66TH EDITION

AMERICAN LIBRARY DIRECTORY™

2013-2014

American Library Directory™
66th Edition

Publisher
Thomas H. Hogan

Vice President, Content
Dick Kaser

Director, ITI Reference Group
Owen O'Donnell

Managing Editor
Beverley McDonough

Associate Editor
Jennifer Williams

Operations Manager, Tampa Editorial
Debra James

Associate Project Coordinator, Tampa Editorial
Paula Watts

66th Edition

American Library Directory™

2013-2014
VOL. 2

South Carolina–Wyoming & Territories
Libraries In Canada
Library Networks, Consortia & Schools
Organization Index
Personnel Index

 Information Today, Inc.

ISSN 0065-910X

Set ISBN: 978-1-57387-467-0
Vol. 1 ISBN: 978-1-57387-465-6
Vol. 2 ISBN: 978-1-57387-466-3

Library of Congress Catalog Card Number: 23-3581

Information Today, Inc.
143 Old Marlton Pike
Medford, NJ 08055-8750
Phone: 800-300-9868 (Customer Service)
           800-409-4929 (Editorial)
Fax: 609-654-4309
E-mail (orders): custserv@infotoday.com
Web Site: www.infotoday.com

Printed and bound in the United States of America

US $369.50
ISBN 13: 978-1-57387-467-0
36950>

9 781573 874670

CONTENTS

VOLUME 1

VOLUME 2

PREFACE

Now in its 66th edition, the *American Library Directory*™ is edited and compiled by Information Today, Inc. Published biennially from 1908 until 1978, the directory is now updated year-round to reflect the increased importance of documenting changes in library income, personnel, expenditures, and automation capabilities.

ARRANGEMENT AND COVERAGE

The major section of the directory is a listing of public, academic, government, and special libraries in the United States and regions administered by it and in Canada. Arranged geographically, the entries are alphabetized by state, region, or province, then by city, and finally by the institution or library name.

Each state, region, and province opens with statistical information regarding public libraries. These statistics were supplied by the state, regional, or provincial library.

Entries include the name and address of the library, names of key personnel, and information on the library's holdings. In addition, the entries for the majority of libraries provide information on some or all of these additional areas: Income; Expenditures including salaries; E-Mail; Subject Interests; Special Collections; Automation; and Publications. Also included in each entry is a Standard Address Number (SAN), a unique address identification code. For SAN assignments or questions, contact SAN@bowker.com. See the sample entry on page xi for a comprehensive guide to information that can be included in each entry.

Information within each library entry came either from the library itself or from public sources. Each library received a copy of the previous edition's entry for updating; if the material was not returned, the data were verified, as much as possible, through research. Entries verified from public sources are indicated by an asterisk (*) following the library name.

Libraries that the editors have learned about since the previous edition are sent questionnaires. If the library returns the form with sufficient information, it is included. Such entries, either new libraries or simply new to the directory, are indicated by a section indicator (§) to the left of the classification letter that precedes the entry.

Each library listed is identified by a code that indicates the type of library it is. The following codes are used:

A — Armed Forces
C — College and University
E — Electronic
G — Government, from local to federal
J — Community College
L — Law
M — Medical
P — Public and State Libraries
R — Religious
S — Special, including industry and company libraries as well as libraries serving associations, clubs, foundations, institutes, and societies.

ADDITIONAL SECTIONS

Library Award Recipients 2012. This section includes awards for outstanding librarianship or services, major development grants, and research projects.

Volume 2 of the directory serves as a support or auxiliary to the Library Section, and includes a variety of information:

1. *Networks, Consortia, and Other Cooperative Library Organizations* includes automation networks, statewide networking systems, book processing and purchasing centers, and other specialized cooperating organizations. Entries indicate the number of members and the primary functions of each.

2. *Library Schools and Training Courses* includes community college, college, and university library science programs. Entries indicate entrance requirements, tuition, type of training offered, degrees and hours offered, and special courses offered. A dagger (†) indicates a program accredited by the American Library Association Committee on Accreditation.

3. *Library Systems* provides a listing of all state and provincial library systems. A brief statement indicating system functions within the state or province precedes the alphabetically arranged list of the state or province's systems. Cities are also included so that the user can locate a system's entry in the Library Section of the directory, or in cases where the state is followed by (N), in the Network Section of the directory.

4. *Libraries for the Blind and Physically Handicapped* provides a listing of all libraries designated by the National Library Service for the Blind and Physically Handicapped as regional and subregional libraries serving print handicapped patrons. It also includes Canadian libraries that have facilities for assisting these patrons.

5. *Libraries Serving the Deaf and Hearing Impaired* provides a similar listing of all libraries that have indicated that they have a TDD reference service for deaf patrons. The list is arranged by state and then by library name. The city is included so the user can find the entry in the Library Section and determine the TDD number as well as other services by reading the paragraph, "Special Services for the Deaf" in the library's entry.

6. *State and Provincial Public Library Agencies* indicates name, address, person-in-charge, and telephone number of the state agency that is responsible for public libraries.

7. *State School Library Agencies* indicates the same information for the state agency that is responsible for elementary and high school programs.

8. The *Interlibrary Loan Code for the United States* is reprinted with the permission of the American Library Association.

9. *United States Armed Forces Libraries Overseas* is a listing, by military branch, of all overseas libraries and is arranged in geographic order. Entries include the name, address, person-in-charge, and Standard Address Number (SAN) of each library.

10. The *Organization Index* provides an alphabetical listing of all libraries and networks. Cross-references are included as needed.

11. The *Personnel Index* is an alphabetical listing of individuals who are included within entries for libraries, consortia, and library schools.

RELATED SERVICES

American Library Directory™ is also available online at **www.americanlibrarydirectory.com**. You can identify all libraries that meet certain criteria such as holdings, staff size, expenditures, income, and more with a single search. Visit the site and take advantage of our free trial offer.

The editors have made every effort to include all material submitted as accurately and completely as possible within the confines of format and scope. However, the publishers do not assume and hereby disclaim any liability to any party for any loss or damage caused by errors or omissions in the *American Library Directory*™ whether such errors and omissions resulted from negligence, accident, or any other cause. In the event of a publication error, the sole responsibility of the publisher will be the entry of corrected information in succeeding editions.

ACKNOWLEDGEMENTS

The editors wish to thank all of those who responded to our requests for information; without their efforts, the *American Library Directory*™ could not be published.

The editors also wish to express their appreciation for the cooperation of the officers of the state, regional, and provincial libraries who have provided statistics and other information concerning libraries in their areas.

Beverley McDonough
Managing Editor

Return this form to:

Information Today, Inc.

American Library Directory™
630 Central Avenue
New Providence, NJ 07974
Fax: 908-219-0192

AMERICAN LIBRARY DIRECTORY™
EDITORIAL REVISION FORM

Library Name: _____

The library listing is found on page number: _____

☐ Please check here if you are nominating this library for a new listing in the directory

General Information

Address: _____

City: _____ State/Country: _____ Postal Code: _____

Phone: _____ Fax: _____

E-Mail: _____ Web Site: _____

Brief Description: _____

Personnel

☐ Addition   ☐ Deletion   ☐ Correction

First Name: _____ Last Name: _____ Title: _____

☐ Addition   ☐ Deletion   ☐ Correction

First Name: _____ Last Name: _____ Title: _____

☐ Addition   ☐ Deletion   ☐ Correction

First Name: _____ Last Name: _____ Title: _____

☐ Addition   ☐ Deletion   ☐ Correction

First Name: _____ Last Name: _____ Title: _____

(Continued on back)

Other Information

Indicate other information to be added to or corrected in this listing. Please be as specific as possible, noting erroneous data to be deleted.

_____

_____

_____

_____

_____

_____

_____

Verification

Data for this listing will not be updated without the following information.

Your First Name: _____   Your Last Name: _____

Organization Name: _____

Address: _____

City: _____   State/Country: _____   Postal Code: _____

Phone: _____   E-Mail: _____

Indicate if you are a: ☐ Representative of this organization   ☐ User of this directory   ☐ Other

If other, please specify: _____

**Thank you for helping Information Today, Inc. maintain the most up-to-date information
available. Please return by fax to 908-219-0192.**

SAMPLE ENTRY

[1]**P** [2]McNeil & Foster, [3]Prescott Memorial Library, [4]500 Terra Cotta Dr, 85005-3126. [5]SAN 360-9070. [6]Tel: 602-839-9108. Toll Free Tel: 800-625-3848. FAX: 602-839-2020. TDD: 602-839-9202. E-mail: mcneilfoster@prescott.org. Web Site: www.fosterpress.com. [7]*Dir* Troy Alan; Tel: 602-839-5522; *Asst Dir* Tasha Brunnell; *Tech Serv* Beverly Greene; *Pub Servs* Tanya Peeley. Subject Specialists: *Bus* Cecil Brown; *Folklore* Peggy Shoree.

[8]Staff 20 (MLS 15, Non-MLS 5)

[9]Founded 1903. Pop served 92,540; Circ 210,000

[10]July 2012-Jun 2013 Income (Main Library and Branch(es)) $750,500, State $600,000, City $150,500. Mats Exp $118,400, Books $53,400, Per/Ser (Incl. Access Fees) $60,000, Micro $2,000, AV Equip $3,000. Sal $97,100 (Prof $32,000)

[11]**Library Holdings:** Bk Vols 110,000; Bk Titles 72,000; Per subs 245

[12]**Special Collections:** Local History (Lehi College)

[13]**Subject Interests:** Child psychology, genetics

[14]**Automation Activity & Vendor Info:** (Acquisitions) Innovative Interfaces Inc.; (Cataloging) Innovative Interfaces Inc.; (Circulation) Gaylord

[15]**Database Vendor:** EBSCO Online, OCLC WorldCat

[16]Wireless access

[17]Mem of Southwestern Library System

[18]Partic in Amigos Library Services, Inc.; Library Interchange Network (LINK)

[19]Special Services for the Deaf-TDD. Staff member who knows sign language; projector & captioned films

[20]Friends of Library Group

[21]**Bookmobiles:** 1

[22]**Branches:** 1

EASTSIDE, 9807 Post St, 85007-3184. SAN 360-9083. Tel 602-839-9178; *Librn* Linda Rhodes

Library Holdings: Bk Vols 23,000

---

1. Classification key (see "Arrangement & Coverage" in the Preface for explanation).
2. Official library name.
3. Other name by which library may be known.
4. Address.
5. SAN (Standard Address Number).
6. Communication information.
7. Personnel.
8. Number and professional status of staff.
9. Library background—Data on enrollment and the highest degree offered are included for academic libraries.
10. Income figures—Library income is broken down by source when reported.
   Expenditure figures—Material expenditure figures are requested for AV equipment, books, electronic reference materials (including access fees), manuscripts and archives, microforms, other print materials, periodicals/serials (including access fees), and preservation. In addition, salary figures are broken down by professional status when given.

11. Library holdings.
12. Special collections.
13. Subject interests.
14. Automation activity and vendor.
15. Database vendor.
16. Library with wireless access.
17. Library system to which the library belongs.
18. Networks in which the library participates.
19. Special services.
20. Friends of Library Group.
21. Bookmobiles.
22. Branches (or departmental libraries for academic libraries)—Entries include library name, address, name of librarian, and number of book volumes. Branch libraries are listed under the library of which they are a part.

LIBRARY COUNT

Provided here are totals for major types of libraries in the United States, its territories, and Canada. Included are counts for public, academic, armed forces, government, and special libraries. Excluded from the counts are branch, departmental, and divisional libraries not listed with a full address in the directory. Some categories, such as academic, provide counts for specialized libraries such as law or medical libraries. As counts for only certain types of libraries are given, these subcategories do not add up to the total count for each type of library.

PUBLIC—Each public library is counted once and then each branch is counted separately. Because the organization of systems varies from state to state, the method of counting these libraries varies also. In some cases, the libraries forming the systems were designated as member libraries, while in others they were given as branch libraries. In yet other instances, systems maintain branches as well as member libraries. If listed in this directory as a branch, the library was recorded in the branch count; however, member libraries were counted independently and recorded in the number of public libraries. Special public libraries are also included in the Total Special Libraries count.

ACADEMIC—The figure for academic libraries includes all libraries listed in the directory as part of academic institutions, whether they are main, departmental, or special. Specialized libraries and library departments at these colleges, such as law, medical, religious, or science libraries, are also counted in the Total Special Libraries figure.

GOVERNMENT and ARMED FORCES—Counts include all government and armed forces-realted libraries listed in the directory, including specialized ones. Those libraries that are also defined as special libraries are included in the Total Special Libraries figure.

NOTE: Branch records for academic and government libraries are no longer counted within these breakdowns, causing some discrepancy when comparing figures with previous editions. This does not affect the total number of libraries listed in the *American Library Directory*™.

SPECIAL—The special libraries count includes only specialized libraries that are not public, academic, armed forces, or government institutions. The Total Special Libraries count includes all law, medical, religious, business, and other special libraries found in the *American Library Directory*™ regardless of who operates them.

LIBRARIES IN THE UNITED STATES

A. PUBLIC LIBRARIES......................................*16,835
    Public Libraries, excluding Branches.....................9,640
        Main Public Libraries that have branches........1,412
    Public Library Branches......................................7,195

B. ACADEMIC LIBRARIES..................................*3,703
    Community College Libraries................................1,139
        Departmental...201
        Law..2
        Medical...6
        Religious..11
    University & College...2,564
        Departmental..1,279
        Law...183
        Medical...235
        Religious...239

C. ARMED FORCES LIBRARIES............................*265
    Air Force...76
        Medical..6

    Army...123
        Medical...25
    Marine..12
    Navy...54
        Law..1
        Medical...11

D. GOVERNMENT LIBRARIES............................*1,006
    Law...384
    Medical..140

E. SPECIAL LIBRARIES (Excluding Public, Academic, Armed Forces, and Government)..........................*6,373
    Law...793
    Medical...1,285
    Religious...484

F. TOTAL SPECIAL LIBRARIES (Including Public, Academic, Armed Forces, and Government)...........7,616

Total Law...1,363
Total Medical...1,708
Total Religious..964

G. **TOTAL LIBRARIES COUNTED (*)**...................28,182

LIBRARIES IN REGIONS
ADMINISTERED BY THE UNITED STATES

A. **PUBLIC LIBRARIES**...*28
Public Libraries, excluding Branches..........................11
   Main Public Libraries that have branches..............3
Public Library Branches...17

B. **ACADEMIC LIBRARIES**.......................................*37
Community College Libraries...4
   Departmental...3
   Medical...0
University & College..33
   Departmental...21
   Law..3
   Medical...2
   Religious...1

C. **ARMED FORCES LIBRARIES**.................................*2
Air Force...1
Army..1
Navy..0

D. **GOVERNMENT LIBRARIES**....................................*4
Law..1
Medical..1

E. **SPECIAL LIBRARIES** (Excluding Public, Academic,
Armed Forces, and Government)...............................*6
Law..3
Medical..1
Religious..1

F. **TOTAL SPECIAL LIBRARIES** (Including Public,
Academic, Armed Forces, and Government).................14
Total Law...7
Total Medical...4
Total Religious...2

G. **TOTAL LIBRARIES COUNTED (*)**..........................77

LIBRARIES IN CANADA

A. **PUBLIC LIBRARIES**.......................................*2,013
Public Libraries, excluding Branches.........................793
   Main Public Libraries that have branches...........138
Public Library Branches..1,220

B. **ACADEMIC LIBRARIES**.....................................*339
Community College Libraries..81
   Departmental...14
   Medical...0
   Religious...2
University & College..258
   Departmental...177
   Law..16
   Medical...20
   Religious...32

C. **GOVERNMENT LIBRARIES**................................*250
Law..37
Medical...7

D. **SPECIAL LIBRARIES** (Excluding Public, Academic,
Armed Forces, and Government)..............................*756
Law..95
Medical..161
Religious...25

E. **TOTAL SPECIAL LIBRARIES** (Including Public,
Academic, Armed Forces, and Government)...........870
Total Law..148
Total Medical..188
Total Religious..82

F. **TOTAL LIBRARIES COUNTED (*)**.....................3,358

SUMMARY

TOTAL UNITED STATES LIBRARIES................28,182

**TOTAL LIBRARIES ADMINISTERED
  BY THE UNITED STATES**..................................77

TOTAL CANADIAN LIBRARIES........................3,358

GRAND TOTAL OF LIBRARIES LISTED.............31,617

Library Award Recipients 2012

Listed below are major awards given to libraries and librarians in the calendar year 2012. These entries were selected from the more inclusive list of scholarships and grant awards found in the *Library and Book Trade Almanac*, 58th edition (Information Today, Inc., 2013). Included here are awards for outstanding librarianship or service, development grants, and research projects larger than an essay or monograph. Awards are listed alphabetically by organization.

American Association of School Librarians (AASL)

AASL/BAKER & TAYLOR DISTINGUISHED SERVICE AWARD ($3,000). For outstanding contributions to librarianship and school library development. Donor: Baker & Taylor Books. Winner: Sharon Coatney.

American Library Association (ALA)

BETA PHI MU AWARD ($1,000). For distinguished service in library education. Donor: Beta Phi Mu International Library Science Honorary Society. Winner: Mary M. Wagner.

EQUALITY AWARD ($1,000). To an individual or group for an outstanding contribution that promotes equality in the library profession. Donor: Scarecrow Press. Winner: Patricia M.Y. Wong.

ELIZABETH FUTAS CATALYST FOR CHANGE AWARD ($1,000). A biennial award to recognize a librarian who invests time an dtalent to make positive change in the profession of librarianship. Donor: Elizabeth Futas Memorial Fund. Winner: Lyn Hopper.

LOLETA D. FYAN PUBLIC LIBRARY RESEARCH GRANT (up to $10,000). For projects in public library development. Donor: Fyan Estate. Winner: Carmen Patlan, Waukegan (Illinois) Public Library, for the proposed "Promotoras Ambassador Program" which will establish outreach to underserved Latino residents.

GALE CENGAGE LEARNING FINANCIAL DEVELOPMENT AWARD ($2,500). To a library organization for a financial development project to secure new funding resources for a public or academic library. Donor: Gale Cengage Learning. Winner: Cedar Rapids (Iowa) Public Library Foundation.

KEN HAYCOCK AWARD FOR PROMOTING LIBRARIANSHIP ($1,000). For significant contribution to public recognition and appreciation of librarianship through professional performance, teaching, or writing. Winner: Jeanne Drewes, Library of Congress.

JOHN AMES HUMPHRY/OCLC/FOREST PRESS AWARD ($1,000). To one or more individuals for significant contributions to international librarianship. Donor: OCLC/Forest Press. Winner: Jane Kinney Meyers.

JOSEPH W. LIPPINCOTT AWARD ($1,000). For distinguished service to the library profession. Donor: Joseph W. Lippincott, III. Winner: Carla J. Stoffle.

MARSHALL CAVENDISH EXCELLENCE IN LIBRARY PROGRAMMING AWARD ($2,000). To recognize either a school library or public library that demonstrates excellence in library programming by providing programs that have community impact and respond to community need. Donor: Marshall Cavendish. Winner: Waukegan (Illinois) Public Library for its Early Learning Center.

SCHOLASTIC LIBRARY PUBLISHING NATIONAL LIBRARY WEEK GRANT ($3,000). For the best public awareness campaign in support of National Library Week. Donor: Scholastic Library Publishing. Winner: Sacramento (California) Public Library.

H. W. WILSON LIBRARY STAFF DEVELOPMENT GRANT ($3,500). To a library organization for a program to further its staff development goals and objectives. Donor: H. W. Wilson Company. Winner: Virginia Beach Public Library for its staff training program "Petting Zoo."

Association for Library Collections and Technical Services (ALCTS)

ESTHER J. PIERCY AWARD ($1,500). To a librarian with no more than ten years' experience for contributions and leadership in the field of library collections and technical services. Donor: YBP Library Services. Winner: Timothy Strawn.

PAUL BANKS AND CAROLYN HARRIS PRESERVATION AWARD ($1,500). To recognize the contribution of a professional preservation specialist who has been active in the field of preservation and/or conservation for library and/or archival materials. Donor: Preservation Technologies. Winner: Julie Allen Page.

ULRICH SERIALS LIBRARIANSHIP AWARD ($1,500). For distinguished contributions to serials librarianship. Sponsor: ProQuest. Winner: Valerie Bross.

Association for Library Service to Children (ALSC)

ALSC/BOOK WHOLESALERS, INC. BWI SUMMER READING PROGRAM GRANT ($3,000). To an ALSC member for implementation of an outstanding public library summer reading program for children. Donor: Book Wholesalers, Inc. Winner: Wichita Falls (Texas) Public Library.

ALSC/CANDLEWICK PRESS "LIGHT THE WAY: LIBRARY OUTREACH TO THE UNDERSERVED GRANT" ($3,000). To a library conducting exemplary outreach to underserved populations.

Donor: Candlewick Press. Winner: Memphis (Tennessee) Public Library and Information Center for its "Read With Me, Sign With Me" project.

Association of College and Research Libraries (ACRL)

ACRL ACADEMIC OR RESEARCH LIBRARIAN OF THE YEAR AWARD ($5,000). For outstanding contribution to academic and research librarianship and library development. Donor: YBP Library Services. Winner: Paula Kaufman.

ACRL/CLS PROQUEST INNOVATION IN COLLEGE LIBRARIANSHIP AWARD ($3,000). To academic librarians who show a capacity for innovation in the areas of programs, services, and operations; or creating innovations for library colleagues that facilitate their ability to better serve the library's community. Winners: Anne Burke, Adrienne Lai, and Adam Rogers, North Carolina State University Libraries.

ACRL/EBSS DISTINGUISHED EDUCATION AND BEHAVIORAL SCIENCES LIBRARIAN AWARD ($2,500). To an academic librarian who has made an outstanding contribution as an education and/or behavioral sciences librarian through accomplishments and service to the profession. Donor: John Wiley & Sons. Winner: Scott Walter.

EXCELLENCE IN ACADEMIC LIBRARIES AWARD ($3,000). To recognize outstanding community college, college, and university libraries. Donor: YBP Library Services. Winners: (university) Grand Valley State University, Allendale, Michigan; (college) Champlain College, Burlington, Vermont; (community college) Seattle (Washington) Central Community College.

MARTA LANGE/CQ PRESS AWARD ($1,000). To recognize an academic or law librarian for contributions to bibliography and information service in law or political science. Donor: CQ Press. Winner: John Eaton.

Black Caucus of the American Library Association (BCALA)

DEMCO/BCALA EXCELLENCE IN LIBRARIANSHIP AWARD. To a librarian who has made significant contributions to promoting the status of African Americans in the library profession. Winner: Andrew P. Jackson (Sekou Molefi Baako).

Library Leadership and Management Association (LLAMA)

JOHN COTTON DANA LIBRARY PUBLIC RELATIONS AWARDS. To libraries or library organizations of all types for public relations programs or special projects ended during the preceding year. Donors: H. W. Wilson Foundation and EBSCO. Winners: Arlington (Texas) Public Library; Cedar Rapids (Iowa) Public Library; Cleve J. Fredricksen Library, Camp Hill, Pennsylvania; Contra Costa County Library, Pleasant Hill, California; Emily Jones Pointer

Library, Hernando, Mississippi; King County Library System, Issaquah, Washington; Minnesota Department of Transportation, Saint Paul; Utah Valley University, Orem.

Public Library Association (PLA)

EBSCO EXCELLENCE IN SMALL AND/OR RURAL PUBLIC SERVICE AWARD ($1,000). Honors a library serving a population of 10,000 or less that demonstrates excellence of service to its community as exemplified by an overall service program or a special program of significant accomplishment. Donor: EBSCO. Winner: Kinsley (Kansas) Public Library.

ALLIE BETH MARTIN AWARD ($3,000). To honor a public librarian who has demonstrated extraordinary range and depth of knowledge about books or other library materials and has distinguished ability to share that knowledge. Donor: Baker & Taylor. Winner: Kaite Mediatore Stover, Kansas City (Missouri) Public Library.

Reference and User Services Association (RUSA)

VIRGINIA BOUCHER-OCLC DISTINGUISHED ILL LIBRARIAN AWARD ($2,000). To a librarian for outstanding professional achievement, leadership, and contributions to interlibrary loan and document delivery. Winner: Cyril Oberlander, Milne Library, State University of New York, Geneseo.

GALE CENGAGE AWARD FOR EXCELLENCE IN BUSINESS LIBRARIANSHIP ($3,000). For distinguished activities in the field of business librarianship. Donor: Gale Cengage Learning. Winner: Rita W. Moss.

ISADORE GILBERT MUDGE-GALE CENGAGE AWARD ($5,000). For distinguished contributions to reference librarianship. Donor: Gale Cengage Learning. Winner: Robert Kieft.

CANADA

Canadian Library Association (CLA)

CLA ELIZABETH DAFOE SCHOLARSHIP ($C5,000). Winner: Grant Hurley.

CLA/KEN HAYCOCK AWARD FOR PROMOTING LIBRARIANSHIP (C$1,000). For significant contributions to the public recognition and appreciation of librarianship. Winner: Pilar Martinez.

CLA OUTSTANDING SERVICE TO LIBRARIANSHIP AWARD. Donor: Bowker. Winner: Ken Roberts.

CLA/H. W. WILSON SCHOLARSHIP ($2,000). Winner: Leila Meshgini.

KEY TO SYMBOLS AND ABBREVIATIONS

KEY TO SYMBOLS

A - Armed Forces libraries
C - College and university libraries
E - Electronic libraries
G - Government libraries
J - Community college libraries
L - Law libraries
M - Medical libraries
P - Public and state libraries
R - Religious libraries
S - Special libraries
* - No response received directly from the library; data gathered from other sources
§ - New library and/or listed for the first time
† - Library school program accredited by the American Library Association Committee on Accreditation

KEY TO ABBREVIATIONS

A-tapes - Audio Tapes
Acad - Academic, Academy
Acctg - Accounting
Acq - Acquisition Librarian, Acquisitions
Actg - Acting
Ad - Adult Services Librarian
Add - Address
Admin - Administration, Administrative
Adminr - Administrator
Adv - Adviser, Advisor, Advisory
Advan - Advanced, Advancement
Aeronaut - Aeronautics
AFB - Air Force Base
Agr - Agricultural, Agriculture
Ala - Alabama
Alta - Alberta
Am - America, American
Ann - Annual, Annually
Anthrop - Anthropology
APO - Air Force Post Office, Army Post Office
Approp - Appropriation
Approx - Approximate, Approximately
Appt - Appointment
Archaeol - Archaeology
Archit - Architecture
Ariz - Arizona
Ark - Arkansas
Asn - Association
Assoc - Associate
Asst - Assistant
AV - Audiovisual, Audiovisual Materials
Ave - Avenue
BC - British Columbia
Bd - Binding, Bound
Behav - Behaviorial
Bibliog - Bibliographic, Bibliographical, Bibliography
Bibliogr - Bibliographer
Biog - Biographer, Biographical, Biography

Biol - Biology
Bk(s) - Book(s)
Bkmobile - Bookmobile
Bldg - Building
Blvd - Boulevard
Bot - Botany
Br - Branch, Branches
Bro - Brother
Bur - Bureau
Bus - Business
Calif - California
Can - Canada, Canadian
Cap - Capital
Cat(s) - Cataloging Librarian, Cataloging, Catalog(s)
Cent - Central
Ch - Children, Children's Librarian, Children's Services
Chem - Chemical, Chemistry
Chmn - Chairman
Cht(s) - Chart(s)
Circ - Circulation
Cler - Clerical Staff
Co - Company
Col - College
Coll - Collection, Collections
Colo - Colorado
COM - Computer Output Microform
Commun - Community
Comn - Commission
Comt - Committee
Conn - Connecticut
Conserv - Conservation
Consult - Consultant
Coop - Cooperates, Cooperating, Cooperation, Cooperative, Corporate
Coord - Coordinating
Coordr - Coordinator
Corp - Corporation
Coun - Council
CP - Case Postale

Ct - Court
Ctr - Center, Centre
Curric - Curriculum
DC - District of Columbia
Del - Delaware
Den - Denominational
Dent - Dentristry
Dep - Deputy, Depository
Dept - Department
Develop - Development
Dir - Director
Div - Division
Doc - Document, Documents
Dr - Doctor, Drive
E - East
Econ - Economic
Ed - Edited, Edition, Editor
Educ - Education, Educational
Elem - Elementary
Eng - Engineering
Enrl - Enrollment
Ent - Entrance
Environ - Environmental
Equip - Equipment
ERDA - Energy Research & Development Administration
Est - Estimate, Estimation
Estab - Established
Excl - Excluding
Exec - Executive
Exp - Expenditure
Ext - Extension of Telephone
Fac - Faculty, Facilities
Fed - Federal
Fedn - Federation
Fel - Fellowship
Fla - Florida
Flm - Films
Flr - Floor
Found - Foundation
FPO - Fleet Post Office

Fr - French
Fs - Filmstrips
Ft - Fort
FT - Full Time
FTE - Full Time Equivalent
Ga - Georgia
Gen - General, Generated
Geog - Geographical, Geography
Geol - Geological, Geology
Govt - Government
Grad - Graduate
Hist - Historical, History
Hort - Horticulture
Hq - Headquarters
Hrs - Hours
Hwy - Highway, Highways
Hydrol - Hydrology
Ill - Illinois
ILL - Interlibrary Loan
Illustr - Illustrator, Illustration
Inc - Income, Incorporated
Incl - Including
Ind - Indiana
Indust - Industrial, Industry
Info - Information
Ins - Insurance
Inst - Institute, Institutions
Instrul - Instructional
Instr - Instructor
Intl - International
Jr - Junior
Juv - Juvenile
Kans - Kansas
Ky - Kentucky
La - Louisiana
Lab - Laboratories, Laboratory
Lang(s) - Language(s)
Lectr - Lecturer
Legis - Legislative, Legislature
Libr - Libraries, Library
Librn - Librarian
Lit - Literary, Literature
Ltd - Limited
Mag(s) - Magazine(s)
Man - Manitoba
Mass - Massachusetts
Mat(s) - Material(s)
Math - Mathematical, Mathematics
Md - Maryland
Med - Medical, Medicine
Media - Media Specialist
Mem - Member
Metaphys - Metaphysical, Metaphysics
Metrop - Metropolitan
Mgr - Manager, Managerial
Mgt - Management
Mich - Michigan
Micro - Microform
Mil - Military
Misc - Miscellaneous
Miss - Mississippi
Minn - Minnesota
Mkt - Marketing
Mo - Missouri
Ms - Manuscript, Manuscripts
Mus - Museum
N - North

NASA - National Aeronautics & Space Administration
Nat - National
NB - New Brunswick
NC - North Carolina
NDak - North Dakota
NE - Northeast, Northeastern
Nebr - Nebraska
Nev - Nevada
New Eng - New England
Newsp - Newspaper, Newspapers
Nfld - Newfoundland
NH - New Hampshire
NJ - New Jersey
NMex - New Mexico
Nonfict - nonfiction
NS - Nova Scotia
NW - Northwest, Northwestern
NY - New York
Oceanog - Oceanography
Off - Office
Okla - Oklahoma
Ont - Ontario
Ore - Oregon
Ornith - Ornithology
Pa - Pennsylvania
Pac - Pacific
Partic - Participant, Participates
Per(s) - Periodical(s)
Pharm - Pharmacy
Philos - Philosophical, Philosophy
Photog - Photograph, Photography
Phys - Physical
Pkwy - Parkway
Pl - Place
PO - Post Office
Polit Sci - Political Science
Pop - Population
PR - Puerto Rico
Prep - Perparation, Preparatory
Pres - President, Presidents
Presv - Preservation
Proc - Process, Processing
Prof - Professional, Professor
Prog - Program, Programming
Prov - Province, Provincial
Psychiat - Psychiatrist, Psychiatry, Psychiatric
Psychol - Psychological, Psychology
PT - Part Time
Pub - Public
Pub Rel - Public Relations Head
Publ(s) - Publisher, Publishing, Publication(s)
Pvt - Private
Qtr - Quarter
Que - Quebec
R&D - Research & Development
Rd - Road
Read - Readable
Rec - Record, Recording, Records
Ref - Reference
Relig - Religion, Religious
Rep - Representative
Reprod - Reproduction
Req - Requirement
Res - Research, Resource, Resources
RI - Rhode Island
RLIN - Research Libraries Information Network

Rm - Room
Rpt(s) - Report(s)
RR - Rural Route
Rte - Route
S - South
Sal - Salary
SAN - Standard Address Number
Sask - Saskatchewan
SC - South Carolina
Sch - School
Sci - Science, Scientific
Sci Fict - Science Fiction
SDak - South Dakota
SE - Southeast, Southeastern
Secy - Secretary
Sem - Semester, Seminary
Ser - Serials, Serials Librarian
Serv(s) - Service(s)
Soc - Social, Society, Societies
Sociol - Sociology
Spec - Special, Specialist
Sq - Square
Sr - Senor, Senior, Sister
St - Saint, Street
Sta - Station
Sub(s) - Subscription(s)
Subj - Subject, Subjects
Sup - Supplies
Supv - Supervising, Supervision
Supvr - Supervisor
Supvry - Supervisory
SW - Southwest, Southwestern
Syst - System, Systems
TDD - Telecomm. Device for the Deaf
Tech - Technical, Technician, Technology
Tel - Telephone
Tenn - Tennessee
Tex - Texas
Theol - Theological, Theology
Tpk - Turnpike
Treas - Treasurer
TTY - Teletypewriter
TV - Television
TVA - Tennessee Valley Authority
UN - United Nations
Undergrad - Undergraduate
Univ - University
US - United States
VPres - Vice President
V-tapes - Video Tapes
Va - Virginia
Vet - Veteran
VF - Vertical Files
VI - Virgin Islands
Vis - Visiting
Vols - Volumes, Volunteers
Vt - Vermont
W - West
Wash - Washington
Wis - Wisconsin
WLN - Washington Library Network
WVa - West Virginia
Wyo - Wyoming
YA - Young Adult Librarian, Young Adult Services
Zool - Zoology

66TH EDITION

AMERICAN
LIBRARY
DIRECTORY™

2013-2014

Date of Statistics: FY 2009-2010
Population, 2000 Census: 4,012,012
Total Volumes in Public Libraries: 9,423,771
    Volumes Per Capita: 2.35
Total Public Library Circulation: 26,160,419
    Circulation Per Capita: 6.52
Total Public Library Income (including Grants-in-Aid):
    $118,943,647 (available for use in FY 09 operating)
    Source of Income: Mainly public funds
    Expenditures Per Capita: $29.64
Number of County or Multi-county (Regional) Libraries: 42
    county libraries; 2 regional libraries; 1 municipal library
    Counties Served: 46
Number of Bookmobiles in State: 31
**Grants-in-Aid to Public Libraries (including Federal & State
    grants but not construction funds):** $8,560,916
    Federal (Library Services & Technology Act): $2,707,866
    State Aid: $5,853,050 (FY 10)
Formula for Apportionment: Per capita allocation to county
    libraries with a minimum allocation of $60,000

ABBEVILLE

P   ABBEVILLE COUNTY LIBRARY SYSTEM*, 201 S Main St, 29620.
SAN 360-2702. Tel: 864-459-4009. FAX: 864-459-4009. Web Site:
www.abbevillecounty.org. *Dir,* Mary Elizabeth Land; *Br Mgr,* Annette
Greenway
    Library Holdings: Bk Vols 46,000; Per Subs 115
    Subject Interests: Genealogy, Local hist
    Wireless access
    Open Mon & Wed-Fri 9-5:30, Tues 9-8, Sat 9-3
    Friends of the Library Group
    Branches: 2
    CALHOUN FALLS BRANCH, 409 N Tugaloo St, Calhoun Falls, 29628,
    SAN 360-2737. Tel: 864-418-8724. FAX: 864-418-8724. *Br Mgr,* Lois
    Rhodes
      Open Mon, Wed & Thurs 10-2 & 3-6, Tues 3-8, Fri 10-2 & 3-5, Sun 2-5
      Friends of the Library Group
    DONALDS BRANCH, 429 W Main St, Donalds, 29638, SAN 360-2761.
    Tel: 864-379-8568. FAX: 864-379-8568.
      Open Mon 10-1 & 2-8, Tues-Thurs 10-1 & 2-5, Fri 2-5, Sat 10-1
      Friends of the Library Group

AIKEN

P   AIKEN-BAMBERG-BARNWELL-EDGEFIELD REGIONAL LIBRARY
SYSTEM*, 314 Chesterfield St SW, 29801-7171. SAN 359-8861. Tel:
803-642-7575. FAX: 803-642-7597. *Dir,* Mary Jo Dawson; E-mail:
maryjod@abbe-lib.org; *Tech Serv Dir,* Holden Humphrey; E-mail:
holdenh@abbe-lib.org; *Syst Coordr,* Vic McGraner; E-mail:
vicm@abbe-lib.org; *Ch,* Rachel Pirkle; E-mail: rachelp@abbe-lib.org; *Extn
Serv,* Sara Thigpen; E-mail: sarat@abbe-lib.org; Staff 15 (MLS 12,
Non-MLS 3)
    Founded 1958. Pop 207,014
    Library Holdings: AV Mats 26,000; Bk Vols 232,544; Per Subs 367
    Special Collections: South Carolina Coll
    Automation Activity & Vendor Info: (Acquisitions) Ex Libris Group;
    (Cataloging) SirsiDynix; (Circulation) SirsiDynix; (ILL) OCLC Online;
    (OPAC) SirsiDynix
    Wireless access
    Friends of the Library Group
    Branches: 14
    AIKEN COUNTY, 314 Chesterfield St SW, 29801, SAN 359-8896. Tel:
    803-642-2020. Circulation Tel: 803-642-2023. Reference Tel:
    803-642-2022. FAX: 803-642-7570. *Chief Librn,* Michael Swan; *Ch,*
    Jennie Beck; *Ref Serv,* Janet Robinson
      Friends of the Library Group
    BAMBERG COUNTY, 3156 Railroad Ave, Bamberg, 29003-1017. (Mail
    add: PO Box 305, Bamberg, 29003), SAN 359-8926. Tel: 803-245-3022.
    FAX: 803-245-2422. *Libr Mgr,* Jennifer Naimzadeh
      Open Mon-Wed & Fri 10-6, Thurs 10-9, Sat 10-2
      Friends of the Library Group

    BARNWELL COUNTY, 40 Burr St, Barnwell, 29812-1917, SAN
    359-8950. Tel: 803-259-3612. FAX: 803-259-7497. *Chief Librn,* Lisa
    Gillespie
      Special Collections: South Carolina Genealogy
      Friends of the Library Group
    BLACKVILLE BRANCH, 19420 N Sol Blatt Ave, Blackville, 29817, SAN
    359-9985. Tel: 803-284-2295. FAX: 803-284-2295. *Br Mgr,* Terri Mull
      Open Tues & Thurs 10-1 & 2-6, Wed 2-6
      Friends of the Library Group
    NANCY BONNETTE - WAGENER BRANCH LIBRARY, 204 Park St,
    Wagener, 29164, SAN 359-9191. Tel: 803-564-5396. FAX:
    803-564-5396. *Br Mgr,* LaWanda Fulmer
    NANCY CARSON - NORTH AUGUSTA LIBRARY, 135 Edgefield Rd,
    North Augusta, 29841-2423, SAN 359-9132. Tel: 803-279-5767. FAX:
    803-202-3588. *Br Mgr,* Barbara Walker; *Ref,* Derek Marshall
      Friends of the Library Group
    DENMARK BRANCH, 19 Maple Ave, Denmark, 29042, SAN 359-9019.
    Tel: 803-793-4511. FAX: 803-793-4511. *Br Mgr,* Velvet Lace Elrod
      Open Mon & Fri 10-1 & 2-6, Wed 10-1
    EDGEFIELD COUNTY, 105 Courthouse Sq, Edgefield, 29824, SAN
    359-9043. Tel: 803-637-4025. FAX: 803-637-4026. *Chief Librn,* Natalie
    Pulley
    JACKSON BRANCH, 106 Main St, Jackson, 29831-2616, SAN 377-0443.
    Tel: 803-471-3811. FAX: 803-471-3811.
      Open Mon, Wed & Thurs 1-6, Tues 2-6
      Friends of the Library Group
    MIDLAND VALLEY, Nine Hillside Rd, Langley, 29834, SAN 377-046X.
    Tel: 803-593-7379. FAX: 803-593-5253. *Br Mgr,* Barbara Sharpe;
    E-mail: barbaras@abbe-lib.org
      Open Tues-Thurs 1-6, Sat 10-2
    MOBLEY LIBRARY/JOHNSTON BRANCH, 407 Calhoun St, Johnston,
    29832, SAN 359-9078. Tel: 803-275-5157. FAX: 803-275-2754. *Br Mgr,*
    Brenda Bibbs; *Br Mgr,* Jana Rae
      Open Mon 12-8, Tues & Thurs 12-6
      Friends of the Library Group
    NEW ELLENTON BRANCH, 407 Main St, New Ellenton, 29809, SAN
    359-9108. Tel: 803-652-7845. FAX: 803-652-7845. *Br Mgr,* Susan Toole
      Open Mon, Wed & Thurs 1-6, Tues 2-6
    TRENTON BRANCH, 117 Watson Rd, Trenton, 29847, SAN 359-9167.
    Tel: 803-275-2538. *Br Mgr,* Lynn Foster
      Open Tues & Wed 3-6 & Sat 10-2
    WILLISTON BRANCH, 5121 Springfield Rd, Williston, 29853-9762, SAN
    359-9221. Tel: 803-266-3027. FAX: 803-266-3027. *Br Mgr,* Jo Crider
    Bookmobiles: 1

S   SAVANNAH RIVER SITE, Savannah River National Laboratory Applied
Science Library, Bldg 773A, 29808. SAN 327-0815. Tel: 803-725-0069,
803-725-2940. FAX: 803-725-5367. E-mail: library@srs.gov. *Tech Serv
Librn,* Millard Barry Bull; E-mail: Millard.Bull@srnl.doe.gov; Staff 2
(MLS 1, Non-MLS 1)
    Library Holdings: Bk Vols 34,000; Per Subs 215

Subject Interests: Nuclear, Safety, Training
Restriction: Staff use only

C UNIVERSITY OF SOUTH CAROLINA AIKEN*, Gregg-Graniteville
Library, 471 University Pkwy, 29801. SAN 315-4866. Tel: 803-648-6851,
Ext 3465. FAX: 803-641-3302. Web Site: library.usca.edu. *Dir,* Jane H
Tuten; E-mail: janet@usca.edu; *Doc Librn,* Kathy Karn-Carmichael; Tel:
803-641-3320, E-mail: kathyk@usca.edu; *Instruction & Ref Librn,* Deborah
Tritt; Tel: 803-641-3589, E-mail: deboraht@usca.edu; *Mgr, ILL,* Brigitte
Smith; Tel: 803-641-3504, E-mail: brigits@usca.edu; *Circ Mgr,* Robert
Amerson; Tel: 803-641-3485, E-mail: ramerson@usca.edu; *Coll Coordr,*
Natalia Taylor Poppeliers; Tel: 803-641-3492, E-mail: nataliap@usca.edu;
Coordr, Libr Instruction, Kari D Weaver; Tel: 803-641-3261, E-mail:
kariw@usca.edu; *Per Coordr,* Willie Mae Dumas; E-mail:
williemaed@usca.edu; *Ref Coordr,* Kaetrena D Kendrick; Tel:
803-641-3282, E-mail: kaetrenak@usca.edu; *Web Adminr,* Stan Price; Tel:
803-641-3510, E-mail: stanleyp@usca.edu. Subject Specialists: *Govt doc,*
Kathy Karn-Carmichael; Staff 14 (MLS 6, Non-MLS 8)
Founded 1961. Enrl 2,722; Fac 147; Highest Degree: Master
Jun 2007-Jul 2008. Mats Exp $386,581, Books $81,579, Per/Ser (Incl.
Access Fees) $171,148, Micro $6,631, Electronic Ref Mat (Incl. Access
Fees) $118,167, Presv $9,056
Library Holdings: AV Mats 3,455; CDs 930; e-books 3,727; e-journals
41,643; Electronic Media & Resources 181; Microforms 76,276; Bk Titles
125,046; Bk Vols 135,810; Per Subs 1,328; Videos 385
Special Collections: Department of Energy Public Documents Coll;
Gregg-Graniteville Historical Files; Southern History (May Coll); USC
Aiken Archives. State Document Depository; US Document Depository
Automation Activity & Vendor Info: (Acquisitions) Innovative Interfaces,
Inc - Millenium; (Cataloging) Innovative Interfaces, Inc - Millenium;
(Circulation) Innovative Interfaces, Inc; (ILL) OCLC ILLiad; (OPAC)
Innovative Interfaces, Inc - Millenium; (Serials) Innovative Interfaces, Inc -
Millenium
Database Vendor: Alexander Street Press, American Chemical Society,
Cambridge Scientific Abstracts, EBSCOhost, Elsevier, Gale Cengage
Learning, ISI Web of Knowledge, JSTOR, LexisNexis, OCLC FirstSearch,
OVID Technologies, ProQuest, Springer-Verlag, Wiley
Publications: Annual Report; Inter-Intra Library Loan Service Pamphlet;
New Faculty Library Guide
Partic in Carolina Consortium; OCLC Online Computer Library Center,
Inc; Partnership Among South Carolina Academic Libraries; SC Libr
Network; South Carolina Library Network

ALLENDALE

P ALLENDALE-HAMPTON-JASPER REGIONAL LIBRARY*, Allendale
County Library, 158 McNair St, 29810-0280. (Mail add: PO Box 280,
29810-0280), SAN 359-9256. Tel: 803-584-2371, 803-584-3513. FAX:
803-584-8134. Web Site: www.ahjlibrary.org. *Regional Dir,* Beth McNeer;
E-mail: bethmcneer@yahoo.com; Staff 0.88 (MLS 0.88)
Founded 1905. Pop 53,000; Circ 84,574
Library Holdings: Bk Vols 61,279
Automation Activity & Vendor Info: (Cataloging) TLC (The Library
Corporation); (Circulation) TLC (The Library Corporation)
Friends of the Library Group
Branches: 5
ALLENDALE BRANCH, 158 McNair St, 29810-2804. (Mail add: PO Box
280, 29810-0280). Tel: 803-584-2371. FAX: 803-584-8134. *Br Mgr,*
Barbara Reed; Staff 2 (Non-MLS 2)
Library Holdings: Bk Vols 20,000
Open Mon-Wed & Fri 9-5, Thurs 9-8
ESTILL BRANCH, 276 Third Ave, Estill, 29918-4827. (Mail add: PO Box
668, Estill, 29918-0668), SAN 359-9310. Tel: 803-625-4560. FAX:
803-625-3341. *Br Mgr,* Cynthia Gordon; Staff 1 (Non-MLS 1)
Library Holdings: Bk Vols 2,000
Open Mon-Thurs 10-1 & 2-6, Fri 9-1 & 2-5
HAMPTON, 12 Locust St, East Hampton, 29924, SAN 359-9345. Tel:
803-943-7528. FAX: 803-943-3261. *Br Mgr,* Lois Byrd; Staff 3
(Non-MLS 3)
Library Holdings: Bk Vols 16,279
Open Mon-Thurs 11-7, Fri 11-5, Sat 10-2
HARDEEVILLE BRANCH, Main St, Hardeeville, 29927. (Mail add: PO
Box 1837, Hardeeville, 29927-1837), SAN 359-937X. Tel:
843-784-3426. FAX: 843-784-5277. *Br Mgr,* Lynda Cadell; Staff 2
(Non-MLS 2)
Library Holdings: Bk Vols 5,000
Open Mon-Fri 10:30-5:30
Friends of the Library Group
PRATT MEMORIAL, 123-A E Wilson St, Ridgeland, 29936-3602. (Mail
add: PO Drawer 1540, Ridgeland, 29936-1540), SAN 359-940X. Tel:
843-726-7744. FAX: 843-726-7813. *Br Mgr,* Marsha Cleland; Staff 3
(Non-MLS 3)
Library Holdings: Bk Vols 18,000
Open Mon-Fri 10:30-5:30
Bookmobiles: 1

C UNIVERSITY OF SOUTH CAROLINA*, Salkehatchie Library, PO Box
617, 29810-0617. SAN 315-4874. Tel: 803-584-3446, Ext 152. FAX:
803-584-5038. Web Site: www.uscsalkehatchie.sc.edu. *Head Librn,* Dan
Johnson; Tel: 803-584-3446, Ext 153, E-mail: JOHNS943@mailbox.sc.edu;
Staff 2 (MLS 2)
Founded 1965. Enrl 820
Library Holdings: Bk Vols 55,725; Per Subs 153
Special Collections: South Carolina, Five County Area Coll (Allendale,
Bamberg, Barnwell, Colleton & Hampton counties)
Subject Interests: African-Am, Women's studies
Automation Activity & Vendor Info: (Circulation) Innovative Interfaces,
Inc
Publications: Newsletter
Partic in Association of Research Libraries (ARL); Lyrasis
Open Mon-Thurs (Aug-April) 8am-9pm, Fri 8-4:30, Sun 3-7; Mon-Fri
(May-July) 8-4:30

ANDERSON

P ANDERSON COUNTY LIBRARY, 300 N McDuffie St, 29621-5643.
(Mail add: PO Box 4047, 29622-4047), SAN 359-9434. Tel: 864-260-4500.
FAX: 864-260-4510. Web Site: www.andersonlibrary.org. *Dir,* Faith A
Line; E-mail: fline@andersonlibrary.org; *Asst Dir, Head, Ref,* Janet Price;
E-mail: jprice@andersonlibrary.org; *Head, Ch,* Donna Long; E-mail:
dlong@andersonlibrary.org; *Head, Circ,* Mary Montanucci; E-mail:
mmontanucci@andersonlibrary.org; *Head, ILL, Head, Per,* Alex Currin;
E-mail: acurrin@andersonlibrary.org; *Head, Spec Coll,* Laura Holden;
E-mail: lholden@andersonlibrary.org; *Head, Tech Serv,* Susan Manalli;
E-mail: smanalli@andersonlibrary.org; *Coordr, Prog,* H Bistyga; E-mail:
hbistyga@andersonlibrary.org; *Extn Serv,* Pat Pace; E-mail:
ppace@andersonlibrary.org; *Ref Serv, YA,* Kate Walker; E-mail:
kwalker@andersonlibrary.org; Staff 93 (MLS 15, Non-MLS 78)
Founded 1958. Pop 183,924; Circ 644,274
Jul 2012-Jun 2013 Income (Main Library and Branch(s)) $4,550,111, State
$187,126, County $4,242,985, Locally Generated Income $120,000. Mats
Exp $488,443, Books $365,000, Per/Ser (Incl. Access Fees) $27,000, AV
Mat $52,000, Electronic Ref Mat (Incl. Access Fees) $43,943
Library Holdings: AV Mats 24,594; e-books 101; Large Print Bks 6,983;
Bk Vols 336,426; Per Subs 1,079
Special Collections: Foundation Center Cooperating Coll; South Carolina
Coll, bks, microflm & newsp
Subject Interests: SC
Automation Activity & Vendor Info: (Cataloging) Evergreen;
(Circulation) Evergreen; (ILL) OCLC; (OPAC) Evergreen; (Serials)
Evergreen
Database Vendor: Dun & Bradstreet, Gale Cengage Learning, netLibrary,
Newsbank, OCLC FirstSearch, ProQuest
Wireless access
Function: Adult bk club, After school storytime, Audiobks via web, Bk
club(s), Bks on CD, Children's prog, Computer training, Computers for
patron use, Copy machines, Distance learning, Electronic databases & coll,
Fax serv, Holiday prog, ILL available, Online cat, Online ref, Outreach
serv, Photocopying/Printing, Prog for adults, Prog for children & young
adult, Pub access computers, Ref serv in person, Spanish lang bks, Spoken
cassettes & CDs, Story hour, Summer reading prog, Tax forms, Teen prog,
Telephone ref, Web-catalog
Publications: Bookmarks (Newsletter)
Partic in DISCUS; Lyrasis
Special Services for the Deaf - Assistive tech; TTY equip
Special Services for the Blind - Assistive/Adapted tech devices, equip &
products; Audio mat; Talking bks
Open Mon-Thurs 9-9, Fri & Sat 9-6, Sun 2-6
Friends of the Library Group
Branches: 8
BELTON BRANCH, 91 Breazeale St, Belton, 29627, SAN 359-9469. Tel:
864-338-8330. FAX: 864-338-8696. *Br Mgr,* Jennifer Morden; Staff 2
(Non-MLS 2)
Open Mon 11-7:30, Tues 9:30-6, Wed, Fri & Sat 9:30-1 & 2-6, Thurs
9:30-1 & 2-7:30
Friends of the Library Group
JENNIE ERWIN BRANCH, 318 Shirley Ave, Honea Path, 29654, SAN
359-9493. Tel: 864-369-7751. FAX: 864-369-7751. *Br Mgr,* Cheryl
Hughes; Staff 2 (Non-MLS 2)
Open Mon & Wed-Fri 9:30-6, Tues 11-7, Sat 9:30-1:30
IVA BRANCH, 203 W Cruette St, Iva, 29655. (Mail add: PO Box 86, Iva,
26955-0086), SAN 359-9523. Tel: 864-348-6150. FAX: 864-348-6150.
Br Mgr, Becky Thompson; Staff 2 (Non-MLS 2)
Open Mon-Wed & Fri 9:30-6, Thurs 9:30-7, Sat 9:30-1:30
LANDER MEMORIAL REGIONAL, 925 Greenville Dr, Williamston,
29697, SAN 359-9558. Tel: 864-847-5238. FAX: 864-847-5238. *Br Mgr,*
Linda Hiott; Staff 4 (Non-MLS 4)
Open Mon, Tues & Thurs 9:30-8, Wed & Fri 9:30-6, Sat 9:30-1

PENDLETON BRANCH, 650 S Mechanic St, Pendleton, 29670. (Mail add: PO Box 707, Pendleton, 29670-0707), SAN 359-9612. Tel: 864-646-3045. FAX: 864-646-3046. *Br Mgr,* Dani Lubsen; Staff 3 (Non-MLS 3)
Open Mon, Tues & Thurs 9:30-8, Wed & Fri 9:30-6, Sat 9:30-1

PIEDMONT BRANCH, 1407 Hwy 86, Piedmont, 29673, SAN 359-9647. Tel: 864-845-6534. FAX: 864-845-6534. *Br Mgr,* Miranda White; Staff 2 (Non-MLS 2)
Open Mon-Wed & Fri 9:30-6, Thurs 9:30-7, Sat 9:30-1:30 & 2-7:30

POWDERSVILLE, Four Civic Ct, Easley, 29642. (Mail add: PO Box 51325, Powdersville, 29673-2017), SAN 328-7599. Tel: 864-295-2961. FAX: 864-295-2961. *Br Mgr,* Anna Sutton; Staff 2 (Non-MLS 2)
Open Mon, Tues & Thurs 9:30-8, Wed & Fri 9:30-6, Sat 9:30-1:30

WEST SIDE COMMUNITY CENTER BRANCH FACILITY, 1100 W Franklin St, 29624, SAN 378-1623. Tel: 864-260-4660. FAX: 864-260-4660. *Extn Serv, Supv Librn,* Pat Pace; Tel: 864-260-4500, Ext 174; Staff 1.5 (Non-MLS 1.5)
Open Mon-Fri 9-4:30

Bookmobiles: 1. Extn Librn, Pat Pace. Bk titles 6,085

C ANDERSON UNIVERSITY LIBRARY, The Thrift Library, 316 Boulevard, 29621. SAN 315-4882. Tel: 864-231-2050. FAX: 864-231-2191. E-mail: library@andersonuniversity.edu. Web Site: www.andersonuniversity.edu/library. *Dir, Libr Serv,* Kent Millwood; Tel: 864-231-2049, E-mail: kmillwood@andersonuniversity.edu; *Instrul Serv Librn,* Anne Marie Martin; E-mail: annemariemartin@andersonuniversity.edu; *ILL,* Kay Maynard; E-mail: kmaynard@andersonuniversity.edu; *Ref Serv,* Jane Hawley; E-mail: jhawley@andersonuniversity.edu; *Tech Serv,* Cheryl DeHoll; E-mail: cdeholl@andersonuniversity.edu; Staff 7 (MLS 5, Non-MLS 2)
Founded 1911. Enrl 2,339; Fac 4; Highest Degree: Master
Jun 2011-May 2012 Income $628,055. Mats Exp $232,672, Books $73,140, Per/Ser (Incl. Access Fees) $104,730, Micro $297, AV Mat $7,406, Electronic Ref Mat (Incl. Access Fees) $43,581, Presv $3,518
Library Holdings: AV Mats 6,688; e-books 61,000; e-journals 50,000; Electronic Media & Resources 294; Microforms 84,885; Bk Vols 77,153
Automation Activity & Vendor Info: (Cataloging) TLC (The Library Corporation); (Circulation) TLC (The Library Corporation); (Course Reserve) TLC (The Library Corporation); (ILL) OCLC; (OPAC) TLC (The Library Corporation)
Database Vendor: ABC-CLIO, ARTstor, Baker & Taylor, CredoReference, ebrary, EBSCOhost, Facts on File, Gale Cengage Learning, Greenwood Publishing Group, H W Wilson, Hoovers, LexisNexis, Marquis Who's Who, Modern Language Association, netLibrary, OCLC, Oxford Online, ScienceDirect, Springer-Verlag, Springshare, LLC, TLC (The Library Corporation), YBP Library Services
Wireless access
Partic in DISCUS; First Search; OCLC Online Computer Library Center, Inc; Partnership Among South Carolina Academic Libraries

M ANMED HEALTH MEDICAL LIBRARY, 800 N Fant St, 29621-5708. SAN 315-4890. Tel: 864-512-1253. FAX: 864-512-1552. E-mail: library@anmedhealth.org. *Librn,* Clara Elizabeth Addis; E-mail: beth.addis@anmedhealth.org; Staff 1 (MLS 1)
Library Holdings: Bk Vols 150; Per Subs 26
Subject Interests: Med, Nursing, Surgery
Automation Activity & Vendor Info: (Cataloging) Follett Software; (Circulation) Follett Software; (OPAC) Follett Software; (Serials) Follett Software
Database Vendor: PubMed
Wireless access
Function: Copy machines, ILL available, Online cat, Online searches, Photocopying/Printing, Ref serv available
Partic in Docline; National Network of Libraries of Medicine
Open Mon-Fri 8:30-5
Restriction: Hospital employees & physicians only, Non-circulating to the pub

J FORREST COLLEGE LIBRARY, 601 E River St, 29624. Tel: 864-225-7653. FAX: 864-261-7471. Web Site: www.forrestcollege.edu. *Librn,* Darlene Harrington McKay; E-mail: darlenemckay@forrestcollege.edu
Founded 1946. Highest Degree: Associate
Library Holdings: AV Mats 1,082; Bk Vols 2,826; Per Subs 20
Database Vendor: Bowker, CredoReference, ebrary, EBSCOhost, Gale Cengage Learning, ProQuest
Wireless access
Partic in Library & Information Resources Network (LIRN)
Open Mon-Thurs 8am-9pm, Fri 8-5:30

BEAUFORT

P BEAUFORT COUNTY LIBRARY*, 311 Scott St, 29902. (Mail add: 311 Scott Street, 29902). Administration Tel: 843-255-6465. Administration FAX: 843-255-9508. Web Site: www.beaufortcountylibrary.org. *Libr Dir,*

Wlodek Zaryczny; Tel: 843-255-6471, E-mail: wzaryczny@bcgov.net; *Asst Dir,* Jan O'Rourke; Tel: 843-255-6464, E-mail: jorourke@bcgov.net; *Coll Develop,* Kathy Mitchell; Tel: 843-255-6462, E-mail: kathym@bcgov.net; *Mkt & Develop,* Sandra Saad; Tel: 843-255-6467, E-mail: ssaad@bcgov.net; *Syst Spec,* Stuart Forrest; Tel: 843-255-6450, E-mail: sforrest@bcgov.net
Automation Activity & Vendor Info: (Acquisitions) Evergreen
Wireless access
Branches: 5
BEAUFORT BRANCH LIBRARY, 311 Scott St, 29902-5591, SAN 359-9825. Tel: 843-255-6456. Interlibrary Loan Service Tel: 843-255-6466. Reference Tel: 843-255-6458. Administration Tel: 843-255-6443. FAX: 843-255-9426. Interlibrary Loan Service FAX: 843-255-9507. E-mail: refdesk@bcgov.net. *Br Mgr,* Fran Hays; E-mail: fhays@bcgov.net; Staff 10 (MLS 5, Non-MLS 5)
Subject Interests: Local hist
Automation Activity & Vendor Info: (Cataloging) Evergreen; (Circulation) Evergreen; (OPAC) Evergreen
Partic in Lowcounty Libr Fedn; South Carolina Library Network
Friends of the Library Group
BLUFFTON BRANCH LIBRARY, 120 Palmetto Way, Bluffton, 29910, SAN 322-581X. Tel: 843-255-6490. FAX: 843-255-9509. *Br Mgr,* Ann G Rosen; Tel: 843-255-6506, E-mail: annr@bcgov.net; Staff 6 (MLS 4, Non-MLS 2)
Open Mon & Wed 11-8, Tues 11-6, Thurs 1-6, Fri 1-5, Sat 11-5
Friends of the Library Group
HILTON HEAD ISLAND BRANCH, 11 Beach City Rd, Hilton Head Island, 29926, SAN 359-985X. Tel: 843-255-6500. Reference Tel: 843-255-6525. FAX: 843-255-9495. *Br Mgr,* Mary Jo Berkes; E-mail: maryjob@bcgov.net; Staff 12 (MLS 4, Non-MLS 8)
Function: Art exhibits
Open Mon & Wed 10-5, Tues & Thurs 1-8, Fri 1-5, Sat 9-5
Friends of the Library Group
LOBECO BRANCH, 1862 Trask Pkwy, Lobeco, 29931. (Mail add: PO Box 690, Lobeco, 29931-0690), SAN 375-5177. Tel: 843-255-6475. FAX: 843-255-9483. *Br Mgr,* Gina Molter; E-mail: gmolter@bcgov.net; Staff 3 (MLS 1, Non-MLS 2)
Founded 2003
Partic in South Carolina Library Network
Open Mon-Thurs 11-6, Fri & Sat 11-5
Friends of the Library Group
SAINT HELENA BRANCH, 1025 Sea Island Pkwy, Saint Helena Island, 29920. (Mail add: PO Box 339, St Helena Island, 29920), SAN 375-5185. Tel: 843-255-6486. *Br Mgr,* Maria J Benac; E-mail: mbenac@bcgov.net; *Circ Asst,* Carmen Bultron-Griffith; E-mail: carmeng@bcgov.net; *Programmer,* Vera Bradley; E-mail: verab@bcgov.net; Staff 1 (MLS 1)
Function: After school storytime, Bks on CD, Computers for patron use, Electronic databases & coll, Family literacy, ILL available, Music CDs, Outreach serv, Photocopying/Printing, Prog for adults, Prog for children & young adult, Ref serv available, Web-catalog
Open Mon-Thurs 4-8, Sat 9-3:30
Friends of the Library Group

J TECHNICAL COLLEGE OF THE LOWCOUNTRY*, Learning Resources Center, 921 Ribaut Rd, 29902-5441. SAN 320-233X. Tel: 843-525-8304. FAX: 843-525-8346. Web Site: www.tcl.edu/LRC/lrcmain.html. *Head Librn,* Cindy Halsey; E-mail: chalsey@tcl.edu; *Librn,* Sasha Bishop; E-mail: sbishop@tcl.edu; *Libr Spec,* Lauren Faucett; Staff 4 (MLS 2, Non-MLS 2)
Founded 1961. Enrl 1,750; Fac 45; Highest Degree: Associate
Jul 2005-Jun 2006. Mats Exp $63,000
Library Holdings: AV Mats 3,045; e-books 53,000; Bk Vols 23,576; Per Subs 185
Subject Interests: Health sci, Paralegal
Automation Activity & Vendor Info: (Cataloging) SirsiDynix; (Circulation) SirsiDynix; (Course Reserve) SirsiDynix; (OPAC) SirsiDynix
Wireless access
Publications: Check It Out; LRC Information Brochure
Partic in Lyrasis; OCLC Online Computer Library Center, Inc; South Carolina Information & Library Services Consortium (SCILS)
Mon-Thurs 8am-8pm, Fri 8am-11:30am

A UNITED STATES MARINE CORPS*, Air Station Library, PO Box 5018, Elrod Ave, 29906-5018. Tel: 843-228-7682. Interlibrary Loan Service Tel: 843-228-6131. FAX: 843-228-7596. *Librn, Media Spec,* Rose Marie Krauss; E-mail: kraussrm@usmc-mccs.org; Staff 5 (Non-MLS 5)
Founded 1957
Library Holdings: Bk Titles 24,000; Per Subs 90
Special Collections: Children's Stories, Fairytales, Classics; College Textbook; General Fiction & Non-fiction Coll
Subject Interests: City hist, Hist of aircraft, Maintenance of aircraft, Mil art, Mil sci

Wireless access
Open Mon-Fri 9-8, Sat & Sun 12-6

AM   UNITED STATES NAVY*, Naval Hospital Library, One Pickney Blvd, 29902-6148. (Mail add: Commanding Offficer, Education & Training Dept, Naval Hospital, Box 6218-A, 29902-6148). Tel: 843-228-5512. FAX: 843-228-5399. E-mail: ed&trng@med.navy.mil. Web Site: nhbeaufort.med.navy.mil. *Head, Staff Educ & Training Dept,* Lora M Martin; Tel: 843-228-5513, E-mail: lora.martin@med.navy.mil. Subject Specialists: *Med, Nursing educ,* Lora M Martin
Library Holdings: Bk Vols 3,400; Per Subs 15
Subject Interests: Med, Patient educ
Wireless access
Partic in SC Health Info Network

BENNETTSVILLE

P   MARLBORO COUNTY LIBRARY*, 200 John Corry Rd, 29512. SAN 315-4920. Tel: 843-479-5630. FAX: 843-479-5645. E-mail: marlbcolibrary@yahoo.com. Web Site: marlborocountylibrary.org. *Dir,* Sharon Clontz Rowe; *Ch,* Tammy Perkins; *ILL,* Melissa Skipper; *Outreach Serv Librn,* Debra McLaughlin; *Pub Serv,* Cathy Pearson; *Tech Serv,* Bobbie Coxe; Staff 1 (MLS 1)
Founded 1901. Pop 28,147; Circ 47,712
Library Holdings: AV Mats 2,900; Bk Vols 54,307; Per Subs 88
Automation Activity & Vendor Info: (Cataloging) Polaris Library Systems; (Circulation) Polaris Library Systems; (OPAC) Polaris Library Systems
Database Vendor: Polaris Library Systems
Function: ILL available, Photocopying/Printing, Prog for children & young adult, Summer reading prog
Open Mon-Wed 9-6, Thurs & Fri 9-5, Sat 9-1
Bookmobiles: 1

BISHOPVILLE

P   LEE COUNTY PUBLIC LIBRARY*, 200 N Main St, 29010. SAN 315-4939. Tel: 803-484-5921. FAX: 803-484-4177. *Dir,* Dawn Ellen; *Asst Librn,* Melissa Kirven
Founded 1953. Pop 18,929; Circ 40,102
Library Holdings: Bk Vols 30,626; Per Subs 132
Automation Activity & Vendor Info: (Cataloging) TLC (The Library Corporation); (Circulation) TLC (The Library Corporation); (OPAC) TLC (The Library Corporation)
Open Mon-Fri 9-6, Sat 9-3, Sun 1-5
Friends of the Library Group

BLACKSBURG

G   KINGS MOUNTAIN NATIONAL MILITARY PARK LIBRARY, 2625 Park Rd, 29702. SAN 323-7036. Tel: 864-936-7921. FAX: 864-936-9897. Web Site: www.nps.gov/kimo. *In Charge,* Chris Revels
Founded 1931
Library Holdings: Bk Titles 600

BLUFFTON

C   UNIVERSITY OF SOUTH CAROLINA AT BEAUFORT LIBRARY*, One University Blvd, 29909-6085. SAN 315-4912. Tel: 843-208-8022. Interlibrary Loan Service Tel: 843-208-8160. FAX: 843-208-8296. Web Site: www.sc.edu/beaufort/library/. *Distinguished Univ Prof, Libr Dir,* Ellen E Chamberlain; E-mail: ellenc@sc.edu; *Asst Dir, Main Libr,* Melanie Hanes-Ramos; Tel: 843-208-8023, E-mail: hanesml@gwm.sc.edu; *Asst Dir, Br Serv,* Geni Flowers; Tel: 843-521-4122, E-mail: flowers@sc.edu; *Asst Librn, ILL,* Dudley Stutz; Tel: 843-208-8160, E-mail: ddstutz@gwm.sc.edu; *Ref & Info Serv, Web Coordr,* Mae Mendoza; Tel: 843-208-8024; *Circ, Ref,* Mae Mendoza; Tel: 843-521-4126, E-mail: mfmendoz@gwm.sc.edu; Staff 6 (MLS 5, Non-MLS 1)
Founded 1959. Enrl 1,500
Library Holdings: e-books 25,299; Bk Vols 71,178; Per Subs 141
Special Collections: State Document Depository
Subject Interests: SC hist
Automation Activity & Vendor Info: (Acquisitions) Innovative Interfaces, Inc; (Cataloging) Innovative Interfaces, Inc; (Circulation) Innovative Interfaces, Inc; (ILL) Innovative Interfaces, Inc; (OPAC) Innovative Interfaces, Inc
Database Vendor: ABC-CLIO, Agricola, Alexander Street Press, American Chemical Society, BioOne, Cambridge Scientific Abstracts, EBSCO Information Services, Elsevier, Gale Cengage Learning, Grolier Online, H W Wilson, ISI Web of Knowledge, JSTOR, LexisNexis, Nature Publishing Group, Oxford Online, ScienceDirect, TDNet, Wilson - Wilson Web, YBP Library Services
Wireless access
Partic in Lyrasis; OCLC Online Computer Library Center, Inc

CAMDEN

S   CAMDEN ARCHIVES & MUSEUM LIBRARY, 1314 Broad St, 29020-3535. SAN 329-8582. Tel: 803-425-6050. FAX: 803-424-4021. Web Site: www.camdenarchives.org. *Dir,* Howard Branham; Staff 2 (Non-MLS 2)
Founded 1975
Library Holdings: Bk Vols 5,100
Special Collections: South Carolina DAR Library; South Carolina Society Colonial Dames, XVII Century
Subject Interests: Genealogy
Wireless access
Open Mon-Fri 8-5, Sat 10-4
Restriction: In-house use for visitors, Non-circulating to the pub
Friends of the Library Group

P   KERSHAW COUNTY LIBRARY*, Camden Branch, 1304 Broad St, 29020-3595. (Mail add: 632 W DeKalb St, Ste 109, 29020-4254), SAN 359-9914. Tel: 803-425-1508. Administration Tel: 803-424-2352. FAX: 803-425-7180. Administration FAX: 803-424-2046. Web Site: www.kershawcountylibrary.org. *Dir,* Amy Schofield; E-mail: amys@kershawcountylibrary.org; *Br Mgr,* Liz Campbell; E-mail: lizc@kershawcountylibrary.org; *Adult Serv, Ref Librn,* Cristi W Bade; E-mail: cristib@kershawcountylibrary.org; *Pub Serv Mgr,* Steve Parrott; E-mail: stevep@kershawcountylibrary.org; *Syst Mgr,* Erica Peake; E-mail: ericap@kershawcountylibrary.org; *Tech Serv Mgr,* Beatrice Fields; E-mail: beaf@kershawcountylibrary.org; *Ch,* Lauren Decker; E-mail: laurend@kershawcountylibrary.org; Staff 21 (MLS 4, Non-MLS 17)
Founded 1936. Pop 52,647; Circ 108,928
Jul 2005-Jun 2006 Income (Main Library and Branch(s)) $804,608, State $105,294, Federal $38,072, County $628,340, Locally Generated Income $32,902. Mats Exp $169,497, Books $113,300, Per/Ser (Incl. Access Fees) $12,000, AV Mat $17,654, Electronic Ref Mat (Incl. Access Fees) $26,543. Sal $505,700 (Prof $155,000)
Library Holdings: CDs 326; DVDs 300; Large Print Bks 4,280; Bk Titles 73,632; Bk Vols 87,995; Per Subs 190; Talking Bks 1,804; Videos 1,990
Subject Interests: SC
Automation Activity & Vendor Info: (Cataloging) SirsiDynix; (Circulation) SirsiDynix; (OPAC) SirsiDynix
Database Vendor: Baker & Taylor, Booklist Online, BWI, College Source, EBSCOhost, Electric Library, Gale Cengage Learning, Grolier Online, Ingram Library Services, LearningExpress, netLibrary, Newsbank, OCLC WorldCat, ProQuest, ReferenceUSA, SirsiDynix, Sybase
Wireless access
Function: Adult bk club, Adult literacy prog, After school storytime, Bi-weekly Writer's Group, Bks on cassette, Bks on CD, Children's prog, Computers for patron use, Copy machines, e-mail serv, E-Reserves, Electronic databases & coll, Handicapped accessible, Home delivery & serv to Sr ctr & nursing homes, ILL available, Mail & tel request accepted, Online searches, Orientations, Prog for adults, Prog for children & young adult, Senior computer classes, Summer reading prog, Tax forms, VHS videos, Wheelchair accessible
Open Tues-Thurs 9-8, Fri & Sat 9-6, Sun 2-5
Restriction: Off-site coll in storage - retrieval as requested
Friends of the Library Group
Branches: 2
BETHUNE PUBLIC, 206 S Main St, Bethune, 29009. (Mail add: PO Box 446, Bethune, 29009-0446), SAN 359-9949. Tel: 843-334-8420. FAX: 843-334-6981. *Outreach Librn,* Jennifer Kelley; Staff 1 (MLS 1)
   Circ 5,091
   Library Holdings: Large Print Bks 382; Bk Titles 6,784; Bk Vols 6,801; Talking Bks 63; Videos 56
   Automation Activity & Vendor Info: (Circulation) SirsiDynix; (OPAC) SirsiDynix
   Database Vendor: Booklist Online, College Source, EBSCOhost, Electric Library, Gale Cengage Learning, Newsbank, ReferenceUSA
   Function: Bks on cassette, Bks on CD, Children's prog, Computers for patron use, Copy machines, Fax serv, ILL available, Online searches, Summer reading prog, Tax forms, VHS videos
   Open Tues & Thurs 10-7, Sat 10-2
ELGIN BRANCH, 2652 Main St, Elgin, 29045. (Mail add: PO Box 725, Elgin, 29045-0725). Tel: 803-438-7881. FAX: 803-438-4428. *Br Librn,* James Steve Parrott; E-mail: stevep@kershawcountylibrary.org; Staff 3 (MLS 1, Non-MLS 2)
   Founded 1999. Circ 34,150
   Library Holdings: CDs 48; Bk Titles 15,087; Bk Vols 15,329; Per Subs 25; Talking Bks 507; Videos 370
   Automation Activity & Vendor Info: (Cataloging) SirsiDynix; (Circulation) SirsiDynix; (OPAC) SirsiDynix
   Database Vendor: Booklist Online, College Source, EBSCOhost, Electric Library, Gale Cengage Learning, Grolier Online, infoUSA, LearningExpress, netLibrary, OCLC WorldCat, ProQuest, ReferenceUSA
   Function: Accelerated reader prog, Bks on cassette, Bks on CD, Children's prog, Computers for patron use, Copy machines, Electronic

databases & coll, Handicapped accessible, ILL available, Tax forms, VHS videos
Open Mon-Thurs 10-7, Fri & Sat 10-6
Bookmobiles: 1

CENTRAL

C   SOUTHERN WESLEYAN UNIVERSITY*, Claude R Rickman Library, 916 Wesleyan Dr, 29630-9748. (Mail add: PO Box 1020, 907 Wesleyan Dr, 29630-1020), SAN 315-4971. Tel: 864-644-5060. FAX: 864-644-5904. E-mail: library@swu.edu. Web Site: www.swu.edu/library. *Dir, Libr Serv,* Robert E Sears; Tel: 864-644-5064, E-mail: rsears@swu.edu; Staff 6 (MLS 3, Non-MLS 3)
Founded 1906. Enrl 2,400; Highest Degree: Master
Library Holdings: Bk Vols 106,000; Per Subs 515
Special Collections: Genealogical Coll (Upstate South Carolina Families); Wesleyan Historical Coll

CHARLESTON

P   CHARLESTON COUNTY PUBLIC LIBRARY, 68 Calhoun St, 29401. SAN 359-9973. Tel: 843-805-6801. Circulation Tel: 843-805-6833. Interlibrary Loan Service Tel: 843-805-6940. Reference Tel: 843-805-6930. Administration Tel: 843-805-6807. Reference FAX: 843-727-6752. Administration FAX: 843-727-3741. Web Site: www.ccpl.org. *Dir,* Douglas Henderson; E-mail: hendersond@ccpl.org; *Dep Dir,* Cynthia Bledsoe; E-mail: bledsoec@ccpl.org; *Head of Libr,* Darlene Jackson; Tel: 843-805-6808, E-mail: jacksond@ccpl.org; *Acq Mgr, Coll Mgr,* Rodger Smith; Tel: 843-805-6866, E-mail: smithr@ccpl.org; *Info Tech Coordr, Syst Coordr,* Craig Williams; Tel: 843-805-6850, E-mail: williamsc@ccpl.org; *Coordr, Outreach Serv,* Jim Letendre; Tel: 843-805-6883, E-mail: letendrej@ccpl.org; *Ch,* Pam Cadden; Tel: 843-805-6902, E-mail: caddenp@ccpl.org; Staff 70 (MLS 70)
Founded 1930. Pop 330,368; Circ 3,131,596
Jul 2011-Jun 2012 Income (Main Library and Branch(s)) $27,215,432, State $299,716, Federal $21,351, County $12,520,899, Other $14,373,466. Mats Exp $2,023,544, Books $1,334,482, Other Print Mats $13,861, AV Mat $489,745, Electronic Ref Mat (Incl. Access Fees) $185,456. Sal $10,180,013
Library Holdings: Audiobooks 40,154; AV Mats 137,734; Bk Vols 1,026,773; Per Subs 1,410
Subject Interests: Ethnic studies, Local hist
Automation Activity & Vendor Info: (Circulation) SirsiDynix
Wireless access
Publications: Staff Connections (Newsletter)
Partic in Coastnet; Lyrasis
Special Services for the Deaf - Staff with knowledge of sign lang; TTY equip
Open Mon-Thurs 9-8, Fri & Sat 9-6, Sun 2-5
Restriction: Non-resident fee
Friends of the Library Group
Branches: 15
COOPER RIVER MEMORIAL, 3503 Rivers Ave, Charleston Heights, 29405, SAN 360-0009. Tel: 843-744-2489. FAX: 843-747-6904. *Br Mgr,* Sherman Pyatt; Tel: 843-572-4094, E-mail: pyatts@ccpl.org
Open Mon-Thurs 10-8, Fri & Sat 10-6
JOHN L DART BRANCH, 1067 King St, 29403, SAN 360-0068. Tel: 843-722-7550. FAX: 843-727-6784. *Br Mgr,* Cheryl Brinkley; E-mail: brinkleyc@ccpl.org
Open Mon-Sat 10-6
DORCHESTER ROAD REGIONAL, 6325 Dorchester Rd, North Charleston, 29418, SAN 370-9140. Tel: 843-552-6466. FAX: 843-552-6775. *Br Head,* Gerald Moore; E-mail: mooreg@ccpl.org
Open Mon-Thurs 10-8, Fri & Sat 10-6
EDISTO BRANCH, Thomas Hall, Hwy 174, Edisto Island, 29438, SAN 360-0017. Tel: 843-869-2355. FAX: 843-869-2355. *Br Head,* Marilyn Bowman
Open Tues & Thurs 1-5, Sat 10-2
FOLLY BEACH BRANCH, 45 Center St, Folly Beach, 29439, SAN 360-0025. Tel: 843-588-2001. *Br Head,* Dot Osborne
Open Mon & Fri 10-6, Wed 12-8
JAMES ISLAND, 1248 Camp Rd, 29412, SAN 360-0033. Tel: 843-795-6679. *Br Mgr,* Position Currently Open
Open Mon-Thurs 10-8, Fri & Sat 10-6
JOHN'S ISLAND REGIONAL, 3531 Maybank Hwy, John's Island, 29455. Tel: 843-557-1945. FAX: 843-557-0080. *Br Mgr,* Jim McQueen; E-mail: mcqueenj@ccpl.org
Open Mon-Thurs 10-8, Fri & Sat 10-6
MCCLELLANVILLE BRANCH, 222 Baker St, McClellanville, 29458, SAN 360-0041. Tel: 843-887-3699. FAX: 843-887-3144. *In Charge,* Pat Gross; E-mail: grossp@ccpl.org
Open Mon & Thurs 2-6, Tues & Fri 9:30-1 & 2-6, Sat 9:30-2

MOUNT PLEASANT REGIONAL, 1133 Mathis Ferry Rd, Mount Pleasant, 29464, SAN 360-005X. Tel: 843-849-6161. FAX: 843-849-6166. *Br Mgr,* Cindy Schweinfest
Open Mon-Thurs 10-8, Fri & Sat 10-6
OTRANTO ROAD REGIONAL, 2261 Otranto Rd, North Charleston, 29406, SAN 370-9159. Tel: 843-572-4094. FAX: 843-572-4190. *Br Mgr,* Deborah Harris; E-mail: harrisd@ccpl.org
Open Mon-Thurs 10-8, Fri & Sat 10-6
EDGAR ALLAN POE BRANCH, 1921 I'On St, Sullivan's Island, 29482, SAN 360-0076. Tel: 843-883-3914. *Br Head,* Jessica Austin-Scaff
Open Mon & Fri 2-6, Tues, Thurs & Sat 10-2
SAINT ANDREWS REGIONAL, 1735 N Woodmere Dr, 29407, SAN 370-9167. Tel: 843-766-2546. FAX: 843-766-2762. *Br Mgr,* Cynthia Hurd; E-mail: hurdc@ccpl.org
Open Mon-Thurs 10-8, Fri & Sat 10-6
SAINT PAUL'S BRANCH, 5153 Hwy 165, Hollywood, 29449. (Mail add: PO Box 549, Hollywood, 29449), SAN 360-0084. Tel: 843-889-3300. FAX: 843-889-3605. *Br Mgr,* LeeAnn Floss
Open Mon, Wed & Fri 9:30-1 & 2-6, Sat 9:30-3
VILLAGE BRANCH, 430 Whilden St, Mount Pleasant, 29464, SAN 374-5236. Tel: 843-884-9741. FAX: 843-884-5396. *In Charge,* Marvin Stewart; E-mail: stewartm@ccpl.org
Open Mon & Fri 10-6, Tues & Thurs 2-6, Sat 10-2
WEST ASHLEY, 45 Windermere Blvd, 29407, SAN 360-0092. Tel: 843-766-6635. *Br Mgr,* Beth Bell; E-mail: bellb@ccpl.org
Open Mon-Thurs 10-8, Fri & Sat 10-6
Bookmobiles: 1

S   CHARLESTON LIBRARY SOCIETY*, 164 King St, 29401. SAN 315-4998. Tel: 843-723-9912. FAX: 843-723-3500. E-mail: librarysociety@bellsouth.net. *Interim Dir,* D Carol Jones; *Asst Librn,* LeeAnn Floss; *Asst Librn,* Janice Knight; *Asst Librn,* Dedree Syracuse; Staff 4 (MLS 2, Non-MLS 2)
Founded 1748
Jan 2006-Dec 2006 Income $588,000. Mats Exp $29,600, Books $14,000, Per/Ser (Incl. Access Fees) $5,000, Micro $3,000, AV Mat $6,000. Sal $229,000
Library Holdings: CDs 40; DVDs 90; Large Print Bks 750; Bk Titles 130,000; Per Subs 90; Talking Bks 1,800; Videos 2,000
Special Collections: 18th & 19th Century Manuscripts; Agriculture & Confederacy (Hinson Coll), bks, per & clippings; Architecture (Staats Coll); Horticulture (Aiken Garden Club Coll); Newspapers from 1732 to present; Timrod Scrapbooks (Courtenay Coll), bks & photog
Subject Interests: Am Jewish hist, Charleston, Civil War, Early 20th Century fiction, Lit, Revolutionary war, SE Indians
Open Mon-Fri 9:30-5:30, Sat 9:30-2
Restriction: Mem only

S   CHARLESTON MUSEUM LIBRARY*, 360 Meeting St, 29403. SAN 315-5005. Tel: 843-722-2996, Ext 243. FAX: 843-722-1784. Web Site: www.charlestonmuseum.org. *Archivist, Librn,* Jennifer Scheetz; E-mail: jscheetz@charlestonmuseum.org; *Asst Archivist, Asst Librn,* Jennifer McCormick; Tel: 843-722-2996, Ext 244, E-mail: jmccormick@charlestonmuseum.org; Staff 1 (MLS 1)
Founded 1773
Library Holdings: Bk Vols 9,500
Special Collections: Aiken-Rhett House Coll; Heyward-Washington House Coll; Manigault House Coll; Photograph Coll; Postcard Coll; Sheet Music Coll
Subject Interests: Anthropology, Decorative art, Hist of SC low country, Natural hist
Function: Archival coll
Open Mon-Fri 9-4
Restriction: Closed stack, Limited access based on advanced application, Open to pub for ref only

C   CHARLESTON SOUTHERN UNIVERSITY*, L Mendel Rivers Library, 9200 University Blvd, 29406. (Mail add: PO Box 118087, 29423-8087), SAN 315-498X. Tel: 843-863-7938. Reference Tel: 843-863-7946. Administration Tel: 843-863-7945. FAX: 843-863-7947. Web Site: www.csuniv.edu/library/index.html. *Libr Dir,* Sandra Hammond Hughes; Tel: 843-863-7933, E-mail: shughes@csuniv.edu; *Asst Dir, Head, Circ,* Linda P Rousseau; Tel: 843-863-7941, E-mail: lrousseau@csuniv.edu; *Acq, Ser,* Monica Langley; Tel: 843-863-7911, E-mail: mlangley@csuniv.edu; *Archivist,* Enid Causey; Tel: 843-863-7940, E-mail: ecausey@csuniv.edu; *Cat,* Dianne Boykin; Tel: 843-863-7925, E-mail: dboykin@csuniv.edu; *Syst & Electronic Res,* Eileen Lutzow; Tel: 843-863-7951, E-mail: elutzow@csuniv.edu; Staff 15 (MLS 7, Non-MLS 8)
Founded 1966. Enrl 3,135; Fac 98; Highest Degree: Master
Jun 2005-May 2006 Income $932,252. Mats Exp $248,052, Books $66,453, Per/Ser (Incl. Access Fees) $74,201, AV Mat $13,552, Electronic Ref Mat (Incl. Access Fees) $93,568, Presv $278. Sal $500,134
Library Holdings: AV Mats 9,878; e-books 23,000; Bk Vols 250,000; Per Subs 412

Special Collections: South Carolina History; US Document Depository. US Document Depository
Automation Activity & Vendor Info: (Acquisitions) SirsiDynix; (Cataloging) SirsiDynix; (Circulation) SirsiDynix; (Course Reserve) SirsiDynix; (ILL) OCLC; (OPAC) SirsiDynix; (Serials) SirsiDynix
Database Vendor: American Chemical Society, Bowker, Cambridge Scientific Abstracts, CQ Press, EBSCOhost, Gale Cengage Learning, H W Wilson, JSTOR, LexisNexis, McGraw-Hill, Nature Publishing Group, OCLC FirstSearch, Oxford Online, ProQuest
Wireless access
Partic in Lyrasis
Open Mon-Thurs (Winter) 7:45am-Midnight, Fri 7:45am-5, Sat 9-5, Sun 3-Midnight; Mon-Thurs (Summer) 8am-10pm, Fri 8-5, Sat 1-5, Sun 6pm-10pm

C   THE CITADEL*, Daniel Library, 171 Moultrie St, 29409-6140. SAN 360-0122. Tel: 843-953-5116. Circulation Tel: 843-953-6845. Reference Tel: 843-953-2569. FAX: 843-953-5190. Web Site: www.citadel.edu/library. *Interim Dir, Libr Serv,* Elizabeth Connor; E-mail: elizabeth.connor@citadel.edu; *Head, Coll Mgt,* Kirstin Steele; *Tech Serv,* Judith Swartzel; Staff 19 (MLS 8, Non-MLS 11)
Founded 1842. Enrl 3,036; Fac 163; Highest Degree: Master
Library Holdings: AV Mats 6,740; e-books 650; e-journals 28,200; Bk Titles 172,195; Bk Vols 243,600; Per Subs 514
Special Collections: Citadel Publications; German Literature (Hardin Coll); Leadership Coll; World War I (Coulson Coll). US Document Depository
Subject Interests: Mil sci, SC
Automation Activity & Vendor Info: (Acquisitions) Innovative Interfaces, Inc; (Cataloging) Innovative Interfaces, Inc; (Circulation) Innovative Interfaces, Inc; (Course Reserve) Innovative Interfaces, Inc; (ILL) OCLC WorldCat; (Media Booking) Innovative Interfaces, Inc; (OPAC) Innovative Interfaces, Inc; (Serials) Innovative Interfaces, Inc
Database Vendor: EBSCOhost, Elsevier MDL, Gale Cengage Learning, IEEE (Institute of Electrical & Electronics Engineers), Jane's, JSTOR, LexisNexis, OCLC FirstSearch, ProQuest
Wireless access
Partic in Carolina Consortium; Charleston Academic Libraries Consortium; Lyrasis; Partnership Among South Carolina Academic Libraries
Friends of the Library Group

C   COLLEGE OF CHARLESTON*, Marlene & Nathan Addlestone Library, 205 Calhoun St, 29401-3519. (Mail add: 66 George St, 29424), SAN 360-0211. Tel: 843-953-5530. Circulation Tel: 843-953-8001. Reference Tel: 843-953-8000. FAX: 843-953-6319. Web Site: www.cofc.edu/~library. *Dean of Libr,* David Cohen; E-mail: cohend@cofc.edu; *Admin Dir,* Claire Fund; E-mail: fundc@cofc.edu; *Spec Coll Librn,* Marie Ferrara; E-mail: ferrarae@cofc.edu; *Cat,* Martha Stackel; E-mail: stackelm@cofc.edu; *Coll Develop,* Katina Strauch; E-mail: strauchk@cofc.edu; *ILL,* Michael Phillips; E-mail: phillipsm@cofc.edu; *Pub Serv,* Sheila Seaman; E-mail: seamans@cofc.edu; *Ref,* Tom Gilson; E-mail: gilsont@cofc.edu; *Tech Serv,* Robert Neville; E-mail: neviller@cofc.edu; Staff 43 (MLS 19, Non-MLS 24)
Founded 1785. Enrl 11,332; Fac 858; Highest Degree: Master
Jul 2005-Jun 2006 Income $4,841,119. Mats Exp $1,985,457, Books $738,410, Per/Ser (Incl. Access Fees) $1,219,775, Presv $27,272. Sal $1,968,224
Library Holdings: AV Mats 7,020; e-books 68,063; Bk Vols 599,345; Per Subs 4,429
Special Collections: Book Arts; College of Charleston Archives; Jewish Heritage Coll; John Henry Dick Ornithology Coll; South Carolina, books & per. Oral History; State Document Depository; US Document Depository
Subject Interests: Behav sci, Marine sci, Natural sci, Soc sci
Automation Activity & Vendor Info: (Acquisitions) Innovative Interfaces, Inc; (Cataloging) Innovative Interfaces, Inc; (Circulation) Innovative Interfaces, Inc; (Course Reserve) Innovative Interfaces, Inc; (ILL) OCLC ILLiad; (OPAC) Innovative Interfaces, Inc; (Serials) Innovative Interfaces, Inc
Database Vendor: EBSCOhost, Gale Cengage Learning, LexisNexis, OCLC FirstSearch, OVID Technologies
Publications: A Catalog of the Scientific Apparatus at the College of Charleston: 1800-1940; A History of the College of Charleston (1935); Introduction to Bibliography & Research Methods; Mendel; No Problems, Only Challenges: The Autobiography of Theodore S Stern; Proceedings of Southeastern Conferences on Bibliographic Instruction; St Michaels, Charleston 1751-1951 with Supplements 1951-2001; Tales of Charleston, 1930s
Partic in Lyrasis; Partnership Among South Carolina Academic Libraries
Friends of the Library Group
Departmental Libraries:
MARINE RESOURCES, 217 Fort Johnson Rd, Bldg 8, 29412. (Mail add: PO Box 12559, 29422-2559), SAN 360-0246. Tel: 843-953-9370. Interlibrary Loan Service Tel: 843-953-9373. FAX: 843-953-9371. E-mail: mrlcirc@cofc.edu. Web Site: www.mrl.cofc.edu. *Librn II,* Helen Anita Ivy; E-mail: ivyh@cofc.edu; Staff 1 (MLS 1)

Founded 1977
Special Collections: State Document Depository; US Document Depository
Subject Interests: Marine biol, Marine ecology, Marine genomics, Oceanography, Zoology
Database Vendor: ProQuest, ScienceDirect, Springer-Verlag, Thomson - Web of Science, Wiley InterScience
Function: Computers for patron use, Copy machines, E-Reserves, Electronic databases & coll, ILL available, Online cat, Photocopying/Printing, Ref serv available, Web-catalog, Wheelchair accessible
Open Mon-Fri 8:30-5
Restriction: Badge access after hrs, Borrowing privileges limited to fac & registered students, Limited access for the pub, Open to fac, students & qualified researchers

GM DEPARTMENT OF VETERANS AFFAIRS*, Medical Center Library, 109 Bee St, 29401-5799. SAN 315-5072. Tel: 843-789-7274, 843-789-7494. FAX: 843-805-5975. E-mail: charlestonlibrary@va.gov. *Librn,* Margaret Fulsom; E-mail: margaret.fulsom@va.gov; Staff 1 (MLS 1)
Founded 1966
Library Holdings: AV Mats 338; Bk Vols 734; Per Subs 189
Automation Activity & Vendor Info: (Cataloging) CyberTools for Libraries; (Circulation) CyberTools for Libraries; (OPAC) CyberTools for Libraries; (Serials) CyberTools for Libraries
Database Vendor: EBSCOhost, Elsevier, Gale Cengage Learning, McGraw-Hill, Micromedex, OVID Technologies, ProQuest, PubMed, UpToDate
Function: ILL available
Partic in SEND
Open Mon-Fri 8-4:30
Restriction: Circ limited, Circulates for staff only, Non-circulating to the pub, Prof mat only

S   EVENING POST PUBLISHING CO*, Post-Courier Library, 134 Columbus St, 29403. SAN 315-503X. Tel: 843-937-5698. FAX: 843-937-5696. Web Site: www.charleston.net/aboutlibrary.html. *Chief Librn,* Olivia Wallace; *Librn,* Pam Liles; *Librn,* Lathornia Perry
Library Holdings: Bk Vols 3,100; Per Subs 87
Subject Interests: Newsp clipping files, Newsp photogs

S   HUGUENOT SOCIETY OF SOUTH CAROLINA LIBRARY*, 138 Logan St, 29401. SAN 327-0858. Tel: 843-723-3235. FAX: 843-853-8476. E-mail: archivist@huguenotsociety.org. Web Site: www.huguenotsociety.org. *Archivist,* Harriott Cheves Leland
Founded 1885
Library Holdings: Bk Vols 5,000
Publications: Transactions of the Huguenot Society of South Carolina
Open Mon-Fri 9-2
Restriction: Non-circulating

G   MARINE RESOURCES LIBRARY*, 217 Ft Johnson Rd, 29412. (Mail add: PO Box 12559, 29422-2559), SAN 315-5021. Tel: 843-953-9370. FAX: 843-953-9371. Web Site: mrl.cofc.edu. *Librn,* Helen A Ivy; E-mail: ivyh@cofc.edu; Staff 4 (MLS 1, Non-MLS 3)
Library Holdings: Bk Vols 9,000; Per Subs 40
Subject Interests: Marine sci
Database Vendor: Dialog, SirsiDynix
Function: For res purposes
Partic in OCLC-LVIS
Open Mon-Fri 8:30-5

M   MEDICAL UNIVERSITY OF SOUTH CAROLINA LIBRARY*, 171 Ashley Ave, Ste 300, 29425-0001. (Mail add: PO Box 250403, 29425-0403), SAN 360-0270. Tel: 843-792-9211. Circulation Tel: 843-792-2371. Reference Tel: 843-792-2372. FAX: 843-792-7947. Web Site: www.library.musc.edu. *Dir,* Thomas G Basler; E-mail: basler@musc.edu; *Dir of Outreach, Dir, Pub Serv,* David Rivers; *Asst Dir, Pub Serv, Educ Serv,* Bob Poyer; *Asst Dir, Prog & Serv Develop,* Laura Cousineau; *Asst Dir, Res Mgt Serv,* Randall Watts; *Asst Dir, Syst,* Nancy C McKeehan; *Ref Librn,* Teri Lynn Herbert; *Ref Librn,* Candace Moorer; *Archivist,* Jennifer Welch; *Admin Coordr,* Maria Merritt; *Info Res Coordr,* Tara Hayes; *Pub Info Coordr,* Latecia Abraham; *Prog Coordr,* Missy Anderson; *Univ Archivist,* Brooke Fox. Subject Specialists: *Chem,* Teri Lynn Herbert; Staff 55 (MLS 18, Non-MLS 37)
Founded 1824. Enrl 2,366; Fac 986; Highest Degree: Doctorate
Library Holdings: e-books 737; e-journals 15,600; Bk Titles 74,656; Bk Vols 209,293
Special Collections: History of Medicine (Waring Historical Library Coll), bks, mss, oral history, photog; Micro-Circulation (Melvin M Knisely Coll), bks & mss
Subject Interests: Allied health, Behav sci, Consumer health, Dentistry, Environ sci, Med, Natural sci, Nursing, Pharmacology, Soc sci

Automation Activity & Vendor Info: (Acquisitions) Innovative Interfaces, Inc; (Cataloging) Innovative Interfaces, Inc; (Circulation) Innovative Interfaces, Inc; (Course Reserve) Innovative Interfaces, Inc; (Media Booking) Innovative Interfaces, Inc; (OPAC) Innovative Interfaces, Inc; (Serials) Innovative Interfaces, Inc
Database Vendor: Dialog, Gale Cengage Learning, Innovative Interfaces, Inc INN - View, OCLC FirstSearch, OVID Technologies
Publications: MUSCLS
Partic in Charleston Academic Libraries Consortium; Consortium of Southern Biomedical Libraries; National Network of Libraries of Medicine South Central Region; Partnership Among South Carolina Academic Libraries
Departmental Libraries:
WARING HISTORICAL LIBRARY, 175 Ashley Ave, 29425-0001. (Mail add: PO Box 250403, 29425-0403). Tel: 843-792-2288. FAX: 843-792-8619. *Curator,* Susan Hoffius; *Asst Curator,* Kay Carter; *Archivist,* E Brooke Fox; *Digital Archivist,* Jennifer M Welch
    Special Collections: Archives. Oral History
    Subject Interests: Hist of med
    Publications: Waring Library Society (Newsletter)
    Open Mon-Fri 8:30-5
    Friends of the Library Group

S   SOUTH CAROLINA HISTORICAL SOCIETY LIBRARY*, Fireproof Bldg, 100 Meeting St, 29401-2299. SAN 315-5056. Tel: 843-723-3225. FAX: 843-723-8584. E-mail: info@schistory.org. Web Site: www.southcarolinahistoricalsociety.org. *Exec Dir,* Faye Jensen; Tel: 843-723-3225, Ext 10; *Librn,* Lisa Hayes; Tel: 843-723-3225, Ext 12; *Archivist,* Jane Aldrich; Tel: 843-723-3225, Ext 21; Staff 2 (MLS 2)
Founded 1855
Library Holdings: Bk Vols 30,000
Special Collections: Civil War (R Lockwood Tower Coll); Manuscript Coll, includes family, business & organization papers
Subject Interests: Genealogy, Local hist, State hist
Automation Activity & Vendor Info: (OPAC) EOS International
Wireless access
Function: Res libr
Publications: Carologue; South Carolina Historical Magazine; South Carolina Historical Society Manuscript Guide
Open Mon & Wed-Fri 9-4, Tues 9-7:30, Sat 9-2
Restriction: Non-circulating

TRIDENT TECHNICAL COLLEGE
J   BERKELEY CAMPUS LEARNING RESOURCES*, LR-B, PO Box 118067, 29423-8067, SAN 324-797X. Tel: 843-899-8055. FAX: 843-899-8100. Web Site: www.tridenttech.edu/library. *Dean of Libr,* Charnette Singleton; Tel: 843-574-6088, E-mail: charnette.singleton@tridenttech.edu
Founded 1982
    Library Holdings: Bk Titles 4,025; Bk Vols 4,871; Per Subs 67
    Subject Interests: Aircraft maintenance, Cosmetology, Veterinary tech
    Publications: Annual Report
J   MAIN CAMPUS LEARNING RESOURCES CENTER*, LR-M, PO Box 118067, 29423-8067, SAN 360-036X. Tel: 843-574-6089. Interlibrary Loan Service Tel: 843-574-6316. FAX: 843-574-6484. Web Site: www.tridenttech.edu/library. *Dean of Libr,* Charnette Singleton; Tel: 843-574-6087, E-mail: charnette.singleton@tridenttech.edu; *Ref & Coll Develop Librn,* Diane Lohr; E-mail: diane.lohr@tridenttech.edu; *Cat, Circ, Ser,* Patricia Vierthaler; E-mail: patricia.vierthaler@tridenttech.edu; *Circ & ILL,* Itaski Jenkins; *Syst,* Laura Barfield; Staff 15 (MLS 8, Non-MLS 7)
Founded 1964
    Library Holdings: Bk Titles 85,000; Per Subs 175
    Special Collections: Electronics (Sam Photofact Coll)
    Publications: Annual Report
J   PALMER CAMPUS LEARNING RESOURCES CENTER*, LR-P, PO Box 118067, 29423-8067, SAN 360-0335. Tel: 843-722-5540. FAX: 843-720-5614. Web Site: www.tridenttech.edu/library. *Librn,* Erlene Payne; Tel: 843-722-5539, E-mail: erlene.payne@tridenttech.edu; Staff 3 (MLS 1, Non-MLS 2)
Founded 1955. Enrl 1,800
    Library Holdings: Bk Titles 20,492; Bk Vols 24,471; Per Subs 101
    Subject Interests: Archives, Law
    Publications: Annual Report

UNITED STATES NAVY
A   NAVAL CONSOLIDATED BRIG LIBRARY*, Bldg 3107, 1050 Remount Rd, 29406-3515, SAN 360-0459. Tel: 843-743-0306, Ext 3059. FAX: 843-743-0339, 843-743-0364. *Supv Librn,* Michael R Rucker; E-mail: michaelrucker@navy.mil; *Librn & TOC/Instr,* Sylvia Gilliard; E-mail: sylviagilliard@navy.mil
    Library Holdings: Bk Vols 3,600; Per Subs 41

A   NAVAL WEAPONS STATIONS, (WPNSTA) CHASN LIBRARY*, Bldg 732, 2316 Red Bank Rd, Goose Creek, 29445-8601, SAN 360-0513. Tel: 843-764-7900. FAX: 843-764-4054. Web Site: www.nwschs.navy.mil. *Librn,* Vivian Skipworth; E-mail: vivian.skipworth@navy.mil
Founded 1966
Library Holdings: Bk Vols 27,000
Special Collections: Books on Cassette; CD-ROM: Help Wanted USA Classified Ads, microfiche; Educational & Children's Videos; Large Print Coll
Subject Interests: Self develop, Soc issues
Open Tues-Sat 10-5

CHARLESTON AFB

A   UNITED STATES AIR FORCE*, Charleston Air Force Base Library FL4418, 437 SVS/SVMG, 106 W McCaw St, Bldg 215, 29404-4700. SAN 360-0548. Tel: 843-963-3320. FAX: 843-963-3840. *Dir,* Angela Aschenbrenner; *Prog Coordr,* Brittany Page; *Cat,* Carmen Alonso; *Circ Serv,* Angela Bevins; *Tech Serv,* Martha Wiggins; Staff 5 (MLS 1, Non-MLS 4)
Founded 1953
Library Holdings: Bk Vols 32,000; Per Subs 174
Subject Interests: Mil hist, Total quality mgt
Automation Activity & Vendor Info: (Acquisitions) SirsiDynix; (Cataloging) SirsiDynix; (Circulation) SirsiDynix; (ILL) OCLC Online; (OPAC) SirsiDynix
Wireless access
Partic in Lyrasis
Open Mon-Thurs 9-8, Sat 10-5, Sun 1-5

CHERAW

J   NORTHEASTERN TECHNICAL COLLEGE LIBRARY*, 1201 Chesterfield Hwy, 29520-7015. (Mail add: PO Box 1007, 29520-1007), SAN 315-5099. Tel: 843-921-6954. Toll Free Tel: 800-921-6900. FAX: 843-537-6148. Web Site: www.netc.edu/Library.html. *Head Librn,* Esther Brunson; E-mail: eebrunson@netc.edu; *Dean, Instruction Support Serv,* Perry Johnson; Tel: 843-921-6955, Fax: 843-921-6987, E-mail: pjohnson@netc.edu. Subject Specialists: *Acad, Tech,* Esther Brunson; *Admin,* Perry Johnson; Staff 2.4 (MLS 1, Non-MLS 1.4)
Founded 1968. Enrl 631; Fac 30; Highest Degree: Associate
Library Holdings: Audiobooks 48; AV Mats 1,586; Bks on Deafness & Sign Lang 22; CDs 200; DVDs 572; e-books 60,000; Music Scores 1; Bk Titles 26,867; Per Subs 61
Automation Activity & Vendor Info: (Acquisitions) SirsiDynix; (Cataloging) OCLC Connexion; (Circulation) SirsiDynix; (Course Reserve) SirsiDynix; (ILL) OCLC FirstSearch; (OPAC) SirsiDynix; (Serials) SirsiDynix
Database Vendor: EBSCOhost, Facts on File, Gale Cengage Learning, Grolier Online, ProQuest
Wireless access
Function: Audiobks via web, Bks on cassette, Bks on CD, Computers for patron use, Copy machines, e-mail serv, Electronic databases & coll, Free DVD rentals, Handicapped accessible, ILL available, Music CDs, Online cat, Online searches, Orientations, Outside serv via phone, mail, e-mail & web, Photocopying/Printing, Prof lending libr, Pub access computers, Ref & res, Ref serv available, Ref serv in person, Tax forms, Telephone ref, VHS videos, Web-catalog
Partic in Partnership Among South Carolina Academic Libraries; South Carolina Information & Library Services Consortium (SCILS)
Special Services for the Deaf - Bks on deafness & sign lang
Special Services for the Blind - Bks available with recordings; Bks on cassette; Bks on CD; Cassette playback machines; Cassettes; Closed caption display syst; Copier with enlargement capabilities; Integrated libr/media serv; Large print bks
Open Mon-Thurs 7:30am-9pm, Fri 7:30-1
Restriction: Borrowing requests are handled by ILL, Open to pub for ref & circ; with some limitations, Open to students, fac & staff

CHESTER

P   CHESTER COUNTY LIBRARY, 100 Center St, 29706. SAN 360-0572. Tel: 803-377-8145. FAX: 803-377-8146. Web Site: www.chesterlibsc.org. *Ch,* Beth Harris; *Ref,* Judy Bramlett; Staff 6 (MLS 1, Non-MLS 5)
Founded 1900. Pop 36,212; Circ 119,428
Jul 2012-Jun 2013 Income (Main Library and Branch(s)) $744,728, State $60,000, County $684,728. Mats Exp $112,800, Books $78,899, Per/Ser (Incl. Access Fees) $3,000, Other Print Mats $16,099, AV Mat $1,500, Electronic Ref Mat (Incl. Access Fees) $13,302. Sal $543,135 (Prof $45,000)
Library Holdings: AV Mats 4,836; CDs 1,126; DVDs 960; Large Print Bks 2,500; Bk Vols 108,247; Per Subs 90; Videos 35
Special Collections: Oral History
Subject Interests: Local hist, SC hist

Automation Activity & Vendor Info: (Acquisitions) Evergreen; (Cataloging) Evergreen; (Circulation) Evergreen; (Media Booking) EnvisionWare; (OPAC) Evergreen
Database Vendor: EBSCOhost, Gale Cengage Learning, Newsbank, OCLC WebJunction, ReferenceUSA
Wireless access
Open Mon-Fri 10-6, Sat 10-2
Friends of the Library Group
Branches: 2
GREAT FALLS BRANCH, 39 Calhoun St, Great Falls, 29055, SAN 360-0602. Tel: 803-482-2149. FAX: 803-482-3531. *Br Mgr,* Tally Johnson; E-mail: jfk5351@yahoo.com; Staff 2 (Non-MLS 2)
　Library Holdings: Bk Vols 10,000
　Friends of the Library Group
LEWISVILLE COMMUNITY LIBRARY, 3771 Lancaster Hwy, Richburg, 29729. Tel: 803-789-7800. FAX: 803-789-7801. *Librn,* Valerie Taylor; Staff 2 (MLS 1, Non-MLS 1)
　Founded 1997
　Library Holdings: Bk Vols 10,000; Per Subs 10
　Open Mon, Wed & Thurs (Winter) 9-5, Tues 12-7, Sat 9-3; Tues (Summer) 9-5
　Friends of the Library Group
Bookmobiles: 1

CHESTERFIELD

P　CHESTERFIELD COUNTY LIBRARY*, 119 W Main St, 29709-1512. SAN 360-0637. Tel: 843-623-7489. FAX: 843-623-3295. E-mail: chesterfieldcountylibrary@yahoo.com. Web Site: www.youseemore.com/chesterfield. *Dir,* J Drusilla Carter; *Ch,* Dorothy S Hancock; *Tech Serv,* Betty Moss; Staff 12 (MLS 1, Non-MLS 11)
Founded 1968. Pop 43,000
Jul 2006-Jun 2007 Income $402,156, State $85,884, County $316,272. Mats Exp $65,844, Books $10,000, AV Mat $6,000, Electronic Ref Mat (Incl. Access Fees) $8,000. Sal $231,625
Library Holdings: Large Print Bks 991; Bk Titles 19,000; Bk Vols 23,000; Per Subs 229; Talking Bks 295
Special Collections: South Carolina History Coll
Automation Activity & Vendor Info: (Cataloging) TLC (The Library Corporation); (Circulation) TLC (The Library Corporation); (OPAC) TLC (The Library Corporation)
Wireless access
Open Mon-Fri 9-6, Sat 10-2
Friends of the Library Group
Branches: 4
FANNIE D LOWRY MEMORIAL, PO Box 505, Jefferson, 29718-0505, SAN 328-7149. Tel: 843-658-3966. FAX: 843-658-6695. *Br Mgr,* Kim Isgett
　Open Mon, Wed & Fri 12-6
MATHESON LIBRARY, 227 Huger St, Cheraw, 29520, SAN 360-0661. Tel: 843-537-3571. FAX: 843-537-1248. *Br Mgr,* Lynne Walsh
　Library Holdings: Large Print Bks 291; Bk Titles 17,993; Bk Vols 21,199; Per Subs 50; Talking Bks 333
　Open Mon-Fri 9-6, Sat 10-2
　Friends of the Library Group
MCBEE DEPOT LIBRARY, PO Box 506, McBee, 29101, SAN 328-7165. Tel: 843-335-7515. FAX: 843-335-6219. *Br Mgr,* Kim Isgett
　Open Tues & Thurs 10-6
PAGELAND COMMUNITY LIBRARY, 109 W Blakeney St, Pageland, 29728, SAN 360-0696. Tel: 843-672-6930. FAX: 843-672-6670. *Br Mgr,* Millie Bragg; *Br Librn,* Phyllis Mills; Staff 2 (Non-MLS 2)
　Function: Fax serv, ILL available, Photocopying/Printing, Prog for children & young adult
　Open Tues-Fri 10-6, Sat 10-2

CLEMSON

C　CLEMSON UNIVERSITY LIBRARIES*, R M Cooper Library, Box 343001, 29634-3001. SAN 360-0726. Tel: 864-656-3026. Circulation Tel: 864-656-1557. Interlibrary Loan Service Tel: 864-656-5186. Reference Tel: 864-656-3024. Toll Free Tel: 877-886-2389. FAX: 864-656-0758. TDD: 864-656-0359. Web Site: www.clemson.edu/library. *Dean,* Kay L Wall; Tel: 864-656-5169, E-mail: kwall@clemson.edu; *Assoc Dean,* Eric Shoaf; Tel: 864-656-5731, E-mail: shoaf@clemson.edu; *Head, Acq,* Gail Julian; Tel: 864-656-1114, E-mail: gjulian@clemson.edu; *Head, Cat,* Lisa Bodenheimer; Tel: 864-656-1769, E-mail: bodenhl@clemson.edu; *Head, Circ,* Teri Alexander; Tel: 864-656-5172, E-mail: tajff@clemson.edu; *Head, Digital Initiatives & Info Tech,* Chris Vinson; Tel: 864-656-3039, E-mail: vinsonc@clemson.edu; *Head, Ref Serv,* Suzanne Rook-Schilf; Tel: 864-656-6834, E-mail: rook@clemson.edu; *Head, Spec Coll,* Michael Kohl; Tel: 864-656-5176, E-mail: kohl@clemson.edu; *Head, Univ Rec Mgt,* Isaac Wallace; Tel: 864-656-4336, E-mail: wisaac@clemson.edu; Staff 104 (MLS 33, Non-MLS 71)
Founded 1893. Enrl 19,111; Fac 1,150; Highest Degree: Doctorate
Library Holdings: Bk Vols 1,388,093; Per Subs 47,150

Special Collections: National Park Service Directors' Papers; University Archives. US Document Depository
Subject Interests: Rare bks, Textile
Automation Activity & Vendor Info: (Acquisitions) Innovative Interfaces, Inc; (Cataloging) Innovative Interfaces, Inc; (Circulation) Innovative Interfaces, Inc; (OPAC) Innovative Interfaces, Inc; (Serials) Innovative Interfaces, Inc
Database Vendor: EBSCOhost, Gale Cengage Learning, LexisNexis
Wireless access
Function: Res libr
Publications: In Touch
Partic in Association of Southeastern Research Libraries; Carolina Consortium; DISCUS; Lyrasis; Partnership Among South Carolina Academic Libraries
Open Sun Noon-Fri 8pm, Sat 10-8
Departmental Libraries:
GUNNIN ARCHITECTURE LIBRARY, 112 Lee Hall, Clemson University, 29634-0501, SAN 360-0750. Tel: 864-656-3933. FAX: 864-656-3932. Web Site: www.lib.clemson.edu/gunnin. *Head of Libr,* Gypsey Teague; E-mail: gteague@clemson.edu; *Asst Librn,* Kathy Edwards; E-mail: kedwards@clemson.edu; *Circ Mgr,* Christopher Chapman; E-mail: chapma@clemson.edu; *Libr Spec,* Ina Bootle; E-mail: inab@clemson.edu; Staff 7 (MLS 2, Non-MLS 5)
SPECIAL COLLECTIONS UNIT, Strom Thurmond Inst Bldg, Special Collections Box 343001, 29634-3001, SAN 373-7160. Tel: 864-656-3031. FAX: 864-656-0233. Web Site: www.clemson.edu/library/special_collections/index.html. *Head, Spec Coll,* Michael Kohl; Tel: 864-656-5176, E-mail: kohl@clemson.edu; Staff 9 (MLS 8, Non-MLS 1)
　Special Collections: Liberty Corporation Archives; National Park Service Directors
　Subject Interests: SC hist, Textiles
　Function: Archival coll, Computers for patron use, Handicapped accessible, Ref serv available, Scanner
　Restriction: Closed stack, Non-circulating, Open to pub with supv only

CLINTON

C　PRESBYTERIAN COLLEGE, James H Thomason Library, 211 E Maple St, 29325. SAN 315-5102. Tel: 864-833-8299. Reference Tel: 864-833-7080. FAX: 864-833-8315. E-mail: library@presby.edu. Web Site: www.presby.edu/library/. *Dir,* Dave Chatham; *Assoc Dir, Pub Serv,* Dan Lee; Tel: 864-833-8437, E-mail: dlee@presby.edu; *Head, Circ,* Beverly Blalock; *Archivist, Spec Coll Librn,* Teresa Inman; Tel: 864-833-8525, E-mail: tinman@presby.edu; *Coordr, Electronic Serv & Syst,* Abigail Rush; Tel: 864-833-7026, E-mail: asrush@presby.edu; *Ref Serv,* Sara Rowe; E-mail: sfrowe@presby.edu; Staff 5.25 (MLS 5.25)
Founded 1880. Enrl 1,150; Fac 88; Highest Degree: Bachelor
Jul 2007-Jun 2008 Income $787,852. Mats Exp $274,057. Sal $382,692
Library Holdings: Bk Vols 137,314; Per Subs 684
Special Collections: Presbyterian denominational materials
Subject Interests: Caroliniana
Automation Activity & Vendor Info: (Acquisitions) Innovative Interfaces, Inc; (Cataloging) Innovative Interfaces, Inc; (Circulation) Innovative Interfaces, Inc; (Course Reserve) Innovative Interfaces, Inc; (ILL) Clio; (OPAC) Innovative Interfaces, Inc; (Serials) Innovative Interfaces, Inc
Database Vendor: EBSCOhost, Gale Cengage Learning, OCLC FirstSearch
Wireless access
Partic in Lyrasis; Partnership Among South Carolina Academic Libraries

COLUMBIA

CR　ALLEN UNIVERSITY LIBRARY*, 1530 Harden St, 29204. Tel: 803-376-5719. FAX: 803-765-6009. E-mail: library@allenuniversity.edu. Web Site: www.allenuniversity.edu. *Librn,* Vesta Baughman; E-mail: vesta_baughman@yahoo.com
Founded 1870
Library Holdings: Bk Vols 10,000; Per Subs 80
Special Collections: African Methodist Episcopal Church (AME) Coll; African-American Coll

S　BELLE W BARUCH INSTITUTE FOR MARINE & COASTAL SCIENCES LIBRARY*, University of South Carolina, 29208. SAN 372-9427. Tel: 803-777-3927. FAX: 803-777-3935. *Pub Info Coordr,* Anne Miller

C　BENEDICT COLLEGE LIBRARY*, Benjamin F Payton Learning Resources Center, 1600 Harden St, 29204. SAN 315-5137. Tel: 803-705-4364. FAX: 803-748-7539. Web Site: www.benedict.edu. *Dir,* Darlene Zinnerman-Bethea; Tel: 803-705-4773, E-mail: bethead@benedict.edu; *Cat,* Peter Rossi; *Ref,* Bridget Sledge; Staff 11 (MLS 6, Non-MLS 5)
Founded 1870. Enrl 1,371; Fac 87; Highest Degree: Bachelor
Library Holdings: Bk Vols 118,000; Per Subs 320

Special Collections: State Document Depository; US Document Depository
Subject Interests: African-Am studies
Wireless access
Partic in Coop Col Libr Ctr, Inc
Open Mon-Thurs 8:30am-11pm, Fri 8:30-5, Sat 1-5, Sun 3-9

M   **G WERBER BRYAN PSYCHIATRIC HOSPITAL LIBRARY,** 220 Faison Dr, 29203. SAN 315-5145. Tel: 803-935-5395. FAX: 803-935-7110. *Librn,* Theodora Richardson
Founded 1978
Library Holdings: Audiobooks 120; CDs 250; DVDs 125; Large Print Bks 100; Bk Vols 3,500; Per Subs 50; Videos 70
Subject Interests: Psychiat, Psychol
Partic in SC Health Info Network
Open Mon-Fri 10-6:30
Restriction: Staff & patient use
Friends of the Library Group

C   **COLUMBIA COLLEGE*,** J Drake Edens Library, 1301 Columbia College Dr, 29203-9987. SAN 315-5161. Tel: 803-786-3716. Circulation Tel: 803-786-3877. Interlibrary Loan Service Tel: 803-786-3878. Reference Tel: 803-786-3337. FAX: 803-786-3700. Web Site: www.columbiacollegesc.edu. *Dir,* John C Pritchett; E-mail: jpritchett@colacoll.edu; *Mgr, Per,* Kisha McAdams; Tel: 803-786-3712, E-mail: tmcadams@colacoll.edu; *Circ, ILL,* Gina Dempsey; Tel: 803-786-3878, E-mail: gdempsey@colacoll.edu; *Coll Develop,* Lin C Lake; Tel: 803-786-3042, E-mail: linlake@colacoll.edu; *Media Spec,* Betty E McDonald; Tel: 803-786-3712, E-mail: bmmcdonald@colacoll.edu; *Head, User Serv,* Jane Tuttle; Tel: 803-786-3337, E-mail: jtuttle@colacoll.edu; *User Serv,* Sarah Hood; Tel: 803-786-3703, E-mail: shood@colacoll.edu; *User Serv,* Alexandra Leach; Tel: 803-786-3338, E-mail: sleach@colacoll.edu; *Syst Coordr,* Mary R Cross; Tel: 803-786-3691, E-mail: marycross@colacoll.edu; Staff 10 (MLS 6, Non-MLS 4)
Founded 1854. Enrl 1,400; Fac 105; Highest Degree: Master
Jul 2005-Jun 2006 Income $238,285, Locally Generated Income $5,389, Parent Institution $226,150, Other $6,746. Mats Exp $181,127, Books $74,227, Per/Ser (Incl. Access Fees) $42,941, Micro $9,000, AV Mat $12,654, Electronic Ref Mat (Incl. Access Fees) $42,305. Sal $351,159 (Prof $214,565)
Library Holdings: AV Mats 28,494; CDs 941; DVDs 254; Bk Titles 102,743; Bk Vols 146,135; Per Subs 323; Videos 3,183
Special Collections: Local Authors (Peggy Parish & Barbara Johnson); Religious Literature for Children
Subject Interests: Women
Automation Activity & Vendor Info: (Cataloging) Innovative Interfaces, Inc; (Circulation) Innovative Interfaces, Inc; (OPAC) Innovative Interfaces, Inc; (Serials) Innovative Interfaces, Inc
Database Vendor: Baker & Taylor, Checkpoint Systems, Inc, Grolier Online, Innovative Interfaces, Inc INN - View, LexisNexis, OCLC FirstSearch, ProQuest
Wireless access
Partic in Amigos Library Services, Inc; Lyrasis
Open Mon-Thurs 8am-11pm, Fri 8-5, Sat 10-5, Sun 3-11

CR   **COLUMBIA INTERNATIONAL UNIVERSITY,** G Allen Fleece Library, 7435 Monticello Rd, 29203-1599. SAN 315-5153. Tel: 803-807-5115. Circulation Tel: 803-807-5110. Reference Tel: 803-807-5102. FAX: 803-744-1391. E-mail: library@ciu.edu. Web Site: www.ciu.edu/library. *Libr Instruction, Pub Serv Librn, Ref Librn,* Stephanie Solomon; Tel: 803-807-5104, E-mail: ssolomon@ciu.edu; *Cataloger,* Florida Oamil; Tel: 803-807-5107, E-mail: foamil@ciu.edu; *Curric Media/Mats,* Debby Reichel; Tel: 803-807-5159, E-mail: dreichel@ciu.edu; *Ref Spec for Acq,* Nancy Brown; Tel: 803-807-5103, E-mail: nbrown@ciu.edu; *Circ Asst,* Megan Mains; E-mail: mmains@ciu.edu; *Ref Asst,* Kevin Flickner; Tel: 803-807-5112, E-mail: kflickner@ciu.edu; Staff 6 (MLS 4, Non-MLS 2)
Founded 1923. Enrl 931; Fac 65; Highest Degree: Doctorate
Library Holdings: AV Mats 8,000; e-books 15,000; Electronic Media & Resources 100; Microforms 50,000; Bk Titles 114,000; Per Subs 240
Subject Interests: Bus, Counseling, Educ, Intercultural studies, Theol
Automation Activity & Vendor Info: (Acquisitions) Innovative Interfaces, Inc; (Cataloging) OCLC; (Circulation) Innovative Interfaces, Inc; (Course Reserve) Innovative Interfaces, Inc; (ILL) OCLC FirstSearch; (OPAC) Innovative Interfaces, Inc; (Serials) Innovative Interfaces, Inc
Database Vendor: CredoReference, EBSCOhost, Gale Cengage Learning, Gallup, H W Wilson, Ingenta, Innovative Interfaces, Inc INN - View, JayWil Software Development, Inc, LearningExpress, LexisNexis, Medline, Modern Language Association, netLibrary, Newsbank, OCLC ArticleFirst, OCLC FirstSearch, OCLC WorldCat, Oxford Online, ProQuest, RefWorks, TDNet, TLC (The Library Corporation), Wilson - Wilson Web
Wireless access
Function: Archival coll, CD-ROM, Computers for patron use, Copy machines, Distance learning, Doc delivery serv, E-Reserves, Electronic databases & coll, ILL available, Magnifiers for reading, Music CDs, Online

cat, Online searches, Photocopying/Printing, Ref serv available, Spoken cassettes & CDs, Tax forms, VHS videos, Web-catalog, Wheelchair accessible
Partic in Christian Library Consortium; DISCUS; Lyrasis; OCLC Online Computer Library Center, Inc; Partnership Among South Carolina Academic Libraries
Special Services for the Deaf - Bks on deafness & sign lang; Closed caption videos
Special Services for the Blind - Internet workstation with adaptive software; Large screen computer & software
Open Mon-Sat 8am-Midnight

S   **COLUMBIA MUSEUM OF ART*,** Lorick Library, Main & Hampton, 29201. (Mail add: PO Box 2068, 29202-2068), SAN 315-517X. Tel: 803-799-2810. FAX: 803-343-2150. Web Site: www.columbiamuseum.org. *Dir,* Karen Brosius
Founded 1980
Library Holdings: Bk Vols 14,000; Per Subs 30
Special Collections: Art Coll
Restriction: Open by appt only

GM   **DEPARTMENT OF VETERANS AFFAIRS DORN MEDICAL CENTER*,** Medical Library, 6439 Garners Ferry Rd, 29209-1639. SAN 315-5315. Tel: 803-776-4000, Ext 7315. FAX: 803-695-6874. *Librn,* Emily Ginardi
Library Holdings: Bk Vols 1,187; Per Subs 224

C   **ECPI UNIVERSITY*,** Columbia Campus Library, 250 Berryhill Rd, Ste 300, 29210. Tel: 803-772-3333. Toll Free Tel: 800-986-1200. Web Site: students.ecpi.edu/libcot/. *Campus Librn,* Denise Keating; Staff 4 (MLS 1, Non-MLS 3)
Founded 2007. Enrl 165; Fac 22; Highest Degree: Associate
Automation Activity & Vendor Info: (Acquisitions) SIRSI WorkFlows; (Cataloging) SIRSI WorkFlows; (Circulation) SIRSI WorkFlows; (Course Reserve) SIRSI WorkFlows; (ILL) SIRSI WorkFlows; (Media Booking) SIRSI WorkFlows; (OPAC) SIRSI WorkFlows; (Serials) SIRSI WorkFlows
Database Vendor: ABC-CLIO, American Psychological Association (APA), Annual Reviews, Cinahl Information Systems, CredoReference, ebrary, Gale Cengage Learning, Ingram Library Services, Medline, MITINET, Inc, netLibrary, Open Text Corporation, PubMed, Safari Books Online, SirsiDynix, Standard & Poor's, WebMD
Function: Audio & video playback equip for onsite use, Audiobks via web, AV serv, Bks on CD, Computer training, Computers for patron use, Distance learning, e-mail serv, Electronic databases & coll, Handicapped accessible, Health sci info serv, ILL available, Instruction & testing, Learning ctr, Online cat, Online info literacy tutorials on the web & in blackboard, Online ref, Online searches, Orientations, Outreach serv, Outside serv via phone, mail, e-mail & web, Prog for adults, Ref & res, Ref serv available, Telephone ref, Wheelchair accessible, Workshops
Partic in Libr & Info Resources Network (LIRN)
Open Mon-Thurs 9-8
Restriction: Borrowing privileges limited to fac & registered students

M   **JOSEY HEALTH SCIENCES LIBRARY,** Palmetto Health Richland, Five Richland Medical Park, 29203. SAN 315-5234. Tel: 803-434-6312. FAX: 803-434-2651. E-mail: phrlibrary.phrlibrary@palmettohealth.org. *Libr Mgr,* Cynthia D Garrett; *Libr Coordr,* Marline C Robinson; Staff 3 (MLS 1, Non-MLS 2)
Founded 1957
Oct 2011-Sept 2012. Mats Exp $264,624, Books $6,000, Per/Ser (Incl. Access Fees) $172,750, Electronic Ref Mat (Incl. Access Fees) $74,900
Library Holdings: AV Mats 524; CDs 300; e-books 30; e-journals 325; Bk Titles 2,145; Per Subs 275; Videos 100
Subject Interests: Allied health, Med, Nursing
Automation Activity & Vendor Info: (Acquisitions) EBSCO Online; (Cataloging) Marcive, Inc; (Circulation) Follett Software; (OPAC) Follett Software; (Serials) Follett Software
Database Vendor: Cinahl Information Systems, EBSCOhost, Elsevier, Majors, Marcive, Inc, MD Consult, Micromedex, OVID Technologies, PubMed, TDNet, UpToDate
Wireless access
Function: Computers for patron use, Copy machines, Electronic databases & coll, Handicapped accessible, Health sci info serv, ILL available, Mail & tel request accepted, Online ref, Online searches, Orientations, Outside serv via phone, mail, e-mail & web, Photocopying/Printing, Prof lending libr, Ref & res, Ref serv in person, Res libr, Res performed for a fee, Scanner, Spoken cassettes & CDs, Wheelchair accessible
Partic in National Network of Libraries of Medicine
Open Mon-Fri 8:30-5
Restriction: Med staff & students, Open to hospital affiliates only, Open to students, fac & staff, Photo ID required for access, Restricted access, Restricted borrowing privileges, Restricted loan policy, Secured area only open to authorized personnel

R   LUTHERAN THEOLOGICAL SOUTHERN SEMINARY*, Lineberger
Memorial Library, 4201 N Main St, 29203. SAN 315-5218. Tel:
803-461-3220, 803-786-5150. FAX: 803-461-3278. Web Site:
www.ltss.edu. *Dir,* Dr Lynn A Feider; *Assoc Librn,* Leslie Walker; Staff 2
(MLS 2)
Founded 1830. Highest Degree: Master
Library Holdings: Bk Vols 100,000; Per Subs 474
Special Collections: 16th through 18th Century German Pietism
Subject Interests: Relig studies
Automation Activity & Vendor Info: (Acquisitions) Ex Libris Group;
(Cataloging) Ex Libris Group; (Circulation) Ex Libris Group; (Course
Reserve) Ex Libris Group; (OPAC) Ex Libris Group; (Serials) Ex Libris
Group
Database Vendor: EBSCOhost
Wireless access
Partic in Lyrasis; OCLC Online Computer Library Center, Inc
Open Mon-Thurs 8:30am-10pm, Fri 8:30-4:30, Sat 10-4, Sun 5pm-10pm

G   MUNICIPAL ASSOCIATION OF SOUTH CAROLINA*, Library &
Reference Center, 1411 Gervais St, 29201. (Mail add: PO Box 12109,
29211), SAN 372-9443. Tel: 803-933-1206. FAX: 803-933-1299. E-mail:
mail@masc.sc. Web Site: www.masc.sc. *Exec Dir,* Miriam Hair; Tel:
803-933-1204
Library Holdings: Bk Vols 350
Open Mon-Fri 9-5

L   NELSON, MULLINS, RILEY & SCARBOROUGH*, Law Library, 1320
Main St, Ste 1700, 29201. (Mail add: PO Box 11070, 29211-1070), SAN
323-6560. Tel: 803-255-9367. FAX: 803-255-7500. *Librn Mgr,* Monica
Wilson; *Sr Res Spec,* Melanie DuBard; E-mail:
melanie.dubard@nelsonmullins.com; *Res Librn,* Charles Frey; Tel:
843-534-4320, E-mail: charles.frey@nelsonmullins.com; *Res Librn,* Linda
Gray; Tel: 404-817-6228, E-mail: linda.gray@nelsonmullins.com; *Res
Librn,* Mary Jane Slipsky; Tel: 919-877-3858, E-mail:
maryjane.slipsky@nelsonmullins.com; Staff 7 (MLS 4, Non-MLS 3)
Founded 1982
Library Holdings: Bk Titles 3,500; Bk Vols 16,000; Per Subs 124
Subject Interests: Law
Wireless access
Restriction: Not open to pub, Staff use only

S   RESEARCH PLANNING INC LIBRARY*, 1121 Park St, 29201-3137.
(Mail add: PO Box 328, 29202-0328), SAN 372-9397. Tel: 803-256-7322.
FAX: 803-254-6445. E-mail: info@researchplanning.com. Web Site:
www.researchplanning.com. *Librn,* Wendy Early; *Librn,* Mandie Minton
Subject Interests: Maps

P   RICHLAND COUNTY PUBLIC LIBRARY, 1431 Assembly St,
29201-3101. SAN 360-0939. Tel: 803-799-9084. Circulation Tel:
803-929-3441. Reference Tel: 803-929-3400, 803-929-3401. Administration
Tel: 803-929-3422. Automation Services Tel: 803-929-3407. FAX:
803-929-3448. Interlibrary Loan Service FAX: 803-929-3439.
Administration FAX: 803-929-3438. TDD: 800-735-2905. Web Site:
www.myrcpl.com. *Exec Dir,* Melanie Huggins; *Dep Dir,* Valerie
Rowe-Jackson; *Dir, Literacy & Learning,* Tony Tallent; *Chief, Extn Serv,*
Caroline Hipp; *Chief Financial Officer,* Sarah Sullivan; *Chief, Main Libr
Serv,* Teresa Windham; *Coll Mgt Librn,* Nancy Dail; *Commun Outreach
Mgr,* Georgia Coleman; *Develop Mgr,* Tina Gills; *Learning Engagement
Mgr,* Susan Lyon; *Mkt & Communications Mgr,* Padgett Lewis; *Prog &
Partnerships Mgr,* Clo Cammarata; *Virtual Serv Mgr,* Kelly Coulter;
Operations Supvr, Steve Sullivan; *Personnel Adminr,* Richard Brown; *Tech
Adminr,* Bruce Heimburger; Staff 280.82 (MLS 81.4, Non-MLS 199.42)
Founded 1934. Pop 384,504; Circ 4,754,850
Jul 2011-Jun 2012 Income (Main Library and Branch(s)) $21,601,083,
State $338,973, Federal $481, County $20,176,600, Other $1,085,029. Mats
Exp $3,305,619, Books $1,765,675, AV Mat $1,145,221, Electronic Ref
Mat (Incl. Access Fees) $394,723. Sal $10,066,934
Library Holdings: Audiobooks 63,756; DVDs 86,422; e-books 21,940;
e-journals 2; Electronic Media & Resources 1,006,974; Bk Titles
1,120,591; Per Subs 2,397
Special Collections: Oral History
Subject Interests: Local hist
Automation Activity & Vendor Info: (Acquisitions) SirsiDynix;
(Cataloging) SirsiDynix; (Circulation) SirsiDynix; (OPAC) SirsiDynix;
(Serials) SirsiDynix
Database Vendor: CredoReference, EBSCO Auto Repair Reference,
EBSCO Information Services, EBSCOhost, Gale Cengage Learning,
LearningExpress, Newsbank, Overdrive, Inc, Plunkett Research, Ltd,
ReferenceUSA, Safari Books Online, SerialsSolutions, TumbleBookLibrary,
Westlaw
Wireless access
Function: Adult bk club, Art exhibits, Audiobks via web, Bk club(s), Bks
on cassette, Bks on CD, CD-ROM, Children's prog, Computer training,
Computers for patron use, Copy machines, Digital talking bks, e-mail &

chat, E-Reserves, Electronic databases & coll, Exhibits, Fax serv, Free
DVD rentals, Handicapped accessible, Holiday prog, Home delivery & serv
to Sr ctr & nursing homes, Homebound delivery serv, Homework prog,
ILL available, Instruction & testing, Learning ctr, Libr develop, Magnifiers
for reading, Mail & tel request accepted, Music CDs, Newsp ref libr,
Online cat, Online ref, Online searches, Outreach serv, Outside serv via
phone, mail, e-mail & web, OverDrive digital audio bks,
Photocopying/Printing, Preschool outreach, Prog for adults, Prog for
children & young adult, Pub access computers, Res libr, Senior computer
classes, Senior outreach, Spoken cassettes & CDs, Spoken cassettes &
DVDs, Story hour, Summer reading prog, Teen prog, Telephone ref, VHS
videos, Web-catalog, Wheelchair accessible, Workshops
Publications: Magazine (Bi-monthly)
Special Services for the Deaf - TTY equip
Special Services for the Blind - Closed circuit TV magnifier; Computer
access aids; Computer with voice synthesizer for visually impaired persons;
Large print bks; Scanner for conversion & translation of mats; Talking bk
serv referral
Friends of the Library Group
Branches: 10
BLYTHEWOOD BRANCH, 218 McNulty Rd, Blythewood, 29016, SAN
  373-7098. Tel: 803-691-9806. *Br Mgr,* Shirley Carter
JOHN HUGHES COOPER BRANCH, 5317 N Trenholm Rd, 29206, SAN
  360-0963. Tel: 803-787-3462. FAX: 803-787-8040. *Br Mgr,* Ellan
  Jenkinson
EASTOVER BRANCH, 608 Main St, Eastover, 29044, SAN 360-1021.
  Tel: 803-353-8584. *Br Mgr,* DeBarbara Robinson
THE LINK, BALLENTINE, 1321 Dutch Fork Rd, Irmo, 29063. Tel:
  803-781-5026. *Br Mgr,* Heather Green
NORTH MAIN, 5306 N Main St, 29203-6114, SAN 360-1110. Tel:
  803-754-7734. *Br Mgr,* Patricia Mitchell
NORTHEAST REGIONAL, 7490 Parklane Rd, 29223, SAN 325-4372.
  Tel: 803-736-6575. *Br Mgr,* Jacqueline Sligh
SAINT ANDREWS REGIONAL, 2916 Broad River Rd, 29210, SAN
  360-1145. Tel: 803-772-6675. *Br Mgr,* Lin Ko
SANDHILLS, One Summit Pkwy, @ Clemson Rd, 29229, SAN 373-7101.
  Tel: 803-699-9230. FAX: 803-699-0491. *Br Mgr,* Jim Staskowski
SOUTHEAST REGIONAL, 7421 Garners Ferry Rd, 29209, SAN
  373-711X. Tel: 803-776-0855. *Br Mgr,* Sarah Maner
WHEATLEY, 931 Woodrow St, 29205, SAN 360-0998. Tel: 803-799-5873.
  Br Mgr, Barbara Urban

S   SCANA CORP/SOUTH CAROLINA ELECTRIC & GAS CO*, Corporate
Library, Palmetto Ctr, 1426 Main St, 29201. (Mail add: Palmetto Center,
Mail Code 080, 29218-0001), SAN 329-9317. Tel: 803-217-9942. FAX:
803-217-8310. *Coordr,* Patsy G Moss; Fax: 803-933-8067, E-mail:
pmoss@scana.com; Staff 1 (MLS 1)
Founded 1984
Library Holdings: Bk Titles 1,000; Per Subs 35
Subject Interests: Energy
Automation Activity & Vendor Info: (Cataloging) Inmagic, Inc.
Database Vendor: Dialog, LexisNexis
Function: Res libr
Restriction: Not open to pub

S   WILBUR SMITH ASSOCIATES CORPORATE LIBRARY*, 1301 Gervais
St, 29201-3326. (Mail add: PO Box 92, 29202-0092), SAN 327-0734. Tel:
803-251-2055. FAX: 803-251-2064. E-mail: library@wilbursmith.com.
Librn, Res Coordr, Betty Phillips; Staff 1 (MLS 1)
Library Holdings: Bk Vols 17,000; Per Subs 70
Subject Interests: Civil eng, Economics, Planning, Transportation
Restriction: Employee & client use only, Use of others with permission of
librn

GL   SOUTH CAROLINA ATTORNEY GENERAL'S OFFICE LIBRARY*,
1000 Assembly St, Ste 743, 29201-3117. (Mail add: PO Box 11549,
29211), SAN 321-7604. Tel: 803-734-3769. FAX: 803-253-6283. Web Site:
www.scattorneygeneral.org. *Librn,* Amanda Gallego; E-mail:
agallego@ag.state.sc.us; Staff 1 (MLS 1)
Founded 1974
Library Holdings: Bk Titles 800; Bk Vols 4,000
Special Collections: Attorney General's Opinions
Subject Interests: Law
Automation Activity & Vendor Info: (Acquisitions) Mandarin Library
Automation; (Cataloging) Mandarin Library Automation; (Circulation)
Mandarin Library Automation; (OPAC) Mandarin Library Automation;
(Serials) Mandarin Library Automation
Database Vendor: Westlaw
Wireless access
Open Mon-Fri 8:30-5
Restriction: Open to pub for ref only

S   SOUTH CAROLINA COMMISSION ON HIGHER EDUCATION LIBRARY*, 1122 Lady St, Ste 300, 29201-3240. SAN 371-4438. Tel: 803-737-2293. FAX: 803-737-2297. Web Site: www.che.sc.gov. *Librn,* Arik Bjorn; Staff 1 (MLS 1)
Library Holdings: Bk Vols 5,000; Per Subs 25
Wireless access
Restriction: Staff use only

S   SOUTH CAROLINA CONFEDERATE RELIC ROOM & MILITARY MUSEUM LIBRARY*, 301 Gervais St, 29201-3027. SAN 327-7895. Tel: 803-737-8095. FAX: 803-737-8099. Web Site: www.crr.sc.gov. *Dir,* Allen Roberson; *Archivist,* Kristina Dunn; E-mail: kdunn@crr.sc.gov
Library Holdings: Bk Vols 1,300
Open Tues-Sat 10-5

G   SOUTH CAROLINA DEPARTMENT OF ARCHIVES & HISTORY, 8301 Parklane Rd, 29223. SAN 327-0777. Tel: 803-896-6104. Automation Services Tel: 803-896-6100. FAX: 803-896-6198. Web Site: scdah.sc.gov. *Dir, Archives Div,* Steve D Tuttle
Founded 1905
Library Holdings: Microforms 20,000; Bk Vols 5,000
Special Collections: South Carolina Government Records, 1671-present
Wireless access
Publications: Colonial Records of South Carolina; Curriculum Resource Materials; Popular History Booklets; South Carolina Archives Micropublications; State Records of South Carolina; Technical Leaflets on Document Conservation, Historic Preservation & Records Management
Open Tues-Sat 8:30-5

P   SOUTH CAROLINA STATE LIBRARY*, 1430-1500 Senate St, 29201. (Mail add: PO Box 11469, 29211), SAN 360-117X. Tel: 803-734-8666. Circulation Tel: 803-734-8644. Reference Tel: 803-734-8026. FAX: 803-734-8676. Reference FAX: 803-734-4757. TDD: 711-734-4611 (Relay SC). E-mail: reference@statelibrary.sc.gov. Web Site: www.statelibrary.sc.gov. *Dir,* Position Currently Open; *Dir of Finance,* Paula James; Tel: 803-734-8917, E-mail: pjames@statelibrary.sc.gov; *Dir, Communications,* Curtis R Rogers; E-mail: crogers@statelibrary.sc.gov; *Dir, Libr Develop,* Denise Lyons; Tel: 803-734-6061, E-mail: dlyons@statelibrary.sc.gov; *Dir, Organizational Res,* Leesa Benggio; Tel: 803-734-8668, E-mail: lbenggio@statelibrary.sc.gov; *Info Tech Dir,* Bill Croteau; Tel: 803-734-8651; *Librn,* Amanda Stone; Tel: 803-734-4816, E-mail: astone@statelibrary.sc.gov; *ILL Librn,* Faith Keller; Tel: 803-734-8851, E-mail: fkeller@statelibrary.sc.gov; *Database Mgr,* Amy Duernberger; Tel: 803-737-7736, E-mail: aduernberger@statelibrary.sc.gov; *Fed Grants Coordr,* Kathy Sheppard; Tel: 803-734-8653, E-mail: ksheppard@statelibrary.sc.gov; *Web Coordr,* Robert Lindsey; Tel: 803-734-5831, E-mail: rlindsey@statelibrary.sc.gov; *Cataloger,* Wesley Sparks; Tel: 803-734-8662, E-mail: wsparks@statelibrary.sc.gov; *Coll Develop,* Christopher Yates; Tel: 803-734-4618, E-mail: cyates@statelibrary.sc.gov; *Doc,* Elaine Sandberg; Tel: 803-734-8625, E-mail: esandberg@statelibrary.sc.gov; *Info Serv,* Dawn Mullin; Tel: 803-737-3762, E-mail: dmullin@statelibrary.sc.gov; *Libr Develop Consult,* David Sniffin; Tel: 803-734-8646, E-mail: dsniffin@statelibrary.sc.gov; Staff 24 (MLS 18, Non-MLS 6)
Founded 1943. Pop 4,012,012
Library Holdings: AV Mats 5,434; Electronic Media & Resources 650,000; Large Print Bks 21,900; Bk Titles 142,100; Bk Vols 340,617; Per Subs 39; Talking Bks 522,760
Special Collections: ERIC Coll; Foundation Center Regional Coll; Last Copy Fiction; South Carolina Coll; South Carolina Government Publications. State Document Depository; US Document Depository
Subject Interests: Southern hist
Automation Activity & Vendor Info: (Acquisitions) Evergreen; (Cataloging) Evergreen; (Circulation) Evergreen
Database Vendor: Facts on File, Gale Cengage Learning, LearningExpress, McGraw-Hill, netLibrary, Newsbank, OCLC FirstSearch, ProQuest, Safari Books Online
Wireless access
Publications: Annual Accountability Report, 2008-2009; Annual Report, 2006-2007; Continuing Education Opportunities, 2005-2006; Emergency Preparedness & Safety Manual, 2006; Employee Handbook; Library Services & Technology Act (LSTA) PL 108-81 & Amended Information & Guidelines, Federal Fiscal Year 2006 Program Funds, Oct 1, 2006-Sept 30, 2007; More About Talking Book Services; More: The Newsletter for South Carolina Libraries (Bi-monthly); News about Talking Book Services (Quarterly); South Carolina State Library Strategic Plan, Fiscal years 2005-2008; Survey of South Carolina Public Librarian Salaries 2005; Technology Standards for South Carolina Public Libraries 2005
Partic in Lyrasis; SC Libr Network; SCLENDS
Special Services for the Deaf - Bks on deafness & sign lang; TTY equip
Special Services for the Blind - Assistive/Adapted tech devices, equip & products; Computer with voice synthesizer for visually impaired persons; Open bk software on pub access PC
Friends of the Library Group

Branches: 1
TALKING BOOK SERVICES
   See Separate Entry

P   SOUTH CAROLINA STATE LIBRARY*, Talking Book Services, 1430 Senate St, 29201-3710. (Mail add: PO Box 821, 29202-0821), SAN 315-4963. Tel: 803-734-4611. Toll Free Tel: 800-922-7818. FAX: 803-734-4610. TDD: 803-734-7298. E-mail: tbsbooks@statelibrary.sc.gov. *Dir,* Sandy Knowles; *Coll Develop,* Christopher Yates; *Reader Serv,* Kecia Greer; E-mail: kecia@leo.scsl.state.sc.us; *Reader Serv,* Laura Leventis; E-mail: laura@leo.scsl.state.sc.us; Staff 4 (MLS 4)
Founded 1973. Pop 7,744; Circ 250,293
Library Holdings: Large Print Bks 16,789; Bk Titles 67,903; Bk Vols 349,352; Talking Bks 45,160
Special Collections: South Caroliniana, cassette, descriptive v-tapes
Subject Interests: Fiction, Non-fiction
Database Vendor: SirsiDynix
Publications: News about Talking Book Services (Newsletter)
Special Services for the Blind - Assistive/Adapted tech devices, equip & products; Bks & mags in Braille, on rec, tape & cassette; Braille equip; Children's Braille; Closed circuit TV; Computer with voice synthesizer for visually impaired persons; Home delivery serv; Info on spec aids & appliances; Internet workstation with adaptive software; Large print bks & talking machines; Large screen computer & software; Local mags & bks recorded; Machine repair; Magnifiers; Newsletter (in large print, Braille or on cassette); PC for handicapped; Reader equip; Rec & flexible discs; Screen enlargement software for people with visual disabilities; Screen reader software; Soundproof reading booth; Spec cats; Talking bk & rec for the blind cat; Talking bks & player equip; Tel Pioneers equip repair group; Videos on blindness & phys handicaps; ZoomText magnification & reading software
Open Mon-Fri 8:30-5

GL   SOUTH CAROLINA SUPREME COURT LIBRARY*, 1231 Gervais St, 29201-3206. (Mail add: PO Box 11330, 29211-1330), SAN 315-5293. Tel: 803-734-1080. FAX: 803-734-0519. Web Site: www.sccourts.org. *Librn,* Janet F Meyer; Staff 2 (MLS 1, Non-MLS 1)
Founded 1871
Library Holdings: Bk Vols 49,500; Per Subs 115
Special Collections: Court Cases (1918 to present), micro
Subject Interests: SC law
Open Mon-Fri 8:30-5
Restriction: Non-circulating

C   SOUTH UNIVERSITY*, Columbia Campus, Nine Science Ct, 29203. SAN 360-0815. Tel: 803-935-4301, 803-935-4331. Interlibrary Loan Service Tel: 803-935-4330. FAX: 803-935-4382. *Head, Libr & Info Serv,* Amanda Difeterici; *Circ Librn,* Elizabeth Dolinger; E-mail: edolinger@southuniversity.edu; Staff 3 (MLS 2, Non-MLS 1)
Founded 1935. Enrl 1,000; Fac 55; Highest Degree: Master
Library Holdings: AV Mats 1,300; Bk Vols 15,000; Per Subs 100
Subject Interests: Acctg, Behav sci, Counseling, Econ, Hist, Nursing, Paralegal, Soc sci
Automation Activity & Vendor Info: (Acquisitions) Baker & Taylor; (Cataloging) Ex Libris Group; (Circulation) Ex Libris Group
Database Vendor: Baker & Taylor, Booklist Online, Cinahl Information Systems, CQ Press, EBSCOhost, Ex Libris Group, LexisNexis, Loislaw, Micromedex, Modern Language Association, OVID Technologies, Oxford Online, WT Cox
Wireless access
Function: AV serv, CD-ROM, Computers for patron use, Copy machines, Electronic databases & coll, ILL available, Instruction & testing, Learning ctr, Online cat, Online ref, Online searches, Orientations, Photocopying/Printing, Ref & res, Ref serv available, VHS videos, Video lending libr, Workshops
Restriction: Authorized patrons, Borrowing privileges limited to fac & registered students, Circ privileges for students & alumni only, Open to qualified scholars, Open to researchers by request, Open to students, fac, staff & alumni

C   UNIVERSITY OF SOUTH CAROLINA, Thomas Cooper Library, 1322 Greene St, 29208-0103. SAN 360-1234. Tel: 803-777-3142. Circulation Tel: 803-777-3145. Interlibrary Loan Service Tel: 803-777-2805. Information Services Tel: 803-777-4866. Web Site: www.sc.edu/library. *Dean of Libr,* Thomas F McNally; *Admin Dir,* Mary C Horton; *Spec Coll Librn,* Elizabeth Sudduth; *Acq,* Joseph Pukl; *Circ,* Caroline Taylor; *Coll Develop,* Gary Geer; *Ref,* Sharon Verba
Founded 1801. Highest Degree: Doctorate
Special Collections: Archaeology (19th Century), rare bks; EEC; English & American Literature, rare bks; F Scott Fitzgerald, rare bks; Ornithology (18th-20th Century), rare bks; Robert Burns & Scottish Literature, Civil War, rare bks; Scottish Literature. US Document Depository
Automation Activity & Vendor Info: (Acquisitions) Innovative Interfaces, Inc; (Cataloging) Innovative Interfaces, Inc; (Circulation) Innovative Interfaces, Inc; (OPAC) Innovative Interfaces, Inc - Millenium

Wireless access
Publications: Reflections
Partic in Association of Research Libraries (ARL); Association of Southeastern Research Libraries; Lyrasis
Friends of the Library Group
Departmental Libraries:
DIGITAL COLLECTIONS, 1322 Greene St, 29208. Tel: 803-777-2249. Web Site: sc.edu/library/digital/index.php. *Head Librn,* Kate Boyd
EDUCATIONAL FILMS, Thomas Cooper Library, Level 3, Rm 317, 29208. Tel: 803-777-0322, 803-777-2858. Web Site: www.sc.edu/library/edfilms. *Dept Head,* Amy Trepal; E-mail: ajtrepa@mailbox.sc.edu; Staff 1 (Non-MLS 1)
    Library Holdings: Bk Titles 11,000
    Subject Interests: Anthropology, Bus, English, Film studies, Hist, Humanities, Psychol, Sociol
    Open Mon-Fri 8:30-5

CL COLEMAN KARESH LAW LIBRARY, USC Law Ctr, 701 Main St, 29208, SAN 360-1269. Tel: 803-777-5942. Reference Tel: 803-777-5902. FAX: 803-777-9405. E-mail: lawref@law.sc.edu. Web Site: www.law.sc.edu/library. *Dir,* Duncan Alford; E-mail: alfordd@law.sc.edu; *Assoc Dir, Libr Admin,* Pamela Melton; E-mail: prmelton@law.sc.edu; *Assoc Dir, Libr Operations,* Rebekah Maxwell; E-mail: rkmaxwel@law.sc.edu; *Asst Dir, Fac Serv,* Candle Wester; E-mail: westercm@law.sc.edu; *Asst Dir, Legal Res Instruction,* Terrye Conroy; E-mail: conroyt@law.sc.edu; *Head, Access Serv,* Karen Taylor; E-mail: taylorkg@law.sc.edu; *Head, Tech Serv,* Gloria Zinky; Tel: 803-777-5898; *Ref Librn,* Alyson Drake; E-mail: drakeam@law.sc.edu; *Ref Librn,* David Lehmann; E-mail: lehmannd@law.sc.edu; *Ref Librn,* Ellen Richardson; E-mail: erichard@mailbox.sc.edu; Staff 9 (MLS 9)
Founded 1866. Enrl 657; Fac 50; Highest Degree: Doctorate
Jul-Jun
    Library Holdings: AV Mats 2,628; CDs 723; DVDs 80; e-books 29,184; Electronic Media & Resources 256; Microforms 1,496,676; Bk Titles 109,796; Bk Vols 559,256; Per Subs 5,708; Videos 966
    Special Collections: Anglo-American Law; South Carolina Legal History. US Document Depository
    Automation Activity & Vendor Info: (Acquisitions) Innovative Interfaces, Inc - Millenium; (Cataloging) Innovative Interfaces, Inc - Millenium; (Circulation) Innovative Interfaces, Inc - Millenium; (Course Reserve) Innovative Interfaces, Inc - Millenium; (ILL) OCLC; (OPAC) Innovative Interfaces, Inc - Millenium; (Serials) Innovative Interfaces, Inc - Millenium
    Database Vendor: Blackwell's, HeinOnline, JSTOR, LexisNexis, Loislaw, OCLC WorldCat, Westlaw, Wilson - Wilson Web
    Function: Computers for patron use, Copy machines, Doc delivery serv, e-mail serv, Electronic databases & coll, Exhibits, Fax serv, ILL available, Online cat, Online info literacy tutorials on the web & in blackboard, Pub access computers, Ref serv in person, Telephone ref
Partic in Law Library Microform Consortium (LLMC); Lyrasis
Open Mon-Wed 7am-11pm, Thurs 7am-10pm, Fri 7am-9pm, Sat 9-9, Sun 9am-11pm
    Restriction: Open to pub for ref & circ; with some limitations, Pub use on premises
MATH, LeConte College, 3rd Flr, 29208. Tel: 803-777-4741. Web Site: www.sc.edu/library/math.html. *Dept Head,* Danley Reed; Staff 1 (Non-MLS 1)
    Library Holdings: Bk Vols 25,000; Per Subs 150
    Open Mon-Thurs 8am-9pm, Fri 8-5, Sun 2-6
PEDEN MCLEOD LIBRARY, WALTERBORO, 807 Hampton St, Walterboro, 29488. (Mail add: PO Box 1337, Walterboro, 29488-1337), SAN 378-1607. Tel: 843-549-6314. FAX: 843-549-4345. Web Site: uscsalkehatchie.sc.edu/. *Assoc Prof, Librn,* Edwin O Merwin, Jr; E-mail: emerwin@mailbox.sc.edu; Staff 1 (MLS 1)
    Library Holdings: Bk Vols 13,000; Per Subs 25
Partic in Partnership Among South Carolina Academic Libraries
Open Mon-Thurs 8am-9pm, Fri 8-4:30, Sun 3-7
MEDFORD LIBRARY, 476 Hubbard Dr, Lancaster, 29720. (Mail add: PO Box 889, Lancaster, 29721-0889), SAN 315-5625. Tel: 803-313-7000, 803-313-7060. Administration Tel: 803-313-7058. FAX: 803-313-7107. E-mail: Medford@mailbox.sc.edu. Web Site: usclancaster.sc.edu/library. *Dir,* Lorene B Harris; E-mail: lbharris@sc.edu; *Asst Librn,* Rebecca T Freeman; Tel: 803-313-7062, E-mail: rfreeman@mailbox.sc.edu; *Asst Librn,* Kaetrena Davis Kendrick; Tel: 803-313-7061, E-mail: kaetrena@mailbox.sc.edu; Staff 4 (MLS 3, Non-MLS 1)
Founded 1959. Enrl 1,259; Fac 110; Highest Degree: Associate
    Library Holdings: AV Mats 1,547; e-books 35,194; Microforms 53,374; Bk Vols 80,000
    Special Collections: US Document Depository
    Automation Activity & Vendor Info: (Acquisitions) Innovative Interfaces, Inc - Millenium; (Cataloging) Innovative Interfaces, Inc - Millenium; (Circulation) Innovative Interfaces, Inc - Millenium; (Course Reserve) Innovative Interfaces, Inc - Millenium; (ILL) OCLC ILLiad; (Serials) Innovative Interfaces, Inc - Millenium
    Database Vendor: Alexander Street Press, American Chemical Society, American Psychological Association (APA), Annual Reviews, BioOne,

Cambridge Scientific Abstracts, Children's Literature Comprehensive Database Company (CLCD), Cinahl Information Systems, College Source, Community of Science (COS), CQ Press, CredoReference, EBSCOhost, Elsevier, Facts on File, Gale Cengage Learning, IOP, ISI Web of Knowledge, JSTOR, LearningExpress, Medline, Modern Language Association, Nature Publishing Group, OVID Technologies, Oxford Communications, Project MUSE, ProQuest, PubMed, ScienceDirect, Springshare, LLC, TDNet, Thomson - Web of Science
Partic in Carolina Consortium; Charlotte Area Educ Consortium; DISCUS; Partnership Among South Carolina Academic Libraries
Open Mon-Thurs 8am-9pm, Fri 8-4:30, Sun 2-6
MOVING IMAGE RESEARCH COLLECTIONS, 707 Catawba St, 29201-4305. Tel: 803-777-6841. Web Site: www.sc.edu/library/mirc. *Interim Dir,* Mark G Cooper; Tel: 803-777-2271; *Curator, Movietone News,* Greg Wilsbacher; Staff 6 (MLS 2, Non-MLS 4)
    Special Collections: C E Feltner, Jr Coll (newsfilm); Chinese Film; Covington Coll of Commercials & Shorts; Fox Movietone News; Local Television News; Roman Vishniac Coll; SC Dept of Wildlife Films
MUSIC, 813 Assembly St, 29208. Tel: 803-777-5139. FAX: 803-777-1426. Web Site: www.sc.edu/library/music. *Head Librn,* Ana Dubnjakovic; Tel: 803-777-5425, E-mail: ana@mailbox.sc.edu; Staff 5 (MLS 3, Non-MLS 2)
    Library Holdings: Bk Vols 90,000; Per Subs 135
    Special Collections: Center for Southern African American Music; Digital Sheet Music Project; Henry Cowell Coll; Mario Castelnuovo-Tedesco Coll
    Open Mon-Thurs (Winter) 8am-9pm, Fri 8-5, Sat 11-2, Sun 2-5; Mon-Fri (Summer) 9-5

CM SCHOOL OF MEDICINE, 6311 Garners Ferry Rd, 29209. (Mail add: School of Medicine Library, University of South Carolina Bldg 101, 29208). Tel: 803-733-3344. Interlibrary Loan Service Tel: 803-733-3347. Reference Tel: 803-733-3361. Administration Tel: 803-733-3350. FAX: 803-733-1509. E-mail: libweb@uscmed.sc.edu. Web Site: uscm.med.sc.edu/referenceform.htm. *Dir, Libr Serv,* Ruth Riley; E-mail: ruth.riley@uscmed.sc.edu; *Asst Dir, Coll Mgt,* Felicia Yeh; E-mail: felicia.yeh@uscmed.sc.edu; *Asst Dir, Educ & Outreach,* Rozalynd Anderson; E-mail: roz.anderson@uscmed.sc.edu; *Asst Dir, Info Serv,* Laura Kane; E-mail: laura.kane@uscmed.sc.edu; *Head, Access Serv,* Karen McMullen; Tel: 803-733-3321, E-mail: karen.mcmullen@uscmed.sc.edu; *Coll Develop Librn,* Christine Whitaker; Tel: 803-733-3346, E-mail: christine.whitaker@uscmed.sc.edu; *Syst Librn,* Victor Jenkinson; Tel: 803-733-3351, E-mail: victor.jenkinson@uscmed.sc.edu; *Coordr, Ctr for Disability Res Librn,* Steven P Wilson; Tel: 803-733-1501, E-mail: steve.wilson@uscmed.sc.edu; Staff 16 (MLS 9, Non-MLS 7)
Founded 1975. Enrl 556; Fac 263; Highest Degree: Doctorate
    Special Collections: Rare Medical Books
    Subject Interests: Disabilities
    Automation Activity & Vendor Info: (Cataloging) Innovative Interfaces, Inc; (OPAC) Innovative Interfaces, Inc
    Database Vendor: EBSCO Information Services, McGraw-Hill, MD Consult, Nature Publishing Group, OVID Technologies, Oxford Online, PubMed, ScienceDirect, Springer-Verlag, TDNet, Wiley InterScience
Partic in Carolina Consortium; Consortium of Southern Biomedical Libraries; National Network of Libraries of Medicine Southeastern Atlantic Region; Partnership Among South Carolina Academic Libraries
Open Mon-Fri 8am-10pm, Sat 8-8, Sun 1-10
SOUTH CAROLINA POLITICAL COLLECTIONS, 720 College St, 29208. Tel: 803-777-0578. FAX: 803-777-0578. *Dir,* Herb Hartsook; Staff 4 (MLS 4)
    Special Collections: Papers of South Carolinians holding state & national level office post-WWII
    Open Mon-Fri 8:30-5
SOUTH CAROLINIANA, 29208-0103. Tel: 803-777-3131. Interlibrary Loan Service Tel: 803-777-3132. FAX: 803-777-5747. *Interim Dir,* Alan Stokes; E-mail: stokesa@mailbox.sc.edu; Staff 9 (MLS 9)
Founded 1801
    Library Holdings: Bk Vols 101,114; Per Subs 325
    Special Collections: South Caroliniana & Southern Materials
    Subject Interests: SC culture, SC hist
    Publications: Caroliniana Columns; University South Caroliniana Society Annual Report of Gifts to the Collection
    Open Mon-Fri 8:30-5, Sat 9-1
Friends of the Library Group
ELLIOT WHITE SPRINGS BUSINESS LIBRARY, Francis M Hipp-William H Close Bldg, 1705 College St, 29208. Tel: 803-777-6032. FAX: 803-777-6876. Web Site: library.sc.edu/business. *Head of Libr,* Kathy Snediker; E-mail: snediker@mailbox.sc.edu; Staff 3 (MLS 2, Non-MLS 1)
    Open Mon-Thurs 8am-10pm, Fri 8-6, Sat 1-6, Sun 2-10

CONWAY

C   COASTAL CAROLINA UNIVERSITY*, Kimbel Library, 755 Hwy 544, 29526. (Mail add: PO Box 261954, 29528-6054), SAN 315-5331. Tel: 843-349-2402. Circulation Tel: 843-349-2400. Reference Tel: 843-349-2414. FAX: 843-349-2412. Web Site: www.coastal.edu/library. *Dean*, Barbara Burd; E-mail: barbara@coastal.edu; *Head, Libr Tech, Head, Syst*, John Felt; E-mail: john@coastal.edu; *Head, Pub Serv*, Margaret Fain; Tel: 843-349-2410, E-mail: margaret@coastal.edu; *Access Serv Librn*, Jennifer Hughes; Tel: 843-349-2415, E-mail: jhughes@coastal.edu; *Ref & Instruction Librn*, Joshua Bossler; Tel: 843-349-2650, E-mail: joshua@coastal.edu; *Coll Mgt Serv*, Kathy Goodwin; *Govt Doc, Ref Serv*, Ann Hamilton; Tel: 843-349-2409, E-mail: ahamilto@coastal.edu; *ILL, Ref Serv*, Allison Faix; Tel: 843-349-2511, E-mail: afaix@coastal.edu; Staff 19 (MLS 9, Non-MLS 10)
Founded 1954. Enrl 4,500; Highest Degree: Master
Library Holdings: e-journals 13,403; Bk Vols 149,990; Per Subs 500
Special Collections: Marine Science. State Document Depository; US Document Depository
Automation Activity & Vendor Info: (Acquisitions) Innovative Interfaces, Inc; (Cataloging) Innovative Interfaces, Inc; (Circulation) Innovative Interfaces, Inc; (ILL) Innovative Interfaces, Inc; (OPAC) Innovative Interfaces, Inc; (Serials) Innovative Interfaces, Inc
Database Vendor: Gale Cengage Learning, OCLC FirstSearch, OVID Technologies
Wireless access
Open Mon-Thurs 8am-Midnight, Fri 8-5, Sat 10-6, Sun 1-Midnight

P   HORRY COUNTY MEMORIAL LIBRARY*, Administration, 1008 Fifth Ave, 29526. SAN 360-1382. Tel: 843-248-1544. FAX: 843-248-1548. Web Site: www.horry.lib.sc.us. *Dir*, Clif Boyer; *Dep Dir*, Geraldine Gaskill; *Automation Syst Coordr*, Jody Gray; *Coll Develop*, Claire Campana; Tel: 843-248-1550, Fax: 843-248-1549; *Youth Serv*, Elizabeth Shuping; Staff 8 (MLS 3, Non-MLS 5)
Founded 1948. Pop 210,000; Circ 903,583
Jul 2007-Jun 2008. Mats Exp $688,000. Sal $2,522,031
Special Collections: Local History. Oral History
Automation Activity & Vendor Info: (Acquisitions) SirsiDynix; (Cataloging) SirsiDynix; (Circulation) SirsiDynix; (ILL) OCLC; (OPAC) SirsiDynix
Publications: HCML Report
Partic in DISCUS; Lyrasis; OCLC Online Computer Library Center, Inc
Special Services for the Deaf - Staff with knowledge of sign lang
Open Mon-Thurs 9-8, Fri & Sat 9-6, Sun 2-6
Friends of the Library Group
Branches: 10
   AYNOR BRANCH, 500 Ninth Ave, Aynor, 29511, SAN 360-1412. Tel: 843-358-3324. FAX: 843-358-1639. E-mail: aynorlib@yahoo.com. *Br Mgr*, Angela Hemingway; Staff 2 (Non-MLS 2)
   Founded 1948. Circ 30,354
   Open Tues-Thurs 10-7, Fri 10-6, Sat 10-3
   Friends of the Library Group
   BUCKSPORT, 7657 Hwy 701 S, 29527, SAN 375-5703. Tel: 843-397-1950. FAX: 843-397-1951. E-mail: bucksportlib@yahoo.com. *Br Mgr*, E Ann Dion; Staff 1 (Non-MLS 1)
   Founded 1995. Circ 14,848
   Library Holdings: Bk Vols 16,726
   Open Mon-Thurs 12-8, Sat 12-5
   Friends of the Library Group
   CONWAY BRANCH, 801 Main St, 29526. Tel: 843-915-7323. Interlibrary Loan Service Tel: 843-915-7434. Reference Tel: 843-915-7431. TDD: 843-248-1547. E-mail: conwaylibrary@horrycounty.org. *Librn/Mgr*, Jane Bunal
   Circ 183,528
   Special Collections: Local History Coll
   Open Mon-Thurs 9-8, Fri & Sat 9-6, Sun 2-6
   Friends of the Library Group
   Bookmobiles: 1
   GREEN SEA-FLOYDS BRANCH, 5331 Hwy 9, Green Sea, 29545. Tel: 843-392-0994. FAX: 843-392-0996. E-mail: greensealib@yahoo.com. *Br Mgr*, Bob Gants; Staff 2 (Non-MLS 2)
   Founded 2000. Circ 19,260
   Library Holdings: Bk Vols 11,728
   Open Mon-Thurs 11-7, Sat 11-4
   Friends of the Library Group
   LITTLE RIVER BRANCH, Ralph H Ellis County Complex Bldg, 107 Hwy 57 N, Little River, 29566, SAN 375-5711. Tel: 843-399-5541. FAX: 843-399-5542. E-mail: stecros@yahoo.com. *Br Mgr*, Cindy Burgio; Staff 2 (Non-MLS 2)
   Circ 68,767
   Library Holdings: Bk Vols 20,459
   Open Tues-Fri 9-6, Sat 9-2
   Friends of the Library Group

   LORIS BRANCH, 4316 Main St, Loris, 29569, SAN 360-1501. Tel: 843-756-8101. FAX: 843-756-1988. E-mail: lorislibrary@yahoo.com. *Br Mgr*, Frances Prince; Staff 2 (Non-MLS 2)
   Founded 1952. Circ 52,446
   Library Holdings: Bk Vols 27,958
   Open Tues-Thurs 10-7, Fri 10-6, Sat 10-3
   Friends of the Library Group
   NORTH MYRTLE BEACH BRANCH, 910 First Ave S, North Myrtle Beach, 29582, SAN 360-1471. Tel: 843-915-5281. FAX: 843-915-6280. TDD: 843-915-7452. E-mail: nmblibrary@horrycounty.org. *Librn*, Shelley Ridout; Staff 4 (MLS 2, Non-MLS 2)
   Founded 1948. Pop 120,000; Circ 153,903
   Automation Activity & Vendor Info: (Acquisitions) Horizon; (Cataloging) OCLC; (Circulation) Horizon; (OPAC) EBSCO Online
   Function: Art exhibits, Audio & video playback equip for onsite use, Bks on cassette, Bks on CD, Children's prog, Computers for patron use, Copy machines, Digital talking bks, e-mail serv, E-Reserves, Electronic databases & coll, Exhibits, Free DVD rentals, Handicapped accessible, Holiday prog, ILL available, Instruction & testing, Magnifiers for reading, Mail & tel request accepted, Microfiche/film & reading machines, Music CDs, Newsp ref libr, Online cat, Online ref, Online searches, Photocopying/Printing, Preschool outreach, Preschool reading prog, Prog for adults, Prog for children & young adult, Pub access computers, Ref serv available, Ref serv in person, Referrals accepted, Serves mentally handicapped consumers, Spoken cassettes & CDs, Spoken cassettes & DVDs, Story hour, Summer & winter reading prog, Tax forms, Teen prog, Telephone ref, Web-catalog, Wheelchair accessible
   Special Services for the Deaf - TDD equip
   Special Services for the Blind - Audio mat; Bks on cassette; Bks on CD; Digital talking bk; Extensive large print coll; Large print bks; Magnifiers
   Open Mon-Thurs 9-7, Fri 9-6, Sat 9-2
   Restriction: Circ to mem only, In-house use for visitors, Non-resident fee, Open to pub for ref & circ; with some limitations
   Friends of the Library Group
   SOCASTEE, 141 707-Connector Rd, Myrtle Beach, 29588, SAN 372-7874. Tel: 843-215-4700. FAX: 843-215-2801. TDD: 843-215-6764. E-mail: socasteelibrary@horrycounty.org. *Br Librn*, Sharon Eels; *Ref Librn*, Alan Smith; E-mail: smithph@horrycounty.org; Staff 8 (MLS 3, Non-MLS 5)
   Founded 2003. Circ 259,359
   Library Holdings: Bk Vols 59,000
   Function: Adult bk club, Art exhibits, Bk club(s), Bks on cassette, Bks on CD, Children's prog, Computers for patron use, Copy machines, Electronic databases & coll, Free DVD rentals, Holiday prog, ILL available, Instruction & testing, Magnifiers for reading, Music CDs, Notary serv, Online cat, Online ref, Online searches, Photocopying/Printing, Prog for adults, Prog for children & young adult, Pub access computers, Ref serv available, Scanner, Story hour, Summer reading prog, Tax forms, Telephone ref, Video lending libr, Web-catalog
   Open Mon-Thurs 10-8, Fri 10-6, Sat 10-3
   Friends of the Library Group
   SURFSIDE BEACH BRANCH, 410 Surfside Dr, Surfside Beach, 29575, SAN 360-1536. Tel: 843-238-0122. FAX: 843-238-4273. TDD: 843-238-2180. E-mail: surfsidelibrary@yahoo.com. *Librn*, Gwenda Hemingway; Staff 4 (MLS 1, Non-MLS 3)
   Circ 135,856
   Library Holdings: Bk Vols 36,956
   Open Mon-Thurs 9-7, Fri 9-6, Sat 9-2
   Friends of the Library Group
   TECHNICAL SERVICES, Extension Bldg, 1603 Fourth Ave, 29526, SAN 374-4116. Tel: 843-248-1550. FAX: 843-248-1549. *Head, Tech Serv*, Sue McLeod; Staff 4 (Non-MLS 4)
   Founded 1948
   Open Mon-Fri 8-5

C   HORRY-GEORGETOWN TECHNICAL COLLEGE*, Conway Campus Library, 2050 Hwy 501 E, 29526-9521. (Mail add: PO Box 261966, 29528-6066), SAN 315-5323. Tel: 843-349-5268. Reference Tel: 843-349-5394. FAX: 843-347-0552. Web Site: www.hgtc.edu/library. *Dean of Libr*, Peggy E Smith; Tel: 843-349-5269, E-mail: peggy.smith@hgtc.edu; *Acad Prog Librn*, Nicole Romyak; Tel: 843-349-5397, E-mail: nicole.romyak@hgtc.edu; *Ref Librn*, Chris Williams; E-mail: christopher.williams@hgtc.edu; *Libr Spec*, Wendy Nolan; Tel: 843-349-7809, E-mail: wendy.nolan@hgtc.edu; *Libr Spec*, Christi Scott; Tel: 843-349-7596, E-mail: christi.scott@hgtc.edu; *Libr Spec*, Roberta Tyson; Tel: 843-349-5396, E-mail: roberta.tyson@hgtc.edu; Staff 6.5 (MLS 3.5, Non-MLS 3)
Founded 1966. Enrl 4,398; Fac 180; Highest Degree: Associate
Library Holdings: e-books 68,395; Bk Vols 25,233; Per Subs 180
Subject Interests: Civil eng, Computer sci, Cosmetology, Criminal justice, Culinary arts, Early child care, Golf course maintenance
Automation Activity & Vendor Info: (Acquisitions) SirsiDynix; (Cataloging) SirsiDynix; (Circulation) SirsiDynix; (Course Reserve) SirsiDynix; (ILL) OCLC WorldCat; (OPAC) SirsiDynix; (Serials) SirsiDynix

Database Vendor: 3M Library Systems, CQ Press, CredoReference, EBSCOhost, Facts on File, Gale Cengage Learning, JSTOR, LearningExpress, OCLC FirstSearch, OVID Technologies, ProQuest, SirsiDynix
Wireless access
Function: Computers for patron use, Copy machines, e-mail & chat, e-mail serv, Electronic databases & coll, Free DVD rentals, ILL available, Online cat, Online info literacy tutorials on the web & in blackboard, Online ref, Online searches, Orientations, Outside serv via phone, mail, e-mail & web, Photocopying/Printing, Printer for laptops & handheld devices, Ref & res, Ref serv available, Ref serv in person, Telephone ref, Web-catalog, Wheelchair accessible, Workshops
Partic in Lyrasis; OCLC Online Computer Library Center, Inc; Partnership Among South Carolina Academic Libraries; South Carolina Information & Library Services Consortium (SCILS)
Open Mon-Thurs 7:45am-8:45pm, Fri 7:45-12:30
Restriction: Non-circulating of rare bks
Departmental Libraries:
ELIZABETH MATTOCKS CHAPIN MEMORIAL LIBRARY ON THE GRAND STRAND CAMPUS, 3639 Pampas Dr, Myrtle Beach, 29577, SAN 372-5049. Tel: 843-477-2012. Reference Tel: 843-477-2018. FAX: 843-477-2153. *Electronic Res Librn,* Jennifer Williams; Tel: 843-477-2100, E-mail: jennifer.williams@hgtc.edu; *Ref Librn,* Russell Grooms; E-mail: russell.grooms@hgtc.edu; Staff 2.5 (MLS 1.5, Non-MLS 1)
   Founded 1990. Enrl 1,800; Fac 105; Highest Degree: Associate
   Library Holdings: Bk Vols 20,080; Per Subs 153
   Subject Interests: Allied health, Dental, Nursing, Paralegal, Radiology
   Open Mon-Thurs 7:45am-8:45pm, Fri 8am-12:30pm
GEORGETOWN CAMPUS, 4003 S Fraser St, Georgetown, 29440, SAN 372-5030. Tel: 843-520-1424. FAX: 843-520-1462. *Ref Librn,* Amy Harris; Tel: 843-520-1423, E-mail: amy.harris@hgtc.edu; *Tech Asst,* Julia Rivens; Tel: 843-520-1407, E-mail: julia.rivens@hgtc.edu; Staff 1.5 (MLS 0.5, Non-MLS 1)
   Founded 1978. Enrl 900; Fac 25
   Library Holdings: Bk Titles 7,161; Per Subs 87
   Subject Interests: Forestry, Licensed practical nursing, Surgical tech
   Open Mon-Thurs 7:45-6

DARLINGTON

S   DARLINGTON COUNTY HISTORICAL COMMISSION*, 204 Hewitt St, 29532. SAN 370-2103. Tel: 843-398-4710. FAX: 843-398-4742. E-mail: dchc1968@aol.com. *Dir,* Doris G Gandy
   Library Holdings: Bk Vols 10,000
   Subject Interests: Genealogy, Local hist

P   DARLINGTON COUNTY LIBRARY*, 204 N Main St, 29532. SAN 360-1560. Tel: 843-398-4940. FAX: 843-398-4942. Web Site: www.darlington-lib.org. *Dir,* Nancy Ray; E-mail: nray@spiritcom.net; *Br Mgr,* Audrey Tripp; *Ch,* Karen E Moreau; *Circ,* Marjorie C Reason; Staff 7 (MLS 3, Non-MLS 4)
   Founded 1893. Pop 82,309; Circ 233,425
   Library Holdings: Bk Vols 140,000; Per Subs 422
   Special Collections: NUREG
   Automation Activity & Vendor Info: (Cataloging) Polaris Library Systems; (Circulation) Polaris Library Systems; (OPAC) Polaris Library Systems
   Open Mon-Thurs 9-8, Fri 9-5, Sat 10-2, Sun 2-5
   Friends of the Library Group
   Branches: 3
   HARTSVILLE MEMORIAL, 147 W College St, Hartsville, 29550, SAN 360-1595. Tel: 843-332-5115. FAX: 843-332-7071. *Br Mgr,* Audrey Tripp; E-mail: audrey-library@earthlink.net; *Ch,* Lori Strickland; Staff 8 (MLS 1, Non-MLS 7)
   Founded 1930. Pop 44,747; Circ 164,416
   Library Holdings: Bk Vols 90,200; Per Subs 110
   Special Collections: Hartsville Messenger Newspaper (1894-present)
   Function: Adult bk club, Audiobks via web, Bks on cassette, Bks on CD, Children's prog, Computer training, Computers for patron use, Copy machines, Electronic databases & coll, Fax serv, Free DVD rentals, Handicapped accessible, ILL available, Microfiche/film & reading machines, Music CDs, Online cat, OverDrive digital audio bks, Photocopying/Printing, Preschool outreach, Printer for laptops & handheld devices, Prog for children & young adult, Pub access computers, Ref serv available, Story hour, Summer reading prog, Tax forms, Teen prog, Telephone ref, VHS videos, Web-catalog
   Partic in Palmetto Academic Independent Library System (PAILS)
   Open Mon-Thurs 9-8, Fri 9-5, Sat 10-2, Sun 2-5
   Friends of the Library Group
   LAMAR BRANCH, 103 E Main St, Lamar, 29069, SAN 360-1625. Tel: 843-326-5524. FAX: 843-326-7302. *Br Mgr,* Sherry Humphries; Staff 4 (Non-MLS 4)
   Library Holdings: Bk Vols 18,500; Per Subs 36

Open Mon-Thurs 10-7, Fri 10-5, Sat 10-2
Friends of the Library Group
SOCIETY HILL BRANCH, 473 S Main St, Society Hill, 29593. (Mail add: PO Box 60, Society Hill, 29593-0060). Tel: 843-378-0026. FAX: 843-378-0026. E-mail: sochill.lib@gmail.com. *Br Dir,* Kevin Hicks; *Asst Dir,* Donna Chapman; *Circ Mgr,* Terry Brown; *Ad,* Charlene McDonnough; *Youth Serv Librn,* Karen Moreau; Staff 6 (MLS 3, Non-MLS 3)
   Founded 1822. Pop 10,000; Circ 10,500
   Automation Activity & Vendor Info: (Acquisitions) Polaris Library Systems; (Course Reserve) Polaris Library Systems; (ILL) Polaris Library Systems
   Database Vendor: Ebooks Corporation, EBSCO Information Services, EBSCOhost, Gale Cengage Learning, Ingram Library Services, LearningExpress, Polaris Library Systems, ProQuest, Thomson - Web of Science
   Function: Accelerated reader prog, Adult bk club, After school storytime, Art exhibits, Audio & video playback equip for onsite use, Audiobks via web, AV serv, Bks on CD, CD-ROM, Children's prog, Computer training, Computers for patron use, Copy machines, Distance learning, E-Reserves, Electronic databases & coll, Exhibits, Family literacy, Fax serv, Govt ref serv, ILL available, Instruction & testing, Music CDs, Online cat, Online info literacy tutorials on the web & in blackboard, Online ref, Online searches, OverDrive digital audio bks, Photocopying/Printing, Prog for adults, Prog for children & young adult, Pub access computers, Ref & res, Ref serv in person, Scanner, Senior computer classes, Spoken cassettes & CDs, Spoken cassettes & DVDs, Story hour, Summer reading prog, Tax forms, VHS videos, Video lending libr, Web-catalog, Workshops
   Partic in Palmetto Academic Independent Library System (PAILS)
   Open Mon-Thurs 12-2:30 & 3-8, Fri 12-2:30 & 3-5, Sat 10-2
   Restriction: Circ limited, In-house use for visitors, Non-resident fee, Off-site coll in storage - retrieval as requested, Photo ID required for access
   Friends of the Library Group

DENMARK

J   DENMARK TECHNICAL COLLEGE*, Learning Resources Center, 500 Solomon Blatt Blvd, 29042. (Mail add: PO Box 327, 29042-0327), SAN 374-6232. Tel: 803-793-5213. Circulation Tel: 803-793-5214. Reference Tel: 803-793-5215. FAX: 803-793-5942. Web Site: www.denmarktech.edu. *Dir,* Bobbi Jones; E-mail: jonesb@denmarktech.edu; Staff 3 (MLS 2, Non-MLS 1)
   Founded 1948. Enrl 1,200; Fac 36; Highest Degree: Associate
   Library Holdings: Bk Titles 13,000; Per Subs 187
   Automation Activity & Vendor Info: (Circulation) SirsiDynix
   Database Vendor: Gale Cengage Learning, Innovative Interfaces, Inc INN - View, OVID Technologies, Wilson - Wilson Web
   Publications: The Messenger (Newsletter)
   Open Mon-Thurs 8-8, Fri 8-5, Sat 9-1:30, Sun 3-6

C   VOORHEES COLLEGE*, Wright-Potts Library, 5480 Voorhees Rd, 29042. (Mail add: PO Box 678, 29042-0678), SAN 315-534X. Tel: 803-793-3351, Ext 7095. FAX: 803-793-0471. Web Site: www.voorhees.edu. *Librn,* Marie S Martin; *Circ,* Helen Graham; *Tech Serv,* Sue Bradshaw; Staff 4 (MLS 4)
   Founded 1935. Enrl 600; Fac 44; Highest Degree: Bachelor
   Library Holdings: Bk Vols 110,000; Per Subs 213
   Special Collections: Historical Papers; Ten-Year Developmental Study of Episcopal Church Book of Common Prayer; Voorhees College Documents
   Wireless access
   Partic in HBCU Library Alliance; Partnership Among South Carolina Academic Libraries
   Open Mon-Thurs 8am-9:30pm, Fri 8-5, Sat 10-2, Sun 2-8

DILLON

P   DILLON COUNTY LIBRARY*, 600 E Main St, 29536. Tel: 843-774-0330. FAX: 843-774-0733. E-mail: dilloncountylibrary@live.com. Web Site: www.dillon.lib.sc.us. *Dir,* Yolanda Manning McCormick; *Br Mgr,* Christina Fowler; *Ch,* Mavis Jones; Staff 6 (MLS 1, Non-MLS 5)
   Circ 130,000
   Library Holdings: Bk Titles 50,000; Bk Vols 93,000; Per Subs 50
   Subject Interests: Genealogy, Local hist
   Automation Activity & Vendor Info: (Cataloging) Polaris Library Systems; (Circulation) Polaris Library Systems; (OPAC) Polaris Library Systems; (Serials) Polaris Library Systems
   Wireless access
   Open Mon & Tues 9-8, Wed-Fri 9-6, Sat 9-1
   Friends of the Library Group

Branches: 2
LAKE VIEW BRANCH, 207 S Main St, Lake View, 29563. (Mail add: PO Box 704, Lake View, 29563), SAN 360-294X. Tel: 843-759-2692. FAX: 843-759-0061. *Librn,* Mertis Barnett
Open Mon-Fri 10-6, Sat 10-1
Friends of the Library Group
LATTA BRANCH, 101 N Marion St, Latta, 29565-3597, SAN 360-2885. Tel: 843-752-5389. FAX: 843-752-7457. *Br Mgr,* Vanessa Bildon; Staff 2 (Non-MLS 2)
Founded 1914. Pop 29,114; Circ 75,322
Open Mon-Fri 9-6, Sat 9-1
Bookmobiles: 1

DUE WEST

CR　ERSKINE COLLEGE & THEOLOGICAL SEMINARY*, McCain Library, One Depot St, 29639. (Mail add: PO Box 188, 29639-0188), SAN 315-5358. Tel: 864-379-8898. Circulation Tel: 864-379-8714. Interlibrary Loan Service Tel: 864-379-8747. Reference Tel: 864-379-8784. Toll Free Tel: 877-876-4348. FAX: 864-379-2900. E-mail: library@erskine.edu. Web Site: www.erskine.edu/library. *Dir,* John F Kennerly; Tel: 864-379-8788, E-mail: kennerly@erskine.edu; *Circ Mgr,* Betsy L Elsner; E-mail: belsner@erskine.edu; *Syst Coordr,* Brian K Smith; Tel: 864-379-8789, E-mail: keith@erskine.edu; *Acq,* Shirley R Adams; E-mail: adams@erskine.edu; *Archivist, Cat,* Edith M Brawley; Tel: 864-379-8763, E-mail: ebrawley@erskine.edu; *Cat, ILL,* Sara M Morrison; E-mail: morrison@erskine.edu; *Govt Doc, Ref Serv,* Frederick W Guyette; E-mail: fguyette@erskine.edu; Staff 6 (MLS 3, Non-MLS 3)
Founded 1837. Enrl 778; Fac 83; Highest Degree: Doctorate
Library Holdings: AV Mats 1,963; e-books 36,267; e-journals 625; Bk Vols 177,877; Per Subs 1,333
Special Collections: Associate Reformed Presbyterian Church Records. US Document Depository
Subject Interests: Erskiniana, Genealogy, Local hist, Relig
Automation Activity & Vendor Info: (Acquisitions) Innovative Interfaces, Inc; (Cataloging) OCLC CatExpress; (Circulation) Innovative Interfaces, Inc; (Course Reserve) Innovative Interfaces, Inc; (ILL) OCLC; (OPAC) Innovative Interfaces, Inc; (Serials) Innovative Interfaces, Inc
Database Vendor: Alexander Street Press, American Chemical Society, American Psychological Association (APA), Baker & Taylor, BioOne, Blackwell's, Dialog, EBSCOhost, Gale Cengage Learning, IOP, netLibrary, OCLC FirstSearch, Oxford Online, ProQuest
Wireless access
Partic in Carolina Consortium; Council for Christian Colleges & Universities; Lyrasis; OCLC Online Computer Library Center, Inc; Partnership Among South Carolina Academic Libraries

DUNCAN

S　CRYOVAC SEALED AIR CORPORATE LIBRARY*, 100 Rogers Bridge Rd, 29334. (Mail add: PO Box 464, 29334-0464), SAN 315-5366. Tel: 864-433-2313. FAX: 864-433-3636. *Res Librn,* Sherry Davis; Staff 1 (MLS 1)
Founded 1962
Library Holdings: Bk Titles 8,000; Per Subs 225
Special Collections: Cryovac Proprietary Documents (in-house use only)
Subject Interests: Chem, Eng, Food tech, Packaging, Plastics
Partic in Lyrasis

EASLEY

P　PICKENS COUNTY LIBRARY SYSTEM*, 304 Biltmore Rd, 29640. SAN 360-1684. Tel: 864-850-7077. FAX: 864-850-7088. E-mail: reference@pickens.lib.sc.us. Web Site: www.pickens.lib.sc.us. *Dir,* Allison H Anderson; *Pub Serv Mgr,* Jennifer Crenshaw; E-mail: jenniferc@pickens.lib.sc.us; *Syst Mgr,* Phil Mabry; E-mail: philm@pickens.lib.sc.us; *Coll Develop,* Debra Kaniaris; E-mail: debbiek@pickens.lib.sc.us; Staff 26 (MLS 12, Non-MLS 14)
Founded 1935. Pop 110,757; Circ 775,000
Library Holdings: Bk Titles 190,063; Bk Vols 210,527; Per Subs 326
Subject Interests: SC
Automation Activity & Vendor Info: (Cataloging) SirsiDynix; (Circulation) SirsiDynix; (OPAC) SirsiDynix
Wireless access
Open Mon-Thurs 9-9, Fri & Sat 9-6, Sun 2-6
Friends of the Library Group

EDGEFIELD

S　TOMPKINS MEMORIAL LIBRARY*, 104 Courthouse Sq, 29824. SAN 327-8646. Tel: 803-637-4010. FAX: 803-637-2116. E-mail: oedgs@aikenelectric.net. Web Site: oedgs.org. *Dir,* Tonya Browder
Library Holdings: Bk Vols 17,100
Open Mon-Fri 9-4

FLORENCE

P　FLORENCE COUNTY LIBRARY SYSTEM*, 509 S Dargan St, 29506. SAN 360-1838. Tel: 843-662-8424. FAX: 843-661-7544. Reference E-mail: reference@florencelibrary.org. Web Site: www.florencelibrary.org. *Dir,* Ray McBride; *Head, Ref,* Aubrey Carroll; *Head, Tech Serv,* Timothy Anderson; *Sr Ref Librn,* Eliz Caldwell; *Sr Ref Librn,* Christina Stewart; *Extn Serv,* William McRee; *Hist Coll Librn,* Margaret Collar; Staff 18 (MLS 12, Non-MLS 6)
Founded 1925. Pop 185,000; Circ 313,024
Library Holdings: AV Mats 15,121; Bk Vols 310,117; Per Subs 446
Special Collections: Caroliniana. US Document Depository
Subject Interests: Local hist
Automation Activity & Vendor Info: (Acquisitions) SirsiDynix; (Cataloging) SirsiDynix; (Circulation) SirsiDynix; (ILL) OCLC; (OPAC) SirsiDynix; (Serials) SirsiDynix
Wireless access
Partic in Lyrasis
Open Mon-Fri 9-8:30, Sat 9-5:30, Sun 2-5
Friends of the Library Group
Branches: 5
JOHNSONVILLE PUBLIC LIBRARY, 242 S Georgetown Hwy, Johnsonville, 29555, SAN 360-1862. Tel: 843-386-2052. FAX: 843-380-1302. *Br Mgr, Librn II,* Donna Gaye Tanner; E-mail: dtanner@florencelibrary.org; Staff 3 (MLS 1, Non-MLS 2)
Open Mon & Thurs 9:30-7, Tues, Wed & Fri 9:30-5, Sat 10-1
Friends of the Library Group
LAKE CITY PUBLIC LIBRARY, 221 E Main St, Lake City, 29560-2113, SAN 360-1897. Tel: 843-394-8071. FAX: 843-394-1033. *Br Mgr,* Debbie Quesada; Staff 1 (MLS 1)
Library Holdings: Bk Vols 13,000; Per Subs 35
Open Mon-Thurs 9:30-7:30, Fri 9:30-5, Sat 9:30-2, Sun 2-5
Friends of the Library Group
OLANTA PUBLIC LIBRARY, PO Box 263, Olanta, 29114-0263, SAN 360-1919. Tel: 843-396-4287. FAX: 843-396-9317. *Librn,* Annis Raines
Library Holdings: Bk Vols 1,889
Open Mon-Thurs 10-12 & 2-5:30, Fri 2-5:30, Sun 2-5
PAMPLICO PUBLIC LIBRARY, 100 E Main St, Pamplico, 29583. (Mail add: PO Box 476, Pamplico, 29583-0476), SAN 360-1927. Tel: 843-493-5441. FAX: 843-493-0361. *Br Mgr,* Christina Stewart; E-mail: cstewart@florencelibrary.org; Staff 3 (MLS 1, Non-MLS 2)
Pop 1,150; Circ 12,000
Library Holdings: AV Mats 1,068; Braille Volumes 1; CDs 387; DVDs 68; Large Print Bks 183; Bk Vols 15,000; Per Subs 32; Videos 310
Special Collections: South Carolina Coll
Function: Children's prog, Computers for patron use, Copy machines, Fax serv, ILL available, Mail & tel request accepted, Music CDs, Online cat, Photocopying/Printing, Prog for children & young adult, Pub access computers, Ref & res, Ref serv available, Spoken cassettes & CDs, Summer reading prog, Tax forms, Telephone ref, VHS videos, Web-catalog, Wheelchair accessible
Special Services for the Blind - Audio mat; Bks on cassette; Bks on CD; Large print bks; Talking bk serv referral; ZoomText magnification & reading software
Open Mon, Wed, Fri & Sat 10-5, Tues & Thurs 10-7
Friends of the Library Group
TIMMONSVILLE PUBLIC LIBRARY, 111 S Warren St, Timmonsville, 29161-1743. (Mail add: PO Box 160, Timmonsville, 29161-0160), SAN 360-1951. Tel: 843-346-2941. FAX: 843-346-2931. *Librn,* Beverly Bell; *Librn,* Mary S Dorriety
Library Holdings: Bk Vols 8,000
Open Mon-Fri 10-12 & 1-5, Sat 9-1
Bookmobiles: 1. Librn, Kitty Hinnant. Bk vols 5,000

J　FLORENCE-DARLINGTON TECHNICAL COLLEGE LIBRARIES, Wellman, Inc Library, 2715 W Lucas St, 29501. (Mail add: PO Box 100548, 29501-0548), SAN 315-5390. Tel: 843-661-8032. Circulation Tel: 843-661-8033. Interlibrary Loan Service Tel: 843-661-8034. FAX: 843-661-8266. Web Site: www.fdtc/libraries.edu. *Dir of Libr,* Jeronell W Bradley; E-mail: jeronell.bradley@fdtc.edu; *Librn,* Linda B Coe; E-mail: linda.coe@fdtc.edu; Staff 5 (MLS 3, Non-MLS 2)
Founded 1964. Enrl 2,523; Fac 99; Highest Degree: Associate
Jul 2010-Jun 2011 Income (Main Library and Branch(s)) $363,190. Sal $174,795
Library Holdings: AV Mats 2,923; e-books 60,354; Bk Vols 30,891; Per Subs 286
Automation Activity & Vendor Info: (Acquisitions) Innovative Interfaces, Inc; (Cataloging) Innovative Interfaces, Inc; (Circulation) Innovative Interfaces, Inc; (ILL) Innovative Interfaces, Inc; (OPAC) Innovative Interfaces, Inc; (Serials) Innovative Interfaces, Inc
Database Vendor: CredoReference, EBSCO Auto Repair Reference, EBSCOhost, Facts on File, Innovative Interfaces, Inc, netLibrary, Newsbank, OCLC, OCLC WorldCat, OVID Technologies, ProQuest, Springshare, LLC, Westlaw
Wireless access

Partic in Partnership Among South Carolina Academic Libraries
Open Mon-Thurs 7:30am-9pm, Fri 8-4:30, Sun 2-6
Departmental Libraries:
SEGARS LIBRARY HEALTH SCIENCES CAMPUS, 320 W Cheves St,
29501. (Mail add: PO Box 100548, 29501-0501). Tel: 843-676-8575.
Automation Services Tel: 843-661-8043. *Dir,* Jeronell W Bradley; *Librn,*
Linda Coe; E-mail: linda.coe@fdtc.edu; *Media Spec,* Yvette Pierce;
E-mail: yvette.pierce@fdtc.edu; Staff 5 (MLS 3, Non-MLS 2)
Founded 2001. Fac 99; Highest Degree: Associate
Open Mon-Thurs 8:30am-7pm, Fri 8:30-3

C   FRANCIS MARION UNIVERSITY, James A Rogers Library, 4822 East
Palmetto St, 29506. (Mail add: PO Box 100547, 29502), SAN 315-5412.
Tel: 843-661-1300. Circulation Tel: 843-661-1311. Interlibrary Loan
Service Tel: 843-661-4677. Reference Tel: 843-661-1310. FAX:
843-661-1309. Administration FAX: 843-661-4682. Web Site:
www.fmarion.edu/rogerslibrary. *Dean,* Joyce M Durant; E-mail:
jdurant@fmarion.edu; *ILL, Ref Librn,* Stephanie S Thomas; Tel:
843-661-4674, E-mail: sthomas@fmarion.edu; *Archivist, Spec Coll Librn,*
Suzanne Singleton; Tel: 843-661-1319, E-mail: msingleton@fmarion.edu;
Govt Doc, Bernadette J Johnson; Tel: 843-661-1313, E-mail:
bjjohnson@fmarion.edu; *Ref,* Nathan Flowers; Tel: 843-661-1302, E-mail:
nflowers@fmarion.edu; *Tech Serv,* Linda D Becote; Tel: 843-661-1308,
E-mail: lbecote@fmarion.edu; Staff 23 (MLS 8, Non-MLS 15)
Founded 1970. Enrl 4,187; Fac 282; Highest Degree: Master
Jul 2010-Jun 2011 Income (Main Library Only) $1,832,150, State
$1,816,424, Federal $14,675, Other $1,051. Mats Exp $758,970, Books
$22,250, Per/Ser (Incl. Access Fees) $468,874, Other Print Mats $33,414,
Micro $18,510, Electronic Ref Mat (Incl. Access Fees) $205,772, Presv
$10,150. Sal $972,821
Library Holdings: e-books 85,976; e-journals 39,499; Bk Vols 412,491;
Per Subs 1,110
Special Collections: South Caroliniana especially relating to Pee Dee
Area, bks & microfilm. State Document Depository; US Document
Depository
Automation Activity & Vendor Info: (Acquisitions) Innovative Interfaces,
Inc; (Cataloging) Innovative Interfaces, Inc; (Circulation) Innovative
Interfaces, Inc; (Course Reserve) Innovative Interfaces, Inc; (OPAC)
Innovative Interfaces, Inc; (Serials) Innovative Interfaces, Inc - OCLC
Database Vendor: ACM (Association for Computing Machinery),
American Chemical Society, Annual Reviews, Cambridge Scientific
Abstracts, College Source, EBSCOhost, JSTOR, LearningExpress,
LexisNexis, Medline, Mergent Online, netLibrary, Newsbank, OCLC
FirstSearch, OCLC WorldCat, Project MUSE, ScienceDirect,
SerialsSolutions, Standard & Poor's, ValueLine, Wilson - Wilson Web
Wireless access
Publications: The Axis
Partic in Carolina Consortium; Lyrasis; OCLC Online Computer Library
Center, Inc; Partnership Among South Carolina Academic Libraries
Open Mon-Thurs 8am-11pm, Fri 8-5, Sat 9-5, Sun 2:30-11

M   MCLEOD HEALTH, Health Sciences Library, 144 N Ravenel St, 29506.
(Mail add: PO Box 100551, 29501), SAN 315-5420. Tel: 843-777-2275.
FAX: 843-777-2274. *Libr Dir,* Lorraine Reiman; E-mail:
lreiman@mcleodhealth.org; Staff 1 (MLS 1)
Founded 1975
Library Holdings: Per Subs 40
Special Collections: Medical & Nursing Coll
Subject Interests: Allied health fields, Clinical med, Continuing educ in
the health fields, Nursing
Publications: Journal List
Partic in Docline; National Network of Libraries of Medicine
Restriction: Employees only

FORT JACKSON

UNITED STATES ARMY
A   FORT JACKSON MAIN POST LIBRARY*, Thomas Lee Hall Main Post
Library, Bldg 4679, 29207, SAN 360-1986. Tel: 803-751-4816,
803-751-5589. FAX: 803-751-1065. *Chief Librn,* John Anthony Vassallo;
Tech Serv, Sharon Backenstose; Staff 5 (MLS 2, Non-MLS 3)
Founded 1946
Library Holdings: Bk Vols 70,115; Per Subs 50
Subject Interests: Hist, Mil sci
Automation Activity & Vendor Info: (Cataloging) Follett Software
Database Vendor: OCLC FirstSearch
Function: ILL available
Partic in OCLC Online Computer Library Center, Inc
Open Mon-Thurs 11-8, Fri-Sun 11-5
Restriction: Non-circulating to the pub
AM   MONCRIEF ARMY HOSPITAL MEDICAL LIBRARY*, 4500 Stuart St,
29207-5720, SAN 360-2044. Tel: 803-751-2149. FAX: 803-751-2012.
Librn, Steven Leap; E-mail: steven.leap@us.army.mil
Founded 1950
Library Holdings: Bk Vols 2,000; Per Subs 170

Subject Interests: Dental, Med, Nursing
Automation Activity & Vendor Info: (Acquisitions) Ex Libris Group;
(Cataloging) Ex Libris Group; (Circulation) Ex Libris Group; (OPAC) Ex
Libris Group
Partic in Docline; National Network of Libraries of Medicine

A   US ARMY CHAPLAIN CENTER & SCHOOL LIBRARY*, 10100 Lee
Rd, 29207. Tel: 803-751-8828. FAX: 803-751-8393. Web Site:
www.usachcs.army.mil. *Admin Librn, Chief Librn,* Dr Mohammed A Khan,
PhD; E-mail: mohammed.a.khan@conus.army.mil; *Access Serv,* Dixon
Monica, I; Tel: 803-751-8871. Subject Specialists: *World relig,* Dr
Mohammed A Khan, PhD
Library Holdings: CDs 62; DVDs 393; Bk Titles 23,413; Bk Vols 30,164;
Per Subs 26; Videos 73
Special Collections: World Religions Coll
Subject Interests: World relig
Automation Activity & Vendor Info: (Acquisitions) Baker & Taylor;
(Cataloging) LibraryWorld, Inc; (Circulation) LibraryWorld, Inc; (ILL)
OCLC; (OPAC) LibraryWorld, Inc; (Serials) LibraryWorld, Inc
Database Vendor: 3M Library Systems, Baker & Taylor, EBSCOhost,
LibraryWorld, Inc, OCLC FirstSearch
Wireless access
Publications: Monthly New Books List (Current awareness service)
Open Mon-Fri 8-6

GAFFNEY

P   CHEROKEE COUNTY PUBLIC LIBRARY*, 300 E Rutledge Ave,
29340-2227. SAN 360-2079. Tel: 864-487-2711. FAX: 864-487-2752.
E-mail: cherokeelib@spiritcom.net. Web Site:
www.cherokeecountylibrary.org. *Dir,* Lana Gardner; *Circ Mgr,* Meg Stroup;
Ch, Susan Sarratt; *ILL, Ref,* Judy Brown; *Syst Adminr,* Cindy Harry; Staff
6 (MLS 1, Non-MLS 5)
Founded 1902. Pop 44,506; Circ 184,022
Library Holdings: AV Mats 3,000; e-books 40,000; Bk Vols 11,000; Per
Subs 141; Talking Bks 3,000
Special Collections: Arthur Gettys Genealogy Coll; Gladys Coker Fort
Fine Arts Coll; Heritage Room Coll; June Carr Photography Coll;
Raymond & Bright Parker Story Tape Coll; Ruby Cash Garvin South
Carolina Coll
Subject Interests: SC genealogy
Automation Activity & Vendor Info: (Acquisitions) Horizon;
(Cataloging) SirsiDynix; (Circulation) SirsiDynix; (OPAC) SirsiDynix
Database Vendor: ProQuest
Wireless access
Publications: Friendly Notes; Genealogically Speaking
Open Mon-Thurs 9-7, Fri 9-5, Sat 9-4
Friends of the Library Group
Branches: 1
BLACKSBURG BRANCH, 201 S Rutherford St, Blacksburg, 29702, SAN
360-2109. Tel: 864-839-2630. FAX: 864-839-2572. *Br Mgr,* Laura Jones;
E-mail: lsmjones@infoave.net; *Ch,* Lee Anne Batchler; E-mail:
lbatchler@infoave.net; Staff 1 (MLS 1)
Special Collections: James M Bridges Reference Coll
Open Mon-Thurs 10-6, Fri 10-5
Friends of the Library Group
Bookmobiles: 1

C   LIMESTONE COLLEGE*, A J Eastwood Library, 1115 College Dr,
29340. SAN 315-5439. Tel: 864-488-4612. Toll Free Tel: 800-795-7151.
FAX: 864-487-4613. Web Site: lib.limestone.edu. *Dir,* Lori Hetrick; Tel:
864-488-4446, E-mail: lhetrick@limestone.edu; *Outreach & Instruction
Librn,* Lizah Ismail; *Tech Serv Librn,* Steven A Smith; Tel: 864-488-4611,
E-mail: ssmith@limestone.edu; Staff 6 (MLS 3, Non-MLS 3)
Founded 1845. Highest Degree: Bachelor
Jul 2008-Jun 2009 Income $374,000
Library Holdings: e-books 61,757; Bk Vols 68,861; Per Subs 281
Special Collections: Personal Library of Former Limestone College
President (Lee Davis Lodge & Harrison Patillo Griffith)
Automation Activity & Vendor Info: (Acquisitions) SirsiDynix;
(Cataloging) SirsiDynix; (Circulation) SirsiDynix; (Course Reserve)
SirsiDynix; (OPAC) SirsiDynix; (Serials) SirsiDynix
Wireless access
Partic in Carolina Consortium; Lyrasis; Partnership Among South Carolina
Academic Libraries; South Carolina Library Network

GEORGETOWN

P   GEORGETOWN COUNTY LIBRARY*, 405 Cleland St, 29440-3200.
SAN 360-2133. Tel: 843-545-3300. FAX: 843-545-3395. Web Site:
www.gclibrary.org. *Dir,* Dwight McInvaill; Tel: 843-545-3304, E-mail:
dmcinvaill@georgetowncountysc.org; *Asst Dir,* Trudy Bazemore; *Adult
Serv,* Patti Burns; *Ch,* Sheila Sullivan; *Circ,* Mable Hills; *Tech Serv,* Vickie
Jones; Staff 24 (MLS 2, Non-MLS 22)
Founded 1799. Pop 60,000; Circ 169,305

Library Holdings: Bk Vols 141,906; Per Subs 201; Talking Bks 6,953; Videos 10,893
Special Collections: 18th & 19th Century Library Records & Plantation Documents; Bank of Georgetown Records, 1920-1930's; Georgetown County Life 1890-1915, photos; Georgetown Library Society Materials
Subject Interests: Archives, Local hist
Automation Activity & Vendor Info: (Cataloging) Polaris Library Systems; (Circulation) Polaris Library Systems; (OPAC) Polaris Library Systems
Database Vendor: Overdrive, Inc
Wireless access
Function: Art exhibits, Audiobks via web, Bks on cassette, Bks on CD, Children's prog, Computer training, Computers for patron use, Copy machines, Electronic databases & coll, Free DVD rentals, Handicapped accessible, Holiday prog, Home delivery & serv to Sr ctr & nursing homes, ILL available, Jail serv, Mail & tel request accepted, Music CDs, Notary serv, Online cat, Online searches, Outside serv via phone, mail, e-mail & web, OverDrive digital audio bks, Photocopying/Printing, Preschool outreach, Prog for adults, Prog for children & young adult, Ref & res, Ref serv available, Res libr, Satellite serv, Scanner, Spoken cassettes & CDs, Spoken cassettes & DVDs, Summer reading prog, Tax forms, Teen prog, Telephone ref, Wheelchair accessible, Workshops
Publications: A View of Our Past; Books on local history; Friends (Newsletter)
Friends of the Library Group
Branches: 3
ANDREWS BRANCH, 105 N Morgan St, Andrews, 29510, SAN 360-2168. Tel: 803-264-8785. FAX: 803-264-8785. *Mgr,* Dale Wade
Friends of the Library Group
CARVERS BAY, 13048 Choppee Rd, Hemingway, 29554-3318. Tel: 843-558-6654. FAX: 843-558-6680. *Dir,* Marilynn Lace-Robb; E-mail: afussell@georgetowncountry.org
Open Tues, Thurs & Fri 11-7, Wed & Sat 9-5
WACCAMAW, 24 Commerce Lane, Pawleys Island, 29585, SAN 373-1944. Tel: 843-545-3623. FAX: 843-545-3624. *Mgr,* Carlethia Rudolph
Friends of the Library Group
Bookmobiles: 1

GRAMLING

S   RENTAW FOUNDATION, INC LIBRARY, Hwy 176, 29348. (Mail add: PO Box 275, 29348-0275), SAN 321-4850. Tel: 864-472-2750. E-mail: rentawfoundation@windstream.net. *Librn,* Carl Watner
Founded 1981
Library Holdings: Bk Titles 1,800; Per Subs 19
Special Collections: Libertarianism (Rentaw Coll); Robert LeFevre; The Voluntaryist (Newsletter Coll)

GRANITEVILLE

J   AIKEN TECHNICAL COLLEGE LIBRARY*, 2276 Jefferson Davis Hwy, 29829. (Mail add: PO Drawer 696, Aiken, 29802-0696), SAN 315-484X. Tel: 803-593-9954, Ext 1755. Circulation Tel: 803-593-9954, Ext 1330. Interlibrary Loan Service Tel: 803-593-9954, Ext 1312. FAX: 803-593-2169. Web Site: www.atc.edu. *Dir,* Allyson Davis; E-mail: davisa@atc.edu; *Pub Serv,* Ann Adcock; Tel: 803-593-9954, Ext 1312, E-mail: adcocka@atc.edu; *Tech Serv,* Parri Wright; Tel: 803-593-9954, Ext 1335, E-mail: pmwright@atc.edu; Staff 3 (MLS 2, Non-MLS 1)
Founded 1973. Enrl 3,926; Highest Degree: Associate
Library Holdings: AV Mats 1,824; e-books 27,812; Bk Vols 32,898; Per Subs 180
Subject Interests: Computer tech, Health, Indust tech, Occupational tech, Pub serv
Automation Activity & Vendor Info: (Cataloging) NOTIS; (Circulation) NOTIS; (ILL) OCLC; (OPAC) NOTIS
Database Vendor: Gale Cengage Learning
Function: ILL available, Online searches
Partic in Lyrasis
Open Mon-Thurs 8am-9pm, Fri 8-4, Sat 8-Noon
Restriction: Open to students, fac & staff

GREENVILLE

C   BOB JONES UNIVERSITY, J S Mack Library, 1700 Wade Hampton Blvd, 29614. SAN 360-2192. Tel: 864-242-5100, Ext 6000. Circulation Tel: 864-370-1800, Ext 6000. Interlibrary Loan Service Tel: 864-370-1800, Ext 6030. Reference Tel: 864-370-1800, Ext 6015. Automation Services Tel: 864-370-1800, Ext 6010. FAX: 864-232-1729. E-mail: library@bju.edu. Web Site: library.bju.edu, www.bju.edu/library/home.html. *Dir, Libr Serv,* Joseph Lee Allen, Sr; E-mail: jallen@bju.edu; *Head, Tech Serv,* Bryan Tyson; E-mail: btyson@bju.edu; *Instrul Serv Librn,* Nancy McGuire; Tel: 864-370-1800, Ext 6025, E-mail: mcmguir@bju.edu; *Ref Librn,* Jennifer Walton; E-mail: jwalton@bju.edu; *Archivist,* Shannon Brooks; Tel: 864-252-5100, Ext 6050; *Cataloger,* Megan Townley; E-mail: mtownley@bju.edu; Staff 6 (MLS 6)

Founded 1927. Enrl 3,505; Fac 247; Highest Degree: Doctorate
Jun 2011-May 2012. Mats Exp $526,995, Books $160,624, Per/Ser (Incl. Access Fees) $82,023, AV Mat $16,542, Electronic Ref Mat (Incl. Access Fees) $209,540, Presv $8,530. Sal $432,166 (Prof $200,118)
Library Holdings: AV Mats 22,751; CDs 8,311; DVDs 1,677; e-books 30,515; Bk Titles 287,734; Bk Vols 320,545; Per Subs 970; Videos 1,334
Subject Interests: Art, Relig
Automation Activity & Vendor Info: (Acquisitions) Innovative Interfaces, Inc; (Cataloging) Innovative Interfaces, Inc; (Circulation) Innovative Interfaces, Inc; (Course Reserve) Innovative Interfaces, Inc; (OPAC) Innovative Interfaces, Inc; (Serials) Innovative Interfaces, Inc
Database Vendor: American Chemical Society, CQ Press, Dialog, EBSCOhost, Gale Cengage Learning, H W Wilson, Innovative Interfaces, Inc INN - View, IOP, JSTOR, LexisNexis, ProQuest, PubMed, Safari Books Online, ScienceDirect, Springer-Verlag, Springshare, LLC
Wireless access
Function: Photocopying/Printing, Ref serv available
Partic in Lyrasis
Open Mon-Thurs 7:45am-10:15pm, Fri 7:45am-9pm, Sat 9-9
Departmental Libraries:
MUSIC, 1700 Wade Hampton Blvd, 29614. Tel: 864-242-5100, Ext 2705. FAX: 864-467-9302. *Librn,* Carole Eby
Open Mon-Thurs 8am-10pm, Fri 8am-9pm, Sat 9-9

C   ECPI UNIVERSITY*, Greenville Campus Library, 1001 Keys Dr, No 100, 29615-4232. Tel: 864-288-2828. FAX: 864-288-2930. Web Site: students.ecpi.edu. *Librn,* Kristy Glashagel; Staff 3 (MLS 1, Non-MLS 2)
Founded 1999. Enrl 220; Fac 12; Highest Degree: Associate
Library Holdings: e-books 7,000; Bk Titles 4,000; Per Subs 71; Talking Bks 25
Subject Interests: Info tech
Automation Activity & Vendor Info: (Cataloging) Follett Software; (Circulation) Follett Software; (OPAC) Follett Software; (Serials) EBSCO Online
Database Vendor: EBSCOhost, Gale Cengage Learning, netLibrary, ProQuest
Function: Distance learning, For res purposes, ILL available, Mail loans to mem, Outside serv via phone, mail, e-mail & web, Photocopying/Printing, Ref serv available, Telephone ref
Partic in Libr & Info Resources Network (LIRN)
Open Mon-Thurs 8-8, Fri 8:30-1pm, Sat 9-1

S   FLUOR, Greenville Office Library, 100 Fluor Daniel Dr, 29607-2762. SAN 327-0793. Tel: 864-281-4799. FAX: 864-281-6480. *Librn,* Lillian Hyatt; E-mail: lillian.hyatt@fluor.com; Staff 1 (MLS 1)
Library Holdings: Bk Titles 1,000; Per Subs 5
Special Collections: Historical Standards & Codes
Subject Interests: Eng
Automation Activity & Vendor Info: (Cataloging) EOS International; (Circulation) EOS International; (OPAC) EOS International
Database Vendor: Dialog, ebrary, EOS International, IHS, Knovel, RefWorks, Wiley
Wireless access
Function: Doc delivery serv, Electronic databases & coll, ILL available, Online searches, Ref & res, Ref serv available, Res libr, Telephone ref

C   FURMAN UNIVERSITY LIBRARIES*, James B Duke Library, 3300 Poinsett Hwy, 29613-4100. SAN 315-5455. Tel: 864-294-2190. Circulation Tel: 864-294-2265. Interlibrary Loan Service Tel: 864-294-2198. Reference Tel: 864-294-2195. Administration Tel: 864-294-2191. Automation Services Tel: 864-294-3204. FAX: 864-294-3004. Interlibrary Loan Service FAX: 864-294-3560. Web Site: library.furman.edu. *Dir,* Dr Janis M Bandelin; E-mail: janis.bandelin@furman.edu; *Assoc Dir,* Pongracz Sennyey; E-mail: pongracz.sennyey@furman.edu; *Acq/Coll Develop Librn,* Betty Kelly; Tel: 864-294-2712, E-mail: betty.kelly@furman.edu; *Instrul Serv Librn,* Mary Fairbairn; Tel: 864-294-3226, E-mail: mary.fairbairn@furman.edu; *Syst Librn,* Scott Salzman; Tel: 864-294-3204, E-mail: scott.salzman@furman.edu; *Cat,* Nancy Sloan; Tel: 864-294-2197, E-mail: nancy.sloan@furman.edu; *Digicenter,* Jen Haldaman; Tel: 864-294-3733, E-mail: jen.haldaman@furman.edu; *Doc Delivery,* Laura Baker; Tel: 864-294-2277, E-mail: laura.baker@furman.edu; *Electronic Res,* Cris Ferguson; Tel: 864-294-2713, E-mail: cris.ferguson@furman.edu; *Govt Doc,* Libby Young; Tel: 864-294-2260, E-mail: libby.young@furman.edu; *Music,* Jenny Colvin; Tel: 864-294-3797, E-mail: jenny.colvin@furman.edu; *Ref,* Steve Richardson; Tel: 864-294-3227, E-mail: steve.richardson@furman.edu; *Spec Coll & Archives Librn,* DebbieLee Landi; Tel: 864-294-2714, E-mail: debbielee.landi@furman.edu; Staff 29 (MLS 13, Non-MLS 16)
Founded 1826. Enrl 2,673; Highest Degree: Master
Jul 2008-Jun 2009. Mats Exp $1,681,335, Books $546,876, Per/Ser (Incl. Access Fees) $410,916, Micro $15,016, AV Mat $32,778, Electronic Ref Mat (Incl. Access Fees) $675,749, Presv $33,423
Library Holdings: AV Mats 9,833; e-books 14,461; e-journals 249; Bk Titles 489,944; Bk Vols 569,593; Per Subs 1,150

Special Collections: Furman University Archives; Rare Books & Manuscript Colls; South Carolina Baptist History; South Carolina Poetry Archives. US Document Depository

Automation Activity & Vendor Info: (Acquisitions) Innovative Interfaces, Inc; (Cataloging) Innovative Interfaces, Inc; (Circulation) Innovative Interfaces, Inc; (Course Reserve) Innovative Interfaces, Inc; (OPAC) Innovative Interfaces, Inc; (Serials) Innovative Interfaces, Inc

Database Vendor: Alexander Street Press, American Mathematical Society, Annual Reviews, ARTstor, BioOne, CQ Press, ebrary, EBSCO Information Services, Elsevier, Factiva.com, Gale Cengage Learning, H W Wilson, JSTOR, netLibrary, OCLC FirstSearch, ProQuest, Sage, Springer-Verlag, ValueLine, Westlaw, Wiley

Wireless access

Partic in Carolina Consortium; Lyrasis; OCLC Online Computer Library Center, Inc; OCLC Research Library Partnership; Partnership Among South Carolina Academic Libraries

Open Mon-Thurs 8am-1am, Fri 8-6, Sat 10-7, Sun Noon-1am

Friends of the Library Group

Departmental Libraries:

ROBERT J MAXWELL MUSIC LIBRARY, Daniel Music Bldg, 3300 Poinsett Hwy, 29613. Tel: 864-294-3795. FAX: 864-294-3004. Web Site: library.furman.edu/music. *Music,* Jenny Colvin; E-mail: jenny.colvin@furman.edu; Staff 1 (MLS 1)

　Founded 1998

　Library Holdings: CDs 4,158; Bk Titles 13,164; Per Subs 77; Videos 506

SCIENCE LIBRARY, Plyler Hall of Science, 3300 Poinsett Hwy, 29613. Tel: 864-294-2342. *Sci,* Andrea Wright; E-mail: andrea.wright2630@furman.edu

　Founded 1962

　Library Holdings: e-journals 60; Bk Titles 3,654; Per Subs 138; Videos 184

P　GREENVILLE COUNTY LIBRARY SYSTEM, Hughes Main Library, 25 Heritage Green Pl, 29601-2034. SAN 360-2257. Tel: 864-242-5000. Circulation Tel: 864-242-5000, Ext 2213. Interlibrary Loan Service Tel: 864-242-5000, Ext 2276. Reference Tel: 864-242-5000, Ext 2258. Administration Tel: 864-242-5000, Ext 2231. FAX: 864-235-8375. Reference FAX: 864-232-9656. Web Site: www.greenvillelibrary.org. *Exec Dir,* Beverly A James; Tel: 864-527-9231; *Mgr, Access Serv,* Barbara Yonce; Tel: 864-242-5000, Ext 2254; *Human Res Mgr,* Ann Bishop; Tel: 864-242-5000, Ext 2262; *Info Tech Mgr,* Jerry Osteen; Tel: 864-242-5000, Ext 4231; *Youth Serv Mgr,* Karen Allen; Tel: 864-242-5000, Ext 2249; Staff 183.8 (MLS 48.75, Non-MLS 135.05)

Founded 1921. Pop 451,225; Circ 3,617,618

Jul 2011-Jun 2012 Income (Main Library and Branch(s)) $13,100,503, State $330,704, County $12,139,851, Locally Generated Income $546,227, Other $83,721. Mats Exp $1,955,577. Sal $6,302,714

Special Collections: Foundation Center Cooperating Coll (bks, databases, per); Local History & Genealogy (audio tapes, bks, databases, diaries, ledger bks, maps, micro holdings, pamphlets, personal papers, photog, rare bks); Parenting & Early Childhood Coll (bks, DVDs, videos). State Document Depository; US Document Depository

Subject Interests: Genealogy, Law, Local hist, State hist, Textile hist

Wireless access

Function: Adult bk club, After school storytime, Archival coll, Audiobks via web, Bk club(s), Bks on cassette, Bks on CD, CD-ROM, Children's prog, Computer training, Computers for patron use, Copy machines, Digital talking bks, e-mail serv, Electronic databases & coll, Exhibits, Free DVD rentals, Govt ref serv, Handicapped accessible, Health sci info serv, Holiday prog, Home delivery & serv to Sr ctr & nursing homes, Homebound delivery serv, ILL available, Magnifiers for reading, Mail & tel request accepted, Music CDs, Newsp ref libr, Online cat, Online ref, Online searches, Orientations, Outreach serv, Photocopying/Printing, Prog for adults, Prog for children & young adult, Pub access computers, Ref serv available, Ref serv in person, Satellite serv, Senior computer classes, Senior outreach, Spoken cassettes & CDs, Spoken cassettes & DVDs, Story hour, Summer reading prog, Tax forms, Teen prog, Telephone ref, VHS videos, Video lending libr, Web-catalog, Wheelchair accessible, Workshops, Writing prog

Partic in Lyrasis

Special Services for the Deaf - ADA equip; Assisted listening device; Assistive tech; Bks on deafness & sign lang; Closed caption videos; Pocket talkers; Sign lang interpreter upon request for prog; Sorenson video relay syst; TDD equip; TTY equip; Video & TTY relay via computer; Video relay serv

Special Services for the Blind - Accessible computers; Aids for in-house use; Assistive/Adapted tech devices, equip & products; Audio mat; BiFolkal kits; Bks available with recordings; Bks on cassette; Bks on CD; Braille alphabet card; Braille bks; Children's Braille; Closed caption display syst; Closed circuit TV magnifier; Computer access aids; Computer with voice synthesizer for visually impaired persons; Copier with enlargement capabilities; Digital talking bk; Extensive large print coll; Home delivery serv; Internet workstation with adaptive software; Large print & cassettes; Large print bks; Large screen computer & software; Low

vision equip; Magnifiers; Micro-computer access & training; Networked computers with assistive software; PC for handicapped; Playaways (bks on MP3); Scanner for conversion & translation of mats; Screen enlargement software for people with visual disabilities; Screen reader software; Sound rec; Text reader; Videos on blindness & phys handicaps; ZoomText magnification & reading software

Open Mon-Fri 9-9, Sat 9-6, Sun 2-6

Friends of the Library Group

Branches: 11

ANDERSON ROAD (WEST) BRANCH, 2625 Anderson Rd, 29611, SAN 360-2524. Tel: 864-269-5210. FAX: 864-269-3986. *Mgr,* Renita Barksdale

　Open Mon-Thurs 9-9, Fri & Sat 9-6

　Friends of the Library Group

AUGUSTA ROAD (RAMSEY FAMILY BRANCH), 100 Lydia St, 29605, SAN 360-2281. Tel: 864-277-0161. FAX: 864-277-2673. *Mgr,* Kitti McKean

　Open Mon-Thurs 9-9, Fri & Sat 9-6

　Friends of the Library Group

BEREA (SARAH DOBEY JONES) BRANCH, 111 N Hwy 25 Bypass, 29617, SAN 360-2311. Tel: 864-246-1695. FAX: 864-246-1765. *Mgr,* Andy Dykes

　Open Mon-Thurs 9-9, Fri & Sat 9-6

　Friends of the Library Group

FOUNTAIN INN (KERRY ANN YOUNTS CULP) BRANCH, 311 N Main St, Fountain Inn, 29644, SAN 360-2346. Tel: 864-862-2576. FAX: 864-862-6376. E-mail: fountaininn@greenvillelibrary.org. *Mgr,* Julie Phillips; E-mail: jphillips@greenvillelibrary.org

　Open Mon-Thurs 9-9, Fri & Sat 9-6

　Friends of the Library Group

GREER (JEAN M SMITH) BRANCH, 505 Pennsylvania Ave, Greer, 29650, SAN 360-2370. Tel: 864-877-8722. FAX: 864-877-1422. *Mgr,* Stephanie Ditch

　Open Mon-Thurs 9-9, Fri & Sat 9-6

　Friends of the Library Group

MAULDIN (W JACK GREER) BRANCH, 800 W Butler Rd, 29607, SAN 360-2400. Tel: 864-277-7397. FAX: 864-277-7389. *Mgr,* Michael Evans

　Open Mon-Thurs 9-9, Fri & Sat 9-6

　Friends of the Library Group

PELHAM ROAD (F W SYMMES) BRANCH, 1508 Pelham Rd, 29615, SAN 360-2338. Tel: 864-288-6688. FAX: 864-675-9149. *Mgr,* Nancy Murrin

　Open Mon-Thurs 9-9, Fri & Sat 9-6

　Friends of the Library Group

SIMPSONVILLE (HENDRICKS) BRANCH, 626 NE Main St, Simpsonville, 29681, SAN 360-2435. Tel: 864-963-9031. FAX: 864-228-0986. *Mgr,* Jennifer Jenkins

　Open Mon-Thurs 9-9, Fri & Sat 9-6

　Friends of the Library Group

TAYLORS (BURDETTE) BRANCH, 316 W Main St, Taylors, 29687, SAN 360-2494. Tel: 864-268-5955. FAX: 864-268-4275. *Mgr,* Beth Atwood

　Open Mon-Thurs 9-9, Fri & Sat 9-6

　Friends of the Library Group

TRAVELERS REST (SARGENT) BRANCH, 17 Center St, Travelers Rest, 29690, SAN 360-246X. Tel: 864-834-3650. FAX: 864-834-4686. *Mgr,* Amy Grubbs

　Open Mon-Thurs 9-9, Fri & Sat 9-6

　Friends of the Library Group

Bookmobiles: 1

G　GREENVILLE COUNTY PLANNING DEPARTMENT*, Technical Library, 301 University Ridge, Ste 400, 29601. SAN 325-5360. Tel: 864-467-7270. FAX: 864-467-5962. Web Site: www.greenvilleplanning.com. *Librn,* Wanda Johnson

Founded 1964

Library Holdings: Bk Vols 1,000; Per Subs 35

Restriction: Staff use only

M　GREENVILLE HOSPITAL SYSTEM*, Health Sciences Library, 701 Grove Rd, 29605. SAN 360-2559. Tel: 864-455-7176. FAX: 864-455-5696. *Dir,* Fay Towell; Tel: 864-455-3099, E-mail: ftowell@ghs.org; Staff 5 (MLS 3, Non-MLS 2)

Founded 1912

Library Holdings: e-books 30; e-journals 1,500; Bk Titles 5,500; Bk Vols 25,000; Per Subs 400

Subject Interests: Allied health, Med, Mental health, Nursing, Psychiat, Psychol, Rehabilitation med

Automation Activity & Vendor Info: (Cataloging) EOS International; (Serials) EBSCO Online

Database Vendor: EBSCOhost

Wireless access

Open Mon-Thurs 8-6, Fri 8-5

Restriction: Circulates for staff only

Branches:

ROGER C PEACE HOSPITAL LIBRARY, 701 Grove Rd, 29605. Tel: 864-455-7176. FAX: 864-455-5696. *Librn,* Deanna Handley
   Library Holdings: e-books 30; e-journals 2,000; Bk Titles 800; Per Subs 30
   Special Collections: Patient Education Materials
   Subject Interests: Prof mat in rehabilitation med
   Database Vendor: EBSCOhost
   Open Mon-Fri 8:30-5
   Restriction: Circulates for staff only

S   GREENVILLE NEWS-PIEDMONT LIBRARY*, 305 S Main St, 29601-2640. (Mail add: PO Box 1688, 29602-1688), SAN 315-5471. Tel: 864-298-4158. FAX: 864-298-4395. *Librn,* Holly Diaz
   Founded 1956
   Library Holdings: Bk Titles 600; Bk Vols 900; Per Subs 10
   Special Collections: South Carolina, news & photos
   Wireless access
   Restriction: Staff use only

J   GREENVILLE TECHNICAL COLLEGE LIBRARY*, 620 S Pleasantburg Dr, 29607. (Mail add: PO Box 5616, 29607-5616), SAN 315-548X. Tel: 864-250-8319. Interlibrary Loan Service Tel: 864-250-8332. Reference Tel: 864-250-8321. FAX: 864-250-8506. Web Site: www.gvltec.edu/library. *Dir, Pub Serv,* Doris Jones; Tel: 864-250-8018, E-mail: doris.jones@gvltec.edu; *MLIS Ref, Info Literacy Librn,* Lillie Ruegg; E-mail: Lillie.Ruegg@gvltec.edu; *Tech Serv Librn,* Thomas Gore; Tel: 864-250-8320, E-mail: Thomas.Gore@gvltec.edu; Staff 7 (MLS 3, Non-MLS 4)
   Founded 1962. Enrl 12,557; Fac 250; Highest Degree: Associate
   Jul 2010-Jun 2011 Income $709,819. Mats Exp $182,500, Books $80,000, Per/Ser (Incl. Access Fees) $20,000, Electronic Ref Mat (Incl. Access Fees) $82,500. Sal $175,000
   Library Holdings: Audiobooks 55; AV Mats 1,290; e-books 63,000; Bk Titles 56,300; Per Subs 116
   Automation Activity & Vendor Info: (Acquisitions) OCLC; (Cataloging) OCLC; (Circulation) SIRSI WorkFlows; (ILL) OCLC; (Media Booking) SIRSI WorkFlows; (OPAC) SIRSI WorkFlows; (Serials) OCLC
   Database Vendor: Baker & Taylor, CredoReference, EBSCOhost, Gale Cengage Learning, Grolier Online, LexisNexis, Medline, netLibrary, OCLC FirstSearch, OVID Technologies, ProQuest, PubMed, ScienceDirect, Westlaw, YBP Library Services
   Function: ILL available
   Partic in Lyrasis; South Carolina Information & Library Services Consortium (SCILS)
   Special Services for the Blind - ZoomText magnification & reading software
   Open Mon-Thurs 8-8, Fri 8-1

L   NELSON, MULLINS, RILEY & SCARBOROUGH*, Law Library, 104 S Main St, Ste 900, 29601. (Mail add: PO Box 10084, 29603-0084), SAN 323-6609. Tel: 864-250-2300. FAX: 864-232-2925. Web Site: www.nmrs.com. *Librn,* Linda Gray
   Library Holdings: Bk Vols 13,930; Per Subs 20

GREENWOOD

P   GREENWOOD COUNTY LIBRARY, 600 S Main St, 29646. SAN 360-2672. Tel: 864-941-4650. Reference Tel: 864-941-4655. FAX: 864-941-4651. Web Site: www.greenwoodcountylibrary.org. *Dir,* Prudence A Taylor; Tel: 864-941-3030, E-mail: ptaylor@greenwoodcountylibrary.org; *Head, Circ,* Deborah Dillashaw Price; Tel: 864-941-4653, E-mail: ddillashaw@greenwoodcountylibrary.org; *Ref Librn,* Jessica Howard; E-mail: jhoward@greenwoodcountylibrary.org; *Ref Librn,* Allison Read; E-mail: aread@greenwoodcountylibrary.org; *YA Librn,* Tracey Ouzts; E-mail: touzts@greenwoodcountylibrary.org; *Tech Serv Supvr,* Tiffany Crayne; E-mail: tcrayne@greenwoodcountylibrary.org; *Children's Serv Coordr,* LeVerne Fuller; E-mail: lfuller@greenwoodcountylibrary.org; *Coordr of Ref Serv,* Julie Horton; Tel: 864-941-3042, E-mail: jhorton@greenwoodcountylibrary.org; Staff 8 (MLS 6, Non-MLS 2)
   Founded 1901. Pop 69,661; Circ 212,953
   Jul 2011-Jun 2012 Income (Main Library and Branch(s)) $1,728,234, State $70,059, Federal $1,801, County $1,573,000, Other $83,374. Mats Exp $82,748, Books $65,278, Per/Ser (Incl. Access Fees) $5,000, AV Mat $125, Electronic Ref Mat (Incl. Access Fees) $12,345. Sal $835,551 (Prof $281,100)
   Library Holdings: CDs 4,781; DVDs 5,676; e-books 25,607; Electronic Media & Resources 41; Bk Vols 93,370; Per Subs 258
   Special Collections: Greenwood County Historical Society, bks, letters, diaries & photos; Star Fort Chapter DAR Coll
   Subject Interests: Genealogy, Local hist
   Automation Activity & Vendor Info: (Acquisitions) TLC (The Library Corporation); (Cataloging) OCLC WorldCat; (Circulation) TLC (The Library Corporation); (Media Booking) EnvisionWare; (OPAC) TLC (The Library Corporation); (Serials) EBSCO Online

   Database Vendor: Library Ideas, LLC, Overdrive, Inc, ProQuest
   Wireless access
   Function: Adult bk club, Adult literacy prog, After school storytime, Archival coll, Audiobks via web, Bilingual assistance for Spanish patrons, Bk club(s), Bks on CD, Children's prog, Computer training, Computers for patron use, Copy machines, Fax serv, Home delivery & serv to Sr ctr & nursing homes, Mail & tel request accepted, Music CDs, Notary serv, Online cat, Outreach serv, Passport agency, Photocopying/Printing, Preschool outreach, Prog for adults, Pub access computers, Ref & res, Ref serv in person, Story hour, Summer & winter reading prog, Summer reading prog, Tax forms, Teen prog, Telephone ref, Wheelchair accessible
   Partic in DISCUS
   Special Services for the Deaf - Bks on deafness & sign lang
   Special Services for the Blind - Audio mat; Bks on CD; Large print bks
   Open Mon-Wed 9-8, Thurs & Fri 9-5:30, Sat 12-4, Sun 2-5:30
   Friends of the Library Group
   Branches: 2
   NINETY SIX BRANCH, 100 S Cambridge St S, Ninety Six, 29666, SAN 360-2826. Tel: 864-543-4749. FAX: 864-543-4749. *Br Mgr,* Diana Hennessey; E-mail: dhennessey@greenwoodcountylibrary.org; Staff 1 (Non-MLS 1)
      Founded 1976. Pop 1,936
      Function: Handicapped accessible, Photocopying/Printing, Prog for children & young adult, Ref serv available, Summer reading prog, Wheelchair accessible
      Special Services for the Blind - Bks on CD; Large print bks
      Open Mon 9-7:30, Tues-Fri 9-5:30
   WARE SHOALS COMMUNITY LIBRARY, 54 S Greenwood Ave, Ware Shoals, 29692, SAN 360-2850. Tel: 864-456-2813. FAX: 864-456-2813. *Br Mgr,* Melissa Crenshaw; E-mail: mcrenshaw@greenwoodcountylibrary.org; *Media Spec,* Angie Pitts; Staff 2 (MLS 1, Non-MLS 1)
      Founded 1911. Pop 2,363
      Function: Adult literacy prog, AV serv, Handicapped accessible, ILL available, Outside serv via phone, mail, e-mail & web, Photocopying/Printing, Prog for children & young adult, Ref serv available, Serves mentally handicapped consumers, Summer reading prog, Wheelchair accessible
      Open Mon & Wed-Fri 7:30-5, Tues 7:30-7
   Bookmobiles: 1, Head of Circ, Debbie Dillashaw. Bk titles 2,800

M   GREENWOOD GENETIC CENTER LIBRARY*, 101 Gregor Mendel Circle, 29646. SAN 372-9486. Tel: 864-388-1708. FAX: 864-388-1704. Web Site: www.ggc.org. *Librn,* Rachel Collins
   Library Holdings: Bk Vols 3,000; Per Subs 60
   Special Collections: Genetics Rare Book Coll
   Subject Interests: Genetics, Pediatrics
   Open Mon-Fri 9-5

C   LANDER UNIVERSITY*, Larry A Jackson Library, 320 Stanley Ave, 29649-2099. SAN 315-551X. Tel: 864-388-8365. FAX: 864-388-8816. Web Site: www.lander.edu/library. *Dean of Libr Serv,* David Mash, PhD; Tel: 864-388-8035, E-mail: dmash@lander.edu; *Archivist, Ref Librn,* Michael D Berry; Tel: 864-388-8435, E-mail: mberry@lander.edu; *Circ Supvr,* James Laman; *Continuing Res & Cat,* Lisa Wiecki; Tel: 864-388-8043, E-mail: lwiecki@lander.edu; *Govt Doc, Web Serv,* Adam E Haigh; Tel: 864-388-8029, E-mail: ahaigh@lander.edu; Staff 7 (MLS 4, Non-MLS 3)
   Founded 1872. Enrl 3,019; Fac 139; Highest Degree: Master
   Special Collections: South Carolina History (Watson Coll). State Document Depository; US Document Depository
   Automation Activity & Vendor Info: (Acquisitions) Innovative Interfaces, Inc; (Cataloging) Innovative Interfaces, Inc; (Circulation) Innovative Interfaces, Inc; (Course Reserve) Innovative Interfaces, Inc; (ILL) OCLC; (OPAC) Innovative Interfaces, Inc; (Serials) Innovative Interfaces, Inc
   Database Vendor: American Psychological Association (APA), Cinahl Information Systems, EBSCOhost, Gale Cengage Learning, Grolier Online, JSTOR, LexisNexis, Medline, Modern Language Association, netLibrary, Newsbank, OCLC WorldCat, ProQuest, PubMed
   Wireless access
   Partic in Carolina Consortium; DISCUS; Lyrasis; OCLC Online Computer Library Center, Inc; Partnership Among South Carolina Academic Libraries
   Open Mon-Thurs 7:30am-11pm, Fri 7:30-5, Sat 1-5, Sun 5-11

J   PIEDMONT TECHNICAL COLLEGE LIBRARY*, Marion P Carnell Library, 620 N Emerald Rd, Bldg K, 29646. (Mail add: PO Drawer 1467, 29648-1467), SAN 315-5536. Tel: 864-941-8441. Interlibrary Loan Service Tel: 864-941-8577. Reference Tel: 864-941-8657. Administration Tel: 864-941-8442. Toll Free Tel: 800-868-5528, Ext 8441. FAX: 864-941-8558. E-mail: librarian@ptc.edu. Web Site: www.ptc.edu/library. *Dean, Learning Res,* Meredith Daniel; E-mail: daniel.m@ptc.edu; *Circ Mgr,* Mary Louise Wilde; E-mail: wilde.m@ptc.edu; *Libr Spec,* Geneva Tate; Tel: 864-941-8793, E-mail: tate.g@ptc.edu; *Computer Lab Coordr,* Bonnie Graham; Tel: 864-941-8348, E-mail: graham.b@ptc.edu; *Computer Lab Asst,* Brandon White; Tel: 864-941-8792, E-mail: white.b@ptc.edu;

Cataloger, Karen Hoyt; Tel: 864-941-8659, E-mail: hoyt.k@ptc.edu; Staff 4 (MLS 2, Non-MLS 2)
Founded 1966. Enrl 5,811; Highest Degree: Associate
Jul 2007-Jun 2008. Mats Exp $73,557, Books $19,219, Per/Ser (Incl. Access Fees) $17,874, AV Mat $4,446, Electronic Ref Mat (Incl. Access Fees) $2,905
Special Collections: Piedmont Technical College Archives
Subject Interests: Allied health, Bus, Criminal justice, Early childhood educ, Eng tech, Funeral serv, Hort, Indust tech, Nursing, Off syst tech
Automation Activity & Vendor Info: (Acquisitions) SIRSI WorkFlows; (Cataloging) SIRSI WorkFlows; (Circulation) SIRSI WorkFlows; (ILL) OCLC; (OPAC) SIRSI Unicorn; (Serials) SIRSI WorkFlows
Database Vendor: EBSCOhost, Gale Cengage Learning, Grolier Online, netLibrary, Newsbank, OVID Technologies, ProQuest
Wireless access
Function: Archival coll, Art exhibits, Audio & video playback equip for onsite use, AV serv, Bk club(s), Copy machines, Distance learning, e-mail serv, Electronic databases & coll, Handicapped accessible, Health sci info serv, ILL available, Magnifiers for reading, Music CDs, Online searches, Orientations, Outside serv via phone, mail, e-mail & web, Photocopying/Printing, Prof lending libr, Ref serv available, Spoken cassettes & CDs, Spoken cassettes & DVDs, Telephone ref, VHS videos, Video lending libr, Wheelchair accessible, Workshops
Partic in Lyrasis; OCLC Online Computer Library Center, Inc; Partnership Among South Carolina Academic Libraries; South Carolina Information & Library Services Consortium (SCILS)
Special Services for the Deaf - Bks on deafness & sign lang; Closed caption videos
Special Services for the Blind - Audio mat; Bks on cassette; Bks on CD; Cassette playback machines; Cassettes; Computer with voice synthesizer for visually impaired persons; Text reader
Open Mon-Thurs 8am-8:30pm, Fri 8:30-4
Restriction: Authorized patrons, Circ limited, In-house use for visitors, Restricted borrowing privileges, Restricted loan policy, Restricted pub use

M   SELF REGIONAL HEALTHCARE*, Medical Library, 1325 Spring St, 29646. SAN 315-5544. Tel: 864-725-4851. FAX: 864-725-4838. E-mail: library@selfregional.org. *Librn,* Thomas Hill; *Commun Health Info Ctr Coordr,* Dinah Smith; Tel: 864-725-4797, E-mail: communityhealth@selfregional.org. Subject Specialists: *Consumer health,* Dinah Smith; Staff 2 (MLS 1, Non-MLS 1)
Founded 1976
Oct 2008-Sept 2009 Income $186,000, Locally Generated Income $2,000, Parent Institution $184,000. Mats Exp $70,000, Books $6,000, Per/Ser (Incl. Access Fees) $35,500, AV Mat $500, Electronic Ref Mat (Incl. Access Fees) $28,000. Sal $116,000 (Prof $94,000)
Library Holdings: AV Mats 75; CDs 13; e-books 75; e-journals 4,000; Bk Titles 1,302; Per Subs 340; Spec Interest Per Sub 4; Videos 302
Special Collections: Community Health Information Center (consumer health resources)
Subject Interests: Med, Nursing, Pharm, Therapy
Automation Activity & Vendor Info: (Cataloging) Follett Software; (Circulation) Follett Software; (Course Reserve) Follett Software; (Media Booking) Follett Software; (OPAC) Follett Software; (Serials) Follett Software
Database Vendor: A.D.A.M. Inc, Agricola, Cinahl Information Systems, DynaMed, EBSCO Information Services, EBSCOhost, Gallup, Haworth Pres Inc, Infotrieve, Majors, MD Consult, Medlib, Medline, Natural Standard, PubMed, STAT!Ref (Teton Data Systems), TDNet, UpToDate, WebMD, WT Cox
Wireless access
Function: Audio & video playback equip for onsite use, CD-ROM, Computer training, Computers for patron use, Copy machines, Doc delivery serv, e-mail serv, Electronic databases & coll, Fax serv, Handicapped accessible, Health sci info serv, ILL available, Mail & tel request accepted, Mail loans to mem, Online cat, Online ref, Online searches, Orientations, Outreach serv, Outside serv via phone, mail, e-mail & web, Photocopying/Printing, Prof lending libr, Pub access computers, Ref & res, Ref serv available, Ref serv in person, Res libr, Res performed for a fee, Scanner, Spoken cassettes & CDs, VHS videos, Wheelchair accessible
Partic in National Network of Libraries of Medicine; National Network of Libraries of Medicine Southeastern Atlantic Region; SC Health Info Network; SEND; US National Library of Medicine
Open Mon-Fri 8:30-5

HARTSVILLE

C   COKER COLLEGE*, Charles W & Joan S Coker Library-Information Technology Center, 300 E College Ave, 29550. SAN 315-5560. Tel: 843-383-8125. FAX: 843-383-8129. E-mail: library@coker.edu. Web Site: www.coker.edu/library. *Libr Dir,* Alexa Bartel; Staff 4 (MLS 3, Non-MLS 1)
Founded 1908. Enrl 1,100; Fac 3; Highest Degree: Bachelor
Library Holdings: e-books 59,800; Bk Vols 87,000; Per Subs 160
Special Collections: Arents Tobacco Coll

Subject Interests: Music, Video
Function: Art exhibits
Partic in Lyrasis; Palmetto Academic Independent Library System (PAILS); Partnership Among South Carolina Academic Libraries
Special Services for the Deaf - Closed caption videos
Special Services for the Blind - Sound rec
Open Mon-Thurs 8:30am-11pm, Fri 8:30-5, Sat 12-5, Sun 2-11
Restriction: Mem only

S   SONOCO PRODUCTS CO, INC*, Technical Information Center, One N Second St, 29550. (Mail add: PO Box 160, 29551-0160), SAN 315-5579. Tel: 843-383-7000. FAX: 843-339-6120. *Librn,* Kathleen Cooper
Library Holdings: Bk Titles 300; Per Subs 25
Special Collections: Chemical Abstracts; IPC Abstract Bulletins, microfiche; Standards (Federal, Military-ASTM, CCTI, TAPPI)
Subject Interests: Adhesives, Chem tech, Coating tech, Environ eng, Paper tech, Plastic tech, Pulp tech

KINGSTREE

P   WILLIAMSBURG COUNTY LIBRARY*, 215 N Jackson, 29556-3319. SAN 315-5587. Tel: 843-355-9486. FAX: 843-355-9991. *Dir,* Benjamin Hall; *Br Mgr,* Wanda Baxley; Tel: 843-558-7679, Fax: 843-558-0743; *Circ Mgr,* Audrey Williams; *Cat, Circ,* Sandi Arnold; *Ch,* Kimberley Matthews; Staff 0.94 (MLS 0.94)
Founded 1967. Pop 37,217; Circ 52,245
Jul 2005-Jun 2006 Income (Main Library and Branch(s)) $382,615, State $76,652, Federal $26,920, County $260,000, Locally Generated Income $19,043. Mats Exp $97,481, Books $93,758, AV Mat $3,723. Sal $123,543 (Prof $37,618)
Library Holdings: CDs 927; DVDs 614; Large Print Bks 1,065; Bk Vols 54,553; Per Subs 99; Videos 400
Automation Activity & Vendor Info: (Cataloging) TLC (The Library Corporation); (Circulation) TLC (The Library Corporation); (OPAC) TLC (The Library Corporation)
Function: Audio & video playback equip for onsite use, Copy machines, Electronic databases & coll, Handicapped accessible, ILL available, Preschool outreach, Prog for adults, Prog for children & young adult, Ref serv available, Serves mentally handicapped consumers, Spoken cassettes & CDs, Telephone ref, VHS videos
Open Mon-Thurs 9:30-6, Fri 9:30-4, Sat 10-4
Friends of the Library Group
Branches: 1
HEMINGWAY BRANCH, 306 N Main St, Hemingway, 29554, SAN 320-9695. Tel: 843-558-7679. FAX: 843-558-0743. *Br Mgr,* Wanda Baxley
Open Mon-Thurs 10-6, Fri & Sat 11-4
Friends of the Library Group
Bookmobiles: 1. Bookmobile Mgr, Stephanie Watson

J   WILLIAMSBURG TECHNICAL COLLEGE LIBRARY*, 601 MLK Jr Ave, 29556. Tel: 843-355-4172. Toll Free Tel: 800-768-2021. FAX: 843-355-4291. Web Site: www.wiltech.edu/library. *Dir,* Demetra Walker; Tel: 843-355-4131
Library Holdings: Bk Vols 26,500; Per Subs 109
Automation Activity & Vendor Info: (Acquisitions) SirsiDynix; (Cataloging) SirsiDynix; (Circulation) SirsiDynix; (Course Reserve) SirsiDynix; (ILL) OCLC; (OPAC) SirsiDynix; (Serials) SirsiDynix
Database Vendor: Gale Cengage Learning
Wireless access
Partic in Lyrasis
Open Mon-Thurs 8am-9pm, Fri 8-1

LANCASTER

P   LANCASTER COUNTY LIBRARY*, 313 S White St, 29720. SAN 315-5609. Tel: 803-285-1502. FAX: 803-285-6004. E-mail: lanclib@comporium.net. Web Site: www.lanclib.org. *Dir,* Richard A Band; *Asst Dir,* Nancy C Berry; *Librn,* Judy Hunter; *Ch,* Brenda Parker; Staff 15 (MLS 4, Non-MLS 11)
Founded 1907. Pop 61,351; Circ 189,367
Jul 2006-Jun 2007 Income (Main Library and Branch(s)) $874,197, State $123,144, Federal $15,831, County $663,822, Locally Generated Income $35,000, Other $36,400. Mats Exp $147,363, Books $111,331, Per/Ser (Incl. Access Fees) $6,200, Manu Arch $5,000, AV Equip $7,500, AV Mat $6,500, Presv $10,832. Sal $570,735
Library Holdings: Bks on Deafness & Sign Lang 76; DVDs 1,226; Large Print Bks 3,581; Bk Vols 143,425; Per Subs 282; Talking Bks 3,264; Videos 3,095
Subject Interests: Caroliniana, Genealogy, Local hist
Automation Activity & Vendor Info: (Cataloging) TLC (The Library Corporation); (Circulation) TLC (The Library Corporation); (OPAC) TLC (The Library Corporation)
Database Vendor: TLC (The Library Corporation)
Publications: Inventory to Perry Belle Hough Coll

Partic in DISCUS; SC Libr Network
Special Services for the Deaf - Interpreter on staff
Open Mon-Thurs 9-8, Fri 9-5:30, Sat 9-5
Friends of the Library Group
Branches: 1
KERSHAW MEMORIAL, 3855 Fork Hill Rd, Kershaw, 29067, SAN
325-3961. Tel: 803-475-2609. FAX: 803-475-4444. *Librn,* Pat Hinson;
Staff 1 (Non-MLS 1)
Founded 1949. Circ 45,022
Open Mon 1-8, Tues, Wed & Fri 10-5, Thurs 10-8
Bookmobiles: 1

LAURENS

P LAURENS COUNTY LIBRARY*, 1017 W Main St, 29360. SAN
360-2974. Tel: 864-681-7323. FAX: 864-681-0598. Web Site:
www.lcpl.org. *Dir,* Ann Szypulski; E-mail: annszyp@lcpl.org; *Dep Dir,*
Carol L Gaines; Tel: 864-833-1853, E-mail: cgaines@lcpl.org; *Spec Coll
Librn,* Elaine Martin; E-mail: emartin@lcpl.org; *Acq,* Kathryn W Johnson;
E-mail: kjohnson@lcpl.org; *Ch,* Pamela D Bennett; E-mail:
pbennett@lcpl.org; *Pub Serv,* Margaret Kennedy; E-mail:
pkennedy@lcpl.org; *Tech Serv,* Mary Alice Mundy; E-mail:
mmundy@lcpl.org; Staff 19 (MLS 4, Non-MLS 15)
Founded 1929. Pop 71,000; Circ 172,312
Library Holdings: AV Mats 10,200; Bk Vols 122,271; Per Subs 296;
Videos 2,912
Special Collections: Laurens County History & Genealogy Coll; South
Caroliniana Coll, bk & micro
Subject Interests: Local hist
Automation Activity & Vendor Info: (Acquisitions) TLC (The Library
Corporation); (Cataloging) TLC (The Library Corporation); (Circulation)
TLC (The Library Corporation); (OPAC) TLC (The Library Corporation)
Database Vendor: Gale Cengage Learning, Grolier Online, Newsbank,
OCLC FirstSearch, ProQuest, TLC (The Library Corporation)
Wireless access
Function: Archival coll, Handicapped accessible, Home delivery & serv to
Sr ctr & nursing homes, Homebound delivery serv, ILL available,
Magnifiers for reading, Online searches, Photocopying/Printing, Prog for
adults, Prog for children & young adult, Ref serv available, Summer
reading prog, Telephone ref, Wheelchair accessible
Partic in DISCUS; SC Libr Network
Special Services for the Blind - Large print bks; Talking bks
Open Mon, Tues & Thurs 9-8:30, Wed 9-6, Fri 9-5, Sat 9-1
Friends of the Library Group
Branches: 1
CLINTON PUBLIC, 107 Jacobs Hwy, Ste A, Clinton, 29325, SAN
360-3008. Tel: 864-833-1853. FAX: 864-833-9666. *Br Mgr,* Charlie
Miller; Staff 4 (MLS 1, Non-MLS 3)
Library Holdings: Bk Vols 25,000
Friends of the Library Group
Bookmobiles: 1

LEXINGTON

P LEXINGTON COUNTY PUBLIC LIBRARY SYSTEM*, 5440 Augusta
Rd, 29072. SAN 359-9671. Tel: 803-785-2600. Circulation Tel:
803-785-2613. Interlibrary Loan Service Tel: 803-785-2686. Reference Tel:
803-785-2680. FAX: 803-785-2601. Web Site: www.lex.lib.sc.us. *Dir,*
Daniel S MacNeill; Tel: 803-785-2640, E-mail: dmacneill@lex.lib.sc.us;
Dep Dir, Dee Bedenbaugh; Tel: 803-785-2643, E-mail:
dbedenbaugh@lex.lib.sc.us; *Sr Librn,* Mark Mancuso; Tel: 803-785-2673,
E-mail: mmancuso@lex.lib.sc.us; *Automation Syst Coordr,* Cynthia Kent;
Tel: 803-785-2644, E-mail: ckent@lex.lib.sc.us; *ILL, Ref,* Marie Jefferies;
Tel: 803-785-2686, E-mail: mjefferies@lex.lib.sc.us; *Tech Serv,* Barbara
Remack; Tel: 803-785-2624, E-mail: bremack@lex.lib.sc.us; *YA Serv,* Ellen
Stringer; Tel: 803-785-2632, E-mail: estringer@lex.lib.sc.us; Staff 117
(MLS 23, Non-MLS 94)
Founded 1948. Pop 229,751; Circ 1,669,115
Jul 2005-Jun 2006 Income (Main Library and Branch(s)) $5,026,722, State
$413,726, County $4,376,557, Locally Generated Income $236,439. Mats
Exp $1,087,046, Books $631,312, Per/Ser (Incl. Access Fees) $70,579,
Other Print Mats $2,780, AV Equip $83,407, AV Mat $123,517, Electronic
Ref Mat (Incl. Access Fees) $175,451. Sal $3,218,155
Library Holdings: Bk Vols 517,029; Per Subs 2,630; Talking Bks 12,167;
Videos 29,046
Subject Interests: SC genealogy, SC hist
Automation Activity & Vendor Info: (Acquisitions) Polaris Library
Systems; (Cataloging) Polaris Library Systems; (Circulation) Polaris
Library Systems; (OPAC) Polaris Library Systems
Database Vendor: EBSCOhost, Gale Cengage Learning, OCLC
FirstSearch
Function: Handicapped accessible, ILL available, Online searches,
Photocopying/Printing, Prog for adults, Prog for children & young adult,
Ref serv available, Spoken cassettes & CDs, Summer reading prog, VHS
videos, Wheelchair accessible, Workshops

Open Mon-Thurs 8:30-8, Fri & Sat 8:30-5:30, Sun 2-5
Restriction: Non-resident fee
Friends of the Library Group
Branches: 8
BATESBURG-LEESVILLE BRANCH, 203 Armory St, Batesburg, 29006,
SAN 359-9760. Tel: 803-532-9223. FAX: 803-532-2232. *Librn,* Beverly
Windham; E-mail: bwindham@lex.lib.sc.us; Staff 7 (MLS 1, Non-MLS
6)
Open Mon 10:30-7:30, Tues-Fri 8:30-5:30, Sat 9-5, Sun 2-5
Friends of the Library Group
CAYCE-WEST COLUMBIA BRANCH, 1500 Augusta Rd W, Columbia,
29169, SAN 359-9795. Tel: 803-794-6791. FAX: 803-926-5383. *Br Mgr,*
Kelly Poole; E-mail: kpoole@lex.lib.sc.us; *Ref,* Jim Cheatham; E-mail:
jcheatham@lex.lib.sc.us; *Asst Br Mgr,* Jenny Main; E-mail:
jmain@lex.lib.sc.us; Staff 19 (MLS 5, Non-MLS 14)
Open Mon-Thurs 8:30-8, Fri & Sat 8:30-5:30, Sun 2-5
Friends of the Library Group
CHAPIN BRANCH, 129 NW Columbia Ave, Chapin, 29036-9423. (Mail
add: PO Box 700, Chapin, 29036-0700), SAN 359-9701. Tel:
803-345-5479. *Librn,* Patricia Mauldin; E-mail: pmauldin@lex.lib.sc.us;
Staff 7 (MLS 1, Non-MLS 6)
Open Mon & Thurs 12-8, Tues, Wed & Fri 9-5, Sat 9-1
Friends of the Library Group
GASTON BRANCH, 214 S Main St, Gaston, 29053. (Mail add: PO Box
479, Gaston, 29053), SAN 359-9728. Tel: 803-791-3208. FAX:
803-791-3208. *Br Mgr,* Carol Clark; E-mail: cclark@lex.lib.sc.us; Staff 3
(Non-MLS 3)
Open Mon 12-8, Tues & Thurs 10-6, Wed 2-6, Sat 9-2
Friends of the Library Group
GILBERT-SUMMIT BRANCH, 405 Broad St, Gilbert, 29054. (Mail add:
PO Box 341, Gilbert, 29054-0341), SAN 329-5753. Tel: 803-785-5387.
FAX: 803-785-5387. *Br Mgr,* Louise Taylor; Staff 3 (Non-MLS 3)
Open Mon & Wed 11-5, Tues & Thurs 10-7, Sat 9-12
Friends of the Library Group
IRMO BRANCH, 6251 St Andrews Rd, Columbia, 29212-3152, SAN
359-9736. Tel: 803-798-7880. FAX: 803-798-8570. *Sr Br Librn,* Beverly
Windham; *Asst Br Librn,* Rebecca I James; E-mail: bjames@lex.lib.sc.us;
Youth Serv Librn, Melissa A Pityk; E-mail: mpityk@lex.lib.sc.us; *Ref,*
Mary P Gwyn; E-mail: mgwyn@lex.lib.sc.us; Staff 23 (MLS 4,
Non-MLS 19)
Open Mon-Thurs 8:30-8, Fri & Sat 8:30-5:30
Friends of the Library Group
PELION BRANCH, 206 Pine St, Pelion, 29123, SAN 359-9779. Tel:
803-785-3272. FAX: 803-785-7651. Web Site: www.lex.lib.sc.us. *Br Mgr,*
Shirley Sprenne; E-mail: ssprenne@lex.lib.sc.us; Staff 5 (MLS 1,
Non-MLS 4)
Founded 1986
Database Vendor: EBSCO Auto Repair Reference, EBSCO Information
Services, Polaris Library Systems
Open Mon 12-5, Tues, Wed & Fri 9-5, Thurs 1-8, Sat 9-1
Friends of the Library Group
SWANSEA BRANCH, 199 N Lawrence Ave, Swansea, 29160. (Mail add:
PO Box 130, Swansea, 29160-0130), SAN 359-9809. Tel: 803-785-3519.
FAX: 803-785-3519. *Br Mgr,* Edna Terry; E-mail: eterry@lex.lib.sc.us;
Staff 3 (Non-MLS 3)
Open Mon, Tues & Fri 9-5, Thurs 11-5, Sat 9-12
Friends of the Library Group
Bookmobiles: 1

MANNING

P HARVIN CLARENDON COUNTY LIBRARY*, 215 N Brooks St, 29102.
SAN 373-7535. Tel: 803-435-8633. FAX: 803-435-8101. E-mail:
hccl215@yahoo.com. *Dir,* Marilyn Tsirigotis; E-mail:
marilynt@infoave.net; *Adult Serv,* Carrie James; *Cat,* Debbie Wilson; *Ch,*
Jennifer Howard-Kelley; *Circ,* Emma Hilton; Staff 6 (MLS 2, Non-MLS 4)
Founded 1977. Pop 32,500; Circ 48,000
Jul 2005-Jun 2006 Income $408,980, State $65,004, County $318,976,
Locally Generated Income $25,000. Mats Exp $56,520, Books $32,270,
Per/Ser (Incl. Access Fees) $5,000, AV Mat $12,500, Electronic Ref Mat
(Incl. Access Fees) $3,000. Sal $150,667 (Prof $62,421)
Library Holdings: Large Print Bks 300; Bk Titles 30,000; Bk Vols
34,000; Per Subs 85; Talking Bks 500; Videos 500
Special Collections: South Carolina Coll
Automation Activity & Vendor Info: (Cataloging) TLC (The Library
Corporation); (Circulation) TLC (The Library Corporation); (OPAC) TLC
(The Library Corporation); (Serials) TLC (The Library Corporation)
Database Vendor: EBSCOhost, Gale Cengage Learning
Wireless access
Publications: Long-Range Plan
Special Services for the Deaf - Bks on deafness & sign lang
Open Mon & Tues 9-8, Wed-Fri 9-5:30, Sat 10-4:30
Friends of the Library Group
Bookmobiles: 1. Librn, Patrica Ragin. Bk vols 3,000

MARION

P   MARION COUNTY LIBRARY*, 101 E Court St, 29571-3699. SAN
     360-3067. Tel: 843-423-8300. FAX: 843-423-8302. E-mail:
     marionlibr@spiritcom.net. Web Site: www.marioncountylibrary.org. *Dir,*
     Allen Smith; *Ad,* Pat G Koch; *Tech Serv Coordr,* Georgia Lee; *Youth Serv,*
     Catherine J Pruett; Staff 17 (MLS 4, Non-MLS 13)
     Founded 1898. Pop 34,904; Circ 81,669
     Jul 2005-Jun 2006 Income (Main Library and Branch(s)) $621,450, State
     $70,932, City $1,900, Federal $2,486, County $524,460, Locally Generated
     Income $20,663, Other $1,009. Mats Exp $69,920, Books $53,367, AV
     Mat $11,575, Electronic Ref Mat (Incl. Access Fees) $4,978. Sal $343,545
     Library Holdings: AV Mats 2,423; Bk Vols 82,248; Per Subs 202
     Special Collections: South Carolina, bks & micro
     Subject Interests: Hist
     Automation Activity & Vendor Info: (Cataloging) Polaris Library
     Systems; (Circulation) Polaris Library Systems; (OPAC) Polaris Library
     Systems
     Database Vendor: Gale Cengage Learning
     Wireless access
     Function: Archival coll, Handicapped accessible, Home delivery & serv to
     Sr ctr & nursing homes, Homebound delivery serv, ILL available,
     Photocopying/Printing, Prog for children & young adult, Ref serv available,
     Summer reading prog, Telephone ref, Wheelchair accessible
     Publications: History of Marion County
     Partic in Lyrasis
     Special Services for the Deaf - Closed caption videos
     Special Services for the Blind - Computer with voice synthesizer for
     visually impaired persons
     Open Mon & Wed 9:30-8, Tues & Thurs 9:30-6, Fri 9:30-5:30, Sat 9:30-1
     Branches: 2
     MULLINS BRANCH, 210 N Main St, Mullins, 29574, SAN 360-3091.
       Tel: 843-464-9621. FAX: 843-464-5215. *Mgr,* Janye Caesar
       Open Mon & Thurs 12:30-5:30, Tues & Fri 9:30-5:30, Wed 12:30-8, Sat
       9:30-1
     NICHOLS BRANCH, 208 Floyd St, Nichols, 29581, SAN 360-3121. Tel:
       843-526-2641. FAX: 843-526-2641. *Mgr,* Lois Williams
       Open Mon & Fri 1:30-6, Wed 9:30-12:30
     Bookmobiles: 1

MCCORMICK

P   MCCORMICK COUNTY LIBRARY*, 201 Railroad Ave, 29835. (Mail
     add: PO Box 1899, 29835-1899), SAN 315-5633. Tel: 864-852-2821. FAX:
     864-852-2821. Web Site: mccormickcountylibrary.org. *Dir,* Paul Brown
     Founded 1953
     Library Holdings: Bk Vols 30,000; Per Subs 72
     Automation Activity & Vendor Info: (Cataloging) TLC (The Library
     Corporation); (Circulation) TLC (The Library Corporation); (OPAC) TLC
     (The Library Corporation)
     Database Vendor: TLC (The Library Corporation)
     Wireless access
     Open Tues-Thurs 11-8, Fri 9-6, Sat & Sun 1-5
     Friends of the Library Group

MONCKS CORNER

P   BERKELEY COUNTY LIBRARY SYSTEM*, 1003 Hwy 52, 29461.
     (Mail add: PO Box 1239, 29461), SAN 360-3156. Tel: 843-719-4223.
     Circulation Tel: 843-719-4938. Reference Tel: 843-719-4936.
     Administration Tel: 843-719-4224. Web Site: www.berkeley.lib.sc.us. *Dir,*
     Donna Osborne; Tel: 843-719-4243, E-mail: dosborne@berkeley.lib.sc.us;
     Coordr, Youth Serv, Dep Dir, Sharon M Fashion; Tel: 843-719-4227,
     E-mail: sharon@berkeley.lib.sc.us; *District I Supvry Librn,* Florence
     Lewis-Coker; Tel: 843-719-4228, E-mail: florence@berkeley.lib.sc.us; *Spec
     Projects/Pub Relations Librn,* Ramona L Grimsley; Tel: 843-719-4240,
     E-mail: grimsley@berkeley.lib.sc.us; *Tech Serv Librn,* Nanette Hamilton;
     Tel: 843-719-4273, E-mail: nanette@berkeley.lib.sc.us; *YA Librn,* Jan
     Kowal; Tel: 843-719-4278, E-mail: jan@berkeley.lib.sc.us; *Syst Adminr,*
     Gene Brunson; Tel: 843-719-4241. Subject Specialists: *Cataloging,* Nanette
     Hamilton; Staff 11 (MLS 11)
     Founded 1936. Pop 161,486; Circ 453,986
     Jul 2007-Jun 2008 Income (Main Library and Branch(s)) $2,719,895,
     Federal $320,965, County $2,594,312, Locally Generated Income $65,568,
     Other $21,458. Mats Exp $499,402, Books $380,841, AV Mat $89,155,
     Electronic Ref Mat (Incl. Access Fees) $29,406. Sal $1,432,359
     Library Holdings: Audiobooks 2,974; CDs 1,957; DVDs 5,698; Large
     Print Bks 2,816; Bk Titles 114,968; Bk Vols 228,850; Per Subs 240;
     Videos 3,041
     Subject Interests: Berkeley County hist, Genealogy, SC hist
     Automation Activity & Vendor Info: (Circulation) SirsiDynix; (OPAC)
     SirsiDynix
     Function: Adult bk club, Audio & video playback equip for onsite use, Bk
     club(s), Bks on cassette, Bks on CD, Children's prog, Computer training,
     Computers for patron use, Copy machines, e-mail & chat, E-Reserves,
     Electronic databases & coll, Free DVD rentals, Handicapped accessible,
     ILL available, Music CDs, Online cat, Online ref, Online searches,
     Orientations, Outreach serv, Photocopying/Printing, Prog for adults, Prog
     for children & young adult, Pub access computers, Ref serv available,
     Story hour, Summer reading prog, Tax forms, Teen prog, Telephone ref,
     VHS videos, Web-catalog, Wheelchair accessible
     Open Mon-Thurs 9-7, Fri & Sat 9-5
     Restriction: Circ to mem only, In-house use for visitors, Non-resident fee,
     Pub use on premises
     Friends of the Library Group
     Branches: 5
     DANIEL ISLAND, 2301 Daniel Island Dr, Charleston, 29492. Tel:
       843-471-2952. *Br Librn,* William Christopher Johnston; Staff 1 (MLS 1)
       Founded 2007. Circ 54,123
       Function: Bks on cassette, Bks on CD, Children's prog, Computers for
       patron use, Copy machines, e-mail & chat, E-Reserves, Free DVD
       rentals, ILL available, Music CDs, Online cat, Online ref, Online
       searches, Photocopying/Printing, Prog for adults, Prog for children &
       young adult, Pub access computers, Ref serv available, Ref serv in
       person, Story hour, Summer reading prog, Tax forms, Teen prog, VHS
       videos, Wheelchair accessible
       Open Mon & Wed 10-6, Tues & Thurs 11-7, Fri & Sat 9-5
       Restriction: In-house use for visitors
       Friends of the Library Group
     GOOSE CREEK BRANCH, 325 Old Moncks Corner Rd, Goose Creek,
       29445, SAN 360-3180. Tel: 843-572-1376. FAX: 843-572-1376. *Librn,*
       Dianne C Boersma; E-mail: boersma@berkeley.lib.sc.us; Staff 2 (MLS 2)
       Founded 1971. Circ 174,729
       Open Mon-Thurs 9-7, Fri & Sat 9-5
       Friends of the Library Group
     HANAHAN BRANCH, 1274 Yeamans Hall Rd, Hanahan, 29406-2627,
       SAN 360-3210. Tel: 843-747-5400. FAX: 843-747-5400. *Librn,*
       MaryJane Ritter; E-mail: mritter@berkeley.lib.sc.us; Staff 1 (MLS 1)
       Founded 1965. Circ 27,839
       Function: Bks on cassette, Bks on CD, Computers for patron use, Copy
       machines, e-mail & chat, E-Reserves, Electronic databases & coll, Free
       DVD rentals, ILL available, Music CDs, Online cat, Online ref, Online
       searches, Outreach serv, Photocopying/Printing, Prog for children &
       young adult, Pub access computers, Ref serv available, Summer reading
       prog, Tax forms, Telephone ref, VHS videos, Wheelchair accessible
       Open Mon-Thurs 10-6, Fri & Sat 9-5
       Restriction: In-house use for visitors
       Friends of the Library Group
     SAINT STEPHEN BRANCH, 1104 S Main St, Saint Stephen, 29479.
       (Mail add: PO Box 596, Saint Stephen, 29479-0596), SAN 360-3245.
       Tel: 843-567-4862. FAX: 843-567-4862.
       Founded 1955. Circ 13,985
       Function: Bks on cassette, Bks on CD, Children's prog, Computers for
       patron use, Copy machines, e-mail & chat, e-mail serv, E-Reserves,
       Electronic databases & coll, Free DVD rentals, ILL available, Music
       CDs, Online cat, Photocopying/Printing, Pub access computers, Ref serv
       in person, Story hour, Summer reading prog, Tax forms, Telephone ref,
       VHS videos, Wheelchair accessible
       Open Mon-Thurs 10-6, Fri & Sat 9-5
       Friends of the Library Group
     SANGAREE, 595 Sangaree Pkwy, Summerville, 29483. Tel:
       843-695-1208. *Br Librn,* Karen D Altman; E-mail:
       karen@berkeley.lib.sc.us; Staff 1 (MLS 1)
       Founded 2007. Circ 59,781
       Function: Bks on cassette, Bks on CD, Children's prog, Computers for
       patron use, Copy machines, e-mail & chat, E-Reserves, Electronic
       databases & coll, Free DVD rentals, Handicapped accessible, ILL
       available, Music CDs, Online cat, Online ref, Online searches, Outreach
       serv, Photocopying/Printing, Prog for adults, Prog for children & young
       adult, Pub access computers, Ref serv available, Story hour, Summer
       reading prog, Tax forms, Teen prog, VHS videos
       Open Mon & Wed 10-6, Tues & Thurs 11-7, Fri & Sat 9-5
       Restriction: In-house use for visitors

S   SOUTH CAROLINA PUBLIC SERVICE AUTHORITY*, Santee Cooper
     Corporate Library, One Riverwood Dr, 29461. Tel: 843-761-4072. FAX:
     843-761-4112. *Librn,* Suzanne Krebsbach; E-mail:
     smkrebsb@santeecooper.com; Staff 1 (MLS 1)
     Founded 1989
     Library Holdings: e-books 15,000; e-journals 35; Electronic Media &
     Resources 50; Bk Vols 6,000; Per Subs 300
     Subject Interests: Bus, Eng
     Automation Activity & Vendor Info: (Acquisitions) EOS International;
     (Cataloging) EOS International; (Circulation) EOS International; (OPAC)
     EOS International; (Serials) EOS International
     Wireless access
     Open Mon-Fri 7:30-4

MURRELLS INLET

S   BROOKGREEN GARDENS LIBRARY*, 1931 Brookgreen Dr, 29576. (Mail add: PO Box 3368, Pauley's Island, 29585), SAN 320-5118. Tel: 843-235-6000. FAX: 843-235-6003. E-mail: info@brookgreen.org. Web Site: www.brookgreen.org. *Pres,* Robert Jewell; *Curator,* Robin Salmon
Founded 1931
Library Holdings: Bk Titles 2,800; Bk Vols 3,000; Per Subs 75
Special Collections: American Sculptors, archives, clipping files, correspondence, exhibit cat, photogs, taped & transcribed interviews; Brookgreen Gardens, newsp, photogs; Plantation Records, Medical Accounts & Personal Correspondence
Subject Interests: 19th Century Am sculpture, 20th Century Am sculpture, 21st Century Am sculpture, Fauna of the SE US, Flora of the SE US, Hist of SC, Hort, Landscape archit
Restriction: Not open to pub, Staff use only

MYRTLE BEACH

P   CHAPIN MEMORIAL LIBRARY*, 400 14th Ave N, 29577-3612. SAN 329-787X. Tel: 843-918-1275. FAX: 843-918-1288. E-mail: cmldir@scgovdirect.com, itstaff2@scgovdirect.com. Web Site: www.chapinlibrary.org. *Dir,* Briget Livingston; E-mail: cmldir@scgovdirect.com; *Ch,* Sue Ellen Wilson; E-mail: crstaff1@scgovdirect.com; *Ref Librn,* Carolyn Savage; E-mail: refstaff2@scgovdirect.com; Staff 12 (MLS 3, Non-MLS 9)
Founded 1949. Pop 60,000; Circ 200,000
Special Collections: Oral History
Subject Interests: Local hist
Automation Activity & Vendor Info: (Cataloging) Polaris Library Systems; (Circulation) Polaris Library Systems; (OPAC) Polaris Library Systems; (Serials) Polaris Library Systems
Database Vendor: Baker & Taylor, Comprise Technologies, Inc, Dun & Bradstreet, EBSCO Auto Repair Reference, Gale Cengage Learning, Newsbank, Overdrive, Inc
Wireless access
Open Mon & Wed 9-6, Tues & Thurs 9-8, Fri & Sat 9-5
Friends of the Library Group

L   NELSON, MULLINS, RILEY & SCARBOROUGH*, Law Library, Beach First Ctr, 3751 Robert M Grissom Pkwy, 29577. SAN 323-6587. Tel: 843-448-3500. FAX: 843-448-3437. Web Site: www.nelsonmullins.com. *Librn,* Linda Martin
Library Holdings: Bk Titles 10,000; Per Subs 20
Automation Activity & Vendor Info: (Acquisitions) Inmagic, Inc.; (Cataloging) Inmagic, Inc.; (Circulation) Inmagic, Inc.; (Course Reserve) Inmagic, Inc.; (ILL) Inmagic, Inc.; (Media Booking) Inmagic, Inc.; (OPAC) Inmagic, Inc.; (Serials) Inmagic, Inc.
Restriction: Not open to pub, Staff use only

NEWBERRY

C   NEWBERRY COLLEGE*, Wessels Library, 2100 College St, 29108-2197. SAN 315-565X. Tel: 803-321-5229. FAX: 803-321-5232. Web Site: www.newberry.edu/wessels. *Dir, Libr Serv,* Lawrence E Ellis; E-mail: larry.ellis@newberry.edu; *Assoc Dir, Pub Serv,* Kathy Snediker; E-mail: kathy.snediker@newberry.edu; *Assoc Dir, Tech Serv,* Cleta Dunaway; E-mail: cleta.dunaway@newberry.edu; Staff 6 (MLS 3, Non-MLS 3)
Founded 1856. Enrl 1,084; Fac 68; Highest Degree: Bachelor
Jul 2007-Jun 2008 Income $212,378. Mats Exp $82,410. Sal $110,972
Library Holdings: AV Mats 1,928; Bk Vols 83,928; Per Subs 122
Special Collections: Newberry College Materials; Regional Lutheran Materials; South Caroliniana
Automation Activity & Vendor Info: (Cataloging) SirsiDynix; (Circulation) SirsiDynix
Wireless access
Partic in Lyrasis; OCLC Online Computer Library Center, Inc; Partnership Among South Carolina Academic Libraries; SC Found of Independent Cols Consortia
Open Mon-Thurs 8am-11:30pm, Fri 8-4:30, Sat 9-Noon, Sun 3:30-10:30
Restriction: Open to students, fac & staff

P   NEWBERRY COUNTY LIBRARY*, 1300 Friend St, 29108-3400. SAN 360-330X. Tel: 803-276-0854. FAX: 803-276-7478. Web Site: www.newberrylibrary.org. *Dir,* Tucker Neel Taylor; E-mail: tucktaylor@infoave.net; Staff 7 (MLS 1, Non-MLS 6)
Pop 36,108
Library Holdings: Bk Vols 57,876; Per Subs 115
Open Mon & Wed-Fri 9-6, Tues 9-8, Sat 9-4
Friends of the Library Group
Branches: 1
WHITMIRE MEMORIAL, 1510 Church St, Whitmire, 29178, SAN 360-3369. Tel: 803-694-3961. FAX: 803-694-9945. *Mgr,* Linda Bullard
    Library Holdings: Bk Titles 13,639; Per Subs 25

Open Mon-Fri 9-5
Friends of the Library Group

ORANGEBURG

C   CLAFLIN UNIVERSITY*, H V Manning Library, 400 Magnolia St, 29115. SAN 315-5676. Tel: 803-535-5307, 803-535-5309. Circulation Tel: 803-535-5308. Reference Tel: 803-535-5306. FAX: 803-535-5091. E-mail: library@claflin.edu. Web Site: www.claflin.edu/library/index.asp. *Dir,* Marilyn Y Gibbs; E-mail: mgibbs@claflin.edu; Staff 9 (MLS 3, Non-MLS 6)
Enrl 1,701; Fac 9; Highest Degree: Master
Library Holdings: AV Mats 1,141; Bk Vols 161,726; Per Subs 450
Special Collections: Black Life & History (Wilbur R Gregg Black Coll) bks, microfilm; Claflin University Archives/Claflin University History, Minutes of the Methodist Episcopal Church, selected Civil Rights papers
Subject Interests: Hist, Music, Relig studies
Automation Activity & Vendor Info: (Cataloging) Innovative Interfaces, Inc; (Circulation) Innovative Interfaces, Inc; (Course Reserve) Innovative Interfaces, Inc; (OPAC) Innovative Interfaces, Inc; (Serials) Innovative Interfaces, Inc
Database Vendor: Alexander Street Press, American Chemical Society, Baker & Taylor, Blackwell's, Booklist Online, CQ Press, CredoReference, ebrary, EBSCOhost, Facts on File, Gale Cengage Learning, Grolier Online, H W Wilson, Innovative Interfaces, Inc, JSTOR, LexisNexis, Nature Publishing Group, OCLC FirstSearch, ProQuest, YBP Library Services
Wireless access
Open Mon-Thurs 8am-Midnight, Fri 8-6, Sat 10-2, Sun 3-10

J   ORANGEBURG-CALHOUN TECHNICAL COLLEGE*, Gressette Learning Resources Center, 3250 Saint Matthews Rd NE, 29118. SAN 315-5684. Tel: 803-535-1262. FAX: 803-535-1240. Web Site: www.octech.edu/intpages_side.php?pageid=1351. *Libr Dir,* Harris Murray; *Media Spec,* Timothy Felder; *Tech Serv,* Patti Sonefeld; Staff 4 (MLS 2, Non-MLS 2)
Founded 1968
Library Holdings: Audiobooks 247; AV Mats 2,066; e-books 61,270; Bk Vols 13,396; Per Subs 90
Wireless access
Open Mon-Thurs 7:30am-8pm, Fri 7:30-1:30

P   ORANGEBURG COUNTY LIBRARY*, 510 Louis St, 29115-5030. SAN 315-5692. Tel: 803-531-4636. Reference Tel: 803-533-5856, 803-533-5857. FAX: 803-533-5860. E-mail: OCLSNotify@orangeburgcounty.org. Web Site: www.orangeburgcounty.org/ocl. *Dir,* Roberta F Bibbins; Tel: 803-533-5854, E-mail: rbibbins@orangeburgcounty.org; *Asst Dir,* Debra C Allen; *Adult Serv,* Capers Bull, Jr; *Ch,* Lorene Dennis; Staff 7 (MLS 7)
Founded 1937. Pop 84,803; Circ 354,000
Library Holdings: Bk Vols 151,700; Per Subs 310
Subject Interests: Local hist
Automation Activity & Vendor Info: (Cataloging) Polaris Library Systems; (Circulation) Polaris Library Systems; (OPAC) Polaris Library Systems
Database Vendor: Auto-Graphics, Inc, Gale Cengage Learning, Polaris Library Systems
Wireless access
Open Mon & Tues 9-8, Wed-Fri 9-6, Sat 9-5
Friends of the Library Group
Branches: 3
HOLLY HILL BRANCH, 8441 Old State Rd, Hwy 176, Holly Hill, 29059. (Mail add: PO Box 816, Holly Hill, 29059). Tel: 803-496-7177. *Librn,* Margaret Thomas; Tel: 803-531-4636
    Open Mon-Thurs 1-5:30, Fri 9-1
    Friends of the Library Group
MENTOR BRANCH, 2626 Cleveland St, Elloree, 29047. (Mail add: PO Box 510, Elloree, 29047-0510). Tel: 803-897-2162. *Librn,* Margaret Thomas; Tel: 803-531-4636, E-mail: mthomas@orangeburgcounty.org
    Open Mon & Wed 2-5:30, Tues 1:30-5:30, Fri 9-1
    Friends of the Library Group
NORTH BRANCH, 9316 North Rd, Hwy 178, North, 29112. (Mail add: PO Box 10, North, 29112). Tel: 803-247-5880. *Librn,* Margaret Thomas; Tel: 803-531-4636
    Open Mon, Tues & Fri 2-5:30, Wed 9-1:30
    Friends of the Library Group
Bookmobiles: 1. *Librn,* Margaret Thomas

M   REGIONAL MEDICAL CENTER OF ORANGEBURG & CALHOUN COUNTIES*, Medical Library, 3000 St Matthews Rd, 29118. SAN 371-618X. Tel: 803-395-2275. FAX: 803-395-2557. *Librn,* Beth Grubbs; Staff 2 (Non-MLS 2)
Library Holdings: Bk Titles 218
Wireless access
Restriction: Not open to pub

C   SOUTH CAROLINA STATE UNIVERSITY*, Miller F Whittaker Library, 300 College St NE, 29115-4427. (Mail add: PO Box 7491, 29117), SAN 315-5714. Tel: 803-536-7045. Circulation Tel: 803-536-8645. Interlibrary Loan Service Tel: 803-536-8637. Reference Tel: 803-536-8640. FAX: 803-536-8902. Interlibrary Loan Service FAX: 803-516-4892. E-mail: reference@scsu.edu. *Dean of Libr & Info Serv,* Adrienne Webber; E-mail: awebber1@scsu.edu; *Asst Prof, Ref & Info Spec,* Dr Ruth A Hodges; E-mail: rhodges@scsu.edu; *Asst Prof, Ref & Info Spec,* John P Whitted; E-mail: jwhitte1@scsu.edu; *Govt Doc Coordr, Ref & Info Spec,* Doris E Johnson; Tel: 803-536-8642, E-mail: lb_djohnson@scsu.edu; *Instr, Ref & Info Serv,* Deborah C Gramling; Tel: 803-536-8647, E-mail: dcgramling@scsu.edu; *Coordr, Coll Develop,* Cathi Cooper Mack; Tel: 803-536-8633, E-mail: ccoopermack@scsu.edu; Staff 25 (MLS 8, Non-MLS 17)
Founded 1913. Enrl 4,001; Fac 238; Highest Degree: Doctorate
Library Holdings: Bk Vols 303,768; Per Subs 974
Special Collections: Black Coll-Books by & about Blacks; South Carolina State Data Center; South Carolina State University Historical Coll, bks, papers, pictures & memorabilia. Oral History; State Document Depository; US Document Depository
Subject Interests: Educ, Eng, Humanities, Soc sci
Automation Activity & Vendor Info: (Cataloging) Innovative Interfaces, Inc; (Circulation) Innovative Interfaces, Inc; (Course Reserve) Innovative Interfaces, Inc; (OPAC) Innovative Interfaces, Inc; (Serials) Innovative Interfaces, Inc
Database Vendor: Innovative Interfaces, Inc
Publications: Access to Information; Alumni & Retirees of South Carolina State University; Americans with Disabilities; Building Library Skills; Collection Development Policy; Community Awareness; Computerized Information Retrieval Services; How to Locate Books; Interlibrary Loan Services; Library Databases on the World Wide Web; Library Faculty & Staff Handbook; Library Faculty Staff Handbook; Library News & Notes (1 per semester newsletter); Library Research Skills; Library-Faculty Liaison Program; Miller F Whittaker Library - Computer & Information Services; Resources in Educational Administration; Services in the Miller F Whittaker Library; South Carolina State University Historical Collection, brochure; South Carolina State University Historical Trail; Student Library Handbook; The Bulldog Searcher; The Pathfinder
Partic in Dialog Corp; DISCUS; Lyrasis; OCLC Online Computer Library Center, Inc; Partnership Among South Carolina Academic Libraries
Special Services for the Blind - Braille bks; Magnifiers
Open Mon-Thurs 8:30am-Midnight, Fri 8:30-5, Sat 11-6, Sun 3-9

CR   SOUTHERN METHODIST COLLEGE, Lynn Corbett Library, 541 Broughton St, 29115. SAN 315-5722. Tel: 803-534-7826, Ext 106. FAX: 803-534-7827. E-mail: lcl@smcollege.edu. Web Site: www.smcollege.edu/library.php. *Dir,* Christine Gaskin; Staff 1 (MLS 1)
Founded 1964. Enrl 217; Fac 5; Highest Degree: Master
Library Holdings: AV Mats 40; CDs 52; DVDs 48; Electronic Media & Resources 84; Bk Titles 18,900; Bk Vols 21,550; Per Subs 49; Spec Interest Per Sub 12; Videos 194
Special Collections: Southern Methodist Room (Southern Methodist Denominational Information)
Subject Interests: Biblical studies
Wireless access
Function: Archival coll, AV serv, CD-ROM, ILL available, Music CDs, Online searches, Ref & res, Ref serv available, Telephone ref, VHS videos, Wheelchair accessible
Restriction: Mem only

PARRIS ISLAND

A   UNITED STATES MARINE CORPS*, Recruit Depot Station Library, Blvd DeFrance, Bldg 283, 29905-0070. (Mail add: PO Box 5070, 29905-0070), SAN 360-3393. Tel: 843-228-1672. FAX: 843-228-3840. Web Site: www.mccssc.com/lifelong/libraries.html. *Librn, Media Spec,* Rose Marie Krauss; Tel: 843-228-1671, E-mail: kraussrm@usmc-mccs.org
Founded 1940
Special Collections: General Gray Marine Warriors Library
Subject Interests: Biographies, Mil
Wireless access
Open Mon-Wed & Fri 9-7, Thurs 8-7, Sat 12-6, Sun 10-6
Friends of the Library Group

PENDLETON

S   PENDLETON DISTRICT HISTORICAL, RECREATIONAL & TOURISM COMMISSION*, Reference Library, 125 E Queen St, 29670. (Mail add: PO Box 565, 29670-0565), SAN 327-0874. Tel: 864-646-3782. Toll Free Tel: 800-862-1795. FAX: 864-646-2506. E-mail: pendletontourism@bellsouth.net. Web Site: www.pendleton-district.org. *Dir,* Vicki Fletcher
Founded 1966
Library Holdings: Bk Vols 2,000; Per Subs 30; Videos 35

Special Collections: Black Heritage, tapes; Historic Photos of South Carolina; Records of Anderson Cotton Mill (SC, 1895-1963); Speaking of History, tapes. Oral History
Subject Interests: Genealogy
Function: Photocopying/Printing
Publications: Friends of the Pendleton District (Newsletter)
Open Mon-Fri 9-4:30
Restriction: Non-circulating to the pub
Friends of the Library Group

J   TRI-COUNTY TECHNICAL COLLEGE LIBRARY, 7900 Hwy 76, 29670. (Mail add: PO Box 587, 29670-0587), SAN 315-5730. Tel: 864-646-1750. FAX: 864-646-1543. E-mail: library@tctc.edu. Web Site: library.tctc.edu, www.tctc.edu/library.html. *Dir,* Marla Roberson; E-mail: mrobers1@tctc.edu; *Distance Learning & Embedded Librn,* Michele Gregg; E-mail: mgregg@tctc.edu; *Instrul Serv Librn,* Sue Andrus; E-mail: sandrus@tctc.edu; *Ref Serv,* Norman Hoyle; E-mail: nhoyle@tctc.edu; Staff 7 (MLS 4, Non-MLS 3)
Founded 1963. Enrl 4,087; Fac 172; Highest Degree: Associate
Library Holdings: e-books 75,000; Bk Vols 37,948; Per Subs 165
Subject Interests: Ethnic studies, Hist, Literary criticism
Automation Activity & Vendor Info: (Acquisitions) SIRSI WorkFlows; (Cataloging) SIRSI WorkFlows; (Circulation) SIRSI WorkFlows; (ILL) OCLC; (OPAC) SIRSI WorkFlows; (Serials) EBSCO Online
Database Vendor: Alexander Street Press, EBSCOhost, Gale Cengage Learning, Greenwood Publishing Group, Grolier Online, Medline, netLibrary, OCLC ArticleFirst, OCLC WorldCat, ProQuest, RefWorks, SirsiDynix
Wireless access
Function: ILL available, Online cat, Online ref, Ref serv available
Partic in OCLC Online Computer Library Center, Inc; Partnership Among South Carolina Academic Libraries; South Carolina Information & Library Services Consortium (SCILS)
Restriction: 24-hr pass syst for students only

ROCK HILL

J   CLINTON JUNIOR COLLEGE LIBRARY*, 1029 Crawford Rd, 29730-5152. SAN 315-5765. Tel: 803-327-7402, Ext 228. FAX: 803-324-2734. Web Site: www.clintonjuniorcollege.edu. *Dir,* Minora Hicks; Tel: 803-327-7402, Ext 248; *Ref Asst,* Patricia Hinton; E-mail: phinton@clintonjuniorcollege.edu; Staff 3 (MLS 1, Non-MLS 2)
Founded 1894. Enrl 190; Fac 27; Highest Degree: Associate
Library Holdings: AV Mats 100; Bk Vols 9,105; Per Subs 47
Special Collections: African-African American Coll
Automation Activity & Vendor Info: (Acquisitions) Book Systems, Inc; (Cataloging) Book Systems, Inc
Wireless access
Function: Archival coll, AV serv, For res purposes, Handicapped accessible, Homebound delivery serv, Photocopying/Printing, Ref serv available, Telephone ref, Wheelchair accessible
Publications: Campus Communique (Newsletter)
Partic in DISCUS; Partnership Among South Carolina Academic Libraries
Open Mon-Thurs 8am-10pm, Fri 8-5
Restriction: Authorized scholars by appt, Open to fac, students & qualified researchers, Open to pub for ref & circ; with some limitations
Friends of the Library Group

S   MUSEUM OF YORK COUNTY*, Staff Research Library, 4621 Mount Gallant Rd, 29732-9905. SAN 326-3665. Tel: 803-329-2121. FAX: 803-329-5249. E-mail: myco@comporium.net. Web Site: www.yorkcounty.org. *Librn,* Nancy Sambets; Staff 1 (Non-MLS 1)
Library Holdings: Bk Titles 2,000; Per Subs 102
Special Collections: Shikar-Safari Club Library Coll, exploration, travel & adventure bks
Subject Interests: African anthrop, African art, Arts, Native Am of the SE, Natural sci
Publications: Acquisitions List (Monthly); Volunteer Information (Pamphlet)
Restriction: Staff use only

M   PIEDMONT MEDICAL CENTER LIBRARY*, 222 S Herlong Ave, 29732-1158. SAN 320-2348. Tel: 803-329-1234. FAX: 803-980-1353. *Librn,* Joyce Elder; E-mail: joyce.elder@tenethealth.com
Library Holdings: Bk Titles 578; Per Subs 67
Subject Interests: Med, Nursing
Open Mon-Fri 8-5

C   WINTHROP UNIVERSITY*, Ida Jane Dacus Library, 824 Oakland Ave, 29733. SAN 315-5781. Tel: 803-323-2131, 803-323-2274, 803-323-2311. Circulation Tel: 803-323-4502. Interlibrary Loan Service Tel: 803-323-2195. Reference Tel: 803-323-4501. Automation Services Tel: 803-323-2280. FAX: 803-323-2215. Reference FAX: 803-323-3285. Web Site: www.winthrop.edu/dacus. *Dean, Libr Serv,* Dr Mark Y Herring; Tel:

803-323-2232, E-mail: herringm@winthrop.edu; *Asst Dir, Archives,* Andrew Johnston; Tel: 803-323-2302, E-mail: johnstona@winthrop.edu; *Head, Circ,* Nancy White; Tel: 803-323-2335, E-mail: whiten@winthrop.edu; *Head, Monograph & AV Acq,* Antje Mays; E-mail: maysa@winthrop.edu; *Head, Monograph & AV Cat,* Patricia Ballard; Tel: 803-323-2179, E-mail: ballardp@winthrop.edu; *Head, Pub Serv,* Susan R Silverman; Tel: 803-323-2306, E-mail: silvermans@winthrop.edu; *Head, Ref,* Robert M Gorman; Tel: 803-323-2259, E-mail: gormanb@winthrop.edu; *Head, Ser, Acq & Cat,* Gale Teaster; E-mail: teasterg@winthrop.edu; *Libr Develop & Head, Tech Serv,* Dr Ronnie W Faulkner; Tel: 803-323-2262, E-mail: faulknerr@winthrop.edu; *Database Mgt,* Spiro Shetuni; Tel: 803-323-2234, E-mail: shetunis@winthrop.edu; *Ref, Archives & Doc Librn,* Robert Ryals; Tel: 803-323-2257, E-mail: ryalsr@winthrop.edu; *Syst Librn,* Carrie Volk; E-mail: volkc@winthrop.edu; *Access Serv,* Jean Wells; Tel: 803-323-2330, E-mail: wellsj@winthrop.edu; *Doc,* Jacqueline McFadden; Tel: 803-323-2322, E-mail: mcfaddenj@winthrop.edu; *Libr Instruction,* David Weeks; Tel: 803-323-2319, E-mail: weeksd@winthrop.edu; *Spec Coll & Archives Librn,* Gina P White; E-mail: whitegp@winthrop.edu; Staff 30 (MLS 13, Non-MLS 17)

Founded 1886. Enrl 6,480; Fac 542; Highest Degree: Master

Jul 2009-Jun 2010 Income $2,900,000, Locally Generated Income $20,000, Other $50,000. Mats Exp $2,900,000, Books $250,000, Per/Ser (Incl. Access Fees) $202,764, Manu Arch $20,000, Other Print Mats $20,000, Micro $30,263, AV Equip $10,000, AV Mat $20,000, Electronic Ref Mat (Incl. Access Fees) $890,141, Presv $9,396. Sal $1,816,403 (Prof $971,923)

Library Holdings: AV Mats 3,498; DVDs 15,000; e-books 13,940; e-journals 21,689; Bk Titles 366,428; Bk Vols 450,000; Per Subs 1,447; Videos 1,711

Special Collections: Catawba Indians, ms; Draper Manuscript Coll, microfilm; Education Resources Information Center Reports, microfiche; Genealogy, ms; General South Carolina History, ms; League of Nations Documents & Serial Publications, 1919-1946, microfilm; Library of American Civilization, ultrafiche; Library of English Literature, ultrafiche; Local South Carolina History, ms; Rare Books; United Nations Publications, 1946-1980, microprint; Winthrop Universitiy History, archives, ms. Women's History, ms. Oral History; State Document Depository; US Document Depository

Automation Activity & Vendor Info: (Acquisitions) Innovative Interfaces, Inc; (Cataloging) Innovative Interfaces, Inc; (Circulation) Innovative Interfaces, Inc; (Course Reserve) Innovative Interfaces, Inc; (ILL) OCLC Online; (OPAC) Innovative Interfaces, Inc; (Serials) Innovative Interfaces, Inc

Database Vendor: 3M Library Systems, ABC-CLIO, Academy of Political Science, ACM (Association for Computing Machinery), Agricola, Alexander Street Press, American Chemical Society, American Mathematical Society, American Psychological Association (APA), ARTstor, Blackwell's, Bloomberg, Brodart, CountryWatch, CredoReference, EBSCOhost, Gale Cengage Learning, HeinOnline, Innovative Interfaces, Inc, JSTOR, LearningExpress, LexisNexis, netLibrary, OCLC FirstSearch, OCLC WorldCat, ProQuest, PubMed, Sage, ScienceDirect, SerialsSolutions, Wiley, YBP Library Services

Wireless access

Publications: A Guide to the Manuscript & Oral History Collections; A Guide to the Records Documenting the History of Winthrop College; Dacus Focus; Sources of Genealogical Research in the Winthrop College Archives & Special Collections; The Dean's Corner

Partic in Charlotte Area Educ Consortium; Lyrasis; OCLC Online Computer Library Center, Inc; Partnership Among South Carolina Academic Libraries

Open Mon-Thurs 8am-Midnight, Fri 8-6, Sat Noon-6, Sun 1pm-Midnight

Restriction: Open to pub for ref only, Open to students, fac & staff

Friends of the Library Group

P YORK COUNTY LIBRARY*, Rock Hill Public, 138 E Black St, 29731. (Mail add: PO Box 10032, 29731), SAN 360-3423. Tel: 803-981-5858. Circulation Tel: 803-981-5860. Reference Tel: 803-981-5825. Administration Tel: 803-981-5831. Automation Services Tel: 803-981-5834. FAX: 803-981-5866. Web Site: www.yclibrary.org. *Dir,* Colleen Carney; E-mail: colleenc@lyon.york.lib.sc.us; *Br Coordr, Tech Serv,* Shasta Brewer; Tel: 803-981-5832, E-mail: shastab@lyon.york.lib.sc.us; *Commun Relations Librn,* Debra Turner; Tel: 803-981-5837, E-mail: turnerdebra@hotmail.com; *Ch,* Ginger Sawyer; Tel: 803-981-5888; *Ch,* Diane Williams; Tel: 803-981-5840, E-mail: dianew@lyon.york.lib.sc.us; *Circ,* Elliott Worthey; Tel: 803-981-5860; *ILL,* Page Hendrix; E-mail: pageh@lyon.york.lib.sc.us; *YA Serv,* Abbie Carnes; Tel: 803-981-5830; Staff 54 (MLS 12, Non-MLS 42)

Founded 1884. Pop 164,614; Circ 885,354

Library Holdings: AV Mats 13,911; Electronic Media & Resources 18; Bk Vols 276,787; Per Subs 577

Special Collections: Catawba Indian, bks, clippings & micro; Genealogical & Caroliniana (Local, State & General), bks, clippings & micro; Rock Hill & York County History, bks, clippings & micro

Automation Activity & Vendor Info: (Acquisitions) SirsiDynix; (Cataloging) SirsiDynix; (Circulation) SirsiDynix; (OPAC) SirsiDynix

Database Vendor: Gale Cengage Learning, ProQuest, SirsiDynix

Function: Adult bk club, AV serv, Handicapped accessible, Home delivery & serv to Sr ctr & nursing homes, Homebound delivery serv, ILL available, Photocopying/Printing, Prog for adults, Prog for children & young adult, Ref serv available, Summer reading prog, Telephone ref, VHS videos, Wheelchair accessible

Open Mon-Thurs 9-9, Fri & Sat 9-6, Sun (Sept-May) 2-6

Friends of the Library Group

Branches: 4

CLOVER PUBLIC, 107 Knox St, Clover, 29710, SAN 360-3458. Tel: 803-222-3474. FAX: 803-222-6695. *Br Librn,* Tee Cobb; Staff 4 (Non-MLS 4)

Function: Handicapped accessible, Photocopying/Printing, Prog for children & young adult, Ref serv available, Summer reading prog, Telephone ref, Wheelchair accessible

Open Mon-Thurs 10-8, Fri 10-6, Sat 10-2

FORT MILL PUBLIC, 1818 Second Baxter Crossing, Fort Mill, 29708, SAN 360-3482. Tel: 803-547-4114. FAX: 803-547-4852. *Br Mgr,* Karen Manera; Staff 8 (MLS 1, Non-MLS 7)

Function: Photocopying/Printing, Prog for children & young adult, Ref serv available, Summer reading prog, Telephone ref, Wheelchair accessible

Open Mon-Thurs 9-8, Fri & Sat 9-6

LAKE WYLIE PUBLIC, 185 Blucher Circle, Lake Wylie, 29710, SAN 323-5548. Tel: 803-831-7774. FAX: 803-831-7943. *Br Mgr,* Nancy Monts-Rayfield; Staff 5 (Non-MLS 5)

Function: Handicapped accessible, Photocopying/Printing, Prog for children & young adult, Ref serv available, Summer reading prog, Telephone ref, Wheelchair accessible

Open Mon-Thurs 10-8, Fri 10-6, Sat 10-2

YORK PUBLIC, 21 E Liberty St, York, 29745, SAN 360-3512. Tel: 803-684-3751. FAX: 803-684-6223. *Br Mgr,* Rita Vogel; Staff 8 (MLS 2, Non-MLS 6)

Function: Handicapped accessible, Photocopying/Printing, Prog for children & young adult, Ref serv available, Summer reading prog, Telephone ref

Open Mon-Thurs 9-8, Fri & Sat 9-6

Bookmobiles: 1

J YORK TECHNICAL COLLEGE LIBRARY*, Anne Springs Close Library, 452 S Anderson Rd, 29730. SAN 315-579X. Tel: 803-327-8025. Interlibrary Loan Service Tel: 803-981-7247. Administration Tel: 803-981-7075. Information Services Tel: 803-325-2883. Toll Free Tel: 800-922-8324. FAX: 803-327-4535. E-mail: library@yorktech.com. Web Site: www.yorktech.com/library. *Dir,* Kristine Jones; Tel: 803-981-7075, E-mail: kjones@yorktech.edu; *Acq, Cat, Instrul Serv Librn,* Debbie Majoue Jones; Tel: 803-325-2883, E-mail: djones3837@cruiser.yorktech.edu; *Res Coordr,* Samuel Pigford; Tel: 803-981-7247, E-mail: spigford@yorktech.edu; *Cat, Overdues/Circ, Reserves,* Carolyn F Gill; E-mail: cgill@yorktech.edu; *Cat, ILL, Ser,* Phyllis Hefney; E-mail: phefney@yorktech.edu; Staff 5 (MLS 2, Non-MLS 3)

Founded 1964. Enrl 3,700; Highest Degree: Associate

Jul 2006-Jun 2007 Income $356,000, State $350,000, Federal $6,000. Mats Exp $170,000, Books $80,000, Per/Ser (Incl. Access Fees) $15,700, AV Mat $4,300, Electronic Ref Mat (Incl. Access Fees) $70,000

Library Holdings: DVDs 30; e-books 46,000; Electronic Media & Resources 70; Large Print Bks 16; Bk Titles 24,000; Per Subs 460; Talking Bks 80; Videos 927

Special Collections: Electric Vehicles/Alternative Fuel (Alternative Energy Coll); Instructional Development Coll

Subject Interests: Allied health, Bus, Computers, Eng, Eng tech, Liberal arts, Nursing

Automation Activity & Vendor Info: (Acquisitions) SirsiDynix; (Cataloging) SirsiDynix; (Circulation) SirsiDynix; (Course Reserve) SirsiDynix; (ILL) OCLC; (Media Booking) SirsiDynix; (OPAC) SirsiDynix; (Serials) SirsiDynix

Database Vendor: EBSCOhost, Gale Cengage Learning, infoUSA, LearningExpress, netLibrary, Newsbank, OCLC FirstSearch, OCLC WorldCat, ProQuest, Wilson - Wilson Web

Wireless access

Function: CD-ROM, ILL available, Prog for children & young adult, Ref serv available, Referrals accepted, Spoken cassettes & CDs, VHS videos

Partic in Lyrasis; Partnership Among South Carolina Academic Libraries; South Carolina Information & Library Services Consortium (SCILS)

Special Services for the Deaf - Assistive tech; Bks on deafness & sign lang

Special Services for the Blind - Assistive/Adapted tech devices, equip & products; Bks on cassette; Bks on CD; Computer with voice synthesizer for visually impaired persons; Large print bks; Talking bks

Open Mon-Thurs 7:30am-10pm, Fri 7:30-5

Restriction: Open to pub upon request

SAINT GEORGE

P   DORCHESTER COUNTY LIBRARY, 506 N Parler Ave, 29477-2297.
     SAN 360-3547. Tel: 843-563-9189. FAX: 843-563-7823. E-mail:
     info@dcl.lib.sc.us. Web Site: www.dcl.lib.sc.us. *Dir,* Dr Frank A Bruno;
     Dep Dir, Jennie M Redmond; Staff 42 (MLS 8, Non-MLS 34)
     Founded 1953. Pop 100,833; Circ 671,590
     Library Holdings: Audiobooks 1,000; AV Mats 18,079; e-books 4,950;
     Bk Vols 147,568; Per Subs 305
     Subject Interests: SC hist
     Automation Activity & Vendor Info: (Acquisitions) Evergreen;
     (Cataloging) Evergreen; (Circulation) Evergreen; (OPAC) Evergreen
     Database Vendor: ABC-CLIO, EBSCO Information Services, Gale
     Cengage Learning, Greenwood Publishing Group, netLibrary, ProQuest
     Wireless access
     Open Mon-Thurs 9:30-8, Fri 9:30-5, Sat & Sun 1-5
     Friends of the Library Group
     Branches: 1
     SUMMERVILLE BRANCH, 76 Old Trolley Rd, Summerville, 29485,
       SAN 360-3571. Tel: 843-871-5075. FAX: 843-875-4811. *Br Mgr,*
       Rebecca S Westfall; *Asst Br Mgr,* Chris Johnston; *Ch Mgr,* Jason T
       Reed; Staff 6 (MLS 6)
       Founded 1978. Pop 100,000; Circ 600,000
       Open Mon-Thurs 10-8:30, Fri 10-6, Sat 9:30-5, Sun 1-5
       Friends of the Library Group
     Bookmobiles: 1

SAINT MATTHEWS

P   CALHOUN COUNTY LIBRARY*, 900 FR Huff Dr, 29135-1261. SAN
     315-5803. Tel: 803-874-3389. FAX: 803-874-4154. Web Site:
     www.calhouncountylibrary.org. *Dir,* Kristen Setzler Simensen; *Mgr,* Merle
     Govan
     Pop 15,385; Circ 31,407
     Library Holdings: Bk Vols 32,000; Per Subs 139
     Special Collections: Julia Peterkin Coll
     Automation Activity & Vendor Info: (Cataloging) TLC (The Library
     Corporation); (Circulation) TLC (The Library Corporation); (OPAC) TLC
     (The Library Corporation)
     Database Vendor: EBSCO Auto Repair Reference, LearningExpress,
     TDNet
     Partic in Lyrasis
     Open Mon & Wed 10-6, Tues & Thurs 10-8, Fri 10-5, Sat 10-3
     Friends of the Library Group
     Bookmobiles: 1

S   CALHOUN COUNTY MUSEUM & CULTURAL CENTER*, Archives &
     Library, 313 Butler St, 29135. SAN 329-8507. Tel: 803-874-3964. FAX:
     803-874-4790. E-mail: calmus@oburg.net. *Dir,* Debbie Roland
     Library Holdings: Bk Vols 950; Per Subs 12
     Open Mon-Fri 9-4
     Friends of the Library Group

SALUDA

P   SALUDA COUNTY LIBRARY*, 101 S Main St, 29138. SAN 360-3334.
     Tel: 864-445-2267, 864-445-9586. FAX: 864-445-2725. E-mail:
     saluda.library@saludacounty.sc.gov. Web Site: www.saluda.lib.sc.us. *Dir,*
     Pamela Brill; *Libr Assoc,* Debbie Link
     Library Holdings: Bk Titles 19,000; Per Subs 30
     Subject Interests: Folklore
     Automation Activity & Vendor Info: (Cataloging) Follett Software;
     (Circulation) Follett Software
     Open Mon, Thurs & Fri 9-5, Tues 9-8, Wed & Sat 9-1

SHAW AFB

A   UNITED STATES AIR FORCE*, McElveen Library, FL 4803, 400 Shaw
     Dr, 29152. SAN 360-3601. Tel: 803-895-4518. FAX: 803-895-3961.
     E-mail: library@20thfss.com. Web Site:
     www.20thservices.com/library.html. *Dir,* Janet Price; Staff 5 (MLS 1,
     Non-MLS 4)
     Library Holdings: Bk Vols 40,000; Per Subs 76
     Special Collections: Transition Assistant Program-Military
     Subject Interests: Govt res, Mil
     Automation Activity & Vendor Info: (Cataloging) OCLC Online;
     (Circulation) SirsiDynix; (ILL) OCLC Online; (OPAC) SirsiDynix
     Database Vendor: EBSCOhost, Gale Cengage Learning, Jane's,
     netLibrary, Newsbank, OCLC FirstSearch, ProQuest
     Partic in ALA
     Open Mon-Thurs 10-8, Fri 11-6, Sat & Sun 1-5
     Restriction: Limited access for the pub

SPARTANBURG

C   CONVERSE COLLEGE*, Mickel Library, 580 E Main St, 29302. SAN
     315-5811. Tel: 864-596-9020, 864-596-9071. Interlibrary Loan Service Tel:
     864-596-9596. Reference Tel: 864-596-9076. Administration Tel:
     864-596-9072. FAX: 864-596-9075. Web Site:
     www.converse.edu/academics/mickel-library. *Libr Dir,* Wade Woodward;
     E-mail: wade.woodward@converse.edu; *Dir, Archives & Spec Coll,* Dr
     Jeffrey Willis; Tel: 864-596-9216, E-mail: jeff.willis@converse.edu; *Music
     Librn,* Wendi Arms; Tel: 864-596-9074, E-mail: wendi.arms@converse.edu;
     Acq, Supvr, Rebecca Dalton; E-mail: becky.dalton@converse.edu; *Circ
     Supvr,* Rebecca Poole; E-mail: bpoole@converse.edu; *ILL/Doc Delivery
     Supvr,* Richard Morgan; E-mail: dell.morgan@converse.edu; *Coordr, Music
     & Tech Serv,* Darlene Fawver; Tel: 864-596-9025, E-mail:
     darlene.fawver@converse.edu; *Coordr, Ref & Coll,* Mark Collier; E-mail:
     mark.collier@converse.edu; Staff 4.25 (MLS 4, Non-MLS 0.25)
     Founded 1889. Enrl 1,066; Fac 4; Highest Degree: Master
     Jul 2008-Jun 2009. Mats Exp $316,134
     Library Holdings: AV Mats 21,668; e-books 288; e-journals 47,679;
     Microforms 87,519; Bk Vols 155,731; Per Subs 500
     Subject Interests: Educ, Music
     Database Vendor: ARTstor, Baker & Taylor, BioOne, CredoReference,
     EBSCOhost, Gale Cengage Learning, Grolier Online, H W Wilson,
     Innovative Interfaces, Inc, Innovative Interfaces, Inc INN - View, JSTOR,
     LearningExpress, LexisNexis, netLibrary, OCLC FirstSearch, ProQuest
     Wireless access
     Partic in Lyrasis; Partnership Among South Carolina Academic Libraries
     Open Mon-Thurs 8am-11pm, Fri 8-6, Sat 12-5, Sun 1-11

S   MILLIKEN & COMPANY*, Information Center Library, 920 Milliken Rd,
     MS M-470, 29303. SAN 315-5838. Tel: 864-503-1734. FAX:
     864-503-2769. *In Charge,* David Littlejohn; Staff 1 (MLS 1)
     Founded 1960
     Library Holdings: Bk Titles 1,000; Per Subs 20
     Subject Interests: Chem, Textiles
     Wireless access
     Partic in Lyrasis
     Restriction: Co libr, Employees & their associates

C   SHERMAN COLLEGE OF STRAIGHT CHIROPRACTIC*, Tom & Mae
     Bahan Library, 2020 Springfield Rd, 29316-7251. (Mail add: PO Box
     1452, 29304-1452), SAN 321-4842. Tel: 864-578-8770, Ext 253,
     864-578-8770, Ext 254. FAX: 864-599-4860. E-mail: library@sherman.edu.
     Web Site: www.sherman.edu/edu/library-media.asp. *Dir,* Crissy Lewis;
     E-mail: clewis@sherman.edu; Staff 1 (MLS 1)
     Founded 1973. Enrl 325; Fac 39; Highest Degree: Doctorate
     Library Holdings: AV Mats 3,000; Bk Titles 9,900; Per Subs 138
     Special Collections: Chiropractic (B J Palmer Green Coll)
     Subject Interests: Biological, Chiropractic, Clinical sci
     Automation Activity & Vendor Info: (Cataloging) Follett Software;
     (Circulation) Follett Software; (OPAC) Follett Software; (Serials) EBSCO
     Online
     Database Vendor: EBSCOhost, OCLC FirstSearch
     Wireless access
     Function: Audio & video playback equip for onsite use, CD-ROM, Copy
     machines, Electronic databases & coll, ILL available, Online searches,
     Photocopying/Printing, Res libr, Spoken cassettes & CDs, VHS videos
     Partic in Chiropractic Libr Consortium; National Network of Libraries of
     Medicine; OCLC Online Computer Library Center, Inc; Southeastern
     Regional Med Libr Program
     Open Mon-Thurs 7:30-5:30, Fri 7:30-4:30

S   SOUTH CAROLINA SCHOOL FOR THE DEAF & THE BLIND*, Jesse
     Franklin Cleveland Learning Resource Center, 355 Cedar Springs Rd,
     29302-4699. SAN 315-5846. Tel: 864-577-7642, 864-585-7711. Circulation
     Tel: 864-577-7647. FAX: 864-577-7648. TDD: 864-577-7646. *Dir,* Galena
     Gaw; E-mail: ggaw@scsdb.org; *Tech Serv,* Deborah Wright; E-mail:
     dwright@scsdb.org. Subject Specialists: *Blindness, Deafness,* Galena Gaw;
     Deafness, Deborah Wright; Staff 3 (MLS 1, Non-MLS 2)
     Founded 1849
     Library Holdings: Bk Titles 14,826; Per Subs 20
     Special Collections: Captioned Videos; Descriptive Videos
     Subject Interests: Blindness, Deafness
     Automation Activity & Vendor Info: (Cataloging) Follett Software;
     (Circulation) Follett Software; (OPAC) Follett Software
     Function: Accelerated reader prog
     Special Services for the Deaf - Am sign lang & deaf culture; Bks on
     deafness & sign lang; Coll on deaf educ; Deaf publ; High interest/low
     vocabulary bks; Lecture on deaf culture; Sorenson video relay syst; Staff
     with knowledge of sign lang; TTY equip
     Special Services for the Blind - Accessible computers; Audio mat; Bks &
     mags in Braille, on rec, tape & cassette; Bks on cassette; Bks on CD;
     Braille & cassettes; Children's Braille; Closed circuit TV; Computer with

voice synthesizer for visually impaired persons; Descriptive video serv (DVS); Extensive large print coll
Open Mon-Thurs 7:30-7:30, Fri 7:30-4

J   SPARTANBURG COMMUNITY COLLEGE LIBRARY*, Central Campus, 800 Brisack Rd, 29305. (Mail add: PO Drawer 4386, 29305), SAN 315-5854. Tel: 864-592-4615. Interlibrary Loan Service Tel: 864-592-4769. Information Services Tel: 864-592-4761. Toll Free Tel: 866-542-2779. FAX: 864-592-4762. Automation Services FAX: 864-592-4764. Web Site: library.sccsc.edu. *Libr Dir,* Patricia Jordan; E-mail: jordanp@sccsc.edu; *Pub Serv Librn,* Katherine Knott Stiwinter; E-mail: stiwinterk@sccsc.edu; *Tech Serv Librn,* Barbara Scala; *Libr Spec,* Leverne McBeth; Staff 8 (MLS 4, Non-MLS 4)
Enrl 4,000; Fac 120; Highest Degree: Associate
Library Holdings: AV Mats 5,000; Bks on Deafness & Sign Lang 1,500; e-books 21,000; Bk Titles 42,000; Per Subs 283
Subject Interests: Hort, Sensory impaired
Automation Activity & Vendor Info: (Cataloging) SirsiDynix
Wireless access
Open Mon-Thurs 7:30am-9pm, Fri 7:30-1:30, Sat 9-1

P   SPARTANBURG COUNTY PUBLIC LIBRARIES*, 151 S Church St, 29306-3241. SAN 360-3636. Tel: 864-596-3500. Circulation Tel: 864-596-3503. Interlibrary Loan Service Tel: 864-596-3500, Ext 1248. Reference Tel: 864-596-3505. Administration Tel: 864-596-3507. Automation Services Tel: 864-596-3515. FAX: 864-596-3518. Web Site: www.infodepot.org. *Dir,* Todd Stephens; *Asst County Librn,* Jayne Moorman; *Asst County Librn, Pub Serv,* Carole Bledsoe; *Dir, Ch Serv,* Margo Wilson; *Dir of Circ,* Lori Livesay; *Dir, Multimedia & Adult Serv,* Ashley Layne; *Dir, Ref,* Andy Flynt; *Dir of Tech Serv,* Mildred Finch; *Dir, Teen Serv,* Susan Wetter; *Coord, Coll Develop,* Pat Brown; *Coordr of Develop,* Amanda Cochrum; *Coordr, Local Hist & Spec Coll,* Steve Smith; *Coord, Syst & Planning,* Tom Lowrimore; *Coordr, Web Serv,* Jennifer Land; Staff 197 (MLS 34, Non-MLS 163)
Founded 1885. Pop 253,000; Circ 1,726,715
Library Holdings: Bk Vols 825,179
Special Collections: State Document Depository; US Document Depository
Subject Interests: SC hist
Automation Activity & Vendor Info: (Acquisitions) Polaris Library Systems; (Cataloging) Polaris Library Systems; (Circulation) Polaris Library Systems; (ILL) Polaris Library Systems; (OPAC) Polaris Library Systems; (Serials) Polaris Library Systems
Wireless access
Publications: Directory of Clubs and Organizations (Spartanburg County)
Special Services for the Deaf - Captioned film dep; Closed caption videos; High interest/low vocabulary bks
Special Services for the Blind - Bks on CD; Home delivery serv; Large print bks; Playaways (bks on MP3); Recorded bks
Open Mon-Fri 9-9, Sat 9-6, Sun 1:30-6
Friends of the Library Group
Branches: 9
BOILING SPRINGS LIBRARY, 871 Double Bridge Rd, Boiling Springs, 29316, SAN 360-3652. Tel: 864-578-3665. *Br Librn,* Jean Foster
Open Mon, Tues & Thurs 10-8, Wed, Fri & Sat 10-6, Sun 1:30-6
Friends of the Library Group
CHESNEE LIBRARY, 100 Pickens Ave, Chesnee, 29323, SAN 360-3660. Tel: 864-461-2423. *Br Librn,* Jack Underwood
Open Mon, Tues & Thurs 10-8, Wed & Fri 10-6, Sat 10-4
Friends of the Library Group
COWPENS LIBRARY, 181 School St, Cowpens, 29330, SAN 378-164X. Tel: 864-463-0430. *Br Librn,* Joan Blalock
Open Mon & Tues 10-8, Wed-Fri 10-6, Sat 10-4
Friends of the Library Group
INMAN LIBRARY, 50 Mill St, Inman, 29349, SAN 360-3695. Tel: 864-472-8363. *Br Librn,* Ginger Ridings
Open Mon, Tues & Thurs 10-8, Wed & Fri 10-6, Sat 10-4
Friends of the Library Group
LANDRUM LIBRARY, 111 Asbury Dr, Landrum, 29356, SAN 360-3725. Tel: 864-457-2218. *Br Librn,* Lee Morgan
Open Mon, Tues & Thurs 9-8, Wed & Fri 9-6, Sat 9-2
Friends of the Library Group
MIDDLE TYGER LIBRARY, 170 Groce Rd, Lyman, 29365, SAN 360-375X. Tel: 864-439-4759. *Br Librn,* Sherry Henson
Open Mon, Tues & Thurs 10-8, Wed, Fri & Sat 10-6, Sun 1:30-6
Friends of the Library Group
PACOLET LIBRARY, 390 W Main St, Pacolet, 29372, SAN 375-491X. Tel: 864-474-0421. *Br Librn,* Chris Rogers
Open Mon & Tues 10-8, Wed, Thurs & Fri 10-6, Sat 12-4
Friends of the Library Group
WESTSIDE LIBRARY, 525 Oak Grove Rd, 29301, SAN 325-4046. Tel: 864-574-6815. *Br Librn,* Chandra Placer
Open Mon-Thurs 9-9, Fri 9-6, Sat 10-6, Sun 1:30-6
Friends of the Library Group

WOODRUFF LIBRARY, 270 E Hayne St, Woodruff, 29388, SAN 360-3784. Tel: 864-476-8770. *Br Librn,* Cyn Massey
Open Mon, Tues & Thurs 10-8, Wed 10-6, Fri 12-6, Sat 10-4
Friends of the Library Group
Bookmobiles: 1

JR   SPARTANBURG METHODIST COLLEGE*, Marie Blair Burgess Library, 1000 Powell Mill Rd, 29301. SAN 315-5870. Tel: 864-587-4208. FAX: 864-587-4352. Web Site: www.smcsc.edu/library. *Dir,* James Haller; E-mail: hallerje@smcsc.edu
Founded 1911
Library Holdings: Bk Vols 45,500; Per Subs 75
Wireless access
Partic in OCLC Online Computer Library Center, Inc
Open Mon-Thurs 8am-10pm, Fri 8-1:30, Sun 7pm-10pm
Friends of the Library Group

M   SPARTANBURG REGIONAL MEDICAL CENTER*, Health Sciences Library, 101 E Wood St, 29303. SAN 315-5862. Tel: 864-560-6220. FAX: 864-560-6791. Web Site: www.spartanburgregional.com/Services/Pages/HealthSciencesLibrary.aspx. *Mgr, Libr Serv,* Tonia Harris; E-mail: toharris@srhs.com; Staff 2 (MLS 1, Non-MLS 1)
Founded 1962
Library Holdings: Bk Titles 2,000; Per Subs 175
Subject Interests: Allied health, Clinical sci, Med, Nursing
Automation Activity & Vendor Info: (Cataloging) Follett Software; (Circulation) Follett Software; (Serials) Follett Software
Database Vendor: EBSCOhost, STAT!Ref (Teton Data Systems)
Wireless access
Function: Doc delivery serv, ILL available
Partic in National Network of Libraries of Medicine; SE Network of Hospital Librs on Docline
Restriction: Non-circulating to the pub

C   UNIVERSITY OF SOUTH CAROLINA UPSTATE LIBRARY, 800 University Way, 29303. SAN 315-5889. Tel: 864-503-5620. Circulation Tel: 864-503-5611. Reference Tel: 864-503-5638. FAX: 864-503-5601. Web Site: www.uscupstate.edu/library. *Dean of Libr,* Frieda Davison; Tel: 864-503-5610, E-mail: fdavison@uscupstate.edu; *Asst Dean, Pub Serv Librn,* Nancy Lambert; Tel: 864-503-5615, E-mail: nlambert@uscupstate.edu; *Sr Dir, Commun Engagement,* Susan Hodge; Tel: 864-503-5275, E-mail: shodge@uscupstate.edu; *Pub Serv Librn,* Lola Bradley; Tel: 864-503-5006, E-mail: lbradley@uscupstate.edu; *Archives Coordr, Pub Serv Librn,* Laura Karas; Tel: 864-503-5637, E-mail: lkaras@uscupstate.edu; *Pub Serv Librn,* Breanne Kirsch; Tel: 864-503-5613, E-mail: bkirsch@uscupstate.edu; *Coordr, Instruction, Pub Serv Librn,* Andrew Kearns; Tel: 864-503-5403, E-mail: akearns@uscupstate.edu; *Coordr, Libr Support for Distance Educ, Pub Serv Librn,* James LaMee; Tel: 864-503-5991, E-mail: jlamee@uscupstate.edu; *Coordr, Coll Mgt, Pub Serv Librn,* Camille McCutcheon; Tel: 864-503-5612, E-mail: cmccutcheon@uscupstate.edu; *Pub Serv Librn, Ref Serv Coordr,* Karen Swetland; Tel: 864-503-5034, E-mail: kswetland@uscupstate.edu; *Coordr, Electronic Res, Pub Serv Librn,* Chris Vidas; Tel: 864-503-5672, E-mail: cvidas@uscupstate.edu; *Tech Serv Mgr,* Bonnie Brock; Tel: 864-503-5639, E-mail: bbrock@uscupstate.edu; *Coordr, Access Serv,* Mary Kaye Gault; Tel: 864-503-5679, E-mail: mgault@uscupstate.edu; Staff 26 (MLS 12, Non-MLS 14)
Founded 1967. Enrl 5,493; Fac 218; Highest Degree: Master
Library Holdings: AV Mats 7,413; Braille Volumes 11; CDs 840; DVDs 3,701; e-books 153,008; e-journals 63,011; Microforms 48,584; Bk Vols 182,224; Per Subs 572; Videos 2,563
Special Collections: Archives of the Upstate; Hub City Writers Archives; Pre-1900 Publications; Thomas Moore Craig Coll of Southern History & Literature; University Publications
Automation Activity & Vendor Info: (Acquisitions) Innovative Interfaces, Inc; (Circulation) Innovative Interfaces, Inc; (Course Reserve) Innovative Interfaces, Inc; (ILL) OCLC ILLiad; (OPAC) Innovative Interfaces, Inc
Database Vendor: ACM (Association for Computing Machinery), Agricola, American Chemical Society, American Mathematical Society, American Physical Society, American Psychological Association (APA), Annual Reviews, ARTstor, Cambridge Scientific Abstracts, Children's Literature Comprehensive Database Company (CLCD), Cinahl Information Systems, CQ Press, CredoReference, EBSCOhost, Gale Cengage Learning, IOP, ISI Web of Knowledge, JSTOR, LearningExpress, LexisNexis, Medline, netLibrary, OCLC ArticleFirst, OCLC CAMIO, OCLC FirstSearch, OCLC WorldCat, OVID Technologies, Oxford Online, Project MUSE, ProQuest, PubMed, Sage, ScienceDirect, Springer-Verlag, Springshare, LLC, TDNet, Thomson - Web of Science, ValueLine, Wiley InterScience, Wilson - Wilson Web, YBP Library Services
Wireless access
Partic in Carolina Consortium; DISCUS; Lyrasis; Partnership Among South Carolina Academic Libraries

Open Mon-Thurs 7:30am-10pm, Fri 7:30-5, Sat 10-5, Sun 2-10
Restriction: ID required to use computers (Ltd hrs), Restricted borrowing privileges
Departmental Libraries:
UNIVERSITY CENTER OF GREENVILLE LIBRARY, 225 S Pleasantburg Dr, Greenville, 29607-2544. Tel: 864-250-1111. FAX: 864-250-8905. Web Site: www.ucgreenville.org/facilities-a-services/library-services.html. *Pub Serv Librn,* Lola Bradley; Tel: 864-503-5006; *Coordr, Pub Serv Librn,* James LaMee; Tel: 864-503-5991
    Library Holdings: Bk Titles 118; Bk Vols 348

C   WOFFORD COLLEGE*, Sandor Teszler Library, 429 N Church St, 29303-3663. SAN 315-5897. Tel: 864-597-4300. FAX: 864-597-4329. Web Site: www.wofford.edu/sandorteszlerlibrary. *Dean,* Oakley H Coburn; E-mail: coburnoh@wofford.edu; *Acq,* Joyce Arthur; *Archivist,* Phillip Stone; *Cat,* Timothy Brown; *Circ,* Paul Jones; *Coll Develop,* Ibrahim Hanif; *ILL,* Cathey Meghan; *Pub Serv,* Ellen Tillett; *Ref,* Esther Martin; *Ref,* Chris Strauber; *Tech Serv,* Shelley Sperka; Staff 7 (MLS 7)
Founded 1854. Enrl 1,100; Fac 70; Highest Degree: Bachelor
Library Holdings: AV Mats 3,000; e-books 37,594; e-journals 9,514; Bk Vols 195,924; Per Subs 532
Special Collections: 16th & 17th Century Books; Book Arts; Geography & Travel; Historical Coll of Materials related to the SC Conference of the United Methodist Church; Hymns & Hymnody; Press Books; South Caroliniana
Automation Activity & Vendor Info: (Cataloging) Innovative Interfaces, Inc
Partic in Lyrasis; OCLC Online Computer Library Center, Inc
Open Mon-Thurs 8am-Midnight, Fri 8-7, Sat 10-5, Sun 1-Midnight
Friends of the Library Group

SULLIVAN'S ISLAND

S   US NATIONAL PARK SERVICE*, Fort Sumter National Monument Research Library, 1214 Middle St, 29482. SAN 370-2898. Tel: 843-883-3123. FAX: 843-883-3910. Web Site: www.nps.gov. *In Charge,* Richard W Hatcher, III; Tel: 843-883-3123, Ext 22, E-mail: rick_hatcher@nps.gov. Subject Specialists: *Am Civil War,* Richard W Hatcher, III
Founded 1948
Library Holdings: Bk Vols 1,000; Per Subs 8
Function: For res purposes, Res libr
Restriction: In-house use for visitors, Non-circulating, Non-circulating coll, Not a lending libr, Open by appt only

SUMMERVILLE

S   TIMROD LIBRARY*, 217 Central Ave, 29483. SAN 315-5919. Tel: 843-871-4600. FAX: 843-871-4600. *Librn,* Debra Lodge; Staff 4 (MLS 1, Non-MLS 3)
Library Holdings: Bk Vols 40,000
Subject Interests: SC hist
Open Mon-Fri 10-5, Sat 10-2
Restriction: Mem only

SUMTER

J   CENTRAL CAROLINA TECHNICAL COLLEGE LIBRARY*, 506 N Guignard Dr, 29150. SAN 315-5935. Tel: 803-778-6647. FAX: 803-778-7889. E-mail: library@cctech.edu. Web Site: www.cctech.edu/library.htm. *Interim Libr Mgr,* Denise Robinson; E-mail: robinsondk@cctech.edu; *Libr Asst II,* Johnette Brewer; E-mail: brewerjh@cctech.edu; Staff 2 (MLS 2)
Founded 1963. Enrl 3,000; Fac 88; Highest Degree: Associate
Library Holdings: AV Mats 2,770; e-books 53,288; Bk Titles 20,924; Bk Vols 26,157; Per Subs 174
Subject Interests: Early childhood develop, Law, Nursing
Automation Activity & Vendor Info: (Acquisitions) SirsiDynix; (Cataloging) SirsiDynix; (Circulation) SirsiDynix; (Course Reserve) SirsiDynix; (ILL) OCLC; (OPAC) SirsiDynix; (Serials) SirsiDynix
Database Vendor: CredoReference, EBSCOhost, Gale Cengage Learning, Grolier Online, netLibrary, ProQuest, Westlaw
Partic in Lyrasis; OCLC Online Computer Library Center, Inc; Partnership Among South Carolina Academic Libraries; South Carolina Information & Library Services Consortium (SCILS)
Restriction: Circ to mem only

C   MORRIS COLLEGE*, Richardson-Johnson Learning Resources Center, 100 W College St, 29150-3599. SAN 315-5927. Tel: 803-934-3230. FAX: 803-778-2923. Web Site: www.morris.edu. *Dir, Libr Serv,* Margaret N Mukooza; E-mail: mmukooza@morris.edu; *Cat,* Robyn Hall-Agent; E-mail: rhallagent@morris.edu; *Circ,* Beatrice Golden; E-mail: bgolden@morris.edu; *Ref Serv,* Carol Fleury; E-mail: cfleury@morris.edu;

Ser, Mary Dow; E-mail: mdow@morris.edu; Staff 11 (MLS 3, Non-MLS 8)
Founded 1920. Enrl 970; Fac 52; Highest Degree: Bachelor
Jul 2005-Jun 2006 Income $654,370. Mats Exp $289,759. Sal $726,062
Library Holdings: CDs 153; DVDs 110; High Interest/Low Vocabulary Bk Vols 1,700; Bk Vols 74,819; Per Subs 339; Videos 1,760
Special Collections: African American Coll
Automation Activity & Vendor Info: (Acquisitions) SirsiDynix; (Cataloging) OCLC Connexion; (Circulation) SirsiDynix; (Course Reserve) SirsiDynix; (ILL) OCLC WorldCat; (OPAC) SirsiDynix; (Serials) SirsiDynix
Database Vendor: EBSCOhost, Gale Cengage Learning, OCLC WorldCat, ProQuest, SirsiDynix, Wilson - Wilson Web
Function: ILL available
Partic in Lyrasis; OCLC Online Computer Library Center, Inc; Partnership Among South Carolina Academic Libraries
Open Mon-Thurs 8am-10pm, Fri 8-5, Sat 9-4, Sun 3-9
Restriction: Open to students, fac & staff

P   SUMTER COUNTY LIBRARY, 111 N Harvin St, 29150. SAN 315-5943. Tel: 803-773-7273. FAX: 803-773-4875. E-mail: sumtercolib@spiritcom.net. Web Site: www.sumtercountylibrary.org. *Dir,* Robert Harden; E-mail: hardenr@spiritcom.net; *Head, Ch,* Karen Edgar; E-mail: kedgar@spiritcom.net; *Ref Librn,* Rudean Hill; E-mail: ruhill@spiritcom.net; *Ref Librn,* Brandolyn Love; E-mail: loveb@spiritcom.net; *Ref/ILL,* Susan Smith; E-mail: smiths@spiritcom.net; *Ref & Info Serv Coordr, Webmaster,* Ford Simmons; E-mail: simmonsf@spiritcom.net; Staff 9 (MLS 7, Non-MLS 2)
Founded 1917. Pop 104,430; Circ 266,471
Library Holdings: Bk Titles 150,000; Bk Vols 175,000; Per Subs 250
Automation Activity & Vendor Info: (Acquisitions) Polaris Library Systems; (Cataloging) Polaris Library Systems; (Circulation) Polaris Library Systems; (OPAC) Polaris Library Systems; (Serials) Polaris Library Systems
Database Vendor: Polaris Library Systems
Wireless access
Function: Adult bk club, Adult literacy prog, After school storytime, Audiobks via web, Bks on cassette, Bks on CD, CD-ROM, Children's prog, Computer training, Computers for patron use, Copy machines, Electronic databases & coll, Fax serv, ILL available, Music CDs, Online cat, Prog for children & young adult, Pub access computers, Ref serv available, Spoken cassettes & CDs, Story hour, Summer reading prog, Tax forms
Publications: Bibliographies; Bookings (Newsletter)
Friends of the Library Group
Branches: 2
SOUTH SUMTER BRANCH, 337 Manning Ave, 29150, SAN 374-745X. Tel: 803-775-7132. FAX: 803-775-7132. E-mail: ssbranch@spiritcom.net. *Br Mgr,* Geneva Hogan
    Library Holdings: Bk Vols 7,000
    Open Mon-Fri 10-6
WESMARK BRANCH LIBRARY, 180 W Wesmark Blvd, 29150, SAN 371-9545. Tel: 803-469-8110. FAX: 803-469-8347. *Br Mgr,* Mary Pack; E-mail: packm@spiritcom.net
    Library Holdings: Bk Vols 10,000
    Friends of the Library Group
Bookmobiles: 1

C   UNIVERSITY OF SOUTH CAROLINA SUMTER*, J C Anderson Library, 200 Miller Rd, 29150-2498. SAN 315-596X. Tel: 803-775-8727. Circulation Tel: 803-938-3736. FAX: 803-938-3811. Web Site: www.uscsumter.edu, www.uscsumter.edu/library/index.shtml. *Libr Dir,* Sharon Chapman; *Mgr,* Constance Pender
Founded 1966. Enrl 1,500
Library Holdings: Bk Vols 100,000; Per Subs 125
Automation Activity & Vendor Info: (Circulation) Innovative Interfaces, Inc - Millenium
Database Vendor: EBSCOhost, Gale Cengage Learning, Hoovers, Thomson - Web of Science, Thomson Carswell
Wireless access
Open Mon-Thurs 8:30-7
Friends of the Library Group

TIGERVILLE

C   NORTH GREENVILLE UNIVERSITY, Hester Memorial Library, 7801 N Tigerville Rd, 29688. SAN 315-5978. Tel: 864-977-7091. FAX: 864-977-2126. Web Site: www.ngu.edu. *Dir, Libr Serv,* Carla McMahan; *Ref Librn,* Leslie Brown; *Ref Librn,* Mary Poole; *Tech Serv,* Erica Rainey; Staff 14 (MLS 4, Non-MLS 10)
Founded 1892. Enrl 2,200; Fac 200; Highest Degree: Doctorate
Library Holdings: Bk Titles 46,000; Bk Vols 52,000; Per Subs 426
Special Collections: Archives; Edith Duff Miller Bible Museum Coll
Database Vendor: EBSCOhost

Wireless access
Open Mon-Thurs (Fall & Spring) 7:30am-11:30pm, Fri 7:30-4, Sat Noon-5,
Sun 3-11pm; Mon & Tues (Summer) 8:30am- 9pm, Wed-Thurs 8:30-5, Fri
8:30-Noon

UNION

P   UNION COUNTY CARNEGIE LIBRARY, 300 E South St, 29379-2392.
         SAN 315-5986. Tel: 864-427-7140. FAX: 864-427-4687. Web Site:
         www.unionlibrary.org. *Dir,* Ben Loftis; *Tech Serv,* Susan Gregory; Staff 1
         (MLS 1)
         Founded 1904. Pop 30,751; Circ 55,797
         Library Holdings: Bk Vols 59,167; Per Subs 123
         Special Collections: South Caroliniana Coll, bks & micro
         Partic in SCLENDS
         Open Mon-Fri 9-6, Sat 9-3
         Friends of the Library Group

C   UNIVERSITY OF SOUTH CAROLINA AT UNION LIBRARY*, 309 E
         Academy St, 29379-1932. (Mail add: PO Box 729, 29379-0729), SAN
         315-5994. Tel: 864-429-8728. FAX: 864-427-3682. *Dir,* William Fetty;
         E-mail: fettyw@gwm.sc.edu; Staff 1 (MLS 1)
         Founded 1965. Enrl 222; Fac 19
         Library Holdings: Bk Vols 35,000
         Partic in Lyrasis

WAGENER

C   CHRIST CENTRAL INSTITUTE*, Library & Research Center, 110
         Railroad Ave, 29164. (Mail add: PO Box 387, 29164). Tel: 803-564-5902,
         Ext 5018. Web Site: www.ccins.org. *Libr Dir,* Timothy L Skinner; E-mail:
         tskinner@ccins.org; Staff 1 (MLS 1)
         Founded 2010. Highest Degree: Associate
         Library Holdings: Bk Titles 33,000; Per Subs 10
         Special Collections: Greg Humphries Church History Library
         Subject Interests: Relig

WALHALLA

P   OCONEE COUNTY PUBLIC LIBRARY, 501 W South Broad St, 29691.
         SAN 360-3814. Tel: 864-638-4133. FAX: 864-638-4132. Web Site:
         www.oconee.lib.sc.us. *Dir,* Philip Mathews Cheney; E-mail:
         pcheney@oconeesc.com; *Br Mgr,* Heidi Holmes; E-mail:
         hholmes@oconeesc.com; *Br Serv Librn,* K'Lani Green; E-mail:
         kgreen@oconeesc.com; *Tech Serv Librn,* Debbie Kaniaris; E-mail:
         dkaniaris@oconeesc.com; *Youth Serv Librn,* Stacie Powell; E-mail:
         spowell@oconeesc.com; Staff 28 (MLS 6, Non-MLS 22)
         Founded 1948. Pop 74,000; Circ 348,500
         Library Holdings: Bk Vols 202,317; Per Subs 368
         Special Collections: Nuclear Reg Comm; South Carolina Coll
         Subject Interests: Local hist
         Automation Activity & Vendor Info: (Circulation) TLC (The Library
         Corporation)
         Database Vendor: Overdrive, Inc
         Wireless access
         Open Mon & Tues 9-9, Wed-Fri 9-6, Sat 9-1, Sun (Sept-May) 2-5:30
         Friends of the Library Group
         Branches: 3
         SALEM BRANCH, 5-B Park Ave, Salem, 29676, SAN 360-3849. Tel:
            864-944-0912. Administration Tel: 864-944-1450. *Br Mgr,* Meredith
            Wickham; E-mail: mwickham@oconeesc.com
            Open Mon 11:30-7, Tues-Fri 8:30-5
         SENECA BRANCH, 300 E South Second St, Seneca, 29678, SAN
            360-3873. Tel: 864-882-4855. FAX: 864-882-5559. *Br Mgr,* Blair Hinson
            Open Mon & Thurs 9-9, Tues, Wed & Fri 9-6, Sat 9-5
         WESTMINSTER BRANCH, 112 W North Ave, Westminster, 29693, SAN
            360-3903. Tel: 864-647-3215. FAX: 864-647-3233. *Br Mgr,* Leah Price;
            E-mail: leahprice@oconeesc.com
            Open Mon 12:30-9, Tues-Fri 9-6, Sat 9-1
         Bookmobiles: 1. Brenda Lee Bookmobile manager

WALTERBORO

P   COLLETON COUNTY MEMORIAL LIBRARY, 600 Hampton St,
         29488-4098. SAN 315-6001. Tel: 843-549-5621. FAX: 843-549-5122. Web
         Site: www.colletonlibrary.org. *Dir,* Carl K Coffin; Staff 14 (MLS 4,
         Non-MLS 10)
         Founded 1820. Pop 40,610; Circ 99,869
         Jul 2011-Jun 2012 Income (Main Library and Branch(s)) $752,443, State
         $60,000, County $692,443. Mats Exp $103,325, Books $69,433, Per/Ser
         (Incl. Access Fees) $8,500, AV Mat $23,067, Electronic Ref Mat (Incl.
         Access Fees) $2,325. Sal $492,724
         Library Holdings: CDs 369; DVDs 1,328; e-books 5,000; Electronic
         Media & Resources 37; Bk Vols 122,645; Per Subs 145

Special Collections: Oral History
Subject Interests: SC hist
Automation Activity & Vendor Info: (Acquisitions) Evergreen;
(Cataloging) Evergreen
Wireless access
Open Mon-Thurs 9-8, Fri 9-6, Sat 9-5
Friends of the Library Group
Branches: 1
EDISTO BEACH BRANCH, 71 Station Ct, Edisto Beach, 29438. (Mail
   add: PO Box 760, Edisto Beach, 29438). Tel: 843-869-2499. *Br Mgr,*
   Susan Roberts
   Open Tues & Thurs 1-5, Wed 10-12:30 & 1-5
Bookmobiles: 1

WEST COLUMBIA

J   MIDLANDS TECHNICAL COLLEGE LIBRARY*, Airport Library, 1260
         Lexington Dr, 29170-2176. (Mail add: PO Box 2408, Columbia,
         29202-2408), SAN 360-0874. Tel: 803-822-3530. FAX: 803-822-3670.
         E-mail: libstaff@midlandstech.edu. Web Site: www.lib.midlandstech.edu.
         Interim Dir, Florence Mays; Tel: 803-822-3419, E-mail:
         maysf@midlandstech.edu; *Cat Librn,* Susan Bellows; Tel: 803-822-3616,
         E-mail: bellowss@midlandstech.edu; *Pub Serv,* Laura Baker; Tel:
         803-822-3533, E-mail: bakerl@midlandstech.edu; *Pub Serv,* Catherine
         Eckman; Tel: 803-822-3537, E-mail: eckmanc@midlandstech.edu; *Pub
         Serv,* Marilyn Hook; Tel: 803-822-3535, E-mail:
         hookm@midlandstech.edu; *Pub Serv,* Margaret McClellan; Tel:
         803-822-3674, E-mail: mcclellanm@midlandstech.edu; Staff 18 (MLS 10,
         Non-MLS 8)
         Founded 1963. Enrl 10,852; Highest Degree: Associate
         Library Holdings: AV Mats 1,689; e-books 22,176; Bk Vols 97,562; Per
         Subs 423
         Automation Activity & Vendor Info: (Acquisitions) SirsiDynix;
         (Cataloging) SirsiDynix; (Circulation) SirsiDynix; (OPAC) SirsiDynix;
         (Serials) SirsiDynix
         Database Vendor: EBSCOhost, Factiva.com, Gale Cengage Learning,
         LexisNexis, netLibrary, OCLC FirstSearch, ProQuest, Wilson - Wilson Web
         Wireless access
         Partic in Lyrasis
         Special Services for the Deaf - Staff with knowledge of sign lang
         Special Services for the Blind - ZoomText magnification & reading
         software
         Open Mon-Thurs 8am-9pm, Fri 8-4:30, Sat 9-12, Sun 2:30-5:30
         Departmental Libraries:
         BELTLINE LIBRARY, 316 S Beltline Blvd, 2nd Flr, Columbia, 29205.
            (Mail add: PO Box 2408, Columbia, 29202). Tel: 803-738-7000. FAX:
            803-738-7719. *Interim Dir, Pub Serv,* Florence Mays; Tel: 803-790-7512,
            E-mail: maysf@midlandstech.edu; *Coll Develop,* Virginia Brooker; Tel:
            803-738-7626, E-mail: brookerv@midlandstech.edu; *Pub Serv,* Cary
            Lafaye; Tel: 803-738-7762, E-mail: lafayec@midlandstech.edu; *Tech
            Coordr,* Shawn Carraway; Tel: 803-738-7734, E-mail:
            carraways@midlandstech.edu; Staff 18 (MLS 10, Non-MLS 8)
            Founded 1963. Enrl 10,852; Highest Degree: Associate
            Library Holdings: AV Mats 1,689; e-books 22,176; Bk Vols 97,562; Per
            Subs 423
            Automation Activity & Vendor Info: (Course Reserve) SirsiDynix
            Database Vendor: ProQuest
            Special Services for the Deaf - Staff with knowledge of sign lang
            Special Services for the Blind - ZoomText magnification & reading
            software

WINNSBORO

P   FAIRFIELD COUNTY LIBRARY*, 300 W Washington St, 29180. SAN
         360-3938. Tel: 803-635-4971. FAX: 803-635-7715. Web Site:
         www.fairfield.lib.sc.us. *Dir,* Sarah D McMaster; Staff 1 (MLS 1)
         Founded 1938. Pop 23,956; Circ 63,344
         Jul 2010-Jun 2011 Income (Main Library and Branch(s)) $540,534. Mats
         Exp $102,451. Sal $362,251
         Library Holdings: Audiobooks 1,814; CDs 785; DVDs 1,139; Large Print
         Bks 1,965; Bk Vols 77,605; Per Subs 162; Videos 3,347
         Subject Interests: Hist
         Automation Activity & Vendor Info: (Cataloging) Evergreen;
         (Circulation) Evergreen; (OPAC) Evergreen
         Wireless access
         Open Mon-Wed & Fri 9-6, Thurs 9-9, Sat 9-1
         Friends of the Library Group
         Branches: 1
         RIDGEWAY BRANCH, 175 S Palmer St, Ridgeway, 29130. (Mail add: PO
            Box 160, Ridgeway, 29130-0160), SAN 360-3997. Tel: 803-337-2068.
            FAX: 803-337-2068. *Br Mgr,* Margot Kuebler
            Library Holdings: Bk Vols 4,400
            Open Mon-Thurs 2-6
         Bookmobiles: 1

Date of Statistics: FY 2010
Population, 2008 (est.): 814,180
Population Served by Public Libraries: 769,444
    Underserved: 51,565
Total Volumes in Public Libraries: 3,038,330
    Volumes Per Capita: 3.73
Total Public Library Circulation: 5,892,889
    Circulation Per Capita: 7.24
Total Public Library Income: $22,545,845
    Expenditure Per Capita: $26.11
Number of County Libraries: 20
    Counties Unserved: 5
Number of Bookmobiles in State: 6 (public libraries)
Note: Statistics do not include federal funds or statistics supporting public library services provided by the South Dakota State Library

ABERDEEN

M   AVERA ST LUKE'S HOSPITAL*, Paul G Bunker Memorial Medical Library, 305 S State St, 57401-4590. SAN 326-4041. Tel: 605-622-5355. FAX: 605-622-5041. *Assoc Univ Librn, Digital Initiatives & Content Mgt, Assoc Univ Librn, Digital Initiatives & Open Access, Librn,* Roxie Olson; E-mail: roxie.olson@averastlukes.org; Staff 1 (Non-MLS 1)
Library Holdings: Bk Titles 1,500; Bk Vols 1,650; Per Subs 230

S   DACOTAH PRAIRIE MUSEUM*, Ruth Bunker Memorial Library, 21 S Main St, 57402. (Mail add: PO Box 395, 57402-0395), SAN 323-6781. Tel: 605-626-7117. FAX: 605-626-4026. E-mail: dpm@brown.sd.us. Web Site: www.dacotahprairiemuseum.com. *Dir,* Sue Gates
Founded 1970
Library Holdings: Bk Titles 800
Special Collections: Sioux Missionary Work (Riggs Williamson Coll), papers. Oral History
Restriction: Open by appt only

P   ALEXANDER MITCHELL PUBLIC LIBRARY*, Aberdeen Public Library, 519 S Kline St, 57401-4495. SAN 315-6060. Tel: 605-626-7097. FAX: 605-626-3506. E-mail: aml.ill@aberdeen.sd.us, library@aberdeen.sd.us. Web Site: ampl.sdln.net. *Dir,* Pamla J Lingor; *Asst Dir,* Shirley Arment; *Ch,* Nancy Eckert; *Commun Serv,* Cara Romeo; *Tech Serv,* Debbie Werre; E-mail: dwerre@sdln.net; Staff 13 (MLS 2, Non-MLS 11)
Founded 1884. Pop 35,580; Circ 237,334
Jan 2007-Dec 2007 Income $975,025. Mats Exp $103,800, Books $85,250, Per/Ser (Incl. Access Fees) $13,050, AV Mat $5,500. Sal $675,725
Library Holdings: Bk Vols 108,144; Per Subs 364
Special Collections: Genealogy Coll; Germans from Russia Coll; L Frank Baum Coll; Local History Coll; Railroad History Coll
Automation Activity & Vendor Info: (Cataloging) Ex Libris Group; (Circulation) Ex Libris Group; (ILL) Ex Libris Group; (OPAC) Ex Libris Group; (Serials) Ex Libris Group
Database Vendor: netLibrary, Newsbank
Function: Archival coll, Bk club(s), Bks on CD, Children's prog, Copy machines, Electronic databases & coll, Holiday prog, Homebound delivery serv, ILL available, Magnifiers for reading, Music CDs, Newsp ref libr, Notary serv, Prog for adults, Prog for children & young adult, Pub access computers, Story hour, Summer reading prog, Tax forms, Teen prog
Publications: AMPL News
Partic in OCLC Online Computer Library Center, Inc; South Dakota Library Network
Special Services for the Deaf - TDD equip
Special Services for the Blind - Bks on cassette; Bks on CD; Large print bks; Magnifiers
Open Mon-Thurs 9-9, Fri 9-6, Sat 9-5

C   NORTHERN STATE UNIVERSITY*, Beulah Williams Library, 1200 S Jay St, 57401-7198. SAN 315-6079. Tel: 605-626-2645. FAX: 605-626-2473. Web Site: www.northern.edu/library. *Dir,* Robert Russell; Tel: 605-626-7770, E-mail: rrussell@northern.edu; *Librn,* Kristin Echtenkamp; *Librn,* Shari Theroux; *Librn,* Jonna Underwood; *Syst Librn,* Jackie Hanson; *Circ Mgr,* Ardell Melland; Staff 5 (MLS 4, Non-MLS 1)
Founded 1901. Enrl 2,555; Fac 102; Highest Degree: Master
Jul 2006-Jun 2007 Income $929,836, State $606,354, Parent Institution $323,482. Mats Exp $319,823, Books $98,709, Per/Ser (Incl. Access Fees) $31,376, Micro $4,730, AV Mat $8,967, Electronic Ref Mat (Incl. Access Fees) $169,351, Presv $6,690. Sal $519,184 (Prof $240,200)
Library Holdings: Bk Titles 205,765; Per Subs 172
Special Collections: Dorothea Kerr Germans from Russia Coll; Harriet Montgomery Water Resources Coll; SD History Coll; SD National Guard Coll. Oral History; State Document Depository; US Document Depository
Subject Interests: Educ
Automation Activity & Vendor Info: (Acquisitions) Ex Libris Group; (Cataloging) Ex Libris Group; (Circulation) Ex Libris Group; (Course Reserve) Ex Libris Group; (ILL) Ex Libris Group; (Media Booking) Ex Libris Group; (OPAC) Ex Libris Group; (Serials) Ex Libris Group
Database Vendor: Alexander Street Press, American Chemical Society, American Mathematical Society, American Psychological Association (APA), ARTstor, Career Guidance Foundation, College Source, EBSCO Information Services, EBSCOhost, Elsevier, Ex Libris Group, Factiva.com, Gale Cengage Learning, ISI Web of Knowledge, JSTOR, LexisNexis, Modern Language Association, OCLC FirstSearch, OCLC WorldCat, Project MUSE, ProQuest, Thomson - Web of Science, Wilson - Wilson Web
Wireless access
Function: Adult bk club, After school storytime, Archival coll, Art exhibits, Audio & video playback equip for onsite use, Computers for patron use, Copy machines, Distance learning, Doc delivery serv, Electronic databases & coll, Handicapped accessible, ILL available, Online cat, Online info literacy tutorials on the web & in blackboard, Pub access computers, Ref serv available
Partic in Minitex Library Information Network; OCLC Online Computer Library Center, Inc; South Dakota Library Network

J   PRESENTATION COLLEGE LIBRARY*, 1500 N Main, 57401-1299. SAN 360-4020. Tel: 605-229-8468. FAX: 605-229-8430. E-mail: pclibrary@presentation.edu. Web Site: www.presentation.edu/library.htm. *Dir,* Lea Briggs; E-mail: Lea.Briggs@presentation.edu; *Tech Serv,* Karen Maier; Tel: 605-229-8498, E-mail: karen.maier@presentation.edu; *ILL,* Sandy Urbaniak; Staff 2 (MLS 2)
Founded 1951. Enrl 369; Fac 56; Highest Degree: Bachelor
Library Holdings: e-journals 24,787; Bk Titles 41,861; Per Subs 498
Subject Interests: Allied health, Nursing, Relig studies
Automation Activity & Vendor Info: (Circulation) Ex Libris Group
Wireless access
Partic in South Dakota Library Network
Open Mon-Thurs (Fall & Spring) 7:45am-9pm, Fri 7:45-5, Sun 1-9; (Summer) Mon-Fri 8-5

Departmental Libraries:
LAKOTA CAMPUS, PO Box 1070, Eagle Butte, 57625, SAN 376-8716.
Tel: 605-964-4071. FAX: 605-964-1111. *Librn,* Sister Marilyn Dunn;
E-mail: srmarilyn.dunn@presentation.edu
Library Holdings: Bk Titles 1,537; Per Subs 20
Subject Interests: Nursing
Open Mon-Thurs 8-8, Fri 8-5

S   SOUTH DAKOTA SCHOOL FOR THE BLIND & VISUALLY
IMPAIRED*, Library Media Center, 423 17th Ave SE, 57401-7699. SAN
325-4909. Tel: 605-626-2580. Web Site: www.sdsbvi.sdbor.edu. *Librn,* Pat
Geditz
Founded 1900
Library Holdings: Bk Vols 18,311; Per Subs 50
Special Collections: Local School Archive
Subject Interests: Blind, Deaf, Educ of the blind, Learning disabled,
Mentally retarded blind, Physically handicapped, Visually handicapped
Partic in South Dakota Library Network
Special Services for the Blind - Assistive/Adapted tech devices, equip &
products; Talking bks
Open Mon-Fri 8-3:45

ALEXANDRIA

P   ALEXANDRIA PUBLIC LIBRARY*, 421 Main St, 57311. (Mail add: PO
Box 157, 57311-0157). Tel: 605-239-4549. *Librn,* Camille Davies
Pop 598; Circ 5,852
Library Holdings: Bk Vols 6,000

ARLINGTON

P   ARLINGTON COMMUNITY LIBRARY*, 306 S Main St, 57212. (Mail
add: PO Box 345, 57212-0345), SAN 315-6095. Tel: 605-983-5741, Ext
230. *Librn,* Cheryl Anderson; E-mail: cheryl.anderson@k12.sd.us
Pop 992; Circ 2,394
Library Holdings: Bk Vols 20,000
Open Mon, Wed & Fri 8:30-6, Tues & Thurs 8:30-8, Sat 9-Noon

ARMOUR

P   ARMOUR PUBLIC LIBRARY*, Carnegie Library, 915 Main Ave, 57313.
(Mail add: PO Box 396, 57313-0396), SAN 315-6109. Tel: 605-724-2743.
E-mail: info@armoursd.com. *Head of Libr,* Linda Montgomery
Founded 1915. Pop 1,200; Circ 9,350
Library Holdings: Bk Titles 10,400; Per Subs 35
Function: ILL available
Open Mon & Fri 2-5:30, Wed 2-5 & 6-8, Sat 1:30-4:30

BELLE FOURCHE

P   BELLE FOURCHE PUBLIC LIBRARY, 905 Fifth Ave, 57717-1795. SAN
315-6117. Tel: 605-892-4407. E-mail: bfplib@yahoo.com. Web Site:
www.bellefourche.org. *Librn,* Pat Engebretson; *Asst Librn,* Wanda Nelson;
Staff 4 (MLS 1, Non-MLS 3)
Founded 1906. Pop 9,000; Circ 72,000
Library Holdings: Bk Titles 40,668; Per Subs 116
Special Collections: Genealogy; History of South Dakota
Automation Activity & Vendor Info: (Cataloging) Follett Software
Wireless access
Function: Bks on cassette, Bks on CD, Children's prog, Computers for
patron use, Copy machines, Free DVD rentals, Genealogy discussion
group, Home delivery & serv to Sr ctr & nursing homes, Homebound
delivery serv, ILL available, Mail & tel request accepted, Microfiche/film
& reading machines, OverDrive digital audio bks, Prog for adults, Prog for
children & young adult, Pub access computers, Scanner, Story hour,
Summer reading prog, Tax forms, Telephone ref, VHS videos
Partic in South Dakota Library Network
Open Mon-Thurs 10-6, Fri & Sat 10-2
Friends of the Library Group

BERESFORD

P   BERESFORD PUBLIC LIBRARY*, 115 S Third St, 57004-1798. SAN
315-6133. Tel: 605-763-2782. FAX: 605-763-2403. E-mail:
books@bmtc.net. Web Site: www.bmtc.net/~libone. *Dir,* Jane Norling; *Asst
City Librn,* Barb Geyer; *Asst City Librn,* Jane Pederson; *Ch,* Julie Morren;
Staff 2 (Non-MLS 2)
Founded 1923. Pop 2,006; Circ 33,521
Library Holdings: CDs 283; DVDs 328; Bk Titles 32,300; Bk Vols
32,900; Per Subs 83; Videos 600
Special Collections: South Dakota Coll
Automation Activity & Vendor Info: (Cataloging) Follett Software;
(Circulation) Follett Software
Database Vendor: EBSCOhost, Gale Cengage Learning, netLibrary,
ProQuest, PubMed
Wireless access

Function: AV serv, ILL available, Photocopying/Printing, Prog for children
& young adult, Summer reading prog, Workshops
Partic in Minitex Library Information Network; South Dakota Library
Network
Open Mon, Wed & Fri 1-6, Tues & Thurs 10-8, Sat 9-5

BOWDLE

P   REVEREND MARTIN BIEBER PUBLIC LIBRARY, 1075 N Third Ave,
57428. (Mail add: PO Box 280, 57428-0280), SAN 315-615X. Tel:
605-285-6464. E-mail: rmbpubliclibrary@yahoo.com. *Librn,* Mona
Kennedy
Founded 1971
Library Holdings: Bk Vols 10,523
Wireless access
Open Tues 12-7, Wed-Fri 12-6, Sat 1-5

BRITTON

P   BRITTON PUBLIC LIBRARY*, 759 Seventh St, 57430. (Mail add: PO
Box 299, 57430-0299), SAN 315-6168. Tel: 605-448-2800. FAX:
605-448-2497. E-mail: library@brittonsd.com. *Librn,* Sue Bull
Pop 1,393; Circ 21,970
Library Holdings: AV Mats 250; Bk Vols 15,000; Per Subs 20
Open Mon-Fri 8-6

BROOKINGS

M   BROOKINGS HEALTH SYSTEM*, Medical Library, 300 22nd Ave,
57006-2496. SAN 328-5766. Tel: 605-696-9000. FAX: 605-697-7380. *Dir,
Med Health Info,* Pam Weckwerth
Library Holdings: Bk Titles 400

P   BROOKINGS PUBLIC LIBRARY, 515 Third St, 57006. SAN 315-6176.
Tel: 605-692-9407. FAX: 605-692-9386. Web Site:
www.brookingslibrary.org. *Dir,* Elvita Landau; E-mail: elandau@sdln.net;
Young Adult Serv Coordr, Alison Bruinsma; E-mail: abruinsma@sdln.net;
Adult Serv, Nita Gill; E-mail: ngill@sdln.net; *Ch,* Katherine Eberline;
E-mail: keberline@sdln.net; *Commun Serv,* Rae Brecht; E-mail:
rbrecht@sdln.net; *Tech Serv,* Cathy Enlow; E-mail: cenlow@sdln.net; Staff
19 (MLS 5, Non-MLS 14)
Founded 1913. Pop 31,965; Circ 297,940
Jan 2011-Dec 2011 Income (Main Library Only) $1,003,855, City
$928,114, County $25,000, Locally Generated Income $50,741. Mats Exp
$136,287, Books $86,342, Per/Ser (Incl. Access Fees) $8,216, AV Mat
$23,852, Electronic Ref Mat (Incl. Access Fees) $12,418. Sal $511,944
(Prof $200,745)
Library Holdings: AV Mats 16,455; e-books 8,855; Bk Titles 105,561;
Per Subs 199
Special Collections: South Dakota History & Literature (South Dakota
Coll)
Automation Activity & Vendor Info: (Cataloging) Ex Libris Group;
(Circulation) Ex Libris Group; (ILL) Ex Libris Group; (OPAC) Ex Libris
Group; (Serials) Ex Libris Group
Database Vendor: EBSCOhost, Gale Cengage Learning, netLibrary,
ProQuest
Wireless access
Function: Adult bk club, Audiobks via web, Bk club(s), Bks on CD,
CD-ROM, Computers for patron use, Copy machines, Digital talking bks,
Free DVD rentals, Home delivery & serv to Sr ctr & nursing homes,
Homebound delivery serv, ILL available, Microfiche/film & reading
machines, Music CDs, Notary serv, Online cat, OverDrive digital audio
bks, Preschool reading prog, Prog for adults, Prog for children & young
adult, Story hour, Summer & winter reading prog, Tax forms, Teen prog
Publications: News & Events at Brookings Public Library (Newsletter)
Partic in OCLC Online Computer Library Center, Inc; South Dakota
Library Network
Open Mon-Thurs 10-9, Fri & Sat 10-5:30, Sun 1-5
Friends of the Library Group

C   SOUTH DAKOTA STATE UNIVERSITY*, Hilton M Briggs Library, 1300
N Campus Dr, Box 2115, 57007-1098. SAN 360-408X. Tel: 605-688-5106.
Reference Tel: 605-688-5107. Toll Free Tel: 800-786-2038. FAX:
605-688-6133. E-mail: blref@sdstate.edu. Web Site:
www.sdstate.edu/library. *Chief Univ Librn,* Kristi Tornquist; E-mail:
kristi.tornquist@sdstate.edu; *Head, Pub Serv,* Mary Kraljic; Tel:
605-688-4049, E-mail: mary.kraljic@sdstate.edu; *Head, Tech Serv,* Mary
Caspers-Graper; Tel: 605-688-5565, E-mail:
mary.caspers.graper@sdstate.edu; *Access Serv,* Mary Kraljic; Tel:
605-688-4049, E-mail: mary.kraljic@sdstate.edu; *Archives, Spec Coll,*
Stephen Van Buren; Tel: 605-688-4906, E-mail:
stephen.vanburen@sdstate.edu; *Cat,* Lisa Lindell; Tel: 605-688-5561,
E-mail: lisa.lindell@sdstate.edu; *Govt Doc,* Vickie Mix; Tel: 605-688-5958,
E-mail: vickie.mix@sdstate.edu; *Info Serv,* Melissa Clark; Tel:
605-688-5955, E-mail: melissa.clark@sdstate.edu; *Info Serv,* Elizabeth Fox;
Tel: 605-688-5569, E-mail: elizabeth.fox@sdstate.edu; *Info Serv,* Linda

Kott; Tel: 605-688-5957, E-mail: linda.kott@sdstate.edu; *Info Serv,* Nancy Marshall; Tel: 605-688-5093, E-mail: nancy.marshall@sdstate.edu; *ILL,* Rachel Manzer; Tel: 605-688-5573, E-mail: rachel.manzer@sdstate.edu; *Ser,* Carlene Aro; Tel: 605-688-5567, E-mail: carlene.aro@sdstate.edu; *Syst,* Fei Xu; Tel: 605-688-5560, E-mail: fei.xu@sdstate.edu; Staff 30 (MLS 13, Non-MLS 17)
Founded 1884. Enrl 12,725; Fac 650; Highest Degree: Doctorate
Jul 2010-Jun 2011 Income $3,630,045. Mats Exp $1,482,942. Sal $1,354,647 (Prof $791,768)
Library Holdings: Bk Vols 668,000
Special Collections: Elizabeth Cook-Lynn Coll; George Norby Coll; Marghab Rare Book Coll; Senator Tom Daschle Papers; South Dakota Farm Bureau & Farmers Union Locals Records. State Document Depository; US Document Depository
Automation Activity & Vendor Info: (Acquisitions) Ex Libris Group; (Cataloging) Ex Libris Group; (Circulation) Ex Libris Group; (ILL) Ex Libris Group; (OPAC) Ex Libris Group; (Serials) Ex Libris Group
Database Vendor: EBSCOhost, Elsevier, Gale Cengage Learning, JSTOR, LexisNexis, OCLC FirstSearch, OVID Technologies, Project MUSE, ProQuest
Wireless access
Partic in Minitex Library Information Network; South Dakota Library Network
Open Mon-Thurs 7:45am-Midnight, Fri 7:45am-9pm, Sat 1-9, Sun 1pm-Midnight

BUFFALO

P   NORTHWEST REGIONAL LIBRARY*, 410 Ramstand St, 57720. (Mail add: PO Box 26, 57720-0026), SAN 315-6125. Tel: 605-375-3835. E-mail: hclibrary@sdplains.com. *Dir,* Vicki Anderson; Staff 1 (Non-MLS 1)
Founded 2005. Pop 1,353; Circ 10,000
Library Holdings: Bk Vols 25,000
Partic in South Dakota Library Network
Open Mon 10-6, Tues 9:30-5:30, Fri 3-5:30
Bookmobiles: 1

CANTON

P   CANTON PUBLIC LIBRARY, 225 N Broadway, 57013-1715. SAN 315-6184. Tel: 605-987-5831. FAX: 605-764-5831. *Dir,* Edith Nelson; *Libr Asst,* Iris Schultz; Staff 5 (MLS 1, Non-MLS 4)
Founded 1912. Pop 4,000
Library Holdings: Bk Vols 35,548; Per Subs 73
Automation Activity & Vendor Info: (Circulation) Follett Software
Database Vendor: Overdrive, Inc
Open Mon, Tues & Thurs (Winter) 10-8, Wed & Fri 10-5, Sat 10-2; Mon-Wed & Fri (Summer) 10-5:30, Thurs 10-8, Sat 10-2
Friends of the Library Group

CENTERVILLE

P   CENTERVILLE COMMUNITY LIBRARY, 421 Florida, 57014. (Mail add: PO Box 100, 57014-0100), SAN 315-6192. Tel: 605-563-2540. FAX: 605-563-2615. *Dir,* Lindsey Hansen; *Sch Librn,* Linda Holmberg
Founded 1935. Pop 921; Circ 3,300
Jan 2007-Dec 2007 Income $42,500. Mats Exp $6,250, Books $4,500, Per/Ser (Incl. Access Fees) $300, Micro $50, AV Mat $800, Electronic Ref Mat (Incl. Access Fees) $600. Sal $18,000
Library Holdings: CDs 600; DVDs 580; Large Print Bks 400; Bk Titles 27,138; Bk Vols 28,212; Per Subs 47; Talking Bks 800; Videos 700
Special Collections: Centennial Book - History of Centerville, 100 yrs; Centerville Journal Newspapers since 1903; High School Annuals
Subject Interests: Pioneer hist of Turner Co
Automation Activity & Vendor Info: (Acquisitions) Follett Software; (Cataloging) Follett Software; (Circulation) Follett Software
Function: Homebound delivery serv
Open Mon & Wed 8:30-8:30, Tues, Thurs & Fri 8:30-5:30, Sat 10-12

CLEAR LAKE

P   CLEAR LAKE CITY LIBRARY*, 125 Third Ave S, 57226. (Mail add: PO Box 199, 57226-0199), SAN 315-6206. Tel: 605-874-2013. E-mail: library@itctel.com. Web Site: www.clearlakesd.net/library/. *Librn,* Pam Taylor; *Tech Master & Adv, Libr Tech,* Adam Desenfants
Founded 1899. Pop 4,522; Circ 9,396
Library Holdings: Bk Titles 17,300; Per Subs 48
Special Collections: State Document Depository
Partic in Dewey
Open Mon & Wed 12-8, Thurs & Fri 4-8

CRAZY HORSE

S   CRAZY HORSE MEMORIAL LIBRARY, 12151 Avenue of the Chiefs, 57730-9506. SAN 315-6141. Tel: 605-673-4681. FAX: 605-673-2185. Web Site: www.crazyhorse.org. *Librn,* Marguerite Cullum; Tel: 605-673-4681, Ext 285, E-mail: marguerite.cullum@crazyhorse.org
Founded 1973
Library Holdings: Bk Titles 6,302
Subject Interests: Art, Art hist, Hist, N Am Indians, Western US hist
Publications: Newsletter (Quarterly)

CUSTER

P   CUSTER COUNTY LIBRARY, 447 Crook St, Ste 4, 57730-1509. SAN 315-6214. Tel: 605-673-4803. FAX: 605-673-2385. E-mail: cuslib@gwtc.net. Web Site: www.custercountysd.com/countylibrary. *Dir,* Doris Ann Mertz
Founded 1943. Pop 8,217; Circ 37,711
Special Collections: Black Hills Area History Coll; George Armstrong Custer Coll
Automation Activity & Vendor Info: (Acquisitions) Follett Software; (Cataloging) Follett Software; (Circulation) Follett Software; (OPAC) Follett Software
Database Vendor: EBSCOhost, LearningExpress, ProQuest, SirsiDynix, World Book Online
Wireless access
Open Mon, Tues, Thurs & Fri 11-5:30, Wed 3-7, Sat 10-3

G   DEPARTMENT OF CORRECTIONS*, Star Academy Center Library, 12279 Brady Dr, 57730. SAN 326-4440. Tel: 605-673-2521. FAX: 605-673-5489. *In Charge,* Mary Turner
Library Holdings: Bk Titles 1,900
Open Mon-Fri 7am-Noon
Restriction: Students only
Friends of the Library Group

DE SMET

P   HAZEL L MEYER MEMORIAL LIBRARY*, 114 First St, 57231. (Mail add: PO Box 156, 57231-0156), SAN 315-6222. Tel: 605-854-3842. FAX: 605-854-3842. *Dir,* Mary Purintun
Founded 1937. Pop 1,800; Circ 30,887
Library Holdings: Bks on Deafness & Sign Lang 10; High Interest/Low Vocabulary Bk Vols 50; Bk Titles 19,797; Bk Vols 20,395; Per Subs 72; Spec Interest Per Sub 20
Special Collections: Harvey Dunn Original Paintings (5); Laura Ingalls Wilder Memorabilia
Special Services for the Blind - Audio mat; Large print bks
Open Mon, Tues, Thurs & Fri 12:30-5, Wed 12:30-6

DEADWOOD

P   DEADWOOD PUBLIC LIBRARY*, 435 Williams St, 57732-1113. SAN 315-6230. Tel: 605-578-2821. FAX: 605-578-2071. E-mail: dwdlib@sdln.net. Web Site: dwdlib.sdln.net. *Dir,* Jeanette Lundquist; E-mail: jlundquist@sdln.net; *Reader Serv,* Mary Kay Bullard; *Reader Serv,* Carol Hauck-Reif; Staff 3 (MLS 1, Non-MLS 2)
Founded 1895. Pop 2,885; Circ 15,634
Library Holdings: High Interest/Low Vocabulary Bk Vols 256; Bk Titles 14,481; Bk Vols 14,652; Per Subs 61
Special Collections: Black Hills History; Centennial Archive Coll, black & white photogs; Historic Local Newspapers, micro/newsp; Round Table Club scrapbooks; South Dakota History
Subject Interests: Local hist, SDak
Automation Activity & Vendor Info: (Cataloging) PALS; (Circulation) PALS; (ILL) PALS; (OPAC) PALS
Database Vendor: Gale Cengage Learning, OCLC FirstSearch, ProQuest
Publications: Index to Deadwood Newspapers (Local historical information)
Partic in South Dakota Library Network
Special Services for the Blind - Large screen computer & software

DELL RAPIDS

P   CARNEGIE PUBLIC LIBRARY*, 513 N Orleans Ave, 57022-1637. SAN 315-6249. Tel: 605-428-3280. E-mail: plibrary@siouxvalley.net. *Dir,* Deb Huska; E-mail: deb_huska@hotmail.com; Staff 3 (Non-MLS 3)
Founded 1910. Pop 2,980; Circ 35,818
Library Holdings: Bk Titles 19,520; Bk Vols 21,688; Per Subs 60
Subject Interests: SDak hist
Friends of the Library Group

EDGEMONT

P   EDGEMONT PUBLIC LIBRARY, 412 Second Ave, 57735. (Mail add: PO Box A, 57735), SAN 315-6257. Tel: 605-662-7712. FAX: 605-662-7922. E-mail: edgemont@gwtc.net. *Libr Dir,* Ashley Cortney; *Asst Librn,* Agnes Reecy
Founded 1916. Pop 870; Circ 7,539
Library Holdings: Bk Titles 22,855; Bk Vols 23,440; Per Subs 12
Special Collections: South Dakota Coll
Subject Interests: Local hist
Automation Activity & Vendor Info: (Circulation) Follett Software
Wireless access
Open Mon-Fri 9-5

ELLSWORTH AFB

A   UNITED STATES AIR FORCE*, Holbrook Library, Ellsworth Air Force Base FL4690, 28 FSS/FSDL, 2650 Doolittle Dr, Bldg 3910, 57706-4820. SAN 360-4144. Tel: 605-385-1686, 605-385-1688. Administration Tel: 605-385-1687. FAX: 605-385-4467. Web Site: www.ellsworthfss.com/holbrook-library. *Libr Dir, Supvry Librn,* Jeanne M Stoltenburg; E-mail: jeanne.stoltenburg@ellsworth.af.mil; *Syst Spec,* Tim Herdt; E-mail: tim.herdt@ellsworth.af.mil; Staff 2 (MLS 1, Non-MLS 1)
Founded 1969. Pop 4,659
Library Holdings: Audiobooks 1,095; AV Mats 2,563; CDs 500; DVDs 1,000; e-books 5,971; Bk Titles 40,000; Bk Vols 42,180; Per Subs 25; Videos 250
Automation Activity & Vendor Info: (Acquisitions) SirsiDynix; (Cataloging) SIRSI WorkFlows; (Circulation) SIRSI WorkFlows; (Course Reserve) SirsiDynix; (ILL) OCLC FirstSearch; (Media Booking) SirsiDynix; (OPAC) SIRSI-iBistro; (Serials) SirsiDynix
Database Vendor: EBSCO Auto Repair Reference, Gale Cengage Learning, Jane's, netLibrary, OCLC FirstSearch, SirsiDynix
Wireless access
Function: Audio & video playback equip for onsite use, Audiobks via web, Bks on CD, Children's prog, Computer training, Computers for patron use, e-mail & chat, e-mail serv, Electronic databases & coll, Free DVD rentals, Holiday prog, Homework prog, ILL available, Libr develop, Music CDs, Online cat, Online searches, Orientations, Outreach serv, OverDrive digital audio bks, Preschool outreach, Prog for adults, Prog for children & young adult, Pub access computers, Ref & res, Ref serv available, Ref serv in person, Scanner, Story hour, Summer & winter reading prog, Summer reading prog, Tax forms, Teen prog, VHS videos, Web-catalog, Wheelchair accessible
Publications: LARP (Annual report)
Open Mon-Fri 9:30-7, Sat 9:30-5

EUREKA

P   KATHRYN SCHULKOSKI LIBRARY*, 613 Seventh St, 57437. (Mail add: PO Box 655, 57437-0655), SAN 315-6273. Tel: 605-284-2863. E-mail: kslibrary@valleytel.net. *City Librn,* Susan Fischer
Founded 1932. Pop 2,900; Circ 10,232
Library Holdings: Large Print Bks 65; Bk Vols 13,311; Per Subs 15; Talking Bks 49; Videos 281
Open Mon & Wed 7pm-9pm, Thurs 3-5, Sat 2-5

FAITH

P   FAITH PUBLIC LIBRARY*, 204 W Fifth St, 57626. (Mail add: PO Box 172, 57626-0172), SAN 326-5587. Tel: 605-967-2262. FAX: 605-967-2153. Web Site: www.faith.k12.sd.us/default.htm. *Librn,* Angela Ostrander; Staff 1 (Non-MLS 1)
Founded 1924. Pop 576; Circ 24,059
Library Holdings: Bk Vols 16,000
Special Collections: South Dakota. Oral History
Automation Activity & Vendor Info: (Cataloging) Follett Software; (Circulation) Follett Software
Partic in South Dakota Library Network
Open Mon, Tues & Thurs 8-7, Wed & Fri 8-3
Friends of the Library Group

FLANDREAU

P   MOODY COUNTY RESOURCE CENTER*, 610 W Community Dr, 57028. SAN 315-6281. Tel: 605-997-3326. FAX: 605-997-2457. *Commun Librn,* Erica Rorvik; E-mail: erica.rorvik@k12.sd.us
Founded 1988. Circ 21,800
Library Holdings: Bk Titles 25,000; Per Subs 37
Special Collections: South Dakota Author Coll
Subject Interests: Local newsp
Open Mon & Fri 9-5, Tues-Thurs 9-8, Sat 9-2

Branches: 1
COLMAN BRANCH, 120 N Main Ave, Colman, 57017. (Mail add: PO Box 188, Colman, 57017-0188), SAN 321-8740. Tel: 605-534-3154. *Librn,* Janelle Steffen
Open Wed 2-5 & 7-9, Sat 10-12 & 1-4

FORT MEADE

GM   DEPARTMENT OF VETERANS AFFAIRS LIBRARY*, VA Black Hills Health Care System, 113 Comanche Rd, 57741-1099. SAN 315-629X. Tel: 605-720-7055. FAX: 605-720-7054. *Mgr,* Debbie Mailloux
Library Holdings: Bk Vols 7,400; Per Subs 300
Special Collections: Medical Coll
Publications: Newsletter (Bi-annually)
Partic in South Dakota Library Network
Open Mon-Fri 7:30-4:15

FREEMAN

P   FREEMAN PUBLIC LIBRARY, 322 S Main St, 57029. (Mail add: PO Box I, 57029-0080), SAN 315-6311. Tel: 605-925-7003. FAX: 605-925-7127. E-mail: freemanlibrary@goldenwest.net. Web Site: www.freemanlibrary.org. *Dir,* LeAnn L Kaufman; Staff 1 (Non-MLS 1)
Founded 1939. Pop 1,317; Circ 16,155
Library Holdings: CDs 154; DVDs 304; Bk Titles 14,326; Videos 766
Special Collections: Freeman, SD materials
Subject Interests: Germans in Russia from SDak, Hutterites, Mennonites, SDak hist
Automation Activity & Vendor Info: (Cataloging) Follett Software; (Circulation) Follett Software
Database Vendor: EBSCOhost, LearningExpress, LexisNexis, Medline, netLibrary, Newsbank, OCLC WorldCat, ProQuest, PubMed, WebMD, World Book Online
Wireless access
Function: Adult bk club, Bks on cassette, Bks on CD, Children's prog, Computers for patron use, Copy machines, Electronic databases & coll, Handicapped accessible, ILL available, Photocopying/Printing, Story hour, Summer reading prog
Partic in South Dakota Library Network
Open Mon, Wed & Fri 9-5:30, Tues & Thurs 9-7, Sat 9-2:30
Friends of the Library Group

GETTYSBURG

P   POTTER COUNTY FREE PUBLIC LIBRARY*, 106 E Commercial Ave, 57442-1507. SAN 315-6338. Tel: 605-765-9518. Web Site: www.pottercountylibrary.blogspot.com. *Librn,* Peggy Williams; *Asst Librn,* Dorothy Mink
Founded 1923. Pop 3,900; Circ 33,000
Library Holdings: Large Print Bks 900; Bk Vols 17,220; Per Subs 40; Talking Bks 800
Special Collections: Potter County Obituaries 1883-2006
Wireless access
Special Services for the Blind - Large print bks; Talking bks
Open Mon-Fri 10-5, Sat 9-12

GREGORY

P   GREGORY PUBLIC LIBRARY*, 112 E Fifth, 57533-1463. SAN 315-6346. Tel: 605-835-8531. FAX: 605-835-9575. *Librn,* Diane Althoff; Tel: 605-835-8858
Founded 1926. Pop 1,384; Circ 14,000
Jan 2005-Dec 2005 Income $18,000. Mats Exp $3,000. Sal $8,300
Library Holdings: AV Mats 1,100; Large Print Bks 200; Bk Titles 10,327; Bk Vols 11,705; Per Subs 11; Talking Bks 75
Special Collections: Oral History
Subject Interests: Local hist
Open Mon 2-7, Wed 12-8, Thurs 2-7, Sat 9-5
Friends of the Library Group

HIGHMORE

P   HYDE COUNTY LIBRARY*, 107 Commercial SE, 57345. (Mail add: PO Box 479, 57345-0479), SAN 315-6354. Tel: 605-852-2514. *Librn,* Tina Hamlin
Founded 1918. Pop 1,500; Circ 19,630
Library Holdings: Bk Vols 13,457; Per Subs 35
Function: AV serv, Res libr
Special Services for the Blind - Bks on cassette; Large print bks
Open Mon-Fri 12-5

HILL CITY

P   HILL CITY PUBLIC LIBRARY*, 488 Main, 57745. (Mail add: PO Box 88, 57745). Tel: 605-574-4529. FAX: 605-574-4529. E-mail: hillcitylibrary@hillcitysd.org. Web Site: hillcitysd.org. *Librn,* Paula Demars; E-mail: pdemars@hillcitysd.org
Library Holdings: Bk Vols 16,000; Per Subs 40
Automation Activity & Vendor Info: (Cataloging) Follett Software; (Circulation) Follett Software; (OPAC) Follett Software
Wireless access
Wireless service available at summertime only
Open Mon, Tues, Thurs & Fri 9-5, Wed 9-7, Sat 9-2

HOT SPRINGS

GM   DEPARTMENT OF VETERANS AFFAIRS LIBRARY*, 500 N Fifth St, 57747. SAN 315-6370. Tel: 605-745-2013. FAX: 605-745-2082. *Libr Tech,* Gerald Collogan
Founded 1905
Library Holdings: Bk Vols 4,400; Per Subs 43
Subject Interests: Med
Open Mon-Fri 8-4:30
Restriction: Staff use only

P   HOT SPRINGS PUBLIC LIBRARY*, 2005 Library Dr, 57747-2767. SAN 315-6362. Tel: 605-745-3151. FAX: 605-745-6813. E-mail: hsplib@gwtc.net. Web Site: www.hotspringspubliclibrary.com. *Dir,* Cynthia Messenger
Founded 1898. Circ 16,278
Library Holdings: Bk Vols 25,000
Subject Interests: SDak hist
Automation Activity & Vendor Info: (Cataloging) Follett Software; (Circulation) Follett Software; (OPAC) Follett Software; (Serials) Follett Software
Wireless access
Open Mon, Thurs & Fri 10-5:30, Tues & Wed 12-7, Sat 10-2
Friends of the Library Group

S   NATIONAL PARK SERVICE*, Wind Cave Library, 26611 US Hwy 385, 57747. Tel: 605-745-4600. FAX: 605-745-4207. Web Site: www.nps.gov/wica. *Librn,* Mary Laycock
Library Holdings: Bk Vols 2,600
Subject Interests: Cultural hist, Natural hist, Regional hist, SDak Indians
Function: Res libr
Restriction: Staff use only

HURON

P   HURON PUBLIC LIBRARY*, 521 Dakota Ave S, 57350. SAN 315-6400. Tel: 605-353-8530. FAX: 605-353-8531. Web Site: hpllib.sdln.net. *Dir,* Colleen Smith; E-mail: csmith@sdln.net; *Ch,* Ruth Hemen; *Ref,* Melinda Ellenson; *Tech Serv,* Eileen Deckert; Staff 8 (MLS 1, Non-MLS 7)
Founded 1907. Pop 12,000; Circ 131,000
Jan 2006-Dec 2006 Income $543,059, City $536,358, County $6,701. Mats Exp $72,500, Books $55,000, Per/Ser (Incl. Access Fees) $10,000, AV Mat $7,500. Sal $212,000 (Prof $164,000)
Library Holdings: AV Mats 2,800; Bk Titles 94,000; Per Subs 162; Talking Bks 3,262
Special Collections: Local Newspaper, 1888-present on microfilm. State Document Depository
Subject Interests: SDak hist
Automation Activity & Vendor Info: (Acquisitions) Ex Libris Group; (Cataloging) Ex Libris Group; (Circulation) Ex Libris Group; (ILL) Ex Libris Group; (OPAC) Ex Libris Group
Database Vendor: EBSCOhost, Gale Cengage Learning, OCLC FirstSearch, ProQuest
Function: Bk club(s), Bks on cassette, Bks on CD, CD-ROM, Children's prog, Computers for patron use, Copy machines, Doc delivery serv, Electronic databases & coll, Handicapped accessible, ILL available, Magnifiers for reading, Online cat, Preschool outreach, Prog for adults, Prog for children & young adult, Ref serv available, Senior outreach, Summer reading prog, Tax forms, Teen prog, VHS videos, Video lending libr, Wheelchair accessible
Partic in South Dakota Library Network
Special Services for the Deaf - Bks on deafness & sign lang; Closed caption videos; High interest/low vocabulary bks
Special Services for the Blind - Large print bks; Talking bks
Open Mon-Thurs 9-7, Fri 9-5, Sat 10-5 (10-1 Summer)
Friends of the Library Group

INTERIOR

S   NATIONAL PARK SERVICE*, Badlands National Park Library, PO Box 6, 57750. SAN 315-6419. Tel: 605-433-5361. FAX: 605-433-5248. *Librn,* Megan Cherry
Founded 1965
Library Holdings: Bk Titles 1,000; Bk Vols 1,300
Subject Interests: Badlands, Fossils, Nat Park Serv, Natural hist, SDak Indians
Restriction: Staff use only

IPSWICH

P   MARCUS P BEEBE MEMORIAL LIBRARY*, 120 Main St, 57451. (Mail add: PO Box 304, 57451-0304), SAN 315-6427. Tel: 605-426-6707. E-mail: mpblibrary@abe.midco.net. *Librn,* Ruby Bosanko
Founded 1886. Pop 2,000; Circ 13,580
Jan 2010-Dec 2010 Income $21,650. Mats Exp $2,200. Sal $10,300
Library Holdings: Bk Vols 18,086; Per Subs 19
Wireless access
Open Tues-Sat 2-6

KADOKA

P   JACKSON COUNTY LIBRARY*, 910 Main St, 57543. (Mail add: PO Box 368, 57543-0368), SAN 360-4381. Tel: 605-837-2689. *Librn,* Terry Stout
Founded 1962. Pop 2,846; Circ 10,783
Library Holdings: AV Mats 88; Bk Titles 14,819; Bk Vols 20,445; Per Subs 18; Videos 63
Branches: 2
INTERIOR BRANCH, PO Box 24, Interior, 57750, SAN 360-4411. *Librn,* Margaret Sampson
    Library Holdings: Bk Titles 3,915; Bk Vols 4,048
LONG VALLEY BRANCH, PO Box 21, Long Valley, 57547, SAN 360-4446. Tel: 605-462-6259. *Librn,* Patty Hamar
    Library Holdings: Bk Titles 1,275; Bk Vols 1,345

KENNEBEC

P   KENNEBEC PUBLIC LIBRARY*, 203 S Main St, 57544. (Mail add: PO Box 61, 57544-0061), SAN 315-6435. Tel: 605-869-2207. *Librn,* Pat Halverson
Pop 700; Circ 12,810
Library Holdings: AV Mats 156; Bk Vols 13,575
Open Mon-Fri 2:30-5:30

KEYSTONE

G   MOUNT RUSHMORE NATIONAL MEMORIAL LIBRARY*, Bldg 31, Ste 1, 13000 Hwy 244, 57751. SAN 326-2006. Tel: 605-574-2523. Administration Tel: 605-574-3115. FAX: 605-574-2307. Web Site: www.nps.gov/moru. *Librn,* Herbert Tuggle
Founded 1963
Library Holdings: Bk Titles 1,300
Open Mon-Fri 2-4

KYLE

J   OGLALA LAKOTA COLLEGE*, Woksape Tipi-Learning Resources Center, Three Mile Creek Rd, 57752. (Mail add: PO Box 310, 57752-0310), SAN 321-2319. Tel: 605-455-6069. FAX: 605-455-6070. E-mail: library@olc.edu. Web Site: library.olc.edu/index.html. *Dir,* LaVera Rose; Tel: 605-455-6064, E-mail: lrose@olc.edu; *Asst Dir,* Sharon Running Hawk; E-mail: srunninghawk@olc.edu; *Outreach Coordr,* Theresa Bettelyoun; E-mail: tbettelyoun@olc.edu; *Asst Archivist,* Agnes Gay; E-mail: agay@olc.edu; *Res Tech,* Lorelle Knight; E-mail: lknight@olc.edu; Staff 3 (Non-MLS 3)
Founded 1970
Library Holdings: Bk Titles 34,000; Per Subs 80
Special Collections: Oral History
Subject Interests: Archives
Wireless access
Publications: Policy & Procedures Manual, library instruction & skills; Specialized Bibliographies of North American Indians & related archival materials
Partic in Minn Interlibr Telecommunication Exchange; OCLC Online Computer Library Center, Inc; South Dakota Library Network
Open Mon-Fri 8:30-5
Departmental Libraries:
EAGLE NEST COLLEGE CENTER, PO Box 350, Wanblee, 57577, SAN 321-5407. Tel: 605-462-6274. FAX: 605-462-6105. *Dir,* Georgia Rooks
    Library Holdings: Bk Vols 1,500
    Open Mon-Thurs 8:30-8, Fri 8:30-5
EAST WAKPAMNI COLLEGE CENTER, PO Box 612, Batesland, 57716, SAN 321-5857. Tel: 605-288-1834, 605-862-2032. FAX: 605-288-1828. *Dir,* Phinet Red Owl
    Library Holdings: Bk Vols 1,100
    Open Mon-Thurs 8:30-8, Fri 8:30-5

HE SAPA COLLEGE CENTER, 127 Knollwood Dr, Rapid City, 57709.
Tel: 605-342-1513. FAX: 605-342-8547. *Dir,* Shirley Lewis
Library Holdings: Bk Vols 1,500
Open Mon-Thurs 8:30-8, Fri 8:30-5
LACREEK COLLEGE CENTER, PO Box 629, Martin, 57551, SAN
321-5881. Tel: 605-685-6407. FAX: 605-685-6887. *Dir,* Pearl Cottier
Library Holdings: Bk Vols 1,300
Open Mon-Thurs 8:30-8, Fri 8:30-5
NURSING COLLEGE CENTER, PO Box 861, Pine Ridge, 57770, SAN
321-592X. Tel: 605-867-5856. FAX: 605-867-5724. *In Charge,* Sarah
Danner
Library Holdings: Bk Vols 2,000
Open Mon-Thurs 8:30-8, Fri 8:30-5
OGLALA/WHITE CLAY COLLEGE CENTER, PO Box 19, Oglala,
57764, SAN 321-5903. Tel: 605-867-5780. FAX: 605-867-1243. *Dir,*
Donna Red Ear Horse
Library Holdings: Bk Vols 1,000
Open Mon-Thurs 8:30-8, Fri 8:30-5
PAHIN SINTE COLLEGE CENTER, PO Box 220, Porcupine, 57772,
SAN 321-589X. Tel: 605-867-5404. FAX: 605-867-1242. *Dir,* Janice
Richards
Library Holdings: Bk Vols 1,200
Open Mon-Thurs 8:30-8, Fri 8:30-5
PASS CREEK COLLEGE CENTER, PO Box 630, Allen, 57714, SAN
321-5849. Tel: 605-455-2757. FAX: 605-455-2428. *Dir,* Collette Ruff
Library Holdings: Bk Vols 1,300
Open Mon-Thurs 8:30-8, Fri 8:30-5
PEJUTA HAKA COLLEGE CENTER, PO Box 370, 57752-0370, SAN
321-5865. Tel: 605-455-2450. FAX: 605-455-2671. *Dir,* Steve Hernandez
Library Holdings: Bk Vols 1,400
Open Mon-Thurs 8:30-8, Fri 8:30-5
PINE RIDGE COLLEGE CENTER, PO Box 439, Pine Ridge, 57770,
SAN 321-5911. Tel: 605-867-5893. FAX: 605-867-1241. *Dir,* Shirley
Brewer
Library Holdings: Bk Vols 2,500
Open Mon-Thurs 8:30-8, Fri 8:30-5
WOUNDED KNEE COLLEGE CENTER, PO Box 230, Manderson,
57756, SAN 321-5873. Tel: 605-867-5352. FAX: 605-867-1245. *Dir,*
Karen White Butterfly
Library Holdings: Bk Vols 1,100
Open Mon-Thurs 8:30-8, Fri 8:30-5

LAKE ANDES

P LAKE ANDES CARNEGIE PUBLIC LIBRARY*, Fifth & Main St,
57356. (Mail add: PO Box 248, 57356-0248), SAN 315-6443. Tel:
605-487-7524. *Librn,* Mary Carda; *Asst Librn,* William Pontius
Founded 1912. Pop 1,500; Circ 6,358
Jan 2005-Dec 2005 Income $25,505, State $17,131, City $8,257, Other
$117. Mats Exp $5,219. Sal $13,060
Library Holdings: AV Mats 167; Bk Vols 10,866; Per Subs 23
Wlreless access
Open Mon, Tues & Thurs-Sat 1-5:30, Wed 10-12:30 & 1-5:30

LEAD

P PHOEBE APPERSON HEARST LIBRARY*, 315 W Main, 57754-1604.
SAN 315-6451. Tel: 605-584-2013. Web Site: leadlib.sdln.net. *Dir,* Lee
Ann Paananen
Founded 1894. Pop 3,817; Circ 18,454
Library Holdings: Bk Titles 17,574; Per Subs 60; Talking Bks 1,157;
Videos 766
Special Collections: Curran Coll; Foreign Language Coll; Local History &
Mining Records; Ralph G Cartwright Coll
Automation Activity & Vendor Info: (Cataloging) Ex Libris Group;
(Circulation) Ex Libris Group
Wireless access
Partic in South Dakota Library Network
Open Mon-Wed 10:30-6:30, Thurs & Fri 11-5, Sat 9-1

LEMMON

P LEMMON PUBLIC LIBRARY*, 303 First Ave W, 57638. (Mail add: PO
Box 120, 57638-0120), SAN 315-646X. Tel: 605-374-5611. *Librn,* Carol
Rafferty
Pop 1,500; Circ 14,200
Library Holdings: Bk Vols 35,000; Per Subs 33
Automation Activity & Vendor Info: (Circulation) Follett Software
Open Mon, Tues, Fri & Sat 1:30-5, Wed 9-5, Thurs 1:30-8

LEOLA

P LEOLA PUBLIC LIBRARY*, 802 Main St, 57456. SAN 315-6478. Tel:
605-439-3383. *Actg Librn,* Barb Guthmiller; *Asst City Librn,* Alice Bonnet
Founded 1968. Pop 521; Circ 57,018
Library Holdings: Bk Vols 6,392; Per Subs 10

Special Collections: Oral History
Open Tues-Sat 9-5

LETCHER

P LETCHER PUBLIC LIBRARY*, 105 W Main St, 57359. SAN 325-0091.
Tel: 605-248-2689. *Librn,* Vera Fouberg
Founded 1924. Pop 150; Circ 2,500
Library Holdings: Bk Titles 2,800
Subject Interests: SDak hist

MADISON

C DAKOTA STATE UNIVERSITY*, Karl E Mundt Library, 820 N
Washington Ave, 57042-1799. SAN 315-6494. Tel: 605-256-5203.
Interlibrary Loan Service Tel: 605-256-5205. Reference Tel: 605-256-7128.
FAX: 605-256-5208. E-mail: reference@dsu.edu. Web Site:
www.departments.dsu.edu/library. *Acq/Syst Librn, Assoc VPres/Dir,* Ethelle
S Bean; Tel: 605-256-5207, E-mail: ethelle.bean@dsu.edu; *Prof, Digital
Design/Access Librn,* Rise Smith; E-mail: rise.smith@dsu.edu; *Ref &
Instruction Librn,* Mary Francis; Tel: 605-256-5845, E-mail:
mary.francis@dsu.edu; Staff 6 (MLS 3, Non-MLS 3)
Founded 1881. Enrl 2,329; Fac 93; Highest Degree: Doctorate
Library Holdings: Bk Titles 77,117; Bk Vols 178,240; Per Subs 382
Special Collections: Senator Karl E Mundt Archives; South Dakota Coll;
University Archives. Oral History
Automation Activity & Vendor Info: (Acquisitions) Ex Libris Group;
(Cataloging) Ex Libris Group; (Circulation) Ex Libris Group; (ILL) Ex
Libris Group; (Media Booking) Ex Libris Group; (OPAC) Ex Libris Group;
(Serials) Ex Libris Group
Database Vendor: 3M Library Systems, ABC-CLIO, ACM (Association
for Computing Machinery), Agricola, Baker & Taylor, Cambridge
Scientific Abstracts, College Source, Community of Science (COS), CQ
Press, CRC Press/Taylor & Francis CRCnetBASE, Dialog, ebrary,
EBSCOhost, Ex Libris Group, Gale Cengage Learning, IEEE (Institute of
Electrical & Electronics Engineers), ISI Web of Knowledge,
LearningExpress, LexisNexis, Medline, netLibrary, Newsbank, OCLC
ArticleFirst, OCLC CAMIO, OCLC FirstSearch, OCLC WorldCat, OVID
Technologies, Oxford Online, ProQuest, PubMed, Safari Books Online,
ScienceDirect, SerialsSolutions, Thomson - Web of Science, WebMD, YBP
Library Services
Wireless access
Function: Adult bk club, Archival coll, Art exhibits, Audio & video
playback equip for onsite use, AV serv, Bk club(s), Bks on CD, Computers
for patron use, Copy machines, Digital talking bks, Distance learning, Doc
delivery serv, e-mail & chat, e-mail serv, Electronic databases & coll,
Equip loans & repairs, Exhibits, Fax serv, Free DVD rentals, ILL available,
Instruction & testing, Mail & tel request accepted, Mail loans to mem,
Online cat, Online info literacy tutorials on the web & in blackboard,
Online ref, Online searches, Orientations, Outreach serv,
Photocopying/Printing, Pub access computers, Ref & res, Ref serv
available, Ref serv in person, Satellite serv, Scanner, Tax forms, Telephone
ref, Web-catalog, Workshops
Partic in OCLC Online Computer Library Center, Inc; South Dakota
Library Network
Restriction: 24-hr pass syst for students only, In-house use for visitors,
Open to pub for ref & circ; with some limitations, Open to students, fac &
staff

M MADISON COMMUNITY HOSPITAL*, Health Science Library, 917 N
Washington Ave, 57042. SAN 329-2509. Tel: 605-256-6551. FAX:
605-256-6469. *Librn,* Teresa Simons
Library Holdings: Bk Titles 40; Bk Vols 44; Per Subs 15

P MADISON PUBLIC LIBRARY*, 209 E Center St, 57042-2998. SAN
315-6508. Tel: 605-256-7525. FAX: 605-256-7526. E-mail:
madisonpubliclibrary@gmail.com. Web Site: madisonpublic.sdln.net. *Dir,*
Nancy Sabbe; Staff 1 (MLS 1)
Founded 1906. Pop 11,276; Circ 60,000
Jan 2005-Dec 2005 Income $317,891, City $306,730, County $5,400,
Locally Generated Income $5,761. Mats Exp $108,550, Books $79,196, AV
Mat $24,535, Electronic Ref Mat (Incl. Access Fees) $4,819. Sal $120,475
(Prof $40,449)
Library Holdings: AV Mats 5,239; Bk Titles 49,950; Per Subs 139;
Talking Bks 3,200; Videos 2,000
Special Collections: South Dakota-Lake County (Dakota Coll)
Automation Activity & Vendor Info: (Circulation) Ex Libris Group
Partic in South Dakota Library Network
Open Mon-Thurs 10-9, Fri & Sat 10-5

MARTIN

P BENNETT COUNTY LIBRARY*, 101 Main St, 57551. (Mail add: PO
Box 190, 57551-0190), SAN 315-6516. Tel: 605-685-6556. *Dir,* Marsha
Fyler
Founded 1951. Pop 4,000; Circ 19,304

Library Holdings: Audiobooks 900; Bk Vols 30,000; Per Subs 30
Automation Activity & Vendor Info: (Circulation) Follett Software
Wireless access
Open Mon-Fri 8-5, Sat 9:30-4
Friends of the Library Group

MARVIN

P   BLUE CLOUD ABBEY LIBRARY*, 46561 147th St, 57251. (Mail add:
PO Box 98, 57251-0098), SAN 315-6524. Tel: 605-398-9200. FAX:
605-398-9201. E-mail: abbey@bluecloud.org. Web Site:
www.bluecloud.org. *Librn,* Fr Odilo Burkhardt; Staff 2 (MLS 1, Non-MLS
1)
Founded 1950. Pop 9,500
Library Holdings: Bk Vols 35,000; Per Subs 100
Subject Interests: Hist, Indian studies, Scriptures, Theol

MILBANK

P   GRANT COUNTY PUBLIC LIBRARY*, 207 E Park Ave, 57252-2497.
SAN 315-6532. Tel: 605-432-6543. FAX: 605-432-4635. E-mail:
gclibrary21@hotmail.com. Web Site: grantcountylibrary.com. *Dir,* Robin M
Schrupp; *Tech Serv,* Mary Kay Lee; Staff 6 (Non-MLS 6)
Founded 1979. Pop 8,200; Circ 108,137
Jan 2005-Dec 2005 Income $229,588, County $222,860, Locally Generated
Income $6,728. Mats Exp $40,422, Books $33,279, Per/Ser (Incl. Access
Fees) $2,500, Other Print Mats $1,000, AV Equip $395, AV Mat $3,248.
Sal $154,642
Library Holdings: AV Mats 3,986; Bks on Deafness & Sign Lang 25;
CDs 115; DVDs 257; High Interest/Low Vocabulary Bk Vols 96; Large
Print Bks 3,504; Bk Titles 51,032; Bk Vols 52,044; Per Subs 75; Talking
Bks 1,883; Videos 1,515
Special Collections: Old County Newspapers on Microfilm
Subject Interests: Maps
Automation Activity & Vendor Info: (Acquisitions) Follett Software;
(Cataloging) Follett Software; (Circulation) Follett Software; (ILL) PALS
Database Vendor: Baker & Taylor, EBSCOhost, Gale Cengage Learning,
Grolier Online, netLibrary, OCLC WebJunction, OCLC WorldCat,
ProQuest, ReferenceUSA, WebMD
Wireless access
Function: Adult literacy prog, AV serv, Handicapped accessible, Home
delivery & serv to Sr ctr & nursing homes, ILL available, Magnifiers for
reading, Online searches, Photocopying/Printing, Prog for children &
young adult, Ref serv available, Satellite serv, Summer reading prog,
Telephone ref, Wheelchair accessible
Partic in South Dakota Library Network
Special Services for the Deaf - Adult & family literacy prog; Assistive
tech; Bks on deafness & sign lang
Special Services for the Blind - Aids for in-house use; Assistive/Adapted
tech devices, equip & products; Audio mat; Bks on cassette; Bks on CD;
Braille bks; Computer with voice synthesizer for visually impaired persons;
Large print & cassettes; Large print bks; Low vision equip; Magnifiers;
Talking bks; Videos on blindness & phys handicaps
Open Mon-Thurs 10-8, Fri 10-5, Sat 10-2

MILLER

P   HAND COUNTY LIBRARY*, 402 N Broadway, 57362-1438. SAN
315-6540. Tel: 605-853-3693. FAX: 605-853-2201. E-mail:
db.hcl@midconetwork.com. *Dir,* Ray Caffee; E-mail:
db.hcl@midconetwork.com; *Librn,* Debra Bushfield; Staff 3 (MLS 1,
Non-MLS 2)
Founded 1947. Pop 4,948; Circ 57,345
Library Holdings: Bk Titles 26,000; Bk Vols 35,000; Per Subs 108
Special Collections: Local Newspapers, micro
Subject Interests: Authors, SDak bks
Automation Activity & Vendor Info: (Cataloging) Follett Software;
(Circulation) Follett Software; (OPAC) Follett Software
Function: ILL available
Partic in South Dakota Library Network
Open Mon & Thurs 11-6, Wed 11-7, Fri 11-5, Sat 11-3
Friends of the Library Group

MISSION

C   SINTE GLESKA UNIVERSITY LIBRARY*, E Hwy 18, 57555. (Mail
add: PO Box 107, 57555-0107), SAN 315-6559. Tel: 605-856-8100,
605-856-8112. FAX: 605-856-2011. E-mail: sgulibrary2@sinte.edu. Web
Site: www.sintegleska.edu. *Dir,* Rachel Lindvall; E-mail:
rachell@sintegleska.edu; *Cat,* Diana Dillon; *Circ,* Elsie Hollow Horn Bear;
ILL, Ken Wike; *Ref,* Kathi Her Many Horses; *Youth Serv,* Beverly Olson
Founded 1972. Enrl 850; Fac 60; Highest Degree: Master
Library Holdings: Bk Vols 48,800; Per Subs 372
Special Collections: Unkiciksuyape (Native American coll). Municipal
Document Depository; State Document Depository
Subject Interests: Educ, Environ, Law, Native Am studies

Automation Activity & Vendor Info: (Cataloging) Ex Libris Group
Function: Adult literacy prog, After school storytime, Audio & video
playback equip for onsite use, CD-ROM, Handicapped accessible, Health
sci info serv, Homebound delivery serv, ILL available, Newsp ref libr,
Online searches, Orientations, Photocopying/Printing, Prog for children &
young adult, Ref serv available, Spoken cassettes & DVDs, Summer
reading prog, VHS videos, Video lending libr, Workshops
Partic in American Indian Higher Education Consortium; Ex Libris Aleph;
Minn Interlibr Telecommunication Exchange; South Dakota Library
Network
Open Mon-Thurs 8am-10pm, Fri 8-5, Sun 1-5

MITCHELL

C   DAKOTA WESLEYAN UNIVERSITY*, George & Eleanor McGovern
Library, 1201 McGovern Ave, 57301. SAN 315-6567. Tel: 605-995-2618.
FAX: 605-995-2893. E-mail: library@dwu.edu. Web Site:
www.dwu.edu/library. *Dir, Learning Res,* Kevin J Kenkel; Tel:
605-995-2617, E-mail: kekenkel@dwu.edu; *Univ Archivist,* Laurie
Langland; Tel: 605-995-2134, E-mail: lalangla@dwu.edu; Staff 5 (MLS 2,
Non-MLS 3)
Founded 1885. Enrl 782; Fac 44; Highest Degree: Master
Library Holdings: AV Mats 21,500; CDs 625; DVDs 455; e-books
56,235; e-journals 664; Microforms 64,815; Bk Titles 70,215; Bk Vols
84,095; Per Subs 175; Videos 1,800
Special Collections: Senator Franis Case Coll, political papers; Senator
George McGovern Coll, personal papers & political photog; Western
History & Literature (Jennewein Western Library Coll)
Automation Activity & Vendor Info: (Acquisitions) Ex Libris Group;
(Cataloging) Ex Libris Group; (Circulation) Ex Libris Group; (ILL) Ex
Libris Group; (OPAC) Ex Libris Group; (Serials) Ex Libris Group
Database Vendor: Annual Reviews, BioOne, Cambridge Scientific
Abstracts, Children's Literature Comprehensive Database Company
(CLCD), Cinahl Information Systems, CQ Press, CredoReference,
EBSCOhost, Ex Libris Group, Gale Cengage Learning, JSTOR,
LexisNexis, McGraw-Hill, netLibrary, Newsbank, OCLC FirstSearch,
OCLC WorldCat, ProQuest, ScienceDirect, Wiley InterScience, World
Book Online
Wireless access
Function: Archival coll, Audio & video playback equip for onsite use, AV
serv, Computers for patron use, Distance learning, Electronic databases &
coll, Free DVD rentals, Handicapped accessible, ILL available, Music CDs,
Online cat, Photocopying/Printing, Ref & res, Scanner, VHS videos
Partic in Minitex Library Information Network; OCLC Online Computer
Library Center, Inc; South Dakota Library Network
Special Services for the Deaf - Assistive tech
Open Mon-Thurs (Winter) 7:30am-10pm, Fri 7:30-5, Sat 10-4, Sun
6pm-10pm; Mon-Fri (Summer) 7:30-5

P   MITCHELL PUBLIC LIBRARY*, 221 N Duff St, 57301-2596. SAN
315-6583. Tel: 605-995-8480. FAX: 605-995-8482. Web Site:
mitlib.sdln.net. *Dir,* Jackie Hess; E-mail: jhess@sdln.net; *Ch,* Lori Wagner;
Circ, Cindy Meinen; *Circ,* Linda Rishling; *ILL,* Sandra Spanos; *Tech Serv,*
Lajeane Jons; Staff 7 (MLS 1, Non-MLS 6)
Founded 1903. Pop 15,254; Circ 141,722
Jan 2010-Dec 2010 Income $718,467, City $699,457, County $6,500,
Locally Generated Income $12,510. Mats Exp $92,194, Books $72,713,
Per/Ser (Incl. Access Fees) $7,626, AV Mat $6,200, Electronic Ref Mat
(Incl. Access Fees) $5,655. Sal $260,023 (Prof $50,316)
Library Holdings: Audiobooks 858; CDs 1,151; DVDs 382; Large Print
Bks 1,573; Microforms 562; Bk Vols 69,264; Per Subs 145; Videos 288
Special Collections: Mitchell Area Archives, newspapers; South Dakota
Coll
Automation Activity & Vendor Info: (Cataloging) Ex Libris Group;
(Circulation) Ex Libris Group; (ILL) Ex Libris Group; (OPAC) Ex Libris
Group
Database Vendor: Gale Cengage Learning, Ingram Library Services,
LearningExpress, OCLC FirstSearch, OCLC WorldCat, ProQuest
Wireless access
Function: Audiobks via web, Bk club(s), Bks on cassette, Bks on CD,
Children's prog, Computers for patron use, Copy machines, e-mail & chat,
Electronic databases & coll, Free DVD rentals, Handicapped accessible,
ILL available, Magnifiers for reading, Online cat, Photocopying/Printing,
Preschool outreach, Prog for adults, Prog for children & young adult, Pub
access computers, Story hour, Summer reading prog, Tax forms, VCDs,
VHS videos, Web-catalog
Partic in OCLC Online Computer Library Center, Inc; South Dakota
Library Network
Open Mon-Thurs (Winter) 10-9, Fri & Sat 10-6, Sun 2-5; Mon (Summer)
10-9, Tues-Sat 10-6
Restriction: Non-circulating coll, Non-resident fee

M   QUEEN OF PEACE HOSPITAL LIBRARY*, 525 N Foster, 57301. SAN
315-6575. Tel: 605-995-2462. FAX: 605-995-2441. *Dir,* Pat Sudbeck
Founded 1918

Library Holdings: Bk Vols 1,000; Per Subs 35
Subject Interests: Med, Nursing
Restriction: Not open to pub, Staff use only, Students only

MOBRIDGE

P   A H BROWN PUBLIC LIBRARY*, 521 N Main St, 57601-2130. SAN
315-6591. Tel: 605-845-2808. E-mail: ahbrown@westriv.com. *Libr Dir,*
Karla Bieber
Founded 1930. Circ 10,132
Library Holdings: Bk Vols 20,000; Per Subs 43
Special Collections: South Dakota Coll
Subject Interests: Local hist
Open Mon-Fri 9-6, Thurs 6pm-8pm, Sat 9-12

NEW HOLLAND

R   CHRISTIAN REFORMED CHURCH LIBRARY*, PO Box 3, 57364. SAN
315-6613. Tel: 605-243-2346. *Librn,* Sharon Hofstee
Founded 1947
Library Holdings: Bk Vols 3,000

NEWELL

P   NEWELL PUBLIC LIBRARY*, 208 Girard, 57760. (Mail add: PO Box
54, 57760-0054), SAN 315-6621. Tel: 605-456-2179. Web Site:
www.newell.lib.ia.us. *Librn,* Glynda Smith; *Curator,* Linda Velder
Founded 2009. Circ 6,046
Jan 2006-Dec 2006 Income $20,715, City $19,812, Locally Generated
Income $903. Mats Exp $5,464. Sal $7,696
Library Holdings: Bk Vols 16,000; Per Subs 20; Videos 571
Automation Activity & Vendor Info: (Cataloging) Library Concepts
Wireless access
Open Mon 2-6, Tues-Fri 1:30-5, Wed (Summer) 10am-10:30pm

ONIDA

P   SULLY AREA LIBRARY*, PO Box 205, 57564-0205. SAN 315-663X.
Tel: 605-258-2133. FAX: 605-258-2361. Web Site:
www.sullybuttes.k12.sd.us. *Librn,* Jackie Aspelin; E-mail:
jackie.aspelin@k12.sd.us
Pop 800; Circ 16,000
Library Holdings: Bk Vols 20,000; Per Subs 30
Automation Activity & Vendor Info: (Cataloging) Winnebago Software
Co; (Circulation) Winnebago Software Co; (OPAC) Winnebago Software
Co
Wireless access
Open Mon, Wed & Fri 8-4, Tues 8-8, Thurs 8-5

PARKER

P   PARKER PUBLIC LIBRARY*, 115 N Main Ave, 57053. (Mail add: PO
Box 576, 57053-0576), SAN 315-6648. Tel: 605-297-5552. E-mail:
parkerlib@iw.net. *Dir,* Linda M Chaney; E-mail:
librarychaney@hotmail.com
Founded 1904. Pop 1,022; Circ 20,000
Jan 2010-Dec 2010 Income $59,894, City $58,875, Other $1,019. Mats
Exp $3,335, Books $2,940, AV Mat $395. Sal $34,756
Library Holdings: Audiobooks 375; Bks on Deafness & Sign Lang 3;
Braille Volumes 2; CDs 10; DVDs 307; Large Print Bks 600; Bk Vols
1,500; Per Subs 27; Videos 700
Special Collections: Vietnam Conflict Coll
Subject Interests: Christian fiction, SDak hist
Wireless access
Special Services for the Blind - Audio mat; Bks on cassette; Bks on CD;
Large print bks
Open Mon-Fri 9-12 & 2:30-5:30, Sat 9-12

PHILIP

P   HAAKON COUNTY PUBLIC LIBRARY*, 140 S Howard Ave, 57567.
(Mail add: PO Box 481, 57567). Tel: 605-859-2442. *Dir,* Annie Brunskill
Library Holdings: Bk Vols 10,000
Wireless access
Open Mon-Fri 11-5
Friends of the Library Group

PIERRE

P   RAWLINS MUNICIPAL LIBRARY*, 1000 E Church St, 57501. SAN
315-6656. Tel: 605-773-7421. FAX: 605-773-7423. Web Site:
rpllib.sdln.net. *Dir,* Beverly Lewis; *Cat,* Lisa Pfeiffer; *Ch,* Pat Weeldreyer;
Circ, Judy Ulvestad; Staff 9 (MLS 1, Non-MLS 8)
Founded 1905. Pop 19,000; Circ 156,300
Library Holdings: Audiobooks 4,700; AV Mats 275; CDs 1,100; DVDs
7,900; Large Print Bks 3,100; Bk Titles 63,000; Per Subs 120
Special Collections: History (South Dakota Coll); Lewis & Clark Coll

Automation Activity & Vendor Info: (Acquisitions) Ex Libris Group;
(Cataloging) Ex Libris Group; (Circulation) Ex Libris Group; (Course
Reserve) Ex Libris Group; (ILL) Ex Libris Group; (Media Booking) Ex
Libris Group; (OPAC) Ex Libris Group; (Serials) Ex Libris Group
Wireless access
Partic in South Dakota Library Network
Open Mon-Thurs (Sept-May) 10-9, Fri & Sat 10-6, Sun 1-5; Mon-Thurs
(June-Aug) 9-9, Fri 9-6, Sat 10-6, Sun 1-5

G   SOUTH DAKOTA DEPARTMENT OF GAME, FISH & PARKS
DIVISION OF WILDLIFE*, Natural Heritage Program Library, 523 E
Capitol, 57501. SAN 372-9508. Tel: 605-773-4345. FAX: 605-773-6245.
Actg Dir, Dave Ode; E-mail: dave.ode@state.sd.us; *Database Mgr,* Doug
Backlund
Library Holdings: Bk Vols 4,000; Per Subs 60
Subject Interests: Natural hist
Restriction: Open by appt only

G   SOUTH DAKOTA STATE HISTORICAL SOCIETY*, State Archives, 900
Governors Dr, 57501-2217. SAN 315-6664. Tel: 605-773-3804. FAX:
605-773-6041. E-mail: archref@state.sd.us. Web Site:
www.sdhistory.org/archives.htm. *Librn,* Marvene Riis; Tel: 605-773-4233.
E-mail: marvene.riis@state.sd.us; Staff 1 (Non-MLS 1)
Founded 1901
Library Holdings: Bk Titles 7,164; Bk Vols 13,770; Per Subs 188
Special Collections: Dakota & Western Indians Coll, photog, newsp
Subject Interests: Plains Indians, SDak hist, SDak Western Am
Automation Activity & Vendor Info: (OPAC) Ex Libris Group
Database Vendor: OCLC FirstSearch
Partic in OCLC Online Computer Library Center, Inc; South Dakota
Library Network
Open Mon-Fri 9-4:30
Restriction: Non-circulating

P   SOUTH DAKOTA STATE LIBRARY, 800 Governors Dr, 57501-2294.
SAN 360-4500. Tel: 605-773-3131. Circulation Tel: 605-773-5071.
Reference Tel: 605-773-5070. Administration Toll Free Tel: 800-423-6665
(South Dakota only). Administration FAX: 605-773-6962. E-mail:
library@state.sd.us. Web Site: library.sd.gov. *State Librn,* Dan Siebersma;
E-mail: dan.siebersma@state.sd.us; *Asst State Librn, Access Serv,* Colleen
Kirby; E-mail: colleen.kirby@state.sd.us; *Asst State Librn, Develop Serv,*
Daria Bossman; E-mail: daria.bossman@state.sd.us; *Coll Serv Librn,* Stacia
McGourty; E-mail: stacia.mcgourty@state.sd.us; *Res Serv Librn,* Brenda
Hemmelman; E-mail: brenda.hemmelman@state.sd.us; *Coordr, Ch & Youth
Serv,* Jasmine Rockwell; E-mail: jasmine.rockwell@state.sd.us; *Continuing
Educ Coordr,* Kathleen Slocum; E-mail: kathleen.slocum@state.sd.us;
Electronic Res Coordr, Julie Erickson; E-mail: julie.erickson@state.sd.us;
Electronic Res Coordr, Jane Healy; E-mail: jane.healy@state.sd.us; *Sch
Libr Coordr,* Mary Johnson; E-mail: mary.johnson@state.sd.us; *Sch Libr
Coordr,* Joan Upell; E-mail: joan.upell@state.sd.us; Staff 14 (MLS 10,
Non-MLS 4)
Founded 1913
Jul 2010-Jun 2011 Income $2,761,077, State $1,870,139, Federal $830,123,
Other $60,815
Library Holdings: Bk Vols 16,915; Per Subs 110; Talking Bks 82,527
Special Collections: State Document Depository; US Document
Depository
Subject Interests: Librarianship, Native Am hist, SDak hist
Automation Activity & Vendor Info: (Acquisitions) Ex Libris Group;
(Cataloging) Ex Libris Group; (Circulation) Ex Libris Group; (Course
Reserve) Ex Libris Group; (ILL) Ex Libris Group; (Media Booking) Ex
Libris Group; (OPAC) Ex Libris Group; (Serials) Ex Libris Group
Database Vendor: Gale Cengage Learning, ProQuest
Partic in OCLC Online Computer Library Center, Inc; South Dakota
Library Network; Western Council of State Libraries, Inc
Special Services for the Blind - Audio mat; Bks & mags in Braille, on rec,
tape & cassette; Braille bks; Dep for Braille Inst; Digital talking bk;
Newsletter (in large print, Braille or on cassette); Production of talking
bks; Radio reading serv; Talking bk & rec for the blind cat; Talking bk
serv referral; Talking bks; Talking bks & player equip; Textbks & bks
about music in Braille & large print
Open Mon-Fri 8-5
Branches: 1

P   BRAILLE & TALKING BOOK PROGRAM, McKay Bldg, 800 Governors
Dr, 57501-2294, SAN 315-6699. Tel: 605-773-3131. Administration
FAX: 605-773-6962. E-mail: library@state.sd.us. *Asst State Librn, Access
Serv,* Colleen Kirby; Tel: 605-773-5051, E-mail:
colleen.kirby@state.sd.us; *Prog Asst, Braille & Talking Bks,* Connie
Sullivan; E-mail: connie.sullivan@state.sd.us; Staff 8 (MLS 1, Non-MLS
7)
Founded 1968. Pop 5,739; Circ 112,964
Library Holdings: Bk Titles 58,788; Bk Vols 121,525
Special Collections: Dakota Language Coll; South Dakota Coll

Automation Activity & Vendor Info: (Cataloging) Keystone Systems, Inc (KLAS); (Circulation) Keystone Systems, Inc (KLAS); (OPAC) Keystone Systems, Inc (KLAS)
Partic in Minitex Library Information Network
Publications: Prairie Trails
Open Mon-Fri 8-5

GL   SOUTH DAKOTA SUPREME COURT*, Law Library, 500 E Capitol Ave, 57501-5070. SAN 315-6702. Tel: 605-773-4899. *Librn,* Sheridan Cash Anderson
Library Holdings: Bk Vols 30,000
Database Vendor: Westlaw
Open Mon-Fri 8-5

PLANKINTON

P   PLANKINTON COMMUNITY LIBRARY*, PO Box 190, 57368. SAN 315-6710. Tel: 605-942-7600. FAX: 605-942-7453. *Librn,* Teresa Olson
Pop 750; Circ 5,380
Library Holdings: Bk Vols 6,000
Open Mon-Fri 4-6

PRESHO

P   PRESHO PUBLIC LIBRARY*, 108 N Main St, 57568. SAN 315-6737. Tel: 605-895-2443. *Librn,* Laverne Olson
Pop 950; Circ 4,379
Library Holdings: Bk Vols 9,000
Open Mon-Sat 2-5

RAPID CITY

C   NATIONAL AMERICAN UNIVERSITY*, Thomas Jefferson Library, 321 Kansas City St, 57701-3692. SAN 315-6753. Tel: 605-394-4943. Toll Free Tel: 800-843-8892. FAX: 605-394-4871. Web Site: www.national.edu. *Dir,* Patricia Weiss; E-mail: pweiss@national.edu; *Circ,* Suzanne Brown; Staff 3 (MLS 1, Non-MLS 2)
Founded 1964. Enrl 1,500; Fac 40; Highest Degree: Master
Library Holdings: Bk Vols 35,000; Per Subs 157
Special Collections: Legal Resources; Veterinary Clinics of North America
Subject Interests: Acctg, Paralegal, Veterinary tech
Automation Activity & Vendor Info: (OPAC) Ex Libris Group
Database Vendor: Gale Cengage Learning, OCLC FirstSearch, ProQuest
Function: ILL available
Partic in OCLC Online Computer Library Center, Inc; South Dakota Library Network
Open Mon-Thurs 7:30am-10pm, Fri 7:30-4:30, Sat 10-3, Sun 10-6
Restriction: Open to students, fac & staff

P   RAPID CITY PUBLIC LIBRARY*, 610 Quincy St, 57701-3630. SAN 315-6761. Tel: 605-394-6139. Administration Tel: 605-394-6139, Ext 216. FAX: 605-394-4064. Web Site: www.rapidcitylibrary.org. *Dir,* Greta Chapman; E-mail: gchapman@rcplib.org; *Asst Dir,* Terri Davis; Tel: 605-394-6139, Ext 223, E-mail: tdavis@rcplib.org; *Circ Librn, Tech Serv Librn,* Sean Minkel; *Digital Librn, Emerging Tech Librn,* Stephanie Bents; *Ref/Coll Librn,* Morgan Sohl; *Supvr,* Jason Walker; Tel: 605-394-6139, Ext 243, E-mail: jwalker@rcplib.org; Staff 38 (MLS 12, Non-MLS 26)
Founded 1903. Pop 90,000; Circ 424,642
Jan 2007-Dec 2007 Income $3,036,692, City $2,560,402, County $328,217, Locally Generated Income $148,073. Mats Exp $417,825. Sal $1,855,275
Library Holdings: AV Mats 12,970; e-books 9,471; Bk Vols 157,892; Per Subs 392; Videos 12,970
Special Collections: Rapid City Society for Genealogical Research Coll. State Document Depository
Automation Activity & Vendor Info: (Acquisitions) Ex Libris Group; (Cataloging) Ex Libris Group; (Circulation) Ex Libris Group; (OPAC) Ex Libris Group
Wireless access
Partic in OCLC Online Computer Library Center, Inc; South Dakota Library Network
Open Mon-Thurs 9-8, Fri & Sat 9-6, Sun 12-6
Friends of the Library Group

M   RAPID CITY REGIONAL HOSPITAL*, Medical Library, 353 Fairmont Blvd, 57701. (Mail add: PO Box 6000, 57709-6000), SAN 315-677X. Tel: 605-719-7101. FAX: 605-719-1578. E-mail: library@rcrh.org. Web Site: www.rcrh.org/library. *Dir,* Patricia Hamilton; Staff 1 (MLS 1)
Founded 1926
Library Holdings: e-books 30; e-journals 1,200; Bk Vols 8,000; Per Subs 25
Special Collections: ANA Publications; Consumer Health
Subject Interests: Health admin, Med, Nursing
Database Vendor: EBSCOhost, Medline, Micromedex, Natural Standard, OCLC WorldCat, OVID Technologies, PubMed, WebMD
Wireless access

Function: Bks on cassette, Bks on CD, CD-ROM, Computers for patron use, Copy machines, Doc delivery serv, e-mail serv, Fax serv, Health sci info serv, ILL available, Online searches, Orientations, Outreach serv, Photocopying/Printing, VHS videos, Video lending libr
Partic in ICON Library Consortium; National Network of Libraries of Medicine
Restriction: Circ limited, Hospital employees & physicians only, In-house use for visitors, Med & nursing staff, patients & families, Med staff & students, Non-circulating coll

C   SOUTH DAKOTA SCHOOL OF MINES & TECHNOLOGY*, Devereaux Library, 501 E Saint Joseph St, 57701-3995. SAN 360-456X. Tel: 605-394-2418. Reference Tel: 605-394-2419. Administration Tel: 605-394-1255. Automation Services Tel: 605-394-1259. FAX: 605-394-1256. E-mail: library.reference@sdsmt.edu. Web Site: library.sdsmt.edu. *Dir,* Patricia M Andersen; E-mail: patricia.andersen@sdsmt.edu; *Assoc Librn, Coll Mgr, Syst Librn,* Cindy L Davies; E-mail: cindy.davies@sdsmt.edu; *Bus & Finance Mgr, Coordr, Outreach Serv, Coordr, Pub Serv,* Janet L Taylor; Tel: 605-394-1262, E-mail: janet.taylor@sdsmt.edu; *Coordr, ILL,* Scott Hall; E-mail: scott.hall@sdsmt.edu; *Cat, Spec Coll & Archives Librn,* Donna B Neal; E-mail: donna.neal@sdsmt.edu; *Circ,* Karen M Vieira; E-mail: karen.vieira@sdsmt.edu; *Circ,* Josh Wilkinson; E-mail: josh.wilkinson@sdsmt.edu; *Ref Serv, Spec Coll & Archives Librn,* Dick Beshara; E-mail: richard.beshara@sdsmt.edu; *Ser,* Lois Zens; E-mail: lois.zens@sdsmt.edu; Staff 10 (MLS 2, Non-MLS 8)
Founded 1885. Enrl 2,200; Fac 175; Highest Degree: Doctorate
Library Holdings: AV Mats 2,456; Bk Titles 133,382; Bk Vols 212,062; Per Subs 527
Special Collections: Black Hills & Western South Dakota Mining History, (Black Hills Special Coll Area), maps; School History, 1885 to date. US Document Depository
Subject Interests: Eng, Mining, Sci, Tech
Automation Activity & Vendor Info: (Acquisitions) Ex Libris Group; (Cataloging) Ex Libris Group; (Circulation) Ex Libris Group; (Course Reserve) Ex Libris Group; (ILL) Ex Libris Group; (Media Booking) Ex Libris Group; (OPAC) Ex Libris Group; (Serials) Ex Libris Group
Database Vendor: American Chemical Society, Baker & Taylor, Blackwell's, EBSCOhost, H W Wilson, IEEE (Institute of Electrical & Electronics Engineers), ISI Web of Knowledge, Knovel, LearningExpress, LexisNexis, netLibrary, Newsbank, OCLC FirstSearch, OCLC WorldCat, ProQuest, Thomson - Web of Science, Wilson - Wilson Web
Wireless access
Function: Audio & video playback equip for onsite use, Audiobks via web, Bks on cassette, Bks on CD, CD-ROM, Electronic databases & coll, Free DVD rentals, ILL available, Music CDs, Online cat, Online ref, Photocopying/Printing, Ref serv available, Res libr, Spoken cassettes & CDs, Spoken cassettes & DVDs, Telephone ref, VHS videos
Publications: What's Happening Blog (Online only)
Partic in Minitex Library Information Network; OCLC Online Computer Library Center, Inc; South Dakota Library Network
Open Mon-Thurs 7am-Midnight, Fri 7-5, Sat Noon-5, Sun Noon-Midnight
Restriction: Borrowing requests are handled by ILL, Non-circulating of rare bks, Non-resident fee
Friends of the Library Group

J   WESTERN DAKOTA TECHNICAL INSTITUTE LIBRARY*, 800 Mickelson Dr, 57703. SAN 320-9849. Tel: 605-718-2904. FAX: 605-718-2537. Web Site: www.wdt.edu. *Librn,* Debbie Arne; E-mail: deb.arne@wdt.edu; *Asst Librn,* Vickie Lass; E-mail: vickie.lass@wdt.edu; Staff 2 (Non-MLS 2)
Founded 1968. Enrl 1,053; Fac 78; Highest Degree: Associate
Library Holdings: AV Mats 200; e-books 6,631; Bk Titles 11,968; Per Subs 70
Special Collections: Departmental Coll; Teen Prep
Subject Interests: Agr, Biographies, Bus mgt, Career, Carpentry, Computer network specialist, Electronics, Fiction, Law enforcement, Native Am, Nursing, Paralegal, SDak, State law, Vocational
Automation Activity & Vendor Info: (Acquisitions) Ex Libris Group; (Cataloging) Ex Libris Group; (Circulation) Ex Libris Group; (Course Reserve) Ex Libris Group; (ILL) Ex Libris Group; (Media Booking) Ex Libris Group; (OPAC) Ex Libris Group; (Serials) Ex Libris Group
Wireless access
Partic in South Dakota Library Network
Open Mon-Thurs 7:30-7, Fri 7:30-4

REDFIELD

P   REDFIELD CARNEGIE LIBRARY, Five E Fifth Ave, 57469-1243. SAN 315-6788. Tel: 605-472-4555. FAX: 605-472-4559. E-mail: carnegie2@hotmail.com. Web Site: www.redfield-sd.com/library.html. *Librn,* Betty Baloun
Library Holdings: Bk Vols 17,000; Per Subs 54
Automation Activity & Vendor Info: (Cataloging) Follett Software; (Circulation) Follett Software; (OPAC) Follett Software

Function: Homebound delivery serv, ILL available, Photocopying/Printing, Ref serv available
Open Mon 12-5 & 7-9, Tues 10-12, 1-5 & 7-9, Wed & Fri 12-5, Thurs & Sat 10-12 & 1-5

G   SOUTH DAKOTA DEVELOPMENTAL CENTER, Redfield Library, 17267 W Third St, 57469-1001. SAN 328-4786. Tel: 605-472-2400. FAX: 605-472-4457. *Dir,* Ted Williams
Library Holdings: Bk Vols 500
Subject Interests: Spec educ
Partic in South Dakota Library Network
Restriction: Private libr

SIOUX FALLS

S   ARGUS LEADER LIBRARY*, 200 S Minnesota Ave, 57104. (Mail add: PO Box 5034, 57117-5034), SAN 370-6184. Tel: 605-331-2200. FAX: 605-331-2294. Web Site: www.argusleader.com. *Librn,* Ron Wuertz
Library Holdings: Bk Titles 170; Bk Vols 295
Open Mon-Fri 8-5
Restriction: Private libr

C   AUGUSTANA COLLEGE, Mikkelsen Library, 2001 S Summit Ave, 57197-0001. SAN 315-6796. Tel: 605-274-4921. FAX: 605-274-5447. E-mail: augielibrarians@gmail.com. Web Site: library.augie.edu. *Dir, Libr Serv,* Ronelle Thompson; E-mail: ronelle.thompson@augie.edu; *Asst Dir, Tech Serv,* Deborah A Hagemeier; Tel: 605-274-5354, E-mail: deb.hagemeier@augie.edu; *Bibliog Instruction/Ref,* Lisa Brunick; E-mail: lisa.brunick@augie.edu; *Cat, Govt Doc,* Kay Christensen; Tel: 605-274-5357, E-mail: kay.christensen@augie.edu; *Circ, ILL,* Jan Brue Enright; Tel: 605-274-4493, E-mail: jan.enright@augie.edu; *Media Serv,* Judith Howard; Tel: 605-274-4920, E-mail: judith.howard@augie.edu; Staff 13 (MLS 6, Non-MLS 7)
Founded 1860. Enrl 1,809; Fac 150; Highest Degree: Master
Aug 2010-Jul 2011 Income (Main Library Only) $965,171, Locally Generated Income $15,625, Parent Institution $872,914, Other $76,632. Mats Exp $456,258, Books $27,362, Per/Ser (Incl. Access Fees) $215,043, Micro $1,973, AV Equip $764, AV Mat $7,178, Electronic Ref Mat (Incl. Access Fees) $92,094, Presv $1,976. Sal $538,914 (Prof $301,131)
Library Holdings: AV Mats 7,283; e-books 17,788; e-journals 5,135; Microforms 8,117; Bk Vols 204,033; Per Subs 412; Videos 2,991
Special Collections: Center for Western Studies; Norwegian Coll. US Document Depository
Automation Activity & Vendor Info: (Acquisitions) Ex Libris Group; (Cataloging) Ex Libris Group; (Circulation) Ex Libris Group; (Course Reserve) Ex Libris Group; (ILL) OCLC; (Media Booking) Ex Libris Group; (OPAC) Ex Libris Group; (Serials) Ex Libris Group
Database Vendor: American Chemical Society, American Physical Society, American Psychological Association (APA), ARTstor, Baker & Taylor, BioOne, Cinahl Information Systems, CQ Press, CredoReference, ebrary, EBSCOhost, Ex Libris Group, Facts on File, Gale Cengage Learning, ISI Web of Knowledge, JSTOR, LearningExpress, LexisNexis, Modern Language Association, Nature Publishing Group, OCLC CAMIO, OCLC FirstSearch, OCLC WorldCat, Oxford Online, Project MUSE, ProQuest, PubMed, Sage, ScienceDirect, Springshare, LLC, Wiley InterScience
Wireless access
Function: E-Reserves, Govt ref serv
Partic in Minitex Library Information Network; OCLC Online Computer Library Center, Inc; South Dakota Library Network
Open Mon-Thurs 7:30am-Midnight, Fri 7:30-6, Sat 9-5, Sun 11am-Midnight
Friends of the Library Group
Departmental Libraries:
CENTER FOR WESTERN STUDIES, 2201 S Summit Ave, 57197. (Mail add: PO Box 727, 57197-0727), SAN 329-3033. Tel: 605-274-4007. FAX: 605-274-4999. E-mail: cws@augie.edu. *Exec Dir,* Arthur R Huseboe; *Dir,* Tim Hoheisel; *Dir,* Harry F Thompson. Subject Specialists: *Lit,* Arthur R Huseboe; *Hist,* Tim Hoheisel; *Lit,* Harry F Thompson
Founded 1970. Enrl 1,800; Highest Degree: Master
Library Holdings: Bk Titles 32,000; Bk Vols 35,000; Per Subs 30; Spec Interest Per Sub 20
Special Collections: Episcopal Diocese of SD Archives; United Church of Christ SD Conference Archives; Upper Great Plains. Oral History
Subject Interests: Hist, Lit, Northern Prairie Plains
Partic in OCLC Online Computer Library Center, Inc; South Dakota Library Network
Publications: A New South Dakota History; CWS Newsletter; The Geography of South Dakota; Yanktonai Sioux Water Colors & other books about Plains Indians & Western History
Open Mon-Fri 8-12 & 1-5, Sat 10-2
Restriction: Non-circulating to the pub
Friends of the Library Group

R   FIRST BAPTIST CHURCH LIBRARY*, 1401 S Covell Ave, 57105. SAN 315-680X. Tel: 605-336-0966. FAX: 605-336-3294. *Librn,* Cathy Schock
Library Holdings: Bk Vols 3,300; Per Subs 15
Open Mon-Fri 8-5
Friends of the Library Group

R   FIRST LUTHERAN CHURCH LIBRARY*, 327 S Dakota, 57104. SAN 315-6818. Tel: 605-336-3734. FAX: 605-336-8370. Web Site: www.flcsf.org. *Librn,* Barbara Siebelts
Founded 1920
Library Holdings: Bk Titles 6,600; Per Subs 3
Subject Interests: Relig studies
Open Tues, Thurs & Fri 9-1, Wed 5-8, Sun 8:15-12:30

S   SIOUXLAND HERITAGE MUSEUMS, Pettigrew Museum Library, 200 W Sixth St, 57104. SAN 315-6907. Tel: 605-367-4210. FAX: 605-367-6004. E-mail: museum@minnehahacounty.org. Web Site: www.siouxlandmuseums.com. *Dir,* William J Hoskins; Staff 3 (Non-MLS 3)
Founded 1926
Library Holdings: Bk Titles 10,000; Per Subs 10
Special Collections: Local & Regional History Coll; Populism, Bimetalism, Maverick Politics 1880-1920; R F Pettigrew Papers & Private Library, bks, pamphlets, pvt papers
Subject Interests: Especially pioneering through pre-World War II, Hist of Sioux Falls, SDak state, Surrounding region
Function: Archival coll, Photocopying/Printing, Res libr
Publications: Sioxland Heritage Museums Report (Newsletter)
Special Services for the Deaf - TTY equip
Restriction: Not a lending libr, Open by appt only

P   SIOUXLAND LIBRARIES*, 200 N Dakota Ave, 57104. (Mail add: PO Box 7403, 57117-7403), SAN 315-6885. Tel: 605-367-8700. Interlibrary Loan Service Tel: 605-367-8720. Administration Tel: 605-367-8701. Automation Services Tel: 605-367-8728. FAX: 605-367-4312. Web Site: www.siouxlandlib.org. *Dir,* Mary Johns; E-mail: mjohns@siouxfalls.org; *Asst Dir, Admin,* Joan Reddy; Tel: 605-367-8721, E-mail: jreddy@siouxfalls.org; *Asst Dir, Pub Serv,* Cynthia Winn; Tel: 605-367-8725, E-mail: cwinn@siouxfalls.org; *Asst Dir, Tech Serv,* Jodi Fick; Tel: 605-367-8713, E-mail: jfick@siouxfalls.org; *Coll Develop Librn,* Deb Yoder; Tel: 605-367-8727, E-mail: dyoder@siouxfalls.org; *Info Serv Librn,* Jane Huwe; Tel: 605-367-8722, E-mail: jhuwe@siouxfalls.org; *Info Serv Librn,* Heather Stephenson; Tel: 605-367-8718, E-mail: hstephenson@siouxfalls.org; *Sr Librn/Youth Serv,* Jim Oliver; Tel: 605-367-8719, E-mail: joliver@siouxfalls.org; *Tech Serv Librn,* Vicki Biggerstaff; Tel: 605-367-8703, E-mail: vbiggerstaff@siouxfalls.org; *Tech Serv Librn,* Donna Cranmer; Tel: 605-367-8712, E-mail: dcranmer@siouxfalls.org; *Youth Serv Librn,* Karen Wiechmann; Tel: 605-367-8708, E-mail: kweichmann@siouxfalls.org; *Circ Mgr,* Monique Christensen; Tel: 605-367-8723, E-mail: mchristensen@siouxfalls.org; *ILL,* Alysia Boysen; E-mail: aboysen@siouxfalls.org; Staff 17 (MLS 17)
Founded 1886. Pop 183,454; Circ 1,711,237
Jan 2008-Dec 2008 Income (Main Library and Branch(s)) $5,724,391, State $29,775, City $4,729,587, County $778,815, Locally Generated Income $186,214. Mats Exp $609,867, Books $317,569, Per/Ser (Incl. Access Fees) $40,357, AV Mat $212,318, Electronic Ref Mat (Incl. Access Fees) $39,623. Sal $3,163,564
Library Holdings: Audiobooks 19,014; AV Mats 21; CDs 5,667; DVDs 15,525; e-books 12,875; Electronic Media & Resources 43; Large Print Bks 6,207; Microforms 1,213; Bk Titles 116,195; Bk Vols 293,428; Per Subs 778; Videos 9,825
Special Collections: State & Regional History & Genealogy (Caille Room). State Document Depository
Subject Interests: Foreign lang, SDak hist
Automation Activity & Vendor Info: (Acquisitions) Horizon; (Cataloging) Horizon; (Circulation) Horizon; (ILL) OCLC; (Media Booking) Horizon; (OPAC) Horizon; (Serials) Horizon
Database Vendor: 3M Library Systems, Baker & Taylor, BWI, Dun & Bradstreet, EBSCO Auto Repair Reference, EBSCOhost, Ingram Library Services, LearningExpress, LexisNexis, Marcive, Inc, netLibrary, Newsbank, OCLC FirstSearch, OCLC WorldCat, Overdrive, Inc, ProQuest, PubMed, SirsiDynix, Sybase, Telus, ValueLine
Wireless access
Function: Adult bk club, After school storytime, Art exhibits, Audiobks via web, Bk club(s), Bks on cassette, Bks on CD, Children's prog, Computer training, Computers for patron use, Copy machines, e-mail serv, Electronic databases & coll, Fax serv, Free DVD rentals, Games & aids for the handicapped, Handicapped accessible, Holiday prog, Home delivery & serv to Sr ctr & nursing homes, Homebound delivery serv, ILL available, Large print keyboards, Magnifiers for reading, Mail & tel request accepted, Music CDs, Online cat, Online ref, Online searches, Orientations, Outreach serv, Outside serv via phone, mail, e-mail & web, OverDrive digital audio bks, Photocopying/Printing, Prof lending libr, Prog for adults, Prog for children & young adult, Ref serv available, Spoken cassettes & CDs,

Spoken cassettes & DVDs, Story hour, Summer reading prog, Tax forms, Teen prog, Telephone ref, VHS videos, Video lending libr, Web-catalog, Wheelchair accessible
Partic in Minitex Library Information Network; OCLC Online Computer Library Center, Inc; South Dakota Library Network
Special Services for the Deaf - Bks on deafness & sign lang; Closed caption videos; Deaf publ; Staff with knowledge of sign lang; TDD equip; TTY equip
Special Services for the Blind - Audio mat; BiFolkal kits; Bks on cassette; Bks on CD; Computer with voice synthesizer for visually impaired persons; Descriptive video serv (DVS); Home delivery serv; Large print bks; Magnifiers; ZoomText magnification & reading software
Open Mon-Thurs 9-9, Fri 9-6, Sat 9-5, Sun (Sept-May) 1-5
Restriction: Non-circulating coll, Non-resident fee
Branches: 11
BALTIC BRANCH, 213 St Olaf, Baltic, 57003. (Mail add: PO Box 326, Baltic, 57003-0326), SAN 329-577X. Tel: 605-529-5415. FAX: 605-529-5415. *In Charge,* Kathy Faith; E-mail: kfaith@siouxfalls.org; Staff 1 (Non-MLS 1)
Open Mon 3-7, Tues & Thurs 2:30-6:30, Sat 9-12
BRANDON BRANCH, 305 S Splitrock, Brandon, 57005-1651, SAN 327-960X. Tel: 605-582-2390. FAX: 605-582-8760. *In Charge,* Peggy Lind; E-mail: plind@siouxfalls.org; Staff 1 (Non-MLS 1)
Open Mon-Thurs 10-8, Fri & Sat 10-5
CAILLE BRANCH, 4100 Carnegie Circle, 57106-2320, SAN 375-5606. Tel: 605-367-8144. FAX: 605-362-2816. *Br Librn,* Carin Schleicher; Tel: 605-367-8714, E-mail: cschleicher@siouxfalls.org; Staff 1 (MLS 1)
Open Mon-Thurs 10-9, Fri 10-6, Sat 10-5, Sun (Sept-May) 1-5
COLTON BRANCH, 325 E Fourth, Colton, 57018. (Mail add: PO Box 338, Colton, 57018-0338), SAN 322-6115. Tel: 605-446-3519. FAX: 605-446-3519. *In Charge,* Jennifer Brynjulson; E-mail: jbrynjulson@siouxfalls.org; Staff 1 (Non-MLS 1)
Open Tues & Thurs 3:30-6:30, Wed 4-7, Sat 9-12
CROOKS BRANCH, 900 N West Ave, Crooks, 57020-6402, SAN 360-4179. Tel: 605-543-5296. FAX: 605-543-5297. *In Charge,* Bev Liesinger; E-mail: bliesinger@siouxfalls.org; Staff 1 (Non-MLS 1)
Function: Photocopying/Printing
Open Mon 4-8, Tues & Fri 12:30-5, Wed 9-5, Sat 10-1
GARRETSON BRANCH, 649 Main St, Garretson, 57030-0392. (Mail add: PO Drawer N, Garretson, 57030-0392), SAN 322-6107. Tel: 605-594-6619. FAX: 605-594-6619. *In Charge,* Bev Liesinger; Staff 1 (Non-MLS 1)
Open Tues 10-1 & 3-6, Wed 5-8, Thurs 3-6, Sat 10-1
HARTFORD - WEST CENTRAL BRANCH, 705 E Second St, Hartford, 57033. (Mail add: PO Box 248, Hartford, 57033-0248), SAN 322-6093. Tel: 605-528-3223. FAX: 605-528-3702. Web Site: www.westcentral.edu. *In Charge,* Jo Ann Miles; E-mail: joann.miles@k12.sd.us; Staff 1 (Non-MLS 1)
Open Mon, Wed & Fri 8-11:15 & 11:45-5, Tues & Thurs 8-11:15 & 11:45-8, Sat 9-1
HUMBOLDT BRANCH, 201 S Main St, Humboldt, 57035-0166. (Mail add: PO Box 274, Humboldt, 57035-0274), SAN 322-6085. Tel: 605-363-3361. FAX: 605-363-3361. *In Charge,* Marian Puthoff; Staff 1 (Non-MLS 1)
Open Mon & Fri 3-6, Wed 6-9, Sat 9-12
OAK VIEW, 3700 E Third St, 57103. Tel: 605-367-8060. FAX: 605-367-4343. *Br Librn,* James Borchert
Open Mon-Thurs 10-9, Fri 10-6, Sat 10-5, Sun (Sept-May) 1-5
RONNING BRANCH, 3100 E 49th St, 57103-5877, SAN 375-5614. Tel: 605-367-8140. FAX: 605-371-4144. *Br Mgr,* Jane Taylor; Tel: 605-367-8715, E-mail: jtaylor@siouxfalls.org; Staff 1 (MLS 1)
Open Mon-Thurs 10-9, Fri 10-6, Sat 10-5, Sun (Sept-May) 1-5
VALLEY SPRINGS BRANCH, 401 Broadway Ave, Valley Springs, 57068. (Mail add: PO Box 56, Valley Springs, 57068-0056), SAN 322-6123. Tel: 605-757-6264. FAX: 605-757-6730. *In Charge,* Lavon Schmitt; E-mail: lschmitt@siouxfalls.org; Staff 1 (Non-MLS 1)
Open Tues-Thurs 3-6, Sat 10-1
Bookmobiles: 1
Bookmobiles: 1. Asst Dir for Extn, Jodi Fick

S   SOUTH DAKOTA STATE PENITENTIARY*, Donald M Cole & Jameson Annex Library, 1600 N Dr, 57104-0915, (Mail add: PO Box 5911, 57117-5911), SAN 315-6915. Tel: 605-367-5170, 605-367-5171. *Librn,* Larry Anderson; *Librn,* Michelle Wysuph
Library Holdings: Bk Vols 8,000; Per Subs 20
Open Mon-Fri 8-3
Restriction: Staff & inmates only

G   UNITED STATES GEOLOGICAL SURVEY, Earth Resources Observation & Science Center Library, Mundt Federal Bldg, 47914 252nd St, 57198-0001. SAN 315-632X. Tel: 605-594-2611. FAX: 605-594-6589. Web Site: eros.usgs.gov/#/about_us/library. *Librn,* Carol Deering; Staff 1 (MLS 1)
Founded 1973
Library Holdings: Bk Vols 6,500; Per Subs 24

Subject Interests: Aerial remote sensing in conjuction with geog, Computer graphics, Computer tech, Geog info systs, Geol, Hydrol, Land use planning, Satellite
Wireless access
Partic in OCLC Online Computer Library Center, Inc; South Dakota Library Network
Open Mon-Fri 8-4

CR   UNIVERSITY OF SIOUX FALLS*, Mears Library, 1101 W 22nd St, 57105-1699. SAN 315-6842. Tel: 605-331-6660. Interlibrary Loan Service Tel: 605-331-6664. Web Site: www.usiouxfalls.edu. *Dir, Libr Serv,* Judy Clauson Krull; Tel: 605-331-6661, E-mail: judy.krull@usiouxfalls.edu; *Acq, Per,* Angie Wixon; Tel: 605-331-6614, E-mail: angie.wixon@usiouxfalls.edu; *Circ,* Jennifer Knutson; E-mail: jennifer.knutson@usiouxfalls.edu; Staff 3 (MLS 1, Non-MLS 2)
Founded 1883. Enrl 1,116; Fac 74; Highest Degree: Master
Library Holdings: Bk Titles 57,750; Bk Vols 87,929; Per Subs 378
Special Collections: Baptist, South Dakota
Automation Activity & Vendor Info: (Cataloging) Ex Libris Group
Database Vendor: Gale Cengage Learning, LexisNexis, OCLC FirstSearch, ProQuest
Wireless access
Partic in OCLC Online Computer Library Center, Inc; South Dakota Library Network
Open Mon-Thurs 8am-10pm, Fri 8-5, Sat 10-2, Sun 2-10

M   WEGNER HEALTH SCIENCE INFORMATION CENTER*, 1400 W 22nd St, Ste 100, 57105. SAN 377-6263. Tel: 605-357-1400. Toll Free Tel: 800-521-2987. FAX: 605-357-1490. E-mail: wegner@usd.edu. Web Site: www.usd.edu/wegner. *Dir,* Anne Moore; E-mail: anne.moore@usd.edu; *Head, Ref,* Anna Gieschen; *Outreach Serv Librn,* Molly Youngkin; *Cat Mgr,* Vicki Carlson; *Circ Supvr,* Linda Robinson; Staff 6 (MLS 3, Non-MLS 3)
Founded 1998
Library Holdings: AV Mats 2,291; Bk Vols 16,011; Per Subs 545
Special Collections: Children's Coll; Ethics Coll; History of Medicine
Subject Interests: Health, Spec educ
Automation Activity & Vendor Info: (Acquisitions) Ex Libris Group; (Cataloging) Ex Libris Group; (Circulation) Ex Libris Group; (ILL) Ex Libris Group; (OPAC) Ex Libris Group; (Serials) Ex Libris Group
Database Vendor: Cinahl Information Systems, DynaMed, EBSCOhost, Gale Cengage Learning, MD Consult, Medline, Micromedex, Natural Standard, OCLC FirstSearch, OCLC WorldCat, OVID Technologies, ProQuest, PubMed, ScienceDirect
Wireless access
Function: Audio & video playback equip for onsite use, AV serv, Doc delivery serv, Handicapped accessible, Health sci info serv, Homebound delivery serv, ILL available, Online searches, Photocopying/Printing, Ref serv available, Wheelchair accessible
Publications: Wegner Wellness (Newsletter)
Partic in Minitex Library Information Network; National Network of Libraries of Medicine South Central Region; OCLC Online Computer Library Center, Inc; South Dakota Library Network
Open Mon-Thurs 8am-10pm, Fri 8-5, Sat 10-5, Sun 2-10

SISSETON

P   SISSETON MEMORIAL LIBRARY*, 305 E Maple St, 57262-1524. (Mail add: PO Box 289, 57262-0289), SAN 315-694X. Tel: 605-698-7391. E-mail: sislib@venturecomm.net. *Librn,* Mary Ann Cameron
Founded 1907. Pop 11,161; Circ 26,171
Library Holdings: Bk Vols 15,000; Per Subs 72
Special Collections: Bing & Grondahl Christmas Plate Coll; South Dakota History
Automation Activity & Vendor Info: (Cataloging) Winnebago Software Co; (Circulation) Winnebago Software Co
Wireless access
Open Mon & Thurs 10-8, Tues & Wed 10-6, Fri 10-5, Sat 9-12

C   SISSETON WAHPETON COLLEGE LIBRARY*, Agency Village, PO Box 689, 57262-0698. SAN 322-9483. Tel: 605-698-3966, Ext 1320. FAX: 605-698-3132. Web Site: www.swc.tc. *Librn,* Delight Robertson; E-mail: drobertson@swc.tc; *Asst Librn,* Bonnye Flammond; Staff 1 (Non-MLS 1)
Founded 1979. Enrl 227; Fac 17; Highest Degree: Associate
Library Holdings: Bk Titles 14,500; Per Subs 160; Talking Bks 114; Videos 782
Special Collections: Indians of North America Coll; Sisseton-Wahpeton Sioux Tribe
Automation Activity & Vendor Info: (Cataloging) TLC (The Library Corporation); (Circulation) TLC (The Library Corporation); (Serials) EBSCO Online
Database Vendor: EBSCOhost
Wireless access
Partic in South Dakota Library Network

Open Mon-Fri (Winter) 8-4:30; Mon-Fri (Summer) 8-6
Restriction: Pub use on premises
Friends of the Library Group

SPEARFISH

P   GRACE BALLOCH MEMORIAL LIBRARY*, 625 N Fifth St,
57783-2311. SAN 315-6958. Tel: 605-642-1330. Web Site: spflib.sdln.net.
Dir, Amber Wilde
Founded 1945. Pop 13,250; Circ 136,500
Library Holdings: Bk Titles 55,247; Per Subs 146
Special Collections: South Dakota History Coll. Oral History
Automation Activity & Vendor Info: (Circulation) Ex Libris Group
Partic in South Dakota Library Network
Open Mon-Thurs (Winter) 10-8, Fri 10-5, Sat 9-5, Sun 5-8; Mon-Thurs
(Summer) 9-7, Fri 9-5, Sat 9-2
Friends of the Library Group

C   BLACK HILLS STATE UNIVERSITY*, E Y Berry Library-Learning
Center, 1200 University St, Unit 9676, 57799-9676. SAN 315-6966. Tel:
605-642-6250. Circulation Tel: 605-642-6834. FAX: 605-642-6298. Web
Site: iis.bhsu.edu/lis/index.cfm. *Dir,* Rajeev Bukralia; Tel: 605-642-6360,
E-mail: librarydirector@bhsu.edu; *Ref Librn,* Scott Ahola; Tel:
605-642-6359; *Spec Coll Librn,* Roberta Sago; Tel: 605-642-6361; *Acq,*
Sarah Freng; *Cat,* Michael Tolan; Tel: 605-642-6356; *Circ,* Amber Wilde;
Tel: 605-642-6834; *ILL,* Karen Stacy; Tel: 605-642-6357; *Per,* Becky
Cooper; Tel: 605-642-6362; Staff 5 (MLS 3, Non-MLS 2)
Founded 1883. Enrl 3,800; Fac 122; Highest Degree: Master
Library Holdings: e-books 13,000; e-journals 17,000; Bk Titles 206,000
Special Collections: ARROW, Inc Coll; Congressman E Y Berry Papers;
Leland Case Western Historical Studies. State Document Depository; US
Document Depository
Wireless access
Partic in Minitex Library Information Network; South Dakota Library
Network
Open Mon-Thurs 7:30am-11pm, Fri 7:30-5, Sat 10-5, Sun 2-11
Friends of the Library Group

SPENCER

P   HANSON-MCCOOK COUNTY REGIONAL LIBRARY, 306 Main St,
57374. (Mail add: PO Box 227, 57374-0227), SAN 315-6974. Tel:
605-246-2740. E-mail: hmlibrary@triotel.net. *Dir,* Cherie Schroeder
Pop 9,829; Circ 35,792
Library Holdings: Bk Vols 19,995
Open Fri 8-12 & 1-5
Bookmobiles: 1

SPRINGFIELD

S   MIKE DURFEE STATE PRISON*, Carl G Lawrence Library, 1412 Wood
St, 57062. SAN 370-5412. Tel: 605-369-2201, 605-369-4318. FAX:
604-369-2813. *Librn,* Mark Stoebner; E-mail: mark.stoebner@state.sd.us
Library Holdings: Bk Vols 30,000; Per Subs 50

STURGIS

P   STURGIS PUBLIC LIBRARY*, 1040 Second St, 57785-1595. SAN
315-6990. Tel: 605-347-2624. FAX: 605-720-7211. E-mail:
sturgispubliclibrary@yahoo.com. Web Site: www.cityofriders.com. *Dir,*
Julie Moore; E-mail: jmoore@sdlm.net; *Ch,* Kathy Dykstra; *Ref,* Grace
Hammond; Staff 3 (Non-MLS 3)
Founded 1922. Pop 24,253; Circ 77,652
Library Holdings: Bk Titles 31,000; Bk Vols 38,000; Per Subs 140
Special Collections: Dakota Coll. Oral History
Subject Interests: SDak Black Hills region
Publications: Audiovisual Catalog
Mem of Woodlands Library Cooperative
Partic in South Dakota Library Network
Open Mon-Thurs 9-7, Fri & Sat 9-4
Friends of the Library Group
Bookmobiles: 1

TIMBER LAKE

P   DEWEY COUNTY LIBRARY*, 212 Main, 57656. (Mail add: PO Box 68,
57656-0068), SAN 360-4624. Tel: 605-865-3541. *Dir,* Margaret Salzer;
E-mail: m_salzer@hotmail.com
Pop 5,300; Circ 17,015
Library Holdings: Bk Titles 21,500; Bk Vols 23,000; Per Subs 15
Special Collections: Regional History Coll
Wireless access
Function: Wheelchair accessible
Open Mon-Fri 9-12 & 1-5

TYNDALL

P   TYNDALL PUBLIC LIBRARY, PO Box 26, 57066-0026. SAN 315-7008.
Tel: 605-589-3266. *Librn,* Sue Gough
Founded 1917. Pop 1,500; Circ 14,930
Library Holdings: Bk Vols 13,098
Open Tues, Wed & Fri 1-5, Thurs 12-5

VERMILLION

S   AMERICAN INDIAN RESEARCH PROJECT*, Joseph Harper Cash
Memorial Library, University of South Dakota, 414 E Clark St, 12 Dakota
Hall, 57069. SAN 329-9228. Tel: 605-677-5209. FAX: 605-677-6525.
E-mail: iais@usd.edu. Web Site: www.usd.edu/iais. *Dir,* Dr Mark Daniels
Library Holdings: Bk Vols 5,000; Per Subs 35
Subject Interests: Agr, Am Indian culture, Am Indian issues, Ethnic
groups, Hist, Music, Politics, Rapid City flood, Relig, Veterans
Publications: Index to the American Indian Research Project; Index to the
South Dakota Oral History Collection
Restriction: Open by appt only

S   W H OVER MUSEUM, 1110 University St, 57069. (Mail add: 414 E
Clark, 57069), SAN 371-4446. Tel: 605-677-5228. E-mail:
whover@usd.edu. Web Site: www.usd.edu/whover.
Founded 1883
Library Holdings: Bk Vols 2,000
Open Mon-Fri 10:30-5, Sat 10:30-4:30, Sun 1-4:30

C   UNIVERSITY OF SOUTH DAKOTA*, University Libraries, 414 E Clark
St, 57069. SAN 360-4713. Tel: 605-677-5371. FAX: 605-677-6834.
E-mail: library@usd.edu. Web Site: www.usd.edu/library. *Dean of Libr,*
Position Currently Open; *Digital Access Mgr, Librn,* David Alexander;
E-mail: david.alexander@usd.edu; *Librn, License/Contract Negotiator,* Joe
Edelen; E-mail: joe.edelen@usd.edu; *Coll Develop, Librn, Sci,* Barbara
Gauger; E-mail: barbara.gauger@usd.edu; *Bus Serv, Distance Educ, Librn,*
Stephen Johnson; E-mail: stephen.johnson@usd.edu; *Coordr, Info Literacy,
Librn,* Carol Leibiger; E-mail: c.leibiger@usd.edu; *Instruction & Educ Res,
Librn,* Margaret Miller; E-mail: margaret.b.miller@usd.edu; *Archives &
Spec Coll Librn,* Dan Daily; Tel: 605-677-8867, E-mail:
dan.daily@usd.edu; *Health Sci Librn, Tech Librn,* Danielle Loftus; E-mail:
danielle.loftus@usd.edu; *Health Sci Librn,* David Midyette; E-mail:
david.midyette@usd.edu; *Instruction Librn,* Alan Aldrich; E-mail:
alan.aldrich@usd.edu; *Instruction Librn,* Deedra Holdhusen; E-mail:
deedra.holdhusen@usd.edu. Subject Specialists: *Archives, Hist,* Dan Daily;
Art, Health sci, Danielle Loftus; *Anthropology, Health sci,* David Midyette;
Staff 29 (MLS 11, Non-MLS 18)
Founded 1882. Enrl 9,243; Highest Degree: Doctorate
Jul 2007-Jun 2008 Income (Main Library Only) $2,776,751, State
$1,887,961, Parent Institution $888,790. Mats Exp $960,196, Books
$153,818, Per/Ser (Incl. Access Fees) $496,987, Micro $5,748, Electronic
Ref Mat (Incl. Access Fees) $293,643, Presv $10,000. Sal $1,512,479 (Prof
$782,099)
Library Holdings: AV Mats 19,686; CDs 5,491; DVDs 746; Microforms
740,794; Bk Titles 362,262; Bk Vols 550,778; Per Subs 1,509; Videos
6,220
Special Collections: Country Schools Survey; Herman P Chilson Western
Americana Coll; Mahoney Music Coll; South Dakota History & Historical
Maps (Richardson Archives). State Document Depository; US Document
Depository
Automation Activity & Vendor Info: (Acquisitions) Ex Libris Group;
(Cataloging) Ex Libris Group; (Circulation) Ex Libris Group; (ILL) OCLC
ILLiad; (OPAC) Ex Libris Group
Database Vendor: ABC-CLIO, ACM (Association for Computing
Machinery), American Chemical Society, American Mathematical Society,
Blackwell's, Bowker, Cambridge Scientific Abstracts, EBSCOhost,
Elsevier, Gale Cengage Learning, ISI Web of Knowledge, JSTOR,
LexisNexis, netLibrary, OCLC FirstSearch, OCLC WorldCat, OVID
Technologies, Oxford Online, Project MUSE, ProQuest, ValueLine, Wiley
InterScience
Wireless access
Publications: Coyote Connection (Newsletter); Extension Express
(Newsletter); Guide to the I D Weeks Library for USD Faculty & Staff;
Guide to the I D Weeks Library Resources; I D Weeks Library Serials List;
USD Internet Guide: Navigating Internet Services; Volante Index
Open Mon-Thurs 7:30am-2am, Fri 7:30am-11pm, Sat 10am-11pm, Sun
10am-2am
Departmental Libraries:
CL   MCKUSICK LAW LIBRARY, 414 E Clark St, 57069-2390, SAN
360-4772. Tel: 605-677-5259. Circulation Tel: 605-677-5363,
605-677-6354. Interlibrary Loan Service Tel: 605-677-6372. Reference
Tel: 605-677-6355. FAX: 605-677-5417. E-mail: lllibrary@usd.edu. Web
Site: www.usd.edu/lawlib. *Dir,* John F Hagemann; Tel: 605-677-5041,
E-mail: jhageman@usd.edu; *Acq,* Lynette Simonsen; *Cat, ILL,* Doris
Hodgen; *Circ,* Erma Larson; *Ref,* Candice Spurlin; *Ser,* Karyl Knodel;
Staff 10 (MLS 7, Non-MLS 3)

Founded 1901. Enrl 225; Fac 19; Highest Degree: Doctorate
Library Holdings: Bk Vols 200,000
Subject Interests: Agr law, Arts, Family law, Health law, Indian law, Water law
Partic in Mid-America Law Library Consortium; Minn Interlibr Telecommunication Exchange; OCLC Online Computer Library Center, Inc
Open Mon-Thurs 7:30am-10pm, Fri 7:30-4:30, Sat & Sun 12-4
Restriction: Open to pub for ref only

NATIONAL MUSIC MUSEUM LIBRARY, 414 E Clark St, 57069-2390, SAN 326-7695. Tel: 605-677-5306. FAX: 605-677-6995. E-mail: smm@usd.edu. Web Site: www.nmmusd.org. *Interim Exec Dir,* Margaret Downie Banks; E-mail: margaret.banks@usd.edu; Staff 11 (MLS 1, Non-MLS 10)
Founded 1973. Enrl 6; Fac 4; Highest Degree: Master
Library Holdings: Bk Titles 10,000; Per Subs 50
Subject Interests: Music, Musical instruments, Musicology
Publications: National Music Museum (Newsletter)
Restriction: Non-circulating, Not a lending libr, Open by appt only, Open to pub by appt only, Open to qualified scholars, Open to researchers by request, Researchers by appt only

CM   WEGNER HEALTH SCIENCE INFORMATION CENTER, Sanford School of Medicine, 414 E Clark, 57069-2390, SAN 315-7016. Tel: 605-677-5348. Interlibrary Loan Service Tel: 605-677-5349. Reference Tel: 605-677-5121. FAX: 605-677-5124. E-mail: library@usd.edu. Web Site: www.usd.edu/lhsl/. *Health Sci Librn,* Barbara Harvey; E-mail: Barbara.Harvey@usd.edu; *Health Sci Librn,* Timmy Johnson; Staff 6 (MLS 2, Non-MLS 4)
Founded 1907. Enrl 860; Fac 190; Highest Degree: Doctorate
Library Holdings: AV Mats 271; e-journals 14,500; Bk Titles 28,036; Bk Vols 91,247; Per Subs 677
Special Collections: History of Medicine Archives; Rare Books. US Document Depository
Subject Interests: Allied health, Basic sci, Clinical med, Nursing
Automation Activity & Vendor Info: (Acquisitions) Ex Libris Group; (Cataloging) Ex Libris Group; (Circulation) Ex Libris Group; (Course Reserve) Ex Libris Group; (ILL) Ex Libris Group; (Media Booking) Ex Libris Group; (OPAC) Ex Libris Group; (Serials) Ex Libris Group
Partic in South Dakota Library Network
Publications: Accession List; Library Handbook
Open Mon-Fri 8am-Midnight, Sat 10-5, Sun 11am-Midnight

P   VERMILLION PUBLIC LIBRARY*, 18 Church St, 57069-3093. SAN 315-7024. Tel: 605-677-7060. FAX: 605-677-7160. E-mail: vpl@sdln.net. Web Site: vpl.sdln.net. *Dir,* Jane A Larson; E-mail: jlarson@sdln.net; *Ch, Coordr, Teen Serv, Youth/Young Adult Librn,* Joyce Moore; E-mail: jamoore@sdln.net; *Adult Serv,* Linda Calleja; E-mail: lcalleja@sdln.net; *Cat,* Wendy Nilson; E-mail: wnilson@sdln.net; Staff 4 (MLS 2, Non-MLS 2)
Founded 1903. Pop 14,300; Circ 98,752
Jan 2008-Dec 2008 Income $506,097, City $491,815, County $3,000, Locally Generated Income $11,282. Mats Exp $92,000, Books $72,000, Per/Ser (Incl. Access Fees) $5,000, AV Mat $15,000. Sal $231,167 (Prof $110,491)
Library Holdings: Audiobooks 4,082; AV Mats 444; CDs 970; DVDs 926; Large Print Bks 2,500; Microforms 250; Bk Titles 85,741; Per Subs 157; Videos 3,173
Automation Activity & Vendor Info: (Acquisitions) Ex Libris Group; (Cataloging) Ex Libris Group; (Circulation) Ex Libris Group; (Course Reserve) Ex Libris Group; (ILL) Ex Libris Group; (Media Booking) Ex Libris Group; (OPAC) Ex Libris Group; (Serials) Ex Libris Group
Database Vendor: EBSCO Auto Repair Reference, EBSCO Information Services, EBSCOhost, Elsevier, Ex Libris Group, Gale Cengage Learning, LearningExpress, OCLC WebJunction, OCLC WorldCat, ProQuest, ReferenceUSA, SirsiDynix
Wireless access
Publications: EAI Index, General Periodical Index, MGI, RapidCity, Journal Index, Health Index, Business Index (Index to educational materials)
Partic in South Dakota Library Network
Special Services for the Deaf - TDD equip
Special Services for the Blind - Audio mat; Bks on cassette; Bks on CD; Cassette playback machines; Cassettes; Copier with enlargement capabilities; Extensive large print coll; Home delivery serv; Large print bks; Lending of low vision aids; Magnifiers; Playaways (bks on MP3); Rec; Recorded bks; Ref serv; Screen enlargement software for people with visual disabilities; Sound rec
Open Mon-Thurs 10-9, Fri 10-6, Sat 10-5, Sun 1-5
Friends of the Library Group

VIBORG

P   VIBORG CITY PUBLIC LIBRARY*, 110 Main St, 57070. Tel: 605-326-5481. *Librn,* Dawn Kludt
Library Holdings: Bk Vols 14,000; Per Subs 12

Wireless access
Open Mon-Fri 1-6, Sat 9-12

WAGNER

P   WAGNER PUBLIC LIBRARY*, 106 Sheridan Ave SE, 57380-9701. (Mail add: Box 6, Rte 1, 57380-9701), SAN 315-7032. Tel: 605-384-5248. FAX: 605-384-5248. E-mail: wpublib@hcinet.net. *Librn,* Anne Podhradsky
Founded 1914. Circ 14,000
Library Holdings: AV Mats 95; Large Print Bks 950; Bk Titles 16,877; Bk Vols 17,390; Per Subs 53; Talking Bks 165
Automation Activity & Vendor Info: (Cataloging) Follett Software; (OPAC) Follett Software
Partic in South Dakota Library Network
Open Mon-Fri 9-12 & 1-5, Sat 9-12

WALL

P   WALL COMMUNITY LIBRARY, 407 Main St, 57790. (Mail add: PO Box 131, 57790-0131). Tel: 605-279-2929. E-mail: wallcomlib@gwtc.net. *Libr Dir,* Wendy Brunnemann; Staff 0.5 (Non-MLS 0.5)
Library Holdings: Audiobooks 70; DVDs 100; Large Print Bks 107; Bk Vols 10,000; Per Subs 2
Wireless access
Function: Adult bk club, Audiobks via web, Bk club(s), Bks on cassette, Bks on CD, Computers for patron use, Copy machines, Free DVD rentals, ILL available, Online cat, Online searches, OverDrive digital audio bks, Preschool reading prog, Prog for adults, Prog for children & young adult, Pub access computers, Ref serv in person, Story hour, Summer & winter reading prog, Summer reading prog
Open Wed 12-7, Thurs 9-12:30 & 1:30-5, Fri 8-1

WATERTOWN

S   LAKE AREA TECHNICAL INSTITUTE LIBRARY*, L H Timmerman Library, PO Box 730, 57201-0730. SAN 327-0955. Tel: 605-882-5284, Ext 231. FAX: 605-882-6299. Web Site: www.lakeareatech.edu. *Librn,* Nicki Yackley-Franken
Library Holdings: Bk Vols 1,500; Per Subs 113
Subject Interests: Agr
Wireless access
Open Mon-Thurs 7:30am-9pm, Fri 7:30-4

P   WATERTOWN REGIONAL LIBRARY*, 160 Sixth St NE, 57201-2778. (Mail add: PO Box 250, 57201-0250), SAN 315-7040. Tel: 605-882-6220. FAX: 605-882-6221. E-mail: adminwat@sdln.net. Web Site: watweb.sdln.net. *Dir,* Michael C Mullin; *Asst Librn,* Ann Bailey; *Cat,* Selma Mitchell; *Ch,* Linda Bauman; *Circ,* Ellen Heisner; *Spec Serv,* Bev Moore; Staff 7 (MLS 3, Non-MLS 4)
Founded 1899. Pop 20,237; Circ 227,488
Jan 2008-Dec 2008 Income $842,760, City $801,060, Other $41,700. Mats Exp $111,600, Books $107,700, Electronic Ref Mat (Incl. Access Fees) $3,900. Sal $570,300 (Prof $295,450)
Library Holdings: AV Mats 4,398; Bk Titles 63,476; Bk Vols 67,046; Per Subs 226
Special Collections: Dakota Territory Coll
Subject Interests: Watertown hist
Automation Activity & Vendor Info: (Acquisitions) Ex Libris Group; (Cataloging) OCLC; (Circulation) Ex Libris Group; (ILL) OCLC; (OPAC) Ex Libris Group
Wireless access
Function: Art exhibits, Audiobks via web, Bks on cassette, Bks on CD, CD-ROM, Children's prog, Computer training, Computers for patron use, Copy machines, Electronic databases & coll, Fax serv, Free DVD rentals, Handicapped accessible, Home delivery & serv to Sr ctr & nursing homes, Homebound delivery serv, ILL available, Music CDs, Online cat, Photocopying/Printing, Prog for adults, Prog for children & young adult, Pub access computers, Ref serv available, Scanner, Senior computer classes, Serves mentally handicapped consumers, Spoken cassettes & CDs, Story hour, Summer reading prog, Tax forms, Teen prog, Telephone ref, VHS videos, Wheelchair accessible
Partic in OCLC Online Computer Library Center, Inc; South Dakota Library Network
Open Mon-Thurs 9:30-9, Fri 9:30-6, Sat 9:30-5, Sun 1-5
Friends of the Library Group

WAUBAY

P   WAUBAY PUBLIC LIBRARY, 94 N Main St, 57273. (Mail add: PO Box 446, 57273-0446). Tel: 605-947-4748. FAX: 605-947-4748. *Librn,* Erika Welch
Library Holdings: Bk Vols 7,500
Open Mon-Fri 11-5, Sat 10-2

WEBSTER

P   WEBSTER PUBLIC LIBRARY*, 800 Main St, 57274-1494. SAN
315-7059. Tel: 605-345-3263. *Dir,* Anne Fossum
Founded 1930. Pop 1,956; Circ 17,750
Jan 2007-Dec 2007 Income $48,000. Mats Exp $7,450, Books $5,100,
Per/Ser (Incl. Access Fees) $1,200, AV Mat $500, Electronic Ref Mat
(Incl. Access Fees) $650. Sal $37,000 (Prof $22,000)
Library Holdings: AV Mats 448; CDs 40; Bk Vols 32,000; Per Subs 59;
Talking Bks 402
Special Collections: South Dakota History Coll
Open Mon, Tues, Thurs & Fri 1:30-5:30 & 7-9, Wed 1:30-5:30, Sat 9-11

WESSINGTON

P   WESSINGTON PUBLIC LIBRARY, 240 Wessington St, 57381. (Mail
add: PO Box 108, 57381-0108), SAN 315-7067. Tel: 605-458-2596.
E-mail: wesspublib@venturecomm.net. *Dir,* Donna Runge
Founded 1937. Pop 800; Circ 4,700
Library Holdings: Bk Titles 4,665; Per Subs 16
Special Collections: South Dakota History; South Dakota Poetry,
pamphlets; South Dakota State Laws
Open Wed & Sat 1-5

WESSINGTON SPRINGS

P   WESSINGTON SPRINGS CARNEGIE LIBRARY*, 109 W Main St,
57382. (Mail add: PO Box 336, 57382), SAN 315-7075. Tel:
605-539-1803. *Librn,* Barb Horsley
Founded 1918. Pop 1,203; Circ 8,299
Library Holdings: Bk Titles 18,200; Per Subs 30
Special Collections: Books By or About South Dakotans & South Dakota;
Old Newspapers (local)
Open Mon & Wed 1-6 & 7-8:30, Thurs 2-5, Fri 10-11:30 & 1-6

WINNER

P   TRIPP COUNTY LIBRARY-GROSSENBURG MEMORIAL*, 442 S
Monroe St, 57580. SAN 360-4837. Tel: 605-842-0330. *Librn,* Sandy
Hansen; E-mail: sandy_hansen@hotmail.com
Founded 1921. Pop 6,430; Circ 50,685
Library Holdings: DVDs 700; Bk Vols 49,000; Per Subs 15; Talking Bks
1,000; Videos 2,000
Special Collections: County; South Dakota History & Tripp County
History Colls, bks, pamphlets, photog
Subject Interests: Agr, Archit, Art
Automation Activity & Vendor Info: (Cataloging) Winnebago Software
Co; (Circulation) Winnebago Software Co; (OPAC) Winnebago Software
Co
Open Mon 9:30-8, Tues-Fri 9:30-5:30
Friends of the Library Group
Branches: 1
COLOME BRANCH, 217 Main St, Colome, 57528. (Mail add: PO Box
285, Colome, 57528-0285), SAN 360-4861. *Librn,* Verlas Vavra
Library Holdings: Bk Vols 1,036

WOONSOCKET

P   WOONSOCKET COMMUNITY LIBRARY*, PO Box 428, 57385-0428.
SAN 315-7083. Tel: 605-796-1412. E-mail: woonlib@santel.net. *Librn,* Pat
Larson
Founded 1918. Pop 850; Circ 4,522
Library Holdings: AV Mats 210; Bk Vols 5,274; Per Subs 22
Database Vendor: LearningExpress
Open Mon & Fri (Winter) 9-5, Tues & Thurs 9-1, Wed 9-6; Mon-Fri
(Summer) 1:30-5, Wed 1:30-6

YANKTON

M   AVERA SACRED HEART HOSPITAL*, Medical Library, 501 Summit St,
57078-9967. SAN 320-2356. Tel: 605-668-8384. FAX: 605-668-8488.
Librn, Barbara Papik; E-mail: bpapik@shhservices.com; Staff 1 (MLS 1)
Founded 1975
Library Holdings: Bk Titles 275; Per Subs 40
Subject Interests: Allied health, Hospital admin, Med, Nursing
Wireless access
Open Mon-Thurs 8-3, Fri 8-12

C   MOUNT MARTY COLLEGE LIBRARY*, 1105 W Eighth St,
57078-3724. SAN 315-7091. Tel: 605-668-1555. FAX: 605-668-1357. Web
Site: www.mtmc.edu. *Dir,* Sandra Brown; E-mail: sbrown@mtmc.edu; *Cat,
Circ,* Diane Dvorak; *ILL, Per,* Aimee Huntley; Staff 3 (MLS 1, Non-MLS
2)
Founded 1936. Highest Degree: Master
Library Holdings: Bk Vols 77,959; Per Subs 327
Subject Interests: Relig studies
Automation Activity & Vendor Info: (Circulation) Ex Libris Group
Wireless access
Partic in Minitex Library Information Network; OCLC Online Computer
Library Center, Inc; South Dakota Library Network
Open Mon-Thurs 7:30am-10pm, Fri 7:30-5, Sat 1-5, Sun 1-10

P   YANKTON COMMUNITY LIBRARY*, 515 Walnut, 57078-4042. SAN
315-7121. Tel: 605-668-5275. FAX: 605-668-5277. E-mail:
ycllibrary@sdln.net. Web Site: ycllib.sdln.net. *Dir,* Kathy Jacobs; *Asst Dir,
Ch,* Beck Pittenger; *Circ, Sr Libr Asst,* Joyce Brunken; *Tech Serv,* Linda
Dobrovolny
Founded 1902. Pop 21,652; Circ 178,344
Jan 2006-Dec 2006 Income $518,000, City $500,000, County $18,000.
Mats Exp $94,000, Books $52,000, Per/Ser (Incl. Access Fees) $8,900, AV
Mat $8,600, Electronic Ref Mat (Incl. Access Fees) $24,500. Sal $334,000
(Prof $86,900)
Library Holdings: Bk Titles 64,000; Bk Vols 75,000; Per Subs 160
Special Collections: State Document Depository
Subject Interests: Genealogy, Local hist, SDak hist
Automation Activity & Vendor Info: (Acquisitions) Ex Libris Group;
(Cataloging) Ex Libris Group; (Circulation) Ex Libris Group; (ILL) Ex
Libris Group; (Media Booking) Ex Libris Group; (OPAC) Ex Libris Group;
(Serials) Ex Libris Group
Partic in South Dakota Library Network
Open Mon-Thurs (Winter) 10-9, Sat 10-5, Sun 1-5; Mon & Tues (Summer)
10-9, Wed & Thurs 10-6, Fri & Sat 10-5
Friends of the Library Group

Date of Statistics: FY 2011-2012
Population, 2010 Census (est.): 6,346,105
Population Served by Public Libraries: 6,346,105
Total Volumes in Public Libraries: 18,253,025
  Volumes Per Capita: 3.47
Total Public Library Circulation: 26,501,693
  Circulation Per Capita: 2.39
Total Public Library Income: $109,515,536
Income per Capita: $17.25
  Source of Income: Mainly public funds; federal, state & local
  Expenditures: $71,407,786

Expenditure Per Capita: $11.25
Number of County or Multi-county (Regional) Libraries: 9
  multi-county, 4 metropolitan
  Counties Served: 95
Number of Bookmobiles in State: 3
Grants-in-Aid to Public Libraries:
  Federal (Library Services & Technology Act): $3,493,286
  State Aid: $7,452,700
PLEASE NOTE: In reality, Tennessee does not give direct state aid
  to public libraries. Most of the state money flows through the
  regional library system where a percentage goes to regional
  salaries and benefits.

ADAMSVILLE

P   IRVING MEEK JR MEMORIAL LIBRARY*, 204 W Main St, 38310.
     (Mail add: PO Box 303, 38310-0303), SAN 315-713X. Tel: 731-632-3572.
     FAX: 731-632-3572. Web Site: www.irvingmeekjrmemoriallibrary.org/. *Dir,*
     Marsha Jernigan Hutcherson
     Founded 1961. Pop 7,050; Circ 33,000
     Library Holdings: AV Mats 1,442; Bk Vols 19,993; Per Subs 45
     Special Collections: Buford Pusser Memorabilia
     Subject Interests: Fossils, Shells
     Mem of Hatchie River Regional Library
     Open Mon & Fri 9-5, Tues & Thurs 9-6, Sat 9-Noon

ALAMO

P   CROCKETT MEMORIAL LIBRARY, 258 E Church St, 38001-1108.
     SAN 315-7148. Tel: 731-696-4220. FAX: 731-696-5107. *Dir,* Linda Rice
     Founded 1968
     Library Holdings: Bk Vols 20,000
     Subject Interests: Local hist
     Automation Activity & Vendor Info: (Circulation) Auto-Graphics, Inc;
     (ILL) Auto-Graphics, Inc
     Database Vendor: Booklist Online, Electric Library, Ingram Library
     Services, LearningExpress, WebMD
     Wireless access
     Open Mon-Wed & Fri 10-5, Thurs 10-6, Sat 10-4
     Friends of the Library Group

ALTAMONT

P   ALTAMONT PUBLIC LIBRARY*, Hwy 56, 37301. (Mail add: PO Box
     228, 37301-0228), SAN 315-7156. Tel: 931-692-2457. FAX:
     931-692-2457. E-mail: altamontlib@blomand.net. *Librn,* Ann F Nunley
     Library Holdings: Bk Vols 5,000
     Open Mon 8:30-12, Wed & Fri 8:30-4:30

ARDMORE

P   ARDMORE PUBLIC LIBRARY*, 25836 Main St, 38449. (Mail add: PO
     Box 517, 38449-0517), SAN 376-7000. Tel: 931-427-4883. FAX:
     931-427-3818. E-mail: ardmorelib@ardmore.net. *Dir,* Verlin Collins; Staff
     3 (Non-MLS 3)
     Founded 1977. Pop 2,813; Circ 51,042
     Jul 2011-Jun 2012 Income $80,938, City $77,288, County $3,650
     Library Holdings: Bk Vols 49,502; Per Subs 21
     Automation Activity & Vendor Info: (Cataloging) Follett Software;
     (Circulation) Follett Software
     Open Mon-Fri 9-6, Sat 9-1
     Friends of the Library Group

ARLINGTON

P   SAM T WILSON PUBLIC LIBRARY*, 11968 Walker St, 38002. SAN
     378-4452. Tel: 901-867-1943. Web Site:
     www.townofarlington.org/index.asp?nid=61. *Dir,* Alda Boster
     Library Holdings: Bk Titles 20,000
     Function: Bks on CD
     Open Mon 11-7, Tues-Thurs & Sat 10-6

ARNOLD AFB

A   UNITED STATES AIR FORCE*, Arnold Engineering Development Center
     Technical Library, FL 2804, 100 Kindel Dr, Ste C212, 37389-3212. SAN
     360-5078. Tel: 931-454-4430. Interlibrary Loan Service Tel: 931-454-5431.
     Administration Tel: 931-454-4429. Automation Services Tel: 931-454-7220.
     FAX: 931-454-5421. *Mgr,* Gay D Goethert; Tel: 931-454-4429, E-mail:
     gay.goethert@arnold.af.mil; *Ref,* Sharon Butcher; E-mail:
     sharon.butcher@arnold.af.mil; *Syst Coordr,* Emily Moore; E-mail:
     emily.moore@arnold.af.mil; Staff 3 (MLS 3)
     Founded 1952
     Library Holdings: AV Mats 918; e-journals 33; Bk Vols 27,429; Per Subs
     273
     Special Collections: NACA Technical Reports; NACA Wartime Reports
     Subject Interests: Aerospace sci, Astronomy, Chem, Eng, Math, Optics,
     Physics, Pollution
     Automation Activity & Vendor Info: (Acquisitions) SirsiDynix;
     (Cataloging) SirsiDynix; (Circulation) SirsiDynix; (OPAC) SirsiDynix;
     (Serials) SirsiDynix
     Database Vendor: OCLC FirstSearch
     Partic in Lyrasis; OCLC Online Computer Library Center, Inc
     Restriction: Not open to pub

ASHLAND CITY

P   CHEATHAM COUNTY PUBLIC LIBRARY*, 188 County Services Dr,
     Ste 200, 37015-1726. SAN 315-7172. Tel: 615-792-4828. FAX:
     615-792-2054. Web Site: www.cheathamlibrary.com. *Dir,* Mary Linger;
     Staff 7 (MLS 1, Non-MLS 6)
     Founded 1967. Pop 23,789
     Library Holdings: Bk Titles 25,000; Per Subs 55
     Special Collections: Oral History
     Automation Activity & Vendor Info: (Acquisitions) Book Systems, Inc;
     (Cataloging) Auto-Graphics, Inc; (Course Reserve) Auto-Graphics, Inc;
     (ILL) Auto-Graphics, Inc
     Wireless access
     Mem of Red River Regional Library
     Special Services for the Blind - Audio mat
     Open Mon, Wed & Fri 9:30-5, Tues & Thurs 9:30-8, Sat 9:30-3
     Friends of the Library Group

ATHENS

P   **EDWARD GAUCHE FISHER PUBLIC LIBRARY***, 1289 Ingleside Ave, 37303. SAN 315-7199. Tel: 423-745-7782. FAX: 423-745-1763. Web Site: www.fisherlibrary.org. *Dir,* Julie Forkner; E-mail: julieforkner@bellsouth.net; *Head, Ref,* Amberly Cole; E-mail: egfreference@bellsouth.net; Staff 13 (MLS 2, Non-MLS 11)
Founded 1969. Pop 50,000; Circ 117,414
Library Holdings: Bk Vols 102,000; Per Subs 80; Videos 1,600
Automation Activity & Vendor Info: (Cataloging) SirsiDynix; (Circulation) SirsiDynix; (OPAC) SirsiDynix
Wireless access
Function: For res purposes, ILL available, Online searches, Prog for children & young adult, Ref serv available, Summer reading prog, Telephone ref, Wheelchair accessible
Mem of Ocoee River Regional Library
Open Mon, Tues & Thurs 9:30-8, Wed & Fri 9:30-5:30, Sat 10-5
Friends of the Library Group

P   **OCOEE RIVER REGIONAL LIBRARY***, (Formerly Fort Loudoun Regional Library Center), 718 George St NW, 37303-2214. SAN 315-7180. Tel: 423-745-5194. Toll Free Tel: 800-624-1982. FAX: 423-745-8086. Web Site: state.tn.us/tsla/regional/FLRL/index.htm. *Dir,* Beth Mercer; E-mail: Beth.Mercer@tn.gov; Staff 8 (MLS 2, Non-MLS 6)
Founded 1939. Pop 439,074; Circ 1,886,988
Jul 2005-Jun 2006 Income $668,450. Mats Exp $665,450
Library Holdings: Bk Vols 264,949
Special Collections: Tennessee Library History Coll (History of Tennessee Regional Service & Public Library Development)
Automation Activity & Vendor Info: (Cataloging) SirsiDynix; (Circulation) SirsiDynix; (ILL) Auto-Graphics, Inc; (OPAC) SirsiDynix
Database Vendor: Gale Cengage Learning
Function: Home delivery & serv to Sr ctr & nursing homes, Homebound delivery serv, ILL available, Libr develop, Prof lending libr, Workshops
Member Libraries: Audrey Pack Memorial Library; Benton Public Library; Blount County Public Library; Calhoun Public Library; Clyde W Roddy Library; Copperhill Public Library; Ducktown Community Library; Edward Gauche Fisher Public Library; Englewood Public Library; Etowah Carnegie Public Library; Graysville Public Library; Greenback Public Library; Harriman Public Library; Lenoir City Public Library; Loudon Public Library; Madisonville Public Library; Meigs County - Decatur Public Library; Niota Public Library; Oliver Springs Public Library; Philadelphia Public Library; Rockwood Public Library; Sweetwater Public Library; Tellico Plains Public Library; Vonore Public Library
Partic in Tenn-Share
Open Mon-Fri 8-4:30
Bookmobiles: 1

C   **TENNESSEE WESLEYAN COLLEGE***, Merner-Pfeiffer Library, 23 Coach Farmer Dr, 37303. (Mail add: PO Box 40, 37371-0040), SAN 315-7202. Tel: 423-746-5250. Interlibrary Loan Service Tel: 423-746-5251. FAX: 423-746-5272. E-mail: library@twcnet.edu. Web Site: www.twcnet.edu/library. *Assoc Dean, Libr & Info Serv,* Sandra Clariday; Tel: 423-746-5249, E-mail: sclariday@twcnet.edu; *Assoc Dir,* Julie Adams; E-mail: adamsj@twcnet.edu; *Pub Serv Librn,* Carolynn Sarah Roy; Tel: 423-252-1103, E-mail: sroy@twcnet.edu; Staff 7 (MLS 3, Non-MLS 4)
Founded 1857. Enrl 793; Fac 52; Highest Degree: Bachelor
Library Holdings: AV Mats 3,550; e-books 30,000; Bk Titles 85,926; Bk Vols 109,699; Per Subs 809
Special Collections: Methodist Church History (Cooke Memorial Coll)
Automation Activity & Vendor Info: (Acquisitions) Innovative Interfaces, Inc; (Cataloging) Innovative Interfaces, Inc; (Circulation) Innovative Interfaces, Inc; (ILL) Innovative Interfaces, Inc; (OPAC) Innovative Interfaces, Inc; (Serials) Innovative Interfaces, Inc
Database Vendor: Alexander Street Press, ARTstor, CredoReference, EBSCOhost, Gale Cengage Learning, JSTOR, netLibrary, Newsbank, OCLC FirstSearch, OCLC WorldCat, Project MUSE, PubMed, SerialsSolutions
Wireless access
Function: Archival coll, E-Reserves, Electronic databases & coll, Handicapped accessible, ILL available, Orientations, Ref serv available, Telephone ref
Partic in Appalachian Col Asn; Lyrasis; Tenn-Share
Open Mon-Fri (Winter) 8am-9pm, Sun 2-8; Mon-Thurs 8-8, Fri (Summer) 8-4
Restriction: Open to pub for ref & circ; with some limitations, Open to students, fac & staff

BEAN STATION

P   **BEAN STATION PUBLIC LIBRARY***, 895 Broadway Dr, 37708. (Mail add: PO Box 100, 37708-0100), SAN 361-011X. Tel: 865-993-3068. FAX: 865-993-3068. *Dir,* Ada Rhea; Staff 1 (Non-MLS 1)
Library Holdings: Bk Vols 9,242
Open Mon, Tues, Thurs & Fri 9-5, Wed 10-6

BEERSHEBA SPRINGS

P   **BEERSHEBA SPRINGS PUBLIC LIBRARY***, Hwy 56, 37305. (Mail add: PO Box 192, 37305-0192), SAN 315-7210. Tel: 931-692-3029. FAX: 931-692-3029. E-mail: beershebalib@blomand.net. *Dir,* Melissa Scruggs
Library Holdings: Bk Vols 3,000
Open Mon-Wed 10-5, Fri 10-4
Friends of the Library Group

BENTON

P   **BENTON PUBLIC LIBRARY***, PO Box 128, 37307-0128. SAN 315-7229. Tel: 423-338-4536. *Dir,* Wannell Beard
Library Holdings: Bk Vols 3,600
Mem of Ocoee River Regional Library
Open Mon, Wed & Fri 9-4:30

BLAINE

P   **BLAINE PUBLIC LIBRARY***, 220 Indian Ridge Rd, 37709. (Mail add: PO Box 66, 37709-0066), SAN 370-4394. Tel: 865-933-0845. FAX: 865-933-0845. E-mail: blnlibr@bellsouth.net. *Dir,* Cindy Chandler
Pop 1,700; Circ 9,081
Library Holdings: CDs 10; DVDs 20; Large Print Bks 150; Bk Vols 6,811; Per Subs 13; Talking Bks 40; Videos 150
Function: CD-ROM, Digital talking bks, Handicapped accessible, Health sci info serv, Homebound delivery serv, ILL available, Music CDs, Online searches, Photocopying/Printing, Prog for children & young adult, Ref serv available, Spoken cassettes & CDs, Spoken cassettes & DVDs, Summer reading prog, Telephone ref
Special Services for the Blind - Aids for in-house use; Bks on cassette; Bks on CD; Talking bks
Open Mon, Wed & Fri 9-5, Tues 9-3

BLOUNTVILLE

J   **NORTHEAST STATE COMMUNITY COLLEGE**, Wayne G Basler Library, 2425 Hwy 75, 37617-6350. (Mail add: PO Box 246, 37617-0246), SAN 376-7922. Tel: 423-354-2429. FAX: 423-323-0254. Web Site: www.northeaststate.edu/library. *Dean,* Duncan A Parsons; E-mail: daparsons@northeaststate.edu; *Pub Serv Librn, Acq,* Annis Evans; *Pub Serv Librn, Outreach,* Christina Peters; *Pub Serv Librn, Per,* Virginia Salmon; *Pub Serv Librn, Tech Serv,* Christopher Demas; *Pub Serv Librn, Tech Serv,* John Grubb; Staff 12.5 (MLS 6, Non-MLS 6.5)
Founded 1966. Enrl 4,423; Fac 320; Highest Degree: Associate
Jul 2011-Jun 2012 Income $952,470. Mats Exp $158,660
Library Holdings: Bk Vols 64,454; Per Subs 322
Automation Activity & Vendor Info: (Cataloging) Innovative Interfaces, Inc; (Circulation) Innovative Interfaces, Inc; (OPAC) Innovative Interfaces, Inc
Wireless access

P   **SULLIVAN COUNTY PUBLIC LIBRARY***, 1655 Blountville Blvd, 37617. (Mail add: PO Box 510, 37617-0510). Tel: 423-279-2714. FAX: 423-279-2836. Web Site: www.wrlibrary.org/sullivan. *Dir,* Theresa McMahan; Tel: 423-279-2715, E-mail: tmcmahan@wrlibrary.org; *Asst Dir,* Amy Lippo; Tel: 423-279-2716, E-mail: alippo@wrlibrary.org; *Br Mgr,* Margaret Elsea; E-mail: melsea@wrlibrary.org; *Asst Br Mgr,* June Feathers; *Cat,* Ellen Price; *Cat,* Fran Pyeatt; Staff 6 (MLS 1, Non-MLS 5)
Founded 1946. Pop 83,322; Circ 167,196
Library Holdings: Bk Vols 123,354; Per Subs 161
Special Collections: Sullivan County History
Subject Interests: Genealogy, Tenn hist
Automation Activity & Vendor Info: (Cataloging) SirsiDynix; (Circulation) SirsiDynix
Database Vendor: SirsiDynix
Wireless access
Function: Telephone ref
Mem of Holston River Regional Library
Partic in SouthWest Information Network Group (SWING)
Open Mon, Wed, Fri & Sat 9-5, Tues & Thurs 9-6:30
Friends of the Library Group
Branches: 4
BLOOMINGDALE BRANCH, 3230 Van Horn St, Kingsport, 37660, SAN 360-5132. Tel: 423-288-1310. FAX: 423-288-1310. *Br Mgr,* Angela Taylor; E-mail: ataylor@wrlibrary.org; *Asst Br Mgr,* Karen Matney; Staff 2 (Non-MLS 2)
Pop 87,933; Circ 147,230
Open Mon-Sat 9-5
COLONIAL HEIGHTS BRANCH, 149 Pactolus Rd, Kinsgport, 37663, SAN 360-5191. Tel: 423-239-1100. FAX: 423-239-1100. *Br Mgr,* Jo McDavid; E-mail: jmcdavid@wrlibrary.org; *Asst Br Mgr,* Betty Hill
Founded 1961
Library Holdings: Bk Vols 15,000

Open Mon-Sat 9-5
Friends of the Library Group
SULLIVAN GARDENS BRANCH, 104 Bluegrass Dr, Kingsport, 37660,
SAN 360-5221. Tel: 423-349-5990. FAX: 423-349-5990. *Br Mgr,* Peggy
Sutherland; E-mail: psutherland@wrlibrary.org; *Asst Br Mgr,* Nancy
Shelton; E-mail: nshelton@wrlibrary.org
Open Mon-Sat 9-5
Friends of the Library Group
THOMAS MEMORIAL BRANCH, 481 Cedar St, Bluff City, 37618, SAN
360-5167. Tel: 423-538-1980. FAX: 423-538-1980. *Br Mgr,* Kathryn
Nichols; E-mail: knichols@wrlibrary.org; *Asst Br Mgr,* Position Currently
Open
Open Mon-Sat 9-5
Friends of the Library Group

BOLIVAR

P   BOLIVAR-HARDEMAN COUNTY LIBRARY, 213 N Washington St,
38008-2020. SAN 315-7237. Tel: 731-658-3436. Administration Tel:
731-658-9045. FAX: 731-658-4660. Web Site: www.hardemanlibrary.org.
Dir, Louise Manhein; E-mail: louise@hardemanlibrary.org; *Local Hist
Librn,* Janette Tigner. Subject Specialists: *Theol,* Louise Manhein;
Genealogy, Local hist, Janette Tigner; Staff 1 (MLS 1)
Founded 1952. Pop 24,451
Jul 2012-Jun 2013 Income (Main Library Only) $154,450, City $74,136,
County $80,314. Sal $90,130 (Prof $24,500)
Library Holdings: AV Mats 8,374; DVDs 586; Large Print Bks 3,292; Bk
Vols 41,522; Per Subs 75; Talking Bks 1,947; Videos 3,588
Special Collections: Quinnie Armour Books Rare Civil War Coll, bks;
Roy Black Book Coll
Subject Interests: Genealogy, Local hist
Automation Activity & Vendor Info: (Acquisitions) Follett Software;
(Cataloging) Follett Software; (Circulation) Follett Software; (ILL)
Auto-Graphics, Inc; (OPAC) Auto-Graphics, Inc
Database Vendor: Auto-Graphics, Inc, OCLC FirstSearch
Wireless access
Function: Story hour, Tax forms, VHS videos, Web-catalog
Mem of Hatchie River Regional Library
Open Mon & Wed-Fri 8-5, Tues 8-7, Sat 9-4
Friends of the Library Group

BRENTWOOD

P   THE BRENTWOOD LIBRARY*, A Center for Fine Arts, 8109 Concord
Rd, 37027. SAN 325-092X. Tel: 615-371-0090. Circulation Tel:
615-371-0090, Ext 8070. Reference Tel: 615-371-0090, Ext 8200.
Administration Tel: 615-371-0090, Ext 8000. FAX: 615-371-2238. E-mail:
reference@brentwood-tn.org. Web Site: www.brentwood-tn.org/library. *Dir,*
Susan Earl; Tel: 615-371-0090, Ext 8010, E-mail: earls@brentwood-tn.org;
Head, Ref & Acq, Mary Barksdale; Tel: 615-371-0090, Ext 8130, E-mail:
barksdalem@brentwood-tn.org; *Ref & Teen Librn,* Cara Huwieler; Tel:
615-371-0090, Ext 8130, E-mail: huwielerc@brentwood-tn.org; *Ref Librn,
Spec Coll Librn,* Holly Hebert; Tel: 615-371-0090, Ext 8230, E-mail:
heberth@brentwood-tn.org; *Libr Serv Mgr,* Missy Dillingham; Tel:
615-371-0090, Ext 8380, E-mail: dillinghamm@brentwood-tn.org; *Circ
Serv Supvr,* Heather Lanier; Tel: 615-371-0090, Ext 8600, E-mail:
lanierh@brentwood-tn.org; Staff 33 (MLS 7, Non-MLS 26)
Founded 1978. Pop 37,060; Circ 678,533
Jul 2010-Jun 2011 Income $2,259,720, City $2,102,770, County $71,950,
Other $85,000. Mats Exp $351,000, Books $203,500, Per/Ser (Incl. Access
Fees) $10,000, AV Mat $83,500, Electronic Ref Mat (Incl. Access Fees)
$54,000. Sal $890,945
Library Holdings: AV Mats 28,334; CDs 10,456; DVDs 17,878;
Electronic Media & Resources 60; Bk Vols 202,467; Per Subs 200
Special Collections: Art Lending Library; Brentwood Local History
Automation Activity & Vendor Info: (Acquisitions) SIRSI WorkFlows;
(Cataloging) SIRSI WorkFlows; (Circulation) SIRSI WorkFlows; (ILL)
SIRSI WorkFlows; (OPAC) SIRSI WorkFlows; (Serials) SIRSI WorkFlows
Database Vendor: 3M Library Systems, Baker & Taylor, Booklist Online,
BWI, EBSCOhost, Evanced Solutions, Inc, Gale Cengage Learning, Ingram
Library Services, LearningExpress, Newsbank, OCLC FirstSearch, OCLC
WorldCat, Overdrive, Inc, ProQuest, ReferenceUSA, TumbleBookLibrary,
World Book Online
Wireless access
Partic in Nashville Area Libr Alliance; Tenn-Share
Open Mon-Thurs 9-8, Fri 9-6, Sat 10-6, Sun 1-6
Friends of the Library Group

BRICEVILLE

P   BRICEVILLE PUBLIC LIBRARY*, 921 Andy's Ridge Rd, 37710. (Mail
add: PO Box 361, 37710-0361), SAN 315-7245. Tel: 865-426-6220. FAX:
865-426-6220. E-mail: bricevillepubliclibrary@comcast.net. Web Site:
www.orgsites.com/tn/briceville-public-library. *Dir,* Lynette C Seeber; *Asst
Librn,* Daphne Windham
Library Holdings: Bk Vols 3,000

Automation Activity & Vendor Info: (Cataloging) Brodart; (Circulation)
Brodart
Function: ILL available
Open Mon-Fri 12-6
Friends of the Library Group

BRISTOL

M   BRISTOL REGIONAL MEDICAL CENTER LIBRARY, One Medical
Park Blvd, 37621-8964. SAN 377-5410. Tel: 423-844-4440. FAX:
423-844-4443. E-mail: library@wellmont.org. *Librn,* Sharon Brown;
E-mail: sharon.brown@wellmont.org
Library Holdings: Bk Vols 1,000; Per Subs 150
Partic in Med Libr Asn, Southern Chapter; SEND; Tennessee Health
Science Library Association
Open Mon-Fri 8-4:30

C   KING COLLEGE*, The E W King Library, 1350 King College Rd, 37620.
SAN 315-727X. Tel: 423-652-4716. Interlibrary Loan Service Tel:
423-652-4795. Administration Tel: 423-652-4791. FAX: 423-652-4871.
E-mail: library@king.edu. Web Site: www.king.edu/library. *Dir,* Julie A
Roberson; Tel: 423-652-6301, E-mail: jarobers@king.edu; *Electronic Serv
Librn,* Andrea Coles; Tel: 423-652-4897, E-mail: aacoles@king.edu; *Access
Serv,* Crystal L Davidson; E-mail: cldavids@king.edu; *Access Serv,* Sean
Taylor; Tel: 423-652-4790, E-mail: sctaylor@king.edu; *Acq of
Monographs,* Anna P Slagle; E-mail: apslagle@king.edu; *Info Serv Spec,*
James Wilcox; Tel: 423-224-3379, E-mail: jawilcox@king.edu; *Ref & Libr
Instruction,* Jenny Horton; Tel: 423-652-6325, E-mail: jlhorton@king.edu;
Tech Serv, Betty Curtis; Tel: 423-652-4792, E-mail: becurtis@king.edu;
Staff 8 (MLS 3, Non-MLS 5)
Founded 1867. Enrl 1,500; Fac 90; Highest Degree: Master
Library Holdings: Bk Vols 94,080; Per Subs 463
Special Collections: Southern Presbyterian History Coll
Subject Interests: Bus, Classics, Educ, Lit, Missiology, Nursing, Relig
studies
Automation Activity & Vendor Info: (Acquisitions) Innovative Interfaces,
Inc; (Cataloging) Innovative Interfaces, Inc; (Circulation) Innovative
Interfaces, Inc; (Course Reserve) Innovative Interfaces, Inc; (ILL)
Innovative Interfaces, Inc; (Media Booking) Innovative Interfaces, Inc;
(OPAC) Innovative Interfaces, Inc; (Serials) Innovative Interfaces, Inc
Database Vendor: EBSCOhost, Gale Cengage Learning, LexisNexis,
OCLC FirstSearch
Wireless access
Publications: Accession List; Library Brochure; Library Newsletter;
Subject Bibliographies
Partic in Holston Associated Librs Consortium
Open Mon-Thurs 7:30am-Midnight, Fri 8-5, Sat 11-6, Sun 2-Midnight

BROWNSVILLE

P   ELMA ROSS PUBLIC LIBRARY*, 1011 E Main St, 38012-2652. SAN
315-7288. Tel: 731-772-9534. FAX: 731-772-5416. E-mail:
elmarosslibrary@bellsouth.net. *Dir,* Katherine Lee Horn; *Asst Dir,* Sherry
Glidewell; Staff 2 (MLS 2)
Founded 1910. Pop 19,797; Circ 34,950
Jul 2005-Jun 2006 Income $109,853, City $52,323, County $57,530. Mats
Exp $8,941, Books $7,446, Per/Ser (Incl. Access Fees) $1,495. Sal $67,169
(Prof $53,177)
Library Holdings: Large Print Bks 500; Bk Vols 27,000; Per Subs 60;
Talking Bks 300
Special Collections: Disadvantaged Grant-Core Careers; Literacy Bank for
Adults
Subject Interests: Genealogy, W Tenn genealogy
Automation Activity & Vendor Info: (Cataloging) Follett Software;
(Circulation) Follett Software; (ILL) Auto-Graphics, Inc
Database Vendor: Gale Cengage Learning
Partic in Tenn Share
Open Mon 10-8, Tues-Fri 10-5, Sat 1-5
Friends of the Library Group

BYRDSTOWN

P   PICKETT COUNTY PUBLIC LIBRARY*, 79 Pickett Square Annex,
38549. SAN 315-730X. Tel: 931-864-6281. FAX: 931-864-7078. E-mail:
pickettlib@twlakes.net. Web Site: www.pickettlibrary.org. *Dir,* Laura
Winningham
Founded 1961. Circ 12,000
Library Holdings: Bk Titles 12,000; Per Subs 13
Automation Activity & Vendor Info: (Circulation) Book Systems, Inc
Mem of Falling Water River Regional Library
Open Mon-Fri 8:30-5, Sat 9-2
Friends of the Library Group

CALHOUN

P CALHOUN PUBLIC LIBRARY, 746 Hwy 163, 37309. (Mail add: PO Box 115, 37309-0115), SAN 315-7318. Tel: 423-336-2348. FAX: 423-336-1527. E-mail: calhoun_c@bellsouth.net. *Dir,* Kristi Swafford
Library Holdings: Bk Titles 5,000; Per Subs 12
Automation Activity & Vendor Info: (Acquisitions) LibraryWorld, Inc; (Cataloging) LibraryWorld, Inc; (Circulation) LibraryWorld, Inc
Database Vendor: LibraryWorld, Inc
Wireless access
Mem of Ocoee River Regional Library
Open Mon 9-6, Wed 9-5, Tues & Thurs 9-8

CAMDEN

P BENTON COUNTY PUBLIC LIBRARY*, 121 S Forrest Ave, 38320-2055. SAN 315-7326. Tel: 731-584-4772. FAX: 731-584-1098. E-mail: bentoncolibrary@bellsouth.net. Web Site: www.bcpl-tn.org. *Dir,* Position Currently Open; *Children/Youth Librn,* Susan Tyner; *Circ Librn,* Janet Wooden; *Circ/Bk Proc Librn,* Hildegard Needes; *Computer Lab Librn/Circ,* Jessica Milligan; *Tech/Cat Librn,* Linda Wyatt
Pop 16,000
Special Collections: Benton County Genealogy & History Coll
Automation Activity & Vendor Info: (Cataloging) ComPanion Corp; (Circulation) ComPanion Corp; (OPAC) ComPanion Corp
Wireless access
Mem of Obion River Regional Library
Open Mon, Wed, Fri & Sat 9-5, Tues & Thurs 9-8
Friends of the Library Group
Branches: 1
BIG SANDY BRANCH, 12 Front St, Big Sandy, 38221. (Mail add: PO Box 115, Big Sandy, 38221-0115), SAN 377-7464. Tel: 731-593-0225. FAX: 731-593-0226. *Br Mgr,* Elizabeth Cooper
Library Holdings: Bk Vols 5,000
Automation Activity & Vendor Info: (Cataloging) Winnebago Software Co; (Circulation) Winnebago Software Co
Open Mon-Fri 9-5
Friends of the Library Group

CARTHAGE

P SMITH COUNTY PUBLIC LIBRARY*, 215 Main St N, 37030. SAN 360-5345. Tel: 615-735-1326. FAX: 615-735-2317. E-mail: smithpubliclibrary@comcast.net. *Dir,* Elaine West; E-mail: elainesmithlibrary@comcast.net
Pop 15,356
Library Holdings: Large Print Bks 500; Bk Vols 22,000; Per Subs 32; Talking Bks 150; Videos 1,000
Subject Interests: Genealogy
Automation Activity & Vendor Info: (Acquisitions) Book Systems, Inc; (Cataloging) Book Systems, Inc; (Circulation) Book Systems, Inc; (OPAC) Book Systems, Inc
Mem of Falling Water River Regional Library
Open Mon 8-4:30, Tues 8-6, Wed-Fri 8-4, Sat 9-12
Branches: 1
GORDONSVILLE BRANCH, 63 E Main St, Gordonsville, 38563-0217. (Mail add: PO Box 217, Gordonsville, 38563-0217), SAN 360-537X. Tel: 615-683-8063. FAX: 615-683-8063. E-mail: grdlib@COMCAST.NET. *Br Mgr,* Kay Bennett
Library Holdings: AV Mats 150; Bk Vols 6,000; Per Subs 14
Open Mon, Tues, Thurs & Fri 8:30-4:30, Wed 8:30-12

CARYVILLE

P CARYVILLE PUBLIC LIBRARY*, 4839 Old Hwy 63, Ste 2, 37714-4105. SAN 315-7334. Tel: 423-562-1108. FAX: 423-562-1096. E-mail: caypl@comcast.net. Web Site: caryvillepubliclibrary.org. *Dir,* Robyn Turner
Founded 1966. Pop 2,500; Circ 13,500
Library Holdings: Bk Titles 9,000; Per Subs 16
Automation Activity & Vendor Info: (Acquisitions) Book Systems, Inc; (Cataloging) Book Systems, Inc; (Circulation) Book Systems, Inc; (ILL) Book Systems, Inc
Wireless access
Function: Bks on cassette, Bks on CD, Computers for patron use, Copy machines, Free DVD rentals, Handicapped accessible, ILL available, Music CDs, OverDrive digital audio bks, Prog for children & young adult, Pub access computers, Spoken cassettes & CDs, Spoken cassettes & DVDs, Story hour, Summer reading prog, Tax forms, VHS videos, Wheelchair accessible
Partic in Tenn-Share
Special Services for the Deaf - Bks on deafness & sign lang
Special Services for the Blind - Bks on CD
Open Mon-Fri 9-1 & 2-6
Restriction: Borrowing requests are handled by ILL
Friends of the Library Group

CELINA

P CLAY COUNTY PUBLIC LIBRARY, 116 Guffey St, 38551-9802. SAN 315-7342. Tel: 931-243-3442. FAX: 931-243-4876. E-mail: claycountylibrary@hotmail.com. Web Site: sites.google.com/site/claycountypubliclibrary. *Dir,* Judith Cutright; Staff 2 (Non-MLS 2)
Pop 7,676; Circ 92,458
Jul 2007-Jun 2008 Income $69,076. Mats Exp $8,000. Sal $34,126
Library Holdings: Audiobooks 886; Bks on Deafness & Sign Lang 10; CDs 661; DVDs 1,753; Bk Titles 22,400; Per Subs 45; Talking Bks 502; Videos 1,959
Automation Activity & Vendor Info: (Circulation) Book Systems, Inc; (ILL) Auto-Graphics, Inc
Database Vendor: Ingram Library Services
Wireless access
Mem of Falling Water River Regional Library
Open Mon, Tues, Thurs & Fri 8:30-4:30, Wed 3-8, Sat 9-1
Friends of the Library Group

CENTERVILLE

P HICKMAN COUNTY PUBLIC LIBRARY*, J B Walker Memorial Library, 120 W Swan St, 37033. SAN 315-7350. Tel: 931-729-5130. FAX: 931-729-6950. E-mail: hclib1@bellsouth.net. Web Site: www.hickmancountylibrary.net. *Dir,* Mary B Pruett; *Asst Dir,* David Dansby
Founded 1939
Library Holdings: Bk Vols 22,000; Per Subs 70
Automation Activity & Vendor Info: (Cataloging) Book Systems, Inc; (Circulation) Book Systems, Inc; (Course Reserve) Book Systems, Inc
Database Vendor: Gale Cengage Learning
Open Mon 10:30-7, Tues, Wed & Fri 9-5:30, Thurs & Sat 9-2
Branches: 1
EAST HICKMAN PUBLIC LIBRARY, 5009 Hwy 100, Lyles, 37098, SAN 377-7820. Tel: 931-670-5767. FAX: 931-670-1933. *Dir,* Mary Beth Pruett; *Br Mgr,* Mina Dressler
Open Tues, Wed & Fri 9:30-5, Thurs 11-7, Sat 9-2

CHARLESTON

S OLIN CORP*, Information Resource Center, 1186 Lower River Rd, 37310. (Mail add: PO Box 248, 37310), SAN 327-8565. Tel: 423-336-4347. Reference Tel: 423-336-4481. FAX: 423-336-4194. *Mgr, Libr Serv,* Connie Jean Upton; E-mail: cjupton@olin.com; *Info Spec,* Nancy Darlene Sneed; E-mail: ndsneed@olin.com; Staff 2 (Non-MLS 2)
Founded 1976
Library Holdings: Bk Titles 5,000; Per Subs 100
Subject Interests: Mkt
Database Vendor: Dialog
Function: Res libr
Restriction: Not open to pub

CHATTANOOGA

SR AMG INTERNATIONAL LIBRARY, 6815 Shallowford Rd, 37421-1755. SAN 375-720X. Tel: 423-894-6060, Ext 262. FAX: 423-510-8074. *Libr Dir, VPres,* Dale Anderson; Tel: 423-894-6060, Ext 238, Fax: 423-894-9511, E-mail: dalea@amgpublishers.com; *Libr Mgr,* Dr Warren Patrick Baker; Tel: 423-894-6060, Ext 254, E-mail: warrenb@amgpublishers.com; Staff 1 (Non-MLS 1)
Library Holdings: Bk Titles 32,000; Bk Vols 32,500
Special Collections: Christian World Pulpit, bd editions
Wireless access
Function: Ref serv available, Res libr
Open Mon-Fri 8-5
Restriction: In-house use for visitors, Not a lending libr, Open to students

P CHATTANOOGA-HAMILTON COUNTY BICENTENNIAL LIBRARY*, 1001 Broad St, 37402-2652. SAN 360-540X. Tel: 423-757-5310. Circulation Tel: 423-757-5315. Interlibrary Loan Service Tel: 423-757-5379. Administration Tel: 423-757-5320. Automation Services Tel: 423-757-0576. FAX: 423-757-4994. Automation Services FAX: 423-757-4854. TDD: 423-757-5053. E-mail: library@lib.chattanooga.gov. Web Site: www.lib.chattanooga.gov. *Interim Dir,* Eva M Johnston; E-mail: johnston_e@lib.chattanooga.gov; *Spec Coll Librn,* Mary Helms; Tel: 423-757-5317, E-mail: helms_m@lib.chattanooga.gov; *Mgr, Main Libr,* Robert Drake; Tel: 423-757-5426, E-mail: drake_robert@lib.chattanooga.gov; *Circ,* Chuck Brown; E-mail: brown_chuck@lib.chattanooga.gov; *Info Serv,* Mary Jane Spehar; Tel: 423-757-5429, E-mail: spehar@lib.chattanooga.gov; Staff 18 (MLS 18)
Founded 1905. Pop 309,936; Circ 820,598
Jul 2010-Jun 2011 Income (Main Library and Branch(s)) $6,106,152, State $107,800, City $2,777,468, County $2,777,468, Locally Generated Income $291,963, Other $148,953. Mats Exp $609,697, Books $308,124, Per/Ser

(Incl. Access Fees) $62,765, AV Mat $74,690, Electronic Ref Mat (Incl. Access Fees) $162,394, Presv $1,724. Sal $3,159,963 (Prof $914,240)
Library Holdings: Audiobooks 6,074; AV Mats 21,347; Bks on Deafness & Sign Lang 129; Braille Volumes 5; CDs 2,978; DVDs 10,961; e-books 1,245; Electronic Media & Resources 46; Large Print Bks 10,835; Microforms 1,407; Music Scores 81; Bk Titles 310,517; Bk Vols 414,296; Per Subs 933; Videos 11,046
Special Collections: Genealogy Coll; Interviews Chattanooga & Hamilton County History; Tennesseana (Tennessee Room Coll), bks & microflm. Oral History
Automation Activity & Vendor Info: (Acquisitions) Polaris Library Systems; (Cataloging) Polaris Library Systems; (Circulation) Polaris Library Systems; (OPAC) Polaris Library Systems; (Serials) Polaris Library Systems
Database Vendor: 3M Library Systems, Auto-Graphics, Inc, Baker & Taylor, BookLetters LLC, CredoReference, EBSCO Auto Repair Reference, EBSCO Information Services, EBSCOhost, Gale Cengage Learning, H W Wilson, infoUSA, Ingram Library Services, LearningExpress, LexisNexis, McGraw-Hill, OCLC WorldCat, Overdrive, Inc, Polaris Library Systems, ProQuest, ReferenceUSA, TumbleBookLibrary
Wireless access
Publications: A Brief Guide to Genealogical Materials; Bibliographies; Friends of the Library Newsletter; Volumes (Bi-monthly)
Partic in Lyrasis; OCLC Online Computer Library Center, Inc
Special Services for the Deaf - Bks on deafness & sign lang; Captioned film dep; High interest/low vocabulary bks
Open Mon & Tues 9-9, Wed & Thurs 9-7, Fri & Sat 9-6
Friends of the Library Group
Branches: 4
EASTGATE, 5900 Bldg, 5705 Marlin Rd, Ste 1500, 37411, SAN 360-5434. Tel: 423-757-5310. Circulation Tel: 423-855-2689. FAX: 423-855-2696. *Librn,* Margaret Curtis; Tel: 423-855-2686, E-mail: curtis_m@lib.chattanooga.gov
   Library Holdings: Bk Vols 37,271
   Open Mon-Thurs & Sat 9-6
NORTHGATE, 520 Northgate Mall, 37415-6924, SAN 360-5469. Tel: 423-757-5310. Circulation Tel: 423-870-0635. FAX: 423-870-0619. *Librn,* Carol Green; Tel: 423-870-0632, E-mail: green_c@lib.chattanooga.gov
   Library Holdings: Bk Vols 43,871
   Open Mon-Thurs & Sat 9-6
OOLTEWAH-COLLEGEDALE, 9318 Apison Pike, Ooltewah, 37363, SAN 372-784X. Tel: 423-757-5310. Circulation Tel: 423-396-9300. FAX: 423-396-9334. *Librn,* Joanne Stanfield; Tel: 423-396-9223, E-mail: stanfield_j@lib.chattanooga.gov
   Library Holdings: Bk Vols 47,400
   Open Mon-Fri 9-6
SOUTH CHATTANOOGA, 925 W 39th St, 37410, SAN 360-5493. Tel: 423-757-5310. FAX: 423-825-7239. *Head of Libr,* Greg DeFriese; E-mail: defriese_g@lib.chattanooga.gov
   Library Holdings: Bk Vols 19,556
   Open Mon-Fri 9-6

J   CHATTANOOGA STATE COMMUNITY COLLEGE, Augusta R Kolwyck Library, 4501 Amnicola Hwy, 37406-1097. SAN 315-7369. Tel: 423-697-4448. Interlibrary Loan Service Tel: 423-697-2577. Reference Tel: 423-697-4436. FAX: 423-697-4409. Web Site: library.chattanoogastate.edu. *Dean,* Susan L Jennings; Tel: 423-697-2576, E-mail: susan.jennings@chattanoogastate.edu; *Access Serv,* Tisa Houck; E-mail: tisa.houck@chattanoogastate.edu; *Tech Serv,* Pamela P Temple; Tel: 423-697-3291, E-mail: pamela.temple@chattanoogastate.edu; Staff 7 (MLS 7)
Founded 1965. Fac 500; Highest Degree: Associate
Library Holdings: AV Mats 5,606; Bk Titles 55,414; Bk Vols 67,802; Per Subs 314; Talking Bks 521
Subject Interests: Allied health, Environ sci, Law, Off automation
Automation Activity & Vendor Info: (Acquisitions) Ex Libris Group; (Cataloging) Ex Libris Group; (Circulation) Ex Libris Group; (Course Reserve) Ex Libris Group; (ILL) OCLC; (Media Booking) Ex Libris Group; (OPAC) Ex Libris Group; (Serials) Ex Libris Group
Database Vendor: Alexander Street Press, Career Guidance Foundation, Discovery Education, EBSCOhost, Gale Cengage Learning, JSTOR, LexisNexis, netLibrary, OCLC FirstSearch, Oxford Online, ProQuest, STAT!Ref (Teton Data Systems), Wilson - Wilson Web
Wireless access
Partic in Lyrasis; TBR Consortium; Tenn-Share
Special Services for the Deaf - Bks on deafness & sign lang; Captioned film dep; High interest/low vocabulary bks
Special Services for the Blind - Talking bks

S   CHATTANOOGA TIMES FREE PRESS LIBRARY*, 400 E 11th St, 37403. (Mail add: PO Box 1447, 37401), SAN 324-1009. Tel: 423-757-6238. Circulation Tel: 423-757-6200. FAX: 423-668-5067. Web Site: www.timesfreepress.com. *Librn,* Jackie Punneo

Founded 1963
Library Holdings: Bk Titles 200; Bk Vols 400
Subject Interests: Clippings dealing with local nat news, Photog dealing with local nat news
Database Vendor: LexisNexis, ProQuest
Restriction: Not open to pub

C   ELECTRONIC COMPUTER PROGRAMMING COLLEGE INC LIBRARY*, 3805 Brainerd Rd, 37411. SAN 375-443X. Tel: 423-624-0077. FAX: 423-624-1575. Web Site: ecpconline.com. *Dir,* Bill Faour; E-mail: billf@ecpconline.com; *Librn,* Gayla C Brewer; Staff 1 (MLS 1)
Library Holdings: Bk Vols 3,500; Per Subs 10; Videos 122
Special Collections: Travel & Tourism Coll, videos
Subject Interests: Computer sci, Electronics, Travel tourism
Open Mon, Tues & Thurs 8:30am-9:30pm, Wed 8:30-5, Fri 8:30-1:30

M   ERLANGER HEALTH SYSTEM LIBRARY*, 975 E Third St, 37403. SAN 360-5523. Tel: 423-778-7246. Interlibrary Loan Service Tel: 423-778-6525. FAX: 423-778-7247. E-mail: library@erlanger.org. Web Site: www.erlanger.org. *Mgr,* Langhorne Waterhouse; E-mail: langhorne.waterhouse@erlanger.org; Staff 4 (MLS 1, Non-MLS 3)
Founded 1940
Library Holdings: Bk Vols 9,000; Per Subs 320
Special Collections: History of Medicine Coll
Subject Interests: Cancer, Hospital admin, Med, Nursing, Orthopedics, Pediatrics, Plastic surgery, Surgery
Automation Activity & Vendor Info: (Cataloging) Follett Software; (Circulation) Follett Software; (OPAC) Follett Software
Publications: LibNews (Newsletter)
Partic in Docline; Lyrasis; Tennessee Health Science Library Association
Open Mon-Fri 8-4

R   FIRST CENTENARY UNITED METHODIST CHURCH LIBRARY*, 419 McCallie Ave, 37402. (Mail add: PO Box 208, 37401-0208), SAN 328-6282. Tel: 423-756-2021. FAX: 423-266-9742. Web Site: www.firstcentenary.com.
Founded 1967
Library Holdings: Bk Vols 2,000
Partic in CSLA
Open Mon-Fri 8-4:30

GL   HAMILTON COUNTY GOVERNMENTAL LAW LIBRARY*, City County Courts Bldg, 600 Market St, Rm 305, 37402. SAN 315-7393. Tel: 423-209-7595. FAX: 423-209-7596. *Librn,* Martha Wilson
Founded 1953
Library Holdings: Bk Vols 13,000
Special Collections: Federal & State Codes Coll; West Reporter Coll
Open Mon-Thurs 9-4, Fri 10-2

S   HOUSTON MUSEUM OF DECORATIVE ARTS*, 201 High St, 37403. SAN 315-7407. Tel: 423-267-7176. FAX: 423-267-7177. E-mail: houston@chattanooga.net. Web Site: www.thehoustonmuseum.com. *Dir,* Amy Frierson
Founded 1961
Library Holdings: Bk Vols 550
Restriction: Not open to pub, Staff use only

S   HUNTER MUSEUM OF ART*, Reference Library, Ten Bluff View, 37403-1197. SAN 315-7415. Tel: 423-267-0968. FAX: 423-267-9844. Web Site: huntermuseum.org. *Chief Curator,* Ellen Simak
Founded 1959
Library Holdings: Bk Titles 1,300; Bk Vols 1,500; Per Subs 38
Subject Interests: Am art, Antiques, Archit
Open Mon, Tues, Fri & Sat 10-5, Wed & Sun 12-5, Thurs 10-8

L   MILLER & MARTIN PLLC*, Law Library, Volunteer Bldg, Ste 1000, 832 Georgia Ave, 37402-2289. SAN 372-1841. Tel: 423-756-6600. Toll Free Tel: 800-275-7303. FAX: 423-785-8480. Web Site: www.millermartin.com. *Libr Serv Dir,* Gail Sisson; E-mail: gsisson@millermartin.com; *Librn,* Virginia Hughes; E-mail: ghughes@millermartin.com; Staff 2 (MLS 1, Non-MLS 1)
Library Holdings: Bk Vols 30,000; Per Subs 20; Videos 200
Subject Interests: Corporate, Employment, Labor, Litigation, Real estate
Restriction: Not open to pub

     MOCCASIN BEND MENTAL HEALTH INSTITUTE
M   HEALTH SCIENCES LIBRARY*, 100 Moccasin Bend Rd, 37405, SAN 360-5612. Tel: 423-785-3365. FAX: 423-785-3364. *Librn,* Ione Crowe; E-mail: ione.crowe@state.tn.us
Founded 1961
Library Holdings: Bk Vols 1,000; Per Subs 50

Subject Interests: Activity therapy, Nursing, Pastoral counseling, Pharmacology, Psychiat, Psychol, Sociol
Partic in Chattanooga Health Educ Libr Prog; Southeastern Regional Med Libr Program
Open Mon-Fri 8-4:30

M   PATIENT LIBRARY*, 100 Moccasin Bend Rd, 37405, SAN 360-5647. Tel: 423-785-3365. FAX: 423-785-3364. *Librn,* Ione Crowe; E-mail: ione.crowe@state.tn.us
Library Holdings: Bk Vols 3,000
Partic in Tennessee Health Science Library Association
Open Mon-Fri 8-4:30

S   NATIONAL MODEL RAILROAD ASSOCIATION*, A C Kalmbach Memorial Library, 4121 Cromwell Rd, 37421-2119. SAN 373-871X. Tel: 423-894-8144. FAX: 423-899-4869. E-mail: lib@hq.nmra.org. Web Site: www.nmra.org/library. *Dir,* Brent L Lambert; *Res Serv,* Thomas Mossbeck
Founded 1986
Library Holdings: Bk Titles 7,000; Per Subs 250; Videos 900
Special Collections: Kentlein-Porter Coll, data, photos, recs; Model Railroad Kit Instructions & Catalogs (Walthers Coll); Nashville, Chattanooga & Saint Louis Railway Blueprint Coll
Subject Interests: Railroads
Open Mon-Fri 8:30-5
Restriction: Not a lending libr
Friends of the Library Group

CR   RICHMONT GRADUATE UNIVERSITY*, Poindexter Library, 1815 McCallie Ave, 37404-3026. Tel: 423-648-2408. Toll Free Tel: 888-267-4073. FAX: 423-265-7375. E-mail: library@psy.edu. Web Site: richmont.edu/services/libraries. *Assoc Dir of Libr,* Ron Bunger; E-mail: rbunger@richmont.edu; Staff 2 (MLS 1, Non-MLS 1)
Enrl 55; Highest Degree: Master
Library Holdings: AV Mats 47,000; e-books 14,126; e-journals 17,185; Bk Vols 16,657; Per Subs 13; Videos 4,000
Automation Activity & Vendor Info: (Cataloging) Follett Software; (Circulation) Follett Software; (ILL) OCLC Connexion; (Media Booking) Follett Software; (OPAC) Follett Software
Database Vendor: American Psychological Association (APA), EBSCOhost, netLibrary, ProQuest
Wireless access
Open Mon-Thurs 8:30-5:30, Fri 8:30-4:30, Sat 9-12

CR   TENNESSEE TEMPLE UNIVERSITY*, Cierpke Memorial Library, 1815 Union Ave, 37404. SAN 315-7423. Tel: 423-493-4250. Circulation Tel: 423-493-4253. Reference Tel: 423-493-4252. Administration Tel: 423-493-4251. FAX: 423-493-4497. E-mail: cierpke@prodigy.net. Web Site: www.tntemple.edu/library. *Dir, ILL Librn, Ref Librn,* Kevin Wayne Woodruff; E-mail: woodruk@tntemple.edu. Subject Specialists: *Bible, Greek,* Kevin Wayne Woodruff; Staff 2 (MLS 1, Non-MLS 1)
Founded 1946. Enrl 325; Fac 30; Highest Degree: Doctorate
Library Holdings: e-journals 1,000; Bk Vols 196,000; Per Subs 50
Special Collections: Rare Out of Print Books; Religious Education Materials
Subject Interests: Arts, Relig studies, Sci
Automation Activity & Vendor Info: (Acquisitions) Ex Libris Group; (Cataloging) Ex Libris Group; (Circulation) Ex Libris Group; (ILL) OCLC; (OPAC) Ex Libris Group
Database Vendor: American Psychological Association (APA), EBSCOhost, Gale Cengage Learning, OCLC ArticleFirst, OCLC FirstSearch, OCLC WorldCat, OCLC-RLG, ProQuest
Wireless access
Partic in Lyrasis
Special Services for the Deaf - Staff with knowledge of sign lang
Open Mon, Tues & Thurs 9am-11pm, Wed & Fri 9-5, Sat 1-5
Friends of the Library Group

G   TENNESSEE VALLEY AUTHORITY*, Research Library-Chattanooga, 1101 Market St, LP 4A-C, 37402. SAN 315-7431. Tel: 423-751-4913. FAX: 423-751-4914. E-mail: corplibchatt@tva.gov. *Librn,* Ann Holder; *Acq, Cat,* Kathy Moree; Staff 2 (MLS 1, Non-MLS 1)
Founded 1957
Library Holdings: Bk Titles 25,000; Bk Vols 35,000; Per Subs 20
Subject Interests: Electric power production, Electric power transmission, Environ studies, River operations
Function: Res libr
Publications: Desktop Library News (Monthly newsletter); Nuclear Power Current Awareness List (Monthly); Power Current Awareness List (Monthly)
Partic in OCLC Online Computer Library Center, Inc
Open Mon-Fri 8-4:45
Restriction: External users must contact libr, Limited access for the pub

C   UNIVERSITY OF TENNESSEE AT CHATTANOOGA LIBRARY*, T Cartter & Margaret Rawlings Lupton Library, 615 McCallie Ave, Dept 6456, 37403-2598. SAN 315-744X. Tel: 423-425-4501. Reference Tel:

423-425-4510. Administration Tel: 423-425-4506. FAX: 423-425-4775. Web Site: www.lib.utc.edu. *Dean,* Theresa Liedtka; Tel: 423-425-4506, E-mail: theresa-liedtka@utc.edu; *Asst Dean, Head, Mat Proc,* Michael Bell; E-mail: mike-bell@utc.edu; *Head, Access Serv,* Colleen Harris; E-mail: colleen-harris@utc.edu; *Head, Info Tech,* Jason Griffey; E-mail: jason-griffey@utc.edu; *Head, Ref,* Virginia Cairns; E-mail: virginia-cairns@utc.edu; *Instrul Design Librn,* Caitlin Shanley; E-mail: caitlin-shanley@utc.edu; *ILL Librn,* Melanie Dunn; E-mail: melanie-dunn@utc.edu; *Ref & Instruction Librn,* Bo Baker; E-mail: bo-baker@utc.edu; *Ref & Instruction Librn,* Lane Wilkinson; E-mail: lane-wilkinson@utc.edu; *Ref & Instruction Librn,* Beverly Simmons; E-mail: beverly-simmons@utc.edu; *Ref Serv Librn,* Sarla Murgai; E-mail: sarla-murgai@utc.edu; *Coordr, Cat,* Valarie Adams; E-mail: valarie-adams@utc.edu; *Electronic Res,* Charles Remy; E-mail: charles-remy@utc.edu; *Ref & Libr Instruction,* Priscilla Seaman; E-mail: priscilla-seaman@utc.edu; *Spec Coll & Archives Librn,* Steven Cox; E-mail: steven-cox@utc.edu; *Web Serv,* Andrea Schurr; E-mail: andrea-schurr@utc.edu; Staff 31 (MLS 17, Non-MLS 14)
Founded 1872. Enrl 10,781; Fac 403; Highest Degree: Doctorate
Jul 2010-Jun 2011. Mats Exp $1,285,071. Sal $1,235,411 (Prof $803,619)
Library Holdings: AV Mats 20,327; Microforms 1,312,167; Bk Titles 459,132; Bk Vols 516,293; Per Subs 9,946
Subject Interests: Civil War, Local hist, Southern lit
Automation Activity & Vendor Info: (Acquisitions) VTLS, Inc; (Cataloging) VTLS, Inc; (Circulation) VTLS, Inc; (Course Reserve) VTLS, Inc; (ILL) OCLC ILLiad; (OPAC) VTLS, Inc; (Serials) VTLS, Inc
Database Vendor: 3M Library Systems, ARTstor, Cambridge Scientific Abstracts, Dialog, EBSCOhost, Gale Cengage Learning, JSTOR, LexisNexis, OCLC FirstSearch, OCLC WorldCat, OVID Technologies, ProQuest, SerialsSolutions, STAT!Ref (Teton Data Systems), Swets Information Services, Westlaw, Wiley, Wilson - Wilson Web
Wireless access
Publications: Annual Statistical Report
Partic in Lyrasis; OCLC Online Computer Library Center, Inc; Tenn Acad Libr Collaborative

CLARKSVILLE

C   AUSTIN PEAY STATE UNIVERSITY*, Felix G Woodward Library, 601 E College St, 37044. (Mail add: PO Box 4595, 37040), SAN 315-7474. Tel: 931-221-7346. Interlibrary Loan Service Tel: 931-221-7679. Toll Free Tel: 800-250-1890. FAX: 931-221-7296. E-mail: librarian@apsu.edu. Web Site: library.apsu.edu. *Dir, Libr Serv,* Joe Weber; Tel: 931-221-7618, E-mail: weberj@apsu.edu; *Database/Network Serv Librn,* Deborah Fetch; Tel: 931-221-7617, E-mail: fetchd@apsu.edu; *Digital Serv Librn,* Gina Garber; Tel: 931-221-7028, E-mail: garberg@apsu.edu; *Electronic Res Librn,* Michael Hooper; Tel: 931-221-7092, E-mail: hooperm@apsu.edu; *Instruction Librn,* Christina Chester-Fangman; Tel: 931-221-1267, E-mail: chester-fangmanc@apsu.edu; *Instruction Librn,* Inga A Filippo; Tel: 931-221-7381, E-mail: filippoi@apsu.edu; *Instruction Librn,* Sharon Johnson; Tel: 931-221-7914, E-mail: johnsons@apsu.edu; *Instrul Tech Librn,* Nancy Gibson; Tel: 931-221-6166, E-mail: gibsonn@apsu.edu; *Access Serv Coordr,* Elaine W Berg; Tel: 931-221-6405, E-mail: berge@apsu.edu; *Coordr, Instrul Serv,* Philenese H Slaughter; Tel: 931-221-7741, E-mail: slaughterp@apsu.edu; *Libr Assessment Coordr,* Lori E Buchanan; Tel: 931-221-7017, E-mail: buchananl@apsu.edu; *Res Mgt Coordr,* D Sean Hogan; Tel: 931-221-1325, E-mail: HoganD@apsu.edu; Staff 26 (MLS 13, Non-MLS 13)
Founded 1969. Enrl 10,188; Fac 300; Highest Degree: Master
Library Holdings: AV Mats 5,969; e-books 55,000; e-journals 29,000; Microforms 673,000; Bk Titles 193,000; Bk Vols 219,000; Per Subs 695
Special Collections: Clarksville Photograph Coll; Dorothy Dix Coll; Dr Joseph Milton Henry Papers; Robert Penn Warren Coll; The Hillman Papers
Automation Activity & Vendor Info: (Acquisitions) Innovative Interfaces, Inc - Millenium; (Cataloging) Innovative Interfaces, Inc - Millenium; (Circulation) Innovative Interfaces, Inc - Millenium; (Course Reserve) Innovative Interfaces, Inc - Millenium; (ILL) OCLC ILLiad; (OPAC) Innovative Interfaces, Inc - Millenium; (Serials) Innovative Interfaces, Inc - Millenium
Database Vendor: ABC-CLIO, Agricola, Alexander Street Press, American Mathematical Society, ARTstor, Blackwell's, Cambridge Scientific Abstracts, CQ Press, EBSCO Information Services, EBSCOhost, Facts on File, Gale Cengage Learning, H W Wilson, IOP, JSTOR, LexisNexis, netLibrary, Newsbank, OCLC FirstSearch, OCLC WorldCat, OVID Technologies, ProQuest, PubMed, RefWorks, STN International, Westlaw, Wilson - Wilson Web
Wireless access
Partic in Lyrasis; Nashville Area Libr Alliance; Tenn Share
Open Mon-Thurs (Fall & Spring) 7:30am-9pm, Fri 7:30-6, Sat 10-5, Sun 1-9; Mon-Fri (Summer) 7:30-6:30, Sat 10-5, Sun 1-9
Friends of the Library Group

P **CLARKSVILLE-MONTGOMERY COUNTY PUBLIC LIBRARY***, 350 Pageant Lane, Ste 501, 37040. SAN 320-2364. Tel: 931-648-8826. FAX: 931-648-8831. Web Site: www.clarksville.org. *Dir,* Pamela Murphy; E-mail: director@clarksville.org; *Asst Dir,* Martha Hendricks; Staff 20 (MLS 1, Non-MLS 19)
Founded 1894. Pop 147,202; Circ 754,737
Jul 2006-Jun 2007 Income $1,782,067, County $1,527,251, Other $254,816. Mats Exp $313,830, Books $201,960, Per/Ser (Incl. Access Fees) $8,300, Micro $1,200, AV Equip $1,100, AV Mat $64,270, Electronic Ref Mat (Incl. Access Fees) $37,000. Sal $908,561 (Prof $61,016)
Library Holdings: CDs 10,722; DVDs 4,720; Electronic Media & Resources 37; Large Print Bks 4,587; Bk Vols 269,851; Per Subs 128; Videos 12,534
Special Collections: Brown Harvey Genealogy Room; Family & Tennessee History, bks & microfilm
Automation Activity & Vendor Info: (Acquisitions) TLC (The Library Corporation); (Cataloging) TLC (The Library Corporation); (Circulation) TLC (The Library Corporation); (OPAC) TLC (The Library Corporation)
Database Vendor: BWI, EBSCO Information Services, Ingram Library Services, LexisNexis, Newsbank, Overdrive, Inc, ProQuest, TLC (The Library Corporation), WT Cox
Wireless access
Function: Accelerated reader prog, Art exhibits, Audiobks via web, AV serv, Bilingual assistance for Spanish patrons, Bk reviews (Group), Bks on cassette, Bks on CD, CD-ROM, Children's prog, Computer training, Computers for patron use, Copy machines, Digital talking bks, e-mail serv, E-Reserves, Electronic databases & coll, Fax serv, Free DVD rentals, Genealogy discussion group, Handicapped accessible, Holiday prog, ILL available, Mail & tel request accepted, Mail loans to mem, Music CDs, Online cat, Online ref, Online searches, Orientations, Outside serv via phone, mail, e-mail & web, OverDrive digital audio bks, Photocopying/Printing, Prog for adults, Prog for children & young adult, Pub access computers, Ref serv available, Senior computer classes, Spoken cassettes & CDs, Spoken cassettes & DVDs, Tax forms, Teen prog, Telephone ref, VHS videos, Video lending libr, Web-catalog, Wheelchair accessible
Publications: Friends of the Library Newsletter
Mem of Red River Regional Library
Open Mon-Thurs 9-8, Fri & Sat 9-6, Sun 1-5
Restriction: Non-resident fee
Friends of the Library Group

M **GATEWAY MEDICAL CENTER HEALTH SCIENCE LIBRARY***, 651 Dunlop Lane, 37040. (Mail add: PO Box 31629, 37040). Tel: 931-502-2085. FAX: 931-502-2086. *Librn, Libr Dir,* Jennifer Layton; E-mail: Jennifer_Layton@todaysgateway.com; Staff 1 (MLS 1)
Library Holdings: DVDs 116; e-journals 5; Bk Titles 601; Per Subs 27; Videos 123
Automation Activity & Vendor Info: (Cataloging) Marcive, Inc; (Circulation) LibraryWorld, Inc; (OPAC) LibraryWorld, Inc
Database Vendor: EBSCOhost, MD Consult
Function: Computers for patron use, Doc delivery serv, Electronic databases & coll, Handicapped accessible, Health sci info serv, ILL available, Photocopying/Printing
Open Mon-Fri 9-9
Restriction: Badge access after hrs, In-house use for visitors, Lending to staff only, Med & nursing staff, patients & families, Non-circulating to the pub

S **THE LEAF-CHRONICLE CO LIBRARY***, 200 Commerce St, 37040. (Mail add: PO Box 31029, 37040-0018), SAN 327-0998. Tel: 931-245-0274, 931-552-1808, Ext 274. FAX: 931-552-5859. Web Site: www.theleafchronicle.com.
Library Holdings: Bk Vols 200

P **RED RIVER REGIONAL LIBRARY***, (Formerly Warioto Regional Library Center), 1753A Alpine Dr, 37040-6729. SAN 315-7482. Tel: 931-645-9531. FAX: 931-645-6695. *Dir,* Becky Bailey; E-mail: becky.bailey@tn.gov; Staff 8 (MLS 2, Non-MLS 6)
Founded 1947. Pop 339,766; Circ 869,320
Library Holdings: Bk Titles 154,006; Per Subs 60
Automation Activity & Vendor Info: (Acquisitions) Book Systems, Inc; (Cataloging) Book Systems, Inc; (Circulation) Book Systems, Inc
Publications: Word from Warioto (Bi-monthly); Word from Warioto (Newsletter)
Member Libraries: Cheatham County Public Library; Clarksville-Montgomery County Public Library; Dickson County Public Library; Edward Ward Carmack Sumner County Public Library; Gorham-Macbane Public Library; Houston County Public Library; Humphreys County Public Library; Martin Curtis Hendersonville Public Library; Portland Public Library; Stewart County Public Library; White House Inn Library & Museum
Open Mon-Fri 8-4:30

CLEVELAND

P **CLEVELAND BRADLEY COUNTY PUBLIC LIBRARY**, 795 Church St NE, 37311-5295. SAN 315-7490. Tel: 423-472-2163. FAX: 423-339-9791. E-mail: info@clevelandlibrary.org. Web Site: www.clevelandlibrary.org. *Dir,* Andrew Hunt; E-mail: director@clevelandlibrary.org; *Coordr, Info Tech,* David Ingram; E-mail: david@clevelandlibrary.org; *Vols Serv Coordr,* Mary Ellen Stinchfield; E-mail: volunteers@clevelandlibrary.org; *Ch,* Parks Keisha; *Circ,* Toni Swink; E-mail: tswink@clevelandlibrary.org; *Ref,* Wilbertine Scott; E-mail: wscott@clevelandlibrary.org; *Tech Serv,* Misty Eubank; E-mail: meubank@clevelandlibrary.org; Staff 9 (MLS 4, Non-MLS 5)
Founded 1923. Pop 98,963; Circ 421,792
Jul 2011-Jun 2012 Income (Main Library and Branch(s)) $1,251,008, State $2,943, City $567,933, Federal $2,670, County $567,933, Locally Generated Income $74,738, Other $34,791. Mats Exp $201,807, Books $83,625, Per/Ser (Incl. Access Fees) $7,848, AV Mat $27,331, Electronic Ref Mat (Incl. Access Fees) $27,212. Sal $693,453
Library Holdings: Audiobooks 7,175; AV Mats 7,972; e-books 25,553; Electronic Media & Resources 7; Microforms 4,150; Bk Vols 133,743; Per Subs 154
Special Collections: Corn Cherokee Coll; Tennessee Genealogy Coll. Oral History
Subject Interests: Cherokee Indians
Automation Activity & Vendor Info: (Cataloging) TLC (The Library Corporation); (Circulation) SIRSI WorkFlows; (ILL) Auto-Graphics, Inc; (OPAC) SIRSI-iBistro
Database Vendor: CountryWatch, EBSCO Auto Repair Reference, EBSCOhost, ProQuest, TumbleBookLibrary, Westlaw, WT Cox
Wireless access
Function: Archival coll, Art exhibits, Audio & video playback equip for onsite use, Audiobks via web, AV serv, Bk club(s), Bks on cassette, Bks on CD, Children's prog, Computer training, Computers for patron use, Copy machines, Digital talking bks, e-mail serv, Electronic databases & coll, Family literacy, Fax serv, Free DVD rentals, Handicapped accessible, Holiday prog, Homebound delivery serv, ILL available, Mail & tel request accepted, Microfiche/film & reading machines, Music CDs, Outreach serv, OverDrive digital audio bks, Preschool outreach, Preschool reading prog, Prog for adults, Prog for children & young adult, Pub access computers, Ref serv available, Senior computer classes, Spoken cassettes & CDs, Spoken cassettes & DVDs, Story hour, Summer reading prog, Tax forms, Teen prog, Telephone ref, VHS videos
Publications: Friends of the Library Newsletter; Genealogical Books
Special Services for the Deaf - Video & TTY relay via computer
Special Services for the Blind - Bks on cassette; Bks on CD; Closed circuit TV magnifier; Large print bks
Open Mon-Thurs 9-9, Fri & Sat 9-6, Sun 1-5
Restriction: Borrowing requests are handled by ILL, ID required to use computers (Ltd hrs), In-house use for visitors
Friends of the Library Group
Branches: 1
HISTORY BRANCH & ARCHIVES, 833 N Ocoee St, 37311. Tel: 423-479-8367. E-mail: hbranch@clevelandlibrary.org. *Archives Mgr,* Treasure Swanson; Staff 4 (MLS 1, Non-MLS 3)
  Library Holdings: Bk Titles 6,500; Per Subs 25
  Database Vendor: EBSCO Information Services
  Function: Archival coll, Electronic databases & coll, Ref serv available, Telephone ref
  Open Mon 9-12 & 1-8, Tues & Wed 9-12 & 1-5, Thurs 1-8, Fri & Sat 9-2, Sun 1-5
  Restriction: Not a lending libr
Bookmobiles: 1. Libr Dir, Andrew Hunt. Bk titles 2500

J **CLEVELAND STATE COMMUNITY COLLEGE LIBRARY***, 3535 Adkisson Dr, 37312-2813. (Mail add: PO Box 3570, 37320-3570), SAN 376-2947. Tel: 423-478-6209. FAX: 423-478-6255. E-mail: library@clevelandstatecc.edu. Web Site: www.clscc.cc.tn.us/library/index.html. *Dir, Libr Serv,* Mary Evelyn Lynn; E-mail: melynn@clevelandstatecc.edu; *Ref & Instruction Librn,* Alan Goslen; E-mail: agoslen@clevelandstatecc.edu; *Acq, Coll Develop, Ref Serv,* Janet Caruth; E-mail: jcaruth@clevelandstatecc.edu; *Cat,* Sandy Hixson; E-mail: shixson@clevelandstatecc.edu; *Circ,* Terri Engebretson; E-mail: tengebretson@clevelandstatecc.edu; *ILL Coordr,* Slade Scoggins; E-mail: sscoggins@clevelandstatecc.edu; Staff 7 (MLS 3, Non-MLS 4)
Founded 1967. Enrl 2,224; Fac 120; Highest Degree: Associate
Library Holdings: AV Mats 11,662; Bks on Deafness & Sign Lang 15; e-books 30,000; Bk Vols 70,000; Per Subs 210
Special Collections: Bill Breuer Archives. US Document Depository
Subject Interests: Hist, Legal assisting, Nursing
Automation Activity & Vendor Info: (Cataloging) OCLC Connexion; (Circulation) Ex Libris Group; (Course Reserve) Ex Libris Group; (ILL) OCLC WorldCat; (OPAC) Ex Libris Group; (Serials) Ex Libris Group
Database Vendor: Agricola, ARTstor, Baker & Taylor, Cinahl Information Systems, CQ Press, EBSCOhost, Ex Libris Group, Gale Cengage Learning, H W Wilson, Ingram Library Services, JSTOR, Majors, Marcive, Inc,

netLibrary, Newsbank, OCLC FirstSearch, OCLC WorldCat, ProQuest, PubMed, Safari Books Online, SerialsSolutions, Westlaw, Wiley
Wireless access
Function: Distance learning, For res purposes, Games & aids for the handicapped, Govt ref serv, ILL available, Large print keyboards, Photocopying/Printing, Ref serv available
Partic in Lyrasis; Tenn-Share
Special Services for the Blind - Assistive/Adapted tech devices, equip & products
Open Mon-Thurs (Winter) 7:30am-10pm, Fri 7:30-4:30, Sat 10-2; Mon-Thurs (Summer) 7:30-7:30, Fri 7:30-4:30

S   RED CLAY STATE HISTORIC AREA LIBRARY*, 1140 Red Clay Park Rd SW, 37311. SAN 374-7646. Tel: 423-478-0339. FAX: 423-614-7251. *In Charge,* Carol Crabtree
Library Holdings: Bk Vols 600
Subject Interests: Native Am culture, Native Am hist, Native Am lit
Restriction: Not a lending libr, Open to pub for ref only, Open to pub upon request

C   WILLIAM G SQUIRES LIBRARY*, 260 11th St NE, 37311. SAN 315-7512. Tel: 423-614-8550. FAX: 423-614-8555. E-mail: library@leeuniversity.edu. Web Site: www.leeuniversity.edu/library. *Dir,* Barbara McCullough; Tel: 423-614-8567, E-mail: mccullough@leeuniversity.edu; *Asst Dir,* Dr Louis Morgan; E-mail: lmorgan@leeuniversity.edu; *Acq,* Brenda Armstrong; E-mail: barmstrong@leeuniversity.edu; Staff 14 (MLS 6.5, Non-MLS 7.5)
Founded 1941. Enrl 4,300; Fac 175; Highest Degree: Master
Library Holdings: Bk Vols 150,000; Per Subs 400
Special Collections: Dixon Pentecostal Research Center Coll
Subject Interests: Educ, Music, Pentecostalism, Relig studies
Automation Activity & Vendor Info: (Acquisitions) Innovative Interfaces, Inc - Millenium; (Cataloging) OCLC; (Circulation) Innovative Interfaces, Inc - Millenium; (Course Reserve) Innovative Interfaces, Inc - Millenium; (ILL) OCLC; (OPAC) Innovative Interfaces, Inc - Millenium; (Serials) Innovative Interfaces, Inc
Database Vendor: Alexander Street Press, American Chemical Society, American Psychological Association (APA), ARTstor, BCR: Christian Periodical Index, BioOne, CountryWatch, CredoReference, ebrary, EBSCOhost, Gale Cengage Learning, JSTOR, LearningExpress, Newsbank, OCLC FirstSearch, OCLC WorldCat, Plunkett Research, Ltd, Project MUSE, ScienceDirect
Wireless access
Publications: Library Newsletter (Online only)
Partic in Appalachian Col Asn; Lyrasis; OCLC Online Computer Library Center, Inc
Library serves Lee University & Pentecostal Theological Seminary
Open Mon-Thurs 8am-Midnight, Fri 8-8, Sat 11-8, Sun 2-8

CLINTON

P   CLINCH RIVER REGIONAL LIBRARY, 130 N Main St, Ste 2, 37716-3691. SAN 315-7539. Tel: 865-457-0931. FAX: 865-457-8546. *Dir,* Susan Simmons Byrne; E-mail: susan.simmons@tn.gov; Staff 5 (MLS 2, Non-MLS 3)
Founded 1946
Automation Activity & Vendor Info: (Cataloging) Auto-Graphics, Inc
Function: Prof lending libr, Workshops
Restriction: Not open to pub

P   CLINTON PUBLIC LIBRARY, 118 S Hicks St, 37716-2826. SAN 315-7547. Tel: 865-457-0519. FAX: 865-457-4233. E-mail: clinton_library@comcast.net. Web Site: www.clintonpubliclibrary.org. *Dir,* Essy Day; Staff 9 (MLS 2, Non-MLS 7)
Founded 1898. Pop 28,970; Circ 97,170
Jul 2011-Jun 2012 Income $254,400, City $80,400, County $159,000, Locally Generated Income $15,000
Library Holdings: Bk Vols 50,400; Per Subs 61
Special Collections: Genealogy Research Coll
Automation Activity & Vendor Info: (Acquisitions) Auto-Graphics, Inc; (Cataloging) Auto-Graphics, Inc; (Circulation) Auto-Graphics, Inc; (Media Booking) Auto-Graphics, Inc; (OPAC) Auto-Graphics, Inc
Database Vendor: Auto-Graphics, Inc, Gale Cengage Learning
Wireless access
Function: Adult bk club, Audiobks via web, Bk club(s), Bks on CD, Children's prog, Computer training, Computers for patron use, Copy machines, E-Reserves, Electronic databases & coll, Family literacy, Fax serv, Free DVD rentals, Handicapped accessible, ILL available, Microfiche/film & reading machines, Online cat, Online ref, Online searches, OverDrive digital audio bks, Photocopying/Printing, Preschool outreach, Preschool reading prog, Prog for adults, Prog for children & young adult, Pub access computers, Ref serv available, Ref serv in person, Spanish lang bks, Story hour, Summer & winter reading prog, Summer reading prog, Tax forms, Teen prog, Web-catalog, Wheelchair accessible, Winter reading prog, Workshops

Special Services for the Deaf - Adult & family literacy prog; Bks on deafness & sign lang
Special Services for the Blind - Large print bks
Open Mon-Thurs 10-7, Fri 10-5, Sat 10-3
Friends of the Library Group

COALFIELD

P   COALFIELD PUBLIC LIBRARY*, 112 Jerry Jones, 37719. (Mail add: PO Box 97, 37719-0097). Tel: 865-435-4275. FAX: 865-435-4275. E-mail: coalfieldlibrary@yahoo.com. *Dir,* Leota Hawks
Library Holdings: Bk Vols 10,000
Open Tues & Thurs 2-8, Fri 10-4, Sat 10-2

COALMONT

P   COALMONT PUBLIC LIBRARY, 7426 State Rte 56, 37313-0334. (Mail add: PO Box 334, 37313-0334), SAN 376-6993. Tel: 931-592-9373. FAX: 931-592-9373. *Dir,* Brinda Franceine Adams; Staff 1 (Non-MLS 1)
Founded 1960. Pop 2,500; Circ 2,500
Library Holdings: Bk Vols 6,000
Automation Activity & Vendor Info: (Cataloging) Surpass; (Circulation) Surpass; (ILL) Auto-Graphics, Inc
Wireless access
Function: Computers for patron use, Copy machines, e-mail & chat, e-mail serv, Electronic databases & coll, Fax serv, Free DVD rentals, Handicapped accessible, ILL available, Online cat, Online searches, OverDrive digital audio bks, Photocopying/Printing, Prog for children & young adult, Pub access computers, Serves mentally handicapped consumers, Story hour, Summer reading prog, Wheelchair accessible
Partic in Tenn Share
Open Mon 11-5, Wed & Thurs 10-5
Restriction: Authorized patrons

COLLEGEDALE

C   SOUTHERN ADVENTIST UNIVERSITY*, McKee Library, 4851 Industrial Dr, 37315. (Mail add: PO Box 629, 37315-0629), SAN 360-5671. Tel: 423-236-2788. Interlibrary Loan Service Tel: 423-236-2791. Reference Tel: 423-236-2794. FAX: 423-236-1788. Web Site: library.southern.edu. *Dir of Libr,* Genevieve Cottrell; Tel: 423-236-2795, E-mail: gcottrell@southern.edu; *Bibliog Instr, Pub Serv,* Marge Seifert; E-mail: meseifrt@southern.edu; *Distance Educ, ILL,* Ann Greer; Tel: 423-236-2791, E-mail: atgreer@southern.edu; *Electronic Res,* Daniel Maxwell; Tel: 423-236-2009, E-mail: dmaxwell@southern.edu; *Media Spec, Reserves,* Frank Di Memmo; Tel: 423-236-2727, E-mail: dimemmo@southern.edu; *Per,* Patricia Beaman; Tel: 423-236-2789, E-mail: pbeaman@southern.edu; *Syst Adminr,* Ron Miller; Tel: 423-236-2796, E-mail: rsmiller@southern.edu; *Tech Serv,* Stanley Cottrell; Tel: 423-236-2798, E-mail: scottrell@southern.edu; Staff 11 (MLS 6, Non-MLS 5)
Founded 1890. Enrl 2,153; Fac 120; Highest Degree: Master
Library Holdings: AV Mats 6,410; Bks on Deafness & Sign Lang 100; e-books 25,000; Bk Vols 154,987; Per Subs 1,047
Special Collections: Abraham Lincoln (Dr Vernon Thomas Memorial Coll), bks, letters, mss, newsp, pamphlets, pictures, maps, paintings & artifacts; Civil War (Dr Vernon Thomas Memorial Coll), bks, letters, mss, newsp, pamphlets, pictures & maps; Seventh Day Adventist Church Publications, bks, per, micro & archives
Subject Interests: Bus, Computing, Educ, Nursing, Relig
Automation Activity & Vendor Info: (Acquisitions) Ex Libris Group; (Cataloging) Ex Libris Group; (Circulation) Ex Libris Group; (Course Reserve) Ex Libris Group; (ILL) OCLC WorldCat; (OPAC) Ex Libris Group; (Serials) Ex Libris Group
Database Vendor: ARTstor, EBSCOhost, Gale Cengage Learning, JSTOR, LexisNexis, netLibrary, OCLC FirstSearch, OCLC WorldCat, OVID Technologies, ProQuest, ScienceDirect, SerialsSolutions, STN International, Wilson - Wilson Web
Wireless access
Partic in Adventist Librs Info Coop; Lyrasis; OCLC Online Computer Library Center, Inc; Tenn-Share
Open Mon-Thurs (Fall & Winter) 8am-11pm, Fri 8-12, Sun Noon-11; Mon-Thurs (Summer) 9-9, Fri 9-Noon, Sun 2-9

COLLIERVILLE

P   LUCIUS E & ELSIE C BURCH LIBRARY*, Collierville Burch Library, 501 Poplar View Pkwy, 38017. SAN 378-4428. Tel: 901-457-2600. Circulation Tel: 901-457-2602. Reference Tel: 901-457-2601. FAX: 901-854-5893. Web Site: www.colliervillelibrary.org. *Dir,* Deanna Britton; E-mail: dbritton@ci.collierville.tn.us; *Head, Ad Ref Serv,* Kathryn Leache; *Head, Circ,* Rachel Carder; *Head, Youth Serv,* Jodi Hall; Staff 14.417 (MLS 3, Non-MLS 11.417)
Founded 1956. Pop 45,152; Circ 345,914
Library Holdings: Bk Vols 113,785

Automation Activity & Vendor Info: (Acquisitions) Polaris Library Systems; (Cataloging) Polaris Library Systems; (Circulation) Polaris Library Systems; (ILL) Polaris Library Systems; (OPAC) Polaris Library Systems
Database Vendor: Baker & Taylor, EBSCO Information Services, Gale Cengage Learning, LearningExpress, OCLC, Overdrive, Inc, ProQuest
Wireless access
Function: Adult bk club, Art exhibits, Audiobks via web, Bk club(s), Bks on CD, CD-ROM, Children's prog, Computer training, Computers for patron use, Copy machines, Digital talking bks, Electronic databases & coll, Exhibits, Games & aids for the handicapped, Handicapped accessible, Holiday prog, ILL available, Libr develop, Magnifiers for reading, Mus passes, Online cat, Online searches, Orientations, Outreach serv, OverDrive digital audio bks, Photocopying/Printing, Preschool outreach, Prog for adults, Prog for children & young adult, Pub access computers, Ref & res, Ref serv available, Ref serv in person, Scanner, Senior computer classes, Story hour, Summer reading prog, Tax forms, Teen prog, Telephone ref, Visual arts prog, Web-catalog, Wheelchair accessible, Workshops, Writing prog
Partic in Wolf River Library Consortium
Special Services for the Blind - Accessible computers; Aids for in-house use; Assistive/Adapted tech devices, equip & products; Bks on CD; Computer access aids; Computer with voice synthesizer for visually impaired persons; Copier with enlargement capabilities; HP Scan Jet with photo-finish software; Info on spec aids & appliances; Internet workstation with adaptive software; Large screen computer & software; Large type calculator; Low vision equip; Magnifiers; Mags & bk reproduction/duplication; Open bk software on pub access PC; PC for handicapped; Photo duplicator for making large print; Premier adaptive tech software; Reader equip; Reading & writing aids; Recorded bks; Ref serv; Scanner for conversion & translation of mats; Screen enlargement software for people with visual disabilities; Screen reader software; Talking calculator; Talking machines
Open Mon-Thurs 10-8, Fri & Sat 10-6, Sun 1-5
Restriction: ID required to use computers (Ltd hrs), Non-resident fee, Restricted borrowing privileges
Friends of the Library Group

COLUMBIA

P   BUFFALO RIVER REGIONAL LIBRARY, 104 E Sixth St, 38401-3359. SAN 315-7555. Tel: 931-388-9282. Toll Free Tel: 800-331-8487. FAX: 931-388-1762. *Dir,* Marion K Bryant; E-mail: marion.bryant@tn.gov; *Asst Dir,* Roben Mounger; *Acq, Cat,* Kim Henderson; E-mail: kim.henderson@tn.gov; Staff 4 (MLS 2, Non-MLS 2)
Founded 1954. Pop 461,257
Library Holdings: Audiobooks 1,574; Bk Vols 139,925
Automation Activity & Vendor Info: (Cataloging) Auto-Graphics, Inc; (ILL) Auto-Graphics, Inc
Wireless access
Open Mon-Fri 8-4:30
Restriction: Circ limited

J   COLUMBIA STATE COMMUNITY COLLEGE*, Finney Memorial Library, 1665 Hampshire Pike, 38401. SAN 315-7563. Tel: 931-540-2560. Reference Tel: 931-540-2556. FAX: 931-540-2565. E-mail: library@columbiastate.edu. Web Site: columbiastate.edu/library. *Dir, Libr Serv,* Kathy Breeden; Tel: 931-540-2555, E-mail: breeden@columbiastate.edu; *Cat, ILL,* Lyn Bayless; Tel: 931-540-2559, E-mail: bayless@columbiastate.edu; *Ref Serv,* Anne Scott; Tel: 931-540-2851, E-mail: ascott12@columbiastate.edu; Staff 7 (MLS 3, Non-MLS 4)
Founded 1966. Enrl 4,580
Jul 2010-Jun 2011. Mats Exp $125,100, Books $50,000, Per/Ser (Incl. Access Fees) $10,000, Micro $300, AV Mat $5,000, Electronic Ref Mat (Incl. Access Fees) $60,000. Sal $290,000 (Prof $175,000)
Library Holdings: AV Mats 5,500; e-books 65,000; Bk Vols 72,500; Per Subs 220; Talking Bks 600
Automation Activity & Vendor Info: (Acquisitions) Ex Libris Group; (Cataloging) Ex Libris Group; (Circulation) Ex Libris Group; (Course Reserve) Ex Libris Group; (ILL) OCLC Online; (OPAC) Ex Libris Group; (Serials) Ex Libris Group
Database Vendor: Alexander Street Press, ARTstor, EBSCOhost, Gale Cengage Learning, H W Wilson, netLibrary, Newsbank, Oxford Online, ProQuest, Safari Books Online, Wilson - Wilson Web
Partic in Lyrasis; OCLC Online Computer Library Center, Inc; Tenn-Share
Open Mon-Thurs 7:45am-8pm, Fri 7:45-4:15, Sat 12-4

P   MAURY COUNTY PUBLIC LIBRARY*, 211 W Eighth St, 38401. SAN 360-5701. Tel: 931-375-6501. FAX: 931-375-6519. Web Site: www.maurycountylibrary.org. *Dir,* Elizabeth Potts
Pop 63,888
Library Holdings: Bk Vols 78,808; Per Subs 214
Subject Interests: Genealogy, Local hist, Maury County, Mules, Tenn hist

Open Mon-Wed 8-8, Thurs-Sat 9-5
Friends of the Library Group
Branches: 1
MOUNT PLEASANT BRANCH, 200 Hay Long Ave, Mount Pleasant, 38474. (Mail add: PO Box 71, Mount Pleasant, 38474-0071), SAN 360-5736. Tel: 931-379-3752. FAX: 931-379-3774. *Dir,* Janice Jones
Pop 6,000
Library Holdings: Bk Vols 10,000
Open Mon & Wed 10-9, Tues, Thurs, Fri & Sat 10-5

COOKEVILLE

P   FALLING WATER RIVER REGIONAL LIBRARY*, (Formerly Upper Cumberland Regional Library), 208 E Minnear St, 38501-3949. SAN 315-7598. Tel: 931-526-4016. FAX: 931-528-3311. *Dir,* Faith A Holdredge; E-mail: Faith.Holdredge@tn.gov; Staff 9 (MLS 2, Non-MLS 7)
Founded 1946. Pop 162,561; Circ 723,893
Library Holdings: Bk Vols 119,020
Automation Activity & Vendor Info: (Acquisitions) Book Systems, Inc; (Cataloging) Book Systems, Inc; (Circulation) Book Systems, Inc; (Course Reserve) Book Systems, Inc; (ILL) Book Systems, Inc; (Media Booking) Book Systems, Inc; (OPAC) Book Systems, Inc; (Serials) Book Systems, Inc
Member Libraries: Charles Ralph Holland Memorial Library; Clay County Public Library; Fentress County Public Library; Justin Potter Public Library; Macon County Public Library; Millard Oakley Library; Pickett County Public Library; Putnam County Library System; Smith County Public Library
Open Mon-Fri 8-4:30

P   PUTNAM COUNTY LIBRARY SYSTEM*, 50 E Broad St, 38501. SAN 315-7571. Tel: 931-526-2416. FAX: 931-372-8517. Web Site: www.pclibrary.org. *Dir,* Diane Duncan; E-mail: dianed@pclibrary.org; *Dir, Ch Serv,* Dale Stapp; *Adult Serv, Asst Dir, YA Serv,* Nicole Pugh; *Tech Coordr,* Brian Page; Staff 3 (MLS 2, Non-MLS 1)
Founded 1923. Pop 62,315; Circ 355,000
Library Holdings: AV Mats 8,050; Bk Titles 86,374; Per Subs 139; Talking Bks 3,293
Subject Interests: Genealogy
Automation Activity & Vendor Info: (Cataloging) TLC (The Library Corporation); (Circulation) TLC (The Library Corporation)
Database Vendor: Gale Cengage Learning
Mem of Falling Water River Regional Library
Special Services for the Deaf - TDD equip
Special Services for the Blind - Bks on cassette; Braille bks
Open Mon & Tues 9-8, Wed-Fri 9-6, Sat 10-5, Sun 1-5
Friends of the Library Group
Branches: 3
ALGOOD BRANCH, 125 Fourth Ave, Algood, 38506-5224, SAN 376-7337. Tel: 931-537-3240. FAX: 931-372-8517. E-mail: algood@pclibrary.org. *Br Mgr,* Kathy Keller
Founded 1980
Library Holdings: Bk Titles 1,390; Bk Vols 4,000
Open Mon-Fri 12-4
Friends of the Library Group
BAXTER BRANCH, Baxter City Hall, 200 Main St, Baxter, 38544-0335, SAN 376-8147. Tel: 931-858-1888. E-mail: baxter@pclibrary.org. *Br Mgr,* Sarah Lewis
Founded 1958
Library Holdings: Bk Titles 2,781; Bk Vols 5,000
Open Mon-Fri 12-6
Friends of the Library Group
MONTEREY BRANCH, 401 E Commercial Ave, Monterey, 38574, SAN 376-8155. Tel: 931-839-2103. FAX: 931-839-2103. E-mail: mntlib@pclibrary.org. Web Site: www.pclibrary.org. *Br Mgr,* Doylenne Farley
Library Holdings: Bk Titles 4,215
Open Mon-Fri 10-5, Sat 10-2
Friends of the Library Group

C   TENNESSEE TECHNOLOGICAL UNIVERSITY*, Angelo & Jennette Volpe Library, 1100 N Peachtree Ave, 38505. (Mail add: TTU Campus Box 5066, 38505), SAN 315-758X. Tel: 931-372-3326. Interlibrary Loan Service Tel: 931-372-3710. FAX: 931-372-6112. Web Site: www.tntech.edu/library. *Dean of Libr & Learning Assistance,* Dr Douglas Bates; Tel: 931-372-3408, E-mail: dbates@tntech.edu; *Head, Circ,* Charlene McClain; *Head, Govt Pub, Maps & Micro,* Regina Lee; Tel: 931-372-6105; *Head, ILL,* Sonya Bowman; E-mail: sbowman@tntech.edu; *Bus/Educ/Humanities Librn,* Nancy Mielke; *Cat Librn,* Mei-Xiang Hu; *Distance Learning, Soc Sci Librn,* David Hajdik; *Website Mgr,* April Crockett; *Coordr, Bibliog Control & Libr Automation,* Susan LaFever; Tel: 931-372-6110, E-mail: slafever@tntech.edu; *Coordr, Media Serv,* Patricia B McGee; *Archivist,* Mancil Johnson; *Electronic & Multimedia Spec,* Gary Bradford; *Media Spec,* Ed Beason; Staff 26 (MLS 11, Non-MLS 15)
Founded 1915. Enrl 10,871; Fac 409; Highest Degree: Doctorate

Jul 2008-Jun 2009 Income $3,468,849, State $3,001,804, Federal $55,447, Locally Generated Income $57,744, Other $353,854. Mats Exp $1,295,476, Electronic Ref Mat (Incl. Access Fees) $353,854. Sal $1,127,111 (Prof $668,353)

Library Holdings: AV Mats 38,196; e-books 27,719; e-journals 103,770; Electronic Media & Resources 37; Microforms 1,512,400; Bk Vols 353,405; Per Subs 1,405

Special Collections: Harding Studio Coll; Joe L Evins Coll; Tennessee History Coll; Upper Cumberland History Coll. US Document Depository

Subject Interests: Eng

Automation Activity & Vendor Info: (Acquisitions) Innovative Interfaces, Inc; (Cataloging) Innovative Interfaces, Inc; (Circulation) Innovative Interfaces, Inc; (ILL) OCLC WorldCat; (OPAC) Innovative Interfaces, Inc; (Serials) Innovative Interfaces, Inc

Database Vendor: Cambridge Scientific Abstracts, EBSCO Information Services, Elsevier MDL, Gale Cengage Learning, netLibrary, OVID Technologies, ProQuest, SerialsSolutions, STAT!Ref (Teton Data Systems), Wiley, Wilson - Wilson Web

Wireless access

Partic in Lyrasis; OCLC Online Computer Library Center, Inc; Tenn Share

Special Services for the Blind - ZoomText magnification & reading software

Open Mon-Thurs (Winter) 7:45am-Midnight, Fri 7:45-6, Sat 10-6, Sun 1-Midnight; Mon-Thurs (Summer) 7:30am-10pm, Fri 7:30-4:30, Sun 2-10

Friends of the Library Group

CORDOVA

R   MID-AMERICA BAPTIST THEOLOGICAL SEMINARY*, The Ora Byram Allison Memorial Library, 2095 Appling Rd, 38016. SAN 321-4583. Tel: 901-751-3007. Administration Tel: 901-751-8453. Toll Free Tel: 800-968-4508. FAX: 901-751-8454. *Dir, Libr Serv,* Terrence Neal Brown; E-mail: tbrown@mabts.edu; *Head, Circ,* Mary Teed; Staff 6 (MLS 1, Non-MLS 5)
Founded 1972. Enrl 442; Fac 22; Highest Degree: Doctorate
Library Holdings: Bk Titles 81,758; Bk Vols 150,000; Per Subs 972
Subject Interests: Missions, Semitic lang
Partic in Dialog Corp; Lyrasis; OCLC Online Computer Library Center, Inc
Open Mon-Fri 8-4:30

S   NATIONAL COTTON COUNCIL OF AMERICA LIBRARY, 7193 Goodlett Farms Pkwy, 38016. (Mail add: PO Box 2995, 38088-2995), SAN 315-8748. Tel: 901-274-9030. FAX: 901-725-0510. Web Site: www.cotton.org. *Prog Coordr,* Fred Johnson
Founded 1950
Library Holdings: Bk Vols 500
Special Collections: History of the National Cotton Council. Oral History
Subject Interests: Agr, Biol, Cotton, Econ, Govt
Publications: Cotton's Week
Restriction: Open by appt only

COSBY

P   COSBY COMMUNITY LIBRARY*, 3292 Cosby Hwy, 37722-0052. Tel: 423-487-5885. FAX: 423-487-5885. E-mail: cosbylib@planetc.com. *Dir,* Sandra Foster
Library Holdings: Bk Vols 8,000
Automation Activity & Vendor Info: (Cataloging) Follett Software; (Circulation) Follett Software; (OPAC) Follett Software
Open Mon, Wed & Thurs 12-6

COVINGTON

P   TIPTON COUNTY PUBLIC LIBRARY*, 300 W Church Ave, 38019-2729. SAN 315-761X. Tel: 901-476-8289. FAX: 901-476-0008. E-mail: tiptonpl@covingtontn.com. *Dir,* Susan Cheairs; E-mail: scheairs@covingtontn.com; Staff 1 (Non-MLS 1)
Founded 1938. Pop 58,000
Library Holdings: DVDs 400; Bk Vols 50,000; Per Subs 30
Subject Interests: County genealogy, State
Database Vendor: Inspire, ReferenceUSA
Function: After school storytime, AV serv, Bks on cassette, Bks on CD, Children's prog, Computer training, Computers for patron use, Copy machines, Fax serv, Free DVD rentals, Handicapped accessible, ILL available, Music CDs, Outreach serv, Photocopying/Printing, Preschool outreach, Prog for children & young adult, Pub access computers, Story hour, Summer reading prog, Tax forms, Teen prog, VHS videos, Wheelchair accessible
Open Mon-Fri 9:30-5:30, Sat 9:30-3

CROSSVILLE

P   ART CIRCLE PUBLIC LIBRARY, CUMBERLAND COUNTY*, 154 E First St, 38555-4696. SAN 315-7628. Tel: 931-484-6790. FAX: 931-484-2350. Web Site: www.artcircle.crossville.com. *Libr Serv Dir,* Debra H Kokes; Tel: 931-484-6790, Ext 221, E-mail:

dhkokes@crossville.com; *Dep Dir,* James S Houston; Tel: 931-484-6790, Ext 228, Fax: 931-707-8956, E-mail: jhouston@crossville.com; *Ch,* Patricia J Dalton; E-mail: pjdalton@crossville.com; *Ref Serv,* Margo L Brown; E-mail: mlbrown@crossville.com
Founded 1898. Pop 49,000; Circ 125,000
Jul 2005-Jun 2006 Income $346,892
Library Holdings: Bk Titles 42,000; Per Subs 120
Automation Activity & Vendor Info: (Acquisitions) Book Systems, Inc; (Cataloging) Book Systems, Inc; (Circulation) Book Systems, Inc; (ILL) Auto-Graphics, Inc; (OPAC) Auto-Graphics, Inc
Database Vendor: ProQuest, ReferenceUSA
Open Mon, Tues, Thurs & Fri 8-7, Wed & Sat 8-4
Friends of the Library Group

DANDRIDGE

P   DANDRIDGE MEMORIAL LIBRARY*, 1235 Circle Dr, 37725-4750. (Mail add: PO Box 339, 37725-0339), SAN 315-7636. Tel: 865-397-9758. FAX: 865-397-0950. *Dir,* Billie Jean Chambers; *Asst Dir,* Lois Redmond
Founded 1942. Pop 47,593; Circ 54,862
Jul 2009-Jun 2010 Income $113,416, City $44,787, County $68,242, Other $387. Mats Exp $3,925, Books $3,244, Per/Ser (Incl. Access Fees) $681. Sal $73,419
Library Holdings: Audiobooks 225; AV Mats 826; Bks on Deafness & Sign Lang 11; DVDs 94; Microforms 506; Bk Vols 20,885; Per Subs 45; Talking Bks 720; Videos 945
Subject Interests: Genealogy
Automation Activity & Vendor Info: (Acquisitions) Follett Software; (Cataloging) Follett Software; (Circulation) Follett Software
Database Vendor: Auto-Graphics, Inc
Open Mon & Wed-Fri 7:30-5:30
Friends of the Library Group

DAYTON

C   BRYAN COLLEGE LIBRARY*, 585 Bryan Dr, 37321. (Mail add: PO Box 7000, 37321-7000), SAN 315-7652. Tel: 423-775-7307, FAX: 423-775-7309. Web Site: www.bryan.edu. *Dir,* Laura Kaufmann; Tel: 423-775-7196, E-mail: kaufmala@bryan.edu; *ILL, Pub Serv,* Lavonne Johnson; Tel: 423-775-7228, E-mail: johnsovo@bryan.edu; Staff 2.25 (MLS 2.25)
Founded 1930. Enrl 900; Fac 45; Highest Degree: Bachelor
Library Holdings: Bk Vols 113,000
Automation Activity & Vendor Info: (Cataloging) OCLC; (Circulation) Ex Libris Group; (Course Reserve) Ex Libris Group; (ILL) OCLC; (OPAC) Ex Libris Group; (Serials) SerialsSolutions
Wireless access
Partic in Appalachian Col Asn; Lyrasis; OCLC Online Computer Library Center, Inc; Tenn-Share
Open Mon-Thurs (Winter) 7:45am-11pm, Fri 7:45-5, Sat 1-5, Sun 2-11; Mon-Fri (Summer) 8-4:30

P   CLYDE W RODDY LIBRARY*, 371 First Ave, 37321-1499. SAN 315-7644. Tel: 423-775-8406. FAX: 423-775-8422. *Dir,* Kaye Madewell; E-mail: kmadewell@clydewroddy.org
Library Holdings: Bk Vols 35,000; Per Subs 42
Automation Activity & Vendor Info: (Cataloging) Book Systems, Inc; (Circulation) Book Systems, Inc; (OPAC) Book Systems, Inc
Mem of Ocoee River Regional Library
Open Mon, Wed & Fri 8:30-5, Tues & Thurs 8:30-8:30
Friends of the Library Group

DECATUR

P   MEIGS COUNTY - DECATUR PUBLIC LIBRARY*, 120 E Memorial Dr, 37322. (Mail add: PO Box 187, 37322-0187), SAN 315-7660. Tel: 423-334-3332. FAX: 423-334-1816. E-mail: meigslibrary@hotmail.com. *Dir,* Judith K Reynolds; Staff 2 (Non-MLS 2)
Pop 10,000; Circ 12,000
Library Holdings: Bks on Deafness & Sign Lang 20; Bk Vols 16,000
Automation Activity & Vendor Info: (Cataloging) SirsiDynix; (Circulation) SirsiDynix
Mem of Ocoee River Regional Library
Special Services for the Deaf - TDD equip
Special Services for the Blind - Talking bks
Open Mon & Fri 9-5, Tues-Thurs 9-7, Sat 10-2
Friends of the Library Group

DECATURVILLE

P   DECATUR COUNTY LIBRARY*, Court Sq, 20 W Market St, 38329. (Mail add: PO Box 396, 38329-0396), SAN 315-7679. Tel: 731-852-3325. FAX: 731-852-2351. E-mail: dcldsl@tds.net. Web Site: www.decaturcountylibrary.org. *Dir,* Athalia Boroughs Taylor; E-mail: taylora@decaturcountytn.org; *Cat,* Amber Ruth Taylor; *Circ,* Mildred Crawley; *Circ,* Patty Wyatt; Staff 4 (Non-MLS 4)

Founded 1942. Pop 3,111; Circ 39,630
Jul 2005-Jun 2006 Income $65,300, City $300, Federal $7,000, County $58,000. Mats Exp $11,500, Books $4,500, AV Mat $7,000. Sal $30,386
Library Holdings: Bks on Deafness & Sign Lang 15; Large Print Bks 4,000; Bk Titles 23,000; Per Subs 27; Talking Bks 250
Automation Activity & Vendor Info: (Acquisitions) Follett Software; (Cataloging) Auto-Graphics, Inc; (Circulation) Follett Software
Database Vendor: EBSCOhost, Gale Cengage Learning
Wireless access
Function: Archival coll, Handicapped accessible, Home delivery & serv to Sr ctr & nursing homes, ILL available, Newsp ref libr, Photocopying/Printing, Prog for children & young adult, Summer reading prog, Wheelchair accessible
Mem of Hatchie River Regional Library
Open Mon, Thurs & Fri 10-5, Tues 10-7, Wed 10-2, Sat 9:30-12:30
Friends of the Library Group

DEER LODGE

P   DEER LODGE PUBLIC LIBRARY*, 110 Corrine Ave, 37726-4239. (Mail add: PO Box 37, 37726-0037), SAN 376-7558. Tel: 423-965-3029. E-mail: deerlodgepl@highland.net. *Dir,* Sharon L Waschevski
Pop 2,000; Circ 2,374
Library Holdings: AV Mats 119; Bk Vols 6,000
Open Mon-Thurs 3-6

DEL RIO

P   MARIE ELLISON MEMORIAL LIBRARY*, 480 S Hwy 107, 37727-9625. SAN 370-6737. Tel: 423-487-5929. FAX: 423-487-5929. E-mail: delriolib@planetc.com. *Librn,* Leslie Gibbens
Founded 1984. Circ 5,890
Library Holdings: Bk Titles 8,000
Automation Activity & Vendor Info: (Cataloging) Follett Software; (Circulation) Follett Software
Open Mon, Wed & Fri 12-7

DICKSON

P   DICKSON COUNTY PUBLIC LIBRARY*, 206 Henslee Dr, 37055-2020. SAN 315-7687. Tel: 615-446-8293. FAX: 615-446-9130. *Dir,* Position Currently Open
Founded 1933. Pop 43,017; Circ 102,991
Library Holdings: CDs 6,732; DVDs 8,086; e-books 3,675; Bk Vols 77,488; Per Subs 110
Subject Interests: Genealogy, Local hist
Automation Activity & Vendor Info: (Acquisitions) Book Systems, Inc; (Cataloging) Book Systems, Inc; (Circulation) Book Systems, Inc; (ILL) Book Systems, Inc; (OPAC) Book Systems, Inc; (Serials) Book Systems, Inc
Wireless access
Mem of Red River Regional Library
Open Mon, Wed, Fri & Sat 9-6, Tues & Thurs 9-8, Sun 2-5
Friends of the Library Group

DOVER

P   STEWART COUNTY PUBLIC LIBRARY*, 102 Natcor Dr, 37058. SAN 315-7695. Tel: 931-232-3127. FAX: 931-232-3159. Web Site: www.stewartcountypubliclibrary.com. *Dir,* Pamela Ford; E-mail: pam.ford@mchsi.com; *Asst Dir,* Sandy Brake
Founded 1942
Library Holdings: Bk Titles 31,000; Per Subs 19
Automation Activity & Vendor Info: (Acquisitions) Follett Software; (Cataloging) Follett Software; (Circulation) Follett Software
Wireless access
Mem of Red River Regional Library
Open Mon, Tues & Thurs 8-8, Fri 8-4, Sat 9-3
Friends of the Library Group

DRESDEN

P   NED R MCWHERTER WEAKLEY COUNTY LIBRARY*, 341 Linden St, 38225-1400. SAN 315-7709. Tel: 731-364-2678. FAX: 731-364-2599. E-mail: weakleycolibrary@frontier.com. *Libr Dir,* Candy McAdams; *Principal Asst Librn,* Carol Tippins; *Asst Librn,* Karen Gertsch. Subject Specialists: *Genealogy,* Carol Tippins
Founded 1943. Circ 21,377
Library Holdings: Bk Vols 16,000; Per Subs 27
Special Collections: Ned R McWherter Room
Automation Activity & Vendor Info: (Cataloging) Follett Software; (Circulation) Winnebago Software Co
Wireless access
Mem of Obion River Regional Library
Partic in Tenn-Share

Open Mon-Fri 9-5, Sat 9-2
Friends of the Library Group

DUCKTOWN

P   DUCKTOWN COMMUNITY LIBRARY*, 331 Main St, 37326. (Mail add: PO Box 369, 37326-0369), SAN 315-7717. Tel: 423-496-4004. *Librn,* Diane Meeks
Pop 3,577; Circ 6,281
Library Holdings: Bk Vols 3,411; Videos 184
Mem of Ocoee River Regional Library
Open Tues & Thurs 1:30-4:30

DUNLAP

P   SEQUATCHIE COUNTY PUBLIC LIBRARY*, 227 Cherry St W, 37327-5207. SAN 315-7725. Tel: 423-949-2357. FAX: 423-949-6619. *Dir,* Betty Worley; E-mail: bworley@sequatchiecountylibrary.org; *Asst Dir,* Donna Moore; E-mail: dmoore3@sequatchiecountylibrary.org
Founded 1959. Pop 10,846
Library Holdings: AV Mats 1,626; Bk Vols 16,557
Automation Activity & Vendor Info: (Cataloging) Book Systems, Inc; (Circulation) Book Systems, Inc
Open Mon 8-5:30, Tues & Wed 8-5, Fri 8-4:30, Sat 8-Noon
Friends of the Library Group

DYERSBURG

J   DYERSBURG STATE COMMUNITY COLLEGE*, Learning Resource Center, 1510 Lake Rd, 38024. SAN 315-7733. Tel: 731-286-3225. FAX: 731-286-3228. E-mail: lrc@dscc.edu. Web Site: www.dscc.edu/lrc. *Dean,* Robert Lhota; Tel: 731-286-3226, E-mail: lhota@dscc.edu; *Br Coordr,* Tanga McCullough; Tel: 731-475-3100, Fax: 901-475-0008, E-mail: tanga@dscc.edu; *Mgr, Tech Support,* Crouch Linda; Tel: 731-286-3223, E-mail: crouch@dscc.edu; *Librn,* Teresa Johnson; Tel: 731-286-3352, E-mail: tjohnson@dscc.edu; *Media Spec,* Ken Teutsch; Tel: 731-286-3227, E-mail: teutsch@dscc.edu; *Tech Serv,* Rodney Alford; Tel: 731-286-3272, E-mail: alford@dscc.edu; Staff 6 (MLS 2, Non-MLS 4)
Founded 1969. Enrl 1,800; Fac 55; Highest Degree: Associate
Library Holdings: AV Mats 2,176; e-books 41,000; Bk Vols 43,871; Per Subs 109
Automation Activity & Vendor Info: (Cataloging) Follett Software; (Circulation) Follett Software; (Course Reserve) Follett Software; (OPAC) Follett Software; (Serials) Follett Software
Database Vendor: EBSCOhost, Gale Cengage Learning, LexisNexis, OCLC FirstSearch
Function: Res libr
Partic in Lyrasis; Tenn-Share; West Tennessee Academic Library Consortium
Special Services for the Blind - Assistive/Adapted tech devices, equip & products

P   MCIVER'S GRANT PUBLIC LIBRARY*, 204 N Mill, 38024-4631. SAN 315-7741. Tel: 731-285-5032. FAX: 731-285-9332. E-mail: publib@bellsouth.net. Web Site: mciversgrantpubliclibrary.org. *Dir,* Dara Gonzales
Pop 34,663
Library Holdings: AV Mats 1,100; CDs 775; DVDs 375; Bk Vols 38,000; Per Subs 50; Videos 800
Special Collections: Microfilm of State Gazette; Small Genealogy Coll
Automation Activity & Vendor Info: (Cataloging) Follett Software; (Circulation) Follett Software
Wireless access
Open Mon 10-6, Tues-Sat 10-5

EAST RIDGE

P   EAST RIDGE CITY LIBRARY*, 1517 Tombras Ave, 37412-2716. SAN 315-775X. Tel: 423-867-7323. E-mail: library@eastridgetn.org. Web Site: www.eastridgetn.org. *Dir,* Susan Macrellis; *Asst Dir,* Norine Bolt
Pop 25,000; Circ 15,000
Library Holdings: Bk Vols 20,000; Per Subs 12
Automation Activity & Vendor Info: (Acquisitions) Follett Software; (Cataloging) Follett Software; (Circulation) Follett Software; (Course Reserve) Follett Software; (ILL) Follett Software; (Media Booking) Follett Software; (OPAC) Follett Software; (Serials) Follett Software
Publications: Library Journal; Publisher's Weekly
Open Mon-Thurs 10-8:30, Fri & Sat 10-6, Sun 2-5
Friends of the Library Group

ELIZABETHTON

P   ELIZABETHTON-CARTER COUNTY PUBLIC LIBRARY*, 201 N Sycamore St, 37643. SAN 315-7768. Tel: 423-547-6360. FAX: 423-542-1510. Web Site: www.eccpl.org. *Dir,* Joyce H White; E-mail: jwhite@eccpl.org; *Asst Dir,* Sharon Walker; E-mail: swalker@eccpl.org;

Ch, Ashlee Williams; E-mail: awilliams@eccpl.org; Staff 9 (MLS 1, Non-MLS 8)
Founded 1929. Pop 58,622; Circ 126,188
Library Holdings: Bk Vols 58,639; Per Subs 75
Special Collections: Tennessee History
Automation Activity & Vendor Info: (Acquisitions) Ex Libris Group; (Cataloging) Ex Libris Group; (Circulation) Ex Libris Group; (OPAC) Ex Libris Group
Open Mon & Thurs 10-8, Tues, Wed & Fri 10-6, Sat 10-4
Friends of the Library Group

ENGLEWOOD

P   ENGLEWOOD PUBLIC LIBRARY*, 35 Carroll, 37329. (Mail add: PO Box 834, 37329-0834), SAN 315-7792. Tel: 423-887-7152. E-mail: engpl@comcast.net. *Dir,* Bennie Raper
Library Holdings: Bk Vols 6,000
Mem of Ocoee River Regional Library
Partic in Colorado Library Consortium
Open Mon & Fri 11-5, Tues & Thurs 12-6, Sat 10-4

ERIN

P   HOUSTON COUNTY PUBLIC LIBRARY*, 21 Spring St, 37061-4073. (Mail add: PO Box 183, 37061-0183), SAN 315-7806. Tel: 931-289-3858. FAX: 931-289-4967. *Librn,* Kay French
Pop 6,871
Library Holdings: Bk Vols 14,500; Per Subs 10
Automation Activity & Vendor Info: (Circulation) Follett Software
Mem of Red River Regional Library
Partic in Tenn Libr Asn
Open Mon, Wed & Fri 10-5, Tues & Thurs 9-5, Sat 9-12
Friends of the Library Group

ERWIN

P   UNICOI COUNTY PUBLIC LIBRARY*, 201 Nolichucky Ave, 37650-1237. SAN 315-7814. Tel: 423-743-6533. FAX: 423-743-0275. E-mail: ucpl@wrlibrary.org. Web Site: www.wrlibrary.org/Library/uupage.html. *Dir,* Angie Georgeff; E-mail: ageorgeff@wrlibrary.org; *Circ & Ref,* Leanne Dynneson; *Circ & Ref,* Ruth Van Sickle; *Outreach & Children's Serv,* Pat Barraclough; Staff 5 (MLS 1, Non-MLS 4)
Founded 1921. Pop 17,713; Circ 85,119
Library Holdings: Bk Vols 32,000; Per Subs 10
Special Collections: Unicoi County History Coll
Automation Activity & Vendor Info: (Acquisitions) Innovative Interfaces, Inc; (Cataloging) Innovative Interfaces, Inc; (Circulation) Innovative Interfaces, Inc; (ILL) Innovative Interfaces, Inc; (OPAC) Innovative Interfaces, Inc
Database Vendor: Gale Cengage Learning
Mem of Holston River Regional Library
Special Services for the Blind - Audio mat; Bks on cassette; Bks on CD; Large print bks; Large screen computer & software; Magnifiers
Open Mon-Fri 10-6, Sat 11-3
Restriction: Visually impaired students, teachers & their parents

ETOWAH

P   ETOWAH CARNEGIE PUBLIC LIBRARY*, 723 Ohio Ave, 37331. SAN 315-7822. Tel: 423-263-9475. FAX: 423-263-4271. E-mail: library@cityofetowahtn.com. Web Site: etowahlibrary.com. *Dir,* Lorie Waters; Staff 1 (Non-MLS 1)
Founded 1915. Pop 10,000
Library Holdings: Bk Titles 10,000; Bk Vols 11,000; Per Subs 20
Automation Activity & Vendor Info: (Acquisitions) SirsiDynix; (Cataloging) SirsiDynix; (Circulation) SirsiDynix; (OPAC) SirsiDynix
Mem of Ocoee River Regional Library
Open Mon & Thurs 9:30-8, Tues, Wed & Fri 9:30-5:30, Sat 10-2

FAYETTEVILLE

P   FAYETTEVILLE-LINCOLN COUNTY PUBLIC LIBRARY*, 306 Elk Ave N, 37334. SAN 315-7830. Tel: 931-433-3286. FAX: 931-433-0063. *Dir,* Charlotte Brown; E-mail: charliebrown@fpunet.com
Pop 26,483
Library Holdings: Bk Vols 36,000; Per Subs 50
Automation Activity & Vendor Info: (Acquisitions) Book Systems, Inc; (Cataloging) Book Systems, Inc; (Circulation) Book Systems, Inc; (ILL) Book Systems, Inc; (OPAC) Book Systems, Inc
Wireless access
Mem of Stones River Regional Library
Open Mon-Sat 8-5
Friends of the Library Group

FRANKLIN

P   WILLIAMSON COUNTY PUBLIC LIBRARY*, 1314 Columbia Ave, 37064-3626. SAN 360-5760. Tel: 615-794-3105. Circulation Tel: 615-595-1277. Reference Tel: 615-595-1243. Administration Tel: 615-595-1250. Automation Services Tel: 615-595-1241. FAX: 615-595-1245. Circulation FAX: 615-595-1202. Reference FAX: 615-595-1247. Automation Services FAX: 615-595-1203. E-mail: ref@williamson-tn.org. Web Site: lib.williamson-tn.org. *Dir,* Dolores Greenwald; Tel: 615-595-1240, E-mail: dgreenwald@williamson-tn.org; *Asst Dir,* Julie Duke; Tel: 615-595-1281, E-mail: jduke@williamson-tn.org; *Assoc Dir, Tech Serv,* Kathy Ossi; E-mail: kossi@williamson-tn.org; *Main Libr Coordr,* Mrs Jeffie Nicholson; Tel: 615-595-1269, E-mail: jnicholson@williamson-tn.org; Staff 27 (MLS 14, Non-MLS 13)
Founded 1927. Pop 106,780; Circ 593,838
Jul 2009-Jun 2010 Income (Main Library and Branch(s)) $1,547,041. Mats Exp $147,534, Books $88,228, Per/Ser (Incl. Access Fees) $8,000, AV Mat $37,772, Electronic Ref Mat (Incl. Access Fees) $13,534
Library Holdings: AV Mats 1,653; Bks on Deafness & Sign Lang 236; CDs 555; DVDs 4,536; e-books 7,187; Electronic Media & Resources 14; High Interest/Low Vocabulary Bk Vols 591; Large Print Bks 3,436; Bk Vols 160,598; Per Subs 171; Talking Bks 5,921; Videos 4,813
Special Collections: African-American Genealogy & Photograph Coll; Civil War Coll; Edythe Rucker Whitley Historical & Genealogical Coll; Local Authors Coll; Williamson County Local History & Genealogy
Automation Activity & Vendor Info: (Acquisitions) Innovative Interfaces, Inc; (Cataloging) Innovative Interfaces, Inc; (Circulation) Innovative Interfaces, Inc; (ILL) Auto-Graphics, Inc; (OPAC) Innovative Interfaces, Inc
Database Vendor: Facts on File, Gale Cengage Learning, Hoovers, Innovative Interfaces, Inc, ProQuest, ValueLine
Wireless access
Function: Adult bk club, Archival coll, Art exhibits, Bi-weekly Writer's Group, Bk club(s), Bks on cassette, Bks on CD, Chess club, Children's prog, Computer training, Computers for patron use, Digital talking bks, Electronic databases & coll, Exhibits, Fax serv, Free DVD rentals, Handicapped accessible, Holiday prog, ILL available, Large print keyboards, Magnifiers for reading, Mail & tel request accepted, Notary serv, Online cat, Online ref, Outside serv via phone, mail, e-mail & web, OverDrive digital audio bks, Photocopying/Printing, Prog for adults, Prog for children & young adult, Pub access computers, Ref serv in person, Scanner, Spoken cassettes & CDs, Story hour, Summer reading prog, Tax forms, Teen prog, Telephone ref, VHS videos, Workshops
Publications: Community Service Directory of Williamson County
Open Mon-Thurs 9-8, Fri & Sat 9-5:30, Sun 1-5:30
Restriction: Registered patrons only
Friends of the Library Group
Branches: 5
BETHESDA, 4905 Bethesda Rd, Thompson Station, 37179-9231, SAN 372-3992. Tel: 615-790-1887. FAX: 615-790-8426. *Br Head,* Susan Fisher; E-mail: sfisher@williamson-tn.org; Staff 1 (Non-MLS 1)
    Library Holdings: Bk Vols 11,172
    Open Tues, Wed & Fri 9:30-5:30, Thurs 11-7, Sat 10-2
    Friends of the Library Group
COLLEGE GROVE COMMUNITY, 8607 Horton Hwy, College Grove, 37046. Tel: 615-368-3222. E-mail: collegegrovelib@williamson-tn.org. Web Site: lib.williamson-tn.org/CollegeGrove/collegegrove.htm. *Br Head,* Janice Bobo; Tel: 615-776-5490, E-mail: jbobo@williamson-tn.org
    Library Holdings: Bk Vols 2,500
    Open Mon & Wed-Fri 9-5, Tues 1-7
    Friends of the Library Group
FAIRVIEW BRANCH, 2240 Fairview Blvd, Fairview, 37062-9011, SAN 360-5825. Tel: 615-224-6087. FAX: 615-799-1399. *Br Head,* Kathy Grimenstein; E-mail: kgrimenstein@williamson-tn.org; Staff 1 (MLS 1)
    Library Holdings: Bk Vols 19,778
    Function: Satellite serv
    Open Tues & Thurs 9-7, Wed & Fri 9-5:30, Sat 9-5
    Friends of the Library Group
LEIPER'S FORK, 5333 Old Hwy 96, 37064-9357, SAN 370-0011. Tel: 615-794-7019. FAX: 615-591-6976. *Br Head,* Emily Anglin; E-mail: eanglin@williamson-tn.org; Staff 1 (Non-MLS 1)
    Library Holdings: Bk Vols 12,053
    Open Tues, Wed & Fri 10-6, Thurs 11-7, Sat 10-4
    Friends of the Library Group
NOLENSVILLE BRANCH, 915 Oldham Dr, Nolensville, 37135. (Mail add: PO Box 577, Nolensville, 37135-0577), SAN 328-7181. Tel: 615-776-5490. FAX: 615-776-3626. *Br Head,* Janice Bobo; E-mail: jbobo@williamson-tn.org; Staff 1 (Non-MLS 1)
    Library Holdings: Bk Vols 15,754
    Open Tues, Wed & Fri 9-6, Thurs 10-7, Fri 10-6, Sat 9-3
    Friends of the Library Group

GAINESBORO

P   CHARLES RALPH HOLLAND MEMORIAL LIBRARY*, Jackson
     County Public Library, 205 West Hull Ave, 38562. (Mail add: PO Box
     647, 38562), SAN 315-7849. Tel: 931-268-9190. FAX: 931-268-5706.
     E-mail: jacksonctylibrary@yahoo.com. *Dir,* Mary Cooper
     Founded 1959. Pop 11,211
     Library Holdings: Bk Vols 11,000; Per Subs 36
     Special Collections: Local History. Oral History
     Mem of Falling Water River Regional Library
     Open Mon-Fri 9:30-4:30, Sat 10-3

GALLATIN

P   EDWARD WARD CARMACK SUMNER COUNTY PUBLIC
     LIBRARY*, 658 Hartsville Pike, 37066-2509. SAN 315-7857. Tel:
     615-452-1722. FAX: 615-451-3319. E-mail: ewclib@bellsouth.net. *Librn,*
     Judy Baggett; *Ch,* Patience Cole
     Pop 33,400; Circ 67,766
     Library Holdings: Bk Vols 35,000; Per Subs 25
     Special Collections: Oral History
     Automation Activity & Vendor Info: (Cataloging) Book Systems, Inc;
     (Circulation) Book Systems, Inc
     Publications: College for this Community; Daniel Smith; James
     Winchester
     Mem of Red River Regional Library
     Open Tues & Thurs 10-7, Wed & Fri 9-5, Sat 9-3
     Friends of the Library Group

J   VOLUNTEER STATE COMMUNITY COLLEGE LIBRARY, Learning
     Resources Center, 1480 Nashville Pike, 37066-3188. SAN 324-7783. Tel:
     615-230-3400. Circulation Tel: 615-230-3402. Reference Tel:
     615-230-3405. Toll Free Tel: 888-335-8722. FAX: 615-230-3410. E-mail:
     librarian@volstate.edu. Web Site: www.volstate.edu/library. *Coll Develop,
     Dir,* Louise R Kelly; Tel: 615-230-3400, Ext 3412, E-mail:
     louise.kelly@volstate.edu; *Instrul Serv Librn, Ref Serv,* Livy I Simpson;
     Tel: 615-230-3400, Ext 3414, E-mail: livy.simpson@volstate.edu;
     Automated Syst Coordr, Cataloger, ILL Librn, Julie G Brown; Tel:
     615-230-3400, Ext 3438, E-mail: julie.brown@volstate.edu; *Acq,* Donna
     Warden; Tel: 615-230-3400, Ext 3407, E-mail: donna.warden@volstate.edu;
     Admin Serv, Victoria G Comer; Tel: 615-230-3400, Ext 3496, E-mail:
     vicki.comer@volstate.edu; *Circ Serv,* Phillip Hailey; Tel: 615-230-3400,
     Ext 3402, E-mail: phillip.hailey@volstate.edu; *Circ Serv,* Michael
     Hitzelberger; Tel: 615-230-3400, Ext 3409, E-mail:
     michael.hitzelberger@volstate.edu; *Circ Serv,* Ann Kirkpatrick; Tel:
     615-230-3400, Ext 3402, E-mail: ann.kirkpatrick@volstate.edu; *Circ Serv,*
     Rebecca Loftis; Tel: 615-230-3400, Ext 3409, E-mail:
     rebecca.loftis@volstate.edu; *Distance Educ, Electronic Res,* Jane K
     Armour; Tel: 615-230-3400, Ext 3406, E-mail: jane.armour@volstate.edu;
     Pub Serv, Lynda A Vincent; Tel: 615-230-3400, Ext 3415, E-mail:
     lynda.vincent@volstate.edu; *Tech Serv,* Marguerite Voorhies; Tel:
     615-230-3400, Ext 3404, E-mail: marguerite.voorhies@volstate.edu; Staff
     12 (MLS 4, Non-MLS 8)
     Founded 1971. Enrl 8,177; Fac 155; Highest Degree: Associate
     Jul 2011-Jun 2012 Income $756,996. Mats Exp $191,884, Books $47,169,
     Per/Ser (Incl. Access Fees) $28,942, Micro $8,900, AV Mat $10,718,
     Electronic Ref Mat (Incl. Access Fees) $94,967, Presv $1,188. Sal
     $480,822 (Prof $255,081)
     Library Holdings: AV Mats 2,018; e-books 150,000; Bk Titles 43,837;
     Per Subs 175
     Automation Activity & Vendor Info: (Acquisitions) Innovative Interfaces,
     Inc - Millenium; (Cataloging) Innovative Interfaces, Inc - Millenium;
     (Circulation) Innovative Interfaces, Inc - Millenium; (Course Reserve)
     Innovative Interfaces, Inc - Millenium; (ILL) OCLC FirstSearch; (OPAC)
     Innovative Interfaces, Inc - Millenium; (Serials) Innovative Interfaces, Inc -
     Millenium
     Database Vendor: Alexander Street Press, ARTstor, CQ Press,
     EBSCOhost, Facts on File, Gale Cengage Learning, JSTOR, netLibrary,
     Newsbank, OCLC FirstSearch, Oxford Online, ProQuest, Westlaw
     Wireless access
     Function: Audio & video playback equip for onsite use, Bks on CD,
     Computers for patron use, Copy machines, Distance learning, Doc delivery
     serv, e-mail serv, Electronic databases & coll, Handicapped accessible, ILL
     available, Instruction & testing, Libr develop, Magnifiers for reading, Mail
     & tel request accepted, Online cat, Online info literacy tutorials on the web
     & in blackboard, Online ref, Online searches, Orientations, Outside serv
     via phone, mail, e-mail & web, Pub access computers, Ref & res, Ref serv
     available, Ref serv in person, Scanner, Telephone ref, VHS videos,
     Wheelchair accessible
     Partic in Nashville Area Libr Alliance; Tenn Share
     Special Services for the Deaf - Assistive tech; Bks on deafness & sign
     lang; Closed caption videos
     Special Services for the Blind - Accessible computers; Aids for in-house
     use; Audio mat; Bks on CD; Cassette playback machines; Computer with
     voice synthesizer for visually impaired persons; Copier with enlargement

capabilities; Internet workstation with adaptive software; Magnifiers; PC
for handicapped; Screen enlargement software for people with visual
disabilities; ZoomText magnification & reading software
Open Mon-Thurs (Fall & Spring) 7:30am-9pm, Fri 7:30-4:30, Sat 8-4;
Mon-Thurs (Summer) 7:30am-9pm, Fri 7:30-4:30, Sat 8-Noon
Restriction: Borrowing requests are handled by ILL, Non-circulating coll

GATLINBURG

P   ANNA PORTER PUBLIC LIBRARY*, 207 Cherokee Orchard Rd,
     37738-3417. SAN 315-7873. Tel: 865-436-5588. FAX: 865-436-5588. Web
     Site: www.annaporterpl.org. *Dir,* Kenton Temple; E-mail:
     kt@annaporterpl.org; Staff 4 (MLS 1, Non-MLS 3)
     Pop 4,000
     Library Holdings: Bk Titles 27,000; Per Subs 56
     Special Collections: Crafts; Smoky Mountain Region
     Automation Activity & Vendor Info: (Cataloging) Follett Software;
     (Circulation) Follett Software; (OPAC) Follett Software
     Database Vendor: OCLC FirstSearch
     Open Mon & Wed-Fri 10-5, Tues 10-8, Sat 10-1
     Friends of the Library Group

S   US NATIONAL PARK SERVICE*, Great Smoky Mountains National Park
     Library, 107 Park Headquarters Rd, 37738. SAN 370-2863. Tel:
     865-436-1296. FAX: 865-436-1220. *Librn,* Annette Hartigan
     Library Holdings: Bk Vols 7,200
     Special Collections: Naturalists Journals. Oral History
     Restriction: Open to others by appt, Staff use only

GERMANTOWN

P   GERMANTOWN COMMUNITY LIBRARY*, 1925 Exeter Rd,
     38138-2815. SAN 378-4436. Tel: 901-757-7323. Circulation Tel:
     901-757-7323, Ext 7477. Reference Tel: 901-757-7323, Ext 7465.
     Information Services Tel: 901-757-7323, Ext 7481. FAX: 901-756-9940.
     Web Site: www.germantown-library.org. *Dir,* Melody Pittman; Tel:
     901-757-7323, Ext 7480, E-mail: mpittman@germantown-tn.gov; *Asst Dir,*
     Raymond Wheeldon; Tel: 901-757-7323, Ext 7479; *Children & Young
     Adult Supvr,* Jan Colbert; Tel: 901-757-7323, Ext 7468; *Cat,*
     Sylvia-Michelle Hostetter; Tel: 901-757-7323, Ext 7476; *Off Mgr/Circ
     Supvr,* Diana Hostetter; *Ref Serv,* Kathleen Raymond; Tel: 901-757-7323,
     Ext 7478; *Tech Serv,* Tom Langston; Staff 24 (MLS 2.5, Non-MLS 21.5)
     Pop 40,977; Circ 289,225
     Library Holdings: Audiobooks 2,529; AV Mats 2,639; CDs 978; DVDs
     3,327; Electronic Media & Resources 40; Large Print Bks 3,649; Bk Vols
     155,506; Per Subs 220; Videos 762
     Automation Activity & Vendor Info: (Cataloging) SirsiDynix;
     (Circulation) SirsiDynix; (Course Reserve) SirsiDynix; (ILL) OCLC;
     (Serials) SirsiDynix
     Wireless access
     Special Services for the Blind - Accessible computers; Assistive/Adapted
     tech devices, equip & products; Bks on cassette; Bks on CD; Computer
     with voice synthesizer for visually impaired persons; Large print bks;
     Magnifiers; Screen enlargement software for people with visual disabilities;
     Screen reader software
     Open Mon-Thurs 9:30-9, Fri & Sat 9:30-6, Sun 1-6
     Friends of the Library Group

GLEASON

P   GLEASON MEMORIAL LIBRARY*, 105 College St, 38229. (Mail add:
     116 N Cedar St, 38229-7228), SAN 315-7881. Tel: 731-648-9020. FAX:
     731-648-9020. *Dir,* Kathy Tucker
     Library Holdings: Bk Titles 2,500; Bk Vols 2,600
     Mem of Obion River Regional Library
     Open Mon-Thurs 10-5

GRAND JUNCTION

P   BOBBY MARTINDALE MEMORIAL LIBRARY*, 103 Washington Ave,
     38039. (Mail add: PO Box 751, 38039-0751), SAN 376-7027. Tel:
     731-764-2716. *Dir,* Loretta Crowder-Bell
     Founded 1982. Pop 306; Circ 3,013
     Library Holdings: Bk Vols 4,663
     Mem of Hatchie River Regional Library
     Open Tues-Thurs & Sat 9-2
     Friends of the Library Group

GRAYSVILLE

P   GRAYSVILLE PUBLIC LIBRARY*, 151 Mill St, 37338-5044. (Mail add:
     PO Box 100, 37338-0100), SAN 315-789X. Tel: 423-775-0966. FAX:
     423-775-6952. E-mail: graysvillelibrary@usa.com. *Dir,* Debbie Pelfrey
     Library Holdings: Bk Vols 4,080
     Mem of Ocoee River Regional Library
     Open Mon, Tues, Thurs & Fri 8-5

GREENBACK

P   GREENBACK PUBLIC LIBRARY*, 6889 Morganton Rd, 37742-4143.
SAN 315-7903. Tel: 865-856-2841. FAX: 865-856-2841. Web Site:
www.discoveret.org/greenbkl. *Dir,* Clara Sue Hammontree; E-mail:
cshammon@esper.com
Pop 1,200; Circ 10,377
Library Holdings: AV Mats 190; CDs 35; DVDs 122; Large Print Bks
1,500; Bk Vols 7,000; Per Subs 15; Talking Bks 20; Videos 255
Function: Audio & video playback equip for onsite use, Computer
training, Copy machines, Digital talking bks, e-mail serv, E-Reserves, Fax
serv, Handicapped accessible, ILL available, Online ref, Online searches,
Photocopying/Printing, Preschool outreach, Prog for children & young
adult, Senior computer classes, Spoken cassettes & CDs, Spoken cassettes
& DVDs, Summer reading prog, Tax forms, Video lending libr
Mem of Ocoee River Regional Library
Open Tues, Wed & Fri 9-5, Thurs 11-7
Friends of the Library Group

GREENEVILLE

S   THE T ELMER COX LIBRARY*, 229 N Main St, 37745. Tel:
423-638-9866. E-mail: grv@ggcpl.org. Web Site: www.ggcpl.org/cox.htm.
Mgr, Don Miller; *Asst Librn,* Mitzi Bible
Special Collections: Historical & Genealogical Coll
Open Mon 10-6, Tues-Thurs 10-5, Fri 10-4, Sat 10-1

P   GREENEVILLE GREEN COUNTY PUBLIC LIBRARY*, 210 N Main St,
37745-3816. SAN 315-7911. Tel: 423-638-5034. FAX: 423-638-3841.
E-mail: grv@ggcpl.org. Web Site: www.ggcpl.org. *Dir,* Madge Walker;
Staff 1 (MLS 1)
Founded 1908. Pop 54,406; Circ 96,608
Library Holdings: Bk Vols 50,000; Per Subs 125
Automation Activity & Vendor Info: (Acquisitions) Ex Libris Group;
(Cataloging) Ex Libris Group; (Circulation) Ex Libris Group; (Course
Reserve) Ex Libris Group; (ILL) Ex Libris Group; (Media Booking) Ex
Libris Group; (OPAC) Ex Libris Group; (Serials) Ex Libris Group
Open Mon & Thurs 9:30-7, Tues, Wed & Fri 9:30-5, Sat 9:30-2
Friends of the Library Group

C   TUSCULUM COLLEGE*, Thomas J Garland Library, Hwy 107, 60
Shiloh Rd, 37743. (Mail add: PO Box 5005, Greenville, 37743-0001), SAN
360-585X. Tel: 423-636-7320. Toll Free Tel: 800-729-0256. FAX:
423-787-8498. E-mail: library@tusculum.edu. Web Site:
library.tusculum.edu. *Libr Dir,* Myron J Smith, Jr; Tel: 423-636-7320, Ext
5260, 5148, E-mail: jsmith@tusculum.edu; *Asst Dir, Distance Learning,
Webmaster,* Anne Reever Osborne; Tel: 423-636-7320, Ext 5801, E-mail:
aosborne@tusculum.edu; *Info Literacy Librn,* Kathy Hipps; Tel:
423-636-7320, Ext 5123; *Pub Serv Librn,* Marsha Griffith; Tel:
423-636-7320, Ext 5122, E-mail: mgriffit@tusculum.edu; *Ref Librn,*
Charles Tunstall; Tel: 423-636-7320, Ext 5124, E-mail:
ctunstal@tusculum.edu; *Coordr, Tech Serv,* Carolyn Parker; E-mail:
cparker@tusculum.edu; Staff 6 (MLS 5, Non-MLS 1)
Founded 1794. Enrl 2,290; Fac 78; Highest Degree: Master
Library Holdings: DVDs 25; e-books 120,000; e-journals 29,388; Bk Vols
92,595; Per Subs 206; Videos 800
Special Collections: Childrens Literature; Library Books prior to 1900;
Warren W Hobbie Civic Arts Coll
Subject Interests: Bus & mgt, Educ
Automation Activity & Vendor Info: (Cataloging) Innovative Interfaces,
Inc; (Circulation) Innovative Interfaces, Inc; (Course Reserve) Innovative
Interfaces, Inc; (ILL) Innovative Interfaces, Inc; (Media Booking)
Innovative Interfaces, Inc; (OPAC) Innovative Interfaces, Inc; (Serials)
Innovative Interfaces, Inc
Database Vendor: Alexander Street Press, American Psychological
Association (APA), ARTstor, ebrary, EBSCOhost, Gale Cengage Learning,
Greenwood Publishing Group, Hoovers, JSTOR, LexisNexis, netLibrary,
ProQuest, SerialsSolutions, Standard & Poor's
Wireless access
Publications: Reel'n Page (Newsletter)
Partic in Appalachian Col Asn; Lyrasis; OCLC Online Computer Library
Center, Inc; Tenn Share
Open Mon-Thurs 8am-10pm, Fri 8-5, Sat 9am-Noon, Sun 6pm-10pm
Departmental Libraries:
KNOXVILLE CAMPUS, 1305 Centerpoint Blvd, Knoxville, 37932. Tel:
865-693-1177, Ext 5016. Toll Free Tel: 800-729-0116, Ext 5016. FAX:
865-531-0524. E-mail: tcknoxlib@tusculum.edu. *Br Operations Adminr,*
Mary Hartman Halliburton; E-mail: mhalliburton@tusculum.edu; Staff 3
(MLS 1, Non-MLS 2)
Founded 1794. Enrl 1,650; Fac 50; Highest Degree: Master
Library Holdings: Bk Vols 4,000; Per Subs 20; Videos 30
Open Mon-Thurs 11-8, Sat 8:30-1

G   US DEPARTMENT OF THE INTERIOR, NATIONAL PARK SERVICE*,
Andrew Johnson National Historic Site Library, 121 Monument Ave,
37743. SAN 325-0911. Tel: 423-638-3711. FAX: 423-798-0754. *Adminr,*
Kendra Hinkle
Library Holdings: Bk Vols 653
Special Collections: Andrew Johnson Coll; Civil War Coll; National Parks
Coll; Presidential History Coll; Tennessee History Coll
Subject Interests: Hist presv, Hist sites, Nat parks, Presidents (US), State
hist
Open Mon-Fri 7:30-4
Restriction: Staff use only, Use of others with permission of librn

GREENFIELD

P   DR NATHAN PORTER PUBLIC LIBRARY*, 228 N Front St,
38230-9998. SAN 376-3277. Tel: 731-235-9932. FAX: 731-235-9932. Web
Site: www.nathanporterlibrary.org. *Dir,* Sandra Dowland
Library Holdings: AV Mats 250; Large Print Bks 1,250; Bk Titles 1,300;
Per Subs 28; Videos 400
Automation Activity & Vendor Info: (Circulation) Winnebago Software
Co
Database Vendor: Gale Cengage Learning
Wireless access
Function: Adult bk club, Copy machines, Electronic databases & coll, Fax
serv, Handicapped accessible, ILL available, Music CDs, Senior computer
classes, Spoken cassettes & CDs, Summer reading prog, Tax forms, VHS
videos, Wheelchair accessible
Mem of Obion River Regional Library
Partic in Tenn Libr Asn
Open Tues-Fri 9-5, Sat 9-12

HALLS

P   HALLS PUBLIC LIBRARY, 110 N Church St, 38040-1502. (Mail add:
PO Box 236, 38040-0236), SAN 321-6330. Tel: 731-836-5302. E-mail:
citylibrary@bellsouth.net. *Dir,* Violet Burks
Founded 1980
Library Holdings: Bk Titles 10,000; Per Subs 10
Special Collections: US Tax Cases 1913-current
Open Mon-Fri 12-5, Sat 10-3

HARRIMAN

P   HARRIMAN PUBLIC LIBRARY*, 601 Walden St, 37748-2506. SAN
315-7938. Tel: 865-882-3195. FAX: 865-882-3188. E-mail:
harrimanlibrary@comcast.net. Web Site: www.harrimanlibrary.org. *Dir,*
Barbara Pelfrey; *Ch,* Tammie Edwards; E-mail: tedwardshpl@comcast.net
Library Holdings: Bk Titles 20,000; Per Subs 45
Automation Activity & Vendor Info: (Cataloging) SirsiDynix;
(Circulation) SirsiDynix; (ILL) SirsiDynix; (OPAC) SirsiDynix
Mem of Ocoee River Regional Library
Open Mon-Thurs 9-5, Fri & Sat 9-1
Friends of the Library Group

J   ROANE STATE COMMUNITY COLLEGE LIBRARY*, 276 Patton Lane,
37748. SAN 321-3412. Tel: 865-882-4553. Circulation Tel: 865-882-4646.
FAX: 865-882-4562. E-mail: librarystaff@rscc.edu. Web Site:
www.rscc.cc.tn.us/library/. *Dir,* Becky Brunton; Tel: 865-882-4551, E-mail:
bruntonBI@roanestate.edu; *Cat,* Rosemary Ellis; Tel: 865-354-4464; *Ref,*
Robert Benson; Tel: 865-354-4254, E-mail: BensonRM@roanestate.edu;
Staff 8 (MLS 4, Non-MLS 4)
Founded 1971. Enrl 3,376; Fac 175
Library Holdings: Bk Titles 50,000; Bk Vols 52,500; Per Subs 560
Database Vendor: SirsiDynix
Open Mon-Thurs 8am-10pm, Fri 8-5, Sat 9-1

HARROGATE

C   LINCOLN MEMORIAL UNIVERSITY*, Carnegie Vincent Library,
Cumberland Gap Pkwy, Box 2012, 37752. SAN 315-7946. Tel:
423-869-7079. Toll Free Tel: 800-325-0900, Ext 7079. FAX:
423-869-6426. E-mail: library@lmunet.edu. Web Site: www.lmunet.edu.
Dir, Gabriel Morley; *Asst Univ Librn, Pub Serv,* Melissa Byrd; *Acq of New
Ser,* Robyn Williams; Tel: 423-869-6218, E-mail:
robyn.williams@lmunet.edu; *Bibliog Instr,* Crystal Goldman; *Circ,* Karen
Loving; Tel: 423-869-6219, E-mail: karen.loving@lmunet.edu; *Distance
Educ,* Janice McDonnell; E-mail: janice.mcdonnell@lmunet.edu; *ILL, Ser,*
Kay Davis; Tel: 423-869-6220, E-mail: kay.davis@lmunet.edu; *Tech Serv,*
Kathy Brunsma; Tel: 423-869-6221, E-mail: kathy.brunsma@lmunet.edu;
Staff 8 (MLS 5, Non-MLS 3)
Founded 1897. Enrl 1,500; Fac 45; Highest Degree: Master
Library Holdings: Bk Titles 142,290; Bk Vols 187,915; Per Subs 119,000
Special Collections: Jesse Stuart Coll; Lincoln Memorial University
Authors
Subject Interests: Civil War, Lincolniana

Automation Activity & Vendor Info: (Acquisitions) Ex Libris Group; (Cataloging) Ex Libris Group; (Circulation) Ex Libris Group; (Course Reserve) Ex Libris Group; (ILL) Ex Libris Group; (Media Booking) Ex Libris Group; (OPAC) Ex Libris Group; (Serials) Ex Libris Group
Function: For res purposes
Partic in Appalachian Col Asn; Knoxville Area Health Sciences Library Consortium; Lyrasis; Tenn Share
Open Mon-Thurs 8am-12am, Fri 8-4:30, Sat 10-5

HARTSVILLE

P   FRED A VAUGHT MEMORIAL PUBLIC LIBRARY*, 211 White Oak St, 37074-1420. SAN 315-7954. Tel: 615-374-3677. FAX: 615-374-4553. *Dir,* Mary Carpenter; E-mail: maryl@isdn.net
Founded 1961. Pop 7,300; Circ 30,000
Library Holdings: Bk Titles 30,000; Per Subs 25
Automation Activity & Vendor Info: (Cataloging) Book Systems, Inc; (Circulation) Book Systems, Inc; (ILL) Book Systems, Inc; (OPAC) Book Systems, Inc
Mem of Stones River Regional Library
Open Mon, Thurs & Fri 9-5, Tues 9-8, Sat 8-1

HENDERSON

P   CHESTER COUNTY PUBLIC LIBRARY*, 1012 East Main St, 38340-0323. SAN 315-7962. Tel: 731-989-4673. FAX: 731-989-4673. E-mail: chester_library@bellsoulth.net. *Dir,* Nancy Canada
Pop 15,540
Library Holdings: Bk Titles 11,000
Automation Activity & Vendor Info: (Circulation) Follett Software
Mem of Hatchie River Regional Library
Partic in Tenn Libr Asn
Open Mon-Wed & Fri 9:30-5, Thurs 12-7, Sat 9:30-12:30
Friends of the Library Group

C   FREED-HARDEMAN UNIVERSITY*, Loden-Daniel Library, 158 E Main St, 38340-2399. SAN 315-7970. Tel: 731-989-6067. FAX: 731-989-6065. E-mail: library@fhu.edu. Web Site: www.fhu.edu/library. *Dir,* Hope Shull; E-mail: hshull@fhu.edu; *Cat, Rare Bks,* Sharon Jennette; *Circ,* Shirley Eaton; *Per,* Teresa Hanger; *Ref Serv,* Wade Osburn; *Tech Coordr,* John Wilson; Staff 5 (MLS 5)
Founded 1869. Enrl 1,800; Fac 106; Highest Degree: Master
Library Holdings: e-books 14,000; Bk Vols 150,000; Per Subs 1,460
Special Collections: Religion (Restoration Library Coll), bks & tapes. Oral History
Automation Activity & Vendor Info: (Acquisitions) Ex Libris Group; (Cataloging) Ex Libris Group; (Circulation) Ex Libris Group; (Course Reserve) Ex Libris Group; (ILL) Ex Libris Group; (Media Booking) Ex Libris Group; (OPAC) Ex Libris Group; (Serials) Ex Libris Group
Partic in Lyrasis; OCLC Online Computer Library Center, Inc
Open Mon-Thurs 7:30am-11:30pm, Fri 7:30-5:30, Sat 10-5:30, Sun 1-4:30 & 7-11:30

HENDERSONVILLE

P   MARTIN CURTIS HENDERSONVILLE PUBLIC LIBRARY*, 140 Saundersville Rd, 37075-3525. SAN 315-7989. Tel: 615-824-0656. FAX: 615-824-3112. *Dir,* Lelani Sabo; Staff 10 (MLS 2, Non-MLS 8)
Founded 1965. Pop 72,505; Circ 189,740
Jul 2005-Jun 2006 Income $277,967, City $25,000, County $252,967. Sal $204,667
Library Holdings: AV Mats 5,726; Bk Titles 46,000; Per Subs 125
Wireless access
Mem of Red River Regional Library
Open Mon & Thurs 10-8, Tues & Wed 10-6, Sat 10-2
Friends of the Library Group

HOHENWALD

P   LEWIS COUNTY PUBLIC LIBRARY*, 15 Kyle Ave, 38462-1434. SAN 315-7997. Tel: 931-796-5365. FAX: 931-796-7739. E-mail: lewislibrary@bellsoulth.net. *Libr Dir,* Crystal Nash; Staff 1 (Non-MLS 1)
Founded 1951. Pop 12,161; Circ 30,539
Jul 2010-Jun 2011 Income $94,157, State $14,034, County $80,123. Mats Exp $12,305, Books $9,307, Per/Ser (Incl. Access Fees) $1,205, AV Equip $1,500, AV Mat $293. Sal $51,416 (Prof $26,059)
Library Holdings: Audiobooks 343; Bks on Deafness & Sign Lang 32; DVDs 207; Large Print Bks 1,628; Microforms 441; Bk Titles 25,836; Per Subs 48; Videos 247
Special Collections: Hohenwald, Tennessee History Coll; Lewis County, Tennessee History Coll; Local Newspaper (Lewis County Herald Coll-1915 to present), micro
Subject Interests: County hist, Lewis & Clark expedition, State hist
Automation Activity & Vendor Info: (Acquisitions) Book Systems, Inc; (ILL) Auto-Graphics, Inc
Wireless access

Function: Adult literacy prog, Audiobks via web, Bks on cassette, Bks on CD, Children's prog, Computer training, Computers for patron use, Copy machines, Electronic databases & coll, Free DVD rentals, Handicapped accessible, ILL available, Orientations, Outreach serv, OverDrive digital audio bks, Photocopying/Printing, Preschool outreach, Prog for adults, Prog for children & young adult, Pub access computers, Ref serv available, Story hour, Summer reading prog, Teen prog, VHS videos, Wheelchair accessible
Special Services for the Deaf - Bks on deafness & sign lang
Special Services for the Blind - Audio mat; Bks available with recordings; Bks on cassette; Bks on CD; Large print bks
Open Tues, Wed, Fri & Sat 9-5, Thurs 11-7
Restriction: Non-resident fee
Friends of the Library Group

HUMBOLDT

P   HUMBOLDT PUBLIC LIBRARY, 115 S 16th Ave, 38343-3403. SAN 315-8004. Tel: 731-784-2383. FAX: 731-784-0582. Web Site: www.humboldtpublic.org. *Dir,* Diane Wright; E-mail: diane@humboldtpublic.org
Pop 13,911; Circ 89,598
Jul 2011-Jun 2012 Income $166,140, City $151,090, Federal $5,050, County $10,000. Mats Exp $27,902, Books $21,902, Per/Ser (Incl. Access Fees) $1,000, AV Equip $5,000. Sal $111,211
Library Holdings: Audiobooks 2,003; Braille Volumes 50; CDs 455; DVDs 2,000; Microforms 113; Bk Vols 33,000; Per Subs 77; Videos 2,004
Special Collections: Music CD's
Automation Activity & Vendor Info: (Acquisitions) Auto-Graphics, Inc; (Cataloging) Auto-Graphics, Inc; (Circulation) Auto-Graphics, Inc; (Course Reserve) Auto-Graphics, Inc; (ILL) Auto-Graphics, Inc; (OPAC) Auto-Graphics, Inc; (Serials) Auto-Graphics, Inc
Database Vendor: Auto-Graphics, Inc
Wireless access
Function: Home delivery & serv to Sr ctr & nursing homes
Mem of Obion River Regional Library
Open Mon & Wed-Fri 9-5, Tues 9-7, Sat 10-4
Friends of the Library Group

HUNTINGDON

P   CARROLL COUNTY LIBRARY*, 625 High St, Ste 102, 38344-3903. SAN 315-8012. Tel: 731-986-1919. FAX: 731-986-1335. *Dir,* Karen Pierce; E-mail: kpierce@aeneas.net; *Ch,* Janet Welch; *Circ,* Sally Wilson
Founded 1950. Pop 28,400; Circ 64,683
Library Holdings: Bk Vols 25,000; Per Subs 41
Special Collections: Genealogy, History (Tennessee Coll), Literacy
Automation Activity & Vendor Info: (Acquisitions) Follett Software; (Cataloging) Follett Software; (Circulation) Follett Software; (Course Reserve) Follett Software; (ILL) Follett Software; (Media Booking) Follett Software; (OPAC) Follett Software; (Serials) Follett Software
Mem of Obion River Regional Library
Open Mon-Thurs 9-5:30, Fri 9-5, Sat 9-12

HUNTSVILLE

P   HUNTSVILLE PUBLIC LIBRARY*, 314 Court House Sq, 37756. (Mail add: PO Box 180, 37756-0180), SAN 376-2963. Tel: 423-663-9230. E-mail: huntsvillepl@highland.net. *Dir,* Sharon Kay Reed; Staff 1 (Non-MLS 1)
Founded 1986. Pop 20,000; Circ 16,500
Library Holdings: Bk Titles 7,000; Per Subs 12
Open Mon & Wed 12-5, Tues 10-3, Thur & Sat 10-2, Fri 1-6

JACKSBORO

P   JACKSBORO PUBLIC LIBRARY, 585 Main St, Ste 201, 37757. (Mail add: PO Box 460, 37757-0460), SAN 315-8020. Tel: 423-562-3675. FAX: 423-562-9587. E-mail: director@jacksboropubliclibrary.org, library@jacksboropubliclibrary.org. Web Site: www.jacksboropubliclibrary.org. *Dir,* Gregory Smith; Staff 3 (Non-MLS 3)
Founded 1976. Pop 7,329; Circ 40,148
Jul 2010-Jun 2011 Income $94,495, City $80,500, County $9,400, Locally Generated Income $4,595
Library Holdings: Audiobooks 692; Bks on Deafness & Sign Lang 30; DVDs 2,936; e-books 27,849; Electronic Media & Resources 18; Large Print Bks 818; Bk Titles 12,255; Per Subs 38
Automation Activity & Vendor Info: (Circulation) Follett Software; (ILL) Auto-Graphics, Inc
Database Vendor: Gale Cengage Learning
Open Mon-Sat 10-6; Mon-Sat (Winter) 9-5

JACKSON

P   HATCHIE RIVER REGIONAL LIBRARY*, (Formerly Shiloh Regional Library), 63 Executive Dr, 38305. SAN 315-808X. Tel: 731-668-0710. FAX: 731-668-6663. *Dir,* Carla Jacobs; E-mail: carla.jacobs@tn.gov
Founded 1956. Pop 188,198; Circ 586,655
Library Holdings: Bk Vols 115,795
Subject Interests: Tenn
Member Libraries: Bobby Martindale Memorial Library; Bolivar-Hardeman County Library; Chester County Public Library; Decatur County Library; Everett Horn Public Library; Hardin County Library; Irving Meek Jr Memorial Library; Jack McConnico Memorial Library; Jackson-Madison County Library; Lee Ola Roberts Public Library; Middleton Community Library; Parsons Public Library
Open Mon-Fri 8-4:30

M   JACKSON-MADISON COUNTY GENERAL HOSPITAL*, Learning Center, 620 Skyline Dr, 38301. SAN 320-586X. Tel: 731-541-4140. FAX: 731-541-6983. E-mail: learnctr@gmail.com. *Libr Tech,* Becky Parks; Staff 1 (Non-MLS 1)
Founded 1972
Library Holdings: Bk Titles 1,500; Per Subs 200
Subject Interests: Hospital admin, Med, Nursing, Nutrition, Pathology, Phys therapy, Radiology, Respiratory therapy, Surgery
Database Vendor: EBSCOhost, MD Consult, Medline, PubMed, UpToDate
Wireless access
Function: Computers for patron use, Copy machines, Fax serv, Online ref, Photocopying/Printing, Pub access computers, Ref serv available
Open Mon-Fri 8:15-4:30
Restriction: Access at librarian's discretion, Badge access after hrs, Borrowing requests are handled by ILL, Lending to staff only, Limited access for the pub, Med & nursing staff, patients & families, Non-circulating to the pub, Not a lending libr, Open to pub for ref only, Open to pub with supv only, Pub use on premises, Ref only to non-staff, Restricted pub use

P   JACKSON-MADISON COUNTY LIBRARY*, 433 E Lafayette St, 38301-6386. SAN 315-8039. Tel: 731-425-8600. FAX: 731-425-8609. Web Site: www.jmcl.tn.org. *Dir,* Position Currently Open; *Spec Coll Librn,* Jack Darrell Wood; *Ch,* Jennifer Hanson; *Media Spec,* Michael Baker; *Tech Serv, YA Serv,* Patty Williams; Staff 20 (MLS 3, Non-MLS 17)
Founded 1903. Pop 91,837; Circ 194,720
Library Holdings: AV Mats 11,806; Bk Vols 115,520; Per Subs 211
Special Collections: Genealogy, bks, micro; Jackson Area Business History Coll; Local & State History (Tennessee Room Coll), bks, micro
Automation Activity & Vendor Info: (Cataloging) TLC (The Library Corporation); (Circulation) TLC (The Library Corporation); (OPAC) TLC (The Library Corporation)
Database Vendor: EBSCOhost, Gale Cengage Learning, LearningExpress, Newsbank, TLC (The Library Corporation), World Book Online
Wireless access
Mem of Hatchie River Regional Library
Open Mon-Sat 10-6
Friends of the Library Group

J   JACKSON STATE COMMUNITY COLLEGE LIBRARY*, 2046 North Pkwy, 38301. SAN 315-8047. Tel: 731-425-2609. Interlibrary Loan Service Tel: 901-425-2609, Ext 327. Reference Tel: 731-425-2609, Ext 572. FAX: 731-425-2625. Web Site: library.jscc.edu. *Dir,* Scott Cohen; Tel: 731-425-2615, E-mail: scohen@jscc.edu; *Acq, Circ,* Gloria Hester; Tel: 731-425-3520, Ext 328, E-mail: ghester@jscc.edu; *Cat, Ref,* Joyce Johnston; Tel: 731-424-3520, Ext 325, E-mail: jjohnston@jscc.edu; Staff 7 (MLS 4, Non-MLS 3)
Founded 1967. Enrl 2,797; Fac 120; Highest Degree: Associate
Jul 2005-Jun 2006 Income $371,000. Mats Exp $69,200, Books $31,000, Per/Ser (Incl. Access Fees) $32,000, Micro $2,400, AV Mat $2,800, Presv $1,000. Sal $297,000 (Prof $19,200)
Library Holdings: AV Mats 2,594; DVDs 96; e-books 47,000; Bk Titles 53,000; Bk Vols 62,386; Per Subs 180; Talking Bks 1,398; Videos 1,196
Subject Interests: Agr, Careers, Eng tech, Health sci, Indust eng, Tenn hist
Automation Activity & Vendor Info: (Cataloging) SirsiDynix; (Circulation) SirsiDynix; (OPAC) SirsiDynix
Database Vendor: EBSCOhost, Gale Cengage Learning, LexisNexis, OCLC FirstSearch, SirsiDynix, Wilson - Wilson Web
Function: Ref serv available
Partic in West Tennessee Academic Library Consortium
Open Mon-Thurs (Fall & Spring) 7:30am-8:45pm, Fri 7:30-4:15, Sat 10-1:30

C   LAMBUTH UNIVERSITY*, Luther L Gobbel Library, 705 Lambuth Blvd, 38301. SAN 315-8063. Tel: 731-425-3270. Circulation Tel: 731-425-3289. Interlibrary Loan Service Tel: 731-425-3448. FAX: 731-425-3200. Web Site: www.lambuth.edu/academics/library/library.html. *Dir,* Dr Pamela Dennis; Tel: 731-425-3479, E-mail: dennis@lambuth.edu; *Coordr, Media Serv,* James Barham; Tel: 731-425-3293, E-mail: barham-j@lambuth.edu; *Acq, Archivist,* Jackie Wood; Tel: 731-425-3290, E-mail: wood-j@lambuth.edu; *Circ, Media Serv,* Elaine E Walker; Tel: 731-425-3298, E-mail: walker@lambuth.edu; *Coll Develop, Ref,* Sammy Chapman; Tel: 731-425-3270, E-mail: chapman@lambuth.edu; *ILL, Ser,* Rex West; E-mail: west@lambuth.edu; *Syst Adminr, Tech Serv,* Laura Simpson; Tel: 731-425-3292, E-mail: simpson@lambuth.edu. Subject Specialists: *Archives, Genealogy, Music,* Dr Pamela Dennis; *Libr sci,* Jackie Wood; *Bus, Libr sci,* Sammy Chapman; Staff 7 (MLS 3, Non-MLS 4)
Founded 1843. Enrl 805; Fac 50; Highest Degree: Bachelor
Library Holdings: AV Mats 649; CDs 270; e-books 41,641; Music Scores 1,229; Bk Titles 106,454; Bk Vols 113,005; Per Subs 392
Special Collections: US Document Depository
Subject Interests: Civil War, Methodism
Automation Activity & Vendor Info: (Acquisitions) Ex Libris Group; (Cataloging) Ex Libris Group; (Circulation) Ex Libris Group; (Course Reserve) Ex Libris Group; (ILL) OCLC; (OPAC) Ex Libris Group; (Serials) Ex Libris Group
Database Vendor: EBSCOhost, Gale Cengage Learning, LexisNexis, OCLC FirstSearch
Function: ILL available
Partic in Lyrasis; OCLC Online Computer Library Center, Inc; Soline; Tenn-Share; West Tennessee Academic Library Consortium
Open Mon-Thurs (Winter) 7:30am-11pm, Fri 7:30-4:30, Sat 12-4, Sun 4-11; Mon-Fri (Summer) 8:30-4:30
Restriction: Circ limited

C   LANE COLLEGE LIBRARY*, 545 Lane Ave, 38301-4598. SAN 315-8071. Tel: 731-426-7654. FAX: 731-426-7591. Web Site: www.lanecollege.edu. *Head Librn,* Lan Wang; Tel: 731-426-7593, E-mail: lwang@lanecollege.edu; Staff 5 (MLS 2, Non-MLS 3)
Founded 1882. Enrl 768; Fac 48; Highest Degree: Bachelor
Library Holdings: Bk Vols 84,000; Per Subs 339
Special Collections: Black Studies, AV, bks; Haitian Art; Juvenile. Oral History
Automation Activity & Vendor Info: (Cataloging) LibraryWorld, Inc; (Circulation) LibraryWorld, Inc; (OPAC) LibraryWorld, Inc; (Serials) LibraryWorld, Inc
Publications: Library Usage Manual; Staff Manual
Partic in West Tennessee Academic Library Consortium

GL TENNESSEE STATE LAW LIBRARY*, Supreme Court Bldg, 6 Hwy 45 By-Pass, 38301. SAN 320-4227. Tel: 731-423-5849. *Librn,* Debbie Durham
Library Holdings: Bk Vols 30,000; Per Subs 30
Open Mon-Fri 8:30-4:30

C   UNION UNIVERSITY*, Emma Waters Summar Library, 1050 Union University Dr, 38305-3697. SAN 315-8098. Tel: 731-661-5070. Reference Tel: 731-661-6571. FAX: 731-661-5175. E-mail: library@uu.edu. Web Site: www.uu.edu/library. *Dir,* Anna Beth Morgan; Tel: 731-661-5410, E-mail: amorgan@uu.edu; *Cat Librn,* Mary Platt; Tel: 731-661-5414, E-mail: mplatt@uu.edu; *Instrul Serv Librn, Syst Librn,* Dr Jenny Lowery; Tel: 731-661-5058, E-mail: jlowery@uu.edu; *Outreach Librn,* T Parker; E-mail: tparker@uu.edu; *Pub Serv Librn,* Melissa Moore; Tel: 731-661-5408, E-mail: mmoore@uu.edu; *Ser/Electronic Res Librn,* Jeannie Byrd; Tel: 731-661-5339, E-mail: jbyrd@uu.edu; *Circ Serv Mgr,* Margaret Duncan; E-mail: mduncan@uu.edu; *Evening Circ Supvr,* Ellen Kimbro; *Coll Develop Coordr,* Beth Lynn; *Project Coordr,* Paul Sorrell; Staff 13.5 (MLS 7, Non-MLS 6.5)
Enrl 2,495; Fac 174; Highest Degree: Doctorate
Library Holdings: AV Mats 14,131; e-books 35,779; Bk Vols 149,255; Per Subs 713
Special Collections: Fonville Neville Coll; R G Lee Coll; West Tennessee Baptist Coll
Automation Activity & Vendor Info: (Acquisitions) Ex Libris Group; (Cataloging) Ex Libris Group; (Circulation) Ex Libris Group; (Course Reserve) Ex Libris Group; (ILL) OCLC Online; (OPAC) Ex Libris Group; (Serials) Ex Libris Group
Database Vendor: Dialog, EBSCOhost, Gale Cengage Learning, LexisNexis, netLibrary, OCLC FirstSearch, OVID Technologies, ProQuest, SerialsSolutions, Wilson - Wilson Web
Wireless access
Publications: The Compass (Newsletter)
Partic in Lyrasis; OCLC Online Computer Library Center, Inc; West Tennessee Academic Library Consortium
Open Mon-Thurs 7am-12:30am, Fri 7-5, Sat 11-5, Sun 2-5 & 8pm-12:30am
Friends of the Library Group

JAMESTOWN

P   FENTRESS COUNTY PUBLIC LIBRARY*, 306 S Main St, 38556-3845.
SAN 315-8101. Tel: 931-879-7512. Reference Tel: 931-879-1720. FAX:
931-879-6984. E-mail: fcpublib@twlakes.net. Web Site:
fentresscountylibrary.com. *Dir,* Leslie Pullins; *Asst Dir,* Chestene Tauber
Pop 14,826
Library Holdings: Bk Titles 18,000; Per Subs 28
Mem of Falling Water River Regional Library
Open Mon-Thurs 8-6, Fri 8-5, Sat 9-2
Friends of the Library Group

JASPER

P   JASPER PUBLIC LIBRARY*, 14 W Second St, 37347-3409. SAN
315-811X. Tel: 423-942-3369. FAX: 423-942-6383. Web Site:
www.jasperpubliclibrary.org. *Dir,* Carolyn Stewart; E-mail:
carolynstewart@bellsouth.net; Staff 1 (Non-MLS 1)
Founded 1968. Pop 3,210; Circ 10,878
Library Holdings: AV Mats 5,000; DVDs 301; Bk Vols 26,000; Per Subs
52; Talking Bks 2,000; Videos 3,349
Automation Activity & Vendor Info: (Cataloging) Surpass; (Circulation)
Surpass; (OPAC) Surpass
Open Mon 8:30-8, Tues, Wed & Fri 8:30-5, Sat 8:30-2

JEFFERSON CITY

C   CARSON-NEWMAN COLLEGE*, Stephens-Burnett Memorial Library,
1634 Russell Ave, 37760. (Mail add: Box 70000, 37760), SAN 315-8136.
Tel: 865-471-3335. FAX: 865-471-3450. Web Site:
www.cn.edu/academics/resources/library. *Dean,* Bruce G Kocour; Tel:
865-471-3336; *Dir, Media Serv,* Donnie Newman; Tel: 865-471-3220;
Instrul Serv/Ref Librn, Alison R Jones; Tel: 865-471-3340; *Ref &
Instruction Librn,* Kelli Williams; Tel: 865-471-3338; *Access Serv,* Shelia
Gaines; Tel: 865-471-3534; *Acq,* Sylvia Sawyer; *Archivist, Spec Coll,*
Albert Lang; Tel: 865-471-3542; *Tech Serv,* Lori Thornton; Tel:
865-471-3339; Staff 7 (MLS 5, Non-MLS 2)
Founded 1851. Enrl 2,200; Fac 120; Highest Degree: Master
Special Collections: US Document Depository
Subject Interests: Baptist mat, Family counseling, Marriage
Automation Activity & Vendor Info: (Cataloging) Innovative Interfaces,
Inc - Millenium; (Circulation) Innovative Interfaces, Inc - Millenium;
(Course Reserve) Innovative Interfaces, Inc - Millenium; (ILL) Innovative
Interfaces, Inc - Millenium; (OPAC) Innovative Interfaces, Inc - Millenium
Database Vendor: Alexander Street Press, American Chemical Society,
Annual Reviews, ARTstor, BioOne, CountryWatch, CQ Press,
CredoReference, ebrary, EBSCOhost, Facts on File, Gale Cengage
Learning, Greenwood Publishing Group, Ingram Library Services,
Innovative Interfaces, Inc, JSTOR, LexisNexis, McGraw-Hill, netLibrary,
Newsbank, OCLC FirstSearch, ProQuest, PubMed, Standard & Poor's,
Wiley InterScience
Wireless access
Publications: Carson-Newman Baptist
Partic in Appalachian Libr Info Coop; Lyrasis; OCLC Online Computer
Library Center, Inc; Tenn Share
Open Mon-Thurs 7:45am-Midnight, Fri 7:45-5, Sat 10-5, Sun 3-Midnight;
Mon, Wed & Fri (Summer) 8-5, Tues & Thurs 8am-9pm, Sat 12-5

P   JEFFERSON CITY PUBLIC LIBRARY*, 1427 Russell Ave, 37760. SAN
315-8128. Tel: 865-475-9094. FAX: 865-475-1253. TDD: 865-475-9094.
Dir, Barbara C Shelton; *Asst Librn,* Donna Phillips; Staff 2 (MLS 1,
Non-MLS 1)
Pop 22,905; Circ 30,748
Library Holdings: Bk Vols 28,482; Per Subs 62
Automation Activity & Vendor Info: (Cataloging) Follett Software;
(Circulation) Follett Software; (ILL) Auto-Graphics, Inc; (OPAC) Follett
Software
Special Services for the Deaf - TTY equip
Open Mon, Wed & Fri 10-5, Tues & Thurs 11:30-6:30, Sat 9-2
Friends of the Library Group

JELLICO

P   JELLICO PUBLIC LIBRARY*, 104 N Main St, 37762-2004. SAN
315-8144. Tel: 423-784-7488. FAX: 423-784-8745. *Dir,* Mark J Tidwell
Library Holdings: Bk Vols 12,000; Per Subs 120
Open Mon-Thurs 12-5, Fri 10-3

JOHNSON CITY

EAST TENNESSEE STATE UNIVERSITY

CM   JAMES H QUILLEN COLLEGE OF MEDICINE LIBRARY*, Maple St,
Bldg 4, 37614. (Mail add: PO Box 70693, 37614-0693), SAN 360-5949.
Tel: 423-439-6252. Circulation Tel: 423-439-6253. Interlibrary Loan
Service Tel: 423-439-7032. Reference Tel: 423-439-6246, 423-439-6254.
FAX: 423-439-7025. E-mail: medref@etsu.edu. Web Site:

com.etsu.edu/medlib. *Dir,* Biddanda (Suresh) P Ponnappa; Tel:
423-439-6355, E-mail: ponnappa@etsu.edu; *Res Mgr,* Martha Whaley;
Tel: 423-439-8069, E-mail: whaleym@etsu.edu; *Pub Serv Mgr,* Richard
Wallace; Tel: 423-439-8071, E-mail: wallacer@etsu.edu. Subject
Specialists: *Hist of med,* Martha Whaley; Staff 15 (MLS 5, Non-MLS
10)
Founded 1975. Fac 4; Highest Degree: Master
Library Holdings: Bk Vols 45,336; Per Subs 618
Special Collections: History of Medicine Coll; Long Coll
Automation Activity & Vendor Info: (Acquisitions) Ex Libris Group;
(Cataloging) Ex Libris Group; (Circulation) Ex Libris Group; (Course
Reserve) Ex Libris Group; (OPAC) Ex Libris Group; (Serials) Ex Libris
Group
Database Vendor: 3M Library Systems, Blackwell's, Cambridge
Scientific Abstracts, EBSCOhost, Elsevier MDL, Gale Cengage Learning,
ISI Web of Knowledge, JSTOR, LexisNexis, OVID Technologies,
ProQuest, PubMed, ScienceDirect, STAT!Ref (Teton Data Systems),
UpToDate, Wiley
Function: Res libr
Partic in Consortium of Southern Biomedical Libraries; Tenn-Share;
Tri-Cities Area Health Sciences Libraries Consortium
Open Mon-Thurs 8am-Midnight, Fri 8-8, Sat 10-6, Sun 1-Midnight

C   SHERROD LIBRARY, Seehorn Dr & Lake St, 37614-0204. (Mail add: PO
Box 70665, 37614-1701), SAN 360-5914. Tel: 423-439-4337. Circulation
Tel: 423-439-4303. Interlibrary Loan Service Tel: 423-439-6998.
Reference Tel: 423-439-4307. Automation Services Tel: 423-439-4713.
FAX: 423-439-5222. Reference FAX: 423-439-4720. E-mail:
refdesk@etsu.edu. Web Site: sherrod.etsu.edu. *Dean,* Patricia Van Zandt;
E-mail: vanzandt@etsu.edu; *Asst Dean, Grad Prog Librn,* Marie Jones;
Tel: 423-439-4336, E-mail: jonesmf@etsu.edu; *Head, Acq,* Kelly
Hensley; Tel: 423-439-5815, Fax: 423-439-4410, E-mail:
hensleyk@etsu.edu; *Head, Govt Doc,* Mark Ellis; Tel: 423-439-4715,
E-mail: ellism@etsu.edu; *Head, Ref,* Kathy Campbell; Tel:
423-439-5629, E-mail: campbeka@etsu.edu; *Distance Educ Librn,*
Joanna Anderson; Tel: 423-439-4714, E-mail: andersonjm@etsu.edu; *Fac
Outreach Librn,* Rebecca Tolley-Stokes; Tel: 423-439-4365, E-mail:
tolleyst@etsu.edu; *Student Serv Librn,* Leslie Adebonojo; Tel:
423-439-4308, E-mail: adebonol@etsu.edu; *Syst Librn,* Celia Szarejko;
E-mail: szarejko@etsu.edu; *Cat,* Katy Libby; Tel: 423-439-6992, Fax:
423-439-4410, E-mail: libby@etsu.edu; *Electronic Res,* Jerry Shuttle; Tel:
423-439-6996, Fax: 423-439-4410, E-mail: shuttle@etsu.edu; *ILL,* Alison
DePollo; E-mail: depollo@etsu.edu; Staff 14 (MLS 12, Non-MLS 2)
Founded 1911. Enrl 14,662; Fac 866; Highest Degree: Doctorate
Jul 2011-Jun 2012 Income $3,369,230. Mats Exp $1,325,796, Books
$136,617, Per/Ser (Incl. Access Fees) $647,945, AV Mat $22,185,
Electronic Ref Mat (Incl. Access Fees) $518,704, Presv $345. Sal
$1,441,364 (Prof $639,540)
Library Holdings: AV Mats 22,056; e-books 79,932; Bk Vols 487,474;
Per Subs 476
Special Collections: State Document Depository; US Document
Depository
Subject Interests: Sports
Automation Activity & Vendor Info: (Acquisitions) Innovative
Interfaces, Inc; (Cataloging) Innovative Interfaces, Inc; (Circulation)
Innovative Interfaces, Inc; (Course Reserve) Innovative Interfaces, Inc;
(OPAC) Innovative Interfaces, Inc; (Serials) Innovative Interfaces, Inc
Function: ILL available
Partic in Lyrasis; OCLC Online Computer Library Center, Inc;
OCLC-LVIS; TBR Consortium; Tenn Share; Tennessee Health Science
Library Association
Special Services for the Deaf - TDD equip
Special Services for the Blind - Reader equip
Friends of the Library Group

R   EMMANUEL SCHOOL OF RELIGION LIBRARY*, One Walker Dr,
37601-9438. SAN 315-8152. Tel: 423-926-1186. Interlibrary Loan Service
Tel: 423-461-1543. FAX: 423-926-6198. E-mail: library@esr.edu. Web
Site: www.esr.edu/library.htm. *Librn,* Thomas E Stokes; *Asst Librn,* John
Mark Wade; *Circ,* Marsha Conner; *ILL,* Chris Quillen; Staff 2 (MLS 2)
Founded 1965. Enrl 150; Fac 10; Highest Degree: Doctorate
Library Holdings: AV Mats 1,415; Bk Vols 116,314; Per Subs 712
Special Collections: Discipliana Coll, historical materials pertaining to the
Christian Churches & Churches of Christ
Automation Activity & Vendor Info: (Cataloging) TLC (The Library
Corporation); (Circulation) TLC (The Library Corporation); (Course
Reserve) TLC (The Library Corporation); (ILL) OCLC; (OPAC) TLC (The
Library Corporation); (Serials) TLC (The Library Corporation)
Partic in Lyrasis; Tri-Cities Area Health Sciences Libraries Consortium
Open Mon-Thurs 7:30am-10pm, Fri 7:30-5, Sat 9-4

P   HOLSTON RIVER REGIONAL LIBRARY*, (Formerly Watauga Regional
Library), 2700 S Roan St, Ste 435, 37601-7587. SAN 315-8179. Tel:
423-926-2951. FAX: 423-926-2956. *Dir,* Nancy Renfro; E-mail:
nrenfro@wrlibrary.org; Staff 6 (MLS 1, Non-MLS 5)

Founded 1942. Pop 415,063
Special Collections: Local History Coll; Professional Resources Coll
Automation Activity & Vendor Info: (Acquisitions) Ex Libris Group;
(Cataloging) Ex Libris Group; (Circulation) Ex Libris Group; (ILL) OCLC
Online; (OPAC) Ex Libris Group; (Serials) Ex Libris Group
Database Vendor: Gale Cengage Learning
Member Libraries: Bristol Public Library; Johnson City Public Library;
Kingsport Public Library & Archives; Mosheim Public Library; Sullivan
County Public Library; Unicoi County Public Library; Washington County
- Jonesborough Library
Special Services for the Blind - Integrated libr/media serv
Open Mon-Fri 8-4:30

P   JOHNSON CITY PUBLIC LIBRARY*, 100 W Millard St, 37604. SAN
315-8160. Tel: 423-434-4450. Circulation Tel: 423-434-4455. Reference
Tel: 423-434-4454. FAX: 423-434-4469. Web Site: www.jcpl.net. *Dir,*
Robert Swanay; Tel: 423-434-4457, E-mail: rswanay@jcpl.net; *Asst Dir,
Adm Serv,* Cathy Griffith; Tel: 423-434-4463, E-mail: cgriffith@jcpl.net;
Cat Librn, Linda Heck Blanton; Tel: 423-434-4462, E-mail:
lblanton@jcpl.net; *Adult Serv Mgr,* Holly Russo; Tel: 423-434-4354,
E-mail: hrusso@jcpl.net; *Circ Mgr,* Gina Thayer-Coleman; Tel:
423-434-4465, E-mail: gcoleman@jcpl.net; *Info Tech Mgr,* Eric Jon Job;
Tel: 423-434-4468, E-mail: ejjob@jcpl.net; *Tech Serv Mgr,* Esther
Pawlowicz; Tel: 423-434-4343, E-mail: estherp@jcpl.net; *Youth Serv Mgr,*
Betty Cobb; Tel: 423-434-4350, E-mail: bcobb@jcpl.net; Staff 38 (MLS 8,
Non-MLS 30)
Founded 1895. Pop 71,183; Circ 409,205
Jul 2009-Jun 2010 Income (Main Library Only) $1,713,819, City
$1,475,750, Federal $15,000, County $100,000, Locally Generated Income
$120,140. Mats Exp $159,035, Books $93,090, AV Mat $27,479,
Electronic Ref Mat (Incl. Access Fees) $4,944. Sal $1,182,078
Library Holdings: AV Mats 10,475; Microforms 19,045; Bk Vols
130,954; Per Subs 371
Subject Interests: Local hist
Automation Activity & Vendor Info: (Acquisitions) Innovative Interfaces,
Inc - Millenium; (Cataloging) OCLC; (Circulation) Innovative Interfaces,
Inc - Millenium; (ILL) OCLC; (OPAC) Innovative Interfaces, Inc -
Millenium; (Serials) EBSCO Online
Database Vendor: EBSCO Auto Repair Reference, Gale Cengage
Learning, OCLC FirstSearch
Wireless access
Mem of Holston River Regional Library
Open Mon-Thurs 9-8, Fri & Sat 9-6, Sun (Sept-May) 1-6
Friends of the Library Group

L   LEGAL AID OF EAST TENNESSEE LIBRARY*, 311 W Walnut St,
37604. (Mail add: PO Box 360, 37605-0360), SAN 320-2372. Tel:
423-928-8311. Toll Free Tel: 800-821-1312. FAX: 423-928-9488. Web
Site: www.laet.org. *Exec Dir,* David Yoder
Founded 1977
Library Holdings: Bk Vols 2,000; Per Subs 37
Open Mon-Fri 8-12 (1-5 Summer)

M   MOUNTAIN STATES HEALTH ALLIANCE*, Johnson City Medical
Center Learning Resources Center, 400 N State of Franklin Rd,
37604-6094. SAN 371-6481. Tel: 423-431-1691. FAX: 423-431-1692.
E-mail: medicallibrary@msha.com. Web Site:
www.msha.com/facility.cfm?id=47. *Coordr,* Bobbi Kahan; Staff 3 (MLS 2,
Non-MLS 1)
Founded 1981
Library Holdings: Bk Titles 850; Per Subs 25
Subject Interests: Cancer, Med, Nursing, Pediatrics, Surgery
Database Vendor: EBSCOhost, Gale Cengage Learning
Partic in Med Libr Asn, Southern Chapter; National Network of Libraries
of Medicine South Central Region; SEND; Tennessee Health Science
Library Association; Tri-Cities Area Health Sciences Libraries Consortium
Open Mon-Fri 6am-4:30pm

JONESBOROUGH

P   WASHINGTON COUNTY - JONESBOROUGH LIBRARY*, 200 Sabin
Dr, 37659-1306. SAN 360-6007. Tel: 423-753-1800. FAX: 423-753-1802.
Web Site: www.wrlibrary.org/Libraries/washco.htm. *Dir,* Patricia H Beard;
E-mail: pbeard@wrlibrary.org; *Br Mgr,* Dorothy Linton; E-mail:
dlinton@wrlibrary.org; *Br Mgr,* Lusetta Slagle; Staff 14.25 (MLS 3,
Non-MLS 11.25)
Founded 1896. Pop 45,003; Circ 113,042
Library Holdings: AV Mats 6,153; e-books 773; Bk Vols 73,969; Per
Subs 72
Special Collections: Railroad Coll
Subject Interests: Genealogy, Local hist
Automation Activity & Vendor Info: (Acquisitions) Ex Libris Group;
(Cataloging) Ex Libris Group; (Circulation) Ex Libris Group; (Course
Reserve) Ex Libris Group; (ILL) Auto-Graphics, Inc; (Media Booking) Ex
Libris Group; (OPAC) Ex Libris Group; (Serials) Ex Libris Group

Database Vendor: ProQuest
Function: Adult literacy prog, Fax serv, ILL available,
Photocopying/Printing, Prog for adults, Prog for children & young adult,
Ref serv available, Summer reading prog, Tax forms
Mem of Holston River Regional Library
Partic in SouthWest Information Network Group (SWING); Tenn-Share
Special Services for the Blind - Audio mat; Bks on cassette; Large print
bks; Talking bks
Open Mon & Thurs 9-8, Tues, Wed & Fri 9-6, Sat 9-2
Friends of the Library Group
Branches: 1
GRAY BRANCH, 5026 Bobby Hicks Hwy, Gray, 37615-3461, SAN
360-6031. Tel: 423-477-1550. FAX: 423-477-1553. *Br Mgr,* Lusetta
Slagle; Tel: 423-477-1559, E-mail: lslagle@wrlibrary.org; Staff 5 (MLS
1, Non-MLS 4)
Founded 1968
Automation Activity & Vendor Info: (Acquisitions) Innovative
Interfaces, Inc - Millenium; (Cataloging) Innovative Interfaces, Inc -
Millenium; (Circulation) Innovative Interfaces, Inc - Millenium; (OPAC)
Innovative Interfaces, Inc - Millenium; (Serials) Innovative Interfaces, Inc
- Millenium
Mem of Holston River Regional Library
Open Mon, Wed & Thurs 9-6, Tues 9-8, Fri 9-5, Sat 9-12
Friends of the Library Group

KINGSPORT

S   EASTMAN CHEMICAL CO*, Library & Information Services, Bldg
150B, PO Box 1972, 37662-5150. SAN 371-6805. Tel: 423-229-1845.
FAX: 423-229-6114. Web Site: www.eastman.com. *Supvr,* Mary Fanslow;
Librn, Gail Preslar; Staff 10 (MLS 4, Non-MLS 6)
Founded 1944
Library Holdings: Bk Vols 10,000
Wireless access
Open Mon-Fri 8-5
Branches:
BUSINESS LIBRARY, Bldg 280, Lincoln St, 37662-5280. (Mail add: PO
Box 431, 37662-0431), SAN 360-6155. Tel: 423-229-2071. FAX:
423-224-0111. E-mail: buslib@eastman.com. *Info Spec,* Gail Preslar; Tel:
423-229-6117
Founded 1947
Library Holdings: Bk Vols 3,000; Per Subs 300
Special Collections: Company Annual Reports; Resources for Doing
Business Outside USA (culture, customs, government restrictions, etc);
State Industrial Directories
Subject Interests: Bus mgt, Economics, Indust relations, Mkt
RESEARCH LIBRARY, Bldg 150B, 37662. (Mail add: PO Box 1972,
37662-5150), SAN 360-6120. Tel: 423-229-4290. FAX: 423-224-0519.
E-mail: reslib@eastman.com. *Team Mgr,* Debra Bledsoe; *Info Scientist,*
Mike Ramsey
Founded 1944
Library Holdings: Bk Titles 24,000; Per Subs 850
Special Collections: Beilstein Coll; Chemical Abstracts; Four Million
US & Foreign Patents; Government Reports
Subject Interests: Fiber tech, Organ chem incl polymers, Pharmaceutical
chem, Textile tech
Open Mon-Fri 7-4:30

M   HOLSTON VALLEY MEDICAL CENTER, Health Science Library, 130
W Ravine Rd, 37660. SAN 327-1013. Tel: 423-224-6870. FAX:
423-224-6014. E-mail: library@wellmont.org. Web Site:
www.wellmont.org. *Librn,* Sharon M Brown; E-mail:
sharon.brown@wellmont.org
Library Holdings: Bk Titles 1,000; Bk Vols 1,000; Per Subs 175
Subject Interests: Allied health, Med, Nursing
Partic in SE-Atlantic Regional Med Libr Servs; Tennessee Health Science
Library Association; Tri-Cities Area Health Sciences Libraries Consortium
Open Mon-Fri 8-4:30

P   KINGSPORT PUBLIC LIBRARY & ARCHIVES, J Fred Johnson
Memorial Library, 400 Broad St, 37660-4292. SAN 360-6066. Tel:
423-224-2539. FAX: 423-224-2558. E-mail: kptlib@wrlibrary.org. Web
Site: www.kingsportlibrary.org. *Mgr,* Helen Whittaker; Tel: 423-229-9488,
E-mail: hwhittaker@wrlibrary.org; *Asst Mgr,* Hannah Powell; E-mail:
hpowell@wrlibrary.org; *Hist Coll Librn,* Helen Hamilton; E-mail:
hhamilton@wrlibrary.org; *Archivist,* Brianne Wright; Tel: 423-224-2559,
E-mail: bwright@wrlibrary.org; *Cat,* Lennea Hickam; Tel: 423-229-9369,
E-mail: lhickam@wrlibrary.org; *Ref Serv,* Tina Spencer; E-mail:
tspencer@wrlibrary.org; Staff 8 (MLS 5, Non-MLS 3)
Founded 1921. Pop 44,905; Circ 237,389
Jul 2009-Jun 2010 Income $1,196,200. Mats Exp $144,000. Sal $896,700
Library Holdings: Bk Vols 177,790; Per Subs 354
Special Collections: Archives of the City of Kingsport; First Tennessee
Bank Small Business Center; Job & College Info Center; Palmer Regional
History Coll

Subject Interests: Local hist
Automation Activity & Vendor Info: (Acquisitions) Innovative Interfaces, Inc - Millenium; (Cataloging) Auto-Graphics, Inc; (Circulation) Innovative Interfaces, Inc - Millenium; (ILL) OCLC; (OPAC) Innovative Interfaces, Inc - Millenium; (Serials) Ex Libris Group
Database Vendor: Evanced Solutions, Inc, Gale Cengage Learning, H W Wilson, Innovative Interfaces, Inc, Overdrive, Inc, ProQuest, TumbleBookLibrary, World Book Online
Wireless access
Function: Adult bk club, Archival coll, Audiobks via web, Bks on cassette, Bks on CD, Children's prog, Computer training, Computers for patron use, Copy machines, Digital talking bks, e-mail & chat, E-Reserves, Electronic databases & coll, Exhibits, Free DVD rentals, Games & aids for the handicapped, Handicapped accessible, Health sci info serv, Holiday prog, Home delivery & serv to Sr ctr & nursing homes, Homebound delivery serv, ILL available, Magnifiers for reading, Mail & tel request accepted, Music CDs, Online cat, Online ref, Online searches, Outreach serv, OverDrive digital audio bks, Photocopying/Printing, Preschool outreach, Prof lending libr, Prog for adults, Prog for children & young adult, Pub access computers, Ref & res, Ref serv available, Ref serv in person, Scanner, Senior computer classes, Senior outreach, Spoken cassettes & CDs, Spoken cassettes & DVDs, Story hour, Summer reading prog, Tax forms, Teen prog, Telephone ref, VCDs, VHS videos, Web-catalog, Wheelchair accessible, Workshops
Publications: Footnotes (Friends of Library quarterly newsletter); Kingsport Public Library (Monthly newsletter)
Mem of Holston River Regional Library
Partic in Tenn-Share
Special Services for the Deaf - Bks on deafness & sign lang; High interest/low vocabulary bks; TTY equip
Special Services for the Blind - Assistive/Adapted tech devices, equip & products; Home delivery serv
Open Mon-Thurs 9-8, Fri & Sat 9-5:30
Restriction: Restricted borrowing privileges
Friends of the Library Group

KINGSTON

P   KINGSTON PUBLIC LIBRARY*, 10004 Bradford Way, 37763. SAN 315-8217. Tel: 865-376-9905. FAX: 865-376-2301. E-mail: directorkpl@bellsouth.net. Web Site: kpltn.org. *Dir,* Steve Jacks; *Asst Dir,* Diana Cash; *Ch,* Barbara Thorbjornsen
Founded 1947. Pop 15,000; Circ 45,000
Library Holdings: Bk Vols 21,000; Per Subs 35
Special Collections: Oral History
Subject Interests: County genealogy, Hist, Tenn hist
Automation Activity & Vendor Info: (Cataloging) SirsiDynix; (Circulation) SirsiDynix; (ILL) SirsiDynix
Open Mon-Thurs 9-7, Fri 9-5:30, Sat 10-4
Friends of the Library Group

KINGSTON SPRINGS

P   SOUTH CHEATHAM PUBLIC LIBRARY*, 358 N Main St, 37082. (Mail add: PO Box 310, 37082-0310), SAN 373-9317. Tel: 615-952-4752. FAX: 615-952-3803. E-mail: soucpl@comcast.net. Web Site: www.kingstonspringslibrary.org. *Dir,* Janet Walker; Staff 4 (MLS 1, Non-MLS 3)
Founded 1986. Pop 14,948; Circ 32,140
Library Holdings: Large Print Bks 230; Bk Vols 16,400; Per Subs 18; Videos 675
Special Collections: Juvenile Poetry (Brewton/Blackburn Coll). Oral History
Automation Activity & Vendor Info: (Cataloging) Book Systems, Inc; (ILL) Auto-Graphics, Inc
Special Services for the Deaf - High interest/low vocabulary bks; TTY equip
Open Mon, Tues & Thurs 10-8, Wed, Fri & Sat 10-4:30
Friends of the Library Group

KNOXVILLE

M   COVENANT HEALTH, Fort Sanders Regional Medical Center-Medical/Nursing Library, 1915 White Ave, 3rd Flr, 37916. SAN 315-8241. Tel: 865-541-1293. FAX: 865-541-1762. *Librn,* Nedra Johnson Cook; E-mail: ncook@covhlth.com; Staff 1 (MLS 1)
Founded 1949
Library Holdings: e-books 70; e-journals 2,000; Bk Titles 4,500; Per Subs 88
Special Collections: Historical Nursing Coll; National League for Nursing Coll
Subject Interests: Nursing
Database Vendor: EBSCO Information Services, EBSCOhost, Gale Cengage Learning, JSTOR, Majors, Marcive, Inc, Micromedex, OVID Technologies, ProQuest, PubMed, STAT!Ref (Teton Data Systems), WebMD, Westlaw, Wiley InterScience, World Book Online

Function: Doc delivery serv, Health sci info serv, ILL available, Online searches, Photocopying/Printing, Ref serv available, Telephone ref
Partic in Docline; Knoxville Area Health Sciences Library Consortium; SE Network of Hospital Librs on Docline; Tenn-Share; Tennessee Health Science Library Association
Open Mon-Fri 8:30-5
Restriction: Private libr

R   FIRST CHRISTIAN CHURCH*, Winona Roehl Library, 211 W Fifth Ave, 37917. SAN 315-8233. Tel: 865-522-0545. FAX: 865-521-6266. Web Site: www.achurch.com. *In Charge,* Mary Topping
Founded 1955
Library Holdings: Bk Vols 3,514
Special Collections: Local Poetry (Elizabeth Merchant Coll); Stanley Jones Coll
Publications: Christmount Voice; Disciple; Tennessee Christian

CR   JOHNSON BIBLE COLLEGE*, Glass Memorial Library, 7900 Johnson Dr, 37998. Tel: 865-251-2277. FAX: 865-251-2278. E-mail: library@johnsonu.edu. Web Site: www.johnsonu.edu. *Dir,* Carrie Beth Lowe; E-mail: CBLowe@johnsonu.edu; *Asst Librn,* Jon Hale; E-mail: JHale@johnsonu.edu; *Circ,* Heidi Berryhill; *Per,* Denny Eaton; E-mail: deaton@jbc.edu; *Tech Serv,* Jan Christy; E-mail: jchristy@jbc.edu; Staff 5 (MLS 2, Non-MLS 3)
Founded 1893. Enrl 821; Fac 63; Highest Degree: Master
Library Holdings: AV Mats 14,372; e-books 31,442; Microforms 19,531; Bk Titles 73,240; Bk Vols 108,126; Per Subs 395
Special Collections: Religion (Restoration Movement)
Automation Activity & Vendor Info: (Acquisitions) TLC (The Library Corporation); (Cataloging) TLC (The Library Corporation); (Circulation) TLC (The Library Corporation); (OPAC) TLC (The Library Corporation)
Database Vendor: Alexander Street Press, ARTstor, EBSCOhost, Gale Cengage Learning, Greenwood Publishing Group, H W Wilson, JSTOR, netLibrary, OCLC FirstSearch, OCLC WorldCat, ProQuest, Swets Information Services, Wiley, Wilson - Wilson Web
Wireless access
Partic in Appalachian Col Asn; Christian Library Consortium; Tenn Share
Open Mon-Thurs (Fall & Spring) 7:45am-10:30pm, Fri 7:45-5, Sat 10-5; Mon & Tues (Summer) 8-6, Wed & Fri 8-5, Thurs 8-8

GL   KNOX COUNTY GOVERNMENTAL LAW LIBRARY*, Honorable Sharon J Bell Library, M-99 City County Bldg, 400 Main St, 37902. SAN 327-6694. Tel: 865-215-2368. FAX: 865-215-2920, 865-215-4283. *Actg Chief Librn,* Katherine Meredith Douglas; E-mail: meredith.douglas@knoxcounty.org
Library Holdings: Bk Vols 60,000
Subject Interests: Legal
Database Vendor: Westlaw
Open Mon-Fri 8:30-6
Restriction: Access at librarian's discretion, Authorized patrons, Circ to mem only

P   KNOX COUNTY PUBLIC LIBRARY SYSTEM*, Lawson McGhee Library-East Tennessee History Center, 500 W Church Ave, 37902-2505. SAN 360-618X. Tel: 865-215-8750. Interlibrary Loan Service Tel: 865-215-8746. Reference Tel: 865-215-8700. Administration Tel: 865-215-8701. Automation Services Tel: 865-215-8711. FAX: 865-215-8742. TDD: 865-215-8733, 865-215-8765. E-mail: reference@knoxlib.org. Web Site: www.knoxlib.org. *Dir,* Larry Frank; E-mail: lfrank@knoxlib.org; *Asst Dir,* Myretta Black; *Bus Librn, Ref Librn,* Thomas Whisman; *Hist Coll Librn,* Steve Cotham; Tel: 865-215-8808, E-mail: scotham@knoxlib.org; *Archives Mgr, Archivist,* Doris Martinson; Tel: 865-215-8804, E-mail: dmartinson@knoxlib.org; *Automation Syst Mgr,* Sally Lodico; E-mail: slodico@knoxlib.org; *Cent Libr Mgr,* Nelda Hill; Tel: 865-215-8729, E-mail: nhill@knoxlib.org; *Mgr, Coll Develop,* Nancy Petersen; *Mgr, Ref Serv,* Janet Drumheller; Tel: 865-215-8723, E-mail: jdrumheller@knoxlib.org; *Circ Supvr,* Stephanie Faulkner; *Planning, Res Projects Coordr,* Rene Jordan; Tel: 865-215-8716, E-mail: rjordan@knoxlib.org; *Communications Adminr, Pub Relations,* Mary Pomeroy Claiborne; Tel: 865-215-8767, E-mail: mclaiborne@knoxlib.org; *ILL,* Willa Reister; E-mail: wreister@knoxlib.org; Staff 27 (MLS 27)
Founded 1886. Pop 430,019; Circ 406,752
Jul 2008-Jun 2009 Income (Main Library and Branch(s)) $12,645,721, State $5,000, County $12,285,560, Locally Generated Income $355,161. Mats Exp $2,356,936, Electronic Ref Mat (Incl. Access Fees) $121,989. Sal $8,274,621
Library Holdings: AV Mats 22,127; e-books 57; Electronic Media & Resources 78; Microforms 39,757; Bk Vols 1,040,078; Per Subs 1,122
Special Collections: History & Genealogy of Tennessee & the Southeast (Calvin M McClung Historical Coll); Knox County Archives. US Document Depository
Automation Activity & Vendor Info: (Cataloging) SirsiDynix; (Circulation) SirsiDynix; (OPAC) SirsiDynix
Wireless access

Function: Adult bk club, After school storytime, Archival coll, Art exhibits, Audiobks via web, AV serv, Bk club(s), Bks on cassette, Bks on CD, Bus archives, Children's prog, Citizenship assistance, Computer training, Computers for patron use, Copy machines, Digital talking bks, e-mail serv, E-Reserves, Electronic databases & coll, Exhibits, Fax serv, Genealogy discussion group, Handicapped accessible, Homebound delivery serv, ILL available, Instruction & testing, Jazz prog, Mail & tel request accepted, Music CDs, Online cat, Online ref, Online searches, Outreach serv, OverDrive digital audio bks, Photocopying/Printing, Prog for adults, Prog for children & young adult, Pub access computers, Ref & res, Ref serv available, Ref serv in person, Spoken cassettes & CDs, Spoken cassettes & DVDs, Story hour, Summer reading prog, Teen prog, Telephone ref, VHS videos, Video lending libr, Web-catalog, Wheelchair accessible, Workshops

Partic in Lyrasis; OCLC Online Computer Library Center, Inc; Tenn-Share
Special Services for the Deaf - TDD equip
Special Services for the Blind - Audio mat; Bks on cassette; Bks on CD; Digital talking bk; Duplicating spec requests; Extensive large print coll; Home delivery serv; Integrated libr/media serv; Large print & cassettes; Large print bks; Magnifiers; PC for handicapped; Recorded bks; Sound rec; Talking bk serv referral
Open Mon, Tues & Thurs 10-8, Wed, Fri & Sat 10-5:30
Restriction: Non-circulating coll, Non-circulating of rare bks
Friends of the Library Group
Branches: 17
BURLINGTON BRANCH, 4614 Asheville Hwy, 37914, SAN 360-621X. Tel: 865-525-5431. FAX: 865-525-4648. *Br Mgr,* Jeff Johnston
Circ 63,132
Library Holdings: Bk Vols 19,804
Open Mon 1-8, Tues & Wed 10-5:30, Thurs 12-5:30, Fri 1-5:30
CARTER BRANCH, 9036 Asheville Hwy, 37924, SAN 360-6244. Tel: 865-933-5438. FAX: 865-932-1221. *Br Mgr,* Melanie Reseigh
Circ 31,814
Library Holdings: Bk Vols 16,367
Open Tues 12-8, Wed, Thurs & Sat 10-6
CEDAR BLUFF BRANCH, 9045 Cross Park Dr, Cedar Bluff, 37923, SAN 377-6522. Tel: 865-470-7033. FAX: 865-470-0927. *Br Mgr,* Jackie Hill; Staff 1 (MLS 1)
Circ 309,824
Library Holdings: Bk Vols 85,974
Open Mon 10-8, Tues-Fri 10-5:30, Thurs 12-8, Sat 1-5
CORRYTON BRANCH, 7733 Corryton Rd, Corryton, 37721-9802, SAN 360-6279. Tel: 865-688-1501. FAX: 865-687-7568. *Br Mgr,* Patricia Sue Walker
Circ 9,920
Library Holdings: Bk Vols 17,079
Open Mon, Tues, Thurs & Fri 1:30-5:30
FARRAGUT BRANCH, 417 N Campbell Station Rd, Farragut, 37922, SAN 360-6333. Tel: 865-777-1750. FAX: 865-777-1751. *Br Mgr,* Marilyn Jones; Staff 1 (MLS 1)
Circ 302,942
Library Holdings: Bk Vols 68,619
Open Mon, Wed-Fri 10-5:30, Tues 10-8, Sat 1-5
FOUNTAIN CITY BRANCH, 5300 Stanton Rd, 37918, SAN 360-6368. Tel: 865-689-2681. FAX: 865-689-3481. *Br Mgr,* Elizabeth Nelson; Staff 1 (MLS 1)
Circ 119,967
Library Holdings: Bk Vols 36,291
Open Mon, Wed-Fri 10-5:30, Tues 12-8, Sat 1-5
HALLS BRANCH, 4518 E Emory Rd, 37938, SAN 360-6392. Tel: 865-922-2552. FAX: 865-922-6543. *Br Mgr,* Sally Dill; Staff 1 (MLS 1)
Circ 136,457
Library Holdings: Bk Vols 41,754
Open Mon-Wed & Fri 10-5:30, Thurs 12-8, Sat 10-2
KARNS BRANCH, 7516 Oak Ridge Hwy, 37931-3333, SAN 360-6422. Tel: 865-470-8663. FAX: 865-693-7858. *Mgr,* Karen Van Rij
Circ 87,938
Library Holdings: Bk Vols 33,403
Open Tues 12-8, Wed & Thurs 10-6, Sat 10-5:30
MASCOT BRANCH, 2010 Library Rd, Mascot, 37806-9999, SAN 360-6457. Tel: 865-933-2620. FAX: 865-933-4239. *Br Mgr,* Ralph McGhee
Circ 30,227
Library Holdings: Bk Vols 16,553
Open Mon-Thurs 2-6
MURPHY BRANCH, L T Ross Bldg, 2247 Western Ave, 37921-5756, SAN 360-649X. Tel: 865-521-7812. FAX: 865-521-0962. *Br Mgr,* Sandra Chandler
Circ 9,469
Library Holdings: Bk Vols 10,928
Open Tues & Wed 10-5, Thurs 2-6

NORTH KNOXVILLE BRANCH, 2901 Ocoee Trail, 37917-3233, SAN 360-6511. Tel: 865-525-7036. FAX: 865-525-0796. *Br Mgr,* Tammie Morgan
Circ 50,397
Library Holdings: Bk Vols 25,355
NORWOOD BRANCH, 1110 Merchants Dr, 37912-4704, SAN 360-6546. Tel: 865-688-2454. FAX: 865-688-0677. *Br Mgr,* Honaker Laura
Circ 68,653
Library Holdings: Bk Vols 31,537
Open Mon 12-8, Tues-Thurs 10:30-5:30, Sat 1-5
HOWARD PINKSTON BRANCH, 7732 Martin Mill Pike, 37920. Tel: 865-573-0436. FAX: 865-573-1351. *Br Mgr,* Vicki Evans
Circ 57,009
Library Holdings: Bk Titles 25,191
Open Mon & Thurs 10-6, Tues 12-8, Sat 10-5:30
POWELL BRANCH, 330 W Emory Rd, 37938-4010, SAN 360-6570. Tel: 865-947-6210. FAX: 865-938-6466. *Br Mgr,* Carol Swaggerty; Staff 1 (MLS 1)
Circ 151,464
Library Holdings: Bk Vols 43,786
Open Mon & Wed-Fri 10-5:30, Tues 12-8, Sat 10-2
SEQUOYAH BRANCH, 1140 Southgate Rd, 37919-7646, SAN 360-6600. Tel: 865-525-1541. FAX: 865-525-3148. *Br Mgr,* Jan Miller
Circ 34,279
Library Holdings: Bk Vols 18,519
Open Mon 12-8, Tues, Thurs & Sat 9:30-5:30
SOUTH KNOXVILLE BRANCH, 4500 Chapman Hwy, 37920-4359, SAN 360-6635. Tel: 865-573-1772. FAX: 865-579-4912. *Br Mgr, Ch,* Fredda Williams; Staff 1 (MLS 1)
Circ 88,803
Library Holdings: Bk Vols 32,865
Open Mon-Wed & Fri 10-5:30, Thurs 12-8, Sat 1-5
WEST KNOXVILLE BRANCH, 100 Golf Club Rd, 37919-4801, SAN 360-6724. Tel: 865-588-8813. FAX: 865-588-7580. *Br Mgr,* Rebecca Dames; Staff 1 (MLS 1)
Circ 215,909
Library Holdings: Bk Vols 61,824
Open Mon-Wed & Fri 10-5:30, Thurs 12-8, Sat 10-2

C   KNOXVILLE COLLEGE*, Alumni Memorial Library, 901 Knoxville College Dr, 37921. SAN 315-8276. Tel: 865-524-6554. Circulation Tel: 865-524-6553. FAX: 865-524-6549. Web Site: www.knoxvillecollege.edu. *Dir,* Carolyn Ashkar; E-mail: caskhar@knoxvillecollege.edu; Staff 2 (MLS 2)
Founded 1876. Enrl 500; Fac 30; Highest Degree: Bachelor
Library Holdings: Bk Vols 97,000; Per Subs 205
Open Mon-Thurs 8am-10pm, Fri 8-5, Sat 10-2, Sun 3-10

G   KNOXVILLE-KNOX COUNTY METROPOLITAN PLANNING COMMISSION LIBRARY, City & County Bldg, Ste 403, 400 Main St, 37902-2476. SAN 326-5684. Tel: 865-215-2500. Reference Tel: 865-215-3829. FAX: 865-215-2068. E-mail: contact@knoxmpc.org. Web Site: www.knoxmpc.org. *Info & Res Mgr,* Terry Gilhula; E-mail: terry.gilhula@knoxmpc.org; Staff 2 (MLS 1, Non-MLS 1)
Founded 1975
Library Holdings: DVDs 216; Bk Titles 10,000; Per Subs 93; Videos 48
Subject Interests: Urban affairs
Automation Activity & Vendor Info: (Cataloging) New Generation Technologies Inc. (LiBRARYSOFT); (Circulation) New Generation Technologies Inc. (LiBRARYSOFT); (OPAC) New Generation Technologies Inc. (LiBRARYSOFT)
Function: ILL available, Photocopying/Printing, Ref serv available, Telephone ref
Publications: Catalogue of M P C Publications; Monthly Acquisitions
Restriction: Internal circ only, Open to pub for ref only, Pub use on premises

G   MUNICIPAL TECHNICAL ADVISORY SERVICE LIBRARY*, Univ Tennessee Conference Ctr Bldg, 600 Henley St, Ste 120, 37996-4105. SAN 327-6678. Tel: 865-974-0411. FAX: 865-974-0423. Web Site: www.mtas.utk.edu. *Info Res Mgr,* Frances Adams-O'Brien; Tel: 865-974-9842, E-mail: frances.adams-obrien@tennessee.edu; *Tech Serv,* Becky Smeltzer; Tel: 865-974-9841, E-mail: becky.smeltzer@tennessee.edu; Staff 3 (MLS 2, Non-MLS 1)
Founded 1950
Library Holdings: Bk Vols 10,000; Per Subs 120
Special Collections: City Ordinances; Municipal Law
Subject Interests: Municipal
Database Vendor: OCLC FirstSearch
Function: Res libr
Publications: Directory of Tennessee Municipal Officials
Partic in Lyrasis; Tenn-Share
Open Mon-Fri 8:30-5:30
Restriction: Not a lending libr

S   NATIONAL COLLEGE OF BUSINESS & TECHNOLOGY*, Knoxville Campus Library, 8415 Kingston Pike, 37919. Tel: 865-539-2011. FAX: 865-539-2049. E-mail: gborio@national-college.edu. Web Site: www.ncbt.edu/library. *Librn,* Gail Borio; E-mail: gborio@national-college.edu; Staff 1 (MLS 1)
Enrl 350; Highest Degree: Associate
Automation Activity & Vendor Info: (Cataloging) LibraryWorld, Inc; (Circulation) LibraryWorld, Inc; (OPAC) LibraryWorld, Inc
Function: Prog for adults
Open Mon-Fri 8am-10pm
Restriction: Open to students, fac & staff

J   PELLISSIPPI STATE TECHNICAL COMMUNITY COLLEGE*, Library Services, 10915 Harding Valley Rd, 37933. (Mail add: PO Box 22990, 37933-0990), SAN 327-8050. Tel: 865-694-6516. Reference Tel: 865-539-7107. FAX: 865-694-6625. E-mail: askref@pstcc.edu. Web Site: www.pstcc.edu/library. *Dir, Libr Serv,* Peter Nerzak; Tel: 865-694-6517, E-mail: pnerzak@pstcc.edu; *Acq, Coll Develop,* Karen Cornell; Tel: 865-694-6621, E-mail: kcornell@pstcc.edu; *Cat,* Jane Cameron; Tel: 865-694-6520, E-mail: jcameron@pstcc.edu; *Cat, Media Spec, Ref Serv,* Nina McPherson; Tel: 865-539-7237, E-mail: nmcpherson@pstcc.edu; *Circ,* Jean Jackson; Tel: 865-539-7047, E-mail: jejackson@pstcc.edu; *Ref Serv,* Rick Bower; Tel: 865-539-7106, E-mail: rbower@pstcc.edu. Subject Specialists: *Communications syst, Computer sci, Info tech,* Peter Nerzak; *Art, Educ, Interior design,* Karen Cornell; *Math, Sciences,* Jane Cameron; *Civil eng, Electrical eng, GIS,* Nina McPherson; *Hist, Sign lang, Women's studies,* Jean Jackson; *Communications, Lit, Paralegal studies,* Rick Bower; Staff 11 (MLS 7, Non-MLS 4)
Founded 1979. Enrl 6,000; Highest Degree: Associate
Library Holdings: Audiobooks 1,926; AV Mats 2,500; CDs 125; e-books 55,000; e-journals 5,000; Bk Titles 70,000; Per Subs 200; Videos 2,000
Automation Activity & Vendor Info: (Acquisitions) Innovative Interfaces, Inc - Millenium; (Cataloging) Innovative Interfaces, Inc - Millenium; (Circulation) Innovative Interfaces, Inc - Millenium; (Course Reserve) Innovative Interfaces, Inc - Millenium; (ILL) OCLC Online; (OPAC) Innovative Interfaces, Inc - Millenium; (Serials) Innovative Interfaces, Inc - Millenium
Database Vendor: 3M Library Systems, Alexander Street Press, American Psychological Association (APA), ARTstor, Baker & Taylor, CountryWatch, CQ Press, CredoReference, ebrary, EBSCOhost, Gale Cengage Learning, H W Wilson, JSTOR, Knovel, LexisNexis, McGraw-Hill, Modern Language Association, netLibrary, Newsbank, OCLC FirstSearch, OCLC WorldCat, Oxford Online, ProQuest, Safari Books Online, Springshare, LLC, Westlaw, Wilson - Wilson Web, WT Cox
Wireless access
Function: Audiobks via web, e-mail serv, Electronic databases & coll, Handicapped accessible, ILL available, Online cat, Online ref, Online searches, Outside serv via home, mail, e-mail & web, Photocopying/Printing, Ref serv available, Scanner, Telephone ref, Web-catalog
Partic in Lyrasis; OCLC Online Computer Library Center, Inc; Tenn-Share
Open Mon-Thurs 7:30-7:30, Fri 7:30-6, Sat 10-4
Restriction: Open to students, fac & staff

C   SOUTH COLLEGE LIBRARY*, 3904 Lonas Dr, 37909. SAN 328-5758. Tel: 865-251-1750, 865-251-1832. Web Site: www.southcollegetn.edu. *Head Librn,* Mel McHugh; *Acq Librn,* Michael Schneider; *Cat Librn,* Kathleen Kitzmiller; *Ref Librn,* Anya Furman; *Ref Librn,* Joy Johnson; Staff 5 (MLS 4, Non-MLS 1)
Enrl 750; Highest Degree: Master
Library Holdings: CDs 90; DVDs 175; e-books 28,000; e-journals 12,000; Bk Vols 7,800; Per Subs 226; Videos 830
Subject Interests: Allied health, Bus, Law
Wireless access
Function: Electronic databases & coll, Online cat, Orientations
Open Mon-Thurs 8am-9:30pm, Fri 8-4, Sat 8-1
Restriction: Not open to pub, Open to students, fac & staff

TENNESSEE VALLEY AUTHORITY

L   LEGAL RESEARCH CENTER*, 400 W Summit Hill Dr, 37922, SAN 360-6813. Tel: 865-632-6613. FAX: 865-632-6718. *Librn,* Deborah Cherry; E-mail: dacherry@tva.gov; Staff 5 (MLS 5)
Founded 1935
Library Holdings: Bk Vols 26,000; Per Subs 13
Subject Interests: Case law, Eminent domain, Energy, Environment, Fed practice, Fed statutory, Procurement, Pub utilities, Water law
Partic in Dialog Corp; Vutext; Westlaw
Open Mon-Fri 8-4:30
Restriction: Not open to pub, Staff use only

S   TVA RESEARCH LIBRARY-KNOXVILLE*, WT CC - K, 400 W Summit Hill Dr, 37902, SAN 360-6759. Tel: 865-632-3464. Interlibrary Loan Service Tel: 423-751-4916. FAX: 865-632-4475. E-mail: corplibknox@tva.gov. *Ref Librn,* Nancy Proctor; Tel: 865-632-7865, E-mail: njproctor@tva.gov; Staff 1 (MLS 1)

Founded 1933
Library Holdings: Bk Vols 16,685
Special Collections: TVA History Coll
Subject Interests: Econ develop, Electric power production, Flood control
Partic in Dialog Corp; Fedlink; OCLC Online Computer Library Center, Inc
Publications: Environmental & Corporate Current Awareness Lists
Restriction: Open to pub by appt only

CL   UNIVERSITY OF TENNESSEE*, Joel A Katz Law Library, Taylor Law Center, 1505 W Cumberland Ave, 37996-1800. SAN 360-6937. Tel: 865-974-7419. Reference Tel: 865-974-3771. FAX: 865-974-6571, 865-974-6595. Web Site: www.law.utk.edu/library/. *Dir,* William J Beintema; Tel: 865-974-4381, E-mail: beintema@tennessee.edu; *Assoc Dir, Head, Tech Serv,* D Cheryn Picquet; Tel: 865-974-6729, E-mail: dpicquet@utk.edu; *Head, Cat,* Reba A Best; Tel: 865-974-6728, E-mail: rbest2@tennessee.edu; *Head, Pub Serv,* Sibyl Marshall; Tel: 865-974-5906, E-mail: smarshal@utk.edu; *Mgr, Network Serv,* Bill Hodges; Tel: 865-974-2547, E-mail: bhodges@utk.edu; *Supvr, Govt Docs,* Dawn Adkins; Tel: 865-974-6724, E-mail: dadkins@tennessee.edu; *Acq,* M Loretta Price; Tel: 865-974-9746, E-mail: mprice@utk.edu; *Cat,* Carol Collins; Tel: 865-974-6552, E-mail: ccollin1@utk.edu; *Electronic Res,* Cathy Cochran; Tel: 865-974-0236, E-mail: cochran@utk.edu; Staff 22 (MLS 9, Non-MLS 13)
Founded 1890. Enrl 478; Fac 35; Highest Degree: Doctorate
Library Holdings: Bk Titles 95,337; Bk Vols 483,372; Per Subs 6,363
Special Collections: US Document Depository
Automation Activity & Vendor Info: (Acquisitions) Innovative Interfaces, Inc; (Cataloging) Innovative Interfaces, Inc; (Circulation) Innovative Interfaces, Inc; (Course Reserve) Innovative Interfaces, Inc; (OPAC) Innovative Interfaces, Inc; (Serials) Innovative Interfaces, Inc
Database Vendor: Gale Cengage Learning, Innovative Interfaces, Inc INN - View, LexisNexis, OCLC FirstSearch, Wilson - Wilson Web
Wireless access
Function: Res libr
Partic in Association of Research Libraries (ARL); Lyrasis
Open Mon-Thurs (Winter) 7am-Midnight, Fri 7am-10pm, Sat 8:30am-10pm, Sun 8:30am-Midnight; Mon-Thurs (Summer) 8am-10pm, Fri 8-8, Sat 12-5, Sun 12-10
Friends of the Library Group

M   UNIVERSITY OF TENNESSEE GRADUATE SCHOOL OF MEDICINE*, Preston Medical Library & Learning Resource Center, 1924 Alcoa Hwy, Box U-111, 37920. SAN 315-8284. Tel: 865-305-9525. FAX: 865-305-9527. E-mail: library@mc.utmck.edu. Web Site: gsm.utmck.edu/library. *Dir,* Sandy Oelschlegel; Tel: 865-305-6615, E-mail: soelschl@mc.utmck.edu; *Circ, Med Librn, Ref,* Cynthia Vaughn; Tel: 865-305-9526, E-mail: cvaughn@mc.utmck.edu; *Bibliog Instr, Coll Develop, Ref,* Martha Earl; Tel: 865-305-6616, E-mail: mearl@utmck.edu; *ILL,* Laura Wolfe; E-mail: lwolfe@utmck.edu; *Ser, Web Adminr,* J Michael Lindsay; Tel: 865-305-9528; Staff 8 (MLS 4, Non-MLS 4)
Founded 1969. Enrl 180; Highest Degree: Doctorate
Library Holdings: e-books 200; e-journals 4,000; Bk Titles 3,750; Per Subs 150
Subject Interests: Biochem, Cancer, Clinical med, Dentistry, Hematology, Immunology, Perinatology, Trauma
Automation Activity & Vendor Info: (Cataloging) Ex Libris Group; (Circulation) Ex Libris Group; (OPAC) Ex Libris Group; (Serials) EBSCO Online
Database Vendor: Cinahl Information Systems, DynaMed, EBSCOhost, Gale Cengage Learning, MD Consult, Medline, Micromedex, OCLC WorldCat, OVID Technologies, PubMed, STAT!Ref (Teton Data Systems), UpToDate
Wireless access
Function: Workshops
Partic in Knoxville Area Health Sciences Library Consortium; Tenn Share
Open Mon-Thurs 8:30am-9pm, Fri 8:30-5, Sat 9-5, Sun 2-10
Restriction: Badge access after hrs, Non-circulating to the pub

C   UNIVERSITY OF TENNESSEE, KNOXVILLE*, John C Hodges University Libraries, 1015 Volunteer Blvd, 37996-1000. SAN 360-6848. Tel: 865-974-4127. Circulation Tel: 865-974-4351. Interlibrary Loan Service Tel: 423-974-4240. Reference Tel: 865-974-4171. FAX: 865-974-4259. Web Site: www.lib.utk.edu. *Dean of Libr,* Barbara I Dewey; E-mail: bdewey@utk.edu; *Assoc Dean,* Jillian Keally; Tel: 865-974-6600, E-mail: jkeally@utk.edu; *Asst Dean,* Pauline Bayne; Tel: 865-974-4465, E-mail: pbayne@utk.edu; *Head, Res Serv,* Rita Smith; Fax: 865-974-9242, E-mail: rsmith19@utk.edu; *Coll Mgt Librn,* Linda Phillips; Tel: 865-974-4702, E-mail: lphilli6@utk.edu; *Bus Mgr,* Kenneth Wise; Tel: 865-974-2359, E-mail: kwise@utk.edu; *Syst Coordr,* William Britten; Tel: 865-974-4304, E-mail: wbritten@utk.edu; *Access Serv,* David Atkins; Tel: 865-974-6866, E-mail: datkins@utk.edu; Staff 170 (MLS 63, Non-MLS 107)
Founded 1794. Enrl 23,986; Fac 1,477; Highest Degree: Doctorate

Library Holdings: Bk Vols 2,319,379; Per Subs 32,099
Special Collections: Alex Haley Coll; Cherokee Indians; Congressional Papers; Congreve; Early Imprints; Early Voyages & Travel; Nineteenth Century American Fiction; Radiation Biology; Tennessee World War II Veterans. Oral History; State Document Depository; US Document Depository
Automation Activity & Vendor Info: (Acquisitions) Ex Libris Group; (Cataloging) Ex Libris Group; (Circulation) Ex Libris Group; (Course Reserve) Ex Libris Group; (ILL) Ex Libris Group; (Media Booking) Ex Libris Group; (OPAC) Ex Libris Group; (Serials) Ex Libris Group
Wireless access
Publications: Library Development Review (Annually); Library Friends (Newsletter); Mission & Strategic Plan (Annually); The UTK Librarian (Newsletter); The UTK Library Record (Annual report)
Partic in Association of Research Libraries (ARL); Center for Research Libraries; Digital Libr Fedn; Lyrasis; OCLC Online Computer Library Center, Inc
Special Services for the Deaf - TTY equip
Special Services for the Blind - Braille equip
Open Mon-Thurs 7:30am-10pm, Fri 7:30-6, Sat 10-6, Sun (Summer) 1-10
Friends of the Library Group
Departmental Libraries:
AGRICULTURE-VETERINARY MEDICINE, A-113 Veterinary Teaching Hospital, 2407 Joe Johnson Dr, 37996-4541, SAN 360-6902. Tel: 865-974-7338. FAX: 865-974-4732. E-mail: agvetlib@utk.edu. Web Site: www.lib.utk.edu/branches. *Br Mgr,* Sandra Leach; Tel: 865-974-7922, E-mail: sandra-leach@utk.edu; *Libr Supvr-Popular Libr,* Allison Roberts; Tel: 865-974-0356, E-mail: robertsa@utk.edu; *Govt Doc, Tech Serv,* Barbara Doyle-Maher; Tel: 865-974-4735, E-mail: doyle-maher@utk.edu; *Ref Serv Librn,* Peter Fernandez; Tel: 865-974-2886, E-mail: pfernand@utk.edu; *Ref Serv Librn,* Ann Viera; Tel: 865-974-9015, E-mail: annviera@utk.edu; Staff 7 (MLS 3, Non-MLS 4)
Friends of the Library Group
GEORGE F DEVINE MUSIC LIBRARY, 301 Music Bldg, 1741 Volunteer Blvd, 37996-2600, SAN 360-6961. Tel: 865-974-3474. FAX: 865-974-0564. E-mail: musiclib@utk.edu. Web Site: www.lib.utk.edu/music. *Librn,* Pauline S Bayne; E-mail: pbayne@utk.edu; *Librn,* Chris Durman; Tel: 865-974-7542, E-mail: cdurman@utk.edu; *Librn,* Nathalie Hristov; Tel: 865-974-9893, E-mail: mhristov@utk.edu; *Librn,* Matt Jordan; Tel: 865-974-4051, E-mail: mjordan3@utk.edu; *Librn,* Connie Steigenga; Tel: 865-974-9946, E-mail: willow1@utk.edu; Staff 4 (MLS 2, Non-MLS 2)
Founded 1965
Special Collections: Barry McDonald Music Coll, scores; Canadian Composers' Information File; Opera Libretti, Programs & Ballet Programs (Earl W Quintrell Coll)
Open Mon-Thurs (Fall & Spring) 8am-10pm, Fri 8-5, Sat 1-5, Sun 2-10; Mon-Thurs (Summer) 8am-9pm, Fri 8-5, Sun 2-9
Friends of the Library Group
MAP LIBRARY, 15 Hoskins Bldg, 37996-4006, SAN 372-7777. Tel: 865-974-4315. FAX: 865-974-3925. E-mail: maplib@utk.edu. Web Site: www.lib.utk.edu/~cic. *Librn,* Gregory March; E-mail: gmarch@utk.edu; *Supvr,* Eric Arnold; E-mail: arnold@utk.edu
Friends of the Library Group
SERIALS, 1015 Volunteer Blvd, 37996-1000. Tel: 865-974-4236. FAX: 865-974-0551. Web Site: www.utk.edu/libraries.
Friends of the Library Group
SPECIAL COLLECTIONS, 121 Hodges Library, 1015 Volunteer Blvd, 37996-1000, SAN 372-7793. Tel: 865-974-4480. E-mail: special@utk.edu. Web Site: www.lib.utk.edu/special. *Dept Head,* Jennifer Benedetto Beals; E-mail: jbeals@utk.edu; *Res Serv Spec,* Elizabeth Dunham; E-mail: edunham@utk.edu; *Res Serv Spec,* Bill Eigelsbach; E-mail: weigelsb@utk.edu; *Res Serv Spec,* Nick Wyman; E-mail: dwyman@utk.edu; *Archivist,* Alesha Shumar; E-mail: ashumar@utk.edu; *Acq Asst,* Justin Eastwood; Staff 7 (MLS 2, Non-MLS 5)
Function: Archival coll
Open Mon-Fri 9-5:30
Restriction: Non-circulating coll
Friends of the Library Group

LA FOLLETTE

P   LA FOLLETTE PUBLIC LIBRARY*, 201 S Tennessee Ave, 37766-3606. SAN 315-8330. Tel: 423-562-5154. FAX: 423-562-0013. E-mail: laflib@comcast.net. Web Site: lafollettepubliclibrary.org. *Librn,* Nancy J Green; Staff 1 (Non-MLS 1)
Library Holdings: Audiobooks 122; Braille Volumes 1; CDs 256; DVDs 1,376; Large Print Bks 101; Bk Titles 12,318; Per Subs 46; Talking Bks 50; Videos 1,062
Automation Activity & Vendor Info: (Cataloging) Book Systems, Inc; (Circulation) Book Systems, Inc
Database Vendor: EBSCOhost
Wireless access
Friends of the Library Group

LA VERGNE

P   LA VERGNE PUBLIC LIBRARY, 5063 Murfreesboro Rd, 37086-0177. SAN 322-7464. Tel: 615-793-7303. FAX: 615-793-7307. Web Site: catalog.lavergnetn.gov. *Dir,* Teresa Wilberscheid; E-mail: twilberscheid@lavergnetn.gov
Founded 1979. Pop 36,985; Circ 152,991
Library Holdings: Audiobooks 2,116; CDs 574; DVDs 1,492; Large Print Bks 647; Bk Vols 59,881; Per Subs 83; Videos 1,693
Automation Activity & Vendor Info: (Cataloging) Book Systems, Inc; (Circulation) Book Systems, Inc; (OPAC) Book Systems, Inc
Database Vendor: American Physical Society, EBSCOhost, Gale Cengage Learning, LearningExpress, Newsbank, ProQuest
Wireless access
Function: Adult bk club, After school storytime, Bks on CD, Children's prog, Computers for patron use, Copy machines, E-Reserves, Electronic databases & coll, Fax serv, Free DVD rentals, Genealogy discussion group, Handicapped accessible, Holiday prog, Instruction & testing, Music CDs, Online cat, Online searches, Outreach serv, Photocopying/Printing, Preschool outreach, Prog for adults, Prog for children & young adult, Pub access computers, Spanish lang bks, Story hour, Summer reading prog, Tax forms, Teen prog, VHS videos, Video lending libr, Web-catalog, Wheelchair accessible
Open Mon, Tues & Thurs 9-8, Wed, Fri & Sat 9-5

LAFAYETTE

P   MACON COUNTY PUBLIC LIBRARY*, 311 Church St, 37083-1607. SAN 360-702X. Tel: 615-666-4340. FAX: 615-666-8932. *Dir,* Julia Marshall; *Asst Librn,* Joyce Huddleston
Founded 1957. Pop 20,000; Circ 40,000
Library Holdings: Bk Vols 22,000; Per Subs 46
Automation Activity & Vendor Info: (Circulation) Book Systems, Inc
Mem of Falling Water River Regional Library
Open Mon-Wed & Fri 9-5:45, Thurs 12-8, Sat 8-1:45
Friends of the Library Group
Branches: 1
RED BOILING SPRINGS BRANCH, 335 E Main St, Red Boiling Springs, 37150-0033, SAN 360-7054. Tel: 615-699-3701. FAX: 615-699-3777. E-mail: rbslib@nctc.com. *Br Mgr,* Victoria Kindle
Open Mon 12-6, Wed & Thurs 10-11:30 & 12-5:30, Fri 10-11:30 & 12-4:30, Sat 10-2
Friends of the Library Group

LAKE CITY

P   LAKE CITY PUBLIC LIBRARY*, 226 N Main St, 37769. (Mail add: PO Box 157, 37769-0157), SAN 315-8349. Tel: 865-426-6762. FAX: 865-426-9235. E-mail: lakecitylibrary@comcast.net. Web Site: orgsites.com/tn/lakecitypubliclibrary. *Librn,* Norma Day
Library Holdings: Bk Titles 800; Bk Vols 32,000; Per Subs 35
Open Mon & Tues 9:30-6, Thurs, Fri & Sat 1-6
Friends of the Library Group

LAWRENCEBURG

P   LAWRENCE COUNTY PUBLIC LIBRARY*, 519 E Gaines St, 38464-3599. SAN 315-8357. Tel: 931-762-4627. FAX: 931-766-1597. Web Site: www.co.lawrence.tn.us/departments/library/county_library.htm. *Dir,* Teresa Newton
Founded 1941. Pop 35,303; Circ 114,552
Library Holdings: Bk Vols 44,842; Per Subs 127
Special Collections: Oral History
Automation Activity & Vendor Info: (Circulation) Brodart; (ILL) Brodart
Open Mon, Thurs & Fri 9-5:30, Tues & Wed 9-8, Sat 9-2:30
Branches: 1
LORETTO BRANCH, 102 S Main St, Loretto, 38469-2110. (Mail add: PO Box 338, Loretto, 38469-0338), SAN 377-7847. Tel: 931-853-7323. FAX: 931-853-7324. E-mail: llibrary@lorettotel.net. *Dir,* Judy Henkel
Library Holdings: Bk Vols 6,000; Per Subs 20; Talking Bks 70; Videos 70
Automation Activity & Vendor Info: (Cataloging) Book Systems, Inc; (Circulation) Book Systems, Inc; (OPAC) Book Systems, Inc
Open Tues 10-6, Wed & Thur 12-6, Fri 1-5, Sat 9-3

LEBANON

C   CUMBERLAND UNIVERSITY, Doris & Harry Vise Library, One Cumberland Sq, 37087. SAN 315-8365. Tel: 615-547-1299. Toll Free Tel: 800-467-0562. FAX: 615-444-2569. E-mail: library@cumberland.edu. Web Site: www.cumberland.edu/library. *Dean of Libr,* Eloise Hitchcock; Tel: 615-547-1351, E-mail: ehitchcock@cumberland.edu; *Ref & Instruction Librn,* Position Currently Open; *Ref & Instruction Librn,* Amber Woodard; Tel: 615-547-1354, E-mail: awoodard@cumberland.edu; *Libr Asst,* Ashli Thomas; Tel: 615-547-1354, E-mail: athomas@cumberland.edu; Staff 5 (MLS 3, Non-MLS 2)

Founded 1842. Enrl 1,355; Fac 61; Highest Degree: Master
Library Holdings: AV Mats 2,131; e-books 113,128; Microforms 1,184;
Bk Vols 28,595; Per Subs 270
Special Collections: Childrens Literature Coll; Nobel Laureate Coll;
Stockton Archives; Tennessee Room
Subject Interests: Liberal arts, Tenn hist
Automation Activity & Vendor Info: (Cataloging) Surpass; (Circulation)
Surpass; (ILL) OCLC FirstSearch; (OPAC) Surpass; (Serials) Surpass
Database Vendor: Baker & Taylor, Cambridge Scientific Abstracts, CQ
Press, EBSCOhost, Gale Cengage Learning, Ingram Library Services,
JSTOR, LexisNexis, netLibrary, OCLC FirstSearch, OCLC WorldCat,
Oxford Online, ProQuest, RefWorks
Wireless access
Function: For res purposes
Partic in Lyrasis; Nashville Area Libr Alliance; OCLC Online Computer
Library Center, Inc; Tenn Share
Open Mon-Thurs 7:30am-10pm, Fri 7:30-4:30, Sun 2-10
Restriction: Non-circulating to the pub

P   LEBANON-WILSON COUNTY LIBRARY*, 108 S Hatton Ave,
       37087-3590. SAN 360-7089. Tel: 615-444-0632. FAX: 615-444-0535.
       E-mail: lebanonlibrary@wilsoncolibrary.com. Web Site: lebanonlibrary.net.
       Dir, Alesia Burnley; *Asst Dir,* Nancy Fowler
       Founded 1938. Pop 59,604; Circ 258,779
       Library Holdings: Audiobooks 3,553; Bk Vols 56,481; Per Subs 92;
       Videos 1,433
       Automation Activity & Vendor Info: (Cataloging) TLC (The Library
       Corporation); (Circulation) TLC (The Library Corporation)
       Wireless access
       Function: Bk club(s), Computers for patron use, Copy machines, Free
       DVD rentals, Handicapped accessible, ILL available, Magnifiers for
       reading, Online cat, OverDrive digital audio bks, Photocopying/Printing,
       Preschool outreach, Prog for adults, Prog for children & young adult, Pub
       access computers, Story hour, Summer reading prog, Tax forms, Teen prog,
       Web-catalog, Wheelchair accessible
       Mem of Stones River Regional Library
       Open Mon, Tues & Thurs 8:30-8, Wed, Fri & Sat 8:30-5
       Branches: 1
       WATERTOWN BRANCH, 206 Public Sq, Watertown, 37184-1422, SAN
          360-7119. Tel: 615-237-9700. FAX: 615-237-9700. E-mail:
          watertown@wilsoncolibrary.com. *Br Mgr,* Pamela Moore
          Pop 34,511
          Library Holdings: Audiobooks 701; Large Print Bks 408; Bk Vols
          15,900; Per Subs 39; Videos 1,244
          Function: Children's prog, Computers for patron use, Copy machines,
          Fax serv, Free DVD rentals, Magnifiers for reading, Prog for children &
          young adult, Pub access computers, Story hour, Tax forms, VHS videos,
          Video lending libr
          Open Mon & Wed-Sat 9:30-5, Tues 12-8

LENOIR CITY

P   LENOIR CITY PUBLIC LIBRARY*, 100 W Broadway, 37771. (Mail add:
       PO Box 1156, 37771-1156), SAN 315-8373. Tel: 865-986-3210. *Librn,*
       Kaye Hathcock; E-mail: kayehathcock@hotmail.com
       Founded 1928
       Library Holdings: Bk Vols 25,000; Per Subs 40
       Mem of Ocoee River Regional Library
       Open Mon-Fri 10-6, Sat 9-1
       Friends of the Library Group

LEWISBURG

P   MARSHALL COUNTY MEMORIAL LIBRARY*, 310 Old Farmington
       Rd, 37091. SAN 315-8381. Tel: 931-359-3335. FAX: 931-359-5866. *Dir,*
       Jan Allen
       Founded 1944. Pop 26,000; Circ 150,000
       Library Holdings: Bk Titles 47,000; Per Subs 90
       Subject Interests: Archit, Art, Educ, Genealogy, Hist, Med, Relig studies
       Open Mon, Tues & Thurs 9-8, Wed & Fri 9-5, Sat 9-3

LEXINGTON

P   EVERETT HORN PUBLIC LIBRARY*, 702 W Church St, 38351-1713.
       SAN 315-839X. Tel: 731-968-3239. FAX: 731-968-4134. E-mail:
       librarye@bellsouth.net. Web Site: www.everetthornlibrary.netfirms.com.
       Dir, Dinah Harris; Staff 1 (Non-MLS 1)
       Founded 1949. Pop 25,000
       Library Holdings: Bk Titles 26,342; Per Subs 45
       Automation Activity & Vendor Info: (Cataloging) Follett Software;
       (Circulation) Follett Software
       Mem of Hatchie River Regional Library
       Open Mon, Wed & Fri 9-5, Tues & Thurs 9-6, Sat 9-3

LINDEN

P   PERRY COUNTY PUBLIC LIBRARY*, Rte 10, 37096-9802. (Mail add:
       Box 3A, 37096-9802), SAN 360-7178. Tel: 931-589-5011. FAX:
       931-589-6210. E-mail: perrycolib@netease.net. *Dir,* Dorothy Pevahouse
       Pop 6,111
       Library Holdings: Bk Titles 20,000
       Automation Activity & Vendor Info: (Cataloging) Follett Software;
       (Circulation) Follett Software
       Open Mon, Tues, Thurs & Fri 9-5, Wed 9-Noon
       Branches: 1
       LOBELVILLE BRANCH, 85 W Seventh St, Lobelville, 37097, SAN
          360-7208. Tel: 931-593-3111. FAX: 931-593-2089. E-mail:
          lobelvillelibrary@netease.net. *Br Mgr,* Angie McGee
          Library Holdings: Bk Vols 5,000
          Open Mon-Fri 10-5

LIVINGSTON

P   MILLARD OAKLEY LIBRARY*, 107 E Main St, 38570. SAN 315-8403.
       Tel: 931-823-1888. FAX: 931-403-0798. Web Site:
       www.overtoncolibrary.com. *Dir,* Cynthia Carmack; Staff 4 (Non-MLS 4)
       Founded 1966. Pop 20,100
       Jul 2005-Jun 2006 Income $121,338, City $5,000, County $116,338
       Library Holdings: Audiobooks 1,034; DVDs 1,972; Bk Vols 26,422; Per
       Subs 30
       Special Collections: Extensive Genealogy Area & Support System; Local
       Newpapers, Early 1900's to present, microfilm
       Automation Activity & Vendor Info: (Circulation) TLC (The Library
       Corporation); (OPAC) TLC (The Library Corporation)
       Wireless access
       Function: ILL available
       Mem of Falling Water River Regional Library
       Open Mon & Thurs 10-7, Tues, Wed & Fri 9-5, Sat 9-2
       Friends of the Library Group

LOUDON

P   LOUDON PUBLIC LIBRARY*, 210 River Rd, 37774. SAN 315-842X.
       Tel: 865-458-3161. FAX: 865-458-3161. E-mail:
       loudonlibrary@bellsouth.net. *Librn,* Tammy Smallen
       Library Holdings: Bk Vols 10,000; Per Subs 12
       Automation Activity & Vendor Info: (Acquisitions) SirsiDynix;
       (Cataloging) SirsiDynix; (Circulation) SirsiDynix
       Mem of Ocoee River Regional Library
       Open Mon-Fri 9:30-5:30, Sat 9-2

P   TELLICO VILLAGE PUBLIC LIBRARY*, 304 Lakeside Plaza,
       37774-4160. Tel: 865-458-8762. FAX: 865-458-8762. Web Site:
       www.tvlibrary.org. *Dir,* Becky Haile
       Founded 1997
       Library Holdings: CDs 200; Bk Vols 8,000; Per Subs 52; Talking Bks
       800
       Automation Activity & Vendor Info: (Cataloging) SirsiDynix;
       (Circulation) SirsiDynix; (OPAC) SirsiDynix
       Open Mon 10-5, Tues & Wed 10-6, Thurs & Fri 9-5, Sat 10-12

LUTTRELL

P   LUTTRELL PUBLIC LIBRARY*, 115 Park Rd, 37779. SAN 315-8438.
       Tel: 865-992-0208. FAX: 865-992-4354. E-mail:
       luttrelllibrary@comcast.net. *Dir,* Gloria Fox
       Library Holdings: Bk Titles 5,000
       Open Mon-Wed & Fri 9-6, Sat 9-1

LYNCHBURG

P   MOORE COUNTY PUBLIC LIBRARY*, PO Box 602, 37352-0602. Tel:
       931-759-7285. FAX: 931-759-6393. Web Site: moorecolibrary.com. *Dir,*
       Peggy Gold; E-mail: pgold@bellsouth.net; Staff 3 (Non-MLS 3)
       Founded 1953. Pop 5,740; Circ 25,331
       Library Holdings: Bk Titles 23,280; Per Subs 10
       Special Collections: Reagor Motlow Papers Coll
       Automation Activity & Vendor Info: (Cataloging) Book Systems, Inc;
       (Circulation) Book Systems, Inc; (OPAC) Book Systems, Inc
       Function: Ref serv available
       Mem of Stones River Regional Library
       Special Services for the Deaf - TDD equip
       Special Services for the Blind - Bks on cassette
       Open Mon, Wed & Fri 9-5, Tues 12-8, Sat 9-12

LYNNVILLE

P   ROBERT B JONES MEMORIAL LIBRARY*, 135 Main St, 38472. (Mail add: PO Box 66, 38472-0066), SAN 376-6918. Tel: 931-273-3466. *In Charge,* Bobby Allen Hollis
Pop 345; Circ 4,656
Library Holdings: AV Mats 56; Bk Titles 2,000; Bk Vols 4,544
Open Tues-Fri 4-6, Sat 10-1

MADISONVILLE

JR   HIWASSEE COLLEGE*, Hardwick Johnston Memorial Library, 225 Hiwassee College Dr, 37354. SAN 315-8489. Tel: 423-442-2001. Toll Free Tel: 800-356-2187. FAX: 423-420-1896. E-mail: library@hiwassee.edu. Web Site: www.hiwassee.edu/library. *Dir, Libr Serv,* Curtis Chapmin; Tel: 423-442-2001, Ext 1266, E-mail: chapminc@hiwassee.edu; *Circ,* Barbara Carringer; Tel: 423-442-2001, Ext 1267; Staff 4 (MLS 2, Non-MLS 2)
Founded 1849. Enrl 400; Fac 26; Highest Degree: Associate
Library Holdings: e-books 74,000; e-journals 22,000; Bk Vols 30,000; Per Subs 106; Videos 255
Automation Activity & Vendor Info: (Acquisitions) Innovative Interfaces, Inc; (Cataloging) Innovative Interfaces, Inc; (Circulation) Innovative Interfaces, Inc; (Course Reserve) Innovative Interfaces, Inc; (ILL) Innovative Interfaces, Inc; (Media Booking) Innovative Interfaces, Inc; (OPAC) Innovative Interfaces, Inc; (Serials) Innovative Interfaces, Inc
Database Vendor: Alexander Street Press, ARTstor, EBSCOhost, Gale Cengage Learning, JSTOR, netLibrary
Wireless access
Open Mon-Thurs 8-8, Fri 8-5, Sun 4-8
Friends of the Library Group

P   MADISONVILLE PUBLIC LIBRARY*, 4023 Hwy 411 N, Unit C, 37354-1535. SAN 315-8497. Tel: 423-442-4085. FAX: 423-442-8121. Web Site: www.madisonvillelibrary.org. *Dir,* Kim Hicks; E-mail: Kim.Hicks@madisonvillelibrary.org; *Asst Dir,* Kim Johnson; E-mail: Kim.Johnson@madisonvillelibrary.org; Staff 6 (Non-MLS 6)
Founded 1915. Pop 15,122; Circ 143,000
Library Holdings: AV Mats 3,000; Bks on Deafness & Sign Lang 10; Large Print Bks 1,000; Bk Titles 28,000; Per Subs 70; Talking Bks 1,200
Special Collections: Genealogy Coll. State Document Depository; US Document Depository
Automation Activity & Vendor Info: (Cataloging) SIRSI WorkFlows; (Circulation) SIRSI Unicorn; (OPAC) SirsiDynix
Database Vendor: Gale Cengage Learning, Newsbank, ProQuest
Wireless access
Function: Archival coll, AV serv, For res purposes, Handicapped accessible, Home delivery & serv to Sr ctr & nursing homes, Homebound delivery serv, ILL available, Large print keyboards, Newsp ref libr, Online searches, Photocopying/Printing, Prog for children & young adult, Ref serv available, Summer reading prog, Telephone ref, Wheelchair accessible
Mem of Ocoee River Regional Library
Special Services for the Deaf - Bks on deafness & sign lang; Closed caption videos
Special Services for the Blind - Audio mat; Bks available with recordings; Bks on cassette; Bks on CD; Computer with voice synthesizer for visually impaired persons; Copier with enlargement capabilities; Extensive large print coll; Info on spec aids & appliances; Integrated libr/media serv; Large print & cassettes; Large print bks; Large screen computer & software; Magnifiers; Ref serv; Screen enlargement software for people with visual disabilities; Talking bks; Videos on blindness & phys handicaps
Open Tues, Wed & Fri 10:30-4:30, Thurs 10:30-7:30, Sat 9-Noon
Friends of the Library Group

MANCHESTER

P   COFFEE COUNTY-MANCHESTER LIBRARY*, 1005 Hillsboro Hwy, 37355-2099. SAN 376-7310. Tel: 931-723-5143. FAX: 931-723-0713. Web Site: www.coffeecountylibrary.org. *Dir,* Sherryl Roberts; E-mail: director@coffeecountylibrary.org
Library Holdings: Bk Titles 56,000; Per Subs 53
Automation Activity & Vendor Info: (Cataloging) SirsiDynix; (Circulation) SirsiDynix; (ILL) Auto-Graphics, Inc; (OPAC) SirsiDynix
Mem of Stones River Regional Library
Open Mon, Tues & Thurs 9-9, Wed, Fri & Sat 9-5
Friends of the Library Group

MARTIN

P   OBION RIVER REGIONAL LIBRARY*, (Formerly Reelfoot Regional Library Center), 542 N Lindell St, 38237. (Mail add: PO Box 168, 38237-0168), SAN 315-8519. Tel: 731-587-2347. FAX: 731-587-0027. *Dir,* Position Currently Open; Staff 2 (MLS 2)
Founded 1942. Pop 179,930; Circ 873,558
Library Holdings: Bk Titles 80,000; Bk Vols 120,000
Automation Activity & Vendor Info: (Acquisitions) Follett Software; (Cataloging) Follett Software; (Circulation) Follett Software

Publications: Library Lines (Quarterly)
Member Libraries: Benton County Public Library; C E Weldon Public Library; Carroll County Library; Dr Nathan Porter Public Library; Gibson County Memorial Library; Gleason Memorial Library; Humboldt Public Library; McKenzie Memorial Library; Ned R McWherter Weakley County Library; Obion County Public Library; Sharon Public Library; W G Rhea Public Library
Open Mon-Fri 8-4:30

C   UNIVERSITY OF TENNESSEE AT MARTIN*, Paul Meek Library, Ten Wayne Fisher Dr, 38238. SAN 315-8527. Tel: 731-881-7070. Circulation Tel: 731-881-7092. Interlibrary Loan Service Tel: 731-881-7068. Reference Tel: 731-881-7065. Automation Services Tel: 731-881-7060. FAX: 731-881-7074. Web Site: www.utm.edu/library.php. *Dir,* Mary Vaughan Carpenter; E-mail: maryc@utm.edu; *Head, Circ,* Samuel S Richardson; Tel: 731-881-7061, E-mail: richardson@utm.edu; *Syst Librn,* James R Nance; Tel: 731-881-7093, E-mail: jimnance@utm.edu; *Acq,* Dr Linda K Butler; Tel: 731-881-7096, E-mail: lbutler@utm.edu; *Archivist, Curator,* Richard L Saunders; Tel: 731-881-7094, E-mail: saunders@utm.edu; *Cat,* Georgia I Baskett; Tel: 731-881-7079, E-mail: gbaskett@utm.edu; *Coll Develop, ILL,* Earlene J Moore; Tel: 731-881-7067, E-mail: ejmoore@utm.edu; *Per, Ref Serv,* Patricia L Greer; Tel: 731-881-7064, E-mail: patgreer@utm.edu; Staff 10 (MLS 10)
Founded 1900. Enrl 6,300; Fac 270; Highest Degree: Master
Library Holdings: CDs 2,849; DVDs 3,029; e-books 44,941; Bk Titles 371,877; Bk Vols 524,119; Per Subs 964; Videos 4,571
Special Collections: Congressman Ed Jones Papers; Governor Ned Ray McWherter Personal & Legislative Papers; Harry Harrison Kroll Coll; Holland McCombs Coll; Weakley County Chancery Records. US Document Depository
Automation Activity & Vendor Info: (Acquisitions) Innovative Interfaces, Inc; (Cataloging) Innovative Interfaces, Inc; (Circulation) Innovative Interfaces, Inc; (Course Reserve) Innovative Interfaces, Inc; (ILL) Innovative Interfaces, Inc; (OPAC) Innovative Interfaces, Inc; (Serials) Innovative Interfaces, Inc
Database Vendor: Agricola, EBSCOhost, Elsevier MDL, Gale Cengage Learning, JSTOR, LexisNexis, netLibrary, OCLC FirstSearch, ProQuest, STN International, Westlaw
Wireless access
Partic in Lyrasis; OCLC Online Computer Library Center, Inc
Open Mon-Thurs (Fall & Spring) 7:50am-11pm, Fri 7:50-6, Sat 12-5, Sun 2-11; Mon-Thurs (Summer) 7:50am-10pm, Fri 7:50-5, Sat 1-5, Sun 2-10
Friends of the Library Group

P   C E WELDON PUBLIC LIBRARY*, 100 Main St, 38237-2445. SAN 315-8500. Tel: 731-587-3148. FAX: 731-587-4674. Web Site: www.ceweldonlibrary.org. *Dir,* Roberta Peacock; Staff 3 (Non-MLS 3)
Founded 1925. Pop 32,896; Circ 60,628
Library Holdings: Bk Vols 45,000
Special Collections: Tennessee Genealogical Colls
Automation Activity & Vendor Info: (Cataloging) Follett Software; (Circulation) Follett Software; (OPAC) Follett Software
Wireless access
Function: Adult bk club, Adult literacy prog, Art exhibits, Audio & video playback equip for onsite use, AV serv, Bk club(s), CD-ROM, Doc delivery serv, Handicapped accessible, Homebound delivery serv, ILL available, Magnifiers for reading, Music CDs, Online searches, Orientations, Photocopying/Printing, Prog for adults, Prog for children & young adult, Provide serv for the mentally ill, Ref & res, Ref serv available, Serves mentally handicapped consumers, Spoken cassettes & CDs, Spoken cassettes & DVDs, Summer reading prog, Telephone ref, VHS videos, Video lending libr, Wheelchair accessible
Publications: C E Weldon Public Library Newsletter
Mem of Obion River Regional Library
Open Mon-Wed & Fri 9:30-5:30, Thurs 9:30-8, Sat 9:30-12
Restriction: Authorized patrons
Friends of the Library Group

MARYVILLE

P   BLOUNT COUNTY PUBLIC LIBRARY*, 508 N Cusick St, 37804-5714. SAN 315-8535. Tel: 865-982-0981. FAX: 865-977-1142. Web Site: www.korrnet.org/bcpl. *Dir,* Kathryn Pagles; *Dir, Coll Develop,* Laura Hutchens; *Bus & Finance Mgr,* Jennifer Headrick-York; *Mgr, Ref Serv,* Kathleen Christy; *Head, Circ,* Becky Barry; *Ch,* Jean Closz; Staff 13 (MLS 4, Non-MLS 9)
Founded 1919. Pop 113,000; Circ 738,547
Jul 2007-Jun 2008 Income $2,052,138, City $876,735, County $876,735, Locally Generated Income $298,668. Mats Exp $306,522, Books $208,522, Per/Ser (Incl. Access Fees) $30,000, AV Mat $40,000, Electronic Ref Mat (Incl. Access Fees) $28,000. Sal $1,268,777
Library Holdings: AV Mats 25,739; e-books 3,362; Bk Vols 158,021; Per Subs 411
Subject Interests: Genealogy, Local hist

Automation Activity & Vendor Info: (Cataloging) SirsiDynix; (Circulation) SirsiDynix; (OPAC) SirsiDynix
Wireless access
Function: Art exhibits, Audiobks via web, Bks on cassette, Bks on CD, Children's prog, Computers for patron use, Copy machines, Electronic databases & coll, Exhibits, Free DVD rentals, Handicapped accessible, ILL available, Music CDs, Online cat, Prog for adults, Prog for children & young adult, Pub access computers, Summer reading prog, Tax forms, VHS videos, Wheelchair accessible
Mem of Ocoee River Regional Library
Special Services for the Deaf - TDD equip
Special Services for the Blind - Scanner for conversion & translation of mats; Videos on blindness & phys handicaps
Open Mon-Thurs 9-9, Fri & Sat 9-5:30, Sun 1-5:30
Friends of the Library Group

M   BLOUNT MEMORIAL HOSPITAL*, L R Lingeman Memorial Medical Library, 907 E Lamar Alexander Pkwy, 37804. SAN 315-8543. Tel: 865-977-5520. FAX: 865-981-2473. *Librn,* Rebecca Marcum; Staff 1 (MLS 1)
Founded 1947
Library Holdings: Bk Titles 1,000; Per Subs 80
Subject Interests: Consumer health, Med, Nursing
Partic in Knoxville Area Health Sciences Library Consortium; National Network of Libraries of Medicine Greater Midwest Region
Open Mon-Fri 9-2:30

C   MARYVILLE COLLEGE*, Lamar Memorial Library, 502 E Lamar Alexander Pkwy, 37804-5907. SAN 315-8551. Tel: 865-981-8256. Circulation Tel: 865-981-8099. FAX: 865-981-8267. Web Site: www.maryvillecollege.edu/library. *Dir,* Angela Myatt Quick; Tel: 865-981-8038, E-mail: angela.quick@maryvillecollege.edu; *Asst Dir, Tech Serv Librn,* Debbie Nichols; Tel: 865-981-8255, E-mail: debbie.nichols@maryvillecollege.edu; *Coll Develop Librn,* Dori May; Tel: 865-981-8074, E-mail: dori.may@maryvillecollege.edu; *Ref & Instruction Librn,* Roger Myers; Tel: 865-981-5259, E-mail: roger.myers@maryvillecollege.edu; *Circ Coordr,* Marina Jaffe; E-mail: marina.jaffe@maryvillecollege.edu; *Computing Coordr/Evening Supvr,* Neena Teaster; Tel: 865-981-8258, E-mail: neena.teaster@maryvillecollege.edu; Staff 6 (MLS 4, Non-MLS 2)
Founded 1819. Enrl 1,083; Fac 80; Highest Degree: Bachelor
Automation Activity & Vendor Info: (Acquisitions) Innovative Interfaces, Inc - Millenium; (Cataloging) Innovative Interfaces, Inc - Millenium; (Circulation) Innovative Interfaces, Inc - Millenium; (Course Reserve) Innovative Interfaces, Inc - Millenium; (ILL) OCLC; (OPAC) Innovative Interfaces, Inc - Millenium; (Serials) Innovative Interfaces, Inc - Millenium
Database Vendor: ABC-CLIO, Alexander Street Press, American Chemical Society, American Mathematical Society, American Psychological Association (APA), Annual Reviews, ARTstor, Baker & Taylor, BioOne, CQ Press, EBSCO Information Services, EBSCOhost, Gale Cengage Learning, Innovative Interfaces, Inc, JSTOR, LexisNexis, Modern Language Association, netLibrary, OCLC WorldCat, Oxford Online, Project MUSE, ProQuest, Standard & Poor's
Wireless access
Partic in Appalachian Col Asn; Lyrasis; Tenn-Share
Special Services for the Deaf - Bks on deafness & sign lang; Closed caption videos; Deaf publ
Special Services for the Blind - Computer with voice synthesizer for visually impaired persons; Copier with enlargement capabilities; Dragon Naturally Speaking software; Internet workstation with adaptive software; Low vision equip
Open Mon-Thurs 7:30am-Midnight, Fri 7:30-5, Sat 10-4, Sun 1-Midnight

R   NEW PROVIDENCE PRESBYTERIAN CHURCH*, Alexander-Smith Library, 703 W Broadway Ave, 37801. SAN 315-856X. Tel: 865-983-0182. FAX: 865-681-0804. E-mail: mail@newprovidencepres.org. Web Site: www.newprovidencepres.org. *Librn,* Bob Thurman
Founded 1951
Library Holdings: Bk Titles 7,110
Subject Interests: Children's videos, Church hist, Family, Fine arts, Relig, Travel
Open Mon-Fri 8-5

MAYNARDVILLE

P   MAYNARDVILLE PUBLIC LIBRARY*, 296 Main St, 37807-3400. SAN 315-8578. Tel: 865-992-7106. FAX: 865-992-0202. E-mail: mayna2bk@comcast.net. Web Site: www.maynardville.com/library. *Dir,* Chantay Collins; Staff 1.5 (Non-MLS 1.5)
Pop 19,076; Circ 63,203
Library Holdings: Bks on Deafness & Sign Lang 10; DVDs 20; Large Print Bks 400; Bk Titles 18,418; Videos 150
Subject Interests: Local hist

Automation Activity & Vendor Info: (Cataloging) Surpass; (Circulation) Surpass; (Course Reserve) Surpass; (ILL) Auto-Graphics, Inc; (OPAC) Auto-Graphics, Inc
Database Vendor: Gale Cengage Learning
Function: Bk club(s), Copy machines, e-mail serv, Fax serv, Handicapped accessible, ILL available, Online searches, Photocopying/Printing, Prog for children & young adult, Ref serv available, Summer reading prog, VHS videos
Open Mon & Fri 8-5, Tues & Thurs 10-7, Sat 9-1
Restriction: Access at librarian's discretion
Friends of the Library Group

MCKENZIE

C   BETHEL UNIVERSITY*, Burroughs Learning Center, 325 Cherry Ave, 38201. SAN 315-8454. Tel: 731-352-4083. Interlibrary Loan Service Tel: 731-352-6915. Reference Tel: 731-352-6926. FAX: 731-352-4070. E-mail: library@bethelu.edu. Web Site: www.bethelu.edu/library. *Dir,* Jill Whitfill; Tel: 731-352-6913, E-mail: whitfillj@bethelu.edu; *Electronic Res & Cat Librn,* Jennifer Green; *Outreach/Pub Serv Librn,* Elizabeth Whitaker; *Admin Mgr,* Melissa Jackson; *Circ Supvr,* Rhonda Allen; *Acq, Cat, Tech Serv,* Kim Jackson; Staff 5 (MLS 2, Non-MLS 3)
Enrl 650; Fac 32; Highest Degree: Master
Library Holdings: Bk Vols 64,193; Per Subs 340
Special Collections: Cumberland Presbyterian History
Automation Activity & Vendor Info: (Cataloging) LibraryWorld, Inc; (Circulation) LibraryWorld, Inc; (ILL) OCLC
Database Vendor: EBSCOhost, ProQuest
Wireless access
Partic in West Tennessee Academic Library Consortium
Open Mon-Thurs 8am-10pm, Fri 8-4:30, Sun 6pm-10pm

P   MCKENZIE MEMORIAL LIBRARY*, 15 N Broadway, 38201-2101. SAN 315-8462. Tel: 731-352-5741. FAX: 731-352-5741. *Dir,* Terri Wilson; E-mail: mcklib@mckenzielibrary.com
Founded 1957. Pop 10,000
Library Holdings: Bk Vols 8,000; Per Subs 32
Subject Interests: Hist
Mem of Obion River Regional Library
Open Mon-Tues & Thurs-Fri 9-5

MCMINNVILLE

P   THE W H & EDGAR MAGNESS COMMUNITY HOUSE & LIBRARY*, 118 W Main St, 37110. SAN 315-8470. Tel: 931-473-2428. FAX: 931-473-6778. E-mail: magnesslib@blomand.net. Web Site: www.magnesslibrary.org. *Dir,* Mary Robbins
Founded 1931. Pop 38,296; Circ 68,000
Library Holdings: Bk Vols 41,000
Special Collections: Business & Community Development Coll; Education Coll; Genealogy Coll; Horticulture Coll; Southern Heritage Coll; Tennessee History Coll
Automation Activity & Vendor Info: (Acquisitions) Surpass; (Cataloging) Surpass; (Circulation) Surpass
Function: Adult bk club, After school storytime, Art exhibits, Audio & video playback equip for onsite use, Bk club(s), CD-ROM, Computer training, Copy machines, Fax serv, Genealogy discussion group, Handicapped accessible, ILL available, Mail & tel request accepted, Music CDs, Photocopying/Printing, Preschool outreach, Prof lending libr, Prog for adults, Prog for children & young adult, Ref serv available, Senior computer classes, Serves mentally handicapped consumers, Spoken cassettes & CDs, Spoken cassettes & DVDs, Summer reading prog, Tax forms, Telephone ref, VHS videos, Video lending libr, Wheelchair accessible, Workshops
Open Mon & Tues 8-8, Wed-Fri 8-5, Sat 8-3

MEMPHIS

S   AMERICAN CONTRACT BRIDGE LEAGUE*, Albert H Morehead Memorial Library, 2990 Airways Blvd, 38116-3847. SAN 371-9464. Tel: 901-332-5586, Ext 1240. FAX: 901-398-7754. E-mail: service@acbl.org. Web Site: www.acbl.org. *Actg Librn,* Kate Sides
Founded 1969
Library Holdings: Bk Titles 3,200; Per Subs 500
Open Mon-Fri 8-4:30

CM   BAPTIST COLLEGE OF HEALTH SCIENCES*, Health Sciences Library, 1003 Monroe, 38104. SAN 360-7232. Tel: 901-572-2677. FAX: 901-572-2674. *Librn,* Patricia Irby; E-mail: patricia.irby@bchs.edu; *Librn,* Richard Owen; E-mail: richard.owen@bchs.edu; Staff 2 (Non-MLS 2)
Founded 1991. Enrl 850; Fac 60; Highest Degree: Master
Library Holdings: AV Mats 2,000; Bk Titles 11,000; Per Subs 250
Subject Interests: Allied health, Nursing

Automation Activity & Vendor Info: (Cataloging) EOS International; (Circulation) EOS International; (OPAC) EOS International; (Serials) EOS International
Database Vendor: EBSCOhost
Partic in OCLC Online Computer Library Center, Inc
Open Mon-Thurs 7:30am-10:30pm, Fri & Sat 7:30-6, Sun 1-6

S   BUCKMAN LABORATORIES INTERNATIONAL, INC*, Knowledge Resource Center, 1256 N McLean Blvd, 38108. SAN 315-8608. Tel: 901-272-8585. Interlibrary Loan Service Tel: 901-272-8378. FAX: 901-272-8583. E-mail: krc@buckman.com. Web Site: www.buckman.com. *Mgr, Libr Serv,* Maureen Fitzer. Subject Specialists: *Leather,* Maureen Fitzer; Staff 4 (MLS 4)
Founded 1948
Library Holdings: Bk Titles 20,000; Per Subs 600
Subject Interests: Corrosion, Leather, Microbiology, Paper, Pulp, Water treatment
Automation Activity & Vendor Info: (Acquisitions) Robert A Schless & Co. Inc (NOTEbookS); (Cataloging) Robert A Schless & Co. Inc (NOTEbookS); (Circulation) Robert A Schless & Co. Inc (NOTEbookS); (ILL) OCLC; (OPAC) Robert A Schless & Co. Inc (NOTEbookS); (Serials) Robert A Schless & Co. Inc (NOTEbookS)
Database Vendor: Dialog, Dun & Bradstreet, Elsevier, infoUSA, LexisNexis, OCLC FirstSearch, OCLC WorldCat, ScienceDirect, STN International
Wireless access
Function: Computers for patron use, Copy machines, Doc delivery serv, e-mail serv, Electronic databases & coll, ILL available, Mail & tel request accepted, Online cat, Online searches, Outside serv via phone, mail, e-mail & web, Photocopying/Printing, Ref & res, Res libr, Scanner, Spoken cassettes & CDs, VHS videos
Partic in Lyrasis; Memphis Area Libr Coun
Open Mon-Fri 8:30-5
Restriction: Co libr, External users must contact libr, In-house use for visitors, Not open to pub, Open to pub by appt only, Open to researchers by request, Researchers by appt only, Restricted borrowing privileges

M   CAMPBELL FOUNDATION LIBRARY*, 1211 Union Ave, Ste 510, 38104. SAN 325-5085. Tel: 901-759-3271. FAX: 901-759-3278. *Librn,* Joan Crowson; E-mail: jcrowson@utmem.edu
Library Holdings: Bk Titles 714; Bk Vols 850; Per Subs 54
Subject Interests: Orthopedics
Partic in SERMLP
Open Mon-Fri 8:30-4:30

CR   CHRISTIAN BROTHERS UNIVERSITY, Plough Library, 650 E Pkwy South, 38104. SAN 315-8616. Tel: 901-321-3432. FAX: 901-321-3219. E-mail: library@cbu.edu. Web Site: www.cbu.edu/library. *Dir,* Kay Cunningham; E-mail: kay.cunningham@cbu.edu; *Acq & Pub Serv Librn,* Maya Berry; E-mail: mberry2@cbu.edu; *Electronic Serv Librn,* Deborah Babb; E-mail: dbabb@cbu.edu; *Instruction Librn,* Benjamin Head; E-mail: bhead@cbu.edu; *Tech Serv Librn,* Julie Gilmore; E-mail: jgilmore@cbu.edu; *ILL & Evening Circ Coordr,* Melissa Verble; E-mail: mverble@cbu.edu; *Per Coordr,* Barbara Hill; E-mail: bhill@cbu.edu; Staff 7 (MLS 5, Non-MLS 2)
Founded 1871. Enrl 1,400; Fac 109; Highest Degree: Master
Library Holdings: e-books 70,000; Microforms 61,361; Bk Titles 80,500; Bk Vols 97,000; Per Subs 301
Special Collections: Bro. Leo O'Donnell Archives
Subject Interests: Educ, Eng, Relig
Automation Activity & Vendor Info: (Acquisitions) Ex Libris Group; (Cataloging) Ex Libris Group; (Circulation) Ex Libris Group; (Course Reserve) Ex Libris Group; (OPAC) Ex Libris Group
Database Vendor: Alexander Street Press, ASCE Research Library, CQ Press, CredoReference, EBSCOhost, Gale Cengage Learning, JSTOR, LearningExpress, LexisNexis, McGraw-Hill, MD Consult, Mergent Online, OCLC CAMIO, OCLC FirstSearch, OCLC WorldCat, OVID Technologies, Oxford Online, PubMed, SerialsSolutions
Wireless access
Function: Copy machines, Electronic databases & coll
Partic in Lyrasis; Tenn-Share; West Tennessee Academic Library Consortium
Open Mon-Thurs 7:45am-11pm, Fri 7:45-4:30, Sun 1-11

S   COMMERCIAL APPEAL NEWS LIBRARY*, 495 Union Ave, 38103. SAN 325-3627. Tel: 901-529-2781. Toll Free Tel: 800-444-6397. FAX: 901-529-6460. E-mail: library@commercialappeal.com. Web Site: www.commercialappeal.com. *Dir,* Rosemary Nelms; *Librn,* Jan Smith; Staff 2 (MLS 2)
Founded 1841
Library Holdings: Bk Titles 2,000; Per Subs 200
Special Collections: Clipping Coll
Database Vendor: Dialog, Factiva.com, LexisNexis, Newsbank, ProQuest, Westlaw
Partic in Tenn-Share

C   CRICHTON COLLEGE*, J W & Dorothy Bell Library, 255 N Highland St, 38111. SAN 315-873X. Tel: 901-320-9770. FAX: 901-320-9785. Web Site: www.crichton.edu. *Dir,* Pam Walker; E-mail: pwalker@crichton.edu; *Asst Librn,* Alice Ruleman; Staff 2 (MLS 1, Non-MLS 1)
Founded 1947. Enrl 1,023; Fac 42; Highest Degree: Bachelor
Library Holdings: AV Mats 1,079; Bk Vols 50,000; Per Subs 361
Subject Interests: Biblical studies, Biol, English, Organizational mgt, Pre-nursing, Psychol, Teacher educ
Automation Activity & Vendor Info: (Cataloging) Follett Software; (Circulation) Follett Software; (ILL) OCLC; (OPAC) Follett Software
Database Vendor: Gale Cengage Learning, OCLC FirstSearch, ProQuest
Partic in Tenn Share
Open Mon-Thurs 8am-9pm, Fri 8-5, Sat 10-5

GM   DEPARTMENT OF VETERANS AFFAIRS-MEMPHIS*, Medical Library, 1030 Jefferson Ave, 38104-2193. SAN 315-8861. Tel: 901-523-8990, Ext 5883. Interlibrary Loan Service Tel: 901-523-8990, Ext 5881. FAX: 901-577-7338. E-mail: vhamemliblns@va.gov. *Chief Librn,* Mary Virginia Taylor; E-mail: maryvirginia.taylor@va.gov; *Libr Tech,* Barry W Powell, Sr; E-mail: barry.powell@va.gov; Staff 2 (MLS 1, Non-MLS 1)
Founded 1941
Library Holdings: AV Mats 1,036; Bk Vols 1,586; Per Subs 305
Subject Interests: Med, Nursing, Patient health educ, Spinal cord injury
Function: Health sci info serv, ILL available, Online searches, Ref serv available
Open Mon-Fri 8-4:30
Restriction: Circulates for staff only, In-house use for visitors, Prof mat only, Restricted borrowing privileges, Restricted loan policy

S   DIXON GALLERY & GARDENS LIBRARY*, 4339 Park Ave, 38117. SAN 315-8624. Tel: 901-761-5250. FAX: 901-682-0943. Web Site: www.dixon.org. *Educ Curator,* Margarita Sandino; E-mail: msandino@dixon.org
Founded 1976
Jan 2005-Dec 2005 Income $7,500, Parent Institution $5,000, Other $2,500. Mats Exp $7,500, Books $2,500, Per/Ser (Incl. Access Fees) $1,000, AV Equip $500, AV Mat $1,000, Electronic Ref Mat (Incl. Access Fees) $2,500
Library Holdings: AV Mats 200; Bk Vols 5,750; Per Subs 15
Special Collections: Decorative Arts; French & American Impressionist Art; Horticulture; Warda S Stout German Porcelain Coll, bks
Automation Activity & Vendor Info: (Acquisitions) LibraryWorld, Inc; (Cataloging) LibraryWorld, Inc; (Circulation) LibraryWorld, Inc
Function: Archival coll, For res purposes, Photocopying/Printing, Ref serv available
Restriction: Open by appt only

L   GLANKLER BROWN*, Law Library, One Commerce Sq, Ste 1700, 38103. SAN 371-5957. Tel: 901-525-1322. FAX: 901-525-2389. *Librn,* Donna Windham; Tel: 901-576-1806, E-mail: dwindham@glankler.com; Staff 1 (Non-MLS 1)
Library Holdings: Bk Vols 10,000; Per Subs 250
Open Mon-Fri 8:30-5

CR   HARDING UNIVERSITY GRADUATE SCHOOL OF RELIGION*, L M Graves Memorial Library, 1000 Cherry Rd, 38117. SAN 315-8659. Tel: 901-761-1354. E-mail: hgslib@hugsr.edu. Web Site: www.hugsr.edu. *Librn,* Don Meredith; *Assoc Librn,* Sheila Owen; Staff 4 (MLS 2, Non-MLS 2)
Founded 1958. Enrl 80
Library Holdings: Bk Vols 126,500; Per Subs 589
Subject Interests: Biblical studies, Christian doctrine, Church hist, Counseling, Missions, Philosophy, Relig educ
Automation Activity & Vendor Info: (Acquisitions) Ex Libris Group; (Cataloging) Ex Libris Group; (Circulation) Ex Libris Group; (Course Reserve) Ex Libris Group; (ILL) Ex Libris Group; (Media Booking) Ex Libris Group; (OPAC) Ex Libris Group; (Serials) Ex Libris Group
Database Vendor: American Psychological Association (APA), OCLC ArticleFirst, OCLC FirstSearch, OCLC WorldCat
Wireless access
Partic in Lyrasis
Open Mon, Tues & Thurs 8am-9pm, Wed & Fri 8-5, Sat 10-4

S   HARDWOOD FOREST FOUNDATION LIBRARY*, 6830 Raleigh LaGrange Rd, 38134. (Mail add: PO Box 34518, 38184-0518), SAN 372-9567. Tel: 901-507-0312. FAX: 901-382-6419. Web Site: www.hardwoodforest.org. *Exec Dir,* Crystal Oldham; E-mail: coldham@hardwoodforest.org
Library Holdings: Bk Vols 2,650
Open Mon-Fri 7:30-4:30

S KRAFT FOOD INGREDIENTS CORP*, Technical Center Library, 8000 Horizon Center Blvd, 38133. SAN 372-8595. Tel: 901-381-6500. Toll Free Tel: 800-458-8324. FAX: 901-381-6524, 901-381-6628. Web Site: www.kraftfoodingredients.com. *Librn,* Betty Murphy; Tel: 901-381-6503
Library Holdings: Bk Vols 4,000; Per Subs 50

M LE BONHEUR CHILDREN'S MEDICAL CENTER*, Health Sciences Library, 50 N Dunlap Ave, 38103. SAN 324-6949. Tel: 901-572-3167. FAX: 901-572-5290. E-mail: library@lebonheur.org. *Dir,* Leigh Hays
Founded 1952
Library Holdings: Bk Titles 1,200; Per Subs 140
Subject Interests: Pediatrics
Publications: Guide for Users; Newsletter (Monthly)
Partic in Docline

C LEMOYNE-OWEN COLLEGE*, Hollis F Price Library, 807 Walker Ave, 38126. SAN 315-8675. Tel: 901-435-1354. Circulation Tel: 901-435-1352. FAX: 901-435-1374. Web Site: www.loc.edu. *Coll Develop, Dir,* Annette C Berhe-Hunt; Tel: 901-435-1351, E-mail: annette_berhe@loc.edu; *Ref & Circ Librn,* Cassandra Jackson; Tel: 901-435-1355; Staff 5 (MLS 3, Non-MLS 2)
Founded 1870. Enrl 1,050; Fac 70; Highest Degree: Master
Library Holdings: Bk Titles 66,000; Bk Vols 86,250; Per Subs 420
Special Collections: Sweeney Coll, bks
Subject Interests: African-Am
Automation Activity & Vendor Info: (Acquisitions) SirsiDynix; (Cataloging) SirsiDynix; (Circulation) SirsiDynix
Publications: Classified bibliography of Sweeney Coll
Partic in Lyrasis; West Tennessee Academic Library Consortium
Open Mon-Thurs 7:45am-9pm, Fri 7:45-6, Sat 9-4

S MEMPHIS BOTANIC GARDEN FOUNDATION, INC*, Goldsmith Civic Garden Center - Sybile Malloy Memorial, 750 Cherry Rd, 38117. SAN 325-8769. Tel: 901-576-4100. FAX: 901-682-1561. Web Site: www.memphisbotanicgarden.com. *Dir, Operations,* Dr Stan Meyer; E-mail: plantmanstan@hotmail.com
Founded 1964
Library Holdings: Bk Vols 2,500; Per Subs 30
Subject Interests: Hort
Open Mon-Fri (March-Oct) 9-6, Sun 11-6; Mon-Sat (Nov-Feb) 9-4:30, Sun 11-4:30
Restriction: Open to pub for ref only

S MEMPHIS BROOKS MUSEUM OF ART LIBRARY*, Overton Park, 1934 Poplar Ave, 38104. SAN 315-8594. Tel: 901-544-6200. FAX: 901-725-4071. E-mail: brooks@brooksmuseum.org. Web Site: brooksmuseum.org/library. *In Charge,* Marilyn Masler; *Librn,* Wendy Trenthem
Founded 1950
Library Holdings: Bk Vols 6,741
Special Collections: Decorative Arts Coll; Dr Louis Levey Coll, prints; Kress Coll; Morrie Moss Coll; The Julie Isenberg Coll
Subject Interests: Am Art 19th-20th Centuries, Art hist
Restriction: Staff use only

S MEMPHIS COLLEGE OF ART*, G Pillow Lewis Memorial Library, 1930 Poplar Ave, 38104. SAN 315-8683. Tel: 901-272-5131. FAX: 901-272-5104. *Head of Librn,* Leslie Holland; E-mail: lholland@mca.edu; *Curator,* Karla Strickland
Founded 1936
Library Holdings: Bk Titles 16,000; Per Subs 120
Subject Interests: Fine arts
Automation Activity & Vendor Info: (Cataloging) Follett Software; (Circulation) Follett Software
Database Vendor: Cambridge Scientific Abstracts, Gale Cengage Learning
Partic in Memphis Area Libr Coun; Tenn Share
Open Mon-Thurs 8-8, Fri 8-4, Sat 10-1, Sun 1-3

S MEMPHIS PINK PALACE MUSEUM LIBRARY*, 3050 Central Ave, 38111-3399. SAN 315-8705. Tel: 901-320-6322. FAX: 901-320-6391. Web Site: www.memphismuseums.org. *Coll Develop,* Ron Brister
Founded 1967
Library Holdings: Bk Titles 5,200
Special Collections: Burge Civil War Coll; Pink Palace Museum Archives
Subject Interests: Archaeology, Botany, Geol, Hist, Zoology
Open Mon-Thurs 9-4
Restriction: Staff use only

P MEMPHIS PUBLIC LIBRARY & INFORMATION CENTER*, Benjamin L Hooks Central Library, 3030 Poplar Ave, 38111-3527. SAN 360-7291. Tel: 901-415-2700. Circulation Tel: 901-415-2702. Interlibrary Loan Service Tel: 901-415-2704. Administration Tel: 901-415-2749. Automation Services Tel: 901-415-2801. FAX: 901-323-7108. Interlibrary Loan Service FAX: 901-323-7637. Automation Services FAX: 901-323-7275. TDD: 901-415-2701. Web Site: www.memphislibrary.org. *Dir of Libr,* E Keenon McCloy; E-mail: mccloyk@memphislibrary.org; *Dep Dir,* Fred Bannerman-Williams; E-mail: bannermanwf@memphislibrary.org; *Asst Dir, Libr Communications,* Stephanie Jones; Tel: 901-415-2847, E-mail: joness@memphislibrary.org; *Asst Dir, Outreach & Spec Projects,* Aurelia Kyles; Tel: 901-415-2871, E-mail: kylesa@memphislibrary.org; *Asst Dir, Support Serv,* Debby McElroy-Clark; E-mail: mcelroyd@memphislibrary.org; *Sr Mgr, Bus/Sci Dept,* Ruth Morrison; Tel: 901-415-2736, E-mail: morrisonr@memphislibrary.org; *Circ Sr Mgr/ILL,* Ann Delphin; Tel: 901-415-2705, E-mail: delphina@memphislibrary.org; *Sr Mgr, Hist/Genealogy Dept,* Wayne Dowdy; Tel: 901-415-2744, E-mail: dowdyw@memphislibrary.org; *Sr Mgr, Humanities Dept,* Gina Milburn; Tel: 901-415-2726, E-mail: milburng@memphislibrary.org; *Sr Mgr, LINC,* Ron Reid; Tel: 901-415-2716, E-mail: reidr@memphislibrary.org; *Senior Mgr, East Region,* Norvel Adams-Walker; E-mail: adamswalkern@memphislibrary.org; *Regional Mgr, North Region,* Position Currently Open; *Regional Mgr, South Region,* Chris Marszalek; E-mail: marszalekc@memphislibrary.org; *Coordr, Youth Serv,* Mary Seratt; Tel: 901-415-2839, E-mail: serattm@memphislibrary.org; *Acq,* Cindy Soenksen; Tel: 901-415-2817, E-mail: soenksenc@memphislibrary.org; *Children's Coll Develop,* Ann Andrews; Tel: 901-415-2712, E-mail: andrewsa@memphislibrary.org; *Mgr, Coll Develop,* Alan Stewart; *Head Cataloger,* Position Currently Open
Founded 1893. Pop 808,113; Circ 2,480,472
Library Holdings: AV Mats 154,217; e-books 16; Electronic Media & Resources 16; Bk Titles 1,398,697; Bk Vols 1,637,596
Special Collections: Afro-American Memphis (Beale Street, WC Handy, J Ashton Hayes, Blair T Hunt, George W Lee, Ethyl Venson Colls); Christian Coll; Commerce & Industry (Rees V Downs, Henry A Montgomery Colls); E H Crump Coll; Family History (Duke-Bedford, Farrow, Price-Davis, Trezevant Colls); Folk History (Morris Solomon, WW Busby, John Ogden Carley, Memphis Historical Society Colls); Health Information Center; Louise Mercer Coll; Mary Love Coll; Maxine Smith Coll; Memphis & Shelby County Archives; Photographs (Poland & Coovert Colls); Politics & Government (Samuel Bates, Robert Cohn, Mayer Henry Loeb, Sen Kennth McKellar, Judge John D Martin, Commissioner James Moore, Page/Lenox, Commissioner Jack W Ramsay, Tennessee Valley Authority Colls); Public Health (Memphis Crippled Childern's Hospital School, Rev George C Harris, Yellow Fever Colls); Religion (Rabbi James A Wax); The Arts (Hugh Higbee Huhn, Sarah B Kennedy, Florence McIntyre, Walter Malone, Music Miscellany, Julia Raine, Searcy Family Colls); War History (William W Goodman, Colton Greene, Memphians During War, Memphis Belle, Gideon J Pillow Colls); William Fowler Coll. Oral History; State Document Depository; US Document Depository
Subject Interests: Archit, Art, Memphis hist
Automation Activity & Vendor Info: (Acquisitions) SirsiDynix; (Cataloging) SirsiDynix; (Circulation) SirsiDynix; (Serials) SirsiDynix
Database Vendor: Gale Cengage Learning
Wireless access
Publications: Friends Newletter; Getting Ready for Summer; InfoDATES; Library Calendar; Library Matters; Program Highlights (Channel 18); Staff Newslinc; WYPL Program Guide
Partic in Dialog Corp; Dow Jones News Retrieval; Lyrasis
Open Mon-Thurs 9-9, Fri & Sat 9-6, Sun 1-5
Friends of the Library Group
Branches: 22
BARTLETT BRANCH, 5884 Stage Rd, Bartlett, 38134, SAN 360-7593. Tel: 901-386-8968. FAX: 901-386-2358. *Br Mgr,* Gay Cain; E-mail: caing@memphislibrary.org
Pop 40,000; Circ 324,968
Library Holdings: Bk Vols 782,306
Open Mon-Thurs 10-8, Fri & Sat 10-6, Sun 1-5
Friends of the Library Group
CHEROKEE, 3300 Sharpe, 38111, SAN 360-7623. Tel: 901-743-3655. FAX: 901-743-9030. *Br Mgr,* Sara Ellen Reid
Circ 23,886
Library Holdings: Bk Vols 28,025
Open Mon-Thurs & Sat 10-6
Friends of the Library Group
CHILDREN'S DEPARTMENT, 3030 Poplar Ave, 38111-3527. Tel: 901-415-2739. FAX: 901-323-7108. *Coordr, Youth Serv,* Mary M Seratt; E-mail: serattm@memphislibrary.org; Staff 12.5 (MLS 5, Non-MLS 7.5)
Function: Children's prog, Computers for patron use, Copy machines, Exhibits, Handicapped accessible, Music CDs, Online cat, Online ref, Orientations, Preschool outreach, Prog for children & young adult, Story hour, Summer reading prog, Web-catalog, Wheelchair accessible
Open Mon-Thurs 9-9, Fri & Sat 9-6, Sun 1-5
Friends of the Library Group
CORDOVA BRANCH, 8457 Trinity Rd, Cordova, 38018, SAN 360-7674. Tel: 901-754-8443. FAX: 901-754-6874. *Br Mgr,* Phillips Williams; E-mail: williamsp@memphislibrary.org
Circ 380,585
Library Holdings: Bk Vols 114,118

Open Mon-Thurs 10-9, Fri & Sat 10-6
Friends of the Library Group

COSSITT BRANCH, 33 S Front, 38103-2499, SAN 360-7682. Tel:
901-526-1712. FAX: 901-526-0730. *Mgr,* Inger Upchurch
Founded 1888. Circ 14,838
Library Holdings: Bk Vols 10,422
Open Mon-Fri 10-5
Friends of the Library Group

CORNELIA CRENSHAW MEMORIAL LIBRARY, 531 Vance Ave,
38126-2116, SAN 360-8131. Tel: 901-525-1643. FAX: 901-525-0390.
Mgr, Inger Upchurch
Founded 1939. Circ 12,925
Library Holdings: Bk Vols 22,670
Open Mon-Thurs & Sat 10-5
Friends of the Library Group

EAST SHELBY BRANCH, 7200 E Shelby Dr, 38125. Tel: 901-751-7360.
Br Mgr, Louis Alen; *Br Mgr,* Debra Stevens
Open Mon-Sat 10-6

FRAYSER BRANCH, 3712 Argonne, 38127-4414, SAN 360-7712. Tel:
901-357-4115. FAX: 901-358-0360. *Mgr,* Arlene Handerson; *Mgr,* Dean
Moore; E-mail: moored@memphislibrary.org
Circ 50,330
Library Holdings: Bk Vols 34,026
Open Mon-Wed 10-7, Thurs-Sat 10-6
Friends of the Library Group

GASTON PARK, 1040 S Third, 38106-2002, SAN 360-7747. Tel:
901-942-0836. FAX: 901-942-5667. *Br Mgr,* Inger Upchurch
Founded 1978. Circ 11,013
Library Holdings: Bk Vols 12,848
Open Mon-Thurs 10-5, Sat 12-5
Friends of the Library Group

HISTORY & TRAVEL, 3030 Poplar Ave, 38111. Tel: 901-415-2742. FAX:
901-323-7981. *Actg Mgr,* Thomas Jones
Special Collections: Memphis Coll
Subject Interests: Genealogy, Hist, Travel
Open Mon-Thurs 9-9, Fri & Sat 9-6, Sun 1-5
Friends of the Library Group

HOLLYWOOD, 1530 N Hollywood, 38108, SAN 360-7836. Tel:
901-323-6201. FAX: 901-323-5610. *Br Mgr,* Jennifer Poindexter; E-mail:
poindexterj@memphislibrary.org
Circ 18,604
Library Holdings: Bk Vols 24,617
Open Mon-Sat 10-6
Friends of the Library Group

HUMANITIES, 3030 Poplar Ave, 38111. Tel: 901-415-2726. FAX:
901-323-7206. *Mgr,* Gina Milburn; E-mail:
milburng@memphislibrary.org
Open Mon-Thurs 9-9, Fri & Sat 9-6, Sun 1-5
Friends of the Library Group

LEVI, 3676 Hwy 61 S, 38109-8296, SAN 360-7860. Tel: 901-789-3140.
FAX: 901-789-3141. *Br Mgr,* Margaret Hicks; E-mail:
hicksm@memphislibrary.org
Circ 18,408
Library Holdings: Bk Vols 21,099
Open Mon & Tues 10-6, Wed, Thurs & Sat 10-5
Friends of the Library Group

NORTH, 1192 Vollintine, 38107-2899, SAN 360-7925. Tel: 901-276-6631.
FAX: 901-726-0731. *Br Mgr,* Carol Hogan
Founded 1961. Circ 20,992
Library Holdings: Bk Vols 25,732
Open Mon-Thurs 10-6, Fri & Sat 11-6
Friends of the Library Group

PARKWAY VILLAGE, 4655 Knight Arnold Rd, 38118-3234, SAN
360-795X. Tel: 901-363-8923. FAX: 901-794-2344. *Br Mgr,* Sara Ellen
Reid; E-mail: reids@memphislibrary.org
Founded 1966. Circ 74,654
Library Holdings: Bk Vols 54,980
Open Mon-Thurs 10-7, Fri & Sat 10-6
Friends of the Library Group

POPLAR-WHITE STATION, 5094 Poplar, 38117-7629, SAN 360-7984.
Tel: 901-415-2777. FAX: 901-682-8975. *Br Mgr,* Lisa Ingram; *Youth
Serv Librn,* Michelle Allen; *Circ Supvr,* Barbara Matthews; Staff 4 (MLS
1, Non-MLS 3)
Circ 149,596
Library Holdings: Bk Vols 52,643
Open Mon-Thurs 10-7, Fri & Sat 10-5
Friends of the Library Group

RALEIGH BRANCH, 3157 Powers Rd, 38128, SAN 360-8018. Tel:
901-386-5333. FAX: 901-371-9495. *Mgr,* Freda Hopkins; *Mgr,* Mollie
Howard
Circ 98,716
Library Holdings: Bk Vols 48,985
Open Mon-Thurs 10-9, Fri & Sat 10-6
Friends of the Library Group

RANDOLPH BRANCH, 3752 Given, 38122, SAN 360-8042. Tel:
901-452-1068. FAX: 901-454-9594. *Br Mgr,* Maggie Farmer; E-mail:
farmerm@memphislibrary.org; *Br Librn,* Mattie Gray
Founded 1956. Circ 35,274
Library Holdings: Bk Vols 30,563
Open Mon 10-7, Tues-Sat 10-6
Friends of the Library Group

SCIENCE, BUSINESS, 3030 Poplar Ave, 38111. Tel: 901-415-2734.
Nonprofit Res Librn, Supvr, Pub Serv, Jessie W Marshall; *Agency Mgr,*
Ruth W Morrison; Tel: 901-415-2736; Staff 7 (MLS 6, Non-MLS 1)
Special Collections: Job & Career Centre; NonProfit Resource
Information Center; Personal Finance Coll; Small Business Center. State
Document Depository; US Document Depository
Subject Interests: Bus, Govt publ
Open Mon-Thurs 9-9, Fri & Sat 9-6, Sun 1-5
Friends of the Library Group

SOUTH, 1929 S Third St, 38109, SAN 360-8107. Tel: 901-946-8518.
FAX: 901-946-1435. *Br Mgr,* Pam Nickleberry-Brooks; E-mail:
brooksp@memphislibrary.org
Circ 29,631
Library Holdings: Bk Vols 36,608
Database Vendor: Gale Cengage Learning
Open Mon-Thurs 10-6, Fri & Sat 10-5
Friends of the Library Group

WHITEHAVEN, 4120 Mill Branch Rd, 38116, SAN 360-8166. Tel:
901-396-9700. FAX: 901-332-6150. *Br Mgr,* Toni Braswell
Circ 140,769
Library Holdings: Bk Vols 103,973
Open Mon-Thurs 10-9, Fri & Sat 10-6
Friends of the Library Group

CR   MEMPHIS THEOLOGICAL SEMINARY LIBRARY*, 168 E Parkway S,
38104. SAN 315-8713. Tel: 901-458-8232. Reference Tel: 901-334-5814.
Administration Tel: 901-334-5812. Information Services Tel: 901-334-5858.
FAX: 901-452-4051. E-mail: library@memphisseminary.edu. Web Site:
www.memphisseminary.edu/library. *Dir,* Steven R Edscorn; E-mail:
sedscorn@memphisseminary.edu; *Asst Dir,* Jane Williamson; E-mail:
jwilliamson@memphisseminary.edu; *Acq,* Melissa Hamblin; Tel:
901-334-5824, E-mail: mhamblin@memphisseminary.edu; *Cat,* Megan
Kettner; Tel: 901-334-5825, E-mail: mkettner@memphisseminary.edu; *Circ,*
Mildred Saulsberry; Tel: 901-334-5813, E-mail:
msaulsberry@memphisseminary.edu; Staff 5 (MLS 3, Non-MLS 2)
Founded 1956. Enrl 349; Fac 15; Highest Degree: Doctorate
Aug 2007-Jul 2008. Mats Exp $329,180, Books $35,135, Per/Ser (Incl.
Access Fees) $44,136, AV Mat $1,652, Electronic Ref Mat (Incl. Access
Fees) $12,847. Sal $196,031 (Prof $126,086)
Library Holdings: Microforms 1,252; Bk Vols 72,148; Per Subs 376;
Videos 950
Special Collections: C S Lewis Coll; Christian Missions (R Pierce Beaver
Coll); Cumberland Presbyterian History; Martin Luther King, Jr, papers
Subject Interests: Baptist, Methodism, Presbyterianism
Automation Activity & Vendor Info: (Acquisitions) SirsiDynix;
(Cataloging) SirsiDynix; (Circulation) SirsiDynix; (Course Reserve)
SirsiDynix; (OPAC) SirsiDynix
Database Vendor: Gale Cengage Learning, OCLC FirstSearch, OCLC
WorldCat
Open Mon-Thurs 8-7:30, Fri 8-3, Sat 8:30-12:30

M   METHODIST HEALTHCARE*, Leslie M Stratton Medical Library, 1265
Union Ave, 38104-3499. SAN 315-8721. Tel: 901-726-7899. FAX:
901-726-8254. *Dir,* Judy Watts; *Mgr,* Glenda Mendina; Staff 1 (MLS 1)
Founded 1951
Library Holdings: Bk Titles 1,084; Bk Vols 5,000; Per Subs 164
Subject Interests: Clinical med
Automation Activity & Vendor Info: (Acquisitions) CyberTools for
Libraries; (Cataloging) CyberTools for Libraries; (Circulation) CyberTools
for Libraries; (ILL) CyberTools for Libraries; (Media Booking) CyberTools
for Libraries; (OPAC) CyberTools for Libraries
Partic in Medical Library Association (MLA); Tennessee Health Science
Library Association
Open Mon-Fri 8-4:30
Restriction: Staff use only

A   PT BOATS, INC, WW II PT Boats Museum & Library, 1384 Cordova
Cove, Ste 2, 38138-2200. (Mail add: PO Box 38070, Germantown,
38183-0070), SAN 326-1700. Tel: 901-755-8440. E-mail:
ptboats@ptboats.org. Web Site: www.ptboats.org. *VPres,* Alyce N Guthrie;
Coordr, Don Shannon; Tel: 508-678-1100
Founded 1946
Library Holdings: Bk Titles 230; Bk Vols 430; Per Subs 20
Special Collections: Two Restored PT Boats
Function: Res libr
Publications: PT Squadrons, Bases, Tenders ALL HANDS (Newsletter)
Restriction: Not a lending libr, Open by appt only

C   RHODES COLLEGE*, Paul Barret Jr Library, 2000 North Pkwy,
     38112-1694. SAN 315-8810. Tel: 901-843-3900. Interlibrary Loan Service
     Tel: 901-843-3770. Reference Tel: 901-843-3927. Administration Tel:
     901-843-3901. Information Services Tel: 901-843-3745. FAX:
     901-843-3404. Web Site: www.rhodes.edu. *Dir, Electronic Res, Info Serv,*
     Darlene Brooks; E-mail: brooksd@rhodes.edu; *Assoc Dir, Libr Serv,*
     William Short; Tel: 901-843-3792, E-mail: short@rhodes.edu; *Head, Cat,*
     Janice Tankersley; Tel: 901-843-3891, E-mail: tankersley@rhodes.edu; *Info
     Serv Librn,* Lee Boulie; E-mail: bouliel@rhodes.edu; *Info Serv Librn,* Greg
     Paraham; E-mail: parahamg@rhodes.edu; *Info Serv Librn,* Nikki Rech;
     E-mail: rechn@rhodes.edu; *Archivist, Spec Coll,* Elizabeth Gates; Tel:
     901-843-3902, E-mail: archives@rhodes.edu; *Acq,* Janet James; Tel:
     901-843-3903, E-mail: jamesjc@rhodes.edu; *Cat, Coll Develop,* Rachel
     Feinman; Tel: 901-843-3893, E-mail: feinmanr@rhodes.edu; *Info Serv, ILL,*
     Kenan Padgett; E-mail: padgettk@rhodes.edu. Subject Specialists: *Eng,
     Music, Theatre,* William Short; *Am studies, Gender studies,* Janice
     Tankersley; *Art, Environ studies,* Lee Boulie; *Chem, Econ,* Greg Paraham;
     Anthropology, Modern lang, Psychol, Nikki Rech; *Hist,* Elizabeth Gates;
     Am studies, Janet James; *Film studies, Neuroscience,* Rachel Feinman;
     Biochem, Urban studies, Kenan Padgett; Staff 8 (MLS 8)
     Founded 1848. Enrl 1,560; Fac 120; Highest Degree: Bachelor
     Library Holdings: AV Mats 7,000; e-books 64,000; e-journals 4,011;
     Electronic Media & Resources 8,339; Bk Titles 191,927; Bk Vols 275,000;
     Talking Bks 417; Videos 6,771
     Special Collections: 19th & 20th Century English & American Literature
     (Walter Armstrong Rare Book Coll), autographed first editions; Art
     (Clough Hansen Art Memorial for Teaching), paintings, objects d'art
     Subject Interests: Liberal arts
     Automation Activity & Vendor Info: (Acquisitions) SirsiDynix;
     (Cataloging) SirsiDynix; (Circulation) SirsiDynix; (ILL) OCLC; (OPAC)
     SirsiDynix; (Serials) SirsiDynix
     Database Vendor: Alexander Street Press, American Chemical Society,
     American Psychological Association (APA), ARTstor, Baker & Taylor,
     BioOne, Blackwell's, Cambridge Scientific Abstracts, CQ Press,
     CredoReference, EBSCO Information Services, EBSCOhost, Elsevier, Facts
     on File, Gale Cengage Learning, H W Wilson, IEEE (Institute of Electrical
     & Electronics Engineers), Infotrieve, Ingenta, JSTOR, LearningExpress,
     LexisNexis, Modern Language Association, Nature Publishing Group,
     netLibrary, Newsbank, Newsbank-Readex, OCLC FirstSearch, OCLC
     WorldCat, Oxford Online, Project MUSE, ProQuest, Sage, ScienceDirect,
     SerialsSolutions, SirsiDynix, Swets Information Services, Wiley
     InterScience, Wilson - Wilson Web
     Wireless access
     Partic in Lyrasis; Oberlin Group; OCLC Online Computer Library Center,
     Inc
     Open Mon-Thurs 7:30am-2am, Fri 7:30-6, Sat 10-5, Sun 10am-2am;
     Mon-Fri (Summer) 8-5

M   SAINT JUDE CHILDREN'S RESEARCH HOSPITAL*, Biomedical
     Library, 262 Danny Thomas Pl, 38105-3678. SAN 315-8772. Tel:
     901-595-3388. Interlibrary Loan Service Tel: 901-495-3389. FAX:
     901-595-3117. E-mail: library@stjude.org. Web Site:
     www.stjude.org/library. *Dir,* Jan Orick; Staff 5 (MLS 3, Non-MLS 2)
     Founded 1962
     Library Holdings: Bk Vols 2,500; Per Subs 500
     Subject Interests: Cancer, Immunology, Molecular biol, Pediatrics,
     Virology
     Automation Activity & Vendor Info: (Cataloging) EOS International;
     (Circulation) EOS International; (OPAC) EOS International; (Serials) EOS
     International
     Partic in National Network of Libraries of Medicine; OCLC Online
     Computer Library Center, Inc
     Open Mon-Fri 8-5

S   SCHERING-PLOUGH HEALTH CARE, INC*, Research & Development
     Library, 3030 Jackson Ave, 38112-2020. (Mail add: PO Box 377,
     38101-0377), SAN 328-624X. Tel: 901-320-2702. FAX: 901-320-3017.
     Librn, Martha Hurst; E-mail: martha.hurst@spcorp.com
     Library Holdings: Bk Titles 3,000; Per Subs 60
     Automation Activity & Vendor Info: (Cataloging) Inmagic, Inc.;
     (Circulation) Inmagic, Inc.
     Restriction: Not open to pub

L   SHELBY COUNTY LAW LIBRARY*, Shelby County Courthouse, 140
     Adams Ave, Rm 334, 38103. SAN 315-8691. Tel: 901-527-7041.
     Administration Tel: 901-527-8498. FAX: 901-522-8935. E-mail:
     lawlibrary@bellsouth.net. Web Site: www.shelbycountylawlibrary.com.
     Adminr, Gary L Johnson; Fax: 901-522-8936; Staff 3 (MLS 2, Non-MLS
     1)
     Founded 1970
     Library Holdings: Bk Vols 51,000
     Special Collections: Early English Law Coll; Early Laws of North
     Carolina Coll; Statutes at Large for First Congress of the United States
     Coll

Database Vendor: Westlaw
Wireless access
Function: Ref serv available
Open Mon-Fri 8-4:30
Restriction: Non-circulating to the pub

CM   SOUTHERN COLLEGE OF OPTOMETRY LIBRARY*, 1245 Madison
     Ave, 38104. SAN 315-8802. Tel: 901-722-3237. FAX: 901-722-3292. *Dir
     of Libr Serv,* Dr Sharon E Tabachnick; Tel: 901-722-3238, E-mail:
     stabachnick@sco.edu; *Asst Dir, Libr Serv,* Rosemary Gordon; Tel:
     901-722-3239, E-mail: rgordon@sco.edu. Subject Specialists: *Educ
     psychol,* Dr Sharon E Tabachnick; Staff 2 (MLS 2)
     Founded 1938. Enrl 470; Fac 56; Highest Degree: Doctorate
     Library Holdings: AV Mats 1,662; Bk Titles 15,000; Bk Vols 15,613; Per
     Subs 162
     Special Collections: Oral History
     Subject Interests: Ophthalmology, Optics, Optometry
     Automation Activity & Vendor Info: (Acquisitions) Cuadra Associates;
     (Cataloging) Cuadra Associates; (OPAC) Cuadra Associates; (Serials)
     Cuadra Associates
     Database Vendor: Dialog, EBSCO Information Services, EBSCOhost
     Wireless access
     Partic in Asn for Vision Sci Librns
     Produce the Visionet online index of vision literature citations which
     contains citations not covered by other indices, available on the Internet at
     visionet.sco.edu
     Open Mon-Thurs (Winter) 8am-10:30pm, Fri 8-6, Sat 12-6, Sun 1-10;
     Mon-Fri (Summer) 8-4:30

J   SOUTHWEST TENNESSEE COMMUNITY COLLEGE*, Parrish Library,
     170 Myrtle St, 38103. (Mail add: PO Box 708, 38101-0780), SAN
     315-8799. Tel: 901-333-5135. Toll Free Tel: 877-717-7822. FAX:
     901-333-5141. Web Site: southwest.tn.edu/library. *Exec Dir,* Carolyn Head;
     Tel: 901-333-5938, E-mail: cshead@southwest.tn.edu; *Assoc Dir,* Vivian
     Stewart; Tel: 901-333-5067, E-mail: vstewart@southwest.tn.edu; *Librn,*
     Alice Thompson; Tel: 901-333-5945, E-mail: afduncan@southwest.tn.edu;
     Ref, Regina Massey; Tel: 901-333-5140, E-mail:
     rmassey@southwest.tn.edu; Staff 5 (MLS 2, Non-MLS 3)
     Founded 1972. Enrl 4,000; Fac 200
     Library Holdings: Music Scores 808; Bk Titles 42,493; Bk Vols 45,917;
     Per Subs 288; Videos 5,219
     Subject Interests: Allied health, Behav sci, Educ, Ethnic studies, Soc sci
     Automation Activity & Vendor Info: (Circulation) SirsiDynix
     Database Vendor: Gale Cengage Learning, SirsiDynix, Wilson - Wilson
     Web
     Partic in TBR Consortium
     Open Mon-Thurs (Winter) 7am-9pm, Fri 7-4:30, Sat 8:30-12:30;
     Mon-Thurs 8-8, Fri (Summer) 8-4:30
     Departmental Libraries:
     GEORGE FREEMAN LIBRARY, 5983 Macon Cove, 38134, SAN
     315-8829. Tel: 901-333-4706. Reference Tel: 901-333-4733. FAX:
     901-333-4566. *Exec Dir,* Carolyn Head; Tel: 901-333-4732, E-mail:
     cshead@southwest.tn.edu; *Assoc Dir, Libr Admin,* Vivian Stewart; Fax:
     901-333-5141, E-mail: vstewart@southwest.tn.edu; *Pub Serv Mgr,*
     Virginia Anne Howard; E-mail: ahoward@southwest.tn.edu; *Tech Serv
     Team Leader,* Emmer T Swauncy; Tel: 901-333-4437, E-mail:
     eswauncy@southwest.tn.edu; *Circ,* Lisa Lumpkin; Tel: 901-333-4105,
     E-mail: llumpkin@southwest.tn.edu; *Per,* Regina N Massey; Tel:
     901-333-5140, E-mail: rmassey@southwest.tn.edu; *Tech Serv,* Stephen
     Beeko; Tel: 901-333-4732, E-mail: sbeeko@southwest.tn.edu; Staff 13
     (MLS 6, Non-MLS 7)
     Founded 2000. Enrl 11,566; Highest Degree: Associate
     Library Holdings: CDs 1,866; Music Scores 838; Bk Vols 35,761; Per
     Subs 147; Talking Bks 1,768; Videos 1,544
     Subject Interests: Allied health, Computer, Eng, Paralegal
     Automation Activity & Vendor Info: (Cataloging) SirsiDynix;
     (Circulation) SirsiDynix; (Course Reserve) SirsiDynix; (ILL) SirsiDynix;
     (OPAC) SirsiDynix; (Serials) SirsiDynix
     Database Vendor: LexisNexis, OCLC FirstSearch, ProQuest
     Open Mon-Thurs (Winter) 7am-9pm, Fri 7-4:30, Sat 8:30-12:30;
     Mon-Thurs (Summer) 8-8, Fri 8-4:30
     GILL LIBRARY, 3833 Mountain Terrace, 38127. Tel: 901-333-5979. FAX:
     901-333-5980. Web Site: www.southwest.tn.edu/library/gill_lib.htm. *Exec
     Dir,* Carolyn Head; E-mail: cshead@southwest.tn.edu; *Assoc Dir,* Vivian
     Stewart; E-mail: vstewart@southwest.tn.edu
     Library Holdings: Music Scores 45; Bk Titles 3,254; Per Subs 42;
     Videos 293
     Automation Activity & Vendor Info: (Cataloging) Innovative Interfaces,
     Inc; (Circulation) Innovative Interfaces, Inc
     Database Vendor: EBSCOhost
     Open Mon-Thurs 8am-9pm, Fri 8-4:30
     Friends of the Library Group
     SOUTHEAST CENTER LIBRARY, 5396 Mendenhall Mall, 38115. Tel:
     901-333-6037. FAX: 901-333-6038. Web Site:
     www.southwest.tn.edu/library/southeast_lib.htm. *Exec Dir,* Carolyn Head;

E-mail: cshead@southwest.tn.edu; *Assoc Dir,* Vivian Stewart; E-mail: vstewart@southwest.tn.edu
Library Holdings: Music Scores 92; Bk Titles 2,903; Per Subs 37; Videos 272
Automation Activity & Vendor Info: (Cataloging) Innovative Interfaces, Inc; (Circulation) Innovative Interfaces, Inc
Database Vendor: EBSCOhost
Open Mon-Thurs 8am-9pm, Fri 8-4:30, Sat 8:30-12:30
WHITEHAVEN CENTER LIBRARY, 3035 Directors Row, Bldg 6, 38131. Tel: 901-333-6442. FAX: 901-333-6441. Web Site: www.southwest.tn.edu/library/whitehaven.htm. *Exec Dir,* Carolyn Head; E-mail: cshead@southwest.tn.edu; *Assoc Dir,* Vivian Stewart; E-mail: vstewart@southwest.tn.edu
Library Holdings: AV Mats 475; Music Scores 148; Bk Titles 1,681; Per Subs 29; Videos 292
Automation Activity & Vendor Info: (Cataloging) Innovative Interfaces, Inc; (Circulation) Innovative Interfaces, Inc
Database Vendor: EBSCOhost
Open Mon-Thurs 8am-9pm, Fri 8-4:30

A   UNITED STATES ARMY*, Corps of Engineers Memphis District Library, B-202 Clifford Davis Federal Bldg, 167 N Main St, 38103-1899. SAN 360-8379. Tel: 901-544-3584. FAX: 901-544-3792. *In Charge,* Janet Wilson; Tel: 901-544-3134
Founded 1932
Library Holdings: Bk Titles 5,850; Per Subs 275
Subject Interests: Civil eng, Econ, Environ studies, Hydrol, Lower Miss Valley, Water res
Publications: Periodical List
Partic in Dialog Corp; OCLC Online Computer Library Center, Inc
Restriction: Open to pub for ref only

C   UNIVERSITY LIBRARIES, UNIVERSITY OF MEMPHIS*, 126 Ned R McWherter Library, 38152-3250. SAN 360-8190. Circulation Tel: 901-678-2205. Interlibrary Loan Service Tel: 901-678-2262. Reference Tel: 901-678-2208. Administration Tel: 901-678-2201. Automation Services Tel: 901-678-2356. Interlibrary Loan Service FAX: 901-678-2511. Administration FAX: 901-678-8218. Web Site: www.memphis.edu/libraries. *Dean, Univ Libr,* Dr Sylverna V Ford; E-mail: sford@memphis.edu; *Assoc Dean,* Annelle R Huggins; Tel: 901-678-4482, E-mail: ahuggins@memphis.edu; *Head, Br Libr, Music Librn,* Anna Neal; Tel: 901-678-4412, E-mail: abneal@memphis.edu; *Head, Cat,* Elizabeth McDonald; Tel: 901-678-8237, E-mail: emcdnld1@memphis.edu; *Head, Circ,* Stacey J Smith; Tel: 901-678-8201, E-mail: sjsmith1@memphis.edu; *Head, Coll Mgt,* Kevin Merriman; Tel: 901-678-8234, E-mail: kmerriman@memphis.edu; *Head Govt Publ,* Mary Freilich; Tel: 901-678-8203, E-mail: freilich@memphis.edu; *Head, Instrul Serv,* Margaret Robinson; Tel: 901-678-8206, E-mail: merobnsn@memphis.edu; *Head, Libr Info Syst Dept,* Dr John E Evans; Tel: 901-678-4485, E-mail: jevans@memphis.edu; *Curator, Head, Presv & Spec Coll,* Edwin G Frank; Tel: 901-678-2210, E-mail: efrank@memphis.edu; *Coll Develop Librn,* Steven Knowlton; Tel: 901-678-8234, E-mail: sknwlton@memphis.edu; *Electronic Res Librn,* RaShauna Brannon; Tel: 901-678-8226, E-mail: rnbrnnon@memphis.edu; *ILL Librn,* Susan Wood; Tel: 901-678-8223, E-mail: swood1@memphis.edu; *Web Serv Librn,* Yue Xu; Tel: 901-678-4465, E-mail: yxu1@memphis.edu; Staff 85 (MLS 20, Non-MLS 65)
Founded 1914. Enrl 23,000; Fac 735; Highest Degree: Doctorate
Jul 2006-Jun 2007 Income (Main and Other College/University Libraries) $7,100,000
Library Holdings: Bk Vols 1,311,471; Per Subs 11,541
Special Collections: 1968 Memphis Sanitation Strike Coll; 19th & 20th Century US & European Theatre History Coll; 20th Century American Circus Coll; Confederate Historical Association Coll; Edmund Orgill Coll; Edward Meeman Coll; Election Campaign Material, local, state & national; Ethnic Populations for the Mid-South; Freedman's Bureau of the US War Department; Jefferson Davis-Joel Addison Hayes Family Coll; Jesse Hill Ford Coll; John Faulkner Coll; Lower Mississippi Delta Development Center, papers; Lower Mississippi Valley History, Literature & Culture, A-tapes, bks, ephemera, films, maps, ms, pamphlets, photog, sheet music, V-tapes; Margaret Polk Coll (Memphis Bell), scrapbks; Memphis Commercial Appeal Coll, photog; Memphis Typographical Union Coll; Mississippi River Boatmen; Oral Histories - Blues & Jazz; Overton Park Expressway Controversy Coll; Press Scimitar, clipping file; Public Management Science Coll; Robert R Church Family Coll; Rock & Roll & Elvis Presley (Jerry Hopkins Coll); Southern Writers; Tennessee Politicians; Tennessee Valley Authority; Watkins Overton Coll; West Tennessee Historical Society (Elizabeth Avery Meriwether Family Coll); Women Leaders of Memphis. State Document Depository; UN Document Depository; US Document Depository
Automation Activity & Vendor Info: (Acquisitions) Innovative Interfaces, Inc; (Cataloging) Innovative Interfaces, Inc; (Circulation) Innovative Interfaces, Inc; (Course Reserve) Innovative Interfaces, Inc; (ILL) OCLC ILLiad; (OPAC) Innovative Interfaces, Inc; (Serials) Innovative Interfaces, Inc

Database Vendor: Dialog, Gale Cengage Learning, LexisNexis, OCLC FirstSearch, OVID Technologies, ProQuest, SirsiDynix, TLC (The Library Corporation)
Wireless access
Publications: The UOML News (Newsletter)
Partic in Association of Southeastern Research Libraries; Lyrasis; OCLC Online Computer Library Center, Inc; Tenn Acad Libr Collaborative; Tenn Share
Special Services for the Blind - Reader equip
Open Mon-Thurs (Spring-Fall) 7:30am-Midnight, Fri 7:30-6, Sat 10-6, Sun 1-10
Restriction: Open to pub for ref & circ; with some limitations
Friends of the Library Group
Departmental Libraries:
COMMUNICATION SCIENCES, 807 Jefferson St, Rm 110, 38105-5042, SAN 360-8344. Tel: 901-678-5846. FAX: 901-678-8281. Web Site: www.memphis.edu/ausplibrary/index.php. *Br Mgr,* John Swearengen; E-mail: jmswrngn@memphis.edu; Staff 1 (Non-MLS 1)
Library Holdings: Bk Vols 8,130; Per Subs 86
Open Mon-Fri 8-4:30
Friends of the Library Group
MATHEMATICS, 341 Dunn Hall, 38152, SAN 373-5540. Tel: 901-678-2385. FAX: 901-678-2480. Web Site: exlibris.memphis.edu/math/index.html. *Circ & Ref,* Rose Moore; Staff 1 (Non-MLS 1)
Library Holdings: Bk Vols 30,699; Per Subs 283
Open Mon-Thurs (Fall & Spring) 8-6, Fri 8-4:30; Mon-Fri (Summer) 8-4:30
Friends of the Library Group
MUSIC, 115 Music Bldg, 38152, SAN 360-831X. Tel: 901-678-2330. FAX: 901-678-3096. Web Site: exlibris.memphis.edu/music/index.html. *Head, Br Libr, Music Librn,* Anna Neal; Tel: 901-678-4412, E-mail: abneal@memphis.edu; Staff 3 (MLS 1, Non-MLS 2)
Library Holdings: Bk Vols 43,092; Per Subs 174
Open Mon-Thurs (Fall & Spring) 7:45am-9pm, Fri 7:45-4:30, Sat 10-2, Sun 6pm-9pm; Mon-Thurs (Summer) 8-8, Fri 8-4:30, Sat 10-2
Friends of the Library Group

L   THE UNIVERSITY OF MEMPHIS, Cecil C Humphreys School of Law Library, One N Front St, 38103. SAN 360-828X. Tel: 901-678-2426. FAX: 901-678-5293. Web Site: www.memphis.edu/law/library/index.php. *Asst Prof of Law, Assoc Dean, Info, Dir, Law Libr,* D R Jones; Tel: 901-678-3244; *Asst Dir, Pub Serv,* Whitney Curtis; Tel: 901-678-4937, E-mail: wcurtis1@memphis.edu; *Asst Dir, Tech Serv,* Beth Behrens; Tel: 901-678-2749, E-mail: bbehrens@memphis.edu; Staff 12 (MLS 4, Non-MLS 8)
Automation Activity & Vendor Info: (Acquisitions) Innovative Interfaces, Inc - Millenium; (Cataloging) Innovative Interfaces, Inc - Millenium; (Circulation) Innovative Interfaces, Inc - Millenium; (Course Reserve) Innovative Interfaces, Inc - Millenium; (ILL) OCLC ILLiad; (OPAC) Innovative Interfaces, Inc - Millenium; (Serials) Innovative Interfaces, Inc - Millenium
Wireless access
Open Mon-Fri 7:30-6

CM   UNIVERSITY OF TENNESSEE-MEMPHIS*, Health Sciences Library & Biocommunications Center, 877 Madison Ave, 38163. SAN 360-8409. Tel: 901-448-5634. Interlibrary Loan Service Tel: 901-448-5847. Reference Tel: 901-448-5404. Administration Tel: 901-448-5694. Toll Free Tel: 877-747-0004. FAX: 901-448-7235. E-mail: utlibrary@utmem.edu. Web Site: library.utmem.edu. *Dir,* Dr Thomas Singarella; E-mail: tsingarella@utmem.edu; *Instrul Serv Librn,* Brenda Green; Tel: 901-448-4759, E-mail: bfgreen@utmem.edu; Staff 27 (MLS 11, Non-MLS 16)
Founded 1913. Enrl 2,600; Fac 790; Highest Degree: Doctorate
Library Holdings: e-journals 2,000; Bk Titles 48,760; Bk Vols 187,000; Per Subs 1,400
Special Collections: History of Medicine; Tennessee Authors (Wallace Memorial Coll)
Subject Interests: Allied health, Dentistry, Med, Nursing, Pharm, Soc work
Automation Activity & Vendor Info: (Acquisitions) Innovative Interfaces, Inc; (Cataloging) Innovative Interfaces, Inc; (Circulation) Innovative Interfaces, Inc; (Course Reserve) Innovative Interfaces, Inc; (ILL) Innovative Interfaces, Inc; (Media Booking) Innovative Interfaces, Inc; (OPAC) Innovative Interfaces, Inc; (Serials) Innovative Interfaces, Inc
Database Vendor: Dialog, Gale Cengage Learning, Innovative Interfaces, Inc INN - View, OVID Technologies
Partic in Dialog Corp; Lyrasis; National Network of Libraries of Medicine; Southeastern Regional Med Libr Program
Open Mon-Thurs (Winter) 8am-Midnight, Fri 8am-11pm, Sat 8-5, Sun 2-Midnight; Mon-Fri (Summer) 8-5

MIDDLETON

P   MIDDLETON COMMUNITY LIBRARY*, 110 Bolton Ave, 38052-3403. (Mail add: PO Box 40, 38052), SAN 376-7035. Tel: 731-376-0680. FAX: 731-376-0680. E-mail: midcomlib@excite.com. *Dir,* Cynthia Scott
Library Holdings: Bk Titles 5,000; Per Subs 12
Automation Activity & Vendor Info: (Cataloging) Winnebago Software Co; (Circulation) Winnebago Software Co
Mem of Hatchie River Regional Library
Open Tues-Fri 12-5:30, Sat 9-1
Friends of the Library Group

MILAN

P   MILDRED G FIELDS MEMORIAL LIBRARY*, Milan Public Library, 1075 E Van Hook St, 38358-2892. SAN 315-8888. Tel: 731-686-8268, 731-723-3747. FAX: 731-686-3207. Web Site: www.milantennessee.com. *Dir,* Dot Bruce; E-mail: dbruce27@bellsouth.net
Founded 1950. Pop 13,309; Circ 33,425
Library Holdings: Bk Vols 40,000; Per Subs 75
Automation Activity & Vendor Info: (Cataloging) Follett Software; (Circulation) Follett Software; (Serials) Follett Software
Open Mon & Tues 9-6, Wed & Fri 9-5, Sat 9-Noon
Friends of the Library Group

MILLIGAN COLLEGE

C   MILLIGAN COLLEGE*, P H Welshimer Memorial Library, 200 Blowers Blvd, 37682. (Mail add: PO Box 600, 37682), SAN 315-8970. Tel: 423-461-8703. Circulation Tel: 423-461-8697. Reference Tel: 423-461-8900. FAX: 423-461-8984. E-mail: library@milligan.edu. Web Site: www.milligan.edu. *Coll Develop, Dir,* Gary F Daught; Staff 3 (MLS 3)
Founded 1881. Enrl 964; Fac 79; Highest Degree: Master
Library Holdings: AV Mats 3,394; CDs 650; DVDs 691; e-books 40,176; e-journals 6,850; Bk Titles 135,253; Bk Vols 142,591; Per Subs 463; Videos 1,336
Special Collections: Restoration History (Restoration of New Testament Christianity)
Subject Interests: Educ, Humanities, Relig studies
Automation Activity & Vendor Info: (Acquisitions) Innovative Interfaces, Inc; (Cataloging) Innovative Interfaces, Inc; (Circulation) Innovative Interfaces, Inc; (Course Reserve) Innovative Interfaces, Inc; (ILL) Innovative Interfaces, Inc; (Media Booking) Innovative Interfaces, Inc; (OPAC) Innovative Interfaces, Inc; (Serials) Innovative Interfaces, Inc
Partic in Appalachian Col Asn; Holston Assoc Librs, Inc; Lyrasis; OCLC Online Computer Library Center, Inc

MILLINGTON

P   MILLINGTON PUBLIC LIBRARY*, 4858 Navy Rd, 38053. SAN 378-4444. Tel: 901-872-1585. FAX: 901-872-2554. E-mail: millingtonpubliclibrary@hotmail.com. Web Site: www.ci.millington.tn.us/library. *Dir,* Brian Miller; E-mail: brianm@lssi.com
Library Holdings: Bk Titles 49,362
Wireless access
Function: Children's prog
Open Mon 1-5, Tues & Thurs 12-8, Wed, Fri & Sat 10-6

A   NAVY PERSONNEL RESEARCH, STUDIES & TECHNOLOGY*, Spishock Library, 5761 Commitment Loop, Bldg 785, 38055. (Mail add: Bureau of Naval Personnel, 5720 Integrity Dr, Bupers 1, 38055), SAN 334-5122. Tel: 901-874-2115. FAX: 901-874-2720. E-mail: NPRST_library@navy.mil. Web Site: 69.63.217.2/N10006Staff/OPAC. *Admin Librn,* Genni Arledge; E-mail: genni.arledge@navy.mil; Staff 1 (MLS 1)
Founded 1953
Library Holdings: e-journals 16; Bk Titles 10,000; Bk Vols 15,000; Per Subs 30
Subject Interests: Statistics
Automation Activity & Vendor Info: (Circulation) EOS International; (OPAC) EOS International
Database Vendor: EBSCOhost, OCLC WorldCat
Function: ILL available
Publications: Accession List; Journal List (Annually)
Partic in Fedlink; OCLC Online Computer Library Center, Inc; OCLC-LVIS
Open Mon-Fri 8:30-4
Restriction: In-house use for visitors

MINOR HILL

P   MINOR HILL PUBLIC LIBRARY*, PO Box 69, 38473. SAN 315-890X. Tel: 931-565-3699. *Dir,* Marie Jones
Circ 7,028

Library Holdings: Bk Vols 3,500
Open Mon, Tues, Thurs & Fri 3-8, Sat 9-Noon

MONTEAGLE

P   MAY JUSTUS MEMORIAL LIBRARY*, 24 Dixie Lee Ave, 37356. (Mail add: PO Box 78, 37356), SAN 315-8918. Tel: 931-924-2638. FAX: 931-924-3628. E-mail: mayjustuslib@blomand.net. *Dir,* Karen Tittle; Staff 1 (Non-MLS 1)
Founded 1960. Pop 1,500; Circ 18,000
Library Holdings: Bk Titles 14,000
Database Vendor: Gale Cengage Learning
Open Mon 10-6, Tues-Fri 8-4

MORRISTOWN

P   MORRISTOWN-HAMBLEN LIBRARY*, 417 W Main St, 37814-4686. SAN 315-8942. Tel: 423-586-6410. FAX: 423-587-6226. E-mail: library@lcs.net. Web Site: www.morristownhamblenlibrary.org. *Dir,* Position Currently Open; *Asst Dir, Youth Serv Librn,* Christina Mosley; Staff 10.25 (MLS 2, Non-MLS 8.25)
Founded 1925. Pop 61,026; Circ 257,606
Jul 2007-Jun 2008 Income (Main Library and Branch(s)) $546,230, State $5,000, City $228,500, Federal $15,925, County $238,500, Locally Generated Income $58,305. Mats Exp $58,781. Sal $278,399
Library Holdings: Audiobooks 2,946; e-books 28; Microforms 1,570; Bk Titles 127; Bk Vols 128,091; Per Subs 153; Videos 8,113
Automation Activity & Vendor Info: (Cataloging) Biblionix; (Circulation) Biblionix; (OPAC) Biblionix
Wireless access
Function: Audiobks via web, Bks on cassette, Bks on CD, Children's prog, Computers for patron use, Copy machines, Electronic databases & coll, Fax serv, Handicapped accessible, ILL available, Photocopying/Printing, Preschool outreach, Prog for adults, Prog for children & young adult, Story hour, Summer reading prog, VHS videos
Open Mon, Wed, Fri & Sat 9-5:30, Tues & Thurs 9-8
Restriction: Non-resident fee
Friends of the Library Group
Branches: 1
DAVIS HOMES BRANCH LIBRARY, 1149 Kennedy Circle, 37814-5406, SAN 324-3281. Tel: 423-581-3413. Web Site: www.geocities.com/davishomeslibrary. *Br Mgr,* Theresa Lane
Circ 13,065
Library Holdings: Bk Vols 11,279
Automation Activity & Vendor Info: (Cataloging) Biblionix; (Circulation) Biblionix
Open Mon-Fri 1-5
Friends of the Library Group

J   WALTERS STATE COMMUNITY COLLEGE*, R Jack Fishman Library, 500 S Davy Crockett Pkwy, 37813-6899. SAN 315-8969. Tel: 423-585-2600. Circulation Tel: 423-585-6903. Reference Tel: 423-585-6946. Toll Free Tel: 800-225-4770. FAX: 423-585-6959. Web Site: www.ws.edu/library. *Dean of Libr,* Douglas Cross; Tel: 423-585-6901; E-mail: doug.cross@ws.edu; *Dir,* Jim Damewood; E-mail: jim.damewood@ws.edu; *Circ,* Shirley Parker; E-mail: shirley.parker@ws.edu; *Ref,* Samuel Richardson; E-mail: sam.richardson@ws.edu; Staff 4 (MLS 4)
Founded 1970. Highest Degree: Associate
Library Holdings: Bk Titles 41,570; Bk Vols 47,865; Per Subs 189; Spec Interest Per Sub 189
Automation Activity & Vendor Info: (Acquisitions) TLC (The Library Corporation); (Cataloging) TLC (The Library Corporation); (Circulation) TLC (The Library Corporation); (Course Reserve) TLC (The Library Corporation); (ILL) OCLC; (OPAC) TLC (The Library Corporation)
Database Vendor: EBSCOhost, Gale Cengage Learning, LexisNexis, OCLC FirstSearch
Partic in Lyrasis
Open Mon-Fri 8-4:15

MOSHEIM

P   MOSHEIM PUBLIC LIBRARY*, 730 Main St, 37818. SAN 376-2971. Tel: 423-422-7937. FAX: 423-422-6492. E-mail: mostaff@mosheimlib.org. Web Site: www.mosheimlib.org. *Dir,* Cindy Fink; E-mail: cfink@mosheimlib.org
Founded 1981. Pop 2,500
Library Holdings: Bk Titles 13,000
Mem of Holston River Regional Library
Open Mon-Thurs 12:30-6, Fri 12:30-5

MOUNT CARMEL

P   MOUNT CARMEL LIBRARY*, 100 1/2 Main St, 37645-9999. (Mail add: PO Box 1421, 37645-1421), SAN 376-6330. Tel: 423-357-4011. FAX: 423-357-4011. E-mail: mtcarmellibrary@msn.com.
Pop 4,200
Library Holdings: Bk Vols 3,500
Open Mon 12-8, Tues-Fri 12-6, Sat 10-2
Friends of the Library Group

MOUNT JULIET

P   MOUNT JULIET-WILSON COUNTY PUBLIC*, Harvey Freeman Public Library, 2765 N Mount Juliet Rd, 37122. (Mail add: PO Box 319, 37122-0319), SAN 360-7143. Tel: 615-758-7051. FAX: 615-758-2439. E-mail: mt.julietlibrary@comcast.net. Web Site: www.mtjulietlibrary.net. *Dir,* Nancy Armstrong; Staff 8 (MLS 1, Non-MLS 7)
Pop 53,532; Circ 369,697
Library Holdings: Audiobooks 2,600; DVDs 3,600; e-books 17,000; Microforms 7,300; Bk Titles 64,500; Per Subs 70
Automation Activity & Vendor Info: (Cataloging) TLC (The Library Corporation); (Circulation) TLC (The Library Corporation)
Wireless access
Open Mon, Tues & Thurs 9-8, Wed, Fri & Sat 9-5
Friends of the Library Group

MOUNTAIN CITY

P   JOHNSON COUNTY PUBLIC LIBRARY*, 219 N Church St, 37683-1522. (Mail add: PO Box 107, 37683-0107), SAN 315-8977. Tel: 423-727-6544. FAX: 423-727-0319. Web Site: www.jocopl.org. *Dir,* Linda Icenhour; E-mail: licenhour@jocopl.org; *Asst Dir,* Laura Hayworth; E-mail: lhayworth@jocopl.org
Pop 13,745
Library Holdings: Bk Vols 17,000; Per Subs 20
Automation Activity & Vendor Info: (Cataloging) Ex Libris Group; (Circulation) Ex Libris Group; (OPAC) Ex Libris Group
Partic in Midwest Collaborative for Library Services (MCLS)
Open Mon, Wed, Thurs & Fri 9-5, Tues 9-8, Sat 9-1
Friends of the Library Group

MOUNTAIN HOME

GM   JAMES H QUILLEN VA MEDICAL CENTER*, Medical Library 142 D, Lamont & Sidney Sts, 37684. SAN 315-8985. Tel: 423-926-1171, Ext 7452, 423-926-1171, Ext 7453. FAX: 423-979-3440. *Librn,* Patsy S Ellis; E-mail: patsy.ellis@va.gov
Founded 1904
Library Holdings: Bk Vols 2,946; Per Subs 238
Partic in Vets Admin Libr Network
Open Mon-Fri 7:45-4:30

MUNFORD

P   MUNFORD-TIPTON MEMORIAL LIBRARY*, 87 College St, 38058-6412. (Mail add: PO Box B, 38058-1902), SAN 376-7566. Tel: 901-837-2665. E-mail: munford@bigriver.net. *Dir,* Geraldine Simmons
Jul 2005-Jun 2006 Income $33,999, City $19,399, County $14,600. Mats Exp $13,101. Sal $20,898
Library Holdings: Bk Vols 1,200
Open Mon-Wed & Fri 1-5, Thurs 1-7, Sat 9-Noon

MURFREESBORO

R   FIRST BAPTIST CHURCH LIBRARY*, 200 E Main St, 37130. SAN 315-8993. Tel: 615-893-2514. FAX: 615-895-5804. E-mail: office@fbcmboro.org. Web Site: www.fbcmboro.org. *Librn,* Juana Cates; Staff 19 (MLS 4, Non-MLS 15)
Founded 1843
Library Holdings: Bk Vols 18,398; Per Subs 31
Special Collections: Children's Coll
Subject Interests: Church curriculum, Relig studies
Open Wed 9-12, Sun 8-11 & 5-7

P   LINEBAUGH PUBLIC LIBRARY SYSTEM OF RUTHERFORD COUNTY*, 105 W Vine St, 37130-3673. SAN 360-8581. Tel: 615-893-4131. Circulation Tel: 615-893-4131, Ext 115. Reference Tel: 615-893-4131, Ext 117. FAX: 615-848-5038. Web Site: www.linebaugh.org. *Dir,* Rita Shacklett; Tel: 615-893-4131, Ext 112, E-mail: rshacklett@linebaugh.org; *Circ Supvr,* Hank Williams; *Ref Supvr,* LIsa Ramsay; *Coll Develop Coordr,* Annie Herlocker; *Youth Serv Spec,* Joan Hemphill; Staff 33 (MLS 4, Non-MLS 29)
Founded 1948. Pop 192,407; Circ 858,862
Jul 2005-Jun 2006 Income (Main Library Only) $1,344,884, City $526,979, County $670,701, Locally Generated Income $91,696. Mats Exp $192,000, Books $169,500, Per/Ser (Incl. Access Fees) $22,500. Sal $817,511

Library Holdings: e-books 497; Bk Vols 140,565; Per Subs 100
Subject Interests: Genealogy, Local hist
Automation Activity & Vendor Info: (Acquisitions) SirsiDynix; (Cataloging) SirsiDynix; (Circulation) SirsiDynix; (ILL) Auto-Graphics, Inc; (OPAC) SirsiDynix
Database Vendor: Gale Cengage Learning
Mem of Stones River Regional Library
Partic in Tenn Share
Open Mon-Thurs 9-9, Fri & Sat 9-5, Sun 1-6
Friends of the Library Group
Branches: 2
EAGLEVILLE BICENTENNIAL BRANCH, 317 Hwy 99 E, Eagleville, 37060, SAN 376-7019. Tel: 615-274-2626. FAX: 615-274-2626. E-mail: eaglelib@bellsouth.net. *Br Mgr,* Donna Jordon; E-mail: djordon@linebaugh.org
Library Holdings: Bk Vols 12,000
Open Mon, Tues & Thurs 1-7, Fri 1-5, Sat 9-4
SMYRNA PUBLIC, 400 Enon Springs Rd W, Smyrna, 37167, SAN 360-8611. Tel: 615-459-4884. FAX: 615-459-2370. Web Site: www.linebaugh.org. *Br Mgr,* Carol Kersey; Tel: 615-459-2700, E-mail: ckersey@linebaugh.org; *Youth Serv,* Sandy Kaiser; Staff 13 (MLS 1, Non-MLS 12)
Founded 1960. Pop 25,162; Circ 210,533
Library Holdings: Bk Vols 67,384; Per Subs 160
Open Mon-Thurs 9-8, Fri & Sat 9-5
Friends of the Library Group

C   MIDDLE TENNESSEE STATE UNIVERSITY*, James E Walker Library, MTSU, PO Box 13, 37132. SAN 360-8522. Tel: 615-898-2817. Circulation Tel: 615-898-2650. Interlibrary Loan Service Tel: 615-898-5104. Administration Tel: 615-898-2772. Circulation FAX: 615-904-8225. Interlibrary Loan Service FAX: 615-898-5551. Administration FAX: 615-904-8505. Web Site: library.mtsu.edu. *Admin Librn, Interim Dir,* William Black; E-mail: wblack@mtsu.edu; *Dean of Libr,* Position Currently Open; *Access Serv Librn,* Mayo Taylor; Tel: 615-898-5605, E-mail: taylorm@mtsu.edu; *Acq Librn,* Rachel Kirk; Tel: 615-904-8518, E-mail: rakirk@mtsu.edu; *Cat Librn,* Jane Davis; Tel: 615-898-2529, E-mail: jdavis@mtsu.edu; *Coll Develop Librn,* Suzanne Mangrum; Tel: 615-904-8517, E-mail: smangrum@mtsu.edu; *Electronic Res Librn,* Mary Ellen Pozzebon; Tel: 615-898-2526, E-mail: mepozzeb@mtsu.edu; *Ref & Instruction Librn,* Sharon Parente; Tel: 615-898-2549, E-mail: sparente@mtsu.edu; *Spec Coll Librn,* Alan Boehm; Tel: 615-904-8501, E-mail: aboehm@mtsu.edu; *Syst Librn,* David Robinson; Tel: 615-898-2572, E-mail: robinson@mtsu.edu; *Supvr, Per,* Gale McLean; Tel: 615-898-2819, E-mail: wmclean@mtsu.edu; *Circ/Reserves,* Neil Scott; Tel: 615-898-2539, E-mail: nscott@ulibnet.mtsu.edu; *Coordr, Coll Mgt,* Virginia Vesper; Tel: 615-898-2806, E-mail: vvesper@mtsu.edu; Staff 26 (MLS 26)
Founded 1912. Enrl 22,322; Fac 794; Highest Degree: Doctorate
Library Holdings: Bk Vols 748,888; Per Subs 4,144
Special Collections: Artists Books Coll; Tennesseana
Subject Interests: Artists bks, Civil War, Tenn hist
Publications: Library Update (Newsletter)
Partic in Lyrasis; Nashville Area Libr Alliance; OCLC Online Computer Library Center, Inc
Adaptive Technology Center for students with disabilities
Open Mon-Thurs (Winter) 7:30am-Midnight, Fri 7:30-5, Sat 8-5, Sun 1-Midnight; Mon-Thurs (Summer) 7:30am-10pm, Fri 7:30-4:30, Sat 8-4:30, Sun 2-10
Departmental Libraries:
CENTER FOR POPULAR MUSIC, John Bragg Mass Communication Bldg, Rm 140, 1301 E Main St, 37132. (Mail add: PO Box 41, 37133-0041), SAN 323-8199. Tel: 615-898-2449. Reference Tel: 615-898-5513. FAX: 615-898-5829. E-mail: ctrpopmu@mtsu.edu. Web Site: popmusic.mtsu.edu. *Dir,* Paul Wells; E-mail: pfwells@mtsu.edu; *Librn,* Grover Baker; Tel: 615-898-5512, E-mail: gbaker@mtsu.edu; *Mgr, Recorded Media Coll,* W Martin Fisher; Tel: 615-898-5509, E-mail: wmfisher@mtsu.edu; *Mgr, Ser,* Amy Hunsberger; Tel: 615-898-2755, E-mail: hunsberg@mtsu.edu; *Archivist, Coordr, Res Coll,* Lucinda Poole Cockrell; Tel: 615-898-5884, E-mail: lcockrel@mtsu.edu; Staff 4.8 (MLS 1.8, Non-MLS 3)
Founded 1985
Library Holdings: AV Mats 171,000; CDs 9,000; DVDs 100; Microforms 2,900; Music Scores 78,000; Bk Vols 14,000; Per Subs 200; Spec Interest Per Sub 200; Videos 1,200
Special Collections: 18th & Early 19th Century British Music Imprints (Alfred Moffatt Coll); 19th Century American Songsters & Song Broadsides (Kenneth S Goldstein Coll); Rare Books (Gospel Song Books, Hymnbooks, Instrumental Music Books, Sacred & Secular Oblong Song Books, School Text Hillbilly Song Folios, Text-Only Hymnals); Ray Avery Coll, photogs, sheet music, sound recs; Sheet Music, Late 18th Century to Present; Tennessee Music (John S Mitchell Coll), bks, sheet music, sound recs
Subject Interests: Popular music, Vernacular religious music
Automation Activity & Vendor Info: (Cataloging) Ex Libris Group; (OPAC) Ex Libris Group

Function: Archival coll, Audio & video playback equip for onsite use, Res libr
Partic in Lyrasis
Open Mon-Fri 8-4:30
Restriction: Closed stack, Non-circulating

P   STONES RIVER REGIONAL LIBRARY*, (Formerly Highland Rim Regional Library Center), 2118 E Main St, 37130. SAN 315-9000. Tel: 615-893-3380. FAX: 615-895-6727. *Dir,* BettyJo Jarvis; E-mail: Bttyjo.Jarvis@state.tn.us
Founded 1945. Pop 466,511; Circ 2,252,907
Jul 2005-Jun 2006 Income $529,350, State $502,100, Federal $27,250. Mats Exp $97,300, Per/Ser (Incl. Access Fees) $250
Library Holdings: Bk Vols 30,000
Automation Activity & Vendor Info: (Acquisitions) Brodart; (Cataloging) Brodart; (Circulation) Brodart; (Course Reserve) Brodart; (ILL) Brodart; (Media Booking) Brodart; (OPAC) Brodart; (Serials) Brodart
Member Libraries: Argie Cooper Public Library; Cannon County Library System; Coffee County Lannom Memorial Public Library; Coffee County-Manchester Library; Fayetteville-Lincoln County Public Library; Franklin County Library; Fred A Vaught Memorial Public Library; Lebanon-Wilson County Library; Linebaugh Public Library System of Rutherford County; Moore County Public Library
Open Mon-Fri 8-4:30

GM   ALVIN C YORK VETERANS ADMINISTRATION MEDICAL CENTER*, Library Service (142D), 3400 Lebanon Pike, 37129. SAN 315-9019. Tel: 615-893-1360, Ext 6142. FAX: 615-867-5778. *Dir,* Dr Gary Linn; Staff 2 (MLS 1, Non-MLS 1)
Library Holdings: Bk Vols 5,900; Per Subs 300
Subject Interests: Clinical med, Geriatrics, Nursing, Psychiat
Partic in OCLC Online Computer Library Center, Inc
Open Mon-Fri 7:30-4

NASHVILLE

JR   AMERICAN BAPTIST COLLEGE OF THE AMERICAN BAPTIST THEOLOGICAL SEMINARY*, T L Holcomb Library, 1800 Baptist World Center Dr, 37207-4952. SAN 315-9027. Tel: 615-256-1463. Circulation Tel: 615-687-6899. Reference Tel: 615-687-6893. FAX: 615-226-7855. Web Site: www.abcnash.edu. *Dir of Libr Serv,* Janet Walsh; Tel: 615-687-6904, E-mail: jwalsh@abcnash.edu; Staff 1 (MLS 1)
Founded 1924
Library Holdings: Bk Vols 32,000; Per Subs 200
Subject Interests: Ethnic studies, Relig studies
Automation Activity & Vendor Info: (Acquisitions) Book Systems, Inc; (Circulation) Book Systems, Inc
Publications: IMPRINTS
Open Mon-Thurs (Winter) 8:30-8, Fri 8:30-5, Sat 8:30-12; Mon-Fri (Summer) 9-5
Friends of the Library Group

C   THE ART INSTITUTE OF TENNESSEE-NASHVILLE LIBRARY*, 100 Centerview Dr, Ste 250, 37214. SAN 378-4312. Tel: 615-874-1067. Toll Free Tel: 866-747-5770. FAX: 615-874-3530. Web Site: www.artinstitutes.edu/nashville. *Librn,* Kristin Junik
Library Holdings: Bk Vols 2,000
Automation Activity & Vendor Info: (Cataloging) Ex Libris Group; (Circulation) Ex Libris Group; (OPAC) Ex Libris Group
Database Vendor: EBSCOhost, ProQuest

M   BAPTIST HOSPITAL*, Medical Library, 2000 Church St, 37236. SAN 315-9051. Tel: 615-284-5373. FAX: 615-284-5861. Web Site: baptistnashville-dl.slis.ua.edu. *Librn,* Marilyn Teolis; E-mail: marilyn.teolis@baptisthospital.com; Staff 1 (MLS 1)
Founded 1948
Library Holdings: Bk Vols 3,000; Per Subs 160
Special Collections: Internal Medicine emphasis
Subject Interests: Clinical med, Consumer health, Healthcare mgt, Nursing
Publications: Newsletter
Partic in National Network of Libraries of Medicine; OCLC Online Computer Library Center, Inc
Open Mon-Fri 8-4:30

S   BARBERSHOP HARMONY SOCIETY, Old Songs Library, 110 Seventh Ave N, 37203. SAN 318-0514. Tel: 615-823-3993. Toll Free Tel: 800-876-7464, Ext 4127. FAX: 615-313-7619. E-mail: library@barbershop.org. *Libr & Licensing Mgr,* Janice Bane
Founded 1965
Library Holdings: Bk Titles 200,000
Special Collections: 78 RPM Barbershop Records (Lou Reed & William Spengler Colls); Old Music (Edison & Columbia Cylinder Records)

Subject Interests: Old lyrical sheet music
Partic in Tri-County Libr Council, Inc

G   CHARLES BASS CORRECTIONAL COMPLEX LIBRARY*, Main-Site No 1, 7177 Cockrill Bend Industrial Rd, 37243-0470. SAN 371-6783. Tel: 615-350-3361, Ext 1195. FAX: 615-350-3319. *Coordr,* Lakesha Robinson
Founded 1979
Library Holdings: Bk Titles 3,500; Per Subs 60
Subject Interests: Fiction, Hist, Sci fict
Open Mon-Fri 7:30-3:30
Branches:
MTCX ANNEX-SITE NO 2, 7466 Centennial Blvd-Extended, 32243-0466, SAN 377-7480. Tel: 615-350-3361, Ext 2201. FAX: 615-350-3395. *In Charge,* Lakesha Robinson
Founded 1946
Open Mon-Thurs 12-8

C   BELMONT UNIVERSITY*, Lila D Bunch Library, 1900 Belmont Blvd, 37212-3757. SAN 315-9078. Tel: 615-460-6782. Interlibrary Loan Service Tel: 615-460-5597. Reference Tel: 615-460-5498. Administration Tel: 615-460-6424. Information Services Tel: 615-460-6033. FAX: 615-460-5641. Interlibrary Loan Service FAX: 615-460-5482. Web Site: library.belmont.edu. *Dir,* Dr Ernest William Heard; E-mail: ernest.heard@belmont.edu; *Coll Mgt Librn,* Sue Mazaros; *Educ Res Librn, Electronic Res Librn,* Courtney Fuson; E-mail: courtney.fuson@belmont.edu; *Music Librn,* Timothy Gmeiner; Tel: 615-460-5495, E-mail: tim.gmeiner@belmont.edu; *Ref Librn,* Rachel Scott; E-mail: rachel.scott@belmont.edu; *Ref Librn,* Judy Williams; Tel: 615-460-6610, E-mail: judy.williams@belmont.edu; *Circ Mgr,* Vance Joel Wilson; Tel: 615-460-5596, E-mail: vance.wilson@belmont.edu; *Coordr of Ref Serv,* Jenny Rushing; E-mail: jenny.rushing@belmont.edu; Staff 16 (MLS 6, Non-MLS 10)
Founded 1951. Enrl 3,350; Fac 200; Highest Degree: Doctorate
Library Holdings: Bk Vols 242,545; Per Subs 1,106
Subject Interests: Educ, Lit, Music, Natural sci, Nursing, Relig studies, Soc & behav sci
Automation Activity & Vendor Info: (Acquisitions) Ex Libris Group; (Cataloging) Ex Libris Group; (Circulation) Ex Libris Group; (Course Reserve) Ex Libris Group; (ILL) OCLC; (OPAC) Ex Libris Group; (Serials) Ex Libris Group
Partic in OCLC Online Computer Library Center, Inc
Open Mon-Thurs (Winter) 7:30am-11pm, Fri 7:30-6, Sat 9-6, Sun 2-11; Mon-Thurs (Summer) 7:30am-9pm, Fri 7:30-4:30, Sat 12-4:30, Sun 5-9

S   BROWN & CALDWELL LIBRARY*, 501 Great Circle Rd, Ste 150, 37228. SAN 370-4076. Tel: 615-255-2288. FAX: 615-256-8332. Web Site: brownandcaldwell.com.
Founded 1947
Library Holdings: Bk Vols 3,000; Per Subs 20
Subject Interests: Air pollution, Ecology, Environment, Hazardous waste mgt, Wastewater
Restriction: Not open to pub

S   COUNTRY MUSIC HALL OF FAME & MUSEUM*, Frist Library & Archives, 222 Fifth Ave S, 37203. SAN 315-9086. Tel: 615-416-2036. FAX: 615-255-2245. E-mail: reference@countrymusichalloffame.com. Web Site: www.countrymusichalloffame.com. *Dir,* Carolyn Tate; Tel: 615-416-2009, E-mail: ctate@countrymusichalloffame.com; *Assoc Librn,* Becky Miley; *Coll Mgr,* Tracy Landino; E-mail: tlandino@countrymusichalloffame.com
Founded 1967
Library Holdings: Bk Titles 10,000; Per Subs 450
Special Collections: Country Music & The Music Industry Coll, A-tapes; Nashville Chapter Coll; National Academy of Recording Arts & Sciences; Roy Acuff Coll. Oral History
Subject Interests: Anglo-Am folksong, Commercial popular music in gen, Country music, Culture, Early commercial recording, Folklore, Law, Music copyright, Recorded sound tech, Southern hist
Publications: Journal of Country Music
Restriction: Open by appt only
Friends of the Library Group

SR   E C DARGAN LIBRARY, One Lifeway Plaza, 37234-0142. SAN 315-906X. Tel: 615-251-2000. Circulation Tel: 615-251-2137. Administration Tel: 615-251-2751. FAX: 615-277-8433. E-mail: library@lifeway.com. Web Site: library.lifeway.com. *Librn/Mgr,* Stephen Gateley; E-mail: steve.gateley@lifeway.com; Staff 0.75 (MLS 0.75)
Founded 1933
Oct 2012-Sept 2013. Mats Exp $215,000, Books $6,000, Per/Ser (Incl. Access Fees) $1,300, Electronic Ref Mat (Incl. Access Fees) $4,000
Library Holdings: CDs 100; DVDs 100; e-books 100; e-journals 100; Bk Vols 41,200; Per Subs 75; Videos 150
Special Collections: Scofield Photographic Coll, slides; Sunday School Board/LifeWay Press Coll
Subject Interests: Biblical, Corp hist, Relig educ

Automation Activity & Vendor Info: (Cataloging) OCLC Connexion; (Circulation) TLC (The Library Corporation); (ILL) OCLC FirstSearch; (OPAC) TLC (The Library Corporation)
Database Vendor: Bowker, EBSCOhost
Wireless access
Partic in Tenn Share
Open Mon-Thurs 8:30-2:30

R   DISCIPLES OF CHRIST HISTORICAL SOCIETY LIBRARY & ARCHIVES*, 1101 Nineteenth Ave S, 37212-2196. SAN 315-9108. Tel: 615-327-1444. FAX: 615-327-1445. E-mail: mail@discipleshistory.org. Web Site: www.discipleshistory.org. *VPres, Libr & Info Serv,* Sara Harwell; Staff 5 (MLS 1, Non-MLS 4)
Founded 1941
Library Holdings: Bk Titles 37,000
Subject Interests: Christian churches, Churches of Christ, Disciples of Christ, Hist, Related relig groups
Automation Activity & Vendor Info: (Cataloging) Ex Libris Group; (OPAC) Ex Libris Group; (Serials) Ex Libris Group
Database Vendor: OCLC FirstSearch
Function: Archival coll, Res libr
Publications: Discipliana (Quarterly); Stream Lines (Newsletter)
Partic in Lyrasis; OCLC Online Computer Library Center, Inc
Open Mon-Fri 8-4:30
Restriction: Circ to mem only

C   FISK UNIVERSITY, John Hope & Aurelia E Franklin Library, Fisk University, 1000 17th Ave N, 37208-3051. SAN 315-9116. Tel: 615-329-8730. Circulation Tel: 615-329-8640. Interlibrary Loan Service Tel: 615-329-8734. FAX: 615-329-8761. Web Site: www.fisk.edu. *Dean, Univ Libr,* Dr Jessie Carney-Smith, PhD; E-mail: jcsmith@fisk.edu; *Spec Coll Librn,* Position Currently Open; *Asst Librn, Tech Serv,* Cheryl Hamberg; Tel: 615-329-8733, E-mail: chamberg@fisk.edu; *Night Supvr,* Ester McShepard; E-mail: emcshepa@fisk.edu; *Archives Asst,* Mattie McHollin; Tel: 615-329-8838, E-mail: mmchollin@fisk.edu; *Libr Asst,* Susie Harris; Tel: 615-329-8640, E-mail: sharris@fisk.edu; *Libr Asst,* Michael Powell; Tel: 615-329-8734, E-mail: mpowell@fisk.edu; *Libr Asst,* Vanessa Smith; Tel: 615-329-8646, E-mail: vsmith@fisk.edu; Staff 9 (MLS 4, Non-MLS 5)
Founded 1866. Highest Degree: Master
Special Collections: Black Literature (Charles W Chesnutt, James Weldon Johnson, Naomi Madgett, Louise Meriweather); Civil Rights & Politics (Slater King, John Mercer Langston, James Carroll Napier & William L Dawson); Music & Musical Literature (George Gershwin Coll); Music (W C Handy, Scott Joplin, Fisk Jubilee Singers & John W Work); Sociology (WEB DuBois, Marcus Garvey & Charles S Johnson). Oral History; US Document Depository
Subject Interests: African-Am culture, African-Am hist, African-Am lit
Automation Activity & Vendor Info: (Cataloging) Innovative Interfaces, Inc; (Circulation) Innovative Interfaces, Inc; (OPAC) Innovative Interfaces, Inc; (Serials) Innovative Interfaces, Inc
Database Vendor: American Psychological Association (APA), EBSCOhost, Gale Cengage Learning, Innovative Interfaces, Inc, JSTOR, LexisNexis, Marcive, Inc, OCLC FirstSearch, OCLC WorldCat, Oxford Online, PubMed
Wireless access
Function: Archival coll, Art exhibits, Doc delivery serv, Orientations, Photocopying/Printing, Ref serv available, Workshops
Partic in Lyrasis; Nashville Area Libr Alliance; Tenn-Share
Open Mon-Thurs 7:45-10, Fri 7:45-5, Sat 1-5, Sun 2-10
Restriction: In-house use for visitors

C   FREE WILL BAPTIST BIBLE COLLEGE*, Welch Library, 3630 W End Ave, 37205. (Mail add: 3606 W End Ave, 37205), SAN 315-9124. Tel: 615-844-5274. FAX: 615-269-6028. *Mgr,* Margaret Evans Hampton; Tel: 615-844-5284, E-mail: library@fwbbc.edu; *Librn,* Carol Ketteman Reid; E-mail: creid@fwbbc.edu; Staff 2 (MLS 1, Non-MLS 1)
Founded 1942. Enrl 330; Highest Degree: Bachelor
Library Holdings: e-books 3,000; Bk Titles 52,000; Bk Vols 64,000; Per Subs 300
Special Collections: Free Will Baptist Historical Coll
Subject Interests: Bible, Theol
Automation Activity & Vendor Info: (Acquisitions) Follett Software; (Cataloging) Follett Software; (Circulation) Follett Software; (Course Reserve) Follett Software; (ILL) Follett Software; (Media Booking) Follett Software; (OPAC) Follett Software; (Serials) Follett Software
Database Vendor: EBSCOhost, Gale Cengage Learning, OVID Technologies
Publications: Acquisitions (Monthly)
Partic in Christian Libr Network; Nashville Area Libr Alliance; Tenn-Share
Open Mon, Tues & Thurs 7:45am-11pm, Wed 7:45-6:30, Fri 8-4:30, Sat 12:30-4:30

JEWISH FEDERATION LIBRARIES

R   AKIVA LIBRARY, 809 Percy Warner Blvd, 37205, SAN 360-8670. Tel: 615-356-1880. FAX: 615-356-1850. *Librn,* Jackie Gregory; Tel: 615-356-1880, Ext 19; Staff 1 (MLS 1)
Library Holdings: Bk Vols 4,000
Special Collections: Judaica Coll
Open Mon-Fri 8-4:30

R   ARCHIVES OF THE JEWISH FEDERATION OF NASHVILLE & MIDDLE TENNESSEE*, 801 Percy Warner Blvd, 37205, SAN 360-8719. Tel: 615-356-3242, Ext 255. FAX: 615-352-0056. E-mail: library@jewishnashville.org. *Dir,* Annette Ratkin; *Asst Librn,* Leona Fleischer; Staff 2 (MLS 1, Non-MLS 1)
Founded 1979
Sept 2005-Aug 2006 Income $1,000
Library Holdings: Bk Titles 6,500
Special Collections: Community History Coll; Holocaust Oral Histories Coll; Manuscripts; Older Nashvillians Oral Histories; Record Groups; Small Coll
Publications: A Guide for Teaching the History of the Jews of Nashville, Tennessee

R   JEWISH COMMUNITY CENTER LIBRARY*, 801 Percy Warner Blvd, 37205, SAN 360-8700. Tel: 615-356-3242, Ext 255. FAX: 615-352-0056. E-mail: library@jewishnashville.org. *In Charge,* Carrie Mills Small; Tel: 615-354-1699; Staff 1 (Non-MLS 1)
Library Holdings: Bk Vols 2,450
Special Collections: Holocaust Coll; Israel Coll; Judaica Coll; Large Print Coll; Russian Coll
Automation Activity & Vendor Info: (Cataloging) Surpass; (Circulation) Surpass
Friends of the Library Group

R   TEMPLE LIBRARY*, 5015 Harding Rd, 37205, SAN 360-8735. Tel: 615-352-7620. FAX: 615-352-9365.
Founded 1876
Library Holdings: Large Print Bks 30; Bk Vols 8,300; Spec Interest Per Sub 6; Talking Bks 12
Special Collections: Easy Books & Young People's Coll
Subject Interests: Am Jewish hist, Holocaust, Israel, Judaism
Automation Activity & Vendor Info: (Cataloging) Surpass

J   JOHN A GUPTON COLLEGE*, Memorial Library, 1616 Church St, 37203. SAN 315-9132. Tel: 615-327-3927. FAX: 615-321-4518. Web Site: www.guptoncollege.com. *Dir,* William P Bruce; E-mail: pbruce@guptoncollege.edu; Staff 1 (MLS 1)
Founded 1946. Enrl 60; Fac 14; Highest Degree: Associate
Library Holdings: Bk Titles 3,228; Bk Vols 4,050; Per Subs 55
Special Collections: Funeral Service/Grief Psychology
Subject Interests: Mortuary sci
Automation Activity & Vendor Info: (Cataloging) LibraryWorld, Inc; (OPAC) LibraryWorld, Inc
Database Vendor: Gale Cengage Learning
Open Mon & Thurs 8:30-8:30, Tues & Wed 8:30-4:30
Friends of the Library Group

SR   VIRGINIA DAVIS LASKEY RESEARCH LIBRARY, 1008 19th Ave S, 37212-2126. Tel: 615-340-7477. FAX: 615-340-7551. Web Site: www.scarrettbennett.org. *Res Librn,* Stephen Gateley; E-mail: sgateley@scarrittbennett.org; Staff 1 (MLS 1)
Founded 2007
Library Holdings: AV Mats 275; Bk Vols 12,000; Per Subs 167
Special Collections: Methodist Women's Division Coll; Scarritt College Archives, cats, col files, newsletters, photog, student rec, yearbks
Subject Interests: Hymnody, Methodist hist, Missionaries, Missions, Multiculturalism, Spirituality, Women's issues
Automation Activity & Vendor Info: (Cataloging) TLC (The Library Corporation)
Database Vendor: TLC (The Library Corporation)
Wireless access
Function: Audio & video playback equip for onsite use, Computers for patron use, Copy machines, ILL available, Scanner
Publications: LibraryWise @ Laskey (Newsletter)
Open Tues-Thurs 12:30-4:30, Fri 8-4:30
Restriction: Non-circulating of rare bks, Open to pub for ref & circ; with some limitations, Researchers by appt only
Friends of the Library Group

C   LIPSCOMB UNIVERSITY, Beaman Library, One University Park Dr, 37204-3951. SAN 315-9094. Tel: 615-966-1793. Circulation Tel: 615-966-6032. Interlibrary Loan Service Tel: 615-966-6033. Reference Tel: 615-966-6037. Administration Tel: 615-966-5837. Toll Free Tel: 800-333-4358, Ext 1793. FAX: 615-966-5874. Web Site: library.lipscomb.edu. *Dir,* Carolyn T Wilson; E-mail: carolyn.wilson@lipscomb.edu; *Cat Librn,* Elizabeth Heffington; Tel: 615-966-5803, E-mail: elizabeth.heffington@lipscomb.edu; *Electronic Res/Ser Librn,* Kayce D Gill; Tel: 615-966-5763, E-mail:

kayce.gill@lipscomb.edu; *Ref Librn,* Julie Harston; Tel: 615-966-5717, E-mail: julie.harston@lipscomb.edu; *Tech Coordr,* Eunice F Wells; Tel: 615-966-5836, E-mail: eunice.wells@lipscomb.edu; *Archivist,* Marie P Byers; Tel: 615-966-6031, E-mail: marie.byers@lipscomb.edu; *Circ,* Anna Leta Moss; Tel: 615-966-5717; Staff 10 (MLS 6, Non-MLS 4)
Founded 1891. Enrl 4,300; Fac 300; Highest Degree: Doctorate
May 2011-Jun 2012 Income $771,478. Mats Exp $420,035, Books $75,577, Per/Ser (Incl. Access Fees) $229,379, Electronic Ref Mat (Incl. Access Fees) $115,079. Sal $390,665 (Prof $292,095)
Library Holdings: e-books 18,000; Microforms 391,030; Bk Vols 232,907; Per Subs 719
Special Collections: Bailey Hymnology Coll; C E W Dorris Coll; Herald of Truth Videotapes
Subject Interests: Bibliog instruction, Relig
Automation Activity & Vendor Info: (Acquisitions) Innovative Interfaces, Inc; (Cataloging) Innovative Interfaces, Inc; (Circulation) Innovative Interfaces, Inc; (Course Reserve) Innovative Interfaces, Inc; (OPAC) Innovative Interfaces, Inc; (Serials) Innovative Interfaces, Inc
Database Vendor: 3M Library Systems, ABC-CLIO, ACM (Association for Computing Machinery), American Chemical Society, American Mathematical Society, American Psychological Association (APA), Annual Reviews, Atlas Systems, Blackwell's, CQ Press, EBSCO Information Services, EBSCOhost, Elsevier, Facts on File, Gale Cengage Learning, Greenwood Publishing Group, Grolier Online, H W Wilson, Haworth Pres Inc, IEEE (Institute of Electrical & Electronics Engineers), Ingram Library Services, Innovative Interfaces, Inc, Innovative Interfaces, Inc INN - View, LexisNexis, Marquis Who's Who, McGraw-Hill, Medlib, Modern Language Association, netLibrary, OCLC FirstSearch, OCLC WorldCat, OVID Technologies, Oxford Online, ProQuest, ScienceDirect, Standard & Poor's, Wiley, YBP Library Services
Wireless access
Partic in Lyrasis; Nashville Area Libr Alliance; Tenn Share
Open Mon-Thurs (Winter) 7:30am-12:30am, Fri 7:30-5, Sat 10-6, Sun 1-5 & 7:30pm-12:30am; Mon-Fri (Summer) 8-5, Sat 12-5
Friends of the Library Group

M   MEHARRY MEDICAL COLLEGE LIBRARY, Kresge Learning Resource Center, 1005 Dr D B Todd Jr Blvd, 37208. SAN 315-9140. Tel: 615-327-6728. Reference Tel: 615-327-6454. FAX: 615-327-6448. Web Site: www.mmc.edu/library. *Libr Dir,* Fatima Barnes; Tel: 615-327-5770, E-mail: fbarnes@mmc.edu; *Access Serv Librn,* Amelia Whitehead; Tel: 615-327-6326, E-mail: awhitehead@mmc.edu; *Coordr, Coll Develop, Coordr, Electronic Res, Coordr, Tech Serv,* Donald Dryden; Tel: 615-327-6465, E-mail: ddryden@mmc.edu; *Archivist,* Christyne Douglas; Tel: 615-327-6470, E-mail: cdouglas@mmc.edu; *Ref Serv,* Savi Ranganathan; E-mail: srangathan@mmc.edu; Staff 6 (MLS 5, Non-MLS 1)
Founded 1940
Library Holdings: AV Mats 330; e-books 1,979; e-journals 4,176; Bk Titles 10,287; Bk Vols 66,248; Per Subs 4,176
Special Collections: Black Medical History
Subject Interests: Biomed sci, Sciences
Automation Activity & Vendor Info: (Cataloging) OCLC; (Circulation) SirsiDynix; (OPAC) SirsiDynix; (Serials) SirsiDynix
Database Vendor: 3M Library Systems, Annual Reviews, CredoReference, ebrary, EBSCOhost, Elsevier MDL, Gale Cengage Learning, MD Consult, Nature Publishing Group, netLibrary, OCLC, OVID Technologies, PubMed, RefWorks, ScienceDirect, SerialsSolutions, SirsiDynix, STAT!Ref (Teton Data Systems), Swets Information Services, UpToDate, WebMD, Wiley InterScience
Wireless access
Function: Res libr
Partic in OCLC Online Computer Library Center, Inc; SE-Atlantic Regional Med Libr Servs
Open Mon-Fri 8am-1am, Sat & Sun Noon-1am

M   METROPOLITAN NASHVILLE GENERAL HOSPITAL*, Health Sciences Library, 1818 Albion St, 37208. SAN 327-652X. Tel: 615-341-4100. FAX: 615-341-4501. Web Site: www.nashville.gov/general_hospitalcontactus.htm. *Librn,* Glenda L Perry; E-mail: glenda.perry@gh.nashville.gov; Staff 1 (MLS 1)
Library Holdings: Bk Titles 500; Per Subs 50
Subject Interests: Med, Nursing, Surgery
Partic in National Network of Libraries of Medicine; Tennessee Health Science Library Association
Open Mon-Fri 8:30-4:30

P   NASHVILLE PUBLIC LIBRARY, 615 Church St, 37219-2314. SAN 360-912X. Tel: 615-862-5760. FAX: 615-862-5771. Web Site: www.library.nashville.org. *Dir,* Kent L Oliver; *Main Libr Adminr,* Jena Schmid; Tel: 615-862-5806; *Br Adminr,* Larry Price; *Emerging Technologies Adminr,* Tricia Bengel; *Head, Ref,* Ron Perry; *Spec Coll Librn,* Andrea Blackman; *Admin Serv,* Chase Adams; *Archivist,* Ken Fieth; *Ch,* Lindsey Wesson; *Coll Develop,* Noel Rutherford; *Res, Spec Projects,* Elyse Adler

Founded 1904. Pop 635,475; Circ 4,340,657
Special Collections: Children's International Coll; Deaf Services Coll; Government Archives; Local Genealogy & History (Nashville); Naff (Drama Coll). Oral History; State Document Depository
Subject Interests: Bus, Grants, Tenn hist
Automation Activity & Vendor Info: (Acquisitions) Innovative Interfaces, Inc; (Cataloging) Innovative Interfaces, Inc; (Circulation) Innovative Interfaces, Inc; (OPAC) Innovative Interfaces, Inc; (Serials) Innovative Interfaces, Inc
Database Vendor: Innovative Interfaces, Inc INN - View
Wireless access
Partic in Lyrasis; OCLC Online Computer Library Center, Inc
Friends of the Library Group
Branches: 23
BELLEVUE, 650 Colice Jeanne Rd, 37221-2811, SAN 360-9146. Tel: 615-862-5854. FAX: 615-862-5758. *Br Mgr,* Heidi Berg
    Library Holdings: Bk Vols 59,142
    Friends of the Library Group
BORDEAUX, 4000 Clarksville Pike, 37218-1912, SAN 360-9154. Tel: 615-862-5856. FAX: 615-862-5748. *Br Mgr,* Verlon Malone
    Library Holdings: Bk Vols 70,073
    Friends of the Library Group
CARNEGIE NORTH, 1001 Monroe St, 37208-2543, SAN 360-9162. Tel: 615-862-5858. FAX: 615-862-5749. *Br Coordr,* Verlon Malone
    Library Holdings: Bk Vols 16,060
    Friends of the Library Group
DONELSON, 2315 Lebanon Rd, 37214-3410, SAN 360-9189. Tel: 615-862-5859. FAX: 615-862-5799. *Br Mgr,* Chris Morin
    Library Holdings: Bk Vols 53,485
    Friends of the Library Group
EAST, 206 Gallatin Rd, 37206-3240, SAN 360-9219. Tel: 615-862-5860. FAX: 615-862-5807. *Br Mgr,* Linda Harrison
    Library Holdings: Bk Vols 31,880
    Friends of the Library Group
EDGEHILL, 1409 12th Ave S, 37203-4903, SAN 360-9243. Tel: 615-862-5861. FAX: 615-862-5840. *Br Mgr,* Rebecca Whipple
    Library Holdings: Bk Vols 18,376
    Friends of the Library Group
EDMONDSON PIKE, 5501 Edmondson Pike, 37211-5808. Tel: 615-880-3957. FAX: 615-880-3961. *Br Mgr,* Emily Dye
    Library Holdings: Bk Vols 124,905
    Friends of the Library Group
GOODLETTSVILLE BRANCH, 205 Rivergate Pkwy, Goodlettsville, 37072, SAN 360-9278. Tel: 615-862-5862. FAX: 615-862-5798. *Br Mgr,* Jennifer Hunsicker
    Library Holdings: Bk Vols 42,319
    Friends of the Library Group
GREEN HILLS, 3701 Benham Ave, 37215-2121, SAN 360-9308. Tel: 615-862-5863. FAX: 615-862-5881. *Br Mgr,* Susan Perry
    Library Holdings: Bk Vols 127,747
    Friends of the Library Group
HADLEY PARK, 1039 28th Ave N, 37208-2809, SAN 360-9332. Tel: 615-862-5865. FAX: 615-862-5887. *Br Mgr,* Linda Emerson
    Library Holdings: Bk Vols 26,394
    Friends of the Library Group
HERMITAGE BRANCH, 3700 James Kay Lane, Hermitage, 37076-3429. Tel: 615-880-3951. FAX: 615-880-3955. *Br Mgr,* Gloria Coleman
    Library Holdings: Bk Vols 120,902
    Friends of the Library Group
INGLEWOOD, 4312 Gallatin Rd, 37216-2192, SAN 360-9367. Tel: 615-862-5866. FAX: 615-862-5888. *Br Mgr,* Suzanne Robinson
    Library Holdings: Bk Vols 38,056
    Friends of the Library Group
LIBRARY SERVICE FOR THE DEAF & HARD OF HEARING, 615 Church St, 37219-2314, SAN 328-7246. Tel: 615-862-5750. Toll Free Tel: 800-342-3262. FAX: 615-862-5494. *Mgr,* Sandy Cohen
    Library Holdings: Bk Vols 12,773
    Special Services for the Deaf - Bks on deafness & sign lang; TDD equip
Z ALEXANDER LOOBY BRANCH, 2301 Rosa L Parks Blvd, 37228-1221, SAN 360-9391. Tel: 615-862-5867. FAX: 615-862-5797. *Br Mgr,* Jessica Piper
    Library Holdings: Bk Vols 27,006
    Friends of the Library Group
MADISON BRANCH, 610 Gallatin Pike S, Madison, 37115-4013, SAN 360-9421. Tel: 615-862-5868. FAX: 615-862-5889. *Br Mgr,* DeAnza Williams
    Library Holdings: Bk Vols 89,425
    Friends of the Library Group
METROPOLITAN GOVERNMENT ARCHIVES, 3801 Green Hills Village Dr, 37215-2610, SAN 328-7262. Tel: 615-862-5880. FAX: 615-862-5883. *Archivist,* Kenneth Fieth
    Friends of the Library Group

NASHVILLE TALKING LIBRARY, 505 Heritage Dr, Madison, 37115-2688, SAN 328-722X. Tel: 615-862-5874. FAX: 615-862-5796. *Mgr,* Michael Wagner
Special Services for the Blind - Radio reading serv
Friends of the Library Group
OLD HICKORY BRANCH, 1010 Jones St, Old Hickory, 37138-2915, SAN 360-9456. Tel: 615-862-5869. FAX: 615-862-5896. *Br Mgr,* Ronnie Pugh
Library Holdings: Bk Vols 31,299
Friends of the Library Group
MARY & CHARLES W PRUITT BRANCH, 117 Charles E Davis Blvd, 37210-2745, SAN 375-2941. Tel: 615-862-5985. FAX: 615-862-6745. *Br Mgr,* Ibiba Okpara
Library Holdings: Bk Vols 19,322
Friends of the Library Group
RICHLAND PARK, 4711 Charlotte Ave, 37209-3404, SAN 360-9480. Tel: 615-862-5870. FAX: 615-862-5897. *Br Mgr,* Deborah Hynes
Library Holdings: Bk Vols 51,470
Friends of the Library Group
SOUTHEAST, 2325 Hickory Highlands Dr, Antioch, 37013-2101, SAN 373-1987. Tel: 615-862-5871. FAX: 615-862-5756. *Br Mgr,* Edward Todd
Library Holdings: Bk Vols 81,455
Friends of the Library Group
THOMPSON LANE, 380 Thompson Lane, 37211-2485, SAN 360-9510. Tel: 615-862-5873. FAX: 615-862-5898. *Br Mgr,* Kyle Barber
Library Holdings: Bk Vols 40,653
Friends of the Library Group
WATKINS COMMUNITY, 612 17th Ave N, 37203-2878, SAN 375-295X. Tel: 615-862-5872. FAX: 615-862-6746. *Br Coordr,* Deborah Hynes
Library Holdings: Bk Vols 7,757
Friends of the Library Group

L   NASHVILLE SCHOOL OF LAW LIBRARY*, 4013 Armory Oaks Dr, 37204. SAN 321-6144. Tel: 615-256-3684. FAX: 615-244-2383. Web Site: www.nashvilleschooloflaw.net. *Librn,* Janet W Naff; *Libr Coordr,* Amy Hennemann; Staff 1 (MLS 1)
Founded 1911
Library Holdings: Bk Titles 165; Bk Vols 16,500; Per Subs 15
Special Collections: Judge Shriver Coll
Wireless access
Publications: Annual Barrister; Annual Catalog
Open Mon-Thurs (Winter) 8:30am-11pm, Fri & Sat 8:30-6; Mon-Thurs (Summer) 8-5

J   NASHVILLE STATE TECHNICAL COMMUNITY COLLEGE*, Mayfield Library, 120 White Bridge Rd, 37209-4515. SAN 315-9167. Tel: 615-353-3555. FAX: 615-353-3558. Web Site: www.nscc.edu/academics/library. *Dean, Learning Res,* Margaret Faye Jones; Tel: 615-353-3556, E-mail: faye.jones@nscc.edu; *Instruction Librn,* Emily Bush; Tel: 615-353-3559, E-mail: emily.bush@nscc.edu; *Cat, Ref Serv, Ser,* Sally Robertson; Tel: 615-353-3270, E-mail: sally.robertson@nscc.edu; *Ref Serv,* Charles May; Tel: 615-353-3557, E-mail: charles.may@nscc.edu; *Tech Serv,* Faye Vaughn; Tel: 615-353-3560, E-mail: faye.vaughn@nscc.edu; *Libr Asst,* Allison Boyd; Tel: 615-353-3472, E-mail: allison.boyd@nscc.edu; *Libr Asst,* Pamela Gadd; Tel: 615-353-3552, E-mail: pamela.gadd@nscc.edu; *Libr Asst,* Andrew Mason; E-mail: andrew.mason@nscc.edu; Staff 4 (MLS 3, Non-MLS 1)
Founded 1969. Enrl 9,000; Fac 182; Highest Degree: Associate
Automation Activity & Vendor Info: (Acquisitions) SirsiDynix; (Cataloging) SirsiDynix; (Circulation) SirsiDynix; (Course Reserve) SirsiDynix; (ILL) SirsiDynix; (Media Booking) SirsiDynix; (OPAC) SirsiDynix; (Serials) SirsiDynix
Database Vendor: Alexander Street Press, ARTstor, Baker & Taylor, Checkpoint Systems, Inc, Cinahl Information Systems, College Source, EBSCOhost, Facts on File, Ingram Library Services, JSTOR, Newsbank, OCLC FirstSearch, OCLC WorldCat, Oxford Online, ProQuest, Safari Books Online, SirsiDynix, Westlaw, Wilson - Wilson Web
Wireless access
Function: Computers for patron use, Copy machines, Electronic databases & coll, Exhibits, ILL available, Learning ctr, Online cat, Photocopying/Printing
Publications: Annotated AV Lists, Library Guide
Partic in Lyrasis
Open Mon-Thurs 7:30am-8pm, Fri 7:30-4:30, Sat 9-2
Restriction: Co libr

M   SAINT THOMAS HOSPITAL*, Julius Jacobs Health Sciences Library, 4220 Harding Rd, 37202. (Mail add: PO Box 380, 37202-0380), SAN 315-9175. Tel: 615-222-6658. Information Services Tel: 615-222-3051. FAX: 615-222-6765. E-mail: jjlibrar@stthomas.org. Web Site: www.stthomas.org/healthserviceslibrary.php. *Managing Librn,* Jan Haley; E-mail: jhaley@stthomas.org; Staff 1 (MLS 1)

Founded 1961
Jul 2005-Jun 2006. Mats Exp $217,000
Library Holdings: Bk Vols 3,148; Per Subs 266
Special Collections: St Thomas Hospital Archival Coll
Automation Activity & Vendor Info: (Cataloging) EOS International; (Circulation) EOS International; (OPAC) EOS International; (Serials) EOS International
Database Vendor: Gale Cengage Learning, OVID Technologies, ScienceDirect
Function: Res libr
Partic in Mid-Tennessee Health Science Librarians Association; Tenn Share; Tennessee Health Science Library Association

SR SOUTHERN BAPTIST HISTORICAL LIBRARY & ARCHIVES, 901 Commerce St, Ste 400, 37203-3630. SAN 326-1417. Tel: 615-244-0344. FAX: 615-782-4821. Web Site: www.sbhla.org. *Dir,* Bill Sumners; E-mail: bill@sbhla.org; *Archivist,* Taffey Hall; E-mail: taffey@sbhla.org; Staff 4 (MLS 2, Non-MLS 2)
Founded 1938
Library Holdings: AV Mats 4,000; DVDs 175; Electronic Media & Resources 66; Microforms 19,000; Bk Vols 40,000; Per Subs 255
Special Collections: Primitive Baptist holdings; Southern Baptist Convention Archives Depository; Southern Baptist Convention Leaders' Papers
Subject Interests: Baptist hist
Automation Activity & Vendor Info: (Cataloging) Ex Libris Group; (Circulation) Ex Libris Group; (OPAC) Ex Libris Group; (Serials) Ex Libris Group
Database Vendor: Ex Libris Group, OCLC
Wireless access
Function: Res libr
Open Mon-Fri 8-4

S   TENNESSEAN LIBRARY & ARCHIVES*, 1100 Broadway, 37203. SAN 315-9205. Tel: 615-259-8000. Web Site: www.tennessean.com. *Mgr, Ref Serv, Spec Coll & Archives Librn,* Christine Irizarry; E-mail: Christine.irizarry@tennessean.com; *Spec Coll & Archives Librn,* Chantay Steptoe; E-mail: csteptoe@tennessean.com
Founded 1939
Library Holdings: Bk Vols 1,900; Per Subs 35
Special Collections: The Tennessean & Nashville Banner, microfilm, clipping files, photo prints, negatives, bound volumes, card indexes, electronic archives
Subject Interests: Journalism, Local hist
Function: Archival coll, Newsp ref libr
Restriction: By permission only, Co libr, In-house use for visitors, Open by appt only, Open to researchers by request, Restricted access

S   TENNESSEE DEPARTMENT OF CORRECTIONS*, Tennessee Prison for Women Library, 3881 Stewarts Lane, 37218-5256. SAN 371-7364. Tel: 615-741-1255. FAX: 615-253-6323, 615-741-1245. *In Charge,* Earlene Guida; Staff 1 (MLS 1)
Library Holdings: Bk Titles 13,000; Bk Vols 17,000; Per Subs 10
Special Collections: Children's Coll; Law Library
Special Services for the Deaf - Bks on deafness & sign lang; High interest/low vocabulary bks; Staff with knowledge of sign lang

GL TENNESSEE GENERAL ASSEMBLY, OFFICE OF LEGAL SERVICES*, Legislative Library, G-12 War Memorial Bldg, 37243-0059. SAN 370-4181. Tel: 615-741-5816. FAX: 615-741-1146. Web Site: www.legislature.state.tn.us/. *Assoc Librn,* Eddie Weeks; E-mail: eddie.weeks@legislature.state.tn.us; *Dir, Libr Serv,* Tomi Hall; Tel: 615-741-3057; Staff 2 (MLS 1, Non-MLS 1)
Founded 1977
Library Holdings: Bk Vols 6,000; Per Subs 30; Spec Interest Per Sub 25
Special Collections: Acts of the Tennessee Legislature 1827-Present
Subject Interests: Tenn legis mat
Function: Archival coll
Open Mon-Fri 8-4

P   TENNESSEE REGIONAL LIBRARY FOR THE BLIND & PHYSICALLY HANDICAPPED*, 403 Seventh Ave N, 37243-0313. SAN 315-9256. Tel: 615-741-3915. Toll Free Tel: 800-342-3308. FAX: 615-532-8856. E-mail: tsla.tbph@state.tn.us. Web Site: www.state.tn.us/sos/statelib/lbph. *Dir,* Ruth Hemphill; Tel: 615-741-3917, E-mail: ruth.hemphill@state.tn.us; *Asst Dir,* Donna Cirenza; Tel: 615-741-6748, E-mail: donna.cirenza@state.tn.us; Staff 14 (MLS 2, Non-MLS 12)
Founded 1970
Library Holdings: Braille Volumes 26,237; Per Subs 126; Talking Bks 220,925; Videos 1,003
Function: Bks on cassette, Handicapped accessible, Online ref, VHS videos, Video lending libr
Publications: Window to the World (Newsletter)

Special Services for the Blind - Bks & mags in Braille, on rec, tape & cassette; Bks on cassette; Braille & cassettes; Braille alphabet card; Braille bks; Braille equip; Cassette playback machines; Cassettes; Children's Braille; Copier with enlargement capabilities; Descriptive video serv (DVS); Large print & cassettes; Large print bks; Mags & bk reproduction/duplication; Newsletter (in large print, Braille or on cassette); Newsline for the Blind; Recorded bks; Ref serv; Talking bks; Talking bks & player equip
Open Mon-Fri 8-4:30
Restriction: Registered patrons only

GL   TENNESSEE STATE LAW LIBRARY*, Law Library, Supreme Ct Bldg, 401 Seventh Ave N, 37219-1407. SAN 315-9264. Tel: 615-741-2016. FAX: 615-741-7186. *Librn,* Stephen M Jackson
Founded 1938
Library Holdings: Bk Titles 50,000; Bk Vols 55,000; Per Subs 30
Subject Interests: Present, Tenn law
Automation Activity & Vendor Info: (Cataloging) Inmagic, Inc.
Function: Res libr

P   TENNESSEE STATE LIBRARY & ARCHIVES, 403 Seventh Ave N, 37243-0312. SAN 360-960X. Tel: 615-741-2764. FAX: 615-532-2472, 615-741-6471. E-mail: reference.tsla@tn.gov. Web Site: www.tennessee.gov/tsla. *Archivist, State Librn,* Charles A Sherrill; E-mail: chuck.sherrill@tn.gov; *Asst State Librn, Admin,* Ashley Bowers; Tel: 615-532-2398; *Dir, Regional Libr, Planning & Develop,* Lynette Sloan; Tel: 615-741-3158, E-mail: lynette.sloan@state.tn.us; *Dir of Archival Tech Serv,* Carmack Cathi; Tel: 615-253-3468, E-mail: cathi.carmak@state.tn.us; *Dir, Presv Serv,* Carol Roberts; Tel: 615-741-2997, E-mail: carol.roberts@state.tn.us; *Dir, Pub Serv,* Gordon Belt; Tel: 615-253-6468, E-mail: gordon.belt@state.tn.us; *Dir of Tech Serv,* Stephanie Sutton; Tel: 615-253-3462, E-mail: stephanie.sutton@state.tn.us; *Regional Mgr,* Becky Bailey; *Regional Mgr,* Marion Bryant; Tel: 931-388-9282, E-mail: marion.bryant@state.tn.us; *Regional Mgr,* Susan Simmons Byrne; Tel: 865-457-0931, E-mail: susan.simmons@state.tn.us; *Regional Mgr,* Mary Carpenter; Tel: 731-587-2347, E-mail: susan.blakely@state.tn.us; *Regional Mgr,* Faith Holdredge; Tel: 931-836-2209, E-mail: faith.holdredge@state.tn.us; *Regional Mgr,* Carla Jacobs; Tel: 731-668-0710, E-mail: carla.jacobs@state.tn.us; *Regional Mgr,* BettyJo Jarvis; Tel: 615-893-3380, E-mail: bettyjo.jarvis@state.tn.us; *Regional Mgr,* Beth Allen Mercer; Tel: 800-624-1982, E-mail: beth.mercer@tn.gov; *Regional Mgr,* Nancy Roark; E-mail: nancy.renfro@tn.gov; *Asst State Archivist,* Wayne Moore; Tel: 615-741-2561, E-mail: wayne.moore@state.tn.us; Staff 156 (MLS 54, Non-MLS 102)
Founded 1854
Library Holdings: AV Mats 220,587; Braille Volumes 25,331; Electronic Media & Resources 766; Large Print Bks 11,397; Bk Vols 325,436; Per Subs 372; Talking Bks 149,683; Videos 904
Special Collections: Genealogy Coll; Popular Sheet Music (Rose Music); Southeastern US Maps; Tennessee County & Public Records; Tennessee Newspapers. Oral History; State Document Depository; US Document Depository
Subject Interests: Govt, SE US hist, Tenn politics
Automation Activity & Vendor Info: (Acquisitions) TLC (The Library Corporation); (Cataloging) OCLC; (ILL) Auto-Graphics, Inc; (OPAC) TLC (The Library Corporation); (Serials) TLC (The Library Corporation)
Database Vendor: Gale Cengage Learning, OCLC FirstSearch
Wireless access
Publications: List of Tennessee State Publications (Quarterly); Tennessee Minimum Standards for Non-Metropolitan Public Libraries; Tennessee Public Library Directory & Statistics (Annually); Tennessee Public Library Trustee Manual; Tennessee State Library & Archives: Guide to Resources & Services; Tennessee Summer Reading Program (Annually)
Partic in Lyrasis
Special Services for the Blind - Bks & mags in Braille, on rec, tape & cassette; Braille alphabet card; Cassette playback machines; Children's Braille; Closed circuit TV magnifier; Copier with enlargement capabilities; Descriptive video serv (DVS); Info on spec aids & appliances; Large print bks; Newsletter (in large print, Braille or on cassette); Talking bks & player equip
Open Tues-Sat 8-4:30
Branches: 1
LIBRARY FOR THE BLIND & PHYSICALLY HANDICAPPED
  See Separate Entry under Tennessee Regional Library for the Blind & Physically Handicapped

S   TENNESSEE STATE MUSEUM LIBRARY*, Polk Cultural Ctr, 505 Deaderick St, 37243-1120. SAN 321-4532. Tel: 615-741-2692. Toll Free Tel: 800-407-4324. FAX: 615-741-7231. E-mail: info@tnmuseum.org. Web Site: www.tnmuseum.org. *Librn,* Dan Pomeroy
Founded 1977
Library Holdings: Bk Vols 1,600; Per Subs 25
Special Collections: Weesner Coll on Archaeology & American Indians
Subject Interests: Am mat culture, Archaeology, Art, Artists
Restriction: Open to pub for ref only

C   TENNESSEE STATE UNIVERSITY*, Brown-Daniel Library, 3500 John A Merritt Blvd, 37209. SAN 315-9272. Tel: 615-963-5211. Circulation Tel: 615-963-5064. Interlibrary Loan Service Tel: 615-963-5206. Reference Tel: 615-963-5201. Administration Tel: 615-963-5212. FAX: 615-963-5216. Reference FAX: 615-963-5224. Web Site: www.tnstate.edu/library. *Dean, Libr & Media Ctr,* Dr Yildiz Barlas Binkley; E-mail: ybinkley@tnstate.edu; *Asst Dir, Coll Develop,* Glenda Alvin; Tel: 615-963-5230, Fax: 615-963-1368, E-mail: galvin@tnstate.edu; *Asst Dir, Pub Serv,* Dr Murle Kenerson; Tel: 615-963-5203, E-mail: mkenerson@tnstate.edu; *Head, Cat,* Barbara Taylor; Tel: 615-963-5236, Fax: 615-963-1368, E-mail: btaylor@tnstate.edu; *Head, Ref (Info Serv),* Fletcher Moon; Tel: 615-963-5205, E-mail: fmoon@tnstate.edu; *Head, Spec Coll,* Sharon Hull; Tel: 615-963-5219, E-mail: shull@tnstate.edu; *Syst Librn,* Sherry Ge; Tel: 615-963-5237, E-mail: xge@tnstate.edu; *Coordr,* Dr Helen Chen; Tel: 615-963-7185, Fax: 615-963-7193, E-mail: hchen@tnstate.edu; *Coordr, Media Spec,* Karen Gupton; Tel: 615-963-5743, Fax: 615-963-5745, E-mail: kgupton@tnstate.edu; *ILL,* Nancy Henthorne; E-mail: nhenthorne@tnstate.edu; *Webmaster,* Phil Yan; Tel: 615-963-5213, E-mail: pyan@tnstate.edu. Subject Specialists: *Info tech,* Dr Yildiz Barlas Binkley; *Info tech,* Phil Yan; Staff 38 (MLS 18, Non-MLS 20)
Founded 1912. Enrl 8,807; Fac 510; Highest Degree: Doctorate
Jul 2008-Jun 2009 Income $2,537,764, State $1,817,500, Federal $620,264, Locally Generated Income $100,000. Mats Exp $2,537,764, Books $385,000, Per/Ser (Incl. Access Fees) $613,000, Micro $50,000, Electronic Ref Mat (Incl. Access Fees) $1,486,764, Presv $3,000. Sal $1,354,390 (Prof $963,330)
Library Holdings: CDs 379; DVDs 960; e-books 168,866; e-journals 365; Electronic Media & Resources 210; Microforms 101,140; Bk Titles 402,971; Per Subs 1,637; Videos 4,011
Special Collections: Black History Coll; Jazz Recordings; Tennessee History; Tennessee State University History, art objects, bks, micro, pamphlets, per, pictures & newsp files. US Document Depository
Subject Interests: Agr, Art, Astronomy, Biol, Bus, Criminal justice, Educ, Eng, Ethnic studies, Govt affairs, Hist, Music, Nursing, Sociol
Automation Activity & Vendor Info: (Acquisitions) Innovative Interfaces, Inc; (Cataloging) Innovative Interfaces, Inc; (Circulation) Innovative Interfaces, Inc; (Course Reserve) Innovative Interfaces, Inc; (ILL) Innovative Interfaces, Inc; (Media Booking) Innovative Interfaces, Inc; (OPAC) Innovative Interfaces, Inc; (Serials) Innovative Interfaces, Inc - OCLC
Database Vendor: 3M Library Systems, ABC-CLIO, Agricola, Alexander Street Press, ARTstor, Baker & Taylor, Blackwell's, Cambridge Scientific Abstracts, ebrary, EBSCOhost, Elsevier MDL, Factiva.com, Gale Cengage Learning, IEEE (Institute of Electrical & Electronics Engineers), Infotrieve, ISI Web of Knowledge, JSTOR, LexisNexis, netLibrary, Newsbank, OVID Technologies, ProQuest, PubMed, ReferenceUSA, ScienceDirect, SerialsSolutions, Springer-Verlag, TLC (The Library Corporation), ValueLine, Westlaw, Wiley, Wilson - Wilson Web
Wireless access
Function: Accelerated reader prog
Publications: Accession List; Annual Report; Newsletter; Student Handbooks
Partic in Lyrasis; NALA; TBR Consortium; Tenn Acad Libr Collaborative; Tenn Share
Special Services for the Deaf - TDD equip
Special Services for the Blind - Closed circuit TV
Open Mon-Thurs 7:30am-10pm, Fri 7:30-4:30, Sat 10-6, Sun 2pm-10pm
Friends of the Library Group

C   TREVECCA NAZARENE UNIVERSITY*, Waggoner Library, 73 Lester Ave, 37210-4227. (Mail add: 333 Murfreesboro Rd, 37210-2834), SAN 315-9280. Tel: 615-248-1214. Reference Tel: 615-248-1570. FAX: 615-248-1452. Web Site: library.trevecca.edu. *Dir, Libr Serv,* Ruth T Kinnersley; Tel: 615-248-1491, E-mail: rkinnersley@trevecca.edu; *Info Literacy & Ref Librn,* Priscilla Speer; Tel: 615-248-1347, E-mail: pspeer@trevecca.edu; *Instrul Res Ctr Librn,* Karla Wardlow; Tel: 615-248-1548, E-mail: kwardlow@trevecca.edu; *Ser Librn,* Annette Harber; Tel: 615-248-1338, E-mail: aharber@trevecca.edu; *Archivist, Spec Coll Librn,* Andrea Gales; Tel: 615-248-1798, E-mail: agales@trevecca.edu; *Syst Librn,* Paula Mate; Tel: 615-248-7732, E-mail: pmate@trevecca.edu; *Tech Serv Librn,* Beth Purtee; Tel: 615-248-1455, E-mail: bpurtee@trevecca.edu; *Coordr, Instrul Res Ctr,* Judy Bivens; Tel: 615-248-1206, E-mail: jbivens@trevecca.edu; Staff 10.5 (MLS 8, Non-MLS 2.5)
Founded 2000. Enrl 2,300; Fac 231; Highest Degree: Doctorate
Library Holdings: AV Mats 3,573; e-books 20,795; Music Scores 682; Bk Vols 98,032; Per Subs 3,250
Subject Interests: Bus, Educ, Relig
Automation Activity & Vendor Info: (Acquisitions) Innovative Interfaces, Inc; (Cataloging) Innovative Interfaces, Inc; (Circulation) Innovative Interfaces, Inc; (Course Reserve) Innovative Interfaces, Inc; (ILL) Innovative Interfaces, Inc; (OPAC) Innovative Interfaces, Inc; (Serials) Innovative Interfaces, Inc

Database Vendor: Dialog, ebrary, EBSCOhost, Gale Cengage Learning, netLibrary, ProQuest, Wilson - Wilson Web
Wireless access
Publications: Brochures; Handbook; Newsletter
Partic in Christian Library Consortium; Lyrasis; Nashville Area Libr Alliance; Tenn Share
Open Mon-Thurs (Fall & Spring) 8am-Midnight, Fri 8-6, Sat 10-5, Sun 2-5 & 8-Midnight; Mon-Thurs (Summer) 10-8, Fri 10-6, Sat 10-5

R   UNITED METHODIST PUBLISHING HOUSE LIBRARY*, 201 Eighth Ave S, 37203. SAN 315-9302. Tel: 615-749-6335. FAX: 615-749-6128.
Tech Serv, Duane Diehl; Staff 1 (MLS 1)
Founded 1945
Library Holdings: Bk Titles 21,000; Bk Vols 40,000; Per Subs 300
Subject Interests: Methodistica, Theol, United Methodist publishing
Partic in Lyrasis
Open Mon-Fri 9-3:30

G   US COURT OF APPEALS FOR THE SIXTH CIRCUIT*, Harry Phillips Memorial Library, United States Courthouse, Rm A-830, 110 Ninth Ave S, 37203. SAN 326-7946. Tel: 615-736-7492. FAX: 615-736-2045. *Librn,* Position Currently Open; Staff 2 (MLS 1, Non-MLS 1)
Founded 1981
Library Holdings: Bk Vols 26,509
Automation Activity & Vendor Info: (Acquisitions) SirsiDynix; (Cataloging) SirsiDynix; (ILL) OCLC; (OPAC) SirsiDynix; (Serials) SirsiDynix
Open Mon-Fri 8-4:30

C   UNIVERSITY OF TENNESSEE COLLEGE OF SOCIAL WORK LIBRARY AT NASHVILLE*, 193-E Polk Ave, Ste 292, 37210. SAN 372-7785. Tel: 615-251-1774. FAX: 615-742-1085. Web Site: www.lib.utk.edu/~swn. *Librn,* Elsie Pettit; E-mail: epettit1@utk.edu
Library Holdings: Bk Vols 19,000; Per Subs 60
Wireless access
Open Mon-Thurs 8-1 & 2-8:30, Fri 8-1 & 2-4:30, Sat 12-4
Friends of the Library Group

SR   UPPER ROOM DEVOTIONAL LIBRARY*, 1908 Grand Ave, 37212. (Mail add: PO Box 340004, 37203-0004), SAN 315-9329. Tel: 615-340-7110. FAX: 615-340-7257. Web Site: www.upperroom.org. *Dean,* Tom Albin; E-mail: talbin@gbod.org; Staff 2 (MLS 1, Non-MLS 1)
Founded 1949
Library Holdings: Bk Titles 8,500; Per Subs 35
Subject Interests: Hymnals, Spiritual formation
Database Vendor: EBSCOhost
Wireless access
Open Mon-Fri 8-4:30

S   USW INTERNATIONAL UNION LIBRARY*, 3340 Perimeter Hill Dr, 37211. SAN 326-1832. Tel: 615-834-8590, Ext 720. FAX: 615-831-6792. Web Site: www.usw.org. *Info Spec,* Mary Dimoff; E-mail: mdimoff@usw.org
Library Holdings: Bk Vols 10,754; Per Subs 70
Special Collections: International Union, Allied Industrial Workers of America (AIW) Archives; Oil Chemical & Atomic Workers International Union (OCAW) Archives; United Paperworkers International Union (UPIU) Oral History Series, audio, microfilm, video cassette
Publications: USW @ Work
Partic in LexisNexis
Open Mon-Fri 8:30-4:30
Restriction: Staff use only

C   VANDERBILT UNIVERSITY, Jean & Alexander Heard Library, 419 21st Ave S, 37203-2427. SAN 360-8794. Tel: 615-322-7100. Interlibrary Loan Service Tel: 615-322-2408. FAX: 615-343-8279. Web Site: www.library.vanderbilt.edu. *Dean of Libr,* Connie Vinita Dowell; *Assoc Dean,* Jody Combs; *Assoc Dean,* Bill Hook; *Assoc Dean,* Larry Reeves; *Asst Dean, Coll,* Nancy Godleski; *Assoc Dean, Tech Serv,* Roberta Winjum; *Dir of Financial Affairs, Libr,* Jean Klockenkemper; *Spec Project Dir,* Celia Walker; Staff 184 (MLS 58, Non-MLS 126)
Founded 1873. Enrl 12,721; Fac 3,526; Highest Degree: Doctorate
Jul 2010-Jun 2011. Mats Exp $11,063,708. Sal $10,239,563
Library Holdings: Bk Vols 3,467,542; Per Subs 55,260
Special Collections: UN Document Depository; US Document Depository
Automation Activity & Vendor Info: (Acquisitions) SirsiDynix; (Cataloging) SirsiDynix; (Circulation) SirsiDynix; (Course Reserve) SirsiDynix; (ILL) OCLC ILLiad; (OPAC) SirsiDynix
Wireless access
Partic in Association of Southeastern Research Libraries; Lyrasis; Nashville Area Libr Alliance; OCLC Online Computer Library Center, Inc; Tenn-Share

Departmental Libraries:
CENTRAL LIBRARY, 419 21st Ave S, 37203-2427. Tel: 615-322-2800. Circulation Tel: 615-322-2893. Interlibrary Loan Service Tel: 615-322-2408. Administration Tel: 615-322-2664. FAX: 615-343-7451. Interlibrary Loan Service FAX: 615-343-7276. Web Site: www.library.vanderbilt.edu/central. *Dir,* Bill Hook; E-mail: bill.hook@vanderbilt.edu; *Assoc Dir, Head, Ref,* David Carpenter; Tel: 615-322-3618, E-mail: david.carpenter@vanderbilt.edu; *Head, Govt Docs & Media Serv,* Larry Romans; Tel: 615-322-2838, E-mail: larry.romans@vanderbilt.edu; *Instruction Coordr,* Melinda Brown; Tel: 615-322-6285, E-mail: melinda.brown@vanderbilt.edu; *Bibliographer, Coordr, Media Serv, Webmaster,* Frank Lester; Tel: 615-322-2838, E-mail: frank.lester@vanderbilt.edu; *Bibliographer,* Yvonne Boyer; Tel: 615-322-6284, E-mail: yvonne.boyer@vanderbilt.edu; *Bibliographer,* Peter Brush; Tel: 615-343-4838, E-mail: peter.w.brush@vanderbilt.edu; *Bibliographer,* Paula Covington; Tel: 615-322-6282, E-mail: paula.covington@vanderbilt.edu; *Bibliographer,* Deborah Lilton; Tel: 615-343-4237; *Bibliographer,* Pamela Morgan; Tel: 615-343-3081, E-mail: pamela.j.morgan@vanderbilt.edu; *Bibliographer,* Ramona Romero; Tel: 615-343-4236, E-mail: ramona.romero@vanderbilt.edu; *Bibliographer,* Susan Widmer; E-mail: susan.l.widmer@vanderbilt.edu. Subject Specialists: *Commun studies, Govt info, Polit sci,* Larry Romans; *Gender studies, Women's studies,* Melinda Brown; *Film studies,* Frank Lester; *Art, Fr (Lang), Italian (Lang),* Yvonne Boyer; *Asian studies, Hist,* Peter Brush; *Latin Am studies, Portuguese, Spanish,* Paula Covington; *African-Am studies, English, Theatre,* Deborah Lilton; *Psychol, Sociol,* Pamela Morgan; *Anthropology, Classics, Philosophy,* Ramona Romero; *Arabic studies, Economics, Germanic & Slavic (Lang),* Susan Widmer; Staff 25 (MLS 13, Non-MLS 12)
Founded 1873
Library Holdings: AV Mats 7,411; CDs 841; DVDs 3,376; Bk Vols 1,424,255; Per Subs 1,714; Videos 3,194
Special Collections: 18th Century French Literature (Morris Wachs Coll); 20th Century French Literature (Pascal Pia Coll); 20th Century French Theater (Gilbert Sigaux Coll); WT Bandy Center for Baudelaire & Modern French Studies. UN Document Depository; US Document Depository
Subject Interests: Art, Humanities
Database Vendor: Alexander Street Press, Annual Reviews, ARTstor, Blackwell's, Cambridge Scientific Abstracts, CountryWatch, ebrary, EBSCOhost, Elsevier MDL, Haworth Pres Inc, Ingenta, ISI Web of Knowledge, JSTOR, LexisNexis, netLibrary, Newsbank-Readex, OCLC FirstSearch, OCLC WorldCat, OVID Technologies, Oxford Online, Project MUSE, ProQuest, Sage, ScienceDirect, Westlaw, Wiley, Wilson - Wilson Web
Open Mon-Thurs (Fall & Spring) 7:30am-Midnight, Fri 7:30am-10pm, Sat 9am-10pm, Sun 11am-Midnight; Mon-Thurs (Summer) 7:30am-9pm, Fri 7:30-7, Sat 11-7, Sun 11-9

CR   DIVINITY LIBRARY, 419 21st Ave S, 37203-2427, SAN 360-8913. Tel: 615-322-2865. FAX: 615-343-8279. Web Site: divinity.library.vanderbilt.edu. *Dir,* William Hook; E-mail: bill.hook@vanderbilt.edu; *Assoc Dir, Coll Develop Officer,* Eileen Crawford; *Pub Serv Coordr,* Margaret Ann Trotter; *Divinity Cataloger,* Jill Brown; *Ref & Info Serv,* Chris Benda; *Coll Asst,* Charlotte Lew; *Pub Serv Asst,* Janis Lee; Staff 8 (MLS 4, Non-MLS 4)
Founded 1894. Enrl 275; Fac 29; Highest Degree: Doctorate
Jul 2011-Jun 2012 Income $1,151,301, Locally Generated Income $4,500, Parent Institution $1,146,801. Mats Exp $223,376, Books $110,000, Per/Ser (Incl. Access Fees) $26,326, Electronic Ref Mat (Incl. Access Fees) $85,050, Presv $2,000. Sal $425,832
Library Holdings: Bk Vols 220,332; Per Subs 373
Special Collections: Judaica Coll; Kelly Miller Smith Coll
Subject Interests: Relig studies, Theol
Automation Activity & Vendor Info: (Acquisitions) SirsiDynix; (Cataloging) SirsiDynix; (Circulation) SirsiDynix; (ILL) OCLC ILLiad; (OPAC) SirsiDynix; (Serials) SirsiDynix
Partic in OCLC Online Computer Library Center, Inc
Publications: Franz Rosenzweig: His Life & Work; Lectionary Readings for Reference & Reflection; Nahum Glatzer Archivesï¿½ Register; Vanderbilt University Libraryï¿½ Brief History of the Judaica Collection

CM   ANNETTE & IRWIN ESKIND BIOMEDICAL LIBRARY, 2209 Garland Ave, 37232-8340, SAN 315-9337. Tel: 615-936-1410. Interlibrary Loan Service Tel: 615-936-1405. Administration Tel: 615-936-1402. FAX: 615-936-1384. Interlibrary Loan Service FAX: 615-936-1407. Web Site: www.mc.vanderbilt.edu/biolib. *Dir,* Nunzia B Giuse; Tel: 615-936-1402, E-mail: nunzia.giuse@vanderbilt.edu; *Admin Serv, Assoc Dir,* Frances Lynch; Tel: 615-936-2617, E-mail: frances.lynch@vanderbilt.edu; *Assoc Dir for Operations,* Annette Williams; Tel: 615-936-3931, E-mail: annette.williams@vanderbilt.edu; *Assoc Dir, Res,* Nila Sathe; Tel: 615-936-5790, E-mail: nila.sathe@vanderbilt.edu; *Asst Dir, Doc Delivery, Info Serv,* Dan E McCollum; Tel: 615-936-6176, E-mail: dan.mccollum@vanderbilt.edu; Staff 42 (MLS 18, Non-MLS 24)
Founded 1906. Highest Degree: Doctorate
Library Holdings: e-books 790; e-journals 3,235; Bk Vols 202,110; Per Subs 4,325

Special Collections: History of Medicine, artifacts, bks, mss, pictures; Hypnotism (Albert Moll Coll), bks, clippings, reprints, theses; International Neuropsychopharmacology Archives; Nutrition History (Goldberger-Sebrell Coll, Helen Mitchell Coll, Franklin C Bing Coll, Neige Todhunter Culinary Coll, William J Darby Coll, American Society of Nutrition Scientists Archives), bks, clipping, mss, photogs; VUMC Archives; VUMC History, artifacts, bks, clippings, dissertations (University of Nashville), mss, photogs
Partic in Consortium of Southern Biomedical Libraries; Nashville Area Libr Alliance; National Network of Libraries of Medicine Southeastern Atlantic Region; OCLC Online Computer Library Center, Inc
Open Mon-Thurs 7am-Midnight, Fri 7am-10pm, Sat 8am-9pm, Sun Noon-Midnight
Restriction: Restricted access

CL   ALYNE QUEENER MASSEY LAW LIBRARY, 131 21st Ave S, 37203, SAN 315-9345. Tel: 615-322-2568. Reference Tel: 615-343-8737. Administration Tel: 615-322-2187. FAX: 615-343-1265. Administration FAX: 615-322-6629. Web Site: www.law.vanderbilt.edu/library. *Asst Dean,* Martin Cerjan; Tel: 615-322-0020, E-mail: martin.cerjan@law.vanderbilt.edu; *Assoc Dir,* Mary Miles Prince; Tel: 615-322-0021, E-mail: mary.miles.prince@law.vanderbilt.edu; *Access Serv,* James Kelly; Tel: 615-343-0208, E-mail: jim.kelly@vanderbilt.edu; *Acq,* William M Walker; Tel: 615-343-4079, E-mail: william.walker@law.vanderbilt.edu; *Cat, Doc,* Linda Tesar; Tel: 615-322-0022, E-mail: linda.tesar@law.vanderbilt.edu; *Ref,* Stephen Jordan; Tel: 615-322-3814, E-mail: stephen.jordan@law.vanderbilt.edu
Founded 1874
Special Collections: US Document Depository
Partic in OCLC Online Computer Library Center, Inc
Open Mon-Thurs 7am-Midnight, Fri 7am-10pm, Sat 9am-10pm, Sun 9am-Midnight

THE PEABODY LIBRARY, 230 Appleton Pl, PMB 135, 37203, SAN 360-8972. Tel: 615-322-8095, 615-322-8098. Administration Tel: 615-322-8866. FAX: 615-343-7923. Web Site: www.library.vanderbilt.edu/peabody. *Interim Dir,* Bill Hook; Tel: 615-322-8096, E-mail: bill.hook@vanderbilt.edu; *Librn,* Leslie J Foutch; Tel: 615-343-7541; *Librn,* Lee Ann Lannom; Tel: 615-343-2915, E-mail: lee.ann.lannom@vanderbilt.edu; Staff 8 (MLS 3, Non-MLS 5)
Founded 1886. Enrl 1,659; Fac 131; Highest Degree: Doctorate
Library Holdings: Bk Vols 222,697; Per Subs 372
Special Collections: Child Study (Peabody Coll of Books on Children); Curriculum Laboratory; Juvenile Literature Coll
Subject Interests: Educ, Human develop, Leadership, Psychol, Pub policy, Spec educ
Database Vendor: OCLC FirstSearch, OVID Technologies
Open Mon-Thurs (Winter) 7:30am-2am, Fri 7:30-6, Sat 10-8, Sun 11am-2am; Mon-Fri (Summer) 8-6, Sat 12-6, Sun 2-6
Friends of the Library Group

SCIENCE & ENGINEERING, 3200 Stevenson Ctr, 419 21st Ave S, 37240-0007, SAN 378-2247. Tel: 615-322-2775. Interlibrary Loan Service Tel: 615-344-2408. Reference Tel: 615-322-2717. FAX: 615-343-7249. E-mail: sciren@vanderbilt.edu. Web Site: www.library.vanderbilt.edu/science. *Dir,* Tracy Primich; Tel: 615-343-6043; *Coll Mgr,* Machelle Keen; Tel: 615-322-4165, E-mail: angela.m.keen@vanderbilt.edu; *Circ Supvr,* Debra Stephens; Tel: 615-322-4905, E-mail: debra.stephens@vanderbilt.edu; *Ref Librn, Tech Coordr,* Richard Stringer-Hye; Tel: 615-343-4395, E-mail: richard.stringer-hye@vanderbilt.edu; *Ref Librn,* Jon Erickson; Tel: 615-343-7105, E-mail: jon.erickson@vanderbilt.edu; *Ref Librn,* Kitty Porter; Tel: 615-343-7106, E-mail: kitty.porter@vanderbilt.edu; *Ref Librn,* Carlin Sappenfield; Tel: 615-343-7107, E-mail: carlin.sappenfield@vanderbilt.edu. Subject Specialists: *Biol, Molecular biol, Patents,* Jon Erickson; *Chem,* Kitty Porter; *Astronomy, Math, Physics,* Carlin Sappenfield; Staff 8 (MLS 5, Non-MLS 3)
Library Holdings: Bk Vols 348,776; Per Subs 2,005
Special Collections: US Patent & Trademark Depository Library. UN Document Depository; US Document Depository
Partic in Lyrasis; OCLC Online Computer Library Center, Inc
Restriction: Open to pub upon request
Friends of the Library Group

SPECIAL COLLECTIONS & UNIVERSITY ARCHIVES, 419 21st Ave S, 37203-2427, SAN 360-9065. Tel: 615-322-2807. E-mail: archives@vanderbilt.edu. Web Site: www.library.vanderbilt.edu/speccol. *Dir, Spec Coll,* Juanita Murray; E-mail: juanita.g.murray@vanderbilt.edu; *Assoc Dir,* Kathleen Smith; E-mail: kathleen.i.smith@vanderbilt.edu; Staff 3 (MLS 3)
Library Holdings: Bk Vols 43,000
Special Collections: 20th Century Film (Delbert Mann Coll); American Literature & Criticism, 1920 to Present (Jesse E Wills Fugitive-Agrarian Coll); Sevier & Rand Coll; Theatre, Music & Dance (Francis Robinson Coll)
Subject Interests: Hist, Performing arts, Politics, Southern lit
Function: Archival coll, Exhibits

Open Mon-Fri 8-4:30
Restriction: Closed stack, Non-circulating, Off-site coll in storage - retrieval as requested, Photo ID required for access

WALKER MANAGEMENT LIBRARY, Owen Graduate School of Management, 401 21st Ave S, 37203, SAN 328-9737. Tel: 615-322-2970. Circulation Tel: 615-343-3340. Reference Tel: 615-322-3960. Administration Tel: 615-322-3635. FAX: 615-343-0061. Web Site: management.library.vanderbilt.edu/. *Dir,* Hilary A Craiglow; Tel: 615-323-4182, E-mail: hilary.craiglow@owen.vanderbilt.edu; *Librn,* Sara Byrd; Tel: 615-322-2546; *Librn,* Rahn Huber; Tel: 615-343-4084, E-mail: rahn.huber@owen.vanderbilt.edu; *Admin Serv,* Elaine Hill; Tel: 615-343-4109, E-mail: elaine.hill@owen.vanderbilt.edu; *Mgr, Access Serv,* Brent Tenpenny; Tel: 615-343-7324, E-mail: brent.tenpenny@owen.vanderbilt.edu; *Operations Mgr,* Deborah Brooks; Tel: 615-343-4108, E-mail: deborah.brooks@owen.vanderbilt.edu; *Evening Supvr,* Joseph Collins; Tel: 615-343-5946; *Access Serv, Doc Delivery,* Laura Norris; Tel: 615-343-6036, E-mail: laura.norris@owen.vanderbilt.edu; *Tech Serv,* Sylvia Grant; Tel: 615-343-8252, E-mail: sylvia.grant@owen.vanderbilt.edu; Staff 10 (MLS 5, Non-MLS 5)
Enrl 545; Highest Degree: Doctorate
Library Holdings: Bk Vols 58,381; Per Subs 1,102
Special Collections: Career Planning & Placement Resource Coll
Subject Interests: Corp info
Function: Doc delivery serv, For res purposes, Homebound delivery serv, ILL available, Newsp ref libr, Outside serv via phone, mail, e-mail & web, Photocopying/Printing, Ref serv available, Res libr
Restriction: Access for corporate affiliates, Mem organizations only
Friends of the Library Group

ANNE POTTER WILSON MUSIC LIBRARY, Blair School of Music, 2400 Blakemore Ave, 37212, SAN 360-9006. Tel: 615-322-7695. Reference Tel: 615-322-7696. FAX: 615-343-0050. Web Site: www.library.vanderbilt.edu/music. *Libr Dir,* Holling Smith-Borne; Tel: 615-322-5227, E-mail: holling.j.smith-borne@vanderbilt.edu; *Educ & Outreach Music Librn,* Sara J Beutter Manus; Tel: 615-322-8686, E-mail: sara.manus@vanderbilt.edu; *Asst Librn, Ref,* Robert Rich; Tel: 615-322-7171; *Music Cataloger,* Jacob Schaub; Tel: 615-322-3022, E-mail: jacob.schaub@vanderbilt.edu. Subject Specialists: *Music,* Holling Smith-Borne; *Music,* Sara J Beutter Manus; *Music,* Jacob Schaub; Staff 5 (MLS 3, Non-MLS 2)
Founded 1945. Enrl 205; Pop 11,000; Fac 56; Highest Degree: Bachelor
Library Holdings: CDs 14,000; DVDs 800; Music Scores 22,000; Bk Vols 47,000; Per Subs 170; Videos 750
Special Collections: Digital Coll of East African Recordings; Seminar in Piano Teaching, Lectures, Master Classes, Recitals, 1970-76, a-tapes
Publications: Newsletter (Annually)
Open Mon-Thurs 8am-11pm, Fri 8am-9pm, Sun 2-10
Restriction: Authorized patrons, Authorized scholars by appt, Borrowing privileges limited to fac & registered students, Borrowing requests are handled by ILL, In-house use for visitors
Friends of the Library Group

S   WATKINS COLLEGE OF ART & DESIGN LIBRARY*, 2298 Rosa L Parks Blvd (MetroCenter), 37228. SAN 315-9361. Tel: 615-383-4848. Circulation Tel: 615-277-7427. FAX: 615-383-4849. Web Site: www.watkins.edu. *Dir,* Beverly Stark; Tel: 615-277-7426, E-mail: bstark@watkins.edu; *Asst Librn,* Virginia Allision
Founded 1885
Jul 2005-Jun 2006. Mats Exp $18,500, Books $10,000, Per/Ser (Incl. Access Fees) $5,000, AV Mat $2,000, Electronic Ref Mat (Incl. Access Fees) $1,500. Sal $32,000
Library Holdings: AV Mats 3,173; Bk Titles 17,000; Bk Vols 20,000; Per Subs 60; Spec Interest Per Sub 56
Subject Interests: Art, Film, Graphic design, Interior design, Photog
Automation Activity & Vendor Info: (Cataloging) LibraryWorld, Inc; (Circulation) LibraryWorld, Inc; (Serials) EBSCO Online
Partic in Tenn Share
Open Mon-Thurs 7:45am-9:30pm, Fri 7:45-4, Sun 1-6
Friends of the Library Group

R   WEST END SYNAGOGUE*, 3810 W End Ave, 37205. SAN 360-876X. Tel: 615-269-4592. Toll Free Tel: 888-335-8993. FAX: 615-269-4695. E-mail: office@westendsyn.org. Web Site: www.westendsyn.org. *Librn,* Susan Pankowsky
Founded 1874
Library Holdings: Bk Vols 15,000
Subject Interests: Holocaust, Israel, Judaism

NEWBERN

P   NEWBERN CITY LIBRARY*, 220 E Main St, 38059-1528. SAN 315-937X. Tel: 731-627-3153. FAX: 731-627-3129. *Dir,* Janice Peevyhouse
Founded 1969. Pop 3,000; Circ 31,372
Library Holdings: Bk Vols 12,000; Per Subs 47

Automation Activity & Vendor Info: (Cataloging) Follett Software; (Circulation) Follett Software; (ILL) Follett Software
Open Mon 11-7, Tues-Sat 11-5

NEWPORT

P   STOKELY MEMORIAL LIBRARY*, 383 E Broadway, 37821-3105. SAN 315-9388. Tel: 423-623-3832. FAX: 423-623-3832. *Dir,* Meschelyn Barrett; E-mail: meschelyn@charter.net
Pop 34,329; Circ 84,632
Library Holdings: Bk Vols 35,000; Per Subs 30
Special Collections: James Stokely Coll
Subject Interests: Genealogy
Automation Activity & Vendor Info: (Acquisitions) Winnebago Software Co; (Cataloging) Winnebago Software Co; (Circulation) Winnebago Software Co
Open Mon-Sat 10-5
Friends of the Library Group

NIOTA

P   NIOTA PUBLIC LIBRARY*, 11 E Main St, 37826. (Mail add: PO Box 146, 37826-0146), SAN 315-9396. Tel: 423-568-2613. FAX: 423-568-3026. E-mail: nio_lib@yahoo.com. *Dir,* Eva Brakebill
Pop 1,303; Circ 19,051
Library Holdings: Bk Vols 5,000; Per Subs 39
Mem of Ocoee River Regional Library
Open Mon & Thurs 2:30-5:30, Tue & Fri 12:30-6, Sat 9-12

NORRIS

P   BETTY ANNE JOLLY NORRIS COMMUNITY LIBRARY*, One Norris Sq, 37828. (Mail add: PO Box 1110, 37828-1110), SAN 315-940X. Tel: 865-494-6800. E-mail: norrispl@comcast.net. Web Site: www.discoveret.org/norrispl/. *Dir,* Patrisha Austin-Halsey
Founded 1934. Pop 1,446; Circ 16,777
Library Holdings: AV Mats 1,217; Bk Vols 19,456; Per Subs 49
Open Mon, Tues, Thurs, Fri & Sun 12-6
Friends of the Library Group

OAK RIDGE

S   CHILDREN'S MUSEUM OF OAK RIDGE*, Regional Appalachian Center - Media Library, 461 W Outer Dr, 37830-3714. (Mail add: PO Box 5766, 37831-5766), SAN 326-727X. Tel: 865-482-1074. FAX: 865-481-4889. E-mail: chmor@bellsouth.net. Web Site: www.childrensmuseumofoakridge.org. *Exec Dir,* Maryann Damos
Library Holdings: Bk Vols 2,520; Per Subs 20
Special Collections: Oak Ridge, Anderson & Roane Counties (personal papers, scrapbooks, photographs & oral history tapes)
Publications: An Appalachian Studies Teacher's Manual; An Encyclopedia of East Tennessee; Anderson County Tennessee: A Pictorial History; Oak Ridge and Me: From Youth to Maturity; Ridges & Valleys: A Mini-Encyclopedia of Anderson County; These Are Our Voices: The Story of Oak Ridge, Tennessee, 1943-1970
Restriction: Open by appt only

SR   FIRST UNITED METHODIST CHURCH*, Jones Memorial Library, 1350 Oak Ridge Tpk, 37830. SAN 371-6171. Tel: 865-483-4357. E-mail: library@fumcor.org. Web Site: www.fumcor.org/library. *Librn,* Susan Ekkebus; Staff 1 (MLS 1)
Founded 1967
Library Holdings: Braille Volumes 2; CDs 120; DVDs 173; e-books 20; Large Print Bks 450; Bk Vols 6,354; Spec Interest Per Sub 22; Talking Bks 65; Videos 202
Automation Activity & Vendor Info: (Cataloging) JayWil Software Development, Inc; (OPAC) JayWil Software Development, Inc
Wireless access
Open Mon-Fri 9-5, Sun 9-1
Restriction: External users must contact libr, Open to pub for ref & circ; with some limitations, Use of others with permission of librn
Friends of the Library Group

S   OAK RIDGE NATIONAL LABORATORY*, ORNL Research Library, Bldg 4500N, MS-6191, Bethel Valley Rd, 37830. (Mail add: PO Box 2008, 37831-6191), SAN 360-9960. Tel: 865-574-6744. FAX: 865-574-6915. E-mail: library@ornl.gov. Web Site: www.ornl.gov/info/library. *Dir of Libr,* Conrad Bob; Tel: 865-574-4872, E-mail: conradre@ornl.gov; *Tech Serv Team Leader,* Cynthia Manley; Tel: 865-574-0082, E-mail: manleycg@ornl.gov; Staff 14 (MLS 8, Non-MLS 6)
Founded 1946
Library Holdings: e-books 9,000; e-journals 3,394; Bk Vols 77,000; Per Subs 535
Special Collections: DOE Scientific & Technical Reports
Subject Interests: Biol, Chem, Climate, Ecology, Energy, Eng, Environ sci, Fusion energy, Mat sci, Neutron sci, Nuclear sci, Physics, Robotics

Automation Activity & Vendor Info: (OPAC) Ex Libris Group
Database Vendor: Cambridge Scientific Abstracts, Dialog, EBSCOhost, JSTOR, LexisNexis
Function: Res libr
Partic in Knoxville Area Health Sciences Library Consortium; Univ of Tenn Knoxville
Restriction: Staff use only

P   OAK RIDGE PUBLIC LIBRARY*, 1401 Oak Ridge Tpk, 37830-6224. (Mail add: PO Box 1, 37831-0001), SAN 315-9469. Tel: 865-425-3455. Reference Tel: 865-425-3465. FAX: 865-425-3429. Web Site: www.orpl.org. *Dir,* Kathy E McNeilly; E-mail: kmcneilly@cortn.org; *Asst Dir,* Marie Stooksbury; *Ch,* Michaela Miller; *Circ,* Virginia Bayne; *ILL,* Teresa Fortney; *Ref,* Susannah Howard; *Tech Serv,* Martha Lux; Staff 23 (MLS 6, Non-MLS 17)
Founded 1944. Pop 27,514; Circ 176,906
Jul 2009-Jun 2010 Income $1,354,049. Sal $906,762
Library Holdings: AV Mats 4,673; CDs 7,141; DVDs 4,314; Per Subs 216; Videos 4,737
Special Collections: Center for Oak Ridge Oral History Coll; Oak Ridge Room. Oral History; State Document Depository
Subject Interests: Local authors, Local hist, Small bus
Automation Activity & Vendor Info: (Acquisitions) SirsiDynix; (Cataloging) SirsiDynix; (Circulation) SirsiDynix; (OPAC) SirsiDynix; (Serials) SirsiDynix
Wireless access
Function: Archival coll, Art exhibits, AV serv, Bks on cassette, Bks on CD, CD-ROM, Children's prog, Computer training, Computers for patron use, Copy machines, e-mail serv, E-Reserves, Electronic databases & coll, Home delivery & serv to Sr ctr & nursing homes, ILL available, Magnifiers for reading, Music CDs, Online cat, Online ref, Photocopying/Printing, Prog for adults, Pub access computers, Ref & res, Ref serv available, Senior computer classes, Spoken cassettes & CDs, Spoken cassettes & DVDs, Story hour, Summer reading prog, Tax forms, Telephone ref, VHS videos, Video lending libr, Web-catalog, Wheelchair accessible
Publications: Annual report; Orplines (Newsletter)
Partic in Tenn-Share
Open Mon-Thurs 10-9, Fri 10-6, Sat 9-6, Sun 2-6
Restriction: Non-circulating coll, Non-resident fee
Friends of the Library Group

G   UNITED STATES DEPARTMENT OF ENERGY*, Office of Scientific & Technical Information, One Science.gov Way, 37830. (Mail add: PO Box 62, 37831-0062), SAN 315-9477. Tel: 865-576-1188. Toll Free Tel: 800-553-6847. FAX: 865-576-3609. Web Site: www.osti.gov. *Dir,* Walter L Warnick; E-mail: warnickw@osti.gov; *Dep Dir, Mgr,* R Charles Morgan
Library Holdings: Bk Vols 4,700,000; Per Subs 50
Special Collections: US Department of Energy Research & Development Reports and Monographs
Publications: Radio Active Waste Mgmt

OAKDALE

P   OAKDALE PUBLIC LIBRARY*, 212 Queen St, 37829-3137. (Mail add: PO Box 190, 37829-0190), SAN 315-9485. Tel: 423-369-2595, 423-369-3524. FAX: 423-369-2595. E-mail: oakdalelib@highland.net. *Dir,* Norma A Mathis
Pop 268; Circ 2,686
Library Holdings: Bk Vols 3,042
Open Mon-Wed 5-9

OLIVER SPRINGS

P   OLIVER SPRINGS PUBLIC LIBRARY, 610 Walker Ave, 37840. SAN 315-9515. Tel: 865-435-2509. FAX: 865-730-6476. E-mail: os_publibrary@comcast.net. Web Site: oliverspringscity.com/library.html. *Libr Dir,* Larrisa Walker
Pop 3,500; Circ 5,000
Library Holdings: Bk Titles 5,000
Subject Interests: Local hist
Database Vendor: SirsiDynix
Wireless access
Function: Copy machines, Free DVD rentals, Handicapped accessible, ILL available, Photocopying/Printing, Preschool reading prog, Story hour, Summer reading prog
Mem of Ocoee River Regional Library
Open Mon-Fri 10-6
Restriction: Authorized patrons

ONEIDA

P   SCOTT COUNTY PUBLIC LIBRARY*, Oneida Public, 290 S Main St, 37841-2605. SAN 315-9523. Tel: 423-569-8634. FAX: 423-569-3062. E-mail: oneidapl@highland.net. *Dir,* Dawn Claiborne
Pop 16,618; Circ 17,620

Library Holdings: AV Mats 895; Bk Vols 12,415; Per Subs 38
Open Mon, Wed & Fri 9-5, Tues 10-7, Thurs 1-7, Sat 9-12

PALMER

P   PALMER PUBLIC LIBRARY*, 2115 Main St, 37365-9999. SAN 315-9531. Tel: 931-779-5292. FAX: 931-779-2334. E-mail: palmerlib@blomand.net. Web Site: www.state.tn.us/cgi-bin/library. *Dir,* Susan Faye Sissom
Founded 1956. Pop 726
Library Holdings: AV Mats 183; Bk Titles 3,200; Bk Vols 7,589
Automation Activity & Vendor Info: (Cataloging) Book Systems, Inc; (Circulation) Book Systems, Inc; (OPAC) Book Systems, Inc
Open Mon 1-5, Tues & Thurs 9:30-6

PARIS

P   W G RHEA PUBLIC LIBRARY*, 400 W Washington St, 38242-3903. SAN 315-954X. Tel: 731-642-1702. FAX: 731-642-1777. E-mail: library@rheapubliclibrary.com. Web Site: www.rheapubliclibrary.com. *Dir,* Connie McSwain; E-mail: conniemcswain@bellsouth.net; *Asst Dir,* Freda Reddick; E-mail: fredareddick@bellsouth.net
Founded 1960. Pop 31,185; Circ 79,618
Library Holdings: Bks on Deafness & Sign Lang 31; CDs 861; Bk Titles 51,854; Per Subs 100; Talking Bks 2,179
Subject Interests: Genealogy
Automation Activity & Vendor Info: (Circulation) Winnebago Software Co; (OPAC) Winnebago Software Co
Mem of Obion River Regional Library
Open Mon, Wed, Fri & Sat 9-5, Tues & Thurs 9-7
Friends of the Library Group

PARROTTSVILLE

P   PARROTTSVILLE COMMUNITY LIBRARY*, PO Box 147, 37843. Tel: 423-625-8990. FAX: 423-625-8990. E-mail: pvillelib@planetc.com. *Dir,* Kim Murphy
Library Holdings: Bk Vols 25,000
Automation Activity & Vendor Info: (Cataloging) Follett Software; (Circulation) Follett Software; (OPAC) Follett Software
Open Mon, Wed & Fri 12:30-6:30

PARSONS

P   PARSONS PUBLIC LIBRARY*, 105 Kentucky Ave S, 38363-2517. SAN 315-9566. Tel: 731-847-6988. FAX: 731-847-3476. E-mail: parsonslib@netease.net. Web Site: www.geocities.com/athens/troy/3469. *Dir,* Maxine Wheat
Pop 6,000
Library Holdings: Bk Vols 14,000; Per Subs 12
Automation Activity & Vendor Info: (Cataloging) Follett Software; (Circulation) Follett Software; (OPAC) Follett Software
Mem of Hatchie River Regional Library
Open Tues, Thurs & Fri 10:30-4:30, Sat 10-2
Friends of the Library Group

PETROS

P   PETROS PUBLIC LIBRARY*, 208 Main St, 37845. (Mail add: PO Box 147, 37845-0147), SAN 315-9574. Tel: 423-324-2825. E-mail: petrospl1@highland.net. *Dir,* Pat Chamblee
Pop 4,676
Library Holdings: Bk Vols 9,111
Open Mon & Wed 9:30-5, Thurs 9:30-4:30

PHILADELPHIA

P   PHILADELPHIA PUBLIC LIBRARY*, 714 Thompson St, 37846. (Mail add: PO Box 117, 37846-0117), SAN 376-2955. Tel: 865-458-9493. FAX: 865-458-9493. E-mail: phpl@esper.com. *Dir,* Kim Roberts; Staff 1 (Non-MLS 1)
Pop 550
Library Holdings: Bk Titles 7,375
Function: Online searches, Photocopying/Printing, Summer reading prog
Mem of Ocoee River Regional Library
Open Tues-Fri 9-5

PIGEON FORGE

P   PIGEON FORGE PUBLIC LIBRARY*, 2449 Library Dr, 37876. Tel: 865-429-7490. FAX: 865-429-7495. E-mail: info@pfpl.net. Web Site: www.pfpl.net. *Dir,* Dr JoAn Trentham; Staff 1 (MLS 1)
Founded 2001. Pop 5,000
Library Holdings: AV Mats 5,500; Bk Vols 30,000; Per Subs 86
Special Collections: White House Memorabilia (Tennessee Darling Coll). Oral History

Automation Activity & Vendor Info: (Cataloging) Book Systems, Inc; (Circulation) Book Systems, Inc; (Course Reserve) Book Systems, Inc; (ILL) Book Systems, Inc; (OPAC) Book Systems, Inc
Wireless access
Function: Handicapped accessible, ILL available, Magnifiers for reading
Special Services for the Blind - Reader equip
Open Mon 9-6, Tues & Thurs 8-8, Wed & Fri 8-6, Sat 9-5
Friends of the Library Group

PIKEVILLE

P   BLEDSOE COUNTY PUBLIC LIBRARY, 478 Cumberland Ave, 37367. (Mail add: PO Box 465, 37367-0465), SAN 315-9582. Tel: 423-447-2817. FAX: 423-447-3002. Web Site: www.bledsoelibrary.com. *Dir,* Carolyne Knight; E-mail: cknightbcpl@bledsoe.net
Founded 1952. Pop 12,500; Circ 17,720
Library Holdings: Bk Titles 14,000; Per Subs 16
Automation Activity & Vendor Info: (Acquisitions) Book Systems, Inc
Wireless access
Open Mon, Wed & Thurs 10-6, Tues & Fri 10-5, Sat 9-2

S   TENNESSEE DEPARTMENT OF CORRECTIONS*, Southeastern Tennessee State Regional Correction Facility Library, 1045 Horsehead Rd, 37367. Tel: 423-881-3251. FAX: 423-881-4226. *In Charge,* Rick Hassler
Library Holdings: Bk Vols 7,000; Per Subs 14
Open Mon-Fri 7-6:30, Sat & Sun 7-1:30

PINEY FLATS

S   ROCKY MOUNT HISTORICAL ASSOCIATION LIBRARY, 200 Hyder Hill Rd, 37686-4630. (Mail add: PO Box 160, 37686-0160), SAN 326-3223. Tel: 423-538-7396. FAX: 423-538-1086. Web Site: www.rockymountmuseum.org. *Exec Dir,* Gary Walrath; E-mail: gwalrath@rockymountmuseum.com
Library Holdings: Bk Vols 3,600
Open Tues-Sat 11-5

PORTLAND

P   PORTLAND PUBLIC LIBRARY*, Elmer Hinton Memorial Library, 301 Portland Blvd, 37148-1229. SAN 315-9590. Tel: 615-325-2279. Reference Tel: 615-325-4015. FAX: 615-325-7061. E-mail: portlandlibrary@bellsouth.net. Web Site: www.portlandtn.com/library.htm. *Dir,* Barbara Russell; E-mail: ehmldirector@bellsouth.net; *Asst Dir, Ch,* Linda Ackerman; *Adult Serv, Tech Serv,* Lori Melching; *Circ,* Margie Boots; *Spec Coll,* Debra Elledge; Staff 5 (Non-MLS 5)
Founded 1953. Pop 30,544; Circ 108,000
Jul 2007-Jun 2008 Income $227,193, State $875, City $25,000, County $161,341, Locally Generated Income $20,426, Other $19,551. Mats Exp $23,592. Sal $132,622
Library Holdings: Audiobooks 1,298; AV Mats 2,387; Bks on Deafness & Sign Lang 12; e-books 911; Large Print Bks 900; Microforms 76; Bk Titles 39,156; Per Subs 100
Special Collections: Civil War Coll; NASA Coll; Tennessee History Coll
Automation Activity & Vendor Info: (Acquisitions) TLC (The Library Corporation); (Cataloging) TLC (The Library Corporation); (Circulation) TLC (The Library Corporation); (Course Reserve) TLC (The Library Corporation); (ILL) Auto-Graphics, Inc; (OPAC) TLC (The Library Corporation)
Database Vendor: Gale Cengage Learning
Wireless access
Function: Adult bk club, After school storytime, Audiobks via web, Bk club(s), Bks on cassette, Bks on CD, Children's prog, Computer training, Computers for patron use, Copy machines, Digital talking bks, Doc delivery serv, e-mail & chat, e-mail serv, E-Reserves, Electronic databases & coll, Fax serv, Free DVD rentals, Handicapped accessible, Holiday prog, Homebound delivery serv, ILL available, Mail & tel request accepted, Music CDs, Newsp ref libr, Notary serv, Online cat, Online searches, Outreach serv, Photocopying/Printing, Preschool outreach, Prog for adults, Prog for children & young adult, Pub access computers, Ref serv available, Scanner, Senior computer classes, Senior outreach, Spoken cassettes & CDs, Spoken cassettes & DVDs, Story hour, Summer reading prog, Tax forms, Teen prog, Telephone ref, VHS videos, Video lending libr, Wheelchair accessible
Mem of Red River Regional Library
Partic in Tenn-Share
Open Tues & Thurs 10-8, Wed & Fri 10-6, Sat 10-2
Friends of the Library Group

PULASKI

P   GILES COUNTY PUBLIC LIBRARY, 122 S Second St, 38478-3285. SAN 315-9604. Tel: 931-363-2720. FAX: 931-424-7032. E-mail: glibrary@bellsouth.net. Web Site: gilescountylibrary.org. *Financial Mgr, Interim Dir,* Cindy Nesbitt; *Ault Prog Librn/Acq,* Christopher Poole; *Ch, Circ Librn,* Barbara Pankey; *YA Librn,* Jessica Barber; *Asst Circ Mgr,* Beth

Armstrong; *Asst Circ/ILL Mgr,* Brianna Wise; *Sci/Tech Prog,* Scott Hardage; Staff 1 (Non-MLS 1)
Founded 1940. Pop 29,036; Circ 85,000
Library Holdings: Bk Titles 40,000; Bk Vols 44,000; Per Subs 90
Special Collections: Census (microfilms); Museum Coll
Subject Interests: Genealogy, Hist, Local hist
Automation Activity & Vendor Info: (Cataloging) Auto-Graphics, Inc; (Circulation) Auto-Graphics, Inc; (ILL) Auto-Graphics, Inc; (OPAC) Auto-Graphics, Inc
Database Vendor: Auto-Graphics, Inc, Gale Cengage Learning
Wireless access
Publications: Bulletin (Quarterly)
Friends of the Library Group
Branches: 2
ELKTON PUBLIC LIBRARY, 110 Main St, Elkton, 38455. (Mail add: PO Box 157, Elkton, 38455-0157), SAN 376-8082. Tel: 931-468-2506. FAX: 931-468-2993. *Br Mgr,* Margie Brooks
  Library Holdings: Bk Vols 500
  Open Mon 8-2, Tues-Thurs 8-4:30
LYNNVILLE BRANCH, 105 Mill St, Lynnville, 38472. Tel: 931-527-0707. *Br Mgr,* Barbara Clayton
  Open Mon, Wed & Fri 10-5, Tues & Thurs 2-7, Sat 10-4, Sun 12-4

C   MARTIN METHODIST COLLEGE*, Warden Memorial Library, 433 W Madison St, 38478-2799. SAN 315-9612. Tel: 931-363-9844. Toll Free Tel: 800-467-1273. FAX: 931-363-9844. E-mail: library@martinmethodist.edu. Web Site: www.martinmethodist.edu/library. *Dir,* Richard Madden; E-mail: rmadden@martinmethodist.edu; *Asst Dir,* Harold Rosenbaum; Tel: 931-363-9843, E-mail: hrosenbaum@martinmethodist.edu; *Acq Mgr, Mgr, ILL, Mgr, Ser,* Martha Kelley; E-mail: mkelley@martinmethodist.edu; *Cat Mgr,* Judy Kelly; E-mail: jkelly@martinmethodist.edu; *Pub Serv Mgr,* Chris VanDoran; E-mail: cvandoran@martinmethodist.edu; Staff 5 (MLS 2, Non-MLS 3)
Founded 1975. Enrl 1,000; Fac 39; Highest Degree: Bachelor
Jul 2005-Jun 2006 Income $87,401. Mats Exp $80,100, Books $28,226, Per/Ser (Incl. Access Fees) $12,772, Micro $7,000, AV Mat $5,091, Electronic Ref Mat (Incl. Access Fees) $27,011. Sal $109,000 (Prof $72,000)
Library Holdings: AV Mats 1,300; DVDs 100; e-books 46,000; Bk Titles 80,000; Bk Vols 84,000; Per Subs 670; Videos 700
Special Collections: Glatzer/Zimmerman Judaica; Gregory McDonald Coll, ms; Methodist History Coll; Psychology (William Fitts Coll); Senator Ross Bass Coll
Subject Interests: Local hist, Methodist hist
Automation Activity & Vendor Info: (Acquisitions) Mandarin Library Automation; (Cataloging) Mandarin Library Automation; (Circulation) Mandarin Library Automation; (ILL) OCLC; (Media Booking) Mandarin Library Automation; (OPAC) Mandarin Library Automation; (Serials) Mandarin Library Automation
Database Vendor: Baker & Taylor, EBSCOhost, Gale Cengage Learning, JSTOR, LexisNexis, netLibrary, OCLC FirstSearch, OVID Technologies, ProQuest
Partic in Lyrasis; Tenn Share
Special Services for the Blind - Braille bks
Open Mon-Thurs (Fall & Spring) 7:30am-10:30pm, Fri 7:30-3:30, Sat 8-Noon, Sun 2-10; Mon & Thurs (Summer) 7:30am-10:30pm, Tues & Wed 7:30-4:30, Fri 7:30-3:30
Restriction: Open to pub for ref & circ; with some limitations

RIDGELY

P   RIDGELY PUBLIC LIBRARY*, 134 N Main St, 38080-1316. SAN 315-9620. Tel: 731-264-5809. FAX: 731-264-5809. *Dir,* Frances Dial
Pop 2,213; Circ 7,504
Library Holdings: Bk Vols 14,699
Wireless access
Open Mon-Fri 1-5

RIPLEY

P   LAUDERDALE COUNTY LIBRARY*, 120 Lafayette St, 38063-1321. SAN 315-9639. Tel: 731-635-1872. FAX: 731-635-8568. E-mail: libraryl@bellsouth.net. *Librn,* Marilyn Tillman
Pop 22,000
Library Holdings: Bk Vols 20,000; Per Subs 24
Subject Interests: Genealogy
Automation Activity & Vendor Info: (Cataloging) Follett Software; (Circulation) Follett Software; (Course Reserve) Follett Software; (ILL) Follett Software
Open Mon-Fri 9-6, Sat 9-12
Friends of the Library Group

ROCKWOOD

P   ROCKWOOD PUBLIC LIBRARY*, 117 N Front St, 37854-2320. SAN 315-9647. Tel: 865-354-1281. FAX: 865-354-4302. Web Site: library.rockwoodtn.org. *Dir,* Margaret Marrs; E-mail: mmarrs@comcast.net
Library Holdings: Bk Vols 36,000; Per Subs 50
Automation Activity & Vendor Info: (Cataloging) Follett Software; (Circulation) Follett Software
Mem of Ocoee River Regional Library
Open Mon, Wed, Fri & Sat 10-5, Tues & Thurs 10-8

ROGERSVILLE

P   H B STAMPS MEMORIAL LIBRARY*, 407 E Main St, 37857. SAN 315-9655. Tel: 423-272-8710. FAX: 423-272-9261. E-mail: hbslib@chartertn.net. *Dir,* Ann M Fields; Staff 7 (MLS 1, Non-MLS 6)
Founded 1954. Pop 55,851; Circ 56,332
Library Holdings: DVDs 684; Large Print Bks 578; Bk Titles 43,000; Bk Vols 44,902; Per Subs 41; Talking Bks 1,269; Videos 2,106
Special Collections: Hawkins County History & Genealogy (H B Stamps Coll); Juno Altom Genealogy Room; Tennessee Valley Authority
Automation Activity & Vendor Info: (Acquisitions) Book Systems, Inc; (Cataloging) Book Systems, Inc; (Circulation) Book Systems, Inc; (Course Reserve) Book Systems, Inc; (ILL) Book Systems, Inc; (Media Booking) Book Systems, Inc; (OPAC) Book Systems, Inc; (Serials) Book Systems, Inc
Open Mon, Wed & Fri 9:30-5, Tues & Thurs 9:30-8, Sat 9-1
Friends of the Library Group
Branches: 1
CHURCH HILL BRANCH, 302 E Main Blvd, Church Hill, 37642. (Mail add: PO Box 37, Church Hill, 37642-0037), SAN 315-7458. Tel: 423-357-4591. FAX: 423-357-8396. E-mail: chulib@chartertn.net. *Dir,* Maureen McDaniel; *Asst Librn,* Joyce Thacker
  Library Holdings: Bk Titles 17,289; Per Subs 42
  Open Mon 9:30-7:30, Tues-Fri 9:30-5:30, Sat 10-2

RUGBY

S   HISTORIC RUGBY*, Thomas Hughes Free Public Library, 5517 Rugby Hwy, 37733. (Mail add: PO Box 8, 37733-0008), SAN 324-1378. Tel: 423-628-2441. FAX: 423-628-2266. E-mail: rugbytn@highland.net. Web Site: www.historicrugby.org. *Exec Dir,* Barbara Stagg
Founded 1881
Library Holdings: Bk Titles 7,000; Per Subs 1,010
Subject Interests: Biog, Etiquette, Poetry, Relig, Travel, Victorian-era hist
Restriction: Not a lending libr

RUTLEDGE

P   RUTLEDGE PUBLIC LIBRARY*, 8030 Rutledge Pk, 37861. (Mail add: PO Box 100, 37861-9804), SAN 361-008X. Tel: 865-828-4784. FAX: 865-828-4784. E-mail: rutlib@planetc.com. *Dir,* Gray Elizabeth
Founded 1946. Pop 16,751
Library Holdings: Bk Vols 35,000; Per Subs 12
Automation Activity & Vendor Info: (Cataloging) Book Systems, Inc; (Circulation) Book Systems, Inc; (OPAC) Book Systems, Inc
Open Mon, Wed & Fri 9-3, Tues & Thurs 1-7

SAVANNAH

P   HARDIN COUNTY LIBRARY, 1365 Pickwick St, 38372. SAN 315-9663. Tel: 731-925-4314, 731-925-6848. FAX: 731-925-7132. *Dir,* Jeanette K Smith; E-mail: jsmith_hardin1@bellsouth.net; *Asst Dir, Ref Serv,* Connie Lewis; E-mail: clewis_hardin1@bellsouth.net; *Circ Librn,* Shelia Alexander; E-mail: salexan_hardin1@bellsouth.net; *Ch,* Betty Stricklin; E-mail: bstrick_hardin1@bellsouth.net; *Tech Serv,* Debbie Brannon; E-mail: dbrannon_hardin1@bellsouth.net; Staff 9 (Non-MLS 9)
Founded 1935. Pop 26,000; Circ 159,191
Jul 2011-Jun 2012 Income $241,919, Federal $6,728, County $199,142, Locally Generated Income $20,711, Other $15,338. Mats Exp $12,520, Books $6,847, Per/Ser (Incl. Access Fees) $2,500, AV Mat $1,598, Electronic Ref Mat (Incl. Access Fees) $1,575. Sal $141,605 (Prof $32,165)
Library Holdings: Audiobooks 1,295; Bks on Deafness & Sign Lang 10; CDs 348; DVDs 1,253; e-books 1; Microforms 572; Bk Vols 39,158; Per Subs 77; Videos 495
Special Collections: Spanish Language Coll, bks, tapes. Oral History
Subject Interests: Local hist, Tenn hist
Automation Activity & Vendor Info: (Acquisitions) Auto-Graphics, Inc; (Cataloging) MITINET, Inc; (Circulation) Auto-Graphics, Inc; (Course Reserve) Auto-Graphics, Inc; (ILL) Auto-Graphics, Inc
Database Vendor: Gale Cengage Learning, Ingram Library Services, MITINET, Inc, ProQuest
Wireless access
Publications: Hardin County Library Newsletter (Monthly)
Mem of Hatchie River Regional Library

Open Mon, Tues & Thurs 9-8, Wed 9-12, Fri 9-5, Sat 9-1
Friends of the Library Group

SELMER

P JACK MCCONNICO MEMORIAL LIBRARY*, 225 Oak Grove Rd,
38375. SAN 315-9671. Tel: 731-645-5571. FAX: 731-645-4874. *Dir,*
Norma Humphries; E-mail: norma_jmc@bellsouth.net; *Librn,* Karan Lea
Taylor; Staff 3 (MLS 1, Non-MLS 2)
Founded 1984. Pop 22,422; Circ 56,861
Library Holdings: AV Mats 1,713; Bk Vols 37,881; Per Subs 44
Special Collections: Historic Old Purdy; Literacy, McNairy Co History;
McNairy Co; photo; Vietnam War; Wild Flower Coll
Subject Interests: Genealogy, State hist
Automation Activity & Vendor Info: (Circulation) Follett Software
Database Vendor: Gale Cengage Learning
Publications: Cemetery Records; Early Marriages; McNairy Co History
Mem of Hatchie River Regional Library
Open Mon & Fri 9-5, Tues & Thurs 9-9, Sat 9-1

SEVIERVILLE

P SEVIER COUNTY PUBLIC LIBRARY SYSTEM*, 321 Court Ave,
37862. SAN 315-968X. Tel: 865-453-3532. Administration Tel:
865-774-6033. FAX: 865-908-6108. Administration FAX: 865-774-6024.
Web Site: www.sevierlibrary.org. *Dir,* Kaurri C Williams; E-mail:
kwilliams@sevierlibrary.org; *Br Mgr, Coordr, Ch Serv,* Virginia Borrelli;
E-mail: gborrelli@sevierlibrary.org; Staff 19 (MLS 1, Non-MLS 18)
Founded 1922. Pop 66,000; Circ 146,288
Library Holdings: Bk Vols 70,112; Per Subs 177
Subject Interests: Genealogy
Automation Activity & Vendor Info: (Cataloging) Book Systems, Inc;
(Circulation) Book Systems, Inc; (OPAC) Book Systems, Inc; (Serials)
Book Systems, Inc
Database Vendor: Gale Cengage Learning, ProQuest, Wilson - Wilson
Web
Function: Homebound delivery serv, ILL available, Photocopying/Printing,
Prog for adults, Prog for children & young adult, Ref serv available,
Summer reading prog, Workshops
Open Mon & Thurs 9-7, Tues, Wed & Fri 9-6, Sat 9-4
Friends of the Library Group
Branches: 2
KODAK BRANCH, 319 W Dumplin Valley Rd, Kodak, 37764. Tel:
865-933-0078. FAX: 865-933-5888. *Br Mgr,* Kelly Hamilton; E-mail:
khamilton@sevierlibrary.org; Staff 3 (Non-MLS 3)
  Library Holdings: Bk Vols 16,000
  Open Mon & Thurs 10:30-7, Tues, Wed & Fri 10:30-6, Sat 10:30-4
  Friends of the Library Group
SEYMOUR BRANCH, 137 W Macon Lane, Seymour, 37865, SAN
320-0647. Tel: 865-573-0728. FAX: 865-573-0662. *Br Mgr, Coordr,
Outreach Serv,* Kelly Hamilton; E-mail: khamilton@sevierlibrary.org
  Library Holdings: Bk Titles 18,000
  Open Mon & Thurs 10:30-7, Tues, Wed & Fri 10:30-6, Sat 10:30-4
  Friends of the Library Group

SEWANEE

C UNIVERSITY OF THE SOUTH*, Jessie Ball DuPont Library, 735
University Ave, 37383-1000. SAN 361-0144. Tel: 931-598-1364.
Circulation Tel: 931-598-1664. Interlibrary Loan Service Tel:
931-598-1363. Reference Tel: 931-598-1368. Administration Tel:
931-598-1265. FAX: 931-598-1702. Web Site: library.sewanee.edu. *Assoc
Provost, Univ Librn,* Todd D Kelley; Tel: 931-598-1777; *Librn,* Vicki Sells;
E-mail: vsells@sewanee.edu; *Assoc Univ Librn,* Jim Dunkly; Tel:
931-598-1267, E-mail: jdunkly@sewanee.edu; *Asst Univ Librn,* Patricia
Thompson; Tel: 931-598-1657, E-mail: pthompso@sewanee.edu; *Asst Univ
Librn, Pub Serv,* Kevin Reynolds; Tel: 931-598-1366, E-mail:
kreynold@sewanee.edu; *Dir, Tech & Info Serv,* Penny Cowan; Tel:
931-598-1573, E-mail: pcowan@sewanee.edu; *Head, Acq, Head, Cat,*
Elizabeth Grant; Tel: 931-598-1663, E-mail: bgrant@sewanee.edu; *Head,
Circ,* Barbara Dykes; Tel: 931-598-1486, E-mail: bdykes@sewanee.edu;
Head, Ref, Kevin Reynolds; Tel: 931-598-1366, E-mail:
kreynold@sewanee.edu; *Head, Ser,* Joe David McBee; Tel: 931-598-1574,
E-mail: dmcbee@sewanee.edu; *Head, Spec Coll & Archives,* Annie
Armour; Tel: 931-598-3213, E-mail: aarmour@sewanee.edu; *Ref Serv,*
Mary O'Neill; Tel: 931-598-1660, E-mail: moneill@sewanee.edu; *Ref Serv,*
Heidi Syler; Tel: 931-598-1709, E-mail: hsyler@sewanee.edu; Staff 15
(MLS 9, Non-MLS 6)
Founded 1857. Enrl 1,415; Fac 137; Highest Degree: Doctorate
Library Holdings: Bk Vols 709,873; Per Subs 2,531
Special Collections: Allen Tate Coll; Anglican Prayer Book; Anglican
Studies; Ayres Architecture; Episcopal Church in Southeast History;
Hudson Stuck Coll; Limited Editions Club Publications; Sewaneena;
Southern Literature & History; Ward Ritchie Coll. US Document
Depository
Subject Interests: Liberal arts, Theol

Automation Activity & Vendor Info: (Acquisitions) Innovative Interfaces,
Inc; (Cataloging) Innovative Interfaces, Inc; (Circulation) Innovative
Interfaces, Inc; (Course Reserve) Innovative Interfaces, Inc; (ILL)
Innovative Interfaces, Inc; (Media Booking) Innovative Interfaces, Inc;
(OPAC) Innovative Interfaces, Inc; (Serials) Innovative Interfaces, Inc
Publications: Friends of the Library (Newsletter)
Partic in Appalachian Col Asn; Asn of Colleges of the South; Lyrasis;
OCLC Online Computer Library Center, Inc
Open Mon-Thurs 7:45am-1am, Fri 7:45am-9pm, Sat 9-6, Sun (Summer)
10am-1am
Friends of the Library Group

SHARON

P SHARON PUBLIC LIBRARY*, 133 E Main St, 38255. (Mail add: PO
Box 235, 38255-0235), SAN 315-9698. Tel: 731-456-2707. FAX:
731-456-2707. E-mail: sharonlibrary@frontiernet.net. *Dir,* Marlow E
Peters; Staff 1 (MLS 1)
Library Holdings: Bk Titles 5,000
Mem of Obion River Regional Library
Open Tues-Fri 9-4:45, Sat 9-12

SHELBYVILLE

P ARGIE COOPER PUBLIC LIBRARY*, 100 S Main St, 37160-3984. SAN
315-9701. Tel: 931-684-7323. FAX: 931-685-4848. Web Site:
www.acolibrary.com. *Dir,* Pat Hastings; E-mail: phastings@bellsouth.net;
Asst Dir, Youth Serv, Margaret Reed; E-mail: mlr617@bellsouth.net; *Spec
Serv,* Betty Fox; *Tech Serv,* Doris Segroves; E-mail: dorisjs@bellsouth.net
Founded 1966. Pop 27,916; Circ 89,000
Library Holdings: Bk Titles 36,000; Bk Vols 50,000; Per Subs 72
Special Collections: History (Early Editions of Newspapers in Bedford
County), micro
Automation Activity & Vendor Info: (Cataloging) Book Systems, Inc;
(Circulation) Book Systems, Inc; (OPAC) Book Systems, Inc
Database Vendor: LearningExpress, ProQuest
Mem of Stones River Regional Library
Open Mon, Tues & Thurs 9-8, Wed, Fri & Sat 9-5
Friends of the Library Group

SHILOH

S NATIONAL PARK SERVICE*, Shiloh National Military Park Study
Library, 1055 Pittsburg Landing Rd, 38376. SAN 315-971X. Tel:
731-689-5275. FAX: 731-689-5450. *Superintendent,* Haywood Harrell;
Chief of Operations, Stacey Allen; E-mail: stacy_allen@nps.gov
Founded 1895
Library Holdings: Bk Titles 1,752; Bk Vols 2,373
Subject Interests: Civil War
Open Mon-Fri 8-5, Sat & Sun 9-8

SIGNAL MOUNTAIN

P SIGNAL MOUNTAIN PUBLIC LIBRARY*, 1114 James Blvd,
37377-2509. SAN 371-7380. Tel: 423-886-7323. FAX: 423-886-3735. Web
Site: www.signalmtntown.org. *Dir,* Karin Glendenning; E-mail:
kglendenning@signalmtntown.org; *Asst Librn,* Dot Timmerman; Staff 5
(MLS 1, Non-MLS 4)
Founded 1970. Pop 7,500; Circ 60,000
Library Holdings: Large Print Bks 804; Bk Vols 22,154; Per Subs 17;
Talking Bks 742; Videos 1,000
Subject Interests: Local hist
Automation Activity & Vendor Info: (Cataloging) Follett Software;
(Circulation) Follett Software; (OPAC) Follett Software
Database Vendor: Gale Cengage Learning, Wilson - Wilson Web
Function: Home delivery & serv to Sr ctr & nursing homes, Homebound
delivery serv, Prog for children & young adult, Summer reading prog
Publications: Speaking Volumes (Bi-monthly)
Special Services for the Blind - Home delivery serv
Open Mon & Thurs 12-8, Tues & Wed 10-6, Sat 10-2
Friends of the Library Group

SMITHVILLE

P JUSTIN POTTER PUBLIC LIBRARY*, 101 S First St, 37166-1706. SAN
361-0209. Tel: 615-597-4359. FAX: 615-597-4329. *Dir,* Kathy Hendrixson
Pop 18,694; Circ 54,403
Jul 2008-Jun 2009 Income (Main Library and Branch(s)) $296,688, City
$500, Federal $2,500, County $138,905, Locally Generated Income
$35,829, Other $118,954. Mats Exp $40,871, Books $35,000, AV Mat
$5,871. Sal $79,967
Library Holdings: AV Mats 4,434; Microforms 556; Bk Vols 33,285; Per
Subs 99; Videos 2,865
Automation Activity & Vendor Info: (Cataloging) Book Systems, Inc;
(Circulation) Book Systems, Inc; (ILL) Book Systems, Inc
Wireless access

Function: Bks on cassette, Bks on CD, Children's prog, Computers for patron use, Copy machines, Holiday prog, ILL available, Music CDs, Notary serv, Photocopying/Printing, Prog for adults, Prog for children & young adult, Story hour, Summer reading prog, Tax forms, Teen prog, VHS videos, Wheelchair accessible
Mem of Falling Water River Regional Library
Open Mon-Wed & Fri 9-5:30, Thurs 9-8, Sat 9-12
Friends of the Library Group
Branches: 2
ALEXANDRIA BRANCH, 109 Public Sq, Alexandria, 37012-2141. (Mail add: PO Box 367, Alexandria, 37012-0367), SAN 361-0233. Tel: 615-529-4124. FAX: 615-529-4124. E-mail: alexlib@dtccom.net. *Br Mgr,* Marie Isles
  Automation Activity & Vendor Info: (Cataloging) Book Systems, Inc; (Circulation) Book Systems, Inc; (OPAC) Book Systems, Inc
  Open Mon-Wed 12-5, Fri 11-5, Sat 8-12
  Friends of the Library Group
LIBERTY BRANCH, PO Box 116, Liberty, 37095. Tel: 615-536-6116. *Br Mgr,* Lawrence Bean
  Open Mon, Wed & Fri 12-5, Sat 9-2

SNEEDVILLE

P HANCOCK COUNTY PUBLIC LIBRARY*, 138 Willow St, 37869. SAN 315-9736. Tel: 423-733-2020. E-mail: hcpl@discoveret.org. Web Site: www.discoveret.org/hcpl. *Dir,* Anita Hopkins
Pop 6,887
Library Holdings: Bk Vols 9,500
Automation Activity & Vendor Info: (Cataloging) Book Systems, Inc; (Circulation) Book Systems, Inc; (OPAC) Book Systems, Inc
Open Mon-Fri 9-5:30

SOMERVILLE

P SOMERVILLE-FAYETTE COUNTY LIBRARY*, 216 W Market St, 38068-1592. SAN 315-9744. Tel: 901-465-5248. FAX: 901-465-5271. Web Site: www.fayettetn.us/library.htm. *Dir,* Laura Winfrey; E-mail: llwinfrey@bellsouth.net; Staff 2 (Non-MLS 2)
Founded 1931. Circ 33,624
Library Holdings: AV Mats 1,064; Bk Titles 30,000; Per Subs 53
Special Collections: Genealogy (Tennessee Coll); Local History (Museum Room)
Automation Activity & Vendor Info: (Circulation) Follett Software
Open Mon-Wed, Fri & Sat 9-5, Thurs 12-8
Friends of the Library Group

SOUTH PITTSBURG

P BEENE-PEARSON PUBLIC LIBRARY*, 208 Elm Ave, 37380-1312. SAN 315-9752. Tel: 423-837-6513. FAX: 423-837-6612. *Dir,* Alicia Stuart; E-mail: astuart@tnii.net; *Asst Librn,* Wilbalene Crocker
Founded 1967. Circ 21,967
Library Holdings: Bk Titles 30,000; Per Subs 19
Open Mon, Wed & Fri 8:30-5, Tues 8-6, Sat 9-2

SPARTA

P WHITE COUNTY PUBLIC LIBRARY*, 11 N Church St, 38583-2299. SAN 315-9779. Tel: 931-836-3613. FAX: 931-836-2570. Web Site: www.wtclibrary.org. *Dir,* Cathy M Farley; E-mail: wcpldirector@frontiernet.net; Staff 4.75 (MLS 1, Non-MLS 3.75)
Founded 1957. Pop 24,039; Circ 65,000
Library Holdings: Bk Titles 23,700; Per Subs 42
Special Collections: Census for White County, micro 8
Automation Activity & Vendor Info: (Cataloging) Book Systems, Inc; (Circulation) Book Systems, Inc; (ILL) Auto-Graphics, Inc; (OPAC) Book Systems, Inc
Database Vendor: Gale Cengage Learning
Wireless access
Open Mon & Wed-Sat 8-5, Tues 8-8
Friends of the Library Group

SPENCER

P BURRITT MEMORIAL LIBRARY*, 427 College St, 38585-0314. (Mail add: PO Box 18, 38585-0018). Tel: 931-946-2575. FAX: 931-946-2575. *Dir,* Donna Beck; E-mail: dbeck1@blomand.net
Pop 4,994; Circ 12,962
Library Holdings: Bk Vols 9,000; Per Subs 18
Open Mon 8-4, Tues & Thurs 12-6, Wed & Fri 10-4

SPRING CITY

P AUDREY PACK MEMORIAL LIBRARY*, 169 W Rhea Ave, 37381. (Mail add: PO Box 382, 37381-0382), SAN 315-9795. Tel: 423-365-9757. FAX: 423-365-2198. *Dir,* Aliceann McCabe; E-mail: audpack@bellsouth.net
Library Holdings: Bk Vols 22,000; Per Subs 20
Automation Activity & Vendor Info: (Acquisitions) Follett Software; (Cataloging) Follett Software; (Circulation) Follett Software; (ILL) Follett Software
Mem of Ocoee River Regional Library
Open Mon, Wed & Fri 10-5, Tues & Thurs 10-7, Sat 10-3
Friends of the Library Group

SPRINGFIELD

P GORHAM-MACBANE PUBLIC LIBRARY*, 405 White St, 37172-2340. SAN 315-9809. Tel: 615-384-5123. FAX: 615-384-0106. E-mail: gorhampl@bellsouth.net. *Dir,* Mary Schmidt; E-mail: mmms1959@yahoo.com; *Ch,* Patricia Bellar
Founded 1923. Pop 44,000; Circ 165,000
Library Holdings: High Interest/Low Vocabulary Bk Vols 400; Bk Vols 45,000; Per Subs 64
Special Collections: Joseph Wellington Byrns Coll
Automation Activity & Vendor Info: (Acquisitions) Book Systems, Inc; (Cataloging) Book Systems, Inc; (Circulation) Book Systems, Inc; (OPAC) Book Systems, Inc; (Serials) Book Systems, Inc
Mem of Red River Regional Library
Open Mon, Wed, Fri & Sat 9-5, Tues & Thurs 9-8, Sun 2:30-5
Friends of the Library Group

STRAWBERRY PLAINS

P PARROTT-WOOD MEMORIAL LIBRARY*, 3133 W Old Andrew Johnson Hwy, 37871. (Mail add: PO Box 399, 37871), SAN 315-9817. Tel: 865-933-1311. FAX: 865-932-3718. *Dir,* Coneen H Ailey
Founded 1955. Pop 4,000; Circ 13,184
Library Holdings: Bk Titles 7,200; Bk Vols 8,500; Per Subs 30; Talking Bks 112
Automation Activity & Vendor Info: (Circulation) Follett Software; (ILL) Auto-Graphics, Inc; (OPAC) Follett Software
Open Mon-Thurs 12-6:30
Friends of the Library Group

SUNBRIGHT

P SUNBRIGHT PUBLIC LIBRARY*, 142 Melton Dr, 37872. SAN 315-9825. Tel: 423-628-2439. FAX: 423-628-2439. E-mail: sunbrightlib@highland.net. Web Site: www.korrnet.org/sunlibry. *Dir,* Lonetta Beshears; E-mail: sunbrightlib@highland.net; Staff 1 (MLS 1)
Circ 2,597
Library Holdings: AV Mats 158; Large Print Bks 250; Bk Vols 6,972; Talking Bks 50
Subject Interests: Civil War, Environ issues, Tenn hist, World War II
Open Mon-Thurs 4:30-6:30, Sat 9:30-1:30

SURGOINSVILLE

P SURGOINSVILLE PUBLIC LIBRARY*, 120 Old Stage Rd, 37873-3145. (Mail add: PO Box 115, 37873-0115), SAN 376-754X. Tel: 423-345-4805. FAX: 423-345-4825. E-mail: surlib@bellsouth.net. *Librn,* Melissa Montgomery
Library Holdings: Bk Titles 5,000; Per Subs 15
Automation Activity & Vendor Info: (Cataloging) Book Systems, Inc; (Circulation) Book Systems, Inc; (OPAC) Book Systems, Inc
Open Mon 10-6, Tues & Thurs 2-6, Wed & Fri 1-5

SWEETWATER

P SWEETWATER PUBLIC LIBRARY*, 210 Mayes Ave, 37874. SAN 315-9833. Tel: 423-337-5274. FAX: 423-337-0552. *Dir,* Beverly Bollenbacher; *Asst Dir,* Wanda Patterson
Library Holdings: AV Mats 556; Bk Vols 33,332; Per Subs 18
Subject Interests: Genealogy, Local hist
Mem of Ocoee River Regional Library
Friends of the Library Group

TAZEWELL

P CLAIBORNE COUNTY PUBLIC LIBRARY*, 1304 Old Knoxville Rd, 37879. (Mail add: PO Box 139, 37879-0139), SAN 315-9841. Tel: 423-626-5414. FAX: 423-626-9481. E-mail: cclibrary@netcommander.com. *Dir,* Sandy Rosenbalm
Pop 29,820
Library Holdings: Bk Vols 18,000; Per Subs 30
Open Mon-Fri 9-5, Sat 9-2

TELLICO PLAINS

P   TELLICO PLAINS PUBLIC LIBRARY, 209 Hwy 165, 37385. (Mail add: PO Box 658, 37385-0658), SAN 315-985X. Tel: 423-253-7388. FAX: 423-253-6274. E-mail: tplibrary@tds.net. *Libr Dir,* Alisandra Snyder; *Libr Dir,* Joy Turner; Staff 0.1 (MLS 0.1)
Founded 1992. Pop 6,000
Oct 2012-Sept 2013 Income $33,000, City $10,000, County $17,000, Locally Generated Income $6,000. Sal $21,000 (Prof $5,000)
Library Holdings: Audiobooks 75; DVDs 450; Large Print Bks 6,000; Bk Vols 18,000
Automation Activity & Vendor Info: (Cataloging) SirsiDynix; (Circulation) SirsiDynix; (ILL) SirsiDynix
Wireless access
Function: Accessibility serv available based on individual needs, Adult literacy prog, After school storytime, Archival coll, Art exhibits, Audiobks via web, AV serv, Bks on CD, Children's prog, Computer training, Computers for patron use, Copy machines, Digital talking bks, e-mail serv, E-Reserves, Fax serv, Free DVD rentals, Games & aids for the handicapped, Handicapped accessible, Holiday prog, ILL available, Instruction & testing, Large print keyboards, Music CDs, Online cat, Online ref, Outreach serv, OverDrive digital audio bks, Photocopying/Printing, Preschool outreach, Preschool reading prog, Prog for adults, Prog for children & young adult, Pub access computers, Ref & res, Ref serv in person, Scanner, Senior computer classes, Story hour, Summer reading prog, Tax forms, Telephone ref, Video lending libr, Wheelchair accessible
Mem of Ocoee River Regional Library
Open Mon-Wed & Fri 10-5, Thurs 10-7, Sat 10-2
Friends of the Library Group

TIPTONVILLE

P   TIPTONVILLE PUBLIC LIBRARY*, 126 Tipton St, 38079-1133. SAN 315-9868. Tel: 731-253-7391. FAX: 731-253-7391. E-mail: tipvle@bellsouth.net. *Dir,* Scarlett Algee
Founded 1940. Pop 3,000
Library Holdings: DVDs 36; Large Print Bks 300; Bk Vols 8,800; Per Subs 25; Videos 400
Open Mon-Fri 12:30-5
Friends of the Library Group

TOWNSEND

P   MARY E TIPPITT MEMORIAL LIBRARY*, 120 Tiger Dr, 37882-4032. Tel: 865-448-1441. FAX: 865-448-1875. E-mail: metmlib@yahoo.com. Web Site: www.discoveret.org/metmlib. *Dir,* Mary Newman; Staff 3 (MLS 1, Non-MLS 2)
Founded 1997. Pop 750; Circ 16,000
Library Holdings: Audiobooks 551; CDs 122; DVDs 239; Large Print Bks 564; Bk Titles 22,935; Bk Vols 23,272; Videos 613
Automation Activity & Vendor Info: (Acquisitions) Mandarin Library Automation; (Cataloging) Mandarin Library Automation; (Circulation) Mandarin Library Automation; (OPAC) Mandarin Library Automation
Function: Adult bk club, After school storytime, Art exhibits, Bks on cassette, Bks on CD, Children's prog, Computers for patron use, Copy machines, Electronic databases & coll, Exhibits, Fax serv, Free DVD rentals, Handicapped accessible, ILL available, Music CDs, Online cat, Photocopying/Printing, Prog for children & young adult, Pub access computers, Ref & res, Scanner, Spoken cassettes & CDs, Spoken cassettes & DVDs, Summer reading prog, Tax forms, VHS videos, Video lending libr, Wheelchair accessible
Open Mon & Tues 9-6, Wed 12-6, Thurs & Fri 9-5
Friends of the Library Group

TRACY CITY

P   TRACY CITY PUBLIC LIBRARY*, 217 Shook St, 37387-0277. SAN 315-9876. Tel: 931-592-9714. FAX: 931-592-9715. E-mail: tcpublib@blomand.net. *Dir,* Leslie Coppinger
Library Holdings: Bk Vols 2,300
Wireless access
Open Mon & Wed Noon-4:30, Fri 9-4
Friends of the Library Group

TRENTON

P   GIBSON COUNTY MEMORIAL LIBRARY*, 303 S High St, 38382-2027. SAN 315-9884. Tel: 731-855-1991. FAX: 731-855-1991. *Dir,* Connie G Bates; E-mail: conniebates@bellsouth.net; Staff 3 (Non-MLS 3)
Founded 1945. Pop 46,315
Library Holdings: Bk Vols 26,000; Per Subs 80; Talking Bks 600
Special Collections: Original County Records
Subject Interests: Formal educ support, Genealogical res, Popular mat
Automation Activity & Vendor Info: (Acquisitions) Follett Software; (Cataloging) Follett Software; (Circulation) Follett Software; (Course Reserve) Follett Software; (ILL) Follett Software; (Media Booking) Follett Software; (OPAC) Follett Software; (Serials) Follett Software
Mem of Obion River Regional Library
Open Mon 9-6, Tues-Fri 9-5, Sat (Jan-Oct) 10-1
Friends of the Library Group

TRIMBLE

P   HAMILTON PARKS PUBLIC LIBRARY*, 74 Parks Plaza, 38259-4106. SAN 376-7752. Tel: 731-297-3601. E-mail: trimblelibrary@hotmail.com. *Dir,* Neda Hinson
Library Holdings: Bk Vols 17,000
Open Tues & Thurs 9-5, Sat 9-1

TULLAHOMA

P   COFFEE COUNTY LANNOM MEMORIAL PUBLIC LIBRARY*, 312 N Collins St, 37388-3229. SAN 315-9906. Tel: 931-454-2404, 931-455-2460. FAX: 931-454-2300. Web Site: www.lannom.org. *Dir,* Susan Stovall; *Asst Dir,* Christie Brookhart
Founded 1947. Pop 21,864; Circ 171,061
Library Holdings: Bk Vols 70,000; Per Subs 106
Special Collections: Genealogy Coll
Subject Interests: Local hist
Automation Activity & Vendor Info: (Acquisitions) SirsiDynix; (Cataloging) SirsiDynix; (Circulation) SirsiDynix; (ILL) SirsiDynix; (Media Booking) SirsiDynix; (OPAC) SirsiDynix; (Serials) SirsiDynix
Mem of Stones River Regional Library
Open Mon, Tues & Thurs 9-9, Wed, Fri & Sat 9-5, Sun 1-5

J   MOTLOW STATE COMMUNITY COLLEGE LIBRARIES*, Clayton-Glass Library, Ledford Mill Rd, 37388. (Mail add: PO Box 8500, Lynchburg, 37352-8500), SAN 315-9914. Circulation Tel: 931-393-1670. Reference Tel: 931-393-1665. Administration Tel: 931-393-1663. Toll Free Tel: 800-654-4877, Ext 1670. FAX: 931-393-1516. TDD: 931-393-1621. E-mail: library@mscc.edu. Web Site: www.mscc.edu/library. *Dir of Libr,* Allen Stuart Gaetjens; E-mail: sgaetjens@mscc.edu; *Tech Serv Coordr,* Paula Standridge; Tel: 931-393-1669, E-mail: pstandridge@mscc.edu; *Circ,* Roger Merritt; E-mail: rmerritt@mscc.edu; *ILL,* Joyce Davenport Bateman; Tel: 931-393-1660, E-mail: jbateman@mscc.edu; *Ref Serv,* Zoe Rascoe; E-mail: zrascoe@mscc.edu; Staff 6 (MLS 2, Non-MLS 4)
Founded 1969. Enrl 5,000; Fac 200; Highest Degree: Associate
Jul 2009-Jun 2010 Income (Main Library and Branch(s)) $120,378. Mats Exp $106,605, Books $24,855, Per/Ser (Incl. Access Fees) $9,000, AV Mat $8,000, Electronic Ref Mat (Incl. Access Fees) $64,750. Sal $319,300 (Prof $148,472)
Library Holdings: e-books 56,000; Bk Vols 58,049; Per Subs 110
Special Collections: Oral History
Automation Activity & Vendor Info: (Cataloging) Innovative Interfaces, Inc - Millenium; (Circulation) Innovative Interfaces, Inc - Millenium; (Course Reserve) Innovative Interfaces, Inc - Millenium; (OPAC) Innovative Interfaces, Inc - Millenium; (Serials) Innovative Interfaces, Inc - Millenium
Database Vendor: EBSCO Information Services, Gale Cengage Learning, JSTOR, LexisNexis, netLibrary, OCLC ArticleFirst, SirsiDynix
Wireless access
Partic in Lyrasis; TBR Consortium
Special Services for the Deaf - TDD equip
Open Mon-Thurs (Winter) 7:30-9, Fri 7:30-4:30, Sun 1-5; Mon-Fri (Summer) 8-4:30
Departmental Libraries:
FAYETTEVILLE CENTER LIBRARY, 1802 Winchester Hwy, Fayetteville, 37334. (Mail add: PO Box 616, Fayetteville, 37334-0618), SAN 373-9201. Tel: 931-438-0028. FAX: 931-438-0619. Web Site: www.mscc.edu/library/faylib.html. *Br Coordr,* Debbie Logan; E-mail: dlogan@mscc.edu; Staff 1 (Non-MLS 1)
Highest Degree: Associate
Library Holdings: Bk Vols 3,500
MCMINNVILLE CENTER LIBRARY, 225 Cadillac Lane, McMinnville, 37110, SAN 373-921X. Tel: 931-815-2113. FAX: 931-668-2172. Web Site: www.mscc.edu/library/mcmlib.html. *Br Coordr,* Nancy Jones; E-mail: njones@mscc.edu; Staff 1 (Non-MLS 1)
Open Mon-Thurs (Fall & Spring) 8-7, Fri 8-2; Mon-Thurs (Summer) 8-4, Fri 8-1:30
SMYRNA CENTER LIBRARY, 5002 Motlow College Blvd, Smyrna, 37167. Tel: 615-220-7815. *Br Librn,* A Paige Hendrickson; E-mail: phendrickson@mscc.edu; Staff 1 (MLS 1)
Founded 2006
Library Holdings: Bk Vols 2,704
Automation Activity & Vendor Info: (ILL) OCLC
Open Mon-Thurs 8am-9pm, Fri 8-2, Sat 9-3, Sun 1-5

S   TENNESSEE CORRECTION ACADEMY LIBRARY*, 1314 S Jackson
St, 37388. (Mail add: Box 1510, 37388-1510), SAN 373-6113. Tel:
931-461-7693. FAX: 931-461-7757. *Librn,* Scott Ulm
Founded 1984
Library Holdings: Bk Vols 2,000
Special Collections: Corrections, bks, flm, policies. State Document
Depository
Open Mon-Thurs 7-4:30, Fri 7am-11:30am

C   UNIVERSITY OF TENNESSEE SPACE INSTITUTE LIBRARY*, Helen
& Arthur Mason Library, Library, MS-25, 411 B H Goethert Pkwy,
37388-9700. SAN 315-9922. Circulation Tel: 931-393-7315. Reference Tel:
931-393-7316. FAX: 931-393-7518. E-mail: library@utsi.edu. Web Site:
www.utsi.edu/library. *Libr Dir,* Emily S Moore; E-mail: emoore@utsi.edu;
ILL, Brenda Brooks; E-mail: bbrooks@utsi.edu; Staff 2 (MLS 1, Non-MLS
1)
Founded 1965. Enrl 238; Fac 27; Highest Degree: Doctorate
Jul 2010-Jun 2011. Mats Exp $41,100, Books $1,000, Per/Ser (Incl. Access
Fees) $5,000, Electronic Ref Mat (Incl. Access Fees) $35,000, Presv $100
Library Holdings: Bk Vols 25,000; Per Subs 158
Special Collections: Thomas Jefferson Coll
Subject Interests: Aviation, Computer sci, Eng, Eng mgt, Mat sci, Math,
Nanotechnologies, Physics
Automation Activity & Vendor Info: (ILL) OCLC FirstSearch
Wireless access
Partic in Lyrasis
Restriction: Open to students, fac & staff

UNION CITY

P   OBION COUNTY PUBLIC LIBRARY*, 1221 E Reelfoot Ave,
38261-5097. SAN 315-9930. Tel: 731-885-7000, 731-885-9411. FAX:
731-885-9638. Web Site: www.oclibrary.org. *Interim Dir,* Curt True;
E-mail: curt.true@oclibrary.org; *Educ Dir,* Angie Fitzgerald; E-mail:
angie.heitman@oclibrary.org; *Circ Mgr,* Karen White; E-mail:
karen.white@oclibrary.org; Staff 2 (MLS 1, Non-MLS 1)
Founded 1939. Pop 32,213; Circ 164,591
Jul 2006-Jun 2007 Income $558,338, City $152,339, County $304,677,
Locally Generated Income $101,322. Mats Exp $64,880, Books $46,800,
AV Equip $9,000. Sal $372,300 (Prof $104,741)
Library Holdings: AV Mats 2,642; Bk Titles 81,517; Per Subs 157
Special Collections: Oral History
Database Vendor: Alexander Street Press, Checkpoint Systems, Inc, Facts
on File, Gale Cengage Learning, ProQuest
Wireless access
Function: Ref serv available
Mem of Obion River Regional Library
Open Mon, Tues & Thurs 9-7:30, Wed 9-6, Fri 9-5, Sat 9-3:30
Friends of the Library Group

VONORE

P   VONORE PUBLIC LIBRARY*, 611 Church St, 37885-0308. SAN
373-6636. Tel: 423-884-6729. FAX: 423-884-6729. E-mail:
vonoreplibrary@tds.net. *Librn,* Reynelda Gentry
Founded 1978. Pop 3,000; Circ 10,750
Library Holdings: Bk Titles 9,500; Per Subs 14
Automation Activity & Vendor Info: (Acquisitions) SirsiDynix;
(Cataloging) SirsiDynix; (Circulation) SirsiDynix; (ILL) SirsiDynix
Mem of Ocoee River Regional Library
Open Tues, Wed & Fri 10-5, Thurs 10-6, Sat 10-3

WARTBURG

P   WARTBURG PUBLIC LIBRARY*, 514 Spring St, 37887. (Mail add: PO
Box 366, 37887-0366). Tel: 423-346-2479. FAX: 423-346-2479. E-mail:
wartburgpl@highland.net. *Dir,* Judy Williams
Library Holdings: AV Mats 87; Bk Vols 16,453; Videos 319
Open Mon, Wed & Fri 11-5:30, Tues & Thurs 10:15-5

WASHBURN

P   WASHBURN PUBLIC LIBRARY*, Hwy 131, 37888-9708. (Mail add: PO
Box 129, 37888-0129). Tel: 865-497-2506. FAX: 865-497-2506. E-mail:
washburnlib@planetc.com. *Librn,* Amanda Williams
Library Holdings: Bk Vols 5,300; Per Subs 15
Automation Activity & Vendor Info: (Acquisitions) Book Systems, Inc;
(Cataloging) Book Systems, Inc; (Circulation) Book Systems, Inc; (Course
Reserve) Book Systems, Inc
Open Mon, Wed & Fri 9-5

WAVERLY

P   HUMPHREYS COUNTY PUBLIC LIBRARY*, 201 Pavo Ave,
37185-1529. SAN 315-9957. Tel: 931-296-2143. FAX: 931-296-6520. *Dir,*
Ethel Carmical; E-mail: ethelcarmical@bellsouth.net
Pop 15,957
Library Holdings: Bk Vols 40,000; Per Subs 30
Automation Activity & Vendor Info: (Circulation) Book Systems, Inc;
(ILL) Auto-Graphics, Inc; (OPAC) Book Systems, Inc
Mem of Red River Regional Library
Open Mon-Fri 10-5
Friends of the Library Group

WAYNESBORO

P   WAYNE COUNTY PUBLIC LIBRARY*, Hwy 64 East, 38485. (Mail add:
PO Box 630, 38485-0630), SAN 315-9965. Tel: 931-722-5537. FAX:
931-722-5537. *Dir,* Katherine Motika Morris
Pop 16,800; Circ 56,642
Library Holdings: DVDs 350; Large Print Bks 550; Bk Vols 24,000; Per
Subs 43; Talking Bks 285; Videos 400
Automation Activity & Vendor Info: (Acquisitions) Book Systems, Inc;
(Cataloging) Book Systems, Inc; (Circulation) Book Systems, Inc
Open Mon-Fri 10-6, Sat 10-2
Branches: 2
CLIFTON BRANCH, 300 E Water St, Clifton, 38425-0501. Tel:
931-676-3678. FAX: 931-676-3678. E-mail: cliftonlibrary@tds.net. Web
Site: cityofclifton.com. *Mgr,* Sissy Pogue; E-mail: cliftonlibrary@tds.net;
Asst Librn, Elaine Chubb
Library Holdings: Bk Vols 2,000
Open Tues-Fri 10:30-5:30, Sat 10-2
COLLINWOOD DEPOT, 101 E Depot St, Collinwood, 38450. (Mail add:
PO Box 410, Collinwood, 38450-0410). Tel: 931-724-2498. FAX:
931-724-2498. E-mail: collinwoodlibrary@tds.net. Web Site:
cityofcollinwood.org. *Br Mgr,* Tammy West
Library Holdings: Bk Vols 6,000; Per Subs 13; Talking Bks 50; Videos
300
Open Tues-Fri 10:30-5:30, Sat 10-2

WESTMORELAND

P   WESTMORELAND PUBLIC LIBRARY*, 2305 Epperson Springs Rd,
37186. (Mail add: PO Box 685, 37186-0685), SAN 376-2939. Tel:
615-644-2026. FAX: 615-644-2026. *Dir,* Willie Ruth Borders
Library Holdings: Bk Vols 15,000; Per Subs 300
Automation Activity & Vendor Info: (Cataloging) Book Systems, Inc;
(Circulation) Book Systems, Inc; (OPAC) Book Systems, Inc
Open Mon 11-6, Tues & Wed 10-6, Fri 10-5, Sat 10-3
Friends of the Library Group

WHITE HOUSE

P   WHITE HOUSE INN LIBRARY & MUSEUM*, 412 Hwy 76, 37188.
SAN 376-3110. Tel: 615-672-0239. Web Site: www.cityofwhitehouse.com.
Dir, Judy Speight; E-mail: judyspeight@bellsouth.net; *Ch,* Sherry Tackett;
E-mail: sherrytackett@bellsouth.net
Founded 1987. Pop 12,667; Circ 54,400
Jul 2006-Jun 2007 Income $162,690
Library Holdings: Bks on Deafness & Sign Lang 25; CDs 310; DVDs
354; e-books 3,375; Large Print Bks 617; Bk Titles 16,657; Per Subs 39;
Talking Bks 516; Videos 1,051
Special Collections: Gardening (Lida Kirby Ragland Memorial Coll);
Home Improvement/Renovation (W A Ragland Memorial Coll); Louis
L'Amour Coll
Automation Activity & Vendor Info: (Cataloging) Auto-Graphics, Inc;
(Circulation) Book Systems, Inc; (ILL) Auto-Graphics, Inc; (OPAC) Book
Systems, Inc
Wireless access
Function: Adult bk club, Bks on cassette, Bks on CD, CD-ROM,
Children's prog, Computers for patron use, Copy machines, Fax serv, Free
DVD rentals, Handicapped accessible, ILL available, Music CDs, Prog for
adults, Prog for children & young adult, Summer reading prog, Tax forms,
Telephone ref, VHS videos, Wheelchair accessible
Mem of Red River Regional Library
Partic in Tenn Libr Asn
Special Services for the Deaf - Bks on deafness & sign lang; Closed
caption videos
Special Services for the Blind - Bks on cassette; Bks on CD; Large print
bks; Talking bks
Open Mon-Wed & Fri 10-5:30, Thurs 12-8, Sat 10-4
Restriction: Circ to mem only, In-house use for visitors

WHITE PINE

P   WHITE PINE PUBLIC LIBRARY*, 1708 Main St, 37890. SAN 315-9973.
Tel: 865-674-6313. FAX: 865-674-8511. *Dir,* Betty Jo Moore
Founded 1920. Pop 12,343; Circ 28,367
Library Holdings: Bk Vols 10,500; Per Subs 36
Subject Interests: Local hist
Automation Activity & Vendor Info: (Cataloging) Follett Software;
(Circulation) Follett Software; (ILL) Follett Software; (OPAC) Follett
Software
Open Mon, Wed & Thurs 8:30-5:30, Fri 9-3
Friends of the Library Group

WHITEVILLE

P   LEE OLA ROBERTS PUBLIC LIBRARY*, 140 W Main St, 38075. (Mail
add: PO Box 615, 38075-0615), SAN 315-9981. Tel: 731-254-8834. FAX:
731-254-8805. *Dir,* Brenda Pirtle; *Tech Serv,* Bill Wernet
Library Holdings: Bk Vols 8,500
Mem of Hatchie River Regional Library
Open Mon-Fri 9-12 & 12:30-5, Sat 10-2
Friends of the Library Group

WHITWELL

P   ORENA HUMPHREY PUBLIC LIBRARY*, 900 Main St, Ste 1,
37397-5249. SAN 315-999X. Tel: 423-658-6134. FAX: 423-658-7726. *Dir,*
Linda Powell; E-mail: lindapwl@bellsouth.net; *Asst Librn,* Linda Shirley
Founded 1959. Pop 7,400
Library Holdings: Bk Vols 14,500; Per Subs 50
Automation Activity & Vendor Info: (Acquisitions) Surpass; (Cataloging)
Surpass; (Circulation) Surpass
Open Mon 8:30-6:30, Tues & Wed 8:30-5, Fri 8:30-4:30, Sat 8:30-1:30

WINCHESTER

P   FRANKLIN COUNTY LIBRARY*, 105 S Porter St, 37398-1546. SAN
361-0268. Tel: 931-967-3706. FAX: 931-962-1477. *Dir,* Diane K Krauth;
E-mail: dianekrauth@bellsouth.net
Founded 1925. Pop 39,270
Library Holdings: Bk Vols 40,000
Subject Interests: Local genealogy, Local hist

Automation Activity & Vendor Info: (Cataloging) Auto-Graphics, Inc;
(Circulation) Book Systems, Inc; (ILL) Auto-Graphics, Inc
Mem of Stones River Regional Library
Open Mon, Wed, Fri & Sat 9-5, Tues & Thurs 9-8
Friends of the Library Group

WINFIELD

P   WINFIELD LIBRARY*, 24961 Scott Hwy, 37892. (Mail add: PO Box 38,
37892-0038), SAN 376-6845. Tel: 423-569-9047. FAX: 423-569-2569.
E-mail: towlib@highland.net. *Dir,* Darlene King
Library Holdings: Bk Vols 6,000
Open Tues 9:30-5:30, Wed 9:30-2:30, Thurs 10-6, Fri 10-2

WOODBURY

P   CANNON COUNTY LIBRARY SYSTEM*, Dr & Mrs J F Adams
Memorial Library, 212 College St, 37190. SAN 316-0009. Tel:
615-563-5861. FAX: 615-563-2140. E-mail: cannonlib@dtccom.net. *Dir,*
Rita M Allen; Staff 2.65 (MLS 0.8, Non-MLS 1.85)
Founded 1963. Pop 13,900
Library Holdings: Bk Vols 27,000
Subject Interests: County hist, Genealogy, Local hist
Automation Activity & Vendor Info: (Acquisitions) Book Systems, Inc;
(Cataloging) Book Systems, Inc; (OPAC) Book Systems, Inc
Wireless access
Mem of Stones River Regional Library
Special Services for the Deaf - Adult & family literacy prog; Bks on
deafness & sign lang; Closed caption videos; High interest/low vocabulary
bks; TTY equip
Special Services for the Blind - Magnifiers; Talking bks
Open Mon, Wed, Fri & Sat 9-4, Tues 9-8, Thurs 9-6
Friends of the Library Group
Branches: 1
ABURNTOWN BRANCH LIBRARY, 73 E Main St, Auburntown, 37016.
Tel: 615-464-2622. FAX: 615-464-2623. E-mail: cannonlib@dtccom.net.
Web Site: www.cannoncolibrary.org. *Dir,* Rita M Allen; *Br Mgr,* Patti
Chappell; Staff 0.575 (Non-MLS 0.575)
Library Holdings: AV Mats 100; Bk Vols 4,000; Per Subs 10
Mem of Stones River Regional Library
Open Mon, Wed & Fri 10-4

Date of Statistics: FY 2010
Population, 2009 (est): 24,782,302
Population Served by Public Libraries: 23,047,854
Total Volumes in Public Libraries: 46,911,133
Total Public Library Circulation: 119,019,073
Total Public Library Expenditures: $443,059,639
  Expenditures Per Capita: $19.22 (population served); $17.88
  (total population)
Number of Counties Served: 248
Number of Counties Unserved: 6
Number of Bookmobiles in State: 8
Appropriation for Statewide Library Development (FY 2012)
  State: $119,136
  Federal LSTA: $4,931,736
Appropriation for Library Resource Sharing and TexShare (FY 2012)
  State: $1,540,947
  Federal: $5,125,250 (including grants)
  Other: 2,000,000

ABERNATHY

P   ABERNATHY PUBLIC LIBRARY*, 811 Ave D, 79311-3400. (Mail add:
      PO Box 310, 79311-0310), SAN 316-0017. Tel: 806-298-4138. FAX:
      806-298-2968. E-mail: library@cityofabernathy.org. Web Site:
      wtls.tsl.state.tx.us/abernathy. *Librn,* Sharla Ann Middleton; Staff 0.5
      (Non-MLS 0.5)
      Founded 1951. Pop 3,413; Circ 4,169
      Oct 2010-Sept 2011. Mats Exp $5,445
      Library Holdings: Audiobooks 68; DVDs 280; Bk Titles 9,426; Videos
      184
      Automation Activity & Vendor Info: (Cataloging) Follett Software
      Wireless access
      Function: Bks on CD, Computers for patron use, Copy machines, e-mail
      & chat, Electronic databases & coll, Free DVD rentals, Handicapped
      accessible, ILL available, Online cat, Photocopying/Printing, VHS videos,
      Wheelchair accessible
      Mem of West Texas Library System
      Open Mon, Wed & Fri 9-12 & 1-5

ABILENE

C   ABILENE CHRISTIAN UNIVERSITY*, Margaret & Herman Brown
      Library, 221 Brown Library, ACU Box 29208, 79699-9208. SAN
      361-0322. Tel: 325-674-2344. Circulation Tel: 325-674-2316. Interlibrary
      Loan Service Tel: 325-674-2398. Reference Tel: 325-674-2941. FAX:
      325-674-2202. Web Site: www.acu.edu/library. *Dean of Libr,* Dr Mark
      Tucker; E-mail: mark.tucker@acu.edu; *Asst Dir,* Dr Mark McCallon;
      E-mail: mccallonm@acu.edu; *Head, Pub Serv,* Karen Hendrick; E-mail:
      hendrick@acu.edu; *Librn,* Craig Churchill; E-mail: churchillc@acu.edu;
      Cat, Jana Davis; E-mail: davisj@acu.edu; *Cat,* Gary Oliver; E-mail:
      oliverg@acu.edu; *Electronic Serv, Ser,* Melissa Johnson; E-mail:
      johnsonm@acu.edu; *Govt Doc,* Laura Baker; E-mail: bakerl@acu.edu; *ILL,*
      Ellen Schoenrock; E-mail: schoenrocke@acu.edu; *Ref,* Virginia Bailey;
      E-mail: baileyv@acu.edu; *Spec Coll & Archives Librn,* Carisse Berryhill;
      E-mail: carisse.berryhill@acu.edu. Subject Specialists: *Theol,* Craig
      Churchill; Staff 25 (MLS 11, Non-MLS 14)
      Founded 1906. Enrl 4,786; Fac 227; Highest Degree: Doctorate
      Library Holdings: AV Mats 65,213; Bks on Deafness & Sign Lang 395;
      CDs 1,942; e-books 33,760; e-journals 2,113; Electronic Media &
      Resources 500; Large Print Bks 33; Music Scores 3,360; Bk Titles
      200,949; Bk Vols 498,551; Per Subs 2,417; Talking Bks 19; Videos 3,500
      Special Collections: Austin Taylor Hymn Book Coll; Bibles; Burleson
      Congressional Papers; Church Historical & Archival Materials; Donner
      Library of Americanism; Herald of Truth Radio & Television Archives;
      Robbins Railroad Coll; Sewell Bible Library. Oral History; US Document
      Depository
      Subject Interests: Educ, Humanities, Relig studies
      Automation Activity & Vendor Info: (Acquisitions) SirsiDynix;
      (Cataloging) SirsiDynix; (Circulation) SirsiDynix; (Course Reserve)
      SirsiDynix; (OPAC) SirsiDynix; (Serials) SirsiDynix
      Database Vendor: OCLC FirstSearch, SirsiDynix

Wireless access
Function: Archival coll, AV serv, Distance learning, Doc delivery serv,
Govt ref serv, Handicapped accessible, ILL available, Magnifiers for
reading, Online searches, Photocopying/Printing, Ref serv available
Publications: Library Friends News (Newsletter); Restoration Serials Index
(Bibliographies)
Partic in Abilene Library Consortium; Llano Estacado Info Access
Network (LEIAN); OCLC Online Computer Library Center, Inc; Tex
Independent Cols & Univ Librs; TexSHARE - Texas State Library &
Archives Commission
Special Services for the Blind - Braille equip; Internet workstation with
adaptive software; Magnifiers; PC for handicapped; Reader equip; Scanner
for conversion & translation of mats; ZoomText magnification & reading
software
Open Mon-Thurs 8am-Midnight, Fri 8-5, Sat 10-5
Friends of the Library Group

P   ABILENE PUBLIC LIBRARY, 202 Cedar St, 79601-5793. SAN
      361-0357. Tel: 325-676-6025. Circulation Tel: 325-677-2474. Interlibrary
      Loan Service Tel: 325-437-4561. Administration Tel: 325-676-6328.
      Information Services Tel: 325-676-6021. Administration FAX:
      325-676-6024. Web Site: www.abilenetx.com/apl. *Head, Info Serv,* Janis
      Test; Tel: 325-676-6017, E-mail: janis.test@abilenetx.com; *Head, Tech
      Serv, ILL,* Janet Bailey; Tel: 352-676-6063, E-mail:
      janet.bailey@abilenetx.com; *City Librn,* Ricki V Brown; E-mail:
      ricki.brown@abilenetx.com; *Customer Serv Mgr,* Marie Noe; Tel:
      325-437-4537, E-mail: marie.noe@abilenetx.com; *Ref,* Dennis Miller; Tel:
      325-676-6026, E-mail: dennis.miller@abilenetx.com. Subject Specialists:
      Bus, Dennis Miller; Staff 35 (MLS 11, Non-MLS 24)
      Founded 1899. Pop 117,179; Circ 922,985
      Oct 2010-Sept 2011 Income (Main Library and Branch(s)) $2,447,680,
      State $19,580, City $2,427,350, Other $750. Mats Exp $436,676, Books
      $314,325, AV Mat $47,201, Electronic Ref Mat (Incl. Access Fees)
      $75,150. Sal $1,403,451
      Library Holdings: CDs 13,515; DVDs 25,080; e-books 685; Bk Titles
      175,790; Bk Vols 274,832; Per Subs 156
      Special Collections: West Texas Digital Archives. Oral History
      Subject Interests: Genealogy
      Automation Activity & Vendor Info: (Acquisitions) SIRSI WorkFlows;
      (Cataloging) OCLC; (Circulation) SIRSI WorkFlows; (ILL) OCLC;
      (OPAC) SIRSI-iBistro; (Serials) SIRSI WorkFlows
      Database Vendor: Baker & Taylor, CQ Press, EBSCOhost, Evanced
      Solutions, Inc, Facts on File, Gale Cengage Learning, Greenwood
      Publishing Group, Hoovers, Newsbank, OCLC FirstSearch, OCLC
      WorldCat, Overdrive, Inc, ProQuest, SirsiDynix, Tech Logic, ValueLine
      Wireless access
      Partic in Abilene Library Consortium
      Special Services for the Blind - Accessible computers; Assistive/Adapted
      tech devices, equip & products; Bks on CD; Computer with voice
      synthesizer for visually impaired persons; Large print bks; Large screen
      computer & software; Screen enlargement software for people with visual
      disabilities

Open Mon, Tues & Thurs 9-9, Wed, Fri & Sat 9-6
Friends of the Library Group
Branches: 2
MOCKINGBIRD BRANCH, 1214 N Mockingbird, 79603. Tel:
325-437-7323. Administration Tel: 325-437-2665. *Br Mgr,* Anne Ellis;
E-mail: anne.ellis@abilenetx.com; *Ch,* Darla Casella; E-mail:
darla.casella@abilenetx.com; Staff 2 (MLS 2)
Founded 2009. Circ 135,626
Function: Bk club(s), Bks on CD, Children's prog, Computer training,
Computers for patron use, Copy machines, Free DVD rentals,
Handicapped accessible, ILL available, Large print keyboards, Online
cat, Online searches, OverDrive digital audio bks, Preschool outreach,
Prog for adults, Prog for children & young adult, Pub access computers,
Story hour, Summer reading prog, Tax forms, Teen prog, Wheelchair
accessible
SOUTH BRANCH LIBRARY, 1401 S Danville, 79605, SAN 371-3024.
Tel: 325-698-7565. FAX: 325-698-7621. *Br Mgr,* Tremain Jackson; Tel:
325-698-7378, E-mail: tremain.jackson@abilenetx.com; *Ch,* Alysa Crow;
E-mail: alysa.crow@abilenetx.com; Staff 6 (MLS 2, Non-MLS 4)
Founded 1998
Friends of the Library Group

P   BIG COUNTRY LIBRARY SYSTEM*, 202 Cedar St, 79601-5793. SAN
316-0033. Tel: 325-676-6021. Interlibrary Loan Service Tel: 325-676-6023.
Toll Free Tel: 800-588-2311 (Texas only). FAX: 325-676-6028. Toll Free
FAX: 800-588-8322 (Texas only). Web Site: www.bclstx.org. *Coordr,* John
Pecoraro; E-mail: john.pecoraro@abilenetx.com; *Asst Coordr,* Terri
Blackwell; Tel: 325-676-6022, E-mail: terri.blackwell@abilenetx.com; Staff
4 (MLS 1, Non-MLS 3)
Founded 1970. Pop 443,971
Database Vendor: SirsiDynix
Wireless access
Function: ILL available, Libr develop, Workshops
Publications: Horizons (Newsletter)
Member Libraries: Abilene Public Library; Breckenridge Library;
Callahan County Library; City County Library of Munday; Coke County
Library; Coleman Public Library; Comanche Public Library; Crockett
County Public Library; Cross Plains Public Library; De Leon City County
Library; Eden Public Library; Haskell County Library; Irion County
Library; Ranger City Library; Rotan Public Library; Scurry County
Library; Shackelford County Library; Stamford Carnegie Library; Sterling
County Public Library; Stonewall County Library; Sutton County Library;
Sweetwater County-City Library; The Depot Public Library; Winters Public
Library
Partic in Tex Share; Texas Navigator Group
Open Mon-Fri 8-5

R   CRESCENT HEIGHTS BAPTIST CHURCH LIBRARY*, 1902 N
Mockingbird Lane, 79603. SAN 316-0041. Tel: 325-677-3749. E-mail:
chbc1902@aol.com. *Asst Librn,* Dwanna Nichols
Founded 1959
Library Holdings: Bk Vols 2,460
Open Mon-Thurs 9-12 & 1-4, Fri 9-12, Sun 10:45-12:30

C   HARDIN-SIMMONS UNIVERSITY, Richardson Library, 2341 Hickory
St, 79698. (Mail add: PO Box 16195, 79698-6195), SAN 316-0068. Tel:
325-670-1236. Circulation Tel: 325-670-1578. Interlibrary Loan Service
Tel: 325-670-1244. Reference Tel: 325-671-2151. Administration Tel:
325-670-1230. FAX: 325-677-8351. Web Site: rupert.alc.org/library. *Dean,*
Alice Specht; Tel: 325-670-1229; *Assoc Dir, Ref,* Elizabeth Worley; Tel:
325-670-1237; *Theological Librn,* Teresa Ellis; *Cat, Tech Serv,* Belinda
Norvell; *Govt Doc, Per,* Ellen Simmons; *ILL,* Leta Tillman; *Media Spec,*
Gary Stephenson; *Music,* Dr James Floyd; Staff 17 (MLS 7, Non-MLS 10)
Founded 1892. Enrl 2,200; Fac 148; Highest Degree: Doctorate
Jun 2010-May 2011 Income $1,300,000. Mats Exp $352,000. Sal $493,000
(Prof $322,000)
Library Holdings: CDs 5,022; DVDs 1,216; e-books 27,498; e-journals
41,404; Music Scores 7,710; Bk Titles 209,914; Per Subs 450; Videos
2,500
Special Collections: Local Historical Photography Archives; Printing of
Carl Hertzog; Southwest History Coll, bks, micro; Texana Coll. Oral
History; US Document Depository
Subject Interests: Educ, English, Environ, Music, Theol
Automation Activity & Vendor Info: (Acquisitions) SirsiDynix;
(Cataloging) SirsiDynix; (Circulation) SirsiDynix; (Course Reserve)
SirsiDynix; (ILL) SirsiDynix; (OPAC) SirsiDynix; (Serials) SirsiDynix
Database Vendor: EBSCOhost, LexisNexis, OCLC FirstSearch, ProQuest
Wireless access
Publications: Friends of the Richardson Library Imprint
Partic in Abilene Library Consortium; Llano Estacado Info Access
Network (LEIAN); OCLC Online Computer Library Center, Inc;
TexSHARE - Texas State Library & Archives Commission
Open Mon-Thurs 7:30am-Midnight, Fri 7:30-5, Sat 1-5, Sun 3-Midnight
Friends of the Library Group

M   HENDRICK MEDICAL CENTER*, Sellers Health Sciences Library, 1900
Pine St, 79601. SAN 327-6821. Tel: 325-670-2375. FAX: 325-670-2422.
Web Site: www.ehendrick.org/sellers/index.htm. *Coordr,* Jean Snodgrass
Library Holdings: AV Mats 1,000; Bk Titles 1,200
Automation Activity & Vendor Info: (Acquisitions) Follett Software;
(Cataloging) Follett Software; (Circulation) Follett Software; (Course
Reserve) Follett Software; (ILL) Follett Software; (Media Booking) Follett
Software; (OPAC) Follett Software; (Serials) Follett Software
Database Vendor: EBSCOhost
Partic in Medical Library Association (MLA)
Open Mon-Fri 8:30-11:30 & 12:30-4:30

C   MCMURRY UNIVERSITY*, Jay-Rollins Library, Sayles Blvd & S 14th,
79605. (Mail add: One McMurry University, Box 218, 79697-0218), SAN
316-0084. Tel: 325-793-4692. FAX: 325-793-4930. Web Site:
www.mcm.edu/academic/depts/library/libraryhome.htm. *Dir,* Terry S
Young; Tel: 325-793-4690, E-mail: tyoung@mcm.edu; *ILL/Ref Librn,* Dr
Keith Waddle; Tel: 325-793-4683, E-mail: waddle.keith@mcm.edu; *Acq,*
Lynn Roberts; *Cat,* Nancy F Shanafelt; Staff 3 (MLS 3)
Founded 1923. Enrl 1,411; Fac 90; Highest Degree: Bachelor
Library Holdings: Bk Titles 128,602; Bk Vols 171,838; Per Subs 240
Special Collections: E L & A W Yeats Coll; Hunt Library of Texana &
Southwest
Subject Interests: 20th Century Am popular culture, 20th Century British,
African-Am studies, Am, Relig studies, Spanish-Am lit
Automation Activity & Vendor Info: (Acquisitions) SirsiDynix;
(Cataloging) SirsiDynix; (Circulation) SirsiDynix; (Course Reserve)
SirsiDynix; (OPAC) SirsiDynix; (Serials) SirsiDynix
Database Vendor: Agricola, American Chemical Society, Cinahl
Information Systems, CQ Press, EBSCO Information Services,
EBSCOhost, Gale Cengage Learning, LexisNexis, Newsbank, OCLC
FirstSearch, OCLC WorldCat, ProQuest, SirsiDynix, WT Cox
Wireless access
Partic in Abilene Library Consortium; Llano Estacado Info Access
Network (LEIAN); OCLC Online Computer Library Center, Inc
Open Mon-Thurs 7:30am-11pm, Fri 7:30-5, Sun 3-11
Friends of the Library Group

ADDISON

S   MARY KAY INC*, Information Resources, 16251 Dallas Pkwy, 75001.
SAN 324-3613. Tel: 972-687-6300. FAX: 972-687-1613. Web Site:
www.marykay.com. *Mgr,* Cecilia Armas; Staff 4 (MLS 3, Non-MLS 1)
Founded 1976
Library Holdings: Bk Vols 500; Per Subs 120
Subject Interests: Cosmetics, Dermatology, Direct selling, Mkt, Skin care
Automation Activity & Vendor Info: (Acquisitions) Inmagic, Inc.;
(Cataloging) Inmagic, Inc.; (Circulation) Inmagic, Inc.; (OPAC) Inmagic,
Inc.; (Serials) Inmagic, Inc.
Wireless access
Restriction: Staff use only

ALAMO

P   SARGEANT FERNANDO DE LA ROSA MEMORIAL LIBRARY*, 416
N Tower Rd, 78516-2317. SAN 322-7529. Tel: 956-787-6160. FAX:
956-787-5154. Web Site: www.alamo.lib.tx.us. *Dir,* Victoria Gonzalez;
E-mail: victoria@alamo.lib.tx.us; Staff 1 (Non-MLS 1)
Founded 1980
Library Holdings: Bk Titles 27,000; Bk Vols 28,000; Per Subs 54
Wireless access
Mem of Hidalgo County Library System
Special Services for the Deaf - Bks on deafness & sign lang
Open Mon-Thurs 9-9, Fri 9-5
Friends of the Library Group

ALBANY

S   THE OLD JAIL ART CENTER*, Green Art Research Library, 201 S
Second St, 76430. Tel: 325-762-2269. FAX: 325-762-2260. E-mail:
archivist@theoldjailartcenter.org. Web Site: www.theoldjailartcenter.org.
Archivist, Librn, Molly Sauder
Library Holdings: Bk Vols 2,500
Wireless access
Partic in Abilene Library Consortium
Open Tues-Sat 10-5, Sun 2-5
Restriction: Non-circulating

P   SHACKELFORD COUNTY LIBRARY*, 402 N Second St, 76430. (Mail
add: PO Box 2167, 76430-0445), SAN 316-0092. Tel: 325-762-2672. FAX:
325-762-2672. E-mail: albanypubliclibrary@hotmail.com. *Dir,* Linda
Adams; *Acq, Librn,* Carolyn Waller
Founded 1956. Pop 3,915
Library Holdings: Bk Vols 8,200; Talking Bks 300

Automation Activity & Vendor Info: (Cataloging) Follett Software; (Circulation) Follett Software
Mem of Big Country Library System
Open Mon-Fri 11:30-5:30

ALEDO

P   EAST PARKER COUNTY LIBRARY*, 201 FM 1187 N, 76008. SAN 372-5847. Tel: 817-441-6545. FAX: 817-441-5787. E-mail: info@epclibrary.com, libdirector@epclibrary.com. Web Site: www.epclibrary.com. *Dir,* Leslie Walstrom; *Librn,* Anita Bond; *Librn,* Julie Howell
Founded 1988. Pop 17,500
Library Holdings: Bk Titles 1,800
Special Collections: Parker County History Coll, bks
Wireless access
Mem of North Texas Library Partners
Open Tues-Fri 10-6, Sat 11-3
Friends of the Library Group

ALICE

P   ALICIA SALINAS CITY OF ALICE PUBLIC LIBRARY*, 401 E Third St, 78332. SAN 361-0446. Tel: 361-664-9506. FAX: 361-668-3248. Web Site: www.youseemore.com/alice/default.asp. *Dir,* Position Currently Open; *Cat,* Noemi Garza
Founded 1932. Pop 34,000; Circ 259,000
Library Holdings: Bk Vols 99,000; Per Subs 175
Subject Interests: Spanish lang, Tex hist
Automation Activity & Vendor Info: (Acquisitions) TLC (The Library Corporation); (Cataloging) TLC (The Library Corporation); (Circulation) TLC (The Library Corporation); (OPAC) TLC (The Library Corporation); (Serials) TLC (The Library Corporation)
Wireless access
Open Mon, Wed, Fri & Sat 9-6, Tues & Thurs 9-8
Friends of the Library Group
Branches: 2
    ORANGE GROVE SCHOOL & PUBLIC LIBRARY, PO Box 534, Orange Grove, 78372, SAN 361-0470. Tel: 361-384-2330, Ext 505, 361-384-2461. *Librn,* Lisa Jurecek
    Library Holdings: Bk Vols 26,000
    Open Mon-Fri 8:30-4
    PREMONT PUBLIC LIBRARY, 115 S Agnes St, Premont, 78375. (Mail add: PO Box 829, Premont, 78375-0829), SAN 361-0500. Tel: 361-348-3815. *Br Mgr,* Mona Wilson; Staff 1 (MLS 1)
    Library Holdings: Bk Titles 3,200
    Open Mon & Wed 1-6, Tues, Thurs & Fri 1-5
    Friends of the Library Group

ALLEN

P   ALLEN PUBLIC LIBRARY*, 300 N Allen Dr, 75013. SAN 316-0106. Tel: 214-509-4900. Reference Tel: 214-509-4905. FAX: 214-509-4950. Web Site: www.allenlibrary.org. *Dir,* Jeff Timbs; E-mail: jtimbs@cityofallen.org; Staff 11 (MLS 11)
Founded 1967. Pop 79,000; Circ 509,400
Oct 2005-Sept 2006 Income $1,780,777, State $10,166, City $1,731,611, County $33,000, Locally Generated Income $6,000. Mats Exp $211,810, Books $146,000, Per/Ser (Incl. Access Fees) $28,000, AV Mat $20,910, Electronic Ref Mat (Incl. Access Fees) $16,900. Sal $1,043,168
Library Holdings: AV Mats 11,171; Bk Titles 121,000; Bk Vols 123,600; Per Subs 150
Automation Activity & Vendor Info: (Acquisitions) SirsiDynix; (Cataloging) SirsiDynix; (Circulation) SirsiDynix; (OPAC) SirsiDynix; (Serials) SirsiDynix
Open Mon-Thurs 10-9, Fri & Sat 10-6, Sun 1-5
Friends of the Library Group

ALPINE

P   ALPINE PUBLIC LIBRARY*, 203 N Seventh St, 79830. SAN 361-0535. Tel: 432-837-2621. FAX: 432-837-2501. E-mail: alpinepl@sbcglobal.net. Web Site: alpinepubliclibrary.org. *Dir,* Paige Delaney; *Ch Serv Librn,* Mary Beth Garrett; E-mail: aplkids@sbcglobal.net
Founded 1947. Pop 7,780; Circ 51,907
Library Holdings: Bk Titles 30,000; Bk Vols 50,000
Special Collections: Genealogical Coll
Subject Interests: World War II
Wireless access
Mem of Texas Trans-Pecos Regional Library System
Open Mon-Fri 9:30-5:30, Sat 10-1
Friends of the Library Group

Branches: 1
    MARATHON PUBLIC, 106 N Third St E, Marathon, 79842. (Mail add: PO Box 177, Marathon, 79842-0177), SAN 361-056X. Tel: 432-386-4136. FAX: 432-386-4136. E-mail: marathonpl@sbcglobal.net. *Br Mgr,* Carol Townsend
    Library Holdings: Bk Titles 8,000
    Automation Activity & Vendor Info: (Cataloging) Biblionix; (Circulation) Biblionix
    Open Mon-Fri 11-5
    Friends of the Library Group

C   SUL ROSS STATE UNIVERSITY*, Bryan Wildenthal Memorial Library, PO Box C-109, 79832-0001. SAN 316-0114. Tel: 432-837-8123. FAX: 432-837-8400. Web Site: www.sulross.edu/library. *Dean,* Don Dowdey; E-mail: ddowdey@sulross.edu; *Dir of Tech Serv,* Ross Burns; *Access Serv,* Andrea Cancellare; E-mail: acancellare@sulross.edu; *Bibliog Instr,* Renee Goodvin; *ILL,* Linda Epps; Staff 18 (MLS 7, Non-MLS 11)
Founded 1920. Enrl 2,274; Fac 136; Highest Degree: Master
Library Holdings: Bk Vols 221,000; Per Subs 1,245
Special Collections: Archives of the Big Bend. State Document Depository
Subject Interests: Big Bend region of Tex
Automation Activity & Vendor Info: (Acquisitions) SirsiDynix
Wireless access
Partic in OCLC Online Computer Library Center, Inc; TexSHARE - Texas State Library & Archives Commission
Open Mon-Thurs 8am-9pm, Fri 8-5, Sat & Sun 12-9

ALTO

P   STELLA HILL MEMORIAL LIBRARY*, 158 W San Antonio St, 75925. (Mail add: PO Box 98, 75925-0098), SAN 316-0122. Tel: 936-858-4343. E-mail: altolibrary@gmail.com. *Dir,* Virginia Singletary; *Librn,* Joyce Hopkins
Founded 1957. Pop 1,045; Circ 4,500
Library Holdings: Bk Vols 13,000
Special Collections: Local Hist (incl negatives)
Wireless access
Open Tues & Thurs 1-5 (9-1 Summer), Sat 9-1

ALVARADO

P   ALVARADO PUBLIC LIBRARY*, 210 N Baugh St, 76009. SAN 370-5064. Tel: 817-783-7323. FAX: 817-783-7323. E-mail: librarydirector@sbcglobal.net. Web Site: www.alvaradopubliclibrary.org. *Dir,* Leanna Cowan; Staff 3 (Non-MLS 3)
Founded 1989. Pop 4,289
Library Holdings: Audiobooks 670; Bks on Deafness & Sign Lang 11; CDs 447; DVDs 1,287; Large Print Bks 176; Microforms 64; Bk Titles 25,456; Bk Vols 25,882; Per Subs 15; Videos 1,862
Automation Activity & Vendor Info: (Cataloging) Evergreen; (Circulation) Evergreen; (OPAC) Evergreen
Mem of North Texas Library Partners
Open Mon-Fri 10-7, Sat 10-1

ALVIN

J   ALVIN COMMUNITY COLLEGE LIBRARY*, 3110 Mustang Rd, 77511. SAN 316-0130. Tel: 281-756-3559. Circulation Tel: 281-756-3562. Reference Tel: 281-756-3561. FAX: 281-756-3854. Web Site: library.alvincollege.edu. *Dir,* Tom Bates; E-mail: tbates@alvincollege.edu. Subject Specialists: *Criticism, Lit,* Tom Bates; Staff 2 (MLS 2)
Founded 1948. Enrl 3,800; Fac 102; Highest Degree: Associate
Library Holdings: Bk Titles 12,100; Bk Vols 26,000; Per Subs 43; Spec Interest Per Sub 23
Automation Activity & Vendor Info: (Cataloging) SirsiDynix; (Circulation) SirsiDynix; (Course Reserve) SirsiDynix; (OPAC) SirsiDynix; (Serials) SirsiDynix
Database Vendor: Gale Cengage Learning, Westlaw
Wireless access
Partic in TexSHARE - Texas State Library & Archives Commission
Special Services for the Deaf - TDD equip
Special Services for the Blind - Computer with voice synthesizer for visually impaired persons
Open Mon-Thurs (Fall & Spring) 7:30am-9pm, Fri 7:30-5, Sun 2-6; Mon-Thurs (Summer) 7:30am-9pm
Restriction: Open to students

ALVORD

P   ALVORD PUBLIC LIBRARY*, 117 N Wickham St, 76225-5325. (Mail add: PO Box 323, 76225-0323), SAN 376-4699. Tel: 940-427-2842. FAX: 940-427-2948. E-mail: alvordpl@hotmail.com. Web Site: www.orgsites.com/tx/alvordpubliclibrary. *Libr Dir,* Randy Dunaway; Staff 1 (Non-MLS 1)
Founded 1982. Pop 4,028; Circ 5,317

Library Holdings: Audiobooks 517; AV Mats 2,366; DVDs 615; Bk Vols 15,643; Per Subs 17; Videos 1,104
Special Collections: Antiques & Collectibles Books & Price Guides; Local History & Genealogy Coll; Texas Non-Fiction & Biography Books Coll
Automation Activity & Vendor Info: (Acquisitions) LRMS, Inc (Library Resource Management Systems); (Cataloging) LRMS, Inc (Library Resource Management Systems); (Circulation) LRMS, Inc (Library Resource Management Systems); (Course Reserve) LRMS, Inc (Library Resource Management Systems); (ILL) LRMS, Inc (Library Resource Management Systems); (Media Booking) LRMS, Inc (Library Resource Management Systems); (OPAC) LRMS, Inc (Library Resource Management Systems); (Serials) LRMS, Inc (Library Resource Management Systems)
Database Vendor: EBSCOhost, Gale Cengage Learning, netLibrary, OCLC WorldCat, ProQuest
Mem of North Texas Library Partners
Partic in TexSHARE - Texas State Library & Archives Commission
Open Wed-Fri 9-5, Sat 9-12

AMARILLO

J   AMARILLO COLLEGE LIBRARY*, 2201 S Washington, 79109. (Mail add: PO Box 447, 79178-0001), SAN 361-0594. Tel: 806-371-5400. Toll Free Tel: 866-371-5468. FAX: 806-371-5470. E-mail: library-help@actx.edu. Web Site: www.actx.edu/library. *Dir,* Mark Hanna; *Acq,* Barbara Sherrill; *Bibliog Instr,* Jana Comerford; *Circ,* Marian Daniels; *ILL,* Nan Kemp; *Libr Instr, Outreach Prog,* Khaki Hoover; *Pub Serv,* Lil Withrow; *Tech Serv,* Karen F McIntosh; Staff 10 (MLS 6, Non-MLS 4)
Founded 1929. Enrl 9,229; Fac 581; Highest Degree: Associate
Library Holdings: e-books 28,000; Bk Vols 40,000
Automation Activity & Vendor Info: (Acquisitions) SirsiDynix; (Cataloging) SirsiDynix; (Circulation) SirsiDynix; (Course Reserve) SirsiDynix; (OPAC) SirsiDynix; (Serials) SirsiDynix
Database Vendor: OCLC FirstSearch, SirsiDynix
Wireless access
Partic in Harrington Library Consortium; Llano Estacado Info Access Network (LEIAN); TexSHARE - Texas State Library & Archives Commission
Open Mon-Fri 7:30am-9pm, Sun 2-6

S   AMARILLO GLOBE-NEWS LIBRARY*, 900 Harrison, 79166-2091. SAN 316-0157. Tel: 806-376-4488, Ext 3331. FAX: 806-373-0810. Web Site: amarillo.com. *Librn,* Rita Leatherman; Tel: 806-345-3331
Library Holdings: Bk Vols 200
Special Collections: Archives, microfilm, newsps
Restriction: Not open to pub

S   AMARILLO MUSEUM OF ART*, 2200 S Van Buren St, 79109-2407. (Mail add: PO Box 447, 79178), SAN 316-0149. Tel: 806-371-5050. FAX: 806-373-9235. E-mail: amoa@actx.edu. Web Site: www.amarilloart.org. *Dir of Develop,* Kay Kennedy
Founded 1972
Library Holdings: Bk Vols 527
Subject Interests: Archit, Art
Open Tues-Fri 10-5, Sat & Sun 1-5
Restriction: Open to pub for ref only

P   AMARILLO PUBLIC LIBRARY*, 413 E Fourth Ave, 79101. (Mail add: PO Box 2171, 79105-2171), SAN 361-0659. Tel: 806-378-3054. Interlibrary Loan Service Tel: 806-378-3053. FAX: 806-378-9327. TDD: 806-378-9328. Web Site: www.amarillolibrary.org. *Dir,* Donna Littlejohn; Tel: 806-378-3050, E-mail: donna.littlejohn@amarillolibrary.org; *Asst Dir,* Amanda Barrera; Tel: 806-378-9330, E-mail: amanda.barrera@amarillolibrary.org; *Spec Coll Librn,* Robert Groman; E-mail: rob.groman@amarillolibrary.org; *Acq,* Terri Jolly; E-mail: terri.jolly@amarillolibrary.org; *AV,* Sam Jones; E-mail: sam.jones@amarillolibrary.org; *Cat,* Marian Cole; E-mail: marian.cole@amarillolibrary.org; *Circ,* Jennifer Myers; E-mail: jennifer.myers@amarillolibrary.org; *ILL,* Joan Morris; E-mail: joan.morris@amarillolibrary.org; *Ref,* Judith Sample; E-mail: judith.sample@amarillolibrary.org; *Tech Serv,* John Titus; Tel: 806-378-9331, E-mail: john.titus@amarillolibrary.org; Staff 71 (MLS 11, Non-MLS 60)
Founded 1902. Pop 179,287; Circ 2,030,752
Library Holdings: Bk Titles 632,473; Bk Vols 768,319; Per Subs 227
Special Collections: Southwestern History (William H Bush & Laurence J Fitzsimon Coll), bks, maps. State Document Depository
Subject Interests: Genealogy
Automation Activity & Vendor Info: (Acquisitions) SirsiDynix; (Cataloging) SirsiDynix; (Circulation) SirsiDynix; (Course Reserve) SirsiDynix; (ILL) SirsiDynix; (OPAC) SirsiDynix; (Serials) SirsiDynix
Database Vendor: Gale Cengage Learning, OCLC FirstSearch, SirsiDynix
Wireless access

Function: AV serv, Handicapped accessible, ILL available, Music CDs, Prog for adults, Prog for children & young adult, Ref serv available, Spoken cassettes & CDs, Summer reading prog, Wheelchair accessible
Publications: Bibliography of the Bush-FitzSimon-McCarty Southwestern Collections
Partic in Harrington Library Consortium; OCLC Online Computer Library Center, Inc
Special Services for the Deaf - TTY equip
Open Mon-Thurs 9-9, Fri & Sat 9-6, Sun 2-6
Restriction: Non-resident fee
Friends of the Library Group
Branches: 4
EAST BRANCH, 2232 E 27th St, 79103, SAN 361-0683. Tel: 806-342-1589. FAX: 806-342-1591. *Librn,* Cindy Dockery
   Library Holdings: Bk Vols 121,181
   Open Mon & Tues 12-9, Wed-Fri 9-6, Sun 2-6
   Friends of the Library Group
NORTH BRANCH, 1500 NE 24th St, 79107, SAN 361-0713. Tel: 806-381-7931. FAX: 806-381-7929. *Br Mgr,* Zetta Riles
   Library Holdings: Bk Vols 129,811
   Subject Interests: Genealogy
   Open Mon & Tues 12-9, Wed-Fri 9-6, Sun 2-6
   Friends of the Library Group
NORTHWEST BRANCH, 6100 W Ninth, 79106-0700. Tel: 806-359-2035. FAX: 806-359-2037. *Br Mgr,* Sam Jones
   Library Holdings: Bk Vols 212,000
   Open Mon & Tues Noon-9, Wed-Sat 9-6, Sun 2-6
   Friends of the Library Group
SOUTHWEST BRANCH, 6801 W 45th St, 79109, SAN 361-0748. Tel: 806-359-2094. FAX: 806-359-2096. *Br Mgr,* Valisa McHugh
   Library Holdings: e-books 2,368; Bk Vols 547,646
   Subject Interests: Genealogy
   Open Mon-Thurs 9-9, Fri & Sat 9-6, Sun 2-6
   Friends of the Library Group

R   DIOCESE OF AMARILLO*, Diocesan Archives, 1800 N Spring St, 79107. (Mail add: PO Box 5644, 79117-5644), SAN 372-9605. Tel: 806-383-2243, Ext 120. Toll Free Tel: 800-658-6643. FAX: 806-383-8452. Web Site: www.amarillodiocese.org. *Archivist,* Susan Garner; E-mail: sgarner@amarillodiocese.org
Founded 1926
Library Holdings: Bk Titles 50; Bk Vols 1,107; Spec Interest Per Sub 3
Special Collections: Catholic Church History, Panhandle of Texas; Diocese of Amarillo Bishop's Colls; Genealogy; Official Catholic Directory, 1925-present
Subject Interests: Catholic studies, Relig
Wireless access
Function: Archival coll
Restriction: Open by appt only, Open to researchers by request
Friends of the Library Group

L   POTTER COUNTY LAW LIBRARY*, 501 S Filmore, Ste 2B, 79101. SAN 327-8042. Tel: 806-379-2347. *Librn,* Susan Montgomery
Library Holdings: Bk Vols 50,000
Open Mon-Fri 8-4:30

M   TEXAS TECH UNIVERSITY HEALTH SCIENCES CENTER AT AMARILLO*, Harrington Library, 1400 Wallace Blvd, 79106. SAN 371-6996. Tel: 806-354-5448. FAX: 806-354-5430. Web Site: www.ttuhsc.edu/libraries. *Assoc Dir,* Cheryl Simonsen; E-mail: cheryl.simonsen@ttuhsc.edu; *Asst Dir,* Terri Wilson; Staff 6 (MLS 3, Non-MLS 3)
Founded 1977
Library Holdings: AV Mats 3,500; e-journals 24,000; Bk Titles 15,259; Per Subs 40
Database Vendor: EBSCOhost, Elsevier, netLibrary, OVID Technologies, RefWorks, Wiley
Wireless access
Partic in Tex Share; US National Library of Medicine
Open Mon-Thurs 7:30am-11pm, Fri 7:30am-8pm, Sat 9-5, Sun 2-10
Friends of the Library Group

ANAHUAC

P   CHAMBERS COUNTY LIBRARY SYSTEM*, 202 Cummings St, 77514. (Mail add: PO Box 520, 77514-0520), SAN 361-0772. Tel: 409-267-8261. FAX: 409-267-3783. E-mail: ccls@co.chambers.tx.us. Web Site: www.chambers.lib.tx.us. *County Librn,* Valerie Jensen; E-mail: vjensen@co.chambers.tx.us; Staff 2 (MLS 2)
Founded 1950. Pop 24,167; Circ 159,768
Jan 2011-Dec 2011 Income (Main Library and Branch(s)) $438,609. Mats Exp $56,139, Books $42,622, Per/Ser (Incl. Access Fees) $2,278, Micro $184, AV Mat $8,660, Electronic Ref Mat (Incl. Access Fees) $800. Sal $353,897 (Prof $44,355)

Library Holdings: Bk Titles 80,145; Bk Vols 103,373; Per Subs 104; Videos 4,177
Subject Interests: Chambers County hist, Texana
Automation Activity & Vendor Info: (Cataloging) Follett Software; (Circulation) Follett Software; (ILL) OCLC ILLiad; (OPAC) Follett Software; (Serials) Follett Software
Wireless access
Open Mon-Fri 8-5
Friends of the Library Group
Branches: 3
CHAMBERS COUNTY LIBRARY, 202 Cummings St, 77514. (Mail add: PO Box 520, 77514-0520). Tel: 409-267-2554. FAX: 409-267-5181. *County Librn,* Valerie Jensen; E-mail: vjensen@co.chambers.tx.us; Staff 13 (MLS 2, Non-MLS 11)
Founded 1950
Automation Activity & Vendor Info: (Cataloging) Auto-Graphics, Inc; (Circulation) Auto-Graphics, Inc; (Course Reserve) Auto-Graphics, Inc
Open Mon-Fri 8-5, Sat & Sun 9-1
Friends of the Library Group
JUANITA HARGRAVES MEMORIAL BRANCH, 924 Hwy 124, Winnie, 77665. (Mail add: PO Box 597, Winnie, 77665-0597), SAN 361-0802. Tel: 409-296-8245. FAX: 409-296-8243. *Br Librn,* Scott Crawford; E-mail: scrawford@co.chambers.tx.us; Staff 3 (Non-MLS 3)
Open Mon, Wed & Fri 8-5, Tues & Thurs 10-7, Sat 9-1
Friends of the Library Group
WEST CHAMBERS BRANCH, 10616 Eagle Dr, Mont Belvieu, 77580-1289. (Mail add: PO Box 1289, 77514-0520), SAN 361-0829. Tel: 281-576-2245, 409-576-2550. FAX: 281-576-2496. *Br Mgr,* Adrienne Cain; E-mail: acain@co.chambers.tx.us; Staff 3 (Non-MLS 3)
Open Mon-Fri 8-5, Sat & Sun 9-1
Friends of the Library Group

ANDREWS

P   ANDREWS COUNTY LIBRARY, 109 NW First St, 79714. SAN 316-0254. Tel: 432-523-9819. FAX: 432-523-4570. Web Site: www.andrews.lib.tx.us. *Dir,* Liz Stottlemyre; E-mail: lstottlemyre@andrews.lib.tx.us; *Asst Dir,* Sarah Pando; Staff 7 (MLS 2, Non-MLS 5)
Founded 1950. Pop 13,025; Circ 84,550
Library Holdings: Bk Vols 67,325; Per Subs 80
Automation Activity & Vendor Info: (Acquisitions) Biblionix; (Cataloging) Biblionix; (Circulation) Biblionix; (OPAC) Biblionix
Database Vendor: Baker & Taylor, Brodart, BWI, EBSCOhost, Ingram Library Services, OCLC FirstSearch
Function: Adult literacy prog, Handicapped accessible, Home delivery & serv to Sr ctr & nursing homes, Homebound delivery serv, ILL available, Photocopying/Printing, Prog for children & young adult, Summer reading prog
Mem of West Texas Library System
Special Services for the Deaf - Bks on deafness & sign lang
Special Services for the Blind - Bks on CD; Large print bks
Open Mon-Thurs 9-8, Fri 9-6, Sat 10-3
Friends of the Library Group

ANGLETON

L   BRAZORIA COUNTY LAW LIBRARY*, 111 E Locust St, Ste 315-A, 77515. SAN 372-1914. Tel: 979-864-1225. FAX: 979-864-1226. *Dir,* Angela Wollam; E-mail: angelaw@brazoria-county.com
Library Holdings: Bk Vols 10,000; Per Subs 20
Database Vendor: LexisNexis, Westlaw
Wireless access
Open Mon-Fri 8-5

P   BRAZORIA COUNTY LIBRARY SYSTEM, 451 N Velasco, Ste 250, 77515. (Mail add: Bldg 29-A, Ste 250, 111 E Locust St, 77515-4642), SAN 361-0837. Tel: 979-864-1505. FAX: 979-864-1298. E-mail: bcls@bcls.lib.tx.us. Web Site: bcls.lib.tx.us. *Dir,* Catherine H Threadgill; Tel: 979-864-1509, E-mail: cthreadg@bcls.lib.tx.us; *Asst Dir,* Lisa Marie Loranc; Tel: 979-864-1510, E-mail: lloranc@bcls.lib.tx.us; *Adult Coordr,* Thomas West; Tel: 979-864-1507, E-mail: twest@bcls.lib.tx.us; *Children's Coordr,* Sara Joiner; Tel: 979-864-1826, E-mail: sjoiner@bcls.lib.tx.us; *Tech Serv,* Sylvia Drake; Tel: 979-864-1544, Fax: 979-864-1273, E-mail: sdrake@bcls.lib.tx.us; Staff 28 (MLS 15, Non-MLS 13)
Founded 1941. Pop 319,973; Circ 1,460,912
Oct 2010-Sept 2011 Income (Main Library and Branch(s)) $6,079,534, State $57,494, City $555,804, County $5,038,575, Locally Generated Income $427,661. Mats Exp $923,487, Books $855,233, AV Mat $68,254. Sal $4,094,907
Library Holdings: Audiobooks 24,036; AV Mats 179; DVDs 20,901; e-books 388; e-journals 2; Bk Titles 181,363; Bk Vols 527,358; Per Subs 838
Special Collections: Brazoria County History Coll; State History (Texana Coll)

Subject Interests: Genealogy
Automation Activity & Vendor Info: (Acquisitions) Polaris Library Systems; (Cataloging) Polaris Library Systems; (Circulation) Polaris Library Systems; (ILL) Polaris Library Systems; (OPAC) Polaris Library Systems; (Serials) Polaris Library Systems
Database Vendor: ALLDATA Online, Baker & Taylor, Brodart, BWI, EBSCOhost, Facts on File, Gale Cengage Learning, H W Wilson, infoUSA, Ingram Library Services, LearningExpress, netLibrary, OCLC FirstSearch, OCLC WorldCat, Overdrive, Inc, Polaris Library Systems, ProQuest, ReferenceUSA, World Book Online, WT Cox
Wireless access
Function: Accelerated reader prog, Adult bk club, Audiobks via web, AV serv, Bilingual assistance for Spanish patrons, Bk club(s), Bks on CD, CD-ROM, Children's prog, Computer training, Computers for patron use, Copy machines, Digital talking bks, Electronic databases & coll, Exhibits, Fax serv, Free DVD rentals, Handicapped accessible, Holiday prog, Homework prog, ILL available, Microfiche/film & reading machines, Online cat, Online ref, Online searches, Outside serv via phone, mail, e-mail & web, OverDrive digital audio bks, Photocopying/Printing, Preschool outreach, Preschool reading prog, Prog for adults, Prog for children & young adult, Ref serv available, Ref serv in person, Scanner, Senior computer classes, Spanish lang bks, Spoken cassettes & CDs, Spoken cassettes & DVDs, Story hour, Summer reading prog, Tax forms, Teen prog, Telephone ref, VHS videos, Web-catalog, Wheelchair accessible
Publications: Library Newsletter; Union List of Periodicals
Friends of the Library Group
Branches: 11
ALVIN BRANCH, 105 S Gordon, Alvin, 77511, SAN 361-0896. Tel: 281-388-4300. FAX: 281-388-4305. E-mail: alvin@bcls.lib.tx.us. *Br Head,* Danna Kay Wilson; Tel: 281-388-4301, E-mail: dawilson@bcls.lib.tx.us; Staff 2 (MLS 1, Non-MLS 1)
Open Mon, Wed & Fri 10-6, Tues & Thurs 10-8, Sat 10-5
Friends of the Library Group
ANGLETON BRANCH, 401 E Cedar St, 77515-4652, SAN 361-0861. Tel: 979-864-1519. Information Services Tel: 979-864-1520. FAX: 979-864-1518. E-mail: angleton@bcls.lib.tx.us. *Br Head,* Layna L Lewis; E-mail: layna@bcls.lib.tx.us; *Asst Br Librn, Ref Librn,* Mrs Stephanie Carter; Tel: 979-864-1513, E-mail: stephaniec@bcls.lib.tx.us; *Ch,* Emma Lou O'Bannon; Staff 3 (MLS 2, Non-MLS 1)
Open Mon & Tues 9-8, Wed-Sat 9-6
Friends of the Library Group
BRAZORIA BRANCH, 620 S Brooks, Brazoria, 77422-9022. (Mail add: PO Drawer 1550, Brazoria, 77422-1550), SAN 361-0926. Tel: 979-798-2372. FAX: 979-798-4013. *Br Mgr,* Jo Conway; E-mail: jconway@bcls.lib.tx.us; *Ch,* Allison Percival; E-mail: apercival@bcls.lib.tx.us; Staff 2 (Non-MLS 2)
Open Mon & Wed 10-6, Tues & Thurs 10-8, Sat 10-5
Friends of the Library Group
CLUTE BRANCH, 215 N Shanks, Clute, 77531-4122, SAN 361-0950. Tel: 979-265-4582. FAX: 979-265-8496. *Br Mgr,* Carolyn Weatherly; E-mail: cweather@bcls.lib.tx.us; Staff 1 (Non-MLS 1)
Open Mon & Wed 10-6, Tues & Thurs 10-8, Sat 10-5
Friends of the Library Group
DANBURY BRANCH, 1702 N Main St, Danbury, 77534. (Mail add: PO Box 159, Danbury, 77534-0159). Tel: 979-922-1905. FAX: 979-922-1905. E-mail: danbury@bcls.lib.tx.us. Web Site: bcls.lib.tx.us. *Br Mgr,* Kandy Taylor-Hille; E-mail: kandyt@bcls.lib.tx.us; Staff 1 (Non-MLS 1)
Automation Activity & Vendor Info: (OPAC) Polaris Library Systems
Open Tues & Thurs 1-8, Wed & Fri 10-6, Sat 10-5
FREEPORT BRANCH, 410 Brazosport Blvd, Freeport, 77541, SAN 361-0985. Tel: 979-233-3622. FAX: 979-233-4300. *Br Librn,* Cindy Yell; E-mail: cindyy@bcls.lib.tx.us; *Ch,* Rebecca Watts; Staff 2 (MLS 1, Non-MLS 1)
Open Mon & Wed 10-6, Tues & Thurs 10-8, Sat 10-5
Friends of the Library Group
LAKE JACKSON BRANCH, 250 Circle Way, Lake Jackson, 77566, SAN 361-1019. Tel: 979-415-2590. FAX: 979-415-2993. *Br Head,* Nancy Hackney; E-mail: nhackney@bcls.lib.tx.us; *Asst Br Librn, Ref Librn,* Susan Wheeler; E-mail: susanw@bcls.lib.tx.us; *Ch,* Michelle Delgado; E-mail: michelled@bcls.lib.tx.us; Staff 3 (MLS 3)
Library Holdings: Bk Vols 96,040
Database Vendor: Polaris Library Systems
Open Mon, Wed & Thurs 10-8, Tues & Fri 10-6, Sat 10-5
Friends of the Library Group
MANVEL BRANCH, 20514B Hwy 6, Manvel, 77578, SAN 361-1027. Tel: 281-489-7596. FAX: 281-489-7596. *Br Mgr,* Melissa Neibuhr; E-mail: mneibuhr@bcls.lib.tx.us; *Ch,* Geri Swanzy; E-mail: gswanzy@bcls.lib.tx.us; Staff 2 (MLS 1, Non-MLS 1)
Open Mon & Wed 10-6, Tues & Thurs 1-8, Sat 10-5
Friends of the Library Group
PEARLAND BRANCH, 3522 Liberty Dr, Pearland, 77581, SAN 361-1043. Tel: 281-485-4876. FAX: 281-485-5576. E-mail: pearland@bcls.lib.tx.us. *Br Librn,* Andrew Fearn; E-mail:

afearn@bcls.lib.tx.us; *Asst Br Librn/Ref,* Kristen Stewart; *Ch,* Jennifer Trusty; Staff 3 (MLS 3)
Open Mon-Wed 10-9, Thurs-Sat 10-6
Friends of the Library Group
SWEENY BRANCH, 205 W Ashley-Wilson Rd, Sweeny, 77480, SAN 361-1078. Tel: 979-548-2567. FAX: 979-548-2597. E-mail: sweeny@bcls.lib.tx.us. *Br Mgr,* Leslie Smith; E-mail: leslies@bcls.lib.tx.us; Staff 1 (Non-MLS 1)
Open Tues & Thurs 10-8, Wed & Fri 10-6, Sat 10-5
Friends of the Library Group
WEST COLUMBIA BRANCH, 518 E Brazos, West Columbia, 77486, SAN 361-1108. Tel: 979-345-3394. FAX: 979-345-3652. E-mail: west@bcls.lib.tx.us. *Br Mgr,* Melissa Fichera; E-mail: mfichera@bcls.lib.tx.us; Staff 1 (Non-MLS 1)
Open Mon & Wed 10-8, Tues & Thurs 10-6, Sat 10-5
Friends of the Library Group

ANSON

P   ANSON PUBLIC LIBRARY*, 1137 12th St, 79501. SAN 316-0262. Tel: 325-823-2711. FAX: 325-823-2711. E-mail: aplibrary@hotmail.com. *Librn,* Durell Wilson
Founded 1962. Pop 2,615; Circ 5,716
Library Holdings: Bk Vols 13,800
Automation Activity & Vendor Info: (Cataloging) LibLime; (Circulation) LibLime; (OPAC) LibLime
Wireless access
Open Mon-Thurs 10-5
Friends of the Library Group

ARANSAS PASS

P   ED & HAZEL RICHMOND PUBLIC LIBRARY*, 110 N Lamont St, 78336-3698. SAN 316-0270. Tel: 361-758-2350. *Librn,* James McCoy
Founded 1943. Pop 11,092; Circ 15,847
Library Holdings: Bk Titles 17,103; Bk Vols 17,319; Per Subs 10
Subject Interests: Texana
Automation Activity & Vendor Info: (Cataloging) Follett Software; (Circulation) Follett Software; (OPAC) Follett Software
Wireless access
Mem of San Patricio County Library System
Open Mon, Tues, Thurs & Fri 8:30-5, Wed 8:30-7, Sat 11-3
Friends of the Library Group

ARCHER CITY

P   ARCHER PUBLIC LIBRARY, 105 N Center, 76351. (Mail add: PO Box 1574, 76351-1574), SAN 316-0289. Tel: 940-574-4954. *Dir,* Cheryl Beesinger
Founded 1968. Pop 9,274; Circ 23,827
Library Holdings: Bk Vols 16,300
Automation Activity & Vendor Info: (Acquisitions) Book Systems, Inc; (Cataloging) Book Systems, Inc; (Circulation) Book Systems, Inc; (Course Reserve) Book Systems, Inc; (OPAC) Book Systems, Inc; (Serials) Book Systems, Inc
Wireless access
Mem of North Texas Library Partners
Open Mon-Wed & Fri 9-5:30, Thurs 1-9

ARLINGTON

C   ARLINGTON BAPTIST COLLEGE*, Earl K Oldham Library, 3001 W Division, 76012-3425. SAN 316-0300. Tel: 817-461-8741, Ext 127. FAX: 817-274-1138. E-mail: abclibrary@abconline.org. Web Site: www.abconline.edu. *Dir,* Jill Botticelli; *Asst Librn,* Amy Schaeffer; Staff 3 (MLS 1, Non-MLS 2)
Founded 1939. Enrl 250; Fac 20; Highest Degree: Doctorate
Library Holdings: AV Mats 812; Bk Vols 31,000; Per Subs 280
Subject Interests: Music, Relig studies
Automation Activity & Vendor Info: (Cataloging) Follett Software; (Circulation) Follett Software; (OPAC) Follett Software
Wireless access
Open Mon, Tues & Thurs (Fall & Spring) 7am-9pm, Wed & Fri 7-4; Mon-Thurs (Summer) 7-4, Fri 8-4

P   ARLINGTON PUBLIC LIBRARY SYSTEM*, George W Hawkes Central Library, 101 E Abram St, MS 10-0100, 76010-1183. SAN 361-1132. Tel: 817-459-6900. Interlibrary Loan Service Tel: 817-459-6905. Administration Tel: 817-459-6903, 817-459-6961. Automation Services Tel: 817-459-6909, 817-459-6917. Information Services Tel: 817-459-6926. FAX: 817-459-6936. Interlibrary Loan Service FAX: 817-459-6917. Administration FAX: 817-459-6902. Web Site: www.arlingtonlibrary.org. *Dir,* Cary Siegfried; Tel: 817-459-6916, Fax: 817-459-6902, E-mail: cary.siegfried@arlington.gov; *Early Childhood Librn,* Laureen Jacobs; *Teen Librn,* Jenny Ethington; *User Experience Librn,* Mark Dellenbaugh; *Libr Serv Mgr,* Marc Marchand; *Libr Serv Mgr,* Debi Wood; *Youth Serv Mgr,*

Sharon Granado; *Admin Serv Coordr,* Lee Shgeir; *Adminr,* Christopher Brown; Tel: 817-459-6914, E-mail: christopher.brown@.arlington.gov; *Adminr, Info Tech,* Saralyn Shone; Tel: 817-459-6922, E-mail: shones@pub-lib.ci.arlington.tx.us; *Adminr,* Norma Zuniga; *Circ,* James Pool; Tel: 817-459-6910, E-mail: poolj@pub-lib.ci.arlington.tx.us; Staff 89 (MLS 14, Non-MLS 75)
Founded 1923. Pop 353,597; Circ 500,689
Oct 2006-Sept 2007. Mats Exp $843,866, Books $591,408, Per/Ser (Incl. Access Fees) $50,195, AV Mat $118,683, Electronic Ref Mat (Incl. Access Fees) $83,580
Library Holdings: AV Mats 46,102; Bks on Deafness & Sign Lang 32; Large Print Bks 8,157; Bk Titles 237,334; Bk Vols 570,029; Per Subs 842; Talking Bks 14,154
Special Collections: US Document Depository
Subject Interests: Careers, Deaf, Foreign lang, Genealogy, Hearing impaired, Texana
Automation Activity & Vendor Info: (Acquisitions) Polaris Library Systems; (Cataloging) Polaris Library Systems; (Circulation) Polaris Library Systems; (OPAC) Polaris Library Systems
Database Vendor: EBSCOhost, Gale Cengage Learning, LearningExpress, Newsbank, ReferenceUSA, TDNet
Function: Govt ref serv, ILL available, Large print keyboards, Magnifiers for reading, Photocopying/Printing, Prog for children & young adult, Ref serv available, Res libr, Summer reading prog, Telephone ref, Wheelchair accessible
Mem of North Texas Library Partners
Partic in Tex Share
Special Services for the Deaf - Assistive tech; Bks on deafness & sign lang; Deaf publ
Special Services for the Blind - Assistive/Adapted tech devices, equip & products; Audio mat; Bks on CD; Closed circuit TV; Closed circuit TV magnifier; Computer with voice synthesizer for visually impaired persons; Large print bks; Large screen computer & software; Magnifiers; PC for handicapped; Reader equip; Screen enlargement software for people with visual disabilities; Talking bks; Videos on blindness & phys handicaps
Open Mon-Thurs 9-9, Fri & Sat 9-6, Sun (Sept-May) 2-6
Friends of the Library Group
Branches: 6
EAST ARLINGTON, 1624 New York Ave, 76010-4795, SAN 361-1191. Tel: 817-275-3321. FAX: 817-795-0726. *Br Mgr,* Marc Marchand; Tel: 817-459-6792, E-mail: marchandm@ci.arlington.tx.us; Staff 9 (MLS 3, Non-MLS 6)
Founded 1970. Pop 353,597; Circ 220,934
Library Holdings: AV Mats 7,107; Large Print Bks 29; Bk Titles 52,710; Bk Vols 61,856; Per Subs 86
Special Collections: Children's Learning Center Coll; GED/ESL; Multicultural Coll
Function: ILL available, Magnifiers for reading, Photocopying/Printing, Prog for children & young adult, Ref serv available, Summer reading prog, Wheelchair accessible
Open Mon-Thurs 10-8, Fri & Sat 10-5
Friends of the Library Group
LAKE ARLINGTON, 4000 W Green Oaks Blvd, 76016-4442, SAN 328-7289. Tel: 817-478-3762. FAX: 817-561-9823. *Br Mgr, Pub Serv Coordr,* Shana Fry; *Ch,* Dawn Reyes; Staff 11 (MLS 3, Non-MLS 8)
Founded 1986. Pop 353,597; Circ 500,689
Library Holdings: AV Mats 7,621; Large Print Bks 287; Bk Titles 58,972; Bk Vols 73,828; Per Subs 88; Talking Bks 2,360
Function: ILL available, Magnifiers for reading, Photocopying/Printing, Prog for children & young adult, Ref serv available, Summer reading prog
Open Mon-Thurs 10-8, Fri & Sat 10-5
Friends of the Library Group
NORTHEAST, 1905 Brown Blvd, 76006-4605, SAN 361-1167. Tel: 817-277-5573. FAX: 817-276-8649. *Br Mgr,* Marc Marchand; E-mail: marchandm@ci.arlington.tx.us; *Adult Serv,* Melissa Dease; *Ch,* Laureen Jacobs; E-mail: ljacobs@ci.arlington.tx.us; Staff 11 (MLS 3, Non-MLS 8)
Founded 1997. Pop 353,597; Circ 500,689
Library Holdings: AV Mats 5,200; Large Print Bks 324; Bk Titles 58,565; Bk Vols 69,591; Per Subs 96
Function: Adult literacy prog, Handicapped accessible, ILL available, Magnifiers for reading, Photocopying/Printing, Prog for children & young adult, Ref serv available, Summer reading prog
Open Mon-Thurs 9-9, Fri & Sat 9-6
Friends of the Library Group
SOUTHEAST, 900 SE Green Oaks Blvd, 76018-1708. Tel: 817-459-6395. FAX: 817-472-6495. *Librn II,* David Jackson; E-mail: jacksond@ci.arlington.tx.us; Staff 6 (Non-MLS 6)
Pop 353,597; Circ 500,689
Library Holdings: Bk Vols 25,000
Function: Handicapped accessible, ILL available, Magnifiers for reading, Photocopying/Printing, Prog for children & young adult, Ref serv available, Summer reading prog

Open Mon-Thurs 10-8, Fri & Sat 10-5, Sun (Sept-May) 2-6
Friends of the Library Group
SOUTHWEST, 3111 SW Green Oaks Blvd, 76017. Tel: 817-459-6386. *Br Mgr,* Derek Perdue
Open Mon-Thurs 10-8, Fri & Sat 10-5
WOODLAND WEST, 2837 W Park Row Dr, 76013-2261, SAN 361-1221. Tel: 817-277-5265. FAX: 817-795-4741. *Br Mgr,* Robert Linan; Staff 8 (MLS 2, Non-MLS 6)
Founded 1996. Pop 353,597; Circ 500,689
Library Holdings: AV Mats 5,038; Large Print Bks 298; Bk Titles 45,267; Bk Vols 50,955; Per Subs 68; Talking Bks 1,988
Function: Handicapped accessible, ILL available, Magnifiers for reading, Photocopying/Printing, Prog for children & young adult, Ref serv available, Summer reading prog
Open Mon-Thurs 10-8, Fri & Sat 10-5
Friends of the Library Group

R   FIRST BAPTIST CHURCH*, Meredith Memorial Library, 301 S Center St, Ste 500, 76010. SAN 316-0327. Tel: 817-277-6353. FAX: 817-276-6499. Web Site: www.fbca.org. *Librn,* Barbara Pritcher; E-mail: barbara.pritcher@fbca.org
Library Holdings: Bk Vols 9,000; Per Subs 15
Automation Activity & Vendor Info: (Cataloging) Library Concepts
Wireless access
Open Wed 9-12 & 5-7:30, Thurs 9-12, Sun 8-12:30

J   TARRANT COUNTY COLLEGE*, Southeast Campus Library, 2100 Southeast Pkwy, 76018. Tel: 817-515-3081. Circulation Tel: 817-515-3082. Reference Tel: 817-515-3084. FAX: 817-515-3183. Web Site: library.tccd.edu. *Dir, Libr Serv,* Mark Dolive; Tel: 817-515-3083, E-mail: mark.dolive@tccd.edu; *Librn,* Kenneth Evans; Tel: 817-515-3085, E-mail: kenneth.evans@tccd.edu; *Librn,* JoTisa Klemm; Tel: 817-515-3388, E-mail: jotisa.klemm@tccd.edu; *Pub Serv Librn,* Vidya Krishnaswamy; Tel: 817-515-3086, E-mail: vidya.krishnaswamy@tccd.edu; *Pub Serv Librn,* James Foreman; Tel: 817-515-3089, E-mail: james.foreman@tccd.edu; Staff 5 (MLS 5)
Founded 1996. Enrl 14,780; Fac 350; Highest Degree: Associate
Library Holdings: DVDs 62; e-books 36,000; Bk Titles 47,200; Per Subs 100
Automation Activity & Vendor Info: (Acquisitions) Ex Libris Group; (Cataloging) Ex Libris Group; (Circulation) Ex Libris Group; (Course Reserve) Ex Libris Group; (ILL) Ex Libris Group; (OPAC) Ex Libris Group; (Serials) Ex Libris Group
Wireless access
Open Mon-Thurs (Fall & Spring) 7am-10pm, Fri 8-5, Sat 9-3; Mon-Thurs (Summer) 7:45am-10pm

C   UNIVERSITY OF TEXAS AT ARLINGTON LIBRARY, 702 Planetarium Pl, 76019. (Mail add: PO Box 19497, 76019-0497), SAN 316-0343. Tel: 817-272-3000. Circulation Tel: 817-272-3395. Interlibrary Loan Service Tel: 817-272-3344. Reference Tel: 817-272-3394. Administration Tel: 817-272-1413. Toll Free Tel: 888-565-9023. FAX: 817-272-5797. Web Site: www.uta.edu/library. *Dean of Libr,* Rebecca Bichel; Tel: 817-272-0368, E-mail: rbichel@uta.edu; Staff 47 (MLS 43, Non-MLS 4)
Founded 1895. Enrl 33,439; Fac 1,450; Highest Degree: Doctorate
Sept 2011-Aug 2012 Income $11,943,183. Mats Exp $5,160,654, Books $792,321, Per/Ser (Incl. Access Fees) $4,242,733, Presv $40,000. Sal $5,586,465 (Prof $2,954,232)
Library Holdings: e-books 431,340; e-journals 39,245; Microforms 1,483,541; Bk Vols 1,208,411; Per Subs 72,378; Videos 8,881
Special Collections: Cartographic Library; Fort Worth Star Telegram Coll; Mexico & MesoAmerica, bks, doc; Organized Labor in Texas & the Southwest, doc; Photographic Archives; Robertson's Colony, doc; Texas & the Mexican War, bks, cartography, doc, maps; Virginia Garrett Cartographic History Coll. Oral History; US Document Depository
Automation Activity & Vendor Info: (Acquisitions) Ex Libris Group; (Cataloging) Ex Libris Group; (Circulation) Ex Libris Group; (Course Reserve) Ex Libris Group; (ILL) OCLC ILLiad; (OPAC) Ex Libris Group; (Serials) Ex Libris Group
Database Vendor: Alexander Street Press, Amigos Library Services, ARTstor, EBSCOhost, Elsevier, Emerald, Factiva.com, IEEE (Institute of Electrical & Electronics Engineers), JSTOR, LexisNexis, netLibrary, Newsbank, OCLC FirstSearch, OCLC WorldCat, OVID Technologies, Project MUSE, ProQuest, PubMed, ReferenceUSA, ScienceDirect, SerialsSolutions, Springer-Verlag, Standard & Poor's, Thomson - Web of Science, Wiley, Wilson - Wilson Web
Publications: Compass Rose (Newsletter)
Partic in OCLC Online Computer Library Center, Inc; Phoenix Group; TexSHARE - Texas State Library & Archives Commission; UT Sys Electronic Ref Ctr
Special Services for the Deaf - Assistive tech
Special Services for the Blind - Assistive/Adapted tech devices, equip & products
Friends of the Library Group

ASPERMONT

P   STONEWALL COUNTY LIBRARY*, 516 S Washington St, 79502. (Mail add: PO Box H, 79502-0907), SAN 324-7597. Tel: 940-989-2730. FAX: 940-989-2730. E-mail: stonewall.lib@gmail.com. Web Site: www.stonewall-library.com. *Librn,* Patti Sedberry; *Asst Librn,* Dana Martin
Founded 1962. Pop 2,340; Circ 18,192
Library Holdings: Bk Titles 11,345; Bk Vols 11,684
Automation Activity & Vendor Info: (Cataloging) LibLime; (Circulation) LibLime
Wireless access
Mem of Big Country Library System
Partic in Tex Share
Open Tues-Thurs 8-11:30 & 12:30-5
Friends of the Library Group

ATHENS

P   HENDERSON COUNTY*, Clint W Murchison Memorial Library, 121 S Prairieville, 75751. SAN 316-0351. Tel: 903-677-7295. FAX: 903-677-7275. E-mail: librarian@co.henderson.tx.us. Web Site: co.henderson.tx.us/ips/cms/countyoffices/ClintWMurchisonLibrary. *Head Librn,* Lorie Lee; *Asst Librn,* Erin Holyfield
Founded 1972. Pop 49,132; Circ 96,182
Library Holdings: Bk Titles 49,075; Bk Vols 53,024; Per Subs 57
Automation Activity & Vendor Info: (Circulation) Follett Software
Wireless access
Open Mon-Fri 9-5, Sat 9-1
Friends of the Library Group

J   TRINITY VALLEY COMMUNITY COLLEGE LIBRARY*, Ginger Murchison Learning Resource Center, 100 Cardinal Dr, 75751-2765. SAN 316-036X. Tel: 903-675-6260. FAX: 903-675-6207. Web Site: www.tvcc.edu. *Dir,* Janice Sutton; Tel: 903-675-6229, E-mail: jsutton@tvcc.edu; *Ref,* Karla Bryan; Staff 2 (MLS 2)
Founded 1946. Highest Degree: Associate
Library Holdings: e-books 29,000; Bk Vols 28,000; Per Subs 150; Videos 2,000
Special Collections: Athens Review, bound vols, microfilm
Automation Activity & Vendor Info: (Acquisitions) SirsiDynix; (Cataloging) SirsiDynix; (Circulation) SirsiDynix; (Course Reserve) SirsiDynix; (ILL) SirsiDynix; (Media Booking) SirsiDynix; (OPAC) SirsiDynix; (Serials) SirsiDynix
Open Mon-Thurs (Fall & Spring) 7:45-7:45, Fri 7:45-4:15, Sun 2-5; Mon & Tues (Summer) 7:45-7:45, Wed & Thurs 7:45-4:15
Departmental Libraries:
ANDERSON COUNTY, 2970 Hwy 19 N, Palestine, 75802. (Mail add: PO Box 2530, Palestine, 75802-2530), SAN 370-372X. Tel: 903-729-0256. FAX: 903-729-2325. *Librn,* Charles Dobroski; E-mail: cdobroski@tvcc.edu
Library Holdings: Bk Titles 18,000; Per Subs 131
Open Mon-Thurs (Fall & Spring) 8-7, Fri 8-4; Mon-Thurs (Summer) 8-6

JM   HEALTH OCCUPATIONAL, 800 Ed Hall Dr, Kaufman, 75142, SAN 370-3738. Tel: 972-932-4309. FAX: 972-932-5010. *In Charge,* Glada M Norris; E-mail: norris@tvcc.edu
Library Holdings: Bk Titles 2,013; Per Subs 41
Partic in TexSHARE - Texas State Library & Archives Commission
Open Mon-Fri (Fall & Spring) 7:30-4:30, Mon-Thurs (Summer) 7:30-4:30
KAUFMAN COUNTY, PO Box 668, Terrell, 75160-0668, SAN 370-3746. Tel: 972-563-4929. FAX: 972-563-1667. *Librn,* Deanna Thompson; E-mail: thompson@tvcc.edu; Staff 1 (MLS 1)
Library Holdings: Bk Titles 6,200; Per Subs 60
Open Mon-Thurs 8-7, Fri (Fall & Spring) 8-4

ATLANTA

P   ATLANTA PUBLIC LIBRARY*, 101 W Hiram St, 75551. SAN 376-4451. Tel: 903-796-2112. FAX: 903-799-4067. E-mail: aplib@sbcglobal.net. Web Site: www.atlantalib.com. *Librn,* Jackie Icenhower
Library Holdings: Bk Vols 42,000; Per Subs 30
Wireless access
Open Mon 10-8, Tues-Fri 10-6, Sat 10-2
Friends of the Library Group

AUBREY

P   AUBREY AREA LIBRARY*, 226 Countryside Dr, 76227. SAN 376-4672. Tel: 940-365-9162. FAX: 940-365-9411. E-mail: library@aubreytx.gov. *Dir,* Kathy Gilson; *Admin Serv,* Elaine Turrubiarte
Library Holdings: Bk Titles 17,000
Automation Activity & Vendor Info: (Cataloging) Evergreen; (Circulation) Evergreen; (OPAC) Evergreen
Wireless access

Mem of North Texas Library Partners
Open Tues-Thurs 10-7, Sat 10-3
Friends of the Library Group

AUSTIN

R THE ARCHIVES OF THE EPISCOPAL CHURCH*, 606 Rathervue Pl,
78705. (Mail add: PO Box 2247, 78768-2247), SAN 372-9664. Tel:
512-472-6816. FAX: 512-480-0437. E-mail:
research@episcopalarchives.org. Web Site: www.episcopalarchives.org. *Dir,*
Mark J Duffy; Staff 7 (MLS 5, Non-MLS 2)
Founded 1940
Library Holdings: Bk Vols 12,000; Per Subs 50
Special Collections: Book of Common Prayer. Oral History
Open Mon-Thurs 9-4:45
Friends of the Library Group

J AUSTIN COMMUNITY COLLEGE, Library Services Administration,
1212 Rio Grande, 78701. SAN 316-0386. Tel: 512-223-3085. FAX:
512-223-3431. E-mail: library@austincc.edu. Web Site: library.austincc.edu.
Dean, Libr Serv, Julie Todaro; Tel: 512-223-3071, E-mail:
jtodaro@austincc.edu; *Head Librn, Tech Serv & Automation,* Cherry
Luedtke; Tel: 512-223-8682, Fax: 512-223-8611, E-mail:
clue@austincc.edu; *Automation Syst Adminr,* Melissa Airoldi; Tel:
512-223-8683, Fax: 512-223-8611, E-mail: airoldi@austincc.edu; Staff 9.08
(MLS 3.78, Non-MLS 5.3)
Founded 1973. Enrl 44,100; Fac 2,107; Highest Degree: Associate
Library Holdings: AV Mats 16,875; e-books 40,357; Bk Vols 150,182;
Per Subs 1,312
Special Collections: Multicultural Coll
Subject Interests: Health sci
Automation Activity & Vendor Info: (Acquisitions) Innovative Interfaces,
Inc; (Cataloging) Innovative Interfaces, Inc; (Circulation) Innovative
Interfaces, Inc; (Course Reserve) Innovative Interfaces, Inc; (ILL)
Innovative Interfaces, Inc; (Media Booking) Innovative Interfaces, Inc;
(OPAC) Innovative Interfaces, Inc; (Serials) Innovative Interfaces, Inc
Wireless access
Publications: Library Instruction; Pathfinders; Study Guides
Partic in TexSHARE - Texas State Library & Archives Commission
Special Services for the Blind - Computer with voice synthesizer for
visually impaired persons
Departmental Libraries:
CYPRESS CREEK CAMPUS LIBRARY, 1555 Cypress Creek Rd, Cedar
Park, 78613, SAN 377-5852. Circulation Tel: 512-223-2030. Reference
Tel: 512-223-2037. FAX: 512-223-2035. *Head Librn,* Terry Barksdale;
Tel: 512-223-2135, E-mail: tbarksda@austincc.edu; *Ref Librn,* Jonathan
Buckstead; Tel: 512-223-2132, E-mail: jrb@austincc.edu; *Ref Librn,*
Linda Clement; Tel: 512-223-2033, E-mail: lclement@austincc.edu; *Ref
Librn,* Molly Dahlstrom Ledbetter; Tel: 512-223-2137, E-mail:
mdahlstr@austincc.edu; Staff 8.28 (MLS 4.68, Non-MLS 3.6)
Open Mon-Fri 7:30am-9pm, Sat 8-5, Sun 12-6
EASTVIEW CAMPUS LIBRARY, 3401 Webberville Rd, 78702, SAN
377-5879. Tel: 512-223-5119. Circulation Tel: 512-223-5109. Reference
Tel: 512-223-5116. FAX: 512-223-5111. *Head Librn,* Margaret Peloquin;
Tel: 512-223-5117, E-mail: peloquin@austincc.edu; *Ref Librn,* Steve
Self; Tel: 512-223-5134, E-mail: ses@austincc.edu; *Ref Librn,* Cary
Sowell; Tel: 512-223-5232, E-mail: cary@austincc.edu; Staff 9.35 (MLS
4.25, Non-MLS 5.1)
Open Mon-Fri 7:30am-9pm, Sat 8-5, Sun 12-6
NORTHRIDGE CAMPUS LIBRARY, 11928 Stone Hollow Dr, 78758,
SAN 321-7949. Tel: 512-223-4740. Circulation Tel: 512-223-4746.
Reference Tel: 512-223-4744. FAX: 512-223-4902. *Head Librn,* Melinda
Townsel; Tel: 512-223-4731, E-mail: mtownsel@austincc.edu; *Ref Librn,*
Teresa Ashley; Tel: 512-223-4742, E-mail: tashley@austincc.edu; *Ref
Librn,* Ashley Carr; Tel: 512-223-4869, E-mail: acarr@austincc.edu; Staff
8.35 (MLS 4.05, Non-MLS 4.3)
Open Mon-Fri 7:30am-9pm, Sat 8-5, Sun 12-6
PINNACLE CAMPUS LIBRARY, 7748 Hwy 290 W, 78736, SAN
377-5836. Tel: 512-223-8113. Reference Tel: 512-223-8150. FAX:
512-223-8223. *Head Librn,* Leigh Kilman; Tel: 512-223-8114, E-mail:
lkilman@austincc.edu; *Ref Librn,* Barbara Jorge; Tel: 512-223-8091,
E-mail: bjorge@austincc.edu; *Ref Librn,* Nathan Tinnin; Tel:
512-223-8130, E-mail: tinnin@austincc.edu; Staff 6.05 (MLS 3.45,
Non-MLS 2.6)
Open Mon-Thurs 7:30am-9pm, Fri 7:30-5
RIO GRANDE CAMPUS LIBRARY, 1212 Rio Grande, 78701, SAN
321-7930. Tel: 512-223-3085. Circulation Tel: 512-223-3067. Reference
Tel: 512-223-3068. FAX: 512-223-3430. *Head Librn,* Carrie Gits; Tel:
512-223-3066; *Ref Librn,* Jon Luckstead; Tel: 512-223-3089, E-mail:
jluckste@austincc.edu; *Ref Librn,* Red Wassenich; Tel: 512-223-3074,
E-mail: redwass@austincc.edu; Staff 7.88 (MLS 3.68, Non-MLS 4.2)
Open Mon-Thurs 7:30am-9pm, Fri 7:30-5, Sat 9-1
RIVERSIDE CAMPUS LIBRARY, 1020 Grove Blvd, 78741, SAN
321-7957. Tel: 512-223-6001. Circulation Tel: 512-223-6006. Reference
Tel: 512-223-6005. FAX: 512-223-6703. *Head Librn,* Jennifer Weber;

Tel: 512-223-6603, E-mail: jweber@austincc.edu; *Ref Librn,* Lola
Cowling; Tel: 512-223-6134, E-mail: lcowling@austincc.edu; *Ref Librn,*
Donna Meadows; Tel: 512-223-6004, E-mail: dcm@austincc.edu; *Ref
Librn,* Terese Morgan; Tel: 512-223-6181, E-mail:
tmorgan@austincc.edu; Staff 8.1 (MLS 4, Non-MLS 4.1)
Open Mon-Fri 7:30am-9pm, Sat 8-5, Sun 12-6
ROUND ROCK CAMPUS LIBRARY, 4400 College Park Dr, Round
Rock, 78665. Tel: 512-223-0115. Circulation Tel: 512-223-0104.
Reference Tel: 512-223-0105. FAX: 512-223-0903. *Head Librn,* Sheila
Henderson; Tel: 512-223-0116; *Ref Librn,* Sylvia Owens; Tel:
512-223-0118, E-mail: sowens@austincc.edu; *Ref Librn,* Betsy Young;
Tel: 512-223-0119, E-mail: byoung1@austincc.edu; Staff 7 (MLS 3,
Non-MLS 4)
Open Mon-Fri 7:30am-9pm, Sat 8-5, Sun 12-6
SOUTH AUSTIN CAMPUS LIBRARY, 1820 W Stassney Lane, 78745.
Tel: 512-223-9183. Circulation Tel: 512-223-9180. Reference Tel:
512-223-9181. FAX: 512-223-9190. *Head Librn,* Pam Spooner; Tel:
512-223-9184, E-mail: pspooner@austincc.edu; *Ref Librn,* Adrian
Whatley; Tel: 512-223-9179, E-mail: aerb@austincc.edu; *Ref Librn,* Dave
Wilson; Tel: 512-223-9185, E-mail: dwilson3@austincc.edu; Staff 8.1
(MLS 3, Non-MLS 5.1)
Open Mon-Fri 7:30am-9pm, Sat 8-5, Sun 12-6

CR AUSTIN GRADUATE SCHOOL OF THEOLOGY*, David Worley
Library, 7640 Guadalupe St, 78752-1333. SAN 328-3860. Tel:
512-476-2772. FAX: 512-476-3919. Web Site:
www.austingrad.edu/academics_library.html. *Dir,* Todd M Hall; E-mail:
thall@austingrad.edu; Staff 1 (MLS 1)
Enrl 100; Fac 4; Highest Degree: Master
Library Holdings: Bk Titles 22,500; Bk Vols 25,000; Per Subs 120
Special Collections: Showalter Coll
Subject Interests: Biblical studies
Automation Activity & Vendor Info: (Cataloging) Follett Software;
(Circulation) Follett Software
Database Vendor: EBSCOhost
Partic in Tex Share
Open Mon, Tues & Thurs 8:30-5 Wed & Fri 8:30-4
Friends of the Library Group

CR AUSTIN PRESBYTERIAN THEOLOGICAL SEMINARY*, David L &
Jane Stitt Library, 100 E 27th St, 78705-5797. SAN 316-0394. Tel:
512-472-6736. Circulation Tel: 512-404-4879. Toll Free Tel: 800-777-6127.
FAX: 512-322-0901. E-mail: library@austinseminary.edu. Web Site:
www.austinseminary.edu. *Dir,* Timothy D Lincoln; *Assoc Dir,* Helen
Kennedy; *Pub Serv,* Lila Parrish; Staff 9 (MLS 5, Non-MLS 4)
Founded 1902. Enrl 183; Highest Degree: Doctorate
Library Holdings: Bk Vols 157,211; Per Subs 450
Special Collections: Rumble Communion Token Coll
Subject Interests: Biblical studies
Automation Activity & Vendor Info: (Cataloging) Ex Libris Group;
(Circulation) Ex Libris Group; (Course Reserve) Ex Libris Group; (OPAC)
Ex Libris Group; (Serials) Ex Libris Group
Database Vendor: EBSCOhost
Wireless access
Open Mon-Thurs (Winter) 8am-10pm; Mon-Fri (Summer) 8-5

P AUSTIN PUBLIC LIBRARY*, Faulk Central Library, 800 Guadalupe St,
78701. (Mail add: PO Box 2287, 78768-2287), SAN 361-1256. Tel:
512-974-7400. Interlibrary Loan Service Tel: 512-974-7399. Administration
Tel: 512-974-7449. Administration FAX: 512-974-7403. Web Site:
www.ci.austin.tx.us/library. *Dir,* Brenda Branch; Tel: 512-974-7444; *Asst
Dir, Pub Serv,* Toni Lambert; Tel: 512-974-7466; *Asst Dir, Support Serv,*
Dana McBee; Tel: 512-974-7431; *Cent Libr Serv Mgr,* David Spradling;
Tel: 512-974-7437; Staff 120 (MLS 28, Non-MLS 92)
Founded 1926. Pop 777,559; Circ 4,316,785
Library Holdings: Bk Vols 1,465,765; Per Subs 1,064
Special Collections: Austin History Center. Oral History
Automation Activity & Vendor Info: (Acquisitions) SirsiDynix;
(Circulation) SirsiDynix; (ILL) OCLC WorldCat
Database Vendor: 3M Library Systems, EBSCOhost, Factiva.com, Gale
Cengage Learning, netLibrary, OCLC WorldCat, ReferenceUSA,
SirsiDynix
Wireless access
Partic in Dialog Corp; OCLC Online Computer Library Center, Inc
Special Services for the Deaf - Staff with knowledge of sign lang
Special Services for the Blind - Reader equip
Open Mon-Thurs 10-9, Fri & Sat 10-6, Sun 12-6
Friends of the Library Group
Branches: 21
AUSTIN HISTORY CENTER, 810 Guadalupe St, 78701. (Mail add: PO
Box 2287, 78768-2287), SAN 323-9306. Tel: 512-974-7480. Reference
Tel: 512-974-7385. FAX: 512-974-7483. E-mail:
ahc_reference@austintexas.gov, ahc_reference@ci.austin.tx.us. Web Site:
www.austinhistorycenter.org. *Mgr,* Mike Miller; Tel: 512-974-7436,
E-mail: mike.miller@ci.austin.tx.us; Staff 15 (MLS 6, Non-MLS 9)

Founded 1955. Pop 750,525
Library Holdings: Bk Titles 13,500; Bk Vols 36,000; Per Subs 200
Special Collections: Architectural Archives; blueprints; drawings; photo images; Charles Whitman Coll; O Henry (O'Quinn-O Henry Coll), bks, ms; Texas Governor E M Pease Papers; Travis County Historical Resource Depository; Women's Suffrage (Jane Y McCallum Coll), blueprints, drawings, ms. Oral History
Function: Archival coll
Publications: An Austin Album; Austin & Travis County: A Pictorial History, 1839-1939; Lucadia Pease & the Governor; Pease Porridge Hot; Waterloo Scrapbook
Open Tues-Sat 10-6, Sun 12-6
Friends of the Library Group
CARVER, 1161 Angelina St, 78702, SAN 361-1280. Tel: 512-974-1010. FAX: 512-974-1021. *Managing Librn,* Steve Reich; Tel: 512-974-1020, E-mail: steve.reich@ci.austin.tx.us; Staff 6.5 (MLS 1, Non-MLS 5.5)
Pop 9,529; Circ 48,256
Library Holdings: Bk Vols 33,000
Subject Interests: African-Am hist
Open Mon-Thurs 10-9, Sat 10-5, Sun 2-6
EUSTASIO CEPEDA, 651 N Pleasant Valley Rd, 78702, SAN 361-1310. Tel: 512-974-7372. FAX: 512-974-7329. *Managing Librn,* Sulema Vielma; E-mail: sulema.vielma@ci.austin.tx.us; Staff 5 (MLS 1, Non-MLS 4)
Founded 1998. Pop 4,532; Circ 51,319
Library Holdings: Bk Vols 18,511
Special Collections: Adult Literacy Coll
Open Mon-Thurs 10-9, Sat 10-5
WILL HAMPTON BRANCH AT OAK HILL, 5125 Convict Hill Rd, 78749, SAN 377-7995. Tel: 512-974-9900. FAX: 512-974-9902. *Managing Librn,* Irma Flores-Manges; E-mail: irma.flores-manges@ci.austin.tx.us; Staff 11 (MLS 1, Non-MLS 10)
Founded 1997. Pop 66,453; Circ 413,200
Open Mon-Wed 10-9, Fri 10-6, Sat 10-5
HOWSON, 2500 Exposition Blvd, 78703, SAN 361-1345. Tel: 512-974-8800. FAX: 512-479-8554. *Managing Librn,* Bonita Snyder-Jones; E-mail: bonita.snyder-jones@ci.austin.tx.us; Staff 6 (MLS 2, Non-MLS 4)
Pop 23,483; Circ 148,619
Library Holdings: Bk Vols 35,000
Open Mon-Wed 10-9, Fri 10-6, Sat 10-5
LITTLE WALNUT CREEK, 835 W Rundberg Lane, 78758, SAN 361-137X. Tel: 512-974-9860. FAX: 512-974-9865. *Regional Br Operations Mgr,* Tom Moran; E-mail: tom.moran@ci.austin.tx.us; Staff 10 (MLS 2, Non-MLS 8)
Pop 41,258; Circ 101,862
Library Holdings: Bk Vols 54,000
Open Mon-Thurs 10-9, Sat 10-5, Sun 2-6
MANCHACA ROAD, 5500 Manchaca Rd, 78745, SAN 361-140X. Tel: 512-974-8700. FAX: 512-974-8701. *Regional Br Operations Mgr,* Patti Fowler; E-mail: patti.fowler@ci.austin.tx.us; Staff 8.075 (MLS 2, Non-MLS 6.075)
Founded 1974. Pop 14,500; Circ 116,490
Library Holdings: Bk Vols 70,000; Per Subs 155
Open Mon-Thurs 10-9, Sat 10-5, Sun 2-6
MILWOOD, 12500 Amherst Dr, 78727, SAN 377-8010. Tel: 512-974-9880. FAX: 512-974-9884. *Managing Librn,* Pamela Bowles; E-mail: pamela.bowles@ci.austin.tx.us; Staff 11.625 (MLS 2, Non-MLS 9.625)
Pop 37,725; Circ 333,885
Open Mon-Thurs 10-9, Sat 10-5
NORTH VILLAGE, 2505 Steck Ave, 78757, SAN 361-1493. Tel: 512-974-9960. FAX: 512-974-9965. *Managing Librn,* Kathleen Kanarski; E-mail: kathleen.kanarski@ci.austin.tx.us; Staff 7 (MLS 2, Non-MLS 5)
Pop 24,966; Circ 146,434
Library Holdings: Bk Vols 29,000
Open Mon-Wed 10-9, Fri 10-6, Sat 10-5
OAK SPRINGS, 3101 Oak Springs Dr, 78702, SAN 361-1523. Tel: 512-974-9920. FAX: 512-974-9924. *Managing Librn,* Deborah Coronado; E-mail: deborah.coronado@ci.austin.tx.us; Staff 6 (MLS 1, Non-MLS 5)
Pop 11,994; Circ 44,807
Library Holdings: Bk Vols 29,500
Special Collections: Workplace Literary Coll
Open Mon-Wed 10-9, Fri 10-6, Sat 10-5
OLD QUARRY, 7051 Village Center Dr, 78731, SAN 361-1558. Tel: 512-345-4435. FAX: 512-794-0459. *Managing Librn,* Patricia Campbell; E-mail: patricia.campbell@ci.austin.tx.us; Staff 7.5 (MLS 1, Non-MLS 6.5)
Pop 39,949; Circ 204,529
Library Holdings: Bk Vols 39,000
Open Mon-Thurs 10-9, Sat 10-5
PLEASANT HILL, 211 E William Cannon Dr, 78745, SAN 361-1582. Tel: 512-974-3940. FAX: 512-444-6237. *Managing Librn,* Ben Sorrels; E-mail: ben.sorrels@ci.austin.tx.us; Staff 7 (MLS 2, Non-MLS 5)
Pop 40,074; Circ 200,041

Library Holdings: Bk Vols 38,000
Open Mon-Thurs 10-9, Sat 10-5
DANIEL E RUIZ BRANCH, 1600 Grove Blvd, 78741, SAN 361-1566. Tel: 512-974-7500. FAX: 512-386-9146. *Regional Br Operations Mgr,* Elva Garza; E-mail: elva.garza@ci.austin.tx.us; Staff 9 (MLS 2, Non-MLS 7)
Pop 42,671; Circ 113,615
Library Holdings: Bk Vols 25,000
Open Mon-Thurs 10-9, Sat 10-5
ST JOHN, 7500 Blessing Ave, 78752. Tel: 512-974-7570. FAX: 512-380-7055. *Libr Dir,* Michael Abramov; E-mail: michael.abramov@ci.austin.tx.us; Staff 6.5 (MLS 1, Non-MLS 5.5)
Pop 32,635; Circ 59,629
Open Mon-Wed 10-9, Fri 10-6, Sat 10-4
SOUTHEAST AUSTIN COMMUNITY BRANCH, 5803 Nuckols Crossing Rd, 78744, SAN 377-8037. Tel: 512-462-1452. FAX: 512-447-7639. *Managing Librn,* Paola Ferate-Soto; E-mail: paola.ferate-soto@ci.austin.tx.us; Staff 6.5 (MLS 1, Non-MLS 5.5)
Founded 1998. Pop 35,164; Circ 66,699
Open Mon-Wed 10-9, Fri 10-6, Sat 10-5
SPICEWOOD SPRINGS, 8637 Spicewood Springs Rd, 78759, SAN 326-8454. Tel: 512-974-3800. FAX: 512-974-3801. *Managing Librn,* Nancy Toombs; E-mail: nancy.toombs@ci.austin.tx.us; Staff 13.75 (MLS 2, Non-MLS 11.75)
Founded 1985. Pop 45,426; Circ 381,797
Library Holdings: Bk Vols 55,000; Per Subs 110
Special Collections: Chinese (Traditional & Simplified)
Subject Interests: Chinese lang
Open Mon-Wed 10-9, Fri 10-6, Sat 10-5
TERRAZAS, 1105 E Cesar Chavez St, 78702, SAN 361-1612. Tel: 512-974-3625. FAX: 512-479-8558. *Managing Librn,* Eric Travis; Tel: 512-974-3636, E-mail: eric.travis@ci.austin.tx.us; Staff 6.5 (MLS 1, Non-MLS 5.5)
Pop 9,882; Circ 69,490
Library Holdings: Bk Vols 27,690
Open Mon-Wed 10-9, Fri 10-6, Sat 10-5
TWIN OAKS, 1800 S Fifth St, 78704, SAN 361-1647. Tel: 512-974-9980. FAX: 512-974-9988. *Managing Librn,* Anita Fudell; E-mail: anita.fudell@ci.austin.tx.us; Staff 8 (MLS 2, Non-MLS 6)
Pop 46,200; Circ 104,647
Library Holdings: Bk Vols 23,000
Open Mon-Wed 10-9, Fri 10-6, Sat 10-5
UNIVERSITY HILLS, 4721 Loyola Lane, 78723, SAN 328-9117. Tel: 512-974-9940. FAX: 512-974-9944. *Managing Librn,* Frank Schmitzer; E-mail: frank.schmitzer@ci.austin.tx.us; Staff 6.75 (MLS 1, Non-MLS 5.75)
Founded 1986. Pop 26,492; Circ 63,379
Library Holdings: Bk Vols 29,356
Open Mon-Thurs 10-9, Sat 10-5
WINDSOR PARK, 5833 Westminster Dr, 78723, SAN 361-1671. Tel: 512-974-9840. FAX: 512-974-9844. *Managing Librn,* D J Harris; Tel: 512-974-9841, E-mail: dj.harris@ci.austin.tx.us; Staff 7 (MLS 2, Non-MLS 5)
Pop 23,874; Circ 99,371
Library Holdings: Bk Titles 48,000; Bk Vols 54,000
Partic in Tex Share
Open Mon-Wed 10-9, Fri 10-6, Sat 10-5
YARBOROUGH, 2200 Hancock Dr, 78756, SAN 361-1469. Tel: 512-454-7208. FAX: 512-458-3047. *Regional Br Operations Mgr,* Diane Palan; E-mail: diane.palan@ci.austin.tx.us; Staff 8.25 (MLS 2, Non-MLS 6.25)
Pop 33,317; Circ 230,938
Library Holdings: Bk Vols 30,000
Open Mon-Thurs 10-9, Sat 10-5

L   BROWN MCCARROLL, LLP LIBRARY*, 111 Congress Ave, Ste 1400, 78701-4043. SAN 329-1375. Tel: 512-472-5456. Reference Tel: 512-370-3440. FAX: 512-479-1101. Web Site: www.brownmccarroll.com. *Dir,* Kamie Oehrle; *Ref Librn,* D John Conger; Tel: 512-370-3449, E-mail: jconger@mailbmc.com; *Tech Serv,* Lisa B Bailey; Tel: 512-370-3377, E-mail: lbailey@mailbmc.com; Staff 3 (MLS 2, Non-MLS 1)
Founded 1933
Library Holdings: Bk Titles 400; Bk Vols 4,500; Per Subs 50
Subject Interests: Bankruptcy, Bus law, Environ law, Litigation, Product liability, Torts
Automation Activity & Vendor Info: (Acquisitions) Inmagic, Inc.; (Cataloging) Inmagic, Inc.; (Serials) Inmagic, Inc.
Database Vendor: LexisNexis
Function: Res libr
Open Mon-Fri 8-5:30

SR   CATHOLIC ARCHIVES OF TEXAS*, 1600 N Congress, 78711. (Mail add: PO Box 13124, Capitol Sta, 78711), SAN 316-0580. Tel: 512-476-6296. FAX: 512-476-3715. E-mail: archives@tx.cat.org,

cat@onr.com. Web Site: www.onr.com/user/cat. *Dir,* Susan Eason; *Archivist,* Eric J Hartmann; Staff 2 (MLS 2)
Founded 1924
Library Holdings: Microforms 7,000; Bk Vols 2,000; Per Subs 12
Special Collections: Catholic Parishes in Texas; Catholic Texas Newspapers (1890 to present); Early Anglo & French Missionaries in Texas; General Information on Texas Catholic Institutions & Organizations; Notre Dame Archives & New Orleans Diocesan Archives, photostats; Spanish Period Documents; Texas Catholic Conference Records, 1964-1990; Texas Coll (Mexican Period); Texas Knights of Columbus Records, 1882-1990; Volunteers for Education & Social Services Records, 1972-2001
Publications: Guide to the Records of Texas Catholic Conference; Guide to the Spanish & Mexican Manuscripts Collection; Our Catholic Heritage in Texas, Journal of Texas Catholic History & Culture; Texas Catholic Historical Society Newsletter
Restriction: Open by appt only

P   CENTRAL TEXAS LIBRARY SYSTEM, INC, 5555 N Lamar Blvd, Ste L115, 78751. SAN 316-0416. Tel: 512-583-0704. FAX: 512-583-0709. Web Site: www.ctls.net. *Exec Dir,* Patricia Tuohy; Tel: 512-583-0704, Ext 12, E-mail: pat.tuohy@ctls.net; *Dep Dir,* Laurie Mahaffey; E-mail: Laurie.mahaffey@ctls.net; *Youth Serv Spec,* Kim Lehman; E-mail: kim.lehman@ctls.net; Staff 6 (MLS 6)
Founded 1971. Pop 2,101,209
Special Collections: Large Print Book Coll
Wireless access
Publications: CTLS Bulletin (Bi-monthly); CTLS Newsletter (Bi-monthly)
Member Libraries: Austin Public Library; B J Hill Library; Bastrop Public Library; Bee Cave Public Library; Black Bridge Library; Blanco County South Library District; Bremond Public Library & Visitors Center; Buda Public Library; Buffalo Public Library; Burnet County Library System; Cedar Park Public Library; Copperas Cove Public Library; D Brown Memorial Library; Dr Eugene Clark Public Library; Dripping Springs Community Library; Elgin Public Library; Elroy Community Library; Fairfield Library Association, Inc; Fayette Public Library; Florence Public Library; Gatesville Public Library; Gibbs Memorial Library; Giddings Public Library; Groesbeck Maffett Public Library; Harrie P Woodson Memorial Library; Hewitt Public Library; Hillsboro City Library; J B Nickells Memorial Library; Jennie Trent Dew Library; Johnson City Library District; Jonestown Community Library; Killeen City Library System; Kyle Public Library; Lago Vista Public Library; Lake Travis Community Library; Lake Whitney Public Library; Lampasas Public Library; Leander Public Library; Lena Armstrong Public Library; Liberty Hill Public Library; Llano County Library System; Lucy Hill Patterson Memorial Library; Madison County Library; McGinley Memorial Public Library; Meridian Public Library; Moody Community Library; Mount Calm Public Library; Nancy Carol Roberts Memorial Library; Nancy Nail Memorial Library; Navasota Public Library; Nellie Pederson Civic Library; Pauline & Jane Chilton Memorial Public Library; Pflugerville Community Library; Robertson County Library; Round Rock Public Library; Round Top Library Association Inc; Salado Public Library; San Marcos Public Library; San Saba County Library; Schulenburg Public Library; Smith-Welch Memorial Library; Smithville Public Library; Teague Public Library; Teinert Memorial Public Library; Temple Public Library; Tri-Community Library; Valley Mills Public Library; Waco-McLennan County Library System; Wells Branch Community Library; West Public Library; Westbank Community Library District; Wimberley Village Library
Special Services for the Blind - Large print bks
Open Mon-Fri 8-5
Restriction: Circ to mem only
Friends of the Library Group

C   CONCORDIA UNIVERSITY TEXAS LIBRARY, CTX Library, 11400 Concordia University Dr, 78726. SAN 316-0432. Tel: 512-313-5050. Administration Tel: 512-313-5051. Web Site: www.concordia.edu/library. *Dir, Libr Serv,* Mikail McIntosh-Doty; E-mail: mikail.doty@concordia.edu; *Ref Librn,* Position Currently Open; *Tech Serv Librn,* Marcus X Fry; E-mail: marcus.fry@concordia.edu; Staff 3.5 (MLS 3, Non-MLS 0.5)
Founded 1926. Enrl 2,600; Fac 49; Highest Degree: Master
Jul 2012-Jun 2013 Income $149,000. Mats Exp $149,000, Books $19,500, Per/Ser (Incl. Access Fees) $36,100, AV Equip $1,000, AV Mat $500, Electronic Ref Mat (Incl. Access Fees) $64,500. Sal $148,500 (Prof $128,000)
Library Holdings: Audiobooks 25; AV Mats 2,416; CDs 125; DVDs 105; e-books 99,000; e-journals 66,000; Electronic Media & Resources 96; Large Print Bks 25; Microforms 2,000; Music Scores 20; Bk Titles 46,000; Bk Vols 53,000; Per Subs 230
Automation Activity & Vendor Info: (Cataloging) Ex Libris Group; (Circulation) Ex Libris Group; (Course Reserve) Ex Libris Group; (ILL) OCLC FirstSearch; (OPAC) Ex Libris Group
Database Vendor: Amigos Library Services, Baker & Taylor, Bowker, Brodart, Children's Literature Comprehensive Database Company (CLCD), Cinahl Information Systems, CredoReference, EBSCOhost, Facts on File, Gale Cengage Learning, Greenwood Publishing Group, Hoovers, JSTOR,

LexisNexis, Medline, Mergent Online, netLibrary, Newsbank, OCLC, OCLC FirstSearch, OCLC WorldCat, ProQuest, Sage, Standard & Poor's, STAT!Ref (Teton Data Systems), Wiley
Wireless access
Function: ILL available, Learning ctr, Online cat, Online info literacy tutorials on the web & in blackboard, Photocopying/Printing, Ref & res
Publications: Concordia University Press
Partic in Amigos Library Services, Inc; TexSHARE - Texas State Library & Archives Commission
Open Mon-Thurs (Fall & Spring) 7:30am-11pm, Fri 7:30-5, Sat Noon-4, Sun 2-10
Restriction: Use of others with permission of librn

R   EPISCOPAL THEOLOGICAL SEMINARY OF THE SOUTHWEST*, Booher Library, 501 E 32nd St, 78705. (Mail add: PO Box 2247, 78768-2247), SAN 316-0467. Tel: 512-472-4133, 512-478-5212. FAX: 512-472-4620. E-mail: library@ssw.edu. Web Site: www.ssw.edu. *Dir,* Donald E Keeney; Staff 2 (MLS 2)
Founded 1951. Enrl 125; Fac 9; Highest Degree: Master
Library Holdings: Bk Titles 97,719; Bk Vols 123,347; Per Subs 260
Special Collections: History, Literature & Culture of Latin Culture (Sophie H Winterbotham Coll); Lutheran Seminary Program in the Southwest (LSPS), Seminex Library; Nineteenth Century English Literature-Fine Editions (Charles L Black Coll); Spanish Language Texts
Subject Interests: Biblical studies, Church hist, Cultural studies, Hispanic
Automation Activity & Vendor Info: (Acquisitions) SirsiDynix; (Cataloging) SirsiDynix; (Circulation) SirsiDynix; (Course Reserve) SirsiDynix; (ILL) SirsiDynix; (Media Booking) SirsiDynix; (OPAC) SirsiDynix; (Serials) SirsiDynix
Wireless access
Open Mon-Thurs 8am-10pm, Fri 8-6:30, Sat 9-5:30, Sun 2-10; Mon-Fri (Summer) 8:15-4:45
Friends of the Library Group

SR   FIRST UNITED METHODIST CHURCH LIBRARY*, 1201 Lavaca, 78701-1831. SAN 328-5367. Tel: 512-478-5684. FAX: 512-478-6169. Web Site: www.fumcaustin.org. *Librn,* Sharon Doss
Library Holdings: Bk Vols 2,800; Per Subs 15
Wireless access
Restriction: Open by appt only

S   O HENRY MUSEUM LIBRARY*, 409 E Fifth St, 78701. SAN 320-8893. Tel: 512-472-1903. FAX: 512-472-7102. Web Site: www.cityofaustin.org/ohenry. *Curator,* Valerie Bennett; E-mail: valerie.bennett@ci.austin.tx.us
Library Holdings: Bk Vols 1,000
Special Collections: O Henry Coll by William Sidney Porter; Poetry Coll, 19th Century
Open Wed-Sun 12-5
Restriction: Non-circulating
Friends of the Library Group

C   HOUSTON-TILLOTSON UNIVERSITY*, Downs-Jones Library, 900 Chicon St, 78702-3430. SAN 316-0483. Tel: 512-505-3081. Interlibrary Loan Service Tel: 512-505-3078. Reference Tel: 512-505-3088. FAX: 512-505-3190. Web Site: aa.htu.edu/Library.aspx. *Dir,* Patricia A Wilkins; E-mail: pawilkins@htu.edu; Staff 4 (MLS 4)
Founded 1891. Highest Degree: Bachelor
Library Holdings: Bk Vols 91,375; Per Subs 301
Special Collections: Afro-American History (Schomburg Coll), micro; Religion (Heinsohn Coll)
Automation Activity & Vendor Info: (Acquisitions) Ex Libris Group; (Cataloging) Ex Libris Group; (Circulation) Ex Libris Group; (OPAC) Ex Libris Group; (Serials) Ex Libris Group
Database Vendor: 3M Library Systems, Amigos Library Services, EBSCOhost, Ex Libris Group, JSTOR, netLibrary, ProQuest
Wireless access
Publications: Recent Acquisitions List; Student Library Handbook
Open Mon-Thurs 8am-10pm, Fri 8-5, Sun 1-9

S   IBM CORP*, Library Information Resource Center, 11501 Burnet Rd, 78758. SAN 316-0491. Tel: 512-833-9279. *Coop Librn,* Amanda Stites; Staff 3 (MLS 1, Non-MLS 2)
Founded 1967
Library Holdings: Bk Titles 9,000; Bk Vols 11,000; Per Subs 300
Subject Interests: Computer sci, Electronic eng, Electronics, Eng, Math
Wireless access
Restriction: Co libr

L   JACKSON WALKER, LLP*, Law Library, 100 Congress Ave, Ste 1100, 78701-4099. SAN 327-5426. Tel: 512-236-2306. FAX: 512-236-2002. Web Site: www.jw.com. *Law Librn,* Judith B Hamner; Staff 2 (MLS 1, Non-MLS 1)

Founded 1980
Library Holdings: Bk Vols 50,000; Per Subs 200
Automation Activity & Vendor Info: (Acquisitions) EOS International; (Cataloging) EOS International; (OPAC) EOS International; (Serials) EOS International
Wireless access
Function: Res libr
Partic in Dialog Corp; Westlaw
Restriction: Staff use only

G　LYNDON BAINES JOHNSON LIBRARY & MUSEUM*, 2313 Red River St, 78705. SAN 361-1760. Tel: 512-721-0200. Administration FAX: 512-721-0170. E-mail: johnson.library@nara.gov. Web Site: www.lbjlibrary.org. *Dir,* Mark K Updegrove; E-mail: mark.updegrove@nara.gov; *Dep Dir,* Christina Houston; Tel: 512-721-0206, E-mail: tina.houston@nara.gov; Staff 29 (MLS 4, Non-MLS 25)
Founded 1971
Library Holdings: Bk Vols 17,911
Special Collections: Federal Agency & Commission Records, mss, reels, audiovisual materials, & museum objects; Lyndon B Johnson (Oral History Coll), tape, transcribed; Personal Papers of Famous Individuals such as Wright Patman, Drew Pearson, John B Connally, William Westmoreland, Wright Patman, Joseph A Califano, Ramsey Clark, William McC Martin, Lawrence F O'Brien, Walt W Rostow, mss, Oral History
Subject Interests: 20th Century Am, Career of Lyndon B Johnson, Econ, Johnson administration, Johnson family, Politics, Presidency, Soc hist, US Presidency, Vietnam War
Wireless access
Function: Archival coll, ILL available, Photocopying/Printing, Wheelchair accessible
Publications: Guide to Foreign Policy at the Lyndon B Johnson Library (Archives guide); Historical Materials in the Lyndon Baines Johnson Library (Archives guide); Materials in the LBJ Library Pertaining to [Subject] (Archives guide)
Open Mon-Sun 9-5 (Museum); Mon-Fri 9-5 (Archives)
Restriction: Photo ID required for access, Restricted loan policy
Friends of the Library Group

P　LAKE TRAVIS COMMUNITY LIBRARY, 2300 Lohman's Spur, Ste 100, 78734. SAN 376-4737. Tel: 512-263-2885. FAX: 512-535-3044. Web Site: www.laketravislibrary.org. *Libr Dir,* Morgan McMillian; E-mail: librarian@laketravis.lib.tx.us; Staff 5 (MLS 1, Non-MLS 4)
Founded 1985. Pop 22,500; Circ 150,000
Automation Activity & Vendor Info: (Acquisitions) Biblionix; (Cataloging) Biblionix; (Circulation) Biblionix; (OPAC) Biblionix
Database Vendor: Gale Cengage Learning, ProQuest, World Book Online
Wireless access
Function: Adult bk club, After school storytime, Audiobks via web, Bi-weekly Writer's Group, Bk club(s), Bks on cassette, Bks on CD, Children's prog, Computer training, Computers for patron use, Copy machines, e-mail & chat, Electronic databases & coll, Family literacy, Free DVD rentals, Genealogy discussion group, Holiday prog, ILL available, Instruction & testing, Music CDs, Notary serv, Online cat, Online ref, Online searches, Outreach serv, Photocopying/Printing, Preschool outreach, Prog for adults, Prog for children & young adult, Pub access computers, Ref serv available, Ref serv in person, Scanner, Senior computer classes, Spoken cassettes & CDs, Spoken cassettes & DVDs, Story hour, Tax forms, Teen prog, Telephone ref, VHS videos, Web-catalog, Wheelchair accessible, Workshops, Writing prog
Mem of Central Texas Library System, Inc
Open Mon & Tues 10-7, Wed-Fri 10-6, Sat 10-4, Sun 1-4
Friends of the Library Group

L　MCGINNIS, LOCHRIDGE & KILGORE, LLP*, Law Library, 600 Congress Ave, Ste 2100, 78701. SAN 372-1566. Tel: 512-495-6000. FAX: 512-495-6093. Web Site: www.mcginnislaw.com. *Librn,* Joan O'Mara; E-mail: jomara@mcginnislaw.com
Library Holdings: Bk Vols 6,500; Per Subs 50
Automation Activity & Vendor Info: (Cataloging) Inmagic, Inc.
Database Vendor: LexisNexis, Westlaw
Wireless access
Restriction: Staff use only

S　ELISABET NEY MUSEUM LIBRARY, 304 East 44th St, 78751. SAN 320-8745. Tel: 512-458-2255. FAX: 512-453-0638. Web Site: www.elisabetneymuseum.org. *Educ Coordr,* Colin Haymes. Subject Specialists: *Austin, Tex hist,* Colin Haymes
Founded 1911
Library Holdings: Bk Titles 320
Special Collections: Elisabet Ney Correspondence Coll
Subject Interests: 19th Century Am art, 19th Century Am hist, 19th Century European art, 19th Century European hist, Texan
Restriction: Open by appt only

G　PUBLIC UTILITY COMMISSION OF TEXAS LIBRARY*, 1701 N Congress, 7th Flr, 78701. (Mail add: PO Box 13326, 78711-3326), SAN 327-5582. Tel: 512-936-7080. FAX: 512-936-7079. E-mail: library@puc.state.tx.us. Web Site: www.puc.state.tx.us. *Librn,* Carol Maxwell; Tel: 512-936-7075; Staff 1 (MLS 1)
Founded 1975
Library Holdings: Bk Vols 8,000; Per Subs 25
Special Collections: Electric Power Research Institute Research Reports
Automation Activity & Vendor Info: (Cataloging) Biblionix; (OPAC) Biblionix; (Serials) Biblionix
Function: For res purposes
Open Mon-Fri 8-5
Restriction: Non-circulating to the pub

S　REGIONAL FOUNDATION LIBRARY*, 1009 E 11th St, 2nd Flr, 78702. SAN 316-0475. Tel: 512-475-7373. E-mail: rfl@austin.utexas.edu. Web Site: www.utexas.edu/diversity/ddce/rfl/index.php. *Librn,* Allison Supancic; E-mail: allison.supancic@mail.utexas.edu; Staff 2 (MLS 1, Non-MLS 1)
Founded 1962
Library Holdings: Bk Titles 800; Per Subs 2; Spec Interest Per Sub 2
Subject Interests: Evaluation, Grants, Volunteerism
Open Mon-Fri 8-5
Restriction: Non-circulating

C　SAINT EDWARDS UNIVERSITY*, Scarborough-Phillips Library, 3001 S Congress Ave, 78704-6489. SAN 361-1825. Tel: 512-448-8469. Interlibrary Loan Service Tel: 512-448-8738. Reference Tel: 512-448-8474. FAX: 512-448-8737. Web Site: library.stedwards.edu. *Dir,* Pongracz Sennyey; Tel: 512-448-8470, E-mail: pongracz@stedwards.edu; *Head, Pub Serv,* Margaret Warner; Tel: 512-428-1024, E-mail: margyw@stedwards.edu; *Archivist, Curator, Spec Coll,* April Sullivan; *Acq, Cat, Tech Serv,* Tina Buck; Tel: 512-464-8825, E-mail: tinab@stedwards.edu; *Libr Instruction,* Anna Stewart; Tel: 512-428-1096, E-mail: annas@stedwards.edu; *Ser,* Todd Butler; Tel: 512-233-1679, E-mail: toddb@stedwards.edu. Subject Specialists: *Soc sci,* Margaret Warner; *Nat sci,* Tina Buck; *Bus,* Anna Stewart; *Philosophy, Relig,* Todd Butler; Staff 18 (MLS 9, Non-MLS 9)
Founded 1889. Enrl 4,651; Fac 140; Highest Degree: Master
Jul 2007-Jun 2008 Income $1,501,019. Mats Exp $434,996, Books $80,701, Per/Ser (Incl. Access Fees) $114,382, Micro $6,109, AV Mat $6,717, Electronic Ref Mat (Incl. Access Fees) $216,921, Presv $10,166. Sal $875,796 (Prof $557,113)
Library Holdings: Microforms 6,073; Bk Vols 161,644; Per Subs 1,909; Videos 3,362
Automation Activity & Vendor Info: (Acquisitions) Innovative Interfaces, Inc; (Cataloging) Innovative Interfaces, Inc - OCLC; (Circulation) Innovative Interfaces, Inc; (Course Reserve) Innovative Interfaces, Inc; (ILL) OCLC ILLiad; (Media Booking) Innovative Interfaces, Inc; (OPAC) Innovative Interfaces, Inc - OCLC; (Serials) Innovative Interfaces, Inc
Database Vendor: EBSCOhost, JSTOR, LexisNexis, OCLC FirstSearch, OCLC WorldCat, ProQuest, SerialsSolutions
Wireless access
Partic in OCLC Online Computer Library Center, Inc
Special Services for the Blind - Reader equip
Restriction: Open to researchers by request
Friends of the Library Group

SR　SAINT ELIAS ORTHODOX CHURCH LIBRARY*, 408 E 11th St, 78701. SAN 328-395X. Tel: 512-476-2314. FAX: 512-476-2314. Web Site: www.st-elias.org.
Library Holdings: Bk Vols 1,500
Subject Interests: Theol
Wireless access
Function: Ref serv available, Res libr
Restriction: Mem only

G　TEXAS COMMISSION ON ENVIRONMENT QUALITY LIBRARY*, 12100 Park 35 Circle, MC-196, 78753. (Mail add: PO Box 13087, 78711-3087), SAN 316-0629. Tel: 512-239-0020. FAX: 512-239-0022. Web Site: www.tceq.state.tx.us. *Head Librn,* Vonda K Todd; Tel: 512-239-0024, E-mail: vonda.todd@tceq.state.tx.us; *Librn,* John Conger; E-mail: john.conger@tceq.state.tx.us; Staff 2 (MLS 2)
Founded 1964
Library Holdings: Bk Titles 60,000; Bk Vols 66,000; Per Subs 250
Special Collections: Civil Engineering (United States Corps of Engineers Coll); Engineers & United States Bureau of Reclamation Papers; Geology (United States Geological Survey Papers); Water Resources Development (Texas Water Development Board Publications)
Subject Interests: Air, Fields of sci relating to water resources, Geol, Hazardous waste, Hydraulic eng, Land use, Outdoor recreation, Problems, Solid waste, Water quality, Weather modification
Automation Activity & Vendor Info: (Cataloging) SirsiDynix; (Circulation) SirsiDynix; (OPAC) SirsiDynix; (Serials) SirsiDynix

Open Mon-Fri 8-12 & 1-5
Restriction: Open to pub for ref only

GM TEXAS DEPARTMENT OF STATE HEALTH SERVICES, Library &
Information Services Program, 1100 W 49th St, 78756-3199. (Mail add:
PO Box 149347, Mailcode 1955, 78714-9347), SAN 316-0696. Tel:
512-776-7559. FAX: 512-776-7474 (AV Library), 512-776-7683. E-mail:
library@dshs.state.tx. Web Site: www.dshs.state.tx.us/library/default.shtm.
AV, Librn, Team Leader, Elizabeth DeLeon; Tel: 512-776-2787, E-mail:
elizabeth.deleon@dshs.state.tx.us; *AV, Librn,* Kelli Kennedy; Tel:
512-776-7260, E-mail: kelli.kennedy@dshs.state.tx.us; *Librn,* David
McLellan; Tel: 512-776-2882, E-mail: david.mclellan@dshs.state.tx.us;
Librn, Team Leader, Carolyn Medina; E-mail:
carolyn.medina@dshs.state.tx.us; *Mgr,* Cindy Faries; Tel: 512-776-6492,
E-mail: cindy.faries@dshs.state.tx.us; Staff 9 (MLS 4, Non-MLS 5)
Founded 1958
Library Holdings: AV Mats 6,000; Bk Titles 10,400; Bk Vols 20,000; Per
Subs 250
Special Collections: Disabilities & Rehabilitation; Early Childhood
Intervention; Health & Safety; Texas Health Statistics
Automation Activity & Vendor Info: (Cataloging) EOS International;
(Circulation) EOS International; (OPAC) EOS International; (Serials) EOS
International
Partic in National Network of Libraries of Medicine
Open Mon-Fri 8-5
Restriction: Circ limited

G TEXAS EDUCATION AGENCY*, 1701 N Congress Ave, 78701-1494.
SAN 321-9259. Tel: 512-463-9050. FAX: 512-475-3447. *Chief Librn,*
Linda Kemp; Staff 2 (MLS 2)
Founded 1968
Library Holdings: Bk Vols 20,000; Per Subs 250
Special Collections: ERIC Coll, micro
Subject Interests: Pub sch educ
Wireless access
Function: Res libr
Restriction: Non-circulating, Open by appt only

G TEXAS GENERAL LAND OFFICE*, Archives & Records Division
Library, Stephen F Austin Bldg, 1700 N Congress Ave, 78701. SAN
372-9613. Tel: 512-463-5277. FAX: 512-475-4619. Web Site:
www.glo.texas.gov. *In Charge,* Mark Lambert
Founded 1836
Library Holdings: Bk Vols 400
Special Collections: Map Coll; Pub Lands Archives; Spanish Coll
Open Mon-Fri 8-5
Restriction: Non-circulating

G TEXAS HISTORICAL COMMISSION LIBRARY*, 1511 Colorado,
78701. (Mail add: PO Box 12276, 78711-2276), SAN 326-5323. Tel:
512-463-8817. Administration Tel: 512-936-4323. FAX: 512-936-0237.
Administration FAX: 512-463-8222. Web Site:
www.thc.state.tx.us/thclibrary/libdefault.shtml.
Founded 1998
Library Holdings: Bk Titles 3,500; Bk Vols 5,000; Per Subs 30
Special Collections: Archeological Surveys & Reports; National Register
in Texas Files; National Register in Texas Files; Official Texas Historical
Marker Files. Oral History
Subject Interests: Archaeology, Archit
Automation Activity & Vendor Info: (Cataloging) Follett Software
Restriction: By permission only, Circulates for staff only, External users
must contact libr, Not a lending libr, Open by appt only, Open to pub by
appt only, Open to pub for ref only, Researchers by appt only, Staff use,
pub by appt, Visitors must make appt to use bks in the libr

S TEXAS LEGISLATIVE REFERENCE LIBRARY*, State Capitol Bldg,
1100 N Congress Ave, Rm 2N-3, 78701. (Mail add: PO Box 12488,
78711-2488), SAN 316-0513. Tel: 512-463-1252. FAX: 512-475-4626.
E-mail: lrl.service@lrl.state.tx.us. Web Site: www.lrl.state.tx.us. *Dir,* Mary
Camp
Founded 1969
Library Holdings: Bk Vols 50,000
Special Collections: Texas Legislative Bills 1973-Present; Texas State
Documents
Subject Interests: Law, Legislation, Polit sci, Pub affairs
Open Mon-Fri 8-5
Restriction: Ref only

M TEXAS MEDICAL ASSOCIATION*, Knowledge Center Library, 401 W
15th, 78701-1680. SAN 316-0661. Tel: 512-370-1300. E-mail:
tma.library@texmed.org. Web Site: www.texmed.org. *Dir,* Claire Duncan;
E-mail: claire.duncan@texmed.org; *Librn,* Barbara Tims; Staff 8 (MLS 4,
Non-MLS 4)
Founded 1922

Library Holdings: Bk Vols 800; Per Subs 80
Special Collections: History of medicine in Texas
Subject Interests: Clinical med
Automation Activity & Vendor Info: (Cataloging) EOS International;
(OPAC) EOS International; (Serials) EOS International
Function: Ref serv available, Res libr
Publications: CME Resource Catalog; Library Services Guide for
Community Users; Library Services: A Guide for TMA Members
Partic in Docline; National Network of Libraries of Medicine; S Cent
Regional Med Libr Program
Restriction: Mem only, Non-circulating
Friends of the Library Group

S TEXAS NATURAL RESOURCES INFORMATION SYSTEM*, Steven F
Austin State Bldg, Rm B40, 1700 N Congress Ave, 78701. (Mail add: PO
Box 13231, 78711-3231), SAN 323-4657. Tel: 512-463-8337. FAX:
512-463-7274. Web Site: www.tnris.org.
Library Holdings: Bk Vols 1,000; Per Subs 12
Function: Res libr
Restriction: Non-circulating, Open by appt only

S TEXAS SCHOOL FOR THE BLIND*, Learning Resource Center Library,
1100 W 45th St, 78756. SAN 326-3819. Tel: 512-454-8631. FAX:
512-206-9450. Web Site: www.tsbvi.edu. *Librn,* Renee Toy; Staff 4 (MLS
1, Non-MLS 3)
Library Holdings: Bk Vols 10,600; Per Subs 50
Special Collections: Special Education for visually handicapped
Automation Activity & Vendor Info: (Cataloging) Follett Software;
(Circulation) Follett Software
Restriction: Students only

GL TEXAS STATE LAW LIBRARY*, Tom C Clark Bldg, 205 W 14th St,
78701-1614. (Mail add: PO Box 12367, 78711-2367), SAN 316-0718. Tel:
512-463-1722. FAX: 512-463-1728. Web Site: www.sll.state.tx.us. *Dir,*
Dale Propp; Staff 7 (MLS 7)
Founded 1971
Library Holdings: Bk Vols 130,000; Per Subs 275
Special Collections: US Document Depository
Subject Interests: Law, Legal hist
Wireless access
Open Mon-Fri 8-5
Friends of the Library Group

P TEXAS STATE LIBRARY & ARCHIVES COMMISSION*, 1201 Brazos
St, 78701. (Mail add: PO Box 12927, 78711-2927), SAN 361-1914. Tel:
512-463-5460. Interlibrary Loan Service Tel: 512-463-5406. Reference Tel:
512-463-5455. Toll Free Tel: 800-252-9386 (Tex only). Administration
FAX: 512-463-5436. E-mail: info@tsl.state.tx.us. Web Site:
www.tsl.state.tx.us. *Dir, State Librn,* Peggy D Rudd; E-mail:
peggy.rudd@tsl.state.tx.us; *Asst State Librn,* Edward Seidenberg; E-mail:
eseidenberg@tsl.state.tx.us; *Chief Financial Officer, Dir of Admin Serv Div,*
Vincent Houston; *Dir, Libr Develop & Networking,* Deborah Littrell; Tel:
512-463-5456, Fax: 512-463-8800, E-mail: dlittrell@tsl.state.tx.us; *Info
Tech Dir,* Manuel Alvarez; Tel: 512-463-5481, E-mail:
manuel.alvarez@tsl.state.tx.us; *State Rec Mgr,* Position Currently Open;
State Archivist, Jelain Chubb; Tel: 512-463-5467, E-mail:
jchubb@tsl.state.tx.us; *Talking Bks,* Ava M Smith; Tel: 512-463-5428, Fax:
512-936-0685, E-mail: amsmith@tsl.state.tx.us; Staff 97 (MLS 58,
Non-MLS 39)
Founded 1909
Library Holdings: e-books 28,281; Bk Vols 2,000,000; Per Subs 352
Special Collections: Broadside Coll; History Coll, maps, ms; Professional
Librarianship Coll; Texas & Federal Government Documents Coll. State
Document Depository; US Document Depository
Subject Interests: Fed govt, Genealogy, Pub policy, State govt, Texana
Automation Activity & Vendor Info: (Cataloging) OCLC Connexion;
(Circulation) SirsiDynix; (ILL) OCLC WorldCat; (OPAC) SirsiDynix;
(Serials) SirsiDynix
Database Vendor: EBSCOhost, Gale Cengage Learning, netLibrary,
OCLC FirstSearch, OCLC WebJunction, OCLC WorldCat, ProQuest,
SirsiDynix
Wireless access
Function: Archival coll, Distance learning, Govt ref serv, Homebound
delivery serv, ILL available, Libr develop, Online searches, Prof lending
libr, Summer reading prog, Workshops
Publications: Instruction Manuals; Library Developments (Online only);
Texas Academic Library Statistics
Special Services for the Blind - Bks & mags in Braille, on rec, tape &
cassette; Large print & cassettes; Local mags & bks recorded; Machine
repair; Newsletter (in large print, Braille or on cassette); Production of
talking bks; Reader equip; Ref serv; Talking bks; Talking bks & player
equip; Tel Pioneers equip repair group; Volunteer serv
Open Mon-Fri 8-5

Restriction: Circ limited, Closed stack, Non-circulating coll
Friends of the Library Group
Branches: 1
SAM HOUSTON REGIONAL LIBRARY & RESEARCH CENTER, 650
FM 1011, Liberty, 77575. (Mail add: PO Box 310, Liberty, 77575-0310),
SAN 326-4505. Tel: 936-336-8821. E-mail:
samhoustoncenter@tsl.state.tx.us. Web Site: www.tsl.state.tx.us/shc. *Dir,*
Position Currently Open; *Archivist, Curator,* Lisa Meisch; E-mail:
lisa.meisch@tsl.state.tx.us; *Pub Serv,* Darlene Mott; E-mail:
darlene.mott@tsl.state.tx.us
Founded 1977
Sept 2008-Aug 2009 Income $210,000. Sal $165,871 (Prof $110,000)
Library Holdings: Bk Titles 6,138; Per Subs 11
Special Collections: Papers of Martin Dies, archives; Papers of Price
Daniel, archives; Sam Houston Images (Jean Houston Baldwin Coll).
Oral History
Function: Archival coll, For res purposes
Open Tues-Fri 8-5, Sat 9-4
Restriction: Non-circulating to the pub
Friends of the Library Group

P   TEXAS STATE LIBRARY & ARCHIVES COMMISSION, Talking Book
Program, 1201 Brazos, 78711. (Mail add: PO Box 12927, 78711-2927),
SAN 316-0726. Tel: 512-463-5458. Toll Free Tel: 800-252-9605 (TX only).
FAX: 512-936-0685. E-mail: tbp.services@tsl.state.tx.us. Web Site:
www.texastalkingbooks.org. *Regional Librn,* Ava M Smith; Tel:
512-463-5428, E-mail: amsmith@tsl.state.tx.us; *Coll Develop Librn,* Lisa
Hendricks; E-mail: lhendricks@tsl.state.tx.us; *Reader Serv Mgr,* Stacey
Hathaway-Bell; E-mail: shbell@tsl.state.tx.us; *Automation Syst Coordr,*
Jennifer Ronsen; E-mail: jronsen@tsl.state.tx.us; *Pub Awareness Coordr,*
Ruth Wedergren; Tel: 512-463-5452, E-mail: rwedergren@tsl.state.tx.us;
Staff 47.7 (MLS 11.6, Non-MLS 36.1)
Founded 1931
Library Holdings: Audiobooks 438,480; Braille Volumes 66,713; Large
Print Bks 25,500; Bk Titles 33,292
Special Collections: Audio Books; Braille Books; Disability Information;
Large Print Books; Spanish & Other Languages Coll
Wireless access
Function: Web-Braille
Special Services for the Blind - Assistive/Adapted tech devices, equip &
products; Audio mat; Bks & mags in Braille, on rec, tape & cassette; Bks
on cassette; Braille & cassettes; Braille alphabet card; Braille bks; Cassette
playback machines; Children's Braille; Digital talking bk; Extensive large
print coll; Home delivery serv; Info on spec aids & appliances; Large print
bks; Machine repair; Mags & bk reproduction/duplication; Newsletter (in
large print, Braille or on cassette); Production of talking bks; Tel Pioneers
equip repair group; Volunteer serv; Web-Braille
Open Mon-Fri 8-5
Restriction: Visually impaired students, teachers & their parents
Friends of the Library Group

S   3M LIBRARY & INFORMATION SERVICES*, Austin Information
Services, Bldg 130-1-N, 6801 Riverplace Blvd, 78726-9000. SAN
326-3673. Tel: 512-984-2124. FAX: 512-984-3237. *Head Librn,* Erika
Mittag; Staff 3 (MLS 2, Non-MLS 1)
Founded 1984
Library Holdings: Bk Titles 8,000; Per Subs 200
Subject Interests: Electronics
Automation Activity & Vendor Info: (Cataloging) Ex Libris Group;
(Circulation) Ex Libris Group; (OPAC) Ex Libris Group
Database Vendor: Dialog, Factiva.com
Open Mon-Fri 7:30-4:30

L   TRAVIS COUNTY LAW LIBRARY*, Travis City Admin Bldg, 314 W
11th, Rm 140, 78701-2112. SAN 374-6070. Tel: 512-854-4569. FAX:
512-854-9887. Web Site: www.traviscountylawlibrary.org. *Ref Serv,* Josie
Arjona; E-mail: josie.arjona@co.travis.tx.us; *Ref Serv,* Judy Helms; Tel:
512-854-9045, Fax: 512-473-9082, E-mail: judy.helms@co.travis.tx.us; *Ref
Serv,* Geri Krohn; Tel: 512-854-9273, Fax: 512-473-9082; Staff 6 (MLS 2,
Non-MLS 4)
Founded 1983
Library Holdings: Bk Titles 360; Bk Vols 12,000; Per Subs 20
Special Collections: Texas & Federal Law Coll
Automation Activity & Vendor Info: (Cataloging) Cuadra Associates;
(OPAC) Cuadra Associates
Database Vendor: LexisNexis, Westlaw
Function: For res purposes
Open Mon-Fri 8-5
Restriction: Circ limited, Non-circulating to the pub, Prof mat only

C   UNIVERSITY OF TEXAS AT AUSTIN*, Center for Transportation
Research Library, 1616 Guadalupe St, Ste 4.202, 78701. SAN 372-9648.
Tel: 512-232-3126. FAX: 512-232-3088. E-mail: ctrlib@uts.cc.utexas.edu.
Web Site: library.ctr.utexas.edu/index.html. *Mgr, Libr Serv,* Louise

Rosenzweig; Tel: 512-232-3138, E-mail:
louise.rosenzweig@engr.utexas.edu; Staff 2 (Non-MLS 2)
Library Holdings: CDs 220; Bk Vols 25,000; Per Subs 10; Videos 10
Special Collections: NAFTA Research; Texas Department of
Transportation Research; TRB, FHWA, State DOT Materials
Subject Interests: Transportation eng
Automation Activity & Vendor Info: (Cataloging) Inmagic, Inc.
Open Mon-Fri 8-12 & 1-5

C   UNIVERSITY OF TEXAS LIBRARIES*, Perry-Castaneda Library, 101 E
21st St, 78713. (Mail add: PO Box P, 78713-8916), SAN 361-1973. Tel:
512-495-4350. FAX: 512-495-4296. Web Site: www.lib.utexas.edu. *Vice
Provost & Dir,* Dr Fred M Heath; Staff 138 (MLS 138)
Founded 1883. Enrl 51,426; Fac 2,432; Highest Degree: Doctorate
Library Holdings: Bk Vols 8,482,207; Per Subs 48,096
Special Collections: US Document Depository
Automation Activity & Vendor Info: (Acquisitions) Innovative Interfaces,
Inc
Partic in ALA; Association of Research Libraries (ARL); Center for
Research Libraries; Coun of Libr Info Resources; Digital Libr Fedn;
Greater Western Library Alliance; OCLC Online Computer Library Center,
Inc; OCLC Research Library Partnership; TexSHARE - Texas State Library
& Archives Commission
Friends of the Library Group
Departmental Libraries:
ACQUISITIONS DEPARTMENT, PO Box P, PCL 2 306, S5450,
78713-8916. Tel: 512-495-4143. FAX: 512-495-4410. *Head Librn,*
Position Currently Open
ARCHITECTURE & PLANNING, Mail Code S5430, BTL 200,
78713-8916. (Mail add: PO Box P, 78713-8916). Tel: 512-495-4620.
Reference Tel: 512-495-4623. Web Site: www.lib.utexas.edu/apl/. *Head
Librn,* Beth Dodd; Tel: 512-495-4623, E-mail:
dodd.beth@austin.utexas.edu; Staff 2 (MLS 2)
Founded 1912
Library Holdings: Bk Vols 88,000; Per Subs 240
Special Collections: Alexander Architectural Archive
Subject Interests: Archit, Architectural hist, City planning, Interior
design, Landscape archit, Regional planning
NETTIE LEE BENSON LATIN AMERICAN COLLECTION, Sid
Richardson Hall 1-108, 78713-8916, SAN 361-2309. Tel: 512-495-4520.
Circulation Tel: 512-495-4522. FAX: 512-495-4568. E-mail:
blac@lib.utexas.edu. Web Site: www.lib.utexas.edu/benson/contacts.html.
Head Librn, Ann Hartness; *Asst Head Librn,* Margo Gutierrez; *Librn,*
Pamela Mann; *Librn,* Craig Schroer; *Archivist,* Christian Kelleher;
Bibliographer, Donald Gibbs
Library Holdings: Bk Vols 888,670
Special Collections: Afro-Jamaican Folklore (Joseph G Moore Coll);
Americo Paredes papers; Author collections of Sor Juana Ines de la
Cruz; Brazilian Music (David P Appleby Coll); Central American
Materials (Arturo Taracena Flores Coll; Roberto Carpio Nicolle Coll);
Cultural History & Literature of Brazil, Chile & the Rio de las Plata
Region (Manuel Gondra, Simon Lucuix & Pedro Martinez Reales Colls);
Joaquin Fernandez de Lizardi, Alfonso Reyes, Jose Angel Gutierrez,
Julian Samora Library, Jose Toribio Medina & Many Literary Figures of
Mexico, Argentina, Brazil, Chile & Peru; Jose Cardenas & Intercultural
Development Research Association Archives; Julio Cortazar Literary
Papers; Letters of Santa Anna & Pancho Villa; Manuscripts from 16th to
20th Century, incl 16th Century Relaciones Geograficas; Martin Fierro
Coll; Media Materials of Chile, Bolivia & Peru (Diego Munoz Coll);
Mexican Cultural History & Literature (Genaro Garcia, Joaquin Garcia
Icazbalceta, Juan Hernandez y Davalos, Sanchez Navarro, Lazaro de la
Garza, Pablo Salce Arrendondo & W B Stephens Colls); Papers of Six
Mexican Presidents & Other 19th Century Mexican Figures; Presidential
Papers of League of United Latin American Citizens; St John d'el Rey
Mining Company Archives
Subject Interests: Latin Am studies
Partic in OCLC Online Computer Library Center, Inc
Publications: Catalog of the Latin American Collection
BUREAU OF ECONOMIC GEOLOGY, PUBLICATIONS SALES
OFFICE & RESOURCE CENTER, 10100 Burnet Rd, Bldg 130,
78758-4445. (Mail add: Box X, University Sta, 78713-8916). Tel:
512-471-7144, 512-475-9513. Reference Tel: 512-471-0302. Toll Free
Tel: 888-839-4365. FAX: 512-471-0140. Toll Free FAX: 888-839-6277.
E-mail: begmail@beg.utexas.edu. Web Site:
www.beg.utexas.edu/info/info_res.php. *In Charge,* Amanda Masterson;
Tel: 512-471-2794, E-mail: amanda.masterson@beg.utexas.edu; Staff 1
(MLS 1)
Special Collections: Bureau Contract Reports; Historical Geology
(Girard Coll); South Texas/Coastal Geology (W Armstrong Price Coll);
Unpublished Open-File Documents, letter rpts, maps, theses; Virgil E
Barnes Coll, aerial photos, geologic maps
Subject Interests: Gas, Geol, Geophysics, Geoscience, Oil, Tex
Function: Archival coll, Bks on CD, Computers for patron use, Mail &
tel request accepted, Online cat, Res libr, Wheelchair accessible

Open Mon-Fri 8-5
Restriction: Circ limited, Circulates for staff only, In-house use for visitors, Non-circulating coll, Not a lending libr
CENTER FOR AMERICAN HISTORY, SRH 2-101, D1100, University of Texas at Austin, 78712. Tel: 512-495-4515. Reference Tel: 512-495-4532. Information Services Tel: 512-495-4518. FAX: 512-495-4542. Web Site: www.cah.utexas.edu. *Dir,* Don E Carleton; *Assoc Dir,* Alison M Beck; *Asst Dir,* Patrick Cox; *Asst Dir,* Brenda Gunn; *Head, Archives & Ms,* Stephanie Malmros; *Head, Ref,* Katherine Fox
Library Holdings: Bk Vols 150,000; Per Subs 103
Special Collections: American History Coll; Congressional History Coll; Eugene C Barker Texas History Coll; John Nance Garner House & Museum (Uvalde, Texas); Research & Collections Division; Sam Rayburn Library & Museum (Bonham, Texas); The George W Littlefield Southern History Coll; University of Texas Archives; Western Americana Coll; Winedale Historical Center (Round Top, Texas). Oral History
Subject Interests: Archives, Hist of old south, Imprints, Manuscripts, Music, Newsps, Oral hist, Tex
Publications: Newsletter
Open Mon-Fri 9-5
Friends of the Library Group
CLASSICS, Waggener Hall 1, 78713, SAN 361-2457. Tel: 512-495-4690. *Librn,* Gina Giovannone
Library Holdings: Bk Vols 27,292
COLLECTIONS DEPOSIT LIBRARY, PO Box P, CDL, SS461, 78713-8916. Tel: 512-495-4694. FAX: 512-495-4651. *Supvr,* Jeff Newberry
EAST ASIAN LIBRARY PROGRAM, PO Box P, PCL4-114, S5431, 78713-8916. Tel: 512-495-4325. *Head Librn,* Meng-fen Su; E-mail: msu@mail.utexas.edu; Staff 5 (MLS 2, Non-MLS 3)
Library Holdings: Bk Vols 104,000
Subject Interests: China, Japan, Korea
FINE ARTS, Doty Fine Arts Bldg 3-200, 23rd & Trinity, 78713. (Mail add: Fine Arts Library, One University Sta S5437, 78712), SAN 361-2511. Tel: 512-495-4480. FAX: 512-495-4490. Web Site: www.lib.utexas.edu/fal. *Librn,* David Hunter; Tel: 512-495-4475, E-mail: david.hunter@mail.utexas.edu; *Librn,* Beth Kerr; Tel: 512-495-4482, E-mail: bethkerr@mail.utexas.edu; *Librn,* Laura Schwartz; Tel: 512-495-4476, E-mail: lschwartz@austin.utexas.edu. Subject Specialists: *Music,* David Hunter; *Dance,* Beth Kerr; *Art,* Laura Schwartz; Staff 30 (MLS 3, Non-MLS 27)
Founded 1979
Library Holdings: AV Mats 50,000; Bk Vols 300,000; Per Subs 600
Special Collections: Historical Music Recordings Coll
Subject Interests: Art, Dance, Music
Function: AV serv, Ref serv available, Res libr
Open Mon-Thurs 8am-10pm, Fri 8-5, Sat 1-5, Sun 1-10
Friends of the Library Group
INTERLIBRARY SERVICES DEPARTMENT, PO Box P, PCL1-343, S5463, 78713-8916. Tel: 512-495-4134. Interlibrary Loan Service Tel: 512-495-4131. FAX: 512-495-4283. *In Charge,* Wendy Nesmith
JAMAIL CENTER FOR LEGAL RESEARCH, University of Texas School of Law, 727 E Dean Keeton St, 78705-3224, SAN 361-2783. Tel: 512-471-7726. Reference Tel: 512-471-6220. Administration Tel: 512-471-7735. FAX: 512-471-0243. Web Site: tarlton.law.utexas.edu. *Dir,* Roy M Mersky; E-mail: rmersky@mail.law.utexas.edu; *Assoc Dir,* Brian Quigley; *Asst Dir,* Tobe Liebert; *Asst Dir,* Cathy Mantor-Ramirez; *Head, Cat,* Barbara Washecka; *Head, Res Serv,* Kumar Percy; *Head, Spec Coll,* Michael Widener; *Access Serv,* Abigail Schultz; *Acq,* Pierrette Moreno; *Ref Serv,* Mark Holman; *Ref Serv,* Marlyn Robinson; Staff 19 (MLS 16, Non-MLS 3)
Founded 1886
Library Holdings: Bk Vols 1,012,401; Per Subs 7,492
Special Collections: ABA Gavel Committee Award entries; Holdings of Foreign Countries (Western Europe, Latin America, Middle East); Law & Popular Culture Coll; Papers of Tom C Clark, Assoc Justice, Supreme Court of the United States
Subject Interests: Constitutional law, Human rights, Intl law
Partic in OCLC Online Computer Library Center, Inc; RLIN (Research Libraries Information Network)
Publications: Annual report; Tarlton Law Library Legal History Series
Friends of the Library Group
LIFE SCIENCE (BIOLOGY, PHARMACY), Main Bldg 220, 78713, SAN 361-266X. Tel: 512-495-4630. FAX: 512-495-4638. Web Site: www.lib.utexas.edu/lsl/. *Head Librn,* Nancy Elder; Tel: 512-495-4635, E-mail: n.elder@mail.utexas.edu
Library Holdings: Bk Vols 220,000; Per Subs 1,800
Subject Interests: Biological sci, Pharm
MALLET CHEMISTRY LIBRARY, Welch Hall 2.132, 78712. (Mail add: 105 E 24th St, Stop S5433, 78712-1577), SAN 361-2422. Tel: 512-495-4600. Web Site: www.lib.utexas.edu/chem. *Librn,* David Flaxbart; Staff 3 (MLS 1, Non-MLS 2)
Library Holdings: Bk Vols 101,000
Subject Interests: Chem, Chem eng, Food sci

MARINE SCIENCE, Marine Science Institute, 750 Channelview Dr, Port Aransas, 78373-5015, SAN 371-5965. Tel: 361-749-6723, 361-749-6778. FAX: 361-749-6725. Web Site: www.lib.utexas.edu/msl. *Head Librn,* Liz DeHart; E-mail: liz@utmsi.utexas.edu; Staff 2 (MLS 1, Non-MLS 1)
Founded 1946. Fac 13; Highest Degree: Doctorate
Library Holdings: Bk Vols 40,000; Per Subs 100
Subject Interests: Ecosystems, Environ toxicology, Marine biosciences, Marine culture systs, Marine sci
Function: Doc delivery serv, For res purposes, Handicapped accessible, ILL available, Online searches, Photocopying/Printing, Ref serv available
Partic in Association of Research Libraries (ARL)
Publications: Contributions in Marine Science
Open Mon-Fri 8-5
Restriction: Circ limited, In-house use for visitors, Internal circ only, Non-circulating to the pub, Open to pub for ref only, Open to students, fac & staff
MCKINNEY ENGINEERING LIBRARY, One University Sta S5435, ECJ 1.300, 78712, SAN 316-0742. Tel: 512-495-4511. FAX: 512-495-4507. E-mail: englib@lib.utexas.edu. Web Site: www.lib.utexas.edu/engin. *Head Librn,* Susan Ardis; E-mail: s.ardis@mail.utexas.edu; *Asst Librn,* Larayne Dallas; E-mail: ldallas@austin.utexas.edu; *Instruction Librn, Sci Librn,* Robyn Rosenberg; *Circ Supvr,* Claudia Fuentes
Library Holdings: Bk Vols 165,000
Special Collections: Engineering Industry Standards, micro; Master Catalog Service; Patents, micro; US Patents
MIDDLE EASTERN LIBRARY PROGRAM, 21st & Speedway, 78713. (Mail add: PO Box P, 78713-8916). Tel: 512-495-4322. FAX: 512-495-4296. *Librn,* Roberta L Dougherty; Staff 5 (MLS 1, Non-MLS 4)
Library Holdings: Bk Vols 319,200
Subject Interests: Islamic world
Publications: Arabic & Persian Periodicals in the Middle East Collection
PERRY-CASTANEDA LIBRARY (MAIN LIBRARY), 101 E 21st St, 78712-1266. (Mail add: PO Box P, UT Station, 78713-8916). Tel: 512-495-4350. Web Site: www.lib.utexas.edu/pcl/. *Vice Provost & Dir,* Dr Fred M Heath; *Circ,* Suzanne McAnna; *Doc,* Paul Rascoe; *ILL,* Wendy Nesmith; *Per,* William Kopplin; *Ref,* Jenifer Flaxbart
PHYSICS-MATHEMATICS-ASTRONOMY, Robert L Moore Hall 4-200, 78713, SAN 361-2635. Tel: 512-495-4610. FAX: 512-495-4611. E-mail: pma@lib.utexas.edu. Web Site: www.lib.utexas.edu/pma. *Librn,* Molly White
Library Holdings: Bk Vols 112,100
POPULATION RESEARCH CENTER LIBRARY, Main Bldg 1800, G1800, 78712, SAN 361-2759. Tel: 512-471-8332. Information Services Tel: 512-471-8299. FAX: 512-471-4886. Web Site: www.prc.utexas.edu. *Dir,* Mark Hayward; E-mail: mhayward@prc.utexas.edu; *Asst Dir,* Stephen Trejo; E-mail: trejo@eco.utexas.edu; *Mrg, Admin Serv,* Mary De La Garza; E-mail: marydlg@prc.utexas.edu
Founded 1971
Library Holdings: Bk Vols 35,000
Special Collections: World Fertility Survey, publ depository
Subject Interests: Demography, Domestic demography, Educ, Family life, Human ecology, Latin Am, Relig, Soc policy
Publications: Handbook of National Population Census: Africa & Asia; International Population Census Bibliography: 1965-68; Latin America & the Caribbean, North America, Oceania & Europe; Revision & Update: 1945-1977
HARRY RANSOM CENTER, 300 W 21st St, 78712. (Mail add: University of Texas, PO Box 7219, 78713-7219), SAN 361-2724. Tel: 512-471-8944. Reference Tel: 512-471-9119. Automation Services Tel: 512-471-8903. Reference FAX: 512-471-2899. Administration FAX: 512-471-9646. E-mail: info@hrc.utexas.edu, reference@hrc.utexas.edu. Web Site: www.hrc.utexas.edu. *Dir,* Dr Thomas F Staley; E-mail: tfs@austin.utexas.edu; *Assoc Dir & Hobby Found Librn,* Dr Richard W Oram; E-mail: roram@austin.utexas.edu; Staff 28 (MLS 17, Non-MLS 11)
Founded 1957
Library Holdings: Bk Titles 800,000; Per Subs 276
Special Collections: 17th & 18th Century First Editions, T J Wise Forgeries (Wrenn Library); 17th-20th Century First Editions; 18th Century First Editions & Source Materials (Aitken Library); A A Knopf Library & Archives; Author Colls of James Agee, Maxwell Anderson, W H Auden, H E Bates, Samuel Beckett, Arnold Bennett, Edmund Blunden, E B & Robert Browning, A Burgess, Byron, J B Cabell, Conrad, Hart Crane, E E Cummings, Edward Dahlberg, J F Dobie, Norman Douglas, A C Doyle, T S Eliot, Faulkner, Fitzgerald, C S Forester, E M Forster, John Fowles, Galsworthy, Goyen, Robert Graves, Graham Greene, D Hare, Lillian Hellman, Hemingway, Hergesheimer, W H Hudson, Huxley, Jacobson, Jeffers, Joyce, Adrienne Kennedy, D H Lawrence, T E Lawrence, Sinclair Lewis, Arthur Machen, Louis MacNeice, E L Masters, Maugham, David Mamet, George Meredith, James Michener, Arthur Miller, Henry Miller, Marianne Moore, Morley, Nabokov, Eugene O'Neill, Poe, Pound, Powys, Priestley, Prokosch, Purdy, Sassoon, Scott, Sexton, G B Shaw, Isaac Bashevis Singer, The Sitwells, C P Snow, Steinbeck, Tom Stoppard, Dylan Thomas, Tennessee

Williams, Tutuola, W C Williams, W B Yeats & Louis Zukofsky; Barrie, Eliot, Galsworthy, Shaw, Wilde, Yeats (T E Hanley Library); David O Selznick Archives; Don Delillo Coll; Edward Laroque Tinker Archives; Gernsheim Photography Coll; History of Science Coll; McManus-Young Magic Coll; Norman Mailer Coll; Robert De Niro Coll; Science Fiction (Currey Coll); Southwest Pacificana (Grattan Coll); Terrence McNally Coll; Theatre History & Dramatic Literature (Kemble, Garrick, P T Barnum, Houdini, Norman Bel Geddes Theatre Arts Library); Watergate (Woodward & Bernstein Coll)
Subject Interests: Am lit, British lit, Fr lit, Hist of photog, Performing arts
Restriction: Non-circulating coll
Friends of the Library Group
SERIALS ACQUISITIONS UNIT, PO Box P, 78713-8916. Tel: 512-495-4222. FAX: 512-495-4296. *Supvr,* Popma Kim; *Acq,* Hugh Banter; *Cat,* Alisha Little
SOUTH ASIAN LIBRARY PROGRAM, PCL 3 313, 78713, SAN 371-4985. Tel: 512-495-4329. FAX: 512-495-4397. *Librn,* Merry Burlingham; Staff 3 (MLS 1, Non-MLS 2)
Library Holdings: Bk Vols 300,000
WALTER GEOLOGY LIBRARY, Geology 4-202, 78713-8916, SAN 361-2546. Tel: 512-495-4680. FAX: 512-495-4102. E-mail: georequests@lib.utexas.edu. Web Site: www.lib.utexas.edu/geo. *Librn,* Dennis Trombatore
Library Holdings: Bk Vols 134,100
Special Collections: Tobin Geologic Maps Coll
Open Mon-Thurs (Spring & Fall) 8am-10pm, Fri 8-6, Sat 1-5, Sun 2-10; Mon-Fri (Summer) 8-5, Sun 1-7
WASSERMAN PUBLIC AFFAIRS LIBRARY, Sid Richardson Hall 3.243, S5442, 78712-1282. Tel: 512-495-4400. Reference Tel: 512-495-4401. FAX: 512-471-4697. E-mail: lib-hr@lib.utexas.edu. Web Site: www.lib.utexas.edu/pal. *Librn,* Stephen Littrell; Tel: 512-495-4401, E-mail: s.littrell@mail.utexas.edu
Library Holdings: Bk Vols 250,000
Special Collections: Governmental Financial Statements & Annual Reports. State Document Depository; US Document Depository
Subject Interests: Pub admin, Pub policy, Tex

P   WELLS BRANCH COMMUNITY LIBRARY*, 15001 Wells Port Dr, 78728. Tel: 512-989-3188. FAX: 512-989-3533. E-mail: wblibrarian@sbcglobal.net. Web Site: www.wblibrary.org. *Dir,* Donita Carlquist; E-mail: director@wblibrary.org; Staff 2 (MLS 1, Non-MLS 1)
Founded 1998. Pop 17,800; Circ 34,218
Library Holdings: AV Mats 6,000; CDs 500; Large Print Bks 300; Bk Titles 35,000; Per Subs 50
Wireless access
Mem of Central Texas Library System, Inc
Open Mon-Thurs 10-8, Fri & Sat 10-6, Sun 1-6
Friends of the Library Group

P   WESTBANK COMMUNITY LIBRARY DISTRICT*, 1309 Westbank Dr, 78746. SAN 372-6789. Tel: 512-327-3045. Circulation Tel: 512-314-3588. Interlibrary Loan Service Tel: 512-314-3593. Reference Tel: 512-314-3582. Administration Tel: 512-314-3580. FAX: 512-327-3074. Web Site: www.westbanklibrary.com. *Dir,* Mary Jo Finch; E-mail: maryjo@westbanklibrary.com; *Coll Develop, Head, Tech Serv,* Tristan Boyd; Tel: 512-314-3590, E-mail: tristan@westbanklibrary.com; *Cat/Ref Librn,* Donna Woods; Tel: 512-314-3583, E-mail: donna@westbanklibrary.com; *Pub Relations Librn,* Trina Bolfing; E-mail: trina@westbanklibrary.com; *Ref & Prog Librn,* Sharon Temple; E-mail: sharon@westbanklibrary.com; *Br Mgr,* Mary Jo Finch; Tel: 512-381-1404; *Prog & Pub Relations Supvr,* Kristi Floyd; Tel: 512-314-3583, E-mail: kristi@westbanklibrary.com; *Ref & Info Supvr,* Rhonda Kuiper; E-mail: rhoda@westbanklibrary.com; *Tech Coordr,* Tom Watson; Tel: 512-314-3584, E-mail: tom@westbanklibrary.com; Staff 7 (MLS 6, Non-MLS 1)
Founded 1984. Pop 29,268; Circ 713,438
Jan 2010-Dec 2010 Income $1,675,471, State $13,172, Locally Generated Income $291,183, Other $1,371,116. Mats Exp $258,812, Books $151,247, Other Print Mats $55,935, Electronic Ref Mat (Incl. Access Fees) $51,630. Sal $803,046
Library Holdings: Audiobooks 5,782; CDs 5,782; DVDs 9,696; e-books 440; Electronic Media & Resources 58; Large Print Bks 650; Bk Titles 57,886; Bk Vols 76,415; Per Subs 228; Videos 9,696
Automation Activity & Vendor Info: (Cataloging) Biblionix; (Circulation) Biblionix; (ILL) Biblionix; (OPAC) Biblionix
Database Vendor: EBSCO Information Services, Gale Cengage Learning, ProQuest
Wireless access
Function: Adult bk club, After school storytime, Art exhibits, Audiobks via web, Bk club(s), Bks on CD, Chess club, Children's prog, Computers for patron use, Copy machines, e-mail & chat, E-Reserves, Electronic databases & coll, Fax serv, Free DVD rentals, Genealogy discussion group, Holiday prog, ILL available, Mail & tel request accepted, Online cat, Online info literacy tutorials on the web & in blackboard, Online ref,

OverDrive digital audio bks, Photocopying/Printing, Prog for adults, Prog for children & young adult, Ref serv in person, Senior outreach, Story hour, Summer reading prog, Tax forms, Telephone ref, Web-catalog, Wheelchair accessible
Publications: Annual report (Annually); Newflash (Bi-monthly); The Dragon's Tale (Bi-monthly); The Teen Scene (Bi-monthly)
Mem of Central Texas Library System, Inc
Partic in Tex Share
Open Mon, Tues, Thurs & Fri 10-6, Wed 10-8, Sat 10-4, Sun 1-6
Restriction: Non-resident fee
Friends of the Library Group
Branches: 1
LAURA BUSH COMMUNITY LIBRARY, 9411 Bee Cave Rd, 78733. Tel: 512-381-1400. Circulation Tel: 512-381-1401. Interlibrary Loan Service Tel: 512-381-1403. Administration Tel: 512-381-1404. FAX: 512-381-1421. *Br Mgr,* Position Currently Open. Subject Specialists: *Human resources,* Position Currently Open
Founded 2009
Automation Activity & Vendor Info: (Acquisitions) Biblionix; (Cataloging) Biblionix; (Circulation) Biblionix; (Course Reserve) Biblionix; (ILL) Biblionix; (OPAC) Biblionix
Function: Adult bk club, After school storytime, Art exhibits, Bk club(s), Bks on CD, Computer training, Computers for patron use, Copy machines, e-mail & chat, E-Reserves, Electronic databases & coll, Exhibits, Fax serv, Free DVD rentals, Genealogy discussion group, ILL available, Online cat, Online ref, Orientations, Photocopying/Printing, Prog for adults, Prog for children & young adult, Pub access computers, Ref & res, Ref serv in person, Scanner, Spoken cassettes & CDs, Spoken cassettes & DVDs, Story hour, Summer reading prog, Tax forms, Teen prog, Telephone ref, Web-catalog, Wheelchair accessible, Writing prog
Restriction: Circ to mem only, Non-resident fee

L   WRIGHT & GREENHILL PC*, Law Library, 221 W Sixth St, Ste 1800, 78701-3495. SAN 375-0221. Tel: 512-476-4600, Ext 327. FAX: 512-476-5382. Web Site: www.wrightgreenhill.com. *Librn,* Julie Erisson; Staff 2 (MLS 1, Non-MLS 1)
Library Holdings: Bk Vols 5,000; Per Subs 50
Restriction: Staff use only

AZLE

P   AZLE MEMORIAL LIBRARY*, 333 W Main St, 76020. SAN 316-0750. Tel: 817-444-7216. FAX: 817-444-7064. E-mail: library@ci.azle.tx.us. *Dir,* Curren McLane; E-mail: cmclane@ci.azle.tx.us; *Children's & YA Librn,* Stefanie Bara; E-mail: sbara@ci.azle.tx.us
Founded 1964. Pop 12,000; Circ 110,744
Library Holdings: AV Mats 8,334; Bk Vols 43,000; Per Subs 100
Subject Interests: Local hist
Automation Activity & Vendor Info: (Cataloging) Polaris Library Systems; (Circulation) Polaris Library Systems; (OPAC) Polaris Library Systems
Database Vendor: 3M Library Systems, Baker & Taylor, Polaris Library Systems
Mem of North Texas Library Partners
Open Mon, Wed & Fri 9-6, Tues & Thurs 9-8, Sat 9-2, Sun 2-5
Friends of the Library Group

BAIRD

P   CALLAHAN COUNTY LIBRARY*, 100 W Fourth St, B-1, 79504-5305. SAN 316-0769. Tel: 325-854-5875. FAX: 325-854-5841. *Librn,* Sonia Walker; E-mail: sonia.walker@callahancounty.org
Founded 1937. Pop 3,470
Library Holdings: AV Mats 303; Bk Titles 17,000; Bk Vols 34,653; Per Subs 16
Mem of Big Country Library System
Open Mon-Fri 1-5

BALCH SPRINGS

P   BALCH SPRINGS PUBLIC LIBRARY*, 12450 Elam Rd, 75180. SAN 376-4478. Tel: 972-913-3000. FAX: 972-286-8856. Web Site: www.balchsprings.lib.tx.us. *Dir,* Sandra Gallion; E-mail: sgallion@cityofbalchsprings.com; Staff 3 (Non-MLS 3)
Founded 1969. Pop 19,000; Circ 19,920
Library Holdings: Bks on Deafness & Sign Lang 15; Bk Titles 31,000; Per Subs 26
Wireless access
Special Services for the Blind - Cassettes
Open Mon 10-7, Thurs & Fri 10-5, Sat 11-3
Friends of the Library Group

BALLINGER

P   CARNEGIE LIBRARY OF BALLINGER, 204 N Eighth St, 76821. SAN
     316-0777. Tel: 325-365-3616. FAX: 325-365-5004. E-mail:
     carnegie.library@verizon.net. Web Site: www.carnegieofballinger.com. *Dir,*
     Kenna Clark; Staff 1 (Non-MLS 1)
     Founded 1909. Pop 6,602; Circ 25,500
     Library Holdings: Audiobooks 397; CDs 147; DVDs 24; Large Print Bks
     967; Bk Titles 13,340; Per Subs 15; Videos 325
     Automation Activity & Vendor Info: (Cataloging) LibLime; (Circulation)
     LibLime; (ILL) OCLC WorldCat
     Database Vendor: Plunkett Research, Ltd
     Wireless access
     Function: Bks on CD, Computers for patron use, Copy machines, Fax
     serv, Free DVD rentals, ILL available, Music CDs, Online cat,
     Photocopying/Printing, Prog for children & young adult, Pub access
     computers, Scanner, Spanish lang bks, Story hour, Summer reading prog
     Open Mon-Wed 9-5, Thurs 9-7

BALMORHEA

P   BALMORHEA PUBLIC LIBRARY*, 102 SW Main St, 79718. (Mail add:
     PO Box 355, 79718-0355), SAN 316-0785. Tel: 432-375-2522. FAX:
     432-375-0225. *Head Librn,* Rosa Dominguez
     Founded 1927. Pop 650
     Library Holdings: Bk Vols 4,139
     Wireless access
     Open Mon-Thurs 9-12 & 1-3, Fri 9-12:30

BANDERA

P   ALBERT & BESSIE MAE KRONKOSKY LIBRARY OF BANDERA
     COUNTY*, 515 Main St, 78003. (Mail add: PO Box 1568, 78003-1568),
     SAN 316-0793. Tel: 830-796-4213. FAX: 830-796-3449. E-mail:
     banderalibrary@gmail.com. Web Site: www.banderalibrary.org. *Dir,* John
     Hegemier; Staff 3 (Non-MLS 3)
     Founded 1934. Pop 9,025; Circ 35,000
     Library Holdings: Bk Vols 27,393; Per Subs 53
     Special Collections: Genealogy; Texana
     Automation Activity & Vendor Info: (Cataloging) Follett Software;
     (Circulation) Follett Software; (OPAC) Follett Software
     Wireless access
     Function: ILL available, Photocopying/Printing, Ref serv available
     Special Services for the Blind - Bks on cassette; Large print bks
     Open Mon & Wed-Fri 10-6, Tues 10-8, Sat 9-1
     Friends of the Library Group

BARTLETT

P   TEINERT MEMORIAL PUBLIC LIBRARY*, 337 N Dalton St, 76511.
     (Mail add: PO Box 12, 76511-0012), SAN 316-0815. Tel: 254-527-3208.
     FAX: 254-527-0217. E-mail: bartlib@sbcglobal.net. *Dir,* Valerie Bartlett;
     Staff 1 (Non-MLS 1)
     Founded 1976. Pop 1,600; Circ 45,000
     Library Holdings: AV Mats 400; Large Print Bks 300; Bk Vols 12,000;
     Per Subs 40
     Special Collections: Texana (Texas History). Oral History
     Subject Interests: Local hist
     Automation Activity & Vendor Info: (Acquisitions) Follett Software;
     (Cataloging) Follett Software; (Circulation) Follett Software; (OPAC)
     Follett Software; (Serials) Follett Software
     Wireless access
     Mem of Central Texas Library System, Inc
     Open Mon-Fri 9-5, Sat 9-12

BASTROP

P   BASTROP PUBLIC LIBRARY*, 1100 Church St, 78602. (Mail add: PO
     Box 670, 78602-0670), SAN 316-0823. Tel: 512-321-5441. Administration
     Tel: 512-303-0934. FAX: 512-321-3163. Web Site: www.bastroplibrary.org.
     Dir, Mickey DuVall; E-mail: mickey@bastroplibrary.org; *Asst Dir,* Sheilah
     Kosco; E-mail: skosco@bastroplibrary.org; *Cat,* Cookie Adkins; E-mail:
     cookie@bastroplibrary.org; *Ch,* Bonnie Ueckert; E-mail:
     bonniej@bastroplibrary.org; *Circ,* Linda Jenkins; E-mail:
     ljenkins@bastroplibrary.org; *ILL,* Kathy Lindsey; E-mail:
     kathyl@bastroplibrary.org; Staff 8 (MLS 2, Non-MLS 6)
     Founded 1972. Pop 27,000; Circ 192,700
     Oct 2010-Sept 2011 Income $626,246, State $8,893, City $608,853,
     County $8,500. Mats Exp $40,380, Books $26,250, Per/Ser (Incl. Access
     Fees) $6,000, AV Mat $7,630, Electronic Ref Mat (Incl. Access Fees)
     $500. Sal $461,300 (Prof $104,000)
     Library Holdings: Bks on Deafness & Sign Lang 13; CDs 587; DVDs
     1,617; e-books 28,290; Electronic Media & Resources 14; High
     Interest/Low Vocabulary Bk Vols 7; Large Print Bks 2,561; Bk Titles
     33,385; Bk Vols 35,648; Per Subs 91; Talking Bks 744; Videos 2,002
     Special Collections: Texana

Subject Interests: Genealogy, Local hist
Automation Activity & Vendor Info: (Acquisitions) Biblionix;
(Cataloging) Biblionix; (Circulation) Biblionix; (ILL) Biblionix; (OPAC)
Biblionix
Database Vendor: Gale Cengage Learning, OCLC FirstSearch
Wireless access
Function: Adult bk club, Audiobks via web, Bilingual assistance for
Spanish patrons, Children's prog, Citizenship assistance, Computer training,
Computers for patron use, Copy machines, Exhibits, Holiday prog, Home
delivery & serv to Sr ctr & nursing homes, ILL available, Music CDs,
Online cat, Photocopying/Printing, Prog for adults, Prog for children &
young adult, Pub access computers, Ref serv available, Ref serv in person,
Senior computer classes, Story hour, Summer reading prog, Tax forms,
Teen prog, Telephone ref, Web-catalog, Wheelchair accessible, Workshops
Mem of Central Texas Library System, Inc
Open Mon, Wed & Fri 10-6, Tues & Thurs 1-9, Sat 10-4
Restriction: Authorized patrons
Friends of the Library Group

BAY CITY

P   BAY CITY PUBLIC LIBRARY*, 1100 Seventh St, 77414. SAN 316-0831.
     Tel: 979-245-6931. FAX: 979-245-2614. E-mail: director@baycitytxlib.org.
     Web Site: www.baycitytxlib.org. *Dir,* Ann Moor; *Asst Dir,* Sue Hall; *Acq,*
     Janet Davis; *Cat,* Marjorie Carson; *Ch,* Andrea Savage; *Ref Serv,* Ramona
     Torres; Staff 11 (MLS 1, Non-MLS 10)
     Founded 1913. Pop 29,258
     Jan 2011-Dec 2011 Income (Main Library and Branch(s)) $344,288, State
     $3,000, City $40,000, Federal $3,000, County $165,000, Locally Generated
     Income $133,288. Mats Exp $51,900, Books $40,000, Per/Ser (Incl. Access
     Fees) $4,000, Micro $2,000, AV Equip $5,900. Sal $185,660 (Prof
     $40,000)
     Library Holdings: Bk Vols 70,000; Per Subs 65
     Subject Interests: Genealogy, Texana
     Automation Activity & Vendor Info: (Cataloging) Auto-Graphics, Inc;
     (Circulation) Auto-Graphics, Inc; (OPAC) Auto-Graphics, Inc
     Wireless access
     Function: ILL available, Photocopying/Printing, Prog for children & young
     adult, Ref serv available, Summer reading prog, Telephone ref, Wheelchair
     accessible
     Publications: Friends (newsletter)
     Open Mon-Thurs 10-7, Fri 10-6, Sat 10-4
     Friends of the Library Group
     Branches: 1
     SARGENT BRANCH, FM 457, Sargent, 77414, SAN 374-4442. Tel:
     979-245-3032. FAX: 979-245-7297. *Br Mgr,* Lynn Wilson
     Founded 1985
          Library Holdings: Bk Titles 6,553; Per Subs 62
          Subject Interests: Resorts
     Open Wed 10-4, Thurs & Fri 1-6, Sat 10-2
     Friends of the Library Group

BAYTOWN

J   LEE COLLEGE LIBRARY*, 150 Lee Dr, 77520. (Mail add: PO Box 818,
     77522), SAN 316-084X. Tel: 281-425-6379. FAX: 281-425-6557. Web
     Site: www.lee.edu/library. *Libr Dir,* Paul A Arrigo; Tel: 281-425-6447,
     E-mail: parrigo@lee.edu; *Outreach Serv Librn,* Lisa Reynold; *Distance
     Educ,* Jeanie Colson; Tel: 281-425-6497, E-mail: jcolson@lee.edu; *Govt
     Doc, Ser,* Julie Sayles; *Tech Serv,* Beverly Li; Staff 5 (MLS 5)
     Founded 1935. Enrl 6,087; Fac 198; Highest Degree: Associate
     Sept 2010-Aug 2011. Mats Exp $205,310, Books $96,653, Per/Ser (Incl.
     Access Fees) $53,400, Electronic Ref Mat (Incl. Access Fees) $55,257. Sal
     $496,613 (Prof $323,622)
     Library Holdings: AV Mats 3,838; e-books 43,017; Bk Vols 96,653; Per
     Subs 340
     Special Collections: Law Library Coll; Lee College Archives. Oral
     History; US Document Depository
     Subject Interests: Film studies, Local hist, Tex gulf coast
     Automation Activity & Vendor Info: (Cataloging) Polaris Library
     Systems; (Circulation) Polaris Library Systems; (Course Reserve) Polaris
     Library Systems; (OPAC) Polaris Library Systems; (Serials) Polaris Library
     Systems
     Wireless access
     Publications: Faculty Library Handbook; Student & Library Handbook
     Partic in TexSHARE - Texas State Library & Archives Commission
     Open Mon-Thurs 7:30-7, Fri 7:30-2, Sat 10-2
     Friends of the Library Group

P   STERLING MUNICIPAL LIBRARY*, Mary Elizabeth Wilbanks Ave,
     77520. SAN 316-0858. Tel: 281-427-7331. FAX: 281-420-5347. TDD:
     281-427-7331. E-mail: smlib@sml.lib.tx.us. Web Site: baytownlibrary.org.
     City Librn, Katherine Skinner Brown; *Ch,* Martin Shupla; *Teen Librn,*
     Lesley Washburn; *Mgr, Mat Serv,* Lisa S Coker; E-mail:
     lcoker@sml.lib.tx.us; *Coordr, Extn Serv,* Susan Chandler; *Coordr, Ref*

Serv-Adult, Cherie Morgan; *Pub Serv Adminr,* Jamie Eustace; Staff 10 (MLS 10)
Founded 1961. Pop 93,304; Circ 629,000
Library Holdings: Bk Vols 180,000; Per Subs 150
Special Collections: Oral History
Subject Interests: Local hist
Automation Activity & Vendor Info: (Cataloging) Innovative Interfaces, Inc; (Circulation) Innovative Interfaces, Inc; (OPAC) Innovative Interfaces, Inc; (Serials) Innovative Interfaces, Inc
Database Vendor: EBSCOhost, Gale Cengage Learning, OCLC FirstSearch
Wireless access
Function: ILL available
Publications: Brighter Horizons, a journal of SML/Literacy Volunteers of America Students
Special Services for the Deaf - Bks on deafness & sign lang; Closed caption videos; High interest/low vocabulary bks; TTY equip; Videos & decoder
Special Services for the Blind - Computer with voice synthesizer for visually impaired persons
Open Mon-Thurs 10-9, Fri & Sat 10-6, Sun 1-5
Friends of the Library Group

BEAUMONT

S   ART MUSEUM OF SOUTHEAST TEXAS LIBRARY, 500 Main St, 77701. (Mail add: PO Box 3703, 77704-3703), SAN 316-0874. Tel: 409-832-3432. FAX: 409-832-8508. E-mail: info@amset.org. Web Site: www.amset.org. *Educ Curator,* Sandra Laurette; E-mail: slaurette@amset.org
Founded 1950
Library Holdings: Bk Vols 3,859
Subject Interests: Anthropology, Archaeology, Archit, Art, Cultural hist, Humanities
Wireless access
Open Mon-Fri 10-5, Sat & Sun 12-5
Restriction: Non-circulating

S   BEAUMONT ENTERPRISE LIBRARY*, 380 Main St, 77701-2331. (Mail add: PO Box 3071, 77704-3071), SAN 370-4084. Tel: 409-833-3311. FAX: 409-838-2857. *Librn,* Terry Maillet-Jones; Staff 2 (Non-MLS 2)
Library Holdings: DVDs 5; Electronic Media & Resources 4; Microforms 2; Bk Titles 250
Subject Interests: Clip file, Ref mat
Restriction: Employees only

P   BEAUMONT PUBLIC LIBRARY SYSTEM*, 801 Pearl St, 77701. (Mail add: PO Box 3827, 77704), SAN 361-2872. Tel: 409-981-5911. FAX: 409-838-6838. TDD: 409-832-1761. Web Site: www.beaumontlibrary.org. *Libr Adminr,* Paul Eddy; Tel: 409-981-5912, E-mail: peddy@ci.beaumont.tx.us; *Asst Admin,* Geri Roberts; E-mail: groberts@ci.beaumont.tx.us; Staff 25 (MLS 7, Non-MLS 18)
Founded 1926. Pop 114,332
Library Holdings: Bk Vols 345,345; Per Subs 126
Automation Activity & Vendor Info: (Acquisitions) SirsiDynix; (Cataloging) SirsiDynix; (Circulation) SirsiDynix; (OPAC) SirsiDynix; (Serials) SirsiDynix
Wireless access
Partic in TexSHARE - Texas State Library & Archives Commission
Open Mon-Fri 10-8
Friends of the Library Group
Branches: 6
BEAUMONT PUBLIC, 801 Pearl St, 77701. (Mail add: PO Box 3827, 77704-3827). Tel: 409-838-6606. *Asst Admin,* Geri Roberts; Tel: 409-833-7308, E-mail: groberts@ci.beaumont.tx.us; *Ch,* Robin Smith
Oct 2010-Sept 2011 Income $939,539, State $13,639, City $893,900, Locally Generated Income $32,000
Library Holdings: Bk Vols 135,000
Automation Activity & Vendor Info: (Cataloging) SirsiDynix; (Circulation) SirsiDynix; (OPAC) SirsiDynix
Database Vendor: ProQuest
Open Mon-Fri 10-9
Friends of the Library Group
THEODORE R JOHNS SR BRANCH LIBRARY, 4255 Fannett Rd, 77705. (Mail add: PO Box 3827, 77704-3827), SAN 375-0159. Tel: 409-842-5233. FAX: 409-842-5422. *Br Mgr,* Gwendolyn Pierre; E-mail: gpierre@ci.beaumont.tx.us
Open Mon-Thurs 9-8, Fri & Sat 9-6
Friends of the Library Group
LITERACY DEPOT, 1205 Franklin St, 77701. (Mail add: PO Box 3827, 77704-3827), SAN 378-2123. Tel: 409-835-7924. FAX: 409-838-6734.
Br Mgr, Barbara S Beard
Open Mon-Thurs 9-8, Fri 9-5
Friends of the Library Group

R C MILLER MEMORIAL, 1605 Dowlen Rd, 77706. (Mail add: PO Box 3827, 77704-3827), SAN 361-2899. Tel: 409-866-9487. FAX: 409-866-3720. *Br Mgr,* Jim D Shoemaker; *Ch,* Lori Nock; *Ref Serv,* Rosie Postelnek
Automation Activity & Vendor Info: (Acquisitions) SirsiDynix; (Cataloging) SirsiDynix
Open Mon-Thurs 9-8, Fri & Sat 9-6
TYRRELL HISTORICAL, 695 Pearl St, 77701. (Mail add: PO Box 3827, 77704-3827), SAN 361-2937. Tel: 409-833-2759. FAX: 409-833-5828.
Br Mgr, William Grace. Subject Specialists: *Archives, Genealogy,* William Grace; Staff 4 (MLS 1, Non-MLS 3)
Library Holdings: Per Subs 44
Special Collections: Archives Coll; Genealogy Coll; Local History Coll
Subject Interests: Genealogy, Texana
Function: Copy machines
Open Mon-Sat 9-6
Restriction: Closed stack
Friends of the Library Group
ELMO WILLARD BRANCH, 3590 E Lucas, 77708. (Mail add: PO Box 3827, 77704-3827), SAN 378-214X. Tel: 409-892-4988. FAX: 409-898-4088. *Br Mgr,* Kunwoo Choi
Founded 1998
Library Holdings: Bk Vols 43,000
Automation Activity & Vendor Info: (Cataloging) SirsiDynix; (Circulation) SirsiDynix; (OPAC) SirsiDynix
Open Mon-Thurs 9-8, Fri & Sat 9-6
Friends of the Library Group

C   LAMAR UNIVERSITY*, Mary & John Gray Library, 211 Redbird Lane, 77705. (Mail add: PO Box 10021, 77710-0021), SAN 316-0920. Tel: 409-880-8118. Circulation Tel: 409-880-8134. Interlibrary Loan Service Tel: 409-880-8987. Reference Tel: 409-880-1898. FAX: 409-880-2318. Web Site: library.lamar.edu. *Dir of Libr Serv,* David Carroll; Tel: 409-880-8159, E-mail: david.carroll@lamar.edu; *Govt Doc Librn,* Theresa Hefner-Babb; Tel: 409-880-2135, E-mail: theresa.hefner-babb@lamar.edu; *Circ Supvr,* Fay Sands; Tel: 409-880-8133, E-mail: fay.sands@lamar.edu; *ILL Supvr,* Severa Norris; E-mail: severa.norris@lamar.edu; *Reserves/Per Supvr,* Annette Stanfield; Tel: 409-880-8980, E-mail: annette.stanfield@lamar.edu; *Coordr, Cat,* Jon Tritsch; Tel: 409-880-7299, E-mail: jon.tritsch@lamar.edu; *Coordr, Coll Develop & Acq,* Sarah Tusa; Tel: 409-880-8125, E-mail: sarah.tusa@lamar.edu; *Coordr, Media Serv,* Mark Asteris; Tel: 409-880-8064, E-mail: mark.asteris@lamar.edu; *Coordr of Ref Serv,* Karen Nichols; Tel: 409-880-8131, E-mail: karen.nichols@lamar.edu; *Univ Archivist,* Penny Clark; Tel: 409-880-8660, E-mail: penny.clark@lamar.edu; Staff 43 (MLS 13, Non-MLS 30)
Founded 1923. Enrl 14,119; Fac 464; Highest Degree: Doctorate
Library Holdings: Bks on Deafness & Sign Lang 466; Bk Titles 367,958; Bk Vols 432,130; Per Subs 1,800
Special Collections: Big Thicket National Preserve Coll; Cookery Coll; Petroleum Refining Coll; Texana Coll. State Document Depository; US Document Depository
Subject Interests: Bus, Computer sci, Deaf educ, Educ, Eng, Nursing
Automation Activity & Vendor Info: (Acquisitions) SirsiDynix; (Cataloging) SirsiDynix; (Circulation) SirsiDynix; (Course Reserve) SirsiDynix; (ILL) OCLC ILLiad; (Media Booking) Dymaxion; (OPAC) SirsiDynix; (Serials) SirsiDynix
Database Vendor: OCLC FirstSearch
Wireless access
Publications: From the Stacks (Library Newsletter)
Partic in Amigos Library Services, Inc; TexSHARE - Texas State Library & Archives Commission
Special Services for the Deaf - Assistive tech; TTY equip
Special Services for the Blind - Accessible computers; Assistive/Adapted tech devices, equip & products; Large screen computer & software; Reader equip
Open Mon-Thurs & Sun (Winter) 7:30am-2am, Fri 7:30-6, Sat 10-7; Mon-Thurs (Summer) 7:30am-9pm, Fri 7:30-6, Sun 2-9
Friends of the Library Group

SR   SAINT MARK'S PARISH LIBRARY*, 680 Calder, 77701-2398. SAN 316-0947. Tel: 409-832-3405. FAX: 409-832-8045. Web Site: www.stmarksbeaumont.org. *Librn,* Ginger Clark
Library Holdings: Bk Vols 1,000
Wireless access
Function: Res libr
Open Mon-Thurs 8-5, Fri 8-4, Sat 9-12, Sun 8-1
Restriction: Non-circulating

BEDFORD

P   BEDFORD PUBLIC LIBRARY*, 2424 Forest Ridge Dr, 76021. SAN 316-0955. Tel: 817-952-2335. Reference Tel: 817-952-2342. Administration Tel: 817-952-2330. FAX: 817-952-2396. Web Site: www.bedfordlibrary.org. *Dir,* Maria Redburn; E-mail: Maria.Redburn@ci.bedford.tx.us; *Tech Serv Mgr,* Barbara Glassford Johnson; Tel: 817-952-2360, E-mail:

bjohnson@ci.bedford.tx.us; *Commun Serv Supvr,* Jean E Green; Tel:
817-952-2370, E-mail: jgreen@ci.bedford.tx.us; *Adult Serv,* Susan L Neal;
E-mail: sneal@ci.bedford.tx.us; Staff 14 (MLS 5, Non-MLS 9)
Founded 1964. Pop 48,000; Circ 393,231
Library Holdings: AV Mats 13,633; Bks on Deafness & Sign Lang 34;
e-books 26,048; Large Print Bks 3,208; Bk Titles 75,744; Bk Vols 94,740;
Per Subs 239; Spec Interest Per Sub 10; Talking Bks 2,379
Special Collections: Bedford History Coll
Automation Activity & Vendor Info: (Acquisitions) Innovative Interfaces,
Inc; (Cataloging) Innovative Interfaces, Inc; (Circulation) Innovative
Interfaces, Inc; (OPAC) Innovative Interfaces, Inc; (Serials) Innovative
Interfaces, Inc
Database Vendor: EBSCOhost, Gale Cengage Learning, netLibrary,
OCLC FirstSearch
Wireless access
Function: ILL available
Special Services for the Blind - Low vision equip
Open Mon, Wed & Thurs 10-9, Tues 10-6, Fri & Sat 10-5, Sun 1-5
Friends of the Library Group

BEE CAVE

P   BEE CAVE PUBLIC LIBRARY*, 4000 Galleria Pkwy, 78738. SAN
378-4398. Tel: 512-767-6624. Circulation Tel: 512-767-6620. FAX:
512-767-6629. E-mail: library@beecavetexas.gov. Web Site:
pl.beecavetexas.gov. *Dir,* Barbara Hathaway; E-mail:
bhathaway@beecavetexas.gov; Staff 6 (MLS 1, Non-MLS 5)
Founded 2005. Pop 3,100; Circ 157,000
Function: Adult bk club, Bk club(s), Bks on CD, Children's prog,
Computers for patron use, Copy machines, Family literacy, Fax serv, Free
DVD rentals, Handicapped accessible, Holiday prog, ILL available, Online
cat, Outreach serv, Photocopying/Printing, Prog for adults, Prog for
children & young adult, Pub access computers, Ref serv in person, Senior
outreach, Story hour, Summer reading prog, Teen prog, Telephone ref,
Web-catalog, Wheelchair accessible
Mem of Central Texas Library System, Inc
Open Tues-Thurs 10-7, Fri 10-5, Sat 1-5

BEEVILLE

P   JOE BARNHART BEE COUNTY PUBLIC LIBRARY*, 110 W Corpus
Christi St, 78102-5604. SAN 316-0963. Tel: 361-362-4901. FAX:
361-358-8694. Web Site: www.bclib.org. *Dir,* Sarah Milnarich; E-mail:
director@bclib.org; *Pub Serv Librn,* Cynthia Blatherwick; *ILL Coordr,*
Kathy Outten; *Tech Spec,* Roland Diaz. Subject Specialists: *German, Hist,
Intl relations,* Sarah Milnarich; Staff 4 (MLS 2, Non-MLS 2)
Founded 1939. Pop 25,114; Circ 59,832
Library Holdings: Bk Vols 40,000; Per Subs 100
Automation Activity & Vendor Info: (Cataloging) TLC (The Library
Corporation); (Circulation) TLC (The Library Corporation); (ILL) OCLC
CatExpress; (OPAC) TLC (The Library Corporation); (Serials) TLC (The
Library Corporation)
Database Vendor: EBSCOhost, Gale Cengage Learning, LearningExpress,
Newsbank, OCLC WorldCat, OVID Technologies, ProQuest, TLC (The
Library Corporation), Westlaw, Westlaw Business
Wireless access
Function: Games & aids for the handicapped, ILL available, Online
searches, Photocopying/Printing, Prog for adults, Prog for children &
young adult, Ref serv available, Summer reading prog, Wheelchair
accessible
Special Services for the Blind - Braille equip; Computer with voice
synthesizer for visually impaired persons
Open Mon & Wed 9-6, Tues & Thurs 9-9, Fri & Sat 9-5

J   COASTAL BEND COLLEGE*, Grady C Hogue Learning Resource Center
Library, 3800 Charco Rd, 78102-2110. SAN 316-0971. Tel: 361-354-2737,
361-354-2740. FAX: 361-354-2719. Web Site: www.coastalbend.edu. *Dir,*
Sarah Milnarich; Tel: 361-354-2741; *Head, Circ,* Ray Benavides; *Ref Serv,*
Marvin Southworth; Staff 5 (MLS 3, Non-MLS 2)
Founded 1967. Enrl 3,016; Fac 155
Library Holdings: Bk Vols 48,000; Per Subs 230
Special Collections: Texana Coll
Automation Activity & Vendor Info: (Acquisitions) EOS International;
(Cataloging) EOS International; (Circulation) EOS International; (Course
Reserve) EOS International; (ILL) OCLC; (OPAC) EOS International;
(Serials) EOS International
Database Vendor: OCLC FirstSearch
Wireless access
Publications: BookSampler (monthly) (Newsletter); Recent Titles
(quarterly) (Newsletter)
Partic in Coastal Bend Health Info Network; OCLC Online Computer
Library Center, Inc; TexSHARE - Texas State Library & Archives
Commission
Open Mon-Thurs 8-5, Fri 8-4

BELLAIRE

P   BELLAIRE CITY LIBRARY*, 5111 Jessamine, 77401-4498. SAN
316-098X. Tel: 713-662-8160. Reference Tel: 713-662-8166. FAX:
713-662-8169. Web Site: www.ci.bellaire.tx.us/index.aspx. *Dir,* Mary
Cohrs; E-mail: malford@ci.bellaire.tx.us; *Ch,* Missy Dixon; Tel:
713-662-8164, E-mail: mstraub@ci.bellaire.tx.us; *Ref,* Terri Mote; E-mail:
tmote@ci.bellaire.tx.us; Staff 3 (MLS 3)
Founded 1951. Pop 17,206; Circ 165,000
Oct 2011-Sept 2012 Income $617,403, City $590,403, Locally Generated
Income $27,000. Mats Exp $63,184, Books $37,800, Per/Ser (Incl. Access
Fees) $4,725, AV Mat $9,975, Electronic Ref Mat (Incl. Access Fees)
$10,684. Sal $497,066
Library Holdings: Audiobooks 2,354; AV Mats 3,062; CDs 590; DVDs
1,876; e-books 6,298; Bk Titles 67,910; Bk Vols 72,032; Per Subs 123
Subject Interests: Local hist
Automation Activity & Vendor Info: (Acquisitions) Innovative Interfaces,
Inc; (Cataloging) Innovative Interfaces, Inc; (Circulation) Innovative
Interfaces, Inc; (Course Reserve) Innovative Interfaces, Inc; (ILL)
Innovative Interfaces, Inc; (OPAC) Innovative Interfaces, Inc; (Serials)
Innovative Interfaces, Inc
Wireless access
Function: Audio & video playback equip for onsite use, Audiobks via
web, Bks on cassette, Bks on CD, Children's prog, Computer training,
Computers for patron use, Copy machines, Digital talking bks, E-Reserves,
Fax serv, Free DVD rentals, Holiday prog, ILL available, Mail & tel
request accepted, Mail loans to mem, Music CDs, Online cat, OverDrive
digital audio bks, Photocopying/Printing, Preschool outreach, Prog for
adults, Prog for children & young adult, Pub access computers, Scanner,
Senior computer classes, Senior outreach, Story hour, Summer reading
prog, Tax forms, Teen prog, Telephone ref, VHS videos
Partic in Houston Area Database Consortium; Houston Area Library
Automated Network
Open Mon, Tues & Thurs 9-8, Wed 9-6, Fri 1-5 (9-1 Summer), Sat 9-5
Friends of the Library Group

BELLVILLE

P   BELLVILLE PUBLIC LIBRARY*, 12 W Palm, 77418-1446. SAN
316-0998. Tel: 979-865-3731. FAX: 979-865-2060. *Dir,* Aimee Ladewig;
Staff 5 (Non-MLS 5)
Founded 1968
Library Holdings: Bk Titles 33,018; Bk Vols 33,898; Per Subs 20
Automation Activity & Vendor Info: (Cataloging) Follett Software;
(Circulation) Follett Software
Open Mon & Tues 1:30-5:30, Wed & Thurs 9:30-5:30, Sat 9-1

BELTON

P   LENA ARMSTRONG PUBLIC LIBRARY*, 301 E First Ave, 76513.
(Mail add: PO Box 120, 76513-0120), SAN 316-1005. Tel: 254-933-5830.
Administration Tel: 254-933-5832. FAX: 254-933-5831. Web Site:
www.ci.belton.tx.us. *Dir,* Kim Adele Kroll; E-mail: kkroll@ci.belton.tx.us;
Staff 5 (MLS 2, Non-MLS 3)
Founded 1899. Pop 19,700; Circ 46,631
Oct 2009-Sept 2010 Income $242,034. Mats Exp $20,000. Sal $196,858
(Prof $56,218)
Library Holdings: Audiobooks 186; CDs 641; DVDs 135; Electronic
Media & Resources 25; Large Print Bks 1,737; Bk Titles 26,346; Bk Vols
27,056; Per Subs 10; Videos 902
Special Collections: Genealogy Coll
Subject Interests: Genealogy, Local hist
Automation Activity & Vendor Info: (Cataloging) Biblionix; (Circulation)
Biblionix
Database Vendor: EBSCOhost
Wireless access
Function: Audiobks via web, Bks on cassette, Bks on CD, Children's
prog, Computers for patron use, Copy machines, Distance learning, e-mail
serv, Electronic databases & coll, Handicapped accessible, ILL available,
Online cat, Online searches, Outreach serv, Photocopying/Printing, Scanner,
Senior outreach, Story hour, Summer reading prog, Tax forms, Telephone
ref, VHS videos, Wheelchair accessible
Mem of Central Texas Library System, Inc
Special Services for the Blind - Bks on cassette; Bks on CD; Cassette
playback machines; Copier with enlargement capabilities; Extensive large
print coll; Internet workstation with adaptive software; Large print &
cassettes; Large print bks; Large screen computer & software; Magnifiers;
PC for handicapped; Ref serv; Screen enlargement software for people with
visual disabilities
Open Mon & Fri 10-5, Tues-Thurs 11-6, Sat 9-2
Restriction: Open to pub for ref & circ; with some limitations
Friends of the Library Group

R   CEDARBRAKE LIBRARY*, 5602 State Hwy 317 N, 76513. (Mail add: PO Box 58, 76513). Tel: 254-780-2436. FAX: 254-780-2436. E-mail: cedarbrake@austindiocese.org. *Dir,* Abby Jimenez; *Asst Dir,* Beverly Collins
Library Holdings: Bk Titles 1,000
Subject Interests: Church, Devotions, Prayer, Spirituality
Wireless access
Open Mon-Fri 9-5

CR   UNIVERSITY OF MARY HARDIN-BAYLOR*, Townsend Memorial Library, 900 College St, UMHB Sta, Box 8016, 76513-2599. SAN 316-1013. Tel: 254-295-4637. Interlibrary Loan Service Tel: 254-295-5004. Reference Tel: 254-295-4641. Toll Free Tel: 877-316-3313. FAX: 254-295-4642. E-mail: library@umhb.edu. Web Site: umhblib.umhb.edu. *Dir,* Denise Karimkhani; Tel: 254-295-4636, E-mail: dkarimkhani@umhb.edu; *Head, Pub Serv,* Anne Price; Tel: 254-295-4639, E-mail: aprice@umhb.edu; *Head, Ref,* Dorothy Planas; E-mail: dplanas@umhb.edu; *Head, Tech Serv,* Teresa Buck; Tel: 254-295-4640, E-mail: tbuck@umhb.edu; *Electronic Serv, Ref & Instrul Serv, Instr Coordr,* Kathy Harden; Tel: 254-295-4161, E-mail: kharden@umhb.edu; *Ref Serv, Ser,* Paige Alfonzo; Tel: 254-295-5011, E-mail: palfonzo@umhb.edu; Staff 11 (MLS 6, Non-MLS 5)
Founded 1845. Enrl 3,000; Fac 140; Highest Degree: Doctorate
Jun 2009-May 2010 Income $812,933. Mats Exp $689,000, Books $267,000, Per/Ser (Incl. Access Fees) $403,000, Micro $19,000. Sal $367,188 (Prof $227,720)
Library Holdings: AV Mats 6,500; Bks on Deafness & Sign Lang 102; CDs 2,200; DVDs 3,000; e-books 26,700; High Interest/Low Vocabulary Bk Vols 202; Large Print Bks 35; Music Scores 1,303; Bk Titles 212,800; Per Subs 878; Talking Bks 474; Videos 200
Special Collections: Baptist Coll; Local History Coll; Texas & Mexican History Coll
Subject Interests: Baptist, Baptist women, Educ, Nursing
Automation Activity & Vendor Info: (Acquisitions) Innovative Interfaces, Inc; (Cataloging) Innovative Interfaces, Inc - OCLC; (Circulation) Innovative Interfaces, Inc; (Course Reserve) Innovative Interfaces, Inc; (ILL) Innovative Interfaces, Inc - OCLC; (OPAC) Innovative Interfaces, Inc; (Serials) Innovative Interfaces, Inc
Database Vendor: ACM (Association for Computing Machinery), American Chemical Society, American Psychological Association (APA), Amigos Library Services, Baker & Taylor, CQ Press, EBSCOhost, Gale Cengage Learning, H W Wilson, Hoovers, JSTOR, LexisNexis, OCLC FirstSearch, OCLC WorldCat, PubMed, Safari Books Online, ScienceDirect, Wilson - Wilson Web
Wireless access
Function: Archival coll, Audio & video playback equip for onsite use, Bks on cassette, Bks on CD, Computers for patron use, Copy machines, Electronic databases & coll, Free DVD rentals, ILL available, Learning ctr, Mail & tel request accepted, Music CDs, Online cat, Online ref, Online searches, Orientations, Photocopying/Printing, Pub access computers, Ref serv available, Spoken cassettes & CDs, Spoken cassettes & DVDs, Telephone ref, VHS videos
Publications: Handbook
Partic in Leian; Texas Council of Academic Libraries; TexSHARE - Texas State Library & Archives Commission
Open Mon-Thurs 7:30am-1am, Fri 7:30-5, Sat 10-6, Sun 2pm-1am
Restriction: Non-circulating of rare bks

BENBROOK

P   BENBROOK PUBLIC LIBRARY*, 1065 Mercedes, 76126. SAN 378-3693. Tel: 817-249-6632. Automation Services Tel: 817-249-3930. FAX: 817-249-3326. Web Site: www.benbrooklibrary.org. *Dir,* Michael Baldwin; E-mail: mikeb@benbrooklibrary.org; *Adult Serv,* Lori Batchelor; E-mail: lorib@benbrooklibrary.org; *Youth Serv,* Miranda Bauer; E-mail: mirandaw@benbrooklibrary.org; Staff 3 (MLS 3)
Founded 1999. Pop 25,000; Circ 80,000
Oct 2009-Sept 2010 Income $725,061. Mats Exp $88,000, Books $50,000, Per/Ser (Incl. Access Fees) $10,000, AV Mat $8,000, Electronic Ref Mat (Incl. Access Fees) $20,000. Sal $250,000 (Prof $200,000)
Library Holdings: Bk Titles 24,000; Bk Vols 30,000; Per Subs 100
Automation Activity & Vendor Info: (Acquisitions) Horizon; (Cataloging) Horizon; (Circulation) Horizon; (OPAC) Horizon
Database Vendor: infoUSA, Plunkett Research, Ltd, ReferenceUSA
Wireless access
Function: ILL available, Photocopying/Printing, Prog for adults, Prog for children & young adult, Ref serv available, Spoken cassettes & CDs, Summer reading prog, Telephone ref, Wheelchair accessible
Mem of North Texas Library Partners
Open Tues-Thurs 10-7, Fri 10-5, Sat 10-6
Friends of the Library Group

BERTRAM

JOANNE COLE-MITTE MEMORIAL LIBRARY*, 170 N Gabriel St, 78605. SAN 361-3232. Tel: 512-355-2113. FAX: 512-355-3323. *Dir,* Ann Brock; E-mail: abrock@burnetcountylibrary.org
Library Holdings: Bk Vols 10,000
Database Vendor: TLC (The Library Corporation)
Open Mon-Fri 10-6
Friends of the Library Group

BIG LAKE

P   REAGAN COUNTY LIBRARY, 300 Courthouse Sq, 76932. SAN 316-1021. Tel: 325-884-2854. E-mail: rclibrary@reagancounty.org. Web Site: www.rclibrary.net. *Librn,* Linda Rees; *Asst Librn,* Rosa Ramirez; Staff 2 (MLS 1, Non-MLS 1)
Founded 1937. Pop 3,006; Circ 7,260
Library Holdings: Bk Titles 19,572; Per Subs 40
Automation Activity & Vendor Info: (Cataloging) Biblionix; (Circulation) Biblionix
Wireless access
Function: Audiobks via web, Bks on CD, Children's prog, Citizenship assistance, Computers for patron use, Copy machines, E-Reserves, Electronic databases & coll, Handicapped accessible, ILL available, OverDrive digital audio bks, Photocopying/Printing, Pub access computers, Summer reading prog, Tax forms, Web-catalog, Wheelchair accessible
Open Mon & Wed 8:30-5, Tues & Thurs 8:30-7, Fri 8:30-4

BIG SPRING

GM   DEPARTMENT OF VETERANS AFFAIRS*, Medical Center Library, 300 Veterans Blvd, 79720. SAN 316-1072. Tel: 432-263-7361. FAX: 432-268-5064. Web Site: www.med.va.gov. *Librn,* Samie Pequeno; E-mail: samie.pequeno@med.va.gov
Founded 1950
Library Holdings: Bk Vols 1,015; Per Subs 66
Partic in Vets Admin Libr Network
Restriction: Not open to pub

J   HOWARD COUNTY JUNIOR COLLEGE*, Anthony Hunt Library & Learning Resource Center, 1001 Birdwell Lane, 79720. SAN 316-1056. Tel: 432-264-5090. FAX: 432-264-5094. Web Site: www.howardcollege.edu/library. *Dean of Libr,* William Luis Kincade; Tel: 432-264-5092, E-mail: wkincade@howardcollege.edu; Staff 3.5 (MLS 1, Non-MLS 2.5)
Founded 1945. Enrl 2,236; Highest Degree: Associate
Library Holdings: Bk Vols 32,000; Per Subs 62
Automation Activity & Vendor Info: (Cataloging) LibLime; (Circulation) LibLime; (OPAC) LibLime
Wireless access
Function: ILL available
Open Mon-Thurs (Winter) 7:30am-9pm, Fri 7:30-3, Sun 1-5; Mon-Thurs (Summer) 7am-9pm, Sun 1-5
Departmental Libraries:
SOUTHWEST COLLEGIATE INSTITUTE FOR THE DEAF - LIBRARY, 3200 Ave C, 79720, SAN 328-817X. Tel: 432-218-4056. FAX: 432-264-3726. *Libr Supvr,* Sonia Gonzales; E-mail: sgonzales@howardcollege.edu; Staff 1 (Non-MLS 1)
Founded 1980. Enrl 170; Highest Degree: Associate
Library Holdings: Bks on Deafness & Sign Lang 946; Bk Titles 3,035; Bk Vols 3,262; Per Subs 100
Special Collections: Deafness, AV mat, bks, per. Oral History
Database Vendor: EBSCOhost, Gale Cengage Learning, OCLC FirstSearch, OVID Technologies
Special Services for the Deaf - Staff with knowledge of sign lang
Open Mon, Wed & Thurs 8-5, Tues 8-5 & 6-8, Fri 8-3

P   HOWARD COUNTY LIBRARY*, Dora Roberts Library, 500 Main St, 79720-2532. SAN 316-1064. Tel: 432-264-2260. FAX: 432-264-2263. Web Site: www.howard-county.lib.tx.us. *Dir,* Hollis McCright; *Cat,* Martha Vierra; *Ref,* Johnny Schafer; Staff 6 (MLS 1, Non-MLS 5)
Founded 1907. Pop 33,200; Circ 161,147
Oct 2009-Sept 2010 Income $362,000. Mats Exp $40,000, Books $35,000, Per/Ser (Incl. Access Fees) $2,000, Micro $300. Sal $162,073
Library Holdings: AV Mats 1,850; Bks on Deafness & Sign Lang 35; DVDs 1,200; Large Print Bks 1,997; Bk Titles 63,831; Bk Vols 70,292; Per Subs 52; Videos 1,257
Special Collections: Texana
Automation Activity & Vendor Info: (Cataloging) LibLime; (Circulation) LibLime; (OPAC) LibLime
Wireless access
Function: Adult bk club, Adult literacy prog, Children's prog, Copy machines, Electronic databases & coll, Fax serv, Genealogy discussion group, Handicapped accessible, ILL available, Mail & tel request accepted, Photocopying/Printing, Summer reading prog, Tax forms

Mem of West Texas Library System
Special Services for the Deaf - Adult & family literacy prog; Bks on deafness & sign lang; High interest/low vocabulary bks
Special Services for the Blind - Bks on CD
Open Mon-Fri 10-6, Sat (Sept-May) 10-2
Friends of the Library Group

M   TEXAS DEPARTMENT OF HEALTH & HUMAN SERVICES*, Big Spring State Hospital Professional Library, 1901 N Hwy 87, 79720. SAN 316-1048. Tel: 432-267-8216, 432-268-7215. FAX: 432-268-7401. Web Site: www.dshs.state.tx.us. *Dir, Info Mgt,* Elizabeth Correa; Tel: 432-268-7400
Founded 1973
Sept 2005-Aug 2006. Mats Exp $13,000
Library Holdings: Bk Vols 1,000
Subject Interests: Psychiat med, Psychiat treatment
Restriction: Not open to pub

BLANCO

P   BLANCO COUNTY SOUTH LIBRARY DISTRICT*, James A & Evelyn Williams Memorial Library, 1118 Main St, 78606. Tel: 830-833-4280. FAX: 830-833-2680. E-mail: blanlib@moment.net. Web Site: www.blancolib.org. *Librn,* Crystal Spybuck; Staff 47 (MLS 1, Non-MLS 46)
Founded 1938. Pop 5,500; Circ 27,000
Automation Activity & Vendor Info: (Cataloging) Follett Software; (Circulation) Follett Software
Wireless access
Function: Adult bk club, Art exhibits, Audio & video playback equip for onsite use, Bks on cassette, Bks on CD, Computer training, Computers for patron use, Copy machines, e-mail serv, Electronic databases & coll, Fax serv, Free DVD rentals, ILL available, Mail & tel request accepted, Music CDs, OverDrive digital audio bks, Photocopying/Printing, Prog for adults, Scanner, Spoken cassettes & CDs, Story hour, Summer reading prog, Tax forms, VHS videos, Web-catalog, Writing prog
Mem of Central Texas Library System, Inc
Special Services for the Blind - Large print bks; Large screen computer & software; Screen enlargement software for people with visual disabilities; Talking bks & player equip
Open Mon, Wed & Fri 10-6, Tues & Thurs 12-8, Sat 10-4, Sun (Fall-Spring) 2-6
Restriction: In-house use for visitors, Non-circulating of rare bks, Photo ID required for access
Friends of the Library Group

BOERNE

P   BOERNE PUBLIC LIBRARY*, Patrick Heath Public Library, 451 N Main St, Bldg 100, 78006. SAN 316-1102. Tel: 830-249-3053. FAX: 830-249-8410. E-mail: librarian@boernelibrary.org. Web Site: www.boernelibrary.org. *Dir,* Kelly W Skovbjerg; E-mail: skovbjerg@boerne.lib.tx.us; *Asst Libr Dir,* Natalie Morgan; E-mail: morgan@boernelibrary.org; Staff 3 (MLS 3)
Founded 1952. Pop 26,200; Circ 165,600
Oct 2010-Sept 2011 Income $574,600, City $451,600, County $123,000. Mats Exp $43,320, Books $30,817, Per/Ser (Incl. Access Fees) $3,319, AV Mat $7,589, Electronic Ref Mat (Incl. Access Fees) $1,595. Sal $348,699 (Prof $158,131)
Library Holdings: AV Mats 4,189; Bk Vols 39,535; Per Subs 68
Subject Interests: German lang, Local hist, Spanish (Lang), Texana
Automation Activity & Vendor Info: (Cataloging) Biblionix; (Circulation) Biblionix; (OPAC) Biblionix
Database Vendor: EBSCOhost, Gale Cengage Learning, OCLC FirstSearch
Wireless access
Open Mon & Tues 9-8, Wed & Thurs 9-6, Fri 9-5, Sat 9-3
Friends of the Library Group

BONHAM

P   BONHAM PUBLIC LIBRARY*, 305 E Fifth St, 75418-4002. SAN 316-1110. Tel: 903-583-3128. FAX: 903-583-8030. E-mail: bonlib@cableone.net. Web Site: www.cobon.net/plgi.htm. *Librn,* Barbara McCutcheon; Staff 4 (Non-MLS 4)
Founded 1901. Pop 7,338; Circ 51,788
Jan 2010-Dec 2010. Mats Exp $42,400, Books $14,000, Other Print Mats $400, AV Equip $4,000, AV Mat $24,000. Sal $44,000
Library Holdings: Audiobooks 4,000; AV Mats 4,000; CDs 500; DVDs 800; Bk Titles 36,000; Bk Vols 38,000; Per Subs 84
Special Collections: Oral History
Automation Activity & Vendor Info: (Cataloging) Book Systems, Inc; (Circulation) Book Systems, Inc; (OPAC) Book Systems, Inc
Database Vendor: OCLC FirstSearch
Open Mon 10-7, Tues-Fri 8-5, Sat 9-1

S   SAM RAYBURN LIBRARY & MUSEUM*, 800 W Sam Rayburn Dr, 75418-4103. (Mail add: PO Box 309, 75418-0309), SAN 316-1129. Tel: 903-583-2455. FAX: 903-583-7394. Web Site: www.cah.utexas.edu. Founded 1957
Library Holdings: Bk Vols 20,000
Special Collections: Life & Career of Speaker Sam Rayburn, historical memorabilia, interviews, micro. Oral History
Open Mon-Fri 9-5, Sat 10-2
Friends of the Library Group

GM VA NORTH TEXAS HEALTH CARE SYSTEM*, Library Service - Sam Rayburn Memorial Veterans Center, 1201 E Ninth St, 75418. SAN 316-1137. Tel: 903-583-6302. FAX: 903-583-6694. *Libr Tech,* Deann Hicks; E-mail: elizabeth.hicks@va.gov; Staff 1 (MLS 1)
Library Holdings: Bk Titles 1,060; Per Subs 115
Restriction: Not open to pub

BORGER

J   FRANK PHILLIPS COLLEGE, James W Dillard Library, 1301 Roosevelt St, 79008. (Mail add: PO Box 5118, 79008-5118), SAN 316-1145. Tel: 806-457-4200, Ext 787. FAX: 806-457-4230. Web Site: www.fpctx.edu. *Libr Dir,* Jason Price; Staff 1 (MLS 1)
Founded 1948. Enrl 1,200; Fac 56; Highest Degree: Associate
Library Holdings: AV Mats 1,124; e-books 29,000; Electronic Media & Resources 70; Bk Titles 14,000; Per Subs 25
Special Collections: Rare
Automation Activity & Vendor Info: (Cataloging) SirsiDynix; (Circulation) SirsiDynix; (OPAC) SirsiDynix
Wireless access
Function: AV serv, Handicapped accessible, Homebound delivery serv, ILL available, Online searches, Photocopying/Printing, Ref serv available, Wheelchair accessible
Partic in Harrington Library Consortium
Open Mon-Thurs 8-5, Fri 8-4

P   HUTCHINSON COUNTY LIBRARY*, 625 N Weatherly, 79007-3621. SAN 361-302X. Tel: 806-273-0126. FAX: 806-273-0128. *Dir,* Carolyn Wilkinson; E-mail: bor_carolynw@hotmail.com; *Asst Dir,* Debbie Cauthon; E-mail: debbiecauthon@mail.com; Staff 7 (Non-MLS 7)
Founded 1938. Pop 22,617; Circ 104,511
Library Holdings: Bk Titles 53,482; Bk Vols 58,894; Per Subs 175
Subject Interests: Genealogy, Tex
Automation Activity & Vendor Info: (Acquisitions) SIRSI-DRA
Wireless access
Partic in Harrington Library Consortium
Open Mon-Thurs 10-7, Fri 10-5, Sat 10-2
Friends of the Library Group
Branches: 2
FRITCH BRANCH, 205 N Cornell, Fritch, 79036, SAN 361-3054. Tel: 806-857-3752. FAX: 806-857-0940. E-mail: fritchlibrary@yahoo.com. *Br Mgr,* Delena Burks; Staff 1 (Non-MLS 1)
    Library Holdings: Bk Vols 8,895
    Open Mon-Fri 9-12:30 & 1:30-5
    Friends of the Library Group
STINNETT BRANCH, 500 S Main St, Stinnett, 79083. (Mail add: PO Box 478, Stinnett, 79083-0478), SAN 361-3089. Tel: 806-878-4013. FAX: 806-878-4014. *Br Mgr,* Debra Hukill
    Library Holdings: Bk Vols 11,738
    Open Mon-Fri 9-11:45 & 1-5
    Friends of the Library Group

BOWIE

P   BOWIE PUBLIC LIBRARY*, 301 Walnut St, 76230. SAN 316-1161. Tel: 940-872-2681. FAX: 940-872-6418. E-mail: bowiepubliclibrary@yahoo.com. *Dir,* Jackie Lowrie; Staff 4 (Non-MLS 4)
Founded 1926. Pop 6,000; Circ 60,000
Jan 2011-Dec 2011 Income $223,000, City $213,000, Other $10,000. Mats Exp $23,200, Books $20,000, Micro $700, AV Mat $2,500
Library Holdings: Bk Titles 34,000; Per Subs 66
Automation Activity & Vendor Info: (Cataloging) Follett Software; (Circulation) Follett Software; (OPAC) Follett Software
Mem of North Texas Library Partners
Open Tues, Wed & Fri 9-5, Thurs 12-7, Sat 9-3
Friends of the Library Group

BOYD

P   RAYMOND JORDAN BOYD PUBLIC LIBRARY*, 101 W Rock Island Ave, 76023-3001. (Mail add: PO Box 1238, 76023-1238), SAN 376-4680. Tel: 940-433-5580. FAX: 940-433-8253. E-mail: boydpublib@yahoo.com. *Librn,* Doris Autry
Pop 3,995
Library Holdings: AV Mats 450; Bk Vols 12,000; Per Subs 18

Mem of North Texas Library Partners
Open Mon, Wed & Fri 10-3, Tues 10-7, Thurs 3-7
Friends of the Library Group

BRACKETTVILLE

P   KINNEY COUNTY PUBLIC LIBRARY*, 510 S Ellen, 78832. (Mail add:
PO Box 975, 78832), SAN 324-1270. Tel: 830-563-2884. FAX:
830-563-2312. E-mail: kclibrary4772@sbcglobal.net. *Dir,* Sara Terrazas;
Staff 3 (Non-MLS 3)
Founded 1973. Pop 3,413; Circ 18,220
Library Holdings: AV Mats 265; Large Print Bks 325; Bk Titles 9,891;
Per Subs 21
Subject Interests: Genealogy, Local hist
Automation Activity & Vendor Info: (Cataloging) Biblionix
Database Vendor: OVID Technologies, TLC (The Library Corporation)
Wireless access
Function: Homebound delivery serv, ILL available, Magnifiers for reading,
Prog for children & young adult, Ref serv available, Satellite serv, Summer
reading prog
Special Services for the Blind - Talking bks
Open Mon & Fri 9-5, Tues-Thurs 10-6, Sat 10-2
Friends of the Library Group

BRADY

P   F M (BUCK) RICHARDS MEMORIAL LIBRARY*, 1106 S Blackburn
St, 76825. SAN 316-117X. Tel: 325-597-2617. FAX: 325-597-0461.
E-mail: rchmlib@centex.net. *Dir,* Ann Shuffler; Staff 4 (Non-MLS 4)
Founded 1928. Pop 8,694; Circ 53,823
Library Holdings: AV Mats 49; Bk Titles 20,474; Bk Vols 23,222; Per
Subs 13
Automation Activity & Vendor Info: (Cataloging) Follett Software;
(Circulation) Follett Software; (OPAC) Follett Software
Function: ILL available, Photocopying/Printing, Ref serv available
Open Mon, Wed-Fri 10-5:30, Tues 12-7, Sat 10-1
Friends of the Library Group

BRECKENRIDGE

P   BRECKENRIDGE LIBRARY*, 209 N Breckenridge Ave, 76424. SAN
316-1188. Tel: 254-559-5505. FAX: 254-559-5505. E-mail:
brecklibrary@att.net. Web Site: www.brecklibrary.org/index.html. *Dir,* Judy
Credicott; *Admin Senior Librn,* Teresa Fitch; Staff 2 (Non-MLS 2)
Founded 1924. Pop 9,800; Circ 14,640
Library Holdings: CDs 27; High Interest/Low Vocabulary Bk Vols 65;
Large Print Bks 1,243; Bk Titles 21,225; Bk Vols 22,250; Per Subs 48;
Spec Interest Per Sub 15; Talking Bks 929; Videos 92
Special Collections: Rare & Out-of-Print Books; Texas Coll, 1940-present
Subject Interests: Hist
Automation Activity & Vendor Info: (Cataloging) Winnebago Software
Co; (Circulation) Winnebago Software Co
Mem of Big Country Library System
Open Mon-Thurs 11-6, Fri 8:30-3:30
Restriction: Residents only
Friends of the Library Group

BREMOND

P   BREMOND PUBLIC LIBRARY & VISITORS CENTER*, 115 S Main St,
76629. (Mail add: PO Box 132, 76629-0132). Tel: 254-746-7752. FAX:
254-746-7065. E-mail: bremondpubliclibrary@yahoo.com. Web Site:
www.bremondtxlibrary.com. *Libr Dir,* Theresa Ann Crawford; *Librn,*
DeAnna LaFaver
Founded 1998. Pop 2,000; Circ 2,911
Library Holdings: Audiobooks 65; Large Print Bks 211; Bk Titles 8,887
Automation Activity & Vendor Info: (Cataloging) Biblionix; (Circulation)
Biblionix; (OPAC) Biblionix
Wireless access
Function: Accelerated reader prog, Adult bk club, After school storytime,
Art exhibits, Audio & video playback equip for onsite use, Bk club(s), Bk
reviews (Group), Bks on cassette, Bks on CD, CD-ROM, Children's prog,
Citizenship assistance, Computer training, Computers for patron use, Copy
machines, e-mail & chat, e-mail serv, Electronic databases & coll, Family
literacy, Fax serv, Handicapped accessible, Holiday prog, Home delivery &
serv to Sr ctr & nursing homes, Homebound delivery serv, Homework
prog, ILL available, Jail serv, Libr develop, Literacy & newcomer serv,
Mail & tel request accepted, Online cat, Online searches, Outreach serv,
Photocopying/Printing, Preschool outreach, Prog for adults, Prog for
children & young adult, Pub access computers, Ref & res, Scanner, Senior
outreach, Story hour, Summer reading prog, Tax forms, Teen prog,
Wheelchair accessible, Workshops
Mem of Central Texas Library System, Inc
Open Mon & Tues 10-5, Wed-Fri 12-5, Sat 10-1
Restriction: Registered patrons only
Friends of the Library Group

BRENHAM

SR   BAPTIST GENERAL CONVENTION OF TEXAS*, Texas Baptist
Historical Museum Library, 10405 FM 50, 77833. SAN 328-0519. Tel:
979-836-5117. *Dir,* Phil Hassell; E-mail: pshassell@gmail.com
Library Holdings: Bk Titles 250
Special Collections: Tex Baptist Convention Doc. Oral History
Publications: Flowers & Fruits in the Wilderness
Open Tues-Sat 10-4

J   BLINN COLLEGE LIBRARY*, W L Moody Jr Library, 800 Blinn Blvd,
77833. (Mail add: 902 College Ave, 77833), SAN 316-1196. Tel:
979-830-4250. FAX: 979-830-4222. Web Site: www.blinn.edu/library. *Dir,*
Linda C Flynn; E-mail: lflynn@blinn.edu; *Ref & Circ Librn,* Jason
Bontrager; *Ref & Instruction Librn,* Brian Carpenter; *Ref & Instruction
Librn,* Jayne Kitterman; *Ref & Instruction Librn,* Brad Meyer; *Br Coordr,*
Mary Castle; *Cat,* Robin Chaney; *Ref & Libr Instruction,* Ann Bay; *Ref &
Libr Instruction,* Barbara Treptow; Staff 8 (MLS 8)
Founded 1883. Enrl 14,000; Fac 315; Highest Degree: Associate
Library Holdings: AV Mats 10,800; Bk Vols 170,000; Per Subs 2,000
Special Collections: College Archives; Film/Theater Coll; Local History
Coll
Subject Interests: Germans in Tex, Local hist
Automation Activity & Vendor Info: (Acquisitions) VTLS, Inc;
(Cataloging) VTLS, Inc; (Circulation) VTLS, Inc; (Course Reserve) VTLS,
Inc; (ILL) OCLC; (OPAC) VTLS, Inc; (Serials) VTLS, Inc
Database Vendor: Alexander Street Press, Amigos Library Services,
Backstage Library Works, Baker & Taylor, Bowker, Career Guidance
Foundation, Checkpoint Systems, Inc, ebrary, EBSCO Information
Services, EBSCOhost, Facts on File, Gale Cengage Learning, Greenwood
Publishing Group, Marcive, Inc, Modern Language Association, Oxford
Online, Project MUSE, ProQuest, VTLS, Inc
Wireless access
Partic in Tex Share
Open Mon-Thurs 7:45am-9:30pm, Fri 7:45-5, Sun 5:30pm-9:30pm

P   NANCY CAROL ROBERTS MEMORIAL LIBRARY*, 100 W MLK Jr
Pkwy, 77833. SAN 316-120X. Tel: 979-337-7201. FAX: 979-337-7209.
E-mail: ncrml@swbell.net. Web Site: www.brenhamlibrary-online.org. *Dir,*
Charles Suessmuth; Tel: 979-337-7202; Staff 1 (MLS 1)
Founded 1901. Pop 30,373; Circ 66,747
Library Holdings: Bk Vols 45,360; Per Subs 66; Talking Bks 2,250
Special Collections: Oral History
Subject Interests: Germans in Tex, Texana
Automation Activity & Vendor Info: (Cataloging) ComPanion Corp;
(Circulation) ComPanion Corp
Mem of Central Texas Library System, Inc
Partic in Tex Share
Open Mon-Thurs 9-7, Fri & Sat 9-5

BRIDGE CITY

P   BRIDGE CITY PUBLIC LIBRARY*, 101 Parkside Dr, 77611. SAN
376-4079. Tel: 409-735-4242. FAX: 409-738-2127. E-mail:
bclib@bridgecitytex.com. Web Site: www.bridgecitypubliclibrary.com. *Dir,*
Mary Montgomery; Staff 1 (Non-MLS 1)
Founded 1991
Library Holdings: Bk Vols 18,000; Per Subs 40
Automation Activity & Vendor Info: (Cataloging) Follett Software;
(Circulation) Follett Software; (OPAC) Follett Software
Wireless access
Open Mon-Wed 10-6, Thurs 1-7, Fri 9-2
Friends of the Library Group

BRIDGEPORT

P   BRIDGEPORT PUBLIC LIBRARY*, John A & Katherine G Jackson
Municipal Library, 2159 Tenth St, 76426. SAN 316-1226. Tel:
940-683-4412. *Dir, Libr Serv,* Jackie Lowrie; E-mail:
jlowrie@cityofbridgeport.net; Staff 4 (MLS 1, Non-MLS 3)
Founded 1960. Pop 16,005; Circ 64,570
Oct 2010-Sept 2011 Income $357,000, City $171,000, County $15,000,
Parent Institution $171,000. Mats Exp $22,236, Books $16,000, Per/Ser
(Incl. Access Fees) $2,000, AV Mat $4,000, Electronic Ref Mat (Incl.
Access Fees) $236. Sal $108,000 (Prof $48,000)
Library Holdings: AV Mats 1,400; Bks on Deafness & Sign Lang 10;
CDs 580; DVDs 642; Large Print Bks 2,000; Bk Titles 33,000; Bk Vols
33,750; Per Subs 29; Talking Bks 751; Videos 35
Automation Activity & Vendor Info: (Cataloging) Evergreen;
(Circulation) Evergreen; (OPAC) EnvisionWare
Wireless access
Mem of North Texas Library Partners
Open Mon, Wed & Fri 10-6, Tues & Thurs 10-7, Sat 10-2
Friends of the Library Group

BROOKS AFB

AM UNITED STATES AIR FORCE*, The Aeromedical Library, 2511 Kennedy Circle, No 155, 78235-5116. SAN 361-3178. Tel: 210-536-3321. FAX: 210-536-3239. *Head of Libr,* Joseph J Franzello; E-mail: joseph.franzello@brooks.af.mil; *Syst Coordr,* John Whitney; Tel: 210-536-3323, E-mail: john.whitney@brooks.af.mil; Staff 9 (MLS 3, Non-MLS 6)
Founded 1918
Library Holdings: Bk Titles 41,613; Bk Vols 43,138; Per Subs 431
Special Collections: History of Aerospace Medicine Coll
Subject Interests: Aerospace med, Cognitive sci, Environ med, Microbiology, Physiology, Psychol, Radiation sci
Automation Activity & Vendor Info: (Cataloging) SirsiDynix; (Circulation) SirsiDynix
Database Vendor: Dialog, EBSCOhost
Publications: Armstrong Researcher (Newsletter)
Partic in Medical Library Association (MLA)
Open Mon-Fri 7:30-4:15

BROWNFIELD

P KENDRICK MEMORIAL LIBRARY*, 301 W Tate, 79316-4387. SAN 316-1234. Tel: 806-637-3848. E-mail: kendrick@door.net. *Dir,* Lupe Serna
Founded 1957. Pop 12,000; Circ 60,550
Library Holdings: Bk Vols 33,000; Per Subs 20
Automation Activity & Vendor Info: (Cataloging) LibLime; (Circulation) LibLime
Wireless access
Function: Adult literacy prog
Mem of West Texas Library System
Open Mon-Fri 9-5:30
Friends of the Library Group

BROWNSVILLE

P BROWNSVILLE PUBLIC LIBRARY SYSTEM*, 2600 Central Blvd, 78520-8824. SAN 375-5541. Tel: 956-548-1055. FAX: 956-548-0684. TDD: 800-735-2989. E-mail: info@bpl.us. Web Site: www.bpl.us. *Dir of Libr Serv, Head Librn,* Juan J Guerra; E-mail: jua@cob.us; *Br Mgr,* Marisol Vidales; *Automation Syst Coordr,* James McCoy; *Ch,* Brenda Trevino; *Ref Serv,* Jose Gonzalez; *Tech Serv,* Corinna Chapa; Staff 6 (MLS 5, Non-MLS 1)
Library Holdings: Bk Titles 122,771; Bk Vols 143,755; Per Subs 250
Subject Interests: Genealogy, Local hist, Texana
Automation Activity & Vendor Info: (Acquisitions) SirsiDynix; (Cataloging) SirsiDynix; (Circulation) SirsiDynix
Special Services for the Deaf - TDD equip
Open Mon-Thurs 10-9, Fri & Sat 10-6, Sun 1-8
Friends of the Library Group

C UNIVERSITY OF TEXAS AT BROWNSVILLE & TEXAS SOUTHMOST COLLEGE LIBRARY, 80 Fort Brown St, 78521. SAN 371-4187. Tel: 956-882-8221. Interlibrary Loan Service Tel: 956-882-7591. Reference Tel: 956-882-7205. Administration Tel: 956-882-8223. FAX: 956-882-5495. E-mail: library@utb.edu. Web Site: www.utb.edu/library. *Univ Librn,* Annabel Trevino; Tel: 956-882-8296, E-mail: annabel.trevino@utb.edu; *Librn,* Joel Chirinos; Tel: 956-882-7465, E-mail: joel.chirinos@utb.edu; *Librn,* Raquel Estrada; Tel: 956-882-7267, E-mail: raquel.estrada@utb.edu; *Librn,* Jessica Harris; Tel: 956-882-7281, E-mail: jessica.harris@utb.edu; *Librn,* Justin Lawrence; *Librn,* Ezequiel Melgoza; E-mail: ezequiel.melgoza@utb.edu; *Librn,* Liliana Sanchez; Tel: 956-882-6576, E-mail: liliana.sanchez@utb.edu; *Librn,* Mark Williams; Tel: 956-882-7108, E-mail: mark.williams@utb.edu; *Mgr, Tech Serv,* Bashir Tiwana; Tel: 956-882-7757, E-mail: bashir.tiwana@utb.edu; Staff 9 (MLS 9)
Founded 1926. Enrl 9,308; Highest Degree: Doctorate
Library Holdings: e-books 8,000; e-journals 35,000; Bk Titles 175,000; Per Subs 7,000
Special Collections: Brownsville, Cameron County, Lower Rio Grande Valley & Northeast Mexico History Coll
Subject Interests: Genealogy, Local hist
Automation Activity & Vendor Info: (Acquisitions) Innovative Interfaces, Inc; (Cataloging) Innovative Interfaces, Inc; (Circulation) Innovative Interfaces, Inc; (Course Reserve) Innovative Interfaces, Inc; (ILL) Innovative Interfaces, Inc; (OPAC) Innovative Interfaces, Inc; (Serials) LS 2000
Database Vendor: Baker & Taylor, EBSCOhost, Gale Cengage Learning, LexisNexis, OCLC FirstSearch, OVID Technologies, ProQuest, TLC (The Library Corporation), Wilson - Wilson Web
Wireless access
Function: Telephone ref
Publications: Annual Report; Newsletter; Orientation Manuals
Partic in OCLC Online Computer Library Center, Inc; TexSHARE - Texas State Library & Archives Commission
Friends of the Library Group

BROWNWOOD

P BROWNWOOD PUBLIC LIBRARY*, 600 Carnegie Blvd, 76801-7038. SAN 316-1277. Tel: 325-646-0155. FAX: 325-646-6503. E-mail: dir@brownwoodpubliclibrary.com. Web Site: www.brownwoodpubliclibrary.com. *Dir,* Mathew P McConnell; Staff 8 (MLS 1, Non-MLS 7)
Founded 1904. Pop 38,750; Circ 78,865
Library Holdings: Bk Vols 78,000; Per Subs 120
Automation Activity & Vendor Info: (Cataloging) Follett Software; (Circulation) Follett Software; (OPAC) Follett Software
Open Mon, Wed & Fri 9-6, Tues & Thurs 9-8, Sat 9-1

C HOWARD PAYNE UNIVERSITY, Walker Memorial Library, 1000 Fisk Ave, 76801. SAN 316-1285. Tel: 325-649-8602. Interlibrary Loan Service Tel: 325-649-8096. FAX: 325-649-8904. E-mail: library@hputx.edu. Web Site: library.hputx.edu. *Dean of Libr,* Nancy Anderson; Tel: 325-649-8610, E-mail: nanderson@hputx.edu; *Pub Serv,* Wade Kinnin; Tel: 325-649-8095, E-mail: wkinnin@hputx.edu; *Ref,* Laura Coulter; Tel: 325-649-8091, E-mail: lcoulter@hputx.edu; *Tech Serv,* Mary Dunham; Tel: 325-649-8093, E-mail: mdunham@hputx.edu; Staff 8 (MLS 4, Non-MLS 4)
Founded 1889. Enrl 1,171; Fac 73; Highest Degree: Master
Library Holdings: CDs 1,879; e-books 45,000; Bk Titles 87,000; Bk Vols 121,000; Per Subs 598; Videos 472
Special Collections: US Document Depository
Subject Interests: Bus, Educ, Relig, Sociol
Automation Activity & Vendor Info: (Acquisitions) SirsiDynix; (Cataloging) SirsiDynix; (Circulation) SirsiDynix; (Course Reserve) SirsiDynix; (ILL) OCLC Online; (OPAC) SirsiDynix; (Serials) SirsiDynix
Database Vendor: American Chemical Society, Amigos Library Services, Annual Reviews, Baker & Taylor, BioOne, College Source, CQ Press, CredoReference, EBSCOhost, Facts on File, Gale Cengage Learning, JSTOR, LexisNexis, Newsbank, OCLC FirstSearch, OCLC WorldCat, Oxford Online, Project MUSE, ProQuest, PubMed, SirsiDynix, WT Cox
Wireless access
Partic in Abilene Library Consortium; Llano Estacado Info Access Network (LEIAN); OCLC Online Computer Library Center, Inc; Tex Independent Cols & Univ Librs; TexSHARE - Texas State Library & Archives Commission
Open Mon-Thurs 7:30am-11:00pm, Fri 7:30-5, Sat 12-5, Sun (Fall/Spring) 3-11; Mon-Fri (Summer) 8-5
Restriction: Authorized patrons

BRYAN

P BRYAN COLLEGE STATION PUBLIC LIBRARY SYSTEM, 201 E 26th St, 77803-5356. SAN 316-1293. Tel: 979-209-5600. Administration Tel: 979-209-5614. FAX: 979-209-5610. Web Site: www.bcslibrary.org. *Dir, Libr Serv,* Larry D Koeninger; Tel: 979-209-5611, E-mail: lkoeninger@bryantx.gov; *Ref & Ad Serv Librn,* Position Currently Open; *Automation Coordr,* Wendell Gragg; *Tech Serv,* Kimberly Bridges; E-mail: kbridges@bryantx.gov; Staff 12 (MLS 12)
Founded 1903. Pop 140,000; Circ 731,924
Library Holdings: AV Mats 6,200; Bk Titles 176,084; Bk Vols 235,323; Per Subs 524; Talking Bks 3,600
Subject Interests: Ballet, Genealogy, Humanities, Local hist, Tex, Tex poets
Automation Activity & Vendor Info: (Cataloging) Polaris Library Systems; (Circulation) Polaris Library Systems; (OPAC) Polaris Library Systems
Database Vendor: Polaris Library Systems
Wireless access
Function: Handicapped accessible, ILL available, Music CDs, Online searches, Photocopying/Printing, Prog for children & young adult, Ref serv available, Spoken cassettes & CDs, Summer reading prog, Telephone ref
Open Mon-Thurs 10-7, Fri & Sat 9-5, Sun 1:30-5:30
Friends of the Library Group
Branches: 2
CARNEGIE HISTORY CENTER, 111 S Main St, 77803. Tel: 979-209-5630. *Br Mgr,* Nancy Ross; Tel: 979-209-5631, E-mail: nross@bryantx.gov; *Archives,* Lou Vonne Johnson; E-mail: lvjohnson@bryantx.gov; Staff 2 (MLS 2)
Library Holdings: Bk Vols 13,428
Subject Interests: Genealogy
Open Tues & Thurs 10-7, Wed & Fri 10-5
LARRY J RINGER LIBRARY, 1818 Harvey Mitchell Pkwy S, College Station, 77840, SAN 323-7702. Tel: 979-764-3416. FAX: 979-764-6379. *Br Mgr,* Kathy Nixie; Tel: 979-764-3625, E-mail: knixie@bryantx.gov; Staff 7 (MLS 7)
Founded 1987. Pop 140,000; Circ 389,404
Database Vendor: Baker & Taylor, EBSCOhost, Gale Cengage Learning, Overdrive, Inc
Open Mon & Wed 9-9, Tues & Thurs 9-7, Fri & Sat 9-5, Sun 1:30-5:30
Friends of the Library Group

BUDA

P　　BUDA PUBLIC LIBRARY*, Basil Anthony Moreau Memorial Library, 303 Main St, 78610. (Mail add: PO Box 608, 78610-0608), SAN 376-4818. Tel: 512-295-5899. FAX: 512-295-6525. E-mail: budalibrary@budalibrary.org, librarian@budalibrary.org. Web Site: www.budalibrary.org. *Dir,* Melinda Hodges; *Ch,* Martha Sanders; *Circ Coordr,* Lupe Herrera; E-mail: lupe@budalibrary.org; Staff 5 (MLS 2, Non-MLS 3)
　　Founded 1980
　　Library Holdings: Audiobooks 2,036; DVDs 673; Large Print Bks 837; Bk Titles 22,084; Bk Vols 23,944; Per Subs 68; Videos 802
　　Automation Activity & Vendor Info: (Cataloging) Biblionix; (Circulation) Biblionix; (OPAC) Biblionix
　　Function: AV serv, ILL available, Prog for children & young adult, Summer reading prog, Wheelchair accessible
　　Mem of Central Texas Library System, Inc
　　Open Mon-Thurs 10-8, Fri & Sat 10-5
　　Friends of the Library Group

BUFFALO

P　　BUFFALO PUBLIC LIBRARY*, Hwy 79, 75831. (Mail add: PO Box 1290, 75831-1290), SAN 376-4826. Tel: 903-322-4146. FAX: 903-322-3253. E-mail: buffalo@members.ctls.net. *Librn,* Sandra Dawkins; *Asst Librn,* Dorothy Hartley; *Children's Coordr,* Debbie Rust
　　Library Holdings: Bk Vols 25,000
　　Mem of Central Texas Library System, Inc
　　Open Mon-Thurs 8-5, Fri 8-12
　　Friends of the Library Group

BULLARD

P　　BULLARD COMMUNITY LIBRARY, 211 W Main, 75757. (Mail add: PO Box 368, 75757-0368). Tel: 903-894-6125. FAX: 903-894-6125. Web Site: www.bullardlibrary.org. *Dir,* Joanne Marie Buendtner; E-mail: director@bullardlibrary.org; Staff 1 (Non-MLS 1)
　　Founded 1976. Pop 2,000
　　Special Collections: Local History Coll
　　Subject Interests: Genealogy
　　Automation Activity & Vendor Info: (Cataloging) Book Systems, Inc; (Circulation) Book Systems, Inc; (ILL) OCLC FirstSearch; (OPAC) Book Systems, Inc
　　Wireless access
　　Function: Adult bk club, Archival coll, Audiobks via web, Bk club(s), Bks on CD, Children's prog, Computer training, Computers for patron use, Copy machines, e-mail & chat, Electronic databases & coll, Family literacy, Free DVD rentals, Holiday prog, Online cat, Outreach serv, OverDrive digital audio bks, Photocopying/Printing, Preschool outreach, Printer for laptops & handheld devices, Prog for adults, Prog for children & young adult, Pub access computers, Scanner, Story hour, Summer reading prog, Teen prog, Workshops
　　Partic in TexSHARE - Texas State Library & Archives Commission
　　Open Mon 10-9, Tues & Thurs 10-6, Fri 10-4, Sat 10-2
　　Friends of the Library Group

BULVERDE

P　　BULVERDE AREA RURAL LIBRARY DISTRICT, Bulverde-Spring Branch Library, 131 Bulverde Crossing, 78163. SAN 376-4184. Tel: 830-438-4864. FAX: 830-980-3362. E-mail: bul207@gvtc.com. Web Site: www.bsblibrary.org, www.bulverdespringbranchlibrary.org. *Dir,* Susan Herr; *Ad,* Sam Salas; *Youth Serv Librn,* Oster Janeth; Staff 2 (MLS 2)
　　Founded 1986. Pop 23,000; Circ 257,579
　　Library Holdings: AV Mats 8,042; Braille Volumes 75; Large Print Bks 2,054; Bk Titles 44,968; Bk Vols 47,335; Per Subs 63
　　Automation Activity & Vendor Info: (Acquisitions) Biblionix; (Cataloging) Biblionix; (Circulation) Biblionix; (ILL) OCLC FirstSearch; (OPAC) Follett Software
　　Wireless access
　　Function: Accessibility serv available based on individual needs, Adult bk club, Adult literacy prog, Art exhibits, Audiobks via web, Bilingual assistance for Spanish patrons, Bk club(s), Bks on CD, Children's prog, Citizenship assistance, Computer training, Computers for patron use, Copy machines, E-Reserves, Electronic databases & coll, Equip loans & repairs, Exhibits, Fax serv, Free DVD rentals, Handicapped accessible, ILL available, Large print keyboards, Magnifiers for reading, Music CDs, Newsp ref libr, Online cat, Online searches, OverDrive digital audio bks, Photocopying/Printing, Prog for adults, Prog for children & young adult, Pub access computers, Ref serv available, Ref serv in person, Scanner, Spanish lang bks, Story hour, Summer reading prog, Tax forms, Teen prog, Wheelchair accessible
　　Friends of the Library Group

BUNA

P　　BUNA PUBLIC LIBRARY*, 1042 Texas Hwy 62 S, 77612. (Mail add: PO Box 1571, 77612-1571), SAN 375-555X. Tel: 409-994-5501. FAX: 409-994-4737. E-mail: buna.library@sbcglobal.net, www.bunalibrary.org. *Dir,* Lena White; Staff 1 (Non-MLS 1)
　　Founded 1973. Pop 8,807; Circ 18,352
　　Library Holdings: AV Mats 1,500; Bk Titles 24,853; Per Subs 6
　　Wireless access
　　Special Services for the Deaf - Bks on deafness & sign lang
　　Open Mon & Tues 10-5:30, Wed 10-4, Thurs 10-4:30, Fri 10-5
　　Friends of the Library Group

BURKBURNETT

P　　BURKBURNETT LIBRARY, 215 E Fourth St, 76354-3446. SAN 316-1315. Tel: 940-569-2991. FAX: 940-569-1620. *Dir,* Teri Pickrel; E-mail: tpickrel@burkburnett.org; Staff 2 (Non-MLS 2)
　　Founded 1967. Pop 10,927; Circ 34,989
　　Library Holdings: Audiobooks 1,221; CDs 700; DVDs 1,698; Bk Titles 32,156; Per Subs 10; Videos 752
　　Special Collections: Native American History & Literature; Spanish Language Materials; Wordless Picture Books
　　Subject Interests: Genealogy, Hist, Texana
　　Automation Activity & Vendor Info: (Cataloging) Book Systems, Inc; (Circulation) Book Systems, Inc; (OPAC) Book Systems, Inc
　　Wireless access
　　Function: Children's prog, Computers for patron use, Copy machines, Free DVD rentals, Genealogy discussion group, ILL available, Microfiche/film & reading machines, Music CDs, Photocopying/Printing, Preschool reading prog, Prog for children & young adult, Spoken cassettes & CDs, Summer reading prog, Tax forms, Teen prog, VHS videos
　　Mem of North Texas Library Partners
　　Partic in Tex Share
　　Open Tues & Thurs 10-8, Wed & Fri 10-6, Sat 10-2
　　Friends of the Library Group

BURLESON

P　　BURLESON PUBLIC LIBRARY, 248 SW Johnson Ave, 76028. SAN 316-1323. Tel: 817-426-9210. Circulation Tel: 817-426-9209. Reference Tel: 817-426-9207. Administration Tel: 817-426-9206. FAX: 817-426-9371. E-mail: library@burlesontx.com. Web Site: www.burlesonlibrary.com. *Dir,* Rodney Bland; E-mail: rbland@burlesonlibrary.com; Staff 10.5 (MLS 4.5, Non-MLS 6)
　　Founded 1971. Pop 36,600; Circ 433,072
　　Library Holdings: Bk Titles 64,590; Per Subs 100
　　Automation Activity & Vendor Info: (Acquisitions) SirsiDynix; (Cataloging) SirsiDynix; (Circulation) SirsiDynix; (Course Reserve) SirsiDynix; (ILL) SirsiDynix; (OPAC) SirsiDynix; (Serials) SirsiDynix
　　Wireless access
　　Function: AV serv, Handicapped accessible, ILL available, Prog for children & young adult, Ref serv available, Summer reading prog, Wheelchair accessible
　　Mem of North Texas Library Partners
　　Partic in MetrOPAC Consortium
　　Open Mon-Thurs 10-8, Fri 10-6, Sat 10-4
　　Friends of the Library Group

BURNET

P　　BURNET COUNTY LIBRARY SYSTEM*, Herman Brown Free Library, 100 E Washington St, 78611. SAN 361-3208. Tel: 512-715-5228. FAX: 512-715-5249. E-mail: bcls@burnetcountylibrary.org. Web Site: www2.youseemore.com/burnet. *Dir,* Betsy Engelbrecht
　　Founded 1948. Pop 23,000; Circ 180,622
　　Library Holdings: Bk Titles 65,000; Bk Vols 80,000; Per Subs 250
　　Special Collections: Oral History
　　Subject Interests: Genealogy, Texana
　　Automation Activity & Vendor Info: (Cataloging) TLC (The Library Corporation); (Circulation) TLC (The Library Corporation); (Course Reserve) TLC (The Library Corporation); (ILL) TLC (The Library Corporation); (OPAC) TLC (The Library Corporation); (Serials) TLC (The Library Corporation)
　　Mem of Central Texas Library System, Inc
　　Partic in Tex Share
　　Open Mon-Fri 10-6, Sat 10-3
　　Friends of the Library Group
　　Branches: 2
　　MARBLE FALLS PUBLIC BRANCH, 101 Main St, Marble Falls, 78654, SAN 361-3291. Tel: 830-693-3023. FAX: 830-693-3987. Web Site: www.marblefallslibrary.org. *Dir,* Mary Jackson; E-mail: mjackson@burnetcountylibrary.org
　　　Library Holdings: Bk Vols 43,000
　　　Database Vendor: TLC (The Library Corporation)

Open Mon-Fri 10-6, Sat 10-3
Friends of the Library Group
OAKALLA PUBLIC LIBRARY, 29011 FM 963, Oakalla, 78608, SAN
376-9496. Tel: 512-556-9085. FAX: 512-556-9085. *Libr Asst,* Joan
Eaton; E-mail: eatonjoan7@hotmail.com
Library Holdings: Bk Vols 9,017
Open Mon 5:30pm-8:30pm, Tues 5pm-8pm, Sat 10-1
Friends of the Library Group

CALDWELL

P   HARRIE P WOODSON MEMORIAL LIBRARY*, 704 W Hwy 21,
77836-1129. SAN 316-1331. Tel: 979-567-4111. FAX: 979-567-4962.
E-mail: library@caldwelltx.gov. *Librn,* Evelyn Evans; *Asst Librn,* Mary
Kuehn
Circ 17,877
Library Holdings: Bk Titles 16,000; Per Subs 15
Automation Activity & Vendor Info: (Cataloging) Biblionix; (Circulation)
Biblionix; (OPAC) Biblionix
Wireless access
Mem of Central Texas Library System, Inc
Open Mon 10-7, Tues-Fri 9-6
Friends of the Library Group

CAMERON

P   CAMERON PUBLIC LIBRARY*, 304 E Third St, 76520. SAN 316-1358.
Tel: 254-697-2401. FAX: 254-697-2401. E-mail: camlib7@hotmail.com.
Librn, Maurina Corley; *Asst Librn,* Linda Layne
Founded 1953. Pop 11,890; Circ 29,035
Library Holdings: Bk Titles 18,000; Bk Vols 35,118; Per Subs 50
Special Collections: DAR Genealogy, vols, mss; Local History Coll; Texas
History Coll
Wireless access
Open Mon 11-7, Tues-Fri 10-6
Friends of the Library Group

CAMP WOOD

P   CAMP WOOD PUBLIC LIBRARY*, 117 S Nueces, 78833-0828. (Mail
add: PO Box 138, 78833-0138), SAN 378-3936. Tel: 830-597-3208. FAX:
830-597-3208. Web Site: www.campwood.com/library.htm. *Dir,* Dixie
Frizzell; *Librn,* Annette Hutto
Pop 1,523
Library Holdings: AV Mats 8,000; Bk Vols 8,000; Videos 660
Automation Activity & Vendor Info: (Cataloging) Biblionix; (Circulation)
Biblionix
Wireless access
Open Mon, Wed & Fri 10-2, Tues & Thurs 1-5
Friends of the Library Group

CANADIAN

P   HEMPHILL COUNTY LIBRARY*, 500 Main St, 79014. SAN 316-1366.
Tel: 806-323-5282. FAX: 806-323-6102. E-mail: staff@hemphillcl.org. *Dir,*
April Dillon; E-mail: staff@hemphillcl.org; *Ch,* Zandi Rankin; E-mail:
jzrankin@yahoo.com; Staff 1 (MLS 1)
Founded 1927. Pop 3,300
Library Holdings: Bk Titles 37,957; Per Subs 72; Talking Bks 1,379;
Videos 729
Special Collections: Local Newspaper since 1887, micro
Subject Interests: Local hist
Automation Activity & Vendor Info: (Cataloging) SirsiDynix;
(Circulation) SirsiDynix; (OPAC) SirsiDynix
Wireless access
Partic in Harrington Library Consortium
Open Mon & Thurs 8:30-6, Tues, Wed & Fri 8:30-5, Sat 9-12
Friends of the Library Group

CANTON

P   VAN ZANDT COUNTY LIBRARY*, 317 First Monday Lane, 75103.
SAN 320-7498. Tel: 903-567-4276. FAX: 903-567-6981. E-mail:
vanzandtcolibrary@hotmail.com. Web Site: vanzandtlibrary.org. *Librn,*
Susie Pulley
Pop 38,000
Library Holdings: Bk Vols 44,697; Per Subs 60
Special Collections: Genealogy Coll; Local History Coll; Texas Coll
Automation Activity & Vendor Info: (Cataloging) Follett Software;
(Circulation) Follett Software
Wireless access
Open Mon-Fri 10-5:45, Sat 9:30-12:45
Friends of the Library Group

CANYON

P   CANYON AREA LIBRARY, 1501 Third Ave, 79015. SAN 316-1374. Tel:
806-655-5015. FAX: 806-655-5032. Web Site: www.canyonlibrary.org.
Head Librn, Sandra Munger; E-mail: smunger@canyontx.com; *Librn,*
Noreen Taylor; E-mail: ntaylor@canyontx.com; Staff 6 (MLS 2, Non-MLS
4)
Founded 1928. Pop 35,516; Circ 93,845
Oct 2010-Sept 2011 Income $376,486, State $6,212, City $302,264,
County $50,000, Locally Generated Income $8,010, Other $10,000. Mats
Exp $35,635, Books $24,939, Per/Ser (Incl. Access Fees) $2,449, AV Mat
$7,249, Electronic Ref Mat (Incl. Access Fees) $998. Sal $212,732 (Prof
$111,000)
Library Holdings: Audiobooks 1,116; CDs 1,796; DVDs 1,056; e-books
502; Electronic Media & Resources 61; Large Print Bks 1,693; Bk Titles
45,825; Bk Vols 49,087; Per Subs 70; Videos 985
Special Collections: Texas Coll
Automation Activity & Vendor Info: (Cataloging) SirsiDynix;
(Circulation) SirsiDynix; (ILL) SirsiDynix; (OPAC) SirsiDynix
Database Vendor: Agricola, Amigos Library Services, EBSCOhost, Gale
Cengage Learning, Ingram Library Services, LearningExpress, netLibrary,
Newsbank, OCLC FirstSearch, Overdrive, Inc, ProQuest,
TumbleBookLibrary, World Book Online
Wireless access
Function: Adult bk club, Bks on cassette, Bks on CD, Computer training,
Computers for patron use, Copy machines, Electronic databases & coll,
Free DVD rentals, Handicapped accessible, Homebound delivery serv, ILL
available, Music CDs, Online cat, OverDrive digital audio bks, Prog for
adults, Prog for children & young adult, Ref serv available, Summer
reading prog, Tax forms, VHS videos
Partic in Harrington Library Consortium
Open Mon & Thurs 10-8, Tues & Wed 10-6, Fri 10-5:30, Sat 10-2
Friends of the Library Group

S   PANHANDLE-PLAINS HISTORICAL MUSEUM*, Research Center,
2503 Fourth Ave, 79015. (Mail add: WT Box 60967, 79016), SAN
328-6169. Tel: 806-651-2254. FAX: 806-651-2260. Administration FAX:
806-651-2250. Web Site: www.panhandleplains.org. *Dir, Res,* Warren
Stricker; E-mail: wstricker@pphm.wtamu.edu; Staff 1.5 (MLS 1, Non-MLS
0.5)
Library Holdings: Bk Vols 15,000
Special Collections: Oral History
Subject Interests: Hist of the Tex Panhandle-Plains region, Local hist,
Okla Panhandle & Eastern NMex, Petroleum indust, Ranching,
Southwestern art & artists, State & local govt
Wireless access
Function: Archival coll, Copy machines, Res libr
Open Mon-Thurs 1-5, Fri 10-12 & 1-5
Restriction: Closed stack, Non-circulating

C   WEST TEXAS A&M UNIVERSITY*, Cornette Library, University Dr &
26th St, 79016. (Mail add: WTAMU Box 60748, 79016-0001), SAN
316-1382. Tel: 806-651-2229. Circulation Tel: 806-651-2223. Interlibrary
Loan Service Tel: 806-651-2406. Reference Tel: 806-651-2215. FAX:
806-651-2213. Web Site: www.wtamu.edu/library. *Dir,* Shawna
Kennedy-Witthar; Tel: 806-651-2227, E-mail: switthar@wtamu.edu; *Asst
Dir,* Linda Chenoweth; Tel: 806-651-2212, E-mail:
lchenoweth@wtamu.edu; *Head, Acq,* Gonda Stayton; Tel: 806-651-2218,
E-mail: gdstayton@wtamu.edu; *Head, Cat,* Mary Rausch; Tel:
806-651-2219, E-mail: mrausch@wtamu.edu; *Head, Circ,* Beth Vizzini;
Tel: 806-651-2223, E-mail: bavizzini@wtamu.edu; *Doc Librn,* Carolyn
Ottoson; Tel: 806-651-2204, E-mail: cottoson@wtamu.edu; *Ref Librn,*
Steve Ely; E-mail: sely@wtamu.edu; *Per, Spec Coll Librn,* Sidnye Johnson;
Tel: 806-651-2209, E-mail: sjohnson@wtamu.edu; *Evening/Weekend Librn,*
Martha Allred; E-mail: mallred@wtamu.edu; *Evening/Weekend Librn,*
Amada Vidaurri; *Coordr, ILL,* Pam Wilson; Tel: 806-651-2211, E-mail:
pwilson@wtamu.edu; Staff 23 (MLS 8, Non-MLS 15)
Founded 1910. Enrl 7,900; Fac 242; Highest Degree: Doctorate
Sept 2006-Aug 2007 Income $1,793,649, State $1,238,987, Locally
Generated Income $548,905, Other $5,757. Mats Exp $772,390, Books
$111,791, Per/Ser (Incl. Access Fees) $282,871, Micro $61,448, AV Mat
$7,217, Electronic Ref Mat (Incl. Access Fees) $305,965, Presv $3,098. Sal
$732,061 (Prof $448,216)
Library Holdings: AV Mats 1,927; Bk Titles 740,579; Bk Vols 1,096,057;
Per Subs 19,022
Special Collections: American History (Library of American Civilization),
micro; English History (British House of Commons Sessional Papers &
Hansard's British Parliamentary Debates), micro; English Literature
(Library of English Literature, Parts 1-4), micro; Loula Grace Erdmen
Papers; Sheffy Coll, regional hist; Texas Panhandle & Great Plains (Dr L F
Sheffy Memorial); Western Americana (Xerox UM Western Americana),
micro. Oral History; State Document Depository; US Document Depository
Automation Activity & Vendor Info: (Acquisitions) Ex Libris Group;
(Cataloging) Ex Libris Group; (Circulation) Ex Libris Group; (Course

Reserve) Ex Libris Group; (ILL) OCLC ILLiad; (Media Booking) Ex Libris Group; (OPAC) Ex Libris Group; (Serials) Ex Libris Group
Database Vendor: ABC-CLIO, Amigos Library Services, Annual Reviews, Baker & Taylor, Blackwell's, Bowker, Checkpoint Systems, Inc, Cinahl Information Systems, EBSCOhost, Elsevier, Ex Libris Group, Gale Cengage Learning, Grolier Online, H W Wilson, ISI Web of Knowledge, JSTOR, LexisNexis, Marcive, Inc, Marquis Who's Who, McGraw-Hill, netLibrary, OCLC FirstSearch, OCLC WorldCat, OVID Technologies, Project MUSE, ProQuest, ScienceDirect, Springer-Verlag, Standard & Poor's, Swets Information Services, ValueLine, Westlaw, Wiley
Wireless access
Publications: Newsletter; Quick Guides
Partic in Llano Estacado Info Access Network (LEIAN)
Special Services for the Blind - VisualTek equip
Open Mon-Thurs 7:45am-11pm, Fri 7:45-5, Sat 10-5, Sun 2-11
Friends of the Library Group

CANYON LAKE

P   TYE PRESTON MEMORIAL LIBRARY, 16311 S Access Rd, 78133-5301. SAN 324-1238. Tel: 830-964-3744. FAX: 830-964-3126. Web Site: www.tpml.org. *Dir*, Roxanna Deane; E-mail: roxanna@tpml.org; *Pub Serv Coordr*, Brenda Coulter; E-mail: coulter@tpml.org; *Youth Serv Coordr*, Jo Johnstone; E-mail: jo@tpml.org; Staff 6 (MLS 1, Non-MLS 5)
Founded 1977. Pop 23,561; Circ 115,606
Jul 2010-Jun 2011 Income $457,288, Locally Generated Income $425,923, Other $31,365. Mats Exp $35,108, Books $26,957, AV Mat $7,864. Sal $178,318 (Prof $40,000)
Library Holdings: Audiobooks 2,170; DVDs 2,315; e-books 540; Bk Vols 30,739
Automation Activity & Vendor Info: (Acquisitions) Biblionix; (Cataloging) Biblionix; (Circulation) Biblionix; (OPAC) Biblionix
Wireless access
Function: Adult bk club, Adult literacy prog, Art exhibits, Audiobks via web, Bks on cassette, Bks on CD, Children's prog, Computer training, Computers for patron use, Copy machines, Electronic databases & coll, Exhibits, Family literacy, Fax serv, Free DVD rentals, Genealogy discussion group, Handicapped accessible, Homebound delivery serv, ILL available, Magnifiers for reading, Online cat, Photocopying/Printing, Preschool outreach, Prog for adults, Prog for children & young adult, Pub access computers, Scanner, Spoken cassettes & CDs, Story hour, Summer reading prog, Tax forms, Teen prog, Web-catalog
Special Services for the Blind - Computer with voice synthesizer for visually impaired persons; Reader equip; ZoomText magnification & reading software
Open Mon-Thurs 9-8:30, Fri & Sat 10-5
Friends of the Library Group

CARRIZO SPRINGS

P   DIMMIT COUNTY PUBLIC LIBRARY, 200 N Ninth St, 78834. SAN 376-4141. Tel: 830-876-5788. FAX: 830-876-3890. E-mail: carrizo.librarian@gmail.com. Web Site: www.carrizosprings.lib.tx.us. *Libr Dir*, Evelyn W McDonald; Tel: 830-876-1174; Staff 3 (Non-MLS 3)
Founded 1980. Pop 10,460
Library Holdings: Bk Vols 22,539; Per Subs 41
Automation Activity & Vendor Info: (Acquisitions) Follett Software; (Cataloging) Follett Software; (Circulation) Follett Software; (Course Reserve) Follett Software; (ILL) Follett Software; (OPAC) Follett Software; (Serials) Follett Software
Wireless access
Function: Bks on cassette, Bks on CD, CD-ROM, Children's prog, Computers for patron use, Copy machines, e-mail serv, Fax serv, Free DVD rentals, Genealogy discussion group, ILL available, Magnifiers for reading, Music CDs, Photocopying/Printing, Pub access computers, Summer reading prog, Tax forms, VHS videos, Wheelchair accessible
Open Mon-Fri 8-5
Friends of the Library Group

CARROLLTON

P   CARROLLTON PUBLIC LIBRARY*, 1700 Keller Springs Rd, 75006. SAN 319-3268. Tel: 972-466-4800. Administration Tel: 972-466-3362. FAX: 972-466-4265. Web Site: www.cityofcarrollton.com/library. *Syst Adminr*, Jan Sapp; Tel: 972-466-3591, E-mail: jan.sapp@cityofcarrollton.com; *Access Serv*, Cynthia Lyman; Tel: 972-466-4812, E-mail: cynthia.lyman@cityofcarrollton.com; *Acq*, Lana Kelley; Tel: 972-466-4704, E-mail: lana.kelley@cityofcarrollton.com; *Info Serv*, Terri Allison; E-mail: terri.allison@cityofcarrollton.com; *Info Serv*, Lynette Jones; Tel: 972-466-4814, E-mail: lynette.jones@cityofcarrollton.com; *Youth Serv*, Kelly Burns; Tel: 972-466-4717, E-mail: kelly.burns@cityofcarrollton.com; Staff 27.75 (MLS 15, Non-MLS 12.75)
Founded 1963. Pop 121,000; Circ 761,078

Oct 2008-Sept 2009 Income $134,832, State $54,232, County $80,600. Mats Exp $417,537, Per/Ser (Incl. Access Fees) $116,656, AV Equip $240,720, Electronic Ref Mat (Incl. Access Fees) $60,161. Sal $2,178,897
Library Holdings: AV Mats 16,035; e-books 1,172; Bk Titles 140,067; Bk Vols 208,000
Special Collections: Genealogy Coll; Local History Coll
Automation Activity & Vendor Info: (Acquisitions) Innovative Interfaces, Inc; (Cataloging) Innovative Interfaces, Inc; (Circulation) Innovative Interfaces, Inc; (ILL) Innovative Interfaces, Inc; (OPAC) Innovative Interfaces, Inc; (Serials) Innovative Interfaces, Inc
Database Vendor: EBSCOhost, Gale Cengage Learning, OCLC FirstSearch
Wireless access
Function: ILL available
Partic in Tex Share
Open Mon 10-9, Tues, Fri & Sat 10-6, Wed 12-9, Sun 2-6
Friends of the Library Group

CARTHAGE

P   SAMMY BROWN LIBRARY*, 522 W College St, 75633. SAN 316-1412. Tel: 903-693-6741. FAX: 903-693-4503. Web Site: www.carthagetexas.com/library. *Dir*, Debbie Godwin; E-mail: dgodwin@sammybrown.org
Founded 1962. Pop 22,350
Oct 2009-Sept 2010 Income $44,000. Mats Exp $6,800. Sal $42,300 (Prof $24,000)
Library Holdings: CDs 1,206; DVDs 2,000; Bk Titles 48,862; Per Subs 44
Automation Activity & Vendor Info: (Cataloging) Follett Software; (Circulation) Follett Software
Wireless access
Open Mon-Fri 9-6, Sat 9-1
Friends of the Library Group

J   PANOLA COLLEGE*, M P Baker Library, 1109 W Panola St, 75633. SAN 316-1404. Tel: 903-693-2052. Interlibrary Loan Service Tel: 903-693-2091. Reference Tel: 903-693-1181. FAX: 903-693-1115. Web Site: www.panola.edu/library.htm. *Dir, Libr Serv*, Zeny Jett; Tel: 903-693-2005, E-mail: zjett@panola.edu; *AV, Media Spec*, Phillip Scholl; Tel: 903-693-1146; *Cat, Tech Serv*, Mary Kay Davis; Tel: 903-693-1162; *Circ*, Sharon Hill; Tel: 903-693-1155, E-mail: shill@panola.edu; *Distance Educ*, Cristie Ferguson; Tel: 903-693-2091, E-mail: cferguson@panola.edu; *Evening Circ*, May Whitten; Tel: 903-693-1119, E-mail: mwhitten@panola.edu; *Ref*, Sherri Baker; E-mail: sherri.baker@panola.edu; Staff 7 (MLS 3, Non-MLS 4)
Founded 1947. Enrl 1,981; Fac 70; Highest Degree: Associate
Special Collections: East Texas Documents & Genealogies, oral hist
Automation Activity & Vendor Info: (Cataloging) SirsiDynix; (Circulation) SirsiDynix; (Course Reserve) SirsiDynix; (Media Booking) SirsiDynix; (OPAC) SirsiDynix; (Serials) SirsiDynix
Database Vendor: Amigos Library Services, EBSCOhost, Elsevier, Gale Cengage Learning, Grolier Online, H W Wilson, LearningExpress, OCLC ArticleFirst, OCLC FirstSearch, OCLC WorldCat, OVID Technologies, ProQuest, ScienceDirect, Wiley InterScience, WT Cox
Function: Archival coll, Art exhibits, Bks on CD, Computers for patron use, Copy machines, Distance learning, Doc delivery serv, e-mail & chat, E-Reserves, Electronic databases & coll, Exhibits, ILL available, Instruction & testing, Music CDs, Online cat, Online info literacy tutorials on the web & in blackboard, Online ref, Orientations, Photocopying/Printing, Ref & res, Ref serv available, Ref serv in person, Scanner, Spoken cassettes & CDs, Spoken cassettes & DVDs, Tax forms, Telephone ref, VHS videos, Web-catalog, Workshops
Publications: Library Annual (Annual report); M P Baker Library Staff Handbook
Partic in Amigos Library Services, Inc; OCLC Online Computer Library Center, Inc; TexSHARE - Texas State Library & Archives Commission
Special Services for the Deaf - Assistive tech
Open Mon-Thurs (Winter) 7:30am-9pm, Fri 7:30-4:30, Sun 4-9; Mon-Thurs (Summer) 7:30-5, Fri 7:30-12:30
Restriction: Open to fac, students & qualified researchers

CASTROVILLE

P   CASTROVILLE PUBLIC LIBRARY, 802 London St, 78009. SAN 316-1420. Tel: 830-931-4095. FAX: 830-931-9050. Web Site: www.castrovillelibrary.org. *Libr Dir*, Kim Davis; E-mail: dirpublicsvcs@castrovilletx.gov; *Librn*, Catherine Prazak; E-mail: cathy.prazak@castrovillelibrary.org; *IT Mgr*, Gerardo Flores, II; E-mail: itspecialist@castrovilletx.gov; *Youth Serv Coordr*, Debbie Krueger; E-mail: debbie.krueger@castrovillelibrary.org; Staff 3 (MLS 1, Non-MLS 2)
Founded 1962. Pop 3,059
Library Holdings: Audiobooks 595; DVDs 1,103; Large Print Bks 1,203; Bk Titles 12,966
Special Collections: Oral History

Subject Interests: Genealogy, Local hist
Automation Activity & Vendor Info: (Cataloging) Biblionix; (Circulation) Biblionix; (ILL) Biblionix
Wireless access
Function: Accelerated reader prog, Adult bk club, Audiobks via web, Bk club(s), Bks on CD, Children's prog, Computer training, Computers for patron use, Copy machines, Distance learning, Family literacy, Fax serv, Free DVD rentals, ILL available, Online cat, OverDrive digital audio bks, Photocopying/Printing, Preschool outreach, Prog for adults, Prog for children & young adult, Pub access computers, Ref serv available, Ref serv in person, Scanner, Senior computer classes, Senior outreach, Story hour, Summer reading prog, Tax forms, Teen prog, Wheelchair accessible
Open Mon-Thurs 10-6, Fri 10-5, Sat 10-4
Friends of the Library Group

CEDAR HILL

C   NORTHWOOD UNIVERSITY LIBRARY*, Cedar Hill Campus, 1114 W FM 1382, 75104. SAN 361-3410. Tel: 972-293-5436. FAX: 972-293-7026. Web Site: www.northwood.edu. *Dir,* Kaethryn Duncan
Founded 1967. Enrl 751; Fac 30; Highest Degree: Bachelor
Library Holdings: Bk Vols 10,500; Per Subs 160
Special Collections: Advertising; Automotive Marketing; Business Management; Fashion Merchandising; Hotel & Restaurant; Management
Subject Interests: Acctg, Econ, Fashion
Restriction: Staff use only, Students only

P   ZULA BRYANT WYLIE PUBLIC LIBRARY*, 225 Cedar St, 75104-2655. SAN 361-4107. Tel: 972-291-7323. Circulation Tel: 972-291-7323, Ext 1315. Reference Tel: 972-291-7323, Ext 1313. FAX: 972-291-5361. E-mail: library@cedarhilltx.com. Web Site: www.zulabwylielib.org. *Ch,* Toni Simmons; Tel: 972-291-7323, Ext 1312; *Ref Serv, Syst Librn,* Dan Watkins; Tel: 972-291-7323, Ext 1311, E-mail: watkd@cedarhilltx.com; Staff 12 (MLS 2, Non-MLS 10)
Founded 1948. Pop 43,151; Circ 119,365
Oct 2007-Sept 2008 Income $844,630, State $9,336, City $835,294. Mats Exp $102,040, Books $45,410, Per/Ser (Incl. Access Fees) $3,356, Micro $1,200, AV Mat $35,140, Electronic Ref Mat (Incl. Access Fees) $16,934. Sal $353,970
Library Holdings: Audiobooks 3,018; Braille Volumes 119; CDs 1,898; DVDs 1,293; e-books 28,281; Large Print Bks 1,913; Microforms 11; Bk Titles 54,254; Bk Vols 55,068; Per Subs 110; Videos 2,860
Special Collections: Spanish Language Coll
Subject Interests: Local hist
Automation Activity & Vendor Info: (Acquisitions) Innovative Interfaces, Inc - Millenium; (Cataloging) Innovative Interfaces, Inc - Millenium; (Circulation) Innovative Interfaces, Inc - Millenium; (OPAC) Innovative Interfaces, Inc - Millenium
Database Vendor: Amigos Library Services, CountryWatch, EBSCOhost, Gale Cengage Learning, LearningExpress, netLibrary, Newsbank, OCLC FirstSearch, OCLC WorldCat, ProQuest, ReferenceUSA, ValueLine
Wireless access
Function: Bk club(s), Bks on cassette, Bks on CD, Children's prog, Computers for patron use, Copy machines, Electronic databases & coll, Fax serv, Holiday prog, ILL available, Music CDs, Notary serv, Online cat, Online ref, Photocopying/Printing, Preschool outreach, Prog for adults, Prog for children & young adult, Pub access computers, Ref & res, Ref serv in person, Story hour, Summer reading prog, Teen prog, Telephone ref, VHS videos
Special Services for the Deaf - Bks on deafness & sign lang; Closed caption videos
Special Services for the Blind - Audio mat; Bks & mags in Braille, on rec, tape & cassette; Bks available with recordings; Bks on cassette; Bks on CD; Braille bks; Large print bks
Open Mon, Tues & Thurs 10-9, Wed & Fri 10-6, Sat 10-5
Friends of the Library Group

CEDAR PARK

P   CEDAR PARK PUBLIC LIBRARY*, 550 Discovery Blvd, 78613. SAN 325-5158. Tel: 512-401-5600. Circulation Tel: 512-401-5602, 512-401-5604, 512-401-5606. Interlibrary Loan Service Tel: 512-401-5638. Reference Tel: 512-401-5608. Administration Tel: 512-401-5624. FAX: 512-259-5236. E-mail: library@cedarparktx.us. Web Site: www.cedarparktx.us. *Dir,* Pauline P Lam; E-mail: pauline.lam@cedarparktx.us; *Pub Serv Librn,* Sarah Whited; E-mail: sarah.whited@cedarparktx.us; *Operations Mgr,* Julia Mitschke; Tel: 512-401-5648, E-mail: julia.mitschke@cedarparktx.us; *Ch,* Kit Coates; Tel: 512-401-5634, E-mail: kit.coates@cedarparktx.us; *Pub Serv,* Nancy Pendleton; Tel: 512-401-5640, E-mail: nancy.pendleton@cedarparktx.us; Staff 23.5 (MLS 5.25, Non-MLS 18.25)
Founded 1981. Pop 52,058; Circ 573,685
Oct 2010-Sept 2011 Income $1,322,469, State $200,000, City $1,092,469, Locally Generated Income $30,000. Mats Exp $132,126, Books $82,240,

Per/Ser (Incl. Access Fees) $7,000, AV Mat $38,826, Electronic Ref Mat (Incl. Access Fees) $4,060. Sal $791,332
Library Holdings: AV Mats 4,713; CDs 1,744; DVDs 2,468; Large Print Bks 1,239; Bk Titles 91,434; Bk Vols 106,056; Per Subs 217; Talking Bks 5,740; Videos 2,468
Subject Interests: Texana
Automation Activity & Vendor Info: (Cataloging) SirsiDynix; (Circulation) SirsiDynix; (ILL) OCLC FirstSearch; (OPAC) SirsiDynix
Database Vendor: EBSCOhost, Gale Cengage Learning, netLibrary, OCLC FirstSearch, OCLC WorldCat, ProQuest, ReferenceUSA, SirsiDynix
Wireless access
Function: Adult bk club, Bks on cassette, Bks on CD, Children's prog, Computers for patron use, Copy machines, Electronic databases & coll, Fax serv, ILL available, Music CDs, Online cat, Photocopying/Printing, Prog for adults, Prog for children & young adult, Story hour, Summer reading prog, Tax forms, Teen prog, Web-catalog
Mem of Central Texas Library System, Inc
Partic in Amigos Library Services, Inc; Tex Share
Open Mon-Thurs 9-9, Fri & Sat 9-5, Sun 1-6
Friends of the Library Group

CELESTE

P   CELESTE PUBLIC LIBRARY*, 400 E Cockrell St, 75423-9669. Tel: 903-568-0556. *Librn,* Yancy Wehmeyer; E-mail: ywehmeyer@texoma.net
Library Holdings: Bk Titles 4,200
Open Wed 4-5:30, Thurs 2:30-5:30

CELINA

P   CELINA PUBLIC LIBRARY*, 142 N Ohio St, 75009. SAN 376-4494. Tel: 972-382-8655. FAX: 972-382-3736. *Librn,* Linda Shaw; E-mail: lshaw@celina-tx.gov; Staff 1 (Non-MLS 1)
Founded 1992. Pop 6,222
Library Holdings: Bk Titles 10,900; Bk Vols 11,150; Per Subs 30
Subject Interests: Educ
Automation Activity & Vendor Info: (Acquisitions) Follett Software; (Cataloging) Follett Software; (Circulation) Follett Software; (Course Reserve) Follett Software; (ILL) Follett Software; (OPAC) Follett Software; (Serials) Follett Software
Open Tues 10-8, Wed & Thurs 10-6, Fri & Sat 10-4

CENTER

P   FANNIE BROWN BOOTH MEMORIAL LIBRARY, 619 Tenaha St, 75935. SAN 316-1439. Tel: 936-598-5522. FAX: 936-598-7854. Web Site: www.centerlibrary.org. *Libr Dir,* Sandra Davis; E-mail: fbbl.sandra@yahoo.com; *Asst Librn,* Catherine Spann; Fax: fbbl.catherine@yahoo.com; Staff 2 (Non-MLS 2)
Pop 5,678; Circ 19,458
Sept 2008-Aug 2009 Income $111,771, State $3,998, City $48,000, Locally Generated Income $59,773. Mats Exp $11,951, Books $9,300, AV Mat $2,651. Sal $49,185
Library Holdings: Audiobooks 604; Bks-By-Mail 68; Bks on Deafness & Sign Lang 6; Braille Volumes 14; CDs 850; DVDs 903; Large Print Bks 604; Microforms 69; Bk Titles 15,462; Bk Vols 16,059; Per Subs 8; Spec Interest Per Sub 5; Videos 857
Special Collections: Texas History Coll. Municipal Document Depository
Automation Activity & Vendor Info: (Cataloging) Follett Software; (Circulation) Follett Software; (OPAC) Follett Software
Wireless access
Function: Accelerated reader prog
Open Tues-Fri 10-6, Sat 9-12
Friends of the Library Group

CENTERVILLE

P   LEON COUNTY LIBRARY*, Elmer P & Jewel Ward Memorial Library, 207 E Saint Mary's, 75833. (Mail add: PO Box 567, 75833-0567). Tel: 903-536-3726. FAX: 903-536-2329. *Dir,* Susie Stone
Pop 15,703
Library Holdings: Bk Vols 10,000
Open Mon 12-2, Tues 9-7, Wed 10-3, Thurs & Fri 9-5

CHANDLER

CHANDLER PUBLIC LIBRARY*, 900 E Hwy 31, 75758. (Mail add: PO Box 301, 75758), SAN 323-6994. Tel: 903-849-4122. FAX: 903-849-4122. E-mail: chandlerpublib@yahoo.com. Web Site: www.chandlerpublib.org. *Librn,* Nancy Bertholf; Staff 1 (MLS 1)
Pop 2,000
Library Holdings: Bk Titles 1,500; Per Subs 32
Automation Activity & Vendor Info: (Acquisitions) Follett Software; (Cataloging) Follett Software; (Circulation) Follett Software
Wireless access

Open Mon-Fri 10-6, Sat 9-1
Friends of the Library Group

CHARLOTTE

P   CHARLOTTE PUBLIC LIBRARY*, 77 Yule St, 78011. (Mail add: PO Box 757, 78011), SAN 376-4206. Tel: 830-277-1212. FAX: 830-277-1212. E-mail: charlottepublib@vtxb.com. *Librn,* Anna Estrada; E-mail: anna.estrada@us.army.mil; Staff 1 (MLS 1)
Founded 1984
Library Holdings: Bk Titles 9,000; Bk Vols 10,100
Wireless access
Open Mon-Fri 8-5 (11-5 Summer)
Friends of the Library Group

CHICO

P   CHICO PUBLIC LIBRARY INC*, 106 W Jacksboro, 76431. (Mail add: PO Box 707, 76431-0707), SAN 376-4648. Tel: 940-644-2330. FAX: 940-644-2330. *Dir,* Karen Hornsby
Founded 1973
Library Holdings: Bk Vols 20,371
Automation Activity & Vendor Info: (Cataloging) Book Systems, Inc; (Circulation) Book Systems, Inc; (OPAC) Book Systems, Inc
Wireless access
Mem of North Texas Library Partners
Open Mon & Fri 10-6, Tues-Thurs 1-5, Sat 9-12

CHILDRESS

P   CHILDRESS PUBLIC LIBRARY*, 117 Ave B NE, 79201-4509. SAN 316-1455. Tel: 940-937-8421. FAX: 940-937-8421. *Dir,* Judy Faye McKeever; E-mail: judymck@hotmail.com; Staff 2 (Non-MLS 2)
Founded 1900. Pop 7,532; Circ 14,877
Jan 2011-Dec 2011 Income $62,680, City $22,500, County $36,217, Other $3,963. Sal $36,917
Library Holdings: AV Mats 432; Large Print Bks 200; Bk Vols 18,028; Talking Bks 412
Wireless access
Function: Telephone ref
Open Mon-Fri 10-6
Friends of the Library Group

CISCO

J   CISCO COLLEGE*, Maner Memorial Library, 101 College Heights, 76437. SAN 316-1463. Tel: 254-442-5026. Administration Tel: 254-442-5001. FAX: 254-442-5100. Web Site: www.cisco.edu. *Dir, Libr Serv,* Heather Williamson; E-mail: hwilliamson@cisco.edu; Staff 10 (MLS 2, Non-MLS 8)
Founded 1940. Enrl 3,516; Highest Degree: Associate
Library Holdings: AV Mats 2,000; CDs 153; DVDs 127; e-books 36,398; e-journals 40; Electronic Media & Resources 99; Music Scores 200; Bk Titles 27,127; Bk Vols 16,005; Per Subs 190
Special Collections: Local History Archives, bks, clippings, local newsp, oral hist, maps; Old West, Native Americans & US Military History (Randy Steffen Coll), bks, per; Texas Coll, bks, per. Oral History
Automation Activity & Vendor Info: (Acquisitions) ComPanion Corp; (Cataloging) ComPanion Corp; (Circulation) ComPanion Corp; (Course Reserve) ComPanion Corp; (Media Booking) ComPanion Corp; (OPAC) ComPanion Corp; (Serials) ComPanion Corp
Database Vendor: EBSCOhost, Gale Cengage Learning, Hoovers, netLibrary, OCLC FirstSearch, OCLC WorldCat, Oxford Online, ProQuest, Wilson - Wilson Web
Wireless access
Function: Archival coll, Art exhibits, Audio & video playback equip for onsite use, AV serv, CD-ROM, Copy machines, Distance learning, E-Reserves, Electronic databases & coll, Equip loans & repairs, Handicapped accessible, ILL available, Magnifiers for reading, Music CDs, Online info literacy tutorials on the web & in blackboard, Online searches, Orientations, Photocopying/Printing, Ref serv available, Satellite serv, Telephone ref, Wheelchair accessible
Publications: FYI (Newsletter); Maner Messenger (Newsletter)
Partic in TexSHARE - Texas State Library & Archives Commission
Special Services for the Blind - Large screen computer & software; ZoomText magnification & reading software
Open Mon-Thurs 7:30am-11pm, Fri 7:30-6, Sun 7pm-11pm
Restriction: Open to pub for ref & circ; with some limitations, Photo ID required for access
Friends of the Library Group
Departmental Libraries:
    ABILENE EDUCATIONAL CENTER LIBRARY, 717 E Industrial Blvd, Abilene, 79602. Tel: 325-794-4481. *Br Librn,* Marissa Jurkis; Tel: 325-794-4466, E-mail: mjurkis@cisco.edu; Staff 3 (MLS 1, Non-MLS 2)
    Founded 2004. Enrl 2,637; Highest Degree: Associate

Function: Audio & video playback equip for onsite use, AV serv, Copy machines, E-Reserves, Electronic databases & coll, ILL available, Online info literacy tutorials on the web & in blackboard, Online searches, Orientations, Photocopying/Printing, Ref serv available, Telephone ref, VHS videos, Workshops
Partic in Tex Share
Open Mon-Thurs 7:30am-9pm, Fri 8-2 (8-Noon Summer)
Restriction: Open to pub for ref only

P   CISCO PUBLIC LIBRARY*, 600 Ave G, 76437. SAN 316-1471. Tel: 254-442-1020. E-mail: clibrary@txol.net. *Librn,* Janet Hounshell
Circ 4,029
Library Holdings: Bk Vols 20,000
Wireless access
Open Mon, Wed & Fri 12:30-5:30

CLARENDON

P   GABIE BETTS BURTON MEMORIAL LIBRARY*, 217 S Kearney, 79226. (Mail add: PO Box 783, 79226-0783), SAN 316-148X. Tel: 806-874-3685. FAX: 806-874-9750. *Librn,* Jerri Shields; E-mail: clajerri@amaonline.com
Founded 1923. Pop 4,100; Circ 26,393
Library Holdings: Bk Titles 30,000; Per Subs 20
Automation Activity & Vendor Info: (Cataloging) SIRSI-DRA; (Circulation) SIRSI-DRA; (OPAC) SIRSI-DRA
Wireless access
Partic in Harrington Library Consortium
Open Mon-Fri 9-5
Friends of the Library Group

J   CLARENDON COLLEGE LIBRARY*, 1122 College Dr, 79226. (Mail add: PO Box 968, 79226-0968), SAN 316-1498. Tel: 806-874-4813. Circulation Tel: 806-874-4814. Toll Free Tel: 800-687-9737. FAX: 806-874-5080. Web Site: clarendoncollege.edu. *Dir,* Reagan Silva; *Asst Dir,* Annis Stavenhagen; Staff 3 (MLS 1, Non-MLS 2)
Founded 1898. Enrl 1,413; Fac 37; Highest Degree: Associate
Library Holdings: e-books 1,900; Bk Titles 25,267; Bk Vols 26,500; Per Subs 90
Special Collections: Clarendon Coll. Oral History
Subject Interests: Tex
Automation Activity & Vendor Info: (Acquisitions) SirsiDynix; (Cataloging) SirsiDynix; (Circulation) SirsiDynix; (Course Reserve) SirsiDynix; (ILL) SirsiDynix; (Media Booking) SirsiDynix; (OPAC) SirsiDynix; (Serials) SirsiDynix
Database Vendor: EBSCOhost, Gale Cengage Learning, netLibrary, Newsbank, OVID Technologies
Function: AV serv, Distance learning, Doc delivery serv, Handicapped accessible, Homebound delivery serv, ILL available, Magnifiers for reading, Online searches, Orientations, Outside serv via phone, mail, e-mail & web, Spoken cassettes & CDs, Telephone ref, Web-Braille, Workshops
Publications: Faculty Handbook; Student Handout
Partic in Harrington Library Consortium; Tex Share
Open Mon-Thurs 7:45am-8pm, Fri 7:45-4, Sun 4-8
Restriction: Open to pub for ref & circ; with some limitations

CLARKSVILLE

P   RED RIVER COUNTY PUBLIC LIBRARY*, 307 N Walnut, 75426-3038. (Mail add: PO Box 508, 75426-0508), SAN 316-1501. Tel: 903-427-3991. FAX: 903-427-3991. E-mail: rrlibrary@email.com. Web Site: www.rrlibrary.org. *Dir,* Lisa Cornelius
Founded 1961. Pop 12,000
Library Holdings: Audiobooks 900; DVDs 1,010; Large Print Bks 650; Bk Vols 34,107; Per Subs 25
Automation Activity & Vendor Info: (Cataloging) Book Systems, Inc; (Circulation) Book Systems, Inc; (OPAC) Book Systems, Inc
Wireless access
Open Mon & Wed-Fri 12-5:30, Tues 9-12 & 1-5:30, Sat 9-12
Friends of the Library Group

CLAUDE

P   CLAUDE PUBLIC LIBRARY*, 100 Trice St, 79019. SAN 316-151X. Tel: 806-226-7881. FAX: 806-226-7881. *Librn,* June Adcock; E-mail: karetha@hotmail.com
Founded 1979. Pop 1,895; Circ 2,049
Library Holdings: Bk Vols 9,684
Partic in Harrington Library Consortium
Open Mon-Thurs 12-5

CLEBURNE

P   CLEBURNE PUBLIC LIBRARY*, 302 W Henderson St, 76033. (Mail add: PO Box 677, 76033-0657), SAN 316-1528. Tel: 817-645-0934. FAX: 817-556-8816. E-mail: library@cleburne.net. Web Site:

www.ci.cleburne.tx.us/library.aspx. *Librn, Mgr,* Tina Williams; Tel: 817-645-0936, E-mail: tina.williams@cleburne.net; Staff 7 (MLS 2, Non-MLS 5)
Founded 1905. Pop 29,889; Circ 284,579
Library Holdings: AV Mats 1,033; Bks on Deafness & Sign Lang 20; Bk Titles 41,846; Bk Vols 44,067; Per Subs 80; Talking Bks 740
Special Collections: Carnegie Library Coll, rare bks; Genealogy (Cleburne & Johnson County History Coll)
Automation Activity & Vendor Info: (Cataloging) TLC (The Library Corporation); (Circulation) TLC (The Library Corporation)
Database Vendor: ProQuest, ReferenceUSA, World Book Online
Wireless access
Function: Homebound delivery serv, ILL available
Mem of North Texas Library Partners
Special Services for the Deaf - Adult & family literacy prog; Bks on deafness & sign lang; High interest/low vocabulary bks; TTY equip
Special Services for the Blind - Home delivery serv
Open Mon & Thurs 10-8:30, Tues & Wed 10-6, Fri 10-5, Sat 10-2
Friends of the Library Group

S   LAYLAND MUSEUM*, Research Library & Archives, 201 N Caddo St, 76031. SAN 370-1689. Tel: 817-645-0940. FAX: 817-641-4161. E-mail: museum@cleburne.net.
Founded 1963
Library Holdings: Bk Vols 3,000
Special Collections: Texana (Layland Book Coll)
Subject Interests: N Cent Tex hist
Wireless access
Function: For res purposes
Open Mon-Fri 9-5
Friends of the Library Group

CLEVELAND

P   AUSTIN MEMORIAL LIBRARY*, 220 S Bonham Ave, 77327-4591. SAN 316-1536. Tel: 281-592-3920. FAX: 281-593-0361. E-mail: aml@austinmemlib.org. Web Site: www.austinmemlib.org. *Libr Dir,* Mary Cohn
Founded 1952. Pop 7,200; Circ 42,000
Library Holdings: Bk Vols 46,000
Subject Interests: Genealogy, Tex
Automation Activity & Vendor Info: (Acquisitions) SirsiDynix; (Cataloging) SirsiDynix; (Circulation) SirsiDynix; (Course Reserve) SirsiDynix; (ILL) SirsiDynix; (OPAC) SirsiDynix; (Serials) SirsiDynix
Partic in TexSHARE - Texas State Library & Archives Commission
Open Mon-Fri 9-6

P   TARKINGTON COMMUNITY LIBRARY*, 3032 Fm 163 Rd, 77327. (Mail add: PO Box 1682, 77328-1682). Tel: 281-592-5136. FAX: 281-592-5136. E-mail: tarklib@sbcglobal.net. Web Site: www.tarkingtoncommunitylibrary.org. *Dir,* Ruth Stetson
Founded 1996. Pop 8,100
Library Holdings: Bk Titles 13,000; Per Subs 4
Automation Activity & Vendor Info: (Cataloging) Follett Software; (Circulation) Follett Software
Wireless access
Open Mon & Wed-Fri 12-5, Sat 10-1

CLIFTON

P   NELLIE PEDERSON CIVIC LIBRARY*, 403 W Third St, 76634. (Mail add: PO Box 231, 76634-0231). Tel: 254-675-6495. FAX: 254-675-3175. E-mail: cliftonlib@cliftontexas.us. Web Site: www.cliftonlib.com. *Libr Dir,* Dr Shirley A Dahl. Subject Specialists: *Lit,* Dr Shirley A Dahl; Staff 1 (Non-MLS 1)
Pop 6,700; Circ 10,000
Library Holdings: Bk Vols 10,000
Automation Activity & Vendor Info: (Cataloging) Follett Software; (Circulation) Follett Software; (OPAC) Follett Software
Wireless access
Mem of Central Texas Library System, Inc
Partic in TexSHARE - Texas State Library & Archives Commission
Open Mon-Wed 12-5:30, Thurs & Fri 12-5
Friends of the Library Group

CLINT

P   CLINT ISD PUBLIC LIBRARY*, 12625 Alameda Ave, 79836. (Mail add: 14521 Horizon Blvd, El Paso, 79928). Tel: 915-926-8017. FAX: 915-851-3895. Web Site: www.clintweb.net. *Librn,* Beatriz Delgado; E-mail: beatriz.delgado@clint.net; Staff 1 (MLS 1)
Circ 8,888
Library Holdings: Bk Vols 8,000; Per Subs 104
Automation Activity & Vendor Info: (Cataloging) Follett Software; (Circulation) Follett Software; (OPAC) Follett Software

Wireless access
Mem of Texas Trans-Pecos Regional Library System
Open Mon-Thurs (Winter) 7:30am-8pm, Sat 8-Noon; Mon-Fri (Summer) 8-4

CLYDE

P   CLYDE PUBLIC LIBRARY*, 125 Oak St, 79510-4702. (Mail add: PO Box 1779, 79510-1779), SAN 324-7457. Tel: 325-893-5315. FAX: 325-893-5315. *Dir,* Linda Cavanaugh
Founded 1972. Pop 6,406; Circ 7,072
Library Holdings: Bk Titles 10,577; Per Subs 6
Special Collections: Texas (Callahan County Coll)
Automation Activity & Vendor Info: (Cataloging) LibLime; (Circulation) LibLime; (OPAC) LibLime
Wireless access
Function: ILL available
Mem of Central Kansas Library System
Open Tues 10-6, Wed & Fri 1-5, Thurs 10-5, Sat 10-2
Friends of the Library Group

COLDSPRING

P   COLDSPRING AREA PUBLIC LIBRARY*, 14221 State Hwy 150 W, 77331. (Mail add: PO Box 1756, 77331-1756), SAN 329-0891. Tel: 936-653-3104. FAX: 936-653-4628. E-mail: capl@eastex.net. Web Site: www.coldspringlibrary.com. *Head Librn,* Pamela Neely; *Asst Librn,* Debbie Brooks; Staff 2 (Non-MLS 2)
Founded 1983. Pop 714; Circ 13,684
Library Holdings: AV Mats 92; Bks on Deafness & Sign Lang 12; DVDs 270; Large Print Bks 1,130; Bk Titles 18,883; Per Subs 27; Talking Bks 638; Videos 1,148
Special Collections: Genealogy Coll; Spanish Language Books; Texas Coll
Automation Activity & Vendor Info: (Acquisitions) ComPanion Corp; (Cataloging) ComPanion Corp; (Circulation) ComPanion Corp
Wireless access
Function: Video lending libr
Partic in Tex Share
Special Services for the Deaf - Bks on deafness & sign lang
Special Services for the Blind - Magnifiers
Open Tues 10-7, Wed-Fri 10-5, Sat 10-1
Friends of the Library Group

COLEMAN

P   COLEMAN PUBLIC LIBRARY*, 402 Commercial Ave, 76834-4202. SAN 316-1544. Tel: 325-625-3043. FAX: 325-625-3629. E-mail: colemanlibrary@yahoo.com, cpl@web-access.net. Web Site: www.colemanlibrary.com. *Librn,* Sue Dossey; *Asst Librn,* Cindy Dempsey; Staff 3 (Non-MLS 3)
Pop 9,710; Circ 39,260
Library Holdings: Audiobooks 1,829; AV Mats 2,253; CDs 580; DVDs 882; Large Print Bks 600; Bk Titles 32,824; Bk Vols 34,560; Per Subs 20
Special Collections: Local History/Genealogy Coll; Mac Woodward Texas Coll; Texana; Walter Gann Coll; World War II Coll
Automation Activity & Vendor Info: (Cataloging) LibLime; (Circulation) LibLime
Wireless access
Mem of Big Country Library System
Open Tues & Thurs 10-6, Wed & Fri 12-6, Sat 9-12
Friends of the Library Group

COLLEGE STATION

L   RICHARDS & ASSOCIATES LIBRARY*, 4723 Stonebriar Circle, 77842. (Mail add: PO Box 10350, 77842-0350), SAN 372-9699. Tel: 979-985-5990. FAX: 979-690-6196. Web Site: www.hwyrail.com. *Librn,* Hoy A Richards; E-mail: hoyrich@aol.com
Library Holdings: Bk Titles 2,000; Bk Vols 3,200
Subject Interests: Law
Publications: Monthly National Newsletter
Restriction: Staff use only

C   TEXAS A&M UNIVERSITY LIBRARIES*, Sterling C Evans Library & Library Annex, 5000 TAMU, 77843-5000. Tel: 979-845-8111. Circulation Tel: 979-845-3731. Interlibrary Loan Service Tel: 979-845-5641. Reference Tel: 979-845-3826. FAX: 979-845-6238. Web Site: library.tamu.edu. *Dean,* Charles Gilreath; E-mail: charles-gilreath@library.tamu.edu; *Cat,* Jeanette Ho; Tel: 979-845-5438, E-mail: jaho@library.tamu.edu; *Coll Develop & Acq,* Carmelita Pickett; Tel: 979-862-1033, E-mail: cpickett@library.tamu.edu; *Digital Initiatives,* Michael Bolton; Tel: 979-845-5751, E-mail: michael.bolton@library.tamu.edu; *Digital Serv & Scholarly Communications,* Holly Mercer; Tel: 979-862-2534, E-mail: hmercer@library.tamu.edu; *Doc Delivery, ILL,* Lan Yang; Tel: 978-862-1904, E-mail: zyang@library.tamu.edu; *Sci, Eng & Liaison Serv,* Sandra Tucker; Tel: 979-862-1043, E-mail: s-tucker@library.tamu.edu;

User Serv & Learning & Outreach, Susan Goodwin; Tel: 979-458-0114, E-mail: sgoodwin@library.tamu.edu. Subject Specialists: *Eng, Sci,* Sandra Tucker; *Humanities, Soc sci,* Susan Goodwin; Staff 139 (MLS 80, Non-MLS 59)
Founded 1876. Enrl 49,861; Fac 80; Highest Degree: Doctorate
Library Holdings: Bk Vols 4,088,969; Per Subs 91,580
Special Collections: Maps & GIS. Oral History; State Document Depository; US Document Depository
Automation Activity & Vendor Info: (Acquisitions) Ex Libris Group; (Cataloging) Ex Libris Group
Database Vendor: ABC-CLIO, EBSCOhost, Gale Cengage Learning, LexisNexis, OCLC FirstSearch, RefWorks, YBP Library Services
Wireless access
Partic in Center for Research Libraries; Digital Libr Fedn; Greater Western Library Alliance; Houston Area Research Library Consortium
Friends of the Library Group
Departmental Libraries:
CUSHING MEMORIAL LIBRARY & ARCHIVES, 5000 TAMU, 77843-5000. Tel: 979-845-1951. FAX: 979-845-1441. E-mail: cushing-library@tamu.edu. *Interim Dir,* Larry Mitchell; E-mail: mitchell@library.tamu.edu; *Asst Univ Archivist,* Mary Manning; E-mail: MManning@library.tamu.edu; *Coordr of Res Serv, Curator,* Cait Coker; E-mail: CCoker@library.tamu.edu; *Curator,* Rebecca Hankins; *Curator,* Todd Samuelson; *Coll Mgt Lectr,* Robin Hutchison; *Rare Bk Cataloger,* Felicia Piscitelli; E-mail: FPiscitelli@library.tamu.edu; Staff 8.75 (MLS 4, Non-MLS 4.75)
Founded 1994. Enrl 48,112; Highest Degree: Doctorate
Library Holdings: Bk Vols 180,000
Special Collections: Americana Coll; Illustration, Military History (Ragan Coll); Literary Coll (R Kipling, S Maugham, M Arnold, Sea Fiction, R Fuller, A E Coppard, P G Wodehouse, et al); Local Texas History Coll; Mexican Colonial Coll; Nautical Archaeology/Naval Architecture, Botanicals, Incunables & Fore Edge Paintings (Loran Laughlin Coll); Nineteenth Century Prints (Kelsey Coll); Ornithology (Kincaid Coll); Political Papers of Texans (eg, William Clements Papers); Printing History Coll; Range Livestock (Jeff Dykes Coll); Science Fiction Coll; Texas A&M Coll; Texas Agriculture (TAES/TAEX Archives). Oral History
Function: Archival coll, Art exhibits, Exhibits, Handicapped accessible, Mail & tel request accepted, Online cat, Online ref, Online searches, Ref serv in person, Telephone ref, VHS videos, Workshops
Open Mon-Fri 8-6, Sat 9-1
Restriction: Non-circulating
Friends of the Library Group
CM   MEDICAL SCIENCES, University & Olsen Blvd, 77843-4462. (Mail add: 4462 TAMU, 77843-4462). Tel: 979-845-7428. FAX: 979-845-7493. *Dir,* Position Currently Open; Staff 25 (MLS 13, Non-MLS 12)
Founded 1940. Enrl 48,039; Highest Degree: Doctorate
Sept 2009-Aug 2010 Income $3,845,961, State $1,918,395, Other $1,927,566. Mats Exp $2,213,371. Sal $1,509,262
Library Holdings: Bk Vols 119,698; Per Subs 1,633
Subject Interests: Biol, Veterinary med
Automation Activity & Vendor Info: (Acquisitions) Ex Libris Group; (Cataloging) Ex Libris Group; (Circulation) Ex Libris Group; (Course Reserve) Docutek; (ILL) OCLC ILLiad; (OPAC) Ex Libris Group; (Serials) Ex Libris Group
Database Vendor: Agricola, Alexander Street Press, American Chemical Society, American Mathematical Society, American Physical Society, American Psychological Association (APA), Amigos Library Services, ARTstor, Blackwell's, Cambridge Scientific Abstracts, Cinahl Information Systems, Community of Science (COS), CRC Press/Taylor & Francis CRCnetBASE, Dialog, DynaMed, ebrary, EBSCOhost, Elsevier, Gale Cengage Learning, IEEE (Institute of Electrical & Electronics Engineers), ISI Web of Knowledge, JSTOR, Lexi-Comp, LexisNexis, Medline, OCLC ArticleFirst, OCLC FirstSearch, OCLC WorldCat, OVID Technologies, PubMed, ScienceDirect, Scopus, SerialsSolutions, Wiley, Wilson - Wilson Web
Function: Res libr
Partic in SCAMeL; Tex A&M Univ Consortium of Med Librs; TexSHARE - Texas State Library & Archives Commission
Publications: TAMU Medical Sciences Library Newsletter
POLICY SCIENCES & ECONOMICS, 1016 Annenberg Presidential Conference Ctr, 77843-5002. Tel: 979-862-3544. FAX: 979-862-3791. E-mail: pseldesk@library.tamu.edu. *Dir,* Leslie J Reynolds; E-mail: leslie.reynolds@tamu.edu; Staff 3 (MLS 1, Non-MLS 2)
Founded 1997
Library Holdings: Bk Vols 6,000; Per Subs 50; Videos 400
Automation Activity & Vendor Info: (Cataloging) Ex Libris Group; (Circulation) Ex Libris Group; (OPAC) Ex Libris Group
Partic in Tex Share
Open Mon-Thurs 8am-9pm, Fri 8-5, Sun 1-9
WEST CAMPUS LIBRARY, Olsen Blvd, Bldg 1511, 77843-5001. (Mail add: 5001 TAMU, 77843-5001). Tel: 979-845-2111. Circulation Tel: 979-862-1983. FAX: 979-862-2977. Web Site: wcl.library.tamu.edu. *Dir,* Leslie Reynolds; Tel: 979-458-0138, E-mail: leslie.reynolds@tamu.edu;

Asst Prof, Bus Ref, Jennifer Foster; Tel: 979-862-1982, E-mail: jrfoster@tamu.edu; *Assoc Prof, Bus Ref,* Michael M Smith; Tel: 979-845-2902, E-mail: michaelsmith@tamu.edu; *Asst Prof, Bus Ref,* Joel Thornton; Tel: 979-862-8933, E-mail: joelthor@lib-gw.tamu.edu. Subject Specialists: *Mgt,* Jennifer Foster; *Acctg, Info, Mkt,* Michael M Smith; *Acctg, Finance,* Joel Thornton; Staff 4 (MLS 4)
Founded 1994. Enrl 46,000; Highest Degree: Doctorate
Subject Interests: Bus
Function: Bks on CD, Computers for patron use, Copy machines, E-Reserves, Electronic databases & coll, ILL available, Magnifiers for reading, Online cat, Online ref, Photocopying/Printing, Ref serv available, Wheelchair accessible
Open Mon-Thurs Midnight-Midnight, Fri Midnight-10pm, Sat 1-5, Sun Noon-Midnight
Restriction: Borrowing privileges limited to fac & registered students, In-house use for visitors, Open to pub for ref & circ; with some limitations
Friends of the Library Group

COLORADO CITY

P   MITCHELL COUNTY PUBLIC LIBRARY*, 340 Oak St, 79512. SAN 316-1552. Tel: 325-728-3968. FAX: 325-728-3912. Web Site: www.mitchellcountylibrary.org. *Dir,* Brigada Hiser
Founded 1926. Pop 9,000; Circ 23,981
Library Holdings: AV Mats 573; Bk Titles 35,159; Bk Vols 38,331; Per Subs 23; Talking Bks 1,350
Wireless access
Open Mon 10-6, Tues-Fri 9-5:30
Friends of the Library Group

COLUMBUS

P   NESBITT MEMORIAL LIBRARY*, 529 Washington St, 78934-2326. SAN 316-1560. Tel: 979-732-3392. FAX: 979-732-3392. E-mail: library@columbustexas.net. Web Site: www.columbustexas.net/library. *Interim Dir,* Nancy Koehl; Tel: 979-732-5514; *Asst Librn,* Susan Archuletta; Staff 3 (Non-MLS 3)
Founded 1979. Pop 6,629; Circ 44,334
Library Holdings: Bk Titles 41,000; Per Subs 40
Subject Interests: Archit, Art, Hist, Tex hist
Automation Activity & Vendor Info: (Cataloging) Follett Software; (Circulation) Follett Software
Wireless access
Open Mon-Fri 9-6, Sat 9-4
Friends of the Library Group

COMANCHE

P   COMANCHE PUBLIC LIBRARY*, 311 N Austin St, 76442. (Mail add: PO Box 777, 76442-0777), SAN 316-1579. Tel: 325-356-2122. FAX: 325-356-2122 (Must call first). E-mail: comanchepl@verizon.net. Web Site: www.comanchepubliclibrary.com. *Dir,* Margaret T Waring; Staff 3 (Non-MLS 3)
Founded 1960. Pop 9,000; Circ 17,600
Oct 2010-Sept 2011 Income $115,822, State $4,700, City $55,561, County $55,561. Mats Exp $6,271. Sal $66,200
Library Holdings: Bk Titles 24,980; Bk Vols 26,532; Per Subs 15
Special Collections: Genealogy Coll; State & Local History Coll, bks, maps, microfilm, photographs
Subject Interests: Area hist, Genealogy
Wireless access
Function: Bk club(s), Computers for patron use, Copy machines, e-mail serv, Electronic databases & coll, ILL available, Photocopying/Printing, Pub access computers, Ref serv in person, Summer reading prog, Tax forms, Telephone ref, Web-catalog, Wheelchair accessible
Mem of Big Country Library System
Partic in TexSHARE - Texas State Library & Archives Commission
Open Mon & Tues 9-6, Wed & Fri 9-5, Sat 9-12
Friends of the Library Group

COMFORT

P   COMFORT PUBLIC LIBRARY*, 701 High St, 78013. (Mail add: PO Box 536, 78013-0036), SAN 316-1587. Tel: 830-995-2398. FAX: 830-995-5574. E-mail: library@comfort.txed.net. Web Site: www.comfort-library.txed.net. *Dir,* Patricia Miles; *Asst Dir,* Tracy Ahrens; Staff 3 (Non-MLS 3)
Founded 1956. Pop 7,981; Circ 18,974
Library Holdings: Bk Titles 17,161; Bk Vols 18,434; Per Subs 30
Subject Interests: Local hist, Texana
Automation Activity & Vendor Info: (Cataloging) Biblionix; (Circulation) Biblionix
Database Vendor: EBSCOhost, Gale Cengage Learning, OCLC FirstSearch, OCLC WorldCat, TLC (The Library Corporation), Wilson - Wilson Web

Wireless access
Function: ILL available
Open Tues, Thurs & Fri 12-6, Wed 11-8, Sat 9-1
Friends of the Library Group

COMMERCE

P   COMMERCE PUBLIC LIBRARY*, 1210 Park St, 75428. (Mail add: PO
           Box 308, 75429-0308), SAN 316-1595. Tel: 903-886-6858. FAX:
           903-886-7239. E-mail: commerce@koyote.com. Web Site:
           www.commercepubliclibrary.org. *Dir*, Gayle Gordon; Staff 5 (MLS 1,
           Non-MLS 4)
           Founded 1954. Pop 19,252; Circ 38,234
           Oct 2010-Sept 2011 Income $105,139, State $1,898, City $57,520, County
           $4,000, Locally Generated Income $41,721. Mats Exp $8,806, Books
           $4,301, Per/Ser (Incl. Access Fees) $375, AV Mat $3,899, Electronic Ref
           Mat (Incl. Access Fees) $231. Sal $69,602
           Library Holdings: Audiobooks 1,435; AV Mats 3,900; Bks on Deafness &
           Sign Lang 29; CDs 600; DVDs 149; Electronic Media & Resources 50;
           Large Print Bks 1,811; Microforms 186; Bk Titles 32,847; Per Subs 35;
           Videos 1,450
           Special Collections: Commerce History Coll, bks, maps, newsp, photogs;
           Texas History Coll
           Automation Activity & Vendor Info: (Cataloging) Book Systems, Inc;
           (Circulation) Book Systems, Inc; (OPAC) Book Systems, Inc
           Wireless access
           Function: Adult literacy prog, Archival coll, Bks on cassette, Bks on CD,
           Children's prog, Computer training, Computers for patron use, Electronic
           databases & coll, Fax serv, ILL available, Mus passes, Music CDs, Notary
           serv, Online cat, Online ref, Online searches, Photocopying/Printing, Prog
           for adults, Prog for children & young adult, Pub access computers, Senior
           computer classes, Story hour, Summer reading prog, Tax forms, Telephone
           ref, VHS videos
           Publications: The Pictorial History of Commerce, 1885-2010
           Partic in TexSHARE - Texas State Library & Archives Commission
           Open Mon, Wed & Fri 10-5, Tues & Thurs 10-6, Sat 9-12
           Friends of the Library Group

C   TEXAS A&M UNIVERSITY-COMMERCE*, James Gilliam Gee Library,
           2600 S Neal St, 75429. (Mail add: PO Box 3011, 75429-3011), SAN
           361-3534. Tel: 903-886-5717. Circulation Tel: 903-886-5718. Interlibrary
           Loan Service Tel: 903-886-5741. Reference Tel: 903-885-5720. Toll Free
           Tel: 866-386-4333. FAX: 903-886-5434. Web Site:
           www.tamu-commerce.edu/library. *Dir*, Gregory A Mitchell; Tel:
           903-886-5716, E-mail: greg_mitchell@tamu-commerce.edu; *Assoc Dir*,
           Gail Johnston; Tel: 903-886-5715, E-mail:
           gail_johnston@tamu-commerce.edu; *Head, Access Serv*, Sue Weatherbee;
           Tel: 903-886-5414, E-mail: sue_weatherbee@tamu-commerce.edu; *Head,
           Cat*, Dione Mahan; Tel: 903-886-5730, E-mail:
           dione_mahan@tamu-commerce.edu; *Head, ILL*, Jake Pichnarcik; E-mail:
           jacob_pichnarcik@tamu-commerce.edu; *Head, Ref*, Sarah Northam; Tel:
           903-886-5719; *Head, Ser*, Susan Andrews; Tel: 903-886-5733, E-mail:
           susan_andrews@tamu-commerce.edu; *Head, Spec Coll & Archives*, Andrea
           Weddle; Tel: 903-886-5463; *Head, Syst*, Marsha Keenan; Tel:
           903-886-5727, E-mail: marsha_keenan@tamu-commerce.edu; *Head, Tech
           Serv*, Tamara Remhof; *Digital Coll Librn*, Adam Northam; Tel:
           903-468-8738, E-mail: adam_northam@tamu-commerce.edu; *Educ Librn*,
           Scott Lancaster; Tel: 903-468-8139, E-mail:
           scott_lancaster@tamu-commerce.edu; *Tech Librn*, Sean Anderson; Tel:
           903-468-8661, E-mail: sean_anderson@tamu-commerce.edu; *Univ
           Archivist*, John Atabaev; *Acq*, Sandy Hayes; Tel: 903-886-5734, E-mail:
           sandy_hayes@tamu-commerce.edu; *Ref Serv*, Sarah Northam; Tel:
           903-886-5714, E-mail: sarah_northam@tamu-commerce.edu; *Ref Serv*,
           Emily Witsell. Subject Specialists: *Eng, Sci*, John Atabaev; *Sciences*, Sandy
           Hayes; *Bus*, Sarah Northam; *Govt doc, Humanities, Soc sci*, Emily Witsell;
           Staff 18 (MLS 16, Non-MLS 2)
           Founded 1894. Enrl 9,430; Fac 505; Highest Degree: Doctorate
           Sept 2008-Aug 2009 Income (Main Library and Branch(s)) $2,375,000,
           Locally Generated Income $800,000, Parent Institution $1,500,000, Other
           $75,000. Mats Exp $1,388,000, Books $342,000, Per/Ser (Incl. Access
           Fees) $530,000, Electronic Ref Mat (Incl. Access Fees) $489,000, Presv
           $27,000. Sal $1,366,085 (Prof $887,773)
           Library Holdings: CDs 4,322; DVDs 80; e-books 42,836; e-journals
           22,000; Electronic Media & Resources 126; Bk Titles 644,413; Bk Vols
           1,090,021; Per Subs 1,667; Videos 198
           Special Collections: Aviation (Jeana Yeager/Voyager Coll); Foreign
           Diplomatic Service (Ambassador Fletcher Warren Papers); Jazz (Louise
           Tobin/Peanuts Hucko Coll); Music (Ruby Allmond Coll); Texas Literature
           (Elithe Hamilton Kirkland Papers); Texas Poetry (Faye Carr Adams Coll);
           Texas Political History (A M Aiken, T C Chaddick & Celia M Wright
           Colls); US Government & Politics (Congressman Ray Roberts Papers).
           Oral History; State Document Depository; US Document Depository
           Automation Activity & Vendor Info: (Acquisitions) Innovative Interfaces,
           Inc - Millenium; (Cataloging) Innovative Interfaces, Inc - Millenium;
           (Circulation) Innovative Interfaces, Inc - Millenium; (Course Reserve)

Innovative Interfaces, Inc - Millenium; (OPAC) Innovative Interfaces, Inc -
Millenium; (Serials) Innovative Interfaces, Inc - Millenium
Wireless access
Function: Archival coll, Audio & video playback equip for onsite use,
Computers for patron use, Copy machines, Distance learning, Doc delivery
serv, e-mail & chat, Electronic databases & coll, Exhibits, Govt ref serv,
Handicapped accessible, ILL available, Large print keyboards, Music CDs,
Online cat, Online info literacy tutorials on the web & in blackboard,
Online ref, Pub access computers, Ref serv available, Ref serv in person,
Scanner, Tax forms
Partic in OCLC Online Computer Library Center, Inc; Phoenix Group; Tex
Share
Special Services for the Blind - Braille equip; Computer with voice
synthesizer for visually impaired persons
Open Mon-Thurs (Fall) 7:30am-Midnight, Fri 7:30am-8pm, Sat 10-4, Sun
2pm-Midnight
Restriction: Non-circulating of rare bks
Departmental Libraries:
METROPLEX COMMUTER FACILITY LIBRARY, 2600 Motley Dr,
  Mesquite, 75150, SAN 361-4913. Tel: 972-882-7535, 972-882-7537.
  FAX: 972-882-7536. Web Site:
  www.tamu-commerce.edu/library/branch/metro/. *Br Mgr*, Craig Wheeler;
  E-mail: craig_wheeler@tamu-commerce.edu; Staff 1 (MLS 1)
  Founded 1978. Enrl 1,800; Highest Degree: Doctorate
  Library Holdings: Bk Titles 19,730; Bk Vols 28,868; Per Subs 98
  Partic in OCLC Online Computer Library Center, Inc

CONROE

P   MONTGOMERY COUNTY MEMORIAL LIBRARY SYSTEM*, 104 I-45
           N, 77301-2720. SAN 361-3593. Tel: 936-788-8377. Circulation Tel:
           936-788-8360. Reference Tel: 936-788-8361. FAX: 936-788-8398. Web
           Site: www.countylibrary.org. *Dir*, Jerilynn A Williams; Tel: 936-788-8377,
           Ext 237, E-mail: jeri.williams@countylibrary.org; *Asst Dir*, Sarah Booth;
           Tel: 936-788-8377, Ext 236, E-mail: sarah.booth@countylibrary.org; *Bus
           Mgr*, Lana Beathard; Tel: 936-788-8377, Ext 238, E-mail:
           lana.beathard@countylibrary.org; *Tech Serv Mgr*, Linda Gambrill; Tel:
           936-788-8377, Ext 229, E-mail: linda.gambrill@countylibrary.org; *Adult
           Serv Coordr*, Gregory Tramel; Tel: 936-788-8377, Ext 250, E-mail:
           greg.tramel@countylibrary.org; *Children's Serv Coordr*, Laura Harper; Tel:
           936-788-8377, Ext 242, E-mail: laura.harper@coountylibrary.org; *Circ
           Coordr*, Terry Melton; Tel: 936-788-8377, Ext 244, E-mail:
           terry.melton@countylibrary.org; *Coll Develop Coordr*, Andrea Yang; Tel:
           936-538-8130, E-mail: andrea.yang@countylibrary.org; *Mkt & Prog
           Coordr*, Melissa Baker; Tel: 936-788-8377, Ext.266, E-mail:
           melissa.baker@countylibrary.org; Staff 139.5 (MLS 47.5, Non-MLS 92)
           Founded 1948. Pop 447,029; Circ 2,035,288
           Oct 2009-Sept 2010 Income (Main Library and Branch(s)) $8,723,140,
           State $112,341, County $8,434,188, Locally Generated Income $176,611.
           Mats Exp $964,590, Books $593,022, Per/Ser (Incl. Access Fees) $74,000,
           Micro $6,000, AV Mat $165,108, Electronic Ref Mat (Incl. Access Fees)
           $121,460, Presv $5,000. Sal $4,660,961 (Prof $2,327,091)
           Library Holdings: AV Mats 58,964; Electronic Media & Resources
           53,949; Bk Titles 346,746; Bk Vols 561,845; Per Subs 1,246
           Subject Interests: Genealogy
           Automation Activity & Vendor Info: (Cataloging) SirsiDynix;
           (Circulation) SirsiDynix; (OPAC) SirsiDynix
           Database Vendor: Amigos Library Services, Gale Cengage Learning,
           ProQuest, ReferenceUSA, SirsiDynix, ValueLine, World Book Online, WT
           Cox
           Wireless access
           Open Mon-Thurs 9-9, Fri & Sat 9-5
           Friends of the Library Group
           Branches: 6
           R F MEADOR BRANCH, 709 W Montgomery, Willis, 77378, SAN
             371-9820. Tel: 936-442-7740. FAX: 936-856-3360. *Br Mgr*, Twillia J
             Liles; E-mail: twillia.liles@countylibrary.org; Staff 7 (MLS 2, Non-MLS
             5)
             Library Holdings: Bk Vols 55,548
             OpenMon-Wed 9-6, Thurs 9-8, Fri & Sat 9-5
             Friends of the Library Group
           GEORGE & CYNTHIA WOODS MITCHELL LIBRARY, 8125 Ashlane
             Way, The Woodlands, 77382. Tel: 281-364-4298. Toll Free Tel:
             936-442-7728. FAX: 281-362-0772. *Br Mgr*, Tim Walker; Tel:
             936-442-7728, Ext 307, E-mail: tim.walker@countylibrary.org; Staff 24.5
             (MLS 9.5, Non-MLS 15)
             Library Holdings: Bk Titles 290,526; Bk Vols 707,802
             Open Mon-Thurs 9-9, Fri & Sat 9-5
           MALCOLM PURVIS LIBRARY, 510 Melton St, Magnolia, 77354, SAN
             326-7415. Tel: 936-788-8324. FAX: 936-788-8304. *Br Mgr*, Barbara
             Appleby; Staff 10 (MLS 3, Non-MLS 7)
             Library Holdings: Bk Vols 64,325
             Open Mon 9-8, Tues-Thurs 9-6, Fri & Sat 10-4
             Friends of the Library Group

SOUTH BRANCH, 2101 Lake Robbins Dr, The Woodlands, 77380, SAN 361-3658. Tel: 281-364-4294. FAX: 936-788-8372. *Br Mgr,* Catherine Pells; Tel: 936-442-7727, E-mail: catherine.pells@countylibrary.org; Staff 22.7 (MLS 8.5, Non-MLS 14.2)
   Library Holdings: Bk Vols 136,549
   Open Mon-Thurs 9-9, Fri & Sat 9-5
   Friends of the Library Group
CHARLES B STEWART - WEST BRANCH, 202 Bessie Price Owen Dr, Montgomery, 77356, SAN 329-630X. Tel: 936-442-7718, 936-788-8314. FAX: 936-788-8349. *Br Mgr,* Beverly Christopher; E-mail: beverly.christopher@countylibrary.org; Staff 13.13 (MLS 5, Non-MLS 8.13)
   Library Holdings: Bk Vols 59,636
   Open Mon, Tues, Thurs 9-8, Wed 9-6, Fri & Sat 9-5
   Friends of the Library Group
R B TULLIS BRANCH, 21569 US Hwy 59, New Caney, 77357, SAN 361-3623. Tel: 281-577-8968. FAX: 281-577-8992. *Br Mgr,* Dave Eames; Staff 21.5 (MLS 8, Non-MLS 13.5)
   Library Holdings: Bk Vols 74,190
   Open Mon, Tues & Thurs 9-9, Wed 9-6, Fri & Sat 9-5
   Friends of the Library Group

CONVERSE

P   CONVERSE PUBLIC LIBRARY*, 601 S Seguin Rd, 78109. (Mail add: PO Box 36, 78109-0036), SAN 376-4192. Tel: 210-659-4160. FAX: 210-659-4160. E-mail: librarian@conversetx.net. Web Site: www.converset.net. *Dir,* Robert Ayala; Staff 2 (Non-MLS 2)
   Pop 13,650; Circ 26,000
   Library Holdings: Bks on Deafness & Sign Lang 20; DVDs 550; Large Print Bks 400; Bk Vols 20,000; Videos 650
   Automation Activity & Vendor Info: (Cataloging) Follett Software; (Circulation) Follett Software
   Function: Audio & video playback equip for onsite use, Bilingual assistance for Spanish patrons, Children's prog, Computers for patron use, Copy machines, e-mail serv, Handicapped accessible, Homework prog, ILL available, Instruction & testing, Online ref, Online searches, Photocopying/Printing, Prog for children & young adult, Pub access computers, Ref serv available, Referrals accepted, Story hour, Summer reading prog, Tax forms, VHS videos, Video lending libr, Wheelchair accessible
   Open Mon, Tues, Thurs & Fri 9-6, Wed 10-7, Sat 10-2
   Restriction: Authorized patrons, Circ to mem only, In-house use for visitors, Lending limited to county residents, Open to pub for ref & circ; with some limitations, Photo ID required for access, Restricted access

COOPER

P   DELTA COUNTY PUBLIC LIBRARY*, 300 W Dallas Ave, 75432-1632. SAN 376-7981. Tel: 903-395-4575. FAX: 903-395-4556. E-mail: deltalib@neto.com. *Asst Dir,* Karen Falls; *Asst Librn,* Sylvia Wood
   Founded 1983. Pop 4,600
   Library Holdings: Bks on Deafness & Sign Lang 37; Bk Titles 20,001; Bk Vols 20,068; Per Subs 30
   Automation Activity & Vendor Info: (Cataloging) Follett Software; (Circulation) Follett Software; (OPAC) Follett Software
   Function: ILL available, Photocopying/Printing
   Partic in Tex Share
   Special Services for the Deaf - Adult & family literacy prog
   Special Services for the Blind - Large print bks; Talking bks
   Open Tues & Wed 10-5, Thurs 11-6, Fri 10-4
   Friends of the Library Group

COPPELL

P   COPPELL PUBLIC LIBRARY*, William T Cozby Library, 177 N Hertz Rd, 75019. SAN 361-4131. Tel: 972-304-3655. Reference Tel: 972-304-3658. Administration Tel: 972-304-3626. FAX: 972-304-3622. E-mail: library@coppelltx.gov. Web Site: www.coppelltx.gov. *Dir,* Vicki Chiavetta; E-mail: vchiavetta@coppelltx.gov; *Asst Dir,* Jane Darling; Tel: 972-304-3660, E-mail: jdarling@coppelltx.gov; *Librn Supvr,* Kevin Carrothers; *Librn Supvr,* Ellen Ko; Tel: 972-304-3656, E-mail: eko@coppelltx.gov; Staff 20.5 (MLS 9, Non-MLS 11.5)
   Pop 39,224; Circ 611,821
   Oct 2008-Sept 2009 Income $1,688,547, State $15,862, City $1,672,685. Mats Exp $262,647
   Library Holdings: AV Mats 13,119; e-books 26,539; Bk Titles 67,022; Bk Vols 81,271; Per Subs 180
   Automation Activity & Vendor Info: (Acquisitions) SirsiDynix; (Cataloging) SirsiDynix; (Circulation) SirsiDynix; (OPAC) SirsiDynix; (Serials) SirsiDynix
   Wireless access
   Function: Adult bk club, After school storytime, Art exhibits, Audiobks via web, Bk club(s), Bks on CD, Chess club, Children's prog, Computers for patron use, Copy machines, Electronic databases & coll, Free DVD rentals, Holiday prog, Homework prog, ILL available, Online searches,

Prog for adults, Prog for children & young adult, Pub access computers, Ref serv in person, Story hour, Summer reading prog, Tax forms, Teen prog, Wheelchair accessible, Workshops
   Open Mon-Thurs 10-9, Fri 10-6, Sat 10-5, Sun 1-5

COPPERAS COVE

P   COPPERAS COVE PUBLIC LIBRARY*, 501 S Main St, 76522. SAN 316-1609. Tel: 254-547-3826. FAX: 254-542-7279. Web Site: www.ci.copperas-cove.tx.us. *Dir,* Margaret Handrow; E-mail: mhandrow@ci.copperas-cove.tx.us; *Asst Dir,* Terry Swenson; E-mail: tswenson@ci.copperas-cove.tx.us; Staff 1 (MLS 1)
   Founded 1959. Pop 31,300; Circ 127,648
   Library Holdings: Bk Titles 66,388; Bk Vols 68,387
   Subject Interests: Texana
   Automation Activity & Vendor Info: (Cataloging) Follett Software; (Circulation) Follett Software
   Database Vendor: Gale Cengage Learning, ProQuest
   Wireless access
   Mem of Central Texas Library System, Inc
   Open Mon, Wed & Fri 10-5:30, Tues & Thurs 10-9, Sat 10-5
   Friends of the Library Group

CORPUS CHRISTI

M   CHRISTUS SPOHN HEALTH SYSTEM*, Health Sciences Library, 2606 Hospital Blvd, 78405. SAN 316-1706. Tel: 361-902-4197, 361-902-4990. FAX: 361-902-4198. *Librn,* Leta J Dannelley; E-mail: leta.dannelley@christushealth.org; Staff 1 (MLS 1)
   Founded 1972
   Library Holdings: Bk Vols 5,000; Per Subs 148
   Subject Interests: Allied health sci, Med, Nursing
   Automation Activity & Vendor Info: (Cataloging) EOS International; (Circulation) EOS International; (OPAC) EOS International; (Serials) EOS International
   Database Vendor: Baker & Taylor, EBSCOhost, EOS International, Majors, OVID Technologies
   Wireless access
   Function: Health sci info serv
   Partic in National Network of Libraries of Medicine
   Restriction: Not open to pub

S   CORPUS CHRISTI MUSEUM OF SCIENCE & HISTORY*, 1900 N Chaparral, 78401. SAN 316-1641. Tel: 361-826-4650. FAX: 361-884-7392. Web Site: www.ccmuseum.com. *Librn,* Jesenia Guerra; Tel: 361-826-4663, E-mail: jeseniag@cctexas.com; Staff 1 (Non-MLS 1)
   Founded 1957
   Library Holdings: Bk Vols 20,000; Per Subs 35
   Special Collections: 1930's pictorial history of Corpus Christi; Children's Fiction (Horatio Alger, Tom Swift & others); Law Coll-19th & 20th Centuries; Library Archival Material (mid 19th century); Museological Coll; Natural History (Netting Periodicals Coll)
   Subject Interests: Anthropology, Archaeology, Hist, Museology, Natural hist
   Open Tues-Sat 10-5, Sun 12-5

P   CORPUS CHRISTI PUBLIC LIBRARIES*, Central Library, 805 Comanche, 78401. SAN 361-3682. Tel: 361-826-7000. Interlibrary Loan Service Tel: 361-880-7050. Administration Tel: 361-826-7070. FAX: 361-826-7046. E-mail: libraries@cclibraries.com. Web Site: www.cclibraries.com. *Dir,* Position Currently Open; *Spec Coll Librn,* Margaret Rose; *Automation Syst Coordr,* Alen Hatley; *Ch,* Patricia Harera; Tel: 361-880-7020; *Tech Serv,* Karen Van Kirk; Staff 17 (MLS 17)
   Founded 1909. Pop 280,000; Circ 1,400,000
   Library Holdings: AV Mats 7,892; Bk Vols 376,395; Per Subs 622
   Special Collections: State Document Depository
   Subject Interests: Genealogy, Hispanic genealogy, Local hist
   Database Vendor: EBSCOhost, Gale Cengage Learning
   Partic in Tex State Libr Communications Network
   Open Tues-Sat 10-6
   Friends of the Library Group
   Branches: 4
   JANET F HARTE PUBLIC, 2629 Waldron Rd, 78418, SAN 361-3712. Tel: 361-937-6569. FAX: 361-937-5222. *Librn,* Cynthia Tunches; Staff 1 (MLS 1)
      Library Holdings: Bk Titles 36,000; Bk Vols 40,000
      Open Mon-Thurs 10-9, Fri & Sat 10-6
      Friends of the Library Group
   BEN F MCDONALD BRANCH, 4044 Greenwood Dr, 78416, SAN 361-3747. Tel: 361-826-2356. *Br Mgr,* Dorothea Castanon; Staff 2 (MLS 1, Non-MLS 1)
      Library Holdings: Audiobooks 767; CDs 248; DVDs 435; High Interest/Low Vocabulary Bk Vols 53; Large Print Bks 210; Bk Vols 23,000

Open Mon-Wed 10-8, Thurs-Sat 10-6
Friends of the Library Group
NORTHWEST BRANCH, 3202 McKinzie Rd, 78410, SAN 361-3763. Tel:
361-241-9329. *Ch,* Jean Meador; Staff 2 (MLS 2)
Pop 25,000
Open Mon-Wed 10-8, Thurs-Sat 10-6
PARKDALE, 1230 Carmel Pkwy, 78411, SAN 361-3771. Tel:
361-853-9961. *Librn,* Michelle Balis
Pop 109,000; Circ 480,000
Open Mon 2-9, Tues-Thurs 10-9, Fri & Sat 10-6
Friends of the Library Group

J   DEL MAR COLLEGE*, William F White Jr Library, 101 Baldwin Blvd,
78404. SAN 361-3801. Tel: 361-698-1310. Interlibrary Loan Service Tel:
361-698-1932. Reference Tel: 361-698-1311. Administration Tel:
361-698-1308. Automation Services Tel: 361-698-1951. FAX:
361-698-1182. Administration FAX: 361-698-1949. Automation Services
FAX: 361-698-2133. TDD: 361-698-1174. Web Site: library.delmar.edu.
Dir, Christine Tetzlaff-Belhasen; Tel: 361-698-1307, E-mail:
chris@delmar.edu; *Head, Ref Serv,* Sally Bickley; E-mail:
sbickley@delmar.edu; *Head, Tech Serv,* Susan Harvey; Tel: 361-698-1183,
Fax: 361-698-1158, E-mail: sharvey@delmar.edu; *Ref Librn,* Alan Berecka;
E-mail: aberecka@delmar.edu; *Automation Syst Coordr,* Merry Bortz;
E-mail: mbortz@delmar.edu; *Access Serv,* Daniel Cayce; E-mail:
dcayce@delmar.edu; Staff 30.1 (MLS 5.7, Non-MLS 24.4)
Founded 1937. Enrl 12,200; Fac 450; Highest Degree: Associate
Sept 2009-Aug 2010 Income (Main and Other College/University
Libraries) $2,015,805. Mats Exp $2,015,805, Books $111,000, Per/Ser
(Incl. Access Fees) $112,000, Micro $4,000, AV Equip $2,000, AV Mat
$63,000, Electronic Ref Mat (Incl. Access Fees) $89,000, Presv $1,500. Sal
$1,397,776 (Prof $489,349)
Library Holdings: AV Mats 15,363; e-books 31,339; Electronic Media &
Resources 98; Microforms 9,381; Bk Vols 188,777; Per Subs 774
Automation Activity & Vendor Info: (Cataloging) SirsiDynix;
(Circulation) SirsiDynix; (Course Reserve) SirsiDynix; (ILL) SirsiDynix;
(OPAC) SirsiDynix; (Serials) SirsiDynix
Database Vendor: EBSCO Auto Repair Reference, EBSCOhost, Electric
Library, Gale Cengage Learning, netLibrary, Newsbank, OCLC FirstSearch,
OVID Technologies, SirsiDynix, Westlaw
Wireless access
Partic in Amigos Library Services, Inc; OCLC Online Computer Library
Center, Inc; TexSHARE - Texas State Library & Archives Commission
Special Services for the Deaf - Bks on deafness & sign lang; Closed
caption videos; Video & TTY relay via computer
Special Services for the Blind - Internet workstation with adaptive
software; Large print bks; Talking bks
Open Mon-Thurs 7:30am-10pm, Fri 7:30-5, Sat 9-6, Sun 1-7
Departmental Libraries:
BARTH LEARNING RESOURCE CENTER, 4101 Old Brownsville Rd,
78405. (Mail add: 101 Baldwin Blvd, 78404). Tel: 361-698-1753.
Circulation Tel: 361-698-1754. Reference Tel: 361-698-1877. FAX:
361-698-1795. Web Site: library.delmar.edu. *Ref Librn,* Lisa Muilenburg;
Tel: 361-698-1742, E-mail: lmuilenb1@delmar.edu; Staff 4 (MLS 1,
Non-MLS 3)
Library Holdings: Bk Vols 18,017
Automation Activity & Vendor Info: (Cataloging) SirsiDynix;
(Circulation) SirsiDynix; (OPAC) SirsiDynix; (Serials) SirsiDynix
Database Vendor: EBSCOhost, ProQuest
Open Mon-Thurs 7:30am-10pm, Fri 7:30-5, Sat 9-6, Sun 1-7

M   DRISCOLL CHILDREN'S HOSPITAL, Robert Bell Parrish Medical
Library, 3533 S Alameda St, 78411-1721. (Mail add: PO Box 6530,
78466-6530), SAN 316-1692. Tel: 361-694-5467. FAX: 361-808-2141.
Web Site: www.dchstx.org/dchweb/education/content/
robert_bell_parrish_medical_libr.asp, www.dchstx.org/medlib. *Librn,* Dr
Paula Scott; E-mail: paula.scott@dchstx.org; *Info Spec,* Cindy Munoz;
E-mail: Cindy.Munoz@dchstx.org; Staff 2 (MLS 1, Non-MLS 1)
Library Holdings: e-journals 244; Bk Titles 1,300; Per Subs 80
Subject Interests: Pediatric med
Automation Activity & Vendor Info: (Acquisitions) Innovative Interfaces,
Inc; (Cataloging) Innovative Interfaces, Inc; (Circulation) Innovative
Interfaces, Inc
Database Vendor: Cinahl Information Systems, DynaMed, EBSCOhost,
Innovative Interfaces, Inc, MD Consult, Medline, Micromedex, OCLC
ArticleFirst, OCLC FirstSearch, OCLC WorldCat, OVID Technologies,
PubMed, Sage, ScienceDirect, Springer-Verlag, UpToDate, Wiley
InterScience
Wireless access
Function: Electronic databases & coll, Fax serv, ILL available, Online cat,
Online searches, Photocopying/Printing, Prof lending libr, Ref & res, Ref
serv in person, Scanner
Restriction: Circulates for staff only, Hospital employees & physicians
only

TEXAS A&M UNIVERSITY-CORPUS CHRISTI
C   ART MUSEUM OF SOUTH TEXAS LIBRARY*, 1902 N Shoreline,
78401-1164, SAN 316-1617. Tel: 361-825-3500. FAX: 361-825-3520.
Web Site: www.artmuseumofsouthtexas.org. *Dir,* Joseph Schenk
Founded 1965
Library Holdings: Bk Titles 1,000; Per Subs 10
Subject Interests: Art hist
Open Tues-Sat 10-5, Sun 1-5
Restriction: Non-circulating to the pub

C   MARY & JEFF BELL LIBRARY*, 6300 Ocean Dr, 78412-5501, SAN
316-1676. Tel: 361-825-2643. Interlibrary Loan Service Tel:
361-825-2340. Reference Tel: 361-825-2609. FAX: 361-825-5973. Web
Site: rattler.tamucc.edu. *Dir,* Christine Shupala; E-mail:
christine.shupala@tamucc.edu; *Assoc Dir,* Edward Kownslar; E-mail:
edward.kownslar@tamucc.edu; *Archivist, Spec Coll Librn,* Dr Thomas
Kreneck; E-mail: thomas.kreneck@tamucc.edu
Founded 1973. Highest Degree: Doctorate
Library Holdings: Bk Vols 433,185; Per Subs 1,706
Special Collections: 18th, 19th & 20th Century Books (Texas-Southwest
Coll); 19th Century Maps & Land Title Papers of South Texas &
Northern Mexico (Charles F H Von Blucher Coll); Sarita Kenedy East
Estate (Turcotte Coll); South Texas (Dan E Kilgore Coll), bks, mss;
South Texas (Dr Hector P Garcia Coll), mss; Southwest & Mexico in
Fine Binding (Sanders Key Stroud II Memorial Coll); Texas Legislature
(L Dewitt Hale Coll); University History Coll; Veracruz, Mexico
Archives (Archivo Notaria de Jalapa, Archivo Paroquial de Cordoba)
Automation Activity & Vendor Info: (Acquisitions) Innovative
Interfaces, Inc; (Cataloging) Innovative Interfaces, Inc; (Circulation)
Innovative Interfaces, Inc; (Serials) Innovative Interfaces, Inc
Function: Archival coll, Distance learning, Doc delivery serv, For res
purposes, Govt ref serv, Handicapped accessible, Health sci info serv,
ILL available, Online searches, Photocopying/Printing
Partic in OCLC Online Computer Library Center, Inc
Friends of the Library Group

S   THE TEXAS STATE MUSEUM OF ASIAN CULTURES &
EDUCATIONAL CENTER*, 1809 N Chaparral, 78401. SAN 371-2974.
Tel: 361-882-2641. FAX: 361-882-5718. E-mail:
executivedirector@asianculturesmuseum.org. Web Site:
www.asianculturesmuseum.org. *Managing Dir,* Joye LaBarrett
Library Holdings: Bk Vols 1,100
Special Collections: Billie Chandler Coll
Function: Ref serv available
Open Tues-Sat 10-4
Restriction: Non-circulating

A   UNITED STATES NAVY*, Naval Air Station Library, NAS Dr, 78419.
SAN 361-395X. Tel: 361-961-3574. *Librn,* Sharon Faith Scott; E-mail:
sharon.f.scott@navy.mil
Founded 1941
Library Holdings: CDs 9; DVDs 40; Bk Vols 34,000; Per Subs 72;
Talking Bks 396; Videos 219
Special Collections: Aviation Coll; Military Coll; World War II
Wireless access
Restriction: Mil only

CORRIGAN

P   MICKEY REILY PUBLIC LIBRARY*, 604 S Mathews St, 75939. SAN
316-1757. Tel: 936-398-4156. FAX: 936-398-5113. *Dir,* LaDonna Ray;
E-mail: lray_409@yahoo.com; *Asst Dir,* Tommye Wright; Staff 3
(Non-MLS 3)
Founded 1970. Pop 1,724; Circ 4,000
Library Holdings: Bk Titles 25,918; Bk Vols 28,160; Per Subs 45
Subject Interests: Local hist
Automation Activity & Vendor Info: (Cataloging) Surpass; (Circulation)
Surpass
Database Vendor: Gale Cengage Learning
Wireless access
Partic in Tex Share
Open Mon 12-7, Tues-Fri 10:30-5:30

CORSICANA

P   CORSICANA PUBLIC LIBRARY*, 100 N 12th St, 75110. SAN
316-1765. Tel: 903-654-4810, 903-654-4813. FAX: 903-654-4814. E-mail:
library@ci.corsicana.tx.us. Web Site: www.ci.corsicana.tx.us. *Dir,* Chad
Freeze; E-mail: cfreeze@ci.corsicana.tx.us; *Head, Tech Serv,* Barbara
Honea; E-mail: bhonea@ci.corsicana.tx.us; Staff 7 (MLS 2, Non-MLS 5)
Founded 1901. Pop 48,000; Circ 112,273
Library Holdings: Bk Titles 55,450; Bk Vols 64,342; Per Subs 5,362
Subject Interests: Genealogy
Automation Activity & Vendor Info: (Cataloging) Book Systems, Inc;
(Circulation) Book Systems, Inc; (Course Reserve) Book Systems, Inc;
(OPAC) Book Systems, Inc

Open Mon & Tues 10-8, Wed-Fri 10-6, Sat 10-4
Restriction: 24-hr pass syst for students only
Friends of the Library Group

J NAVARRO COLLEGE*, Richard M Sanchez Library, 3200 W Seventh
Ave, 75110-4899. SAN 316-1773. Tel: 903-875-7442. FAX: 903-875-7449.
Web Site: navarrocollege.edu/library.php. *Dir of Libr,* Tim Kevil; Staff 3
(MLS 3)
Founded 1946. Enrl 4,360; Fac 86; Highest Degree: Associate
Library Holdings: Bk Vols 60,500; Per Subs 290
Special Collections: Indian Artifacts (R S Reading Coll); Samuels Hobbit
Coll. US Document Depository
Subject Interests: Bus admin, Computer sci, Electronics, Fine arts, Law,
Law enforcement, Liberal arts, Med lab tech, Nursing, Occupational
therapy, Sci, Soc sci
Automation Activity & Vendor Info: (Cataloging) SirsiDynix;
(Circulation) SirsiDynix; (OPAC) SirsiDynix
Database Vendor: EBSCOhost, Gale Cengage Learning, LexisNexis,
netLibrary, OCLC FirstSearch, ProQuest, Westlaw
Wireless access
Partic in Tex Share
Open Mon-Thurs (Winter) 7:30am-9pm, Fri 7:30-5, Sat 8-12, Sun 5-8;
Mon-Fri (Summer) 7:30-5

COTULLA

P ALEXANDER MEMORIAL LIBRARY*, 201 S Center St, 78014-2255.
SAN 316-179X. Tel: 830-879-2601. FAX: 830-879-2601. E-mail:
librarian@cotulla.lib.tx.us. Web Site: www.cotulla.lib.tx.us. *Dir,* Clara Jo
Horton; *Asst Dir,* Lori Gunstream
Founded 1936. Pop 5,000; Circ 16,000
Library Holdings: Audiobooks 740; AV Mats 1,215; Bks on Deafness &
Sign Lang 11; CDs 570; DVDs 700; Large Print Bks 450; Bk Titles
17,150; Per Subs 10; Videos 750
Database Vendor: EBSCOhost, Gale Cengage Learning, ProQuest
Wireless access
Open Tues, Thurs & Fri 11-6, Wed 3-8, Sat 9-12

CRANDALL

P CRANDALL-COMBINE COMMUNITY LIBRARY*, 13385 FM 3039,
75114. (Mail add: PO Box 128, 75114-0128). Tel: 972-427-8170. FAX:
972-427-8171. Web Site:
crandall-isdtx.booksys.net/opac/crandall-combine/index.html,
www.crandall-isd.net. *Dir,* Donna Gillespie; E-mail:
donna_gillespie@crandall-isd.net
Pop 5,526; Circ 6,668
Library Holdings: AV Mats 592; e-books 3; Large Print Bks 210; Bk
Titles 21,191; Bk Vols 24,581; Per Subs 25
Automation Activity & Vendor Info: (Cataloging) Book Systems, Inc;
(Circulation) Book Systems, Inc
Database Vendor: Amigos Library Services, EBSCOhost, Gale Cengage
Learning
Wireless access
Partic in TexSHARE - Texas State Library & Archives Commission
Open Mon & Wed (Winter) 7:30-4:30, Tues & Thurs 7:30-7, Fri 7:30-3:30,
Sat 9-1; Mon & Wed (Summer) 8-5:30, Tues & Thurs 8-7

CRANE

P CRANE COUNTY LIBRARY*, 701 S Alford St, 79731-2521. SAN
316-1803. Tel: 432-558-1142. FAX: 432-558-1144. E-mail:
cranecountylibrary@yahoo.com. *Dir,* Paula C Frymire; E-mail:
pcfry40@yahoo.com
Founded 1950. Pop 3,500; Circ 30,000
Oct 2010-Sept 2011 Income $143,000. Mats Exp $21,842, Books $14,000,
Other Print Mats $2,500, AV Mat $5,200, Electronic Ref Mat (Incl. Access
Fees) $142. Sal $30,000
Library Holdings: AV Mats 600; Bks-By-Mail 100; CDs 60; DVDs 200;
Large Print Bks 200; Bk Titles 29,115; Per Subs 86; Talking Bks 600;
Videos 500
Special Collections: Christian Fiction Coll; Multicultural & Spanish Coll;
Texana; Western Coll
Database Vendor: EBSCOhost, OCLC FirstSearch
Wireless access
Mem of West Texas Library System
Open Mon, Wed & Thurs 9-5, Tues 12-8, Fri 9-1

CROCKETT

P CROCKETT PUBLIC LIBRARY*, 709 E Houston Ave, 75835-2124. SAN
316-1811. Tel: 936-544-3089. FAX: 936-544-4139. Web Site:
www.crockettlibrary.com. *Libr Dir,* Sharlene Hoffmaster; *Technology Tech,*
James Sutton; E-mail: jcsutton@crockettlibrary.com
Founded 1904. Pop 23,700; Circ 44,119
Library Holdings: Bk Vols 39,000; Per Subs 56

Special Collections: Houston County (Genealogy Coll); Rare Books Coll;
Texana Coll; Texas History & Literature Coll
Subject Interests: Genealogy
Automation Activity & Vendor Info: (Cataloging) Biblionix; (Circulation)
Biblionix; (OPAC) Biblionix
Wireless access
Open Mon, Tues & Thurs 8:30-7, Wed 8:30-5, Sat 9-1

S HOUSTON COUNTY HISTORICAL COMMISSION ARCHIVES*,
Courthouse Annex, 401 E Goliad, 75835-4035. SAN 371-6295. Tel:
936-544-3255, Ext 238. FAX: 936-544-8053. *Chairperson,* Maxine R
Moore
Founded 1978
Library Holdings: Bk Vols 26,802; Per Subs 49
Special Collections: Obituaries 1998-2004
Subject Interests: Civil War, Genealogy, Indians, Texana
Wireless access
Publications: History of Houston County; Houston County Maps to
Cemeteries & Special Locations; Mini History Brochure; Supplement to
Houston County (Texas) Cemetaries, 3rd Edition
Open Mon-Fri 8-4
Restriction: Restricted pub use

CROSBYTON

P CROSBY COUNTY LIBRARY*, 114 W Aspen St, 79322. SAN 316-1838.
Tel: 806-675-2673. FAX: 806-675-2673. E-mail:
crosbycountylibrary@yahoo.com. *Dir,* Janelle Berry
Founded 1960. Pop 8,859; Circ 22,000
Library Holdings: AV Mats 200; Bk Vols 9,000; Per Subs 15
Automation Activity & Vendor Info: (Acquisitions) LibLime;
(Cataloging) LibLime; (Circulation) LibLime
Wireless access
Mem of West Texas Library System
Open Mon-Thurs 9-12 & 1-5
Branches: 2
LORENZO BRANCH, 409 Van Buren, Lorenzo, 79343-2553. (Mail add:
PO Box 430, Lorenzo, 79343-0430), SAN 373-9465. Tel: 806-634-5639.
FAX: 806-634-5639. E-mail: library2read@yahoo.com. *Dir,* Joan Stone
Library Holdings: Bk Vols 6,000; Per Subs 56
Automation Activity & Vendor Info: (Acquisitions) LibLime;
(Cataloging) LibLime; (Circulation) LibLime
Open Mon & Tues 10-5, Thurs 10-4
RALLS BRANCH, 813 Main St, Ralls, 79357. (Mail add: PO Box 608,
Ralls, 79357-0608), SAN 373-9473. Tel: 806-253-2755. FAX:
806-253-2755. E-mail: rallslibrary2006@yahoo.com. *Librn,* Eva Lozano;
Asst Librn, Linda Isbell
Library Holdings: Bk Vols 12,000
Mem of West Texas Library System
Open Mon & Tues 9-6, Wed-Fri 9-5

S CROSBY COUNTY PIONEER MEMORIAL MUSEUM LIBRARY*, 101
W Main St, 79322. SAN 316-1846. Tel: 806-675-2331. E-mail:
ccpmm@door.net. Web Site: www.crosbycountymuseum.com. *Dir,* Verna
Anne Wheeler; Staff 3 (MLS 2, Non-MLS 1)
Founded 1958
Library Holdings: Bk Titles 300
Special Collections: Rare Books. Oral History
Subject Interests: Genealogy, Ranch hist, Regional hist, Tex hist, Tex
Indians
Publications: A History of Crosby County Tx; Aunt Hanks Rock House
Kitchen; Estacado, The Cradle of Culture & Civilization on the Staked
Plains of Texas; Gone But Not Forgotten, The Cemetery Survey of Crosby
County; History of Black families in Crosby Co Tx; McNeill SR Ranch,
100 years in Blanco Canyon; Spikes & Ellis Through the Years; Sun
Rising on the West, the Saga of Henry Clay & Elizabeth Smith; Teachers
Manuals, 3-5th Grade Level; The Bridwell Site Archaeology in Crosby Co
Tx; The Bridwell Site Archaeology in Crosby County

CROSS PLAINS

P CROSS PLAINS PUBLIC LIBRARY*, 149 N Main St, 76443. (Mail add:
PO Box 333, 76443-0333), SAN 376-4028. Tel: 254-725-7722. FAX:
254-725-6629. E-mail: cppl@windstream.net. Web Site:
www.crossplainslibrary.com. *Dir,* Linda Burns; Staff 1 (Non-MLS 1)
Library Holdings: Bk Vols 15,400; Per Subs 19
Wireless access
Mem of Big Country Library System
Open Mon-Fri 1-5

CROWELL

P FOARD COUNTY LIBRARY*, 110 E California St, 79227. (Mail add:
PO Box 317, 79227-0317), SAN 316-1854. Tel: 940-684-1250. FAX:
940-684-1250. *Dir,* Jackie Diggs
Pop 2,211

Library Holdings: Bk Titles 14,835; Bk Vols 16,760; Per Subs 20
Automation Activity & Vendor Info: (Cataloging) Follett Software; (Circulation) Follett Software; (OPAC) Follett Software
Mem of North Texas Library Partners
Friends of the Library Group

CROWLEY

P CROWLEY PUBLIC LIBRARY, 409 S Oak St, 76036. SAN 371-7674. Tel: 817-297-6707. Circulation Tel: 817-297-6707, Ext 2000. Interlibrary Loan Service Tel: 817-297-6707, Ext 2060. Administration Tel: 817-297-6707, Ext 2090. Information Services Tel: 817-297-6707, Ext 2030. FAX: 817-297-1554. Web Site: ci.crowley.tx.us. *Dir,* Cristina Winner; Staff 2 (MLS 1, Non-MLS 1)
Founded 1989
Library Holdings: Bks on Deafness & Sign Lang 40; Bk Titles 35,000; Per Subs 72
Special Collections: Deaf Education (Sign Language) Coll
Automation Activity & Vendor Info: (Acquisitions) Evergreen; (Cataloging) Evergreen; (Circulation) Evergreen; (OPAC) Evergreen; (Serials) Evergreen
Wireless access
Mem of North Texas Library Partners
Special Services for the Deaf - Bks on deafness & sign lang; Videos & decoder
Open Tues & Thurs 10-8, Wed, Fri & Sat 10-5
Friends of the Library Group

CRYSTAL CITY

P CRYSTAL CITY MEMORIAL LIBRARY*, 101 E Dimmit St, 78839-3505. SAN 375-3174. Tel: 830-374-0036. FAX: 830-374-2123. E-mail: cctxlib@yahoo.com. *Dir,* Teresa Ramirez; E-mail: ccpl_librarian_teresa@yahoo.com; Staff 1 (Non-MLS 1)
Founded 1948
Library Holdings: Bk Titles 6,000; Bk Vols 9,000
Special Collections: History (La Rosa Unida Coll), vf. Oral History
Wireless access
Open Mon-Fri 8-5
Friends of the Library Group

CUERO

P CUERO PUBLIC LIBRARY*, 207 E Main St, 77954. SAN 316-1862. Tel: 361-275-2864. FAX: 361-275-2864. E-mail: library@cityofcuero.com. *Dir,* Barbara Jacob
Pop 7,100; Circ 12,788
Library Holdings: Bk Vols 21,000; Per Subs 17
Automation Activity & Vendor Info: (Cataloging) Follett Software; (Circulation) Follett Software; (OPAC) Follett Software
Wireless access
Open Mon-Fri 8:30-5:30, Sat 9-12

DAINGERFIELD

P DAINGERFIELD PUBLIC LIBRARY*, 207 Jefferson St, 75638. SAN 316-1889. Tel: 903-645-2823. FAX: 903-645-7478. E-mail: daingerfieldpubliclibrary@hotmail.com. *Dir,* Earlene Walton; Staff 2 (Non-MLS 2)
Pop 3,000; Circ 19,053
Library Holdings: Bk Vols 20,000; Per Subs 16
Automation Activity & Vendor Info: (Cataloging) LibLime; (Circulation) LibLime
Wireless access
Open Mon-Fri 8-12 & 1-5
Friends of the Library Group

DALHART

P DALLAM-HARTLEY COUNTY LIBRARY*, 420 Denrock Ave, 79022. SAN 316-1897. Tel: 806-244-2761. FAX: 806-244-2761. *Dir,* Gail Holmes; Staff 1 (Non-MLS 1)
Founded 1908. Pop 10,200; Circ 35,000
Library Holdings: Bk Vols 28,000; Per Subs 15
Automation Activity & Vendor Info: (Cataloging) SirsiDynix; (Circulation) SirsiDynix; (OPAC) SirsiDynix
Partic in Harrington Library Consortium
Special Services for the Blind - Bks on CD; Large print bks
Open Mon 12-8, Tues-Fri 9:30-5:30
Friends of the Library Group

DALLAS

L AKIN, GUMP, STRAUSS, HAUER & FELD LIBRARY*, 1700 Pacific Ave, Ste 4100, 75201-4618. SAN 325-5395. Tel: 214-969-4628. FAX: 214-969-4343. Web Site: www.akingump.com. *Librn,* Wendy Lyons; E-mail: wlyons@akingump.com
Library Holdings: Bk Vols 30,000; Per Subs 100
Database Vendor: LexisNexis, Westlaw
Wireless access
Open Mon-Fri 8-5

SR ALL SAINTS CATHOLIC CHURCH*, Parish Resource Library, 5231 Meadowcreek at Arapaho, 75248-4046. SAN 329-1383. Tel: 972-778-0327. FAX: 972-233-5401. E-mail: library@allsaintsdallas.org. Web Site: allsaintslibrary.follettdestiny.com, www.allsaintsdallas.org/page_2.aspx?id=189537. *Librn,* Maria Isabel Garcia; E-mail: marisabel@smu.edu; Staff 1 (MLS 1)
Founded 1979
Jul 2010-Jun 2011 Income $8,598, Locally Generated Income $4,098, Parent Institution $4,500. Mats Exp $4,500, Books $1,256, Per/Ser (Incl. Access Fees) $393, AV Equip $670, AV Mat $625, Presv $1,556. Sal $15,200 (Prof $15,200)
Library Holdings: Audiobooks 19; AV Mats 4,056; CDs 641; DVDs 670; Electronic Media & Resources 187; Large Print Bks 43; Bk Titles 13,936; Bk Vols 16,528; Per Subs 30; Spec Interest Per Sub 21; Videos 983
Special Collections: Antique Bibles; Antique Books; Parish Archives
Subject Interests: Catholic lit, Christian lit
Automation Activity & Vendor Info: (Acquisitions) Follett Software; (Cataloging) Follett Software; (Circulation) Follett Software; (OPAC) Follett Software
Publications: Acquisitions list; Bibliographies; Newsletter (Bi-monthly)
Open Mon & Fri 9:30-12:30, Tues & Thurs 9:30-12:30 & 7-9, Sat 4:30-7, Sun 8:30-1:30 & 4:30-7
Restriction: Mem only
Friends of the Library Group

S AMERICAN FIRE SPRINKLER ASSOCIATION LIBRARY*, 12750 Merit Dr, No 350, 75251. SAN 328-3143. Tel: 214-349-5965. FAX: 214-343-8898. E-mail: afsainfo@firesprinkler.org. Web Site: www.firesprinkler.org. *Pub Relations,* Montalvo D'Arcy
Library Holdings: Bk Vols 40
Restriction: Staff use only

C ARGOSY UNIVERSITY*, Dallas Library, Heritage Sq, 5001 Lyndon B Johnson Freeway, 75244. Tel: 214-459-2215. FAX: 214-672-8106. Web Site: www.argosyu.edu/dallaslib.htm. *Actg Dir,* Jennifer Hosteler
Library Holdings: Bk Vols 4,000; Per Subs 100; Videos 150
Automation Activity & Vendor Info: (Acquisitions) Ex Libris Group; (Cataloging) Ex Libris Group; (Circulation) Ex Libris Group; (Course Reserve) Ex Libris Group; (ILL) Ex Libris Group; (Media Booking) Ex Libris Group; (OPAC) Ex Libris Group; (Serials) Ex Libris Group
Wireless access
Open Mon-Fri 7:30am-10:30pm, Sat 8:30-6, Sun Noon-5

C THE ART INSTITUTE OF DALLAS*, Mildred M Kelley Library, Two North Park E, 8080 Park Lane, Ste 100, 75231-5993. SAN 321-4737. Tel: 214-692-8080. Reference Tel: 469-587-1403. FAX: 214-692-8106. Web Site: www.aidlrc.aiiresources.com. *Dir, Libr Serv,* Lisa Casto; Tel: 469-587-1246, E-mail: castol@aii.edu; *Tech Serv,* Richard Schlaudroff; Tel: 469-587-1244; Staff 4 (MLS 2, Non-MLS 2)
Founded 1981. Enrl 2,000; Fac 150; Highest Degree: Master
Library Holdings: Bk Titles 30,000; Bk Vols 35,000; Per Subs 260
Special Collections: Anime Coll; Manga Coll
Subject Interests: Computer art, Culinary arts, Fashion design, Graphic design, Interior design, Video production
Automation Activity & Vendor Info: (Circulation) Ex Libris Group; (OPAC) Ex Libris Group
Database Vendor: OCLC FirstSearch, Wilson - Wilson Web
Wireless access
Function: Ref serv available
Restriction: Borrowing privileges limited to fac & registered students, Borrowing requests are handled by ILL, In-house use for visitors

CM BAYLOR HEALTH SCIENCES LIBRARY*, 3302 Gaston Ave, 75246. SAN 316-1935. Tel: 214-828-8151. FAX: 214-820-2095. Web Site: www.bcd.tamhsc.edu/library. *Dir,* Cindy Scroggins; Tel: 214-828-8930, E-mail: cscroggins@bcd.tamhsc.edu; *Assoc Dir,* Rosanna Ratliff; E-mail: rratliff@bcd.tamhsc.edu; *Asst Dir, Tech Serv,* Matthew Christy; E-mail: mchristy@bcd.tamhsc.edu; *ILL Coordr,* Mandrell Bufford; E-mail: interlibloan@bcd.tamhsc.edu; Staff 12.5 (MLS 4.5, Non-MLS 8)
Subject Interests: Dentistry, Med, Nursing
Automation Activity & Vendor Info: (Acquisitions) Ex Libris Group; (Cataloging) Ex Libris Group; (Circulation) Ex Libris Group; (Course

Reserve) Ex Libris Group; (ILL) Ex Libris Group; (OPAC) Ex Libris
Group
Database Vendor: American Chemical Society, Amigos Library Services,
Annual Reviews, Baker & Taylor, Cinahl Information Systems, DynaMed,
EBSCOhost, Elsevier, Ex Libris Group, Haworth Pres Inc, ISI Web of
Knowledge, LexisNexis, Majors, Medline, Micromedex, Natural Standard,
Nature Publishing Group, OCLC WorldCat, OVID Technologies, PubMed,
Sage, Scopus, Springer-Verlag, UpToDate, Wiley InterScience
Wireless access
Partic in Healthline
Open Mon-Thurs 7am-9pm, Fri 7-6, Sat 10-6, Sun 1-6

R   CHURCH OF THE INCARNATION*, Marmion Library, 3966 McKinney
Ave, 75204-2099. SAN 316-2001. Tel: 214-521-5101, Ext 25. FAX:
214-528-7209. E-mail: info@incarnation.org. Web Site:
www.incarnation.org. *Librn,* Jo Ann Bell; E-mail: jbell@incarnation.org;
Staff 2 (Non-MLS 2)
Founded 1955
Library Holdings: Bk Vols 12,500; Per Subs 25
Subject Interests: Adult fiction, Biog, Children's lit, Hist, Relig studies
Restriction: Mem only

P   COCKRELL HILL PUBLIC LIBRARY*, 4125 W Clarendon, 75211. SAN
376-4443. Tel: 214-330-9935. FAX: 214-330-5483. E-mail:
library@cockrell-hill.tx.us. *Dir,* Janice Grupe; Staff 2 (MLS 2)
Pop 45,000
Library Holdings: Bk Titles 13,000; Bk Vols 11,250
Special Services for the Blind - Bks on cassette; Talking bks
Open Tues & Fri 11-6:30, Wed & Thurs 11-7

CR   CRISWELL COLLEGE, Wallace Library, 4010 Gaston Ave, 75246. SAN
320-751X. Tel: 214-818-1378. Toll Free Tel: 800-899-0012, Ext 1378.
FAX: 214-818-1310. E-mail: library@criswell.edu. Web Site:
www.criswell.edu. *Dir,* Philip Nott; Staff 3 (MLS 2, Non-MLS 1)
Founded 1976. Enrl 300; Highest Degree: Master
Library Holdings: Bk Vols 70,000; Per Subs 300
Special Collections: Baptist History & Theology
Automation Activity & Vendor Info: (Acquisitions) OCLC; (Cataloging)
OCLC; (Circulation) OCLC; (Course Reserve) OCLC; (ILL) OCLC;
(OPAC) OCLC; (Serials) OCLC
Database Vendor: OCLC FirstSearch, OCLC WorldCat
Wireless access
Partic in OCLC Online Computer Library Center, Inc; TexSHARE - Texas
State Library & Archives Commission
Open Mon, Tues & Thurs 7:30am-9:45pm, Wed 7:30-5, Fri 7:30-4

CR   DALLAS BAPTIST UNIVERSITY, Vance Memorial Library, 3000
Mountain Creek Pkwy, 75211-9299. SAN 316-2044. Tel: 214-333-5213.
Circulation Tel: 214-333-5320. Interlibrary Loan Service Tel:
214-333-5389. Reference Tel: 214-333-5221. Administration Tel:
214-333-5220. Toll Free Tel: 800-483-7048. FAX: 214-333-5323.
Interlibrary Loan Service FAX: 214-333-8887. E-mail: lib_circ@dbu.edu,
lib_ref@dbu.edu. Web Site: www.dbu.edu/library. *Dir,* Debra Collins;
E-mail: debrac@dbu.edu; *Dir, Distance Educ,* Debbi Richard; Tel:
214-333-5225, E-mail: debbi@dbu.edu; *Asst Dir, Ref Librn,* Scott Jeffries;
Tel: 214-333-5211, E-mail: scottj@dbu.edu; *Cat Librn, Syst,* Sharon
Dehnel; Tel: 214-333-5392, E-mail: sharond@dbu.edu; *Ref Librn,* John
Jaeger; Tel: 214-333-5212, E-mail: johnja@dbu.edu; *Coordr, Pub Serv, Ref
Librn,* Linda Stephenson; Tel: 214-333-5522, E-mail: lindas@dbu.edu; *Tech
Serv Librn,* Donna Daniel; Tel: 214-333-5299, E-mail: donnad@dbu.edu;
Circ Supvr, Frankie Hendricks; E-mail: frankieh@dbu.edu; *Supvr, Govt
Docs,* Jinja Rho; Tel: 214-333-5214, E-mail: jinja@dbu.edu; *Supvr, ILL,*
Loraine Walston; E-mail: loraine@dbu.edu; *Supvr, Ser,* Zack Prince; Tel:
214-333-5298, E-mail: zprince@dbu.edu; *Archivist,* Mary Fox; Tel:
214-333-5210, E-mail: mary@dbu.edu; Staff 12.5 (MLS 8, Non-MLS 4.5)
Founded 1898. Enrl 5,622; Fac 126; Highest Degree: Doctorate
Jun 2011-May 2012. Mats Exp $321,422, Books $10,646, Per/Ser (Incl.
Access Fees) $79,369, AV Mat $523, Electronic Ref Mat (Incl. Access
Fees) $126,711
Library Holdings: AV Mats 8,255; e-books 52,719; e-journals 23,398;
Microforms 520,430; Bk Titles 160,545; Bk Vols 226,594; Per Subs 360
Special Collections: Baptist Coll; ERIC, microfiche; Evangelical Coll;
Library of American Literature, ultrafiche; Library of English Literature,
ultrafiche. US Document Depository
Subject Interests: Bus, Educ, Evangelicalism, Music, Natural sci, Relig
Automation Activity & Vendor Info: (Acquisitions) Ex Libris Group;
(Cataloging) Ex Libris Group; (Circulation) Ex Libris Group; (Course
Reserve) Ex Libris Group; (ILL) Ex Libris Group; (OPAC) Ex Libris
Group; (Serials) Ex Libris Group
Database Vendor: Amigos Library Services, EBSCOhost, Gale Cengage
Learning, H W Wilson, JSTOR, LexisNexis, Marcive, Inc, Marquis Who's
Who, netLibrary, Newsbank, OCLC, OCLC ArticleFirst, OCLC CAMIO,
OCLC FirstSearch, OCLC WorldCat, ProQuest, Sage, Wilson - Wilson
Web

Wireless access
Function: Archival coll, Audio & video playback equip for onsite use,
Computers for patron use, Copy machines, Distance learning, Doc delivery
serv, e-mail serv, Electronic databases & coll, Handicapped accessible, ILL
available, Learning ctr, Mail loans to mem, Music CDs, Online cat, Online
ref, Online searches, Photocopying/Printing, Ref & res, Ref serv available,
Ref serv in person, VHS videos
Partic in Amigos Library Services, Inc; Christian Library Consortium;
Llano Estacado Info Access Network (LEIAN); Tex Independent Cols &
Univ Librs; TexSHARE - Texas State Library & Archives Commission
Open Mon-Fri 6:45am-11pm, Sat 7:30-5, Sun 2:30-11
Restriction: Borrowing privileges limited to fac & registered students,
External users must contact libr

CR   DALLAS CHRISTIAN COLLEGE*, C C Crawford Memorial Library,
2700 Christian Pkwy, 75234. SAN 316-2060. Tel: 972-241-3371. FAX:
972-241-8021. E-mail: library@dallas.edu. Web Site:
www.dallas.edu/library/index.cfm. *Dir of Libr Serv,* Jane Reynolds; E-mail:
jreynolds@dallas.edu; Staff 2 (MLS 1, Non-MLS 1)
Founded 1950. Enrl 300; Fac 17; Highest Degree: Bachelor
Library Holdings: e-books 25,000; e-journals 3,600; Bk Vols 30,000; Per
Subs 425; Videos 410
Special Collections: History & Writings of the Restoration Movement
Subject Interests: Biblical studies, Relig, Theol
Database Vendor: EBSCOhost, OCLC FirstSearch
Wireless access
Function: Res libr
Partic in Amigos Library Services, Inc; Christian Libr Network; OCLC
Online Computer Library Center, Inc
Open Mon-Fri 8am-10pm, Sat 9-5

J   DALLAS COUNTY COMMUNITY COLLEGE DISTRICT*, Bill J Priest
Institute for Economic Development, 1402 Corinth St, 75215. Tel:
214-860-5779. Web Site: www.billpriestinstitute.org. *Ref Librn,* Linda
Baker; *Circ Mgr,* Paula Pereira; *Circ Coordr,* Susan Smith; E-mail:
s.smith@dccc.edu
Founded 1989
Library Holdings: Bk Titles 5,000; Per Subs 40
Subject Interests: Bus, Planning
Automation Activity & Vendor Info: (Acquisitions) Innovative Interfaces,
Inc - Millenium; (Cataloging) Innovative Interfaces, Inc - Millenium;
(Circulation) Innovative Interfaces, Inc - Millenium; (Course Reserve)
Innovative Interfaces, Inc - Millenium; (ILL) Innovative Interfaces, Inc -
Millenium; (OPAC) Innovative Interfaces, Inc - Millenium; (Serials)
Innovative Interfaces, Inc - Millenium
Wireless access
Open Mon-Fri 8-4:30

L   DALLAS COUNTY LAW LIBRARY*, George Allen Courts Bldg, 600
Commerce St, Ste 292, 75202-4606. SAN 316-2087. Tel: 214-653-7481.
FAX: 214-653-6103. E-mail: lawlibrary@dallascounty.org. Web Site:
www.dallascounty.org. *Dir,* Mary Rankin; *Assoc Dir,* David Wilkinson;
Law Bk Coordr, Andrew Cross; Tel: 214-653-6947; *Tech Serv &
Automation,* Reese Belew; Tel: 214-653-6013, E-mail:
rbelew@dallascounty.org; Staff 7 (MLS 4, Non-MLS 3)
Oct 2010-Sept 2011 Income $860,000. Mats Exp $354,000, Books
$302,000, Electronic Ref Mat (Incl. Access Fees) $52,000. Sal $440,000
Library Holdings: Bk Vols 82,600
Automation Activity & Vendor Info: (Cataloging) OCLC; (ILL) OCLC
Database Vendor: LexisNexis, OCLC WorldCat, Westlaw
Open Mon-Fri 8-5

S   DALLAS HISTORICAL SOCIETY, G B Dealey Library, PO Box 150038,
Hall of State in Fair Park, 75315-0038. Tel: 214-421-4500. FAX:
214-421-7500. Web Site: www.dallashistory.org. *Archivist, Res,* Samantha
Dodd; Tel: 214-239-8141, Fax: 214-239-8146, E-mail:
samantha@dallashistory.org; Staff 1 (Non-MLS 1)
Founded 1922
Library Holdings: Bk Vols 14,807
Special Collections: 1936 Texas Centennial Coll; Maps of Dallas & the
Southwest, 1800-2000; Personal Papers of Thomas B Love, Joseph W
Bailey, Hatton W Sumners, Sarah Horton Cockrell, Ann McClarmonde
Chase, Margaret Scruggs Caruth, Jesse Daniel Ames, John M Moore,
Elmer Scott, George W Biggs, G B Dealey & Sam Acheson; Photographs
of Dallas & Texas from 1870 to 2000 (J Johnson & C E Arnold Colls);
Photos of Historic Sites & Courthouses of Texas ca. 1936-40 (R M Hayes
Coll); Photos of Texas, 1895-6 (Henry Stark Coll); Social & Urban History
of Dallas; Spanish ms (P P Martinez Coll)
Function: Archival coll
Publications: Guide to Fair Park, Dallas; Legacies: A History Journal for
Dallas & North Central Texas; When Dallas Became a City: The Letters of
John Milton McCoy, 1870-1881
Restriction: Non-circulating, Not a lending libr, Open by appt only, Photo
ID required for access

S   **DALLAS MUNICIPAL ARCHIVES***, City Hall, Rm 5-D South, 1500 Marilla St, 75201. SAN 371-1900. Tel: 214-670-3738. FAX: 214-670-5029. *Archivist,* John H Slate; E-mail: john.slate@dallascityhall.com
Special Collections: Dallas City Government Records Coll
Function: Archival coll
Restriction: Open by appt only

S   **DALLAS MUSEUM OF ART***, Mildred R & Frederick M Mayer Library, 1717 N Harwood, 75201. SAN 316-2125. Tel: 214-922-1277. FAX: 214-954-0174. E-mail: library@dallasmuseumofart.org. Web Site: www.dallasmuseumofart.org. *Dir, Libr & Imaging Serv,* Jacqueline Allen; Tel: 214-922-1276, E-mail: jallen@dallasmuseumofart.org; *Librn,* Mary Leonard; Staff 3 (MLS 2, Non-MLS 1)
Founded 1938
Library Holdings: Bk Titles 62,000; Bk Vols 92,000; Per Subs 110
Subject Interests: African, Contemporary, Gen art hist, Pre-Columbian art
Automation Activity & Vendor Info: (Cataloging) Ex Libris Group; (Circulation) Ex Libris Group; (OPAC) Ex Libris Group
Database Vendor: OCLC FirstSearch
Function: Ref serv available
Publications: Exhibition Catalogues
Partic in OCLC Online Computer Library Center, Inc
Restriction: Non-circulating to the pub

P   **DALLAS PUBLIC LIBRARY***, 1515 Young St, 75201-5499. SAN 361-4379. Tel: 214-670-1400. Circulation Tel: 214-670-1740. Interlibrary Loan Service Tel: 214-670-1741. Administration Tel: 214-670-7809. Information Services Tel: 214-670-1700. FAX: 214-670-7839. Circulation FAX: 214-670-1738. Interlibrary Loan Service FAX: 214-670-1752. TDD: 214-670-1716. E-mail: info@dallaslibrary.org. Web Site: dallaslibrary.org. *Dir of Libr,* Mary Jo Giudice; *Asst Dir, Pub Serv,* Miriam Rodriguez; E-mail: miriam.rodriguez@dallaslibrary.org; *Asst Dir, Res Mgt Serv,* Corinne Hill; Tel: 214-670-1774, E-mail: corinne.hill@dallaslibrary.org; *Head, Govt Info,* Johanna Johnson; Tel: 214-670-1468, Fax: 214-670-1451, E-mail: government@dallaslibrary.org; *Librn,* Greg Browder; E-mail: business@dallaslibrary.org; *Music Librn,* Tina Murdock; E-mail: art@dallaslibrary.org; *Cat Mgr,* Andrew Wright; *Mgr,* Laverne Brown; E-mail: business@dallaslibrary.org; *Mgr,* Victor Kralisz; Tel: 214-670-1643, 670-1668, Fax: 214-670-1654, E-mail: art@dallaslibrary.org; *Mgr, Youth Serv,* Position Currently Open; *Asst Mgr,* Mark Gilman; E-mail: government@dallaslibrary.org; *Asst Mgr,* Rachel Howell; E-mail: texas@dallaslibrary.org; *Asst Mgr,* Theresa Huff; E-mail: history@dallaslibrary.org; *Asst Mgr,* Sharon McCollins; E-mail: childrens@dallaslibrary.org; *Asst Mgr,* Davin Pate; Tel: 214-670-1608, Fax: 214-670-1647, E-mail: business@dallaslibrary.org; *Archivist,* Brian Collins; Tel: 214-670-1435, E-mail: texas@dallaslibrary.org; *Govt Doc,* Charlotte Bagh; E-mail: government@dallaslibrary.org; *Libr Assoc,* Jill Azaria; *Libr Assoc,* Darlene Brimmage; *Spec Coll & Archives Librn,* Carol Roark; E-mail: texas@dallaslibrary.org. Subject Specialists: *Maps, Patents,* Johanna Johnson; *Gas, Petroleum,* Greg Browder; *Bus,* Laverne Brown; *Fine arts, Humanities,* Victor Kralisz; *Municipal ref,* Mark Gilman; *Archives, Fine bks, Texana,* Rachel Howell; *Hist,* Theresa Huff; *Children's lit,* Sharon McCollins; *Bus,* Davin Pate; *Fed docs,* Charlotte Bagh; *Archives, Fine bks, Texana,* Carol Roark; Staff 111 (MLS 107, Non-MLS 4)
Founded 1901. Pop 1,306,350; Circ 5,703,875
Library Holdings: Audiobooks 28,860; AV Mats 130,453; Bk Titles 1,755,802; Bk Vols 2,056,540; Per Subs 3,650; Videos 113,477
Special Collections: Automobile Repair Manual Coll; Black Dallas History (Juanita Craft Coll, Dallas Negro Chamber of Commerce Coll); Business Histories; Children's Literature Coll, hist & rare children's bks & per; Classical Literature (Louie N Bromberg Coll); Classical Recordings (Rual Askew Coll); Dallas Black History (John & Ethelyn M Chisum Coll), diaries, mss, photogs; Dallas Theater Center; Dance (Juana De Laban Coll, Jerry Bywaters Coll); Dance (Mary Bywaters Coll), dance progs, mss, pamphlets, per; Fashion (Bergdorf Goodman Coll), bks, clippings, micro, pamphlets, photogs; Genealogy, bks, micro, per; Grants (Cooperating Coll of the Foundation Center), bks, looseleaf, microfiche; History of Printing, early printing, bks; Lakewood Area History, oral hist; Oil & Gas (Hamon Oil & Gas Resource Center), bks, per, databases; Poetry Society of Texas' Coll, bks & chapbooks; Sears Catalog, micro; Standards & Specifications, bks, micro & pamphlets; Texas & Dallas, archives, bks, clippings, maps, micro, per, photogs; Theater (William Ely Hill Coll, Interstate Theatre Coll, Margo Jones Coll), bks, clippings, disc recordings, micro, pamphlets, per, photogs, slides; US Marshal Clinton T Peoples Coll, scrapbks, photogs, correspondence concerning law enforcement in Texas; US Serial Set. Oral History; State Document Depository; US Document Depository
Automation Activity & Vendor Info: (ILL) OCLC; (OPAC) Polaris Library Systems
Function: Archival coll, Art exhibits, Bus archives, Govt ref serv, ILL available, Prog for adults, Prog for children & young adult, Ref serv available
Publications: Catalog of Large Type Books - Dallas Pub Libr Syst; Dallas Public Library: The First 75 Years; Dallas WPA Guide & History; In

Beauty it is Finished, The McDermott Collection of Navajo Blankets; Long Range Plan for Public Library Service: A Self Study; Reminiscences, A Glimpse of Old East Dallas; The Cartoonist's Art: Editorial Cartoons by Ficklen, McClanahan, Taylor & DeOre; The Dallas Public Library: Celebrating a Century of Services, 1901-2001
Partic in OCLC Online Computer Library Center, Inc; Tex Share; Tex State Libr Communications Network
Special Services for the Deaf - Staff with knowledge of sign lang; TDD equip
Special Services for the Blind - BiFolkal kits; Children's Braille; Closed circuit TV; Reader equip; Talking bks; ZoomText magnification & reading software
Open Mon-Thurs 9-9, Fri & Sat 9-5, Sun 1-5
Restriction: Non-resident fee
Friends of the Library Group
Branches: 23
ARCADIA PARK, 1302 N Justin Ave, 75211-1142. Tel: 214-670-6446. FAX: 214-670-7502. E-mail: arcadiapark@dallaslibrary.org. Web Site: dallaslibrary2.org/branch/arcadia.php. *Br Mgr,* Sandra King; *Librn,* Mary McCorcle; *Ch,* May Shen; Staff 3 (MLS 3)
Library Holdings: Bk Vols 68,000
Automation Activity & Vendor Info: (Cataloging) Polaris Library Systems; (Circulation) Polaris Library Systems; (Course Reserve) Polaris Library Systems
Open Mon 7:45am-8pm, Tues-Fri 7:45-5, Sat 10-5
AUDELIA ROAD, 10045 Audelia Rd, 75238-1999, SAN 361-4409. Tel: 214-670-1350. FAX: 214-670-0790. E-mail: audeliaroad@dallaslibrary.org. Web Site: dallaslibrary2.org/branch/audelia.php. *Br Mgr,* Lynn Moore; Staff 5 (MLS 3, Non-MLS 2)
Library Holdings: Bk Vols 95,377
Open Tues, Fri & Sat 10-6, Wed & Thurs 12-8
Friends of the Library Group
BACHMAN LAKE, 9480 Webb Chapel Rd, 75220-4496, SAN 361-4883. Tel: 214-670-6376. FAX: 214-670-6614. E-mail: bachmanlake@dallaslibrary.org. Web Site: dallaslibrary2.org/branch/bachman.php. *Br Mgr,* Val Armstrong; Staff 3 (MLS 2, Non-MLS 1)
Founded 1961
Library Holdings: Bk Vols 60,000
Open Tues & Wed 12-8, Thurs-Sat 10-6
Friends of the Library Group
DALLAS WEST, 2332 Singleton Blvd, 75212-3790, SAN 361-4468. Tel: 214-670-6445. FAX: 214-670-6618. E-mail: dallaswest@dallaslibrary.org. Web Site: dallaslibrary2.org/branch/dallaswest.php. ; Staff 2 (MLS 2)
Library Holdings: Bk Vols 33,000
Open Tues, Fri & Sat 10-6, Wed & Thurs 12-8
PAUL LAURENCE DUNBAR LANCASTER-KIEST BRANCH, 2008 E Kiest St, 75216-4448, SAN 361-4646. Tel: 214-670-1952. FAX: 214-670-0588. E-mail: lancasterkiest@dallaslibrary.org. Web Site: dallaslibrary2.org/branch/lancaster.php. *Br Mgr,* Betty Leal
Library Holdings: Bk Vols 48,565
Open Tues & Thurs 12-8, Wed, Fri & Sat 10-6
Friends of the Library Group
FOREST GREEN, 9015 Forest Lane, 75243-4114, SAN 361-4492. Tel: 214-670-1335. FAX: 214-670-5597. E-mail: forestgreen@dallaslibrary.org. Web Site: dallaslibrary2.org/branch/forest.php. *Br Mgr,* Katherine Stone; Staff 2 (MLS 2)
Library Holdings: Bk Vols 41,391
Open Tues & Thurs 12-8, Wed, Fri & Sat 10-6
Friends of the Library Group
FRETZ PARK, 6990 Belt Line Rd, 75240-7963, SAN 361-4522. Tel: 214-670-6421. FAX: 214-670-6621. E-mail: fretzpark@dallaslibrary.org. Web Site: dallaslibrary2.org/branch/fretz.php. *Br Mgr,* Kitty Stone; Staff 9 (MLS 3, Non-MLS 6)
Library Holdings: Bk Vols 66,000
Function: Adult bk club, Bks on CD, Children's prog, Computers for patron use, Copy machines, ILL available, Music CDs, Online cat, Online ref, Photocopying/Printing, Story hour, Summer reading prog, Web-catalog
Open Tues & Wed 12-8, Thurs-Sat 10-6
Friends of the Library Group
HAMPTON-ILLINOIS, 2951 S Hampton Rd, 75224, SAN 361-4557. Tel: 214-670-7646. FAX: 214-670-7652. E-mail: hamptonillinois@dallaslibrary.org. Web Site: dallaslibrary2.org/branch/hampton.php. *Br Mgr,* Ann Beaver; Staff 4 (MLS 3, Non-MLS 1)
Library Holdings: Bk Vols 83,131
Open Mon 7:45am-8pm, Tues-Fri 7:45-5, Sat 10-5
Friends of the Library Group
HIGHLAND HILLS, 3624 Simpson Stuart Rd, 75241-4399, SAN 361-4565. Tel: 214-670-0987. FAX: 214-670-0318. E-mail: highlandhills@dallaslibrary.org. Web Site:

dallaslibrary2.org/branch/highland.php. *Br Mgr,* Betty Leal; Staff 2 (MLS 2)
Library Holdings: Bk Vols 46,100
Open Tues & Wed 12-8, Thurs-Sat 10-6
Friends of the Library Group
MARTIN LUTHER KING JR BRANCH, 2922 Martin Luther King Jr Blvd, 75215-2393, SAN 361-4670. Tel: 214-670-0344. FAX: 214-670-0319. E-mail: martinlutherkingjr@dallaslibrary.org. Web Site: dallaslibrary2.org/branch/martin.php. *Asst Br Mgr,* Ora Hankins; Staff 2 (MLS 2)
Library Holdings: Bk Vols 36,740
Open Tues & Wed 12-8, Thurs-Sat 10-6
Friends of the Library Group
KLEBERG-RYLIE, 1301 Edd Rd, 75253-4010, SAN 376-947X. Tel: 214-670-8471. FAX: 214-670-8474. E-mail: klebergrylie@dallaslibrary.org. Web Site: dallaslibrary2.org/branch/kleberg.php. *Br Mgr,* Lynn Craddock; Staff 3 (MLS 3)
Open Tues & Thurs 12-8, Wed, Fri & Sat 10-6
Friends of the Library Group
LAKEWOOD, 6121 Worth St, 75214-4497, SAN 361-4611. Tel: 214-670-1376. FAX: 214-670-5701. E-mail: lakewood@dallaslibrary.org. Web Site: dallaslibrary2.org/branch/lakewood.php. *Br Mgr,* Christina Worden; *Asst Br Mgr,* Kerri Whitmer; Staff 9 (MLS 3, Non-MLS 6)
Library Holdings: Bk Vols 52,676
Automation Activity & Vendor Info: (Acquisitions) Polaris Library Systems; (Cataloging) Polaris Library Systems
Open Tues & Thurs 12-8, Wed, Fri & Sat 10-6
Friends of the Library Group
LOCHWOOD, 11221 Lochwood Blvd, 75218. Tel: 214-670-8403. FAX: 214-670-8405. E-mail: lochwood@dallascityhall.com. Web Site: dallaslibrary2.org/branch/lochwood.php.
Library Holdings: Bk Vols 70,170
Open Tues, Fri & Sat 10-6, Wed & Thurs 12-8
Friends of the Library Group
MOUNTAIN CREEK, 6102 Mountain Creek Pkwy, 75249, SAN 374-4477. Tel: 214-670-6704. FAX: 214-670-6780. E-mail: mountaincreek@dallaslibrary.org. Web Site: dallaslibrary2.org/branch/mountain.php. *Br Mgr,* Sandra King
Library Holdings: Bk Vols 60,473
Open Tues, Fri & Sat 10-6, Wed & Thurs 12-8
Friends of the Library Group
NORTH OAK CLIFF, 302 W Tenth St, 75208-4617, SAN 361-4581. Tel: 214-670-7555. FAX: 214-670-7548. E-mail: northoakcliff@dallaslibrary.org. Web Site: dallaslibrary2.org/branch/north.php. *Asst Br Mgr,* Thomas Finley
Library Holdings: Bk Vols 64,372
Open Tues & Thurs 12-8, Wed, Fri & Sat 10-6
Friends of the Library Group
OAK LAWN, 4100 Cedar Springs Rd, 75219-3522, SAN 361-4700. Tel: 214-670-1359. FAX: 214-670-5703. E-mail: oaklawn@dallaslibrary.org. Web Site: dallaslibrary2.org/branch/oaklawn.php. *Br Mgr,* Christina Worden
Library Holdings: Bk Vols 46,221
Open Tues, Fri & Sat 10-6, Wed & Thurs 12-8
Friends of the Library Group
PARK FOREST, 3421 Forest Lane, 75234-7776, SAN 361-4735. Tel: 214-670-6333. FAX: 214-670-6623. E-mail: parkforest@dallaslibrary.org. Web Site: dallaslibrary2.org/branch/park.php. *Br Mgr,* Sharon Martin
Library Holdings: Bk Vols 65,356
Open Tues & Thurs 12-8, Wed, Fri & Sat 12-6
Friends of the Library Group
PLEASANT GROVE, 7310 Lake June Rd, 75217, SAN 361-476X. Tel: 214-670-0965. E-mail: pleasantgrove@dallaslibrary.org. Web Site: dallaslibrary.org/pleasant.htm. *Br Mgr,* Lynette Robertson; *Librn,* Will Mayer; Staff 2 (MLS 2)
Library Holdings: Bk Vols 53,150
Open Tues & Thurs 12-8, Wed, Fri & Sat 10-6
Friends of the Library Group
POLK-WISDOM, 7151 Library Lane, 75232-3899, SAN 361-4794. Tel: 214-670-1947. FAX: 214-670-0589. E-mail: polkwisdom@dallaslibrary.org. Web Site: dallaslibrary.org/polk.htm. *Br Mgr,* Cosette Ratliff; Staff 2 (MLS 2)
Library Holdings: Bk Vols 63,548
Open Tues & Thurs 12-8, Wed, Fri & Sat 10-6
PRESTON ROYAL BRANCH, 5626 Royal Lane, 75229-5599, SAN 361-4824. Tel: 214-670-7128. FAX: 214-670-7135. E-mail: prestonroyal@dallaslibrary.org. Web Site: dallaslibrary2.org/branch/preston.php. *Br Mgr,* Paige Boe
Library Holdings: Bk Vols 71,770
Open Tues, Fri & Sat 10-6, Wed & Thurs 12-8
Friends of the Library Group

RENNER FRANKFORD BRANCH, 6400 Frankford Rd, 75252-5747, SAN 328-7300. Tel: 214-670-6100. FAX: 214-670-6090. E-mail: rennerfrankford@dallaslibrary.org. Web Site: dallaslibrary.org/renner.htm. *Br Mgr,* Laverne Brown; Staff 2 (MLS 2)
Library Holdings: Bk Vols 80,165
Open Tues, Fri & Sat 10-6, Wed & Thurs 12-8
Friends of the Library Group
SKILLMAN SOUTHWESTERN, 5707 Skillman St, 75206, SAN 376-9488. Tel: 214-670-6078. FAX: 214-670-6184. E-mail: skillmansouthwestern@dallaslibrary.org. Web Site: dallaslibrary2.org/branch/skillman.php. *Asst Mgr,* Deborah Rubin; Staff 6 (MLS 1, Non-MLS 5)
Library Holdings: Bk Vols 56,844
Open Tues & Wed 12-8, Thurs-Sat 10-6
Friends of the Library Group
SKYLINE, 6006 Everglade, 75227-2799, SAN 361-4859. Tel: 214-670-0938. FAX: 214-670-0321. E-mail: skyline@dallaslibrary.org. Web Site: dallaslibrary.org/skyline.htm. *Br Mgr,* Ginger Allen; Staff 2 (MLS 2)
Library Holdings: Bk Vols 50,000
Open Tues & Thurs 12-8, Wed, Fri & Sat 10-6
Friends of the Library Group
Bookmobiles: 1

CR   DALLAS THEOLOGICAL SEMINARY, Turpin Library, 3909 Swiss Ave, 75204. SAN 316-2168. Tel: 214-841-3750. FAX: 214-841-3745. Web Site: library.dts.edu. *Dir,* Marvin Hunn; Tel: 214-841-3751, E-mail: mhunn@dts.edu; *Dir of Tech Serv,* Jessie Zhong; Tel: 214-841-3746, E-mail: jzhong@dts.edu; *Coll Develop Librn,* Jefferson Webster; Tel: 214-841-3748, E-mail: jwebster@dts.edu; *ILL, Ref,* Debbie Hunn; Tel: 214-841-3752, E-mail: dhunn@dts.edu; *Pub Serv, Spec Coll,* Lolana Thompson; Tel: 214-841-3755, E-mail: lthompson@dts.edu; Staff 5 (MLS 3, Non-MLS 2)
Founded 1924. Highest Degree: Doctorate
Library Holdings: AV Mats 11,707; e-books 11,302; e-journals 2,269; Microforms 56,034; Bk Vols 231,007; Per Subs 632
Automation Activity & Vendor Info: (Cataloging) SirsiDynix; (Circulation) SirsiDynix
Wireless access
Function: Res libr
Partic in TexSHARE - Texas State Library & Archives Commission
Open Mon-Thurs 7:30am-10pm, Fri 7:30-6, Sat 9-6

S   DEGOLYER & MACNAUGHTON LIBRARY, 5001 Spring Valley Rd, Ste 800 East, 75244. SAN 316-2184. Tel: 214-368-6391. FAX: 214-369-4061. Web Site: www.demac.com. *Librn,* Deborah Buchel
Founded 1939
Library Holdings: Bk Titles 9,000; Per Subs 50
Subject Interests: Econ, Energy minerals, Eng, Geol, Natural gas, Petroleum
Publications: 20th Century Petroleum Statistics
Restriction: Staff use only

GM   DEPARTMENT OF VETERANS AFFAIRS NORTH TEXAS HEALTH CARE SYSTEM, Library Service, 4500 S Lancaster Rd, 75216. SAN 316-2737. Tel: 214-857-1245. Interlibrary Loan Service Tel: 214-857-1248. E-mail: ntxlibrary@va.gov. *Chief,* Jack Raines; Tel: 214-857-1250; *Librn,* Shirley Campbell; Tel: 214-857-1251, E-mail: shirley.campbell2@va.gov; *Librn,* Teresa Hanson; Tel: 214-857-2169, E-mail: teresaann.hanson@va.gov. Subject Specialists: *Consumer health,* Teresa Hanson; Staff 3 (MLS 3)
Founded 1940
Library Holdings: AV Mats 700; Bk Titles 5,000; Per Subs 350
Subject Interests: Med
Automation Activity & Vendor Info: (OPAC) Inmagic, Inc.
Database Vendor: EBSCOhost, UpToDate
Open Mon-Fri 7:30-4:30

R   EAST DALLAS CHRISTIAN CHURCH, Haggard Memorial Library, 629 N Peak St, 75246. (Mail add: PO Box 140009, 75214-0009), SAN 316-2206. Tel: 214-824-8185. FAX: 214-824-8583. Web Site: www.edcc.org. *Librn,* Marcille McKelvy
Library Holdings: Bk Vols 8,000
Subject Interests: Disciples of Christ hist, Doctrine, Relig mat
Wireless access
Restriction: Mem only

J   EL CENTRO COLLEGE*, Educational Resources Center, 801 Main St, 75202-3605. SAN 316-2214. Tel: 214-860-2174. Circulation Tel: 214-860-2175. FAX: 214-860-2440. E-mail: icl5610@dcccd.edu. Web Site: www.dcccd.edu, www.elcentrocollege.edu/library. *Asst Dean,* Dr Norman Howden; Tel: 214-860-2176, E-mail: nxh5610@dcccd.edu; *Librn,* Linda Baker; E-mail: lib5610@dcccd.edu; *Librn,* Margarette Jones; E-mail:

mmj5610@dcccd.edu; *Coordr, Access Serv,* Josy Thomas; *Circ,* Cindy Hernandez; Staff 13.5 (MLS 6.5, Non-MLS 7)
Founded 1966. Enrl 9,700; Fac 137
Library Holdings: Bk Titles 69,471; Bk Vols 76,814
Subject Interests: Allied health, Culinary arts, Ethnic studies, Nursing
Automation Activity & Vendor Info: (Acquisitions) Innovative Interfaces, Inc; (Circulation) Innovative Interfaces, Inc; (OPAC) Innovative Interfaces, Inc
Database Vendor: Gale Cengage Learning, Innovative Interfaces, Inc INN - View, LexisNexis, netLibrary, ProQuest
Wireless access
Function: Computers for patron use, e-mail & chat, Electronic databases & coll, Online ref, Photocopying/Printing, Scanner, Telephone ref, Web-catalog, Wheelchair accessible
Partic in Tex Share
Open Mon-Thurs 8am-8:30pm, Fri 8-4:30, Sat 10-2:30, Sun 12-3
Restriction: Open to fac, students & qualified researchers, Use of others with permission of librn

G   ENVIRONMENTAL PROTECTION AGENCY*, Sunder Ram Library, EPA Region 6, 1445 Ross Ave, Ste 1200, 75202. SAN 316-2222. Tel: 214-665-6424. FAX: 214-665-8574. E-mail: region6.library@epa.gov. Web Site: www.epa.gov/libraries/region6.html. *Librn,* Beth Wagner; Staff 1 (MLS 1)
Founded 1971
Library Holdings: Bk Titles 2,600; Per Subs 2
Special Collections: EPA Documents; Risk Assessment; USDA Soil Surveys for Arkansas, Louisiana, Oklahoma, New Mexico & Texas
Subject Interests: Environ issues
Automation Activity & Vendor Info: (Cataloging) OCLC Online
Database Vendor: Dialog, LexisNexis
Wireless access
Function: Govt ref serv, ILL available, Photocopying/Printing, Ref serv available
Partic in OCLC-LVIS
Open Mon-Fri 9-12 & 1-4
Restriction: Circulates for staff only, In-house use for visitors, Open to pub for ref & circ; with some limitations, Photo ID required for access

S   FEDERAL RESERVE BANK OF DALLAS LIBRARY*, 2200 N Pearl, 75201. SAN 316-2257. Tel: 214-922-6000. FAX: 214-922-5222. *Mgr,* Fanying Kong; Staff 4 (MLS 4)
Founded 1921
Library Holdings: Bk Titles 19,000; Per Subs 750
Subject Interests: Banking, Economics, Finance, Labor, Petroleum, Southwest region
Automation Activity & Vendor Info: (Acquisitions) SirsiDynix; (Cataloging) SirsiDynix; (Circulation) SirsiDynix; (ILL) OCLC; (OPAC) SirsiDynix; (Serials) SirsiDynix
Database Vendor: Bloomberg, Dialog, EBSCOhost, Elsevier, Factiva.com, Hoovers, JSTOR, LexisNexis, McGraw-Hill, OCLC, Oxford Online, ProQuest, SerialsSolutions, SirsiDynix, Thomson - Web of Science, Wiley
Wireless access
Restriction: Open by appt only, Open to pub for ref only

R   FIRST BAPTIST CHURCH OF DALLAS*, Truett Memorial Library, 1707 San Jacinto, 75201. SAN 316-2273. Tel: 214-969-2442. E-mail: truettlibrary@firstdallas.org. Web Site: www.firstdallas.org/library. *Dir,* Ruth Turner
Founded 1898
Library Holdings: CDs 707; DVDs 1,193; Bk Titles 13,000
Special Collections: Children's Library; Contemporary Christian Nonfiction; Inspirational Fiction
Subject Interests: Archives, Missions hist, Relig
Automation Activity & Vendor Info: (Cataloging) Book Systems, Inc; (Circulation) Book Systems, Inc; (OPAC) Book Systems, Inc
Wireless access
Open Mon, Tues & Thurs 9-4, Wed 9-6, Sun 8:30-12:30 & 4-5:45

L   GARDERE & WYNNE*, Law Library, 1601 Elm St, Ste 3000, 75201. SAN 372-1582. Tel: 214-999-4738. FAX: 214-999-3738. E-mail: whike@gardere.com. Web Site: www.gardere.com. *Dir,* Kellie Whitaker
Library Holdings: Bk Vols 8,000; Per Subs 200
Wireless access
Restriction: Private libr

CR   GRADUATE INSTITUTE OF APPLIED LINGUISTICS LIBRARY*, 7500 W Camp Wisdom Rd, 75236-5699. SAN 326-6125. Tel: 972-708-7416. FAX: 972-708-7292. E-mail: library_dallas@gial.edu. Web Site: www.gial.edu/library. *Acq of New Ser, Dir,* Ferne Weimer; E-mail: library_dallas@gial.edu; *ILL,* Carole Unseth; *Pub Serv,* Barbara Thomas; Staff 7 (MLS 3, Non-MLS 4)
Founded 1972. Enrl 112; Fac 26; Highest Degree: Master

Library Holdings: e-journals 61; Electronic Media & Resources 271; Bk Titles 36,000; Bk Vols 52,367; Per Subs 100
Subject Interests: Linguistics
Automation Activity & Vendor Info: (Cataloging) Follett Software; (Circulation) Follett Software; (ILL) OCLC FirstSearch; (OPAC) Follett Software
Database Vendor: Amigos Library Services, Cambridge Scientific Abstracts, EBSCOhost, OCLC FirstSearch, Wiley InterScience
Wireless access
Partic in Christian Library Consortium; Southwest Area Theological Library Association (SWATLA); TexSHARE - Texas State Library & Archives Commission
Open Mon-Thurs 8am-10pm, Fri 8-5, Sat 9-5
Restriction: Badge access after hrs, In-house use for visitors, Open to fac, students & qualified researchers

L   HAYNES & BOONE LLP*, Law Library, 2323 Victory Ave, Ste 700, 75219. SAN 326-6044. Tel: 214-651-5711. Web Site: www.haynesboone.com. *Supvr,* David Bader; Tel: 214-651-5709, Fax: 214-200-0801, E-mail: david.bader@haynesboone.com; *Librn,* Riva Laughlin; Tel: 713-547-2828, E-mail: riva.laughlin@haynesboone.com; *Librn,* Jennifer Stephens; Tel: 214-651-5233, E-mail: jennifer.stephens@haynesboone.com; *Librn,* Stephanie Towery; Tel: 512-867-8473, E-mail: stephanie.towery@haynesboone.com. Subject Specialists: *Bus,* David Bader; Staff 7 (MLS 5, Non-MLS 2)
Founded 1970
Library Holdings: Bk Titles 6,900; Bk Vols 60,000; Per Subs 130
Automation Activity & Vendor Info: (Acquisitions) Inmagic, Inc.; (Cataloging) Inmagic, Inc.; (Serials) Inmagic, Inc.
Database Vendor: Dialog, LexisNexis, OCLC FirstSearch, Westlaw
Wireless access
Open Mon-Fri 8:30-5

S   HELLMUTH, OBATA & KASSABAUM, INC LIBRARY*, 2711 N Haskell, Ste 2250, 75204. SAN 327-5469. Tel: 214-720-6000. FAX: 214-720-6005. Web Site: www.hok.com. *In Charge,* Kurt Griesbach; Staff 1 (MLS 1)
Library Holdings: Bk Vols 1,000
Subject Interests: Archit, Eng, Interior design, Planning
Open Mon-Fri 8:30-5:30
Restriction: Not open to pub

SR   HIGHLAND PARK PRESBYTERIAN CHURCH*, Meyercord Library, 3821 University Blvd, 75205. SAN 327-5647. Tel: 214-526-7457. Web Site: www.hppc.org. *Assoc Librn,* Rachel Venechanos; Tel: 214-526-4277, E-mail: rachel.venechanos@hppc.org
Library Holdings: Bk Vols 16,752
Special Collections: Civil War Pioneers (James Spearman Coll); Unique Birds (Marianne Roach Coll)
Subject Interests: Relig
Open Mon, Wed, Thurs & Fri 9-1, Sun 9-12:30

R   HIGHLAND PARK UNITED METHODIST CHURCH LIBRARY*, 3300 Mockingbird Lane, 75205. SAN 316-2354. Tel: 214-521-3111, Ext 273. FAX: 214-520-6451. Web Site: www.hpumc.org. *Librn,* Ann L Williams; E-mail: williama@hpumc.org; Staff 1 (Non-MLS 1)
Founded 1950
Library Holdings: Bk Vols 18,000; Per Subs 14
Special Collections: Large Print Books
Subject Interests: Arts, Educ, Hist, Nature, Psychol, Relig, Travel
Open Mon-Wed 9-12 & 1-3, Sun 8-12:15

S   INSTITUTE FOR CREATION RESEARCH LIBRARY, 1806 Royal Lane, 75229. (Mail add: PO Box 59029, 75229), SAN 326-4580. Tel: 214-615-8300. FAX: 214-615-8299. Web Site: www.icr.org. *Librn,* Mary Smith
Library Holdings: Bk Titles 5,200; Per Subs 40
Special Collections: Religion (Harald F J Ellingson Coll)

L   JACKSON WALKER LLP*, Law Library, 901 Main St, Ste 6000, 75202. SAN 372-1604. Tel: 214-953-6038. FAX: 214-953-5822. Web Site: www.jw.com. *Librn,* Ann H Jeter; E-mail: ajeter@jw.com
Library Holdings: Bk Titles 5,000; Bk Vols 35,000; Per Subs 200
Automation Activity & Vendor Info: (Acquisitions) EOS International; (Cataloging) EOS International; (OPAC) EOS International; (Serials) EOS International
Wireless access
Restriction: Not open to pub

L   JONES DAY*, Law Library, 2727 N Harwood St, 75201-1515. SAN 316-2435. Tel: 214-969-4823. FAX: 214-969-5100. Web Site: www.jonesday.com. *Regional Mgr, Libr Serv,* Kim Serna; *Asst Mgr, Libr Serv,* Anne Leather; *Librn,* John L Adams; Staff 3 (MLS 3)
Library Holdings: Bk Vols 60,203

Database Vendor: Bloomberg, Dialog, LexisNexis, Westlaw
Open Mon-Fri 9-5:30

L   K&L GATES LIBRARY*, 1717 Main St, Ste 2800, 75201. SAN
321-7906. Tel: 214-939-5510. FAX: 214-939-5849. Web Site:
www.klgates.com. *Mgr, Libr Serv,* Angela Kennedy; *Asst Librn,* Debra
Burress; Staff 2 (MLS 2)
Library Holdings: Bk Vols 9,920; Per Subs 400
Subject Interests: Law
Wireless access
Partic in Dialog Corp; IRSC; Pacer; Westlaw

SR   MANKOFF RESOURCE CENTER*, Tycher Library, 7900 Northaven Rd,
75230. SAN 326-2820. Tel: 214-739-2737. FAX: 214-750-6473. Web Site:
www.jewishdallas.org. *Librn,* Judy Borejdo; E-mail: jborejdo@jfgd.org;
Staff 2 (MLS 1, Non-MLS 1)
Library Holdings: Bk Vols 5,000
Subject Interests: Foreign lang
Function: Newsp ref libr
Open Sun-Thurs 10-2
Friends of the Library Group

J   MOUNTAIN VIEW COLLEGE*, Learning Resources Center, 4849 W
Illinois, 75211-6599. SAN 316-2451. Tel: 214-860-8669. Reference Tel:
214-860-8527. FAX: 214-860-8667. E-mail: mvclibrary@dcccd.edu. Web
Site: www.mountainviewcollege.edu/library/pages/default.aspx. *Dean,* S
James Corvey; Tel: 214-860-8525; *Dir,* Toby Baldwin; E-mail:
tobaldwin@dcccd.edu; *Acq, Coll Develop, Ref Serv,* Margaret Knox; *Coll
Develop, Pub Serv, Ref Serv,* Position Currently Open; Staff 3 (MLS 3)
Founded 1970. Enrl 6,876; Fac 83; Highest Degree: Associate
Library Holdings: AV Mats 1,706; e-books 28,000; Bk Titles 46,596; Bk
Vols 51,118; Per Subs 200
Subject Interests: Aviation
Automation Activity & Vendor Info: (Acquisitions) Innovative Interfaces,
Inc - OCLC; (Cataloging) Innovative Interfaces, Inc; (Circulation)
Innovative Interfaces, Inc; (Course Reserve) Innovative Interfaces, Inc;
(ILL) Innovative Interfaces, Inc; (Media Booking) Innovative Interfaces,
Inc; (OPAC) Innovative Interfaces, Inc; (Serials) Innovative Interfaces, Inc
Database Vendor: 3M Library Systems, Amigos Library Services, Baker
& Taylor, Bowker, Cinahl Information Systems, College Source,
EBSCOhost, Electric Library, Facts on File, H W Wilson, Innovative
Interfaces, Inc, Mergent Online, netLibrary, OCLC FirstSearch, OCLC
WorldCat, Oxford Online, ProQuest, Wilson - Wilson Web, YBP Library
Services
Wireless access
Function: ILL available, Magnifiers for reading, Photocopying/Printing,
Ref serv available, Telephone ref, Wheelchair accessible
Partic in TexSHARE - Texas State Library & Archives Commission
Special Services for the Blind - Closed circuit TV; Computer with voice
synthesizer for visually impaired persons
Open Mon-Thurs 8am-9pm, Fri 8-4:30, Sat (Fall & Spring) 8:30-1:30

S   MUSEUM OF NATURE & SCIENCE*, E W Mudge Ornithology Library,
1318 S Second Ave, 75315. (Mail add: PO Box 151469, 75315), SAN
372-6940. Tel: 214-428-5555. FAX: 214-428-4356. Web Site:
www.dallasdino.org. *Curator,* Anthony Fiorillo. Subject Specialists: *Earth
sci,* Anthony Fiorillo
Founded 1985
Library Holdings: Bk Titles 1,557; Bk Vols 2,839
Special Collections: Illustrated Ornithological Works from 1556 to present
(Mudge Coll) bks; Travel Histories from 1600 to present (Mudge Coll) bks
Restriction: Open by appt only

S   MUSEUM OF THE AMERICAN RAILROAD*, Fair Park, 1105
Washington St, 75210. (Mail add: PO Box 153259, 75315-3259), SAN
372-977X. Tel: 214-428-0101. FAX: 214-426-1937. E-mail:
info@dallasrailwaymuseum.com. Web Site:
www.dallasrailwaymuseum.com. *Exec Dir,* Robert H LaPrelle; Staff 1
(MLS 1)
Library Holdings: Bk Titles 500; Bk Vols 700
Special Collections: Railroad Technical Manuals
Subject Interests: Energy, Railroads
Function: Res libr
Open Wed-Sun 10-5
Restriction: Not a lending libr

SR   OAK CLIFF PRESBYTERIAN CHURCH LIBRARY*, 6000 S Hampton
Rd, 75232. SAN 371-991X. Tel: 214-339-2211. FAX: 214-339-3500. Web
Site: www.ocpres.com. *Librn,* Shirley Campbell; Staff 1 (MLS 1)
Library Holdings: Bk Vols 3,500
Subject Interests: Relig
Restriction: Mem only
Friends of the Library Group

S   OMNICOM MANAGEMENT SERVICES, Information Services
Department, 1999 Bryan St, Ste 3200, 75201. SAN 316-2656. Tel:
214-259-2517. FAX: 214-259-2508. Web Site: www.omnicomdallas.com.
Dir, Michelle Walker; Staff 3 (MLS 1, Non-MLS 2)
Founded 1968
Library Holdings: Bk Vols 2,500; Per Subs 150
Subject Interests: Advertising, Beverages, Consumer, Demographics,
Hospitality, Mkt, Packaged goods, Promotions, Restaurant, Retail, Travel
Automation Activity & Vendor Info: (Cataloging) Surpass; (Circulation)
Surpass
Wireless access
Restriction: Staff use only

SR   PARK CITIES BAPTIST CHURCH*, Media Library, 3933 Northwest
Pkwy, 75225-3333. (Mail add: PO Box 12068, 75225-0068), SAN
378-1267. Tel: 214-860-1500. FAX: 214-860-1538. Web Site:
www.pcbc.org. *Librn,* Beth Andrews; Tel: 214-860-3993, E-mail:
bsandrews@pcbc.org; Staff 4 (MLS 2, Non-MLS 2)
Founded 1944. Pop 8,000; Circ 18,000
Library Holdings: Bk Vols 20,000; Per Subs 35
Subject Interests: Theol
Automation Activity & Vendor Info: (Cataloging) Follett Software;
(Circulation) Follett Software; (OPAC) Follett Software
Open Tues & Thurs 9-1, Wed 9-7, Sun 8:45-11am

M   PARKLAND HEALTH & HOSPITAL SYSTEM*, Fred Bonte Library,
5201 Harry Hines Blvd, 75235. SAN 316-2486. Tel: 214-590-0066. FAX:
214-590-2720. *Librn, Sr Adminr,* Yvonne Wesley; *Sr Admin Assoc,* Pamela
White
Library Holdings: Bk Vols 8,023; Per Subs 50
Subject Interests: Radiology
Wireless access
Restriction: Staff use only

C   PAUL QUINN COLLEGE*, Zale Library, 3837 Simpson Stuart Rd, 75241.
SAN 316-8328. Tel: 214-379-5576. FAX: 214-379-5456. Web Site:
www.pqc.edu. *Dir,* Clarice Weeks; Tel: 214-379-5565
Library Holdings: Bk Vols 80,000; Per Subs 163
Special Collections: Afro-American Ethnic & Cultural Coll; AME Church
Archives; College Archives
Automation Activity & Vendor Info: (Cataloging) Ex Libris Group;
(Circulation) Ex Libris Group; (OPAC) Ex Libris Group
Wireless access
Open Mon-Thurs 8am-11pm, Fri 8-5:30, Sat 9-4, Sun 2-6

R   PLEASANT GROVE CHRISTIAN CHURCH LIBRARY*, 1324 Pleasant
Dr, 75217. SAN 316-2494. Tel: 214-391-3159. FAX: 214-391-3150. *Librn,*
Mary Simms
Library Holdings: Bk Vols 5,300
Restriction: Mem only, Not open to pub

S   RAYTHEON CO, North Building Library, 13510 N Central Expressway,
MS 211, 75243. (Mail add: PO Box 660246, 75266), SAN 361-5367. Tel:
972-344-5036. FAX: 972-344-5042. *Principal Tech Librn,* Kathy L
Nordhaus; Staff 1 (MLS 1)
Founded 1950
Library Holdings: Bk Titles 10,275; Per Subs 187
Special Collections: IEEE Periodicals from their beginning date
Subject Interests: Computer sci, Defense, Electrical eng, Math
Automation Activity & Vendor Info: (Cataloging) SirsiDynix;
(Circulation) SirsiDynix; (ILL) OCLC
Database Vendor: ProQuest
Wireless access
Function: Res libr
Restriction: Staff & customers only

S   RAYTHEON, INC*, North Building Technical Library, 13510 N Central
Expressway, MS 211, 75243-1108. SAN 370-0070. Tel: 972-344-5034.
Administration Tel: 972-344-5036. FAX: 972-344-5042. *Sr Tech Librn,*
Jackie Florimonte; Staff 2 (MLS 2)
Automation Activity & Vendor Info: (Cataloging) SirsiDynix;
(Circulation) SirsiDynix
Wireless access
Function: Res libr
Restriction: Employees only

J   RICHLAND COLLEGE LIBRARY*, 12800 Abrams Rd, 75243-2199.
SAN 316-2524. Tel: 972-238-6081. E-mail: richlandlibrary@dcccd.edu.
Web Site: www.richlandcollege.edu/library. *Dir of Libr Serv,* Lenni
Henderson; Tel: 972-238-6107, E-mail: lhenderson@dcccd.edu; *Instrul Serv
Librn,* Gary Duke; *Instrul Serv Librn,* Amy Ferguson; *Instrul Serv Librn,*
Alice Fulbright; *Instrul Serv Librn,* Sharlee Jeser-Skaggs; *Coll Develop,*
Cynthia Clements; Staff 19 (MLS 8, Non-MLS 11)

Founded 1972. Enrl 14,145
Library Holdings: Bk Titles 78,800; Bk Vols 91,000; Per Subs 210
Automation Activity & Vendor Info: (Acquisitions) Innovative Interfaces, Inc; (Cataloging) Innovative Interfaces, Inc; (Circulation) Innovative Interfaces, Inc; (Course Reserve) Innovative Interfaces, Inc; (ILL) Innovative Interfaces, Inc; (Media Booking) Innovative Interfaces, Inc; (OPAC) Innovative Interfaces, Inc; (Serials) Innovative Interfaces, Inc
Database Vendor: Innovative Interfaces, Inc INN - View
Wireless access
Partic in Tex Share
Open Mon-Thurs (Fall) 8am-9:30pm, Fri 8-4:30, Sat 2-4; Mon-Thurs (Summer) 8am-9pm, Fri 8-4:30

SOUTHERN METHODIST UNIVERSITY
CR   BRIDWELL LIBRARY-PERKINS SCHOOL OF THEOLOGY, 6005 Bishop Blvd, 75205. (Mail add: PO Box 750476, 75275-0476), SAN 361-5189. Tel: 214-768-3483. Circulation Tel: 214-768-3441. Interlibrary Loan Service Tel: 214-768-3984. Reference Tel: 214-768-4046. FAX: 214-768-4295. E-mail: bridadmin@smu.edu. Web Site: www.smu.edu/bridwell. *Dir & J S Bridwell Endowed Librn,* Roberta Schaafsma; *Assoc Dir,* James McMillin; *Head, Spec Coll,* Daniel Slive; *Ref Librn,* Jane Elder; *Ref & Digital Librn,* Christine Willard; Staff 20 (MLS 11, Non-MLS 9)
Founded 1915
Library Holdings: Microforms 138,000; Bk Vols 375,200; Per Subs 1,120
Special Collections: 15th Century Printing Coll; Bible Coll; Methodism Coll; Savonarola Coll
Subject Interests: Bibles, Fine binding, Methodist hist, Reformation, Theol
Automation Activity & Vendor Info: (Cataloging) Ex Libris Group; (Circulation) Ex Libris Group; (Course Reserve) Ex Libris Group; (ILL) OCLC ILLiad; (OPAC) Ex Libris Group
Partic in OCLC Online Computer Library Center, Inc; Southwest Area Theological Library Association (SWATLA)
Publications: Exhibition Catalogs
Open Mon-Thurs 8am-11pm, Fri 8-6, Sat 10-6, Sun 2-10
Friends of the Library Group
C   CENTRAL UNIVERSITY LIBRARIES*, 6414 Robert S Hyer Lane, 75275. (Mail add: PO Box 750135, 75275-0135). Tel: 214-768-2401. Circulation Tel: 214-768-2329. Interlibrary Loan Service Tel: 214-768-2328. Reference Tel: 214-768-2326. Automation Services Tel: 214-768-3229. FAX: 214-768-3815. Reference FAX: 214-768-1842. Web Site: www.smu.edu/cul. *Dean & Dir,* Gillian McCombs; E-mail: gmccombs@smu.edu; *Dir, Scholarly Resources & Res Serv,* Patricia Van Zandt; Tel: 214-768-4960, E-mail: pvanzandt@smu.edu; Staff 33 (MLS 33)
Founded 1915. Enrl 10,938; Fac 1,040; Highest Degree: Doctorate
Library Holdings: Bk Vols 2,168,033; Per Subs 14,732
Special Collections: State Document Depository; US Document Depository
Subject Interests: Classics, Geol, SW art, Texana, Theatre, Transportation, Western Americana
Automation Activity & Vendor Info: (Acquisitions) Ex Libris Group; (Cataloging) Ex Libris Group; (Circulation) Ex Libris Group; (Course Reserve) Ex Libris Group; (ILL) OCLC ILLiad; (OPAC) Ex Libris Group; (Serials) Ex Libris Group
Partic in OCLC Online Computer Library Center, Inc; TexSHARE - Texas State Library & Archives Commission
Friends of the Library Group
C   DEGOLYER LIBRARY OF SPECIAL COLLECTIONS*, 6404 Robert S Hyer Lane, 75275. (Mail add: PO Box 750396, 75275). Tel: 214-768-3234. FAX: 214-768-1565. E-mail: degolyer@mail.smu.edu. Web Site: www.smu.edu/cul/degolyer. *Dir,* Russell Martin; E-mail: rlmartin@smu.edu; *Cataloger/Ref Librn,* Cynthia Franco; Tel: 214-768-3605, E-mail: cafranco@smu.edu; *Archivist,* Pamalla Anderson; Tel: 214-768-0829, E-mail: andersonp@smu.edu; *Archivist,* Joan Gosnell; Tel: 214-768-2261, E-mail: jgosne@smu.edu; *Curator,* Anne Peterson; Tel: 214-768-2661, E-mail: apeterso@masmu.edu. Subject Specialists: *Women's hist,* Pamalla Anderson; *Photog,* Anne Peterson; Staff 6 (MLS 3, Non-MLS 3)
Library Holdings: Bk Titles 143,326
Special Collections: Archives of Women of the Southwest; Belo Archives; Budner Theodore Roosevelt Coll; Horton Foote Archive; JC Penney Archives; Modern Authors Coll; Photographs; Railroads (Baldwin Archives); SMU Archives; Stanley Marcus Archive; Texana; Texas Instruments Coll; Trade Catalogs; Transportation Coll; Western Americana Coll
Subject Interests: Bus hist, Travel, Voyages, Western Americana
Partic in OCLC Online Computer Library Center, Inc
Publications: Book Club of Texas; Informal Publications & Guides to the Collections; The DeGolyer Library Publication Series
Restriction: Closed stack, Non-circulating of rare bks

C   FONDREN LIBRARY*, 6414 Robert S Hyer Lane, 75275. (Mail add: PO Box 750135, 75275-0135). Tel: 214-768-2401. Circulation Tel: 214-768-2329. Interlibrary Loan Service Tel: 214-768-2328. Reference Tel: 214-768-2326. Automation Services Tel: 214-768-3229. FAX: 214-768-3815. Reference FAX: 214-768-1842. Web Site: www.smu.edu/cul/flc. *Dean, Dir,* Gillian McCombs; E-mail: gmccombs@smu.edu; *Dir, Scholarly Resources & Res Serv,* Patricia Van Zandt; Tel: 214-768-4960, E-mail: pvanzandt@smu.edu. Subject Specialists: *Physics,* Patricia Van Zandt
Enrl 10,938; Fac 1,040; Highest Degree: Doctorate
Library Holdings: Bk Vols 1,857,141; Per Subs 14,732
Special Collections: State Document Depository; US Document Depository
Subject Interests: Am hist, Anthropology, Classical studies, Contemporary biog & lit, Earth sci, Economics, English lit (18th Century), English lit (19th Century), Humanities, Polit sci, Sciences, Soc sci, Tex hist
Automation Activity & Vendor Info: (Acquisitions) Ex Libris Group
Database Vendor: YBP Library Services
C   HAMON ARTS LIBRARY*, 6101 N Bishop Blvd, 75275. (Mail add: PO Box 750356, 75275-0356). Tel: 214-768-1855. Circulation Tel: 214-768-3813. Reference Tel: 214-768-1853. FAX: 214-768-1800. Web Site: www.smu.edu/cul/hamon/index.asp. *Interim Dir, Music Librn,* Jon Haupt; E-mail: jhaupt@smu.edu; *Film, Theatre & Communications Librn, Head, Jones Film & Video Coll,* Amy Turner; E-mail: aeturner@smu.edu; *Head, Spec Coll,* Sam Ratcliffe; E-mail: sratclif@smu.edu; *Art & Dance Librn,* Beverly Mitchell; E-mail: bmitchel@smu.edu; *Supvr, AV Serv & Coll,* Maristella Feustle; E-mail: mfeustle@mail.smu.edu; *Curator, Spec Coll,* Ellen Buie Niewyk; E-mail: eniewyk@smu.edu. Subject Specialists: *Music,* Jon Haupt; *Communications, Film, Theatre,* Amy Turner; *Art, Art hist, Dance,* Beverly Mitchell
Founded 1990
Library Holdings: AV Mats 38,541; Bk Vols 157,726; Per Subs 300
Automation Activity & Vendor Info: (Cataloging) Ex Libris Group; (Circulation) Ex Libris Group
C   INSTITUTE FOR STUDY OF EARTH & MAN READING ROOM*, N L Heroy Science Hall, Rm 129, 3225 Daniels Ave, 75275. (Mail add: PO Box 750274, 75275-0274). Tel: 214-768-2430. FAX: 214-768-4289. Web Site: www.smu.edu/cul/isemrr. *Librn,* John Phinney; E-mail: jphinney@smu.edu
Library Holdings: Bk Vols 9,840; Per Subs 30
Automation Activity & Vendor Info: (Cataloging) Ex Libris Group; (Circulation) Ex Libris Group

L   STRASBURGER & PRICE LLP LIBRARY*, 901 Main St, Ste 4300, 75202. SAN 373-6555. Tel: 214-651-4300. FAX: 214-651-4330. Web Site: www.strasburger.com. *Librn,* Donna Bostic; E-mail: donna.bostic@strasburger.com
Founded 1939
Library Holdings: Bk Vols 40,000; Per Subs 1,500
Special Collections: Law; Texas Law
Automation Activity & Vendor Info: (Cataloging) Inmagic, Inc.
Wireless access
Restriction: Staff use only

M   CHARLES C TANDY MD HEALTH SCIENCES LIBRARY*, 1441 N Beckley Ave, 75203. SAN 316-2427. Tel: 214-947-2330. FAX: 214-947-2334. E-mail: library@mhd.com. Web Site: www.methodisthealthsystem.org/library. *Dir,* Dr William L Smith; E-mail: billsmith@mhd.com; *Coordr, Libr Serv,* Sharon West; Tel: 214-947-2341, Fax: 214-947-2343, E-mail: sharonwest@mhd.com; Staff 2 (MLS 2)
Library Holdings: Bk Titles 2,700; Per Subs 180
Subject Interests: Clinical med
Automation Activity & Vendor Info: (Acquisitions) CyberTools for Libraries; (Cataloging) CyberTools for Libraries; (Circulation) CyberTools for Libraries; (ILL) CyberTools for Libraries; (OPAC) CyberTools for Libraries; (Serials) CyberTools for Libraries
Database Vendor: EBSCOhost
Function: Archival coll, Bus archives, Doc delivery serv, For res purposes, Handicapped accessible, Health sci info serv, Home delivery & serv to Sr ctr & nursing homes, Homebound medical serv, ILL available, Mail loans to mem, Online searches, Outside serv via phone, mail, e-mail & web, Photocopying/Printing, Prog for adults, Telephone ref, Wheelchair accessible
Partic in Docline; Healthline
Restriction: Co libr

R   TEMPLE EMANU-EL*, Alex F Weisberg Library, 8500 Hillcrest Rd, 75225. SAN 361-5308. Tel: 214-706-0000. FAX: 214-706-0025. Web Site: www.tedallas.org/education/libraries/index.html. *Dir,* Nancy Rivin; E-mail: nrivin@tedallas.org
Founded 1957
Library Holdings: AV Mats 350; Bk Vols 12,000; Per Subs 30
Subject Interests: Judaica, Related humanities

Automation Activity & Vendor Info: (Cataloging) Follett Software; (Circulation) Follett Software
Open Sun-Thurs 9-1
Branches:
WILLIAM P BUDNER YOUTH LIBRARY, 8500 Hillcrest Rd, 75225.
Dir, Nancy Rivin; Tel: 214-706-0000, Ext 155, E-mail: nrivin@tedallas.org
Library Holdings: Bk Vols 5,000
Subject Interests: Judaica, Youth

M   TEXAS HEALTH PRESBYTERIAN HOSPITAL LIBRARY*, Green Learning Center, 820 Walnut Hill Lane, 75231. SAN 371-8816. Tel: 214-345-2310. FAX: 214-345-2350. E-mail: thdmedicallibrary@texashealth.org. *Med Librn,* Molly Montgomery; *Med Librn,* Cathy Nakashima; *Med Librn,* Jeanette Prasifka; Staff 3 (MLS 3)
Founded 1966
Library Holdings: Bk Titles 311; Bk Vols 650; Per Subs 181
Subject Interests: Allied health, Healthcare admin, Med, Nursing
Wireless access
Function: Health sci info serv, Online searches, Ref serv available
Open Mon-Fri 8-5
Restriction: In-house use for visitors, Internal circ only, Med & nursing staff, patients & families, Non-circulating to the pub, Restricted borrowing privileges

M   TEXAS SCOTTISH RITE HOSPITAL, The Brandon Carrell Medical Library, 2222 Welborn St, 75219-3993. SAN 329-1340. Tel: 214-559-5000, 214-559-7875. FAX: 214-559-7835. *Libr Serv Mgr,* Mary Nelson Peters; E-mail: mary.peters@tsrh.org; Staff 1 (MLS 1)
Founded 1979
Library Holdings: Bk Titles 800; Per Subs 100
Special Collections: History of Pediatric Orthopedics
Subject Interests: Neurology, Orthopedics, Pediatrics
Automation Activity & Vendor Info: (Cataloging) Marcive, Inc; (OPAC) Professional Software; (Serials) EBSCO Online
Database Vendor: EBSCOhost, PubMed
Wireless access
Function: Computers for patron use, Copy machines, Doc delivery serv, Electronic databases & coll, Handicapped accessible, Health sci info serv, Online cat, Online searches, Orientations, Wheelchair accessible
Partic in Health Libraries Information Network; S Cent Regional Med Libr Program
Restriction: Employees only, External users must contact libr, In-house use for visitors

CM   TEXAS WOMAN'S UNIVERSITY, F W & Bessie Dye Memorial Library, 5500 Southwestern Medical Ave, 75235-7200. SAN 316-2621. Tel: 214-689-6580. FAX: 214-689-6583. Web Site: www.twu.edu/library. *Coordr,* Oliphant Eula; E-mail: eoliphant@twu.edu; Staff 7 (MLS 3, Non-MLS 4)
Founded 1966
Library Holdings: Bk Vols 12,000; Per Subs 160
Subject Interests: Health studies, Nursing, Occupational therapy, Phys therapy
Automation Activity & Vendor Info: (Acquisitions) Ex Libris Group; (Cataloging) Ex Libris Group; (Circulation) Ex Libris Group; (Course Reserve) Ex Libris Group; (OPAC) Ex Libris Group; (Serials) Ex Libris Group
Wireless access
Partic in OCLC Online Computer Library Center, Inc
Open Mon-Thurs 8am-9pm, Fri 8-5, Sat 10-2
Friends of the Library Group

L   THOMPSON & KNIGHT*, Law Library, 1722 Routh St, Ste 1500, 75201. SAN 316-263X. Tel: 214-969-1350. FAX: 214-969-1751. Web Site: www.tklaw.com. *Mgr, Libr Res,* Linda Will; E-mail: linda.will@tklaw.com; Staff 8 (MLS 3, Non-MLS 5)
Founded 1914
Library Holdings: Bk Titles 2,500; Bk Vols 40,000
Automation Activity & Vendor Info: (Cataloging) EOS International
Database Vendor: Dialog, EBSCOhost, LexisNexis, Westlaw
Wireless access
Function: ILL available
Restriction: Open to staff only

S   UNI-BELL PVC PIPE ASSOCIATION LIBRARY*, 2711 LBJ Freeway, Ste 1000, 75234. SAN 323-5254. Tel: 972-243-3902. FAX: 972-243-3907. E-mail: info@uni-bell.org. Web Site: www.uni-bell.org. *Exec Dir,* Bruce Holland; E-mail: bholland@uni-bell.org
Founded 1971
Library Holdings: Bk Vols 7,000
Wireless access
Restriction: Staff & mem only

CM   UNIVERSITY OF TEXAS SOUTHWESTERN MEDICAL CENTER LIBRARY, 5323 Harry Hines Blvd, 75390-9049. SAN 316-2729. Tel: 214-648-2001. FAX: 214-648-2826. Web Site: www.utsouthwestern.edu/library. *Asst VPres, Libr Serv,* Laurie L Thompson; Tel: 214-648-2626, E-mail: laurie.thompson@utsouthwestern.edu; *Dep Dir,* Kelly Gonzalez; E-mail: kelly.gonzalez@utsouthwestern.edu; *Coll Develop, Electronic Res,* Mori Lou Higa; Tel: 214-648-2989, E-mail: mori.lou.higa@utsouthwestern.edu; Staff 21 (MLS 18, Non-MLS 3)
Founded 1943. Enrl 3,429; Fac 4,056; Highest Degree: Doctorate
Library Holdings: e-journals 56,000; Bk Titles 75,146; Bk Vols 84,725
Special Collections: History of Health Sciences Coll
Subject Interests: Biomed sci
Wireless access
Function: Res libr
Partic in National Network of Libraries of Medicine South Central Region; OCLC Online Computer Library Center, Inc; South Central Academic Medical Libraries Consortium; Tex Share; UT-System
Restriction: Not a lending libr

DAYTON

P   JONES PUBLIC LIBRARY*, 801 South Cleveland, Ste A, 77535. SAN 375-3328. Tel: 936-258-7060. FAX: 936-258-7634. E-mail: library@daytontx.com. *Dir,* Rose Klimitchek
Founded 1980. Pop 20,000; Circ 54,812
Library Holdings: Bk Titles 29,000; Per Subs 66
Wireless access
Open Mon-Thurs 9:30-5:30, Fri & Sat 10-2
Friends of the Library Group

DE LEON

P   DE LEON CITY COUNTY LIBRARY*, 125 E Reynosa St, 76444-1862. SAN 316-2788. Tel: 254-893-2417. FAX: 254-893-4915. E-mail: dllib@cctc.net. *Head of Librn,* Rebecca Hurteau; *Asst Librn,* Mary Young
Pop 4,231
Library Holdings: Bk Vols 10,710
Automation Activity & Vendor Info: (Cataloging) LibLime; (Circulation) LibLime
Wireless access
Mem of Big Country Library System
Partic in TexSHARE - Texas State Library & Archives Commission
Open Mon-Fri 9-5

DECATUR

P   DECATUR PUBLIC LIBRARY*, 1700 Hwy 51 S, 76234-9292. SAN 316-2796. Tel: 940-627-5512. FAX: 940-627-2905. E-mail: director@decaturpubliclibrary.com. Web Site: www.decaturpubliclibrary.com. *Dir,* Cecilia Hurt Barham; *Ch,* Diane Oswald; Staff 4 (MLS 2, Non-MLS 2)
Founded 1970. Pop 19,765; Circ 110,428
Oct 2006-Sept 2007 Income $348,582. Mats Exp $41,390, Books $36,000, AV Mat $5,000, Electronic Ref Mat (Incl. Access Fees) $390. Sal $199,316 (Prof $98,256)
Library Holdings: Bk Titles 41,295; Bk Vols 44,753; Per Subs 50
Special Collections: Texas Coll
Automation Activity & Vendor Info: (Cataloging) Evergreen; (Circulation) Evergreen; (OPAC) Evergreen
Wireless access
Function: Adult literacy prog, AV serv, Home delivery & serv to Sr ctr & nursing homes, ILL available, Online searches, Photocopying/Printing, Prog for children & young adult, Ref serv available, Spoken cassettes & CDs, Spoken cassettes & DVDs, Summer reading prog, Video lending libr, Wheelchair accessible
Mem of North Texas Library Partners
Open Mon, Tues & Thurs 10-8, Wed & Fri 10-6, Sat 10-2
Friends of the Library Group

DEER PARK

P   DEER PARK PUBLIC LIBRARY*, 3009 Center St, 77536-5099. SAN 316-280X. Tel: 281-478-7208. FAX: 281-478-7212. Web Site: catalog.library.deerparktx.org/polaris/. *Dir,* Rebecca Pool; *Asst Dir,* Shannon Burke; *Ch,* Peggy Warnock; *ILL,* Connie Laybourn; Staff 4 (MLS 2, Non-MLS 2)
Founded 1962. Pop 31,000; Circ 163,567
Library Holdings: AV Mats 2,519; Bk Vols 57,300; Per Subs 250
Special Collections: CAER Coll
Subject Interests: Commun awareness, Emergency response
Automation Activity & Vendor Info: (Cataloging) Polaris Library Systems; (Circulation) Polaris Library Systems; (OPAC) Polaris Library Systems
Open Mon & Wed 10-6, Tues & Thurs 10-9, Fri & Sat 10-5
Friends of the Library Group

DEL RIO

P   VAL VERDE COUNTY LIBRARY*, 300 Spring St, 78840. SAN
316-2850. Tel: 830-774-7595. FAX: 830-774-7607. E-mail:
library@vvcl.lib.tx.us, valverdecountylibrary@yahoo.com. *County Librn,*
Christopher Kuechmann; *Ch,* Sandra Reed; *Circ Librn, Circ Supvr,* Victor
Cirilo; *Coll Librn, Tech Serv,* Adrian Gonzalez; *Coll Librn, Tech Serv,*
Rosa Martinez; *Circ Mgr, Info Serv Librn,* Daniel Ramos; *Ref Librn, YA
Serv,* Ivone Bukowski; *Weekend Librn,* Paty Martinez; *Coll Serv, Tech
Serv,* Elaine Neal; Staff 6 (MLS 1, Non-MLS 5)
Founded 1940. Pop 48,000; Circ 90,000
Oct 2008-Sept 2009 Income $541,702, State $4,535, County $501,159,
Locally Generated Income $26,608, Other $9,400. Mats Exp $83,362,
Books $73,676, Other Print Mats $7,078, Electronic Ref Mat (Incl. Access
Fees) $2,608. Sal $387,038 (Prof $41,954)
Library Holdings: AV Mats 3,000; e-books 1,500; Electronic Media &
Resources 100; Bk Titles 70,000; Bk Vols 100,000; Per Subs 200
Special Collections: John R Brinkley Coll; Local History (Del Rio Coll)
Subject Interests: Local hist, Texana
Automation Activity & Vendor Info: (Cataloging) Follett Software;
(Circulation) Follett Software; (ILL) OCLC FirstSearch; (OPAC) Follett
Software
Database Vendor: Amigos Library Services, Baker & Taylor, EBSCOhost,
Gale Cengage Learning, Ingram Library Services, netLibrary, Newsbank,
OCLC FirstSearch, OCLC WorldCat, ProQuest
Function: Adult bk club, After school storytime, Archival coll, Audio &
video playback equip for onsite use, Bilingual assistance for Spanish
patrons, Bk reviews (Group), Bks on cassette, Bks on CD, Children's prog,
Computer training, Computers for patron use, Copy machines, E-Reserves,
Electronic databases & coll, Family literacy, Fax serv, Handicapped
accessible, ILL available, Mail & tel request accepted, Music CDs, Online
cat, Preschool outreach, Prog for adults, Prog for children & young adult,
Ref serv available, Scanner, Senior computer classes, Summer reading
prog, Teen prog, Telephone ref, VHS videos, Video lending libr,
Web-catalog, Wheelchair accessible
Open Mon-Thurs 10-7, Fri 10-6, Sat & Sun 1-5
Friends of the Library Group

DEL VALLE

P   ELROY COMMUNITY LIBRARY*, 13512 Fm 812, 78617. (Mail add:
16415 Greenwood Dr, 78617). Tel: 512-243-1981. Administration Tel:
514-243-7371. Administration FAX: 512-243-7371. *Librn,* Jean Phipps
Library Holdings: Bk Vols 3,150
Mem of Central Texas Library System, Inc
Open Mon-Fri 10-8, Sat 10-5

DELL CITY

P   GRACE GREBING PUBLIC LIBRARY*, 110 N Main, 79837. (Mail add:
PO Box 37, 79837-0037), SAN 376-4362. Tel: 915-964-2468,
915-964-2495, Ext 3000. FAX: 915-964-2468. *Librn,* Julia Layton; E-mail:
laytonj@delcity.com
Library Holdings: Bk Vols 16,346; Per Subs 28
Automation Activity & Vendor Info: (Cataloging) Follett Software;
(Circulation) Follett Software; (ILL) Follett Software; (OPAC) Follett
Software
Wireless access
Mem of Texas Trans-Pecos Regional Library System
Open Mon-Fri 7:30-3:30

DENISON

P   DENISON PUBLIC LIBRARY*, 300 W Gandy St, 75020-3153. SAN
316-2877. Tel: 903-465-1797. FAX: 903-465-1130. Web Site:
www.youseemore.com/denison. *Dir,* Alvin R Bailey; *Assoc Dir/Librn,*
Laura Haworth; *Asst Dir,* Dixie Foster; *Adminr,* Kathleen M Boatright;
E-mail: boatrightk@grayson.edu; *Youth Serv Coordr,* Joyce Ullah; *Circ,*
Loretta Hall; *Tech Serv,* Steve McGowen; Staff 3 (MLS 3)
Founded 1936. Pop 22,300; Circ 162,151
Oct 2008-Sept 2009 Income $674,642, City $659,800, County $2,000,
Locally Generated Income $12,842. Mats Exp $99,992, Books $77,486,
Per/Ser (Incl. Access Fees) $11,095, Other Print Mats $1,000, Micro
$3,943, AV Mat $6,468. Sal $385,256 (Prof $150,544)
Library Holdings: Bk Titles 98,097; Per Subs 149
Special Collections: Area History & Books by Area Authors (Texoma
Coll), print, bks, pamphlet
Subject Interests: Genealogy
Automation Activity & Vendor Info: (Acquisitions) Biblionix;
(Cataloging) Biblionix
Database Vendor: EBSCOhost
Wireless access
Open Mon, Wed & Fri 9-6, Tues & Thurs 9-9, Sat 9-1, Sun 1-5
Friends of the Library Group

J   GRAYSON COUNTY COLLEGE LIBRARY*, 6101 Grayson Dr,
75020-8299. SAN 316-2885. Tel: 903-463-8637. FAX: 903-465-4123. Web
Site: grayson.edu/cms/library. *Dir,* Gary Paikowski; E-mail:
paikowski@grayson.edu; *Asst Dir,* Lisa Hebert; *Ref Librn,* Roland
Commons; Staff 4 (MLS 4)
Founded 1965. Enrl 3,843; Fac 126
Library Holdings: Bk Titles 60,000; Per Subs 50
Automation Activity & Vendor Info: (Cataloging) TLC (The Library
Corporation); (Circulation) TLC (The Library Corporation); (ILL) OCLC;
(OPAC) TLC (The Library Corporation)
Wireless access
Open Mon-Thurs 7:30am-8pm, Fri 7:30-4, Sun 1-5

DENTON

P   DENTON PUBLIC LIBRARY*, Emily Fowler Central Library, 502
Oakland St, 76201. Tel: 940-349-8752. Interlibrary Loan Service Tel:
940-349-8760. Administration Tel: 940-349-8755. Automation Services Tel:
940-349-8772. FAX: 940-349-8101. Administration FAX: 940-349-8123.
E-mail: library@cityofdenton.com. Web Site: www.dentonlibrary.com. *Dir,*
Eva D Poole; Tel: 940-349-8750, E-Mail: eva.poole@cityofdenton.com; *Sr
Librn, Cat & Tech Serv,* Jennifer Reaves; E-mail:
jennifer.reaves@cityofdenton.com; *Br Mgr,* Terri Gibbs; Tel: 940-349-8776,
E-mail: terri.gibbs@cityofdenton.com; *Genealogy Serv,* Kathy Strauss; Tel:
940-349-8257, E-mail: kathy.strauss@cityofdenton.com; Staff 49.5 (MLS
19, Non-MLS 30.5)
Founded 1949. Pop 122,830; Circ 1,406,873
Oct 2010-Sept 2011 Income (Main Library and Branch(s)) $4,881,113,
State $45,375, City $4,575,365, Locally Generated Income $226,000, Other
$34,373. Mats Exp $588,258. Sal $3,033,279
Special Collections: Genealogy Coll; Texas & Denton History Coll,
archives, bks, clippings, maps, micro, pamphlets, photog
Automation Activity & Vendor Info: (Acquisitions) Innovative Interfaces,
Inc; (Cataloging) Innovative Interfaces, Inc; (Circulation) Innovative
Interfaces, Inc; (ILL) Innovative Interfaces, Inc; (OPAC) Innovative
Interfaces, Inc; (Serials) Innovative Interfaces, Inc
Wireless access
Partic in OCLC Online Computer Library Center, Inc
Special Services for the Deaf - Assistive tech
Special Services for the Blind - ZoomText magnification & reading
software
Open Mon, Wed, Fri & Sat 9-6, Tues & Thurs 9-9, Sun 1-5
Friends of the Library Group
Branches: 2
NORTH BRANCH, 3020 N Locust, 76209. Tel: 940-349-8752. FAX:
940-387-5367. E-mail: library@cityofdenton.com. *Br Head,* Kimberly
Wells; Tel: 940-349-8796, E-mail: kimberly.wells@cityofdentonon.com;
Sr Librn, WyLaina Hildreth; Tel: 940-349-8774, E-mail:
wylaina.hildreth@cityofdenton.com
Open Mon-Wed 9-9, Thurs-Sat 9-6, Sun 1-5
SOUTH BRANCH, 3228 Teasley Lane, 76210, SAN 376-1452. Tel:
940-349-8752. FAX: 940-349-8383. E-mail: library@cityofdenton.com.
Br Head, Stacy Sizemore; Tel: 940-349-8761, E-mail:
stacy.sizemore@cityofdenton.com; *Sr Librn,* Jess Turner; Tel:
940-349-8256, E-mail: jess.turner@cityofdenton.com
Open Mon 12-9, Tues & Thurs-Sat 9-6, Wed 9-9, Sun 1-5
Friends of the Library Group

C   TEXAS WOMAN'S UNIVERSITY LIBRARIES, Mary Evelyn
Blagg-Huey Library, 304 Administration Dr, 76204. (Mail add: TWU Sta,
PO Box 425528, 76204-5528), SAN 361-5634. Tel: 940-898-3701.
Circulation Tel: 940-898-3719. Interlibrary Loan Service Tel:
940-898-3758. Administration Tel: 940-898-3748. Toll Free Tel:
866-385-5541. FAX: 940-898-3764. Interlibrary Loan Service FAX:
940-898-3762. E-mail: reference@mail.twu.edu. Web Site:
www.twu.edu/library. *Dean of Libr,* Sherilyn Bird; E-mail:
sbird1@twu.edu; *Asst Dean, Libr,* Connie Maxwell; Tel: 940-898-3707,
E-mail: cmaxwell@twu.edu; *Asst Dean, Libr,* Kristine Reed; Tel:
940-898-3767, Fax: 940-898-3809, E-mail: kreed2@twu.edu; *Dir, Libr Info
Tech & Technical Support,* David Schuster; Tel: 940-898-3909, E-mail:
dschuster@twu.edu; *Coordr, Archives & Spec Coll,* Kimberly Johnson; Tel:
940-898-3743, E-mail: kjohnson27@twu.edu; Staff 24 (MLS 23, Non-MLS
1)
Founded 1901. Enrl 13,277; Fac 769; Highest Degree: Doctorate
Library Holdings: AV Mats 12,200; CDs 1,144; DVDs 1,081; e-books
125,000; e-journals 47,971; Electronic Media & Resources 184;
Microforms 19,387; Bk Titles 561,852; Bk Vols 686,588; Per Subs 2,473;
Videos 4,936
Special Collections: Book Art Coll; Children's Coll; Children's Historical
Coll; Cookbook Coll; History of Texas Women Coll; Texas Association of
Women's Clubs; Texas Federation of Women's Clubs; Texas Women's Hall
of Fame; WASP Archive; Whirly Girls Coll; Woman's Coll. Oral History
Subject Interests: Arts, Educ, Health professions, Humanities,
Kinesiology, Mgt, Nursing, Occupational therapy, Phys therapy, Sci, Soc
sci

Automation Activity & Vendor Info: (Acquisitions) Ex Libris Group; (Cataloging) Ex Libris Group; (Circulation) Ex Libris Group; (Course Reserve) Ex Libris Group; (ILL) OCLC ILLiad; (OPAC) Ex Libris Group; (Serials) Ex Libris Group

Database Vendor: ABC-CLIO, Alexander Street Press, American Chemical Society, American Mathematical Society, American Psychological Association (APA), Amigos Library Services, Atlas Systems, Backstage Library Works, Baker & Taylor, Bowker, Career Guidance Foundation, Checkpoint Systems, Inc, Children's Literature Comprehensive Database Company (CLCD), Cinahl Information Systems, CQ Press, CredoReference, ebrary, EBSCOhost, Elsevier, Emerald, Ex Libris Group, Facts on File, Gale Cengage Learning, H W Wilson, Haworth Pres Inc, infoUSA, Ingenta, Jane's, JSTOR, LexisNexis, Marquis Who's Who, Medline, Mergent Online, Modern Language Association, Natural Standard, Nature Publishing Group, Newsbank, OCLC, OCLC FirstSearch, OCLC WorldCat, OVID Technologies, Oxford Online, Paratext, Plunkett Research, Ltd, Project MUSE, ProQuest, PubMed, RefWorks, Sage, ScienceDirect, Scopus, Springer-Verlag, Springshare, LLC, STAT!Ref (Teton Data Systems), Wiley, Wiley InterScience, Wilson - Wilson Web, WT Cox, YBP Library Services

Wireless access

Function: Archival coll, Distance learning, e-mail & chat, Electronic databases & coll, Exhibits, Handicapped accessible, ILL available, Microfiche/film & reading machines, Online cat, Pub access computers, Scanner, Telephone ref

Partic in Amigos Library Services, Inc; Federation of North Texas Area Universities; OCLC Online Computer Library Center, Inc; Statewide California Electronic Library Consortium (SCELC); Tex Share

Open Mon-Thurs 7:30am-Midnight, Fri 7:30am-10pm, Sat 9-6, Sun 2pm-Midnight

Restriction: Borrowing requests are handled by ILL

Friends of the Library Group

C   UNIVERSITY OF NORTH TEXAS LIBRARIES*, PO Box 305190, 76203-5190. SAN 361-5510. Tel: 940-565-2413. Interlibrary Loan Service Tel: 940-565-2495. Reference Tel: 940-565-3245. Administration Tel: 940-565-3025. Toll Free Tel: 800-735-2989. FAX: 940-369-8760. E-mail: circ@library.unt.edu. Web Site: www.library.unt.edu. *Dean of Libr,* Martin Halbert; E-mail: martin.halbert@unt.edu; *Assoc Dean,* Cathy Hartman; Tel: 940-565-3269, E-mail: cathy.hartman@unt.edu; *Asst Dean for Coll Mgt,* Sian Brannon; Tel: 940-891-6945, E-mail: sian.brannon@unt.edu; *Asst Dean, Digital Libr,* Mark Phillips; Tel: 940-565-2415, E-mail: mark.phillips@unt.edu; *Asst Dean, External Relations,* Dreanna Belden; Tel: 940-369-8740, E-mail: dreanna.belden@unt.edu; *Asst Dean, Finance & Admin,* Susan Paz; Tel: 940-369-8165; *Asst Dean, Spec Libr,* Sue Parks; Tel: 940-369-7249, E-mail: sue.parks@unt.edu; *Asst Dean, Pub Serv,* Suzanne Sears; Tel: 940-565-2868; *Dir, Fac & Syst,* Scott Jackson; Tel: 940-565-3024, E-mail: scott.jackson@unt.edu

Founded 1890. Enrl 36,000; Fac 1,993; Highest Degree: Doctorate

Library Holdings: Microforms 3,877,996; Bk Vols 1,825,148

Special Collections: Jean-Baptiste Lully Coll; Miniature Book Coll; Portal to Texas History Electronic Coll; Weaver Coll. Oral History; State Document Depository; US Document Depository

Automation Activity & Vendor Info: (Acquisitions) Innovative Interfaces, Inc; (Cataloging) Innovative Interfaces, Inc; (Circulation) Innovative Interfaces, Inc; (Course Reserve) Innovative Interfaces, Inc; (ILL) Innovative Interfaces, Inc; (Media Booking) Innovative Interfaces, Inc; (OPAC) Innovative Interfaces, Inc; (Serials) Innovative Interfaces, Inc

Database Vendor: ABC-CLIO, ACM (Association for Computing Machinery), Agricola, Alexander Street Press, American Chemical Society, American Mathematical Society, American Physical Society, American Psychological Association (APA), Amigos Library Services, Annual Reviews, ASCE Research Library, Baker & Taylor, Bowker, Cambridge Scientific Abstracts, Coutts Information Service, CQ Press, CRC Press/Taylor & Francis CRCnetBASE, CredoReference, Dun & Bradstreet, Elsevier, Emerald, Gale Cengage Learning, H W Wilson, Haworth Pres Inc, Hoovers, IBISWorld, Infotrieve, Innovative Interfaces, Inc, IOP, ISI Web of Knowledge, JSTOR, LexisNexis, McGraw-Hill, Nature Publishing Group, netLibrary, Newsbank-Readex, OCLC, OCLC FirstSearch, OCLC WorldCat, Plunkett Research, Ltd, Project MUSE, ProQuest, PubMed, ReferenceUSA, RefWorks, Safari Books Online, Sage, ScienceDirect, SerialsSolutions, Springer-Verlag, Standard & Poor's, Thomson - Web of Science, ValueLine, Wiley InterScience, YBP Library Services

Wireless access

Departmental Libraries:

DALLAS CAMPUS LIBRARY, 7400 University Hills Blvd, Dallas, 75241. Tel: 972-780-3625. FAX: 972-780-3676. *Librn,* Brenda Robertson; Tel: 972-780-3625, Ext 1617; Staff 2 (MLS 2)

Founded 1999

Library Holdings: Bk Titles 756; Videos 132

Open Mon-Thurs 8-8, Fri 8-5, Sat 9-5

DENVER CITY

P   YOAKUM COUNTY LIBRARY*, 205 W Fourth St, 79323. SAN 316-2907. Tel: 806-592-2754. FAX: 806-592-2439. E-mail: ycdc_79323@hotmail.com. *Librn,* Pat McNabb; *Asst Librn,* Ginger Wilson

Founded 1957. Pop 8,000; Circ 63,130

Library Holdings: Bk Vols 45,000; Per Subs 70

Automation Activity & Vendor Info: (Cataloging) Follett Software; (Circulation) Follett Software

Mem of West Texas Library System

Open Mon-Fri 9-5:30

DESOTO

P   DESOTO PUBLIC LIBRARY, 211 E Pleasant Run Rd, Ste C, 75115-3939. SAN 370-7423. Tel: 972-230-9656. Circulation Tel: 972-230-9665. Reference Tel: 972-230-9661. Administration Tel: 972-230-9658. Automation Services Tel: 972-230-9660. FAX: 972-230-5797. Web Site: www.desototexas.gov/library. *Dir,* Lucile Dade; E-mail: ldade@desototexas.gov; *Adult Ref Librn,* Angela Alford; E-mail: aalford@desototexas.gov; *Circ Supvr,* Marquenez Runnels; E-mail: mrunnels@desototexas.gov; *Syst Coordr,* Sharon Castleberry; E-mail: scastleberry@desototexas.gov; Staff 9 (MLS 4, Non-MLS 5)

Founded 1943. Pop 50,000

Library Holdings: Bk Titles 80,000; Per Subs 125

Automation Activity & Vendor Info: (Cataloging) Polaris Library Systems; (Circulation) Polaris Library Systems; (OPAC) Polaris Library Systems

Database Vendor: EBSCOhost, Newsbank, OCLC FirstSearch, OCLC WorldCat, ReferenceUSA

Wireless access

Open Mon-Thurs 10-8, Fri 10-6, Sat 9-5

Friends of the Library Group

DEVINE

P   DRISCOLL PUBLIC LIBRARY*, 202 E Hondo Ave, 78016. (Mail add: c/o City of Devine, 303 S Teel Dr, 78016), SAN 316-2915. Tel: 830-663-2993. FAX: 830-663-6380. E-mail: driscoll.library@gmail.com. *Dir,* Barbara Moore

Founded 1965. Pop 7,362; Circ 15,783

Library Holdings: Bk Titles 19,000; Per Subs 20

Automation Activity & Vendor Info: (Cataloging) Biblionix; (Circulation) Biblionix; (OPAC) Biblionix

Wireless access

Open Mon & Thurs 12-7, Tues & Wed 10-6, Fri 12-5

Friends of the Library Group

DIBOLL

P   TLL TEMPLE MEMORIAL LIBRARY*, 300 Park St, 75941. SAN 316-2923. Tel: 936-829-5497. FAX: 936-829-5465. Web Site: www.tlltemplememoriallibrary.org. *Dir,* Brenda C Russell; E-mail: bcr@consolidated.net; Staff 6 (MLS 1, Non-MLS 5)

Founded 1961. Pop 5,470; Circ 32,436

Library Holdings: Bk Titles 32,000; Bk Vols 34,000; Per Subs 46

Special Collections: Large Print Coll; Texana Material (John S Redditt Texas Coll). Oral History

Automation Activity & Vendor Info: (Acquisitions) Follett Software; (Cataloging) Follett Software; (Circulation) Follett Software

Wireless access

Function: Accelerated reader prog, Adult bk club, After school storytime, Archival coll, Art exhibits, Audio & video playback equip for onsite use, AV serv, Bilingual assistance for Spanish patrons, Bks on cassette, Bks on CD, Children's prog, Computers for patron use, Copy machines, Handicapped accessible, Home delivery & serv to Sr ctr & nursing homes, Homebound delivery serv, ILL available, Magnifiers for reading, Notary serv, Outreach serv, Prog for adults, Prog for children & young adult, Story hour, Summer reading prog, Tax forms, Teen prog, Telephone ref, VHS videos, Wheelchair accessible

Open Mon (Winter) 9-7, Tues-Fri 9-5:30, Sat 10-2; Mon-Fri (Summer) 9-5:30, Sat 10-2

Restriction: Circ to mem only

Friends of the Library Group

DICKINSON

P   DICKINSON PUBLIC LIBRARY*, 4411 Hwy 3, 77539. SAN 316-2931. Tel: 281-534-3812. Web Site: www.dickinsonpubliclibrary.org. *Dir,* Vicki McCallister; *Asst Dir,* Kathy Soehl; Staff 1 (MLS 1)

Founded 1966. Pop 20,826; Circ 89,839

Oct 2010-Sept 2011 Income $10,177, State $6,177, City $4,000. Mats Exp $3,221

Library Holdings: Audiobooks 1,132; Bk Titles 35,782; Bk Vols 36,889; Per Subs 79; Videos 1,147

Automation Activity & Vendor Info: (Cataloging) Book Systems, Inc;
(Circulation) Book Systems, Inc; (OPAC) Book Systems, Inc
Wireless access
Partic in Houston Area Research Library Consortium; OCLC Online
Computer Library Center, Inc
Open Mon, Wed & Fri 10-5, Tues & Thurs 10-6, Sat 10-2
Friends of the Library Group

DILLEY

P   DILLEY PUBLIC LIBRARY*, 231 W FM 117, 78017. (Mail add: PO
Box 230, 78017-0230), SAN 378-3960. Tel: 830-965-1951. FAX:
830-965-4131. E-mail: dilpublibrary@yahoo.com. *Dir,* Norma Herrera; *Asst
Librn,* Ermulinda Garcia
Pop 3,674; Circ 6,256
Library Holdings: AV Mats 200; Bk Titles 15,000
Automation Activity & Vendor Info: (Cataloging) Follett Software;
(Circulation) Follett Software; (OPAC) Follett Software
Wireless access
Open Mon-Fri 8-5
Friends of the Library Group

DIME BOX

P   BLACK BRIDGE LIBRARY*, Dime Box Library, 1079 S F Austin Blvd,
77853. (Mail add: PO Box 157, 77853-0157). Tel: 979-884-0124. FAX:
979-884-0106. *Dir,* Tracy Juel; E-mail: tracy.juel@dimebox.txed.net
Library Holdings: Bk Vols 18,000
Wireless access
Mem of Central Texas Library System, Inc
Open Mon-Fri (Winter) 8-5; Tues & Thurs (Summer) 12-6, Wed 10-6

DIMMITT

P   RHOADS MEMORIAL LIBRARY*, 103 SW Second St, 79027. SAN
316-294X. Tel: 806-647-3532. FAX: 806-647-1038. E-mail:
rhoadsmlibrary@gmail.com. Web Site: www.rhoadsmemoriallibrary.org.
Dir, Marie Howell; *Asst Dir,* Sulema Oltivero; Staff 2 (Non-MLS 2)
Founded 1971. Pop 8,285; Circ 13,413
Library Holdings: AV Mats 607; Bk Titles 15,782; Bk Vols 20,000; Per
Subs 40; Talking Bks 526
Automation Activity & Vendor Info: (Cataloging) SirsiDynix;
(Circulation) SirsiDynix; (OPAC) SirsiDynix
Wireless access
Partic in Harrington Library Consortium
Open Tues-Fri 9-6, Sat 9-12

DONNA

P   DONNA PUBLIC LIBRARY*, 301 S Main St, 78537. SAN 316-2958.
Tel: 956-464-2221. FAX: 956-464-2172. E-mail: library@donna.lib.tx.us.
Web Site: www.donna.lib.tx.us. *Dir,* Bruce Kalter; *Asst Dir,* Elodia Rios
Founded 1938. Pop 17,366; Circ 50,134
Library Holdings: Bk Vols 45,715; Talking Bks 254
Special Collections: Spanish Coll; Texas Coll
Automation Activity & Vendor Info: (Cataloging) TLC (The Library
Corporation); (Circulation) TLC (The Library Corporation); (OPAC) TLC
(The Library Corporation)
Database Vendor: Newsbank
Wireless access
Publications: Monthly Calendar; Newsletter (Quarterly)
Mem of Hidalgo County Library System
Open Mon & Fri 8-5, Tues-Thurs 8-8
Friends of the Library Group

DRIPPING SPRINGS

P   DRIPPING SPRINGS COMMUNITY LIBRARY*, 501 Sportsplex Dr,
78620. SAN 376-480X. Tel: 512-858-7825. FAX: 512-858-2639. Web Site:
www.dscl.org. *Dir,* Cara Russell; *Ch,* Marie Kimbrough; Staff 5 (MLS 1,
Non-MLS 4)
Founded 1986. Pop 20,000; Circ 65,561
Jan 2005-Dec 2005 Income $196,540, County $15,570, Locally Generated
Income $15,930, Other $165,040. Mats Exp $23,421, Books $12,078,
Per/Ser (Incl. Access Fees) $2,405, AV Mat $8,938. Sal $97,018
Library Holdings: Bk Titles 40,000; Per Subs 69; Talking Bks 990;
Videos 910
Automation Activity & Vendor Info: (Acquisitions) Biblionix;
(Cataloging) Biblionix; (Circulation) Biblionix
Database Vendor: EBSCOhost, Gale Cengage Learning, OCLC
FirstSearch, ProQuest
Wireless access
Function: Electronic databases & coll, Handicapped accessible, ILL
available, Music CDs, Photocopying/Printing, Prog for children & young
adult, Summer reading prog, Telephone ref, VHS videos
Mem of Central Texas Library System, Inc

Open Mon-Wed 9-7, Thurs 9-8, Fri 9-1, Sat 10-5
Restriction: Non-resident fee
Friends of the Library Group

DUBLIN

P   DUBLIN PUBLIC LIBRARY*, 206 W Blackjack St, 76446. (Mail add:
PO Box 427, 76446-2204), SAN 316-2966. Tel: 254-445-4141. FAX:
254-445-2176. E-mail: dublin.library@ci.dublin.tx.us,
dublinlib@yahoo.com. Web Site: dublinlibrary.org. *Dir,* Sandra Thomas;
Asst Librn, Adina Dunn
Founded 1952. Pop 3,887; Circ 10,734
Oct 2010-Sept 2011 Income $59,319, City $41,853, Locally Generated
Income $15,466, Other $2,000. Mats Exp $6,868, Books $5,368, Per/Ser
(Incl. Access Fees) $200, Micro $200, AV Mat $1,000, Electronic Ref Mat
(Incl. Access Fees) $100. Sal $54,000
Library Holdings: AV Mats 600; Large Print Bks 200; Bk Titles 17,500;
Bk Vols 18,690; Per Subs 30; Talking Bks 200
Special Collections: Erath County Genealogical Society Coll; Local
History Archives
Subject Interests: Genealogy
Automation Activity & Vendor Info: (Acquisitions) AmLib Library
Management System; (Cataloging) AmLib Library Management System;
(OPAC) AmLib Library Management System
Wireless access
Open Tues-Fri 9-6, Sat 9-2

DUMAS

P   KILLGORE MEMORIAL LIBRARY*, Moore County Library, 124 S Bliss
Ave, 79029-3889. SAN 361-5723. Tel: 806-935-4941. FAX: 806-935-3324.
Web Site: www.mocolib.net. *Dir,* Angela Wakefield; E-mail:
director@mocolib.net; Staff 5 (Non-MLS 5)
Founded 1936. Pop 19,875; Circ 97,713
Library Holdings: Bks on Deafness & Sign Lang 12; High Interest/Low
Vocabulary Bk Vols 45; Bk Titles 54,720; Bk Vols 60,506; Per Subs 60
Special Collections: Texas
Partic in Harrington Library Consortium
Open Mon & Thurs 9-8, Tues, Wed & Fri 9-6, Sat 9-1
Friends of the Library Group
Branches: 2
BRITAIN MEMORIAL, PO Box 180, Sunray, 79086-0180, SAN
361-5758. Tel: 806-948-5501. FAX: 806-948-5369. E-mail:
bml@moorecountytexas.com. *Br Mgr,* Deborah Mi
Library Holdings: Bk Titles 49,872
CACTUS BRANCH, 407 Sherri, Cactus, 79013. (Mail add: PO Box 99,
Cactus, 79013-0099). Tel: 806-966-3706. FAX: 806-966-3291. E-mail:
cbl@mocolib.net.
Library Holdings: Bk Titles 3,750
Automation Activity & Vendor Info: (Cataloging) SirsiDynix;
(Circulation) SirsiDynix
Open Mon-Thurs 10-6, Fri 10-5

DUNCANVILLE

P   DUNCANVILLE PUBLIC LIBRARY*, 201 James Collins Blvd, 75116.
SAN 320-8362. Tel: 972-780-5050. Circulation Tel: 972-780-5051.
Reference Tel: 972-780-5052. FAX: 972-780-4958. Web Site:
www.youseemore.com/duncanville. *Librn,* Carla Wolf Bryan; E-mail:
cbryan@ci.duncanville.tx.us; *Ch,* Urla Morgan; *Pub Serv,* Elaine Patrick
Founded 1955. Pop 36,000; Circ 125,000
Library Holdings: Bk Titles 97,000; Bk Vols 105,500; Per Subs 141
Special Collections: Texana; Texas Heritage Resource Center. Oral History
Subject Interests: Genealogy
Automation Activity & Vendor Info: (Acquisitions) TLC (The Library
Corporation); (Cataloging) TLC (The Library Corporation); (Circulation)
TLC (The Library Corporation); (OPAC) TLC (The Library Corporation)
Publications: Duncanville History Videos; Duncanville Treasures Videos
Open Tues-Thurs 10-8, Fri 10-6, Sat 10-5
Friends of the Library Group

EAGLE LAKE

P   EULA & DAVID WINTERMANN LIBRARY*, 101 N Walnut Ave,
77434. SAN 316-2974. Tel: 979-234-5411. FAX: 979-234-5442. E-mail:
wintermannlib@elc.net. *Librn,* Vicki L Powers; Staff 1 (Non-MLS 1)
Founded 1975. Pop 5,610; Circ 15,000
Library Holdings: AV Mats 846; Large Print Bks 120; Bk Titles 16,500;
Bk Vols 17,000; Per Subs 33; Talking Bks 327
Automation Activity & Vendor Info: (Cataloging) Follett Software;
(Circulation) Follett Software
Open Mon-Fri 10-6, Sat 10-2
Friends of the Library Group

EAGLE PASS

P   EAGLE PASS PUBLIC LIBRARY*, 589 Main St, 78852. SAN 316-2982.
Tel: 830-773-2516. FAX: 830-773-4204. E-mail:
librarian@eaglepass.lib.tx.us. Web Site: www.eaglepass.lib.tx.us. *Dir,*
Thomas D Eggers; Staff 1 (MLS 1)
Founded 1939. Pop 40,000
Library Holdings: Bk Titles 60,000; Per Subs 75
Special Collections: Spanish Coll; Texana Coll
Wireless access
Open Mon, Wed & Fri 10-6, Tues & Thurs 10-8, Sat 1-5
Friends of the Library Group

EASTLAND

P   EASTLAND CENTENNIAL MEMORIAL LIBRARY*, 210 S Lamar St,
76448-2794. SAN 316-2990. Tel: 254-629-2281. E-mail:
library@eastland.net.
Founded 1904. Pop 10,838
Library Holdings: Bk Titles 13,092; Bk Vols 15,506
Automation Activity & Vendor Info: (Cataloging) Follett Software;
(Circulation) Follett Software; (OPAC) Follett Software
Open Mon-Fri 12-5

GL TEXAS STATE COURT OF APPEALS*, Eleventh Supreme Judicial
District Law Library, County Courthouse, 100 W Main St, Ste 300, 76448.
SAN 328-6088. Tel: 254-629-2638. FAX: 254-629-2191. Web Site:
www.11thcoa.courts.state.tx.us. *Librn,* Sherry Williamson; E-mail:
sherry.williamson@courts.state.tx.us
Restriction: Open to staff only

EDEN

P   EDEN PUBLIC LIBRARY, 117 Market St, 76837. (Mail add: PO Box
896, 76837-0896), SAN 376-4931. Tel: 325-869-7761. FAX:
325-869-8212. E-mail: eden.library@verizon.net. Web Site:
www.edentexas.com. *Librn,* Tanya Garcia; Staff 1 (Non-MLS 1)
Library Holdings: Bk Vols 20,060
Automation Activity & Vendor Info: (Cataloging) LibLime; (Circulation)
LibLime; (OPAC) LibLime
Wireless access
Mem of Big Country Library System
Open Mon 10:30-5:30, Wed 10:30-5, Fri 11-5:30
Friends of the Library Group

EDINBURG

L   HIDALGO COUNTY LAW LIBRARY*, Courthouse, 100 N Closner,
78539. SAN 328-4743. Tel: 956-318-2155. FAX: 956-381-4269. Web Site:
www.co.hidalgo.tx.us. *Librn,* Angie Chapa; E-mail:
angie.chapa@co.hidalgo.tx.us
Library Holdings: Bk Titles 22,000
Database Vendor: Westlaw
Open Mon-Fri 8-5

R   RIO GRANDE BIBLE INSTITUTE & LANGUAGE SCHOOL*, Richard
Wade & Glen Vyck McKinney Library, 4300 US Hwy 281, 78539-9650.
SAN 316-3016. Tel: 956-380-8100. Circulation Tel: 956-380-8138.
Administration Tel: 956-380-8128. Automation Services Tel: 956-380-8178.
FAX: 956-380-8101. E-mail: biblioteca@riogrande.edu. Web Site:
www.riogrande.edu/English/library.html. *Librn,* Donna Antoniuk; *Librn,*
Maria E Cano; Staff 3 (MLS 2, Non-MLS 1)
Founded 1952. Enrl 200; Fac 21; Highest Degree: Master
Library Holdings: AV Mats 986; Bk Titles 15,850; Bk Vols 31,458; Per
Subs 88; Videos 1,924
Subject Interests: Christian theol works in the Spanish lang, Missions
Automation Activity & Vendor Info: (Cataloging) Follett Software;
(Circulation) Follett Software; (OPAC) Follett Software; (Serials) Follett
Software
Wireless access
Function: Archival coll, Photocopying/Printing, Prof lending libr
Open Mon & Wed 8-11:45, 1-5:45 & 7-8:45, Tues & Thurs 8-9, 10-11:45,
1-5:45 & 7-8:45, Fri 8-11:45 & 1-5:45, Sat 1-5:45
Restriction: Open to students, Pub use on premises

P   DUSTIN MICHAEL SEKULA MEMORIAL LIBRARY*, 1906 S Closner
Blvd, 78539. SAN 316-3008. Tel: 956-383-6246. Interlibrary Loan Service
Tel: 956-383-6247. FAX: 956-318-3123. Web Site: www.edinburg.lib.tx.us.
Dir, Leticia S Leija; *Asst Dir,* Jose Tamez; *Librn,* Clemente Garcia;
E-mail: clem@edinburg.lib.tx.us; *Automation Librn,* Jaime Cardoza;
E-mail: jaime@edinburg.lib.tx.us; *Ch,* Alexa Tressler; E-mail:
alexa@edinburg.lib.tx.us; *Circ,* Elma Guerrero; E-mail:
elma@edinburg.lib.tx.us; *ILL,* Raul Martinez; E-mail:
raul@edinburg.lib.tx.us; *Ref Serv, Ad,* Omero Morales; E-mail:
omero@edinburg.lib.tx.us; *Tech Serv,* Amy Navarro; E-mail:

amy@edinburg.lib.tx.us. Subject Specialists: *Computer tech,* Jaime
Cardoza; *Adult, Mil,* Omero Morales; Staff 10 (MLS 2, Non-MLS 8)
Founded 1967. Pop 64,328; Circ 314,800
Library Holdings: Bk Titles 90,662; Bk Vols 95,000; Per Subs 215
Special Collections: Bilingual-Bicultural (Spanish), bk, flm, per; Literacy
& Adult Basis Education, bk, per, videocassettes; Texana, bk, flm, per
Subject Interests: Ethnic studies, Hist, Spanish, Texana
Automation Activity & Vendor Info: (Cataloging) TLC (The Library
Corporation); (Circulation) TLC (The Library Corporation); (OPAC) TLC
(The Library Corporation)
Database Vendor: EBSCOhost, Gale Cengage Learning, OCLC
FirstSearch
Wireless access
Mem of Hidalgo County Library System
Open Mon-Thurs 8am-9pm, Fri 8-5, Sat 11-3, Sun 1-5
Friends of the Library Group

C   THE UNIVERSITY OF TEXAS-PAN AMERICAN LIBRARY*, 1201 W
University Dr, 78541-2999. SAN 361-5812. Tel: 956-665-3306. Circulation
Tel: 956-665-2005. Reference Tel: 956-665-2752. Administration Tel:
956-665-5005. FAX: 956-665-5396. TDD: 956-665-2763. Web Site:
www.lib.panam.edu. *Dean of Libr,* Dr Farzaneh Razzaghi; Tel:
956-665-2755, E-mail: farzaneh@panam.edu; *Assoc Libr Dir,* Ricardo
Peralez; Tel: 956-665-2758, E-mail: rickp@panam.edu; *Head, Ref,* Jane
Goodman; E-mail: ngoodman@panam.edu; *Coll Develop Librn,* John
Asbell; Tel: 956-665-5282, E-mail: jasbell@panam.edu; *Syst Librn,* Daniel
David McGinnis; Tel: 956-665-2878, E-mail: ddm@panam.edu; *Archivist,
Spec Coll,* Janette Garcia; Tel: 956-665-2990, E-mail: janette@panam.edu;
Doc, Dr David Mizener; Staff 58 (MLS 19, Non-MLS 39)
Founded 1927. Enrl 17,337; Fac 884; Highest Degree: Doctorate
Sept 2006-Aug 2007. Mats Exp $2,110,000, Books $780,000, Per/Ser (Incl.
Access Fees) $785,000, Micro $65,000, AV Mat $10,000, Electronic Ref
Mat (Incl. Access Fees) $450,000, Presv $20,000. Sal $2,057,708 (Prof
$1,012,460)
Library Holdings: AV Mats 25,174; Bks on Deafness & Sign Lang 710;
CDs 1,109; DVDs 212; e-books 45,742; e-journals 33,158; Electronic
Media & Resources 1,319; Bk Vols 598,008; Per Subs 1,846; Videos 5,679
Special Collections: De la Gauza papers; Depository for the Texas
Regional Historical Resource Depository Program, Cameron, Hidalgo, Jim
Hogg, Starr, Webb, Willacy & Zapata Counties; Lower Rio Grande Valley
Coll; Rare Books; Shary papers; University Archives. State Document
Depository; US Document Depository
Subject Interests: Lower Rio Grande Valley
Automation Activity & Vendor Info: (Acquisitions) Innovative Interfaces,
Inc; (Cataloging) Innovative Interfaces, Inc - OCLC; (Circulation)
Innovative Interfaces, Inc; (ILL) Innovative Interfaces, Inc; (OPAC)
Innovative Interfaces, Inc; (Serials) Innovative Interfaces, Inc
Database Vendor: Baker & Taylor, Cambridge Scientific Abstracts,
EBSCOhost, Elsevier MDL, Gale Cengage Learning, ISI Web of
Knowledge, JSTOR, LexisNexis, netLibrary, OCLC FirstSearch, OCLC
WorldCat, OVID Technologies, ProQuest, PubMed, SerialsSolutions,
WebMD, Wiley, Wilson - Wilson Web
Wireless access
Publications: Reflections/Reflecciones (Newsletter)
Partic in OCLC Online Computer Library Center, Inc; Paisano Consortium;
TexSHARE - Texas State Library & Archives Commission; UT-System
Special Services for the Deaf - Assisted listening device
Special Services for the Blind - Assistive/Adapted tech devices, equip &
products
Open Mon-Thurs (Winter) 7:30am-Midnight, Fri 7:30-7, Sat 11-8, Sun
1-Midnight; Mon-Thurs (Summer) 7:30am-11pm, Fri 7:30-5, Sat 10-6
Restriction: Borrowing privileges limited to fac & registered students

EDNA

P   JACKSON COUNTY MEMORIAL LIBRARY*, 411 N Wells St, Rm 121,
77957-2734. SAN 316-3024. Tel: 361-782-2162. FAX: 361-782-6708.
E-mail: jclibrary@jcml-tx.org. Web Site: www.jcml-tx.org. *Dir,* Cherie
Robinson
Pop 15,000
Library Holdings: Bk Titles 40,000; Per Subs 26
Automation Activity & Vendor Info: (Cataloging) Follett Software;
(Circulation) Follett Software
Open Mon-Wed 8:30-5, Thurs 8:30-7, Fri 9-1

EL PASO

J   EL PASO COMMUNITY COLLEGE LIBRARY*, PO Box 20500,
79998-0500. SAN 361-5847. Automation Services Tel: 915-831-2132.
FAX: 915-831-2484. Web Site: www.epcc.edu/library/library.htm. *Dir of
Tech Serv,* Luis Chaparro
Subject Interests: Allied health fields, Mexican-Am mats
Automation Activity & Vendor Info: (Acquisitions) Innovative Interfaces,
Inc; (Cataloging) Innovative Interfaces, Inc; (Circulation) Innovative
Interfaces, Inc; (Course Reserve) Innovative Interfaces, Inc; (ILL)

Innovative Interfaces, Inc; (OPAC) Innovative Interfaces, Inc; (Serials) Innovative Interfaces, Inc
Database Vendor: EBSCOhost, Gale Cengage Learning, OCLC FirstSearch, ProQuest
Wireless access
Partic in Del Norte Biosciences Library Consortium; Dialog Corp; OCLC Online Computer Library Center, Inc
Departmental Libraries:
MISSION DEL PASO CAMPUS LIBRARY, 10700 Gateway East, Rm C-102, 79927. (Mail add: PO Box 20500, 79998-0500). Circulation Tel: 915-831-7057. Reference Tel: 915-831-7040. FAX: 915-831-7041. Web Site: www.epcc.edu/Library/MDP. *Head Librn,* Norma Ballenger; Tel: 915-831-7052; *Supvr,* Sonia Aragon
   Library Holdings: AV Mats 1,302; Bk Vols 24,714
   Automation Activity & Vendor Info: (Acquisitions) Innovative Interfaces, Inc; (Cataloging) Innovative Interfaces, Inc; (Circulation) Innovative Interfaces, Inc; (OPAC) Innovative Interfaces, Inc
   Database Vendor: ARTstor, Baker & Taylor, BioOne, CQ Press, EBSCOhost, Gale Cengage Learning, LexisNexis, OCLC WorldCat, ProQuest, PubMed, TDNet
   Special Services for the Deaf - Sorenson video relay syst
   Special Services for the Blind - Accessible computers; Internet workstation with adaptive software; Telesensory - Genie Pro screen enlarger
   Open Mon-Thurs (Winter) 7:30am-8pm, Fri 7:30-4, Sat 9-1; Mon-Thurs (Summer) 8-5, Fri 8-4
RIO GRANDE CAMPUS LIBRARY, 1111 N Oregon, 79902. (Mail add: PO Box 20500, 79998). Tel: 915-831-4019. *Head Librn,* Charlotte Hollis; E-mail: chollis@epcc.edu; *Pub Serv Librn,* Rebecca Perales; E-mail: rperale4@epcc.edu; *Pub Serv Librn,* G Kristin Sanchez; E-mail: gsanc127@epcc.edu; Staff 9.75 (MLS 5.5, Non-MLS 4.25)
   Enrl 5,600; Fac 7; Highest Degree: Associate
   Library Holdings: AV Mats 1,945; Bk Vols 22,500
   Open Mon-Thurs 7:30am-8:30pm, Fri 7:30-2, Sat 9-3, Sun 1-5
TRANSMOUNTAIN CAMPUS LIBRARY, 9570 Gateway Blvd N, 79924. Tel: 915-831-5092. *Head Librn,* Alberto Villegas; Tel: 915-831-5198, E-mail: albertov@epcc.edu; *Librn,* Deas Campbell; *Librn,* Carlos Humphreys; Staff 3 (MLS 3)
   Library Holdings: AV Mats 3,994; Bk Vols 50,494
   Open Mon-Thurs 7:30am-10pm, Fri 7:30-5, Sat 9-5, Sun 12-4
VALLE VERDE CAMPUS LIBRARY, 919 Hunter St, 79915. (Mail add: PO Box 20500, 79998). Tel: 915-831-2442, 915-831-2645. *Head Librn,* Luis Chaparro; Tel: 915-831-2132, E-mail: lchapa13@epcc.edu; *Pub Serv Librn,* Kerry Ann Gardner; Tel: 915-831-2255
   Library Holdings: AV Mats 2,649; DVDs 1,918; e-books 24,600; Bk Titles 47,443; Bk Vols 56,474
   Open Mon-Thurs 7am-10pm, Fri 7-4, Sat 9-4, Sun 12-4
P   NORTHWEST CAMPUS-JENNA WELCH & LAURA BUSCH COMMUNITY LIBRARY, 6701 S Desert Blvd, 79932. Tel: 915-831-8840. FAX: 915-831-8816. Web Site: dnn.epcc.edu/nwlibrary. *Head Librn,* Monica Wong; *Librn,* Anna Hernandez; *Ref Librn,* Lourdes Garcia; *Supvr, Pub Serv,* Terri Zarate
   Oct 2010-Sept 2011 Income $664,000, County $15,000, Other $649,000. Mats Exp $38,000. Sal $290,200 (Prof $195,000)
   Library Holdings: AV Mats 1,643; Bk Titles 25,000
   Open Mon-Thurs 7:30am-8pm, Fri 7:30-4, Sat 10-4

GL   EL PASO COUNTY LAW LIBRARY*, The Robert J Galvan Law Library, 500 E San Antonio St, Rm 1202, 79901. Tel: 915-546-2245. FAX: 915-542-0440. E-mail: eplawlibrary@epcounty.com. Web Site: www.co.el-paso.tx.us/lawlibrary. *Librn,* Lynn Sanchez; E-mail: lsanchez@epcounty.com; *Asst Librn,* Vicky Corona; E-mail: vcorona@co.el-paso.tx.us
   Library Holdings: Bk Vols 30,000; Per Subs 49
   Wireless access
   Partic in SW Law Librs
   Open Mon-Fri 8-6
   Friends of the Library Group

S   EL PASO MUSEUM OF ART*, Algur H Meadows Art Library, One Art Festival Plaza, 79901. SAN 316-3067. Tel: 915-532-1707. FAX: 915-532-1010. Web Site: www.elpasoartmuseum.org. *In Charge,* Tracy Fontenot
   Library Holdings: Bk Vols 11,000; Per Subs 24
   Special Collections: Renaissance & Baroque Artists Coll
   Subject Interests: Gen, Modern art
   Restriction: Open to pub by appt only

P   EL PASO PUBLIC LIBRARY*, 501 N Oregon St, 79901. SAN 361-5901. Tel: 915-543-5401. FAX: 915-543-5410. Web Site: www.elpasolibrary.org. *Dir,* Dionne Mack-Harvin; Tel: 915-543-5413, E-mail: mackdx@elpasotexas.gov; *Dep Dir of Libr - Main Libr,* Mark Pumphrey; E-mail: pumphreyme@elpasotexas.gov; *Dep Dir of Libr - Spec Projects,* Ivonne Jimenez; Tel: 915-543-5412, E-mail: jimenezir@elpasotexas.gov;

Coordr, Ch Serv, Laurel Indalecio; Tel: 915-543-5470, E-mail: indaleciol@elpasotexas.gov; Staff 168.56 (MLS 43, Non-MLS 125.56)
Founded 1894. Pop 609,415; Circ 2,445,641
Sept 2008-Aug 2009 Income (Main Library and Branch(s)) $8,566,198, State $450,010, City $7,991,362, Federal $98,595, Locally Generated Income $26,231. Mats Exp $691,000, Books $461,298, Per/Ser (Incl. Access Fees) $133,202, Micro $17,000, AV Mat $24,500, Electronic Ref Mat (Incl. Access Fees) $55,000. Sal $7,145,530 (Prof $3,520,112)
Library Holdings: Bk Vols 931,884; Per Subs 355
Special Collections: Raza Coll. State Document Depository; US Document Depository
Subject Interests: Genealogy, Literacy, Local archit, Local hist, Local photog, Mexican Revolutionary, Spanish
Automation Activity & Vendor Info: (Acquisitions) SirsiDynix; (Cataloging) SirsiDynix; (Circulation) SirsiDynix; (ILL) SirsiDynix; (OPAC) SirsiDynix; (Serials) SirsiDynix
Database Vendor: Gale Cengage Learning, ValueLine
Wireless access
Publications: Great Constellations, Tom Lea Bibliography; Henry C Trost, Architect of the Southwest
Mem of Texas Trans-Pecos Regional Library System
Partic in TexSHARE - Texas State Library & Archives Commission
Special Services for the Deaf - Assistive tech
Special Services for the Blind - Assistive/Adapted tech devices, equip & products; Children's Braille; Talking bks
Open Mon-Thurs 10-7, Fri 11-6, Sat 10-6, Sun 12-6
Friends of the Library Group
Branches: 11
ESPERANZA ACOSTA MORENO REGIONAL, 12480 Pebble Hills Blvd, 79938. Tel: 915-921-7001. FAX: 915-856-2977. *Regional Br Mgr,* Ellen Eyberg; E-mail: eybergec@elpasotexas.gov
   Open Mon & Sat 10-6, Tues-Thurs 10-7, Fri 1-6
   Friends of the Library Group
ARMIJO, 620 E Seventh Ave, 79901, SAN 361-5936. Tel: 915-533-1333. FAX: 915-532-1758. E-mail: Armijo@elpasotexas.gov. *Br Mgr,* Martha Andrade; E-mail: andrademi@elpasotexas.gov
   Open Mon 10-6, Tues-Thurs 10-7, Fri 1-6, Sat 10-6
   Friends of the Library Group
RICHARD BURGES REGIONAL, 9600 Dyer, 79924, SAN 361-5960. Tel: 915-759-2400. FAX: 915-759-2424. E-mail: RichardBurges@elpasotexas.gov. *Br Mgr,* Steve Roehling; E-mail: roehlingsr@elpasotexas.gov
   Open Mon & Sat 10-6, Tues-Thurs 10-7, Fri 1-6
   Friends of the Library Group
JOSE CISNEROS CIELO VISTA, 1300 Hawkins, 79907-6803, SAN 361-5995. Tel: 915-594-7680. *Br Mgr,* Cindy McPeters
   Open Mon & Sat 10-6, Tues-Thurs 10-7, Fri 1-6
   Friends of the Library Group
CLARDY FOX BRANCH, 5515 Robert Alva, 79905, SAN 361-6029. Tel: 915-772-0501. FAX: 915-772-7941. *Br Mgr,* Suzanne Marrufo; E-mail: marrufosx@elpasotexas.gov
   Subject Interests: Spanish lang
   Open Mon & Sat 10-6, Tues-Thurs 10-7, Fri 1-6
   Friends of the Library Group
JUDGE EDWARD S MARQUEZ MISSION VALLEY BRANCH, 610 N Yarbrough Dr, 79915, SAN 361-6053. Tel: 915-591-3391. FAX: 915-591-8334. E-mail: judgemarquez@elpasotexas.gov. *Br Mgr,* Fernando Racelis; E-mail: racelisfx@elpasotexas.gov
   Subject Interests: Spanish lang
   Database Vendor: EBSCOhost
   Open Tues & Wed 12-8, Thurs & Sat 10-6, Fri 1-6
   Friends of the Library Group
MEMORIAL PARK, 3200 Copper Ave, 79930, SAN 361-6088. Tel: 915-566-1034. FAX: 915-564-3944. E-mail: memorialpark@elpasotexas.gov. *Br Mgr,* Janie Villasana; E-mail: villasanajc@elpasotexas.gov
   Open Mon & Sat 10-6, Tues-Thurs 10-7, Fri 1-6
   Friends of the Library Group
IRVING SCHWARTZ BRANCH, 1865 Dean Martin, 79936. Tel: 915-857-0594. FAX: 915-857-7218. E-mail: schwartz@elpasotexas.gov. *Br Mgr,* Martha Herrera; E-mail: herreama@elpasotexas.gov
   Open Mon & Sat 10-6, Tues-Thurs 10-7, Fri 1-6
   Friends of the Library Group
DORRIS VAN DOREN REGIONAL, 551 Redd Rd, 79912. Tel: 915-875-0700. FAX: 915-585-1524. E-mail: dorrisVanDoren@elpasotexas.gov. Web Site: www.elpasotexas.gov/library. *Br Mgr,* Patricia Hernandez; E-mail: hernapl@elpasotexas.gov
   Subject Interests: Spanish lang
   Open Tues & Wed 11-8, Thurs & Sat 10-6, Fri 1-6
   Friends of the Library Group

WESTSIDE, 125 Belvidere, 79912, SAN 361-6118. Tel: 915-581-2024. FAX: 915-833-4785. E-mail: westside2@elpasotexas.gov. *Br Mgr,* Cheryl Bernero; E-mail: berneroca@elpasotexas.gov
Open Mon & Sat 10-6, Tues-Thurs 10-7, Fri 1-6
Friends of the Library Group

YSLETA, 9321 Alameda, 79907, SAN 361-6142. Tel: 915-858-0905. FAX: 915-860-8017. E-mail: ysleta@elpasotexas.gov. *Br Mgr,* Aimee Camp; E-mail: campaj@elpasotexas.gov
Subject Interests: Spanish lang
Open Mon & Sat 10-6, Tues-Thurs 10-7, Fri 1-6
Friends of the Library Group
Bookmobiles: 1. Libr Servs Supvr, Sal Gutierrez. Bk titles 51,734

R   FIRST PRESBYTERIAN CHURCH LIBRARY*, 1340 Murchison St, 79902. SAN 316-3083. Tel: 915-533-7551. FAX: 915-534-7167. Web Site: www.pep.org. *In Charge,* Lynette Meyer
Founded 1957
Library Holdings: Bk Titles 3,700
Subject Interests: Hist, Theol
Open Mon-Thurs 8-5, Fri 8-3, Sun 8-12

S   THE GREEN HOUSE CANCER RESOURCE CENTER*, 10460 Vista del Sol, Ste 101, 79925. Tel: 915-562-7660. FAX: 915-562-7841. E-mail: greenhse@rgcf.org. Web Site: www.rgcf.org. *Adminr,* Izzy Mora
Founded 1998
Library Holdings: Bk Vols 6,500
Subject Interests: Cancer, Food & nutrition, Psychosocial aspects, Self help
Function: Audio & video playback equip for onsite use, Bks on cassette, Bks on CD, CD-ROM, Computers for patron use
Open Mon-Fri 9-5
Restriction: Circ to mem only

L   MOUNCE & GREEN, MEYERS, SAFI & GALATZAN*, Law Library, 100 N Stanton, Ste 1000, 79901. SAN 372-1647. Tel: 915-532-2000. FAX: 915-541-1597. Web Site: mgmsg.com. *Librn,* Sylvia T Contreras
Library Holdings: Bk Vols 15,000; Per Subs 15
Restriction: Staff use only

G   NATIONAL PARK SERVICE*, Chamizal National Memorial Library, 800 S San Marcial, 79905. SAN 326-3282. Tel: 915-532-7273, Ext 111. FAX: 915-532-7240. *Curator, Librn,* Catherine Johnson; Tel: 915-532-7273, Ext 110, E-mail: catherine_johnson@nps.gov
Library Holdings: Bk Titles 1,000; Bk Vols 1,500
Special Collections: Museum Collection. Conatins history of the surveying of international boundary, national park service, theater, music and border region
Function: Ref serv available
Open Mon-Fri 8-4:30
Restriction: Non-circulating to the pub

S   SCOTTHULSE, PC*, Law Library, 201 E Main Dr, Ste 1100, 79901. (Mail add: PO Box 99123, 79999-9123), SAN 326-4513. Tel: 915-533-2493. FAX: 915-546-8333. Web Site: scotthulse.com. *In Charge,* Mariana Marrazas
Library Holdings: Bk Titles 650; Bk Vols 15,800; Per Subs 57
Subject Interests: Labor
Publications: Acquisitions List
Restriction: Staff use only

P   TEXAS TRANS-PECOS REGIONAL LIBRARY SYSTEM*, El Paso Public Library, 501 Oregon St N, 79901-1103. SAN 316-3121. Tel: 915-543-5465. FAX: 915-543-5473. *Coordr,* Barbara Valle; E-mail: vallebk@elpasotexas.gov; Staff 3 (MLS 2, Non-MLS 1)
Founded 1969
Sept 2005-Aug 2006 Income $380,721. Mats Exp $149,000. Sal $158,847 (Prof $130,000)
Member Libraries: Alpine Public Library; City of Presidio Library; Clint ISD Public Library; El Paso Public Library; Fort Hancock County Public Library; Fort Stockton Public Library; Grace Grebing Public Library; Imperial Public Library; Iraan Public Library; Jeff Davis County Library; Marfa Public Library; Reeves County Library; Terrell County Public Library; Van Horn City County Library
Partic in Tex State Libr
Open Mon-Fri 8-4:30

AM   UNITED STATES ARMY*, William Beaumont Army Medical Library, WBAMC/MCHM, NTL, 5005 N Piedras St, Rm 2D01, 79920-5001. SAN 361-6177. Tel: 915-742-2537, 915-742-2580. FAX: 915-742-1534. E-mail: wbamc-library@amedd.army.mil. Web Site: wbamclib.amedd.army.mil. *Librn,* Joy Marion; E-mail: joy.b.marion@us.army.mil; Staff 2 (MLS 1, Non-MLS 1)
Founded 1922

Library Holdings: Bk Vols 3,800; Per Subs 165
Special Collections: Military Medical History
Subject Interests: Dentistry, Med, Nursing, Orthopedics, Surgery
Automation Activity & Vendor Info: (Cataloging) Ex Libris Group; (Circulation) Ex Libris Group
Publications: Library Bulletin (Quarterly)
Partic in National Network of Libraries of Medicine; OCLC Online Computer Library Center, Inc
Restriction: Not open to pub, Staff use only

C   UNIVERSITY OF TEXAS AT EL PASO LIBRARY*, 500 W University Ave, 79968-0582. SAN 361-6231. Tel: 915-747-5683. Circulation Tel: 915-747-5672. Interlibrary Loan Service Tel: 915-747-5678. Reference Tel: 915-747-5643. FAX: 915-747-5345. Interlibrary Loan Service FAX: 915-747-5327. E-mail: libraryadmin@utep.edu. Web Site: www.libraryweb.utep.edu. *Assoc VPres, Info Res & Planning,* Robert Stakes; Tel: 915-747-6710, E-mail: rlstakes@utep.edu; *Assoc Librn Dir, Coll & Bibliog Serv,* Carol M Kelley; Tel: 915-747-6710, E-mail: ckelley@utep.edu; *Assoc Librn Dir, Pub Serv,* Luke Jastrzebski; Tel: 915-747-6723, E-mail: ljastrzebski@utep.edu; *Asst Dir, Tech Serv/Cat,* Nancy Hill; Tel: 915-747-6722, E-mail: nhill@utep.edu; *Head, Admin Serv,* Sebastian Diaz; Tel: 915-747-6721, E-mail: sdiaz@utep.edu; *Head, Libr Info Res Serv,* Mary Duffy; Tel: 915-747-6739, E-mail: mduffy@utep.edu; *Access Serv,* Antonio Rodarte; Tel: 915-747-6700, E-mail: arodarte@utep.edu; *Spec Coll & Archives Librn,* Claudia Rivers; Tel: 915-747-6725, E-mail: crivers@utep.edu. Subject Specialists: *Polit sci, Pub admin,* Carol M Kelley; *Hist,* Luke Jastrzebski; *English, Music,* Nancy Hill; *Educ,* Sebastian Diaz; *Sci fict,* Mary Duffy; *Humanities,* Antonio Rodarte; *Sociol, Southwest,* Claudia Rivers; Staff 25 (MLS 21, Non-MLS 4)
Founded 1919. Enrl 16,901; Fac 1,177; Highest Degree: Doctorate
Library Holdings: AV Mats 3,648; e-books 67,761; e-journals 84,202; Microforms 53,893; Bk Titles 773,998; Bk Vols 839,429; Per Subs 3,172
Special Collections: Mexican History Manuscripts Coll, micro; Military History (SLA Marchall Coll); Onamastics Coll; Printing & Bookmaking (Carl Hertzog Coll), bks & papers. Oral History; State Document Depository; US Document Depository
Subject Interests: Art, Border studies, Chicano studies, Composition, Eng, Environ studies, Geol, Hist, Judaica, Mexico, Psychol, Rare bks, Southwest, Southwest region, Southwestern anthrop, Southwestern archit, Western stories
Automation Activity & Vendor Info: (Acquisitions) Innovative Interfaces, Inc; (Cataloging) Innovative Interfaces, Inc; (Circulation) Innovative Interfaces, Inc; (Course Reserve) Innovative Interfaces, Inc; (ILL) Innovative Interfaces, Inc; (Media Booking) Innovative Interfaces, Inc; (OPAC) Innovative Interfaces, Inc; (Serials) Innovative Interfaces, Inc
Database Vendor: ACM (Association for Computing Machinery), Alexander Street Press, American Chemical Society, Amigos Library Services, ARTstor, BioOne, Blackwell's, Cambridge Scientific Abstracts, Children's Literature Comprehensive Database Company (CLCD), EBSCOhost, Elsevier, Emerald, HeinOnline, IEEE (Institute of Electrical & Electronics Engineers), Ingenta, Innovative Interfaces, Inc, ISI Web of Knowledge, JSTOR, LexisNexis, Marcive, Inc, Mergent Online, Modern Language Association, Nature Publishing Group, netLibrary, OCLC WorldCat, Oxford Online, Project MUSE, ProQuest, RefWorks, Sage, ScienceDirect, SerialsSolutions, Wiley InterScience
Wireless access
Function: Res libr
Publications: Keywords (Newsletter)
Partic in Association of Research Libraries (ARL); TexSHARE - Texas State Library & Archives Commission
Special Services for the Blind - Accessible computers; Aids for in-house use; Assistive/Adapted tech devices, equip & products
Open Mon-Thurs 7am-1am, Fri 7am-8pm, Sat 9-6, Sun Noon-1am
Restriction: Open to students, fac & staff
Friends of the Library Group

ELDORADO

P   SCHLEICHER COUNTY PUBLIC LIBRARY, 201 SW Main St, 76936. (Mail add: PO Box 611, 76936-0611), SAN 376-4036. Tel: 325-853-3767. FAX: 325-853-2963. *Librn,* Linda Thomas; Staff 1 (Non-MLS 1)
Library Holdings: Bk Vols 10,000
Automation Activity & Vendor Info: (Acquisitions) Biblionix; (Cataloging) Biblionix; (Circulation) Biblionix
Wireless access
Open Mon-Fri 9-1 & 2-5

ELECTRA

P   ELECTRA PUBLIC LIBRARY*, 401 N Waggoner, 76360. SAN 316-3148. Tel: 940-495-2208. FAX: 940-495-4143. *Dir,* Terry Holbert; E-mail: terryholbert@yahoo.com; *Asst Librn,* Patti Oakley; Staff 2 (MLS 2)
Founded 1925. Pop 3,000; Circ 34,898

Library Holdings: AV Mats 4,456; Bk Titles 20,005; Bk Vols 20,074; Per Subs 54
Special Collections: Hometown Genealogy
Automation Activity & Vendor Info: (Cataloging) Book Systems, Inc; (Circulation) Book Systems, Inc; (OPAC) Book Systems, Inc
Mem of North Texas Library Partners
Special Services for the Blind - Bks on CD; Large print bks
Open Mon-Fri 10-6
Friends of the Library Group

ELGIN

P   ELGIN PUBLIC LIBRARY*, 404 N Main St, 78621. SAN 376-4842. Tel: 512-281-5678. FAX: 512-285-3015. E-mail: librarylisa@elgin.lib.ia.us. Web Site: www.elginpubliclibrary.org. *Dir,* Sandy Ott; Staff 4 (Non-MLS 4)
Founded 1986. Pop 28,239; Circ 80,922
Library Holdings: AV Mats 3,816; CDs 160; Large Print Bks 1,159; Bk Titles 40,762; Bk Vols 42,821; Per Subs 55; Talking Bks 914; Videos 1,495
Automation Activity & Vendor Info: (Cataloging) Follett Software; (Circulation) Follett Software; (OPAC) Follett Software
Mem of Central Texas Library System, Inc
Partic in Tex Share
Open Tues & Thurs 10-7, Wed & Fri 10-6, Sat 10-4
Friends of the Library Group

ELSA

P   ELSA PUBLIC LIBRARY*, 711 N Hidalgo St, 78543. (Mail add: PO Box 1447, 78543-1447), SAN 316-3156. Tel: 956-262-3061. Reference Tel: 956-262-5130. FAX: 956-262-3066. Web Site: www.elsa.lib.tx.us. *Dir,* Hilda Molina; E-mail: hilda@elsa.lib.tx.us; *Head, Ref,* Blanca Garza; *Tech Serv Mgr,* Mateo Castillo; *Ch,* Patty Flores
Founded 1974. Pop 9,500; Circ 38,869
Library Holdings: Bk Titles 27,000; Per Subs 28; Talking Bks 125; Videos 785
Automation Activity & Vendor Info: (Cataloging) SirsiDynix; (Circulation) SirsiDynix
Database Vendor: OCLC FirstSearch, OCLC WorldCat
Wireless access
Function: ILL available
Mem of Hidalgo County Library System
Open Mon-Thurs 9-6, Fri 8:30-5

EMORY

P   RAINS COUNTY PUBLIC LIBRARY*, 150 Doris Briggs Pkwy, 75440-3012. (Mail add: PO Box 189, 75440-0189), SAN 376-4486. Tel: 903-473-5000, Ext 283. FAX: 903-473-1703. *Librn,* Wendy Byrd; E-mail: wendy.byrd@co.raines.tx.us
Library Holdings: Bk Vols 17,000; Per Subs 15
Automation Activity & Vendor Info: (Cataloging) Book Systems, Inc; (Circulation) Book Systems, Inc
Wireless access
Open Mon, Wed & Fri 10-5, Tues & Thurs 12-8, Sat 10-12
Friends of the Library Group

ENNIS

P   ENNIS PUBLIC LIBRARY, 501 W Ennis Ave, 75119-3803. SAN 316-3164. Tel: 972-875-5360. FAX: 972-878-9649. Web Site: www.ennispubliclibrary.com. *Dir,* Raymon Lowry; Staff 6 (MLS 1, Non-MLS 5)
Founded 1939. Pop 18,500; Circ 93,000
Library Holdings: Bks on Deafness & Sign Lang 13; Bk Titles 34,300; Bk Vols 35,000; Per Subs 96
Special Collections: Ennis Historic Archives; Superconducting Super Collidor Archives
Subject Interests: Genealogy, Tex hist
Automation Activity & Vendor Info: (Cataloging) Book Systems, Inc; (Circulation) Book Systems, Inc; (OPAC) Book Systems, Inc; (Serials) Book Systems, Inc
Wireless access
Function: ILL available
Partic in TexSHARE - Texas State Library & Archives Commission
Open Mon-Wed & Fri 10-6, Thurs 10-8, Sat 10-2
Friends of the Library Group

EULESS

P   EULESS PUBLIC LIBRARY*, 201 N Ector Dr, 76039-3595. SAN 316-3172. Tel: 817-685-1679. Circulation Tel: 817-685-1481. Reference Tel: 817-685-1489. FAX: 817-267-1979. Web Site: www.eulesstx.gov/library. *Dir,* Kate Lyon; Tel: 817-685-1482, E-mail: klyon@eulesstx.gov; *Adult Serv,* Susan Neal; Tel: 817-685-1484; *Ch,* Rachel Feltenberger; Tel: 617-685-1486; Staff 28 (MLS 5, Non-MLS 23)

Founded 1961. Pop 52,000; Circ 375,000
Library Holdings: Bk Titles 80,000; Bk Vols 109,000; Per Subs 290
Automation Activity & Vendor Info: (Cataloging) Polaris Library Systems; (Circulation) Polaris Library Systems; (ILL) Polaris Library Systems; (OPAC) Polaris Library Systems
Wireless access
Mem of North Texas Library Partners
Open Mon, Tues & Thurs 10-9, Wed 10-6, Fri & Sat 10-5, Sun 1-5
Friends of the Library Group

EVERMAN

P   EVERMAN PUBLIC LIBRARY*, 100 N Race St, 76140. (Mail add: 212 N Race St, 76140-3297), SAN 376-4621. Tel: 817-551-0726. FAX: 817-551-1999. Web Site: www.evermantx.net/library. *Libr Mgr,* Obed Rodriguez; E-mail: rodriguezobed@yahoo.com; *Libr Asst,* Elizabeth Ann Kendrick; Staff 1 (Non-MLS 1)
Founded 1987. Pop 5,888; Circ 17,357
Library Holdings: AV Mats 1,500; CDs 358; DVDs 700; High Interest/Low Vocabulary Bk Vols 1,000; Large Print Bks 700; Bk Titles 68,000; Per Subs 15; Talking Bks 350; Videos 1,165
Automation Activity & Vendor Info: (Acquisitions) Book Systems, Inc; (Cataloging) Book Systems, Inc; (Circulation) Book Systems, Inc; (Course Reserve) Book Systems, Inc; (ILL) Book Systems, Inc; (Media Booking) Book Systems, Inc; (OPAC) Book Systems, Inc; (Serials) Book Systems, Inc
Database Vendor: OCLC FirstSearch, OCLC WorldCat
Function: CD-ROM, Copy machines, Digital talking bks, e-mail serv, Electronic databases & coll, Handicapped accessible, ILL available, Magnifiers for reading, Mail & tel request accepted, Photocopying/Printing, Prog for children & young adult, Serves mentally handicapped consumers, Spoken cassettes & CDs, Summer reading prog, Tax forms, Telephone ref, VHS videos, Video lending libr, Wheelchair accessible
Mem of North Texas Library Partners
Partic in TexSHARE - Texas State Library & Archives Commission
Open Tues-Thurs 12-8, Fri 12-4, Sat 10-4
Restriction: Access at librarian's discretion, Access for corporate affiliates, Authorized patrons, Authorized scholars by appt, Circ limited, Circ to mem only, Internal use only, Non-circulating coll, Non-circulating of rare bks, Non-circulating to the pub, Pub use on premises, Restricted loan policy, Restricted pub use, Use of others with permission of librn
Friends of the Library Group

FAIRFIELD

P   FAIRFIELD LIBRARY ASSOCIATION, INC*, Mary Moody Northern Municipal Library, 350 W Main, 75840. Tel: 903-389-3574. FAX: 903-389-5636. E-mail: fairfield@members.ctls.net, fairlib1@yahoo.com. *Libr Dir,* John Stevens
Founded 1966. Pop 8,100; Circ 37,000
Library Holdings: Bk Titles 24,451; Per Subs 56
Special Collections: Genealogy; Texas
Wireless access
Mem of Central Texas Library System, Inc
Open Tues-Fri 9:30-5:30

FALFURRIAS

P   ED RACHAL MEMORIAL LIBRARY*, 203 S Calixto Mora Ave, 78355. SAN 316-3202. Tel: 361-325-2144. FAX: 361-325-3743. E-mail: gracielamorales1948@yahoo.com. *Librn,* Enola Garza; E-mail: enolagarza@yahoo.com; Staff 4 (MLS 3, Non-MLS 1)
Founded 1960. Pop 8,005; Circ 55,068
Library Holdings: AV Mats 3,000; Large Print Bks 600; Microforms 300; Bk Vols 38,000; Per Subs 56
Subject Interests: English, Genealogy, Law, Lit
Automation Activity & Vendor Info: (Cataloging) Follett Software; (Circulation) Follett Software; (OPAC) Follett Software
Open Mon-Fri 8-5

FALLS CITY

P   FALLS CITY PUBLIC LIBRARY*, 206 N Irvin, 78113. (Mail add: PO Box 220, 78113-0220), SAN 376-4214. Tel: 830-254-3361. FAX: 830-254-3954. E-mail: fcpublib@yahoo.com. *Dir,* Dixie Mutz
Founded 1975. Pop 1,091
Library Holdings: AV Mats 850; Bk Titles 13,636; Bk Vols 13,924; Per Subs 38; Talking Bks 113
Automation Activity & Vendor Info: (Acquisitions) Biblionix; (Cataloging) Biblionix; (Circulation) Biblionix
Mem of Karnes County Library System
Open Mon-Fri 11:30-5:30

P   KARNES COUNTY LIBRARY SYSTEM*, Falls City Public Library, 206
N Irvin, 78113. (Mail add: PO Box 190, 78113-0190), SAN 316-5388. Tel:
830-254-3361. FAX: 830-254-3954. *Dir,* Dixie Mutz
Founded 1969
Special Collections: Holchak & McClane Coll, scrapbooks; Local History
(M S Yeater Coll), biog, papers
Member Libraries: Falls City Public Library; Karnes City Public Library;
Kenedy Public Library; Runge Public Library
Open Mon-Fri 9-11am

FARMERS BRANCH

J   BROOKHAVEN COLLEGE*, Learning Resources Center, 3939 Valley
View, 75244-4997. SAN 316-3210. Tel: 972-860-4854. Circulation Tel:
972-860-4863. Reference Tel: 972-860-4862. FAX: 972-860-4675. E-mail:
bhref-grp@dcccd.edu. Web Site: www.brookhavencollege.edu/library.
Dean, Sarah Ferguson; E-mail: sferguson@dcccd.edu; *Librn,* Ann Coder;
Librn, Sue Crowson; *Librn,* John Flores; *Librn,* Linda Kleen; *Librn,* Larry
McClung; *Librn,* Lois Wagenseil; Staff 5 (MLS 5)
Founded 1978. Enrl 4,946; Fac 241
Library Holdings: Bk Titles 55,603; Bk Vols 55,890; Per Subs 119
Special Collections: Plotkin Holocaust Coll
Automation Activity & Vendor Info: (Acquisitions) Innovative Interfaces,
Inc; (Cataloging) Innovative Interfaces, Inc; (Circulation) Innovative
Interfaces, Inc; (Course Reserve) Innovative Interfaces, Inc; (ILL)
Innovative Interfaces, Inc; (Media Booking) Innovative Interfaces, Inc;
(OPAC) Innovative Interfaces, Inc; (Serials) Innovative Interfaces, Inc
Database Vendor: Amigos Library Services, EBSCOhost, Innovative
Interfaces, Inc, netLibrary, ProQuest
Wireless access
Open Mon-Thurs 8am-9:30pm, Fri 8-3:30, Sat 10-3 (10-2 Summer)

P   FARMERS BRANCH MANSKE LIBRARY*, 13613 Webb Chapel,
75234-3756. SAN 316-3229. Tel: 972-247-2511. FAX: 972-247-9606. Web
Site: www.farmersbranch.info/library. *Dir,* Belinda Jacks
Founded 1961. Pop 27,600; Circ 29,800
Library Holdings: Bk Titles 88,000; Bk Vols 108,000; Per Subs 250
Subject Interests: Tex hist
Automation Activity & Vendor Info: (Cataloging) SirsiDynix;
(Circulation) SirsiDynix; (OPAC) SirsiDynix
Wireless access
Partic in Dialog Corp; Dow Jones News Retrieval
Open Mon-Thurs 10-9, Fri & Sat 10-6, Sun 1-5

FARMERSVILLE

P   CHARLES J RIKE MEMORIAL LIBRARY*, 203 Orange St, 75442.
(Mail add: PO Box 352, 75442-0352), SAN 322-8053. Tel: 972-782-6681.
FAX: 972-782-7608. Web Site: www.rikelibrary.com. *Librn,* Trisha Dowell;
E-mail: t.dowell@ci.farmersville.tx.us
Founded 1979. Pop 3,000; Circ 26,557
Library Holdings: Bk Titles 28,000
Automation Activity & Vendor Info: (Cataloging) Biblionix; (Circulation)
Biblionix
Open Tues & Thurs 8:30-6, Wed & Fri 8:30-4, Sat 9-2

FERRIS

P   FERRIS PUBLIC LIBRARY*, 301 E Kent St, 75125. SAN 316-3237. Tel:
972-544-3696. Web Site: www.ferris.lib.tx.us.
Founded 1971. Pop 2,600; Circ 2,700
Library Holdings: Bk Titles 15,000; Per Subs 35
Subject Interests: Genealogy
Automation Activity & Vendor Info: (Cataloging) Book Systems, Inc;
(Circulation) Book Systems, Inc; (OPAC) Book Systems, Inc
Wireless access
Partic in TexSHARE - Texas State Library & Archives Commission
Open Mon-Wed 9-5, Thurs 10-5:30

FLATONIA

P   FLATONIA PUBLIC LIBRARY, 208 N Main St, 78941. (Mail add: PO
Box 656, 78941-0656). Tel: 361-772-2088. Administration Tel:
361-217-0342, 361-865-2600. *Head Librn,* Evelyn C Miller; E-mail:
evelynlib@yahoo.com
Founded 1988. Pop 1,397; Circ 2,936
Jan 2012-Jan 2013 Income $2,500
Library Holdings: Large Print Bks 75; Bk Vols 10,000
Wireless access
Open Mon-Fri 3:30-5:30

FLORENCE

P   FLORENCE PUBLIC LIBRARY*, Eula Hunt Beck Public Library, 207 E
Main St, 76527-4048. (Mail add: PO Box 430, 76527-0430), SAN
376-4834. Tel: 254-793-2672. FAX: 254-793-2102. E-mail:
fllib@vvm.com. *Libr Dir,* Charlotte Summers; Staff 1 (MLS 1)
Library Holdings: Bk Vols 16,177; Per Subs 5
Wireless access
Mem of Central Texas Library System, Inc
Open Mon-Fri 8:30-12, Sat 1-5:30

FLORESVILLE

P   SAM FORE JR WILSON COUNTY PUBLIC LIBRARY*, One Library
Lane, 78114. SAN 316-3245. Tel: 830-393-7361. Administration Tel:
830-393-7360. FAX: 830-393-7337. E-mail:
librarian@wilsoncounty.lib.tx.us. *Dir,* Nicki Stohr; E-mail:
librarian@wilsoncounty.lib.tx.us; *Asst Librn, ILL,* Cynthia Peck; E-mail:
assistant@wilsoncounty.lib.tx.us; *Circ Serv Team Leader,* Sheri Mantei;
Cataloger, Vanessa Marrero; *Circ Asst,* Nicole Sauceda. Subject
Specialists: *Genealogy,* Nicki Stohr; Staff 4.5 (MLS 1, Non-MLS 3.5)
Founded 1934. Pop 37,529; Circ 78,036
Library Holdings: AV Mats 3,612; Bk Titles 34,342; Per Subs 37
Special Collections: Texas Reference (local hist & genealogy mat)
Subject Interests: County genealogy, County hist, Texana
Automation Activity & Vendor Info: (Cataloging) Biblionix; (Circulation)
Biblionix; (ILL) OCLC FirstSearch
Database Vendor: OCLC WorldCat
Wireless access
Function: Children's prog, Computers for patron use, Copy machines, Fax
serv, ILL available, Music CDs, Printer for laptops & handheld devices,
Summer reading prog, Tax forms, VHS videos, Winter reading prog
Partic in Tex Share
Open Mon-Wed 9-6, Thurs 9-8, Fri 9-5, Sat 9-1
Friends of the Library Group

FLOWER MOUND

P   FLOWER MOUND PUBLIC LIBRARY*, 3030 Broadmoor Lane, 75022.
SAN 376-4702. Tel: 972-874-6200. FAX: 972-874-6466. E-mail:
fmpl@flower-mound.com. Web Site: fmlibrary.net. *Dir,* Sue Compton; Tel:
972-874-6151, E-mail: sue.compton@flower-mound.com; *Mgr, Ad Serv,*
Becky Getting; Tel: 972-874-6152, E-mail:
becky.getting@flower-mound.com; *Mgr, Ch Serv,* Sue Ridnour; Tel:
972-874-6153, E-mail: sue.ridnour@flower-mound.com; *Mgr, Tech Serv,*
Victoria Kemp; Tel: 972-874-6154, E-mail:
victoria.kemp@flower-mound.com; Staff 23 (MLS 8, Non-MLS 15)
Founded 1984. Pop 64,669; Circ 483,632
Oct 2010-Sept 2011 Income $1,292,104, State $13,222, City $1,278,882.
Mats Exp $168,983, Books $80,687, Per/Ser (Incl. Access Fees) $67,276,
AV Mat $21,020. Sal $1,035,189
Library Holdings: Audiobooks 2,634; AV Mats 12,133; Bks on Deafness
& Sign Lang 31; Braille Volumes 1; CDs 1,900; DVDs 6,198; e-books
2,751; Electronic Media & Resources 30,721; Large Print Bks 1,237; Bk
Titles 78,208; Bk Vols 91,163; Per Subs 197; Talking Bks 249; Videos 943
Automation Activity & Vendor Info: (Acquisitions) Polaris Library
Systems; (Cataloging) Polaris Library Systems; (Circulation) Polaris
Library Systems; (OPAC) Polaris Library Systems
Wireless access
Mem of North Texas Library Partners
Open Mon-Wed 9-9, Thurs 9-5, Fri & Sat 11-5, Sun 1-5
Friends of the Library Group

FLOYDADA

P   FLOYD COUNTY LIBRARY*, 111 S Wall St, 79235. SAN 361-638X.
Tel: 806-983-4922. FAX: 806-983-4922. E-mail: floydlib@amaonline.com.
Librn, Sandra Crawford; Staff 2 (MLS 2)
Pop 10,516; Circ 29,960
Library Holdings: Bk Vols 17,000; Per Subs 20
Automation Activity & Vendor Info: (Cataloging) Follett Software;
(Circulation) Follett Software; (OPAC) Follett Software
Wireless access
Mem of West Texas Library System
Open Mon-Fri 8-5
Friends of the Library Group
Branches: 1
LOCKNEY BRANCH, 124 S Main, Lockney, 79241. (Mail add: PO Box
249, Lockney, 79241-0249), SAN 361-641X. Tel: 806-652-3561. *Librn,*
Neta Marble
Library Holdings: Bk Titles 14,000; Per Subs 12
Automation Activity & Vendor Info: (Cataloging) LibLime;
(Circulation) LibLime; (OPAC) LibLime
Partic in Tex Share
Mem of West Texas Library System

Open Mon-Fri 1-5
Friends of the Library Group

FORNEY

P   FORNEY PUBLIC LIBRARY*, Ellen Brooks West Memorial Library, 800
FM 741 S, 75126. SAN 376-4400. Tel: 972-564-7027. FAX:
972-564-5616. Web Site: www.forneyisd.net. *Librn,* Jo Weiner; E-mail:
jo.weiner@forneyisd.net
Library Holdings: Bk Titles 14,500; Bk Vols 16,000; Per Subs 12
Open Mon, Wed & Thurs 8-7, Tues 8-5, Fri 8-3:45, Sat 10-2

FORT BLISS

UNITED STATES ARMY

A   MICKELSEN COMMUNITY LIBRARY*, Mickelsen Library, Bldg 2E
Sheridan Rd, 79916, SAN 361-6444. Tel: 915-568-6156. Administration
Tel: 915-568-3089. Information Services Tel: 915-568-1491. FAX:
915-568-5754. Web Site: www.blissmwr.com/library. *Chief Librn,*
Michael W McDaniel; E-mail: michael.w.mcdaniel2@us.army.mil; Staff
5 (MLS 1, Non-MLS 4)
Founded 1942
Library Holdings: Bk Titles 34,370; Bk Vols 34,788; Per Subs 65
Subject Interests: Mil hist, Southwest
Automation Activity & Vendor Info: (Acquisitions) Innovative
Interfaces, Inc - Millenium; (Cataloging) Innovative Interfaces, Inc -
Millenium; (Circulation) Innovative Interfaces, Inc - Millenium; (Course
Reserve) Innovative Interfaces, Inc - Millenium; (ILL) OCLC; (OPAC)
Innovative Interfaces, Inc - Millenium
Function: Audio & video playback equip for onsite use, Electronic
databases & coll, Handicapped accessible, ILL available, Prog for
children & young adult, Spoken cassettes & CDs, Summer reading prog,
Tax forms, VHS videos, Wheelchair accessible
Partic in Fedlink; OCLC Online Computer Library Center, Inc; Tralinet;
United States Army Training & Doctrine Command
Publications: Library Handbook
Open Mon-Fri 8-6, Sat 9-6
Restriction: Authorized patrons

A   SERGEANTS MAJOR ACADEMY LEARNING RESOURCES
CENTER*, Commandant USASMA, Biggs Field, 11291 Sgt E Churchill
St, 79918-8002, SAN 361-6568. Tel: 915-744-8176, 915-744-8451.
Administration Tel: 915-744-8122. FAX: 915-744-8484. E-mail:
atss-scr@conus.army.mil. Web Site: usasma.bliss.army.mil. *Supvry Librn,*
Angelica Garcia; E-mail: angelica.garcia1@us.army.mil; Staff 5 (MLS 2,
Non-MLS 3)
Founded 1972
Library Holdings: Bk Titles 29,601; Bk Vols 39,655; Per Subs 249
Special Collections: Army Unit History Coll; Autographed Coll
Subject Interests: Mil hist, Mil sci
Automation Activity & Vendor Info: (Cataloging) SIRSI WorkFlows;
(Circulation) SIRSI WorkFlows; (ILL) OCLC FirstSearch; (OPAC)
SIRSI-iLink
Database Vendor: Baker & Taylor, EBSCOhost, JSTOR, OCLC
FirstSearch, OCLC WorldCat, ProQuest, SirsiDynix, WT Cox
Partic in Fedlink; OCLC Online Computer Library Center, Inc; Tradoc
Publications: LRC Brochure (Research guide); Periodical Holdings
(Union list of periodicals)
Open Mon-Thurs 7:30-6, Fri 7:30-4:30, Sat 9-1
Restriction: Circ limited, Pub use on premises

FORT DAVIS

P   JEFF DAVIS COUNTY LIBRARY*, 100 Memorial Sq, 79734. (Mail add:
PO Box 1054, 79734-1054), SAN 376-4338. Tel: 432-426-3802. FAX:
432-426-2225. E-mail: librarian426@sbcglobal.net. *Librn,* Toi Fisher
Library Holdings: Bk Vols 41,000; Per Subs 42
Automation Activity & Vendor Info: (Cataloging) Follett Software;
(Circulation) Follett Software; (OPAC) Follett Software
Wireless access
Mem of Texas Trans-Pecos Regional Library System
Open Mon-Fri 10-6
Friends of the Library Group

S   NATIONAL PARK SERVICE*, Fort Davis National Historic Site Library,
101 Lt Flipper Dr, 79734. (Mail add: PO Box 1379, 79734-0015), SAN
323-8709. Tel: 432-426-3224. Reference Tel: 432-426-3224, Ext 25. FAX:
432-426-3122. Web Site: www.nps.gov/foda.
Founded 1963
Library Holdings: Bk Titles 2,500
Special Collections: Military Career of Lt Henry O Flipper; Oral History
(Reminiscences of Second & Third Generation Fort Descendents); The
Buffalo Soldiers & Colonel Benjamin H Grierson, 10th US Cavalry;
Western US Military History. Oral History
Function: Res libr
Restriction: Open by appt only, Open to researchers by request, Staff use
only

FORT HANCOCK

P   FORT HANCOCK COUNTY PUBLIC LIBRARY*, 101 School Dr,
79839. (Mail add: PO Box 98, 79839-0098), SAN 376-4354. Tel:
915-769-3811, Ext 1306. FAX: 915-769-3940. *Dir,* Galindo Lily; E-mail:
lgalindo@forthancockisd.net; Staff 1 (Non-MLS 1)
Founded 1990. Pop 1,200
Library Holdings: Bk Vols 12,500; Per Subs 21
Automation Activity & Vendor Info: (Cataloging) Follett Software;
(Circulation) Follett Software; (OPAC) Follett Software
Mem of Texas Trans-Pecos Regional Library System
Open Mon-Fri 8-4

FORT HOOD

UNITED STATES ARMY

A   CASEY MEMORIAL LIBRARY, 72nd St & 761st Tank Battalion, Bldg
3202, 76544-5024. Tel: 254-287-0025. Circulation Tel: 254-287-4921.
Reference Tel: 254-287-5202. FAX: 254-288-4029. Web Site:
www.hoodmwr.com/casey_library.htm. *Dir,* Pamela Shelton; E-mail:
pamela.a.shelton.naf@mail.mil; *Syst Librn,* Jane Mohammadi; E-mail:
jane.l.mohammadi.naf@mail.mil; *Pub Serv,* Jennifer Hauschildt; E-mail:
jennifer.k.hauschildt.naf@mail.mil; *Ref Serv,* George R Jung; E-mail:
george.r.jung.naf@mail.mil; Staff 18 (MLS 5, Non-MLS 13)
Founded 1942
Oct 2011-Sept 2012 Income $1,200,000. Mats Exp $103,000, Books
$60,000, Per/Ser (Incl. Access Fees) $15,000, AV Mat $20,000,
Electronic Ref Mat (Incl. Access Fees) $8,000. Sal $550,000 (Prof
$300,000)
Library Holdings: CDs 1,200; DVDs 5,000; e-books 5,000; Bk Titles
70,000; Bk Vols 90,000; Per Subs 204
Subject Interests: Gen reading, Grad, Mil sci, Undergrad studies
Automation Activity & Vendor Info: (Cataloging) Innovative Interfaces,
Inc - Millenium; (Circulation) Innovative Interfaces, Inc - Millenium;
(ILL) OCLC Connexion; (OPAC) Innovative Interfaces, Inc - Millenium
Function: Audio & video playback equip for onsite use, Bks on cassette,
Bks on CD, Computer training, Computers for patron use, Copy
machines, Govt ref serv, ILL available, Music CDs, Prog for adults, Prog
for children & young adult, Ref & res, Summer reading prog, Tax forms,
Telephone ref, Video lending libr
Partic in OCLC Online Computer Library Center, Inc; Worldcat
Open Mon-Thurs 10-8, Fri & Sat 10-6, Sun 12-8

AM   MEDICAL LIBRARY*, Bldg 36000, Carl R Darnall Medical Ctr,
76544-5063, SAN 361-6657. Tel: 254-288-8366. FAX: 254-288-8368.
Librn, Beatrice Nichols; *Asst Librn,* Cathy Newell
Founded 1952
Library Holdings: Bk Vols 8,000; Per Subs 195
Subject Interests: Basic sci, Dentistry, Med, Specialities, Surgical
Automation Activity & Vendor Info: (Cataloging) Ex Libris Group;
(Circulation) Ex Libris Group; (OPAC) Ex Libris Group
Partic in Dialog Corp; Docline; National Network of Libraries of
Medicine; OCLC Online Computer Library Center, Inc; S Cent Regional
Libr Prog
Restriction: Staff use only

FORT SAM HOUSTON

UNITED STATES ARMY

AM   BROOKE ARMY MEDICAL CENTER LIBRARY, Medical Library
MCHE-EDL, 3551 Roger Brooke Dr, Bldg 3600, Rm 371-17,
78234-6200, SAN 361-6711. Tel: 210-916-1119. Interlibrary Loan
Service Tel: 210-916-5673. Administration Tel: 210-916-0285.
Information Services Tel: 210-916-2182. FAX: 210-916-5709. E-mail:
medicallibrary.bamc@amedd.army.mil. Web Site:
www.bamc.amedd.army.mil. *Librn,* Beverly Rakowitz; E-mail:
beverly.rakowitz@amedd.army.mil; *Cat,* Craig Wilcox; E-mail:
robert.wilcox@amedd.army.mil; *ILL,* Karen Degroat; *Ser,* Grace
McFarland; Staff 5 (MLS 1, Non-MLS 4)
Founded 1914
Library Holdings: Bk Vols 1,500; Per Subs 173
Subject Interests: Clinical med, Dentistry, Nursing
Automation Activity & Vendor Info: (Acquisitions) Ex Libris Group;
(Cataloging) Ex Libris Group; (Circulation) Ex Libris Group; (OPAC) Ex
Libris Group; (Serials) Ex Libris Group
Database Vendor: Dialog, DynaMed, EBSCOhost, Elsevier, Ex Libris
Group, OCLC WorldCat, OVID Technologies, ScienceDirect, UpToDate
Function: Res libr
Restriction: Staff use only

A   KEITH A CAMPBELL MEMORIAL LIBRARY*, 2601 Harney Rd, Ste
29, 78234-5029, SAN 361-6770. Tel: 210-221-4387, 210-221-4702.
Automation Services Tel: 210-221-4170. FAX: 210-227-5921. Web Site:
www.campbellmemoriallibraryfsh.com. *Libr Mgr,* Robbye Durham;
E-mail: robbye.durham@us.army.mil; *Ref Librn,* Susan Weart Artiglia;
E-mail: susan.artiglia@us.army.mil; *Ref Librn,* Dena Melvin; E-mail:
dena.melvin@us.army.mil; Staff 3 (MLS 3)

Founded 1918
Library Holdings: Bk Titles 82,000; Bk Vols 98,000; Per Subs 245
Subject Interests: Mil hist, Patient educ
Automation Activity & Vendor Info: (Cataloging) Innovative Interfaces, Inc; (Circulation) Innovative Interfaces, Inc; (ILL) OCLC Online; (Media Booking) Baker & Taylor; (OPAC) Innovative Interfaces, Inc - Millenium
Database Vendor: CountryWatch, EBSCO Auto Repair Reference, EBSCOhost, Gale Cengage Learning, Innovative Interfaces, Inc, OCLC WorldCat, WT Cox
Function: Bks on cassette, Bks on CD, Children's prog, Computers for patron use, Copy machines, Electronic databases & coll, Fax serv, Free DVD rentals, Handicapped accessible, ILL available, Masonic res mat, Music CDs, Online cat, Online searches, Orientations, Photocopying/Printing, Preschool outreach, Prog for children & young adult, Ref serv available, Ref serv in person, Scanner, Spoken cassettes & CDs, Spoken cassettes & DVDs, Story hour, Summer reading prog, Tax forms, Telephone ref, VHS videos, Wheelchair accessible
Partic in OCLC Online Computer Library Center, Inc
Open Tues-Fri 9-8, Sat & Sun 11-8
Restriction: Authorized personnel only, Borrowing requests are handled by ILL, Circ to mem only, In-house use for visitors

AM INSTITUTE OF SURGICAL RESEARCH LIBRARY, 3698 Chambers Pass, Bldg 3611, 78234-6315. Tel: 210-539-4559. FAX: 210-539-1460. E-mail: isr.library@amedd.army.mil. *Libr Mgr,* Gerri Trumbo; *Libr Tech,* Frank Hernandez
Library Holdings: e-journals 121; Bk Vols 3,000; Per Subs 125
Subject Interests: Med
Automation Activity & Vendor Info: (Cataloging) Ex Libris Group
Database Vendor: Medline, PubMed
Restriction: Staff use only

AM STIMSON LIBRARY*, Medical Department Center & School, 3630 Stanley Rd, Bldg 2840, Ste 106, 78234-6100, SAN 361-6746. Tel: 210-221-6900. Interlibrary Loan Service Tel: 210-221-6230. Reference Tel: 210-221-6249. FAX: 210-221-8264. E-mail: stimson.library@amedd.army.mil. Web Site: ameddlib.amedd.army.mil, digitallib.amedd.army.mil, www.cs.amedd.army.mill/stimlib. *Dir,* Norma L Sellers; E-mail: norma.sellers@amedd.army.mil; *Ref,* Joan Bares; *Tech Serv,* Anne Mitchell; Staff 11 (MLS 4, Non-MLS 7)
Founded 1932
Library Holdings: e-journals 8,000; Bk Titles 30,000; Bk Vols 60,000; Per Subs 600
Subject Interests: Allied health, Anesthesiology, Healthcare admin, Mil med, Nursing, Pub health
Automation Activity & Vendor Info: (Acquisitions) Ex Libris Group; (Cataloging) Ex Libris Group; (Circulation) Ex Libris Group; (Course Reserve) Ex Libris Group; (ILL) Ex Libris Group; (OPAC) Ex Libris Group; (Serials) Ex Libris Group
Database Vendor: DynaMed, ebrary, EBSCOhost, MD Consult, Medline, Natural Standard, netLibrary, OCLC WorldCat, OVID Technologies, UpToDate
Function: ILL available
Partic in Coun of Res & Acad Librs; Fedlink; Health Oriented Libraries of San Antonio (HOLSA)
Restriction: Not open to pub

FORT STOCKTON

P FORT STOCKTON PUBLIC LIBRARY*, 500 N Water St, 79735. SAN 316-327X. Tel: 432-336-3374. FAX: 432-336-6648. E-mail: info@fort-stockton.lib.tx.us. Web Site: www.fort-stockton.lib.tx.us. *County Librn, Dir,* Elva Valadez; E-mail: director@fort-stockton.lib.tx.us; *Acq, Asst Dir, Cat,* Debra Whitfield; E-mail: dwhitfield@fort-stockton.lib.tx.us; *AV Coll, Syst Adminr,* Sarah Pacheco; E-mail: sbernal@fort-stockton.lib.tx.us; *Circ,* Rebecca Gonzalez; E-mail: gonzalez@fort-stockton.lib.tx.us; *Circ,* Patsy Quintella; E-mail: pquintella@fort-stockton.lib.tx.us; Staff 7 (Non-MLS 7)
Founded 1911. Pop 12,000; Circ 120,000
Jan 2011-Dec 2011 Income $7,000. Mats Exp $4,088, AV Equip $3,007, AV Mat $1,081
Library Holdings: AV Mats 1,226; CDs 733; DVDs 754; Large Print Bks 1,064; Music Scores 85; Bk Titles 48,144; Bk Vols 52,218; Per Subs 164; Videos 2,234
Subject Interests: Genealogy, Southwest
Automation Activity & Vendor Info: (Acquisitions) LibLime; (Cataloging) LibLime; (Circulation) LibLime; (ILL) OCLC; (OPAC) LibLime
Database Vendor: EBSCOhost, netLibrary, Newsbank, OCLC FirstSearch, OCLC WorldCat
Wireless access
Function: ILL available
Publications: FSPL Monthly News; Young Adult Writers & Artists (YAWA) (Annually)
Mem of Texas Trans-Pecos Regional Library System
Open Mon, Wed & Fri 9-6, Tues & Thurs 10-8, Sat 9-3
Friends of the Library Group

FORT WORTH

S BELL HELICOPTER TEXTRON, INC, Engineering & XworX Library, 600 E Hurst Blvd, 76053. (Mail add: PO Box 482, MS 1302, 76101-0482), SAN 316-330X. Tel: 817-280-3608. FAX: 817-278-3608. *Sr Librn,* Donald A Welch; E-mail: dwelch@bh.com; Staff 1 (MLS 1)
Founded 1955
Library Holdings: Bk Titles 3,200; Per Subs 20
Special Collections: Centers of Excellence for Rotary Wing Study & Technology
Subject Interests: Aeronaut, Astronautics, Aviation, Composite mat, Helicopters
Wireless access
Restriction: Staff use only
Branches:
ILS LIBRARY, 3000 S Norwood Dr, Hurst, 76053. (Mail add: PO Box 482, 76101-0482), SAN 372-9923. Tel: 817-280-2001.

P BLUE MOUND COMMUNITY LIBRARY*, 1600 Bell Avenue, 76131-1002. SAN 316-1099. Tel: 817-847-4095. FAX: 817-232-8050. E-mail: bluemoundlib2004@sbcglobal.net. *Librn,* Billie Hamilton
Pop 2,500; Circ 5,745
Library Holdings: Bk Vols 13,000; Per Subs 10
Automation Activity & Vendor Info: (Cataloging) Follett Software; (Circulation) Follett Software
Mem of North Texas Library Partners
Open Tues-Fri 10-5, Sat 10-2

S BOTANICAL RESEARCH INSTITUTE OF TEXAS LIBRARY*, 500 E Fourth St, 76102. SAN 374-6631. Tel: 817-332-4441. FAX: 817-332-4112. E-mail: info@brit.org. Web Site: www.brit.org/library. *Librn,* Gary L Jennings; E-mail: gjennings@brit.org; Staff 1 (MLS 1)
Founded 1987
Library Holdings: Bk Titles 18,000; Bk Vols 75,000; Per Subs 1,100
Special Collections: Botany, Taxonomy (Lloyd Shinners Coll in Systematic Botany)
Wireless access
Function: Ref serv available
Publications: Journal of the Botanical Research Institute of Texas; SIDA Botanical Miscellaney
Partic in Amigos Library Services, Inc
Open Mon-Fri 9-5

S AMON CARTER MUSEUM OF AMERICAN ART, Research Library, 3501 Camp Bowie Blvd, 76107-2695. SAN 316-3318. Tel: 817-738-1933. Reference Tel: 817-989-5040. FAX: 817-989-5079. E-mail: library@cartermuseum.org. Web Site: www.cartermuseum.org/library. *Libr Dir,* Samuel Duncan; *Archivist, Ref Serv Mgr,* Jonathan Frembling; E-mail: jon.frembling@cartermuseum.org; Staff 2 (MLS 1, Non-MLS 1)
Founded 1961
Library Holdings: Microforms 66,000; Bk Titles 50,000; Bk Vols 55,000; Per Subs 120
Special Collections: 19th-century US Newspapers, micro; American Artist & Photographer Coll, bio/ephemera files; American Illustrated Book Coll; Archives of American Art Associated Research Center, unrestricted micro; Auction Catalogs; Eliot Porter Archives; Laura Gilpin Archives; Roman Bronze Works Archives
Subject Interests: Am art, Am photog, Hist of the Am West
Automation Activity & Vendor Info: (Cataloging) Ex Libris Group; (OPAC) Ex Libris Group
Function: Archival coll, Art exhibits, Computers for patron use, Copy machines, Doc delivery serv, e-mail serv, Electronic databases & coll, Exhibits, ILL available, Microfiche/film & reading machines, Newsp ref libr, Online searches, Outside serv via phone, mail, e-mail & web, Pub access computers, Ref & res, Ref serv available, Ref serv in person, Res libr, Scanner
Partic in Amigos Library Services, Inc; Cultural District Library Consortium (CDLC); OCLC Online Computer Library Center, Inc; OCLC Research Library Partnership
Open Wed & Fri 11-4, Thurs 11-7
Restriction: Closed stack, Lending to staff only, Non-circulating to the pub, Open to pub with supv only, Pub use on premises, Restricted borrowing privileges

P FORT WORTH LIBRARY*, Central Library, 500 W Third St, 76102. SAN 361-6800. Tel: 817-871-7701. Circulation Tel: 817-871-7715. Interlibrary Loan Service Tel: 817-871-7731. Administration Tel: 817-871-7705. FAX: 817-871-7734. TDD: 817-871-8926. E-mail: librarywebmail@fortworthgov.org. Web Site: www.forthworthtexas.gov. *Dir,* Dr Gleneice A Robinson; Tel: 817-871-7706; *Circ Supvr,* Virginia Gonzalez; Tel: 817-871-7795; *Tech Coordr,* Edward McCree; Tel: 817-871-8960; *Adult Serv,* Loretta Hart; *Genealogy Serv,* Donna Kruse; Tel: 817-871-7740; Staff 209 (MLS 80, Non-MLS 129)
Founded 1901

Library Holdings: Bk Titles 990,293; Bk Vols 2,240,515; Per Subs 1,392
Special Collections: Bookplates; Early Children's Books; Earth Science; Fort Worth History/Archives; Genealogy Coll; Popular Sheet Music; Postcards. Oral History; State Document Depository; US Document Depository
Automation Activity & Vendor Info: (Cataloging) SirsiDynix; (Circulation) SirsiDynix; (OPAC) SirsiDynix; (Serials) SirsiDynix
Database Vendor: Dialog, EBSCOhost, Gale Cengage Learning, LexisNexis, OCLC FirstSearch, SirsiDynix
Wireless access
Mem of North Texas Library Partners
Special Services for the Deaf - TDD equip
Open Mon, Wed, Fri & Sat 10-6, Tues & Thurs 12-8, Sun 1-5
Restriction: Residents only
Friends of the Library Group
Branches: 13
BOLD - BUTLER OUTREACH LIBRARY DIVISION, 1801 North/South Freeway, 76102-5742. (Mail add: 500 W Third St, 76102-7305). Tel: 817-338-1467.
   Library Holdings: Bk Vols 1,263
   Open Tues-Sat 9-6
   Friends of the Library Group
DIAMOND HILL/JARVIS BRANCH, 1300 NE 35th St, 76106, SAN 323-8385. Tel: 817-624-7331. FAX: 817-625-4029. *Librn,* Mary Sexton
   Library Holdings: Bk Vols 49,977
   Partic in Tex Share
   Open Mon 12-8, Tues-Sat 10-6
   Friends of the Library Group
EAST BERRY, 4300 E Berry St, 76105, SAN 361-6959. Tel: 817-536-1945. FAX: 817-536-6253. *Br Mgr,* Mary Sikes; Staff 7 (MLS 2, Non-MLS 5)
   Library Holdings: Bk Vols 53,699
   Open Mon, Tues & Thurs 10-6, Wed 12-8, Sat 10-8
   Friends of the Library Group
EAST REGIONAL, 6301 Bridge St, 76105, SAN 376-9321. Tel: 817-871-6436. FAX: 817-871-6440. *Mgr,* Barbara Henderson; Staff 6 (MLS 3, Non-MLS 3)
   Founded 1943
   Library Holdings: Bk Vols 56,991
   Open Mon & Wed 12-8, Tues, Thurs & Sat 10-6
   Friends of the Library Group
ESKILLS LIBRARY & JOB CENTER, 5651 E Lancaster, 76112, SAN 361-6835. Tel: 817-451-0916. FAX: 817-496-8931. *Librn,* L G Swift
   Library Holdings: Bk Vols 67,449
   Open Mon 4-8, Tues-Thurs 10-6, Fri 1-5
   Friends of the Library Group
NORTHSIDE, 601 Park St, 76106, SAN 361-686X. Tel: 817-626-8241. FAX: 817-625-0702. *Librn,* Sarah Harris
   Library Holdings: Bk Vols 46,225
   Open Tues & Thurs 11-8, Wed, Fri & Sat 10-6
   Friends of the Library Group
RIDGLEA, 3628 Bernie Anderson Ave, 76116-5403, SAN 361-7017. Tel: 817-737-6619. FAX: 817-763-8404. *Librn,* Rebecca Caldow
   Library Holdings: Bk Vols 95,152
   Open Mon 12-8, Tues, Wed, Fri & Sat 10-6
   Friends of the Library Group
RIVERSIDE, 2913 Yucca Ave, 76111, SAN 361-6894. Tel: 817-392-5560. FAX: 817-392-5403. *Mgr,* Dr George Thadathil; E-mail: george.thadathil@fortworthgov.org; Staff 3 (MLS 3)
   Founded 1966
   Library Holdings: Bk Vols 55,413
   Special Collections: Spanish Coll; Vietnamese Coll, bks, CDs, DVDs
   Function: Adult literacy prog, Audiobks via web, AV serv, Bilingual assistance for Spanish patrons, Bks on CD, Children's prog, Citizenship assistance, Computer training, Computers for patron use, Copy machines, e-mail serv, E-Reserves, Electronic databases & coll, Family literacy, Handicapped accessible, ILL available, Literacy & newcomer serv, Magnifiers for reading, Mail & tel request accepted, Mus passes, Music CDs, Online cat, Orientations, OverDrive digital audio bks, Photocopying/Printing, Prog for children & young adult, Pub access computers, Ref & res, Ref serv in person, Senior computer classes, Spoken cassettes & CDs, Spoken cassettes & DVDs, Story hour, Summer reading prog, Tax forms, Teen prog, Telephone ref, Wheelchair accessible
   Open Mon, Wed, Fri & Sat 10-6, Tues 12-8
   Friends of the Library Group
SEMINARY SOUTH, 501 E Bolt St, 76110, SAN 361-6924. Tel: 817-926-0215. FAX: 817-926-1703. *Librn,* Peter Fekety; *Asst Librn,* Doreen Boyd; Staff 6 (MLS 2, Non-MLS 4)
   Library Holdings: Bk Vols 66,333
   Open Mon, Wed, Thurs & Sat 10-6, Tues 12-8
   Friends of the Library Group
SHAMBLEE, 1062 Evans Ave, 76104-5135, SAN 361-6916. Tel: 817-392-5580. FAX: 817-392-5583. *Br Mgr,* Sheila Barnett
   Library Holdings: Bk Vols 32,337

Open Mon 9-8, Tues, Wed, Fri & Sat 10-6
Friends of the Library Group
SOUTHWEST REGIONAL, 4001 Library Lane, 76109, SAN 328-7327. Tel: 817-782-9853. FAX: 817-732-8714. *Br Mgr,* L G Swift
   Library Holdings: Bk Vols 131,489
   Open Mon, Wed & Sat 10-6, Tues & Thurs 12-8
   Friends of the Library Group
SUMMERGLEN, 4205 Basswood Blvd, 76137-1402. Tel: 817-232-0478. FAX: 817-232-1065. *Br Mgr,* Robert Rinkin
   Library Holdings: Bk Vols 43,744
   Automation Activity & Vendor Info: (Cataloging) Follett Software; (Circulation) Follett Software; (ILL) Follett Software; (OPAC) Follett Software
   Partic in Tex Share
   Open Mon-Wed & Sat 10-6, Thurs 12-8
   Friends of the Library Group
WEDGWOOD, 3816 Kimberly Lane, 76133, SAN 361-6983. Tel: 817-292-3368. FAX: 817-346-1862. *Br Mgr,* Sylvia Polk; Staff 4.5 (MLS 4, Non-MLS 0.5)
   Founded 1962. Circ 277,105
   Library Holdings: Bk Titles 23,400; Bk Vols 35,498; Per Subs 38
   Automation Activity & Vendor Info: (Cataloging) Horizon; (Circulation) Horizon; (OPAC) Horizon
   Open Mon & Wed-Fri 10-6, Tues 12-8
   Friends of the Library Group

S   FORT WORTH MUSEUM OF SCIENCE & HISTORY LIBRARY, 1600 Gendy St, 76107. SAN 316-3369. Tel: 817-255-9305. FAX: 817-255-9595. Web Site: www.fortworthmuseum.org. *Archivist, Res Librn,* Tiffany Schureman; E-mail: tschureman@fwmsh.org; Staff 1 (MLS 1)
   Founded 1954
   Library Holdings: Bk Vols 6,000
   Special Collections: Institutional Archives; Stock Show & Rodeo History 1938 to 1999 (Fort Worth Stock Show Archives)
   Subject Interests: Archaeology, Astronomy, Ethnology, Geol, Local hist, Museology, Natural sci, Texana
   Function: Archival coll, For res purposes, Photocopying/Printing, Ref serv available, Res libr, Telephone ref
   Restriction: Circ limited, Closed stack, In-house use for visitors, Non-circulating to the pub, Open by appt only

R   INDEPENDENT BAPTIST COLLEGE LIBRARY*, 5101 Western Center Blvd, 76137. SAN 324-1858. Tel: 817-514-6364. FAX: 817-281-8257. E-mail: ibcsvbc@juno.com. *Librn,* Beverly Dotson
   Founded 1964
   Library Holdings: Bk Vols 12,000; Per Subs 50
   Subject Interests: Bible, Educ, Music, Theol
   Restriction: Students only

L   KELLY, HART & HALLMAN*, Law Library, Chase Bldg, 201 Main St, Ste 2500, 76102. SAN 372-1639. Tel: 817-332-2500. FAX: 817-878-9280. Web Site: www.khh.com. *Librn,* Amy E Yawn; Fax: 817-878-9822, E-mail: amy_yawn@khh.com
   Library Holdings: Bk Vols 18,000; Per Subs 45
   Subject Interests: General law
   Wireless access
   Restriction: Staff use only

S   KIMBELL ART MUSEUM LIBRARY, 3333 Camp Bowie Blvd, 76107. SAN 316-3415. Tel: 817-332-8451. FAX: 817-877-1264. Web Site: www.kimbellart.org. *Librn,* Chia-Chun Shih; *Assoc Librn,* Stephen R Gassett
   Founded 1967
   Library Holdings: Bk Vols 45,000; Per Subs 155
   Subject Interests: Ancient to early 20th Century art (excluding Am)
   Automation Activity & Vendor Info: (Acquisitions) Ex Libris Group; (Cataloging) OCLC WorldCat; (ILL) OCLC WorldCat; (OPAC) Ex Libris Group; (Serials) OCLC WorldCat
   Database Vendor: Amigos Library Services, Ex Libris Group, JSTOR, OCLC, OCLC WorldCat, OCLC-RLG
   Partic in Cultural District Library Consortium (CDLC); OCLC Online Computer Library Center, Inc

A   NAVY GENERAL LIBRARY PROGRAM, NAS Fort Worth JRB Library, 1802 Doolittle Ave, NAS Fort Worth JRB, 76127. SAN 361-5480. Tel: 817-782-7735. FAX: 817-782-7219. E-mail: jrblibrary@yahoo.com. *Dir,* Patricia Elaine Tellman; E-mail: patricia.tellman@navy.mil; Staff 3 (MLS 1, Non-MLS 2)
   Library Holdings: Bk Vols 31,000; Per Subs 15
   Subject Interests: Mil hist
   Automation Activity & Vendor Info: (Cataloging) EOS International; (Circulation) EOS International; (OPAC) EOS International
   Database Vendor: EBSCO Information Services, Gale Cengage Learning

Wireless access
Restriction: Not open to pub

P NEIGHBORHOOD LIBRARY*, 1310 W Allen Ave, 76110. Tel: 817-921-5999. E-mail: theneighborhoodlibrary@gmail.com. Web Site: www.theneighborhoodlibrary.org. *Dir,* Berlene Milburn
Library Holdings: Bk Vols 13,000
Open Tues-Thurs 4-8, Sat 10-4

P NORTH TEXAS LIBRARY PARTNERS*, 6320 Southwest Blvd, Ste 101, 76109-3961. SAN 316-3458. Tel: 817-377-4440. FAX: 817-377-8020. Web Site: www.ntxlibpartners.org. *Exec Dir,* Carolyn Davidson Brewer; E-mail: cbrewer@ntrls.org; Staff 4 (MLS 4)
Founded 1994
Sept 2005-Aug 2006 Income $872,984, State $174,597, Federal $698,387
Publications: Connections Newsletter (Newsletter); Glossary; Membership Directory; Menu Allocation Guidebook; New Director's Packet; Professional Collection Catalog; Resource Manual; System Assembly Rep Info Pack
Member Libraries: Alvarado Public Library; Alvord Public Library; Archer Public Library; Arlington Public Library System; Aubrey Area Library; Azle Memorial Library; Benbrook Public Library; Betty Foster Public Library; Bicentennial City-County Public Library; Blue Mound Community Library; Bowie Public Library; Bridgeport Public Library; Burkburnett Library; Burleson Public Library; Carnegie City-County Library; Chico Public Library Inc; Cleburne Public Library; Crowley Public Library; Decatur Public Library; Denton Public Library; Dublin Public Library; East Parker County Library; Edwards Public Library; Electra Public Library; Euless Public Library; Everman Public Library; Flower Mound Public Library; Foard County Library; Fort Worth Library; Gladys Johnson Ritchie Library; Grandview Public Library; Grapevine Public Library; Haltom City Public Library; Hood County Public Library; Hurst Public Library; Joshua Public Library; Justin Community Library; Keller Public Library; Kennedale Public Library; Krum Public Library; Lake Cities Library; Lewisville Public Library System; Library of Graham; Little Elm Public Library; Mansfield Public Library; Mary Lou Reddick Public Library; Newark Public Library; Nocona Public Library; North Richland Hills Public Library; Olney Community Library & Arts Center; Pilot Point Community Library; Raymond Jordan Boyd Public Library; Richland Hills Public Library; River Oaks Public Library; Roanoke Public Library; Saginaw Public Library; Sanger Public Library; Somervell County Library; Southlake Public Library; Springtown Public Library; Stephenville Public Library; The Colony Public Library; Thompson-Sawyer Public Library; Tom Burnett Memorial Library; University of North Texas Health Science Center at Fort Worth; Watauga Public Library; Weatherford Public Library; White Settlement Public Library; Wichita Falls Public Library
Open Mon-Fri 8-5
Friends of the Library Group

M JOHN PETER SMITH HOSPITAL*, Medical Library, 1500 S Main St, 76104. SAN 316-3490. Tel: 817-921-3431, Ext 5088. FAX: 817-923-0718. E-mail: medicallibrary@jpshealth.org. Web Site: www.jpshealth.org. *Mgr,* Leslie Herman
Founded 1960
Library Holdings: e-books 10,377; e-journals 10,091; Bk Vols 20,000; Per Subs 300
Subject Interests: Dental surgery, Family practice, Gynecology, Internal med, Nursing, Obstetrics, Pediatrics, Psychiat, Radiology
Wireless access
Partic in Healthline; SCC/MLA
Open Mon-Fri 8-5

R SOUTHWESTERN BAPTIST THEOLOGICAL SEMINARY LIBRARIES*, A Webb Roberts Library, 2001 W Seminary Dr, 76115-2157. (Mail add: PO Box 22490, 76122-0490), SAN 361-7106. Tel: 817-923-1921, Ext 4000. Interlibrary Loan Service Tel: 817-923-1921, Ext 2750. FAX: 817-921-8765. E-mail: rlcirc@swbts.edu. Web Site: www.swbts.edu/libraries. *Dean of Libr,* Dr Berry Driver; E-mail: bdriver@swbts.edu; *Assoc Dean, Ref Serv,* Dr Robert L Phillips; E-mail: rphillips@swbts.edu; *Acq,* Dr Glenn Wittig; *Archivist,* Allison Kirchner; *Cat,* Jeanne Kennedy; *Pub Serv,* Tiffany Norris; *Ser,* Bill Taylor. Subject Specialists: *Church hist, Theol,* Dr Berry Driver; Staff 10 (MLS 10)
Founded 1908. Enrl 3,400; Fac 141; Highest Degree: Doctorate
Library Holdings: Bk Vols 464,586; Per Subs 736
Special Collections: Baptist History (James M Carroll, George W Truett & M E Dodd Coll), mss files; Hymnals
Subject Interests: Relig educ, Sacred music, Theol
Automation Activity & Vendor Info: (Acquisitions) SirsiDynix; (Cataloging) SirsiDynix; (Circulation) SirsiDynix; (Course Reserve) SirsiDynix; (OPAC) SirsiDynix; (Serials) SirsiDynix
Publications: New Titles List
Partic in OCLC Online Computer Library Center, Inc; TexSHARE - Texas State Library & Archives Commission

Departmental Libraries:
KATHRYN SULLIVAN BOWLD MUSIC LIBRARY, 1809 W Broadus, Rm 113, 76115-2157. Tel: 817-923-1921, Ext 2070. FAX: 817-921-8762. *Librn,* Dr Fang-Lan Hsieh; E-mail: fhsieh@swbts.edu, Subject Specialists: *Church music,* Dr Fang-Lan Hsieh
Library Holdings: Bk Titles 21,546
Special Collections: George Stebbins Memorial; Hymnals
Subject Interests: Church, Relig scores, Sacred music

TARRANT COUNTY COLLEGE
J JENKINS GARRETT LIBRARY-SOUTH CAMPUS*, 5301 Campus Dr, 76119, SAN 361-7289. Tel: 817-515-4524. FAX: 817-515-4436. Web Site: www.tccd.edu. *Dir, Libr Serv,* Linda Jenson; E-mail: t; *Asst Dir,* Erik France; *Circ Mgr,* Jeanne Wright; *Pub Serv,* Lynda De los Santos; *Pub Serv,* Jennifer Jackson; Staff 5 (MLS 5)
Founded 1967. Enrl 7,142; Fac 175
Library Holdings: Bk Vols 65,747; Per Subs 268
Open Mon-Thurs 7:45am-10pm, Fri 7:45-3, Sat 9-3

J NORTHWEST CAMPUS WALSH LIBRARY*, 4801 Marine Creek Pkwy, 76179, SAN 361-7254. Tel: 817-515-7725. FAX: 817-515-7720. Web Site: www.tccd.edu. *Dir,* Sandra McCurdy; E-mail: sandra.mccurdy@tccd.edu; *Asst Dir, Libr Serv,* Jim Baxter; E-mail: jim.baxter@tccd.edu; *Pub Serv,* Danelle Ellis; E-mail: danelle.ellis@tccd.edu; Staff 10 (MLS 4, Non-MLS 6)
Founded 1975. Enrl 8,100; Fac 90; Highest Degree: Associate
Library Holdings: Bk Vols 41,024; Per Subs 200
Open Mon-Thurs (Fall) 7am-10pm, Fri 7-5, Sat 8-5; Mon-Thurs (Summer) 7am-10pm

GL TARRANT COUNTY LAW LIBRARY*, 100 W Weatherford, Rm 420, 76196-0800. SAN 316-3504. Tel: 817-884-1481. FAX: 817-884-1509. Web Site: www.tarrantcounty.com/law_library/. *Dir,* Sharon Wayland; E-mail: swayland@tarrantcounty.com; *Asst Dir,* Peggy Martindale; Staff 5 (MLS 3, Non-MLS 2)
Founded 1942
Library Holdings: Bk Titles 3,500; Bk Vols 55,000; Per Subs 270
Automation Activity & Vendor Info: (Cataloging) EOS International; (Circulation) EOS International
Publications: library guide
Open Mon-Fri 8-5

C TEXAS CHRISTIAN UNIVERSITY, Mary Couts Burnett Library, 2913 Lowden St, TCU Box 298400, 76129. SAN 361-7319. Tel: 817-257-7106. Circulation Tel: 817-257-7112. Reference Tel: 817-257-7117. FAX: 817-257-7282. TDD: 817-257-7716. E-mail: library@tcu.edu. Web Site: library.tcu.edu. *Dean,* Dr June Koelker; E-mail: j.koelker@tcu.edu; *Assoc Dean,* Tracy Hull; *Dir, Admin Serv,* James Lutz; *Dir, Libr Syst,* Kerry Bouchard; *Head, Acq,* Dennis Odom; *Head, Cat,* Sally Sorensen; *Head, Circ,* Cheryl Sassman; *Head, Coll Develop,* Dennis Gibbons; *Head, Ref,* Brenda Barnes; Tel: 817-257-5430, E-mail: b.barnes@tcu.edu; *Music & Media Librn,* Cari Alexander; *Spec Coll Librn,* Roger Rainwater; *Cat,* Sara Dillard; *Info Tech,* Stephanie Folse; *ILL,* Kay Edmondson; Staff 26 (MLS 23, Non-MLS 3)
Founded 1873. Enrl 9,725; Fac 532; Highest Degree: Doctorate
Jun 2011-May 2012. Mats Exp $5,078,094, Books $949,040, Per/Ser (Incl. Access Fees) $4,107,935, Presv $21,119. Sal $2,672,129 (Prof $1,518,732)
Library Holdings: AV Mats 67,260; Bk Vols 1,363,887; Per Subs 75,302
Special Collections: International Piano Competition (Van Cliburn Foundation Archives), AV mat; Juvenile Literature (The Erisman-Odom Coll of Juvenile Literature in Series); Literature (William Luther Lewis Coll); United States History (Amon G Carter Archives); United States History (James C Wright Jr Archives). State Document Depository; US Document Depository
Subject Interests: Chem, English, Hist, Lit, Music, Nursing, Psychol, Theol
Automation Activity & Vendor Info: (Acquisitions) Ex Libris Group; (Cataloging) Ex Libris Group; (Circulation) Ex Libris Group; (Course Reserve) Ex Libris Group; (ILL) OCLC; (OPAC) Ex Libris Group; (Serials) Ex Libris Group
Database Vendor: ACM (Association for Computing Machinery), Alexander Street Press, American Chemical Society, American Mathematical Society, American Physical Society, American Psychological Association (APA), Amigos Library Services, Annual Reviews, ARTstor, Baker & Taylor, BioOne, Bowker, Cinahl Information Systems, ebrary, EBSCO Information Services, EBSCOhost, Elsevier, Ex Libris Group, Factiva.com, Gale Cengage Learning, Hoovers, IBISWorld, IEEE (Institute of Electrical & Electronics Engineers), IOP, ISI Web of Knowledge, JSTOR, LexisNexis, Marcive, Inc, Mergent Online, Modern Language Association, Nature Publishing Group, Newsbank, Newsbank-Readex, OCLC ArticleFirst, OCLC FirstSearch, OCLC WorldCat, Oxford Online, Project MUSE, ProQuest, PubMed, RefWorks, Sage, ScienceDirect, SerialsSolutions, Standard & Poor's, Thomson - Web of Science, ValueLine, Wiley, Wiley InterScience, YBP Library Services
Wireless access

Function: Res libr
Publications: Windows
Partic in Amigos Library Services, Inc; Statewide California Electronic Library Consortium (SCELC); TexSHARE - Texas State Library & Archives Commission
Special Services for the Blind - Closed circuit TV magnifier
Restriction: Restricted pub use
Friends of the Library Group

M   TEXAS HEALTH HARRIS METHODIST FORT WORTH HOSPITAL*, 1301 Pennsylvania Ave, 76104. SAN 316-3393. Tel: 817-250-2118. Interlibrary Loan Service Tel: 817-250-3167. Reference Tel: 817-250-2917. FAX: 817-250-5119. Interlibrary Loan Service FAX: 817-250-3054. E-mail: thswmedicallibrary@texashealth.org. *Dir,* Scarlett Burchfield; Tel: 817-250-2916, E-mail: scarlettburchfield@texashealth.org; *Asst Admin, Circ, Head, ILL,* Coy Bowen; E-mail: coybowen@texashealth.org; *Head, Ref, Instr,* Gay Taber; E-mail: gaytaber@texashealth.org; *Outreach Serv Librn, Per, Ref,* Jamie Furrh; Tel: 817-250-3191; *Acq,* Claire Kamego; E-mail: clairekamego@texashealth.org; Staff 5 (MLS 4, Non-MLS 1)
Founded 1948
Library Holdings: Bk Titles 10,000; Bk Vols 10,400; Per Subs 330
Subject Interests: Internal med, Surgery
Wireless access
Function: Doc delivery serv, For res purposes, Homebound delivery serv, ILL available, Photocopying/Printing
Partic in Healthline; S Cent Regional Med Libr Program; Tarrant County Consortium of Health Sci Libr
Restriction: Co libr, Employees & their associates, In-house use for visitors, Lending to staff only, Med staff only, Open to pub for ref only, Restricted borrowing privileges

C   TEXAS WESLEYAN UNIVERSITY*, Eunice & James L West Library, 1201 Wesleyan St, 76105. SAN 316-3512. Tel: 817-531-4800. Interlibrary Loan Service Tel: 817-531-4803. Reference Tel: 817-531-4802. Administration Tel: 817-531-4821. FAX: 817-531-4806. Web Site: westlibrary.txwes.edu. *Univ Librn,* Cindy Potter; E-mail: cpotter@txwes.edu; *Univ Archivist,* Louis Sherwood, Jr; Tel: 817-531-4822, E-mail: lsherwood@txwes.edu; *Acq Librn, Asst Dir,* David Thurston; Tel: 817-531-4813, E-mail: dthurston@txwes.edu; *Per, Syst Librn,* Shelley Almgren; Tel: 817-531-4816, E-mail: salmgren@txwes.edu; *Libr Operations Coordr,* Sheri Parker; E-mail: sparker@txwes.edu; Staff 12 (MLS 6, Non-MLS 6)
Founded 1891. Enrl 1,792; Fac 142; Highest Degree: Master
Jun 2006-May 2007. Mats Exp $174,876, Books $55,262, Per/Ser (Incl. Access Fees) $109,590, Electronic Ref Mat (Incl. Access Fees) $10,024. Sal $407,822 (Prof $231,931)
Library Holdings: AV Mats 5,261; CDs 150; e-books 32,819; Music Scores 8,169; Bk Titles 196,210; Bk Vols 227,215; Per Subs 287
Special Collections: Bobby Bragen Baseball Memorabillia Coll; Joe Brown Theatre Coll, microfiche; Music Scores; Twyla Miranda Juvenile Coll
Subject Interests: Lit
Automation Activity & Vendor Info: (Acquisitions) SirsiDynix; (Cataloging) SirsiDynix; (Circulation) SirsiDynix; (Course Reserve) SirsiDynix; (OPAC) SirsiDynix; (Serials) SirsiDynix
Database Vendor: Academy of Political Science, American Psychological Association (APA), EBSCOhost, Elsevier, Gale Cengage Learning, Hoovers, netLibrary, OCLC WorldCat, ProQuest, STAT!Ref (Teton Data Systems), TDNet, ValueLine, Wilson - Wilson Web
Wireless access
Function: Archival coll, Audio & video playback equip for onsite use, Copy machines, Electronic databases & coll, ILL available, Online ref, Online searches, Orientations, Ref & res, Telephone ref, VHS videos
Partic in OCLC Online Computer Library Center, Inc; Tex Share
Open Mon-Thurs (Fall & Winter) 7:30am-10pm, Fri 7:30-5, Sat 8-5, Sun 1-10; Mon-Thurs (Summer) 7:30-7, Fri 7:30-5, Sat & Sun 12-6
Restriction: Open to students, fac & staff, Photo ID required for access, Private libr

R   TRAVIS AVENUE BAPTIST CHURCH LIBRARY*, 800 W Berry St, 76110. SAN 316-3520. Tel: 817-924-4266. FAX: 817-921-9620. Web Site: www.travis.org. *Librn,* Cornelia Pim
Library Holdings: Bk Vols 1,250
Restriction: Mem only

A   UNITED STATES ARMY*, Corps of Engineers Fort Worth District Technical Library, 819 Taylor St, Rm 2C02, 76102. SAN 361-7408. Tel: 817-886-1013. FAX: 817-886-6401. *Librn,* Carolyn Solomon
Founded 1950
Library Holdings: Bk Vols 5,000; Per Subs 10
Special Collections: Civil & Military Design Reports; Law (Federal, Texas); State of Texas Water Resources Reports
Subject Interests: Eng, Environ studies, Legal, Soil survey

Partic in OCLC Online Computer Library Center, Inc
Restriction: Staff use only

G   UNITED STATES DEPARTMENT OF HOUSING & URBAN DEVELOPMENT*, Region VI Library, 801 Cherry St Unit 45, Ste 2500, 76102. SAN 321-0235. Tel: 817-978-5924. FAX: 817-978-5563. *Librn,* Debbie Holland
Library Holdings: Bk Vols 8,500
Special Collections: Federal Reporters; Law; State Statutes; Housing & Urban Affairs Coll, microfiche
Subject Interests: Housing, Law
Restriction: Non-circulating, Staff use only

G   UNITED STATES DEPARTMENT OF JUSTICE*, Bureau of Prisons Federal Medical Center Library, 3150 Horton Rd, 76119. SAN 316-3539. Tel: 817-534-8400, Ext 3214. FAX: 817-413-3376. *Libr Tech,* Joanne Santorio
Founded 1938
Library Holdings: Bk Vols 2,000
Subject Interests: Fiction, Law, Non-fiction
Restriction: Not open to pub

CM UNIVERSITY OF NORTH TEXAS HEALTH SCIENCE CENTER AT FORT WORTH*, Gibson D Lewis Health Science Library, 3500 Camp Bowie Blvd, 76107-2699. SAN 316-3466. Tel: 817-735-2070. Circulation Tel: 817-735-2465. Interlibrary Loan Service Tel: 817-735-2491. Administration Tel: 817-735-2380. Toll Free Tel: 800-687-5302. FAX: 817-763-0325. Interlibrary Loan Service FAX: 817-763-0408. Administration FAX: 817-735-5158. Web Site: library.hsc.unt.edu. *Libr Dir,* Daniel E Burgard; Tel: 817-735-2589, E-mail: Daniel.Burgard@unthsc.edu; *Dep Dir,* Lisa Smith; Tel: 817-735-2589, E-mail: Lisa.Smith@unthsc.edu; *Access Serv Librn,* Laura Gutierrez; *Digital Projects Librn,* Danelle Orange; *Electronic Res Librn,* Alexis Ackel; *Instruction Librn,* Michele Whitehead; *Ref Librn,* Kathy Broyles; E-mail: Kathy.Broyles@unthsc.edu; *Syst Librn,* Mike Pullin; *Tech Serv Librn,* Tim Mason; Tel: 817-735-2466, E-mail: tim.mason@unthsc.edu; *Web Librn,* Clayton Crenshaw; Staff 22 (MLS 11, Non-MLS 11)
Founded 1970. Enrl 1,800; Fac 250; Highest Degree: Doctorate
Sept 2008-Aug 2009. Mats Exp $2,800,000
Library Holdings: e-books 1,200; e-journals 18,000; Bk Titles 12,000; Bk Vols 14,800
Special Collections: History of Osteopathic Medicine; Texas Osteopathic Medical Association Archives; William G Sutherland Coll. Oral History
Subject Interests: Allied health prof, Med, Osteopathic med, Pub health
Automation Activity & Vendor Info: (Acquisitions) Innovative Interfaces, Inc; (Cataloging) OCLC Connexion; (Circulation) Innovative Interfaces, Inc; (OPAC) Innovative Interfaces, Inc; (Serials) EBSCO Online
Database Vendor: Amigos Library Services, Annual Reviews, Blackwell's, Cambridge Scientific Abstracts, Checkpoint Systems, Inc, Cinahl Information Systems, Dialog, EBSCO Information Services, EBSCOhost, Elsevier, Gale Cengage Learning, Innovative Interfaces, Inc, ISI Web of Knowledge, JSTOR, Majors, Nature Publishing Group, netLibrary, OCLC ArticleFirst, OCLC FirstSearch, OCLC WorldCat, OVID Technologies, Oxford Online, PubMed, RefWorks, ScienceDirect, SerialsSolutions, Springer-Verlag, STAT!Ref (Teton Data Systems), Swets Information Services, Wiley, YBP Library Services
Wireless access
Function: Audio & video playback equip for onsite use, Computers for patron use, Copy machines, Doc delivery serv, E-Reserves, Electronic databases & coll, Health sci info serv, ILL available, Online cat, Online ref, Online searches, Outreach serv, Photocopying/Printing, Ref serv available, VHS videos, Web-catalog
Publications: Acquisition List; Bibliography of Faculty Publications (Bibliographies); Collection Catalog; Library Guide; Library Handbook; New Books List (Audio-visual catalog); On-Line Services Guide; Oral History Collection CAT; Research Guide
Mem of North Texas Library Partners
Partic in Healthline; National Network of Libraries of Medicine South Central Region; South Central Academic Medical Libraries Consortium; TexSHARE - Texas State Library & Archives Commission

P   WESTWORTH VILLAGE CITY LIBRARY*, 101 Seymour Ave, 76114. Tel: 817-738-2248. *Mgr,* Glenda Block
Library Holdings: Bk Vols 17,561
Open Mon-Wed & Fri 1-6, Sat 10-3

FRANKLIN

P   ROBERTSON COUNTY LIBRARY*, Franklin Carnegie Library, 315 E Decherd St, 77856. (Mail add: PO Box 1027, 77856-1027), SAN 316-3547. Tel: 979-828-4331. E-mail: carnegie@valornet.com. *Librn & Info Dir,* Melanie Redden
Pop 1,884
Library Holdings: Large Print Bks 1,000; Bk Titles 8,500; Bk Vols 9,000; Per Subs 2; Talking Bks 62

Automation Activity & Vendor Info: (Cataloging) LRMS, Inc (Library Resource Management Systems); (Circulation) LRMS, Inc (Library Resource Management Systems)
Wireless access
Mem of Central Texas Library System, Inc
Open Mon-Fri 8-Noon
Friends of the Library Group

FRANKSTON

P   FRANKSTON DEPOT LIBRARY & MUSEUM, 159 W Railroad St, 75763. (Mail add: PO Box 639, 75763-0639), SAN 376-4435. Tel: 903-876-4463. FAX: 903-876-3226. *Librn,* Carolyn A Wheeler
Founded 1985
Library Holdings: Bk Vols 16,000; Per Subs 30
Automation Activity & Vendor Info: (Cataloging) Biblionix; (Circulation) Biblionix; (OPAC) Biblionix
Open Tues & Sat 9-5, Thurs 10-7 (9-6 Winter)
Friends of the Library Group

FREDERICKSBURG

S   ADMIRAL NIMITZ NATIONAL MUSEUM OF THE PACIFIC WAR*, Center for Pacific War Studies, 328 E Main St, 78624-4612. SAN 374-4620. Tel: 830-997-4379, Ext 262. FAX: 830-997-8092. Web Site: www.pacificwarmuseum.org.
Founded 1978
Library Holdings: Bk Titles 4,500
Special Collections: Admiral Chester Nimitz Coll, bks, paper, photogs; World War II Pacific Coll, bks, maps, paper, photogs, posters; World War II Vet. Oral History
Restriction: Open by appt only
Friends of the Library Group

P   PIONEER MEMORIAL LIBRARY*, 115 W Main St, 78624. SAN 316-3555. Tel: 830-997-6513. FAX: 830-997-6514. E-mail: library@gillespiecounty.org. Web Site: www.pmlfbg.com. *Libr Dir,* Brian MacWithey; Staff 1 (MLS 1)
Founded 1966. Pop 19,635; Circ 88,693
Library Holdings: Bk Vols 45,000; Per Subs 75
Special Collections: German Coll
Automation Activity & Vendor Info: (Cataloging) TLC (The Library Corporation); (Circulation) TLC (The Library Corporation); (OPAC) TLC (The Library Corporation)
Wireless access
Open Mon, Tues & Thurs 9-6, Wed 9-7, Fri & Sat 9-2
Friends of the Library Group

FREEPORT

S   DOW CHEMICAL LIBRARY*, Business Intelligence Center, Business Intelligence Ctr, B-1210, 2301 Brazosport Blvd, 77541. SAN 316-3563. Tel: 979-238-2011, 979-238-4854. *Mgr,* Jeff Hart; *Libr Tech,* JoAnne Scott; *Info Res,* Gary McNamee; Tel: 979-238-4881; *Info Spec,* Carl Wolfe; Staff 4 (MLS 1, Non-MLS 3)
Founded 1944
Library Holdings: Bk Titles 10,000; Bk Vols 12,000; Per Subs 47
Subject Interests: Chem, Commerce, Eng, Indust, Proprietary res
Automation Activity & Vendor Info: (Acquisitions) SirsiDynix; (Cataloging) SirsiDynix; (Circulation) SirsiDynix; (OPAC) SirsiDynix; (Serials) SirsiDynix
Database Vendor: Dialog, Factiva.com, LexisNexis, OCLC WorldCat, ScienceDirect, STN International
Partic in OCLC Online Computer Library Center, Inc

FRESNO

S   CHAMPION TECHNOLOGIES TECHNICAL LIBRARY*, 3130 FM 521 Rd, 77545. Tel: 281-710-9401. FAX: 281-710-9415. *Res Librn,* Donna K Hopkins; E-mail: donna.hopkins@champ-tech.com; Staff 1.5 (MLS 1, Non-MLS 0.5)
Library Holdings: Bk Titles 331
Subject Interests: Gas, Oil, Petroleum products
Automation Activity & Vendor Info: (Cataloging) EOS International; (Circulation) EOS International; (OPAC) EOS International
Database Vendor: American Chemical Society, Elsevier
Wireless access
Function: CD-ROM, Copy machines, Electronic databases & coll
Restriction: Not a lending libr, Not open to pub, Prof mat only

FRIENDSWOOD

P   FRIENDSWOOD PUBLIC LIBRARY, 416 S Friendswood Dr, 77546-3897. SAN 316-358X. Tel: 281-482-7135. FAX: 281-482-2685. E-mail: frpublib@friendswood.lib.tx.us. Web Site: www.friendswood.lib.tx.us. *Dir,* Mary Booker Perroni; E-mail:

maryp@friendswood.lib.tx.us; *Circ Mgr,* Mary Keever; E-mail: mkeever@ci.friendswood.tx.us; *Ch,* Pat Akes; E-mail: pjakes@friendswood.lib.tx.us; *Ref,* Donald LeBlanc; E-mail: reflib@friendswood.lib.tx.us; *Ref & Info Serv, Web Coordr,* Matthew Riley; E-mail: mriley@friendswood.lib.tx.us; *Tech Serv,* Keith Rogers; E-mail: krogers@friendswood.lib.tx.us; *YA Serv,* Christina Hicks; E-mail: librariansti@gmail.com; Staff 7 (MLS 3, Non-MLS 4)
Founded 1968. Pop 35,000; Circ 350,892
Library Holdings: AV Mats 9,296; CDs 1,932; DVDs 1,880; Large Print Bks 603; Bk Titles 79,140; Bk Vols 83,419; Per Subs 143; Talking Bks 2,807
Automation Activity & Vendor Info: (Cataloging) SirsiDynix; (Circulation) SirsiDynix; (ILL) OCLC Online
Database Vendor: EBSCOhost, Facts on File, OCLC FirstSearch
Wireless access
Function: Adult bk club, Bk club(s), Children's prog, Computer training, Computers for patron use, Copy machines, Digital talking bks, E-Reserves, Electronic databases & coll, ILL available, Online cat, OverDrive digital audio bks, Preschool outreach, Prog for adults, Prog for children & young adult, Story hour, Summer reading prog, Tax forms, Teen prog, Telephone ref, Web-catalog, Wheelchair accessible
Friends of the Library Group

FRIONA

P   FRIONA PUBLIC LIBRARY*, 109 W Seventh St, 79035-2548. SAN 316-3598. Tel: 806-250-3200. FAX: 806-250-2185. Web Site: www.hlc-lib.org. *Dir,* Darla Bracken; E-mail: fridarla19@yahoo.com; *Asst Librn,* Brenda Patterson
Founded 1963. Pop 3,854
Library Holdings: Bk Vols 35,000; Per Subs 75
Automation Activity & Vendor Info: (Cataloging) SirsiDynix; (Circulation) SirsiDynix; (OPAC) SirsiDynix
Database Vendor: SirsiDynix
Publications: Friends of the Library (Bi-annually)
Partic in Harrington Library Consortium; OCLC Online Computer Library Center, Inc
Special Services for the Blind - Reader equip
Open Mon-Fri 9-6
Friends of the Library Group

FRISCO

J   COLLIN COLLEGE*, Preston Ridge Campus Library, 9700 Wade Blvd, 75035. Tel: 972-377-1560, 972-377-1577. FAX: 972-377-1511. Web Site: www.collin.edu/library. *Exec Dir,* John Mullin; E-mail: jmullin@collin.edu
Library Holdings: AV Mats 9,171; CDs 1,000; DVDs 3,000; Electronic Media & Resources 700; Bk Vols 52,133; Per Subs 330; Talking Bks 1,500; Videos 4,200
Automation Activity & Vendor Info: (Acquisitions) Polaris Library Systems; (Cataloging) Polaris Library Systems; (Circulation) Polaris Library Systems; (Course Reserve) Polaris Library Systems; (ILL) Polaris Library Systems; (OPAC) Polaris Library Systems; (Serials) Polaris Library Systems
Database Vendor: EBSCOhost, Gale Cengage Learning, JSTOR, LexisNexis, OCLC WorldCat, ProQuest, PubMed, ReferenceUSA, Safari Books Online, Wilson - Wilson Web
Wireless access
Open Mon-Thurs 7:45am-9:45pm, Fri 7:45-5, Sat 9-4, Sun 1-5

P   FRISCO PUBLIC LIBRARY*, 6101 Frisco Square Blvd, Ste 3000, 75034-3000. SAN 378-4606. Tel: 972-292-5669. FAX: 972-292-5699. Web Site: www.friscolibrary.com. *Dir, Libr Serv,* Shelley Holley; E-mail: sholley@friscotexas.gov; *Mgr, Ad Serv,* Rachel Dalton; *Mgr, Circ Serv,* Adela Arteaga; *Mgr, Mat Serv,* Nigel Boeg; *Mgr, Youth Serv,* Mayra Diaz; *Syst Coordr,* Gary Werchan; Staff 8 (MLS 8)
Pop 102,000; Circ 1,200,000
Oct 2009-Sept 2010. Mats Exp $525,000
Library Holdings: Audiobooks 5,566; AV Mats 27,944; CDs 6,788; DVDs 15,590; e-books 7,344; Large Print Bks 2,437; Bk Titles 89,034; Bk Vols 132,095; Per Subs 74; Talking Bks 5,566; Videos 15,590
Automation Activity & Vendor Info: (Acquisitions) SirsiDynix; (Cataloging) SirsiDynix; (Circulation) SirsiDynix; (OPAC) SirsiDynix
Database Vendor: Baker & Taylor, Brodart, BWI, Checkpoint Systems, Inc, EBSCOhost, Facts on File, Gale Cengage Learning, infoUSA, netLibrary, OCLC WorldCat, Overdrive, Inc, ProQuest, ReferenceUSA, SirsiDynix, World Book Online
Wireless access
Function: Adult bk club, After school storytime, Audio & video playback equip for onsite use, Audiobks via web, Bilingual assistance for Spanish patrons, Bk club(s), Bk reviews (Group), Bks on cassette, Bks on CD, CD-ROM, Children's prog, Computer training, Computers for patron use, Copy machines, Digital talking bks, Doc delivery serv, e-mail & chat, e-mail serv, E-Reserves, Electronic databases & coll, Fax serv, Free DVD rentals, Handicapped accessible, Homework prog, ILL available, Instruction

& testing, Libr develop, Mail & tel request accepted, Music CDs, Newsp ref libr, Notary serv, Online cat, Online ref, Online searches, Orientations, Outreach serv, Outside serv via phone, mail, e-mail & web, OverDrive digital audio bks, Photocopying/Printing, Preschool outreach, Prog for adults, Prog for children & young adult, Pub access computers, Ref & res, Ref serv available, Ref serv in person, Scanner, Senior computer classes, Spoken cassettes & CDs, Spoken cassettes & DVDs, Story hour, Summer reading prog, Tax forms, Teen prog, Telephone ref, Web-catalog, Wheelchair accessible, Workshops
Partic in TexSHARE - Texas State Library & Archives Commission
Open Mon-Thurs 10-9, Fri & Sat 10-6, Sun 1-5
Restriction: In-house use for visitors
Friends of the Library Group

GAINESVILLE

P   COOKE COUNTY LIBRARY*, 200 S Weaver St, 76240-4790. SAN 316-361X. Tel: 940-668-5530. FAX: 940-668-5533. Web Site: cookecountylibrary.org. *Dir,* Jennifer Johnson-Spence; Staff 7 (MLS 1, Non-MLS 6)
Founded 1893. Pop 29,841; Circ 70,353
Oct 2010-Sept 2011 Income $366,767, State $6,645, County $300,000, Locally Generated Income $60,122. Mats Exp $54,185, Books $32,000, Per/Ser (Incl. Access Fees) $3,185, Micro $2,000, AV Equip $5,000, AV Mat $9,500, Electronic Ref Mat (Incl. Access Fees) $2,500. Sal $178,145 (Prof $50,435)
Library Holdings: Audiobooks 1,146; AV Mats 3,824; Bks on Deafness & Sign Lang 13; CDs 390; DVDs 1,211; Electronic Media & Resources 51; Large Print Bks 513; Microforms 557; Bk Titles 60,268; Bk Vols 69,903; Per Subs 55; Videos 1,467
Special Collections: Local History Coll
Subject Interests: Genealogy, Local hist
Automation Activity & Vendor Info: (Acquisitions) Book Systems, Inc; (Cataloging) Book Systems, Inc; (Circulation) Book Systems, Inc; (OPAC) Book Systems, Inc; (Serials) EBSCO Online
Wireless access
Function: Accelerated reader prog, Archival coll, Children's prog, Computers for patron use, Electronic databases & coll, Fax serv, Homework prog, ILL available, Online cat, Photocopying/Printing, Prog for children & young adult, Pub access computers, Ref & res, Spoken cassettes & CDs, Spoken cassettes & DVDs, Story hour, Summer reading prog, Tax forms, Telephone ref, VHS videos, Wheelchair accessible
Open Mon, Wed, Thurs & Fri 9-6, Tues 10-7, Sat 10-4
Friends of the Library Group

J   NORTH CENTRAL TEXAS COLLEGE LIBRARY*, 1525 W California St, 76240-0815. SAN 316-3601. Tel: 940-668-4283. E-mail: nctccorinth@nctc.edu. Web Site: www.nctc.edu. *Dir of Libr Serv,* Diane Roether; Staff 2 (MLS 2)
Enrl 9,000; Fac 88
Library Holdings: e-books 15,000; Bk Titles 50,000; Per Subs 52
Special Collections: Cooke County History Coll
Automation Activity & Vendor Info: (Cataloging) SirsiDynix; (Circulation) SirsiDynix; (OPAC) SirsiDynix; (Serials) SirsiDynix
Publications: Bibliographies; Faculty Handbook
Open Mon-Thurs (Summer) 8-4:30, Fri 8-3; Mon-Thurs (Winter) 7:30am-9pm, Fri 7:30am-3pm, Sun 1-5

GALVESTON

J   GALVESTON COLLEGE*, David Glenn Hunt Memorial Library, 4015 Ave Q, 77550. SAN 316-3636. Tel: 409-944-1240. Reference Tel: 409-944-1242. FAX: 409-944-1521. E-mail: learningresourcecenter@gc.edu. Web Site: www.gc.edu. *Dir, Libr & Learning Res,* Dr Alan Uyehara; E-mail: auyehara@gc.edu; *Ref,* Gracie Otin; E-mail: gotin@gc.edu; Staff 3 (MLS 3)
Founded 1967. Enrl 2,300
Library Holdings: e-books 28,281; Bk Titles 37,000; Per Subs 241
Subject Interests: Educ, Lit, Local hist, Nursing
Automation Activity & Vendor Info: (Cataloging) EOS International; (Circulation) EOS International; (OPAC) EOS International; (Serials) EOS International
Database Vendor: EBSCOhost, Gale Cengage Learning, netLibrary
Wireless access
Open Mon-Thurs (Winter) 8am-9pm, Fri 8-5, Sat 9-Noon; Mon-Thurs (Summer) 7:30am-9pm

P   ROSENBERG LIBRARY*, 2310 Sealy Ave, 77550. SAN 316-3652. Tel: 409-763-8854. Circulation Tel: 409-763-8854, Ext 111. Reference Tel: 409-763-8854, Ext 115. Administration Tel: 409-763-8854, Ext 121. FAX: 409-763-0275. E-mail: admin@rosenberg-library.org. Web Site: www.rosenberg-library.org. *Exec Dir,* John Augelli; Tel: 409-763-8854, Ext 114, E-mail: jaugelli@rosenberg-library.org; *Head, Adult Serv, Head, Tech Serv,* Poom Sunhachawi-Taylor; Tel: 409-763-8854, Ext 140, E-mail: ptaylor@rosenberg-library.org; *Head, Ch,* Karen Stanley; Tel:

409-763-8854, Ext 119, E-mail: kstanley@rosenberg-library.org; *Head, Circ,* Carolyn Williams; Tel: 409-763-8854, Ext 141, E-mail: cwilliams@rosenberg-library.org; *Head, Spec Coll,* Casey Greene; Tel: 409-763-8854, Ext 117, E-mail: cgreene@rosenberg-library.org; *Archivist,* Carol Wood; E-mail: cwood@rosenberg-library.org; *ILL, Ref,* Delo White; *YA Serv,* Gavin Sheaffer; Tel: 409-763-8854, Ext 116; Staff 10 (MLS 8, Non-MLS 2)
Founded 1904. Pop 67,299; Circ 234,781
Oct 2006-Sept 2007 Income $3,024,134, State $17,807, City $1,627,658, County $486,250, Locally Generated Income $892,419. Mats Exp $276,688, Books $172,220, Per/Ser (Incl. Access Fees) $18,405, Micro $1,600, AV Mat $71,113, Electronic Ref Mat (Incl. Access Fees) $12,400, Presv $950. Sal $1,201,525
Library Holdings: AV Mats 17,918; Bk Vols 160,724; Per Subs 354
Special Collections: Early Texas & Galveston (Museum Coll); Galveston & Texas History, archit drawings, hist doc, maps, photogs; Rare Books (Colonel Milo Pitcher Fox & Agness Peel Fox Rare Room), bks, maps, mss
Subject Interests: Early Texas & Galveston hist
Automation Activity & Vendor Info: (Acquisitions) SirsiDynix; (Cataloging) SirsiDynix; (Circulation) SirsiDynix
Wireless access
Publications: A Descriptive Catalog of the Cartographic Collection of the Rosenberg Library; Fragile Empires: The Texas Correspondence of Samuel Swartwout & James Morgan, 1836-1856; Julius Stockfleth: Gulf Coast Marine & Landscape Painter; Manuscript Sources in the Rosenberg Library
Open Mon-Thurs 9-9, Fri & Sat 9-6
Friends of the Library Group

C   TEXAS A&M UNIVERSITY AT GALVESTON, Jack K Williams Library, 200 Seawolf Pkwy, 77553. (Mail add: PO Box 1675, 77553-1675), SAN 316-3644. Tel: 409-740-4560. Interlibrary Loan Service Tel: 409-740-4564. Reference Tel: 409 740 4568. Automation Services Tel: 409-740-4571. FAX: 409-740-4702. E-mail: library@tamug.edu. Web Site: www.tamug.edu/library. *Digital Initiatives Librn,* Natalie H Wiest; Tel: 409-740-4567, E-mail: wiestn@tamug.edu; *Electronic Res Librn,* Cantrelle Mills; E-mail: millsc@tamug.edu; *Interim Dir,* David Baca; E-mail: bacad@tamug.edu; Staff 7 (MLS 3, Non-MLS 4)
Founded 1972. Enrl 2,000; Fac 91; Highest Degree: Doctorate
Sept 2011-Aug 2012 Income $1,070,387, State $289,702, Locally Generated Income $751,342, Other $29,343. Mats Exp $469,179, Books $14,781, Per/Ser (Incl. Access Fees) $453,972, AV Mat $426. Sal $308,315 (Prof $177,718)
Library Holdings: AV Mats 2,492; DVDs 761; e-journals 10,000; Microforms 54,187; Bk Vols 93,748; Per Subs 400; Spec Interest Per Sub 200
Special Collections: Galveston Bay Information Center
Subject Interests: Marine biol, Maritime, Oceanography, Transportation
Automation Activity & Vendor Info: (Acquisitions) Ex Libris Group; (Cataloging) Ex Libris Group; (Circulation) Ex Libris Group; (Course Reserve) Ex Libris Group; (ILL) Ex Libris Group; (Media Booking) Ex Libris Group; (OPAC) Ex Libris Group; (Serials) Ex Libris Group
Database Vendor: Agricola, American Chemical Society, American Mathematical Society, American Psychological Association (APA), Amigos Library Services, Annual Reviews, Blackwell's, Bowker, Cambridge Scientific Abstracts, Career Guidance Foundation, Checkpoint Systems, Inc, College Source, Community of Science (COS), ebrary, EBSCO Information Services, EBSCOhost, Elsevier, Ex Libris Group, Gale Cengage Learning, Jane's, JSTOR, LexisNexis, Marquis Who's Who, McGraw-Hill, Nature Publishing Group, OCLC FirstSearch, OCLC WorldCat, OVID Technologies, ProQuest, PubMed, ScienceDirect, Springer-Verlag, Standard & Poor's, Wiley
Wireless access
Partic in TexSHARE - Texas State Library & Archives Commission
Open Mon-Thurs 7am-2am, Fri 8-5, Sat 10-6, Sun Noon-2 am

A   UNITED STATES ARMY*, Galveston District Corps of Engineers Library, 2000 Fort Point Rd, Rm 308, 77553. SAN 361-7432. Tel: 409-766-3196. FAX: 409-766-3905. Web Site: www.swg.usace.army.mil/library. *Librn,* Clark Bartee; E-mail: clark.bartee@usace.army.mil; Staff 1 (MLS 1)
Library Holdings: Bk Vols 10,616; Per Subs 136
Special Collections: Archeological Reports; Civil Works Reports (Annual Reports of the C of E 1871-Present); Congressional Documents (1900-Present); Design Memoranda; Environmental Impact Statements & Assessments
Subject Interests: Dredging, Ecology, Environ res, Flood control, Flood plain studies, Law, Navigation, Shoreline studies, Soils, Water res
Partic in OCLC Online Computer Library Center, Inc

CM   UNIVERSITY OF TEXAS MEDICAL BRANCH*, Moody Medical Library, 301 University Blvd, 77555-1035. SAN 316-3687. Tel: 409-772-1971. Circulation Tel: 409-772-2385. Reference Tel: 409-772-2372. FAX: 409-762-9782. Web Site: library.utmb.edu. *Dir,* Brett Kirkpatrick; Tel: 409-772-2371, E-mail: bkirkpat@utmb.edu; *Assoc Dir,*

Patricia Ciejka; Tel: 409-772-8745, E-mail: pciejka@utmb.edu; *Cat,* Mira Greene; E-mail: megreene@utmb.edu; Staff 49 (MLS 9, Non-MLS 40) Founded 1891

Library Holdings: Bk Titles 95,833; Bk Vols 251,937; Per Subs 5,820

Special Collections: History of Medicine & Archives

Subject Interests: Allied health sci, Med, Nursing

Automation Activity & Vendor Info: (Acquisitions) Ex Libris Group; (Cataloging) Ex Libris Group; (Circulation) Ex Libris Group; (OPAC) Ex Libris Group; (Serials) Ex Libris Group

Database Vendor: Dialog, EBSCOhost, LexisNexis, OCLC FirstSearch, OVID Technologies

Function: Doc delivery serv

Partic in Houston Area Research Library Consortium; National Network of Libraries of Medicine; Tex Health Sci Libr Consortium; UT Syst Librns Open Mon-Thurs 7:30am-12am, Fri 7:30-6, Sat 9-6, Sun Noon-9

GARDEN RIDGE

P   GARDEN RIDGE LIBRARY*, 9400 Municipal Pkwy, 78266. Tel: 210-651-6570. Web Site: www.ci.garden-ridge.tx.us/library.htm. *Libr Dir,* Linda Crosland

Library Holdings: AV Mats 750; DVDs 700; Large Print Bks 200; Bk Vols 15,000; Talking Bks 550

Automation Activity & Vendor Info: (Acquisitions) Softlink America; (Cataloging) Softlink America

Open Mon-Wed 10-6, Thurs 10-8, Fri & Sat 10-5

GARLAND

C   AMBERTON UNIVERSITY, Library Resource Center, 1700 Eastgate Dr, 75041. Tel: 972-279-6511, Ext 136. FAX: 972-686-5567. E-mail: library@amberton.edu. *Dir, Libr Serv,* Judy Maxine Gibson; E-mail: jgibson@amberton.edu; *Librn,* Patricia Porter; Tel: 972-279-6511, Ext 138, E-mail: pporter@amberton.edu; Staff 6 (MLS 2, Non-MLS 4) Founded 1971. Enrl 1,500; Highest Degree: Master

Library Holdings: e-books 121,001; Bk Vols 15,000; Per Subs 4

Subject Interests: Bus admin, Counseling, Ethics, Human relations

Database Vendor: EBSCOhost, Gale Cengage Learning, OCLC FirstSearch

Wireless access

Function: For res purposes

Partic in TexSHARE - Texas State Library & Archives Commission Open Mon-Thurs 10-6:30, Fri & Sat 10-1:30

P   NICHOLSON MEMORIAL LIBRARY SYSTEM, Central Library, 625 Austin St, 75040-6365. SAN 361-7467. Tel: 972-205-2500. Reference Tel: 972-205-2501. FAX: 972-205-2523. Web Site: www.nmls.lib.tx.us. *Dir of Libr,* Claire Bausch; Tel: 972-205-2543, E-mail: gbpayne@garlandtx.gov; *Asst Dir,* Constance Moss; E-mail: cmoss@garlandtx.gov; *Cent Libr Mgr,* Will Massey; *Circ Supvr,* Leticia Cromley; *Pub Serv Adminr,* Kathleen Cizek; Tel: 972-205-2546, E-mail: kcizek@garlandtx.gov; *Tech Serv Coordr,* Kathi Mehan

Founded 1933. Pop 228,060; Circ 1,549,358

Oct 2010-Sept 2011 Income (Main Library and Branch(s)) $5,822,227, State $44,634, City $5,777,593. Mats Exp $970,096, Books $687,721, AV Mat $120,258, Electronic Ref Mat (Incl. Access Fees) $162,117. Sal $3,704,692

Library Holdings: Audiobooks 8,801; CDs 8,029; DVDs 42,512; e-books 10,586; Large Print Bks 5,405; Microforms 23; Bk Titles 177,850; Bk Vols 348,465; Per Subs 774

Automation Activity & Vendor Info: (Acquisitions) SirsiDynix; (Cataloging) SIRSI WorkFlows; (Circulation) SIRSI WorkFlows; (ILL) OCLC WorldCat; (OPAC) SirsiDynix; (Serials) SirsiDynix

Database Vendor: Brodart, EBSCOhost, Gale Cengage Learning, LearningExpress, OCLC WorldCat, Overdrive, Inc, ProQuest, SirsiDynix, TDNet, TumbleBookLibrary, ValueLine

Wireless access

Publications: ACCESS (Newsletter)

Open Mon-Thurs 10-9, Fri & Sat 10-6, Sun 2-6

Friends of the Library Group

Branches: 3

NORTH GARLAND BRANCH, 3845 N Garland Ave, 75040, SAN 372-7920. Tel: 972-205-2803. *Br Mgr,* Dianne Dupont
    Open Tues & Thurs 1-9, Wed, Fri & Sat 10-6

SOUTH GARLAND BRANCH LIBRARY, 4845 Broadway Blvd, 75043. Tel: 972-205-3920. *Br Mgr,* Bill Raley; Staff 11 (MLS 6, Non-MLS 5)
    Open Tues & Thurs 1-9, Wed, Fri & Sat 10-6
    Friends of the Library Group

WALNUT CREEK BRANCH LIBRARY, 3319 Edgewood, 75042-7118, SAN 361-7521. Tel: 972-205-2587. *Br Mgr,* Becky Crow
    Open Tues & Thurs 1-9, Wed, Fri & Sat 10-6

GATESVILLE

P   GATESVILLE PUBLIC LIBRARY*, 111 N Eighth St, 76528. SAN 316-375X. Tel: 254-865-5367. FAX: 254-248-0986. Web Site: www.ci.gatesville.tx.us/library. *Librn,* Faye Nichols; E-mail: faye.nichols@ci.gatesville.tx.us; Staff 4 (MLS 1, Non-MLS 3) Founded 1970. Pop 16,000; Circ 40,975

Library Holdings: Bk Titles 42,170; Bk Vols 48,000; Per Subs 40

Subject Interests: Genealogy, Local hist, Tex

Automation Activity & Vendor Info: (Cataloging) Book Systems, Inc; (Circulation) Book Systems, Inc; (OPAC) Book Systems, Inc

Wireless access

Mem of Central Texas Library System, Inc

Open Mon, Wed & Fri 8:30-6, Tues & Thurs 8:30-8, Sat 8:30-4:30

Friends of the Library Group

GEORGE WEST

P   LIVE OAK COUNTY LIBRARY*, George West Branch, 402 N Houston St, 78022. SAN 361-7556. Tel: 361-449-1124. E-mail: librarygw@gmail.com. Web Site: liveoak.biblionix.com/atoz/catalog. *Dir,* Sherrie Smith; Staff 4 (Non-MLS 4)

Special Collections: US Document Depository

Automation Activity & Vendor Info: (Cataloging) Follett Software; (Circulation) Follett Software

Function: Copy machines, Home delivery & serv to Sr ctr & nursing homes, ILL available, Photocopying/Printing, Spoken cassettes & CDs, Summer reading prog, Tax forms, VHS videos, Video lending libr Open Mon-Thurs 11:30-6, Fri 1-5, Sat 9-1

Restriction: Open to pub for ref & circ; with some limitations

Branches: 1

THREE RIVERS, 102 Leroy St, Three Rivers, 78071, SAN 361-7580. Tel: 361-786-3037. E-mail: librarytr@gmail.com. *Dir,* Sherrie Smith; Tel: 361-449-1124
    Open Mon-Thurs 11:30-6, Fri 1-5, Sat 9-1

GEORGETOWN

P   GEORGETOWN PUBLIC LIBRARY*, 402 W Eighth St, 78626-5503. SAN 316-3768. Circulation Tel: 512-930-3551. Reference Tel: 512-930-3627. FAX: 512-930-3764. TDD: 512-930-3507. E-mail: gpl@georgetowntx.org. Web Site: www.library.georgetowntx.org. *Dir, Libr Serv,* Eric P Lashley; E-mail: epl@georgetowntx.org; *Ch,* Rosa Garcia; E-mail: rxg@georgetowntx.org; Staff 19 (MLS 5, Non-MLS 14) Founded 1967. Pop 30,000; Circ 159,648

Library Holdings: CDs 1,500; Large Print Bks 1,789; Bk Vols 80,966; Per Subs 118; Videos 4,400

Subject Interests: Genealogy, Local hist, Tex hist

Automation Activity & Vendor Info: (Cataloging) Biblionix; (Circulation) Biblionix; (OPAC) Biblionix

Database Vendor: Gale Cengage Learning, netLibrary

Wireless access

Function: ILL available

Special Services for the Blind - Bks on cassette; Bks on CD Open Mon-Thurs 9-8, Fri 9-6, Sat 9-5, Sun 12-5

Friends of the Library Group

C   SOUTHWESTERN UNIVERSITY*, A Frank Smith Jr Library Center, 1100 E University Ave, 78626. (Mail add: PO Box 770, 78627-0770), SAN 316-3776. Tel: 512-863-1561. Circulation Tel: 512-863-1563. Interlibrary Loan Service Tel: 512-863-1638. Administration Tel: 512-863-1635. FAX: 512-863-8198. Web Site: www.southwestern.edu/library. *Dean of Libr,* Lynne M Brody; Tel: 512-863-1214, E-mail: brodyl@southwestern.edu; *Head, Acq, Head, Coll Serv,* Dana Hendrix; Tel: 512-863-1241, E-mail: hendrixd@southwestern.edu; *Head, Cat,* Hong Yu; E-mail: yuh@southwestern.edu; *Head, Circ,* Carol Fonken; Tel: 512-863-1550, E-mail: fonkenc@southwestern.edu; *Head, Media Serv,* Paul Sicard; *Head, Per,* Amy Anderson; *Head, Ref,* Joan Parks; E-mail: parksj@southwestern.edu; *Head, Spec Coll,* Kathryn Stallard; E-mail: stallark@southwestern.edu; *Head, Syst & Web Mgt,* Jesse Saunders; E-mail: saunderj@southwestern.edu; *Cat Librn,* Theresa Zelasko; E-mail: zelaskot@southwestern.edu; Staff 10 (MLS 9, Non-MLS 1) Founded 1840. Enrl 1,301; Fac 166; Highest Degree: Bachelor

Library Holdings: AV Mats 17,260; e-books 34,784; Microforms 63,602; Bk Vols 378,865; Per Subs 1,112

Special Collections: Bertha Dobie Papers; Hymnals (Meyer Coll); J Frank Dobie Coll; John G Tower Papers; Rare Books Coll (Bewick, Bible, Blake); Texana (Clark Coll)

Automation Activity & Vendor Info: (Acquisitions) Ex Libris Group; (Cataloging) Ex Libris Group; (Circulation) Ex Libris Group; (OPAC) Ex Libris Group; (Serials) Ex Libris Group

Database Vendor: EBSCOhost, Gale Cengage Learning, JSTOR, LexisNexis, netLibrary, OCLC FirstSearch, OCLC WorldCat, Oxford Online

Wireless access

Publications: Bibliographic Series; Exhibit Catalogs; Handbook; Summer Reading List
Partic in Leian; National Institute for Technology & Liberal Education (NITLE); OCLC Online Computer Library Center, Inc; TexSHARE - Texas State Library & Archives Commission

GIDDINGS

P GIDDINGS PUBLIC LIBRARY*, 276 N Orange St, 78942-3317. SAN 316-3784. Tel: 979-542-2716. FAX: 979-542-1879. Web Site: www.giddings.net. *Dir,* Pamela Hutchinson; E-mail: pamelahutchinson@hotmail.com
Founded 1920. Pop 5,105; Circ 33,707
Library Holdings: AV Mats 400; Bks on Deafness & Sign Lang 20; Large Print Bks 606; Bk Titles 35,000; Bk Vols 36,000; Per Subs 54; Talking Bks 789
Special Collections: Baseball Coll; Indian Artifact Display; Large Print Coll, audio cassettes, videos
Subject Interests: Cookery, Gardening, Genealogy, Handicrafts, Local hist, Texana
Automation Activity & Vendor Info: (Cataloging) Follett Software; (Circulation) Follett Software; (ILL) OCLC
Wireless access
Mem of Central Texas Library System, Inc
Partic in TexSHARE - Texas State Library & Archives Commission
Open Mon-Fri 10-6, Sat 10-1
Friends of the Library Group

GILMER

P UPSHUR COUNTY LIBRARY*, 702 W Tyler St, 75644. SAN 316-3792. Tel: 903-843-5001. FAX: 903-843-3995. *Librn,* Mark Warren; Staff 5 (MLS 1, Non-MLS 4)
Founded 1929. Pop 33,000
Library Holdings: Bk Titles 61,632; Bk Vols 63,813; Per Subs 77
Special Collections: Library of America
Subject Interests: Civil War, Local genealogy, Texana
Automation Activity & Vendor Info: (Cataloging) TLC (The Library Corporation); (Circulation) TLC (The Library Corporation); (OPAC) TLC (The Library Corporation)
Database Vendor: TLC (The Library Corporation)
Wireless access
Function: Bks on cassette, Bks on CD, Children's prog, Computers for patron use, Copy machines, Electronic databases & coll, Handicapped accessible, Holiday prog, Homework prog, ILL available, Mail & tel request accepted, Music CDs, Orientations, Photocopying/Printing, Preschool outreach, Prof lending libr, Prog for adults, Prog for children & young adult, Ref serv available, Tax forms, Telephone ref, Video lending libr
Special Services for the Deaf - Bks on deafness & sign lang
Special Services for the Blind - Audio mat; Bks available with recordings; Copier with enlargement capabilities; Extensive large print coll
Open Mon-Fri 9-6, Sat 9-1
Friends of the Library Group

GLADEWATER

P LEE PUBLIC LIBRARY*, Gladewater Public Library, 312 W Pacific, 75647-2135. SAN 316-3806. Tel: 903-845-2640. FAX: 903-845-2648. *Dir,* Vickey Green; Staff 4 (MLS 1, Non-MLS 3)
Founded 1937. Pop 8,950; Circ 31,502
Library Holdings: Bk Titles 31,813; Bk Vols 32,213; Per Subs 15
Special Collections: Texana (John Ben Shepperd Jr Coll)
Automation Activity & Vendor Info: (Cataloging) Follett Software; (Circulation) Follett Software
Open Mon-Fri 9:30-5:30
Friends of the Library Group

GLEN ROSE

P SOMERVELL COUNTY LIBRARY*, 108 Allen Dr, 76043. SAN 376-4583. Tel: 254-897-4582. FAX: 254-897-9882. E-mail: somlib@hotmail.com. *Librn,* Peggy Oldham; Staff 4 (Non-MLS 4)
Oct 2009-Sept 2010 Income $247,303, County $241,506, Other $5,797. Mats Exp $31,200, Books $22,000, AV Mat $9,200. Sal $126,820 (Prof $40,280)
Library Holdings: Audiobooks 903; DVDs 70; Bk Titles 38,243; Per Subs 40
Wireless access
Mem of North Texas Library Partners
Partic in Tex Share
Open Mon & Wed 10-6, Tues & Thurs 9-7, Fri 9-5, Sat 10-3

GOLDTHWAITE

P JENNIE TRENT DEW LIBRARY, 1101 Hutchings St, 76844. (Mail add: PO Box 101, 76844-0101). Tel: 325-648-2447. FAX: 325-648-2447. E-mail: librarian@jtdlibrary.net. Web Site: jtdlibrary.net. *Dir,* Deb Flowers
Pop 4,723; Circ 13,763
Library Holdings: Bk Titles 10,079; Bk Vols 11,123
Automation Activity & Vendor Info: (Cataloging) Biblionix; (Circulation) Biblionix
Wireless access
Mem of Central Texas Library System, Inc
Partic in Central Texas Digital Consortium
Open Mon & Wed-Fri 1-6, Tues 10-7, Sun 12-6
Friends of the Library Group

GOLIAD

P GOLIAD COUNTY LIBRARY*, 320 S Commercial St, 77963. (Mail add: PO Box 1025, 77963-1025), SAN 316-3814. Tel: 361-645-2291. FAX: 361-645-8956. *Librn,* Claudine Janota
Founded 1958. Pop 7,104; Circ 25,000
Library Holdings: AV Mats 412; Bk Vols 25,571; Per Subs 50
Subject Interests: Tex hist
Automation Activity & Vendor Info: (Cataloging) Follett Software; (Circulation) Follett Software; (OPAC) Follett Software
Wireless access
Open Mon-Fri 8-5
Friends of the Library Group

GONZALES

P GONZALES PUBLIC LIBRARY, 415 St Matthew, 78629-4037. (Mail add: PO Box 220, 78629-0220), SAN 316-3822. Tel: 830-672-6315. Administration Tel: 830-672-9433. FAX: 830-672-8735. Web Site: cityofgonzales.org. *Libr Dir,* Caroline C Helms; E-mail: caroline_helms@yahoo.com; Staff 3 (Non-MLS 3)
Pop 7,471; Circ 27,000
Apr 2008-Mar 2009 Income $179,280, City $158,280, Locally Generated Income $14,000, Other $7,000. Mats Exp $92,798, Books $49,350, Per/Ser (Incl. Access Fees) $1,100, AV Mat $38,348, Electronic Ref Mat (Incl. Access Fees) $4,000. Sal $86,481
Library Holdings: Audiobooks 744; AV Mats 16; Bks on Deafness & Sign Lang 25; DVDs 1,890; Large Print Bks 531; Bk Titles 28,670; Per Subs 65
Special Collections: Genealogy Coll; Texana Coll
Automation Activity & Vendor Info: (Cataloging) Follett Software; (Circulation) Follett Software; (ILL) OCLC FirstSearch; (OPAC) Follett Software
Wireless access
Open Mon 11-7, Tues-Fri 9-5, Sat 9-12
Friends of the Library Group

GOODFELLOW AFB

A UNITED STATES AIR FORCE*, Goodfellow Base Library FL 3030, 17 FSS/FSDL, Bldg 712, 271 Fort Phantom Hill Ave, 76908-4711. SAN 361-7645. Tel: 325-654-5049. Circulation Tel: 325-654-3232. FAX: 325-654-4731. E-mail: gafblibrary@suddenlinkmail.com. Web Site: www.gafblibrary.org. *Librn,* Cindy Tews; E-mail: cindy.tews@goodfellow.af.mil; Staff 8 (MLS 1, Non-MLS 7)
Founded 1942
Library Holdings: Audiobooks 1,146; AV Mats 1,855; Bk Vols 26,660; Per Subs 129
Automation Activity & Vendor Info: (Cataloging) OCLC Connexion; (Circulation) ComPanion Corp; (ILL) OCLC
Database Vendor: Amigos Library Services, EBSCOhost, Faulkner Information Services, Gale Cengage Learning, Newsbank, OCLC, Overdrive, Inc, ProQuest, Safari Books Online, TumbleBookLibrary
Wireless access
Restriction: Not open to pub

GORMAN

P CHARLIE GARRETT MEMORIAL LIBRARY*, 103 S Fisher St, 76454. (Mail add: PO Box 236, 76454-0236). Tel: 254-734-3301, 254-734-4305. *Dir,* Susanne Lipson
Pop 3,580
Library Holdings: Bk Vols 11,443
Wireless access
Open Mon-Fri 3-5
Friends of the Library Group

GRAHAM

P   LIBRARY OF GRAHAM*, 910 Cherry St, 76450-3547. SAN 316-3830.
Tel: 940-549-0600. FAX: 940-549-8624. E-mail: library@grahamtexas.net.
Web Site: www.grahamtexas.net/library. *Dir*, Sherrie R Gibson; E-mail:
sherrie@grahamtexas.net; *Ch*, Betsy Keith; Staff 6 (Non-MLS 6)
Founded 1911. Pop 8,716; Circ 111,518
Library Holdings: AV Mats 3,389; Large Print Bks 2,187; Bk Titles
40,946; Bk Vols 43,399; Per Subs 94; Talking Bks 1,781
Special Collections: Texana Coll; Young County Coll. Oral History
Automation Activity & Vendor Info: (Cataloging) Book Systems, Inc;
(Circulation) Book Systems, Inc; (ILL) OCLC; (OPAC) Book Systems, Inc
Database Vendor: Baker & Taylor, Facts on File, OCLC WorldCat
Wireless access
Mem of North Texas Library Partners
Open Mon-Fri 10-6, Sat 10-2
Friends of the Library Group

GRANBURY

P   HOOD COUNTY PUBLIC LIBRARY*, 222 N Travis, 76048. SAN
316-3849. Tel: 817-573-3569. FAX: 817-573-3969. E-mail:
patron@co.hood.tx.us. *Libr Dir*, Courtney Kincaid; Staff 6 (MLS 2,
Non-MLS 4)
Pop 51,182; Circ 108,000
Library Holdings: Bk Titles 39,900; Per Subs 75
Automation Activity & Vendor Info: (Cataloging) TLC (The Library
Corporation); (Circulation) TLC (The Library Corporation)
Wireless access
Function: Bks on CD, Children's prog, Computers for patron use, Free
DVD rentals, ILL available, Photocopying/Printing, Prog for children &
young adult, Spoken cassettes & CDs, Spoken cassettes & DVDs, Summer
reading prog, Tax forms, VHS videos, Video lending libr
Mem of North Texas Library Partners
Open Mon 10-7, Tues 10-9, Wed-Sat 10-6
Friends of the Library Group

GRAND PRAIRIE

P   GRAND PRAIRIE PUBLIC LIBRARY SYSTEM*, 901 Conover Dr,
75051. SAN 316-3857. Tel: 972-237-5700. Administration Tel:
972-237-5702. Information Services Tel: 972-237-5701. FAX:
972-237-5750. E-mail: infodesk@gptx.org. Web Site: www.gptx.org/library.
Dir, Kathy Ritterhouse; E-mail: kritterh@gptx.org; *Head, Ref*, Linda
Stidham; E-mail: lstidham@gptx.org; *Head, Tech Serv*, Jennifer Douglas;
E-mail: jlatham@gptx.org; *Ref & ILL Librn*, Tanya Slaughter; E-mail:
tpomeroy@gptx.org; *Libr Serv Mgr*, Jennifer Walker; E-mail:
jwalker@gptx.org; *Communications, Advocacy & Outreach Serv Coordr*,
Elisabeth McMahon; E-mail: emcmahon@gptx.org; *Ch*, Melissa Perez;
E-mail: mperez@gptx.org; *Ref Serv*, Anne Felix; E-mail: afelix@gptx.org;
Staff 34 (MLS 13, Non-MLS 21)
Founded 1937. Pop 137,500; Circ 341,750
Library Holdings: Bk Vols 166,005; Per Subs 425
Special Collections: Local History, bks, doc, micro, ms, photog, slides,
tapes
Automation Activity & Vendor Info: (Acquisitions) SirsiDynix;
(Cataloging) SirsiDynix; (Circulation) SirsiDynix; (OPAC) SirsiDynix
Wireless access
Open Mon, Tues & Thurs 10-9, Wed 10-6, Sat 9-6, Sun 1-5
Friends of the Library Group
Branches: 2
BOWLES LIFE CENTER BRANCH, 2750 Graham St, 75050. Tel:
972-237-5740. *Br Librn*, Christie Gibrich; E-mail: cgibrich@gptx.org
  Library Holdings: Bk Titles 10,000
  Automation Activity & Vendor Info: (Cataloging) Horizon;
(Circulation) Horizon
  Open Mon, Tues & Thurs 2-9, Wed & Sat 10-6
BETTY WARMACK BRANCH LIBRARY, 760 Bardin Rd, 75052. Tel:
972-237-5772. Circulation Tel: 972-237-5770. FAX: 972-237-5779. *Br
Mgr*, Debra Holster; E-mail: dholster@gptx.org
  Library Holdings: Bk Vols 35,000; Per Subs 95
  Automation Activity & Vendor Info: (Cataloging) Horizon;
(Circulation) Horizon; (OPAC) Horizon
  Open Mon, Tues & Thurs 1-9, Wed & Sat 9-6, Sun 1-5
  Friends of the Library Group

S   LOCKHEED MARTIN MISSILES & FIRE CONTROL*, Technical
Library, 1701 W Marshall Dr, 75051. (Mail add: PO Box 650003, Dallas,
75265-0003), SAN 316-2745. Tel: 972-603-7155. Interlibrary Loan Service
Tel: 972-603-9404. Reference Tel: 972-603-7318. FAX: 972-603-0182.
Chief Librn, Sherry Daniel Siler; E-mail: sherry.siler@lmco.com; *Doc
Delivery*, Ming-Pei Eades; E-mail: ming-pei.eades@lmco.com; *Ref Serv*,
Kay Nichols; E-mail: kay.nichols@lmco.com; Staff 3 (MLS 3)
Founded 1949

Library Holdings: Audiobooks 120; e-books 550; Bk Titles 27,000; Per
Subs 80
Special Collections: Vought History Coll
Subject Interests: Aeronautical eng, Aerospace, Defense, Electronics
Automation Activity & Vendor Info: (Cataloging) SirsiDynix;
(Circulation) SirsiDynix; (ILL) OCLC; (OPAC) SirsiDynix; (Serials)
SirsiDynix
Partic in Amigos Library Services, Inc
Restriction: Co libr

GRAND SALINE

P   GRAND SALINE PUBLIC LIBRARY*, 201 E Pacific Ave, 75140. SAN
320-8478. Tel: 903-962-5516. FAX: 903-962-6866. *Librn*, Kelli Bryant
Founded 1966. Pop 5,000
Library Holdings: Bk Vols 22,000
Automation Activity & Vendor Info: (Cataloging) LibLime; (Circulation)
LibLime; (OPAC) LibLime
Wireless access
Open Tues-Fri 9-5
Friends of the Library Group

GRANDVIEW

P   GRANDVIEW PUBLIC LIBRARY*, 112 S Third St, 76050. (Mail add:
PO Box 694, 76050-0694). Tel: 817-866-3995. FAX: 817-866-2037.
E-mail: grandviewpubliclibrary@yahoo.com. Web Site:
www.grandviewlibrary.net. *Dir*, Joey Plew
Pop 1,346; Circ 2,003
Library Holdings: Bk Vols 11,000; Talking Bks 400
Automation Activity & Vendor Info: (Cataloging) Book Systems, Inc;
(Circulation) Book Systems, Inc
Wireless access
Mem of North Texas Library Partners
Open Mon, Wed & Thurs 12-5, Tues 12-7

GRAPELAND

P   GRAPELAND PUBLIC LIBRARY*, 212 N Oak St, 75844. (Mail add: PO
Box 879, 75844). Tel: 936-687-3425. FAX: 936-687-3461. Web Site:
www.grapelandlib.org. *Librn*, Alice Ormiston
Circ 1,374
Library Holdings: AV Mats 81; CDs 143; DVDs 231; Bk Titles 9,259;
Videos 196
Subject Interests: Genealogy, Regional hist
Automation Activity & Vendor Info: (Cataloging) Surpass; (Circulation)
Surpass; (OPAC) Surpass
Wireless access
Open Mon 3-8, Tues-Thurs 10-2, Fri 10-1

GRAPEVINE

P   GRAPEVINE PUBLIC LIBRARY*, 1201 Municipal Way, 76051. SAN
316-3881. Tel: 817-410-3400. FAX: 817-410-3084. Web Site:
www.grapevine.lib.tx.us. *Dir*, Janis Roberson; Tel: 817-410-3410, E-mail:
janisr1@airmail.net; *Libr Mgr*, David Coulter; Tel: 817-410-3415, E-mail:
dcoulter@grapevine.lib.tx.us; *Librn*, Nancy Maxwell; Tel: 817-410-3429,
E-mail: nmaxwell@grapevine.lib.tx.us; *Ref Librn II*, Erica Stone; Tel:
817-410-3403, E-mail: estone@grapevinetexas.gov; *Ref Librn II*, Linda
Tervino; Tel: 817-410-3403, E-mail: ltrevino@grapevinetexas.gov; *Cat*,
Ron Tester; *Ch*, Leigh Burnham; Tel: 817-410-3405, E-mail:
lburnham@grapevine.lib.tx.us; Staff 7 (MLS 7)
Founded 1923. Pop 50,514; Circ 330,975
Oct 2010-Sept 2011 Income $1,655,128. Mats Exp $1,572,880, Books
$1,449,043, Per/Ser (Incl. Access Fees) $20,000, AV Mat $35,337,
Electronic Ref Mat (Incl. Access Fees) $68,000, Presv $500. Sal
$1,192,323 (Prof $527,655)
Library Holdings: AV Mats 1,997; CDs 7,931; DVDs 7,930; e-books
36,000; Electronic Media & Resources 2,750; Bk Titles 130,480; Bk Vols
150,510; Per Subs 150; Talking Bks 8,624; Videos 2,846
Special Collections: Oral History
Subject Interests: Genealogy, Tex
Automation Activity & Vendor Info: (Acquisitions) SirsiDynix;
(Cataloging) SirsiDynix; (Circulation) SirsiDynix; (OPAC) SirsiDynix
Wireless access
Mem of North Texas Library Partners
Special Services for the Blind - Reader equip
Open Mon-Thurs 10-9, Fri 10-6, Sat 10-5, Sun 2-6
Friends of the Library Group

GREENVILLE

P   W WALWORTH HARRISON PUBLIC LIBRARY*, One Lou Finney
Lane, 75401-5988. SAN 316-3903. Tel: 903-457-2992. FAX:
903-457-2961. *Dir*, Paul Phelan; Staff 4 (MLS 2, Non-MLS 2)
Founded 1904. Pop 25,051; Circ 99,000

Library Holdings: AV Mats 1,780; Bk Vols 48,500; Per Subs 86; Talking Bks 1,444
Subject Interests: Genealogy, Local hist
Automation Activity & Vendor Info: (Cataloging) TLC (The Library Corporation); (Circulation) TLC (The Library Corporation); (OPAC) TLC (The Library Corporation)
Database Vendor: EBSCOhost, Gale Cengage Learning, netLibrary, OCLC FirstSearch
Function: ILL available
Open Mon, Tues & Thurs 10-8, Wed, Fri & Sat 10-6
Restriction: No access to competitors
Friends of the Library Group

L   MORGAN & GOTCHER LAW OFFICE LIBRARY*, 2610 Stonewall St, 75401-4258. (Mail add: PO Box 556, 75403-0556), SAN 372-9796. Tel: 903-455-3183. FAX: 903-454-4654.
Library Holdings: Bk Vols 5,000; Per Subs 15
Restriction: Staff use only

GROESBECK

P   GROESBECK MAFFETT PUBLIC LIBRARY*, 601 W Yeagua St, 76642-1658. SAN 316-392X. Tel: 254-729-3667. FAX: 254-729-2345. Web Site: www.groesbecklibrary.org. *Libr Dir,* Rhonda J Bass; Staff 3 (MLS 1, Non-MLS 2)
Founded 1976. Pop 7,500
Library Holdings: Bks on Deafness & Sign Lang 10; High Interest/Low Vocabulary Bk Vols 50; Large Print Bks 350; Bk Titles 21,045; Per Subs 66
Special Collections: Limestone County History Coll; Ray A Walter Coll. Oral History
Automation Activity & Vendor Info: (Acquisitions) Baker & Taylor; (Cataloging) Biblionix; (Circulation) Biblionix; (ILL) OCLC WorldCat
Database Vendor: LearningExpress, OCLC FirstSearch, OCLC WebJunction, OCLC WorldCat
Wireless access
Mem of Central Texas Library System, Inc
Special Services for the Deaf - Adult & family literacy prog; Assisted listening device; Assistive tech; Bks on deafness & sign lang; High interest/low vocabulary bks
Special Services for the Blind - Talking bks & player equip; Videos on blindness & phys handicaps
Open Mon-Fri 11:30-5:30, Sat 10-1

GROVES

P   GROVES PUBLIC LIBRARY*, 5600 W Washington St, 77619. SAN 325-0113. Tel: 409-962-6281. FAX: 409-962-3379. Web Site: cigrovestx.com/libraryhome.php. *Dir,* Deborah Harper; E-mail: dharper@cigrovestx.com; *Asst Librn,* Louella Neeb
Founded 1930. Pop 17,008; Circ 50,000
Library Holdings: Bk Vols 40,000; Per Subs 52
Automation Activity & Vendor Info: (Cataloging) Follett Software; (Circulation) Follett Software; (OPAC) Follett Software
Partic in TexSHARE - Texas State Library & Archives Commission
Special Services for the Deaf - Bks on deafness & sign lang; High interest/low vocabulary bks; Spec interest per
Open Mon-Thurs 8:30-6, Fri 8:30-5, Sat 11-3

GROVETON

P   GROVETON PUBLIC LIBRARY*, 126 W First, 75845. (Mail add: PO Box 399, 75845-0399), SAN 376-4095. Tel: 936-642-2483. *Asst Librn,* Evelyn Hyland
Library Holdings: Large Print Bks 120; Bk Titles 7,500; Videos 130
Automation Activity & Vendor Info: (Cataloging) Follett Software; (Circulation) Follett Software
Open Mon-Fri 8-12

GRUVER

P   GRUVER CITY LIBRARY*, 504 King St, 79040. (Mail add: PO Box 701, 79040-0701), SAN 316-3938. Tel: 806-733-2191. FAX: 806-733-2419. E-mail: gruverlibrary@antden.com. *Dir,* Carolyn Fletcher
Founded 1961. Pop 1,444; Circ 3,036
Library Holdings: Bk Vols 14,097
Partic in Harrington Library Consortium
Open Mon, Wed & Fri 2-6, Tues & Thurs 9-1

GUTHRIE

P   GUTHRIE CSD & KING COUNTY CONSOLIDATED LIBRARY*, Hwy 82, 79236. (Mail add: PO Box 70, 79236-0070), SAN 376-4249. Tel: 806-596-4466. FAX: 806-596-4088. Web Site: www.guthriejags.net/district/library.php. *Librn,* JoAnn Shipman; E-mail: joannshipman@esc17.net

Pop 363; Circ 3,000
Library Holdings: AV Mats 1,000; Bk Vols 17,000; Per Subs 45; Videos 1,507
Wireless access
Mem of West Texas Library System
Open Mon-Fri 8-4:30

HALE CENTER

P   HALE CENTER PUBLIC LIBRARY*, 609 Main St, 79041. (Mail add: PO Box 214, 79041-0214), SAN 316-3946. Tel: 806-839-2055. FAX: 806-839-2055. E-mail: hcplibrary@yahoo.com. *Librn,* Linda Chapman; Staff 1 (MLS 1)
Pop 2,000; Circ 5,234
Library Holdings: Bk Vols 20,000
Special Collections: Texas Heritage Resource Center
Automation Activity & Vendor Info: (Cataloging) LibLime; (Circulation) LibLime; (OPAC) LibLime
Wireless access
Mem of West Texas Library System
Open Mon, Wed & Fri 9-12 & 1-5:30
Friends of the Library Group

HALLETTSVILLE

P   FRIENCH SIMPSON MEMORIAL LIBRARY*, 705 E Fourth St, 77964-2828. SAN 316-3954. Tel: 361-798-3243. FAX: 361-798-5833. E-mail: fsmlib@cmaaccess.com. *Dir,* Carol Morisak; *Ch,* Brenda Lincke-Fisseler; Staff 4 (Non-MLS 4)
Founded 1962. Pop 3,800; Circ 45,000
Library Holdings: Bk Titles 23,800; Per Subs 35
Subject Interests: Genealogy, Local hist
Automation Activity & Vendor Info: (Cataloging) Follett Software; (Circulation) Follett Software; (OPAC) Follett Software
Wireless access
Open Tues & Thurs 8:30-5:30, Wed & Fri 11:30-5:30, Sat 9-12
Friends of the Library Group

HALTOM CITY

P   HALTOM CITY PUBLIC LIBRARY*, 4809 Haltom Rd, 76117-3622. (Mail add: PO Box 14277, 76117-0277), SAN 316-3962. Tel: 817-222-7787. Circulation Tel: 817-222-7785. Reference Tel: 817-222-7786. Administration Tel: 817-222-7790. FAX: 817-834-1446. E-mail: info@haltomcitytx.com. Web Site: www.haltomcitytx.com/library. *Dir, Libr Serv,* Lesly M Smith; Tel: 817-222-7791, E-mail: lmsmith@haltomcitytx.com; *Asst Libr Dir, Cat,* Ann Rethard; Tel: 817-222-7792, E-mail: arethard@haltomcitytx.com; *Sr Librn, Ad Serv,* Position Currently Open; *Sr Librn, Coll Develop,* Grant Vaden; Tel: 817-222-7813, E-mail: gvaden@haltomcitytx.com; *Librn, Adult Serv,* Dean Hodges; Tel: 817-222-7758, E-mail: dhodges@haltomcitytx.com; *Children's Librn, Circ Serv,* Becky Deaton; Tel: 817-222-7815, E-mail: bdeaton@haltomcitytx.com; *Outreach Serv Librn,* Allison Long; Tel: 817-222-7814, E-mail: along@haltomcitytx.com; *Acq,* Dianne Elrod; Tel: 817-222-7793, E-mail: delrod@haltomcitytx.com; Staff 22 (MLS 2, Non-MLS 20)
Founded 1961. Pop 39,812; Circ 333,170
Oct 2008-Sept 2009 Income $1,113,689, State $13,424, City $1,087,360, Locally Generated Income $12,905. Mats Exp $125,000, Books $105,000, Per/Ser (Incl. Access Fees) $3,000, AV Mat $15,000, Electronic Ref Mat (Incl. Access Fees) $2,000
Library Holdings: Bk Vols 114,000
Automation Activity & Vendor Info: (Cataloging) SirsiDynix; (Circulation) SirsiDynix; (OPAC) SirsiDynix
Database Vendor: SirsiDynix
Wireless access
Function: Adult literacy prog, Bks on cassette, Bks on CD, Children's prog, Computers for patron use, Copy machines, E-Reserves, Electronic databases & coll, Fax serv, Free DVD rentals, Handicapped accessible, Holiday prog, Home delivery & serv to Sr ctr & nursing homes, Homebound delivery serv, ILL available, Music CDs, Online cat, Outreach serv, Photocopying/Printing, Preschool outreach, Prog for adults, Prog for children & young adult, Pub access computers, Ref serv in person, Senior outreach, Story hour, Summer reading prog, Tax forms, Teen prog, Telephone ref, VHS videos, Writing prog
Mem of North Texas Library Partners
Partic in MetrOPAC Consortium
Open Tues-Thurs 10-8, Fri 10-6, Sat 10-5
Friends of the Library Group

HAMILTON

P   HAMILTON PUBLIC LIBRARY*, 201 N Pecan St, 76531. SAN 376-4796. Tel: 254-386-3474. FAX: 254-386-4447. E-mail: hpl@htcomp.net. Web Site: www.hamilton-public-library.org. *Dir,* Nancy Diaz; Staff 3 (Non-MLS 3)

Pop 7,603; Circ 19,983
Library Holdings: DVDs 500; Large Print Bks 240; Bk Titles 17,420; Per Subs 10; Talking Bks 650; Videos 1,000
Automation Activity & Vendor Info: (Cataloging) Follett Software; (Circulation) Follett Software
Database Vendor: EBSCOhost, OCLC FirstSearch
Function: ILL available
Special Services for the Blind - Aids for in-house use
Open Tues & Fri 9-5, Wed & Thurs 9-6, Sat 9-12
Friends of the Library Group

HARKER HEIGHTS

P   HARKER HEIGHTS PUBLIC LIBRARY*, 400 Indian Trail, 76548. SAN 376-4788. Tel: 254-259-5491. FAX: 254-699-4772. E-mail: circulation@ci.harker-heights.tx.us. Web Site: www.ci.harker-heights.tx.us. *Dir,* Lisa D Youngblood; Tel: 254-699-1776, E-mail: lyoungblood@harkerheights.com; Staff 10 (MLS 2, Non-MLS 8)
Pop 18,000
Oct 2009-Sept 2010 Income $576,100, City $42,311. Mats Exp $9,107. Sal $394,000
Library Holdings: Bk Titles 53,131; Per Subs 40
Automation Activity & Vendor Info: (Cataloging) Follett Software; (Circulation) Follett Software; (OPAC) Follett Software
Wireless access
Function: Ref serv available
Open Mon-Thurs 9-8, Fri & Sat 9-6
Friends of the Library Group

HARLINGEN

P   HARLINGEN PUBLIC LIBRARY, 410 76 Dr, 78550. SAN 316-3997. Tel: 956-216-5800. Circulation Tel: 956-216-5810. Reference Tel: 956-216-5821. FAX: 956-430-6654. Web Site: harlingen.biblionix.com. *Dir,* Ruben Rendon; E-mail: rrendon@harlingenlibrary.com; Staff 16.5 (MLS 3, Non-MLS 13.5)
Founded 1920. Pop 83,505; Circ 148,460
Oct 2011-Sept 2012 Income $1,061,571, State $13,083, City $1,035,051, Other $13,437. Mats Exp $117,021, Books $83,639, Per/Ser (Incl. Access Fees) $20,795, Electronic Ref Mat (Incl. Access Fees) $12,587. Sal $688,389 (Prof $60,710)
Library Holdings: Audiobooks 8,574; AV Mats 5,838; Electronic Media & Resources 53; Bk Titles 120,148; Bk Vols 142,351; Per Subs 284
Subject Interests: Genealogy, Railroad hist, Spanish, Tex hist
Automation Activity & Vendor Info: (Acquisitions) Biblionix; (Cataloging) Biblionix; (Circulation) Biblionix; (ILL) Biblionix; (OPAC) Biblionix
Wireless access
Function: Archival coll, Art exhibits, Audio & video playback equip for onsite use, Audiobks via web, AV serv, Bks on CD, CD-ROM, Chess club, Children's prog, Computer training, Computers for patron use, Copy machines, e-mail serv, E-Reserves, Electronic databases & coll, Exhibits, Fax serv, Free DVD rentals, Genealogy discussion group, Handicapped accessible, Holiday prog, ILL available, Magnifiers for reading, Microfiche/film & reading machines, Music CDs, Newsp ref libr, Online cat, Online ref, Online searches, Orientations, Outreach serv, OverDrive digital audio bks, Photocopying/Printing, Prog for adults, Prog for children & young adult, Pub access computers, Ref & res, Ref serv available, Ref serv in person, Scanner, Spanish lang bks, Story hour, Summer & winter reading prog, Summer reading prog, Tax forms, Teen prog, Telephone ref, Web-catalog, Winter reading prog
Special Services for the Deaf - TDD equip
Special Services for the Blind - Reader equip
Open Mon-Thurs 10-9, Fri-Sun 1-5
Restriction: Circ to mem only, Non-circulating coll, Open to pub for ref & circ; with some limitations
Friends of the Library Group

J   TEXAS STATE TECHNICAL COLLEGE*, J Gilbert Leal Learning Resource Center, 1902 N Loop 499, 78550. SAN 316-4012. Tel: 956-364-4609. Interlibrary Loan Service Tel: 956-364-4608. Reference Tel: 956-364-4708. Administration Tel: 956-364-4611. Toll Free Tel: 800-852-8784. FAX: 956-364-5149. Administration FAX: 956-364-5150. E-mail: library@harlingen.tstc.edu. Web Site: www.harlingen.tstc.edu/library. *Dir,* Nancy Hendricks; E-mail: nancy.hendricks@harlingen.tstc.edu; *Tech Serv Librn,* Kelly Withrow; Tel: 956-364-4612, E-mail: kelly.withrow@harlingen.tstc.edu; Staff 11 (MLS 2, Non-MLS 9)
Founded 1969. Enrl 5,800; Fac 150; Highest Degree: Associate
Sept 2008-Aug 2009. Sal $360,452 (Prof $220,860)
Library Holdings: AV Mats 31; Bks on Deafness & Sign Lang 30; CDs 567; DVDs 142; e-books 53,707; e-journals 10,041; Bk Titles 31,600; Bk Vols 34,720; Per Subs 320; Videos 179
Subject Interests: Allied health

Automation Activity & Vendor Info: (Acquisitions) SIRSI-iBistro; (Cataloging) SIRSI-iBistro; (Circulation) SIRSI-iLink; (ILL) OCLC; (OPAC) SirsiDynix
Database Vendor: 3M Library Systems, Baker & Taylor, EBSCOhost, Gale Cengage Learning, OCLC WorldCat, ProQuest, PubMed
Wireless access
Function: Copy machines, Web-catalog, Wheelchair accessible
Special Services for the Blind - Reader equip
Open Mon-Thurs 7:30am-8pm, Fri 7:30-5, Sat 10-4, Sun 1-4

HASKELL

P   HASKELL COUNTY LIBRARY*, 300 N Ave E, 79521-5706. SAN 316-4020. Tel: 940-864-2747, FAX: 940-864-6164. E-mail: haskell.library@yahoo.com. *Librn,* Joan Frazier; Staff 1 (Non-MLS 1)
Founded 1902. Pop 6,093; Circ 14,500
Library Holdings: AV Mats 325; Large Print Bks 500; Bk Titles 9,217; Bk Vols 9,840; Per Subs 8; Talking Bks 1,275
Subject Interests: Local county hist, Local genealogy, Local hist
Automation Activity & Vendor Info: (Cataloging) LibLime; (Circulation) LibLime
Wireless access
Mem of Big Country Library System
Open Mon-Thurs 9-5:30, Fri 9-4:30
Friends of the Library Group

HAWKINS

P   ALLEN MEMORIAL PUBLIC LIBRARY*, 121 E Blackbourn Ave, 75765. (Mail add: PO Box 329, 75765-0329), SAN 370-7431. Tel: 903-769-2241. *Dir,* Pam McKenzie; E-mail: pmck4848@aol.com
Founded 1988. Pop 5,936
Library Holdings: Bk Vols 14,921; Per Subs 12
Open Mon & Wed 8:30-4:30, Tues & Thurs 10-6, Sat 11-2

P   HOLLY COMMUNITY LIBRARY*, 1620 FM 2869, Teaching Library, 75765. Tel: 903-769-5142. *Librn,* Lin Dunham; *Librn,* Adelle Holland
Library Holdings: AV Mats 400; Bk Titles 13,000; Talking Bks 600
Open Tues, Fri & Sat 10-2

HEARNE

P   SMITH-WELCH MEMORIAL LIBRARY*, 105 W Fifth St, 77859. SAN 316-4047. Tel: 979-279-5191. FAX: 979-279-6212. E-mail: info@swmlibrary.com. Web Site: www.hearnepubliclibrary.org. *Dir,* Kelly Hover; Staff 3 (Non-MLS 3)
Pop 4,852; Circ 172,127
Library Holdings: Audiobooks 166; DVDs 38; Bk Titles 10,446; Bk Vols 14,203; Per Subs 5
Automation Activity & Vendor Info: (Cataloging) Follett Software; (Circulation) Follett Software
Wireless access
Mem of Central Texas Library System, Inc
Open Mon-Fri 8:30-5:30

HEBBRONVILLE

P   JIM HOGG COUNTY PUBLIC LIBRARY*, 210 N Smith Ave, 78361. SAN 316-4055. Tel: 361-527-3421. FAX: 361-527-3421.
Pop 5,109; Circ 8,000
Library Holdings: Bk Vols 13,000; Per Subs 42
Automation Activity & Vendor Info: (Cataloging) Follett Software; (Circulation) Follett Software
Wireless access
Open Mon-Fri 9-5

HEMPHILL

P   J R HUFFMAN PUBLIC LIBRARY*, 375 Sabine St, 75948. Tel: 409-787-4829. FAX: 409-787-2957. E-mail: jrhuffman@yahoo.com. Web Site: www.hemphilltxlibrary.com. *Dir,* Vicky Ostrom
Founded 1994. Pop 1,242; Circ 27,526
Library Holdings: Bk Vols 17,000; Per Subs 20
Special Collections: Forestry, Dr Hiram Arnold Coll; Genealogical Research & Family History Coll
Subject Interests: Local hist, Tex hist, Westerns
Automation Activity & Vendor Info: (Acquisitions) Follett Software; (Cataloging) Follett Software; (Circulation) Follett Software; (OPAC) Follett Software
Partic in TexSHARE - Texas State Library & Archives Commission
Open Mon-Fri 9:30-5
Friends of the Library Group

HEMPSTEAD

P   WALLER COUNTY LIBRARY*, 2331 11th St, 77445-6724. SAN 316-4063. Tel: 979-826-7658. FAX: 979-826-7657. Web Site: www.wallercolibrary.com. *Libr Dir,* Shannon B Hausinger; Staff 5 (MLS 1, Non-MLS 4)
Founded 1834. Pop 36,000; Circ 70,000
Jan 2010-Dec 2010 Income (Main Library and Branch(s)) $301,000. Mats Exp $27,000. Sal $218,000 (Prof $47,000)
Library Holdings: Large Print Bks 1,200; Bk Titles 30,106; Per Subs 11
Wireless access
Open Mon-Fri 9-5, Sat 9-12
Branches: 1
BROOKSHIRE PATTISON BRANCH, 3815 Sixth St, Brookshire, 77423. Tel: 281-375-5550. FAX: 281-934-3516. E-mail: blibrary@consolidated.net. *Br Mgr,* Lynda Fairchild; Staff 4 (Non-MLS 4)
    Library Holdings: AV Mats 1,000; Bk Titles 20,000
    Open Mon-Wed 9-5, Thurs 1-7, Fri 8:30-4, Sat 9-12

HENDERSON

P   RUSK COUNTY LIBRARY*, 106 E Main St, 75652. SAN 361-767X. Tel: 903-657-8557. FAX: 903-657-7637. Web Site: www.rclib.org. *Dir,* Pamela Pipkin; E-mail: pipkinp@rclib.org; Staff 10 (MLS 1, Non-MLS 9)
Founded 1937. Pop 48,887; Circ 318,406
Library Holdings: AV Mats 3,159; DVDs 90; Large Print Bks 2,288; Bk Titles 59,300; Bk Vols 64,679; Per Subs 139
Special Collections: Texas Heritage Resource Center
Subject Interests: Hist, Rusk county genealogy
Automation Activity & Vendor Info: (Acquisitions) TLC (The Library Corporation); (Cataloging) TLC (The Library Corporation); (Circulation) TLC (The Library Corporation); (OPAC) TLC (The Library Corporation)
Wireless access
Function: AV serv, ILL available, Photocopying/Printing, Prog for children & young adult, Ref serv available, Summer reading prog, Wheelchair accessible
Publications: The County Line (newsletter of Friends of RCML)
Open Mon & Thurs 8:30-8, Tues & Wed 8:30-6, Fri 9-5
Friends of the Library Group
Branches: 3
MCMILLAN MEMORIAL, 401 S Commerce St, Overton, 75684. (Mail add: P.O. Box 290, Overton, 75684), SAN 361-770X. Tel: 903-834-6318. FAX: 903-834-6937. *Br Mgr,* Jann Smith; E-mail: smithj@rclib.org; Staff 3 (Non-MLS 3)
    Library Holdings: AV Mats 1,549; Large Print Bks 806; Bk Titles 20,439; Bk Vols 21,300; Per Subs 32
    Function: Bk reviews (Group), Bks on cassette, Bks on CD, Children's prog, Computer training, Computers for patron use, Copy machines, Electronic databases & coll, Fax serv, Free DVD rentals, Handicapped accessible, Holiday prog, ILL available, Music CDs, Online cat, OverDrive digital audio bks, Photocopying/Printing, Preschool outreach, Preschool reading prog, Prog for adults, Prog for children & young adult, Pub access computers, Ref & res, Ref serv in person, Scanner, Senior computer classes, Spoken cassettes & CDs, Summer reading prog, Tax forms, Teen prog, VHS videos, Wheelchair accessible
    Open Mon-Wed & Fri 8-5, Thurs 10-7
    Friends of the Library Group
MORROW, 111 W Rusk, Mount Enterprise, 75681. (Mail add: PO Box 367, Mount Enterprise, 75681-0360), SAN 361-7734. Tel: 903-822-3532. *Asst Librn,* Ann Fuller; Staff 2 (Non-MLS 2)
    Library Holdings: AV Mats 1,016; Large Print Bks 646; Bk Titles 13,494; Bk Vols 13,933; Per Subs 25
    Function: ILL available, Photocopying/Printing, Summer reading prog
    Open Mon-Fri 8-5
    Friends of the Library Group
TATUM PUBLIC, 335 Hood, Tatum, 75691. (Mail add: PO Box 1087, Tatum, 75691-1087), SAN 361-7769. Tel: 903-947-2211. FAX: 903-947-3215. *Libr Mgr,* Janet Breedlove; Staff 2.5 (Non-MLS 2.5)
    Library Holdings: AV Mats 1,199; Large Print Bks 938; Bk Titles 15,528; Bk Vols 16,109; Per Subs 27
    Automation Activity & Vendor Info: (Cataloging) TLC (The Library Corporation); (Circulation) TLC (The Library Corporation); (OPAC) TLC (The Library Corporation); (Serials) TLC (The Library Corporation)
    Function: ILL available, Photocopying/Printing, Summer reading prog, Wheelchair accessible
    Open Mon-Fri 8-5

HENRIETTA

P   EDWARDS PUBLIC LIBRARY*, 210 W Gilbert St, 76365-2816. SAN 316-4098. Tel: 940-538-4791. FAX: 940-538-5861. Web Site: www.edwardspl.org. *Dir,* Norma Jean Ruiz-Hearne; E-mail: norma.hearne@sbcglobal.net; Staff 2 (MLS 1, Non-MLS 1)
Founded 1932. Pop 10,450; Circ 44,292
Library Holdings: Bk Titles 31,466; Bk Vols 32,356; Per Subs 70

Automation Activity & Vendor Info: (Cataloging) Follett Software; (Circulation) Follett Software; (OPAC) Follett Software
Database Vendor: EBSCOhost
Wireless access
Partic in Tex Share
Open Mon-Wed & Fri 9-12:30 & 1:30-5, Thurs 9-8

HEREFORD

P   DEAF SMITH COUNTY LIBRARY*, 211 E Fourth St, 79045. SAN 316-4101. Tel: 806-364-1206. FAX: 806-363-7063. Web Site: www.deafsmithcolib.org. *Dir,* Martha Russell; Staff 5 (Non-MLS 5)
Founded 1910. Pop 18,561
Oct 2010-Sept 2011. Mats Exp $56,212. Sal $48,754
Library Holdings: AV Mats 2,752; Large Print Bks 2,350; Bk Vols 64,919; Per Subs 138; Talking Bks 1,965
Subject Interests: Adult basic educ, Spanish
Automation Activity & Vendor Info: (Cataloging) SirsiDynix; (Circulation) SirsiDynix; (OPAC) SirsiDynix
Wireless access
Partic in Harrington Library Consortium
Open Mon & Thurs 9-9, Tues, Wed & Fri 9-6, Sat 9-1
Friends of the Library Group

HEWITT

P   HEWITT PUBLIC LIBRARY*, 100 Zuni Dr, 76643. SAN 376-477X. Tel: 254-666-2442. FAX: 254-666-6025. E-mail: library@cityofhewitt.com. Web Site: www.cityofhewitt.com. *Dir,* Waynette Ditto; Staff 3 (MLS 2, Non-MLS 1)
Founded 1984. Pop 17,416
Library Holdings: High Interest/Low Vocabulary Bk Vols 763; Large Print Bks 340; Bk Vols 38,000
Automation Activity & Vendor Info: (Acquisitions) Follett Software; (Cataloging) Follett Software; (Circulation) Follett Software; (OPAC) Follett Software
Wireless access
Function: Photocopying/Printing, Prog for children & young adult, Summer reading prog
Mem of Central Texas Library System, Inc
Open Mon-Thurs 10-8, Fri 10-5, Sat 10-1
Friends of the Library Group

HIDALGO

P   HIDALGO PUBLIC LIBRARY*, 710 E Texano Dr, 78557. Tel: 956-843-2093. FAX: 956-843-8841. E-mail: librarian@hidalgo.lib.tx.us. Web Site: www.hidalgo.lib.tx.us. *Dir,* Eduardo Lopez; E-mail: eddie@hidalgo.lib.tx.us; *Asst Dir,* Nicole Mckelvy; Staff 3 (MLS 0, Non-MLS 3)
Founded 1998. Pop 18,785
Oct 2008-Sept 2009 Income $240,899, State $6,081, City $215,235, County $19,583. Mats Exp $6,129. Sal $158,757
Library Holdings: Bk Titles 13,099; Bk Vols 14,128; Per Subs 15; Talking Bks 116; Videos 375
Automation Activity & Vendor Info: (Acquisitions) TLC (The Library Corporation); (Cataloging) TLC (The Library Corporation); (Circulation) TLC (The Library Corporation); (ILL) TLC (The Library Corporation); (OPAC) TLC (The Library Corporation)
Wireless access
Function: Adult literacy prog, After school storytime, Bilingual assistance for Spanish patrons, Bks on cassette, Bks on CD, CD-ROM, Children's prog, Computer training, Computers for patron use, Copy machines, Distance learning, e-mail serv, Electronic databases & coll, Fax serv, Free DVD rentals, Handicapped accessible, Holiday prog, ILL available, Instruction & testing, Magnifiers for reading, Mail & tel request accepted, Online cat, Online ref, Online searches, Photocopying/Printing, Prog for children & young adult, Pub access computers, Ref & res, Ref serv in person, Scanner, Spoken cassettes & CDs, Story hour, Summer & winter reading prog, Tax forms, Telephone ref, VHS videos, Video lending libr, Wheelchair accessible
Mem of Hidalgo County Library System
Open Mon-Thurs 10-8, Fri 10-5, Sat 10-2

HIGGINS

P   HIGGINS PUBLIC LIBRARY*, 201 N Main St, 79046. SAN 316-411X. Tel: 806-852-2214. FAX: 806-852-2214. Web Site: www.hlc-lib.org/higgins. *Dir,* Joanie Smith; E-mail: joanslibrary@hotmail.com
Pop 3,486
Library Holdings: Bk Titles 12,000; Bk Vols 12,250; Per Subs 15; Talking Bks 475
Partic in Harrington Library Consortium
Special Services for the Blind - Talking bks

HIGHLAND PARK

P   HIGHLAND PARK LIBRARY*, 4700 Drexel Dr, 75205-3198. SAN 316-1994. Tel: 214-559-9400. FAX: 214-559-9335. E-mail: hplibrary@hptx.org. Web Site: www.hplibrary.info. *Dir,* Bonnie N Case; E-mail: bcase@hptx.org; Staff 1 (MLS 1)
Founded 1930. Pop 8,800; Circ 76,315
Oct 2010-Sept 2011 Income $573,250. Mats Exp $69,160, Books $51,500, Per/Ser (Incl. Access Fees) $4,000, Micro $160, AV Mat $7,500, Electronic Ref Mat (Incl. Access Fees) $6,000. Sal $347,820
Library Holdings: AV Mats 1,972; CDs 1,169; DVDs 533; e-books 1,300; Large Print Bks 630; Bk Titles 35,542; Bk Vols 37,115; Per Subs 55; Talking Bks 2,076; Videos 1,656
Automation Activity & Vendor Info: (Cataloging) TLC (The Library Corporation); (Circulation) TLC (The Library Corporation); (OPAC) TLC (The Library Corporation)
Database Vendor: TLC (The Library Corporation)
Wireless access
Function: Copy machines, E-Reserves, Electronic databases & coll, Handicapped accessible, ILL available, Music CDs, Online searches, Photocopying/Printing, Prog for children & young adult, Ref & res, Ref serv available, Spoken cassettes & CDs, Spoken cassettes & DVDs, Summer reading prog, Tax forms, VHS videos, Wheelchair accessible
Special Services for the Deaf - Bks on deafness & sign lang; High interest/low vocabulary bks
Special Services for the Blind - Audio mat; Bks on cassette; Bks on CD; Cassettes; Copier with enlargement capabilities; Extensive large print coll; Large print bks; Talking bks; Videos on blindness & phys handicaps
Open Tues-Sat 9:30-5:30
Friends of the Library Group

HILLSBORO

J   HILL COLLEGE LIBRARY*, 112 Lamar Dr, 76645. SAN 316-4128. Tel: 254-659-7831. FAX: 254-582-7591. E-mail: library@hillcollege.edu. Web Site: www.hillcollege.edu. *Dir,* Joe Shaughnessy; Staff 4 (MLS 1, Non-MLS 3)
Founded 1962. Enrl 1,958; Fac 84
Library Holdings: Bk Titles 39,000; Bk Vols 42,000; Per Subs 183
Special Collections: Civil War Research Center. Oral History
Subject Interests: Behav sci, Cosmetology, Humanities, Microelectronics, Nursing, Soc sci, Vocational tech
Automation Activity & Vendor Info: (Acquisitions) Mandarin Library Automation; (Cataloging) Mandarin Library Automation; (Circulation) Mandarin Library Automation; (Course Reserve) Mandarin Library Automation; (ILL) Mandarin Library Automation; (Media Booking) Mandarin Library Automation; (OPAC) Mandarin Library Automation; (Serials) Mandarin Library Automation
Database Vendor: EBSCOhost, Gale Cengage Learning, LexisNexis, ProQuest
Wireless access
Open Mon-Thurs 7:30am-10pm, Fri 7:30-4, Sun 2-10
Departmental Libraries:
JOHNSON COUNTY CAMPUS, 2112 Mayfield Pkwy, Cleburne, 76033. Tel: 817-641-9887. FAX: 817-556-2142. Web Site: www.hillcollege.edu. *Librn,* Kevin Henard; Tel: 817-760-5831, E-mail: khenard@hillcollege.edu
     Library Holdings: Bk Vols 10,239; Per Subs 65
     Open Mon-Thurs (Winter) 7:30am-9:30pm, Fri 7:30-4, Sat 9-5:30; Mon-Wed (Summer) 7:30am-8:30pm, Thurs 7:30-5, Sat 11-3

P   HILLSBORO CITY LIBRARY*, 118 S Waco St, 76645. SAN 316-4136. Tel: 254-582-7385. FAX: 254-582-7765. Web Site: www.hillsborotx.org/city-departments/library. *Dir,* Susan S Mann; *Asst Librn,* Russell W Keelin; *Tech Serv,* Nanette Miller; E-mail: nmiller@hillsborotx.org
Library Holdings: Bk Titles 48,000; Per Subs 105
Subject Interests: Tex
Automation Activity & Vendor Info: (Cataloging) Biblionix; (Circulation) Biblionix; (OPAC) Biblionix
Wireless access
Mem of Central Texas Library System, Inc
Partic in Tex ILL Syst
Open Mon & Thurs 9-7, Tues, Wed & Fri 9-5, Sat 9-12
Friends of the Library Group

HITCHCOCK

P   GENEVIEVE MILLER HITCHCOCK PUBLIC LIBRARY*, 8005 Barry Ave, 77563-3238. SAN 376-4109. Tel: 409-986-7814. FAX: 409-986-6353. Web Site: www.hitchcockpubliclibrary.org. *Dir,* Joyce Kliemann; Staff 5 (MLS 1, Non-MLS 4)
     Library Holdings: Audiobooks 300; DVDs 500; Bk Vols 33,000; Per Subs 16

Automation Activity & Vendor Info: (Cataloging) Surpass; (Circulation) Surpass
Wireless access
Open Tues, Wed & Fri 10-5, Thurs 10-6, Sat 10-3
Friends of the Library Group

HOLLAND

P   B J HILL LIBRARY*, 402 W Travis St, 76534-3015. (Mail add: PO Box 217, 76534-0217). Tel: 254-657-2884. FAX: 254-657-2845. *Dir,* Cindie Gunn; E-mail: cgunn@holland.isd.tenet.edu; *Librn,* Holly Naizer
Library Holdings: Bk Vols 10,400
Automation Activity & Vendor Info: (Cataloging) Follett Software; (Circulation) Follett Software
Wireless access
Mem of Central Texas Library System, Inc
Open Tues-Fri 9-5
Friends of the Library Group

HONDO

P   HONDO PUBLIC LIBRARY*, 1011 19th St, 78861-2431. SAN 324-1289. Tel: 830-426-5333. FAX: 830-426-7089. Web Site: www.cityofhondo.com. *Dir,* Dorothy Saathoff; E-mail: d.saathoff@yahoo.com
Founded 1967. Pop 8,481; Circ 30,439
Oct 2010-Sept 2011 Income $265,000. Mats Exp $16,400, Books $13,100, Per/Ser (Incl. Access Fees) $2,500, AV Mat $800
Library Holdings: Bk Titles 19,018; Bk Vols 19,164; Per Subs 92
Special Collections: Caregivers' Resource Center; Celebration of Life Coll; Local Newspaper (Hondo Anvil Herald 1900-present)
Automation Activity & Vendor Info: (Cataloging) Biblionix; (Circulation) Biblionix
Database Vendor: Baker & Taylor, BWI, Gale Cengage Learning
Wireless access
Function: Accelerated reader prog, Adult bk club, Adult literacy prog, Archival coll, Bilingual assistance for Spanish patrons, Bks on cassette, Bks on CD, Children's prog, Computer training, Computers for patron use, Copy machines, Fax serv, Free DVD rentals, Handicapped accessible, ILL available, Mail & tel request accepted, Mail loans to mem, Newsp ref libr, Notary serv, Online cat, Online searches, Photocopying/Printing, Preschool outreach, Prog for children & young adult, Pub access computers, Ref serv in person, Senior computer classes, Serves mentally handicapped consumers, Spoken cassettes & CDs, Story hour, Summer reading prog, Tax forms, VHS videos, Wheelchair accessible
Open Mon & Thurs 8:30-6, Tues & Wed 8:30-7, Fri 8:30-5, Sat 9-12
Restriction: Pub use on premises
Friends of the Library Group

HONEY GROVE

P   HALL-VOYER FOUNDATION*, Bertha Voyer Memorial Library, 500 N Sixth St, 75446. (Mail add: PO Box 47, 75446), SAN 316-4144. Tel: 903-378-2206. FAX: 903-378-2208. Web Site: www.honeygrovelibrary.org. *Dir,* Pattie Mayfield; E-mail: mayfield@honeygrove.org
Founded 1962. Pop 3,000; Circ 16,091
Library Holdings: Bk Titles 21,263; Per Subs 40
Automation Activity & Vendor Info: (Circulation) LibLime
Wireless access
Open Tues & Thurs 10-7, Wed & Fri 10-5, Sat 10-2
Friends of the Library Group

HOOKS

P   HOOKS PUBLIC LIBRARY*, 108 W First St, 75561. (Mail add: PO Box 1540, 75561-1540), SAN 375-5126. Tel: 903-547-3365. E-mail: hplib@windstream.net. *Dir,* Shannon Heflin; Staff 1 (Non-MLS 1)
Founded 1990. Pop 3,500
Library Holdings: Bk Titles 12,576
Special Collections: Hooks Family Geneaology
Subject Interests: Tex
Automation Activity & Vendor Info: (Cataloging) LibraryWorld, Inc; (Circulation) LibraryWorld, Inc; (OPAC) LibraryWorld, Inc
Function: AV serv, Handicapped accessible, Home delivery & serv to Sr ctr & nursing homes, ILL available, Photocopying/Printing, Prog for children & young adult, Summer reading prog, Wheelchair accessible
Open Mon 4pm-7pm, Tues & Wed 10-5, Thurs 1-6, Fri 10-1
Restriction: Open to pub for ref & circ; with some limitations, Pub use on premises

HOUSTON

S   AMERICAN BRAHMAN BREEDERS ASSOCIATION LIBRARY*, 3003 South Loop W, Ste 140, 77054. SAN 371-022X. Tel: 713-349-0854. FAX: 713-349-9795. E-mail: abba@brahman.org. Web Site: www.brahman.org. *VPres,* Chris Shivers; E-mail: cshivers@brahman.org

Library Holdings: Bk Vols 3,800; Per Subs 28
Restriction: Mem only

S   AMERICAN HOTEL & LODGING ASSOCIATION, Information Center, 229 C N Hilton Hotel & College, University of Houston, 77204-3028. SAN 377-2950. Tel: 713-743-2515. Toll Free Tel: 888-743-2515. Information Services FAX: 713-743-3774. E-mail: informationcenter@ahla.com. Web Site: www.ahla.com/information. *Dir,* Lydia Westbrook; *Mgr,* Tamika Figgs
Founded 1988
Library Holdings: Bk Vols 3,000; Per Subs 30
Special Collections: AH&LA Archives
Subject Interests: Hospitality, Lodging, Travel
Database Vendor: EBSCOhost, Elsevier MDL, LexisNexis, OCLC WorldCat, ProQuest
Wireless access
Restriction: Open by appt only

S   ART INSTITUTE OF HOUSTON LIBRARY*, 14400 Northwest Freeway, 77040. SAN 375-4316. Tel: 713-353-4142. FAX: 713-966-2701. Web Site: www.artinstitutes.edu/houston/student-life/library.aspx. *Dir,* Elene Gedevanishvili; E-mail: egedevanishvili@aii.edu; Staff 4 (MLS 3, Non-MLS 1)
Library Holdings: Bk Vols 30,000; Per Subs 147
Special Collections: Culinary Coll
Subject Interests: Applied art
Automation Activity & Vendor Info: (Cataloging) Ex Libris Group; (Circulation) Ex Libris Group; (ILL) OCLC; (OPAC) Follett Software
Database Vendor: ebrary, Wilson - Wilson Web
Wireless access
Partic in Amigos Library Services, Inc; OCLC Online Computer Library Center, Inc
Open Mon-Thurs 7am-10pm, Fri 7-7, Sat 9-5

L   BAKER & BOTTS LLP*, Law Library, One Shell Plaza, 910 Louisiana St, 77002. SAN 316-4160. Tel: 713-229-1643. Interlibrary Loan Service Tel: 713-229-1412. FAX: 713-229-1522. Web Site: www.bakerbotts.com. *Ref,* Emily Clement; *Ref,* Cynthia Montalvo; *Ref,* Richard Pravata
Founded 1872
Library Holdings: Bk Vols 80,000
Special Collections: Corporate Law Coll; Securities Coll; Tax Coll; Utilities Coll
Database Vendor: LexisNexis, Westlaw
Publications: Library Notes (Monthly); User Location Guide to Baker & Botts Library
Partic in D&B; Dialog Corp; LivEdgar; Westlaw
Open Mon-Fri 8:30-5

S   BAKER HUGHES-HOUSTON TECHNOLOGY CENTER*, HTC Library, 2001 Rankin Rd, 77073. SAN 316-4667. Tel: 713-625-6583. FAX: 713-625-5710. Web Site: 69.63.217.25/b95002staff/opac/index.asp. *Info Res Spec,* Gilberto Morales; E-mail: gilberto.morales@bakerhughes.com. Subject Specialists: *Geophysics,* Gilberto Morales; Staff 1 (MLS 1)
Jan 2010-Dec 2010. Mats Exp $34,000, Per/Ser (Incl. Access Fees) $2,000, Other Print Mats $12,000, Electronic Ref Mat (Incl. Access Fees) $20,000. Sal Prof $56,000
Library Holdings: AV Mats 12; CDs 180; e-journals 39; Electronic Media & Resources 25; Bk Titles 5,645; Per Subs 10; Spec Interest Per Sub 25; Videos 726
Subject Interests: Chem, Drilling, Eng, Geol, Geophysics, Petroleum eng, Reservoir eng
Automation Activity & Vendor Info: (Acquisitions) TLC (The Library Corporation); (Cataloging) EOS International; (Circulation) EOS International; (OPAC) EOS International; (Serials) EOS International
Database Vendor: American Chemical Society, American Physical Society, Elsevier, IEEE (Institute of Electrical & Electronics Engineers), IHS, Infotrieve, Ingenta
Open Mon-Thurs 7:30-4:30, Fri 7:30-4
Restriction: Staff use only

L   CHAMBERLAIN, HRDLICKA, WHITE, WILLIAMS & MARTIN*, Law Library, 1200 Smith St, Ste 1400, 77002. SAN 371-6287. Tel: 713-658-2547. Toll Free Tel: 800-342-5829. FAX: 713-658-2553. E-mail: firm@chamberlainlaw.com. Web Site: www.chamberlainlaw.com. *Librn,* Susan Earley; Staff 2 (MLS 1, Non-MLS 1)
Library Holdings: Bk Vols 20,000; Per Subs 90

SR   CHAPELWOOD UNITED METHODIST CHURCH*, Carey B Sayers Memorial Library, 11140 Greenbay St, 77024-6798. SAN 328-4751. Tel: 713-354-4427, 713-465-3467. FAX: 713-365-2808. Web Site: www.chapelwood.org. *Dir,* Kris Jodon; Tel: 713-465-3467, Ext 127; Staff 2 (MLS 2)
Founded 1955

Library Holdings: Bks on Deafness & Sign Lang 10; Large Print Bks 90; Bk Vols 15,000; Per Subs 5; Talking Bks 75
Special Collections: Vidio & Audio Coll
Subject Interests: Relig
Automation Activity & Vendor Info: (Cataloging) Book Systems, Inc
Wireless access
Open Mon-Thurs & Sun 8:30-4:30, Fri 8:30-1:30

S   CHEVRON GLOBAL LIBRARY HOUSTON*, 3901 Briarpark Dr, 77042. SAN 361-7971. Tel: 713-954-6007. FAX: 713-954-6907. E-mail: libhou@chevron.com. *Mgr,* Nan Dubbelde; *Librn,* Debra Clay; *Librn,* Paula Marks; *Librn,* Margy Walsh; Staff 10 (MLS 7, Non-MLS 3)
Founded 1974
Library Holdings: Bk Vols 50,000; Per Subs 150
Special Collections: Society of Petroleum Engineers, preprints
Subject Interests: Exploration, Geol, Personnel, Petrochem bus, Petroleum eng, Petroleum indust statistics, Production
Wireless access
Publications: Acquisitions List (Bi-monthly)
Partic in Dialog Corp; Dow Jones News Retrieval
Restriction: Open by appt only

L   CHEVRON LAW LIBRARY, 1400 Smith St, 7th Flr, 77002. SAN 323-6536. Tel: 713-372-9116. FAX: 713-372-9282. *Chief Librn,* Frederick A Riemann; E-mail: fariemann@chevron.com; Staff 1 (MLS 1)
Founded 1933
Publications: Acquisitions List (Monthly)

GL   CITY OF HOUSTON*, Legal Dept Library, 900 Bagby, 4th Flr, 77002. (Mail add: PO Box 1562, 77251-1562), SAN 361-7793. Tel: 832-393-6354. FAX: 713-247-1017. *In Charge,* Evangeline Bell
Founded 1907
Library Holdings: Bk Titles 11,100
Subject Interests: Municipal law
Wireless access
Partic in Houston Area Law Libr; Westlaw

R   CONGREGATION BETH YESHURUN*, Cantor Rubin Kaplan Memorial Library, 4525 Beechnut Blvd, 77096. SAN 316-4306. Tel: 713-666-1884. FAX: 713-666-2924. *Librn,* Monica Woolf; Staff 6 (MLS 1, Non-MLS 5)
Library Holdings: Bk Vols 50,000
Subject Interests: Holocaust, Judaica
Automation Activity & Vendor Info: (Acquisitions) Follett Software; (Cataloging) Follett Software; (Circulation) Follett Software; (Course Reserve) Follett Software; (ILL) Follett Software; (Media Booking) Follett Software; (OPAC) Follett Software; (Serials) Follett Software
Open Mon & Wed 8-3:15 & 4-6, Tues, Thurs & Fri 8-3:15

§S   CONOCOPHILLIPS LIBRARY NETWORK, 600 N Dairy Ashford, OF 2047, 77079. Tel: 281-293-4972. FAX: 281-293-4574. E-mail: Houston.Library@conocophillips.com. *Dir,* Joyce Foegelle; E-mail: Joyce.L.Foegelle@conocophillips.com; Staff 2 (MLS 1, Non-MLS 1)
Library Holdings: e-books 1,000; e-journals 100; Bk Vols 15,000; Per Subs 20
Subject Interests: Geol, Geophysics, Petroleum eng
Automation Activity & Vendor Info: (Cataloging) VTLS, Inc; (Circulation) VTLS, Inc; (ILL) OCLC; (OPAC) VTLS, Inc; (Serials) VTLS, Inc
Database Vendor: ebrary, EBSCO Information Services, EBSCOhost, Elsevier, Scopus, SerialsSolutions, Springer-Verlag, VTLS, Inc, Wiley, Wiley InterScience
Function: Doc delivery serv, Electronic databases & coll, For res purposes, ILL available, Online cat, Online searches, Orientations, Ref serv available, Res libr, Web-catalog
Partic in Amigos Library Services, Inc; OCLC Online Computer Library Center, Inc
Restriction: Authorized patrons, Authorized personnel only, Employees & their associates, Employees only, Internal circ only, Internal use only, Not open to pub

GM   DEPARTMENT OF VETERANS AFFAIRS MEDICAL CENTER*, Medical Library, 2002 Holcombe Blvd, 77030. SAN 316-5027. Tel: 713-794-7856. FAX: 713-794-7456. Web Site: www.houston.va.gov. *Dir of Educ,* Paulette Wilson; E-mail: paulette.wilson@va.gov
Library Holdings: Bk Vols 3,000; Per Subs 500
Automation Activity & Vendor Info: (Cataloging) Inmagic, Inc.; (Circulation) Inmagic, Inc.; (OPAC) Inmagic, Inc.
Database Vendor: EBSCOhost
Open Mon-Fri 7:30-4:30
Restriction: Staff use only

C   DEVRY UNIVERSITY*, Houston Library, 11125 Equity Dr, 77041. Tel: 713-973-3137. FAX: 713-896-7650. Web Site: www.hou.devry.edu/campus_library.html. *Libr Dir,* Lloyd Wedes; E-mail: lwedes@devry.edu

Library Holdings: Bk Titles 12,000
Open Mon-Thurs 8am-9pm, Fri 8-7, Sat 9-5

R   FIRST PRESBYTERIAN CHURCH*, Ewing Memorial Library, 5300
Main St, 77004-6877. SAN 316-4365. Tel: 713-620-6541. FAX:
713-620-6550. Web Site: www.fpchouston.org. *Librn,* Dorothy Murphey
Founded 1951
Library Holdings: Bk Titles 3,000; Bk Vols 3,200
Subject Interests: Relig studies
Publications: Christianity Today; Presbyterian Outlook; Presbyterians
Today
Open Mon-Fri 8:30-4:30
Restriction: Not open to pub

S   FUGRO, INC*, Corporate Library, 6100 Hillcroft, 77081. (Mail add: PO
Box 740010, 77274-0010), SAN 316-4640. Tel: 713-369-5500. FAX:
713-369-5570. *Bibliog Instr, Librn, Online Serv,* Pat Farnell
Founded 1966
Library Holdings: CDs 50; e-journals 20; Bk Titles 8,100; Bk Vols
12,000; Per Subs 75
Special Collections: Geotechnics (Company Reports & Proceedings of
Geotechnical Conferences); Related publications; Special technical files
Subject Interests: Geol, Geophysics, Geotech eng, Land, Offshore soil
investigations
Automation Activity & Vendor Info: (Cataloging) LibraryWorld, Inc
Publications: McClelland Engineers Library System A to Z (handbook);
New in the Library
Partic in Dialog Corp; OCLC Online Computer Library Center, Inc
Open Mon-Fri 7:30-5
Restriction: Not open to pub, Staff use only

L   GARDERE, WYNNE & SEWELL LIBRARY*, 1000 Louisiana, Ste 3400,
77002. SAN 372-980X. Tel: 713-276-5500. FAX: 713-276-6736. E-mail:
fabtr@gardere.com. Web Site: www.gardere.com. *Librn,* Trisha Petite
Library Holdings: Bk Vols 10,000; Per Subs 50

S   GULF PUBLISHING CO LIBRARY*, Two Green Plaza, Ste 1020, 77046.
(Mail add: PO Box 2608, 77252-2608), SAN 316-4446. Tel: 713-529-4301.
FAX: 713-520-4433. E-mail: publications@gulfpub.com. Web Site:
www.gulfpub.com. *Dir of Circ,* Suzanne McGehee
Founded 1947
Library Holdings: Bk Vols 3,065; Per Subs 95
Subject Interests: Petrochem indust, Petroleum
Wireless access
Open Mon-Fri 8-5

S   H O K, INC*, Resource Library, 2800 Post Oak Blvd, 77056. SAN
316-4241. Tel: 713-407-7700. FAX: 713-407-7809. Web Site:
www.hok.com.
Founded 1968
Library Holdings: Bk Vols 3,000
Subject Interests: Archit, Art, Construction, Eng, Planning
Wireless access
Partic in Dialog Corp; SDC Search Serv; Vutext
Open Mon-Fri 8-5
Restriction: Staff use only

S   HALLIBURTON ENERGY SERVICES*, Houston Technical Library, 3000
N Sam Houston Pkwy E, 77032. SAN 324-1866. Tel: 281-871-4544. FAX:
281-871-4575. *Librn,* Becky L Bolliger; Staff 1 (Non-MLS 1)
Founded 1979
Library Holdings: Bk Titles 9,000; Bk Vols 11,000; Per Subs 105
Special Collections: Association & Industry Standards; Military
Specifications; Society of Petroleum Engineers Coll; United States Patents
Coll (1972-present)
Subject Interests: Chem, Electronics, Eng
Automation Activity & Vendor Info: (Cataloging) Inmagic, Inc.; (OPAC)
Inmagic, Inc.
Database Vendor: Dialog, STN International
Publications: Acquisitions List (Monthly); Brief Guide to the Technical
Information Center; Master Serials List
Partic in Amigos Library Services, Inc
Restriction: Open by appt only

GL   HARRIS COUNTY LAW LIBRARY*, Congress Plaza, 1019 Congress,
17th Flr, 77002. SAN 316-4454. Tel: 713-755-5183. Web Site:
www.hctx.net/law. *Assoc Law Librn,* Judith Jackson
Founded 1913
Library Holdings: Bk Vols 100,000
Automation Activity & Vendor Info: (Cataloging) EOS International;
(OPAC) EOS International; (Serials) EOS International
Wireless access
Open Mon-Fri 8-7

P   HARRIS COUNTY PUBLIC LIBRARY*, 8080 El Rio, 77054. SAN
361-8129. Tel: 713-749-9000. FAX: 713-749-9090. TDD: 713-755-7396.
Web Site: www.hcpl.net. *Libr Dir,* Rhoda L Goldberg; Tel: 713-749-9011,
E-mail: rhoda.goldberg@hcpl.net; *Asst Dir, Technology & Tech Serv,* Gene
Rollins; Tel: 713-749-9020, E-mail: grollins@hcpl.net; *Asst Dir, Support
Serv,* Ronald Lucik; Tel: 713-749-9050, E-mail: rlucik@hcpl.net; *Acq
Librn,* Linda Rima; Tel: 713-749-9041, E-mail: lrima@hcpl.net; *Tech Serv
Mgr,* Bill Jarvis; Tel: 713-749-9040, E-mail: bjarvis@hcpl.net; *Adult Serv
Spec,* Elaine Plotkin; Tel: 713-749-9030, E-mail: eplotkin@hcpl.net; *Ch
Serv Spec,* Stephanie Borgman; Tel: 713-749-9036, E-mail:
sborgman@hcpl.net; Staff 121 (MLS 104, Non-MLS 17)
Founded 1921. Pop 1,453,512; Circ 11,485,172
Mar 2009-Feb 2010 Income (Main Library and Branch(s)) $25,783,888,
State $285,954, County $25,301,914, Locally Generated Income $148,680,
Other $47,340. Mats Exp $3,645,405, Books $2,511,415, Per/Ser (Incl.
Access Fees) $120,472, Other Print Mats $184,553, AV Mat $393,344,
Electronic Ref Mat (Incl. Access Fees) $435,621. Sal $18,066,672
Library Holdings: Audiobooks 53,074; AV Mats 3,000; CDs 90,754;
DVDs 98,456; e-books 75,283; Microforms 200,000; Bk Titles 306,648;
Bk Vols 1,909,707; Per Subs 3,480; Videos 23,244
Automation Activity & Vendor Info: (Acquisitions) SirsiDynix;
(Cataloging) SirsiDynix; (Circulation) SirsiDynix; (Course Reserve)
SirsiDynix; (ILL) OCLC; (Media Booking) SirsiDynix; (OPAC)
SirsiDynix; (Serials) SirsiDynix
Database Vendor: Agricola, American Physical Society, Amigos Library
Services, Backstage Library Works, Booklist Online, Brodart, EBSCO
Information Services, EBSCOhost, Electric Library, Evanced Solutions,
Inc, Gale Cengage Learning, infoUSA, Ingram Library Services,
LearningExpress, Loislaw, Marcive, Inc, Medline, netLibrary, Newsbank,
OCLC FirstSearch, OCLC WebJunction, OCLC WorldCat, Overdrive, Inc,
ProQuest, ReferenceUSA, Safari Books Online, SirsiDynix, Sybase,
TumbleBookLibrary, ValueLine, Wilson - Wilson Web, World Book Online
Wireless access
Function: Ref serv available
Special Services for the Deaf - TDD equip
Friends of the Library Group
Branches: 25
ALDINE BRANCH, 11331 Airline Dr, 77037, SAN 361-8153. Tel:
281-445-5560. FAX: 281-445-8625. *Br Mgr,* Clara Maynard; Staff 4
(MLS 3, Non-MLS 1)
Founded 2001. Circ 266,883
Library Holdings: Audiobooks 580; AV Mats 104; CDs 1,875; DVDs
2,454; Bk Vols 67,091; Per Subs 147; Videos 470
Open Mon 1-8, Tues & Thurs 10-7, Wed 10-8, Fri 1-6, Sat 10-5
Friends of the Library Group
ATASCOCITA, 19520 Pinehurst Trails Dr, Humble, 77346, SAN 376-9461.
Tel: 281-812-2162. FAX: 281-812-2135. *Br Mgr,* Beth Krippel; Staff 4
(MLS 4)
Circ 483,185
Library Holdings: Audiobooks 1,213; AV Mats 230; CDs 3,687; DVDs
4,063; Microforms 48,150; Bk Vols 84,567; Per Subs 162; Videos 2,560
Open Mon & Thurs 10-9, Tues 1-9, Wed 10-6, Fri 1-6, Sat 10-5, Sun
1-5
Friends of the Library Group
BALDWIN BOETTCHER BRANCH, 22248 Aldine Westfield Rd,
Humble, 77338, SAN 322-5704. Tel: 281-821-1320. FAX: 281-443-8068.
TDD: 281-443-4827. *Br Mgr,* Bonnie Langan; Staff 4 (MLS 4)
Founded 1986. Circ 645,634
Library Holdings: Audiobooks 1,417; AV Mats 165; CDs 2,609; DVDs
3,220; Bk Vols 59,480; Per Subs 167; Videos 1,417
Special Services for the Deaf - TDD equip
Open Mon 1-8, Tues & Thurs 10-7, Wed 10-8, Fri 1-6, Sat 10-5
Friends of the Library Group
BARBARA BUSH BRANCH, 6817 Cypresswood Dr, Spring, 77379, SAN
361-8242. Tel: 281-376-4610. FAX: 281-376-0820. E-mail: cc@hcpl.net.
Web Site: www.hcpl.net/branchinfo/cc/ccinfo.htm. *Br Mgr,* Nancy
Agafitei; Staff 9 (MLS 9)
Founded 2002. Pop 186,000; Circ 1,297,303
Library Holdings: Audiobooks 1,189; AV Mats 351; CDs 4,061; DVDs
5,628; Microforms 144,800; Bk Vols 165,033; Per Subs 177; Videos
1,836
Special Services for the Blind - Closed circuit TV magnifier; Reader
equip
Open Mon 1-9, Tues-Thurs 10-9, Fri 10-6, Sat 10-5, Sun 1-5
Friends of the Library Group
CLEAR LAKE CITY-COUNTY FREEMAN BRANCH, 16616 Diana
Lane, 77062, SAN 361-8307. Tel: 281-488-1906. FAX: 281-286-3931.
Br Mgr, Karen Akkerman; Staff 11.5 (MLS 10.5, Non-MLS 1)
Founded 2004. Circ 1,278,022
Library Holdings: Audiobooks 724; AV Mats 76; CDs 7,036; DVDs
8,986; Microforms 29,840; Bk Vols 152,164; Per Subs 198; Videos 1,160
Open Mon-Wed 10-9, Thurs 1-9, Fri 10-6, Sat 10-5, Sun 1-5
Friends of the Library Group

CROSBY BRANCH, 135 Hare Rd, Crosby, 77532, SAN 361-8218. Tel: 281-328-3535. FAX: 281-328-5590. *Librn,* Diane Barker; Staff 2 (MLS 2)
Founded 1987. Circ 126,329
Library Holdings: Audiobooks 959; AV Mats 154; CDs 1,494; DVDs 2,490; Bk Vols 43,135; Per Subs 90; Videos 1,020
Open Mon 12-8, Tues & Thurs 10-6, Fri 1-6, Sat 10-5
Friends of the Library Group

CY-FAIR COLLEGE BRANCH, 9191 Barker Cypress Rd, Cypress, 77433. Tel: 281-290-3210. FAX: 281-290-5288. *Dir,* Mick Stafford
Founded 2003. Circ 1,174,718
Library Holdings: Audiobooks 1,602; AV Mats 285; CDs 5,774; DVDs 8,101; Bk Vols 154,057; Per Subs 208; Videos 2,132
Open Mon-Thurs 7am-10pm, Fri 7-4:30, Sat 8-6, Sun 1-6

FAIRBANKS BRANCH, 7122 N Gessner, 77040, SAN 361-8277, Tel: 713-466-4438. FAX: 281-466-9757. *Br Mgr,* Luanna Adams; Staff 2 (MLS 2)
Founded 1970. Circ 309,914
Library Holdings: Audiobooks 506; AV Mats 160; CDs 1,896; DVDs 2,798; Bk Vols 47,638; Per Subs 94; Videos 838
Open Mon 1-9, Tues-Thurs 10-6, Fri 1-6, Sat 10-5
Friends of the Library Group

OCTAVIA FIELDS MEMORIAL, 1503 S Houston Ave, Humble, 77338, SAN 361-8455. Tel: 281-446-3377. FAX: 281-446-4203. *Br Mgr,* Fayth Brady; Staff 4 (MLS 4)
Founded 2001. Circ 427,052
Library Holdings: Audiobooks 1,042; AV Mats 137; CDs 2,132; DVDs 1,042; Bk Vols 84,048; Per Subs 151; Videos 2,131
Open Mon 1-7, Tues & Thurs 10-9, Wed 10-7, Fri 1-6, Sat 10-5
Friends of the Library Group

GALENA PARK BRANCH, 1500 Keene St, Galena Park, 77547, SAN 361-8331. Tel: 713-450-0982. FAX: 713-451-1131. *Br Supvr,* Robert Fierro; Staff 2 (Non-MLS 2)
Founded 1996. Circ 60,884
Library Holdings: Audiobooks 373; AV Mats 37; CDs 1,119; DVDs 1,568; Bk Vols 31,549; Per Subs 106; Videos 604
Open Mon, Wed & Thurs 10-6, Tues 12-8, Sat 9-1
Friends of the Library Group

HIGH MEADOWS, 4500 Aldine Mail Rte, 77039, SAN 361-834X. Tel: 281-590-1456. FAX: 281-987-3560. *Br Mgr,* Bilal Salahuddin; Staff 3 (MLS 2, Non-MLS 1)
Founded 1983. Circ 102,474
Library Holdings: Audiobooks 508; AV Mats 135; CDs 1,504; DVDs 1,712; Bk Vols 44,796; Per Subs 131; Videos 818
Open Mon 1-8, Tues & Wed 10-7, Thurs 10-8, Fri 1-6, Sat 10-5
Friends of the Library Group

JACINTO CITY BRANCH, 921 Akron, Jacinto City, 77029, SAN 361-8366. Tel: 713-673-3237. FAX: 713-671-0458. *Br Mgr,* Stephanie Orr; Staff 2 (MLS 1, Non-MLS 1)
Founded 1992. Circ 71,416
Library Holdings: Audiobooks 357; AV Mats 129; CDs 1,114; DVDs 1,900; Bk Vols 27,487; Per Subs 100; Videos 762
Open Mon & Fri 1-6, Tues & Wed 10-6, Thurs 10-8, Sat 10-2
Friends of the Library Group

KATY BRANCH, 5414 Franz Rd, Katy, 77493, SAN 361-8390. Tel: 281-391-3509. FAX: 281-391-1927. *Br Mgr,* Angel Hill; Staff 3 (MLS 3)
Founded 2003. Circ 337,709
Library Holdings: Audiobooks 748; AV Mats 140; CDs 2,536; DVDs 3,525; Bk Vols 66,545; Per Subs 144; Videos 1,124
Open Mon & Tues 10-7, Wed 1-8, Thurs 10-6, Fri 1-6, Sat 10-5
Friends of the Library Group

KINGWOOD BRANCH, 4400 Bens View Lane, Kingwood, 77339, SAN 361-8404. Tel: 281-360-6804. FAX: 281-360-2093. *Br Mgr,* Christi Whittington; Staff 8 (MLS 8)
Founded 1983. Circ 534,967
Library Holdings: Audiobooks 753; AV Mats 144; CDs 4,505; DVDs 5,229; Microforms 36,155; Bk Vols 111,763; Per Subs 131; Videos 1,267
Open Mon 1-9, Tues & Thurs 10-6, Fri 1-6, Sat 10-5
Friends of the Library Group

LAPORTE BRANCH, 600 S Broadway, LaPorte, 77571, SAN 361-8420. Tel: 281-471-4022. FAX: 281-470-0839. *Br Mgr,* Myra Wilson; Staff 4 (MLS 4)
Founded 1929. Circ 187,171
Library Holdings: Audiobooks 1,331; AV Mats 155; CDs 2,198; DVDs 2,951; Bk Vols 71,878; Per Subs 134; Videos 1,770
Open Mon 1-9, Tues-Thurs 10-7, Fri 1-6, Sat 10-5
Friends of the Library Group

MAUD SMITH MARKS BRANCH, 1815 Westgreen Blvd, Katy, 77450, SAN 373-529X. Tel: 281-492-8592. FAX: 281-492-3420. *Br Mgr,* Sylvia Powers; Staff 4 (MLS 4)
Founded 1993. Circ 604,310
Library Holdings: Audiobooks 509; AV Mats 128; CDs 3,384; DVDs 4,355; Bk Vols 82,453; Per Subs 172; Videos 845
Open Mon 1-9, Tues 10-9, Wed & Thurs 10-6, Fri 1-6, Sat 10-5
Friends of the Library Group

NORTH CHANNEL, 15741 Wallisville Rd, 77049, SAN 361-8633. Tel: 281-457-1631. *Br Mgr,* Carolyn Dial; E-mail: cdial@hcpl.net; Staff 6 (MLS 3, Non-MLS 3)
Founded 1994. Circ 380,615
Library Holdings: Bk Vols 70,190
Open Mon 1-8, Tues-Thurs 10-8, Fri 1-6, Sat 10-5, Sun 1-5
Friends of the Library Group

NORTHWEST, 11355 Regency Green Dr, Cypress, 77429, SAN 370-0216. Tel: 281-890-2665. FAX: 281-469-4718. *Br Mgr,* Deborah Sica; Staff 3 (MLS 3)
Founded 1984. Circ 534,967
Library Holdings: Audiobooks 254; AV Mats 103; CDs 2,953; DVDs 3,833; Bk Vols 66,233; Per Subs 124; Videos 475
Open Mon 1-8, Tues & Thurs 10-6, Wed 10-8, Fri 1-6, Sat 10-5
Friends of the Library Group

SOUTH HOUSTON BRANCH, 607 Ave A, South Houston, 77587, SAN 361-848X. Tel: 713-941-2385. FAX: 713-947-7389. *Br Supvr,* Clara Lopez; Staff 2 (Non-MLS 2)
Founded 1991. Circ 102,987
Library Holdings: Audiobooks 426; AV Mats 67; CDs 1,335; DVDs 2,059; Bk Vols 295,598; Per Subs 91; Videos 646
Open Mon 1-8, Tues-Thurs 10-6, Sat 10-5
Friends of the Library Group

SPRING BRANCH MEMORIAL, 930 Corbindale, 77024, SAN 361-851X. Tel: 713-464-1633. FAX: 713-973-2654. *Br Mgr,* Karen Hayes; Staff 3 (MLS 3)
Founded 1975. Circ 478,289
Library Holdings: Audiobooks 732; AV Mats 95; CDs 4,346; DVDs 4,122; Bk Vols 75,107; Per Subs 95; Videos 772
Open Mon 1-9, Tues 10-9, Wed & Thurs 10-6, Fri 1-6, Sat 10-5
Friends of the Library Group

STRATFORD BRANCH, 509 Stratford, Highlands, 77562, SAN 361-8544. Tel: 281-426-3521. FAX: 281-426-4354. *Br Supvr,* Sarah Davis; Staff 2 (Non-MLS 2)
Founded 1928. Circ 64,738
Library Holdings: Audiobooks 62; AV Mats 87; CDs 1,101; DVDs 1,930; Bk Vols 19,598; Per Subs 59; Videos 137
Open Mon 12-8, Tues-Thurs 10-6, Fri 1-6, Sat 9-1
Friends of the Library Group

TOMBALL BRANCH, 30555 Tomball Pkwy, Tomball, 77375, SAN 361-8579. Tel: 832-559-4200. FAX: 832-559-4248. *Co-Dir,* Wendy Schneider; Staff 8 (MLS 7, Non-MLS 1)
Founded 2005. Circ 693,809
Library Holdings: Audiobooks 1,567; AV Mats 255; CDs 4,330; DVDs 5,371; Bk Vols 118,454; Per Subs 142; Videos 2,311
Open Mon-Thurs 8am-9:30pm, Fri 8-6, Sat 10-5
Friends of the Library Group

KATHERINE TYRA BRANCH, 16719 Clay Rd, 77084, SAN 361-8161. Tel: 281-550-0885. FAX: 281-550-3304. *Br Mgr,* Sandra Silvey; Staff 4 (MLS 4)
Founded 1983. Circ 645,634
Library Holdings: Audiobooks 107; AV Mats 127; CDs 3,407; DVDs 4,165; Bk Vols 70,647; Per Subs 192; Videos 246
Open Mon 1-8, Tues & Thurs 10-6, Wed 10-8, Fri 1-6, Sat 10-5, Sun 1-5
Friends of the Library Group

WEST UNIVERSITY, 6108 Auden, 77005, SAN 361-8609. Tel: 713-668-8273. FAX: 713-667-2264. *Br Mgr,* Margaret Ann Triandaflyllis; Staff 3 (MLS 3)
Founded 1963. Circ 338,595
Library Holdings: Audiobooks 87; AV Mats 104; CDs 1,789; DVDs 3,063; Bk Vols 40,586; Per Subs 103; Videos 50
Open Mon 10-8, Tues-Thurs 10-6, Fri 1-6, Sat 10-5
Friends of the Library Group

PARKER WILLIAMS BRANCH, 10851 Scarsdale Blvd, Ste 510, 77089, SAN 373-5281. Tel: 281-484-2036. FAX: 281-481-0729. *Br Mgr,* Mary Murray; Staff 3 (MLS 3)
Founded 1993. Circ 343,234
Library Holdings: Audiobooks 821; AV Mats 110; CDs 2,358; DVDs 4,644; Bk Vols 69,742; Per Subs 139; Videos 1,326
Open Mon 1-9, Wed 10-9, Thurs 10-6, Fri 1-6, Sat 10-5
Friends of the Library Group

S THE HERITAGE SOCIETY LIBRARY*, 1100 Bagby, 77002. SAN 327-5388. Tel: 713-655-1912. FAX: 713-655-9249. Web Site: www.heritagesociety.org. *Curator,* Wallace Saage; E-mail: wsaage@heritagesociety.org
Library Holdings: Bk Vols 1,500
Subject Interests: City hist, Decorative art, Tex hist
Function: Ref serv available
Restriction: Non-circulating, Open by appt only

S   HESS CORP*, US Exploration & Production - Technical Library, 500 Dallas St, Level 2, 77002. SAN 370-9809. Tel: 713-609-5000. FAX: 713-609-5549. *Supv Librn,* Kelly Cook; E-mail: kcook@hess.com
Library Holdings: Bk Vols 3,000; Per Subs 30
Open Mon-Fri 8-4:45
Restriction: Not open to pub

S   HIRSCH LIBRARY, MUSEUM OF FINE ARTS, HOUSTON*, 1001 Bissonnet St, 77005-1803. (Mail add: PO Box 6826, 77265-6826), SAN 316-4683. Tel: 713-639-7325. Toll Free Tel: 800-388-8164. FAX: 713-639-7707. E-mail: hirsch@mfah.org. Web Site: www.mfah.org/research/hirsch-library. *Dir,* Jon Evans; Tel: 713-639-7393, E-mail: jevans@mfah.org; *Archivist,* Lorraine A Stuart; E-mail: lstuart@mfah.org; Staff 12 (MLS 6, Non-MLS 6)
Library Holdings: Bk Titles 90,000; Bk Vols 110,000; Per Subs 315
Special Collections: Bayou Bend Library; Museum Archives; Texana
Subject Interests: Art hist, Decorative art, Fine arts
Automation Activity & Vendor Info: (Acquisitions) Ex Libris Group; (Cataloging) Ex Libris Group; (Circulation) Ex Libris Group; (OPAC) Ex Libris Group
Database Vendor: OCLC FirstSearch, Wilson - Wilson Web
Wireless access
Function: For res purposes
Open Tues, Wed & Fri 10-5, Thurs 10-9, Sat 12-5
Restriction: Open to pub for ref only

M   HOUSTON ACADEMY OF MEDICINE, Texas Medical Center Library, 1133 John Freeman Blvd, 77030. SAN 316-4470. Tel: 713-795-4200. Circulation Tel: 713-799-7147. Interlibrary Loan Service Tel: 713-799-7105. Reference Tel: 713-799-7161. Administration Tel: 713-799-7108. FAX: 713-790-7052. Circulation FAX: 713-799-7149. Interlibrary Loan Service FAX: 713-797-7056. Reference FAX: 713-797-0163. Web Site: www.library.tmc.edu. *Exec Dir,* Maximilian Buja; E-mail: l.maximilian.buja@exch.library.tmc.edu; *Sr Assoc Dir, Operations,* Deborah Halsted; Fax: 713-799-7163, E-mail: deborah.halsted@exch.library.tmc.edu; *Assoc Dir, Coll Develop,* Dean James; Tel: 713-799-7122, E-mail: dean.james@exch.library.tmc.edu; *Assoc Dir, Info Tech,* J Chris Young; Tel: 713-799-7803, E-mail: chris.young@exch.library.tmc.edu; *Assoc Dir, Ref & Outreach,* Lisa M Berry; Tel: 713-799-7164, E-mail: lisa.berry@exch.library.tmc.edu; *Asst Dir, Circ,* Jesse Gonzalez; Tel: 713-799-7148, E-mail: jesse.gonzalez@exch.library.tmc.edu; *Mgr, ILL,* Alisa Hemphill; E-mail: alisa.hemphill@exch.library.tmc.edu; Staff 53 (MLS 23, Non-MLS 30)
Founded 1949. Highest Degree: Doctorate
Library Holdings: e-books 12,000; e-journals 8,215; Bk Vols 357,023; Per Subs 32
Special Collections: John P McGovern Historical Coll & Research Center
Subject Interests: Consumer health, Med res, Nursing, Patient info
Automation Activity & Vendor Info: (Acquisitions) Ex Libris Group; (Cataloging) Ex Libris Group; (Circulation) Ex Libris Group; (OPAC) Ex Libris Group; (Serials) SerialsSolutions
Database Vendor: Cambridge Scientific Abstracts, EBSCOhost, Elsevier MDL, Gale Cengage Learning, JSTOR, OCLC FirstSearch, OCLC WorldCat, OVID Technologies, ProQuest, PubMed, ScienceDirect, SerialsSolutions, Swets Information Services, Wiley
Wireless access
Function: Prof lending libr
Partic in SCAMeL; Tex Health Sci Libr Consortium; TexSHARE - Texas State Library & Archives Commission
Open Mon-Thurs 7am-10pm, Fri 7am-9pm, Sat 9-5, Sun 1-10
Restriction: Private libr
Friends of the Library Group

CR   HOUSTON BAPTIST UNIVERSITY*, Moody Memorial Library, 7502 Fondren Rd, 77074-3298. SAN 316-4497. Tel: 281-649-3435. Circulation Tel: 281-649-3304. Interlibrary Loan Service Tel: 281-649-3181. Reference Tel: 281-649-3180. Administration Tel: 281-649-3177. Automation Services Tel: 281-649-3182. FAX: 281-649-3489. Web Site: www.hbu.edu/moody. *Dir,* Ann A Noble; E-mail: aanoble@hbu.edu; *Syst Coordr,* Dean Riley; E-mail: dmriley@hbu.edu; *Bibliog Instr, Ser,* Diane Casebier; Tel: 281-649-3178, E-mail: dcasebier@hbu.edu; *Cat,* Bonita Crider; Tel: 281-649-3179, E-mail: bcrider@hbu.edu; *ILL, Ref,* Kristin Fance; E-mail: kfance@hbu.edu; *Ref & Instruction,* Position Currently Open; Staff 9.75 (MLS 6, Non-MLS 3.75)
Founded 1963. Enrl 2,403; Fac 120; Highest Degree: Master
Jun 2008-May 2009 Income $1,094,715. Mats Exp $701,791, Books $132,629, Per/Ser (Incl. Access Fees) $314,784, AV Equip $15,147, Electronic Ref Mat (Incl. Access Fees) $234,157, Presv $5,074. Sal $522,713
Library Holdings: AV Mats 9,968; CDs 1,989; DVDs 1,208; e-books 51,064; e-journals 60,147; Bk Vols 237,996; Videos 3,565
Special Collections: Gilbert & Sullivan (Linder Coll); History & Literature (Palmer Bradley Coll); History (Hicks Memorial Coll)
Subject Interests: Baptist hist, Southwest, Tex, Victorian lit

Automation Activity & Vendor Info: (Acquisitions) SirsiDynix; (Cataloging) SirsiDynix; (Circulation) SirsiDynix; (Course Reserve) SirsiDynix; (ILL) OCLC; (OPAC) SirsiDynix
Database Vendor: 3M Library Systems, Alexander Street Press, American Chemical Society, Amigos Library Services, Annual Reviews, Bowker, Cinahl Information Systems, College Source, CountryWatch, CQ Press, CredoReference, Discovery Education, EBSCO Information Services, EBSCOhost, Elsevier, Gale Cengage Learning, H W Wilson, IOP, JSTOR, LexisNexis, Medline, Mergent Online, Modern Language Association, Newsbank, OCLC FirstSearch, OCLC WorldCat, OVID Technologies, ProQuest, PubMed, ReferenceUSA, ScienceDirect, SirsiDynix, Standard & Poor's, STAT!Ref (Teton Data Systems), STN International, ValueLine
Wireless access
Function: Audio & video playback equip for onsite use, Computers for patron use, Copy machines, Electronic databases & coll, ILL available, Online cat, Ref serv available
Partic in Tex Share
Open Mon-Thurs 7:30am-11pm, Fri 7:30-5, Sat 12-6, Sun 2-8
Restriction: Open to pub for ref only, Open to students, fac, staff & alumni

S   HOUSTON CHRONICLE LIBRARY*, 801 Texas Ave, 77002. (Mail add: PO Box 4260, 77210), SAN 316-4500. Tel: 713-220-7171. E-mail: info@copyright.com. Web Site: www.houstonchronicle.com. Staff 2 (MLS 2)
Founded 1961
Library Holdings: Bk Vols 2,000; Per Subs 14
Subject Interests: News files, Texana
Database Vendor: Factiva.com, LexisNexis, ProQuest
Open Mon-Fri 7:30-7:30
Restriction: Co libr, Not open to pub

HOUSTON COMMUNITY COLLEGE*, Coleman Campus Library, 1900 Pressler St, 77030. Tel: 713-718-7399. FAX: 713-718-7396.
Highest Degree: Associate
Library Holdings: AV Mats 2,750; e-books 19,000; Bk Vols 9,051; Per Subs 120
Open Mon-Thurs 7:30am-9pm, Fri 7:30-4, Sat 9-1

HOUSTON COMMUNITY COLLEGE - CENTRAL COLLEGE
J   CENTRAL CAMPUS LIBRARY*, 1300 Holman, 77004, SAN 316-4519. Tel: 713-718-6133. Information Services Tel: 713-718-6141. FAX: 713-718-6154. E-mail: aska.librarian@hccs.edu. Web Site: library.hccs.edu. *Chairperson,* Ronald Homick; E-mail: ron.homick@hccs.edu; *Librn,* Marcia Braun; E-mail: marcia.braun@hccs.edu; *Librn,* Leo Cavazos; E-mail: leo.cavazos@hccs.edu; *Librn,* Len Cazares; E-mail: len.cazares@hccs.edu; *Librn,* Stephanie Emesih; E-mail: stephanie.emesih@hccs.edu
Founded 1972. Enrl 70,000; Fac 980
Library Holdings: AV Mats 4,161; e-books 19,000; Bk Vols 56,924; Per Subs 97
Subject Interests: Med
Automation Activity & Vendor Info: (Acquisitions) Innovative Interfaces, Inc; (Cataloging) Innovative Interfaces, Inc; (Circulation) Innovative Interfaces, Inc - Millenium; (Course Reserve) Innovative Interfaces, Inc; (Media Booking) Innovative Interfaces, Inc; (OPAC) Innovative Interfaces, Inc; (Serials) Innovative Interfaces, Inc
Database Vendor: Baker & Taylor, EBSCOhost, Gale Cengage Learning, JSTOR, netLibrary, OCLC FirstSearch, OCLC WorldCat, OVID Technologies, ProQuest, Wilson - Wilson Web
Partic in OCLC Online Computer Library Center, Inc
Open Mon-Thurs (Fall & Spring) 7:30am-9pm, Fri 7:30-4, Sat 9-3

E   WILLIE LEE GAY HALL ERC - SOUTH CAMPUS*, 1990 Airport Blvd, 77051. Tel: 713-718-6693. FAX: 713-718-6655. *Librn,* Amy Sisson; E-mail: amy.sisson@hccs.edu
Library Holdings: e-books 30,000; Bk Vols 100; Per Subs 19
Open Mon-Thurs 8am-9pm

HOUSTON COMMUNITY COLLEGE - NORTHEAST COLLEGE
J   CODWELL CAMPUS LIBRARY*, 555 Community College Dr, 77013-6127. Tel: 713-718-8354. Reference Tel: 713-718-8320. FAX: 713-718-8330. *Chairperson,* Gwendolyn Richard; E-mail: gwendolyn.richard@hccs.edu; *Librn,* Denise Coles; E-mail: denise.coles@hccs.edu; *Librn,* James Smith; E-mail: james.smith@hccs.edu
Highest Degree: Associate
Library Holdings: AV Mats 1,912; e-books 19,000; Bk Vols 16,526; Per Subs 134
Automation Activity & Vendor Info: (Acquisitions) Innovative Interfaces, Inc; (Cataloging) Innovative Interfaces, Inc; (Circulation) Innovative Interfaces, Inc - Millenium; (Course Reserve) Innovative Interfaces, Inc; (ILL) Innovative Interfaces, Inc; (Media Booking)

Innovative Interfaces, Inc; (OPAC) Innovative Interfaces, Inc; (Serials) Innovative Interfaces, Inc

Open Mon-Thurs 8am-9pm, Fri 8-4:30, Sat 9-3, Sun 12-4

J NORTH FOREST CAMPUS LIBRARY*, 7525 Tidwell Rd, 77016-4413. Tel: 713-635-0427. *Chairperson,* Gwendolyn Richard; E-mail: gwendolyn.richard@hccs.edu; *Librn,* Mildred Joseph
   Automation Activity & Vendor Info: (Acquisitions) Innovative Interfaces, Inc; (Cataloging) Innovative Interfaces, Inc; (Circulation) Innovative Interfaces, Inc - Millenium; (Course Reserve) Innovative Interfaces, Inc; (ILL) Innovative Interfaces, Inc; (Media Booking) Innovative Interfaces, Inc; (OPAC) Innovative Interfaces, Inc; (Serials) Innovative Interfaces, Inc
   Open Mon-Thurs 5pm-9pm

J NORTHLINE LIBRARY*, 8001 Fulton St, 77022. Tel: 713-718-8045. Reference Tel: 713-718-8061. FAX: 713-718-8063. *Dir, Libr Serv,* Gwendolyn Richard; E-mail: gwen.richard@hccs.edu; *Librn,* Lawrence Anderson; E-mail: lawrence.anderson@hccs.edu; *Librn,* Jennifer Stidham; E-mail: jennifer.stidham@hccs.edu
   Library Holdings: AV Mats 1,079; e-books 19,000; Bk Vols 14,687; Per Subs 74
   Automation Activity & Vendor Info: (Acquisitions) Innovative Interfaces, Inc; (Cataloging) Innovative Interfaces, Inc; (Circulation) Innovative Interfaces, Inc - Millenium; (Course Reserve) Innovative Interfaces, Inc; (ILL) Innovative Interfaces, Inc; (Media Booking) Innovative Interfaces, Inc; (OPAC) Innovative Interfaces, Inc; (Serials) Innovative Interfaces, Inc
   Open Mon-Thurs 8am-9pm, Fri & Sat 8-4:30, Sun 12-4; Mon-Thurs (Summer) 8am-9pm, Fri 8-4:30

J PINEMONT CAMPUS LIBRARY*, 1265 Pinemont, 77018-1303. Tel: 713-718-8443. FAX: 713-718-8438. *NE Dir of Libr Serv,* Gwendolyn Richard; E-mail: gwen.richard@hccs.edu; *Librn,* Tolley Reeves; E-mail: tolley.reeves@hccs.edu
   Library Holdings: AV Mats 144; e-books 19,000; Bk Vols 1,187; Per Subs 48
   Automation Activity & Vendor Info: (Acquisitions) Innovative Interfaces, Inc; (Cataloging) Innovative Interfaces, Inc; (Circulation) Innovative Interfaces, Inc - Millenium; (Course Reserve) Innovative Interfaces, Inc; (ILL) Innovative Interfaces, Inc; (Media Booking) Innovative Interfaces, Inc; (OPAC) Innovative Interfaces, Inc; (Serials) Innovative Interfaces, Inc
   Open Mon-Thurs 8am-9pm, Fri 8-4:30

HOUSTON COMMUNITY COLLEGE - NORTHWEST COLLEGE

J KATY CAMPUS LIBRARY*, 1550 Foxlake Dr, 77084-6029. Tel: 713-718-5747. FAX: 281-492-6075. *Librn,* Cynthia Belmar; Tel: 713-718-5849, E-mail: cynthia.belmar@hccs.edu; *Librn,* Daniel Dylla; Staff 3 (MLS 2, Non-MLS 1)
   Library Holdings: AV Mats 1,768; e-books 30,000; Bk Vols 16,000; Per Subs 68
   Automation Activity & Vendor Info: (Acquisitions) Innovative Interfaces, Inc; (Cataloging) Innovative Interfaces, Inc; (Circulation) Innovative Interfaces, Inc - Millenium; (Course Reserve) Innovative Interfaces, Inc; (ILL) Innovative Interfaces, Inc; (Media Booking) Innovative Interfaces, Inc; (OPAC) Innovative Interfaces, Inc; (Serials) Innovative Interfaces, Inc
   Open Mon-Thurs 7:30am-9pm, Fri 7:30-4
   Restriction: Open to students, fac & staff, Pub use on premises

J SPRING BRANCH CAMPUS LIBRARY*, 1010 W Sam Houston Pkwy N, 77043-5008. Tel: 713-718-5655. Reference Tel: 713-718-5434, 713-718-7502. Administration Tel: 713-718-5849. FAX: 713-718-5745. *Librn,* Peggy Edwards; E-mail: peggy.edwards@hccs.edu; *Librn,* Melba Martin; Tel: 713-718-5656, E-mail: melba.martin@hccs.edu; Staff 5 (MLS 3, Non-MLS 2)
   Library Holdings: AV Mats 1,779; e-books 29,000; Bk Vols 16,529; Per Subs 65
   Automation Activity & Vendor Info: (Acquisitions) Innovative Interfaces, Inc; (Cataloging) Innovative Interfaces, Inc; (Circulation) Innovative Interfaces, Inc - Millenium; (Course Reserve) Innovative Interfaces, Inc; (ILL) Innovative Interfaces, Inc; (Media Booking) Innovative Interfaces, Inc; (OPAC) Innovative Interfaces, Inc; (Serials) Innovative Interfaces, Inc
   Open Mon-Thurs 7:30am-9pm, Fri 7:30-4, Sat (Aug-May) 9-1
   Restriction: Open to students, fac & staff, Pub use on premises

HOUSTON COMMUNITY COLLEGE - SOUTHWEST COLLEGE

E ALIEF CENTER*, 2811 Hayes Rd, 77082. Tel: 713-718-6941. FAX: 713-718-6932. *Chairperson,* Dennis Klappersack; E-mail: dennis.klappersack@hccs.edu; *Librn,* Jo Blair; E-mail: jo.blair@hccs.edu
   Open Mon-Thurs 7:30am-9pm, Fri 7:30-1, Sat 9-1

E ALIEF CONTINUING EDUCATION CENTER*, 13803 Bissonnet, 77083. Tel: 713-718-5447. *Chairperson,* Dennis Klappersack; E-mail: dennis.klappersack@hccs.edu; *Librn,* Cathy Montoya; E-mail: cathy.montoya@hccs.edu
   Automation Activity & Vendor Info: (Acquisitions) Innovative Interfaces, Inc; (Cataloging) Innovative Interfaces, Inc; (Circulation)

Innovative Interfaces, Inc - Millenium; (Course Reserve) Innovative Interfaces, Inc; (ILL) Innovative Interfaces, Inc; (Media Booking) Innovative Interfaces, Inc; (OPAC) Innovative Interfaces, Inc; (Serials) Innovative Interfaces, Inc
Open Mon-Fri (Sept-May) 7:30-5

E MISSOURI CITY (SIENNA) CAMPUS*, 5855 Sienna Springs Way, Missouri City, 77459. Tel: 713-718-2942. FAX: 713-718-2474. *Chairperson,* Dennis Klappersack; E-mail: dennis.klappersack@hccs.edu; *Librn,* Daphene Keys
   Open Mon-Thurs (Sept-May) 7:30-9pm, Fri 7:30-1

J STAFFORD CAMPUS LIBRARY*, 9910 Cash Rd, Stafford, 77477-4405. Tel: 713-718-7823. Reference Tel: 713-718-7824. FAX: 713-718-6723. *Chairperson,* Dennis Klappersack; E-mail: dennis.klappersack@hccs.edu; *Librn,* Trudy Cleveland; E-mail: trudy.cleveland@hccs.edu; *Librn,* Bill Hord; E-mail: bill.hord@hccs.edu
   Library Holdings: AV Mats 608; Bk Vols 18,486; Per Subs 81
   Automation Activity & Vendor Info: (Acquisitions) Innovative Interfaces, Inc; (Cataloging) Innovative Interfaces, Inc; (Circulation) Innovative Interfaces, Inc - Millenium; (Course Reserve) Innovative Interfaces, Inc; (ILL) Innovative Interfaces, Inc; (Media Booking) Innovative Interfaces, Inc; (OPAC) Innovative Interfaces, Inc; (Serials) Innovative Interfaces, Inc
   Open Mon-Thurs 7:30am-9pm, Fri 7:30-3, Sat (Fall & Spring) 10-2

J WEST LOOP CENTER LIBRARY*, 5601 West Loop S, 77081-2221. Tel: 713-718-7880. FAX: 713-718-7881. *Chairperson,* Dennis Klappersack; E-mail: dennis.klappersack@hccs.edu; *Librn,* Kathleen Dillon; E-mail: kathleen.dillon@hccs.edu
   Library Holdings: AV Mats 472; Bk Vols 18,270; Per Subs 110
   Automation Activity & Vendor Info: (Acquisitions) Innovative Interfaces, Inc; (Cataloging) Innovative Interfaces, Inc; (Circulation) Innovative Interfaces, Inc - Millenium; (Course Reserve) Innovative Interfaces, Inc; (ILL) Innovative Interfaces, Inc; (Media Booking) Innovative Interfaces, Inc; (OPAC) Innovative Interfaces, Inc; (Serials) Innovative Interfaces, Inc
   Open Mon-Thurs 7:30am-9pm, Fri 7:30-1, Sat 8-1

S HOUSTON MUSEUM OF NATURAL SCIENCE LIBRARY*, One Hermann Circle Dr, 77030-1799. SAN 316-4543. Tel: 713-639-4600, 713-639-4670. FAX: 713-639-4767. Web Site: www.hmns.org. *VPres, Coll,* Lisa Rebori; E-mail: lrebori@hmns.org
   Founded 1969
   Library Holdings: Bk Vols 8,000; Per Subs 80
   Special Collections: Malacology
   Restriction: Open by appt only

P HOUSTON PUBLIC LIBRARY, 500 McKinney Ave, 77002-2534. SAN 361-8692. Tel: 832-393-1313. Circulation Tel: 832-393-2222. Interlibrary Loan Service Tel: 832-393-1447. Administration Tel: 832-393-1300. FAX: 832-393-1324. Interlibrary Loan Service FAX: 832-393-1474. TDD: 832-393-1539. Web Site: www.houstonlibrary.org. *Dir,* Dr Rhea Lawson, PhD; *Dep Dir, Admin,* Roosevelt Weeks; Tel: 832-393-1327, E-mail: roosevelt.weeks@houstontx.gov; *Dep Dir, Pub Serv,* Meller Langford; Tel: 832-393-1329, E-mail: meller.langford@houstontx.gov; Staff 473 (MLS 93, Non-MLS 380)
   Founded 1901. Pop 2,231,335; Circ 7,352,410
   Jul 2011-Jun 2012 Income (Main Library and Branch(s)) $32,352,534. Mats Exp $4,600,000. Sal $23,318,022
   Library Holdings: Audiobooks 33,249; CDs 100,131; DVDs 92,369; Electronic Media & Resources 51,941; Large Print Bks 18,402; Microforms 23,300; Music Scores 550; Bk Vols 1,560,121; Per Subs 3,755
   Special Collections: Architectural Coll; Archives & Manuscripts Department (Houston Metropolitan Research Center) contains 12,000 linear ft of archival material & 1.5 million photographs & negatives related to Houston including manuscript Coll; Bibles, Civil War, Salvation Army, Milsap Coll; Early Houston & Texas Maps; Early Printing & Illuminated Manuscript (Annette Finnigan Coll); Juvenile Literature (Norma Meldrum, Special Coll & Historical Juvenile Coll); Petroleum (Barton, Dumble, & DeWolf Coll); Posters; Sheet Music (Max Hornstein, Adele Margulies, Henry Thayer & Edna Joseph Coll); Texana (Maresh & Blake Coll). Oral History; State Document Depository; US Document Depository
   Subject Interests: Archit, Art, Genealogy
   Automation Activity & Vendor Info: (Acquisitions) Innovative Interfaces, Inc - Millenium; (Cataloging) Innovative Interfaces, Inc - Millenium; (Circulation) Innovative Interfaces, Inc - Millenium; (OPAC) Innovative Interfaces, Inc - Millenium; (Serials) Innovative Interfaces, Inc - Millenium Wireless access
   Function: Archival coll, Audiobks via web, Bilingual assistance for Spanish patrons, Bk club(s), Bks on CD, Bus archives, Children's prog, Computer training, Computers for patron use, Electronic databases & coll, Genealogy discussion group, ILL available, Music CDs, Online cat, Online ref, Online searches, Prog for adults, Prog for children & young adult, Pub access computers, Senior computer classes, Spoken cassettes & CDs, Story hour, Summer reading prog, Tax forms, Teen prog, Telephone ref
   Partic in Houston Area Library Automated Network

Special Services for the Deaf - Captioned film dep; Spec interest per; TTY equip

Special Services for the Blind - Reader equip

Open Mon-Thurs 10-8, Sat 10-5

Friends of the Library Group

Branches: 42

THE AFRICAN AMERICAN LIBRARY AT THE GREGORY SCHOOL, 1300 Victor St, 77019. Tel: 832-393-1440. Web Site: www.thegregoryschool.org/library.html. *Mgr*, Hellena Stokes; E-mail: hellena.stokes@houstontx.gov; Staff 7 (MLS 2, Non-MLS 5)

Founded 2009

Library Holdings: Bk Vols 5,000

Special Collections: Photographs, manuscripts, oral history, government papers & records

Subject Interests: African-Am hist & culture

Open Mon-Thurs 10-6, Sat 10-5

Restriction: Non-circulating, Researchers only

J S BRACEWELL NEIGHBORHOOD LIBRARY, 9002 Kingspoint Dr, 77089, SAN 361-9230. Tel: 832-393-2580. FAX: 832-393-2581.

Founded 1970

Open Tues & Wed 10-6, Thurs 12-8, Fri 1-5, Sat 10-5

Friends of the Library Group

CARNEGIE NEIGHBORHOOD LIBRARY, 1050 Quitman, 77009. (Mail add: 500 McKinney Ave, 77002), SAN 361-9265. Tel: 832-393-1720. FAX: 832-393-1721.

Founded 1982

Open Mon & Thurs 11-7, Tues, Wed & Fri 10-6

Friends of the Library Group

CLAYTON LIBRARY CENTER FOR GENEALOGICAL RESEARCH, 5300 Caroline, 77004-6896, SAN 361-8846. Tel: 832-393-2600. Web Site: www.houstonlibrary.org/clayton. *Br Mgr*, Susan D Kaufman; Tel: 832-393-2602, Fax: 832-393-2601, E-mail: susan.kaufman@houstontx.gov; Staff 9 (MLS 3, Non-MLS 6)

Library Holdings: CDs 200; Bk Vols 85,000; Per Subs 2,648

Subject Interests: Genealogy

Partic in OCLC Online Computer Library Center, Inc

Publications: In-house Bibligraphies

Open Tues & Thurs 10-6, Wed 10-8, Fri & Sat 10-5

Restriction: Non-circulating

Friends of the Library Group

EVERETT COLLIER REGIONAL LIBRARY, 6200 Pinemont, 77092, SAN 326-7563. Tel: 832-393-1740. FAX: 832-393-1741.

Function: Adult bk club

Open Mon & Wed 12-8, Tues & Thurs 10-6, Fri 1-5, Sat 10-5

Friends of the Library Group

AMANDA E DIXON NEIGHBORHOOD LIBRARY, 8002 Hirsch, 77016, SAN 361-929X. Tel: 832-393-1760.

Open Tues & Wed 10-6, Thurs 12-8, Fri 1-5, Sat 10-5

Friends of the Library Group

FIFTH WARD NEIGHBORHOOD LIBRARY, 4014 Market St, 77020, SAN 361-932X. Tel: 832-393-1770.

Open Mon-Thurs 2-6, Fri 2-5

Friends of the Library Group

PATRICIO FLORES NEIGHBORHOOD LIBRARY, 110 N Milby, 77003, SAN 361-9338. Tel: 832-393-1780.

Open Tues & Wed 10-6, Thurs 12-8, Fri 1-5, Sat 10-5

Friends of the Library Group

MORRIS FRANK NEIGHBORHOOD LIBRARY, Brays Oaks Towers Bldg, 1013 Fondren, 77096, SAN 361-9346. Tel: 832-393-2410.

Founded 1984

Open Mon & Thurs 11-6, Tues 12-8, Wed 10-6, Fri 1-5

Friends of the Library Group

ELEANOR K FREED MONTROSE NEIGHBORHOOD LIBRARY, 4100 Montrose, 77006. Tel: 832-393-1800. FAX: 832-393-1801.

Open Tues & Wed 10-6, Thurs 12-8, Fri 1-5, Sat 10-5

Friends of the Library Group

HEIGHTS NEIGHBORHOOD LIBRARY, 1302 Heights Blvd, 77008, SAN 361-9354. Tel: 832-393-1810. Reference Tel: 832-393-1818. Administration Tel: 832-393-1812. FAX: 832-393-1811.

Function: Bks on CD, Children's prog, Computer training, Free DVD rentals, Handicapped accessible, Holiday prog, Homework prog, Music CDs, Online cat, OverDrive digital audio bks, Photocopying/Printing, Prog for adults, Prog for children & young adult, Pub access computers, Ref serv in person, Spoken cassettes & CDs, Spoken cassettes & DVDs, Story hour, Summer & winter reading prog, Tax forms, Wheelchair accessible

Open Mon & Wed 12-8, Tues & Thurs 10-6, Fri 1-5, Sat 10-5

DAVID M HENINGTON ALIEF REGIONAL LIBRARY, 7979 S Kirkwood, 77072, SAN 322-5682. Tel: 832-393-1820.

Open Mon & Wed 12-8, Tues & Thurs 10-6, Fri 1-5, Sat 10-5

Friends of the Library Group

ARNOLD L HILLENDAHL NEIGHBORHOOD LIBRARY, 2436 Gessner Dr, 77080, SAN 361-9419. Tel: 832-393-1940.

Subject Interests: African-Am, Chinese lang, Korean (Lang), Spanish lang, Vietnamese (Lang)

Open Tues & Wed 10-6, Thurs 12-8, Fri 1-5, Sat 10-5

Friends of the Library Group

HOUSTON METROPOLITAN RESEARCH CENTER, ARCHIVES & LOCAL HISTORY, Julia Ideson Bldg, 500 McKinney, 77002, SAN 361-8722. Tel: 832-393-1658, 832-393-1659. Reference Tel: 832-393-1313. Administration Tel: 832-393-1665. *Lea Archivist, Mgr*, Liz Sargent; Staff 3 (MLS 1, Non-MLS 2)

Founded 1854

Special Collections: Regional Historical Records for Texas State Depository (select records of 5 surrounding counties)

Function: Archival coll, Res libr

Open Mon, Tues & Thurs 10-6, Wed 10-8, Sat 10-5

Restriction: Closed stack, Non-circulating coll

Friends of the Library Group

HPL EXPRESS DISCOVERY GREEN, 1500 McKinney, R2, 77010.

Open Fri & Sat 12-5

Friends of the Library Group

HPL EXPRESS SOUTHWEST, 6400 High Star, 77074. Tel: 832-393-2660.

Open Mon & Thurs 11-6, Tues 12-8, Wed 10-6, Fri 1-5

Friends of the Library Group

W L D JOHNSON NEIGHBORHOOD LIBRARY, 3517 Reed Rd, 77051, SAN 361-9443. Tel: 832-393-2550.

Open Tues & Wed 10-6, Thurs 12-8, Fri 1-5, Sat 10-5

Friends of the Library Group

J FRANK JUNGMAN NEIGHBORHOOD LIBRARY, 5830 Westheimer Rd, 77057, SAN 361-9478. Tel: 832-393-1860.

Open Tues & Wed 10-6, Thurs 12-8, Fri 1-5, Sat 10-5

Friends of the Library Group

BELLE SHERMAN KENDALL NEIGHBORHOOD LIBRARY, 609 N Eldridge, 77079, SAN 361-9532. Tel: 832-393-1880.

Open Mon & Wed 12-8, Tues & Thurs 10-6, Fri 1-5, Sat 10-5

Friends of the Library Group

LAKEWOOD NEIGHBORHOOD LIBRARY, 8815 Feland St, 77028, SAN 361-9591. Tel: 832-393-2530.

Founded 1963

Open Mon & Thurs 11-6, Tues 12-8, Wed 10-6, Fri 1-5

Friends of the Library Group

ADELE BRISCOE LOOSCAN NEIGHBORHOOD LIBRARY, 2510 Willowick Rd, 77027, SAN 361-9621. Tel: 832-393-1900.

Open Mon & Thurs 11-6, Tues 12-8, Wed 10-6, Fri 1-5

Friends of the Library Group

FRANK O MANCUSO NEIGHBORHOOD LIBRARY, 6767 Bellfort, 77087, SAN 361-963X. Tel: 832-393-1920.

Open Mon & Thurs 11-6, Tues 12-8, Wed 10-6, Fri 1-5

Friends of the Library Group

EVA ALICE MCCRANE KASHMERE GARDENS NEIGHBORHOOD LIBRARY, 5411 Pardee, 77026, SAN 361-9508. Tel: 832-393-2450.

Founded 1971

Open Tues & Wed 10-6, Thurs 12-8, Fri 1-5, Sat 10-5

Friends of the Library Group

MCGOVERN-STELLA LINK NEIGHBORHOOD LIBRARY, 7405 Stella Link, 77025. Tel: 832-393-2630.

Open Mon & Wed 12-8, Tues & Thurs 10-6, Fri 1-5, Sat 10-5

LUCILE Y MELCHER NEIGHBORHOOD LIBRARY, 7200 Keller St, 77012, SAN 361-9656. Tel: 832-393-2480.

Open Tues & Wed 10-6, Thurs 12-8, Fri 1-5, Sat 10-5

Friends of the Library Group

GEORGE B MEYER SR NEIGHBORHOOD LIBRARY, 5005 W Bellfort, 77035, SAN 361-9680. Tel: 832-393-1840.

Open Tues & Wed 10-6, Thurs 12-8, Fri 1-5, Sat 10-5

Friends of the Library Group

NETTIE MOODY NEIGHBORHOOD LIBRARY, 9525 Irvington Blvd, 77076, SAN 361-9710. Tel: 832-393-1950.

Open Mon & Thurs 11-6, Tues 12-8, Wed 10-6, Fri 1-5

Friends of the Library Group

OAK FOREST NEIGHBORHOOD LIBRARY, 1349 W 43rd St, 77018, SAN 361-9745. Tel: 832-393-1960. Administration Tel: 832-393-1963. FAX: 832-393-1961.

Founded 1961

Function: Bk club(s), Children's prog, Computers for patron use, Copy machines, Free DVD rentals, Handicapped accessible, ILL available, Music CDs, Online cat, OverDrive digital audio bks, Photocopying/Printing, Prog for adults, Pub access computers, Story hour, Summer reading prog, Tax forms, Teen prog, Wheelchair accessible

Open Tues & Wed 10-6, Thurs 12-8, Fri 1-5, Sat 10-5

PARK PLACE REGIONAL LIBRARY, 8145 Park Place Blvd, 77017, SAN 361-977X. Tel: 832-393-1970.

Open Mon & Wed 12-8, Tues & Thurs 10-6, Fri 1-5, Sat 10-5

Friends of the Library Group

PLEASANTVILLE NEIGHBORHOOD LIBRARY, 1520 Gellhorn Dr, 77029, SAN 361-980X. Tel: 832-393-2330.

Open Mon & Thurs 11-6, Tues 12-8, Wed 10-6, Fri 1-5

Friends of the Library Group

ELIZABETH L RING NEIGHBORHOOD LIBRARY, 8835 Long Point Rd, 77055, SAN 361-9834. Tel: 832-393-2000.
Open Mon & Thurs 11-6, Tues 12-8, Wed 10-6, Fri 1-5
Friends of the Library Group

JUDSON W ROBINSON JR WESTCHASE NEIGHBORHOOD LIBRARY, 3223 Wilcrest, 77042, SAN 371-9669. Tel: 832-393-2011.
Open Mon & Thurs 11-6, Tues 12-8, Wed 10-6, Fri 1-5
Friends of the Library Group

SCENIC WOODS REGIONAL LIBRAY, 10677 Homestead Rd, 77016, SAN 326-758X. Tel: 832-393-2030.
Open Mon & Wed 12-8, Tues & Thurs 10-6, Fri 1-5, Sat 10-5
Friends of the Library Group

BEULAH SHEPARD–ACRES HOMES NEIGHBORHOOD LIBRARY, 8501 W Montgomery Rd, 77088, SAN 361-9176. Tel: 832-393-1700.
Founded 1976
Open Mon & Thurs 11-6, Tues 12-8, Wed 10-6, Fri 1-5
Friends of the Library Group

LONNIE E SMITH NEIGHBORHOOD LIBRARY, 3624 Scott St, 77004, SAN 361-9893. Tel: 832-393-2050.
Open Mon & Thurs 11-6, Tues 12-8, Wed 10-6, Fri 1-5
Friends of the Library Group

STANAKER NEIGHBORHOOD LIBRARY, 611 S Sgt Macario Garcia, 77011.
Open Mon & Thurs 11-6, Tues 12-8, Wed 10-6, Fri 1-5

SHERMAN E STIMLEY BLUE RIDGE NEIGHBORHOOD LIBRARY, 7007 W Fuqua, 77489. Tel: 832-393-2370.
Founded 1999
Open Mon & Thurs 11-6, Tues 12-8, Wed 10-6, Fri 1-5
Friends of the Library Group

CLIFF TUTTLE NEIGHBORHOOD LIBRARY, 702 Kress, 77020, SAN 361-9958. Tel: 832-393-2100.
Open Tues & Wed 10-6, Thurs 12-8, Fri 1-5, Sat 10-5
Friends of the Library Group

WILLIAM A VINSON NEIGHBORHOOD LIBRARY, 3810 W Fuqua, 77045, SAN 361-9982. Tel: 832-393-2120.
Open Tues & Wed 10-6, Thurs 12-8, Fri 1-5, Sat 10-5
Friends of the Library Group

M E WALTER NEIGHBORHOOD LIBRARY, 7660 Clarewood, 77036, SAN 362-0018. Tel: 832-393-2500.
Open Tues & Wed 10-6, Thurs 12-8, Fri 1-5, Sat 10-5
Friends of the Library Group

ALICE MCKEAN YOUNG NEIGHBORHOOD LIBRARY, 5260 Griggs Rd, Palm Center, 77021, SAN 362-0042. Tel: 832-393-2140.
Open Tues & Wed 10-6, Thurs 12-8, Fri 1-5, Sat 10-5
Friends of the Library Group

S   JACOBS ENGINEERING LIBRARY, 5995 Rogerdale Rd, 77072. SAN 316-4616. Tel: 832-351-7025. FAX: 832-351-7700. *Librn,* Sara Davis; E-mail: sara.davis@jacobs.com; Staff 1 (MLS 1)
Founded 1964
Library Holdings: CDs 15; Bk Titles 1,500; Per Subs 25
Subject Interests: Chem eng, Environ eng
Automation Activity & Vendor Info: (Cataloging) EOS International; (Circulation) EOS International; (OPAC) EOS International
Open Mon-Thurs 8-4:30, Fri 8-12
Restriction: Open to pub upon request

L   JONES DAY*, Law Library, 717 Texas St, Ste 3300, 77002. Tel: 832-239-3939. FAX: 832-239-3600. Web Site: www.jonesday.com. *Librn,* Kimberly Serna; E-mail: ktserna@jonesday.com
Library Holdings: Bk Titles 357; Per Subs 57
Restriction: Staff use only

S   KELLOGG, BROWN & ROOT LIBRARY*, 601 Jefferson Ave, 77002. SAN 316-4772. Tel: 713-753-8466. FAX: 713-753-6226. *Mgr,* John Galloway; Staff 1 (MLS 1)
Library Holdings: Bk Vols 20,000; Per Subs 200
Subject Interests: Chem, Petrochem, Petroleum eng
Publications: Acquisitions list (quarterly)
Restriction: Staff use only

S   LOCKWOOD, ANDREWS & NEWNAM, INC*, Information Resource Center, 2925 Briarpark Dr, Ste 400, 77042. SAN 327-3857. Tel: 713-266-6900. FAX: 713-266-2089. Web Site: www.lan-inc.com. *Adminr,* Marji Pool; E-mail: mlpool@lan-inc.com
Library Holdings: Bk Vols 1,500; Per Subs 40
Subject Interests: Archit, Eng
Restriction: Staff use only

J   LONE STAR COLLEGE SYSTEM*, Automated Library Services, 20515 State Hwy 249, Bldg 11, Rm 11437, 77070-2607. SAN 316-4713. Tel: 281-290-2843. FAX: 281-290-2979. Web Site: www.lonestar.edu/library. *Dir,* Carol Steinmetz; E-mail: carol.l.steinmetz@lonestar.edu; *Head, Cat,* Peter Applin; Tel: 281-290-3717, E-mail: peter.applin@lonestar.edu;

Authority Control Librn, Kathleen Whitsitt; Tel: 281-290-2842, E-mail: kathleen.s.whitsitt@lonestar.edu; Staff 9.5 (MLS 3, Non-MLS 6.5)
Founded 1973
Automation Activity & Vendor Info: (Acquisitions) SirsiDynix; (Cataloging) SirsiDynix; (Circulation) SirsiDynix; (Course Reserve) SirsiDynix; (OPAC) SirsiDynix; (Serials) SirsiDynix
Database Vendor: SirsiDynix
Wireless access
Partic in OCLC Online Computer Library Center, Inc
Open Mon-Fri (Winter) 7-5; Mon-Thurs (Summer) 7-5
Departmental Libraries:
CYFAIR LIBRARY, 9191 Barker Cypress Rd, Cypress, 77433. Tel: 281-290-3214, 281-290-3219. E-mail: cyfairlibrary@lonestar.edu. *Libr Dir,* Mick Stafford; E-mail: michael.d.stafford@lonestar.edu; *Asst Dir, Ch,* Melanie Metzger; E-mail: melanie.r.metzger@lonestar.edu; *Ch,* Krissy Conn; E-mail: kristen.s.conn@lonestar.edu; *Ref Librn,* Monica Norem; E-mail: monica.r.norem@lonestar.edu
Open Mon-Thurs 7am-10pm, Fri & Sat 8-6, Sun 1-6; Mon-Thurs (Summer) 7am-10pm, Fri 9-5, Sat 10-6, Sun 1-6
KINGWOOD COLLEGE LIBRARY, 20000 Kingwood Dr, Kingwood, 77339, SAN 325-352X. Tel: 281-312-1691. FAX: 281-312-1456. E-mail: Kingwood.LRC-Ref@LoneStar.edu. *Dean,* Peggy Whitley; Tel: 281-312-1493, E-mail: peggy.whitly@lonestar.edu; *Ref,* Rebecca Bradley; Staff 11 (MLS 11)
Founded 1984. Enrl 11,000; Fac 140; Highest Degree: Associate
Library Holdings: e-books 39,000; Bk Vols 40,000; Per Subs 350
Automation Activity & Vendor Info: (Acquisitions) Horizon; (Cataloging) Horizon; (Circulation) Horizon; (Course Reserve) Horizon; (OPAC) Horizon; (Serials) Horizon
Open Mon-Thurs 7am-9pm, Fri 7-4:30, Sat 9-2
MONTGOMERY COLLEGE LIBRARY, 3200 College Park Dr, Conroe, 77384, SAN 376-222X. Tel: 936-273-7388, 936-273-7392. Circulation Tel: 936-273-7387. Reference Tel: 936-273-7390. FAX: 936-273-7395. E-mail: mclr@lonestar.edu. *Dir,* Janice Lucas Peyton, PhD; *Ref,* Gary Church; Tel: 936-273-7389, E-mail: gary.church@lonestar.edu; *Ref,* Cheryl Mansfield-Egans; Tel: 936-273-7393, E-mail: cheryl.mansfield-egans@lonestar.edu; *Ref Serv,* Deborah Cox; Tel: 936-273-7490, E-mail: debbie.cox@lonestar.edu; *Ref Serv,* Daniel Stevens; Tel: 936-273-7487, E-mail: daniel.stevens@lonestar.edu. Subject Specialists: *Biol sci,* Gary Church; *Bus,* Cheryl Mansfield-Egans; *English, Humanities,* Deborah Cox; *Liberal arts,* Daniel Stevens; Staff 5 (MLS 5)
Founded 1995. Enrl 11,500; Fac 402; Highest Degree: Associate
Library Holdings: AV Mats 3,016; CDs 87; e-books 41,500; Bk Vols 43,114; Per Subs 462; Talking Bks 96
Special Collections: McKay Everett (Children's Coll)
Database Vendor: Baker & Taylor, JSTOR, netLibrary, Newsbank, OCLC FirstSearch, Westlaw
Function: Art exhibits, Audio & video playback equip for onsite use, Distance learning, For res patrons, ILL available
Open Mon-Thurs 7:30am-9:30pm, Fri 7:30-7:30, Sat 9-4, Sun 1-6
Restriction: Authorized patrons, Fee for pub use, Non-circulating coll
NORTH HARRIS COLLEGE LIBRARY, 2700 W W Thorne Dr, 77073, SAN 323-6943. Tel: 281-618-5491. Reference Tel: 281-618-5707. FAX: 281-618-5695. E-mail: nhc.libweb@lonestar.edu. *Dir,* Pradeep Lele; Tel: 281-618-5497; *Head, Ref,* Dr Carolyn Jacobs; Tel: 281-618-5487; *Doc, Ref Librn,* Virginia Rigby; Tel: 281-618-5490; *Ref & Acq Librn,* Karen Parker; *Ref & Instruction Librn,* Olia Palmer; Tel: 281-618-5487; *Ref & Tech Librn,* Norma Drepaul; Staff 13 (MLS 6, Non-MLS 7)
Founded 1972. Enrl 11,000; Fac 390; Highest Degree: Associate
Library Holdings: AV Mats 11,869; Bk Vols 101,000; Per Subs 1,041
Special Collections: ERIC Junior College Fiche Coll. US Document Depository
Publications: Library Dateline
Open Mon-Thurs 7:30am-9:30pm, Fri 7:30-4:30, Sat 9-5, Sun 1-6
TOMBALL COLLEGE LIBRARY, 30555 Tomball Pkwy, Tomball, 77375-4036, SAN 323-696X. Tel: 832-559-4206. Reference Tel: 832-559-4211. FAX: 832-559-4248. E-mail: tcref@LoneStar.edu. *Dir,* Pam Shafer; Tel: 832-559-4217, E-mail: Pamela.N.Shafer@lonestar.edu; *Ref Librn,* Elizabeth Gault; E-mail: Elizabeth.K.Gault@lonestar.edu; *Circ,* Margaret Dawson
Founded 1988. Enrl 11,000; Fac 209; Highest Degree: Associate
Library Holdings: Bk Titles 24,486; Bk Vols 32,469; Per Subs 486
Open Mon-Thurs (Fall & Spring) 8am-9:30pm, Fri 8-6, Sat 10-5
THE UNIVERSITY CENTER LIBRARY, 3232 College Park Dr, The Woodlands, 77384. Tel: 281-618-7140, 936-273-7562. FAX: 936-273-7616. Web Site: www.lonestar.edu. *Ref Librn,* Scott Gilbert; E-mail: scott.a.gilbert@lonestar.edu
Library Holdings: e-books 42,000
Open Mon-Thurs 8am-9pm, Fri & Sat 8-5

S   LUNAR & PLANETARY INSTITUTE, Center for Information & Research Services, 3600 Bay Area Blvd, 77058-1113. SAN 362-0107. Tel: 281-486-2182. Administration Tel: 281-486-2136. FAX: 281-486-2186. E-mail: library@lpi.usra.edu. Web Site:

www.lpi.usra.edu/library/library.html. *Mgr,* Mary Ann Hager; E-mail:
mhager@hou.usra.edu; *Tech Serv,* David Bigwood; Tel: 281-486-2134,
E-mail: dbigwood@hou.usra.edu; Staff 4 (MLS 1, Non-MLS 3)
Founded 1969
Library Holdings: Bk Titles 23,000; Bk Vols 55,000; Per Subs 140
Special Collections: Maps & Imagery of the Solar System
Subject Interests: Astronomy, Geol, Space sci
Automation Activity & Vendor Info: (Cataloging) EOS International;
(Circulation) EOS International; (OPAC) EOS International
Database Vendor: OCLC FirstSearch
Wireless access
Function: Res libr
Open Mon-Fri 8-5

S   MENIL FOUNDATION*, The Menil Collection Library, 1500 Branard St,
77006. (Mail add: 1511 Branard St, 77006), SAN 373-6164. Tel:
713-525-9420. FAX: 713-525-9444. E-mail: library@menil.org. Web Site:
www.menil.org. *Dir,* Eric Wolf; *Cat,* Rita Marsales; Tel: 713-525-9424.
Subject Specialists: *Art hist,* Eric Wolf; *Art hist,* Rita Marsales; Staff 2
(MLS 2)
Founded 1987
Library Holdings: Bk Titles 25,000; Bk Vols 30,000; Per Subs 80
Special Collections: Rare Book Room
Subject Interests: Art hist
Automation Activity & Vendor Info: (Cataloging) Follett Software
Database Vendor: JSTOR, OCLC FirstSearch, Wilson - Wilson Web
Function: Res libr
Restriction: Open by appt only
Friends of the Library Group

S   NACE INTERNATIONAL LIBRARY*, 1440 S Creek Dr, 77084-4906.
SAN 316-0807. Tel: 281-228-6200. FAX: 281-228-6300. E-mail:
firstservice@mail.nace.org. Web Site: www.nace.org. *Librn,* Suzanne
Moreno
Founded 1945
Library Holdings: Bk Titles 2,000; Per Subs 40
Special Collections: Corrosion Abstracts: 1962 to date; Corrosion: 1982 to
date; Materials Performance: 1962 to date
Subject Interests: Corrosion
Wireless access
Function: Ref serv available
Open Mon-Fri 7:30-4:15
Restriction: Mem only

G   NASA*, Johnson Space Center Scientific & Technical Information Center,
2101 NASA Pkwy, 77058-3696. SAN 316-4691. Tel: 281-483-4245. FAX:
281-244-6624. E-mail: jsc-sticnter@mail.nasa.gov. *Supvr,* Christa George;
Tel: 281-483-2491, E-mail: christa.george-1@nasa.gov; Staff 11 (MLS 4,
Non-MLS 7)
Founded 1962
Library Holdings: e-books 7,000; e-journals 317; Electronic Media &
Resources 105; Bk Vols 12,000; Per Subs 90
Special Collections: NASA, JSC & Other Proprietary Government
Publications
Subject Interests: Aeronaut, Astronautics, Computer sci, Earth resources,
Eng, Guidance, Life sci, Math, Navigation, Physics, Space med, Space sci,
Space shuttles, Space sta, Telemetry
Automation Activity & Vendor Info: (Acquisitions) SirsiDynix;
(Cataloging) SirsiDynix; (Circulation) SirsiDynix; (OPAC) SirsiDynix
Partic in OCLC Online Computer Library Center, Inc
Restriction: Not open to pub

S   OCCIDENTAL OIL & GAS CORP LIBRARY*, Five Greenway Plaza, Ste
B-1, 77046. SAN 357-7082. Tel: 713-215-7667. FAX: 713-215-7528.
Librn, Mitra Kia; E-mail: mitra_kia@oxy.com; Staff 2 (MLS 1, Non-MLS
1)
Founded 1953
Library Holdings: Bk Titles 30,000; Per Subs 25
Subject Interests: Exploration, Production of petroleum
Database Vendor: Dialog, EBSCO Information Services, LexisNexis
Restriction: Staff use only

S   PIERCE, GOODWIN, ALEXANDER & LINVILLE LIBRARY*, 3131
Briarpark, Ste 200, 77042. SAN 328-4395. Tel: 713-622-1444. FAX:
713-968-9333. Web Site: www.pgal.com. *In Charge,* Kathleen Truong
Library Holdings: Bk Vols 580
Subject Interests: Archit
Restriction: Not open to pub

S   PITNEY BOWES MANAGEMENT SERVICES, Information Services
/ Library - Houston, 3333 Hwy 6 S, 77082. (Mail add: PO Box 1380,
77251-1380), SAN 316-4829. Tel: 281-544-7510. FAX: 281-544-8121.
E-mail: libreq@shell.com. *Mgr,* Frances Brown; Tel: 281-544-9156,
E-mail: frances.brown@shell.com; Staff 6 (MLS 5, Non-MLS 1)

Founded 1947
Library Holdings: Bk Titles 60,000; Per Subs 70
Automation Activity & Vendor Info: (Acquisitions) Cuadra Associates;
(Cataloging) Cuadra Associates; (Circulation) Cuadra Associates; (Serials)
Cuadra Associates
Database Vendor: American Chemical Society, Dialog, Dun & Bradstreet,
EBSCO Information Services, Elsevier, Factiva.com, Knovel, Open Text
Corporation, OVID Technologies, ScienceDirect, Scopus, Springer-Verlag,
STN International, Westlaw
Wireless access
Restriction: Co libr, Not open to pub

S   PLANNING & FORECASTING CONSULTANTS LIBRARY*, PO Box
820228, 77282-0228. SAN 372-9915. Tel: 281-497-2179. FAX:
281-497-4128. *Mgr,* Dale Steffes; E-mail: dalesteffes@comcast.net
Library Holdings: Bk Vols 1,500; Per Subs 38
Subject Interests: Energy, Natural gas

S   RESURRECTION METROPOLITAN COMMUNITY CHURCH*, Botts
Memorial Library & Archives, 2025 W 11th St, 77008. SAN 329-2916.
Tel: 713-861-9149. FAX: 713-861-2520. Web Site:
www.resurrectionmcc.org. *Dir,* Melissa Rogers
Founded 1979
Jan 2005-Dec 2005 Income $3,000. Mats Exp $1,300, Books $300, Manu
Arch $500, Presv $500
Library Holdings: Bks on Deafness & Sign Lang 15; Bk Vols 20,000; Per
Subs 75,000
Special Collections: Gay/Lesbian Publications; Newspaper Clippings;
Organzational Files to the 1960's; Periodicals, 1940-present. Oral History
Subject Interests: Homosexuality, Relig
Publications: Archive Quarterly (Newsletter); MCC Newsletter; Monthly
Status Report
Restriction: Open by appt only

C   RICE UNIVERSITY, Fondren Library, 6100 Main, MS-44, 77005. (Mail
add: PO Box 1892, 77251-1892), SAN 316-506X. Tel: 713-348-5113.
Circulation Tel: 713-348-4021. Interlibrary Loan Service Tel:
713-348-2284. Administration Tel: 713-348-4022. FAX: 713-348-5258.
Interlibrary Loan Service FAX: 713-348-4117. E-mail: reference@rice.edu.
Web Site: library.rice.edu. *Vice Provost & Univ Librn,* Sara Lowman;
E-mail: lowman@rice.edu; *Asst Univ Librn, Libr Core Syst & Serv,* Diane
Butler; Tel: 713-348-4400, E-mail: dianeb@rice.edu; *Asst Univ Librn, Res
Serv,* Kerry Keck; Tel: 713-348-2926, E-mail: keckker@rice.edu; *Asst Univ
Librn, Tech Serv,* Melinda Reagor Flannery; Tel: 713-348-3773, E-mail:
reagor@rice.edu; *Exec Dir, Digital Scholarship Serv,* Geneva Henry; Tel:
713-348-2480, E-mail: ghenry@rice.edu; *Head of Doc Delivery,* Randolph
Tibbits; Tel: 713-348-8827, E-mail: tibbits@rice.edu; *Head, Acq,* Janice
Lindquist; Tel: 713-348-4023, E-mail: jlindq@rice.edu; *Head, Cat &
Metadata Serv,* Jiun Kuo; Tel: 713-348-2568, E-mail: kuo@rice.edu; *Head,
Circ,* Virginia Martin; Tel: 713-348-2573, E-mail: martin@rice.edu; *Head,
Kelley Ctr for Govt Pub & Micro,* Esther Crawford; Tel: 713-348-6212,
E-mail: crawford@rice.edu; *Head, Presv Serv,* Andrew Damico; Tel:
713-348-2602, E-mail: adamico@rice.edu; *Head, Ref,* Sandra Edwards; Tel:
713-348-2504, E-mail: edwards@rice.edu; *Head, Spec Coll & Archives,*
Lee Pecht; Tel: 713-348-2120, E-mail: pecht@rice.edu; Staff 60 (MLS 28,
Non-MLS 32)
Founded 1912. Enrl 5,760; Fac 650; Highest Degree: Doctorate
Jul 2010-Jun 2011 Income $15,909,137. Mats Exp $9,927,963, Books
$2,643,981, Per/Ser (Incl. Access Fees) $6,667,217, Presv $46,181. Sal
$5,396,539 (Prof $3,741,490)
Library Holdings: e-books 88,665; e-journals 99,705; Microforms
3,394,890; Bk Vols 2,711,120; Per Subs 57,238
Special Collections: 18th & 19th Century British Maritime & Naval
History, ms; 18th Century British Drama (Axson Coll), rare bks; 19th &
20th Century Texas (Judge James L Autry, Gen William Hamman,
Mirabeau B Lamar Journal, Harris Masterson, John P Osterhout, Walter B
& Estelle B Sharp, J Russell Wait, E O Lovett, Hutcheson Family, Stuart
Family, Townsend Family, William W Watkin & Anderson-Greenwood
Colls); Americas Coll; Architecture (William Ward Watkin Papers, William
Cannady, Anderson Todd, Arthur E Jones & Charles Tapley Architectural
Records); Cruikshank Coll; Fine & Performing Arts (Ann Holmes Fine
Arts Archive, Ensemble Theater Records, Marion Kessel Performing Arts,
Vera Prasilova Scott Portraiture Colls, Arthur Hall & Paul Cooper Papers,
Sacred Music Coll); Historical Maps & Atlases; History of Aeronautics
(Anderson Coll); History of Science, rare bks; Limited Edition Coll; Local
& Texas History (Masterson Coll, Clarence Wharton, Marguerite Johnston
Barnes, Tanglewood/William G Farrington, ChampionsGolf Club, South
Main Alliance Records); Maximilian & Carlotta Coll; Military Intelligence
& Espionage Coll; Modern American Literature (Larry McMurtry, David
Westheimer, William Goyen, J P Miller & Thornton Wilder Colls); Oil &
Gas (Panhandle Eastern, Merchants & Planters Oil Co, Huffington Pol Co,
El Paso Natural Gas); Papermaking Coll; Rice University (Julian S Huxley
& Juliette Huxley Papers); Texas Entrepreneurs/Business (Dillingham
Family, Walter W & Ella F Fondren, Groce Family, Gus S Wortham,

family & business, Merchants & Planters Oil Co, Baker & Botts Historical Archives, William L Clayton Papers, Brown & Root Records); Texas Politics (Oveta Culp Hobby Papers, Billie Carr, Frankie Randolph, Fagan Dickson, Walter Hall, William Clayton & Albert Thomas Colls); US Civil War & Slavery, diaries, doc, imprints, letters, photog; William Martin Religious Right Coll. State Document Depository; US Document Depository

Automation Activity & Vendor Info: (Acquisitions) SirsiDynix; (Cataloging) SirsiDynix; (Circulation) SirsiDynix; (Course Reserve) Atlas Systems - Ares; (ILL) OCLC ILLiad; (OPAC) SirsiDynix; (Serials) SirsiDynix

Database Vendor: EBSCO Discovery Service, OCLC FirstSearch, SerialsSolutions
Wireless access

Function: Archival coll, Audio & video playback equip for onsite use, Bks on CD, Computer training, Computers for patron use, Copy machines, Doc delivery serv, e-mail & chat, E-Reserves, Electronic databases & coll, Exhibits, Govt ref serv, ILL available, Microfiche/film & reading machines, Music CDs, Online cat, Online ref, Orientations, Photocopying/Printing, Res libr, Scanner, Tax forms, Telephone ref, VHS videos, Video lending libr, Web-catalog, Workshops

Publications: Flyleaf; News from Fondren
Partic in Association of Research Libraries (ARL); Coalition for Networked Information (CNI); Coun of Libr Info Resources; Digital Libr Fedn; Greater Western Library Alliance; Inter-University Consortium for Political & Social Research (ICPSR); OCLC Online Computer Library Center, Inc; Scholarly Publ & Acad Resources Coalition; TexSHARE - Texas State Library & Archives Commission

Restriction: Open to pub for ref & circ; with some limitations, Open to students, fac & staff, Photo ID required for access
Friends of the Library Group

SR **SAINT LUKE THE EVANGELIST CATHOLIC CHURCH***, Community Resource Library, 11011 Hall Rd, 77089. SAN 327-3717. Tel: 281-481-4251. FAX: 281-481-8780. Web Site: www.stlukescatholic.com. *Librn,* Marcia Birsinger
Library Holdings: Bk Titles 320; Bk Vols 750
Wireless access

R **SAINT MARTIN'S EPISCOPAL CHURCH***, Parish Library, 717 Sage Rd, 77056. SAN 316-4802. Tel: 713-621-3040. FAX: 713-622-5701, Web Site: www.stmartinsepiscopal.org. *Librn,* Ann Moss
Founded 1959
Library Holdings: Bk Vols 13,000
Open Wed 10-2, Sun 8:30-1

J **SAN JACINTO COLLEGE NORTH***, Doctor Edwin E Lehr Library, 5800 Uvalde Rd, 77049-4599. SAN 362-0131. Tel: 281-459-7116. FAX: 281-459-7166. Web Site: www.sjcd.edu. *Dir,* Jan C Crenshaw; E-mail: jan.crenshaw@sjcd.edu; *Pub Serv,* Karyn Jones; *Ref,* Madelyn C Garner; Staff 4 (MLS 4)
Founded 1974. Enrl 6,000; Highest Degree: Associate
Library Holdings: High Interest/Low Vocabulary Bk Vols 200; Bk Vols 80,000; Per Subs 17,145
Special Collections: Law Library; Texana Coll
Automation Activity & Vendor Info: (Cataloging) Innovative Interfaces, Inc - Millenium; (Circulation) Innovative Interfaces, Inc - Millenium; (Course Reserve) Innovative Interfaces, Inc - Millenium; (OPAC) Innovative Interfaces, Inc - Millenium; (Serials) Innovative Interfaces, Inc - Millenium
Database Vendor: Amigos Library Services, EBSCOhost, Loislaw, Mergent Online, Standard & Poor's, Westlaw
Wireless access
Special Services for the Blind - Reader equip
Open Mon-Thurs 7:30am-9pm, Fri 7:30-3, Sat 11-2, Fri (Summer) 7:30-Noon

J **SAN JACINTO COLLEGE SOUTH***, Parker Williams Library, 13735 Beamer Rd, 77089-6099. SAN 362-0166. Tel: 281-922-3416. FAX: 281-922-3470. Web Site: www.sjcd.edu. *Dir,* Richard McKay; E-mail: richard.mckay@sjcd.edu; *Ref,* Larry Gainor; E-mail: larry.gainor@sjcd.edu; *Ref,* Jane Stimson; E-mail: jane.stimson@sjcd.edu; Staff 9 (MLS 3, Non-MLS 6)
Founded 1979. Enrl 9,100; Fac 339; Highest Degree: Associate
Library Holdings: Bk Vols 63,000; Per Subs 101
Special Collections: Texana
Subject Interests: Am lit, British lit, Health sci, Texana
Automation Activity & Vendor Info: (Cataloging) OCLC Online; (Circulation) Innovative Interfaces, Inc - Millenium; (ILL) OCLC Online; (OPAC) Innovative Interfaces, Inc - Millenium
Database Vendor: EBSCOhost, Gale Cengage Learning, netLibrary, OVID Technologies, ProQuest, STAT!Ref (Teton Data Systems)
Wireless access

Function: For res purposes, Handicapped accessible, ILL available, Photocopying/Printing, Telephone ref
Partic in TexSHARE - Texas State Library & Archives Commission
Open Mon-Thurs 8am-9pm, Fri 8-3, Sat 10-1

S **SHELL OIL CO***, Tax Library, 910 Louisiana St, Ste 4353, 77002. (Mail add: PO Box 2463, 77252-2463), SAN 362-0247. Tel: 713-241-2155. FAX: 713-241-7029. Web Site: www.shell.com. *Librn,* Lito Llamas
Library Holdings: Bk Vols 3,000
Automation Activity & Vendor Info: (Cataloging) Sydney
Restriction: Staff use only

M **SHRINERS' HOSPITALS FOR CHILDREN-HOUSTON, LIBRARY***, 6977 Main St, 77030-3701. SAN 316-4837. Tel: 713-793-3918. FAX: 713-793-3779. *Librn,* Carl Martin; Staff 1 (MLS 1)
Founded 1963
Library Holdings: Bk Vols 1,000; Per Subs 22
Restriction: Staff use only

CL **SOUTH TEXAS COLLEGE OF LAW***, The Fred Parks Law Library, 1303 San Jacinto St, 77002-7000. SAN 316-4845. Tel: 713-646-1711. Interlibrary Loan Service Tel: 713-646-1792. Reference Tel: 713-646-1712. Administration Tel: 713-646-1729. FAX: 713-659-2217. E-mail: stclill@stcl.edu. Web Site: www.stcl.edu/library/libhome.html. *Dir, Libr Serv,* David G Cowan; *Computer Instrul Serv Librn,* Susan Spillman; *Publ & Ref Librn,* Adrienne Cobb; *Sr Cat Librn,* Barbara Szalkowski; *Spec Coll Librn,* Heather Kushnerick; *ILL, Ref Serv,* Heather Waltman; *Ref Serv,* Jessica Alexander; *Ref Serv, Ser,* Mary Lippold; *Ref Serv,* Monica Ortale; Staff 9 (MLS 9)
Founded 1924. Enrl 1,200; Fac 55; Highest Degree: Doctorate
Library Holdings: Bk Titles 79,719; Bk Vols 500,000; Per Subs 4,326
Special Collections: Law School Archives; Rare Book Coll. US Document Depository
Automation Activity & Vendor Info: (Acquisitions) Innovative Interfaces, Inc; (Cataloging) Innovative Interfaces, Inc; (Circulation) Innovative Interfaces, Inc; (ILL) Innovative Interfaces, Inc; (OPAC) Innovative Interfaces, Inc; (Serials) Innovative Interfaces, Inc
Publications: Accession List (Monthly); Footnotes (Newsletter); Journal Holdings; Library Guides
Partic in OCLC Online Computer Library Center, Inc; Westlaw
Open Mon-Thurs 7:30am-Midnight, Fri 7:30am-10pm, Sat 8:30am-10pm, Sun 10-10

M **TEXAS CHILDREN'S HOSPITAL***, Pi Beta Phi Patient/Family Library, 6621 Fannin St, MC-W16277, 77030. SAN 316-490X. Tel: 832-826-1619. FAX: 832-825-1601. Web Site: www.texaschildrenshospital.org. *Libr Coordr,* Julia D Allison; E-mail: jdalliso@texaschildrenshospital.org
Founded 1984
Library Holdings: Bk Vols 5,000
Subject Interests: Bks for all ages, Children's lit, Med, Movies, Parenting
Wireless access
Open Mon-Fri 8-5, Sat 10-3
Friends of the Library Group

C **TEXAS SOUTHERN UNIVERSITY***, Robert James Terry Library, 3100 Cleburne Ave, 77004. SAN 362-0255. Tel: 713-313-7402. Interlibrary Loan Service Tel: 713-313-1085. Administration Tel: 713-313-4420. FAX: 713-313-1080. Web Site: www.tsu.edu. *Interim Dir,* Norma Bean; *Acq Librn,* Margaret Tunstall; Tel: 713-313-7152; *Circ Librn,* Marion Ferguson; Tel: 713-313-4417; *Ref Librn,* Ronald Keys; Tel: 713-313-4424; *Archivist, Coordr, Spec Coll,* Bernard Forrester; Tel: 713-313-4416; *Ser,* Leocadia Hooks; Tel: 713-313-4423; Staff 10 (MLS 10)
Founded 1947. Enrl 6,522; Fac 458; Highest Degree: Doctorate
Library Holdings: Microforms 504,149; Bk Vols 261,506; Per Subs 1,774
Special Collections: Barbara Jordan Archives; Heartman Collection; Traditional African Art Gallery; University Archives. State Document Depository
Automation Activity & Vendor Info: (Acquisitions) Ex Libris Group; (Cataloging) Ex Libris Group; (Circulation) Ex Libris Group; (Course Reserve) Ex Libris Group; (ILL) Ex Libris Group; (Media Booking) Ex Libris Group; (OPAC) Ex Libris Group; (Serials) Ex Libris Group
Publications: Catalog of the Traditional African Art Gallery
Partic in Houston Area Research Library Consortium; OCLC Online Computer Library Center, Inc; TexSHARE - Texas State Library & Archives Commission
Open Mon-Thurs (Summer) 7am-10pm, Fri 7am-8pm, Sat 9-6, Sun 12-9
Departmental Libraries:

CL **THURGOOD MARSHALL SCHOOL OF LAW LIBRARY**, 3100 Cleburne Ave, 77004, SAN 362-028X. Tel: 713-313-7125. FAX: 713-313-4483. Web Site: www.tsulaw.edu/library. *Dir,* DeCarlous Spearman; Tel: 713-313-7328, E-mail: dspearman@tsulaw.edu; *Acq,* Gwen Henderson; Tel: 713-313-1157; *Cat, Tech Serv,* Evelyn Beard; Tel: 713-313-1005; *Govt Doc,* Olusola Babatunde; Tel: 713-313-1978; *Ref,* Nanette Collins; Tel: 713-313-1106; Staff 9 (MLS 3, Non-MLS 6)
Founded 1948. Enrl 400; Fac 25; Highest Degree: Doctorate

Library Holdings: Bk Titles 350,000; Per Subs 2,500
Automation Activity & Vendor Info: (Acquisitions) Innovative
Interfaces, Inc; (Cataloging) Innovative Interfaces, Inc; (Circulation)
Innovative Interfaces, Inc; (Course Reserve) Innovative Interfaces, Inc;
(ILL) Innovative Interfaces, Inc; (Media Booking) Innovative Interfaces,
Inc; (OPAC) Innovative Interfaces, Inc; (Serials) Innovative Interfaces,
Inc
Database Vendor: LexisNexis, Westlaw
Open Mon-Thurs 7am-Midnight, Fri 7am-10pm, Sat 9am-10pm, Sun
Noon-Midnight

M   TIRR MEMORIAL HERMANN*, Rehabilitation & Research Library,
1333 Moursund Ave, 77030. SAN 316-4934. Tel: 713-797-5947. FAX:
713-797-7549. Web Site: www.memorialhermann.org. *Librn,* Brenda Eames
Founded 1969
Library Holdings: Bk Vols 2,500; Per Subs 25
Special Collections: Polio & Post-Polio
Subject Interests: Head injury, Rehabilitation, Spinal cord injury
Wireless access
Function: Res libr, Telephone ref
Restriction: Not open to pub, Ref only to non-staff

L   UNITED STATES COURTS LIBRARY*, 515 Rusk Ave, Rm 6311, 77002.
SAN 372-1620. Tel: 713-250-5696. FAX: 713-250-5091. Web Site:
www.lb5.uscourts.gov. *Librn,* Andrew Jackson; *Librn,* Ching-Cheng C
Ting; E-mail: tina_ting@ca5.uscourts.gov
Library Holdings: Bk Vols 50,000; Per Subs 70
Automation Activity & Vendor Info: (Acquisitions) SirsiDynix;
(Cataloging) SirsiDynix; (Serials) SirsiDynix
Wireless access
Publications: Library guide; newsletter
Restriction: Non-circulating, Not open to pub

UNIVERSITY OF HOUSTON
C   M D ANDERSON LIBRARY*, 114 University Libraries, 77204-2000. Tel:
713-743-9800. FAX: 713-743-9811. Web Site: info.lib.uh.edu. *Dean of
Libr,* Dana Rooks; E-mail: drooks@uh.edu; *Assoc Dean of Libr,* Linda
Thompson; *Assoc Dean, Personnel Planning & Syst,* John Lehner; *Assoc
Dean, Pub Serv,* Marilyn Myers; *Prog Dir, Coll,* Miranda Bennett; *Spec
Coll Librn,* Pat Bozeman; *ILL Coordr,* Nora Dethloff; *Archivist,* Richard
Dickerson; Staff 60 (MLS 60)
Founded 1927. Enrl 34,663; Fac 2,953; Highest Degree: Doctorate
Library Holdings: Bk Vols 2,298,433; Per Subs 21,845
Special Collections: American History (Israel Shreve Coll), papers;
Architecture (Franzheim Memorial Coll); Bibliography & History of
Printing; British & American Authors (A Huxley, Thurber, Jeffers,
Patchen, Updike, Lowry & McMurtry Colls); City of Houston (George
Fuermann Coll); Creative Writing & Performing Arts Archive; History of
Science (Jadish Hehra Coll); James E & Miriam A Ferguson Coll,
papers; James V Allred Coll of Texas gubernatorial papers; Texana &
Western Americana (W B Bates Coll), bks, mss. State Document
Depository; US Document Depository
Subject Interests: Chem, Computer sci, Eng
Automation Activity & Vendor Info: (Acquisitions) Innovative
Interfaces, Inc; (Cataloging) Innovative Interfaces, Inc; (Circulation)
Innovative Interfaces, Inc; (Course Reserve) Innovative Interfaces, Inc;
(ILL) Innovative Interfaces, Inc; (Media Booking) Innovative Interfaces,
Inc; (OPAC) Innovative Interfaces, Inc; (Serials) Innovative Interfaces,
Inc
Partic in Association of Research Libraries (ARL); Center for Research
Libraries
Publications: Public-Access Computer Systems Review
Open Mon-Thurs 7:45am-10pm, Fri 7:45-5, Sat & Sun 1-6
C   WILLIAM R JENKINS ARCHITECTURE & ART LIBRARY*, 122
Architecture Bldg, 77204-4000, SAN 362-0417. Tel: 713-743-2340.
Interlibrary Loan Service Tel: 713-743-9720. FAX: 713-743-9917. Web
Site: www.info.lib.uh.edu/local/arch.htm. *Coordr,* Catherine Essinger;
E-mail: cwessinger@uh.edu
Library Holdings: Bk Vols 80,000; Per Subs 225
Subject Interests: Archit, Art, Landscape archit, Urban design
Partic in Amigos Library Services, Inc; Association of Research Libraries
(ARL); Houston Area Research Library Consortium; Texas Council of
Academic Libraries; TexSHARE - Texas State Library & Archives
Commission
Open Mon-Fri 7:45am-10pm, Fri 7:45-5, Sat & Sun 1-6
C   MUSIC LIBRARY*, 220 Moores School of Music Bldg, 77204-4017.
(Mail add: 114 University Libraries, 77204-2000). Tel: 713-743-3197.
FAX: 713-743-9918. E-mail: musiclib@uh.edu. Web Site:
info.lib.uh.edu/music. *Dir,* Ericka Patillo; Tel: 713-743-3770; Staff 4
(MLS 2, Non-MLS 2)
Founded 1968. Highest Degree: Doctorate
Library Holdings: Bk Vols 54,000; Per Subs 195
Automation Activity & Vendor Info: (Acquisitions) Innovative
Interfaces, Inc; (Cataloging) Innovative Interfaces, Inc; (Circulation)

Innovative Interfaces, Inc; (Course Reserve) Innovative Interfaces, Inc;
(ILL) OCLC ILLiad; (Media Booking) Innovative Interfaces, Inc;
(OPAC) Innovative Interfaces, Inc; (Serials) Innovative Interfaces, Inc
Function: Handicapped accessible, ILL available, Ref serv available
Partic in Association of Research Libraries (ARL); Tex Share
Open Mon-Fri 7:45-5

CM   OPTOMETRY LIBRARY*, 505 J Davis Armistead Bldg, 77204-2020,
SAN 362-0441. Tel: 713-743-1910. FAX: 713-743-2001. Web Site:
info.lib.uh.edu/local/optometr.htm. *Librn,* Suzanne Ferimer; Tel:
713-743-1912, E-mail: sferimer@uh.edu
Library Holdings: Bk Vols 10,000; Per Subs 137
Subject Interests: Ophthalmology, Optometry, Physiological optics,
Vision sci
Partic in Association of Research Libraries (ARL)
Open Mon-Fri 7-6

CL   THE O'QUINN LAW LIBRARY, 12 Law Library, 77204-6054. Tel:
713-743-2300. Interlibrary Loan Service Tel: 713-743-2286. Reference
Tel: 713-743-2327. Administration Tel: 713-743-2331. FAX:
713-743-2296. Web Site: www.law.uh.edu/libraries. *Dir,* Spencer Simons;
Assoc Dir, Mon Yin Lung; *Head, Acq & Coll Serv,* Marek Waterstone;
Head, Cat & Ser, Yuxin Li; *Head, Doc Serv,* Helen E Boyce; *Instrul
Serv Librn,* Christopher Dykes; *Ref Serv,* Lauren Schroeder; Staff 12
(MLS 10, Non-MLS 2)
Founded 1947. Enrl 1,100; Fac 46; Highest Degree: Doctorate
Library Holdings: e-books 21,925; Electronic Media & Resources 26;
Microforms 1,670,675; Bk Titles 125,251; Bk Vols 569,358; Per Subs
2,598; Videos 175
Special Collections: Congressional Publications (CIS Microfiche
Library); Texas Supreme Court Briefs. US Document Depository
Subject Interests: Admiralty law, Energy law, Intellectual property law,
Intl trade, Maritime law, Taxes
Automation Activity & Vendor Info: (Acquisitions) Innovative
Interfaces, Inc; (Cataloging) Innovative Interfaces, Inc; (Circulation)
Innovative Interfaces, Inc; (OPAC) Innovative Interfaces, Inc; (Serials)
Innovative Interfaces, Inc
Partic in Association of Research Libraries (ARL); TexSHARE - Texas
State Library & Archives Commission
Open Mon-Thurs 7:30am-Midnight, Fri 7:30am-11pm, Sat 9-8, Sun
9am-11pm
Restriction: Pub use on premises

C   UNIVERSITY OF HOUSTON - CLEAR LAKE, Neumann Library, 2700
Bay Area Blvd, 77058-1098. SAN 362-0468. Tel: 281-283-3930.
Circulation Tel: 281-283-4050. Interlibrary Loan Service Tel:
281-283-3906. Information Services Tel: 281-283-3910. FAX:
281-283-3937. E-mail: library@uhcl.edu. Web Site: www.uhcl.edu/library.
Exec Dir, Karen Wielhorski; *Assoc Dir,* Martha Steele; Tel: 281-283-3912,
E-mail: steelem@uhcl.edu; *Assoc Dir, Digital Serv,* Karen Berrish; Tel:
281-283-3919, E-mail: berrish@uhcl.edu; *Assoc Dir, Tech Serv,* Martha
Hood; Tel: 281-283-3920, E-mail: hood@uhcl.edu; *ILL,* Frances Weeks;
Staff 35 (MLS 14, Non-MLS 21)
Founded 1973. Enrl 7,700; Fac 339; Highest Degree: Master
Library Holdings: e-books 48,000; Bk Titles 287,000; Bk Vols 500,000;
Per Subs 1,400
Special Collections: Early English Books (Pollard & Redgrave Coll)
Subject Interests: Acctg, Environ, Software eng, Space sci
Automation Activity & Vendor Info: (Acquisitions) Innovative Interfaces,
Inc; (Cataloging) Innovative Interfaces, Inc; (Circulation) Innovative
Interfaces, Inc; (Course Reserve) Innovative Interfaces, Inc; (ILL)
Innovative Interfaces, Inc; (OPAC) Innovative Interfaces, Inc; (Serials)
Innovative Interfaces, Inc
Wireless access
Function: Wheelchair accessible
Partic in TexSHARE - Texas State Library & Archives Commission
Special Services for the Blind - Computer with voice synthesizer for
visually impaired persons; Internet workstation with adaptive software
Open Mon-Thurs 8am-Midnight, Fri 8-5, Sat 9-5, Sun 1-5

C   UNIVERSITY OF HOUSTON-DOWNTOWN, W I Dykes Library, One
Main St, 77002. SAN 362-0492. Tel: 713-221-8181, 713-221-8182.
Circulation Tel: 713-221-8186. Reference Tel: 713-221-8187.
Administration Tel: 713-221-8011. Automation Services Tel: 713-221-8054.
FAX: 713-221-8037. Web Site: www.uhd.edu/library/index.html. *Exec Dir,
Libr Serv,* Pat Ensor; E-mail: ensorp@uhd.edu; Staff 35.5 (MLS 15.5,
Non-MLS 20)
Founded 1974. Enrl 12,918; Fac 642; Highest Degree: Master
Sept 2011-Aug 2012 Income $3,924,014. Mats Exp $2,041,937, Books
$238,988, Per/Ser (Incl. Access Fees) $68,261, AV Mat $23,293, Electronic
Ref Mat (Incl. Access Fees) $1,544,355, Presv $6,741. Sal $1,371,959
(Prof $752,786)
Library Holdings: AV Mats 3,536; e-books 232,372; e-journals 83,241;
Electronic Media & Resources 347,107; Microforms 5,688; Bk Titles
134,410; Bk Vols 179,213; Per Subs 9,731; Videos 3,536
Automation Activity & Vendor Info: (Acquisitions) Innovative Interfaces,
Inc - Millenium; (Cataloging) Innovative Interfaces, Inc - Millenium;

(Circulation) Innovative Interfaces, Inc - Millenium; (ILL) OCLC; (OPAC) Innovative Interfaces, Inc - Millenium; (Serials) Innovative Interfaces, Inc - Millenium

Database Vendor: Alexander Street Press, ARTstor, ebrary, EBSCOhost, Gale Cengage Learning, Hoovers, JSTOR, LexisNexis, Newsbank, OCLC WorldCat, Project MUSE, ProQuest, PubMed, Springer-Verlag, Westlaw, Wiley InterScience

Wireless access

Function: Audio & video playback equip for onsite use, Bks on CD, Computers for patron use, Copy machines, Distance learning, e-mail serv, E-Reserves, Electronic databases & coll, Handicapped accessible, ILL available, Music CDs, Online cat, Online info literacy tutorials on the web & in blackboard, Orientations, Pub access computers, Ref serv available, Ref serv in person, Spoken cassettes & CDs, Spoken cassettes & DVDs, VCDs, VHS videos, Wheelchair accessible

Partic in Houston Area Research Library Consortium; OCLC Online Computer Library Center, Inc; TexSHARE - Texas State Library & Archives Commission

Special Services for the Blind - Bks on CD

Open Mon-Thurs (Fall & Spring) 7am-10pm, Fri 7-6, Sat 9-6, Sun 1-6; Mon-Thurs (Summer) 7am-9:30pm, Fri 7-5, Sat 1-5

Restriction: Limited access for the pub

C   UNIVERSITY OF SAINT THOMAS, Robert Pace & Ada Mary Doherty Library, 1100 W Main, 77006. (Mail add: 3800 Montrose Blvd, 77006), SAN 362-0522. Tel: 713-525-2192. Circulation Tel: 713-525-2180. Interlibrary Loan Service Tel: 713-525-6926. Reference Tel: 713-525-2188. Automation Services Tel: 713-525-2183. FAX: 713-525-3886. E-mail: reference @stthom.edu. Web Site: www.stthom.edu/public/index.asp?page_ID=1467. *Dean of Libr,* James Piccininni; E-mail: jpicci@stthom.edu; *Coll Develop Librn,* Nicholas Kowalski; Tel: 713-525-2182, Fax: 713-525-2186, E-mail: kowalsn@stthom.edu; *Electronic Res Librn,* Loan Nguyen; Tel: 713-525-2189, E-mail: ltnguyen1@stthom.edu; *Info Literacy Librn,* Joseph Goetz; Tel: 713-942-5972, E-mail: goetzj@stthom.edu; *ILL Librn,* Fr George Hosko; E-mail: loans@stthom.edu; *Pub Serv Librn,* Emily Couvillon; Tel: 713-525-3891, E-mail: couvile@stthom.edu; *Tech Serv Librn,* Jesus Serrato; E-mail: serratj@stthom.edu; *Circ Supvr,* Natalie Aquila; E-mail: aquilan@stthom.edu; *Circ Supvr,* Silvia Coy; E-mail: coys@stthom.edu; *Archives Coordr,* Betty Fisher; Tel: 713-525-3895, Fax: 713-525-2117, E-mail: fisheb@stthom.edu; *Archives Coordr,* Betty Kaffenberger; Tel: 713-525-3895, Fax: 713-525-2117, E-mail: kaffenb@stthom.edu; *Acq,* Pat Gerson; Tel: 713-525-2191, E-mail: gerson@stthom.edu; Staff 10 (MLS 6, Non-MLS 4)

Founded 1947. Enrl 3,246; Fac 141; Highest Degree: Doctorate

Library Holdings: AV Mats 2,045; e-books 98,281; Microforms 608,076; Bk Vols 250,263; Per Subs 58,041

Special Collections: Philosophy (Thomistic Studies Coll)

Automation Activity & Vendor Info: (Acquisitions) SirsiDynix; (Cataloging) SirsiDynix; (Circulation) SirsiDynix; (Course Reserve) SirsiDynix; (OPAC) SirsiDynix; (Serials) EBSCO Online

Database Vendor: American Chemical Society, Amigos Library Services, Annual Reviews, ARTstor, Baker & Taylor, BioOne, Cinahl Information Systems, CountryWatch, CQ Press, CredoReference, ebrary, EBSCOhost, Elsevier, Gale Cengage Learning, H W Wilson, JSTOR, LexisNexis, McGraw-Hill, Medline, Mergent Online, netLibrary, Newsbank, OCLC, OCLC FirstSearch, OCLC WorldCat, OVID Technologies, ProQuest, PubMed, RefWorks, Sage, SirsiDynix, Springer-Verlag, Springshare, LLC, Standard & Poor's, Westlaw, Wilson - Wilson Web, YBP Library Services

Wireless access

Function: Archival coll, CD-ROM, Computers for patron use, Copy machines, e-mail & chat, E-Reserves, Electronic databases & coll, Exhibits, ILL available, Instruction & testing, Literacy & newcomer serv, Magnifiers for reading, Online cat, Online info literacy tutorials on the web & in blackboard, Online ref, Online searches, Orientations, Outside serv via phone, mail, e-mail & web, Ref & res, Ref serv available, Ref serv in person, Summer reading prog, VHS videos, Workshops

Publications: Folio

Partic in OCLC Online Computer Library Center, Inc; Tex Independent Cols & Univ Librs; Tex Share

Open Mon-Thurs 7:45am-Midnight, Fri & Sat 10-9, Sun 1pm-Midnight

Restriction: Circ limited, Non-circulating coll, Non-circulating of rare bks, Open to pub for ref & circ; with some limitations, Open to students, fac & staff, Photo ID required for access

Friends of the Library Group

Departmental Libraries:

CARDINAL BERAN LIBRARY AT SAINT MARY'S SEMINARY, 9845 Memorial Dr, 77024-3498, SAN 362-0581. Tel: 713-686-4345, Ext 248, 713-686-4345, Ext 265. FAX: 713-681-7550. E-mail: beran@smseminary.com. Web Site: www.smseminary.com. *Chair,* Dr Mary Kelleher; E-mail: kellehe@stthom.edu; *Generalist Librn,* Nicolas Castellanos; E-mail: castelno@stthom.edu; *Generalist Librn,* Ashley Pitts; E-mail: pittsa@stthom.edu; Staff 3.8 (MLS 2.8, Non-MLS 1)

Founded 1954. Fac 8; Highest Degree: Master

Library Holdings: Bk Vols 64,000; Per Subs 315

Subject Interests: Relig studies, Theol

Restriction: Borrowing privileges limited to fac & registered students, Photo ID required for access

UNIVERSITY OF TEXAS

CM   M D ANDERSON CANCER CENTER RESEARCH MEDICAL LIBRARY*, 1400 Pressler St, 77030-3722, SAN 362-0646. Tel: 713-792-2282. Interlibrary Loan Service Tel: 713-745-4531. FAX: 713-563-3650. Web Site: www3.mdanderson.org/library. *Exec Dir,* Stephanie Fulton; Tel: 713-792-2293, E-mail: sfulton@mdanderson.org; *Sr Ref Librn, Webmaster,* Ron Hutchins; Tel: 713-745-4334, E-mail: rhutchin@mdanderson.org; *Coll Mgr,* Sherry Widdoes; Tel: 713-792-2812, E-mail: swiddoes@mdanderson.org; *Mgr, Info Serv,* Clara Fowler; *Info Tech Mgr,* Wes Browning; Tel: 713-745-1545, E-mail: wbrownin@mdanderson.org; *Info Tech Mgr,* Marlene Caldwell; Tel: 713-745-5158, E-mail: mcaldwe@mdanderson.org; *Sr Info Spec,* Greg Pratt; Tel: 713-745-5156, E-mail: gfpratt@mdanderson.org; *Archivist,* Javier F Garza; Tel: 713-792-2285, E-mail: jjgarza@mdanderson.org; *Cat,* Linda Olewine; Tel: 713-745-3086, E-mail: lolewine@mdanderson.org; *Doc Delivery,* Roxanne Dolen; Tel: 713-745-7432, E-mail: rdolen@mdanderson.org; Staff 13 (MLS 10, Non-MLS 3)

Founded 1941

Library Holdings: AV Mats 849; CDs 32; e-books 42,257; e-journals 20,786; Bk Titles 17,496; Bk Vols 20,431; Per Subs 670

Special Collections: Historical Resources Center; Leland Clayton Barbee History of Cancer Coll, early treatises, rare bks. Oral History

Subject Interests: Cancer, Radiology

Automation Activity & Vendor Info: (Acquisitions) Ex Libris Group; (Cataloging) Ex Libris Group; (Circulation) Ex Libris Group; (Course Reserve) Ex Libris Group; (ILL) OCLC ILLiad; (OPAC) Ex Libris Group; (Serials) Ex Libris Group

Database Vendor: Dialog, EBSCOhost, Gale Cengage Learning, JSTOR, netLibrary, OCLC FirstSearch, OVID Technologies

Function: Archival coll, Distance learning, Doc delivery serv, Health sci info serv, Homebound delivery serv, ILL available, Online searches, Photocopying/Printing, Ref serv available, Res libr

Partic in Tex Health Sci Libr Consortium

Publications: NewsBytes (Newsletter)

Open Mon-Fri 7:30-7

CM   HEALTH SCIENCE CENTER AT HOUSTON, DENTAL BRANCH LIBRARY*, 6516 M D Anderson Blvd, Rm 133, 77030. (Mail add: PO Box 20068, 77225-0068), SAN 362-0611. Tel: 713-500-4094. FAX: 713-500-4100. Web Site: www.db.uth.tmc.edu/education/library. *Asst Libr Dir,* Janet Peri; Tel: 713-500-4204; Staff 4 (MLS 1, Non-MLS 3)

Founded 1943. Fac 180; Highest Degree: Doctorate

Library Holdings: Bk Titles 14,937; Bk Vols 32,246; Per Subs 204

Special Collections: Dentistry (Historical Coll), first editions & rare bks

Subject Interests: Dentistry

Partic in OCLC Online Computer Library Center, Inc

Open Mon-Fri 8-5

CM   SCHOOL OF PUBLIC HEALTH LIBRARY*, 1200 Herman Pressler Blvd, 77030-3900. (Mail add: PO Box 20186, 77225-0186), SAN 316-5019. Tel: 713-500-9121. Interlibrary Loan Service Tel: 713-500-9130. Reference Tel: 713-500-9131. FAX: 713-500-9125. Web Site: www.sph.uth.tmc.edu/library. *Dir, Ref,* Helena M VonVille; E-mail: helena.m.vonville@uth.tmc.edu; *Acq,* Elaine Wilson; *Cat, Tech Serv,* Richard Guinn; *ILL,* Xuan Pang; *Pub Serv,* Angel Hooper; Staff 4 (MLS 4)

Founded 1969. Enrl 1,500; Fac 145; Highest Degree: Doctorate

Library Holdings: Bk Titles 55,000; Bk Vols 72,000; Per Subs 250

Special Collections: International Census Statistics; Pan American Health Organization; World Health Organization

Subject Interests: Epidemiology, Health econ, Health promotion, HIV-AIDS, Infectious diseases, Nutrition, Pub health

Automation Activity & Vendor Info: (Acquisitions) Ex Libris Group; (Cataloging) Ex Libris Group; (Circulation) Ex Libris Group; (OPAC) Ex Libris Group; (Serials) Ex Libris Group

Partic in National Network of Libraries of Medicine South Central Region; OCLC Online Computer Library Center, Inc; S Cent Regional Med Libr Program; Tex Health Sci Libr Consortium; TexSHARE - Texas State Library & Archives Commission; UT Syst Librns

Open Mon-Thurs 8-7, Fri 8-5, Sat 12-6

S   UNIVERSITY OF TEXAS-HOUSTON HEALTH SCIENCE CENTER*, UT Psychiatry Library, 2800 S McGregor Way, 77021. SAN 316-4950. Tel: 713-741-6043. FAX: 713-741-6050. Web Site: www.uth.tmc.edu. *Dir,* Felicia S Chuang; Staff 1 (MLS 1)

Founded 1959

Library Holdings: Bk Titles 12,883; Per Subs 77

Special Collections: Psychiatry (Eugen Kahn Memorial Coll)

Subject Interests: Aging, Psychiat, Substance abuse

Automation Activity & Vendor Info: (Acquisitions) Ex Libris Group; (Cataloging) Ex Libris Group; (Circulation) Ex Libris Group; (Course

Reserve) Ex Libris Group; (ILL) Ex Libris Group; (OPAC) Ex Libris Group; (Serials) Ex Libris Group
Database Vendor: EBSCOhost, OVID Technologies
Partic in Tex Health Sci Libr Consortium; TexSHARE - Texas State Library & Archives Commission
Restriction: Pub use on premises

L VINSON & ELKINS*, Law Library, 3055 First City Tower, 1001 Fannin, 77002-6760. SAN 316-5035. Tel: 713-758-2678. FAX: 713-615-5211. Web Site: www.velaw.com. *Librn,* Susan Yancey; *Cat,* Patricia Huntsman
Founded 1917
Library Holdings: Bk Vols 145,000
Database Vendor: Dialog, LexisNexis, Westlaw
Restriction: Staff use only

L JACKSON WALKER LAW LIBRARY, 1401 McKinney, Ste 1900, 77010. SAN 372-1612. Tel: 713-752-4479. FAX: 713-752-4221. *Law Librn,* Caren Zentner Luckie; E-mail: cluckie@jw.com; *Libr Asst,* Sarah Gutierrez; Tel: 713-752-4317, E-mail: sgutierrez@jw.com; Staff 2 (MLS 1, Non-MLS 1)
Library Holdings: Bk Vols 7,500; Per Subs 30
Automation Activity & Vendor Info: (Cataloging) EOS International; (OPAC) EOS International; (Serials) EOS International
Database Vendor: Dialog, LexisNexis, Westlaw
Restriction: Not open to pub

S WEATHER RESEARCH CENTER LIBRARY*, 5104 Caroline, 77004. SAN 370-3037. Tel: 713-529-3076. FAX: 713-528-3538. E-mail: wrc@wxresearch.org. Web Site: www.wxresearch.com, www.wxresearch.org. *Dir,* Jill F Hasling
Library Holdings: Bk Vols 900; Per Subs 6,500
Subject Interests: Meteorology
Restriction: Open by appt only

L WEIL, GOTSHAL & MANGES LLP*, Law Library, 700 Louisiana St, Ste 1600, 77002. SAN 374-6607. Tel: 713-546-5131. FAX: 713-224-9511. Web Site: www.weil.com. *Dir,* Elizabeth Black Berry; Tel: 713-546-5055, E-mail: elizabeth.berry@weil.com; *Asst Librn,* Debra Milligen; Staff 2 (MLS 2)
Founded 1985
Library Holdings: Bk Vols 8,000
Automation Activity & Vendor Info: (Cataloging) Sydney; (Circulation) Sydney
Wireless access
Restriction: Staff use only

R WINDWOOD PRESBYTERIAN CHURCH LIBRARY*, 10555 Spring Cypress Rd, 77070. SAN 316-1870. Tel: 281-257-7860. FAX: 281-378-4041. E-mail: windwood@windwoodpc.org. Web Site: www.windwoodpc.org.
Founded 1971
Library Holdings: Bk Vols 650
Restriction: Mem only

M WINSTON & STRAWN LIBRARY*, 1111 Louisiana St, 25th Fl, 77002. SAN 320-8737. Tel: 713-787-1400. FAX: 713-787-1440. *Librn,* Caralinn Cole
Library Holdings: Bk Vols 9,000; Per Subs 100
Subject Interests: Copyrights, Franchises, Patents, Trademarks, Unfair competition
Partic in BRS
Open Mon-Fri 9-5:30

HOWE

P HOWE COMMUNITY LIBRARY*, 315 S Collins Freeway, 75459. SAN 376-4540. Tel: 903-532-3350. FAX: 903-532-3351. E-mail: howelibrary2@howeisd.net. Web Site: www.howeisd.net. *Dir,* Becky Hogenson; *Librn,* Terry McLaughlin; *Librn,* Joyce Park; Staff 3 (MLS 1, Non-MLS 2)
Founded 1982. Pop 6,638; Circ 38,637
Library Holdings: AV Mats 1,540; Bk Vols 34,000; Per Subs 90; Videos 1,330
Automation Activity & Vendor Info: (Cataloging) Follett Software; (Circulation) Follett Software; (OPAC) Follett Software
Open Mon-Wed & Fri (Winter) 8-5:30, Thurs 8-6, Sat 9-12; Mon-Wed & Fri (Summer) 9-5, Thurs 9-6, Sat 9-12
Friends of the Library Group

HUBBARD

P WILKES MEMORIAL LIBRARY*, Sixth St, 76648. Tel: 254-576-2527. FAX: 785-899-6411. *Librn,* Linda Jordon; Staff 1 (Non-MLS 1)
Library Holdings: Bk Titles 10,000
Open Wed 10-4, Sat 10-5

HUNTINGTON

P MCMULLEN MEMORIAL LIBRARY*, 906 N Main St, 75949. (Mail add: PO Box 849, 75949-0849). Tel: 936-876-4516. FAX: 936-876-4516. *Dir,* Debra Bashaw; E-mail: dbashaw@consolidated.net
Library Holdings: AV Mats 2,000; Bk Vols 25,000; Per Subs 12
Open Mon & Wed-Fri 8-4, Tues 8-7, Sat 10-2
Friends of the Library Group

HUNTSVILLE

M HUNTSVILLE MEMORIAL HOSPITAL*, Medical Library Resource Center, 110 Memorial Hospital Dr, 77340. (Mail add: PO Box 4001, 77342-4001), SAN 316-5086. Tel: 936-435-7520. FAX: 936-291-4218. *Dir,* Roxann Langston
Founded 1966
Library Holdings: Bk Titles 2,300; Bk Vols 2,500; Per Subs 5
Special Collections: CIBA; Video Coll
Subject Interests: Med, Nursing
Partic in National Network of Libraries of Medicine
Open Mon-Fri 7:30-4

P HUNTSVILLE PUBLIC LIBRARY*, 1216 14th St, 77340. SAN 316-5094. Tel: 936-291-5470. FAX: 936-291-5418. Web Site: www.myhuntsvillelibrary.com. *Dir,* Linda Dobson
Founded 1967. Pop 23,936; Circ 63,440
Library Holdings: Bk Vols 65,000; Per Subs 100
Special Collections: Adult Education; Genealogy; Ornithology
Automation Activity & Vendor Info: (Cataloging) SirsiDynix; (Circulation) SirsiDynix; (OPAC) SirsiDynix
Wireless access
Open Mon-Thurs 10-6, Fri 9-5, Sat 10-2
Friends of the Library Group

C SAM HOUSTON STATE UNIVERSITY*, Newton Gresham Library, 1830 Bobby K Marks Dr, 77340. (Mail add: PO Box 2281, 77041), SAN 316-5108. Tel: 936-294-1614. Interlibrary Loan Service Tel: 936-294-1616. Administration Tel: 936-294-1613. FAX: 936-294-3780. Web Site: library.shsu.edu. *Dir,* Ann H Holder; E-mail: lib_ahh@shsu.edu; *Head, Acq,* Teri L Oparanozie; Tel: 936-294-1623, E-mail: lib_tlo@shsu.edu; *Head, Circ,* Linda S Meyer; Tel: 936-294-3551, E-mail: lib_lsm@shsu.edu; *Head, Ref,* Lynn M McMain; Tel: 936-294-3734, E-mail: lib_lmm@shsu.edu; *Head, Tech Serv,* Janice P Lange; Tel: 936-294-1620, E-mail: lib_jpl@shsu.edu; *ILL Librn,* Ann Jerabek; Tel: 936-294-3528, Fax: 936-294-1597, E-mail: lib_jaj@shsu.edu; *Coordr, Cat,* Linda Turney; Tel: 936-294-3503, E-mail: lmt012@shsu.edu; *Archivist,* Barbara A Kievit-Mason; Tel: 936-294-3699, E-mail: lib_bak@shsu.edu; *Ser Cataloger,* Glenda Griffin; Staff 22 (MLS 14, Non-MLS 8)
Founded 1879. Enrl 16,000; Highest Degree: Doctorate
Library Holdings: AV Mats 21,848; e-books 24,310; Bk Vols 1,202,263; Per Subs 4,521
Special Collections: Col John W Thomason Coll; Criminology (Bates, Bennett, Colfield, Eliasburg & McCormick Coll); Gertrude Stein Coll; Mark Twain Coll; Texana & the Southwest (Shettles Coll); Texana Coll; Texas (J L Clark Coll). State Document Depository; US Document Depository
Subject Interests: Criminal justice, Educ, Texana
Automation Activity & Vendor Info: (Acquisitions) SirsiDynix; (Cataloging) SirsiDynix; (Circulation) SirsiDynix; (OPAC) SirsiDynix; (Serials) SirsiDynix
Database Vendor: Dialog, EBSCOhost, Gale Cengage Learning, LexisNexis, OCLC FirstSearch, SirsiDynix, TLC (The Library Corporation)
Wireless access
Publications: Newsletter
Open Mon-Wed (Fall & Spring) 7:30am-1am, Thurs 7:30am-Midnight, Fri 7:30-6, Sat 10-7, Sun 2pm-1am; Mon-Wed (Summer) 7:30am-11pm, Thurs 7:30am-10pm, Fri 7:30-6, Sat 10-5, Sun 2-11

HURST

P HURST PUBLIC LIBRARY*, 901 Precinct Line Rd, 76053. SAN 316-5124. Tel: 817-788-7300. FAX: 817-590-9515. Web Site: www.ci.hurst.tx.us/lib. *City Librn,* Susan Andrews; E-mail: sandrews@ci.hurst.tx.us; *Adult Serv,* Ramona DeMeglio; *Ch,* Beverly Kirkendall; E-mail: bkirkend@ci.hurst.tx.us; *Circ,* Mary DeLeon; *Tech Serv,* Janet Young; E-mail: jyoung@ci.hurst.tx.us; Staff 23.5 (MLS 10, Non-MLS 13.5)
Founded 1959. Pop 40,000; Circ 329,375
Oct 2009-Sept 2010 Income $1,968,770, State $29,294, City $1,939,023, Other $453. Mats Exp $248,243, Books $143,101, Other Print Mats $60,545, Electronic Ref Mat (Incl. Access Fees) $44,597
Library Holdings: AV Mats 15,489; e-books 27; Bk Titles 99,067; Bk Vols 109,387; Per Subs 243; Talking Bks 2,249
Special Collections: Oral History
Subject Interests: Local hist

Automation Activity & Vendor Info: (Acquisitions) SirsiDynix; (Cataloging) SirsiDynix; (Circulation) SirsiDynix; (Course Reserve) SirsiDynix; (OPAC) SirsiDynix
Wireless access
Mem of North Texas Library Partners
Open Mon, Wed, Fri & Sat 10-6, Tues & Thurs 10-9
Friends of the Library Group

J   TARRANT COUNTY COLLEGE*, Northeast Campus Learning Resource Center, 828 Harwood Rd, 76054-3219. SAN 361-722X. Tel: 817-515-6477. Circulation Tel: 817-515-6627. Reference Tel: 817-515-6629. Administration FAX: 817-515-6275. Web Site: library.tccd.edu. *Dir, Libr Serv,* Dr Steven W Hagstrom; Tel: 817-515-6637, E-mail: steven.hagstrom@tccd.edu; *Mgr, Network Serv,* Paul Gray; Tel: 817-515-6623, E-mail: paul.gray@tccd.edu; *Ref Serv Librn,* Beth Mullins; Tel: 817-515-6314, E-mail: beth.mullins@tccd.edu; *Ref Serv Librn,* Judie Smith; Tel: 817-515-6625, E-mail: judie.smith@tccd.edu; Staff 6 (MLS 5, Non-MLS 1)
Founded 1968. Enrl 15,000; Fac 250; Highest Degree: Associate
Sept 2007-Aug 2008 Income $786,110. Mats Exp $828,298, Books $80,000, Per/Ser (Incl. Access Fees) $35,000, Other Print Mats $18,140, Micro $15,000, Electronic Ref Mat (Incl. Access Fees) $35,000. Sal $645,158
Library Holdings: Bk Vols 68,500; Per Subs 275
Subject Interests: Bus, Humanities, Sci tech, Soc sci
Automation Activity & Vendor Info: (Acquisitions) Ex Libris Group; (Cataloging) Ex Libris Group; (Circulation) Ex Libris Group; (Course Reserve) Ex Libris Group; (ILL) Ex Libris Group; (Media Booking) Ex Libris Group; (OPAC) Ex Libris Group; (Serials) Ex Libris Group
Database Vendor: Ex Libris Group
Wireless access
Function: Computers for patron use, Copy machines, Distance learning, Electronic databases & coll, Online ref, Photocopying/Printing, Ref & res, Ref serv available
Open Mon-Thurs 7:45am-10pm, Fri & Sat 7:45am-9pm, Sun 12-5
Restriction: Non-circulating coll, Open to pub for ref & circ; with some limitations

HUTCHINS

P   HUTCHINS-ATWELL PUBLIC LIBRARY*, 300 N Denton, 75141-9404. (Mail add: PO Box 888, 75141-0888), SAN 361-4042. Tel: 972-225-4711. FAX: 972-225-4593. *Librn,* Cheryl Hawkins; Staff 2 (MLS 2)
Library Holdings: Bk Titles 32,011; Per Subs 8
Automation Activity & Vendor Info: (Cataloging) Book Systems, Inc; (Circulation) Book Systems, Inc; (OPAC) Book Systems, Inc
Wireless access
Open Tues-Thurs 9-5:30, Sat 10-1

IDALOU

P   IDALOU COMMUNITY LIBRARY*, 210 Main St, 79329. (Mail add: PO Box 138, 79329-0138), SAN 376-4257. Tel: 806-892-2114. E-mail: idaloulibrary04@yahoo.com. *Dir,* Ester Espinoza
Jan 2010-Dec 2010 Income $1,175, City $975, Locally Generated Income $200. Mats Exp $200
Library Holdings: Bk Vols 12,000
Automation Activity & Vendor Info: (Cataloging) Follett Software; (Circulation) Follett Software; (OPAC) Follett Software
Open Mon, Tues & Thurs 1-7, Wed 1-6, Fri 1-5

IMPERIAL

P   IMPERIAL PUBLIC LIBRARY*, 223 W Farm Rd 11, 79743. (Mail add: PO Box 307, 79743-0307), SAN 376-4370. Tel: 432-536-2236. FAX: 432-536-2236. E-mail: imperiallib107@hotmail.com. *Dir,* Maxie King
Library Holdings: Bk Vols 15,000; Per Subs 15
Automation Activity & Vendor Info: (Cataloging) Follett Software; (Circulation) Follett Software
Wireless access
Mem of Texas Trans-Pecos Regional Library System
Open Mon-Thurs 8-6

INDUSTRY

P   INDUSTRY PUBLIC LIBRARY*, West End Public Library, 1646 N Main St, 78944. (Mail add: PO Box 179, 78944-0179). Tel: 979-357-4434. FAX: 979-357-4470. E-mail: westlib@industryinet.com.
Library Holdings: AV Mats 840; Bk Titles 9,000; Talking Bks 200
Automation Activity & Vendor Info: (Cataloging) Follett Software; (Circulation) Follett Software
Wireless access
Open Mon & Wed 8-5, Thurs 9-6, Sat 8:30-12:30

INGLESIDE

P   INGLESIDE PUBLIC LIBRARY*, 2775 Waco St, 78362. (Mail add: PO Drawer 400, 78362-0400), SAN 316-5159. Tel: 361-776-5355. FAX: 361-776-2264. *Dir,* Belinda Cassanova
Founded 1933. Pop 8,547; Circ 25,868
Library Holdings: Bk Titles 30,000
Special Collections: Municipal Libr Coll
Subject Interests: Oceanography, Texana
Wireless access
Mem of San Patricio County Library System
Open Mon & Thurs 8:30-6, Tues & Wed 8:30-7, Fri 8:30-5, Sat 9-4
Friends of the Library Group

IOWA PARK

P   TOM BURNETT MEMORIAL LIBRARY*, 400 W Alameda, 76367. SAN 320-5134. Tel: 940-592-4981. FAX: 940-592-4664. Web Site: www.iowapark.com/dept/library. *Dir,* Sue Maness
Founded 1962. Pop 6,431
Library Holdings: AV Mats 160; CDs 101; DVDs 586; Large Print Bks 445; Bk Titles 14,986; Per Subs 4; Videos 814
Subject Interests: Genealogy
Automation Activity & Vendor Info: (Cataloging) Book Systems, Inc; (Circulation) Book Systems, Inc; (OPAC) Book Systems, Inc
Mem of North Texas Library Partners
Open Tues & Thurs 10-8, Wed & Fri 10-5, Sat 10-2

IRAAN

P   IRAAN PUBLIC LIBRARY*, 120 W Fifth St, 79744. (Mail add: PO Box 638, 79744-0638), SAN 316-5167. Tel: 432-639-2235. FAX: 432-639-2276. E-mail: iraanlibrary@yahoo.com. *Librn,* Minnie Quintero
Founded 1950. Pop 1,500
Library Holdings: Bk Titles 15,900; Per Subs 26
Automation Activity & Vendor Info: (Cataloging) Book Systems, Inc; (Circulation) Book Systems, Inc; (OPAC) Book Systems, Inc
Wireless access
Mem of Texas Trans-Pecos Regional Library System
Open Mon-Thurs 9-5, Fri 8-4

IRVING

C   DEVRY UNIVERSITY LIBRARY*, Irving Campus Library, 4800 Regent Blvd, 75063-2440. SAN 316-2192. Tel: 972-929-9336. Circulation Tel: 972-929-9346. FAX: 972-929-6778. Web Site: www.dal.devry.edu/library.html. *Head Librn,* Naana Otaa-Gyamfi; Staff 1 (MLS 1)
Founded 1969. Highest Degree: Master
Library Holdings: e-books 11,500; Bk Titles 14,481; Per Subs 62
Subject Interests: Acctg, Bus operations, Computer sci, Electronics, Telecommunication
Automation Activity & Vendor Info: (Cataloging) Ex Libris Group; (Circulation) Ex Libris Group; (OPAC) Ex Libris Group
Database Vendor: EBSCOhost, LexisNexis, ProQuest
Wireless access
Publications: New Books Lists
Open Mon-Thurs 8am-9pm, Fri 8-7, Sat 9-5
Restriction: Non-circulating to the pub

P   IRVING PUBLIC LIBRARY*, 801 W Irving Blvd, 75015. (Mail add: PO Box 152288, 75015-2288), SAN 362-0670. Tel: 972-721-2606. Circulation Tel: 972-721-2440. Interlibrary Loan Service Tel: 972-721-4629. Administration Tel: 972-721-2628, 972-721-2639. Automation Services Tel: 972-721-2580. FAX: 972-721-2463. Circulation FAX: 972-721-2491. Interlibrary Loan Service FAX: 972-721-4771. Reference FAX: 972-721-8040. E-mail: reference@cityofirving.org. Web Site: www.cityofirving.org/library. *Dir,* Chris Michalski; E-mail: cmichals@cityofirving.org; *Libr Serv Mgr-Br,* Deborah Vaden; Tel: 972-721-2457, E-mail: dvaden@cityofirving.org; *Libr Serv Mgr-Cent,* Christine Dobson; Tel: 972-721-2748, E-mail: cdobson@cityofirving.org; *Libr Serv Mgr-Tech Serv,* Michael Ayres; Tel: 972-721-2439, Fax: 972-721-2329, E-mail: mayres@cityofirving.org; *Sr Archivist,* Jan Hart; Tel: 972-721-3729, E-mail: jhart@cityofirving.org; Staff 81 (MLS 22, Non-MLS 59)
Founded 1961. Pop 201,950; Circ 1,377,286
Library Holdings: AV Mats 343,118; Bk Titles 253,320; Bk Vols 531,380; Per Subs 1,089; Talking Bks 31,808; Videos 36,067
Subject Interests: Genealogy, Local hist
Automation Activity & Vendor Info: (Acquisitions) SirsiDynix; (Cataloging) SirsiDynix; (Circulation) SirsiDynix; (Course Reserve) SirsiDynix; (ILL) OCLC ILLiad; (OPAC) SirsiDynix; (Serials) SirsiDynix
Database Vendor: EBSCOhost, Gale Cengage Learning, Greenwood Publishing Group, infoUSA, netLibrary, Overdrive, Inc, ProQuest
Wireless access

Function: Adult bk club, Adult literacy prog, After school storytime, Archival coll, Bilingual assistance for Spanish patrons, Bks on cassette, Bks on CD, CD-ROM, Children's prog, Computer training, Computers for patron use, Copy machines, Electronic databases & coll, Fax serv, Free DVD rentals, Handicapped accessible, ILL available, Music CDs, Online cat, Online searches, OverDrive digital audio bks, Photocopying/Printing, Prog for adults, Prog for children & young adult, Pub access computers, Story hour, Summer reading prog, Tax forms, Teen prog, Telephone ref, VHS videos, Wheelchair accessible
Partic in Amigos Library Services, Inc; OCLC Online Computer Library Center, Inc; TexSHARE - Texas State Library & Archives Commission
Open Mon-Thurs 10-9, Fri & Sat 10-6, Sun 1-5
Friends of the Library Group
Branches: 3
EAST, 440 S Nursery Rd, 75060. (Mail add: PO Box 152288, 75015-2288). Tel: 972-721-3722. FAX: 972-721-3724. *Br Mgr,* Carol Danielson; E-mail: cdanielson@cityofirving.org; *Sr Librn,* Corine Barbarena; E-mail: cbarbarena@cityofirving.org; Staff 2 (MLS 2)
  Circ 61,964
  Library Holdings: Bk Vols 21,212
  Subject Interests: Mat in Spanish
  Open Mon & Wed, Noon-8, Tues & Thurs 10-6
  Friends of the Library Group
NORTHWEST, 2928 N Beltline Rd, 75062. (Mail add: PO Box 152288, 75060-2288), SAN 362-0700. Tel: 972-721-2691. FAX: 972-721-3637. *Mgr,* Tracy Bearden; E-mail: tbearden@cityofirving.org; *Sr Librn,* Deborah Brown; E-mail: dbrown@cityofirving.org; Staff 2 (MLS 2)
  Circ 156,232
  Library Holdings: Bk Vols 57,042
  Open Tues & Thurs 12-9, Wed, Fri & Sat 10-6
  Friends of the Library Group
VALLEY RANCH, 401 Cimmaron Trail, 75063-4680. (Mail add: PO Box 152288, 75015-2288), SAN 376-950X. Tel: 972-721-4669. FAX: 972-831-0672. *Mgr,* Patty Mount; E-mail: pmount@cityofirving.org; *Sr Librn,* Stephanie Gimble; Staff 3 (MLS 3)
  Circ 284,643
  Library Holdings: Bk Vols 71,788
  Open Mon, Wed, Fri & Sat 10-6, Tues & Thurs 12-9, Sun 1-5
  Friends of the Library Group
Bookmobiles: 1. Mgr, Deborah Vaden. Bk titles 7,017

J NORTH LAKE COLLEGE LIBRARY*, 5001 N MacArthur Blvd, 75062. SAN 324-2064. Tel: 972-273-3400. FAX: 972-273-3431. E-mail: ekc7610@dcccd.edu. Web Site: www.northlakecollege.edu/library. *Head Librn,* Dr Enrique Chamberlain; E-mail: ekc7610@dcccd.edu; *Librn,* Jane Bell; *Circ,* Olga Henson
  Library Holdings: Bk Vols 50,000; Per Subs 325
  Automation Activity & Vendor Info: (Cataloging) Innovative Interfaces, Inc; (Circulation) Innovative Interfaces, Inc; (OPAC) Innovative Interfaces, Inc
  Wireless access
  Open Mon-Thurs 8-8, Fri 8-4

CR UNIVERSITY OF DALLAS, William A Blakley Library, 1845 E Northgate Dr, 75062-4736. SAN 316-5175. Tel: 972-721-5328. Circulation Tel: 972-721-5329. Interlibrary Loan Service Tel: 972-721-5057. Reference Tel: 972-721-5315. Automation Services Tel: 972-721-5040. FAX: 972-721-4010. Web Site: www.udallas.edu/library. *Dir, Libr Serv & Univ Res,* Dr Robert Scott Dupree; E-mail: scott@udallas.edu; *Assoc Dir,* Nettie L Baker; Tel: 972-721-4031, E-mail: nettie@udallas.edu; *Head, Cat,* Lely White; Tel: 972-721-5310, E-mail: lely@udallas.edu; *Cataloger/Ref Librn,* Melissa Randall; Tel: 972-721-5397, E-mail: mrandall@udallas.edu; *Access Serv, Syst Librn,* Cherie Hohertz; E-mail: chohertz@udallas.edu; *Acq, Supvr,* Deborah Hathaway; Tel: 972-721-4122, E-mail: dhathaw@udallas.edu; *Circ Coordr,* Christopher Kirk; Tel: 972-721-4128, E-mail: ckirk@udallas.edu; *ILL,* Alice Puro; E-mail: apuro@udallas.edu; *Ref,* Carolyn Mauzy; Tel: 972-721-5350, E-mail: cmauzy@udallas.edu; *Ser,* Susan Vaughan; Tel: 972-721-4130, E-mail: svaughan@udallas.edu. Subject Specialists: *Lit,* Dr Robert Scott Dupree; *Libr admin,* Nettie L Baker; *German studies,* Lely White; *Drama, English,* Melissa Randall; *Music,* Cherie Hohertz; *English lit,* Christopher Kirk; *Sociol,* Carolyn Mauzy; *Bus, Hist,* Susan Vaughan; Staff 8 (MLS 7, Non-MLS 1)
  Founded 1956. Enrl 2,843; Fac 134; Highest Degree: Doctorate
  Jun 2011-May 2012. Mats Exp $521,335, Books $102,064, Per/Ser (Incl. Access Fees) $198,992, Electronic Ref Mat (Incl. Access Fees) $217,497, Presv $2,782. Sal $613,392 (Prof $307,777)
  Library Holdings: AV Mats 162; CDs 1,124; DVDs 204; e-books 31,764; e-journals 50; Microforms 75,340; Bk Titles 210,375; Bk Vols 372,071; Per Subs 453; Videos 907
  Special Collections: Index Thomisticus; Jacques Migne; Patrologiae Cursus Completus, micro; Political Philosophy (Kendall Memorial Library Coll)
  Subject Interests: Bus mgt, Liberal arts, Philosophy, Polit sci, Theol

Automation Activity & Vendor Info: (Acquisitions) SirsiDynix; (Cataloging) SirsiDynix; (Circulation) SirsiDynix; (Course Reserve) SirsiDynix; (ILL) OCLC ILLiad; (OPAC) SirsiDynix; (Serials) SirsiDynix
Database Vendor: ABC-CLIO, ACM (Association for Computing Machinery), Agricola, American Chemical Society, American Mathematical Society, American Psychological Association (APA), Amigos Library Services, Annual Reviews, ARTstor, Baker & Taylor, EBSCOhost, Gale Cengage Learning, Hoovers, infoUSA, Ingenta, IOP, JSTOR, LexisNexis, Medline, Mergent Online, Modern Language Association, netLibrary, OCLC FirstSearch, OCLC WorldCat, Project MUSE, ProQuest, PubMed, ReferenceUSA, ScienceDirect, Scopus, SerialsSolutions, SirsiDynix, Standard & Poor's, ValueLine, WebMD, YBP Library Services
Wireless access
Function: Distance learning, Doc delivery serv, For res purposes, ILL available, Ref serv available, Telephone ref
Partic in Amigos Library Services, Inc; OCLC Online Computer Library Center, Inc; TexSHARE - Texas State Library & Archives Commission
Open Mon-Thurs 8am-Midnight, Fri 8am-10pm, Sat 9-6, Sun 1pm-Midnight
Restriction: Open to students, fac & staff

ITALY

P S M DUNLAP MEMORIAL LIBRARY*, 300 W Main St, 76651. SAN 316-5183. Tel: 972-483-6481. E-mail: dunlaplibrary@hotmail.com. Web Site: www.ci.italy.tx.us/index.php. *Librn,* Kathryn French
  Pop 2,400
  Library Holdings: Bk Vols 21,000; Per Subs 26
  Open Tues-Sat 9-5

JACKSBORO

P GLADYS JOHNSON RITCHIE LIBRARY*, 626 W College St, 76458-1655. SAN 376-4656. Tel: 940-567-2240. FAX: 940-567-2240. Web Site: www.jacksboro.lib.tx.us. *Librn,* Delyn Lewis; E-mail: dlewis@jacksboro.lib.tx.us
  Pop 8,763; Circ 57,757
  Library Holdings: Bk Vols 25,000; Per Subs 14
  Automation Activity & Vendor Info: (Cataloging) Follett Software; (Circulation) Follett Software; (OPAC) Follett Software
  Mem of North Texas Library Partners
  Open Mon-Wed & Fri 9-6, Thurs 9-7, Sat 9-12

JACKSONVILLE

R BAPTIST MISSIONARY ASSOCIATION THEOLOGICAL SEMINARY*, Kellar Library, 1530 E Pine St, 75766-5407. (Mail add: PO Box 670, 75766-0670), SAN 316-5191. Tel: 903-586-2501, Ext 232. Information Services Tel: 903-586-2501. Toll Free Tel: 800-259-5673. FAX: 903-586-0378. Web Site: www.bmats.edu. *Dir,* James C Blaylock; E-mail: jblaylock@bmats.edu; Staff 3 (MLS 1, Non-MLS 2)
  Founded 1957. Enrl 145; Fac 10; Highest Degree: Master
  May 2010-Apr 2011 Income $136,468. Mats Exp $19,676, Books $3,709, Per/Ser (Incl. Access Fees) $8,525, Electronic Ref Mat (Incl. Access Fees) $5,468, Presv $1,974. Sal $100,801 (Prof $46,165)
  Library Holdings: AV Mats 7,470; CDs 404; DVDs 5,126; e-books 28,281; Bk Titles 62,924; Bk Vols 75,000; Per Subs 272; Videos 877
  Special Collections: Annuals of Baptist Yearly Meetings, bk, micro
  Subject Interests: Hist, Relig studies
  Wireless access
  Open Mon, Tues & Thurs 7:45am-9:30pm, Wed & Fri 7:45-4:45, Sat 9-12 & 1-4
  Friends of the Library Group

P JACKSONVILLE PUBLIC LIBRARY*, 502 S Jackson St, 75766. SAN 316-5213. Tel: 903-586-7664. FAX: 903-586-3397. E-mail: director@jacksonvillelibrary.com. Web Site: www.jacksonvillelibrary.com. *Dir,* Barbara Crossman; *Head, Circ,* Marshia Walker; *Ch,* Peggy Jo Jones; *Tech Serv,* David Emprimo; Staff 8 (Non-MLS 8)
  Founded 1913. Pop 13,553; Circ 82,303
  Library Holdings: Bk Vols 58,321; Per Subs 105
  Subject Interests: Cherokee County, Tex
  Automation Activity & Vendor Info: (Circulation) Book Systems, Inc
  Database Vendor: EBSCOhost
  Wireless access
  Open Mon & Thurs 12-8, Tues, Wed & Fri 10-6, Sat 10-2
  Friends of the Library Group

J LON MORRIS COLLEGE*, Simon & Louise Henderson Library, 800 College Ave, 75766. SAN 316-5221. Tel: 903-589-4024. FAX: 903-586-8562. Web Site: www.lonmorris.edu/lmc-library-482.php. *Dir,* Linda Gray; E-mail: lgray@lonmorris.edu; Staff 4.5 (MLS 1, Non-MLS 3.5)
  Library Holdings: Bk Vols 26,000; Per Subs 70

Automation Activity & Vendor Info: (Cataloging) TLC (The Library Corporation); (Circulation) TLC (The Library Corporation); (OPAC) TLC (The Library Corporation)
Wireless access
Partic in Forest Trail Library Consortium, Inc; Tex Share
Open Mon-Thurs (Fall & Spring) 7:45am-11pm, Fri 7:45-5, Sat 12-7, Sun 4-11; Mon-Thurs (Summer) 8:30-4:30

JASPER

P   JASPER PUBLIC LIBRARY*, 175 E Water St, 75951. SAN 316-5248. Tel: 409-384-3791. FAX: 409-384-5881. Web Site: www.jaspertx.org. *Dir,* Denise Milton; E-mail: dmilton22@hotmail.com; Staff 5 (MLS 1, Non-MLS 4)
Founded 1936. Pop 7,838
Library Holdings: Bks on Deafness & Sign Lang 10; Large Print Bks 1,008; Bk Titles 32,420; Bk Vols 35,486; Per Subs 69; Talking Bks 1,425
Automation Activity & Vendor Info: (Circulation) ComPanion Corp; (OPAC) ComPanion Corp; (Serials) EBSCO Online
Wireless access
Mem of Carl Elliott Regional Library System
Special Services for the Blind - Bks on cassette; Bks on CD
Open Mon-Fri 10-6, Sat 10-5
Friends of the Library Group

JAYTON

P   KENT COUNTY LIBRARY*, 156 W Fourth St, 79528. (Mail add: PO Box 28, 79528-0028), SAN 316-5256. Tel: 806-237-3287. FAX: 806-237-2511. E-mail: klibrary@caprock-spur.com. *Dir,* Dana Brinkman; Staff 1 (MLS 1)
Founded 1961. Pop 1,110; Circ 5,179
Library Holdings: Bk Vols 25,000
Wireless access

JEFFERSON

P   JEFFERSON CARNEGIE LIBRARY*, 301 W Lafayette, 75657. SAN 316-5264. Tel: 903-665-8911. FAX: 903-665-8911. E-mail: carnegielibrary@sbcglobal.net. Web Site: www.jeffersoncarnegielibrary.com. *Dir,* Peter Kuchta; Staff 2 (MLS 1, Non-MLS 1)
Founded 1907. Pop 9,000; Circ 12,000
Jan 2007-Dec 2007 Income $46,287, City $14,500, Locally Generated Income $31,787. Mats Exp $6,743, Books $4,368, AV Mat $2,375. Sal $11,699
Library Holdings: CDs 88; Large Print Bks 549; Bk Titles 12,116; Per Subs 2; Talking Bks 918; Videos 478
Automation Activity & Vendor Info: (Acquisitions) Book Systems, Inc; (Cataloging) Book Systems, Inc; (Circulation) Book Systems, Inc; (ILL) OCLC FirstSearch; (OPAC) Book Systems, Inc
Wireless access
Open Mon-Thurs 10-6, Fri 10-5
Friends of the Library Group

JOHNSON CITY

P   JOHNSON CITY LIBRARY DISTRICT*, 209 Nugent St, 78636. (Mail add: PO Box 332, 78636-0332), SAN 316-5272. Tel: 830-868-4469. FAX: 830-868-4469. E-mail: jclib@moment.net. Web Site: www.moment.net/~jclib. *Dir,* Maggie Goodman; Staff 2 (Non-MLS 2)
Founded 1940. Pop 2,500; Circ 9,109
Library Holdings: Bk Titles 14,000; Per Subs 15
Special Collections: L B Johnson Coll; Texana; Texas Authors
Automation Activity & Vendor Info: (Cataloging) Follett Software; (Circulation) Follett Software
Wireless access
Mem of Central Texas Library System, Inc
Open Mon-Fri 9-7, Sat 9-2
Friends of the Library Group

S   NATIONAL PARK SERVICE*, Lyndon B Johnson National Historical Park, 100 Lady Bird Lane, 78636. (Mail add: PO Box 329, 78636-0329), SAN 316-5280. Tel: 830-868-7128, Ext 260. FAX: 830-868-7863. Web Site: www.nps.gov/lyjo. *Librn,* Rosa Lara; E-mail: rosa_lara@nps.gov
Founded 1975
Library Holdings: Bk Titles 3,000; Per Subs 29
Special Collections: Oral History
Subject Interests: Hill County hist, Life, Natural hist subjects, Tex frontier, Times of Lyndon B Johnson
Restriction: Non-circulating to the pub, Open to pub by appt only, Open to researchers by request

JONESTOWN

P   JONESTOWN COMMUNITY LIBRARY*, 18649 FM1431, Ste 10A, 78645. SAN 376-4850. Tel: 512-267-7511. FAX: 512-267-4572. *Dir,* Marji Smith; *Head Librn,* Dara Repass; Staff 2 (MLS 1, Non-MLS 1)
Founded 1991. Pop 2,500
Library Holdings: AV Mats 324; High Interest/Low Vocabulary Bk Vols 450; Bk Vols 10,803; Per Subs 10; Videos 324
Automation Activity & Vendor Info: (Cataloging) Follett Software; (Circulation) Follett Software
Mem of Central Texas Library System, Inc
Open Mon, Wed & Fri 9-6, Tues & Thurs 9-8, Sat 10-2

JOSHUA

P   JOSHUA PUBLIC LIBRARY*, 907 S Broadway, 76058. Tel: 817-202-8324, 817-426-7547. FAX: 817-202-9134.
Circ 12,558
Library Holdings: AV Mats 252; Bk Titles 17,502; Per Subs 68; Talking Bks 58
Automation Activity & Vendor Info: (Cataloging) Follett Software; (Circulation) Follett Software; (ILL) Follett Software; (OPAC) Follett Software
Mem of North Texas Library Partners
Open Mon & Thurs (Winter) 8-8, Tues 8-4, Wed & Fri 8-6, Sat 9-12; Mon (Summer) 12-8, Tues-Fri 10-5, Sat 9-12

JOURDANTON

P   JOURDANTON COMMUNITY LIBRARY*, 1101 Campbell Ave, 78026. SAN 316-5302. Tel: 830-769-3087. FAX: 830-769-4082. E-mail: jourdlib@txun.net. *Dir,* Dorothy Manning
Founded 1976
Library Holdings: Bk Vols 25,000; Per Subs 60
Special Collections: Texana
Automation Activity & Vendor Info: (Cataloging) Follett Software; (Circulation) Follett Software
Special Services for the Deaf - Bks on deafness & sign lang; Spec interest per
Open Mon-Fri 9-6, Sat 9-1
Friends of the Library Group

JUNCTION

P   KIMBLE COUNTY LIBRARY*, 208 N Tenth St, 76849. SAN 316-5310. Tel: 325-446-2342. FAX: 325-446-3615. Web Site: www.kc-library.org. *Dir,* Sylvia Lawler
Founded 1933. Pop 4,063; Circ 22,642
Library Holdings: Bk Titles 20,000; Per Subs 15
Subject Interests: Tex
Automation Activity & Vendor Info: (Cataloging) LibLime; (Circulation) LibLime
Wireless access
Open Mon, Tues & Thurs 9-6, Wed 9-5, Fri 9-4
Friends of the Library Group

JUSTIN

P   JUSTIN COMMUNITY LIBRARY*, 408 Pafford St, 76247-9442. (Mail add: PO Box 877, 76247-0877), SAN 376-4664. Tel: 940-648-3649. FAX: 940-648-8423. E-mail: justinlibrary@verizon.net. *Dir,* Stacey Rogers
Founded 1986. Pop 4,000; Circ 3,500
Library Holdings: Audiobooks 301; Bks on Deafness & Sign Lang 10; DVDs 696; Large Print Bks 200; Bk Titles 16,200; Videos 1,386
Automation Activity & Vendor Info: (Cataloging) Evergreen; (Circulation) Evergreen
Wireless access
Function: Bks on cassette, Bks on CD, Children's prog, Computers for patron use, Copy machines, Free DVD rentals, Handicapped accessible, ILL available, Photocopying/Printing, Pub access computers, Scanner, Story hour, Summer reading prog, Tax forms, VHS videos, Wheelchair accessible
Mem of North Texas Library Partners
Open Mon-Fri 12-6, Sat 10-1
Restriction: Non-circulating coll
Friends of the Library Group

KARNES CITY

P   KARNES CITY PUBLIC LIBRARY*, 302 S Panna Maria, 78118. SAN 316-5329. Tel: 830-780-2539. FAX: 830-780-3790. E-mail: kclibrary@sbcglobal.net. *Dir,* Amy McCarley
Founded 1972. Pop 4,623; Circ 48,655
Library Holdings: Bk Titles 17,000; Per Subs 30
Automation Activity & Vendor Info: (Cataloging) Follett Software; (Circulation) Follett Software
Wireless access

Mem of Karnes County Library System
Open Mon-Fri 9-5:30

KAUFMAN

P   KAUFMAN COUNTY LIBRARY*, 3790 S Houston St, 75142-2033. SAN
316-5345. Tel: 972-932-6222. FAX: 972-932-0681. Web Site:
www.kaufmancountylibrary.org. *Dir,* Yasma Holland; Staff 3 (MLS 1,
Non-MLS 2)
Founded 1970. Pop 12,000; Circ 21,000
Library Holdings: Bk Titles 44,000; Per Subs 22
Automation Activity & Vendor Info: (Cataloging) Follett Software;
(Circulation) Follett Software
Wireless access
Open Mon-Wed 10-6, Thurs 10-7, Fri 10-5, Sat 9-1
Friends of the Library Group

KEENE

C   SOUTHWESTERN ADVENTIST UNIVERSITY*, Chan Shun Centennial
Library, 101 W Magnolia St, 76059. SAN 316-5353. Tel: 817-202-6242.
FAX: 817-556-4722. Web Site: library.swau.edu. *Dir, Univ Librn,* Cristina
Thomsen; E-mail: thomsenc@swau.edu; *Assoc Librn, Electronic Res &
Tech Serv,* Marsha Rasmussen; Tel: 817-202-6603, E-mail:
marshar@swau.edu; *Assoc Librn, Pub Serv & Spec Coll,* Alfredo Vergel;
Tel: 817-202-6521, E-mail: avergel@swau.edu; Staff 5 (MLS 3, Non-MLS
2)
Founded 1894. Enrl 900; Fac 60; Highest Degree: Master
Library Holdings: AV Mats 1,900; Bk Vols 110,000; Per Subs 460
Special Collections: Seventh-day Adventist Church History
Subject Interests: Bus, Elem educ, Liberal arts, Nursing
Automation Activity & Vendor Info: (Acquisitions) TLC (The Library
Corporation); (Cataloging) TLC (The Library Corporation); (Circulation)
TLC (The Library Corporation); (Course Reserve) TLC (The Library
Corporation); (OPAC) TLC (The Library Corporation); (Serials) EOS
International
Database Vendor: Agricola, EBSCOhost, Gale Cengage Learning,
LexisNexis, netLibrary, OCLC FirstSearch, OCLC WorldCat, OVID
Technologies, ProQuest, PubMed, TLC (The Library Corporation)
Wireless access
Partic in Adventist Library Information Cooperative (ALICE); Amigos
Library Services, Inc; Tex Share
Open Mon-Thurs 8am-11pm, Fri 8-2, Sun Noon-11pm

KELLER

P   KELLER PUBLIC LIBRARY, 640 Johnson Rd, 76248. SAN 325-1527.
Tel: 817-743-4800. FAX: 817-743-4890. Web Site: www.kellerlibrary.org.
Dir, Jana Prock; E-mail: jprock@cityofkeller.com; *Pub Serv Mgr,* Carolyn
Booker; Staff 20 (MLS 5, Non-MLS 15)
Founded 1972. Pop 40,055; Circ 490,789
Oct 2011-Sept 2012 Income $1,381,545
Library Holdings: Bk Titles 80,000; Bk Vols 82,000; Per Subs 160
Automation Activity & Vendor Info: (Acquisitions) Horizon;
(Cataloging) Horizon; (Circulation) Horizon; (OPAC) Horizon
Database Vendor: EBSCOhost, LearningExpress, Medline, netLibrary,
Overdrive, Inc, ReferenceUSA
Wireless access
Function: Adult bk club, Audiobks via web, Bks on CD, Children's prog,
Computer training, Computers for patron use, Copy machines, Electronic
databases & coll, Free DVD rentals, Music CDs, Online cat, Online
searches, Prog for adults, Prog for children & young adult, Ref & res,
Scanner, Story hour, Summer reading prog, Tax forms, Telephone ref
Special Services for the Deaf - Bks on deafness & sign lang; Spec interest
per
Special Services for the Blind - Bks on CD; Magnifiers
Open Mon-Wed 10-8, Thurs & Fri 10-6, Sat & Sun 12-5
Friends of the Library Group

KENDALIA

P   KENDALIA PUBLIC LIBRARY*, 2610-B Hwy 473, 78027-2010. (Mail
add: PO Box 399, 78027-0399), SAN 316-5361. Tel: 830-336-2002. FAX:
830-336-2002. Web Site: www.kendalialibrary.com. *Dir,* Donna Jonas;
E-mail: djonas@gvtc.com; Staff 1 (Non-MLS 1)
Founded 1961. Pop 1,802; Circ 2,695
Jan 2010-Dec 2010 Income $28,467, County $23,893, Other $4,574. Sal
$14,393
Library Holdings: Bk Vols 9,946; Per Subs 5; Talking Bks 652
Automation Activity & Vendor Info: (Cataloging) Follett Software;
(Circulation) Follett Software; (OPAC) Follett Software
Wireless access
Function: Res libr
Open Mon 10-5, Wed 9-6, Fri 1-5

KENDLETON

C   BAY RIDGE CHRISTIAN COLLEGE LIBRARY*, 3626 FM 2919, PO
Box 726, 77451-0726. SAN 316-537X. Tel: 979-532-3982. FAX:
979-532-4352. *VPres,* Tracy Walker
Founded 1967
Library Holdings: Bk Vols 1,200
Special Collections: Warner Coll
Open Mon-Fri 8-2

KENEDY

P   KENEDY PUBLIC LIBRARY*, 303 W Main St, 78119. Tel:
830-583-3313. FAX: 830-583-3270. E-mail: kenedylibrary@sbcglobal.net.
Dir, Sylvia Pena; Staff 1 (MLS 1)
Library Holdings: Bk Vols 19,000; Per Subs 25
Automation Activity & Vendor Info: (Cataloging) Biblionix; (Circulation)
Biblionix
Wireless access
Mem of Karnes County Library System
Open Mon-Fri 9-5:30

KENNEDALE

P   KENNEDALE PUBLIC LIBRARY, 316 W Third St, 76060-2202. Tel:
817-985-2136. FAX: 817-483-0660. *Dir,* Gwen Bevill
Pop 7,000
Library Holdings: AV Mats 1,133; Bk Vols 16,000; Per Subs 14; Videos
454
Automation Activity & Vendor Info: (Cataloging) Evergreen;
(Circulation) Evergreen; (OPAC) Evergreen
Wireless access
Mem of North Texas Library Partners
Partic in North Texas Library Consortium (NTLC)
Open Tues-Thurs 10-8, Fri & Sat 10-5
Friends of the Library Group

KERMIT

P   WINKLER COUNTY LIBRARY*, 307 S Poplar St, 79745-4300. SAN
362-0824. Tel: 432-586-3841. FAX: 432-586-2462. *Librn,* Laurie
Shropshire
Founded 1929. Pop 8,015
Library Holdings: Bk Vols 62,000; Per Subs 35
Automation Activity & Vendor Info: (Cataloging) LibLime; (Circulation)
LibLime
Mem of West Texas Library System
Open Mon-Fri 10-6
Branches: 1
WINK BRANCH, 207 Roy Orbison Dr, Wink, 79789. (Mail add: PO Box
608, Wink, 79789-0608), SAN 362-0859. Tel: 432-527-3691. *Librn,*
Pauline Kline
Open Mon-Fri 12-5

KERRVILLE

P   BUTT-HOLDSWORTH MEMORIAL LIBRARY*, 505 Water St, 78028.
SAN 316-5396. Tel: 830-257-8422. FAX: 830-792-5552. Web Site:
www.bhmlibrary.org/. *Libr Dir,* Daniel Schwartz; E-mail:
dan.schwartz@kerrvilletx.gov; *Head, Pub Serv,* Lolita Holczer; E-mail:
lolita.holczer@kerrvilletx.gov; *Circ Serv Supvr,* Mary L Meyers; E-mail:
mary.meyers@kerrvilletx.gov; *Ref,* Patricia Gordinier; E-mail:
pat.gordinier@kerrvilletx.gov; Staff 5 (MLS 5)
Founded 1967. Pop 47,860
Library Holdings: Bk Titles 152,711; Per Subs 300
Special Collections: Texana Coll. Oral History
Automation Activity & Vendor Info: (Acquisitions) Innovative Interfaces,
Inc; (Cataloging) Innovative Interfaces, Inc; (Circulation) Innovative
Interfaces, Inc; (OPAC) Innovative Interfaces, Inc
Wireless access
Open Mon, Wed & Sat 10-6, Tues & Thurs 10-8, Fri 12-6, Sun 1-5
Friends of the Library Group

S   MUSEUM OF WESTERN ART LIBRARY*, 1550 Bandera Hwy,
78028-9547. (Mail add: PO Box 294300, 78029-4300), SAN 370-7342.
Tel: 830-896-2553. FAX: 830-257-5206. E-mail:
mrademacher@mowatx.com. Web Site: www.americanwesternart.org.
Librn, Fred Egloff; *Asst Librn,* Nancy Doig; *Tech Serv,* Terry Laurendine;
Tech Serv, Cindy Terry; Staff 1 (MLS 1)
Founded 1983
Library Holdings: Bk Titles 6,000; Per Subs 10
Subject Interests: Hist of the Am West, Western art
Function: Res libr
Publications: Special Indexes Listing Periodical
Open Tues-Sat 10-4

C SCHREINER UNIVERSITY*, W M Logan Library, 2100 Memorial Blvd,
78028-5697. SAN 316-5418. Tel: 830-792-7312. FAX: 830-792-7448.
E-mail: library@schreiner.edu. Web Site: library.schreiner.edu. *Dir,* Dr
Candice Scott; Tel: 830-792-7318, E-mail: cscott@schreiner.edu; *Asst Dir,*
Mary MacWithey; Tel: 830-792-7313, E-mail:
memacwithey@schreiner.edu; *Ref Librn,* Conner Baldwin; Tel:
830-792-7314, E-mail: connerb@schreiner.edu; *Spec Coll Librn,* Sara
Schmidt; Tel: 830-792-7337, E-mail: spschmidt@schreiner.edu; Staff 4
(MLS 4)
Founded 1967. Enrl 1,013; Fac 72; Highest Degree: Master
Library Holdings: Bk Titles 120,000; Bk Vols 160,000; Per Subs 260
Special Collections: Schreiner University Coll; Texas Hill Country Coll
Subject Interests: Liberal arts
Automation Activity & Vendor Info: (Acquisitions) Ex Libris Group;
(Cataloging) Ex Libris Group; (Circulation) Ex Libris Group; (Course
Reserve) Ex Libris Group; (OPAC) Ex Libris Group; (Serials) Ex Libris
Group
Function: Archival coll, Audio & video playback equip for onsite use,
Computers for patron use, Copy machines, e-mail serv, Electronic
databases & coll, Fax serv, Mail & tel request accepted, Online ref,
Photocopying/Printing, Pub access computers, Ref & res, Scanner, Tax
forms, Wheelchair accessible
Partic in Coun of Res & Acad Librs; OCLC Online Computer Library
Center, Inc
Open Mon-Thurs (Fall & Spring) 7:30am-Midnight, Fri 7:30-4, Sat 12-4,
Sun 3-12; Mon-Thurs (Summer) 7:30-6, Fri 7:30-4

KILGORE

J KILGORE COLLEGE*, Randolph C Watson Library, 1100 Broadway,
75662. SAN 316-5434. Tel: 903-983-8237. FAX: 903-983-8638. Web Site:
kcfac.kilgore.edu/library. *Dir,* Kathy Fair; Tel: 903-983-8639, E-mail:
kfair@kilgore.edu; *Ref Serv,* Susan Wilson; Tel: 903-983-8239, E-mail:
swilson@kilgore.edu; Staff 9 (MLS 5, Non-MLS 4)
Founded 1935. Enrl 4,911; Fac 145; Highest Degree: Associate
Library Holdings: e-books 50,000; e-journals 7,000; Bk Vols 85,000; Per
Subs 80
Special Collections: Habenicht Texana Coll; Hill Texana Coll; Spear Coll
(American & English Literature)
Automation Activity & Vendor Info: (Acquisitions) Ex Libris Group;
(Cataloging) Ex Libris Group; (Circulation) Ex Libris Group; (Course
Reserve) Ex Libris Group; (OPAC) Ex Libris Group; (Serials) Ex Libris
Group
Database Vendor: EBSCOhost, Gale Cengage Learning, LexisNexis,
ProQuest
Wireless access
Partic in OCLC Online Computer Library Center, Inc; Tex Share
Open Mon-Thurs (Fall & Spring) 7:30am-9pm, Fri 7:30-4, Sun 2-5; Mon
& Wed (Summer) 7-4:30, Tues & Thurs 7am-8pm, Fri 7-4
Friends of the Library Group

P KILGORE PUBLIC LIBRARY*, 301 Henderson Blvd, 75662-2799. SAN
362-0883. Tel: 903-984-1529. FAX: 903-983-1779. *Dir,* Linda Johnson;
E-mail: kpljohnson@cablelynx.com; Staff 5 (Non-MLS 5)
Founded 1933. Pop 14,037; Circ 65,796
Library Holdings: AV Mats 1,098; Large Print Bks 1,889; Bk Vols
38,923; Per Subs 79; Talking Bks 1,758
Automation Activity & Vendor Info: (Cataloging) Book Systems, Inc;
(Circulation) Book Systems, Inc
Function: Handicapped accessible, Home delivery & serv to Sr ctr &
nursing homes, Homebound delivery serv, ILL available,
Photocopying/Printing, Prog for adults, Prog for children & young adult,
Summer reading prog, Telephone ref, Wheelchair accessible
Open Mon-Thurs 9-6, Fri & Sat 9-4
Friends of the Library Group

KILLEEN

J CENTRAL TEXAS COLLEGE*, Oveta Culp Hobby Memorial Library,
Bld 102, 6200 W Central Texas Expressway, 76549. (Mail add: PO Box
1800, 76540-1800), SAN 316-5469. Tel: 254-526-1237. Circulation Tel:
254-526-1621. Reference Tel: 254-526-1871. Toll Free Tel: 800-223-4760,
Ext 1237 (Instate), 800-792-3348, Ext 1237 (Out of state). FAX:
254-526-1878. Web Site: www.ctcd.edu/library/pg-lib6.htm. *Dean of Libr,*
Deba Swan; Tel: 254-526-1475, E-mail: deborah.swan@ctcd.edu; *Dir,*
Multimedia Serv, Mark Plasterer; Tel: 254-526-1537, E-mail:
mark.plasterer@ctcd.edu; *Asst Dir, Libr Serv,* Alan Withoff; Tel:
254-526-1872, E-mail: alan.withoff@ctcd.edu; *Ref Librn,* Ina Kelley; *Tech
Serv Librn,* Angela Campbell; Staff 21 (MLS 5, Non-MLS 16)
Founded 1967. Enrl 5,890; Fac 332; Highest Degree: Associate
Library Holdings: Bk Titles 73,504; Bk Vols 80,044; Per Subs 448
Subject Interests: Educ, Law
Automation Activity & Vendor Info: (Cataloging) SirsiDynix;
(Circulation) SirsiDynix; (OPAC) SirsiDynix; (Serials) SirsiDynix
Database Vendor: EBSCOhost, ProQuest

Wireless access
Open Mon-Thurs 7:30am-9:30pm, Fri 7:30-4:30, Sat 11-5, Sun 1-8

P KILLEEN CITY LIBRARY SYSTEM*, 205 E Church Ave, 76541. SAN
316-5477. Tel: 254-501-8990. Circulation Tel: 254-501-8996. Reference
Tel: 254-501-8808. Administration Tel: 254-501-8994. FAX: 254-501-7704.
E-mail: library@ci.killeen.tx.us. *Dir,* Deanna A Frazee; Tel: 254-501-8995,
E-mail: dfrazee@ci.killeen.tx.us; *Asst Dir,* Dawn M Harris; Tel:
254-501-8966, E-mail: dharris@ci.killeen.tx.us; *Br Mgr,* Hellena Barkley;
Tel: 254-501-7875, E-mail: hbarkley@ci.killeen.tx.us; *Ref Librn,* Kim
Miller; Tel: 254-501-8949, E-mail: kmiller@ci.killeen.tx.us; *Circ Supvr,*
Debbie Eubanks; E-mail: deubanks@ci.killeen.tx.us; *Ch,* Theresa
Campbell; Tel: 254-501-8959, E-mail: tcampbell@ci.killeen.tx.us; *Ch,* Amy
Gibson; Tel: 254-501-7874, E-mail: agibson@ci.killeen.tx.us; *Circ,* Annie
Lowe; E-mail: hlowe@ci.killeen.tx.us; Staff 29 (MLS 4, Non-MLS 25)
Founded 1958. Pop 100,976; Circ 317,403
Library Holdings: Bk Titles 89,000; Bk Vols 114,000; Per Subs 112
Subject Interests: Automotive repair, Children, County hist, Genealogy,
Local hist, Mechanics, Texana
Automation Activity & Vendor Info: (Cataloging) SirsiDynix;
(Circulation) SirsiDynix; (OPAC) SirsiDynix
Database Vendor: Agricola, EBSCOhost, Gale Cengage Learning,
netLibrary, SirsiDynix, STAT!Ref (Teton Data Systems)
Function: ILL available
Mem of Central Texas Library System, Inc
Open Mon & Tues 10-8, Wed-Sat 10-6
Restriction: In-house use for visitors, Non-circulating coll, Open to pub
for ref & circ; with some limitations
Friends of the Library Group

C TEXAS A&M UNIVERSITY CENTRAL TEXAS*, Hobby Memorial
Library, 1901 S Clear Creek Rd, 76549. SAN 316-5450. Tel:
254-526-1244, 254-526-1618, 254-526-1619. FAX: 254-526-1589,
254-526-1993. E-mail: library@ct.tamus.edu. Web Site:
www.ct.tamus.edu/departments/library/index.php. *Dir of Libr Serv,* Mark
Harris; E-mail: harrism@ct.tamus.edu; *Instruction & Ref Librn,* Bridgit
McCafferty; Tel: 254-526-1617, E-mail: bmccaffe@ct.tamus.edu; *Circ, ILL,
Per,* Cynthia Scott; Tel: 254-526-1618, E-mail: cynthia.scott@ct.tamus.edu;
Circ, Tech Serv, Inez Edwards; Tel: 254-526-1676, E-mail:
iedwards@ct.tamus.edu; Staff 6 (MLS 2, Non-MLS 4)
Founded 1973. Enrl 1,879; Fac 60; Highest Degree: Master
Sept 2007-Aug 2008 Income $280,406, State $276,660, Locally Generated
Income $3,746. Mats Exp $160,662, Books $72,013, Per/Ser (Incl. Access
Fees) $26,828, Micro $2,880, AV Mat $19,688, Electronic Ref Mat (Incl.
Access Fees) $39,253. Sal $177,264 (Prof $99,149)
Library Holdings: AV Mats 1,161; Bk Titles 32,455; Bk Vols 35,666; Per
Subs 58
Special Collections: Crime & Juvenile Delinquency, micro; Energy
Management (Solar Energy), docs
Automation Activity & Vendor Info: (Acquisitions) SirsiDynix;
(Cataloging) SirsiDynix; (Circulation) SirsiDynix; (Course Reserve)
SirsiDynix; (ILL) OCLC ILLiad; (Media Booking) SirsiDynix; (OPAC)
SirsiDynix; (Serials) SirsiDynix
Database Vendor: SirsiDynix
Wireless access
Function: Archival coll, Art exhibits, Audio & video playback equip for
onsite use, AV serv, Bks on cassette, CD-ROM, Computers for patron use,
Copy machines, Distance learning, Doc delivery serv, e-mail serv,
E-Reserves, Electronic databases & coll, Equip loans & repairs,
Handicapped accessible, ILL available, Instruction & testing, Large print
keyboards, Mail & tel request accepted, Mail loans to mem, Music CDs,
Online cat, Online info literacy tutorials on the web & in blackboard,
Online ref, Online searches, Orientations, Outside serv via phone, mail,
e-mail & web, Photocopying/Printing, Pub access computers, Ref & res,
Tax forms, Telephone ref, VCDs, VHS videos, Web-catalog, Wheelchair
accessible
Partic in Amigos Library Services, Inc
Open Mon-Thurs 7:30am-9:30pm, Fri 7:30-4:30, Sat 11-5, Sun 1-8

KINGSVILLE

P ROBERT J KLEBERG PUBLIC LIBRARY*, 220 N Fourth St, 78363.
SAN 316-5493. Tel: 361-592-6381. E-mail:
kpldirector@kleberglibrary.com. Web Site: www.kleberglibrary.com. *Dir,*
Robert Rodriguez; *Asst Admin,* Ruth Valdez; *Acq,* Hector Vela; *Ch,*
Danielle Friend; *Circ,* Andrea Vidaurri; *Ref,* Mary Ann Escamilla; Staff 6
(MLS 1, Non-MLS 5)
Founded 1907. Pop 35,600; Circ 82,135
Library Holdings: Bks on Deafness & Sign Lang 22; Bk Titles 58,000;
Per Subs 135
Special Collections: Genealogy Reference; Texas Reference
Automation Activity & Vendor Info: (Cataloging) TLC (The Library
Corporation); (Circulation) TLC (The Library Corporation); (OPAC) TLC
(The Library Corporation)
Wireless access

Open Tues-Fri 8-6, Sat 9-1
Friends of the Library Group

C   TEXAS A&M UNIVERSITY-KINGSVILLE*, James C Jernigan Library,
700 University Blvd, MSC 197, 78363-8202. SAN 316-5507. Tel:
361-593-3416. FAX: 361-593-4093. Web Site: www.tamuk.edu/library. *Libr
Dir,* Dr Carol Tipton; Tel: 361-539-3528, E-mail: c-tipton@tamuk.edu;
Prof & Assoc Dir of Pub Serv, Dr Maria de Jesus Ayala-Schueneman; Tel:
361-593-3097, E-mail: mari.ayala-schueneman@tamuk.edu; *Prof & Assoc
Dir of Syst & Tech Serv,* Bruce Schueneman; Tel: 361-593-4082, E-mail:
bruce.schueneman@tamuk.edu
Founded 1925. Enrl 6,130; Fac 225; Highest Degree: Doctorate
Library Holdings: e-journals 13,700; Bk Vols 681,013; Per Subs 1,400
Special Collections: Bilingual Education Coll; Botany (Runyon Coll);
Western Americana (McGill Coll). Oral History; State Document
Depository; UN Document Depository; US Document Depository
Automation Activity & Vendor Info: (Acquisitions) Innovative Interfaces,
Inc; (Cataloging) Innovative Interfaces, Inc; (Circulation) Innovative
Interfaces, Inc; (Course Reserve) Innovative Interfaces, Inc; (ILL)
Innovative Interfaces, Inc; (Media Booking) Innovative Interfaces, Inc;
(OPAC) Innovative Interfaces, Inc; (Serials) Innovative Interfaces, Inc
Wireless access
Partic in OCLC Online Computer Library Center, Inc
Open Mon-Thurs (Fall) 7am-1am, Fri 7-5, Sat 12-6, Sun 1pm-1am;
Mon-Thurs (Summer) 7:30am-10pm, Fri 7:30-5, Sat 12-5, Sun 3-10

A   UNITED STATES NAVY*, Naval Air Station Library, 500 Moffett Ave,
No 104, 78363-5034. SAN 362-0948. Tel: 361-516-6271. FAX:
361-516-6971. *Mgr,* Vickie Jacobson; E-mail: vickie.jacobson@navy.mil
Founded 1943
Library Holdings: Bk Vols 13,000; Per Subs 34
Special Collections: Military History Coll
Automation Activity & Vendor Info: (Cataloging) EOS International;
(Circulation) EOS International
Restriction: Mil only, Staff use only

KINGVILLE

J   COASTAL BEND COLLEGE*, Kingsville Campus Library, 1814 S
Brahma Blvd, 78363. Tel: 361-592-1615. Web Site: lrc.coastalbend.edu,
www.coastalbend.edu. *Distance Learning Librn,* Jennifer Jimenez
Library Holdings: Bk Vols 500
Automation Activity & Vendor Info: (Acquisitions) EOS International;
(Cataloging) EOS International; (Circulation) EOS International; (Course
Reserve) EOS International; (ILL) OCLC; (OPAC) EOS International;
(Serials) EOS International

KIRBYVILLE

P   KIRBYVILLE PUBLIC LIBRARY*, 210 S Elizabeth St, 75956. (Mail
add: PO Box 567, 75956-0567), SAN 316-5515. Tel: 409-423-4653. FAX:
409-423-5545. E-mail: kirbyvillelibrary@sbcglobal.net. Web Site:
www.kirbyvillelibrary.org. *Dir,* Tammy Johnson; Staff 3 (Non-MLS 3)
Founded 1937. Pop 3,776; Circ 10,205
Library Holdings: Bk Titles 18,000; Bk Vols 19,000; Per Subs 39
Automation Activity & Vendor Info: (Acquisitions) Surpass; (Cataloging)
Surpass; (Circulation) Surpass; (OPAC) Surpass
Wireless access
Open Mon 10-6, Tues-Fri 10-5
Friends of the Library Group

KOUNTZE

P   KOUNTZE PUBLIC LIBRARY*, 800 S Redwood Ave, 77625. SAN
316-5523. Tel: 409-246-2826. FAX: 409-246-4659. Web Site:
www.kountzelibrary.org. *Dir,* Laverne Crysel; E-mail:
lcrysel@kountzelibrary.org
Pop 10,000; Circ 17,668
Library Holdings: Bk Vols 18,486; Per Subs 20
Automation Activity & Vendor Info: (Cataloging) Follett Software;
(Circulation) Follett Software; (OPAC) Follett Software
Wireless access
Open Mon 9-6, Tues-Fri 8:30-5:30, Sat 9:30-12:30
Friends of the Library Group

KRUM

P   KRUM PUBLIC LIBRARY, 803 E McCart St, 76249-6823. (Mail add: PO
Box 780, 76249-0780), SAN 376-4567. Tel: 940-482-3455. FAX:
940-482-0088. Web Site: www.krumlibrary.org. *Dir,* Donna Pierce; Staff 1
(MLS 1)
Founded 1979. Pop 5,261; Circ 20,502
Oct 2011-Sept 2012 Income $96,514, City $83,903, County $12,611. Mats
Exp $9,482, Books $9,000, Electronic Ref Mat (Incl. Access Fees) $482.
Sal $62,003 (Prof $28,924)

Library Holdings: Audiobooks 418; CDs 350; DVDs 392; Large Print
Bks 290; Bk Titles 19,900; Per Subs 10; Videos 1,163
Automation Activity & Vendor Info: (Cataloging) Evergreen;
(Circulation) Evergreen; (OPAC) Evergreen
Database Vendor: Amigos Library Services
Wireless access
Mem of North Texas Library Partners
Partic in North Texas Library Consortium (NTLC)
Special Services for the Deaf - Assistive tech
Special Services for the Blind - Assistive/Adapted tech devices, equip &
products
Open Mon-Wed & Fri 11-6, Sat 10-3
Friends of the Library Group

KYLE

P   KYLE PUBLIC LIBRARY*, 409 W Blanco St, 78640. (Mail add: PO Box
2349, 78640-0366), SAN 316-5531. Tel: 512-268-7411. FAX:
512-268-0021. E-mail: library@cityofkyle.com. Web Site:
www.kylelibrary.com. *Dir,* Connie Brooks; Staff 14 (MLS 2, Non-MLS 12)
Founded 1958. Pop 18,672
Library Holdings: AV Mats 1,669; DVDs 433; Large Print Bks 510; Bk
Titles 28,708; Bk Vols 30,405; Per Subs 42; Videos 5,166
Special Collections: Katherine Ann Porter Coll
Automation Activity & Vendor Info: (Acquisitions) Book Systems, Inc;
(Cataloging) Book Systems, Inc; (Circulation) Book Systems, Inc; (OPAC)
Book Systems, Inc
Wireless access
Function: Audio & video playback equip for onsite use, Computer
training, Copy machines, Digital talking bks, e-mail serv, Fax serv, Online
searches, Photocopying/Printing, Prof lending libr, Prog for adults, Prog for
children & young adult, Ref & res, Ref serv available, Senior computer
classes, Spoken cassettes & CDs, Spoken cassettes & DVDs, Summer
reading prog, Tax forms, Telephone ref, VHS videos, Video lending libr
Mem of Central Texas Library System, Inc
Open Mon 10-5, Tues & Thurs 10-8, Wed & Fri 10-6, Sat 9-3
Friends of the Library Group

LA FERIA

P   BAILEY H DUNLAP MEMORIAL PUBLIC LIBRARY*, 400 S Main St,
78559. Tel: 956-797-1242. FAX: 956-797-5408. *Dir,* Lori Vogt
Pop 6,231; Circ 16,668
Library Holdings: Bk Vols 17,000; Per Subs 40
Automation Activity & Vendor Info: (Cataloging) SirsiDynix;
(Circulation) SirsiDynix; (OPAC) SirsiDynix
Database Vendor: SirsiDynix
Open Mon, Wed & Fri 12-6, Tues & Thurs 12-8, Sat 9-3

LA GRANGE

P   FAYETTE PUBLIC LIBRARY, 855 S Jefferson, 78945. SAN 316-5558.
Tel: 979-968-3765. FAX: 979-968-5357. E-mail: library@cityoflg.com.
Web Site: www.cityoflg.com/library.htm. *Dir,* Sherie Knape; *Librn,* Carol
Jenkins; *Asst Librn,* Maria Rocha; *Archivist, Curator,* Donna Green;
E-mail: archives@cityoflg.com; *Archivist, Asst Curator,* Brandii Cruz; Staff
5.5 (Non-MLS 5.5)
Pop 5,500; Circ 83,500
Library Holdings: Audiobooks 438; Bks on Deafness & Sign Lang 10;
CDs 902; DVDs 3,503; Large Print Bks 440; Bk Titles 19,856; Bk Vols
20,519; Per Subs 62; Videos 3,350
Special Collections: Texana Coll
Subject Interests: Local hist archives
Automation Activity & Vendor Info: (Cataloging) Book Systems, Inc;
(Circulation) Book Systems, Inc; (ILL) OCLC; (OPAC) Book Systems, Inc
Database Vendor: ProQuest
Wireless access
Function: Archival coll, Bks on cassette, Bks on CD, Children's prog,
Computers for patron use, Copy machines, Exhibits, Free DVD rentals,
ILL available, Microfiche/film & reading machines, Music CDs, Newsp ref
libr, Online cat, OverDrive digital audio bks, Photocopying/Printing,
Preschool reading prog, Pub access computers, Ref serv in person, Story
hour, Summer reading prog, Tax forms, Telephone ref, VHS videos,
Web-catalog, Wheelchair accessible
Mem of Central Texas Library System, Inc
Open Tues-Thurs 10-6, Fri 10-5, Sat 10-1, Sun 1-5
Friends of the Library Group

LA JOYA

P   LA JOYA MUNICIPAL LIBRARY*, 925 S Leo Ave, 78560. (Mail add:
PO Box H, City Hall, 78560-0180). Tel: 956-581-4533. Circulation Tel:
956-580-7022. FAX: 956-580-7023. E-mail: lj_staff@yahoo.com. *Libr Dir,*
Susana Villegas
Founded 1999. Pop 5,322
Library Holdings: Bk Vols 11,200; Talking Bks 23

Mem of Hidalgo County Library System
Open Mon-Thurs 9-6, Fri 9-5, Sat 9-3

LA MARQUE

P   LA MARQUE PUBLIC LIBRARY*, 1011 Bayou Rd, 77568-4195. SAN
     316-5566. Tel: 409-938-9270. FAX: 409-938-9277. Web Site:
     www.ci.la-marque.tx.us. *Dir,* Cynthia Hart; *Asst Dir, Ref Serv,* Tom
     Hansen; *Ch,* Margaret Little; Staff 1 (MLS 1)
     Founded 1946. Pop 23,691
     Library Holdings: AV Mats 2,954; Bk Titles 39,962; Per Subs 50
     Automation Activity & Vendor Info: (Cataloging) Biblionix; (Circulation)
     Biblionix
     Wireless access
     Open Tues & Thurs 10-7, Wed 10-6, Fri & Sat 9-4
     Friends of the Library Group

LA PORTE

S   SAN JACINTO MUSEUM OF HISTORY*, Albert & Ethel Herzstein
     Library, One Monument Circle, 77571-9585. SAN 321-8155. Tel:
     281-479-2421. FAX: 281-479-2866. E-mail:
     library@sanjacinto-museum.org. Web Site:
     www.sanjacinto-museum.org/herzstein_library. *Dir,* Lisa A Struthers;
     E-mail: lstruthers@sanjacinto-museum.org; Staff 2 (MLS 1, Non-MLS 1)
     Founded 1939
     Library Holdings: Bk Vols 19,500; Per Subs 35
     Subject Interests: Tex hist
     Automation Activity & Vendor Info: (Cataloging) EOS International;
     (OPAC) EOS International
     Function: Archival coll, Photocopying/Printing, Ref serv available
     Restriction: Non-circulating, Open to pub by appt only

LACKLAND AFB

A   UNITED STATES DEPARTMENT OF THE AIR FORCE*, Defense
     Language Institute, English Language Center Library, Bldg 7445, Rm 105,
     2230 Andrews Ave, 78236. SAN 316-5574. Tel: 210-671-2767. FAX:
     210-671-1014. *Librn,* Patricia Arnold; E-mail: patricia.arnold.3@us.af.mil;
     Staff 3 (MLS 1, Non-MLS 2)
     Founded 1967
     Library Holdings: Bk Vols 8,000; Per Subs 41
     Special Collections: English as a Second Language Coll
     Subject Interests: Teaching English as a second lang to foreign mil
     students from various allied countries
     Automation Activity & Vendor Info: (Cataloging) Mandarin Library
     Automation; (Circulation) Mandarin Library Automation
     Database Vendor: EBSCOhost, Gale Cengage Learning, OCLC
     FirstSearch
     Wireless access
     Function: ILL available
     Restriction: Open to students, fac & staff

M   WILFORD HALL MEDICAL CENTER LIBRARY*, 59MDW/SGN,
     78236-5300. SAN 362-0972. Tel: 210-292-7204. Circulation Tel:
     210-292-5776. FAX: 210-292-7030. *Librn,* Rita Smith; Tel: 210-292-5771,
     E-mail: rita.smith@lackland.af.mil; *Asst Librn,* Debra Ragan; Tel:
     210-292-5770, E-mail: debra.ragan@lackland.af.mil; *ILL,* Doris Perez; Tel:
     210-292-5777, E-mail: doris.perez@lackland.af.mil; Staff 3 (MLS 3)
     Founded 1950
     Library Holdings: Bk Titles 9,500; Per Subs 333
     Subject Interests: Clinical med, Dentistry, Nursing
     Automation Activity & Vendor Info: (Cataloging) Ex Libris Group;
     (Circulation) Ex Libris Group
     Database Vendor: Dialog, EBSCOhost, LexisNexis, OCLC FirstSearch,
     OVID Technologies, ProQuest
     Partic in Docline; OCLC Online Computer Library Center, Inc
     Restriction: Mil only, Staff use only

LAGO VISTA

P   LAGO VISTA PUBLIC LIBRARY*, 5803 Thunderbird, Ste 40, 78645.
     Tel: 512-267-3868. FAX: 512-267-4855. E-mail: lvlibrary@austin.rr.com.
     Web Site: www.lagovista.lib.tx.us. *Dir,* Jan Steele; *Asst Librn,* Louise
     Morris; *Asst Librn,* Carol Ann Rawlins; Staff 1 (MLS 1)
     Pop 6,500; Circ 14,189
     Library Holdings: Bk Titles 14,916; Bk Vols 17,200; Per Subs 42
     Automation Activity & Vendor Info: (Acquisitions) Biblionix;
     (Cataloging) Biblionix; (Circulation) Biblionix; (Course Reserve) Biblionix;
     (ILL) Biblionix
     Wireless access
     Function: Archival coll, ILL available, Music CDs, Photocopying/Printing,
     Prog for adults, Pub access computers, Senior computer classes, Story
     hour, Summer reading prog, Tax forms, Video lending libr, Web-catalog,
     Wheelchair accessible, Workshops, Writing prog
     Mem of Central Texas Library System, Inc

Partic in Tex Share
Open Mon, Wed & Fri 10-6, Tues & Thurs 10-8, Sat 10-2
Friends of the Library Group

LAGUNA VISTA

P   LAGUNA VISTA PUBLIC LIBRARY*, 1300 Palm Blvd, 78578. Tel:
     956-943-7155. FAX: 956-943-2371. E-mail: library@lvtexas.us. Web Site:
     www.lvlibrary.org. *Dir,* Pura Mireles; Staff 2 (Non-MLS 2)
     Pop 2,024; Circ 2,259
     Library Holdings: Bk Vols 15,000; Per Subs 55
     Wireless access
     Function: Handicapped accessible, Photocopying/Printing, Summer reading
     prog, Wheelchair accessible
     Special Services for the Deaf - Bks on deafness & sign lang
     Open Mon-Fri 9-6
     Friends of the Library Group

LAKE DALLAS

P   LAKE CITIES LIBRARY*, 302 S Shady Shores Rd, 75065-3609. SAN
     376-4559. Tel: 940-497-3566. FAX: 940-497-3567. Web Site:
     www.lakecitieslibrary.org. *Dir,* Barbara Thompson; E-mail:
     bthompson@lakecitieslibrary.org; *Tech Serv Dir,* Lanita Noland; Staff 5.675
     (MLS 2, Non-MLS 3.675)
     Founded 1975
     Library Holdings: Bk Vols 46,562; Per Subs 37
     Automation Activity & Vendor Info: (Cataloging) Follett Software;
     (Circulation) Follett Software; (OPAC) Follett Software
     Wireless access
     Function: CD-ROM, Handicapped accessible, Home delivery & serv to Sr
     ctr & nursing homes, Homebound delivery serv, ILL available, Music CDs,
     Online searches, Prog for children & young adult, Spoken cassettes &
     CDs, Summer reading prog, VHS videos, Wheelchair accessible,
     Workshops
     Mem of North Texas Library Partners
     Open Tues-Thurs 10-8, Fri & Sat 10-6
     Friends of the Library Group

LAKE JACKSON

J   BRAZOSPORT COLLEGE LIBRARY*, 500 College Dr, 77566. SAN
     316-5582. Tel: 979-230-3310. Reference Tel: 979-230-3406. FAX:
     979-230-3185. Web Site: www.brazosport.edu. *Dir,* Tami Wisofsky; Tel:
     979-230-3308, E-mail: tami.wisofsky@brazosport.edu; *Ref Librn,* Brent
     Cooper; Tel: 979-230-3366, E-mail: brent.cooper@brazosport.edu; *Ser
     Librn,* JoAnne Alcorn; Tel: 979-230-3259, E-mail:
     jo.anne.alcorn@brazosport.edu; *Tech Serv Librn,* Michael Mitchell; Tel:
     979-230-3309, E-mail: michael.mitchell@brazosport.edu; Staff 6 (MLS 4,
     Non-MLS 2)
     Founded 1968. Enrl 4,022; Fac 68; Highest Degree: Bachelor
     Library Holdings: e-books 46,000; Bk Titles 60,000; Bk Vols 70,000; Per
     Subs 350
     Special Collections: Children's Coll; New Book Coll; Rare Book Coll;
     Small Business Development Coll
     Automation Activity & Vendor Info: (Cataloging) SirsiDynix;
     (Circulation) SirsiDynix; (ILL) OCLC; (OPAC) SirsiDynix; (Serials)
     SirsiDynix
     Database Vendor: EBSCOhost, Gale Cengage Learning, netLibrary,
     Newsbank, OCLC FirstSearch, OCLC WorldCat, ProQuest, SirsiDynix,
     Wilson - Wilson Web
     Wireless access
     Partic in Tex Share
     Open Mon-Thurs 7:30am-9:30pm, Fri 7:30-Noon

LAKE WORTH

P   MARY LOU REDDICK PUBLIC LIBRARY*, 7005 Charbonneau Rd,
     76135. SAN 316-5590. Tel: 817-237-9681. FAX: 817-237-9671. *Librn,*
     Lara Strother
     Pop 5,000; Circ 18,684
     Library Holdings: Bk Vols 22,000; Per Subs 22
     Automation Activity & Vendor Info: (Cataloging) Biblionix; (Circulation)
     Biblionix; (OPAC) Biblionix
     Wireless access
     Mem of North Texas Library Partners
     Open Tues & Fri 9-5, Wed & Thurs 9-7, Sat 9-1
     Friends of the Library Group

LAKEHILLS

P   LAKEHILLS AREA LIBRARY, 7200 FM 1283, 78063. SAN 378-3952.
     Tel: 830-510-2777. FAX: 830-510-2777. E-mail: llca1@juno.com. *Dir,*
     Dorothy Steelman; Staff 2 (MLS 1, Non-MLS 1)
     Founded 1999
     Library Holdings: Bk Titles 19,039; Per Subs 127

Automation Activity & Vendor Info: (Acquisitions) Biblionix;
(Cataloging) Biblionix; (Circulation) Biblionix; (Course Reserve) Biblionix
Database Vendor: Gale Cengage Learning
Wireless access
Function: Children's prog, Computer training, Free DVD rentals,
Handicapped accessible, Pub access computers, Senior computer classes,
Story hour, Summer reading prog, Tax forms, VHS videos, Wheelchair
accessible
Open Mon & Thurs 10-8, Tues, Wed & Fri 10-5, Sat 10-2

LAMESA

P   DAWSON COUNTY LIBRARY*, 511 N Third St, 79331. (Mail add: PO
Box 1264, 79331-1264), SAN 316-5604. Tel: 806-872-6502. FAX:
806-872-2435. Web Site: www.dclib.lib.tx.us. *Dir,* Debbie Garza; E-mail:
dgarza@lamesa.esc17.net
Founded 1933. Pop 14,000; Circ 129,871
Library Holdings: AV Mats 1,722; Bks on Deafness & Sign Lang 10;
e-books 19,000; Large Print Bks 1,246; Bk Titles 40,200; Per Subs 75;
Talking Bks 2,585
Special Collections: Genealogy, Texas Heritage
Automation Activity & Vendor Info: (Acquisitions) Follett Software;
(Cataloging) Follett Software; (Circulation) Follett Software; (OPAC)
Follett Software
Wireless access
Mem of West Texas Library System
Open Mon & Tues 9:30-6:30, Wed-Fri 9:30-5:30, Sat 9:30-12:30

LAMPASAS

P   LAMPASAS PUBLIC LIBRARY*, 201 S Main, 76550-2843. SAN
316-5612. Tel: 512-556-3251. FAX: 512-556-4065. E-mail:
library@cityoflampasas.com. Web Site: www.cityoflampasas.com/library.
Dir, Subia Shanda; Staff 3 (Non-MLS 3)
Founded 1902. Pop 7,948; Circ 50,358
Library Holdings: Audiobooks 464; Large Print Bks 828; Bk Titles
26,607; Bk Vols 26,996; Per Subs 30; Videos 593
Automation Activity & Vendor Info: (Cataloging) Biblionix; (Circulation)
Biblionix; (OPAC) Biblionix
Database Vendor: OCLC FirstSearch
Wireless access
Mem of Central Texas Library System, Inc
Open Mon & Wed-Fri 10-5:30, Tues 10-7, Sat 10-2

LANCASTER

J   CEDAR VALLEY COLLEGE LIBRARY*, 3030 N Dallas Ave,
75134-3799. SAN 321-3501. Tel: 972-860-8140. FAX: 972-860-8221. Web
Site: www.cedarvalleycollege.edu. *Assoc Dean,* Edna White; Tel:
972-860-8152, E-mail: ewhite@dcccd.edu; *Librn,* Dana Corbin; Tel:
972-860-2973, E-mail: dcorbin@dcccd.edu; *Librn,* Kim Ross; Tel:
972-860-8150, E-mail: kross@dcccd.edu; *Librn,* Jeffrey Stagner; E-mail:
jstagner@dcccd.edu. Subject Specialists: *English lit,* Dana Corbin; *Hist,*
Kim Ross; *Hist,* Jeffrey Stagner; Staff 3 (MLS 3)
Founded 1977. Highest Degree: Associate
Library Holdings: AV Mats 50,000; Bk Titles 47,585; Per Subs 200
Subject Interests: Automotive, Commercial music, Mkt, Veterinary tech
Automation Activity & Vendor Info: (Circulation) Innovative Interfaces,
Inc; (OPAC) Innovative Interfaces, Inc
Database Vendor: Innovative Interfaces, Inc INN - View
Wireless access
Partic in OCLC Online Computer Library Center, Inc; Tex Share
Open Mon-Thurs 8am-9pm, Fri 8-4:30, Sat 9-12
Restriction: In-house use for visitors, Open to students, fac & staff

P   LANCASTER VETERANS MEMORIAL LIBRARY*, 1600 Veterans
Memorial Pkwy, 75134. SAN 376-4419. Tel: 972-227-1080. FAX:
972-227-5560. Web Site: www.lancastertxlib.org. *Dir,* Cami Loucks;
E-mail: cloucks@lancaster-tx.com; *Asst Dir,* Jimi Davis; E-mail:
jdavis@lancaster-tx.com; Staff 8.5 (MLS 2, Non-MLS 6.5)
Founded 1923. Pop 33,550
Library Holdings: High Interest/Low Vocabulary Bk Vols 15,314; Bk Vols
63,000; Per Subs 99
Special Collections: Genealogy Coll
Subject Interests: Local hist
Automation Activity & Vendor Info: (Acquisitions) Innovative Interfaces,
Inc; (Cataloging) Innovative Interfaces, Inc; (Circulation) Innovative
Interfaces, Inc; (OPAC) Innovative Interfaces, Inc
Open Mon 2-9, Tues & Thurs 10-9, Wed 10-6, Fri 10-4, Sat 10-5
Friends of the Library Group

LAREDO

J   LAREDO COMMUNITY COLLEGE*, Harold R Yeary Library, West End
Washington St, 78040. SAN 316-5620. Tel: 956-721-5816. Circulation Tel:
956-721-5275. Interlibrary Loan Service Tel: 956-721-5845. Reference Tel:

956-721-5274. FAX: 956-721-5447. Reference E-mail:
reference_desk@laredo.edu. Web Site: www.laredo.edu/library. *Libr Dir,*
Thomas Walter LaFleur; Tel: 956-721-5283, E-mail: tlafleur@laredo.edu;
Cat/Ref Librn, Cathy Craig; Tel: 956-721-5813, Fax: 956-721-5447,
E-mail: cathy.craig@laredo.edu; *Per/Circ Librn,* Analiza Perez-Gomez; Tel:
956-721-5842, Fax: 956-721-5447, E-mail: analiza.perez@laredo.edu; *Ref
& ILL Librn,* William H Wisner; Tel: 956-721-5281, E-mail:
bwisner@laredo.edu; *Acq, Supvr,* Esmeralda Chapa; Tel: 956-721-5277,
E-mail: echapa@laredo.edu; *Circ Supvr,* Terry Dominguez; Tel:
956-721-5275, E-mail: tdominguez@laredo.edu; *Govt Pub & Info Supvr,*
Christine Bautista; Tel: 956-721-5841, E-mail: pvasquez@laredo.edu;
Ref/ILL Supvr, Albert Bustos; Tel: 956-721-5845, E-mail:
abustos@laredo.edu; *Supvr, Ser,* Pat Delapass; Tel: 956-721-5276, E-mail:
pdelapass@laredo.edu; *Coordr, Acq,* Juanita Perez; Tel: 956-721-5961,
E-mail: juanita.perez@laredo.edu; *Automated Syst Coordr,* Jose Eddie
Perez; Tel: 956-721-5282, E-mail: eddiep@laredo.edu; *Coordr, Ser,*
Cynthia Y Navarro; Tel: 956-721-5961, E-mail:
cynthia.navarro@laredo.edu; *Ref Coordr,* Roxanne Garza; Tel:
956-721-5280, E-mail: roxgarza@laredo.edu; *Cat Spec,* Dinorah Ramon;
Tel: 956-721-5272, E-mail: dramon@laredo.edu; *Cat Tech,* Melina
Villarreal; Tel: 956-721-5269, E-mail: melina.ramirez@laredo.edu; *Circ
Asst,* Rosa H Rios; Tel: 956-721-5275, E-mail: rosa.rios@laredo.edu; *Libr
Mat Proc Spec,* Valeriano Hernandez; Tel: 956-721-5279, E-mail:
vhernandez@laredo.edu. Subject Specialists: *Bibliog instruction,* Analiza
Perez-Gomez; *Art, Bibliog instruction,* William H Wisner; *Govt doc,*
Christine Bautista; *Automation, Networking,* Jose Eddie Perez; Staff 7
(MLS 6, Non-MLS 1)
Founded 1947. Enrl 10,029; Fac 205; Highest Degree: Associate
Sept 2010-Aug 2010 Income $1,390,751, State $248,000, Federal
$306,074, Locally Generated Income $836,677. Mats Exp $272,920, Books
$36,636, Per/Ser (Incl. Access Fees) $86,169, Manu Arch $5,050, Micro
$5,336, AV Equip $10,987, AV Mat $1,118, Electronic Ref Mat (Incl.
Access Fees) $124,794, Presv $2,830. Sal $830,180 (Prof $306,074)
Library Holdings: AV Mats 15; Bks on Deafness & Sign Lang 49; Braille
Volumes 30; CDs 83; DVDs 540; Electronic Media & Resources 23; Large
Print Bks 148; Microforms 11,045; Music Scores 11; Bk Titles 94,313; Bk
Vols 113,367; Per Subs 415; Videos 1,214
Special Collections: Laredo Archives; Old Fort MacIntosh Records
Subject Interests: Behav sci, Soc sci, Voc-tech
Automation Activity & Vendor Info: (Acquisitions) SIRSI-iBistro;
(Cataloging) SIRSI-iBistro; (Circulation) SIRSI-iBistro; (Course Reserve)
SIRSI-iBistro; (ILL) OCLC WorldCat; (Media Booking) SIRSI-iBistro;
(OPAC) SIRSI-iBistro; (Serials) SIRSI-iBistro
Database Vendor: 3M Library Systems, ABC-CLIO, Amigos Library
Services, Baker & Taylor, Checkpoint Systems, Inc, Cinahl Information
Systems, College Source, CQ Press, EBSCOhost, Gale Cengage Learning,
H W Wilson, netLibrary, OCLC FirstSearch, OCLC WorldCat, Project
MUSE, ProQuest, SirsiDynix, Wilson - Wilson Web, YBP Library Services
Wireless access
Publications: Library E-News (Online only); Yeary Library Tidings
Newsletter (Newsletter)
Partic in Tex Share
Special Services for the Blind - Computer with voice synthesizer for
visually impaired persons; Reader equip
Open Mon-Thurs (Winter) 7:30am-9pm, Fri 7:30-12, Sat & Sun 1-5;
Mon-Thurs (Summer) 7:30am-9pm, Fri 7:30-12
Restriction: Authorized patrons
Departmental Libraries:
SENATOR JUDITH ZAFFIRINI LIBRARY (SOUTH LIBRARY), 5500 S
Zapata Hwy, 78046. Circulation Tel: 956-794-4275. Reference Tel:
956-794-4274. Administration Tel: 956-721-5816. FAX: 956-794-4375.
Web Site: www.laredo.edu/library. *Libr Dir,* Thomas Walter LaFleur; Tel:
956-721-5816, Fax: 956-721-5447, E-mail: tlafleur@laredo.edu; *South
Campus Librn (1),* Rachel Bohmfalk; E-mail: rbohmfalk@laredo.edu;
Circ Asst, San Juanita Ibarra; E-mail: sanjuanita.ibarra@laredo.edu;
Computer Lab Asst, Santiago Fonseca; Tel: 956-794-4267, E-mail:
santiago.fonseca@laredo.edu. Subject Specialists: *Bibliog instruction,*
Rachel Bohmfalk; *Automation, Computers, Networking,* Santiago Fonseca
Jan 2010-Aug 2011 Income Locally Generated Income $360,507. Mats
Exp $47,243, Books $26,672, Per/Ser (Incl. Access Fees) $15,998, Micro
$60, AV Equip $3,848, AV Mat $508, Presv $157
Library Holdings: Audiobooks 1; AV Mats 10; Bks on Deafness &
Sign Lang 23; CDs 62; DVDs 972; Large Print Bks 130; Microforms
167; Bk Titles 36,017; Bk Vols 37,199; Per Subs 84; Videos 154
Open Mon-Thurs 7:30am-9pm, Fri 7:30-12, Sat & Sun 1-5; Mon-Thurs
(Summer) 7:30am-9pm, Fri 7:30-12

P   LAREDO PUBLIC LIBRARY*, 1120 E Calton Rd, 78041. SAN
316-5639. Tel: 956-795-2400. FAX: 956-795-2403. Web Site:
laredolibrary.org, lpl@laredolibrary.org. *Dir,* Maria G Soliz; E-mail:
mgsoliz@laredolibrary.org; *Asst Dir,* Homero Vazquez-Garcia; Tel:
956-795-2420, E-mail: homero@laredolibrary.org; *Pub Serv Mgr,* Rena
Ren; E-mail: rena@laredolibrary.org; *Ref Librn,* Robert Brown; E-mail:
robert@laredolibrary.org; *Ref Librn,* Pam Burrell; E-mail:
pam@laredolibrary.org; *Spec Coll Librn,* Joe Moreno; E-mail:

jmoreno@laredolibrary.org; *Cat,* Kelly Simms; E-mail:
kelly@laredolibrary.org; *Tech Serv,* Anne Mente; E-mail:
anne@laredolibrary.org; Staff 38 (MLS 8, Non-MLS 30)
Founded 1951. Pop 208,754; Circ 472,113
Library Holdings: Audiobooks 5,848; AV Mats 11,037; Bks on Deafness
& Sign Lang 3,870; Braille Volumes 13; CDs 6,296; DVDs 12,812;
e-books 357; Electronic Media & Resources 80; Large Print Bks 3,056;
Microforms 1,052; Bk Vols 26,000; Per Subs 337; Talking Bks 150
Special Collections: Funding Information Library (Foundation Center
Cooperating Coll); Laredo Historical Coll, bks, clippings
Subject Interests: Grantsmanship, Local authors, Webb County hist
Automation Activity & Vendor Info: (Acquisitions) SirsiDynix;
(Cataloging) SirsiDynix; (Circulation) SirsiDynix; (ILL) OCLC; (OPAC)
SirsiDynix; (Serials) EBSCO Online
Database Vendor: EBSCOhost, Facts on File, infoUSA, LearningExpress,
Medline, ProQuest, PubMed, ReferenceUSA, SirsiDynix
Wireless access
Function: Archival coll, Art exhibits, BA reader (adult literacy), Bilingual
assistance for Spanish patrons, Bk club(s), Bks on cassette, Bks on CD,
CD-ROM, Citizenship assistance, Computer training, Computers for patron
use, Copy machines, Digital talking bks, Distance learning, e-mail serv,
E-Reserves, Electronic databases & coll, Equip loans & repairs, Exhibits,
Free DVD rentals, Games & aids for the handicapped, Handicapped
accessible, Holiday prog, Homework prog, ILL available, Instruction &
testing, Magnifiers for reading, Mail & tel request accepted, Music CDs,
Newsp ref libr, Online info literacy tutorials on the web & in blackboard,
Online searches, Orientations, Outreach serv, Outside serv via phone, mail,
e-mail & web, OverDrive digital audio bks, Passport agency,
Photocopying/Printing, Preschool outreach, Prog for adults, Prog for
children & young adult, Pub access computers, Ref & res, Ref serv
available, Ref serv in person, Referrals accepted, Satellite serv, Senior
computer classes, Senior outreach, Serves mentally handicapped
consumers, Specialized serv in classical studies, Spoken cassettes & CDs,
Spoken cassettes & DVDs, Story hour, Summer reading prog, Tax forms,
Teen prog, Telephone ref, VCDs, VHS videos, Video lending libr, Visual
arts prog, Web-catalog, Wheelchair accessible, Workshops
Publications: Bookletters (Monthly newsletter)
Special Services for the Blind - Assistive/Adapted tech devices, equip &
products; Bks on cassette; Bks on CD; Computer with voice synthesizer
for visually impaired persons; Large print bks; Talking bks
Open Mon, Fri & Sat 9-6, Tues-Thurs 9-8, Sun 1-5
Friends of the Library Group
Bookmobiles: 2

C   TEXAS A&M INTERNATIONAL UNIVERSITY*, Sue & Radcliffe
Killam Library, 5201 University Blvd, 78041-1900. SAN 316-5647. Tel:
956-326-2400. Circulation Tel: 956-326-2112. Interlibrary Loan Service
Tel: 956-326-2117. Reference Tel: 956-326-2138. FAX: 956-326-2399. *Dir,*
Douglass Ferrier; E-mail: douglas.ferrier@tamiu.edu; *Head, Pub Serv,* John
Maxstadt; Tel: 956-326-2116, E-mail: jmaxstadt@tamiu.edu; *Acq Librn,*
Rogelio Hinojosa; Tel: 956-326-2123, E-mail: rhinojosa@tamiu.edu; *Govt
Doc Librn,* Rodney Webb; Tel: 956-326-2119, E-mail: rwebb@tamiu.edu;
Access Serv Librn, Ref Librn, Malynda Dalton; *Ref Librn, Spec Coll Librn,*
Jeanette Hatcher; Tel: 956-326-2404, E-mail: jhatcher@tamiu.edu; Staff 25
(MLS 8, Non-MLS 17)
Founded 1970. Enrl 3,052; Fac 138; Highest Degree: Doctorate
Library Holdings: e-books 65,000; e-journals 8,000; Bk Titles 260,000;
Bk Vols 300,000; Per Subs 1,000
Special Collections: Laredo Spanish Archives on MF; Raza Unida Papers.
State Document Depository; US Document Depository
Subject Interests: Intl trade, Nursing
Automation Activity & Vendor Info: (Acquisitions) Ex Libris Group;
(Cataloging) Ex Libris Group; (Circulation) Ex Libris Group; (Course
Reserve) Ex Libris Group; (OPAC) Ex Libris Group; (Serials) Ex Libris
Group
Database Vendor: EBSCOhost, Gale Cengage Learning, OCLC
FirstSearch
Wireless access
Publications: Newsletter
Partic in TexSHARE - Texas State Library & Archives Commission
Open Mon-Thurs 7:30am-Midnight, Fri 10-5, Sat 9-6, Sun 1-Midnight

LAROSITA

P   STARR COUNTY PUBLIC LIBRARY*, Larosita Branch, 4192 W Hwy
83, 78582. SAN 376-1045. Tel: 956-849-4453. *Br Mgr,* Imelda Escobar
Open Mon-Fri 8-5
Friends of the Library Group

LAUGHLIN AFB

A   UNITED STATES AIR FORCE, Laughlin Air Force Base Library, 201
Mitchell Blvd, Bldg 223, 78843-2125. SAN 362-1030. Tel: 830-298-5119.
Reference Tel: 830-298-4377. Administration Tel: 830-298-5757. E-mail:
laughlin.library@laughlin.af.mil. Web Site:

laughlinservices.com/?page_id=44. *Head Librn,* Sue A Blankemeyer;
E-mail: sue.blankemeyer@us.af.mil
Library Holdings: Audiobooks 772; CDs 554; DVDs 1,080; Bk Titles
20,895; Bk Vols 21,650; Per Subs 100; Videos 223
Special Collections: AFSO21 (Lean Initiative); Career Transition
Assistance Coll; Language & Culture Coll; Military, Chief of Staff Coll
Automation Activity & Vendor Info: (Cataloging) Softlink America;
(Circulation) Softlink America; (ILL) OCLC; (OPAC) Softlink America;
(Serials) Softlink America
Database Vendor: CountryWatch, EBSCO Auto Repair Reference,
EBSCOhost, Gale Cengage Learning, Newsbank, OCLC, Safari Books
Online
Wireless access
Open Mon-Thurs 9-7:30, Fri 9-5, Sat 12-5

LEAGUE CITY

P   HELEN HALL LIBRARY*, 100 W Walker, 77573-3899. SAN 316-5671.
Tel: 281-554-1111. Circulation Tel: 281-554-1120. Interlibrary Loan
Service Tel: 281-554-1104. Reference Tel: 281-554-1101. Administration
Tel: 281-554-1107. Automation Services Tel: 281-554-1126. FAX:
281-554-1118. Reference FAX: 281-554-1117. Web Site:
leaguecitylibrary.org. *City Librn,* Shelley Leader; Tel: 281-554-1109,
E-mail: shelley.leader@leaguecitylibrary.org; *Asst City Librn,* Bruce
Compton; E-mail: bruce.compton@leaguecitylibrary.org; *Asst City Librn,*
Jeannie Kunzinger; Tel: 281-554-1116, E-mail:
jeannie.kunzinger@leaguecitylibrary.org; *Ad,* Jenny Brewer; Tel:
281-554-1108, E-mail: jenny.brewer@leaguecitylibrary.org; *Ch,* Patti
Conrad; Tel: 281-554-1115, E-mail: patti.conrad@leaguecitylibrary.org;
Commun Relations Librn, Elizabeth Hopkins; Tel: 281-554-1106, E-mail:
elizabeth.hopkins@leaguecitylibrary.org; *Local Hist Librn,* Caris Brown;
Tel: 281-554-1105, E-mail: caris.brown@leaguecitylibrary.org; *Tech Serv
Librn,* Maggie Walk; Tel: 281-554-1127, E-mail:
maggie.walk@leaguecitylibrary.org; *Teen Librn,* Lindsay Faust; Tel:
281-554-1102, E-mail: lindsay.faust@leaguecitylibrary.org; *Youth Serv
Librn,* Bonnie Keith; Tel: 281-554-1112, E-mail:
bonnie.keith@leaguecitylibrary.org; *Info Tech,* Neal Burt; Tel:
281-554-1125, E-mail: nburt@leaguecitylibrary.org; Staff 10 (MLS 9,
Non-MLS 1)
Founded 1972. Pop 83,000; Circ 776,647
Oct 2009-Sept 2010 Income $2,292,814, State $29,530, City $2,173,567,
County $89,717. Mats Exp $313,350, Books $213,530, Per/Ser (Incl.
Access Fees) $13,000, AV Mat $62,250, Electronic Ref Mat (Incl. Access
Fees) $24,570. Sal $1,327,342
Library Holdings: Braille Volumes 91; CDs 6,885; DVDs 15,781;
Electronic Media & Resources 1; Large Print Bks 5,161; Microforms 2;
Music Scores 111; Bk Titles 139,414; Bk Vols 169,728; Per Subs 268;
Talking Bks 3,128
Automation Activity & Vendor Info: (Acquisitions) SirsiDynix;
(Cataloging) SirsiDynix; (Circulation) SirsiDynix
Database Vendor: Facts on File, Gale Cengage Learning
Wireless access
Function: Audiobks via web, Bk club(s), Bk reviews (Group), Bks on
cassette, Bks on CD, Children's prog, Computers for patron use, Copy
machines, ILL available, Mail & tel request accepted, Music CDs, Online
cat, Online searches, Outreach serv, OverDrive digital audio bks,
Photocopying/Printing, Preschool outreach, Prog for adults, Prog for
children & young adult, Pub access computers, Ref serv available, Senior
computer classes, Spoken cassettes & CDs, Story hour, Summer reading
prog, Tax forms, Teen prog, Telephone ref
Publications: League City: A History from 1913-1924, vol 2
Open Mon-Thurs 10-9, Fri & Sat 10-6, Sun 1-5
Friends of the Library Group

LEAKEY

P   REAL COUNTY PUBLIC LIBRARY*, Leakey Library, 225 Main St,
78873. (Mail add: PO Box 488, 78873-0488), SAN 376-4125. Tel:
830-232-5199. FAX: 830-232-5913. E-mail: rcplea@hctc.net. Web Site:
leakeylibrary.org. *Co-Dir,* Mary Boedeker; *Co-Dir,* Gale Huckaby
Founded 1991
Library Holdings: Bk Vols 10,000
Wireless access
Special Services for the Blind - Home delivery serv; Large print &
cassettes; Talking bks
Friends of the Library Group

LEANDER

P   LEANDER PUBLIC LIBRARY*, 1011 S Bagdad Rd, 78641. SAN
375-5118. Tel: 512-259-5259. E-mail: leanderpl@leander.lib.tx.us. Web
Site: www.leander.lib.tx.us. *Dir,* Priscilla Donovan; Staff 5 (MLS 3,
Non-MLS 2)
Founded 1987. Pop 26,500; Circ 140,000

Library Holdings: AV Mats 5,000; CDs 120; Large Print Bks 1,500; Bk Titles 38,000; Bk Vols 40,000; Per Subs 107; Talking Bks 2,000; Videos 3,000
Automation Activity & Vendor Info: (Cataloging) TLC (The Library Corporation); (Circulation) TLC (The Library Corporation)
Wireless access
Mem of Central Texas Library System, Inc
Open Mon-Thurs 9-9, Fri & Sat 9-7, Sun 12-6

LEON VALLEY

P   LEON VALLEY PUBLIC LIBRARY*, 6425 Evers Rd, 78238-1453. SAN 372-5944. Tel: 210-684-0720. FAX: 210-684-2088. E-mail: librarian@leonvalley.lib.tx.us. Web Site: www.leonvalley.lib.tx.us. *Librn,* Joyce Miller Trent; *Asst Librn,* Sherry Watson; Staff 3 (MLS 1, Non-MLS 2)
Founded 1977. Pop 10,000; Circ 64,500
Library Holdings: Bk Titles 50,000; Per Subs 100
Special Collections: Leon Valley Historical Society. Oral History
Automation Activity & Vendor Info: (Cataloging) Biblionix; (Circulation) Biblionix; (OPAC) Biblionix
Wireless access
Special Services for the Deaf - Bks on deafness & sign lang
Open Tues & Thurs 10-8, Wed & Fri 10-6, Sat 10-2
Friends of the Library Group

LEONARD

P   LEONARD PUBLIC LIBRARY*, 102 S Main St, 75452. (Mail add: PO Box 1188, 75452-1188), SAN 376-6500. Tel: 903-587-2391. FAX: 903-587-0311. E-mail: info@leonardlibrary.net. Web Site: www.leonardlibrary.net. *Dir,* Rosey Farhood; E-mail: rosie@leonardlibrary.net
Library Holdings: Bk Vols 24,000
Automation Activity & Vendor Info: (Cataloging) Follett Software; (Circulation) Follett Software
Open Tues 10-7, Wed-Fri 2-7, Sat 10-2
Friends of the Library Group

LEVELLAND

P   HOCKLEY COUNTY MEMORIAL LIBRARY*, 811 Austin St, 79336. (Mail add: 802 Houston St, Ste 108, 79336-3705), SAN 316-568X. Tel: 806-894-6750. FAX: 806-894-6917. E-mail: hockleycountymemoriallibrary@gmail.com. *Dir,* Kay Daniel; E-mail: kdaniel@hockleycounty.org; *Asst Librn,* Nora Honesto; E-mail: nhonesto@hockleycounty.org; Staff 2 (Non-MLS 2)
Founded 1946. Pop 24,500; Circ 67,115
Library Holdings: Bk Titles 37,517; Bk Vols 43,479; Per Subs 77
Subject Interests: Tex hist
Automation Activity & Vendor Info: (Cataloging) Follett Software; (Circulation) Follett Software
Mem of West Texas Library System
Partic in TexSHARE - Texas State Library & Archives Commission
Open Mon-Wed & Fri 9-5, Thurs 9-7
Branches: 1
SUNDOWN BRANCH, 207 E Richardson, Sundown, 79372. (Mail add: PO Box 600, Sundown, 79372-0600), SAN 375-6025. Tel: 806-229-3133. E-mail: librarian@sundowntx.com. *Librn,* Pamela Elam; Staff 1 (Non-MLS 1)
Circ 5,815
Library Holdings: Bk Titles 6,334; Bk Vols 6,627
Automation Activity & Vendor Info: (Acquisitions) LibLime; (Cataloging) LibLime; (Circulation) LibLime; (OPAC) LibLime; (Serials) LibLime
Open Mon-Fri 9-1 & 2-5

J   SOUTH PLAINS COLLEGE LIBRARY, 1401 S College Ave, Box E, 79336. SAN 316-5698. Tel: 806-716-2300, 806-716-2330. Circulation Tel: 806-716-2299. Administration Tel: 806-716-2304. FAX: 806-894-5274. Web Site: www.southplainscollege.edu/library. *Dir of Libr Serv,* Jim Belcher; E-mail: jbelcher@southplainscollege.edu; *Pub Serv Librn,* Katherine Anderson; Tel: 806-716-2303, E-mail: kanderson@southplainscollege.edu; *Pub Serv Librn,* Ann Hebisen; Tel: 806-716-2298, E-mail: ahebisen@southplainscollege.edu; *Tech Serv Librn,* Hope Elizabeth Beyer; Tel: 806-716-2302, E-mail: hbeyer@southplainscollege.edu; Staff 7 (MLS 7)
Founded 1958. Enrl 9,600; Highest Degree: Associate
Sept 2011-Aug 2012 Income $856,058. Mats Exp $268,500. Sal $421,000
Library Holdings: Audiobooks 132; AV Mats 2,687; e-books 55,000; Microforms 300; Bk Vols 98,000; Per Subs 270
Automation Activity & Vendor Info: (Acquisitions) Ex Libris Group; (Cataloging) Ex Libris Group; (Circulation) Ex Libris Group; (Course Reserve) Ex Libris Group; (ILL) OCLC FirstSearch; (OPAC) Ex Libris Group; (Serials) Ex Libris Group

Database Vendor: Agricola, Amigos Library Services, ARTstor, Baker & Taylor, Booklist Online, Cinahl Information Systems, CredoReference, ebrary, EBSCO Auto Repair Reference, EBSCOhost, Ex Libris Group, Gale Cengage Learning, LearningExpress, LexisNexis, Newsbank, OCLC, OCLC WorldCat, ProQuest, STAT!Ref (Teton Data Systems), Westlaw
Wireless access
Partic in OCLC Online Computer Library Center, Inc; TexSHARE - Texas State Library & Archives Commission; US National Library of Medicine
Special Services for the Blind - Magnifiers
Open Mon-Wed (Winter) 7:45am-8:30pm, Thurs & Fri 7:45-4, Sun 2-6; Mon-Wed (Summer) 8-6, Thurs 8-4, Fri 8-3

LEWISVILLE

S   AMERICAN DONKEY & MULE SOCIETY LIBRARY, 1346 Morningside Ave, 75057. (Mail add: PO Box 1210, 75067), SAN 324-0983. Tel: 972-219-0781. FAX: 972-219-0781. E-mail: lovelongears@hotmail.com. Web Site: www.lovelongears.com. *Librn,* Betty Posey. Subject Specialists: *Equine,* Betty Posey
Founded 1967
Library Holdings: Bk Titles 1,000
Special Collections: Breed Association Coll (private); Historical: Studbooks
Subject Interests: Donkeys, Horses, Mules
Restriction: Open by appt only

P   LEWISVILLE PUBLIC LIBRARY SYSTEM*, 1197 W Main at Civic Circle, 75067. (Mail add: PO Box 299002, 75029-9002), SAN 316-5701. Tel: 972-219-3566. Circulation Tel: 972-219-3576. Reference Tel: 972-219-3779. FAX: 972-219-5094. Web Site: library.cityoflewisville.com. *Dir,* Ann Wiegand; Tel: 972-219-3571, E-mail: awiegand@cityoflewisville.com; *Ref & Adult Serv Supvr,* Jennifer Bekker; Tel: 972-219-3721, E-mail: jbekker@cityoflewisville.com; *Youth Serv Supvr,* Patricia Peters; Tel: 972-219-3691, E-mail: ppeters@cityoflewisville.com; Staff 7 (MLS 7)
Founded 1968. Pop 86,100
Oct 2009-Sept 2010 Income $1,724,213, State $24,900, City $1,699,313. Mats Exp $131,425, Books $81,772, Manu Arch $200, AV Equip $10,453, Electronic Ref Mat (Incl. Access Fees) $39,000. Sal $1,115,472 (Prof $39,700)
Library Holdings: AV Mats 21,887; e-books 27,267; Bk Vols 176,499; Per Subs 90
Special Collections: Children's Enrichment, bk, flm. Oral History
Subject Interests: Local oral hist
Automation Activity & Vendor Info: (Acquisitions) SirsiDynix; (Cataloging) SirsiDynix; (Circulation) SirsiDynix; (OPAC) SirsiDynix
Database Vendor: SirsiDynix
Wireless access
Function: AV serv, ILL available, Magnifiers for reading, Photocopying/Printing, Prog for adults, Prog for children & young adult, Ref serv available, Summer reading prog, Telephone ref, Wheelchair accessible
Mem of North Texas Library Partners
Special Services for the Deaf - TTY equip
Open Mon-Thurs 10-9, Fri & Sat 11-5, Sun 1-5
Friends of the Library Group

LIBERTY

P   LIBERTY MUNICIPAL LIBRARY*, 1710 Sam Houston Ave, 77575-4741. SAN 316-571X. Tel: 936-336-8901. FAX: 936-336-2414. *Dir,* Dana G Abshier; E-mail: dabshier@cityofliberty.org; *Admin Serv, Asst Admin, Cat,* Betty Boyd; *AV,* DeAnn Joerg; *Ch, Circ,* Sue Lintleman; *Ref Serv,* Margaret Michel; Staff 6 (Non-MLS 6)
Founded 1940. Pop 8,173
Library Holdings: Bk Vols 42,000; Per Subs 80
Automation Activity & Vendor Info: (Cataloging) Follett Software; (Circulation) Follett Software
Wireless access
Open Mon-Thurs 10-6, Fri 1-5, Sat 10-4
Friends of the Library Group

LIBERTY HILL

P   LIBERTY HILL PUBLIC LIBRARY*, 355 Loop 332, 78642. (Mail add: PO Box 1072, 78642-1072). Tel: 512-778-6400. FAX: 512-778-5822. E-mail: librarian@lhpl.org. Web Site: www.lhpl.org. *Dir,* Sandy Schultz; Staff 2 (Non-MLS 2)
Founded 2002. Pop 11,000; Circ 32,000
Automation Activity & Vendor Info: (Acquisitions) Biblionix; (Cataloging) Biblionix; (Circulation) Biblionix; (OPAC) Biblionix
Wireless access
Function: Children's prog, Computers for patron use, Copy machines, e-mail & chat, e-mail serv, Fax serv, Free DVD rentals, Handicapped accessible, Holiday prog, ILL available, Music CDs, Online cat, Online ref, Online searches, Photocopying/Printing, Preschool outreach, Prog for

adults, Prog for children & young adult, Ref & res, Ref serv available, Ref serv in person, Spoken cassettes & CDs, Spoken cassettes & DVDs, Story hour, Summer reading prog, Teen prog, Telephone ref, VHS videos, Video lending libr, Web-catalog
Mem of Central Texas Library System, Inc
Open Mon-Wed & Fri 10-5, Thurs 10-8, Sat 10-3

LINDALE

P   LINDALE LIBRARY*, 200 E Hubbard St, 75771. (Mail add: PO Box 1570, 75771-1570). Tel: 903-882-1900, FAX: 903-882-1236. E-mail: info@lindalelibrary.org. Web Site: www.lindalelibrary.org. *Dir,* Carrie Custer
Founded 1993
Library Holdings: Audiobooks 1,500; AV Mats 147; Bks on Deafness & Sign Lang 12; CDs 60; DVDs 1,500; e-books 28,281; Large Print Bks 300; Bk Vols 55,100; Per Subs 10
Automation Activity & Vendor Info: (Cataloging) Book Systems, Inc; (Circulation) Book Systems, Inc; (ILL) OCLC FirstSearch; (OPAC) Book Systems, Inc
Database Vendor: Brodart
Wireless access
Partic in TexSHARE - Texas State Library & Archives Commission
Open Tues-Thurs 10-6, Fri & Sat 10-4
Friends of the Library Group

LITTLE ELM

P   LITTLE ELM PUBLIC LIBRARY*, 100 W Eldorado Pkwy, 75068. Tel: 214-975-0430. Administration Tel: 214-975-0435. FAX: 972-377-5546. E-mail: library@littleelm.org. Web Site: www.littleelm.org/library. *Libr Dir,* Tina Irene Hager; E-mail: thager@littleelm.org; *Ref/Tech Serv Librn,* Laurie McKee; E-mail: lmckee@littleelm.org; *Youth Serv Librn,* Heather Perry; *Circ Asst,* Marian Lanum; Staff 7.5 (MLS 2, MLS 2, Non-MLS 1.75, Non-MLS 1.75)
Founded 1998. Pop 24,000; Circ 34,857
Automation Activity & Vendor Info: (Cataloging) SirsiDynix; (Circulation) SirsiDynix; (OPAC) SirsiDynix
Wireless access
Function: Adult literacy prog, Art exhibits, Audio & video playback equip for onsite use, Bks on cassette, Bks on CD, CD-ROM, Children's prog, Computer training, Computers for patron use, Copy machines, Distance learning, e-mail & chat, e-mail serv, E-Reserves, Electronic databases & coll, Exhibits, Family literacy, Fax serv, Free DVD rentals, Holiday prog, ILL available, Instruction & testing, Music CDs, Online cat, Online searches, Outreach serv, Outside serv via phone, mail, e-mail & web, Photocopying/Printing, Preschool outreach, Prog for adults, Prog for children & young adult, Pub access computers, Ref & res, Ref serv available, Ref serv in person, Referrals accepted, Scanner, Senior computer classes, Senior outreach, Spoken cassettes & CDs, Spoken cassettes & DVDs, Story hour, Summer reading prog, Tax forms, Teen prog, Telephone ref, VHS videos, Video lending libr, Visual arts prog, Wheelchair accessible, Workshops, Writing prog
Mem of North Texas Library Partners
Special Services for the Blind - Bks on cassette; Bks on CD; Large print bks; Talking bks
Open Mon & Wed 10-5:30, Tues & Thurs 10-8, Sat 10-3
Friends of the Library Group

LITTLEFIELD

P   LAMB COUNTY LIBRARY*, 110 E Sixth St, 79339. SAN 316-5728. Tel: 806-385-5223. FAX: 806-385-0030. E-mail: lambkaren1@winstream.net. Web Site: wtls.tsl.state.tx.us/littlefield. *Dir,* Karen Varner
Pop 6,500
Library Holdings: Bk Vols 11,700; Per Subs 28
Automation Activity & Vendor Info: (Cataloging) LibLime; (Circulation) LibLime
Mem of West Texas Library System
Open Mon-Fri 8:30-5, Sat 9-12
Friends of the Library Group

LIVINGSTON

P   MURPHY MEMORIAL LIBRARY*, 601 W Church St, 77351. SAN 316-5736. Tel: 936-327-4252. FAX: 936-327-4162. E-mail: library@murphymemlib.org. Web Site: www.murphymemlib.org. *Librn,* Priscilla E Emrich; E-mail: priscillaemrich@murphymemlib.org; Staff 1 (MLS 1)
Founded 1969. Pop 5,433; Circ 66,878
Library Holdings: AV Mats 1,210; Large Print Bks 1,031; Bk Titles 21,587; Bk Vols 22,560; Per Subs 25; Talking Bks 488
Special Collections: World War I & World War II Aviation
Wireless access
Open Mon-Fri 10-6, Sat 10-2
Friends of the Library Group

LLANO

P   LLANO COUNTY LIBRARY SYSTEM*, Llano County Public Library, 102 E Haynie, 78643. SAN 362-109X. Tel: 325-247-5248. FAX: 325-247-1778. Web Site: www.llano-library-system.net. *Dir,* Dian Ray; E-mail: dian@llano-library-system.net; Staff 9 (Non-MLS 9)
Founded 1939. Pop 17,044; Circ 123,998
Library Holdings: Bk Titles 30,149; Bk Vols 49,745; Per Subs 58
Special Collections: Oral History
Subject Interests: Genealogy
Automation Activity & Vendor Info: (Cataloging) Follett Software; (Circulation) Follett Software; (OPAC) Follett Software
Mem of Central Texas Library System, Inc
Partic in TexSHARE - Texas State Library & Archives Commission
Open Mon-Fri 9-5:30, Sat 10-1
Friends of the Library Group
Branches: 2
KINGSLAND BRANCH, 125 W Polk, Kingsland, 78639, SAN 362-112X. Tel: 325-388-3170. *Br Mgr,* Denise Reed; E-mail: dreed.klib@yahoo.com
Open Mon-Fri 9-5:30, Sat 9-Noon
Friends of the Library Group
LAKE SHORE, 7346 Ranch Rd 261, Buchanan Dam, 78609, SAN 376-2297. Tel: 325-379-1174. FAX: 325-379-3054. E-mail: lakeshore.library@gmail.com. *Br Mgr,* Pat Taylor
Open Mon-Fri 8:30-12 & 1-5:30
Friends of the Library Group

LOCKHART

P   DR EUGENE CLARK PUBLIC LIBRARY*, Lockhart Public Library, 217 S Main St, 78644-2742. (Mail add: PO Box 209, 78644-0209), SAN 316-5744. Tel: 512-398-3223. FAX: 512-376-2258. Web Site: www.clark-library-lockhart.org. *Dir, Libr Serv,* Bertha Martinez
Pop 13,000; Circ 88,000
Library Holdings: AV Mats 6,406; Bk Vols 37,677; Per Subs 175; Videos 4,001
Special Collections: Dr Eugene Clark Special Coll; Lockhart Post-Register Coll. Oral History
Subject Interests: Tex
Automation Activity & Vendor Info: (Cataloging) Follett Software
Wireless access
Mem of Central Texas Library System, Inc
Open Mon, Wed & Fri 9-6, Tues & Thurs 9-8, Sat 9-3
Friends of the Library Group

LONE OAK

P   LONE OAK AREA PUBLIC LIBRARY*, 102 Jones St, 75453. (Mail add: PO Box 501, 75453-0501). Tel: 903-662-4565. FAX: 903-662-0955. E-mail: library@cumbytel.com. Web Site: loneoaklibrary.org. *Librn,* Christene Barrow
Pop 1,073
Library Holdings: AV Mats 100; Bk Titles 8,000; Talking Bks 200
Automation Activity & Vendor Info: (Acquisitions) Book Systems, Inc; (Cataloging) Book Systems, Inc; (Circulation) Book Systems, Inc; (Course Reserve) Book Systems, Inc; (OPAC) Book Systems, Inc
Wireless access
Open Tues-Fri 10-5, Sat 10-2

LONGVIEW

R   FIRST BAPTIST CHURCH*, John L Whorton Media Center Library, 209 E South, 75601. SAN 316-5779. Tel: 903-758-0681, Ext 117. FAX: 903-753-0936. Web Site: www.fbcl.org. *Dir, Media Serv,* Donna Hutchison
Founded 1942
Library Holdings: Bk Vols 30,000; Per Subs 14
Subject Interests: Am hist, Biblical, Cookbks, Inspirational, Tex hist, World hist
Automation Activity & Vendor Info: (Cataloging) Library Concepts; (Circulation) Library Concepts; (OPAC) Library Concepts
Open Mon & Tues 9-12, Wed 9-12 & 5-6, Sun 9am-10:30am

M   GOOD SHEPHERD MEDICAL CENTER*, Medical Library, 700 E Marshall Ave, 75601. SAN 375-7676. Tel: 903-315-2165. FAX: 903-315-2034. Web Site: www.goodsheperdhealth.org. *Librn,* Meredith Burks; E-mail: mburks@gsmc.org; Staff 1 (Non-MLS 1)
Oct 2010-Sept 2011 Income $33,192
Library Holdings: Bk Titles 75
Database Vendor: PubMed
Wireless access
Open Mon-Fri 8-4:30

CR   LETOURNEAU UNIVERSITY*, Margaret Estes Library, 2100 S Mobberly Ave, 75602-3524. (Mail add: PO Box 7001, 75607-7001), SAN 316-5787. Tel: 903-233-3260. Reference Tel: 903-233-3271. FAX:

903-233-3263. Web Site: www.letu.edu. *Dir,* Ginger Specian; *Circ Supvr,* Linda Haynie; Tel: 903-233-3268, E-mail: lindahaynie@letu.edu; *Tech Serv,* Judy Williams; Tel: 903-233-3269, E-mail: judywilliams@letu.edu; Staff 7 (MLS 6, Non-MLS 1)
Founded 1946. Enrl 3,983; Fac 84; Highest Degree: Master
Library Holdings: AV Mats 4,969; e-books 500; e-journals 22,546; Bk Titles 73,852; Bk Vols 94,251; Per Subs 527
Special Collections: Harmon General Hospital Coll, newsp, rpts; Robert G LeTourneau Archives & Museum, bks, flm
Subject Interests: Aviation, Biblical studies, Eng, Humanities
Automation Activity & Vendor Info: (Cataloging) OCLC; (ILL) OCLC
Database Vendor: Dialog, EBSCOhost, LexisNexis, OCLC FirstSearch
Wireless access
Partic in TexSHARE - Texas State Library & Archives Commission
Open Mon-Thurs (Winter) 7:30am-Midnight, Fri 7:30-5, Sat 10-6, Sun 1pm-Midnight; Mon-Thurs (Summer) 8-6, Fri 8-5, Sat 10-5

P   LONGVIEW PUBLIC LIBRARY*, 222 W Cotton St, 75601-6348. SAN 362-1189. Tel: 903-237-1350. Reference Tel: 903-237-1352. Administration Tel: 903-237-1341. FAX: 903-237-1327. Web Site: www.longviewlibrary.com. *Dir,* Kara Spitz; Tel: 903-237-1340, E-mail: kspitz@longview.lib.tx.us; *Head, Circ,* Katherine Jordan; Tel: 903-237-1355, E-mail: kjordan@longview.lib.tx.us; Staff 23 (MLS 7.5, Non-MLS 15.5)
Founded 1932. Pop 121,730; Circ 278,608
Library Holdings: Bk Titles 139,743; Per Subs 187
Special Collections: East Texas; Oil Field Production Records. US Document Depository
Subject Interests: Genealogy, Texana
Database Vendor: EBSCOhost, Gale Cengage Learning, Newsbank
Wireless access
Function: ILL available
Open Mon, Wed, Fri & Sat 10-6, Tues & Thurs 10-9, Sun 1-5
Friends of the Library Group

LOS FRESNOS

P   ETHEL L WHIPPLE MEMORIAL LIBRARY*, 402 W Ocean Blvd, 78566. SAN 316-5795. Tel: 956-233-5330. FAX: 956-233-3203. Web Site: www.los-fresnos.lib.tx.us. *Dir,* Angie Lugo; E-mail: angie@los-fresnos.lib.tx.us
Pop 26,000
Library Holdings: Bk Titles 27,699; Bk Vols 30,000; Per Subs 25
Automation Activity & Vendor Info: (Acquisitions) TLC (The Library Corporation); (Cataloging) TLC (The Library Corporation); (Circulation) TLC (The Library Corporation); (Course Reserve) TLC (The Library Corporation); (ILL) TLC (The Library Corporation); (OPAC) TLC (The Library Corporation); (Serials) TLC (The Library Corporation)
Open Mon-Thurs (Winter) 10-7, Fri 10-5; Mon-Thurs (Summer) 10-6, Fri 10-5
Friends of the Library Group

LUBBOCK

M   COVENANT HEALTH SYSTEM*, Covenant Medical Library, 3615 19th St, 79410. SAN 316-5825. Tel: 806-725-0602. FAX: 806-723-7363. Web Site: www.covenanthealth.org. *Med Librn,* Susan Warner; E-mail: swarner@covhs.org; Staff 2 (MLS 1, Non-MLS 1)
Library Holdings: e-books 75; e-journals 4,200; Bk Titles 7,000; Per Subs 300
Subject Interests: Allied health, Med, Nursing
Automation Activity & Vendor Info: (Cataloging) CyberTools for Libraries; (Circulation) CyberTools for Libraries; (OPAC) CyberTools for Libraries
Database Vendor: EBSCOhost
Wireless access
Partic in National Network of Libraries of Medicine South Central Region
Open Mon-Fri 8:30-5

R   FIRST CHRISTIAN CHURCH LIBRARY*, 2323 Broadway, 79401. SAN 316-5809. Tel: 806-763-1995. FAX: 806-763-5904. Web Site: www.fcclubbock.org. *Adminr,* Dan Elliott
Founded 1948
Library Holdings: Bk Vols 4,950
Automation Activity & Vendor Info: (Cataloging) Book Systems, Inc; (Circulation) Book Systems, Inc; (OPAC) Book Systems, Inc
Open Tues, Thurs & Sun 10-2

M   GRACE MEDICAL CENTER*, Health Information Library, 2412 50th St, 79412. SAN 324-220X. Tel: 806-788-4026. FAX: 806-788-4284. *Dir,* Gena Pittman
Library Holdings: Bk Titles 400
Subject Interests: Med, Nursing
Open Mon-Thurs 8-5, Fri 8-4:30
Restriction: Staff use only

C   LUBBOCK CHRISTIAN UNIVERSITY LIBRARY, 5601 19th St, 79407-2009. SAN 316-5817. Tel: 806-720-7326. E-mail: library@lcu.edu. Web Site: theportal.lcu.edu/Library/Pages/Library.aspx. *Dir,* Rebecca Vickers; *Assoc Librn, Coll Develop, Per,* Paula Gannaway; E-mail: paula.gannaway@lcu.edu; *Automation Librn,* Barbara Slate; Staff 4 (MLS 4)
Founded 1957. Enrl 2,000; Fac 80; Highest Degree: Master
Library Holdings: Bk Vols 126,000; Per Subs 550
Subject Interests: Relig studies
Automation Activity & Vendor Info: (Acquisitions) SirsiDynix; (Cataloging) SirsiDynix; (Circulation) SirsiDynix; (Course Reserve) SirsiDynix; (OPAC) SirsiDynix; (Serials) SirsiDynix
Database Vendor: SirsiDynix
Wireless access
Partic in TexSHARE - Texas State Library & Archives Commission
Restriction: In-house use for visitors

P   LUBBOCK PUBLIC LIBRARY*, Mahon (Main), 1306 Ninth St, 79401. SAN 362-1278. Tel: 806-775-2834. Interlibrary Loan Service Tel: 806-775-2857. FAX: 806-775-2827. Web Site: www.lubbocklibrary.com. *Dir,* Jane Clausen; E-mail: jclausen@mylubbock.us; *Mat Mgr,* Janet Henderson; Staff 53 (MLS 13, Non-MLS 40)
Founded 1966
Library Holdings: Bk Titles 206,336; Bk Vols 417,633; Per Subs 164
Subject Interests: Genealogy
Automation Activity & Vendor Info: (Circulation) SirsiDynix; (OPAC) SirsiDynix; (Serials) SirsiDynix
Database Vendor: OCLC FirstSearch
Wireless access
Publications: Exploring New Worlds
Mem of West Texas Library System
Open Mon-Wed 9-9, Thurs-Sat 9-6, Sun 1-5
Friends of the Library Group
Branches: 3
BOBBIE GEAN & T J PATTERSON BRANCH, 1836 Parkway Dr, 79403. Tel: 806-767-3300. FAX: 806-767-3302. *Br Mgr,* Helen Viser
    Library Holdings: Bk Titles 51,018
    Open Mon & Tues 12-9, Wed-Sat 9-6
    Friends of the Library Group
GODEKE, 6707 Slide Rd, 79424, SAN 362-1308. Tel: 806-792-6566. FAX: 806-767-3762. *Br Mgr,* Lorraine Lord; Tel: 806-775-3748, E-mail: llord@mylubbock.us
    Library Holdings: Bk Vols 103,768
    Open Mon & Tues 12-9, Wed-Sat 9-6
    Friends of the Library Group
GROVES, 5520 19th St, 79416, SAN 377-662X. Tel: 806-767-3734. FAX: 806-795-9641. *Br Mgr,* Nancy Cammack; E-mail: ncammack@mylubbock.us
    Library Holdings: Bk Titles 61,182
    Open Mon & Tues 12-9, Wed-Sat 9-6

CL   TEXAS TECH UNIVERSITY*, School of Law Library, School of Law Bldg, 1802 Hartford Ave, 79409. SAN 362-1456. Tel: 806-742-3957. FAX: 806-742-1629. Web Site: www.law.ttu.edu/lawlibrary/library. *Dir,* Arturo L Torres
Founded 1967. Highest Degree: Doctorate
Library Holdings: Bk Vols 225,220; Per Subs 2,114
Subject Interests: Commercial law
Automation Activity & Vendor Info: (Acquisitions) Innovative Interfaces, Inc; (Cataloging) Innovative Interfaces, Inc; (Circulation) Innovative Interfaces, Inc; (Course Reserve) Innovative Interfaces, Inc; (OPAC) Innovative Interfaces, Inc; (Serials) Innovative Interfaces, Inc
Database Vendor: LexisNexis, Westlaw
Wireless access
Partic in OCLC Online Computer Library Center, Inc; Westlaw
Open Mon-Thurs 7:30-Midnight, Fri 7:30am-9pm, Sat 9-9, Sun 10am-Midnight

CM   TEXAS TECH UNIVERSITY HEALTH SCIENCES CENTER*, Preston Smith Library of the Health Sciences, 3601 Fourth St, 79430-7781. SAN 321-2432. Tel: 806-743-2200. Administration Tel: 806-743-2203. FAX: 806-743-2218. Web Site: www.ttuhsc.edu/libraries. *Exec Dir,* Richard C Wood; E-mail: richard.wood@ttuhsc.edu; *Circ,* Sharon Beckham; *Pub Serv,* Candia Thew; *Ser,* Joseph Blackburn; Staff 59 (MLS 19, Non-MLS 40)
Founded 1971. Enrl 1,547; Fac 516; Highest Degree: Doctorate
Library Holdings: Bk Vols 289,736; Per Subs 2,144
Special Collections: Oral History
Subject Interests: Allied health, Med, Nursing
Automation Activity & Vendor Info: (Acquisitions) CyberTools for Libraries; (Cataloging) CyberTools for Libraries; (Circulation) CyberTools for Libraries; (Course Reserve) CyberTools for Libraries; (OPAC) CyberTools for Libraries; (Serials) CyberTools for Libraries

Database Vendor: EBSCOhost, Gale Cengage Learning, OVID Technologies
Publications: Newsletter
Partic in SCAMeL
Open Mon-Thurs 7:30am-Midnight, Fri 7:30am-10pm, Sat 9am-10pm, Sun 1pm-Midnight
Friends of the Library Group
Departmental Libraries:
DELIA MONTES-GALLO LIBRARY OF THE HEALTH SCIENCES, 4800 Alberta Ave, El Paso, 79905, SAN 316-3113. Tel: 915-545-6650. FAX: 915-545-6656. *Assoc Dir,* Rebecca Ruddock
Founded 1976
Subject Interests: Med
Friends of the Library Group
ODESSA CAMPUS, 800 W Fourth St, Odessa, 79763, SAN 322-5739. Tel: 432-335-5172. FAX: 432-335-5170.
Library Holdings: Bk Titles 11,500; Per Subs 200
Open Mon-Fri 7:30am-10pm, Sat 10-5, Sun 1-10
Friends of the Library Group

C   TEXAS TECH UNIVERSITY LIBRARIES*, 18th & Boston Ave, 79409-0002. SAN 362-1391. Tel: 806-742-2261. Circulation Tel: 806-742-2265. Reference Tel: 806-742-2236. Toll Free Tel: 888-270-3369. FAX: 806-742-0737. Web Site: www.library.ttu.edu. *Dean,* Dr Donald Dyal; E-mail: donald.dyal@ttu.edu; *Assoc Dean of Libr,* Jennifer Spurrier; *Assoc Dean of Libr,* Robert Sweet; *Cat,* Jayne Sappington; *Rare Bks,* Bruce Cammack; Staff 57 (MLS 51, Non-MLS 6)
Founded 1923. Enrl 24,000; Fac 871; Highest Degree: Doctorate
Library Holdings: Bk Vols 1,700,000
Special Collections: Archive of Turkish Oral Narrative; CNN World News Report Archive; Institute for Studies in Pragmatism; Southwest Coll; Vietnam Archive. State Document Depository; US Document Depository
Automation Activity & Vendor Info: (Acquisitions) Ex Libris Group; (Cataloging) Ex Libris Group; (Circulation) Ex Libris Group; (Course Reserve) Ex Libris Group; (OPAC) Ex Libris Group; (Serials) Ex Libris Group
Database Vendor: EBSCOhost, ISI Web of Knowledge, LexisNexis, OCLC FirstSearch, Wilson - Wilson Web
Function: Res libr
Publications: ACCESS (Newsletter); Guides to Library Collections; Library News; Southwest Chronicle (Newsletter); Texas Tech University Library

P   WEST TEXAS LIBRARY SYSTEM*, 1306 Ninth St, 79401-2798. SAN 316-5833. Tel: 806-775-2858. Toll Free Tel: 800-848-3146. FAX: 806-775-2856. Web Site: wtls.tsl.state.tx.us/wtls. *Coordr, Librn III,* Nancy Hill; Tel: 806-775-2854, E-mail: nhill@mail.ci.lubbock.tx.us; *Asst Coordr, Librn II,* Barbara Blake; *ILL Librn,* Sally Quiroz
Founded 1969. Pop 704,540
Publications: In The Wind (newsletter)
Member Libraries: Abernathy Public Library; Andrews County Library; City of Wolfforth Library; Cochran County Love Memorial Library; Crane County Library; Crosby County Library; Dawson County Library; Dickens County-Spur Public Library; Ector County Library; Floyd County Library; Gaines County Library; Guthrie CSD & King County Consolidated Library; Hale Center Public Library; Hockley County Memorial Library; Howard County Library; Kendrick Memorial Library; Lamb County Library; Lubbock Public Library; Martin County Library; Midland County Public Library; Muleshoe Area Public Library; Olton Area Public Library; Post Public Library; Rankin Public Library; Slaton City Library; Springlake-Earth Community Library; Unger Memorial Library; Ward County Library; Winkler County Library; Yoakum County Library
Partic in OCLC Online Computer Library Center, Inc
Open Mon-Fri 8-5

LUFKIN

C   ANGELINA COLLEGE LIBRARY*, 3500 S First St, 75904. (Mail add: PO Box 1768, 75902-1768), SAN 316-5841. Tel: 936-633-5219. FAX: 936-633-5442. Web Site: www.angelina.edu. *Dir,* Anet Avery-Sublett; E-mail: jsublett@angelina.edu; *Tech Serv,* Candace Powell; E-mail: cpowell@angelina.edu; Staff 4 (MLS 3, Non-MLS 1)
Founded 1968
Library Holdings: e-books 33,300; Bk Titles 38,641; Per Subs 45
Automation Activity & Vendor Info: (Acquisitions) SirsiDynix; (Cataloging) SirsiDynix; (Circulation) SirsiDynix; (Course Reserve) SirsiDynix; (OPAC) SirsiDynix; (Serials) SirsiDynix
Database Vendor: EBSCOhost, Gale Cengage Learning
Wireless access
Partic in Amigos Library Services, Inc; TexSHARE - Texas State Library & Archives Commission
Open Mon-Thurs 7:30am-9pm, Fri 7:30-4, Sun 1:30-5:30

R   FIRST UNITED METHODIST CHURCH LIBRARY*, 805 E Denman Ave, 75901. SAN 328-6142. Tel: 936-639-3141. FAX: 936-639-3667. E-mail: iheermans@lufkinfirst.com. Web Site: www.lufkinfumc.org.
Library Holdings: Bk Vols 7,000
Subject Interests: Relig
Wireless access
Open Mon-Thurs 8-4:30

P   KURTH MEMORIAL LIBRARY*, 706 S Raguet, 75904. SAN 316-585X. Tel: 936-630-0560. FAX: 936-639-2487. Web Site: cityoflufkin.com/library. *Dir,* Lorraine Simoneau; E-mail: lsimoneau@cityoflufkin.com; *Asst Dir,* Martha Coleman; *Genealogy Librn,* Cindy McMullen; *Ref,* Michelle Jacobson. Subject Specialists: *Genealogy,* Cindy McMullen; Staff 12 (MLS 2, Non-MLS 10)
Founded 1932. Pop 70,000; Circ 74,413
Library Holdings: Bk Vols 60,000; Per Subs 80
Subject Interests: Genealogy, Local hist, Spanish lit
Automation Activity & Vendor Info: (Cataloging) SirsiDynix; (Circulation) SirsiDynix; (OPAC) SirsiDynix
Wireless access
Open Mon 10-7, Tues-Thurs 9-6, Fri 9-5:30, Sat 9-1
Friends of the Library Group

LULING

R   FIRST BAPTIST CHURCH*, E F Walker Memorial Library, 218 N Magnolia, 78648-2342. (Mail add: PO Box 90, 78648-0090), SAN 316-5884. Tel: 830-875-2227. *Librn,* Lucille Matthews
Founded 1957
Library Holdings: AV Mats 95; Bk Titles 2,776; Bk Vols 5,000

P   J B NICKELLS MEMORIAL LIBRARY*, 215 S Pecan St, 78648. SAN 316-5892. Tel: 830-875-2813. E-mail: lullib78648@yahoo.com. *Librn,* Nancy Gilchrist; Staff 2 (MLS 1, Non-MLS 1)
Founded 1969. Pop 5,060; Circ 38,380
Apr 2010-Mar 2011 Income $110,000. Mats Exp $8,600, Books $7,000, AV Equip $1,600. Sal $93,750 (Prof $31,980)
Library Holdings: AV Mats 578; Bks on Deafness & Sign Lang 10; DVDs 1,200; Large Print Bks 700; Bk Titles 20,000; Per Subs 19; Talking Bks 250; Videos 400
Subject Interests: Tex
Automation Activity & Vendor Info: (Cataloging) Biblionix; (Circulation) Biblionix; (OPAC) Biblionix
Wireless access
Mem of Central Texas Library System, Inc
Open Mon, Wed & Fri 10-5, Tues & Thurs 12-8, Sat 10-1
Friends of the Library Group

LUMBERTON

P   LUMBERTON PUBLIC LIBRARY*, 130 E Chance Rd, 77657. SAN 376-4885. Tel: 409-755-7400. Web Site: www.lumbertonpubliclibrary.org. *Dir,* Lon Nickles; Staff 4 (Non-MLS 4)
Founded 1994. Pop 16,900; Circ 56,764
Special Collections: Texana
Automation Activity & Vendor Info: (Acquisitions) ComPanion Corp; (Cataloging) ComPanion Corp; (Circulation) ComPanion Corp; (OPAC) ComPanion Corp
Database Vendor: ComPanion Corp
Wireless access
Function: Audio & video playback equip for onsite use, Bks on cassette, Bks on CD, CD-ROM, Children's prog, Computer training, Computers for patron use, Copy machines, Electronic databases & coll, Equip loans & repairs, Free DVD rentals, Games & aids for the handicapped, Home delivery & serv to Sr ctr & nursing homes, ILL available, Magnifiers for reading, Music CDs, Newsp ref libr, Online cat, Online searches, Photocopying/Printing, Pub access computers, Ref & res, Ref serv available, Scanner, Senior computer classes, Spoken cassettes & CDs, Spoken cassettes & DVDs, Story hour, Summer reading prog, Tax forms, VHS videos, Web-catalog, Workshops
Open Mon-Fri 10-6, Sat 10-1
Friends of the Library Group

LYTLE

P   LYTLE PUBLIC LIBRARY*, 19325 Farm Rd, No 2790, 78052. (Mail add: PO Box 831, 78052-0831), SAN 376-415X. Tel: 830-709-4142. FAX: 830-772-3675. E-mail: lytle_library@sbcglobal.net. *Dir,* Cassandra Cortez; Staff 1 (Non-MLS 1)
Founded 1972. Pop 4,500; Circ 19,000
Library Holdings: Bk Vols 21,000
Automation Activity & Vendor Info: (Cataloging) Biblionix; (Circulation) Biblionix
Open Mon, Wed & Fri 9:30-5:30, Tues & Thurs 11-7

MABANK

P   TRI-COUNTY LIBRARY*, 132 E Market St, 75147-2307. (Mail add: PO Box 1770, 75147-1770), SAN 376-4389. Tel: 903-887-9622. FAX: 903-887-3396. E-mail: tricountylibrary2002@yahoo.com. Web Site: www.tricountylibrary.org. *Dir,* Claire Stout; E-mail: clairehere2000@yahoo.com
Founded 1991. Pop 3,718
Library Holdings: CDs 31; DVDs 48; Large Print Bks 350; Bk Titles 22,000; Bk Vols 25,000; Per Subs 26; Talking Bks 517
Special Collections: Genealogy Coll
Automation Activity & Vendor Info: (Cataloging) Follett Software; (Circulation) Follett Software
Wireless access
Open Mon & Wed-Fri 9-5:30, Tues 9-7, Sat 9-3
Friends of the Library Group

MADISONVILLE

P   MADISON COUNTY LIBRARY*, 605 S May, 77864. SAN 316-599X. Tel: 936-348-6118. FAX: 936-348-6118. E-mail: mclib@madisoncountytx.org. Web Site: www.madisoncountylib.org. *Librn,* Veronica Grooms
Pop 10,000; Circ 25,375
Library Holdings: Bk Vols 25,000; Per Subs 45
Subject Interests: Genealogy
Automation Activity & Vendor Info: (Cataloging) Biblionix; (Circulation) Biblionix
Wireless access
Mem of Central Texas Library System, Inc
Open Mon, Wed & Fri 9-5, Tues 11-7
Friends of the Library Group

MALAKOFF

P   RED WALLER COMMUNITY LIBRARY, 109 Mitcham St, 75148. (Mail add: PO Box 1177, 75148-1177), SAN 316-6007. Tel: 903-489-1818. Administration Tel: 903-489-0699. FAX: 903-489-2517. *Dir,* Charlotte Regester; Staff 1.5 (Non-MLS 1, Non-MLS 0.5)
Founded 1972. Pop 7,535
Library Holdings: AV Mats 1,061; Large Print Bks 1,000; Bk Titles 32,062; Bk Vols 32,162; Per Subs 46; Talking Bks 456
Special Collections: Bicentennial Package (American Issues Forum Coll); Malakoff History Coll. Oral History
Automation Activity & Vendor Info: (Cataloging) LibraryWorld, Inc; (Circulation) LibraryWorld, Inc
Function: AV serv, Games & aids for the handicapped, Handicapped accessible, ILL available, Libr develop, Magnifiers for reading, Photocopying/Printing, Prof lending libr, Prog for children & young adult, Ref serv available, Summer reading prog, Telephone ref, Wheelchair accessible, Workshops
Open Mon 1-5, Tues-Fri 9:30-5
Friends of the Library Group

MANSFIELD

P   MANSFIELD PUBLIC LIBRARY*, 104 S Wisteria St, 76063. SAN 316-6015. Tel: 817-473-4391. FAX: 817-453-4975. E-mail: mpl@mansfield-tx.gov. Web Site: www.mansfield-tx.gov/departments/library. *City Librn,* Steve Standefer; E-mail: steve.standefer@mansfield-tx.gov; *Ad,* Pat Young; E-mail: pat.young@mansfield-tx.gov; *Tech Serv Librn,* John Miller; E-mail: john.miller@mansfield-tx.gov; *Youth Serv Librn,* Annette Weber; E-mail: annette.weber@mansfield-tx.gov; Staff 3 (MLS 3)
Pop 55,950
Automation Activity & Vendor Info: (Cataloging) Follett Software; (Circulation) Follett Software
Database Vendor: Brodart, Newsbank, ReferenceUSA, WT Cox
Function: Accelerated reader prog, Adult bk club, Art exhibits, Audiobks via web, Bk club(s), Bks on cassette, Bks on CD, Children's prog, Computers for patron use, Copy machines, e-mail serv, E-Reserves, Electronic databases & coll, Exhibits, Free DVD rentals, Handicapped accessible, ILL available, Music CDs, Outside serv via phone, mail, e-mail & web, Photocopying/Printing, Prog for adults, Prog for children & young adult, Pub access computers, Ref serv available, Res libr, Spoken cassettes & CDs, Spoken cassettes & DVDs, Story hour, Summer reading prog, Tax forms, Teen prog, VHS videos, Wheelchair accessible, Workshops
Special Services for the Blind - Audio mat; Bks available with recordings; Bks on cassette; Bks on CD; Large print bks; Talking bk & rec for the blind cat; Talking bk serv referral; Talking bks & player equip
Open Mon 10-8, Tue, Wed & Fri 10-6, Thurs 10-8, Sat 10-4
Friends of the Library Group

MARFA

P   MARFA PUBLIC LIBRARY*, 115 E Oak St, 79843. (Mail add: PO Drawer U, 79843-0609), SAN 316-6023. Tel: 432-729-4631. FAX: 432-729-3424. *Dir,* Rene Meck; *Asst Libr Dir,* Maggie Marquez; *Librn,* Joyce Poenisch; Staff 3 (Non-MLS 3)
Founded 1947. Pop 2,800; Circ 31,306
Library Holdings: Bk Titles 32,148; Per Subs 22
Special Collections: Genealogy & Texana Coll; Junior Historian Files; Local & Border Regional History
Automation Activity & Vendor Info: (Cataloging) Follett Software; (Circulation) Follett Software; (OPAC) Follett Software
Wireless access
Mem of Texas Trans-Pecos Regional Library System
Open Mon-Fri 9-5, Sat 10-1
Friends of the Library Group

MARION

P   MARION ISD COMMUNITY LIBRARY*, 500 Bulldog Blvd, 78124. (Mail add: PO Box 619, 78124-0619), SAN 376-4133. Tel: 830-914-2803, Ext 430, 830-914-4268. *Libr Dir,* Christy Loomis; *Commun Coordr,* Amy Herndon; E-mail: aherndon@marion.txed.net; Staff 2 (MLS 1, Non-MLS 1)
Library Holdings: Audiobooks 321; DVDs 1,003; e-books 64; Bk Vols 18,385; Per Subs 40; Videos 430
Automation Activity & Vendor Info: (Cataloging) Follett Software; (Circulation) Follett Software; (OPAC) Follett Software
Wireless access
Function: Accelerated reader prog, Adult bk club, Adult literacy prog, Bk club(s), Bks on CD, Children's prog, Computers for patron use, Copy machines, Digital talking bks, Distance learning, e-mail serv, Electronic databases & coll, Free DVD rentals, Handicapped accessible, Health sci info serv, Holiday prog, Homework prog, Online cat, Online ref, Online searches, Orientations, Photocopying/Printing, Preschool outreach, Prog for adults, Prog for children & young adult, Pub access computers, Ref & res, Senior outreach, Story hour, Summer reading prog, Teen prog, VHS videos, Video lending libr, Wheelchair accessible, Winter reading prog
Open Mon & Fri 8-4, Tues-Thurs 8-8, Sat 12-4
Restriction: Lending limited to county residents
Friends of the Library Group

MARLIN

P   PAULINE & JANE CHILTON MEMORIAL PUBLIC LIBRARY*, Marlin Public Library, 400 Oakes St, 76661. SAN 316-6031. Tel: 254-883-6602. Web Site: www.marlinpubliclibrary.com. *Dir,* Phyllis Macmillan; E-mail: phyllis@marlinpubliclibrary.com; Staff 2 (MLS 1, Non-MLS 1)
Founded 1925. Pop 5,597; Circ 16,000
Library Holdings: Bk Vols 14,000
Wireless access
Mem of Central Texas Library System, Inc
Open Tues & Thurs 10-7, Wed & Fri 10-5:30, Sat 10-2

MARSHALL

CR   EAST TEXAS BAPTIST UNIVERSITY*, Mamye Jarrett Library, 1209 N Grove St, 75670-1498. SAN 316-6066. Tel: 903-923-2256. Circulation Tel: 903-923-2264. Interlibrary Loan Service Tel: 903-923-2259. Reference Tel: 903-923-2262. Administration Tel: 903-923-2257. Information Services Tel: 903-923-2263. FAX: 903-935-3447. Web Site: www.etbu.edu/library. *Dir, Libr Serv,* Cynthia L Peterson; E-mail: cpeterson@etbu.edu; *Head, Access Serv,* Annie Henderson; E-mail: ahenderson@etbu.edu; *Mgr, ILL, Mgr, Tech Serv,* Steve Horton; E-mail: shorton@etbu.edu; Staff 6.5 (MLS 3, Non-MLS 3.5)
Founded 1917. Enrl 1,116; Fac 75; Highest Degree: Bachelor
Jun 2009-May 2010 Income $554,143. Mats Exp $230,515, Books $31,323, Per/Ser (Incl. Access Fees) $10,362, Micro $7,000, AV Mat $2,000, Electronic Ref Mat (Incl. Access Fees) $179,830. Sal $207,455
Library Holdings: AV Mats 45,159; CDs 2,091; DVDs 163; e-books 99,542; e-journals 23,000; Electronic Media & Resources 41,458; Music Scores 6,518; Bk Vols 122,904; Per Subs 100; Videos 1,138
Special Collections: Alumni Coll; Baptist Coll; College of Marshall/East Texas Baptist College/East Texas Baptist University History Coll, doc, newsp, photog, yearbks; Cope Coll of Texana; Dr & Mrs T C Gardner (Gardner Baptist Training Union Coll), memorabilia, papers; East Texas Ante-Bellum History Coll; H L Mencken (Joseph C Goulden Coll); Lentz Coll of Texana; Rare Books
Subject Interests: Baptists, Local hist, Texana, Univ hist
Automation Activity & Vendor Info: (Acquisitions) SirsiDynix; (Cataloging) SirsiDynix; (Circulation) SirsiDynix; (Course Reserve) SirsiDynix; (ILL) OCLC; (OPAC) SirsiDynix; (Serials) SirsiDynix
Database Vendor: Alexander Street Press, American Chemical Society, Amigos Library Services, ARTstor, Baker & Taylor, BioOne, Bowker, CountryWatch, CQ Press, CredoReference, ebrary, EBSCOhost, Faulkner Information Services, Gale Cengage Learning, Grolier Online, Ingram Library Services, JSTOR, LexisNexis, Nature Publishing Group, netLibrary,

Newsbank, Newsbank-Readex, OCLC ArticleFirst, OCLC CAMIO, OCLC FirstSearch, OCLC WorldCat, Oxford Online, ProQuest, ScienceDirect, SirsiDynix, Springshare, LLC, STAT!Ref (Teton Data Systems), Wiley InterScience, WT Cox, YBP Library Services
Wireless access
Function: Archival coll, Audio & video playback equip for onsite use, Electronic databases & coll, Handicapped accessible, ILL available, Instruction & testing, Online cat, Online info literacy tutorials on the web & in blackboard, Online ref, Outside serv via phone, mail, e-mail & web, Photocopying/Printing, Prog for adults, Ref & res, Ref serv available, Ref serv in person, Telephone ref, VHS videos, Web-catalog, Wheelchair accessible, Workshops
Publications: BiblioTech (Newsletter); Library Handbook for Faculty (Annually)
Partic in Amigos Library Services, Inc; Statewide California Electronic Library Consortium (SCELC); Tex Independent Cols & Univ Librs; Texas Council of Academic Libraries; TexSHARE - Texas State Library & Archives Commission
Open Mon-Thurs 7:30am-Midnight, Fri 7:30-4:30, Sat 10-3, Sun 4-Midnight
Restriction: Authorized patrons, Borrowing privileges limited to fac & registered students, Circ limited, Limited access for the pub, Open to pub for ref & circ; with some limitations, Open to pub with supv only, Open to qualified scholars, Open to students, fac, staff & alumni, Photo ID required for access, Res pass required for non-affiliated visitors
Friends of the Library Group

S   HARRISON COUNTY HISTORICAL MUSEUM*, Inez Hatley Hughes Research Library, 117 E Bowie St, 75670. (Mail add: PO Box 1987, 75671), SAN 327-7992. Tel: 903-938-2680. FAX: 903-927-2534. E-mail: easttexaskin@yahoo.com. Web Site: www.harrisoncountymuseum.org/research_library.
Founded 1965
Library Holdings: Bk Titles 2,500; Bk Vols 3,000
Special Collections: Census Records; High School Yearbooks; Marshall Telephone Books & City Directories; Pictures; Scrapbooks
Subject Interests: Civil War, Genealogy, Hist, Law, Local hist, Med
Wireless access
Function: Archival coll
Publications: Ancestor Issues (Newsletter)
Open Wed-Fri 10-4

P   MARSHALL PUBLIC LIBRARY, 300 S Alamo Blvd, 75670. SAN 316-6082. Tel: 903-935-4465. FAX: 903-935-4463. Web Site: www.marshallpubliclibrary.org. Dir, Anna Lane; Staff 7 (MLS 2, Non-MLS 5)
Founded 1969. Pop 58,399; Circ 63,022
Library Holdings: Bk Titles 52,432; Bk Vols 56,323; Per Subs 80
Special Collections: Local Newspaper, 1849-present, micro; Texana
Automation Activity & Vendor Info: (Acquisitions) TLC (The Library Corporation); (Cataloging) TLC (The Library Corporation); (Circulation) TLC (The Library Corporation); (OPAC) TLC (The Library Corporation)
Database Vendor: TLC (The Library Corporation)
Wireless access
Function: Bks on cassette, Bks on CD, Children's prog, Computer training, Computers for patron use, Copy machines, Free DVD rentals, ILL available, Music CDs, Online cat, Preschool reading prog, Pub access computers, Story hour, Summer reading prog, Tax forms, Wheelchair accessible
Open Mon, Tues & Thurs 10-7:30, Wed & Fri 10-5:30, Sat 10-3:30
Friends of the Library Group

C   WILEY COLLEGE*, Thomas Winston Cole Sr Library, 711 Wiley Ave, 75670-5151. SAN 316-6090. Tel: 903-927-3275. FAX: 903-934-9333. Web Site: www.wileyc.edu. Dir, Alma Ravenell; Assoc Dir, Position Currently Open; Staff 3 (MLS 2, Non-MLS 1)
Founded 1873. Enrl 1,400; Highest Degree: Bachelor
Library Holdings: Bk Vols 90,000; Per Subs 306
Special Collections: Black Studies (Schomburg Coll of Negro Literature & History), portion of the print coll on microfilm; Wiley College Memorabilia. State Document Depository; US Document Depository
Partic in Coop Col Libr Ctr, Inc
Open Mon-Thurs 8am-11pm, Fri 8-5, Sat 10-2, Sun 6pm-10pm

MART

P   NANCY NAIL MEMORIAL LIBRARY*, 124 S Pearl St, 76664-1425. Tel: 254-876-2465. FAX: 254-876-2465. E-mail: nancynaillibrary@att.net. Web Site: www.martlibrary.org. Dir, Pat Curry; Staff 1 (Non-MLS 1)
Pop 3,731; Circ 7,725
Library Holdings: Audiobooks 158; CDs 36; DVDs 145; Large Print Bks 749; Bk Titles 16,337; Videos 409
Wireless access
Mem of Central Texas Library System, Inc
Open Mon-Fri 1-5

MASON

P   MASON COUNTY LIBRARY*, M Beven Eckert Memorial Library, 410 Post Hill, 76856. (Mail add: PO Box 1785, 76856-1785), SAN 316-6104. Tel: 325-347-5446. FAX: 325-347-6562. E-mail: masonlibrary@verizon.net. Dir, Patty Grote; Staff 1 (Non-MLS 1)
Pop 3,356; Circ 9,884
Library Holdings: Bk Vols 10,000; Per Subs 14
Automation Activity & Vendor Info: (Cataloging) LibLime; (Circulation) LibLime
Wireless access
Open Mon-Fri 10-6
Friends of the Library Group

MATADOR

P   MOTLEY COUNTY LIBRARY*, 1105 Main St, 79244. (Mail add: PO Box 557, 79244-0557), SAN 325-2922. Tel: 806-347-2717. Librn, Mary Ann Potts
Founded 1981. Pop 1,200; Circ 4,711
Library Holdings: Bk Titles 9,613; Bk Vols 10,583
Subject Interests: Genealogy, Tex hist
Wireless access
Special Services for the Deaf - Bks on deafness & sign lang; High interest/low vocabulary bks
Open Mon 2-5, Tues-Thurs 1-6, Fri 9-2
Friends of the Library Group

MATHIS

P   MATHIS PUBLIC LIBRARY*, 103 Lamar St, 78368. SAN 316-6112. Tel: 361-547-6201. FAX: 361-547-6201. E-mail: mathispubliclibrary@yahoo.com. Librn, Norma Ovalle
Pop 7,416; Circ 8,679
Library Holdings: AV Mats 973; Bk Titles 18,000; Bk Vols 19,000; Per Subs 30; Videos 779
Automation Activity & Vendor Info: (Cataloging) Biblionix; (Circulation) Biblionix
Wireless access
Open Mon 2-6, Tues 9-6, Wed & Thurs 11-6, Fri 1-6
Friends of the Library Group

MAUD

P   MAUD PUBLIC LIBRARY*, 134 Main St, 75567-0388. (Mail add: PO Box 100, 75567-0100), SAN 376-4524. Tel: 903-585-5255. FAX: 903-585-5255. Librn, Pam Smith
Pop 1,016; Circ 2,867
Library Holdings: Bk Titles 15,000; Talking Bks 60; Videos 300
Automation Activity & Vendor Info: (Acquisitions) LibraryWorld, Inc; (Cataloging) LibraryWorld, Inc
Wireless access
Open Mon-Thurs 9-2, Fri 9-1
Friends of the Library Group

MCALLEN

R   FIRST BAPTIST CHURCH LIBRARY*, 1200 Beech Ave, 78501. SAN 316-5914. Tel: 956-686-7418. FAX: 956-630-4940. E-mail: office@fbcmcallen.com. Web Site: www.fbcmcallen.com. Interim Mgr, Chlista Cox
Library Holdings: Bk Vols 6,700
Subject Interests: Biog, Children's mat, Fiction, Relig

P   MCALLEN MEMORIAL LIBRARY*, 601 N Main, 78501-4666. SAN 316-5930. Tel: 956-688-3300. FAX: 956-688-3301. E-mail: genref@mcallen.net, ReferenceLibrarian@mcallen.net. Web Site: www.mcallenlibrary.net. Libr Dir, Jose A Gamez; Tel: 956-688-3300, Ext 112, E-mail: jgamez@mcallen.net; Asst Dir, Pub Serv, Kate Horan; E-mail: khoran@mcallen.net; Head, Circ, John J Donohue; E-mail: jdonohue@mcallen.net; Ch, Michelle Shelton; Acq, Supvr, Judy M Perry; E-mail: jperry@mcallen.net; Cat Supvr, David Pardue; E-mail: dpardue@mcallen.net; Acq, Rachel Reyes; E-mail: rreyes@mcallen.net; ILL, Nancy Davis; E-mail: ndavis@mcallen.net; Staff 17.5 (MLS 16, Non-MLS 1.5)
Founded 1932. Pop 168,000; Circ 536,627
Library Holdings: CDs 11,474; DVDs 10,559; e-books 76; Electronic Media & Resources 69; Bk Titles 322,868; Bk Vols 359,321; Per Subs 1,366
Special Collections: Libros en Espanol; Mexican-American Coll; Mexico Coll; Texas Coll
Subject Interests: Genealogy, Mexico, Tex
Automation Activity & Vendor Info: (Acquisitions) SirsiDynix; (Cataloging) SirsiDynix; (Circulation) SirsiDynix; (ILL) OCLC; (OPAC) SirsiDynix; (Serials) SirsiDynix

Database Vendor: Amigos Library Services, Baker & Taylor, EBSCOhost, ProQuest, SirsiDynix
Wireless access
Publications: Beginnings - A First Course in Spanish (Library handbook)
Mem of Hidalgo County Library System
Partic in OCLC Online Computer Library Center, Inc
Special Services for the Deaf - TDD equip
Special Services for the Blind - Bks on cassette; Braille bks; Reader equip
Open Mon-Thurs 9-9, Fri & Sat 9-6, Sun 1-6
Friends of the Library Group
Branches: 2
LARK, 2601 Lark Ave, 78504. (Mail add: PO Box 220, 78505-0220). Tel: 956-688-3320. FAX: 956-688-3346. *Br Mgr,* Jennifer Lee; E-mail: jlee@mcallen.net; Staff 10 (MLS 1, Non-MLS 9)
Library Holdings: Bk Vols 7,500
Open Mon-Thurs 10-9, Fri & Sat 10-5, Sun 1-9
Friends of the Library Group
PALM VIEW, 3401 Jordan Ave, 78503. (Mail add: PO Box 220, 78505-0220). Tel: 956-688-3322. FAX: 956-688-3366. *Br Mgr,* Sylvia Marichalar; E-mail: smarichalar@mcallen.net; Staff 3 (MLS 2, Non-MLS 1)
Founded 2001
Library Holdings: Bk Vols 11,000
Open Mon-Thurs 10-9, Fri & Sat 10-5, Sun 1-9

C   SOUTH TEXAS COLLEGE LIBRARY*, Pecan Campus, 3201 W Pecan Blvd, 78501-6661. SAN 325-0687. Tel: 956-872-8330. Administration Tel: 956-872-2645. FAX: 956-872-7202. Web Site: library.southtexascollege.edu. *Interim Assoc Dean,* Cody Gregg; E-mail: cgregg@southtexascollege.edu; *Dir, Pub Serv,* Noemi Garza; *Dir of Tech Serv,* Jesus Campos; *Librn,* Minerva Alvarez; Tel: 956-872-3442, E-mail: malvarez1@southtexascollege.edu; *Librn,* Shawn Anderson; *Librn,* Angelica Maria Garcia; E-mail: amgarcia@southtexascollege.edu; *Librn,* Jose Noriega; *Librn,* Joshua Wallace; Tel: 956-872-2623, E-mail: jjwallac@southtexascollege.edu; Staff 62 (MLS 5, Non-MLS 57)
Founded 1984. Highest Degree: Associate
Library Holdings: Bk Titles 50,000; Per Subs 300
Automation Activity & Vendor Info: (Acquisitions) SirsiDynix; (Cataloging) SirsiDynix; (Circulation) SirsiDynix; (Course Reserve) SirsiDynix; (ILL) SirsiDynix; (Media Booking) SirsiDynix; (OPAC) SirsiDynix; (Serials) SirsiDynix
Partic in Paisano Consortium
Open Mon-Thurs 7am-10pm, Fri 7-5, Sat 9-6, Sun 1-6

MCCAMEY

P   UPTON COUNTY PUBLIC LIBRARY*, 212 W Seventh St, 79752. (Mail add: PO Box 1377, 79752-1377), SAN 316-5949. Tel: 432-652-8718. FAX: 432-652-3858. *Dir,* Mary Glenn; Staff 1 (Non-MLS 1)
Founded 1939. Pop 2,650; Circ 22,770
Library Holdings: Bk Vols 16,500; Per Subs 34
Special Collections: Texana Coll
Automation Activity & Vendor Info: (Cataloging) Follett Software; (Circulation) Follett Software
Open Mon-Thurs 9-5

MCGREGOR

P   MCGINLEY MEMORIAL PUBLIC LIBRARY*, 317 S Main St, 76657. SAN 372-7599. Tel: 254-840-3732. FAX: 254-840-2624. *Librn,* Trella Hughes; E-mail: thughes@members.ctls.net; Staff 1 (Non-MLS 1)
Founded 1983. Pop 5,000; Circ 8,000
Library Holdings: Bk Titles 13,500; Bk Vols 14,500; Per Subs 10
Automation Activity & Vendor Info: (Cataloging) Follett Software; (Circulation) Follett Software
Wireless access
Mem of Central Texas Library System, Inc
Open Tues 2-7, Wed & Fri 8:30-1:30, Thurs 12-5
Friends of the Library Group

MCKINNEY

J   COLLIN COLLEGE*, Central Park Campus Library, 2200 W University, 75071. Tel: 972-548-6860, 972-548-6868. Reference Tel: 972-548-6869. FAX: 972-548-6844. E-mail: cplibrary@collin.edu. Web Site: www.collin.edu/library. *Exec Dir,* Bobbie Long; Staff 5 (MLS 5)
Founded 1986
Library Holdings: Bk Vols 48,000
Automation Activity & Vendor Info: (Acquisitions) Polaris Library Systems; (Cataloging) Polaris Library Systems; (Circulation) Polaris Library Systems; (Course Reserve) Polaris Library Systems; (ILL) Polaris Library Systems; (OPAC) Polaris Library Systems
Database Vendor: LexisNexis, Wilson - Wilson Web
Open Mon-Thurs 7:45am-9:45pm, Fri 7:45-5, Sat 10-5, Sun 1-4

L   COLLIN COUNTY LAW LIBRARY*, Courthouse, Ste 10216, 2100 Bloomdale Rd, 75071. SAN 372-1671. Tel: 972-548-4260. FAX: 972-547-5734. E-mail: lawlib@co.collin.tx.us. Web Site: www.co.collin.tx.us. *Law Librn,* Lori Bull Dodds; E-mail: ldodds@co.collin.tx.us; *Asst Law Librn,* Ellen Heavner; Tel: 972-548-4255, E-mail: eheavner@co.collin.tx.us; Staff 2 (MLS 2)
Library Holdings: Bk Vols 25,000; Per Subs 15
Database Vendor: LexisNexis, Westlaw
Wireless access
Open Mon-Fri 8-5

P   MCKINNEY MEMORIAL PUBLIC LIBRARY*, 101 E Hunt St, 75069. SAN 316-5973. Tel: 972-547-7323. FAX: 972-542-0868. Web Site: www.mckinneypubliclibrary.org. *Dir,* Beth A Scudder; E-mail: bscudder@mckinneytexas.org; *Youth Serv Librn,* Position Currently Open; *Pub Serv,* Amy Albrecht; Staff 38 (MLS 11, Non-MLS 27)
Founded 1928. Pop 115,000; Circ 630,000
Library Holdings: Bk Vols 130,000
Subject Interests: Genealogy, Texana
Database Vendor: Baker & Taylor, Brodart, SirsiDynix
Wireless access
Open Mon-Thurs 10-9, Fri & Sat 10-6, Sun 1-5
Friends of the Library Group
Branches: 1
JOHN & JUDY GAY LIBRARY, 6861 W Eldorado Pkwy, 75070-5637. *Br Mgr,* Lisa Bailey; Tel: 972-547-2020, E-mail: lbailey@mckinneytexas.org
Open Tues 12-8, Wed-Sat 10-6
Friends of the Library Group

MCLEAN

P   LOVETT MEMORIAL LIBRARY*, 302 N Main, 79057. (Mail add: PO Box 8, 79057-0008), SAN 316-5981. Tel: 806-779-2851. FAX: 806-779-3241. E-mail: mcleanpl@centramedia.net. *Librn,* Sally Bohlar; Staff 1 (Non-MLS 1)
Founded 1957. Pop 1,387; Circ 19,929
Library Holdings: Bk Titles 13,160
Automation Activity & Vendor Info: (Cataloging) SirsiDynix; (Circulation) SirsiDynix; (OPAC) SirsiDynix
Wireless access
Open Mon-Fri 10-5

MEDINA

P   MEDINA COMMUNITY LIBRARY, 13948 State Hwy 16 N, 78055. (Mail add: PO Box 300, 78055-0300), SAN 378-4002. Tel: 830-589-2825. FAX: 830-589-7514. E-mail: medinalib@gmail.com. Web Site: www.medinacommunitylibrary.us. *Actg Dir,* Mary Ellen Lindstrom
Founded 2001
Library Holdings: Bk Titles 11,000; Per Subs 50
Special Collections: Local Plant & Wildlife Coll
Subject Interests: Local hist, Tex
Automation Activity & Vendor Info: (Cataloging) Biblionix; (Circulation) Biblionix; (OPAC) Biblionix
Wireless access
Open Mon & Thurs 10-6, Tues, Wed & Fri 10-5, Sat 10-1

MELISSA

P   CITY OF MELISSA PUBLIC LIBRARY*, Melissa Public Library, 3411 Barker Ave, 75454. SAN 376-4532. Tel: 972-837-4540. FAX: 972-837-2006. E-mail: librarian@cityofmelissa.com. Web Site: www.cityofmelissa.com. *Libr Dir,* Lorelei Perkins; E-mail: lperkins@cityofmelissa.com; *Libr Asst,* Victoria Villegas; Staff 1 (Non-MLS 1)
Founded 1994. Pop 5,300
Library Holdings: Bks on Deafness & Sign Lang 10; CDs 40; DVDs 174; Large Print Bks 180; Bk Vols 12,000; Videos 562
Automation Activity & Vendor Info: (Acquisitions) LRMS, Inc (Library Resource Management Systems); (Cataloging) LRMS, Inc (Library Resource Management Systems); (Circulation) LRMS, Inc (Library Resource Management Systems); (OPAC) LRMS, Inc (Library Resource Management Systems)
Wireless access
Function: Bks on CD, Children's prog, Computers for patron use, Copy machines, Electronic databases & coll, Exhibits, Fax serv, Free DVD rentals, Genealogy discussion group, Handicapped accessible, Holiday prog, ILL available, Notary serv, Online cat, Photocopying/Printing, Prog for children & young adult, Story hour, Summer reading prog, Wheelchair accessible, Workshops, Writing prog
Open Mon 9-6, Tues, Wed & Fri 10-6, Thurs 12-8, Sat 10-3
Restriction: Authorized patrons
Friends of the Library Group

MEMPHIS

P   MEMPHIS PUBLIC LIBRARY*, 303 S Eight St, 79245. SAN 316-6120.
Tel: 806-259-2062. FAX: 806-259-2062. *Librn,* Jacqulyn Owens
Pop 5,594; Circ 18,500
Library Holdings: Bk Vols 20,300; Per Subs 30
Automation Activity & Vendor Info: (Cataloging) SirsiDynix;
(Circulation) SirsiDynix; (OPAC) SirsiDynix
Wireless access
Open Mon & Fri 1-6, Tues & Thurs 9-12 & 1-6, Sat 9-1

MENARD

P   MENARD PUBLIC LIBRARY*, 100 E Mission, 76859. (Mail add: PO
Box 404, 76859-0404), SAN 316-6139. Tel: 325-396-2717. FAX:
325-396-2717. E-mail: menardpl@verizon.net. *Dir,* Denise Murry
Pop 2,252; Circ 13,333
Library Holdings: Bk Vols 11,000; Per Subs 12
Automation Activity & Vendor Info: (Cataloging) Follett Software;
(Circulation) Follett Software
Open Mon-Thurs 10-1 & 2-5
Friends of the Library Group

MERCEDES

P   DR HECTOR P GARCIA MEMORIAL LIBRARY, 434 S Ohio St, 78570.
SAN 316-6147. Tel: 956-565-2371. FAX: 956-565-9458. *Dir,* Marisol
Vidales; *Asst Librn,* Socorro Gracia; Staff 2 (MLS 1, Non-MLS 1)
Founded 1940. Pop 24,178; Circ 26,451
Oct 2010-Sept 2011 Income $350,597. Mats Exp $17,305, Books $12,963,
Per/Ser (Incl. Access Fees) $895, AV Mat $3,161, Electronic Ref Mat
(Incl. Access Fees) $286. Sal $242,340 (Prof $79,024)
Library Holdings: Electronic Media & Resources 49; Large Print Bks
1,120; Bk Titles 35,172; Bk Vols 39,258; Per Subs 67
Subject Interests: Spanish lang, Tex
Automation Activity & Vendor Info: (Cataloging) TLC (The Library
Corporation); (Circulation) TLC (The Library Corporation); (OPAC) TLC
(The Library Corporation)
Wireless access
Mem of Hidalgo County Library System
Partic in TexSHARE - Texas State Library & Archives Commission
Open Mon-Thurs 9-8, Fri 9-6, Sat 11-3

MERIDIAN

P   MERIDIAN PUBLIC LIBRARY*, 118 N Main St, 76665. (Mail add: PO
Box 679, 76665-0679). Tel: 254-435-9100. FAX: 254-435-9800. E-mail:
meridian@members.ctls.net. *Head Librn,* Sarita Ellis
Founded 2000. Pop 1,490
Library Holdings: Audiobooks 350; Large Print Bks 200; Bk Vols 17,000
Special Collections: Chronicler of Folk Music (J T Lomax Coll)
Subject Interests: Texana
Automation Activity & Vendor Info: (Cataloging) Biblionix; (Circulation)
Biblionix
Wireless access
Function: ILL available
Mem of Central Texas Library System, Inc
Open Tues 10-7, Wed-Fri 10-6, Sat 10-3

MERKEL

P   MERKEL PUBLIC LIBRARY*, 100 Kent St, 79536. Tel: 325-928-5054.
FAX: 325-928-3171. E-mail: merkelibrary@merkeltexas.com. Web Site:
www.merkeltexas.com/public_library.html. *Librn,* Rose Fields; E-mail:
fieldsrose@merkeltexas.com.com
Pop 2,433
Library Holdings: Bk Vols 2,000
Automation Activity & Vendor Info: (Cataloging) Follett Software;
(Circulation) Follett Software
Partic in Tex Share
Open Mon-Thurs 12:30-5:30

MERTZON

P   IRION COUNTY LIBRARY*, PO Box 766, 76941-0766. SAN 376-4044.
Tel: 325-835-2704. FAX: 325-835-2008. E-mail: iclibrary@hotmail.com.
Web Site: bcls.tsl.state.tx.us/irion. *Dir,* T Kae Hampton
Pop 1,739
Library Holdings: Bk Vols 9,090; Per Subs 10
Automation Activity & Vendor Info: (Cataloging) Follett Software;
(Circulation) Follett Software
Mem of Big Country Library System
Open Mon-Fri 1:30-5:30

MESQUITE

S   DALLAS COUNTY COMMUNITY COLLEGE DISTRICT*, Education
Resources Support Services, 4343 Interstate 30, 75150. SAN 324-2102.
Tel: 972-860-7700. FAX: 972-860-4062. Web Site: www.dcccd.edu. *Dir,*
Paul E Dumont; E-mail: pdumont@dcccd.edu
Automation Activity & Vendor Info: (Acquisitions) Innovative Interfaces,
Inc; (Cataloging) Innovative Interfaces, Inc; (Circulation) Innovative
Interfaces, Inc; (Course Reserve) Innovative Interfaces, Inc; (ILL)
Innovative Interfaces, Inc; (Media Booking) Innovative Interfaces, Inc;
(OPAC) Innovative Interfaces, Inc; (Serials) Innovative Interfaces, Inc
Database Vendor: EBSCOhost, ProQuest, Wilson - Wilson Web
Open Mon-Fri 8:30-5

J   EASTFIELD COLLEGE LIBRARY*, 3737 Motley Dr, 75150-2033. SAN
316-6163. Tel: 972-860-7168. Web Site: www.eastfieldcollege.com,
www.efc.dcccd.edu. *Dean, Educ Res,* Karla Greer; Tel: 972-860-7173,
E-mail: kgreer@dcccd.edu; *Coll Develop,* Judith Wayne; Tel:
972-860-7176, E-mail: jwayne@dcccd.edu; *ILL,* Donna Smith; Staff 12.92
(MLS 4, Non-MLS 8.92)
Founded 1970. Enrl 5,540; Fac 303; Highest Degree: Associate
Library Holdings: AV Mats 2,832; e-books 28,602; Electronic Media &
Resources 159; Bk Vols 58,712; Per Subs 219
Automation Activity & Vendor Info: (Acquisitions) Innovative Interfaces,
Inc; (Cataloging) Innovative Interfaces, Inc; (Circulation) Innovative
Interfaces, Inc; (Course Reserve) Innovative Interfaces, Inc; (ILL)
Innovative Interfaces, Inc; (Media Booking) Innovative Interfaces, Inc;
(OPAC) Innovative Interfaces, Inc; (Serials) Innovative Interfaces, Inc
Wireless access
Open Mon-Thurs 7:30am-10pm, Fri 7:30-5, Sat 9-2

P   MESQUITE PUBLIC LIBRARY*, 300 W Grubb Dr, 75149. SAN
316-6171. Tel: 972-216-6220. FAX: 972-216-6740. E-mail:
mainbr@library.mesquite.tx.us. Web Site: www.library.mesquite.tx.us. *Dir,*
Jeannie Johnson; E-mail: jjohnson@cityofmesquite.com; *Br Mgr,* Jane
Brown; *Adult Ref Librn, AV Librn,* Cheryl Hollingsworth; *Ch,* Christine
Thomson; *Supvr, Pub Serv,* Virginia Mundt; *Supvr, Tech Serv,* Susan
Harding; *Adult Ref, ILL,* Ed Odom; Staff 14 (MLS 10, Non-MLS 4)
Founded 1963. Pop 139,824; Circ 476,916
Oct 2007-Sept 2008 Income (Main Library and Branch(s)) $2,213,084
Library Holdings: Bk Titles 162,705; Bk Vols 199,502; Per Subs 273
Subject Interests: Genealogy
Automation Activity & Vendor Info: (Cataloging) SirsiDynix;
(Circulation) SirsiDynix; (OPAC) SirsiDynix
Database Vendor: ALLDATA Online, Mergent Online
Wireless access
Function: Adult bk club, Audiobks via web, Bks on cassette, Bks on CD,
CD-ROM, Children's prog, Computer training, Computers for patron use,
Copy machines, Electronic databases & coll, Free DVD rentals,
Handicapped accessible, Holiday prog, ILL available, Music CDs, Online
cat, Prog for adults, Prog for children & young adult, Pub access
computers, Ref & res, Spoken cassettes & CDs, Story hour, Summer
reading prog, Tax forms, Teen prog, Telephone ref, VHS videos
Open Mon, Tues & Thurs 9-8, Wed, Fri & Sat 9-6
Friends of the Library Group
Branches: 1
NORTH BRANCH, 2600 Oates Dr, 75150, SAN 328-7556. Tel:
972-681-0465. FAX: 972-681-0467. *Br Mgr,* Jane Brown; *Ch,* Christi
Monis; *Ref Librn,* Beverly Yunker
Open Mon, Wed & Thurs 10-8, Tues, Fri & Sat 10-6
Friends of the Library Group

MEXIA

P   GIBBS MEMORIAL LIBRARY*, 305 E Rusk St, 76667-2398. SAN
316-618X. Tel: 254-562-3231. FAX: 254-472-0140. Reference E-mail:
ref@gibbslibrary.com. Web Site: www.gibbslibrarymexia.org. *Dir,*
ShienDee Pullman; Staff 5 (Non-MLS 5)
Founded 1903. Pop 13,702; Circ 51,000
Library Holdings: AV Mats 2,370; CDs 656; DVDs 352; Large Print Bks
2,000; Bk Vols 43,000; Per Subs 34; Talking Bks 1,000; Videos 871
Special Collections: War of the Rebellion
Subject Interests: Genealogy, Local hist
Automation Activity & Vendor Info: (Cataloging) Biblionix; (Circulation)
Biblionix; (ILL) OCLC FirstSearch
Database Vendor: EBSCOhost
Wireless access
Function: Bks on CD
Mem of Central Texas Library System, Inc
Open Mon-Fri 10-6, Sat 10-4
Friends of the Library Group

MIAMI

P   ROBERTS COUNTY LIBRARY, 300 W Commercial St, 79059. SAN 316-6198. Tel: 806-868-4791. *Librn,* Evelyn Huff
Pop 2,081; Circ 6,465
Library Holdings: Bk Vols 13,200
Wireless access
Open Tues, Thurs & Fri (Winter) 2-5; Mon-Fri (Summer) 1-5

MIDLAND

J   MIDLAND COLLEGE*, Murray Fasken Learning Resource Center, 3600 N Garfield, 79705. SAN 316-621X. Tel: 432-685-4560. FAX: 432-685-6710. Web Site: www.midland.edu. *Dir,* John Deats; Tel: 432-685-4726, E-mail: jdeats@midland.edu; *Automation Syst Coordr, Tech Serv,* Cecilia Miranda; *Circ,* Emma King; *Electronic Res,* Debby West; *Per,* Joan Williams; *Pub Serv,* Aline Collins; *Tech Serv,* Ellen Fino; Staff 4 (MLS 4)
Founded 1973. Enrl 4,600; Fac 185
Library Holdings: e-books 10,890; Bk Titles 49,274; Bk Vols 62,610; Per Subs 311
Subject Interests: Health sci libr, Law
Automation Activity & Vendor Info: (Acquisitions) SirsiDynix; (Cataloging) SirsiDynix; (Circulation) SirsiDynix; (Course Reserve) SirsiDynix; (ILL) SirsiDynix; (Media Booking) SirsiDynix; (OPAC) SirsiDynix; (Serials) SirsiDynix
Publications: LRC Bulletin; New Acquisitions Lists
Partic in Llano Estacado Info Access Network (LEIAN)
Open Mon-Thurs (Fall & Spring) 8am-10pm, Fri 8-5, Sat 10-3; Mon-Thurs (Summer) 7am-10pm

P   MIDLAND COUNTY PUBLIC LIBRARY*, 301 W Missouri, 79701. SAN 316-6228. Tel: 432-688-4320. FAX: 432-688-4939. E-mail: reference@co.midland.tx.us/. Web Site: www.co.midland.tx.us/library. *Dir,* John Trischitti, III; *Asst Dir,* J'Nevelyn White; E-mail: white@co.midland.tx.us; *Spec Coll Librn,* Marie Humphrey; *Br Coordr,* Alice White; *AV,* Barbara Edson; E-mail: edson@co.midland.tx.us; *Cat,* Pat Brashear; *Ch,* Jennifer Harris; *Circ,* Sharon Rowland; E-mail: beman@co.midland.tx.us; *ILL,* Becky Naranjo; *Per,* Barbara Kimber-Durr; E-mail: periodicals@co.midland.tx.us; Staff 41 (MLS 6, Non-MLS 35)
Founded 1903. Pop 116,009; Circ 405,807
Oct 2005-Sept 2006 Income (Main Library and Branch(s)) $1,380,324. Mats Exp $215,388, Books $149,932, Per/Ser (Incl. Access Fees) $20,172, Micro $3,999, AV Mat $41,285. Sal $786,970 (Prof $199,710)
Library Holdings: AV Mats 10,634; Bk Vols 265,948; Per Subs 445
Subject Interests: Genealogy, Petroleum
Automation Activity & Vendor Info: (Cataloging) OCLC; (Circulation) TLC (The Library Corporation); (OPAC) TLC (The Library Corporation)
Database Vendor: EBSCOhost, netLibrary, OCLC FirstSearch, OVID Technologies
Publications: Friends of the Library Newsletter (Bi-annually)
Mem of West Texas Library System
Partic in OCLC Online Computer Library Center, Inc
Open Mon-Thurs (Winter) 9-9, Fri & Sat 9-6; Mon (Summer) 9-9, Tues-Sat 9-6
Friends of the Library Group
Branches: 1
MIDLAND CENTENNIAL, Imperial Shopping Ctr, 3211 W Wadley, Ste 4B, 79705-6232, SAN 370-4998. Tel: 432-699-0629. E-mail: branch@co.midland.tx.us. *Librn,* Alice White
    Library Holdings: Bk Vols 15,216
    Open Mon-Thurs 9-8, Fri & Sat 9-6

S   PETROLEUM MUSEUM LIBRARY & HALL OF FAME*, Archives Center, 1500 Interstate 20 W, 79701. SAN 370-1905. Tel: 432-683-4403. FAX: 432-683-4509. Web Site: www.petroleummuseum.org, www.petroleummuseum.org/Archives/Archives.html. *Exec Dir,* Kathy Shannon; E-mail: kshannon@petroleummuseum.org; *Dir, Libr & Archives,* Leslie Meyer; E-mail: lmeyer@petroleummuseum.org
Library Holdings: Bk Titles 2,500; Per Subs 25
Special Collections: Oil & Gas Industry History; Photograph Archive; Samuel Myers Coll, oil industry, county histories, research mat used for writing of The Permian Basin. Oral History
Subject Interests: Local hist
Function: Ref serv available
Publications: Museum Memo (Quarterly)
Open Mon-Fri 10-5

MIDLOTHIAN

P   A H MEADOWS LIBRARY*, 921 S Ninth St, 76065-3636. SAN 376-4516. Tel: 972-775-3417. FAX: 972-775-5630. *Librn,* Susie Casstevens; E-mail: susie_casstevens@midlothian-isd.net; Staff 2 (MLS 2)
Library Holdings: Bk Vols 38,000; Per Subs 72

Automation Activity & Vendor Info: (Acquisitions) Follett Software; (Cataloging) Follett Software; (Circulation) Follett Software; (OPAC) Follett Software
Wireless access
Open Mon-Thurs 8-8, Fri 8-4, Sat 10-4

MINEOLA

P   MINEOLA MEMORIAL LIBRARY, INC*, 301 N Pacific St, 75773. SAN 316-6244. Tel: 903-569-2767. FAX: 903-569-6511. Web Site: netls.tsl.state.tx.us/mineola. *Dir,* Position Currently Open; Staff 1 (MLS 1)
Founded 1950. Pop 9,527
Library Holdings: Bk Titles 42,010; Per Subs 36
Automation Activity & Vendor Info: (Cataloging) Biblionix; (Circulation) Biblionix; (OPAC) Biblionix
Wireless access
Open Tues-Thurs 9-5:30, Fri 9-5, Sat 9-4
Friends of the Library Group

MIRANDO CITY

P   WEBB COUNTY LIBRARY*, Hwy 359, 78369. Tel: 361-586-4626. FAX: 361-586-5060. *Dir,* Mario Cortinas; *Supvr,* Melda Cartinas
Library Holdings: Bk Titles 2,500
Open Mon-Fri 8-5

MISSION

P   SPEER MEMORIAL LIBRARY*, 801 E 12th St, 78572. SAN 316-6260. Tel: 956-580-8750. FAX: 956-580-8756. E-mail: library@missiontexas.us. Web Site: www.mission.lib.tx.us. *Libr Dir,* Mayra Rocha; E-mail: mayra@missiontexas.us; *Ch,* Lisa Rivera; *Ref,* Rosaura Alvarez
Pop 105,795; Circ 176,638
Library Holdings: Bk Vols 160,000; Per Subs 103
Subject Interests: Bilingual, English lang, Genealogy, Spanish lang, Tex
Automation Activity & Vendor Info: (Cataloging) TLC (The Library Corporation); (Circulation) TLC (The Library Corporation)
Wireless access
Mem of Hidalgo County Library System
Open Mon-Thurs 8am-9pm, Fri & Sat 8-5, Sun 12-5
Friends of the Library Group

MONAHANS

P   WARD COUNTY LIBRARY*, 409 S Dwight, 79756. SAN 316-6279. Tel: 432-943-3332. FAX: 432-943-3332. E-mail: wardlibrary@hotmail.com. Web Site: www.wcl.lib.tx.us. *Dir,* Bonnie Moore; Staff 3 (Non-MLS 3)
Pop 10,507; Circ 30,264
Library Holdings: AV Mats 3,828; Large Print Bks 1,100; Bk Vols 63,706; Per Subs 25
Automation Activity & Vendor Info: (Circulation) Follett Software
Wireless access
Mem of West Texas Library System
Open Tues & Thurs 8-7, Wed, Fri & Sat 8-5
Friends of the Library Group
Branches: 2
BARSTOW BRANCH, PO Box 74, Barstow, 79719-0074. Tel: 432-445-5205. E-mail: barcolib@yahoo.com. *Librn,* Margie Gonzales
    Library Holdings: Bk Vols 1,300
    Open Mon & Fri 3-6, Tues, Wed & Thurs 2-6
GRANDFALLS PUBLIC, 209 Ave D, Grandfalls, 79742. (Mail add: PO Box 262, Grandfalls, 79742-0262). Tel: 432-547-2861. FAX: 432-547-2861. E-mail: grandfallslibrary@yahoo.com. *Librn,* Kellie Acosta
    Library Holdings: Bk Titles 6,900
    Open Mon-Fri 8-5

MOODY

P   MOODY COMMUNITY LIBRARY*, 108 Fifth St, 76557. (Mail add: PO Box 57, 76557-0057). Tel: 254-853-2004. FAX: 254-853-9704. Web Site: www.moody.lib.tx.us. *Librn,* Kathy Ellis; E-mail: kathyellismcl@hotmail.com
Pop 1,400; Circ 2,500
Library Holdings: DVDs 50; Bk Vols 15,000; Talking Bks 50; Videos 100
Wireless access
Mem of Central Texas Library System, Inc
Open Mon & Wed 9-2, Tues 1-5, Thurs 1-7, Sat 9-1

MORTON

P   COCHRAN COUNTY LOVE MEMORIAL LIBRARY*, 318 S Main, 79346-3006. SAN 316-6287. Tel: 806-266-5051. FAX: 806-266-8057. E-mail: cclmlibrary@hotmail.com. *Dir,* Irene Sealy; Staff 1 (Non-MLS 1)
Pop 3,952; Circ 7,748
Jan 2006-Dec 2006 Income $70,327. Mats Exp $9,400. Sal $20,738

Library Holdings: Bks on Deafness & Sign Lang 5; CDs 327; Bk Vols 14,000; Per Subs 15; Videos 25
Automation Activity & Vendor Info: (Acquisitions) LibLime; (Cataloging) LibLime; (Circulation) LibLime; (Course Reserve) LibLime; (ILL) LibLime; (Media Booking) LibLime; (OPAC) LibLime; (Serials) LibLime
Wireless access
Function: Accelerated reader prog, Adult bk club, Archival coll
Mem of West Texas Library System
Open Mon-Fri 9-Noon & 1-5
Restriction: Access at librarian's discretion, Authorized patrons

MOUNT CALM

P   MOUNT CALM PUBLIC LIBRARY*, 222 Allyn Ave, 76673. (Mail add: PO Box 84, 76673-0084), SAN 376-4745. Tel: 254-993-2761. *Librn,* Kathleen Franklin
Pop 320
Library Holdings: Bk Vols 14,000; Per Subs 10
Automation Activity & Vendor Info: (Cataloging) Biblionix; (Circulation) Biblionix
Mem of Central Texas Library System, Inc
Open Mon & Thurs 12-5:30, Tues 9-5, Sat 10-12

MOUNT PLEASANT

P   MOUNT PLEASANT PUBLIC LIBRARY*, 213 N Madison, 75455. SAN 316-6295. Tel: 903-575-4180. FAX: 903-577-8000. E-mail: library@mpcity.org. Web Site: www.mpcity.net/library-public.htm. *Dir,* Brenda Bynum; E-mail: bbynum@mpcity.org; Staff 4 (Non-MLS 4)
Founded 1968. Pop 14,000; Circ 83,429
Library Holdings: AV Mats 1,757; Large Print Bks 1,258; Bk Titles 29,438; Bk Vols 30,599; Per Subs 60; Talking Bks 1,028
Special Collections: Cross Family Indian Artifact Coll; Newspaper Coll (1923-1967), microfilm; Pioneers & Heroes of Titus County, Online Database; Titus County Genealogical Society Coll
Subject Interests: Local hist
Automation Activity & Vendor Info: (Cataloging) Book Systems, Inc; (Circulation) Book Systems, Inc; (OPAC) Book Systems, Inc
Wireless access
Function: AV serv, Home delivery & serv to Sr ctr & nursing homes, Homebound delivery serv, ILL available, Online searches, Photocopying/Printing, Prog for adults, Prog for children & young adult, Ref serv available, Summer reading prog, Telephone ref, Wheelchair accessible, Workshops
Publications: Pleasant Reading (Newsletter)
Special Services for the Blind - Bks on cassette; Bks on CD; Large print bks; Ref serv
Open Mon-Fri 9-6, Sat 9-1
Friends of the Library Group

J   NORTHEAST TEXAS COMMUNITY COLLEGE*, Learning Resource Center, Farm-to-Market Rd 1735, 75456. (Mail add: PO Box 1307, 75456-1307), SAN 328-106X. Tel: 903-572-1911. FAX: 903-572-7017. E-mail: lrc@ntcc.edu. Web Site: unicorn.ntcc.edu. *Dir,* Lonnie Beene; Tel: 903-572-1911, Ext 454, E-mail: lbeene@ntcc.edu; *Librn,* Ronald Bowden; Tel: 903-572-1911, Ext 452, E-mail: rbowden@ntcc.edu; Staff 6 (MLS 3, Non-MLS 3)
Founded 1985. Enrl 2,512; Fac 71; Highest Degree: Associate
Library Holdings: Bk Titles 28,396; Bk Vols 31,801; Per Subs 270
Automation Activity & Vendor Info: (Cataloging) SirsiDynix; (Circulation) SirsiDynix; (OPAC) SirsiDynix
Database Vendor: EBSCOhost
Wireless access
Function: ILL available
Partic in TexSHARE - Texas State Library & Archives Commission
Open Mon-Thurs (Fall & Spring) 8am-9pm, Fri 8-Noon, Sun 1:30-5:30; Mon & Tues (Summer) 7:30-6, Wed & Thurs 7:30-7:30, Fri 8am-Noon

MOUNT VERNON

P   FRANKLIN COUNTY LIBRARY*, 100 Main St, 75457. (Mail add: PO Box 579, 75457-0579), SAN 376-4397. Tel: 903-537-4916. FAX: 903-537-4319. E-mail: flibrary@mt-vernon.com. Web Site: www.mt-vernon.com/~library. *Dir,* Lisa Lawrence
Library Holdings: Bk Vols 30,000; Per Subs 50
Automation Activity & Vendor Info: (Cataloging) Follett Software; (Circulation) Follett Software; (OPAC) Follett Software
Wireless access
Open Mon 9-6, Tues-Fri 9-5, Sat 9-12
Friends of the Library Group

MUENSTER

P   MUENSTER PUBLIC LIBRARY*, 418 N Elm St, 76252. SAN 316-6309. Tel: 940-759-4291. FAX: 940-759-2250. E-mail: muensterlibrary@ntin.net. *Dir,* Stephanie Wright
Founded 1965. Pop 3,000; Circ 17,563
Library Holdings: Bk Titles 16,964; Bk Vols 17,417; Per Subs 28
Automation Activity & Vendor Info: (Cataloging) Book Systems, Inc; (Circulation) Book Systems, Inc
Wireless access
Open Tues & Thurs 10-6:30, Wed 1:30-5:30, Sat 10:30-2:30
Friends of the Library Group

MULESHOE

P   MULESHOE AREA PUBLIC LIBRARY*, 322 W Second, 79347. SAN 316-6317. Tel: 806-272-4707. FAX: 806-272-5031. Web Site: www.mapl.lib.tx.us. *Librn,* Dyan Dunagan; *Asst Librn,* Position Currently Open
Founded 1964. Pop 5,158; Circ 41,409
Library Holdings: Bk Vols 27,000; Per Subs 30
Special Collections: Audio-visual Coll; Large Print Coll; Paperback Coll; Southwest Coll; Spanish Coll; Texas Coll
Automation Activity & Vendor Info: (Cataloging) LibLime; (Circulation) LibLime
Wireless access
Mem of West Texas Library System
Open Mon-Fri 9-6
Friends of the Library Group

MUNDAY

P   CITY COUNTY LIBRARY OF MUNDAY*, 32 Munday Ave, 76371. (Mail add: PO Box 268, 76371-0268), SAN 316-6325. Tel: 940-422-4877. Pop 5,700; Circ 9,900
Library Holdings: Bk Vols 7,080
Automation Activity & Vendor Info: (Cataloging) Follett Software; (Circulation) Follett Software; (OPAC) Follett Software
Wireless access
Mem of Big Country Library System
Partic in Abilene Major Resource Syst
Open Mon-Thurs 8-5

NACOGDOCHES

P   NACOGDOCHES PUBLIC LIBRARY*, 1112 North St, 75961-4482. SAN 316-6341. Tel: 936-559-2970. FAX: 936-569-8282. Web Site: npl.sfasu.edu. *Dir,* Anne Barker; E-mail: abarker@npl.sfasu.edu; *Asst Dir,* Mercedes Franks; E-mail: franksm@npl.sfasu.edu; Staff 7.5 (MLS 2, Non-MLS 5.5)
Founded 1974. Pop 64,000; Circ 197,217
Oct 2010-Sept 2011 Income $565,000, City $505,000, Locally Generated Income $60,000. Mats Exp $109,970, Books $66,750, Per/Ser (Incl. Access Fees) $3,000, AV Equip $3,220, Electronic Ref Mat (Incl. Access Fees) $37,000. Sal $372,040 (Prof $90,000)
Library Holdings: AV Mats 9,000; CDs 2,622; DVDs 1,160; Electronic Media & Resources 50; Large Print Bks 3,500; Bk Vols 77,000; Per Subs 107; Talking Bks 3,150; Videos 493
Automation Activity & Vendor Info: (Cataloging) SirsiDynix; (Circulation) SirsiDynix; (ILL) OCLC; (Media Booking) Baker & Taylor; (OPAC) SirsiDynix; (Serials) SirsiDynix
Wireless access
Special Services for the Blind - Audio mat; Bks on cassette; Bks on CD
Open Mon & Thurs 9:30-8, Tues, Wed & Fri 9:30-5:30, Sat 10-3
Friends of the Library Group

C   STEPHEN F AUSTIN STATE UNIVERSITY, Ralph W Steen Library, 1936 North St, 75962. (Mail add: PO Box 13055, SFA Sta, 75962-3055), SAN 316-635X. Tel: 936-468-4636. Circulation Tel: 936-468-1497. Interlibrary Loan Service Tel: 936-468-1720. Administration Tel: 936-468-4101. FAX: 936-468-7610. Web Site: library.sfasu.edu. *Dir,* Shirley Dickerson; E-mail: sdickerson@sfasu.edu; *Asst Dir, Dir, E Tex Res Ctr, Spec Coll & Archives Librn,* Linda Reynolds; Tel: 936-468-1562, E-mail: lreynolds@sfasu.edu; *Head Acq/ILL Serv,* Barbara Olds; Tel: 936-468-1720, E-mail: Bolds@sfasu.edu; *Head, Cat,* Ellen Caplan; Tel: 936-468-1762; *Head, Libr Syst,* Reginald Gossett; Tel: 936-468-1488, E-mail: gossettregin@sfasu.edu; *Head, Ref,* Susan Clarke; Tel: 936-468-1459, E-mail: Sclarke@sfasu.edu; *Archivist,* Jennifer Brancato; Tel: 936-468-1841, E-mail: jmbrancato@sfasu.edu; *Ref Serv,* Carol Scamman; Tel: 936-468-1710, E-mail: scammancarol@sfasu.edu; *Webmaster,* Wade Carter; Tel: 936-468-1444, E-mail: wcarter@sfasu.edu; *Web Serv,* Kreg Mosier; Tel: 936-468-2853, E-mail: Kmosier@sfasu.edu. Subject Specialists: *Ill,* Barbara Olds; *Humanities,* Carol Scamman; Staff 46 (MLS 18, Non-MLS 28)
Founded 1923. Enrl 11,569; Fac 648; Highest Degree: Doctorate
Library Holdings: Bk Titles 463,133; Bk Vols 549,952; Per Subs 2,458

Special Collections: Business Documents & Papers of Major East Texas
Lumber Companies; East Texas History, bk, mss; The Texas Tides Coll.
Oral History; State Document Depository; US Document Depository
Subject Interests: Forestry
Automation Activity & Vendor Info: (Acquisitions) SirsiDynix;
(Circulation) SirsiDynix; (Serials) SirsiDynix
Database Vendor: Dialog, Gale Cengage Learning, LexisNexis, OCLC
FirstSearch, OVID Technologies, SirsiDynix, TLC (The Library
Corporation), Wilson - Wilson Web
Publications: Guide to Special Collections
Partic in BRS; Dialog Corp
Open Mon-Thurs 7am-1am, Fri 7-6, Sat 10-8, Sun Noon-1am

S   STERNE-HOYA HOUSE MUSEUM & LIBRARY*, 211 S Lanana St,
       75961-0012. (Mail add: PO Box 635030, 75963-5030), SAN 316-6333.
       Tel: 936-560-5426. FAX: 936-569-9813. *Mgr,* Brian W Bray; Staff 2 (MLS
       1, Non-MLS 1)
       Founded 1958. Pop 35,000
       Library Holdings: Bk Vols 5,000
       Special Collections: Texas Coll
       Subject Interests: Children's lit
       Open Tues-Sat 10-4
       Restriction: Non-circulating

NAPLES

P   NAPLES PUBLIC LIBRARY*, 103 Walnut St, 75568. (Mail add: PO Box
       705, 75568-0705). Tel: 903-897-2964. FAX: 903-897-2964. E-mail:
       naples_public_library@hotmail.com. *Librn,* Joyce Charlton
       Pop 1,496; Circ 4,343
       Library Holdings: Bk Vols 12,000; Per Subs 10
       Wireless access
       Open Mon-Fri 12-5
       Friends of the Library Group

NAVASOTA

P   NAVASOTA PUBLIC LIBRARY*, 1411 E Washington Ave, 77868-3240.
       SAN 316-6376. Tel: 936-825-6744. FAX: 936-825-4106. *Dir,* Cheryl
       Franklin; Staff 2 (MLS 1, Non-MLS 1)
       Founded 1954. Pop 7,400; Circ 54,211
       Library Holdings: Bk Vols 31,250; Per Subs 36
       Special Collections: Texana Coll
       Subject Interests: Local genealogy, Local hist
       Automation Activity & Vendor Info: (Cataloging) Follett Software;
       (Circulation) Follett Software; (OPAC) Follett Software
       Mem of Central Texas Library System, Inc
       Open Mon 3:30-7:30, Tues-Fri 9-6, Sat 9-12
       Friends of the Library Group
       Branches: 1
       HORLOCK HOUSE HISTORY CENTER, 1215 E Washington Ave,
       77868. Tel: 936-825-7055. *Dir,* Cheryl Franklin
          Subject Interests: Local genealogy, Local hist
          Restriction: Open by appt only

NEDERLAND

P   MARION & ED HUGHES PUBLIC LIBRARY*, 2712 Nederland Ave,
       77627-7015. SAN 320-2623. Tel: 409-722-1255. FAX: 409-721-5469. Web
       Site: www.ned.lib.tx.us. *Dir, Libr Serv,* Victoria L Klehn; E-mail:
       vklehn@ned.lib.tx.us; *Cat,* Molly Hall; *ILL,* Anne Flowers; Staff 3 (MLS
       1, Non-MLS 2)
       Founded 1930. Pop 17,422; Circ 115,379
       Library Holdings: AV Mats 3,358; Bk Titles 47,694; Bk Vols 55,388; Per
       Subs 72; Talking Bks 2,455
       Subject Interests: La Accadian hist, Nederland
       Automation Activity & Vendor Info: (Cataloging) Innovative Interfaces,
       Inc; (Circulation) Innovative Interfaces, Inc; (OPAC) Innovative Interfaces,
       Inc; (Serials) Innovative Interfaces, Inc
       Open Mon 1-9, Tues-Fri 10-6, Sat 10:30-2
       Friends of the Library Group

NEW BOSTON

P   NEW BOSTON PUBLIC LIBRARY*, 127 N Ellis St, 75570-2905. SAN
       376-446X. Tel: 903-628-5414. FAX: 903-628-9739. E-mail:
       nbpl127@yahoo.com. Web Site: newbostonlibrary.org. *Dir,* Christine
       Woodrow
       Library Holdings: Bk Vols 15,553; Per Subs 40
       Automation Activity & Vendor Info: (Cataloging) Follett Software;
       (Circulation) Follett Software
       Open Mon, Tues & Thurs 10-6, Wed & Fri 9-5, Sat 9-1
       Friends of the Library Group

NEW BRAUNFELS

P   NEW BRAUNFELS PUBLIC LIBRARY, 700 E Common St, 78130-5689.
       SAN 316-6392. Tel: 830-221-4300. Reference Tel: 830-221-4312.
       Administration Tel: 830-221-4322. FAX: 830-608-2151. E-mail:
       reference@nbtexas.org. Web Site: www.nbtexas.org/library. *Dir,* Gretchen
       Pruett; E-mail: gpruett@nbtexas.org; *Adult Serv,* Alix Samuels; Tel:
       830-221-4316, E-mail: asamuels@nbtexas.org; *Ch,* Debbie Martin; Tel:
       830-221-4313, E-mail: dmartin@nbtexas.org; *Coll Develop,* Ben Pensiero;
       Tel: 830-221-4325, E-mail: bpensiero@nbtexas.org; *Pub Serv,* Lynn
       Thompson; Tel: 830-221-4315, E-mail: lthompson@nbtexas.org; *Youth
       Serv,* Kit Ward-Crixell; Tel: 830-221-4319, E-mail:
       kwardcrixell@nbtexas.org; Staff 12 (MLS 7, Non-MLS 5)
       Founded 1928. Pop 57,000; Circ 756,549
       Oct 2010-Sept 2011 Income $1,507,646, State $11,981, City $1,446,476,
       Other $49,189. Mats Exp $172,745, Books $121,500, AV Mat $37,197,
       Electronic Ref Mat (Incl. Access Fees) $14,048. Sal $786,215
       Library Holdings: Audiobooks 4,357; CDs 3,035; DVDs 7,920; e-books
       1,042; Large Print Bks 5,197; Microforms 202; Bk Vols 90,540; Per Subs
       193
       Special Collections: Texana Coll
       Automation Activity & Vendor Info: (Cataloging) Biblionix; (Circulation)
       Biblionix; (ILL) OCLC Connexion; (OPAC) Biblionix
       Database Vendor: EBSCO Information Services, EBSCOhost, Gale
       Cengage Learning, OCLC WorldCat, Overdrive, Inc, ProQuest
       Wireless access
       Function: Adult bk club, Adult literacy prog, Archival coll, Audiobks via
       web, Bi-weekly Writer's Group, Bilingual assistance for Spanish patrons,
       Bk club(s), Bk reviews (Group), Bks on CD, Children's prog, Computer
       training, Computers for patron use, Copy machines, Digital talking bks,
       Distance learning, e-mail serv, E-Reserves, Electronic databases & coll,
       Family literacy, Fax serv, Free DVD rentals, Govt ref serv, Handicapped
       accessible, Homebound delivery serv, Homework prog, ILL available,
       Instruction & testing, Large print keyboards, Magnifiers for reading, Mail
       & tel request accepted, Music CDs, Online cat, Online ref, Online
       searches, Outreach serv, OverDrive digital audio bks,
       Photocopying/Printing, Preschool outreach, Printer for laptops & handheld
       devices, Prog for adults, Prog for children & young adult, Pub access
       computers, Ref & res, Ref serv in person, Scanner, Senior computer
       classes, Story hour, Summer reading prog, Tax forms, Teen prog,
       Telephone ref, Web-catalog, Wheelchair accessible
       Open Mon-Thurs 9-9, Fri 9-6, Sat 9-5, Sun 1-5
       Friends of the Library Group

NEW WAVERLY

P   NEW WAVERLY PUBLIC LIBRARY*, 9372 State Hwy 75 S, 77358.
       SAN 376-4117. Tel: 936-344-2198. FAX: 936-344-2198. E-mail:
       nwpublib@txun.net. *Dir,* Becky Powell
       Library Holdings: Bk Vols 8,500; Per Subs 12
       Wireless access
       Open Mon, Wed & Fri 12:30-4:30, Tues 9:30-7, Thurs 12:30-6, Sat 9-12
       Friends of the Library Group

NEWARK

P   NEWARK PUBLIC LIBRARY*, Godfrey Pegues Public Library, 207
       Hudson St, 76071. (Mail add: PO Box 1219, 76071-1219), SAN 376-4729.
       Tel: 817-489-2224. FAX: 817-489-3472. E-mail:
       newarklibtxus@sbcglobal.net. Web Site:
       www.newarktexas.com/library.html. Staff 1 (Non-MLS 1)
       Founded 1988. Pop 1,000; Circ 9,000
       Library Holdings: Bk Titles 10,100
       Automation Activity & Vendor Info: (Acquisitions) Follett Software;
       (Cataloging) Follett Software; (Circulation) Follett Software; (Course
       Reserve) Follett Software
       Wireless access
       Function: Adult bk club, Bks on cassette, Bks on CD, Children's prog,
       Computer training, Computers for patron use, Copy machines, e-mail &
       chat, e-mail serv, Electronic databases & coll, Fax serv, Free DVD rentals,
       Handicapped accessible, Magnifiers for reading, Notary serv, Online cat,
       Online searches, Photocopying/Printing, Prog for adults, Prog for children
       & young adult, Pub access computers, Ref serv available, Ref serv in
       person, Scanner, Senior computer classes, Story hour, Summer reading
       prog, VHS videos, Video lending libr, Wheelchair accessible, Workshops
       Open Mon, Tues, Thurs & Fri 3-7, Sat 9-1

NEWTON

P   NEWTON COUNTY PUBLIC LIBRARY, 212 High St, 75966. SAN
       375-3727. Tel: 409-379-8300. FAX: 409-379-2798. E-mail:
       newtonlibrary@hotmail.com. *Dir, Libr & Media Serv,* Sharon Long; Staff 2
       (Non-MLS 2)
       Founded 1974. Pop 14,946; Circ 24,390
       Library Holdings: AV Mats 600; Bk Vols 17,000; Per Subs 15; Videos
       894

Wireless access
Function: AV serv, Handicapped accessible, ILL available, Prog for children & young adult, Summer reading prog, Wheelchair accessible
Special Services for the Deaf - Bks on deafness & sign lang; High interest/low vocabulary bks
Special Services for the Blind - Talking bks
Open Mon-Fri 8:30-5
Restriction: Clients only, Open to pub for ref & circ; with some limitations
Friends of the Library Group
Branches: 1
DEWEYVILLE PUBLIC LIBRARY, 212 State Hwy 272, Deweyville, 77614. (Mail add: PO Box 801, Deweyville, 77614-0801). Tel: 409-746-0222. FAX: 409-746-9955. E-mail: dewpublib@hotmail.com. *Librn,* Janelle Horton
   Library Holdings: Bk Titles 6,000
   Automation Activity & Vendor Info: (Cataloging) Biblionix; (Circulation) Biblionix
   Partic in Tex Share
   Open Tues & Thurs 9-5, Wed & Fri 10-5

NIXON

P   NIXON PUBLIC LIBRARY*, 401 N Nixon Ave, 78140. SAN 316-6414. Tel: 830-582-1913. FAX: 830-582-1713. *Librn,* Sally Brassell
   Pop 2,008; Circ 8,500
   Library Holdings: Bk Vols 11,000; Per Subs 12
   Automation Activity & Vendor Info: (Cataloging) Follett Software; (Circulation) Follett Software; (OPAC) Follett Software
   Wireless access
   Open Mon-Fri 12-5
   Friends of the Library Group

NOCONA

P   NOCONA PUBLIC LIBRARY*, Ten Cooke St, 76255. SAN 376-4591. Tel: 940-825-6373. FAX: 940-825-4587. *Dir,* Jayne McCall; *Asst Dir,* Sharon Martinez
   Pop 3,198; Circ 15,049
   Library Holdings: Bk Vols 22,000; Per Subs 20
   Automation Activity & Vendor Info: (Cataloging) Follett Software; (Circulation) Follett Software
   Mem of North Texas Library Partners
   Open Mon-Fri 9-5:30
   Friends of the Library Group

NORTH RICHLAND HILLS

P   NORTH RICHLAND HILLS PUBLIC LIBRARY*, 9015 Grand Ave, 76180. SAN 316-344X. Tel: 817-427-6800. Circulation Tel: 817-427-6816. Reference Tel: 817-427-6814. FAX: 817-427-6808. Web Site: www.library.nrhtx.com. *Dir,* Steven L Brown; E-mail: sbrown@nrhtx.com; *Adult Serv,* Brenda Talley; *Ch,* Liz Brockman; Tel: 817-427-6818; *Circ,* Margaret Ragus; *Tech Serv,* Todd Humble; Tel: 817-427-6822; Staff 9.9 (MLS 9.9)
   Founded 1971. Pop 66,100; Circ 764,195
   Oct 2008-Sept 2009 Income $1,978,832, State $19,964, City $1,923,868, Locally Generated Income $35,000. Mats Exp $318,337, Books $256,290, AV Mat $18,000, Electronic Ref Mat (Incl. Access Fees) $44,047
   Library Holdings: Bk Vols 194,821; Per Subs 188
   Special Collections: Digital Historic Photo Archives
   Automation Activity & Vendor Info: (Cataloging) Innovative Interfaces, Inc; (Circulation) Innovative Interfaces, Inc; (ILL) OCLC ILLiad; (OPAC) Innovative Interfaces, Inc; (Serials) Innovative Interfaces, Inc
   Database Vendor: Innovative Interfaces, Inc, ReferenceUSA
   Wireless access
   Publications: Off the Shelf (Newsletter)
   Mem of North Texas Library Partners
   Open Mon-Thurs 9-9, Fri 9-6, Sat 9-5

ODEM

P   ODEM PUBLIC LIBRARY*, 516 Voss Ave, 78370. SAN 316-6422. Tel: 361-368-7388. FAX: 361-368-7388. E-mail: odempl@stx.rr.com. *Dir,* Donna Hutchins; Staff 1 (Non-MLS 1)
   Founded 1934. Pop 3,448
   Library Holdings: AV Mats 375; Bk Titles 9,409; Bk Vols 9,759; Per Subs 20
   Automation Activity & Vendor Info: (Cataloging) Follett Software; (Circulation) Follett Software
   Function: Adult literacy prog, CD-ROM, Digital talking bks, Handicapped accessible, ILL available, Magnifiers for reading, Music CDs, Online searches, Prog for children & young adult, Ref serv available, Spoken cassettes & CDs, Summer reading prog, Telephone ref, VHS videos, Wheelchair accessible
   Mem of San Patricio County Library System

Special Services for the Blind - Aids for in-house use; Audio mat; Bks on cassette; Bks on CD; Cassettes; Large print bks; Magnifiers; Talking bks
Open Mon, Wed & Fri 9-5, Sat 9-12
Friends of the Library Group

ODESSA

P   ECTOR COUNTY LIBRARY*, 321 W Fifth St, 79761-5066. SAN 316-6430. Tel: 432-332-0633. Circulation Tel: 432-332-0633, Ext 4000. Reference Tel: 432-332-0633, Ext 4001. Administration Tel: 432-332-0633, Ext 4020. FAX: 432-377-6502. Reference FAX: 432-332-4211. E-mail: library@ector.lib.tx.org. Web Site: www.ector.lib.tx.us. *Dir,* Rebbecca Taylor; E-mail: rtaylor@ector.lib.tx.us; *Spec Coll Librn,* Doris Baker; Tel: 432-332-0633, Ext 4015; *Syst & Cat Librn,* Joseph White; E-mail: jwhite@ector.lib.tx.us; *AV,* Ronald Roloff; Tel: 432-332-0633, Ext 4017, E-mail: rroloff@ector.lib.tx.us; *Ch,* Lynette Nickell; Tel: 432-332-0633, Ext 4013, E-mail: lnickell@ector.lib.tx.us. Subject Specialists: *Genealogy, SW hist,* Doris Baker; *Cataloging,* Joseph White; Staff 26 (MLS 4, Non-MLS 22)
   Founded 1938. Pop 121,123; Circ 696,820
   Library Holdings: Bk Titles 109,370; Bk Vols 128,570; Per Subs 320
   Subject Interests: Genealogy, Local hist, SW hist
   Automation Activity & Vendor Info: (Cataloging) SirsiDynix; (Circulation) SirsiDynix; (OPAC) SirsiDynix
   Database Vendor: Gale Cengage Learning, ProQuest, TLC (The Library Corporation)
   Wireless access
   Mem of West Texas Library System
   Special Services for the Deaf - Bks on deafness & sign lang; High interest/low vocabulary bks
   Special Services for the Blind - Bks on cassette; Talking bks
   Open Mon & Tues 8:30am-8:30pm, Wed 9-6
   Friends of the Library Group

J   ODESSA COLLEGE, Murry H Fly Learning Resources Center, 201 W University Blvd, 79764. SAN 316-6457. Tel: 432-335-6640. Interlibrary Loan Service Tel: 432-335-6644. Reference Tel: 432-335-6645. Administration Tel: 432-335-6641. Automation Services Tel: 432-335-6642. FAX: 432-335-6610. Web Site: www.odessa.edu/dept/library. *Dir,* Carolyn Petersen; E-mail: cpetersen@odessa.edu; *Pub Serv Dir,* Donna Clark; E-mail: dclark@odessa.edu; *Ser Dir,* Patricia Quintero; Tel: 915-335-6350, E-mail: pquintero@odessa.edu; *Tech Serv Dir,* Susan Elliott; E-mail: selliott@odessa.edu; Staff 4 (MLS 4)
   Founded 1946. Enrl 4,591; Fac 120; Highest Degree: Associate
   Sept 2011-Aug 2012 Income $595,378. Mats Exp $201,058, Books $115,500, Per/Ser (Incl. Access Fees) $43,532, Electronic Ref Mat (Incl. Access Fees) $39,626, Presv $2,400. Sal $338,448 (Prof $198,698)
   Library Holdings: AV Mats 5,752; e-books 48,293; Bk Titles 50,000; Bk Vols 58,794; Per Subs 352
   Automation Activity & Vendor Info: (Acquisitions) SirsiDynix; (Cataloging) SirsiDynix; (Circulation) SirsiDynix; (Course Reserve) SirsiDynix; (OPAC) SirsiDynix; (Serials) SirsiDynix
   Database Vendor: EBSCOhost, Gale Cengage Learning, OCLC FirstSearch
   Wireless access
   Publications: Faculty Handbook; Permian Basin Directory of Library Resources; Student Brochure (Library handbook); Student Handbook
   Partic in Leian; TexSHARE - Texas State Library & Archives Commission
   Open Mon-Thurs 7:30am-9:30pm, Fri 7:30-1, Sun 2-5

S   THE PRESIDENTIAL ARCHIVES, The Leadership Library, 4919 E University Blvd, 79762. SAN 316-6465. Tel: 432-363-7737. FAX: 432-552-2851. Web Site: www.thepresidentialmuseum.com. *Dir,* Charles Cotten
   Founded 1964
   Library Holdings: Bk Titles 6,000
   Special Collections: Constitutional Government; Elective Processes
   Subject Interests: The Presidency, all aspects
   Open Tues-Sat 10-5
   Restriction: Non-circulating

C   UNIVERSITY OF TEXAS OF THE PERMIAN BASIN*, J Conrad Dunagan Library, 4901 E University Blvd, 79762. SAN 316-6473. Tel: 432-552-2370. FAX: 432-552-2374. Web Site: www.utpb.edu/library/index. *Dir,* Charlene Shults; Tel: 432-552-2371, E-mail: shults_c@utpb.edu; Staff 5 (MLS 5)
   Founded 1973. Enrl 2,193; Fac 83; Highest Degree: Master
   Library Holdings: e-books 97; Bk Titles 274,000; Per Subs 700
   Special Collections: J Frank Dobie Coll, bks & papers; Texana; Texas Writers Coll
   Automation Activity & Vendor Info: (Cataloging) Innovative Interfaces, Inc; (Circulation) Innovative Interfaces, Inc; (OPAC) Innovative Interfaces, Inc

Partic in Leian; TexSHARE - Texas State Library & Archives Commission; Univ Tex Syst
Open Mon-Thurs 8am-11pm, Fri 8-5, Sat 10-7

OLNEY

P   OLNEY COMMUNITY LIBRARY & ARTS CENTER*, 807 W Hamilton St, 76374. (Mail add: PO Box 67, 76374-0067), SAN 316-6481. Tel: 940-564-5513. FAX: 940-564-3453. *Dir,* Kathy Gilmore; E-mail: kathy.gilmore@esc9.net; Staff 6 (Non-MLS 6)
Pop 4,082; Circ 55,071
Library Holdings: Bk Vols 32,069; Per Subs 85
Special Collections: Spanish-Bilingual Coll; Texas Coll; World War II Coll. Oral History
Automation Activity & Vendor Info: (Cataloging) Follett Software; (Circulation) Follett Software; (OPAC) Follett Software
Wireless access
Function: Archival coll, Art exhibits, Distance learning, Handicapped accessible, Homework prog, ILL available, Large print keyboards, Online searches, Photocopying/Printing, Prog for children & young adult, Spoken cassettes & CDs, Spoken cassettes & DVDs, Summer reading prog, VHS videos, Wheelchair accessible
Mem of North Texas Library Partners
Open Mon-Thurs (Winter) 8-8, Fri 8-5, Sat 8-12; Mon-Thurs (Summer) 9-8, Fri 9-5, Sat 9-12
Friends of the Library Group

OLTON

P   OLTON AREA LIBRARY*, 701 Main St, 79064. (Mail add: PO Box 675, 79064), SAN 321-6160. Tel: 806-285-7772. FAX: 806-285-7790. E-mail: oltonlib@amaonline.com. *Dir,* Linda Roper; Staff 2 (Non-MLS 2)
Founded 1982. Pop 4,634
Library Holdings: Bk Vols 10,000
Automation Activity & Vendor Info: (Acquisitions) Biblionix; (Cataloging) Biblionix; (Circulation) Biblionix
Wireless access
Mem of West Texas Library System
Open Mon & Wed-Fri 9-5:30, Tues 1-8
Friends of the Library Group

ONALASKA

P   ONALASKA PUBLIC LIBRARY*, 372 South FM 356, 77360. (Mail add: PO Box 880, 77360). Tel: 936-646-2665. FAX: 936-646-2665. E-mail: library@cityofonalaska.us. Web Site: cityofonalaska.us/public_library.htm. *Head Librn,* Jenny Quintin
Founded 2002
Library Holdings: CDs 200; DVDs 50; Bk Vols 9,211
Automation Activity & Vendor Info: (Cataloging) MC2 Systems; (Circulation) MC2 Systems
Wireless access
Open Mon-Fri 9-6, Sat 10-2
Friends of the Library Group

ORANGE

J   LAMAR STATE COLLEGE-ORANGE LIBRARY*, Ron E Lewis Library, 410 Front St, 77630-5796. SAN 370-6982. Tel: 409-882-3352. FAX: 409-883-7552. Web Site: library.lsco.edu. *Dir, Libr & Learning Res,* Mary McCoy; Tel: 409-882-3083, E-mail: mary.mccoy@lsco.edu; *Electronic Res Librn,* Marilyn Greene; Tel: 409-882-3084, E-mail: marilyn.greene@lsco.edu; *Tech Serv Librn,* Aubrey Kapranos; Tel: 409-882-3953, E-mail: aubrey.kapranos@lsco.edu; *Tech Serv Mgr,* Kungwha Kim; Tel: 409-882-3080, E-mail: kungwha.kim@lsco.edu; *Evening Supvr, Libr Tech III,* China Burks; Tel: 409-882-3081, E-mail: china.burks@lsco.edu; *Libr Tech III,* Josie Solis; E-mail: josie.solis@lsco.edu; *Libr Tech-Media Serv,* Position Currently Open.
Subject Specialists: *Govt, Hist, Proc tech,* Mary McCoy; *Nursing,* Marilyn Greene; *English, Math,* Aubrey Kapranos; Staff 5.5 (MLS 3, Non-MLS 2.5)
Founded 1969. Enrl 2,600; Fac 56; Highest Degree: Associate
Library Holdings: DVDs 1,200; Bk Titles 46,000
Special Collections: Local History (Orange County Coll)
Automation Activity & Vendor Info: (Acquisitions) SIRSI WorkFlows; (Cataloging) SIRSI WorkFlows; (Circulation) SIRSI WorkFlows; (ILL) OCLC FirstSearch; (OPAC) SIRSI WorkFlows
Database Vendor: Alexander Street Press, American Psychological Association (APA), Amigos Library Services, Bowker, College Source, Gale Cengage Learning, LexisNexis, OCLC FirstSearch, OCLC WorldCat, ProQuest, Sage, SerialsSolutions
Wireless access
Function: Archival coll, Art exhibits, AV serv, Copy machines, Electronic databases & coll, ILL available, Learning ctr, Online cat, Online info literacy tutorials on the web & in blackboard, Ref serv available, Scanner
Partic in OCLC Online Computer Library Center, Inc

Special Services for the Deaf - Closed caption videos; TDD equip
Special Services for the Blind - Accessible computers; Aids for in-house use; Computer access aids; Computer with voice synthesizer for visually impaired persons; Internet workstation with adaptive software; Low vision equip; PC for handicapped; Reader equip; Screen enlargement software for people with visual disabilities; Screen reader software
Restriction: Borrowing privileges limited to fac & registered students, Borrowing requests are handled by ILL, Circ privileges for students & alumni only

P   ORANGE PUBLIC LIBRARY*, 220 N Fifth St, 77630. SAN 316-6511. Tel: 409-883-1086. Reference Tel: 409-883-1053. FAX: 409-883-1057. E-mail: reference@orangetexas.org. Web Site: www.orangetexas.net/library.html. *Dir,* Brenna Manasco; E-mail: bmanasco@orangetexas.org; *Ch Serv Librn, Ref,* Karen Phares; *Acq,* Pam Williams; Staff 1 (Non-MLS 1)
Founded 1958. Pop 18,381
Special Collections: Large Print Children's Books; SE Texas & SW Louisiana Genealogy
Automation Activity & Vendor Info: (Cataloging) SirsiDynix; (Circulation) SirsiDynix; (OPAC) SirsiDynix
Function: Audio & video playback equip for onsite use, Bks on cassette, Bks on CD, Free DVD rentals, Holiday prog, ILL available, Online cat, Photocopying/Printing, Preschool outreach, Prog for children & young adult, Ref serv available, Summer reading prog, Tax forms, Teen prog, Telephone ref, VHS videos, Wheelchair accessible
Partic in OCLC Online Computer Library Center, Inc
Special Services for the Deaf - Accessible learning ctr; Adult & family literacy prog; Am sign lang & deaf culture; Assisted listening device; Captioned film dep; Closed caption videos; Coll on deaf educ; Deaf publ; Described encaptioned media prog; FullTalk; Interpreter on staff; Lecture on deaf culture; Pocket talkers; Sorenson video relay syst; Spec interest per; Staff with knowledge of sign lang; TDD equip; TTY equip; Video & TTY relay via computer; Video relay serv; Videos & decoder
Open Mon & Wed-Fri 10-5, Tues 10-8
Restriction: Circ to mem only, Non-resident fee, Open to pub for ref & circ; with some limitations
Friends of the Library Group

OZONA

P   CROCKETT COUNTY PUBLIC LIBRARY*, 1201 Ave G, 76943. (Mail add: PO Box 3030, 76943-3030), SAN 316-652X. Tel: 325-392-3565. FAX: 325-392-2941. E-mail: crockco@verizon.net. Web Site: bcls.tsl.state.tx.us/crockett. *Dir,* Louise Ledoux; Staff 4 (Non-MLS 4)
Founded 1985. Pop 4,000
Jan 2011-Dec 2011 Income $170,333. Mats Exp $16,000, Books $10,000, Per/Ser (Incl. Access Fees) $500, AV Mat $5,500. Sal $117,539
Library Holdings: AV Mats 3,000; CDs 659; Large Print Bks 5,000; Bk Titles 28,388; Bk Vols 32,610; Per Subs 10
Automation Activity & Vendor Info: (Cataloging) LibLime; (Circulation) LibLime
Mem of Big Country Library System
Open Mon & Thurs 9-9, Tues & Wed 9-6, Fri 9-5
Friends of the Library Group

PADUCAH

P   BICENTENNIAL CITY-COUNTY PUBLIC LIBRARY*, County Courthouse, Eighth St, 79248. (Mail add: PO Drawer AD, 79248-1197), SAN 372-7440. Tel: 806-492-2006. FAX: 806-492-2006. *Dir,* Curtis Burton; Staff 1 (Non-MLS 1)
Founded 1977. Pop 1,797; Circ 8,419
Library Holdings: Bk Vols 18,000
Special Collections: Genealogy (Texas & various USA Coll); Local History (Cottle Co & Area Coll)
Automation Activity & Vendor Info: (Acquisitions) Follett Software; (Cataloging) Follett Software; (Circulation) Follett Software; (Course Reserve) Follett Software; (ILL) Follett Software; (OPAC) Follett Software; (Serials) Follett Software
Mem of North Texas Library Partners
Open Mon, Wed & Fri 10-5, Tues 9-12 & 1-5, Thurs 10-12 & 1-5
Friends of the Library Group

PAINT ROCK

P   HARRY BENGE CROZIER MEMORIAL LIBRARY*, 184 W Moss St, 76866. SAN 375-4812. Tel: 325-732-4320. E-mail: hbclib@yahoo.com. *Libr Dir,* Barbara Herring; *Librn,* Karen Sedlak; Tel: 325-456-1420
Founded 1971. Pop 309; Circ 1,083
Library Holdings: Audiobooks 38; AV Mats 15; Bk Titles 2,783
Wireless access
Open Tues & Thurs 1-5

PALACIOS

P   PALACIOS LIBRARY, INC*, 326 Main St, 77465. SAN 316-6538. Tel: 361-972-3234. FAX: 361-972-2142. Web Site: www.palacioslibrary.org. *Dir,* Vikijane Bear; E-mail: vikijane@palacioslibrary.org; *Asst Librn,* Jane Kinzle; Staff 3 (Non-MLS 3)
Pop 9,400
Library Holdings: Bk Titles 34,000; Per Subs 10
Automation Activity & Vendor Info: (Cataloging) Book Systems, Inc; (Circulation) Book Systems, Inc; (OPAC) Book Systems, Inc
Wireless access
Open Mon-Wed 9-6, Thurs & Fri 1-6, Sat 9-2
Friends of the Library Group
Branches: 1
BLESSING BRANCH, 812 Tenth St, Blessing, 77419. Tel: 361-588-7717. FAX: 361-588-7717. E-mail: blessing_branch@palacioslibrary.org. *Librn,* Robin Griffith
Founded 1988
Library Holdings: Bk Vols 32,912
Open Mon & Tues 1-6, Wed & Fri 1-4

PALESTINE

P   PALESTINE PUBLIC LIBRARY*, 2000 S Loop 256, Ste 42, 75801. SAN 316-6546. Tel: 903-729-4121. Administration Tel: 903-729-8087. FAX: 903-729-4062. Web Site: www.palestine.lib.tx.us. *Interim Dir,* Theresa Holden; E-mail: tholden@palestine.lib.tx.us; *Ref Librn,* Ana Sanchez; E-mail: asanchez@palestine.lib.tx.us; *Spec Coll Librn,* Karla Lang; E-mail: klang@palestine.lib.tx.us; *Circ Supvr, ILL,* Rachel Menjiver; E-mail: rmenjiver@palestine.lib.tx.us; *Youth Serv,* Jamie E King; E-mail: jking@palestine.lib.tx.us; Staff 9 (MLS 2, Non-MLS 7)
Founded 1882. Pop 38,208; Circ 199,908
Library Holdings: AV Mats 5,417; Bk Vols 77,499; Per Subs 99
Special Collections: Anderson County, Texas Coll; Civil War Coll; Texana Coll
Subject Interests: Genealogy
Automation Activity & Vendor Info: (Cataloging) TLC (The Library Corporation); (Circulation) TLC (The Library Corporation); (OPAC) TLC (The Library Corporation)
Database Vendor: EBSCOhost, OCLC FirstSearch
Wireless access
Open Mon & Thurs 12-8, Tues 10-8, Wed & Fri 10-6, Sat 10-4
Friends of the Library Group

PAMPA

P   LOVETT MEMORIAL LIBRARY*, 111 N Houston, 79065. (Mail add: PO Box 342, 79066-0342), SAN 316-6562. Tel: 806-669-5780. FAX: 806-669-5782. E-mail: library@centramedia.net. *Dir,* Misty Guy; Staff 11 (MLS 2, Non-MLS 9)
Founded 1954. Pop 17,887; Circ 81,396
Oct 2009-Sept 2010 Income $523,837, State $7,641, City $491,196, County $5,000, Locally Generated Income $20,000. Mats Exp $34,552, Books $22,839, Per/Ser (Incl. Access Fees) $5,500, AV Mat $4,193, Electronic Ref Mat (Incl. Access Fees) $2,020. Sal $199,107
Library Holdings: Large Print Bks 1,000; Bk Titles 42,633; Per Subs 69; Talking Bks 2,045
Subject Interests: Local hist, Spanish
Automation Activity & Vendor Info: (Cataloging) SirsiDynix; (Circulation) SirsiDynix; (OPAC) SirsiDynix
Database Vendor: EBSCOhost, Gale Cengage Learning, OCLC FirstSearch, SirsiDynix, Wilson - Wilson Web
Wireless access
Function: Handicapped accessible, ILL available, Photocopying/Printing, Prog for children & young adult, Ref serv available, Summer reading prog, Telephone ref, Wheelchair accessible
Partic in Harrington Library Consortium; Tex Share
Open Mon-Thurs 9-9, Fri & Sat 9-6, Sun 2-6
Friends of the Library Group

PANHANDLE

P   CARSON COUNTY PUBLIC LIBRARY*, 401 Main, 79068. (Mail add: PO Box 339, 79068-0339), SAN 362-1510. Tel: 806-537-3742. FAX: 806-537-3780. E-mail: ccl@amaonline.com. *Librn Dir,* Mary Hare
Founded 1937. Pop 3,000; Circ 93,000
Library Holdings: AV Mats 3,123; Bk Titles 43,075; Bk Vols 51,652; Per Subs 106
Automation Activity & Vendor Info: (Cataloging) SirsiDynix; (ILL) OCLC WorldCat
Wireless access
Partic in Harrington Library Consortium
Open Mon 9-7, Tues-Fri 9-5

Branches: 3
GROOM BRANCH, 201 Broadway St, Groom, 79039. (Mail add: PO Box 308, Groom, 79039-0308), SAN 362-1545. Tel: 806-248-7353. FAX: 806-248-7353. E-mail: groomlib@amaonline.com. *Br Librn,* Tina Painter
Open Mon-Thurs 1-5, Fri 9-1
Friends of the Library Group
SKELLYTOWN BRANCH, N Main St, Skellytown, 79080. (Mail add: PO Box 92, Skellytown, 79080-0092), SAN 362-157X. Tel: 806-848-2551. FAX: 806-848-2551. *Br Librn,* Darlene Ledford
Open Mon-Thurs 1-5, Fri 9-1
WHITE DEER BRANCH, 200 Fourth St, White Deer, 79097. (Mail add: PO Box 85, White Deer, 79097-0085), SAN 362-160X. Tel: 806-883-7121. FAX: 806-883-7121. *Br Librn,* Beverly Warminski
Open Mon, Wed & Thurs 1-5, Tues & Fri 9-1

PARIS

M   ESSENT CORP*, Paris Regional Medical Center-North Library, 865 DeShong Dr, 75462-2097. (Mail add: 820 Clarksville St, 75460), SAN 316-6570. FAX: 903-782-2802. *In Charge,* Lisa House
Founded 1923
Library Holdings: Bk Titles 3,500; Per Subs 15
Special Collections: Texana
Open Mon-Fri 8-3

J   PARIS JUNIOR COLLEGE, Mike Rheusadil Learning Center, 2400 Clarksville St, 75460. SAN 316-6589. Tel: 903-782-0215, 903-782-0415. FAX: 903-782-0356. Web Site: www.parisjc.edu. *Dir of Libr Serv,* Carl Covert; E-mail: ccovert@parisjc.edu; *Off-Campus Librn,* Jay Strickland; Tel: 903-453-6435, Fax: 903-454-3380; *Tech Serv Librn,* Joe Jackson; Tel: 903-782-0437, E-mail: jjackson@parisjc.edu; Staff 8 (MLS 3, Non-MLS 5)
Founded 1924. Enrl 3,621; Fac 326; Highest Degree: Associate
Library Holdings: AV Mats 2,941; Bk Titles 39,250; Bk Vols 42,957; Per Subs 329
Special Collections: A M Aikin Archives; William Owens Coll
Subject Interests: County hist, Genealogy, Local hist
Automation Activity & Vendor Info: (Cataloging) Horizon; (Circulation) Horizon; (Course Reserve) Horizon; (OPAC) Horizon
Database Vendor: EBSCOhost, Facts on File, Gale Cengage Learning, Springshare, LLC
Wireless access
Partic in TexSHARE - Texas State Library & Archives Commission
Open Mon-Thurs 8am-10pm, Fri 8-5, Sun 5-9

P   PARIS PUBLIC LIBRARY*, 326 S Main St, 75460. SAN 316-6597. Tel: 903-785-8531. FAX: 903-784-6325. Web Site: www.paristexas.gov. *Dir,* Priscilla McAnally; E-mail: pmcanally@ci.paris.tx.us; *Ch,* Emily Kirkman; Staff 11 (MLS 1, Non-MLS 10)
Founded 1926. Circ 332,750
Library Holdings: Bk Vols 86,689; Per Subs 104
Automation Activity & Vendor Info: (Cataloging) Polaris Library Systems; (Circulation) Polaris Library Systems; (OPAC) Polaris Library Systems
Wireless access
Open Mon 1-5, Tues & Thurs 10-8, Wed, Fri & Sat 9-6
Friends of the Library Group

PASADENA

P   PASADENA PUBLIC LIBRARY*, 1201 Jeff Ginn Memorial Dr, 77506-4895. SAN 362-1634. Tel: 713-477-0276. FAX: 713-475-7005. Web Site: ppltx.net. *Actg Librn,* Wayne Holt; E-mail: wholt@ci.pasadena.tx.us; *Coll Develop Officer,* Lisa Jackson; *ILL,* William Simpson; *Youth & Teen Serv,* Richard Clark; Staff 36.25 (MLS 9.5, Non-MLS 26.75)
Founded 1953. Pop 146,439; Circ 440,458
Library Holdings: Bk Vols 118,231; Per Subs 295; Talking Bks 3,289; Videos 13,794
Special Collections: Geneology Room
Subject Interests: Local hist
Automation Activity & Vendor Info: (Cataloging) Innovative Interfaces, Inc; (Circulation) Innovative Interfaces, Inc; (OPAC) Innovative Interfaces, Inc; (Serials) Innovative Interfaces, Inc
Database Vendor: EBSCOhost, Gale Cengage Learning, Innovative Interfaces, Inc INN - View
Wireless access
Publications: Booklets, Brochures & Bookmarks; Newsletter (Monthly)
Geneology room
Open Mon, Wed, Fri & Sat 10-6, Tues & Thurs 10-9
Friends of the Library Group
Branches: 1
FAIRMONT, 4330 Fairmont, 77504-3306, SAN 372-7068. Tel: 281-998-1095. FAX: 281-998-1583. *Br Mgr,* Kathy Johnson; E-mail: kjohnson@ci.pasadena.tx.us; Staff 9 (MLS 3, Non-MLS 6)
Founded 1992. Circ 234,031

Open Mon-Fri 2-6
Friends of the Library Group

J   SAN JACINTO COLLEGE*, Lee Davis Library, 8060 Spencer Hwy, 77505. SAN 362-1693. Tel: 281-476-1850. FAX: 281-478-2734. Web Site: www.sjcd.edu. *Dir, Libr Serv,* Karen Blankenship; *Automation Syst Coordr,* Abraham Korah; Staff 6 (MLS 6)
Founded 1961. Enrl 7,336; Fac 500; Highest Degree: Associate
Library Holdings: Bk Vols 157,000; Per Subs 300
Special Collections: Pomeroy Archives on Area History
Automation Activity & Vendor Info: (Cataloging) Innovative Interfaces, Inc - Millenium; (Circulation) Innovative Interfaces, Inc - Millenium; (Course Reserve) Innovative Interfaces, Inc - Millenium; (OPAC) Innovative Interfaces, Inc - Millenium; (Serials) Innovative Interfaces, Inc - Millenium
Database Vendor: Wilson - Wilson Web
Wireless access
Partic in Tex Share
Special Services for the Blind - Reader equip

CM   TEXAS CHIROPRACTIC COLLEGE*, Mae Hilty Memorial Library, 5912 Spencer Hwy, 77505. SAN 316-6619. Tel: 281-998-6049. Interlibrary Loan Service Tel: 281-998-6052. Reference Tel: 281-998-6054. Administration Tel: 281-998-6098. FAX: 281-487-4168. Web Site: www.txchiro.edu. *Dir,* Caroline Webb; E-mail: cwebb@txchiro.edu; *Asst Circ Librn,* Sharon Lazorwitz; *Circ,* Sherry Mahana; E-mail: smahana@txchiro.edu; *Pub Serv,* Karen Bulow; E-mail: kbulow@txchiro.edu; Staff 5 (MLS 3, Non-MLS 2)
Founded 1908. Enrl 1,908; Fac 42; Highest Degree: Doctorate
Library Holdings: Bk Titles 11,500; Bk Vols 14,000; Per Subs 175
Special Collections: Chiropractic Coll, bks
Subject Interests: Chiropractic, Med, Natural sci
Automation Activity & Vendor Info: (Cataloging) Follett Software; (Circulation) Follett Software; (Course Reserve) Follett Software; (OPAC) Follett Software
Wireless access
Partic in Chiropractic Libr Consortium; Docline; National Network of Libraries of Medicine; OCLC Online Computer Library Center, Inc
Open Mon-Thurs 7am-10pm, Fri 7-4, Sun 12-8
Friends of the Library Group

PEARSALL

P   PEARSALL PUBLIC LIBRARY*, 200 E Trinity St, 78061. SAN 316-6627. Tel: 830-334-2496. FAX: 830-334-9194. *Dir,* David Medrano; E-mail: dmedrano@cityofpearsall.org
Founded 1962. Pop 7,000; Circ 56,214
Library Holdings: Bk Titles 39,093; Bk Vols 65,607; Per Subs 16
Automation Activity & Vendor Info: (Cataloging) Follett Software; (Circulation) Follett Software
Wireless access
Open Mon-Fri 9-6

PECOS

P   REEVES COUNTY LIBRARY*, 505 S Park St, 79772-3735. SAN 316-6635. Tel: 432-445-5340. FAX: 432-445-1028. E-mail: pecosbill@suddenlinkmail.com. *Librn,* Sally Perry; *Asst Librn,* Rosie Gonzalez; Staff 3 (MLS 1, Non-MLS 2)
Founded 1937. Pop 11,842; Circ 40,000
Library Holdings: Bks on Deafness & Sign Lang 10; High Interest/Low Vocabulary Bk Vols 2,500; Bk Titles 35,000; Bk Vols 39,060; Per Subs 40; Spec Interest Per Sub 10
Special Collections: State Document Depository
Subject Interests: Educ K-12, Recreational, Southwest, Spanish, Tex
Automation Activity & Vendor Info: (Cataloging) Book Systems, Inc; (Circulation) Book Systems, Inc
Database Vendor: EBSCOhost
Wireless access
Mem of Texas Trans-Pecos Regional Library System
Special Services for the Deaf - Bks on deafness & sign lang; Videos & decoder
Special Services for the Blind - Audio mat
Open Mon-Fri 9-6, Sat 9-12
Friends of the Library Group

PERRYTON

P   PERRY MEMORIAL LIBRARY*, 22 SE Fifth Ave, 79070. SAN 316-6643. Tel: 806-435-5801. FAX: 806-435-4266. E-mail: persan@usa.com. *Dir,* Sandra Sears; *Assoc Librn,* Linda Sue Johnson; Staff 2 (Non-MLS 2)
Founded 1925. Pop 10,000; Circ 72,966
Library Holdings: Bk Vols 37,500; Per Subs 10
Special Collections: Texas Coll
Subject Interests: Hist

Automation Activity & Vendor Info: (Cataloging) SirsiDynix; (Circulation) SirsiDynix; (OPAC) SirsiDynix
Wireless access
Open Mon & Thurs 9:30-8, Tues, Wed & Fri 9:30-5:30, Sat 9:30-1

PETERSBURG

P   PETERSBURG PUBLIC LIBRARY, 1614 Main St, 79250. (Mail add: PO Box 65, 79250-0065). Tel: 806-667-3657. *Librn,* Shirley Overstreet
Pop 2,532; Circ 6,048
Jan 2011-Dec 2011 Income $3,000
Library Holdings: Bk Vols 10,000
Open Tues & Thurs 1:30-5, Sat 9-12

PFLUGERVILLE

P   PFLUGERVILLE COMMUNITY LIBRARY*, 102 Tenth St, 78660. SAN 372-5685. Tel: 512-251-9185. Circulation Tel: 512-251-9185, Ext 12. Information Services Tel: 512-251-9185, Ext 11. FAX: 512-990-8791. E-mail: library@cityofpflugerville.com. Web Site: www.cityofpflugerville.com/library. *Dir,* Kathy Freiheit; Staff 12 (MLS 5, Non-MLS 7)
Founded 1981. Pop 46,936; Circ 283,000
Library Holdings: Bk Vols 60,000
Subject Interests: Texana
Automation Activity & Vendor Info: (Cataloging) Biblionix; (Circulation) Biblionix; (OPAC) Biblionix
Wireless access
Mem of Central Texas Library System, Inc
Open Mon-Thurs 10-9, Fri 10-6, Sat 10-4, Sun 1-6
Friends of the Library Group

PHARR

P   HIDALGO COUNTY LIBRARY SYSTEM*, c/o Pharr Memorial LIbrary, 121 E Cherokee St, 78577-4826. SAN 316-5922. Tel: 956-787-3966. FAX: 956-787-3345. Web Site: www.hcls.lib.tx.us. *Pres,* Adolfo Garcia; E-mail: adolfo@pharr.lib.tx.us; Staff 1 (MLS 1)
Founded 1971. Pop 506,919
Member Libraries: Donna Public Library; Dr Hector P Garcia Memorial Library; Dustin Michael Sekula Memorial Library; Elsa Public Library; Hidalgo Public Library; La Joya Municipal Library; Mayor Joe V Sanchez Public Library; McAllen Memorial Library; San Juan Public Library; Sargeant Fernando de la Rosa Memorial Library; Speer Memorial Library
Open Mon-Thurs 8am-9pm, Fri 8-5, Sat 11-3, Sun 1-5

G   PHARR MEMORIAL LIBRARY*, 121 E Cherokee St, 78577-4826. SAN 316-6651. Tel: 956-787-3966. FAX: 956-787-3345. E-mail: staff@pharr.lib.tx.us. Web Site: www.pharr-tx.gov/departments/pharr-library. *Dir,* Adolfo Garcia; E-mail: adolfo@pharr.lib.tx.us; Staff 22 (MLS 2, Non-MLS 20)
Founded 1960. Pop 73,000
Library Holdings: Bk Vols 85,000; Per Subs 70
Special Collections: Large Print Coll; Spanish Coll (Spanish language materials); Texas Coll
Automation Activity & Vendor Info: (Acquisitions) TLC (The Library Corporation); (Cataloging) TLC (The Library Corporation); (Circulation) TLC (The Library Corporation); (OPAC) TLC (The Library Corporation)
Database Vendor: EBSCO Auto Repair Reference, EBSCOhost, LearningExpress, ProQuest, TumbleBookLibrary
Wireless access
Function: Computers for patron use, Prog for children & young adult, Ref serv available, Summer reading prog
Open Mon-Thurs 9-9, Fri & Sat 9-6, Sun 1-6
Friends of the Library Group

PILOT POINT

P   PILOT POINT COMMUNITY LIBRARY*, 324 S Washington St, 76258. (Mail add: PO Box 969, 76258-0969). Tel: 940-686-5004. FAX: 940-686-2833. E-mail: library@cityofpilotpoint.org. Web Site: www.pilotpointlibrary.org. *Dir,* Phyllis Tillery
Library Holdings: Bk Vols 18,000; Per Subs 25
Automation Activity & Vendor Info: (Cataloging) Follett Software; (Circulation) Follett Software
Wireless access
Function: AV serv, Bks on CD, Children's prog, Copy machines, ILL available
Mem of North Texas Library Partners
Partic in Tex Share
Open Tues-Fri 8:30-5:30, Sat 9-2
Friends of the Library Group

PINELAND

P   ARTHUR TEMPLE SR MEMORIAL LIBRARY*, 106 Timberland Hwy, 75968. SAN 316-666X. Tel: 409-584-2546. FAX: 409-584-3206. E-mail: atsmlibrary@valornet.com, home.valornet.com/atsmlibrary. *Dir,* Donna Nichols
Founded 1969. Pop 7,200; Circ 33,559
Library Holdings: AV Mats 2,039; Bk Vols 23,000; Per Subs 16; Videos 1,200
Automation Activity & Vendor Info: (Cataloging) Follett Software; (Circulation) Follett Software; (OPAC) Follett Software
Wireless access
Open Mon & Wed-Fri 9-4, Tues 10-5
Friends of the Library Group

PITTSBURG

P   PITTSBURG-CAMP COUNTY PUBLIC LIBRARY*, 613 Quitman St, 75686-1035. SAN 316-6678. Tel: 903-856-3302. FAX: 903-856-0591. E-mail: info@pittsburglibrary.org. Web Site: www.pittsburglibrary.org. *Libr Dir,* Nancy Murillo; Staff 1 (Non-MLS 1)
Founded 1973. Pop 12,238; Circ 85,000
Oct 2008-Sept 2009 Income $156,230, City $74,858, County $74,858, Locally Generated Income $6,514. Mats Exp $155,236, Books $8,690, AV Mat $3,178. Sal $81,568
Library Holdings: Bk Vols 27,749; Per Subs 50
Special Collections: Genealogy Coll
Automation Activity & Vendor Info: (Acquisitions) Book Systems, Inc; (Cataloging) Book Systems, Inc; (Circulation) Book Systems, Inc; (OPAC) Book Systems, Inc
Wireless access
Open Mon-Thurs 9-5:30, Fri 9-5, Sat (Oct-May) 9-12:45
Friends of the Library Group

PLAINS

P   YOAKUM COUNTY LIBRARY*, 901 Ave E, 79355. (Mail add: PO Box 419, 79355-0419), SAN 316-6686. Tel: 806-456-8725. FAX: 806-456-7056. *Librn,* Pat McNabb; *Asst Librn,* Dolores Davis; Staff 6 (MLS 3, Non-MLS 3)
Founded 1957. Pop 3,500
Library Holdings: Bk Vols 38,000; Per Subs 47
Special Collections: Texas History Coll
Automation Activity & Vendor Info: (Cataloging) Follett Software; (Circulation) Follett Software
Publications: Appraisal; Booklist; Publishers Weekly
Mem of West Texas Library System
Open Mon-Fri 9-5:30

PLAINVIEW

P   UNGER MEMORIAL LIBRARY*, 825 Austin St, 79072-7235. SAN 316-6694. Tel: 806-296-1148. Administration Tel: 806-296-1149. FAX: 806-291-1245. Web Site: unger.myplainview.com/index.htm. *Librn,* John Sigwald; E-mail: johnsigwald@texasonline.net; Staff 1 (MLS 1)
Founded 1960. Pop 35,000; Circ 52,000
Oct 2010-Sept 2011 Income $398,500, City $389,000, County $9,500. Mats Exp $57,600, Books $40,000, Per/Ser (Incl. Access Fees) $9,000, AV Mat $5,000, Electronic Ref Mat (Incl. Access Fees) $600, Presv $3,000. Sal $157,000 (Prof $51,000)
Library Holdings: Bk Vols 50,000; Per Subs 110
Special Collections: Hale County Cemetery Records, online database; Plainview & Hale County History Coll
Subject Interests: Genealogy
Automation Activity & Vendor Info: (Cataloging) Surpass; (Circulation) Surpass; (ILL) OCLC; (OPAC) Surpass
Wireless access
Function: Bilingual assistance for Spanish patrons, Bks on cassette, Bks on CD, Children's prog, Computers for patron use, Copy machines, Free DVD rentals, Genealogy discussion group, Handicapped accessible, ILL available, Notary serv, Online cat, Photocopying/Printing, Printer for laptops & handheld devices, Prog for children & young adult, Pub access computers, Ref serv in person, Scanner, Spoken cassettes & CDs, Story hour, Summer reading prog, Tax forms, Telephone ref, Web-catalog, Wheelchair accessible
Publications: Unger Ululations (Newsletter)
Mem of West Texas Library System
Partic in TexSHARE - Texas State Library & Archives Commission
Open Mon, Wed & Fri (Winter) 9-6, Tues & Thurs 9-9, Sat 9-5; Mon-Fri (Summer) 9-6
Friends of the Library Group

C   WAYLAND BAPTIST UNIVERSITY*, Mabee Learning Resources Center, 1900 W Seventh, 79072-6957. SAN 316-6708. Tel: 806-291-3700. FAX: 806-291-1964. Web Site: www.wbu.edu/lrc. *Dir,* Dr Polly Lackey; E-mail: lackeyp@wbu.edu; *Distance Serv Librn,* Dann Wigner; Tel: 806-291-3701,
E-mail: wignerd@wbu.edu; *Coll Develop,* John Elliott; Tel: 806-291-3704, E-mail: elliottj@wbu.edu; Staff 4 (MLS 3, Non-MLS 1)
Founded 1910. Enrl 3,408; Fac 133; Highest Degree: Master
Library Holdings: Bk Vols 130,044; Per Subs 466
Automation Activity & Vendor Info: (Cataloging) SirsiDynix; (Circulation) SirsiDynix; (OPAC) SirsiDynix
Database Vendor: Amigos Library Services, EBSCOhost, JSTOR, OCLC FirstSearch, ProQuest, SirsiDynix
Partic in Harrington Library Consortium; OCLC Online Computer Library Center, Inc
Open Mon-Thurs 7:45am-11pm, Fri 7:45-4, Sat 10-5, Sun 2-5 & 7:30pm-10pm

PLANO

J   COLLIN COLLEGE*, Spring Creek Campus Library, 2800 E Spring Creek Pkwy, 75074. SAN 328-0276. Tel: 972-881-5860. Interlibrary Loan Service Tel: 972-881-5749. Reference Tel: 972-881-5985. FAX: 972-881-5911. Web Site: www.collin.edu/library. *Exec Dir,* Linda Kyprios; Tel: 972-881-5726, E-mail: lkyprios@collin.edu; *Tech Serv Dir,* John Schanot; Tel: 972-881-5628, Fax: 972-881-5610, E-mail: jschanot@collin.edu; *ILL,* Sandy Marton; Tel: 972-881-5931, Fax: 972-881-5866, E-mail: smarton@collin.edu; Staff 11 (MLS 6, Non-MLS 5)
Founded 1985. Highest Degree: Associate
Library Holdings: Bk Vols 180,000; Per Subs 937
Automation Activity & Vendor Info: (Cataloging) Polaris Library Systems; (Circulation) Polaris Library Systems
Wireless access
Function: Art exhibits, Audio & video playback equip for onsite use, Digital talking bks, Distance learning, For res purposes, Handicapped accessible, ILL available, Magnifiers for reading, Music CDs, Orientations, Prog for adults, Ref serv available, Spoken cassettes & CDs, Telephone ref, VHS videos, Wheelchair accessible, Workshops
Partic in OCLC Online Computer Library Center, Inc
Open Mon-Thurs 7:45am-9:45pm, Fri 7:45-5, Sat 8-5, Sun 1-5
Restriction: In-house use for visitors

P   PLANO PUBLIC LIBRARY SYSTEM, Library Administration, 2501 Coit Rd, 75075. SAN 316-6724. Tel: 972-769-4208. FAX: 972-769-4269. Web Site: www.planolibrary.org. *Dir,* Cathy Ziegler; E-mail: cathyz@plano.gov; *Tech Serv Mgr,* Julie Torstad; Tel: 972-769-4291, Fax: 972-769-4121, E-mail: juliet@plano.gov; *Pub Relations Coordr,* Tammy Korns; Tel: 972-769-4211, E-mail: tammyko@plano.gov; Staff 8 (MLS 7, Non-MLS 1)
Founded 1965. Pop 265,347; Circ 3,909,121
Oct 2011-Sept 2012. Sal $2,706,074
Special Collections: Archives; Genealogy Coll; Local History Coll; Texana Coll
Automation Activity & Vendor Info: (Acquisitions) Polaris Library Systems; (Cataloging) Polaris Library Systems; (Circulation) Polaris Library Systems; (OPAC) Polaris Library Systems; (Serials) Polaris Library Systems
Database Vendor: EBSCOhost, Facts on File, Gale Cengage Learning, JSTOR, LearningExpress, OCLC FirstSearch
Wireless access
Publications: Plano, Texas: The Early Years (Local historical information)
Open Mon-Thurs 9-9, Fri 9-6, Sat 10-6, Sun 1-5
Friends of the Library Group
Branches: 6
MARIBELLE M DAVIS LIBRARY, 7501-B Independence Pkwy, 75025, SAN 378-0317. Tel: 972-208-8000. FAX: 972-208-8037. *Libr Mgr,* Brent Bloechle; E-mail: brentb@plano.gov; *Head Librn,* Dexter Goodman; E-mail: dexterg@plano.gov; *Ch,* Cecily Ponce de Leon; E-mail: cecilyp@plano.gov; Staff 8.5 (MLS 8.5)
Founded 1998. Pop 65,000
Open Mon-Thurs 9-9, Fri 9-6, Sat 10-6, Sun 1-5
Friends of the Library Group
W O HAGGARD JR LIBRARY, 2501 Coit Rd, 75075, SAN 370-0003. Tel: 972-769-4250. FAX: 972-769-4256. *Mgr,* Libby Holtmann; E-mail: libbyh@plano.gov; *Head Librn,* Teri Arce; E-mail: teria@plano.gov; *Ch,* Ramarie Beaver; E-mail: ramarieb@plano.gov; Staff 10 (MLS 10)
Founded 1989. Pop 65,000
Subject Interests: Consumer health, Sci
Open Mon-Thurs 9-9, Fri 9-6, Sat 10-6, Sun 1-5
Friends of the Library Group
GLADYS HARRINGTON LIBRARY, 1501 E 18th St, 75074, SAN 321-1401. Tel: 972-941-7175. FAX: 972-941-7292. *Libr Mgr,* Danita Barber; E-mail: danitab@plano.gov; *Head Librn,* Eva Gonzalez; E-mail: evag@plano.gov; *Ch,* Julie Conner; E-mail: juliec@plano.gov; Staff 7.5 (MLS 7.5)
Founded 1969. Pop 43,000
Open Mon-Thurs 9-9, Fri 9-6, Sat 10-6, Sun 1-5
Friends of the Library Group

MUNICIPAL REFERENCE, 1520 Ave K, 75074, SAN 375-5673. Tel: 972-941-7377. FAX: 972-941-7453. *Librn,* Bob Loftin; E-mail: bobl@plano.gov; Staff 1 (MLS 1)
Founded 1991
Open Mon-Fri 8-5
Friends of the Library Group

CHRISTOPHER A PARR LIBRARY, 6200 Windhaven Pkwy, 75093. Tel: 972-769-4300. FAX: 972-769-4304. *Libr Mgr,* April Hill; E-mail: aprilh@plano.gov; *Librn Supvr,* Position Currently Open; *Ch,* Connie Charron; Staff 7 (MLS 7)
Founded 2001. Pop 43,000
Open Mon-Thurs 9-9, Fri 9-6, Sat 10-6, Sun 1-5
Friends of the Library Group

L E R SCHIMELPFENIG LIBRARY, 5024 Custer Rd, 75023, SAN 321-141X. Tel: 972-769-4200. FAX: 972-769-4210. *Libr Mgr,* Melissa Perez; E-mail: melissape@plano.gov; *Head Librn,* Jennifer Strange; E-mail: jennifers@plano.gov; *Ch,* Donna Cifarelli; E-mail: donnac@plano.gov; Staff 7.5 (MLS 7.5)
Founded 1980. Pop 43,000
Subject Interests: Law, Sci
Open Mon-Thurs 9-9, Fri 9-6, Sat 10-6, Sun 1-5
Friends of the Library Group

PLEASANTON

P   PLEASANTON PUBLIC LIBRARY*, 321 N Main, 78064. SAN 316-6732. Tel: 830-569-3622. FAX: 830-569-6082. Web Site: www.ppltx.org. *Dir,* Diana Guthrie; E-mail: dguthrie405@att.net; *Asst City Librn,* Kathleen Guerra; *Head, Circ,* Gina Stewart; *Cat,* Danielle Rangel; Staff 4 (MLS 1, Non-MLS 3)
Founded 1950
Library Holdings: Bks on Deafness & Sign Lang 20; Large Print Bks 500; Bk Titles 35,000; Bk Vols 36,500; Per Subs 70; Talking Bks 2,000
Special Collections: Texana
Automation Activity & Vendor Info: (Acquisitions) Biblionix; (Cataloging) Biblionix; (Circulation) Biblionix; (ILL) OCLC ILLiad; (OPAC) Biblionix; (Serials) Biblionix
Wireless access
Function: ILL available
Open Mon-Fri 9-6, Sat 9-1
Friends of the Library Group

PONDER

P   BETTY FOSTER PUBLIC LIBRARY*, 405 Shaffner St, 76259. Tel: 940-479-2683. FAX: 940-479-2314. E-mail: bettyfosterpubliclibrary@pondertx.com. *Actg Dir,* Shelly Bannister
Circ 8,346
Library Holdings: Bk Vols 8,000
Automation Activity & Vendor Info: (Acquisitions) Evergreen; (Cataloging) Evergreen; (Circulation) Evergreen; (ILL) Evergreen; (Serials) Evergreen
Mem of North Texas Library Partners
Open Tues & Wed 10-6, Thurs 10-7, Fri 12-6, Sat 9-1
Friends of the Library Group

PORT ARANSAS

P   ELLIS MEMORIAL LIBRARY*, 700 W Ave A, 78373. SAN 376-4303. Tel: 361-749-4116. FAX: 361-749-5679. E-mail: eml@cityofportaransas.org. *Dir,* Kathy Caldwell; Staff 4 (MLS 1, Non-MLS 3)
Pop 3,370
Library Holdings: Bk Vols 16,500; Per Subs 80

PORT ARTHUR

M   CHRISTUS ST MARY HOSPITAL*, Health Science Library, 3600 Gates Blvd, 77642-3850. (Mail add: PO Box 3696, 77643-3696), SAN 322-7537. Tel: 409-989-5150, 409-989-5804. FAX: 409-989-5137. *Health Info Coordr,* Sanford Herine
Library Holdings: Bk Titles 22,000
Subject Interests: Dentistry, Dermatology, Pathology, Radiology
Restriction: Staff use only

C   LAMAR STATE COLLEGE, Gates Memorial Library, 317 Stilwell Blvd, 77640. (Mail add: PO Box 310, 77641-0310), SAN 378-0716. Tel: 409-984-6222. Interlibrary Loan Service Tel: 409-984-6218. Reference Tel: 409-984-6220. FAX: 409-984-6008. Web Site: library.lamarpa.edu. *Dean of Libr,* Peter B Kaatrude; Tel: 409-984-6216, E-mail: kaatrpb@lamarpa.edu; *Coordr,* Jimmet G Lawrence; E-mail: jimmet.lawrence@lamarpa.edu; *Acq, Automation Syst Coordr,* Patty Oltremari; Tel: 409-984-6225, E-mail: oltremari.patricia@lamarpa.edu; *Distance Educ,* Chad Clark; Tel: 409-984-6224, E-mail: clarkce@lamarpa.edu; *ILL,* Myra A Thompson; E-mail: myra.thompson@lamarpa.edu; Staff 9 (MLS 3, Non-MLS 6)
Founded 1909. Enrl 3,000; Fac 135; Highest Degree: Associate

Sept 2012-Aug 2013 Income $510,000. Mats Exp $190,000, Books $90,000, Per/Ser (Incl. Access Fees) $25,000, AV Equip $5,000, AV Mat $15,000, Electronic Ref Mat (Incl. Access Fees) $35,000, Presv $2,000. Sal $300,000 (Prof $175,000)
Library Holdings: AV Mats 2,000; Bks on Deafness & Sign Lang 10; e-books 28,000; e-journals 32,000; Bk Titles 45,000; Bk Vols 60,000; Per Subs 200
Special Collections: Music Heritage (Janis Joplin Coll); Texana Coll
Subject Interests: Careers, Law, Nursing, Undergrad studies
Automation Activity & Vendor Info: (Acquisitions) EOS International; (Cataloging) EOS International; (Circulation) EOS International; (Course Reserve) EOS International; (ILL) EOS International; (OPAC) EOS International; (Serials) EOS International
Database Vendor: Amigos Library Services, Baker & Taylor, Cinahl Information Systems, EBSCOhost, Gale Cengage Learning, LexisNexis, Marcive, Inc, Medline, Newsbank, OCLC FirstSearch, OCLC WorldCat, OVID Technologies, ProQuest, Westlaw
Wireless access
Partic in TexSHARE - Texas State Library & Archives Commission
Special Services for the Deaf - ADA equip; Assisted listening device; Assistive tech; Bks on deafness & sign lang; Closed caption videos; Interpreter on staff; Pocket talkers; Sign lang interpreter upon request for prog; Staff with knowledge of sign lang; Video & TTY relay via computer
Special Services for the Blind - Accessible computers; Assistive/Adapted tech devices, equip & products; Audio mat; Bks available with recordings; Compressed speech equip; Computer access aids; Computer with voice synthesizer for visually impaired persons; Copier with enlargement capabilities; Digital talking bk; Ednalite Hi-Vision scope; Internet workstation with adaptive software; Magnifiers
Open Mon-Thurs 7:30-7:30, Fri 7:30-5

P   PORT ARTHUR PUBLIC LIBRARY*, 4615 Ninth Ave, 77642. SAN 362-1723. Tel: 409-985-8838. Circulation Tel: 409-985-8838, Ext 2238. Reference Tel: 409-985-8838, Ext 2240. FAX: 409-985-5969. Web Site: www.pap.lib.tx.us. *Dir,* Jose Martinez; Tel: 409-985-8838, Ext 2234; *Asst Dir,* Rick Whitaker; Tel: 409-985-8838, Ext 2241; *Head, Cat,* Janell Farris; Tel: 409-985-8838, Ext 2229; *Ch,* Carolyn Thibodeaux; Tel: 409-985-8838, Ext 2237; *Circ Supvr,* Steven Williams; Staff 18 (MLS 3, Non-MLS 15)
Founded 1918. Pop 56,827
Library Holdings: CDs 1,782; e-books 1,700; Large Print Bks 5,250; Bk Titles 161,230; Bk Vols 182,000; Per Subs 205; Videos 3,860
Special Collections: Port Arthur History Archives (includes historical photos of Port Arthur people & places; information on Arthur Stilwell, John W "Bet-A-Million" Gates, Janis Joplin, Jimmy Johnson, Robert Rauschenberg, Karen Silkwood & other notables who have called Port Arthur home. Oral History
Automation Activity & Vendor Info: (Cataloging) Innovative Interfaces, Inc; (Circulation) Innovative Interfaces, Inc
Database Vendor: Gale Cengage Learning
Wireless access
Publications: Friends Newsletter
Special Services for the Blind - Talking bks
Open Mon-Thurs 9-9, Fri 9-6, Sat 9-5, Sun (Sept-May) 2-5
Friends of the Library Group

PORT ISABEL

P   PORT ISABEL PUBLIC LIBRARY*, 213 Yturria St, 78578. SAN 316-6783. Tel: 956-943-1822. FAX: 956-943-4638. Web Site: pilibrary.net. *Libr Dir,* Carolyn Bogardus; *Asst Dir,* Ida Tellez; *Ch,* Marilyn Ponder; *Circ,* Carmen Tadeo
Pop 20,000; Circ 28,465
Library Holdings: Bk Titles 24,245; Bk Vols 26,057; Per Subs 72
Automation Activity & Vendor Info: (Cataloging) Biblionix; (Circulation) Biblionix
Wireless access
Open Mon & Tues (Winter) 8:30-5:30, Wed 9-6, Thurs 10-7, Fri 10-5, Sat 9-1; Mon-Fri (Summer) 9-6
Friends of the Library Group

PORT LAVACA

P   CALHOUN COUNTY LIBRARY*, 200 W Mahan, 77979. SAN 362-1782. Tel: 361-552-7323. Reference Tel: 361-552-7250. FAX: 361-552-4926. Web Site: www.cclibrary.org. *Dir,* Noemi Cruz; E-mail: ncruz@cclibrary.org; Staff 1 (Non-MLS 1)
Founded 1962. Pop 21,300; Circ 105,999
Jan 2011-Dec 2011 Income (Main Library and Branch(s)) $423,558. Mats Exp $42,000
Library Holdings: Bk Titles 76,749; Bk Vols 111,867; Per Subs 167
Automation Activity & Vendor Info: (Cataloging) Follett Software; (Circulation) Follett Software
Publications: Booklist; Library Journal; Public Libraries
Open Tues & Thurs 10-8, Wed & Fri 10-6, Sat 9-1
Friends of the Library Group

Branches: 3
POINT COMFORT BRANCH, One Lamar St, Point Comfort, 77978.
(Mail add: PO Box 424, Point Comfort, 77978-0424), SAN 362-1812.
Tel: 361-987-2954. FAX: 361-987-2954. *Librn,* Grace Bradley; E-mail:
gbradley@cclibrary.org; Staff 2 (MLS 1, Non-MLS 1)
Pop 780
Library Holdings: Bk Vols 15,000; Per Subs 30
Open Tues 9-1:30 & 2-6, Wed & Thurs 10:30-1:30 & 2-6 Fri 10-3, Sat
9-2
PORT O'CONNOR BRANCH, Hwy 185 & Sixth St, Port O'Connor,
77982. (Mail add: PO Box 424, Port O'Connor, 77982), SAN 370-4564.
Tel: 361-983-4365. FAX: 316-983-4365. *Librn,* Shirley Gordon; E-mail:
sgordon@cclibrary.org; Staff 1 (Non-MLS 1)
Pop 1,182
Library Holdings: Bk Vols 25,000; Per Subs 8
Friends of the Library Group
SEADRIFT BRANCH, 103 W Dallas, Seadrift, 77983. (Mail add: PO Box
576, Seadrift, 77983), SAN 362-1847. Tel: 361-785-4241. FAX:
361-785-2346. *Librn,* C J Garriott; Staff 1 (Non-MLS 1)
Pop 1,230
Library Holdings: Bk Vols 12,000
Friends of the Library Group

PORT NECHES

P   EFFIE & WILTON HEBERT PUBLIC LIBRARY*, 2025 Merriman St,
77651. SAN 320-5150. Tel: 409-722-4554. FAX: 409-719-4296. Web Site:
www.ptn.lib.tx.us. *Dir,* Mark Durham; Staff 1 (MLS 1)
Founded 1934. Pop 13,944
Library Holdings: Bk Vols 60,000; Per Subs 105
Subject Interests: Acadian genealogy, Texana
Automation Activity & Vendor Info: (Acquisitions) Innovative Interfaces,
Inc; (Cataloging) Innovative Interfaces, Inc; (Circulation) Innovative
Interfaces, Inc; (OPAC) Innovative Interfaces, Inc
Open Mon-Thurs 8:30-8:30, Fri 9-5, Sun 2:30-8:30
Friends of the Library Group

PORTLAND

P   BELL-WHITTINGTON PUBLIC LIBRARY*, 2400 Memorial Pkwy,
78374. SAN 316-6805. Tel: 361-777-0921. FAX: 361-643-6411. E-mail:
bwpubliclibrary@gmail.com. Web Site: www.portlandtxlibrary.com. *Dir,*
RoseAleta Laurell; E-mail: rlaurell@portlandtx.com; Staff 4 (MLS 4)
Founded 1934. Pop 12,000; Circ 80,000
Library Holdings: Bk Vols 40,000; Per Subs 70
Special Collections: Oral History
Subject Interests: Antique collecting, Archit, Art, Educ, Genealogy
Automation Activity & Vendor Info: (Cataloging) LibLime; (Circulation)
LibLime; (OPAC) LibLime
Wireless access
Publications: Annual Report
Mem of San Patricio County Library System
Partic in Tex Share
Open Mon-Thurs 9-8, Fri 9-5, Sat 10-2
Friends of the Library Group

POST

P   POST PUBLIC LIBRARY*, 105 E Main St, 79356-3299. SAN 316-6813.
Tel: 806-990-2149. E-mail: postpublic@yahoo.com. *Librn,* Peggy Ashley;
Staff 1.5 (Non-MLS 1.5)
Founded 1966. Pop 5,182; Circ 16,530
Library Holdings: Bk Titles 14,940; Bk Vols 14,983; Per Subs 12
Special Collections: US Document Depository
Subject Interests: Tex
Wireless access
Mem of West Texas Library System
Open Mon & Thurs 9:30-5, Tues, Wed & Fri 12-5

POTEET

P   POTEET PUBLIC LIBRARY*, 500 Ave H, 78065. (Mail add: PO Box
380, 78065-0380), SAN 316-6821. Tel: 830-742-8917. FAX:
830-742-3988. *Dir,* Gloria O Solis
Pop 6,402
Library Holdings: Bk Titles 9,500; Per Subs 25
Special Collections: Texana Coll
Wireless access
Special Services for the Deaf - Bks on deafness & sign lang; Captioned
film dep; High interest/low vocabulary bks; Spec interest per
Open Mon-Fri 8-12 & 1-5
Friends of the Library Group

POTTSBORO

P   POTTSBORO AREA PUBLIC LIBRARY*, 104 N Main, 75076. (Mail
add: PO Box 477, 75076-0477), SAN 376-4427. Tel: 903-786-8274. FAX:
903-786-8274. E-mail: library@cityofpottsboro.com. *Dir,* Fern Watson;
E-mail: ewatson@cityofpottsboro.com
Founded 1985. Pop 2,000; Circ 4,000
Library Holdings: Bk Vols 15,000; Per Subs 3
Automation Activity & Vendor Info: (Cataloging) Biblionix; (Circulation)
Biblionix
Wireless access
Open Mon-Fri 1-5, Sat 10-2
Friends of the Library Group

PRAIRIE LEA

P   TRI-COMMUNITY LIBRARY*, 6910 Hwy 80, 78661. (Mail add: PO Box
44, 78661-0044). Tel: 512-488-2164. FAX: 512-488-9006. Web Site:
www.prairielea.txed.net/library/index.html. *Dir,* Lulu Ivarra; E-mail:
ivarral@plisd.net; Staff 1 (Non-MLS 1)
Library Holdings: Audiobooks 100; Bk Vols 8,000; Per Subs 15
Mem of Central Texas Library System, Inc
Open Mon & Wed (Winter) 7:30-3, Tues & Thurs 7:30am-8pm, Fri 7:30-2;
Tues & Thurs (Summer) 10-8

PRAIRIE VIEW

J   PRAIRIE VIEW A&M UNIVERSITY*, John B Coleman Library, PO Box
519, MS 1040, 77446-0519. SAN 316-683X. Tel: 936-261-1500. FAX:
936-261-1539. Web Site: www.pvamu.edu. *Dir, Libr Serv,* Dr Rosie
Albritton; E-mail: rlalbritton@pvamu.edu; *Asst Dir, Pub Serv,* Juanita
Walker; Tel: 936-261-1531, E-mail: jcwalker@pvamu.edu; *Asst Dir, Tech
Serv,* Helen Yeh; Tel: 936-261-1533, E-mail: hyyeh@pvamu.edu; *Univ
Archivist,* Phyllis Earles; Tel: 936-261-1516, E-mail: plearles@pvamu.edu
Founded 1878. Enrl 5,243; Fac 273; Highest Degree: Doctorate
Library Holdings: Bk Vols 333,057; Per Subs 872
Special Collections: Black Heritage of the West Coll; Black Lawless Coll;
Blacks in the US Military Coll
Subject Interests: Biol, Bus, Educ, Eng, Nursing
Automation Activity & Vendor Info: (Acquisitions) Ex Libris Group;
(Cataloging) Ex Libris Group; (Circulation) Ex Libris Group; (Course
Reserve) Ex Libris Group; (OPAC) Ex Libris Group; (Serials) Ex Libris
Group
Partic in Houston Area Research Library Consortium; OCLC Online
Computer Library Center, Inc; TexSHARE - Texas State Library &
Archives Commission
Open Mon-Thurs (Spring & Fall) 7am-Midnight, Fri & Sat 8-5, Sun
1pm-Midnight; Mon-Thurs (Summer) 8am-9pm, Fri & Sat 8-5
Friends of the Library Group

PRESIDIO

P   CITY OF PRESIDIO LIBRARY*, 1200 E O'Reilly St, 79845. (Mail add:
PO Box 2440, 79845-2440), SAN 376-432X. Tel: 432-229-3317. FAX:
432-229-4640. *Dir,* Carmen Elguezabal; E-mail: carmen_el@yahoo.com;
Staff 2 (Non-MLS 2)
Pop 4,169; Circ 7,700
Library Holdings: Bk Vols 11,000; Per Subs 20
Automation Activity & Vendor Info: (Circulation) Follett Software;
(OPAC) Follett Software
Wireless access
Mem of Texas Trans-Pecos Regional Library System
Open Mon-Fri 9-1 & 2-6, Sat (Nov-Aug) 10-2

PROSPER

P   PROSPER COMMUNITY LIBRARY*, 700 N Coleman Rd, 75078. (Mail
add: PO Box 219, 75078-0219). Tel: 469-219-2499. FAX: 972-346-9115.
Web Site: www.prospertx.gov/prosperlibrary.aspx. *In Charge,* Linda Shaw;
E-mail: linda_shaw@prospertx.gov; Staff 3 (MLS 1, Non-MLS 2)
Founded 2001
Library Holdings: AV Mats 50; Bk Titles 12,530; Bk Vols 13,794; Per
Subs 40
Automation Activity & Vendor Info: (Cataloging) Follett Software;
(Circulation) Follett Software
Wireless access
Open Mon-Thurs (Winter) 9-8, Fri 9-4:30, Sat 10-3, Sun 1-5; Mon
(Summer) 10-8, Tues-Thurs 10-6, Sat 10-3, Sun 1-5
Friends of the Library Group

QUANAH

P   THOMPSON-SAWYER PUBLIC LIBRARY*, 403 W Third St, 79252.
SAN 376-4613. Tel: 940-663-2654. *Librn,* Janice Davis
Library Holdings: Bk Vols 25,000; Per Subs 12

Automation Activity & Vendor Info: (Cataloging) Follett Software; (Circulation) Follett Software
Wireless access
Mem of North Texas Library Partners
Open Tues & Wed 9:30-11:30 & 12:30-5:30, Thurs & Fri 12:30-5:30, Sat 9:30-3:30
Friends of the Library Group

QUEMADO

P   QUEMADO PUBLIC LIBRARY*, 19791 N Hwy 277, 78877. (Mail add: PO Box 210, 78877-0210), SAN 376-4168. Tel: 830-757-1313. FAX: 830-757-3322. E-mail: quemado.librarian@gmail.com. *Librn,* Carmen Broussard
Library Holdings: Bk Vols 14,000; Per Subs 15
Automation Activity & Vendor Info: (Cataloging) Follett Software; (Circulation) Follett Software
Open Mon-Fri 12-6

QUITAQUE

P   CAPROCK PUBLIC LIBRARY*, 104 N First, 79255. (Mail add: PO Box 487, 79255-0487), SAN 376-6519. Tel: 806-455-1225. FAX: 806-455-1225. E-mail: libqui1@yahoo.com. *Librn,* Arlene Hinkle
Library Holdings: Bk Vols 11,000
Open Tues-Fri 7:30-5
Friends of the Library Group

QUITMAN

P   QUITMAN PUBLIC LIBRARY*, 202 East Goode St, 75783-2533. (Mail add: PO Box 1677, 75783-1677), SAN 320-8486. Tel: 903-763-4191. FAX: 903-763-2532. E-mail: qlibrary@texascellnet.com. Web Site: www.quitmanlibrary.org. *Dir of Libr Serv,* Delene H Allen; E-mail: delene460@hotmail.com; *Adult Serv, Asst Librn, Cat,* Martha Fregia; *Asst Librn, Cat, Ch,* Stephanie Fetty; *AV Coll, Cat, Circ Media,* Melissa Frosch; *Cat, Circ, Coll Develop,* Georgia V Hoffpauir; Staff 5 (Non-MLS 5)
Founded 1975. Pop 2,030; Circ 29,000
Oct 2007-Sept 2008 Income $90,000. Mats Exp $90,000
Library Holdings: AV Mats 2,500; Bks-By-Mail 75; Bks on Deafness & Sign Lang 25; Braille Volumes 10; DVDs 50; High Interest/Low Vocabulary Bk Vols 2,000; Large Print Bks 980; Bk Titles 28,000; Bk Vols 28,500; Per Subs 20; Talking Bks 1,050; Videos 2,500
Special Collections: Adult Continuing Education: ESL, GED, ASL, Adult Literacy (ACE Project Coll); American Sign Language Coll; Genealogy (Wood County Genealogy Society Coll); Texas Section; Trade Materials for Homeschoolers (Homeschool Section Coll). Municipal Document Depository
Subject Interests: Adult literacy, Am sign lang, Brazil, Genealogy, Texana
Automation Activity & Vendor Info: (Acquisitions) Biblionix; (Cataloging) Biblionix; (Circulation) Biblionix; (Course Reserve) Biblionix; (ILL) OCLC FirstSearch; (Media Booking) OCLC ILLiad; (OPAC) Biblionix; (Serials) Biblionix
Database Vendor: EBSCOhost, OCLC FirstSearch, OCLC WorldCat, ProQuest
Wireless access
Function: Adult literacy prog, AV serv, BA reader (adult literacy), Handicapped accessible, Home delivery & serv to Sr ctr & nursing homes, Homebound delivery serv, ILL available, Magnifiers for reading, Photocopying/Printing, Prog for children & young adult, Summer reading prog, Wheelchair accessible
Special Services for the Deaf - Adult & family literacy prog; Bks on deafness & sign lang; Closed caption videos; Deaf publ; High interest/low vocabulary bks; Spec interest per; Staff with knowledge of sign lang
Special Services for the Blind - Audio mat; Bks on cassette; Bks on CD; Braille bks; Extensive large print coll; Large print bks; Lending of low vision aids; Magnifiers; Talking bks; Videos on blindness & phys handicaps
Open Tues-Fri 10-6
Friends of the Library Group

RANDOLPH AFB

A   UNITED STATES AIR FORCE*, Randolph Air Force Base Library, Bldg 598, Fifth St E, 78150-4424. SAN 362-1901. Tel: 210-652-2617. FAX: 210-652-3261. Interlibrary Loan Service E-mail: library@rafblibrary.org. Web Site: rafblibrary.org. *Dir,* Dr Gail Trevino; Tel: 210-652-8901, E-mail: gail.trevino@randolph.af.mil; Staff 3 (MLS 2, Non-MLS 1)
Founded 1933
Library Holdings: Bk Titles 48,983; Per Subs 140
Special Collections: Air War College; Embry-Riddle Coll; Project Warrior; Texana
Subject Interests: Mil hist, Prof develop, Tex
Automation Activity & Vendor Info: (Acquisitions) Softlink America; (Cataloging) Softlink America; (Circulation) Softlink America; (Course Reserve) Softlink America; (ILL) OCLC; (OPAC) Softlink America; (Serials) Softlink America
Database Vendor: OCLC FirstSearch
Wireless access
Partic in Coun of Res & Acad Librs
Restriction: Circ to mil employees only
Friends of the Library Group

RANGER

P   RANGER CITY LIBRARY*, 718 Pine St, 76470. Tel: 254-647-1880. FAX: 254-647-3070. E-mail: rcl@txol.net. Web Site: rangercitylibrary.com. *Librn,* Diana McCullough
Library Holdings: Bk Vols 12,000; Per Subs 12
Wireless access
Mem of Big Country Library System
Open Mon 10-7:30, Tues-Fri 10-6

J   RANGER COLLEGE*, Golemon Library & Learning Resources Center, 1100 College Circle, 76470-3298. SAN 316-6880. Tel: 254-647-1414. FAX: 254-647-1656. E-mail: rclibrary@rangercollege.edu. Web Site: www.rangercollege.edu/Library. *Librn,* Cherie Beltran; *Asst Librn,* Avery Garrison; Staff 2 (MLS 1, Non-MLS 1)
Founded 1926. Enrl 1,200; Highest Degree: Associate
Library Holdings: AV Mats 262; Bk Vols 30,000; Per Subs 75
Special Collections: Robert E Howard Coll
Automation Activity & Vendor Info: (Cataloging) Follett Software; (Circulation) Follett Software
Database Vendor: EBSCOhost, Gale Cengage Learning, OVID Technologies
Wireless access
Publications: Learning Resources Newsletter
Partic in TexSHARE - Texas State Library & Archives Commission
Open Mon-Thurs 8am-9pm, Fri 8-1, Sun 4-9

RANKIN

P   RANKIN PUBLIC LIBRARY*, 310 E Tenth St, 79778. (Mail add: PO Box 6, 79778-0006), SAN 316-6899. Tel: 432-693-2881. FAX: 432-693-2667. *Dir,* Celia Hooker
Founded 1950. Pop 1,000; Circ 15,600
Library Holdings: Bk Vols 16,000; Per Subs 15
Automation Activity & Vendor Info: (Cataloging) Follett Software; (Circulation) Follett Software
Publications: Newsletter
Mem of West Texas Library System
Open Mon-Thurs 9:30-5
Branches: 1
MIDKIFF PUBLIC, 12701 No FM 2401, Midkiff, 79755. (Mail add: PO Box 160, Midkiff, 79755). Tel: 432-535-2311. FAX: 432-535-2312. *Librn,* Teresa Latzel
Pop 100
Open Tues & Thurs 10:30-5:30

RAYMONDVILLE

P   REBER MEMORIAL LIBRARY*, 193 N Fourth, 78580-1994. SAN 316-6902. Tel: 956-689-2930. FAX: 956-689-6476. *Librn,* Virginia Barron
Pop 21,000; Circ 43,423
Library Holdings: Bk Vols 48,000; Per Subs 22
Automation Activity & Vendor Info: (Cataloging) Follett Software; (Circulation) Follett Software
Wireless access
Open Mon-Fri 9-6 (8-5 Summer)

RED OAK

P   RED OAK PUBLIC LIBRARY*, 200 Lakeview Pkwy, 75154. (Mail add: PO Box 393, 75154-0393), SAN 378-4487. Tel: 469-218-1230. FAX: 469-218-1231. E-mail: librarian@redoaktx.org. Web Site: www.redoakpubliclibrary.org. *Dir,* Theresa McNutt
Library Holdings: Bk Vols 10,500; Videos 700
Automation Activity & Vendor Info: (Acquisitions) Polaris Library Systems
Wireless access
Open Mon-Thurs 11-7, Fri & Sat 1-5

REFUGIO

P   DENNIS M O'CONNOR PUBLIC LIBRARY, 815 S Commerce St, 78377. SAN 316-6929. Tel: 361-526-2608. FAX: 361-526-2608. *Librn,* Tina McGuill
Pop 7,980; Circ 23,668
Library Holdings: AV Mats 769; Bk Titles 21,574; Bk Vols 23,635; Per Subs 53
Special Collections: Texas Room

Automation Activity & Vendor Info: (Cataloging) Follett Software; (Circulation) Follett Software
Wireless access
Open Mon-Fri 8-5

RHOME

P   RHOME PUBLIC LIBRARY*, 265 BC Rhome Ave, 76078. Tel: 817-636-2767. Web Site: www.cityofrhome.com/library.html. *Librn,* Linda Gillespie
Library Holdings: Bk Vols 2,000
Open Tues-Fri 1-5, Sat 10:30-2:30

RICHARDSON

SR   FIRST UNITED METHODIST CHURCH LIBRARY*, 503 N Central Expressway, 75080. SAN 328-5111. Tel: 972-301-0143. Administration Tel: 972-235-4056. FAX: 972-341-0140. E-mail: library@fumcr.com. *Librn,* Rosanna Whitfield
Founded 1959
Jul 2005-Jun 2006. Mats Exp $1,200
Library Holdings: Bk Titles 7,000
Restriction: Mem only

P   RICHARDSON PUBLIC LIBRARY, 900 Civic Center Dr, 75080. SAN 316-6945. Tel: 972-744-4350. Circulation Tel: 972-744-4363. Interlibrary Loan Service Tel: 972-744-4357. Reference Tel: 972-744-4355. FAX: 972-744-5806. Web Site: www.richardsonpubliclibrary.com. *Dir of Libr Serv,* Steve Benson; E-mail: steve.benson@cor.gov; *Asst Dir,* Susan Allison; E-mail: susan.allison@cor.gov; *ILL Librn,* Jane Nearing; E-mail: jane.nearing@cor.gov; *Commun Serv Supvr,* Janet Vance; Tel: 972-744-4376, E-mail: janet.vance@cor.gov; *Supvr, Ad Serv,* Hanna Jurecki; Tel: 972-744-4377, E-mail: hanna.jerecki@cor.gov; *Supvr, Tech Serv,* Yolanda Medina; Tel: 972-744-4368, E-mail: yolanda.medina@cor.gov; *Supvr, Youth Serv,* Tamara Golubski; Tel: 972-744-4383, E-mail: tamara.golubski@cor.gov; Staff 26 (MLS 17, Non-MLS 9)
Founded 1959. Pop 99,800; Circ 1,440,000
Oct 2011-Sept 2012 Income $3,310,000, City $3,300,000, Locally Generated Income $10,000. Mats Exp $432,000, Books $230,000, Per/Ser (Incl. Access Fees) $90,000, Micro $10,000, AV Mat $45,000, Electronic Ref Mat (Incl. Access Fees) $57,000. Sal $2,130,000
Library Holdings: Audiobooks 7,057; AV Mats 31,250; CDs 6,670; DVDs 17,000; e-books 1,600; High Interest/Low Vocabulary Bk Vols 1,050; Large Print Bks 10,000; Bk Titles 175,000; Bk Vols 230,000; Per Subs 275
Special Collections: Richardson Local History Coll, clippings, local govt publs, photog, scrapbks; World Language Materials Coll (Chinese, Korean, Vietnamese, Hindi, Urdu, Spanish, French & Russian)
Automation Activity & Vendor Info: (Acquisitions) SirsiDynix; (Cataloging) SirsiDynix; (Circulation) SirsiDynix; (OPAC) SirsiDynix; (Serials) SirsiDynix
Database Vendor: Baker & Taylor, BookLetters LLC, Bowker, EBSCOhost, Gale Cengage Learning, infoUSA, netLibrary, Newsbank, OCLC WorldCat, ProQuest, ReferenceUSA, SirsiDynix
Wireless access
Publications: Bibliographies
Open Mon-Thurs 10-9, Fri & Sat 10-6, Sun 2-6
Friends of the Library Group

C   UNIVERSITY OF TEXAS AT DALLAS, Eugene McDermott Library, 800 W Campbell Rd, 75080. (Mail add: PO Box 830643, MC33, 75083-0643), SAN 362-1995. Tel: 972-883-2950. Circulation Tel: 972-883-2953. Interlibrary Loan Service Tel: 972-883-2900. Reference Tel: 972-883-2955. Administration Tel: 972-883-2960. FAX: 972-883-2473. Web Site: www.utdallas.edu/library. *Dir of Libr,* Ellen Derey Safley; Tel: 972-883-2916, E-mail: safley@utdallas.edu; *Assoc Dir, Syst,* Jean Vik; Tel: 972-883-2623, Fax: 972-883-2988, E-mail: jvik@utdallas.edu; *Assoc Dir, Tech Serv,* Debbie Montgomery; Tel: 972-883-2963, E-mail: debmontg@utdallas.edu; *Head, Circ Serv,* Debbie Gilbert-Stadigh; E-mail: deborah@utdallas.edu; *Head, ILL,* Kristen Palmiere; E-mail: kxp125430@utdallas.edu; *Head, Info Literacy,* Loreen Henry; Tel: 972-883-2126, E-mail: loreen@utdallas.edu; *Head, Ref Serv,* Linda Snow; Tel: 972-883-2626, E-mail: snow@utdallas.edu; *Spec Coll Librn,* Paul Oelkrug; Tel: 972-883-2553, Fax: 972-883-4590, E-mail: oelkrug@utdallas.edu. Subject Specialists: *Mgt,* Loreen Henry; *Arts, Humanities,* Linda Snow; Staff 30 (MLS 25, Non-MLS 5)
Founded 1969. Enrl 19,900; Fac 500; Highest Degree: Doctorate
Library Holdings: AV Mats 5,646; CDs 2,107; e-books 1,094,541; e-journals 66,163; Bk Titles 1,888,627; Bk Vols 2,643,393; Per Subs 718; Videos 8,765
Special Collections: CAT/Air America Archives; Eugene & Margaret McDermott Coll; General James H Doolittle Military Aviation Library; History of Aviation Coll; History of the Book; Louise B Belsterling Botanical Library; Wineburgh Philatelic Research Library. US Document Depository

Automation Activity & Vendor Info: (Acquisitions) Ex Libris Group; (Cataloging) Ex Libris Group; (Circulation) Ex Libris Group; (Course Reserve) Docutek; (ILL) OCLC ILLiad; (OPAC) Ex Libris Group; (Serials) Ex Libris Group
Database Vendor: Baker & Taylor, Cambridge Scientific Abstracts, Dialog, EBSCOhost, Factiva.com, Gale Cengage Learning, JSTOR, LexisNexis, netLibrary, OCLC FirstSearch, OCLC WorldCat, ProQuest
Special Services for the Deaf - Assistive tech
Special Services for the Blind - Dragon Naturally Speaking software
Friends of the Library Group
Departmental Libraries:
CALLIER LIBRARY, 1966 Inwood Rd, Dallas, 75235, SAN 362-2029. Tel: 214-905-3165. Interlibrary Loan Service Tel: 214-883-2900. FAX: 214-905-3143. E-mail: callierlibrary@utdallas.edu. Web Site: callierlibrary.utdallas.edu, www.utdallas.edu/library/callier. *Sr Librn,* Wanda Tanghlyn; E-mail: wxt120330@utdallas.edu. Subject Specialists: *Communication disorders,* Wanda Tanghlyn; Staff 1 (MLS 1)
Library Holdings: Bk Vols 4,800
Subject Interests: Audiology, Deaf educ, Speech-lang pathology
Function: Computers for patron use, Doc delivery serv, e-mail & chat, E-Reserves, Electronic databases & coll, ILL available, Online cat, Online searches, Orientations, Outside serv via phone, mail, e-mail & web, Photocopying/Printing, Scanner, Spoken cassettes & CDs, Spoken cassettes & DVDs, VHS videos
Restriction: Fee for pub use, In-house use for visitors, Open to pub for ref only, Open to students, fac & staff

RICHLAND HILLS

P   RICHLAND HILLS PUBLIC LIBRARY*, 6724 Rena Dr, 76118-6297. SAN 316-3482. Tel: 817-299-1860. FAX: 817-299-1863. E-mail: library@richlandhills.com. Web Site: www.richlandhills.com. *Dir,* Theresa Tillery; *Asst Dir,* Jo Anne Mitchell; Staff 6 (MLS 1, Non-MLS 5)
Founded 1960. Pop 8,132; Circ 42,290
Oct 2008-Sept 2009 Income $292,931, State $6,300, City $271,685, Locally Generated Income $179, Other $14,767. Mats Exp $30,685, Books $11,996, Per/Ser (Incl. Access Fees) $2,587, Other Print Mats $1,468, AV Mat $1,336, Electronic Ref Mat (Incl. Access Fees) $256. Sal $193,462 (Prof $71,768)
Library Holdings: Audiobooks 767; Bks on Deafness & Sign Lang 20; CDs 607; DVDs 873; Electronic Media & Resources 52; Large Print Bks 760; Bk Titles 31,746; Bk Vols 32,963; Per Subs 98; Videos 1,020
Special Collections: Large Print Coll
Subject Interests: Local hist
Automation Activity & Vendor Info: (Cataloging) Horizon; (Circulation) Horizon; (OPAC) Horizon
Database Vendor: SirsiDynix
Function: Bks on cassette, Bks on CD, Children's prog, Computers for patron use, Copy machines, Electronic databases & coll, Free DVD rentals, Health sci info serv, Holiday prog, ILL available, Magnifiers for reading, Mail & tel request accepted, Music CDs, Online cat, Photocopying/Printing, Prog for adults, Prog for children & young adult, Pub access computers, Ref serv available, Story hour, Summer reading prog, Tax forms, Teen prog, Telephone ref, VHS videos, Wheelchair accessible
Mem of North Texas Library Partners
Special Services for the Deaf - Closed caption videos
Special Services for the Blind - Bks on cassette; Bks on CD; Large print bks
Open Mon, Wed & Fri 10-6, Tues & Thurs 1-9, Sat 10-2
Friends of the Library Group

RICHMOND

P   FORT BEND COUNTY LIBRARIES*, George Memorial Library, 1001 Golfview Dr, 77469-5199. SAN 362-2088. Tel: 281-342-4455. Circulation Tel: 281-341-2606. Interlibrary Loan Service Tel: 281-341-2605. Reference Tel: 281-341-2604. Administration Tel: 281-341-2603. FAX: 281-341-2688. Reference FAX: 281-341-2689. Automation Services FAX: 281-341-2685. TDD: 281-341-2669. E-mail: dfojtik@fortbend.lib.tx.us. Web Site: www.fortbend.lib.tx.us. *Libr Dir,* Clara Russell; Tel: 281-341-2618, E-mail: crussell@fortbend.lib.tx.us; *Asst Dir,* Joanne Downing; Tel: 281-341-2617, E-mail: jdowning@fortbend.lib.tx.us; *Bus Librn,* Patty Gonzales; Tel: 281-341-2644, E-mail: pgonzales@fortbend.lib.tx.us; *Outreach Serv Librn,* Sanchez Jorge; Tel: 281-344-3818, E-mail: jsanchez@fortbend.lib.tx.us; *Syst & Cat Librn,* Debra Lewis; Tel: 281-341-2633, E-mail: dlewis@fortbend.lib.tx.us; *Mgr,* Sample Daniel; Tel: 281-341-2646, E-mail: dsample@fortbend.lib.tx.us; *Staff Develop Coordr,* Myra Ponville; Tel: 281-341-2622, E-mail: mponville@fortbend.lib.tx.us; *Tech Coordr,* Jill Sumpter; Tel: 281-341-2630, E-mail: jsumpter@fortbend.lib.tx.us; *Ch,* Susan King; Tel: 281-341-2634, E-mail: sking@fortbend.lib.tx.us; *Circ,* Mary Beth Winograd; Tel: 281-341-2695, E-mail: mwinograd@fortbend.lib.tx.us; *Coll Develop, Ad,* Lorri Lessey; Tel: 281-341-2640, E-mail: llessey@fortbend.lib.tx.us; *Distance Educ,* Danea Hall; Tel: 281-341-2692, Fax: 281-341-2690, E-mail:

dhall@fortbend.lib.tx.us; *Pub Info Officer,* Joyce Claypool Kennerly, V; Tel: 281-341-2611, E-mail: jkennerly@fortbend.lib.tx.us; *Ref Serv, Ad,* Kenny Chao; Tel: 281-341-2653, E-mail: kchao@fortbend.lib.tx.us; *YA Serv,* Teresa Thiim; Tel: 281-341-2613, E-mail: tthiim@fortbend.lib.tx.us. Subject Specialists: *Genealogy, Local hist,* Sample Daniel; Staff 87 (MLS 19, Non-MLS 68)

Founded 1947. Pop 548,000; Circ 569,333

Oct 2009-Sept 2010 Income (Main Library Only) $12,523,357, State $141,277, County $12,327,480, Locally Generated Income $54,600. Mats Exp $542,091, Books $191,520, Per/Ser (Incl. Access Fees) $31,517, Micro $10,210, AV Equip $12,306, AV Mat $58,629, Electronic Ref Mat (Incl. Access Fees) $237,909. Sal $2,813,736 (Prof $1,183,711)

Library Holdings: Audiobooks 11,367; AV Mats 23,263; Braille Volumes 165; CDs 9,379; DVDs 7,332; e-books 22,697; Large Print Bks 5,652; Microforms 23; Bk Titles 125,799; Bk Vols 175,523; Per Subs 323; Videos 5,382

Special Collections: Civil War Coll; Genealogy & Local History Coll; Regional Historical Resource Depository of Texas; Restoration (George Carriage Coll); Texana

Automation Activity & Vendor Info: (Acquisitions) SirsiDynix; (Cataloging) SirsiDynix; (Circulation) SirsiDynix; (ILL) SirsiDynix; (OPAC) SirsiDynix; (Serials) SirsiDynix

Database Vendor: ALLDATA Online, Amigos Library Services, BookLetters LLC, Brodart, BWI, CountryWatch, CQ Press, EBSCO Auto Repair Reference, EBSCOhost, Facts on File, Gale Cengage Learning, infoUSA, Ingram Library Services, LearningExpress, Marcive, Inc, netLibrary, OCLC FirstSearch, OCLC WorldCat, Overdrive, Inc, ProQuest, ReferenceUSA, SerialsSolutions, SirsiDynix, Standard & Poor's, ValueLine, WebFeat, WebMD, World Book Online, WT Cox

Wireless access

Publications: Annual Report; Calendar of Library Events (Monthly); Public Newsletter (Quarterly); Staff Newsletter

Special Services for the Deaf - TDD equip

Open Mon-Thurs 9-9, Fri & Sat 9-5, Sun 1-5

Friends of the Library Group

Branches: 9

CINCO RANCH, 2620 Commercial Center Blvd, Katy, 77494. Tel: 281-395-1311. FAX: 281-395-6377. TDD: 281-693-7845. *Librn,* Virginia Harrell; Tel: 281-633-4600, E-mail: vharrell@fortbend.lib.tx.us; Staff 23 (MLS 5, Non-MLS 18)

Founded 1999. Pop 548,000; Circ 773,664

Oct 2009-Sept 2010. Mats Exp $244,539, Books $148,592, Per/Ser (Incl. Access Fees) $9,768, AV Mat $28,453, Electronic Ref Mat (Incl. Access Fees) $57,726. Sal $604,188 (Prof $193,071)

Library Holdings: Audiobooks 3,929; AV Mats 12,920; CDs 5,073; DVDs 4,967; Large Print Bks 855; Bk Titles 73,072; Bk Vols 109,178; Per Subs 186; Videos 1,213

Open Mon 12-9, Tues & Thurs 10-9, Wed 10-6, Fri 12-5, Sat 10-5

Friends of the Library Group

FIRST COLONY, 2121 Austin Pkwy, Sugar Land, 77479-1219, SAN 374-4345. Tel: 281-265-4444. FAX: 281-265-4440. TDD: 281-565-0798. *Br Mgr,* Janna Raven; Tel: 281-265-0969, E-mail: jraven@fortbend.lib.tx.us; Staff 26 (MLS 5, Non-MLS 21)

Pop 548,000; Circ 760,286

Oct 2009-Sept 2010. Mats Exp $232,427, Books $144,721, Per/Ser (Incl. Access Fees) $10,912, AV Mat $34,407, Electronic Ref Mat (Incl. Access Fees) $42,387. Sal $663,586 (Prof $194,217)

Library Holdings: Audiobooks 3,575; AV Mats 11,734; CDs 4,878; DVDs 4,755; Large Print Bks 765; Bk Titles 69,728; Bk Vols 99,312; Per Subs 153; Videos 676

Database Vendor: Wilson - Wilson Web

Special Services for the Deaf - TDD equip

Open Mon 12-9, Tues-Thurs 10-9, Fri 12-5, Sat 9-5

Friends of the Library Group

FORT BEND COUNTY LAW LIBRARY, 401 Jackson, 77469, SAN 370-9205. Tel: 281-341-3718. FAX: 281-342-0734. *Librn,* Melissa Salnave; E-mail: msalnave@fortbend.lib.tx.us; Staff 1 (MLS 1)

Founded 1989. Pop 548,000

Oct 2009-Sept 2010 Income $224,908. Mats Exp $134,576, Books $80,036, Per/Ser (Incl. Access Fees) $1,967, Electronic Ref Mat (Incl. Access Fees) $52,573. Sal $51,135

Library Holdings: Bk Titles 713; Bk Vols 765; Per Subs 16

Database Vendor: LexisNexis, Westlaw

Open Mon-Fri 8-5

ALBERT GEORGE BRANCH, 9230 Gene St, Needville, 77461-8313, SAN 362-2118. Tel: 979-793-4270. FAX: 281-342-5992. TDD: 979-793-3672. *Br Mgr,* Patricia Dittrich; E-mail: pdittrich@fortbend.lib.tx.us; Staff 4 (MLS 1, Non-MLS 3)

Founded 1974. Pop 548,000; Circ 56,849

Oct 2009-Sept 2010. Mats Exp $78,528, Books $44,279, Per/Ser (Incl. Access Fees) $2,955, AV Mat $9,758, Electronic Ref Mat (Incl. Access Fees) $21,536. Sal $121,270 (Prof $42,233)

Library Holdings: Audiobooks 779; AV Mats 3,888; CDs 1,462; DVDs 1,618; Large Print Bks 206; Bk Titles 62,043; Bk Vols 83,647; Per Subs 81; Videos 371

Special Services for the Deaf - TDD equip

Open Mon 12-8, Tues 10-8, Wed & Thurs 10-6, Fri 12-5, Sat 9-1

Friends of the Library Group

MAMIE GEORGE BRANCH, 320 Dulles Ave, Stafford, 77477-4799, SAN 362-2142. Tel: 281-491-8086. FAX: 281-242-5793. *Br Mgr,* Barbara Barton; Tel: 281-242-7398, E-mail: bbarton@fortbend.lib.tx.us; Staff 4 (MLS 1, Non-MLS 3)

Founded 1974. Pop 548,000; Circ 114,838

Oct 2009-Sept 2010. Mats Exp $84,230, Books $46,962, Per/Ser (Incl. Access Fees) $2,834, AV Mat $10,341, Electronic Ref Mat (Incl. Access Fees) $24,093. Sal $122,469 (Prof $49,859)

Library Holdings: Audiobooks 1,295; AV Mats 5,143; CDs 1,742; DVDs 2,162; Large Print Bks 404; Bk Titles 27,154; Bk Vols 35,115; Per Subs 50; Videos 757

Subject Interests: Music

Database Vendor: Project MUSE

Open Mon 12-8, Tues-Thurs 10-6, Fri 12-5

Friends of the Library Group

BOB LUTTS FULSHEAR SIMONTON BRANCH, 8100 FM 359 S, Fulshear, 77441. (Mail add: PO Box 907, Fulshear, 77441-0907), SAN 373-2762. Tel: 281-346-1432. FAX: 281-346-1265. TDD: 281-346-1281. *Br Mgr,* Dana Brittain; Tel: 281-346-2384, E-mail: dbrittain@fortbend.lib.tx.us; Staff 6 (MLS 1, Non-MLS 5)

Pop 548,000; Circ 81,976

Oct 2009-Sept 2010. Mats Exp $178,337, Books $108,007, Per/Ser (Incl. Access Fees) $9,515, AV Mat $15,971, Electronic Ref Mat (Incl. Access Fees) $44,844. Sal $169,024 (Prof $41,400)

Library Holdings: Audiobooks 1,436; AV Mats 5,871; CDs 2,144; DVDs 2,431; Large Print Bks 260; Bk Titles 37,512; Bk Vols 45,400; Per Subs 104; Videos 946

Open Mon 12-8, Tues & Wed 9-6, Thurs 9-8, Fri 12-5, Sat 9-5

Restriction: Authorized patrons

Friends of the Library Group

MISSOURI CITY BRANCH, 1530 Texas Pkwy, Missouri City, 77489-2170, SAN 373-2754. Tel: 281-499-4100. FAX: 281-261-5829. TDD: 281-261-5944. *Br Mgr,* Shearron-Hawkins Cecilia; Tel: 281-261-3044, E-mail: cshawkins@fortbend.lib.tx.us; Staff 16 (MLS 4, Non-MLS 12)

Founded 1992. Circ 241,547

Oct 2009-Sept 2010. Mats Exp $178,337, Books $108,007, Per/Ser (Incl. Access Fees) $9,515, AV Mat $15,971, Electronic Ref Mat (Incl. Access Fees) $44,844. Sal $387,014 (Prof $153,183)

Library Holdings: Audiobooks 2,028; AV Mats 9,366; CDs 3,570; DVDs 3,933; Large Print Bks 489; Bk Titles 62,043; Bk Vols 83,647; Per Subs 171; Videos 1,004

Special Services for the Deaf - TDD equip

Open Mon 12-9, Tues & Wed 10-9, Thurs 10-6, Fri 12-5, Sat 10-5

Restriction: Access at librarian's discretion

Friends of the Library Group

SIENNA BRANCH, 8411 Sienna Springs Blvd, Missouri City, 77459. Tel: 281-238-2900. FAX: 281-238-2902. *Br Mgr,* David Lukose; Tel: 281-238-2912, E-mail: dlukose@fortbend.lib.tx.us; Staff 27 (MLS 8, Non-MLS 19)

Pop 548,000; Circ 225,679

Oct 2009-Sept 2010. Mats Exp $202,906, Books $148,132, Per/Ser (Incl. Access Fees) $9,734, AV Mat $36,986, Electronic Ref Mat (Incl. Access Fees) $8,054. Sal $610,547 (Prof $259,122)

Library Holdings: Audiobooks 2,603; AV Mats 11,742; CDs 3,734; DVDs 7,277; Large Print Bks 430; Bk Titles 75,350; Bk Vols 105,602; Per Subs 1,415; Videos 11,915

SUGAR LAND BRANCH, 550 Eldridge Rd, Sugar Land, 77478. Tel: 281-277-8934. FAX: 281-277-8945. TDD: 281-277-8963. *Br Mgr,* Cindy Ruggeri; Tel: 281-277-8943, E-mail: cruggeri@fortbend.lib.tx.us; Staff 20 (MLS 4, Non-MLS 16)

Founded 1999. Pop 548,000; Circ 563,268

Oct 2009-Sept 2010. Mats Exp $215,750, Books $141,743, Per/Ser (Incl. Access Fees) $9,759, AV Mat $24,417, Electronic Ref Mat (Incl. Access Fees) $39,831. Sal $536,309 (Prof $185,558)

Library Holdings: Audiobooks 3,994; AV Mats 11,348; CDs 4,213; DVDs 3,712; Large Print Bks 373; Bk Titles 75,350; Bk Vols 105,602; Per Subs 154; Videos 3,305

Open Mon 12-9, Tues & Thurs 10-9, Wed 10-6, Fri 12-5, Sat 10-5

Friends of the Library Group

RIO GRANDE CITY

P   RIO GRANDE CITY PUBLIC LIBRARY*, 591 E Canales St, 78582-3588. SAN 372-7580. Tel: 956-487-4389. FAX: 956-487-7390. E-mail: rgclibrary@yahoo.com. Web Site: www.rgclibrary.org. *Dir,* Norma Gomez Fultz; *Asst Br Mgr,* Leticia Guerra; Staff 4 (Non-MLS 4)

Founded 1990. Pop 11,923

Library Holdings: Bk Titles 35,000; Per Subs 55

Automation Activity & Vendor Info: (Cataloging) Biblionix; (Circulation) Biblionix; (OPAC) Follett Software

Wireless access

Function: Photocopying/Printing, Preschool outreach, Prog for children & young adult, Provide serv for the mentally ill, Serves mentally handicapped consumers, Spoken cassettes & CDs, Summer reading prog, Tax forms, VHS videos
Publications: Library Update
Open Mon-Thurs 8:30-7, Fri 8:30-5:30
Friends of the Library Group

RIO HONDO

P   RIO HONDO PUBLIC LIBRARY*, 121 N Arroyo Blvd, 78583. (Mail add: PO Box 740, 78583-0740), SAN 376-4311. Tel: 956-748-3322. FAX: 956-748-3322. Web Site: www.cityofriohondo.com/library. *Dir,* Maria Turner; E-mail: mjturner@riohondo.com; Staff 2 (Non-MLS 2)
Library Holdings: Bk Titles 25,000; Per Subs 18
Automation Activity & Vendor Info: (Cataloging) Biblionix; (Circulation) Biblionix; (OPAC) Biblionix
Wireless access
Open Mon-Fri 12-6, Sat 9-12

RIVER OAKS

P   RIVER OAKS PUBLIC LIBRARY*, 4900 River Oaks Blvd, 76114. SAN 316-6961. Tel: 817-624-7344. FAX: 817-624-6214. E-mail: ropl59@yahoo.com. Web Site: www.riveroakslibrary.com. *Librn,* Mary Earwood; E-mail: maryearwood@charter.net; Staff 7 (Non-MLS 7)
Founded 1959. Pop 6,900; Circ 58,207
Library Holdings: AV Mats 2,100; Bks on Deafness & Sign Lang 125; Large Print Bks 700; Bk Vols 28,292; Per Subs 30; Talking Bks 500
Wireless access
Mem of North Texas Library Partners
Restriction: Residents only
Friends of the Library Group

ROANOKE

P   ROANOKE PUBLIC LIBRARY*, 308 S Walnut St, 76262. SAN 373-2800. Tel: 817-491-2691. FAX: 817-491-2729. E-mail: library@roanoketexas.com. Web Site: www.roanoketexas.com. *Dir,* Jesse Ephraim; E-mail: jephraim@roanoketexas.com; *Asst City Librn,* Debra Wallace; Staff 4 (MLS 1, Non-MLS 3)
Founded 1979. Pop 8,700; Circ 57,800
Library Holdings: CDs 692; DVDs 476; Large Print Bks 1,595; Bk Titles 39,200; Per Subs 20; Videos 3,198
Special Collections: Texana. Oral History
Automation Activity & Vendor Info: (Acquisitions) Book Systems, Inc; (Cataloging) Book Systems, Inc; (Circulation) Book Systems, Inc; (OPAC) Book Systems, Inc
Database Vendor: EBSCOhost, Facts on File, Gale Cengage Learning, infoUSA, netLibrary, Newsbank, OCLC FirstSearch, Wilson - Wilson Web
Wireless access
Function: Adult literacy prog, AV serv, CD-ROM, Digital talking bks, Homebound delivery serv, ILL available, Music CDs, Online searches, Prog for adults, Prog for children & young adult, Provide serv for the mentally ill, Ref serv available, Spoken cassettes & CDs, Summer reading prog, VHS videos, Wheelchair accessible
Mem of North Texas Library Partners
Partic in Midwest Collaborative for Library Services (MCLS)
Special Services for the Deaf - Bks on deafness & sign lang; High interest/low vocabulary bks
Open Mon-Thurs 10-9, Fri & Sat 10-6
Restriction: Non-resident fee, Residents only
Friends of the Library Group

ROBERT LEE

P   COKE COUNTY LIBRARY*, 706 Austin St, 76945. (Mail add: PO Box 637, 76945-0637), SAN 316-697X. Tel: 325-453-2495. E-mail: cokelib@wcc.net. *Librn,* Beth Prather
Pop 3,367; Circ 6,532
Library Holdings: AV Mats 28; Bk Vols 11,000
Mem of Big Country Library System
Partic in Tex Share
Open Tues & Fri 8-12, Wed 8-4, Thurs 1-5

ROBSTOWN

P   NUECES COUNTY KEACH FAMILY LIBRARY*, 100 Terry Shamsie Blvd, 78380. SAN 362-2177. Tel: 361-387-3431. FAX: 361-387-7964. Web Site: ncl-lsweb.nueces.esc2.net. *Dir,* Ida Gonzalez-Garza; Tel: 361-387-4817, E-mail: ida.garza@co.nueces.tx.us; *Ref Librn, Youth Serv,* Laura Chapa; E-mail: laura.chapa@co.nueces.tx.us. Subject Specialists: *Children, Youth,* Laura Chapa; Staff 10.5 (MLS 2, Non-MLS 8.5)
Founded 1976. Pop 31,819; Circ 41,062
Oct 2010-Sept 2011 Income $441,033, Locally Generated Income $393,033, Other $48,000. Mats Exp $83,000, Books $50,000, Other Print

Mats $2,000, AV Equip $1,000, AV Mat $15,000, Electronic Ref Mat (Incl. Access Fees) $15,000. Sal $203,240 (Prof $50,212)
Library Holdings: Audiobooks 426; AV Mats 119; Bks-By-Mail 136; Bks on Deafness & Sign Lang 14; CDs 169; DVDs 1,699; e-journals 7; Large Print Bks 99; Microforms 83; Bk Titles 32,046; Per Subs 49; Spec Interest Per Sub 1; Videos 230
Special Collections: Robstown Record Newspaper Coll, microfilm
Automation Activity & Vendor Info: (Acquisitions) TLC (The Library Corporation); (Cataloging) TLC (The Library Corporation); (Circulation) TLC (The Library Corporation); (ILL) TLC (The Library Corporation); (Media Booking) TLC (The Library Corporation); (OPAC) TLC (The Library Corporation)
Database Vendor: 3M Library Systems, Baker & Taylor, Brodart, EBSCO Information Services, EBSCOhost, Facts on File, Gale Cengage Learning, Grolier Online, H W Wilson, LearningExpress, McGraw-Hill, netLibrary, OCLC FirstSearch, OCLC WorldCat, TLC (The Library Corporation)
Function: Accelerated reader prog, Adult bk club, Adult literacy prog, After school storytime
Special Services for the Deaf - Bks on deafness & sign lang
Special Services for the Blind - Bks on cassette; Bks on CD
Open Mon-Thurs 10:30-8, Fri & Sat 10-3
Branches: 1
BISHOP BRANCH, 115 S Ash, Bishop, 78343, SAN 362-2207. Tel: 361-584-2222. FAX: 361-584-2225.
    Founded 2002. Pop 3,126
    Function: Accelerated reader prog
    Open Mon-Thurs 12-5

ROCKDALE

P   LUCY HILL PATTERSON MEMORIAL LIBRARY*, 201 Ackerman St, 76567. SAN 316-7003. Tel: 512-446-3410. FAX: 512-446-5597. E-mail: pattersonlib@rockdalecityhall.com. Web Site: www.rockdalelibrarytx.org. *Dir,* Melanie Todd; *Asst Librn,* Karen Newton; Staff 4 (Non-MLS 4)
Founded 1953. Pop 11,906; Circ 32,368
Library Holdings: AV Mats 1,281; Bk Titles 24,824; Bk Vols 28,396; Per Subs 14; Videos 336
Special Collections: Dr George Hill Patterson Coll (First Editions)
Mem of Central Texas Library System, Inc
Open Tues, Wed & Fri 10-6, Thurs 10-8, Sat 10-2
Friends of the Library Group

ROCKPORT

P   ARANSAS COUNTY PUBLIC LIBRARY*, 701 E Mimosa, 78382-4150. SAN 316-7011. Tel: 361-790-0153. FAX: 361-790-0150. Web Site: www.acplibrary.org. *Dir,* Iris Sanchez; E-mail: isanchez@aransascounty.org; Staff 5 (MLS 3, Non-MLS 2)
Founded 1956. Pop 22,497; Circ 70,000
Jan 2011-Dec 2011 Income $176,000. Mats Exp $160,475, Books $19,500. Sal $105,000
Library Holdings: CDs 146; DVDs 250; Large Print Bks 865; Bk Titles 46,000; Per Subs 13; Talking Bks 371; Videos 623
Subject Interests: Local hist
Automation Activity & Vendor Info: (Cataloging) Surpass; (Circulation) Surpass
Wireless access
Function: Computers for patron use, Copy machines, ILL available, Magnifiers for reading, Online cat, Photocopying/Printing, Prog for children & young adult, Summer reading prog, Tax forms, Telephone ref, VHS videos, Wheelchair accessible
Special Services for the Deaf - Bks on deafness & sign lang
Special Services for the Blind - Bks on cassette; Bks on CD; Large print bks; Magnifiers
Open Mon-Fri 9-6, Sat 10-2
Friends of the Library Group

ROCKSPRINGS

P   CLAUD H GILMER MEMORIAL LIBRARY*, 206 N Hwy 377, 78880. (Mail add: PO Box 157, 78880-0157). Tel: 830-683-8130. FAX: 830-683-8131. Web Site: www.rockspringsisd.net/library/library.htm. *Dir,* Lisa Scroggins; E-mail: lisa.scroggins@rockspringsisd.net; *Asst Dir,* Annie Haynes; E-mail: annie.haynes@rockspringsisd.net; Staff 3 (Non-MLS 3)
Pop 1,500; Circ 37,734
Library Holdings: AV Mats 350; Bk Titles 23,000; Per Subs 62; Talking Bks 55
Automation Activity & Vendor Info: (Cataloging) Follett Software; (Circulation) Follett Software
Wireless access
Function: Distance learning, Handicapped accessible, ILL available, Photocopying/Printing, Prog for children & young adult, Ref serv available, Summer reading prog, Wheelchair accessible
Special Services for the Deaf - Bks on deafness & sign lang; High interest/low vocabulary bks

Open Mon, Tues, Thurs & Fri (Winter) 8-6, Wed 8-8, Sat 9-12; Mon-Fri (Summer) 9-2
Restriction: Open to pub for ref & circ; with some limitations, Open to students, fac & staff, Pub use on premises

ROCKWALL

P   ROCKWALL COUNTY LIBRARY, 1215 E Yellowjacket Lane, 75087. SAN 316-7038. Tel: 972-204-7700. Reference Tel: 972-204-7770. FAX: 972-204-7709. E-mail: rocklib@rocklib.com. Web Site: www.rocklib.com, www.rockwallcountytexas.com/library. *Dir,* Marcine McCulley; *Ch Serv Librn,* Doreen Miller; *Generalist Librn,* Lindsey Snelling; *Ref Librn,* Alan Pippin; *Ref Librn,* Chantal Walvoord; *Circ Supvr,* Eileen Conway; Staff 7 (MLS 6, Non-MLS 1)
Founded 1945. Pop 78,000; Circ 367,316
Library Holdings: Audiobooks 3,720; CDs 1,876; DVDs 3,580; Large Print Bks 1,781; Bk Titles 60,510; Bk Vols 68,838; Per Subs 121
Subject Interests: Genealogy, Texana
Automation Activity & Vendor Info: (Acquisitions) Polaris Library Systems; (Cataloging) Polaris Library Systems; (Circulation) Polaris Library Systems; (OPAC) Polaris Library Systems
Database Vendor: TLC (The Library Corporation)
Wireless access
Function: Audiobks via web, Bks on CD, Citizenship assistance, Computer training, Electronic databases & coll, Handicapped accessible, ILL available, Literacy & newcomer serv, Magnifiers for reading, Prog for children & young adult, Pub access computers, Summer reading prog
Open Mon & Wed 10-6, Tues & Thurs 10-8, Fri 10-5, Sat 10-4
Friends of the Library Group

ROMA

P   STARR COUNTY PUBLIC LIBRARY*, Roma Branch, 1705 N Athens, 78584. SAN 376-1053. Tel: 956-849-0072. *Librn,* Eliama Cantu
Library Holdings: Bk Vols 9,500
Wireless access
Open Mon-Fri 9-6

ROSEBUD

P   D BROWN MEMORIAL LIBRARY*, 203 N Second St, 76570. (Mail add: PO Box 479, 76570), SAN 316-7046. Tel: 254-583-2328. FAX: 254-583-2328. E-mail: rosebud@members.ctls.net. Web Site: www.dbrownlibrary.org. *Dir,* Fran Hargrove; Staff 1 (Non-MLS 1)
Pop 1,600
Library Holdings: Bk Vols 12,000
Automation Activity & Vendor Info: (Cataloging) Biblionix; (Circulation) Biblionix; (OPAC) Biblionix
Wireless access
Mem of Central Texas Library System, Inc
Open Tues & Wed 12-7

ROTAN

P   ROTAN PUBLIC LIBRARY*, 404 E Sammy Baugh, 79546-3820. SAN 320-5169. Tel: 325-735-3362. E-mail: rotan.library@gmail.com. *Dir of Libr Serv,* Helen Elkins; Staff 1 (Non-MLS 1)
Founded 1978. Pop 4,719; Circ 8,333
Library Holdings: Bk Titles 10,679; Bk Vols 11,599; Per Subs 4
Special Collections: Genealogy Coll; Local History Coll; Texas Heritage Resource Center (Southwest Coll)
Automation Activity & Vendor Info: (Cataloging) LibLime; (Circulation) LibLime
Wireless access
Function: Homebound delivery serv
Mem of Big Country Library System
Open Tues & Wed 9-5:30, Thurs 9-1

ROUND ROCK

E   EMERSON PROCESS MANAGEMENT ELIBRARY, 1100 W Louis Henna Blvd, 78681. SAN 374-6674. Tel: 512-834-7255. Web Site: www.emersonprocess.com. *E-Libr Mgr,* Jane Bitter; E-mail: jane.bitter@emerson.com; Staff 1 (MLS 1)
Founded 1984
Library Holdings: Bk Titles 500; Per Subs 40
Automation Activity & Vendor Info: (Cataloging) Inmagic, Inc.; (Circulation) Inmagic, Inc.
Database Vendor: Dialog
Restriction: Employees & their associates

P   ROUND ROCK PUBLIC LIBRARY*, 216 E Main St, 78664. SAN 316-7054. Tel: 512-218-7000, 512-218-7003. Circulation Tel: 512-218-7001. Interlibrary Loan Service Tel: 512-218-7009. Administration Tel: 512-218-7005. Information Services Tel: 512-218-7006. FAX: 512-218-7061. Circulation FAX: 512-218-3272. Web Site:

www.roundrocktexas.gov/library. *Libr Mgr,* Michelle Cervantes; E-mail: mcervantes@round-rock.tx.us; *Librn II,* Jane Dance; E-mail: jdance@round-rock.tx.us; *Librn II,* Theresa Faris; *Librn II,* Geeta Halley; Tel: 512-218-7014, E-mail: ghalley@round-rock.tx.us; *Librn II,* Pat McElveon; E-mail: pmcelveen@round-rock.tx.us; *Mgr, Ch Serv,* Janette Johnston; Tel: 512-218-7002, E-mail: jj@round-rock.tx.us; Staff 12 (MLS 11, Non-MLS 1)
Founded 1963. Pop 75,000; Circ 510,000
Oct 2009-Sept 2010 Income $2,393,937, State $28,261, City $2,365,676. Sal $1,650,162
Library Holdings: AV Mats 10,578; Bk Titles 182,791; Per Subs 255
Special Collections: Fire Department Historical Room; Williamson County Genealogical Society Coll. Oral History
Subject Interests: Local hist, Texana
Automation Activity & Vendor Info: (Cataloging) Horizon; (Circulation) Horizon; (OPAC) Horizon
Database Vendor: EBSCOhost, Gale Cengage Learning, OCLC FirstSearch, SirsiDynix
Wireless access
Publications: Bibliographies
Mem of Central Texas Library System, Inc
Partic in TexSHARE - Texas State Library & Archives Commission
Open Mon-Thurs 9-9, Fri & Sat 9-6, Sun 1-6
Friends of the Library Group

ROUND TOP

P   ROUND TOP LIBRARY ASSOCIATION INC*, Round Top Family Library, 206 W Mill St, 78954. (Mail add: PO Box 245, 78954-0245). Tel: 979-249-2700. FAX: 979-249-2563. E-mail: info@ilovetoread.org. Web Site: ilovetoread.org. *Dir,* Barbara Smith; E-mail: barbara@ilovetoread.org
Founded 2000. Pop 1,177
Library Holdings: AV Mats 1,200; Bk Titles 12,000; Per Subs 12; Talking Bks 300
Special Collections: ByBee Texas Heritage Coll. Oral History
Automation Activity & Vendor Info: (Cataloging) Follett Software; (Circulation) Follett Software; (Course Reserve) Follett Software; (ILL) Follett Software; (OPAC) Follett Software
Mem of Central Texas Library System, Inc
Open Tues-Fri 1:30-5:30, Sat & Sun 1-4
Friends of the Library Group

S   UNIVERSITY OF TEXAS AT AUSTIN CENTER FOR AMERICAN HISTORY*, Winedale Historical Center Library, 3738 FM 2714, 78954. (Mail add: PO Box 11, 78954-0011), SAN 327-8530. Tel: 979-278-3530. FAX: 979-278-3531. E-mail: winedale@austin.utexas.edu. Web Site: www.cah.utexas.edu. *Dir,* Dr Don E Carleton; *Admin Mgr,* Barbara B White; E-mail: barbara.white@austin.utexas.edu
Founded 1969
Library Holdings: Bk Vols 1,000
Subject Interests: Antiques, Hist
Open Mon-Fri 8-5
Restriction: Non-circulating to the pub

ROWLETT

P   ROWLETT PUBLIC LIBRARY*, 3900 Main St, 75088-5075. SAN 361-4190. Tel: 972-412-6161. FAX: 972-412-6153. Web Site: www.rowlett.com/library. *Interim Dir,* Joyce Baumbach; Staff 8 (MLS 2.5, Non-MLS 5.5)
Pop 54,869
Library Holdings: Bk Titles 102,651
Automation Activity & Vendor Info: (Cataloging) SirsiDynix; (Circulation) SirsiDynix; (OPAC) SirsiDynix
Wireless access
Open Mon-Thurs 9:30-8:30, Fri & Sat 9:30-5:30
Friends of the Library Group

RUNGE

P   RUNGE PUBLIC LIBRARY*, 311 N Helena, 78151. (Mail add: PO Box 37, 78151-0037), SAN 316-7062. Tel: 830-239-4192. FAX: 830-239-4629. E-mail: librarian@runge.lib.tx.us. *Dir,* Betty J Plant; Staff 1 (Non-MLS 1)
Founded 1966. Pop 1,955
Library Holdings: Bk Titles 14,448; Per Subs 54
Subject Interests: Texana
Automation Activity & Vendor Info: (Cataloging) Biblionix; (Circulation) Biblionix
Mem of Karnes County Library System
Open Mon, Wed & Fri 9:30-5:30, Tues & Thurs 1-5

RUSK

P   SINGLETARY MEMORIAL LIBRARY*, 207 E Sixth St, 75785. SAN
316-7089. Tel: 903-683-5916. FAX: 903-683-5964. E-mail:
mtl_19@hotmail.com. *Libr Dir,* Amy Darrington
Founded 1902. Pop 4,633; Circ 17,000
Library Holdings: Bk Vols 20,000; Per Subs 20
Special Collections: Cherokee County Genealogy; Texana
Automation Activity & Vendor Info: (Cataloging) Book Systems, Inc;
(Circulation) Book Systems, Inc
Wireless access
Open Mon-Fri 10-6
Friends of the Library Group

SABINAL

P   SABINAL PUBLIC LIBRARY*, 412 N Center St, 78881. (Mail add: PO
Box 245, 78881-0245), SAN 378-3928. Tel: 830-988-2911. FAX:
830-988-2633. E-mail: sabinallibrary@yahoo.com. *Dir,* Caroline
Habermacher
Founded 1978. Pop 2,076
Library Holdings: Bk Vols 12,000
Automation Activity & Vendor Info: (Cataloging) SirsiDynix;
(Circulation) SirsiDynix
Open Mon-Fri 1-5
Friends of the Library Group

SACHSE

P   SACHSE PUBLIC LIBRARY*, 3815 Sachse Rd, Ste C, 75048. SAN
361-4220. Tel: 972-530-8966. FAX: 972-495-7682. Web Site:
www.cityofsachse.com.
Library Holdings: Bk Vols 30,000; Per Subs 15
Automation Activity & Vendor Info: (Cataloging) Brodart; (Circulation)
Brodart
Wireless access
Open Mon-Thurs 12-8, Fri 12-6, Sat 10-4
Friends of the Library Group

SAGINAW

P   SAGINAW PUBLIC LIBRARY*, The John Ed Keeter Public Library of
Saginaw, 355 W McLeroy Blvd, 76179. (Mail add: PO Box 79070,
76179-0070), SAN 316-7097. Tel: 817-232-0300. FAX: 817-232-9134.
E-mail: library@ci.saginaw.tx.us. Web Site: www.ci.saginaw.tx.us. *Dir,*
Paula Sallforf
Founded 1964. Pop 15,857; Circ 126,338
Library Holdings: Bk Vols 53,000; Per Subs 85
Special Collections: Large Print Coll; Local History Coll; Western Coll
Automation Activity & Vendor Info: (Cataloging) Evergreen;
(Circulation) Evergreen; (OPAC) Evergreen
Wireless access
Mem of North Texas Library Partners
Open Tues & Thurs 9-8, Wed, Fri & Sat 9-6
Friends of the Library Group

SALADO

P   SALADO PUBLIC LIBRARY*, 1151 N Main St, 76571. (Mail add: PO
Box 1178, 76571-1178). Tel: 254-947-9191. FAX:
254-947-9146. E-mail: spl@vvm.com. Web Site: www.saladolibrary.org.
Dir, Marsha McGuire; Staff 5 (MLS 2, Non-MLS 3)
Founded 1985. Pop 6,529; Circ 47,747
Library Holdings: Audiobooks 1,870; AV Mats 3,908; CDs 1,115; DVDs
1,843; e-books 2,800; e-journals 1,200; Large Print Bks 800; Bk Titles
16,988; Bk Vols 18,230; Per Subs 31; Videos 649
Automation Activity & Vendor Info: (Cataloging) Biblionix; (Circulation)
Biblionix; (ILL) OCLC FirstSearch; (OPAC) Biblionix
Database Vendor: Baker & Taylor, EBSCOhost, Ingram Library Services,
OCLC FirstSearch
Wireless access
Function: Art exhibits, Bilingual assistance for Spanish patrons, Bk
club(s), Bks on CD, Children's prog, Computer training, Computers for
patron use, Copy machines, E-Reserves, Electronic databases & coll, Fax
serv, Free DVD rentals, ILL available, Magnifiers for reading, Online cat,
Online searches, Prog for adults, Prog for children & young adult, Tax
forms, VHS videos, Web-catalog
Mem of Central Texas Library System, Inc
Open Mon-Fri 10-6, Sat 10-5
Friends of the Library Group

SAN ANGELO

C   ANGELO STATE UNIVERSITY LIBRARY, Porter Henderson Library,
2025 S Johnson, 76904-5079. (Mail add: ASU Station #11013,
76909-1013), SAN 316-7119. Tel: 325-942-2222. Circulation Tel:

325-486-6523. Interlibrary Loan Service Tel: 325-486-6551. Reference Tel:
325-486-6534. FAX: 325-942-2198. E-mail: library@angelo.edu,
reference@angelo.edu. Web Site: www.angelo.edu/services/library. *Exec
Dir, Libr Serv,* Dr Maurice G Fortin; E-mail: maurice.fortin@angelo.edu;
Asst Dir, Access Serv, Angela L Skaggs; Tel: 325-486-6524, E-mail:
angela.skaggs@angelo.edu; *Asst Dir, Ref & Instruction Serv,* Mark Allan;
Tel: 325-486-6535, E-mail: mark.allan@angelo.edu; *Head, Spec Coll &
Programming,* Suzanne O Campbell; Tel: 325-486-6553, E-mail:
suzanne.campbell@angelo.edu; *Head, Tech Serv,* Janetta Paschal; Tel:
325-486-6530, E-mail: janetta.paschal@angelo.edu; *Asst Head, Spec Coll
& Prog, Univ Archivist,* Shannon Sturm; Tel: 325-486-6555, E-mail:
shannon.sturm@angelo.edu; *Acq Librn,* Janice (Jenny) Hock; Tel:
325-486-6525, E-mail: janice.hock@angelo.edu; *Electronic Ser Librn,*
Susan G Elkins; Tel: 325-486-6548, E-mail: susan.elkins@angelo.edu; *Govt
Info/Ref Librn,* Sarah Schmidt; Tel: 325-486-6527, E-mail:
sarah.schmidt@angelo.edu; *Multimedia Support Librn,* Antonella Ward;
Tel: 325-486-6540, E-mail: antonella.ward@angelo.edu; Staff 10 (MLS 8,
Non-MLS 2)
Founded 1928. Enrl 7,084; Fac 360; Highest Degree: Master
Sept 2011-Aug 2012 Income $2,786,966. Mats Exp $1,269,902. Sal
$1,025,431 ($533,952)
Library Holdings: AV Mats 20,905; CDs 1,077; DVDs 90; e-books
23,712; e-journals 44,855; Microforms 735,046; Bk Titles 291,249; Bk
Vols 446,096; Per Subs 858; Videos 7,037
Special Collections: State Document Depository; US Document
Depository
Subject Interests: SW hist, Tex hist, W Tex
Automation Activity & Vendor Info: (Acquisitions) Ex Libris Group;
(Cataloging) Ex Libris Group; (Circulation) Ex Libris Group; (Course
Reserve) Ex Libris Group; (ILL) Ex Libris Group; (OPAC) Ex Libris
Group; (Serials) Ex Libris Group
Wireless access
Partic in OCLC Online Computer Library Center, Inc
Friends of the Library Group

S   FORT CONCHO NATIONAL HISTORIC LANDMARK*, Research
Library & Archives, 630 S Oakes St, 76903-7099. SAN 321-0219. Tel:
325-481-2646. FAX: 325-657-4531. E-mail: hqtrs@fortconcho.com. Web
Site: www.fortconcho.com. *Librn,* Evelyn Lemons; Tel: 325-657-4442;
Staff 1 (MLS 1)
Founded 1969
Library Holdings: Bk Titles 6,000; Per Subs 20
Special Collections: Architectural Coll (Oscar Ruffini Papers); Boyd
Cornick Papers; Fort Concho History; Fort Concho Museum Records;
George Gibson Huntt Papers; M C Ragsdale Photograph Coll; Military
History; San Angelo Coll; Texas Photographers Coll, prints; William G
Wedemeyer Photograph Coll; William S Veck Papers. Oral History
Publications: Fort Concho Guidon (Newsletter)
Restriction: Open by appt only, Open to pub for ref only

P   TOM GREEN COUNTY LIBRARY SYSTEM*, 113 W Beauregard,
76903. SAN 362-2231. Tel: 915-655-7321. FAX: 915-659-4027. TDD:
915-659-3247. E-mail: infodesk@co.tom-green.tx.us. Web Site:
www.co.tom-green.tx.us. *Dir,* Larry D Justiss; E-mail:
larry.justiss@co.tom-green.tx.us; *Assoc Dir,* Martha McCloskey; E-mail:
martha.mccoskey@co.tom-green.tx.us; *Acq,* Mary Crudup; *Adult Serv,*
Wanda Green; *Ch,* Sally Meyers; *ILL,* Aurora Nombrano; Staff 32 (MLS 5,
Non-MLS 27)
Founded 1923. Pop 104,398; Circ 545,084
Library Holdings: AV Mats 5,980; Large Print Bks 4,096; Bk Titles
172,769; Bk Vols 304,428; Per Subs 368; Talking Bks 3,338
Subject Interests: Local hist
Automation Activity & Vendor Info: (Acquisitions) Infor Library &
Information Solutions; (Cataloging) Infor Library & Information Solutions;
(Circulation) Infor Library & Information Solutions; (ILL) OCLC Online;
(OPAC) Infor Library & Information Solutions
Database Vendor: EBSCOhost, Gale Cengage Learning, LexisNexis,
netLibrary, OCLC FirstSearch, Westlaw
Function: AV serv, Distance learning, Handicapped accessible, Home
delivery & serv to Sr ctr & nursing homes, Homebound delivery serv, ILL
available, Libr develop, Outside serv via phone, mail, e-mail & web,
Photocopying/Printing, Prog for children & young adult, Ref serv available,
Summer reading prog, Telephone ref, Wheelchair accessible
Special Services for the Deaf - TDD equip; TTY equip
Friends of the Library Group
Branches: 2
ANGELO WEST, 3013 Vista del Arroyo, 76904, SAN 362-2266. Tel:
915-659-6436. *Librn,* Dorthy Stapleton; Staff 1 (Non-MLS 1)
Library Holdings: Bk Vols 43,386
Friends of the Library Group
NORTH ANGELO, 3001 N Chadbourne, 76904, SAN 362-2290. Tel:
915-653-8412. *Br Mgr,* Marilyn Hendricks; Staff 1 (MLS 1)
Library Holdings: Bk Vols 18,162
Friends of the Library Group
Bookmobiles: 1

J   HOWARD COLLEGE - SAN ANGELO LIBRARY*, 3501 N US Hwy 67, 76905. Tel: 325-481-8300, Ext 309. FAX: 325-481-8321. Web Site: www.howardcollege.edu. *Librn,* Denise Coonrod; *Librn,* Kleo Hidalgo; Staff 1 (MLS 1)
Enrl 944; Highest Degree: Associate
Library Holdings: Bk Titles 2,679; Per Subs 55
Automation Activity & Vendor Info: (Cataloging) LibLime; (Circulation) LibLime
Database Vendor: EBSCOhost, Gale Cengage Learning, OCLC FirstSearch, OVID Technologies
Wireless access
Open Mon-Thurs (Fall & Spring) 7:30am-8pm, Fri 8-3; Mon-Thurs (Summer) 7:30-6

M   SHANNON MEDICAL CENTER LIBRARY*, Pharmacy Dept Library, 120 E Harris, 76903. SAN 316-7135. Tel: 325-653-6741. Administration Tel: 325-657-5214. FAX: 325-657-5401. Web Site: www.shannonhealth.com. *Asst Dir,* Stephanie McCann
Library Holdings: Bk Vols 100; Per Subs 20
Partic in National Network of Libraries of Medicine
Restriction: Staff use only

SAN ANTONIO

L   AKIN, GUMP, STRAUSS, HAUER & FELD LLP, 300 Convent St, Ste 1500, 78205. SAN 373-6199. Tel: 210-281-7130. FAX: 210-224-2035. Web Site: www.akingump.com.
Library Holdings: Bk Vols 20,000
Database Vendor: LexisNexis, Westlaw
Open Mon-Fri 8-4:30
Restriction: Staff use only

R   ARCHDIOCESE OF SAN ANTONIO*, Catholic Archives of San Antonio, 2718 W Woodlawn, 78228-5195. (Mail add: PO Box 28410, 78228-0410), SAN 329-1502. Tel: 210-734-1609, 210-734-2620, Ext 1103. *Archivist,* Brother Edward J Loch; E-mail: eloch@archsa.org; Staff 1 (Non-MLS 1)
Founded 1974. Highest Degree: Master
Jul 2007-Jun 2008 Income $42,000, Locally Generated Income $2,000, Parent Institution $40,000. Mats Exp $4,095, Per/Ser (Incl. Access Fees) $95, Micro $2,000, AV Equip $1,000, Presv $1,000. Sal $20,000
Library Holdings: DVDs 10; Microforms 800; Music Scores 50; Bk Titles 300; Bk Vols 500; Per Subs 4; Videos 100
Special Collections: Bexar Archives; Camargo Mexico; Chancery Papers, papers & microfilm; Orphanage (restricted); Papal Visit, papers, video; Vital Statistics, Sacramental Records, originals & microfilm, newsp. Oral History
Publications: ACDA Newsletter; Archival Outlook; Texas Catholic Historical Newsletter
Restriction: Open by appt only, Restricted access

R   ASSUMPTION SEMINARY LIBRARY*, 2600 W Woodlawn, 78228-5122. (Mail add: PO Box 28240, 78228-0201), SAN 316-7151. Tel: 210-734-5137. FAX: 210-734-2324. Web Site: www.assumptionseminary.org.
Founded 1952
Library Holdings: Bk Vols 20,500; Per Subs 140
Wireless access
Function: Ref serv available
Restriction: Not open to pub, Open to students

M   BAPTIST HEALTH SYSTEM*, Bruce A Garrett Medical Library, 8400 Datapoint Dr, 78229. SAN 327-8301. Tel: 210-297-7639. FAX: 210-297-0716. Web Site: www.bshp.edu/current-students/library.aspx. *Dir,* DeDe Rios; Staff 1 (MLS 1)
Library Holdings: Bk Titles 3,400; Per Subs 80
Subject Interests: Nursing
Wireless access
Open Mon-Thurs (Winter) 7:30-6, Fri 7:30-5; Mon-Thurs (Summer) 7:30-5, Fri 7-3

CR   BAPTIST UNIVERSITY OF THE AMERICAS*, Learning Resource Center, 8019 S Pan Am Expressway, 78224-1397. SAN 321-1843. Tel: 210-924-4338, Ext 233. FAX: 210-924-2701. E-mail: reference.desk@bua.edu. Web Site: www.bua.edu. *Dir, Learning Res,* Teresa Martinez; E-mail: tmartinez@bua.edu
Founded 1955
Library Holdings: Bk Titles 16,500; Bk Vols 25,361; Per Subs 207
Special Collections: Neal Coll
Subject Interests: Theol in Spanish
Automation Activity & Vendor Info: (OPAC) Follett Software
Database Vendor: OCLC FirstSearch
Open Mon, Tues & Thurs 8:30am-10:30pm, Wed & Fri 8:30-5, Sat 8:30-7, Sun 9pm-Midnight

GL   BEXAR COUNTY LAW LIBRARY*, Bexar County Courthouse, 5th Flr, 100 Dolorosa, 78205. SAN 316-7178. Tel: 210-227-8822. FAX: 210-271-9614. *Dir,* James M Allison
Library Holdings: Bk Vols 77,000; Per Subs 86
Database Vendor: Westlaw
Open Mon-Fri 8-4:45

M   BEXAR COUNTY MEDICAL LIBRARY ASSOCIATION*, 6243 IH 10 W, 6th Flr, 78201. (Mail add: PO Box 5519, 78201-0519), SAN 316-7186. Tel: 210-301-4391. FAX: 210-301-2150. E-mail: bcms@bcms.org. Web Site: www.bcms.org.
Founded 1912
Library Holdings: Per Subs 40
Wireless access
Restriction: Not open to pub
Friends of the Library Group

M   CHRISTUS SANTA ROSA HEALTH CARE*, Harold S Toy MD Memorial Health Science Library, 333 N Santa Rosa St, 78207-3198. SAN 316-7429. Tel: 210-704-2284. FAX: 210-704-3177. *Coordr,* Jann Harrison
Founded 1949
Library Holdings: Bk Titles 1,989; Bk Vols 2,000; Per Subs 126
Subject Interests: Family practice, Hematology, Med, Nursing, Oncology, Orthopedics, Pediatrics
Partic in Docline

SR   CONGREGATION AGUDAS ACHIM*, Goldie & Joe Tills Library, 16550 Huebner Rd, 78248. SAN 316-7216. Tel: 210-479-0307. FAX: 210-479-0295. Web Site: www.agudas-achim.org. *In Charge,* Lynn Waghalter
Library Holdings: Bk Titles 2,529; Bk Vols 2,632
Special Collections: Judaica Coll
Automation Activity & Vendor Info: (Cataloging) Follett Software
Open Mon & Wed 4-6, Sun 9-12

L   COX SMITH MATTHEWS INC*, Law Library, 112 E Pecan, Ste 1800, 78205-1521. SAN 316-7291. Tel: 210-554-5500. FAX: 210-226-8395. Web Site: www.coxsmith.com. *Mgr, Libr Serv,* Elizabeth Prike; Staff 2 (MLS 1, Non-MLS 1)
Library Holdings: Bk Vols 51,000; Per Subs 500
Subject Interests: Banking, Bankruptcy, Corporate, Estate planning, Fed litigation, Gas, Health, Intellectual property, Labor, Oil, Tax, Tex litigation
Automation Activity & Vendor Info: (Acquisitions) Inmagic, Inc.; (Cataloging) Inmagic, Inc.; (Circulation) Inmagic, Inc.
Database Vendor: LexisNexis, Westlaw
Wireless access
Restriction: Access at librarian's discretion

S   DAUGHTERS OF THE REPUBLIC OF TEXAS LIBRARY AT THE ALAMO*, 300 Alamo Plaza, 78205. (Mail add: PO Box 1401, 78295-1401), SAN 316-7224. Tel: 210-225-1071. FAX: 210-212-8514. E-mail: drtl@drtl.org. Web Site: www.drtl.org. *Dir,* Leslie Stapleton; E-mail: lstapleton@drtl.org; *Asst Dir,* Martha Utterback; E-mail: mutterback@drtl.org; *Archivist,* Caitlin Donnelly; E-mail: cdonnelly@drtl.org; Staff 8 (MLS 5, Non-MLS 3)
Founded 1945
Library Holdings: Bk Titles 31,922; Per Subs 134
Special Collections: Photograph Coll; San Antonio through 1950; Viceregal Mexico & Early Texas Manuscript Coll
Subject Interests: Tex hist: Republic period, the Alamo, US Mexican war
Automation Activity & Vendor Info: (Acquisitions) EOS International; (Cataloging) EOS International; (OPAC) EOS International; (Serials) EOS International
Database Vendor: EOS International
Function: Archival coll, Photocopying/Printing, Prog for adults, Res libr, Web-catalog
Partic in Council of Research & Academic Libraries
Open Mon-Fri 9-5
Restriction: Non-circulating coll, Open to pub for ref only, Photo ID required for access

S   EXPRESS NEWS CORP*, San Antonio Express-News Library, 301 Ave E, 78205. (Mail add: PO Box 2171, 78297-2171), SAN 316-7364. Tel: 210-250-3274. FAX: 210-250-3157. Web Site: www.mysanantonio.com. *In Charge,* Michael Knoop; Tel: 210-250-3279, E-mail: mknoop@express-news.net; Staff 4 (MLS 3, Non-MLS 1)
Founded 1962
Library Holdings: Bk Vols 1,000
Special Collections: Digital Photo & Clip Archives
Subject Interests: Current events, Local hist
Database Vendor: LexisNexis, Newsbank
Restriction: Not open to pub

L FULBRIGHT & JAWORSKI LIBRARY*, 300 Convent St, Ste 2200,
   78205-3792. SAN 323-6269. Tel: 210-224-5575. Web Site:
   www.fulbright.com. *Librn,* Kathy Darrow; Staff 1 (MLS 1)
   Library Holdings: Bk Vols 30,000; Per Subs 60
   Database Vendor: LexisNexis, Westlaw
   Open Mon-Fri 8:30-5:30

S INTERCULTURAL DEVELOPMENT RESEARCH ASSOCIATION
   LIBRARY*, 5815 Callaghan Rd, Ste 101, 78228. SAN 329-4161. Tel:
   210-444-1710. FAX: 210-444-1714. E-mail: sarah.aleman@idra.org. Web
   Site: www.idra.org.
   Library Holdings: Bk Vols 500; Per Subs 4
   Subject Interests: Early childhood, Educ
   Automation Activity & Vendor Info: (Cataloging) Follett Software;
   (Circulation) Follett Software
   Wireless access
   Function: For res purposes
   Open Mon-Fri 8-5
   Restriction: Not a lending libr

S MCNAY ART MUSEUM LIBRARY, 6000 N New Braunfels Ave, 78209.
   (Mail add: PO Box 6069, 78209-0069), SAN 316-7283. Tel: 210-805-1727.
   Administration Tel: 210-805-1728. FAX: 210-824-0218. *Semmes Found
   Head Librn,* Ann Jones; *Asst Librn,* Craig Bunch; Staff 3.5 (MLS 2,
   Non-MLS 1.5)
   Founded 1954
   Library Holdings: Bk Vols 26,000; Per Subs 41
   Special Collections: Tobin Theatre Arts & Rare Book Coll
   Subject Interests: 19th Century art hist, 20th Century art hist, 21st
   Century art hist
   Automation Activity & Vendor Info: (Acquisitions) EOS International;
   (Cataloging) EOS International; (Circulation) EOS International; (OPAC)
   EOS International; (Serials) EOS International
   Database Vendor: EBSCOhost, JSTOR, Marcive, Inc
   Wireless access
   Restriction: Non-circulating

M METHODIST HEALTHCARE*, Methodist Healthcare Health Services
   Library, 7700 Floyd Curl Dr, 78229. SAN 316-7461. Tel: 210-575-4583.
   Toll Free FAX: 866-773-7611. *Mgr,* Catherine Dikcis; Staff 1 (MLS 1)
   Founded 1967
   Special Collections: Medical
   Open Mon-Fri 8-5

M NORTHEAST BAPTIST HOSPITAL*, Dr Leroy & Norma Bates
   Memorial Library, 8811 Village Dr, 78217. SAN 372-9990. Tel:
   210-297-2000, 210-297-2639.
   Library Holdings: Bk Vols 300
   Subject Interests: Nutrition
   Restriction: Staff use only

J NORTHWEST VISTA COLLEGE*, Library/Learning Resource Center,
   Redbud Hall, 3535 N Ellison Dr, 78251. SAN 375-4170. Tel:
   210-486-4500. Interlibrary Loan Service Tel: 210-486-4578. Reference Tel:
   210-486-4513. FAX: 210-486-9105. Web Site:
   www.alamo.edu/nvc/lrc/default.htm. *Dean, Learning Res,* Christine
   Crowley; Tel: 210-486-4572; *Ref Serv,* Nancy Kaida; Tel: 210-486-4571,
   E-mail: nkaida@alamo.edu; *Ref Serv,* Judy McMillan; Tel: 210-486-4567,
   E-mail: jmcmillan@alamo.edu; *Ref Serv,* Linda Reeves; Tel: 210-486-4569,
   E-mail: lreeves3@alamo.edu; *Tech Serv,* Karen Weiskittel; Tel:
   210-486-4558, E-mail: kweiskittel@alamo.edu; Staff 13 (MLS 9,
   Non-MLS 4)
   Founded 1998. Enrl 14,500; Highest Degree: Associate
   Sept 2008-Aug 2009. Mats Exp $327,000, Books $80,000, Per/Ser (Incl.
   Access Fees) $12,000, AV Mat $35,000, Electronic Ref Mat (Incl. Access
   Fees) $200,000. Sal $450,000 (Prof $320,000)
   Library Holdings: Audiobooks 50; AV Mats 8,500; CDs 1,500; DVDs
   2,300; e-books 35,000; Electronic Media & Resources 100; Music Scores
   25; Bk Vols 28,000; Per Subs 100; Videos 1,800
   Automation Activity & Vendor Info: (Acquisitions) Innovative Interfaces,
   Inc; (Cataloging) Innovative Interfaces, Inc; (Circulation) Innovative
   Interfaces, Inc; (ILL) OCLC; (OPAC) Innovative Interfaces, Inc; (Serials)
   EBSCO Online
   Database Vendor: Alexander Street Press, Amigos Library Services,
   ARTstor, Baker & Taylor, Bowker, CQ Press, CredoReference,
   EBSCOhost, Facts on File, Gale Cengage Learning, JSTOR, Newsbank,
   OCLC FirstSearch, OCLC WorldCat, Oxford Online, ProQuest, Safari
   Books Online, Sage, SerialsSolutions, Wilson - Wilson Web, YBP Library
   Services
   Wireless access
   Function: Bks on CD, Copy machines, Electronic databases & coll,
   Handicapped accessible, ILL available, Music CDs, Online cat, Ref & res,
   Wheelchair accessible
   Partic in Council of Research & Academic Libraries; Tex Share

Special Services for the Blind - Accessible computers; Assistive/Adapted
tech devices, equip & products; Copier with enlargement capabilities;
Internet workstation with adaptive software; Screen enlargement software
for people with visual disabilities; Talking bks & player equip; ZoomText
magnification & reading software
Open Mon-Thurs 8am-9pm, Fri 8-5, Sat 9-5
Restriction: Open to pub for ref & circ; with some limitations

SR DONALD E O'SHAUGHNESSY LIBRARY*, Oblate School of Theology,
   285 Oblate Dr, 78216-6693. SAN 316-7305. Tel: 210-341-1368.
   Administration Tel: 210-341-1366. FAX: 210-979-6520. Administration
   FAX: 210-341-4519. E-mail: library@ost.edu. Web Site: www.ost.edu. *Dir,*
   Fr Donald J Joyce; E-mail: djoyce@ost.edu; Staff 6 (MLS 2, Non-MLS 4)
   Founded 1903. Enrl 144; Fac 18; Highest Degree: Doctorate
   Jul 2006-Jul 2007. Mats Exp $76,992, Books $36,000, Other Print Mats
   $31,992, AV Mat $140, Electronic Ref Mat (Incl. Access Fees) $9,000. Sal
   $140,000
   Library Holdings: AV Mats 215; Bk Vols 85,000; Per Subs 425
   Special Collections: Faculty Dissertations; Missions Documents; Rare
   Books Coll
   Subject Interests: Relig studies
   Automation Activity & Vendor Info: (Acquisitions) Ex Libris Group;
   (Cataloging) Ex Libris Group; (Circulation) Ex Libris Group; (Course
   Reserve) Ex Libris Group; (ILL) OCLC; (OPAC) Ex Libris Group;
   (Serials) Ex Libris Group
   Database Vendor: EBSCOhost, OCLC FirstSearch
   Function: For res purposes, Handicapped accessible, ILL available, Online
   searches
   Publications: Offerings (College journal)
   Partic in Council of Research & Academic Libraries; OCLC Online
   Computer Library Center, Inc; TexSHARE - Texas State Library &
   Archives Commission
   Open Mon & Fri 7:30-5:30, Tues-Thurs 7:30am-9pm, Sat 11-5
   Restriction: Open to pub upon request, Open to students, fac & staff

C OUR LADY OF THE LAKE UNIVERSITY*, Sueltenfuss Library, 411
   SW 24th St, 78207-4689. SAN 362-2320. Tel: 210-434-6711, Ext 2324.
   Circulation Tel: 210-434-6711, Ext 2325. Reference Tel: 210-434-6711,
   Ext 8236. Administration Tel: 210-431-3917. FAX: 210-436-1616. Web
   Site: library.ollusa.edu, www.ollusa.edu. *Dean of Libr, Dir,* Dr Paul Frisch;
   E-mail: frisp@lake.ollusa.edu; *Asst Libr Dir,* Judith Larson; E-mail:
   larsj@lake.ollusa.edu; *Head, Tech Serv,* Carolyn Ellis Gonzalez; E-mail:
   gonzca@lake.ollusa.edu; *Instrul Serv Librn,* Dr Kimberly Gibson; E-mail:
   gibsk@lake.ollusa.edu; *Archivist,* Antoinette Garza; E-mail:
   garza@lake.ollusa.edu. Subject Specialists: *Hist,* Dr Paul Frisch; *Hist,*
   Judith Larson; *Communications,* Dr Kimberly Gibson; *English,* Antoinette
   Garza; Staff 7 (MLS 6, Non-MLS 1)
   Founded 1896. Enrl 4,024; Fac 181; Highest Degree: Doctorate
   Library Holdings: AV Mats 3,369; Bks on Deafness & Sign Lang 52;
   e-books 21,059; Bk Vols 143,874; Per Subs 724; Talking Bks 15
   Special Collections: History of the Southwest (Texana)
   Subject Interests: Educ, Leadership, Mexican-Am, Psychol, Soc work
   Automation Activity & Vendor Info: (Acquisitions) SirsiDynix;
   (Cataloging) SirsiDynix; (Circulation) SirsiDynix; (Course Reserve)
   SirsiDynix; (ILL) SirsiDynix; (OPAC) SirsiDynix; (Serials) SirsiDynix
   Database Vendor: EBSCOhost, Gale Cengage Learning, LexisNexis,
   Newsbank, OCLC FirstSearch, OVID Technologies, ProQuest
   Wireless access
   Partic in Coun of Res & Acad Librs; OCLC Online Computer Library
   Center, Inc; Tex Share
   Open Mon-Thurs (Spring & Fall) 8am-Midnight, Fri 8-6, Sat 11-6, Sun
   11am-Midnight; Mon-Thurs (Winter) 8am-9pm, Fri 8-6, Sat 11-6, Sun 11-9

J PALO ALTO COLLEGE*, Ozuna Library & Academic Center, 1400 W
   Villaret St, 78224-2499. SAN 372-4921. Tel: 210-486-3901. Interlibrary
   Loan Service Tel: 210-486-3555. Reference Tel: 210-486-3557. FAX:
   210-486-9184. Interlibrary Loan Service FAX: 210-486-3556. Web Site:
   www.alamo.edu/pac. *Dean, Learning Res,* Tina Mesa; E-mail:
   emesa@alamo.edu; *Chair, Libr & Info Studies,* Camille F Fiorillo; Tel:
   210-486-3560, E-mail: cfiorillo@alamo.edu; *Automation Syst Librn, Coll
   Mgt, Tech Serv,* Position Currently Open; *Lead Access Serv Librn,* Cynthia
   Sanchez; Tel: 210-486-3579, E-mail: csanchez@alamo.edu; *Lead Ref
   Librn,* Irene F Scharf; Tel: 210-486-3574, E-mail: ischarf@alamo.edu; *Circ
   Supvr, ILL,* Anna M Rodriguez; E-mail: arodriguez799@alamo.edu; *Circ
   Supvr, ILL,* Shelby Rogers, II; E-mail: srogers2@alamo.edu; *Acq Tech,*
   Robert Jakubowski; Tel: 210-486-3562, E-mail: rjakubowski@alamo.edu;
   Learning Res Spec, Veronica Buendia; Tel: 210-486-3564, E-mail:
   vbuendia@alamo.edu; Staff 16 (MLS 11, Non-MLS 5)
   Founded 1985. Enrl 7,822; Fac 11; Highest Degree: Associate
   Aug 2007-Jul 2008 Income $1,263,742. Mats Exp $282,383, Books
   $48,179, Per/Ser (Incl. Access Fees) $43,000, Micro $31,000, Electronic
   Ref Mat (Incl. Access Fees) $65,000. Sal $744,381
   Library Holdings: AV Mats 3,199; DVDs 182; e-books 28,059; Bk Titles
   119,294; Per Subs 284; Videos 3,011

Special Collections: US Document Depository
Automation Activity & Vendor Info: (Acquisitions) Innovative Interfaces, Inc; (Cataloging) Innovative Interfaces, Inc; (Circulation) Innovative Interfaces, Inc; (Course Reserve) Innovative Interfaces, Inc; (ILL) Innovative Interfaces, Inc; (Media Booking) Innovative Interfaces, Inc; (OPAC) Innovative Interfaces, Inc; (Serials) Innovative Interfaces, Inc
Database Vendor: EBSCOhost, Grolier Online, Innovative Interfaces, Inc INN - View, OCLC WorldCat, ProQuest
Wireless access
Partic in Tex Share
Special Services for the Deaf - Bks on deafness & sign lang
Special Services for the Blind - Accessible computers; Aids for in-house use; Computer access aids; Computer with voice synthesizer for visually impaired persons; Magnifiers; Ref serv; Screen enlargement software for people with visual disabilities; Screen reader software; Text reader
Open Mon-Thurs 7:45am-9pm, Fri 7:45-5, Sun 1-9

S   MINNIE STEVENS PIPER FOUNDATION*, Student Aid Center Library, 1250 NE Loop 410, Ste 810, 78209-1539. SAN 326-5943. Tel: 210-525-8494. FAX: 210-341-6627. E-mail: mspf@mspf.org. Web Site: www.mspf.org. *Dir,* Joyce M Ellis
Founded 1961
Library Holdings: Bk Vols 5,000
Special Collections: College/University Catalogs & Reference Books on Scholarships, Careers & Grants
Function: Res libr
Publications: Compendium of Texas College & Financial Aid Calendar
Open Mon-Fri 8:30-12 & 1-4:30

SR   SAINT MARK'S EPISCOPAL CHURCH*, Bishop Jones Library, 315 E Pecan St, 78205. SAN 328-5847. Tel: 210-226-2426. FAX: 210-226-2468. E-mail: stmarks@stmarks-sa.org. Web Site: www.stmarks-sa.org. *Info Tech,* Emmet Faulk; E-mail: efaulkjr@stmarks-sa.org
Library Holdings: Bk Vols 5,600
Special Collections: Jack Kent Coll, bks
Subject Interests: Relig
Wireless access
Restriction: Mem only

SAINT MARY'S UNIVERSITY
C   LOUIS J BLUME LIBRARY, One Camino Santa Maria, 78228-8608, SAN 362-2479. Tel: 210-436-3441. Reference Tel: 210-436-3508. FAX: 210-436-3782. Web Site: library.stmarytx.edu/acadlib, www.stmarytx.edu. *Dir,* Dr H Palmer Hall; *Assoc Dir,* Caroline Byrd; *Asst Dir, Tech Serv,* Margaret Sylvia; *Circ Mgr,* Nettie Lucio; *Bibliog Instr, Ref,* Diane Duesterhoeft; *Bibliog Instr, Ref,* Necia Wolff; *Cat,* Jill Crane; *Govt Doc,* Kathy Amen; *Per,* Marcella Lesher; Staff 8 (MLS 8)
Founded 1852. Enrl 4,300; Fac 194; Highest Degree: Doctorate
Library Holdings: AV Mats 17,500; CDs 7,800; DVDs 2,500; e-books 72,000; e-journals 47,000; Bk Titles 252,000; Bk Vols 270,000; Per Subs 1,100
Special Collections: Hilaire Belloc Coll & G K Chesterton Coll (complete sets of 1st editions); Old Spanish Trail Highway; Peninsular Wars Coll; Political Buttons Coll; Spanish Archives of Laredo, Texas. Municipal Document Depository; State Document Depository; US Document Depository
Subject Interests: Ethic studies, Hist, Law
Automation Activity & Vendor Info: (Acquisitions) Innovative Interfaces, Inc - Millenium; (Cataloging) Innovative Interfaces, Inc - Millenium; (Circulation) Innovative Interfaces, Inc - Millenium; (Course Reserve) Innovative Interfaces, Inc - Millenium; (ILL) Innovative Interfaces, Inc - Millenium; (OPAC) Innovative Interfaces, Inc - Millenium; (Serials) Innovative Interfaces, Inc - Millenium
Partic in Coun of Res & Acad Librs; Novanet
Open Mon-Thurs (Fall & Spring) 7:45am-Midnight, Fri 7:45-5, Sat 9-5, Sun 1pm-Midnight; Mon-Thurs (Summer) 8am-9pm, Fri 8-4, Sun 1-9
CL   SARITA KENNEDY EAST LAW LIBRARY*, One Camino Santa Maria, 78228-8605, SAN 362-2509. Tel: 210-436-3435. FAX: 210-436-3240. Web Site: www.stmarytx.edu. *Dir,* Robert H Hu; Tel: 210-431-2056, E-mail: rhu@stmarytx.edu; *Cat,* Lee Unterborn; *Ref,* Mike Martinez, Jr; Tel: 210-436-3435, Ext 1374; *Ref,* Garry Stillman; Tel: 210-436-3435, Ext 1366; Staff 8 (MLS 8)
Founded 1927. Enrl 600; Fac 25
Library Holdings: Bk Titles 32,873; Bk Vols 338,904; Per Subs 3,474
Special Collections: Anglo American Law Coll
Automation Activity & Vendor Info: (Cataloging) SirsiDynix; (Circulation) SirsiDynix; (OPAC) SirsiDynix
Partic in Westlaw
Open Mon-Fri (Fall & Winter) 7am-Midnight, Sat 9am-10pm, Sun 10am-Midnight; Mon-Fri (Summer) 8am-10pm, Sat 9am-10pm, Sun 10am-10pm
Friends of the Library Group

J   ST PHILIP'S COLLEGE*, Learning Resource Center, 1801 Martin Luther King Dr, 78203-2098. SAN 316-7321. Tel: 210-486-2330. Circulation Tel: 210-486-2555. Administration Tel: 210-485-0000. FAX: 210-486-2335. Web Site: www.accd.edu/spc/lrc. *Ref,* Reuben Kaller; *Chair,* Lillian Turner; *Librn,* Kimbel May; *Librn,* Kelli Wilder; *Automation Syst Coordr,* Jill M Zimmerman; *Archivist,* Rebecca Barnard; *Ser,* Anna L Delgado; *Tech Serv,* Lucy E Duncan; Staff 14 (MLS 8, Non-MLS 6)
Founded 1898. Enrl 8,644; Fac 498
Library Holdings: e-journals 1,050; Bk Vols 117,737
Special Collections: African-American Coll
Automation Activity & Vendor Info: (Acquisitions) Innovative Interfaces, Inc; (Cataloging) Innovative Interfaces, Inc; (Circulation) Innovative Interfaces, Inc; (Course Reserve) Innovative Interfaces, Inc; (ILL) Innovative Interfaces, Inc; (Media Booking) Innovative Interfaces, Inc; (OPAC) Innovative Interfaces, Inc; (Serials) Innovative Interfaces, Inc
Publications: Basic Instruction in Word Perfect 7.0; How to Use the NOTIS OPAC; PowerPoint Library Orientation; Templates for CD-ROM Programs
Partic in Coun of Res & Acad Librs; Tex Coun of Commun/Jr Col Librns; TexSHARE - Texas State Library & Archives Commission
Special Services for the Blind - Assistive/Adapted tech devices, equip & products
Open Mon-Thurs 7am-9pm, Fri 7-5, Sat 8-5

S   SAN ANTONIO ART LEAGUE & MUSEUM*, Museum Gallery Archives, 130 King William St, 78204. SAN 316-733X. Tel: 210-223-1140. E-mail: saalm@att.net. Web Site: www.saalm.org. *Pres,* Helen Fey
Library Holdings: Bk Vols 350
Special Collections: Davis Coll
Subject Interests: Artist's biog, Hist, How-to
Function: Res libr
Open Tues-Sat 10-3

J   SAN ANTONIO COLLEGE, Library Department, 1001 Howard St, 78212. (Mail add: 1300 San Pedro Ave, 78212-4299), SAN 316-7348. Tel: 210-486-0554. Circulation Tel: 210-486-0582. Interlibrary Loan Service Tel: 210-486-0572. Administration Tel: 210-486-0902. E-mail: eref@alamo.edu. Web Site: www.alamo.edu/sac/library. *Dean, Learning Res,* Dr Alice Johnson; E-mail: ajohnson@alamo.edu; *Dir,* Eileen Oliver; Tel: 210-486-1577, E-mail: eoliver@alamo.edu; *Coll Develop Librn, Instrul Serv Librn,* Thomas Bahlinger; Fax: 210-486-0568, E-mail: tbahlinger@alamo.edu; *Web Coordr,* Dr Karen Balcom; E-mail: kbalcom@alamo.edu; *Ref,* Tom Kuykendall; E-mail: tkuykendall@alamo.edu; Staff 9.5 (MLS 8.5, Non-MLS 1)
Founded 1926. Enrl 24,313; Fac 972; Highest Degree: Associate Sept 2008-Aug 2009. Mats Exp $616,000
Library Holdings: AV Mats 8,724; Bks on Deafness & Sign Lang 533; CDs 1,726; DVDs 6,998; e-books 35,148; e-journals 25,735; Bk Vols 168,601; Per Subs 121; Talking Bks 739
Special Collections: 18th Century British Literature (Morrison Coll); McAllister Coll; Texana Coll. US Document Depository
Automation Activity & Vendor Info: (Acquisitions) Innovative Interfaces, Inc; (Cataloging) Innovative Interfaces, Inc; (Circulation) Innovative Interfaces, Inc; (Course Reserve) Innovative Interfaces, Inc; (ILL) OCLC; (OPAC) Innovative Interfaces, Inc; (Serials) EBSCO Online
Database Vendor: Alexander Street Press, Amigos Library Services, ARTstor, Baker & Taylor, CQ Press, CRC Press/Taylor & Francis CRCnetBASE, CredoReference, EBSCOhost, Facts on File, Gale Cengage Learning, H W Wilson, JSTOR, LexisNexis, netLibrary, OVID Technologies, Oxford Online, Project MUSE, ProQuest, Safari Books Online, SerialsSolutions, Wilson - Wilson Web
Wireless access
Partic in Council of Research & Academic Libraries; Tex Share
Special Services for the Blind - Computer with voice synthesizer for visually impaired persons

S   SAN ANTONIO CONSERVATION SOCIETY FOUNDATION LIBRARY*, 107 King William St, 78204. SAN 316-7356. Tel: 210-224-6163. FAX: 210-224-6168. Web Site: www.saconservation.org. *Librn,* Beth Standifird; Fax: 210-354-0070, E-mail: bstandifird@saconservation.org; Staff 1 (MLS 1)
Founded 1970
Library Holdings: Microforms 59; Bk Vols 5,542; Per Subs 10
Special Collections: Dorothy Matthies Postcards (early San Antonio views); Ernst Raba Photographs (1870s-1920s San Antonio); Robert H H Hugman River Walk Architectural Drawings Coll; San Antonio City Directories, 1881-1935, micro, 1938-2002, bk; Sanborn Fire Insurance Maps, San Antonio 1885, 1896, 1904, 1911, 1912, microfilm, 1956, print
Subject Interests: Architectural hist, Restoration techniques, San Antonio, Tex hist
Function: Res libr, Telephone ref
Open Mon-Thurs 9:30-3:30
Restriction: Non-circulating to the pub, Pub use on premises

R   **SAN ANTONIO FIRST BAPTIST CHURCH***, Wallace Library, 515 McCullough St, 78215. SAN 316-7259. Tel: 210-226-0363, Ext 219. FAX: 210-299-2633. E-mail: library@fbcsa.org. Web Site: www.sbcsa.org. *In Charge,* Christie Ethington; Staff 7 (MLS 1, Non-MLS 6)
Founded 1939
Library Holdings: Bks on Deafness & Sign Lang 10; Bk Titles 16,500; Bk Vols 18,037; Per Subs 10
Subject Interests: Baptist hist, Theol
Automation Activity & Vendor Info: (Cataloging) Follett Software; (Circulation) Follett Software
Restriction: Mem only

P   **SAN ANTONIO PUBLIC LIBRARY,** 600 Soledad, 78205-2786. SAN 362-2533. Tel: 210-207-2500. Administration Tel: 210-207-2644. FAX: 210-207-2603. E-mail: librarywebadmin@sanantonio.gov. Web Site: www.sanantonio.gov/library. *Dir,* Ramiro S Salazar; E-mail: ramiro.salazar@sanantonio.gov; *Asst Dir, Pub Serv,* Dale McNeill; Tel: 210-207-2661, E-mail: dale.mcneill@sanantonio.gov; *Asst Dir, Support Serv,* Kathy Donellan; Tel: 210-207-2572, E-mail: kathy.donellan@sanantonio.gov; *Libr Serv Adminr,* Teresa Jensen; Tel: 210-207-2829, E-mail: teresa.jensen@sanantonio.gov; *Pub Relations Mgr,* Beth Graham; Tel: 210-207-2638, E-mail: elizabeth.graham@sanantonio.gov; *Br Serv Coordr,* Joel Bangilan; Tel: 210-207-2560, E-mail: joel.bangilan@sanantonio.gov; *Br Serv Coordr,* Kate Gray; Tel: 210-207-2661, E-mail: kate.gray@sanantonio.gov; *Br Serv Coordr,* Cheryl Sheehan; Tel: 210-207-2587, E-mail: cheryl.sheehan@sanantonio.gov; *Coordr, Ch Serv,* Viki Ash; Tel: 210-207-2620, E-mail: viki.ash@sanantonio.gov; *Coordr, Teen Serv,* Jennifer Velasquez; Tel: 210-207-2567, E-mail: jennifer.velasquez@sanantonio.gov; Staff 130 (MLS 124, Non-MLS 6)
Founded 1903. Pop 1,578,000; Circ 6,601,175
Oct 2010-Sept 2011 Income (Main Library and Branch(s)) $32,000,000. Mats Exp $32,000,000
Library Holdings: Bk Titles 552,610; Bk Vols 1,687,881; Per Subs 1,000
Special Collections: Latino Special Coll; Texana Coll. State Document Depository; US Document Depository
Automation Activity & Vendor Info: (Acquisitions) Innovative Interfaces, Inc; (Cataloging) OCLC Online; (Circulation) Innovative Interfaces, Inc; (ILL) OCLC Online; (OPAC) Innovative Interfaces, Inc
Wireless access
Publications: Young Pegasus (children's original poetry book)
Special Services for the Deaf - Bks on deafness & sign lang; Captioned film dep; High interest/low vocabulary bks; TTY equip
Open Mon-Thurs 9-9, Fri & Sat 9-5, Sun 11-5
Friends of the Library Group
Branches: 29
BAZAN, 2200 W Commerce St, 78207, SAN 362-2800. Tel: 210-225-1614. *Br Mgr,* Raymond Villarreal; E-mail: raymond.villarreal@sanantonio.gov; Staff 5 (MLS 3, Non-MLS 2)
Founded 1977. Pop 60,000; Circ 74,000
Function: After school storytime, Audiobks via web, Bilingual assistance for Spanish patrons, Bks on cassette, Bks on CD, Children's prog, Citizenship assistance, Computer training, Computers for patron use, Copy machines, Digital talking bks, e-mail serv, Electronic databases & coll
Open Mon & Wed 12-8, Tues & Thurs-Sat 10-6
Restriction: ID required to use computers (Ltd hrs), In-house use for visitors, Non-resident fee, Open to pub for ref & circ; with some limitations
Friends of the Library Group
BROOK HOLLOW, 530 Heimer Rd, 78232, SAN 362-2584. Tel: 210-496-6315. *Mgr,* Beth Schorlemer
Open Mon & Wed 12-8, Tues & Thurs-Sun 10-6
CARVER, 3350 E Commerce, 78220, SAN 362-2835. Tel: 210-225-7801. FAX: 210-472-3480. *Mgr,* Ronnie Delgado
Open Mon, Wed & Fri-Sun 10-6, Tues & Thurs 12-8
CHILDREN'S DEPARTMENT, 600 Soledad, 78205-2786. Tel: 210-207-2621. FAX: 210-207-2555. *Children's Coordr,* Viki Ash
Open Mon-Thurs 9-9, Fri & Sat 9-5, Sun 11-5
CODY, 11441 Vance Jackson, 78230, SAN 362-2630. Tel: 210-696-6396. FAX: 210-696-6273. *Mgr,* Hayley Latshaw
Open Mon, Wed & Fri-Sun 10-6, Tues & Thurs 12-8
COLLINS GARDEN, 200 N Park, 78204, SAN 322-5542. Tel: 210-225-0331. *Mgr,* Pamela Longoria
Open Mon, Wed & Fri-Sun 10-6, Tues & Thurs 12-8
CORTEZ, 2803 Hunter Blvd, 78224, SAN 362-2843. Tel: 210-922-7372. FAX: 210-932-1495. *Mgr,* Ignacio Albarracin
Open Mon, Wed & Fri-Sun 10-6, Tues & Thurs 12-8
FOREST HILLS, 5245 Ingram, 78228, SAN 329-6520. Tel: 210-431-2544. FAX: 210-434-3524. *Mgr,* Jimmy Jimenez
Open Mon & Wed 12-8, Tues & Thurs-Sun 10-6
GOVERNMENT DOCUMENTS, 600 Soledad, 78205-2786. Tel: 210-207-2500. FAX: 210-207-2552.
Open Mon-Thurs 9-9, Fri & Sat 9-5, Sun 11-5

GREAT NORTHWEST, 9050 Wellwood, 78251, SAN 374-6755. Tel: 210-684-5251. FAX: 210-543-9025. *Mgr,* Roberto Zapata
Open Mon & Wed 12-8, Tues & Thurs-Sat 10-6
GUERRA, 7978 Military Dr W, 78227. Tel: 210-673-1492. FAX: 210-673-3862. *Mgr,* Dexter Katzman
Open Mon, Wed & Fri-Sun 10-6, Tues & Thurs 12-8
JOHNSTON, 6307 Sun Valley, 78237, SAN 362-2851. Tel: 210-674-8410. *Mgr,* Diane Backhus
Open Mon & Wed 12-8, Tues & Thurs-Sat 10-6
LANDA, 233 Bushnell Ave, 78212, SAN 362-286X. Tel: 210-732-8369. FAX: 210-737-9662. *Mgr,* Michael Kaminski
Open Mon & Wed 12-8, Tues & Thurs-Sun 10-6
LAS PALMAS, 515 Castroville, 78237, SAN 362-2894. Tel: 210-434-6394. FAX: 210-435-5479. *Mgr,* Rebecca A Alvarez
Open Mon & Wed 12-8, Tues & Thurs-Sun 10-6
MAVERICK, 8700 Mistic Park, 78254. Tel: 210-680-9346. FAX: 210-680-9311. *Mgr,* Jef Martin
Open Mon, Wed & Fri-Sun 10-6, Tues & Thurs 12-8
MCCRELESS, 1023 Ada St, 78223, SAN 362-2924. Tel: 210-207-9170. FAX: 210-207-9175. *Mgr,* Cammie Brantley; Staff 3 (MLS 3)
Founded 1966. Circ 18,000
Open Mon & Wed 12-8, Tues & Thurs-Sun 10-6
MEMORIAL, 3222 Culebra, 78228, SAN 362-2932. Tel: 210-432-6783. FAX: 210-435-5471. *Mgr,* Jimmy Jimenez
Open Mon, Wed & Fri-Sun 10-6, Tues & Thurs 12-8
MISSION, 3134 Roosevelt Ave, 78214. Tel: 210-207-2704. FAX: 210-207-2704. *Br Mgr,* Elma Nieto-Rodriguez
Open Mon, Wed & Fri-Sun 10-6, Tues & Thurs 12-8
OAKWELL, 4134 Harry Wurzbach, 78209, SAN 362-2959. Tel: 210-828-2569. FAX: 210-821-6923. *Mgr,* Tracey Knouse
Open Mon, Wed & Fri-Sun 10-6, Tues & Thurs 12-8
PAN AMERICAN, 1122 W Pyron Ave, 78221, SAN 362-2983. Tel: 210-924-8164. FAX: 210-932-1489. *Mgr,* Rebecca Johnson
Open Mon & Wed 12-8, Tues & Thurs-Sun 10-6
PARMAN, 20735 Wilderness Oak, 78258. Tel: 210-207-2703. FAX: 210-207-2703. *Br Mgr,* Haley Holmes
Open Mon, Wed & Fri-Sun 10-6, Tues & Thurs 12-8
MOLLY PRUITT LIBRARY, 5110 Walzem Rd, 78218. Tel: 210-650-1122. FAX: 210-650-1291. *Br Mgr,* Mariya Rodriguez
Open Mon, Wed & Fri-Sun 10-6, Tues & Thurs 12-8
SAN PEDRO, 1315 San Pedro Ave, 78212, SAN 362-3017. Tel: 210-733-1454. FAX: 210-738-9471. *Br Mgr,* Dan Stanford; Staff 7 (MLS 2, Non-MLS 5)
Open Mon, Wed & Fri-Sun 10-6, Tues & Thurs 12-8
SEMMES, 15060 Judson Rd, 78247. Tel: 210-650-9540. FAX: 210-650-4079. *Mgr,* Jamie Flowers
Open Mon, Wed & Thurs-Sun 10-6, Tues & Thurs 12-8
TEEN SERVICES, 600 Soledad, 78205-2786. Tel: 210-207-2678. FAX: 210-207-2553. *Mgr,* Jennifer Velasquez
Open Mon-Thurs 9-9, Fri & Sat 9-5, Sun 11-5
TEXANA & GENEALOGY, 600 Soledad, 78205-2786. Tel: 210-207-2500. E-mail: genealogydesk@sanantonio.gov. ; Staff 6 (MLS 5, Non-MLS 1)
Library Holdings: Bk Vols 108,535; Per Subs 586
Special Collections: Municipal Document Depository; Oral History
Subject Interests: Genealogy, Hist, Texana
Open Mon-Thurs 9-9, Fri & Sat 9-5, Sun 11-5
Friends of the Library Group
THOUSAND OAKS, 4618 Thousand Oaks, 78233, SAN 328-865X. Tel: 210-657-5205. FAX: 210-657-6874. *Mgr,* Jamie Flowers
Open Mon & Wed 12-8, Tues & Thurs-Sun 10-6
WESTFALL, 6111 Rosedale Ct, 78201, SAN 362-3041. Tel: 210-344-2373. FAX: 210-344-4699. *Mgr,* Michael Kaminski
Open Mon & Wed 12-8, Tues & Thurs-Sun 10-6
Bookmobiles: 2

S   **SAN ANTONIO SCOTTISH RITE LIBRARY***, 308 Ave E, 78298. (Mail add: PO Box 2239, 78298-2239). Tel: 210-222-0133. Toll Free Tel: 866-222-9293. FAX: 210-222-0136. Web Site: albertpikedemolay.org. *In Charge,* Jerry Nowotny; E-mail: nowot@hotmail.com
Library Holdings: Bk Titles 4,000
Wireless access
Open Mon-Fri 8-5
Restriction: Not a lending libr

S   **THOMAS BAKER SLICK MEMORIAL LIBRARY***, SwRI Library, 6220 Culebra Rd, MS 84, 78238-5166. SAN 316-7453. Tel: 210-522-2125. FAX: 210-522-5479. E-mail: libraryrequest@swri.org. *Dir,* Sally Crash; Staff 3 (MLS 3)
Founded 1948
Library Holdings: Electronic Media & Resources 10,000
Automation Activity & Vendor Info: (Acquisitions) Ex Libris Group; (Cataloging) Ex Libris Group; (Circulation) Ex Libris Group; (ILL) Ex Libris Group; (OPAC) Ex Libris Group; (Serials) SerialsSolutions
Database Vendor: Amigos Library Services, CISTI Source, CredoReference, Elsevier, Emerald, Ex Libris Group, IEEE (Institute of

Electrical & Electronics Engineers), IOP, ISI Web of Knowledge, Jane's, Nature Publishing Group, ScienceDirect, SerialsSolutions, Springer-Verlag, Thomson - Web of Science, Wiley InterScience
Wireless access
Partic in Amigos Library Services, Inc; Council of Research & Academic Libraries
Open Mon-Fri 8-5

S SOUTHWEST SCHOOL OF ARTS LIBRARY*, 300 Augusta, 78205. SAN 326-6133. Tel: 210-224-1848. FAX: 210-224-9337. E-mail: information@swschool.org. Web Site: www.swschool.org. *Librn,* Beck Whitehead
Founded 1965. Enrl 2,000; Fac 70
Special Collections: American Fabrics Quarterly, 1948-1967; The Flying Needle (complete set) 1969-1991
Wireless access
Restriction: Non-circulating

S TEXAS BIOMEDICAL RESEARCH INSTITUTE*, Preston G Northrup Memorial Library, 7620 NW Loop 410, 78227-5301. (Mail add: PO Box 760549, 78245-0549). Administration Tel: 210-258-9502, 210-258-9593. Administration FAX: 210-670-3313. E-mail: library@txbiomed.org. *Dir,* Jayson L Felty; E-mail: jfelty@txbiomed.org; *ILL,* Mary Ann Smith; E-mail: msmith@txbiomed.org; *Libr Tech,* Mary F Orsborn; Tel: 210-258-9749, E-mail: morsborn@txbiomed.org; Staff 4 (MLS 2, Non-MLS 2)
Founded 1947
Jan 2010-Dec 2010 Income $958,080. Mats Exp $951,368. Sal $286,865
Library Holdings: Bk Titles 5,000; Bk Vols 6,000; Per Subs 300
Subject Interests: Basic biomed sci, Primatology, Res
Automation Activity & Vendor Info: (Acquisitions) Ex Libris Group; (Cataloging) Ex Libris Group; (Circulation) Ex Libris Group; (ILL) OCLC ILLiad; (OPAC) Ex Libris Group; (Serials) Ex Libris Group
Database Vendor: Annual Reviews, BioOne, Elsevier, ISI Web of Knowledge, Majors, Marcive, Inc, OCLC Openly Informatics, OCLC WorldCat, PubMed, ScienceDirect, Wiley, YBP Library Services
Wireless access
Function: For res purposes
Partic in ARIEL; Docline; National Network of Libraries of Medicine South Central Region
Open Mon-Fri 8-5
Restriction: Lending to staff only, Limited access for the pub

C TRINITY UNIVERSITY*, Coates Library, One Trinity Pl, 78212-7200. SAN 362-3130. Tel: 210-999-8121. Circulation Tel: 210-999-8127. Interlibrary Loan Service Tel: 210-999-8473. Reference Tel: 210-999-7213. FAX: 210-999-8182. Interlibrary Loan Service FAX: 210-999-8021. Web Site: lib.trinity.edu. *Dir, Ctr for Learning & Tech,* Ronnie C Swanner; Tel: 210-999-7356, E-mail: rswanner@trinity.edu; *Univ Librn,* Diane J Graves; E-mail: diane.graves@trinity.edu; *Asst Univ Librn, Pub Serv,* Christopher W Nolan; E-mail: cnolan@trinity.edu; *Head, Coll Develop, Acq & Res Sharing,* Beatrice Caraway; Tel: 210-999-7292, E-mail: bcaraway@trinity.edu; *Head, Discovery Serv,* Jane Costanza; Tel: 210-999-7612, E-mail: jane.costanza@trinity.edu; *Acq,* Brenda Sheffield; Tel: 210-999-8173, Fax: 210-999-8120, E-mail: bsheffie@trinity.edu; *ILL,* Maria McWilliams; E-mail: mmcwilli@trinity.edu; Staff 13 (MLS 11, Non-MLS 2)
Founded 1869. Enrl 2,431; Fac 278; Highest Degree: Master
Jun 2010-May 2011 Income $3,896,983. Mats Exp $2,890,348, Books $406,446, Per/Ser (Incl. Access Fees) $1,402,865, Micro $27,779, AV Mat $36,445, Electronic Ref Mat (Incl. Access Fees) $996,419, Presv $20,394. Sal $1,509,891 (Prof $734,548)
Library Holdings: AV Mats 54,498; CDs 10,129; DVDs 4,872; e-books 122,304; Microforms 307,774; Music Scores 18,056; Bk Titles 706,229; Bk Vols 918,588; Per Subs 1,911; Videos 5,681
Special Collections: American Literature (Helen Miller Jones Coll); Archives of Monterrey & the State of Nuevo Leon, Mexico, micro; Greek & Roman Art & Architecture (Denman Coll); Latin America (Hilton Coll); Space Exploration (Campbell Coll & Maloney Coll); Texana (Beretta Coll & Nixon Coll); Trinity University Archives. State Document Depository; US Document Depository
Automation Activity & Vendor Info: (Acquisitions) Innovative Interfaces, Inc; (Cataloging) Innovative Interfaces, Inc - Millenium; (Circulation) Innovative Interfaces, Inc - Millenium; (Course Reserve) Docutek; (ILL) OCLC ILLiad; (OPAC) Innovative Interfaces, Inc; (Serials) Innovative Interfaces, Inc - Millenium
Database Vendor: ACM (Association for Computing Machinery), Alexander Street Press, American Chemical Society, American Mathematical Society, American Psychological Association (APA), Amigos Library Services, ARTstor, BioOne, Cambridge Scientific Abstracts, CIOS (Communication Institute for Online Scholarship), EBSCOhost, Elsevier, Gale Cengage Learning, Innovative Interfaces, Inc, JSTOR, LexisNexis, Marcive, Inc, netLibrary, Newsbank, OCLC FirstSearch, OCLC WorldCat, Oxford Online, ProQuest, PubMed, RefWorks, Standard & Poor's, TDNet, ValueLine, Wiley, Wilson - Wilson Web, YBP Library Services

Wireless access
Function: Archival coll, Audio & video playback equip for onsite use, AV serv, Computers for patron use, Copy machines, Doc delivery serv, e-mail serv, E-Reserves, Electronic databases & coll, Free DVD rentals, Govt ref serv, Handicapped accessible, ILL available, Music CDs, Online info literacy tutorials on the web & in blackboard, Online searches, Photocopying/Printing, Ref serv available, Spoken cassettes & DVDs, Telephone ref, Wheelchair accessible, Writing prog
Partic in Associated Colleges of the South; Coun of Res & Acad Librs; NITLE; Oberlin Group; Texas Council of Academic Libraries
Open Mon-Thurs 8am-Midnight, Fri 8-6, Sat 10-6, Sun 10am-Midnight
Restriction: 24-hr pass syst for students only, In-house use for visitors, Limited access for the pub, Non-circulating coll, Non-circulating of rare bks, Open to students, fac, staff & alumni, Private librn, Restricted borrowing privileges, Restricted loan policy

A UNITED STATES AIR FORCE*, AFIWC Library, 102 Hall Blvd, No 2, 78243-7168. SAN 320-4235. Tel: 210-977-2804. FAX: 210-977-6621. *Librn,* Emily Mardis; Staff 6 (MLS 1, Non-MLS 5)
Founded 1994
Library Holdings: Bk Vols 20,000; Per Subs 20
Special Collections: Air War College; Project Warrior
Subject Interests: Electronic warfare, Electronics, Eng
Automation Activity & Vendor Info: (Cataloging) SirsiDynix; (Circulation) SirsiDynix
Database Vendor: EBSCOhost, OCLC FirstSearch, ProQuest
Open Mon-Fri 7-3

C UNIVERSITY OF TEXAS AT SAN ANTONIO LIBRARIES*, One UTSA Circle, 78249-0671. SAN 316-7496. Tel: 210-458-7506. Circulation Tel: 210-458-2440, 210-458-4574. Interlibrary Loan Service Tel: 210-458-5501. Reference Tel: 210-458-2446, 210-458-4573. Interlibrary Loan Service FAX: 210-458-4571. Administration FAX: 210-458-7577. E-mail: librarycolldev@utsa.edu. Web Site: www.lib.utsa.edu. *Dean of Librs,* Dr Krisellen Maloney; Tel: 210-458-4889, E-mail: krisellen.maloney@utsa.edu; *Asst Dean, Coll & Assessments,* Posie Aagaard; *Asst Dean, Info & Tech Mgt,* Barbara Jakubowski; Tel: 210-458-5509, E-mail: barbara.jakubowski@utsa.edu; *Asst Dean, Pub Serv,* Jan Kemp; *Head, Acq,* Judy Garrison; Tel: 210-458-5507, E-mail: judy.garrison@utsa.edu; Staff 90 (MLS 20, Non-MLS 70)
Founded 1972. Enrl 30,000; Highest Degree: Doctorate
Library Holdings: e-journals 35,000; Bk Vols 1,800,000; Per Subs 2,000
Special Collections: Texana, especially San Antonio & South Texas. State Document Depository; US Document Depository
Automation Activity & Vendor Info: (Acquisitions) Ex Libris Group; (Cataloging) Ex Libris Group; (Circulation) Ex Libris Group; (Course Reserve) Ex Libris Group; (ILL) Ex Libris Group; (Media Booking) Ex Libris Group; (OPAC) Ex Libris Group; (Serials) Ex Libris Group
Database Vendor: EBSCOhost, Gale Cengage Learning, OCLC FirstSearch, ProQuest, Wilson - Wilson Web
Partic in Coun of Res & Acad Librs; TexSHARE - Texas State Library & Archives Commission
Open Sun 10am-Fri 10pm, Sat 9-9
Friends of the Library Group

CM UNIVERSITY OF TEXAS HEALTH SCIENCE CENTER AT SAN ANTONIO LIBRARIES, Dolph Briscoe Library, 7703 Floyd Curl Dr, MSC 7940, 78229-3900. SAN 362-3165. Tel: 210-567-2400. Circulation Tel: 210-567-2440. Interlibrary Loan Service Tel: 210-567-2460. Reference Tel: 210-567-2450. Automation Services Tel: 210-567-2410. FAX: 210-567-2490. Interlibrary Loan Service FAX: 210-567-2463. Web Site: www.library.uthscsa.edu. *Executive Dir of Libr,* Rajia Tobia; *Dir of Briscoe Libr & Outreach Serv,* Jonquil Feldman; E-mail: feldman@uthscsa.edu; *Dir, Libr Tech & Hist Coll,* Luke Rosenberger; E-mail: rosenberger@uthscsa.edu; *Asst Dir, Digital & Spec Coll,* Anne Comeaux; E-mail: comeaux@uthscsa.edu; *Asst Dir, Ramirez Libr,* Greysi Reyna; E-mail: reynag@uthscsa.edu; *Head, Access Serv,* Chris Gaspard; E-mail: sifuentes@uthscsa.edu; *Head, Coll Res,* John Weed; E-mail: weedj@uthscsa.edu; *Head, Educ & Info Serv,* Katie Prentice; E-mail: prenticek@uthscsa.edu; *Head, Outreach Serv,* Peg Seger; E-mail: segerp@uthscsa.edu; *Cat Librn,* Lisa Finnie; E-mail: finnie@uthscsa; *Cat & Acq,* Andrea Schorr; E-mail: schorr@uthscsa.edu; *Curric Liaison Librn,* Angela Myatt; E-mail: myatta@uthscsa.edu; *Electronic Res/Ser Librn,* Dana Whitmire; E-mail: whitmired@uthscsa.edu; *Ramirez Librn,* Kathleen Carter; E-mail: carterk3@uthscsa.edu; *Spec Projects Librn,* Susan Hunnicutt; E-mail: hunnicutt@uthscsa.edu; *Syst Librn,* Eric Willman; E-mail: willman@uthscsa.edu; *Web Serv Librn,* Kelley Minars; E-mail: minars@uthscsa.edu; Staff 50 (MLS 17, Non-MLS 33)
Founded 1966. Enrl 3,123; Fac 1,722; Highest Degree: Doctorate
Library Holdings: AV Mats 1,640; e-books 8,978; e-journals 19,855; Bk Titles 104,230; Bk Vols 219,801
Special Collections: History of Medicine Coll
Subject Interests: Allied health, Dentistry, Med, Nursing

Automation Activity & Vendor Info: (Acquisitions) Innovative Interfaces, Inc; (Cataloging) Innovative Interfaces, Inc; (Circulation) Innovative Interfaces, Inc; (ILL) OCLC ILLiad; (OPAC) Innovative Interfaces, Inc; (Serials) Innovative Interfaces, Inc
Database Vendor: American Chemical Society, American Psychological Association (APA), Amigos Library Services, Annual Reviews, ARTstor, Checkpoint Systems, Inc, Cinahl Information Systems, CISTI Source, Dialog, ebrary, EBSCOhost, Elsevier, Gale Cengage Learning, Ingenta, Innovative Interfaces, Inc, ISI Web of Knowledge, JSTOR, Majors, McGraw-Hill, MD Consult, Medline, Micromedex, Natural Standard, Nature Publishing Group, netLibrary, OCLC Openly Informatics, OCLC WorldCat, OVID Technologies, Oxford Online, ProQuest, PubMed, RefWorks, ScienceDirect, Scopus, Springer-Verlag, STAT!Ref (Teton Data Systems), Thomson - Web of Science, UpToDate, WebMD, Wiley InterScience, YBP Library Services
Wireless access
Function: Archival coll, Art exhibits, Audio & video playback equip for onsite use, Bk club(s), Computers for patron use, Copy machines, Doc delivery serv, e-mail & chat, Electronic databases & coll, Exhibits, Handicapped accessible, Health sci info serv, ILL available, Mail & tel request accepted, Online cat, Online ref, Online searches, Orientations, Outreach serv, Photocopying/Printing, Pub access computers, Ref serv available, Ref serv in person, Scanner, Telephone ref, Web-catalog, Wheelchair accessible
Publications: Annual Report: The Libraries (Annual report); News from The Libraries (Newsletter); Newsletter of the Friends of the P I Nixon Medical Historical Library (Annually)
Partic in Coun of Res & Acad Librs; National Network of Libraries of Medicine South Central Region; OCLC Online Computer Library Center, Inc; TexSHARE - Texas State Library & Archives Commission
Open Mon-Thurs 7am-Midnight, Fri 7am-10pm, Sat 9am-10pm, Sun 10am-Midnight
Restriction: 24-hr pass syst for students only, Badge access after hrs, In-house use for visitors
Friends of the Library Group

CR UNIVERSITY OF THE INCARNATE WORD*, JE & LE Mabee Library, 4301 Broadway, UPO Box 297, 78209-6397. SAN 316-7275. Tel: 210-829-6010. Circulation Tel: 210-805-5896, 210-829-3836. Interlibrary Loan Service Tel: 210-829-3838. Reference Tel: 210-829-3835. Administration Tel: 210-829-3837. FAX: 210-829-6041. Web Site: library.uiwtx.edu. *Dean,* Dr Cheryl Anderson; E-mail: cheryla@uiwtx.edu; *Dir, Pub Serv,* Dell Davis; Tel: 210-829-6054, E-mail: dmdavis@uiwtx.edu; *Dir of Tech Serv,* Mary L Jinks; Tel: 210-829-3839, E-mail: marydlg@uiwtx.edu; *Cat Librn,* Melissa Rucker; Tel: 210-829-6097, E-mail: melissa@uiwtx.edu; *Info Literacy Librn,* Leslie Todd; Tel: 210-829-3841, E-mail: todd@uiwtx.edu; *AV,* Farhad L Moshiri; Tel: 210-829-3842, E-mail: moshiri@uiwtx.edu; *Syst Adminr,* Philip Hernandez; Tel: 210-829-3843, E-mail: prhernan@uiwtx.edu; Staff 20 (MLS 10, Non-MLS 10)
Founded 1897. Enrl 7,000; Highest Degree: Doctorate
Library Holdings: AV Mats 15,415; Bks on Deafness & Sign Lang 500; e-books 23,754; Bk Titles 272,159; Per Subs 17,018
Special Collections: Unique & Limited Editions, Rare Books
Subject Interests: Ezra Pound, Texana, Women's studies
Automation Activity & Vendor Info: (Acquisitions) Ex Libris Group; (Cataloging) Ex Libris Group; (Circulation) Ex Libris Group; (ILL) Ex Libris Group; (OPAC) Ex Libris Group; (Serials) Ex Libris Group
Database Vendor: EBSCOhost, Gale Cengage Learning, LexisNexis, netLibrary, OCLC FirstSearch, OVID Technologies, ProQuest
Wireless access
Partic in Coun of Res & Acad Librs; Phoenix Group; TexSHARE - Texas State Library & Archives Commission
Open Mon-Thurs 7:30am-Midnight, Fri 7:30am-9pm, Sat 8am-9pm, Sun 2pm-Midnight
Restriction: Open to fac, students & qualified researchers, Photo ID required for access

SAN AUGUSTINE

P SAN AUGUSTINE PUBLIC LIBRARY*, 413 E Columbia St, 75972-2111. SAN 316-7526. Tel: 936-275-5367. FAX: 936-275-5049. E-mail: sauglib@yahoo.com. Web Site: www.salibrary.org. *Dir,* Adrienne Montgomery; Staff 1 (MLS 1)
Founded 1973. Pop 8,086; Circ 19,000
Library Holdings: Bk Vols 19,949; Per Subs 26
Special Collections: Genealogy (Tex Heritage), bk, micro. Oral History
Automation Activity & Vendor Info: (Cataloging) Follett Software; (Circulation) Follett Software
Wireless access
Publications: Caucasian Cemeteries of San Augustine County, Texas, 3 vols; Probate cases of San Augustine County, Texas (1828-1940)
Open Mon-Fri 8:30-5, Sat 9-2
Friends of the Library Group

SAN BENITO

P SAN BENITO PUBLIC LIBRARY, 101 W Rose St, 78586-5169. SAN 316-7534. Tel: 956-361-3860. FAX: 956-361-3867. Web Site: www.cityofsanbenito.com/library.htm. *Libr Dir,* Gerardo Salazar; E-mail: gsalazar@cityofsanbenito.com; Staff 1 (MLS 1)
Founded 1936. Pop 30,000; Circ 73,500; Fac 5
Library Holdings: Bk Titles 32,000; Bk Vols 34,000; Per Subs 110
Automation Activity & Vendor Info: (Acquisitions) Biblionix; (Cataloging) Biblionix; (Circulation) Biblionix; (Course Reserve) Biblionix; (OPAC) Biblionix
Wireless access
Function: Accelerated reader prog
Open Mon-Thurs 10-7, Fri 10-5, Sat 12-5
Friends of the Library Group

SAN DIEGO

P DUVAL COUNTY-SAN DIEGO PUBLIC LIBRARY*, 315 S Dr Dunlap St, 78384. (Mail add: PO Box 1062, 78384-1062), SAN 376-429X. Tel: 361-279-8201. FAX: 361-279-8212. Web Site: www.duvalco.lib.tx.us. *Libr Dir,* B J Alaniz; E-mail: bjalaniz@mail.com; Staff 1 (Non-MLS 1)
Founded 1994. Pop 12,578
Library Holdings: AV Mats 229; High Interest/Low Vocabulary Bk Vols 5,000; Bk Vols 16,000; Per Subs 26
Automation Activity & Vendor Info: (Cataloging) ComPanion Corp; (Circulation) ComPanion Corp
Wireless access
Function: Bks on cassette, Children's prog, Computers for patron use, Copy machines, e-mail serv, Electronic databases & coll, Handicapped accessible, ILL available, Magnifiers for reading, Photocopying/Printing, Preschool outreach, Ref serv in person, Summer reading prog, Tax forms, VHS videos, Wheelchair accessible
Open Mon-Thurs 3-8, Fri 3-6, Sat 10-5
Friends of the Library Group
Branches: 2
BENAVIDES BRANCH, 131 Mesquite St, Benavides, 78341. (Mail add: PO Box R, Benavides, 78341-0918). Tel: 361-256-4646. FAX: 361-256-4646. *Br Mgr,* Janie Saenz
Library Holdings: Bk Vols 3,500
Open Tues-Fri 4-8, Sat 10-2
Friends of the Library Group
FREER BRANCH, 608 Carolyn St, Freer, 78357. (Mail add: PO Box 1203, Freer, 78357). Tel: 361-394-5350. FAX: 361-394-5350. *Br Mgr,* Esmeralda Canales; E-mail: amycanales42@yahoo.com
Library Holdings: AV Mats 30; Bk Vols 4,000
Database Vendor: EBSCOhost
Open Mon-Fri 3-7
Friends of the Library Group

SAN JUAN

P SAN JUAN PUBLIC LIBRARY*, 1010 S Standard St, 78589. SAN 378-4479. Tel: 956-702-0926. FAX: 956-783-3444. Web Site: www.youseemore.com/sanjuan; E-mail: stevec@lssi.com; *Dir,* Steve Coffman; E-mail: stevec@lssi.com; Staff 7 (MLS 1, Non-MLS 6)
Pop 44,500
Library Holdings: Bk Vols 20,000
Automation Activity & Vendor Info: (Cataloging) SirsiDynix; (Circulation) SirsiDynix; (OPAC) SirsiDynix
Mem of Hidalgo County Library System
Open Mon-Thurs 8-6, Fri & Sat 9-5

SAN MARCOS

P SAN MARCOS PUBLIC LIBRARY*, 625 E Hopkins, 78666. SAN 316-7550. Tel: 512-393-8200. E-mail: smpl@sanmarcostx.gov. Web Site: www.sanmarcostx.gov/library. *Dir of Libr,* Stephanie Langenkamp; *Head, Tech Serv,* Arro Smith; *Commun Serv, Outreach Serv Librn,* Susan Smith; *Tech Serv Librn,* Sandra Bailey; *Mgr, Patron Serv,* Diane Insley; *Adult Serv,* Robin Wood; *Ch,* Ashley Schimelman; Staff 19 (MLS 7, Non-MLS 12)
Founded 1966. Pop 64,000; Circ 405,000
Library Holdings: Bk Vols 148,995; Per Subs 230
Special Collections: San Marcos-Hays County Coll
Automation Activity & Vendor Info: (Acquisitions) TLC (The Library Corporation); (Cataloging) TLC (The Library Corporation); (Circulation) TLC (The Library Corporation); (OPAC) TLC (The Library Corporation)
Wireless access
Function: Adult bk club, Adult literacy prog, Archival coll, Computer training, Copy machines, Electronic databases & coll, Handicapped accessible, ILL available, Learning ctr, Magnifiers for reading, Preschool outreach, Prog for adults, Prog for children & young adult, Summer reading prog, Tax forms, Telephone ref
Publications: Calender of Events (Monthly)

Mem of Central Texas Library System, Inc
Friends of the Library Group

C   TEXAS STATE UNIVERSITY-SAN MARCOS*, Albert B Alkek Library,
Wood & Talbot St, 78666-4604. (Mail add: 601 University Dr,
78666-4684), SAN 362-322X. Tel: 512-245-2133. Circulation Tel:
512-245-3681. Reference Tel: 512-245-2685. FAX: 512-245-3002. E-mail:
library@txstate.edu. Web Site: www.library.txstate.edu. *Assoc VPres for
Univ Libr,* Joan Heath; *Dir, Res & Learning Serv,* Position Currently Open;
Acq, Paivi Rentz; E-mail: pr11@txstate.edu; *Cat,* Elaine Sanchez; E-mail:
es02@txstate.edu; *Computer Serv,* Todd C Peters; E-mail:
tp09@txstate.edu; Staff 33 (MLS 29, Non-MLS 4)
Founded 1899. Enrl 27,171; Fac 1,394; Highest Degree: Doctorate
Library Holdings: e-journals 38,946; Bk Titles 1,432,812; Bk Vols
3,741,467; Per Subs 5,370
Special Collections: J Frank Dobie, John Graves, Preston Jones, Larry L
King, Elithe Hamilton Kirkland (Southwestern Writers Coll); Wittliff
Gallery of Southwestern & Mexican Photography. State Document
Depository; US Document Depository
Automation Activity & Vendor Info: (Acquisitions) Innovative Interfaces,
Inc - Millenium; (Cataloging) Innovative Interfaces, Inc - Millenium;
(Circulation) Innovative Interfaces, Inc - Millenium; (Course Reserve)
Docutek; (ILL) OCLC ILLiad; (OPAC) Innovative Interfaces, Inc -
Millenium; (Serials) Innovative Interfaces, Inc - Millenium
Wireless access
Partic in Coun of Res & Acad Librs; OCLC Online Computer Library
Center, Inc; Tex Share
Open Mon-Wed 7:30am-1am, Thurs 7:30am-Midnight, Fri 7:30am-10pm,
Sat 9-6, Sun 1-1

SAN SABA

P   SAN SABA COUNTY LIBRARY*, Rylander Memorial Library, 103 S
Live Oak, 76877. SAN 316-7569. Tel: 325-372-3079. FAX: 325-372-3079.
E-mail: rylander@co.san-saba.tx.us. Web Site: www.sansabalibrary.org.
Librn, Mary Lee Calder; Staff 1 (Non-MLS 1)
Pop 5,540; Circ 16,055
Library Holdings: Bk Vols 13,000; Per Subs 25
Automation Activity & Vendor Info: (Cataloging) Biblionix; (Circulation)
Biblionix
Wireless access
Mem of Central Texas Library System, Inc
Open Mon-Fri 11-5, Sat 10-2
Friends of the Library Group

SANDERSON

P   TERRELL COUNTY PUBLIC LIBRARY*, Courthouse Sq, 109
Hackberry, 79848. (Mail add: PO Drawer 250, 79848-0250), SAN
376-4346. Tel: 432-345-2294. FAX: 432-345-2144. E-mail:
library@co.terrell.tx.us. *Dir,* Christina Valles
Library Holdings: Bk Titles 28,000; Per Subs 32
Automation Activity & Vendor Info: (Cataloging) Follett Software;
(Circulation) Follett Software
Wireless access
Mem of Texas Trans-Pecos Regional Library System
Open Mon-Fri 1-6, Sat 2-5
Friends of the Library Group

SANGER

P   SANGER PUBLIC LIBRARY, 501 Bolivar St, 76266. SAN 370-7350. Tel:
940-458-3257. E-mail: library@sangertexas.org. Web Site:
www.sanger.lib.tx.us. *Dir,* Victoria Elieson; Staff 1.5 (MLS 1.5)
Founded 1970. Pop 9,325; Circ 39,200
Oct 2010-Sept 2011 Income $150,655, State $5,012, City $122,473,
County $16,331, Locally Generated Income $4,339, Other $2,500. Mats
Exp $14,350, Books $10,596, Per/Ser (Incl. Access Fees) $1,145, Micro
$276, AV Mat $2,133, Electronic Ref Mat (Incl. Access Fees) $200. Sal
$112,324 (Prof $52,000)
Library Holdings: Audiobooks 840; CDs 353; DVDs 1,042; Microforms
86; Bk Titles 17,850; Bk Vols 18,034; Per Subs 19; Videos 724
Special Collections: Sanger Courier, microfilm
Subject Interests: Local hist
Automation Activity & Vendor Info: (Cataloging) Evergreen;
(Circulation) Evergreen; (OPAC) Evergreen
Wireless access
Function: Adult bk club, Bks on cassette, Bks on CD, Children's prog,
Computer training, Computers for patron use, Copy machines, e-mail serv,
E-Reserves, Free DVD rentals, Homebound delivery serv, ILL available,
Magnifiers for reading, Microfiche/film & reading machines, Music CDs,
Online cat, Photocopying/Printing, Ref serv in person, Scanner, Spanish
lang bks, Story hour, Summer reading prog, Tax forms, VHS videos,
Web-catalog
Mem of North Texas Library Partners

Partic in North Texas Library Consortium (NTLC)
Open Mon-Thurs 10-6, Fri 10-5, Sat 10-2
Restriction: Authorized scholars by appt
Friends of the Library Group

SANTA ANNA

P   SANTA ANNA LIBRARY, 606 Wallis Ave, 76878-2031. SAN 316-7577.
Tel: 325-348-3395. *Librn,* Alice Spillman
Founded 1907. Pop 1,000; Circ 12,000
Jan 2012-Dec 2012 Income $28,084, County $500, Locally Generated
Income $24,584, Other $3,000
Library Holdings: Bk Vols 25,000
Subject Interests: Local hist
Wireless access
Open Mon & Wed-Fri 9:30-4, Tues 9:30-Noon

SANTA FE

P   MAE S BRUCE LIBRARY*, 13302 Sixth, 77510-9148. (Mail add: PO
Box 950, 77510-0950), SAN 326-1816. Tel: 409-925-5540. FAX:
409-925-8697. E-mail: library@maebrucelibrary.org. Web Site:
www.maebrucelibrary.org. *Librn,* Brenda Cheatham; E-mail:
bccheatham@yahoo.com; Staff 3 (MLS 1, Non-MLS 2)
Founded 1973. Pop 13,783; Circ 37,000
Library Holdings: Bk Vols 28,000; Per Subs 18; Talking Bks 700
Automation Activity & Vendor Info: (Cataloging) Follett Software;
(Circulation) Follett Software
Partic in Houston Area Database Consortium
Open Mon-Wed & Fri 10-6, Thurs 12-8, Sat 10-1:30
Friends of the Library Group

SCHERTZ

P   SCHERTZ PUBLIC LIBRARY*, 798 Schertz Pkwy, 78154. SAN
324-1556. Tel: 210-619-1700. FAX: 210-619-1711. E-mail:
librarian@schertz.com. Web Site: www.schertzlibrary.org. *Libr Mgr,*
Melissa Uhlhorn; Staff 17.5 (MLS 4, Non-MLS 13.5)
Founded 1978. Pop 58,000; Circ 300,000
Library Holdings: Bk Titles 65,000; Per Subs 160
Subject Interests: Genealogy, Texana
Database Vendor: Polaris Library Systems
Wireless access
Function: ILL available, Photocopying/Printing, Prog for children & young
adult, Ref serv available, Summer reading prog, Wheelchair accessible
Open Mon-Thurs 10-8, Fri 10-6, Sat & Sun 12-6

SCHULENBURG

P   SCHULENBURG PUBLIC LIBRARY*, 310 Simpson, 78956. SAN
316-7585. Tel: 979-743-3345. *Librn,* Cindy Lytle; *Asst Librn,* Donna Holub
Pop 2,730; Circ 18,000
Library Holdings: Audiobooks 20; DVDs 1,000; Large Print Bks 150; Bk
Vols 30,000; Per Subs 20
Wireless access
Mem of Central Texas Library System, Inc
Open Mon 10-8, Tues-Fri 10-6, Sat 9-12
Friends of the Library Group

SEAGOVILLE

P   SEAGOVILLE PUBLIC LIBRARY*, 702 N Hwy 175, 75159-1774. SAN
316-7593. Tel: 972-287-7720. FAX: 972-287-3891. E-mail:
info@seagovillelibrary.org. Web Site: www.seagovillelibrary.org. *Librn,*
Elizabeth Gant
Founded 1942
Library Holdings: AV Mats 802; Bks on Deafness & Sign Lang 23; High
Interest/Low Vocabulary Bk Vols 100; Large Print Bks 394; Bk Titles
28,822; Bk Vols 29,749; Per Subs 18; Talking Bks 444
Automation Activity & Vendor Info: (Cataloging) Follett Software;
(Circulation) Follett Software; (OPAC) Follett Software
Open Mon & Thurs 11-7, Tues & Fri 10-5, Wed 11-6, Sat 9-1
Friends of the Library Group

SEALY

P   VIRGIL & JOSEPHINE GORDON MEMORIAL LIBRARY*, 917 N
Circle Dr, 77474. SAN 324-2188. Tel: 979-885-7469. FAX: 979-885-7469.
E-mail: gordonlib@sbcglobal.net. *Librn,* Joyce Williams; *Asst Librn,*
Guadalupe Amaya; Staff 2 (Non-MLS 2)
Pop 9,000; Circ 111,514
Library Holdings: AV Mats 2,420; CDs 66; DVDs 164; Large Print Bks
280; Bk Titles 29,307; Bk Vols 30,767; Per Subs 20; Videos 1,304
Wireless access

Function: Adult bk club, Copy machines, Fax serv, ILL available, Photocopying/Printing, Prog for children & young adult, Summer reading prog, Tax forms, VHS videos, Workshops
Open Mon-Thurs 10-5:30, Sat 9-1
Friends of the Library Group

SEGUIN

P   SEGUIN-GUADALUPE COUNTY PUBLIC LIBRARY*, 707 E College St, 78155-3217. SAN 316-7615. Tel: 830-401-2422. FAX: 830-401-2477. E-mail: library@seguintexas.gov. Web Site: www.seguin.lib.tx.us. *Libr Dir,* Jacki Gross; Tel: 830-401-2466, E-mail: jacki@seguin.lib.tx.us; *Asst Libr Dir,* Silvia DeLourdes Christy; Tel: 830-401-2426, E-mail: silviac@seguin.lib.tx.us; Staff 9 (MLS 3, Non-MLS 6)
Founded 1930. Pop 48,359; Circ 226,268
Oct 2009-Sept 2010 Income $586,448, City $377,259, County $162,249, Other $39,593. Sal $288,789
Library Holdings: AV Mats 5,098; Large Print Bks 3,692; Bk Titles 65,730; Bk Vols 71,498; Per Subs 104
Special Collections: Guadalupe County Land Records, micro; Historic Photographs (Kubala Coll); Old Seguin Newspapers, micro-filmed
Subject Interests: Guadalupe County hist, Local hist
Automation Activity & Vendor Info: (OPAC) Biblionix
Database Vendor: Agricola, Baker & Taylor, EBSCOhost, Gale Cengage Learning, Medline, netLibrary, Newsbank, OCLC FirstSearch, ProQuest, SirsiDynix, ValueLine
Wireless access
Function: Computer training, Copy machines, Electronic databases & coll, Fax serv, Free DVD rentals, ILL available, Prog for children & young adult, Ref serv available, Spoken cassettes & CDs, Summer reading prog, Tax forms, VHS videos
Open Mon-Thurs 9-9, Fri & Sat 9-5
Friends of the Library Group

C   TEXAS LUTHERAN UNIVERSITY*, Blumberg Memorial Library, 1000 W Court St, 78155-5978. SAN 316-7623. Tel: 830-372-8100. FAX: 830-372-8156. Web Site: www.tlu.edu. *Librn,* Martha Rinn; E-mail: mrinn@tlu.edu; *Asst Librn,* Vicki Eckhardt; *Electronic Res, Syst Librn,* Sally Carol-Ricks; *Instruction & Outreach, Pub Serv,* Mark Dibble; Staff 5 (MLS 5)
Founded 1891. Enrl 1,473; Fac 64; Highest Degree: Bachelor
Library Holdings: Bk Vols 102,400; Per Subs 597
Special Collections: American Lutheran Church; German Literature & Culture. US Document Depository
Subject Interests: Gen liberal arts, Relig studies, State hist
Automation Activity & Vendor Info: (Acquisitions) Ex Libris Group; (Cataloging) Ex Libris Group; (Circulation) Ex Libris Group; (OPAC) Ex Libris Group; (Serials) Ex Libris Group
Database Vendor: EBSCOhost, Gale Cengage Learning, OCLC FirstSearch, OVID Technologies, OVID Technologies
Publications: Library guide; Library newsletter
Partic in Coun of Res & Acad Librs; OCLC Online Computer Library Center, Inc; Tex Share
Open Mon-Thurs 7:45am-11pm, Fri 7:45-5, Sat 1-5, Sun 1:45-11

SEMINOLE

P   GAINES COUNTY LIBRARY*, 704 Hobbs Hwy, 79360. SAN 362-3289. Tel: 432-758-4007. FAX: 432-758-4024. Web Site: wtls.tsl.state.tx.us/seminole. *Libr Dir,* Jane Bering; E-mail: gainescountylibrary1@yahoo.com; Staff 5 (MLS 1, Non-MLS 4)
Founded 1957. Pop 17,526; Circ 68,157
Oct 2009-Sept 2010 Income (Main Library and Branch(s)) $329,302, State $7,809, County $320,837, Other $656. Mats Exp $42,732, Books $31,003, Per/Ser (Incl. Access Fees) $4,243, AV Mat $5,472, Electronic Ref Mat (Incl. Access Fees) $2,014. Sal $191,749 (Prof $41,000)
Library Holdings: Audiobooks 1,584; AV Mats 2,495; Large Print Bks 1,872; Bk Titles 37,833; Bk Vols 38,648; Per Subs 59
Subject Interests: Gaines County hist, Local hist, Mennonites, Spanish lang
Automation Activity & Vendor Info: (Acquisitions) LibLime; (Cataloging) LibLime; (Circulation) LibLime; (OPAC) LibLime; (Serials) EBSCO Online
Database Vendor: Agricola, Baker & Taylor, EBSCOhost, Gale Cengage Learning, H W Wilson, LibLime, Medline, netLibrary, OCLC FirstSearch, OCLC WorldCat, ProQuest, Wilson - Wilson Web
Wireless access
Mem of West Texas Library System
Open Mon & Wed-Fri (Winter) 9-6, Tues 9-8; Mon-Fri (Summer) 9-6
Branches: 1
SEAGRAVES BRANCH, 311 Hill St, Seagraves, 79359. (Mail add: PO Box 366, Seagraves, 79359-0366), SAN 362-3319. Tel: 806-546-2480. FAX: 806-546-3053. *Br Mgr,* Toni Polyak; Staff 1.5 (Non-MLS 1.5)
Founded 1958
Open Mon-Fri 8:30-5:30

SEVEN POINTS

P   LIBRARY AT CEDAR CREEK LAKE*, 410 E Cedar Creek Pkwy, 75143-8397. (Mail add: PO Box 43711, 75143-0711). Tel: 903-432-4185. FAX: 903-432-4108. E-mail: cedarcreeklibrary@embarqmail.com. Web Site: wwww.cedarcreeklibrary.com. *Dir,* Saondra Price; Staff 4 (MLS 1, Non-MLS 3)
Pop 6,510; Circ 70,000
Library Holdings: Bk Vols 38,000; Per Subs 14
Automation Activity & Vendor Info: (Acquisitions) LibLime; (Cataloging) LibLime; (Circulation) LibLime; (Course Reserve) LibLime; (ILL) LibLime
Wireless access
Function: Adult bk club, Adult literacy prog, BA reader (adult literacy), Bk club(s), Bks on cassette, Children's prog, Copy machines, Distance learning, Electronic databases & coll, Fax serv, Free DVD rentals, Health sci info serv, Homebound delivery serv, ILL available, Music CDs, Online info literacy tutorials on the web & in blackboard, Online searches, Photocopying/Printing, Preschool outreach, Prog for children & young adult, Ref serv available, Senior computer classes, Senior outreach, Summer reading prog, Tax forms, Teen prog, Telephone ref, VHS videos, Video lending libr
Open Mon, Wed & Fri 9-5, Tues & Thurs 9-7, Sat 9-1
Friends of the Library Group

SHAMROCK

P   SHAMROCK PUBLIC LIBRARY*, 712 N Main St, 79079. SAN 316-764X. Tel: 806-256-3921. FAX: 806-256-3921. Web Site: www.shamrocklibrary.org. *Dir,* Melanie Starr King; E-mail: melanieking2003@yahoo.com
Pop 3,000; Circ 12,057
Library Holdings: Bk Vols 22,000; Per Subs 32
Wireless access
Partic in Harrington Library Consortium
Open Mon-Fri 1-5
Friends of the Library Group

SHEPHERD

P   SHEPHERD PUBLIC LIBRARY*, 30 N Liberty St, 77371-2460. SAN 376-4087. Tel: 936-628-3515. FAX: 936-628-6608. Web Site: shepherdpubliclibrary.org. *Dir,* Diana Wilkinson; E-mail: thedirector@shepherdpubliclibrary.org; Staff 1 (Non-MLS 1)
Founded 1963. Pop 2,212; Circ 24,787
Oct 2009-Sept 2010 Income $28,088. Mats Exp $10,409, Books $4,929, Per/Ser (Incl. Access Fees) $5,480. Sal $52,506 (Prof $20,000)
Library Holdings: Audiobooks 328; DVDs 605; Bk Titles 17,604; Bk Vols 17,614
Wireless access
Open Mon, Wed & Fri 9-5, Tues & Thurs 12-5
Friends of the Library Group

SHEPPARD AFB

UNITED STATES AIR FORCE
A   882ND TRAINING GROUP ACADEMIC LIBRARY*, 882 TRG/TSOL, 939 Missile Rd Bldg 1900, 76311-2245, SAN 362-3408. Tel: 940-676-3802. FAX: 940-676-4025. *Librn,* Linda Fryar; E-mail: linda.fryar@sheppard.af.mil; Staff 2 (MLS 1, Non-MLS 1)
Founded 1958
Library Holdings: Bk Vols 10,000; Per Subs 80
Subject Interests: Dentistry, Med, Nursing
Automation Activity & Vendor Info: (OPAC) Surpass
Open Mon-Fri 7-4:30
A   SHEPPARD AIR FORCE BASE LIBRARY*, 425 Third Ave, Bldg 312, 76311-3043, SAN 362-3343. Tel: 940-676-6152. FAX: 940-855-8854. E-mail: askthelibrary@sheppard.com.
Founded 1949
Library Holdings: DVDs 1,500; Bk Vols 30,000; Per Subs 140
Subject Interests: Gen, Juv, Mil tech
Automation Activity & Vendor Info: (Acquisitions) Softlink America; (Cataloging) Softlink America; (Circulation) Softlink America; (ILL) OCLC WorldCat; (OPAC) Softlink America; (Serials) Softlink America
Open Mon-Fri 10-9, Sat & Sun 10:30-6

SHERIDAN

P   SHERIDAN MEMORIAL LIBRARY*, 5805 Logan Park Dr, 77475. (Mail add: PO Box 274, 77475-0274), SAN 372-7335. Tel: 979-234-5154. FAX: 979-234-5154. E-mail: sheridanlib@elc.net. Web Site: sheridanmemoriallibrary.org. *Dir,* Marjorie Rychlik; Staff 1 (Non-MLS 1)
Founded 1971. Pop 5,811
Library Holdings: AV Mats 600; CDs 207; DVDs 900; High Interest/Low Vocabulary Bk Vols 50; Large Print Bks 150; Bk Titles 8,500; Per Subs 3
Subject Interests: Genealogy, Tex

Automation Activity & Vendor Info: (Cataloging) Follett Software;
(Circulation) Follett Software; (OPAC) Follett Software
Wireless access
Function: AV serv
Open Mon-Thurs 12-5
Restriction: Access at librarian's discretion
Friends of the Library Group

SHERMAN

C   AUSTIN COLLEGE, George T & Gladys H Abell Library Center, 900 N
Grand Ave, Ste 6L, 75090-4402. SAN 316-7658. Tel: 903-813-2490.
Circulation Tel: 903-813-2236. Interlibrary Loan Service Tel:
903-813-2395. Reference Tel: 903-813-2556. FAX: 903-813-2297. Web
Site: abell.austincollege.edu/abell. *Dir,* John R West; E-mail:
jwest@austincollege.edu; *Assoc Dir,* Dr Carolyn Vickrey; E-mail:
cvickrey@austincollege.edu; *Coordr, Bibliog Serv,* LadyJane Hickey; Tel:
903-813-2237, E-mail: lhickey@austincollege.edu; *Coordr, Electronic Res,*
Shannon Fox; Tel: 903-813-2559, E-mail: sfox@austincollege.edu;
Archivist, Justin Banks; Tel: 903-813-2557, E-mail:
jbanks@austincollege.edu; Staff 5 (MLS 5)
Founded 1849. Enrl 1,330; Fac 109; Highest Degree: Master
Library Holdings: AV Mats 6,693; e-books 27,271; e-journals 3,325;
Microforms 121,415; Bk Vols 227,019; Per Subs 5,714
Special Collections: Texas & Southwest Studies (Pate Texana, Margaret
White Hoard, Rex & Mary Strickland & Lewis F Russell Colls). Oral
History
Automation Activity & Vendor Info: (Acquisitions) SirsiDynix;
(Cataloging) SirsiDynix; (Circulation) SirsiDynix; (Course Reserve)
SirsiDynix; (ILL) OCLC; (OPAC) SirsiDynix; (Serials) SirsiDynix
Database Vendor: 3M Library Systems, ABC-CLIO, ACM (Association
for Computing Machinery), American Chemical Society, American
Mathematical Society, Amigos Library Services, Annual Reviews,
Backstage Library Works, Baker & Taylor, BioOne, CountryWatch, CQ
Press, CRC Press/Taylor & Francis CRCnetBASE, CredoReference,
EBSCO Information Services, EBSCOhost, Elsevier, Gale Cengage
Learning, H W Wilson, IOP, JSTOR, Knovel, LexisNexis, Marcive, Inc,
netLibrary, Newsbank, OCLC FirstSearch, OCLC WorldCat, Oxford
Online, Project MUSE, ProQuest, PubMed, Sage, ScienceDirect,
SirsiDynix, Springer-Verlag, ValueLine, Wiley, Wilson - Wilson Web, WT
Cox
Wireless access
Function: Archival coll, Art exhibits, Audio & video playback equip for
onsite use, Computers for patron use, Copy machines, Doc delivery serv,
e-mail serv, Electronic databases & coll, Exhibits, ILL available, Online
cat, Photocopying/Printing, Ref serv available, VHS videos, Web-catalog,
Wheelchair accessible
Partic in Amigos Library Services, Inc; OCLC Online Computer Library
Center, Inc; Statewide California Electronic Library Consortium (SCELC);
Tex Independent Cols & Univ Librs; TexSHARE - Texas State Library &
Archives Commission
Open Mon-Thurs 7:45am-Midnight, Fri 7:45-6, Sat 1-5, Sun 1-Midnight;
Mon-Fri (Summer) 9-4

R   NORTH PARK BAPTIST CHURCH LIBRARY*, 2605 Rex Cruse Dr,
75092. SAN 362-3467. Tel: 903-892-8429. FAX: 903-893-4463. E-mail:
churchoffice@northparknet.com. Web Site: www.northparknet.com. *Librn,*
Doris Lee
Founded 1958
Library Holdings: Bk Titles 4,774; Per Subs 12
Wireless access
Restriction: Mem only
Friends of the Library Group

P   SHERMAN PUBLIC LIBRARY*, 421 N Travis, 75090-5975. SAN
316-7674. Tel: 903-892-7240. FAX: 903-892-7101. Web Site:
www.barr.org/sherman.htm. *Dir,* Jacqueline Banfield; E-mail:
jbanfield@grayson.edu; *Ch,* Jennifer Cummings; *Pub Serv,* Susan Banner;
Ref Serv, Michael Miller; Staff 4 (MLS 4)
Founded 1911. Pop 38,407; Circ 225,538
Library Holdings: AV Mats 19,360; Bk Vols 128,907; Per Subs 139
Special Collections: Grayson County Historical Resources for Texas State
Library; Hilmer H Flemming Manuscripts; Mattie Davis Lucas
Manuscripts. Oral History
Open Mon & Wed 9-6, Tues & Thurs 9-8, Fri 10-6, Sat 11-5
Friends of the Library Group

SHINER

P   SHINER PUBLIC LIBRARY*, 115 E Wolters/Second St, 77984-0308.
(Mail add: PO Box 1602, 77984-1602), SAN 376-4281. Tel: 361-594-3044.
FAX: 361-594-4249. E-mail: shinercc@shinertx.com. Web Site:
www.shinertx.com. *Dir,* Paula Sue Pekar
Founded 1994

Library Holdings: AV Mats 1,295; Bk Vols 14,000; Per Subs 54; Talking
Bks 200
Automation Activity & Vendor Info: (Cataloging) Follett Software;
(Circulation) Follett Software
Open Mon-Thurs 8-5, Fri & Sat 8am-11am
Friends of the Library Group

SILSBEE

P   SILSBEE PUBLIC LIBRARY*, Santa Fe Park, 77656. SAN 316-7682.
Tel: 409-385-4831. FAX: 409-385-7382. E-mail: spl@cityofsilsbee.com.
Dir, Diane Rutledge; *Asst Libr Dir,* Crystal Mallet
Pop 26,500; Circ 74,330
Library Holdings: Bk Titles 24,413; Bk Vols 48,500; Per Subs 20
Automation Activity & Vendor Info: (Cataloging) Book Systems, Inc;
(Circulation) Book Systems, Inc
Wireless access
Open Mon-Fri 9-6, Sat 9-1
Friends of the Library Group

SINTON

P   SAN PATRICIO COUNTY LIBRARY SYSTEM*, 313 N Rachal St, Rm
226, 78387-2663. SAN 316-7704. Tel: 361-364-6199. FAX: 361-364-6117.
E-mail: librarysanpat@yahoo.com. Web Site: stls.lib.tx.us. *Ch,* Kippy Edge;
Staff 2 (MLS 1, Non-MLS 1)
Founded 1973. Pop 53,000
Library Holdings: Bk Titles 900; Bk Vols 1,000
Special Collections: Puppet Coll
Member Libraries: Bell-Whittington Public Library; Ed & Hazel
Richmond Public Library; Ingleside Public Library; Odem Public Library;
Taft Public Library
Open Mon-Fri 8-12 & 1-5

P   SINTON PUBLIC LIBRARY*, 100 N Pirate Blvd, 78387. SAN 316-7712.
Tel: 361-364-4545. FAX: 361-364-5711. Web Site: sintonpl@sbcglobal.net.
Libr Dir, Yolanda Bustamante; Staff 3 (Non-MLS 3)
Founded 1927. Pop 7,239; Circ 16,670
Oct 2009-Sept 2010 Income $172,000. Mats Exp $13,002, Books $12,600,
AV Equip $90, AV Mat $312. Sal $128,000 (Prof $36,384)
Library Holdings: AV Mats 1,450; Bks on Deafness & Sign Lang 7; Bk
Titles 18,077; Bk Vols 18,756; Per Subs 43
Special Collections: Texana Coll
Automation Activity & Vendor Info: (Cataloging) Follett Software;
(Circulation) Follett Software
Wireless access
Open Mon 9-8, Tues-Fri 9-6, Sat 10-2
Friends of the Library Group

S   ROB & BESSIE WELDER WILDLIFE FOUNDATION LIBRARY*,
10620 Hwy 77 N, 78387. (Mail add: PO Box 1400, 78387-1400), SAN
316-7720. Tel: 361-364-2643. FAX: 361-364-2650. E-mail:
welderfoundation@welderwildlife.org. Web Site: www.welderwildlife.org.
Dir, Terry Blankenship; *Librn,* Kay Drawe
Founded 1954
Library Holdings: Bk Titles 7,849; Bk Vols 12,005; Per Subs 80; Videos
119
Special Collections: Ornithology (Alexander Wetmore Coll); Rare Book
Coll
Subject Interests: Ecology, Environ & conserv, Nat hist, Ornithology,
Range mgt, Sci
Wireless access
Publications: Newsletter (biennial); Student Symposiums
Restriction: Open by appt only

SLATON

P   SLATON CITY LIBRARY*, 200 W Lynn, 79364-4136. SAN 376-4230.
Tel: 806-828-2008. FAX: 806-828-2029. E-mail: slatlib@odsy.net. *Librn,*
Kim Balch
Library Holdings: Bk Vols 8,500; Per Subs 30
Mem of West Texas Library System
Open Mon-Fri 9:30-1 & 2-5:30

SMILEY

P   STELLA HART MEMORIAL PUBLIC LIBRARY*, PO Box 88,
78159-0088. SAN 316-7739. Tel: 830-587-6101. E-mail:
smileylibrary@gvec.net. *Librn,* Susy Parker; Staff 1 (Non-MLS 1)
Founded 1938. Pop 861; Circ 1,702
Library Holdings: Audiobooks 200; Large Print Bks 200; Bk Vols 9,000;
Videos 25
Wireless access
Open Mon & Thurs 8-11 & 1-5, Tues 8am-10am

SMITHVILLE

P   SMITHVILLE PUBLIC LIBRARY*, 507 Main St, 78957. SAN 316-7755. Tel: 512-237-3282, Ext 2401. FAX: 512-237-4549. Web Site: www.ci.smithville.tx.us/public-library.aspx. *Dir,* Judy Bergeron; E-mail: jmbergeron13@yahoo.com; Staff 7 (Non-MLS 7)
Founded 1929. Pop 4,000; Circ 75,000
Library Holdings: AV Mats 100; Bks on Deafness & Sign Lang 20; High Interest/Low Vocabulary Bk Vols 150; Large Print Bks 700; Bk Titles 30,000; Bk Vols 32,000; Per Subs 30
Special Collections: Genealogy Coll; Handmade Quilts; Literacy Coll; Media Library; Texian Coll; Video Coll
Automation Activity & Vendor Info: (Cataloging) Biblionix; (Circulation) Biblionix
Function: Alaskana res
Mem of Central Texas Library System, Inc
Special Services for the Blind - Magnifiers
Open Mon & Wed 10-6, Tues & Thurs 10-7, Fri 10-5, Sat 9-1
Friends of the Library Group

SNYDER

P   SCURRY COUNTY LIBRARY, 1916 23rd St, 79549-1910. SAN 316-7763. Tel: 325-573-5572. FAX: 325-573-1060. E-mail: sclibrary@att.net. *Dir,* Linda Jones; *Asst Dir,* Sharon Sumruld; Staff 4 (Non-MLS 4)
Founded 1958. Pop 10,000; Circ 90,000
Library Holdings: Bk Vols 66,000; Per Subs 57
Subject Interests: Genealogy, Southwest
Automation Activity & Vendor Info: (Cataloging) LibLime; (Circulation) LibLime
Wireless access
Mem of Big Country Library System
Partic in Tex Share
Open Mon, Wed & Fri 10-6, Tues & Thurs 10-9, Sat 10-5
Friends of the Library Group

J   WESTERN TEXAS COLLEGE, Learning Resource Center, 6200 S College Ave, 79549. SAN 316-7771. Tel: 325-574-7678. FAX: 325-573-9321. Web Site: www.wtc.edu. *Dir, Libr & Media Serv,* Howard Marks; *Supvr, Pub Serv,* Glenda Boyd; Staff 5 (Non-MLS 5)
Founded 1971. Highest Degree: Associate
Library Holdings: Bk Vols 31,548; Per Subs 78
Automation Activity & Vendor Info: (Circulation) Auto-Graphics, Inc
Database Vendor: EBSCOhost, Gale Cengage Learning, netLibrary, OCLC FirstSearch, ProQuest
Wireless access
Function: AV serv, ILL available, Photocopying/Printing, Ref serv available, Res libr
Partic in TexSHARE - Texas State Library & Archives Commission
Open Mon-Thurs 8-5, Fri 8-4
Restriction: Open to students, fac & staff, Pub use on premises

SONORA

P   SUTTON COUNTY LIBRARY*, 306 E Mulberry St, 76950. SAN 376-401X. Tel: 325-387-2111. FAX: 325-387-9044. E-mail: suttonlibrary@seabridge.net. *Librn,* Florie Gonzales; *Asst Librn,* C Monica Buitron; Staff 4 (MLS 2, Non-MLS 2)
Oct 2009-Sept 2010 Income $170,800, State $5,800, County $165,000. Sal $133,925 (Prof $44,786)
Library Holdings: AV Mats 2,600; Bk Titles 19,421; Per Subs 26
Automation Activity & Vendor Info: (Cataloging) LibLime; (Circulation) LibLime
Mem of Big Country Library System
Open Mon-Fri 9-5:30
Friends of the Library Group

SOURLAKE

P   ALMA M CARPENTER PUBLIC LIBRARY*, 300 S Ann, 77659. SAN 316-778X. Tel: 409-287-3592. FAX: 409-287-4777. E-mail: amclibrary@cmaaccess.com. *Dir,* Sherry Williams
Pop 5,000; Circ 10,600
Library Holdings: Bk Titles 17,217; Per Subs 33
Special Collections: Texas Coll
Automation Activity & Vendor Info: (Cataloging) Surpass; (Circulation) Surpass; (OPAC) Surpass
Open Mon-Fri 9-6

SOUTHLAKE

P   SOUTHLAKE PUBLIC LIBRARY*, 1400 Main St, Ste 130, 76092-7640. Tel: 817-748-8243. Reference Tel: 817-748-8247. Administration Tel: 817-748-8384. Web Site: www.southlakelibrary.org. *Adminr,* Kerry McGeath; E-mail: kmcgeath@ci.southlake.tx.us; *Pub Serv Librn,* Cynthia Pfledderer; *Adult Serv,* Maria Cameron; E-mail: mcameron@ci.southlake.tx.us; Staff 8 (MLS 3, Non-MLS 5)
Founded 2001. Pop 25,000; Circ 125,000
Library Holdings: AV Mats 600; Electronic Media & Resources 12; Large Print Bks 250; Bk Titles 40,000; Bk Vols 45,000; Per Subs 150; Talking Bks 350
Automation Activity & Vendor Info: (Acquisitions) SirsiDynix; (Cataloging) SirsiDynix; (Circulation) SirsiDynix
Function: Handicapped accessible, Homebound delivery serv, ILL available, Large print keyboards, Libr develop, Magnifiers for reading, Outside serv via phone, mail, e-mail & web, Photocopying/Printing, Prog for adults, Prog for children & young adult, Ref serv available, Summer reading prog, Telephone ref, Wheelchair accessible, Workshops
Mem of North Texas Library Partners
Open Mon-Thurs 10-8, Fri & Sat 10-6
Friends of the Library Group

SPEARMAN

P   HANSFORD COUNTY LIBRARY*, 122 Main St, 79081. SAN 316-7798. Tel: 806-659-2231. FAX: 806-659-5042. E-mail: hansfordcountylibrary@yahoo.com. Web Site: www.hansfordcountylibrary.org. *Dir,* Margaret Ruttman; E-mail: marrut40@hotmail.com; *Asst Dir,* Liz Miser; E-mail: mommymiser1@juno.com; Staff 3 (Non-MLS 3)
Founded 1932. Pop 3,878; Circ 33,540
Library Holdings: AV Mats 680; Large Print Bks 395; Bk Titles 25,467; Bk Vols 30,332; Per Subs 20; Talking Bks 947
Special Collections: Oral History
Database Vendor: SirsiDynix
Wireless access
Partic in Harrington Library Consortium
Open Mon-Fri 9:30-5:30 (9:30-5 Summer)
Friends of the Library Group

SPRINGLAKE

P   SPRINGLAKE-EARTH COMMUNITY LIBRARY*, 472 Farm Rd 302, 79082. (Mail add: PO Box 259, Earth, 79031-0259). Tel: 806-257-3357. FAX: 806-257-3927. Web Site: www.springlake-earth.org. *Dir,* Linda Thompson; E-mail: thompson@springlake-earth.org
Pop 1,858; Circ 28,223
Library Holdings: Bk Vols 15,110; Per Subs 32
Automation Activity & Vendor Info: (Cataloging) ComPanion Corp; (Circulation) ComPanion Corp; (OPAC) ComPanion Corp
Mem of West Texas Library System
Open Mon (Winter) 8-5, Tues-Thurs 8-4:30; Mon-Thurs (Summer) 10-4

SPRINGTOWN

P   SPRINGTOWN PUBLIC LIBRARY*, 626 N Main St, 76082-2541. SAN 376-463X. Tel: 817-523-5862. FAX: 817-523-5922. *Dir,* Jackie M McGauchie; E-mail: jmcgauchie@cityofspringtown.com; *Librn,* Katherine Crabtree; *Librn,* Donna Leonard
Oct 2010-Sept 2011 Income $20,457, County $16,000, Other $4,457. Mats Exp $4,750. Sal $68,125 (Prof $32,109)
Library Holdings: Bk Titles 16,875; Bk Vols 16,915; Per Subs 12
Automation Activity & Vendor Info: (Cataloging) Polaris Library Systems; (Circulation) Polaris Library Systems
Mem of North Texas Library Partners
Open Mon & Sat 9-1, Tues 10-7, Wed-Fri 11-6
Friends of the Library Group

SPUR

P   DICKENS COUNTY-SPUR PUBLIC LIBRARY*, 415 E Hill St, 79370-2511. (Mail add: PO Box 282, 79370-0282), SAN 376-4222. Tel: 806-271-3714. FAX: 806-271-4341. E-mail: library2@caprock-spur.com. *Librn,* Merla Watson; Staff 0.5 (Non-MLS 0.5)
Pop 1,088
Library Holdings: Bk Vols 15,821; Spec Interest Per Sub 15
Automation Activity & Vendor Info: (Acquisitions) LibLime; (Cataloging) LibLime; (Circulation) LibLime
Database Vendor: Amigos Library Services, Baker & Taylor, Brodart, EBSCO Information Services
Wireless access
Function: Bks on cassette, Bks on CD, Computers for patron use, Copy machines, Distance learning, Electronic databases & coll, Exhibits, Fax serv, Free DVD rentals, Handicapped accessible, Holiday prog, Homebound delivery serv, ILL available, Mail & tel request accepted, Online cat, Photocopying/Printing, Prog for adults, Prog for children & young adult, Pub access computers, Ref serv available, Scanner, Spoken cassettes & CDs, Spoken cassettes & DVDs, Summer reading prog, VHS videos, Video lending libr, Wheelchair accessible
Mem of West Texas Library System

Open Mon-Thurs 12-5
Friends of the Library Group

STAMFORD

P   **STAMFORD CARNEGIE LIBRARY***, 600 E McHarg St, 79553. SAN 316-7801. Tel: 325-773-2532. FAX: 325-773-2654. E-mail: stamlib@stamfordtexas.net. *Dir,* Lucile Frazier
Founded 1910. Pop 5,000; Circ 12,180
Oct 2009-Sept 2010 Income $8,993, City $4,246, Other $4,747. Mats Exp $4,000. Sal $14,246
Library Holdings: Audiobooks 60; CDs 36; DVDs 429; Bk Titles 12,196; Per Subs 14
Automation Activity & Vendor Info: (Cataloging) Follett Software; (Circulation) Follett Software
Mem of Big Country Library System
Open Mon-Fri 12:30-6

STANTON

P   **MARTIN COUNTY LIBRARY***, 200 N Saint Mary, 79782. (Mail add: PO Box 1187, 79782-1187), SAN 316-781X. Tel: 432-756-2472. FAX: 432-756-2681. E-mail: mclibstanton@yahoo.com. *Librn,* Kaye Smith
Founded 1929. Pop 4,500; Circ 25,000
Library Holdings: Bk Vols 23,000
Automation Activity & Vendor Info: (Cataloging) LibLime; (Circulation) LibLime
Wireless access
Mem of West Texas Library System
Open Mon-Fri 8:30-5:30
Friends of the Library Group

STEPHENVILLE

P   **STEPHENVILLE PUBLIC LIBRARY**, 174 N Columbia, 76401-3492. SAN 316-7828. Tel: 254-918-1240. FAX: 254-918-1208. Web Site: www.stephenvillepubliclibrary.org. *Dir,* Mary Meredith; E-mail: mmeredith@ci.stephenville.tx.us
Founded 1903. Pop 18,000; Circ 66,019
Library Holdings: DVDs 2,500; Large Print Bks 2,000; Bk Vols 31,000; Per Subs 30; Talking Bks 750
Automation Activity & Vendor Info: (Cataloging) AmLib Library Management System; (Circulation) AmLib Library Management System
Wireless access
Mem of North Texas Library Partners
Open Tues, Wed & Fri 10-6, Thurs 12-8, Sat 8-4
Friends of the Library Group

C   **TARLETON STATE UNIVERSITY LIBRARY**, Dick Smith Library, 201 Saint Felix, 76401. (Mail add: Box T-0450, 76402), SAN 316-7836. Tel: 254-968-9246. Circulation Tel: 254-968-9450. Interlibrary Loan Service Tel: 254-968-9660. Reference Tel: 254-968-9249. Automation Services Tel: 254-968-9466. Information Services Tel: 254-968-9938. Toll Free Tel: 866-339-5555. FAX: 254-968-9467. E-mail: reference@tarleton.edu. Web Site: www.tarleton.edu/library. *Univ Librn,* Donna D Savage; E-mail: dsavage@tarleton.edu; *Assoc Dir, Libr Admin Serv,* Trudy Carlson; Tel: 254-968-9455, E-mail: carlson@tarleton.edu; *Asst Dir, Coll Mgt,* Tracy Holtman; E-mail: holtman@tarleton.edu; *Asst Dir, User Serv,* Jennifer Barrera; Tel: 254-968-9248, E-mail: barrera@tarleton.edu; *Access Serv Librn,* Position Currently Open; *Acq Librn,* Jodee Tennyson; Tel: 254-968-9475, E-mail: tennyso@tarleton.edu; *Cat Librn,* Melissa Cookson; Tel: 254-968-9339, E-mail: cookson@tarleton.edu; *Periodicals Librn,* Amy Castillo; Tel: 254-968-9868, E-mail: acastillo@tarleton.edu; *Ref/Outreach Librn,* Yvonne Mulhern; Tel: 254-968-9934, E-mail: mulhern@tarleton.edu; *Syst Librn,* Position Currently Open; *Coordr, Instruction & Outreach,* Cathy Wilterding; Tel: 254-968-9456, E-mail: wilterding@tarleton.edu; *Coordr of Ref Serv,* Jodie Baker; Tel: 254-968-9987, E-mail: jbaker@tarleton.edu; *Coordr, Spec Serv,* Amanda Pape; Tel: 254-968-9251, E-mail: pape@tarleton.edu; *Coll Archivist,* Gary Spurr; Tel: 254-968-1808, E-mail: spurr@tarleton.edu; Staff 14.5 (MLS 13.5, Non-MLS 1)
Founded 1899. Enrl 10,200; Fac 600; Highest Degree: Doctorate
Sept 2011-Aug 2012 Income $2,300,000. Mats Exp $1,000,000. Sal $1,300,000
Special Collections: Agricultural, Experiment Station Reports; Texana Coll. State Document Depository
Subject Interests: Agr, Bus, Econ, Educ, Hist, Mgt, Sci tech
Automation Activity & Vendor Info: (Acquisitions) SirsiDynix; (Cataloging) SirsiDynix; (Circulation) SirsiDynix; (Course Reserve) SirsiDynix; (ILL) OCLC ILLiad; (OPAC) SirsiDynix; (Serials) SirsiDynix
Database Vendor: ABC-CLIO, Agricola, Alexander Street Press, American Chemical Society, American Psychological Association (APA), Amigos Library Services, Annual Reviews, Baker & Taylor, BioOne, Cambridge Scientific Abstracts, Checkpoint Systems, Inc, Children's Literature Comprehensive Database Company (CLCD), Cinahl Information Systems, CredoReference, EBSCOhost, Electric Library, Elsevier, Elsevier

MDL, Emerald, Ex Libris Group, Gale Cengage Learning, H W Wilson, Haworth Pres Inc, IEEE (Institute of Electrical & Electronics Engineers), Ingenta, IOP, ISI Web of Knowledge, JSTOR, LexisNexis, Medline, Mergent Online, Modern Language Association, Nature Publishing Group, netLibrary, Newsbank, OCLC ArticleFirst, OCLC FirstSearch, OCLC WorldCat, Project MUSE, ProQuest, PubMed, Sage, ScienceDirect, Scopus, SirsiDynix, Springer-Verlag, Standard & Poor's, STAT!Ref (Teton Data Systems), STN International, Swets Information Services, Thomson - Web of Science, ValueLine, Westlaw, Wiley, Wilson - Wilson Web, YBP Library Services
Wireless access
Function: Computers for patron use, Copy machines, Distance learning, Doc delivery serv, E-Reserves, Electronic databases & coll, Fax serv, Handicapped accessible, Online cat, Online info literacy tutorials on the web & in blackboard, Photocopying/Printing, Satellite serv, Scanner
Partic in Tex Share
Special Services for the Blind - Assistive/Adapted tech devices, equip & products
Open Mon-Thurs 7am-Midnight, Fri 7am-8pm, Sat 10-6, Sun Noon-Midnight
Friends of the Library Group

STERLING CITY

P   **STERLING COUNTY PUBLIC LIBRARY***, 301 Main, 76951. (Mail add: PO Box 1130, 76951-1130). Tel: 325-378-2212. FAX: 325-378-3303. E-mail: stcolib@verizon.net. *Dir,* Suzanne Davis
Pop 1,364; Circ 3,598
Library Holdings: Bk Titles 20,000; Per Subs 35
Automation Activity & Vendor Info: (Cataloging) LibLime; (ILL) OCLC FirstSearch
Wireless access
Mem of Big Country Library System
Open Mon-Thurs 9-5

STRATFORD

P   **SHERMAN COUNTY PUBLIC LIBRARY***, 719 N Main, 79084. (Mail add: PO Box 46, 79084-0046), SAN 316-7844. Tel: 806-366-2200. FAX: 806-366-7551. E-mail: lib2200@xit.net. Web Site: www.shermancountylibrary.org. *Dir,* Sandra C Baskin; Staff 2 (Non-MLS 2)
Founded 1957. Pop 2,858; Circ 9,208
Library Holdings: Bk Titles 27,000; Per Subs 36
Special Collections: Texas Coll
Automation Activity & Vendor Info: (Cataloging) SirsiDynix; (Circulation) SirsiDynix
Wireless access
Partic in Harrington Library Consortium
Open Mon 9-7, Tues-Thurs 9-6, Fri 9-1
Friends of the Library Group

SUGAR LAND

S   **FLUOR CORP***, Knowledge Services Center, One Fluor Daniel Dr, 77478. (Mail add: PO Box 5014, 77487), SAN 316-4381. Tel: 281-263-1000. FAX: 281-263-3777. Web Site: www.fluor.com. *Mgr,* Doris Brooks; Tel: 281-263-2245, E-mail: doris.brooks@fluor.com
Founded 1973
Library Holdings: Bk Titles 4,000; Per Subs 20
Subject Interests: Chem eng, Civil eng, Offshore eng, Petroleum eng
Automation Activity & Vendor Info: (Cataloging) EOS International
Database Vendor: EBSCOhost
Wireless access
Restriction: Not open to pub

SULPHUR SPRINGS

P   **SULPHUR SPRINGS PUBLIC LIBRARY**, 611 N Davis St, 75482. SAN 316-7852. Tel: 903-885-4926. FAX: 903-439-1052. Web Site: www.sslibrary.org. *Dir,* Hope Cain; Staff 5 (MLS 1, Non-MLS 4)
Pop 35,371; Circ 29,900
Library Holdings: Bk Vols 50,591
Special Collections: St Clair Music Box Coll (Leo St Clair's Coll)
Database Vendor: ProQuest
Wireless access
Open Mon-Wed & Fri 9-6, Thurs 11-8, Sat 9-1
Friends of the Library Group

SUNNYVALE

P   **SUNNYVALE PUBLIC LIBRARY***, 402 Tower Pl, 75182. SAN 361-428X. Tel: 972-226-4491. FAX: 972-203-0310. E-mail: library@townofsunnyvale.org. *Dir,* Doris Padgett; Staff 3 (Non-MLS 3)
Pop 4,000; Circ 42,000

Library Holdings: Audiobooks 91; Bks on Deafness & Sign Lang 12; Braille Volumes 38; DVDs 732; High Interest/Low Vocabulary Bk Vols 15; Large Print Bks 340; Bk Titles 41,800; Bk Vols 42,777; Per Subs 80; Spec Interest Per Sub 4; Videos 2,077
Automation Activity & Vendor Info: (Cataloging) Book Systems, Inc; (Circulation) Book Systems, Inc
Wireless access
Partic in Tex Share
Open Tues-Sat 10-7
Friends of the Library Group

SWEETWATER

P   SWEETWATER COUNTY-CITY LIBRARY*, 206 Elm St, 79556. SAN 316-7860. Tel: 325-235-4978. FAX: 325-235-4979. E-mail: swaterlib@sbcglobal.net. Web Site: www.sweetwaterlibrary.org. *Dir,* Rebecca Brock
Founded 1907. Pop 16,744; Circ 53,500
Library Holdings: e-books 150; Bk Titles 38,597; Per Subs 30
Automation Activity & Vendor Info: (Cataloging) LibLime; (Circulation) LibLime
Wireless access
Mem of Big Country Library System
Open Mon 1-6, Tues-Fri 9-5, Sat 9-1
Friends of the Library Group

J   TEXAS STATE TECHNICAL COLLEGE LIBRARY*, 300 Homer K Taylor Dr, 79556. SAN 316-7879. Tel: 325-235-7406. FAX: 325-235-7462. Web Site: www.tstc.edu. *Dir,* Steve Perry; Staff 1 (MLS 1)
Library Holdings: e-books 8,100; Bk Titles 11,405; Bk Vols 12,495; Per Subs 22
Subject Interests: Computer maintenance, Computer sci, Electronics, Robotics, Telecommunication
Wireless access
Publications: New Titles List (Monthly)
Open Mon-Thurs (Fall) 8-7, Fri 8-1

TAFT

P   TAFT PUBLIC LIBRARY, 501 Green Ave, 78390-2711. (Mail add: PO Box 416, 78390-0416), SAN 316-7895. Tel: 361-528-3512. FAX: 361-528-3515. *Librn,* Mary Griffin; E-mail: mgriffin@cityoftaft.net
Pop 5,117; Circ 13,515
Library Holdings: Bk Vols 15,900; Per Subs 10
Special Collections: Texana-Spanish Coll
Automation Activity & Vendor Info: (Cataloging) Follett Software; (Circulation) Follett Software
Mem of San Patricio County Library System
Open Mon, Wed, Fri 8-5, Tues & Thurs 10-7
Friends of the Library Group

TAHOKA

P   CITY COUNTY LIBRARY, 1717 Main St, 79373. (Mail add: PO Box 1018, 79373-1018), SAN 376-4273. Tel: 806-561-4050. FAX: 806-561-4051. E-mail: tahokalibry@yahoo.com. Web Site: wtls.tsl.state.tx.us/tahoka. *Dir,* Claudia Guin; Staff 1 (Non-MLS 1)
Pop 5,500; Circ 11,000
Library Holdings: Bk Vols 10,000
Automation Activity & Vendor Info: (Cataloging) LibLime; (Circulation) LibLime
Wireless access
Function: Bks on cassette, Bks on CD, Children's prog, Computer training, Computers for patron use, Copy machines, Electronic databases & coll, Fax serv, Free DVD rentals, Handicapped accessible, Homebound delivery serv, ILL available, Mail & tel request accepted, Notary serv, Online cat, Photocopying/Printing, Preschool reading prog, Pub access computers, Ref serv available, Story hour, Summer reading prog, Tax forms, Telephone ref, VHS videos, Video lending libr, Web-catalog, Wheelchair accessible
Open Mon-Fri 9-1 & 2-6

TAYLOR

P   TAYLOR PUBLIC LIBRARY, 801 Vance St, 76574. SAN 316-7909. Tel: 512-352-3434. FAX: 512-352-8080. Web Site: tx-taylor4.civicplus.com/index.aspx?nid=25. *Dir,* Karen Ellis; E-mail: karen.ellis@taylortx.gov; *Tech Librn,* Betty Thomson; E-mail: betty.thompson@taylortx.gov; Staff 7 (MLS 2, Non-MLS 5)
Founded 1899. Pop 15,014; Circ 91,408
Oct 2011-Sept 2012 Income $420,000. Mats Exp $40,000
Library Holdings: AV Mats 755; CDs 425; DVDs 661; Bk Vols 46,115; Per Subs 39; Videos 377
Special Collections: Taylor Local History
Automation Activity & Vendor Info: (Cataloging) Biblionix; (Circulation) Biblionix

Wireless access
Function: Archival coll, Children's prog, Computers for patron use, Copy machines, E-Reserves, Electronic databases & coll, Holiday prog, ILL available, Microfiche/film & reading machines, Online cat, Photocopying/Printing, Prog for adults, Prog for children & young adult, Pub access computers, Ref serv available, Senior outreach, Spanish lang bks, Spoken cassettes & CDs, Spoken cassettes & DVDs, Story hour, Summer reading prog, Tax forms, Teen prog, VHS videos, Video lending libr, Wheelchair accessible
Open Mon & Thurs 9-8, Tues, Wed & Fri 9-6, Sat 9-2
Friends of the Library Group

TEAGUE

P   TEAGUE PUBLIC LIBRARY*, 400 Main St, 75860. SAN 316-7917. Tel: 254-739-3311. FAX: 254-739-3118. E-mail: teague.library@glade.net. Web Site: www.teaguelibrary.org. *Dir,* Melissa Satterwhite; Staff 3 (Non-MLS 3)
Pop 10,086; Circ 52,085
Library Holdings: Bk Titles 23,300; Bk Vols 28,978; Per Subs 40
Special Collections: Texas History Coll
Automation Activity & Vendor Info: (Cataloging) Biblionix; (Circulation) Biblionix
Wireless access
Mem of Central Texas Library System, Inc
Open Mon-Fri 8:30-5:30, Sat 9-12
Friends of the Library Group

TEMPLE

S   CZECH HERITAGE MUSEUM & GENEALOGY CENTER LIBRARY, 119 W French Ave, 76501. SAN 327-7984. Tel: 254-899-2935. FAX: 254-742-0294. Web Site: www.czechmuseum.org.
Founded 2000
Library Holdings: Bk Titles 23,000
Special Collections: Czech Language Coll
Subject Interests: Fiction, Genealogy, Geog, Hist
Wireless access
Function: Ref serv available
Open Mon-Fri 8-12 & 1-5

GM   DEPARTMENT OF VETERANS AFFAIRS*, Central Texas Veterans Health Care System Library Service, 1901 Veterans Memorial Dr, 14LIB-T, 76504. SAN 362-3556. Tel: 254-743-0607. Circulation Tel: 254-743-0606. Reference Tel: 254-743-0609. Administration Tel: 254-743-0533. Toll Free Tel: 800-423-2111, Ext 40606 (TX only). FAX: 254-743-0183. *Supv Librn,* Joanne Greenwood; *Libr Tech,* Barbara Hart; Staff 3 (MLS 2, Non-MLS 1)
Founded 1942
Library Holdings: AV Mats 500; CDs 50; e-journals 67; Electronic Media & Resources 10; Large Print Bks 100; Bk Titles 3,800; Per Subs 100
Special Collections: Local History Coll
Subject Interests: Allied health, Med, Nursing
Automation Activity & Vendor Info: (Cataloging) Ex Libris Group; (Circulation) Ex Libris Group; (OPAC) Ex Libris Group
Database Vendor: Gale Cengage Learning, ProQuest
Function: Archival coll, Audio & video playback equip for onsite use, Copy machines, Doc delivery serv, e-mail serv, Electronic databases & coll, Fax serv, Govt ref serv, Health sci info serv, ILL available, Learning ctr, Online ref, Online searches, Orientations, Photocopying/Printing, Res libr, Telephone ref, VHS videos
Publications: New Additions List (Accession list)
Partic in Docline; TAMU Consortium of Med Librs
Open Mon-Fri 8-4:30
Restriction: Non-circulating to the pub

S   RAILROAD & HERITAGE MUSEUM LIBRARY*, 315 West Ave B, 76501. SAN 316-7933. Tel: 254-298-5172. FAX: 254-298-5171. Web Site: www.rrhm.org. *Archivist,* Craig Ordner; Tel: 254-298-5190, E-mail: craig.rrhm@sbcglobal.net; *Curator,* Amy Mitchell; E-mail: amy.rrhm@sbcglobal.net
Founded 1973
Library Holdings: Bk Titles 5,000
Special Collections: Santa Fe Railroad Engineer Tracings, 1896-1980; Springer Railroad Timetables & Passes
Subject Interests: Archit, Area pioneer hist, Art, Employees, Railroads, Women vet
Open Mon 10-2, Tues-Fri 10-4
Restriction: In-house use for visitors

M   SCOTT & WHITE HEALTHCARE, Richard D Haines Medical Library, 2401 S 31st, MS-AG-302, 76508. SAN 316-7941. Tel: 254-724-2228. Reference Tel: 254-724-2374, 254-724-6271. FAX: 254-724-4229. E-mail: library@sw.org. Web Site: www.sw.org/library/library.htm. *Dir,* Julie Bolin; Staff 7 (MLS 5, Non-MLS 2)
Founded 1919

Library Holdings: e-books 55,000; e-journals 30,000; Bk Titles 4,000; Per Subs 300
Special Collections: Nursing (Laura Cole Coll)
Automation Activity & Vendor Info: (Cataloging) Ex Libris Group; (Circulation) Ex Libris Group
Database Vendor: EBSCOhost, Elsevier, Medline, Natural Standard, Nature Publishing Group, OCLC FirstSearch, OCLC WorldCat, OVID Technologies, ProQuest, PubMed, ScienceDirect, SerialsSolutions, STAT!Ref (Teton Data Systems), UpToDate
Wireless access
Partic in Amigos Library Services, Inc; National Network of Libraries of Medicine; National Network of Libraries of Medicine South Central Region; TAMU Consortium of Med Librs
Restriction: Med staff only

J   TEMPLE COLLEGE*, Hubert M Dawson Library, 2600 S First St, 76504. SAN 316-795X. Tel: 254-298-8426. FAX: 254-298-8430. E-mail: library@templejc.edu. Web Site: www.templejc.edu/library/library.html. *Dir,* Kathy Fulton; E-mail: kf@templejc.edu; *Assoc Dir,* Paul Haire; *Ref,* Todd Hively; Staff 5 (MLS 3, Non-MLS 2)
Founded 1926. Enrl 2,500; Fac 152; Highest Degree: Associate
Library Holdings: AV Mats 3,064; CDs 744; DVDs 603; e-books 48,751; Bk Vols 57,771; Per Subs 305; Videos 1,485
Automation Activity & Vendor Info: (Acquisitions) Ex Libris Group; (Cataloging) Ex Libris Group; (Circulation) Ex Libris Group; (Course Reserve) Ex Libris Group; (OPAC) Ex Libris Group; (Serials) Ex Libris Group
Database Vendor: CQ Press, ebrary, EBSCOhost, Facts on File, Gale Cengage Learning, netLibrary, OCLC FirstSearch, ProQuest, STAT!Ref (Teton Data Systems)
Wireless access
Partic in Tex Share
Open Mon-Thurs (Fall) 7:45am-9pm, Fri 8-4, Sun 2-6; Mon & Thurs (Summer) 7:45-6, Tues & Wed 7am-9pm, Fri 8-4

S   TEMPLE DAILY TELEGRAM LIBRARY*, Ten S Third St, 76501-7619. (Mail add: PO Box 6114, 76503-6114), SAN 373-000X. Tel: 254-778-4444. FAX: 254-778-4444. E-mail: tdt@temple-telegram.com. Web Site: www.temple-telegram.com. *Librn,* Mary Lopez
Library Holdings: Bk Vols 100
Subject Interests: Local hist
Restriction: Open to staff only

P   TEMPLE PUBLIC LIBRARY*, 100 W Adams Ave, 76501-7641. SAN 316-7968. Tel: 254-298-5556. Reference Tel: 254-298-5702. FAX: 254-298-5328. TDD: 254-298-5569. Web Site: www.templelibrary.us. *Dir,* Judy Duer; Tel: 254-298-5707, E-mail: jduer@ci.temple.tx.us; *Outreach Serv Librn,* Diane Wolfe; Tel: 254-298-5288, E-mail: dwolfe@ci.temple.tx.us; *Ch,* Erin Gaines; Tel: 254-298-5289, E-mail: egaines@ci.temple.tx.us; *Circ,* Mary Garza; Tel: 254-298-5706, E-mail: mgarza@ci.temple.tx.us; *Coll Develop,* Donna Holloman; Tel: 254-298-5284, E-mail: dholloman@ci.temple.tx.us; *Ref Serv, Ad,* Nancy Williams; Tel: 254-298-5333, E-mail: nwilliams@ci.temple.tx.us; *Tech Serv,* Leon Perkins; Tel: 254-298-5560, E-mail: lperkins@ci.temple.tx.us; Staff 28.36 (MLS 4.5, Non-MLS 23.86)
Founded 1900. Pop 60,118; Circ 448,328
Oct 2008-Sept 2009 Income $1,588,594, State $19,468, City $1,537,932, Locally Generated Income $3,722, Other $27,472. Mats Exp $209,676, Books $161,878, Per/Ser (Incl. Access Fees) $16,185, Micro $3,600, AV Mat $23,270, Electronic Ref Mat (Incl. Access Fees) $4,743. Sal $811,837 (Prof $290,673)
Library Holdings: Audiobooks 6,992; Electronic Media & Resources 54; Bk Titles 130,641; Bk Vols 150,546; Per Subs 202; Videos 9,206
Special Collections: Adult Education; Career & Job Information; Genealogy Coll; Large-Print Coll; Local Authors Coll
Subject Interests: Temple hist
Automation Activity & Vendor Info: (Acquisitions) TLC (The Library Corporation); (Cataloging) TLC (The Library Corporation); (Circulation) TLC (The Library Corporation); (OPAC) TLC (The Library Corporation)
Database Vendor: EBSCOhost, Gale Cengage Learning, Medline, OCLC FirstSearch, TLC (The Library Corporation), Wilson - Wilson Web
Wireless access
Function: Adult bk club, AV serv, Bk reviews (Group), Bks on cassette, Bks on CD, CD-ROM, Children's prog, Computers for patron use, Copy machines, E-Reserves, Electronic databases & coll, Handicapped accessible, Home delivery & serv to Sr ctr & nursing homes, ILL available, Magnifiers for reading, Mail & tel request accepted, Music CDs, Newsp ref libr, Online cat, Online searches, Outreach serv, Photocopying/Printing, Preschool outreach, Prog for children & young adult, Pub access computers, Ref serv available, Senior outreach, Spoken cassettes & CDs, Spoken cassettes & DVDs, Story hour, Summer & winter reading prog, Summer reading prog, Tax forms, Teen prog, Telephone ref, VHS videos, Wheelchair accessible
Mem of Central Texas Library System, Inc

Partic in TexSHARE - Texas State Library & Archives Commission
Special Services for the Deaf - TDD equip
Special Services for the Blind - Audio mat; BiFolkal kits; Bks on cassette; Bks on CD; Computer with voice synthesizer for visually impaired persons; Extensive large print coll; Large print bks; Magnifiers; Recorded bks; Text reader
Open Mon-Thurs 10-9, Fri 10-6, Sat 10-5, Sun 1-9
Friends of the Library Group
Bookmobiles: 1. Librn, Diane Wolfe. Bk titles 3,809

TERRELL

P   RITER C HULSEY PUBLIC LIBRARY, 301 N Rockwall, 75160-2618. SAN 316-7976. Tel: 972-551-6663. FAX: 972-551-6662. E-mail: library@cityofterrell.org. Web Site: www.cityofterrell.org/library.htm. *Dir,* Rebecca W Sullivan; Staff 3 (MLS 2, Non-MLS 1)
Founded 1904. Pop 34,204; Circ 90,121
Oct 2012-Sept 2013 Income $545,109, City $465,609, County $67,500, Locally Generated Income $12,000. Mats Exp $30,625, Books $19,125, Per/Ser (Incl. Access Fees) $2,200, AV Mat $3,700, Electronic Ref Mat (Incl. Access Fees) $5,600. Sal $280,398 (Prof $108,142)
Library Holdings: Bk Titles 62,481; Bk Vols 69,160; Per Subs 84; Talking Bks 1,945; Videos 2,187
Subject Interests: Genealogy, Kaufman county hist
Automation Activity & Vendor Info: (Cataloging) Polaris Library Systems; (Circulation) Polaris Library Systems; (ILL) OCLC; (OPAC) Polaris Library Systems
Database Vendor: Gale Cengage Learning
Wireless access
Function: Adult bk club, Adult literacy prog, Audio & video playback equip for onsite use, Audiobks via web, Bilingual assistance for Spanish patrons, Bks on CD, Citizenship assistance, Computer training, Computers for patron use, Copy machines, Electronic databases & coll, Exhibits, Fax serv, Free DVD rentals, Handicapped accessible, Home delivery & serv to Sr ctr & nursing homes, ILL available, Mail & tel request accepted, Microfiche/film & reading machines, Online cat, Orientations, Photocopying/Printing, Preschool outreach, Printer for laptops & handheld devices, Prog for children & young adult, Pub access computers, Ref & res, Story hour, Summer reading prog, Tax forms, Telephone ref, Web-catalog, Wheelchair accessible
Open Mon & Tues 10-8, Wed & Thurs 10-6, Fri 1-5
Friends of the Library Group

J   SOUTHWESTERN CHRISTIAN COLLEGE, Doris Johnson Library, Hogan Steward Learning Ctr, 200 Bowser St, 75160-3400. (Mail add: PO Box 10, 75160-9002), SAN 316-7984. Tel: 972-524-3341. FAX: 972-563-7133. Web Site: www.swcc.edu/library.htm. *Dir,* Doris Johnson; Tel: 972-524-3341, Ext 141; *Cat,* Trinita Rollie; Tel: 972-524-3341, Ext 109; Staff 2 (MLS 1, Non-MLS 1)
Founded 1948. Enrl 206; Fac 24; Highest Degree: Doctorate
Library Holdings: AV Mats 5,170; CDs 41; Electronic Media & Resources 1,058; Microforms 31,800; Bk Titles 34,765; Bk Vols 34,817; Per Subs 190; Talking Bks 6; Videos 141
Special Collections: African-American Studies Coll; Bible & Religious Studies Coll
Subject Interests: African-Am studies, Arts
Automation Activity & Vendor Info: (Acquisitions) SirsiDynix; (Cataloging) SirsiDynix; (Circulation) SirsiDynix; (OPAC) SirsiDynix
Wireless access
Publications: A Library Handbook
Partic in TexSHARE - Texas State Library & Archives Commission
Open Mon, Tues, Thurs & Fri 8am-9pm, Wed 8-5

M   TERRELL STATE HOSPITAL*, Patient Library, 1200 E Brin Ave, 75160-2938. (Mail add: PO Box 70, 75160-9000), SAN 376-0316. Tel: 972-563-6452, Ext 8616. FAX: 972-551-8371. *Dir,* Jill Mormon; Tel: 972-551-8525, Ext 8525
Library Holdings: Bk Titles 11,000; Bk Vols 11,500; Per Subs 4
Open Mon-Fri 8-5

TEXARKANA

J   TEXARKANA COLLEGE*, Palmer Memorial Library, 2500 N Robison Rd, 75599. SAN 316-8018. Tel: 903-832-5565, Ext 3215. FAX: 903-831-7429. Web Site: www.texarkanacollege.edu/library. *Pub Serv Librn/Interim Dir of Libr Serv,* Dru-Ann Merriman; E-mail: dru-ann.merriman@texarkanacollege.edu; *Circ Supvr,* Holly Cook; E-mail: holly.cook@texarkanacollege.edu; *Acq,* Mary Young; Tel: 903-832-5565, Ext 3115, E-mail: marym.young@texarkanacollege.edu; *Govt Doc,* Katy Elkins; Tel: 903-832-5565, Ext 3028, E-mail: katy.elkins@texarkanacollege.edu; *Per,* Vivian Osborne; Tel: 903-832-5565, Ext 3231, E-mail: vivian.osborne@texarkanacollege.edu; *Pub Serv Asst,* Melba Surman; Tel: 903-832-5565, Ext 3075, E-mail: melba.surman@texarkanacollege.edu; Staff 8 (MLS 1, Non-MLS 7)
Founded 1927. Enrl 3,671; Fac 205; Highest Degree: Associate

Library Holdings: Microforms 216,300; Bk Titles 38,837; Bk Vols 50,495; Per Subs 490
Special Collections: Interstate Commerce (Transportation Coll); Rare Books Coll. US Document Depository
Subject Interests: Nursing
Automation Activity & Vendor Info: (Acquisitions) Innovative Interfaces, Inc; (Cataloging) Innovative Interfaces, Inc; (Circulation) Innovative Interfaces, Inc; (Course Reserve) Innovative Interfaces, Inc; (ILL) Innovative Interfaces, Inc; (Media Booking) Innovative Interfaces, Inc; (OPAC) Innovative Interfaces, Inc; (Serials) Innovative Interfaces, Inc
Wireless access
Partic in OCLC Online Computer Library Center, Inc; Tex Share; Tex State Libr Communications Network
Open Mon-Thurs 7:30am-9pm, Fri 7:30-4, Sun 1-9

S　TEXARKANA MUSEUMS SYSTEM*, Wilbur Smith Research Library & Archives, 219 N State Line Ave, 75501-5606. (Mail add: PO Box 2343, 75504-2343), SAN 316-8026. Tel: 903-793-4831. FAX: 903-793-7108. E-mail: texarkanamuseums@cableone.net. Web Site: www.texarkanamuseums.org. *Archivist, Curator,* Jamie Simmons; Staff 5 (MLS 3, Non-MLS 2)
Founded 1971
Library Holdings: Bk Vols 1,400; Per Subs 10
Special Collections: City Directories Coll; Local Architectural Blue Prints Coll; Local Map Coll; Regional Photograph Coll; Wilbur Smith Coll. Oral History
Subject Interests: Antiques, Ark, State
Wireless access
Function: Archival coll, Bus archives, Photocopying/Printing, Res libr, Telephone ref
Restriction: Access at librarian's discretion, Non-circulating to the pub, Open by appt only

P　TEXARKANA PUBLIC LIBRARY*, 600 W Third St, 75501-5054. SAN 316-8034. Tel: 903-794-2149. FAX: 903-794-2139. Web Site: www.txar-publib.org. *Dir,* Alice Coleman; E-mail: acoleman@cableone.net; Staff 12 (MLS 3, Non-MLS 9)
Founded 1925. Pop 62,200; Circ 159,692
Oct 2006-Sept 2007 Income $787,660, State $60,836, City $653,186, Locally Generated Income $64,301, Other $9,337. Mats Exp $734,089, Books $99,901, Other Print Mats $18,168, AV Mat $18,168, Electronic Ref Mat (Incl. Access Fees) $6,436. Sal $455,525 (Prof $54,371)
Library Holdings: AV Mats 5,394; Bk Titles 74,542; Bk Vols 89,651; Per Subs 139; Videos 6,804
Special Collections: Genealogy Coll
Subject Interests: Genealogy
Automation Activity & Vendor Info: (Acquisitions) SirsiDynix; (Cataloging) SirsiDynix; (Circulation) SirsiDynix; (OPAC) SirsiDynix
Database Vendor: EBSCOhost, LearningExpress, ProQuest
Wireless access
Function: AV serv, CD-ROM, Computer training, Copy machines, Equip loans & repairs, ILL available, Learning ctr, Music CDs
Special Services for the Deaf - TTY equip
Special Services for the Blind - Closed circuit TV; Reader equip
Open Mon-Thurs 9-9, Fri & Sat 9-5
Friends of the Library Group

C　TEXAS A&M UNIVERSITY-TEXARKANA*, John F Moss Library, 7101 University Ave, 75503. SAN 321-2378. Tel: 903-223-3088. Circulation Tel: 903-838-4541, Ext 3215. Interlibrary Loan Service Tel: 903-223-3094. Reference Tel: 903-223-3091. FAX: 903-334-6695. Web Site: library.tamut.edu. *Dir,* Teri Stover; E-mail: teri.stover@tamut.edu; *Tech Serv Librn,* Ginger Mann; Tel: 903-223-3090, E-mail: ginger.mann@tamut.edu; *Acq,* Becky Power; Tel: 903-223-3089, E-mail: becky.power@tamut.edu; *Computer Spec,* Arthur Christy; Tel: 903-223-3159, E-mail: arthur.christy@tamut.edu; *Cat Asst,* Gwen Darden; Tel: 903-223-3093, E-mail: gwen.darden@tamut.edu; *Ref Asst,* Neisha Federick; E-mail: neisha.federick@tamut.edu; Staff 10 (MLS 2, Non-MLS 8)
Founded 1971. Enrl 1,637; Fac 63; Highest Degree: Doctorate
Library Holdings: e-books 53,000; Electronic Media & Resources 78; Microforms 132,220; Bk Titles 120,000; Bk Vols 140,000; Per Subs 404
Special Collections: US Document Depository
Automation Activity & Vendor Info: (Acquisitions) Innovative Interfaces, Inc; (Cataloging) Innovative Interfaces, Inc; (Circulation) Innovative Interfaces, Inc; (Course Reserve) Innovative Interfaces, Inc; (ILL) Innovative Interfaces, Inc; (Media Booking) Innovative Interfaces, Inc; (OPAC) Innovative Interfaces, Inc; (Serials) Innovative Interfaces, Inc
Database Vendor: OCLC FirstSearch
Wireless access
Partic in OCLC Online Computer Library Center, Inc; Tex State Libr Communications Network; TexSHARE - Texas State Library & Archives Commission
Open Mon-Thurs 7:30am-10pm, Fri 7:30-5, Sat 10-2, Sun 2-6
Friends of the Library Group

TEXAS CITY

J　COLLEGE OF THE MAINLAND LIBRARY*, 1200 Amburn Rd, 77591-2499. SAN 316-8042. Tel: 409-938-1211, Ext 205. FAX: 409-938-8918. Web Site: libguides.com.edu. *Dir, Libr Instruction, Webmaster,* Kathryn Park; Tel: 409-938-1211, Ext 201, E-mail: kpark@com.edu; *Tech Serv Librn,* Kathleen Goldfarb; Tel: 409-938-1211, Ext 202, E-mail: kgoldfarb@com.edu; Staff 2 (MLS 2)
Founded 1967. Enrl 3,700; Highest Degree: Associate
Library Holdings: e-books 44,098; Bk Titles 43,640; Bk Vols 50,615; Per Subs 183
Special Collections: Texana
Automation Activity & Vendor Info: (Acquisitions) Ex Libris Group; (Cataloging) Ex Libris Group; (Circulation) Ex Libris Group; (OPAC) Ex Libris Group
Wireless access
Open Mon-Thurs 8am-9pm, Fri 8-5, Sat 9-1

P　MOORE MEMORIAL PUBLIC LIBRARY*, 1701 Ninth Ave N, 77590. SAN 316-8069. Tel: 409-643-5979. FAX: 409-948-1106. Web Site: www.texascity-library.org. *Dir,* Beth Ryker Steiner; E-mail: esteiner@texas-city-tex.org; *Head, Tech Proc,* Samantha Johnson; *Ch,* Kayla Jackson; Staff 6 (MLS 3, Non-MLS 3)
Founded 1928. Pop 50,565; Circ 212,000
Library Holdings: Bk Vols 140,000; Per Subs 180
Special Collections: Oral History
Subject Interests: Genealogy, Texana
Automation Activity & Vendor Info: (Cataloging) Inlex; (Cataloging) SirsiDynix; (Circulation) SirsiDynix; (Circulation) Inlex; (OPAC) SirsiDynix; (OPAC) Inlex
Database Vendor: SirsiDynix
Wireless access
Open Mon-Wed 9-9, Thurs & Fri 9-6, Sat 10-4
Friends of the Library Group

TEXLINE

P　TEXLINE PUBLIC LIBRARY*, 517 S Second St, 79087. (Mail add: PO Box 356, 79087-0356), SAN 323-469X. Tel: 806-362-4849. *In Charge,* Kay Hefley
Founded 1980. Pop 789; Circ 1,275
Library Holdings: Large Print Bks 48; Bk Titles 2,059; Bk Vols 2,080
Wireless access
Function: Summer reading prog
Open Mon-Fri 9-5
Friends of the Library Group

THE COLONY

P　THE COLONY PUBLIC LIBRARY, 6800 Main St, 75056-1133. SAN 376-4605. Tel: 972-625-1900. Circulation Tel: 972-625-1900, Ext 2. Reference Tel: 972-625-1900, Ext 3. Administration Tel: 972-624-3184. FAX: 972-624-2245. E-mail: library@thecolonypl.org. Web Site: thecolonypl.org. *Dir,* Joan L Sveinsson; Staff 6 (MLS 6)
Founded 1982. Pop 43,667; Circ 159,777
Oct 2010-Sept 2011 Income $951,611, City $903,265, County $48,346. Mats Exp $104,006, Books $53,381, AV Mat $9,190, Electronic Ref Mat (Incl. Access Fees) $41,435. Sal $606,973
Library Holdings: AV Mats 7,901; e-books 2,091; Electronic Media & Resources 2,684; Bk Titles 61,047; Bk Vols 72,453; Per Subs 116
Special Collections: Local History, maps, books, genealogies of original settlers, photographs & documents
Automation Activity & Vendor Info: (Cataloging) Auto-Graphics, Inc; (Circulation) Auto-Graphics, Inc; (OPAC) Auto-Graphics, Inc
Database Vendor: Dun & Bradstreet, EBSCOhost, Facts on File, Gale Cengage Learning, Mergent Online, OCLC WorldCat, Overdrive, Inc, ProQuest, TumbleBookLibrary
Wireless access
Function: Adult bk club, Art exhibits, Audiobks via web, Bilingual assistance for Spanish patrons, Bk club(s), Bks on cassette, Bks on CD, CD-ROM, Children's prog, Computers for patron use, Copy machines, Digital talking bks, Distance learning, E-Reserves, Electronic databases & coll, Fax serv, Free DVD rentals, Handicapped accessible, Holiday prog, Homework prog, ILL available, Mail & tel request accepted, Microfiche/film & reading machines, Music CDs, Online cat, Online searches, OverDrive digital audio bks, Preschool outreach, Preschool reading prog, Prog for adults, Prog for children & young adult, Pub access computers, Ref serv available, Ref serv in person, Spanish lang bks, Story hour, Summer reading prog, Tax forms, Teen prog, Telephone ref, VHS videos, Web-catalog, Wheelchair accessible, Workshops
Mem of North Texas Library Partners
Open Tues & Thurs 10-9, Wed 1-9, Fri & Sat 10-5, Sun 1-5
Friends of the Library Group

THROCKMORTON

P   THE DEPOT PUBLIC LIBRARY*, 120 E Chestnut St, 76483-5901. (Mail
    add: PO Box 6, 76483-0006). Tel: 940-849-3076. FAX: 940-849-3076.
    Web Site: www.throckmortontx.org. *Librn,* Linda Northam
    Pop 1,727; Circ 3,070
    Library Holdings: Bk Vols 9,000
    Automation Activity & Vendor Info: (Cataloging) Biblionix; (Circulation)
    Biblionix
    Mem of Big Country Library System
    Open Mon & Wed 9-1, Tues 9-1 & 3-6, Thurs 9-4:30

TRINITY

P   BLANCHE K WERNER PUBLIC LIBRARY*, 203 Prospect Dr, 75862.
    (Mail add: PO Box 1168, 75862-1168), SAN 316-8093. Tel: 936-594-2087.
    FAX: 936-594-9513. E-mail: plibrary@valornet.com. Web Site:
    www.blanchekwernerpubliclibrary.org. *Dir,* Melvin R Shelly; E-mail:
    bkwld@valornet.com; Staff 2.25 (Non-MLS 2.25)
    Founded 1961. Pop 12,966; Circ 26,000
    Library Holdings: Large Print Bks 2,605; Bk Titles 25,760; Bk Vols
    27,015; Per Subs 12; Talking Bks 800; Videos 1,309
    Special Collections: Texana Coll
    Automation Activity & Vendor Info: (Acquisitions) Follett Software;
    (Cataloging) Follett Software; (Circulation) Follett Software; (OPAC)
    Follett Software
    Wireless access
    Partic in TexSHARE - Texas State Library & Archives Commission
    Open Mon-Fri 1-6, Sat 9-2
    Friends of the Library Group

TROUP

P   CAMERON J JARVIS TROUP MUNICIPAL LIBRARY*, 102 S Georgia,
    75789-2020. (Mail add: PO Box 721, 75789-0721), SAN 375-5568. Tel:
    903-842-3101. FAX: 903-842-2890. E-mail: tlibrary@trouptx.com. Web
    Site: www.trouplibrary.org. *Dir,* Melanie Brumit; Staff 7 (MLS 1,
    Non-MLS 6)
    Founded 1992. Pop 6,800
    Library Holdings: Bk Vols 23,081; Per Subs 10
    Automation Activity & Vendor Info: (Cataloging) Book Systems, Inc;
    (Circulation) Book Systems, Inc; (OPAC) Book Systems, Inc
    Open Tues, Wed & Fri 1-5, Thurs 3-7, Sat 9-1
    Friends of the Library Group

TULIA

P   SWISHER COUNTY LIBRARY*, 127 SW Second St, 79088. SAN
    316-8107. Tel: 806-995-3447. FAX: 806-995-2206. E-mail:
    swishercountylibrary@gmail.com. Web Site: www.harringtonlc.org/swisher.
    Dir, Terri McCasland; Staff 2 (Non-MLS 2)
    Founded 1922. Pop 7,854
    Library Holdings: Bk Titles 20,462; Bk Vols 27,597; Per Subs 30
    Special Collections: Texana Coll
    Automation Activity & Vendor Info: (Cataloging) SirsiDynix;
    (Circulation) SirsiDynix
    Wireless access
    Open Mon 11-8, Tues & Wed 9-6, Thurs & Fri 9-5

TURKEY

P   TURKEY PUBLIC LIBRARY, Sixth & Lyles St, 79261. (Mail add: PO
    Box 415, 79261-0415). Tel: 806-423-1033. FAX: 806-423-1221. *Librn,*
    Fredia Fuston; Tel: 806-423-1092, E-mail: frefuston@caprock-spur.com
    Pop 400
    Jul 2011-Jun 2012 Income $4,100, City $3,600, County $500. Sal $3,600
    Library Holdings: Audiobooks 28; Bks on Deafness & Sign Lang 1;
    Braille Volumes 1; Large Print Bks 23; Bk Vols 6,712; Videos 24
    Wireless access
    Open Mon-Fri 8-12 & 1-5

TYLER

M   EAST TEXAS MEDICAL CENTER*, Bell-Marsh Memorial Library, 100
    S Beckham Ave, 75701. SAN 316-8131. Tel: 903-531-8685. FAX:
    903-535-6464. Web Site: www.etmc.org. *Coordr,* Laurie Coats
    Founded 1951
    Library Holdings: Bk Titles 725; Per Subs 7
    Subject Interests: Med
    Wireless access
    Restriction: Med staff only, Not open to pub

P   NOONDAY COMMUNITY LIBRARY INC*, 16662 CR 196, 75703. Tel:
    903-939-0540. FAX: 903-939-0540. *Dir,* Loretta Applegate
    Circ 5,266
    Library Holdings: AV Mats 300; Bk Titles 14,000; Talking Bks 350

    Automation Activity & Vendor Info: (Acquisitions) Book Systems, Inc;
    (Cataloging) Book Systems, Inc; (Circulation) Book Systems, Inc; (Course
    Reserve) Book Systems, Inc; (ILL) Book Systems, Inc; (OPAC) Book
    Systems, Inc
    Wireless access
    Open Tues-Fri 12-5

L   RAMEY & FLOCK, PC*, Law Firm Library, 100 E Ferguson St, Ste 500,
    75702. SAN 373-7403. Tel: 903-597-3301. FAX: 903-597-2413. E-mail:
    ramey@ramey-flock.com. Web Site: www.ramey-flock.com. *Librn,* Kay
    Moore; Staff 1 (MLS 1)
    Founded 1922
    Library Holdings: Bk Titles 1,010; Bk Vols 10,000; Per Subs 10
    Partic in Westlaw
    Restriction: Staff use only

C   TEXAS COLLEGE*, D R Glass Library, 2404 N Grand Ave, 75702-4500.
    SAN 316-814X. Tel: 903-593-8311, Ext 2237. FAX: 903-526-4426. Web
    Site: www.texascollege.edu. *Dir of Libr Serv,* Joyce Arps; Staff 2 (MLS 2)
    Founded 1894. Enrl 500; Fac 54; Highest Degree: Bachelor
    Library Holdings: Bk Titles 60,000; Bk Vols 88,000; Per Subs 150
    Subject Interests: African-Am studies
    Automation Activity & Vendor Info: (Acquisitions) TLC (The Library
    Corporation); (Cataloging) TLC (The Library Corporation); (Circulation)
    TLC (The Library Corporation); (Course Reserve) TLC (The Library
    Corporation); (ILL) TLC (The Library Corporation); (Media Booking) TLC
    (The Library Corporation); (OPAC) TLC (The Library Corporation);
    (Serials) TLC (The Library Corporation)
    Wireless access
    Partic in Coop Col Libr Ctr, Inc
    Open Mon-Thurs 8am-9pm, Fri 8-5, Sat 2-5, Sun 4-7

J   TYLER JUNIOR COLLEGE*, Vaughn Library, 1327 S Baxter St, 75701.
    (Mail add: PO Box 9020, 75711-9020), SAN 316-8174. Tel: 903-510-2502,
    903-510-2503. Interlibrary Loan Service Tel: 903-510-2304. Reference Tel:
    903-510-3149. Administration Tel: 903-510-2759. Information Services Tel:
    903-510-2501. Toll Free Tel: 800-687-5680, Ext 2503. FAX:
    903-510-2639. Web Site: www.tjc.edu/library. *Dir, Libr Serv,* Marian D
    Jackson; E-mail: mjac@tjc.edu; *Acq/Archives Librn,* Robin Insalaco; Tel:
    903-510-2549, E-mail: rins@tjc.edu; *Outreach Serv Librn,* Candy Dyson;
    Tel: 903-510-2308, E-mail: cdys@tjc.edu; *Re/Ser Librn,* Leif Pierson;
    E-mail: lpie@tjc.edu; *Cat Mgr,* Lilly Smith; Tel: 903-510-2645, E-mail:
    lsmi2@tjc.edu; *Circ Mgr,* Daniel McKenzie; E-mail: dmck@tjc.edu;
    ILL/Electronic Ref Serv Coordr, Clarice Martin; E-mail: cmar@tjc.edu;
    Automation Tech, John Dougay; Tel: 903-510-2577, E-mail: jdou@tjc.edu;
    Libr Tech, Elisa S Mullenax; Tel: 903-510-2309, E-mail: emul@tjc.edu;
    Staff 29 (MLS 5, Non-MLS 24)
    Founded 1926. Enrl 11,936; Fac 550; Highest Degree: Associate
    Library Holdings: Bk Vols 101,427; Per Subs 325
    Special Collections: Al Herrington Native American Indian Coll; Allied
    Health Sciences Coll; Dr Tom Smith Native American Indian Coll; Legal
    Assistant Coll; Texas History Coll
    Automation Activity & Vendor Info: (Acquisitions) SirsiDynix;
    (Cataloging) SirsiDynix; (Circulation) SirsiDynix; (Course Reserve)
    SirsiDynix; (ILL) OCLC; (Media Booking) SirsiDynix; (OPAC)
    SirsiDynix; (Serials) SirsiDynix
    Database Vendor: Amigos Library Services, Cinahl Information Systems,
    ebrary, EBSCO Information Services, EBSCOhost, Gale Cengage Learning,
    Gallup, H W Wilson, Hoovers, Medline, MITINET, Inc, netLibrary, OCLC
    FirstSearch, OCLC WorldCat, ProQuest, SirsiDynix, Westlaw
    Wireless access
    Function: Archival coll, Art exhibits, Audio & video playback equip for
    onsite use, Bks on CD, Computers for patron use, Copy machines,
    Distance learning, e-mail serv, Electronic databases & coll, Exhibits,
    Handicapped accessible, Health sci info serv, ILL available, Learning ctr,
    Mail & tel request accepted, Online cat, Online info literacy tutorials on
    the web & in blackboard, Online ref, Online searches, Orientations,
    Outreach serv, Photocopying/Printing, Pub access computers, Ref serv
    available, Ref serv in person, Scanner, Telephone ref, VHS videos
    Partic in TexSHARE - Texas State Library & Archives Commission
    Open Mon-Thurs 7:30am-9:30pm, Fri 7:30-5, Sat 10-2, Sun 1-5
    Restriction: ID required to use computers (Ltd hrs), In-house use for
    visitors, Open to pub for ref & circ; with some limitations, Open to
    students, fac & staff, Photo ID required for access

S   TYLER MUSEUM OF ART LIBRARY*, 1300 S Mahon, 75701-3499.
    SAN 316-8182. Tel: 903-595-1001. FAX: 903-595-1055. Web Site:
    www.tylermuseum.org. *Dir,* Kim Bush-Tomio
    Founded 1971
    Library Holdings: Bk Vols 3,000; Spec Interest Per Sub 3
    Subject Interests: Archit, Art, Design
    Publications: Catalogs on selected exhibitions organized by Tyler Museum
    Restriction: Non-circulating

P   TYLER PUBLIC LIBRARY*, 201 S College Ave, 75702-7381. SAN
    316-8115. Tel: 903-593-7323. FAX: 903-531-1329. E-mail:
    library@tylertexas.com. Web Site: www.tylerlibrary.com. *City Librn,* Chris
    Albertson; E-mail: citylibn@tylertexas.com; *Access Serv Librn,* Lori
    Lawrence; E-mail: accesslibn@tylertexas.com; *Res Serv Librn,* Pauline
    Eng; E-mail: resourcelibn@tylertexas.com; *Circ Supvr,* Malissia Meador;
    E-mail: circlibn@tylertexas.com; *Coll Develop Assoc,* Lara Tabri; E-mail:
    colldev@tylertexas.com; Staff 6 (MLS 3, Non-MLS 3)
    Founded 1899. Pop 98,872; Circ 280,181
    Library Holdings: Bk Titles 145,749; Bk Vols 183,195; Per Subs 510
    Special Collections: Local & Family History Coll
    Automation Activity & Vendor Info: (Acquisitions) SirsiDynix;
    (Cataloging) SirsiDynix; (Circulation) SirsiDynix; (Course Reserve)
    SirsiDynix; (ILL) SirsiDynix; (Media Booking) SirsiDynix; (OPAC)
    SirsiDynix; (Serials) SirsiDynix
    Wireless access
    Function: Accelerated reader prog, Adult bk club, Audio & video
    playback equip for onsite use, Audiobks via web, AV serv, Bks on cassette,
    Bks on CD, CD-ROM, Children's prog, Computers for patron use, Copy
    machines, e-mail serv, Electronic databases & coll, Free DVD rentals,
    Genealogy discussion group, Handicapped accessible, ILL available,
    Magnifiers for reading, Mail & tel request accepted, Music CDs, Online
    cat, Prog for adults, Prog for children & young adult, Pub access
    computers, Spoken cassettes & CDs, Spoken cassettes & DVDs, Story
    hour, Summer reading prog, Telephone ref, Wheelchair accessible
    Publications: Calendar (Bi-monthly)
    Open Mon & Wed 9-6, Tues & Thurs 10-7, Fri 9-5, Sat 10-5, Sun 1-5
    Restriction: Non-resident fee
    Friends of the Library Group

C   UNIVERSITY OF TEXAS AT TYLER LIBRARY*, Robert R Muntz
    Library, 3900 University Blvd, 75799. SAN 316-8158. Tel: 903-566-7342.
    Interlibrary Loan Service Tel: 903-566-7396. Reference Tel: 903-566-7343.
    Administration Tel: 903-566-7161. FAX: 903-566-2513. Administration
    FAX: 903-565-5562. E-mail: library@uttyler.edu. Web Site:
    library.uttyler.edu. *Libr Dir,* Jeanne Standley; Tel: 903-566-7351, E-mail:
    jstandley@uttyler.edu; *Acq/Coll Develop Librn,* Tiffany LeMaistre; Tel:
    903-565-5614, E-mail: tlemaistre@uttyler.edu; *Cat/Ref Librn,* Vicki Betts;
    Tel: 905-566-7344, E-mail: vbetts@uttyler.edu; *Circ/Interlibr Serv Librn,*
    Penny Reynolds; E-mail: preynold@uttyler.edu; *Instruction/Distance Educ
    Librn,* Vandy Dubre; Tel: 903-566-7167, E-mail: vdubre@uttyler.edu;
    Ref/Outreach Librn, Angel Rivera; Tel: 903-566-7165, E-mail:
    arivera@uttyler.edu; *Univ Archivist,* Terra Bianchi; Tel: 903-565-5849,
    E-mail: tbianchi@uttyler.edu; Staff 23 (MLS 10, Non-MLS 13)
    Founded 1973. Enrl 6,476; Fac 388; Highest Degree: Doctorate
    Library Holdings: e-books 252,000; e-journals 51,308; Bk Vols 157,000;
    Per Subs 495
    Special Collections: State Document Depository
    Database Vendor: A.D.A.M. Inc, ABC-CLIO, ACM (Association for
    Computing Machinery), Alexander Street Press, American Chemical
    Society, American Mathematical Society, American Physical Society,
    American Psychological Association (APA), Amigos Library Services,
    Annual Reviews, ARTstor, ASCE Research Library, Baker & Taylor,
    Cinahl Information Systems, EBSCO Information Services, EBSCOhost,
    Elsevier MDL, Emerald, Gale Cengage Learning, IEEE (Institute of
    Electrical & Electronics Engineers), ISI Web of Knowledge, JSTOR,
    LexisNexis, netLibrary, OCLC FirstSearch, OVID Technologies, ProQuest,
    RefWorks, Sage, ScienceDirect, Springer-Verlag, Springshare, LLC,
    Westlaw, Wiley InterScience, Wilson - Wilson Web, WT Cox
    Wireless access
    Partic in Amigos Library Services, Inc; Tex Share; UT-System
    Open Mon-Thurs 7:30am-Midnight, Fri 7:30-5, Sat 9-6, Sun 1pm-Midnight

CM UNIVERSITY OF TEXAS HEALTH SCIENCE CENTER AT TYLER,
    Watson W Wise Medical Research Library, 11937 US Hwy 271, 75708.
    SAN 321-6462. Tel: 903-877-2865. Interlibrary Loan Service Tel:
    903-877-7354. Reference Tel: 903-877-2864. FAX: 903-877-5412. E-mail:
    library@uthct.edu. Web Site: library.uthct.edu. *Dir of Libr Serv,* Thomas B
    Craig; E-mail: thomas.craig@uthct.edu; *Circ, ILL, Libr Asst,* Lisa Garred;
    E-mail: lisa.garred@uthct.edu; Staff 1 (MLS 1)
    Founded 1979. Fac 89
    Library Holdings: AV Mats 100; Bk Titles 2,000; Bk Vols 2,101; Per
    Subs 31,000; Spec Interest Per Sub 4,500
    Subject Interests: Biochem, Cardiology, Environ health, Molecular biol,
    Occupational health, Oncology, Primary health care, Pub health, Pulmonary
    Automation Activity & Vendor Info: (Acquisitions) Ex Libris Group;
    (Cataloging) Ex Libris Group; (Circulation) Ex Libris Group; (OPAC) Ex
    Libris Group; (Serials) Ex Libris Group
    Database Vendor: American Chemical Society, Amigos Library Services,
    Annual Reviews, Blackwell's, EBSCO Information Services, EBSCOhost,
    Elsevier, Gale Cengage Learning, Haworth Pres Inc, Ingenta, IOP, JSTOR,
    Majors, MD Consult, Medline, Nature Publishing Group, netLibrary,
    OCLC FirstSearch, OVID Technologies, Oxford Online, PubMed,
    ScienceDirect, SerialsSolutions, Springer-Verlag, STAT!Ref (Teton Data
    Systems), Wiley InterScience

Wireless access
Publications: Acquisitions List (Bi-monthly); Newsletter (Bi-monthly)
Partic in National Network of Libraries of Medicine South Central Region;
TexSHARE - Texas State Library & Archives Commission
Open Mon-Fri 8-5

UNIVERSAL CITY

P   UNIVERSAL CITY PUBLIC LIBRARY*, 100 Northview Dr, 78148-4150.
    SAN 375-3883. Tel: 210-659-7048. FAX: 210-945-9221. Web Site:
    www.universalcitytexas.com/library. *Dir,* Pamela Woody; E-mail:
    library@universalcitytexas.com; Staff 3.5 (MLS 1.5, Non-MLS 2)
    Founded 1985. Pop 18,000; Circ 36,129
    Library Holdings: AV Mats 1,200; Large Print Bks 689; Bk Vols 28,000;
    Per Subs 47; Talking Bks 700
    Automation Activity & Vendor Info: (Cataloging) Biblionix; (Circulation)
    Biblionix; (OPAC) Biblionix
    Open Mon & Wed 12-8, Tues & Thurs 10-6, Fri & Sat 10-4
    Friends of the Library Group

UTOPIA

P   UTOPIA MEMORIAL LIBRARY*, 800 Main St, 78884. (Mail add: PO
    Box 677, 78884-0677), SAN 378-3944. Tel: 830-966-3448. FAX:
    830-966-3412. E-mail: utopiabk@swtexas.net. *Dir,* Connie Lanphier
    Founded 1972. Pop 2,418; Circ 4,000
    Oct 2006-Sept 2007 Income $15,200. Mats Exp $12,500
    Library Holdings: Bk Titles 11,000; Bk Vols 20,000; Per Subs 12;
    Talking Bks 539; Videos 700
    Automation Activity & Vendor Info: (Cataloging) LRMS, Inc (Library
    Resource Management Systems); (Circulation) LRMS, Inc (Library
    Resource Management Systems)
    Open Mon & Thurs 9-12 & 1-5, Tues, Wed & Fri 9-3

UVALDE

P   EL PROGRESO MEMORIAL LIBRARY*, 301 W Main St, 78801. SAN
    362-3610. Tel: 830-278-2017. FAX: 830-278-4940. Web Site:
    www.elprogreso.org. *Dir,* Susan Anderson; E-mail:
    lsmanderson@hotmail.com; *Asst Librn,* Olga Zamora; *Cat,* Lucy Sandoval;
    Ch, Martha Carreon; *Circ,* Leticia Ruiz
    Founded 1903. Pop 25,000; Circ 89,399
    Library Holdings: AV Mats 1,674; Large Print Bks 1,101; Bk Titles
    55,000; Bk Vols 60,000; Per Subs 90; Talking Bks 1,440
    Special Collections: Uvalde Historical Archive
    Subject Interests: County hist, Local hist
    Automation Activity & Vendor Info: (Cataloging) TLC (The Library
    Corporation); (Circulation) TLC (The Library Corporation); (OPAC) TLC
    (The Library Corporation)
    Wireless access
    Function: Archival coll, Home delivery & serv to Sr ctr & nursing homes,
    Homebound delivery serv, Photocopying/Printing, Prog for children &
    young adult, Summer reading prog, Wheelchair accessible
    Special Services for the Blind - Bks on cassette; Bks on CD; Home
    delivery serv; Volunteer serv
    Open Mon-Wed 10-6, Thurs 10-8, Fri & Sat 10-1
    Restriction: Residents only
    Friends of the Library Group

J   SOUTHWEST TEXAS JUNIOR COLLEGE*, Will C Miller Memorial
    Library, 2401 Garner Field Rd, 78801. SAN 316-8190. Tel: 830-591-7367.
    Administration Tel: 830-591-7301. FAX: 830-591-4186. Web Site:
    library.swtjc.cc.tx.us. *Dir, Libr Serv,* Karen Baen; E-mail:
    krbaen@swtjc.edu; *Cat/Ref Librn,* Landra Fowler; Tel: 830-591-7251,
    E-mail: llfowler@swtjc.edu; Staff 12 (MLS 3, Non-MLS 9)
    Founded 1945. Enrl 5,000; Fac 85; Highest Degree: Associate
    Library Holdings: AV Mats 210; e-books 28,000; Bk Titles 42,300; Bk
    Vols 44,200; Per Subs 355
    Subject Interests: Archives, Texana
    Automation Activity & Vendor Info: (Cataloging) TLC (The Library
    Corporation); (Circulation) TLC (The Library Corporation); (OPAC) TLC
    (The Library Corporation)
    Database Vendor: CredoReference, EBSCOhost, Gale Cengage Learning,
    ProQuest
    Wireless access
    Restriction: Open to pub for ref & circ; with some limitations

VALLEY MILLS

P   VALLEY MILLS PUBLIC LIBRARY*, 405 Fifth St, 76689. (Mail add:
    PO Box 25, 76689-0025). Tel: 254-932-6370. FAX: 254-932-5608. E-mail:
    vmpl@yahoo.com. Web Site: valleymillslibrary.org. *Librn,* Kathleen Hale
    Pop 1,103; Circ 1,653
    Library Holdings: e-books 77; Bk Vols 7,800
    Automation Activity & Vendor Info: (Cataloging) Follett Software;
    (Circulation) Follett Software

Mem of Central Texas Library System, Inc
Open Tues-Sat (Fall & Winter) 10-5; Tues-Fri (Summer) 10-6, Sat 10-3

VAN ALSTYNE

P   VAN ALSTYNE PUBLIC LIBRARY*, 151 W Cooper St, 75495. (Mail
add: PO Box 247, 75495-0247), SAN 375-5576. Tel: 903-482-5991. FAX:
903-482-1316. E-mail: info@vanalstynepl.lib.tx.us. *Dir,* Tracy Luscombe;
Col Librn, YA Librn, Judy Spence; E-mail: jesmile333@aol.com; *Cat,*
Aaron Emdy; *Ch,* Emily Kendrick; Staff 3.5 (MLS 1, Non-MLS 2.5)
Founded 1969. Pop 5,934; Circ 36,687
Oct 2006-Sept 2007 Income $148,579, State $2,114, City $137,845,
County $2,000, Locally Generated Income $6,620. Mats Exp $6,802,
Books $5,667, Other Print Mats $1,135. Sal $104,064 (Prof $34,236)
Library Holdings: Audiobooks 595; AV Mats 2,900; Bk Titles 30,777; Bk
Vols 37,221; Per Subs 25
Special Collections: Grayson County Community College Materials; Local
History Coll
Automation Activity & Vendor Info: (Cataloging) Book Systems, Inc;
(Circulation) Book Systems, Inc; (OPAC) Book Systems, Inc
Special Services for the Blind - Accessible computers; Bks on cassette;
Bks on CD; Computer with voice synthesizer for visually impaired
persons; Dragon Naturally Speaking software; Extensive large print coll;
Magnifiers
Open Mon & Wed 10-6, Tues 10-8, Thurs 12-8, Sat 10-2
Friends of the Library Group

VAN HORN

P   VAN HORN CITY COUNTY LIBRARY*, 410 Crockett St, 79855. (Mail
add: PO Box 129, 79855-0129), SAN 316-8204. Tel: 432-283-2855. FAX:
432-283-8316. *Librn,* Leticia M Hernandez
Library Holdings: Bk Vols 18,000; Per Subs 20
Automation Activity & Vendor Info: (Cataloging) Follett Software;
(Circulation) Follett Software
Mem of Texas Trans-Pecos Regional Library System
Open Mon, Tues & Thurs (Winter) 9-7, Wed 10-6, Fri 9-5; Mon-Fri
(Summer) 8-5

VEGA

P   OLDHAM COUNTY PUBLIC LIBRARY*, 914 Main St, 79092. (Mail
add: PO Box 640, 79092-0640), SAN 375-4944. Tel: 806-267-2635. FAX:
806-267-2635. E-mail: oldhamlibrary@amaonline.com. Web Site:
www.hlc-lib.org/vega. *Librn,* Carolyn Richardson; *Asst Librn,* Zachary
Rouse; Staff 1 (Non-MLS 1)
Founded 1987. Pop 1,100; Circ 1,430
Library Holdings: Large Print Bks 152; Bk Vols 12,600; Per Subs 10;
Talking Bks 145; Videos 50
Special Collections: Texas Sesquicentennial
Wireless access
Partic in Harrington Library Consortium
Open Mon, Wed & Fri 12-6, Sat 9-1
Friends of the Library Group

VERNON

P   CARNEGIE CITY-COUNTY LIBRARY*, 2810 Wilbarger St, 76384. SAN
316-8212. Tel: 940-552-2462. FAX: 940-552-6206. E-mail:
carnegieccl@hotmail.com. *Dir,* Beth Railsback
Founded 1903. Pop 13,711; Circ 53,000
Library Holdings: AV Mats 2,600; Bk Vols 30,000; Per Subs 60
Automation Activity & Vendor Info: (Acquisitions) Book Systems, Inc;
(Cataloging) Book Systems, Inc; (Circulation) Book Systems, Inc; (Course
Reserve) Book Systems, Inc; (ILL) Book Systems, Inc; (OPAC) Book
Systems, Inc; (Serials) Book Systems, Inc
Wireless access
Mem of North Texas Library Partners
Open Tues & Thurs 10-6, Wed & Fri 10-5, Sat 9-12

M   NORTH TEXAS STATE HOSPITAL*, Medical Library, 4730 College Dr,
76384. SAN 316-8522. Tel: 940-552-4117. FAX: 940-553-2515. *Dir,* Mark
Smithwick; *Librn,* Marcia Williams; E-mail:
marcia.williams@dshs.state.tx.us
Founded 1961
Library Holdings: Bk Vols 1,000; Per Subs 30
Special Collections: Clinical Neurology (Baker Coll); Harvard Classics;
Medical (Ciba Coll); Nobel Prize Library; Pictures (Metropolitan
Miniatures), albums; Remotivation Materials; Scientific American
Medicine; Stereoscopic Atlas of Human Anatomy (Bassett Coll)
Subject Interests: Hist, Mental health filmstrips, Nursing, Pharmacology,
Philosophy, Psychiat, Psychol
Partic in S Cent Regional Med Libr Program
Restriction: Med staff only

J   VERNON COLLEGE*, Wright Library, 4400 College Dr, 76384. SAN
329-7853. Tel: 940-552-6291, Ext 2220. FAX: 940-552-0288. E-mail:
librarian@vernoncollege.edu. Web Site: www.vernoncollege.edu/library.
Dir, Libr Serv, Marian Grona; *Librn,* Stephen Stafford; *Circ,* Pam Garvin;
Media Spec, Gene Frommelt; *Ref,* Suzanne Butler; *Tech Serv,* Patti Jouett;
Staff 7 (MLS 2, Non-MLS 5)
Founded 1972. Enrl 2,109; Fac 76; Highest Degree: Associate
Library Holdings: Bk Vols 28,000; Per Subs 79
Automation Activity & Vendor Info: (Cataloging) TLC (The Library
Corporation); (Circulation) TLC (The Library Corporation); (OPAC) TLC
(The Library Corporation)
Database Vendor: OVID Technologies
Wireless access
Open Mon-Thurs 7:30am-9:30pm, Fri 7:30am-Noon, Sat 8-2, Sun 1-8

VICTORIA

C   UNIVERSITY OF HOUSTON*, Victoria College Library, 2602 N Ben
Jordan St, 77901-5699. SAN 316-8247. Tel: 361-570-4177. FAX:
361-570-4155. Web Site: www.vcuhvlibrary.uhv.edu. *Dir,* Dr Joe F
Dahlstrom; Tel: 361-570-4150, E-mail: dahlstromj@uhv.edu; *Head, Pub
Serv,* Karen Locher; *Head, Tech Serv,* Gail Crockett; *Spec Coll Librn,*
Sheron Barnes; *Bibliog Instr,* David Ticen; *Cat,* Laurie Neuerburg;
Distance Educ, Lori Williamson; *Media Spec,* Jennifer Foster; Staff 24
(MLS 8, Non-MLS 16)
Founded 1925. Enrl 4,050; Fac 166; Highest Degree: Master
Library Holdings: Bk Titles 202,000; Bk Vols 287,000; Per Subs 285
Special Collections: Local History Coll; Texas Coll. State Document
Depository
Subject Interests: Behav sci, Computer sci, Soc sci
Automation Activity & Vendor Info: (Acquisitions) SirsiDynix;
(Cataloging) SirsiDynix; (Circulation) SirsiDynix; (Course Reserve)
SirsiDynix; (ILL) SirsiDynix; (OPAC) SirsiDynix
Publications: Library acquisitions (monthly booklist); serials list
Partic in OCLC Online Computer Library Center, Inc; Tex Share
Open Mon-Thurs 7:45am-10pm, Fri 7:45-5, Sat & Sun 1-6

P   VICTORIA PUBLIC LIBRARY*, 302 N Main, 77901-6592. SAN
316-8255. Tel: 361-485-3304. Circulation Tel: 361-485-3301. Information
Services Tel: 361-485-3302, 361-485-3307. FAX: 361-485-3295. E-mail:
comments@victoriatx.org. Web Site: www.victoriapubliclibrary.org. *Dir,*
Dayna Williams-Capone; *Head, Ch,* Erica Ien; *Head, Info Serv,* Catherine
Muehlbrad; *Head, Tech Serv,* Jo Ann Oliphant; *Electronic Serv Librn,*
Katherine Henley; Staff 31 (MLS 9, Non-MLS 22)
Founded 1932. Pop 82,000
Library Holdings: AV Mats 10,500; e-books 2,210; Bk Titles 128,000; Bk
Vols 149,000; Per Subs 312
Special Collections: Great Plains-Texas, New Mexico & Arizona (Claude
K McCan Coll of the Great Plains)
Automation Activity & Vendor Info: (Acquisitions) SirsiDynix;
(Cataloging) SirsiDynix; (Circulation) SirsiDynix; (OPAC) SirsiDynix
Database Vendor: Gale Cengage Learning, OCLC FirstSearch, SirsiDynix
Wireless access
Open Mon, Tues & Thurs 9-9, Wed 9-5:30, Fri & Sat 9-5
Friends of the Library Group

VIDOR

P   VIDOR PUBLIC LIBRARY*, 440 E Bolivar, 77662. SAN 316-8263. Tel:
409-769-7148. FAX: 409-769-5782. *Dir,* Colette Turner
Founded 1974. Pop 11,440; Circ 46,143
Library Holdings: AV Mats 2,295; Bk Vols 38,000; Per Subs 30; Videos
2,000
Special Collections: Genealogy Coll; Texana, bks. US Document
Depository
Automation Activity & Vendor Info: (Cataloging) Follett Software;
(Circulation) Follett Software
Open Mon-Fri 8-5
Friends of the Library Group

VILLAGE MILLS

P   WILDWOOD HERITAGE MUSEUM & LIBRARY*, 92 Cypress Bend Dr,
77663. (Mail add: PO Box 774, 77663-0774), SAN 375-3611. Tel:
409-834-2924. *Librn,* Clara Beth Urban
Founded 1988
Library Holdings: Bk Vols 10,000
Open Mon-Fri 8-5

WACO

S   THE ART CENTER OF WACO LIBRARY, 1300 College Dr, 76708. SAN
320-8753. Tel: 254-752-4371. FAX: 254-752-3506. E-mail:
director@artcenterwaco.org. Web Site: www.artcenterwaco.org. *Exec Dir,*
Mark Arnold; Staff 2 (MLS 2)
Founded 1972

Library Holdings: Bk Vols 1,500
Subject Interests: Archit, Contemporary art
Open Tues-Sat 10-5, Sun 1-5
Restriction: Open to pub for ref only

C   BAYLOR UNIVERSITY LIBRARIES*, 1312 S Third St, 76798. (Mail add: One Bear Pl, No 97148, 76798-7148), SAN 362-3726. Tel: 254-710-2112. Circulation Tel: 254-710-6702. Interlibrary Loan Service Tel: 254-710-3054. Reference Tel: 254-710-2122. FAX: 254-710-3116. Interlibrary Loan Service FAX: 254-710-1710. E-mail: libraryquestions@baylor.edu. Web Site: www.baylor.edu/lib. *Dean, Univ Libr, VPres, Info Tech,* Pattie Orr; Tel: 254-710-3590, E-mail: pattie_orr@baylor.edu; Staff 127 (MLS 20, Non-MLS 107)
Founded 1845. Enrl 14,174; Fac 804; Highest Degree: Doctorate
Library Holdings: AV Mats 128,845; e-books 394,559; e-journals 68,607; Microforms 2,213,631; Bk Vols 2,521,216
Special Collections: Armstrong Browning Library (Library of record of research materials relating to Robert & Elizabeth Barrett Browning); Baylor Library Digital Coll (Digital versions of unique materials in areas of collection strength); The Texas Coll (Premier research collection on Texas & Texas-related subjects); W.R. Poage Legislative Library (Collects congressional records and personal papers related to the political history of Central Texas). Oral History; State Document Depository; UN Document Depository; US Document Depository
Subject Interests: 19th Century, Church-state, Fine arts, Hist, Law, Lit, Music, Relig studies, Sci eng
Automation Activity & Vendor Info: (Acquisitions) Innovative Interfaces, Inc; (Cataloging) Innovative Interfaces, Inc; (Circulation) Innovative Interfaces, Inc; (Course Reserve) Innovative Interfaces, Inc; (ILL) OCLC ILLiad; (OPAC) Innovative Interfaces, Inc; (Serials) Innovative Interfaces, Inc
Wireless access
Partic in Center for Research Libraries; Greater Western Library Alliance; OCLC Online Computer Library Center, Inc
Friends of the Library Group
Departmental Libraries:
ARMSTRONG BROWNING LIBRARY, 710 Speight Ave, 76798-7152. (Mail add: One Bear Pl, No 97152, 76798-7152), SAN 362-3734. Tel: 254-710-3566. FAX: 254-710-3552. Web Site: www.baylor.edu/abl/. *Dir, Librn/Curator of Ms,* Rita Patteson; Tel: 254-710-4967, E-mail: rita_patteson@baylor.edu; *Librn/Curator of Bks & Printed Mat,* Cynthia Burgess; Tel: 254-710-4959, E-mail: cyndie_burgess@baylor.edu; *Outreach Librn,* Avery Sharp; Tel: 254-710-4964, E-mail: avery_sharp@baylor.edu; Staff 6 (MLS 3, Non-MLS 3)
Founded 1918
Library Holdings: Music Scores 1,500; Bk Vols 25,000; Per Subs 22
Special Collections: 19th-Century Theological Pamphlets; A Joseph Armstrong Coll; Browning Contemporaries Coll; Browning Family Coll; Charles Dickens Coll; Edward Dowden Coll; Edward Robert Bulwer Lytton Coll; Elizabeth Barrett Browning Coll; John Forster Coll; John Henry Newman & Francis William Newman Colls; John Ruskin Coll; Joseph Milsand Archive; Matthew Arnold Coll; Ralph Waldo Emerson Coll; Robert Browning Coll; Wilfred Meynell Family Coll
Subject Interests: 19th Century Am lit, 19th Century British lit, 19th Century women poets
Function: Archival coll, Art exhibits, Audio & video playback equip for onsite use, Handicapped accessible, Res libr
Publications: Armstrong Browning Library Newsletter; Baylor Browning Interests (irregular); Studies in Browning and His Circle (Annually)
Open Mon-Fri 9-5, Sat 10-2
Restriction: Closed stack, Internal use only, Non-circulating, Photo ID required for access
Friends of the Library Group
CM   MABEL PETERS CARUTH LEARNING RESOURCE CENTER, Louise Herrington School of Nursing, 3700 Worth St, Dallas, 75246, SAN 362-3807. Tel: 214-820-2100. FAX: 214-820-4770. Web Site: www.baylor.edu/lib. *Dir,* Susan Gerding Bader; E-mail: susan_bader@baylor.edu; *Asst Dir,* Jean Hillyer; E-mail: jean_hillyer@baylor.edu; Staff 3 (MLS 2, Non-MLS 1)
Enrl 350; Fac 35; Highest Degree: Doctorate
Jun 2008-May 2009. Mats Exp $61,289
Library Holdings: Bk Vols 5,826; Per Subs 135
Automation Activity & Vendor Info: (Cataloging) Innovative Interfaces, Inc - Millenium; (Circulation) Innovative Interfaces, Inc - Millenium; (Media Booking) Innovative Interfaces, Inc - Millenium; (OPAC) Innovative Interfaces, Inc - Millenium; (Serials) Innovative Interfaces, Inc - Millenium
Database Vendor: Cinahl Information Systems, EBSCOhost, Micromedex, PubMed, STAT!Ref (Teton Data Systems)
Open Mon-Thurs 8am-11pm, Fri 8-5, Sat 8-4, Sun 1-11
Restriction: Badge access after hrs
CROUCH FINE ARTS LIBRARY, 1312 S Third St, 76798. (Mail add: One Bear Pl, No 97148, 76798-7148), SAN 362-3793. Tel: 254-710-2164. *Fine Arts Librn,* Sha Towers; Tel: 254-710-6673, E-mail: sha_towers@baylor.edu

Special Collections: 18th & 19th Century English Books on Music & Scores; 18th Century Editions of Ensemble Music; Cecil R Porter Organ Music Coll; Contemporary Christian Sound Recordings (Bob Darden Coll); David W Guion Coll, ms; Francis G Spencer Coll of American Printed Music; Manuscripts of Kurt Kiser; Mrs J W Jennings Coll of Medieval Music Manuscripts; Ouseley Library; Travis Johnson Coll
Friends of the Library Group
J M DAWSON CHURCH-STATE RESEARCH CENTER, Carroll Library Bldg, 1311 S Fifth St, 76798-7308. (Mail add: One Bear Pl, No 97308, 76798-7308), SAN 326-8020. Tel: 254-710-1510. FAX: 254-710-1571. *Dir,* Position Currently Open
Library Holdings: Bk Vols 15,809; Per Subs 235
Special Collections: Church & State Coll; E S James Coll; James E Wood Jr Coll; Joseph Martin Dawson Coll; Leo Pfeffer Coll
Function: Res libr
Publications: Church & State in Scripture, History & Constitutional Law; Church-State Relations & Religious Liberty in Mexico: Historical & Contemporary Perspectives; Ecumenical Perspectives on Church & State; Genesis & the Millennium: An Essay on Religion Pluralism in the Twenty-First Century; International Perspectives on Freedom & Equality of Religious Belief; Jewish-Christian Relations in Today's World; New Religious Movements & Religious Liberty in America; Problems & Conflicts Between Law & Morality in a Free Society; Readings on Church & State; Reflections on Church & State; Religion & Politics; Religion, the State, & Education; Religious Liberty in Northern Europe in the Twenty-First Century; The Contours of Church & State in the Thought of John Paul II; The First Freedom: Religion & the Bill of Rights; The Role of Government in Monitoring & Regulating Religion in Public Life; The Role of Religion in the Making of Public Policy; The Separation of Church & State Defended: Selected Writings of James E Wood, Jr; Welfare Reform & Faith-Based Organizations
Open Mon-Fri 8-5
JESSE H JONES LIBRARY, 1312 S Third, 76798. (Mail add: One Bear Pl, No 97148, 76798-7148), SAN 372-8455. *Asst Dean & Dir, Central Libr,* Jeff A Steely; Tel: 254-710-2464, Fax: 254-710-3116, E-mail: jeffrey_steely@baylor.edu; *Govt Doc Librn, Ref & Libr Instruction Unit Leader,* Sinai Wood; Tel: 254-710-4606, E-mail: sinai_wood@baylor.edu
Friends of the Library Group
MOODY MEMORIAL LIBRARY, 1312 S Third, 76798. (Mail add: One Bear Pl, No 97148, 76798-7148), SAN 362-370X. *Asst Dean & Dir, Central Libr,* Jeff A Steely; Tel: 254-710-2464, Fax: 254-710-3116, E-mail: jeffrey_steely@baylor.edu; *Assoc Dir, Cent Libr,* Beth Farwell; Tel: 254-710-3679, E-mail: beth_farwell@baylor.edu; *Assoc Prof & Dir, Cent Libr Spec Coll,* Kathy Hillman; *Access Serv Unit Leader,* Ken Carriveau; *Cat & Metadata Serv Unit Leader,* Bruce Evans
Friends of the Library Group
W R POAGE LEGISLATIVE LIBRARY, BAYLOR COLLECTIONS OF POLITICAL MATERIALS, 201 Baylor Ave, 76706. (Mail add: One Bear Pl, No 97153, 76798-7153), SAN 372-8463. Tel: 254-710-3540. FAX: 254-710-3059. E-mail: poage_library@baylor.edu. Web Site: www.baylor.edu/lib/poage. *Dir,* Ben Rogers; E-mail: ben_rogers@baylor.edu; *Project & Events Coordr,* Mary Goolsby; Tel: 254-710-6735, E-mail: mary-goolsby@baylor.edu; *Archivist,* Benna Ball; Tel: 247-710-3767, E-mail: benna_ball@baylor.edu; Staff 6 (MLS 3, Non-MLS 3)
Founded 1979
Library Holdings: Bk Titles 21,598; Bk Vols 23,786
Special Collections: Abraham Lincoln (Jack Hightower Coll); Biles Editorial Cartoons Coll, 1965-1985; Campaign Materials, Buttons & Papers (Bob Platt & Ben Guttery Colls); Commodity Futures Trading Commission, 1982-1992 (Fowler West Papers); Congressional Papers (W R Poage 1936-1978, Marvin Leath 1989-1991, W R Smith, Jack E Hightower 1975-1985, Thomas A Pickett, John V Dowdy Sr 1952-1972, Hatton Summers, Alan W Steelman 1972-1976, O C Fisher 1943-1974, Ed Lee Goossett 1944-1952 & Sam B Hall Jr 1975-1985); District Judge Impeachment Papers (O P Carrillo Coll); Extremist Organizations (Tiller Papers); Federal 5th Circuit Court New Orleans Papers, 1978-1998 (Sam Johnson Coll); Kennedy Assassination Papers, 1963-1998 (Penn Jones Jr Coll; Jack White Coll; Bob Platt Coll & Jack Hightower Coll); Personal Papers: Paul Hoch; L N Stewart; Ed Nichols; Meadowbrook Farm; Jack White; Project 9-11 Coll; Signed Editions (Jack Hightower Coll; Bob Poage Coll); Texas Circuit Court (Bob Thomas Papers); Texas Lieutenant Governor, 1991-1999 (Bob Bullock Papers, 1929-2004); Texas State Legislature Papers (Donald G Adams, E Ray Kirkpatrick 1946-1952 & Allen D Place, Jr); Texas State Senate (Chet Edwards Papers & Jack Hightower Coll; Kip Averitt); Texas Supreme Court Papers (Charles W Barrow Coll; Jack Hightower Coll); US Agriculture Committee Papers (Hyde Murray 1958-1978 & John Hogan 1978-1998; Fowler West, 1963-1982)
Subject Interests: 20th Century politics, JFK assassination, Terrorism
Open Mon-Fri 9-12 & 1-5
Friends of the Library Group
TEXAS COLLECTION, 1429 S Fifth St, 76706. (Mail add: One Bear Pl, No 97142, 76798-7142), SAN 362-3823. Tel: 254-710-1268. FAX: 254-710-1368. E-mail: txcoll@baylor.edu. Web Site:

www.baylor.edu/lib/texas. *Dir,* John Wilson; E-mail:
john_wilson@baylor.edu; *Librn,* Michael Toon; E-mail:
michael_toon@baylor.edu; *Libr Assoc,* Amie Oliver; Staff 3 (MLS 2,
Non-MLS 1)
Founded 1923. Fac 3; Highest Degree: Doctorate
Library Holdings: Bk Titles 93,917; Bk Vols 129,000; Per Subs 1,101
Special Collections: Newsfilm Archive, KWTX-TV, Waco; Regional
Historical Resource Depository; Texas State Publications & Documents
Depository. Oral History; State Document Depository
Function: ILL available, Wheelchair accessible
Open Mon-Fri 8-5
Restriction: Authorized scholars by appt, Borrowing privileges limited
to fac & registered students, Circ limited, Closed stack, In-house use for
visitors, Non-circulating coll, Non-circulating of rare bks
Friends of the Library Group

CL SHERIDAN & JOHN EDDIE WILLIAMS LEGAL RESEARCH &
TECHNOLOGY CENTER, 1114 S University Parks Dr, One Bear Pl,
No 97128, 76798-7128, SAN 362-3769. Tel: 254-710-2168. FAX:
254-710-2294. Web Site: www.baylor.edu/law/library. *Dir,* Brandon
Quarles; *Assoc Dir,* Matt Cordon; *Cat & Govt Doc Librn,* Lesley Wilson;
Ref Librn, Rachel Little
Library Holdings: Bk Titles 26,446; Bk Vols 112,091; Per Subs 2,212
Special Collections: Frank M Wilson Rare Book Coll
Automation Activity & Vendor Info: (Acquisitions) Innovative
Interfaces, Inc; (Cataloging) Innovative Interfaces, Inc; (Circulation)
Innovative Interfaces, Inc; (Course Reserve) Innovative Interfaces, Inc;
(ILL) Innovative Interfaces, Inc; (OPAC) Innovative Interfaces, Inc;
(Serials) Innovative Interfaces, Inc
Partic in Amigos Library Services, Inc; TexSHARE - Texas State Library
& Archives Commission
Open Mon-Thurs 7am-Midnight, Fri 7am-10pm, Sat 8am-10pm, Sun
1pm-Midnight

GM DEPARTMENT OF VETERANS AFFAIRS*, Medical Center Library,
4800 Memorial Dr, 76711. SAN 316-8336. Tel: 254-297-3272. FAX:
254-297-5335. *Librn,* JoAnn Greenwood
Library Holdings: Bk Vols 2,300; Per Subs 200
Database Vendor: ProQuest, UpToDate
Open Mon-Fri 8-4:30

S MASONIC GRAND LODGE LIBRARY & MUSEUM OF TEXAS*, 715
Columbus, 76701-1349. (Mail add: PO Box 446, 76703-0446), SAN
316-828X. Tel: 254-753-7395. FAX: 254-753-2944. E-mail:
gs@grandlodgeoftexas.org. Web Site: www.grandlodgeoftexas.org. *Librn,*
Barbara Mechell
Founded 1873
Library Holdings: Bk Titles 36,000
Subject Interests: Masonry, Tex hist
Open Mon-Fri 8:30-4
Restriction: Mem only, Open to pub for ref only
Friends of the Library Group

J MCLENNAN COMMUNITY COLLEGE LIBRARY*, 1400 College Dr,
76708-1498. SAN 316-8301. Tel: 254-299-8000. Reference Tel:
254-299-8323. FAX: 254-299-8026. Web Site: www.mclennan.edu/library.
Dir, Dan Martinsen, PhD; Tel: 254-299-8333, E-mail:
dmartinsen@mclennan.edu; *Sr Librn, Ref,* Sharon K Kenan; Tel:
254-299-8343, E-mail: skenan@mclennan.edu; *Coll Develop Librn,* Terri
Hugo; Tel: 254-299-8389, E-mail: thugo@mclennan.edu; *Online Serv
Librn,* Gail Woodward; E-mail: gwoodward@mclennan.edu; *Ref Librn,* Jo
Pendleton; E-mail: jpendleton@mclennan.edu; Staff 15 (MLS 5, Non-MLS
10)
Founded 1968. Enrl 8,500; Fac 200; Highest Degree: Associate
Sept 2006-Aug 2007 Income $931,581. Mats Exp $283,160, Books
$82,500, Per/Ser (Incl. Access Fees) $72,500, Electronic Ref Mat (Incl.
Access Fees) $128,160. Sal $380,727 (Prof $189,466)
Library Holdings: Bk Vols 82,591; Per Subs 430
Subject Interests: Law
Automation Activity & Vendor Info: (Cataloging) SirsiDynix;
(Circulation) SirsiDynix; (Course Reserve) SirsiDynix; (OPAC) SirsiDynix
Database Vendor: Agricola, EBSCOhost, Gale Cengage Learning,
netLibrary, Newsbank, OCLC WorldCat, ProQuest, PubMed,
SerialsSolutions, SirsiDynix, STAT!Ref (Teton Data Systems), Westlaw,
Wilson - Wilson Web
Wireless access
Partic in Tex State Libr
Open Mon-Thurs 7:30am-10pm, Fri 8-5, Sat 9-3, Sun 3-9

GL MCLENNAN COUNTY LAW LIBRARY*, 500 Washington, 76701. SAN
316-831X. Tel: 254-757-5191.
Library Holdings: Bk Vols 8,000
Database Vendor: LexisNexis, Westlaw
Wireless access

Function: Res libr
Open Mon-Fri 8-5

S TEXAS RANGER HALL OF FAME & MUSEUM*, Texas Ranger
Research Center, 100 Texas Ranger Trail, 76706. (Mail add: PO Box 2570,
76702-2570), SAN 362-3971. Tel: 254-750-8631. Toll Free Tel:
254-750-8639. Toll Free Tel: 877-750-8631. FAX: 254-750-8629. E-mail:
trhf@eramp.net. Web Site: www.texasranger.org. *Dep Dir,* Christina
Stopka; *Librn,* Christy Smith; Staff 2 (MLS 1, Non-MLS 1)
Founded 1976
Library Holdings: Bk Vols 2,400
Special Collections: Ex-Texas Ranger Association Papers; Frank Hamer
Papers (Bonnie & Clyde); M D "Kelly" Rogers Coll; M T "Lone Wolf"
Gonzaullas Papers; Texarkana Phantom Killer. Oral History
Subject Interests: Law enforcement
Automation Activity & Vendor Info: (Cataloging) TLC (The Library
Corporation)
Function: Res libr
Restriction: Non-circulating, Open by appt only

J TEXAS STATE TECHNICAL COLLEGE*, Waco Library, 3801 Campus
Dr, 76705. SAN 362-3858. Tel: 254-867-4846. Interlibrary Loan Service
Tel: 254-867-2351. Reference Tel: 254-867-2342. Administration Tel:
254-867-2349. Automation Services Tel: 254-867-2348. FAX:
254-867-2339. Web Site: walib.tstc.edu. *Dir,* Linda S Koepf; E-mail:
linda.koepf@tstc.edu; *Tech Serv,* Lianna Dick; Staff 9 (MLS 2, Non-MLS
7)
Founded 1967. Enrl 4,700; Fac 250; Highest Degree: Associate
Library Holdings: DVDs 100; Bk Titles 64,000; Bk Vols 68,000; Per
Subs 310; Videos 2,500
Special Collections: Eric Documents; FAA Aerospace Collection;
Industrial & Safety Standards; Texas College Catalog; Texas Phone Books
Subject Interests: Auto repairs, Aviation piloting, Computer, Electronics,
Food serv, Hazardous mat, Laser mechanics, Nuclear tech, Occupational
health, Occupational safety
Automation Activity & Vendor Info: (Acquisitions) SirsiDynix;
(Cataloging) SirsiDynix; (Circulation) SirsiDynix; (Course Reserve)
SirsiDynix; (ILL) SirsiDynix; (Media Booking) SirsiDynix; (OPAC)
SirsiDynix; (Serials) SirsiDynix
Wireless access
Publications: Periodicals By Technology
Partic in TexSHARE - Texas State Library & Archives Commission
Open Mon-Thurs 8-8, Fri 8-5, Sat & Sun 1-6
Restriction: Open to students, fac & staff

P WACO-MCLENNAN COUNTY LIBRARY SYSTEM*, 1717 Austin Ave,
76701-1794. SAN 362-3882. Tel: 254-750-5941. Circulation Tel:
254-750-5943. Interlibrary Loan Service Tel: 254-750-5955. Reference Tel:
254-750-5944. Administration Tel: 254-750-5990. FAX: 254-750-5940.
E-mail: referencewaco@ci.waco.tx.us. Web Site:
www.waco-texas.com/city_depts/libraryservices/libraryservices.htm. *Dir,*
James A Karney; E-mail: jamesk@ci.waco.tx.us; *Assoc Dir,* Jackie
Dodson; E-mail: jdodson@ci.waco.tx.us; *Ch,* Linda Bogusch; Tel:
254-750-5942, E-mail: lbogusch@ci.waco.tx.us; *Circ,* Naomi Tran; E-mail:
naomit@ci.waco.tx.us; *Genealogy Serv,* Bill Buckner; Tel: 254-750-5945,
E-mail: bbuckner@ci.waco.tx.us; *ILL,* Michael Duncan; E-mail:
mduncan@ci.waco.tx.us; *Ref Serv,* Barbara Frank; E-mail:
bfrank@ci.waco.tx.us; *Tech Serv,* Linda Howell; Tel: 254-750-5993,
E-mail: lhowell@ci.waco.tx.us; Staff 53 (MLS 16, Non-MLS 37)
Founded 1898. Pop 188,085; Circ 623,376
Oct 2008-Sept 2009 Income (Main Library and Branch(s)) $3,677,731,
State $35,825, City $2,787,040, Federal $93,880, County $557,408, Locally
Generated Income $101,726, Other $101,852. Mats Exp $402,394. Sal
$1,611,959
Library Holdings: Audiobooks 9,344; CDs 2,188; DVDs 6,240; e-books
31,245; Microforms 91,989; Bk Vols 289,416; Per Subs 767
Special Collections: Grants Resource Center; Local Newspaper (Waco
Tribune-Herald & Predecessors: 1890-Present), microfilm. Municipal
Document Depository; Oral History
Subject Interests: Genealogy, Local hist
Automation Activity & Vendor Info: (Acquisitions) SirsiDynix;
(Cataloging) SirsiDynix; (Circulation) SirsiDynix; (ILL) OCLC; (OPAC)
SirsiDynix
Database Vendor: EBSCOhost, Gale Cengage Learning, netLibrary,
OCLC FirstSearch, OCLC WorldCat, ProQuest, ReferenceUSA, STAT!Ref
(Teton Data Systems), Wilson - Wilson Web
Wireless access
Mem of Central Texas Library System, Inc
Open Mon-Thurs 10-9, Fri & Sat 10-6
Friends of the Library Group
Branches: 3
EAST WACO, 901 Elm, 76704-2659, SAN 362-3912. Tel: 254-750-8620.
FAX: 254-750-8413. *Mgr,* Billie Farley
  Library Holdings: Audiobooks 991; CDs 372; DVDs 3,140; Bk Vols
  41,000

Subject Interests: African-Am hist
Open Mon 10-9, Tues-Sat 10-6
Friends of the Library Group
R B HOOVER LIBRARY, 1428 Wooded Acres Dr, 76710, SAN 362-4005.
Tel: 254-745-6018. FAX: 254-745-6019. *Mgr,* William Buckner; Tel:
254-750-5945
Library Holdings: Audiobooks 2,533; DVDs 3,122; Bk Vols 57,052
Open Mon-Wed, Fri & Sat 10-6, Thurs 10-9
SOUTH WACO, 2737 S 18th St, 76706, SAN 362-403X. Tel:
254-750-8621. FAX: 254-750-8606. *Mgr,* Robert Kelly; Staff 1 (MLS 1)
Library Holdings: Audiobooks 1,836; CDs 352; DVDs 3,494; Bk Vols
40,650
Open Mon & Wed-Sat 10-6, Tues 10-9

S   WACO TRIBUNE-HERALD LIBRARY*, 900 Franklin, 76701. SAN
373-0018. Tel: 254-757-5757. FAX: 254-757-0302. Web Site:
wacotrib.com. *Librn,* Kathy Wigfall
Library Holdings: Bk Vols 225
Subject Interests: Genealogy, Local hist
Restriction: Open by appt only

WAELDER

P   WAELDER PUBLIC LIBRARY*, 310 North Ave E, 78959. (Mail add: PO
Box 428, 78959-0428), SAN 316-8344. Tel: 830-788-7167. FAX:
830-788-7541. *Head Librn,* Doris Burney
Pop 904
Library Holdings: Bk Vols 9,000
Automation Activity & Vendor Info: (Cataloging) Follett Software;
(Circulation) Follett Software
Open Mon-Fri 1-5

WALLER

P   MELANEE SMITH MEMORIAL LIBRARY*, 2103 Main St, 77484. Tel:
936-372-3961. Web Site: www.wallertexas.com/library.htm. *Librn,* Sandra
Chambers; E-mail: schambers@wallertexas.com
Library Holdings: Bk Titles 12,000
Wireless access
Open Tues-Fri 9-12 & 1-5, Sat 9-12
Friends of the Library Group

WALLIS

P   AUSTIN COUNTY LIBRARY SYSTEM*, Knox Memorial Library, 6730
Railroad, 77485. (Mail add: PO Box 519, 77485-0519), SAN 362-4064.
Tel: 979-478-6813. FAX: 979-478-6813. Web Site:
www.knoxmemoriallibrary.org. *Dir,* Gloria Havemann; *Asst Librn,* Lyndsey
Martinez
Pop 3,375
Library Holdings: AV Mats 1,198; Bk Vols 15,500; Per Subs 40; Videos
1,806
Automation Activity & Vendor Info: (Cataloging) Follett Software;
(Circulation) Follett Software
Wireless access
Function: CD-ROM, ILL available, Music CDs, Photocopying/Printing,
Prog for children & young adult, Spoken cassettes & CDs, VHS videos
Open Mon-Thurs 9-6, Sat 9-12

WASHINGTON

S   STAR OF THE REPUBLIC MUSEUM LIBRARY*, 23200 Park Rd 12,
77880. (Mail add: PO Box 317, 77880-0317), SAN 326-2448. Tel:
936-878-2461, Ext 234. FAX: 936-878-2462. E-mail: star@blinn.edu. Web
Site: www.starmuseum.org. *Dir,* Houston McGaugh
Founded 1970
Library Holdings: Bk Titles 3,000; Per Subs 20
Open Mon-Fri 10-5
Restriction: Non-circulating

WASKOM

P   WASKOM PUBLIC LIBRARY*, 103 Waskom Ave, 75692-9281. (Mail
add: PO Box 1187, 75692-1187). Tel: 903-687-3041. E-mail:
waskomlibrary@eastex.net. Web Site: www.waskompubliclibrary.org. *Dir,*
Willa Bose
Pop 4,812
Library Holdings: AV Mats 20; Bk Titles 6,957; Talking Bks 171
Automation Activity & Vendor Info: (Acquisitions) Follett Software;
(Cataloging) Follett Software; (Circulation) Follett Software; (ILL) Follett
Software; (OPAC) Follett Software
Partic in Tex Share
Open Mon-Fri 12:30-4:30, Sat 10-1

WATAUGA

P   WATAUGA PUBLIC LIBRARY*, 7109 Whitley Rd, 76148-2024. SAN
375-4804. Tel: 817-514-5855. Circulation Tel: 817-514-5864. Reference
Tel: 817-514-5865, 817-514-5866. FAX: 817-581-3910. E-mail:
library@ci.watauga.tx.us. Web Site:
www.ci.watauga.tx.us/library/libindex.htm. *Dir,* Lana Ewell; E-mail:
lewell@cowtx.org; *Ch,* Laura Cleveland; *Pub Serv,* Connie Barnes; Staff
14 (MLS 3, Non-MLS 11)
Founded 1983. Pop 141,467; Circ 227,273
Library Holdings: Bk Titles 40,000; Per Subs 80
Function: ILL available, Photocopying/Printing, Prog for children & young
adult, Ref serv available
Publications: Calendar (Monthly) (Newsletter)
Mem of North Texas Library Partners
Partic in TexSHARE - Texas State Library & Archives Commission
Special Services for the Deaf - Bks on deafness & sign lang; Captioned
film dep; High interest/low vocabulary bks
Special Services for the Blind - Bks on cassette; Large print bks;
Magnifiers
Open Mon & Thurs 12-8, Tues & Wed 10-6, Fri & Sat 9-5
Friends of the Library Group

WAXAHACHIE

P   NICHOLAS P SIMS LIBRARY*, 515 W Main, 75165-3235. SAN
316-8352. Tel: 972-937-2671. FAX: 972-937-4409. E-mail:
info@simslib.org. Web Site: www.simslib.org. *Dir,* Susan A Maxwell;
E-mail: dir@simslib.org; *Asst Dir,* Barbara Claspell; E-mail:
asstdir@simslib.org; *Ch,* Allison Bain; E-mail: children@simslib.org; *YA
Librn,* Connie Colston; E-mail: ya@simslib.org; *Adult Serv,* Nelda Curlin;
E-mail: adultlibraryservices@simslib.org; *Ref,* Samantha Estey; Staff 12
(MLS 4, Non-MLS 8)
Founded 1904. Pop 28,000; Circ 214,143
Oct 2008-Sept 2009 Income $1,486,621, City $1,274,000. Mats Exp
$187,687, Books $122,500, Per/Ser (Incl. Access Fees) $7,000, Micro
$1,500, AV Mat $44,687, Electronic Ref Mat (Incl. Access Fees) $12,000.
Sal $694,593 (Prof $178,500)
Library Holdings: AV Mats 6,795; Bk Titles 119,216; Bk Vols 130,364;
Per Subs 198; Videos 2,663
Subject Interests: Local genealogy
Automation Activity & Vendor Info: (Cataloging) SirsiDynix;
(Circulation) SirsiDynix; (OPAC) SirsiDynix
Database Vendor: Amigos Library Services, Gale Cengage Learning,
ProQuest, ReferenceUSA, SirsiDynix, ValueLine
Wireless access
Function: Adult bk club, AV serv, Bks on cassette, Bks on CD, Bus
archives, Chess club, Children's prog, Computer training, Computers for
patron use, Copy machines, Electronic databases & coll, Exhibits, Fax serv,
Free DVD rentals, Handicapped accessible, Health sci info serv, Holiday
prog, Homework prog, ILL available, Magnifiers for reading, Mail & tel
request accepted, Music CDs, Newsp ref libr, Online cat, Orientations,
Outreach serv, Photocopying/Printing, Preschool outreach, Prog for adults,
Prog for children & young adult, Pub access computers, Ref & res, Ref
serv available, Ref serv in person, Res performed for a fee, Scanner, Senior
computer classes, Senior outreach, Spoken cassettes & CDs, Spoken
cassettes & DVDs, Story hour, Summer reading prog, Tax forms, Teen
prog, VHS videos, Video lending libr, Web-catalog, Wheelchair accessible
Partic in TexSHARE - Texas State Library & Archives Commission
Open Tues 9:30-8, Wed-Fri 9:30-6, Sat 9:30-2:30
Friends of the Library Group

C   SOUTHWESTERN ASSEMBLIES OF GOD UNIVERSITY, P C Nelson
Memorial Library, 1200 Sycamore, 75165-2342. SAN 316-8360. Tel:
972-825-4761. FAX: 972-923-0488. E-mail: library@sagu.edu. Web Site:
www.sagu.edu/library. *Dir,* Eugene Holder; *Asst Dir, Circ & Ref, ILL,* John
Palmer; E-mail: jpalmer@sagu.edu; *Coll Develop Librn,* Marcy Mapes
Founded 1927. Highest Degree: Master
Library Holdings: Bk Titles 96,000; Bk Vols 115,000; Per Subs 609
Special Collections: Charismatic Authors, History & Materials
(Pentecostal Alcove), bks & per. Oral History
Subject Interests: Educ, Relig studies
Automation Activity & Vendor Info: (Acquisitions) TLC (The Library
Corporation); (Cataloging) TLC (The Library Corporation); (Circulation)
TLC (The Library Corporation); (Course Reserve) TLC (The Library
Corporation); (ILL) OCLC WorldCat; (OPAC) TLC (The Library
Corporation)
Database Vendor: Agricola, American Psychological Association (APA),
Amigos Library Services, Atlas Systems, Baker & Taylor, EBSCOhost,
Gale Cengage Learning, OCLC FirstSearch, OCLC WorldCat, ProQuest
Wireless access
Special Services for the Deaf - Bks on deafness & sign lang
Open Mon-Thurs (Fall) 7:30am-11pm, Fri 7:30-5, Sat 10am-11pm, Sun
1-5; Mon-Fri (Summer) 8-5

WEATHERFORD

J   WEATHERFORD COLLEGE LIBRARY*, 225 College Park Dr, 76086.
SAN 316-8379. Tel: 817-594-5471, 817-598-6252. Reference Tel:
817-598-6425. Information Services Tel: 817-598-6453. FAX:
817-598-6369, 817-599-9305. TDD: 817-598-6254. Web Site:
www.wc.edu/library. *Dir,* Martha Tandy; E-mail: mtandy@wc.edu; *Asst
Dir,* Dr Henry Wang; Fax: 817 598-9005, E-mail: hwang@wc.edu; *Ref
Librn,* Jeff Dunn; E-mail: jdunn@wc.edu; *Tech Serv Librn,* Ann Halligan;
Tel: 817-598-6250, E-mail: ahalligan@wc.edu; Staff 4 (MLS 4)
Founded 1869. Fac 212; Highest Degree: Associate
Sept 2009-Aug 2010 Income $672,878. Mats Exp $248,768, Books
$89,700, Per/Ser (Incl. Access Fees) $44,250, Manu Arch $1,000, AV
Equip $58,428, AV Mat $24,000, Electronic Ref Mat (Incl. Access Fees)
$30,390, Presv $1,000. Sal $366,115 (Prof $218,309)
Library Holdings: Audiobooks 226; AV Mats 2,201; CDs 330; DVDs
1,802; e-books 28,000; Bk Titles 57,716; Per Subs 370; Talking Bks 20
Special Collections: Ranching in the Southwest
Subject Interests: Tex counties hist
Automation Activity & Vendor Info: (Acquisitions) SIRSI WorkFlows;
(Cataloging) SIRSI WorkFlows; (Circulation) SIRSI WorkFlows; (ILL)
OCLC WorldCat; (OPAC) SIRSI WorkFlows; (Serials) SIRSI WorkFlows
Database Vendor: EBSCOhost, JSTOR, SirsiDynix
Wireless access
Partic in Tex Share
Special Services for the Deaf - TTY equip
Special Services for the Blind - Braille equip; Braille servs; Closed circuit
TV
Open Mon-Thurs (Fall & Spring) 7:30am-9pm, Fri 8-4, Sat 9-5;
Mon-Thurs (Summer) 7:30am-8pm, Fri 8am-12pm

P   WEATHERFORD PUBLIC LIBRARY*, 1014 Charles St, 76086-5098.
SAN 316-8387. Tel: 817-598-4150. Reference Tel: 817-598-4151.
Administration Tel: 817-598-4159. FAX: 817-598-4161. Web Site:
www.weatherford.lib.tx.us. *Dir,* Dale Fleeger; Tel: 817-598-4269; *ILL, Ref
Serv,* Jean E Bennett; *Ref Serv,* Cherie Kendrick; *Tech Serv,* Patricia
Cromwell; Tel: 817-598-4158. Subject Specialists: *Genealogy,* Jean E
Bennett; Staff 5 (MLS 4, Non-MLS 1)
Founded 1959. Pop 61,500; Circ 310,000
Library Holdings: AV Mats 9,051; Bk Vols 96,000; Per Subs 200; Videos
3,696
Special Collections: Parker County Historical & Genealogical Coll
Automation Activity & Vendor Info: (Cataloging) Follett Software;
(Circulation) Follett Software
Function: ILL available
Mem of North Texas Library Partners
Open Mon-Fri 10-6, Sat 2-6
Friends of the Library Group

WEIMAR

P   WEIMAR PUBLIC LIBRARY*, One Jackson Sq, 78962-2019. SAN
316-8395. Tel: 979-725-6608. FAX: 979-725-9033. E-mail:
weimarlibrary@hotmail.com. Web Site: www.weimarlibrary.org. *Libr Dir,*
Cindy Kahlden
Founded 1964. Pop 3,146; Circ 13,992
Library Holdings: e-books 50; Bk Vols 20,000; Per Subs 13
Automation Activity & Vendor Info: (Cataloging) Follett Software;
(Circulation) Follett Software; (OPAC) Follett Software
Open Mon & Thurs 8-6:30, Tues, Wed & Fri 8-4:30, Sun 12-3

WELLINGTON

P   COLLINGSWORTH PUBLIC LIBRARY*, 711 15th St, 79095. SAN
316-8409. Tel: 806-447-2116. FAX: 806-447-5240. E-mail:
collingsworth@usa.com. Web Site: collingsworthpubliclibrary.info. *Librn,*
Vicki Decker
Founded 1924. Pop 5,000; Circ 5,831
Library Holdings: Bk Titles 20,850; Per Subs 75
Automation Activity & Vendor Info: (Cataloging) SirsiDynix;
(Circulation) SirsiDynix; (ILL) SirsiDynix; (OPAC) SirsiDynix
Wireless access
Special Services for the Deaf - Spec interest per
Open Mon & Thurs (Winter) 8am-8:30pm, Tues, Wed & Fri 8-5:30;
Mon-Fri (Summer) 9:30-5:30
Friends of the Library Group

WELLS

P   RUBE SESSIONS MEMORIAL LIBRARY*, 298 Rusk Ave, 75976. (Mail
add: PO Box 120, 75976). Tel: 936-867-4757. FAX: 936-867-4760. E-mail:
rubelib@gmail.com. Web Site: www.sessions.lib.tx.us. *Librn,* Ellen
Hamlett; Staff 1 (Non-MLS 1)
Founded 1975. Pop 10,000; Circ 6,000

Library Holdings: Audiobooks 38; AV Mats 265; Bks on Deafness &
Sign Lang 3; CDs 23; DVDs 102; Large Print Bks 509; Bk Titles 8,541;
Talking Bks 6; Videos 96
Automation Activity & Vendor Info: (Acquisitions) Biblionix;
(Cataloging) Biblionix; (Circulation) Biblionix; (Course Reserve) Biblionix
Wireless access
Function: Bks on cassette, Bks on CD, Children's prog, Copy machines,
Exhibits, Fax serv, Handicapped accessible, Mail & tel request accepted,
Music CDs, Photocopying/Printing, Preschool outreach, Prog for adults,
Prog for children & young adult, Pub access computers, Ref serv available,
Ref serv in person, Scanner, Spoken cassettes & CDs, Story hour, Summer
reading prog, Tax forms, Teen prog, VHS videos, Wheelchair accessible,
Workshops
Special Services for the Deaf - Bks on deafness & sign lang; Closed
caption videos
Special Services for the Blind - Bks on cassette; Bks on CD; Large print
bks
Open Tues 9-7, Wed-Fri 9-5, Sat 9-3

WESLACO

P   MAYOR JOE V SANCHEZ PUBLIC LIBRARY*, 525 S Kansas Ave,
78596-6215. SAN 316-8425. Tel: 956-968-4533. Administration Tel:
956-973-3144. FAX: 956-973-1641. Interlibrary Loan Service FAX:
956-968-8922. Web Site: www.weslacopl.us. *Dir,* Arnold Becho; Staff 11
(MLS 1, Non-MLS 10)
Founded 1948. Pop 53,000; Circ 65,104
Library Holdings: AV Mats 2,285; Bk Titles 50,104; Bk Vols 57,196; Per
Subs 85
Special Collections: Texana Coll, bk & tape. Oral History
Subject Interests: Hispanic
Automation Activity & Vendor Info: (Circulation) TLC (The Library
Corporation)
Database Vendor: EBSCOhost, Gale Cengage Learning
Wireless access
Mem of Hidalgo County Library System
Open Mon-Thurs 8-8, Fri 8-5, Sat 11-5
Friends of the Library Group

WEST

P   WEST PUBLIC LIBRARY*, 209 W Tokio Rd, 76691. (Mail add: PO Box
513, 76691-0513), SAN 375-3484. Tel: 254-826-3070. FAX:
254-826-4473. E-mail: westpl@wacool.net. *Librn,* Henrietta Meurer; Staff
2 (Non-MLS 2)
Founded 1984. Pop 4,279; Circ 136,400
Library Holdings: AV Mats 380; Bks on Deafness & Sign Lang 20; High
Interest/Low Vocabulary Bk Vols 2,000; Large Print Bks 400; Bk Vols
30,000; Talking Bks 270
Automation Activity & Vendor Info: (Cataloging) Follett Software;
(Circulation) Follett Software
Mem of Central Texas Library System, Inc
Special Services for the Deaf - Bks on deafness & sign lang
Open Mon, Tues & Thurs 3-7, Wed 10-3, Sat 9-12
Friends of the Library Group

WEST TAWAKONI

P   TAWAKONI AREA PUBLIC LIBRARY*, 340 W Hwy 276, 75474-2644.
SAN 323-6668. Tel: 903-447-3445. FAX: 903-447-3445. E-mail:
tapl42@hotmail.com. Web Site: www.tawakonilibrary.com. *Dir,* Vicki Lynn
Wallace; Staff 2 (Non-MLS 2)
Founded 1982. Pop 4,891; Circ 18,427
Library Holdings: Bk Titles 26,583; Bk Vols 26,803; Per Subs 141
Special Collections: Texas Literature (Texana Coll). Oral History
Automation Activity & Vendor Info: (Acquisitions) LibraryWorld, Inc;
(Cataloging) LibraryWorld, Inc; (Circulation) Follett Software
Wireless access
Function: Bks on cassette, Bks on CD, Children's prog, Computers for
patron use, Copy machines, e-mail serv, Fax serv, Free DVD rentals,
Handicapped accessible, Holiday prog, ILL available,
Photocopying/Printing, Scanner, Summer reading prog, Tax forms,
Wheelchair accessible
Open Tues, Wed & Fri 11-5, Thurs 10-5, Sat 10-3
Friends of the Library Group

WHARTON

J   WHARTON COUNTY JUNIOR COLLEGE, J M Hodges Library, 911
Boling Hwy, 77488-3298. SAN 316-8441. Tel: 979-532-6953. Interlibrary
Loan Service Tel: 979-532-6509. FAX: 979-532-6527. E-mail:
wcjclibrary@wcjc.edu. Web Site: www.wcjc.edu. *Dir, Libr Serv,*
Kwei-Feng Hsu; E-mail: kweih@wcjc.edu; *Pub Serv Librn,* Leslie
Kolojaco; Tel: 979-532-6356, E-mail: kolojacol@wcjc.edu; *Acq,* Janice
Gensler; *Cat,* Rosie Nunez; *Circ,* Veronica Garcia; *Computer Lab Tech,* Liz
Jasso; Tel: 979-532-6332, E-mail: lizj@wcjc.edu; Staff 2 (MLS 2)

Founded 1946. Enrl 7,500
Library Holdings: DVDs 500; e-books 28,000; Electronic Media & Resources 45; Bk Titles 55,000; Bk Vols 55,800; Per Subs 110; Videos 2,000
Automation Activity & Vendor Info: (Cataloging) EOS International; (Circulation) EOS International; (OPAC) EOS International
Database Vendor: Agricola, Alexander Street Press, Amigos Library Services, Baker & Taylor, BioOne, CQ Press, EBSCOhost, EOS International, Facts on File, Gale Cengage Learning, JSTOR, LearningExpress, LexisNexis, Marcive, Inc, OCLC WorldCat, OVID Technologies, Oxford Online, ProQuest, PubMed
Wireless access
Partic in TexSHARE - Texas State Library & Archives Commission
Open Mon-Thurs 7:30am-9pm, Fri 7:30-4

P   WHARTON COUNTY LIBRARY*, 1920 N Fulton, 77488. SAN 362-4153. Tel: 979-532-8080. Web Site: www.whartonco.lib.tx.us. *Dir,* Barbara J Goodell; E-mail: bgoodell@whartonco.lib.tx.us; *Asst Dir,* Geraldine Smaistrla; *Ch,* Linda Hines; Staff 2 (MLS 2)
Founded 1938. Pop 41,467; Circ 203,978
Library Holdings: Bk Vols 85,790; Per Subs 114
Automation Activity & Vendor Info: (Cataloging) TLC (The Library Corporation); (Circulation) TLC (The Library Corporation); (OPAC) TLC (The Library Corporation)
Open Mon & Tues 9-8, Wed-Fri 9-6, Sat 9-3
Friends of the Library Group
Branches: 3
EAST BERNARD BRANCH, 746 Clubside Dr, East Bernard, 77435. Tel: 979-335-6142. *Librn,* Agnes Minks; E-mail: aminks@whartonco.lib.tx.us
Library Holdings: Bk Vols 9,794
Open Mon & Wed-Fri 11:30-5:30, Tues 10-6, Sat 9-12
Friends of the Library Group
EL CAMPO BRANCH, 200 W Church St, El Campo, 77437-3316, SAN 362-4218. Tel: 979-543-2362. *Librn,* Aileen Terry; E-mail: aterry@whartonco.lib.tx.us
Library Holdings: Bk Vols 36,270
Open Mon 10-8, Tues-Fri 10-6, Sat 9-1
LOUISE BRANCH, 803 Third St, Louise, 77455. (Mail add: PO Box 36, Louise, 77455-0036), SAN 362-4242. Tel: 979-648-2018. *Librn,* Jessie Gonzales
Library Holdings: Bk Vols 5,740
Open Tues 9-11:30 & 12:30-4, Wed 1-5, Thurs 1-3

WHEELER

P   WHEELER PUBLIC LIBRARY*, 306 S Canadian St, 79096. (Mail add: PO Box 676, 79096-0676), SAN 316-845X. Tel: 806-826-5977. FAX: 806-826-5977. E-mail: wheelerlibrary@centramedia.net. *Librn,* Teresa Watts
Pop 1,922; Circ 18,347
Library Holdings: Bk Vols 40,000
Open Mon-Fri 12-5:30

WHITE SETTLEMENT

P   WHITE SETTLEMENT PUBLIC LIBRARY*, 8215 White Settlement Rd, 76108-1604. SAN 376-4710. Tel: 817-367-0166. FAX: 817-246-8184. E-mail: wsplib@wstx.us. Web Site: www.whitesettlement.lib.tx.us. *Mgr,* Teresa McBrayer; E-mail: tgmcbrayer@charter.net
Library Holdings: Bk Vols 70,000; Per Subs 80
Automation Activity & Vendor Info: (Cataloging) Mandarin Library Automation; (Circulation) Mandarin Library Automation
Mem of North Texas Library Partners
Open Mon & Thurs 10-8, Tues & Wed 10-6, Sat 10-2
Friends of the Library Group

WHITEHOUSE

P   WHITEHOUSE COMMUNITY LIBRARY, INC*, 107 Bascom Rd, 75791-3230. SAN 376-4508. Tel: 903-839-2949. E-mail: whitehouselibrary@hotmail.com. *Libr Dir,* Sandra Knackstedt; Staff 0.75 (Non-MLS 0.75)
Founded 1983. Pop 7,000; Circ 14,000
Oct 2006-Sept 2007 Income $46,400, City $38,400, Locally Generated Income $8,000. Sal $21,840 (Prof $12,376)
Library Holdings: Bk Vols 30,000; Per Subs 30
Automation Activity & Vendor Info: (Acquisitions) Book Systems, Inc; (Cataloging) Book Systems, Inc; (Circulation) Book Systems, Inc; (OPAC) Book Systems, Inc
Wireless access
Function: Accelerated reader prog, Audio & video playback equip for onsite use, Bk club(s), Bks on cassette, Bks on CD, Children's prog, Computer training, Computers for patron use, Copy machines, Fax serv, Free DVD rentals, Holiday prog, ILL available, Music CDs, Notary serv, Photocopying/Printing, Prog for adults, Prog for children & young adult,

Ref serv available, Senior computer classes, Spoken cassettes & CDs, Spoken cassettes & DVDs, Summer reading prog, Tax forms, VHS videos, Video lending libr, Wheelchair accessible, Workshops
Open Mon, Tues, Thurs & Fri 12-6, Sat 11-4

WHITESBORO

P   WHITESBORO PUBLIC LIBRARY*, 308 W Main, 76273. SAN 316-8468. Tel: 903-564-5432. FAX: 903-564-6105. E-mail: whlibrary@yahoo.com. Web Site: whitesboropl.org. *Dir,* Virginia Garvin
Founded 1969. Pop 3,197; Circ 30,796
Library Holdings: Bk Vols 28,000; Per Subs 12
Special Collections: Genealogy Coll
Automation Activity & Vendor Info: (Cataloging) Follett Software; (Circulation) Follett Software
Open Mon, Wed & Fri 9-5:30, Tues & Thurs 9-8, Sat 9-2
Friends of the Library Group

WHITEWRIGHT

P   WHITEWRIGHT PUBLIC LIBRARY*, 200 Grand St, 75491. (Mail add: PO Box 984, 75491-0984), SAN 316-8476. Tel: 903-364-2955. FAX: 903-364-5680. E-mail: wwpl@texoma.net. Web Site: www.whitewright.lib.tx.us. *Librn,* Chris Ely
Circ 19,000
Library Holdings: Bk Vols 20,000; Per Subs 12
Automation Activity & Vendor Info: (Cataloging) Follett Software; (Circulation) Follett Software
Open Mon-Wed & Fri 10-12 & 1-5:30, Thurs 10-12 & 1-7

WHITNEY

P   LAKE WHITNEY PUBLIC LIBRARY*, 106 N Colorado St, 76692-2213. (Mail add: PO Box 2050, 76692-2050), SAN 376-4753. Tel: 254-694-4639. FAX: 254-694-0896. E-mail: whitney@members.ctls.net. Web Site: www.whitneylibrary.org. *Dir,* Denise Carter; Staff 1 (Non-MLS 1)
Library Holdings: Audiobooks 400; Bk Vols 11,000; Videos 600
Wireless access
Mem of Central Texas Library System, Inc
Open Mon-Fri 10-5, Sat 9-1
Friends of the Library Group

WICHITA FALLS

C   MIDWESTERN STATE UNIVERSITY, George Moffett Library, 3410 Taft Ave, 76308-2099. SAN 316-8492. Circulation Tel: 940-397-4753. Interlibrary Loan Service Tel: 940-397-4174. Reference Tel: 940-397-4758. Administration Tel: 940-397-4757. Toll Free Tel: 800-259-8518. FAX: 940-397-4689. E-mail: msulib@mwsu.edu. Web Site: library.mwsu.edu. *Dir,* Clara M Latham; E-mail: clara.latham@mwsu.edu; *Head, Ref,* Violet Allison Breen; Tel: 940-397-4171, E-mail: allison.breen@mwsu.edu; *Cat,* Terri Decker; Tel: 940-397-4175, E-mail: terri.decker@mwsu.edu; *Ch,* Andrea L Williams; Tel: 940-397-4698, E-mail: andrea.williams@mwsu.edu; *Coll Develop,* Dan Winslow; Tel: 940-397-4169; *Doc,* Ryan Samuelson; Tel: 940-397-4177, E-mail: ryan.samuelson@mwsu.edu; *ILL,* Ashley Tipton; E-mail: ashley.tipton@mwsu.edu; *Media Spec,* Christopher Henderson; Tel: 940-397-4696, E-mail: chris.henderson@mwsu.edu. Subject Specialists: *English, Hist,* Violet Allison Breen; *Hist,* Terri Decker; *Children's educ, Children's lit,* Andrea L Williams; *Govt info, Humanities,* Ryan Samuelson; *Nonprint mat, Soc studies,* Christopher Henderson; Staff 14 (MLS 9, Non-MLS 5)
Founded 1922. Enrl 6,200; Fac 221; Highest Degree: Master
Sept 2011-Aug 2012 Income $612,469. Mats Exp $542,875, Books $105,000, Per/Ser (Incl. Access Fees) $96,000, Micro $31,000, AV Mat $8,875, Electronic Ref Mat (Incl. Access Fees) $292,000, Presv $10,000. Sal $581,000 (Prof $448,000)
Library Holdings: AV Mats 15,000; e-books 52,000; Bk Titles 321,887; Bk Vols 480,000; Per Subs 1,200
Special Collections: Americana (Library of American Civilization), ultrafiche; English Literature (Library of English Literature to Early 20th Century), ultrafiche; Missouri-Kansas-Texas Railroad Map Coll; Nolan A Moore III Heritage of Print Coll. State Document Depository; US Document Depository
Subject Interests: Educ, Hist, US
Automation Activity & Vendor Info: (Acquisitions) Ex Libris Group; (Cataloging) Ex Libris Group; (Circulation) Ex Libris Group; (Course Reserve) Ex Libris Group; (ILL) Ex Libris Group; (OPAC) Ex Libris Group; (Serials) Ex Libris Group
Database Vendor: EBSCOhost, Gale Cengage Learning, JSTOR, OCLC FirstSearch, OVID Technologies
Wireless access
Function: For res purposes
Publications: Libra (Newsletter)
Partic in OCLC Online Computer Library Center, Inc; TexSHARE - Texas State Library & Archives Commission

Special Services for the Deaf - TDD equip; TTY equip; Videos & decoder
Open Mon-Thurs 7:45am-2am, Fri 7:45-5, Sat 10-6, Sun 2pm-2am
Restriction: Non-circulating to the pub

S   OIL INFORMATION LIBRARY OF WICHITA FALLS*, 718 Lamar St,
      76301-6877. SAN 316-8549. Tel: 940-322-4241. FAX: 940-322-8695. *Exec
      Dir,* Gail Baldon Phillips; Staff 1 (MLS 1)
      Founded 1966
      Library Holdings: Bk Vols 1,200
      Subject Interests: Gas records, Geol data, Maps, Oil records
      Function: Res libr
      Open Mon-Fri 8:30-5

P   WICHITA FALLS PUBLIC LIBRARY*, 600 11th St, 76301-4604. SAN
      316-8484. Tel: 940-767-0868. Circulation Tel: 940-767-0868, Ext 221.
      Interlibrary Loan Service Tel: 940-767-0868, Ext 230. Reference Tel:
      940-767-0868, Ext 234. FAX: 940-720-6672. Information Services FAX:
      940-720-6659. E-mail: ill@wfpl.net. Web Site: www.wfpl.net. *Adminr,*
      Lesley Daly; Tel: 940-767-0868, Ext 229, E-mail: lesley.daly@wfpl.net;
      Asst Admin, Head, Ref (Info Serv), Rebecca Morrison; Tel: 940-767-0868,
      Ext 233, E-mail: becky.morrison@wfpl.net; *Network Adminr,* Annette
      Britain; Tel: 940-767-0868, Ext 246, E-mail: annette.britain@wfpl.net;
      Head, Circ, Lana Horner; Tel: 940-767-0868, Ext 225, E-mail:
      lana.horner@wfpl.net; *Acq Librn, Head, Coll Develop,* Andrew Jelen; Tel:
      940-767-0868, Ext 228, E-mail: andrew.jelen@wfpl.net; *Ch,* Erin Warzala;
      Tel: 940-767-0868, Ext 244, E-mail: erin.warzala@wfpl.net; *Ref Librn,*
      Graham Tedesco-Blair; Tel: 940-767-0868, Ext 232, E-mail:
      graham.tedesco-blair@wfpl.net; *Tech Serv Librn,* Rich Maruscsak; Tel:
      940-767-0868, Ext 241, E-mail: rich.maruscsak@wfpl.net; *ILL & Distance
      Libr Serv Spec,* Mary McQueen; E-mail: mary.mcqueen@wfpl.net;
      Cataloger, Carolyn Haines; Tel: 940-767-0868, Ext 231, E-mail:
      carolyn.haines@wfpl.net. Subject Specialists: *Genealogy,* Andrew Jelen;
      Staff 17 (MLS 10, Non-MLS 7)
      Founded 1918. Pop 125,000; Circ 377,807
      Library Holdings: Bk Titles 148,000; Bk Vols 154,000; Per Subs 86
      Special Collections: Texana & Southwest (Texas Coll)
      Subject Interests: Genealogy, Tex hist
      Automation Activity & Vendor Info: (Acquisitions) SirsiDynix;
      (Cataloging) SirsiDynix; (Circulation) SirsiDynix; (OPAC) SirsiDynix
      Database Vendor: EBSCOhost, Gale Cengage Learning, OCLC
      FirstSearch, Wilson - Wilson Web
      Publications: Check It Out (Newsletter)
      Mem of North Texas Library Partners
      Open Mon-Wed 9-8, Thurs-Fri 9-5, Sat 9-2
      Friends of the Library Group

WILMER

P   ELVIS MAXINE GILLIAM MEMORIAL PUBLIC LIBRARY, 205 E
      Beltline Rd, 75172. SAN 361-4344. Tel: 972-441-3713. FAX:
      972-525-3914. E-mail: wilmerlibrary@cityofwilmer.com. Web Site:
      wilmerlibrary.org. *Libr Dir,* Jennifer Ramirez; E-mail:
      jramirez@cityofwilmer.com; *Libr Asst,* Jennifer Dominguez; E-mail:
      jdominguez@cityofwilmer.com; Staff 1 (MLS 1)
      Founded 1966. Pop 1,800
      Library Holdings: Bk Vols 16,493; Per Subs 10
      Automation Activity & Vendor Info: (Cataloging) Book Systems, Inc;
      (Circulation) Book Systems, Inc; (OPAC) Book Systems, Inc
      Wireless access
      Function: Bilingual assistance for Spanish patrons, Bks on cassette, Bks
      on CD, Computer training, Computers for patron use, Copy machines, Fax
      serv, Free DVD rentals, Genealogy discussion group, ILL available, Online
      cat, Outside serv via phone, mail, e-mail & web, Photocopying/Printing,
      Pub access computers, Senior computer classes, Spanish lang bks, Summer
      reading prog, Tax forms, Telephone ref, VHS videos, Wheelchair
      accessible
      Open Mon-Wed & Fri 9-6, Thurs 9-8, Sat 10-2
      Friends of the Library Group

WIMBERLEY

P   WIMBERLEY VILLAGE LIBRARY*, 400 FM 2325, 78676-5009. (Mail
      add: PO Box 1240, 78676-1240), SAN 320-264X. Tel: 512-847-2188.
      FAX: 512-847-1467. Web Site: www.wimberleylibrary.org. *Dir,* Carolyn
      Manning
      Founded 1975. Pop 12,666; Circ 18,000
      Library Holdings: Bk Titles 20,000; Bk Vols 21,635; Per Subs 55
      Special Collections: History (Herrick Arnold Coll)
      Publications: Wimberley - A Way of Life, 1985
      Mem of Central Texas Library System, Inc
      Open Mon & Wed 10-8, Tues, Thurs & Sat 10-6
      Friends of the Library Group

WINNSBORO

P   GILBREATH MEMORIAL LIBRARY*, 916 N Main St, 75494. SAN
      316-8557. Tel: 903-342-6866. E-mail: gml@winnsborolibrary.org. Web
      Site: www.winnsborolibrary.org. *Dir,* Vickie Martin; *Asst Dir,* Diane Fite;
      Staff 3 (Non-MLS 3)
      Pop 7,825; Circ 68,764
      Oct 2010-Sept 2011 Income $420,418, State $17,888, City $402,530
      Library Holdings: AV Mats 1,938; Large Print Bks 938; Bk Titles 29,103;
      Bk Vols 29,718; Per Subs 45; Talking Bks 1,018
      Automation Activity & Vendor Info: (Cataloging) Book Systems, Inc;
      (Circulation) Book Systems, Inc
      Wireless access
      Open Tues-Fri 8:30-6, Sat 8:30-12
      Friends of the Library Group

WINTERS

P   WINTERS PUBLIC LIBRARY*, 120 N Main, 79567. SAN 316-8565. Tel:
      325-754-4251. E-mail: winterspl@netscape.net. *Dir, Libr Serv,* Judi Rusk;
      Staff 1 (Non-MLS 1)
      Founded 1954. Pop 4,500; Circ 8,500
      Library Holdings: Bk Titles 15,600
      Subject Interests: Hist
      Publications: Big Country Major Resource News; Forecast
      Mem of Big Country Library System
      Open Mon-Thurs 1-6, Sat 10-12

WOLFE CITY

P   WOLFE CITY PUBLIC LIBRARY*, 203 E Williams St, 75496. (Mail
      add: PO Box 109, 75496-0109), SAN 316-8573. Tel: 903-496-7311. FAX:
      903-496-7311. E-mail: wclibrary02@yahoo.com. Web Site:
      www.wolfecitylibrary.com. *Dir,* Angela Scarlett; Staff 1 (Non-MLS 1)
      Pop 3,700
      Library Holdings: Bk Titles 23,000
      Open Mon 10-5:30, Tues 10-6, Wed 10-4, Thurs & Fri 1-5:30, Sat 10-1
      Friends of the Library Group

WOLFFORTH

P   CITY OF WOLFFORTH LIBRARY*, 508 E Hwy 62-82, 79382-7001.
      (Mail add: PO Box 36, 79382-0036), SAN 376-4265. Tel: 806-866-9280.
      FAX: 806-833-6932. E-mail: library@wolfforthtx.us. Web Site:
      wolfforthtx.us. *Dir,* Andi Powers; *Librn,* Stephanie Murdock
      Library Holdings: AV Mats 200; Bk Titles 25,000; Per Subs 6
      Automation Activity & Vendor Info: (Acquisitions) LibLime;
      (Cataloging) LibLime; (Circulation) LibLime
      Wireless access
      Mem of West Texas Library System
      Open Mon-Fri 9-8, Sat 1-5
      Friends of the Library Group

WOODVILLE

P   ALLAN SHIVERS LIBRARY & MUSEUM*, 302 N Charlton St, 75979.
      SAN 316-8581. Tel: 409-283-3709. FAX: 409-283-5258. Web Site:
      allanshiverslibrary.com. *Dir,* Rosemary Mosey-Bunch; Staff 1 (MLS 1)
      Founded 1966. Pop 20,000; Circ 55,111
      Library Holdings: Audiobooks 2,000; CDs 242; DVDs 1,181; Large Print
      Bks 5,170; Bk Vols 39,000; Per Subs 48
      Automation Activity & Vendor Info: (Acquisitions) SirsiDynix;
      (Cataloging) SirsiDynix; (Circulation) SirsiDynix
      Wireless access
      Open Mon-Fri 9-4, Sat 10-2
      Friends of the Library Group

WYLIE

P   RITA & TRUETT SMITH PUBLIC LIBRARY*, 300 Country Club Rd,
      Bldg 300, 75098. SAN 316-859X. Tel: 972-516-6250. E-mail:
      libinfo@wylietexas.gov. Web Site: www.wylietexas.gov. *Dir,* Rachel
      Orozco; *Supvr, Pub Serv,* Donna Shirley
      Founded 1970. Pop 9,200; Circ 55,105
      Library Holdings: Bk Vols 45,000; Per Subs 50
      Automation Activity & Vendor Info: (Cataloging) TLC (The Library
      Corporation); (Circulation) TLC (The Library Corporation); (OPAC) TLC
      (The Library Corporation)
      Wireless access
      Publications: Library Notes (monthly)
      Open Mon, Tues & Thurs 12-8, Wed 9-6, Fri 11-5, Sat 9-4
      Friends of the Library Group

YOAKUM

P CARL & MARY WELHAUSEN LIBRARY*, 810 Front St, 77995-3058. SAN 316-8603. Tel: 361-293-5001. FAX: 361-293-7091. E-mail: librarian@cityofyoakum.org. Web Site: www.cityofyoakum.org/Library.html. *Librn,* Lynn Mixon
Pop 5,517; Circ 21,618
Library Holdings: AV Mats 1,194; DVDs 300; Microforms 150; Bk Vols 16,968; Per Subs 1; Talking Bks 800; Videos 1,500
Special Collections: Genealogy Coll
Automation Activity & Vendor Info: (Cataloging) Follett Software; (Circulation) Follett Software
Open Mon-Fri 9-6
Friends of the Library Group

YORKTOWN

P YORKTOWN PUBLIC LIBRARY*, 103 W Main, 78164-5000. (Mail add: PO Box 308, 78164-0308), SAN 316-8611. Tel: 361-564-3232. FAX: 361-564-3232. *Libr Dir,* Beth Riedesel; E-mail: yplbeth@yahoo.com; Staff 1 (Non-MLS 1)
Founded 1939. Pop 2,090; Circ 9,200
Library Holdings: Audiobooks 200; AV Mats 425; Braille Volumes 3; CDs 100; DVDs 75; Large Print Bks 250; Bk Titles 18,500; Per Subs 35; Videos 450
Automation Activity & Vendor Info: (Cataloging) Follett Software; (Circulation) Follett Software; (ILL) Follett Software; (OPAC) Follett Software
Wireless access
Function: Adult bk club, Art exhibits, Audio & video playback equip for onsite use, Bks on cassette, Bks on CD, CD-ROM, Children's prog, Computers for patron use, Copy machines, Distance learning, e-mail serv, Electronic databases & coll, Exhibits, Fax serv, Free DVD rentals, Handicapped accessible, Home delivery & serv to Sr ctr & nursing homes, Homebound delivery serv, ILL available, Magnifiers for reading, Mail & tel request accepted, Music CDs, Newsp ref libr, Photocopying/Printing, Preschool outreach, Prog for adults, Prog for children & young adult, Pub access computers, Ref serv available, Ref serv in person, Referrals accepted, Spoken cassettes & CDs, Spoken cassettes & DVDs, Story hour, Summer reading prog, Tax forms, Telephone ref, VHS videos, Wheelchair accessible, Workshops
Partic in Tex Share
Special Services for the Deaf - Bks on deafness & sign lang; Closed caption videos
Special Services for the Blind - Accessible computers; Audio mat; Bks available with recordings; Bks on cassette; Bks on CD; Cassettes; Home delivery serv; Large print bks; Magnifiers; Ref serv; Sound rec
Open Mon 1-9, Tues & Wed 1-6, Thurs 9-9
Friends of the Library Group

ZAPATA

P ZAPATA COUNTY PUBLIC LIBRARY*, 901 Kennedy St, 78076. (Mail add: 2806 Stop28A, 78076-2836), SAN 325-173X. Tel: 956-765-5351. FAX: 956-765-1578. E-mail: zcplibr@yahoo.com. *Dir,* Aida R Garcia; E-mail: zcplibr@yahoo.com; *Asst Librn,* Amalia Navarro; *Ch,* Maria Yanira Garcia; E-mail: yanira7_98@yahoo.com; Staff 3 (Non-MLS 3)
Founded 1983. Pop 12,200
Library Holdings: CDs 500; DVDs 200; Bk Vols 28,000; Per Subs 48; Talking Bks 175; Videos 300
Special Collections: Genealogical Records, microfiche, microfilm; Texas History Coll
Database Vendor: EBSCOhost, OCLC FirstSearch
Open Mon & Tues 9-7, Wed & Thurs 9-6, Fri 9-4, Sat 8-12
Friends of the Library Group
Branches: 1
A L BENNAVIDES BRANCH, 301 Lincoln Ave, San Ygnacio, 78067. (Mail add: PO Box 219, San Ygnacio, 78067-0219), SAN 376-9879. Tel: 956-765-5611, Ext 26. *Br Mgr,* Ismael Valdez
Library Holdings: Bk Vols 5,000; Per Subs 10
Open Mon-Fri 3-6

Date of Statistics: FY 2011
Population, 2011 (est.): 2,776,469
Population Served by Public Libraries: 2,775,406
Total Volumes in Public Libraries: 8,013,937
    Volumes Per Capita: 2.89
Total Public Library Circulation: 37,903,928
    Circulation Per Capita: 13.66
Total Public Library Income (not including Grants-in-Aid):
    $85,025,697
    Source of Income: Public funds
    Expenditure Per Capita: $32.08
Number of County Libraries: 26
Number of Bookmobiles in State: 9
Grants-in-Aid to Public Libraries:
    Federal (Library Services & Technology Act): $538,189
    State Aid: $904,117

AMERICAN FORK

P   AMERICAN FORK CITY LIBRARY, 64 S 100 East, 84003. SAN 316-862X. Tel: 801-763-3070. FAX: 801-763-3073. Web Site: www.afcity.org. *Dir,* Sheena Parker; E-mail: sheena@afcity.net; Staff 20 (MLS 1, Non-MLS 19)
Pop 26,263; Circ 301,750
Jul 2011-Jun 2012 Income $748,129, State $7,486, City $686,022, Other $54,621. Mats Exp $58,638, Books $46,944, AV Mat $2,868. Sal $576,924
Library Holdings: Audiobooks 3,009; CDs 893; DVDs 2,401; Large Print Bks 736; Bk Vols 97,080; Per Subs 93; Videos 2,361
Automation Activity & Vendor Info: (Cataloging) SirsiDynix; (Circulation) SirsiDynix; (OPAC) SirsiDynix
Database Vendor: SirsiDynix
Wireless access
Function: Computers for patron use, Copy machines, e-mail & chat, Electronic databases & coll, Fax serv, Free DVD rentals, Holiday prog, Homework prog, ILL available, Learning ctr, Music CDs, Online cat, OverDrive digital audio bks, Photocopying/Printing, Preschool reading prog, Prog for adults, Prog for children & young adult, Pub access computers, Ref & res, Spanish lang bks, Story hour, Summer reading prog, Tax forms, Teen prog, VHS videos, Video lending libr, Wheelchair accessible, Winter reading prog
Partic in Pioneer
Open Mon-Thurs 9-9, Fri & Sat 10-6
Restriction: Circ to mem only, In-house use for visitors, Non-resident fee
Friends of the Library Group

S   NATIONAL PARK SERVICE*, Timpanogos Cave National Monument Library, RR 3, Box 200, 84003-9803. SAN 321-8376. Tel: 801-756-5239. FAX: 801-756-5661. *In Charge,* Mike Gosse; E-mail: tica_ranger_activities@nps.gov
Founded 1966
Library Holdings: Bk Titles 925
Subject Interests: Cave related subjs, Caves, Natural res, The Environment

BEAVER

P   BEAVER PUBLIC LIBRARY*, 55 W Center St, 84713. (Mail add: PO Box 192, 84713), SAN 316-8638. Tel: 435-438-5274. FAX: 435-438-5826. *Dir,* Angela Edwards; Staff 1 (Non-MLS 1)
Founded 1920. Pop 2,618; Circ 19,016
Jul 2008-Jun 2009 Income $70,809, State $6,176, City $46,261, County $17,400, Locally Generated Income $972. Mats Exp $8,187, Books $7,418, AV Mat $769. Sal $39,709
Library Holdings: AV Mats 413; Large Print Bks 80; Bk Vols 18,394; Per Subs 26; Talking Bks 326
Automation Activity & Vendor Info: (Acquisitions) Follett Software; (Cataloging) Follett Software; (Circulation) Follett Software; (Course Reserve) Follett Software; (OPAC) Follett Software
Wireless access
Open Mon-Thurs 10-6, Fri & Sat 11-3

BRIGHAM CITY

S   ATK LAUNCH SYSTEMS*, PO Box 707, 84302-0707. SAN 316-8662. Tel: 435-863-6819. FAX: 435-863-6023. Web Site: www.atk.com. *Librn,* Diane Nielson; Tel: 435-863-2132, E-mail: diane.nielson@atk.com; *Librn,* Ellen Wagstaff; Tel: 435-863-6819, E-mail: ellen.wagstaff@atk.com
Library Holdings: Bk Vols 100,000; Per Subs 50
Subject Interests: Solid propellant rocket tech
Automation Activity & Vendor Info: (Cataloging) EOS International; (Circulation) EOS International; (ILL) OCLC; (OPAC) EOS International
Database Vendor: Dialog
Open Mon-Fri 7-3:30

P   BRIGHAM CITY LIBRARY*, 26 E Forest, 84302-2198. SAN 316-8646. Tel: 435-723-5850. FAX: 435-723-2813. Web Site: bcpl.lib.ut.us. *Dir,* Susan H Hill; E-mail: susan@peachy.bcpl.lib.ut.us; *Adult Serv,* Elizabeth Schow; *Circ,* Elizabeth Schow; *Ch,* Connie Edwards; *Ch,* Michele Schumann; *Ref,* Susan Behring; Staff 4 (MLS 1, Non-MLS 3)
Founded 1915. Pop 15,619; Circ 172,233
Library Holdings: Bk Titles 50,577; Bk Vols 56,907; Per Subs 176
Special Collections: Box Elder History, bks & pamphlets; Mormon History; Mormon Religion
Automation Activity & Vendor Info: (Cataloging) Follett Software; (Circulation) Follett Software; (OPAC) Follett Software
Partic in Pioneer
Open Mon-Thurs 10-9, Fri & Sat 10-6
Friends of the Library Group

CASTLE DALE

P   EMERY COUNTY LIBRARY, 115 N 100 East, 84513. (Mail add: PO Box 515, 84513-0515), SAN 316-8670. Tel: 435-381-2554. FAX: 435-381-2699. Web Site: www.emerycounty.com/library, www.lib.emerycounty.com. *Asst County Dir,* Roxanne Noyes; *Asst Librn,* Jaki Collard
Pop 10,651; Circ 109,268
Library Holdings: Bk Vols 134,130
Automation Activity & Vendor Info: (Acquisitions) Book Systems, Inc; (Cataloging) Book Systems, Inc; (Circulation) Book Systems, Inc; (Course Reserve) Book Systems, Inc; (ILL) Book Systems, Inc; (OPAC) Book Systems, Inc; (Serials) Book Systems, Inc
Partic in Pioneer
Open Mon-Fri 10-6
Branches: 7
CLEVELAND BRANCH, 45 W Main, Cleveland, 84518. (Mail add: PO Box 275, Cleveland, 84518-0275). Tel: 435-653-2204. FAX: 435-653-2104. *Librn,* Loyette Holdaway; *Asst Librn,* Tina Bradley
Open Mon-Fri 9:30-5:30
ELMO BRANCH, 15 S 100 East, Elmo, 84521. (Mail add: PO Box 217, Elmo, 84521). Tel: 435-653-2558. FAX: 435-653-2553. *Librn,* Bonnie Day; *Asst Librn,* Marilyn Olsen
Open Mon-Fri 9:30-5:30

EMERY BRANCH, 100 N Center, Emery, 84522. (Mail add: PO Box 127, Emery, 84522-0127). Tel: 435-286-2474. FAX: 435-286-2434. *Librn,* Marian Mangum; *Asst Librn,* Denise Allen
Open Mon-Fri 9:30-5:30

FERRON BRANCH, 55 N 200 West, Ferron, 84523. (Mail add: PO Box 850, Ferron, 84523-0850). Tel: 435-384-2637. FAX: 435-384-2876. *Librn,* Colleen Murdock; *Asst Librn,* Becky Jewkes
Open Mon-Fri 9:30-5:30

GREEN RIVER BRANCH, 85 S Long St, Green River, 84525. (Mail add: PO Box 510, Green River, 84525-0510). Tel: 435-564-3349. FAX: 435-564-3399. *Librn,* Cheri Packer; *Asst Librn,* Jolene Dalton
Open Mon-Fri 9:30-5:30

HUNTINGTON BRANCH, 92 S Main, Huntington, 84528. (Mail add: PO Box 794, Huntington, 84528-0794). Tel: 435-687-9590. FAX: 435-687-9510. *Librn,* Flora Motte; *Asst Librn,* Kay Jeffs
Open Mon-Fri 9:30-5:30

ORANGEVILLE BRANCH, 125 S Main, Orangeville, 84537. (Mail add: PO Box 628, Orangeville, 84537-0628). Tel: 435-748-2726. FAX: 435-748-2736. *Dir,* Carole Larsen; *Asst Librn,* Hoffman Melodie
Open Mon-Fri 9:30-5:30

CEDAR CITY

P   CEDAR CITY PUBLIC LIBRARY IN THE PARK*, 303 N 100 East, 84720. SAN 316-8689. Tel: 435-586-6661. FAX: 435-865-7280. Web Site: cedarcitylibrary.org. *Dir,* Steven D Decker; E-mail: dsteve@cedarcity.org; *Ch,* Crystal Bilyeu; *Ch,* Pat Mills; *Tech Serv,* Sherry Bohman; Staff 1 (MLS 1)
Founded 1914. Pop 22,000; Circ 230,000
Library Holdings: Bk Vols 66,000; Per Subs 68
Special Collections: Local Newspaper Coll, micro; Rare Book Coll. Oral History
Subject Interests: Consumer guides, Hist, Relig studies, Sci
Automation Activity & Vendor Info: (Cataloging) TLC (The Library Corporation); (Circulation) TLC (The Library Corporation); (OPAC) TLC (The Library Corporation)
Database Vendor: LearningExpress
Open Mon-Thurs 9-9, Fri & Sat 9-6

C   SOUTHERN UTAH UNIVERSITY, Gerald R Sherratt Library, 351 W University Blvd, 84720. SAN 316-8697. Tel: 435-865-8240. Interlibrary Loan Service Tel: 435-586-7938. Reference Tel: 435-865-8040. Administration Tel: 435-586-7947. FAX: 435-865-8152. Interlibrary Loan Service FAX: 435-865-8531. E-mail: library@suu.edu. Web Site: library.suu.edu. *Dean of Libr Serv,* Dr John Eye; Tel: 435-865-8392, Fax: 435-865-8152, E-mail: eye@suu.edu; *Dept Chair,* Vik G Brown; Tel: 435-586-7952, E-mail: brown_v@suu.edu; *Libr Media Prog Dir,* Verlene Schafer; Tel: 435-865-8031, E-mail: verleneschafer@suu.edu; *Electronic Res Librn,* Steven Irving; Tel: 435-586-5480, E-mail: stevenirving@suu.edu; *Instruction Librn,* Philip Roche; Tel: 435-865-8734, E-mail: roche@suu.edu; *New Technologies Librn,* Richard Eissinger; Tel: 435-586-5435, E-mail: eissinger@suu.edu; *Access Serv, Ref Librn,* Scott W Lanning; Tel: 435-865-8156, E-mail: lanning@suu.edu; *Spec Coll Librn,* Janet B Seegmiller; Tel: 435-586-7945, E-mail: seegmiller@suu.edu; *Spec Projects Librn,* Matthew Nickerson; Tel: 435-586-1955, E-mail: nickerson@suu.edu; *Tech Serv Librn,* Loralyn O Felix; Tel: 435-586-7946, E-mail: felix@suu.edu; *Network Adminr,* Julie Wood; Tel: 435-586-8052, E-mail: juliewood@suu.edu. Subject Specialists: *Electronics, Tech,* Dr John Eye; *Art, Hist, Music,* Vik G Brown; *Educ, Geog, Soc sci,* Verlene Schafer; *Lang, Philosophy, Relig,* Steven Irving; *Am lit, Eng lit,* Philip Roche; *Criminal justice, Nursing, Phys sci,* Richard Eissinger; *Bus,* Scott W Lanning; *Communication, Theatre, US hist,* Janet B Seegmiller; *Biol,* Matthew Nickerson; *Home econ, Interdisciplinary studies, Lit,* Loralyn O Felix; Staff 9.25 (MLS 7.25, Non-MLS 2)
Founded 1897. Enrl 6,612; Fac 250; Highest Degree: Master
Jul 2010-Jun 2011 Income $2,262,694. State $2,086,877, Other $175,517. Mats Exp $2,133,934, Books $245,190, Per/Ser (Incl. Access Fees) $101,967, Electronic Ref Mat (Incl. Access Fees) $116,180, Presv $5,383. Sal $1,105,400 (Prof $611,470)
Library Holdings: AV Mats 11,879; e-books 11,484; Microforms 38,720; Bk Vols 296,655; Per Subs 43,845
Special Collections: Dixie National Forest Coll; Grand Staircase-Escalante National Monument Coll; Howard R Driggs Coll; Iron Mining District; Michael O Leavitt Coll; Mountain West Digital Library; Opera Scores & Books of the 19th Century (Victorian Room); Shakespeare Coll; Southern Paiute Indian Coll; Southern Utah History Coll; US Geology Maps; William R Palmer Coll. Oral History; State Document Depository; US Document Depository
Subject Interests: Music, Opera, Shakespeare, Sibelius, Utah hist
Automation Activity & Vendor Info: (Cataloging) SirsiDynix; (Circulation) SirsiDynix; (Course Reserve) SirsiDynix; (ILL) OCLC; (OPAC) SirsiDynix; (Serials) SirsiDynix
Database Vendor: 3M Library Systems, ACM (Association for Computing Machinery), Alexander Street Press, American Chemical Society, Annual Reviews, BioOne, CRC Press/Taylor & Francis CRCnetBASE,

CredoReference, Dialog, EBSCOhost, Foundation Center, Gale Cengage Learning, H W Wilson, IOP, LexisNexis, Medline, Mergent Online, netLibrary, OCLC FirstSearch, OCLC WorldCat, Oxford Online, Project MUSE, ProQuest, PubMed, Safari Books Online, Sage, SerialsSolutions, SirsiDynix, Wilson - Wilson Web, YBP Library Services
Wireless access
Function: Computers for patron use, Copy machines, Doc delivery serv, E-Reserves, Electronic databases & coll, Exhibits, Handicapped accessible, ILL available, Photocopying/Printing, Pub access computers, Ref serv available, Ref serv in person, Web-catalog, Wheelchair accessible
Publications: Gerald R Sherratt Library Annual Report; Historical Topography A New Look at Old Sites on Mountain Meadows (Local historical information); InterLink (Newsletter); Journal of the Wooden O Symposium (College journal); SUU Departmental Histories (Local historical information)
Special Services for the Blind - Accessible computers; Bks on CD; Computer with voice synthesizer for visually impaired persons; Dragon Naturally Speaking software
Open Mon-Thurs 7am-12pm, Fri 7-7, Sat 11-7, Sun 2-10
Friends of the Library Group

J   SOUTHWEST APPLIED TECHNOLOGY COLLEGE, Campus Library, 510 W 800 S, 84720. Tel: 435-586-2899. FAX: 435-586-2873. E-mail: info@swatc.edu. Web Site: www.swatc.edu.
Founded 1987. Pop 1,000; Highest Degree: Certificate
Library Holdings: Bk Titles 3,000
Wireless access
Open Mon-Thurs 8-8, Fri 8-3
Restriction: Open to students, fac & staff, Photo ID required for access, Private libr

DELTA

P   DELTA CITY LIBRARY*, 76 N 200 W, 84624-9424. SAN 316-8727. Tel: 435-864-4945. FAX: 435-864-4313. Web Site: www.stacksandtracks.lib.state.ut.us. *Coll Develop, Librn,* Deb Greathouse; E-mail: dgreat2@frontiernet.net; Staff 5 (Non-MLS 5)
Founded 1920. Pop 3,186; Circ 47,010
Library Holdings: AV Mats 2,228; Bks on Deafness & Sign Lang 15; High Interest/Low Vocabulary Bk Vols 300; Large Print Bks 155; Bk Titles 29,015; Per Subs 32
Automation Activity & Vendor Info: (Cataloging) OCLC Online; (Circulation) Follett Software
Open Mon-Fri 2-8, Sat 1-5

DUCHESNE

P   DUCHESNE LIBRARY*, 130 S Center St, 84021. (Mail add: P O Box 169, 84021-0169). Tel: 435-738-2800. FAX: 435-738-2802. Web Site: duchesne.utah.gov/county-services/library/duchesne-library.html. *Libr Dir/Br Mgr,* Cornel Thomas; E-mail: cthomas@duchesne.utah.gov; Staff 1 (MLS 1)
Founded 2007. Pop 17,000; Circ 45,000
Jan 2012-Dec 2012 Income County $553,750. Mats Exp $14,700, Books $107,700, Per/Ser (Incl. Access Fees) $7,000. Sal $206,764 (Prof $83,690)
Branches: 1
ROOSEVELT BRANCH, 70 W Lagoon 44-4, Roosevelt, 84066-2841, SAN 316-9103. Tel: 435-722-4441. FAX: 435-722-3386. *Br Mgr,* Lorie Womack; E-mail: lwomack@duchesne.utah.gov; *Asst Br Mgr,* Stephen Moon
Circ 52,209
Library Holdings: Bk Vols 52,000; Per Subs 45
Automation Activity & Vendor Info: (Acquisitions) Follett Software; (Cataloging) Follett Software; (Circulation) Follett Software; (Course Reserve) Follett Software; (ILL) Follett Software; (Media Booking) Follett Software; (OPAC) Follett Software; (Serials) Follett Software
Partic in Pioneer
Open Mon-Thurs 10-7, Fri & Sat 10-5

DUGWAY

A   UNITED STATES ARMY DUGWAY PROVING GROUND*, Dugway Post Library, 5124 Kister Ave, IMWE-DUG-MWL MS1, 84022-1097. SAN 362-4277. Tel: 435-831-2178. Interlibrary Loan Service Tel: 435-831-2633. Administration Tel: 435-831-2179. Automation Services Tel: 435-831-2765. FAX: 435-831-3543. TDD: 435-831-2123. E-mail: dpg.lib@us.army.mil. Web Site: mylibraryus.fmwr.net. *Dir,* Michael Beier; E-mail: michael.beier@us.army.mil; *Asst Dir, Cataloger,* John Crawford; E-mail: john.d.crawford2@us.army.mil; *Coordr, ILL, Coordr, Youth Serv,* Melissa Johnson; E-mail: melissa.ann.johnson@us.army.mil; Staff 3 (MLS 2, Non-MLS 1)
Library Holdings: CDs 475; DVDs 1,400; Electronic Media & Resources 50; Bk Titles 27,000; Bk Vols 28,000; Per Subs 50; Talking Bks 1,100; Videos 750
Special Collections: Utah Coll

Automation Activity & Vendor Info: (Cataloging) Innovative Interfaces, Inc - Millenium; (Circulation) Innovative Interfaces, Inc - Millenium; (ILL) OCLC; (OPAC) Innovative Interfaces, Inc - Millenium; (Serials) Innovative Interfaces, Inc - Millenium

Database Vendor: CountryWatch, EBSCO Information Services, Factiva.com, Facts on File, Gale Cengage Learning, netLibrary, Newsbank, OCLC FirstSearch, OCLC WorldCat, Overdrive, Inc, ProQuest, SirsiDynix
Wireless access

Function: After school storytime, Audio & video playback equip for onsite use, Audiobks via web, Children's prog, Computer training, Computers for patron use, Copy machines, Digital talking bks, Electronic databases & coll, Fax serv, Free DVD rentals, ILL available, Music CDs, Online cat, Online searches, Orientations, OverDrive digital audio bks, Photocopying/Printing, Prog for adults, Prog for children & young adult, Pub access computers, Ref & res, Ref serv in person, Scanner, Spoken cassettes & CDs, Story hour, Summer reading prog, VHS videos
Open Mon-Fri 9-7

A   WEST DESERT TECHNICAL INFORMATION CENTER*, Dugway Proving Ground Tech Library, TEDT-DPW-DST, MS No 5, 4531 B St, Rm 116, 84022-5005. SAN 362-4307. Tel: 435-831-3822. FAX: 435-831-3813. E-mail: atec.wdticdpg@mail.mil. Web Site: www.dugway.army.mil/index.php/index/content/id/67.htm. *Lead Librn,* Tracy Elizabeth Lay; Tel: 435-831-5009, E-mail: tracy.lay@us.army.mil; Staff 1 (MLS 1)
Founded 1950
Library Holdings: e-journals 18; Bk Titles 65,000; Bk Vols 3,000; Per Subs 2
Special Collections: Dugway Documents Coll (Fort Detrick, Tropic Test Center, Deseret Test Center, Dugway Proving Ground, Joint/CINC Operational Testing & Chemical-Biological Data Source Books)
Subject Interests: Biol, Chem, Chem-Bio defense, Eng, Math, Meteorology, Munitions, Statistics, Zoology
Automation Activity & Vendor Info: (Cataloging) SirsiDynix; (Circulation) SirsiDynix; (ILL) OCLC FirstSearch; (OPAC) SirsiDynix
Database Vendor: American Chemical Society, Dialog, OCLC WorldCat
Function: Doc delivery serv, For res purposes, ILL available, Online searches, Orientations, Ref serv available, Res libr
Partic in Fedlink; OCLC Online Computer Library Center, Inc
Restriction: Not open to pub, Open to mil & govt employees only, Researchers by appt only, Restricted access

EAGLE MOUNTAIN

P   EAGLE MOUNTAIN PUBLIC LIBRARY*, 1650 E Stagecoach Run, 84005. Tel: 801-789-6623. FAX: 801-789-6653. E-mail: eaglemtnlibrary@emcity.org. Web Site: www.eaglemountaincity.com. *City Librn,* Michele Graves; E-mail: mgraves@emcity.org; *Asst City Librn,* Susan White; *Libr Tech,* Heather Davis
Founded 1999. Pop 12,000
Jul 2005-Jun 2006. Mats Exp $9,000
Library Holdings: DVDs 130; Bk Titles 12,324; Talking Bks 560; Videos 1,000
Automation Activity & Vendor Info: (Cataloging) ComPanion Corp; (Circulation) ComPanion Corp
Function: Handicapped accessible, Online searches, Photocopying/Printing, Prog for children & young adult, Ref serv available, Summer reading prog, VHS videos, Wheelchair accessible
Open Mon-Thurs 10-6:30, Sat 10-2

EPHRAIM

P   EPHRAIM PUBLIC LIBRARY*, 30 S Main St, 84627. SAN 316-8735. Tel: 435-283-4544. *Dir,* Erickson Betsy
Pop 5,500; Circ 44,755
Library Holdings: CDs 1,448; DVDs 91; Bk Vols 33,000; Per Subs 48; Videos 986
Automation Activity & Vendor Info: (Acquisitions) Follett Software; (Cataloging) Follett Software; (Circulation) Follett Software; (OPAC) Follett Software
Partic in Pioneer; Utah Libr Asn
Open Mon-Fri 11-9, Sat 10-2
Friends of the Library Group

J   SNOW COLLEGE, Karen H Huntsman Library, 141 E Center St, 84627. (Mail add: 150 E College Ave, Box 1025, 84627-1550), SAN 316-8743. Tel: 435-283-7363. Reference Tel: 435-283-7361. Administration Tel: 435-283-7365. Toll Free Tel: 800-848-3399. FAX: 435-283-7369. E-mail: library@snow.edu. Web Site: www.lib.snow.edu. *Dir of Librn,* Jon Ostler; E-mail: jon.ostler@snow.edu; *Pub Serv Librn,* Zachary Allred; E-mail: zachary.allred@snow.edu; *Tech Serv Librn,* Lynn Anderson; Tel: 435-283-7366, E-mail: lynn.anderson@snow.edu; *Circ Mgr,* Nikki Elizabeth; E-mail: nikki.elizabeth@snow.edu; *Circ Mgr,* Alexa Pollock; E-mail: alexa.pollock@snow.edu; *Evening/Weekend Supvr,* Charlynn Christensen; E-mail: charlynn.christensen@snow.edu; *Evening/Weekend*

Supvr, Julia Herbert; E-mail: julia.herbert@snow.edu; *Learning Commons Supvr,* Adrian Peterson; E-mail: adrian.peterson@snow.edu; *Libr Syst Adminr,* Dave Peterson; Tel: 435-283-7360, E-mail: dave.peterson@snow.edu; Staff 5 (MLS 3, Non-MLS 2)
Founded 1888. Enrl 3,484; Highest Degree: Bachelor
Library Holdings: Bk Titles 50,000; Bk Vols 50,203; Per Subs 264
Special Collections: Childrens Literature (Demont & Arlea Howell Childrens Literature Coll); Sanpete County & Snow College History (Ruth C Olsen Coll)
Automation Activity & Vendor Info: (Acquisitions) SirsiDynix; (Cataloging) SirsiDynix; (Circulation) SirsiDynix; (Course Reserve) SirsiDynix; (ILL) OCLC; (OPAC) SirsiDynix; (Serials) SirsiDynix
Database Vendor: Alexander Street Press, Annual Reviews, CredoReference, ebrary, EBSCOhost, Facts on File, Gale Cengage Learning, LexisNexis, Mergent Online, netLibrary, OCLC FirstSearch, ProQuest, Safari Books Online, SirsiDynix, Tech Logic, Wilson - Wilson Web, YBP Library Services
Wireless access
Function: Art exhibits, Audio & video playback equip for onsite use, Bks on CD, Copy machines, Free DVD rentals, ILL available, Mail & tel request accepted, Microfiche/film & reading machines, Music CDs, Online ref, Photocopying/Printing, Ref serv available, Ref serv in person, Res libr, Scanner
Publications: Overdue Notes (Newsletter)
Partic in Utah Academic Library Consortium
Open Mon-Thurs 7:30am-1am, Fri 7:30-7, Sat Noon-6, Sun 5-11; Mon-Thurs (Summer) 8-8, Fri 8-5, Sat Noon-5, Sun 5-10

FARMINGTON

P   DAVIS COUNTY LIBRARY*, 38 S 100 East, 84025. (Mail add: PO Box 115, 84025-0115), SAN 362-4331. Tel: 801-451-2322. FAX: 801-451-9561. Web Site: www.co.davis.ut.us/library. *Dir,* Chris Sanford; *Asst Dir,* Jerry Meyer; *Head, Tech Serv,* Mary Moore; *Site Mgr,* Shirleen Wiscombe; *Circ Supvr,* Jeni Hall; *Cataloger, Tech Serv Supvr,* Malayna Paskett; Staff 116 (MLS 6, Non-MLS 110)
Founded 1946. Pop 300,827. Circ 2,842,728
Library Holdings: AV Mats 79,495; Bk Vols 606,290
Automation Activity & Vendor Info: (Acquisitions) SirsiDynix; (Cataloging) SIRSI WorkFlows; (Circulation) SIRSI WorkFlows; (ILL) OCLC; (OPAC) SIRSI-iBistro
Database Vendor: Alexander Street Press, Baker & Taylor, BookLetters LLC, Comprise Technologies, Inc, EBSCO Auto Repair Reference, EBSCOhost, Factiva.com, Gale Cengage Learning, LearningExpress, Newsbank, OCLC FirstSearch, OCLC WorldCat, Overdrive, Inc, ProQuest, ReferenceUSA, SirsiDynix
Wireless access
Function: Computers for patron use, ILL available, Music CDs, Online cat, OverDrive digital audio bks, Prog for adults, Prog for children & young adult, Story hour, Summer reading prog, Tax forms
Partic in OCLC Online Computer Library Center, Inc
Open Mon-Thurs 10-9, Fri & Sat 10-6
Restriction: Lending limited to county residents, Non-resident fee, Open to pub for ref & circ; with some limitations
Branches: 6
CENTERVILLE BRANCH, 45 S 400 West, Centerville, 84014. Tel: 801-294-4054. *Br Librn,* Bradley Maurer; *Circ Supvr,* Nancy Barton
Founded 2006. Circ 337,586
Open Mon-Thurs 10-9, Fri & Sat 10-6
CENTRAL BRANCH, 155 N Wasatch Dr, Layton, 84041, SAN 329-6342. Tel: 801-547-0729. *Br Librn,* Marilyn Getts; *Circ Supvr,* Ellen Peterson; *Ref Supvr,* Meledie Durans
Founded 1988. Circ 488,847
Open Mon-Thurs 10-9, Fri & Sat 10-6
KAYSVILLE BRANCH, 44 N Main St, Kaysville, 84037, SAN 316-8832. Tel: 801-544-2826. FAX: 801-544-5646. *Br Librn,* Lynnette Mills; *Circ Supvr,* Karen Bass
Founded 1920. Circ 298,793
Open Mon-Thurs 10-9, Fri & Sat 10-6
NORTH BRANCH, 562 S 100 East, Clearfield, 84015, SAN 362-4366. Tel: 801-825-6662. *Br Librn,* Patricia York; *Circ Supvr,* Theresa Kimball
Founded 1975. Circ 281,925
Open Mon-Thurs 10-9, Fri & Sat 10-6
NORTHWEST BRANCH, 1875 S 2000 West, Syracuse, 84075-9359. Tel: 801-825-7080. FAX: 801-825-7083. *Br Librn,* Matt Goff; *Circ Supvr,* Lori Gardiner
Founded 2003. Circ 414,045
Open Mon-Thurs 10-9, Fri & Sat 10-6
SOUTH BRANCH, 725 S Main St, Bountiful, 84010, SAN 362-4390. Tel: 801-295-8732. *Br Librn,* Carrie Murphy; *Circ Supvr,* Kimberley Matheson; *Ref Supvr,* Chelsa Echeverria
Founded 1969. Circ 543,725
Open Mon-Thurs 10-9, Fri & Sat 10-6

FILLMORE

P PRESIDENT MILLARD FILLMORE LIBRARY*, 25 S 100 W, 84631. (Mail add: PO Box 529, 84631-0529), SAN 316-8751. Tel: 435-743-5314. FAX: 435-743-6710. E-mail: info@fillmorelibrary.org. *Dir,* Stephanie Aleman
Pop 2,253; Circ 36,561
Library Holdings: Bk Vols 27,000; Per Subs 14
Automation Activity & Vendor Info: (Cataloging) Follett Software; (Circulation) Follett Software; (OPAC) Follett Software
Partic in Pioneer
Open Mon-Thurs 10-6, Fri 10-5, Sat 9-1
Friends of the Library Group

GARLAND

P GARLAND PUBLIC LIBRARY*, 86 W Factory St, 84312. (Mail add: PO Box 147, 84312-0147), SAN 316-876X. Tel: 435-257-3117. FAX: 435-257-1217. E-mail: garlandlib@yahoo.com. *Libr Dir,* Teresa Clark; *Asst Librn,* Danielle Rasmussen; *Ch,* Torie Cutler
Founded 1914. Pop 1,900
Library Holdings: Bk Vols 11,000; Per Subs 23
Subject Interests: Agr, Hist, Lit
Automation Activity & Vendor Info: (Cataloging) Follett Software; (Circulation) Follett Software; (ILL) Follett Software; (OPAC) Follett Software
Partic in Pioneer
Open Tues-Fri 1-7, Sat 10-2
Friends of the Library Group

GUNNISON

P GUNNISON CIVIC LIBRARY*, 38 W Center St, 84634. (Mail add: PO Box 790, 84634-0790), SAN 323-939X. Tel: 435-528-3104. FAX: 435-528-3145. E-mail: gunnlibrary@gunnisoncity.org. Web Site: gunnlibrary.org. *Librn,* Carolyn Childs
Founded 1945. Pop 2,000; Circ 12,074
Library Holdings: Bk Vols 15,000
Automation Activity & Vendor Info: (Cataloging) Follett Software; (Circulation) Follett Software; (OPAC) Follett Software
Open Mon-Wed 1-5, Thurs 3-7, Sat 11-3
Friends of the Library Group

S UTAH DEPARTMENT OF CORRECTIONS*, Central Utah Correctional Facility Library, PO Box 898, 84634-0898. Tel: 435-528-6000. FAX: 435-528-6234. *Librn,* Alvin Hatch; E-mail: ahatch@utah.gov
Library Holdings: Bk Vols 20,000; Per Subs 10
Automation Activity & Vendor Info: (Cataloging) Follett Software; (Circulation) Follett Software

HEBER CITY

P WASATCH COUNTY LIBRARY*, 465 E 1200 South, 84032-3943. SAN 316-8778. Tel: 435-654-1511. FAX: 435-654-6456. Web Site: www.wasatch.lib.ut.us. *Dir,* Kristen Bowcutt; E-mail: kbowcutt@co.wasatch.ut.us; Staff 8 (Non-MLS 8)
Founded 1919. Pop 13,500; Circ 75,000
Library Holdings: Bks on Deafness & Sign Lang 20; Bk Vols 34,500; Per Subs 60
Automation Activity & Vendor Info: (Cataloging) SirsiDynix; (Circulation) SirsiDynix; (OPAC) SirsiDynix
Open Mon-Fri 9:30-8, Sat 9:30-1:30
Friends of the Library Group

HELPER

P HELPER CITY LIBRARY, 19 S Main, 84526. SAN 325-1861. Tel: 435-472-5601. FAX: 435-472-3064. *Librn,* Leila Andrews; Staff 1 (Non-MLS 1)
Founded 1935. Pop 2,200
Library Holdings: Audiobooks 381; AV Mats 200; Bks on Deafness & Sign Lang 26; DVDs 49; Large Print Bks 92; Bk Titles 12,356; Per Subs 21; Talking Bks 381; Videos 285
Automation Activity & Vendor Info: (Cataloging) Follett Software; (Circulation) Follett Software; (OPAC) Follett Software
Wireless access
Partic in Pioneer
Open Mon-Fri 10-6, Sat (Summer) 10-2
Friends of the Library Group

HIGHLAND

P HIGHLAND CITY LIBRARY*, 5400 W Civic Center Dr, Ste 2, 84003. Tel: 801-772-4528. FAX: 801-756-6903. E-mail: highlandlibrary@highlandcity.org. Web Site: highlandcitylibrary.org. *Dir,*

Kent Slade; E-mail: kslade@highlandcity.org; *Asst Librn,* Michelle DeKorver; Staff 5 (MLS 1, Non-MLS 4)
Founded 2008. Pop 15,000; Circ 175,000
Jul 2011-Jun 2012 Income $240,000, City $210,000, Locally Generated Income $30,000. Mats Exp $240,000, Books $25,500, Per/Ser (Incl. Access Fees) $2,000, AV Mat $8,500, Electronic Ref Mat (Incl. Access Fees) $750. Sal $127,369 (Prof $51,000)
Library Holdings: Audiobooks 587; AV Mats 2,246; CDs 155; DVDs 1,384; Large Print Bks 50; Bk Titles 24,335; Bk Vols 28,383; Per Subs 25
Subject Interests: Nutritional supplements
Automation Activity & Vendor Info: (Acquisitions) Polaris Library Systems; (Cataloging) OCLC CatExpress; (Circulation) Polaris Library Systems; (OPAC) Polaris Library Systems; (Serials) Polaris Library Systems
Database Vendor: EBSCOhost, Overdrive, Inc, ProQuest
Wireless access
Function: Audiobks via web, Bks on CD, Children's prog, Free DVD rentals, Handicapped accessible, ILL available, Online cat, OverDrive digital audio bks, Photocopying/Printing, Prog for children & young adult, Pub access computers, Ref serv available, Story hour, Summer reading prog, Teen prog, Wheelchair accessible
Open Mon-Thurs 10-9, Fri & Sat 10-6
Friends of the Library Group

HILL AFB

A UNITED STATES AIR FORCE*, Gerrity Memorial Library, 75 MSG/SVMG, Bldg 440, 7415 Eighth St, 84056-5006. SAN 362-4455. Tel: 801-777-2533, 801-777-3833. FAX: 801-777-6667. *Asst Librn,* Rose Burton; E-mail: rose.burton@hill.af.mil; Staff 5 (MLS 1, Non-MLS 4)
Founded 1941
Library Holdings: Bk Vols 40,404; Per Subs 107
Subject Interests: Aeronautical, Gen coll recreational for adults, Gen coll tech, Space, Western hist
Automation Activity & Vendor Info: (Cataloging) SirsiDynix; (Circulation) SirsiDynix
Wireless access
Open Mon, Fri & Sat 10-6, Tues-Thurs 9-8

HYRUM

P HYRUM LIBRARY*, 50 W Main, 84319. (Mail add: PO Box B, 84319-0310), SAN 316-8794. Tel: 435-245-6411. FAX: 435-245-0180. Web Site: www.hyrumlibrary.com. *Dir,* Virginia Tremayne; *Asst Librn,* Jill Baxter; *Circ Librn,* Diane Harris; *Ch,* Deliliah Sant; *Youth Serv,* Angie Anderson
Founded 1969. Pop 16,500; Circ 309,000
Jul 2008-Jun 2009 Income $216,970, State $7,879, City $198,724, Federal $6,484, Other $3,883. Mats Exp $36,200, Books $26,500, Per/Ser (Incl. Access Fees) $1,200, AV Mat $8,500. Sal $119,776
Library Holdings: Audiobooks 2,160; CDs 1,128; DVDs 1,083; Large Print Bks 173; Bk Vols 46,248; Per Subs 53; Talking Bks 67; Videos 3,723
Subject Interests: Hist
Automation Activity & Vendor Info: (Cataloging) Follett Software; (Circulation) Follett Software; (Course Reserve) Follett Software; (OPAC) Follett Software
Wireless access
Open Mon-Fri 12-7, Sat 2-5

KANAB

P KANAB CITY LIBRARY*, 374 N Main St, 84741-3259. Tel: 435-644-2394, 435-644-3518. FAX: 435-644-2822. E-mail: kancitlib@xpressweb.com. Web Site: kanablibrary.org. *Dir,* Dicki Robinson
Library Holdings: AV Mats 660; Bks on Deafness & Sign Lang 12; CDs 263; DVDs 150; Large Print Bks 57; Bk Titles 32,623; Per Subs 47; Talking Bks 1,247; Videos 1,214
Special Collections: Grandstaircase Oral Histories; South West Coll. Oral History
Subject Interests: Southwest
Automation Activity & Vendor Info: (Acquisitions) Follett Software; (Cataloging) OCLC CatExpress; (Circulation) Follett Software; (Course Reserve) Follett Software; (ILL) OCLC WorldCat; (OPAC) Follett Software
Wireless access
Open Mon & Fri 10-5, Tues-Thurs 10-7, Sat 10-2
Friends of the Library Group

LEHI

P LEHI CITY LIBRARY*, 120 N Center St, 84043. SAN 316-8840. Tel: 801-768-7150. FAX: 801-766-8856. E-mail: library@lehi-ut.gov. Web Site: www.lehicity.com. *Dir,* Kristi Seely; Staff 8 (MLS 1, Non-MLS 7)
Founded 1917. Pop 21,000; Circ 180,000
Library Holdings: Bk Vols 71,000; Per Subs 108
Automation Activity & Vendor Info: (Acquisitions) TLC (The Library Corporation); (Cataloging) TLC (The Library Corporation); (Circulation)

TLC (The Library Corporation); (OPAC) TLC (The Library Corporation); (Serials) TLC (The Library Corporation)
Database Vendor: TLC (The Library Corporation)
Partic in Pioneer
Open Mon-Thurs 9-9, Fri & Sat 10-6

LEWISTON

P　　LEWISTON PUBLIC LIBRARY*, 33 S Main, 84320. (Mail add: PO Box 36, 84320-0036), SAN 316-8859. Tel: 435-258-5515. FAX: 435-258-2141. Web Site: www.lewiston-ut.org. *Dir*, Chris Martinez; E-mail: cmartinez@lewiston-ut.org
Founded 1936. Pop 1,400; Circ 7,299
Library Holdings: Bk Vols 20,000; Per Subs 30
Open Mon, Tues & Thurs 12-7, Wed 9-1 & 6pm-9pm, Fri & Sat 10-3

LOGAN

P　　LOGAN LIBRARY*, 255 N Main, 84321-3914. SAN 316-8867. Tel: 435-716-9123. Circulation Tel: 435-716-9121. Interlibrary Loan Service Tel: 435-716-9129. Reference Tel: 435-716-9120. FAX: 435-716-9145. Web Site: library.loganutah.org. *Dir*, Robert Shupe; Tel: 435-716-9130, E-mail: rshupe@loganutah.org; *Assoc Librn, Genealogy*, Jason Cornelius; Tel: 435-716-9143; *Sr Librn, Tech Serv*, Janet Fiesinger; *Acq*, Karen Clark; *Ch*, Becky Smith; *Computer Serv*, Melanie Liechty; *Electronic Res*, Kara Huggard; *Ref*, Patricia Record; Staff 9 (MLS 7, Non-MLS 2)
Founded 1916. Pop 43,675; Circ 776,295
Library Holdings: Bk Vols 179,293; Per Subs 155
Special Collections: Everton Genealogy Coll
Automation Activity & Vendor Info: (Cataloging) SirsiDynix; (Circulation) SirsiDynix; (OPAC) SirsiDynix
Database Vendor: OCLC FirstSearch, ProQuest, SirsiDynix
Wireless access
Partic in OCLC Online Computer Library Center, Inc
Special Services for the Blind - Internet workstation with adaptive software; Magnifiers
Open Mon-Thurs 10-9, Fri & Sat 10-6
Friends of the Library Group

C　　UTAH STATE UNIVERSITY*, Merrill-Cazier Library, 3000 Old Main Hill, 84322-3000. SAN 362-448X. Tel: 435-797-2631. Circulation Tel: 435-797-2633. Interlibrary Loan Service Tel: 435-797-2680. Reference Tel: 435-797-2678. FAX: 435-797-2880. Interlibrary Loan Service FAX: 435-797-2677. Web Site: library.usu.edu. *Dean of Libr*, Richard Clement; Tel: 435-797-2631, E-mail: richard.clement@usu.edu; *Assoc Dean, Pub Serv*, John Elsweiler; Tel: 435-797-2636, E-mail: john.elsweiler@usu.edu; *Assoc Dean, Tech Serv*, Betty Rozum; Tel: 435-797-2632, E-mail: betty.rozum@usu.edu; *Assoc Dir, Spec Coll & Archives*, Brad Cole; Tel: 435-797-8268, E-mail: brad.cole@usu.edu; *Head, Cat*, Cheryl Adams; Tel: 435-797-2667, E-mail: cheryl.adams@usu.edu; *Head, Coll Develop*, Jennifer Duncan; Tel: 435-797-8148, E-mail: jennifer.duncan@usu.edu; *Head, Digital Libr Serv*, Cheryl Walters; Tel: 435-797-2623, E-mail: cheryl.walters@usu.edu; *Head, Patron Serv*, Vicki Read; Tel: 435-797-2914, E-mail: vicki.read@usu.edu; *Head, Ref*, Flora Shrode; Tel: 435-797-8033, E-mail: flora.shrode@usu.edu; *Head, Govt Doc*, John Walters; Tel: 435-797-2683, E-mail: john.walters@usu.edu; *Bus Mgr*, Becky Olson; E-mail: becky.olson@usu.edu; *Coordr, ILL*, Carol Kochan; Tel: 435-797-2676, E-mail: carol.kochan@usu.edu; *Info Tech*, Todd Hugie; Tel: 435-797-2638, E-mail: todd.hugie@usu.edu; Staff 47 (MLS 35, Non-MLS 12)
Founded 1888. Enrl 24,500; Fac 834; Highest Degree: Doctorate Jul 2005-Jun 2006 Income (Main Library Only) $7,579,000. Mats Exp $3,759,000, Books $625,000, Per/Ser (Incl. Access Fees) $2,489,000, AV Mat $20,000, Electronic Ref Mat (Incl. Access Fees) $625,000. Sal $2,819,000 (Prof $1,872,000)
Library Holdings: AV Mats 39,299; e-books 175,000; e-journals 27,000; Bk Titles 693,239; Bk Vols 1,574,000; Per Subs 12,369
Special Collections: Archives of Society of American Range Management; Berten Wendell Allred Western Americana Library; Blanche Browning Rich Coll, rec; Briant H Stringham Papers, mss; Compton Photograph Coll; Cowboy Poetry Coll; Czechoslovakia (Masaryk Coll & Spencer Taggart Coll); Daryl Chase Coll; Dolly Sitton Bentley Memorial Coll; Edgar B Brossard Papers, mss; Fife Folklore Coll; Frederick P Champ Papers, mss; Gunn McKay Congressional Papers, mss; Hand Folklore Coll; Jack London Coll; Medical Artifacts & Books (Robert & Mary Ann Simmons McDill Coll); Ridgway Coll; Utah Woolgrowers Association Archives, mss; Utah, Mormons & Southern Idaho; Western American Literature (David & Beatrice C Evans Coll); Yoder Folklore Coll. Oral History; State Document Depository; US Document Depository
Subject Interests: Agr, Environ studies, Natural sci, Space studies, Western Am art
Automation Activity & Vendor Info: (Acquisitions) SirsiDynix; (Cataloging) SirsiDynix; (Circulation) SirsiDynix; (Course Reserve) Docutek; (OPAC) SirsiDynix; (Serials) SirsiDynix

Database Vendor: Dialog, EBSCOhost, LexisNexis, OVID Technologies, ProQuest, SirsiDynix, Wilson - Wilson Web
Partic in Utah Academic Library Consortium
Friends of the Library Group
Departmental Libraries:
ANN CARROLL MOORE CHILDREN'S LIBRARY, 6700 Old Main Hill, 84322. Tel: 435-797-3093. *Librn*, Vaughn Larson
　Library Holdings: Bk Vols 21,501
　Partic in Greater Western Library Alliance
　Open Mon-Thurs 7-Midnight, Fri 7-6, Sat 11-7, Sun 11-Midnight
REGIONAL DEPOSITORY COLLECTION OF US GOVERNMENT DOCUMENTS, 3000 Old Main Hill, 84322-3000. Tel: 435-797-2684. *Head, Doc Serv*, John Walters; Tel: 435-797-2683, E-mail: john.walters@usu.edu; *Librn*, Stephen Weiss; Tel: 435-797-3661, E-mail: steve.weiss@usu.edu
　Open Mon-Fri 8-5
YOUNG EDUCATIONAL TECHNOLOGY CENTER, UMC 2845 - 170 EDUC, Utah State University, 84322-2845. Tel: 435-797-3377. *Librn*, Nathan M Smith

MANTI

P　　MANTI PUBLIC LIBRARY*, Two S Main St, 84642-1349. SAN 316-8883. Tel: 435-835-2201. FAX: 435-835-2202. Web Site: www.mantiutah.org/manti_city/library.html. *Dir*, Connie Alder; Staff 3 (Non-MLS 3)
Founded 1910. Pop 3,500; Circ 23,000
Library Holdings: Bk Vols 25,240; Per Subs 38
Subject Interests: Local hist
Automation Activity & Vendor Info: (Cataloging) ComPanion Corp; (Circulation) ComPanion Corp; (Course Reserve) ComPanion Corp; (OPAC) ComPanion Corp
Wireless access
Partic in Pioneer
Open Mon-Fri 10-7, Sat 10-3
Friends of the Library Group

MILFORD

P　　MILFORD PUBLIC LIBRARY*, 400 S 100 West, 84751. (Mail add: PO Box 69, 84751-0069). Tel: 435-387-5039. FAX: 435-387-5027. *Librn*, Sherri Yardley; E-mail: sherbear51@hotmail.com
Library Holdings: AV Mats 519; Bk Vols 17,761; Talking Bks 267
Automation Activity & Vendor Info: (Cataloging) Follett Software; (Circulation) Follett Software
Open Mon-Fri 11-6

MINERSVILLE

P　　MINERSVILLE PUBLIC LIBRARY*, 40 W Main St, 84752. (Mail add: PO Box 250, 84752-0250). Tel: 435-386-2267. FAX: 435-386-1813. E-mail: mlibrary@infowest.com. *Dir*, Melinda C Dalton
Library Holdings: Bk Vols 10,000; Talking Bks 200
Automation Activity & Vendor Info: (Cataloging) Follett Software; (Circulation) Follett Software
Database Vendor: OCLC FirstSearch
Open Mon 1-7, Tues-Fri 1-5

MOAB

P　　GRAND COUNTY PUBLIC LIBRARY*, 257 E Center St, 84532. SAN 316-8891. Tel: 435-259-5421. FAX: 435-259-1380. E-mail: info@moablibrary.org. Web Site: www.moablibrary.org. *Dir*, Carrie Valdes; Staff 7 (MLS 1, Non-MLS 6)
Founded 1912. Pop 8,500; Circ 140,000
Library Holdings: Audiobooks 2,070; AV Mats 6,128; Bks on Deafness & Sign Lang 20; CDs 846; DVDs 1,615; Large Print Bks 924; Bk Titles 44,469; Bk Vols 49,465; Per Subs 105; Videos 1,728
Special Collections: Foundation Center (Grantwriting Resources); Mountaineering (Chouinard Coll)
Subject Interests: Hispanic
Automation Activity & Vendor Info: (Cataloging) LibLime; (Circulation) LibLime; (OPAC) LibLime
Wireless access
Partic in Pioneer
Special Services for the Deaf - Assistive tech
Special Services for the Blind - Assistive/Adapted tech devices, equip & products
Open Mon-Fri 9-8, Sat 9-5
Friends of the Library Group

MONROE

P　　MONROE PUBLIC LIBRARY, 55 N Main St, 84754. (Mail add: PO Box 120, 84754-0120). Tel: 435-527-4019. FAX: 435-527-4622. E-mail: monroecitylibrary@yahoo.com. Web Site: monroecitylibrary.booksys.net.

Dir, Sandra Spendlove; E-mail: monroedirector@yahoo.com; Staff 4 (Non-MLS 4)

Founded 1928. Pop 2,256; Circ 11,462

Library Holdings: Bk Vols 11,000; Per Subs 12; Talking Bks 900

Automation Activity & Vendor Info: (Cataloging) Book Systems, Inc; (Circulation) Book Systems, Inc; (OPAC) Book Systems, Inc

Wireless access

Function: Bks on CD, Children's prog, Computers for patron use, Copy machines, Free DVD rentals, Handicapped accessible, ILL available, Online cat, OverDrive digital audio bks, Photocopying/Printing, Preschool reading prog, Summer reading prog, VHS videos

Open Tues-Sat 1-6

MONTICELLO

P   SAN JUAN COUNTY LIBRARY*, Monticello Branch, 80 N Main St, 84535. (Mail add: PO Box 66, 84535-0066), SAN 362-4609. Tel: 435-587-2281. FAX: 435-587-2281. E-mail: mlibrary@sanjuancounty.org. Web Site: www.sanjuancounty.org/library.html. *Librn,* Rick Richardson

Pop 9,606; Circ 18,800

Library Holdings: Bk Vols 18,603; Per Subs 45

Automation Activity & Vendor Info: (Cataloging) Follett Software; (Circulation) Follett Software

Open Mon-Sat 1:30-9

Branches: 1

BLANDING BRANCH, 25 W 300 South, Blanding, 84511-3829, SAN 362-4633. Tel: 435-678-2335. FAX: 435-678-2335. E-mail: blibrary@sanjuancounty.org. *Dir,* Lana Latham

Library Holdings: Bk Vols 12,500; Per Subs 40

Open Mon-Thurs 12-7, Fri 2-6, Sat 10-2

MORGAN

P   MORGAN COUNTY LIBRARY*, 50 N 100 W, 84050. (Mail add: PO Box 600, 84050-0600), SAN 316-8905. Tel: 801-829-3481. FAX: 801-829-6176. *Dir,* Valerie Hancock; Staff 3.4 (Non-MLS 3.4)

Pop 8,909; Circ 93,065

Library Holdings: Bk Vols 30,871; Per Subs 49

Special Collections: Morgan County Historical Society Coll

Automation Activity & Vendor Info: (Acquisitions) Follett Software; (Cataloging) Follett Software; (Circulation) Follett Software; (OPAC) Follett Software

Database Vendor: EBSCOhost

Wireless access

Open Mon-Thurs 12-7, Fri & Sat 12-5

Friends of the Library Group

MOUNT PLEASANT

P   MT PLEASANT PUBLIC LIBRARY*, 24 E Main St, 84647-1429. SAN 316-8913. Tel: 435-462-3240. FAX: 435-462-9115. E-mail: mtpleasantlib@gmail.com. Web Site: www.mtpleasantlib.org. *Libr Dir,* Laurie Hansen; E-mail: lauriemplibrary@gmail.com

Founded 1917. Circ 60,987

Library Holdings: Bk Vols 23,000

Automation Activity & Vendor Info: (Cataloging) Follett Software; (Circulation) Follett Software; (OPAC) Follett Software

Function: After school storytime, Audiobks via web, Bks on cassette, Bks on CD, CD-ROM, Children's prog, Computer training, Computers for patron use, Copy machines, Digital talking bks, Doc delivery serv, e-mail & chat, e-mail serv, Electronic databases & coll, Fax serv, Free DVD rentals, Holiday prog, ILL available, Instruction & testing, Mail & tel request accepted, Music CDs, Newsp ref libr, Online cat, Online ref, Online searches, Outside serv via phone, mail, e-mail & web, OverDrive digital audio bks, Photocopying/Printing, Preschool reading prog, Prog for children & young adult, Pub access computers, Ref & res, Ref serv available, Ref serv in person, Scanner, Spoken cassettes & CDs, Spoken cassettes & DVDs, Story hour, Summer reading prog, Tax forms, Teen prog, VCDs, VHS videos, Video lending libr, Web-catalog

Open Mon-Thurs 10:30-8, Sat 12-4

Friends of the Library Group

MURRAY

P   MURRAY PUBLIC LIBRARY*, 166 E 5300 South, 84107-6075. SAN 362-4668. Tel: 801-264-2580. FAX: 801-264-2586. Web Site: www.murraylibrary.org. *Dir,* Daniel J Barr; Tel: 801-264-2585, E-mail: dbarr@murray.utah.gov; *Asst Dir,* Danny O'Rourke; *Circ Supvr,* Sharon Williams; *Adult Serv,* David Brown; *Cat,* Helene Richardson; *Ch,* Ellen Wells; Staff 15 (MLS 4, Non-MLS 11)

Founded 1910. Pop 34,024; Circ 265,084

Library Holdings: AV Mats 9,200; Bk Titles 72,000; Per Subs 116

Automation Activity & Vendor Info: (Cataloging) SirsiDynix; (Circulation) SirsiDynix; (OPAC) SirsiDynix

Open Mon-Thurs 10-9, Fri & Sat 10-6

Friends of the Library Group

NEPHI

P   NEPHI PUBLIC LIBRARY*, 21 E First N, 84648-1501. SAN 316-8921. Tel: 435-623-1312. FAX: 435-623-5443. *Librn,* Barbara Lovell; E-mail: blovell@nephi.utah.gov; *Ch,* Deborah Hall; E-mail: dwhall@nephi.utah.gov; Staff 4 (Non-MLS 4)

Pop 5,045; Circ 60,760

Library Holdings: Bks on Deafness & Sign Lang 10; Large Print Bks 15; Bk Titles 24,030; Talking Bks 1,515; Videos 601

Automation Activity & Vendor Info: (Cataloging) Follett Software; (Circulation) Follett Software

Open Mon-Thurs 11-7, Fri 1-5, Sat 10-2

Friends of the Library Group

NEWTON

P   NEWTON TOWN LIBRARY, 51 South Center St, 84327. Tel: 435-563-9283. E-mail: newtonlib@comcast.net. Web Site: home.comcast.net~newtonlib. *Dir,* Sarah Rigby; *Librn,* Cheri Ballard; *Librn,* Michelle Furgeson

Library Holdings: AV Mats 142; Bk Vols 15,000

Open Mon 3-7, Tues & Wed 3-6, Thurs 10-1 & 3-7, Sat 12-4

NORTH LOGAN

P   NORTH LOGAN CITY LIBRARY*, 475 E 2500 North, 84341-1523. Tel: 435-755-7169. FAX: 435-227-0032. Web Site: www.northloganlibrary.org. *Dir,* Sue Randleman; Tel: 435-755-7091, E-mail: quackonover@yahoo.com; Staff 3 (MLS 2, Non-MLS 1)

Pop 9,683; Circ 215,866; Fac 8

Library Holdings: Bk Vols 54,000; Per Subs 78

Automation Activity & Vendor Info: (Cataloging) Follett Software; (Circulation) Follett Software

Open Mon 12-4, Tues-Fri 10-7, Sat 12-4

Friends of the Library Group

OGDEN

C   STEVENS HENAGER COLLEGE LIBRARY*, 1890 S 1350 W, 84401. (Mail add: PO Box 9428, 84409-0428), SAN 316-8956. Tel: 801-622-1567. FAX: 801-621-0853. *Admin Dir,* Marjorie Anderson; E-mail: marjorie.anderson@stevenshenager.edu; Staff 1 (Non-MLS 1)

Founded 1891. Enrl 800; Highest Degree: Master

Library Holdings: Audiobooks 25; DVDs 200; e-books 50; High Interest/Low Vocabulary Bk Vols 150; Bk Titles 1,800; Per Subs 110; Talking Bks 15; Videos 450

Subject Interests: Acctg, Bus, Computers, Graphic arts, Med, Nursing

Database Vendor: Cinahl Information Systems, EBSCOhost, LearningExpress, Newsbank, ProQuest

Wireless access

Function: Audio & video playback equip for onsite use, Computer training, Copy machines, Distance learning, Handicapped accessible, Homework prog, Learning ctr, Online ref, Online searches, Orientations, VHS videos

Partic in Utah Libr Asn

Open Mon-Thurs 8am-10pm, Fri 8-5

Restriction: Open to students, fac & staff

G   UTAH SCHOOL FOR THE DEAF & BLIND*, Educational Resource Center, 742 Harrison Blvd, 84404. SAN 323-7281. Tel: 801-629-4817. FAX: 801-629-4896. Web Site: www.usdb.org. *Dir,* Hollie Murdock; *Librn,* Mary Jo White

Library Holdings: Bk Titles 30,000; Bk Vols 37,000; Per Subs 10

Automation Activity & Vendor Info: (Cataloging) Follett Software; (Circulation) Follett Software

Open Mon-Fri 8-5

Branches:

EDUCATIONAL RESOURCE CENTER - SALT LAKE EXTENSION, 1655 E 3300 South, Salt Lake City, 84106. Tel: 801-464-2040. FAX: 801-464-2016. *Librn,* Position Currently Open

Library Holdings: Bk Vols 30,000

Open Mon-Fri 8-4:45

P   WEBER COUNTY LIBRARY SYSTEM*, 2464 Jefferson Ave, 84401-2464. SAN 362-4722. Tel: 801-337-2617. Toll Free Tel: 888-618-0564. FAX: 801-337-2615. TDD: 801-337-2614. Web Site: www.weberpl.lib.ut.us. *Dir,* Lynnda Wangsgard; *Assoc Dir,* Karen Burton; *Asst Dir,* Scott Jones; *Asst Dir,* Kevin Pendleton; *Circ Mgr,* Brannigan Cheney; *Tech Serv Mgr,* Monyee Yip; Staff 21 (MLS 20, Non-MLS 1)

Founded 1903. Pop 213,247; Circ 1,346,481

Jan 2007-Dec 2007 Income (Main Library and Branch(s)) $7,002,620, State $41,252, Federal $3,769, County $6,835,806, Locally Generated Income $121,793. Mats Exp $1,008,647, Books $706,469, Per/Ser (Incl. Access Fees) $37,363, Other Print Mats $1,203, Micro $30,367, AV Mat

$143,241, Electronic Ref Mat (Incl. Access Fees) $90,004. Sal $3,310,883 (Prof $1,281,683)

Library Holdings: Audiobooks 8,591; AV Mats 40,097; Bks on Deafness & Sign Lang 496; CDs 21,965; DVDs 9,908; High Interest/Low Vocabulary Bk Vols 1,072; Large Print Bks 4,293; Microforms 11,644; Music Scores 405; Bk Titles 169,824; Bk Vols 329,696; Per Subs 998; Talking Bks 8,591; Videos 13,962

Special Collections: Utah & Western History (Ava J Cooper Spec Coll)

Automation Activity & Vendor Info: (Acquisitions) Innovative Interfaces, Inc; (Cataloging) Innovative Interfaces, Inc; (Circulation) Innovative Interfaces, Inc; (ILL) OCLC; (OPAC) Innovative Interfaces, Inc; (Serials) Innovative Interfaces, Inc

Database Vendor: ALLDATA Online, Baker & Taylor, Bowker, CQ Press, EBSCO Auto Repair Reference, EBSCOhost, Gale Cengage Learning, Grolier Online, H W Wilson, Innovative Interfaces, Inc, LearningExpress, LexisNexis, OCLC FirstSearch, ReferenceUSA, Westlaw, Wilson - Wilson Web, World Book Online

Wireless access

Special Services for the Deaf - Bks on deafness & sign lang; TDD equip; TTY equip

Special Services for the Blind - Assistive/Adapted tech devices, equip & products; Closed circuit TV; Radio reading serv

Open Mon-Thurs 10-9, Fri & Sat 10-6, Sun 1-5

Friends of the Library Group

Branches: 3

NORTH BRANCH, 475 E 2600 North, North Ogden, 84414-2833, SAN 362-4765. Tel: 801-782-8800. FAX: 801-782-8801. *Librn,* Ann Booth; Staff 3 (MLS 3)

Pop 44,887; Circ 197,070

Library Holdings: AV Mats 5,428; Bks on Deafness & Sign Lang 120; High Interest/Low Vocabulary Bk Vols 323; Large Print Bks 582; Bk Titles 49,299; Bk Vols 55,562; Per Subs 80; Talking Bks 5,428

Open Mon-Thurs 10-9, Fri & Sat 10-6, Sun 1-5

Friends of the Library Group

OGDEN VALLEY BRANCH, 131 S 7400 East, Huntsville, 84317-9309, SAN 377-0281. Tel: 801-745-2220. FAX: 801-745-2221. *Librn,* Karen Burton; Staff 2 (MLS 2)

Pop 3,609; Circ 73,235

Library Holdings: AV Mats 4,851; Bks on Deafness & Sign Lang 75; High Interest/Low Vocabulary Bk Vols 260; Large Print Bks 286; Bk Titles 43,157; Bk Vols 47,419; Per Subs 110; Talking Bks 1,057

Open Mon-Thurs 10-9, Fri & Sat 10-6, Sun 1-5

Friends of the Library Group

SOUTHWEST BRANCH, 1950 W 4800 South, Roy, 84067-2627, SAN 362-4781. Tel: 801-773-2556. FAX: 801-773-2557. *Librn,* Vernon Waters; Staff 2 (MLS 2)

Pop 59,302; Circ 179,962

Library Holdings: AV Mats 6,034; Bks on Deafness & Sign Lang 90; High Interest/Low Vocabulary Bk Vols 113; Large Print Bks 474; Bk Titles 44,985; Bk Vols 50,528; Per Subs 90; Talking Bks 1,199

Open Mon-Thurs 10-9, Fri & Sat 10-6

Friends of the Library Group

C WEBER STATE UNIVERSITY*, Stewart Library, 2901 University Circle, 84408-2901. SAN 316-8972. Tel: 801-626-6403. Circulation Tel: 801-626-6545. Interlibrary Loan Service Tel: 801-626-6384. Reference Tel: 801-626-6415. Toll Free Tel: 877-306-3140. FAX: 801-626-7045. Interlibrary Loan Service FAX: 801-626-8521. Web Site: library.weber.edu. *Univ Librn,* Joan Hubbard; Tel: 801-626-6405, E-mail: jhubbard@weber.edu; *Head, Cat,* Stella Chang; Tel: 801-626-6869, E-mail: schang@weber.edu; *Head, Circ,* Sandi Andrews; Tel: 801-626-6546, E-mail: sandrews@weber.edu; *Head, Ref,* Kathy Payne; Tel: 801-626-6511, E-mail: klpayne@weber.edu; *Bus Librn,* Edward Hahn; Tel: 801-626-8662, E-mail: edwardhahn@weber.edu; *Curator, Spec Coll & Archives Librn,* John Sillito; *Instrul Serv Librn,* Carol Hansen; Tel: 801-626-8709, E-mail: chansen@weber.edu; *ILL, Media Coordr,* Misty Allen; Tel: 801-626-7820, E-mail: mallen4@weber.edu; *Syst Adminr,* Chris Hauser; Tel: 801-626-6104, E-mail: chauser@weber.edu; *G* Megan Davis; Tel: 801-626-6069, E-mail: megandavis1@weber.edu. Subject Specialists: *Art, Humanities,* Joan Hubbard; *Econ,* Edward Hahn; *Hist, Relig, Women studies,* John Sillito; *Educ,* Evan Christensen; *Applied sci, Phys sci,* JaNae Kinikin; *Behav sci,* Wade Kotter; Staff 46 (MLS 15, Non-MLS 31) Founded 1924. Enrl 18,821; Fac 450; Highest Degree: Master

Library Holdings: Bk Vols 533,759; Per Subs 1,711

Special Collections: Hyrum & Ruby Wheelwright Coll (Mormon Literature); James A Howell Coll (Literature); Utah Construction/Utah International Coll. State Document Depository; US Document Depository

Automation Activity & Vendor Info: (Acquisitions) SirsiDynix; (Cataloging) SirsiDynix; (Circulation) SirsiDynix; (Course Reserve) SirsiDynix; (ILL) OCLC; (Media Booking) SirsiDynix; (OPAC) SirsiDynix; (Serials) SirsiDynix

Database Vendor: EBSCOhost, LexisNexis, OCLC FirstSearch, OVID Technologies, ProQuest, SirsiDynix, TLC (The Library Corporation), Wilson - Wilson Web

Wireless access

Publications: Colophon, Friends of the Stewart Library Newsletter

Partic in Dialog Corp; OCLC Online Computer Library Center, Inc; Utah Academic Library Consortium

Open Mon-Thurs 7am-11pm, Fri 7am-8pm, Sat 9-8, Sun 1-9

Friends of the Library Group

OREM

P OREM PUBLIC LIBRARY*, 58 N State St, 84057-5596. SAN 316-8980. Tel: 801-229-7050. Interlibrary Loan Service Tel: 801-229-7175. FAX: 801-229-7130. TDD: 801-229-7104. Web Site: www.oremlibrary.org. *Dir,* Louise Wallace; E-mail: lgwallace@orem.org; *Div Mgr,* Megan Spencer; *Cat,* Dale Burns; *Cat,* Sue Phelps; *Cat,* Evelyn Schmidt; *Ch,* Patricia Castelli; *Info Tech,* Clarke Hoover; *Media Spec,* James Scarborough; *Outreach Prog,* Janet Low; *Teen Serv,* Lanell Reeder; Staff 44 (MLS 8, Non-MLS 36) Founded 1940. Pop 84,324; Circ 1,398,697

Library Holdings: Bk Vols 280,000; Per Subs 255

Subject Interests: Flm classics, Relig studies

Automation Activity & Vendor Info: (Acquisitions) SirsiDynix; (Cataloging) SirsiDynix; (Circulation) SirsiDynix; (OPAC) SirsiDynix

Database Vendor: EBSCOhost, Factiva.com, Newsbank, SirsiDynix

Partic in Pioneer

Open Mon-Fri 9-9, Sat 9-6

Friends of the Library Group

C UTAH VALLEY UNIVERSITY LIBRARY, 800 W University Pkwy, 84058-5999. Tel: 801-863-8751. Circulation Tel: 801-863-8886. Reference Tel: 801-863-8840. FAX: 801-863-7065. Web Site: www.uvu.edu/library. *Dir of Libr,* Michael J Freeman; E-mail: michael.freeman@uvu.edu; *Asst Dir, Pub Serv,* Lesli Baker; Tel: 801-863-8286, E-mail: bakerle@uvu.edu; *Asst Dir, Syst & Tech Serv,* Tim Rowley; Tel: 801-863-8107, E-mail: rowleyti@uvu.edu; *Res Serv Librn,* Jacques D'Emal; Tel: 801-863-8058, E-mail: demalja@uvu.edu; *Bibliog Instr,* Benjamin Wilson; Tel: 801-863-8423, E-mail: wilsonbn@uvu.edu; *Media Spec,* Trevor Young; Tel: 801-863-6846, E-mail: youngtr@uvu.edu; *Ref,* Annie Smith; Tel: 801-863-8752, E-mail: smithan@uvu.edu; *Ref,* Kim Rollins; Tel: 801-863-7326, E-mail: Kim.Rollins@uvu.edu; *Ref Serv, Ad,* Debbie Short; Tel: 801-863-6336, E-mail: shortde@uvu.edu; *Spec Coll,* Catherine McIntyre; Tel: 801-863-8821, E-mail: mcintyca@uvu.edu; *Syst,* Mark Stevens; Tel: 801-863-8155, E-mail: stevenma@uvu.edu; *Tech Serv,* Keith Rowley; Tel: 801-863-8780, E-mail: rowleyke@uvu.edu. Subject Specialists: *Math,* Michael J Freeman; *Educ,* Lesli Baker; *Eng, Trades,* Tim Rowley; *Psychol, Sociol,* Jacques D'Emal; *Bus, Criminal justice,* Benjamin Wilson; *Sci,* Trevor Young; *Lit,* Annie Smith; *Commun, Dance, Theatre,* Kim Rollins; *Health, Nursing,* Debbie Short; *Hist, Polit sci,* Catherine McIntyre; *Computer sci,* Mark Stevens; *Arts, Philosophy, Relig,* Keith Rowley; Staff 15 (MLS 12, Non-MLS 3) Founded 1978. Enrl 33,395; Fac 519; Highest Degree: Master Jul 2010-Jun 2011 Income $3,134,000, State $220,000, Parent Institution $2,914,000. Mats Exp $788,000, Books $290,000, Per/Ser (Incl. Access Fees) $439,000, AV Equip $5,000, AV Mat $30,000, Electronic Ref Mat (Incl. Access Fees) $24,000. Sal $1,154,000 (Prof $719,000)

Library Holdings: Bks on Deafness & Sign Lang 683; CDs 5,411; DVDs 19,527; e-books 16,477; e-journals 68,000; Microforms 800; Music Scores 2,215; Bk Vols 212,102; Per Subs 532

Special Collections: Ethics; LDS Religion Coll. Oral History

Subject Interests: Computer sci, Educ, Lit, Trades

Automation Activity & Vendor Info: (Acquisitions) SirsiDynix; (Cataloging) SirsiDynix; (Circulation) SirsiDynix; (Course Reserve) SirsiDynix; (ILL) OCLC ILLiad; (OPAC) SirsiDynix; (Serials) SirsiDynix

Database Vendor: ACM (Association for Computing Machinery), Alexander Street Press, American Chemical Society, American Mathematical Society, Dialog, ebrary, EBSCOhost, Gale Cengage Learning, IEEE (Institute of Electrical & Electronics Engineers), JSTOR, LexisNexis, netLibrary, OVID Technologies, Oxford Online, Project MUSE, ProQuest, PubMed, Safari Books Online, Sage, ScienceDirect, SirsiDynix, Wilson - Wilson Web

Wireless access

Function: Art exhibits, Computer training, Computers for patron use, Copy machines, Doc delivery serv, e-mail & chat, e-mail serv, E-Reserves, Electronic databases & coll, Equip loans & repairs, Exhibits, Fax serv, Free DVD rentals, Games & aids for the handicapped, Handicapped accessible, ILL available, Instruction & testing, Music CDs, Online cat, Online info literacy tutorials on the web & in blackboard, Online ref, Online searches, Orientations, Outside serv via phone, mail, e-mail & web, Photocopying/Printing, Pub access computers, Ref & res, Ref serv available, Ref serv in person, Referrals accepted, Res libr, Telephone ref, VHS videos, Video lending libr, Web-catalog, Wheelchair accessible, Workshops, Writing prog

Partic in Utah Academic Library Consortium

PANGUITCH

P   GARFIELD COUNTY-PANGUITCH CITY LIBRARY, 25 S 200 E, 84759. (Mail add: PO Box 75, 84759-0075), SAN 377-2780. Tel: 435-676-2431. FAX: 435-676-2758. E-mail: info@panguitchlibrary.org (www.panguitchlibrary.org). Web Site: www.panguitchlibrary.org. *Librn,* Brinda Bair
Pop 1,500
Library Holdings: Bk Vols 48,000
Automation Activity & Vendor Info: (Circulation) SIRSI WorkFlows; (OPAC) SIRSI WorkFlows
Wireless access
Partic in Pioneer; Utah Libr Asn
Special Services for the Blind - Home delivery serv
Open Mon-Fri 1-6
Branches: 1
ESCALANTE BRANCH, 90 N 100 West, Escalante, 84726. (Mail add: PO Box 173, Escalante, 84726-0173). Tel: 435-826-4220. Web Site: library.utah.gov/panguitch.html. *Br Mgr,* Raymond Christian
   Library Holdings: Bk Vols 15,000
   Open Mon-Thurs 3-5 & 6pm-8pm, Fri 10-12 & 1-3

PARK CITY

P   PARK CITY LIBRARY*, 1255 Park Ave, 84060. (Mail add: PO Box 668, 84060-0668), SAN 322-6794. Tel: 435-615-5600. FAX: 435-615-4903. Web Site: www.parkcitylibrary.org. *Dir,* Linda L Tillson; Tel: 435-615-5605, E-mail: ltillson@parkcity.org; *Ref Serv, Ad,* Jasmina Jusic; Tel: 435-615-5602, E-mail: jasmina.jusic@parkcity.org; *Youth Serv,* Heather Reynolds; Tel: 435-615-5603, E-mail: hreynolds@parkcity.org; Staff 14 (MLS 4, Non-MLS 10)
Founded 1917. Pop 8,044; Circ 89,174
Library Holdings: Bk Vols 71,164; Per Subs 196
Special Collections: Park City History Coll; Skiing Coll
Subject Interests: Local hist
Automation Activity & Vendor Info: (OPAC) TLC (The Library Corporation)
Database Vendor: EBSCOhost, ReferenceUSA
Wireless access
Function: Art exhibits, Audio & video playback equip for onsite use, Audiobks via web, Bks on cassette, Bks on CD, Children's prog, Computers for patron use, Copy machines, e-mail serv, Electronic databases & coll, Free DVD rentals, Handicapped accessible, ILL available, Magnifiers for reading, Music CDs, Online cat, OverDrive digital audio bks, Prog for adults, Prog for children & young adult, Pub access computers, Senior computer classes, Spoken cassettes & CDs, Spoken cassettes & DVDs, Story hour, Summer reading prog, Tax forms, Teen prog, VHS videos, Web-catalog
Partic in OCLC Online Computer Library Center, Inc
Open Mon-Thurs 10-9, Fri & Sat 10-6, Sun 1-5
Friends of the Library Group

P   SUMMIT COUNTY LIBRARY*, 6505 N Landmark Dr, Ste 100, 84098-6009. Tel: 435-615-3900. FAX: 435-615-3905. Web Site: library.utah.gov/summit.html, www.summit.lib.ut.us. *Dir,* Diana Skousen; Tel: 435-615-3902, E-mail: dskousen@co.summit.ut.us; *Tech Serv,* Pat Darcey; Tel: 435-615-3901, E-mail: pdarcey@co.summit.ut.us; *Youth Serv,* Linda Schmida; Tel: 435-615-3903, E-mail: lschmida@co.summit.ut.us
Pop 26,935
Jan 2005-Dec 2005 Income (Main Library and Branch(s)) $823,336. Mats Exp $111,500, Books $77,000, Per/Ser (Incl. Access Fees) $9,500, AV Mat $25,000. Sal $345,000
Library Holdings: Large Print Bks 125; Bk Titles 47,222; Per Subs 84
Wireless access
Open Mon-Thurs 10-8, Fri & Sat 10-6
Friends of the Library Group
Branches: 2
COALVILLE BRANCH, 10 N Main, Coalville, 84017. (Mail add: PO Box 206, Coalville, 84017-0206). Tel: 435-336-3070. FAX: 435-336-2062. *Br Mgr,* Yvonne Judd; E-mail: yjudd@co.summit.ut.us
   Library Holdings: Bk Titles 12,867; Per Subs 34
   Open Mon-Thurs 10-6, Fri-Sat 10-3
KAMAS BRANCH, 110 N Main, Kamas, 84036. (Mail add: PO Box 1053, Kamas, 84036-1053). Tel: 435-783-4351, Ext 3080. FAX: 435-783-6693. *Br Mgr,* Donna Davis; Tel: 435-615-3080, E-mail: ddavis@co.summit.ut.us
   Library Holdings: Bk Titles 23,019; Per Subs 43
   Open Mon-Thurs 10-7, Fri 10-5, Sat 10-3
Bookmobiles: 1. Outreach Servs Librn, Dennis Willie

PAROWAN

P   PAROWAN PUBLIC LIBRARY*, 16 S Main St, 84761. (Mail add: PO Box 427, 84761-0427), SAN 316-8999. Tel: 435-477-3491. FAX: 435-477-8671. *Librn,* Kristen Robinson
Founded 1915. Pop 2,200; Circ 57,208

Library Holdings: AV Mats 498; Bk Titles 25,000; Per Subs 55
Subject Interests: Hist of Parowan
Automation Activity & Vendor Info: (Acquisitions) Follett Software; (Cataloging) Follett Software; (Circulation) Follett Software; (ILL) Follett Software; (Media Booking) Follett Software; (OPAC) Follett Software; (Serials) Follett Software
Partic in Pioneer
Open Mon, Wed & Thurs 1-9, Tues & Fri 10-9, Sat 10-6

PAYSON

P   PAYSON CITY LIBRARY*, 66 S Main St, 84651-2223. SAN 316-9006. Tel: 801-465-5220. FAX: 801-465-5208. Web Site: payson.org. *Dir,* Linda Collard; E-mail: lindac@payson.org; *Ch,* Sherry Gay
Founded 1878. Pop 9,776; Circ 41,413
Library Holdings: Bk Vols 38,580; Per Subs 74
Special Collections: US Constitution Materials Coll
Automation Activity & Vendor Info: (Cataloging) Follett Software; (Circulation) Follett Software; (OPAC) Follett Software
Partic in Pioneer
Open Mon-Thurs 10-8, Fri & Sat 11-5
Friends of the Library Group

PLEASANT GROVE

P   PLEASANT GROVE PUBLIC LIBRARY*, 30 E Center St, 84062-2234. SAN 316-9014. Tel: 801-785-3950. FAX: 801-785-9734. Web Site: www.plgrove.org/library/index.html. *Librn,* April H Harrison; E-mail: harrison.ah@gmail.com
Pop 23,000; Circ 210,000
Library Holdings: Bk Vols 85,000; Per Subs 50
Subject Interests: Local hist
Automation Activity & Vendor Info: (Acquisitions) SirsiDynix; (Cataloging) SirsiDynix; (Circulation) SirsiDynix; (OPAC) SirsiDynix; (Serials) SirsiDynix
Open Mon-Thurs 10-9, Fri & Sat 10-6
Friends of the Library Group

PRICE

J   COLLEGE OF EASTERN UTAH LIBRARY*, 451 E & 400 N, 84501. SAN 316-9030. Tel: 435-613-5209, 435-637-2120. FAX: 435-613-5863. Web Site: www.ceu.edu/library. *Dir,* Lori Brassaw; Tel: 435-613-5328, E-mail: lori.brassaw@ceu.edu; *Acq,* Denise Reid; Tel: 435-613-5278, E-mail: denise.reid@ceu.edu; *Cat,* Sherill Shaw; Tel: 435-613-5208, E-mail: sherill.shaw@ceu.edu; *Circ,* Aimee Lauritsen; Tel: 435-613-5646, E-mail: aimee.lauritsen@ceu.edu; Staff 6 (MLS 2, Non-MLS 4)
Founded 1938. Enrl 1,250; Fac 70; Highest Degree: Associate
Library Holdings: Bk Vols 50,000; Per Subs 100
Subject Interests: Local hist, Utah hist
Automation Activity & Vendor Info: (Acquisitions) SirsiDynix; (Cataloging) SirsiDynix; (Circulation) SirsiDynix; (Course Reserve) SirsiDynix; (ILL) OCLC FirstSearch; (OPAC) SirsiDynix; (Serials) SirsiDynix
Database Vendor: Agricola, ALLDATA Online, American Chemical Society, American Mathematical Society, American Physical Society, BioOne, Canadian Reference Centre, Cinahl Information Systems, CIOS (Communication Institute for Online Scholarship), CISTI Source, CQ Press, CRC Press/Taylor & Francis CRCnetBASE, ebrary, EBSCO Auto Repair Reference, EBSCOhost, H W Wilson, IEEE (Institute of Electrical & Electronics Engineers), JSTOR, netLibrary, OCLC FirstSearch, OCLC WorldCat, OVID Technologies, ProQuest, ReferenceUSA, Safari Books Online, SirsiDynix, WebFeat
Wireless access
Partic in Utah Academic Library Consortium
Special Services for the Deaf - TTY equip
Special Services for the Blind - Reader equip
Open Mon-Thurs 8am-10pm, Fri 8-5, Sat 10-6, Sun 2-10
Friends of the Library Group

P   PRICE CITY LIBRARY*, 159 E Main St, 84501-3046. SAN 316-9049. Tel: 435-636-3188. FAX: 435-637-2905. Web Site: www.priceutah.net. *Librn,* Norma Rae Procarione; E-mail: norma@priceutah.net; *Asst Librn,* Diana Bordea
Founded 1914. Pop 8,000; Circ 40,000
Library Holdings: Bk Vols 50,000; Per Subs 52
Subject Interests: Heritage, Local hist
Automation Activity & Vendor Info: (Cataloging) Follett Software; (Circulation) Follett Software; (OPAC) Follett Software
Partic in Pioneer
Open Mon-Thurs (Winter) 9-7:45, Fri 9-4:45, Sat 11-3:45; Mon-Thurs (Summer) 9-6:45, Fri 9-4:45

PROVO

BRIGHAM YOUNG UNIVERSITY

CL HOWARD W HUNTER LAW LIBRARY*, 256 JRCB, 84602-8000, SAN
362-4846. Tel: 801-422-3593. Interlibrary Loan Service Tel:
801-422-5481. FAX: 801-422-0404. Web Site: www.law2.byu.edu. *Dir,*
Kory Staheli; E-mail: stahelik@lawgate.byu.edu; *Dep Dir,* Gary Hill;
E-mail: hillg@lawgate.byu.edu; *Assoc Dir, Access Serv,* Laurie Urquiaga;
E-mail: urquiagal@lawgate.byu.edu; *Acq,* Bonnie Geldmacher; *Cat,* Curt
E Conklin; *Coll Develop,* Kory Staheli; *Govt Doc,* Galen L Fletcher; *Info
Tech,* David Armond; *Ref,* Steve Averett; *Ref,* Dennis Sears; *Ser,* Teresa
Odam; Staff 11 (MLS 10, Non-MLS 1)
Founded 1972. Enrl 470; Fac 40; Highest Degree: Doctorate
Library Holdings: AV Mats 1,380; e-books 3,027; Bk Titles 125,828;
Bk Vols 345,402; Per Subs 4,121
Special Collections: State Document Depository; US Document
Depository
Subject Interests: Am Commonwealth law, Biblical law, British
Commonwealth law, Comparative law, Constitutional law, Family law,
Feminist legal issues, Foreign law, Native Am law
Automation Activity & Vendor Info: (Acquisitions) SirsiDynix;
(Cataloging) SirsiDynix; (Circulation) SirsiDynix; (Course Reserve)
SirsiDynix; (ILL) SirsiDynix; (OPAC) SirsiDynix; (Serials) SirsiDynix
Database Vendor: LexisNexis, Westlaw
Partic in Association of Research Libraries (ARL); RLIN (Research
Libraries Information Network); Westlaw
Open Mon-Fri (Winter) 6am-Midnight, Sat 6am-11pm; Mon-Sat
(Summer) 8-8

C HAROLD B LEE LIBRARY*, 2060 HBLL, 84602. (Mail add: 2060 Lee
Library, 84602), SAN 362-4811. Tel: 801-422-2927. Circulation Tel:
801-422-6061. Interlibrary Loan Service Tel: 801-422-6344.
Administration Tel: 801-422-2905. Information Services Tel:
801-422-7652. FAX: 801-422-0466. Web Site: www.library.byu.edu. *Univ
Librn,* Randy J Olsen; E-mail: randy_olsen@byu.edu; *Assoc Univ Librn,*
H Julene Butler; E-mail: julene_butler@byu.edu; *Asst Univ Librn, Spec
Coll Librn,* Scott Duvall; E-mail: scott_duvall@byu.edu; *Asst Univ Librn,
Coll Develop, Tech Serv,* Robert Murdoch; E-mail:
robert_murdoch@byu.edu; *Asst Univ Librn, Pub Serv,* Terry Dahlin;
E-mail: terry_dahlin@byu.edu; *Chair,* Jeff Belliston; *Librn,* Brian
Champion; *Librn,* Mike Hunter; *Librn,* Gail King; *Librn,* Connie Lamb;
Librn, Marvin Wiggins; *Coll Develop, Librn,* Tom Wright; *Acq,* Bill
Slater; *Bus Librn,* Leticia Camacho; *Bus Librn,* H Kirk Memmott; *Cat,*
Roger Flick; *Circ,* Kathy Hansen; *Ch,* Marsha Broadway; *Humanities &
Soc Sci Librn,* Gary Gillum; *Humanities & Soc Sci Librn,* Mark Grover;
Humanities & Soc Sci Librn, Richard Hacken; *Humanities & Soc Sci
Librn,* Robert Means; *Humanities & Soc Sci Librn,* Christiane Ramsey;
Humanities & Soc Sci Librn, Julie Williamsen; *Info Res,* Michael
Whitchurch; *ILL,* Nancy Alder; *Music,* David Day; *Sci,* John Christensen;
Sci, Richard Jensen; *Ser,* Dennis Bernards. Subject Specialists: *Hist,*
Mike Hunter; *Asia,* Gail King; *Near Eastern studies,* Connie Lamb; *Soc
sci & issues,* Marvin Wiggins; *Educ,* Tom Wright; *Mgt,* Leticia
Camacho; *Mgt,* H Kirk Memmott; *Ancient hist,* Gary Gillum; *Latin Am,*
Mark Grover; *European hist, European studies,* Richard Hacken; *English
lit,* Robert Means; *Fine arts, Humanities,* Christiane Ramsey; Staff 159
(MLS 87, Non-MLS 72)
Founded 1875. Enrl 28,400; Fac 1,330; Highest Degree: Doctorate
Library Holdings: Bk Titles 3,120,238; Bk Vols 3,121,030; Per Subs
22,714
Special Collections: Can; Children's; Herman Melville; Incunabula;
Literature; Middle American Linguistics (William Gates Coll); Modern
Fine Press; Mormon & Western Americana; Robert Burns; Victorian
Literature; Walt Whitman; Welsh Languages & Literature; William
Wordsworth. Oral History; State Document Depository; US Document
Depository
Automation Activity & Vendor Info: (Acquisitions) SirsiDynix;
(Cataloging) SirsiDynix; (Circulation) SirsiDynix; (OPAC) SirsiDynix;
(Serials) SirsiDynix
Partic in Association of Research Libraries (ARL); Center for Research
Libraries; RLIN (Research Libraries Information Network); SDC Search
Serv; Utah Academic Library Consortium
Open Mon-Fri 7am-12am, Sat 8am-12am
Friends of the Library Group

P PROVO CITY LIBRARY*, 550 N University Ave, 84601-1618. SAN
316-9057. Tel: 801-852-6661. FAX: 801-852-6688. Web Site:
www.provo.lib.ut.us, www.provolibrary.com, www.provolibrary.com.
Dir, Gene Nelson; Tel: 801-852-6663; *Mgr, Ad Serv,* Carla Zollinger; Tel:
801-852-6673; *Mgr, Ch Serv,* Carla Morris; Tel: 801-852-6672; *Mgr, Tech
Serv,* Sharon Kuttler; Tel: 801-852-6676; Staff 20 (MLS 9, Non-MLS 11)
Founded 1904. Pop 115,000; Circ 1,471,000
Library Holdings: AV Mats 40,000; Bk Vols 240,000
Subject Interests: LDS relig, Utah, Utah County hist
Automation Activity & Vendor Info: (Circulation) SirsiDynix
Publications: Calendar (Monthly)

Open Mon-Fri 9-9, Sat 9-6
Friends of the Library Group

J PROVO COLLEGE LIBRARY*, 1450 W 820 N, Rm 111, 84601. SAN
378-2174. Tel: 801-818-8959. FAX: 801-375-9728. Web Site:
www.provocollege.edu. *Dir,* Alan Overstreet; E-mail:
alano@provocollege.edu. Subject Specialists: *Anthropology,* Alan
Overstreet; Staff 2 (MLS 1, Non-MLS 1)
Founded 1996. Enrl 500; Fac 50; Highest Degree: Associate
Jul 2008-Jun 2009 Income $36,943. Mats Exp $41,673, Books $3,900,
Per/Ser (Incl. Access Fees) $6,773, AV Equip $1,000, Electronic Ref Mat
(Incl. Access Fees) $30,000
Library Holdings: Bk Titles 3,017; Bk Vols 3,386; Per Subs 70; Videos
219
Subject Interests: Acctg, Bus mgt, Computer sci, Criminal justice, Dental
assisting, Graphic design, Med asst, Network mgt, Nursing, Pharmacology,
Phys therapy
Database Vendor: ebrary, Elsevier, OCLC WorldCat, OVID Technologies,
ProQuest
Wireless access
Function: Instruction & testing
Partic in Libr & Info Resources Network (LIRN)
Open Mon-Thurs 7:30am-9pm, Fri 8-Noon
Restriction: Open to students, fac & staff

S UTAH STATE HOSPITAL*, Patients Library, 1300 E Center St,
84606-3554. (Mail add: PO Box 270, 84603-0270), SAN 316-9065. Tel:
801-344-4400. FAX: 801-344-4225. Web Site: www.hsush.state.ut.us. *Dir,*
Marilyn Bonnett
Library Holdings: Bk Vols 6,500; Per Subs 25
Automation Activity & Vendor Info: (Cataloging) Follett Software;
(Circulation) Follett Software
Wireless access
Open Tues & Thurs 1-5, Sat 9-12

RICHFIELD

P RICHFIELD PUBLIC LIBRARY*, 83 E Center St, 84701. SAN 316-9081.
Tel: 435-896-5169. FAX: 435-896-6512. *Librn,* Linda Fields; E-mail:
linda@richfieldcity.com; *Ch,* Robin Davis; Staff 1 (Non-MLS 1)
Founded 1915. Pop 7,044; Circ 56,542
Jul 2006-Jun 2007 Income $128,000, State $6,000, City $122,000. Mats
Exp $14,100, Books $12,500, AV Mat $1,600. Sal $27,540
Library Holdings: DVDs 85; High Interest/Low Vocabulary Bk Vols 49;
Large Print Bks 358; Bk Vols 35,155; Per Subs 80; Talking Bks 1,465;
Videos 1,393
Automation Activity & Vendor Info: (Acquisitions) Follett Software;
(Cataloging) Follett Software; (Circulation) Follett Software
Wireless access
Friends of the Library Group

RICHMOND

P RICHMOND PUBLIC LIBRARY*, 38 W Main, 84333-1409. (Mail add:
PO Box 202, 84333-0202), SAN 316-909X. Tel: 435-258-5525. FAX:
435-258-3604. *Dir,* Harriet H Coalter; E-mail:
harriet.henderson@richmondgov.com; *Dep Dir,* Liz Triplett; E-mail:
elizabeth.triplett@richmondgov.com
Pop 2,000; Circ 6,934
Library Holdings: Bk Vols 18,000; Per Subs 10
Automation Activity & Vendor Info: (Cataloging) Follett Software;
(Circulation) Follett Software
Open Mon 3-6, Tues & Thurs 10-12 & 2-8, Wed 2-6, Fri 2-5, Sat 9-1

SAINT GEORGE

G BUREAU OF LAND MANAGEMENT*, Arizona Strip Library, 345 E
Riverside Dr, 84790. SAN 316-9111. Tel: 435-688-3200. FAX:
435-688-3252, 435-688-3258, 435-688-3358.
Founded 1966
Library Holdings: Bk Titles 500; Per Subs 19
Subject Interests: Conserv, Grazing, Land, Range, Recreation, Wildlife
mgt
Open Mon-Fri 7:45-5, Sat 9-5
Restriction: Open to staff only

C DIXIE STATE COLLEGE OF UTAH*, Val A Browning Library, 225 S
700 E, 84770. SAN 316-912X. Tel: 435-652-7714. Reference Tel:
435-634-2081. FAX: 435-656-4169. Web Site: library.dixie.edu. *Dir,*
William Baer; Tel: 435-652-7711, E-mail: baer@dixie.edu; *Head, Cat,*
David Zielke; Tel: 435-652-7716, E-mail: zielke@dixie.edu; *Head, Spec
Coll, Ref Serv,* Bonnie Percival; Tel: 435-652-7718, E-mail:
bpercival@dixie.edu; *Acq,* Deaun Kimber; Tel: 435-652-7721, E-mail:
kimber_d@dixie.edu; *Acq,* Carole Williams; Tel: 435-652-7715, E-mail:
willc@dixie.edu; *Circ,* Ellen Bonadurer; Tel: 435-652-7713, E-mail:
bonadure@dixie.edu; *ILL,* Shannon Broad; Tel: 435-652-7720, E-mail:

broad@dixie.edu; *Ref Serv,* Martha Talman; Tel: 435-652-7722, E-mail: talman@dixie.edu; *Ser,* Shannon Broad; Tel: 435-652-2720, E-mail: broad@dixie.edu; *Syst Coordr,* Rob Snyder; Tel: 435-652-7719, E-mail: snyder@dixie.edu. Subject Specialists: *Communications, Sci tech,* William Baer; *Bus, Math,* David Zielke; *Allied health,* Bonnie Percival; *English, Fine arts, Lit,* Martha Talman; *Computer tech, Info tech, Math,* Rob Snyder; Staff 11 (MLS 4, Non-MLS 7)
Founded 1912. Enrl 4,017; Highest Degree: Bachelor
Library Holdings: Bk Vols 100,000; Per Subs 314
Special Collections: Mormon & Southwest History. Oral History
Subject Interests: Allied health prof, Bus, Computer tech, Humanities, Info tech, Soc sci
Automation Activity & Vendor Info: (Acquisitions) SirsiDynix; (Cataloging) SirsiDynix; (Circulation) SirsiDynix; (Course Reserve) SirsiDynix; (OPAC) SirsiDynix; (Serials) SirsiDynix
Database Vendor: EBSCOhost, Gale Cengage Learning, LexisNexis, ProQuest, Wilson - Wilson Web
Partic in Utah Academic Library Consortium
Open Mon-Thurs 8am-10pm, Fri 8-5, Sat 10-5, Sun 3-8

P   WASHINGTON COUNTY LIBRARY SYSTEM*, 88 West 100 South, 84770-3490. SAN 316-9138. Tel: 435-634-5737. Administration Tel: 435-256-6326. FAX: 435-634-5741. Web Site: www.washco.lib.ut.us. *Dir,* Britton Lund; Tel: 435-256-6331, E-mail: blund@washco.lib.ut.us; *Ch,* Grace Mann; Tel: 435-256-6329, E-mail: gmann@washco.lib.ut.us; *Spec Coll Librn,* Brenda Brown; Tel: 435-256-6328, E-mail: bbrown@washco.lib.ut.us; *Circ Supvr,* Michelle Hughes; E-mail: mhughes@washco.lib.ut.us; *Ref Serv,* Wendy Uribe; Tel: 435-256-6320, E-mail: wuribe@washco.lib.ut.us; Staff 37 (MLS 1, Non-MLS 36)
Founded 1912. Pop 140,000; Circ 1,060,712
Library Holdings: Bk Vols 106,567; Per Subs 250
Special Collections: Local Histories & Diaries (WPA Pioneer Diary Coll), bks & pamphlets
Automation Activity & Vendor Info: (Cataloging) SirsiDynix; (Circulation) SirsiDynix; (OPAC) SirsiDynix
Wireless access
Publications: Newsletter
Partic in Metropolitan Library Service Agency
Open Mon-Thurs 10-8, Fri & Sat 10-6
Friends of the Library Group
Branches: 6
ENTERPRISE BRANCH, 393 S 200 E, Enterprise, 84725. (Mail add: PO Box 160, Enterprise, 84725-0160), SAN 371-3725. Tel: 435-878-2574. FAX: 435-878-2725. *Br Mgr,* Susan Staheli
   Library Holdings: Bk Vols 12,000
   Open Mon 10-6, Tues-Thurs 10-7, Fri 10-6, Sat 10-3
HURRICANE BRANCH, 36 S 300 West, Hurricane, 84737-2100, SAN 325-4011. Tel: 435-635-4621. FAX: 435-635-3845. *Br Mgr,* Lauren Stoddard; E-mail: lstoddard@washco.lib.ut.us
   Library Holdings: Bk Vols 41,042
   Open Mon-Thurs 10-7, Fri & Sat 10-6
NEW HARMONY VALLEY BRANCH, 34 S 2900 East, New Harmony, 84757. Tel: 435-867-0065. FAX: 435-867-0222. *Br Mgr,* Bonnie Mellor; E-mail: bmellor@washco.lib.ut.us
   Library Holdings: Bk Titles 5,000
   Open Mon & Tues 10-6, Wed & Thurs 12-7, Fri 10-3
   Friends of the Library Group
SANTA CLARA BRANCH, 1099 N Lava Flow Dr, 84770-0999. Tel: 435-986-0432. FAX: 435-986-0436. *Br Mgr,* Abe King; Tel: 435-256-6327, E-mail: aking@washco.lib.ut.us
   Library Holdings: Bk Titles 35,076
   Automation Activity & Vendor Info: (OPAC) SirsiDynix
   Open Mon-Thurs 10-7, Fri & Sat 10-6
SPRINGDALE BRANCH, 126 Lion Blvd, Springdale, 84767. (Mail add: PO Box 479, Springdale, 84767), SAN 371-3733. Tel: 435-772-3676. FAX: 435-772-3124. *Br Mgr,* Robert Snyder; E-mail: rob.snyder@washco.lib.ut.us; *Cataloger,* Kristey Black
   Library Holdings: Bk Vols 12,000
   Open Mon, Wed & Fri 10-6, Tues & Thurs 10-8, Sat 10-5
   Friends of the Library Group
WASHINGTON BRANCH, 220 N 300 E, Washington City, 84780. Tel: 435-627-2706. FAX: 435-627-2776. *Br Mgr,* Alan Anderson; E-mail: aanderson@washco.lib.ut.us

SALINA

P   SALINA PUBLIC LIBRARY*, 90 W Main St, 84654. SAN 316-9146. Tel: 435-529-7753. FAX: 435-529-1235. E-mail: publiclibrary@salinacity.org. Web Site: www.salinacity.org. *Librn,* Becky Lopshire
Pop 4,900; Circ 19,861
Library Holdings: Bk Titles 11,250; Bk Vols 11,500; Per Subs 30
Automation Activity & Vendor Info: (Cataloging) Follett Software; (Circulation) Follett Software
Open Mon-Thurs 12-7, Fri & Sat 1-5

SALT LAKE CITY

THE CHURCH OF JESUS CHRIST OF LATTER-DAY SAINTS
SR   BOCA RATON FAMILY HISTORY CENTER*, 1530 W Camino Real, Boca Raton, 33486. (Mail add: 1199 SW Ninth Ave, Boca Raton, 33486), SAN 375-278X. Tel: 561-395-6644. FAX: 561-395-8957. *Dir,* Brother Donald W Jennings
Founded 1979
Library Holdings: Microforms 4,000; Bk Titles 800; Per Subs 10
Special Collections: New York Death Indexes
Subject Interests: Genealogy
Open Mon & Wed 10-5, Tues 3-9
SR   CHURCH HISTORY LIBRARY & ARCHIVES*, 50 E North Temple, 84150, SAN 362-4935. Tel: 801-240-2272. FAX: 801-240-1845. E-mail: www.lds.org/churchhistory/askalibrarian. Web Site: www.lds.org/churchhistory. *Dir,* Christine Cox; Tel: 801-240-3603; *Coll Develop,* Matt Heiss; Tel: 801-240-5944. Subject Specialists: *Church hist,* Christine Cox; Staff 180 (MLS 25, Non-MLS 155)
Founded 1830
Library Holdings: AV Mats 41,000; Bk Titles 250,000; Bk Vols 300,000; Per Subs 799
Special Collections: Church of Jesus Christ of Latter-Day Saints, mss, publs, records. Oral History
Subject Interests: Mormon hist, Mormon theol, Utah hist
Automation Activity & Vendor Info: (OPAC) Innovative Interfaces, Inc; (Serials) Innovative Interfaces, Inc
Function: Photocopying/Printing, Telephone ref
Publications: Index to Periodicals of the Church of Jesus Christ of Latter-Day Saints
Restriction: Circulates for staff only
SR   FAMILY HISTORY LIBRARY*, 35 N West Temple St, Rm 344, 84150-3440, SAN 362-496X. Tel: 801-240-2584. Toll Free Tel: 800-346-6044. FAX: 801-240-3718. TDD: 801-240-6745. E-mail: help@productsupport.familysearch.org. Web Site: www.familysearch.org. *Dir,* Raymond S Wright, III; *Pub Relations,* Elaine Hasleton; Staff 200 (MLS 110, Non-MLS 90)
Founded 1894
Library Holdings: Electronic Media & Resources 943; Bk Titles 888,979; Per Subs 4,500
Special Collections: Oral History
Subject Interests: Family hist, Genealogy, Local hist
Publications: Country & State Research Outlines; Family History Centers Address List; Family History Materials List; International Genealogical Index; International Genealogical Index (micro); Patron Aids
Special Services for the Deaf - Staff with knowledge of sign lang
Open Mon 8-5, Tues-Sat 8am-9pm

GM   DEPARTMENT OF VETERANS AFFAIRS MEDICAL CENTER*, Medical Library, 500 Foothill Dr, 84148. SAN 362-577X. Tel: 801-584-1209. FAX: 801-584-1251. *Chief Librn,* Kirk Davis
Library Holdings: Bk Titles 7,000; Bk Vols 8,500; Per Subs 350
Subject Interests: Allied health, Med, Psychiat, Related fields, Surgery
Partic in BRS; Dialog Corp; Midcontinental Regional Med Libr Network
Open Mon-Fri 7-6

L   FABIAN & CLENDENIN, Law Library, 215 S State St, Ste 1200, 84111-2323. SAN 372-1906. Tel: 801-531-8900. FAX: 801-596-2814. Web Site: www.fabianlaw.com. *Librn,* Michelle Hardgrave
Library Holdings: Bk Vols 40,000; Per Subs 100
Restriction: Staff use only

M   INTERMOUNTAIN HEALTH CARE, LDS Hospital Medical Library, Eighth Ave & C St, 84143-0001. SAN 316-9219. Tel: 801-408-1054. FAX: 801-408-5287. E-mail: docline@imail.org. *Librn,* Dave Castelli; Tel: 801-507-5142; *Librn,* Robin Nielsen; *Librn,* Carol Tripp; Staff 3 (MLS 3)
Founded 1945
Library Holdings: Bk Vols 1,500; Per Subs 280
Subject Interests: Med
Database Vendor: EBSCOhost
Partic in National Network of Libraries of Medicine Midcontinental Region; Utah Health Sciences Library Consortium
Restriction: Staff use only

S   INTERNATIONAL SOCIETY DAUGHTERS OF UTAH PIONEERS*, Museum & Library, 300 N Main St, 84103-1699. SAN 375-7811. Tel: 801-532-6479. FAX: 801-538-1119. E-mail: info@dupinternational.org. *Librn,* Carol Dee Buchmiller; Staff 1 (MLS 1)
Library Holdings: Bk Titles 1,800
Special Collections: Histories of Pioneers to 1869 & Western History
Restriction: Open to pub for ref only

J   **LDS BUSINESS COLLEGE LIBRARY***, 95 N 300 West, 84101-3500. SAN 316-9200. Tel: 801-524-8149. FAX: 801-524-1900. Web Site: www.ldsbc.edu. *Dir,* Karen Hales; E-mail: khales@ldsbc.edu
Founded 1975. Enrl 1,300; Fac 18; Highest Degree: Associate
Library Holdings: Bk Vols 7,500; Per Subs 100
Subject Interests: Acctg, Computer, Computer tech, Econ, Interior design, Med asst, Relig studies, Secretarial
Automation Activity & Vendor Info: (Cataloging) SirsiDynix; (Circulation) SirsiDynix; (OPAC) SirsiDynix
Database Vendor: ProQuest
Wireless access
Open Mon & Fri 7:30-5, Tues-Thurs 7:30-5, Sat 10-3
Restriction: In-house use for visitors

S   **NATIONAL SOCIETY OF SONS OF UTAH PIONEERS***, Sons of Utah Pioneers Library, 3301 E 2920 S, 84109. SAN 323-7176. Tel: 801-484-4441. Toll Free Tel: 888-827-2746. FAX: 801-484-2067. Web Site: www.sonsofutahpioneers.org. *Cat, Dir,* Marilyn Johnson
Founded 1981
Library Holdings: Bk Titles 6,000; Spec Interest Per Sub 25
Special Collections: Western USA Local History Coll, 1600 to date
Subject Interests: Biographies, Family hist, Local hist
Function: Res libr
Publications: Pioneer (Magazine)
Open Tues-Thurs 9-4
Restriction: Non-circulating

M   **PRIMARY CHILDREN'S MEDICAL CENTER LIBRARY***, 100 N Mario Capecchi Dr, 84113. SAN 323-6617. Tel: 801-662-1390. FAX: 801-662-1393. *Sr Med Librn,* Emily Eresuma; *Asst Med Librn,* Michelle Hill. Subject Specialists: *Pediatrics,* Emily Eresuma; Staff 2 (MLS 2)
Library Holdings: Bk Titles 1,500; Per Subs 240
Subject Interests: Pediatrics
Database Vendor: EBSCOhost, UpToDate
Wireless access
Partic in Utah Health Sciences Library Consortium
Open Mon-Fri 8:30-5:30

L   **RAY QUINNEY & NEBEKER PC***, Law Library, 36 S State St, Ste 1400, 84111. (Mail add: PO Box 45385, 84145-0385), SAN 372-1817. Tel: 801-532-1500. FAX: 801-532-7543. Web Site: www.rqn.com. *Head Librn,* Gwendolyn Mulks; E-mail: gmulks@rqn.com
Library Holdings: Bk Vols 15,000
Restriction: Staff use only

M   **SAINT MARK'S HOSPITAL***, Medical Library, 1200 E 3900 South, 84124. SAN 326-2367. Tel: 801-268-7004. FAX: 801-270-3417. Web Site: www.stmarkshospital.com. *Librn,* Helen Chang; Staff 0.8 (MLS 0.8)
Library Holdings: Bk Titles 600; Per Subs 75; Videos 40
Subject Interests: Healthcare
Automation Activity & Vendor Info: (OPAC) LibraryWorld, Inc; (Serials) EBSCO Online
Database Vendor: EBSCOhost
Wireless access
Partic in Docline
Open Mon-Fri 8-6

P   **SALT LAKE CITY PUBLIC LIBRARY***, 210 E 400 S, 84111-3280. SAN 362-4994. Tel: 801-524-8200. FAX: 801-322-8194. Circulation FAX: 801-322-8188. Reference FAX: 801-322-8191. Administration FAX: 801-322-8196. TDD: 801-364-4669. Web Site: www.slcpl.org. *Dir,* Position Currently Open; *Exec Dir,* Position Currently Open; *Assoc Dir, Br & Ch,* Patty Steed; Tel: 801-524-8202, E-mail: psteed@slcpl.org; *Assoc Dir, Libr Experiences,* Deborah Ehrman; Tel: 801-524-8204, E-mail: dehrman@slcpl.org; *Circ Mgr,* Frances Brummett; Tel: 801-322-8110, E-mail: fbrummett@slcpl.org; *Human Res Mgr,* Shelly Chapman; Tel: 801-524-8225, E-mail: schapman@slcpl.org; *Mgr, Communications & Libr Innovation,* Julianne Hancock; Tel: 801-524-8219, E-mail: jhancock@slcpl.org; *Tech Serv Mgr,* Becky Butler; Tel: 801-524-8521, Fax: 801-322-8185, E-mail: bbutler@slcpl.org; Staff 181.4 (MLS 36, Non-MLS 145.4)
Founded 1898. Pop 186,440; Circ 3,854,418
Jul 2010-Jun 2011 Income (Main Library and Branch(s)) $13,432,554. Mats Exp $1,885,395, Books $943,647, AV Mat $631,293, Electronic Ref Mat (Incl. Access Fees) $310,455. Sal $6,738,025
Library Holdings: AV Mats 185,949; Bk Vols 767,711; Per Subs 2,385
Special Collections: Foundations; Grants; Salt Lake City Coll
Automation Activity & Vendor Info: (Acquisitions) Innovative Interfaces, Inc; (Cataloging) Innovative Interfaces, Inc; (Circulation) Innovative Interfaces, Inc; (ILL) Innovative Interfaces, Inc; (OPAC) BiblioCommons; (Serials) Innovative Interfaces, Inc
Database Vendor: Baker & Taylor, Checkpoint Systems, Inc, Corbis, EBSCOhost, Factiva.com, Gale Cengage Learning, Innovative Interfaces, Inc, netLibrary, OCLC WorldCat, ReferenceUSA

Wireless access
Function: Accessibility serv available based on individual needs, Adult bk club, After school storytime, Art exhibits, Audiobks via web, AV serv, Bilingual assistance for Spanish patrons, Bk reviews (Group), Bks on CD, Children's prog, Computer training, Computers for patron use, Copy machines, e-mail & chat, Electronic databases & coll, Exhibits, Free DVD rentals, Homework prog, ILL available, Mus passes, Music CDs, Online cat, Online searches, Outreach serv, OverDrive digital audio bks, Photocopying/Printing, Preschool outreach, Prog for adults, Prog for children & young adult, Story hour, Summer reading prog, Tax forms, Teen prog, Visual arts prog, Web-catalog, Workshops, Writing prog
Publications: Events Calendar (Monthly)
Partic in OCLC Online Computer Library Center, Inc
Special Services for the Deaf - TDD equip
Open Mon-Thurs 9-9, Fri & Sat 9-6, Sun 1-5
Friends of the Library Group
Branches: 5
ANDERSON-FOOTHILL, 1135 S 2100 E, 84108. (Mail add: 210 E 400 S, 84111), SAN 322-5763. Tel: 801-594-8611. FAX: 801-322-8181.
Founded 1985
Open Mon-Thurs 10-9, Fri & Sat 10-6
Friends of the Library Group
CHAPMAN, 577 S 900 W, 84104-1302. (Mail add: 210 E 400 S, 84111), SAN 362-5028. Tel: 801-594-8623. FAX: 801-322-8180.
Founded 1912
Open Mon-Thurs 10-9, Fri & Sat 10-6
Friends of the Library Group
DAY-RIVERSIDE, 1575 W 1000 N, 84116. (Mail add: 210 E 400 S, 84111), SAN 362-5052. Tel: 801-594-8632. FAX: 801-322-8182.
Founded 1965
Open Mon-Thurs 10-9, Fri & Sat 10-6, Sun 1-5
Friends of the Library Group
SPRAGUE, 2131 S 1100 E, 84106-2806. (Mail add: 210 E 400 S, 84111), SAN 362-5087. Tel: 801-594-8640. FAX: 801-322-8183.
Founded 1914
Open Mon-Thurs 10-9, Fri & Sat 10-6, Sun 1-5
Friends of the Library Group
CORINNE & JACK SWEET, 455 F St, 84103. (Mail add: 210 E 400 S, 84111), SAN 322-5771. Tel: 801-594-8651. FAX: 801-322-8184.
Founded 1985
Open Mon-Thurs 10-9, Fri & Sat 10-6
Friends of the Library Group

J   **SALT LAKE COMMUNITY COLLEGE LIBRARIES***, Markosian Library, 4600 S Redwood Rd, 84123-3197. (Mail add: PO Box 30808, 84130-0808), SAN 316-9324. Tel: 801-957-4195. Circulation Tel: 801-957-4602. Reference Tel: 801-957-4610. FAX: 801-957-4414. Web Site: libweb.slcc.edu. *Dean, Learning Res,* Tiffany Evans, PhD; Tel: 801-957-4905, E-mail: tiffany.evans@slcc.edu; *Head, Syst,* Truc Tran; Tel: 801-957-4607, E-mail: truc.tran@slcc.edu; *Head, Tech Serv,* Eloise G Vanderhooft; Tel: 801-957-4588, E-mail: eloise.vanderhooft@slcc.edu; Staff 34 (MLS 9, Non-MLS 25)
Founded 1948. Enrl 60,000; Fac 314; Highest Degree: Associate
Library Holdings: AV Mats 28,682; Bks on Deafness & Sign Lang 204; e-books 6,300; High Interest/Low Vocabulary Bk Vols 219; Bk Titles 76,315; Bk Vols 91,570; Per Subs 721
Special Collections: Health Science Coll
Subject Interests: Gen educ, Indust, Nursing, Sci tech
Automation Activity & Vendor Info: (Cataloging) SirsiDynix; (Circulation) SirsiDynix; (Course Reserve) SirsiDynix; (OPAC) SirsiDynix; (Serials) SirsiDynix
Database Vendor: EBSCOhost, ProQuest, Westlaw, Wilson - Wilson Web
Wireless access
Partic in OCLC Online Computer Library Center, Inc; Utah Academic Library Consortium
Open Mon-Thurs 7:30-9:30, Fri 7:30-5, Sat 9-5

P   **SALT LAKE COUNTY LIBRARY SERVICES***, 2197 E Fort Union Blvd, 84121-3139. SAN 362-5117. Tel: 801-943-4636. FAX: 801-942-6323. Web Site: www.slcolibrary.org. *Dir,* James D Cooper; Tel: 801-944-7504; *Assoc Dir, Finance & Operations,* Mike Stoker; *Assoc Dir, Prog, Outreach & Ref,* Susan Hamada; Tel: 801-944-7513, E-mail: shamada@slcolibrary.org; *Assoc Dir, Coll Mgt,* Marsha Leclair-Marzolf; *Assoc Dir, Tech,* Gretchen Freeman; *Human Res Mgr,* Tamara Springer; *Mkt & Commun Relations Mgr,* Scott Russell; Staff 322 (MLS 90, Non-MLS 232)
Founded 1938. Pop 753,597; Circ 12,749,312
Library Holdings: Bk Vols 2,000,000; Per Subs 7,000
Automation Activity & Vendor Info: (Acquisitions) SirsiDynix; (Cataloging) SirsiDynix; (Circulation) SirsiDynix; (Media Booking) SirsiDynix; (OPAC) SirsiDynix; (Serials) SirsiDynix
Wireless access
Publications: Library Links (Newsletter); Library Links (Quarterly); Staff Matters (Newsletter); Staff Matters (Monthly)
Partic in OCLC Online Computer Library Center, Inc

Special Services for the Deaf - TTY equip
Open Mon-Thurs 10-9, Fri & Sat 10-6
Branches: 19
ALTA READING ROOM, Alta Community Ctr, Sandy, 84092-6001, SAN
362-515X. Tel: 801-742-2068. *Coordr,* Penee Lynn; *Coordr,* Sara Shaw
Open Mon, Wed & Fri 6-9
BINGHAM CREEK, 4834 W 9000 South, West Jordan, 84088-2213, SAN
377-7413. Tel: 801-944-7684. Circulation Tel: 801-944-7685. FAX:
801-282-0943. E-mail: binghamc@slcolibrary.org. *Mgr,* Ruby Cheesman;
Tel: 801-944-7688; Staff 22 (MLS 8, Non-MLS 14)
Circ 1,089,913
Library Holdings: Bk Vols 155,000
Open Mon-Thurs 10-9, Fri & Sat 10-6
COLUMBUS BRANCH, 2530 S 500 East, South Salt Lake City,
84106-1316, SAN 362-5419. Tel: 801-944-7545. Circulation Tel:
801-944-7625. FAX: 801-412-0944. *Mgr,* Darlene Dineen; Tel:
801-944-7606, E-mail: ddineen@slcolibrary.org; Staff 7 (MLS 2,
Non-MLS 5)
Circ 182,742
Library Holdings: Bk Vols 56,000
Open Mon-Thurs 10-9, Fri & Sat 10-6
DRAPER BRANCH, 1136 E Pioneer Rd, Draper, 84020-9628, SAN
362-5168. Tel: 801-944-7548. Circulation Tel: 801-944-7578. FAX:
801-619-9861. *Mgr,* Danette Hantla; Tel: 801-944-7558; Staff 30 (MLS
5, Non-MLS 25)
Circ 296,271
Library Holdings: Bk Vols 47,000
Open Mon-Thurs 10-9, Fri & Sat 10-6
EAST MILLCREEK, 2266 E Evergreen Ave, 84109-2927, SAN 362-5176.
Tel: 801-944-7622. Circulation Tel: 801-944-7623. FAX: 801-278-9016.
Mgr, Suzanne Tronier; Tel: 801-944-7510, E-mail:
stronier@slcolibrary.org; Staff 16 (MLS 6, Non-MLS 10)
Circ 577,013
Library Holdings: Bk Vols 96,400
Open Mon-Thurs 10-9, Fri & Sat 10-6
HERRIMAN BRANCH, 13011 S Pioneer St, Herriman, 84065-8904. Tel:
801-944-7680. Circulation Tel: 801-944-7681. FAX: 801-446-5348. *Mgr,*
Leslie Schow; Tel: 801-944-7682, E-mail: lschow@slcolibrary.org
Open Mon-Thurs 10-9, Fri & Sat 10-6
HOLLADAY, 2150 E Murray-Holladay Rd, 84117-5241, SAN 362-5230.
Tel: 801-944-7627. Circulation Tel: 801-944-7629. FAX: 801-278-8947.
Mgr, Steve Pierson; Tel: 801-944-7524, E-mail: spierson@slcolibrary.org;
Staff 13 (MLS 5, Non-MLS 8)
Circ 569,706
Library Holdings: Bk Vols 113,500
Open Mon-Thurs 10-9, Fri & Sat 10-6
HUNTER BRANCH, 4740 W 4100 South, 84120-4948, SAN 374-8138.
Tel: 801-944-7593. Circulation Tel: 801-944-7594. FAX: 801-968-8350.
Mgr, Jan Elkins; Staff 18 (MLS 6, Non-MLS 12)
Circ 843,640
Library Holdings: Bk Vols 179,700
Open Mon-Thurs 10-9, Fri & Sat 10-6
KEARNS BRANCH, 5350 S 4220 West, Kearns, 84118-4314, SAN
362-5265. Tel: 801-944-7611. FAX: 801-967-8958. *Mgr,* Position
Currently Open; Staff 12 (MLS 4, Non-MLS 8)
Founded 1965. Circ 579,789
Function: Audiobks via web, Bilingual assistance for Spanish patrons,
Bks on CD, Children's prog, Computers for patron use, Copy machines,
e-mail & chat, Electronic databases & coll, Family literacy, Free DVD
rentals, Handicapped accessible, Homework prog, ILL available,
Magnifiers for reading, Music CDs, Online cat, Online ref, Online
searches, Outreach serv, OverDrive digital audio bks, Preschool outreach,
Prog for adults, Prog for children & young adult, Pub access computers,
Ref serv in person, Story hour, Summer reading prog, Tax forms, Teen
prog, Web-catalog, Wheelchair accessible
Open Mon-Thurs 10-9, Fri & Sat 10-6
MAGNA BRANCH, 8339 W 3500 South, Magna, 84044-1870, SAN
362-529X. Tel: 801-944-7547. Circulation Tel: 801-944-7626. FAX:
801-250-6927. *Mgr,* Trish Hull; Tel: 801-944-7657, E-mail:
thull@slcolibrary.org; Staff 8 (MLS 3, Non-MLS 5)
Circ 310,598
Library Holdings: Bk Vols 85,700
Open Mon-Thurs 10-9, Fri & Sat 10-6
PARK BRANCH, 4870 S 2700 West, Taylorsville, 84118-2138, SAN
372-0284. Tel: 801-944-7618. Circulation Tel: 801-944-7638. FAX:
801-965-3907. *Mgr,* Maggie Mills; Staff 15 (MLS 5, Non-MLS 10)
Founded 1990. Circ 615,767
Library Holdings: Bk Vols 105,991
Open Mon-Thurs 10-9, Fri & Sat 10-6
RIVERTON BRANCH, 12877 S 1830 West, Riverton, 84065-3204, SAN
328-7580. Tel: 801-944-7677. Circulation Tel: 801-944-7661. FAX:
801-466-8601. *Mgr,* Christa Warren; Staff 17 (MLS 6, Non-MLS 11)
Circ 692,240
Library Holdings: Bk Vols 109,313
Open Mon-Thurs 10-9, Fri & Sat 10-6

SANDY BRANCH, 10100 S Petunia Way, 1450 East, Sandy, 84092-4380,
SAN 372-0292. Tel: 801-944-7574. Circulation Tel: 801-944-7602.
Reference Tel: 801-944-7601. FAX: 801-572-8247. *Mgr,* Darin Butler;
Tel: 801-944-7600; Staff 41 (MLS 11, Non-MLS 30)
Circ 1,479,008
Library Holdings: Bk Vols 231,175
Open Mon-Thurs 10-9, Fri & Sat 10-6
CALVIN S SMITH BRANCH, 810 E 3300 South, 84106-1534, SAN
362-5354. Tel: 801-944-7630. Circulation Tel: 801-944-7620. FAX:
801-485-3243. *Mgr,* Suzanne Tronier; Staff 6 (MLS 2, Non-MLS 4)
Circ 247,350
Library Holdings: Bk Vols 56,090
Open Mon-Thurs 10-9, Fri & Sat 10-6
SOUTH JORDAN BRANCH, 10673 S Redwood Rd, South Jordan,
84095-2481, SAN 362-5389. Tel: 801-943-4636. Circulation Tel:
801-944-7650. Reference Tel: 801-944-7634. Administration Tel:
801-944-7643. Information Services Tel: 801-944-7634. FAX:
801-254-9047. Web Site:
www.slcolibrary.org/gl/glal/librarySouthJordan.htm. *Mgr,* Dina Wyatt;
E-mail: dwyatt@slcolibrary.org; Staff 5 (MLS 4.5, Non-MLS 0.5)
Founded 1974. Pop 55,557; Circ 1,078,999
Library Holdings: Large Print Bks 496; Bk Vols 94,717; Per Subs 235
Automation Activity & Vendor Info: (Serials) EBSCO Online
Database Vendor: SirsiDynix
Function: Bks on CD, Children's prog, Computers for patron use, Copy
machines, Digital talking bks, e-mail & chat, Electronic databases & coll,
Free DVD rentals, Homebound delivery serv, ILL available, Music CDs,
Online cat, Outreach serv, Photocopying/Printing, Preschool outreach,
Preschool reading prog, Prog for children & young adult, Pub access
computers, Ref serv available, Story hour, Summer reading prog, Teen
prog, Telephone ref, Web-catalog
Open Mon-Thurs 10-9, Fri & Sat 10-6
RUTH V TYLER BRANCH, 8041 S Wood St, 55 West, Midvale,
84047-7559, SAN 362-5443. Tel: 801-944-7641. Reference Tel:
801-944-7642. FAX: 801-565-8012. *Mgr,* Lorraine Jeffrey; Tel:
801-944-7608; Staff 6 (MLS 2, Non-MLS 4)
Circ 228,670
Library Holdings: Bk Vols 65,985
Open Mon-Thurs 10-9, Fri & Sat 10-6
WEST JORDAN BRANCH, 1970 W 7800 South, West Jordan,
84088-4025, SAN 328-7602. Tel: 801-944-7646. Circulation Tel:
801-944-7645. FAX: 801-562-8761. *Mgr,* Nanette Alderman; Tel:
801-944-7633, E-mail: nalderman@slcolibrary.org; Staff 13 (MLS 4,
Non-MLS 9)
Circ 562,827
Library Holdings: Bk Vols 102,691
Open Mon-Thurs 10-9, Fri & Sat 10-6
WEST VALLEY BRANCH, 2880 W 3650 South, West Valley City,
84119-3743, SAN 362-5206. Tel: 801-944-7621. Circulation Tel:
801-944-7631. FAX: 801-969-1782. *Mgr,* Cindy Smiley; Staff 10 (MLS
4, Non-MLS 6)
Circ 366,529
Library Holdings: Bk Vols 84,019
Open Mon-Thurs 10-9, Fri & Sat 10-6
WHITMORE BRANCH, 2197 E Fort Union Blvd, 84121-3139, SAN
362-5478. Tel: 801-944-7533. Circulation Tel: 801-944-7531. Reference
Tel: 801-944-7666. FAX: 801-944-7534. *Mgr,* Kent Dean; Tel:
801-944-7535, E-mail: kdean@slcolibrary.org; Staff 24 (MLS 9,
Non-MLS 15)
Circ 1,089,913
Library Holdings: Bk Vols 207,300
Open Mon-Thurs 10-9, Fri & Sat 10-6

M   SALT LAKE REGIONAL MEDICAL CENTER*, Medical Library, 1050
E South Temple, 84102. SAN 329-2894. Tel: 801-350-4060, 801-350-4111,
801-350-4631. FAX: 801-350-4390. *Dir, Health Info,* Amy Mitchell
Library Holdings: Bk Titles 1,100; Bk Vols 1,250; Per Subs 50
Subject Interests: Med ethics
Partic in Utah Health Sciences Library Consortium
Open Mon-Fri 8-4

L   UNITED STATES COURTS LIBRARY*, US Courthouse, Rm 201, 350 S
Main St, 84101. SAN 372-1892. Tel: 801-524-3505. FAX: 801-524-5375.
Librn, Patricia Hummel
Library Holdings: Bk Vols 18,000
Automation Activity & Vendor Info: (Cataloging) SirsiDynix
Open Mon-Fri 9:30-5
Restriction: Non-circulating to the pub

UNIVERSITY OF UTAH

CM   SPENCER S ECCLES HEALTH SCIENCES LIBRARY*, Bldg 589, 10 N
1900 E, 84112-5890, SAN 362-5680. Tel: 801-581-8771. Circulation Tel:
801-581-8772. Interlibrary Loan Service Tel: 801-581-5282. Reference
Tel: 801-581-5534. Toll Free Tel: 866-581-5534 (UT only). FAX:
801-581-3632. Web Site: library.med.utah.edu. *Dir,* Wayne J Peay;

E-mail: wayne@lib.med.utah.edu; *Dep Dir,* Joan Stoddart; E-mail:
joans@lib.med.utah.edu; Staff 10 (MLS 10)
Founded 1966
Special Collections: History of Medicine, bks & journals. Oral History;
US Document Depository
Subject Interests: Med, Nursing
Automation Activity & Vendor Info: (OPAC) SirsiDynix
Partic in Center for Research Libraries; Greater Western Library
Alliance; Utah Academic Library Consortium
Open Mon-Thurs 7am-11pm, Fri 7am-8pm, Sat 9-8, Sun 11-11
Restriction: In-house use for visitors

C   MARRIOTT LIBRARY*, 295 S 1500 East, 84112-0860, SAN 362-5532.
Tel: 801-581-8558. Circulation Tel: 801-581-8203. Interlibrary Loan
Service Tel: 801-581-6010. Reference Tel: 801-581-6273. FAX:
801-585-7185. Web Site: www.lib.utah.edu. *Dean,* Joyce Ogburn; E-mail:
joyce.ogburn@utah.edu; *Assoc Dean, Budget & Planning,* Ann Marie
Breznay; Tel: 801-581-3852, E-mail: annmarie.breznay@utah.edu; *Assoc
Dean, Res & Learning Serv,* Catherine Soehner; E-mail:
catherine.soehner@utah.edu; *Assoc Dean, Scholarly Res & Coll,* Rick
Anderson; Tel: 801-587-9989, E-mail: rick.anderson@utah.edu; *Assoc
Dean, Spec Coll,* Gregory C Thompson; Tel: 801-581-8863, E-mail:
gregory.c.thompson@utah.edu; *Assoc Dean, Info Tech,* Position Currently
Open; *Head, Scholarly Res,* Maria Hunt; Tel: 801-581-7741, E-mail:
maria.hunt@utah.edu; *Circ Serv Coordr,* Natalie Polson; E-mail:
natalie.polson@utah.edu; *ILL,* Susan Brusik; Fax: 801-585-3464, E-mail:
susan.brusik@utah.edu; Staff 184 (MLS 45, Non-MLS 139)
Founded 1850. Enrl 30,819; Fac 1,555; Highest Degree: Doctorate
Library Holdings: Bk Vols 2,992,502; Per Subs 68,225
Special Collections: 2002 Winter Olympics Coll; Manuscripts Coll;
Multimedia Archives; University Archives; US Patents; Utah Artists
Project. Oral History; State Document Depository; UN Document
Depository; US Document Depository
Subject Interests: Fine arts, Math, Rare bks, Western Americana
Automation Activity & Vendor Info: (Acquisitions) Ex Libris Group;
(Cataloging) Ex Libris Group; (Circulation) Ex Libris Group; (Course
Reserve) Ex Libris Group; (ILL) OCLC ILLiad; (OPAC) Ex Libris
Group
Partic in Association of Research Libraries (ARL); Center for Research
Libraries; OCLC Online Computer Library Center, Inc; Pioneer; Utah
Libr Asn
Publications: Inspirations (Newsletter); Ski Archives (Newsletter)
Friends of the Library Group

CL   S J QUINNEY LAW LIBRARY, 332 S 1400 East, 84112-0731, SAN
362-5591. Circulation Tel: 801-581-6438. Reference Tel: 801-581-6184.
FAX: 801-585-3033. Web Site: www.law.utah.edu/library. *Dir,* Melissa
Bernstein; Tel: 801-581-3386, E-mail: melissa.bernstein@law.utah.edu;
Asst Dir, Head, Coll Develop, Lee Warthen; Tel: 801-581-5344, E-mail:
lee.warthen@law.utah.edu; *Head, Info Serv,* Linda Stephenson; Tel:
801-581-5800, E-mail: linda.stephenson@law.utah.edu; *Head, Info Tech,*
Suzanne Darais; Tel: 801-585-3074, E-mail: suzane.darais@law.utah.edu;
Access Technologies Librn, Valeri Craigle; Tel: 801-585-5475; *Circ
Supvr,* Maura Fowler; Tel: 801-581-6296, E-mail:
maura.fowler@law.utah.edu; *Coordr, ILL & Doc Delivery Serv,* Laura
Ngai; Tel: 801-581-3804, E-mail: laura.ngai@law.utah.edu; Staff 19
(MLS 6, Non-MLS 13)
Founded 1923. Enrl 400; Fac 41; Highest Degree: Doctorate
Library Holdings: Bk Titles 84,000; Bk Vols 230,000; Per Subs 2,300
Special Collections: State Document Depository; US Document
Depository
Subject Interests: Law
Automation Activity & Vendor Info: (Acquisitions) Ex Libris Group;
(Cataloging) Ex Libris Group; (Circulation) Ex Libris Group; (OPAC) Ex
Libris Group; (Serials) Ex Libris Group
Database Vendor: Bloomberg, LexisNexis, Westlaw
Publications: Acquisitions List (Monthly); User Guide

S   UTAH DEPARTMENT OF NATURAL RESOURCES LIBRARY*, 1594
W North Temple, 84114. (Mail add: PO Box 146100, 84114-6100), SAN
372-865X. Tel: 801-537-3333. FAX: 801-537-3400. Web Site:
dnrlibrary.utah.gov. *Librn,* Stephanie Earls; E-mail:
stephanieearls@utah.gov
Library Holdings: Bk Vols 23,000; Per Subs 41
Subject Interests: Natural res
Automation Activity & Vendor Info: (Cataloging) ComPanion Corp
Open Mon-Fri 7:30-4:30
Restriction: Non-circulating to the pub

S   UTAH STATE HISTORICAL SOCIETY*, Utah History Research Center
Library, 300 Rio Grande, 84101-1182. SAN 316-9294. Tel: 801-533-3535.
FAX: 801-533-3504. Web Site: www.history.utah.gov,
www.historyresearch.utah.gov. *Actg Dir, Prog Mgr,* Wilson G Martin; *Coll
Mgr, Librn, Res,* Doug Misner; E-mail: dmisner@utah.gov; *Librn,* Greg
Walz; Staff 4 (MLS 4)
Founded 1939
Library Holdings: Bk Vols 50,000; Per Subs 205

Subject Interests: Mormon hist, Utah hist, Western hist
Automation Activity & Vendor Info: (Cataloging) SirsiDynix
Database Vendor: SirsiDynix
Function: Res libr
Publications: Guide to the Women's History Holdings at the Utah State
Historical Society Library; Guide to Unpublished Materials at the Utah
State Historical Society
Partic in RLIN (Research Libraries Information Network)
Open Mon-Fri 9-4
Restriction: Non-circulating

GL   UTAH STATE LAW LIBRARY*, 450 S State St, W-13, 84111-3101. (Mail
add: PO Box 140220, 84114-0220), SAN 316-9308. Tel: 801-238-7990.
FAX: 801-238-7993. Web Site: www.utcourts.gov/lawlibrary. *Dir,* Jessica
Van Buren; E-mail: jessicavb@email.utcourts.gov; Staff 5 (MLS 2,
Non-MLS 3)
Library Holdings: Bk Titles 3,500; Bk Vols 50,000
Special Collections: State Document Depository; US Document
Depository
Subject Interests: Law
Automation Activity & Vendor Info: (Cataloging) SirsiDynix;
(Circulation) SirsiDynix; (OPAC) SirsiDynix; (Serials) SirsiDynix
Database Vendor: EBSCOhost, Factiva.com, LexisNexis, Westlaw
Function: Ref serv available
Open Mon-Fri 8-5
Restriction: Non-circulating to the pub

P   UTAH STATE LIBRARY DIVISION*, 250 N 1950 West, Ste A,
84116-7901. SAN 362-5710. Tel: 801-715-6777. Toll Free Tel:
800-662-9150. FAX: 801-715-6767. TDD: 901-715-6721. Web Site:
www.library.utah.gov. *State Librn,* Donna Jones Morris; Tel: 801-715-6770,
E-mail: dmorris@utah.gov; *Asst Dir, Mgr, Libr Develop,* Cheryl Mansen;
Tel: 801-715-6747, E-mail: cmansen@utah.gov; *Res Mgr,* Craig Neilson;
Tel: 801-715-6750, E-mail: cneilson@utah.gov; *Govt Info Coordr,* Ray
Matthews; Tel: 801-715-6752, E-mail: raymatthews@utah.gov; *Acq, Circ,*
Roxann Rose; *ILL,* Kristen Stehel; Tel: 801-715-6753, E-mail:
kstehel@utah.gov; *Pub Relations,* Jeri Openshaw; Tel: 801-715-6737,
E-mail: jerio@utah.gov; Staff 67 (MLS 13, Non-MLS 54)
Founded 1957. Pop 2,615,129
Library Holdings: Bk Titles 47,654; Per Subs 83
Special Collections: Local Utah History Coll. State Document Depository
Automation Activity & Vendor Info: (Acquisitions) SirsiDynix;
(Cataloging) SirsiDynix; (Circulation) SirsiDynix; (OPAC) SirsiDynix;
(Serials) SirsiDynix
Database Vendor: OCLC FirstSearch
Publications: Directions for Utah Libraries; Directory of Public Libraries
in Utah; Utah Library Laws; Utah Trustee Manual
Partic in OCLC Online Computer Library Center, Inc; Utah Academic
Library Consortium; Utah Libr Network
Open Mon-Thurs 7-6
Bookmobiles: 9. Incharge, Cheryl Mansen

P   UTAH STATE LIBRARY DIVISION*, Program for the Blind & Disabled,
250 N 1950 West, Ste A, 84116-7901. SAN 316-9316. Tel: 801-715-6789.
Toll Free Tel: 800-453-4293, 800-662-5540. FAX: 801-715-6767. TDD:
801-715-6721. E-mail: blind@utah.gov. Web Site: blindlibrary.utah.gov.
Libr Prog Mgr, Bessie Oakes; E-mail: boakes@utah.gov; Staff 18 (MLS 4,
Non-MLS 14)
Founded 1957. Pop 13,000; Circ 267,000
Library Holdings: Bks on Deafness & Sign Lang 30; High Interest/Low
Vocabulary Bk Vols 1,829; Talking Bks 470,000
Special Collections: Mormon Literature Coll; Western Books Coll
Subject Interests: Mormon lit
Wireless access
Publications: The See Note Newsletter (Quarterly)
Special Services for the Deaf - TDD equip
Special Services for the Blind - Bks & mags in Braille, on rec, tape &
cassette; Descriptive video serv (DVS); Large print bks; Radio reading
serv; Rec & flexible discs
Open Mon-Thurs 7-6

C   WESTMINSTER COLLEGE*, Giovale Library, 1840 S 1300 East,
84105-3697. SAN 316-9340. Tel: 801-832-2250. Interlibrary Loan Service
Tel: 801-832-2262. FAX: 801-832-3109. Web Site:
www.westminstercollege.edu/library. *Dir,* Diane VanderPol; E-mail:
dvanderpol@westminstercollege.edu; *Coll,* David A Hales; E-mail:
dhales@westminstercollege.edu; *Instruction & Outreach,* Kerri Carter;
E-mail: kcarter@westminstercollege.edu; *Ser, Tech Serv,* M Diane Raines;
E-mail: draines@westminstercollege.edu; *Syst,* Jennifer Foy; E-mail:
jfoy@westminstercollege.edu; Staff 9 (MLS 5, Non-MLS 4)
Founded 1875. Enrl 2,800; Fac 132; Highest Degree: Master
Jul 2008-Jun 2009. Mats Exp $287,000, Books $90,000, Per/Ser (Incl.
Access Fees) $65,000, Micro $3,500, AV Mat $16,500, Electronic Ref Mat
(Incl. Access Fees) $112,000

Library Holdings: AV Mats 6,000; e-books 58,000; Bk Vols 124,000
Special Collections: Archival Material Relating to Early History of the College & Early History of the Presbyterian Church in Utah & Southern Idaho
Subject Interests: Modern poets, Utah landscape
Automation Activity & Vendor Info: (Acquisitions) SirsiDynix; (Cataloging) SirsiDynix; (Circulation) SirsiDynix; (Course Reserve) SirsiDynix; (ILL) OCLC ILLiad; (OPAC) SirsiDynix; (Serials) SirsiDynix
Wireless access
Special Services for the Blind - Assistive/Adapted tech devices, equip & products; Computer with voice synthesizer for visually impaired persons; Magnifiers; Reader equip; Scanner for conversion & translation of mats; Screen reader software
Open Mon-Thurs 7:30am-11pm, Fri 7:30-6, Sat 9-6, Sun 1-10
Restriction: Open to pub for ref & circ; with some limitations, Open to students, fac, staff & alumni

SANTAQUIN

P   SANTAQUIN CITY LIBRARY*, 20 W 100 S, 84655. SAN 322-8606. Tel: 801-754-3030. FAX: 801-754-3030. E-mail: contact@santaquinlibrary.org. Web Site: santaquinlibrary.org. *Dir,* Lyn Oryall; Staff 1 (Non-MLS 1)
Founded 1932. Pop 8,500; Circ 37,800
Automation Activity & Vendor Info: (Acquisitions) Follett Software; (Cataloging) Follett Software; (Circulation) Follett Software
Wireless access
Function: Bks on CD, Children's prog, Computers for patron use, Copy machines, Electronic databases & coll, Free DVD rentals, ILL available, Mail & tel request accepted, Online cat, Photocopying/Printing, Pub access computers, Ref & res, Spoken cassettes & CDs, Summer reading prog, Tax forms, Telephone ref, VHS videos
Open Mon-Thurs 12-8, Fri 12-5
Friends of the Library Group

SMITHFIELD

P   SMITHFIELD PUBLIC LIBRARY*, 25 N Main St, 84335-1957. (Mail add: PO Box 35, 84335-0035), SAN 316-9359. Tel: 435-563-3555. Web Site: smithfieldcity.org. *Dir,* Marilyn Benavides; E-mail: mbenavides@smithfieldcity.org; *Asst Librn,* Karen Bowling; *Asst Librn,* Kathy Downs
Pop 7,600; Circ 65,000
Library Holdings: Bk Vols 30,000; Per Subs 32
Automation Activity & Vendor Info: (Cataloging) Follett Software; (Circulation) Follett Software
Mem of Fayette County Library System
Open Mon-Thurs 11-7, Fri 2:30-5, Sat 11-3

SOUTH SALT LAKE

S   TESTING ENGINEERS INTERNATIONAL, INC, TEi-Library Services, 3455 S 500 West, 84115-4234. (Mail add: PO Box 57025, Murray, 84157-0025), SAN 316-9189. Tel: 801-262-2332. FAX: 801-262-2363. E-mail: info@tei-libsvcs.com. Web Site: www.TEi-LibSvcs.com. *Pres,* Matthew MacGregor; E-mail: matt@tei-test.com; *Librn,* Suzanne Turner
Founded 1963
Jan 2008-Dec 2008 Income $125,000, Locally Generated Income $15,000, Parent Institution $75,000, Other $35,000. Mats Exp $75,000, Books $5,000, Per/Ser (Incl. Access Fees) $10,000, Other Print Mats $5,000, AV Equip $5,000, Electronic Ref Mat (Incl. Access Fees) $50,000. Sal $45,000
Library Holdings: CDs 150; DVDs 150; Electronic Media & Resources 25,000; Bk Vols 45,000; Per Subs 25; Videos 50
Special Collections: Industry Standards
Subject Interests: Manufacturing, Sci ref, Test standards
Function: For res purposes, Photocopying/Printing, Prof lending libr
Restriction: By permission only, Fee for pub use, Lending libr only via mail, Photo ID required for access, Restricted access

SPANISH FORK

P   SPANISH FORK PUBLIC LIBRARY, 49 S Main St, 84660-2030. SAN 316-9367. Tel: 801-804-4480. FAX: 801-798-5014. Web Site: www.spanishfork.org. *Dir,* Pam Jackson; *Ch,* Sue Griggs; *Syst Coordr,* Chrissy Henry
Pop 35,000
Library Holdings: AV Mats 10,172; DVDs 3,981; e-books 67; Large Print Bks 1,040; Bk Vols 64,000; Per Subs 91
Automation Activity & Vendor Info: (Circulation) ByWater Solutions; (ILL) OCLC; (OPAC) ByWater Solutions

Wireless access
Open Mon-Thurs 10-8, Fri & Sat 12-6

SPRINGVILLE

P   SPRINGVILLE PUBLIC LIBRARY*, 50 S Main St, 84663. SAN 316-9391. Tel: 801-489-2720. Reference Tel: 801-491-7825. Administration Tel: 801-489-2722. FAX: 801-489-2709. Web Site: springvillelibrary.org. *Dir,* Pamela Vaughn; E-mail: pvaughn@springville.org; *Ch,* Vivian Milius; E-mail: vmilius@springville.org; Staff 4 (MLS 2, Non-MLS 2)
Founded 1916. Pop 20,424
Library Holdings: AV Mats 10,108; Large Print Bks 370; Bk Vols 73,267; Per Subs 150
Special Collections: Local History Coll; Springville History Coll
Automation Activity & Vendor Info: (Cataloging) TLC (The Library Corporation); (Circulation) TLC (The Library Corporation); (OPAC) Wil-Tech Software Ltd
Open Mon-Thurs 10-9, Fri 10-6, Sat 10-4
Friends of the Library Group

TOOELE

P   TOOELE CITY PUBLIC LIBRARY*, 128 W Vine St, 84074-2059. SAN 316-9405. Tel: 435-882-2182. FAX: 435-882-6843. E-mail: library@tooelecity.org. Web Site: www.tooelecity.org/tcl/library.html. *Dir,* Jami Carter; E-mail: jamic@tooelecity.org
Founded 1910. Pop 17,500; Circ 130,781
Library Holdings: Bk Vols 57,373
Special Collections: State Document Depository
Automation Activity & Vendor Info: (Cataloging) Follett Software; (Circulation) Follett Software; (OPAC) Follett Software
Open Tues-Fri 10-8, Sat 10:30-6
Friends of the Library Group

TREMONTON

P   TREMONTON CITY LIBRARY*, 210 N Tremont St, 84337-1329. SAN 316-9413. Tel: 435-257-9525. FAX: 435-257-9526. E-mail: library@tremontoncity.com. Web Site: www.tremontonlibrary.org. *Dir,* Kim L Griffiths; E-mail: library@tremontoncity.com
Pop 6,380; Circ 59,145
Library Holdings: Bk Titles 23,583; Bk Vols 24,165; Per Subs 57
Automation Activity & Vendor Info: (Acquisitions) Follett Software; (Cataloging) Follett Software; (Circulation) Follett Software; (OPAC) Follett Software
Wireless access
Open Mon-Thurs 1-8, Fri 1-7, Sat 9-3
Friends of the Library Group

VERNAL

G   BUREAU OF LAND MANAGEMENT LIBRARY*, 170 S 500 E, 84078. SAN 316-9421. Tel: 435-781-4400. FAX: 435-781-3420.
Library Holdings: Bk Vols 2,000; Per Subs 100
Open Mon-Fri 7:45-4:30

P   UINTAH COUNTY LIBRARY, 204 E 100 N, 84078-2695. SAN 316-943X. Tel: 435-789-0091. FAX: 435-789-6822. E-mail: books@co.uintah.ut.us. Web Site: uintahbuilds.blogspot.com, www.uintah.lib.ut.us. *Dir,* Samuel J Passey; E-mail: passey@co.uintah.ut.us; *Coll Develop,* Darleen Kinsey; Tel: 435-789-0091, Ext 15; Staff 23 (MLS 1, Non-MLS 22)
Founded 1908. Pop 26,155; Circ 524,461
Jan 2006-Dec 2006 Income $1,243,000. Mats Exp $441,000, Books $70,000, Per/Ser (Incl. Access Fees) $8,000, Manu Arch $245,000, AV Mat $30,000, Electronic Ref Mat (Incl. Access Fees) $18,000, Presv $70,000. Sal $721,300 (Prof $64,750)
Library Holdings: CDs 3,421; DVDs 9,809; e-books 5,000; Electronic Media & Resources 1,441; High Interest/Low Vocabulary Bk Vols 500; Large Print Bks 1,313; Music Scores 2,386; Bk Vols 97,592; Per Subs 159
Special Collections: Oral History
Subject Interests: Local hist
Automation Activity & Vendor Info: (Cataloging) SirsiDynix; (Circulation) SirsiDynix; (OPAC) SirsiDynix
Publications: A History of Uintah County: Scratching the Surface; Behind Swinging Doors: Colorful History; Blue Mountain Folks: Their Lives & Legends; Outlaw Trail History Journal; Rivers We Know; Settlements of Uintah County: Digging Deeper
Open Mon-Thurs 10-9, Fri & Sat 10-6

VERMONT

Date of Statistics: FY 2010
Population, 2008 Census (est.): 625,741
Population Served by Public Libraries: 605,850
Total Volumes in Public Libraries: 3,202,125
  Volumes Per Capita: 5.12
Total Public Library Circulation: 4,850,945
  Circulation Per Capita: 7.75
Total Public Library Income (not including Grants-in-Aid):
  $19,904,037
  Source of Income: Public funds + fundraising
  Income Per Capita: $33.92
Federal (Library Services & Technology Act): $36,957
Number of Bookmobiles in State: 5

ALBANY

P   ALBANY TOWN LIBRARY, 530 Main St, 05820. (Mail add: PO Box 194, 05820), SAN 376-4915. Tel: 802-755-6107. *Librn,* Amanda Mason
Library Holdings: Bk Vols 3,000; Per Subs 10
Wireless access
Open Tues 12-4:30 & 6-8, Thurs 12-4:30, Sat 9-12

ALBURG

P   ALBURG PUBLIC LIBRARY*, 16 S Main St, 05440. (Mail add: PO Box 344, 05440), SAN 376-3439. Tel: 802-796-6077. FAX: 802-796-3089. E-mail: alburgpl@fairpoint.net. Web Site: alburghlibrary.org. *Librn,* Marybelle Singer; Staff 2 (Non-MLS 2)
Founded 1917. Pop 2,010
Jan 2010-Dec 2010 Income $78,226. Mats Exp $4,582. Sal $43,000
Library Holdings: Audiobooks 75; DVDs 200; Large Print Bks 400; Bk Vols 12,305; Per Subs 35
Wireless access
Function: Adult bk club, Adult literacy prog, Bk reviews (Group), Bks on cassette, Bks on CD, Children's prog, Computer training, Computers for patron use, Copy machines, Fax serv, Free DVD rentals, Handicapped accessible, Holiday prog, Homebound delivery serv, ILL available, Mail & tel request accepted, Mail loans to mem, Music CDs, Newsp ref libr, Photocopying/Printing, Preschool outreach, Printer for laptops & handheld devices, Prog for adults, Prog for children & young adult, Pub access computers, Senior computer classes, Story hour, Summer reading prog, Tax forms, Teen prog, VHS videos, Video lending libr, Wheelchair accessible, Workshops
Open Mon, Wed & Thurs 1-5, Tues 9-5, Fri 1-9, Sat 10-1
Friends of the Library Group

ARLINGTON

P   MARTHA CANFIELD MEMORIAL FREE LIBRARY*, 528 E Arlington Rd, 05250. (Mail add: PO Box 267, 05250-0267), SAN 316-9456. Tel: 802-375-6153. FAX: 802-375-6153. Web Site: www.marthacanfieldlibrary.org. *Dir,* Phyllis Skidmore; E-mail: phyllis.marthacanfield.org; Staff 2 (Non-MLS 2)
Founded 1803. Pop 3,700; Circ 19,500
Jan 2005-Dec 2005 Income $74,000. Mats Exp $7,000. Sal $27,000 (Prof $18,500)
Library Holdings: AV Mats 800; Large Print Bks 700; Bk Titles 24,000; Per Subs 12
Special Collections: Vermontiana (Dr George Russell Coll), bks, clipping, mss, photog
Automation Activity & Vendor Info: (Cataloging) Follett Software; (Circulation) Follett Software; (OPAC) Follett Software
Wireless access
Function: Art exhibits, Bks on CD, Computers for patron use, Copy machines, Handicapped accessible, Music CDs, Photocopying/Printing, Tax forms, VHS videos

Partic in OCLC Online Computer Library Center, Inc
Open Tues & Thurs 9-8, Wed 9-5, Fri 2-6, Sat 10-3

ASCUTNEY

P   WEATHERSFIELD PROCTOR LIBRARY*, 5181 Rte 5, 05030. (Mail add: PO Box 519, 05030-0519), SAN 362-5869. Tel: 802-674-2863. E-mail: library@weathersfield.org. Web Site: www.weathersfield.org. *Dir,* Amity Aldridge; *Asst Librn,* Lynn Esty
Founded 1902. Pop 2,788
Jul 2006-Jun 2007 Income $42,000. Mats Exp $7,000. Sal $19,500
Library Holdings: AV Mats 288; Bk Vols 6,908; Per Subs 31; Talking Bks 432
Subject Interests: Local hist
Wireless access
Function: ILL available, Online searches, Photocopying/Printing, Prog for children & young adult, Ref & res, Video lending libr, Wheelchair accessible
Open Wed-Fri 12-6, Sat 9-1
Friends of the Library Group

BAKERSFIELD

P   H F BRIGHAM FREE PUBLIC LIBRARY, 104 Main St, 05441. (Mail add: PO Box 5, 05441-0005), SAN 316-9464. Tel: 802-827-4414. Web Site: hfbrighamlibrary.wordpress.com. *Dir,* Cheryll DeRue; *Asst Librn,* Helen Bushey; *Asst Librn,* Mary Schwartz; Staff 3 (MLS 1, Non-MLS 2)
Pop 1,015; Circ 3,692
Library Holdings: Bk Titles 5,850; Per Subs 15
Wireless access
Open Mon 2-7, Wed 2-6, Thurs 9-12 & 2-7, Sat 9-1

BARNARD

P   CHARLES B DANFORTH PUBLIC LIBRARY*, 6208 VT Rte 12, 05031. (Mail add: PO Box 204, 05031-0204), SAN 316-9472. Tel: 802-234-9408. *Librn,* Melissa Strayton; *Libr Tech,* Edwards Margaret
Pop 960; Circ 1,400
Library Holdings: Bk Vols 10,000
Open Wed 6pm-8pm, Sat 10-Noon

BARNET

P   BARNET PUBLIC LIBRARY*, 147 Church St, 05821. (Mail add: PO Box 34, 05821-0034), SAN 316-9480. Tel: 802-633-4436. FAX: 802-633-4436. E-mail: barnetpl@hotmail.com. *Librn,* Sherry Tolle; *Asst Librn,* Dylan Ford; Staff 1 (Non-MLS 1)
Founded 1900. Pop 1,690; Circ 2,596
Library Holdings: AV Mats 125; CDs 25; DVDs 20; Large Print Bks 100; Bk Vols 7,500; Per Subs 12; Talking Bks 150; Videos 50
Special Collections: Large Print Books
Subject Interests: Vt
Wireless access

Function: Handicapped accessible, Home delivery & serv to Sr ctr & nursing homes, Homebound delivery serv, ILL available, Photocopying/Printing, Prog for children & young adult
Special Services for the Blind - Large print bks
Open Mon 6:30-8:30, Tues-Thurs 12:30-4, Sat 10-2

BARRE

P ALDRICH PUBLIC LIBRARY*, Six Washington St, 05641-4227. SAN 316-9499. Tel: 802-476-7550. FAX: 802-479-0450 (Call before sending fax). E-mail: aldrichlibrary@charter.net. Web Site: www.aldrich.lib.vt.us/. *Dir,* Karen E Lane; Tel: 802-476-7550, Ext 307; *Head, Tech Serv,* Mary-Ann S Huang; *Circ Librn,* Mary Ellen Boisvert; *Outreach Serv Librn,* Jacqueline C Walker; *Network Tech, Ref & ILL Librn,* Lee Aura Bonamico; *Youth Serv Librn,* Adrianne Scucces; *Asst Circ Librn,* Nancy Buttura; *Asst Circ Librn,* Mary Gagne; *Asst Circ Librn,* Renate Gelineau; *Asst Circ Librn,* Barbara Menard; Staff 12 (Non-MLS 12)
Founded 1907. Pop 16,893; Circ 53,172
Library Holdings: CDs 2,374; DVDs 2,548; Large Print Bks 1,515; Bk Vols 49,149; Per Subs 112; Talking Bks 1,700
Special Collections: Archives of Barre History; Barre Museum; Vermont History Coll
Subject Interests: Am sculpture, Ethnic hist, European sculpture, Immigration, Indust hist, Labor hist, Political movements
Automation Activity & Vendor Info: (Cataloging) Follett Software; (Circulation) Follett Software; (OPAC) Follett Software
Wireless access
Publications: Barre Granite Heritage with Guide to the Cemeteries (1997) (Local historical information); Barre in Retrospect 1776-1995 (community hist) (Local historical information); Barre, VT; An Annotated Bibliography (1979) (Local historical information); Guide to the Manuscript Holdings of the Archives of Barre History (1997) (Local historical information)
Special Services for the Blind - Bks on cassette; Closed circuit TV magnifier; Home delivery serv; Large print bks
Open Mon-Wed 12-8, Thurs 10-6, Fri 12-6, Sat 10-1
Friends of the Library Group
Branches: 1
EAST BARRE BRANCH, 134 Mill St, East Barre, 05649. (Mail add: Six Washington St, 05641-4227). Tel: 802-476-5118. *Librn,* John Thomas Poeton
Library Holdings: Bk Vols 4,000
Open Tues 9-12, Wed 2-6, Sat 10-1
Friends of the Library Group

S VERMONT GRAND LODGE LIBRARY*, 49 East Rd - Berlin, 05641-5390. Tel: 802-223-1883. FAX: 802-223-2187. E-mail: glsec@vtfreemasons.org. Web Site: www.vtfreemasons.org. *Librn,* Donald C Brown
Library Holdings: Bk Vols 6,000
Open Mon-Thurs 8-4

S VERMONT HISTORICAL SOCIETY LIBRARY*, Vermont History Ctr, 60 Washington St, 05641-4209. SAN 317-073X. Tel: 802-479-8509. FAX: 802-479-8510. E-mail: vhs-library@state.vt.us. Web Site: www.vermonthistory.org. *Librn,* Paul A Carnahan; *Asst Librn,* Marjorie Strong; Staff 2 (MLS 2)
Founded 1838
Library Holdings: Bk Vols 53,000; Per Subs 220
Special Collections: Broadside Coll; Manuscripts Coll; Photograph Coll; Sheet Music Coll
Subject Interests: Genealogy, Lower Can hist, New England, NY hist, Vt
Automation Activity & Vendor Info: (Cataloging) SIRSI WorkFlows; (OPAC) SIRSI Unicorn
Partic in Lyrasis
Open Tues-Fri 9-4:30
Restriction: Non-circulating to the pub

BARTON

P BARTON PUBLIC LIBRARY*, 100 Church St, 05822. (Mail add: PO Box 549, 05822-0549), SAN 316-9510. Tel: 802-525-6524. FAX: 802-525-6524. E-mail: bartonpubliclibrary@yahoo.com. *Librn,* Toni Eubanks
Founded 1914. Pop 1,553
Library Holdings: DVDs 40; Large Print Bks 300; Bk Vols 16,000; Per Subs 35; Talking Bks 300; Videos 300
Function: Homebound delivery serv, ILL available, Prog for children & young adult, Summer reading prog, Telephone ref
Open Mon & Fri 1-7, Wed 9-12 & 1-7
Friends of the Library Group

BELLOWS FALLS

P ROCKINGHAM FREE PUBLIC LIBRARY*, 65 Westminster St, 05101. SAN 316-9529. Tel: 802-463-4270. FAX: 802-463-1566. E-mail: rocklib@sover.net. Web Site: www.rockingham.lib.vt.us. *Dir,* Celina

Houlne; E-mail: celina@rockinghamlibrary.org; Staff 5.35 (MLS 2.25, Non-MLS 3.1)
Founded 1887. Pop 5,100; Circ 51,696
Library Holdings: AV Mats 3,524; Bk Vols 35,265; Per Subs 87
Special Collections: Rockingham Historical Collection
Subject Interests: Genealogy, Local hist
Automation Activity & Vendor Info: (Acquisitions) Baker & Taylor; (Cataloging) Baker & Taylor; (Circulation) LibLime; (OPAC) LibLime; (Serials) LibLime
Database Vendor: Gale Cengage Learning
Wireless access
Open Mon-Wed 10-7, Thurs & Fri 10-5:30, Sat 10-2
Friends of the Library Group

BELMONT

P MOUNT HOLLY TOWN LIBRARY*, 26 Maple Hill Rd, 05730. (Mail add: PO Box 93, 05730-0093), SAN 320-5177. Tel: 802-259-3707. E-mail: mthollylibrary@gmaul.com. *Librn,* Lynne Herbst; Staff 1 (MLS 1)
Founded 1913. Pop 1,350; Circ 1,200
Sept 2008-Aug 2009 Income $8,000
Library Holdings: Audiobooks 300; Large Print Bks 120; Bk Vols 12,000; Videos 200
Database Vendor: Ingram Library Services
Wireless access
Open Mon & Wed 3-7, Sat 9-1, Sun 2-4

BENNINGTON

C BENNINGTON COLLEGE*, Crossett Library, One College Dr, 05201-6001. SAN 362-5923. Tel: 802-440-4610. Circulation Tel: 802-440-4600. Interlibrary Loan Service Tel: 802-440-4605. Reference Tel: 802-440-4737. FAX: 802-440-4580. E-mail: library@bennington.edu. *Librn,* Oceana Wilson; *Coordr, Ser,* Position Currently Open; *Info Tech Librn,* Kathleen Berry; *Instruction Coordr, Ref & Instrul Serv Librn,* Joe Tucker; *Tech Serv Librn,* Vanessa Haverkoch; Tel: 802-440-4602; Staff 4 (MLS 3, Non-MLS 1)
Founded 1932. Enrl 750; Fac 105; Highest Degree: Master
Library Holdings: AV Mats 3,000; Bk Titles 94,000; Bk Vols 100,000; Per Subs 275
Special Collections: Literary Reviews; Photography
Subject Interests: Art, Dance, Lit
Automation Activity & Vendor Info: (Cataloging) Innovative Interfaces, Inc; (Circulation) Innovative Interfaces, Inc; (ILL) OCLC; (OPAC) Innovative Interfaces, Inc
Database Vendor: Gale Cengage Learning, LexisNexis, OCLC FirstSearch, SerialsSolutions
Partic in Lyrasis; Nylink
Open Mon-Thurs 8:30am-9pm, Fri 8:30-5, Sat 10-8, Sun 1-9
Departmental Libraries:
JENNINGS MUSIC LIBRARY, One College Dr, Jennings Music Bldg, 05201, SAN 362-5958. Tel: 802-440-4512. FAX: 802-440-4511. Web Site: bennington.edu/library. *Head Music Librn,* Susan Reiss; E-mail: sreiss@bennington.edu
Library Holdings: CDs 5,000; DVDs 50; Music Scores 8,000; Bk Titles 700; Bk Vols 400; Per Subs 8; Videos 145
Subject Interests: Contemporary chamber music
Automation Activity & Vendor Info: (Circulation) Innovative Interfaces, Inc - OCLC
Restriction: Not open to pub, Open to students, fac & staff

P BENNINGTON FREE LIBRARY*, 101 Silver St, 05201. SAN 316-9545. Tel: 802-442-9051. Web Site: bennington.freelibrary.org. *Dir,* Lynne Fonteneau-McCann; *Cat Librn,* Wendy Sharkey; *Ch, YA Librn,* Linda Donigan; *Ch, YA Librn,* Chris Poggi; *Circ Librn,* Joan Douglass; *Ref Librn,* Karson Kiesinger; *Tech Serv,* Judy Pembroke
Founded 1865. Pop 20,500; Circ 90,336
Library Holdings: Bk Titles 56,105; Per Subs 187
Special Collections: Bennington Banner, 1903-present, flm
Subject Interests: Town hist, Vt hist
Open Mon 10-7, Tues & Wed 10-5, Thurs 1-7, Fri 1-5, Sat 10-5 (10-1 Summer)
Friends of the Library Group

S BENNINGTON MUSEUM, Research Library, 75 Main St, 05201. SAN 316-9553. Tel: 802-447-1571. FAX: 802-442-8305. Web Site: www.benningtonmuseum.org/library.html. *Librn,* Tyler Resch; E-mail: tresch@benningtonmuseum.org
Founded 1928
Library Holdings: Bk Titles 4,500
Special Collections: American Biographical & Genealogical (Rider) Index; Bennington County Census, microfilm; Bennington Town Records & Maps; Bennington's Old First Church Records; Early Vital Records for Southern New England States; Essays & Data on Early Families in New England: Cutter, Savage & Others; Genealogy Columns from Boston Transcript,

Hartford Times; Hemenway's Six-Volume 19th Century Vermont Gazetteer: Town, County & State Histories for Vermont, New England, New York; Military Rosters & Data for Vermont, Nearby States: Revolution, Civil War; Mormon IGI Microfiche for New England (except Maine) & New York; Published Family Histories, New England-Oriented; Registers of New England Historic Genealogical Society, since 1847; The Day Papers: 25 Scrapbooks of Discerning News Clips, 1870-1916; The Harwood Diaries: Rich Details of Life Between 1803 & 1837; US Census Indexes, 1790-1850 for New England, New York & Others; Vermont & Bennington Regional Resources: Aldrich Histories & Child Directories of Vermont Counties, circa 1880; Vermont Vital Records to 1941, microfilm
Subject Interests: Genealogy, Regional hist
Wireless access
Function: Res libr
Open Mon-Sat 1-5
Restriction: Non-circulating
Friends of the Library Group

C   SOUTHERN VERMONT COLLEGE LIBRARY, 982 Mansion Dr, 05201-6002. SAN 316-9561. Tel: 802-447-6311. FAX: 802-447-4695. E-mail: libstaff@svc.edu. Web Site: www.svc.edu. *Dir,* Sarah Sanfilippo; E-mail: ssanfilippo@svc.edu; *Ref Serv,* Andrea Robare; E-mail: arobare@svc.edu; Staff 2 (MLS 2)
Founded 1926. Enrl 524; Highest Degree: Bachelor
Library Holdings: Bk Vols 20,000; Per Subs 95
Subject Interests: Communication, Criminal justice, Healthcare, Nursing, Soc sci
Automation Activity & Vendor Info: (Cataloging) TLC (The Library Corporation); (Circulation) TLC (The Library Corporation); (OPAC) TLC (The Library Corporation)
Partic in Lyrasis
Open Mon-Thurs 7:45am-10pm, Fri 7:45-5, Sat 12-5, Sun 12-10

M   SOUTHWESTERN VERMONT HEALTH CARE*, Health Sciences Library, 100 Hospital Dr, 05201. SAN 362-6016. Tel: 802-447-5120. FAX: 802-447-5388. E-mail: hslibrary@phin.org. *Librn,* Gary Strubel; Staff 1 (MLS 1)
Founded 1969
Library Holdings: Bk Titles 800; Bk Vols 947; Per Subs 37
Subject Interests: Allied health, Basic sci, Biomed sci, Med, Nursing, Surgery
Automation Activity & Vendor Info: (Cataloging) EOS International; (OPAC) EOS International
Database Vendor: EBSCOhost, ProQuest
Publications: Library Newsletter
Partic in Basic Health Sciences Library Network; Health Sciences Libraries of New Hampshire & Vermont; North Atlantic Health Sciences Libraries, Inc
Open Mon-Fri 8-4

G   VERMONT VETERANS HOME LIBRARY*, 325 North St, 05201. SAN 321-1037. Tel: 802-442-6353. FAX: 802-447-2757. *In Charge,* Michele Burgess; Tel: 802-447-6520, E-mail: michele.burgess@state.vt.us
Founded 1884
Library Holdings: Bk Vols 800; Per Subs 25
Special Collections: Civil War Coll
Restriction: Residents only

BENSON

P   BENSON VILLAGE LIBRARY*, 2724 Stage Rd, 05731. (Mail add: PO Box 163, 05731), SAN 376-3455. Tel: 802-537-4181. FAX: 802-537-2612. E-mail: library@benson-vt.com. *Librn,* Jacqueline Lussier
Pop 847
Library Holdings: Bk Vols 4,500; Talking Bks 30
Open Wed 3-7, Sat 11-3

BERLIN

M   CENTRAL VERMONT MEDICAL CENTER*, Health Sciences Library, 130 Fisher Rd, 05602. (Mail add: PO Box 547, Barre, 05641-0547), SAN 316-957X. Tel: 802-371-4205. FAX: 803-371-4575. E-mail: biomed.reference@dartmouth.edu. *Actg Dir,* Cindy Stewart
Founded 1970
Library Holdings: Bk Titles 400; Bk Vols 500; Per Subs 70
Subject Interests: Allied health lit, Med, Nursing
Restriction: Open to pub by appt only

P   VERMONT REGIONAL LIBRARY FOR THE BLIND & PHYSICALLY HANDICAPPED*, Vermont Dept of Libraries Special Services Unit, 578 Paine Turnpike N, 05602. SAN 317-0748. Tel: 802-828-3273. Toll Free Tel: 800-479-1711 (Vermont only). FAX: 802-828-2199. E-mail: ssu@mail.dol.state.vt.us. Web Site: dol.state.vt.us. *Librn,* Teresa Faust; E-mail: teresa.faust@state.vt.us; *Asst Librn,* Jennifer Hart; Staff 4 (MLS 1, Non-MLS 3)

Founded 1976. Pop 1,400; Circ 63,840
Library Holdings: Braille Volumes 119; Bk Titles 8,169; Bk Vols 8,583; Talking Bks 52,184; Videos 348
Special Collections: Handicaps Reference Material
Automation Activity & Vendor Info: (Cataloging) SirsiDynix; (Circulation) SirsiDynix; (ILL) SirsiDynix; (OPAC) SirsiDynix
Special Services for the Blind - BiFolkal kits; Bks & mags in Braille, on rec, tape & cassette; Bks on cassette; Cassette playback machines; Children's Braille; Descriptive video serv (DVS); Digital talking bk; Large print bks; Newsletter (in large print, Braille or on cassette); Newsline for the Blind; Talking bks
Open Mon-Fri 7:45-4:30

BETHEL

P   BETHEL PUBLIC LIBRARY*, 106 Main St, 05032. (Mail add: PO Box 354, 05032-0354), SAN 316-9596. Tel: 802-234-9107. *Librn,* Cathy Day
Founded 1893. Pop 1,980; Circ 10,090
Library Holdings: Bk Vols 12,000; Per Subs 38
Open Mon 2-7 Wed 1-7, Sat 9-1

BONDVILLE

P   WINHALL MEMORIAL LIBRARY*, Two Lower Tayler Hill Rd, 05340. (Mail add: PO Box 738, 05340-0738), SAN 316-960X. Tel: 802-297-9741. *Librn,* Brian Van Horn
Pop 482; Circ 6,400
Library Holdings: Bk Vols 7,000
Special Collections: Cook & needlepoint bks
Open Tues & Thurs 4-7

BRADFORD

P   BRADFORD PUBLIC LIBRARY*, 21 S Main St, 05033. (Mail add: PO Box 619, 05033-0619), SAN 316-9618. Tel: 802-222-4536. *Librn,* Debra Tinkham
Founded 1796. Pop 2,800; Circ 20,330
Jan 2006-Dec 2006 Income $35,000. Mats Exp $10,000, Books $9,000, AV Mat $1,000. Sal $23,000
Library Holdings: Large Print Bks 70; Bk Titles 12,000; Per Subs 25; Talking Bks 50; Videos 100
Special Collections: Historical (Trotter Coll), bks, logs, artifacts
Special Services for the Blind - Talking bks
Open Wed Noon-8, Thurs 11-5, Fri 10-5, Sat 9-2

BRANDON

P   BRANDON FREE PUBLIC LIBRARY*, Four Franklin St, 05733. SAN 316-9626. Tel: 802-247-8230. FAX: 802-247-1212. E-mail: info@brandonpubliclibrary.org. Web Site: www.brandonpubliclibrary.org. *Librn,* Stephanie Choma
Founded 1901. Pop 3,697; Circ 30,800
Library Holdings: AV Mats 2,000; Large Print Bks 400; Bk Titles 18,000; Per Subs 75; Talking Bks 800
Automation Activity & Vendor Info: (Cataloging) Mandarin Library Automation; (Circulation) Mandarin Library Automation; (OPAC) Mandarin Library Automation
Wireless access
Open Tues (Winter) 8:30-8, Wed, Thurs & Fri 8:30-5, Sat 8:30-1; Tues & Wed (Summer) 8:30-8, Thurs & Fri 8:30-5, Sat 8:30-Noon
Friends of the Library Group

BRATTLEBORO

M   BRATTLEBORO MEMORIAL HOSPITAL*, Medical Library, 17 Belmont Ave, 05301. SAN 316-9642. Tel: 802-257-8357. FAX: 802-257-8822. *Med Librn,* Jessie Casella; E-mail: jcsella@bmhvt.org; Staff 1 (MLS 1)
Founded 1970
Oct 2005-Sept 2006 Income $32,470. Mats Exp $13,275, Books $5,225, Per/Ser (Incl. Access Fees) $6,300
Library Holdings: Bk Titles 1,600; Per Subs 62
Subject Interests: Med, Nursing
Partic in Basic Health Sciences Library Network; Health Sciences Libraries of New Hampshire & Vermont; North Atlantic Health Sciences Libraries, Inc
Open Mon & Thurs 9-4:30, Tues 9-3:30

M   BRATTLEBORO RETREAT*, Asa Keyes Medical Library, 75 Linden St, 05301. (Mail add: PO Box 803, 05302-0803), SAN 321-8600. Tel: 802-258-3737, Ext 3221. FAX: 802-258-3796. *Dir, Libr Serv,* Brenda Nichols; E-mail: bnichols@retreathealthcare.org
Library Holdings: Bk Vols 4,500; Per Subs 20
Subject Interests: Behav sci, Child psychology, Eating disorders, Geriatric psychiatry, Partial hospitalization, Substance abuse, Substance treatment
Partic in Health Sciences Libraries of New Hampshire & Vermont
Restriction: Non-circulating to the pub, Open by appt only

P   BROOKS MEMORIAL LIBRARY*, 224 Main St, 05301. SAN 362-6040. Tel: 802-254-5290. Interlibrary Loan Service Tel: 802-254-5290, Ext 107. Reference Tel: 802-254-5290, Ext 109. FAX: 802-257-2309. E-mail: brattlib@brooks.lib.vt.us. Web Site: www.brooks.lib.vt.us, www.youseemore.com/brooksmemorial. *Dir,* Jerry J Carbone; E-mail: jerry@brooks.lib.vt.us; *Cat, Tech Serv,* Leslie Markey; *Ch,* Sandra King; *ILL, Ref,* Jeanne Walsh; Staff 12 (MLS 4, Non-MLS 8)
Founded 1882. Pop 12,005; Circ 180,000
Library Holdings: Audiobooks 4,229; DVDs 2,554; Electronic Media & Resources 35; Bk Vols 72,606; Per Subs 260
Special Collections: Brattleboro & Surrounding Area (Local History Coll), mixed media; Fine Arts Coll (paintings, drawings, bronzes, sculpted marble); Genealogy (Lawson Coll); Gordon Crandall Abenaki Artifacts; Local History (Bratteboro Photo, Porter Thayer Photo & Benjamin Crown Photo Colls); Windam World Affairs Council Archives
Automation Activity & Vendor Info: (Acquisitions) TLC (The Library Corporation); (Cataloging) TLC (The Library Corporation); (Circulation) TLC (The Library Corporation); (OPAC) TLC (The Library Corporation); (Serials) TLC (The Library Corporation)
Database Vendor: EBSCO Auto Repair Reference, EBSCOhost, Gale Cengage Learning, infoUSA, netLibrary, OCLC FirstSearch, Overdrive, Inc, TLC (The Library Corporation)
Wireless access
Publications: Friends of the Library (Quarterly); Friends of the Library, The Brooks Readers
Special Services for the Blind - Extensive large print coll; Large print bks; Low vision equip
Open Mon-Wed 10-9, Thurs 1-6, Fri 10-6, Sat 10-2
Friends of the Library Group

C   SIT GRADUATE INSTITUTE/SIT STUDY ABROAD, Donald B Watt Library, One Kipling Rd, 05302. (Mail add: PO Box 676, 05302-0676), SAN 316-9677. Tel: 802-258-3354. Interlibrary Loan Service Tel: 802-258-3356. Administration Tel: 802-258-3329. Toll Free Tel: 800-257-7751. FAX: 802-258-3248. E-mail: library@sit.edu. Web Site: www.sit.edu/library. *Libr Dir,* Oscar Lanza-Galindo; E-mail: oscar.lanzagalindo@sit.edu; *Archives Coordr,* Shirley L Capron; E-mail: shirley.capron@sit.edu; *Discovery & Access Mgr,* April Sommerville; E-mail: april.sommerville@sit.edu; Staff 3 (MLS 1, Non-MLS 2)
Founded 1967. Enrl 1,250; Fac 35; Highest Degree: Master
Library Holdings: AV Mats 1,600; e-books 15,000; e-journals 12,000; Bk Titles 30,000; Bk Vols 35,000; Per Subs 12,000
Special Collections: Foreign Language & ESL Learning Materials (Language Coll); Rob Cash Memorial Coll; SIETAR Coll; Student's Master Theses Coll
Subject Interests: Area studies, Bicultural studies, Bilingual studies, Educ
Automation Activity & Vendor Info: (Acquisitions) LibLime; (Cataloging) LibLime; (Circulation) Ex Libris Group; (ILL) OCLC ILLiad; (OPAC) LibLime; (Serials) Ex Libris Group
Database Vendor: CQ Press, Ebooks Corporation, ebrary, EBSCOhost, Foundation Center, Gale Cengage Learning, JSTOR, LexisNexis, LibLime, netLibrary, OCLC FirstSearch, OCLC WorldCat, ProQuest, ScienceDirect, YBP Library Services
Wireless access
Function: e-mail & chat, Electronic databases & coll, Free DVD rentals, ILL available, Online cat, Online ref, Online searches
Partic in Westchester Academic Library Directors Organization (WALDO)
Open Mon-Fri 8am-10pm, Sat 10-6, Sun 10-10

BRISTOL

P   LAWRENCE MEMORIAL LIBRARY*, 40 North St, 05443. SAN 376-3358. Tel: 802-453-2366. E-mail: readmorenow@gmavt.net. Web Site: www.lawrencelibrary.net. *Librn,* Nancy Wilson; *Ch,* Marita Bathe-Schine; *YA Librn,* Paulita Washburn; *Circ,* Lynn Goldsmith
Library Holdings: Bk Vols 18,000; Per Subs 30
Automation Activity & Vendor Info: (Cataloging) Book Systems, Inc
Database Vendor: Gale Cengage Learning, ProQuest
Open Mon 10-5, Tues & Thurs 10-8, Wed & Fri 1-5, Sat 9-1

BROOKFIELD

P   BROOKFIELD FREE PUBLIC LIBRARY*, 40 Ralph Rd, 05036. (Mail add: PO Box 469, 05036), SAN 320-2739. Tel: 802-276-3358. FAX: 802-276-3926. E-mail: brookfieldpl@vals.state.vt.us. *Librn,* Florence Barnum; Staff 1 (Non-MLS 1)
Founded 1791. Pop 1,271; Circ 5,979
Library Holdings: Bk Titles 5,000
Special Collections: Brookfield Historical Society, Files
Open Mon & Wed 2:30-6:30, Fri 9-Noon, Sat 9-2

BROWNINGTON

S   ORLEANS COUNTY HISTORICAL SOCIETY, INC*, Old Stone House Library, 109 Old Stone House Rd, 05860. SAN 316-9723. Tel: 802-754-2022. FAX: 802-754-9336. E-mail: library@oldstonehousemuseum.org. Web Site: www.oldstonehousemuseum.org. *Dir,* Peggy Day Gibson; *Librn,* Sarah Dumas
Founded 1853
Library Holdings: Bk Titles 1,500
Special Collections: 19th Century School Textbooks
Subject Interests: Orleans County hist, Vt hist
Automation Activity & Vendor Info: (Cataloging) Mandarin Library Automation; (Circulation) Mandarin Library Automation; (OPAC) Mandarin Library Automation
Wireless access
Restriction: Non-circulating, Open by appt only

BURLINGTON

C   BURLINGTON COLLEGE LIBRARY*, 351 North Ave, 05401. Tel: 802-862-9616. FAX: 802-864-8408. Web Site: www.burlington.edu. *Libr Dir,* Jessica Allard; Staff 1 (MLS 1)
Enrl 200; Highest Degree: Master
Jul 2011-Jun 2012. Mats Exp $29,500. Sal $34,000
Library Holdings: DVDs 1,279; Bk Titles 16,373; Per Subs 50; Videos 748
Special Collections: Frank Manchel Film Study Coll
Subject Interests: Film studies, Transpersonal psychology
Automation Activity & Vendor Info: (ILL) OCLC ILLiad
Database Vendor: ARTstor, Gale Cengage Learning, JSTOR
Wireless access
Partic in Vermont Consortium of Academic Libraries
Open Mon-Thurs 9-9, Fri 9-5, Sat & Sun 10-4

C   CHAMPLAIN COLLEGE LIBRARY*, Miller Information Commons, 163 S Willard St, 05401. (Mail add: PO Box 670, 05401-0670), SAN 316-974X. Tel: 802-860-2717. Interlibrary Loan Service Tel: 802-651-5987. Reference Tel: 802-865-6486. Web Site: www.champlain.edu/library. *Dir,* Janet Cottrell; Tel: 802-865-6492, E-mail: cottrell@champlain.edu; *Assoc Dir, Coll Develop & Acq Librn,* Marie Kascus; Tel: 802-860-2718, E-mail: kascus@champlain.edu; *Cat & Syst Librn,* Michele Melia; *Emerging Tech Librn,* Andy Burkhardt; *Info Literacy Librn,* Sarah Cohen; *Ref & ILL Librn,* Brenda Racht; Tel: 802-651-5987, E-mail: racht@champlain.edu; *Ref/Instruction Librn,* Paula Olsen; Tel: 802-865-6486, E-mail: olsen@champlain.edu; *Circ Mgr,* Tammy Poquette; Tel: 802-865-6489, E-mail: poquette@champlain.edu; *Archives Coordr,* Christina Dunphy. Subject Specialists: *Children's lit,* Marie Kascus; *Bus,* Brenda Racht; *Polit sci,* Paula Olsen; Staff 12 (MLS 5, Non-MLS 7)
Founded 1878. Enrl 2,678; Fac 96; Highest Degree: Master
Library Holdings: e-books 40,000; Bk Vols 40,477; Per Subs 187
Special Collections: Art Book Coll; Champlain Col Hist; Col Archives; Vermontiana
Subject Interests: Bus mgt, Children's lit, Computer sci, Computing, Educ, Travel
Automation Activity & Vendor Info: (Acquisitions) Innovative Interfaces, Inc; (Cataloging) Innovative Interfaces, Inc; (Circulation) Innovative Interfaces, Inc; (Course Reserve) Innovative Interfaces, Inc; (ILL) OCLC; (OPAC) Innovative Interfaces, Inc
Database Vendor: ACM (Association for Computing Machinery), American Psychological Association (APA), ARTstor, Baker & Taylor, Brodart, ebrary, EBSCOhost, Emerald, Facts on File, Faulkner Information Services, Gale Cengage Learning, Hoovers, Innovative Interfaces, Inc, JSTOR, LexisNexis, Mergent Online, netLibrary, Project MUSE, ProQuest, Safari Books Online, ScienceDirect, SerialsSolutions
Wireless access
Partic in Lyrasis
Open Mon-Thurs 7:30am-Midnight, Fri 7:30am-10pm, Sat 10-10, Sun 10am-Midnight

R   EPISCOPAL CHURCH CENTER*, Bishops Library-Rock Point, Five Rock Point Rd, 05408. SAN 316-9774. Tel: 802-863-3431. FAX: 802-860-1562. *Librn,* Elizabeth Allison; E-mail: eallison@dioceseofvermont.org
Founded 1894
Library Holdings: Bk Vols 4,500
Function: For res purposes
Restriction: Open by appt only

P   FLETCHER FREE LIBRARY*, 235 College St, 05401. SAN 316-9782. Tel: 802-863-3403. Reference Tel: 802-865-7217. FAX: 802-865-7227. Web Site: www.fletcherfree.org. *Dir, Syst Adminr,* Robert Coleburn; Tel: 802-865-7218, E-mail: rcoleburn@ci.burlington.vt.us; *Dir,* Amber Collins; Tel: 802-865-7214, E-mail: acollins@ci.burlington.vt.us; *Dir,* Robert Resnik; Tel: 802-865-7222, E-mail: rresnik@ci.burlington.vt.us; *Adult Serv, Outreach Serv Librn,* Barbara Shatara; Tel: 802-865-7211, E-mail: bshatara@ci.burlington.vt.us; *Circ Mgr,* Toni Taginski; E-mail: ttaginski@ci.burlington.vt.us; *Acq,* Susan Bevins; Tel: 802-865-7221, E-mail: sbevins@ci.burlington.vt.us; *Ch,* Christine Demarais; Tel:

802-865-7216, E-mail: cdemarais@ci.burlington.vt.us; *Ch,* Rebecca Goldberg; E-mail: rgoldberg@ci.burlington.vt.us; *ILL,* Pham Nga; E-mail: npham@ci.burlington.vt.us; Staff 23 (MLS 7, Non-MLS 16)
Founded 1873. Pop 38,897; Circ 398,446
Jul 2008-Jun 2009 Income $1,594,245, State $1,721, City $1,592,524. Mats Exp $177,724, Books $132,225, AV Mat $23,494. Sal $830,078
Library Holdings: AV Mats 10,381; Bk Vols 123,543; Per Subs 281
Subject Interests: Local hist
Automation Activity & Vendor Info: (Acquisitions) SirsiDynix; (Cataloging) SirsiDynix; (Circulation) SirsiDynix; (OPAC) SirsiDynix
Wireless access
Publications: BiblioFile (Monthly)
Open Mon, Tues, Thurs & Fri 8:30-6, Wed 8:30-9, Sat 9-5:30, Sun 12-6
Friends of the Library Group

C   UNIVERSITY OF VERMONT LIBRARIES*, Bailey/Howe Library, 538 Main St, 05405-0036. SAN 362-6105. Tel: 802-656-2020. FAX: 802-656-4038. Web Site: library.uvm.edu. *Dean of Libr & Info Serv,* Mara Saule; Tel: 802-656-2003, E-mail: mara.saule@uvm.edu; *Head, Access & Tech Serv,* Paul Philbin; Tel: 802-656-1369, E-mail: paul.philbin@uvm.edu; *Head of Instruction & Info Serv,* Alison Armstrong; *Head, Coll Mgt Serv,* Birdie MacLennan; Tel: 802-656-2016, E-mail: birdie.maclennan@uvm.edu; *Spec Coll & Archives Librn,* Jeffrey Marshall; Tel: 802-656-2595, E-mail: jeffrey.marshall@uvm.edu; Staff 76 (MLS 22, Non-MLS 54)
Founded 1800. Enrl 10,314; Fac 871; Highest Degree: Doctorate
Library Holdings: Bk Vols 1,391,631; Per Subs 3,500
Special Collections: Canadian & United States Army Map Service; Civil War (Rush-Hawkins Coll); Geography, Foreign Affairs, Linguistics & Ecology (George Perkins Marsh Coll), mss; Literature & Personal Correspondence (Dorothy Canfield Fisher Coll), bks, mss; Politics & Government Coll, mss; U S Army Map Service; Vermont Local History, Stevens Family & Bookselling (Henry Stevens Coll), mss; Vermontiana (Wilbur Coll). Can & Prov; State Document Depository; US Document Depository
Automation Activity & Vendor Info: (Acquisitions) Ex Libris Group; (Cataloging) Ex Libris Group; (Circulation) Ex Libris Group; (Course Reserve) Ex Libris Group; (Media Booking) Ex Libris Group
Database Vendor: American Chemical Society, Dialog, Gale Cengage Learning, JSTOR, LexisNexis, OCLC FirstSearch, OVID Technologies
Wireless access
Publications: A Newsletter for Friends of Special Collections; Liber
Partic in Center for Research Libraries; Lyrasis; Northeast Research Libraries Consortium (NERL); OCLC Online Computer Library Center, Inc; Vermont Resource Sharing Network
Open Mon-Thurs 8am-Midnight, Fri 8am-10pm, Sat 10-10, Sun 10am-Midnight
Friends of the Library Group
Departmental Libraries:

CM   DANA MEDICAL LIBRARY, 81 Colchester Ave, 05405, SAN 362-613X. Tel: 802-656-2200. FAX: 802-656-0762. Web Site: library.uvm.edu/dana. *Dir,* Marianne Burke; Tel: 802-656-3483, E-mail: marianne.burke@uvm.edu; Staff 22 (MLS 8, Non-MLS 14)
Library Holdings: Bk Vols 123,767; Per Subs 3,157
Special Collections: Vermont Medical History
Partic in National Network of Libraries of Medicine; Northeast Research Libraries Consortium (NERL); OCLC Online Computer Library Center, Inc
Publications: Dana Medical Library Newsletter
Open Mon-Thurs 7:30-Midnight, Fri 7:30-9, Sat 9-9, Sun 9-Midnight

S   WCAX-TV LIBRARY*, PO Box 4508, 05406-4508. SAN 373-0123. Tel: 802-652-6300. FAX: 802-652-6399. E-mail: news@wcax.com. Web Site: www.wcax.com. *Librn,* Diane Landry; E-mail: landry@wcax.com
Library Holdings: Bk Vols 40; Per Subs 30
Special Collections: News Archives from 1950s; Scripts Online from 1996
Function: Res libr
Restriction: Open by appt only

CABOT

P   CABOT PUBLIC LIBRARY*, 3084 Main St, 05647. (Mail add: PO Box 6, 05647-0006), SAN 316-9820. Tel: 802-563-2721. E-mail: cabotlibrary@yahoo.com. *Co-Dir,* Kathleen Hoyne; *Co-Dir,* Anne C Walker
Pop 1,343; Circ 11,723
Library Holdings: Bk Vols 8,000; Per Subs 34
Automation Activity & Vendor Info: (Acquisitions) LibraryWorld, Inc; (Cataloging) LibraryWorld, Inc; (Circulation) LibraryWorld, Inc
Wireless access
Open Tues 9-6, Wed 2-6, Thurs 11-6, Sat 9-2
Friends of the Library Group

CANAAN

P   ALICE M WARD MEMORIAL LIBRARY*, 27 Park St, 05903. (Mail add: PO Box 134, 05903-0134), SAN 316-9839. Tel: 802-266-7135. FAX: 802-266-8159. *Dir,* Deborah Dagwah
Founded 1930. Pop 1,121; Circ 6,000
Library Holdings: Large Print Bks 158; Bk Vols 12,000; Per Subs 23; Talking Bks 150
Subject Interests: Educ, Hist
Automation Activity & Vendor Info: (Cataloging) Follett Software; (Circulation) Follett Software; (Course Reserve) Follett Software; (ILL) Follett Software; (Media Booking) Follett Software; (OPAC) Follett Software; (Serials) Follett Software
Special Services for the Blind - Home delivery serv
Open Mon-Thurs 12-5, Fri 12-4, Sat 9-1

CASTLETON

P   CASTLETON FREE LIBRARY*, Main St, 05735. (Mail add: PO Box 296, 05735), SAN 316-9847. Tel: 802-468-5574. *Dir,* Jan Jones; *Librn,* Meg Fitch
Pop 3,637; Circ 11,934
Library Holdings: Bk Vols 19,450
Open Mon & Thurs 3-8, Tues & Wed 2-6, Fri 10-6, Sat 10-Noon

C   CASTLETON STATE COLLEGE, Calvin Coolidge Library, 178 Alumni Dr, 05735. SAN 316-9855. Tel: 802-468-1256. Reference Tel: 802-468-1257. FAX: 802-468-1475. Web Site: www.castleton.edu/library. *Dir,* Sandy Duling; *Circ,* Virginia Johnston; *Instruction/Ref Serv,* Charlotte Gerstein; *Instruction/Ref Serv,* Lauren Olewnik; *ILL, Ser,* Frances Ryan; *Media Spec,* Karen Sanborn; *Tech Serv,* Nancy Luzer; Staff 10 (MLS 4, Non-MLS 6)
Founded 1787. Enrl 2,191; Fac 86; Highest Degree: Master
Library Holdings: Bk Vols 160,000; Per Subs 500
Special Collections: Vermontiania. US Document Depository
Automation Activity & Vendor Info: (Acquisitions) SirsiDynix; (Cataloging) SirsiDynix; (Circulation) SirsiDynix; (Course Reserve) SirsiDynix; (OPAC) SirsiDynix; (Serials) SirsiDynix
Wireless access
Partic in Lyrasis
Open Mon-Thurs 8am-11:30pm, Fri 8-5, Sat 10-6, Sun 1-11:30

CHARLOTTE

P   CHARLOTTE LIBRARY*, 115 Ferry Rd, 05445. (Mail add: PO Box 120, 05445-0120), SAN 376-4907. Tel: 802-425-3864. E-mail: charlottelibrary@gmavt.net. Web Site: charlottepubliclibrary.org. *Libr Dir,* Margaret Woodruff; *Head Librn,* Sherrie Simmons
Library Holdings: Bk Vols 16,029; Per Subs 58
Open Mon & Wed 10-7, Tues, Thurs & Fri 10-4, Sat 10-2 (9-1 Summer)
Friends of the Library Group

CHELSEA

P   CHELSEA PUBLIC LIBRARY*, Alden Speare Memorial Library, 296 Rte 110, 05038. (Mail add: PO Box 67, 05038-0067), SAN 316-9871. Tel: 802-685-2188. E-mail: chelsealibrary@charter.com. *Librn,* Nick Clemens; Staff 1 (MLS 1)
Founded 1894. Pop 1,264; Circ 12,366
Library Holdings: Bk Vols 10,000; Per Subs 32
Special Collections: Vermontiania Coll
Partic in Vermont State Libr Syst
Open Mon 10-12 & 1-6, Wed & Fri 1-6, Sat 9:30-12:30

CHESTER

P   WHITING LIBRARY*, 117 Main St, 05143. (Mail add: PO Box 68, 05143-0068), SAN 316-988X. Tel: 802-875-2277. FAX: 802-875-2277. E-mail: whitinglibrary@yahoo.com. *Dir,* Karen Morris; *Ch,* Sharon Tanzer; Staff 3 (MLS 1, Non-MLS 2)
Founded 1892. Pop 3,000; Circ 20,000
Library Holdings: AV Mats 740; Bk Vols 13,850; Per Subs 24; Talking Bks 525
Special Collections: Vermont Coll
Open Mon, Wed & Fri 10-6, Sat 10-2
Friends of the Library Group

CHITTENDEN

P   CHITTENDEN PUBLIC LIBRARY*, Frederic D Barstow Memorial Library, 223 Chittenden Rd, 05737. (Mail add: PO Box 90, 05737-0090), SAN 316-9898. Tel: 802-773-3531. FAX: 802-747-4814. *Librn,* Nina Flood; E-mail: nmflood@yahoo.com
Pop 1,102; Circ 2,080
Library Holdings: Bk Vols 5,400; Per Subs 25

Automation Activity & Vendor Info: (Cataloging) Follett Software; (Circulation) Follett Software
Open Tues & Thurs (Winter) 4-7, Sat 8-12; Mon & Wed (Summer) 1-7, Fri 1-5

COLCHESTER

P   BURNHAM MEMORIAL LIBRARY*, 898 Main St, 05446. SAN 316-9901. Tel: 802-879-7576. FAX: 802-879-5079. E-mail: burnhamlib@colchestervt.gov. Web Site: colchestervt.gov/Library. *Libr Dir,* Rubi Simon; E-mail: rsimon@burnham.lib.vt.us; *Ch, Head, Youth Serv,* Hannah Peacock; E-mail: hpeacock@burnham.lib.vt.us; Staff 10 (MLS 3, Non-MLS 7)
Founded 1902. Pop 17,000; Circ 125,000
Jul 2007-Jun 2008 Income $559,635, City $551,635, Locally Generated Income $8,000. Mats Exp $40,023, Books $31,300, Per/Ser (Incl. Access Fees) $4,000, AV Mat $3,523, Electronic Ref Mat (Incl. Access Fees) $1,200. Sal $314,231
Library Holdings: AV Mats 4,650; Bk Vols 50,072; Per Subs 95
Subject Interests: Local hist
Automation Activity & Vendor Info: (Cataloging) LibLime; (Circulation) LibLime; (OPAC) LibLime
Wireless access
Function: ILL available, Online cat, Prog for adults, Prog for children & young adult, Senior outreach, Wheelchair accessible
Open Mon & Wed 9-9, Tues, Thurs & Fri 9-5, Sat 9-3
Restriction: Non-circulating coll
Friends of the Library Group

C   SAINT MICHAEL'S COLLEGE, Durick Library, One Winooski Park, Box L, 05439-2525. SAN 316-991X. Tel: 802-654-2400. Interlibrary Loan Service Tel: 802-654-2590. Reference Tel: 802-654-2405. Administration Tel: 802-654-2629. Automation Services Tel: 802-654-2402. FAX: 802-654-2630. Web Site: www.smcvt.edu/library. *Dir, Libr & Info Serv,* John K Payne; Tel: 802-654-2401, E-mail: jpayne@smcvt.edu; *Assoc Dir, Circ,* Mark McAteer; Tel: 802-654-2403, E-mail: mmcateer@smcvt.edu; *Assoc Dir, Coll Serv,* Laura Crain; Tel: 802-654-2388, E-mail: lcrain@smcvt.edu; *Assoc Dir, Syst & Metadata,* Stacey Knight; E-mail: sknight3@smcvt.edu; *Head, ILL & Coll Serv,* Kristen Hindes; E-mail: khindes@smcvt.edu; *Ref & Instruction, Ref Coordr,* Michele McCaffrey; Tel: 802-654-2411, E-mail: mmccaffrey@smcvt.edu; *Ref & Instrul Serv, Instr Coordr,* Marilyn Scoville; Tel: 802-654-2410, E-mail: mscoville@smcvt.edu; *Ref & Info Serv, Web Coordr,* Steven Burks; Tel: 802-654-2354, E-mail: sburks@smcvt.edu; *Archivist,* Elizabeth Scott; Tel: 802-654-2540, E-mail: escott@smcvt.edu; Staff 18 (MLS 9, Non-MLS 9)
Founded 1904. Enrl 2,210; Fac 150; Highest Degree: Master
Jul 2012-Jun 2013 Income $1,900,000. Mats Exp $744,147, Books $204,000, Per/Ser (Incl. Access Fees) $364,000, AV Mat $19,700, Electronic Ref Mat (Incl. Access Fees) $154,247, Presv $2,200. Sal $800,000
Library Holdings: AV Mats 12,812; e-books 74,333; e-journals 82,350; Bk Vols 277,282
Special Collections: Saint Michael's College Archives; Society of Saint Edmund Archives
Automation Activity & Vendor Info: (Acquisitions) Ex Libris Group; (Cataloging) Ex Libris Group; (Circulation) Ex Libris Group; (Course Reserve) Ex Libris Group; (ILL) Clio; (OPAC) Ex Libris Group; (Serials) Ex Libris Group
Database Vendor: American Chemical Society, American Mathematical Society, American Psychological Association (APA), ARTstor, BioOne, CQ Press, CredoReference, EBSCO Information Services, EBSCOhost, Ex Libris Group, Gale Cengage Learning, H W Wilson, JSTOR, LexisNexis, netLibrary, OCLC FirstSearch, Project MUSE, ProQuest, RefWorks, ScienceDirect, SerialsSolutions, STN International, ValueLine
Wireless access
Publications: News@YourLibrary (Newsletter)
Partic in ARIEL; Lyrasis; OCLC Online Computer Library Center, Inc; Vermont Automated Libr Syst (VALS); Vermont Consortium of Academic Libraries
Special Services for the Blind - Reader equip
Open Mon-Thurs 7:30am-1am, Fri 7:30-7, Sat 11-7, Sun 10am-1am

CONCORD

P   CONCORD PUBLIC LIBRARY*, 374 Main St, 05824. (Mail add: PO Box 188, 05824-0188), SAN 316-9928. Tel: 802-695-2220. *Librn,* Brenda Regan
Pop 1,224
Library Holdings: Bk Vols 5,000; Per Subs 15
Open Wed 6pm-7:30pm, Sat 9:30-11:30

CORNWALL

P   CORNWALL FREE PUBLIC LIBRARY, 2629 Rte 30, 05753-9340. SAN 316-9936. Tel: 802-462-3615. FAX: 802-462-2606. *Librn,* Susan Johnson
Pop 1,550

Jul 2011-Jun 2012 Income $3,688, City $3,000, Other $688. Mats Exp $6,996
Library Holdings: Audiobooks 172; DVDs 300; Large Print Bks 30; Bk Vols 3,368; Videos 328
Subject Interests: Local authors, Local hist
Wireless access
Open Tues-Fri 9-5

CRAFTSBURY COMMON

P   CRAFTSBURY PUBLIC LIBRARY*, 12 Church St, 05827-9696. (Mail add: PO Box 74, Craftsbury, 05827-0074), SAN 376-3374. Tel: 802-586-9683. FAX: 802-586-9683. E-mail: craftsbury@hotmail.com. Web Site: www.craftsburypubliclibrary.org. *Dir,* Linda Wells; Tel: 802-533-2346; *Youth Serv Coordr,* Barbara Strong; Staff 2 (Non-MLS 2)
Founded 1898. Pop 1,240; Circ 15,857
Library Holdings: DVDs 150; Large Print Bks 50; Bk Titles 14,000; Per Subs 25; Talking Bks 260; Videos 342
Special Collections: General Coll
Open Tues & Fri 10-8, Wed & Sat 9-12, Sun 10-1
Friends of the Library Group

C   STERLING COLLEGE*, Brown Library, 1205 N Craftsbury Rd, 05827. (Mail add: PO Box 72, 16 Sterling Dr, 05827-0072). Tel: 802-586-7711, Ext 129. FAX: 802-586-2596. Web Site: www.sterlingcollege.edu. *Librn,* Petra Vogel; E-mail: pvogel@sterlingcollege.edu; Staff 1 (MLS 1)
Founded 1990. Enrl 100; Fac 15; Highest Degree: Bachelor
Library Holdings: AV Mats 700; Bk Titles 13,220; Bk Vols 14,795; Per Subs 115
Subject Interests: Conserv ecology, Northern studies, Outdoor educ, Sustainable agr
Automation Activity & Vendor Info: (Cataloging) Follett Software; (Circulation) Follett Software; (OPAC) Follett Software
Database Vendor: Gale Cengage Learning, JSTOR, ProQuest, ScienceDirect, SerialsSolutions
Wireless access
Partic in Associated Colleges of Central Kansas; Lyrasis; Vermont Consortium of Academic Libraries
Open Mon-Fri 8-8

CUTTINGSVILLE

P   SHREWSBURY PUBLIC LIBRARY*, 98 Town Hill Rd, 05738. (Mail add: PO Box 396, 05738-0396), SAN 316-9952. Tel: 802-492-3410. E-mail: shrewsburypl@vals.state.vt.us. Web Site: www.shrewsburyvt.org/library.htm. *Dir,* Eleanor Tufano
Founded 1975. Pop 1,100; Circ 3,500
Library Holdings: Bk Vols 8,000
Partic in Vt Libr Asn; Vt Trustees Asn
Open Mon 12:30-2:30, Tues & Thurs 7pm-9pm, Wed 10-5 & 7pm-9pm, Fri 9am-11am, Sat 9:30-12
Friends of the Library Group

DANBY

P   SILAS L GRIFFITH MEMORIAL LIBRARY*, 74 S Main St, 05739. SAN 316-9960. Tel: 802-293-5106. *Librn,* Cheryl Colby
Founded 1908. Pop 1,200; Circ 5,706
Library Holdings: Bk Vols 15,610; Per Subs 18; Talking Bks 69; Videos 359
Open Wed 2-7, Sat 9-12

DANVILLE

P   BRAINERD MEMORIAL LIBRARY*, 4215 Bruce Badger Memorial Hwy, 05828. Tel: 802-748-4423. *Librn,* Elizabeth Szymanik
Founded 1934. Pop 2,289
Library Holdings: Bk Vols 3,000
Function: Photocopying/Printing
Open Mon & Fri 2-4, Wed 2-4 & 6-8

P   POPE MEMORIAL LIBRARY, 121 Park St, 05828. (Mail add: PO Box 260, 05828-0260), SAN 316-9979. Tel: 802-684-2256. E-mail: danville@vals.state.vt.us. Web Site: www.popememoriallibrary.org. *Librn,* Deidre Palmer; Staff 2 (MLS 1, Non-MLS 1)
Founded 1890. Pop 2,200; Circ 12,000
Jan 2006-Dec 2006 Income $47,000, City $17,000, Locally Generated Income $30,000. Mats Exp $4,000. Sal $23,000
Library Holdings: Audiobooks 400; Large Print Bks 300; Bk Titles 11,700; Per Subs 40; Videos 800
Special Collections: Circulating Toy Coll; Vermont Mysteries & Westerns (fiction & nonfiction)
Subject Interests: Genealogical res, Vt hist
Wireless access

Function: Adult bk club, Bks on cassette, Bks on CD, Children's prog, Computers for patron use, Copy machines, Free DVD rentals, Handicapped accessible, Holiday prog, Home delivery & serv to Sr ctr & nursing homes, Homebound delivery serv, Homework prog, ILL available, Instruction & testing, Mail & tel request accepted, Mail loans to mem, Mus passes, Passport agency, Preschool outreach, Prog for adults, Prog for children & young adult, Senior outreach, Summer reading prog, Tax forms, Teen prog, VHS videos, Writing prog
Open Mon & Fri 10-5, Wed 9-7, Sat 9-12

DERBY

P   DAILEY MEMORIAL LIBRARY*, 101 Junior High Dr, 05829. SAN 316-9987. Tel: 802-766-5063. FAX: 802-766-5063. E-mail: derby@vals.state.vt.us. *Dir,* Barbara J Whitehill; Staff 3 (Non-MLS 3)
Founded 1957. Pop 3,951; Circ 13,000
Library Holdings: Audiobooks 256; Large Print Bks 200; Bk Titles 8,479; Bk Vols 12,330; Per Subs 22; Videos 743
Special Collections: Children's Coll, Local History
Automation Activity & Vendor Info: (Acquisitions) LibraryWorld, Inc; (Cataloging) LibraryWorld, Inc; (Circulation) LibraryWorld, Inc
Database Vendor: H W Wilson, OCLC FirstSearch, OCLC WebJunction, Overdrive, Inc, Wilson - Wilson Web
Wireless access
Open Tues & Fri 10-6, Wed & Thurs 10-5, Sat 10-3

DERBY LINE

P   HASKELL FREE LIBRARY, INC*, 93 Caswell Ave, 05830. (Mail add: PO Box 337, 05830-0337). Tel: 802-873-3022. FAX: 802-873-3022. Web Site: www.haskellopera.org. *Dir,* Nancy Rumery; Staff 4 (Non-MLS 4)
Founded 1905. Pop 5,000; Circ 44,000
Library Holdings: Bk Vols 20,000; Per Subs 45
Function: Adult bk club, Art exhibits, Audiobks via web, Bks on cassette, Bks on CD, Children's prog, Computers for patron use, Electronic databases & coll, Free DVD rentals, Handicapped accessible, Holiday prog, Online cat, OverDrive digital audio bks, Prog for adults, Story hour, Summer reading prog, Wheelchair accessible
Special Services for the Blind - Bks on cassette
Open Tues, Wed, Fri & Sat 10-5, Thurs 10-6, Sat 10-2

DORSET

P   DORSET VILLAGE LIBRARY*, Rte 30 & Church St, 05251. (Mail add: PO Box 38, 05251-0038), SAN 317-0004. Tel: 802-867-5774. E-mail: info@dorsetlibrary.org. Web Site: www.dorsetlibraryinfo.org. *Admin Dir,* Gail Woll
Founded 1871. Pop 2,026; Circ 24,000
Library Holdings: DVDs 500; Large Print Bks 700; Bk Titles 21,000; Bk Vols 22,000; Per Subs 75; Talking Bks 1,000; Videos 600
Automation Activity & Vendor Info: (Circulation) Follett Software
Wireless access
Open Mon, Wed & Fri 11-5, Tues & Thurs 11-6, Sat 10-1

EAST BURKE

P   EAST BURKE COMMUNITY LIBRARY*, 368 Rt 114, 05832. (Mail add: PO Box 309, 05832-0309), SAN 317-0047. Tel: 802-626-9823. *Librn,* Charlotte Downs
Pop 1,047; Circ 2,300
Library Holdings: Bk Vols 4,000
Open Mon, Tues & Thurs 1:30-8, Sat 9-Noon
Friends of the Library Group

EAST CORINTH

P   BLAKE MEMORIAL LIBRARY*, 676 Village Rd, 05040. (Mail add: PO Box D, 05040), SAN 317-0063. Tel: 802-439-5338. FAX: 802-439-5338. E-mail: blakemem@tops-tele.com. Web Site: www.blakememorial.org. *Librn,* Ken Linge. Subject Specialists: *English,* Ken Linge; Staff 1 (Non-MLS 1)
Founded 1901. Pop 2,600; Circ 14,000
Library Holdings: AV Mats 330; CDs 50; DVDs 75; Large Print Bks 70; Bk Vols 20,000; Per Subs 24; Videos 600
Automation Activity & Vendor Info: (OPAC) Mandarin Library Automation
Wireless access
Function: Art exhibits, Bk club(s), Bks on cassette, Bks on CD, Children's prog, Computers for patron use, Copy machines, e-mail & chat, e-mail serv, Electronic databases & coll, Fax serv, Free DVD rentals, Handicapped accessible, Health sci info serv, ILL available, Mus passes, Online cat, Online ref, Online searches, Outside serv via phone, mail, e-mail & web, Photocopying/Printing, Preschool outreach, Prog for adults, Prog for children & young adult, Story hour, Summer reading prog, Wheelchair accessible
Open Mon & Wed 2-8, Thurs & Sat 9-12, Fri 2-6

EAST CRAFTSBURY

P   JOHN WOODRUFF SIMPSON MEMORIAL LIBRARY, 1972 E Craftsbury Rd, 05826. (Mail add: 300 Shields Lane, Craftsbury Common, 05827), SAN 317-0071. Tel: 802-586-9692. *Librn,* Sherry Urie; Staff 1 (Non-MLS 1)
Founded 1921. Pop 1,000; Circ 5,000
Library Holdings: Bk Titles 20,000; Per Subs 50
Open Wed & Sat 9-12, 2-5 & 7-8:30, Sun 12-1

EAST DOVER

P   DOVER FREE LIBRARY*, 22 Hollands Rd, 05341-9617. (Mail add: PO Box 267, 05341-0267), SAN 317-008X. Tel: 802-348-7488. E-mail: doverfreelibrary1913@yahoo.com. Web Site: www.doverfreelibrary1913.org. *Librn,* John G Flores; *Ch,* Tamara Hamm
Founded 1913. Pop 1,410; Circ 17,265
Library Holdings: AV Mats 657; Bk Vols 15,000; Per Subs 68; Talking Bks 600
Special Collections: Oral History
Subject Interests: Cookery, Early childhood educ, New England, Parenting
Open Mon & Tues 2-8, Wed-Fri 10-6, Sat 10-2

EAST RYEGATE

P   RYEGATE CORNER PUBLIC LIBRARY*, 18 S Bayley Hazen Rd, 05042. (Mail add: PO Box 332, 05042-0332), SAN 317-1205. Tel: 802-584-3880. *Librn,* Marsha Nelson
Pop 1,000
Library Holdings: Bk Vols 700
Publications: County Journal

ENOSBURG FALLS

P   ENOSBURGH PUBLIC LIBRARY*, 241 Main St, 05450. (Mail add: PO Box 206, 05450-0206), SAN 317-011X. Tel: 802-933-2328. Web Site: enosburghlibrary.org. *Libr Dir,* Maria Harris; Staff 1 (MLS 1)
Pop 2,535; Circ 20,000
Library Holdings: Bk Titles 15,000; Per Subs 47
Wireless access
Open Mon-Fri 10-8, Sat 10-4

ESSEX

P   ESSEX FREE LIBRARY*, Two Browns River Rd, 05451. (Mail add: PO Box 8093, 05451-8093), SAN 317-0128. Tel: 802-879-0313. Web Site: www.townofessex.org. *Librn,* Susan Overfield; *Asst Librn II,* Caitlin Corless; *Asst Librn,* Sherry Somerset; *Tech Serv Librn,* Peggy Wygmans; Staff 4.65 (MLS 1.5, Non-MLS 3.15)
Founded 1929. Pop 19,065; Circ 107,722
Jul 2009-Jun 2010 Income $328,192. Mats Exp $23,567. Sal $188,454
Library Holdings: Bks on Deafness & Sign Lang 14; Bk Titles 31,240; Bk Vols 34,878; Per Subs 72
Automation Activity & Vendor Info: (Acquisitions) Follett Software; (Cataloging) Follett Software; (Circulation) Follett Software; (Media Booking) Follett Software; (OPAC) Follett Software; (Serials) Follett Software
Open Mon, Wed & Fri 10-5, Tues & Thurs 10-8, Sat 10-2
Friends of the Library Group

ESSEX JUNCTION

P   BROWNELL LIBRARY*, Six Lincoln St, 05452-3154. SAN 317-0136. Tel: 802-878-6955. Reference Tel: 802-878-6957. Administration Tel: 802-878-6954. FAX: 802-878-6946. Web Site: www.brownelllibrary.org. *Dir,* Penelope D Pillsbury; E-mail: penny@brownellibrary.org; *Circ Librn,* Alison Pierce; *ILL Librn,* Susan Pierce; *Youth Serv Librn,* Mary L Graf; Tel: 802-878-6956; Staff 5 (MLS 3, Non-MLS 2)
Founded 1897. Pop 14,392; Circ 287,414
Jul 2009-Jun 2010 Income $620,660, State $100, City $605,878, Locally Generated Income $11,134, Other $3,548. Mats Exp $93,120, Books $76,278, AV Mat $12,542, Electronic Ref Mat (Incl. Access Fees) $4,300. Sal $320,787
Library Holdings: Audiobooks 3,883; AV Mats 4,441; Bks on Deafness & Sign Lang 323; Braille Volumes 2; CDs 1,534; e-books 486; Electronic Media & Resources 17; High Interest/Low Vocabulary Bk Vols 7; Large Print Bks 421; Bk Vols 78,111; Per Subs 181; Videos 773
Special Collections: Vermont Local History Coll
Subject Interests: Essex Area hist
Automation Activity & Vendor Info: (Cataloging) Follett Software; (Circulation) Follett Software; (OPAC) Follett Software
Database Vendor: Gale Cengage Learning, World Book Online
Wireless access
Function: Adult bk club, Adult literacy prog, After school storytime, Art exhibits, Audio & video playback equip for onsite use, Audiobks via web, Bk club(s), Bks on cassette, Bks on CD, Children's prog, Computer

training, Computers for patron use, Copy machines, Doc delivery serv, e-mail & chat, e-mail serv, Equip loans & repairs, Exhibits, Free DVD rentals, Games & aids for the handicapped, Handicapped accessible, Home delivery & serv to Sr ctr & nursing homes, Homebound delivery serv, ILL available, Instruction & testing, Magnifiers for reading, Mail & tel request accepted, Mail loans to mem, Mus passes, Music CDs, Online cat, Online ref, Online searches, Orientations, Outside serv via phone, mail, e-mail & web, Photocopying/Printing, Prog for adults, Prog for children & young adult, Provide serv for the mentally ill, Pub access computers, Ref & res, Ref serv in person, Senior computer classes, Senior outreach, Serves mentally handicapped consumers, Spoken cassettes & CDs, Spoken cassettes & DVDs, Story hour, Summer reading prog, Tax forms, Teen prog, Telephone ref, VHS videos, Visual arts prog, Wheelchair accessible, Workshops

Publications: Friends of Brownell (Newsletter)

Special Services for the Blind - Aids for in-house use; Audio mat; Bks on CD; Cassette playback machines; Large print bks; Magnifiers; Reader equip; Talking bks

Open Mon, Wed & Fri 9-9, Tues & Thurs 9-5, Sat (Sept-June) 9-5

Friends of the Library Group

FAIR HAVEN

P FAIR HAVEN FREE LIBRARY*, 107 Main St, 05743. SAN 317-0160. Tel: 802-265-8011. *Librn,* Carol Scott

Founded 1906. Pop 2,936; Circ 16,149

Library Holdings: Bk Vols 15,500; Per Subs 50

Special Collections: Mystery Coll; Vermontiana Coll

Wireless access

Open Mon & Wed 4-8, Tues & Fri 8:30-4:30, Sat 9-1

Friends of the Library Group

FAIRFAX

P FAIRFAX COMMUNITY LIBRARY, 75 Hunt St, 05454. SAN 317-0179. Tel: 802-849-2420. FAX: 802-849-2611. E-mail: fairfaxlibrarian@gmail.com. *Town Librn,* Debbie Landauer; Staff 2 (MLS 1, Non-MLS 1)

Founded 1972. Pop 4,285; Circ 35,000

Library Holdings: Bk Titles 24,000; Per Subs 35

Special Collections: Local History (Fairfax Historical Society Coll)

Automation Activity & Vendor Info: (Acquisitions) Follett Software; (Cataloging) Follett Software; (Circulation) Follett Software; (OPAC) Follett Software

Database Vendor: Gale Cengage Learning, H W Wilson, Overdrive, Inc

Wireless access

Function: Adult bk club, Audiobks via web, Bks on cassette, Bks on CD, Chess club, Children's prog, Computers for patron use, Copy machines, e-mail & chat, Free DVD rentals, Handicapped accessible, Homebound delivery serv, ILL available, Mus passes, Online cat, Online searches, OverDrive digital audio bks, Photocopying/Printing, Prog for adults, Prog for children & young adult, Pub access computers, Ref serv available, Story hour, Summer reading prog, VHS videos, Wheelchair accessible

Open Mon & Wed (Winter) 8-5:30, Tues & Thurs 8-8, Fri 8-3:15, Sat 9-1; Mon, Wed & Fri (Summer) 10-5:30, Tues & Thurs 9-8, Sat 9-1

P GEORGIA PUBLIC LIBRARY*, 1697 Ethan Allen Hwy, 05454. SAN 376-3382. Tel: 802-524-4643. FAX: 802-524-7426. Web Site: www.georgia.lib.vt.us. *Librn,* Susan Webster

Library Holdings: Bk Vols 10,000; Per Subs 55

Automation Activity & Vendor Info: (Cataloging) Follett Software; (Circulation) Follett Software

Open Mon & Wed 9-8, Tues & Thurs 3-8, Fri 9-5, Sat 9-1

Friends of the Library Group

FAIRFIELD

P BENT NORTHROP MEMORIAL LIBRARY*, 164 Park St, 05455. SAN 376-4893. Tel: 802-827-3945. FAX: 802-827-3604. E-mail: bentnorthrop@gmail.com. *Librn,* Kristen Hughes

Founded 1988. Pop 1,880; Circ 8,000

Library Holdings: High Interest/Low Vocabulary Bk Vols 30; Large Print Bks 60; Bk Vols 11,166; Per Subs 10

Automation Activity & Vendor Info: (Cataloging) Brodart; (Circulation) Follett Software

Wireless access

Open Wed & Fri 9-5, Tues & Thurs 3-8:30, Sat 9-1

FAIRLEE

P FAIRLEE PUBLIC LIBRARY, 221 US Rte 5N, 05045-9584. (Mail add: PO Box 125, 05045-0125), SAN 317-0187. Tel: 802-333-4716. FAX: 802-333-4152. E-mail: fairlee.library@gmail.com, fairlee_pub@vals.state.vt.us. Web Site: www.fairleelibrary.com. *Libr Dir,* Hannah Tracy; Staff 1 (MLS 1)

Founded 1898. Pop 1,848; Circ 11,743

Jan 2010-Dec 2010 Income $62,008, City $57,908, Locally Generated Income $4,100. Mats Exp $6,000. Sal $27,250 (Prof $27,250)

Library Holdings: CDs 478; DVDs 511; e-books 1,100; High Interest/Low Vocabulary Bk Vols 21; Large Print Bks 44; Bk Vols 13,911; Per Subs 43

Automation Activity & Vendor Info: (Cataloging) ByWater Solutions; (Circulation) ByWater Solutions

Wireless access

Partic in Green Mountain Library Consortium (GMLC)

Open Tues 9-5, Wed 1-7, Thurs & Fri 1-5, Sat 9-Noon

FERRISBURG

S ROKEBY MUSEUM*, Special Collections Library, 4334 Rte 7, 05456-9711. SAN 317-0209. Tel: 802-877-3406. FAX: 802-877-3406. E-mail: rokeby@comcast.net. Web Site: www.rokeby.org. *Dir,* Jane Williamson

Founded 1962

Special Collections: Abolition, Religious History, Social History & Vermont Folklore (Robinson & Stevens Family Papers, 1770-1960)

Subject Interests: Anti-slavery, Biog, Farming, Fishing, Hist, Hunting, Popular lit, Quaker writings, Sch texts, Spiritualism

Restriction: Open by appt only

FRANKLIN

P HASTON LIBRARY*, 5167 Main St, 05457. (Mail add: PO Box 83, 05457-0083), SAN 321-0952. Tel: 802-285-6505. FAX: 802-285-2181. E-mail: hastonlibrary@franklinvt.net. Web Site: www.hastonlibraryvt.org. *Librn,* Melissa McKinstry; Staff 0.75 (Non-MLS 0.75)

Founded 1907. Pop 1,268; Circ 7,246

Library Holdings: Audiobooks 150; CDs 11; DVDs 143; Electronic Media & Resources 16; Large Print Bks 109; Bk Vols 6,384; Per Subs 15; Videos 230

Automation Activity & Vendor Info: (Circulation) OpenBiblio

Database Vendor: Baker & Taylor, Gale Cengage Learning, H W Wilson, ProQuest

Wireless access

Function: Adult bk club, Bks on cassette, Bks on CD, Children's prog, Computers for patron use, e-mail serv, Electronic databases & coll, Free DVD rentals, Handicapped accessible, Homebound delivery serv, ILL available, Mus passes, Online searches, Photocopying/Printing, Prog for adults, Prog for children & young adult, Pub access computers, Ref serv in person, Story hour, Summer reading prog, Teen prog, Telephone ref, VHS videos, Video lending libr, Wheelchair accessible

Open Mon 10-2, Tues 2-7, Thurs 9-6, Fri 2-6, Sat 9-1

Bookmobiles: 1. *Librn,* Deb Grenon

GAYSVILLE

P BELCHER MEMORIAL LIBRARY*, 4452 VT Rte 107, 05746-0144. (Mail add: PO Box 144, 05746), SAN 376-4060. Tel: 802-234-6608. FAX: 802-234-6608. *Librn,* Mary Ellen Dorman

Pop 618

Library Holdings: Bk Vols 2,500

Open Wed 3-6, Sat 9-Noon

GLOVER

P GLOVER PUBLIC LIBRARY*, 51 Beanhill Rd, 05839. SAN 317-0241. Tel: 802-525-4365. *Librn,* Toni Eubanks

Founded 1909. Pop 982

Library Holdings: Bk Vols 5,600

Open Mon-Thurs 3-6, Sat 10-Noon

GRAFTON

P GRAFTON PUBLIC LIBRARY*, 204 Main St, 05146. (Mail add: PO Box 129, 05146-0129), SAN 317-0268. Tel: 802-843-2404. E-mail: librarian@graftonpubliclibrary.org. Web Site: www.graftonpubliclibrary.org. *Dir,* Michelle Dufort

Founded 1882

Library Holdings: Large Print Bks 12; Bk Titles 25,000; Per Subs 15; Talking Bks 145

Wireless access

Open Mon & Wed 10-1 & 2-5, Tues 10-8, Thurs & Fri 10-1 & 2-8, Sat 9-Noon

Friends of the Library Group

GRANBY

P GRANBY TOWN LIBRARY*, 8960 Granby Rd, 05840. SAN 317-0276. Tel: 802-328-4494. *Librn,* Barbara Brown

Pop 70; Circ 1,000

Library Holdings: Bk Vols 925

Restriction: Open by appt only

GRAND ISLE

P   GRAND ISLE FREE LIBRARY*, Ten Hyde Rd, 05458. SAN 317-0284. Tel: 802-372-4797. E-mail: grandislefreelibrary@hotmail.com. *Librn,* Colleen Bushway
Library Holdings: Bk Vols 6,000
Open Tues 1-8, Wed 9-Noon, Thurs 4-8, Sat 9-3

GREENSBORO

P   GREENSBORO FREE LIBRARY*, 53 Wilson St, 05841. SAN 317-0306. Tel: 802-533-2531. E-mail: greensborofree@yahoo.com. Web Site: www.greensborofreelibrary.org. *Librn,* Mary Metcalf; *Asst Librn,* Debbie Kasper
Pop 770; Circ 9,500
Library Holdings: Bk Titles 9,000
Special Collections: Greensboro Authors
Subject Interests: Craft, Gardening
Wireless access
Function: Audiobks via web, Bks on cassette, Bks on CD, CD-ROM, Children's prog, Computer training, Computers for patron use, Copy machines, e-mail & chat, e-mail serv, Handicapped accessible, ILL available, Online cat, Online ref, Online searches, Photocopying/Printing, VCDs
Publications: Greensboro Free Library Newsletter (Quarterly)
Open Tues (Winter) 10-7, Thurs & Fri 10-5:30, Sat 10-2, Sun 11:30-1:30pm; Mon, Wed-Fri (Summer) 10-4, Tues 10-7, Sat 10-2, Sun 11:30am-1:30pm
Restriction: 24-hr pass syst for students only
Friends of the Library Group

GROTON

P   GROTON FREE PUBLIC LIBRARY*, 1304 Scott Hwy, 05046. SAN 317-0314. Tel: 802-584-3358. E-mail: groton_free@vals.state.vt.us. *Librn,* Marjorie Shane
Founded 1886. Pop 876
Library Holdings: AV Mats 131; Bk Vols 5,350
Automation Activity & Vendor Info: (Cataloging) JayWil Software Development, Inc
Wireless access
Publications: Vermont Library Trustees Publish
Open Mon & Fri 2:30-7, Wed 10-4, Sat 10-Noon
Friends of the Library Group

GUILDHALL

P   GUILDHALL PUBLIC LIBRARY*, Rt 102 N, 05905. (Mail add: PO Box 9, 05905-0009), SAN 317-0322. Tel: 802-676-3054. *Librn,* Valerie Foy
Jul 2009-Jun 2010 Income $6,000. Mats Exp $500
Library Holdings: AV Mats 83; CDs 10; DVDs 25; Bk Vols 5,000; Per Subs 18; Videos 15
Wireless access
Open Mon (Winter) 4-9, Wed 4-8; Mon (Summer) 6pm-8pm, Wed 1-3 & 7pm-8pm
Friends of the Library Group

GUILFORD

P   GUILFORD FREE LIBRARY*, 4024 Guilford Center Rd, 05301. SAN 317-0330. Tel: 802-257-4603. FAX: 802-257-4603. *Librn,* Cathi Wilken
Pop 2,046; Circ 2,150
Library Holdings: Bk Vols 4,500
Special Collections: Guilford, Vermont History & Biography Coll
Subject Interests: Children's prog, Local hist, Sr prog
Function: Handicapped accessible, Homebound delivery serv, ILL available, Prog for adults, Prog for children & young adult, Summer reading prog
Publications: At the Guilford Free Library (Newsletter)
Open Tues 9:30-6, Wed 1-8, Thurs 3-6, Sat 9:30-3

HANCOCK

P   HANCOCK FREE PUBLIC LIBRARY, PO Box 159, 05748-0159. SAN 317-0349. Tel: 802-767-4651. *Librn,* Caroline Meagher; Staff 0.4 (Non-MLS 0.4)
Founded 1920. Pop 340; Circ 1,469
Library Holdings: AV Mats 187; CDs 20; DVDs 260; Bk Titles 3,000; Bk Vols 3,500; Per Subs 8; Talking Bks 50; Videos 900
Wireless access
Open Wed 12:30-5:30, Thurs 12:30-6:30, Sat 9-12
Friends of the Library Group

HARDWICK

P   JEUDEVINE MEMORIAL LIBRARY, 93 N Main St, 05843. (Mail add: PO Box 536, 05843-0536), SAN 317-0357. Tel: 802-472-5948. FAX: 802-472-3793. E-mail: jeudevine@hotmail.com. Web Site: www.jeudevinememoriallibrary.org. *Libr Dir,* Lisa Sammet; Tel: 802-586-7533; *Youth Serv Dir,* Jessica Summer; Staff 2.5 (MLS 2, Non-MLS 0.5)
Founded 1896. Pop 3,010; Circ 16,333
Jul 2011-Jun 2012 Income $90,752, State $100, City $82,864, Federal $148, Locally Generated Income $3,640, Other $4,000. Mats Exp $6,580, Books $4,800, Per/Ser (Incl. Access Fees) $650, AV Mat $600, Electronic Ref Mat (Incl. Access Fees) $530. Sal $59,085 (Prof $24,220)
Library Holdings: Audiobooks 350; Bks-By-Mail 400; Bks on Deafness & Sign Lang 4; CDs 250; DVDs 200; Electronic Media & Resources 12; Large Print Bks 100; Bk Titles 11,436; Per Subs 28; Talking Bks 500; Videos 400
Special Collections: Vermontiana Coll
Automation Activity & Vendor Info: (Cataloging) LibraryWorld, Inc; (Circulation) LibraryWorld, Inc; (ILL) SirsiDynix
Database Vendor: Gale Cengage Learning, Overdrive, Inc, ProQuest
Wireless access
Function: After school storytime, AV serv, Bks on CD, Children's prog, Computer training, Computers for patron use, Copy machines, Digital talking bks, Distance learning, Electronic databases & coll, Free DVD rentals, Holiday prog, Home delivery & serv to Sr ctr & nursing homes, ILL available, Music CDs, Online cat, Online searches, OverDrive digital audio bks, Preschool outreach, Prog for adults, Prog for children & young adult, Pub access computers, Ref & res, Ref serv in person, Senior computer classes, Spoken cassettes & CDs, Spoken cassettes & DVDs, Story hour, Summer & winter reading prog, Summer reading prog, Telephone ref, Video lending libr, Web-catalog, Workshops
Partic in First Search; ProQuest; Vermont Automated Libr Syst (VALS)
Open Mon & Wed 1-7, Tues & Thurs 1-5, Fri 10-5, Sat 10-2
Friends of the Library Group

HARTFORD

P   HARTFORD LIBRARY, 1587 Maple, 05047. (Mail add: PO Box 512, 05047-0512), SAN 317-0373. Tel: 802-296-2568. FAX: 802-296-7452. E-mail: hartford@vals.state.vt.us. Web Site: www.hartfordvtlibrary.org. *Librn,* Anne Dempsey
Founded 1893. Pop 4,500
Library Holdings: Bk Vols 10,000; Per Subs 15
Subject Interests: Harvard Classics, Vt hist
Function: Bks on CD, Children's prog, Computers for patron use, Copy machines, e-mail serv, Electronic databases & coll, Fax serv, Free DVD rentals, Handicapped accessible, Home delivery & serv to Sr ctr & nursing homes, ILL available, Mail & tel request accepted, Online cat, Online ref, Online searches, Outreach serv, OverDrive digital audio bks, Photocopying/Printing, Pub access computers, Scanner, Story hour, Summer reading prog, Tax forms, Telephone ref, Wheelchair accessible
Open Mon, Tues & Thurs 9-6, Wed & Fri Noon-6, Sat 9-Noon

HARTLAND

P   HARTLAND PUBLIC LIBRARIES*, 153 Rte 5, 05048. (Mail add: PO Box 137, 05048-0137), SAN 362-6199. Tel: 802-436-2473. FAX: 802-436-2473. E-mail: hartlandvtlib@vermonttel.net. Web Site: www.hartlandlibraryvt.org. *Dir,* Mary Danko; *Asst Dir,* Theresa Gregory; Staff 4 (MLS 1, Non-MLS 3)
Pop 3,200; Circ 23,902
Library Holdings: Bk Titles 14,115; Per Subs 64
Special Collections: Vermont & Hartland Hist Coll
Automation Activity & Vendor Info: (Cataloging) Mandarin Library Automation; (Circulation) Mandarin Library Automation
Wireless access
Open Tues & Fri 10-6, Wed & Thurs 12-8, Sat 9-2
Friends of the Library Group

HIGHGATE CENTER

P   HIGHGATE PUBLIC LIBRARY*, 17 Mill Hill, 05459. (Mail add: PO Box 76, 05459), SAN 317-0381. Tel: 802-868-3970. FAX: 802-868-4389. E-mail: highgate_public@comcast.net. Web Site: highgatelibrary.wordpress.com. *Libr Dir,* Lisa Comiskey
Library Holdings: Bk Vols 1,500
Open Mon & Thurs 2-6, Tues & Wed 9-12 & 2-6, Sat 9-Noon

HINESBURG

P   CARPENTER-CARSE LIBRARY*, 69 Ballards Corner Rd, 05461. (Mail add: PO Box 127, 05461), SAN 317-039X. Tel: 802-482-2878. E-mail: carpentercarselibrary@gmavt.net. Web Site: www.carpentercarse.org. *Dir,* Susan Barden; *Asst Dir,* Richard Pritsky; *Ad,* Jane Racer; *Youth Serv Librn,*

Position Currently Open; *Circ Supvr,* Judy Curtis; Staff 2.5 (MLS 0.5, Non-MLS 2)
Founded 1947. Pop 4,964; Circ 35,000
Library Holdings: Audiobooks 1,500; CDs 200; DVDs 500; Large Print Bks 500; Bk Vols 26,000; Per Subs 55; Videos 1,000
Special Collections: Vermontiana Coll. Oral History
Automation Activity & Vendor Info: (Acquisitions) LibLime; (Cataloging) LibLime; (Circulation) LibLime; (Course Reserve) LibLime; (ILL) LibLime; (Media Booking) LibLime; (OPAC) LibLime; (Serials) LibLime
Wireless access
Function: Adult bk club, After school storytime, Art exhibits, Audio & video playback equip for onsite use, Audiobks via web, AV serv, Bks on cassette, Bks on CD, CD-ROM, Children's prog, Computer training, Computers for patron use, Copy machines, Digital talking bks, Doc delivery serv, E-Reserves, Electronic databases & coll, Exhibits, Free DVD rentals, Handicapped accessible, Holiday prog, Home delivery & serv to Sr ctr & nursing homes, Homebound delivery serv, ILL available, Mail & tel request accepted, Mus passes, Music CDs, Online cat, Online searches, Outreach serv, OverDrive digital audio bks, Photocopying/Printing, Preschool outreach, Prog for adults, Prog for children & young adult, Pub access computers, Ref serv available, Scanner, Senior outreach, Spoken cassettes & CDs, Spoken cassettes & DVDs, Story hour, Summer reading prog, Teen prog, VHS videos, Video lending libr, Web-catalog, Wheelchair accessible, Workshops
Partic in Green Mountain Library Consortium (GMLC)
Open Mon 10-1, Tues & Thurs 10-8, Wed & Fri 4-8, Sat 10-5 (10-2 Summer)
Restriction: Non-resident fee
Friends of the Library Group
Bookmobiles: 1

HUNTINGTON

P HUNTINGTON PUBLIC LIBRARY, 2156 Main Rd, 05462. (Mail add: PO Box 98, 05462-0098). Tel: 802-434-4583. E-mail: hpl@gmavt.net. Web Site: www.huntingtonpubliclibrary.org. *Dir,* Anne Dannenberg; *Asst Dir,* Wendy DeForest
Founded 1976. Pop 1,609; Circ 4,705
Jul 2012-Jun 2013 Income $43,100. Mats Exp $4,750. Sal $17,880
Library Holdings: AV Mats 60; High Interest/Low Vocabulary Bk Vols 50; Large Print Bks 50; Bk Titles 10,000; Talking Bks 250; Videos 80
Subject Interests: Vt
Automation Activity & Vendor Info: (Cataloging) Follett Software; (Circulation) Follett Software; (OPAC) Follett Software
Function: ILL available
Special Services for the Blind - Large print bks
Open Mon, Tues & Thurs 10-6, Fri 10-2, Sun Noon-5
Friends of the Library Group

HYDE PARK

P LANPHER MEMORIAL LIBRARY*, 141 Main St, 05655. (Mail add: PO Box 196, 05655-0196), SAN 317-0411. Tel: 802-888-4628. E-mail: info@lanpherlibrary.org. Web Site: www.lanpherlibrary.org. *Librn,* Amy Olsen
Founded 1895. Pop 2,823
Library Holdings: Bk Titles 8,500; Per Subs 35
Special Collections: Art & Artist; Bound Local Newspapers 1863-1930; Vermont History, Life & Literature
Open Mon Noon-7, Tues & Fri 1-5, Wed 10-5, Sat 10-1
Friends of the Library Group

IRASBURG

P LEACH PUBLIC LIBRARY*, 130 Park Ave, 05845. (Mail add: PO Box 87, 05845), SAN 325-0482. Tel: 802-754-2526. *Librn,* Laurie Green; Staff 1 (Non-MLS 1)
Founded 1927. Pop 1,098; Circ 5,670
Library Holdings: DVDs 120; Bk Titles 10,000; Bk Vols 10,900; Per Subs 22; Talking Bks 44; Videos 320
Open Mon 3-8, Wed & Thurs 3-6, Sat 10-4

ISLAND POND

P ISLAND POND PUBLIC LIBRARY*, 49 Mill St Extension, 05846. (Mail add: PO Box 422, 05846-0422), SAN 320-5193. Tel: 802-723-6134. FAX: 802-723-6134. *Dir,* John W Zuppa; *Asst Librn,* Michelle Wilcox
Founded 1897. Pop 1,562
Library Holdings: Bk Vols 15,600; Per Subs 7
Wireless access
Open Tues & Thurs 10-7, Wed 2-6, Fri 10-5, Sat 10-2

ISLE LA MOTTE

P ISLE LA MOTTE LIBRARY*, 2238 Main St, 05463. SAN 317-042X. Tel: 802-928-4113. *Librn,* Jeannine Bruley
Founded 1904. Pop 519; Circ 1,058
Library Holdings: Bk Titles 4,200
Subject Interests: Local hist, State hist
Open Fri (Winter) Noon-3:30, Sat 10-Noon; Wed (Summer) 6-8, Fri Noon-5, Sat 10-Noon
Friends of the Library Group

JACKSONVILLE

P WHITINGHAM FREE PUBLIC LIBRARY*, 2948 Vt Rte 100, 05342. (Mail add: PO Box 500, 05342-0500), SAN 317-0438. Tel: 802-368-7506. E-mail: whitingham@vals.state.vt.us. Web Site: www.readwithus.org. *Librn,* Kristine Sweeter; *Asst Librn,* Lisa Barus; *Asst Librn,* Lois Lapointe
Founded 1899. Pop 2,100; Circ 10,000
Library Holdings: AV Mats 1,000; Bk Vols 15,000; Per Subs 20
Open Mon 10-4, Wed 2-7, Thurs 2-6, Sat 9-2
Friends of the Library Group

JAMAICA

P JAMAICA MEMORIAL LIBRARY, 17 Depot St, 05343. (Mail add: PO Box 266, 05343-0266), SAN 317-0446. Tel: 802-874-4901. E-mail: jamaicapl@vals.state.vt.us. Web Site: www.jamaicavtlibrary.org. *Librn,* Victoria Tomkinson
Pop 1,035; Circ 760
Library Holdings: Audiobooks 364; Bk Vols 6,755; Per Subs 10; Videos 267
Special Collections: Vermont & Jamaica (VT) Histories Coll
Wireless access
Open Wed 2-6, Fri 9-1, Sat 10-Noon

JEFFERSONVILLE

P VARNUM MEMORIAL LIBRARY*, 194 Main St, 05464. (Mail add: PO Box 198, 05464-0198). Tel: 802-644-2117. E-mail: varnum_jeff@vals.state.vt.us. *Librn,* Gene Rybicki-Judkins
Founded 1894. Pop 3,000
Jul 2005-Jun 2006 Income $25,000
Library Holdings: DVDs 25; Bk Vols 15,000; Per Subs 23; Talking Bks 150; Videos 200
Open Mon & Tues 1-8, Thurs & Sat 9-12

JERICHO

P DEBORAH RAWSON MEMORIAL LIBRARY*, Eight River Rd, 05465. SAN 329-0964. Tel: 802-899-4962. FAX: 802-899-5257. E-mail: underhill@vals.state.vt.us. Web Site: www.drml.org. *Dir,* Holly Hall; *Ch,* Anne Hawley; Staff 1 (Non-MLS 1)
Pop 8,000; Circ 55,000
Library Holdings: Bk Vols 25,662; Per Subs 60
Automation Activity & Vendor Info: (Cataloging) Follett Software; (Circulation) Follett Software
Wireless access
Open Tues & Thurs 12-8, Wed & Fri 10-6, Sat 10-2, Sun 1-4
Friends of the Library Group

JERICHO CENTER

P JERICHO TOWN LIBRARY*, Seven Jericho Ctr Green, 05465. (Mail add: PO Box 1055, Jericho, 05465-1055). Tel: 802-899-4686. *Librn,* Donna Malinowski
Pop 5,010
Library Holdings: AV Mats 292; Bk Vols 7,455; Per Subs 13; Talking Bks 228
Special Collections: Vermont Coll
Wireless access
Open Mon & Fri 1-5, Wed 10-12 & 2-6, Sat 10-1

JOHNSON

P JOHNSON PUBLIC LIBRARY*, Seven Library Dr, 05656. (Mail add: PO Box 601, 05656-0601), SAN 317-0497. Tel: 802-635-7141. *Librn,* Jeanne Engel
Pop 3,000; Circ 4,950
Library Holdings: Bk Vols 7,500; Per Subs 10
Open Tues, Thurs & Fri 10-5, Wed 11-6, Sat 10-1

C JOHNSON STATE COLLEGE LIBRARY*, 337 College Hill, 05656. SAN 317-0500. Tel: 802-635-1274. FAX: 802-635-1294. Web Site: www.jsc.vsc.edu/library. *Dir,* Joseph Farara; E-mail: joseph.farara@jsc.edu; *Access Serv Librn,* Joanne Edwards; Tel: 802-635-1266; *Pub Serv Librn,* Linda Kramer; Tel: 802-635-1275; *Tech Serv Librn,* Raymond Brior; Tel:

802-635-1495; *Circ Supvr,* Walter Reeve; Tel: 802-635-1273; *ILL Supvr,* Alice Godin; *Govt Doc, Per,* Pamela Gelineau; Tel: 802-635-1271; Staff 7 (MLS 4, Non-MLS 3)
Founded 1866. Enrl 1,700; Fac 62; Highest Degree: Master
Library Holdings: AV Mats 7,500; e-books 6,137; Electronic Media & Resources 25; Bk Vols 109,600; Per Subs 500
Special Collections: State Document Depository; US Document Depository
Subject Interests: Children's lit
Database Vendor: SirsiDynix
Wireless access
Publications: Annual Report; Pathfinders; Serials List
Partic in Lyrasis; Vermont Automated Libr Syst (VALS)
Open Mon-Thurs (Winter) 8am-11pm, Fri 8-6, Sat 10-6, Sun 10am-11pm; Mon-Thurs (Summer) 10-8, Fri 10-4, Sun 1-8

KILLINGTON

P   SHERBURNE MEMORIAL LIBRARY*, PO Box 73, 05751. SAN 317-0519. Tel: 802-422-4251, 802-422-9765. FAX: 802-422-4323. E-mail: information@sherburnelibrary.org. *Dir,* Gail Weymouth; *Ch,* Terry Austin; *YA Librn,* Heather Grev
Pop 900; Circ 20,000
Library Holdings: Bk Vols 18,000
Special Collections: Sherburne Township History Coll
Subject Interests: Alaska, Northern territories, Vt hist
Automation Activity & Vendor Info: (Cataloging) Mandarin Library Automation; (Circulation) Mandarin Library Automation
Open Mon & Fri 10-5:30, Wed 10-8, Tues & Thurs 1-5:30, Sat 9-1

LINCOLN

P   LINCOLN LIBRARY*, 222 W River Rd, 05443. SAN 317-0535. Tel: 802-453-2665. E-mail: lincolnlibraryvt@gmail.com. Web Site: www.lincoln.lib.vt.us. *Dir,* Deborah Gray; Staff 2 (Non-MLS 2)
Pop 1,214; Circ 2,000
Library Holdings: Bk Titles 16,525; Per Subs 68
Automation Activity & Vendor Info: (Acquisitions) LibraryWorld, Inc; (Cataloging) LibraryWorld, Inc; (Circulation) LibraryWorld, Inc
Wireless access
Function: Adult bk club, After school storytime, Art exhibits, Bi-weekly Writer's Group, Bks on cassette, Bks on CD, CD-ROM, Chess club, Children's prog, Computer training, Computers for patron use, Copy machines, e-mail serv, Free DVD rentals, Handicapped accessible, ILL available, Mus passes, Music CDs, Online cat, Online searches, Photocopying/Printing, Prog for adults, Prog for children & young adult, Senior outreach, Summer reading prog, Tax forms, Teen prog, VHS videos, Web-catalog, Workshops
Open Mon 2-6, Wed 10-8, Fri 10-6, Sat 10-4

LOWELL

P   LOWELL COMMUNITY LIBRARY, 2170 Vermont Rte 100, 05847. (Mail add: PO Box 189, 05847-0189), SAN 317-0543. Tel: 802-744-2447. *Librn,* Regine Griswold; Staff 1 (Non-MLS 1)
Founded 1935. Pop 750; Circ 1,200
Jul 2006-Jun 2007 Income $5,500. Mats Exp $3,700, Books $3,500, Per/Ser (Incl. Access Fees) $200. Sal $2,200
Library Holdings: Braille Volumes 2; CDs 10; Large Print Bks 80; Bk Vols 6,000; Per Subs 3; Videos 14
Open Tues 4-6, Sat 10-12

LOWER WATERFORD

P   DAVIES MEMORIAL LIBRARY*, 532 Maple St, 05848. (Mail add: PO Box 56, 05848-0056), SAN 322-8576. Tel: 802-748-4609. *Librn,* Donna Stinehour; Staff 1 (Non-MLS 1)
Founded 1896. Pop 1,210; Circ 1,319
Library Holdings: Bk Vols 3,500; Per Subs 15
Open Mon-Fri 8:15-5:15, Sat 8:15-Noon
Friends of the Library Group

LUDLOW

P   FLETCHER MEMORIAL LIBRARY, 88 Main St, 05149. SAN 317-0551. Tel: 802-228-3517, 802-228-8921. Web Site: www.fletchermemorial.org. *Dir,* Jill Tofferi; *Ref Librn,* Ginger Palmer; *Youth Serv Librn,* Lindsay Gratten
Founded 1901. Pop 3,000; Circ 24,000
Library Holdings: Audiobooks 900; DVDs 200; Bk Vols 14,000; Per Subs 70
Subject Interests: Local hist
Automation Activity & Vendor Info: (Acquisitions) Baker & Taylor; (Cataloging) Baker & Taylor; (Circulation) Baker & Taylor; (OPAC) Follett Software
Database Vendor: Gale Cengage Learning

Wireless access
Open Mon 10-7, Tues & Fri 10-5, Sat 10-1
Friends of the Library Group

P   TYSON LIBRARY*, 286 Dublin Rd, 05149. SAN 376-8023. Tel: 802-228-7157. *Librn,* Betty Jarvi; Tel: 802-228-8037
Library Holdings: Bk Vols 3,500
Partic in Midwest Collaborative for Library Services (MCLS)
Open Tues-Thurs & Sat (May-Sept) 10-12

LUNENBURG

P   ALDEN BALCH MEMORIAL LIBRARY*, 24 E Main St, 05906. (Mail add: PO Box 6, 05906-0006), SAN 317-056X. Tel: 802-892-5365. *Librn,* Theresa A Lewis
Founded 1904. Pop 1,320; Circ 12,517
Jul 2008-Jun 2009 Income $21,500, City $20,000, Locally Generated Income $1,500. Mats Exp $3,250, Books $3,000, Per/Ser (Incl. Access Fees) $100, Other Print Mats $150. Sal $14,000
Library Holdings: AV Mats 200; Bk Vols 8,000; Per Subs 15
Open Tues-Thurs 10-4, Sun 6-8
Friends of the Library Group

LYNDONVILLE

P   COBLEIGH PUBLIC LIBRARY*, 14 Depot St, 05851. (Mail add: PO Box 147, 05851-0147), SAN 317-0578. Tel: 802-626-5475. FAX: 802-626-1167. Web Site: cobleighlibrary.org. *Dir,* Cindy M Karasinski; E-mail: cindyk@cobleighlibrary.org; Staff 4 (Non-MLS 4)
Founded 1904. Pop 9,873; Circ 52,000
Jan 2008-Dec 2008 Income $224,950, City $193,000, Locally Generated Income $3,400, Other $28,550. Mats Exp $15,969, Books $12,500, Per/Ser (Incl. Access Fees) $1,250, AV Mat $1,500, Electronic Ref Mat (Incl. Access Fees) $719. Sal $117,694
Library Holdings: Bk Vols 25,000
Automation Activity & Vendor Info: (Cataloging) TLC (The Library Corporation); (OPAC) TLC (The Library Corporation)
Database Vendor: Gale Cengage Learning
Wireless access
Open Mon 12-5, Tues & Thurs 12-7, Wed & Fri 10-5, Sat 9-1
Friends of the Library Group
Bookmobiles: 1. Librn, Kari Cochran

C   LYNDON STATE COLLEGE, Samuel Read Hall Library, 1001 College Rd, 05851. (Mail add: PO Box 919, 05851), SAN 317-0586. Tel: 802-626-6366. Interlibrary Loan Service Tel: 802-626-6449. Reference Tel: 802-626-6450. FAX: 802-626-6331. E-mail: Library@Lyndonstate.edu. Web Site: library.lyndonstate.edu. *Dir, Libr Serv,* Garet Nelson; Tel: 802-626-6446, E-mail: garet.nelson@lsc.vsc.edu; *Pub Serv Librn,* Graham Sherriff; *Coordr, Acq, Per,* Monique Prive; *Circ Coordr,* Jay Bona; *ILL Coordr,* Tara-jean Samora; *ILL Spec,* Elizabeth Conklin; Staff 6 (MLS 2, Non-MLS 4)
Founded 1911. Enrl 1,200; Fac 83; Highest Degree: Master
Library Holdings: CDs 1,686; DVDs 2,545; e-books 4,572; Microforms 23,413; Bk Vols 87,294; Per Subs 255
Special Collections: Juvenile & Instructional Coll; Vermont Coll
Automation Activity & Vendor Info: (Acquisitions) SirsiDynix; (Cataloging) SirsiDynix; (Circulation) SirsiDynix; (Course Reserve) SirsiDynix; (ILL) SirsiDynix; (Media Booking) SirsiDynix; (OPAC) SirsiDynix; (Serials) SirsiDynix
Database Vendor: Baker & Taylor, CQ Press, CredoReference, EBSCOhost, Gale Cengage Learning, JSTOR, LexisNexis, Medline, Newsbank, OCLC FirstSearch, ProQuest, PubMed, Springshare, LLC
Wireless access
Publications: Annual Report; Faculty Handbook; General Guide; Pathfinders
Partic in Lyrasis; OCLC Online Computer Library Center, Inc
Open Mon-Thurs (Fall-Spring) 8am-11pm, Fri 8-4, Sat 10-5, Sun 1-11; Mon-Fri (Summer) 8-4
Friends of the Library Group

MANCHESTER

P   MARK SKINNER LIBRARY*, 48 West Rd, 05254. (Mail add: PO Box 438, 05254-0438), SAN 317-0594. Tel: 802-362-2607. E-mail: info@markskinnerlibrary.org. Web Site: www.markskinnerlibrary.org. *Dir,* James Knowlton; *Asst Dir,* Cheryl Stillson; *Youth Serv Dir,* Janet Kleinberg; *Database Coordr, ILL, Webmaster,* Susan Swasta; *Youth Serv,* Jan Ketterer; *Adult Prog Coordr, Vols Serv Coordr,* Cindy Waters; Staff 6 (MLS 3, Non-MLS 3)
Founded 1897. Pop 4,359; Circ 46,645
Aug 2008-Jul 2009 Income $323,582, State $500, City $144,000, Federal $50, Locally Generated Income $179,032. Mats Exp $27,622, Books $20,512, Per/Ser (Incl. Access Fees) $590, AV Mat $6,520. Sal $169,985

Library Holdings: Audiobooks 795; Bks on Deafness & Sign Lang 15; DVDs 771; Large Print Bks 403; Microforms 1; Bk Titles 20,788; Bk Vols 21,297; Per Subs 38; Videos 147
Automation Activity & Vendor Info: (Acquisitions) Baker & Taylor; (Cataloging) Follett Software; (Circulation) Follett Software; (OPAC) Follett Software
Database Vendor: Gale Cengage Learning
Wireless access
Function: Adult bk club, Bks on CD, Children's prog, Computers for patron use, Copy machines, ILL available, Mus passes, Online cat, Prog for adults, Prog for children & young adult, Pub access computers, Story hour, Summer reading prog, Tax forms
Open Tues & Thurs 10-6, Wed 10-8, Fri & Sat 10-4

MARLBORO

C   MARLBORO COLLEGE*, Rice-Aron Library, 64 Dalrymple Rd, 05344-0300. (Mail add: PO Box A, 05344-0300), SAN 317-0616. Tel: 802-258-9221. Interlibrary Loan Service Tel: 802-451-7579. Administration Tel: 802-451-7577. FAX: 802-451-7550. E-mail: library@marlboro.edu. Web Site: www.marlboro.edu/resources/library. *Libr Dir,* Emily Alling; E-mail: ealling@marlboro.edu; *Ref Librn, Tech Librn,* Amber Hunt; *Access Serv Spec,* Bonny White; *Tech Serv Spec,* Sharon Reidt; Staff 4 (MLS 3, Non-MLS 1)
Founded 1947. Enrl 369; Fac 50; Highest Degree: Master
Jul 2005-Jun 2006. Mats Exp $91,325, Books $40,806, Per/Ser (Incl. Access Fees) $22,450, AV Mat $2,000, Electronic Ref Mat (Incl. Access Fees) $26,069. Sal $134,442 (Prof $113,059)
Library Holdings: AV Mats 2,990; e-books 50,000; e-journals 40,000; Bk Vols 75,000; Per Subs 150; Talking Bks 186
Special Collections: Rudyard Kipling Coll
Automation Activity & Vendor Info: (Cataloging) ByWater Solutions; (Circulation) ByWater Solutions; (Course Reserve) ByWater Solutions; (ILL) Clio; (OPAC) ByWater Solutions
Database Vendor: Alexander Street Press, Annual Reviews, ARTstor, BioOne, ebrary, EBSCOhost, Elsevier, Gale Cengage Learning, JSTOR, LexisNexis, Marcive, Inc, Nature Publishing Group, OCLC FirstSearch, OCLC WorldCat, Oxford Online, Project MUSE, PubMed, Springshare, LLC
Wireless access
Partic in Lyrasis
Open Mon-Thurs 8:30-5:30 & 6:30-11, Fri 8:30-4:30, Sun 12:30-5:30 & 6:30-11

MARSHFIELD

P   JAQUITH PUBLIC LIBRARY*, Old Schoolhouse Common, 122 School St, 05658. (Mail add: PO Box 227, 05658-0227), SAN 317-0624. Tel: 802-426-3581. FAX: 802-426-3045. E-mail: jaquithpubliclibrary@hotmail.com. *Librn,* Susan Grey
Pop 1,441; Circ 9,175
Library Holdings: Bk Vols 8,000; Per Subs 15
Special Collections: Oral History
Subject Interests: Gen, Local hist
Open Mon 9-12 & 3-6, Tues, Thurs & Fri 3-6, Wed 9-12 & 3-8, Sat 9-12
Friends of the Library Group

MIDDLEBURY

S   AMERICAN MORGAN HORSE INSTITUTE*, Orcutt & Cole Memorial Research Library, 34 Main St, 05482. (Mail add: PO Box 101, 05753), SAN 375-3212. Tel: 802-985-8665. FAX: 802-985-5242. E-mail: info@morganhorseinstitute.com, morganmuseum@gmail.com. Web Site: www.morganmuseum.org. *Curator,* Amber Broderick
Library Holdings: AV Mats 55; Bk Titles 1,500; Bk Vols 2,000
Special Collections: Morgan Horses. Oral History
Subject Interests: Equine
Function: Res libr
Open Tues-Sat 10-5
Friends of the Library Group

P   ILSLEY PUBLIC LIBRARY, 75 Main St, 05753. SAN 317-0632. Tel: 802-388-4095. FAX: 802-388-4367. E-mail: info@ilsleypubliclibrary.org. Web Site: www.ilsleypubliclibrary.org. *Dir,* David Clark; Tel: 802-388-4098, E-mail: david.clark@ilsleypubliclibrary.org; *Librn, Adult Serv & Tech,* Chris Kirby; E-mail: chris.kirby@ilsleypubliclibrary.org; *Youth Serv Librn,* Sarah Lawton; Tel: 802-388-4097, E-mail: sarah.lawton@ilsleypubliclibrary.org; Staff 15 (MLS 3, Non-MLS 12)
Founded 1866. Pop 8,496; Circ 184,010
Jul 2012-Jun 2013 Income (Main Library and Branch(s)) $616,105. Mats Exp $86,409, Books $50,475, Per/Ser (Incl. Access Fees) $4,034, AV Mat $31,400, Electronic Ref Mat (Incl. Access Fees) $500. Sal $311,327 (Prof $137,000)
Library Holdings: Bk Vols 54,500; Per Subs 108
Subject Interests: Local hist

Automation Activity & Vendor Info: (Acquisitions) Innovative Interfaces, Inc - Millenium; (Cataloging) Innovative Interfaces, Inc - Millenium; (Circulation) Innovative Interfaces, Inc - Millenium
Database Vendor: Innovative Interfaces, Inc
Wireless access
Function: Art exhibits, Audio & video playback equip for onsite use, Audiobks via web, Bks on cassette, Bks on CD, Children's prog, Computer training, Computers for patron use, Copy machines, Distance learning, Electronic databases & coll, Equip loans & repairs, Fax serv, Free DVD rentals, Handicapped accessible, Holiday prog, ILL available, Mail & tel request accepted, Microfiche/film & reading machines, Mus passes, Music CDs, OverDrive digital audio bks, Preschool outreach, Prog for adults, Prog for children & young adult, Pub access computers, Ref serv available, Ref serv in person, Scanner, Spoken cassettes & CDs, Story hour, Summer reading prog, Tax forms, Teen prog, Telephone ref, Web-catalog, Wheelchair accessible
Publications: Ilsley Inklings
Open Mon, Wed & Fri 10-6, Tues & Thurs 10-8, Sat 10-4, Sun (Oct-Apr) 1-4
Restriction: Non-resident fee
Friends of the Library Group
Branches: 1
SARAH PARTRIDGE COMMUNITY, 431 E Main St, East Middlebury, 05740. (Mail add: PO Box 330, East Middlebury, 05740-0330). Tel: 802-388-7588. E-mail: sarahpartridge04@hotmail.com. *Librn,* Mona Rogers
Library Holdings: Bk Titles 2,300
Open Tues & Sat 9-Noon, Thurs 2-6
Friends of the Library Group

C   MIDDLEBURY COLLEGE LIBRARY*, 110 Storrs Ave, 05753-6007. SAN 362-6318. Tel: 802-443-5490. Circulation Tel: 802-443-5494. Interlibrary Loan Service Tel: 802-443-5498. Reference Tel: 802-443-5496. FAX: 802-443-2074, 802-443-5698. Web Site: web.middlebury.edu/lis/lib/default.htm. *Dean,* Michael D Roy; Tel: 802-443-5490, E-mail: mdroy@middlebury.edu; *Head, Circ,* Dan Frostman; Tel: 802-443-5798, E-mail: dfrostman@middlebury.edu; *Head, Coll, Head, Digital Libr Initiatives, Head, Per,* Rebecca Irwin; Tel: 802-443-5499, E-mail: rirwin@middlebury.edu; *Head of Ref & Instrul Serv,* Karrie MacFarlane; E-mail: kmacfarlane@middlebury.edu; *Assoc Librn, Ref Serv,* Hans Raum; Tel: 802-443-5493, E-mail: raum@middlebury.edu; *Spec Coll Librn,* Andrew Wentink; Tel: 802-443-5501, E-mail: awentink@middlebury.edu; *Reserves,* Ayers Kallem; *Network Serv, Syst,* Stewart Jim; Staff 54 (MLS 15, Non-MLS 39)
Founded 1800. Enrl 2,406; Fac 305; Highest Degree: Doctorate
Library Holdings: Bk Vols 710,649; Per Subs 2,908
Special Collections: Abernethy American Literature Coll, bks, mss; Archives of Traditional Music Flanders Ballad Coll, bks, mss, recording; Vermont Coll. US Document Depository
Subject Interests: Anglo-Am ballad, European langs
Automation Activity & Vendor Info: (Acquisitions) Innovative Interfaces, Inc; (Cataloging) Innovative Interfaces, Inc; (Circulation) Innovative Interfaces, Inc; (Course Reserve) Innovative Interfaces, Inc; (OPAC) Innovative Interfaces, Inc; (Serials) Innovative Interfaces, Inc
Wireless access
Publications: Friends of the Library Newsletter; Myriad News
Partic in Dialog Corp; Lyrasis; OCLC Online Computer Library Center, Inc
Open Mon-Thurs 7:30am-1am, Fri 7:30am-11pm, Sat 9am-11pm, Sun 9am-1am
Friends of the Library Group
Departmental Libraries:
ARMSTRONG LIBRARY, McCardell Bicentennial Hall, 05753, SAN 362-6377. Tel: 802-443-5449. FAX: 802-443-2016. *Librn,* Carrie M Macfarlane; Tel: 802-443-5018; Staff 3 (MLS 1, Non-MLS 2)
Library Holdings: Bk Vols 108,064
Database Vendor: ABC-CLIO, Alexander Street Press, American Chemical Society, Annual Reviews, Dialog, EBSCO Information Services, EBSCOhost, Gale Cengage Learning, ISI Web of Knowledge, LexisNexis, OCLC FirstSearch, ProQuest, RefWorks, SirsiDynix, Wilson - Wilson Web
Partic in OCLC Online Computer Library Center, Inc
Open Mon-Thurs (Winter) 8am-Midnight, Fri 8-6, Sat 10-6, Sun 10-Midnight; Mon-Fri (Summer) 9-5
Friends of the Library Group

S   THE STEWART-SWIFT RESEARCH CENTER AT THE HENRY SHELDON MUSEUM OF VERMONT HISTORY*, Sheldon Museum Research Center, One Park St, 05753. SAN 317-0659. Tel: 802-388-2117. FAX: 802-388-2112. Web Site: www.henrysheldonmuseum.org. *Exec Dir,* Jan Albers; E-mail: albers@HenrySheldonMuseum.org; Staff 1 (MLS 1)
Founded 1882
Library Holdings: Bk Vols 3,000
Special Collections: Manuscript Coll; Middlebury Newspaper Coll; Sheldon Scrapbooks
Subject Interests: County hist

Function: Archival coll, Res libr
Publications: Treasures Gathered Here: A Guide to the Manuscript
Collection of the Sheldon Museum
Open Tues, Wed & Fri 1-5, Thurs 1-8
Restriction: Closed stack, Non-circulating, Open to pub for ref only

MIDDLETOWN SPRINGS

P   MIDDLETOWN SPRINGS PUBLIC LIBRARY*, 39 West St, 05757-4401.
SAN 320-5185. Tel: 802-235-2435. *Librn,* Kimberley Mathewson; Staff 1
(MLS 1)
Pop 821; Circ 1,774
Library Holdings: Bk Vols 5,472
Mem of Southwest Regional Library Service System
Open Mon & Wed 2-8, Fri & Sat 9-Noon

MILTON

P   MILTON PUBLIC LIBRARY, 39 Bombadier Rd, 05468. SAN 317-0667.
Tel: 802-893-4644. FAX: 802-893-1005. *Dir,* Scott Murphy; *Asst Dir, Ch,*
Kathy Dulac; Staff 7 (Non-MLS 7)
Founded 1898. Pop 10,347; Circ 70,000
Jul 2006-Jun 2007 Income $180,990. Mats Exp $26,978, Books $20,275,
AV Mat $5,998, Electronic Ref Mat (Incl. Access Fees) $705. Sal
$131,284
Library Holdings: CDs 2,988; DVDs 2,477; Electronic Media &
Resources 2; Bk Titles 33,129; Bk Vols 38,000; Per Subs 30
Wireless access
Open Mon, Wed & Thurs 9-8, Tues & Fri 9-5, Sat 9-1
Friends of the Library Group
Bookmobiles: 1. Bk titles 1,643

MONKTON

P   RUSSELL MEMORIAL LIBRARY*, 4333 State Prison Hollow Rd,
05469. (Mail add: PO Box 39, 05469-0039), SAN 317-0675. Tel:
802-453-4471. *Librn,* Deborah Chamberlain
Pop 1,201; Circ 1,223
Library Holdings: Bk Vols 2,365
Wireless access
Open Tues 3-8, Fri 9-1, Sat 9-2

MONTGOMERY CENTER

P   MONTGOMERY TOWN LIBRARY*, 86 Mountain Rd, 05471. (Mail add:
PO Box 448, 05471-0448), SAN 317-0683. Tel: 802-326-3113. E-mail:
montgomery.librarian@gmail.com. Web Site:
www.montgomeryvt.us/library.htm. *Dir, Town Librn,* Tracey Durgan; Staff
0.4 (Non-MLS 0.4)
Pop 992; Circ 4,888
Library Holdings: Audiobooks 400; DVDs 200; Large Print Bks 100; Bk
Vols 7,000; Per Subs 3; Videos 200
Wireless access
Function: Art exhibits, Bks on cassette, Bks on CD, Children's prog,
Computers for patron use, Copy machines, Electronic databases & coll,
Family literacy, Free DVD rentals, Handicapped accessible, ILL available,
Mail & tel request accepted, Mus passes, Outreach serv,
Photocopying/Printing, Prog for adults, Prog for children & young adult,
Pub access computers, Ref serv in person, Senior computer classes, Story
hour, Summer reading prog, Tax forms, Teen prog, VHS videos
Open Mon, Thurs & Fri 10-12, Tues 10-12 & 3-7, Wed 10-12 &
6pm-8pm, Sat 10-2, Sun 12-2
Friends of the Library Group

MONTPELIER

P   KELLOGG-HUBBARD LIBRARY*, 135 Main St, 05602. SAN 317-0691.
Tel: 802-223-3338. FAX: 802-223-3337. E-mail: info@kellogghubbard.org.
Web Site: www.kellogghubbard.org. *Libr Dir,* Robin Sales; *Librn, Network
Tech, Webmaster,* Carol Minkiewicz; *Ch,* Jane Napier; *Ch,* Linda Pruitt;
Circ Librn, Lise Markus; *Outreach Coordr,* Rachael Grossman; *Coordr of
Develop, Prog Coordr,* Rachael Senechal; *Circ,* Roberta Downey; *ILL,*
Scott Lovelette; *Tech Serv,* Ruth McCullough; Staff 10 (MLS 2, Non-MLS
8)
Founded 1894. Pop 8,609; Circ 196,018
Library Holdings: Bk Titles 71,305; Per Subs 100
Automation Activity & Vendor Info: (Cataloging) Follett Software;
(Circulation) Follett Software; (ILL) SirsiDynix; (OPAC) Follett Software
Open Mon-Thurs (Winter) 10-8, Fri & Sat 10-5:30; Mon-Thurs (Summer)
10-8, Fri 10-5:30, Sat 10-1

P   STATE OF VERMONT DEPARTMENT OF LIBRARIES*, 109 State St,
05609-0601. SAN 322-7774. Tel: 802-828-3261. Reference Tel:
802-828-3268. FAX: 802-828-2199. Reference FAX: 802-828-1481.
E-mail: lib.rls@state.vt.us. Web Site: libraries.vermont.gov. *State Librn,*
Martha Reid; Tel: 802-828-3265, E-mail: martha.reid@state.vt.us; *Asst*

State Librn, Christine Friese; Tel: 802-828-2714; E-mail:
christine.friese@state.vt.us; *Dir, Tech & Info Serv,* Sheila Kearns; Tel:
802-828-6952, E-mail: sheila.kearns@state.vt.us; *Tech Serv-Section Head,*
Position Currently Open; *ILL Librn, Ref,* Gerrie Denison; Tel:
802-828-2735, E-mail: gerrie.denison@state.vt.us; *Law Librn,* Paul
Donovan; Tel: 802-828-2734, E-mail: paul.donovan@state.vt.us; *Youth Serv
Libr Consult,* Grace Greene; Tel: 802-828-6954, E-mail:
grace.greene@state.vt.us; Staff 26 (MLS 12, Non-MLS 14)
Library Holdings: Large Print Bks 1,087; Bk Vols 674,949; Per Subs
1,000; Videos 2,923
Special Collections: Children's Book Exhibit Center; Joseph L Wheeler
Library Science Coll. State Document Depository; US Document
Depository
Subject Interests: Law, Vt coll
Automation Activity & Vendor Info: (Cataloging) SirsiDynix
Database Vendor: Foundation Center, Gale Cengage Learning, OCLC,
OCLC FirstSearch, OCLC WebJunction, OCLC WorldCat, ProQuest,
SirsiDynix, Westlaw
Wireless access
Publications: DOL Newsletter (Newsletter); Manual for Vermont Library
Trustees (Library handbook); Vermont Public Library Annual Report
(Library statistics & report); Vermont School Library/Media Center Annual
Report (Library statistics & report)
Partic in Lyrasis
Special Services for the Blind - Braille bks; Descriptive video serv (DVS);
Digital talking bk; Large print bks; Newsletter (in large print, Braille or on
cassette); Talking bks & player equip
Open Mon-Fri 7:45-4:30
Branches: 2
LIBRARY FOR THE BLIND & PHYSICALLY HANDICAPPED
    See Separate Entry under Vermont Regional Library for the Blind &
    Physically Handicapped, Berlin
MIDSTATE LIBRARY SERVICE CENTER, 578 Paine Tpk N, Berlin,
05602, SAN 316-9588. Tel: 802-828-2320. *In Charge,* Jeremiah Kellogg;
Staff 2 (MLS 1, Non-MLS 1)

C   UNION INSTITUTE & UNIVERSITY*, Gary Memorial Library, 62 Ridge
St, Ste 2, 05602. SAN 362-6466. Tel: 802-828-8747. Toll Free Tel:
888-828-8557, Ext 8758. FAX: 802-828-8748. E-mail:
library@myunion.edu. Web Site: www.myunion.edu/library. *Dir,* Matthew
Pappathan; Tel: 802-828-8746, E-mail: Matthew.Pappathan@myunion.edu;
Asst Librn, Jamie Bordeau; E-mail: Jamie.Bordeau@myunion.edu; *Asst
Librn, ILL,* Tess Zimmerman; E-mail: Tess.Zimmerman@myunion.edu; *Ref
Librn,* Susan Whitehead; E-mail: Susan.Whitehead@myunion.edu; *Syst
Librn,* Linda Howell; E-mail: Linda.Howell@myunion.edu; *Tech Serv
Librn,* Philip Armentrout; E-mail: Philip.Armentrout@myunion.edu; Staff 7
(MLS 4, Non-MLS 3)
Founded 1934. Enrl 2,100; Fac 156; Highest Degree: Doctorate
Jul 2006-Jun 2007 Income $605,000. Mats Exp $267,000, Books $30,000,
Per/Ser (Incl. Access Fees) $15,000, AV Equip $5,000, AV Mat $1,000,
Electronic Ref Mat (Incl. Access Fees) $215,000, Presv $1,000. Sal
$215,000 (Prof $155,000)
Library Holdings: AV Mats 500; CDs 100; DVDs 50; e-books 45,000;
e-journals 40,000; Bk Vols 50,000; Videos 350
Subject Interests: Applied psychol, Creative writing, Holistic studies,
Visual arts, Women's studies
Automation Activity & Vendor Info: (Cataloging) EOS International;
(Circulation) EOS International; (ILL) OCLC; (OPAC) EOS International
Database Vendor: Cambridge Scientific Abstracts, EBSCOhost, Gale
Cengage Learning, LexisNexis, OCLC FirstSearch, SerialsSolutions
Partic in Lyrasis

C   VERMONT COLLEGE OF FINE ARTS LIBRARY, 36 College St, 05602.
Tel: 802-828-8512. FAX: 802-828-8514. E-mail: vcfa.library@vcfa.edu.
Web Site: www.vcfa.edu/library. *Dir,* Jim Nolte; Staff 1.75 (MLS 1,
Non-MLS 0.75)
Founded 1935. Enrl 320; Highest Degree: Master
Jul 2012-Jun 2013 Income $100,000
Open Mon-Fri 10:30-1:30
Restriction: Pub use on premises

MORETOWN

P   MORETOWN MEMORIAL LIBRARY*, 897 Rte 100-B, 05660-9120.
SAN 317-0756. Tel: 802-496-9728. E-mail:
moretown_mem@vals.state.vt.us. *Librn,* Margaret Bentley; *Librn,* Lisa
Samson
Pop 1,563; Circ 3,549
Jan 2007-Dec 2007 Income $13,776, City $9,455, Locally Generated
Income $4,321. Mats Exp $6,276, Books $5,445, AV Mat $831. Sal $3,919
Library Holdings: AV Mats 37; CDs 150; DVDs 60; Large Print Bks 24;
Bk Vols 3,965; Per Subs 5
Wireless access
Open Tues & Thurs 3-8, Wed 6pm-8pm, Fri & Sat 10-1
Friends of the Library Group

MORRISVILLE

M   COPLEY HOSPITAL MEDICAL LIBRARY*, 528 Washington Hwy,
    05661. SAN 317-0764. Tel: 802-888-8347. FAX: 802-888-8361. *Librn,*
    Stacy Wein; E-mail: swein@chsi.org
    Founded 1975
    Library Holdings: e-journals 14; Bk Titles 504; Per Subs 65; Talking Bks
    150
    Subject Interests: Consumer health, Med health sci
    Function: ILL available, Photocopying/Printing
    Partic in New Eng Regional Med Libr Serv
    Open Mon-Thurs 7-2:30
    Restriction: In-house use for visitors

P   MORRISTOWN CENTENNIAL LIBRARY*, Seven Richmond St, 05661.
    (Mail add: PO Box 727, 05661-0727), SAN 317-0772. Tel: 802-888-3853.
    E-mail: info@centenniallibrary.org. Web Site: centenniallibrary.org. *Librn,*
    Mary West; *Asst Librn,* Mary LeMieux; *Circ, ILL,* Linda Hartin; *Youth
    Serv,* Rachael Funk; Staff 3 (Non-MLS 3)
    Founded 1890. Pop 5,138; Circ 36,259
    Jul 2008-Jun 2009 Income $169,204, City $88,580. Mats Exp $21,100,
    Per/Ser (Incl. Access Fees) $1,900. Sal $122,500
    Library Holdings: AV Mats 1,000; Large Print Bks 550; Bk Vols 19,000;
    Per Subs 60; Talking Bks 975
    Special Collections: Cheney Civil War Coll
    Automation Activity & Vendor Info: (Cataloging) Follett Software;
    (Circulation) Follett Software
    Wireless access
    Open Tues & Wed 10-7:30, Thurs & Fri 10-5:30, Sat 9-2
    Friends of the Library Group

NEW HAVEN

P   NEW HAVEN COMMUNITY LIBRARY*, 78 North St,Ste 2, 05472.
    (Mail add: PO Box 85, 05472-0085), SAN 317-0780. Tel: 802-453-4015.
    E-mail: nhl@gmavt.net. Web Site: www.nhcl.org. *Librn,* Deborah
    Lundbech; Staff 1 (Non-MLS 1)
    Pop 1,400; Circ 15,525
    Library Holdings: AV Mats 700; Bk Vols 10,000; Per Subs 20
    Special Collections: Vermont Coll
    Automation Activity & Vendor Info: (Cataloging) Follett Software;
    (Circulation) Follett Software
    Open Tues 10-5, Wed & Thurs 1-8, Sat 10-1
    Friends of the Library Group

NEWBURY

P   TENNEY MEMORIAL LIBRARY, INC, 4886 Main St S, 05051. (Mail
    add: PO Box 85, 05051-0085), SAN 317-0802. Tel: 802-866-5366. E-mail:
    tenneylibrary@gmail.com. *Libr Dir,* Luisa Lindsley
    Founded 1896. Pop 975; Circ 3,118
    Library Holdings: Bk Vols 12,700; Per Subs 20
    Special Collections: New England Coll; Town History Coll. State
    Document Depository
    Automation Activity & Vendor Info: (Cataloging) Calico's Lion
    Wireless access
    Open Tues 10-5, Thurs 2-8, Sat 9-4

NEWFANE

P   MOORE FREE LIBRARY*, 23 West St, 05345. (Mail add: PO Box 208,
    05345-0208), SAN 317-0810. Tel: 802-365-7948. FAX: 802-257-0725.
    E-mail: newfanemoore@vals.state.vt.us. Web Site:
    www.moorefreelibrary.org. *Librn,* Meris Morrison
    Founded 1898. Pop 1,700; Circ 5,300
    Oct 2006-Sept 2007 Income $53,000, Locally Generated Income $13,000,
    Other $40,000. Mats Exp $12,000, Books $9,000, AV Mat $3,000. Sal
    $27,000
    Library Holdings: CDs 90; DVDs 200; Large Print Bks 125; Bk Titles
    13,500; Talking Bks 1,000; Videos 400
    Special Collections: Art & Humanities (Robert Crowell Coll); Civil War
    Coll; Vermont Coll
    Subject Interests: Local hist
    Automation Activity & Vendor Info: (Acquisitions) Brodart
    Database Vendor: Gale Cengage Learning
    Wireless access
    Function: Prog for children & young adult, Summer reading prog
    Partic in Vermont Automated Libr Syst (VALS)
    Open Tues-Fri 1-5, Sat 9-1
    Friends of the Library Group

NEWPORT

P   GOODRICH MEMORIAL LIBRARY*, 202 Main St, 05855. SAN
    317-0829. Tel: 802-334-7902. FAX: 802-334-3890. E-mail:
    info@goodrichlibrary.org. Web Site: www.goodrichlibrary.org. *Dir,*

Caroline Nicholson; *Head, Circ,* Ellen LaRouche; *Head, Tech Serv,* Linda
Bussiere; Staff 9 (Non-MLS 9)
Founded 1898. Pop 6,609; Circ 44,600
Library Holdings: AV Mats 900; CDs 400; DVDs 500; High Interest/Low
Vocabulary Bk Vols 50; Large Print Bks 500; Bk Vols 25,000; Per Subs
66; Talking Bks 400
Special Collections: Vermont History Coll, bks, photogs. State Document
Depository
Automation Activity & Vendor Info: (Acquisitions) Mandarin Library
Automation; (Cataloging) Mandarin Library Automation; (Circulation)
Mandarin Library Automation; (Course Reserve) Mandarin Library
Automation; (ILL) Mandarin Library Automation; (OPAC) Mandarin
Library Automation; (Serials) Mandarin Library Automation
Database Vendor: Baker & Taylor, EBSCO Information Services, Gale
Cengage Learning, netLibrary, OCLC FirstSearch, OCLC Openly
Informatics, OCLC WebJunction, OCLC WorldCat
Wireless access
Function: Distance learning, For res purposes, Games & aids for the
handicapped, Home delivery & serv to Sr ctr & nursing homes,
Homebound delivery serv, ILL available, Large print keyboards, Libr
develop, Photocopying/Printing, Prog for children & young adult, Ref serv
available, Serves mentally handicapped consumers, Summer reading prog,
Telephone ref
Special Services for the Deaf - Bks on deafness & sign lang; Captioned
film dep; Closed caption videos; High interest/low vocabulary bks; Staff
with knowledge of sign lang
Special Services for the Blind - Home delivery serv
Open Mon-Fri 10-6, Sat 10-3
Bookmobiles: 1

M   NORTH COUNTRY HEALTH SYSTEM*, Medical Library, 189 Prouty
    Dr, 05855. SAN 317-0837. Tel: 802-334-3256. FAX: 802-334-3240. Web
    Site: www.nchsi.org. *Librn,* Georgia Lee Zaveson; E-mail:
    gzaveson@nchsi.org; Staff 1 (Non-MLS 1)
    Library Holdings: Bk Titles 1,050; Per Subs 65
    Automation Activity & Vendor Info: (Cataloging) Marcive, Inc
    Function: Res libr
    Publications: Medical Reference Serves (Newsletter)
    Partic in Health Sciences Libraries of New Hampshire & Vermont; North
    Country Consortium

NORTH BENNINGTON

P   JOHN G MCCULLOUGH FREE LIBRARY INC*, Two Main St, 05257.
    (Mail add: PO Box 339, 05257-0339), SAN 317-0845. Tel: 802-447-7121.
    FAX: 802-445-1080. E-mail: mclibrary@comcast.net. Web Site:
    www.mccullough.lib.vt.us. *Libr Dir,* Susanne Warren; *Ch,* Bonnie Dundas;
    Staff 4 (MLS 1, Non-MLS 3)
    Founded 1920. Pop 2,400
    Library Holdings: Bk Vols 20,000; Per Subs 35
    Special Collections: Mose Sage Coll
    Subject Interests: Vt hist
    Automation Activity & Vendor Info: (Cataloging) Mandarin Library
    Automation; (Circulation) Mandarin Library Automation; (OPAC)
    Mandarin Library Automation
    Database Vendor: Gale Cengage Learning
    Wireless access
    Function: Homebound delivery serv, ILL available, Prog for children &
    young adult, Summer reading prog
    Partic in Vermont Automated Libr Syst (VALS)
    Open Tues & Wed 1-8, Thurs & Fri 1-6, Sat 10-2
    Friends of the Library Group

NORTH CLARENDON

P   BAILEY MEMORIAL LIBRARY*, 111 Moulton Ave, 05759-9327. SAN
    376-4869. Tel: 802-747-7743. *Librn,* Dorothy Barnes; Staff 2 (Non-MLS 2)
    Pop 2,881
    Library Holdings: AV Mats 320; Bk Vols 10,800; Talking Bks 171
    Mem of Southwest Regional Library Service System
    Open Mon-Wed 12-5, Thurs 10-5, Sat 9-2

NORTH HERO

P   NORTH HERO PUBLIC LIBRARY*, 1395 US Rte Two, 05474. (Mail
    add: PO Box 187, 05474), SAN 317-0861. Tel: 802-372-5458. E-mail:
    nhlibrary@comcast.net. Web Site: www.northherovt.com/library.php. *Librn,*
    Judy Poquette
    Founded 1913. Pop 850; Circ 3,500
    Jul 2009-Jun 2010 Income $35,450. Mats Exp $4,850, Books $3,000,
    Other Print Mats $350, AV Mat $1,500
    Library Holdings: Audiobooks 170; CDs 53; DVDs 500; Large Print Bks
    34; Bk Vols 4,000; Per Subs 5
    Automation Activity & Vendor Info: (Acquisitions) Brodart; (Cataloging)
    Brodart; (Circulation) LibraryWorld, Inc
    Database Vendor: LibraryWorld, Inc

Wireless access
Function: Bi-weekly Writer's Group, Bks on cassette, Bks on CD, Children's prog, Computers for patron use, Copy machines, e-mail serv, Free DVD rentals, Handicapped accessible, ILL available, Music CDs, Photocopying/Printing, Pub access computers, Story hour, Summer reading prog, VHS videos, Video lending libr, Wheelchair accessible
Open Tues 2-7, Thurs 10-3 & Sat 9-1
Friends of the Library Group

NORTH TROY

P   WILLIAM H & LUCY F RAND MEMORIAL LIBRARY, 160 Railroad St, 05859-9492. (Mail add: PO Box 509, 05859-0509), SAN 317-0888. Tel: 802-988-4741. *Libr Dir,* Emily Andrews
Founded 1925. Pop 1,600; Circ 3,526
Library Holdings: Bk Vols 8,000; Per Subs 30
Subject Interests: Local hist, Vt
Wireless access
Open Mon 2-6, Tues & Wed 2:30-6:30, Thurs 9-12, Fri 8-1
Friends of the Library Group

NORTHFIELD

P   BROWN PUBLIC LIBRARY*, 93 S Main St, 05663. SAN 317-0896. Tel: 802-485-4621. FAX: 802-485-4990. E-mail: librarian@brownpubliclibrary.org. Web Site: www.brownpubliclibrary.org. *Dir,* Sue MacMartin; *ILL,* Barbara Hill; *Youth Serv,* Nancy Munno; Staff 1.5 (Non-MLS 1.5)
Founded 1906. Pop 5,740; Circ 21,530
Jul 2008-Jun 2009 Income $103,430, City $91,050, Federal $808, Locally Generated Income $9,572, Other $2,000. Mats Exp $9,871. Sal $66,113
Library Holdings: AV Mats 2,940; Bks on Deafness & Sign Lang 10; High Interest/Low Vocabulary Bk Vols 50; Large Print Bks 200; Bk Vols 21,425; Per Subs 31
Special Collections: Vermont Coll
Automation Activity & Vendor Info: (Cataloging) Ex Libris Group; (Circulation) Ex Libris Group; (OPAC) Ex Libris Group
Database Vendor: Gale Cengage Learning
Wireless access
Open Mon, Wed & Thurs 10-8, Tues 2-8, Fri 2-5, Sat 10-2
Friends of the Library Group

C   NORWICH UNIVERSITY, Kreitzberg Library, 23 Harmon Dr, 05663. SAN 317-090X. Tel: 802-485-2170. Circulation Tel: 802-485-2176. Interlibrary Loan Service Tel: 802-485-2182. Reference Tel: 802-485-2179. Automation Services Tel: 802-485-2171. FAX: 802-485-2173. E-mail: library@norwich.edu. Web Site: www.norwich.edu/academics/library. *Dir,* Ravil Veli; Tel: 802-485-2169, E-mail: rveli1@norwich.edu; *Assoc Dir, Gen Libr Serv,* Greg Sauer; Tel: 802-485-2175, E-mail: gsauer@norwich.edu; *Head, Digital & Distance Educ Serv,* Heidi Steiner; E-mail: hsteiner@norwich.edu; *Head, Instrul Serv,* Nikki Krysak; Tel: 802-485-2168, E-mail: nkrysak@norwich.edu; *Head, Ref & ILL Serv,* Deborah Ahlers; Tel: 802-485-2174, E-mail: deboraha@norwich.edu; *Electronic Res Librn,* John Holm; Tel: 802-485-2523, E-mail: jholm1@norwich.edu; *Web Serv Librn,* Position Currently Open; *Spec Coll Librn, Univ Archivist,* Kelly Nolin; Tel: 802-485-2722, E-mail: knolin@norwich.edu; *Asst Univ Archivist,* Gail Wiese; Tel: 802-485-2924, E-mail: gwiese@norwich.edu; Staff 9 (MLS 9)
Founded 1819. Enrl 3,348; Fac 205; Highest Degree: Master
Jun 2011-May 2012 Income $1,799,097, Parent Institution $1,689,814, Other $109,283. Mats Exp $545,770, Books $102,000, Per/Ser (Incl. Access Fees) $424,500, Manu Arch $3,500, Micro $1,770, AV Mat $10,000, Presv $4,000. Sal $749,598 (Prof $538,448)
Library Holdings: Audiobooks 197; AV Mats 2,699; CDs 404; e-books 281,000; e-journals 54,155; Microforms 73,342; Bk Vols 140,434; Per Subs 352
Special Collections: Military History; Norwichiana. US Document Depository
Subject Interests: Archit, Mil hist
Automation Activity & Vendor Info: (Acquisitions) OCLC; (Cataloging) OCLC; (Circulation) OCLC; (Course Reserve) OCLC; (ILL) OCLC ILLiad; (OPAC) OCLC WorldCat; (Serials) EBSCO Online
Database Vendor: ACM (Association for Computing Machinery), American Chemical Society, American Geophysical Union, American Mathematical Society, Annual Reviews, ASCE Research Library, Bowker, CountryWatch, CQ Press, CredoReference, Dialog, Ebooks Corporation, ebrary, EBSCO Information Services, EBSCOhost, Elsevier, Gale Cengage Learning, Hoovers, Ingenta, IOP, JSTOR, Knovel, LexisNexis, Material ConneXion, McGraw-Hill, Modern Language Association, Newsbank-Readex, OCLC FirstSearch, OCLC Web-scale Management Services, OCLC WorldCat, OVID Technologies, Oxford Online, ProQuest, PubMed, Sage, ScienceDirect, SerialsSolutions, Springer-Verlag, Springshare, LLC, Standard & Poor's, Thomson - Web of Science, Wiley, YBP Library Services
Wireless access

Publications: Friends of Kreitzberg Library (Newsletter); Occasional Papers
Partic in OCLC Online Computer Library Center, Inc; Vermont Automated Libr Syst (VALS); Vermont Consortium of Academic Libraries; Westchester Academic Library Directors Organization (WALDO)
Friends of the Library Group

NORWICH

P   NORWICH PUBLIC LIBRARY, 368 Main St, 05055-9453. (Mail add: PO Box 290, 05055-0290), SAN 317-0918. Tel: 802-649-1184. FAX: 802-649-3470. E-mail: circulation.desk@norwichlibrary.org. Web Site: www.norwichlibrary.org. *Dir,* Lucinda H Walker; E-mail: lucinda.walker@norwichlibrary.org; *Asst Librn,* Lisa Milchman; *Ch,* Beth Reynolds; *Tech Serv Librn,* Nancy Fontaine; Staff 4 (MLS 2, Non-MLS 2)
Founded 1880. Pop 3,544; Circ 67,922
Library Holdings: Bk Vols 28,357
Subject Interests: Local hist
Automation Activity & Vendor Info: (Cataloging) ByWater Solutions; (Circulation) ByWater Solutions; (OPAC) ByWater Solutions
Function: Art exhibits, Audio & video playback equip for onsite use, Audiobks via web, Bk club(s), Bks on cassette, Bks on CD, CD-ROM, Chess club, Children's prog, Computers for patron use, Copy machines, Doc delivery serv, e-mail serv, E-Reserves, Electronic databases & coll, Equip loans & repairs, Fax serv, Free DVD rentals, Handicapped accessible, Homebound delivery serv, ILL available, Instruction & testing, Magnifiers for reading, Mail & tel request accepted, Mus passes, Music CDs, Newsp ref libr, Online cat, Online ref, Online searches, Orientations, Outreach serv, OverDrive digital audio bks, Photocopying/Printing, Preschool outreach, Prog for adults, Prog for children & young adult, Pub access computers, Ref serv available, Senior outreach, Spoken cassettes & CDs, Spoken cassettes & DVDs, Story hour, Summer reading prog, Tax forms, Telephone ref, VHS videos, Video lending libr, Web-catalog, Wheelchair accessible, Workshops
Publications: Book Mark (Monthly newsletter)
Partic in Green Mountain Library Consortium (GMLC); Librarians of the Upper Valley Coop
Open Mon 1-8, Tues, Wed & Fri 10-5:30, Thurs 10-8, Sat 10-3
Friends of the Library Group

ORLEANS

P   JONES MEMORIAL LIBRARY*, One Water St, 05860-1303. (Mail add: PO Box 38, 05860-0038), SAN 317-0926. Tel: 802-754-6660. FAX: 802-754-6660. E-mail: jonesmemorial@comcast.net. *Dir,* Joanne Pariseau
Founded 1950. Pop 4,170; Circ 21,567
Library Holdings: Bk Titles 26,670; Per Subs 23
Wireless access
Publications: Library Journals Adult & Children
Partic in Vermont Automated Libr Syst (VALS)
Open Mon 10-8, Wed & Fri 10-5, Sat 9-1

ORWELL

P   ORWELL FREE LIBRARY, 473 Main St, 05670. (Mail add: PO Box 92, 05670), SAN 376-3463. Tel: 802-948-2041. *Librn,* Kate Hunter
Founded 1896. Pop 1,250
Library Holdings: Audiobooks 20; Bk Vols 2,500; Per Subs 20
Database Vendor: LibraryWorld, Inc
Wireless access
Open Tues 10-4 & 6-8, Thurs 3-6, Fri 11-4, Sat 9-1
Friends of the Library Group

PAWLET

P   PAWLET PUBLIC LIBRARY*, 141 School St, 05761. (Mail add: PO Box 98, 05761), SAN 317-0934. Tel: 802-325-3123. E-mail: pawlet_pub@vals.state.vt.us. *Dir,* Beth Kashner
Pop 1,244
Library Holdings: Bk Vols 10,000; Per Subs 12
Special Collections: Pawlet History; Vermont History
Mem of Southwest Regional Library Service System
Open Tues 11-7, Wed 12:30-7, Thurs 11:30-5, Fri 11:304, Sat 10-1

PEACHAM

P   PEACHAM LIBRARY*, 656 Bayley Hazen Rd, 05862. (Mail add: PO Box 253, 05862-0253), SAN 317-0942. Tel: 802-592-3216. E-mail: peachamlib@fairpoint.net. *Dir,* Becky Jensen; Staff 2 (Non-MLS 2)
Founded 1810. Pop 650; Circ 4,521
Library Holdings: Bk Vols 8,000; Per Subs 45; Videos 500
Wireless access
Open Mon, Wed, Fri & Sat 10-12, Tues & Thurs 1-7
Friends of the Library Group

PITTSFIELD

P   ROGER CLARK MEMORIAL LIBRARY*, 40 Village Green, 05762.
(Mail add: PO Box 743, 05762-0743), SAN 317-0950. Tel: 802-746-4067.
E-mail: pittsfieldvtlibrary@gmail.com. Web Site: www.pittsfieldlibrary.com.
Founded 1901. Pop 249; Circ 2,430
Library Holdings: AV Mats 100; Large Print Bks 20; Bk Vols 4,500
Open Mon & Fri 10-4, Tues 6pm-8pm

PITTSFORD

P   MACLURE LIBRARY*, 840 Arch St, 05763-0060. (Mail add: PO Box 60,
05763-0060), SAN 317-0969. Tel: 802-483-2972. FAX: 802-483-2703.
E-mail: maclurelibrary@comcast.net. Web Site: www.maclurelibrary.org.
Dir, Bonnie Stewart
Circ 18,000
Library Holdings: Bk Vols 15,000; Per Subs 17
Special Collections: Biography Coll; History Coll
Mem of Southwest Regional Library Service System
Open Mon, Tues & Fri 1-6, Wed & Thurs 10-6, Sat 9-Noon

PLAINFIELD

P   CUTLER MEMORIAL LIBRARY*, 151 High St, 05667. (Mail add: PO
Box 186, 05667-0186), SAN 376-799X. Tel: 802-454-8504. E-mail:
cutler.library@yahoo.com. Web Site: cutlerlibrary.org. *Librn,* Loona
Brogan; Staff 1 (Non-MLS 1)
Library Holdings: Bk Vols 7,000
Automation Activity & Vendor Info: (Acquisitions) Brodart; (Cataloging)
Brodart; (OPAC) LibraryWorld, Inc
Database Vendor: LibraryWorld, Inc
Wireless access
Function: Adult bk club, Audio & video playback equip for onsite use,
Audiobks via web, Bks on cassette, Bks on CD, Computers for patron use,
Copy machines, Distance learning, Free DVD rentals, Handicapped
accessible, ILL available, Mus passes, Music CDs, Online cat, Outreach
serv, OverDrive digital audio bks, Photocopying/Printing, Preschool
outreach, Prog for adults, Prog for children & young adult, Pub access
computers, Spoken cassettes & CDs, Story hour, Summer reading prog,
Tax forms, VHS videos, Video lending libr, Wheelchair accessible,
Workshops
Open Tues & Fri 3-6, Wed & Sat 10-3, Thurs 3-8
Friends of the Library Group

C   GODDARD COLLEGE*, Eliot D Pratt Library, 123 Pitkin Rd, 05667.
SAN 317-0985. Tel: 802-322-1603. E-mail: library@goddard.edu. Web
Site: www.goddard.edu. *Dir, Info Access,* Clara Bruns; E-mail:
clara.bruns@goddard.edu; *Info Res & Tech Librn,* Richard Ambelang; Tel:
802-322-1608, E-mail: richard.ambelang@goddard.edu; *Libr Syst & Tech
Serv Coordr,* Helen Linda; Tel: 802-322-1602, E-mail:
helen.linda@goddard.edu; *Mat Access & Acq Coordr,* Paula Tamburello;
Tel: 802-322-1607, E-mail: paula.tamburello@goddard.edu; *Libr Asst,*
Dustin Byerly; Tel: 802-322-1601; Staff 5 (MLS 4, Non-MLS 1)
Founded 1938. Enrl 762; Highest Degree: Master
Library Holdings: e-books 48,000; Bk Vols 51,000
Special Collections: Goddard Archives; Goddard Authors Coll
Automation Activity & Vendor Info: (Acquisitions) VTLS, Inc;
(Cataloging) OCLC; (ILL) OCLC; (OPAC) VTLS, Inc
Database Vendor: CredoReference, ebrary, EBSCOhost, Gale Cengage
Learning, JSTOR, netLibrary, OCLC ArticleFirst, OCLC FirstSearch,
OCLC WorldCat, RefWorks, SerialsSolutions
Wireless access
Function: Distance learning, Doc delivery serv, Electronic databases &
coll, Exhibits, ILL available, Online ref, Pub access computers, Ref serv in
person, Wheelchair accessible, Workshops
Partic in Lyrasis; Vermont Consortium of Academic Libraries
Restriction: Authorized patrons, Borrowing privileges limited to fac &
registered students, Open to pub for ref & circ; with some limitations

POULTNEY

C   GREEN MOUNTAIN COLLEGE LIBRARY*, Griswold Library, One
Brennan Circle, 05764-1078. SAN 317-0993. Tel: 802-287-8225. FAX:
802-287-8222. E-mail: grislibrefdesk@greenmtn.edu. Web Site:
greenmtn.edu/library.aspx. *Dir,* Paul Millette; Tel: 802-287-8224, E-mail:
millettep@greenmtn.edu; *Pub Serv Librn,* Rachel Pusateri; Staff 4 (MLS 3,
Non-MLS 1)
Founded 1834. Enrl 825; Fac 52; Highest Degree: Master
Library Holdings: e-books 40,000; Bk Vols 90,000; Per Subs 300
Special Collections: Welsh Coll, art objects, bks, patterns. State Document
Depository
Subject Interests: Environ liberal arts
Automation Activity & Vendor Info: (OPAC) Ex Libris Group
Database Vendor: Agricola, American Psychological Association (APA),
BioOne, CredoReference, ebrary, JSTOR, LexisNexis, Medline, ProQuest
Wireless access

Partic in OCLC Online Computer Library Center, Inc
Open Mon-Thurs (Winter) 8am-Midnight, Fri 8-8, Sat 10-5, Sun
10am-Midnight; Mon-Fri (Summer) 8-5

P   POULTNEY PUBLIC LIBRARY*, 205 Main St, 05764. SAN 317-1000.
Tel: 802-287-5556. *Dir,* Rebecca Cook
Pop 3,498; Circ 25,928
Library Holdings: AV Mats 798; Bk Vols 13,240; Per Subs 47
Special Collections: Vermont
Automation Activity & Vendor Info: (Cataloging) Mandarin Library
Automation; (Circulation) Mandarin Library Automation
Open Mon-Thurs 2-8, Fri 10-5, Sat 10-1

POWNAL

P   SOLOMON WRIGHT LIBRARY*, 97 Main St, 05261. (Mail add: PO
Box 400, 05261-0400), SAN 317-1019. Tel: 802-823-5400. FAX:
802-823-5400. E-mail: pownal_pub@vals.state.vt.us. Web Site:
www.solomonwrightlibrary.org. *Dir,* Linda Hall; Staff 1 (Non-MLS 1)
Founded 1966. Pop 3,505
Library Holdings: Bk Vols 20,000; Per Subs 30
Special Collections: Sweeney Indian Arrowhead Coll
Subject Interests: Pownal hist
Wireless access
Function: Adult bk club, Audio & video playback equip for onsite use, Bk
club(s), Bks on cassette, Bks on CD, CD-ROM, Computers for patron use,
Copy machines, ILL available, Mus passes, Online searches, Prog for
adults, Prog for children & young adult, Pub access computers, Ref serv
available, Scanner, Summer reading prog, Tax forms, VHS videos,
Wheelchair accessible
Special Services for the Blind - Audio mat; Bks on cassette; Bks on CD;
Large print bks
Open Mon & Wed 6:30-8:30, Tues & Sat 10-2, Thurs & Fri 10-12

PROCTOR

P   PROCTOR FREE LIBRARY*, Four Main St, 05765. SAN 317-1027. Tel:
802-459-3539. FAX: 802-459-3539. E-mail: proctor_free@vals.state.vt.us.
Librn, Lisa Miser
Founded 1881. Pop 1,998; Circ 12,000
Library Holdings: AV Mats 460; Large Print Bks 62; Bk Titles 16,442;
Bk Vols 17,155; Per Subs 20; Talking Bks 398
Special Collections: Realia (Children); Sports Coll; Vermontiana (Papers
of Four Governors from Proctor)
Wireless access
Mem of Southwest Regional Library Service System
Open Mon-Thurs 9-11 & 2-8, Fri 9-12 & 1-5, Sat 9-12
Friends of the Library Group

PROCTORSVILLE

P   CAVENDISH-FLETCHER COMMUNITY LIBRARY*, 573 Main St,
05153. (Mail add: PO Box 266, 05153-0266), SAN 376-3366. Tel:
802-226-7503. FAX: 802-226-7858. Web Site: www.cavendishlibrary.org.
Librn, Kata Welch; E-mail: kwelch@wswsu.org; *Asst Librn,* Donna
Bushey; Staff 1 (Non-MLS 1)
Founded 1990. Pop 844; Circ 5,713
Library Holdings: Audiobooks 374; Bks on Deafness & Sign Lang 5;
CDs 27; DVDs 248; Large Print Bks 63; Bk Titles 12,952; Bk Vols
13,478; Per Subs 34; Videos 280
Automation Activity & Vendor Info: (Cataloging) Follett Software;
(Circulation) Follett Software; (OPAC) Follett Software
Wireless access
Function: Adult bk club, After school storytime, Art exhibits, Audiobks
via web, Bk club(s), Bks on cassette, Bks on CD, Chess club, Computers
for patron use, Copy machines, e-mail & chat, Fax serv, Free DVD rentals,
Homebound delivery serv, ILL available, Mus passes, Music CDs, Online
cat, Photocopying/Printing, Pub access computers, Scanner, Story hour,
Summer reading prog, VHS videos
Partic in Green Mountain Library Consortium (GMLC)
Open Mon & Fri (Winter) 9-6, Tues-Thurs 9-6:30, Sat 12-4; Tues
(Summer) 9-4:30, Wed 9-6:30
Restriction: Circ to mem only

PUTNEY

C   LANDMARK COLLEGE LIBRARY, River Rd S, 05346. SAN 329-1480.
Tel: 802-387-1648. Interlibrary Loan Service Tel: 802-387-6760. FAX:
802-387-6896. E-mail: library@landmark.edu. Web Site:
www.landmark.edu/library. *Dir of Libr Serv,* Jennifer Lann; E-mail:
jlann@landmark.edu; *Acq/Cat/Syst Adminr,* John Kosakowski; Tel:
802-387-6785, E-mail: johnkosakowski@landmark.edu; *Res Serv Librn,*
Kathy Burris; E-mail: kathyburris@landmark.edu; *Archives Coordr, Res
Serv Librn,* Mary Jane MacGuire; Tel: 802-387-6755, E-mail:
mmacguire@landmark.edu; *Evening Res Serv Libr Spec,* Daniel Maravell;

Tel: 802-387-6763, E-mail: danmaravell@landmark.edu; *Circ & ILL*, Position Currently Open; Staff 5 (MLS 3, Non-MLS 2)
Founded 1985. Enrl 470; Fac 100; Highest Degree: Bachelor
Library Holdings: Audiobooks 281; AV Mats 1,918; Bks on Deafness & Sign Lang 58; CDs 154; DVDs 1,368; e-books 83,000; High Interest/Low Vocabulary Bk Vols 1,185; Large Print Bks 63; Bk Titles 25,159; Per Subs 110; Spec Interest Per Sub 19
Special Collections: Learning Disabilities, ADHD & ASD Research Coll
Subject Interests: Asperger's & Autism spectrum disorders (in col students and/or adults), Attention deficit disorder, Col teaching & serv, Learning disabilities
Automation Activity & Vendor Info: (Cataloging) SirsiDynix; (Circulation) SirsiDynix; (Course Reserve) SirsiDynix; (ILL) SirsiDynix; (OPAC) SirsiDynix
Database Vendor: ACM (Association for Computing Machinery), American Psychological Association (APA), ARTstor, Baker & Taylor, EBSCOhost, Facts on File, Gale Cengage Learning, JSTOR, LexisNexis, netLibrary, Newsbank, OCLC FirstSearch, OCLC WorldCat, SerialsSolutions, SirsiDynix
Wireless access
Function: Archival coll, Audio & video playback equip for onsite use, AV serv, Bks on cassette, Bks on CD, Computers for patron use, Copy machines, Digital talking bks, e-mail serv, Electronic databases & coll, Free DVD rentals, ILL available, Music CDs, Online cat, Online ref, Online searches, Orientations, Outside serv via phone, mail, e-mail & web, Photocopying/Printing, Scanner, Telephone ref, VHS videos, Video lending libr
Partic in Asn of Vermont Independent Col; Vermont Consortium of Academic Libraries; Westchester Academic Library Directors Organization (WALDO)
Open Mon-Thurs 8:30am-Midnight, Fri 8:30am-10pm, Sat Noon-5, Sun Noon-Midnight
Restriction: Pub use on premises

P   PUTNEY PUBLIC LIBRARY*, 55 Main St, 05346. SAN 317-1035. Tel: 802-387-4407. *Dir,* Stephen Coronella; *Asst Librn,* Deb Stetson
Pop 2,700; Circ 20,000
Library Holdings: Bk Vols 17,000; Per Subs 14
Automation Activity & Vendor Info: (Cataloging) Follett Software; (Circulation) Follett Software; (OPAC) Follett Software
Open Mon-Fri 10:30-6, Sat 10-1

QUECHEE

P   QUECHEE PUBLIC LIBRARY ASSOCIATION*, 1957 Quechee Main St, 05059. (Mail add: PO Box 384, 05059-0384), SAN 317-0365. Tel: 802-295-1232. FAX: 802-295-1232. E-mail: quelibrary@sover.net. Web Site: quecheelibrary.org. *Librn,* Kate Schaal; Staff 2 (Non-MLS 2)
Founded 1896. Circ 30,183
Jul 2007-Jun 2008 Income $102,140, City $88,140, Locally Generated Income $14,000. Mats Exp $15,700. Sal $63,428
Library Holdings: Large Print Bks 80; Bk Vols 22,000; Per Subs 50
Automation Activity & Vendor Info: (Acquisitions) Follett Software; (Cataloging) Follett Software; (Circulation) Follett Software
Wireless access
Open Mon, Wed & Fri 10-6, Tues & Thurs 2-7, Sat 9-2
Friends of the Library Group

S   VERMONT INSTITUTE OF NATURAL SCIENCE LIBRARY*, 6565 Woodstock Rd, 05059. SAN 317-1892. Tel: 802-359-5000. FAX: 802-359-5001. E-mail: info@vinsweb.org. Web Site: www.vinsweb.org. *VPres, Prog,* Tree Sturman
Founded 1972
Library Holdings: Bk Titles 2,000
Special Collections: Henry Potter Papers; Olin Sewall Pettingill Ornithological Library Billings - Kitteridge Herbarium
Subject Interests: Environ studies, Natural hist, Ornithology
Publications: Hands on Nature - Lingelbach, Waste Away - Vins
Partic in ILL
Restriction: Non-circulating, Staff & mem only

RANDOLPH

P   KIMBALL PUBLIC LIBRARY*, 67 N Main St, 05060. SAN 317-1051. Tel: 802-728-5073. FAX: 802-728-6735. E-mail: info@kimballlibrary.org. Web Site: www.kimballlibrary.org. *Librn,* Amy Grasmick; E-mail: amy@kimballlibrary.org; *Ad,* Lynne Gately; E-mail: lynne@kimballlibrary.org; *Youth Serv Librn,* Judith Flint; E-mail: judith@kimballlibrary.org; Staff 3 (MLS 1, Non-MLS 2)
Founded 1903. Pop 6,047; Circ 47,112
Jul 2006-Jun 2007 Income $169,827, City $126,166, Locally Generated Income $43,661. Mats Exp $19,200, Books $13,000, Per/Ser (Incl. Access Fees) $2,800, Micro $200, AV Mat $3,000, Electronic Ref Mat (Incl. Access Fees) $200. Sal $86,600 (Prof $80,375)

Library Holdings: AV Mats 1,150; DVDs 20; Electronic Media & Resources 3; Large Print Bks 375; Bk Vols 19,200; Per Subs 58; Videos 530
Subject Interests: Vt
Automation Activity & Vendor Info: (Cataloging) LibLime; (Circulation) LibLime; (OPAC) LibLime
Database Vendor: Gale Cengage Learning, ProQuest
Wireless access
Function: Handicapped accessible, Homebound delivery serv, ILL available, Photocopying/Printing, Prog for adults, Prog for children & young adult, Summer reading prog, Wheelchair accessible
Open Mon & Thurs 2-8, Tues, Wed & Fri 10-5, Sat 10-1
Friends of the Library Group

RANDOLPH CENTER

J   VERMONT TECHNICAL COLLEGE*, Hartness Library, Main St, 05061. SAN 317-106X. Tel: 802-728-1237. Toll Free Tel: 800-431-0025. FAX: 802-728-1506. E-mail: Library@vtc.edu. Web Site: www.vtc.vsc.edu. *Dir,* David Sturges; E-mail: dsturges@vtc.vsc.edu; *Asst Dir,* Eileen Gatti; *Fac Librn,* Benjamin Johnson; *Coordr, Remote Serv,* Michael Taylor; *Acq,* Nancy Aitken; *Electronic Res,* Ben Johnson; *Pub Serv,* Becky Lafferty; *Pub Serv,* Ann Schroeder; *Tech Serv,* Julie Taylor; Staff 8 (MLS 3, Non-MLS 5)
Founded 1866. Enrl 970; Fac 67
Library Holdings: Bk Titles 60,000; Per Subs 396; Videos 6,000
Subject Interests: Agr, Archit, Automotive tech, Bus mgt, Civil eng, Computer eng, Construction mgt, Electrical eng, Electronic eng, Eng tech, Hort, Mechanical eng, Nursing
Automation Activity & Vendor Info: (Acquisitions) SirsiDynix; (Cataloging) SirsiDynix; (Circulation) SirsiDynix; (Course Reserve) SirsiDynix; (ILL) SirsiDynix; (Media Booking) SirsiDynix; (OPAC) SirsiDynix; (Serials) SirsiDynix
Database Vendor: EBSCOhost, LexisNexis, Wilson - Wilson Web
Partic in Lyrasis; OCLC Online Computer Library Center, Inc; Vermont Automated Libr Syst (VALS)
Open Mon-Thurs (Sept-May) 7:30am-10pm, Fri 8-4, Sat 12-5, Sun 5-10; Mon-Fri (Summer) 7:30-4:30

READING

P   READING PUBLIC LIBRARY*, 717 Vermont Rte 106, 05062. (Mail add: PO Box 7, 05062-0007), SAN 317-1078. Tel: 802-484-5588. E-mail: reading.public.library@comcast.net. Web Site: www.readinglibrary.org. *Librn,* Tony Pikramenos
Founded 1899. Pop 712; Circ 3,200
Jul 2009-Jun 2010 Income $22,805. Mats Exp $712
Library Holdings: Bk Vols 7,824
Special Collections: Extensive Coll of Bound Harpers & National Geographic Magazines
Wireless access
Function: Wheelchair accessible
Open Tues 10-5, Thurs 12-7, Sat 10-2

READSBORO

P   READSBORO COMMUNITY LIBRARY*, 301 Phelps Lane, 05350. (Mail add: PO Box 248, 05350-0248), SAN 317-1086. Tel: 802-423-5460. FAX: 802-423-9914. E-mail: rebolibrary@hotmail.com. *Commun Librn,* Cyndi Candiloro; *Librn,* Laura Ashbrook
Founded 1874. Pop 850; Circ 4,953
Library Holdings: Bk Vols 5,910; Per Subs 30
Open Mon & Wed 8:30-11:30 & 12-5, Tues & Thurs 8:30-11:30 & 12-8, Fri 8:30-11:30

RICHFORD

P   ARVIN A BROWN PUBLIC LIBRARY*, 88 Main St, 05476-1133. SAN 317-1094. Tel: 802-848-3313. E-mail: arvinabrown@gmail.com. Web Site: www.aabrown.org. *Librn,* Susan Smolinsky; Staff 1 (MLS 1)
Founded 1895. Pop 3,855; Circ 14,963
Jan 2007-Dec 2007 Income $49,869, City $45,000. Mats Exp $5,660, Books $4,560, Per/Ser (Incl. Access Fees) $950, Electronic Ref Mat (Incl. Access Fees) $150. Sal $30,000
Library Holdings: AV Mats 1,523; CDs 109; DVDs 480; Large Print Bks 317; Bk Titles 13,834; Bk Vols 14,235; Per Subs 35; Talking Bks 316; Videos 1,000
Special Collections: Vermont Coll
Automation Activity & Vendor Info: (Cataloging) Follett Software; (Circulation) Follett Software; (OPAC) Follett Software
Function: Bks on cassette, Bks on CD, Children's prog, Computers for patron use, Copy machines, Electronic databases & coll, Free DVD rentals, Handicapped accessible, Holiday prog, Home delivery & serv to Sr ctr & nursing homes, Homebound delivery serv, ILL available, Magnifiers for reading, Mail & tel request accepted, Mus passes, Online cat, Online searches, Photocopying/Printing, Prog for adults, Prog for children &

young adult, Pub access computers, Ref serv available, Summer reading prog, Tax forms, VHS videos, Web-catalog, Wheelchair accessible, Workshops

Special Services for the Deaf - Bks on deafness & sign lang; Closed caption videos

Special Services for the Blind - Bks on cassette; Bks on CD; Large print bks

Open Mon & Fri 10-5, Wed 10-8, Sat 9-1

RICHMOND

P　RICHMOND FREE LIBRARY*, 201 Bridge St, 05477. SAN 317-1108. Tel: 802-434-3036. FAX: 802-434-3223. E-mail: rfl@gmavt.net. *Dir,* Rebecca Mueller; *Asst Librn,* Joan Cleary; *Ch,* L J Kopf; Staff 4 (MLS 1, Non-MLS 3)

Pop 4,090; Circ 44,500

Library Holdings: AV Mats 920; Bk Vols 16,200; Per Subs 83

Automation Activity & Vendor Info: (Cataloging) Follett Software; (Circulation) Follett Software; (Course Reserve) Follett Software; (OPAC) Follett Software

Database Vendor: Gale Cengage Learning

Open Mon & Wed 10-8, Tues & Thurs 1-6, Fri 10-6, Sat 10-2

Friends of the Library Group

ROCHESTER

P　ROCHESTER PUBLIC LIBRARY*, PO Box 256, 05767. SAN 317-1124. Tel: 802-767-3927. E-mail: rochester@vals.state.vt.us. Web Site: www.rochestervtpubliclibrary.com. *Librn,* Jeannette Bair

Founded 1801. Pop 1,201; Circ 15,000

Library Holdings: Large Print Bks 25; Bk Vols 18,500; Talking Bks 600

Special Collections: Ecology Material; Vermont Books

Open Tues & Thurs 12:30-7, Sat 9-1

ROXBURY

P　ROXBURY FREE LIBRARY*, 1491 Roxbury Rd, 05669. (Mail add: PO Box 95, 05669-0095), SAN 376-3447. Tel: 802-485-6860. E-mail: librarianrox@yahoo.com. *Librn,* Joyce Brosseau; Staff 1 (Non-MLS 1)

Founded 1913. Pop 600; Circ 1,000

Jul 2006-Jun 2007 Income $14,456, Locally Generated Income $10,000, Other $4,456. Mats Exp $2,526. Sal $6,499

Library Holdings: Audiobooks 60; DVDs 30; Large Print Bks 20; Bk Titles 5,000; Talking Bks 100; Videos 50

Special Services for the Blind - Large print bks; Large print bks & talking machines

Open Tues 10-12 & 2-6, Thurs 2-7, Sat 10-1

RUTLAND

C　COLLEGE OF SAINT JOSEPH, Giorgetti Library, 71 Clement Rd, 05701. SAN 317-1140. Tel: 802-776-5232. FAX: 802-776-5258. Web Site: www.csj.edu/library.html. *Dir,* Doreen J McCullough; E-mail: doreen.mccullough@csj.edu; Staff 2 (MLS 1, Non-MLS 1)

Founded 1950. Enrl 313; Fac 59; Highest Degree: Master

Jul 2011-Jun 2012. Mats Exp $53,634, Books $1,814, Per/Ser (Incl. Access Fees) $9,853, AV Mat $445, Electronic Ref Mat (Incl. Access Fees) $41,522. Sal $69,276

Library Holdings: AV Mats 25,051; CDs 30; DVDs 306; e-books 79,270; e-journals 49,051; Microforms 19,739; Bk Titles 137,972; Bk Vols 138,600; Per Subs 60; Videos 893

Special Collections: Kyran McGrath Irish Studies Coll; Sister St George Vermont Coll

Subject Interests: Spec educ

Automation Activity & Vendor Info: (Acquisitions) Follett Software; (Cataloging) Follett Software; (Circulation) Follett Software; (Course Reserve) Follett Software; (ILL) Follett Software; (Media Booking) Follett Software; (OPAC) Follett Software; (Serials) Follett Software

Database Vendor: Blackwell's, ebrary, EBSCO Information Services, EBSCOhost, Elsevier, Gale Cengage Learning, JSTOR, LexisNexis, Oxford Online, ProQuest, ScienceDirect, SerialsSolutions

Wireless access

Partic in Vermont Consortium of Academic Libraries

Friends of the Library Group ·

S　MARBLE VALLEY REGIONAL CORRECTIONAL FACILITY*, 167 State St, 05701. SAN 317-1159. Tel: 802-786-5830. FAX: 802-786-5843. *Librn,* Dennis Bonanza; Tel: 802-747-4608, E-mail: Dennis.Bonanza@ahs.state.vt.us

Library Holdings: Bk Vols 4,362; Per Subs 16

Restriction: Staff & inmates only

P　RUTLAND FREE LIBRARY*, Ten Court St, 05701-4058. SAN 317-1167. Tel: 802-773-1860. FAX: 802-773-1825. E-mail: rutlandfree@rutlandfree.org. Web Site: rutlandfree.org. *Dir,* Paula J Baker;

E-mail: paulajb@rutlandfree.org; *Asst Dir,* Ed Graves; *Circ Supvr,* Deborah Higgins; E-mail: debch@rutlandfree.org; *Ch,* June Osowski; Staff 4 (MLS 4)

Founded 1886. Pop 23,380; Circ 203,535

Library Holdings: AV Mats 7,695; Electronic Media & Resources 15; Large Print Bks 2,600; Bk Vols 79,995; Per Subs 231

Special Collections: Vermont & Regional History

Automation Activity & Vendor Info: (Cataloging) SirsiDynix; (Circulation) SirsiDynix; (OPAC) SirsiDynix

Database Vendor: 3M Library Systems, Baker & Taylor, EBSCOhost, Ingram Library Services, Marcive, Inc, OCLC FirstSearch, ReferenceUSA, SirsiDynix

Wireless access

Open Mon (Winter) 9-9, Tues & Wed 11:30-9, Thurs & Fri 9-5:30, Sat 9-5; Mon 9-9, Tues 11:30-5:30, Wed 11:30-9, Thurs & Fri (Summer) 9-5:30, Sat 9-5

Friends of the Library Group

M　RUTLAND REGIONAL MEDICAL CENTER*, Health Science Library, 160 Allen St, 05701. SAN 317-1175. Tel: 802-747-3777. FAX: 802-747-3955. Web Site: www.rrmc.org. *Librn,* Claire LaForce; E-mail: claforce@rrmc.org

Library Holdings: Bk Vols 1,000; Per Subs 90

Subject Interests: Consumer health

Automation Activity & Vendor Info: (Cataloging) CyberTools for Libraries

Database Vendor: EBSCOhost

Partic in Health Sciences Libraries of New Hampshire & Vermont

Open Mon-Fri 8:30-5

SAINT ALBANS

M　NORTHWESTERN MEDICAL CENTER*, June Wakefield Memorial Library, 133 Fairfield St, 05478. (Mail add: PO Box 1370, 05478-1370), SAN 317-1221. Tel: 802-524-8448. Administration Tel: 802-524-5911. FAX: 802-524-1250. E-mail: library@nmcinc.org. Web Site: www.nmcinc.org. *Med Librn,* Heather Hawley; Staff 1 (MLS 1)

Library Holdings: Bk Titles 300; Per Subs 40; Videos 50

Subject Interests: Allied health, Nursing

Automation Activity & Vendor Info: (Cataloging) Marcive, Inc; (Serials) EBSCO Online

Database Vendor: EBSCOhost

Function: Doc delivery serv, For res purposes, Handicapped accessible, ILL available, Photocopying/Printing

Partic in Basic Health Sciences Library Network; Health Sciences Libraries of New Hampshire & Vermont; National Network of Libraries of Medicine New England Region

Restriction: Circulates for staff only

P　SAINT ALBANS FREE LIBRARY*, 11 Maiden Lane, 05478. SAN 317-1248. Tel: 802-524-1507. FAX: 802-524-1514. E-mail: stalbans@vals.state.vt.us. Web Site: www.stalbans.lib.vt.us. *Dir,* MaryPat Larrabee; *Adult Serv,* Roberta Schmidlen; *Ch,* Sarah Allerton; *Ch,* Becky Manahan; Staff 4 (MLS 4)

Founded 1900. Pop 11,500; Circ 42,817

Library Holdings: Bk Titles 22,000; Per Subs 100

Special Collections: Vermontiana

Publications: The Bookworm

Open Mon, Wed & Fri 10-6, Tues & Thurs 10-8, Sat 10-3

Friends of the Library Group

SAINT JOHNSBURY

L　DOWNS RACHLIN MARTIN PLLC*, Law Library, 90 Prospect St, 05819. (Mail add: PO Box 99, 05819-0099), SAN 372-3321. Tel: 802-748-8324. FAX: 802-748-4394. Web Site: www.drm.com. *Libr Serv Dir,* Wynne Browne; E-mail: wbrowne@drm.com

Library Holdings: Bk Vols 8,000; Per Subs 100

Open Mon-Fri 8:30-5

S　FAIRBANKS MUSEUM & PLANETARIUM*, Kitchel Center for the Study of the Northeast Kingdom, 1302 Main St, 05819. SAN 317-1256. Tel: 802-748-2372, Ext 105. FAX: 802-748-3347. E-mail: kitchelcenter@fairbanksmuseum.org. Web Site: www.fairbanksmuseum.org. *Archivist, Librn,* Pat Swartz; E-mail: pswartz@fairbanksmuseum.org

Library Holdings: Bk Titles 1,001; Bk Vols 2,500

Special Collections: Archives Coll; History of Northeast Kingdom of Vermont (Caledonia, Orleans & Essex Counties); Vermont History Coll

Subject Interests: Local hist, Sci

Function: Res libr

Restriction: Not open to pub, Open to others by appt, Staff use only

Friends of the Library Group

S   NORTHEAST REGIONAL CORRECTIONAL FACILITY LIBRARY*,
1270 US Rte 5 S, 05819. SAN 317-1299. Tel: 802-751-1410. FAX:
802-748-1482. *Librn,* Anne Cote; E-mail: annec@doc.state.vt.us
Library Holdings: Bk Vols 8,000; Per Subs 30
Subject Interests: Literacy for adults

P   NORTHEAST REGIONAL LIBRARY*, Vermont Department of Libraries,
23 Tilton Rd, 05819. SAN 317-1264. Tel: 802-748-3428. Web Site:
www.dol.state.vt.us. *Regional Librn,* Michael Roche; E-mail:
michael.roche@mail.dol.state.vt.us; Staff 2 (MLS 2)
Founded 1936
Library Holdings: Bk Vols 75,000
Open Mon-Fri 8:30-5

M   NORTHEASTERN VERMONT REGIONAL HOSPITAL, Marilyn L
Moulton Library, 1315 Hospital Dr, 05819. SAN 369-4658. Tel:
802-748-7501. FAX: 802-748-7527. *Librn,* Betsy Merrill; E-mail:
a.merrill@nvrh.org
Founded 1972
Library Holdings: AV Mats 134; High Interest/Low Vocabulary Bk Vols
202; Bk Titles 1,200; Per Subs 50; Talking Bks 55; Videos 64
Subject Interests: Allied health, Med, Nursing, Substance abuse
Wireless access
Partic in Health Sciences Libraries of New Hampshire & Vermont; North
Atlantic Health Sciences Libraries, Inc; North Country Library Cooperative
Special Services for the Blind - Bks on cassette
Open Mon-Fri 8-4

P   SAINT JOHNSBURY ATHENAEUM*, 1171 Main St, 05819-2289. Tel:
802-748-8291. FAX: 802-748-8086. E-mail: inform@stjathenaeum.org.
Web Site: www.stjathenaeum.org. *Exec Dir,* Irwin Gelber; *Dir,* Lisa Von
Kann; *Ch,* Gloria Molinaroli; *ILL,* Bob Joly; Staff 4 (MLS 1, Non-MLS 3)
Founded 1871. Pop 7,556; Circ 69,584
Jan 2007-Dec 2007 Income $680,524, City $110,000, Locally Generated
Income $570,524. Mats Exp $29,988, Books $20,981, Per/Ser (Incl. Access
Fees) $3,500, AV Mat $4,478, Electronic Ref Mat (Incl. Access Fees)
$529, Presv $500. Sal $254,080
Library Holdings: Audiobooks 1,903; AV Mats 2,022; Large Print Bks
1,000; Bk Vols 44,940; Per Subs 85
Special Collections: Fine Art Hudson River School, 100 wks of art (orgs
& reprod, incl 10 statues)
Automation Activity & Vendor Info: (Acquisitions) Follett Software;
(Cataloging) Follett Software; (Circulation) Follett Software; (ILL) Follett
Software; (Media Booking) Follett Software; (OPAC) Follett Software;
(Serials) Follett Software
Database Vendor: Baker & Taylor, Brodart
Wireless access
Open Mon-Fri 10-5:30, Sat 9:30-5
Friends of the Library Group

SHARON

P   EDWARD K BAXTER MEMORIAL LIBRARY*, 5114 Rte 14, 05065.
(Mail add: PO Box 87, 05065-0087), SAN 317-1329. Tel: 802-763-2875.
E-mail: baxterlibrarysharonvt@yahoo.com. *Librn,* Rachel Clark
Founded 1928. Pop 1,000; Circ 1,420
Library Holdings: Large Print Bks 15; Bk Titles 6,000; Talking Bks 135
Open Tues, Thurs & Fri 2:30-6:30, Sat 10-Noon

SHELBURNE

P   PIERSON LIBRARY, 5376 Shelburne Rd, 05482. SAN 317-1337. Tel:
802-985-5124. Interlibrary Loan Service Tel: 802-264-5019. FAX:
802-985-5129. E-mail: pierson@vals.state.vt.us. Web Site:
www.piersonlibrary.org. *Dir,* Kip Roberson; E-mail:
kroberson@shelburnevt.org; *Circ,* Reginald Condra; E-mail:
rcondra@shelburnevt.org; *ILL,* Linda Huntington; *Tech Serv,* Katie
Martin-Woodard; *Youth Serv,* Katie Bosley; Staff 9 (MLS 1, Non-MLS 8)
Founded 1888. Pop 7,100; Circ 77,591
Jul 2012-Jun 2013 Income $255,723. Mats Exp $40,750. Sal $169,073
Library Holdings: Bk Titles 27,692; Bk Vols 30,267; Per Subs 95;
Talking Bks 832; Videos 629
Automation Activity & Vendor Info: (Acquisitions) Baker & Taylor;
(Cataloging) OCLC CatExpress; (Circulation) ByWater Solutions; (OPAC)
ByWater Solutions
Database Vendor: Gale Cengage Learning, Wilson - Wilson Web, World
Book Online
Wireless access
Function: Adult bk club, Art exhibits, Audiobks via web, Bks on CD,
Children's prog, Computer training, Computers for patron use, Copy
machines, Digital talking bks, Electronic databases & coll, Fax serv, Free
DVD rentals, Handicapped accessible, Holiday prog, Homebound delivery
serv, ILL available, Mus passes, Notary serv, Online cat, OverDrive digital
audio bks, Prog for adults, Prog for children & young adult, Pub access
computers, Story hour, Summer reading prog, Tax forms

Partic in Green Mountain Library Consortium (GMLC)
Open Mon, Wed & Fri 10-5:30, Tues & Thurs 10-8, Sat 10-3
Friends of the Library Group

S   SHELBURNE MUSEUM LIBRARY*, 5555 Shelburne Rd, 05482-7491.
(Mail add: PO Box 10, 05482-0010), SAN 317-1345. Tel: 802-985-3346,
Ext 3379. FAX: 802-985-2331. Web Site: www.shelburnemuseum.org.
Archivist, Librn, Polly Darnell; E-mail: pdarnell@shelburnemuseum.org;
Staff 1 (MLS 1)
Founded 1947
Library Holdings: Bk Vols 6,000; Per Subs 25
Subject Interests: Am art, Antiques, Contemporary design, Decorative art,
Folk art
Function: Archival coll, Res libr
Restriction: Open by appt only

SHELDON

P   SHELDON PUBLIC LIBRARY, 1640 Main St, 05483. (Mail add: PO Box
12, 05483-0012), SAN 376-8007. Tel: 802-933-7323. *Librn,* Yvette
Severance
Pop 2,303; Circ 6,141
Jan 2008-Dec 2008. Mats Exp $3,910, Books $3,679, Other Print Mats
$71, Electronic Ref Mat (Incl. Access Fees) $160. Sal $7,828
Library Holdings: Audiobooks 186; Bk Vols 5,768; Per Subs 26; Videos
70
Wireless access
Open Tues 8-12 & 1-3, Thurs 1-3 & 6pm-8pm, Sat 8-12
Friends of the Library Group

SHOREHAM

P   PLATT MEMORIAL LIBRARY*, 279 Main St, 05770-9759. (Mail add:
PO Box 237, 05770-0237), SAN 317-1353. Tel: 802-897-2647. E-mail:
platt@shoreham.net. Web Site: www.plattlib.org. *Librn,* Dianne Lawson;
Asst Librn, Robin Severy; Staff 0.5 (MLS 0.25, Non-MLS 0.25)
Founded 1823. Pop 1,300
Jan 2008-Dec 2008 Income $31,500, City $26,500, Other $5,000. Mats
Exp $15,182, Books $2,400, AV Mat $500. Sal $16,000
Library Holdings: Bk Titles 11,730; Per Subs 20; Talking Bks 311;
Videos 384
Wireless access
Partic in Vermont Automated Libr Syst (VALS)
Open Mon 11-7, Wed & Thurs 2-7, Sat 9-1
Friends of the Library Group

SOUTH BURLINGTON

S   CHITTENDEN REGIONAL CORRECTIONAL LEARNING CENTER*,
Seven Farrell St, 05403. SAN 316-9758. Tel: 802-863-7356. FAX:
802-863-7473. *Coordr,* John Long
Library Holdings: Bk Vols 4,500
Wireless access
Open Mon 6am-8pm

P   SOUTH BURLINGTON COMMUNITY LIBRARY*, 540 Dorset St,
05403. SAN 317-1361. Tel: 802-652-7080. FAX: 802-652-7013. Web Site:
sbcl.sbschools.net. *Dir,* Louise Murphy; Tel: 802-652-7076, E-mail:
LMurphy@sbschools.net; *Ch,* Meg Paquette; *Supvr, Circ,* Kathy Plageman;
Staff 4 (MLS 1, Non-MLS 3)
Founded 1972. Pop 15,500; Circ 90,000
Jul 2006-Jun 2007 Income $335,840. Mats Exp $34,760. Sal $190,000
Library Holdings: Bk Vols 52,000; Per Subs 123
Automation Activity & Vendor Info: (Cataloging) Follett Software;
(Circulation) Follett Software; (OPAC) Follett Software
Database Vendor: EBSCOhost, Grolier Online
Open Mon, Wed & Thurs 9-9, Tues & Fri 9-5, Sat 10-4
Friends of the Library Group

SOUTH HERO

P   SOUTH HERO COMMUNITY LIBRARY*, 75 South St, 05486. SAN
317-137X. Tel: 802-372-6209. FAX: 802-372-5188. E-mail:
sohero@vals.state.vt.us. *Town Librn,* Diana Cleborne; Staff 2 (MLS 2)
Founded 1974. Pop 1,168; Circ 10,544
Library Holdings: Bk Vols 12,874; Per Subs 12
Open Mon-Fri 8-4, Wed 8-9, Sat 9-Noon
Friends of the Library Group

SOUTH LONDONDERRY

P   SOUTH LONDONDERRY FREE LIBRARY*, 15 Old School St, 05155.
(Mail add: PO Box 95, 05155-0095), SAN 317-1388. Tel: 802-824-3371.
FAX: 802-824-3371. E-mail: southlondonderryfreelibrary@yahoo.com.
Pres, Sherry Clark; *Dir,* Mary Butera; Staff 1 (Non-MLS 1)
Founded 1892. Pop 1,902; Circ 8,102

Jul 2006-Jun 2007 Income $40,000. Mats Exp $7,000, Per/Ser (Incl. Access Fees) $400, AV Mat $500. Sal $23,500 (Prof $17,500)
Library Holdings: AV Mats 500; CDs 400; DVDs 100; Large Print Bks 300; Bk Vols 17,500; Per Subs 50; Talking Bks 200; Videos 75
Subject Interests: Art, Civil War, Classics, Vt
Wireless access
Partic in Vt Libr Asn
Special Services for the Deaf - Adult & family literacy prog; Bks on deafness & sign lang
Special Services for the Blind - Bks available with recordings
Open Mon 10-12 & 1-5, Wed 10-12, 1-5 & 7-9, Fri 1-5, Sat 10-1

SOUTH POMFRET

P   ABBOTT MEMORIAL LIBRARY*, 15 Library St, 05067. (Mail add: PO Box 95, 05067-0095), SAN 317-1396. Tel: 802-457-2236. *Librn,* Cory Smith
Pop 994; Circ 3,750
Library Holdings: Bk Vols 6,000
Special Collections: Thomas Ware Primitive Portraits
Open Tues 10-6, Thurs 10-8, Sat 10-2

SOUTH ROYALTON

P   ROYALTON MEMORIAL LIBRARY, 23 Alexander Pl, 05068. (Mail add: PO Box 179, 05068-0179), SAN 317-1418. Tel: 802-763-7094. Web Site: www.royaltonlibrary.org.
Founded 1923. Pop 2,300; Circ 14,643
Library Holdings: Bk Vols 12,000; Per Subs 40
Automation Activity & Vendor Info: (Cataloging) Mandarin Library Automation; (Circulation) Mandarin Library Automation
Wireless access
Function: Adult bk club, After school storytime, Art exhibits, Audio & video playback equip for onsite use, Audiobks via web, Bks on CD, Children's prog, Computers for patron use, Copy machines, e-mail & chat, Electronic databases & coll, Free DVD rentals, Holiday prog, Home delivery & serv to Sr ctr & nursing homes, Homebound delivery serv, Libr develop, Mus passes, Online cat, Outreach serv, OverDrive digital audio bks, Photocopying/Printing, Preschool reading prog, Pub access computers, Senior outreach, Story hour, Summer reading prog, Video lending libr
Partic in Vermont Automated Libr Syst (VALS)
Open Tues-Fri 12-6, Sat 9-1

CL   VERMONT LAW SCHOOL*, Julien & Virginia Cornell Library, 68 North Windsor, 05068. (Mail add: PO Box 60, 05068-0060), SAN 317-1426. Tel: 802-831-1441. Administration Tel: 802-831-1443. FAX: 802-763-7159. Web Site: vermontlaw.edu/about_the_library.htm. *Dir,* Carl A Yirka; *Librn,* Cynthia Lewis; Tel: 802-831-1444, E-mail: clewis@vermontlaw.edu; *Librn,* Christine Ryan; Tel: 802-831-1448, E-mail: cryan@vermontlaw.edu; *Librn,* Jane Woldow; Tel: 802-831-1449; *Access Serv Librn,* Michele Dill LaRose; Tel: 802-831-1403, E-mail: mlarose@vermontlaw.edu; *ILS Adminr,* Lisa Donadio; Tel: 802-831-1442. Subject Specialists: *Comparative law, Russian law,* Carl A Yirka; *Environ law,* Christine Ryan; Staff 10 (MLS 6, Non-MLS 4)
Founded 1973. Enrl 650; Fac 61; Highest Degree: Doctorate
Library Holdings: Bk Vols 248,283; Per Subs 2,420
Special Collections: Environmental & Historic Preservation Coll. US Document Depository
Subject Interests: Law
Automation Activity & Vendor Info: (Acquisitions) Innovative Interfaces, Inc; (Cataloging) Innovative Interfaces, Inc; (Circulation) Innovative Interfaces, Inc; (ILL) OCLC FirstSearch; (OPAC) Innovative Interfaces, Inc; (Serials) Innovative Interfaces, Inc
Wireless access
Function: Accelerated reader prog
Partic in Lyrasis; New England Law Library Consortium, Inc
Open Mon-Fri 8am-Midnight, Sat & Sun 9am-Midnight
Friends of the Library Group

SOUTH RYEGATE

P   SOUTH RYEGATE PUBLIC LIBRARY, INC*, 140 Church St, 05069. SAN 320-5207. Tel: 802-584-3238. *Librn,* Richard Fraser
Founded 1954. Pop 1,150
Jul 2007-Jun 2008 Income $1,000. Mats Exp $500
Library Holdings: Large Print Bks 80; Bk Vols 6,600; Videos 25
Subject Interests: Ryegate hist
Open Thurs 3-5

SPRINGFIELD

M   SPRINGFIELD HOSPITAL LIBRARY*, 25 Ridgewood Rd, 05156-3057. (Mail add: PO Box 2003, 05156-2003), SAN 320-7544. Tel: 802-885-2151. FAX: 802-885-3959. Web Site: www.springfieldhospital.org. *In Charge,* Linda Hurley; E-mail: lhurley@springfieldhospital.org

Library Holdings: Bk Vols 100; Per Subs 50
Restriction: Not open to pub

P   SPRINGFIELD TOWN LIBRARY*, 43 Main St, 05156. SAN 317-1450. Tel: 802-885-3108. FAX: 802-885-4906. E-mail: springfieldlibrary@hotmail.com. Web Site: www.springfieldtownlibrary.org. *Dir,* Russell Moore; *Adult Serv,* Nancy Tusinski; *Ch,* Cheryl Cox; *Circ, ILL,* Tammy Gould; *Info Tech Coordr,* Christopher Bloomfield; *Ser,* Tracey Pratt; *Tech Serv,* Josephine Coleman; *Circ Asst,* Tracy Obremski; Staff 3 (MLS 1, Non-MLS 2)
Founded 1819. Pop 9,078; Circ 56,716
Jul 2006-Jun 2007 Income $387,280, State $3,166, City $368,381, Locally Generated Income $15,733. Mats Exp $383,665, Books $59,365, AV Mat $5,361, Electronic Ref Mat (Incl. Access Fees) $8,429. Sal $255,242
Library Holdings: AV Mats 3,250; Electronic Media & Resources 16; Bk Vols 43,883; Per Subs 430
Subject Interests: Alternative tech, Machine tool
Automation Activity & Vendor Info: (Cataloging) TLC (The Library Corporation); (Circulation) TLC (The Library Corporation); (OPAC) TLC (The Library Corporation)
Database Vendor: Baker & Taylor, Bowker, CQ Press, EBSCO Auto Repair Reference, EBSCOhost, Gale Cengage Learning, H W Wilson, LearningExpress, ProQuest, ReferenceUSA, TLC (The Library Corporation)
Wireless access
Publications: FOSTL Newsletter (Quarterly)
Partic in Green Mountain Library Consortium (GMLC)
Special Services for the Deaf - ADA equip; Bks on deafness & sign lang; High interest/low vocabulary bks; Sign lang interpreter upon request for prog
Special Services for the Blind - Accessible computers; Audio mat; Bks available with recordings; Bks on cassette; Bks on CD; Cassette playback machines; Closed circuit TV magnifier; Copier with enlargement capabilities; Digital talking bk; Large print & cassettes; Large print bks; Magnifiers; Screen enlargement software for people with visual disabilities; Talking bk serv referral
Open Mon-Thurs 9-8, Fri 9-5, Sat 10-3
Friends of the Library Group

STAMFORD

P   STAMFORD COMMUNITY LIBRARY*, 986 Main Rd, 05352. SAN 317-1469. Tel: 802-694-1379. FAX: 802-694-1636. E-mail: stamlib@mail.sover.net. *Town Librn,* Patricia Carlson; *Librn,* Lee Appelbaum; Staff 2 (MLS 1, Non-MLS 1)
Founded 1960. Circ 11,573
Library Holdings: Bk Vols 9,143
Automation Activity & Vendor Info: (Cataloging) Follett Software; (Circulation) Follett Software; (OPAC) Follett Software
Function: ILL available, Spoken cassettes & CDs, Summer reading prog, VHS videos
Open Mon & Tues 9-2, Wed 9-5, Thurs 9-4:15 & 5-9, Fri 9-3:15

STARKSBORO

P   STARKSBORO PUBLIC LIBRARY*, 2827 Rte 116, 05487. (Mail add: PO Box 124, 05487-0124), SAN 376-3471. Tel: 802-453-3732. E-mail: starksboropl@vals.state.vt.us. *Librn,* Lisa Daudon; Staff 2 (Non-MLS 2)
Pop 1,875
Library Holdings: Bk Vols 4,500; Per Subs 20
Function: ILL available, Photocopying/Printing, Prog for adults, Prog for children & young adult, Wheelchair accessible
Open Mon 10-6, Thurs 10-5, Sat 9-1

STOWE

P   STOWE FREE LIBRARY*, 90 Pond St, 05672. (Mail add: PO Box 1029, 05672-1029), SAN 317-1485. Tel: 802-253-6145. FAX: 802-253-4808. E-mail: info@stowelibrary.org. Web Site: www.stowelibrary.org. *Dir,* Rebekka Mateyk; *Ch,* Julie Pickett; Staff 5.25 (MLS 1.75, Non-MLS 3.5)
Founded 1866. Pop 4,339; Circ 101,837
Jul 2005-Jun 2006 Income $367,420. Mats Exp $40,174, Books $33,200, AV Mat $6,800, Electronic Ref Mat (Incl. Access Fees) $174
Library Holdings: AV Mats 3,582; Bk Vols 26,091; Per Subs 103
Special Collections: Vermont & Stowe History Coll
Database Vendor: Brodart, Ingram Library Services
Wireless access
Function: Handicapped accessible, ILL available, Photocopying/Printing, Prog for adults, Prog for children & young adult, Ref serv available, Spoken cassettes & CDs, Spoken cassettes & DVDs, Summer reading prog
Open Mon, Wed & Fri 9:30-5:30, Tues & Thurs 12-7, Sat 10-3
Friends of the Library Group

STRAFFORD

P   MORRILL MEMORIAL & HARRIS LIBRARY*, 220 Justin Morrill Memorial Hwy, 05072-9730. (Mail add: PO Box 110, 05072-0110), SAN 317-1493. Tel: 802-765-4037. E-mail: strafford@vals.state.vt.us. *Librn,* Rebecca Seibel
Pop 1,045; Circ 8,447
Library Holdings: Bk Vols 11,000
Special Collections: Senator Justin Smith Morrill Coll
Open Mon 1-8, Wed 2-5, Thurs 10-5, Sat 9-Noon

SWANTON

S   NORTHWEST STATE CORRECTIONAL FACILITY*, 3649 Lower Newton Rd, 05488. SAN 317-123X. Tel: 802-524-6771. FAX: 802-527-7534. *In Charge,* Barb Hagen; Tel: 802-527-4342
Founded 1967
Library Holdings: Bk Vols 3,500; Per Subs 1,500

P   SWANTON PUBLIC LIBRARY*, One First St, 05488. SAN 317-1515. Tel: 802-868-7656. E-mail: swanton_pub@vals.state.vt.us. Web Site: www.swantonlibrary.org. *Librn,* Marilyn Barney; *Asst Librn,* Darla Blondo; *Asst Librn,* Joan Martin; *Asst Librn,* Cheryl Messier; *Asst Librn,* Patricia Quilliam
Pop 6,200; Circ 16,707
Library Holdings: Bk Vols 17,000; Per Subs 34
Special Collections: Large Print Books; Local Genealogy Coll; Old Vermont History Coll
Wireless access
Special Services for the Blind - Large print bks
Open Mon & Tues 2-7, Wed & Thurs 10-7, Fri & Sat 10-2

THETFORD

S   THETFORD HISTORICAL SOCIETY LIBRARY*, 16 Library Rd, 05074. (Mail add: PO Box 33, 05074-0033), SAN 325-142X. Tel: 802-785-2068. E-mail: info@thetfordhistoricalsociety.org. *Librn,* Martha Howard; Staff 2 (Non-MLS 2)
Founded 1975
Library Holdings: Bk Vols 4,530
Special Collections: Charles Farnsworth Coll; Ciara Sipprell Photographs; Local Crafts & Trades Coll; Manuscripts; Missionary History Coll; Portraits; School Texts; Thetford Town History Coll; Vermont & New Hampshire Town Histories; Vermont & Thetford Authors Coll. Oral History
Function: Res libr
Open Mon & Thurs 2-4, Tues 10-12
Restriction: Not a lending libr

P   THETFORD TOWN LIBRARY*, Latham Memorial Library, 16 Library Lane, 05074. (Mail add: PO Box 240, 05074-0240), SAN 362-6490. Tel: 802-785-4361. FAX: 802-785-4361. *Librn,* Peter W Blodgett; Staff 1 (MLS 1)
Founded 1876. Pop 2,617; Circ 18,626
Library Holdings: AV Mats 137; Bk Vols 11,987; Per Subs 96; Talking Bks 241
Special Collections: Peabody Coll; Thetford Authors; Vermont Coll
Automation Activity & Vendor Info: (Cataloging) Chancery SMS; (Circulation) Chancery SMS; (OPAC) Chancery SMS
Partic in Librarians of the Upper Valley Coop
Open Mon 2-8:30, Tues 2-5, Wed & Fri 10-5, Thurs 2-8, Sat 9-1
Branches: 2
    GEORGE PEABODY BRANCH, PO Box 190, Post Mills, 05058-0190, SAN 362-6520. Tel: 802-333-9724. *In Charge,* Peter W Blodgett; Staff 1 (MLS 1)
    Library Holdings: AV Mats 19; Bk Vols 6,399; Per Subs 17; Talking Bks 121
    Open Tues 3-8, Wed 2-8:30
    THETFORD HISTORICAL, PO Box 33, 05074-0033. Tel: 802-785-2068. *In Charge,* Marshall Van Norden
    Open Mon 2-4 (Winter); Mon (Summer) 2-4 & Tues 10-12

TINMOUTH

P   TINMOUTH PUBLIC LIBRARY, MountainView Rd, 05773. SAN 376-4001. Tel: 802-446-2498. FAX: 802-446-2498. *Librn,* Ruth Drachman
Library Holdings: Bk Vols 4,000
Mem of Southwest Regional Library Service System
Open Mon 9-12 & 1-5, Thurs 9-12 & 1-8

TOWNSHEND

M   OTIS HEALTH CARE CENTER*, Grace Cottage Hospital Library, 185 Graston Rd, 05353. (Mail add: PO Box 216, 05353-0216). Tel: 802-365-7920, Ext 119. *Dir,* Kathy Stover; E-mail: kstover@otishealthcarecenter.org

Library Holdings: Bk Titles 50
Wireless access
Restriction: Med staff only

P   TOWNSHEND PUBLIC LIBRARY*, 1971 Rte 30, 05353. (Mail add: PO Box 252, 05353-0252), SAN 317-1523. Tel: 802-365-4039. E-mail: info@townshendlibrary.org. Web Site: www.townshendlibrary.org. *Librn,* Karen LaRue; *Libr Asst,* Donna Trumbull
Founded 1899. Pop 1,149; Circ 8,500
Library Holdings: Bk Vols 10,500; Per Subs 15
Special Collections: Vermont History Coll; West River Valley History Coll. State Document Depository
Automation Activity & Vendor Info: (Acquisitions) LibraryWorld, Inc; (Cataloging) LibraryWorld, Inc; (Circulation) LibraryWorld, Inc; (OPAC) LibraryWorld, Inc
Wireless access
Publications: ALA Booklist; Atheneum
Open Mon 1-5, Tues, Fri & Sat 9-1, Wed 1-7
Friends of the Library Group

TUNBRIDGE

P   TUNBRIDGE PUBLIC LIBRARY*, 289 Vt Rte 110, 05077. (Mail add: PO Box 9, 05077-0009), SAN 317-1531. Tel: 802-889-9404. E-mail: tunbridgelibrary@yahoo.com. Web Site: www.tunbridgelibrary.org. *Librn,* Jean Wolfe; Staff 1 (Non-MLS 1)
Jul 2008-Jun 2009 Income $68,500. Mats Exp $2,800. Sal $39,843
Library Holdings: Audiobooks 664; Bk Vols 9,200; Per Subs 10; Videos 714
Special Collections: Vermont Coll
Wireless access
Open Mon & Wed 3-8, Thurs & Fri 3-6, Sat 10-4
Friends of the Library Group

VERGENNES

P   BIXBY MEMORIAL FREE LIBRARY, 258 Main St, 05491. SAN 317-1558. Tel: 802-877-2211. FAX: 802-877-2411. E-mail: bixby_verg@vals.state.vt.us. Web Site: www.bixbylibrary.org. *Dir,* Jane Spencer; E-mail: jane.bixby@comcast.net; *Head Librn,* MacKenzie Ross; *Asst Librn,* Dianne Lawson; E-mail: dianne.bixby@comcast.net; *Youth Serv Librn,* Rachel A Plant; E-mail: rachel.bixby@comcast.net; *Circ,* Sara Howe; *Libr Asst,* Carolyn L Tallen; Staff 6 (MLS 2, Non-MLS 4)
Founded 1912. Pop 7,897; Circ 50,102
Jul 2011-Jun 2012 Income $98,727, City $30,000, Other $68,727. Mats Exp $21,024
Library Holdings: Bks on Deafness & Sign Lang 12; CDs 713; DVDs 896; Large Print Bks 913; Bk Titles 28,520; Per Subs 23
Special Collections: Antiques (Cup Plate Coll); Native American Coll; Paperweight Coll; Stamp Coll; Vermont History Coll
Automation Activity & Vendor Info: (Cataloging) LibraryWorld, Inc; (Circulation) LibraryWorld, Inc; (OPAC) LibraryWorld, Inc
Database Vendor: Brodart, Gale Cengage Learning, LibraryWorld, Inc, ProQuest
Wireless access
Function: Magnifiers for reading, Microfiche/film & reading machines, Mus passes, Newsp ref libr, Online cat, Outreach serv, OverDrive digital audio bks, Photocopying/Printing, Preschool outreach, Preschool reading prog, Prog for adults, Prog for children & young adult, Pub access computers, Ref & res, Ref serv in person, Scanner, Story hour, Summer & winter reading prog, Summer reading prog, Tax forms, Teen prog, VHS videos, Wheelchair accessible, Workshops
Open Mon 12:30-8, Tues & Fri 12:30-5, Wed & Thurs 10-5, Sat 10-2
Restriction: Non-circulating coll, Non-circulating of rare bks, Non-circulating to the pub, Non-resident fee, Open to others by appt, Open to students, Pub use on premises
Friends of the Library Group

VERNON

P   VERNON FREE PUBLIC LIBRARY*, 567 Governor Hunt Rd, 05354-9484. SAN 317-1574. Tel: 802-257-0150. FAX: 802-257-4949. E-mail: veronfreelibrary@comcast.net. Web Site: www.vernonfreelibrary.org. *Dir,* Kristine Berberian; *Ch,* Jean Carr
Founded 1905. Pop 2,141; Circ 15,494
Library Holdings: Bk Vols 17,000; Per Subs 52
Automation Activity & Vendor Info: (Cataloging) Follett Software; (Circulation) Follett Software; (OPAC) Follett Software
Function: Handicapped accessible, Homebound delivery serv, ILL available, Music CDs, Summer reading prog, VHS videos
Open Mon, Wed & Fri 2-5, Tues 9-12 & 2-6:30, Thurs 2-6:30, Sat 9-12

VERSHIRE

P   VERSHIRE COMMUNITY LIBRARY*, Rte 113, 05079. (Mail add: PO Box 112, 05079-0112). Tel: 802-685-9982. E-mail: library@vershare.org. Web Site: www.vershare.org/library. *Dir,* Pamela Mainville
Founded 2002
Library Holdings: Bk Vols 4,000; Talking Bks 70
Open Wed 10-Noon, Thurs 2-5, Sat 10-2

WAITSFIELD

P   JOSLIN MEMORIAL LIBRARY*, 4391 Main St, 05673-6155. (Mail add: PO Box 359, 05673-0359), SAN 317-1590. Tel: 802-496-4205. E-mail: waitsfield@vals.state.vt.us. Web Site: www.joslinmemoriallibrary.com. *Libr Dir,* Joy Worland; *Ch,* Stacy Werner; Staff 2 (MLS 1, Non-MLS 1)
Founded 1913. Pop 2,300; Circ 16,700
Jan 2010-Dec 2010 Income $46,000, City $38,160, Locally Generated Income $7,840. Mats Exp $8,750, Books $8,000, Per/Ser (Incl. Access Fees) $550, AV Mat $200. Sal $24,066
Library Holdings: CDs 10; Bk Vols 9,000; Per Subs 35; Talking Bks 567
Special Collections: Vermont Coll
Database Vendor: Overdrive, Inc
Wireless access
Function: Audio & video playback equip for onsite use, Audiobks via web, AV serv, Bks on cassette, Bks on CD, Bus archives, Children's prog, Computers for patron use, Copy machines, Doc delivery serv, e-mail serv, Electronic databases & coll, Games & aids for the handicapped, Home delivery & serv to Sr ctr & nursing homes, ILL available, Mus passes, Newsp ref libr, Online ref, OverDrive digital audio bks, Photocopying/Printing, Preschool outreach, Prog for adults, Prog for children & young adult, Pub access computers, Ref serv in person, Spoken cassettes & CDs, Story hour, Summer reading prog, Tax forms, Telephone ref, VHS videos, Video lending libr
Partic in Green Mountain Library Consortium (GMLC); Vermont State Libr Syst
Special Services for the Blind - Large print bks
Open Mon-Thurs 12-6, Sat 10-4
Friends of the Library Group

WALLINGFORD

P   GILBERT HART LIBRARY, 14 S Main, 05773. (Mail add: PO Box 69, 05773-0069), SAN 317-1612. Tel: 802-446-2685. FAX: 802-446-2685. E-mail: ghlib@comcast.net. *Dir,* Wendy Savery; Staff 1 (Non-MLS 1)
Founded 1795. Pop 2,300
Library Holdings: DVDs 50; Large Print Bks 128; Bk Vols 19,100; Per Subs 50; Talking Bks 700; Videos 150
Special Collections: Vermontiana Coll
Wireless access
Partic in Green Mountain Library Consortium (GMLC)
Open Tues, Thurs & Fri 10-5, Wed 10-8, Sat 9-Noon
Friends of the Library Group

WARDSBORO

P   WARDSBORO FREE PUBLIC LIBRARY*, 170 Main St, 05355. (Mail add: PO Box 157, 05355-0157), SAN 317-1620. Tel: 802-896-6988. E-mail: wardsboro@vals.state.vt.us. Web Site: www.wardsboropubliclibrary.org. *Librn,* Jill Dean; *Ch,* Amy Dix
Pop 910; Circ 5,391
Library Holdings: Bk Vols 8,000; Talking Bks 200
Open Mon & Thurs 10-1, Tues & Wed 2-7, Sat 9-1
Friends of the Library Group

WARREN

P   WARREN PUBLIC LIBRARY, 413 Main St, 05674. (Mail add: PO Box 287, 05674-0287), SAN 320-5215. Tel: 802-496-3913. FAX: 802-496-2418. E-mail: warrenlibrary@gmavt.net. Web Site: www.warrenlibrary.com. *Librn,* Deborah Kahn; Staff 1.72 (MLS 1, Non-MLS 0.72)
Pop 1,705; Circ 14,444
Jan 2012-Dec 2012 Income $93,017, City $84,487, Other $8,530. Mats Exp $13,125, Books $7,900, Per/Ser (Incl. Access Fees) $1,580, AV Mat $3,525, Electronic Ref Mat (Incl. Access Fees) $120. Sal $53,691 (Prof $33,057)
Library Holdings: Audiobooks 746; DVDs 673; Large Print Bks 10; Bk Vols 8,398; Per Subs 30; Videos 281
Automation Activity & Vendor Info: (Acquisitions) ByWater Solutions; (Cataloging) ByWater Solutions; (Circulation) ByWater Solutions; (OPAC) ByWater Solutions
Database Vendor: Gale Cengage Learning, Newsbank
Wireless access
Function: Adult bk club, Audio & video playback equip for onsite use, Audiobks via web, Bk club(s), Bks on cassette, Bks on CD, Children's prog, Computers for patron use, Copy machines, Distance learning, Electronic databases & coll, Equip loans & repairs, Free DVD rentals, Handicapped accessible, Health sci info serv, Homebound delivery serv, ILL available, Mus passes, Music CDs, Newsp ref libr, Online cat, Online ref, Online searches, OverDrive digital audio bks, Photocopying/Printing, Printer for laptops & handheld devices, Prog for adults, Prog for children & young adult, Pub access computers, Ref serv available, Ref serv in person, Scanner, Spoken cassettes & CDs, Story hour, Summer reading prog, Telephone ref, VHS videos, Video lending libr, Wheelchair accessible, Workshops
Partic in Green Mountain Library Consortium (GMLC); OCLC Online Computer Library Center, Inc
Open Mon & Fri 10-6, Tues (Summer) 10-2, Wed 10-7, Sat 10-4
Friends of the Library Group

WASHINGTON

P   CALEF MEMORIAL LIBRARY, 2964 VT Rte 110, 05675. (Mail add: PO Box 141, 05675-0141), SAN 317-1639. Tel: 802-883-2343. FAX: 802-883-9387. E-mail: caleflibrary@gmail.com. Web Site: caleflibrary.wordpress.com. *Libr Dir,* Sarah Costa; *Libr Asst,* Valerie Ferris
Pop 1,092; Circ 3,048
Library Holdings: Bk Vols 5,900; Per Subs 24
Automation Activity & Vendor Info: (OPAC) ByWater Solutions
Database Vendor: Gale Cengage Learning, H W Wilson, Wilson - Wilson Web
Wireless access
Function: Adult bk club, Audiobks via web, Bks on cassette, Bks on CD, Children's prog, Computer training, Computers for patron use, Copy machines, Distance learning, e-mail & chat, Electronic databases & coll, Free DVD rentals, Homebound delivery serv, Homework prog, ILL available, Literacy & newcomer serv, Mus passes, Online cat, Online searches, Orientations, OverDrive digital audio bks, Prog for children & young adult, Pub access computers, Ref serv available, Scanner, Story hour, Summer reading prog, Telephone ref, VHS videos
Open Mon 11-4, Tues-Thurs 2-7, Sat 9-1

WATERBURY

P   WATERBURY PUBLIC LIBRARY*, 28 N Main St, 05676. SAN 317-1647. Tel: 802-244-7036. Web Site: www.waterburypubliclibrary.com. *Dir,* Mary Kasamatsu
Circ 41,839
Library Holdings: Bk Vols 24,000; Per Subs 60; Talking Bks 704; Videos 857
Special Collections: Vermontiana
Automation Activity & Vendor Info: (Cataloging) TLC (The Library Corporation); (Circulation) TLC (The Library Corporation); (OPAC) TLC (The Library Corporation)
Open Mon-Wed 10-8, Thurs & Fri 10-5, Sat 9-2
Friends of the Library Group

WATERVILLE

P   WATERVILLE TOWN LIBRARY, 850 VT Rte 109, 05492. (Mail add: C/O Alice Godin, 1380 Lapland Rd, 05492-0031), SAN 317-1663. Tel: 802-644-5556. E-mail: librarian@watervillelib.org. Web Site: www.watervillelib.org.
Pop 673; Circ 150
Library Holdings: Bk Vols 3,900
Wireless access
Open Tues & Sat (Summer) 10-2

WELLS

P   WELLS VILLAGE LIBRARY*, Five E Wells Rd, 05774-9791. (Mail add: PO Box 587, 05774-0587), SAN 317-1671. Tel: 802-645-0611. *Librn,* Patricia M Capron
Founded 1944. Pop 902; Circ 1,942
Library Holdings: Bk Vols 6,827
Subject Interests: Adult fiction, Gen juv
Mem of Southwest Regional Library Service System
Special Services for the Blind - Bks on cassette; Large print bks
Open Mon 3-5, Fri 6-8

WELLS RIVER

P   BALDWIN MEMORIAL LIBRARY*, 33 Main St, 05081. (Mail add: PO Box 337, 05081), SAN 317-168X. Tel: 802-757-2693. *Librn,* Peggy Hewes
Pop 1,003; Circ 13,393
Library Holdings: Bk Vols 9,500; Per Subs 25
Special Collections: Martin Luther King Memorial Peace Shelf
Wireless access
Open Mon 9:30-4:30, Wed 1:30-6, Fri 1:30-8, Sun 1-3

WEST BURKE

P   WEST BURKE PUBLIC LIBRARY*, 135 Main St, 05871. (Mail add: PO Box 243, 05871), SAN 317-1698. Tel: 802-467-3328. *Librn,* Kathryn Weed; *Libr Tech,* Jane Davis
Pop 353; Circ 1,750
Library Holdings: AV Mats 25; Bk Vols 5,000; Talking Bks 55
Open Sat (Winter) 1:30-4:30; Wed & Sat (Summer) 1:30-4:30pm

WEST DANVILLE

P   WALDEN COMMUNITY LIBRARY*, 135 Cahoon Farm Rd, 05873. SAN 317-1604. Tel: 802-563-3000. FAX: 802-563-3030. *Librn,* Anne Smith
Founded 1895. Pop 500; Circ 1,000
Library Holdings: Bk Vols 7,000
Special Collections: Vermont Coll
Publications: Walden 200
Open Mon-Fri 10-2, Tues 10-2 & 6-9 (6-9 Summer)

WEST DUMMERSTON

P   LYDIA TAFT PRATT LIBRARY*, 156 West St, 05357-0070. (Mail add: PO Box 70, 05357-0070), SAN 376-8015. Tel: 802-258-9878. E-mail: dummerstonpl@vals.state.vt.us. *Librn,* Melissa Worden
Pop 1,936
Library Holdings: Large Print Bks 60; Bk Titles 4,000; Talking Bks 25
Open Tues (Winter) 2:30-7, Thurs 10-5, Sat 9:30-Noon; Tues (Summer) 2:30-7, Thurs 10-5

WEST FAIRLEE

P   WEST FAIRLEE FREE PUBLIC LIBRARY*, 894 Vt Rte 113, Unit 3, 05083-4405. SAN 317-171X. Tel: 802-333-3502. E-mail: westfairleelibrary@hotmail.com. *Librn,* Viola Farrar
Founded 1908. Pop 337; Circ 900
Library Holdings: AV Mats 232; Bk Titles 7,000; Bk Vols 17,297; Videos 202
Wireless access
Open Wed 6pm-8pm, Fri 2:30-5:30

WEST HARTFORD

P   WEST HARTFORD LIBRARY*, 5133 Rte 14, 05084. (Mail add: PO Box 26, 05084-0026), SAN 317-1728. Tel: 802-295-7992. FAX: 802-295-7992. E-mail: whartfordlibraryvt@gmail.com. *Librn,* Aileen Gillett; Staff 1 (Non-MLS 1)
Founded 1927. Pop 2,500
Jul 2005-Jun 2006 Income $43,606. Mats Exp $6,000. Sal $20,488
Library Holdings: CDs 40; DVDs 88; Large Print Bks 141; Bk Titles 9,879; Per Subs 21; Talking Bks 518; Videos 421
Subject Interests: Local authors, State hist
Database Vendor: Overdrive, Inc
Wireless access
Function: Bks on cassette, Bks on CD, Computers for patron use, Copy machines, Electronic databases & coll, Free DVD rentals, ILL available, Mus passes, Outreach serv, OverDrive digital audio bks, Photocopying/Printing, Pub access computers, Summer reading prog, VHS videos, Wheelchair accessible
Partic in Vermont Automated Libr Syst (VALS)
Open Mon & Tues 12-5, Wed & Fri 12-7, Sat 9-12

WEST RUPERT

P   ROSALIND KESHIN KITTAY PUBLIC LIBRARY*, 2827 Hwy 153, 05768. (Mail add: PO Box 53, 05776-0053). Tel: 802-394-2444. FAX: 802-394-2444. E-mail: rkkittay@myfairpoint.net. Web Site: www.rupertkittaylibrary.com. *Dir,* Thelma Georgeson
Founded 1999. Pop 709
Jan 2010-Dec 2010 Income $25,000
Library Holdings: Bk Vols 4,000
Special Collections: Art Coll
Wireless access
Function: Adult bk club, Art exhibits, Audio & video playback equip for onsite use, Bks on cassette, Bks on CD, Children's prog, Computers for patron use, Copy machines, ILL available, Spoken cassettes & CDs, Spoken cassettes & DVDs, Summer reading prog, VHS videos, Video lending libr, Wheelchair accessible
Open Tues 2:30-5:30, Wed 10-2, Thurs 5-7, Sat 9-12, Sun 1-4

WEST RUTLAND

P   WEST RUTLAND FREE LIBRARY CORP*, 595 Main St, 05777. SAN 317-1736. Tel: 802-438-2964. *Librn,* Barbara Wiskoski
Pop 2,448; Circ 7,899
Jan 2010-Dec 2010. Mats Exp $2,712, Books $1,977, Per/Ser (Incl. Access Fees) $735. Sal $28,734

Library Holdings: Audiobooks 21; DVDs 115; Large Print Bks 103; Bk Vols 10,000; Per Subs 22
Wireless access
Open Mon, Wed & Fri 1:30-5, Tues & Thurs 1:30-7

WEST WINDSOR

P   MARY L BLOOD MEMORIAL LIBRARY*, 41 Brownsville-Hartland Rd, 05037. (Mail add: PO Box 468, Brownsville, 05037-0468), SAN 316-9731. Tel: 802-484-7205. *Librn,* Marcella Barrows
Founded 1901. Pop 932; Circ 5,960
Library Holdings: Bks-By-Mail 476; Bk Vols 5,600; Per Subs 19; Videos 223
Open Wed 4-6, Fri 2-6

WESTFIELD

S   HITCHCOCK MEMORIAL MUSEUM & LIBRARY*, 1252 Rte 100, 05874. (Mail add: PO Box 87, 05874-0087), SAN 376-3420. Tel: 802-744-8258. *Librn,* Tonya Gunn; Staff 1 (Non-MLS 1)
Founded 1899
Library Holdings: AV Mats 15; Bk Vols 8,500
Special Collections: Historic Coll, Natural History
Open Thurs 1-5, Sat 9am-11am

WESTFORD

P   WESTFORD LIBRARY*, 1718 Vermont Rte 128, 05494. (Mail add: PO Box 86, 05494-0086), SAN 376-8031. Tel: 802-878-5639. E-mail: westford_pl@vals.state.vt.us. Web Site: www.westford.lib.vt.us. *Librn,* Victoria Tibbits; Staff 2 (MLS 1, Non-MLS 1)
Founded 1844. Pop 1,740; Circ 8,400
Library Holdings: AV Mats 200; Large Print Bks 25; Bk Vols 8,000; Per Subs 23
Subject Interests: Vt
Function: ILL available
Open Wed 1-7, Thurs 10-6, Fri Noon-6, Sat 10-2
Friends of the Library Group

WESTMINSTER

P   BUTTERFIELD LIBRARY*, 3534 US Rte 5, 05158. (Mail add: PO Box 123, 05158-0123), SAN 317-1744. Tel: 802-722-4891. *Librn,* Linda Fawcett
Founded 1924. Pop 271; Circ 4,583
Library Holdings: Bk Vols 10,000; Per Subs 30
Open Mon 1-4, Tues & Thurs 1:30-7:30

WESTON

P   WILDER MEMORIAL LIBRARY*, 24 Lawrence Hill Rd, 05161. (Mail add: PO Box 38, 05161-0038), SAN 317-1760. Tel: 802-824-4307. E-mail: wilderweston@vals.state.vt.us. *Librn,* Carolyn Mullett
Pop 600; Circ 1,126
Library Holdings: Bk Vols 4,000; Per Subs 10
Open Tues 4-6, Wed & Sat 10-12 & 2-6

WHITE RIVER JUNCTION

GM   DEPARTMENT OF VETERANS AFFAIRS*, Medical Library, 215 N Main St, 05009. SAN 362-6644. Tel: 802-295-9363, Ext 5236. Web Site: www.visn1.med.va.gov/wrj/index.html. *Librn,* Rich DeRosa; E-mail: rich.derosa@va.gov; Staff 1 (MLS 1)
Founded 1940
Library Holdings: DVDs 75; Bk Vols 750; Per Subs 65; Videos 100
Special Collections: medical
Function: CD-ROM, Computer training, Copy machines, Doc delivery serv, e-mail serv, Electronic databases & coll, Fax serv, Govt ref serv, Handicapped accessible, Health sci info serv, ILL available, Online ref, Online searches, Photocopying/Printing, Prof lending libr, Ref & res, Ref serv available, Res libr, Telephone ref, VHS videos, Video lending libr, Wheelchair accessible
Restriction: Open to hospital affiliates only, Restricted access

WILDER

S   THE BERTRAND RUSSELL SOCIETY, INC LIBRARY*, 98 Gillette St, 05088. (Mail add: PO Box 434, 05088-0434), SAN 371-1692. Tel: 802-295-9058. *Librn,* Thomas Stanley; E-mail: tjstanley@myfairpoint.net
Function: ILL available

WILLIAMSTOWN

P   AINSWORTH PUBLIC LIBRARY, 2338 VT Rte 14, 05679. (Mail add: PO Box 236, 05679-0236), SAN 322-6700. Tel: 802-433-5887. FAX: 802-433-2161. E-mail: ainsworthpl@yahoo.com. Web Site:

www.ainsworthlibrary.com. *Dir,* Robert Youngberg; *Asst Librn,* Roberta Tracy; Staff 0.8 (MLS 0.5, Non-MLS 0.3)
Founded 1911. Pop 3,300; Circ 5,817
Library Holdings: Bk Titles 10,290; Per Subs 26
Special Collections: Oral History
Automation Activity & Vendor Info: (Cataloging) Follett Software; (Circulation) Follett Software
Database Vendor: Gale Cengage Learning
Wireless access
Function: Adult bk club
Open Mon, Tues, Thurs & Fri 2-6, Wed 9-6, Sat 9-1
Friends of the Library Group

WILLISTON

P   DOROTHY ALLING MEMORIAL LIBRARY*, 21 Library Lane, 05495. SAN 317-1809. Tel: 802-878-4918. FAX: 802-878-3964. E-mail: daml@williston.lib.vt.us. Web Site: www.williston.lib.vt.us. *Dir,* Marti Fiske; *Asst Dir,* Debbie Roderer; *Head, Tech Serv,* Cindy Weber; *Info Tech, ILL, Ref & Instrul Serv Librn,* Kim Peine; *Ch, Youth Serv,* Jill Coffrin; *Circ,* Barbara Lane; *Patron Serv,* Jen Reichert; *Asst Youth Serv,* Susan Blair; Staff 4.9 (MLS 1, Non-MLS 3.9)
Founded 1905. Pop 9,200; Circ 108,160
Jul 2010-Jun 2011 Income $532,206, City $523,050, Locally Generated Income $6,690, Other $2,466. Mats Exp $58,597, Books $48,800, Per/Ser (Incl. Access Fees) $3,666, Micro $76, AV Mat $2,000, Electronic Ref Mat (Incl. Access Fees) $4,055. Sal $293,920
Library Holdings: Bk Titles 37,621; Bk Vols 44,670
Special Collections: Local History (Williston Coll), bks, photogs, postal cards, scrapbooks, typescripts, oral history
Automation Activity & Vendor Info: (Cataloging) Follett Software; (Circulation) Follett Software; (ILL) Follett Software; (OPAC) Follett Software
Database Vendor: Gale Cengage Learning, Newsbank, OCLC FirstSearch, Overdrive, Inc
Wireless access
Function: Adult bk club, Archival coll, Art exhibits, Audio & video playback equip for onsite use, Audiobks via web, Bk club(s), Bks on cassette, Bks on CD, Children's prog, Computer training, Computers for patron use, Copy machines, Digital talking bks, Exhibits, Fax serv, Free DVD rentals, Handicapped accessible, Home delivery & serv to Sr ctr & nursing homes, Homebound delivery serv, ILL available, Magnifiers for reading, Mail & tel request accepted, Mus passes, Music CDs, Notary serv, Online cat, Outreach serv, OverDrive digital audio bks, Photocopying/Printing, Preschool outreach, Prog for adults, Prog for children & young adult, Pub access computers, Ref serv available, Scanner, Senior outreach, Spoken cassettes & CDs, Story hour, Summer reading prog, Tax forms, Teen prog, Telephone ref, Video lending libr, Web-catalog, Wheelchair accessible, Workshops
Open Mon & Wed 10-8, Tues, Thurs & Fri 10-6, Sat 10-3
Friends of the Library Group
Bookmobiles: 1

WILMINGTON

P   PETTEE MEMORIAL LIBRARY*, 16 S Main St, 05363. (Mail add: PO Box 896, 05363), SAN 317-1817. Tel: 802-464-8557. E-mail: petteelibrary@yahoo.com. Web Site: www.petteelibrary.org. *Librn,* Carol Waseleski; *Asst Librn,* Harriette Hamilton; Staff 3 (MLS 1, Non-MLS 2)
Founded 1895. Pop 2,500; Circ 15,000
Jul 2008-Jun 2009 Income $100,000. Mats Exp $12,500. Sal $49,000
Library Holdings: Audiobooks 400; DVDs 1,400; Bk Titles 10,900; Per Subs 20
Special Collections: Vermont Shelf (books)
Automation Activity & Vendor Info: (Acquisitions) Follett Software; (Cataloging) Follett Software; (Circulation) Follett Software
Wireless access
Partic in Vt Libr Syst
Open Mon & Fri 10-4, Tues-Thurs 12-6, Sat 10-2

WINDHAM

P   WINDHAM TOWN LIBRARY*, Town Hall, 26 Harrington Rd, 05359. (Mail add: 5976 Windham Hill Rd, 05359), SAN 376-334X. Tel: 802-875-2244. E-mail: windlib@vermonttel.net. *Librn,* Beverly Carmichael
Library Holdings: Bk Titles 2,000
Open Wed 12-5

WINDSOR

S   SOUTHEAST STATE CORRECTIONAL FACILITY LIBRARY*, 546 State Farm Rd, 05089. SAN 317-1833. Tel: 802-674-6717. FAX: 802-674-2249. *In Charge,* Maryanne Murphy
Library Holdings: Bk Vols 3,000; Per Subs 18
Restriction: Staff & inmates only

P   WINDSOR PUBLIC LIBRARY, 43 State St, 05089. SAN 317-1841. Tel: 802-674-2556. FAX: 802-674-5767. E-mail: windsorlibrary@comcast.net. Web Site: windsorlibrary.org. *Libr Assoc,* Melissa Ayres; *Ch,* Sarah Tufts; Staff 3 (Non-MLS 3)
Founded 1882. Pop 3,756; Circ 23,000
Library Holdings: Bk Vols 18,000; Per Subs 30
Special Collections: Old Vermont Newspaper Coll; Vermont History Coll
Database Vendor: Gale Cengage Learning, Overdrive, Inc, ProQuest, Wilson - Wilson Web
Wireless access
Open Mon & Wed 9-8, Fri 9-6, Sat 9-1
Friends of the Library Group

WINOOSKI

P   WINOOSKI MEMORIAL LIBRARY*, Champlain Mill, Level 2, One Main St, 05404. SAN 317-1868. Tel: 802-655-6424. FAX: 802-655-6431. E-mail: winooski_memorial@yahoo.com. Web Site: winooskiml.blogspot.com, www.onioncity.com/lib/winlib_home.htm. *Dir, Libr Serv,* Amanda Perry
Founded 1930. Pop 6,800; Circ 17,250
Library Holdings: Bk Vols 13,000; Per Subs 26
Automation Activity & Vendor Info: (Cataloging) Follett Software; (Circulation) Follett Software
Open Tues 10-7, Wed 3-7, Thurs & Fri 10-6, Sat 10-1

WOLCOTT

P   GLEE MERRITT KELLEY COMMUNITY LIBRARY*, 320 School Hill Dr, 05680. (Mail add: PO Box 179, 05680), SAN 317-1884. Tel: 802-472-6551. FAX: 802-472-6295. *Librn,* Sally Gardner; E-mail: sally_gardner@yahoo.com
Founded 1973. Pop 1,619; Circ 27,300
Library Holdings: Bk Vols 12,700; Per Subs 15
Special Collections: Vermont Coll
Open Mon-Thurs 9-6, Sat 9am-11am

C   STERLING COLLEGE*, Center for Northern Studies Library, 479 Cross Rd, 05680-4088. (Mail add: PO Box 72, Craftsbury Common, 05827-0072), SAN 317-1876. Tel: 802-888-3969, 802-888-4331. Web Site: www.sterlingcollege.edu. *Librn,* Petra Vogel; Tel: 802-586-7711, Ext 129, Fax: 802-586-2596, E-mail: pvogel@sterlingcollege.edu; Staff 1 (MLS 1)
Founded 1971. Highest Degree: Bachelor
Library Holdings: Bk Vols 4,000; Per Subs 60
Special Collections: North Polar Regions Coll
Subject Interests: Arctic studies
Automation Activity & Vendor Info: (Cataloging) Follett Software; (Circulation) Follett Software; (OPAC) Follett Software
Database Vendor: Gale Cengage Learning, JSTOR, ProQuest, ScienceDirect, SerialsSolutions
Wireless access

WOODBURY

P   WOODBURY COMMUNITY LIBRARY*, 69 Valley Lake Rd, 05681. (Mail add: PO Box 329, 05681-0329), SAN 376-4923. Tel: 802-472-5710. E-mail: woodbury@vals.state.vt.us. *Dir,* Robert Joly
Library Holdings: Bk Vols 7,000; Per Subs 5
Automation Activity & Vendor Info: (Acquisitions) LibraryWorld, Inc; (Cataloging) LibraryWorld, Inc; (Circulation) LibraryWorld, Inc; (OPAC) LibraryWorld, Inc; (Serials) LibraryWorld, Inc
Database Vendor: Gale Cengage Learning, Wilson - Wilson Web
Wireless access
Open Mon 9:30-8, Tues 9:30-2:30, Wed & Thurs 9:30-2:30 & 6-8, Sat 9-12

WOODSTOCK

P   NORMAN WILLIAMS PUBLIC LIBRARY*, Ten S Park St, 05091. SAN 317-1906. Tel: 802-457-2295. Circulation Tel: 802-457-2295, Ext 113. Reference Tel: 802-457-2295, Ext 125. FAX: 802-457-5181. E-mail: nwpl@normanwilliams.lib.vt.us. Web Site: www.normanwilliams.lib.vt.us. *Dir,* Position Currently Open; *Head, Ch,* Tracey Dugdale; E-mail: tracey@normanwilliams.lib.vt.us; *Circ Mgr,* Lydia Borsch; *Ref Mgr,* Kathy Beaird; Staff 10 (MLS 1, Non-MLS 9)
Founded 1883. Pop 3,232; Circ 66,000
Library Holdings: AV Mats 1,185; Bk Vols 42,303; Per Subs 112; Talking Bks 1,042
Special Collections: Computer Technology (MJUSA Coll); Vermont Genealogy (New England & Local Genealogical Information); Vermont History Discussion Group (Vermont Civil War History Books). Oral History
Subject Interests: Computers, Genealogy, Local hist, State hist
Automation Activity & Vendor Info: (Cataloging) Mandarin Library Automation; (Circulation) Mandarin Library Automation; (OPAC) Mandarin Library Automation

Function: Art exhibits, Audio & video playback equip for onsite use, AV serv, Bk club(s), Computer training, Digital talking bks, Electronic databases & coll, Handicapped accessible, Home delivery & serv to Sr ctr & nursing homes, Homebound delivery serv, ILL available, Magnifiers for reading, Mail & tel request accepted, Online ref, Online searches, Photocopying/Printing, Prog for adults, Prog for children & young adult, Ref serv available, Summer reading prog, Telephone ref, VHS videos, Wheelchair accessible
Partic in Vermont Automated Libr Syst (VALS)
Special Services for the Deaf - Bks on deafness & sign lang
Special Services for the Blind - Bks available with recordings; Bks on cassette; Bks on CD; Braille bks; Copier with enlargement capabilities; Extensive large print coll; Home delivery serv; Internet workstation with adaptive software; Large print bks; Low vision equip; Magnifiers
Open Mon, Fri & Sat 10-5, Tues, Wed & Thurs 10-7
Friends of the Library Group

S   WOODSTOCK HISTORICAL SOCIETY, INC*, John Cotton Dana Library, 26 Elm St, 05091. SAN 327-2621. Tel: 802-457-1822. FAX: 802-457-2811. E-mail: info@woodstockhistorical.org. Web Site: www.woodstockhistorical.org. *Librn,* Jennifer Donaldson; E-mail: jdonaldson@woodstockhistorical.org; *Educ Coordr,* Jennie Shurtleff; Staff 3 (Non-MLS 3)
Founded 1943
Library Holdings: Bk Vols 2,000
Special Collections: Institutional Records, Family Papers & Diaries from Woodstock Area; Large Photography Archive. Oral History
Subject Interests: Genealogy, Local hist
Wireless access
Open Wed-Fri 9:30-4
Restriction: Not a lending libr

Date of Statistics: FY 2007-2008
Population, 2000 Census: 7,078,515
Population Served by Public Libraries: 7,585,662
Total Volumes in Public Libraries: 22,005,535
Volumes Per Capita: 2.95
Total Public Library Circulation: 69,748,939
Total Public Library Expenditures (including Grants-in-Aid):
$269,930,818
Source of Income: Mainly public funds
Expenditures Per Capita: $35.24
Number of County or Multi-county Regional Libraries: 67

Counties Served: 95
Number of Independent Cities: 41
Cities Served: 41
Number of Bookmobiles in State: 31
Grants-in-Aid to Public Libraries:
State Aid: $17,091,761
Formula for Apportionment: Legally established libraries
receive grants based on local support, population, square miles
and number of government units served
Use of Funds: Grants to public libraries and statewide programs
for library development

ABINGDON

J   VIRGINIA HIGHLANDS COMMUNITY COLLEGE LIBRARY*,
Learning Resource Center, 100 VHCC Dr, 24210. (Mail add: PO Box 828,
24212-0828), SAN 317-1930. Tel: 276-739-2542. Circulation Tel:
276-739-2471. Reference Tel: 276-739-2512. Administration Tel:
276-739-2472. FAX: 276-739-2593. E-mail: cdesk@vhcc.edu. Web Site:
www.vhcc.edu/lis/library.htm. *Actg Coordr, Libr & Instrul Serv,* Charles
Boling; Tel: 276-739-2514, E-mail: cboling@vhcc.edu; *Ref & Instrul Serv
Librn,* Joel Rudy, III; E-mail: jrudy@vhcc.edu; *ILL/Circ Supvr,* Reva E
Russell; E-mail: rrussell@vhcc.edu; *Ser,* Joyce P Crusenberry; Tel:
276-739-2470, E-mail: jcrusenberry@vhcc.edu. Subject Specialists: *Hist,*
Joel Rudy, III; Staff 4 (MLS 2, Non-MLS 2)
Founded 1967. Enrl 1,588; Fac 66; Highest Degree: Associate
Library Holdings: Bk Vols 32,500; Per Subs 225
Special Collections: VIVA (Virtual Library of Virginia)
Automation Activity & Vendor Info: (Acquisitions) Ex Libris Group;
(Cataloging) Ex Libris Group; (Circulation) Ex Libris Group; (OPAC) Ex
Libris Group
Database Vendor: Gale Cengage Learning, LexisNexis, OCLC
FirstSearch, OVID Technologies
Wireless access
Partic in SouthWest Information Network Group (SWING); Virginia
Commun Coll Syst; Virtual Library of Virginia
Open Mon-Thurs 8am-9pm, Fri 8-5, Sat 11-3, Sun 2-5

P   WASHINGTON COUNTY PUBLIC LIBRARY*, 205 Oak Hill St, 24210.
SAN 317-1949. Tel: 276-676-6222. Circulation Tel: 276-676-6233.
Reference Tel: 276-676-6298. Administration Tel: 276-676-6383. FAX:
276-676-6235. Web Site: www.wcpl.net. *Dir,* Charlotte L Parsons; E-mail:
charlotte@wcpl.net; *Ch,* Amanda Bailey; Tel: 276-676-6382; *Circ,* Todd
Eastridge; E-mail: teastridge@wcpl.net; *Pub Serv,* Ida Patton; Tel:
276-676-6390, E-mail: ipatton@wcpl.net; *Ref,* William Stein; Tel:
276-676-6389, E-mail: wstein@wcpl.net; *Tech Serv,* Deborah Ledbetter;
Tel: 276-676-6340, E-mail: dledbetter@wcpl.net; Staff 22 (MLS 4,
Non-MLS 18)
Founded 1954. Pop 50,500; Circ 294,637
Library Holdings: Bk Vols 107,657; Per Subs 240
Automation Activity & Vendor Info: (Acquisitions) Innovative Interfaces,
Inc; (Cataloging) Innovative Interfaces, Inc; (Circulation) Innovative
Interfaces, Inc; (OPAC) Innovative Interfaces, Inc; (Serials) Innovative
Interfaces, Inc
Database Vendor: EBSCOhost, Innovative Interfaces, Inc INN - View,
OCLC FirstSearch
Partic in Holston Associated Librs Consortium
Open Mon-Thurs 9-9, Fri & Sat 9-5, Sun 2-5
Friends of the Library Group
Branches: 4
DAMASCUS BRANCH, 126 E Laurel Ave, Damascus, 24236, SAN
329-3211. Tel: 276-475-3820. FAX: 276-475-5081. *Br Mgr,* Deanna
Wolfe; E-mail: dwolfe@wcpl.net; *Asst Br Mgr,* Linda Brown; E-mail:
lbrown@wcpl.net; Staff 2 (Non-MLS 2)

Library Holdings: Bk Vols 22,313; Per Subs 38
Open Mon-Thurs 11-7, Fri 11-5, Sat 9-1
GLADE SPRING BRANCH, 212 Grace St, Glade Spring, 24340. (Mail
add: PO Box 70, Glade Spring, 24340-0070), SAN 320-9504. Tel:
276-429-5626. FAX: 276-429-2740. *Br Mgr,* Pamela Widener; Staff 1
(Non-MLS 1)
Library Holdings: Bk Vols 25,000; Per Subs 52
Open Mon, Wed & Fri 12-5, Tues 2-7, Sat 9-1
HAYTERS GAP, 7720 Hayters Gap Rd, 24210-2823, SAN 375-1430. Tel:
276-944-4442. FAX: 276-944-3011. *Br Mgr,* Kathy Musick; E-mail:
kmusick@wcpl.net; Staff 1 (Non-MLS 1)
Library Holdings: Bk Vols 23,000; Per Subs 49
Open Mon & Thurs 11-7, Tues 11-4, Fri 11-5, Sat 10-2
MENDOTA BRANCH, 2562 Mendota Rd, Mendota, 24270-2018. (Mail
add: PO Box 99, Mendota, 24270-0099), SAN 375-1449. Tel:
276-645-2374. FAX: 276-645-2330. *Br Mgr,* Ray Mullins; E-mail:
rmullins@wcpl.net; Staff 1 (Non-MLS 1)
Library Holdings: Bk Vols 23,000; Per Subs 51
Open Tues-Thurs 12-7, Sat 9-1

ACCOMAC

P   EASTERN SHORE PUBLIC LIBRARY*, 23610 Front St, 23301. (Mail
add: PO Box 360, 23301-0360), SAN 317-1957. Tel: 757-678-7800,
757-787-3400, 757-824-5151. FAX: 757-787-2241. Web Site:
www.espl.org. *Dir,* Carol Vincent; *ILL,* Charle Ricci; E-mail:
cricci@espl.lib.va.us; Staff 6 (MLS 2, Non-MLS 4)
Founded 1957. Pop 45,200; Circ 164,451
Library Holdings: Bk Vols 128,000; Per Subs 108
Special Collections: Local History (Eastern Shore of Virginia Coll), bks,
maps, micro
Subject Interests: Sailing
Automation Activity & Vendor Info: (Cataloging) Auto-Graphics, Inc;
(Circulation) Auto-Graphics, Inc
Partic in Lyrasis
Open Mon-Wed & Fri 9-6, Thurs 9-9, Sat 9-1
Friends of the Library Group
Branches: 3
ISLAND LIBRARY, 4077 Main St, Chincoteague, 23336. Tel:
757-336-3460. *Br Mgr,* Harriet Lonergan
Library Holdings: Bk Vols 8,000
Open Mon & Tues 10-5, Wed, Fri & Sat 1-5, Thurs 4-8
NORTHAMPTON FREE LIBRARY, 7745 Seaside Rd, Nassawadox,
23413. Tel: 757-414-0010. FAX: 757-414-0424. *Dir,* Carol Vincent
Library Holdings: Bk Vols 13,300
Open Mon-Wed & Fri 9-6, Thurs 9-9, Sat 9-1
NORTHAMPTON MEMORIAL LIBRARY, 500 Tazewell Ave, Cape
Charles, 23310. Tel: 757-331-1300. *Br Mgr,* Ann Rutledge
Library Holdings: Bk Vols 9,600
Open Mon-Wed & Fri 10-5, Thurs 10-8, Sat 10-2

ALBERTA

J   SOUTHSIDE VIRGINIA COMMUNITY COLLEGE LIBRARIES*, Julian M Howell Library, 109 Campus Dr, 23821. SAN 362-6709. Tel: 434-949-1064. FAX: 434-949-0013. Web Site: www.sv.vccs.edu/lrs. *Dir,* Jack Ancell; Tel: 434-949-1066, E-mail: jack.ancell@sv.vccs.edu; *Head of Libr,* Earnestine Lewis; E-mail: ernestine.lewis@sv.vccs.edu; *Cat,* Lewis La Verna; *Ser,* Robin Soyars
Founded 1970
Library Holdings: Bk Vols 30,000; Per Subs 270
Automation Activity & Vendor Info: (Acquisitions) Ex Libris Group; (Cataloging) Ex Libris Group; (Course Reserve) Ex Libris Group; (OPAC) Ex Libris Group
Partic in Virginia Commun Coll Syst; Virtual Library of Virginia
Open Mon-Thurs 8am-9pm, Fri 8-4:30

ALEXANDRIA

P   ALEXANDRIA LIBRARY*, 5005 Duke St, 22304. SAN 362-6733. Tel: 703-746-1702. Administration Tel: 703-746-1701. Administration FAX: 703-746-1738. TDD: 703-746-1790. Web Site: www.alexandria.lib.va.us. *Dir,* Rose T Dawson; Tel: 703-746-1777, E-mail: rdawson@alexandria.lib.va.us; *Communications Officer I,* Mark Schwartz; Tel: 703-746-1770, E-mail: mschwartz@alexandria.lib.va.us; *ILL,* Position Currently Open; *Tech Serv,* Lynda Rudd; Tel: 703-746-1764, Fax: 703-746-1747, E-mail: lrudd@alexandria.lib.va.us; Staff 76.39 (MLS 30.52, Non-MLS 45.87)
Founded 1794. Pop 145,011; Circ 1,051,770
Jul 2010-Jun 2011 Income (Main Library and Branch(s)) $6,430,891, State $161,950, City $5,879,455, Federal $26,541, Locally Generated Income $263,785, Other $99,160. Mats Exp $378,225, Books $175,242, Per/Ser (Incl. Access Fees) $37,284, Micro $6,440, AV Mat $43,451, Electronic Ref Mat (Incl. Access Fees) $115,808. Sal $5,288,795
Library Holdings: Audiobooks 13,023; AV Mats 17,071; CDs 14,610; DVDs 8,862; e-books 2,735; Large Print Bks 4,439; Microforms 29; Bk Vols 357,409; Per Subs 618; Talking Bks 14,910; Videos 10,978
Special Collections: Oral History
Subject Interests: Civil War hist, Genealogy, Town hist
Automation Activity & Vendor Info: (Acquisitions) SirsiDynix; (Cataloging) SirsiDynix; (Circulation) SirsiDynix; (Serials) SirsiDynix
Database Vendor: EBSCOhost, Facts on File, Gale Cengage Learning, netLibrary, OCLC FirstSearch, ProQuest, ReferenceUSA, SirsiDynix Wireless access
Function: Archival coll, Audiobks via web, AV serv, Bks on CD, Children's prog, Computers for patron use, Copy machines, e-mail serv, Electronic databases & coll, Handicapped accessible, Home delivery & serv to Sr ctr & nursing homes, Homebound delivery serv, ILL available, Magnifiers for reading, Music CDs, Outreach serv, OverDrive digital audio bks, Photocopying/Printing, Prog for children & young adult, Pub access computers, Ref serv available, Summer reading prog, Telephone ref, Web-catalog, Wheelchair accessible
Partic in Lyrasis; Metro Coun of Govts; Urban Libraries Council (ULC)
Special Services for the Deaf - Assisted listening device; Assistive tech; Bks on deafness & sign lang; Sign lang interpreter upon request for prog; TDD equip
Special Services for the Blind - Assistive/Adapted tech devices, equip & products; Computer with voice synthesizer for visually impaired persons; Descriptive video serv (DVS); Large print bks; Talking bks; ZoomText magnification & reading software
Open Mon-Thurs 10-9, Fri 10-6, Sat 10-5, Sun 1-5
Friends of the Library Group
Branches: 7
   KATE WALLER BARRETT BRANCH, 717 Queen St, 22314, SAN 372-8056. Tel: 703-746-1703. Circulation Tel: 703-746-1722. Reference Tel: 703-746-1721. FAX: 703-746-1709. Reference FAX: 703-746-1708. *Br Mgr,* Position Currently Open; *Circ Serv Mgr,* Sandra Cahill; E-mail: scahill@alexandria.lib.va.us; *Ch,* Elizabeth Springer; E-mail: lspringer@alexandria.lib.va.us; Staff 10.125 (MLS 4.5, Non-MLS 5.625)
Circ 127,958
Jul 2010-Jun 2011. Mats Exp $34,491, Books $24,546, Per/Ser (Incl. Access Fees) $1,755, AV Mat $8,190. Sal $733,112
Library Holdings: Audiobooks 2,201; AV Mats 1,018; CDs 363; DVDs 570; Large Print Bks 755; Bk Vols 70,174; Per Subs 188; Videos 269
Function: Adult bk club, Audiobks via web, Bks on cassette, Bks on CD, Children's prog, Copy machines, Electronic databases & coll, Free DVD rentals, Music CDs, Online cat, OverDrive digital audio bks, Photocopying/Printing, Prog for children & young adult, Pub access computers, Story hour, Summer reading prog, Tax forms, VHS videos
Special Services for the Deaf - ADA equip; Sign lang interpreter upon request for prog
Open Mon 1-9, Tues 10-9, Wed & Thurs 10-7, Fri 10-6, Sat 10-5
Friends of the Library Group
   CHARLES E BEATLEY JR CENTRAL (HQTRS), 5005 Duke St, 22304-2903. Tel: 703-746-1702. Circulation Tel: 703-746-1752. Interlibrary Loan Service Tel: 703-746-1745. Reference Tel:

703-746-1751. Administration Tel: 703-746-1701. Circulation FAX: 703-746-1739. Interlibrary Loan Service FAX: 703-746-1763. Administration FAX: 703-746-1738. TDD: 703-746-1790. *Br Mgr,* Renee Dipilato; Tel: 703-746-1728, E-mail: rdipilato@alexandria.lib.va.us; *Ch,* Julie Fields; Tel: 703-746-1735, E-mail: jfields@alexandria.lib.va.us; *Ref Serv,* Elizabeth Stromme; Tel: 703-746-1746, E-mail: estromme@alexandria.lib.va.us; *YA Serv,* Ginny Rawls; Tel: 703-746-1767, E-mail: grawls@alexandria.lib.va.us; Staff 32.79 (MLS 12.52, Non-MLS 20.27)
Circ 521,379
Jul 2010-Jun 2011. Mats Exp $87,503, Books $64,185, Per/Ser (Incl. Access Fees) $2,404, AV Mat $20,914. Sal $2,173,971
Library Holdings: Audiobooks 5,276; AV Mats 12,483; CDs 7,259; DVDs 3,723; Large Print Bks 2,149; Microforms 29; Bk Titles 156,527; Per Subs 236; Videos 670
Function: Audiobks via web, Bks on cassette, Bks on CD, Children's prog, Computers for patron use, Copy machines, Electronic databases & coll, Free DVD rentals, Handicapped accessible, Homebound delivery serv, ILL available, Music CDs, Online ref, Online searches, Outreach serv, Photocopying/Printing, Prog for children & young adult, Pub access computers, Summer reading prog, Tax forms, VHS videos, Wheelchair accessible
Special Services for the Deaf - Assistive tech; Bks on deafness & sign lang; TDD equip; TTY equip
Special Services for the Blind - Assistive/Adapted tech devices, equip & products
Open Mon-Thurs 10-9, Fri 10-6, Sat 10-5, Sun 1-5
Friends of the Library Group
   ELLEN COOLIDGE BURKE BRANCH, 4701 Seminary Rd, 22304, SAN 362-6792. Tel: 703-746-1704. Circulation Tel: 703-746-1772. Reference Tel: 703-746-1771. FAX: 703-746-1775. *Br Mgr,* Ashley Jefferson; E-mail: ajefferson@alexandria.lib.va.us; *Circ Serv Mgr,* Shahana Parvas; E-mail: sparvas@alexandria.lib.va.us; Staff 8 (MLS 3.25, Non-MLS 4.75)
Circ 113,325
Jul 2010-Jun 2011. Mats Exp $23,834, Books $15,267, Per/Ser (Incl. Access Fees) $1,817, AV Mat $6,750. Sal $542,985
Library Holdings: Audiobooks 1,824; AV Mats 487; CDs 1,549; DVDs 1,645; Large Print Bks 523; Bk Vols 55,965; Per Subs 98; Videos 222
Function: Bks on cassette, Bks on CD, Children's prog, Computer training, Computers for patron use, Copy machines, Free DVD rentals, Music CDs, Online cat, OverDrive digital audio bks, Photocopying/Printing, Pub access computers, Story hour, Summer reading prog, Tax forms, VHS videos
Open Mon 10-9, Tues & Wed 10-7, Thurs 1-9, Fri 10-6, Sat 10-5
Friends of the Library Group
   JAMES M DUNCAN JR BRANCH, 2501 Commonwealth Ave, 22301, SAN 362-6822. Tel: 703-746-1705. Circulation Tel: 703-746-1780. Reference Tel: 703-746-1781. FAX: 703-746-1785. *Br Mgr,* Pat Ryckman; E-mail: pryckman@alexandria.lib.va.us; *Circ Serv Mgr,* Marilyn Doherty; E-mail: mdoherty@alexandria.lib.va.us; *Ch,* Kyle Maier; E-mail: mkyle@alexandria.lib.va.us; Staff 8.875 (MLS 4.25, Non-MLS 4.625)
Circ 251,169
Jul 2010-Jun 2011. Mats Exp $39,553, Books $31,161, Per/Ser (Incl. Access Fees) $793, AV Mat $7,599. Sal $568,430
Library Holdings: Audiobooks 3,722; AV Mats 9,645; CDs 3,548; DVDs 2,924; Large Print Bks 1,012; Bk Titles 75,751; Per Subs 96; Videos 955
Function: Audiobks via web, Bks on CD, Children's prog, Computers for patron use, Copy machines, Electronic databases & coll, Free DVD rentals, Handicapped accessible, Music CDs, OverDrive digital audio bks, Photocopying/Printing, Pub access computers, Summer reading prog, Tax forms, VHS videos, Wheelchair accessible
Open Mon 10-9, Tues & Thurs 10-7, Wed 1-9, Fri 10-6, Sat 10-5
Friends of the Library Group
   LOCAL HISTORY/SPECIAL COLLECTIONS, 717 Queen St, 22314-2420, SAN 362-6857. Tel: 703-746-1706. FAX: 703-746-1720. *Br Mgr,* George Combs; Tel: 703-746-1719, E-mail: gkcombs@alexandria.lib.va.us; Staff 3 (MLS 2, Non-MLS 1)
Circ 15,066
Library Holdings: Bk Titles 17,655
Subject Interests: Civil War, Genealogy, Local hist, State hist
Function: Archival coll, Genealogy discussion group, Handicapped accessible, Ref serv available, Res libr, Wheelchair accessible
Open Mon 1-9, Tues 2-9, Wed 10-7, Fri 10-6
Restriction: Internal circ only, Non-circulating coll, Pub use on premises
Friends of the Library Group
P   TALKING BOOKS, 5005 Duke St, 22304-2903, SAN 362-6768. Tel: 703-746-1760. TDD: 703-746-1790. *Mgr,* Elaine McCaffrey; Staff 2 (Non-MLS 2)
Founded 1968. Circ 7,282
Library Holdings: Braille Volumes 191; Videos 134
Special Collections: Blindness & Other Handicaps Reference Material
Function: Audio & video playback equip for onsite use, Games & aids for the handicapped, Handicapped accessible, Homebound delivery serv,

Magnifiers for reading, Mail loans to mem, Monthly prog for perceptually impaired adults, VHS videos, Web-Braille, Wheelchair accessible
Special Services for the Deaf - Closed caption videos; TDD equip
Special Services for the Blind - Assistive/Adapted tech devices, equip & products; Braille equip; Closed circuit TV; Compressed speech equip; Computer with voice synthesizer for visually impaired persons; Descriptive video serv (DVS); Home delivery serv; Machine repair; Newsline for the Blind; Radio reading serv; Reader equip; Spanish Braille mags & bks; Talking bks & player equip; ZoomText magnification & reading software
Open Mon-Fri 10-5
Friends of the Library Group
TECHNICAL SERVICES, 5005 Duke St, 22304-2903, SAN 372-8048. *Br Mgr,* Lynda Rudd; Tel: 703-746-1764, Fax: 703-746-1747, E-mail: lrudd@alexandria.lib.va.us; Staff 8 (MLS 2, Non-MLS 6)
Open Mon-Fri 9-5

S   AMERICAN CORRECTIONAL ASSOCIATION*, Anthony Travisono Library, 206 N Washington St, 22314. SAN 321-8309. Tel: 703-224-0194. Toll Free Tel: 800-222-5646, Ext 0194. FAX: 703-224-0179. Web Site: www.aca.org. *Dir,* Gabriella Klatt
Founded 1975
Library Holdings: Bk Titles 5,000
Special Collections: Photograph Coll
Subject Interests: Archives, Corrections
Open Mon-Fri 9-4
Restriction: Open to pub for ref only

S   AMERICAN COUNSELING ASSOCIATION*, Professional Library, 5999 Stevenson Ave, 22304. SAN 302-5705. Tel: 703-823-9800. Toll Free Tel: 800-347-6647. FAX: 703-823-0252. Toll Free FAX: 800-473-2329. TDD: 703-823-6862. Web Site: www.counseling.org.
Founded 1952
Library Holdings: Bk Vols 5,000; Per Subs 25
Subject Interests: Counseling
Publications: Bibliographies
Open Mon-Thurs 9:30-3

S   AMERICAN GEOLOGICAL INSTITUTE LIBRARY*, 4220 King St, 22302-1502. SAN 317-2716. Tel: 703-379-2480, Ext 239. FAX: 703-379-7563. Web Site: www.agiweb.org. *Dir,* Sharon Tahirkheli; *Librn,* Lin Rose; E-mail: lnr@agiweb.org
Founded 1967
Library Holdings: Bk Titles 400; Bk Vols 1,600; Per Subs 250
Special Collections: American Geological Institute Publications
Subject Interests: Geol
Wireless access
Restriction: Open by appt only

S   AMERICAN HELICOPTER SOCIETY INTERNATIONAL LIBRARY*, 217 N Washington St, 22314. SAN 329-2649. Tel: 703-684-6777. FAX: 703-739-9279. E-mail: staff@vtol.org. Web Site: www.vtol.org. *Exec Dir,* Michael Hirschberg; *Dep Dir,* Kay Brackins
Founded 1943
Library Holdings: Bk Titles 900; Per Subs 50
Special Collections: History of Vertical Flight (James V Liberatore Coll), archives
Restriction: Mem only

S   AMERICAN PHYSICAL THERAPY ASSOCIATION*, Mary McMillan Library, 1111 N Fairfax St, 4th Flr, 22314-1484. SAN 373-0050. Tel: 703-706-8534. Toll Free Tel: 800-999-2782, Ext 8534. FAX: 703-838-8910. E-mail: inforesources@apta.org. Web Site: www.apta.org. *Dir,* Gini Blodgett; E-mail: giniblodgett@apta.org; Staff 1.6 (MLS 1.6)
Library Holdings: Bk Titles 2,000; Bk Vols 2,500; Per Subs 45
Special Collections: Oral History
Subject Interests: Archives, Rehabilitation
Automation Activity & Vendor Info: (OPAC) Inmagic, Inc.
Database Vendor: Dialog, EBSCOhost, OVID Technologies, ProQuest, PubMed
Function: ILL available, Res libr
Partic in National Network of Libraries of Medicine
Restriction: Circulates for staff only, External users must contact libr, Limited access based on advanced application, Non-circulating of rare bks, Non-circulating to the pub, Open by appt only, Open to researchers by request

R   BETH EL HEBREW CONGREGATION LIBRARY & INFORMATION CENTER*, Lifelong Learning Center, 3830 Seminary Rd, 22304. SAN 317-1973. Tel: 703-370-9400. FAX: 703-370-7730. E-mail: library@bethelhebrew.org. Web Site: www.bethelhebrew.org. *Coordr, Libr Serv,* E J Jarvis
Founded 1964

Library Holdings: DVDs 150; Bk Vols 3,600; Videos 50
Subject Interests: Israel, Judaica, Theol
Automation Activity & Vendor Info: (Cataloging) JayWil Software Development, Inc
Wireless access

S   CENTER FOR NAVAL ANALYSES LIBRARY*, 4825 Mark Center Dr, 22311-1846. SAN 317-1981. Tel: 703-824-2117. Interlibrary Loan Service Tel: 703-824-2110. Reference Tel: 703-824-2120. FAX: 703-824-2200. Web Site: www.cna.org. *Supvr,* Greg Kaminski; Tel: 703-824-2173, E-mail: kaminskg@cna.org; Staff 3 (MLS 1, Non-MLS 2)
Founded 1962
Library Holdings: Bk Vols 15,000; Per Subs 300
Subject Interests: Econ, Math, Mil sci, Polit sci, Statistics
Automation Activity & Vendor Info: (Cataloging) SirsiDynix; (Circulation) SirsiDynix; (ILL) OCLC; (OPAC) SirsiDynix; (Serials) SirsiDynix
Database Vendor: EBSCOhost, OCLC FirstSearch
Publications: Acquisitions Bulletin; Items of Interest; List of Journal Holdings
Partic in Interlibrary Users Association; OCLC Eastern; OCLC Online Computer Library Center, Inc
Open Mon-Fri 8-5

S   COLLINGWOOD LIBRARY & MUSEUM ON AMERICANISM*, 8301 East Blvd Dr, 22308. SAN 376-1762. Tel: 703-765-1652. FAX: 703-765-8390. Web Site: www.collingwoodlibrary.com. *Fac Coordr,* Judie Kunkle; E-mail: curator@collingwoodlibrary.com; Staff 2 (MLS 2)
Founded 1976
Library Holdings: Electronic Media & Resources 19,000; Bk Vols 6,000
Special Collections: "American Heritage" (a semi-monthly publication complete from 1954 volumes 4 through 58 complete); "Harpers Monthly" (Complete set from 1850 rebound)
Open Mon & Wed-Sat 10-4, Sun 1-4
Restriction: Open to pub for ref only

S   EDUCATIONAL RESEARCH SERVICE*, Information Resource Center, 1001 N Fairfax St, Ste 500, 22314. SAN 327-2664. Tel: 703-243-2100. Toll Free Tel: 800-791-9308. FAX: 703-243-1985. Toll Free FAX: 800-791-9309. E-mail: ers@ers.org. Web Site: www.ers.org. *Dir,* Brian Galvin; E-mail: bgalvin@ers.org
Library Holdings: Bk Vols 20,000; Per Subs 150
Automation Activity & Vendor Info: (Cataloging) Inmagic, Inc.; (Circulation) Inmagic, Inc.
Database Vendor: ProQuest
Open Mon-Fri 8:30-5

S   FORT WARD MUSEUM*, Dorothy C S Starr Civil War Research Library, 4301 W Braddock Rd, 22304-1008. SAN 327-2486. Tel: 703-838-4848. FAX: 703-671-7350. Web Site: www.fortward.org. *Dir,* Susan Cumbey; *Curator,* Walton Owen
Library Holdings: Bk Vols 2,500
Subject Interests: Civil War
Restriction: Open by appt only

M   INOVA MOUNT VERNON HOSPITAL*, Robert I McLaughry Health Sciences Library, 2501 Parker's Lane, 22306. SAN 377-2799. Tel: 703-664-7269. FAX: 703-664-7523. E-mail: mvh.library@inova.org. Web Site: inova.org/library. *Librn,* Bea Bobotek
Library Holdings: Bk Vols 1,000; Per Subs 120
Automation Activity & Vendor Info: (Cataloging) SydneyPlus; (OPAC) SydneyPlus
Database Vendor: OVID Technologies
Open Mon, Tues & Thurs 9-5

S   INSTITUTE FOR DEFENSE ANALYSES LIBRARY, 4850 Mark Center Dr, 22311. SAN 317-218X. Tel: 703-845-2087. Tel: 703-820-7194. E-mail: refdesk@ida.org. *Mgr,* Bradley E Gernand; Tel: 703-845-2405, E-mail: bgernand@ida.org; Staff 13.5 (MLS 4.5, Non-MLS 9)
Founded 1960
Library Holdings: e-books 70,000; e-journals 16,000; Bk Titles 21,000; Per Subs 300
Subject Interests: Aeronautical eng, Chem eng, Econ, Math, Physics, Policy analysis, Polit sci
Automation Activity & Vendor Info: (Acquisitions) SydneyPlus; (Cataloging) SydneyPlus; (Circulation) SydneyPlus; (OPAC) SydneyPlus; (Serials) SydneyPlus
Database Vendor: ACM (Association for Computing Machinery), American Chemical Society, American Mathematical Society, American Physical Society, American Psychological Association (APA), Annual Reviews, Blackwell's, CQ Press, ebrary, EBSCO - WebFeat, EBSCO Information Services, EBSCOhost, Elsevier, GalleryWatch, Hoovers, IEEE (Institute of Electrical & Electronics Engineers), IOP, JSTOR, LexisNexis, Marcive, Inc, Marquis Who's Who, Nature Publishing Group, OCLC

WorldCat, OVID Technologies, Oxford Online, PubMed, Safari Books
Online, ScienceDirect, Springer-Verlag, Wiley
Partic in Nat Res Libr Alliance (NRLA)
Restriction: Co libr

S   INTERNATIONAL PERSONNEL MANAGEMENT ASSOCIATION*,
     Center for Human Resources, 1617 Duke St, 22314. SAN 370-5145. Tel:
     703-549-7100. FAX: 703-684-0948. E-mail: cpr@ipma-hr.org. Web Site:
     www.ipma-hr.org. *Dir,* Tina Chaippetta; E-mail: cchiapp@ipma-hr.org
     Library Holdings: Bk Titles 300; Per Subs 10
     Special Collections: Human Resource Issues. State Document Depository;
     US Document Depository
     Publications: Bibliographies; information packets; surveys

S   MPR ASSOCIATES, INC*, Technical Library, 320 King St, 22314-3238.
     SAN 325-8211. Tel: 703-519-0200. FAX: 703-519-0226. E-mail:
     library@mpr.com. *Head Librn,* Danielle Harrison; Tel: 703-519-0567,
     E-mail: dharrison@mpr.com; Staff 4 (MLS 3, Non-MLS 1)
     Library Holdings: Bk Titles 4,200; Per Subs 120
     Automation Activity & Vendor Info: (Acquisitions) Cuadra Associates;
     (Cataloging) Cuadra Associates; (Serials) Cuadra Associates
     Publications: Bulletin (Monthly)
     Open Mon-Fri 9-5

S   NATIONAL SCHOOL BOARDS ASSOCIATION LIBRARY*, 1680 Duke
     St, 22314-3493. SAN 302-7341. Tel: 703-838-6731. FAX: 703-548-5516.
     E-mail: info@nsba.org. Web Site: www.nsba.org. *Mgr, Libr Serv,* Dottie
     Gray; *Librn,* Mary Ternes; Staff 2 (MLS 2)
     Founded 1976
     Library Holdings: Bk Titles 4,000; Per Subs 150
     Special Collections: K-12 Public Education Governance Issues; State
     School Board Associations periodicals
     Subject Interests: Educ

S   NICHOLS PROFESSIONAL LIBRARY*, 4701 Seminary Rd, 22304. SAN
     324-6035. Tel: 703-461-4040. FAX: 703-370-7704. Web Site:
     www.acps.k12.va.us. *Librn,* Peggy Koplitz; E-mail:
     pkoplitz@acps.k12.va.us; Staff 2 (MLS 1, Non-MLS 1)
     Founded 1968
     Library Holdings: Bk Titles 9,500
     Subject Interests: Educ
     Automation Activity & Vendor Info: (Cataloging) Follett Software;
     (Circulation) Follett Software
     Partic in Dialog Corp
     Open Mon-Fri 8:30-4:30

L   OBLON, SPIVAK*, Law Library, 1940 Duke St, 22314-3454. SAN
     374-5961. Tel: 703-412-6391. FAX: 703-413-2220. *Librn,* Jo Burke;
     E-mail: jburke@oblon.com. Subject Specialists: *Patents,* Jo Burke; Staff 1
     (MLS 1)
     Founded 1968
     Database Vendor: LexisNexis, OCLC FirstSearch, STN International,
     Westlaw
     Restriction: Not open to pub, Staff use only

S   SPECIAL LIBRARIES ASSOCIATION, Information Center, 331 S Patrick
     St, 22314-3501. SAN 312-0716. Tel: 703-647-4900. FAX: 703-647-4901.
     E-mail: resources@sla.org. Web Site: www.sla.org. *Dir, Educ & Info Serv,*
     Carolyn Sosnowski; Tel: 703-647-4914, E-mail: csosnowski@sla.org; Staff
     0.5 (MLS 0.5)
     Founded 1909
     Library Holdings: Bk Vols 500; Per Subs 10
     Special Collections: SLA Archives
     Subject Interests: Info sci, Libr sci, Operation of special librs
     Automation Activity & Vendor Info: (Cataloging) Inmagic, Inc.; (Serials)
     Inmagic, Inc.
     Restriction: Open by appt only

A   UNITED STATES ARMY*, Geospatial Information Library, 110 Casey
     Bldg, 7701 Telegraph Rd, 22315-3864. SAN 362-8981. Tel: 703-428-6831.
     FAX: 703-428-6772. *Tech Info Spec,* Allan Wiley
     Library Holdings: Bk Vols 7,000; Per Subs 50
     Special Collections: Map Coll
     Subject Interests: Cartography, Geog, Geol, GIS, Meteorology, Phys sci
     Automation Activity & Vendor Info: (Cataloging) Ex Libris Group;
     (Circulation) Ex Libris Group
     Partic in Fedlink; OCLC Online Computer Library Center, Inc
     Restriction: Not open to pub

A   UNITED STATES DEPARTMENT OF THE ARMY*, Humphreys
     Engineer Center Support Activity Library, CEHEC-ZL Casey Bldg, 7701
     Telegraph Rd, 22315-3860. SAN 337-1522. Tel: 703-428-6388. FAX:
     703-428-6310. E-mail: cehec-im-l@usace.army.mil. Web Site:

www.hecsa.usace.army.mil/hxlibrary. *Dir,* Connie J Wiley; Tel:
703-428-7430, E-mail: connie.j.wiley@usace.army.mil; *Acq,* Donna
Dickerson; *Cat,* Audrey J Thomas; *Electronic Serv,* Phillip Ip; *Eng Librn,*
Deborah E Keller; *Patron Serv,* Barbara J Clark; *Ref Serv,* Robin Baird;
Ser, Jo Ann Soriano. Subject Specialists: *Legal,* Robin Baird; Staff 7 (MLS
5, Non-MLS 2)
Founded 1942
Library Holdings: Bk Titles 100,324; Bk Vols 152,386; Per Subs 427
Special Collections: Civil & Environmental Engineering; Congressional
Materials; Corps of Engineers History & Activities, 1776-present;
Management Coll
Automation Activity & Vendor Info: (Cataloging) Auto-Graphics, Inc;
(Circulation) Auto-Graphics, Inc; (OPAC) Auto-Graphics, Inc; (Serials)
Auto-Graphics, Inc
Database Vendor: Dialog, LexisNexis, OCLC FirstSearch
Function: ILL available

G   UNITED STATES PATENT & TRADEMARK OFFICE*, Scientific &
     Technical Information Center, 400 Dulany St, Rm 1D58, 22314. SAN
     317-2287. Tel: 571-272-3547. FAX: 571-273-0048. Web Site:
     www.uspto.gov/web/patents/sticlibinfo.htm. *Dir,* Anne Hendrickson; *Div
     Chief,* Maxine Brown; *Div Chief,* Arti Shah
     Founded 1836
     Library Holdings: e-journals 17,000; Bk Vols 129,163; Per Subs 300
     Special Collections: Foreign Patents
     Subject Interests: Biochem, Chem eng design, Computer sci, Fed law,
     Foreign patents, Intellectual property law, Mechanical eng design
     Automation Activity & Vendor Info: (Cataloging) SirsiDynix; (OPAC)
     SirsiDynix
     Open Mon-Fri 8-5
     Restriction: Ref only

GL   UNITED STATES TRADEMARK OFFICE LAW LIBRARY*, Trademark
     Law Library, 600 Dulany St, MDE 4B65, 22314-5791. Tel: 571-272-9650.
     FAX: 571-273-0030. E-mail: tm.librarian@uspto.gov. Web Site:
     www.uspto.gov/main/trademarks.htm. *Dir,* Robert A Farina; Tel:
     571-272-9690, Fax: 571-273-9690, E-mail: robert.farina@uspto.gov; *Ref
     Serv Coordr,* Ann Marie Parsons; Tel: 571-272-9694, Fax: 571-273-9694,
     E-mail: ann.parsons@uspto.gov; *Ref Serv,* Jonathan Fiencke; Tel:
     571-272-2759, Fax: 571-273-2759, E-mail: jonathan.fiencke@uspto.gov;
     Ref Serv, Anne Geldermann; Tel: 571-270-1504, Fax: 571-273-1504,
     E-mail: anne.geldermann@uspto.gov; *Ref Serv,* Kate McAloon; Tel:
     571-272-9697, Fax: 571-273-9697, E-mail: kate.mcaloon@uspto.gov; *Ref
     Serv,* Jay Santiago; Tel: 571-272-9699, Fax: 571-273-9699, E-mail:
     jay.santiago@uspto.gov; Staff 6 (MLS 6)
     Founded 1992
     Library Holdings: Bk Titles 1,800; Bk Vols 2,700; Per Subs 185
     Subject Interests: Intellectual property law
     Automation Activity & Vendor Info: (Cataloging) SirsiDynix; (OPAC)
     SirsiDynix
     Database Vendor: Baker & Taylor, Dialog, EBSCOhost, HeinOnline,
     IEEE (Institute of Electrical & Electronics Engineers), Knovel, LexisNexis,
     OCLC, ProQuest, RefWorks, SirsiDynix
     Function: Res libr
     Partic in Fedlink
     Restriction: Staff use only

R   VIRGINIA THEOLOGICAL SEMINARY*, Bishop Payne Library, 3737
     Seminary Rd, 22304-5201. SAN 317-2074. Tel: 703-461-1731. Reference
     Tel: 703-461-1733. FAX: 703-370-0935. E-mail: paynelib@vts.edu. Web
     Site: www.vts.edu/library. *Head Librn,* Mitzi J Budde; E-mail:
     mjbudde@vts.edu. Subject Specialists: *Ecumenism, Relig, Theol,* Mitzi J
     Budde; Staff 10 (MLS 5, Non-MLS 5)
     Founded 1823. Enrl 200; Fac 26; Highest Degree: Doctorate
     Library Holdings: AV Mats 10,937; Electronic Media & Resources 120;
     Music Scores 154; Bk Vols 192,447; Per Subs 1,050
     Special Collections: Anglicanism & Episcopal Church in the USA
     Subject Interests: Relig, Theol
     Automation Activity & Vendor Info: (Acquisitions) Innovative Interfaces,
     Inc; (Cataloging) Innovative Interfaces, Inc; (Circulation) Innovative
     Interfaces, Inc; (Course Reserve) Innovative Interfaces, Inc; (ILL) OCLC;
     (OPAC) Innovative Interfaces, Inc; (Serials) Innovative Interfaces, Inc
     Wireless access
     Partic in OCLC Online Computer Library Center, Inc; Washington
     Theological Consortium
     Restriction: In-house use for visitors

S   VSE CORPORATION LIBRARY-BAV DIVISION*, 2550 Huntington Ave,
     22303-1499. SAN 317-2066. Tel: 703-317-5259. FAX: 703-960-6599. Web
     Site: www.vsecorp.com. *Tech Serv,* Mary Wantrobski; E-mail:
     m.cwantrobski@vsebav.com
     Founded 1979
     Library Holdings: Bk Vols 37,200; Per Subs 10

Special Collections: Military, Industry & Federal Specifications, Standards & Handbooks, micro & CD-ROM; Quality Coll; Vendor Catalogs, micro & CD-ROM; VSMF Engineering Information, micro & CD-ROM
Subject Interests: Eng, Math, Physics
Publications: Very Special Entries (new acquisitions)
Restriction: Not open to pub

R　WESTMINSTER PRESBYTERIAN CHURCH LIBRARY*, 2701 Cameron Mills Rd, 22302. SAN 317-2082. Tel: 703-549-4766. FAX: 703-548-1505. Web Site: wpc-alex.org. *Librn,* Kathy Hunter
Library Holdings: Bk Vols 2,250; Per Subs 11
Restriction: Not open to pub

S　WORLD FOOD LOGISTICS ORGANIZATION LIBRARY*, 1500 King St, Ste 201, 22314. SAN 325-9080. Tel: 703-373-4300. FAX: 703-373-4301. E-mail: email@wflo.org. Web Site: www.wflo.org. *Dir,* Sara L Martin; Staff 1 (Non-MLS 1)
Founded 1943
Library Holdings: Bk Vols 1,000; Per Subs 50
Function: For res purposes

AMELIA

S　AMELIA COUNTY HISTORICAL SOCIETY LIBRARY*, Jackson Bldg, 16501 Church St, 23002. (Mail add: PO Box 113, 23002-0113), SAN 370-9817. Tel: 804-561-3180. *Pres,* Gary Austin; *Librn,* Marilyn Onorati
Library Holdings: Bk Vols 13,000; Per Subs 30
Open Mon, Wed & Fri 10-4

P　JAMES L HAMNER PUBLIC LIBRARY*, 16351 Dunn St, 23002. SAN 322-6611. Tel: 804-561-4559. FAX: 804-561-3174. E-mail: hamner_librarian@tds.net. Web Site: www.ameliacova.us/library.html. *Dir,* Dora Rowe; *Asst Librn,* Susan Gianniny; *Asst Librn,* Sylvia Gray; Staff 5 (MLS 1, Non-MLS 4)
Founded 1972. Pop 9,200; Circ 21,793
Library Holdings: Bk Titles 30,000; Bk Vols 32,000; Per Subs 30
Partic in Virginia Library & Network Information
Open Mon-Wed 10-8, Thurs & Fri 10-6, Sat 10-2

AMHERST

P　AMHERST COUNTY PUBLIC LIBRARY*, 382 S Main St, 24521. (Mail add: PO Box 370, 24521-0370), SAN 362-6946. Tel: 434-946-9488. FAX: 434-946-9348. Web Site: www.acpl.us. *Dir,* Steve Preston; *Head, Pub Serv,* Judy Spencer; *Cat,* Rita Hand; *Ref Serv,* Judy Maxham; *Youth Serv,* Maxine Gasser; Staff 21 (MLS 2, Non-MLS 19)
Founded 1964. Pop 32,000
Special Collections: Virginia History Coll
Automation Activity & Vendor Info: (Cataloging) Horizon; (Circulation) Horizon
Partic in Lyrasis
Open Mon-Wed, Fri & Sat 9-5:30, Tues & Thurs 9-8
Friends of the Library Group
Branches: 1
MADISON HEIGHTS BRANCH, 200 River James Shopping Ctr, Madison Heights, 24572. (Mail add: PO Box 540, Madison Heights, 24572-0540), SAN 362-6970. Tel: 434-846-8171. FAX: 434-846-3102. *Dir,* Steve Preston
Open Mon & Wed 9-9, Tues & Thurs-Sat 9-5:30
Friends of the Library Group

ANNANDALE

J　NORTHERN VIRGINIA COMMUNITY COLLEGE LIBRARIES, 8333 Little River Tpk, 22003. SAN 362-7004. Tel: 703-323-3096. Interlibrary Loan Service Tel: 703-323-3472. FAX: 703-323-3831. Web Site: www.nvcc.edu/library. *Coordr, Tech Serv,* Sandra J Beeson; E-mail: sbeeson@nvcc.edu; Staff 25 (MLS 22, Non-MLS 3)
Founded 1965. Enrl 30,387; Fac 1,037; Highest Degree: Associate
Jul 2011-Jun 2012 Income State $5,743,524. Mats Exp $1,295,848, Books $746,987, Per/Ser (Incl. Access Fees) $79,287, AV Mat $96,924, Electronic Ref Mat (Incl. Access Fees) $372,650. Sal $3,801,519 (Prof $1,708,753)
Library Holdings: Audiobooks 1,651; AV Mats 25,917; Bks on Deafness & Sign Lang 80; CDs 3,243; DVDs 20,506; e-books 32,963; e-journals 30,758; Electronic Media & Resources 147; High Interest/Low Vocabulary Bk Vols 2,752; Music Scores 114; Bk Titles 176,037; Bk Vols 258,878; Per Subs 644
Automation Activity & Vendor Info: (Cataloging) Ex Libris Group; (Circulation) Ex Libris Group; (ILL) OCLC FirstSearch; (OPAC) Ex Libris Group; (Serials) SerialsSolutions
Database Vendor: ABC-CLIO, Agricola, Alexander Street Press, ALLDATA Online, American Chemical Society, American Mathematical Society, American Psychological Association (APA), Annual Reviews, ARTstor, Baker & Taylor, BioOne, Bowker, Cambridge Scientific Abstracts, CQ Press, CredoReference, EBSCOhost, Elsevier, Ex Libris

Group, Factiva.com, Facts on File, Gale Cengage Learning, JSTOR, LearningExpress, LexisNexis, Mergent Online, Nature Publishing Group, netLibrary, OCLC FirstSearch, OCLC WorldCat, Overdrive, Inc, OVID Technologies, Oxford Online, Project MUSE, ProQuest, Safari Books Online, ScienceDirect, SerialsSolutions, STAT!Ref (Teton Data Systems), Westlaw, Wiley InterScience
Wireless access
Partic in Lyrasis; Virtual Library of Virginia (VIVA)
Friends of the Library Group
Departmental Libraries:
ALEXANDRIA CAMPUS, Bisdorf Bldg, Rm 232, 3001 N Beauregard St, Alexandria, 22311, SAN 362-7039. Tel: 703-845-6231. Reference Tel: 703-845-6456. FAX: 703-845-6205. Web Site: www.nvcc.edu/alexandria/library.
Special Collections: ESL Resources
ANNANDALE CAMPUS, 8333 Little River Turnpike, Godwin 300, 22003. Circulation Tel: 703-323-3128. Reference Tel: 703-323-3410. FAX: 703-323-3005. Web Site: www.nvcc.edu/annandale/library. *Assoc Dean, Tech & Learning Res,* Jami L Bryan; Tel: 703-323-3867, E-mail: jbryan@nvcc.edu; Staff 14 (MLS 5, Non-MLS 9)
Fac 5; Highest Degree: Associate
Special Collections: Women's History (Judy Mann DiStefano Coll)
Subject Interests: Admin of justice, Electronic tech, Fire sci, Hotel, Mkt, Restaurant, Tourism, Travel
Open Mon-Thurs 7:45am-9:30pm, Fri 7:45-5, Sat 9-4
EXTENDED LEARNING INSTITUTE, 8000 Forbes Pl, Springfield, 22151. Tel: 703-764-5083. E-mail: ELILearn@nvcc.edu. *ELI Librn/Distance Educ Librn,* Natalie Clewell; E-mail: nclewell@nvcc.edu
LOUDOUN CAMPUS, 1000 Harry Flood Byrd Hwy, Sterling, 20164-8699, SAN 362-7098. Tel: 703-450-2567. FAX: 703-404-7374. *Dean, Learning & Tech Res,* Dr Randolph Fournier; Tel: 703-948-7798; *Librn,* Dana Beltran; Tel: 703-450-2641, E-mail: dbeltran@nvcc.edu; *Librn,* Tamatha Lambert; Tel: 703-450-2642, E-mail: tlambert@nvcc.edu
Subject Interests: Communications, Hort, Interior design, Veterinary tech
Open Mon-Thurs 8am-9pm, Fri 8-4, Sat 9-1
MANASSAS CAMPUS, Colgan Hall, Rm 129, 6901 Sudley Rd, Manassas, 20109-2399, SAN 362-7128. Tel: 703-257-6640. FAX: 703-368-1069. TDD: 703-368-3748. Web Site: www.nvcc.edu/manassas/library. *Dir, Learning & Tech Res,* Dr Tom Hergert; Tel: 703-530-8259, E-mail: thergert@nvcc.edu; *Librn,* Chrystie Greges; Tel: 703-257-6639, E-mail: cgreges@nvcc.edu; *Librn,* Nathan Mueller; Tel: 703-257-6564, E-mail: nmueller@nvcc.edu; Staff 5 (MLS 2, Non-MLS 3)
Open Mon-Thurs (Winter) 8am-9pm, Fri 8-5, Sat 9-1; Mon-Thurs (Summer) 8:30am-9pm, Fri 8:30-5
MEDIA PROCESSING SERVICES, 8333 Little River Tpk, 22003-3796. Tel: 703-323-3294. Interlibrary Loan Service Tel: 703-323-3472. FAX: 703-323-3831. Web Site: www.nvcc.edu/about-nova/directories–offices/administrative-offices/media/index.html. *Head, Cat,* Virginia Graves; Tel: 703-323-3095, E-mail: vagraves@nvcc.edu; *Coordr,* Sandra J Beeson; Tel: 703-323-3096, E-mail: sbeeson@nvcc.edu; *Cat,* Lee Davis; Tel: 703-323-3348, E-mail: ldavis@nvcc.edu

JM　MEDICAL EDUCATION CAMPUS, 6699 Springfield Center Dr, Rm 341, Springfield, 22150. Tel: 703-822-6684. Interlibrary Loan Service Tel: 703-822-6681. Administration Tel: 703-822-6679. Automation Services Tel: 703-822-2099. FAX: 703-822-6612. Web Site: www.nvcc.edu/medical/meclibrary. *Dean, Learning & Tech Res,* Ruth Stanton; E-mail: rstanton@nvcc.edu; *Instrul Serv Librn,* Emily Robinson; Tel: 703-822-9052, E-mail: erobinson@nvcc.edu; *Med Librn,* Carol Lunce; E-mail: clunce@nvcc.edu; *Tech Librn,* Elizabeth DeAngelo; E-mail: edeangelo@nvcc.edu; *Coll Mgr, Libr Spec II,* Andrea McElhenny, Andrea; Tel: 703-822-6683, E-mail: amcelhenny@nvcc.edu; *Acq, Libr Spec II,* Barbara Carroll; Tel: 703-822-0014, E-mail: bcarroll@nvcc.edu; *Libr Spec II, Tech Serv,* Position Currently Open.
Subject Specialists: *Health sci,* Carol Lunce; *Soc work,* Elizabeth DeAngelo; Staff 6 (MLS 3, Non-MLS 3)
Founded 2003. Enrl 3,364; Fac 67; Highest Degree: Associate
Function: Audio & video playback equip for onsite use, CD-ROM, Computer training, Distance learning, E-Reserves, Electronic databases & coll, For res purposes, Handicapped accessible, Health sci info serv, ILL available, Learning ctr, Mail & tel request accepted, Newsp ref libr, Online info literacy tutorials on the web & in blackboard, Online ref, Online searches, Orientations, Outside serv via phone, mail, e-mail & web, Photocopying/Printing, Ref serv available, Telephone ref, VHS videos, Wheelchair accessible
Partic in Virtual Library of Virginia
Open Mon-Thurs 8am-9pm, Fri 8:30-5, Sat 9-1
Restriction: Open to pub for ref & circ; with some limitations, Open to students, fac & staff

J　WOODBRIDGE LIBRARY, 15200 Neabsco Mills Rd, Seefeldt 427, Woodbridge, 22191, SAN 362-7152. Tel: 703-878-5727. Information Services Tel: 703-878-5733. FAX: 703-670-8433. E-mail: wolibrary@nvcc.edu. Web Site: www.nvcc.edu/woodbridge/library. *Librn, Libr Supvr,* Kerry J Cotter; Tel: 703-878-5785, E-mail: kcotter@nvcc.edu; *Ref & Instruction Librn,* Anne Beebe; E-mail:

abeebe@nvcc.edu; *Ref & Instruction Librn,* Russell Grooms; E-mail: rgrooms@nvcc.edu; *Circ Desk Supvr/Stack Mgr,* Karen Williams; E-mail: kcenon@nvcc.edu; *Libr Spec,* Taslima Khatun; E-mail: tkhatun@nvcc.edu; *Libr Spec,* Stephanie Sharkey; E-mail: ssharkey@nvcc.edu

Library Holdings: AV Mats 5,500; Bk Vols 40,000; Per Subs 250
Automation Activity & Vendor Info: (Cataloging) Ex Libris Group; (Circulation) Ex Libris Group; (OPAC) Ex Libris Group
Open Mon-Thurs 8am-9pm, Fri 8-5, Sat 9-3:30; Mon-Thurs (Summer) 8am-9pm, Fri 8-5

APPOMATTOX

P   J ROBERT JAMERSON MEMORIAL LIBRARY*, 106 Main St, 24522. (Mail add: PO Box 789, 24522-0789). Tel: 434-352-5340. FAX: 434-352-0933. E-mail: jrjml@yahoo.com. Web Site: www.jrjml.org. *Dir,* Barry Morris; *Tech Serv,* Martha Charte
Pop 13,705
Library Holdings: AV Mats 1,195; Bk Titles 34,908; Per Subs 57; Talking Bks 2,740
Automation Activity & Vendor Info: (Circulation) TLC (The Library Corporation)
Open Mon, Wed & Fri 9:30-5, Tues & Thurs 9:30-8, Sat 9:30-1
Friends of the Library Group

S   NATIONAL PARK SERVICE*, Appomattox Court House Library, PO Box 218, 24522-0218. SAN 370-2774. Tel: 434-352-8987. FAX: 434-352-8330. Web Site: www.nps.gov/apco/. *In Charge,* Patrick A Schroeder
Library Holdings: Bk Vols 2,500
Open Mon-Thurs 8:30-5

ARLINGTON

S   AIR FORCE ASSOCIATION*, Research Library, 1501 Lee Hwy, 22209-1198. SAN 302-5500. Tel: 703-247-5800. Toll Free Tel: 800-727-3337. FAX: 703-247-5855. *Media Res Ed,* Chequita Wood
Founded 1956
Library Holdings: Bk Vols 5,000
Subject Interests: Mil hist
Restriction: Not a lending libr

S   AMERICAN PSYCHIATRIC ASSOCIATION*, Melvin Sabshin Library & Archives, 1000 Wilson Blvd, Ste 1825, 22209-3901. SAN 302-5748. Tel: 703-907-8648. FAX: 703-907-1084. E-mail: library@psych.org. Web Site: www.psych.org/library. *Dir,* Gary McMillan; Staff 2.5 (MLS 1, Non-MLS 1.5)
Founded 1961
Library Holdings: CDs 100; DVDs 10; e-books 20; e-journals 200; Bk Titles 5,000; Bk Vols 8,000; Per Subs 300; Videos 400
Special Collections: American Psychiatric Association Archives; Kenworthy Video Library; Test & Measurements Coll; Tourney Rare Books Coll. Oral History
Subject Interests: Forensic psychiat & ethics, Hist of psychiat, Psychiat
Automation Activity & Vendor Info: (OPAC) Inmagic, Inc.
Database Vendor: PubMed
Function: Archival coll, Doc delivery serv, Electronic databases & coll, Health sci info serv, ILL available, Mail & tel request accepted, Mail loans to mem, Online searches, Ref & res, Video lending libr
Partic in Asn of Mental Health Librns (AMHL); Mid-Atlantic Chapter-Med Libr Asn; National Network of Libraries of Medicine
Restriction: Authorized scholars by appt, Staff & mem only

C   ARGOSY UNIVERSITY*, Washington DC Library, 1550 Wilson Blvd, Ste 600, 22209. Reference Tel: 703-526-5819. Administration Tel: 703-526-5802. FAX: 703-243-5682. E-mail: auwlibrary@argosyu.edu. Web Site: www.argosy.edu/audclibrary.htm. *Dir, Libr Serv,* Walter Ruf; *Librn,* Raisa Ionin; Staff 2 (MLS 2)
Founded 1994. Enrl 800; Highest Degree: Doctorate
Library Holdings: Bk Vols 2,500; Per Subs 500
Function: Audio & video playback equip for onsite use, ILL available, Ref & res
Open Mon-Fri 8:30am-9:30pm
Restriction: Non-circulating to the pub, Open to students, fac & staff

P   ARLINGTON COUNTY DEPARTMENT OF LIBRARIES, Arlington Public Library, 1015 N Quincy St, 22201. SAN 362-7217. Tel: 703-228-3346, 703-228-3348. Interlibrary Loan Service Tel: 703-228-5991. FAX: 703-228-3354. TDD: 703-228-4611, 703-228-6320. E-mail: libraries@arlingtonva.us. Web Site: www.arlingtonva.us/departments/libraries/librariesmain.aspx. *Dir,* Diane Kresh; *Div Chief, Br Serv,* Susan McCarthy; Tel: 703-228-6334, E-mail: smccar@arlingtonva.us; *Div Chief, Cent Serv,* Margaret Brown; Tel: 703-228-5952, E-mail: mbrown3@arlingtonva.us; *Div Chief, Mat & Tech Mgt,* Anne Gable; Tel: 703-228-5981, E-mail: agable@arlingtonva.us;

Virtual Libr Mgr, Stacia Aho; Tel: 703-228-5968, E-mail: aho@arlingtonva.us; *Coll Develop,* Patricia Alter; Tel: 703-228-5985, E-mail: palter@arlingtonva.us; *ILL,* Lynn Kristianson; E-mail: interlibraryloan@arlingtonva.us
Founded 1937. Pop 209,300; Circ 3,162,135
Jul 2011-Jun 2012 Income (Main Library and Branch(s)) $11,407,803, State $168,893, County $10,549,893, Locally Generated Income $604,017, Other $85,000. Mats Exp $1,262,520. Sal $11,407,803
Library Holdings: Bk Titles 632,517
Special Collections: Children's Illustrators (Francis & Elizabeth Booth Silver Coll); State & Local Data (Virginiana Coll). Oral History
Automation Activity & Vendor Info: (Cataloging) Innovative Interfaces, Inc - Millenium; (Circulation) Innovative Interfaces, Inc - Millenium; (OPAC) Innovative Interfaces, Inc - Millenium
Wireless access
Special Services for the Deaf - Staff with knowledge of sign lang; TDD equip
Special Services for the Blind - Bks on cassette; Computer with voice synthesizer for visually impaired persons; Home delivery serv; Talking bks; Talking bks & player equip
Open Mon-Thurs 9-9, Fri & Sat 9-5, Sun 1-9
Friends of the Library Group
Branches: 10
AURORA HILLS, 735 18th St S, 22202, SAN 362-7241. Tel: 703-228-5715. FAX: 703-892-9378. *Br Mgr,* Sarah Daviau; Tel: 703-228-5716, E-mail: sdaviau@arlingtonva.us
Founded 1973. Circ 158,793
Library Holdings: Bk Vols 44,657
Open Mon & Thurs 10-9, Tues & Wed 1-9, Fri & Sat 10-5
Friends of the Library Group
CENTRAL LIBRARY, 1015 N Quincy St, 22201-4661, SAN 362-7276. Tel: 703-228-5990. Circulation Tel: 703-228-5940. Reference Tel: 703-228-5958. FAX: 703-228-5962. Administration FAX: 703-228-7720. TDD: 703-228-6320. E-mail: libraries@arlingtonva.us. Web Site: www.arlingtonva.us. *Div Chief,* Margaret Brown; Tel: 703-228-5952, E-mail: mbrown3@arlingtonva.us
Founded 1961. Circ 1,155,178
Library Holdings: Bk Vols 330,504
Special Collections: Children's Illustrators; College (Career Coll); Talking Books; Vietnamese Coll
Subject Interests: Art, Local hist, Spanish, Virginiana
Open Mon-Thurs 9am-10pm, Fri & Sat 9-5, Sun 1-9
Friends of the Library Group
CHERRYDALE, 2190 N Military Rd, 22207, SAN 362-7306. Tel: 703-228-6330. FAX: 703-516-4568. *Br Mgr,* Julia Karell; Tel: 703-228-6331, E-mail: jkarell@arlingtonva.us
Library Holdings: Bk Vols 37,378
Open Mon & Thurs 10-9, Tues & Wed 1-9, Fri & Sat 10-5
Friends of the Library Group
COLUMBIA PIKE, 816 S Walter Reed Dr, 22204, SAN 362-7330. Tel: 703-228-5710. FAX: 703-228-5559. *Br Mgr,* Robert Spencer; Tel: 703-228-5711, E-mail: rspenc@arlingtonva.us
Library Holdings: Bk Vols 61,193
Special Collections: Vocational Coll
Open Mon & Wed 10-9, Tues & Sun 1-9, Thurs 10-6, Fri & Sat 10-5
Friends of the Library Group
GLENCARLYN, 300 S Kensington St, 22204, SAN 362-7365. Tel: 703-228-6548. FAX: 703-824-3529. *Br Mgr,* Steven Carr; Tel: 703-228-6547, E-mail: scarr2@arlingtonva.us
Circ 74,917
Library Holdings: Bk Titles 30,817
Open Mon & Thurs 10-9, Tues & Wed 1-9, Fri & Sat 10-5
Friends of the Library Group
HOMEBOUND SERVICE, 1015 N Quincy St, 22201, SAN 329-6296. Tel: 703-228-5960. FAX: 703-228-5998. *Librn,* Suchitra Maitra
Open Mon-Fri 9-5
Friends of the Library Group
PLAZA LIBRARY, 2100 Clarendon Blvd, Lobby, 22201, SAN 329-627X. Tel: 703-228-3352. FAX: 703-228-3354. *Br Mgr,* Michelle Robinson; Tel: 703-228-3708, E-mail: mrobinson@arlingtonva.us
Founded 1989
Library Holdings: Bk Titles 4,646
Function: Computers for patron use, Copy machines, Electronic databases & coll, Govt ref serv, ILL available, Mail & tel request accepted, Notary serv, Online cat, Orientations, Pub access computers, Ref serv in person, Wheelchair accessible
Open Mon-Fri 8-5
Friends of the Library Group
SHIRLINGTON, 4200 Campbell Ave, 22206, SAN 362-739X. Tel: 703-228-6545. FAX: 703-379-6728. *Br Mgr,* Kimberly Knight; Tel: 703-228-6546, E-mail: kbknight@arlingtonva.us
Circ 262,341
Library Holdings: Bk Titles 60,108
Open Mon & Wed 10-9, Tues & Sun 1-9, Thurs 10-6, Fri & Sat 10-5
Friends of the Library Group

VIRTUAL BRANCH, 1015 N Quincy St, 22201. Tel: 703-228-5968.
Automation Activity & Vendor Info: (OPAC) Innovative Interfaces, Inc
- Millenium
Friends of the Library Group
WESTOVER, 1644 N McKinley Rd, 22205, SAN 362-742X. Tel:
703-228-5260. FAX: 703-534-1240. *Br Mgr,* Shari Henry; Tel:
703-228-5261, E-mail: shenry@arlingtonva.us
Circ 301,121
Library Holdings: Bk Titles 58,744
Open Mon & Wed 10-9, Tues 1-9, Thurs 10-6, Fri & Sat 10-5
Friends of the Library Group

S   R L BANKS & ASSOCIATES INC LIBRARY*, 2107 Wilson Blvd, Ste
750, 22201. SAN 373-3475. Tel: 703-276-7522. FAX: 703-276-7732.
E-mail: transport@rlbadc.com. Web Site: www.rlbadc.com. *Librn,* Lorraine
Hart
Library Holdings: Bk Vols 2,000; Per Subs 100
Subject Interests: Eng
Open Mon-Fri 8:45-5:15

S   BUREAU OF NATIONAL AFFAIRS, INC LIBRARY, Bloomberg BNA
Library, (Formerly BNA Inc Library), 1801 S Bell St, Rm 3200, 22202.
SAN 326-9256. Tel: 703-341-3303. Interlibrary Loan Service Tel:
703-341-3317. FAX: 703-341-1636. E-mail: library@bna.com. Web Site:
www.bna.com. *Dir,* Marilyn M Bromley; Tel: 703-341-3307, E-mail:
mbromley@bna.com; *Ref Librn,* Lan Choi; Tel: 703-341-3313, E-mail:
lchoi@bna.com; *Ref Librn,* Catherine A Kitchell; Tel: 703-341-3311,
E-mail: ckitchell@bna.com; *Cat,* Matthew Newton; Tel: 703-341-3308,
E-mail: mnewton@bna.com; *ILL,* Robert Te Tan; Tel: 703-341-3315,
E-mail: rtetan@bna.com; *Tech Serv,* Clare Bailey; Tel: 703-341-3306,
E-mail: cbailey@bna.com; *Libr Tech,* Joe Manley; Tel: 703-341-3312,
E-mail: jmanley@bna.com. Subject Specialists: *Competitive intelligence,*
Marilyn M Bromley; Staff 8 (MLS 6, Non-MLS 2)
Library Holdings: Bk Vols 20,000; Per Subs 900
Special Collections: BNA Publications, non-circulating; State Regulatory
Codes
Subject Interests: Employment, Environ, Healthcare, Human res, Labor,
Law, Tax
Automation Activity & Vendor Info: (Acquisitions) SirsiDynix;
(Cataloging) SirsiDynix; (Circulation) SirsiDynix; (OPAC) SirsiDynix;
(Serials) SirsiDynix
Database Vendor: Bloomberg, Bowker, Carroll Publishing, Dialog,
EBSCOhost, Factiva.com, Gale Cengage Learning, HeinOnline, Hoovers,
LexisNexis, OCLC WorldCat, Plunkett Research, Ltd, SirsiDynix, Westlaw
Wireless access
Function: ILL available
Publications: BNA's Directory of State & Federal Courts, Judges & Clerks
(Annually)

S   CONSUMER ELECTRONICS ASSOCIATION, CEA Research Library,
1919 S Eads St, 22202. SAN 328-1418. Tel: 703-907-7763. E-mail:
info@ce.org. Web Site:
www.ce.org/Research/Products-Services/Research-Library.aspx. *Sr Res
Librn,* Richard Kowalski; *Sr Res Librn,* Katherine Rutkowski; *Mgr,* Angela
Titone; Staff 3 (MLS 3)
Founded 1984
Library Holdings: Bk Vols 1,000; Per Subs 90
Special Collections: Electronic Industries Market
Database Vendor: Factiva.com, Hoovers, LexisNexis
Wireless access
Function: Res performed for a fee
Restriction: Lending to staff only, Mem only

S   COUNCIL ON FOUNDATIONS*, Resource Center, 2121 Crystal Dr, Ste
700, 22202. SAN 375-1031. Tel: 703-879-0600. FAX: 703-879-0800. Web
Site: www.cof.org. *Mgr,* Monte D Edwards; Staff 1 (MLS 1)
Founded 1985
Library Holdings: Bk Titles 3,000; Bk Vols 4,500; Per Subs 15
Subject Interests: Philanthropy
Automation Activity & Vendor Info: (Acquisitions) Inmagic, Inc.;
(Cataloging) Inmagic, Inc.; (Circulation) Inmagic, Inc.; (OPAC) Inmagic,
Inc.; (Serials) Inmagic, Inc.
Function: For res purposes
Partic in Consortium of Foundation Libraries
Restriction: Mem only, Open by appt only

C   DEVRY UNIVERSITY*, Metro DC Library, 2450 Crystal Dr, 22202.
Circulation Tel: 703-414-4068. Toll Free Tel: 866-338-7932. FAX:
703-414-4104. Web Site: www.crys.devry.edu/library.html. *Dir, Libr Serv,*
Jane Carvajal; Tel: 703-414-4095, E-mail: jcarvajal@devry.edu
Library Holdings: e-books 11,000; Electronic Media & Resources 42,000;
Bk Vols 11,500; Per Subs 70

Automation Activity & Vendor Info: (Acquisitions) Ex Libris Group;
(Cataloging) Ex Libris Group; (Circulation) Ex Libris Group; (OPAC) Ex
Libris Group
Database Vendor: netLibrary, ProQuest
Partic in Amigos Library Services, Inc; Georgia Online Database; Illinois
Library & Information Network; SEFLIN - Southeast Florida Library
Information Network, Inc
Open Mon-Wed 8:30am-9pm, Thurs 8:30am-10:30pm, Fri 10-6, Sat 9-1

R   FIRST PRESBYTERIAN CHURCH OF ARLINGTON LIBRARY*, 601 N
Vermont St, 22203. SAN 317-2171. Tel: 703-527-4766. FAX:
703-527-2262. E-mail: fp.church@verizon.net. Web Site:
www.fpcarlington.org. *In Charge,* Ricci Waters
Library Holdings: Bk Vols 2,334
Special Collections: History of First Presbyterian Church
Subject Interests: Christian spirituality, Hebrew Bible, Hist Christianity,
New Testament
Open Mon-Fri 8-4, Sun 8-1

S   FOOD MARKETING INSTITUTE*, Information Service, 2345 Crystal Dr,
Ste 800, 22202. SAN 371-0300. Tel: 202-452-8444. FAX: 202-429-4519.
E-mail: fmi@fmi.org. Web Site: www.fmi.org. *In Charge,* Susan C
Wilkinson; Staff 1 (MLS 1)
Founded 1948
Library Holdings: Bk Vols 3,000; Per Subs 100
Database Vendor: Factiva.com
Wireless access

S   INSURANCE INSTITUTE FOR HIGHWAY SAFETY LIBRARY*, 1005
N Glebe Rd, Ste 800, 22201. SAN 302-6760. Tel: 703-247-1500. FAX:
703-247-1678. Web Site: www.iihs.org. *Librn,* Ellen Sanders; Tel:
703-247-1554, E-mail: esanders@iihs.org; Staff 1 (Non-MLS 1)
Founded 1959
Library Holdings: Bk Titles 20,000; Per Subs 150
Special Collections: US Dept of Transportation Regulatory Docket
Materials
Subject Interests: Transportation
Automation Activity & Vendor Info: (Circulation) Inmagic, Inc.
Database Vendor: LexisNexis
Function: Res libr
Restriction: Circulates for staff only, Co libr, Internal circ only, Not a
lending libr, Not open to pub

C   MARYMOUNT UNIVERSITY*, Emerson G Reinsch Library, 2807 N
Glebe Rd, 22207-4299. SAN 317-2198. Tel: 703-284-1533. Interlibrary
Loan Service Tel: 703-284-1641. Reference Tel: 703-284-1649.
Administration Tel: 703-284-1673. FAX: 703-284-1685. Administration
FAX: 703-526-6820. E-mail: library@marymount.edu. Web Site:
www.marymount.edu/lls. *Dean,* Zary Mostashari, PhD; E-mail:
zary.mostashari@marymount.edu; Staff 13 (MLS 11, Non-MLS 2)
Founded 1950. Enrl 3,609; Fac 350; Highest Degree: Doctorate
Jul 2006-Jun 2007 Income $2,279,016. Mats Exp $770,726, Books
$283,747, Per/Ser (Incl. Access Fees) $200,481, AV Mat $33,152,
Electronic Ref Mat (Incl. Access Fees) $242,200, Presv $11,146. Sal
$1,359,267 (Prof $732,939)
Library Holdings: AV Mats 2,295; e-books 295; e-journals 3,990;
Electronic Media & Resources 108; Bk Titles 155,058; Bk Vols 203,883;
Per Subs 31,082
Special Collections: Economics (Gertrude Hoyt Memorial Coll); John T &
Agnes J Gomatos Reading Room; Wilhelmina Boldt Reading Room
Subject Interests: Educ, Fashion design, Graphic design, Human resource
mgt, Interior design, Nursing, Philosophy, Psychol
Automation Activity & Vendor Info: (Acquisitions) Ex Libris Group;
(Cataloging) Ex Libris Group; (Circulation) Ex Libris Group; (Course
Reserve) Ex Libris Group; (ILL) Ex Libris Group; (OPAC) Ex Libris
Group; (Serials) Ex Libris Group
Wireless access
Publications: Connection
Partic in OCLC Online Computer Library Center, Inc; Virginia Independent
College & University Library Association; Virtual Library of Virginia;
Washington Research Library Consortium

L   WALTER T MCCARTHY LAW LIBRARY*, Court House, 1425 N
Courthouse Rd, Ste 1700, 22201. SAN 317-2120. Tel: 703-228-7005. FAX:
703-228-7360. *Dir,* Patricia Petroccione; E-mail:
ppetroccione@arlingtonva.us; Staff 1 (MLS 1)
Founded 1977
Library Holdings: Bk Vols 22,000; Per Subs 12
Special Collections: All Regional & Federal Reporters; Digests; Form
Books; Old Codes & Acts of Assembly, Virginia; Virginia Treatises
Open Mon-Fri 8:30-4

S   NATIONAL ASSOCIATION OF CHAIN DRUG STORES, 1776 Wilson Blvd, Ste 200, 22209. SAN 375-3131. Tel: 703-549-3001. E-mail: library@nacds.org. *Dir, Knowledge Mgt & Communications,* Betsy Hageman; Staff 1 (MLS 1)
Restriction: Not open to pub

S   NATIONAL GROCERS ASSOCIATION LIBRARY*, 1005 N Glebe Rd, Ste 250, 22201-5758. SAN 327-3539. Tel: 703-516-0700. FAX: 703-516-0115. E-mail: info@nationalgrocers.org. Web Site: www.nationalgrocers.org.
Library Holdings: Bk Vols 1,500
Open Mon-Fri 8:30-5

G   NUCLEAR WASTE TECHNICAL REVIEW BOARD LIBRARY*, 2300 Clarendon Blvd, Ste 1300, 22201. SAN 374-5937. Tel: 703-235-4473. Interlibrary Loan Service Tel: 703-235-4486. FAX: 703-235-4495. *Dir of Admin Serv Div,* Joyce Dory; E-mail: dory@nwtrb.gov; Staff 1 (MLS 1)
Founded 1990
Library Holdings: Bk Vols 6,000; Per Subs 30
Special Collections: Board Meeting Transcripts
Subject Interests: Radioactive waste disposal, Radioactive waste transportation
Automation Activity & Vendor Info: (Cataloging) EOS International; (ILL) OCLC; (OPAC) EOS International; (Serials) EOS International
Function: ILL available, Res libr
Partic in OCLC Online Computer Library Center, Inc
Restriction: Employees only

S   RAND CORP*, RAND-Washington Library, 1200 S Hayes St, 22202. SAN 302-7589. Tel: 703-413-1100, Ext 5330. FAX: 703-414-4729. Web Site: rand.org. *Libr Mgr,* Gail Kouril; E-mail: gkouril@rand.org; *Ref Serv,* Alison Labonte; Staff 2 (MLS 2)
Founded 1950
Library Holdings: Bk Titles 10,000; Per Subs 250
Subject Interests: Econ, Nat defense, Soc sci
Automation Activity & Vendor Info: (Acquisitions) SirsiDynix; (Cataloging) SirsiDynix; (Circulation) SirsiDynix; (OPAC) SirsiDynix; (Serials) SirsiDynix
Database Vendor: EBSCOhost, Gale Cengage Learning, HeinOnline, IEEE (Institute of Electrical & Electronics Engineers), Jane's, JSTOR, Medline, OCLC WorldCat, ProQuest, PubMed, Sage, SerialsSolutions, SirsiDynix, Springer-Verlag, TDNet, Thomson - Web of Science, Wiley InterScience
Partic in Interlibrary Users Association; OCLC Eastern
Restriction: Staff use only

S   UNITED STATES DEPARTMENT OF JUSTICE*, Drug Enforcement Administration Library, 700 Army Navy Dr, 22202. (Mail add: 8701 Morrissette Dr, Springfield, 22152), SAN 302-6396. Tel: 202-307-8932. FAX: 202-307-8939. E-mail: dea.library@usdoj.gov. *Librn,* RoseMary Russo; E-mail: rose.m.russo@usdoj.gov; Staff 3 (MLS 2, Non-MLS 1)
Founded 1960
Library Holdings: Bk Vols 15,000; Per Subs 147
Subject Interests: Drug abuse, Drug laws
Automation Activity & Vendor Info: (OPAC) Horizon
Publications: Acquisition List (Monthly)

GL   UNITED STATES DEPARTMENT OF THE INTERIOR*, Office of Hearings & Appeals Library, 801 N Quincy St, 22203. SAN 317-2260. Tel: 703-235-3804. FAX: 703-235-9014. *Librn,* Theodore Richardson
Founded 1970
Library Holdings: Bk Vols 20,000
Special Collections: Congressional Record, vol 115-1969 to vol 121-1975, micro; Federal Register, 1936-1973, micro, 1973-present, print
Subject Interests: Environ studies, Fed law, Indian probate, Pub lands, Surface mining
Open Mon-Fri 9-5:30
Restriction: Ref only

M   VIRGINIA HOSPITAL CENTER*, Medical Library, 1701 N George Mason Dr, 22205. SAN 327-3571. Tel: 703-558-6524. FAX: 703-558-5343. *Librn,* Kathy Butler; Staff 1 (MLS 1)
Library Holdings: Bk Titles 700; Per Subs 200
Subject Interests: Allied health, Med, Nursing
Database Vendor: OVID Technologies
Restriction: Open to staff only

ASHBURN

S   NATIONAL RECREATION & PARK ASSOCIATION*, Joseph Lee Memorial Library, 22377 Belmont Ridge Rd, 20148. SAN 370-6915. Tel: 703-858-2151, 703-858-2192. FAX: 703-858-0794. Web Site: www.nrpa.org. *Coordr,* Amy Kapp; E-mail: akapp@nrpa.org
Founded 1989

Library Holdings: Bk Titles 5,000
Special Collections: American Institute of Park Executives Coll; American Park Secrets Coll; National Conference on State Parks Coll; National Recreation Association Coll; Playground Association of America Coll
Publications: Thesaurus of Park Recreation & Leisure Service Terms
Open Mon-Fri 8:30-4:45
Restriction: Non-circulating

ASHLAND

C   RANDOLPH-MACON COLLEGE*, McGraw-Page Library, 204 Henry St, 23005. (Mail add: PO Box 5005, 23005-5505), SAN 317-2309. Tel: 804-752-7257. Interlibrary Loan Service Tel: 804-752-3219. FAX: 804-752-3135. Web Site: library.rmc.edu. *Dir,* Dr Virginia E Young; Tel: 804-752-7256, E-mail: gyoung@rmc.edu; Staff 5 (MLS 4, Non-MLS 1)
Founded 1830. Enrl 1,131; Fac 88; Highest Degree: Bachelor
Library Holdings: Microforms 341,771; Bk Vols 196,299; Per Subs 5,657; Videos 4,935
Special Collections: 18th Century European Culture (Casanova & Goudar Coll); Henry Miller Coll; Intellectual History of the Colonial South Coll; Southern History Coll; Virginia Methodism Coll
Automation Activity & Vendor Info: (Acquisitions) SirsiDynix; (Cataloging) SirsiDynix; (Circulation) SirsiDynix; (Course Reserve) SirsiDynix; (ILL) SirsiDynix; (OPAC) SirsiDynix; (Serials) SirsiDynix
Partic in Lyrasis; OCLC Online Computer Library Center, Inc; Richmond Academic Library Consortium; Virginia Independent College & University Library Association

BASSETT

  BASSETT HISTORICAL CENTER*, 3964 Fairystone Park Hwy, 24055. Tel: 276-629-9191. FAX: 276-629-9840. E-mail: historical@brrl.lib.va.us. Web Site: www.bassetthistoricalcenter.com. *Dir,* Pat Ross; *Asst Dir,* Anne Copeland
Founded 1939
Library Holdings: CDs 141; Microforms 477; Bk Vols 19,000; Per Subs 248; Videos 49
Subject Interests: Genealogy, Local hist
Wireless access
Open Mon, Wed & Thurs 10-6, Tues Noon-6, Fri & Sat 10-2
Friends of the Library Group

BEAUMONT

S   BEAUMONT JUVENILE CORRECTIONAL CENTER*, DCE Library, PO Box 8, 23014-0008. SAN 371-8220. Tel: 804-556-7221. FAX: 804-556-7238. *Librn,* Kevin Murray
Library Holdings: Bk Titles 3,500; Bk Vols 4,000; Per Subs 35

BEDFORD

P   BEDFORD PUBLIC LIBRARY SYSTEM*, 321 N Bridge St, 24523-1924. SAN 317-2317. Tel: 540-586-8911. Circulation Tel: 540-586-8911, Ext 2100. Reference Tel: 540-586-8911, Ext 2101. FAX: 540-586-8875. Web Site: www.bplsonline.org. *Dir,* Peggy Bias; Tel: 540-586-8911, Ext 1112, E-mail: director@bplsonline.org; *Libr Serv Librn,* Bernadette Brennan; Tel: 540-586-8911, Ext 2115, E-mail: lslibrarian@bplsonline.org; *Youth Serv Coordr,* Jenifer Golston; Tel: 540-586-8911, Ext 2108, E-mail: yslibrarian@bplsonline.org; *ILL,* Sharon Amstutz; Tel: 540-586-8911, Ext 2113, E-mail: ill@bplsonline.org; *Tech Serv,* Jenny Novalis; Tel: 540-586-8911, Ext 1114, E-mail: techlibrarian@bplsonline.org; Staff 17 (MLS 4, Non-MLS 13)
Founded 1900. Pop 67,800; Circ 471,896
Library Holdings: AV Mats 18,691; Bk Vols 199,186; Per Subs 157
Special Collections: World War II
Subject Interests: Local hist
Automation Activity & Vendor Info: (Acquisitions) TLC (The Library Corporation); (Cataloging) TLC (The Library Corporation); (Circulation) TLC (The Library Corporation); (OPAC) TLC (The Library Corporation)
Database Vendor: Gale Cengage Learning, OCLC FirstSearch
Wireless access
Function: Adult bk club, Art exhibits, Audio & video playback equip for onsite use, Bks on cassette, Bks on CD, Children's prog, Computer training, Computers for patron use, Digital talking bks, Holiday prog, Homebound delivery serv, ILL available, Large print keyboards, Music CDs, Online cat, Photocopying/Printing, Prog for children & young adult, Pub access computers, Story hour, Summer reading prog, Tax forms, Teen prog, Wheelchair accessible
Partic in Lynchburg Area Library Cooperative; Lyrasis
Open Mon, Wed, Fri & Sat 9-5:30, Tues & Thurs 9-8, Sun (Sept-May) 1:30-5:30
Friends of the Library Group

Branches: 5

BIG ISLAND LIBRARY, 1111 Schooldays Rd, Big Island, 24526. Tel:
434-299-5604. FAX: 434-299-6151. Web Site:
www.bplsonline.org/bi/index.html. *Br Mgr,* Carolyn Morehead
Open Mon, Thurs & Fri 10-5, Tues 10-7, Sat 9-12

FOREST LIBRARY, 15583 Forest Rd, Forest, 24551. Tel: 434-525-1817.
Web Site: www.bplsonline.org/fo/index.html. *Br Mgr,* Kate Forsyth
Open Mon, Tues & Thurs 9-9, Wed, Fri & Sat 9-5:30, Sun 1:30-5:30

MONETA/SMITH MOUNTAIN LAKE LIBRARY, 13641 Moneta Rd,
Moneta, 24121. Tel: 540-297-6474. FAX: 540-297-6450. Web Site:
www.bplsonline.org/mo/index.html. *Br Mgr,* Teresa Cook
Open Mon, Wed, Fri & Sat 9-5:30, Tues & Thurs 9-8

MONTVALE LIBRARY, 11575 W Lynchburg-Salem Tpk, Montvale,
24122. (Mail add: PO Box 429, Montvale, 24122). Tel: 540-947-2200.
FAX: 540-947-0300. Web Site: www.bplsonline.org/mv/index.html. *Br
Mgr,* Donna Hackman
Open Mon & Fri 9-5, Tues & Thurs 12-8, Sat 10-1
Friends of the Library Group

STEWARTSVILLE LIBRARY, 45 Cascade Dr, Vinton, 24179. Tel:
540-890-4530. FAX: 434-525-9232. Web Site:
www.bplsonline.org/sv/index.html. *Br Mgr,* Nicole Sheppard
Open Mon & Fri 10-5, Tues & Thurs 10-7, Sat 9-Noon

BERRYVILLE

SR   HOLY CROSS ABBEY LIBRARY*, 901 Cool Spring Lane, 22611-2700.
SAN 317-2325. Tel: 540-955-1425. FAX: 540-955-1356. *Librn,* Fr Vincent
Collins; Staff 1 (MLS 1)
Founded 1950
Library Holdings: Bk Vols 25,000; Per Subs 59
Automation Activity & Vendor Info: (Cataloging) TLC (The Library
Corporation)
Restriction: Open by appt only

BIG STONE GAP

J   MOUNTAIN EMPIRE COMMUNITY COLLEGE*, Wampler Library,
3441 Mountain Empire Rd, 24219. SAN 317-2333. Tel: 276-523-7468.
FAX: 276-523-8220. Web Site: www.mecc.edu/library. *Dir of Libr Serv,*
Terence Michael Gilley; Tel: 276-523-2400, Ext 304, E-mail:
mgilley@me.vccs.edu; *Circ,* Jamie Clark; Tel: 276-523-2400, Ext 305,
E-mail: jclark@me.vccs.edu; *Tech Serv,* Rickey Lawson; Tel:
276-523-2400, Ext 267, E-mail: rlawson@me.vccs.edu; Staff 3 (MLS 1,
Non-MLS 2)
Founded 1972. Enrl 2,136; Fac 86; Highest Degree: Associate
Jul 2009-Jun 2010. Mats Exp $57,575, Books $18,077, Per/Ser (Incl.
Access Fees) $12,497, Micro $683, AV Equip $1,970, AV Mat $11,532,
Electronic Ref Mat (Incl. Access Fees) $12,816
Library Holdings: AV Mats 2,195; e-books 21,333; e-journals 20,000;
Electronic Media & Resources 7,916; Microforms 8,000; Bk Titles 40,006;
Bk Vols 44,136; Per Subs 113
Subject Interests: Criminal justice, Nursing, Respiratory therapy
Automation Activity & Vendor Info: (Acquisitions) Ex Libris Group;
(Cataloging) Ex Libris Group; (Circulation) Ex Libris Group; (OPAC) Ex
Libris Group
Function: Archival coll, Art exhibits, Audiobks via web, Computers for
patron use, Copy machines, Electronic databases & coll, Exhibits, Fax serv,
Handicapped accessible, ILL available, Online cat, Online info literacy
tutorials on the web & in blackboard, Online ref, OverDrive digital audio
bks, Photocopying/Printing
Partic in SouthWest Information Network Group (SWING); Virginia
Commun Coll Syst; Virtual Library of Virginia
Open Mon-Thurs 8am-8:30pm, Fri 8-4:30, Sat 10-2

BLACKSBURG

C   VIRGINIA POLYTECHNIC INSTITUTE & STATE UNIVERSITY
LIBRARIES*, Newman Library, Drill Field Dr, 24062-9001. (Mail add:
PO Box 90001, 24062-9001), SAN 362-7454. Tel: 540-231-6170.
Circulation Tel: 540-231-6340. Reference Tel: 540-231-9232. FAX:
540-231-3946. Web Site: www.lib.vt.edu. *Dean of Libr,* Eileen
Hitchingham; Tel: 540-231-5595, E-mail: hitch@vt.edu; *Assoc Dean, Head,
Circ,* Donald Kenney; E-mail: kenney@vt.edu; *Dir, Digital Libr Prog,* Gail
MacMillan; Tel: 540-231-5252, E-mail: gailmac@vt.edu; *Dir of Libr Res &
Instrul Serv,* Lesley Moyo; Tel: 540-231-2708, E-mail: moyo@vt.edu; *Dir,
Spec Coll,* Aaron Purcell; Tel: 540-231-9672; *Dir, Tech Serv & Coll Mgt,*
Leslie O'Brien; Tel: 540-231-4945, E-mail: lobrien@vt.edu; *Br Head,*
Victoria Kok; Tel: 540-231-6610, E-mail: vkok@vt.edu; *Br Head,* Patrick
Tomlin; Tel: 540-231-9272, E-mail: tomlin@vt.edu; *Coordr, Northern Va
Center Libr & Res & Instrul Serv,* Debbie Cash; Tel: 703-538-8341,
E-mail: dcash@vt.edu; *Syst Coordr,* Curtis Carr; Tel: 540-231-6617,
E-mail: ccarr@vt.edu; Zhiwu Xie. Subject Specialists: *Veterinary med,*
Victoria Kok; Staff 128 (MLS 38, Non-MLS 90)
Founded 1872. Enrl 27,887; Fac 1,371; Highest Degree: Doctorate
Jul 2008-Jun 2009 Income (Main and Other College/University Libraries)
$14,177,077. Mats Exp $7,207,785, Books $1,204,203, Per/Ser (Incl.

Access Fees) $5,335,345, Other Print Mats $615,565, Presv $52,672. Sal
$5,824,624 (Prof $2,447,058)
Library Holdings: CDs 12,975; DVDs 18,185; e-books 192,483;
e-journals 9,302; Microforms 6,329,176; Bk Titles 1,466,099; Bk Vols
2,385,815; Per Subs 22,765
Special Collections: American & British Literature, 1880-1940 (Dayton
Kohler Coll); Appalachian History & Folk Culture, incl Patrick County
Oral History Coll & Blue Ridge Parkway Folk Life Oral History Coll;
Archives of American Aerospace Exploration incl Papers of Melvin N
Gough, Samuel Herrick, Christopher C Kraft, Jr & John T Parsons;
Heraldry (Harry D Temple Coll); History of Technology Coll; History of
Women's Involvement in Architecture (International Archive of Women in
Architecture, incl Papers of Hanna Schroeder, Verena Dietrich, Ilse Koci &
Elise Sundt; Late 19th Century Children's Literature (John H Barnes
Coll); Ornithology (Harold H Bailey Coll); Railroad History Coll;
Sherwood Anderson Coll; Southwest Virginia History
(Black-Kent-Apperson Family Papers, Preston Family Papers & J Hoge
Tyler Papers); Western Americana. State Document Depository; US
Document Depository
Subject Interests: Agr, Archit, Art, Behav sci, Biol, Eng, Humanities,
Phys sci, Soc sci
Automation Activity & Vendor Info: (Cataloging) Innovative Interfaces,
Inc; (Circulation) Innovative Interfaces, Inc; (OPAC) Innovative Interfaces,
Inc; (Serials) Innovative Interfaces, Inc
Database Vendor: Annual Reviews, BioOne, ebrary, EBSCOhost,
Factiva.com, Gale Cengage Learning, Gallup, H W Wilson, Hoovers, IEEE
(Institute of Electrical & Electronics Engineers), Ingenta, JSTOR, Knovel,
LexisNexis, Luna Imaging/Insight, Medline, Modern Language Association,
netLibrary, OCLC FirstSearch, OVID Technologies, Project MUSE,
ProQuest, PubMed, Safari Books Online, Sage, ScienceDirect,
SerialsSolutions, Springer-Verlag, TLC (The Library Corporation), Wiley,
Wiley InterScience, Wilson - Wilson Web
Wireless access
Publications: Off the Shelf
Partic in Consortium for Continuing Higher Educ in Northern Va; NASA
Libraries Information System-NASA Galaxie; National Network of
Libraries of Medicine; OCLC Online Computer Library Center, Inc; Virtual
Library of Virginia
Departmental Libraries:
ART & ARCHITECTURE, Cowgill Hall, 3rd Flr, 24062. Tel:
540-231-9271. Web Site: www.lib.vt.edu/services/branches/artarch. *Librn,*
Heather Gendron; Tel: 540-231-9272, E-mail: heball1@vt.edu
Library Holdings: Bk Vols 77,177
NORTHERN VIRGINIA RESOURCE CENTER, 7054 Haycock Rd, Falls
Church, 22043-2311, SAN 362-7543. Tel: 703-538-8340. FAX:
703-538-8342. E-mail: library@nvc.vt.edu. Web Site: www.lib.vt.edu/nvc.
Librn, Debbie Cash; E-mail: dcash@vt.edu
Library Holdings: Bk Vols 9,300
Open Mon-Thurs 11-10, Fri 11-7, Sat 9-5
CM   VETERINARY MEDICINE, Phase III Duck Pond Dr, 24061-0442. Tel:
540-231-6610. FAX: 540-231-7367. Web Site:
www.lib.vt.edu/services/branches/vetmed. *Librn,* Victoria T Kok; E-mail:
vkok@vt.edu
Library Holdings: Bk Vols 12,620
Partic in Virtual Library of Virginia
Open Mon-Thurs (Winter) 7:30am-11pm, Fri 7:30-6, Sat 9-6, Sun 11-11;
Mon-Thurs (Summer) 8-6, Fri 8-5, Sat 1-6

BLAND

S   BLAND CORRECTIONAL CENTER*, Department of Correctional
Education Library, 256 Bland Farm, 24315-9615. Tel: 276-688-3341, Ext
5162. *Librn,* Harmie E Wiley
Library Holdings: Bk Vols 12,000; Per Subs 40
Open Mon-Fri 1-8

BLUEFIELD

C   BLUEFIELD COLLEGE*, Easley Library, 3000 College Dr, 24605. SAN
317-235X. Tel: 276-326-4238. Reference Tel: 276-326-4269. FAX:
276-326-4288. E-mail: library@bluefield.edu. Web Site:
www.bluefield.edu/library/. *Dir,* Nora Lockett; Tel: 276-326-4237, E-mail:
nlockett@bluefield.edu; *Asst Dir,* Werner Lind; E-mail:
wlind@bluefield.edu; *Electronic Res Librn,* Lynne Bartlett; E-mail:
lbartlett@bluefield.edu; *Circ Supvr,* Tabitha Price; E-mail:
tprice@bluefield.edu; Staff 4 (MLS 3, Non-MLS 1)
Founded 1922. Enrl 700; Fac 46; Highest Degree: Bachelor
Library Holdings: Bk Titles 55,000; Bk Vols 56,000; Per Subs 250
Special Collections: McKenzie Memorial Religion Coll
Automation Activity & Vendor Info: (Acquisitions) Innovative Interfaces,
Inc; (Cataloging) Innovative Interfaces, Inc; (Circulation) Innovative
Interfaces, Inc; (Course Reserve) Innovative Interfaces, Inc; (ILL)
Innovative Interfaces, Inc; (Media Booking) Innovative Interfaces, Inc;
(OPAC) Innovative Interfaces, Inc; (Serials) Innovative Interfaces, Inc

Database Vendor: EBSCOhost, Gale Cengage Learning, LexisNexis, OCLC FirstSearch, OVID Technologies
Function: Ref serv available
Publications: Library Home Pages
Partic in Appalachian Libr Info Coop; Lyrasis; SouthWest Information Network Group (SWING); Virginia Independent College & University Library Association; Virtual Library of Virginia
Open Mon-Thurs 8am-10pm, Fri 8-4, Sat 10-3, Sun 2-10
Restriction: Circ limited

BOYCE

S   RAILWAY MAIL SERVICE LIBRARY, INC, 117 E Main St, 22620-9639. SAN 324-7996. Tel: 540-837-9090. Administration Tel: 202-268-4996. Web Site: www.railwaymailservicelibrary.org. *Curator, Pres,* Dr Frank R Scheer; E-mail: fscheer@railwaymailservicelibrary.org; *VPres, Gen Counsel & Secy of the Corp,* Stuart V Bradley, Jr; E-mail: stuartbradley@comcast.net; *VPres, Libr & Info Serv,* William J Keller; E-mail: gandwk@cybrzn.com; *Law Librn, Webmaster,* Nathan Simmons; *Web Coordr,* Mack Muir; Staff 5 (Non-MLS 5)
Founded 1951
Library Holdings: AV Mats 23; Bk Titles 1,600; Bk Vols 1,700
Special Collections: Chip Komoroske Railroad Book Coll; E B Bergman Schedule of Mall Routes Coll; E J Maloney Marking Device Coll; H E Rankin General Scheme Coll; J R Mundy Postal Lock Coll; L Cohen International Postal Insignia Coll; R R Schmidt Marking Device Coll
Subject Interests: En-route distribution, Postal markings, Transportation of mail
Wireless access
Function: Archival coll, For res purposes, ILL available, Photocopying/Printing, Res libr
Publications: The Catcher Pouch (Newsletter)
Open Sat 10-5
Restriction: Access at librarian's discretion, Closed stack, Non-circulating to the pub, Open by appt only, Open to employees & special libr, Open to fac, students & qualified researchers, Open to pub with supv only, Private libr, Pub use on premises, Restricted loan policy, Use of others with permission of librn
Friends of the Library Group

BOYDTON

P   SOUTHSIDE REGIONAL LIBRARY*, 316 Washington St, 23917. (Mail add: PO Box 10, 23917-0010), SAN 317-2376. Tel: 434-738-6580. FAX: 434-738-6070. Web Site: www.srlib.org. *Dir,* Leigh Lambert; E-mail: llambert@srlib.org; Staff 1 (MLS 1)
Founded 1944. Pop 45,400; Circ 176,676
Library Holdings: Bk Titles 69,688; Bk Vols 130,062; Per Subs 365; Talking Bks 3,245; Videos 1,542
Special Collections: Mecklenburg County Newspapers, late 1800s, micro
Subject Interests: Genealogy
Automation Activity & Vendor Info: (Cataloging) TLC (The Library Corporation); (Circulation) TLC (The Library Corporation); (OPAC) TLC (The Library Corporation)
Database Vendor: OCLC FirstSearch
Partic in Lyrasis
Open Mon 12-6, Tues-Fri 12-5, Sat 9-12
Friends of the Library Group
Branches: 5
R T ARNOLD PUBLIC, 110 E Danville St, South Hill, 23970, SAN 372-7076. Tel: 434-447-8162. FAX: 434-447-4050. *Br Supvr,* Gloria Taylor
Library Holdings: Bk Vols 25,000
Open Mon-Thurs 10-6, Fri 9-5, Sat 9-12
Friends of the Library Group
BUTLER MEMORIAL, 515 Marshall St, Chase City, 23924, SAN 372-7084. Tel: 434-372-4286. FAX: 434-372-0303. *Br Supvr,* Joyce Parcell-Greene
Library Holdings: Bk Vols 24,200
Open Mon, Wed & Fri 10-5, Tues & Thurs 10-8, Sat 10-1, Sun 2-5
Friends of the Library Group
CLARKSVILLE AREA PUBLIC LIBRARY, 914 Virginia Ave, Clarksville, 23927. (Mail add: PO Box 1146, Clarksville, 23927-1146), SAN 372-7092. Tel: 434-374-8692. FAX: 434-374-8200. *Br Supvr,* Eileen Barbieri
Library Holdings: Bk Vols 22,500
Open Mon, Wed & Thurs 10-8, Tues & Fri 10-5, Sat 10-2
Friends of the Library Group
RIPBERGER PUBLIC, 117 S Broad St, Kenbridge, 23944. (Mail add: PO Box 845, Kenbridge, 23944-0845), SAN 372-7106. Tel: 434-676-3456. FAX: 434-676-3211. *Br Supvr,* Roberta Rickers; Staff 7 (Non-MLS 7)
Library Holdings: CDs 113; DVDs 136; Bk Vols 36,000; Talking Bks 637; Videos 350

Special Collections: 16mm Film Coll; Genealogy Coll; Reader's Digest 1930s-present; United Methodist Women's List Coll. State Document Depository
Open Mon, Tues & Thurs 10-6, Fri 10-5, Sat 9-12
Friends of the Library Group
VICTORIA PUBLIC, 1417 Seventh St, Victoria, 23974. (Mail add: PO Drawer W, Victoria, 23974), SAN 372-7114. Tel: 434-696-3416. FAX: 434-696-2895. *Br Supvr,* Kathy Watson
Library Holdings: Bk Vols 20,000
Open Mon, Tues, Thurs & Fri 9-5, Sat 9-12
Friends of the Library Group

BRIDGEWATER

C   BRIDGEWATER COLLEGE*, Alexander Mack Memorial Library, 402 E College St, 22812. SAN 317-2384. Tel: 540-828-5411. Circulation Tel: 540-828-5413. Reference Tel: 540-828-5642. FAX: 540-828-5482. Web Site: www.bridgewater.edu/departments/library. *Dir,* Andrew Pearson; Tel: 540-828-5410, E-mail: apearson@bridgewater.edu; *Info Literacy Librn,* Cori Biddle; Tel: 540-828-5415, E-mail: cbiddle@bridgewater.edu; *Acq Tech,* Laura Adams; E-mail: ladams@bridgewater.edu; *Archivist, Curator,* Dale Harter; Tel: 540-828-5457, E-mail: dharter@bridgewater.edu; *Cat,* Carin Teets; Tel: 540-828-5414, E-mail: cteets@bridgewater.edu; *Circ,* Helen Semones; Tel: 540-515-3782, E-mail: hsemones@bridgewater.edu; *ILL, Ref Serv,* Robert Tout; Tel: 540-828-5672, E-mail: rtout@bridgewater.edu; *Tech Serv,* Roberta Wright; Tel: 540-828-5740, E-mail: rwright@bridgewater.edu; Staff 10 (MLS 6, Non-MLS 4)
Founded 1880. Enrl 1,520; Fac 96; Highest Degree: Bachelor
Library Holdings: AV Mats 6,708; CDs 1,161; DVDs 1,071; Electronic Media & Resources 88; Microforms 2,105; Bk Titles 133,573; Bk Vols 181,238; Per Subs 650; Videos 1,489
Special Collections: Church of the Brethren Material; Old Textbook Coll. US Document Depository
Subject Interests: Genealogy, Local hist
Automation Activity & Vendor Info: (Acquisitions) Innovative Interfaces, Inc; (Cataloging) Innovative Interfaces, Inc; (Circulation) Innovative Interfaces, Inc; (ILL) Innovative Interfaces, Inc; (OPAC) Innovative Interfaces, Inc; (Serials) Innovative Interfaces, Inc
Database Vendor: Annual Reviews, ARTstor, Bowker, EBSCOhost, Elsevier, Factiva.com, Facts on File, Foundation Center, Gale Cengage Learning, ISI Web of Knowledge, JSTOR, Medline, netLibrary, Newsbank, OCLC ArticleFirst, OCLC FirstSearch, OCLC WorldCat, OVID Technologies, Oxford Online, Project MUSE, ProQuest, SerialsSolutions, Standard & Poor's, Swets Information Services, ValueLine, Wiley InterScience, Wilson - Wilson Web
Wireless access
Function: Telephone ref
Partic in Lyrasis; OCLC Online Computer Library Center, Inc; Virtual Library of Virginia
Open Mon-Thurs (Winter) 7:45am-Midnight, Fri 7:45-5, Sat 9-5, Sun 3-11; Mon-Fri (Summer) 7:45-5

BRISTOL

P   BRISTOL PUBLIC LIBRARY, 701 Goode St, 24201-4199. SAN 362-7578. Tel: 276-645-8780. Circulation Tel: 276-821-6133. Interlibrary Loan Service Tel: 276-821-6135. Reference Tel: 276-645-8781, 276-821-6196. FAX: 276-669-5593. Administration FAX: 276-591-1606. E-mail: library@bristol-library.org. Web Site: www.bristol-library.org. *Dir,* Jud B Barry; Tel: 276-645-8782, E-mail: judbarry@bristol-library.org; *Digital Serv Librn,* Christian Trombetta; Tel: 276-645-8792, E-mail: ctrombetta@bristol-library.org; *YA Librn,* Pam Neal; Tel: 276-821-6192, E-mail: pneal@bristol-library.org; *Acq, Cat,* Deborah Moore; Tel: 276-821-6195, E-mail: dmoore@bristol-library.org; *Ch,* Michelle Page; Tel: 276-821-6193, E-mail: mpage@bristol-library.org; Staff 35 (MLS 4, Non-MLS 31)
Founded 1909. Pop 73,000; Circ 372,108
Jul 2011-Jun 2012 Income (Main Library and Branch(s)) $1,886,357, State $139,574, City $1,470,228, Federal $34,617, County $15,000, Locally Generated Income $206,142, Other $10,398, Other $10,398. Mats Exp $136,265, Books $83,948, Per/Ser (Incl. Access Fees) $11,829, AV Mat $32,243, Electronic Ref Mat (Incl. Access Fees) $8,245. Sal $1,186,045 (Prof $201,758)
Library Holdings: AV Mats 247; CDs 2,128; DVDs 6,463; Bk Titles 149,554; Bk Vols 152,607; Per Subs 204; Talking Bks 6,382; Videos 1,369
Subject Interests: Genealogy, Local hist, Tenn, Va
Automation Activity & Vendor Info: (Acquisitions) Innovative Interfaces, Inc; (Cataloging) Innovative Interfaces, Inc; (Circulation) Innovative Interfaces, Inc; (Serials) Innovative Interfaces, Inc
Wireless access
Mem of Holston River Regional Library
Partic in SouthWest Information Network Group (SWING)
Open Mon-Thurs 9-8, Fri & Sat 9-5, Sun 2-5
Friends of the Library Group

Branches: 1
AVOCA, 1550 Volunteer Pkwy, 37620-6000, SAN 362-7608. Tel:
423-968-9663. Circulation Tel: 423-652-7401. FAX: 276-645-8795. *Br
Mgr,* Susan Wolfe; E-mail: swolfe@bristol-library.org; Staff 3 (MLS 1,
Non-MLS 2)
Founded 1974
Library Holdings: Bk Titles 31,121; Bk Vols 31,436
Open Mon-Thurs 11-7, Fri 9-5, Sat 9-12
Friends of the Library Group

C   VIRGINIA INTERMONT COLLEGE*, J F Hicks Memorial Library, 1013
Moore St, 24201. SAN 317-2392. Tel: 276-466-7960. Web Site:
www.vic.edu/library/. *Dir, Libr Serv,* Jonathan Tallman; Tel: 276-466-7959,
E-mail: jtallman@vic.edu; *Circ,* Allison Linder; Tel: 276-466-7955, E-mail:
allisonlinder@vic.edu; *Ref,* William Howard; Tel: 276-466-7958, E-mail:
whoward@vic.edu; Staff 5 (MLS 3, Non-MLS 2)
Founded 1884. Enrl 950; Fac 67; Highest Degree: Bachelor
Library Holdings: e-books 27,594; Bk Vols 64,367; Per Subs 70
Subject Interests: Art, Behav sci, Educ, Horsemanship, Music, Soc sci
Automation Activity & Vendor Info: (OPAC) Innovative Interfaces, Inc
Function: AV serv, ILL available, Photocopying/Printing, Ref serv
available
Partic in Appalachian Col Asn; Holston Assoc Librs, Inc; Virginia
Independent College & University Library Association; Virtual Library of
Virginia
Restriction: Open to pub for ref & circ; with some limitations, Open to
students, fac & staff

BUENA VISTA

CR   SOUTHERN VIRGINIA UNIVERSITY*, Von Canon Library, One
University Hill Dr, 24416. SAN 317-2406. Tel: 540-261-8440. Reference
Tel: 540-261-4241. Administration Tel: 540-261-4234. FAX: 540-261-8496.
Web Site: www.svu.edu. *Dir, Libr Serv,* Christopher Richardson; E-mail:
christopher.richardson@svu.edu; *Asst Dir,* Julie Larsen; E-mail:
julie.larsen@svu.edu; Staff 3 (MLS 3, Non-MLS 2)
Founded 1900. Enrl 750; Fac 50; Highest Degree: Bachelor
Library Holdings: Bk Titles 95,000
Special Collections: Melville Coll; Orson Scott Card; The Church of Jesus
Christ of Latter-Day Saints (Mormon)
Automation Activity & Vendor Info: (Cataloging) Follett Software;
(Circulation) Follett Software; (OPAC) Follett Software
Database Vendor: EBSCOhost, Factiva.com, Gale Cengage Learning,
JSTOR, LexisNexis, OCLC FirstSearch, WT Cox
Wireless access
Function: Archival coll, Audio & video playback equip for onsite use, ILL
available, Online searches, Photocopying/Printing, Ref serv available, VHS
videos
Partic in Virginia Independent College & University Library Association;
Virtual Library of Virginia
Open Mon-Thurs (Fall & Spring) 7:30am-Midnight, Fri 7am-8pm, Sat
10-7; Mon-Fri (Summer) 8:30-5

CAPRON

S   DEERFIELD CORRECTIONAL CENTER*, DCE Library, 21360
Deerfield Dr, 23829. SAN 375-4979. Tel: 434-658-4368. FAX:
434-658-4371. *Librn,* Susan Gillette
Founded 1994
Library Holdings: Bk Titles 12,000; Bk Vols 15,000; Per Subs 30
Automation Activity & Vendor Info: (Circulation) Follett Software
Special Services for the Deaf - Bks on deafness & sign lang; High
interest/low vocabulary bks

CATAWBA

GM   CATAWBA HOSPITAL*, Professional Library, 5525 Catawba Hospital Dr,
24070. (Mail add: PO Box 200, 24070-0200), SAN 321-6004. Tel:
540-375-4300. FAX: 540-375-4348. *Dir, Libr Serv,* Melanie Ham
Founded 1978
Library Holdings: Bk Titles 420; Bk Vols 431; Per Subs 52
Restriction: Staff use only

CEDAR BLUFF

J   SOUTHWEST VIRGINIA COMMUNITY COLLEGE LIBRARY*, Russell
Hall, 599 Community College Rd, 24609. (Mail add: PO Box SVCC,
Richlands, 24641), SAN 317-3976. Tel: 276-964-7265. Interlibrary Loan
Service Tel: 276-964-7738. Information Services Tel: 276-964-7617. FAX:
276-964-7259. Web Site: www.sw.edu/library. *Dir,* Dr Robert Sutherland;
Coordr, Libr Serv, Teresa A Alley; E-mail: teresa.alley@sw.edu; *Ref Serv,*
Diane Phillips; E-mail: diane.phillips@sw.edu; Staff 3 (MLS 3)
Founded 1968. Enrl 2,856; Fac 162; Highest Degree: Associate
Library Holdings: AV Mats 1,592; Bks on Deafness & Sign Lang 25;
e-books 42,000; Bk Vols 43,000; Per Subs 156; Talking Bks 1,422

Automation Activity & Vendor Info: (Cataloging) Ex Libris Group;
(Circulation) Ex Libris Group; (ILL) OCLC; (OPAC) Ex Libris Group;
(Serials) Ex Libris Group
Partic in Virginia Commun Coll Syst; Virtual Library of Virginia
Open Mon-Thurs 7:45am-9pm, Fri 7:45-4:30, Sun 1-5

CHANTILLY

S   NORTHROP GRUMMAN IT-TASC*, TASC Information Resource Center,
4801 Stonecroft Blvd, 20151-3822. SAN 323-7753. Tel: 703-633-8300, Ext
4654. FAX: 703-449-7648. Web Site: www.ngc.com. *Libr Mgr,* Brock
Temanson; E-mail: brock.temanson@ngc.com; *Librn,* Barbara Fischer;
E-mail: barbara.fischer@ngc.com; *Librn,* Barta McCoy; E-mail:
barta.mccoy@ngc.com; Staff 4 (MLS 4)
Founded 1966
Library Holdings: Bk Titles 50,000; Per Subs 450
Automation Activity & Vendor Info: (OPAC) EOS International; (Serials)
EBSCO Online
Database Vendor: ACM (Association for Computing Machinery), Dialog,
EBSCOhost, IEEE (Institute of Electrical & Electronics Engineers), Jane's,
OCLC FirstSearch
Partic in Lyrasis
Restriction: Staff use only

CHARLOTTE COURT HOUSE

P   CHARLOTTE COUNTY LIBRARY*, 112-116 Legrande Ave, 23923.
(Mail add: PO Box 788, 23923-0788), SAN 317-2414. Tel: 434-542-5247.
E-mail: cclibrary@hovac.com. Web Site: www.cclibrary.net. *Librn,* Jim
Watkins; Staff 3 (Non-MLS 3)
Founded 1937. Circ 50,455
Library Holdings: Bk Vols 46,000; Per Subs 130
Partic in Lyrasis
Open Mon, Wed & Fri 9-5, Tues & Thurs 9-6, Sat 10-1
Friends of the Library Group
Branches: 3
KEYSVILLE BRANCH, 300 King St, Keysville, 23947. (Mail add: PO
Box 805, Keysville, 23947-0805), SAN 373-2940. Tel: 434-736-0083. *In
Charge,* Betty Baughan; Staff 2 (Non-MLS 2)
Library Holdings: AV Mats 600; Bk Vols 18,193; Per Subs 12
Open Mon-Fri 10-6, Sat 10-1
Friends of the Library Group
PHENIX BRANCH, Charlotte St, Phenix, 23959. (Mail add: PO Box 187,
Phenix, 23959-0187), SAN 373-2959. Tel: 434-542-4654. *Dir,* Jim
Watkins; *Librn,* Linda LaPratt; Staff 1 (Non-MLS 1)
Library Holdings: AV Mats 600; Bk Titles 2,500; Bk Vols 5,000; Per
Subs 12
Open Mon & Thurs 9-5, Sat 9-Noon
Friends of the Library Group
WYLLIESBURG COMMUNITY, Hwy 15, Wylliesburg, 23976, SAN
373-2932. Tel: 434-735-8812. *Librn,* Betty Baughan; Staff 2 (Non-MLS
2)
Library Holdings: AV Mats 600; Bk Vols 21,770; Per Subs 12
Open Mon, Wed & Fri 9-5, Sat 9-12
Friends of the Library Group

CHARLOTTESVILLE

P   JEFFERSON-MADISON REGIONAL LIBRARY*, Central Library, 201 E
Market St, 22902-5287. SAN 362-7632. Tel: 434-979-7151, Ext 206,
434-979-7151, Ext 207. FAX: 434-971-7035. TDD: 434-293-6848. E-mail:
central@jmrl.org. Web Site: www.jmrl.org. *Dir,* John Halliday; E-mail:
halliday@jmrl.org; *Asst Libr Dir,* Krista Farrell; Fax: 434-979-0278,
E-mail: kfarrell@jmrl.org; *Automation Syst Coordr, Tech Serv,* Phil
Williams; *Ch,* Nancy Cook; *Circ,* David Plunkett; *Coll Develop,* Andrea G
Williams; *Ref,* Joyce MacDonald; *YA Serv,* Timothy Carrier
Founded 1921. Pop 195,000; Circ 1,631,986
Library Holdings: Bk Vols 521,832
Special Collections: Charlottesville/Albemarle Historical Coll
Automation Activity & Vendor Info: (Cataloging) Innovative Interfaces,
Inc; (Circulation) Innovative Interfaces, Inc
Wireless access
Function: Fax serv, Wheelchair accessible
Publications: E-Newsletter; Friends Newsletter
Special Services for the Deaf - TDD equip
Open Mon-Thurs 9-9, Fri & Sat 9-5, Sun 1-5
Friends of the Library Group
Branches: 7
CROZET BRANCH, The Old C&O Sta, PO Box 430, Crozet, 22932-0430,
SAN 362-7667. Tel: 434-823-4050. FAX: 434-823-8399. E-mail:
crozet@jmrl.org. Web Site: www.jmrl.org. *Head of Libr,* Wendy Saz
Open Mon & Tues 1-9, Wed-Sat 9-5

GORDON AVE, 1500 Gordon Ave, 22903-1997, SAN 362-7691. Tel: 434-296-5544. FAX: 434-295-8737. E-mail: gordon@jmrl.org. *Br Mgr,* Meredith Dickens
Open Mon 9-9, Tues 9-6, Wed 12-9, Thurs 10-6, Fri & Sat 10-5
Friends of the Library Group

GREENE COUNTY, 222 Main St, Standardsville, 22973, SAN 362-7721. Tel: 434-985-5227. FAX: 434-985-3315. E-mail: greene@jmrl.org. Web Site: www.jmrl.org. *Head of Libr,* Virginia Reese
Open Mon 1-8, Tues & Thurs 10-6, Fri 1-5, Sat 9-2
Friends of the Library Group

LOUISA COUNTY, 881 Davis Hwy, Mineral, 23117, SAN 362-7756. Tel: 540-894-5853. FAX: 540-894-9810. E-mail: louisa@jmrl.org. Web Site: www.jmrl.org. *Head of Libr,* Gail Ott
Open Mon & Tues 12-7, Wed-Fri 10-5, Sat 9:30-4
Friends of the Library Group

NELSON MEMORIAL, 8521 Thomas Nelson Hwy, Lovingston, 22949. (Mail add: PO Box 321, Lovingston, 22949-0321), SAN 362-7780. Tel: 434-263-5904. FAX: 434-263-5988. E-mail: nelson@jmrl.org. Web Site: www.jmrl.org. *Br Mgr,* Tanith Knight
Open Mon & Tues 12-8, Wed & Thurs 10-5:30, Fri 10-5, Sat 10-2
Friends of the Library Group

NORTHSIDE, 300 Albemarle Sq, 22901-1466, SAN 371-9529. Tel: 434-973-7893. FAX: 434-973-5876. E-mail: northside@jmrl.org. Web Site: www.jmrl.org. *Head of Libr,* Lindsay Ideson
Open Mon & Tues 12-9, Wed & Thurs 10-6, Fri & Sat 10-5, Sun 1-5
Friends of the Library Group

SCOTTSVILLE BRANCH, 330 Bird St, Scottsville, 24590, SAN 362-7810. Tel: 434-286-3541. FAX: 434-286-4744. E-mail: scottsville@jmrl.org. Web Site: www.jmrl.org. *Head of Libr,* Noelle Funk
Open Mon & Tues 1-9, Wed-Sat 9-5
Friends of the Library Group
Bookmobiles: 1. Bk vols 26,980

S THOMAS JEFFERSON FOUNDATION INC*, Jefferson Library, 1329 Kenwood Farm Lane, 22902. (Mail add: PO Box 316, 22902), SAN 327-3512. Tel: 434-984-7540. Reference Tel: 434-984-7543. FAX: 434-984-7546. E-mail: library@monticello.org. Web Site: www.monticello.org/library/index.html. *Found Librn,* Jack Robertson; Tel: 434-984-7545, E-mail: jrobertson@monticello.org; *Assoc Found Librn, Tech Serv,* Endrina Tay; Tel: 434-984-7541, E-mail: etay@monticello.org; *Web Serv Librn,* Eric Johnson; Tel: 434-984-7540, E-mail: ejohnson@monticello.org; *Digital Serv,* Leah Stearns; Tel: 434-984-7550, E-mail: lstearns@monticello.org; *Ref,* Anna Louisa Berkes; Tel: 434-984-7544, E-mail: aberkes@monticello.org; Staff 6 (MLS 4, Non-MLS 2)
Founded 2002
Library Holdings: AV Mats 750; Microforms 1,500; Bk Titles 10,000; Bk Vols 12,500; Per Subs 43
Special Collections: 18th Century Paris (Howard C Rice Coll); Lewis & Clark Literature (Ron Laycock Coll)
Subject Interests: 18th Century Am life
Automation Activity & Vendor Info: (Cataloging) Ex Libris Group; (Circulation) Ex Libris Group; (ILL) OCLC; (OPAC) Ex Libris Group
Function: Ref serv available, Res libr, Web-catalog
Publications: New in Portal (weekly new acquisitions)
Partic in OCLC Eastern
Open Mon-Fri 9-5
Restriction: Open to pub upon request

S NATIONAL RADIO ASTRONOMY OBSERVATORY LIBRARY, 520 Edgemont Rd, 22903-2475. SAN 317-2430. Tel: 434-296-0254. FAX: 434-296-0278. E-mail: library@nrao.edu. Web Site: www.nrao.edu/library. *Head Librn,* Marsha Bishop; *Librn,* Lance Utley; Tel: 434-296-0215.
Subject Specialists: *Astronomy,* Lance Utley; Staff 2 (MLS 2)
Founded 1959
Library Holdings: CDs 422; DVDs 316; e-books 7,200; e-journals 2,295; Bk Titles 20,314; Bk Vols 25,014; Per Subs 1,100
Special Collections: ESO/SEC Atlas of the Southern Sky Coll; NRAO Memo Series (all NRAO internal publs); Observatory, Astronomical Institute & Government Agency Coll
Subject Interests: Astronomy, Astrophysics, Computers, Electronics, Eng, Physics
Automation Activity & Vendor Info: (Acquisitions) EOS International; (Cataloging) OCLC Connexion; (Circulation) EOS International; (ILL) OCLC FirstSearch; (OPAC) EOS International
Database Vendor: Annual Reviews, Dialog, IEEE (Institute of Electrical & Electronics Engineers), IOP, Knovel, Nature Publishing Group, OCLC FirstSearch, OCLC WorldCat, ScienceDirect, Springer-Verlag
Wireless access
Publications: New Titles List (Monthly); Publication Metrics (Annually); Publications List (Quarterly); Publications Statistics (Quarterly); Published Papers (Annual report)

Open Mon-Fri 8-5
Restriction: Authorized personnel only, Authorized scholars by appt, Badge access after hrs, Borrowing requests are handled by ILL, External users must contact libr, In-house use for visitors

J PIEDMONT VIRGINIA COMMUNITY COLLEGE*, Betty Sue Jessup Library, 501 College Dr, 22902. SAN 317-2449. Tel: 434-961-5308. Reference Tel: 434-961-5309. Administration Tel: 434-961-5304. FAX: 434-977-6842. E-mail: reference@pvcc.edu. Web Site: www.pvcc.edu/library. *Coordr, Libr Serv,* Linda Cahill; E-mail: lcahill@pvcc.edu; *Circ/Access Librn,* Crystal Newell; E-mail: cnewell@pvcc.edu; *Ref & Instruction Librn,* Judy Carey Nevin; E-mail: jcareynevin@pvcc.edu; Staff 4 (MLS 3, Non-MLS 1)
Founded 1972. Enrl 4,800; Fac 64; Highest Degree: Associate
Jul 2008-Jun 2009 Income $80,000. Mats Exp $80,000
Library Holdings: e-books 60,000; Bk Titles 36,950; Per Subs 156; Videos 1,849
Automation Activity & Vendor Info: (Acquisitions) Ex Libris Group; (Cataloging) Ex Libris Group; (Circulation) Ex Libris Group; (Course Reserve) Ex Libris Group; (ILL) OCLC; (OPAC) Ex Libris Group
Database Vendor: Annual Reviews, Bowker, Cambridge Scientific Abstracts, Cinahl Information Systems, CQ Press, EBSCOhost, Ex Libris Group, Factiva.com, Gale Cengage Learning, LearningExpress, netLibrary, OCLC FirstSearch, OCLC WorldCat, OVID Technologies, Project MUSE
Wireless access
Publications: Periodical Listing
Partic in Lyrasis; Virginia Commun Coll Syst; Virtual Library of Virginia
Open Mon-Thurs 8am-9:30pm, Fri 8-5, Sat (Fall & Spring) 9-12

S SPERRY MARINE*, Technical Library, 1070 Seminole Trail, 22901. SAN 329-1693. Tel: 434-974-2441. Toll Free Tel: 800-368-2010. FAX: 434-974-2259. *Librn,* Grace Y McKenzie; E-mail: grace_mckenzie@sperry.ngc.com; Staff 1 (Non-MLS 1)
Founded 1956
Library Holdings: Bk Titles 5,800; Per Subs 100
Subject Interests: Electronic eng
Open Mon-Fri 8-5

C UNIVERSITY OF VIRGINIA*, Alderman Library, PO Box 400114, 22904-4114. SAN 362-7845. Tel: 434-924-3021. Circulation Tel: 434-924-3017. Interlibrary Loan Service Tel: 434-924-3875. FAX: 434-924-1431. E-mail: library@virginia.edu. Web Site: www.lib.virginia.edu/. *Univ Librn,* Karin Wittenborg; E-mail: kw7g@virginia.edu; *Dep Univ Librn,* Diane Walker; E-mail: dpw@virginia.edu; *Assoc Univ Librn, Philanthropy & Dir of the Harrison Institute,* Hoke Perkins; E-mail: hp8n@virginia.edu; *Assoc Univ Librn, Production & Tech Serv,* Martha Sites; E-mail: mrs@virginia.edu; *Assoc Univ Librn, Pub Serv & Coll,* Carol Hunter; E-mail: crhsf@virginia.edu; Staff 231 (MLS 67, Non-MLS 164)
Founded 1819. Enrl 19,383; Fac 1,121; Highest Degree: Doctorate
Library Holdings: Bk Vols 2,538,294
Special Collections: State Document Depository; UN Document Depository; US Document Depository
Automation Activity & Vendor Info: (Acquisitions) SirsiDynix; (Cataloging) SirsiDynix; (Circulation) SirsiDynix; (Course Reserve) SirsiDynix; (ILL) OCLC ILLiad; (OPAC) SirsiDynix; (Serials) SirsiDynix
Wireless access
Partic in Lyrasis
Open Mon-Thurs 8am-Midnight, Fri 8am-9pm, Sat 9-8, Sun 10am-Midnight
Friends of the Library Group
Departmental Libraries:
ASTRONOMY, Charles L Brown Sci & Eng Library, 264 Astronomy Bldg, 530 McCormick Rd, 22904. (Mail add: PO Box 400330, 22904-4330), SAN 378-1445. Tel: 434-924-3921. FAX: 434-924-4337. Web Site: www.lib.virginia.edu/science/scilibs/astr-lib.html. *Dir,* Carla H Lee; Tel: 434-243-2390, E-mail: cl9eb@virginia.edu
Library Holdings: Bk Vols 13,796
Restriction: Restricted access
BIOLOGY-PSYCHOLOGY, 290-A Gilmer Hall, 485 McCormick Rd, 22903. (Mail add: PO Box 400400, 22904-4400), SAN 362-8086. Tel: 434-982-5260. FAX: 434-982-5626. Web Site: www.lib.virginia.edu/science/scilibs/bio-psych-lib.html. *Librn,* Sandi Dulaney; E-mail: sandi@virginia.edu
Library Holdings: Bk Vols 32,086
Open Mon-Thurs 9am-10pm, Fri 9-5, Sun 1-8
CHARLES L BROWN SCIENCE & ENGINEERING LIBRARY, Clark Hall, 22903-3188. (Mail add: PO Box 400124, 22904-4124), SAN 362-8213. Tel: 434-924-3628. Circulation Tel: 434-924-7209. FAX: 434-924-4338. E-mail: sciref@virginia.edu. Web Site: www2.lib.virginia.edu/brown/. *Dir,* Carla Lee; E-mail: cl9eb@virginia.edu; *Asst Dir,* Lynda White
Library Holdings: Bk Vols 224,225

CHEMISTRY, 259 Chemistry Bldg, 22903-2454. (Mail add: PO Box 400315, 22904-4315), SAN 362-790X. Tel: 434-924-3159. FAX: 434-924-4338. Web Site: www.lib.virginia.edu/brown/scilibs/chem-lib.html.
Library Holdings: Bk Vols 23,765
Open Mon-Fri 9-5

CLEMONS LIBRARY, PO Box 400710, 22904-4710. Information Services Tel: 434-924-3684. FAX: 434-924-7468. E-mail: clemons@virginia.edu. Web Site: www.lib.virginia.edu/clemons/home.html. *Head of Libr,* Donna Tolson; Tel: 434-982-2957, E-mail: dtolson@virginia.edu
Founded 1982
Library Holdings: Bk Vols 123,820
Subject Interests: Film, Media studies
Special Services for the Blind - Reader equip

DARDEN GRADUATE SCHOOL OF BUSINESS-CAMP LIBRARY, Student Services Bldg, 100 Darden Blvd, 22903. (Mail add: PO Box 6550, 22906-6500), SAN 362-8027. Tel: 434-924-7321. FAX: 434-924-3533. *Dir,* Karen King; E-mail: kmr3m@virginia.edu
Founded 1955. Enrl 500; Fac 85; Highest Degree: Doctorate
Library Holdings: Bk Vols 79,664
Subject Interests: Bus, Economics
Open Mon-Thurs 7:30am-11pm, Fri 7:30-6, Sat 9-6, Sun 11-11

EDUCATION, Ruffner Hall, 3rd Flr, 405 Emmet St S, 22904-4278. (Mail add: PO Box 400278, 22904-4278), SAN 362-7934. Tel: 434-924-7040. Reference Tel: 434-924-7039. FAX: 434-924-3886. E-mail: education_library@virginia.edu. Web Site: www.lib.virginia.edu/education. *Head of Libr,* Kay A Buchanan; Tel: 434-982-2664, E-mail: kaybuchanan@virginia.edu
Founded 1973
Library Holdings: Bk Vols 50,152
Special Collections: ERIC Microfiche Coll
Subject Interests: Educ
Open Mon-Thurs 8am-11pm, Fri 8-6, Sat 10-6, Sun 1-11

FISKE KIMBALL FINE ARTS, Bayly Dr, 22904-4131. (Mail add: PO Box 400131, 22904-4131), SAN 362-7993. Tel: 434-924-6938. FAX: 434-982-2678. E-mail: finearts@virginia.edu. Web Site: www.lib.virginia.edu/fine-arts/index.html. *Head Librn,* Lucie Stylianopoulos; E-mail: lws4n@virginia.edu
Library Holdings: Bk Vols 152,005
Subject Interests: Archit, Art, Drama, Urban planning
Open Mon-Thurs 8am-Midnight, Fri 8-6, Sat 10-6, Sun 1-Midnight

MATHEMATICS, 107 Kerchof Hall, 22903. (Mail add: PO Box 400140, 22904-4140), SAN 362-8116. Tel: 434-924-7806. FAX: 434-924-3104. Web Site: www.lib.virginia.edu/science/scilibs/math-lib.html.
Library Holdings: Bk Vols 33,792
Open Mon-Fri 1-5

CM CLAUDE MOORE HEALTH SCIENCES LIBRARY, Univ Va Health System, 1300 Jefferson Park Ave, 22908. (Mail add: PO Box 800722, 22908-0722), SAN 362-8140. Tel: 434-924-5444. Interlibrary Loan Service Tel: 434-924-0058. Reference Tel: 434-924-5591. Administration Tel: 434-924-5464. FAX: 434-924-0379. Administration FAX: 434-982-4238. Information Services FAX: 434-243-6928. Web Site: www.healthsystem.virginia.edu/internet/library. *Dir,* Gretchen Arnold; E-mail: gvn8r@virginia.edu
Founded 1911. Enrl 1,436; Fac 1,256; Highest Degree: Doctorate
Library Holdings: Bk Vols 134,292
Special Collections: American Lung Association of Virginia Archives; Kerr L White Health Care Coll; Philip S Hench Walter Reed/Yellow Fever Coll
Subject Interests: Behav sci, Med, Med hist, Natural sci, Nursing, Nursing hist, Soc sci
Automation Activity & Vendor Info: (Acquisitions) SirsiDynix; (Cataloging) SirsiDynix; (Circulation) SirsiDynix; (ILL) OCLC; (OPAC) SirsiDynix; (Serials) SirsiDynix
Database Vendor: OVID Technologies
Partic in Association of Southeastern Research Libraries; Lyrasis; National Network of Libraries of Medicine Southeastern Atlantic Region; OCLC Online Computer Library Center, Inc
Publications: The Claude Moore Health Sciences Library Annual Report; The Claude Moore Health Sciences Library Inside Information
Open Mon-Thurs 7:30am-Midnight, Fri 7:30-7, Sat 9-7, Sun Noon-Midnight

CL ARTHUR J MORRIS LAW LIBRARY, 580 Massie Rd, 22903-1789, SAN 362-8051. Tel: 434-924-3384. Circulation Tel: 434-924-3519. Interlibrary Loan Service Tel: 434-924-3511. Reference Tel: 434-924-7465. FAX: 434-982-2232. E-mail: lawlibref@virginia.edu. Web Site: www.law.virginia.edu/library. *Dir,* Taylor Fitchett; Tel: 434-924-7725, Fax: 434-924-7239; *Head, Ref, Res & Instruction,* Kent Olson; Tel: 434-924-4734, E-mail: kco4f@virginia.edu; *Access Serv Librn,* Cathy Palombi; E-mail: ccp7m@virginia.edu; *Bus Res Librn,* Jon Ashley; Tel: 434-924-4730, E-mail: jaa6c@virginia.edu; *Communications & Publ Librn,* Micheal Klepper; Tel: 434-924-3495, E-mail: mtk@virginia.edu; *Digital Coll Librn,* Loren Moulds; Tel: 434-924-3877, E-mail: moulds@virginia.edu; *Intl & Foreign Law Librn,* Xinh Luu; Tel: 434-924-3970, E-mail: xtl5d@virginia.edu; *Res/Emerging Tech Librn,*

Amy Wharton; Tel: 434-924-1816, E-mail: aaw7mh@virginia.edu; *Res Librn,* Leslie Ashbrook; Tel: 434-243-2493, E-mail: la3z@virginia.edu; *Res Librn,* Ben Doherty; Tel: 434-924-7726, E-mail: bad6b@virginia.edu; *Res Librn,* Kristin Glover; Tel: 434-243-2494, E-mail: klg3n@virginia.edu; *Res Librn,* John Roper; Tel: 434-924-4327, E-mail: jhr8v virginia.edu; *Ser Librn,* Kip Gobin; Tel: 434-924-3745, E-mail: krg@virginia.edu; *Syst Librn,* Joe Wynne; Tel: 434-924-4736, E-mail: jjw2w@virginia.edu; Staff 14 (MLS 11, Non-MLS 3)
Enrl 1,106; Fac 79; Highest Degree: Doctorate
Library Holdings: Bk Vols 873,981
Special Collections: US Document Depository
Partic in Lyrasis; OCLC Online Computer Library Center, Inc; Virtual Library of Virginia
Open Mon-Sun 8am-Midnight

MUSIC, Old Cabell Hall, 22904-4175. (Mail add: PO Box 400175, 22904-4175), SAN 362-8175. Tel: 434-924-7041. FAX: 434-924-6033. E-mail: musiclib@virginia.edu. Web Site: www.lib.virginia.edu/MusicLib/index.html. *Dir,* Erin Mayhood; Tel: 434-924-7017, E-mail: elm8s@virginia.edu
Founded 1977. Fac 10; Highest Degree: Doctorate
Library Holdings: Bk Vols 72,275
Open Mon-Thurs 8am-11pm, Fri 8-6, Sat 10-6, Sun 1-11

PHYSICS, 323 Physics Bldg, 22903-2458. (Mail add: PO Box 400714, 22904-4714), SAN 362-8205. Tel: 434-924-6589. Web Site: www.lib.virginia.edu/science/scilibs/phys-lib.html. *Librn,* Vicky Ingram
Library Holdings: Bk Vols 32,623
Open Mon-Fri 9-5

ALBERT & SHIRLEY SMALL SPECIAL COLLECTIONS LIBRARY, PO Box 400113, 22904-4110. Tel: 434-243-1776. FAX: 434-924-4968. Web Site: www.lib.virginia.edu/small/. *Dir,* Nichole Bouche
Library Holdings: Bk Vols 291,930
Open Mon-Thurs 9-9, Fri & Sat 9-5

G VIRGINIA DIVISION OF GEOLOGY & MINERAL RESOURCES LIBRARY*, 900 Natural Resources Dr, Ste 500, 22903-2982. SAN 317-2481. Tel: 434-951-6341. FAX: 434-951-6366. Web Site: www.mme.state.va.us.
Library Holdings: Bk Vols 1,200
Subject Interests: Forestry, Geol, Mineral res

S VIRGINIA TRANSPORTATION RESEARCH COUNCIL LIBRARY*, 530 Edgemont Rd, 22903. SAN 376-1940. Tel: 434-293-1902. FAX: 434-293-4196. E-mail: Library.Circulation@VDOT.Virginia.gov. Web Site: vtrc.virginiadot.org. *Librn,* Ken Winter; Tel: 434-293-1959, E-mail: ken.winter@vdot.virginia.gov
Library Holdings: Bk Vols 32,000; Per Subs 87
Special Collections: Virginia Road & Transportation History
Function: Res libr
Open Mon-Fri 8-5
Restriction: Non-circulating

CHATHAM

P PITTSYLVANIA COUNTY PUBLIC LIBRARY*, 24 Military Dr, 24531. SAN 362-823X. Tel: 434-432-3271. FAX: 434-432-1405. E-mail: info@pcplib.org. Web Site: www.pcplib.org. *Dir,* Diane S Adkins; E-mail: diane.adkins@pcplib.org; *Head, Coll & Acq,* Laverne Campbell; Tel: 434-685-1285, Fax: 434-685-3347, E-mail: laverne.campbell@pcplib.org; *Syst Librn,* David Kahler; E-mail: david.kahler@pcplib.org; Staff 18 (MLS 1, Non-MLS 17)
Founded 1913. Pop 61,745; Circ 320,549
Library Holdings: Audiobooks 2,447; CDs 2,112; DVDs 7,022; e-books 27,660; Electronic Media & Resources 22; Microforms 13; Bk Vols 111,106; Per Subs 212; Talking Bks 2,114
Automation Activity & Vendor Info: (Cataloging) TLC (The Library Corporation); (Circulation) TLC (The Library Corporation); (OPAC) TLC (The Library Corporation)
Database Vendor: Gale Cengage Learning, netLibrary, OCLC FirstSearch, ProQuest
Wireless access
Function: Adult bk club, Bks on CD, Children's prog, Computers for patron use, Copy machines, Electronic databases & coll, Exhibits, Fax serv, Free DVD rentals, Home delivery & serv to Sr ctr & nursing homes, ILL available, Music CDs, Online cat, Photocopying/Printing, Prog for children & young adult, Pub access computers, Senior computer classes, Story hour, Summer reading prog, Tax forms, Teen prog, VHS videos
Open Mon-Thurs 9-8, Fri 9-5, Sat 10-12
Friends of the Library Group
Branches: 3
BROSVILLE CASCADE, 11948 Martinsville Hwy, Danville, 24541, SAN 321-9232. Tel: 434-685-1285. FAX: 434-685-3347. *Br Mgr,* LaVerne Campbell; E-mail: laverne.campbell@pcplib.org; Staff 3 (Non-MLS 3)
Founded 1992

Automation Activity & Vendor Info: (Circulation) TLC (The Library Corporation)

Friends of the Library Group

GRETNA BRANCH LIBRARY, 207 Coffey St, Gretna, 24557. Tel: 434-656-2579. FAX: 434-656-9030. *Br Mgr,* Adrian Badgett; E-mail: adrian.badgett@pcplib.org; Staff 3 (Non-MLS 3)

MT HERMON BRANCH LIBRARY, 2725 Franklin Tpk, Ste J, Danville, 24540. Tel: 434-835-0326. FAX: 434-835-0321. *Br Mgr,* Christine Schrauth; E-mail: christine.schrauth@pcplib.org

Open Mon, Wed & Fri 10-6, Tues & Thurs 2-8, Sat 10-2

Bookmobiles: 1. Outreach Mgr, Myrna Herndon

CHESAPEAKE

P   CHESAPEAKE PUBLIC LIBRARY*, 298 Cedar Rd, 23322-5512. SAN 362-8299. Tel: 757-410-7101, 757-410-7104. Circulation Tel: 757-410-7156. Interlibrary Loan Service Tel: 757-926-5754. Reference Tel: 757-410-7147. Automation Services Tel: 757-410-7170. FAX: 757-410-7112. Circulation FAX: 757-410-7159. Interlibrary Loan Service FAX: 757-410-7122. Reference FAX: 757-410-7150. Web Site: www.chesapeake.lib.va.us. *Dir,* Elizabeth Fowler; Tel: 757-410-7102, E-mail: bfowler@infopeake.org; *Cent Libr Mgr,* James Blanton; Tel: 757-410-7120, E-mail: jblanton@infopeake.org; *Info Syst Mgr,* James A Pearson; Fax: 757-410-7175, E-mail: jpearson@infopeake.org; *Cat Librn,* Jodie Reha; Tel: 757-926-5740, E-mail: jreha@infopeake.org; *Coordr, Circ,* Nancy Kirch; Tel: 757-410-7155, E-mail: njkirch@infopeake.org; *Acq,* Connie Wright; Tel: 757-926-5753, E-mail: cwright@infopeake.org; *Ch,* Martha J Cole; Tel: 757-410-7127, E-mail: mjcole@infopeake.org; Staff 121 (MLS 28, Non-MLS 93)

Founded 1961. Pop 225,255; Circ 2,365,984

Jul 2009-Jun 2010 Income (Main Library and Branch(s)) $8,223,222, State $200,823, City $7,459,942, Federal $73,694, Locally Generated Income $488,652, Other $111. Mats Exp $1,150,035, Books $571,877, Per/Ser (Incl. Access Fees) $83,227, AV Mat $244,812, Electronic Ref Mat (Incl. Access Fees) $250,119. Sal $2,923,501 (Prof $1,388,897)

Library Holdings: Audiobooks 16,769; CDs 24,933; DVDs 45,506; e-books 20,476; Electronic Media & Resources 39; Microforms 110; Bk Vols 487,320; Per Subs 725

Special Collections: Local History (Wallace Memorial Library Coll), bk, micro

Subject Interests: Family, Hist, Law

Automation Activity & Vendor Info: (Cataloging) SirsiDynix; (Circulation) SirsiDynix; (OPAC) SirsiDynix

Database Vendor: EBSCOhost, Gale Cengage Learning, OCLC FirstSearch, SirsiDynix

Wireless access

Function: Art exhibits, Audio & video playback equip for onsite use, Audiobks via web, BA reader (adult literacy), Bk club(s), Bk reviews (Group), Bks on CD, CD-ROM, Children's prog, Computer training, Computers for patron use, Copy machines, e-mail & chat, e-mail serv, E-Reserves, Electronic databases & coll, Exhibits, Fax serv, Free DVD rentals, Handicapped accessible, Holiday prog, Home delivery & serv to Sr ctr & nursing homes, ILL available, Instruction & testing, Legal assistance to inmates, Mail & tel request accepted, Music CDs, Notary serv, Online cat, Online ref, Online searches, Orientations, Outreach serv, Outside serv via phone, mail, e-mail & web, OverDrive digital audio bks, Photocopying/Printing, Preschool outreach, Prog for adults, Prog for children & young adult, Pub access computers, Ref serv available, Ref serv in person, Scanner, Senior computer classes, Senior outreach, Spoken cassettes & CDs, Spoken cassettes & DVDs, Story hour, Summer & winter reading prog, Summer reading prog, Teen prog, Telephone ref, Web-catalog, Wheelchair accessible, Winter reading prog

Special Services for the Blind - Reader equip

Open Mon-Thurs 9-9, Fri & Sat 9-5, Sun 1-5

Friends of the Library Group

Branches: 6

DR CLARENCE V CUFFEE LIBRARY, 2726 Border Rd, 23324-3760. Tel: 757-410-7034. Circulation Tel: 757-410-7036. FAX: 757-410-7044. *Mgr,* Olivia Osei-Sarfo; Tel: 757-410-7040, E-mail: ovoseisa@infopeake.org

Founded 2007

Open Mon-Thurs 9-9, Fri & Sat 9-5, Sun 1-5

Friends of the Library Group

GREENBRIER, 1214 Volvo Pkwy, 23320-7600, SAN 371-9553. Tel: 757-410-7058. Circulation Tel: 757-410-7061. Administration Tel: 757-410-7067. FAX: 757-410-7071. *Br Mgr,* Jean Carideo; E-mail: jacarideo@infopeake.org; *Ch,* Ann Maloney; Tel: 757-410-7065, E-mail: amaloney@infopeake.org; *Ref Librn,* Jessica Fessler; Tel: 757-410-7068, E-mail: jfessler@infopeake.org; *Circ Mgr,* Ann Payne; Tel: 757-410-7070, E-mail: apayne@infopeake.org

Founded 1992

Friends of the Library Group

INDIAN RIVER, 2320 Old Greenbrier Rd, 23325-4916, SAN 362-8353. Tel: 757-410-7001. Circulation Tel: 757-410-7003. FAX: 757-410-7014. *Br Mgr,* Sasha Matthews; Tel: 757-410-7007, E-mail:

srmatthe@infopeake.org; *Circ Mgr,* Cami Myers; Tel: 757-410-7010, E-mail: clmyers@infopeake.org; *Ch,* Jessica Maitland; Tel: 757-410-7005, E-mail: jmaitlan@infopeake.org; *Ref Serv,* Kevin Clement; Tel: 757-410-7008, E-mail: kclement@infopeake.org

Founded 1965

Friends of the Library Group

MAJOR HILLARD LIBRARY, 824 Old George Washington Hwy N, 23323-2214, SAN 362-8329. Tel: 757-410-7075. Circulation Tel: 757-410-7078. FAX: 757-410-7088, 757-410-7089. *Br Mgr,* Susan T Hobbs; Tel: 757-410-7084, E-mail: shobbs@infopeake.org; *Circ Mgr,* Robbie Etheridge; Tel: 757-410-7087, E-mail: retherid@infopeake.org; *Ch,* Hollister Finch; Tel: 757-410-7082, E-mail: hfinch@infopeake.org; *Ref Serv,* Elizabeth Griffing; E-mail: egriffin@infopeake.org

Founded 1977

Friends of the Library Group

RUSSELL MEMORIAL, 2808 Taylor Rd, 23321-2210, SAN 362-8388. Tel: 757-410-7020. Reference Tel: 757-410-7016. FAX: 757-410-7029. *Br Mgr,* Clyde Hunter, Jr; Tel: 757-410-7028, E-mail: chunter@infopeake.org; *Ch,* Elizabeth Hope; Tel: 757-410-7027, E-mail: ejhope@infopeake.org; *Circ Mgr,* Gene Edwards; Tel: 757-410-7023, E-mail: gedwards@infopeake.org; *Ref Serv,* Scott Kurhan, III; E-mail: skurhan@infopeake.org

Founded 1968

Special Collections: Dave Smith Poetry Coll

Subject Interests: Family

Friends of the Library Group

SOUTH NORFOLK MEMORIAL, 1100 Poindexter St, 23324-2447, SAN 362-8418. Tel: 757-410-7052. FAX: 757-410-7055. *Br Mgr,* Position Currently Open; *Librn I, Ref Serv,* Ann Martin; Tel: 757-410-7053, E-mail: amartin@infopeake.org

Founded 1958

Subject Interests: Family

Friends of the Library Group

Bookmobiles: 1

J   TIDEWATER COMMUNITY COLLEGE*, Chesapeake Campus Library, 1428 Cedar Rd, 23322. SAN 362-8442. Circulation Tel: 757-822-5160. Reference Tel: 757-822-5162. FAX: 757-822-5173. Web Site: www.tcc.edu/lrc. *Coordr,* Lois Radford; E-mail: lradford@tcc.edu; Staff 6 (MLS 2, Non-MLS 4)

Founded 1973. Enrl 2,965; Fac 123

Library Holdings: Bk Vols 43,036; Per Subs 239

Subject Interests: Early childhood, Hort

Automation Activity & Vendor Info: (Acquisitions) Ex Libris Group; (Cataloging) Ex Libris Group; (Circulation) Ex Libris Group; (Course Reserve) Ex Libris Group; (ILL) Ex Libris Group; (OPAC) Ex Libris Group; (Serials) Ex Libris Group

Database Vendor: EBSCOhost, OCLC FirstSearch

Partic in Lyrasis; OCLC Online Computer Library Center, Inc; Tidewater Consortium for Continuing Higher Educ

Open Mon-Thurs 8am-9pm, Fri 8-4:30, Sat 9-1

CHESTER

J   JOHN TYLER COMMUNITY COLLEGE LIBRARY, Moyar Hall, M216, 13101 Jefferson Davis Hwy, 23831-5316. SAN 317-2503. Tel: 804-706-5195. Reference Tel: 804-706-5198. FAX: 804-796-4238. E-mail: library@jtcc.edu. Web Site: www.library.jtcc.edu. *Librn,* Linda L Luebke; Tel: 804-706-5202, E-mail: lluebke@jtcc.edu; *ILL, Ref,* Ha Hoang; E-mail: hhoang@jtcc.edu; Staff 7 (MLS 1, Non-MLS 6)

Founded 1967. Enrl 5,415; Highest Degree: Associate

Library Holdings: CDs 193; DVDs 695; Bk Vols 36,156; Per Subs 66; Videos 319

Automation Activity & Vendor Info: (Cataloging) Ex Libris Group; (Circulation) Ex Libris Group; (Course Reserve) Ex Libris Group; (ILL) OCLC; (OPAC) Ex Libris Group

Wireless access

Partic in Lyrasis; Richmond Academic Library Consortium; Virginia Commun Coll Syst

Open Mon-Thurs 7:30am-9pm, Fri 7:30-5, Sat 10-2

Departmental Libraries:

MIDLOTHIAN CAMPUS, Hamel Hall, Rm H202, 800 Charter Colony Pkwy, Midlothian, 23114-4383. Tel: 804-594-1519. Reference Tel: 804-594-1520. FAX: 804-594-1525. *Librn,* Helen McKann; Tel: 804-594-1523, E-mail: hmckann@jtcc.edu; Staff 6 (MLS 1, Non-MLS 5)

Library Holdings: CDs 3; DVDs 368; Bk Vols 18,516; Per Subs 55; Videos 10

Open Mon-Thurs 7:30am-9pm, Fri 7:30-5, Sat 10-2

CHESTERFIELD

P   CHESTERFIELD COUNTY PUBLIC LIBRARY, 9501 Lori Rd, 23832. (Mail add: PO Box 297, 23832-0297), SAN 362-8507. Tel: 804-748-1601. Circulation Tel: 804-748-1774. Reference Tel: 804-748-1603. FAX: 804-751-4679. Web Site: www.library.chesterfield.gov. *Dir,* Michael R

Mabe; E-mail: mabem@chesterfield.gov; *Libr Serv Adminr,* Debra
Winecoff; Tel: 804-751-4475, E-mail: winecoffd@chesterfield.gov; *Libr Serv Adminr, Commun Serv,* Carolyn Sears; Tel: 804-748-1761, E-mail: searsc@chesterfield.gov; *Pub Serv Adminr,* Frank Bridge; Tel: 804-748-1980, E-mail: bridgef@chesterfield.gov; *Pub Serv Adminr,* Nanci Clary; Tel: 804-717-6412, E-mail: claryn@chesterfield.gov; Staff 131 (MLS 26, Non-MLS 105)
Founded 1965. Pop 244,661; Circ 3,474,052
Library Holdings: AV Mats 82,821; Bk Vols 675,692; Per Subs 963
Special Collections: Law Library Coll; Local History Coll
Subject Interests: Civil War, Local hist, Virginiana
Automation Activity & Vendor Info: (Acquisitions) Innovative Interfaces, Inc; (Cataloging) Innovative Interfaces, Inc - Millenium; (Circulation) Innovative Interfaces, Inc; (Serials) Innovative Interfaces, Inc
Database Vendor: EBSCOhost, Gale Cengage Learning, Innovative Interfaces, Inc, ReferenceUSA
Wireless access
Function: Adult bk club, Bk club(s), Bks on CD, Children's prog, Computer training, Computers for patron use, Copy machines, E-Reserves, Electronic databases & coll, Free DVD rentals, Handicapped accessible, Health sci info serv, Holiday prog, ILL available, Jail serv, Music CDs, Online cat, Online ref, Orientations, Outreach serv, OverDrive digital audio bks, Prog for adults, Prog for children & young adult, Pub access computers, Story hour, Summer & winter reading prog, Summer reading prog, Telephone ref, Workshops
Publications: CCPL Annual Report; CCPL Digital Magazine (Monthly); CCPL Program Guide (Monthly newsletter)
Open Mon-Wed 10-9, Thurs 1-9, Fri & Sat 10-5
Friends of the Library Group
Branches: 8
BON AIR, 9103 Rattlesnake Rd, Richmond, 23235, SAN 362-8531. Tel: 804-320-2461. *Br Mgr,* John Twombly; E-mail: twomblyj@chesterfield.gov; *Asst Br Mgr,* Sherie Parker; E-mail: parkers@chesterfield.gov
    Open Mon-Thurs 10-9, Fri & Sat 10-5:30
    Friends of the Library Group
CHESTER BRANCH, 11800 Centre St, Chester, 23831, SAN 362-8566. Tel: 804-748-6314. *Br Mgr,* Elaine Devoss; E-mail: devosse@chesterfield.gov; *Asst Br Mgr,* Janet Records; E-mail: recordsj@chesterfield.gov
    Friends of the Library Group
CLOVER HILL, 6701 Deer Run Rd, Midlothian, 23112, SAN 374-6488. Tel: 804-318-8668. *Br Mgr,* Karen Mann; Tel: 804-318-8642, E-mail: mannk@chesterfield.gov; *Asst Br Mgr,* Jessica Cerny; Tel: 804-318-8406, E-mail: cernyj@chesterfield.gov
    Friends of the Library Group
ENON, 1801 Enon Church Rd, Chester, 23836, SAN 374-6496. Tel: 804-530-3403. *Br Mgr,* Jennifer Hayek; E-mail: hayekj@chesterfield.gov; *Asst Br Mgr,* Kareemah Hamdan; E-mail: hamdank@chesterfield.gov
    Friends of the Library Group
ETTRICK-MATOACA, 4501 River Rd, Petersburg, 23803, SAN 362-8590. Tel: 804-526-8087. *Br Mgr,* Jennifer Hayek; E-mail: hayekj@chesterfield.gov; *Asst Br Mgr,* Karemmah Hamdan; E-mail: hamdank@chesterfield.gov
    Friends of the Library Group
LAPRADE, 9000 Hull St Rd, Richmond, 23236, SAN 362-8620. Tel: 804-276-7755. *Br Mgr,* Ginger Peterman; E-mail: petermang@chesterfield.gov; *Asst Br Mgr,* Megan Hodge; E-mail: hodgem@chesterfield.gov
    Friends of the Library Group
MEADOWDALE, 4301 Meadowdale Blvd, Richmond, 23234, SAN 373-9074. Tel: 804-318-8778. *Br Mgr,* Angela Burt; Tel: 804-318-8755, E-mail: burta@chesterfield.gov
    Friends of the Library Group
MIDLOTHIAN, 521 Coalfield Rd, Midlothian, 23114, SAN 362-8639. Tel: 804-768-7907. *Br Mgr,* Jennifer Shepley; E-mail: shepleyj@chesterfield.gov; *Asst Br Mgr,* Jolynn Holcomb; E-mail: holcombj@chesterfield.gov
    Friends of the Library Group

CHRISTIANSBURG

P   MONTGOMERY-FLOYD REGIONAL LIBRARY SYSTEM*, Christiansburg Library, 125 Sheltman St, 24073. SAN 319-9223. Tel: 540-382-6965. Circulation Tel: 540-382-6965, Ext 15. Administration Tel: 540-382-6967. FAX: 540-382-6964. E-mail: christiansburg@mfrl.org. Web Site: www.mfrl.org. *Dir,* Paula Alston; E-mail: palston@mfrl.org; *Acq Mgr,* Vicki Reedy; E-mail: vreedy@mfrl.org; *Br Mgr,* Pamela Hale; E-mail: phale@mfrl.org; *Bus Mgr,* June Sayers; E-mail: jsayers@mfrl.org; *Coll Develop Mgr,* Anne Greene; E-mail: agreene@mfrl.org; *Prog Mgr,* Linda Spivey; E-mail: lspivey@mfrl.org; Staff 34 (MLS 2, Non-MLS 32)
Founded 1974. Pop 100,200; Circ 781,608
Jul 2005-Jun 2006 Income (Main Library and Branch(s)) $2,155,646, State $273,828, City $23,000, County $1,480,060, Locally Generated Income $377,456, Other $1,302. Mats Exp $472,351

Subject Interests: Genealogy, Local hist
Automation Activity & Vendor Info: (Acquisitions) SirsiDynix; (Cataloging) SirsiDynix; (Circulation) SirsiDynix; (OPAC) SirsiDynix; (Serials) SirsiDynix
Database Vendor: Gale Cengage Learning, Grolier Online, Newsbank, OCLC FirstSearch, ProQuest
Wireless access
Function: Adult bk club, Computer training, Copy machines, Electronic databases & coll, Fax serv, Handicapped accessible, ILL available, Mail & tel request accepted, Music CDs, Online ref, Online searches, Photocopying/Printing, Prog for children & young adult, Tax forms, Telephone ref, VHS videos, Wheelchair accessible
Partic in SouthWest Information Network Group (SWING)
Open Mon-Thurs 9-8, Fri & Sat 10-5, Sun 1-5
Friends of the Library Group
Branches: 3
BLACKSBURG AREA BRANCH, 200 Miller St, Blacksburg, 24060, SAN 362-868X. Tel: 540-552-8246. FAX: 540-552-8265. E-mail: blacksburg@mfrl.org. *Br Supvr,* Elizabeth Sensabaugh; E-mail: esensabaugh@mfrl.org
    Open Mon-Thurs 9-8, Fri & Sat 10-5, Sun (Winter) 1-5
    Friends of the Library Group
MEADOWBROOK PUBLIC, 267 Alleghany Springs Rd, Shawsville, 24162. Tel: 540-268-1964. E-mail: meadowbrook@mfrl.org. *Br Supvr,* Cindy Minnick; E-mail: cminnick@mfrl.org
    Open Mon-Thurs 10-8, Fri & Sat 10-5, Sun (Winter) 1-5
JESSIE PETERMAN MEMORIAL, 321 W Main St, Floyd, 24091, SAN 362-871X. Tel: 540-745-2947. FAX: 540-745-4750. E-mail: floyd@mfrl.org. *Br Supvr,* Cathy Whitten; E-mail: cwhitten@mfrl.org
    Open Mon & Wed 10-6, Tues & Thurs 10-8, Fri & Sat 10-5, Sun (Winter) 1-5
    Friends of the Library Group
Bookmobiles: 1

CLIFTON FORGE

S   CHESAPEAKE & OHIO HISTORICAL SOCIETY ARCHIVES*, C&O Archival Collection, 312 E Ridgeway St, 24422-1325. (Mail add: PO Box 79, 24422-0079), SAN 329-1936. Tel: 540-862-2210. Toll Free Tel: 800-453-2647. FAX: 540-863-9159. Web Site: www.chessieshop.com, www.cohs.org. *Archivist,* Margaret T Whittington
Founded 1969
Special Collections: Chesapeake & Ohio Railway, its predecessors, subsidiaries & successors
Open Mon-Thurs 10-9, Fri, Sat & Sun 10-6
Restriction: Non-circulating

P   CLIFTON FORGE PUBLIC LIBRARY*, 535 Church St, 24422. SAN 317-2511. Tel: 540-863-2519. FAX: 540-863-2520. E-mail: library@cliftonforge.org. *Dir,* Michele Tollie-Porter; E-mail: mtollie@cliftonforge.pa.gov; Staff 1 (Non-MLS 1)
Founded 1972. Pop 4,200; Circ 38,153
Library Holdings: Bk Vols 45,000; Per Subs 54
Automation Activity & Vendor Info: (Cataloging) Polaris Library Systems; (Circulation) Polaris Library Systems; (OPAC) Polaris Library Systems
Wireless access
Open Mon & Thurs 10-7, Tues, Wed & Fri 10-5, Sat 10-1
Friends of the Library Group

J   DABNEY S LANCASTER COMMUNITY COLLEGE LIBRARY-LRC*, 1000 Dabney Dr, 24422. SAN 317-252X. Tel: 540-863-2800. Toll Free Tel: 877-733-7522. FAX: 540-863-2916. Web Site: www.lrc.dslcc.edu/library.htm. *Dir,* Nova Wright; E-mail: nwright@dslcc.edu; Staff 1 (MLS 1)
Founded 1964
Library Holdings: Bk Vols 44,317; Per Subs 250
Subject Interests: Commun col educ, Forestry, Law enforcement, Nursing
Automation Activity & Vendor Info: (Acquisitions) Ex Libris Group; (Circulation) Ex Libris Group; (Course Reserve) Ex Libris Group; (ILL) OCLC; (Media Booking) Ex Libris Group; (OPAC) Ex Libris Group
Database Vendor: OCLC WorldCat
Wireless access
Partic in Lyrasis; Virginia Commun Coll Syst; Virtual Library of Virginia
Open Mon-Thurs 8am-9pm, Fri 8-5, Sun 2-6

COLONIAL HEIGHTS

P   COLONIAL HEIGHTS PUBLIC LIBRARY*, 1000 Yacht Basin Dr, 23834. SAN 317-2538. Tel: 804-520-9384. FAX: 804-524-8740. Web Site: www.colonial-heights.com. *Dir,* Bruce N Hansen; E-mail: hansenb@colonial-heights.com; Staff 5 (Non-MLS 5)
Founded 1968. Pop 16,500; Circ 103,710
Library Holdings: AV Mats 21,000; Bk Vols 41,500; Per Subs 109

Automation Activity & Vendor Info: (Cataloging) Follett Software; (Circulation) Follett Software; (OPAC) Follett Software
Database Vendor: Gale Cengage Learning
Open Mon-Wed 10-8, Thurs-Sat 10-6

COURTLAND

P   BLACKWATER REGIONAL LIBRARY*, Walter Cecil Rawls Library, 22511 Main St, 23837. SAN 362-8744. Tel: 757-653-2821. Administration Tel: 757-653-0298. FAX: 757-653-9374. E-mail: courtland@blackwaterlib.org. Web Site: www.blackwaterlib.org. *Libr Dir,* Yvonne Hilliard-Bradley; E-mail: yvonne@blackwaterlib.org; *Financial Dir,* Stanya Yonker; E-mail: syonker@blackwaterlib.org; *Dir, Human Res,* Betty Britt; E-mail: bjbritt@blackwaterlib.org; *Cat Supvr,* Barbara Powell; *Acq,* Dianne Dunlow; Staff 58 (MLS 3, Non-MLS 55)
Founded 1958. Pop 80,500; Circ 407,000
Library Holdings: Bk Titles 121,729; Bk Vols 245,822; Per Subs 326
Special Collections: Cary Close Memorial Coll (Civil War Reference Materials); Nat Turner (Cole Coll)
Subject Interests: Genealogy, Local hist
Automation Activity & Vendor Info: (Acquisitions) TLC (The Library Corporation); (Cataloging) TLC (The Library Corporation); (Circulation) TLC (The Library Corporation); (OPAC) TLC (The Library Corporation)
Wireless access
Function: AV serv, Bk club(s), Electronic databases & coll, Family literacy, Handicapped accessible, Homebound delivery serv, ILL available, Learning ctr, Online searches, Photocopying/Printing, Prof lending libr, Prog for adults, Prog for children & young adult, Ref serv available, Spoken cassettes & CDs, Spoken cassettes & DVDs, Summer reading prog, VHS videos, Video lending libr, Wheelchair accessible
Open Mon & Wed 9-8, Tues, Thurs & Fri 9-5, Sat 9-12
Friends of the Library Group
Branches: 8
RUTH CAMP CAMPBELL MEMORIAL, 280 N College Dr, Franklin, 23851, SAN 376-1029. Tel: 757-562-4801. FAX: 757-562-0162. E-mail: franklin@blackwaterlib.org. *Br Mgr,* Beryl C Roblin; E-mail: broblin@blackwaterlib.org; Staff 6.5 (MLS 1, Non-MLS 5.5)
Pop 8,500; Circ 116,000
Automation Activity & Vendor Info: (ILL) TLC (The Library Corporation)
Function: Bks on CD, Children's prog, Computer training, Computers for patron use, Copy machines, Electronic databases & coll, Fax serv, Free DVD rentals, Games & aids for the handicapped, Handicapped accessible, Home delivery & serv to Sr ctr & nursing homes, ILL available, Jail serv, Large print keyboards, Magnifiers for reading, Mail & tel request accepted, Music CDs, Online cat, Online ref, Outreach serv, Photocopying/Printing, Preschool outreach, Prog for adults, Prog for children & young adult, Pub access computers, Ref & res, Senior computer classes, Senior outreach, Spoken cassettes & CDs, Spoken cassettes & DVDs, Story hour, Summer reading prog, Tax forms, Teen prog, Telephone ref, VHS videos, Web-catalog, Wheelchair accessible
Open Mon-Thurs 9-8, Fri 9-5, Sat 9-3
Restriction: In-house use for visitors
Friends of the Library Group
CARROLLTON PUBLIC, 14362 New Towne Haven Lane, Carrollton, 23314, SAN 322-5496. Tel: 757-238-2641. FAX: 757-238-3932. E-mail: carrollton@blackwaterlib.org. *Mgr,* Connie Henderson
Founded 1984
Open Mon, Thurs & Fri 9-5, Tues & Wed Noon-8, Sat 9-3
Friends of the Library Group
CLAREMONT PUBLIC, 91 Mancha Ave, Claremont, 23899, SAN 326-8136. Tel: 757-866-8627. Toll Free Tel: 877-866-8627. FAX: 757-866-8628. E-mail: claremont@blackwaterlib.org. *Br Mgr,* Janet Moyer Schaale; *Libr Assoc,* Sue Ehmke
Open Mon 9-6, Tues & Sat 9-1, Thurs & Fri 3-7
Friends of the Library Group
AGNES TAYLOR GRAY BRANCH, 125 Bank St, Waverly, 23890-3235, SAN 362-8795. Tel: 804-834-2192. FAX: 804-834-8671. *Br Mgr,* Laurie Latham
Open Mon 1-5, Tues & Wed 1-8, Thurs 12-5, Fri 9-1, Sat 9-12
Friends of the Library Group
ISLE OF WIGHT COUNTY LIBRARY/SMITHFIELD BRANCH, 255 James St, Smithfield, 23430, SAN 362-8779. Tel: 757-357-2264. FAX: 757-357-0883. E-mail: smithfield@blackwaterlib.org. *Br Mgr,* Karen Zukosky; Tel: 757-357-4856, E-mail: kzukosky@blackwaterlib.org; Staff 8 (Non-MLS 8)
Subject Interests: Genealogy, Local hist
Open Mon-Wed 9-9, Thurs & Fri 9-5, Sat 9-3
Friends of the Library Group
SURRY PUBLIC, 11640 Rolfe Hwy, Surry, 23883-2736, SAN 322-5488. Tel: 757-294-3949. FAX: 757-294-0803. E-mail: surry@blackwaterlib.org. *Librn,* Faye Grandison
Subject Interests: Genealogy
Open Mon & Thurs-Sat 9-1, Tues & Wed 11-8
Friends of the Library Group

TROXLER MEMORIAL, 100 Wilson Ave, Wakefield, 23888. (Mail add: PO Box 279, Wakefield, 23888), SAN 329-7578. Tel: 757-899-6500. FAX: 757-899-2400. *Br Mgr,* Laurie Latham
Open Mon & Tues 1-8, Wed 9-5, Thurs 1-9, Fri 12-5, Sat 9-12
Friends of the Library Group
WINDSOR PUBLIC, 18 Duke St, Windsor, 23487. (Mail add: PO Box 346, Windsor, 23487-0346), SAN 374-8111. Tel: 757-242-3046. FAX: 757-242-3726. E-mail: windsor@blackwaterlib.org. *Librn,* Bonnie Lauver
Open Mon & Thurs 1-7, Tues & Wed 10-5, Fri & Sat 9-1
Friends of the Library Group
Bookmobiles: 1. Karen Blythe

COVINGTON

P   CHARLES P JONES MEMORIAL LIBRARY*, 406 W Riverside St, 24426. SAN 317-2546. Tel: 540-962-3321. FAX: 540-962-8447. Web Site: www.cpjones.org. *Dir,* Lisa Hicks; E-mail: Lisaneace@ntelos.net; *Coll Develop,* Diana Hawkins; Staff 5.03 (MLS 1, Non-MLS 4.03)
Founded 1929. Pop 22,000; Circ 65,000
Library Holdings: Bk Titles 70,000; Per Subs 139
Automation Activity & Vendor Info: (Cataloging) TLC (The Library Corporation); (Circulation) TLC (The Library Corporation); (OPAC) TLC (The Library Corporation)
Database Vendor: ProQuest
Wireless access
Function: Adult bk club, Bks on cassette, Bks on CD, Chess club, Children's prog, Computers for patron use, Copy machines, E-Reserves, Electronic databases & coll, Fax serv, ILL available, Music CDs, Online cat, Online searches, Photocopying/Printing, Prog for adults, Prog for children & young adult, Pub access computers, Spoken cassettes & CDs, Spoken cassettes & DVDs, Summer reading prog, Tax forms, VHS videos, Wheelchair accessible
Open Mon, Wed & Fri 9:30-5:30, Tues & Thurs 9:30-8:30, Sat 9:30-2:30
Friends of the Library Group

CREWE

P   NOTTOWAY COUNTY PUBLIC LIBRARIES*, 414 Tyler St, 23930. SAN 363-1532. Tel: 434-645-9310. FAX: 434-645-8513. E-mail: nottlib@org. Web Site: www.nottlib.org. *Dir,* Nancy Pierce; E-mail: npierce@nottlib.org; *Acq,* Lavonna Gibbs; E-mail: bgibbs@nottlib.org; *Cat,* Emily Beverly; E-mail: ebeverly@nottlib.org; Staff 3 (MLS 1, Non-MLS 2)
Founded 1940. Pop 17,000
Subject Interests: Local hist
Automation Activity & Vendor Info: (Cataloging) TLC (The Library Corporation)
Database Vendor: OCLC FirstSearch
Open Mon-Fri 9-5
Friends of the Library Group
Branches: 3
BLACKSTONE BRANCH, 415 S Main St, Blackstone, 23824, SAN 363-1567. Tel: 434-292-3587. FAX: 434-292-3587. *Librn,* Joyce Norton; Staff 1 (Non-MLS 1)
Library Holdings: Bk Vols 13,229; Per Subs 18
Automation Activity & Vendor Info: (Cataloging) TLC (The Library Corporation); (Circulation) TLC (The Library Corporation); (OPAC) TLC (The Library Corporation)
Database Vendor: Gale Cengage Learning
Open Tues & Thurs 12-6, Wed 12-8, Fri & Sat 10-2
Friends of the Library Group
BURKEVILLE BRANCH, 114 S Agnew, Burkeville, 23922, SAN 363-1575. Tel: 434-767-5555. FAX: 434-767-2652. *Librn,* Agnes McCormick
Library Holdings: Bk Vols 6,456
Open Mon & Thurs 10-5, Tues, Fri & Sat 10-2
Friends of the Library Group
CREWE BRANCH, 400 Tyler St, 23930, SAN 363-1591. Tel: 434-645-8688. FAX: 434-645-8688. *Actg Dir,* Chuck Kostnik; Staff 1 (Non-MLS 1)
Jul 2009-Jun 2010 Income $200,346. Mats Exp $38,665, Books $31,555, AV Mat $7,110
Library Holdings: Audiobooks 673; DVDs 892; Bk Vols 29,615; Per Subs 83
Database Vendor: TLC (The Library Corporation)
Open Mon & Thurs 10-6, Tues & Wed 10-8, Sat 10-2
Friends of the Library Group

CROZIER

G   VIRGINIA DEPARTMENT OF CORRECTIONS, Academy for Staff Development Library, 1900 River Rd W, 23039. SAN 317-4662. Tel: 804-784-6841. FAX: 804-784-6999. *Librn,* Alice Milner; Staff 1 (MLS 1)
Founded 1976
Library Holdings: AV Mats 1,630; Bk Vols 7,500; Per Subs 43
Subject Interests: Corrections, Inmate recovery prog, K-9 training, Leadership mgt

Automation Activity & Vendor Info: (Cataloging) Follett Software
Wireless access
Publications: A/V Catalog; New Materials List (Quarterly)
Partic in Lyrasis
Restriction: Open to dept staff only

CULPEPER

P　CULPEPER COUNTY LIBRARY, 271 Southgate Shopping Ctr,
22701-3215. SAN 317-2562. Tel: 540-825-8691. FAX: 540-825-7486.
E-mail: ccl@cclva.org. Web Site: cclva.org. *Dir,* Susan J Keller; E-mail:
skeller@cclva.org; *Asst Dir,* Dana L Brumbelow; E-mail:
dbrumbelow@cclva.org; *Ch,* Laini Bostian; E-mail: lbostian@cclva.org;
Tech Serv, Elizabeth Hensley; E-mail: ehensley@cclva.org; Staff 7 (MLS 3,
Non-MLS 4)
Founded 1946. Pop 45,500; Circ 491,693
Jul 2011-Jun 2012 Income $789,457, State $148,800, County $580,657.
Mats Exp $122,031, Books $96,231, Per/Ser (Incl. Access Fees) $2,200,
Micro $1,600, Electronic Ref Mat (Incl. Access Fees) $22,000
Library Holdings: Bk Titles 76,000; Per Subs 150
Special Collections: Art Coll; Civil War Coll; Genealogical Coll (Local
History), bks, micro
Automation Activity & Vendor Info: (Acquisitions) TLC (The Library
Corporation); (Cataloging) TLC (The Library Corporation); (Circulation)
TLC (The Library Corporation); (OPAC) TLC (The Library Corporation)
Database Vendor: Baker & Taylor, BookLetters LLC, ebrary, Gale
Cengage Learning, netLibrary, Newsbank, OCLC FirstSearch, OCLC
WorldCat, Overdrive, Inc, ProQuest, TLC (The Library Corporation),
TumbleBookLibrary, World Book Online
Wireless access
Function: Adult bk club, Art exhibits, Audiobks via web, Bks on cassette,
Bks on CD, Children's prog, Computer training, Computers for patron use,
Copy machines, E-Reserves, Electronic databases & coll, Free DVD
rentals, ILL available, Magnifiers for reading, Mail loans to mem, Online
cat, OverDrive digital audio bks, Photocopying/Printing, Preschool
outreach, Prog for adults, Prog for children & young adult, Pub access
computers, Ref serv available, Senior computer classes, Spoken cassettes &
CDs, Spoken cassettes & DVDs, Story hour, Summer reading prog, Tax
forms, Teen prog, Telephone ref, VHS videos, Wheelchair accessible
Special Services for the Deaf - Assisted listening device; Bks on deafness
& sign lang; Pocket talkers
Special Services for the Blind - Assistive/Adapted tech devices, equip &
products; Closed circuit TV magnifier; Large print bks; Low vision equip;
Magnifiers
Open Mon-Thurs 10-9, Fri & Sat 10-5
Friends of the Library Group

CUMBERLAND

P　CUMBERLAND COUNTY PUBLIC LIBRARY*, 1539 Anderson Hwy,
23040-0098. (Mail add: PO Box 98, 23040-0098), SAN 373-8787. Tel:
804-492-5807. FAX: 804-492-9551. E-mail: cumbpublib@yahoo.com. Web
Site: www.cumberlandcountypubliclibrary.org. Staff 1 (MLS 1)
Founded 1967. Pop 9,500; Circ 21,555
Library Holdings: DVDs 68; Large Print Bks 159; Bk Vols 16,531; Per
Subs 27; Talking Bks 138; Videos 627
Automation Activity & Vendor Info: (OPAC) Follett Software
Special Services for the Blind - Closed circuit TV
Open Mon 1-9, Tues-Fri 9-5, Sat 9-1
Friends of the Library Group

DAHLGREN

A　UNITED STATES NAVY*, Dahlgren General Library, Naval Surface
Warfare Ctr, Bldg 1194, 6090 Jenkins Rd, Ste 209, 22448-5000. SAN
362-8809. Tel: 540-653-7474. FAX: 540-653-0260. *Librn,* Christina Posey
Founded 1954
Library Holdings: Bk Vols 18,000; Per Subs 36
Wireless access
Open Mon-Fri 8-6, Sat 10-4

DANVILLE

C　AVERETT UNIVERSITY LIBRARY*, Mary B Blount Library, 344 W
Main St, 24541-2849. SAN 317-2570. Tel: 434-791-5690. Interlibrary Loan
Service Tel: 434-791-5828. Administration Tel: 434-791-5691. Information
Services Tel: 434-791-5692. FAX: 434-791-5637. E-mail:
aclib@averett.edu. Web Site: discover.averett.edu/library. *Dir, Syst Librn,
Web Serv,* Elaine L Day; Tel: 434-791-5696, E-mail:
elaine.day@averett.edu; *Tech Serv Librn,* Jennifer Robinson; Tel:
434-791-5693, E-mail: jrobinson@averett.edu; *Archivist, Ser,* Patrick
Wasley, PhD; E-mail: pwasley@averett.edu; *Access Serv, Ref Serv,* Jim
Verdini; Tel: 434-791-5694, E-mail: jverdini@averett.edu; *Distance Educ,
Electronic Serv, Ref Serv,* Kevin Harden; E-mail:
kevin.harden@averett.edu. Subject Specialists: *Equestrian studies, Sci,*
Elaine L Day; *Children's lit, Communication studies, Journalism,* Jennifer

Robinson; *Art, English lit, Modern lang,* Patrick Wasley, PhD; *Music,
Relig, Theatre,* Jim Verdini; *Bus, Soc sci,* Kevin Harden; Staff 5 (MLS 5)
Founded 1859. Enrl 2,600; Fac 80; Highest Degree: Master
Library Holdings: AV Mats 100,000; e-books 100,000; e-journals 32,840; Bk
Titles 102,736; Bk Vols 116,947; Per Subs 33,098
Special Collections: Averett University Archives; Charles R Hawkins
Papers; Dan Daniel Archives; Danville History Coll. Oral History
Subject Interests: Civil rights era, Local hist
Automation Activity & Vendor Info: (Cataloging) Innovative Interfaces,
Inc; (Circulation) Innovative Interfaces, Inc; (Course Reserve) Innovative
Interfaces, Inc; (ILL) Innovative Interfaces, Inc; (OPAC) Innovative
Interfaces, Inc
Database Vendor: Alexander Street Press, American Chemical Society,
American Psychological Association (APA), ARTstor, Baker & Taylor,
BioOne, Bowker, Cambridge Scientific Abstracts, CQ Press,
CredoReference, ebrary, EBSCOhost, Factiva.com, Gale Cengage Learning,
Innovative Interfaces, Inc, LexisNexis, Mergent Online, Nature Publishing
Group, netLibrary, OCLC FirstSearch, OCLC WorldCat, Oxford Online,
ProQuest, SerialsSolutions, Springshare, LLC
Wireless access
Function: Archival coll, Art exhibits, CD-ROM, Computers for patron use,
Copy machines, Distance learning, e-mail serv, E-Reserves, Electronic
databases & coll, Exhibits, ILL available, Online cat, Online info literacy
tutorials on the web & in blackboard, Online ref, Ref serv available, Ref
serv in person
Publications: Averett Library News (Newsletter)
Partic in Lyrasis; SouthWest Information Network Group (SWING);
Virginia Independent College & University Library Association; Virtual
Library of Virginia
Open Mon-Thurs 8:30am-10pm, Fri 8:30-4:30, Sat 11-4, Sun 1-10
Restriction: In-house use for visitors
Friends of the Library Group

J　DANVILLE COMMUNITY COLLEGE*, Whittington W Clement
Learning Resources Center, 1008 S Main St, 24541-4004. SAN 317-2597.
Tel: 434-797-8453. Reference Tel: 434-797-8555. Toll Free Tel:
800-560-4291 (VA only). FAX: 434-797-8415. Web Site:
www.dcc.vccs.edu/lrc/library/library.htm. *Dir,* William L Dey; Tel:
434-797-8454, E-mail: wdey@dcc.vccs.edu; *Librn,* Barbara Grether;
E-mail: bgrether@dcc.vccs.edu; Staff 9 (MLS 2, Non-MLS 7)
Founded 1968. Enrl 4,000; Fac 51
Jul 2005-Jun 2006. Mats Exp $80,000, Books $59,500, Per/Ser (Incl.
Access Fees) $14,500, Micro $500, AV Mat $5,000, Presv $500
Library Holdings: AV Mats 3,330; Bks on Deafness & Sign Lang 63;
e-journals 8,000; Bk Titles 46,502; Bk Vols 52,218; Per Subs 175
Subject Interests: Local hist
Automation Activity & Vendor Info: (Cataloging) OCLC; (Circulation)
Ex Libris Group; (ILL) OCLC; (OPAC) Ex Libris Group
Database Vendor: EBSCOhost, Gale Cengage Learning
Partic in Lyrasis; OCLC Online Computer Library Center, Inc; Virginia
Commun Coll Syst; Virtual Library of Virginia
Open Mon-Thurs (Winter) 8am-9pm, Fri 8-5, Sun 1-5; Mon-Thurs
(Summer) 8am-9pm, Fri 8-5

P　DANVILLE PUBLIC LIBRARY*, 511 Patton St, 24541. SAN 317-2600.
Tel: 434-799-5195. Circulation Tel: 434-799-5195, Ext 2. Reference Tel:
434-799-5195, Ext 3. Administration Tel: 434-799-5195, Ext 6. FAX:
434-792-5172. Web Site: www.danville-va.gov. *Dir, Libr Serv,* Shelly
Hypes Janosko; E-mail: janossh@ci.danville.va.us; *Principal Librn, Ref,*
Florence Archer; E-mail: archerf@ci.danville.va.us; *Ch,* T Wayne Romano;
E-mail: romantw@ci.danville.va; *Cat,* Donna Cisneros; E-mail:
cisnedl@ci.danville.va.us; *Genealogy Info Spec,* Wilford Burson; *Law Info
Spec,* Rebecca Webb; Staff 18 (MLS 2, Non-MLS 16)
Founded 1923. Pop 48,411; Circ 273,642
Library Holdings: AV Mats 7,000; Bk Vols 131,186
Subject Interests: Genealogy, Local hist
Automation Activity & Vendor Info: (Cataloging) TLC (The Library
Corporation); (Circulation) TLC (The Library Corporation); (OPAC) TLC
(The Library Corporation)
Database Vendor: Gale Cengage Learning, Grolier Online, ProQuest
Wireless access
Function: Handicapped accessible, Homebound delivery serv, ILL
available, Photocopying/Printing, Prog for children & young adult, Ref serv
available, Summer reading prog, Telephone ref, Wheelchair accessible
Open Mon-Thurs 10-8, Fri 9-5, Sat 9-1
Friends of the Library Group
Branches: 2
LAW, 511 Patton St, 24541. Tel: 434-799-5118. FAX: 434-799-5118. *Dir,
Libr Serv,* Alexander Otis; Tel: 434-799-5195, Ext 7, E-mail:
alexaod@ci.danville.va.us; *Law Librn, Supvr,* Rebecca Webb; Staff 1
(Non-MLS 1)
Founded 1987. Pop 48,411
Library Holdings: Bk Titles 300; Bk Vols 25,300
Database Vendor: Westlaw

Function: Handicapped accessible, Photocopying/Printing, Ref serv available, Res libr, Wheelchair accessible
Open Mon-Fri 9-1
Restriction: Non-circulating to the pub
WESTOVER, 94 Clifton St, 24541, SAN 378-1496. Tel: 434-799-5152. *Dir, Libr Serv,* Alexander Otis; Tel: 434-799-5195, Ext 7, E-mail: alexaod@ci.danville.va.us; *Supvr,* Donna Cisneros; *Info Spec,* Denise Hash; *Info Spec,* Patricia Williams; Staff 2 (Non-MLS 2)
Library Holdings: Bk Vols 8,000
Function: Handicapped accessible, Photocopying/Printing, Prog for children & young adult, Ref serv available, Summer reading prog, Wheelchair accessible
Open Mon & Thurs 10-6, Tues & Wed 9-5

M   DANVILLE REGIONAL MEDICAL CENTER*, Ralph R Landes Medical Library, 142 S Main St, 24541. SAN 317-2619. Tel: 434-799-4418. FAX: 434-799-2255. Web Site: www.danvilleregional.com. *Mgr, Libr Serv,* Ann Sasser Evans; Staff 1 (MLS 1)
Library Holdings: Bk Vols 1,000; Per Subs 125
Database Vendor: Cinahl Information Systems, Medline, OVID Technologies
Function: Doc delivery serv, Health sci info serv, ILL available, Online searches, Photocopying/Printing
Publications: RRLibrary Briefs (Newsletter)
Restriction: Open to pub by appt only

DAYTON

S   HARRISONBURG-ROCKINGHAM HISTORICAL SOCIETY LIBRARY*, 382 High St, 22821. (Mail add: PO Box 716, 22821-0716), SAN 327-8719. Tel: 540-879-2616. FAX: 540-879-2616. E-mail: heritag1@shentel.net. *In Charge,* John Sellers
Library Holdings: Bk Vols 1,100
Subject Interests: Genealogy
Open Mon-Sat 10-4

DILLWYN

S   BUCKINGHAM CORRECTIONAL CENTER*, DCE Library, 1349 Correctional Center Rd, 23936. (Mail add: PO Box 430, 23936-0430), SAN 371-6139. Tel: 434-391-5980, Ext 5508. FAX: 434-983-1296. *Librn,* David Jobe; Staff 1 (Non-MLS 1)
Founded 1983
Library Holdings: Bk Titles 13,500; Bk Vols 14,000; Per Subs 43
Automation Activity & Vendor Info: (Acquisitions) Follett Software; (Cataloging) Follett Software; (Circulation) Follett Software; (OPAC) Follett Software
Open Mon-Fri 8-3

S   DILLWYN CORRECTIONAL CENTER*, 1522 Prison Rd, 23936. (Mail add: PO Box 670, 23936-0670), SAN 375-3387. Tel: 434-983-4200, Ext 4883. FAX: 434-983-1821. *In Charge,* Barna Anyadike; Staff 1 (Non-MLS 1)
Founded 1994
Library Holdings: Bk Titles 14,000
Automation Activity & Vendor Info: (Acquisitions) Follett Software; (Cataloging) Follett Software; (Circulation) Follett Software; (OPAC) Follett Software
Open Mon-Sat 8-4, Sun 9am-10am

DUBLIN

J   NEW RIVER COMMUNITY COLLEGE*, Learning Resource Center, 226 Martin Hall, 24084. (Mail add: PO Drawer 1127, 24084-1127), SAN 317-2627. Tel: 540-674-3627. FAX: 540-676-3626. Web Site: www.nr.edu/library/. *Coordr, Libr Serv,* Sandra Smith; Tel: 540-674-3600, Ext 4345, E-mail: nrsmits@nr.edu; *Circ Mgr,* Gary Bryant; Tel: 540-674-3600, Ext 4334, E-mail: nrbryag@nr.edu; *Cat, ILL Librn,* Nadine Shenk; Tel: 540-674-3600, Ext 4336, E-mail: nrshenn@nr.edu; *Ref Librn,* Cornelia Boyd; Tel: 540-674-3600, Ext 4303, E-mail: nrboydc@nr.edu; *Ref & Instruction Librn,* Alison Cockram; Tel: 540-674-3600, Ext 4331, E-mail: nrcocka@nr.edu; *Spec Projects Librn,* Roberta White; Tel: 540-674-3600, Ext 4339, E-mail: nrwhitr@nr.edu; Staff 6 (MLS 3, Non-MLS 3)
Founded 1968. Enrl 2,230; Fac 60
Library Holdings: Bks on Deafness & Sign Lang 250; High Interest/Low Vocabulary Bk Vols 300; Bk Titles 29,185; Bk Vols 34,495; Per Subs 406
Subject Interests: Educ, Hist, Humanities
Automation Activity & Vendor Info: (Acquisitions) Ex Libris Group; (Cataloging) Ex Libris Group; (Circulation) Ex Libris Group; (OPAC) Ex Libris Group
Partic in Virtual Library of Virginia
Special Services for the Deaf - Bks on deafness & sign lang; High interest/low vocabulary bks
Open Mon-Thurs 7:45am-9pm, Fri 7:45-5, Sat 9-1, Sun 1-5

EDINBURG

P   SHENANDOAH COUNTY LIBRARY*, 514 Stoney Creek Blvd, 22824. SAN 322-662X. Tel: 540-984-8200. Reference Tel: 540-984-8200, Ext 201. FAX: 540-984-8207. E-mail: scl@shentel.net. Web Site: www.shenandoah.co.lib.va.us. *Dir,* Robert Whitesides; E-mail: swhiteside@countylib.org; *Asst Dir,* Cathy J Stuter; Tel: 540-984-8200, Ext 205; *Ad,* David Robinson; *Ch,* Diane Cary; E-mail: dcary@countylib.org; *Head, Cat,* Ann Thompson; *Circ Supvr,* Zoe Dellinger; Staff 14 (MLS 2, Non-MLS 12)
Founded 1984. Pop 42,000; Circ 235,000
Jul 2008-Jun 2009 Income (Main Library and Branch(s)) $988,625, State $180,768, County $719,768, Locally Generated Income $88,089. Mats Exp $204,000, Books $104,000, Per/Ser (Incl. Access Fees) $6,300, Manu Arch $3,000, Other Print Mats $1,500, AV Mat $38,000, Electronic Ref Mat (Incl. Access Fees) $45,000, Presv $2,500. Sal $336,752 (Prof $112,000)
Library Holdings: Audiobooks 7,301; Bks on Deafness & Sign Lang 25; CDs 1,902; DVDs 6,162; e-books 300; Electronic Media & Resources 20,140; High Interest/Low Vocabulary Bk Vols 30; Large Print Bks 5,567; Microforms 245; Bk Titles 116,436; Bk Vols 121,321; Per Subs 115; Spec Interest Per Sub 12; Videos 2,800
Special Collections: Mid-Atlantic Germanic Society (MAGS) Coll; Shenandoah Room Coll
Subject Interests: Civil War, Maryland, Shenandoah County, Shenandoah Valley, Va, WVa
Automation Activity & Vendor Info: (Acquisitions) The Library Co-Op, Inc; (Cataloging) TLC (The Library Corporation); (Circulation) TLC (The Library Corporation); (OPAC) TLC (The Library Corporation)
Database Vendor: BWI, infoUSA, LearningExpress, LexisNexis, netLibrary, OCLC ArticleFirst, OCLC WebJunction, ReferenceUSA, TLC (The Library Corporation), ValueLine, WT Cox
Wireless access
Publications: Stoney Creek Current (Newsletter)
Partic in Shenandoah County Libr Syst
Special Services for the Blind - Bks on cassette
Open Mon, Tues & Thurs 10-8, Wed & Fri 10-6, Sat 10-4
Friends of the Library Group
Branches: 5
BASYE-ORKNEY SPRINGS COMMUNITY, Airport Rd, Basye, 22810. (Mail add: PO Box 251, Basye, 22810-0251). Tel: 540-856-8084. FAX: 540-856-2148. E-mail: basyelib@shentel.net. *Dir,* Robert Pasco; Tel: 540-984-8200, Ext 206
Open Mon, Wed, Thurs & Sat 10-2, Tues & Fri 10-2 & 4:30-6:30
FORT VALLEY COMMUNITY, 6190 Woodstock Tower Rd, Fort Valley, 22652. (Mail add: PO Box 120, Fort Valley, 22652-0120). Tel: 540-933-6714. FAX: 540-933-6013. E-mail: ftvallib@shentel.net. *Dir,* Robert Pasco; Tel: 540-984-8200, Ext 206
Open Mon & Thurs 3-8, Wed & Sat 9-2
MT JACKSON COMMUNITY, 5901 Main St, Mount Jackson, 22842. Tel: 540-477-3327. FAX: 540-477-2294. E-mail: mtjlib@shentel.net. *Dir,* Robert Pasco; Tel: 540-984-8200, Ext 206
Open Mon 6-8pm, Tues, Wed & Fri 1:30-5:30, Thurs 1:30-8, Sat 10-4
NEW MARKET AREA, 9417 S Congress St, New Market, 22844. (Mail add: PO Box 452, New Market, 22844). Tel: 540-740-8650. FAX: 540-740-2956. E-mail: nmlib@shentel.net. Web Site: www.shenandoah.co.lib.va.us/new_market_/new_market.htm. *Dir,* Grace Brubaker
Founded 1974
Library Holdings: Bk Vols 5,000; Talking Bks 50
Special Collections: Local History Coll
Open Mon 11-6:30, Tues-Fri 1-4:30, Sat 9:30-12
Friends of the Library Group
STRASBURG COMMUNITY, 195 W King St, Strasburg, 22657. Tel: 540-465-8464. FAX: 540-465-2739. E-mail: stlib@shental.net. *Br Librn,* Pat Orndoff
Open Mon, Wed & Thurs 10-1 & 3-6, Tues 10-1 & 3-8, Fri & Sat 10-4

EMORY

C   EMORY & HENRY COLLEGE, Kelly Library, 30480 Armbrister Dr, 24327. (Mail add: PO Box 948, 24327-0948), SAN 317-2643. Tel: 276-944-6208. Interlibrary Loan Service Tel: 276-944-6210. Reference Tel: 276-944-6209. FAX: 276-944-4592. E-mail: library@ehc.edu. Web Site: library.ehc.edu. *Chief Info Officer, Libr Dir,* Lorraine Abraham; Tel: 276-944-6808, E-mail: labraham@ehc.edu; *Asst Dir, Ref Librn,* Jane Caldwell; E-mail: jcaldwell@ehc.edu; *Electronic Res, Govt Doc Librn,* Jody Hanshew; Tel: 276-944-6213, E-mail: jhanshew@ehc.edu; *Pub Serv Librn,* Patty Greany; E-mail: pcgreany@ehc.edu; *Archivist, Spec Coll Librn,* Robert Vejnar; E-mail: rvejnar@ehc.edu; *Tech Serv Librn,* Janet Kirby; Tel: 276-944-6207, E-mail: jkirby@ehc.edu; Staff 6 (MLS 5, Non-MLS 1)
Founded 1836. Enrl 1,000; Fac 93; Highest Degree: Master
Library Holdings: e-books 78,000; Bk Titles 200,000; Bk Vols 392,000; Per Subs 652

Special Collections: Appalachian Oral History Coll; Methodist Church History (I P Martin Coll); Southwestern Virginiana (Goodrich Wilson Papers). Oral History; US Document Depository
Subject Interests: Liberal arts
Automation Activity & Vendor Info: (Acquisitions) Innovative Interfaces, Inc; (Cataloging) Innovative Interfaces, Inc; (Circulation) Innovative Interfaces, Inc; (ILL) OCLC ILLiad; (Media Booking) Innovative Interfaces, Inc; (OPAC) Innovative Interfaces, Inc; (Serials) Innovative Interfaces, Inc
Database Vendor: Alexander Street Press, ARTstor, BioOne, Cambridge Scientific Abstracts, CredoReference, EBSCOhost, Electric Library, Factiva.com, Gale Cengage Learning, JSTOR, LexisNexis, OCLC FirstSearch, OCLC WorldCat, ProQuest
Wireless access
Partic in Appalachian Col Asn; Holston Assoc Librs, Inc; Lyrasis; Mid-Atlantic Library Alliance (MALiA); Virginia Independent College & University Library Association; Virtual Library of Virginia
Open Mon-Thurs 7:30am-Midnight, Fri 7:30-6, Sat 10-5, Sun 2-Midnight

FAIRFAX

P   FAIRFAX COUNTY PUBLIC LIBRARY*, Administrative Offices, 12000 Government Center Pkwy, Ste 324, 22035-0012. SAN 363-3578. Tel: 703-324-3100. Interlibrary Loan Service Tel: 703-222-3136. FAX: 703-324-8365. Interlibrary Loan Service FAX: 703-222-3137. E-mail: wwwlib@fairfaxcounty.gov. Web Site: www.fairfaxcounty.gov/library. *Dir,* Edwin S Clay, III; E-mail: edwin.clay@fairfaxcounty.gov; *Dep Dir,* Jane Goodwin; *Assoc Dir,* Marianne Gearhart; *Assoc Dir,* Janet Prasher; *Mkt & Communications Mgr,* Mary Mulrenan; *Br Coordr,* Debbie King; *Br Coordr,* Patricia White-Williams; *Coordr, Coll Mgt,* Julie Pringle; *Cat,* Betsy Keefe; *Internet Serv,* Lydia Patrick
Founded 1939
Library Holdings: Bk Vols 2,601,743
Special Collections: Virginia History Coll
Automation Activity & Vendor Info: (Acquisitions) SirsiDynix; (Cataloging) SirsiDynix; (Circulation) SirsiDynix; (Course Reserve) SirsiDynix; (OPAC) SirsiDynix
Database Vendor: EBSCOhost, Gale Cengage Learning, Medline, OCLC ArticleFirst, OCLC FirstSearch, OCLC WorldCat, Overdrive, Inc, ProQuest, PubMed, ValueLine
Wireless access
Publications: Books & Beyond: Fairfax County Public Library's First Fifty Years; Collection Development; Fairfax County Public Library Board of Trustees Policy Manual; Fairfax County Public Library User Study; Information Services Guidelines; Information Services Profile; Materials Availability Study; Page Training Manual; Problem Behavior Manual; Reference Accuracy at the Fairfax County Public Library; Training Checklist for Circulation Staff; Training Checklist for Information Services Staff
Partic in Metrop Wash Libr Coun
Special Services for the Deaf - Assistive tech; TTY equip
Special Services for the Blind - Recorded bks
Open Mon-Fri 8-4:30
Friends of the Library Group
Branches: 22
BURKE CENTRE LIBRARY, 5935 Freds Oak Rd, Burke, 22015-2599. Tel: 703-249-1520. *Br Mgr,* Linda Schlekau
    Open Mon, Wed & Fri 10-6, Tues & Thurs 1-9, Sat 10-5
    Friends of the Library Group
RICHARD BYRD BRANCH, 7250 Commerce St, Springfield, 22150-3499, SAN 363-3969. Tel: 703-451-8055. *Br Mgr,* Sandy Freund
    Open Mon, Wed & Fri 10-6, Tues & Thurs 1-9, Sat 10-5
    Friends of the Library Group
CENTREVILLE REGIONAL, 14200 Saint Germain Dr, Centreville, 20121-2299, SAN 363-3667. Tel: 703-830-2223. *Br Mgr,* Christine Jones
    Open Mon & Wed 1-9, Tues 10-9, Thurs & Fri 10-6, Sat 10-5, Sun 1-5
    Friends of the Library Group
CHANTILLY REGIONAL, 4000 Stringfellow Rd, Chantilly, 20151-2628, SAN 374-7255. Tel: 703-502-3883. *Br Mgr,* Daria Parnes
    Open Mon & Wed 1-9, Tues 10-9, Thurs & Fri 10-6, Sat 10-5, Sun 1-5
    Friends of the Library Group
CITY OF FAIRFAX REGIONAL LIBRARY, 10360 North St, 22030-2514, SAN 363-3632. Tel: 703-293-6227. *Br Mgr,* Kathryn Hoffman
    Subject Interests: Genealogy, Va hist
    Open Mon & Wed 1-9, Tues 10-9, Thurs & Fri 10-6, Sat 10-5, Sun 1-5
    Friends of the Library Group
GREAT FALLS BRANCH, 9830 Georgetown Pike, Great Falls, 22066-2634, SAN 363-3764. Tel: 703-757-8560. *Br Mgr,* Daniela Dixon
    Open Mon, Wed & Fri 10-6, Tues & Thurs 1-9, Sat 10-5
    Friends of the Library Group
PATRICK HENRY BRANCH, 101 Maple Ave E, Vienna, 22180-5794, SAN 363-390X. Tel: 703-938-0405. *Br Mgr,* Sheila Janega
    Open Mon, Wed & Fri 10-6, Tues & Thurs 1-9, Sat 10-5
    Friends of the Library Group

HERNDON FORTNIGHTLY BRANCH, 768 Center St, Herndon, 20170-4640, SAN 363-3780. Tel: 703-437-8855. *Br Mgr,* Nancy Ryan
    Open Mon, Wed & Fri 10-6, Tues & Thurs 1-9, Sat 10-5
    Friends of the Library Group
THOMAS JEFFERSON BRANCH, 7415 Arlington Blvd, Falls Church, 22042-7499, SAN 363-4027. Tel: 703-573-1060. *Br Mgr,* Phyllis Ray
    Open Mon, Wed & Fri 10-6, Tues & Thurs 1-9, Sat 10-5
    Friends of the Library Group
KINGS PARK, 9000 Burke Lake Rd, Burke, 22015-1683, SAN 363-3845. Tel: 703-978-5600. *Br Mgr,* Linda Masnik
    Open Mon, Wed & Fri 10-6, Tues & Thurs 1-9, Sat 10-5
    Friends of the Library Group
KINGSTOWNE BRANCH, 6500 Landsdowne Ctr, Alexandria, 22315-5011. Tel: 703-339-4610. *Br Mgr,* Ted Kavich
    Open Mon, Wed & Fri 10-6, Tues & Thurs 1-9, Sat 10-5
    Friends of the Library Group
LORTON BRANCH, 9520 Richmond Hwy, Lorton, 22079-2124, SAN 363-3853. Tel: 703-339-7385. *Br Mgr,* Susan Larson
    Open Mon, Wed & Fri 10-6, Tues & Thurs 1-9, Sat 10-5
    Friends of the Library Group
DOLLEY MADISON BRANCH, 1244 Oak Ridge Ave, McLean, 22101-2818, SAN 363-3691. Tel: 703-356-0770. *Br Mgr,* Starr Smith
    Open Mon, Wed & Fri 10-6, Tues & Thurs 1-9, Sat 10-5
    Friends of the Library Group
JOHN MARSHALL BRANCH, 6209 Rose Hill Dr, Alexandria, 22310-6299, SAN 363-3810. Tel: 703-971-0010. *Br Mgr,* Kathryn Alleman
    Open Mon, Wed & Fri 10-6, Tues & Thurs 1-9, Sat 10-5
    Friends of the Library Group
GEORGE MASON REGIONAL, 7001 Little River Tpk, Annandale, 22003-5975, SAN 363-3756. Tel: 703-256-3800. *Br Mgr,* Kay Rzasa
    Open Mon & Wed 1-9, Tues 10-9, Thurs & Fri 10-6, Sat 10-5, Sun 1-5
    Friends of the Library Group
OAKTON LIBRARY, 10304 Lynnhaven Pl, Oakton, 22124-1785. Tel: 703-242-4020. *Br Mgr,* Jerilyn Polson
    Open Mon, Wed & Fri 10-6, Tues & Thurs 1-9, Sat 10-5
    Friends of the Library Group
POHICK REGIONAL, 6450 Sydenstricker Rd, Burke, 22015-4274, SAN 328-798X. Tel: 703-644-7333. *Br Mgr,* Jean Johnston
    Open Mon & Wed 1-9, Tues 10-9, Thurs & Fri 10-6, Sat 10-5, Sun 1-5
    Friends of the Library Group
RESTON REGIONAL, 11925 Bowman Towne Dr, Reston, 20190-3311, SAN 363-3934. Tel: 703-689-2700. *Br Mgr,* Andrew Pendergrass
    Open Mon & Wed 1-9, Tues 10-9, Thurs & Fri 10-6, Sat 10-5, Sun 1-5
    Friends of the Library Group
SHERWOOD REGIONAL, 2501 Sherwood Hall Lane, Alexandria, 22306-2799, SAN 363-3993. Tel: 703-765-3645. *Br Mgr,* Denise Morgan
    Open Mon & Wed 1-9, Tues 10-9, Thurs & Fri 10-6, Sat 10-5, Sun 1-5
    Friends of the Library Group
TYSONS-PIMMIT REGIONAL, 7584 Leesburg Pike, Falls Church, 22043-2099, SAN 363-4051. Tel: 703-790-8088. *Br Mgr,* Rita Mayer
    Open Mon & Wed 1-9, Tues 10-9, Thurs & Fri 10-6, Sat 10-5, Sun 1-5
    Friends of the Library Group
MARTHA WASHINGTON BRANCH, 6614 Fort Hunt Rd, Alexandria, 22307-1799, SAN 363-387X. Tel: 703-768-6700. *Br Mgr,* Barbara Rice
    Open Mon & Wed 10-6, Tues & Thurs 1-9, Fri 10-6, Sat 10-5
    Friends of the Library Group
WOODROW WILSON BRANCH, 6101 Knollwood Dr, Falls Church, 22041-1798, SAN 363-4086. Tel: 703-820-8774. *Br Mgr,* Mohammed Esslami
    Open Mon, Wed & Fri 10-6, Tues & Thurs 1-9, Sat 10-5
    Friends of the Library Group

GL   FAIRFAX PUBLIC LAW LIBRARY, Fairfax Bar Association Library, 4110 Chain Bridge Rd, Rm 115, 22030. SAN 321-8384. Tel: 703-246-2170. Administration Tel: 703-246-2175. FAX: 703-591-0310. E-mail: liblawlibrary@fairfaxcounty.gov. Web Site: www.fairfaxcounty.gov/courts/lawlib. *Dir,* Tom Pulver; Staff 3 (MLS 1, Non-MLS 2)
Founded 1956
Library Holdings: CDs 100; High Interest/Low Vocabulary Bk Vols 1,000; Bk Titles 8,000; Bk Vols 80,000; Per Subs 25; Spec Interest Per Sub 25
Special Collections: District of Columbia Coll; Maryland Coll; Virginia Law Coll (Historical Statutes & Session Laws)
Subject Interests: Law
Automation Activity & Vendor Info: (Acquisitions) LibraryWorld, Inc; (Cataloging) LibraryWorld, Inc; (OPAC) LibraryWorld, Inc; (Serials) LibraryWorld, Inc
Database Vendor: HeinOnline, LexisNexis, Westlaw
Wireless access
Function: CD-ROM, Computers for patron use, Copy machines, e-mail serv, Electronic databases & coll, Fax serv, Handicapped accessible, Online cat, Photocopying/Printing, Pub access computers, Web-catalog
Partic in American Association of Law Libraries (AALL)

Open Mon & Thurs 8-7, Tues, Wed & Fri 8-4:30
Restriction: Non-circulating, Not a lending libr

C GEORGE MASON UNIVERSITY LIBRARIES*, Fenwick Library, 4400 University Dr, MSN 2FL, 22030-4444. SAN 362-8833. Tel: 703-993-2250. Circulation Tel: 703-993-2240. Interlibrary Loan Service Tel: 703-993-2228. Reference Tel: 703-993-2210. Administration Tel: 703-993-2491. FAX: 703-993-2200. Interlibrary Loan Service FAX: 703-993-2255. Reference FAX: 703-993-2494. TDD: 703-993-3992. Web Site: library.gmu.edu. *Assoc Dir,* Larry Reeves; *Univ Librn,* John G Zenelis; E-mail: jzenelis@gmu.edu; *Assoc Univ Librn,* Wally Grotophorst; Tel: 703-993-9005, E-mail: wallyg@gmu.edu; *Assoc Univ Librn,* John Walsh; Tel: 703-993-3711, E-mail: jwalsh@gmu.edu; *Dir of Tech Serv,* Meghan Manahan; Tel: 703-993-2445; *Head, Access Serv,* Dorothy Lockaby; E-mail: dlockaby@gmu.edu; *Head, Coll Develop, Presv,* Cynthia Holt; *Head, Ref,* Jamie Coniglio; Tel: 703-993-2207, E-mail: jconigli@gmu.edu; *Head, Ser,* Joseph Becker; *Interim Head, Spec Coll & Archives,* Patty Jordon; *Cat/Metadata Librn,* Friedgard Cowan; *Cat/Metadata Librn,* Ian Fairclough; *Electronic Res Librn,* Betsy Appleton; *Instrul Design Librn,* Jacqueline Sipes; *Syst Librn,* Lara Bushallow; *Web Serv Librn,* Andrew Stevens; Staff 121 (MLS 49, Non-MLS 72) Founded 1957. Enrl 29,889; Fac 2,859; Highest Degree: Doctorate Jul 2006-Jun 2007 Income $14,665,259. Mats Exp $6,688,200, Books $2,153,903, Per/Ser (Incl. Access Fees) $1,402,505, Electronic Ref Mat (Incl. Access Fees) $2,744,436. Sal $5,090,852 (Prof $2,335,912)
Library Holdings: AV Mats 35,246; e-books 100,000; e-journals 30,000; Bk Vols 949,821; Per Subs 5,857
Special Collections: American Theater (Arthur Peterson Coll, Arena Stage Coll, Federal Theatre Project & Robert C Schnitzer Coll); Charles Baptie Photograph Coll; Early Twentieth Century Women's Magazines; Emilie F Miller Papers; Francis J McNamara Coll; GMU Archives; Harold J Morowitz Manuscripts; James Laue Papers; James S Trefil Coll; John N Warfield Coll; John W Burton Coll; Ollie Atkins Photograph Coll; Planned Community Archives (Nan Netherton Papers & Reston Community Archives); Transportation (William L Mertz Coll); Virginia (C Harrison Mann Map Coll & Legislative Papers; William McFarlane Papers). Oral History; State Document Depository; US Document Depository
Automation Activity & Vendor Info: (Acquisitions) Ex Libris Group; (Cataloging) Ex Libris Group; (Circulation) Ex Libris Group; (Course Reserve) Ex Libris Group; (ILL) OCLC Online; (OPAC) Ex Libris Group; (Serials) Ex Libris Group
Database Vendor: 3M Library Systems, ABC-CLIO, ACM (Association for Computing Machinery), Agricola, Alexander Street Press, American Chemical Society, American Psychological Association (APA), Annual Reviews, ARTstor, ASCE Research Library, BioOne, Blackwell's, Bowker, Cambridge Scientific Abstracts, CIOS (Communication Institute for Online Scholarship), College Source, CQ Press, Dialog, Dun & Bradstreet, EBSCO Information Services, EBSCOhost, Elsevier, Factiva.com, Facts on File, Gale Cengage Learning, H W Wilson, Haworth Pres Inc, HeinOnline, Hoovers, IEEE (Institute of Electrical & Electronics Engineers), ISI Web of Knowledge, JSTOR, LexisNexis, Nature Publishing Group, netLibrary, Newsbank, OCLC FirstSearch, OCLC WorldCat, OVID Technologies, Oxford Online, ProQuest, PubMed, ScienceDirect, SerialsSolutions, Springer-Verlag, Standard & Poor's, Swets Information Services, ValueLine, Wiley, Wilson - Wilson Web, YBP Library Services Wireless access
Function: Archival coll, Doc delivery serv, E-Reserves, Govt ref serv, ILL available, Libr develop, Ref serv available, Res libr, Wheelchair accessible
Publications: Fulltext (Newsletter); Research Guides
Partic in Association of Southeastern Research Libraries; Consortium of Southeastern Law Libraries; Lyrasis; OCLC Online Computer Library Center, Inc; Virtual Library of Virginia; Washington Research Library Consortium
Open Mon-Thurs 7:30am-Midnight, Fri 7:30am-9pm, Sat 9-9, Sun 9am-Midnight
Restriction: Open to students, fac & staff, Pub use on premises
Departmental Libraries:
ARLINGTON CAMPUS, 3401 N Fairfax Dr, Arlington, 22201. (Mail add: 4400 University Dr, MSN 1D1, 22030-4444). Tel: 703-993-8188. Reference Tel: 703-993-8230. FAX: 703-993-8142. TDD: 703-993-4970. Web Site: library.gmu.edu/libinfo/acl.html. *Head of Libr,* LeRoy J LaFleur; Tel: 703-993-8268, E-mail: llafleur@gmu.edu
Subject Interests: Conflict analysis & resolution, European Union, Intl trade, Nonprofit mgt
Function: Doc delivery serv, E-Reserves, ILL available, Ref serv available
Special Services for the Deaf - Assistive tech; TTY equip
Special Services for the Blind - Computer with voice synthesizer for visually impaired persons; Dragon Naturally Speaking software; Reader equip; VisualTek equip
Open Mon-Thurs 9am-10pm, Fri 9-7, Sat 10-6, Sun 12-8
Restriction: Open to students, fac & staff, Pub use on premises
JOHNSON CENTER, 4400 University Dr, MSN 1A6, 22030-4444. Tel: 703-993-9060. Reference Tel: 703-993-9070. FAX: 703-993-9063. TDD: 703-993-3992. Web Site: library.gmu.edu/libinfo/jcl.html. *Head of Libr,*

George Oberle; Tel: 703-993-9012, E-mail: goberle@gmu.edu; *Coordr, Circ,* Cynthia Bentley; Tel: 703-993-9057, E-mail: cbentle1@gmu.edu
Subject Interests: Educ, Multimedia, Music
Function: AV serv, E-Reserves, Ref serv available, Wheelchair accessible
Special Services for the Deaf - Assistive tech; Closed caption videos; TTY equip
Special Services for the Blind - Assistive/Adapted tech devices, equip & products; Bks on cassette; Bks on CD; Computer with voice synthesizer for visually impaired persons; Magnifiers; Reader equip; Scanner for conversion & translation of mats
Open Mon-Thurs 7:30am-Midnight, Fri 7:30am-9pm, Sat 9-9, Sun 9am-Midnight
Restriction: Open to students, fac & staff, Pub use on premises
MERCER LIBRARY, PRINCE WILLIAM CAMPUS, 10900 University Blvd, Occoquan Bldg, Rm 104, Manassas, 20110-2203. Tel: 703-993-8340. Reference Tel: 703-993-8342. FAX: 703-993-8349. TDD: 703-993-8365. Web Site: library.gmu.edu/libinfo/pwl.html. *Head of Libr,* Heather Groves Hannan; Tel: 703-993-8344, E-mail: hhannan@gmu.edu
Subject Interests: Admin of justice, Biodefence, Fitness, Health, Recreation, Tourism
Function: Doc delivery serv, ILL available, Ref serv available, Wheelchair accessible
Special Services for the Deaf - Assistive tech; TTY equip
Open Mon-Thurs 8am-10pm, Fri 8-7, Sat 10-5, Sun 1-6
Restriction: Open to students, fac & staff, Pub use on premises
CL SCHOOL OF LAW, 3301 N Fairfax Dr, Arlington, 22201-4426, SAN 362-8906. Tel: 703-993-8120. Reference Tel: 703-993-8076. Administration Tel: 703-993-8106. Automation Services Tel: 703-993-8100. FAX: 703-993-8113. Web Site: www.law.gmu.edu/libtech. *Assoc Dean,* Deborah Keene; Tel: 703-993-8110, E-mail: dkeene@gmu.edu; *Assoc Dir,* Larry Reeves; *Assoc Law Librn,* Femi Cadmus; Tel: 703-993-8107, E-mail: ocadmus1@gmu.edu; *Head, Res Serv,* Iva Futrell; *Head, Tech Serv,* Cynthia Myers; *Fac Serv Librn,* Paul Haas; *Instrul Serv Librn,* Melanie Oberlin; Staff 14 (MLS 7, Non-MLS 7)
Founded 1979. Enrl 742; Highest Degree: Doctorate
Jul 2005-Jun 2006 Income $2,041,426. Mats Exp $877,048, Books $40,316, Per/Ser (Incl. Access Fees) $649,586, Electronic Ref Mat (Incl. Access Fees) $187,146. Sal $834,871 (Prof $543,112)
Library Holdings: Bk Vols 252,590; Per Subs 5,634
Function: AV serv, Doc delivery serv, ILL available, Ref serv available, Res libr, Wheelchair accessible
Partic in Lyrasis
Publications: Law Library Guide (Reference guide); Research Guides
Open Mon-Thurs 8am-11pm, Fri 8am-10pm, Sat 10-8, Sun 11-11
Restriction: Open to students, fac & staff, Pub use on premises

S NATIONAL CLEARINGHOUSE ON CHILD ABUSE & NEGLECT INFORMATION*, 10530 Rosehaven St, Ste 400, 22030. (Mail add: 330 C St SW, Washington, 20447). Tel: 703-385-7565. Toll Free Tel: 800-394-3366. FAX: 703-385-3206. E-mail: nccanch@caliber.com. Web Site: nccanch.acf.hhs.gov. *Head Librn,* John Vogel; Tel: 703-279-6275; Staff 3 (MLS 3)
Library Holdings: Bk Vols 40,000; Per Subs 60
Restriction: Non-circulating, Open by appt only

S NATIONAL RIFLE ASSOCIATION*, ILA Library, 11250 Waples Mill Rd, 22030. SAN 302-7325. Tel: 703-267-3859. FAX: 703-267-3980. Web Site: www.nraila.org. *Librn,* Richard Wahl
Library Holdings: Bk Vols 6,000; Per Subs 75
Restriction: Not open to pub

L ODIN, FELDMAN & PITTLEMAN LIBRARY*, 9302 Lee Hwy, Ste 1100, 22031. SAN 377-3892. Tel: 703-218-2100, 703-218-2362. FAX: 703-218-2160. *Librn,* Andrew Martin
Library Holdings: Bk Vols 11,000; Per Subs 30
Database Vendor: LexisNexis, Westlaw
Partic in VA Law Librs Asn
Open Mon-Fri 8:30-6

FALLS CHURCH

S CENTER FOR HEALTH, ENVIRONMENT & JUSTICE*, 150 S Washington St, Ste 300, 22046. (Mail add: PO Box 6806, 22040), SAN 374-5864. Tel: 703-237-2249. FAX: 703-237-8389. E-mail: chej@chej.org. Web Site: www.chej.org. *Librn,* Barbara Sullivan; *Tech Serv,* Stephen Lester
Founded 1981
Library Holdings: Bk Titles 5,000; Per Subs 58; Spec Interest Per Sub 304
Special Collections: UN Document Depository
Subject Interests: Environ law, Environ sci, Health, Technologies
Function: Res libr
Publications: (Newsletter)

M   INOVA FAIRFAX HOSPITAL*, Jacob D Zylman Health Sciences Library,
3300 Gallows Rd, 22042-3300. SAN 317-2767. Tel: 703-776-3234.
Reference Tel: 703-776-3357. FAX: 703-776-3353. E-mail:
fairfax.library@inova.org. Web Site: www.inova.org/healthlibrary,
www.inova.org/library. *Dir,* Lois H Culler; E-mail: lois.culler@inova.com;
Staff 4.5 (MLS 3.5, Non-MLS 1)
Founded 1966
Library Holdings: CDs 265; DVDs 500; e-books 400; e-journals 2,500;
Electronic Media & Resources 45; Bk Vols 9,000; Per Subs 450; Videos
130
Special Collections: Consumer Health Resources Center
Subject Interests: Consumer health, Healthcare admin, Med, Nursing
Automation Activity & Vendor Info: (Acquisitions) SydneyPlus;
(Cataloging) SydneyPlus; (Circulation) SydneyPlus; (Media Booking)
SydneyPlus; (OPAC) SydneyPlus; (Serials) SydneyPlus
Database Vendor: Dialog, EBSCOhost, Elsevier, MD Consult, Medline,
Micromedex, OVID Technologies, ProQuest, RefWorks, ScienceDirect,
STAT!Ref (Teton Data Systems), Wiley InterScience
Partic in Dialog Corp; National Network of Libraries of Medicine
Open Mon-Fri 8-8, Sat 9-5

L   REED SMITH, LLP*, Law Library, 3110 Fairview Park Dr, Ste 1400,
22042. SAN 372-3348. Tel: 703-641-4200, 703-641-4367. FAX:
703-641-4340. Web Site: www.reedsmith.com. *Librn,* Anne Salzberg
Library Holdings: Bk Vols 3,000; Per Subs 50
Automation Activity & Vendor Info: (Acquisitions) SirsiDynix;
(Cataloging) SirsiDynix; (Circulation) SirsiDynix; (OPAC) SirsiDynix;
(Serials) SirsiDynix
Database Vendor: LexisNexis, Westlaw
Restriction: Staff use only

P   MARY RILEY STYLES PUBLIC LIBRARY*, 120 N Virginia Ave,
22046. SAN 317-2783. Tel: 703-248-5030. Circulation Tel: 703-248-5031.
Reference Tel: 703-248-5035. Administration Tel: 703-248-5032.
Automation Services Tel: 703-248-5174. FAX: 703-248-5144. Web Site:
www.fallschurchva.gov/library. *Dir,* Mary W McMahon; E-mail:
mmcmahon@fallschurchva.gov; Staff 20.5 (MLS 8, Non-MLS 12.5)
Founded 1898. Pop 11,000; Circ 424,191
Jul 2011-Jun 2012 Income $1,634,865, State $138,639, City $1,496,226.
Mats Exp $220,171, Books $129,376, Per/Ser (Incl. Access Fees) $14,564,
AV Mat $26,000, Electronic Ref Mat (Incl. Access Fees) $50,231. Sal
$1,443,627
Library Holdings: Audiobooks 4,254; AV Mats 17,181; CDs 4,214; DVDs
7,653; e-books 1,000; Large Print Bks 1,650; Bk Titles 120,000; Bk Vols
123,698; Per Subs 210; Videos 258
Special Collections: Falls Church History Coll
Automation Activity & Vendor Info: (Acquisitions) Innovative Interfaces,
Inc - Millenium; (Cataloging) Innovative Interfaces, Inc - Millenium;
(Circulation) Innovative Interfaces, Inc - Millenium; (OPAC) Innovative
Interfaces, Inc - Millenium; (Serials) Innovative Interfaces, Inc - Millenium
Database Vendor: 3M Library Systems, Baker & Taylor, Booklist Online,
EBSCOhost, Gale Cengage Learning, infoUSA, Ingram Library Services,
netLibrary, OCLC WorldCat, ProQuest, ReferenceUSA,
TumbleBookLibrary, WT Cox
Wireless access
Function: Adult bk club, AV serv, Bk club(s), Bks on cassette, Bks on
CD, Children's prog, Computer training, Computers for patron use, Copy
machines, e-mail & chat, Electronic databases & coll, Free DVD rentals,
Homebound delivery serv, ILL available, Music CDs, Notary serv, Online
cat, Online ref, Photocopying/Printing, Prog for children & young adult,
Pub access computers, Ref serv available, Ref serv in person, Spoken
cassettes & CDs, Spoken cassettes & DVDs, Story hour, Summer & winter
reading prog, Summer reading prog, Tax forms, Teen prog, Telephone ref,
Video lending libr, Web-catalog
Open Mon, Tues & Thurs 9-9, Wed 1-9, Fri & Sat 9-5, Sun 1-5

AM   UNITED STATES ARMED FORCES MEDICAL LIBRARY*, Office of
the Army Surgeon General Medical Library, Skyline 6, Rm 670, 5109
Leesburg Pike, 22041-3258. SAN 302-7457. Tel: 703-681-8028. Reference
Tel: 703-681-1104, 703-681-8030. FAX: 703-681-8034. E-mail:
afml@tma.osd.mil. Web Site: www.tricare.osd.mil/afml. *Dir,* Diane
Zehnpfennig
Founded 1969
Library Holdings: Bk Titles 18,000; Per Subs 450
Special Collections: Annual Report of the Surgeon General 1818-present
Subject Interests: Hospital admin
Automation Activity & Vendor Info: (Cataloging) EOS International;
(Circulation) EOS International; (ILL) OCLC; (OPAC) EOS International;
(Serials) EOS International
Partic in Docline; OCLC Online Computer Library Center, Inc
Open Mon-Fri 7:30-4

FARMVILLE

P   CENTRAL VIRGINIA REGIONAL LIBRARY*, Farmville-Prince Edward
Library, 217 W Third St, 23901. SAN 371-6791. Tel: 434-392-6924. FAX:
434-392-9784. Web Site: www.centralvirginiaregionallibrary.org. *Dir,*
Peggy Epperson; Staff 2 (MLS 1, Non-MLS 1)
Founded 1993. Pop 34,000; Circ 70,500
Library Holdings: Bk Vols 60,000; Per Subs 45
Special Collections: African-American History Coll
Subject Interests: Local hist
Automation Activity & Vendor Info: (Circulation) Follett Software;
(OPAC) Follett Software
Partic in Lyrasis
Open Mon & Thurs 9-8, Tues & Wed 9-6, Fri & Sat 9-5
Friends of the Library Group
Branches: 1
BUCKINGHAM COUNTY PUBLIC, 1140 Main St, Dillwyn, 23936-8413,
SAN 373-7063. Tel: 434-983-3848. FAX: 434-983-1587. *Br Mgr,* Joyce
Nelson
Founded 1983
Open Mon-Thurs 9-6, Fri & Sat 9-5
Friends of the Library Group

C   LONGWOOD UNIVERSITY*, Janet D Greenwood Library, Redford &
Race St, 23909. (Mail add: 201 High St, 23909), SAN 317-283X. Tel:
434-395-2633. Circulation Tel: 434-395-2433. Interlibrary Loan Service
Tel: 434-395-2446. Reference Tel: 434-395-2435, 434-395-2747.
Administration Tel: 434-395-2431. FAX: 434-395-2453. E-mail:
libweb@longwood.edu. Web Site: www.longwood.edu/library. *Dean of
Libr,* Wendell Barbour; Tel: 434-395-2083; E-mail:
barbourwa@longwood.edu; *Head, Tech Serv,* Patricia Howe; Tel:
434-395-2443, E-mail: howepa@longwood.edu; *Electronic Res Librn,*
Virginia Kinman; Tel: 434-395-2441, E-mail: kinmanvr@longwood.edu;
Instrul & Ref Librn, Liz Kocevar-Weidinger; Tel: 434-395-2445, E-mail:
kocevarweidingerea@longwood.edu; *Reader Serv Librn,* Tammy Hines;
Tel: 434-395-2444, E-mail: hinestm@longwood.edu; *Asst Instrul Design
Librn,* Tatiana Pashkova-Balkenhol; Tel: 434-395-2442, E-mail:
pashkovabalkenholtb@longwood.edu; *Asst Librn, Instruction & Ref,* Mark
Lenker; Tel: 434-395-2257, E-mail: lenkermn@longwood.edu; *Acq Mgr,*
Becky Fisher; Tel: 434-395-2448, E-mail: fisherrh@longwood.edu;
Archives & Rec Mgr, Lydia Williams; Tel: 434-395-2432, E-mail:
williamslc@longwood.edu; *Budget Off Mgr,* Cindy Elliott; Tel:
434-395-2440, E-mail: elliotcb@longwood.edu; *Circ Mgr,* Linda B
Baldwin; Tel: 434-395-2082, E-mail: baldwinlb@longwood.edu; *Reserves
Mgr,* Evelyn Sims; Tel: 434-395-2437, E-mail: simse@longwood.edu; *Mgr,
Ser,* Jenifer Culley; Tel: 434-395-2447, E-mail: culleyjr@longwood.edu;
AV/Multimedia Spec, Benjamin Johnson; Tel: 434-395-2456, E-mail:
johnsonbc@longwood.edu; *Info Syst Spec,* Chris Harper; Tel:
434-395-2438, E-mail: harpercl@longwood.edu; *Info Tech Spec,* Susan
Carroll; Tel: 434-395-2873, E-mail: carrollsk@longwood.edu; *Cat,* Betty
Eike; Tel: 434-395-2449, E-mail: eikeba@longwood.edu; *Circ Asst, ILL,*
Dana Owen; E-mail: owendb@longwood.edu; *Acq Asst,* Florence Southall;
Tel: 434-395-2742, E-mail: southallfs@longwood.edu; *Circ Asst,* Phyllis
Baker; Tel: 434-395-2743, E-mail: bakerdp@longwood.edu; *Circ Asst,*
Suzzane Swisstack; Tel: 434-395-2451, E-mail:
swisstackss@longwood.edu; *Electronic Res Asst,* Mary Fran Bell-Johnson;
Tel: 434-395-2450, E-mail: belljohnmf@longwood.edu; *Ref Asst,* Ruth
Gowin; Tel: 434-395-2741, E-mail: gowinre@longwood.edu
Founded 1839. Enrl 4,800; Fac 210; Highest Degree: Master
Library Holdings: CDs 4,000; DVDs 14,000; e-books 18,000; e-journals
34,000; Bk Titles 275,000; Bk Vols 332,000; Per Subs 35,000
Special Collections: State Document Depository
Automation Activity & Vendor Info: (Cataloging) Innovative Interfaces,
Inc; (Circulation) Innovative Interfaces, Inc
Wireless access
Partic in BRS; Dialog Corp; Dow Jones News Retrieval; Lyrasis; OCLC
Online Computer Library Center, Inc; Source; Specialnet; Virtual Library
of Virginia; Wilsonline
Open Mon-Thurs 8am-Midnight, Fri 8-5, Sat 10-5, Sun 1-Midnight
Friends of the Library Group

FERRUM

C   FERRUM COLLEGE*, Thomas Stanley Library, 150 Wiley Dr, 24088.
(Mail add: PO Box 1000, 24088-1000), SAN 317-2848. Tel: 540-365-4426.
Interlibrary Loan Service Tel: 540-365-4420. Reference Tel: 540-365-4427.
Automation Services Tel: 540 365-4428. FAX: 540-365-4423. Web Site:
www.ferrumlibrary.net. *Dir,* Cy Dillon; E-mail: cdillon@ferrum.edu; *Head,
Pub Serv,* George Loveland; *Head, Tech Serv,* Peggie Barker; *ILL,* Cheryl
Hundley; Staff 4 (MLS 3, Non-MLS 1)
Founded 1913. Enrl 1,000; Highest Degree: Bachelor
Library Holdings: AV Mats 2,086; e-books 100,000; Bk Vols 115,000;
Per Subs 14,600
Special Collections: Archives of Governor & Mrs Thomas B Stanley
Subject Interests: Environ studies, Hist, Relig studies

Automation Activity & Vendor Info: (Acquisitions) Innovative Interfaces, Inc; (Cataloging) Innovative Interfaces, Inc; (Circulation) Innovative Interfaces, Inc; (Course Reserve) Docutek; (ILL) OCLC; (OPAC) Innovative Interfaces, Inc; (Serials) Innovative Interfaces, Inc
Partic in Appalachian Col Asn; Lyrasis; OCLC Online Computer Library Center, Inc; Virginia Independent College & University Library Association; Virtual Library of Virginia
Open Mon-Wed (Winter) 7:45am-Midnight, Thurs 7:45am-11pm, Fri 7:45am-8pm, Sat Noon-8, Sun 2pm-Midnight; Mon-Fri (Summer) 8:30-4:30

FISHERSVILLE

P   AUGUSTA COUNTY LIBRARY*, 1759 Jefferson Hwy, 22939. SAN 317-2856. Tel: 540-885-3961, 540-949-6354. FAX: 540-943-5965. Web Site: www.augustacountylibrary.org. *Dir,* Diantha McCauley; *Asst Dir,* Debbie Sweeney; *Ref,* Barbara Olsen; Staff 3 (MLS 3)
Founded 1977. Pop 70,700; Circ 497,998
Jul 2007-Jun 2008 Income (Main Library and Branch(s)) $1,202,330, State $192,327, County $1,010,003. Mats Exp $192,327, Books $122,327, Per/Ser (Incl. Access Fees) $20,000, AV Mat $50,000
Library Holdings: Audiobooks 6,077; CDs 3,346; DVDs 13,815; Bk Vols 169,628; Per Subs 310; Talking Bks 5,570; Videos 13,167
Automation Activity & Vendor Info: (Cataloging) TLC (The Library Corporation); (Circulation) TLC (The Library Corporation); (OPAC) TLC (The Library Corporation)
Wireless access
Publications: Newsletter (Quarterly)
Partic in Lyrasis; SouthWest Information Network Group (SWING)
Open Mon-Thurs 9-9, Fri & Sat 9-5
Friends of the Library Group
Branches: 1
CHURCHVILLE BRANCH, 3714 Churchville Ave, Churchville, 24421. Tel: 540-245-5287. FAX: 540-245-5290. *Br Mgr,* Jack E Holt; E-mail: jackholt@augustacountylibrary.org; *Ch,* Charlotte Stephenson; Staff 2 (Non-MLS 2)
Founded 2002
Library Holdings: Bk Vols 25,000; Per Subs 26
Automation Activity & Vendor Info: (Serials) EBSCO Online
Database Vendor: EBSCOhost, Gale Cengage Learning, netLibrary
Function: Bk club; CD-ROM, Copy machines, E-Reserves, Electronic databases & coll, Fax serv, Handicapped accessible, Magnifiers for reading, Prog for children & young adult, Spoken cassettes & CDs, Summer reading prog, Tax forms, VHS videos, Wheelchair accessible
Special Services for the Deaf - Closed caption videos
Special Services for the Blind - Bks on cassette; Bks on CD; Large print bks
Open Mon & Tues 12-8, Wed & Thurs 10-6, Sat 10-5
Friends of the Library Group

FORK UNION

P   FLUVANNA COUNTY LIBRARY*, 8880 James Madison Hwy, 23055. (Mail add: PO Box 548, 23055-0548), SAN 317-378X. Tel: 434-842-2230. FAX: 434-842-2230. E-mail: mdrane@fcplva.org. Web Site: www.fcplva.org. *Dir,* Marcia Drane; Staff 5 (MLS 1, Non-MLS 4)
Founded 1968. Pop 24,000; Circ 131,000
Jul 2006-Jun 2007 Income $258,002, State $60,001, County $198,001. Mats Exp $49,000. Sal $129,043
Library Holdings: Bk Vols 44,000; Per Subs 131
Special Collections: Fluvanna County Historical Society Coll
Subject Interests: Local hist
Automation Activity & Vendor Info: (Cataloging) TLC (The Library Corporation); (Circulation) TLC (The Library Corporation); (ILL) TLC (The Library Corporation); (OPAC) TLC (The Library Corporation)
Database Vendor: TLC (The Library Corporation)
Wireless access
Open Mon & Tues 9-6, Wed & Thurs 12-8, Fri 9-5, Sat 9-3
Friends of the Library Group

FORT BELVOIR

G   DAVID D ACKER LIBRARY & KNOWLEDGE REPOSITORY, 9820 Belvoir Rd, 22060. Tel: 703-805-2293. FAX: 703-805-3443. E-mail: library@dau.mil. Web Site: www.dau.mil/library/. *Librn,* Eddie Rozier; Tel: 703-805-5143, E-mail: eddie.rozier@dau.mil; Staff 8 (MLS 4, Non-MLS 4)
Automation Activity & Vendor Info: (Acquisitions) SirsiDynix; (Cataloging) SirsiDynix
Wireless access
Function: ILL available
Restriction: Borrowing privileges limited to fac & registered students, Borrowing requests are handled by ILL

G   DEFENSE TECHNICAL INFORMATION CENTER*, 8725 John J Kingman Rd, Ste 944, 22060-6218. SAN 317-199X. Tel: 703-767-8180. Toll Free Tel: 800-225-3842. FAX: 703-767-9459. Web Site: www.dtic.mil. *Librn,* David Long; E-mail: dlong@dtic.mil
Founded 1958
Library Holdings: Bk Vols 7,000
Special Collections: Technical Reports
Database Vendor: Dialog, LexisNexis, OCLC FirstSearch, OCLC WorldCat, ProQuest, SirsiDynix
Partic in Fedlink; OCLC Online Computer Library Center, Inc
Open Mon-Fri 7-4:30
Restriction: Restricted pub use

UNITED STATES ARMY
A   CENTER FOR ARMY ANALYSIS*, Bldg 1839, 6001 Goethals Rd, 22060-5230, SAN 328-8668. Tel: 703-806-5191. FAX: 703-806-5724. *Dir, Res,* Mary Bushey; E-mail: mary.bushey@us.army.mil; Staff 1 (MLS 1)
Oct 2006-Sept 2007. Mats Exp $77,467, Books $9,000, Per/Ser (Incl. Access Fees) $29,000, Electronic Ref Mat (Incl. Access Fees) $39,467
Library Holdings: Bk Titles 5,400; Per Subs 75
Subject Interests: Computer sci, Mil hist
Automation Activity & Vendor Info: (Cataloging) SirsiDynix; (Circulation) SirsiDynix; (OPAC) SirsiDynix
Database Vendor: EBSCOhost, OCLC FirstSearch
Function: Doc delivery serv, ILL available
Partic in OCLC Online Computer Library Center, Inc
Open Mon-Fri 7:30-4

A   THE INSTITUTE OF HERALDRY LIBRARY*, 9325 Gunston Rd, Ste S113, 22060-5579, SAN 362-6911. Tel: 703-806-4967, 703-806-4975. FAX: 703-656-4964. Web Site: www.tioh.hqda.pentagon.mil. *Res Analyst,* Paul Tuohig
Founded 1961
Library Holdings: Bk Titles 12,000; Bk Vols 26,000; Per Subs 26
Subject Interests: Art, Flags, Heraldry, Insignia, Medallic art, Medals, Mil hist, Seals, Symbolism, Symbols, Uniforms
Restriction: Staff use only

A   VAN NOY LIBRARY, 5966 12th St, Bldg 1024, 22060-5554, SAN 362-8922. Tel: 703-806-3323. Reference Tel: 703-806-3324. Administration Tel: 703-806-0096. Web Site: www.belvoirmwr.com/Facilities/Library/. *Libr Dir,* Daniel Sadowitz; E-mail: daniel.sadowitz@us.army.mil; *Librn,* Donna Ramsey; Tel: 703-806-3238, E-mail: donna.ramsey@us.army.mil; *Coll Mgt Librn,* Stephanie Xander; Tel: 703-806-3273, E-mail: stephanie.xander@us.army.mil; *Tech Serv Librn,* Hyesoon H Kim; Tel: 703-806-0093, E-mail: hyesoon.h.kim@us.army.mil; Staff 4 (MLS 4)
Founded 1939
Oct 2012-Sept 2013. Mats Exp $43,500, Books $35,000, Per/Ser (Incl. Access Fees) $4,500, AV Mat $4,000
Library Holdings: DVDs 2,000; Bk Vols 45,614; Per Subs 108; Talking Bks 1,173
Subject Interests: Adult fiction, Adult non-fiction, Children's fiction, Mil hist
Automation Activity & Vendor Info: (Cataloging) Innovative Interfaces, Inc - Millenium; (Circulation) Innovative Interfaces, Inc - Millenium; (ILL) OCLC WorldCat; (OPAC) Innovative Interfaces, Inc - Millenium
Database Vendor: EBSCO Auto Repair Reference, Gale Cengage Learning, netLibrary, OCLC FirstSearch, OCLC WorldCat
Function: Audiobks via web, Bks on CD, Computers for patron use, Copy machines, Electronic databases & coll, Handicapped accessible, Prog for children & young adult, Summer reading prog
Restriction: Open to mil & govt employees only

FORT EUSTIS

AM   MCDONALD ARMY HEALTH CENTER LIBRARY*, Bldg 576, Jefferson Ave, 23604-5548. SAN 370-243X. Tel: 757-314-7857. FAX: 757-314-7773. *Libr Tech,* Ilianet Berrios
Library Holdings: Bk Titles 400
Open Mon-Fri 7-4

UNITED STATES ARMY
A   AVIATION APPLIED TECHNOLOGY DIRECTORATE, TECHNICAL LIBRARY*, Bldg 401, Rm 100C, 23604-5577, SAN 362-9104. Tel: 757-878-0083. FAX: 757-878-0008. *Tech Info Spec,* George Schultz; E-mail: george.schultz@us.army.mil
Founded 1946
Library Holdings: Bk Vols 5,100; Per Subs 100
Subject Interests: Army aircraft, Aviation safety, Composite structures, Gas turbines, Low-speed aeronaut, Propulsion systs
Partic in OCLC Online Computer Library Center, Inc
Open Tues-Thurs 8-2

A   GRONINGER LIBRARY*, Bldg 1313, Army Transportation Ctr, Washington Blvd, 23604-5107, SAN 362-9163. Tel: 757-878-5017, 757-878-5583. FAX: 757-878-1024. Web Site: www.eustismwr.com. *Librn,* Valerie Fashion; E-mail: valerie.fashion@us.army.mil
Library Holdings: Bk Titles 80,200; Per Subs 60
Special Collections: Genealogy Coll; Military Science Coll
Automation Activity & Vendor Info: (Cataloging) Follett Software; (Circulation) Follett Software
Publications: Library Brochure
Open Mon-Wed 10-7, Thurs 12-9, Fri-Sun 10-5

A   US ARMY TRANSPORTATION MUSEUM LIBRARY*, Besson Hall, 300 Washington Blvd, 23604-5260. SAN 370-2588. Tel: 757-878-1115. FAX: 757-878-5656. Web Site: www.eustis.army.mil. *Dir,* David Hanselman; *Asst Curator,* James Atwater
Library Holdings: Bk Vols 4,500
Open Tues-Sun 9-4
Restriction: Ref only

FORT LEE

A   UNITED STATES ARMY*, The Army Logistics Library, US Army Logistics University, Bldg 12420, 562 Quarters Rd, 23801-1705. SAN 362-9317. Tel: 804-765-4722. Reference Tel: 804-765-8177. FAX: 804-765-4660. E-mail: armyloglib@lee.army.mil. Web Site: www.almc.army.mil/ALU_LIBRARY. *Dir,* Tim Renick; E-mail: tim.renick@us.army.mil; *Coll Develop, Online Serv, Ref,* John Shields; E-mail: john.sheilds1@us.army.mil; *ILL,* Virginia Gordon; E-mail: jennie.gordon@us.army.mil; Staff 5 (MLS 2, Non-MLS 3)
Founded 1971
Library Holdings: Bk Titles 38,000; Bk Vols 40,000; Per Subs 200
Special Collections: Technical Reports
Subject Interests: Computer sci, Logistics, Petroleum
Automation Activity & Vendor Info: (Cataloging) SirsiDynix; (Circulation) SirsiDynix; (ILL) OCLC; (OPAC) SirsiDynix
Database Vendor: EBSCOhost, Medline, ProQuest
Publications: Accessions List (Quarterly); Bibliographies; Library handbook; Periodical Listing
Partic in Dialog Corp; OCLC Online Computer Library Center, Inc
Open Mon-Fri 8-7, Sat 10-5, Sun 12-5

FORT MONROE

S   CASEMATE MUSEUM LIBRARY, 20 Bernard Rd, 23651-1004. (Mail add: PO Box 51341, 23651-0341), SAN 327-4047. Tel: 757-788-3935. FAX: 757-788-3886. Web Site: www-tradoc.army.mil/museum. *Dir,* Claire Samuelson; Tel: 757-788-3391, E-mail: claire.s.samuelson.civ@mail.mil; *Archivist,* David Jeffrey Johnson; E-mail: david.jeffrey.johnson@us.army.mil; Staff 2 (Non-MLS 2)
Founded 1975
Oct 2011-Sept 2012. Mats Exp $304, Books $22, Per/Ser (Incl. Access Fees) $60, Manu Arch $26, Presv $196
Library Holdings: CDs 255; DVDs 131; Microforms 400; Bk Vols 12,600; Per Subs 20; Videos 115
Special Collections: Casemate Newspaper 1965-2011; Coast Artillery School. Oral History
Subject Interests: Local hist, Mil hist
Publications: Casemate Papers (Local historical information); Tales of Old Fort Monroe (Local historical information); The Guns of Fort Monroe (Local historical information)
Open Tues-Fri 9-4, Sat 10-4
Restriction: Non-circulating, Not a lending libr

A   UNITED STATES ARMY*, Fort Monroe Library, Seven Bernard Rd, 23651-5124. SAN 362-9341. Tel: 757-788-2909. FAX: 757-788-2931. Web Site: www-tradoc.monroe.army.mil/library. *Chief Librn,* Karen J Lewis; Tel: 757-788-2967, E-mail: karen.lewis@us.army.mil; *Librn,* Sally A Swan; E-mail: sally.swan@monroe.army.mil; Staff 3 (MLS 3)
Founded 1824
Library Holdings: Bk Vols 4,000; Per Subs 300
Special Collections: Training & Doctrine Command Technical Reports/Studies
Subject Interests: Mil hist, Mil sci
Automation Activity & Vendor Info: (Cataloging) TLC (The Library Corporation); (Circulation) TLC (The Library Corporation); (OPAC) TLC (The Library Corporation)
Database Vendor: EBSCOhost, Gale Cengage Learning, LexisNexis, OCLC FirstSearch
Partic in OCLC Online Computer Library Center, Inc
Open Mon-Fri 8-6

FORT MYER

A   UNITED STATES ARMY*, Fort Myer Post Library, Bldg 417, Rm 120, 239 Sheridan Ave, 22211. SAN 362-9406. Tel: 703-696-3555. Interlibrary Loan Service Tel: 703-696-0000, FAX: 703-696-8587. *Tech Serv,* Cynthia D Earman; E-mail: cynthia.earman@us.army.mil; Staff 1 (MLS 1)
Library Holdings: Bk Vols 45,000; Per Subs 250
Special Collections: Popular Coll
Subject Interests: Computer sci, Juv, Mil hist, Pub admin
Automation Activity & Vendor Info: (Cataloging) EOS International; (Circulation) EOS International; (Course Reserve) EOS International; (OPAC) EOS International; (Serials) EOS International
Database Vendor: EBSCOhost, netLibrary, OCLC FirstSearch
Function: Copy machines, Electronic databases & coll, Fax serv, ILL available, Online searches, Photocopying/Printing
Partic in OCLC Online Computer Library Center, Inc
Open Mon-Wed 11-7, Sat & Sun 12-5

FORT STORY

A   UNITED STATES ARMY*, Fort Story Library, Bldg T-530, Solomons Rd, 23459-5067. SAN 320-9563. Tel: 757-422-7548. Circulation Tel: 757-422-7525. FAX: 757-422-7773. E-mail: ftstory@us.army.mil. *Librn,* Gail Patterson; E-mail: gail.patterson@us.army.mil; Staff 2 (MLS 1, Non-MLS 1)
Library Holdings: Bk Titles 34,000; Per Subs 35
Subject Interests: Mil
Automation Activity & Vendor Info: (Cataloging) Follett Software; (Circulation) Follett Software
Partic in Tralinet
Open Mon-Fri 10-6

FRANKLIN

J   PAUL D CAMP COMMUNITY COLLEGE LIBRARY*, Franklin Campus, 100 N College Dr, 23851-2422. (Mail add: PO Box 737, 23851-0737), SAN 317-2880. Tel: 757-569-6700, 757-569-6737. FAX: 757-569-6736. Web Site: www.pc.vccs.edu. *Dir, Learning Res,* Linza M Weaver; Tel: 757-569-6735, E-mail: lweaver@pc.vccs.edu; Staff 1 (MLS 1)
Founded 1971. Enrl 1,547; Fac 24
Library Holdings: Bk Titles 21,127; Bk Vols 29,083; Per Subs 200
Automation Activity & Vendor Info: (Cataloging) Ex Libris Group; (Circulation) Ex Libris Group; (OPAC) Ex Libris Group
Database Vendor: Gale Cengage Learning, OCLC FirstSearch, OVID Technologies
Function: For res purposes, ILL available, Photocopying/Printing, Ref serv available
Partic in Tidewater Consortium for Continuing Higher Educ; Virginia Commun Coll Syst; Virtual Library of Virginia
Open Mon-Thurs 8:30-7:30, Fri 8-4
Departmental Libraries:
HOBBS SUFFOLK CAMPUS, 271 Kenyon Rd, Suffolk, 23434. (Mail add: PO Box 500, Suffolk, 23439). Tel: 757-925-6300, 757-925-6345. FAX: 757-925-6374. *Dir, Learning Res,* Linza Weaver; E-mail: lweaver@pc.vccs.edu; *Librn,* Troy Hand; Tel: 757-925-6339, E-mail: thand@pc.vccs.edu
Open Mon-Thurs 8:30-7:30, Fri 8:30-4:30

FREDERICKSBURG

P   CENTRAL RAPPAHANNOCK REGIONAL LIBRARY*, Headquarters, 1201 Caroline St, 22401-3761. SAN 317-2899. Tel: 540-372-1144. Administration Tel: 540-372-1160. FAX: 540-373-9411. Web Site: www.librarypoint.org. *Dir,* Donna Cote; *Dep Dir,* Alison Heartwell; *Br Mgr,* Margaret J Beattie; *Mgr, Youth Serv,* Rebecca Purdy; *Head, Ref Serv,* Michele Brown; *Adult Serv Coordr,* Ann Haley; *Youth Serv Coordr,* Caroline Parr; *Cat,* Mary Westbrook; Staff 97.5 (MLS 44, Non-MLS 53.5)
Founded 1969
Jul 2006-Jun 2007 Income (Main Library and Branch(s)) $10,277,286. Mats Exp $1,036,326, Books $935,782, Per/Ser (Incl. Access Fees) $45,247, AV Mat $55,297. Sal $6,140,407 (Prof $2,756,938)
Library Holdings: AV Mats 59,911; Bk Vols 449,772; Per Subs 1,192
Subject Interests: Fredericksburg, Law, Va
Automation Activity & Vendor Info: (Acquisitions) Horizon; (Cataloging) Horizon; (Circulation) Horizon; (Course Reserve) Horizon; (ILL) Horizon; (Media Booking) Horizon; (OPAC) Horizon; (Serials) Horizon
Wireless access
Special Services for the Deaf - TTY equip
Open Mon-Thurs 9-9, Fri & Sat 9-5:30, Sun 1-5:30
Friends of the Library Group

Branches: 7
COOPER BRANCH, 20 Washington Ave, Colonial Beach, 22443-2337, SAN 320-0604. Tel: 804-224-0921. FAX: 804-224-1330. Web Site: www.librarypoint.org. *Br Mgr,* Kitty Norris
Open Tues & Thurs 1-9, Wed 1-5, Fri 9-5, Sat 9-1
Friends of the Library Group

P   FREDERICKSBURG SUBREGIONAL FOR THE BLIND-PHYSICALLY HANDICAPPED, 1201 Caroline St, 22401. Tel: 540-372-1144, Ext 234, 540-372-1160. Toll Free Tel: 800-628-4807, Ext 234. TDD: 540-371-9165. *Head Librn,* Michele Brown; Staff 2 (MLS 1, Non-MLS 1)
Open Mon-Thurs 9-9, Fri & Sat 9-5:30, Sun 1-5:30
MONTROSS BRANCH, 56 Polk St, Montross, 22520-0308, SAN 321-4958. Tel: 804-493-8194. FAX: 804-493-0446. *Br Mgr,* Barbara Maines
Open Tues & Thurs 2-9, Wed & Fri 10-5, Sat 10-2
Friends of the Library Group
NEWTON BRANCH, 22 Coles Point Rd, Hague, 22469, SAN 326-7474. Tel: 804-472-3820. FAX: 804-472-5104. *Br Mgr,* Aimee Dillon; E-mail: adillon@crrl.org
Open Mon & Thurs 9-5, Wed 1-9, Fri 1-5, Sat 9-1
Friends of the Library Group
PORTER BRANCH, 2001 Parkway Blvd, Stafford, 22554-3972, SAN 320-0590. Tel: 540-659-4909. FAX: 540-659-4359. *Br Mgr,* Martha Hutzel
Open Mon, Wed & Thurs 9-9, Tues, Fri & Sat 9-5:30
Friends of the Library Group
SALEM CHURCH, 2607 Salem Church Rd, 22407-6451, SAN 374-7247. Tel: 540-785-9267. FAX: 540-785-9443. *Br Mgr,* Barbara Davison
Open Mon-Thurs 9-9, Fri & Sat 9-5:30, Sun 1-5:30
Friends of the Library Group
SNOW BRANCH, 8740 Courthouse Rd, Spotsylvania, 22553-2513, SAN 324-3087. Tel: 540-507-7565. *Br Mgr,* Shelley Chick-Gravel
Open Mon-Thurs 9-9, Fri & Sat 9-5:30
Friends of the Library Group
Bookmobiles: 1

S   GEORGE WASHINGTON FOUNDATION*, 1201 Washington Ave, 22401. SAN 370-1441. Tel: 540-373-3381. FAX: 540-371-6066. E-mail: mailroom@kenmore.org. Web Site: www.kenmore.org. *Curator,* Gregory Stoner; E-mail: stoner@gwffoundation.org
Library Holdings: Bk Titles 400
Special Collections: George Washington; Lewis Family Coll, 18th Century
Restriction: Open by appt only

J   GERMANNA COMMUNITY COLLEGE*, Cosner Library, 10000 Germanna Point Dr, 22408-9543. Tel: 540-891-3015. FAX: 540-891-3060. E-mail: library@germanna.edu. Web Site: www.gcc.vccs.edu/library. *Coordr, Libr Serv,* Rosemary Blankenship; E-mail: rblankenship@germanna.edu
Library Holdings: Bk Titles 10,000; Per Subs 35
Automation Activity & Vendor Info: (Cataloging) TLC (The Library Corporation); (Circulation) TLC (The Library Corporation); (OPAC) TLC (The Library Corporation)
Open Mon-Thurs 8-8, Fri 8-2, Sat 9-1

S   INTERNATIONAL PARKING INSTITUTE*, Resource Center, 701 Kenmore Ave, 22401-5737. (Mail add: PO Box 7167, 22404-7167), SAN 373-2606. Tel: 540-371-7535. FAX: 540-371-8022. E-mail: ipi@parking.org. Web Site: www.parking.org. *Pres,* Kim Jackson; *In Charge,* Yvonne McCowin
Library Holdings: Bk Vols 1,000
Subject Interests: Law

C   UNIVERSITY OF MARY WASHINGTON*, Simpson Library, 1801 College Ave, 22401-4665. SAN 317-2910. Tel: 540-654-1147. Circulation Tel: 540-654-1748. Interlibrary Loan Service Tel: 540-654-1746. Reference Tel: 540-654-1148. Automation Services Tel: 540-654-1756. FAX: 540-654-1067. Web Site: www.library.umw.edu. *Univ Librn,* Rosemary Arneson; E-mail: rarnes03@umw.edu; *Head, Circ,* Beth Perkins; E-mail: eperkins@umw.edu; *Br Librn,* Jami Bryan; Tel: 540-286-8057, E-mail: jbryan@umw.edu; *Ref & Instrul Serv Librn,* Jack Bales; Tel: 540-654-1780, E-mail: jbales@umw.edu; *Spec Coll Librn,* Carolyn Parsons; Tel: 540-654-1752, E-mail: cparsons@umw.edu; *Syst Librn,* Tim Newman; E-mail: tnewman@umw.edu; *Br Operations Adminr,* Nicole St John; Tel: 540-286-8033, E-mail: nstjohn@umw.edu; *Acq,* Tina Faulconer; Tel: 540-654-1761, E-mail: tfaulcon@umw.edu; *Admin Serv,* Linda Carver; E-mail: lcarver@umw.edu; *Cat,* Charles Balthis; Tel: 540-654-1772, E-mail: cbalthis@umw.edu; *Coll Develop,* Renee Davis; Tel: 540-654-1758, E-mail: rdavis@umw.edu; *Govt Doc,* Phyllis Johnson; Tel: 540-654-1759, E-mail: pjohnson@umw.edu; *ILL,* Carla Bailey; E-mail: cbailey@umw.edu; *Ref,* Christie Glancy; Tel: 540-654-1740, E-mail: cglancy@umw.edu; *Ref,* Karen Nelson; E-mail: knelson@umw.edu; *Ser,* Donna Hudgins; Tel: 540-654-1762, E-mail: dhudgins@umw.edu; Staff 9 (MLS 9)

Founded 1908. Enrl 4,040; Fac 231; Highest Degree: Master
Library Holdings: e-books 42,000; Bk Vols 36,700
Special Collections: Claude Bernard Coll; James Joyce Coll; William Butler Yeats Coll. State Document Depository; US Document Depository
Subject Interests: Archit, Art, Behav sci, Hist, Soc sci
Automation Activity & Vendor Info: (Acquisitions) VTLS, Inc; (Cataloging) VTLS, Inc; (Circulation) VTLS, Inc; (Course Reserve) VTLS, Inc; (ILL) OCLC; (OPAC) VTLS, Inc; (Serials) VTLS, Inc
Partic in Lyrasis; Virtual Library of Virginia
Open Mon-Thurs 8am-Midnight, Fri 8-5, Sat 11-5, Sun Noon-Midnight

M   MARY WASHINGTON HOSPITAL*, Medical Library, 1001 Sam Perry Blvd, 22401-9523. SAN 317-2945. Tel: 540-741-1597. FAX: 540-741-1514. *Med Librn,* Jane Borland; E-mail: 540-741-1598; Staff 2 (MLS 1, Non-MLS 1)
Founded 1974
Library Holdings: Bk Titles 1,000; Per Subs 1,000
Subject Interests: Behav sci, Biomed sci, Hist of med, Med mgt, Nursing, Soc sci
Database Vendor: EBSCOhost, OVID Technologies, UpToDate
Partic in National Network of Libraries of Medicine
Open Mon-Fri 8:30-5

FRONT ROYAL

C   CHRISTENDOM COLLEGE*, St John the Evangelist Library, 263 St Johns Way, 22630. SAN 321-6608. Tel: 540-636-2900, Ext 234. FAX: 540-636-6569. E-mail: library@christendom.edu. *Librn,* Andrew Armstrong; Tel: 540-636-2900, Ext 231; *Ref Serv,* Steven Pilon; Tel: 540-636-2900, Ext 132
Founded 1977. Enrl 160; Fac 15; Highest Degree: Bachelor
Library Holdings: Bk Titles 45,000; Bk Vols 60,000; Per Subs 320
Subject Interests: Hagiography, Rare bks
Automation Activity & Vendor Info: (Acquisitions) Follett Software; (Cataloging) Follett Software; (Circulation) Follett Software; (OPAC) Follett Software
Partic in Lyrasis; OCLC Online Computer Library Center, Inc; Virginia Independent College & University Library Association
Open Mon-Thurs 8am-Midnight, Fri & Sat 1-8, Sun 1-Midnight

P   SAMUELS PUBLIC LIBRARY*, 538 Villa Ave, 22630. SAN 317-2953. Tel: 540-635-3153. FAX: 540-635-7229. Web Site: www.samuelslibrary.net. *Dir,* Mary McGuire Lynch; Tel: 540-635-3153, Ext 110, E-mail: nlynch@samuelslibrary.net; *Dir, Operations,* Eileen Grady; E-mail: egrady@samuelslibrary.net; *Youth Serv Librn,* Michael Ashby; E-mail: childrens@samuelslibrary.net; *Ref,* Nathanael Reed; E-mail: thanreed@samuelslibrary.net; Staff 3 (MLS 3)
Founded 1952. Pop 32,500; Circ 194,371
Jul 2006-Jun 2007 Income $626,610, State $123,961, City $56,593, County $385,000, Locally Generated Income $61,055. Mats Exp $84,609, Books $67,837, Per/Ser (Incl. Access Fees) $7,571, AV Mat $9,201. Sal $333,368
Library Holdings: CDs 504; Bk Vols 75,936; Per Subs 129; Talking Bks 1,891; Videos 2,851
Special Collections: Virginia Coll
Subject Interests: Local hist
Automation Activity & Vendor Info: (Acquisitions) SirsiDynix; (Cataloging) SirsiDynix; (Circulation) SirsiDynix; (OPAC) SirsiDynix
Wireless access
Open Mon-Thurs 10-8, Fri & Sat 10-5, Sun 1-5
Friends of the Library Group

GALAX

P   GALAX-CARROLL REGIONAL LIBRARY*, Galax Public Library, 610 W Stuart Dr, 24333. SAN 317-2961. Tel: 276-236-2042, 276-236-2351. Reference Tel: 276-236-2042, Ext 211. FAX: 276-236-5153. Web Site: galaxcarroll.lib.va.us. *Dir,* Laura A Bryant; E-mail: lbryant@galaxcarroll.lib.va.us; Staff 1 (MLS 1)
Founded 1938. Pop 34,500; Circ 203,459
Library Holdings: Bks on Deafness & Sign Lang 25; Bk Vols 60,000; Per Subs 131
Subject Interests: Carroll County hist, Galax City hist, Genealogy
Automation Activity & Vendor Info: (Cataloging) TLC (The Library Corporation); (Circulation) TLC (The Library Corporation); (OPAC) TLC (The Library Corporation)
Open Mon, Wed & Fri 9-5, Tues & Thurs 9-7, Sat 9-3, Sun 2-5
Branches: 1
CARROLL COUNTY PUBLIC, 101 Beaver Dam Rd, Hillsville, 24343. (Mail add: PO Box 1629, Hillsville, 24343-7629), SAN 321-2696. Tel: 276-728-2228, 276-728-3334. FAX: 276-728-3830. *Dir,* Melanie Hemingway; Tel: 276-236-2351, Fax: 276-236-5153, E-mail: mhemingway@galaxcarroll.lib.va.us; *Asst Dir,* Trish Fore; Tel: 276-236-2042, Fax: 276-236-5153, E-mail: tfore@galaxcarroll.lib.va.us; *Br Mgr,* June Pike

Library Holdings: Bk Titles 37,624
Open Mon 10-8, Tues-Fri 10-6, Sat 10-2

GLENNS

J   RAPPAHANNOCK COMMUNITY COLLEGE LIBRARY*, Glenns
Campus, 12745 College Dr, 23149. SAN 362-9430. Tel: 804-758-6710.
FAX: 804-758-0213. Web Site: www.rcc.vccs.edu/public/library/library.htm.
Col Librn, Loftan Miller; *Cat, ILL,* Bronsene Turner; E-mail:
bturner@rcc.vccs.edu; Staff 4 (MLS 2, Non-MLS 2)
Founded 1971. Enrl 1,500; Highest Degree: Associate
Library Holdings: e-books 35,000; Bk Titles 40,000; Per Subs 300;
Talking Bks 650
Subject Interests: Bus mgr, Nursing
Automation Activity & Vendor Info: (Acquisitions) Ex Libris Group;
(Cataloging) Ex Libris Group; (Circulation) Ex Libris Group; (Course
Reserve) Ex Libris Group; (OPAC) Ex Libris Group
Wireless access
Function: ILL available
Partic in Virginia Commun Coll Syst
Open Mon-Thurs 8:30-8:30, Fri 8:30-3, Sat 9-2

GLOUCESTER

P   GLOUCESTER COUNTY LIBRARY*, 6920 Main St, 23061. (Mail add:
PO Box 2380, 23061-2380), SAN 317-297X. Tel: 804-693-2998.
Administration Tel: 804-693-1480. Automation Services Tel: 804-693-1482.
FAX: 804-693-1477. Web Site: www.gloucesterva.info/lib/home.html. *Dir,
Libr Serv,* Melissa Malcolm; E-mail: mmalcolm@gloucesterva.info; Staff
13.5 (MLS 2, Non-MLS 11.5)
Founded 1933. Pop 35,700; Circ 210,797
Library Holdings: Bks on Deafness & Sign Lang 40; Bk Vols 82,000; Per
Subs 150
Automation Activity & Vendor Info: (Cataloging) TLC (The Library
Corporation); (Circulation) TLC (The Library Corporation); (OPAC) TLC
(The Library Corporation)
Database Vendor: Facts on File, Gale Cengage Learning,
LearningExpress, ProQuest, World Book Online
Wireless access
Function: Adult bk club, Art exhibits, Bk club(s), Bks on cassette, Bks on
CD, Chess club, Children's prog, Computer training, Computers for patron
use, Copy machines, Electronic databases & coll, Fax serv, Handicapped
accessible, ILL available, Music CDs, Online cat, Preschool outreach, Prog
for adults, Prog for children & young adult, Spoken cassettes & CDs, Story
hour, Summer reading prog, Tax forms, Teen prog, Telephone ref, VHS
videos, Wheelchair accessible
Open Mon-Thurs 10-8, Fri & Sat 10-5, Sun 1-5
Friends of the Library Group
Branches: 1
POINT BRANCH, 1720 George Washington Memorial Hwy, Hayes,
23072. (Mail add: PO Box 889, Hayes, 23072). Tel: 804-642-9790. FAX:
804-642-9853. *Dir of Libr Serv,* Melissa Malcolm
Library Holdings: Bk Vols 23,000; Per Subs 20
Function: Computers for patron use, Copy machines, Fax serv
Open Mon & Wed 10-5, Tues & Thurs 10-8, Fri & Sat 10-2
Bookmobiles: 1

GLOUCESTER POINT

C   VIRGINIA INSTITUTE OF MARINE SCIENCE, COLLEGE OF
WILLIAM & MARY, William J Hargis Jr Library, Rte 1208, Greate Rd,
23062. (Mail add: PO Box 1346, 23062-1346), SAN 317-2996. Tel:
804-684-7116. Interlibrary Loan Service Tel: 804-684-7115. FAX:
804-684-7113. Web Site: www.vims.edu/library. *Dir,* Carol Coughlin; Tel:
804-684-7114; *Bibliog Serv, ILL,* Marilyn Lewis; *Pub Serv,* Diane Walker;
Staff 4 (MLS 3, Non-MLS 1)
Founded 1940
Library Holdings: Bk Vols 91,000; Per Subs 366
Special Collections: Expeditions, Sport Fishing & Hunting (Ross H
Walker Coll)
Subject Interests: Chesapeake Bay, Coastal zone, Environ studies,
Estuaries, Fisheries, Geol, Marine biol
Automation Activity & Vendor Info: (Cataloging) OCLC; (Circulation)
SirsiDynix; (OPAC) SirsiDynix
Database Vendor: American Geophysical Union, Annual Reviews,
BioOne, ebrary, EBSCOhost, Elsevier, ISI Web of Knowledge, JSTOR,
LexisNexis, netLibrary, OCLC WorldCat, ProQuest, RefWorks, Safari
Books Online, ScienceDirect, SerialsSolutions, SirsiDynix, Springer-Verlag,
Wiley InterScience
Wireless access
Function: Wheelchair accessible
Partic in Lyrasis; OCLC Online Computer Library Center, Inc; SAILS, Inc;
Virtual Library of Virginia (VIVA)
Open Mon-Fri 9-5

GREAT FALLS

S   INTERNATIONAL CADMIUM ASSOCIATION LIBRARY*, 9222 Jeffery
Rd, 22066. SAN 375-2291. Tel: 703-759-7400. FAX: 703-759-7003. Web
Site: www.cadmium.org. *Sr Consult,* Hugh Morrow; E-mail:
icdamorrow@aol.com
Founded 1980
Library Holdings: Bk Titles 100
Restriction: Mem only

GRUNDY

CL   APPALACHIAN SCHOOL OF LAW LIBRARY*, 1221 Edgewater Dr,
24614-7062. Tel: 276-935-6688, Ext 1308. Interlibrary Loan Service Tel:
276-935-6688, Ext 1311. Reference Tel: 276-935-6688, Ext 1315. Toll Free
Tel: 800-895-7411. FAX: 276-935-7138. Web Site: www.asl.edu/library.
Dir, Charles J Condon; Tel: 276-935-6688, Ext 1309; *Assoc Dir,* Glenna
Owens; Tel: 276-935-6688, Ext 1303; *Access Serv,* Rebecca Belcher; Tel:
276-935-6688, Ext 1311, E-mail: rbelcher@asl.edu; *Coll Mgt,* Elizabeth M
Stanley; Tel: 276-935-6688, Ext 1302; *Pub Serv,* Christopher King; Tel:
276-935-6688, Ext 1314; Staff 5 (MLS 5)
Founded 1997
Library Holdings: Bk Titles 43,258; Bk Vols 116,648; Per Subs 628
Special Collections: Appalachian Coll. US Document Depository
Automation Activity & Vendor Info: (Acquisitions) Innovative Interfaces,
Inc; (Cataloging) Innovative Interfaces, Inc; (Circulation) Innovative
Interfaces, Inc; (Course Reserve) Innovative Interfaces, Inc; (ILL) OCLC
Connexion; (OPAC) Innovative Interfaces, Inc - OCLC; (Serials) Innovative
Interfaces, Inc
Database Vendor: CQ Press, EBSCOhost, Factiva.com, Gale Cengage
Learning, HeinOnline, Innovative Interfaces, Inc, LexisNexis, Loislaw,
Medline, netLibrary, OCLC FirstSearch, ProQuest, Westlaw, YBP Library
Services
Wireless access
Open Mon-Fri 8-5 (9-5 Summer)

P   BUCHANAN COUNTY PUBLIC LIBRARY*, Rte 2, Poetown Rd,
24614-9613. (Mail add: Box 3, 24614-9613), SAN 317-302X. Tel:
276-935-6581. Administration Tel: 276-935-6582. FAX: 276-935-6292.
E-mail: bcpl@bcplnet.org. Web Site: www.bcplnet.org. *Actg Dir, Cat, Tech
Serv,* Edgar F Talbott, III; E-mail: bcpl@bcplnet.org; *Head, Circ,* Gilbert
Jean; E-mail: jeangilbert@bcplnet.org; *Acq, Per, Ref,* Sherry Bright;
E-mail: sherry@bcplnet.org; *Bus Librn, Circ, ILL,* Phyllis Tiller; E-mail:
ptiller@earthlink.net; *Ch, Youth Serv,* Kathy McNalley; E-mail:
bcplkids@bcplnet.org; *Circ, Info Spec,* Bridget D Rife; Tel: 276-935-6582,
E-mail: bridgetrife@bcplnet.org; Staff 6 (Non-MLS 6)
Founded 1960. Pop 26,000; Circ 100,000
Library Holdings: Bk Vols 90,000; Per Subs 155
Subject Interests: Hist, Local hist
Database Vendor: SirsiDynix
Function: Homebound delivery serv, ILL available, Magnifiers for reading,
Photocopying/Printing, Prog for children & young adult, Summer reading
prog
Partic in Lyrasis
Open Mon 1-8, Tues, Wed, Fri & Sat 8:30-5, Thurs 8:30-8
Friends of the Library Group

HALIFAX

P   HALIFAX COUNTY-SOUTH BOSTON REGIONAL LIBRARY*, 177 S
Main St, 24558. (Mail add: PO Box 1729, 24558-1729), SAN 362-9465.
Tel: 434-476-3357. FAX: 434-476-3359. E-mail: hcsblibrary@hotmail.com.
Web Site: www.halifaxlibrary.org. *Dir,* Kenneth Paul Johnson; Staff 11
(MLS 1, Non-MLS 10)
Founded 1961. Pop 37,355; Circ 86,768
Library Holdings: AV Mats 1,682; CDs 161; DVDs 1,000; Large Print
Bks 2,568; Bk Titles 86,000; Bk Vols 130,000; Per Subs 151; Talking Bks
5,595; Videos 1,344
Subject Interests: Art, Local hist
Automation Activity & Vendor Info: (Acquisitions) Polaris Library
Systems; (Cataloging) Polaris Library Systems; (Circulation) Polaris
Library Systems; (OPAC) Polaris Library Systems
Partic in OCLC Online Computer Library Center, Inc
Open Mon-Wed & Fri 9:30-6, Thurs 9:30-8, Sat 9:30-1
Friends of the Library Group
Branches: 1
SOUTH BOSTON PUBLIC LIBRARY, 509 Broad St, South Boston,
24592, SAN 362-949X. Tel: 434-575-4228. FAX: 434-575-4229. Web
Site: www.halifaxlibrary.org/sobo.htm. *Br Mgr,* Woodson Hughes
Library Holdings: Bk Vols 50,000
Open Mon-Wed & Fri 9:30-6, Thurs 11:30-8, Sat 9:30-1
Friends of the Library Group
Bookmobiles: 1

HAMPDEN SYDNEY

C   HAMPDEN SYDNEY COLLEGE, Bortz Library, 257 Via Sacra, HSC
Box 7, 23943. SAN 317-3038. Tel: 434-223-6190. Circulation Tel:
434-223-6192. Reference Tel: 434-223-6302. FAX: 434-223-6351. Web
Site: www.hsc.edu. *Dir,* Cy Dillon; Tel: 434-223-6197; *Asst Dir,* Shaunna
Hunter; Tel: 434-223-6194; *Cat,* Toni H Hamlett; Tel: 434-223-6267;
Media Librn, Brian T Burns; Tel: 434-223-7225; *Pub Serv,* Shaunna
Hunter; Tel: 434-223-6193; Staff 5 (MLS 4, Non-MLS 1)
Founded 1776. Enrl 1,100; Fac 100; Highest Degree: Bachelor
Library Holdings: Bk Vols 251,234; Per Subs 300
Special Collections: John Peter Mettauer Coll. US Document Depository
Subject Interests: Humanities, Local hist
Automation Activity & Vendor Info: (Acquisitions) Innovative Interfaces,
Inc; (Cataloging) Innovative Interfaces, Inc; (Circulation) Innovative
Interfaces, Inc; (Course Reserve) Blackboard Inc; (ILL) OCLC; (OPAC)
Innovative Interfaces, Inc
Wireless access
Partic in OCLC Online Computer Library Center, Inc; Virginia Independent
College & University Library Association; Virtual Library of Virginia
Open Mon-Thurs 8am-1am, Fri 8-6, Sat 9-5, Sun Noon-1am

HAMPTON

GM   DEPARTMENT OF VETERANS AFFAIRS MEDICAL CENTER*,
Medical Library, 100 Emancipation Dr, 23667. SAN 317-3062. Tel:
757-722-9961, Ext 3657. FAX: 757-722-2988, 757-728-7095. Web Site:
www.va.gov/.
Founded 1870
Library Holdings: Bk Vols 12,500; Per Subs 536
Subject Interests: Acute care, Geriatrics, Gerontology, Patient educ mats,
Rehabilitation med
Partic in Tidewater Health Sci Librs

P   HAMPTON PUBLIC LIBRARY*, 4207 Victoria Blvd, 23669-4243. SAN
362-9589. Tel: 757-727-1154. Interlibrary Loan Service Tel: 757-727-1314.
Reference Tel: 757-727-1312. Administration Tel: 757-727-1153. FAX:
757-727-1152. TDD: 757-727-1900. Web Site:
www.hamptonpubliclibrary.org. *Dir,* Robert Carpenter; E-mail:
rcarpenter@hampton.gov; *Coordr, Outreach Serv,* Anita Harrell; E-mail:
aharrell@hampton.gov; *Info Tech,* Brian Ott; E-mail: bott@hampton.gov;
Spec Coll Librn, Gaynell Drummond; E-mail: gdrummond@hampton.gov;
Tech Serv, Rebecca Perry; Tel: 757-727-1218, Fax: 757-727-1151, E-mail:
rperry@hampton.gov; Staff 26 (MLS 10, Non-MLS 16)
Founded 1926. Pop 146,000
Special Collections: Grant Resources Coll; Virginia History & Genealogy
Automation Activity & Vendor Info: (Cataloging) SirsiDynix;
(Circulation) SirsiDynix
Publications: Directory of Community Organizations (Hampton, Newport
News, Poquoson & York Co)
Special Services for the Deaf - TDD equip
Open Mon-Thurs 9-9, Fri & Sat 9-5, Sun 1-5
Friends of the Library Group
Branches: 4
NORTHAMPTON, 936 Big Bethel Rd, 23669, SAN 362-9619. Tel:
757-825-4558. FAX: 757-825-4646. *Br Mgr,* Virginia L Cotter; Staff 3
(MLS 1, Non-MLS 2)
Open Mon-Thurs 9-9, Fri 10-5, Sun 1-5
Friends of the Library Group
PHOEBUS BRANCH, One S Mallory St, 23663, SAN 362-9643. Tel:
757-727-1149. FAX: 757-727-1047. *Br Mgr,* Anita Harrell; Staff 3 (MLS
1, Non-MLS 2)
Database Vendor: SirsiDynix
Special Services for the Deaf - Closed caption videos
Special Services for the Blind - Accessible computers; Bks on CD;
Copier with enlargement capabilities; Free checkout of audio mat; Home
delivery serv; Internet workstation with adaptive software; Large print
bks; Recorded bks
Open Mon-Thurs 10-6, Fri 10-5, Sat 1-5
Friends of the Library Group
WILLOW OAKS, 227 Fox Hill Rd, 23669, SAN 362-9708. Tel:
757-850-5114. FAX: 757-850-5239. *Br Mgr,* Lorraine Bartlett; E-mail:
lbartlett@hampton.gov; Staff 3 (MLS 1, Non-MLS 2)
Open Mon-Thurs 9-9, Fri 9-5, Sat 10-5, Sun 1-5
Friends of the Library Group
GEORGE WYTHE LAW LIBRARY, 101 Kings Way, 2nd Flr, 23669. Tel:
757-728-2065. FAX: www.hamptonpubliclibrary.org/locations/law.html.
E-mail: lawlibrary@georgewythe.hrcoxmal.com. *In Charge,* Lisa Worrall
Library Holdings: Bk Titles 900
Database Vendor: Westlaw
Open Mon-Thurs 12-4
Bookmobiles: 2

C   HAMPTON UNIVERSITY*, William R & Norma B Harvey Library, 130
E Tyler St, 23668. SAN 362-952X. Tel: 757-727-5371. Circulation Tel:
757-727-5372. Interlibrary Loan Service Tel: 757-727-5186. Reference Tel:
757-727-5379. FAX: 757-727-5952. E-mail: ereference@hamptonu.edu.
Web Site: www.hamptonu.edu/universityservices/library. *Dir,* Faye Watkins;
E-mail: faye.watkins@hamptonu.edu; *Cat Librn,* John Curtis; Tel:
757-727-5183, E-mail: john.curtis@hamptonu.edu; *Info Res Librn,* Nicole
Spoor; Tel: 757-727-5179, E-mail: nicole.spoor@hamptonu.edu; *Peabody
Librn,* Gladys Bell; E-mail: gladys.bell@hamptonu.edu; *Ref & Instruction
Librn,* Girija Venkat; E-mail: girija.venkat@hamptonu.edu; *Ref Librn,*
Frank Edgcombe; E-mail: frank.edgcombe@hamptonu.edu; *Virtual Res
Librn,* Peggy Brown; Tel: 757-637-2096, E-mail:
peggy.brown@hamptonu.edu; *Coll Develop,* Alfred Willis; E-mail:
alfred.willis@hamptonu.edu; *Ref, ILL & Gov Doc,* Elizabeth Evans;
E-mail: elizabeth.evans@hamptonu.edu. Subject Specialists: *Bus,* Nicole
Spoor; *African-Am works,* Gladys Bell; *English, Film studies, Humanities,*
Girija Venkat; *Hist, Nursing, Polit sci,* Frank Edgcombe; *Chem, Sci,* Peggy
Brown; *Archit, Art, Music,* Alfred Willis; *Psychol, Sociol,* Elizabeth Evans;
Staff 30 (MLS 10, Non-MLS 20)
Founded 1868. Enrl 5,563; Highest Degree: Doctorate
Library Holdings: e-books 63,000; Bk Vols 341,359
Special Collections: George Foster Peabody Coll. US Document
Depository
Subject Interests: African-Am, Archit, Educ, Nursing, Pharm, Psychol,
Relig, Sciences
Automation Activity & Vendor Info: (Acquisitions) SirsiDynix;
(Cataloging) SirsiDynix; (Circulation) SirsiDynix; (OPAC) SirsiDynix
Database Vendor: ACM (Association for Computing Machinery),
American Chemical Society, American Psychological Association (APA),
Annual Reviews, ARTstor, Blackwell's, Cambridge Scientific Abstracts,
EBSCOhost, Factiva.com, Faulkner Information Services, Hoovers, JSTOR,
LexisNexis, Mergent Online, Micromedex, netLibrary, Newsbank, OCLC
FirstSearch, OCLC WorldCat, OVID Technologies, Project MUSE,
ProQuest, ScienceDirect, Scopus, SerialsSolutions, SirsiDynix, Standard &
Poor's, STAT!Ref (Teton Data Systems), Wiley InterScience, Wilson -
Wilson Web
Partic in Lyrasis; OCLC Online Computer Library Center, Inc; Virginia
Independent College & University Library Association; Virtual Library of
Virginia
Open Mon-Thurs 8:30am-Midnight, Fri 8:30-5, Sat 9-5, Sun 3pm-Midnight
Restriction: Badge access after hrs
Departmental Libraries:
ARCHITECTURE, 130 E Tyler St, 23668. Tel: 757-727-5443. *Librn,*
Norma Sellman; *Coll Develop,* Alfred Willis. Subject Specialists: *Archit,*
Norma Sellman; *Archit, Art, Music,* Alfred Willis
Subject Interests: Archit
Open Mon-Fri 8-5
MUSIC, 130 E Tyler St, 23668. Tel: 757-727-5411. *Music Librn,* Eric
Reif; E-mail: eric.reiff@hamptonu.edu. Subject Specialists: *Music,* Eric
Reif
Open Mon-Fri 8-5

CM   NURSING, 130 E Tyler St, 23668. Tel: 757-727-5353. FAX:
757-727-5423. E-mail: nursing@hamptonu.edu. *Libr Assoc,* Theresa
Brooks; *Ref Serv,* Frank Edgcombe; Tel: 757-727-5371, Fax:
757-727-5952, E-mail: frank.edgcombe@hamptonu.edu
Subject Interests: Communicative disorders, Med, Nursing
Open Mon-Fri 8-5

G   NASA*, Langley Research Center Technical Library, Two W Durand St,
Mail Stop 185, 23681-2199. SAN 317-3046. Tel: 757-864-2356. FAX:
757-864-2375. E-mail: tech-library@larc.nasa.gov. Web Site:
library.larc.nasa.gov. *Mgr,* Carolyn Helmetsie
Founded 1920
Library Holdings: e-books 800; e-journals 1,151; Bk Titles 60,000; Per
Subs 1,100
Subject Interests: Aerospace sci, Aerospace tech
Automation Activity & Vendor Info: (ILL) OCLC ILLiad; (OPAC)
SirsiDynix
Database Vendor: Cambridge Scientific Abstracts, Dialog, OCLC
FirstSearch
Function: Telephone ref
Partic in Federal Library & Information Center Committee (FLICC);
NASA Libraries Information System-NASA Galaxie; OCLC Online
Computer Library Center, Inc
Open Mon-Fri 8-4:30

C   THOMAS NELSON COMMUNITY COLLEGE LIBRARY*, Wythe Hall
228, 99 Thomas Nelson Dr, 23666. (Mail add: PO Box 9407, 23670-0407),
SAN 317-3054. Tel: 757-825-2876. Circulation Tel: 757-825-2877.
Interlibrary Loan Service Tel: 757-825-3878. Reference Tel: 757-825-2878.
FAX: 757-825-2870. Web Site: www.tncc.edu. *Dir,* Aileen Schweitzer; Tel:
757-825-2871, E-mail: schweitzera@tncc.edu; *Acq,* Dyan Vinson; Tel:
757-825-2872, E-mail: vinsond@tncc.edu; *AV,* Ella Belch; Tel:
757-825-2875, E-mail: belche@tncc.edu; *Cat,* Susan Lawlor; Tel:
757-825-3530, E-mail: lawlors@tncc.edu; *Ref Serv, Ad,* Barbara Gibson;

Tel: 757-825-2878, E-mail: gibsonb@tncc.edu; *Ser*, Susan Hoar; Tel: 757-825-3529. Subject Specialists: *Educ, Eng, Math, Natural sci,* Barbara Gibson; Staff 12 (MLS 4, Non-MLS 8)
Founded 1968. Enrl 4,300; Fac 103; Highest Degree: Associate Jul 2005-Jun 2006. Mats Exp $160,000
Library Holdings: Bks on Deafness & Sign Lang 15; High Interest/Low Vocabulary Bk Vols 100; Bk Vols 59,000; Per Subs 346
Special Collections: Accelerated Readers; Paperbacks
Subject Interests: Computer tech, English lit, Ethnic studies, Instrul develop, Nursing, Soc problems
Automation Activity & Vendor Info: (Circulation) Ex Libris Group; (OPAC) Ex Libris Group
Database Vendor: EBSCOhost, Gale Cengage Learning, LexisNexis, OCLC FirstSearch
Partic in Lyrasis; OCLC Online Computer Library Center, Inc; Virginia Commun Coll Syst; Virtual Library of Virginia; Wilsonline
Open Mon-Thurs (Winter) 8am-9pm, Fri 8-4, Sat 9-3; Mon-Thurs 8-8, Fri 8am-12:30pm, Sat (Summer) 9-1

HANOVER

S   HANOVER JUVENILE CORRECTIONAL CENTER*, Department of Correctional Education Library, 7093 Broad Neck Rd, 23069. Tel: 804-537-6682. FAX: 804-537-5491. *Librn,* James Adams
Library Holdings: Bk Vols 64,000; Per Subs 30
Automation Activity & Vendor Info: (Cataloging) Follett Software; (Circulation) Follett Software; (OPAC) Follett Software
Open Mon-Fri 8-4

P   PAMUNKEY REGIONAL LIBRARY*, 7527 Library Dr, 23069. (Mail add: PO Box 119, 23069-0119), SAN 362-9732. Tel: 804-537-6211. FAX: 804-537-6389. TDD: 804-730-6140. E-mail: ask@pamunkeylibrary.org. Web Site: www.pamunkeylibrary.org. *Libr Dir,* Fran Freimarck; *Supv Librn,* Sherida Bradby; *Supv Librn,* Patty Franz; *Supv Librn,* Linda Gosnell; *Supv Librn,* Steven Hartung; *Ref Librn,* Carolyn Garner; *Ref Librn,* Alyce Hackney; *Ref Librn,* Susie Pitts; *Ref Librn,* Jessica Schelleng; *Ref Librn,* Bill Schlimme; Staff 132 (MLS 7, Non-MLS 125)
Founded 1941. Pop 121,959; Circ 943,996
Library Holdings: AV Mats 8,955; Bks on Deafness & Sign Lang 100; Large Print Bks 4,909; Bk Titles 100,000; Bk Vols 399,654; Per Subs 430; Talking Bks 12,494
Special Collections: Virginiana
Automation Activity & Vendor Info: (Circulation) SirsiDynix; (ILL) OCLC FirstSearch; (OPAC) SirsiDynix
Database Vendor: Gale Cengage Learning, OCLC FirstSearch, Wilson - Wilson Web
Function: AV serv, Handicapped accessible, Homebound delivery serv, ILL available, Photocopying/Printing, Prog for children & young adult, Ref serv available, Summer reading prog, Wheelchair accessible
Partic in Richmond Area Network; VA State Libr
Special Services for the Deaf - Closed caption videos; TDD equip
Special Services for the Blind - BiFolkal kits; Bks on cassette; Bks on CD; Large print bks
Friends of the Library Group
Branches: 10
   ATLEE, 9161 Atlee Rd, Mechanicsville, 23116, SAN 378-1925. Tel: 804-559-0654. FAX: 804-559-0645. *Br Mgr,* Toni M Heer; E-mail: theer@pamunkeylibrary.org; *Ref,* Tim Hensley; Staff 16 (MLS 1, Non-MLS 15)
   Founded 1997. Pop 10,000; Circ 200,776
   Library Holdings: Bk Vols 50,000; Per Subs 100
   Special Services for the Deaf - Bks on deafness & sign lang; Closed caption videos; TDD equip
   Special Services for the Blind - BiFolkal kits; Bks on cassette; Bks on CD; Home delivery serv; Large print bks; Ref serv; ZoomText magnification & reading software
   Open Mon-Thurs 10-9, Fri & Sat 10-6
   Friends of the Library Group
   COCHRANE ROCKVILLE BRANCH, 16600 Pouncey Tract Rd, Rockville, 23146. (Mail add: PO Box 220, Rockville, 23146-0220), SAN 362-9856. Tel: 804-749-3146. FAX: 804-749-3631. *Br Mgr,* Donna-Jo Webster; Staff 10 (Non-MLS 10)
   Founded 1985. Pop 4,000; Circ 49,267
   Library Holdings: Bk Vols 18,000; Per Subs 55
   Function: Handicapped accessible, ILL available, Photocopying/Printing, Prog for children & young adult, Ref serv available, Summer reading prog
   Special Services for the Deaf - Bks on deafness & sign lang; Closed caption videos; High interest/low vocabulary bks; TDD equip
   Special Services for the Blind - BiFolkal kits; Bks on cassette; Bks on CD; Large print bks; Videos on blindness & phys handicaps; ZoomText magnification & reading software
   Open Mon-Thurs 10-9, Fri & Sat 10-6
   Friends of the Library Group

   RICHARD S GILLIS JR - ASHLAND BRANCH, 201 S Railroad Ave, Ashland, 23005, SAN 362-9767. Tel: 804-798-4072. FAX: 804-798-6276. *Br Mgr,* Cathy Bach; E-mail: cbach@pamunkeylibrary.org; *Ref Serv,* Alyce Hackney; E-mail: ahackney@pamunkeylibrary.org; Staff 17 (MLS 1, Non-MLS 16)
   Founded 1973. Circ 207,385
   Library Holdings: Bk Vols 45,000; Per Subs 100
   Function: Handicapped accessible, Homebound delivery serv, ILL available, Photocopying/Printing, Prog for children & young adult, Ref serv available, Summer reading prog
   Special Services for the Deaf - Bks on deafness & sign lang; Closed caption videos; High interest/low vocabulary bks; TDD equip
   Special Services for the Blind - BiFolkal kits; Bks on cassette; Bks on CD; Large print bks; Videos on blindness & phys handicaps; ZoomText magnification & reading software
   Open Mon-Thurs 10-9, Fri & Sat 10-6
   Friends of the Library Group
   GOOCHLAND BRANCH, 3075 River Rd W, Goochland, 23063, SAN 362-9791. Tel: 804-556-4774. FAX: 804-556-2941. *Br Mgr,* Janet Melton; E-mail: jmelton@pamunkeylibrary.org; Staff 12 (Non-MLS 12)
   Founded 1977. Pop 10,000; Circ 83,000
   Library Holdings: Bk Vols 23,000; Per Subs 80
   Special Services for the Deaf - Closed caption videos; TDD equip
   Special Services for the Blind - BiFolkal kits; Bks on cassette; Bks on CD; Large print bks; Ref serv; ZoomText magnification & reading software
   Open Mon-Thurs 9-8, Fri 9-6, Sat 9-4
   Friends of the Library Group
   HANOVER BRANCH, 7527 Library Dr, 23069. (Mail add: PO Box 119, 23069-0119), SAN 362-9805. Tel: 804-365-6210. FAX: 804-365-6379. *Br Mgr,* Lisa Ann Morgan; E-mail: lmorgan@pamunkeylibrary.org; Staff 8 (Non-MLS 8)
   Founded 1942. Pop 4,000; Circ 55,200
   Library Holdings: Bks on Deafness & Sign Lang 10; CDs 100; Electronic Media & Resources 15; Large Print Bks 150; Bk Vols 25,000; Per Subs 33; Talking Bks 150; Videos 200
   Special Collections: Virginiana
   Partic in Lyrasis
   Special Services for the Deaf - Bks on deafness & sign lang; Closed caption videos; High interest/low vocabulary bks; TDD equip
   Special Services for the Blind - BiFolkal kits; Bks on cassette; Bks on CD; Large print bks; Videos on blindness & phys handicaps; ZoomText magnification & reading software
   Open Mon-Wed 9-9, Thurs & Fri 9-6, Sat 9-2
   Friends of the Library Group
   LOIS WICKHAM JONES - MONTPELIER BRANCH, 17205 Sycamore Tavern Lane, Montpelier, 23192, SAN 378-1909. Tel: 804-883-7116. FAX: 804-883-5165. *Br Mgr,* Cynthia Seay; E-mail: cseay@pamunkeylibrary.org; Staff 10 (MLS 1, Non-MLS 9)
   Founded 1996. Pop 5,000; Circ 43,378
   Library Holdings: Bk Vols 10,000; Per Subs 44
   Special Services for the Deaf - Bks on deafness & sign lang; Closed caption videos; High interest/low vocabulary bks; TDD equip
   Special Services for the Blind - BiFolkal kits; Bks on cassette; Bks on CD; Large print bks; Videos on blindness & phys handicaps; ZoomText magnification & reading software
   Open Mon-Thurs 9-9, Fri 10-6, Sat 10-2
   Friends of the Library Group
   KING & QUEEN, 450 Newtown Rd, Saint Stephens Church, 23148. (Mail add: PO Box 279, Saint Stephens Church, 23148-0279), SAN 374-5252. Tel: 804-769-1623. FAX: 804-769-9286. *Br Mgr,* Lue Dean Jackson; E-mail: ljackson@pamunkeylibrary.org; Staff 7 (Non-MLS 7)
   Founded 1994. Pop 4,000; Circ 36,210
   Library Holdings: Bk Vols 8,000; Per Subs 35
   Special Services for the Deaf - Bks on deafness & sign lang; Closed caption videos; High interest/low vocabulary bks; TDD equip
   Special Services for the Blind - BiFolkal kits; Bks on cassette; Bks on CD; Large print bks; ZoomText magnification & reading software
   Open Mon-Thurs 12-7, Fri 10-6, Sat 10-2
   MECHANICSVILLE BRANCH, 7179 Stonewall Pkwy, Mechanicsville, 23111, SAN 362-9821. Tel: 804-746-9615. FAX: 804-730-4292. *Br Mgr,* Jaime Stoops; E-mail: jstoops@pamunkeylibrary.org; *Ref,* Jessica Schelleng; E-mail: jschelleng@pamunkeylibrary.org; Staff 17 (MLS 2, Non-MLS 15)
   Founded 1983. Pop 9,000; Circ 166,411
   Library Holdings: Bk Vols 35,000; Per Subs 120
   Special Services for the Deaf - Bks on deafness & sign lang; Closed caption videos; High interest/low vocabulary bks; TDD equip
   Special Services for the Blind - BiFolkal kits; Bks on cassette; Bks on CD; Large print bks; Videos on blindness & phys handicaps; ZoomText magnification & reading software
   Open Mon-Thurs 10-9, Fri & Sat 10-6
   Friends of the Library Group

UPPER KING WILLIAM BRANCH, Sharon Office Park, 694-J Sharon Rd, King William, 23086, SAN 375-6017. Tel: 804-769-3731. FAX: 804-769-1176. *Br Mgr,* Rose Shelley; Staff 8 (MLS 1, Non-MLS 7)
Founded 1995. Pop 4,000; Circ 23,673
Library Holdings: Bk Vols 5,000; Per Subs 44
Function: Handicapped accessible, Homebound delivery serv, ILL available, Photocopying/Printing, Prog for children & young adult, Ref serv available, Summer reading prog, Wheelchair accessible
Special Services for the Deaf - Bks on deafness & sign lang; Closed caption videos; High interest/low vocabulary bks; TDD equip
Special Services for the Blind - BiFolkal kits; Bks on cassette; Bks on CD; Large print bks; Videos on blindness & phys handicaps; ZoomText magnification & reading software
Open Mon, Tues & Thurs 12-8, Wed 10-9, Fri 10-6, Sat 10-4
Friends of the Library Group
WEST POINT BRANCH, 721 Main St, West Point, 23181. (Mail add: PO Box 1680, West Point, 23181-1680), SAN 362-9880. Tel: 804-843-3244. FAX: 804-843-4158. *Br Mgr,* Martha Wood; Staff 9 (Non-MLS 9)
Founded 1989. Pop 2,000; Circ 36,210
Library Holdings: Bk Vols 20,000; Per Subs 30
Function: Handicapped accessible, Homebound delivery serv, ILL available, Photocopying/Printing, Prog for children & young adult, Ref serv available, Summer reading prog, Wheelchair accessible
Special Services for the Deaf - Bks on deafness & sign lang; Closed caption videos; High interest/low vocabulary bks; TDD equip
Special Services for the Blind - BiFolkal kits; Bks on cassette; Bks on CD; Large print bks; Videos on blindness & phys handicaps; ZoomText magnification & reading software
Open Mon-Thurs 11-8, Fri 9-5, Sat 9-2
Friends of the Library Group
Bookmobiles: 1. Mgr, Betty Yarbrough

HARRISONBURG

C EASTERN MENNONITE UNIVERSITY, Sadie A Hartzler Library, 1200 Park Rd, 22802-2462. SAN 317-3070. Tel: 540-432-4175. FAX: 540-432-4977. Web Site: www.emu.edu/library. *Libr Dir,* Beryl H Brubaker; *Instrul Serv Librn,* Stephanie D Bush; *Spec Coll Librn,* Lois B Bowman; *Tech Serv Librn,* Jennifer M Ulrich; *Circ Mgr,* Bonnie W Bowser; *Acq, Syst Adminr,* Audrey J Shenk; *ILL,* Dawn L Nyce; Staff 8 (MLS 3, Non-MLS 5)
Founded 1917. Enrl 1,347; Fac 102; Highest Degree: Master
Jul 2011-Jun 2012. Mats Exp $208,604, Books $44,744, Per/Ser (Incl. Access Fees) $56,469, Micro $2,814, AV Equip $876, AV Mat $9,959, Electronic Ref Mat (Incl. Access Fees) $94,619, Presv $2,324. Sal $436,416 (Prof $210,196)
Library Holdings: AV Mats 4,738; CDs 332; DVDs 1,753; e-books 23,386; e-journals 78,470; Electronic Media & Resources 80; Microforms 74,906; Music Scores 1,195; Bk Vols 168,896; Per Subs 781; Videos 1,461
Special Collections: Anabaptist/Mennonite History, Virginiana (Menno Simons Historical Library & Archives), 16th century bks
Automation Activity & Vendor Info: (Acquisitions) SirsiDynix; (Cataloging) SirsiDynix; (Circulation) SirsiDynix; (ILL) OCLC ILLiad; (OPAC) SirsiDynix; (Serials) SirsiDynix
Database Vendor: Alexander Street Press, American Psychological Association (APA), ARTstor, Baker & Taylor, BioOne, Blackwell's, Cambridge Scientific Abstracts, CredoReference, EBSCOhost, Factiva.com, Gale Cengage Learning, H W Wilson, JSTOR, McGraw-Hill, Medline, Mergent Online, Nature Publishing Group, netLibrary, Newsbank-Readex, OCLC FirstSearch, OCLC WorldCat, Oxford Online, ProQuest, SirsiDynix, Springshare, LLC, STN International, Wiley InterScience, Wilson - Wilson Web, YBP Library Services
Wireless access
Partic in Christian Library Consortium; Lyrasis; OCLC Online Computer Library Center, Inc; Virginia Independent College & University Library Association; Virtual Library of Virginia
Open Mon-Thurs 8am-Midnight, Fri 8-6, Sat Noon-6, Sun 2pm-Midnight

C JAMES MADISON UNIVERSITY LIBRARIES & EDUCATIONAL TECHNOLOGIES*, 800 S Main St, 22807-0001. (Mail add: MSC 1704, 22807), SAN 317-3089. Tel: 540-568-3544. Circulation Tel: 540-568-6150. Interlibrary Loan Service Tel: 540-568-6804. Reference Tel: 540-568-6267. FAX: 540-568-6339. Web Site: www.lib.jmu.edu. *Dean of Libr & Educ Tech,* Ralph Alberico; Tel: 540-568-3828, E-mail: alberira@jmu.edu; *Assoc Dean of Libr & Educ Tech,* Sarah Cheverton; Tel: 540-568-3393, E-mail: cheverse@jmu.edu; *Assoc Dean of Libr & Educ Tech,* Sharon Gasser; Tel: 540-568-6160, E-mail: gasserss@jmu.edu; *Assoc Dean of Libr & Educ Tech,* Sandy Maxfield; Tel: 540-568-6923, E-mail: maxfiesl@jmu.edu; *Dir of East Campus Libr,* John McGehee; Tel: 540-568-3319, E-mail: mcgehejs@jmu.edu; *Dir, Libr Instruction,* Jennifer McCabe; Tel: 540-568-3105, E-mail: mccabeja@jmu.edu; *Dir, Planning & Assessment,* Position Currently Open; *Dir, Pub Serv,* Elizabeth Haworth; Tel: 540-568-5730, E-mail: haworte@jmu.edu; *Head, Acq,* Cheri Duncan; Tel: 540-568-3543, E-mail: duncancj@jmu.edu; *Head, Digital Libr Serv,* Jennifer Keach; Tel: 540-568-8749, E-mail: keachja@jmu.edu; *Music

Librn, Brian Cockburn; Tel: 540-568-9678, E-mail: cockbuba@jmu.edu; *ILL,* Mikki Butcher; Tel: 340-568-6807, E-mail: butcheml@jmu.edu
Founded 1908. Enrl 18,971; Fac 1,340; Highest Degree: Doctorate
Library Holdings: e-books 129,317; Bk Vols 827,959; Per Subs 75,909
Special Collections: State Document Depository; US Document Depository
Subject Interests: Shenandoah Valley hist
Automation Activity & Vendor Info: (Acquisitions) Innovative Interfaces, Inc; (Cataloging) Innovative Interfaces, Inc; (Circulation) Innovative Interfaces, Inc; (ILL) OCLC; (OPAC) Innovative Interfaces, Inc
Wireless access
Partic in Virtual Library of Virginia
Friends of the Library Group
Departmental Libraries:
MUSIC LIBRARY, MSC 7301, 22807. Tel: 540-568-6041, 540-568-6197. FAX: 540-568-7819. E-mail: library-music@jmu.edu. Web Site: www.lib.jmu.edu/music. *Librn,* Brian Cockburn; Tel: 540-568-6978, E-mail: cockbuba@jmu.edu; Staff 3 (MLS 1, Non-MLS 2)
Highest Degree: Doctorate
Library Holdings: Music Scores 18,000; Bk Vols 1,000
Special Collections: Choral Octavo Coll; Gena Branscombe Coll; JMU Performance Coll; Paul Lavalle Coll; Sheet Music Coll
Function: ILL available
Open Mon-Thurs (Winter) 8am-10:45pm, Fri 8-4:45, Sat 1-4:45, Sun 2-10:45; Mon-Fri (Summer) 8-4:45

P MASSANUTTEN REGIONAL LIBRARY*, 174 S Main St, 22801. SAN 362-9910. Tel: 540-434-4475. FAX: 540-434-4382. E-mail: info@mrlib.org. Web Site: www.mrlib.org. *Dir,* Lois Jones; *Asst Libr Dir,* Lora Rose; *Dir of Develop,* Kim Haines; *Tech Serv Mgr,* Patty Liskey; *Ch,* Susan Huffman; E-mail: shuffman@mrlib.org; Staff 48 (MLS 7, Non-MLS 41)
Founded 1928. Pop 131,000; Circ 635,803
Library Holdings: AV Mats 412; Bk Vols 160,000; Per Subs 305
Special Collections: Virginia & Family History (Virginia-Genealogy Coll)
Automation Activity & Vendor Info: (Circulation) SirsiDynix; (OPAC) SirsiDynix
Database Vendor: Gale Cengage Learning, ProQuest
Publications: Check-It-Out (Newsletter); Massanutten Matters (Online only)
Partic in OCLC Eastern; OCLC Online Computer Library Center, Inc; SouthWest Information Network Group (SWING)
Open Mon-Thurs 9:30-8:30, Fri & Sat 9:30-5
Friends of the Library Group
Branches: 6
ELKTON COMMUNITY, 106 N Terrace Ave, Elkton, 22827, SAN 375-5150. Tel: 540-298-2964. FAX: 540-298-0545. *Br Mgr,* Monica Hensley; Tel: monicah@mrlib.org; Staff 2 (Non-MLS 2)
Library Holdings: Bk Vols 26,000; Per Subs 91
Open Mon & Tues 10-5, Wed 2-6, Thurs & Fri 12-5
Friends of the Library Group
GROTTOES BRANCH, 601 Dogwood Ave, Grottoes, 24441. Tel: 540-249-3436. FAX: 540-249-8307. *Br Mgr,* Cheryl Keeler; E-mail: ckeeler@mrlib.org; Staff 2 (Non-MLS 2)
Founded 2000
Library Holdings: Bk Vols 22,775; Per Subs 78
Open Mon-Fri 1:30-6
Friends of the Library Group
NORTH RIVER, 118 Mount Crawford Ave, Bridgewater, 22812, SAN 375-5169. Tel: 540-828-4492. FAX: 540-828-2987. *Br Mgr,* Vicki L Graham; E-mail: vlgraham@mrlib.org; Staff 2 (Non-MLS 2)
Library Holdings: Bk Vols 5,098; Per Subs 56
Open Mon-Wed 1-8, Thurs & Fri 10-6, Sat 10-2, Sun 1-4
Friends of the Library Group
PAGE PUBLIC, 100 Zerkel St, Luray, 22835, SAN 362-9945. Tel: 540-743-6867. *Br Mgr,* Debbie McDonough; E-mail: dmcdonough@mrlib.org; Staff 2 (Non-MLS 2)
Library Holdings: Bk Vols 3,474; Per Subs 23
Open Mon, Wed & Fri 9:30-5, Tues 9:30-6, Thurs 9:30-7, Sat 9:30-2
Friends of the Library Group
SHENANDOAH COMMUNITY, 418 S Third St, Shenandoah, 22849. Tel: 540-652-2665. FAX: 540-652-6245. *Br Mgr,* Ruth Reid
Library Holdings: Bk Vols 14,449; Per Subs 35
Open Mon, Wed, Fri & Sat 10-4, Tues & Thurs 10-4 & 6-8:30
VILLAGE LIBRARY, 113 S Central Ave, Broadway, 22815, SAN 372-8005. Tel: 540-896-1646. FAX: 540-896-9260. *Br Mgr, Br Operations Coordr,* Barbara Andes; E-mail: bandes3@mrlib.org; Staff 2 (Non-MLS 2)
Library Holdings: Bk Vols 6,147; Per Subs 28
Open Mon 10-5 & 7-8:30, Tues-Fri 10-5, Sat 10-2
Friends of the Library Group
Bookmobiles: 1

M RMH HEALTHCARE, Virginia Funkhouser Health Sciences Library, 2010 Health Campus Dr, 22801-3293. SAN 317-3097. Tel: 540-689-1777. Interlibrary Loan Service Tel: 540-689-1772. Administration Tel:

540-689-1771. FAX: 540-689-1770. E-mail: rmhlibrary@rhcc.com. Web Site: www.rmhonline.com/Main/VirginiaFunkhouserHealthSciencesLibrary.aspx. *Dir, Health Sci Libr,* George L Curran, III; E-mail: gcurran@rhcc.com; *Cat, Ref Serv, Ser/ILL,* Megan Khamphavong; E-mail: megan.khamphavong.5324@rhcc.com; Staff 2 (MLS 2)
Founded 1912
Jan 2013-Dec 2013. Mats Exp $347,463, Books $65,000, Per/Ser (Incl. Access Fees) $81,000, AV Mat $12,000, Electronic Ref Mat (Incl. Access Fees) $155,000. Sal $90,480 (Prof $56,160)
Library Holdings: Audiobooks 5; AV Mats 500; DVDs 25; e-books 70; e-journals 2,700; Electronic Media & Resources 15; Bk Vols 5,000; Per Subs 226
Special Collections: Grief Coll-Adult, Children & Teens; Leadership & Governance Coll; Medical Imprints 1792-Early 20th Century (Medical & Nursing Historical Works Coll); Training & Adult Educaton (Learning & Development Coll), AV
Subject Interests: Allied health, Clinical med, Consumer health, Nursing
Automation Activity & Vendor Info: (Acquisitions) Inmagic, Inc.; (Cataloging) Inmagic, Inc.; (Circulation) Inmagic, Inc.; (OPAC) Inmagic, Inc.; (Serials) EBSCO Online
Database Vendor: DynaMed, EBSCO - WebFeat, EBSCOhost, Elsevier, Lexi-Comp, Medline, Micromedex, Natural Standard, OCLC WorldCat, PubMed, STAT!Ref (Teton Data Systems)
Wireless access
Function: Audio & video playback equip for onsite use, AV serv, Bks on CD, Computers for patron use, Copy machines, Doc delivery serv, Electronic databases & coll, Handicapped accessible, Health sci info serv, ILL available, Mail & tel request accepted, Online cat, Online searches, Orientations, Outside serv via phone, mail, e-mail & web, Photocopying/Printing, Pub access computers, Ref serv available, Telephone ref, VHS videos
Partic in Docline; National Network of Libraries of Medicine; OCLC Online Computer Library Center, Inc; Southwestern Virginia Health Information Librarians
Open Mon-Fri 8-4:30
Restriction: Badge access after hrs, Hospital staff & commun

HAYNESVILLE

S   HAYNESVILLE CORRECTIONAL CENTER*, Department of Correctional Education Library, 241 Barnfield Rd, 22472. (Mail add: PO Box 129, 22472-0129). Tel: 804-333-3577, Ext 4713. FAX: 804-333-1295. *Librn,* Edie Hudgins; E-mail: edith.hudgins@vadoc.virginia.gov
Library Holdings: DVDs 94; Bk Vols 10,011; Per Subs 27; Videos 316
Automation Activity & Vendor Info: (Cataloging) Follett Software; (Circulation) Follett Software
Open Mon-Fri 8:30-11 & 1-3

HEATHSVILLE

P   NORTHUMBERLAND PUBLIC LIBRARY, INC, 7204 Northumberland Hwy, 22473. SAN 309-9164. Tel: 804-580-5051. FAX: 804-580-5202. E-mail: library@nplva.org. Web Site: www.nplva.org. *Dir,* Michelle Dotson; E-mail: mdotson@nplva.org; *Ch,* Nancy Webster; E-mail: nwebster@nplva.org; Staff 4 (MLS 1, Non-MLS 3)
Founded 1969. Pop 12,400; Circ 44,000
Library Holdings: High Interest/Low Vocabulary Bk Vols 100; Bk Titles 31,000; Bk Vols 32,000; Per Subs 120; Spec Interest Per Sub 50
Automation Activity & Vendor Info: (Course Reserve) Book Systems, Inc; (OPAC) Book Systems, Inc
Wireless access
Function: Online cat
Open Mon & Tues 9-7, Wed & Fri 9-6, Thurs 9-8, Sat 9-1
Friends of the Library Group

HENRICO

P   HENRICO COUNTY PUBLIC LIBRARY, 1001 N Laburnum Ave, 23223-2705. SAN 363-2199. Tel: 804-290-9000. FAX: 804-222-5566. E-mail: library@henrico.lib.va.us. Web Site: www.henricolibrary.org. *Libr Dir,* Gerald M McKenna; E-mail: gmckenna@henricolibrary.org; *Asst Libr Dir,* Christine M Campbell; E-mail: ccampbell@henricolibrary.org; *Pub Serv Adminr,* Barbara F Weedman; E-mail: bweedman@henricolibrary.org; *Syst Librn,* Position Currently Open; *Children's/Teen Coordr,* Patricia O Muller; E-mail: pmuller@henricolibrary.org; *Coll Develop Coordr,* Ann Theis; E-mail: atheis@henricolibrary.org; *Commun Relations Coordr,* Kara Rothman; E-mail: krothman@henricolibrary.org; *Mat Mgt Coordr,* Joanne Bowman; E-mail: jbowman@henricolibrary.org; *Tech Coordr,* Jennifer Wood; E-mail: jwood@henricolibrary.org; *Controller,* John C Gentry; E-mail: jgentry@henrico.lib.va.us; Staff 166 (MLS 60, Non-MLS 106)
Founded 1966. Pop 306,935; Circ 3,584,375
Jul 2012-Jun 2013 Income (Main Library and Branch(s)) $15,059,497. Mats Exp $1,674,095
Library Holdings: Bk Titles 314,907; Bk Vols 863,149

Automation Activity & Vendor Info: (Acquisitions) SirsiDynix; (Cataloging) SirsiDynix; (Circulation) SirsiDynix; (ILL) SirsiDynix; (Media Booking) SirsiDynix; (OPAC) SirsiDynix; (Serials) SirsiDynix
Database Vendor: Comprise Technologies, Inc, OCLC, Overdrive, Inc, ReferenceUSA
Wireless access
Partic in Lyrasis
Open Mon-Fri 8-4:30
Friends of the Library Group
Branches: 10
DUMBARTON AREA, 6800 Staples Mill Rd, 23228-4930, SAN 363-2229. Tel: 804-290-9400. FAX: 804-266-8986. *Mgr,* Deborah Lammers; E-mail: du_manager@henrico.lib.va.us
Open Mon-Thurs 9-9, Fri & Sat 9-6
Friends of the Library Group
FAIRFIELD AREA LIBRARY, 1001 N Laburnum Ave, 23223-2705. Tel: 804-290-9300. FAX: 804-222-1958. *Mgr,* Michael Hatchett; E-mail: fa_manager@henrico.lib.va.us
Open Mon-Thurs 9-9, Fri & Sat 9-6
Friends of the Library Group
GAYTON BRANCH LIBRARY, 10600 Gayton Rd, 23238-4117, SAN 329-6288. Tel: 804-290-9600. FAX: 804-750-2685. *Br Mgr,* Thomas Bruno; E-mail: ga_manager@henrico.lib.va.us
Open Mon-Wed 10-9, Thurs 1-9, Fri & Sat 10-6
Friends of the Library Group
GLEN ALLEN BRANCH LIBRARY, 10501 Staples Mill Rd, Glen Allen, 23060-3242, SAN 375-5754. Tel: 804-290-9500. FAX: 804-501-2341. *Mgr,* Andrea Brown; E-mail: gl_manager@henrico.lib.va.us
Open Mon-Wed 10-9, Thurs 1-9, Fri & Sat 10-6
Friends of the Library Group
MUNICIPAL GOVERNMENT & LAW LIBRARY, County of Henrico Government Ctr, 4301 E Parham Rd, 23228. (Mail add: PO Box 90775, 23273-0775), SAN 363-2288. Tel: 804-501-4780, 804-501-5155. FAX: 804-672-1948. *Mgr,* Isabel Paul; E-mail: mu_manager@henrico.lib.va.us
Open Mon-Fri 8-4:30
NORTH PARK BRANCH LIBRARY, 8508 Franconia Rd, 23227-1213, SAN 323-813X. Tel: 804-290-9700. FAX: 804-264-7035. *Mgr,* Louise Perry; E-mail: np_manager@henrico.lib.va.us
Open Mon-Wed 10-9, Thurs 1-9, Fri & Sat 10-6
Friends of the Library Group
SANDSTON BRANCH LIBRARY, 23 East Williamsburg Rd, Sandston, 23150-2011, SAN 363-2318. Tel: 804-290-9700. FAX: 804-328-1041. *Mgr,* Donna McDonald; E-mail: sa_manager@henrico.lib.va.us
Open Mon-Wed 10-9, Thurs 1-9, Fri & Sat 10-6
Friends of the Library Group
TUCKAHOE AREA LIBRARY, 1901 Starling Dr, 23229-4564, SAN 363-2342. Tel: 804-290-9100. FAX: 804-270-2293. *Mgr,* Karen S Johnson; E-mail: tu_manager@henrico.lib.va.us
Open Mon-Thurs 9-9, Fri & Sat 9-6
Friends of the Library Group
TWIN HICKORY AREA LIBRARY, 5001 Twin Hickory Rd, Glen Allen, 23059-2509, SAN 373-5265. Tel: 804-290-9200. FAX: 804-364-4624. *Mgr,* Ahmed Tabib; E-mail: tw_manager@henrico.lib.va.us
Open Mon-Thurs 9-9, Fri & Sat 9-6
Friends of the Library Group
VARINA BRANCH LIBRARY, 2001 Library Rd, 23231-5826, SAN 363-2377. Tel: 804-290-9800. FAX: 804-222-4244. *Mgr,* Jean Burchill; E-mail: va_manager@henrico.lib.va.us
Open Mon-Wed 10-9, Thurs 1-9, Fri & Sat 10-6
Friends of the Library Group
Bookmobiles: 1. Carolyn Cook

HERNDON

S   AIRLINE PILOTS ASSOCIATION INTERNATIONAL*, Engineering & Air Safety Resource Center, 535 Herndon Pkwy, 20172-5226. (Mail add: PO Box 1169, 20172-1169), SAN 302-5519. Tel: 703-689-4204. FAX: 703-464-2104. E-mail: easlibrary@alpa.org. Web Site: www.alpa.org. *Actg Librn,* Marvin Ramirez
Library Holdings: Bk Vols 60,000
Special Collections: Federal Aviation Regulations; Jeppesen Flight Charts (worldwide); Videos
Subject Interests: Aviation
Open Mon-Fri 9-5

S   NATIONAL CONCRETE MASONRY ASSOCIATION LIBRARY*, 13750 Sunrise Valley Dr, 20171-3499. SAN 328-3089. Tel: 703-713-1900. FAX: 703-713-1910. E-mail: ncma@ncma.org. Web Site: www.ncma.org. *Managing Librn,* Brittaney KamHong; E-mail: bkamhong@ncma.org
Library Holdings: Bk Vols 4,000; Per Subs 80
Function: Ref serv available
Open Mon-Fri 8-5

HILLSVILLE

S   SOUTHWESTERN VIRGINIA TRAINING CENTER*, Research &
     Training Library, 160 Training Center Rd, 24343. (Mail add: PO Box
     1328, 24343-7328), SAN 321-0197. Tel: 276-728-3121. FAX:
     276-728-3127. Web Site: www.swvtc.dmhmrsas.virginia.gov. *Dir,* Karen
     Poe
     Founded 1976
     Library Holdings: Bk Titles 1,000; Per Subs 20
     Subject Interests: Spec educ

HOPEWELL

P   APPOMATTOX REGIONAL LIBRARY*, Maude Nelson Langhorne
     Library, 209 E Cawson St, 23860. SAN 317-316X. Tel: 804-458-6329,
     804-861-0322. FAX: 804-458-4349. Web Site: www.arls.org. *Dir,* Charles
     Koutnik; E-mail: ckoutnik@arls.org; *Asst Dir,* Scott Firestine; *Ref,* Chris
     Wiegard; Staff 33 (MLS 6, Non-MLS 27)
     Founded 1974. Pop 71,300; Circ 252,405
     Library Holdings: AV Mats 7,846; Bk Titles 122,241; Bk Vols 170,817;
     Per Subs 371; Talking Bks 2,200
     Automation Activity & Vendor Info: (Cataloging) TLC (The Library
     Corporation); (Circulation) TLC (The Library Corporation); (OPAC) TLC
     (The Library Corporation)
     Wireless access
     Open Mon-Thurs 10-9, Fri & Sat 10-6
     Friends of the Library Group
     Branches: 6
     BURROWSVILLE, 18701 James River Dr, Disputanta, 23842. Tel:
       757-866-0659. *Librn,* Darnell Law
       Open Mon 10-1 & 4-8, Tues-Thurs 4-8, Sat 10-1
       Friends of the Library Group
     CARSON BRANCH, 16101 Halligan Park Rd, Carson, 23830, SAN
       328-9869. Tel: 434-246-2900. *Librn,* Darnell Law
       Special Collections: Local Railroad History Coll (Housed in Railroad
       Caboose)
       Open Mon, Tues & Thurs 3-7, Wed 10-12 & 3-7, Fri & Sat 3-6
       Friends of the Library Group
     DINWIDDIE BRANCH, 14103 Boydton Plank Rd, Dinwiddie, 23841.
       (Mail add: PO Box 480, Dinwiddie, 23841), SAN 321-7426. Tel:
       804-469-9450. FAX: 804-469-9450. *Librn,* Darnell Law
       Open Mon, Tues & Thurs 2-7, Wed 10-7, Fri 2-6, Sat 10-1
       Friends of the Library Group
     DISPUTANTA BRANCH, 10010 County Dr, Disputanta, 23842. (Mail
       add: 209 E Cawson St, 23860), SAN 324-2927. Tel: 804-991-2403. FAX:
       804-991-2403. *Librn,* Chandra McPherson
       Open Mon 10-1 & 3-7, Tues-Thurs 3-7, Fri 3-6
       Friends of the Library Group
     MCKENNEY BRANCH, 20707 First St, McKenney, 23872-2703, SAN
       328-9885. Tel: 804-478-4866. FAX: 804-478-4866. *Librn,* Darnell Law
       Open Mon & Thurs 3-7, Tues 10-1 & 3-7, Fri 3-6
       Friends of the Library Group
     ROHOIC, 7301 Boydton Plank Rd, Petersburg, 23803, SAN 324-2935. Tel:
       804-732-4119. FAX: 804-732-4119. *Librn,* Darnell Law
       Open Mon-Wed 3-8, Thurs 10-1 & 3-8, Sat 10-1
       Friends of the Library Group
     Bookmobiles: 1

S   FEDERAL CORRECTIONAL INSTITUTION*, Educational Department
     Library, 1100 River Rd, 23860. (Mail add: PO Box 1000, Petersburg,
     23804-1000), SAN 317-381X. Tel: 804-733-7881. FAX: 804-863-1543.
     Educ Supvr, Janet Morris; Tel: 804-504-7800, Ext 1148
     Library Holdings: Bk Vols 4,000; Per Subs 16
     Subject Interests: Vocational educ, Vocational recreation

INDEPENDENCE

P   WYTHE-GRAYSON REGIONAL LIBRARY*, Grayson County Public,
     147 S Independence Ave, 24348-2800. (Mail add: PO Box 159,
     24348-0159), SAN 362-997X. Tel: 276-773-2761. FAX: 276-773-3289.
     Web Site: wythegrayson.lib.va.us. *Dir,* J Sara Paulk; E-mail:
     jspaulk-wgrl@gmx.com; *Regional Supvr,* Janet Cox; *Br Mgr,* Phyllis
     Bobbit; E-mail: psbobbit-wgrl@gmx.com; Staff 11 (MLS 1, Non-MLS 10)
     Founded 1948
     Special Collections: Oral History
     Subject Interests: Civil War, Genealogy
     Wireless access
     Function: ILL available
     Partic in Lyrasis
     Open Mon, Wed & Fri 9-5:30, Tues & Thurs 9-7, Sat 10-2
     Friends of the Library Group
     Branches: 4
     FRIES PUBLIC, 105 W Main St, Fries, 24330. (Mail add: PO Box 325,
       Fries, 24330-0325), SAN 377-7669. Tel: 276-744-3160. FAX:
       276-744-3160. *Br Supvr,* Autumn Anderson; E-mail:

     aanderson-wgrl@gmx.com; *Circ Librn,* Shelby Johnson; *Circ Librn,*
       Mary Margaret Pack; Staff 2 (Non-MLS 2)
       Function: ILL available
       Open Mon & Thurs 10-7, Tues & Wed 10-6, Sat 10-2
     RURAL RETREAT PUBLIC, 119 N Greever St, Rural Retreat,
       24368-2450. (Mail add: PO Box 279, Rural Retreat, 24368-0279). Tel:
       276-686-8337. FAX: 276-686-8337. *Br Supvr,* Robin LaPrelle; E-mail:
       rlaprelle-wgrl@gmx.com; *Circ Librn,* Belinda Roberts; *Circ Librn,*
       Melissa Swain; Staff 2 (Non-MLS 2)
       Function: ILL available
       Open Mon, Wed & Thurs 3:30-8, Tues 10-5, Sat 10-2
       Friends of the Library Group
     WHITETOP PUBLIC, 16309 Highlands Pkwy, Whitetop, 24292. (Mail
       add: PO Box 17, Whitetop, 24292-0017), SAN 377-7685. Tel:
       276-388-2873. FAX: 276-388-2873. *Br Supvr,* Autumn Anderson;
       E-mail: aanderson-wgrl@gmx.com; *Circ Librn,* Joy Gibney; *Circ Librn,*
       Marlena Phillips; Staff 2 (Non-MLS 2)
       Function: ILL available
       Open Mon-Thurs 11-7, Sat 10-2
       Friends of the Library Group
     WYTHE COUNTY PUBLIC, 300 E Monroe St, Wytheville, 24382-2367,
       SAN 363-0005. Tel: 276-228-4951. FAX: 276-228-6034. *Br Mgr,* Anita
       Wood; E-mail: anitawood-wgrl@gmx.com; Staff 8 (MLS 1, Non-MLS 7)
       Special Collections: Oral History
       Subject Interests: Genealogy
       Function: ILL available
       Open Mon-Thurs 9-8, Fri 9-6, Sat 9-3
       Friends of the Library Group
     Bookmobiles: 1. Outreach Servs, Dexter Edwards

KEYSVILLE

J   SOUTHSIDE VIRGINIA COMMUNITY COLLEGE*, John H Daniel
     Campus Library, 200 Daniel Rd, 23947. Tel: 434-736-2045. FAX:
     434-736-2079. Web Site: www.sv.vccs.edu/lrs. *Dir, Learning Res,* Jack
     Ancell; Tel: 434-949-1066, E-mail: jack.ancell@sv.vccs.edu; *Supvr,* Libby
     Blanton; Tel: 434-736-2044, E-mail: libby.blanton@sv.vccs.edu; *Libr Spec,*
     Rosa Townsend; E-mail: rosa.townsend@southside.edu
     Library Holdings: Bk Vols 34,506; Per Subs 85
     Automation Activity & Vendor Info: (Cataloging) Ex Libris Group;
     (Circulation) Ex Libris Group; (Course Reserve) Ex Libris Group; (OPAC)
     Ex Libris Group
     Partic in Virginia Commun Coll Syst
     Open Mon-Thurs 8am-9pm, Fri 8-4:30

KILMARNOCK

P   LANCASTER COMMUNITY LIBRARY*, 235 School St, 22482-3830.
     (Mail add: PO Box 850, 22482-0850), SAN 317-3178. Tel: 804-435-1729.
     FAX: 804-435-0255. E-mail: library@lancasterlibrary.org. Web Site:
     www.lancasterlibrary.org. *Dir of Libr Serv,* Lindsy Gardner; *Ch,* Tonya
     Carter; E-mail: tmcarter@lancasterlibrary.org; Staff 7 (MLS 1, Non-MLS
     6)
     Founded 1961. Pop 11,567; Circ 107,700
     Jul 2005-Jun 2006 Income $442,559, State $75,955, City $1,000, County
     $73,900, Locally Generated Income $291,704. Mats Exp $64,559, Books
     $36,937, Per/Ser (Incl. Access Fees) $5,200, AV Mat $14,442, Electronic
     Ref Mat (Incl. Access Fees) $7,980. Sal $187,346
     Library Holdings: AV Mats 4,243; Large Print Bks 1,554; Bk Titles
     37,000; Bk Vols 40,000
     Automation Activity & Vendor Info: (Cataloging) TLC (The Library
     Corporation); (Circulation) TLC (The Library Corporation); (OPAC) TLC
     (The Library Corporation)
     Wireless access
     Open Mon & Wed 9-8, Tues, Thurs & Fri 9-6, Sat 10-4
     Friends of the Library Group

KING GEORGE

P   LEWIS EGERTON SMOOT MEMORIAL LIBRARY*, 8562 Dahlgren Rd,
     22485-3503. SAN 317-3186. Tel: 540-775-7951. FAX: 540-775-5292. Web
     Site: www.smoot.org. *Dir,* Robin Tenney; E-mail:
     librarydirector@smoot.org; *Youth Serv Librn,* Katie Pikula; Staff 11 (MLS
     1, Non-MLS 10)
     Founded 1969. Pop 16,600; Circ 61,399
     Library Holdings: Bk Titles 50,000; Bk Vols 52,263; Per Subs 90
     Special Collections: Virginiana. Oral History
     Subject Interests: Va hist
     Open Mon-Thurs 9-9, Fri & Sat 10-5
     Friends of the Library Group

LANCASTER

S   MARY BALL WASHINGTON MUSEUM & LIBRARY, INC*, Genealogy
     & Family Research Center, 8346 Mary Ball Rd, 22503. (Mail add: PO Box
     97, 22503-0097), SAN 317-3194. Tel: 804-462-7280. FAX: 804-462-6107.

E-mail: info@mbwm.org. Web Site: www.mbwm.org. *Exec Dir,* Karen Hart
Founded 1958
Library Holdings: Bk Titles 6,000; Bk Vols 5,000; Per Subs 10
Special Collections: Genealogy Papers & Research Materials, indexed by surname
Subject Interests: Lancaster County, US hist, Va genealogy, Va hist
Function: Computers for patron use, Copy machines, Electronic databases & coll, Online cat, Res performed for a fee
Open Tues-Fri 10-4, Sat 11-3
Restriction: Closed stack, Fee for pub use, Non-circulating, Not a lending libr

LANGLEY AFB

A   UNITED STATES AIR FORCE*, Herbert H Bateman Library-Langley Air Force Base Library FL4800, 42 Ash Ave, 23665. SAN 363-0064. Tel: 757-764-2906. FAX: 757-764-3315. E-mail: 633fss.fsdl@langley.af.mil. Web Site: www.langleylibrary.org. *Dir,* Leslie Smail; Staff 1 (MLS 1)
Founded 1942
Library Holdings: Bk Vols 40,000; Per Subs 80
Subject Interests: Aeronaut, Air Force hist, Mil hist
Automation Activity & Vendor Info: (Cataloging) SIRSI WorkFlows; (Circulation) SIRSI WorkFlows; (ILL) OCLC FirstSearch; (OPAC) SIRSI-iBistro
Database Vendor: CountryWatch
Wireless access
Function: Audiobks via web, Bks on CD, Children's prog, Computers for patron use, Copy machines, Doc delivery serv, Electronic databases & coll, Fax serv, Free DVD rentals, Handicapped accessible, ILL available, Music CDs, Online cat, Orientations, OverDrive digital audio bks, Prog for adults, Prog for children & young adult, Ref serv available, Scanner, Summer reading prog, Web-catalog
Partic in Fedlink; OCLC Online Computer Library Center, Inc
Open Mon-Thurs 10-8, Fri-Sun 12-5
Restriction: Authorized personnel only

LAWRENCEVILLE

S   BRUNSWICK CORRECTIONAL CENTER*, DCE Library, 1147 Planters Rd, PO Box 207C, 23868-3499. SAN 371-9448. Tel: 434-848-4131, Ext 1146. FAX: 434-848-0971. *Regional Librn,* Mary Geist; Staff 1 (MLS 1)
Founded 1982
Library Holdings: Bk Titles 12,000; Bk Vols 12,500; Per Subs 45
Automation Activity & Vendor Info: (Cataloging) Follett Software

P   MEHERRIN REGIONAL LIBRARY*, Brunswick County Library, 133 W Hicks St, 23868. SAN 363-0099. Tel: 434-848-2418. Administration Tel: 434-848-6899. FAX: 434-848-4786. Administration FAX: 434-848-2739. E-mail: bcl@meherrinlib.org. Web Site: meherrinlib.org. *Dir,* Sarah A P Raible; E-mail: sraible@meherrinlib.org; *Exec Mgr,* Marilyn S Marston; Staff 17 (MLS 1, Non-MLS 16)
Founded 1940. Pop 36,000; Circ 140,000
Library Holdings: Bk Vols 80,000; Per Subs 200
Special Collections: Oral History
Automation Activity & Vendor Info: (Circulation) TLC (The Library Corporation); (OPAC) TLC (The Library Corporation)
Database Vendor: Baker & Taylor, EBSCOhost, OCLC FirstSearch, ProQuest
Partic in OCLC Online Computer Library Center, Inc
Open Mon 10-8, Tues-Fri 10-6, Sat 10-1
Friends of the Library Group
Branches: 1
WILLIAM E RICHARDSON JR MEMORIAL LIBRARY, 100 Spring St, Emporia, 23847, SAN 363-0129. Tel: 804-634-2539. FAX: 804-634-5489. E-mail: rml@meherrinlib.org. *Libr & Syst Tech Mgr,* Becky S Walker; E-mail: bwalker@meherrinlib.org; Staff 3 (MLS 1, Non-MLS 2)
Founded 1977
Library Holdings: AV Mats 2,946; CDs 247; DVDs 224; Large Print Bks 981; Bk Vols 43,529; Per Subs 81; Talking Bks 667; Videos 1,612
Automation Activity & Vendor Info: (Cataloging) TLC (The Library Corporation); (ILL) OCLC FirstSearch; (Serials) TLC (The Library Corporation)
Database Vendor: Gale Cengage Learning, ProQuest
Function: After school storytime, Art exhibits, Audio & video playback equip for onsite use, AV serv, Copy machines, Digital talking bks, Electronic databases & coll, Family literacy, Fax serv, Genealogy discussion group, ILL available, Mail & tel request accepted, Music CDs, Newsp ref libr, Online ref, Photocopying/Printing, Prog for adults, Prog for children & young adult, Ref & res, Referrals accepted, Spoken cassettes & CDs, Summer reading prog, Tax forms, Telephone ref, VHS videos, Wheelchair accessible
Open Mon & Wed-Fri 10-6, Tues 10-8, Sat 10-1

Restriction: Non-resident fee
Bookmobiles: 1

C   SAINT PAUL'S COLLEGE*, Russell Memorial Library, 115 College Dr, 23868-1299. SAN 317-3208. Tel: 434-848-1841. FAX: 434-848-1861. Web Site: www.saintpauls.edu. *Dir,* Marc Finney; Tel: 434-848-1840, E-mail: mfinney@saintpauls.edu; *Circ,* Angel Schade; Tel: 434-848-1836, E-mail: aschade@saintpauls.edu; *Pub Serv,* B Roger Keeling; Tel: 434-848-1835, E-mail: bkeeling@saintpauls.edu; Staff 5 (MLS 1, Non-MLS 4)
Enrl 680; Fac 53; Highest Degree: Bachelor
Library Holdings: Bk Titles 44,000; Bk Vols 54,000; Per Subs 245
Special Collections: Black Studies (Schomburg Coll), micro; West Indies (Short Coll)
Automation Activity & Vendor Info: (Acquisitions) SirsiDynix; (Cataloging) SirsiDynix; (Circulation) SirsiDynix; (OPAC) SirsiDynix
Database Vendor: Gale Cengage Learning, ProQuest
Partic in Coop Col Libr Ctr, Inc; Virginia Independent College & University Library Association
Open Mon-Thurs 8am-10pm, Fri 8-5, Sun 2-10

LEBANON

P   RUSSELL COUNTY PUBLIC LIBRARY, 248 W Main St, 24266. (Mail add: PO Box 247, 24266-0247), SAN 317-3216. Tel: 276-889-8044. FAX: 276-889-8045. Web Site: russell.lib.va.us. *Dir,* Kelly McBride; E-mail: kmcbride@russell.lib.va.us; Staff 9 (MLS 2, Non-MLS 7)
Founded 1959. Pop 28,900; Circ 49,558
Jul 2011-Jun 2012 Income (Main Library and Branch(s)) $376,448, State $78,954, City $7,500, Federal $7,622, County $270,572, Locally Generated Income $11,800. Mats Exp $39,980, Books $21,280, Per/Ser (Incl. Access Fees) $2,700, AV Mat $14,500, Electronic Ref Mat (Incl. Access Fees) $1,500. Sal $226,207 (Prof $89,890)
Library Holdings: AV Mats 1,136; CDs 1,034; DVDs 280; Large Print Bks 3,050; Bk Vols 46,480; Per Subs 79; Videos 1,750
Subject Interests: Genealogy, Local hist
Automation Activity & Vendor Info: (Cataloging) TLC (The Library Corporation); (Circulation) TLC (The Library Corporation); (OPAC) TLC (The Library Corporation)
Database Vendor: Gale Cengage Learning, TLC (The Library Corporation)
Wireless access
Partic in SouthWest Information Network Group (SWING)
Open Mon & Tues 9-7, Wed & Fri 10-5:30, Thurs 9-8, Sat 10-2, Sun 2-5
Restriction: Open to pub for ref & circ; with some limitations
Friends of the Library Group
Branches: 1
HONAKER COMMUNITY LIBRARY, Ten Library Dr, Honaker, 24260. Tel: 276-873-6600. FAX: 276-873-5800. *Br Mgr,* Tina Harris; E-mail: tharris@russell.lib.va.us; Staff 1 (Non-MLS 1)
Founded 2001. Pop 7,000
Library Holdings: Bk Vols 11,000; Per Subs 8
Open Mon, Tues & Wed 3-7, Thurs 9-1, Fri 12-5:30, Sun 2-5
Friends of the Library Group

LEESBURG

P   LOUDOUN COUNTY PUBLIC LIBRARY*, Admin Offices, 908A Trailview Blvd SE, 20175-4415. SAN 363-0153. Tel: 703-777-0368. FAX: 703-771-5238, 703-771-5252. E-mail: libraries@loudoun.gov. Web Site: www.lcpl.lib.va.us. *Dir,* Chang Liu; Staff 41 (MLS 41)
Founded 1973. Pop 279,293; Circ 3,602,004
Library Holdings: Bks on Deafness & Sign Lang 311; e-books 41,497; Large Print Bks 8,506; Bk Titles 193,979; Bk Vols 487,554; Per Subs 1,114
Special Collections: American Sign Language (ASL) Coll; English as a Second Language (ESL) Coll
Automation Activity & Vendor Info: (Acquisitions) SirsiDynix; (Cataloging) SirsiDynix; (Circulation) SirsiDynix; (ILL) OCLC; (OPAC) SirsiDynix; (Serials) SirsiDynix
Publications: Welcome to Loudoun County, Services for Citizens with Disabilities
Partic in OCLC Eastern
Special Services for the Deaf - TTY equip
Open Mon-Thurs 10-9, Fri & Sat 10-5, Sun 1-5
Friends of the Library Group
Branches: 8
ASHBURN BRANCH, 43316 Hay Rd, Ashburn, 20147. Tel: 703-737-8100. FAX: 703-737-8101. *Br Mgr,* John Huddy
Founded 2003
Open Mon-Thurs 10-9, Fri & Sat 10-5, Sun 1-5
CASCADES BRANCH, 21030 Whitfield Pl, Potomac Falls, 20165, SAN 371-988X. Tel: 703-444-3228. FAX: 703-444-1336. *Mgr,* Position Currently Open; Staff 11 (MLS 8, Non-MLS 3)
Founded 1992. Circ 1,271,497
Special Services for the Deaf - TTY equip

Open Mon-Thurs 10-9, Fri & Sat 10-5, Sun 1-5
Friends of the Library Group
LOVETTSVILLE BRANCH, 12 N Light St, Lovettsville, 20180. (Mail
add: PO Box 189, Lovettsville, 20180-0189), SAN 328-7645. Tel:
540-822-5824. FAX: 540-822-5998. *Mgr,* Charles V Wood; E-mail:
chuck.wood@loudoun.gov
Special Services for the Deaf - TTY equip
Open Mon-Thurs 10-9, Fri & Sat 10-5
Friends of the Library Group
MIDDLEBURG BRANCH, 101 Reed St, Middleburg, 20117. (Mail add:
PO Box 1823, Middleburg, 20118), SAN 328-7629. Tel: 540-687-5730.
FAX: 540-687-3630. *Mgr,* Sheila Whetzel; E-mail:
sheila.whetzel@loudoun.gov; Staff 2 (MLS 1, Non-MLS 1)
Founded 1984
Special Services for the Deaf - TTY equip
Open Mon-Thurs 10-9, Fri & Sat 10-5
Friends of the Library Group
OUTREACH SERVICES, 380 Old Waterford Rd NW, 20176, SAN
377-6506. Tel: 703-771-5621. FAX: 703-771-5620. Web Site:
library.loudoun.gov. *Mgr,* Jack Frear; Tel: 703-771-3107, Fax:
703-771-5680, E-mail: jack.frear@loudoun.gov; Staff 0.59 (MLS 0.09,
Non-MLS 0.5)
Circ 11,281
Special Services for the Deaf - TDD equip
Open Mon-Fri 9-5
PURCELLVILLE BRANCH, 220 E Main St, Purcellville, 20132-3167,
SAN 363-0218. Tel: 540-338-7235. FAX: 540-338-2629. *Mgr,* Leah
Bromser-Kloeden; E-mail: leah.bromser.kloeden@loudoun.gov; Staff 20
(MLS 4, Non-MLS 16)
Special Services for the Deaf - TTY equip
Open Mon-Thurs 10-9, Fri & Sat 10-5, Sun 1-5
Friends of the Library Group
RUST BRANCH, 380 Old Waterford Rd NW, 20176, SAN 371-9898. Tel:
703-777-0323. FAX: 703-771-5620. *Mgr,* Karim Khan; E-mail:
karim.khan@loudoun.gov; Staff 22.125 (MLS 9.4375, Non-MLS
12.6875)
Founded 1992. Circ 1,290,153
Automation Activity & Vendor Info: (Acquisitions) SirsiDynix
Special Services for the Deaf - Assisted listening device
Open Mon-Thurs 10-9, Fri & Sat 10-5, Sun 1-5
Friends of the Library Group
STERLING BRANCH, 120 Enterprise St, Sterling, 20164, SAN 363-0242.
Tel: 703-430-9500. FAX: 703-430-5935. *Br Mgr,* Valarie Hoover;
E-mail: valarie.hoover@loudoun.gov
Special Services for the Deaf - TDD equip
Open Mon-Thurs 10-9, Fri & Sat 10-5
Friends of the Library Group
Bookmobiles: 1

LEXINGTON

S   STONEWALL JACKSON HOUSE*, Garland Gray Research Center &
Library, Stonewall Jackson House, Eight E Washington St, 24450. SAN
327-3555. Tel: 540-463-2552. FAX: 540-463-4088. E-mail:
sjh1@rockbridge.net. *Dir,* Michael Anne Lynn
Library Holdings: Bk Vols 11,000

S   GEORGE C MARSHALL FOUNDATION RESEARCH LIBRARY, 1600
VMI Parade, 24450-1600. SAN 317-3224. Tel: 540-463-7103. FAX:
540-464-5229. E-mail: marshallfoundation@marshallfoundation.org. Web
Site: www.marshallfoundation.org. *Dir, Libr & Archives,* Paul B Barron;
Tel: 540-463-7103, Ext 129, E-mail: barronpb@marshallfoundation.org;
Archivist, Asst Librn, Jeffrey S Kozak; Tel: 540-463-7103, Ext 122, E-mail:
jkozak@marshallfoundation.org; Staff 2 (MLS 2)
Founded 1964
Library Holdings: Bk Titles 25,000
Special Collections: Cryptography (William Friedman Coll), oral hist,
photos, posters; Marshall Plan; Military-Diplomatic History 1898-1955, ms;
Women's Army Corps
Database Vendor: VTLS, Inc
Wireless access
Function: Archival coll, Res libr
Publications: George C Marshall Research Library Handbook for
Researchers; Manuscript Collections of the George C Marshall Library,
George C Marshall Papers, 1932-1960: A Guide; WWI & WWII Posters in
the George C Marshall Foundation
Open Mon-Fri 9-4:30

P   ROCKBRIDGE REGIONAL LIBRARY*, 138 S Main St, 24450-2316.
SAN 363-0277. Tel: 540-463-4324. FAX: 540-464-4824. E-mail:
rrl@rrlib.net. Web Site: www.rrlib.net. *Dir,* Linda L Krantz; E-mail:
lkrantz@rrlib.net; *Head, Adult Serv,* Margaret Whittington; E-mail:
mwhittington@rrlib.net; *Head, Tech Serv,* Sue Milo; E-mail:
smilo@rrlib.net; *Head, Youth Serv,* Carol Elizabeth Jones; Staff 34 (MLS
3, Non-MLS 31)

Founded 1934. Pop 38,800; Circ 230,137
Library Holdings: CDs 2,380; Bk Vols 160,570; Per Subs 271; Talking
Bks 3,391; Videos 5,956
Subject Interests: Local hist
Automation Activity & Vendor Info: (Acquisitions) TLC (The Library
Corporation); (Cataloging) TLC (The Library Corporation); (Circulation)
TLC (The Library Corporation); (Course Reserve) TLC (The Library
Corporation); (ILL) TLC (The Library Corporation); (Media Booking) TLC
(The Library Corporation); (OPAC) TLC (The Library Corporation);
(Serials) TLC (The Library Corporation)
Database Vendor: Gale Cengage Learning, netLibrary, OCLC FirstSearch,
ProQuest
Function: Ref serv available
Publications: Foundation Annual Report; Library Newsletter
Partic in Lyrasis; SouthWest Information Network Group (SWING)
Special Services for the Blind - Talking bks
Open Mon, Wed & Fri 9-5:30, Tues & Thurs 9-9, Sat 9-1, Sun (Sept-May)
1-5
Friends of the Library Group
Branches: 4
BATH COUNTY PUBLIC, 96 Courthouse Hill Rd, Warm Springs, 24484.
(Mail add: PO Box 250, Warm Springs, 24484-0250), SAN 363-0307.
Tel: 540-839-7286. FAX: 540-839-3058. *Librn,* Sharon Lindsay; E-mail:
slindsay@rrlib.net; *Librn,* Jeannette Robinson; E-mail:
jrobinson@rrlib.net; Staff 3 (Non-MLS 3)
Library Holdings: Bk Vols 30,000; Per Subs 50
Open Mon & Wed-Fri 9-5, Tues 12-8, Sat 9-1
Friends of the Library Group
BUENA VISTA PUBLIC, 2110 Magnolia Ave, Buena Vista, 24416, SAN
363-0331. Tel: 540-261-2715. FAX: 540-261-4822. *Librn,* Anne Johnson;
E-mail: ajohnson@rrlib.net; Staff 2 (Non-MLS 2)
Library Holdings: AV Mats 158; Bk Vols 17,373; Per Subs 49
Open Mon-Wed & Fri 10-5, Thurs 1-7, Sat 10-1
GLASGOW PUBLIC, 1108 Blueridge Rd, Glasgow, 24555. (Mail add: PO
Box 67, Glasgow, 24555), SAN 363-0366. Tel: 540-258-2509. *Librn,*
Barbara Slough; Staff 2 (Non-MLS 2)
Library Holdings: Bk Vols 10,726; Per Subs 23
Open Mon-Wed 10-5:30, Thurs 11:30-7, Sat 10-1
GOSHEN PUBLIC, 1124 Virginia Ave, Goshen, 24439. (Mail add: PO
Box 129, Goshen, 22439), SAN 323-5718. Tel: 540-997-0351. FAX:
540-997-0019. *Librn,* Anne McClung; E-mail: amcclung@rrlib.net; Staff
2 (Non-MLS 2)
Library Holdings: Bk Vols 6,216
Open Mon-Wed 9:30-7, Thurs 9:30-5, Sat 9-1
Friends of the Library Group
Bookmobiles: 1. Extn Librn, Deanie McDonald

C   VIRGINIA MILITARY INSTITUTE*, J T L Preston Library, Letcher Ave,
24450. SAN 317-3232. Tel: 540-464-7228. FAX: 540-464-7279. Web Site:
www.vmi.edu/library/. *Head Librn,* Don Samdahl; E-mail:
samdahldh@vmi.edu; *Head, Archives, Head, Rec Mgt,* Diane Jacob; Tel:
540-464-7566, E-mail: jacobdb@vmi.edu; *Access Serv,* Susan Hastings;
Tel: 540-464-7607, E-mail: hastingssf@vmi.edu; *Doc, Ref Serv,* Janet S
Holly; Tel: 540-464-7296, E-mail: hollyjs@vmi.edu; *ILL,* Valerie Gaylard;
Media Serv, Dave Hess; Staff 7 (MLS 6, Non-MLS 1)
Founded 1839. Enrl 1,300; Fac 106; Highest Degree: Bachelor
Jul 2005-Jun 2006 Income $1,302,961, State $1,224,581, Other $78,380.
Mats Exp $316,257, Books $115,197, Per/Ser (Incl. Access Fees)
$179,656, Micro $10,381, AV Mat $5,603, Presv $5,420. Sal $728,777
(Prof $360,125)
Library Holdings: CDs 1,500; DVDs 395; e-journals 20,426; Bk Vols
216,131; Per Subs 618; Videos 3,360
Special Collections: Civil War; Thomas J (Stonewall) Jackson. US
Document Depository
Automation Activity & Vendor Info: (Serials) Innovative Interfaces, Inc
Database Vendor: Cambridge Scientific Abstracts, EBSCOhost,
Factiva.com, Gale Cengage Learning, JSTOR, LexisNexis, OCLC
FirstSearch, OCLC WorldCat, ProQuest, SerialsSolutions
Wireless access
Partic in Lyrasis; Virtual Library of Virginia
Open Mon-Thurs 8-1, Fri 8am-10pm, Sat 8-5, Sun 1pm-1am
Friends of the Library Group

WASHINGTON & LEE UNIVERSITY
CL   WILBUR C HALL LAW LIBRARY*, Lewis Hall, E Denny Circle, 24450,
SAN 363-0455. Tel: 540-458-8540. Interlibrary Loan Service Tel:
540-458-8553. FAX: 540-458-8967. Web Site: law.wlu.edu/library. *Libr
Dir,* Caroline L Osborne; Tel: 540-458-8545, E-mail:
osbornecl@wlu.edu; *Assoc Librn,* John Doyle; Tel: 540-458-8554,
E-mail: doylej@wlu.edu; *Head, Tech Serv,* John P Bissett; Tel:
540-458-8546, E-mail: bissettj@wlu.edu; *Archivist,* John Jacob; Tel:
540-458-8969, E-mail: jacobj@wlu.edu; *Doc/Ref Serv,* Judy Stinson; Tel:
540-458-8544, E-mail: stinsonj@wlu.edu; Staff 5 (MLS 5)
Founded 1849. Enrl 411; Fac 35; Highest Degree: Doctorate

Jul 2009-Jun 2010 Income (Main Library Only) $784,408. Mats Exp
$1,016,340, Books $72,137, Per/Ser (Incl. Access Fees) $589,669, AV
Mat $8,302, Electronic Ref Mat (Incl. Access Fees) $345,433, Presv
$799. Sal $677,707 (Prof $379,579)
Library Holdings: AV Mats 233,279; Bks on Deafness & Sign Lang 8;
CDs 45; DVDs 444; e-books 7,439; e-journals 1,783; Electronic Media
& Resources 63; Microforms 228,952; Bk Titles 62,616; Bk Vols
467,829; Per Subs 3,055; Videos 460
Special Collections: Appellate Papers (John W Davis Coll); Bankruptcy
(U S Senate Committee on the Judiciary Coll); Early Virginia Legal
Materials (Burks Coll); Frank Parker, Civil Rights Activist; Impeachment
Papers of President Richard M Nixon (Caldwell Butler); Lewis F Powell
Jr Archives; Lewis F Powell Papers; Washington & Lee Law School
Archives
Automation Activity & Vendor Info: (Acquisitions) Innovative
Interfaces, Inc; (Cataloging) Innovative Interfaces, Inc; (Circulation)
Innovative Interfaces, Inc; (Course Reserve) Innovative Interfaces, Inc;
(ILL) OCLC; (OPAC) Innovative Interfaces, Inc; (Serials) Innovative
Interfaces, Inc
Database Vendor: Blackwell's, HeinOnline, Ingenta, Innovative
Interfaces, Inc INN - View, LexisNexis, Springer-Verlag, Swets
Information Services, Westlaw
Partic in OCLC Online Computer Library Center, Inc; Virginia
Independent College & University Library Association
Publications: Acquisitions List; Current Contents; Law Library Guide;
Newsletter
Open Mon-Thurs 8am-9pm, Fri 8-5, Sat 10-5, Sun 1-9

C   UNIVERSITY LIBRARY, 204 W Washington St, 24450-2116. Tel:
540-458-8640. Circulation Tel: 540-458-8643. Interlibrary Loan Service
Tel: 540-458-8645. Reference Tel: 540-458-8644. Administration Tel:
540-458-8642. FAX: 540-458-8964. Web Site: library.wlu.edu. *Univ
Librn,* Terrance J Metz; E-mail: mezt@wlu.edu; *Head, Pub Serv, Ref,*
John Tombarge; Tel: 540-458-8134; *Head, Tech Serv,* Position Currently
Open; *Access Serv Librn,* Elizabeth Anne Teaff; E-mail: teaffe@wlu.edu;
Sr Ref Librn (Info Serv), Richard Grefe; Tel: 540-458-8648; *Electronic
Res Librn,* Position Currently Open; *Humanities Librn,* Yolanda Merrill;
Tel: 540-458-8662; *Rare Bks & Spec Coll Librn,* C Vaughan Stanley;
Tel: 540-458-8649; *Sci Librn,* Mary Abdoney; Tel: 540-458-8647; *Syst
Librn,* Position Currently Open. Subject Specialists: *Humanities,* Yolanda
Merrill; Staff 12 (MLS 9, Non-MLS 3)
Founded 1749. Enrl 1,759; Fac 245; Highest Degree: Bachelor
Jul 2010-Jun 2011. Mats Exp $1,185,230, Books $276,174, Per/Ser (Incl.
Access Fees) $896,206, AV Mat $12,850
Library Holdings: Audiobooks 1,727; AV Mats 14,377; CDs 4,087;
e-books 3,400; e-journals 4,701; Bk Vols 732,593; Per Subs 1,050;
Videos 8,231
Special Collections: Classical Literature; Confederacy (Robert E Lee
Coll); Franklin Society Library; Graham Society Library; W & L
University & Valley of Virginia Manuscripts; Washington Society
Library. US Document Depository
Automation Activity & Vendor Info: (Acquisitions) Innovative
Interfaces, Inc; (Cataloging) Innovative Interfaces, Inc; (Circulation)
Innovative Interfaces, Inc; (Course Reserve) Innovative Interfaces, Inc;
(ILL) OCLC ILLiad; (OPAC) Innovative Interfaces, Inc; (Serials)
Innovative Interfaces, Inc
Partic in Lyrasis; OCLC Online Computer Library Center, Inc; Virginia
Independent College & University Library Association; Virtual Library of
Virginia
Publications: Guide to the Manuscripts Coll
Friends of the Library Group

LOCUST GROVE

J   GERMANNA COMMUNITY COLLEGE*, Locust Grove Campus Library,
2130 Germanna Hwy, 22508-2102. SAN 317-3240. Tel: 540-423-9163.
FAX: 540-423-9159. Web Site: www.germanna.edu/library. *Librn,* Karen
Bowers; Staff 3 (MLS 3)
Founded 1970. Enrl 5,018; Fac 49; Highest Degree: Associate
Library Holdings: e-books 73,894; e-journals 2,086; Bk Vols 31,216; Per
Subs 120
Special Collections: Legacy (Supports Germanna Legacy Lectures)
Subject Interests: Hist, Med, Nursing
Automation Activity & Vendor Info: (Cataloging) OCLC Connexion;
(ILL) OCLC FirstSearch; (OPAC) Ex Libris Group
Wireless access
Partic in Virginia Commun Coll Syst; Virtual Library of Virginia
Special Services for the Blind - Low vision equip
Open Mon-Thurs 8-7, Fri 8-2, Sat 9-2

LYNCHBURG

S   AREVA NP, INC*, Technical Library, 3315 Old Forest Rd, 24501. (Mail
add: PO Box 10935, 24506-0935), SAN 317-3275. Tel: 434-832-2476.
FAX: 434-832-2475. E-mail: library@areva.com. *Res Libr Adminr,* Ella
Carr-Payne; Staff 1 (MLS 1)

Founded 1955
Library Holdings: Bk Titles 75,000; Per Subs 60
Subject Interests: Chem, Computer application, Math, Nuclear sci,
Nuclear tech
Partic in Dialog Corp; OCLC Online Computer Library Center, Inc
Restriction: Not open to pub

M   BARKSDALE MEDICAL LIBRARY*, Virginia Baptist Hospital, 3300
Rivermont Ave, 24503. SAN 323-5203. Tel: 434-200-3147. *Librn,* Claire A
Meissner
Library Holdings: Bk Titles 650; Per Subs 55
Subject Interests: Gynecology, Obstetrics, Oncology, Pediatrics, Psychiat
Database Vendor: EBSCOhost
Partic in Lynchburg Area Library Cooperative; National Network of
Libraries of Medicine Southeastern Atlantic Region; OCLC Online
Computer Library Center, Inc; Southwestern Virginia Health Information
Librarians
Restriction: Not open to pub, Staff use only

J   CENTRAL VIRGINIA COMMUNITY COLLEGE LIBRARY*, Amherst
Hall, Rm 2506, 3506 Wards Rd, 24502-2498. SAN 317-3283. Tel:
434-832-7750. Information Services Tel: 434-832-7752. FAX:
434-386-4677. E-mail: library@cvcc.vccs.edu. Web Site:
www.cvcc.vccs.edu/library. *Coordr, Libr Serv,* Michael T Fein; Tel:
434-832-7751, E-mail: feinm@cvcc.vccs.edu; *Info Serv,* Elizabeth Boothe;
E-mail: boothee@cvcc.vccs.edu; *Tech Serv,* Frances Chambers; Tel:
434-832-7754, E-mail: chambersf@cvcc.vccs.edu; Staff 5 (MLS 3,
Non-MLS 2)
Founded 1967. Enrl 2,200; Fac 95; Highest Degree: Associate
Jul 2005-Jun 2006. Mats Exp $73,000, Books $32,000, Per/Ser (Incl.
Access Fees) $21,000, AV Mat $5,000, Electronic Ref Mat (Incl. Access
Fees) $15,000
Library Holdings: Bk Titles 32,500; Per Subs 200
Subject Interests: Lynchburg area hist
Automation Activity & Vendor Info: (Circulation) Ex Libris Group
Database Vendor: Gale Cengage Learning, OCLC FirstSearch
Wireless access
Publications: Acquisitions List (Quarterly)
Partic in Lynchburg Area Library Cooperative; Lyrasis; SouthWest
Information Network Group (SWING); Virginia Commun Coll Syst;
Virtual Library of Virginia
Open Mon-Thurs 8am-9pm, Fri 8-5, Sat 9-1

M   CENTRAL VIRGINIA TRAINING CENTER*, Professional Library, PO
Box 1098, 24505. SAN 363-051X. Tel: 434-947-6171, 434-947-6871.
FAX: 434-947-2395. Web Site: www.cvtc.dmhmrsas.virginia.gov/. *Dir, Staff
Develop,* Dr Carolyn Robinson; E-mail:
carolyn.robinson@cvtc.dmhmrsas.virginia.gov; Staff 1 (Non-MLS 1)
Founded 1957
Library Holdings: Bk Vols 2,300; Per Subs 70
Subject Interests: Mental retardation
Database Vendor: EBSCOhost, OCLC FirstSearch
Function: ILL available
Partic in Lynchburg Area Library Cooperative
Restriction: Not a lending libr, Pub use on premises

S   GEORGE M JONES LIBRARY ASSOCIATION*, Jones Memorial
Library, 2311 Memorial Ave, 24501. SAN 317-3305. Tel: 434-846-0501.
FAX: 434-846-1572. Web Site: www.jmlibrary.org. *Dir,* Susan Hall Pillow;
E-mail: spillow@jmlibrary.org; *Pub Serv,* Lewis Hobgood Averett; E-mail:
laverett@jmlibrary.org; *Res,* Nancy Jamerson Weiland; E-mail:
nweiland@jmlibrary.org. Subject Specialists: *Genealogical res,* Nancy
Jamerson Weiland; Staff 5 (Non-MLS 5)
Founded 1908
Jul 2005-Jun 2006 Income $160,000. Mats Exp $8,200, Books $3,000,
Per/Ser (Incl. Access Fees) $2,500, Micro $1,200, Presv $1,500. Sal
$148,000
Library Holdings: Bk Titles 1,700; Per Subs 55
Special Collections: Lynchburg Architectural Archives; Personal Family
Papers & Correspondence, Records of Clubs & Organizations, Business
Records (Manuscript Coll)
Subject Interests: Genealogy, Local hist
Database Vendor: ProQuest
Function: For res purposes, Res libr, Wheelchair accessible
Publications: JML Report (Newsletter)
Partic in Lynchburg Area Library Cooperative; OCLC Online Computer
Library Center, Inc
Open Tues & Thurs 1-9, Wed & Fri 1-5, Sat 9-5
Restriction: Non-circulating
Friends of the Library Group

CR   LIBERTY UNIVERSITY LIBRARY*, A Pierre Guillermin Library -
Integrated Learning Resource Center, 1971 University Blvd, 24502. SAN
317-3313. Tel: 434-582-2220. Circulation Tel: 434-582-2506. Interlibrary
Loan Service Tel: 434-582-2442. Reference Tel: 434-592-3362.

Administration Tel: 434-592-3292. FAX: 434-582-2728. Interlibrary Loan Service FAX: 434-582-2017. Web Site: www.liberty.edu/informationservices/ilrc/library/, www.liberty.edu/library. *Dean,* Carl Merat; Tel: 434-592-3751, E-mail: cmerat@liberty.edu; *Assoc Dean,* Lowell A Walters; Tel: 434-592-3294, E-mail: lwalters@liberty.edu; *Head, Info Mgt,* Tom Fesmire; Tel: 434-592-3356, E-mail: twfesmire@liberty.edu; *Head, Pub Serv & Outreach,* Marseille Pride; Tel: 434-592-4012, E-mail: mpride@liberty.edu; *Head, Ref & Instruction,* Randy L Miller; Tel: 434-592-3096, E-mail: rlmiller5@liberty.edu; *Curric Librn,* Rachel Schwedt; Tel: 434-592-3357, E-mail: reschwed@liberty.edu; *Distance Learning Librn,* Jeff Dull; Tel: 434-582-2821, E-mail: jmdull@liberty.edu; *Ref Librn,* Kathryn Cox; Tel: 434-592-4934, E-mail: kcox@liberty.edu. Subject Specialists: *Aviation, Nursing,* Lowell A Walters; *Relig,* Tom Fesmire; *Counseling, Family studies, Psychol,* Randy L Miller; *Educ curric, Fine arts, Juv fiction,* Rachel Schwedt; *Commun studies, Health sci, Kinesiology,* Jeff Dull; *Family & consumer sci,* Kathryn Cox; Staff 42 (MLS 18, Non-MLS 24)
Founded 1971. Enrl 11,054; Fac 354; Highest Degree: Doctorate
Jul 2006-Jun 2007. Mats Exp $693,170, Books $181,945, Per/Ser (Incl. Access Fees) $129,007, Electronic Ref Mat (Incl. Access Fees) $378,572. Sal $1,970,432 (Prof $1,001,361)
Library Holdings: CDs 1,329; DVDs 784; e-books 63,507; e-journals 42,077; Microforms 553,706; Bk Vols 200,626; Per Subs 766; Videos 1,716
Special Collections: Digital Commons; Jerry Falwell Coll
Subject Interests: Relig
Automation Activity & Vendor Info: (Acquisitions) Ex Libris Group; (Cataloging) Ex Libris Group; (Circulation) Ex Libris Group; (Course Reserve) Ex Libris Group; (ILL) OCLC ILLiad; (OPAC) Ex Libris Group; (Serials) EBSCO Online
Database Vendor: ACM (Association for Computing Machinery), Alexander Street Press, American Psychological Association (APA), Annual Reviews, Blackwell's, Bowker, Cambridge Scientific Abstracts, Children's Literature Comprehensive Database Company (CLCD), CountryWatch, CQ Press, EBSCOhost, Emerald, Ex Libris Group, Factiva.com, Facts on File, Gale Cengage Learning, Greenwood Publishing Group, H W Wilson, HeinOnline, IEEE (Institute of Electrical & Electronics Engineers), infoUSA, JSTOR, LexisNexis, Marquis Who's Who, Medline, Modern Language Association, netLibrary, OCLC FirstSearch, OCLC WorldCat, Oxford Online, Project MUSE, ProQuest, PubMed, Safari Books Online, Sage, SBRnet (Sports Business Research Network), ScienceDirect, SerialsSolutions, Standard & Poor's, ValueLine
Wireless access
Function: Archival coll, AV serv, Bks on cassette, Bks on CD, Computers for patron use, Copy machines, Distance learning, Doc delivery serv, Electronic databases & coll, Free DVD rentals, ILL available, Music CDs, Online cat, Online searches, Photocopying/Printing, Pub access computers
Partic in Lynchburg Area Library Cooperative; Lyrasis; Virginia Independent College & University Library Association; Virtual Library of Virginia
Special Services for the Deaf - Sign lang interpreter upon request for prog
Special Services for the Blind - Low vision equip
Open Mon-Thurs 7am-11:45pm, Fri 7am-9pm, Sat 10-9, Sun 1-11:45
Restriction: In-house use for visitors, Open to pub for ref & circ; with some limitations, Open to students, fac & staff

C LYNCHBURG COLLEGE*, Knight-Capron Library, 1501 Lakeside Dr, 24501-3199. SAN 317-3321. Tel: 434-544-8204. Interlibrary Loan Service Tel: 434-544-8441. Reference Tel: 434-544-8575. FAX: 434-544-8499. Web Site: www.lynchburg.edu/library. *Dir, Libr Serv,* Christopher Millson-Martula; Tel: 434-544-8399, E-mail: millsonmartula@lynchburg.edu; *Curric Mat Librn, Head, Ref, Pub Serv Librn,* Christa Poparad; *Instrul Serv Librn,* Elizabeth Henderson; *Archivist, ILL,* Ariel Myers; *Cataloger,* Robyn Williams; *Electronic Res,* Michael Ours; Staff 9.5 (MLS 6, Non-MLS 3.5)
Founded 1903. Enrl 2,400; Fac 150; Highest Degree: Master
Library Holdings: CDs 2,974; DVDs 1,022; e-books 27,000; Bk Titles 175,000; Bk Vols 228,000; Per Subs 473; Videos 2,600
Special Collections: Iron Industry (Capron); Seventeenth, Eighteenth & Nineteenth Century Maps of North America, particularly Virginia (Capron)
Subject Interests: Educ, Nursing
Automation Activity & Vendor Info: (Acquisitions) Innovative Interfaces, Inc - Millenium; (Cataloging) Innovative Interfaces, Inc - OCLC; (Circulation) Innovative Interfaces, Inc - Millenium; (Course Reserve) Innovative Interfaces, Inc - Millenium; (ILL) OCLC ILLiad; (Media Booking) Innovative Interfaces, Inc - Millenium; (OPAC) Innovative Interfaces, Inc - Millenium; (Serials) Innovative Interfaces, Inc - Millenium
Database Vendor: ABC-CLIO, Alexander Street Press, American Chemical Society, American Psychological Association (APA), ARTstor, BioOne, Bowker, Cambridge Scientific Abstracts, Cinahl Information Systems, CQ Press, EBSCOhost, Elsevier, Emerald, Factiva.com, Gale Cengage Learning, Ingenta, JSTOR, LexisNexis, Mergent Online, Modern Language Association, netLibrary, OCLC ArticleFirst, OCLC FirstSearch, OCLC WorldCat, Project MUSE, ProQuest, PubMed, RefWorks, ScienceDirect, SerialsSolutions, STN International, YBP Library Services

Wireless access
Partic in Lynchburg Area Library Cooperative; OCLC Online Computer Library Center, Inc; Virginia Independent College & University Library Association; Virtual Library of Virginia
Open Mon-Thurs 8am-Midnight, Fri 8-7, Sat 11-7, Sun 1-Midnight

M LYNCHBURG GENERAL HOSPITAL*, Health Sciences Library, 1901 Tate Springs Rd, 24501-1167. SAN 327-3792. Tel: 434-200-3147. *Librn,* Claire A Meissner; E-mail: claire.meissner@centrahealth.com
Library Holdings: Bk Vols 1,300; Per Subs 100
Subject Interests: Med, Nursing
Database Vendor: EBSCOhost
Partic in Lynchburg Area Library Cooperative; National Network of Libraries of Medicine Southeastern Atlantic Region; OCLC Online Computer Library Center, Inc; Southwestern Virginia Health Information Librarians
Restriction: Not open to pub, Staff use only

P LYNCHBURG PUBLIC LIBRARY*, 2315 Memorial Ave, 24501. SAN 317-333X. Tel: 434-455-6300. Reference Tel: 434-455-6310. Administration Tel: 434-455-6330. Administration FAX: 434-847-1578. Web Site: www.lynchburgva.gov/publiclibrary. *Dir,* Lynn L Dodge; E-mail: lynn.dodge@lynchburgva.gov; *Cat,* Jane Jobe; *ILL,* Candy Thompson; E-mail: candace.thompson@lynchburgva.gov; *Youth Serv,* Lorry Risinger; E-mail: lorry.risinger@lynchburgva.gov; Staff 8 (MLS 8)
Founded 1966. Pop 65,800; Circ 417,000
Library Holdings: AV Mats 10,000; Bk Vols 150,000; Per Subs 241
Automation Activity & Vendor Info: (Acquisitions) Horizon; (Cataloging) Horizon; (Circulation) Horizon; (ILL) Horizon; (OPAC) Horizon; (Serials) Horizon
Database Vendor: Westlaw
Partic in Lynchburg Information Online Network
Open Mon, Wed, Fri & Sat 9:30-5:30, Tues & Thurs 9:30-9
Friends of the Library Group
Branches: 1
DOWNTOWN, 900 Church St, 24504. Tel: 434-455-3820. FAX: 434-847-1403. *Br Mgr,* Marilyn Martin; E-mail: marilyn.martin@lynchburgva.gov
Library Holdings: Bk Vols 5,000; Per Subs 125
Special Collections: Lynchburg Public Law Library
Open Mon-Fri 9:30-5:30
Friends of the Library Group

C RANDOLPH COLLEGE*, Lipscomb Library, 2500 Rivermont Ave, 24503. SAN 317-3348. Tel: 434-947-8133. FAX: 434-947-8134. Web Site: library.randolphcollege.edu. *Dir,* Theodore J Hostetler; E-mail: thostetler@randolphcollege.edu; *Cat,* Marcia McKenzie; E-mail: mmckenzie@randolphcollege.edu; *Circ,* Adrian Broughman; E-mail: abroughman@randolphcolleg.edu; *Coll Develop,* Lisa Broughman; E-mail: llee@randolphcollege.edu; *ILL/Doc Delivery Serv,* Catherine Lotspeich; E-mail: clotspeich@randolphcollege.edu; *Ref,* Frances Webb; E-mail: fwebb@randolphcollege.edu; *Ser,* Lynne N Weaver; Staff 10 (MLS 3, Non-MLS 7)
Founded 1891. Enrl 620; Fac 70; Highest Degree: Master
Jul 2006-Jun 2007 Income $775,365. Mats Exp $257,206, Books $90,106, Per/Ser (Incl. Access Fees) $126,035, Manu Arch $2,000, Micro $36,272, AV Mat $725, Electronic Ref Mat (Incl. Access Fees) $1,305, Presv $763. Sal $360,953 (Prof $226,997)
Library Holdings: e-books 40,000; Bk Vols 197,000; Per Subs 21,000
Special Collections: Classical Culture (Lipscomb Coll); Lininger, Children's Literature Coll; Pearl S Buck Coll; Writings by Virginia Women
Automation Activity & Vendor Info: (Acquisitions) SirsiDynix; (Cataloging) SirsiDynix; (Circulation) SirsiDynix; (Course Reserve) SirsiDynix; (ILL) OCLC; (OPAC) SirsiDynix; (Serials) SirsiDynix
Database Vendor: American Chemical Society, American Mathematical Society, American Psychological Association (APA), Annual Reviews, ARTstor, Blackwell's, Cambridge Scientific Abstracts, CQ Press, Dialog, EBSCO Information Services, EBSCOhost, Factiva.com, Facts on File, JSTOR, LexisNexis, Modern Language Association, netLibrary, OCLC FirstSearch, OCLC WorldCat, PubMed, RefWorks, SerialsSolutions, SirsiDynix, WebMD
Wireless access
Publications: Collections of Writings by Virginia Women; Lipscomb Library Guide; Quick Library Facts Sheet
Partic in Knight-Ridder Info, Inc; Lynchburg Area Library Cooperative; Lynchburg Information Online Network; Lyrasis; Virginia Independent College & University Library Association; Virtual Library of Virginia

C VIRGINIA UNIVERSITY OF LYNCHBURG*, Mary Jane Cachelin Library, 2058 Garfield Ave, 24501-6417. SAN 317-3356. Tel: 434-528-5276. FAX: 434-528-4257. Web Site: vul.edu/facil_library.html. *Librn,* Swannie Thompson
Founded 1887

Library Holdings: Bk Vols 30,000; Per Subs 50
Open Mon-Thurs 8:30am-9pm, Fri 8:30-5, Sat 8:30-2, Sun 3-9

MADISON

P   MADISON COUNTY LIBRARY, INC*, 402 N Main St, 22727. (Mail
add: PO Box 243, 22727-0243), SAN 317-3445. Tel: 540-948-4720. FAX:
540-948-4919. E-mail: madisonlib@nexet.net. Web Site:
madisoncountyvalibrary.org. *Dir,* Bonnie Utz; *Head, Acq,* Janice Douglas;
Asst Librn, Linda Davis; Staff 8 (Non-MLS 8)
Founded 1937. Pop 13,000; Circ 46,000
Library Holdings: Bk Titles 35,000; Bk Vols 33,000; Per Subs 80
Special Collections: American History (Weaver Coll)
Automation Activity & Vendor Info: (Cataloging) Follett Software;
(Circulation) Follett Software
Wireless access
Open Mon, Wed & Fri 10-5, Tues & Thurs 10-8, Sat 10-2
Friends of the Library Group

MANASSAS

C   ECPI UNIVERSITY*, Northern Virginia Campus-Manassas, 10021 Balls
Ford Rd, 20109. Tel: 703-330-5300, Ext 212. Toll Free Tel: 866-708-6172.
FAX: 703-369-0530. Web Site: www.ecpi.edu. *Librn,* Jonathan Beeker;
E-mail: jbeeker@ecpi.edu
Library Holdings: AV Mats 200; Bk Vols 2,600; Per Subs 45
Automation Activity & Vendor Info: (Cataloging) SirsiDynix;
(Circulation) SirsiDynix; (OPAC) SirsiDynix
Database Vendor: CredoReference, Gale Cengage Learning, netLibrary,
Safari Books Online
Function: Photocopying/Printing
Open Mon-Thurs 9-5, Fri 8-5

S   LOCKHEED MARTIN*, Manassas Library, 9500 Godwin Dr, 20110. SAN
328-1019. Tel: 703-367-6508. FAX: 703-367-4698. *Librn,* Jennifer
Hatfield; E-mail: jennifer.hatfield@lmco.com; Staff 1 (MLS 1)
Founded 1985
Library Holdings: Bk Titles 9,000; Bk Vols 10,000; Per Subs 80
Subject Interests: Computer sci, Electrical eng, Electronic eng, Naval sci
Automation Activity & Vendor Info: (Cataloging) EOS International;
(Circulation) EOS International; (OPAC) EOS International; (Serials) EOS
International
Database Vendor: CRC Press/Taylor & Francis CRCnetBASE, Dialog,
EOS International, IEEE (Institute of Electrical & Electronics Engineers),
IHS, Jane's, LexisNexis, netLibrary, OCLC FirstSearch
Restriction: Open by appt only

S   MANASSAS NATIONAL BATTLEFIELD PARK LIBRARY*, 6511
Sudley Rd, 20109-2005. SAN 370-2995. Tel: 703-361-1339. FAX:
703-361-7106. Web Site: www.nps.gov/mana. *Mus Spec,* Jim Burgess;
E-mail: jim_burgess@nps.gov
Library Holdings: Bk Vols 2,000
Subject Interests: Manuscripts
Restriction: Open by appt only

GL   PRINCE WILLIAM COUNTY CIRCUIT COURT, Law Library, Judicial
Ctr, Rm 039, JU-170, 9311 Lee Ave, 20110-5555. SAN 372-3518. Tel:
703-792-6262. FAX: 703-792-5390. E-mail: lawlibrary@pwcgov.org. *Librn,*
Robert L Davis, III
Founded 1983
Library Holdings: Bk Vols 10,000
Subject Interests: Va Law
Function: Res libr
Open Mon-Thurs 8-5, Fri 8-12:30
Restriction: Non-circulating

MARION

P   SMYTH-BLAND REGIONAL LIBRARY*, 118 S Sheffey St, 24354. SAN
317-3453. Tel: 276-783-2323. Circulation Tel: 276-783-2323, Ext 221.
Interlibrary Loan Service Tel: 276-783-2323, Ext 230. Reference Tel:
276-783-2323, Ext 222. Administration Tel: 276-783-2323, Ext 228,
276-783-2323, Ext 229. Automation Services Tel: 276-783-2323, Ext 231.
FAX: 276-783-5279. Web Site: www.sbrl.org. *Libr Dir,* Patricia M
Hatfield; E-mail: path@sbrl.org; *Exec Asst of Operations,* Brenda J
Umbarger; E-mail: brendau@sbrl.org; *Pub Serv Mgr,* Dora D Dewell;
E-mail: dorad@sbrl.org; *Acctg & Acq Supvr,* Judy Wyant; Tel:
276-783-2323, Ext 224, E-mail: judyw@sbrl.org; *Supvr, Outreach Serv,*
Rita B Copenhaver; Tel: 276-783-2323, Ext 33, E-mail: ritac@sbrl.org;
Tech Serv Supvr, Susan Martin; Tel: 276-783-2323, Ext 226, E-mail:
susanm@sbrl.org; *Supvr, Youth Serv,* Tracey Reed-Armbrister; Tel:
276-783-2323, Ext 223, E-mail: traceyr@sbrl.org; *Syst Adminr,* Sharon K
Dempsey; E-mail: sharond@sbrl.org; Staff 20 (MLS 1, Non-MLS 19)
Founded 1972. Pop 39,900; Circ 203,466

Library Holdings: AV Mats 15,626; Bk Vols 116,795; Per Subs 252;
Videos 9,919
Special Collections: Sherwood Anderson Coll; Southwest Virginia
Heritage Library
Subject Interests: Genealogy, SW Va hist
Automation Activity & Vendor Info: (Acquisitions) TLC (The Library
Corporation); (Cataloging) VTLS, Inc; (Circulation) VTLS, Inc; (ILL)
OCLC FirstSearch; (OPAC) VTLS, Inc; (Serials) VTLS, Inc
Database Vendor: Baker & Taylor, Blackwell's, BWI, EBSCOhost, Gale
Cengage Learning, netLibrary, OCLC FirstSearch, ProQuest, TLC (The
Library Corporation)
Wireless access
Function: Photocopying/Printing, Prog for adults, Prog for children &
young adult, Ref serv available, Serves mentally handicapped consumers,
Spoken cassettes & CDs, Spoken cassettes & DVDs, Summer reading prog,
Telephone ref, VHS videos, Wheelchair accessible
Partic in SouthWest Information Network Group (SWING)
Special Services for the Deaf - Closed caption videos
Special Services for the Blind - Audio mat; Bks available with recordings;
Bks on cassette; Bks on CD; Extensive large print coll; Home delivery
serv; Magnifiers
Open Mon-Thurs 9-8, Fri 9-1, Sat 9-4
Friends of the Library Group
Branches: 3
BLAND COUNTY, 697 Main St, Bland, 24315. (Mail add: PO Box 480,
Bland, 24315-0480), SAN 377-6816. Tel: 276-688-3737. FAX:
276-688-9820. *Br Supvr,* Rebekah Bowling; E-mail: rebekahw@sbrl.org
Founded 1972
    Library Holdings: Bk Vols 27,000; Per Subs 53
    Automation Activity & Vendor Info: (Circulation) VTLS, Inc
    Partic in SouthWest Information Network Group (SWING)
    Special Services for the Deaf - Closed caption videos
    Special Services for the Blind - Audio mat; Bks on cassette; Bks on CD;
    Large print bks
    Open Mon, Wed, Fri & Sat 9:30-4:30, Tues & Thurs 9:30-8
    Friends of the Library Group
CHILHOWIE PUBLIC, 807 Chilhowie St, Chilhowie, 24319. (Mail add:
PO Box 610, Chilhowie, 24319-0610). Tel: 276-646-3404. FAX:
276-646-3406. *Br Supvr,* Linda T Dean
    Open Mon, Tues & Thurs 11-6, Sat 11-2
    Friends of the Library Group
SALTVILLE PUBLIC, 111 Palmer Ave, Saltville, 24370. (Mail add: PO
Box 1033, Saltville, 24370-1033), SAN 375-4839. Tel: 276-496-5514.
FAX: 276-496-4249. Web Site: www.sbrl.org. *Br Supvr,* Kris Sheets;
Staff 2 (Non-MLS 2)
Founded 1985. Pop 5,000; Circ 30,732
    Library Holdings: Bk Titles 10,643; Per Subs 32
    Open Mon-Wed 10-6, Thurs 10-7, Fri 10-2, Sat 10-3
    Friends of the Library Group

M   SOUTHWESTERN VIRGINIA MENTAL HEALTH INSTITUTE
LIBRARY*, Staff & Patients' Library, 340 Bagley Circle, 24354. SAN
363-0633. Tel: 276-783-1200, Ext 161. FAX: 276-783-1247. *Librn,* Ann E
Mathews; Staff 1 (MLS 1)
Jul 2005-Jun 2006 Income $66,455. Mats Exp $12,949. Sal $53,506
Library Holdings: Bk Vols 6,790; Per Subs 90
Subject Interests: Behav med, Psychiat
Partic in Asn of Mental Health Librns (AMHL); Southwestern Virginia
Health Information Librarians; Tri-Cities Area Health Sciences Libraries
Consortium

MARTINSVILLE

P   BLUE RIDGE REGIONAL LIBRARY*, 310 E Church St, 24112-2999.
(Mail add: PO Box 5264, 24115-5264), SAN 363-0692. Tel: 276-403-5430.
Reference Tel: 276-403-5450. FAX: 276-632-1660. E-mail:
martinsville@brrl.lib.va.us. Web Site: www.brrl.lib.va.us. *Dir,* Hal Hubener;
Tel: 276-403-5435, E-mail: hhubener@yahoo.com; *Cat, Coll Develop,* Lisa
Isley; Tel: 276-403-5451; *Ch,* Janet Boucher; Tel: 276-403-5444; *Circ,*
Betty Fulcher; *Electronic Res,* Larry Morrison; Tel: 276-403-5437; *Tech
Serv,* Jane Farley; Tel: 276-403-5434; Staff 47 (MLS 7, Non-MLS 40)
Founded 1923. Pop 89,700; Circ 561,845
Library Holdings: Bk Titles 131,648; Bk Vols 261,699; Per Subs 150;
Talking Bks 9,954
Special Collections: Genealogy (Virginia Coll); Realia (toys)
Automation Activity & Vendor Info: (Acquisitions) TLC (The Library
Corporation); (Cataloging) TLC (The Library Corporation); (Circulation)
TLC (The Library Corporation); (ILL) TLC (The Library Corporation);
(OPAC) TLC (The Library Corporation); (Serials) TLC (The Library
Corporation)
Database Vendor: EBSCOhost, Gale Cengage Learning, OCLC
FirstSearch
Partic in SouthWest Information Network Group (SWING)
Open Mon, Tues & Wed 10-8, Thurs & Fri 10-5:30, Sat 9:30-5
Friends of the Library Group

Branches: 4

BASSETT BRANCH, 3969 Fairystone Park Hwy, Bassett, 24055, SAN 372-7890. Tel: 276-629-2426. FAX: 276-629-3808. E-mail: bassett@brrl.lib.va.us. *Br Mgr,* Karen Thisse; Staff 1 (Non-MLS 1)
Library Holdings: Bk Vols 40,000; Per Subs 32
Open Mon, Wed & Thurs 10-6, Tues 10-8, Fri & Sat 10-2
Friends of the Library Group

COLLINSVILLE BRANCH, 2540 Virginia Ave, Collinsville, 24078, SAN 363-0722. Tel: 276-647-1112. FAX: 276-647-4574. E-mail: collinsville@brrl.lib.va.us. *Br Mgr,* Sandra Shell; Staff 3 (Non-MLS 3)
Library Holdings: Bk Vols 40,000; Per Subs 20
Open Mon & Tues 10-8, Thurs 10-6, Fri 10-5, Sat 10-2
Friends of the Library Group

PATRICK COUNTY, 116 W Blue Ridge St, Stuart, 24171. (Mail add: PO Box 787, Stuart, 24171-0787), SAN 363-0757. Tel: 276-694-3352, 276-694-5427. FAX: 276-694-6744. E-mail: patrick@brrl.lib.va.us. *Br Librn,* Rick Ward; Staff 1 (MLS 1)
Library Holdings: Bk Vols 41,000; Per Subs 58
Open Mon & Wed 10-6, Tues & Thurs 10-8, Fri & Sat 10-2
Friends of the Library Group

RIDGEWAY BRANCH, 900 Vista View Lane, Ridgeway, 24148. (Mail add: PO Box 1210, Ridgeway, 24148-1210), SAN 371-2990. Tel: 276-956-1828. FAX: 276-956-4081. *Br Mgr,* Position Currently Open; Staff 1 (MLS 1)
Library Holdings: Bk Vols 20,000; Per Subs 30
Open Mon, Tues & Fri 10-6
Friends of the Library Group

Bookmobiles: 1. Supvr, Garry Clifton. Bk titles 3,500

J   PATRICK HENRY COMMUNITY COLLEGE*, Lester Library, 645 Patriot Ave, 24115. (Mail add: PO Box 5311, 24115-5311), SAN 317-3488. Tel: 276-656-0228. FAX: 276-656-0327. Web Site: www.ph.vccs.edu. *Dir,* Carolyn Byrd; Tel: 276-656-0211; *Coordr,* Barry Reynolds; Tel: 276-656-0276, E-mail: breynolds@ph.vccs.edu; *Ref,* Becky Westfall; Tel: 276-656-0226, E-mail: bwestfall@ph.vccs.edu; *Tech Serv,* Aileen Martin; Tel: 276-656-0439, E-mail: amartin@ph.vccs.edu; Staff 5 (MLS 2, Non-MLS 3)
Founded 1962. Enrl 1,839; Fac 32
Library Holdings: Bk Titles 32,648; Per Subs 136
Special Collections: Stone Coll (Southern History); Thomas Carter Coll (Literature)
Automation Activity & Vendor Info: (Cataloging) Ex Libris Group; (Circulation) Ex Libris Group; (ILL) OCLC; (OPAC) Ex Libris Group
Database Vendor: Gale Cengage Learning
Partic in Virtual Library of Virginia
Open Mon-Thurs (Winter) 8am-9pm, Fri 8-5, Sat 9am-Noon; Mon-Thurs (Summer) 8-7:30, Fri 8-5

S   VIRGINIA MUSEUM OF NATURAL HISTORY LIBRARY*, 21 Starling Ave, 24112. SAN 375-2194. Tel: 276-634-4172. FAX: 276-634-4199. E-mail: library@vmnh.virginia.gov. Web Site: www.vmnh.net. *Librn,* Mary Catherine Santoro; Staff 1 (MLS 1)
Founded 1993
Library Holdings: Bk Titles 6,000
Wireless access
Open Mon-Fri 9-5
Restriction: Circulates for staff only

MASON NECK

S   GUNSTON HALL PLANTATION LIBRARY & ARCHIVES, 10709 Gunston Rd, 22079-3901. SAN 317-3259. Tel: 703-550-9220. FAX: 703-550-9480. E-mail: library@gunstonhall.org. Web Site: www.gunstonhall.org. *Librn & Archivist,* Mark Whatford. Subject Specialists: *Colonial/constitutional hist,* Mark Whatford
Founded 1970
Library Holdings: Bk Titles 6,000; Bk Vols 7,500; Per Subs 20
Special Collections: 18th Century Library Rare Books; Papers/Documents of Mason family
Subject Interests: Decorative art, Genealogy, George Mason, Mason family, Va hist
Function: Ref serv available, Res libr
Restriction: Open by appt only

MATHEWS

P   MATHEWS MEMORIAL LIBRARY*, Main St, 23109. (Mail add: Po Box 980, 23109-0980), SAN 317-3496. Tel: 804-725-5747. FAX: 804-725-7668. E-mail: staff@mathewslibrary.org. Web Site: www.mathewslibrary.org. *Dir,* Bette Dillehay; Staff 4 (MLS 1, Non-MLS 3)
Founded 1930. Pop 8,430; Circ 26,985
Library Holdings: Bk Titles 35,000; Per Subs 56
Subject Interests: Maritime

Open Mon-Wed & Fri 9-5, Thurs 9-8, Sat 10-2, Sun 1-3
Friends of the Library Group

MCLEAN

S   LMI LIBRARY, 2000 Corporate Ridge, 22102-7805. SAN 328-5561. Tel: 703-917-7214. FAX: 703-917-7474. E-mail: library@lmi.org. *Dir, Libr Serv,* Nancy Eichelman Handy; *Res,* Laura Tyler; *Tech Serv,* Sara Faulk; Staff 4 (MLS 3, Non-MLS 1)
Library Holdings: Audiobooks 50; Bk Titles 8,000; Bk Vols 10,000; Per Subs 400
Special Collections: History of Military Logistics; LMI Reports
Subject Interests: Climate change, Info tech, Logistics, Mgt
Automation Activity & Vendor Info: (Cataloging) Inmagic, Inc.; (Circulation) Inmagic, Inc.; (OPAC) Inmagic, Inc.; (Serials) Inmagic, Inc.
Function: ILL available
Partic in Interlibrary Users Association; OCLC Online Computer Library Center, Inc
Restriction: Borrowing requests are handled by ILL, Employee & client use only

S   FREDDIE MAC CORPORATE INFORMATION RESOURCE CENTER*, 8200 Jones Branch Dr, MS 251, 22102. SAN 375-0396. Tel: 703-903-2773. FAX: 703-903-2755. E-mail: circ@freddiemac.com. *Mgr,* Lois Ireland; Tel: 703-903-3335, E-mail: lois_ireland@freddiemac.com; Staff 4 (MLS 3, Non-MLS 1)
Founded 1991
Library Holdings: Bk Vols 5,500; Per Subs 250
Subject Interests: Finance, Real estate
Automation Activity & Vendor Info: (Acquisitions) EOS International; (Cataloging) EOS International; (Circulation) EOS International; (OPAC) EOS International; (Serials) EOS International
Database Vendor: Dialog, EBSCOhost, LexisNexis, OCLC FirstSearch
Partic in Lyrasis
Open Mon-Fri 8:30-5

L   PILLSBURY WINTHROP SHAW PITTMAN LLP*, Law Library, 1650 Tysons Blvd, 22102. SAN 377-3906. Tel: 703-770-7742. FAX: 703-770-7901. Web Site: www.pillsburylaw.com. *Mgr,* Eileen McCarrier; Staff 2 (MLS 2)
Library Holdings: Bk Vols 4,000; Per Subs 30
Subject Interests: Intellectual property law
Automation Activity & Vendor Info: (Cataloging) Sydney; (Circulation) Sydney; (OPAC) Sydney; (Serials) Sydney

S   USA TODAY LIBRARY*, 7950 Jones Branch Dr, 22108. SAN 372-8684. Tel: 703-854-5588. FAX: 703-854-2112. E-mail: library@usatoday.com. *Dir,* Jeanette Brown
Library Holdings: Bk Vols 5,300; Per Subs 100
Automation Activity & Vendor Info: (Cataloging) Inmagic, Inc.; (Serials) Inmagic, Inc.
Open Mon-Thurs 9am-11pm, Fri 9-6, Sun 11-11
Restriction: Limited access for the pub

L   WATT, TIEDER, HOFFAR & FITZGERALD*, 8405 Greensboro Dr, Ste 100, 22102. (Mail add: 8405 Greensboro Dr, Ste 100, 22102). Tel: 703-749-1019. FAX: 703-893-8029. Web Site: www.wthf.com. *Law Librn,* Barbara Cumming; E-mail: bcumming@wthf.com
Library Holdings: Bk Vols 8,000

MELFA

J   EASTERN SHORE COMMUNITY COLLEGE*, Learning Resources Center, 29300 Lankford Hwy, 23410. SAN 317-3518. Tel: 757-789-1721. Administration Tel: 787-789-1723. FAX: 757-789-1739. Web Site: www.es.vccs.edu. *Dean, Learning Res,* Patricia L Phillips; E-mail: pphillips@es.vccs.edu; *Libr Spec, Media & Tech Serv,* Charles W Killmon; Tel: 757-789-1722, E-mail: ckillmon@es.vccs.edu; *Libr Spec, Pub Serv,* Elizabeth Walraven; E-mail: ewalraven@es.vccs.edu; Staff 3 (MLS 1, Non-MLS 2)
Founded 1964. Enrl 550; Fac 19; Highest Degree: Associate
Library Holdings: Audiobooks 150; AV Mats 1,200; e-books 40,000; e-journals 10,000; Electronic Media & Resources 170; Large Print Bks 300; Bk Vols 25,000; Per Subs 100
Automation Activity & Vendor Info: (Cataloging) OCLC Connexion; (Circulation) Ex Libris Group; (Course Reserve) Ex Libris Group; (ILL) OCLC; (OPAC) Ex Libris Group
Database Vendor: ABC-CLIO, ACM (Association for Computing Machinery), Agricola, American Chemical Society, American Mathematical Society, Blackwell's, Cambridge Scientific Abstracts, Cinahl Information Systems, CQ Press, EBSCOhost, Factiva.com, Facts on File, Gale Cengage Learning, Mergent Online, Modern Language Association, netLibrary, OCLC WorldCat, Overdrive, Inc, OVID Technologies, Oxford Online, Project MUSE
Wireless access

Partic in Virginia Commun Coll Syst; Virginia Tidewater Consortium for Higher Education; Virtual Library of Virginia
Open Mon-Thurs 8-8, Fri 8-4:30

MIDDLEBURG

S   NATIONAL SPORTING LIBRARY, INC*, 102 The Plains Rd, 20118. (Mail add: PO Box 1335, 20118-1335), SAN 317-3526. Tel: 540-687-6542. FAX: 540-687-8540. Web Site: www.nsl.org. *Librn,* Lisa Campbell; E-mail: lcampbell@nsl.org; Staff 1 (MLS 1)
Founded 1954
Library Holdings: DVDs 15; Bk Titles 13,000; Per Subs 23; Videos 73
Special Collections: 16th-19th Century Books on Horses (Huth-Lonsdale-Arundel & Hunersdorf Colls); Foxhunting Papers (Harry Worcester Smith Coll); Sporting Books (John H & Martha Daniel Coll); Woolums Stud Books
Subject Interests: Am sporting art, Am sporting mag, Breeds of horses, British sporting art, English riding, Equine hist, Field sports, Horse sports
Automation Activity & Vendor Info: (OPAC) LibraryWorld, Inc
Function: Archival coll, ILL available, Photocopying/Printing, Res libr
Publications: NSL Newsletter
Partic in Lyrasis; OCLC Online Computer Library Center, Inc
Open Mon 1-4, Tues-Fri 10-4
Restriction: Not a lending libr, Open to pub for ref only
Friends of the Library Group

MIDDLETOWN

J   LORD FAIRFAX COMMUNITY COLLEGE*, Paul Wolk Library, 173 Skirmisher Lane, 22645-1745. SAN 317-3534. Tel: 540-868-7170. Reference Tel: 540-868-7157. Toll Free Tel: 800-906-5322. FAX: 540-868-7171. E-mail: lfcircd@lfcc.edu. Web Site: www.lfcc.edu/libraries. *Dir,* David Gray; Tel: 540-868-7154, E-mail: dgray@lfcc.edu; *Regional Librn,* Joyce Earhart; Tel: 540-868-7157; *Br Mgr,* Linda Harper; Tel: 540-351-1554; *Acq,* Jan Brown; Tel: 540-868-7155; *Circ,* Alice Seabright; Tel: 540-868-7156; *ILL,* Viv Dewitt; Tel: 540-868-7172; Staff 8 (MLS 2, Non-MLS 6)
Founded 1970. Enrl 6,630; Fac 50; Highest Degree: Associate
Library Holdings: Bks on Deafness & Sign Lang 50; Bk Titles 56,500; Bk Vols 58,600; Per Subs 300
Automation Activity & Vendor Info: (Cataloging) Ex Libris Group; (Circulation) Ex Libris Group; (Course Reserve) Ex Libris Group; (ILL) Ex Libris Group; (OPAC) Ex Libris Group; (Serials) Ex Libris Group
Database Vendor: Gale Cengage Learning, OCLC FirstSearch, OVID Technologies, TLC (The Library Corporation)
Function: ILL available
Partic in Lyrasis; Virginia Commun Coll Syst; Virtual Library of Virginia
Open Mon-Thurs 8am-9pm, Fri 8-4:30, Sat 9-1, Sun 1:30-4:30
Departmental Libraries:
BOB G SOWDER LIBRARY, 6480 College St, Warrenton, 20187-8820. Tel: 540-347-6259. E-mail: lffqlib@lfcc.edu. *Dir,* David Gray; E-mail: dgray@lfcc.edu
Function: ILL available, Photocopying/Printing
Open Mon-Thurs 8am-9pm, Fri 8-4:30, Sat 9-1

MILFORD

P   CAROLINE LIBRARY INC*, 17202 Richmond Tpk, 22514. (Mail add: PO Box 9, Bowling Green, 22427-0009). Tel: 804-633-5455. FAX: 804-633-9069. E-mail: carolinelibrary@bealenet.com. Web Site: www.carolinelibrary.org. *Dir,* Kay Brooks; *Asst Dir,* Charlene Harris; *Br Coordr,* Chris Cushing
Pop 22,121
Library Holdings: AV Mats 2,970; Bk Titles 40,000; Per Subs 34
Automation Activity & Vendor Info: (Cataloging) TLC (The Library Corporation); (Circulation) TLC (The Library Corporation); (OPAC) TLC (The Library Corporation)
Database Vendor: Baker & Taylor, Gale Cengage Learning, Grolier Online, netLibrary, OCLC FirstSearch, OCLC WebJunction, ProQuest, TLC (The Library Corporation)
Wireless access
Open Mon-Thurs 8:30-8, Fri 8:30-6, Sat 10-4
Friends of the Library Group
Branches: 3
DAWN, 31046 Richmond Tpk, Hanover, 23069. Tel: 804-632-8341. FAX: 804-632-8848. Web Site: www.carolinelibrary.org.
Library Holdings: Bk Titles 3,000
Open Mon, Wed & Fri 9-6, Tues & Thurs 9-8, Sat 10-4
Friends of the Library Group
LADYSMITH, Ladysmith Village, 7199 Clara Smith Dr, Ruther Glen, 22546. (Mail add: 17202 Richmond Tpk, 22514). Tel: 804-448-0357. FAX: 804-448-3124. *Br Mgr,* Carolyn Wenrich
Library Holdings: Bk Titles 10,000
Open Mon-Wed 9-5, Tues-Thurs 10-8, Fri 10-4, Sat 9-1

PORT ROYAL BRANCH, 419 King St, Port Royal, 22536. Tel: 804-742-5254. FAX: 804-742-5263.
Library Holdings: Bk Titles 2,500
Open Mon, Wed & Fri 1-5
Bookmobiles: 1

MONTEREY

P   HIGHLAND COUNTY PUBLIC LIBRARY*, 31 N Water St, 24465. (Mail add: PO Box 519, 24465). Tel: 540-468-2373. FAX: 540-468-2085. E-mail: mail@highlandlibrary.com. Web Site: highlandlibrary.com. *Dir,* Tomi Herold; Staff 1 (Non-MLS 1)
Founded 1976. Pop 2,400; Circ 28,439
Library Holdings: Audiobooks 948; Bks on Deafness & Sign Lang 11; CDs 698; DVDs 1,124; Electronic Media & Resources 1; Large Print Bks 801; Microforms 68; Bk Vols 15,671; Per Subs 39; Talking Bks 7; Videos 1,040
Special Collections: Forbes Genealogy Coll
Subject Interests: Local genealogy
Automation Activity & Vendor Info: (Acquisitions) Follett Software; (Cataloging) Follett Software; (Circulation) Follett Software; (ILL) OCLC Online; (OPAC) Follett Software
Wireless access
Function: Accelerated reader prog, Adult bk club, Archival coll, Art exhibits, Audio & video playback equip for onsite use, AV serv, Bi-weekly Writer's Group, Bks on cassette, Bks on CD, CD-ROM, Children's prog, Computer training, Computers for patron use, Copy machines, e-mail & chat, Electronic databases & coll, Exhibits, Fax serv, Free DVD rentals, Handicapped accessible, ILL available, Magnifiers for reading, Mail & tel request accepted, Music CDs, Online cat, Photocopying/Printing, Prog for adults, Prog for children & young adult, Pub access computers, Ref serv in person, Spoken cassettes & CDs, Story hour, Summer reading prog, VHS videos, Web-catalog, Wheelchair accessible
Special Services for the Blind - Talking bks
Open Mon & Fri 9-5, Tues & Thurs 9-8, Wed 9-Noon, Sat 9-3
Friends of the Library Group

NARROWS

P   R IRIS BRAMMER PUBLIC LIBRARY*, 109 Mary St, 24124. SAN 317-3569. Tel: 540-726-2884. FAX: 540-726-3050. E-mail: narlibrary@suddenlinkmail.com. *Librn,* Beverly Dent; Staff 1 (Non-MLS 1)
Pop 17,646
Library Holdings: Bk Vols 24,604; Talking Bks 40
Open Mon-Fri 9-5

NEWPORT NEWS

C   CHRISTOPHER NEWPORT UNIVERSITY, Paul & Rosemary Trible Library, One Avenue of the Arts, 23606. SAN 317-3577. Tel: 757-594-7130. Circulation Tel: 757-594-7133. Interlibrary Loan Service Tel: 757-594-8818. Reference Tel: 757-594-7132. FAX: 757-594-7717. Circulation FAX: 757-594-7772. TDD: 757-594-7938. E-mail: library@cnu.edu. Web Site: library.cnu.edu/. *Univ Librn,* Mary Sellen; E-mail: mary.sellen@cnu.edu; *Coll Mgt Librn,* Dr Alicia Willson-Metzger; Tel: 757-594-8948, E-mail: awillson@cnu.edu; *Instruction Librn,* Amy Boykin; Tel: 757-594-7244, E-mail: awboykin@cnu.edu; *ILL Librn,* Jesse Spencer; E-mail: Jesse.spencer@cnu.edu; *Media/ILL Librn,* Johnnie Gray; Tel: 757-594-7249, E-mail: jngray@cnu.edu; *Access Serv,* Beth Young; Tel: 757-594-7134, E-mail: bethany.young@cnu.edu; *Cat,* Steven York; Tel: 757-594-8702, Fax: 757-594-7776; *Pub Serv,* Doris Archer; Tel: 757-594-7245, E-mail: darcher@cnu.edu; Staff 8 (MLS 8)
Founded 1961. Enrl 4,489; Fac 262; Highest Degree: Master
Jul 2005-Jun 2006 Income $2,487,125, State $2,483,307, Other $3,818. Mats Exp $447,498, Books $37,380, Per/Ser (Incl. Access Fees) $215,046, Micro $14,422, AV Mat $8,595, Electronic Ref Mat (Incl. Access Fees) $167,561, Presv $4,494. Sal $758,570 (Prof $404,182)
Library Holdings: e-books 16,000; Bk Vols 401,253; Per Subs 1,027
Special Collections: Josephine Hughes Music Coll; Virginia Authors Coll
Automation Activity & Vendor Info: (Acquisitions) Innovative Interfaces, Inc; (Cataloging) Innovative Interfaces, Inc; (Circulation) Innovative Interfaces, Inc; (Course Reserve) Innovative Interfaces, Inc; (ILL) OCLC ILLiad; (OPAC) Innovative Interfaces, Inc; (Serials) Innovative Interfaces, Inc
Database Vendor: ACM (Association for Computing Machinery), Alexander Street Press, Annual Reviews, ARTstor, BioOne, Bowker, ebrary, EBSCOhost, Facts on File, Gale Cengage Learning, HeinOnline, Innovative Interfaces, Inc, IOP, JSTOR, LexisNexis, Mergent Online, Newsbank, OCLC FirstSearch, OCLC WorldCat, OVID Technologies, Oxford Online, Project MUSE, ProQuest, PubMed, Safari Books Online, Wiley
Wireless access
Function: Archival coll, Computers for patron use, Copy machines, e-mail & chat, Electronic databases & coll, ILL available, Microfiche/film &

reading machines, Music CDs, Online cat, Res libr, Scanner, Web-catalog, Wheelchair accessible
Partic in Virginia Tidewater Consortium for Higher Education; Virtual Library of Virginia

S THOMAS JEFFERSON NATIONAL ACCELERATOR FACILITY LIBRARY*, 12050 Jefferson Ave, ARC 126 (MS-1B), 23606. SAN 317-3615. Tel: 757-269-7525. Interlibrary Loan Service Tel: 757-269-6229. FAX: 757-269-7848. Administration FAX: 757-269-6228. Web Site: www.jlab.org/ir. *Mgr, Info Serv,* Elois A Morgan; E-mail: morgan@jlab.org; *Tech Serv,* Sandra D'Souza; Tel: 757-269-6229, E-mail: dsouza@jlab.org
Founded 1985
Library Holdings: e-journals 4,000; Bk Titles 11,000
Subject Interests: Electrical eng, Math, Nuclear physics
Automation Activity & Vendor Info: (Acquisitions) Ex Libris Group; (Cataloging) Ex Libris Group; (Circulation) Ex Libris Group; (Course Reserve) Ex Libris Group; (ILL) Ex Libris Group; (Media Booking) Ex Libris Group; (OPAC) Ex Libris Group; (Serials) Ex Libris Group
Partic in Lyrasis; Virginia Tidewater Consortium for Higher Education
Open Mon-Fri 8-5
Restriction: Not open to pub, Open by appt only, Photo ID required for access

S LIBRARY AT THE MARINERS' MUSEUM*, 100 Museum Dr, 23606-3759. SAN 317-3585. Tel: 757-591-7782. FAX: 757-591-7310. E-mail: library@mariner.org. Web Site: www.mariner.org. *Dir,* Susan Berg; Tel: 757-581-7780; *Archivist,* Lester Weber; Tel: 757-591-7779; *Pub Serv,* Cathy Williamson; Tel: 757-591-7784; *Tech Serv,* Lisa DuVernay; Tel: 757-591-7788; Staff 9 (MLS 3, Non-MLS 6)
Founded 1930
Library Holdings: Bk Titles 60,000; Bk Vols 92,000; Per Subs 225
Special Collections: Chris Craft Archive; Maritime Vessels, archival items, charts, drawings, maps, photos, ship brochures
Subject Interests: Maritime hist, Naval hist, Navigation, Shipbuilding
Database Vendor: TLC (The Library Corporation)
Function: Ref serv available
Partic in OCLC Eastern; OCLC Online Computer Library Center, Inc
Open Mon-Fri 10-5
Restriction: Not a lending libr
Friends of the Library Group

P NEWPORT NEWS PUBLIC LIBRARY SYSTEM*, 700 Town Center Dr, Ste 300, 23606. SAN 363-0781. Tel: 757-926-1350. Interlibrary Loan Service Tel: 757-247-8505. FAX: 757-926-1365. Interlibrary Loan Service FAX: 757-247-2344. Web Site: www.nngov.com/library. *Dir,* Izabela M Cieszynski; E-mail: icieszynski@nngov.com; *Head, Tech Serv,* Carol Goodwin; *Family & Youth Serv Coordr,* Angelique Simmons; Staff 48 (MLS 16.5, Non-MLS 31.5)
Founded 1891. Pop 193,172; Circ 847,367
Jul 2008-Jun 2009 Income (Main Library and Branch(s)) $6,137,344, State $212,424, City $5,567,157, Federal $133,847, Locally Generated Income $199,391, Other $24,525. Mats Exp $601,106, Books $327,241, Per/Ser (Incl. Access Fees) $44,069, Other Print Mats $1,648, AV Mat $104,681, Electronic Ref Mat (Incl. Access Fees) $123,467. Sal $3,050,555 (Prof $832,204)
Library Holdings: Audiobooks 7,947; CDs 9,794; DVDs 18,227; Electronic Media & Resources 31; Bk Vols 332,572; Per Subs 183
Special Collections: Martha Woodroof Hiden Virginiana Coll; Old Dominion Land Company Coll. Oral History
Subject Interests: Local genealogy, Local hist
Automation Activity & Vendor Info: (Acquisitions) VTLS, Inc; (Cataloging) VTLS, Inc; (Circulation) VTLS, Inc; (OPAC) VTLS, Inc; (Serials) VTLS, Inc
Database Vendor: OCLC FirstSearch
Wireless access
Function: Adult bk club, After school storytime, Archival coll, Art exhibits, Audio & video playback equip for onsite use, Audiobks via web, Bk club(s), Bks on CD, Children's prog, Computer training, Computers for patron use, Copy machines, Doc delivery serv, e-mail & chat, e-mail serv, E-Reserves, Electronic databases & coll, Exhibits, Family literacy, Fax serv, Free DVD rentals, Handicapped accessible, Holiday prog, Home delivery & serv to Sr ctr & nursing homes, Homebound delivery serv, Homework prog, ILL available, Instruction & testing, Jail serv, Mail & tel request accepted, Mail loans to mem, Music CDs, Notary serv, Online cat, Online ref, Online searches, Outreach serv, Outside serv via phone, mail, e-mail & web, Photocopying/Printing, Preschool outreach, Prof lending libr, Prog for adults, Prog for children & young adult, Pub access computers, Ref & res, Ref serv available, Ref serv in person, Referrals accepted, Senior computer classes, Story hour, Summer reading prog, Tax forms, Teen prog, Telephone ref, Web-catalog, Wheelchair accessible, Workshops
Partic in OCLC Online Computer Library Center, Inc
Special Services for the Deaf - TDD equip
Open Mon-Thurs 9-9, Fri & Sat 9-6, Sun 1-5

Restriction: Non-circulating coll, Non-circulating of rare bks, Non-circulating to the pub
Friends of the Library Group
Branches: 5
PEARL BAILEY BRANCH, 2510 Wickham Ave, 23607, SAN 363-096X. Tel: 757-247-8677. FAX: 757-247-2321. *Librn IV,* Anita N Jennings; E-mail: ajennings@nngov.com; Staff 13.8 (MLS 3, Non-MLS 10.8)
Pop 27,649; Circ 68,607
Library Holdings: AV Mats 9,713; Bk Vols 161,753
Function: ILL available, Photocopying/Printing, Prog for children & young adult, Ref serv available, Summer reading prog, Telephone ref
Special Services for the Deaf - TDD equip; TTY equip
Open Mon-Thurs 9-9, Fri & Sat 9-6
Friends of the Library Group
VIRGIL I GRISSOM BRANCH, 366 DeShazor Dr, 23608, SAN 363-0900. Tel: 757-369-3190. FAX: 757-369-3198. *Chief Librn,* Deborah L Wright; E-mail: dwright@nngov.com; *Sr Librn,* Patricia A Manzella; E-mail: pmanzella@nngov.com; Staff 20.88 (MLS 3, Non-MLS 17.88)
Pop 41,875; Circ 270,575
Library Holdings: AV Mats 9,713; Bk Vols 161,753
Function: Handicapped accessible, ILL available, Photocopying/Printing, Prog for children & young adult, Summer reading prog
Special Services for the Deaf - TDD equip; TTY equip
Open Mon-Thurs 9-9, Fri & Sat 9-6, Sun 1-5
Friends of the Library Group
LAW LIBRARY, 2501 Washington Ave, 23607, SAN 363-0846. Tel: 757-926-8678. FAX: 757-926-8824. *Info Serv Spec II,* Lorene Studwell; E-mail: lstudwell@nngov.com
Founded 1964. Pop 182,200
Library Holdings: Bk Vols 13,600
Function: For res purposes, Photocopying/Printing
Open Mon-Fri 8-12 & 1-5
Restriction: Open to pub for ref only
Friends of the Library Group
MAIN STREET, 110 Main St, 23601, SAN 363-0870. Tel: 757-591-4858. FAX: 757-591-7425. *Br Mgr,* Sharon Henderson; E-mail: shenderson@nngov.com; *Librn,* Gregg Grunow; E-mail: ggrunow@nngov.com; Staff 21 (MLS 3, Non-MLS 18)
Circ 234,935
Library Holdings: AV Mats 12,688; Bk Vols 145,671
Special Collections: Martha Hiden Woodroof Virginiana Coll
Subject Interests: Genealogy, Virginiana
Function: Games & aids for the handicapped, Handicapped accessible, Home delivery & serv to Sr ctr & nursing homes, Homebound delivery serv, ILL available, Magnifiers for reading, Photocopying/Printing, Prog for children & young adult, Ref serv available, Summer reading prog, Wheelchair accessible
Special Services for the Deaf - TDD equip; TTY equip
Friends of the Library Group
WEST AVENUE, 30th & West Ave, 23607, SAN 363-0935. Tel: 757-247-8505. FAX: 757-247-2344. *ILL, Sr Librn, YA Serv,* James W Sanderson; E-mail: jsanderson@nngov.com; Staff 6 (MLS 1, Non-MLS 5)
Pop 2,399; Circ 40,314
Library Holdings: AV Mats 4,109; Bk Vols 58,149
Function: ILL available, Photocopying/Printing, Prog for children & young adult, Ref serv available, Summer reading prog, Telephone ref
Special Services for the Deaf - TDD equip; TTY equip
Open Mon 9-6, Tues 12-8, Wed-Fri 10-6
Friends of the Library Group
Bookmobiles: 1. Librn, Sherin Henderson. Bk titles 6,044

M RIVERSIDE REGIONAL MEDICAL CENTER*, Health Sciences Library, 500 J Clyde Morris Blvd, 23601. SAN 327-3733. Tel: 757-240-2400. FAX: 757-240-2401. E-mail: library@rivhs.com. *Librn,* Cassandra Moore; Staff 3 (MLS 1, Non-MLS 2)
Founded 1980
Library Holdings: Bk Vols 5,000; Per Subs 210
Special Collections: Historical Medicine & Nursing
Subject Interests: Allied health, Med, Nursing
Database Vendor: EBSCOhost
Publications: The Library Letter
Open Mon & Wed 7:30am-8pm, Tues & Thurs 7:30am-9pm, Fri 7:30-4, Sat 12-5

S VIRGINIA WAR MUSEUM*, Major George B Collings Memorial, Major George B Collings Memorial Library, 9285 Warwick Blvd, 23607. SAN 321-0200. Tel: 757-247-8523. FAX: 757-247-8627. E-mail: info@warmuseum.org. Web Site: www.warmuseum.org. *Dir,* John V Quarstein
Founded 1923
Library Holdings: Bk Titles 25,000; Per Subs 35
Special Collections: American Military History Coll, 1775-present; German Language Propaganda Publications; World War I - Vietnam Film Coll; World Wars I & II, mags, photogs, scrapbks. Oral History

Function: Res libr
Publications: Film Loan Catalogue
Restriction: Open to pub by appt only

NORFOLK

S CHRYSLER MUSEUM OF ART*, Jean Outland Chrysler Library, 245 W
Olney Rd, 23510-1587. SAN 317-364X. Tel: 757-965-2035. Administration
Tel: 757-664-6202. FAX: 757-664-6201. E-mail: museum@chrysler.org.
Web Site: www.chrysler.org. *Librn,* Laura Christiansen; E-mail:
lchristiansen@chrysler.org; Staff 1 (MLS 1)
Founded 1929
Library Holdings: AV Mats 500; Bk Titles 30,000; Bk Vols 80,000; Per
Subs 250
Special Collections: 18th-20th century auction & exhibition catalogs;
Architecture (Frank A Vanderlip Jr Coll); Knoedler Library
Subject Interests: Am, Art hist, Art nouveau, Decorative art, Drawing,
Glass, Painting, Photog, Sculpture, Textiles, Western European
Automation Activity & Vendor Info: (Cataloging) TLC (The Library
Corporation); (ILL) OCLC; (Serials) EBSCO Online
Partic in Lyrasis
Open Wed-Fri 10-4:45
Restriction: Non-circulating
Friends of the Library Group

CM EASTERN VIRGINIA MEDICAL SCHOOL*, Edward E Brickell Medical
Sciences Library, 740 W Olney Rd, 23501. (Mail add: PO Box 1980,
23501-1980), SAN 317-3658. Tel: 757-446-5840. Circulation Tel:
757-446-5850. Information Services Tel: 757-446-5851. FAX:
757-446-5134. E-mail: library@evms.edu. Web Site:
www.evms.edu/evmslib. *Asst Dean, Libr & Learning Res,* Judith G
Robinson Mercer; Tel: 757-446-5841, E-mail: robinsjg@evms.edu; *Dir,
Libr Serv,* Kerrie Shaw; E-mail: shawks@evms.edu; *Ref/Clinical Librn,*
Susan Harnett; E-mail: harnetsm@evms.edu; *Ref/Clinical Librn,* Kathy
Wheeler; E-mail: wheeleko@evms.edu; *Circ Supvr,* LaVonda Harris; Staff
18 (MLS 8, Non-MLS 10)
Founded 1972. Enrl 993; Fac 351; Highest Degree: Doctorate
Library Holdings: e-journals 1,900; Bk Titles 25,000; Bk Vols 90,000; Per
Subs 700
Subject Interests: Behav sci, Med, Soc sci
Automation Activity & Vendor Info: (Acquisitions) SirsiDynix;
(Cataloging) SirsiDynix; (Circulation) SirsiDynix; (Course Reserve)
SirsiDynix; (ILL) OCLC ILLiad; (Media Booking) SirsiDynix; (OPAC)
SirsiDynix; (Serials) SirsiDynix
Database Vendor: OVID Technologies
Partic in OCLC Online Computer Library Center, Inc; Virginia Independent
College & University Library Association; Virtual Library of Virginia
Open Mon-Thurs 8am-Midnight, Fri 8-6, Sat 9-7, Sun 10am-Midnight
Friends of the Library Group

S FRED HEUTTE HORTICULTURAL LIBRARY*, Norfolk Botanical
Garden Library, c/o Norfolk Botanical Garden, 6700 Azalea Garden Rd,
23518-5337. SAN 317-3690. Tel: 757-441-5830, Ext 359, 757-441-5838.
FAX: 757-441-5828. E-mail: library@nbgs.org. Web Site:
norfolkbotanicalgarden.org. *Librn,* Marcia Oubre. Subject Specialists: *Hort,
Nat sci,* Marcia Oubre
Library Holdings: Bk Vols 3,700; Per Subs 20
Subject Interests: Hort
Function: Handicapped accessible, Wheelchair accessible
Open Mon & Sat 11-3, Sun 1-4
Restriction: Circ to mem only, Pub use on premises

G JOINT FORCES STAFF COLLEGE LIBRARY*, 7800 Hampton Blvd,
23511-1702. SAN 317-3623. Tel: 757-443-6401. FAX: 757-443-6047.
Administration FAX: 757-443-6032. Web Site: www.jfsc.ndu.edu/library.
Dir, Dr Janet Gail Nicula; Tel: 757-443-6400; *Head, Pub Serv,* Loretta
Silvia; Tel: 757-443-6402; *Acq,* Mary Louise O'Brien; Tel: 757-443-6404,
Fax: 757-443-6044; *Cat,* Robert Ellett; Tel: 757-443-6405; Staff 13 (MLS
7, Non-MLS 6)
Founded 1947. Enrl 1,400; Highest Degree: Master
Library Holdings: Bk Vols 136,000; Per Subs 460
Special Collections: US Document Depository
Subject Interests: Econ, Hist, Mil, Mil hist, Nat affairs, Nat security,
Naval hist
Automation Activity & Vendor Info: (Acquisitions) SirsiDynix;
(Cataloging) SirsiDynix; (Circulation) SirsiDynix; (OPAC) SirsiDynix
Database Vendor: EBSCOhost, JSTOR, LexisNexis, OCLC FirstSearch,
OCLC WorldCat, ProQuest, SerialsSolutions, SirsiDynix
Publications: Commandant's Professional Reading List (Research guide);
Periodicals & Recurring Documents (Annually)
Partic in Fedlink; OCLC Online Computer Library Center, Inc; Tidewater
Consortium for Continuing Higher Educ
Open Mon-Thurs 7-5:30, Fri 7-5
Restriction: Open to pub upon request, Photo ID required for access,
Restricted borrowing privileges

S MACARTHUR MEMORIAL LIBRARY & ARCHIVES*, MacArthur Sq,
23510. SAN 317-3674. Tel: 757-441-2965, 757-441-2968. FAX:
757-441-5389. Web Site: www.macarthurmemorial.org. *Archivist,* James W
Zobel; E-mail: james.zobel@norfolk.gov
Founded 1964
Library Holdings: Bk Titles 5,709
Special Collections: D Clayton James Interviews; Facsimiles of papers of
Lewis Beebe, R J Marshall, S J Chamberlain, George Grunert, Edward M
Almond & Facsimiles of Richard K Sutherland; Military Intelligence &
Personal Correspondence (Charles A Willougby Coll), bks, doc, plans,
strategy & tactics of WWII; Military Logistics (H E Eastwood Coll), doc;
Papers of Master Sergeant Paul Rogers, Wendell W Fertig, Bonner F
Fellers & Philip Brougher; Papers of R J Marshall, Jack Napier, Frederic S
Marquardt, Spencer B Akin & Donald Hoover; Philippine Guerrillas,
World War II (Courtney Whitney Coll), doc. Oral History
Subject Interests: Korean War, Occupation of Japan, Philippine
Insurrection, World War I, World War II
Database Vendor: OCLC FirstSearch
Function: Archival coll, Res libr
Publications: Douglas MacArthur Archives & Library (brochure);
MacArthur Report
Open Mon-Fri 10-5
Restriction: Not a lending libr

P NORFOLK PUBLIC LIBRARY, 235 E Plume St, 23510-1706. (Mail add:
Administrative Offices & Service Ctr, 1155 Pineridge Rd, 23502), SAN
363-0994. Tel: 757-664-7323. Circulation Tel: 757-664-7328, Ext 350.
Interlibrary Loan Service Tel: 757-664-7333. Reference Tel: 757-441-1750.
Administration Tel: 757-664-7328. FAX: 757-441-5863. Interlibrary Loan
Service FAX: 757-441-5863. Reference FAX: 757-441-1748. Web Site:
www.npl.lib.va.us. *Dir,* Norman Maas; E-mail: norman.maas@norfolk.gov;
Asst Dir, Pub Serv, Sonal Rastogi; Tel: 757-664-7327, E-mail:
sonal.rastogi@norfolk.gov; *Coll Develop Librn,* Sean Bilby; E-mail:
sean.bilby@norfolk.gov; *Genealogy Librn, Local Hist Librn,* Robert
Hitchings; Tel: 757-664-7485, E-mail: robert.hitchings@norfolk.gov; *Youth
Serv Coordr,* Terri Raymond; Tel: 757-664-7328, Ext 347, E-mail:
terri.raymond@norfolk.gov; *Acq & Cat,* Deborah Folkama; *City Historian,*
Peggy McPhillips; Tel: 757-664-7310, E-mail:
peggy.mcphillips@norfolk.gov; *Govt Doc, Per,* Susan Mercer; Tel:
757-664-7325, E-mail: susan.mercer@norfolk.gov; *ILL,* Laura Dodson;
E-mail: laura.dodson@norfolk.gov; *Pub Relations,* Lori Crowe; *Tech Serv,*
Deborah Folkama; Tel: 757-664-7328, Ext 319, E-mail:
debby.folkama@norfolk.gov. Subject Specialists: *City hist, Genealogy,*
Peggy McPhillips; Staff 22 (MLS 22)
Founded 1870. Pop 234,403; Circ 992,217
Library Holdings: AV Mats 43,476; Music Scores 7,392; Bk Titles
518,552
Special Collections: Virginianna (Sargeant Memorial Room), AV, bk &
micro. US Document Depository
Subject Interests: African-Am lit, Juv lit, Literary studies, Local hist
Automation Activity & Vendor Info: (Acquisitions) SirsiDynix;
(Cataloging) SirsiDynix; (Circulation) SirsiDynix; (ILL) OCLC Connexion;
(OPAC) SirsiDynix
Wireless access
Function: Adult bk club, Bks on cassette, Bks on CD, Children's prog,
Computer training, Computers for patron use, Copy machines, Electronic
databases & coll, Exhibits, Family literacy, Free DVD rentals, Handicapped
accessible, Holiday prog, Homework prog, ILL available, Magnifiers for
reading, Music CDs, Online searches, Photocopying/Printing, Preschool
outreach, Prog for adults, Prog for children & young adult, Rent serv in
person, Senior computer classes, Spoken cassettes & CDs, Spoken cassettes
& DVDs, Story hour, Summer & winter reading prog, Tax forms, Teen
prog, Telephone ref, VHS videos, Wheelchair accessible
Special Services for the Blind - Large print bks
Closed for renovation. Will reopen in 2013.
Friends of the Library Group
Branches: 11
BARRON F BLACK BRANCH, 6700 E Tanners Creek Rd, 23513, SAN
363-1028. Tel: 757-441-5806. FAX: 757-441-5891. *Br Mgr,* Michael
Shaw; E-mail: michael.shaw@norfolk.gov
Library Holdings: AV Mats 881; Bk Vols 25,625
Open Mon-Thurs 10-7, Fri & Sat 10-5
Friends of the Library Group
BLYDEN, 879 E Princess Anne Rd, 23504, SAN 363-1117. Tel:
757-441-2852. FAX: 757-441-1452. *Br Mgr,* Dudley Colbert; E-mail:
dudley.colbert@norfolk.gov; Staff 1 (MLS 1)
Library Holdings: AV Mats 2,084; Bk Vols 14,557
Open Mon-Thurs 10-7, Fri & Sat 10-5
Friends of the Library Group
HORACE C DOWNING BRANCH, 555 E Liberty St, 23523, SAN
363-1052. Tel: 757-441-1968. FAX: 757-441-1994. *Br Mgr,* MaryAnne
Vandivort; E-mail: mary.vandivort@norfolk.gov; Staff 1 (MLS 1)
Library Holdings: AV Mats 1,622; Bk Vols 16,010

Open Mon-Thurs 10-7, Fri & Sat 10-5
Friends of the Library Group
JANAF, 124 Janaf Shopping Ctr, 23502, SAN 363-1176. Tel:
757-441-5660. FAX: 757-441-5715. *Br Mgr,* Jennie Radovsky; E-mail:
jennie.radovsky@norfolk.gov; Staff 1 (MLS 1)
Library Holdings: AV Mats 2,806; Bk Vols 23,228
Open Mon-Thurs 10-7, Fri & Sat 10-5
Friends of the Library Group
JORDAN-NEWBY, 961 Park Ave, 23504, SAN 363-1141. Tel:
757-441-2843. FAX: 757-441-1453. *Br Mgr,* David Dennie; E-mail:
david.dennie@norfolk.gov; Staff 1 (MLS 1)
Library Holdings: AV Mats 1,956; Bk Vols 19,179
Open Mon-Thurs 10-7, Fri & Sat 10-5
Friends of the Library Group
LAFAYETTE, 1610 Cromwell Rd, 23509, SAN 363-1206. Tel:
757-441-2842. FAX: 757-441-1454. *Br Mgr,* Lloyd Ostby; E-mail:
lloyd.ostby@norfolk.gov; Staff 1 (MLS 1)
Library Holdings: AV Mats 2,283; Bk Vols 31,578
Open Mon-Thurs 10-7, Fri & Sat 10-5
Friends of the Library Group
LARCHMONT, 6525 Hampton Blvd, 23508, SAN 363-1230. Tel:
757-441-5335. FAX: 757-441-1451. *Br Mgr,* Donald Gates; E-mail:
donald.gates@norfolk.gov; Staff 1 (MLS 1)
Library Holdings: AV Mats 2,926; Bk Vols 29,740
Open Mon-Thurs 10-7, Fri & Sat 10-5
Friends of the Library Group
LITTLE CREEK, 7853 Tarpon Pl, 23518, SAN 363-1265. Tel:
757-441-1751. FAX: 757-441-1747. *Br Mgr,* Melanie Reeves; E-mail:
melanie.reeves@norfolk.gov; Staff 1 (MLS 1)
Library Holdings: AV Mats 2,707; Bk Vols 27,060
Open Mon-Thurs 10-7, Fri & Sat 10-5
Friends of the Library Group
PARK PLACE, 620 W 29th St, 23508, SAN 363-1087. Tel: 757-664-7330.
FAX: 757-664-7331. *Br Mgr,* Valerie Pierce; E-mail:
valerie.pierce@norfolk.gov
Library Holdings: AV Mats 1,283; Bk Vols 10,737
Open Mon-Thurs 10-7, Fri & Sat 10-5
Friends of the Library Group
MARY D PRETLOW ANCHOR BRANCH LIBRARY, 111 W Ocean
View Ave, 23503-1608, SAN 363-129X. Tel: 757-441-1750. FAX:
757-441-1748. *Br Mgr,* Cynthia Seay; E-mail: cynthia.seay@norfolk.gov;
Staff 5 (MLS 5)
Library Holdings: AV Mats 8,153; Bk Vols 54,332
Open Mon-Thurs 10-9, Fri & Sat 10-5, Sun 1-5
Friends of the Library Group
VAN WYCK, 1368 DeBree Ave, 23517, SAN 363-132X. Tel:
757-441-2844. FAX: 757-441-1456. *Br Mgr,* Sarah Townsend; E-mail:
sarah.townsend@norfolk.gov; Staff 1 (MLS 1)
Library Holdings: AV Mats 3,303; Bk Vols 30,369
Open Mon-Thurs 10-7, Fri & Sat 10-5
Friends of the Library Group
Bookmobiles: 1. In Charge, Bettie Goganious. Bk vols 10,658

C   NORFOLK STATE UNIVERSITY LIBRARY*, Lyman Beecher Brooks
Library, 700 Park Ave, 23504-8010. SAN 317-3712. Tel: 757-823-8517.
Circulation Tel: 757-823-2418. Interlibrary Loan Service Tel:
757-823-2426. Administration Tel: 757-823-8481. Automation Services Tel:
757-823-2334. FAX: 757-823-2431. Administration FAX: 757-823-2092.
Web Site: library.nsu.edu. *Actg Libr Dir,* Tommy L Bogger; E-mail:
tlbogger@nsu.edu; *Head, Info Serv,* Cynthia Baxter-Cooke; Tel:
757-823-2166, E-mail: cbaxter-cooke@nsu.edu; *Head, Libr Syst,* Henry L
Albritton; E-mail: hlalbritton@nsu.edu; *Coordr, Access Serv,* James E
Satchell, III; Tel: 757-823-8796, E-mail: jesatchell@nsu.edu; *Coordr, Info
Serv,* Cynthia Cooke; *Coordr, Tech Serv,* Cynthia L Harrison; Tel:
757-823-2422, E-mail: clharrison@nsu.edu; *Coll Develop Librn,* Marlene
Ballou; *Ref Librn,* Ann D Cannon; Tel: 757-823-2417, E-mail:
adcannon@nsu.edu; *Ref Librn,* Erica D Coleman; Tel: 757-823-2224,
E-mail: edcoleman@nsu.edu; *ILL Supvr,* Manju Majumdar; E-mail:
mmajumdar@nsu.edu; *Access Serv,* Margaret McClenney; Tel:
757-823-8445; *Bibliog Instr,* Craig S Amos; Tel: 757-823-8183, E-mail:
camos@nsu.edu; *Circ/Reserves,* Wilbert Wiggins; *Circ/Reserves,* Phyllis
Williams; *Info Serv,* Cyanna Rodney-Hill; *Info Serv,* Antwanne G Marable;
Tel: 757-823-8445; *Info Serv,* Naomi E White; Tel: 757-823-2438, E-mail:
newhite@nsu.edu; *Tech Serv,* Velma Jones; Tel: 757-823-2429, E-mail:
vdjones@nsu.edu; *Tech Serv,* Kelly S Kerr; Tel: 757-823-2423, E-mail:
kskerr@nsu.edu; *Tech Serv,* E Christina Lee; Tel: 757-823-9061, E-mail:
eclee@nsu.edu; *Tech Serv,* Sheila Oakes Stafford; Tel: 757-823-2423,
E-mail: sostafford@nsu.edu; Staff 28 (MLS 9, Non-MLS 19)
Founded 1935. Enrl 6,000; Fac 350; Highest Degree: Doctorate
Library Holdings: AV Mats 1,828; CDs 587; DVDs 126; e-books 40,000;
e-journals 5,600; Music Scores 177; Bk Titles 288,411; Bk Vols 341,000;
Per Subs 1,395; Videos 194
Special Collections: African American Materials (Herbert A Marshall
Coll); Local & Regional African American Interest, NSU History (Harrison
B Wilson Archives)

Subject Interests: Behav sci, Bus mgt, Chem, Computer sci, Educ, Ethnic
studies, Humanities, Mat sci, Optical eng, Physics, Soc sci, Soc work
Automation Activity & Vendor Info: (Acquisitions) Innovative Interfaces,
Inc; (Cataloging) Innovative Interfaces, Inc; (Circulation) Innovative
Interfaces, Inc; (Course Reserve) Innovative Interfaces, Inc; (ILL)
Innovative Interfaces, Inc; (OPAC) Innovative Interfaces, Inc; (Serials)
Innovative Interfaces, Inc
Wireless access
Function: Archival coll, Distance learning, Doc delivery serv, E-Reserves,
ILL available, Online searches, Photocopying/Printing, Ref serv available,
Scanner, Spoken cassettes & CDs, VCDs, VHS videos, Wheelchair
accessible
Publications: Bibliographic Guides & Pathfinders; Bibliographic
Instruction (handbooks)
Partic in Lyrasis; OCLC Online Computer Library Center, Inc; Virginia
Tidewater Consortium for Higher Education; Virtual Library of Virginia
Special Services for the Deaf - Assistive tech
Special Services for the Blind - Assistive/Adapted tech devices, equip &
products
Open Mon-Thurs 8am-11pm, Fri 8-5, Sat 9-5, Sun 2-9
Restriction: Open to students, fac & staff
Departmental Libraries:
VIRGINIA BEACH HIGHER EDUCATION RESOURCE CENTER, 1881
University Dr, Virginia Beach, 23453-8080. Tel: 757-368-4162. FAX:
757-368-4151. E-mail: vblibrary@nsu.edu. Web Site:
www.nsu.edu/vbhec. *Info Spec,* Karma Gaines-Ra; E-mail:
kgaines-ra@nsu.edu
Database Vendor: EBSCOhost, Factiva.com, Gale Cengage Learning
Open Mon-Fri 8am-10pm, Sat 8-5:30, Sun 2-5

C   OLD DOMINION UNIVERSITY LIBRARIES*, Perry Library, 4427
Hampton Blvd, 23529-0256. SAN 317-3720. Tel: 757-683-4141.
Circulation Tel: 757-683-4154. Interlibrary Loan Service Tel:
757-683-4170. Reference Tel: 757-683-4182. Automation Services Tel:
757-683-4546. FAX: 757-683-5767. Interlibrary Loan Service FAX:
757-683-5035. Web Site: www.lib.odu.edu. *Univ Librn,* Virginia S
O'Herron; E-mail: voherron@odu.edu; *Assoc Univ Librn,* George Fowler;
Tel: 757-683-4159; *Head, Access Serv,* Stuart Frazer; Tel: 757-683-4174,
E-mail: sfrazer@odu.edu; *Head, Bibliog Instr,* Donna Hughes-Oldenburg;
Tel: 757-683-4153, E-mail: dholdenb@odu.edu; *Head, Ref & Res Serv,*
Nancy Schafer; Tel: 757-683-4183, E-mail: nschafer@odu.edu; *Head, Spec
Coll,* Sonia Yaco; Tel: 757-683-4483, E-mail: syaco@odu.edu; *Head, Syst
Develop,* Glenn Bunton; Tel: 757-683-5952, E-mail: gbunton@odu.edu;
Acq & Presv Serv Librn, Frederick Tench; Tel: 757-683-4144, E-mail:
ftench@odu.edu; *Admin Serv,* Morel Fry; Tel: 757-683-4143, E-mail:
mfry@odu.edu; *Coll Develop Officer,* Pam Morgan; Tel: 757-683-4148,
E-mail: pmorgan@odu.edu; Staff 67.5 (MLS 23.5, Non-MLS 44)
Founded 1930. Enrl 23,086; Fac 1,166; Highest Degree: Doctorate
Jul 2008-Jun 2009 Income (Main Library and Branch(s)) $8,893,659. Mats
Exp $4,772,280. Sal $2,589,975 (Prof $1,281,011)
Library Holdings: Bk Vols 1,288,534; Per Subs 14,651
Special Collections: Historical Archives; Recordings; Scottish History
Coll; Tidewater History Coll. State Document Depository; US Document
Depository
Subject Interests: Art, Bus, Contemporary music, Criminal justice, Educ,
Eng, Fine arts, Foreign lang, Geog, Hist, Oceanography, Performing arts,
Philosophy, Polit sci, Regional studies, Relig, Sci, Sociol
Automation Activity & Vendor Info: (Acquisitions) Innovative Interfaces,
Inc; (Cataloging) Innovative Interfaces, Inc; (Circulation) Innovative
Interfaces, Inc; (Course Reserve) Innovative Interfaces, Inc; (ILL)
Innovative Interfaces, Inc; (Media Booking) Innovative Interfaces, Inc;
(OPAC) Innovative Interfaces, Inc; (Serials) Innovative Interfaces, Inc
Database Vendor: 3M Library Systems, ABC-CLIO, American Chemical
Society, American Mathematical Society, American Physical Society,
American Psychological Association (APA), Annual Reviews, BioOne,
Blackwell's, Cambridge Scientific Abstracts, Cinahl Information Systems,
CQ Press, Dun & Bradstreet, Ebooks Corporation, EBSCOhost, Elsevier,
Ex Libris Group, Factiva.com, Facts on File, Gale Cengage Learning, H W
Wilson, Haworth Pres Inc, IEEE (Institute of Electrical & Electronics
Engineers), Infotrieve, Innovative Interfaces, Inc INN - View, ISI Web of
Knowledge, JSTOR, LexisNexis, Library Automation Management,
Marcive, Inc, McGraw-Hill, Medline, Mergent Online, OCLC FirstSearch,
OCLC WorldCat, OVID Technologies, Project MUSE, ProQuest, Sage,
ScienceDirect, The Library Co-Op, Inc, Thomson - Web of Science,
WebMD, Wilson - Wilson Web, YBP Library Services
Wireless access
Function: For res purposes
Publications: Departmental Guides; Instructional Guides; Libnews
(Research guide); Miniguides for Students & Faculty
Partic in Lyrasis; OCLC Online Computer Library Center, Inc; Virtual
Library of Virginia
Open Mon-Thurs (Fall & Spring) 8am-Midnight, Fri 8-7:30, Sat 9-5, Sun
9am-Midnight; Mon-Thurs (Summer) 8am-10pm, Fri 8-7:30, Sat 9-5, Sun
9am-10pm
Friends of the Library Group

Departmental Libraries:
ELISE N HOFHEIMER ART LIBRARY, Diehn Fine & Performing Arts
Ctr, Rm 109, 23529. Tel: 757-683-4059. Web Site:
www.lib.odu.edu/artlib/index.htm. *Libr Spec,* Jessica Ritchie; E-mail:
jhritchi@odu.edu. Subject Specialists: *Art,* Jessica Ritchie
Library Holdings: AV Mats 202; Bk Vols 15,834; Per Subs 94
Open Mon-Thurs 8am-10pm, Fri 8-7:30, Sat 9-5, Sun 1-10

M   SENTARA NORFOLK GENERAL HOSPITAL*, Health Sciences Library,
600 Gresham Dr, 23507. SAN 317-3704. Tel: 757-388-3000,
757-388-3693. FAX: 757-388-2514. E-mail: library@sentara.com. *Librn,*
Suzanne Duncan; E-mail: sxduncan@sentara.com
Founded 1942
Library Holdings: Bk Vols 5,000; Per Subs 260
Subject Interests: Health admin, Med, Nursing
Automation Activity & Vendor Info: (Cataloging) Winnebago Software
Co; (Circulation) Winnebago Software Co
Database Vendor: EBSCOhost
Restriction: Not open to pub

J   TIDEWATER COMMUNITY COLLEGE LEARNING RESOURCES
CENTER*, Thomas W Moss Jr Campus, 300 Granby St, 23510. SAN
377-8304. Tel: 757-822-1100. FAX: 757-822-1106. Web Site:
www.tcc.edu/lrc. *Interim Coordr,* Cherie Carl; Tel: 757-822-1772; *Circ,*
Carolyn Roberts; *Circ Media,* Florence Baines; Tel: 757-822-1124, E-mail:
fbaines@tcc.edu; *Ref Serv,* Jai Stofocik; E-mail: jstofocik@tcc.edu; *Tech
Serv,* Nora Marlow; Tel: 757-822-1105, Fax: 757-822-1105, E-mail:
mmarlow@tcc.edu; Staff 5 (MLS 2, Non-MLS 3)
Founded 1997. Highest Degree: Associate
Library Holdings: Bk Titles 15,000; Per Subs 30
Database Vendor: EBSCOhost, Gale Cengage Learning, OCLC
FirstSearch, OVID Technologies, Wilson - Wilson Web
Function: Ref serv available
Partic in Virtual Library of Virginia
Open Mon-Thurs 8am-9pm, Fri 8-4:30, Sat 9-1

A   UNITED STATES ARMY CORPS OF ENGINEERS*, Norfolk District
Library, 803 Front St, 23510-1096. Tel: 757-201-7562. FAX:
757-201-7870. Web Site: www.nao.usace.army.mil. *District Librn,* Lane
Killam; E-mail: lane.e.killam@usace.army.mil
Library Holdings: Bk Vols 26,000; Per Subs 86
Subject Interests: Sci, Tech
Wireless access
Partic in Illinois Library & Information Network
Restriction: Open to pub by appt only

L   UNITED STATES COURTS LIBRARY, Walter E Hoffman US
Courthouse, 600 Granby St, Rm 319, 23510. SAN 372-3526. Tel:
757-222-7044. FAX: 757-222-7047. *Librn,* Karen J Johnson
Library Holdings: Bk Vols 17,000
Automation Activity & Vendor Info: (Cataloging) SirsiDynix
Open Mon-Fri 8:30-5
Restriction: Ref only

A   UNITED STATES NAVY*, Naval Amphibious Base Library, 1481 D St,
Bldg 3016, 23521. SAN 363-1419. Tel: 757-462-7691. FAX:
757-462-4950. *Librn,* Pauline Reimold; E-mail: pauline.reimold@navy.mil
Founded 1942
Library Holdings: Bk Vols 35,000; Per Subs 85
Special Collections: CLEP Preparation Videos
Subject Interests: Naval hist
Friends of the Library Group

C   VIRGINIA WESLEYAN COLLEGE*, Henry Clay Hofheimer II Library,
1584 Wesleyan Dr, 23502-5599. SAN 317-3755. Tel: 757-455-3224.
Interlibrary Loan Service Tel: 757-455-3254. Reference Tel: 757-455-2132.
Administration Tel: 757-455-3220. Automation Services Tel: 757-455-3262.
Information Services Tel: 757-455-3221. FAX: 757-455-2129. E-mail:
library@vwc.edu. Web Site: www.vwc.edu/library. *Dir,* Sue Erickson;
E-mail: serickson@vwc.edu; *Dir of Tech Serv,* Sandra S Brooks; E-mail:
ssbrooks@vwc.edu; *Res Librn,* Patty Clark; Tel: 757-455-2100, E-mail:
phclark@vwc.edu; *Res Librn,* Stephen Leist; Tel: 757-455-2131, E-mail:
sleist@vwc.edu; *Circ Supvr,* Karen M Devereaux; Tel: 757-455-3219,
E-mail: kmdevereaux@vwc.edu; *AV Coordr,* Karen Hill; Tel:
757-455-3239, E-mail: khill@vwc.edu; *ILL,* Arianne Avery; E-mail:
aavery@vwc.edu; Staff 7.5 (MLS 3, Non-MLS 4.5)
Founded 1966. Enrl 1,151; Fac 85; Highest Degree: Bachelor
Jul 2009-Jun 2010. Mats Exp $229,739, Books $58,825, Per/Ser (Incl.
Access Fees) $102,835, AV Equip $6,801, AV Mat $4,716, Electronic Ref
Mat (Incl. Access Fees) $1,484, Presv $543. Sal $426,970 (Prof $290,000)
Library Holdings: AV Mats 3,599; CDs 422; DVDs 1,102; e-books
56,354; e-journals 35,681; Microforms 15,953; Music Scores 327; Bk
Titles 113,344; Bk Vols 125,896; Per Subs 117; Videos 1,748

Automation Activity & Vendor Info: (Acquisitions) Baker & Taylor;
(Cataloging) TLC (The Library Corporation); (Circulation) TLC (The
Library Corporation); (ILL) OCLC WorldCat; (OPAC) TLC (The Library
Corporation); (Serials) SerialsSolutions
Database Vendor: 3M Library Systems, ABC-CLIO, Alexander Street
Press, American Chemical Society, American Psychological Association
(APA), Baker & Taylor, BioOne, Blackwell's, Cambridge Scientific
Abstracts, CQ Press, EBSCO - WebFeat, EBSCOhost, Elsevier,
Factiva.com, Gale Cengage Learning, H W Wilson, Ingenta, ISI Web of
Knowledge, JSTOR, Knovel, LexisNexis, Mergent Online, Modern
Language Association, netLibrary, OCLC FirstSearch, OCLC WorldCat,
Oxford Online, Project MUSE, ProQuest, RefWorks, ScienceDirect,
Thomson - Web of Science, TLC (The Library Corporation), Wilson -
Wilson Web, YBP Library Services
Wireless access
Function: Archival coll, Art exhibits, AV serv, Bus archives, Computers
for patron use, Copy machines, Electronic databases & coll, Fax serv, Free
DVD rentals, ILL available, Music CDs, Online cat, Photocopying/Printing,
Pub access computers, Ref & res, Telephone ref, VHS videos, Web-catalog
Partic in Lyrasis; Virginia Independent College & University Library
Association; Virginia Tidewater Consortium for Higher Education; Virtual
Library of Virginia
Open Mon-Thurs 8am-Midnight, Fri 8-8, Sat 10-5, Sun 2-Midnight
Restriction: Open to students, fac & staff

S   VIRGINIAN-PILOT LIBRARY*, 150 W Brambleton Ave, 23510-2018.
SAN 371-3040. Tel: 757-446-2242. FAX: 757-446-2974. Web Site:
www.hamptonroads.com/pilotonline. *Librn,* Ann Kinken Johnson
Library Holdings: Bk Vols 2,000
Open Tues-Thurs 1-3
Restriction: Not open to pub

OAKWOOD

S   KEEN MOUNTAIN CORRECTIONAL CENTER*, Department of
Correctional Education Library, State Rd 629, 24631. (Mail add: PO Box
860, 24631-0860), SAN 373-6903. Tel: 276-498-7411, Ext 2055. FAX:
276-498-7341. *Librn,* Mary Marshall
Founded 1990
Library Holdings: Bk Vols 19,000; Per Subs 25
Automation Activity & Vendor Info: (Acquisitions) Follett Software;
(Cataloging) Follett Software; (Circulation) Follett Software; (OPAC)
Follett Software

ORANGE

P   ORANGE COUNTY LIBRARY*, 146A Madison Rd, 22960. SAN
317-3771. Tel: 540-672-3811. FAX: 540-672-5040. E-mail:
ocllibrary@orangecova.com. Web Site: orangecountyva.gov,
tlc.library.net/orange. *Libr Dir,* Kathryn Hill; Tel: 540-661-5444; *Tech
Serv-Section Head,* Teresa Frick; Tel: 540-661-5448, E-mail:
tfrick@orangecova.com; *YA Librn,* Gillian Dawson; Tel: 540-661-5445,
E-mail: gdawson@orangecova.com; *Acq,* Nancy Frost; Tel: 540-661-5446,
E-mail: nfrost@orangecova.com; *Cataloger,* Kelly Dalton; Tel:
540-661-5447, E-mail: kdalton@orangecova.com; Staff 5 (MLS 3,
Non-MLS 2)
Founded 1903. Pop 28,000; Circ 298,000
Jul 2005-Jun 2006 Income (Main Library and Branch(s)) $913,326, State
$159,186, County $542,845, Other $194,945. Mats Exp $158,705, Books
$99,270, Per/Ser (Incl. Access Fees) $5,567, AV Mat $51,468, Electronic
Ref Mat (Incl. Access Fees) $2,400. Sal $487,987 (Prof $143,022)
Library Holdings: AV Mats 19,952; CDs 2,915; DVDs 5,190; Bk Titles
85,600; Bk Vols 117,169; Per Subs 150; Talking Bks 4,740; Videos 6,808
Automation Activity & Vendor Info: (Acquisitions) TLC (The Library
Corporation); (Cataloging) TLC (The Library Corporation); (Circulation)
TLC (The Library Corporation); (OPAC) TLC (The Library Corporation)
Database Vendor: EBSCOhost, TLC (The Library Corporation)
Wireless access
Open Mon-Wed 9:30-8, Thurs & Fri 9:30-5:30, Sat 9:30-1:30
Friends of the Library Group
Branches: 2
GORDONSVILLE BRANCH, 200 S Main St, Gordonsville, 22942. (Mail
add: PO Box 587, Gordonsville, 22942-0587), SAN 377-9939. Tel:
540-832-0712. FAX: 540-832-0849. *Br Mgr,* Billie Crites; Staff 2
(Non-MLS 2)
Founded 1998
Library Holdings: CDs 304; DVDs 1,135; Electronic Media &
Resources 247; Large Print Bks 136; Bk Titles 12,400; Bk Vols 19,089;
Per Subs 17; Talking Bks 412; Videos 908
Open Tues & Wed 9:30-7:30, Thurs & Fri 9:30-5:30, Sat 9:30-1:30
Friends of the Library Group
WILDERNESS, 6421 Flat Run Rd, Locust Grove, 22508. Tel:
540-854-5310, 540-972-1675. FAX: 540-854-5402. E-mail:
willibrary@orangecova.com. *Br Librn,* Michele B Beamer; *Youth Serv*

Librn, Aimee McNulty; E-mail: aslawinski@orangecova.com; Staff 3 (MLS 2, Non-MLS 1)
Founded 1995
Library Holdings: AV Mats 8,450; CDs 923; DVDs 2,098; Electronic Media & Resources 363; Large Print Bks 1,445; Bk Vols 35,211; Per Subs 25; Talking Bks 1,950; Videos 2,453
Subject Interests: Civil War
Function: After school storytime, Audio & video playback equip for onsite use, Bks on cassette, Bks on CD, CD-ROM, Children's prog, Computers for patron use, Copy machines, Free DVD rentals, ILL available, Music CDs, Prog for children & young adult, Summer reading prog, Tax forms
Open Mon-Wed 10-7:30, Thurs & Fri 10-5:30, Sat 10-2
Friends of the Library Group

PEARISBURG

P PEARISBURG PUBLIC LIBRARY*, 209 Fort Branch Rd, 24134. SAN 317-3798. Tel: 540-921-2556. FAX: 540-921-1708. Web Site: www.pearisburg.org/library.htm. *Dir,* Position Currently Open; *Asst Librn,* Birdie B Moye; *Asst Librn,* Lori Porterfield; Staff 2 (Non-MLS 2)
Founded 1963
Library Holdings: Bk Vols 35,777; Per Subs 102
Special Collections: Circulating Art Reproductions; Genealogy, including listings of Giles County cemeteries
Automation Activity & Vendor Info: (Acquisitions) Follett Software; (Cataloging) Follett Software; (Circulation) Follett Software; (Course Reserve) Follett Software; (ILL) Follett Software; (Media Booking) Follett Software; (OPAC) Follett Software; (Serials) Follett Software
Publications: Giles County-Virginia, History-Families
Open Mon 12-8, Tues 12-5, Wed & Fri 9-5, Thurs 9-8, Sat 9-1

PETERSBURG

P PETERSBURG PUBLIC LIBRARY*, 137 S Sycamore St, 23803. SAN 363-1680. Tel: 804-733-2387. FAX: 804-733-7972. Web Site: www.ppls.org. *Dir,* Wayne M Crocker; E-mail: wcrocker@ppls.org; *Cat,* Carolyn T Eubanks; E-mail: ceubank@ppls.org; Staff 4 (MLS 4)
Founded 1924. Pop 33,740; Circ 132,886
Library Holdings: AV Mats 1,631; Bk Titles 105,139; Bk Vols 153,336; Per Subs 229; Talking Bks 1,555
Special Collections: Newspapers since 1800, bd vols & microfilm; Virginia History (Rare Virginiana & Genealogy, Civil War History Coll)
Automation Activity & Vendor Info: (Cataloging) TLC (The Library Corporation); (Circulation) TLC (The Library Corporation); (OPAC) TLC (The Library Corporation)
Open Mon & Wed 9-9, Tues & Thurs-Sat 9-5:30
Friends of the Library Group
Branches: 2
A P HILL BRANCH, 1237 Halifax St, 23803, SAN 363-1710. Tel: 804-733-2391. FAX: 804-733-2391. *Librn,* Amanda Briggs
Library Holdings: Bk Titles 3,774; Bk Vols 12,758; Per Subs 41
Open Mon, Tues & Thurs 3-6, Wed & Fri 10-6
Friends of the Library Group
RODOF SHOLOM BRANCH, 1865 S Sycamore St, 23805, SAN 363-1745. Tel: 804-733-2393. FAX: 804-733-2422. *Librn,* Dana Cragg; E-mail: dcragg@ppls.org; Staff 3 (MLS 1, Non-MLS 2)
Library Holdings: Bk Titles 9,390; Bk Vols 29,389; Per Subs 71
Open Mon, Wed & Fri 9-5:30, Tues & Thurs 9-9
Friends of the Library Group

C RICHARD BLAND COLLEGE LIBRARY*, 11301 Johnson Rd, 23805. SAN 317-3836. Tel: 804-862-6226. Interlibrary Loan Service Tel: 804-862-6228. Reference Tel: 804-862-6227. Administration Tel: 804-862-6208. FAX: 804-862-6125. E-mail: library@rbc.edu. Web Site: www.rbc.edu/library. *Dir,* Dan Ream; E-mail: dream@rbc.edu; *Pub Serv/Ref Librn,* Jacqueline Carrell; *Tech Serv & Pub Serv Librn,* Irene Handy; Staff 3 (MLS 2, Non-MLS 1)
Founded 1960. Enrl 1,634; Fac 33; Highest Degree: Associate
Jul 2008-Jun 2009. Mats Exp $76,962, Books $3,444, Per/Ser (Incl. Access Fees) $6,885, Micro $3,212, AV Mat $310, Electronic Ref Mat (Incl. Access Fees) $12,088, Presv $100
Library Holdings: Audiobooks 18; AV Mats 5,320; CDs 192; DVDs 4,384; e-books 56,829; e-journals 20,000; Electronic Media & Resources 760,000; Microforms 3,854; Bk Titles 57,576; Bk Vols 66,444; Per Subs 98; Videos 863
Special Collections: Southside Virginia Coll
Subject Interests: Geog, Hist, Lit, Music, Philosophy, Psychol, Relig
Automation Activity & Vendor Info: (Cataloging) SirsiDynix; (Circulation) SirsiDynix; (Course Reserve) SirsiDynix; (ILL) OCLC; (OPAC) SirsiDynix; (Serials) SirsiDynix
Database Vendor: ABC-CLIO, American Chemical Society, Annual Reviews, BioOne, Cambridge Scientific Abstracts, CRC Press/Taylor & Francis CRCnetBASE, EBSCOhost, Factiva.com, Gale Cengage Learning, LexisNexis, Nature Publishing Group, netLibrary, OCLC FirstSearch,

OCLC WorldCat, Oxford Online, Project MUSE, Safari Books Online, SirsiDynix, Wiley InterScience
Wireless access
Function: Archival coll, AV serv, Computers for patron use, Copy machines, Electronic databases & coll, Free DVD rentals, Handicapped accessible, ILL available, Music CDs, Online cat, Online ref, Online searches, Orientations, Photocopying/Printing, Pub access computers, Ref serv available, Res libr, Scanner, VHS videos, Wheelchair accessible
Publications: Library Bookmarks (Newsletter)
Partic in Richmond Academic Library Consortium; Virtual Library of Virginia
Open Mon-Thurs 8-8, Fri 8-5, Sun 4-8
Restriction: Limited access for the pub
Friends of the Library Group

M SOUTHSIDE REGIONAL MEDICAL CENTER, Medical Library, 200 Medical Park Blvd, 23805. SAN 317-3828. Tel: 804-765-5663. FAX: 804-765-5664. *Librn,* Joan Pollard; E-mail: joan_pollard@chs.net
Founded 1956
Library Holdings: Bk Vols 400; Per Subs 30
Subject Interests: Med
Wireless access
Partic in Mid-Atlantic Library Alliance (MALiA); National Network of Libraries of Medicine
Open Mon-Thurs 9-3

S UNITED STATES DEPARTMENT OF THE INTERIOR*, Petersburg National Battlefield Library, 5001 Siege Rd, 23803. SAN 317-3844. Tel: 804-732-3531. FAX: 804-732-0835. Web Site: www.nps.gov/pete/. *Curator,* James Blankenship; E-mail: james_blankenship@nps.gov
Founded 1938
Library Holdings: Bk Titles 3,000
Subject Interests: Petersburg hist
Open Mon-Fri 9-5

C VIRGINIA STATE UNIVERSITY*, Johnston Memorial Library, One Hayden Dr, 23806-0001. (Mail add: PO Box 9406, 23806-9406), SAN 363-177X. Tel: 804-524-5040. Circulation Tel: 804-524-5043. Interlibrary Loan Service Tel: 804-524-6944. Reference Tel: 804-524-5582. FAX: 804-524-6959. Circulation FAX: 804-524-5482. *Dean of Libr,* Elsie Wetherington; E-mail: estephens@vsu.edu; *Assoc Librn, Pub Serv,* Michael C Walker; Tel: 804-524-6946, E-mail: mcwalker@vsu.edu; *Assoc Librn, Tech Serv,* Tessa Perry; Tel: 804-524-5580, E-mail: tperry@vsu.edu; *Ref Serv Coordr,* Mary W Bailey; Tel: 804-524-6821, E-mail: mbailey@vsu.edu; *Access Serv & Syst,* Louveller Luster; Tel: 804-524-6945, E-mail: lluster@vsu.edu; *Acq,* Gloria G Harvell; Tel: 804-524-5740, E-mail: gharvell@vsu.edu; *Archivist,* Lucious Edwards; Tel: 804-524-5749, Fax: 805-524-5815, E-mail: ledwards@vsu.edu; *Govt Doc,* Gloria Beck; Tel: 804-524-6945, E-mail: gbeck@vsu.edu; *Ser,* Susan Lobaugh; Tel: 804-542-5042, E-mail: slobaugh@vsu.edu; *Syst Analyst,* Sherod Moses; Tel: 804-524-5942, E-mail: smoses@vsu.edu. Subject Specialists: *Sci tech,* Michael C Walker; *African-Am coll,* Tessa Perry; *Arts, Bus, Humanities,* Mary W Bailey; *Hist,* Lucious Edwards; *Art, Hist, Sociol,* Gloria Beck; *Educ,* Susan Lobaugh; Staff 8 (MLS 6, Non-MLS 2)
Founded 1882. Enrl 5,074; Highest Degree: Doctorate
Library Holdings: CDs 470; DVDs 37; e-books 14,959; e-journals 2,828; Electronic Media & Resources 230; Music Scores 702; Bk Titles 285,353; Bk Vols 310,796; Per Subs 4,437; Videos 1,558
Special Collections: US Document Depository
Subject Interests: African-Am studies, Educ
Automation Activity & Vendor Info: (Acquisitions) VTLS, Inc; (Cataloging) VTLS, Inc; (Circulation) VTLS, Inc; (Course Reserve) Docutek; (ILL) OCLC ILLiad; (OPAC) VTLS, Inc; (Serials) VTLS, Inc
Database Vendor: Cambridge Scientific Abstracts, EBSCOhost, Elsevier MDL, Factiva.com, Gale Cengage Learning, LexisNexis, netLibrary, OCLC FirstSearch, OCLC WorldCat, OVID Technologies, ProQuest, ScienceDirect, SerialsSolutions
Function: Res libr
Publications: InfoNavigator (Newsletter)
Partic in Richmond Academic Library Consortium; Virtual Library of Virginia
Special Services for the Deaf - Assistive tech; Bks on deafness & sign lang; Closed caption videos; TDD equip; TTY equip
Special Services for the Blind - Assistive/Adapted tech devices, equip & products; Audio mat; Bks on cassette; Bks on CD; Braille servs; Cassette playback machines; Cassettes; Closed circuit TV; Ednalite Hi-Vision scope; Handicapped awareness prog; Inspiration software; Internet workstation with adaptive software; Low vision equip; Magnifiers; Reader equip
Open Mon-Thurs 8am-11pm, Fri 8-6, Sat 10-6, Sun 3-11

POQUOSON

P POQUOSON PUBLIC LIBRARY*, 500 City Hall Ave, 23662-1996. SAN 321-0936. Tel: 757-868-3060. Reference Tel: 757-868-3065. FAX: 757-868-3106. E-mail: library@poquoson-va.gov. Web Site:

www.poquoson-va.gov/library. *Dir,* Elizabeth L Tai; Tel: 757-868-3066, E-mail: etai@poquoson-va.gov; Staff 12 (MLS 2, Non-MLS 10)
Founded 1976. Pop 11,800; Circ 208,534
Jul 2006-Jun 2007 Income $1,266,728, State $130,119, City $566,524, Locally Generated Income $566,448, Other $3,637. Mats Exp $61,679, Books $51,589, Per/Ser (Incl. Access Fees) $174, Manu Arch $3,278, Micro $2, AV Mat $6,608, Electronic Ref Mat (Incl. Access Fees) $28. Sal $270,070 (Prof $75,552)
Library Holdings: Audiobooks 1,697; AV Mats 4,865; Bk Vols 51,589; Per Subs 174; Talking Bks 1,409
Automation Activity & Vendor Info: (Acquisitions) SirsiDynix; (Cataloging) SirsiDynix; (Circulation) SirsiDynix; (Course Reserve) SirsiDynix; (ILL) The Library Co-Op, Inc; (OPAC) SirsiDynix
Database Vendor: Gale Cengage Learning, OCLC FirstSearch
Wireless access
Function: Accelerated reader prog, Adult bk club, Adult literacy prog, After school storytime, Art exhibits, AV serv, BA reader (adult literacy), Bk club(s), Bk reviews (Group), Bks on cassette, Bks on CD, CD-ROM, Children's prog, Citizenship assistance, Computer training, Computers for patron use, Copy machines, Digital talking bks, E-Reserves, Electronic databases & coll, Equip loans & repairs, Family literacy, Fax serv, Free DVD rentals, Genealogy discussion group, Govt ref serv, Handicapped accessible, Health sci info serv, Holiday prog, Homework prog, ILL available, Instruction & testing, Large print keyboards, Literacy & newcomer serv, Magnifiers for reading, Mus passes, Music CDs, Newsp ref libr, Notary serv, Online cat, Online ref, Online searches, Orientations, Outreach serv, Outside serv via phone, mail, e-mail & web, Passport agency, Photocopying/Printing, Preschool outreach, Prof lending libr, Prog for adults, Prog for children & young adult, Pub access computers, Ref & res, Ref serv available, Referrals accepted, Scanner, Senior computer classes, Senior outreach, Spoken cassettes & CDs, Spoken cassettes & DVDs, Story hour, Summer reading prog, Tax forms, Teen prog, Telephone ref, VCDs, VHS videos, Video lending libr, Visual arts prog, Web-catalog, Wheelchair accessible, Workshops, Writing prog
Publications: Book Worms; Bookmarks (Newsletter); Friends of Library Newsletter
Open Mon-Thurs 10-9, Fri & Sat 10-5, Sun 1-5
Friends of the Library Group

PORTSMOUTH

S   PORTSMOUTH NAVAL SHIPYARD MUSEUM*, Marshall W Butt Library, Two High St, 23704-3830. (Mail add: 521 Middle St, 23704-3622), SAN 317-3860. Tel: 757-393-8591. FAX: 757-393-5244. Web Site: portsnavalmuseums.com. *Curator,* Corey Thornton; E-mail: thorntonc@portsmouthva.gov
Founded 1949
Library Holdings: Bk Titles 8,000
Subject Interests: Local hist, Naval hist
Function: Archival coll, Photocopying/Printing, Res libr
Restriction: Not a lending libr, Open to others by appt

P   PORTSMOUTH PUBLIC LIBRARY, 601 Court St, 23704-3604. SAN 363-1834. Tel: 757-393-8501. Reference Tel: 757-393-8973. Web Site: www.portsmouthpubliclibrary.org. *Dir,* Todd Elliott; E-mail: elliottt@portsmouthva.gov; *Ch,* Rachel Enrich; Staff 8 (MLS 8)
Founded 1914. Pop 95,500; Circ 371,257
Library Holdings: Bks on Deafness & Sign Lang 274; CDs 1,167; DVDs 6,944; e-books 5; Large Print Bks 8,545; Bk Titles 213,768; Bk Vols 338,939; Per Subs 460; Talking Bks 5,430; Videos 7,039
Special Collections: Lighthouses & Lightships; Local History Coll, bks, doc. Oral History
Automation Activity & Vendor Info: (Acquisitions) Horizon; (Cataloging) Horizon; (Circulation) Horizon; (ILL) OCLC FirstSearch; (OPAC) Horizon
Database Vendor: SirsiDynix
Wireless access
Function: AV serv, Bks on cassette, Bks on CD, CD-ROM, Children's prog, Computer training, Computers for patron use, Copy machines, E-Reserves, Electronic databases & coll, Handicapped accessible, ILL available, Music CDs, Newsp ref libr, Online searches, Photocopying/Printing, Prog for adults, Prog for children & young adult, Pub access computers, Ref serv available, Spoken cassettes & CDs, Summer reading prog, Telephone ref, VHS videos, Wheelchair accessible
Open Mon-Thurs 10-6, Fri & Sat 10-5
Friends of the Library Group
Branches: 3
CHURCHLAND, 4934 High St W, 23703, SAN 363-1869. Tel: 757-686-2538. *Syst Adminr,* Clint Rudy
Automation Activity & Vendor Info: (Acquisitions) SirsiDynix; (Cataloging) SirsiDynix; (Circulation) SirsiDynix
Database Vendor: LearningExpress, ProQuest
Open Mon-Wed 10-8, Thurs 10-6, Fri & Sat 10-5
Friends of the Library Group

CRADOCK, Afton Sq, 28 Prospect Pkwy, 23702, SAN 363-1893. Tel: 757-393-8759. *Br Mgr,* Position Currently Open; Staff 3 (MLS 1, Non-MLS 2)
Library Holdings: CDs 290; DVDs 1,485; Large Print Bks 857; Bk Vols 45,186; Per Subs 43; Talking Bks 773; Videos 1,274
Automation Activity & Vendor Info: (Acquisitions) SirsiDynix; (Cataloging) SirsiDynix; (Circulation) SirsiDynix
Open Mon-Wed 11-7, Thurs & Fri 1-5, Sat 11-3
Friends of the Library Group
MANOR, 1401 Elmhurst Lane, 23701, SAN 363-1923. Tel: 757-465-2916. *Br Mgr,* Mary Goodman; Staff 3 (MLS 1, Non-MLS 2)
Library Holdings: DVDs 1,623; Large Print Bks 1,509; Bk Vols 49,674; Per Subs 36; Talking Bks 1,099; Videos 1,656
Automation Activity & Vendor Info: (Acquisitions) SirsiDynix; (Cataloging) SirsiDynix; (Circulation) SirsiDynix
Special Services for the Deaf - Bks on deafness & sign lang
Open Mon-Wed 10-7:30, Thurs 10-5:30, Fri & Sat 10-5
Friends of the Library Group

J   TIDEWATER COMMUNITY COLLEGE*, Portsmouth Campus Library, 120 Campus Dr, 23701. SAN 363-1958. Circulation Tel: 757-822-2130. Reference Tel: 757-822-2134. FAX: 757-822-2149. Web Site: www.tcc.edu/lrc. *Ref Librn,* Steven Litherland; E-mail: slitherland@tcc.edu; *Ref Librn,* Ruth Shumate; E-mail: rshumate@tcc.edu; *Coordr,* Mary Anne Glanzer; E-mail: mglanzer@tcc.edu; Staff 3 (MLS 3)
Founded 1961. Enrl 3,623; Fac 80; Highest Degree: Associate
Library Holdings: Bk Titles 55,934; Bk Vols 64,070; Per Subs 174
Automation Activity & Vendor Info: (Cataloging) Ex Libris Group; (Circulation) Ex Libris Group; (Course Reserve) Ex Libris Group; (OPAC) Ex Libris Group
Wireless access
Partic in Virtual Library of Virginia
Open Mon-Thurs 7:30am-9pm, Fri 7:30-7, Sat 9-1

AM   UNITED STATES NAVY*, Naval Medical Center Portsmouth, Bldg 1, 4th Flr, 620 John Paul Jones Circle, 23708-2197. SAN 363-2040. Tel: 757-953-5530. Circulation Tel: 757-953-5383. Reference Tel: 757-953-5384. FAX: 757-953-7533. E-mail: nmcp-libraryservices@mar.med.navy.mil. Web Site: www.med.navy.mil/sites/nmcp/pages/default.aspx. *Dept Head,* Jane Pellegrino; E-mail: jane.pellegrino@med.navy.mil; Staff 5 (MLS 3, Non-MLS 2)
Library Holdings: Bk Titles 8,858; Bk Vols 32,117; Per Subs 390
Subject Interests: Allied sci, Dentistry, Med, Nursing
Automation Activity & Vendor Info: (Cataloging) CyberTools for Libraries; (Circulation) CyberTools for Libraries; (OPAC) CyberTools for Libraries
Database Vendor: ProQuest
Publications: Newsletter (in-house)
Partic in OCLC Online Computer Library Center, Inc
Restriction: Authorized patrons, Open by appt only

POWHATAN

P   POWHATAN COUNTY PUBLIC LIBRARY*, 2270 Mann Rd, 23139-5748. SAN 375-8710. Tel: 804-598-5670. FAX: 804-598-5671. Web Site: www.powhatanlibrary.org. *Dir,* Kim Armentrout; E-mail: karmentrout@powhatanlibrary.org
Founded 1975. Pop 22,000
Library Holdings: Bk Vols 54,000; Per Subs 20
Automation Activity & Vendor Info: (Cataloging) TLC (The Library Corporation); (Circulation) TLC (The Library Corporation); (OPAC) TLC (The Library Corporation)
Open Mon-Thurs 9-8, Fri 9-5, Sat 10-3
Friends of the Library Group

PRINCE WILLIAM

P   PRINCE WILLIAM PUBLIC LIBRARY SYSTEM*, 13083 Chinn Park Dr, 22192-5073. SAN 363-0544. Tel: 703-792-6100. FAX: 703-792-4875. TDD: 703-792-6163. Web Site: www.pwcgov.org/library. *Dir,* Richard Murphy; *Coll Develop,* Blair Christolon; Staff 163 (MLS 46, Non-MLS 117)
Founded 1952. Pop 473,000; Circ 3,631,186
Library Holdings: Bk Vols 858,651
Special Collections: Geneaology & Local History Coll; Management & Government Information Center
Subject Interests: Local govt, Local hist
Automation Activity & Vendor Info: (Circulation) Polaris Library Systems
Wireless access
Partic in Lyrasis; OCLC Online Computer Library Center, Inc; SouthWest Information Network Group (SWING)
Special Services for the Deaf - TDD equip

Open Mon-Thurs 10-9, Fri & Sat 10-5
Friends of the Library Group
Branches: 10
BULL RUN REGIONAL, 8051 Ashton Ave, Manassas, 20109-2892, SAN
374-6887. Tel: 703-792-4500. FAX: 703-792-4520. TDD: 703-792-4524.
Br Mgr, Sandra Oliver
Special Services for the Deaf - TDD equip
Open Mon-Thurs 10-9, Fri & Sat 10-5, Sun (Winter) 12-5
Friends of the Library Group
CENTRAL, 8601 Mathis Ave, Manassas, 20110-5229, SAN 329-644X.
Tel: 703-361-8211. FAX: 703-335-2956. TDD: 703-361-7572. *Br Mgr,*
Cathy Atchley
Special Services for the Deaf - TDD equip
Open Mon-Thurs 10-9, Fri & Sat 10-5, Sun (Winter) 12-5
Friends of the Library Group
CHINN PARK REGIONAL, 13065 Chinn Park Dr, 22192-5073, SAN
374-4361. Tel: 703-792-4800. FAX: 703-792-4612. TDD: 703-792-4876.
Br Mgr, Connie Gilman
Special Services for the Deaf - TDD equip
Open Mon-Thurs 10-9, Fri & Sat 10-5, Sun (Winter) 12-5
Friends of the Library Group
DALE CITY NEIGHBORHOOD, 4249 Dale Blvd, Woodbridge,
22193-2414, SAN 326-8284. Tel: 703-792-5670. FAX: 703-670-6152. *Br
Mgr,* Jennifer Harden
Open Mon-Thurs 10-7, Fri & Sat 10-2
DUMFRIES NEIGHBORHOOD, 18007 Dumfries Shopping Plaza,
Dumfries, 22026-2411, SAN 326-8306. Tel: 703-792-5678. FAX:
703-221-7814. *Br Mgr,* Debbie Bittner
Open Mon-Thurs 10-7, Sat 10-2
GAINESVILLE NEIGHBORHOOD, 4603 James Madison Hwy,
Haymarket, 20169-2526, SAN 328-963X. Tel: 703-792-5660. FAX:
703-754-2494. *Br Mgr,* Meredith Murphree
Open Mon-Thurs 10-7, Fri & Sat 10-2
INDEPENDENT HILL NEIGHBORHOOD, 14418 Bristow Rd, Manassas,
20112-3932, SAN 328-9656. Tel: 703-792-5668. FAX: 703-791-2721. *Br
Mgr,* Melanie Erhart
Open Mon-Thurs 10-7, Sat 10-2
LAKE RIDGE NEIGHBORHOOD, 12964 Harbor Dr, Woodbridge,
22192-2930, SAN 326-8322. Tel: 703-792-5675. FAX: 703-491-6661. *Br
Mgr,* Evelyn Casey
Open Mon-Thurs 10-7, Sat 10-2
NOKESVILLE NEIGHBORHOOD, 12993 Fitzwater Dr, Nokesville,
20181-2229, SAN 326-8349. Tel: 703-792-5665. FAX: 703-594-2250. *Br
Mgr,* Dona Swanson
Open Mon-Thurs 10-7, Sat 10-2
POTOMAC COMMUNITY, 2201 Opitz Blvd, Woodbridge, 22191-3377,
SAN 363-0579. Tel: 703-494-8126. FAX: 703-491-2593. *Br Mgr,*
Position Currently Open
Open Mon-Thurs 10-9, Fri & Sat 10-5, Sun (Winter) 12-5
Friends of the Library Group

PROVIDENCE FORGE

P   HERITAGE PUBLIC LIBRARY*, 9001 Blvd, 23140-0008. (Mail add: PO
Box 8, 23140-0008), SAN 324-5780. Tel: 804-966-2480. FAX:
804-966-5982. Web Site: heritagepubliclibrary.org. *Dir,* Alan M Bernstein
Founded 1980. Pop 22,000
Jul 2006-Jun 2007 Income $248,500, State $59,000, County $169,000,
Parent Institution $9,000. Mats Exp $48,000, Books $47,000, Per/Ser (Incl.
Access Fees) $1,000. Sal $130,000 (Prof $46,000)
Library Holdings: Bk Titles 47,000
Special Collections: Religion (Charles Jeffery Smith Coll)
Automation Activity & Vendor Info: (Cataloging) Follett Software;
(Circulation) Follett Software
Open Mon, Tues & Thurs 9-8, Wed & Fri 9-5:30, Sat 9-2
Friends of the Library Group

PULASKI

P   PULASKI COUNTY PUBLIC LIBRARY SYSTEM, 60 W Third St,
24301. SAN 317-3887. Tel: 540-980-7770. Interlibrary Loan Service Tel:
540-994-2460. Reference Tel: 540-994-2456. Administration Tel:
540-994-2451. Automation Services Tel: 540-994-2453. FAX:
540-980-7775. Web Site: www.pclibs.org. *Libr Dir,* Sally Warburton;
E-mail: swarburton@pclibs.org; *Ref Librn/Pub Serv Coordr,* Lucy Glenn;
E-mail: lglenn@pclibs.org; *Youth Serv Librn,* Jenafer Hardy; *Tech Coordr,*
Carol Smith; E-mail: csmith@pclibs.org; Staff 9 (MLS 3, Non-MLS 6)
Founded 1937. Pop 35,170; Circ 79,489
Subject Interests: Pulaski County local hist
Automation Activity & Vendor Info: (Acquisitions) TLC (The Library
Corporation); (Cataloging) TLC (The Library Corporation); (Circulation)
TLC (The Library Corporation); (ILL) OCLC; (OPAC) TLC (The Library
Corporation)

Database Vendor: Baker & Taylor, EBSCOhost, netLibrary, OCLC
FirstSearch, Overdrive, Inc, ProQuest, TLC (The Library Corporation),
TumbleBookLibrary
Wireless access
Function: Audiobks via web, Bk club(s), Bks on CD, Children's prog,
Computers for patron use, Copy machines, E-Reserves, Electronic
databases & coll, Exhibits, Family literacy, Free DVD rentals, Handicapped
accessible, Holiday prog, Home delivery & serv to Sr ctr & nursing homes,
ILL available, Online cat, Online ref, Online searches, Outreach serv,
OverDrive digital audio bks, Photocopying/Printing, Preschool outreach,
Preschool reading prog, Prog for adults, Prog for children & young adult,
Pub access computers, Ref serv available, Scanner, Senior outreach, Story
hour, Summer & winter reading prog, Teen prog
Partic in SouthWest Information Network Group (SWING)
Open Mon 8-8, Tues & Thurs 8-7, Fri 8-5, Sat 9-2
Restriction: Open to pub for ref & circ; with some limitations
Friends of the Library Group
Branches: 1
CHARLES & ONA B FREE MEMORIAL, 300 Giles Ave, Dublin, 24084,
SAN 374-5295. Tel: 540-674-2856. FAX: 540-674-2907. *Br Mgr,* Mia
Catron; E-mail: mcatront@pclibs.org; Staff 1.5 (MLS 0.25, Non-MLS
1.25)
Founded 1989. Pop 2,232
Function: Bks on cassette, Bks on CD, Children's prog, Computers for
patron use, Copy machines, e-mail serv, Electronic databases & coll, Fax
serv, Free DVD rentals, ILL available, Online cat, Preschool outreach,
Ref & res, Spoken cassettes & CDs, Spoken cassettes & DVDs, Summer
reading prog, Tax forms, VHS videos, Web-catalog
Open Mon & Tues 9-7, Wed-Fri 9-5, Sat 9-2
Restriction: Open to pub for ref & circ; with some limitations
Friends of the Library Group

PURCELLVILLE

CR   PATRICK HENRY COLLEGE LIBRARY*, Ten Patrick Henry Circle,
20132. Tel: 540-441-8400. FAX: 540-441-8409. E-mail: library@phc.edu.
Web Site: www.phc.edu/library. Staff 3 (MLS 2, Non-MLS 1)
Founded 2000. Highest Degree: Bachelor
Wireless access
Open Mon-Thurs (Winter) 7:30am-11pm, Fri 7:30-5:30, Sat 10-6; Mon-Fri
(Summer) 8:30-5:30

QUANTICO

G   FEDERAL BUREAU OF INVESTIGATION*, Laboratory Library, 2501
Investigation Pkwy, 22135. SAN 372-6177. Tel: 703-632-8375. FAX:
703-632-8374. E-mail: lablibrary@ic.fbi.gov. *In Charge,* Yvette Trozzi;
Staff 1 (Non-MLS 1)
Founded 1985
Library Holdings: Bk Titles 12,000; Per Subs 450
Special Collections: Forensic Sciences, bks, av, fiche
Publications: Subject Bibliographies
Partic in Dialog Corp; OCLC Online Computer Library Center, Inc

A   LIBRARY OF THE MARINE CORPS*, Gray Research Ctr, 2040
Broadway St, 22134-5107. Tel: 703-784-4409. Reference Tel:
703-784-4411. Automation Services Tel: 703-784-4838. FAX:
703-784-4306. Reference FAX: 703-784-4989. *Dir,* Carol E Ramkey; Tel:
703-784-4764, E-mail: ramkeyce@grc.usmcu.edu; *Head, Archives & Spec
Coll,* Michael Miller; Tel: 703-784-4834, Fax: 703-784-4665, E-mail:
millerm@grc.usmcu.edu; *Head, Breckinridge Libr Br,* Faith C Kanno; Tel:
703-784-0459, Fax: 703-784-4089, E-mail: kannofc@grc.usmcu.edu; *Head,
Virtual Libr Br,* Theresa M Anthony; E-mail: anthonytm@grc.usmcu.edu;
Cat Librn, Janice E Pepper; Tel: 703-784-1839, E-mail:
pepperje@grc.usmcu.edu; *Chief Ref Librn,* Rachel Kingcade; E-mail:
kingcaders@grc.usmcu.edu; *Ref Librn,* Kimberly D Adams; E-mail:
adamskd@grc.usmcu.edu; *Ref Librn,* Patricia S Lane; E-mail:
laneps@grc.usmcu.edu; *Syst Librn,* Monika Lyman; E-mail:
lymanmm@grc.usmcu.edu; *Archivist,* Gregory Cina; Tel: 703-784-4685,
E-mail: cinagl@grc.usmcu.edu; *Archivist,* Dr James Ginther; Fax:
703-784-4665, E-mail: gintherja@grc.usmcu.edu; *Archivist,* Alisa Whitley;
Tel: 703-784-4685, E-mail: whitleyam@grc.usmcu.edu
Special Collections: Personal Papers of the Commandants of the Marine
Corps; US Marine Corps Command Chronologies
Subject Interests: Intl political relations, Leadership, Marine Corps
doctrine, Marine Corps hist, Mil art, Mil sci, Warfighting doctrine
Automation Activity & Vendor Info: (Acquisitions) SirsiDynix;
(Cataloging) SirsiDynix; (Circulation) SirsiDynix; (OPAC) SirsiDynix;
(Serials) SirsiDynix
Database Vendor: Baker & Taylor, EBSCOhost, Gale Cengage Learning,
Jane's, JSTOR, LexisNexis, netLibrary, Newsbank, OCLC FirstSearch,
OCLC WorldCat, ProQuest, SerialsSolutions, SirsiDynix, WT Cox

Wireless access
Partic in Consortium of Naval Libraries (CNL); Federal Library &
Information Center Committee (FLICC); Fedlink; Military Education
Coordination Conference (MECC)

G   UNITED STATES DEPARTMENT OF JUSTICE*, Federal Bureau of
     Investigation Library, MCB No 4, 22135. SAN 317-3895. Tel:
     703-632-3200. FAX: 703-632-3214. E-mail: librarian@fbiacademy.edu.
     Web Site: fbilibrary.fbiacademy.edu. *Dir,* Eugenia B Ryner; Tel:
     702-632-3215, E-mail: eryner@fbiacademy.edu; *Coll Develop, Webmaster,*
     Nzinga Holley-Harris; Tel: 703-632-3218, E-mail:
     nholleyharris@fbiacademy.edu; *ILL, Pub Serv,* Cheryl Weidner; Tel:
     703-632-3204, E-mail: cweidner@fbiacademy.edu; *Govt Doc, Mgt Prog
     Analyst,* Veronica Sacra; Tel: 703-632-3213, E-mail:
     vsacra@fbiacademy.edu; *Tech Info Spec,* Susan Spotteck; Tel:
     703-632-3217; *Tech Serv,* Linda A Cranston; Tel: 703-632-3203, E-mail:
     lcranston@fbiacademy.edu; Staff 6 (MLS 4, Non-MLS 2)
     Founded 1972
     Library Holdings: AV Mats 2,000; Bk Vols 45,000; Per Subs 327
     Special Collections: US Document Depository
     Subject Interests: Criminal justice, Law enforcement, Police
     Automation Activity & Vendor Info: (Acquisitions) Sydney; (Cataloging)
     Sydney; (Circulation) Sydney; (Course Reserve) Sydney; (OPAC) Sydney;
     (Serials) Sydney
     Database Vendor: EBSCOhost, Gale Cengage Learning, ProQuest, Swets
     Information Services, Wilson - Wilson Web
     Function: Audio & video playback equip for onsite use, Bks on CD,
     Computers for patron use, Copy machines, Doc delivery serv, Electronic
     databases & coll, Free DVD rentals, ILL available, Instruction & testing,
     Online cat, Orientations, Ref serv available, VHS videos
     Publications: Subject Bibliographies
     Partic in Fedlink; OCLC Online Computer Library Center, Inc; World
     Criminal Justice Libr Network
     Open Mon-Fri 8-4:30
     Restriction: 24-hr pass syst for students only, By permission only, Not
     open to pub, Restricted access

RADFORD

P   RADFORD PUBLIC LIBRARY*, 30 W Main St, 24141. SAN 317-3917.
     Tel: 540-731-3621. FAX: 540-731-4857. E-mail: library@radford.va.us.
     Web Site: www.radford.va.us/library. *Dir,* Toni Cox; E-mail:
     tonicox@radford.va.us; Staff 7 (MLS 3, Non-MLS 4)
     Founded 1941. Pop 15,940; Circ 141,233
     Library Holdings: Bk Vols 7,500; Per Subs 90
     Special Collections: Adult Low Reading Level Coll
     Subject Interests: Genealogy, Local hist
     Automation Activity & Vendor Info: (Circulation) TLC (The Library
     Corporation); (OPAC) TLC (The Library Corporation)
     Open Mon-Wed 9-8, Thurs 9-6, Fri & Sat 10-5, Sun 2-5
     Friends of the Library Group

C   RADFORD UNIVERSITY*, John Preston McConnell Library, 801 E Main
     St, 24142-0001. (Mail add: PO Box 6881, 24142-6881), SAN 317-3909.
     Tel: 540-831-5471. Circulation Tel: 540-831-5364. Interlibrary Loan
     Service Tel: 540-831-6126, 540-831-6139. Reference Tel: 540-831-5696.
     Automation Services Tel: 540-831-6624. FAX: 540-831-6138. E-mail:
     refdesk@radford.edu. Web Site: lib.radford.edu. *Univ Librn,* David Hayes;
     E-mail: dhayes@radford.edu; *Head, Access Serv,* Beth Johnson; Tel:
     540-831-6648, E-mail: ejohnson82@radford.edu; *Head, Ref & Instruction,*
     Blair Brainard; Tel: 540-831-5688, E-mail: bbrainar@radford.edu; *Coll
     Develop Librn,* Gerald Gordon; Tel: 540-831-6140, E-mail:
     ggordon@radford.edu; *Coordr, Info Tech,* Steve Helm; E-mail:
     shelm@radford.edu; *Coordr, Tech Serv,* Kay Johnson; Tel: 540-831-5703,
     E-mail: kjohnson497@radford.edu; *Cat,* Elizabeth McCormick; Tel:
     540-831-5635, E-mail: emccormick@radford.edu; Staff 35 (MLS 17,
     Non-MLS 18)
     Founded 1913. Enrl 9,157; Fac 581; Highest Degree: Doctorate
     Jul 2007-Jun 2008. Mats Exp $1,469,759, Books $337,925, Per/Ser (Incl.
     Access Fees) $859,679. Sal $1,635,543 (Prof $926,349)
     Library Holdings: AV Mats 25,466; e-books 60,366; e-journals 30,482;
     Bk Vols 384,746; Per Subs 9,935
     Special Collections: Appalachian Coll; Southwestern Virginia Regional
     History Coll. Oral History
     Subject Interests: Bus, Educ, Hist, Music, Nursing, Soc work
     Automation Activity & Vendor Info: (Acquisitions) Innovative Interfaces,
     Inc; (Cataloging) Innovative Interfaces, Inc; (Circulation) Innovative
     Interfaces, Inc; (Course Reserve) Innovative Interfaces, Inc; (ILL) OCLC
     ILLiad; (Media Booking) Innovative Interfaces, Inc; (OPAC) Innovative
     Interfaces, Inc; (Serials) Innovative Interfaces, Inc
     Database Vendor: ABC-CLIO, ACM (Association for Computing
     Machinery), Alexander Street Press, American Chemical Society, American
     Mathematical Society, American Physical Society, American Psychological
     Association (APA), Annual Reviews, ARTstor, Atlas Systems, Baker &
     Taylor, BioOne, Blackwell's, Bowker, Cambridge Scientific Abstracts,

Cinahl Information Systems, CountryWatch, CQ Press, CRC Press/Taylor
& Francis CRCnetBASE, CredoReference, Dun & Bradstreet, EBSCOhost,
Elsevier, Emerald, Factiva.com, Gale Cengage Learning, Gallup, H W
Wilson, HeinOnline, IEEE (Institute of Electrical & Electronics Engineers),
Ingenta, Innovative Interfaces, Inc, IOP, ISI Web of Knowledge, JSTOR,
LexisNexis, Marquis Who's Who, MD Consult, Medline, Mergent Online,
netLibrary, OCLC ArticleFirst, OCLC FirstSearch, OCLC WorldCat, OVID
Technologies, Oxford Online, Project MUSE, ProQuest, PubMed, Safari
Books Online, Sage, SBRnet (Sports Business Research Network),
ScienceDirect, SerialsSolutions, Standard & Poor's, Thomson - Web of
Science, ValueLine, Wiley, Wilson - Wilson Web, YBP Library Services
Wireless access
Function: Audio & video playback equip for onsite use, Computers for
patron use, Copy machines, e-mail serv, E-Reserves, Electronic databases
& coll, ILL available, Magnifiers for reading, Orientations, Outreach serv,
Outside serv via phone, mail, e-mail & web, Photocopying/Printing, Ref &
res, Scanner, Telephone ref, Web-catalog, Wheelchair accessible
Publications: Archives of the Winesett Scholars (Online only)
Partic in Virtual Library of Virginia
Special Services for the Deaf - Bks on deafness & sign lang; Coll on deaf
educ
Special Services for the Blind - VIEW (Visually Impaired Educational
Workstation)
Open Mon-Thurs 7:45am-Midnight, Fri 7:45-7, Sat 10-7, Sun
Noon-Midnight

RESTON

S   HARDWOOD PLYWOOD & VENEER ASSOCIATION LIBRARY, 1825
     Michael Faraday Dr, 20190. SAN 320-8761. Tel: 703-435-2900. FAX:
     703-435-2537. E-mail: hpva@hpva.org. Web Site: www.hpva.org.
     Founded 1921
     Library Holdings: Bk Titles 300; Per Subs 50
     Publications: A Complete Guide to Hardwood Plywood & Face Veneer by
     Ang Schramm; ANSI Standard for Engineered Wood Flooring; ANSI
     Standard for Hardwood & Decorative Plywood; Hardwood Plywood
     Handbook; How to Sell & Install Hardwood Plywood Manual; Inspection
     Testing & Listed Products Manual; Members Bulletin (Monthly); Structural
     Design Guide for Hardwood Plywood; Veneer Species Guide; Where to
     Buy Hardwood Plywood & Veneer (Annually)

S   METRON INC, Scientific Library, 1818 Library St, Ste 600, 20190-5602.
     SAN 375-6858. Tel: 703-787-8700. FAX: 703-787-3518. Web Site:
     www.metsci.com. *In Charge,* Wendy Wang
     Library Holdings: Bk Titles 3,000
     Open Mon-Fri 8-5

S   NORTHROP GRUMMAN MISSION SYSTEMS*, Technology Library,
     12011 Sunset Hills Rd, 20190. SAN 370-7768. Tel: 703-345-7738. FAX:
     703-345-7735. *Mgr,* Norma J Draper; E-mail: norma.j.draper@ngc.com;
     Librn, Cynthia Lemke; E-mail: cynthia.lemke@ngc.com; Staff 2 (MLS 1,
     Non-MLS 1)
     Founded 1982
     Library Holdings: Bk Titles 800; Per Subs 100
     Restriction: Open by appt only

G   UNITED STATES GEOLOGICAL SURVEY LIBRARY*, Clarence King
     Library, National Ctr, Rm 1D100, 12201 Sunrise Valley Dr, 20192. SAN
     317-3968. Circulation Tel: 703-648-4301. Interlibrary Loan Service Tel:
     703-648-6091. Administration Tel: 703-648-6207. Automation Services Tel:
     703-648-6243. Information Services Tel: 703-648-4302. Toll Free Tel:
     888-275-8747, Ext 5. FAX: 703-648-6373. E-mail: library@usgs.gov. Web
     Site: library.usgs.gov. *Br Mgr,* Lisa Adamo; E-mail: ladamo@usgs.gov;
     Tech Serv Mgr, Irena Kavalek; Tel: 703-648-4486, E-mail:
     ikavalek@usgs.gov; *Digital Serv,* Helen (Qi) Tong; E-mail:
     htong@usgs.gov; Staff 11 (MLS 7, Non-MLS 4)
     Founded 1882
     Library Holdings: AV Mats 500; CDs 1,000; DVDs 5,000; e-books 1,000;
     e-journals 1,000; Microforms 10,000; Bk Vols 1,000,000; Per Subs 700
     Special Collections: Gems & Minerals (George F Kunz Coll); Map Coll
     Subject Interests: Cartography, Chem, Environ studies, Geol, Geothermal
     energy, Mineralogy, Oceanography, Paleontology, Petrology, Physics,
     Planetary geology, Remote sensing, Surveying, Water res, Zoology
     Automation Activity & Vendor Info: (Acquisitions) EBSCO Online;
     (Cataloging) SirsiDynix; (Circulation) SirsiDynix; (OPAC) SirsiDynix;
     (Serials) SirsiDynix
     Partic in Dialog Corp; OCLC Online Computer Library Center, Inc

RICHMOND

M   BON SECOURS-SAINT MARY'S HOSPITAL*, Health Sciences Library,
     5801 Bremo Rd, 23226. SAN 322-9017. Tel: 804-281-8247. FAX:
     804-285-2448. *Librn,* Merle L Colglazier; Staff 1 (MLS 1)
     Library Holdings: e-books 200; e-journals 800; Electronic Media &
     Resources 14,000; Bk Vols 1,500; Per Subs 7,000

Automation Activity & Vendor Info: (Cataloging) CyberTools for Libraries; (Circulation) CyberTools for Libraries; (OPAC) CyberTools for Libraries; (Serials) CyberTools for Libraries
Database Vendor: EBSCOhost, Elsevier, MD Consult, OVID Technologies, ScienceDirect, SerialsSolutions
Function: Res libr
Partic in Docline; National Network of Libraries of Medicine
Restriction: Not open to pub

S   BRAILLE CIRCULATING LIBRARY, INC*, 2700 Stuart Ave, 23220. SAN 317-400X. Tel: 804-359-3743. FAX: 804-359-4777. Web Site: www.bclministries.org. *Exec Dir,* Brian J Barton; E-mail: bjbarton77@aol.com
Founded 1925
Library Holdings: Bk Titles 800; Bk Vols 3,000
Subject Interests: Relig
Special Services for the Blind - Braille bks
Open Mon-Fri 9-4

L   CHRISTIAN & BARTON, LLP ATTORNEYS AT LAW*, Law Library, 909 E Main St, 23219. SAN 372-350X. Tel: 804-697-4100. FAX: 804-697-4112. Web Site: www.cblaw.com/. *Librn,* Jane O Bowe; Tel: 804-697-6305, Fax: 804-697-6155, E-mail: jbowe@cblaw.com
Library Holdings: Bk Vols 10,000; Per Subs 200
Database Vendor: LexisNexis, Westlaw
Open Mon-Fri 9-5

SR   CONGREGATION BETH AHABAH MUSEUM & ARCHIVES TRUST*, Beth Ahabah Museum & Archives, 1109 W Franklin St, 23220. SAN 373-8396. Tel: 804-353-2668. FAX: 804-358-3451. E-mail: bama@bethahabah.org. Web Site: www.bethahabah.org. *Exec Dir,* David Farris; *Adminr,* Bonnie Eisenman; Staff 3 (Non-MLS 3)
Founded 1977
Library Holdings: Bk Titles 500
Special Collections: Genealogy Coll; Jefferson Lakeside Country Club; Jewish Community Center; Jewish Community Federation of Richmond; Jewish Family Servs, Beth Sholom Home; National Council of Jewish Women; Rabbi Ariel Goldburg Coll; Rabbi Edward N Calisch Coll
Subject Interests: Genealogy
Publications: Generations (Journal)
Open Mon-Thurs & Sun 10-3
Restriction: Non-circulating

L   DIVISION OF LEGISLATIVE SERVICES REFERENCE CENTER*, General Assembly Bldg, 2nd Flr, 910 Capitol St, 23219. SAN 372-3496. Tel: 804-786-3591. FAX: 804-371-0169, 804-371-8705. Web Site: dls.state.va.us/lrc.htm. *Mgr, Info Serv,* Cheryl Jackson; E-mail: cjackson@leg.state.va.us
Library Holdings: Bk Vols 8,000; Per Subs 150
Open Mon-Fri 8-5

S   FEDERAL RESERVE BANK OF RICHMOND*, Research Library, 701 E Byrd St, 23219. (Mail add: PO Box 27622, 23261-7622), SAN 317-4026. Tel: 804-697-8125. FAX: 804-697-8134. E-mail: rich.reslib@rich.frb.org. *Sr Libr Mgr,* Anne R Hallerman; *Automated Syst & Serv Librn,* Coleen Neary; *Libr Spec,* Charlene Fenner; *Res Librn,* Christian R Pascasio; E-mail: christian.pascasio@rich.frb.org; *Res Librn,* William Perkins; Staff 6 (MLS 3, Non-MLS 3)
Founded 1920
Library Holdings: Bk Titles 20,000; Bk Vols 29,000; Per Subs 325
Subject Interests: Banking, Econ, Finance
Automation Activity & Vendor Info: (Acquisitions) SirsiDynix; (Cataloging) SirsiDynix; (Circulation) SirsiDynix; (OPAC) SirsiDynix; (Serials) SirsiDynix
Database Vendor: Dialog, EBSCOhost, Factiva.com, JSTOR, OCLC WorldCat, ScienceDirect, SirsiDynix
Function: ILL available, Telephone ref
Partic in OCLC Online Computer Library Center, Inc
Restriction: Open by appt only

SR   FIRST BAPTIST CHURCH LIBRARY*, 2709 Monument Ave, 23220. SAN 370-2367. Tel: 804-355-8637, Ext 20. FAX: 804-359-4000. E-mail: library@fbcrichmond.org. Web Site: www.fbcrichmond.org. *Chmn,* David Jackson; *Head, Cat,* Lila Williams; Staff 10 (MLS 1, Non-MLS 9)
Founded 1838
Library Holdings: Large Print Bks 32; Bk Vols 16,500; Per Subs 30
Special Collections: Church Archives
Subject Interests: Authors, Church hist
Automation Activity & Vendor Info: (Cataloging) Book Systems, Inc; (Circulation) Book Systems, Inc; (OPAC) Book Systems, Inc
Special Services for the Deaf - Bks on deafness & sign lang
Open Wed 4-7:30, Sun 8:30-11am
Restriction: Open to pub for ref & circ; with some limitations
Friends of the Library Group

S   GRAND LODGE OF VIRGINIA AF&AM LIBRARY & MUSEUM HISTORICAL FOUNDATION*, Allen E Roberts Masonic Library & Museum, 4115 Nine Mile Rd, 23223-4926. SAN 326-0585. Tel: 804-222-3110. FAX: 804-222-4253. E-mail: library@grandlodgeofvirginia.org. Web Site: www.grandlodgeofvirginia.org. *Librn,* Marie M Barnett. Subject Specialists: *Masonic hist,* Marie M Barnett; Staff 1 (Non-MLS 1)
Founded 1778
Jan 2009-Dec 2009 Income $84,000. Mats Exp $6,850, Books $200, Manu Arch $250, Other Print Mats $600, Electronic Ref Mat (Incl. Access Fees) $300, Presv $5,500. Sal $13,000
Library Holdings: AV Mats 20; CDs 30; Bk Titles 4,900; Bk Vols 9,400; Per Subs 65; Videos 25
Special Collections: Masonic Archival Materials (hist, transactions, bylaws); Museum objects
Subject Interests: Freemasonry
Automation Activity & Vendor Info: (Cataloging) Book Systems, Inc; (OPAC) Book Systems, Inc
Wireless access
Function: Res libr
Publications: The Virginia Masonic Herald (Quarterly)
Restriction: Mem only, Open to pub for ref only

L   HUNTON & WILLIAMS*, Law Library, Riverfront Plaza, E Tower, 951 E Byrd St, 23219-4074. SAN 317-4042. Tel: 804-344-8272. FAX: 804-788-8218. *Librn,* Frosty Owen
Founded 1901
Library Holdings: Bk Vols 65,000; Per Subs 150
Special Collections: Law Memoranda; Records & Briefs; Speeches of Henry W Anderson
Subject Interests: Acctg, Antitrust, Environ, Fed law, Labor law, Real estate, Utilities, Va Law
Automation Activity & Vendor Info: (Cataloging) SydneyPlus; (Circulation) SydneyPlus; (OPAC) SydneyPlus; (Serials) SydneyPlus
Database Vendor: LexisNexis, Westlaw
Partic in Dialog Corp
Restriction: Staff use only

R   INTERNATIONAL MISSION BOARD, SOUTHERN BAPTIST CONVENTION*, Jenkins Research Library, 3806 Monument Ave, 23230-3932. (Mail add: PO Box 6767, 23230-0767), SAN 317-4158. Tel: 804-219-1429.
Founded 1960
Library Holdings: Bk Vols 22,000; Per Subs 600
Special Collections: Southern Baptist Missions History
Subject Interests: Anthropology, Cross-cultural communication, Ethnolinguistic people groups, Future studies, Hist, Hist of missions, Missiology, Politics
Database Vendor: Dialog, LexisNexis, OCLC FirstSearch
Partic in Lyrasis; OCLC Online Computer Library Center, Inc
Restriction: Open by appt only

J   J SARGEANT REYNOLDS COMMUNITY COLLEGE LIBRARY DOWNTOWN CAMPUS-LIBRARY & INFORMATION SERVICES*, 700 E Jackson St, 2nd Flr, 23219-1543. (Mail add: PO Box 85622, 23285-5622), SAN 363-2407. Tel: 804-523-5211. Interlibrary Loan Service Tel: 804-523-5337. Reference Tel: 804-523-5333. Administration Tel: 804-523-5330. FAX: 804-786-6200. Web Site: www.reynolds.edu/library/. *Dir,* Dr Abdul J Miah; E-mail: amiah@reynolds.edu; *Coordr, Libr Serv,* Dr Lillian Hoggard Williams; E-mail: lhwilliams@reynolds.edu; *Acq, Circ,* Neale Foster; E-mail: nfoster@reynolds.edu; *Circ, Coll Mgt, ILL,* Rebekah Goodfellow; E-mail: rgoodfellow@reynolds.edu; *Circ, Media Serv, Ser,* Samuel D Phillips; E-mail: sphillips@reynolds.edu; *Ref,* Khalil Ahmed; E-mail: kahmed@reynolds.edu; Staff 7 (MLS 3, Non-MLS 4)
Founded 1973. Highest Degree: Associate
Library Holdings: Bks on Deafness & Sign Lang 80; CDs 50; Bk Vols 36,500; Per Subs 190; Spec Interest Per Sub 10; Videos 2,500
Special Collections: Business Administration Coll, AV, bks; Film/Video Coll; Health Science Coll
Automation Activity & Vendor Info: (Acquisitions) Ex Libris Group; (Cataloging) Ex Libris Group; (Circulation) Ex Libris Group; (Course Reserve) Ex Libris Group; (ILL) Ex Libris Group; (OPAC) Ex Libris Group
Database Vendor: Factiva.com, Gale Cengage Learning, OCLC FirstSearch, OCLC WorldCat, OVID Technologies, Westlaw
Partic in Richmond Academic Library Consortium; Virginia Commun Coll Syst
Open Mon-Thurs 7:45am-9pm, Fri 7:45-5, Sat 8-12

J   GOOCHLAND CAMPUS-LIBRARY & INFORMATION SERVICES*, 1851 Dickinson Rd, Goochland, 23285. (Mail add: PO Box 85622, 23285-5622), SAN 370-3525. Tel: 804-523-5442. Circulation Tel:

804-523-5419. FAX: 804-556-5750. *Coordr, Tech Serv,* Maureen Hady; E-mail: mhady@reynolds.edu; Staff 1 (MLS 1)
Highest Degree: Associate
Library Holdings: Bk Titles 2,900; Bk Vols 3,500; Per Subs 65
Subject Interests: Automotive, Hort
Automation Activity & Vendor Info: (Acquisitions) Ex Libris Group; (Cataloging) Ex Libris Group; (Circulation) Ex Libris Group; (Course Reserve) Ex Libris Group; (OPAC) Ex Libris Group
Database Vendor: Agricola, ALLDATA Online, EBSCOhost, Factiva.com, Facts on File, JSTOR, Safari Books Online, Westlaw
Partic in Virtual Library of Virginia

J PARHAM CAMPUS-LIBRARY & INFORMATION SERVICES*, 1651 E Parham Rd, 23228. (Mail add: PO Box 85622, 23285-5622), SAN 363-2466. Tel: 804-523-5220. Reference Tel: 804-523-5329. FAX: 804-371-3086. *Dir,* Dr Abdul Miah; Tel: 804-523-5323, E-mail: amiah@reynolds.edu; *Ref Librn,* Mary Denise Woetzel; Tel: 804-523-5325, E-mail: dwoetzel@reynolds.edu; *Coordr, Electronic Res, Coordr, Info Serv,* Hong Wu; E-mail: hwu@reynolds.edu; *Acq,* Jill Brown; Tel: 804-523-5327, E-mail: jbbrown@reynolds.edu; *Circ,* Beverly Glover; Tel: 804-523-5326, E-mail: bglover@reynolds.edu; *Ser,* Lisa Bishop; Tel: 804-523-5328, E-mail: ldbishop@reynolds.edu; Staff 11 (MLS 5, Non-MLS 6)
Founded 1974. Enrl 10,725; Fac 120; Highest Degree: Associate
Library Holdings: Bks on Deafness & Sign Lang 25; High Interest/Low Vocabulary Bk Vols 175; Bk Titles 32,000; Bk Vols 56,000; Per Subs 220; Spec Interest Per Sub 10
Subject Interests: CAD, Electronics, Info syst, Legal assisting, Liberal arts, Semiconductors
Database Vendor: EBSCOhost, Gale Cengage Learning, LexisNexis, OCLC FirstSearch, OVID Technologies
Partic in Lyrasis; SouthWest Information Network Group (SWING); VA Tech Libr Syst; Virginia Commun Coll Syst
Publications: Off the Shelf

P THE LIBRARY OF VIRGINIA, 800 E Broad St, 23219-8000. SAN 363-3128. Tel: 804-692-3592. Circulation Tel: 804-692-3547. Interlibrary Loan Service Tel: 804-692-3532. Reference Tel: 804-692-3777, 804-692-3888 (Archives). Administration Tel: 804-692-3535. FAX: 804-692-3594. Interlibrary Loan Service FAX: 804-692-3537. Reference FAX: 804-692-3556. Web Site: www.lva.virginia.gov, www.virginiamemory.com. *State Archivist, State Librn,* Sandra G Treadway; Tel: 804-692-3597, E-mail: sandra.treadway@lva.virginia.gov; *Dir, Info Tech Serv Div,* Paul Casalaspi; Tel: 804-692-3756, E-mail: paul.casalaspi@lva.virginia.gov; *Dir, Archives, Rec & Coll,* John D Metz; Tel: 804-692-3607, Fax: 804-692-2277, E-mail: john.metz@lva.virginia.gov; *Dir, Pub Serv & Outreach,* Gregg Kimball; Tel: 804-692-3722, E-mail: gregg.kimball@lva.virginia.gov; *Pub Info & Policy Coordr,* Janice Hathcock; E-mail: jan.hathcock@lva.virginia.gov. Subject Specialists: *Hist of state libr, Va hist, Women's hist,* Sandra G Treadway; *Southern agri hist, Vernacular archit,* John D Metz; *Cultural & soc hist of South, Hist of South, Va hist,* Gregg Kimball; Staff 106 (MLS 38, Non-MLS 68)
Founded 1823. Pop 8,136,123
Jul 2011-Jun 2012 Income $33,680,708, State $25,723,804, Federal $4,535,070, Locally Generated Income $922,289, Other $2,499,545. Mats Exp $1,772,000, Books $50,000, Per/Ser (Incl. Access Fees) $70,000, Manu Arch $32,000, Micro $55,000, Electronic Ref Mat (Incl. Access Fees) $65,000, Presv $1,500,000. Sal $9,349,801 (Prof $6,788,110)
Library Holdings: AV Mats 375,732; CDs 1,210; DVDs 190; Electronic Media & Resources 31; Microforms 778,950; Music Scores 5,641; Bk Vols 858,739; Per Subs 636; Spec Interest Per Sub 48; Videos 948
Special Collections: Confederate Imprints; Genealogy Coll; Government & Politics Coll; Virginia & Southern History Coll; Virginia Broadsides; Virginia Maps; Virginia Newspapers; Virginia Picture Coll; Virginia Public Records; Virginia State Documents; Virginia-Related Sheet Music. State Document Depository; US Document Depository
Subject Interests: Archit, Art, Engraving, Govt, Local hist, Politics, Prints, Rare bks, Sheet music, Southern hist
Automation Activity & Vendor Info: (Acquisitions) Ex Libris Group; (Cataloging) Ex Libris Group; (Circulation) Ex Libris Group; (ILL) Ex Libris Group; (OPAC) Ex Libris Group; (Serials) Ex Libris Group
Database Vendor: JSTOR, Mergent Online, Oxford Online, ProQuest, ReferenceUSA
Wireless access
Function: Archival coll, Computers for patron use, e-mail serv, Electronic databases & coll, Exhibits, Handicapped accessible, ILL available, Libr develop, Mail & tel request accepted, Ref serv available, Summer & winter reading prog, Telephone ref, Web-catalog, Wheelchair accessible
Publications: Bibliographical Resources; Broadside (Quarterly); Documentary Editions & Monographs; Historical & Genealogical Research Notes & Guides; Library Statistics; Newsletters (Monthly)
Partic in AIIM (Association for Information & Image Management); Lyrasis; OCLC Online Computer Library Center, Inc; Richmond Academic Library Consortium; Virtual Library of Virginia
Special Services for the Deaf - TTY equip

Special Services for the Blind - Low vision equip; Magnifiers; Reader equip; Screen enlargement software for people with visual disabilities; Screen reader software
Open Mon-Sat 9-5
Restriction: Closed stack

M J STEPHEN LINDSEY MEDICAL LIBRARY*, 1602 Skipwith Rd, 23229-5298. SAN 371-6163. Tel: 804-289-4728. FAX: 804-289-4960. *Med Librn,* Sue E Terminella; E-mail: sue.terminella@hcahealthcare.com; Staff 1 (MLS 1)
Founded 1980
Jan 2010-Dec 2010. Mats Exp $44,000, Books $600, Per/Ser (Incl. Access Fees) $36,800, Electronic Ref Mat (Incl. Access Fees) $6,600. Sal $36,600
Library Holdings: Bk Titles 350; Bk Vols 500; Per Subs 70
Database Vendor: CyberTools for Libraries, OVID Technologies, PubMed, ScienceDirect, UpToDate, Wiley InterScience
Wireless access
Partic in Docline
Restriction: Staff use only

S MUSEUM OF THE CONFEDERACY*, Eleanor S Brockenbrough Library, 1201 E Clay St, 23219. SAN 317-4069. Tel: 804-649-1861. FAX: 804-644-7150. E-mail: library@moc.org. Web Site: www.moc.org. *Dir,* John Coski; *Mgr,* Teresa Roane; Staff 3 (Non-MLS 3)
Founded 1890
Library Holdings: Bk Vols 11,000; Per Subs 10
Special Collections: Archives of the Museum; Confederate Financial Instruments (bonds & currency); Confederate Imprints; Confederate Military Unit Records; Jefferson Davis Coll; Letters of Southern Soldiers & Civilians; Maps; Newspapers; Records of Confederate Monument Associations; Records of the United Confederate Veterans; Records of United Daughters of the Confederacy
Subject Interests: Confederacy, Southern hist
Wireless access
Publications: The Museum of the Confederacy Magazine (Quarterly)
Restriction: Open by appt only

S NATIONAL PARK SERVICE*, Richmond National Battlefield Park Headquarters Library, 3215 E Broad St, 23223. SAN 317-4077. Tel: 804-226-1981. FAX: 804-771-8522. Web Site: www.nps.gov/rich. *Historian,* Robert Krick
Founded 1948
Library Holdings: Bk Vols 1,000
Subject Interests: The Civil War
Special Services for the Deaf - Captioned film dep
Open Mon-Fri 9-5

SR REVEILLE UNITED METHODIST CHURCH LIBRARY*, 4200 Cary Street Rd, 23221. SAN 317-4093. Tel: 804-359-6041. FAX: 804-359-6090. *Librn,* Jake Noland; *Ch,* Diane Hall; Staff 3 (MLS 1, Non-MLS 2)
Library Holdings: Braille Volumes 7; Large Print Bks 49; Bk Vols 9,143; Per Subs 7; Videos 131
Open Mon-Fri 8:30-4:30, Sun 8:30-12:30

S RICHMOND NEWSPAPERS, INC LIBRARY*, 300 E Franklin St, 23219. SAN 317-4123. Tel: 804-649-6224, 804-649-6286. FAX: 804-649-6935. Web Site: www.timesdispatch.com. *Librn,* Charles D Saunders; E-mail: csaunders@timesdispatch.com
Library Holdings: Bk Titles 2,300
Special Collections: Newspapers Back to 1852, microfilm
Database Vendor: LexisNexis, Newsbank
Open Mon-Fri 8:30-5:30

P RICHMOND PUBLIC LIBRARY, 101 E Franklin St, 23219-2193. SAN 363-261X. Tel: 804-646-4256. Circulation Tel: 804-646-2554. Reference Tel: 804-646-7223. Automation Services Tel: 804-646-2559. FAX: 804-646-7685. Interlibrary Loan Service FAX: 804-646-3658. Web Site: www.richmondpubliclibrary.org. *Libr Dir,* Harriet H Coalter; Tel: 804-646-4550, E-mail: harriet.coalter@richmondgov.com; *Coll Develop Mgr,* Melissa Schutt; Tel: 804-646-4807, Fax: 804-646-4757, E-mail: melissa.schutt@richmondgov.com; *Commun Serv Mgr,* Patty Parks; Tel: 804-646-5177, E-mail: patty.parks@richmondgov.com; *Syst Operational Analyst II,* Robert Joe Barbie; E-mail: joe.barbie@richmondgov.com; Staff 36 (MLS 8, Non-MLS 28)
Founded 1924. Pop 200,158; Circ 1,033,146
Jul 2011-Jun 2012 Income (Main Library Only) $2,573,038. Mats Exp $208,571, Books $132,159, Per/Ser (Incl. Access Fees) $15,143, Micro $6,216, Electronic Ref Mat (Incl. Access Fees) $55,053. Sal $2,219,323 (Prof $1,153,702)
Library Holdings: AV Mats 9,170; Bk Vols 278,381
Special Collections: Rare Children's Books; Richmond Authors
Automation Activity & Vendor Info: (Acquisitions) SirsiDynix; (Cataloging) SirsiDynix; (Circulation) SirsiDynix; (ILL) SirsiDynix;

(Media Booking) Right On Programs; (OPAC) SirsiDynix; (Serials)
SirsiDynix
Database Vendor: EBSCOhost
Wireless access
Open Mon-Wed 10-7, Thurs & Fri 10-6, Sat 10-5
Friends of the Library Group
Branches: 9
BELMONT BRANCH, 3100 Ellwood Ave, 23221, SAN 363-2644. Tel:
804-646-1139. Interlibrary Loan Service Tel: 804-646-4867.
Administration Tel: 804-646-4256. Automation Services Tel:
804-646-2559. FAX: 804-646-1105. Interlibrary Loan Service FAX:
804-646-3658. Administration FAX: 804-646-7685. *Commun Serv Mgr,*
Judith Lippy; E-mail: judith.lippy@richmondgov.com; Staff 7 (MLS 2,
Non-MLS 5)
Founded 1956. Circ 141,701
Jul 2011-Jun 2012 Income $250,843. Mats Exp $45,077, Books $42,080,
Per/Ser (Incl. Access Fees) $2,997. Sal $322,411 (Prof $157,975)
Library Holdings: AV Mats 3,277; Bk Vols 31,148
Open Mon & Wed 12-8, Tues, Thurs & Fri 10-6, Sat 10-5
Friends of the Library Group
BROAD ROCK, 4820 Warwick Rd, 23224, SAN 363-2679. Tel:
804-646-8488. Interlibrary Loan Service Tel: 804-646-4867.
Administration Tel: 804-646-4256. Automation Services Tel:
804-646-2559. FAX: 804-646-7014. Circulation FAX: 804-646-3658.
Administration FAX: 804-646-7685. *Commun Serv Mgr,* Cristina
Ramirez; Tel: 804-646-0527, E-mail: cristina.ramirez@richmondgov.com;
Staff 5.5 (MLS 2, Non-MLS 3.5)
Founded 1976. Circ 42,989
Jul 2011-Jun 2012 Income $331,368. Mats Exp $39,262, Books $36,034,
Per/Ser (Incl. Access Fees) $3,228. Sal $307,543 (Prof $85,037)
Library Holdings: AV Mats 2,132; Bk Vols 21,503
Open Mon & Wed 12-8, Tues, Thurs & Fri 10-6, Sat 10-5
Friends of the Library Group
EAST END, 1200 N 25th St, 23223-5250, SAN 363-2709. Tel:
804-646-4474. Interlibrary Loan Service Tel: 804-646-4867.
Administration Tel: 804-646-4256. Automation Services Tel:
804-646-2559. FAX: 804-646-0104. Interlibrary Loan Service FAX:
804-646-3658. Administration FAX: 804-646-7685. *Libr Commun Serv
Mgr,* Veronica Holloway; E-mail: veronica.holloway@richmondgov.com;
Staff 5 (MLS 1, Non-MLS 4)
Founded 1965. Circ 55,233
Jul 2011-Jun 2012 Income $283,959. Mats Exp $29,075, Books $27,061,
Per/Ser (Incl. Access Fees) $2,014. Sal $275,027 (Prof $92,463)
Library Holdings: AV Mats 1,259; Bk Vols 16,157
Open Mon-Fri 10-6, Sat 10-5
Friends of the Library Group
GINTER PARK, 1200 Westbrook Ave, 23227, SAN 363-2733. Tel:
804-646-1236. Interlibrary Loan Service Tel: 804-646-4867.
Administration Tel: 804-646-4256. Automation Services Tel:
804-646-2559. FAX: 804-646-3865. Interlibrary Loan Service FAX:
804-646-3658. Administration FAX: 804-646-7685. *Libr Commun Serv
Mgr,* Kerry Phillips; E-mail: kerry.phillips@richmondgov.com; Staff 5.5
(MLS 1, Non-MLS 4.5)
Founded 1964. Circ 105,737
Jul 2011-Jun 2012 Income $305,352. Mats Exp $39,423, Books $36,335,
Per/Ser (Incl. Access Fees) $3,088. Sal $277,843 (Prof $86,317)
Library Holdings: AV Mats 2,047; Bk Vols 26,419
Open Mon & Wed 12-8, Tues, Thurs & Fri 10-6, Sat 10-5
Friends of the Library Group
HULL STREET, 1400 Hull St, 23224, SAN 328-7173. Tel: 804-646-8699.
Interlibrary Loan Service Tel: 804-646-4867. Administration Tel:
804-646-4256. Automation Services Tel: 804-646-2559. FAX:
804-646-8276. Interlibrary Loan Service FAX: 804-646-3658.
Administration FAX: 804-646-7685. *Libr Commun Serv Mgr,* Khalil Ali;
E-mail: khalil.ali@richmondgov.com; Staff 5 (MLS 1, Non-MLS 4)
Founded 1986. Circ 57,125
Jul 2011-Jun 2012 Income $285,977. Mats Exp $29,540, Books $25,559,
Per/Ser (Incl. Access Fees) $3,981. Sal $268,381 (Prof $103,769)
Library Holdings: AV Mats 1,788; Bk Vols 18,267
Open Mon-Fri 10-6, Sat 10-5
Friends of the Library Group
NORTH AVENUE, 2901 North Ave, 23222, SAN 363-275X. Tel:
804-646-6675. Circulation Tel: 804-646-4867. Administration Tel:
804-646-4256. Automation Services Tel: 804-646-2559. FAX:
804-646-3768. Circulation FAX: 804-646-3658. Administration FAX:
804-646-7685. *Libr Commun Serv Mgr,* Andeberhan Tensae; E-mail:
andeberhan.tensae@richmondgov.com; Staff 5 (MLS 1, Non-MLS 4)
Founded 1983. Circ 69,782
Jul 2011-Jun 2012 Income $269,174. Mats Exp $29,485, Books $27,748,
Per/Ser (Incl. Access Fees) $1,737. Sal $307,580 (Prof $79,109)
Library Holdings: AV Mats 1,575; Bk Vols 20,495
Open Mon 12-8, Tues-Fri 10-6, Sat 10-5
Friends of the Library Group

PUBLIC LAW, 101 E Franklin St, 23219, SAN 372-3976. Tel:
804-646-6500. E-mail: lawlibrary@richmondgov.com. ; Staff 1
(Non-MLS 1)
Jul 2011-Jun 2012 Income $255,435. Mats Exp $172,775. Sal $82,660
Library Holdings: AV Mats 3; Bk Vols 640
Database Vendor: LexisNexis, Westlaw
Open Mon-Wed 10-7, Thurs & Fri 10-6, Sat 10-5
Friends of the Library Group
WEST END, 5420 Patterson Ave, 23226, SAN 363-2768. Tel:
804-646-1877. Circulation Tel: 804-646-4867. Administration Tel:
804-646-4256. Automation Services Tel: 804-646-2559. FAX:
804-646-3769. Circulation FAX: 804-646-3658. Administration FAX:
804-646-7685. *Libr Commun Serv Mgr,* E Brooke Spieldenner; E-mail:
elizabeth.spieldenner@richmondgov.com; Staff 6.47 (Non-MLS 6.47)
Founded 1978. Circ 186,910
Jul 2011-Jun 2012 Income $304,044. Mats Exp $63,255, Books $57,256,
Per/Ser (Incl. Access Fees) $5,999. Sal $298,411
Library Holdings: AV Mats 3,415; Bk Vols 48,606
Open Mon & Wed 10-8, Tues, Thurs & Fri 10-6, Sat 10-5
Friends of the Library Group
WESTOVER HILLS, 1408 Westover Hills Blvd, 23225, SAN 363-2792.
Tel: 804-646-8833. Circulation Tel: 804-646-4867. Administration Tel:
804-646-4256. Automation Services Tel: 804-646-2559. FAX:
804-646-8714. Circulation FAX: 804-646-3658. Administration FAX:
804-646-7685. *Libr Commun Serv Mgr,* Clay Dishon; Tel: 804-646-0652,
E-mail: clay.dishon@richmondgov.com; Staff 5.47 (MLS 1, Non-MLS
4.47)
Founded 1959. Circ 163,593
Jul 2011-Jun 2012 Income $274,911. Mats Exp $45,360, Books $41,543,
Per/Ser (Incl. Access Fees) $3,817. Sal $279,041 (Prof $69,796)
Library Holdings: AV Mats 3,482; Bk Vols 29,597
Open Mon & Wed 12-8, Tues, Thurs & Fri 10-6, Sat 10-5
Friends of the Library Group

R   SAINT PAUL'S EPISCOPAL CHURCH LIBRARY, 815 E Grace St,
     23219. SAN 317-414X. Tel: 804-643-3589. FAX: 804-649-3283. Web Site:
     www.stpauls-episcopal.org.
     Founded 1963
     Library Holdings: Bk Vols 2,500; Per Subs 2
     Subject Interests: Relig studies
     Restriction: Mem only, Not open to pub

L   TROUTMAN SANDERS LLP*, Law Library, 1001 Haxall Point, 23219.
     (Mail add: PO Box 1122, 23218-1122), SAN 372-3925. Tel: 804-697-1200.
     FAX: 804-697-1339. Web Site: www.troutmansanders.com. *Regional Mgr,*
     Carol Goodman; *Ref,* Bill Katz; Staff 3 (MLS 2, Non-MLS 1)
     Automation Activity & Vendor Info: (Cataloging) EOS International;
     (Circulation) EOS International; (OPAC) EOS International; (Serials) EOS
     International
     Database Vendor: LexisNexis
     Function: ILL available
     Restriction: Co libr

R   UNION-PSCE*, Center on Aging Library, 3401 Brook Rd, 23227. SAN
     371-8603. Tel: 804-254-8045. FAX: 804-254-8060. Web Site:
     www.gracefulaging.org. *Dir,* Henry Simmons; E-mail:
     hsimmons@union-psce.edu; Staff 1 (Non-MLS 1)
     Founded 1978. Highest Degree: Doctorate
     Library Holdings: Bk Titles 3,300
     Special Collections: Religion, Aging & Spirituality (Online Annotated
     Bibliography)
     Restriction: Circ limited

R   UNION THEOLOGICAL SEMINARY & PRESBYTERIAN SCHOOL OF
     CHRISTIAN EDUCATION*, William Smith Morton Library, 3401 Brook
     Rd, 23227. Tel: 804-278-4310. Interlibrary Loan Service Tel:
     804-278-4317. Reference Tel: 804-278-4333. Administration Tel:
     804-278-4312. Automation Services Tel: 804-278-4217. FAX:
     804-278-4375. Web Site: library.upsem.edu. *Dir,* Dr Milton J Coalter, Jr;
     Tel: 804-278-4311, E-mail: jcoalter@upsem.edu; *Librn, Acad Computing
     Support, Syst Librn,* Leland Deeds; E-mail: ldeeds@upsem.edu; *Archives
     Librn, Ref Librn,* Paula Skreslet; E-mail: pskreslet@upsem.edu; *Cat Librn,
     Ser Librn,* Irina Topping; Tel: 804-278-4314, E-mail: itopping@upsem.edu;
     Circ Supvr, Rachel Perky; E-mail: rperky@upsem.edu; *ILL, Pub Serv,* Lisa
     Janes; E-mail: lisa.janes@upsem.edu. Subject Specialists: *Hist of
     christianity,* Dr Milton J Coalter, Jr; Staff 11.5 (MLS 5.5, Non-MLS 6)
     Founded 1806. Enrl 344; Fac 28; Highest Degree: Doctorate
     Jul 2007-Jun 2008. Mats Exp $1,451,751, Books $186,468, Per/Ser (Incl.
     Access Fees) $75,410, Manu Arch $2,170, AV Mat $21,573, Electronic Ref
     Mat (Incl. Access Fees) $24,398, Presv $11,701. Sal $919,590
     Library Holdings: AV Mats 59,507; CDs 3,548; DVDs 1,218; e-journals
     225; Microforms 10,669; Bk Vols 272,917; Per Subs 724; Videos 3,417
     Special Collections: Religion (Records of Synod of Virginia), micro;
     William Blake (Norfleet). Oral History

Subject Interests: Biblical studies, Christian educ, Christianity
Automation Activity & Vendor Info: (Acquisitions) Ex Libris Group; (Cataloging) Ex Libris Group; (Circulation) Ex Libris Group; (Course Reserve) Ex Libris Group; (Media Booking) Ex Libris Group; (OPAC) Ex Libris Group; (Serials) Ex Libris Group
Database Vendor: EBSCOhost, OCLC FirstSearch, ProQuest
Wireless access
Function: Archival coll, CD-ROM, Copy machines, Electronic databases & coll, Ref serv in person, VHS videos
Partic in Richmond Academic Library Consortium; Virginia Independent College & University Library Association
Special Services for the Blind - Assistive/Adapted tech devices, equip & products
Open Mon-Thurs 8am-10pm, Fri 8-8, Sat 8-6
Restriction: Open to students, fac & staff, Researchers by appt only, Restricted pub use

S   UNITED DAUGHTERS OF THE CONFEDERACY*, Caroline Meriwether Goodlett Library, 328 North Blvd, 23220-4009. SAN 317-4174. Tel: 804-355-1636. FAX: 804-353-1396. E-mail: hqudc@rcn.com. Web Site: www.hqudc.org. *Coordr, Libr Serv, Res,* Barbara Dunn; *Res,* Laura M Cathcart; E-mail: lcathcart@hqudc.org
Founded 1957
Library Holdings: Bk Vols 2,000
Special Collections: Confederacy letters, diaries, documents, other unpublished material & published books
Subject Interests: Civil War, Confederacy
Restriction: Open by appt only

S   UNITED NETWORK FOR ORGAN SHARING*, Hume-Kauffman Transplantation Library & Archives, 700 N Fourth St, 23219. (Mail add: PO Box 2484, 23218-2484), SAN 374-6658. Tel: 804-782-4846. FAX: 804-782-4893. Web Site: www.unos.org/resources/libraryServices.asp. *Librn,* Lorraine C Sitler; E-mail: librarian@unos.org; Staff 1 (MLS 1)
Founded 1987
Library Holdings: AV Mats 525; Bk Titles 1,020; Bk Vols 1,100; Per Subs 75
Subject Interests: Organ donation, Organ procurement, Organ transplantation, Transplantation
Automation Activity & Vendor Info: (Cataloging) CyberTools for Libraries; (Circulation) CyberTools for Libraries; (OPAC) CyberTools for Libraries; (Serials) CyberTools for Libraries
Partic in Docline; National Network of Libraries of Medicine Southeastern Atlantic Region

GL UNITED STATES COURT OF APPEALS*, Fourth Circuit Library, United States Courthouse, 1000 E Main St, 23219-3517. SAN 317-4182. Tel: 804-916-2319. *Actg Circuit Librn,* Elaine Woodward; Tel: 804-916-2323
Library Holdings: Bk Vols 100,000; Per Subs 300
Special Collections: US Document Depository
Automation Activity & Vendor Info: (Cataloging) SirsiDynix
Partic in Fedlink; LexisNexis; OCLC Online Computer Library Center, Inc; Westlaw
Open Mon-Fri 8:30-5
Restriction: Restricted access

C   UNIVERSITY OF RICHMOND*, Boatwright Memorial Library, 28 Westhampton Way, 23173. SAN 363-2946. Tel: 804-289-8454. Circulation Tel: 804-289-8876. Interlibrary Loan Service Tel: 804-289-8672. Reference Tel: 804-289-8669. Information Services Tel: 804-289-8664. FAX: 804-289-8757. Web Site: library.richmond.edu. *Univ Librn,* Position Currently Open; *Head, Circ, Librn, Emerging Web Tech,* Andy Morton; Tel: 804-287-6047, E-mail: amorton@richmond.edu; *Head, Libr Syst,* Nancy Woodall; Tel: 804-289-8853, E-mail: nwoodall@richmond.edu; *Head, Media Serv,* Paul Porterfield; Tel: 804-289-8453, E-mail: pporterf@richmond.edu; *Head, Instrul Serv Librn, Outreach Serv Librn,* Lucretia McCulley; Tel: 804-289-8670, E-mail: lmcculle@richmond.edu; *Bus Librn,* Littleton Maxwell; Tel: 804-289-8666, E-mail: lmaxwell@richmond.edu; *Coll Develop Librn,* James Gwin; Tel: 804-289-8458, E-mail: jgwin@richmond.edu; *Libr, Humanities & Soc Sci,* Olivia Reinauer; Tel: 804-289-8977, E-mail: oreinaue@richmond.edu; *Libr, Humanities & Soc Sci,* Marcia Whitehead; Tel: 804-289-8823, E-mail: mwhitehe@richmond.edu; *Music Librn,* Linda Fairtile; Tel: 804-287-6849, Fax: 804-287-6899, E-mail: lfairti@richmond.edu; *Sci Librn,* Melanie Hillner; Tel: 804-289-8262; *Soc Sci Librn,* Laura Horne; Tel: 804-289-8851, E-mail: lhorne@richmond.edu; *Customer Serv Supvr,* Ellen Burton; *Distance Educ,* Carrie Ludovico; Tel: 804-287-6647, E-mail: clodovic@richmond.edu; *ILL,* Betty Tobias; E-mail: btobias@richmond.edu; Staff 22 (MLS 18, Non-MLS 4)
Founded 1830. Enrl 3,983; Fac 347; Highest Degree: Master
Jul 2006-Jun 2007. Mats Exp $2,403,921, Books $461,317, Per/Ser (Incl. Access Fees) $1,088,689, AV Mat $50,677, Electronic Ref Mat (Incl. Access Fees) $803,238. Sal $1,955,659 (Prof $1,237,376)

Library Holdings: CDs 10,455; DVDs 5,544; e-books 56,891; e-journals 50,796; Music Scores 16,508; Bk Vols 478,580; Per Subs 2,232; Talking Bks 1,836; Videos 8,544
Special Collections: 19th-20th Century American Literature Coll; Virginia Baptists (Virginia Baptist Historical Society Coll); Virginia History Coll. US Document Depository
Subject Interests: Confederacy, Leadership studies, Relig
Automation Activity & Vendor Info: (Acquisitions) Ex Libris Group; (Cataloging) Ex Libris Group; (Circulation) Ex Libris Group; (Course Reserve) Ex Libris Group; (ILL) Ex Libris Group; (Media Booking) Ex Libris Group; (OPAC) Ex Libris Group; (Serials) Ex Libris Group
Database Vendor: EBSCOhost
Partic in Lyrasis; Virginia Independent College & University Library Association; Virtual Library of Virginia
Friends of the Library Group
Departmental Libraries:
CL WILLIAM T MUSE LAW LIBRARY, 28 Westhampton Way, 23173, SAN 378-4061. Tel: 804-289-8225. Interlibrary Loan Service Tel: 804-287-6555. Reference Tel: 804-289-8685. FAX: 804-289-8683. Administration FAX: 804-287-1845. E-mail: lawrefdesk@richmond.edu. Web Site: law.richmond.edu/librarytech/index.php. *Assoc Dean, Info Tech,* Timothy L Coggins; Tel: 804-289-8218, E-mail: tcoggins@richmond.edu; *Operations Mgr,* Debra Bourlet; *Access Serv,* Gail F Zwirner; Tel: 804-287-6555, E-mail: gzwirner@richmond.edu; *Info Tech,* Paul M Birch; Tel: 804-289-8222, E-mail: pbirch@uofrlaw.richmond.edu; *Ref Serv,* Suzanne B Corriell; Tel: 804-289-8217, E-mail: scorriel@richmond.edu; *Tech Serv,* Sally H Wambold; Tel: 804-289-8226, E-mail: wambold@uofrlaw.richmond.edu; Staff 17 (MLS 7, Non-MLS 10)
Founded 1870. Enrl 465; Fac 25; Highest Degree: Doctorate
Library Holdings: Bk Titles 162,374; Bk Vols 382,741; Per Subs 4,573
Special Collections: Judge Blackwell N Shelley (Retired Judge) Bankruptcy Decisions; Robert R Merhige (Retired Federal District Judge) Papers; Tokoyo War Crimes Trials (International Military Tribunal for the Far East Coll). US Document Depository
Automation Activity & Vendor Info: (Acquisitions) Ex Libris Group; (Cataloging) Ex Libris Group; (Circulation) Ex Libris Group; (Course Reserve) Ex Libris Group; (OPAC) Ex Libris Group; (Serials) Ex Libris Group
Database Vendor: Gale Cengage Learning, LexisNexis, OCLC FirstSearch, Westlaw, Wilson - Wilson Web
Function: Res libr
Partic in Lyrasis; Richmond Academic Library Consortium
Publications: Museletter (Newsletter); Research Guides Series (Research guide)
Open Mon-Thurs 7:30am-Midnight, Fri 7:30am-9pm, Sat 9-9, Sun 10am-Midnight
PARSONS MUSIC LIBRARY, Modlin Center for the Arts, Webb Tower, University of Richmond, 23173, SAN 363-3004. Tel: 804-289-8286. FAX: 804-287-6899. *Librn,* Dr Linda B Fairtile; Tel: 804-287-6849, E-mail: lfairtil@richmond.edu; *Music Libr Assoc,* David Tenenholtz; E-mail: dtenenho@richmond.edu. Subject Specialists: *Music,* Dr Linda B Fairtile; Staff 2 (MLS 1, Non-MLS 1)
Library Holdings: AV Mats 17,000; Music Scores 15,500; Bk Vols 9,000; Per Subs 44
Subject Interests: Ethnomusicology, Jazz, Music hist, Music performance, Music theory, Musicology, Popular music
Function: Audio & video playback equip for onsite use
Open Mon-Thurs 8am-11pm, Fri 8-5, Sat 2-5, Sun 2-11

S   VALENTINE RICHMOND HISTORY CENTER*, 1015 E Clay St, 23219-1590. SAN 317-4212. Tel: 804-649-0711. FAX: 804-643-3510. E-mail: archives@richmondhistorycenter.com. Web Site: www.richmondhistorycenter.com. *Dir, Archives & Photographic Serv,* Meg Hughes; E-mail: mhughes@richmondhistorycenter.com; Staff 2 (MLS 2)
Founded 1898
Library Holdings: Bk Vols 7,400; Per Subs 35
Special Collections: Advertising Art (American Tobacco Co Scrapbooks), lithographs; Architectural Drawings; Art Coll, pen, pencil, watercolor & oil; Engravings (Views of Richmond, Scenic & Historical); Mary Wingfield Scott Photo Coll; Photography (Cook-Lancaster-Scott-Minton-Colonial Studios Coll), negatives, prints
Subject Interests: 19th Century advertising art, Artists, Hist of Richmond, Life of Richmond, Tobacco manufacture
Function: Archival coll, Audio & video playback equip for onsite use, Electronic databases & coll, Online cat, Online searches, Ref & res, Ref serv in person, Res performed for a fee
Publications: In Bondage & Freedom: Antebellum Black Life in Richmond, Virginia; Old Richmond Neighborhoods; Richmond's Hollywood Cemetery; Timeline Newsletter (Bi-annually)
Restriction: Open to researchers by request

GM   **VETERANS HEALTH ADMINISTRATION***, Medical Library 142D, 1201 Broad Rock Blvd, 23249. SAN 317-4220. Tel: 804-675-5142. FAX: 804-675-5252. *Librn,* Susana Hernandez-Kurtulus; Staff 1 (MLS 1)
Library Holdings: AV Mats 450; e-books 700; e-journals 1,500; Bk Titles 1,100; Per Subs 192
Partic in National Network of Libraries of Medicine Midcontinental Region
Special Services for the Blind - Accessible computers
Open Mon-Fri 8-4:30
Restriction: Badge access after hrs

SR   **VIRGINIA BAPTIST HISTORICAL SOCIETY & THE CENTER FOR BAPTIST HERITAGE & STUDIES LIBRARY***, PO Box 34, University of Richmond, 23173. SAN 326-5986. Tel: 804-289-8434. FAX: 804-289-8953. E-mail: theheritagecenter@vbmb.org. Web Site: www.baptistheritage.org. *Acq, Librn,* Fred Anderson; *Pub Serv, Ref,* Darlene Slater; Staff 3 (MLS 3)
Founded 1876
Library Holdings: Bk Vols 25,000
Special Collections: Oral History
Publications: The Virginia Baptist Register (annual journal)
Open Mon-Fri 9-12 & 1-4:30
Friends of the Library Group

C   **VIRGINIA COMMONWEALTH UNIVERSITY LIBRARIES***, 901 Park Ave, 23284-2033. (Mail add: PO Box 2033, 23284-2033), SAN 363-3071. Tel: 804-828-1110. Administration Tel: 804-828-1105. Toll Free Tel: 866-828-2665. FAX: 804-828-0151. TDD: 804-828-1101. Web Site: www.library.vcu.edu. *Univ Librn,* John E Ulmschneider; E-mail: jeulmsch@vcu.edu; *Sr Assoc Univ Librn,* John K Duke; Tel: 804-827-3624, E-mail: jkduke@vcu.edu; *Dir of Libr,* Carol Hansen; Staff 50 (MLS 49, Non-MLS 1)
Founded 1838. Enrl 31,907; Fac 50; Highest Degree: Doctorate
Library Holdings: AV Mats 780,118; e-books 139,541; e-journals 18,325; Microforms 3,211,183; Bk Vols 1,863,214; Per Subs 23,863
Automation Activity & Vendor Info: (Acquisitions) Ex Libris Group; (Cataloging) Ex Libris Group; (Circulation) Ex Libris Group; (Course Reserve) Ex Libris Group; (OPAC) Ex Libris Group
Wireless access
Function: Res libr
Partic in Virtual Library of Virginia
Restriction: Badge access after hrs
Friends of the Library Group
Departmental Libraries:
JAMES CABELL BRANCH LIBRARY, Monroe Park Campus, 901 Park Ave, 23284-2033. (Mail add: PO Box 2033, 23284-2033), SAN 363-3063. Tel: 804-828-1110. Circulation Tel: 804-828-1111. Interlibrary Loan Service Tel: 804-828-1115. Reference Tel: 804-828-1101. Toll Free Tel: 800-828-2665. FAX: 804-828-0151. Web Site: www.library.vcu.edu/jbc. *Dir, Distance Educ, Outreach Serv Librn,* Daniel Ream; Tel: 804-828-6545, E-mail: dream@vcu.edu; *Assoc Univ Librn, Pub Serv,* Patricia Flanagan; Tel: 804-828-9136, E-mail: pflanagan@vcu.edu; *Head, Circ,* Teresa Doherty; Tel: 804-828-1111, E-mail: mtdohert@vcu.edu; *Head, Media Serv, Reserves,* Nell Chenault; Tel: 804-828-2070, E-mail: njchenau@vcu.edu; *Head, Ref & Res Serv,* Mary Ellen Spencer; Tel: 804-828-2729, E-mail: mespencer@vcu.edu; *Head, Spec Coll & Archives,* Position Currently Open
Special Collections: Adele Clark Papers; Book Art; Comics & Cartoon Coll; James Branch Cabell Coll; John Clark Jazz Record Archives; Richmond Architectural History Coll; Richmond Area Development Archives (Richmond Symphony, Richmond YWCA, United Way of Greater Richmond, Richmond Urban Institute); Richmond Black History Archives; Virginia Writers Coll (Helena Caperton, Dabney Stuart, Paul Nagel). State Document Depository; US Document Depository
Subject Interests: Art, Art hist, Behav sci, Biol sci, Educ, Humanities, Journalism, Music, Urban planning
Function: Res libr
Special Services for the Deaf - TDD equip
Friends of the Library Group

CM   TOMPKINS-MCCAW LIBRARY, Medical College of Virginia Campus, 509 N 12th St, 23298-0582, SAN 363-3098. Tel: 804-828-0636. Interlibrary Loan Service Tel: 804-828-0630. Automation Services Tel: 804-828-0032. FAX: 804-828-6089. Interlibrary Loan Service FAX: 804-828-2260. Web Site: www.library.vcu.edu/tml. *Dir,* Position Currently Open; *Asst Dir, Res & Educ,* Position Currently Open; *Head, Coll,* Lynne Turman; Tel: 804-828-0638, E-mail: luturman@vcu.edu; *Head, User Serv,* Position Currently Open; *Fac Mgr, Spec Coll & Archives Librn,* Jodi Koste; Tel: 804-828-9898, E-mail: jlkoste@vcu.edu; *Coordr, Outreach Serv,* Shannon Jones; Tel: 804-828-0626, E-mail: sdjones@vcu.edu. Subject Specialists: *Health sci,* Lynne Turman
Special Collections: Civil War Hospitals in Richmond; Medical Artifacts Coll; Virginia Health Sciences Archives (Harry Warthen, Harry Lyons, Virginia Nurses Association, Virginia Dental Association & Virginia

League for Nursing Colls); Walther Riese Papers; William H Hodgkin Papers; William T Sanger Papers
Subject Interests: Allied health, Dentistry, Med, Med tech, Nursing, Pharm

P   **VIRGINIA DEPARTMENT FOR THE BLIND & VISION IMPAIRED***, Library & Resource Center, 395 Azalea Ave, 23227-3633. SAN 317-4298. Tel: 804-371-3661. Toll Free Tel: 800-552-7015. FAX: 804-371-3508. Web Site: www.vdbvi.org. *Dir,* Barbara McCarthy; E-mail: barbara.mccarthy@dbvi.virginia.gov; Staff 5 (MLS 5)
Founded 1958
Jul 2009-Jun 2010 Income $900,000
Library Holdings: Audiobooks 56,429; Braille Volumes 17,292; Large Print Bks 4,581; Talking Bks 56,429; Videos 572
Special Collections: Print Research Material on Blindness
Special Services for the Blind - Braille bks; Cassette playback machines; Textbks on audio-cassettes
Open Mon-Fri 8:15-5

G   **VIRGINIA DEPARTMENT OF HISTORIC RESOURCES***, Archives-Research Library, 2801 Kensington Ave, 23221. SAN 323-6722. Tel: 804-367-2323, Ext 124. FAX: 804-367-2391. Web Site: www.dhr.virginia.gov. *Archivist,* Quatro Hubbard; E-mail: quatro.hubbard@dhr.virginia.gov. Subject Specialists: *Archaeology, Archit hist, Hist presv,* Quatro Hubbard; Staff 2 (Non-MLS 2)
Founded 1966
Library Holdings: Bk Titles 5,000; Per Subs 80
Special Collections: Ferol Brigg's Scrapbooks; Gilmer Confederate Engineer Maps; Historic Virginia Properties (Architectural Inventory); Wood's Maps of Virginia (1820 Series of Maps)
Subject Interests: Archaeology, Archit hist, Hist presv
Function: Archival coll
Publications: various indexes; Virginia Unpublished Archaeological Reports
Special Services for the Deaf - TDD equip
Open Tues-Thurs 8:30-4:45
Restriction: Non-circulating

S   **VIRGINIA HISTORICAL SOCIETY LIBRARY***, 428 North Blvd, 23220. (Mail add: PO Box 7311, 23221-0311), SAN 317-4263. Tel: 804-358-4901. Interlibrary Loan Service Tel: 804-342-9688. Reference Tel: 804-342-9677. FAX: 804-355-2399. Web Site: www.vahistorical.org. *Pres,* Charles F Bryan, Jr; *Rare Bks, VPres,* Robert F Strohm; *Archivist,* E Lee Shepard; *Conservator,* Stacy Rusch; *Pub Serv,* Frances Pollard; *Tech Serv,* Paulette Schwarting; Staff 55 (MLS 10, Non-MLS 45)
Founded 1831
Jan 2006-Dec 2006 Income $5,755,000, State $200,000, City $11,000, County $29,000, Locally Generated Income $2,942,000, Other $2,573,000. Mats Exp $236,639, Books $29,416, Per/Ser (Incl. Access Fees) $3,470, Manu Arch $38,627, Other Print Mats $12,000, Micro $3,000, AV Equip $48,265, AV Mat $5,224, Electronic Ref Mat (Incl. Access Fees) $13,675, Presv $82,962. Sal $3,263,000 (Prof $2,430,000)
Library Holdings: Bk Titles 70,000; Bk Vols 150,000; Per Subs 350
Special Collections: Confederate Imprints, newsp, sheet music; Maryland Steuart Coll, Confederate Weaponry & Military; Virginia Landscapes; Virginia Portraiture & Museum Objects
Subject Interests: Colonial hist, Confederate hist, Early Am hist, Local hist, State hist
Automation Activity & Vendor Info: (Cataloging) OCLC; (OPAC) Cuadra Associates
Database Vendor: JSTOR, OCLC FirstSearch
Wireless access
Publications: Document Monograph Series; History Notes; Virginia Magazine of History & Biography
Partic in Lyrasis

S   **VIRGINIA MUSEUM OF FINE ARTS LIBRARY***, 200 N Boulevard, 23220-4007. SAN 317-428X. Tel: 804-340-1495. FAX: 804-340-1431. Web Site: www.vmfa.museum/library.html. *Art Librn, Ref Serv Coordr,* Lee B Viverette; Tel: 804-340-1496, E-mail: lee.viverette@vmfa.museum; *Access Serv, Asst Librn,* Nick Curotto; Tel: 804-340-5523, E-mail: nick.curotto@vmfa.museum; Staff 2.5 (MLS 2.5)
Founded 1935
Jul 2010-Jun 2011 Income $307,739, Locally Generated Income $85,030, Parent Institution $212,709, Other $10,000. Mats Exp $130,330, Books $69,330, Per/Ser (Incl. Access Fees) $45,000, Manu Arch $1,000, Electronic Ref Mat (Incl. Access Fees) $14,000, Presv $1,000. Sal $196,563
Library Holdings: CDs 29; DVDs 7; e-journals 20; Bk Titles 82,500; Bk Vols 143,500; Per Subs 251
Special Collections: American Arts (McGlothlin Coll); Art Deco, Art Nouveau (Lewis Coll & Kreuzer Coll); Arts & Crafts (Carol & Fred Brandt Coll); Contemporary Art (Geldzahler Coll); Decorative Arts (Karin Fellowes Coll); East Asian Art (Maxwell Coll); Everett Fahy Western

European Art; Faberge Coll; German Expressionist Art (Fischer Coll); Numismatics (St John Tucker Coll); Oriental Arts (Weedon Coll & Coopersmith Coll); Paul Mellon Pre-1850 British Art Coll. Oral History; State Document Depository
Subject Interests: 20th Century art, African art, Am decorative arts, Ancient art, E Asian art, European art, Indian arts, Numismatics
Automation Activity & Vendor Info: (ILL) OCLC; (OPAC) SirsiDynix
Database Vendor: ARTstor, Cambridge Scientific Abstracts, Ingenta, JSTOR, MITINET, Inc, OCLC FirstSearch, OCLC WorldCat, ProQuest, SirsiDynix, Wiley InterScience, Wilson - Wilson Web
Function: Archival coll
Partic in Lyrasis; OCLC Online Computer Library Center, Inc
Restriction: Circulates for staff only, Open by appt only
Friends of the Library Group

GL   VIRGINIA STATE LAW LIBRARY, Supreme Court Bldg, 2nd Flr, 100 N Ninth St, 23219-2335. SAN 363-2822. Tel: 804-786-2075. FAX: 804-786-4542. E-mail: lawlibrary@courts.state.va.us. Web Site: www.courts.state.va.us/courtadmin/library/home.html. *State Law Librn,* Gail Warren; *Librn,* Benjamin T Almoite; *Librn,* E Terry Long; *Archivist, Librn,* Catherine G OBrion; *Libr Tech,* Janet E Holland; Staff 6 (MLS 4, Non-MLS 2)
Founded 1899
Library Holdings: Bk Vols 100,000; Per Subs 336
Special Collections: 18th Century Legal Treatises; English Reports (Nominative Reports, Mostly Originals). US Document Depository
Automation Activity & Vendor Info: (Cataloging) EOS International; (Circulation) EOS International; (ILL) OCLC; (OPAC) EOS International; (Serials) EOS International
Database Vendor: EBSCOhost, Gale Cengage Learning, HeinOnline, LexisNexis, OCLC FirstSearch, OCLC WorldCat
Function: ILL available
Special Services for the Deaf - TDD equip
Restriction: Not open to pub

G   VIRGINIA STATE POLICE ACADEMY LIBRARY*, 7700 Midlothian Tpke, 23235. (Mail add: PO Box 27472, 23261-7472), SAN 373-2657. Tel: 804-674-2258. FAX: 804-674-2089. *Librn,* Monica Suroosh
Founded 1989
Library Holdings: CDs 75; Bk Vols 4,000; Per Subs 25; Videos 600
Subject Interests: Law enforcement

C   VIRGINIA UNION UNIVERSITY*, L Douglas Wilder Library & Learning Resource Center, 1500 N Lombardy St, 23220. SAN 317-431X. Tel: 804-257-5822. Interlibrary Loan Service Tel: 804-257-5721. Reference Tel: 804-278-4122. Administration Tel: 804-257-5820. FAX: 804-257-5818. E-mail: reference@vuu.edu. Web Site: www.vuu.edu/library/home.htm. *Libr Dir,* Dr Delores Pretlow; Tel: 804-257-5821, E-mail: dzpretlow@vuu.edu; *Tech Serv Librn,* Sara Marrin; Tel: 804-257-5823, E-mail: semarrin@vuu.edu; *Acq, Pub Serv Librn,* Melissa Lauber; Tel: 804-278-4112, E-mail: malauber@vuu.edu; *Electronic Res, Pub Serv Librn,* Shanda Lemon; Tel: 804-278-4120, E-mail: slemon@vuu.edu; *ILL, Pub Serv Librn,* Ronald Shelton; Tel: 804-278-5721, E-mail: rshelton@vuu.edu; *Computer Serv, Pub Serv Librn, Webmaster/Ref Librn,* Pamela Foreman; Tel: 804-278-4119, E-mail: pforeman@vuu.edu; *Archivist/Librn, Spec Coll,* Selicia Allen; Tel: 804-257-4117, E-mail: sngregory@vuu.edu; Staff 12 (MLS 7, Non-MLS 5)
Founded 1865. Enrl 1,318; Fac 84; Highest Degree: Doctorate
Library Holdings: AV Mats 2,988; e-books 43,215; Bk Titles 104,005; Bk Vols 167,216; Per Subs 224; Videos 740
Special Collections: Black Studies (L Douglas Wilder Coll); Black Studies (Schomberg Coll), micro
Subject Interests: Educ, Journalism, Math, Philosophy, Psychol, Relig
Automation Activity & Vendor Info: (Acquisitions) SirsiDynix; (Cataloging) SirsiDynix; (Circulation) SirsiDynix; (ILL) SirsiDynix; (Serials) SirsiDynix
Database Vendor: Gale Cengage Learning, LexisNexis, OCLC FirstSearch, ProQuest
Function: Prof lending libr
Publications: The Resource (Newsletter)
Partic in OCLC Online Computer Library Center, Inc; Virginia Independent College & University Library Association; Virtual Library of Virginia
Open Mon-Thurs 8am-10pm, Fri 8-5, Sat 1-5, Sun 2-10

ROANOKE

P   BOTETOURT COUNTY LIBRARY*, 28 Avery Row, 24012. SAN 324-5179. Tel: 540-977-3433. FAX: 540-977-2407. Web Site: www.botetourt.org. *Dir,* Stephen C Vest; E-mail: svest@botetourt.org; *ILL,* Janet Buttram; *Tech Serv,* Vickie Anway; Staff 10 (MLS 2, Non-MLS 8)
Founded 1979. Pop 24,270; Circ 183,052
Library Holdings: CDs 1,000; Bk Vols 115,324; Per Subs 220; Talking Bks 4,400; Videos 9,600
Automation Activity & Vendor Info: (Cataloging) OCLC; (Circulation) SirsiDynix; (ILL) OCLC; (OPAC) SirsiDynix

Database Vendor: Newsbank
Partic in Lyrasis
Open Mon-Thurs 9-9, Fri & Sat 9-5
Friends of the Library Group
Branches: 2
BUCHANAN BRANCH, 19795 Main St, Buchanan, 24066. (Mail add: PO Box 799, Buchanan, 24066), SAN 324-6248. Tel: 540-254-2538. FAX: 540-254-1793. *Br Mgr,* Janet Buttram; Staff 2 (Non-MLS 2)
Open Mon & Thurs 9-7, Tues, Wed & Fri 9-5, Sat 9-1
Friends of the Library Group
FINCASTLE BRANCH, 11 Academy St, Fincastle, 24090-3316. (Mail add: PO Box 129, Fincastle, 24090-0129), SAN 324-623X. Tel: 540-473-8339. FAX: 540-473-1107. *Br Mgr,* Paige Ware; Staff 2 (Non-MLS 2)
Open Mon & Thurs 9-9, Tues & Wed 9-6, Fri 9-5, Sat 9-1
Friends of the Library Group
Bookmobiles: 1

M   CARILION CLINIC*, Health Sciences Library, Belleview at Jefferson St, 24033. (Mail add: PO Box 13367, 24033-3367), SAN 324-6329. Tel: 540-981-8039. FAX: 540-981-8666. *Librn,* Karen Dillon; E-mail: kdillon@carilion.com
Oct 2009-Sept 2010 Income $496,605. Mats Exp $382,665, Books $16,000, Per/Ser (Incl. Access Fees) $92,248, Electronic Ref Mat (Incl. Access Fees) $274,417. Sal $103,107 (Prof $64,000)
Library Holdings: AV Mats 1,700; CDs 857; DVDs 297; e-books 21,355; Bk Vols 28,741; Per Subs 130; Videos 868
Automation Activity & Vendor Info: (Acquisitions) EOS International; (Cataloging) EOS International; (Circulation) EOS International; (OPAC) EOS International; (Serials) EOS International
Database Vendor: DynaMed, EBSCOhost, Elsevier, EOS International, Majors, MD Consult, Medline, Micromedex, Natural Standard, netLibrary, OCLC WorldCat, OVID Technologies, PubMed, RefWorks, ScienceDirect, STAT!Ref (Teton Data Systems), UpToDate
Wireless access
Partic in Docline; Lyrasis; National Network of Libraries of Medicine; SouthWest Information Network Group (SWING); Southwestern Virginia Health Information Librarians
Restriction: Staff use only

L   GENTRY, LOCKE, RAKES & MOORE LIBRARY*, 800 Sun Trust Plaza, 10 Franklin Rd, 24011-2131. (Mail add: PO Box 40013, 24022-0013), SAN 323-7559. Tel: 540-983-9431.
Open Mon-Fri 8:45-5

S   HISTORY MUSEUM & HISTORICAL SOCIETY OF WESTERN VIRGINIA LIBRARY*, One Market Sq, 3rd Flr, 24011. (Mail add: PO Box 1904, 24008-1904), SAN 329-093X. Tel: 540-342-5770. FAX: 540-224-1256. E-mail: info.hswv@cox.net. Web Site: www.history-museum.org. *Librn,* Betty Lowe
Library Holdings: Bk Titles 1,400; Bk Vols 1,546
Special Collections: Breckinridge, Preston, Trout, Borden, Grant, Tayloe, Deyerle, Campbell, Roanoke Hist, Roanoke Photos, Watts, Eubank
Restriction: Open by appt only

C   HOLLINS UNIVERSITY*, Wyndham Robertson Library, 7950 E Campus Dr, 24020-1000. (Mail add: PO Box 9000, 24020-1000), SAN 317-3143. Tel: 540-362-6591, 540-362-7465. Circulation Tel: 540-362-6090. Interlibrary Loan Service Tel: 540-362-6239. Administration Tel: 540-362-6232. FAX: 540-362-6756. E-mail: askref@hollins.edu. Web Site: www.hollins.edu/library. *Actg Univ Librn, Pub Serv,* Luke Vilelle; Tel: 540-362-6592, E-mail: lvilelle@hollins.edu; *Univ Librn,* Position Currently Open; *Outreach Librn,* Maryke Barber; Tel: 540-362-6328, E-mail: mbarber@hollins.edu; *Interlibrary Serv Coordr,* Jonathan Overturf; E-mail: joverturf@hollins.edu; *Acq,* Lee C Rose; Tel: 540-362-6240, E-mail: lrose@hollins.edu; *Cat,* Lilla Thompson; Tel: 540-362-7467, E-mail: lthompson@hollins.edu; *Circ,* Joesephine Collins; E-mail: collinsjl@hollins.edu; *Info Tech,* Erin Gordon; Tel: 540-362-6653, E-mail: egordon@hollins.edu; *Spec Coll & Archives Librn,* Beth S Harris; Tel: 540-362-6237, E-mail: bharris@hollins.edu; Staff 11 (MLS 5, Non-MLS 6)
Founded 1842. Enrl 1,100; Fac 91; Highest Degree: Master
Library Holdings: AV Mats 5,460; e-books 14,000; Bk Vols 195,340
Special Collections: Benjamin Franklin Coll; Children's Literature (Margaret Wise Brown Coll); French Symbolist Literature (Enid Starkie Coll); Hollins Authors Coll; Incunabula Coll; Paper-Making Coll; Printing Coll; Private Presses; Robert Frost (McVitty Coll). US Document Depository
Subject Interests: Art, Behav sci, Life, Lit, Music, Philosophy, Relig, Soc sci, Women studies
Automation Activity & Vendor Info: (Acquisitions) Innovative Interfaces, Inc; (Cataloging) Innovative Interfaces, Inc; (Circulation) Innovative Interfaces, Inc; (Course Reserve) Innovative Interfaces, Inc; (ILL) OCLC ILLiad; (OPAC) Innovative Interfaces, Inc; (Serials) Innovative Interfaces, Inc

Database Vendor: Alexander Street Press, American Chemical Society, American Psychological Association (APA), ARTstor, Bowker, Cambridge Scientific Abstracts, Children's Literature Comprehensive Database Company (CLCD), CredoReference, EBSCOhost, Factiva.com, Gale Cengage Learning, H W Wilson, JSTOR, LexisNexis, Mergent Online, Newsbank-Readex, OCLC FirstSearch, OCLC WorldCat, Oxford Online, Project MUSE, Springshare, LLC, Wilson - Wilson Web, YBP Library Services
Wireless access
Partic in Lyrasis; Virginia Independent College & University Library Association; Virtual Library of Virginia
Special Services for the Blind - Internet workstation with adaptive software

CM   JEFFERSON COLLEGE OF HEALTH SCIENCES*, Learning Resource Center, 920 S Jefferson St, 24016. SAN 327-9146. Tel: 540-985-8273. Reference Tel: 540-224-4894. FAX: 540-224-4404. Web Site: www.jchs.edu. *Dir,* Ramona Thiss; Tel: 540-985-9828, E-mail: rhthiss@jchs.edu; *Cat,* Crystal Dent; E-mail: cfdent@jchs.edu; *Circ, ILL,* Jose Elacate; Tel: 540-985-9767, E-mail: jelacate@jchs.edu; *Ref Serv,* Jamie Price; Tel: 540-985-4636, E-mail: jbprice2@jchs.edu; Staff 5 (MLS 1, Non-MLS 4)
Library Holdings: Bk Titles 11,000; Per Subs 250
Subject Interests: Allied health, Med, Nursing
Automation Activity & Vendor Info: (Cataloging) EOS International; (Circulation) EOS International; (OPAC) EOS International
Open Mon-Thurs (Winter) 7:30am-8pm, Fri 7:30-5, Sat 11-5; Mon-Fri (Summer) 7:30-6

P   ROANOKE COUNTY PUBLIC LIBRARY*, 3131 Electric Rd SW, 24018-6496. SAN 363-3187. Tel: 540-772-7507. Administration Tel: 540-776-7327. FAX: 540-989-3129. TDD: 540-772-2131. Reference FAX: 540-772-7518. Web Site: www.yourlibrary.us. *Dir,* Diana Rosapepe; *Asst Dir,* Michael Meise; *Head, Ref,* David Webb; *Circ Mgr,* Priscilla Johnson; *Ch,* Wendy Rancier; Staff 8 (MLS 8)
Founded 1945. Pop 92,328; Circ 1,141,376
Library Holdings: Audiobooks 12,872; e-books 47,166; Microforms 516; Bk Vols 315,368; Per Subs 567
Subject Interests: Local hist, Virginiana
Automation Activity & Vendor Info: (Cataloging) SirsiDynix; (Circulation) SirsiDynix; (ILL) OCLC; (OPAC) SirsiDynix
Database Vendor: ebrary, LearningExpress, netLibrary, ProQuest, SirsiDynix
Wireless access
Open Mon-Thurs 9-9, Fri 9-6, Sat 9-5, Sun 1-5
Friends of the Library Group
Branches: 6
BENT MOUNTAIN BRANCH, Brent Mountain Elementary School, PO Box L, Bent Mountain, 24059. Tel: 540-929-4700. FAX: 540-929-4700. *Br Mgr,* Gladys Walters; E-mail: gwalters@roanokecountyva.gov; Staff 2 (Non-MLS 2)
   Library Holdings: Bk Vols 9,850; Per Subs 18
   Open Mon & Fri 1-5, Tues & Thurs 5-9, Wed 9-5, Sat 9-1
   Friends of the Library Group
GLENVAR, 3917 Daugherty Rd, Salem, 24153, SAN 363-3241. Tel: 540-387-6163. FAX: 540-380-3951. *Br Mgr,* John Vest; E-mail: jvest@roanokecountyva.gov; Staff 3 (MLS 1, Non-MLS 2)
   Library Holdings: Bk Vols 50,990; Per Subs 91
   Open Mon-Thurs 9-9, Fri & Sat 9-5
   Friends of the Library Group
HOLLINS, 6624 Peters Creek Rd, 24019, SAN 363-3276. Tel: 540-561-8024. FAX: 540-563-8902. *Br Mgr,* Ann Tripp; E-mail: atripp@roanokecountyva.gov; Staff 6 (MLS 1, Non-MLS 5)
   Library Holdings: Bk Vols 104,928; Per Subs 101
   Open Mon-Thurs 9-9, Fri & Sat 9-5
   Friends of the Library Group
MOUNT PLEASANT, 2918 JAE Valley Rd, 24014, SAN 326-8292. Tel: 540-427-3130. FAX: 540-427-3130. *Br Mgr,* Carol Rodgers; E-mail: crogers@roanokecountyva.gov; Staff 2 (Non-MLS 2)
   Library Holdings: Bk Vols 5,897; Per Subs 32
   Open Mon 9-5, Tues & Thurs 5-9, Wed & Fri 2-6, Sat 9-1
   Friends of the Library Group
VINTON BRANCH, 800 E Washington Ave, Vinton, 24179, SAN 363-3306. Tel: 540-857-5043. FAX: 540-344-3285. *Br Mgr,* Jamie Rowles-Channell; E-mail: jchannell@roanokecountyva.gov; Staff 4 (MLS 1, Non-MLS 3)
   Library Holdings: Bk Vols 80,598; Per Subs 88
   Open Mon-Thurs 9-9, Fri & Sat 9-5
   Friends of the Library Group

C   ROANOKE HIGHER EDUCATION CENTER LIBRARY*, 108 N Jefferson St, Ste 216, 24016. Tel: 540-767-6011. Interlibrary Loan Service Tel: 540-767-6009. Administration Tel: 540-767-6010. FAX: 540-767-6012. E-mail: library@education.edu. Web Site: www.education.edu/library. *Dir of Libr,* Carla Louise James; Tel: 540-767-6010, E-mail: carla.james@education.edu; Staff 3 (MLS 1, Non-MLS 2)

Founded 2000. Enrl 3,000; Highest Degree: Master
Library Holdings: Bk Titles 1,500; Bk Vols 1,750; Per Subs 40
Subject Interests: Distance educ, Early childhood develop, Educ
Automation Activity & Vendor Info: (Acquisitions) VTLS, Inc; (Cataloging) VTLS, Inc; (Circulation) VTLS, Inc; (OPAC) VTLS, Inc; (Serials) VTLS, Inc
Wireless access
Function: CD-ROM, Distance learning, Doc delivery serv, ILL available, Online searches, Orientations, Photocopying/Printing, Ref serv available, Telephone ref, Workshops
Partic in Lyrasis; SouthWest Information Network Group (SWING); Virtual Library of Virginia
Open Mon-Thurs (Winter) 8-8, Fri & Sat 9-4; Mon-Fri (Summer) 9-5
Restriction: Mem organizations only

P   ROANOKE PUBLIC LIBRARIES, 706 S Jefferson St, 24016-5191. SAN 363-3330. Tel: 540-853-2473. Interlibrary Loan Service Tel: 540-853-2477. FAX: 540-853-1781. TDD: 540-853-2641. E-mail: main.library@roanokeva.gov. Web Site: www.roanokegov.com/library. *Dir,* Sheila Umberger; *Head, Tech Serv,* Susan Hayes; *Circ, Pub Serv Librn,* Wendy Allen; *Youth Serv Coordr,* Amber Yopp; Staff 16 (MLS 12, Non-MLS 4)
Founded 1921. Pop 100,600
Library Holdings: Bk Vols 339,685; Per Subs 905
Subject Interests: Civil War, Genealogy, Local hist, Virginiana
Automation Activity & Vendor Info: (Acquisitions) SirsiDynix; (Circulation) SirsiDynix; (Serials) SirsiDynix
Special Services for the Deaf - TDD equip
Open Mon, Tues & Thurs 10-8, Wed 10-6, Fri & Sat 10-5
Friends of the Library Group
Branches: 6
GAINSBORO, 15 Patton Ave NW, 24016, SAN 363-3365. Tel: 540-853-2540. FAX: 540-853-1155. *Librn,* Randi Wines; E-mail: randi.wines@roanokeva.gov; Staff 1 (Non-MLS 1)
   Library Holdings: Bk Vols 25,866
   Subject Interests: African-Am hist
   Open Mon & Tues 10-6, Thurs 10-8, Fri & Sat 10-5
JACKSON PARK, 1101 Morningside St SE, 24013-2515, SAN 363-339X. Tel: 540-853-2640. FAX: 540-853-1156. *Librn,* Nancy Fields; Staff 1 (Non-MLS 1)
   Library Holdings: Bk Vols 30,248
   Open Mon 10-8, Tues & Thurs 10-6, Fri & Sat 10-5
   Friends of the Library Group
LAW LIBRARY, City of Roanoke Courthouse, 315 Church Ave SW, Ste B, 24016, SAN 320-2720. Tel: 540-853-2268. FAX: 540-853-5474. *Librn,* Joseph Klein; Staff 1 (MLS 1)
   Founded 1925
   Library Holdings: Bk Vols 19,195
   Open Mon 8-4:30, Tues-Fri 8am-Noon
MELROSE, 2607 Salem Tpk, 24017, SAN 363-342X. Tel: 540-853-2648. FAX: 540-853-1030. *Librn,* Rushbrooke Gary; Staff 1 (MLS 1)
   Library Holdings: Bk Vols 27,500
   Open Mon & Tues 10-6, Wed 10-8, Fri & Sat 10-5
RALEIGH COURT, 2112 Grandin Rd SW, 24015, SAN 363-3454. Tel: 540-853-2240. FAX: 540-853-1783. *Librn,* Diane Mcguire; Staff 1 (MLS 1)
   Library Holdings: Bk Vols 49,989
   Open Tues & Thurs 10-8, Wed 10-6, Wed 10-5
WILLIAMSON ROAD, 3837 Williamson Rd NW, 24012, SAN 363-3489. Tel: 540-853-2340. FAX: 540-853-1065. *Librn,* Mary Lou Puritz; Staff 1 (MLS 1)
   Library Holdings: Bk Vols 41,886
   Open Tues & Thurs 10-6, Wed 10-8, Fri & Sat 10-5
Bookmobiles: 1

S   ROANOKE TIMES LIBRARY*, 201 W Campbell Ave, 24011. (Mail add: PO Box 2491, 24010-2491), SAN 317-4360. Tel: 540-981-3280. Toll Free Tel: 800-346-1234, Ext 280. FAX: 540-981-3346. Web Site: www.roanoke.com/archives. *Librn,* Belinda Harris; E-mail: belinda.harris@roanoke.com; Staff 2 (MLS 1, Non-MLS 1)
Founded 1956
Library Holdings: Bk Vols 1,000
Subject Interests: Local newspaper data
Database Vendor: Factiva.com, LexisNexis, Newsbank
Function: Newsp ref libr
Partic in News Bank
Restriction: Not open to pub

S   TAUBMAN MUSEUM OF ART*, Fine Arts Library, 110 Salem Ave SE, 24011. SAN 317-4352. Tel: 540-342-5760. FAX: 540-342-5798. Web Site: www.taubmanmuseum.org. *Coll Mgr,* Mary D LaGue; E-mail: mlague@taubmanmuseum.org
Founded 1952

Library Holdings: Bk Vols 2,500
Subject Interests: Fine arts

J   VIRGINIA WESTERN COMMUNITY COLLEGE*, Brown Library, 3095 Colonial Ave SW, 24015-4705. (Mail add: PO Box 40012, 24022-14007), SAN 317-4379. Tel: 540-857-7303. Circulation Tel: 540-857-7242. Interlibrary Loan Service Tel: 540-857-6332. Reference Tel: 540-857-6509. FAX: 540-857-6058. Web Site: www.virginiawestern.edu/library. *Acq & Cat, Interim Dir,* Lynn Hurt; Tel: 540-857-6445, E-mail: lhurt@vw.vccs.edu; *Instruction/Ref Serv, Web Serv,* Laura Milliman; Tel: 540-857-6509, E-mail: lmilliman@vw.vccs.edu; *Archives, Circ & ILL,* Faith Janney; Tel: 540-857-6332, E-mail: fjanney@vw.vccs.edu; Staff 5 (MLS 3, Non-MLS 2)
Founded 1966. Enrl 9,000; Highest Degree: Associate
Library Holdings: Bk Vols 80,000; Per Subs 200
Automation Activity & Vendor Info: (Cataloging) Ex Libris Group; (Circulation) Ex Libris Group
Partic in Virginia Commun Coll Syst; Virtual Library of Virginia
Open Mon-Thurs 7:45am-9:30pm, Fri 7:45-5, Sat 9-1

L   WOODS ROGERS PLC, Law Library, Wells Fargo Tower, Ste 1400, Ten S Jefferson St, 24011. (Mail add: PO Box 14125, 24038-4125), SAN 372-333X. Tel: 540-983-7531. FAX: 540-983-7711. *Info Serv,* Jane Roth Baugh; E-mail: baugh@woodsrogers.com; Staff 1 (MLS 1)
Founded 1892
Library Holdings: Bk Vols 10,000; Per Subs 150; Videos 100
Database Vendor: Bloomberg, Dun & Bradstreet, Fastcase, Medline, PubMed, Westlaw
Wireless access
Open Mon-Fri 8:30-5:30

ROCKY MOUNT

P   FRANKLIN COUNTY PUBLIC LIBRARY*, 355 Franklin St, 24151. SAN 317-4387. Tel: 540-483-3098. FAX: 540-483-6652. Web Site: www.franklincountyva.org/library. *Dir,* David E Bass, III; E-mail: dbass@cablenet-va.com; Staff 3 (MLS 1, Non-MLS 2)
Founded 1975. Pop 48,000; Circ 190,000
Library Holdings: Bk Vols 90,000; Per Subs 220
Subject Interests: Local hist
Automation Activity & Vendor Info: (Cataloging) SirsiDynix; (Circulation) SirsiDynix; (OPAC) SirsiDynix
Database Vendor: ProQuest
Mem of Wilderness Coast Public Libraries
Open Mon, Tues & Thurs 8:30-8, Wed, Fri & Sat 8:30-5

RUSTBURG

P   CAMPBELL COUNTY PUBLIC LIBRARY*, 684 Village Hwy, Lower Level, 24588. (Mail add: PO Box 310, 24588-0310), SAN 317-4409. Tel: 434-332-9560. FAX: 434-332-9697. Web Site: www.campbellcountylibraries.org. *Dir,* Nan Carmack; Tel: 434-332-9658, E-mail: nbcarmack@co.campbell.va.us; *Dep Dir,* Coralee Tuck; Tel: 434-332-9660, E-mail: cctuck@co.campbell.va.us; *Acq, Adult Coll Develop Librn,* Jane S Conner; E-mail: jsconner@co.campbell.va.us; *Tech Serv,* Jordan Welborn; Tel: 434-332-9657; Staff 22 (MLS 4, Non-MLS 18)
Founded 1968. Pop 51,078; Circ 94,510
Jul 2005-Jun 2006 Income (Main Library and Branch(s)) $897,418, State $171,181, County $666,929, Other $59,308. Mats Exp $144,248, Books $118,561, Per/Ser (Incl. Access Fees) $12,020, Micro $1,090, AV Mat $12,577. Sal $572,819 (Prof $187,127)
Library Holdings: CDs 8,630; Bk Titles 87,680; Bk Vols 153,400; Per Subs 285; Talking Bks 3,524; Videos 2,347
Subject Interests: Genealogy
Automation Activity & Vendor Info: (Acquisitions) TLC (The Library Corporation); (Cataloging) TLC (The Library Corporation); (Circulation) TLC (The Library Corporation)
Database Vendor: Gale Cengage Learning
Function: ILL available
Publications: Newsletter (Quarterly)
Partic in Lyrasis; SouthWest Information Network Group (SWING); WYLD Network
Open Mon & Wed-Fri 9-5:30, Tues 9-9, Sat 9-1
Friends of the Library Group
Branches: 3
PATRICK HENRY MEMORIAL, 204 Lynchburg Ave, Brookneal, 24528, SAN 377-0540. Tel: 434-376-3363. FAX: 434-376-1111. *Br Mgr,* Gale Seamster
Founded 1938. Pop 4,000; Circ 16,424
Open Tues 9-7, Wed & Thurs 9-5:30, Sat 9-1
Friends of the Library Group
STAUNTON RIVER MEMORIAL, 500 Washington St, Altavista, 24517, SAN 328-7343. Tel: 434-369-5140. FAX: 434-369-1723. *Br Mgr,* Patrice Robertson
Founded 1956. Pop 5,000; Circ 59,657

Open Mon-Wed & Fri 9-5:30, Thurs 9-7, Sat 9-1
Friends of the Library Group
TIMBROOK BRANCH, 21039 Timberlake Rd, Ste F, Lynchburg, 24502, SAN 325-3988. Tel: 434-239-1190. FAX: 434-237-6784. *Br Mgr,* Judy Gerlinger
Founded 1968. Pop 25,000; Circ 70,005
Open Mon-Wed & Fri 9-6, Thurs 9-7, Sat 10-2
Friends of the Library Group
Bookmobiles: 1

SALEM

GM   DEPARTMENT OF VETERANS AFFAIRS*, Medical Center Library, 1970 Roanoke Blvd, 24153. SAN 363-3519. Tel: 540-982-2463, Ext 2380. FAX: 540-983-1079. *Supv Librn,* Jean Kennedy; E-mail: jean.kennedy1@va.gov; Staff 2 (MLS 2)
Founded 1946
Oct 2006-Sept 2007. Mats Exp $63,090, Books $13,355, Per/Ser (Incl. Access Fees) $42,453, AV Mat $6,271, Electronic Ref Mat (Incl. Access Fees) $1,011
Library Holdings: AV Mats 953; Bk Titles 3,583; Per Subs 23
Subject Interests: Behav sci, Biomed sci, Hospital admin, Nursing, Soc sci
Partic in OCLC Online Computer Library Center, Inc; Valpac
Open Mon-Fri 8-4:30

C   NATIONAL COLLEGE*, Roanoke Valley Campus Library, 1813 E Main St, 24153-4598. SAN 317-4344. Tel: 540-444-4189, 540-986-1800, Ext 189. Toll Free Tel: 800-664-1886. FAX: 540-444-4195. Web Site: www.national-college.edu. *Librn,* Betty W Johnson; E-mail: bjohnson@national-college.edu; Staff 2 (MLS 1, Non-MLS 1)
Founded 1886. Enrl 360; Fac 40; Highest Degree: Master
Dec 2007-Nov 2008 Income (Main Library Only) $3,000
Library Holdings: Bk Vols 23,358
Special Collections: National Colleges History Coll
Subject Interests: Acctg, Bus, Computers, Healthcare mgt, Hospitality, Info tech, Med, Paralegal, Travel
Database Vendor: EBSCOhost
Wireless access
Function: Bks on cassette, Bks on CD, Computers for patron use, Copy machines, Free DVD rentals, Handicapped accessible, Music CDs, Photocopying/Printing, Ref & res
Publications: Newsletter
Partic in SouthWest Information Network Group (SWING)
Open Mon-Fri 8am-10pm, Sat 9-1
Restriction: Borrowing privileges limited to fac & registered students
Departmental Libraries:
CHARLOTTESVILLE CAMPUS LIBRARY, 1819 Emmet St, Charlottesville, 22901. Tel: 434-295-0136. FAX: 434-979-8061. *Librn,* Kerry Ellwanger
Founded 1886
Dec 2010-Nov 2011. Mats Exp $7,080
Library Holdings: AV Mats 53; CDs 6; DVDs 86; Bk Titles 3,480
Automation Activity & Vendor Info: (Cataloging) LibraryWorld, Inc; (Circulation) LibraryWorld, Inc; (OPAC) LibraryWorld, Inc
Database Vendor: Gale Cengage Learning, Thomson - Web of Science
Open Mon-Thurs 8am-9pm, Fri 8-5
KNOXVILLE TENNESSEE CAMPUS LIBRARY
See Separate Entry in Knoxville, TN

C   ROANOKE COLLEGE*, Fintel Library, 220 High St, 24153. SAN 317-4417. Tel: 540-375-2295. Circulation Tel: 540-375-2294. Interlibrary Loan Service Tel: 540-375-2298. Administration Tel: 540-375-2293. Automation Services Tel: 540-375-2575. E-mail: library@roanoke.edu. Web Site: www.roanoke.edu/library. *Dir,* Stan Umberger; E-mail: umberger@roanoke.edu; *Mgr, Info Sys,* Dave Wiseman; E-mail: dcwiseman@roanoke.edu; *Archivist,* Linda Miller; Tel: 540-375-2490, E-mail: lmiller@roanoke.edu; *Lending Serv Librn,* Hany Hosny; E-mail: hosny@roanoke.edu; *Ref,* Rebecca Heller; E-mail: rheller@roanoke.edu; *Tech Serv,* Patricia Powell; Tel: 540-375-2292, E-mail: ppowell@roanoke.edu; Staff 6 (MLS 5, Non-MLS 1)
Founded 1842. Enrl 1,970; Fac 140; Highest Degree: Bachelor
Jul 2007-Jun 2008 Income $1,045,664, Locally Generated Income $125,776, Parent Institution $919,888. Mats Exp $474,710, Books $143,320, Per/Ser (Incl. Access Fees) $182,350, Electronic Ref Mat (Incl. Access Fees) $141,040, Presv $8,000. Sal $461,741 (Prof $318,701)
Library Holdings: e-books 42,343; e-journals 15,839; Bk Vols 172,748; Per Subs 683
Special Collections: Henry F Fowler Coll; Roanoke College Coll. US Document Depository
Automation Activity & Vendor Info: (Acquisitions) Innovative Interfaces, Inc; (Cataloging) Innovative Interfaces, Inc; (Circulation) Innovative Interfaces, Inc; (Course Reserve) Innovative Interfaces, Inc; (ILL) Innovative Interfaces, Inc; (Media Booking) Innovative Interfaces, Inc; (OPAC) Innovative Interfaces, Inc; (Serials) Innovative Interfaces, Inc

Database Vendor: Innovative Interfaces, Inc INN - View
Wireless access
Partic in Lyrasis; Virginia Independent College & University Library
Association; Virtual Library of Virginia

R   SALEM BAPTIST CHURCH LIBRARY*, 103 N Broad St, 24153. SAN
317-4425. Tel: 540-387-0416. FAX: 540-375-6412. E-mail:
salembaptist@salembc.net. Web Site: www.salembc.net/. *Dir,* Pat Hancock
Jan 2006-Dec 2006 Income $600. Mats Exp $600
Library Holdings: CDs 13; Bk Vols 4,500; Talking Bks 35; Videos 290
Automation Activity & Vendor Info: (Cataloging) Book Systems, Inc;
(Circulation) Book Systems, Inc
Open Wed 5:30-7:30, Sun 9-12 & 5:30-7

P   SALEM PUBLIC LIBRARY*, 28 E Main St, 24153. SAN 317-4433. Tel:
540-375-3089. FAX: 540-389-7054. E-mail: library@salemva.gov. Web
Site: www.salemlibrary.info. *Dir,* Janis C Augustine; E-mail:
jaugustine@salemva.gov; *Cat,* Lindsey L Tear; E-mail: ltear@salemva.gov;
Ch, Maureen G Harrill; E-mail: mharrill@salemva.gov; *Circ,* Carol Glosh;
E-mail: cglosh@salemva.gov; *Circ,* Benita Van Cleave; E-mail:
bvancleave@salemva.gov; *Res,* Nancy C Collins; E-mail:
ncollins@salemva.gov; *Teen Serv,* David Butler; E-mail:
dbutler@salemva.gov; Staff 13.5 (MLS 7, Non-MLS 6.5)
Founded 1969. Pop 24,784; Circ 290,390
Jul 2009-Jun 2010 Income $1,099,394, State $162,525, City $936,869.
Mats Exp $197,138, Books $92,615, Per/Ser (Incl. Access Fees) $5,363,
Micro $4,594, AV Mat $64,698, Electronic Ref Mat (Incl. Access Fees)
$29,868. Sal $566,632 (Prof $391,706)
Library Holdings: Audiobooks 7,959; CDs 779; DVDs 9,942; e-books
25,704; Electronic Media & Resources 28; Large Print Bks 5,840; Bk Vols
104,077; Per Subs 99; Videos 1,240
Special Collections: Literature for Visually Handicapped (Listening
Library), cassettes, phonodiscs
Subject Interests: Literacy Vols of Am reading prog
Automation Activity & Vendor Info: (Acquisitions) SirsiDynix;
(Cataloging) SirsiDynix; (Circulation) SirsiDynix; (OPAC) SirsiDynix;
(Serials) SirsiDynix
Database Vendor: Baker & Taylor, BWI, Comprise Technologies, Inc,
EBSCO Auto Repair Reference, Electric Library, Gale Cengage Learning,
LearningExpress, netLibrary, Newsbank, OCLC FirstSearch, OCLC
WebJunction, OCLC WorldCat, ProQuest, ReferenceUSA, SirsiDynix, Tech
Logic
Wireless access
Function: Accelerated reader prog, Adult bk club, Bks on cassette, Bks on
CD, Children's prog, Computer training, Computers for patron use, Copy
machines, Electronic databases & coll, Fax serv, Free DVD rentals,
Handicapped accessible, ILL available, Music CDs, Notary serv, Online
cat, Outreach serv, Outside serv via phone, mail, e-mail & web, Prog for
children & young adult, Pub access computers, Ref serv available, Senior
computer classes, Story hour, Summer reading prog, Tax forms, Teen prog,
Telephone ref, VHS videos, Video lending libr, Wheelchair accessible
Partic in Lyrasis
Open Mon-Thurs 9-9, Fri & Sat 9-5, Sun 1:30-5
Friends of the Library Group

SPOTSYLVANIA

S   FRANCES L N WALLER RESEARCH LIBRARY*, 8956 Courthouse Rd,
22553. (Mail add: PO Box 64, 22553-0064), SAN 328-3372. Tel:
540-507-7112. E-mail: shainc@verizon.net. *Pres,* John Pruitt, Jr
Founded 1964
Library Holdings: Bk Titles 2,500
Subject Interests: Civil War, County hist, Genealogy
Open Mon-Sat 9-5

SPRINGFIELD

S   ARMY TIMES PUBLISHING CO LIBRARY*, 6883 Commercial Dr,
22159. SAN 373-2681. Tel: 703-750-7400 (main), 703-750-9000. FAX:
703-750-8622. Web Site: www.atpco.com. *Librn,* Maneet Asthana; Tel:
703-642-7319, E-mail: masthana@atpco.com; *Librn,* Monica Parkzes; Tel:
703-658-8488, E-mail: mparkzes@atpco.com
Open Mon-Fri 9-5
Restriction: Not open to pub

S   ENSCO, INC*, Information Resource Center, 5400 Port Royal Rd,
22151-2312. SAN 317-445X. Tel: 703-321-4604. Interlibrary Loan Service
Tel: 703-321-4524. FAX: 703-321-4565. *Librn,* Irene Minich
Founded 1972
Library Holdings: Bk Titles 4,000; Per Subs 100
Special Collections: Seismology; Track-Train Dynamics
Subject Interests: Computer sci, Geophysics, Railroad tech, Seismic
detection, Signal processing, Underwater acoustics
Publications: In-house Newsletter

Partic in Dialog Corp
Open Mon-Thurs 9-4

G   UNITED STATES DEPARTMENT OF DEFENSE*, National
Geospatial-Intelligence Agency, 7500 GEOINT Dr, Mail Stop S14-SR,
22150-7500. SAN 321-5830. Tel: 571-557-2400. *Dir,* MaryLynn Francisco;
Tel: 571-557-1594
Special Collections: Bathymetric Surveys; Geodetic Control; Geographic
Names
Publications: Map & Chart Accession List
Open Mon-Fri 6:30-4:30

STATE FARM

S   DEPARTMENT OF CORRECTIONAL EDUCATION*, Powhatan, James
River & Deep Meadow Correctional Center, 1954 State Farm Rd,
23160-9998. SAN 317-4492. Tel: 804-784-3551, Ext 2259. FAX:
804-784-2480. *Librn,* John Buzas; *Librn,* James Riley; *Librn,* Abiodun
Solanke; E-mail: bsolanke@aol.com. Subject Specialists: *Intl librarianship,
Libr instruction,* Abiodun Solanke; Staff 3 (MLS 3)
Founded 1968
Library Holdings: AV Mats 125; Bks on Deafness & Sign Lang 30; Large
Print Bks 300; Bk Titles 13,500; Bk Vols 15,500; Per Subs 350
Special Collections: Black Studies (Paul Robeson Memorial Coll)
Automation Activity & Vendor Info: (Cataloging) Follett Software;
(Circulation) Follett Software

STAUNTON

C   MARY BALDWIN COLLEGE*, Martha S Grafton Library, 109 E
Frederick St, 24401. SAN 317-4506. Tel: 540-887-7085. Circulation Tel:
540-887-7311. Interlibrary Loan Service Tel: 540-887-7317. FAX:
540-887-7137. E-mail: ask@mbc.edu. Web Site: library.mbc.edu. *Dir,*
Carol Creager; Tel: 540-887-7310, E-mail: ccreager@mbc.edu; *Head, Pub
Serv,* Alison Peppers; Tel: 540-887-7299, E-mail: apeppers@mbc.edu;
Archivist, William Pollard; Tel: 540-887-7239, E-mail: wpollard@mbc.edu;
Cat, Ser, Lucy Crews; Tel: 540-887-7088, E-mail: lcrews@mbc.edu; *Circ,*
Christina Daniel; Tel: 540-887-7311, E-mail: cdaniel@mbc.edu; *ILL,*
Megan Bayonet; E-mail: mbayonet@mbc.edu; *Media Serv,* Valerie
Gangwer; Tel: 540-887-7267, E-mail: vgangwer@mbc.edu; *Ref &
Instruction Librn,* Ilka Datig; Tel: 540-887-7299, E-mail: idatig@mbc.edu;
Staff 8 (MLS 4, Non-MLS 4)
Founded 1842. Enrl 1,300; Fac 113; Highest Degree: Master
Library Holdings: AV Mats 9,100; e-books 22,000; e-journals 17,000; Bk
Vols 148,200; Per Subs 337
Special Collections: College History; Mary Julia Baldwin Coll
Subject Interests: Women's studies
Automation Activity & Vendor Info: (Acquisitions) SirsiDynix;
(Cataloging) SirsiDynix; (Circulation) SirsiDynix; (Course Reserve)
SirsiDynix; (ILL) SirsiDynix; (OPAC) SirsiDynix; (Serials) SirsiDynix
Database Vendor: ABC-CLIO, Alexander Street Press, American
Chemical Society, ARTstor, Baker & Taylor, Blackwell's, Cambridge
Scientific Abstracts, Checkpoint Systems, Inc, EBSCOhost, Factiva.com,
Gale Cengage Learning, JSTOR, LexisNexis, Modern Language
Association, netLibrary, OCLC FirstSearch, OCLC WorldCat, ProQuest,
SerialsSolutions, SirsiDynix, Wiley InterScience, Wilson - Wilson Web,
YBP Library Services
Wireless access
Partic in Lyrasis; Virginia Independent College & University Library
Association; Virtual Library of Virginia

P   STAUNTON PUBLIC LIBRARY, One Churchville Ave, 24401. SAN
317-4514. Tel: 540-332-3902. FAX: 540-332-3906. E-mail:
library@ci.staunton.va.us. Web Site: www.stauntonlibrary.org. *Dir,* Ruth S
Arnold; E-mail: arnoldrs@ci.staunton.va.us; *Ad,* Melissa Davidson; E-mail:
davidsonmk@ci.staunton.va.us; *Tech Serv Librn,* Eileen Haigh; E-mail:
haighea@ci.staunton.va.us; Staff 4 (MLS 4)
Founded 1930. Pop 23,473; Circ 397,243
Jul 2011-Jun 2012 Income (Main Library Only) $1,020,770, State
$140,549, City $856,594, Other $23,627. Mats Exp $146,780, Books
$97,578, Per/Ser (Incl. Access Fees) $7,678, Micro $724, AV Mat $29,535,
Electronic Ref Mat (Incl. Access Fees) $11,265. Sal $590,353 (Prof
$181,236)
Library Holdings: Audiobooks 13,262; Microforms 2,085; Bk Vols
149,629; Per Subs 183; Videos 10,782
Subject Interests: Local genealogy, Local hist
Automation Activity & Vendor Info: (Cataloging) TLC (The Library
Corporation); (Circulation) TLC (The Library Corporation); (OPAC) TLC
(The Library Corporation)
Database Vendor: EBSCOhost, Gale Cengage Learning, OCLC
FirstSearch, ProQuest
Wireless access
Function: Adult bk club, After school storytime, Art exhibits, Bks on
cassette, Bks on CD, Children's prog, Computer training, Computers for
patron use, Copy machines, Handicapped accessible, Mus passes, Music

CDs, Online cat, Prog for adults, Prog for children & young adult, Summer reading prog

Partic in Mid-Atlantic Library Alliance (MALiA); Valley Libr Consortium

Special Services for the Deaf - Assisted listening device; Bks on deafness & sign lang; Closed caption videos; Sign lang interpreter upon request for prog; TDD equip

Special Services for the Blind - Magnifiers; Talking bks

Open Mon-Thurs 9-9, Fri & Sat 9-5

Friends of the Library Group

Branches: 1

P   TALKING BOOK CENTER, One Churchville Ave, 24401-3229, SAN 321-6519. Tel: 540-885-6215. Toll Free Tel: 800-995-6215. FAX: 540-332-3906. E-mail: talkingbooks@ci.staunton.va.us. Web Site: talkingbookcenter.org. *Libr Asst III,* Lisa Eye; E-mail: eyela@ci.staunton.va.us

Founded 1982. Pop 250,000

Library Holdings: Talking Bks 29,000; Videos 153

Function: Bks on cassette, Digital talking bks, Wheelchair accessible

Special Services for the Blind - Aids for in-house use; Assistive/Adapted tech devices, equip & products; Audio mat; Bks & mags in Braille, on rec, tape & cassette; Bks on cassette; Braille & cassettes; Braille alphabet card; Braille servs; Cassette playback machines; Cassettes; Copier with enlargement capabilities; Descriptive video serv (DVS); Digital talking bk; Home delivery serv; Info on spec aids & appliances; Local mags & bks recorded; Machine repair; PC for handicapped; Recorded bks; Screen enlargement software for people with visual disabilities; Sound rec; Soundproof reading booth; Talking bk serv referral; Talking bks; Talking bks & player equip; Tel Pioneers equip repair group; Videos on blindness & phys handicaps; ZoomText magnification & reading software

Open Mon-Fri 9-5

Friends of the Library Group

S   WOODROW WILSON PRESIDENTIAL LIBRARY FOUNDATION, 20 N Coalter St, 24401-4332. (Mail add: PO Box 24, 24402-0024), SAN 317-4522. Tel: 540-885-0897. FAX: 540-886-9874. E-mail: info@woodrowwilson.org. Web Site: www.woodrowwilson.org. *Dir, Libr & Archives,* Peggy Dillard; E-mail: pdillard@woodrowwilson.org; Staff 1 (MLS 1)

Founded 1938

Library Holdings: Bk Vols 3,000

Special Collections: Cary T Grayson Coll; Edith Bolling Wilson Papers; Emily Smith Papers; George L Harrison Coll; Historic Photograph Coll; McClure Coll; President Woodrow Wilson Coll; US Political History Coll (late 19th century-early 20th century); Wilson Manuscript Coll

Subject Interests: 19th-20th Centuries, Accomplishments of Foundation since 1925, Decorative art, Hist of Foundation since 1925, Intl relations, Political hist of the US

Wireless access

Function: Archival coll

Open Mon-Fri 9-5

Restriction: Non-circulating, Not a lending libr, Researchers by appt only

STRATFORD

S   JESSIE BALL DUPONT MEMORIAL LIBRARY*, Stratford Hall, 483 Great House Rd, 22558. SAN 321-4753. Tel: 804-493-8038, Ext 8572. FAX: 804-493-8006. Web Site: www.stratfordhall.org. *Dir, Libr & Res Serv,* Judith S Hynson; E-mail: jshynson@stratfordhall.org; Staff 1 (Non-MLS 1)

Founded 1980

Library Holdings: Bk Titles 7,200; Bk Vols 10,200; Per Subs 25

Special Collections: 18th Century America (Shippen Coll), antiquarian bks; 18th Century England (Ditchley Coll), antiquarian bks; Cartes de Visite Coll; Lee Family Manuscripts; Walter Herron Taylor Papers

Subject Interests: Manuscripts, Rare bks

Wireless access

Function: Res libr

Restriction: Authorized scholars by appt

SUFFOLK

P   SUFFOLK PUBLIC LIBRARY SYSTEM*, Morgan Memorial Library, 443 W Washington St, 23434. SAN 317-4530. Tel: 757-514-7323. FAX: 757-539-7155. E-mail: library@city.suffolk.va.us. Web Site: www.suffolk.lib.va.us. *Dir,* Elliot A Drew; E-mail: edrew@city.suffolk.va.us; *Ref,* Sarah Garcia; Staff 17 (MLS 5, Non-MLS 12)

Founded 1959. Pop 79,524; Circ 318,696

Library Holdings: Audiobooks 14,159; e-books 39; Microforms 3; Bk Vols 211,663; Per Subs 266

Special Collections: Black Arts & Literature (Reid Coll)

Automation Activity & Vendor Info: (Cataloging) Polaris Library Systems; (Circulation) Polaris Library Systems; (OPAC) Polaris Library Systems

Database Vendor: EBSCOhost, OCLC FirstSearch

Wireless access

Open Mon & Tues 9-8, Wed-Sat 9-5:30

Friends of the Library Group

Branches: 2

CHUCKATUCK BRANCH, 5881 Godwin Blvd, 23432. (Mail add: PO Box 2278, 23432). Tel: 757-514-7310. *Br Librn,* Chinell Sanders

Library Holdings: Bk Vols 14,083

Open Mon 12-8, Tues-Thurs 10-5

Friends of the Library Group

NORTH SUFFOLK LIBRARY, 2000 Bennett's Creek Park Rd, 23435. Tel: 757-514-7150. *Br Mgr,* Olivia DiLeonardo; *Ch,* Sara Grajek

Library Holdings: Bk Vols 120,000

Open Mon-Wed 9-8:30, Thurs, Fri & Sat 9-5

Friends of the Library Group

Bookmobiles: 1

SWEET BRIAR

C   SWEET BRIAR COLLEGE*, Mary Helen Cochran Library, 134 Chapel Rd, 24595-1200. (Mail add: PO Box 1200, 24595-1200), SAN 363-4175. Tel: 434-381-6138. Interlibrary Loan Service Tel: 434-381-6307. Reference Tel: 434-381-6306. FAX: 434-381-6173. Web Site: www.cochran.sbc.edu. *Dir,* John G Jaffe; E-mail: jgjaffe@sbc.edu; *Assoc Dir,* Lisa Johnston; E-mail: lujohnston@sbc.edu; *Br Coordr,* Ro Putz; E-mail: rputz@sbc.edu; *Head, Cat,* Betty Evans; E-mail: baevans@sbc.edu; *Head, Tech Serv,* Julie Kane; E-mail: jkane@sbc.edu; *Acq,* Joyce Kramar; *Circ,* Shirley Reid; E-mail: spreid@sbc.edu; *Electronic Res,* Liz Kent; E-mail: lkent@sbc.edu; *ILL,* Thelma Jordan; E-mail: tbjordan@sbc.edu; *ILL, Ref,* L Joseph Malloy; E-mail: ljmalloy@sbc.edu; *Media Spec,* Anne Richards; *Per,* LaVerne Paige; Staff 12 (MLS 5, Non-MLS 7)

Founded 1901. Enrl 583; Fac 90; Highest Degree: Bachelor

Library Holdings: Bk Vols 223,218; Per Subs 982

Special Collections: Evelyn D Mullen T E Lawrence Coll; Fletcher Williams Founders Coll; George Meredith Coll; Incunabula; Kellogg Childrens Coll; Vincent Chinese Coll; Virginia Woolf Coll; Wystan Hugh Auden Coll

Automation Activity & Vendor Info: (Acquisitions) SirsiDynix; (Cataloging) SirsiDynix; (Circulation) SirsiDynix; (Serials) SirsiDynix

Publications: Friends of the Library Gazette

Partic in Lynchburg Area Library Cooperative; Lynchburg Information Online Network; Virginia Independent College & University Library Association; Virtual Library of Virginia

Open Mon-Thurs 8am-1am, Fri 8-6, Sat 10-6, Sun 10am-1am

Friends of the Library Group

Departmental Libraries:

JUNIUS P FISHBURN MUSIC LIBRARY, Babcock Fine Arts Bldg, 24595, SAN 363-4191. Tel: 434-381-6250. FAX: 434-381-6173. Founded 1961

Library Holdings: Bk Vols 11,280

Open Mon-Thurs 9am-10pm, Fri 9-3, Sun 6pm-10pm

SHALLENBERGER BOOK ARTS LIBRARY & ARCHIVES, Anne Gary Pannell Ctr, 24595, SAN 363-4205. Tel: 434-381-6294. Founded 1961

Library Holdings: Bk Vols 18,464

Restriction: Open by appt only

TAPPAHANNOCK

P   ESSEX PUBLIC LIBRARY*, 117 N Church Lane, 22560. Tel: 804-443-4945. FAX: 804-443-6444. E-mail: eplva@eplva.org. Web Site: www.eplva.org. *Dir,* Bess Haile

Pop 9,989

Library Holdings: AV Mats 577; Bk Titles 37,000; Per Subs 39; Talking Bks 980

Automation Activity & Vendor Info: (Cataloging) Follett Software; (Circulation) Follett Software; (OPAC) Follett Software

Open Mon & Tues 10-6, Wed & Thurs 10-8, Fri 1-6, Sat 10-4

Friends of the Library Group

TAZEWELL

P   TAZEWELL COUNTY PUBLIC LIBRARY*, 310 E Main St, 24651. (Mail add: PO Box 929, 24651-0929), SAN 363-4264. Tel: 276-988-2541. FAX: 276-988-5980. Web Site: www.tcplweb.org. *Dir,* Laurie S Roberts; Staff 20.5 (MLS 3, Non-MLS 17.5)

Founded 1964. Pop 44,216; Circ 133,847

Jul 2010-Jun 2011 Income (Main Library and Branch(s)) $985,273, State $149,135, County $811,138, Locally Generated Income $25,000. Mats Exp $126,801, Books $63,357, Per/Ser (Incl. Access Fees) $8,227, AV Mat $29,899, Electronic Ref Mat (Incl. Access Fees) $25,318. Sal $458,808 (Prof $125,598)

Library Holdings: Audiobooks 4,173; DVDs 4,920; e-books 18,568; Microforms 56; Bk Vols 99,034; Per Subs 151

Special Collections: Photographic Archive

Subject Interests: Genealogy, Local hist

Automation Activity & Vendor Info: (Acquisitions) Innovative Interfaces, Inc; (Cataloging) Innovative Interfaces, Inc; (Circulation) Innovative Interfaces, Inc; (OPAC) Innovative Interfaces, Inc; (Serials) Innovative Interfaces, Inc
Database Vendor: Gale Cengage Learning, OCLC FirstSearch
Wireless access
Function: Adult bk club, After school storytime, Audiobks via web, Bks on CD, Children's prog, Computers for patron use, Copy machines, Electronic databases & coll, Fax serv, ILL available, OverDrive digital audio bks, Photocopying/Printing, Story hour, Summer & winter reading prog, Tax forms
Publications: Guide to Researching Tazewell County, Virginia Ancestors (Research guide); Tasty Tazewell Traditions: 200 Years of Cooking & History in Tazewell County, Virginia (Local historical information)
Partic in Holston Assoc Librs, Inc; Mid-Atlantic Library Alliance (MALiA)
Open Mon & Thurs 9-8, Tues, Wed & Fri 9-5:30, Sat 10-2, Sun 2-6
Friends of the Library Group
Branches: 2
BLUEFIELD BRANCH, 108 Huffard Dr, Bluefield, 24605, SAN 363-4299. Tel: 276-326-1577. FAX: 276-322-5705. *Br Mgr,* Jill Gates; Staff 5 (Non-MLS 5)
   Open Mon, Wed-Sat 9-5:30, Tues 9-8
   Friends of the Library Group
RICHLANDS BRANCH, 102 Suffolk Ave, Richlands, 24641-2435. (Mail add: PO Box 806, Richlands, 24641-0806), SAN 325-3252. Tel: 276-964-5282. FAX: 276-963-1107. *Br Mgr,* Jami McDonald; Staff 5 (Non-MLS 5)
   Open Mon 12-8, Tues-Sat 9-5:30

URBANNA

P MIDDLESEX COUNTY PUBLIC LIBRARY*, Urbanna Branch, 150 Grace St, 23175. (Mail add: PO Box 189, 23175-0189), SAN 317-4557. Tel: 804-758-5717. FAX: 804-758-5910. Web Site: www.mcplva.org. *Coll Develop, Exec Dir,* Sherry Inabinet; E-mail: inabinet@mcplva.org; Staff 4.4 (MLS 2, Non-MLS 2.4)
Founded 1927. Pop 10,000; Circ 50,200
Jul 2006-Jun 2007 Income $225,000. Mats Exp $32,000. Sal $130,000 (Prof $50,000)
Library Holdings: Audiobooks 2,000; AV Mats 4,525; DVDs 525; Large Print Bks 1,725; Bk Titles 42,000; Bk Vols 49,500; Per Subs 50; Videos 2,000
Special Collections: Chesapeake Bay; Virginia History & Genealogy
Automation Activity & Vendor Info: (Cataloging) TLC (The Library Corporation); (Circulation) TLC (The Library Corporation); (OPAC) TLC (The Library Corporation)
Wireless access
Function: Art exhibits, Bks on cassette, Bks on CD, Chess club, Children's prog, Computer training, Computers for patron use, Copy machines, e-mail serv, Fax serv, Free DVD rentals, ILL serv, Jail serv, Music CDs, Online cat, Online searches, Orientations, Outreach serv, Outside serv via phone, mail, e-mail & web, Photocopying/Printing, Preschool outreach, Prog for adults, Prog for children & young adult, Pub access computers, Ref & res, Ref serv available, Senior computer classes, Spoken cassettes & CDs, Spoken cassettes & DVDs, Story hour, Summer reading prog, Tax forms, Telephone ref, VHS videos, Video lending libr, Web-catalog, Wheelchair accessible
Special Services for the Blind - Large print bks; Talking bks
Open Mon, Wed-Fri 10-5, Tues 10-8, Sat 10-2
Restriction: Non-circulating coll
Friends of the Library Group
Branches: 1
DELTAVILLE BRANCH, 35 Lover's Lane, Deltaville, 23043. Tel: 804-776-7362. FAX: 804-776-7423. *Br Mgr,* Lillian Svetahor; E-mail: svetahor@mcplva.org
   Jul 2008-Jun 2009 Income $284,650, City $7,000, Federal $11,325, County $108,000, Locally Generated Income $108,201, Other $49,124. Mats Exp $37,600, Books $29,000, AV Equip $600, AV Mat $8,000. Sal $180,000 (Prof $78,600)
   Special Collections: Chesapeake Bay Room
   Open Mon & Wed-Fri 10-5, Tues 10-8, Sat 10-2
   Friends of the Library Group

VIENNA

S CENTER FOR CHINESE RESEARCH MATERIALS*, Information Center, 10415 Willow Crest Ct, 22182-1852. SAN 370-9639. Tel: 703-715-2688. FAX: 703-715-7913. E-mail: ccrm703@aol.com. *Dir,* Pingfeng Chi
Publications: Newsletter
Open Mon-Fri 9-5

S KOREAN SCIENTISTS & ENGINEERS ASSOCIATION IN AMERICA LIBRARY*, 1952 Gallows Rd, Ste 300, 22182. SAN 374-9355. Tel: 703-748-1221. FAX: 703-748-1331. E-mail: admin@ksea.org. Web Site: www.ksea.org. *Pres,* Dr Nakhoh Thomas Chung
Library Holdings: Bk Vols 500

S NEWSPAPER ASSOCIATION OF AMERICA*, Information Resource Center, 1921 Gallows Rd, Ste 600, 22182. SAN 317-3925. Tel: 703-902-1692. FAX: 703-902-1691. E-mail: irc@naa.org. Web Site: www.naa.org. *Mgr,* Paul Yachnes; Tel: 703-902-1694, E-mail: yachp@naa.org; Staff 2 (MLS 2)
Founded 1887
Library Holdings: Bk Titles 5,000; Per Subs 50
Special Collections: ANPA Bulletins; Presstime
Subject Interests: Newsp advertising, Newsp indust hist, Newsp publ indust
Automation Activity & Vendor Info: (Cataloging) Inmagic, Inc.; (OPAC) Inmagic, Inc.

L VENABLE LLP LIBRARY*, 8010 Towers Crescent Dr, Ste 300, 22182. SAN 325-3899. Tel: 703-760-1600, 703-760-1621. FAX: 703-821-8949. *Librn,* Kathleen G Lolich; E-mail: kglolich@venable.com; Staff 1 (MLS 1)
Founded 1977
Library Holdings: e-journals 20; Electronic Media & Resources 25; Bk Vols 6,000; Per Subs 15
Subject Interests: Bankruptcy, Corporate law, Employment law, Govt contracts, Labor law, Litigation, Pension & benefit law, Real estate, Securities, Taxation, Transportation
Automation Activity & Vendor Info: (Cataloging) Sydney; (Circulation) Sydney; (Serials) Sydney
Open Mon-Fri 9-5
Restriction: Staff use only

VIRGINIA BEACH

S ASSOCIATION FOR RESEARCH & ENLIGHTENMENT*, Edgar Cayce Foundation Library, 215 67th St, 23451. SAN 317-459X. Tel: 757-428-3588, Ext 7141. FAX: 757-422-4631. E-mail: library@edgarcayce.org. Web Site: www.edgarcayce.org. *Mgr,* Laura Hoff; Staff 5 (MLS 1, Non-MLS 4)
Founded 1940
Library Holdings: Bk Vols 66,000; Per Subs 75
Special Collections: Atlantis (Egerton Sykes Coll); Metaphysics (Andrew Jackson Davis Coll); Readings (Edgar Cayce Coll); San Francisco Metaphysical Library Coll
Subject Interests: Archaeology, Astrology, Comparative relig, Death, Dying, Future life, Health, Metaphysics, Psychic res, Reincarnation, Theosophy, Transpersonal psychology
Automation Activity & Vendor Info: (Cataloging) Follett Software; (Circulation) Follett Software
Publications: Perspective on Consciousness & Psi Research; Venture Inward (ARE magazine)
Open Mon-Sat 9-8, Sun 12-8
Friends of the Library Group

C BRYANT & STRATTON COLLEGE LIBRARY*, 301 Centre Pointe Dr, 23462. SAN 372-5146. Tel: 757-499-7900. FAX: 757-499-9977. Web Site: www.bryantstratton.edu. *Head Librn,* Kathleen A Monaco; E-mail: kamonaco@bryantstratton.edu; *Asst Librn,* Kat J Cannon; E-mail: kjcannon@bryantstratton.edu; *Info Literacy Librn,* Mark A Spivey, PhD; E-mail: maspivey@bryantstratton.edu; Staff 3 (MLS 2, Non-MLS 1)
Founded 1988. Enrl 760; Fac 2; Highest Degree: Bachelor
Library Holdings: Bk Titles 15,000; Per Subs 60
Automation Activity & Vendor Info: (OPAC) Follett Software
Database Vendor: EBSCOhost, Gale Cengage Learning, Mergent Online, netLibrary, ReferenceUSA
Wireless access
Open Mon-Thurs 8:30am-9pm, Sat 10-2
Restriction: Open to students, fac & staff
Departmental Libraries:
RICHMOND CAMPUS, 8141 Hull Street Rd, Richmond, 23235, SAN 372-5332. Tel: 804-745-2444. FAX: 804-745-6884. *Librn,* Rosann Meagher
   Library Holdings: Bk Vols 3,500; Per Subs 45
   Automation Activity & Vendor Info: (Cataloging) Follett Software; (Circulation) Follett Software
   Database Vendor: Westlaw
   Open Mon-Thurs 8am-9pm, Fri 9-2, Sat 9-1

C ECPI UNIVERSITY*, Virginia Beach Main Campus Library, 5555 Greenwich Rd, 23462. SAN 373-8620. Tel: 757-671-7171, Ext 55382. Administration Tel: 757-671-7171, Ext 55215. Toll Free Tel: 866-499-0336. FAX: 757-671-8661. Web Site: ecpilibrary.sirsi.net. *Libr Dir,* Rebecca Tabakin; E-mail: rtabakin@ecpi.edu; Staff 2.5 (MLS 1, Non-MLS 1.5)

Founded 1966. Enrl 1,200; Fac 120; Highest Degree: Master
Library Holdings: e-books 70,000; Per Subs 100
Subject Interests: Bus, Computer sci, Criminal justice, Culinary arts, Health sci, Info sci
Automation Activity & Vendor Info: (Cataloging) SIRSI WorkFlows; (Circulation) SIRSI WorkFlows; (OPAC) SIRSI WorkFlows; (Serials) SIRSI WorkFlows
Database Vendor: ACM (Association for Computing Machinery), Bowker, CredoReference, ebrary, EBSCOhost, Electric Library, Elsevier MDL, Gale Cengage Learning, Hoovers, IEEE (Institute of Electrical & Electronics Engineers), Ingram Library Services, Medline, netLibrary, ProQuest, Safari Books Online, ScienceDirect, Scopus, SirsiDynix
Wireless access
Function: Copy machines, e-mail serv, Electronic databases & coll, Equip loans & repairs, ILL available, Online info literacy tutorials on the web & in blackboard, Orientations, Preschool outreach, Ref serv in person, Scanner, Web-catalog
Partic in Libr & Info Resources Network (LIRN); Lyrasis
Open Mon-Thurs 7:45am-10:30pm, Fri 8:30-5, Sat 9-1:30
Restriction: Borrowing privileges limited to fac & registered students, Open to students, fac & staff, Restricted pub use
Departmental Libraries:
CHARLOTTE CAMPUS
  See Separate Entry in Charlotte, NC
GREENSBORO CAMPUS
  See Separate Entry in Greensboro, NC
GREENVILLE CAMPUS
  See Separate Entry in Greenville, SC
NEWPORT NEWS CAMPUS LIBRARY, 1001 Omni Blvd, Ste 100, Newport News, 23606, SAN 377-0664. Tel: 757-838-9191, Ext 74250. FAX: 757-827-5351. *Librn,* Anthony DiTommaso; Tel: 757-838-9191, Ext 74234, E-mail: aditommaso@ecpi.edu; Staff 2 (MLS 1, Non-MLS 1)
  Highest Degree: Associate
  Library Holdings: Bk Vols 5,800; Per Subs 105
  Open Mon-Thurs 7:30am-10:30pm, Fri 8-3:30, Sat 8:30-1

C   HAMPTON UNIVERSITY*, College of Virginia Beach
       Campus-Information Resource Center, 253 Town Center Dr, 23462. Tel: 757-637-2200. FAX: 757-227-5979. Web Site: www.hamptonu.edu/cofvb. *Dir,* Karianne Sparks; Tel: 757-637-2422
       Library Holdings: Bk Titles 300
       Partic in Virginia Tidewater Consortium for Higher Education; Virtual Library of Virginia
       Open Mon-Fri 7am-10pm, Sat 7am-8pm

S   PROVIDENCE PRESBYTERIAN CHURCH LIBRARY, 5497 Providence Rd, 23464. SAN 328-123X. Tel: 757-420-6159. FAX: 757-420-7553. *Dir,* Karen Cagni
       Founded 1985
       Library Holdings: Bk Titles 1,800
       Open Mon-Fri 9-3

CL   REGENT UNIVERSITY, Law Library, 1000 Regent University Dr, 23464-9800, SAN 329-8108. Tel: 757-352-4450. Interlibrary Loan Service Tel: 757-352-4378. Reference Tel: 757-352-4145. Administration Tel: 757-352-4195. FAX: 757-352-4451. Interlibrary Loan Service FAX: 757-352-4189. E-mail: lawcirc@regent.edu, lawref@regent.edu. Web Site: www.regent.edu/acad/schlaw/library. *Dir,* Margaret L Christiansen; Tel: 757-352-4463, E-mail: margchr@regent.edu; *Asst Dir, Coll Develop,* Marie Summerlin Hamm; Tel: 757-352-4233, E-mail: mariham@regent.edu; *Head, Bibliog Serv,* Teresa A Parker-Bellamy; Tel: 757-352-4370, E-mail: terepar@regent.edu; *Head, Res Serv,* Eric Welsh; Tel: 757-352-4454, E-mail: ericwel@regent.edu; *Supvr, Access Serv,* Nikita Powell; Tel: 757-352-4465, E-mail: nikipow@regent.edu; *Res & Instrul Serv,* William Magee; Tel: 757-352-4098, E-mail: willmag@regent.edu. Subject Specialists: *Advan legal res, Writing,* Marie Summerlin Hamm; *Constitutional law, Legis hist,* Eric Welsh; *Taxation, Va Law,* William Magee; Staff 6 (MLS 5, Non-MLS 1)
       Founded 1986. Enrl 430; Fac 30; Highest Degree: Doctorate
       Jul 2011-Jun 2012 Income $1,349,944, Locally Generated Income $494, Parent Institution $1,349,450. Mats Exp $672,044, Books $16,306, Per/Ser (Incl. Access Fees) $447,282, Micro $137, AV Mat $645, Electronic Ref Mat (Incl. Access Fees) $207,674. Sal $627,549 (Prof $356,520)
       Library Holdings: AV Mats 89; CDs 130; DVDs 581; e-books 34,854; e-journals 1,675; Electronic Media & Resources 28; Microforms 1,006,675; Bk Titles 64,136; Bk Vols 133,009; Per Subs 529; Videos 650
       Special Collections: Early American Political Sermons; First Amendment & Civil Rights Coll; Founders Coll; John Brabner-Smith Library & Papers; Ken North Cannon Law Coll; Ken North Coll; Mary Elizabeth Menefee Law & Film Coll; Ralph Johnson Bunche Coll; Richard Henry Dana, Jr Library
       Subject Interests: Constitutional hist, Constitutional law, Environ law, Family law, Intellectual property law, Intl human rights, Intl law, Intl trade law, Legal hist, Legis hist, Nat security law, Va Law

Automation Activity & Vendor Info: (Acquisitions) Innovative Interfaces, Inc - Millenium; (Cataloging) Innovative Interfaces, Inc - Millenium; (Circulation) Innovative Interfaces, Inc - Millenium; (Course Reserve) Innovative Interfaces, Inc - Millenium; (ILL) Innovative Interfaces, Inc - Millenium; (OPAC) Innovative Interfaces, Inc - Millenium; (Serials) Innovative Interfaces, Inc - Millenium
Database Vendor: Bloomberg, Cassidy Cataloguing Services, Inc, Checkpoint Systems, Inc, Gale Cengage Learning, HeinOnline, Innovative Interfaces, Inc, JSTOR, LexisNexis, Loislaw, Newsbank, OCLC ArticleFirst, OCLC FirstSearch, OCLC WorldCat, Oxford Online, ProQuest, Thomson Carswell, Westlaw
Wireless access
Function: Audio & video playback equip for onsite use, Bks on CD, Computers for patron use, Copy machines, Doc delivery serv, Electronic databases & coll, Handicapped accessible, ILL available, Microfiche/film & reading machines, Online cat, Online ref, Online searches, Orientations, Photocopying/Printing, Pub access computers, Ref serv in person, Res libr, VCDs, Wheelchair accessible
Publications: Law Library Blog (Online only)
Partic in Consortium of Southeastern Law Libraries; Law Library Microform Consortium (LLMC); Lyrasis; Virginia Tidewater Consortium for Higher Education; Virtual Library of Virginia
Special Services for the Deaf - Closed caption videos; Staff with knowledge of sign lang
Special Services for the Blind - Audio mat; Bks on cassette; Bks on CD; Cassette playback machines; Copier with enlargement capabilities; Ref serv; Talking bks
Open Mon-Fri 7:30am-Midnight, Sat 8am-Midnight, Sun 2-Midnight
Restriction: Circ limited, In-house use for visitors, Open to pub for ref & circ; with some limitations, Private libr

C   REGENT UNIVERSITY LIBRARY, 1000 Regent University Dr, 23464. SAN 321-6314. Tel: 757-352-4185. Circulation Tel: 757-352-4150. Interlibrary Loan Service Tel: 757-352-4424. Reference Tel: 757-352-4159. Toll Free Tel: 888-249-1822. FAX: 757-352-4167. Interlibrary Loan Service FAX: 757-352-4179. E-mail: refer@regent.edu. Web Site: www.regent.edu/general/library. *Dean of Libr,* Sara Baron; E-mail: sbaron@regent.edu; *Assoc Dean,* Leanne G Strum; Tel: 757-352-4172, E-mail: leangar@regent.edu; *Head, Pub Serv,* Sandra Yaegle; Tel: 757-352-4165, E-mail: sandyae@regent.edu; *Head, Tech Serv, Librn,* Georgianne Bordner; Tel: 757-352-4493, E-mail: georbor@regent.edu; *Affiliate Librn,* Jason Stuart; Tel: 757-352-4184, E-mail: jstuart@regent.edu; *Asst Librn,* Melody Diehl; Tel: 757-352-4542, E-mail: mdiehl@regent.edu; *ILL,* Patty Hughson; E-mail: patrhug@regent.edu; *Ref Serv,* Harold Henkel; Tel: 757-352-4198, E-mail: harohen@regent.edu. Subject Specialists: *Higher educ,* Sara Baron; *Bus, Leadership,* Leanne G Strum; *Copyright, Educ,* Sandra Yaegle; *Cataloging,* Georgianne Bordner; *Divinity,* Melody Diehl; *Undergrad studies,* Harold Henkel; Staff 23.5 (MLS 7.5, Non-MLS 16)
       Founded 1978. Enrl 5,828; Fac 196; Highest Degree: Doctorate
       Jul 2011-Jun 2012 Income $2,210,394. Mats Exp $754,177, Books $102,498, Per/Ser (Incl. Access Fees) $162,000, AV Mat $3,908, Electronic Ref Mat (Incl. Access Fees) $485,771. Sal $1,323,599
       Library Holdings: AV Mats 11,064; Bks on Deafness & Sign Lang 282; DVDs 11,654; e-books 193,347; e-journals 99,534; Electronic Media & Resources 121; Microforms 593,318; Bk Titles 311,685; Per Subs 525
       Special Collections: Animated Films Coll; Christian Education Association International Coll; Christian Films Research Coll; Clark Hymnology Coll; Dennis Bennett Coll; J Rodman Williams Coll; John Wimber Papers; Matthews Coll; O C Baptista Film Coll; Pentecostal Research Coll; Scott Ross Cultural Coll; Vince Synan Papers; Wellington Boone Coll
       Subject Interests: Biblical studies, Communications, Counseling, Educ, Govt, Hymnology, Leadership studies, Psychol
       Automation Activity & Vendor Info: (Acquisitions) Innovative Interfaces, Inc - Millenium; (Cataloging) Innovative Interfaces, Inc - Millenium; (Circulation) Innovative Interfaces, Inc - Millenium; (Course Reserve) Innovative Interfaces, Inc - Millenium; (ILL) OCLC; (OPAC) Innovative Interfaces, Inc - Millenium; (Serials) Innovative Interfaces, Inc - Millenium
       Database Vendor: ABC-CLIO, Alexander Street Press, American Psychological Association (APA), Baker & Taylor, BCR: Christian Periodical Index, Bowker, CIOS (Communication Institute for Online Scholarship), CQ Press, CredoReference, ebrary, EBSCO Information Services, EBSCOhost, Emerald, Factiva.com, Facts on File, Gale Cengage Learning, H W Wilson, Haworth Pres Inc, Ingenta, Innovative Interfaces, Inc, JSTOR, LexisNexis, McGraw-Hill, Mergent Online, Newsbank, OCLC, OCLC FirstSearch, OCLC WorldCat, Oxford Online, Project MUSE, ProQuest, Safari Books Online, Sage, ScienceDirect, SerialsSolutions, Springer-Verlag, Wiley InterScience, Wilson - Wilson Web, YBP Library Services
Wireless access
Function: Res libr
Publications: Library Link (Newsletter)
Partic in Lyrasis; OCLC Online Computer Library Center, Inc; Virginia Independent College & University Library Association; Virginia Tidewater Consortium for Higher Education; Virtual Library of Virginia (VIVA)

Special Services for the Blind - Screen enlargement software for people with visual disabilities
Open Mon-Fri 7:30am-Midnight, Sat 8am-Midnight, Sun 2pm-Midnight

J   TIDEWATER COMMUNITY COLLEGE*, Virginia Beach Campus
    Learning Resources Center, 1700 College Crescent, 23453. SAN 317-4603.
    Circulation Tel: 757-822-7151. Reference Tel: 757-822-7152. FAX:
    757-427-0327. Web Site: www.tcc.edu/lrc. *Ref Librn,* Kimberly Bateman;
    Ref Librn, Cherie Carl; *Ref Librn,* Todd Elliott; *Ref Librn,* Sarah Jones;
    Staff 9 (MLS 5, Non-MLS 4)
    Founded 1971. Enrl 10,114
    Library Holdings: AV Mats 938; Bk Vols 47,803; Per Subs 241
    Subject Interests: Allied health, Broadcasting, Computer sci, Fire sci,
    Hotel, Institutional mgt, Phys therapy, Radiological tech, Respiratory
    therapy, Restaurant mgt
    Partic in Tidewater Consortium
    Open Mon-Thurs 7:30am-9pm, Fri 7:30-4, Sat 9-5, Sun 1-5

A   UNITED STATES ARMED FORCES SCHOOL OF MUSIC, Library
    Media Center, JEB Little Creek, 1420 Gator Blvd, 23459-2617. SAN
    370-2812. Tel: 757-462-7511. FAX: 757-462-7294. Web Site:
    www.netc.navy.mil/centers/css/som. *Chief Librn,* Russ Girsberger; Tel:
    757-462-5734, E-mail: russ.girsberger@navy.mil; Staff 1 (MLS 1)
    Library Holdings: AV Mats 8,000; Music Scores 25,000; Bk Vols 8,000;
    Per Subs 20
    Special Collections: Broude Coll (Pre-1920)
    Subject Interests: Music analysis, Music scores, Recorded music
    Automation Activity & Vendor Info: (Cataloging) LibraryWorld, Inc;
    (Circulation) LibraryWorld, Inc; (OPAC) LibraryWorld, Inc
    Function: Ref serv available
    Open Mon-Fri 8-3:30
    Restriction: Borrowing privileges limited to fac & registered students, By
    permission only

S   VIRGINIA AQUARIUM & MARINE SCIENCE CENTER*, 717 General
    Booth Blvd, 23451. SAN 328-3631. Tel: 757-385-3474, 757-385-7777.
    FAX: 757-437-6055. Web Site: www.vmsm.com. *Coordr,* Kathleen Reed;
    E-mail: kreed@vbgov.com
    Library Holdings: Bk Vols 1,000; Per Subs 25
    Open Mon-Sun (Winter) 9-5; Mon-Sun (Summer) 9-7

P   VIRGINIA BEACH PUBLIC LIBRARY DEPARTMENT*, Bldg 19,
    Municipal Ctr, 2nd Flr, 2416 Courthouse Dr, 23456. SAN 363-4329. Tel:
    757-385-4321. Interlibrary Loan Service Tel: 757-385-0167. FAX:
    757-385-4220. Web Site: www.vbgov.com. *Dir,* Marcy Sims; E-mail:
    msims@vbgov.com; *Actg Mgr,* Toni Lohman; Staff 41 (MLS 41)
    Founded 1959. Pop 437,778; Circ 2,825,924
    Library Holdings: Bk Vols 717,766
    Special Collections: Princess Anne County (Princess Anne Historical
    Coll), bks, microfilm & microcards
    Automation Activity & Vendor Info: (Circulation) SirsiDynix
    Publications: The Beach: A History of Virginia Beach; Update
    (Newsletter)
    Partic in Dialog Corp; OCLC Online Computer Library Center, Inc
    Friends of the Library Group
    Branches: 15
    BAYSIDE AREA, 936 Independence Blvd, 23455, SAN 363-4590. Tel:
       757-385-2680. *Librn,* Carolyn Caywood; E-mail: ccaywood@vbgov.com;
       Staff 1 (MLS 1)
       Founded 1967. Circ 259,335
       Open Mon-Thurs 10-9, Fri & Sat 10-5
    COLLECTION MANAGEMENT, 4100 Virginia Beach Blvd, 23452, SAN
       322-614X. Tel: 757-385-0170. *Librn,* Toni Lohman; E-mail:
       tlohman@vbgov.com; Staff 5 (MLS 5)
    GREAT NECK AREA, 1251 Bayne Dr, 23454, SAN 363-4620. Tel:
       757-385-2606. Reference Tel: 757-385-2600. Administration Tel:
       757-385-2601. *Librn,* Jacqueline Lewis; E-mail: jlewis@vbgov.com; Staff
       1 (MLS 1)
       Circ 261,867
       Open Mon-Thurs 10-9, Fri & Sat 10-5
    INTERLIBRARY LOAN DIVISION, 4100 Virginia Beach Blvd, 23452,
       SAN 363-4434. Tel: 757-385-0167. Interlibrary Loan Service FAX:
       757-431-3741. *ILL,* Jennifer Thalman; E-mail: jthalman@vbgov.com
    KEMPSVILLE AREA, 832 Kempsville Rd, 23464-2793, SAN 363-4655.
       Tel: 757-385-2627. Web Site: www.vbgov.com/libraries. *Librn,* Denise
       Walker; Tel: 757-385-2614, Fax: 757-495-5401, E-mail:
       dwalker@vbgov.com; Staff 1 (MLS 1)
       Circ 421,516
       Open Mon-Thurs 10-7, Fri & Sat 10-5, Sun (Sept-May) 1-5
    LIBRARY CATALOGING SERVICES, 4100 Virginia Beach Blvd, 23452,
       SAN 363-4442. Tel: 757-385-0170. *Librn,* Sean O'Connell; E-mail:
       soconnel@vbgov.com

MUNICIPAL REFERENCE SERVICES, 4100 Virginia Beach Blvd, 23452,
   SAN 363-4477. Tel: 757-385-4644. E-mail: muniref@vbgov.com. *Librn,*
   Pat Cook; E-mail: pcook@vbgov.com
   Open Mon-Thurs 10-9, Fri & Sat 10-5, Sun (Sept-May) 1-5
MEYERA E OBERNDORF CENTRAL LIBRARY, 4100 Virginia Beach
   Blvd, 23452, SAN 377-0567. Tel: 757-385-0150. Circulation Tel:
   757-385-0120. Interlibrary Loan Service Tel: 757-385-0167.
   Administration Tel: 757-385-0110. Automation Services Tel:
   757-385-0160. FAX: 757-431-3134. Administration FAX: 757-431-3018.
   E-mail: library@vbgov.com. Web Site: www.vbgov.com/libraries. *Cent
   Librn,* Patricia J Cook; Tel: 757-385-0101, E-mail: pcook@vbgov.com
   Open Mon-Thurs 10-9, Fri & Sat 10-5, Sun 1-5
OCEANFRONT AREA, 700 Virginia Beach Blvd, 23451, SAN 363-468X.
   Tel: 757-385-2640. *Librn,* Susan Head
   Circ 190,098
   Open Mon-Thurs 10-9, Fri & Sat 10-5
PUNGO-BLACKWATER LIBRARY, 916 Princess Anne Rd, 23457, SAN
   370-9426. Tel: 757-426-5194. E-mail: libpbstaff@vbgov.com. *Librn,* Jill
   Burr; E-mail: jaburr@vbgov.com
   Circ 65,909
   Open Mon-Thurs 10-9, Fri & Sat 10-5
SOUTH ROSEMONT YOUTH LIBRARY & BOOKMOBILE, 1503
   Competitor Ct, 23456, SAN 363-4418. Tel: 757-385-2650. *Libr Coordr,*
   Liz Lett; E-mail: llett@vbgov.com
   Circ 83,953
   Open Mon-Thurs (Sept-May) 10-9, Fri & Sat 10-5 ; Mon-Thurs
   (June-Aug) 10-6, Fri & Sat 10-5
P   SUBREGIONAL LIBRARY FOR THE BLIND & HANDICAPPED,
   BAYSIDE SPECIAL LIBRARY SERVICES, 936 Independence Blvd,
   23455, SAN 363-4353. Tel: 757-385-2680. Information Services Tel:
   757-385-2684. E-mail: libssbh@vbgov.com. *Dir,* Carolyn Caywood;
   Supvr, Laura Scott
   Founded 1972
   Library Holdings: Bk Vols 14,025
   Special Services for the Deaf - TDD equip
   Open Mon-Thurs 10-9, Fri & Sat 10-5
TECHNOLOGY SERVICES DIVISION, Central Library, 4100 Virginia
   Beach Blvd, 23452, SAN 363-4361. Tel: 757-385-0170. *Tech Mgr,* Nick
   May; E-mail: nmay@vbgov.com
   Founded 1985
   Open Mon-Thurs 10-9, Fri & Sat 10-5, Sun 1-5
WAHAB PUBLIC LAW LIBRARY, Municipal Ctr, Judicial Ctr, Court
   Support Bldg 10B, 2425 Nimmo Pkwy, 23456, SAN 363-4507. Tel:
   757-385-4419. FAX: 757-385-8742. *Librn,* Jean Tancred; E-mail:
   jtancred@vbgov.com
   Circ 1,192
   Open Mon-Fri 8-4:30
WINDSOR WOODS AREA, 3612 S Plaza Trail, 23452, SAN 363-471X.
   Tel: 757-385-2630. *Librn,* Position Currently Open
   Circ 77,415
   Open Mon-Thurs 10-9, Fri & Sat 10-5

WALLOPS ISLAND

G   NASA*, Goddard Space Flight Center, Wallops Flight Facility Library,
    Tech Lib E-105, 23337. SAN 317-4611. Tel: 757-824-1065. FAX:
    757-824-1716. Web Site: www.library.gsfc.nasa.gov/. *Librn,* Roberta Eddy;
    Staff 3 (MLS 1, Non-MLS 2)
    Founded 1959
    Library Holdings: e-journals 2,361; Bk Titles 7,800; Bk Vols 10,000
    Special Collections: Balloon Technology Library
    Subject Interests: Aerospace, Applied sci, Math
    Automation Activity & Vendor Info: (Cataloging) SirsiDynix;
    (Circulation) SirsiDynix; (OPAC) SirsiDynix; (Serials) SirsiDynix
    Publications: Booster
    Open Mon-Fri 8-4:30

WARRENTON

P   FAUQUIER COUNTY PUBLIC LIBRARY*, 11 Winchester St,
    20186-2825. SAN 317-462X. Tel: 540-347-8750. FAX: 540-349-3278.
    Reference FAX: 540-349-2611. Web Site: www.library.fauquiercounty.gov.
    Dir, Maria Del Rosso; Tel: 540-347-8750, Ext 5327, E-mail:
    maria.delrosso@fauquiercounty.gov; *Asst Libr Dir,* Ava K Lee; Tel:
    540-349-1856, E-mail: ava.lee@fauquiercounty.gov; *Coll Mgr,* Fran
    Burke-Urr; Tel: 540-349-1928, E-mail: fran.burke-urr@fauquiercounty.gov;
    Pub Serv Mgr, Dawn Sowers; Tel: 540-349-1253, E-mail:
    dawn.sowers@fauquiercounty.gov; *Support Serv Mgr,* Linda Yowell; Tel:
    540-349-1327, E-mail: linda.yowell@fauquiercounty.gov; *Ad,* Vicky
    Ginther; Tel: 540-349-1793, E-mail: vicky.ginther@fauquiercounty.gov;
    Youth Serv Librn, Jennifer Schultz; Tel: 540-349-1128, E-mail:
    jennifer.schultz@fauquiercounty.gov; Staff 22.88 (MLS 10, Non-MLS
    12.88)
    Founded 1922. Pop 60,400; Circ 457,485

Jul 2006-Jun 2007 Income (Main Library and Branch(s)) $1,991,261, State $201,226, County $1,731,701, Locally Generated Income $58,334. Mats Exp $287,545, Books $147,849, Per/Ser (Incl. Access Fees) $12,925, Micro $427, AV Mat $57,655, Electronic Ref Mat (Incl. Access Fees) $68,689. Sal $1,241,393 (Prof $615,049)

Library Holdings: CDs 1,244; DVDs 1,400; e-books 31,614; Large Print Bks 1,467; Bk Vols 106,714; Per Subs 291; Talking Bks 4,991; Videos 1,891

Subject Interests: Genealogy, Local hist, Va

Automation Activity & Vendor Info: (Acquisitions) Innovative Interfaces, Inc; (Cataloging) Innovative Interfaces, Inc; (Circulation) Innovative Interfaces, Inc; (OPAC) Innovative Interfaces, Inc; (Serials) Innovative Interfaces, Inc

Database Vendor: Baker & Taylor, Children's Literature Comprehensive Database Company (CLCD), infoUSA, Innovative Interfaces, Inc, netLibrary, Newsbank, OCLC FirstSearch, OCLC WorldCat, Oxford Online, ProQuest, ReferenceUSA, Wilson - Wilson Web, World Book Online

Wireless access

Function: Adult bk club, Audiobks via web, Bk club(s), Bks on cassette, Bks on CD, Children's prog, Computer training, Computers for patron use, Copy machines, Handicapped accessible, Holiday prog, Homebound delivery serv, ILL available, Music CDs, Prog for adults, Prog for children & young adult, Pub access computers, Summer reading prog, Teen prog, Telephone ref, VHS videos, Web-catalog, Wheelchair accessible

Partic in SouthWest Information Network Group (SWING)

Open Mon-Wed 10-9, Thurs-Sat 9-5, Sun 1-5

Friends of the Library Group

Branches: 2

BEALETON BRANCH, 10877 Willow Dr N, Bealeton, 22712, SAN 371-9294. Tel: 540-439-9728. FAX: 540-439-9731. *Br Mgr,* Natalie Swart; *Ref Librn,* Beth Stenberg; E-mail: beth.stenberg@fauquiercounty.gov; *Youth Serv Librn,* Helena Richardson; E-mail: helena.richardson@fauquiercounty.gov; Staff 3.12 (MLS 2.82, Non-MLS 0.3)

Founded 1991. Circ 94,993

Library Holdings: CDs 752; DVDs 643; e-books 31,614; Large Print Bks 748; Bk Vols 43,774; Per Subs 107; Talking Bks 2,572; Videos 1,072

Function: Audiobks via web, Bk club(s), Bks on cassette, Bks on CD, Children's prog, Computer training, Computers for patron use, Copy machines, Electronic databases & coll, Handicapped accessible, Holiday prog, ILL available, Music CDs, Online cat, Prog for adults, Prog for children & young adult, Pub access computers, Ref serv available, Spoken cassettes & CDs, Summer reading prog, Teen prog, Telephone ref, VHS videos, Web-catalog, Wheelchair accessible

Open Mon-Wed 10-9, Thurs-Sat 9-5, Sun 1-5

Friends of the Library Group

JOHN MARSHALL BRANCH, 4133 Rectortown Rd, Marshall, 20115, SAN 375-5487. Tel: 540-364-4910. FAX: 540-364-4911. *Br Mgr,* Deborah Cosby; E-mail: deborah.cosby@fauquiercounty.gov; *Outreach Serv Librn,* Johnetta Pruitt; E-mail: johnetta.pruitt@fauquiercounty.gov; Staff 0.94 (MLS 0.94)

Founded 1996. Circ 40,798

Library Holdings: CDs 143; DVDs 328; e-books 31,614; Large Print Bks 412; Bk Vols 26,151; Per Subs 79; Talking Bks 1,385; Videos 832

Function: Adult bk club, Audiobks via web, Bk club(s), Bks on cassette, Bks on CD, Children's prog, Computers for patron use, Copy machines, Handicapped accessible, Holiday prog, Homebound delivery serv, ILL available, Music CDs, Online cat, Preschool outreach, Prog for adults, Prog for children & young adult, Ref serv available, Senior outreach, Spoken cassettes & CDs, Summer reading prog, VHS videos, Web-catalog, Wheelchair accessible

Open Mon-Wed 12-8, Thurs 10-5, Sat & Sun 1-5

Friends of the Library Group

WARSAW

J RAPPAHANNOCK COMMUNITY COLLEGE*, Learning Resource Center, 52 Campus Dr, 22572. SAN 363-4833. Tel: 804-333-6710. FAX: 804-333-0589. Web Site: www.rcc.vccs.edu. *Col Librn, Interim Dean,* Melanie Wick; Tel: 804-333-6714, E-mail: mwick@rcc.vccs.edu; *Pub Serv Mgr,* Linda Taylor; E-mail: ltaylor@rcc.vccs.edu; Staff 12 (MLS 3, Non-MLS 9)

Founded 1973. Enrl 3,100; Fac 29; Highest Degree: Associate

Library Holdings: AV Mats 1,255; e-books 33,000; Large Print Bks 625; Bk Titles 43,000; Bk Vols 49,000; Per Subs 203; Talking Bks 989

Special Collections: Children's Library; Cooperative Law Library; Virginiana Coll

Automation Activity & Vendor Info: (Acquisitions) Ex Libris Group; (Cataloging) OCLC; (Circulation) Ex Libris Group; (Course Reserve) Ex Libris Group; (ILL) OCLC; (Media Booking) Ex Libris Group; (OPAC) Ex Libris Group; (Serials) Ex Libris Group

Function: Distance learning, Doc delivery serv, Handicapped accessible, ILL available, Photocopying/Printing, Workshops

Publications: Learning Resources News (Newsletter)

Partic in Lyrasis; Virginia Commun Coll Syst; Virtual Library of Virginia

Special Services for the Blind - Aids for in-house use; Bks on cassette; Talking bks

Open Mon-Thurs 8:30-8:30, Fri 8:30-3, Sat 9-2

Friends of the Library Group

P RICHMOND COUNTY PUBLIC LIBRARY*, Rappahannock Community College Library Ctr, 52 Campus Dr, 22572. Tel: 804-333-6710. FAX: 804-333-0589. Web Site: www.rcc.vccs.edu/public/library/library_home.htm. *Col Librn,* Melanie Wick; E-mail: mwick@rappahannock.edu; Staff 6 (MLS 2, Non-MLS 4)

Founded 1993. Pop 9,100; Circ 39,909

Library Holdings: AV Mats 1,255; e-books 33,000; Electronic Media & Resources 250; Large Print Bks 303; Bk Titles 43,000; Bk Vols 49,000; Per Subs 110; Talking Bks 550

Special Collections: Virginiana (Virginia History, Local History & Geneaology)

Automation Activity & Vendor Info: (Acquisitions) Ex Libris Group; (Cataloging) Ex Libris Group; (Circulation) Ex Libris Group; (ILL) OCLC Online; (Media Booking) Ex Libris Group; (OPAC) Ex Libris Group; (Serials) Ex Libris Group

Database Vendor: Factiva.com, Gale Cengage Learning, JSTOR, LexisNexis, netLibrary, OCLC FirstSearch, OVID Technologies, Westlaw

Wireless access

Function: Doc delivery serv, Govt ref serv, Handicapped accessible, ILL available, Newsp ref libr, Photocopying/Printing, Prog for children & young adult, Ref serv available, Summer reading prog, Telephone ref, Wheelchair accessible, Workshops

Special Services for the Deaf - Bks on deafness & sign lang

Special Services for the Blind - Bks on cassette; Bks on CD; Talking bks

Open Mon-Thurs 8:30-8:30, Fri 8:30-3, Sat 9-2

Friends of the Library Group

WASHINGTON

P RAPPAHANNOCK COUNTY LIBRARY*, Four Library Rd, 22747. (Mail add: PO Box 55, 22747-0055), SAN 317-4646. Tel: 540-675-3780. FAX: 540-675-1290. Web Site: www.rappahannocklibrary.org. *Dir,* David Shaffer; E-mail: dshaffer@rappahannocklibrary.org; Staff 3 (Non-MLS 3)

Founded 1963. Circ 16,783

Library Holdings: Bk Titles 26,000; Bk Vols 30,000; Per Subs 100

Automation Activity & Vendor Info: (Circulation) Winnebago Software Co; (OPAC) Winnebago Software Co

Open Mon & Wed 10-8, Tues, Thurs & Fri 10-6, Sat 10-2

Friends of the Library Group

WAYNESBORO

S THE KOCH INDUSTRIES INVISTA*, Benger Laboratory Library, DuPont Co, 400 Du Pont Blvd, 22980. SAN 317-4654. Tel: 540-949-2485. FAX: 540-949-2949. *Librn,* Becky Moomau

Founded 1947

Library Holdings: Bk Titles 12,000; Per Subs 90

P WAYNESBORO PUBLIC LIBRARY*, 600 S Wayne Ave, 22980. SAN 363-4868. Tel: 540-942-6746. FAX: 540-942-6753. Web Site: www.waynesboro.va.us/library.html. *Dir,* Zahir M Mahmoud; E-mail: mahmoudz@ci.waynesboro.va.us; *Asst Dir,* Teresa Gilliam; E-mail: gilliamtn@ci.waynesboro.va.us; *Youth Serv Librn,* Bethany E Jones; E-mail: jonesbe@ci.waynesboro.va.us; *Circ Mgr,* Rhonda B Smith; E-mail: smithrb@ci.waynesboro.va.us; *Adult Serv,* Diane H Devoy; E-mail: devoydh@ci.waynesboro.va.us; Staff 11 (MLS 2, Non-MLS 9)

Founded 1915. Pop 20,405; Circ 305,435

Jul 2007-Jun 2008 Income $1,034,289, State $176,137, City $838,152, Locally Generated Income $20,000. Mats Exp $135,682, Books $102,809, Per/Ser (Incl. Access Fees) $9,173, Micro $845, AV Mat $18,522, Electronic Ref Mat (Incl. Access Fees) $3,833, Presv $500. Sal $491,443 (Prof $386,902)

Library Holdings: Audiobooks 3,322; AV Mats 13,206; Bks on Deafness & Sign Lang 82; Braille Volumes 20; CDs 1,093; DVDs 2,398; Electronic Media & Resources 5; High Interest/Low Vocabulary Bk Vols 21; Large Print Bks 6,132; Microforms 1,689; Music Scores 1,163; Bk Titles 162,008; Bk Vols 178,015; Per Subs 141; Spec Interest Per Sub 10; Talking Bks 20; Videos 6,393

Special Collections: Charles Smith Art Coll; George Speck Art Coll, prints; Waynesboro Local History, bks, micro. Oral History

Subject Interests: Genealogy, Local hist

Automation Activity & Vendor Info: (Acquisitions) TLC (The Library Corporation); (Cataloging) TLC (The Library Corporation); (Circulation) TLC (The Library Corporation); (Course Reserve) TLC (The Library Corporation); (OPAC) TLC (The Library Corporation); (Serials) EBSCO Online

Database Vendor: EBSCO Auto Repair Reference, netLibrary, OCLC FirstSearch, ProQuest

Wireless access
Publications: Bookmark (Newsletter); Calendar of Events (Quarterly); The Bookshelf Edition (Newsletter)
Special Services for the Blind - Aids for in-house use; Assistive/Adapted tech devices, equip & products; Audio mat; Bks on cassette; Bks on CD; Braille & cassettes; Braille bks; Braille equip; Home delivery serv; Internet workstation with adaptive software; Large print & cassettes; Large print bks; Large screen computer & software; Magnifiers; Recorded bks; Talking bks
Open Mon-Fri 9-9, Sat 9-5
Friends of the Library Group

WEYERS CAVE

J   BLUE RIDGE COMMUNITY COLLEGE*, Houff Library, One College Lane, 24486. (Mail add: PO Box 80, 24486-0080), SAN 317-4689. Tel: 540-453-2247. Interlibrary Loan Service Tel: 540-453-2245. Reference Tel: 540-453-2309. Administration Tel: 540-453-2269. Information Services Tel: 540-453-2278. FAX: 540-234-9598. TDD: 800-405-8315. Web Site: www.br.vccs.edu. *Dean, Learning Serv,* Frank J Moran; E-mail: moranf@brcc.edu; *Head, Cat,* June Williams; E-mail: williamsj@brcc.edu; *Head, ILL, Purchasing,* Donna S Alexander; E-mail: alexanderd@brcc.edu; *Bibliog Instr, Librn,* Connie Medaris; E-mail: shewmakec@brcc.edu; *Circ,* Martha Livick; E-mail: livickm@brcc.edu; *Info Spec, Ref Serv, Tech Serv,* Sue Ellen Church; E-mail: churchs@brcc.edu; Staff 5 (MLS 3, Non-MLS 2)
Founded 1967. Enrl 2,440; Fac 350; Highest Degree: Associate
Library Holdings: AV Mats 1,784; Bks on Deafness & Sign Lang 20; DVDs 87; Bk Titles 47,557; Bk Vols 50,061; Per Subs 208; Talking Bks 76; Videos 43
Special Collections: Virginia Regional Historical Coll
Subject Interests: Nursing, Veterinary tech
Automation Activity & Vendor Info: (Cataloging) Ex Libris Group; (Circulation) Ex Libris Group; (ILL) OCLC FirstSearch; (OPAC) Ex Libris Group
Database Vendor: Cambridge Scientific Abstracts, Elsevier MDL, Factiva.com, Gale Cengage Learning, JSTOR, LexisNexis, OCLC FirstSearch, OCLC WorldCat, OVID Technologies, ProQuest, PubMed, ScienceDirect
Function: ILL available
Publications: AV Guide; New Accessions; Periodical Listing
Partic in OCLC Online Computer Library Center, Inc; Virginia Commun Coll Syst; Virtual Library of Virginia
Open Mon-Thurs 7:45am-9pm, Fri 7:45-5, Sat 10-3

WILLIAMSBURG

COLLEGE OF WILLIAM & MARY IN VIRGINIA
C   EARL GREGG SWEM LIBRARY*, One Landrum Dr, 23187. (Mail add: PO Box 8794, 23187-8794), SAN 363-4922. Tel: 757-221-3050. Circulation Tel: 757-221-3072. Interlibrary Loan Service Tel: 757-221-3089. Reference Tel: 757-221-3067. FAX: 757-221-2635. Circulation FAX: 757-221-3650. Interlibrary Loan Service FAX: 757-221-3088. Web Site: www.swem.wm.edu. *Dean,* Carrie Lynn Cooper; E-mail: clcooper@wm.edu; *Dir of Coll,* Catherine Reed; Tel: 757-221-7615, E-mail: careed@wm.edu; *Dir, Libr Develop,* Karlene N Jennings; Tel: 757-221-7779, E-mail: knjenn@wm.edu; *Dir, Media Serv,* Troy Davis; Tel: 757-221-2643, E-mail: mtdavi@wm.edu; *Dir, Spec Coll,* Dr Beatriz B Hardy; Tel: 757-221-3054, Fax: 757-221-5440, E-mail: bbhard@wm.edu; *Ref Librn,* Mary S Molineux; Tel: 757-221-3076, E-mail: msmoli@wm.edu; *Head, Acq,* Stephen D Clark; Tel: 757-221-3107, Fax: 757-221-3645, E-mail: sdclar@wm.edu; *Head, Cat,* Trish Kearns; Tel: 757-221-1940, E-mail: pmkear@wm.edu; *Head, Ref,* Donald J Welsh; Tel: 757-221-3068, E-mail: djwels@wm.edu; *Head, Ser,* Jean Sibley; Tel: 757-221-3103, E-mail: bjsibley@wm.edu; *Br Librn,* James T Deffenbaugh; Tel: 757-221-3057, E-mail: jtdeff@wm.edu; *Ref/Govt Doc Librn,* Dr Alan F Zoellner; Tel: 757-221-3065, E-mail: afzoel@wm.edu; *Circ Mgr,* David Morales; *Spec Projects,* Kay Domine; Tel: 757-221-3091, E-mail: kjdomi@wm.edu. Subject Specialists: *Music, Sciences,* James T Deffenbaugh; Staff 67 (MLS 24, Non-MLS 43)
Founded 1693. Enrl 7,036; Fac 567; Highest Degree: Doctorate
Library Holdings: Bk Vols 1,846,385
Special Collections: Books with fore-edge Paintings (Ralph Wark Coll); Dogs (Peter Chapin, Murray & Shirley Horowitz Colls); History of Books & Printing; Seed Catalogs; Tucker-Coleman Papers (Virginia Family), 1675-1956; United States History 17th-19th Centuries (Warren E Burger Coll); Virginia History, 17th-20th Centuries, mss. State Document Depository; US Document Depository
Automation Activity & Vendor Info: (Acquisitions) SirsiDynix; (Cataloging) SirsiDynix; (Circulation) SirsiDynix; (Course Reserve) SirsiDynix; (ILL) SirsiDynix; (OPAC) SirsiDynix; (Serials) SirsiDynix
Partic in Lyrasis
Friends of the Library Group

CL   THE WOLF LAW LIBRARY*, 613 S Henry St, 23187. (Mail add: PO Box 8795, 23187-8795), SAN 363-504X. Tel: 757-221-3255. Reference Tel: 757-221-3257. FAX: 757-221-3051. Web Site: www.wm.edu/law/lawlibrary. *Dir,* James Heller; Tel: 757-221-3252; *Head, Tech Serv,* Kevin Butterfield; *Instrul Serv Librn, Ref, Res,* Christopher Byrne; *Access Serv,* Martha Rush; *Ref Serv,* Frederick Dingledy; *Ref Serv,* Shelley Dowling; *Ref Serv,* Paul Hellyer; *Ref Serv,* Jennifer Sekula; Staff 7.5 (MLS 7.5)
Founded 1779. Enrl 630; Fac 35; Highest Degree: Doctorate
Jul 2008-Jun 2009 Income $2,400,000. Mats Exp $1,200,000. Sal $1,200,000
Library Holdings: Bk Titles 216,000; Bk Vols 406,000; Per Subs 4,000
Special Collections: Thomas Jefferson Law Books. US Document Depository
Subject Interests: Constitutional law, Environ law, Legal hist, Roman law
Automation Activity & Vendor Info: (Acquisitions) SirsiDynix; (Cataloging) SirsiDynix; (Circulation) SirsiDynix; (Course Reserve) SirsiDynix; (ILL) SirsiDynix; (OPAC) SirsiDynix; (Serials) SirsiDynix
Database Vendor: HeinOnline, LexisNexis, Westlaw
Partic in Lyrasis; OCLC Online Computer Library Center, Inc
Open Mon-Thurs (Winter) 7:30am-10pm, Fri 7:30-6, Sat 9-6, Sun 10-10; Mon-Fri (Summer) 8-6, Sat 10-3

S   COLONIAL WILLIAMSBURG FOUNDATION, John D Rockefeller Jr Library, 313 First St, 23185-4306. (Mail add: PO Box 1776, 23187-1776), SAN 363-5139. Tel: 757-565-8500. Circulation Tel: 757-565-8512. Reference Tel: 757-565-8510. FAX: 757-565-8508. E-mail: libref@cwf.org. Web Site: www.history.org. *Dir,* James Horn; Tel: 757-565-8501, E-mail: jhorn@cwf.org; *Assoc Librn,* Douglas Mayo; Tel: 757-565-8521, Fax: 757-565-8538, E-mail: dmayo@cwf.org; *Acq,* Annette Parham; Tel: 757-565-8532, E-mail: aparham@cwf.org; *Circ,* Joann Proper; E-mail: jproper@cwf.org; *Pub Serv,* Juleigh Clark; Tel: 757-565-8511, E-mail: jclark@cwf.org; Staff 10 (MLS 6, Non-MLS 4)
Founded 1933
Library Holdings: Bk Titles 60,000; Bk Vols 83,517; Per Subs 400
Special Collections: Research Query File, 1927 to present; Research Reports
Subject Interests: African-Am, Archit, Customs, Decorative art, Early Am periods, Economics, Govt, Hist presv, Mus studies, Music, Soc life
Automation Activity & Vendor Info: (Acquisitions) SirsiDynix; (Cataloging) SirsiDynix; (Circulation) SirsiDynix; (Course Reserve) SirsiDynix; (ILL) SirsiDynix; (Media Booking) SirsiDynix; (OPAC) SirsiDynix; (Serials) SirsiDynix
Database Vendor: OCLC FirstSearch
Wireless access
Function: For res purposes, ILL available
Publications: Early American History Research Reports from the Colonial Williamsburg Foundation Library, microfiche
Open Mon-Fri 9-5
Restriction: Circ limited, Open to pub for ref only
Branches:
JOHN D ROCKEFELLER JR LIBRARY-SPECIAL COLLECTIONS, 313 First St, 23185-4306. (Mail add: PO Box 1776, 23185-1776). Tel: 757-565-8520. FAX: 757-565-8528. E-mail: speccoll@cwf.org. *Archit Librn,* George Yetter; Tel: 757-565-8522; *Assoc Librn,* Douglas Mayo; Tel: 757-565-8521, E-mail: dmayo@cwf.org; Staff 2.5 (MLS 1.5, Non-MLS 1)
Founded 1929
Library Holdings: Bk Vols 12,500
Special Collections: A Lawrence Kocher Architecture Coll; Alden Hopkins Landscape Architecture Coll; Colonial Virginia & Chesapeake History Coll; Colonial Williamsburg Foundation Coll (1993); Eighteenth Century Music; Eighteenth Century Williamsburg Imprints; Francis Nicholson Papers; John Norton & Sons Papers; Robert Anderson Papers; Shirley Plantation Research Coll; Virginia Colonial Records Project; Webb-Prentis 18th Century Williamsburg Coll; William Blathwayt Papers; Wolcott Coll
Subject Interests: Early Am periods, Hist of Williamsburg Va & Chesapeake region in Colonial
Publications: Collections at the Colonial Williamsburg Foundation Library; Guide to the Manuscript; The Colonial Williamsburg Research Collections in Microform; The William Blathwayt Papers at Colonial Williamsburg, 1631-1722
Open Mon-Fri 9-12 & 1-5
Restriction: Closed stack, Pub use on premises
JOHN D ROCKEFELLER JR LIBRARY-VISUAL RESOURCES, 313 First St, 23185-4306. (Mail add: PO Box 1776, 23187-1776). Tel: 757-565-8540. FAX: 757-565-8548. E-mail: vrc@cwf.org. Web Site: www.colonialwilliamsburg.org. *AV,* Marianne Martin; Tel: 757-565-8541, E-mail: mmartin@cwf.org; Staff 1 (MLS 1)
Founded 1946
Library Holdings: AV Mats 100,000
Special Collections: Colonial Williamsburg Foundation Restoration & Programs; Museum Programs; Williamsburg Activities, History,

Personnel & Collections; Williamsburg's African-American Community in 1940s-1950s (Albert W Durant Coll)

Subject Interests: 18th Century archit, 18th Century decorative arts, 18th Century furnishing, 19th Century folk art, Am decorative arts, Colonial life, Colonial period, English decorative arts, Va-Chesapeake region archit

Restriction: Open by appt only

M   EASTERN STATE HOSPITAL*, Library Services, 4601 Ironbound Rd, 23188. (Mail add: PO Box 8791, 23187-8791), SAN 317-4700. Tel: 757-253-5387. FAX: 757-253-5192. E-mail: libraryservices@esh. Web Site: www.esh.dmhmrsas.virginia.gov. *Mgr,* Judy Harrell; Tel: 757-253-4310, E-mail: judy.harrell@esh.dmhmrsas.virginia.gov; *Mgr,* Sandra Kochersperger; Tel: 757-253-5457, Fax: 757-253-7078, E-mail: sandra.kochersperger@esh.dmhmrsas.virginia.gov; Staff 4 (MLS 1, Non-MLS 3)

Founded 1843

Library Holdings: Bk Titles 17,000; Bk Vols 17,800; Per Subs 343

Special Collections: Galt Papers, mss

Subject Interests: Nursing, Psychiat, Psychol, Soc work

Automation Activity & Vendor Info: (Cataloging) Follett Software; (Circulation) Follett Software; (OPAC) Follett Software

Database Vendor: Dialog, EBSCOhost, OCLC FirstSearch, OVID Technologies

Function: Outside serv via phone, mail, e-mail & web

Publications: Inflow

Partic in Dialog Corp; OCLC Online Computer Library Center, Inc; Tidewater Health Sci Librs

Open Mon-Fri 7:30-4:30

L   NATIONAL CENTER FOR STATE COURTS LIBRARY, 300 Newport Ave, 23185-4147. SAN 317-4719. Tel: 757-259-1826. Toll Free Tel: 800-616-6164. FAX: 757-259-2096. E-mail: library@ncsc.org. Web Site: www.ncsconline.org. *Libr Mgr,* Joan Cochet; E-mail: jcochet@ncsc.org; Staff 1 (Non-MLS 1)

Founded 1973

Library Holdings: Bk Titles 20,000; Bk Vols 40,000

Special Collections: Judicial Administration, videos; National Center for State Courts Reports; State Court Annual Reports

Subject Interests: Court improvement, Court mgt, Judicial admin

Automation Activity & Vendor Info: (Acquisitions) SirsiDynix; (Cataloging) SirsiDynix; (Circulation) SirsiDynix; (OPAC) SirsiDynix; (Serials) SirsiDynix

Database Vendor: Gale Cengage Learning, LexisNexis, OCLC FirstSearch

Publications: Acquisitions List (Quarterly); Video Catalog

Partic in OCLC Online Computer Library Center, Inc

Restriction: Open by appt only

Branches:

DENVER BRANCH, 707 17 St, Ste 2900, Denver, 80202-3429, SAN 375-6661. Tel: 303-293-3063. Toll Free Tel: 800-466-3063. FAX: 303-296-9007.

   Library Holdings: Bk Vols 3,000

   Restriction: Open by appt only

S   OMOHUNDRO INSTITUTE OF EARLY AMERICAN HISTORY & CULTURE*, Kellock Library, Swem Library, One Landrum Dr, 23185. (Mail add: PO Box 8781, 23187-8781), SAN 327-8832. Tel: 757-221-1126. FAX: 757-221-1047. Web Site: www.wm.edu/oieahc. *Archivist, Librn,* Patricia Higgs; E-mail: pvhigg@wm.edu

Library Holdings: Bk Titles 8,730; Per Subs 31

Open Mon-Fri 9-6

Restriction: Non-circulating

P   WILLIAMSBURG REGIONAL LIBRARY, 7770 Croaker Rd, 23188-7064. SAN 317-4727. Tel: 757-259-4040, 757-259-7770. Circulation Tel: 757-259-7753. Reference Tel: 757-259-7720. Administration Tel: 757-259-7777. FAX: 757-259-4079, 757-259-7798. Web Site: www.wrl.org. *Dir,* Dr John A Moorman; E-mail: jmoorman@wrl.org; *Asst Dir,* Genevieve S Owens; Tel: 757-259-7740; E-mail: gowens@mail.wrl.org; *Dir, Adult Serv,* Melissa Simpson; Tel: 757-259-4053, E-mail: msimpson@wrl.org; *Dir, Finance & Gen Serv,* Carrie Binsfeld; Tel: 757-259-4047, E-mail: cbinsfel@wrl.org; *Circ Serv Dir,* Christine White; Tel: 757-259-4063, E-mail: cwhite1@wrl.org; *Digital Serv Dir,* Barry Trott; Tel: 757-259-7747, E-mail: btrott@wrl.org; *Outreach Serv Dir,* Janet Crowther; Tel: 757-259-4066, E-mail: jcrowthe@wrl.org; *Prog Serv Dir,* Patrick Golden; Tel: 757-259-4071, E-mail: pgolden@mail.wrl.org; *Youth Serv Dir,* Noreen Bernstein; Tel: 757-259-4045, E-mail: nbernste@mail.wrl.org; Staff 34 (MLS 34)

Founded 1909. Pop 93,144; Circ 1,176,057

Jul 2011-Jun 2012 Income $5,766,020, State $292,562, City $779,369, County $4,067,456, Locally Generated Income $149,103, Other $477,530. Mats Exp $403,158, Books $210,952, Per/Ser (Incl. Access Fees) $2,540, Micro $5,132, AV Mat $78,423, Electronic Ref Mat (Incl. Access Fees) $106,111. Sal $3,285,529 (Prof $1,480,927)

Library Holdings: Audiobooks 10,734; Bks on Deafness & Sign Lang 92; Braille Volumes 7; CDs 5,538; DVDs 29,698; e-books 2,954; High Interest/Low Vocabulary Bk Vols 31; Large Print Bks 9,751; Microforms 70; Bk Titles 278,490; Bk Vols 352,382; Per Subs 478; Videos 781

Special Collections: Local Documents

Automation Activity & Vendor Info: (Acquisitions) SirsiDynix; (Cataloging) SirsiDynix; (Circulation) SirsiDynix; (OPAC) SirsiDynix

Database Vendor: EBSCOhost, Gale Cengage Learning, infoUSA, OCLC FirstSearch, ReferenceUSA, SirsiDynix

Wireless access

Publications: Ex Libris (Newsletter)

Special Services for the Deaf - TDD equip

Special Services for the Blind - Audio mat; BiFolkal kits; Bks on CD; Large print bks; Low vision equip

Open Mon-Thurs 10-9, Fri 10-6, Sat 10-5, Sun 1-5

Friends of the Library Group

Bookmobiles: 2

WINCHESTER

P   HANDLEY REGIONAL LIBRARY*, 100 W Piccadilly St, 22601. (Mail add: PO Box 58, 22601-0058), SAN 317-4735. Tel: 540-662-9041. FAX: 540-722-4769. Administration FAX: 540-662-9053. E-mail: hlref@handleyregional.org. Web Site: www.handleyregional.org. *Dir,* Trish Ridgeway; Tel: 540-662-9041, Ext 14, Fax: 540-662-9053, E-mail: tridgeway@handleyregional.org; *Bus Mgr,* Ann White; Tel: 540-662-9041, Ext 25; Staff 28 (MLS 8, Non-MLS 20)

Founded 1913. Pop 100,000; Circ 599,345

Library Holdings: AV Mats 22,572; Bk Vols 239,878; Per Subs 315; Talking Bks 4,969; Videos 13,522

Special Collections: Civil War Coll; Rare Local Newspapers; Virginiana Coll

Automation Activity & Vendor Info: (Cataloging) TLC (The Library Corporation); (OPAC) Winnebago Software Co

Database Vendor: EBSCOhost, Gale Cengage Learning, OCLC FirstSearch

Publications: The Friend

Mem of VA State Regional Librs

Open Mon-Wed 10-8, Thurs-Sat 10-5, Sun 1-5

Friends of the Library Group

Branches: 2

MARY JANE & JAMES L BOWMAN BRANCH, 871 Tasker Rd, Stephens City, 22655-2318. (Mail add: PO Box 1300, Stephens City, 22655-1300). Tel: 540-869-9000. Reference Tel: 540-869-9000, Ext 203. Information Services Tel: 540-869-9000, Ext 201. FAX: 540-869-9001. E-mail: hlref@handleyregional.org. Web Site: www.handleyregional.org. ; Staff 4 (MLS 4)

Founded 2001

Automation Activity & Vendor Info: (Acquisitions) TLC (The Library Corporation); (Circulation) TLC (The Library Corporation); (OPAC) TLC (The Library Corporation)

Publications: Handley Regional Library: The First One Hundred Years (Local historical information)

Open Mon-Wed 10-8, Thurs-Sat 10-5, Sun 1-5

Friends of the Library Group

CLARKE COUNTY LIBRARY, 101 Chalmers Ct, Berryville, 22611, SAN 375-5665. Tel: 540-955-5144. FAX: 540-955-3655. E-mail: ccl@handleyregional.org. *Br Mgr,* Laurine Kennedy

Open Mon & Tues 10-8, Wed 10-5, Thurs & Fri 10-1, Sat 10-2

Friends of the Library Group

Bookmobiles: 1

C   SHENANDOAH UNIVERSITY*, Alson H Smith Jr Library, 1460 University Dr, 22601. SAN 317-4743. Tel: 540-665-5424. Reference Tel: 540-665-5421. Toll Free Tel: 877-289-4611. FAX: 540-665-4609. E-mail: library@su.edu. Web Site: www.su.edu/library. *Dir,* Christopher A Bean; Tel: 540-665-4553, E-mail: cbean@su.edu; *Media Spec,* Kenneth Mickie; E-mail: kmickie@su.edu; *Pub Serv,* David McKinney; Tel: 540-665-4634, E-mail: dmckinne@su.edu; *Tech Serv,* Megan Williams; Tel: 540-665-4638, E-mail: mwilliam@su.edu; Staff 14 (MLS 6, Non-MLS 8)

Founded 1875. Enrl 2,500; Fac 210; Highest Degree: Doctorate

Jul 2006-Jun 2007 Income $885,443. Mats Exp $421,300, Books $44,000, Per/Ser (Incl. Access Fees) $210,000, Micro $13,000, AV Equip $18,100, AV Mat $4,000, Electronic Ref Mat (Incl. Access Fees) $125,000, Presv $4,200. Sal $480,000 (Prof $245,000)

Library Holdings: AV Mats 18,600; CDs 2,400; Electronic Media & Resources 72; Music Scores 16,200; Bk Vols 127,000; Per Subs 1,060; Videos 3,600

Special Collections: Religion (Evangelical United Brethren Church Historical Room); Shenandoah University Archives; Shenandoah Valley History

Subject Interests: Civil War, Dance, Educ, Music, Nursing, Phys therapy

Automation Activity & Vendor Info: (Acquisitions) SirsiDynix; (Cataloging) SirsiDynix; (Circulation) SirsiDynix; (Course Reserve)

SirsiDynix; (Media Booking) SirsiDynix; (OPAC) SirsiDynix; (Serials) SirsiDynix

Database Vendor: Gale Cengage Learning, LexisNexis, OCLC FirstSearch, OVID Technologies

Wireless access

Partic in Lyrasis; Shenandoah Valley Independent Cols Libr Coop; Virginia Independent College & University Library Association; Virtual Library of Virginia

Open Mon-Thurs 8-12, Fri 8-8, Sat 10-6, Sun 1pm-Midnight

Friends of the Library Group

WISE

P   LONESOME PINE REGIONAL LIBRARY*, 124 Library Rd SW, 24293-5907. SAN 363-5287. Tel: 276-328-8325. FAX: 276-328-1739. E-mail: reglib@lprlibrary.org. Web Site: www.lprlibrary.org. *Dir,* Amy Bond; E-mail: abond@lprlibrary.org; Staff 61 (MLS 2, Non-MLS 59)
Founded 1958. Pop 108,092; Circ 679,143
Library Holdings: AV Mats 39,759; Bk Vols 399,385; Per Subs 552; Talking Bks 13,142
Subject Interests: Genealogy, SW Va hist
Automation Activity & Vendor Info: (Acquisitions) TLC (The Library Corporation); (Cataloging) TLC (The Library Corporation); (Circulation) TLC (The Library Corporation); (ILL) TLC (The Library Corporation); (OPAC) TLC (The Library Corporation); (Serials) TLC (The Library Corporation)
Database Vendor: ProQuest
Branches: 9
COEBURN COMMUNITY, 111 Third St, Coeburn, 24230. (Mail add: PO Box 2169, Coeburn, 24230-3523), SAN 363-5317. Tel: 276-395-6152. FAX: 276-395-3563. E-mail: ccllib@lprlibrary.org. *Mgr,* Candess Hylton; Staff 5 (Non-MLS 5)
Founded 1972. Circ 73,796
Jul 2005-Jun 2006 Income $173,205, State $27,301, County $103,192, Other $42,712. Mats Exp $12,827, Books $8,602, Per/Ser (Incl. Access Fees) $1,786, AV Mat $2,439. Sal $80,975
Library Holdings: AV Mats 3,089; Bk Vols 35,448; Per Subs 47; Talking Bks 891
Open Mon, Wed, Fri & Sat 8:30-5, Tues & Thurs 8:30-7, Sun 2-5
Friends of the Library Group
JONNIE B DEEL MEMORIAL, 198 Chase St, Clintwood, 24228. (Mail add: PO Box 650, Clintwood, 24228-0650), SAN 363-5309. Tel: 276-926-6617. FAX: 276-926-6795. E-mail: jbdlib@lprlibrary.org. *Br Mgr,* Sheila Phipps; Staff 6 (Non-MLS 6)
Founded 1962. Circ 86,858
Jul 2005-Jun 2006 Income $182,104, State $39,832, County $109,897, Other $32,375. Mats Exp $27,187, Books $18,661, Per/Ser (Incl. Access Fees) $3,382, Micro $110, AV Mat $5,034. Sal $85,738
Library Holdings: AV Mats 3,367; Bk Vols 64,156; Per Subs 65; Talking Bks 1,358
Open Mon, Wed & Fri 8:30-5, Tues 8:30-8, Thurs 11:30-8, Sat 10-2, Sun 2-5
HAYSI PUBLIC, 314 Main St, Haysi, 24256. (Mail add: PO Box CC, Haysi, 24256-0431), SAN 363-5376. Tel: 276-865-4851. FAX: 276-865-5441. E-mail: hpllib@lprlibrary.org. *Br Mgr,* Shirley Hawkins; Staff 3 (Non-MLS 3)
Founded 1970. Circ 29,705
Jul 2005-Jun 2006 Income $126,835, State $16,698, County $82,906, Other $27,231. Mats Exp $7,992, Books $5,279, Per/Ser (Incl. Access Fees) $1,634, AV Mat $1,079. Sal $54,911
Library Holdings: AV Mats 1,145; Bk Vols 17,058; Per Subs 36; Talking Bks 655
Open Mon, Wed & Fri 8:30-5, Tues & Thurs 11-7:30, Sat 10-2
LEE COUNTY PUBLIC, 406 Joslyn Ave, Pennington Gap, 24277, SAN 363-5341. Tel: 276-546-1141. FAX: 276-546-5136. E-mail: lcplib@lprlibrary.org. *Br Mgr,* Audrey Evans; Staff 7 (Non-MLS 7)
Founded 1965. Circ 83,893
Jul 2005-Jun 2006 Income $180,893, State $41,744, County $96,073, Other $43,076. Mats Exp $27,629, Books $19,459, Per/Ser (Incl. Access Fees) $3,500, Micro $126, AV Mat $4,544. Sal $89,279
Library Holdings: AV Mats 3,547; Bk Vols 64,961; Per Subs 66; Talking Bks 1,801
Open Mon, Wed, Fri & Sat 8:30-5, Tues & Thurs 11:30-8, Sun 2-5
J FRED MATTHEWS MEMORIAL, 16552 Wise St, Saint Paul, 24283-3522. (Mail add: PO Box 1976, Saint Paul, 24283-1976), SAN 363-5430. Tel: 276-762-9702. FAX: 276-762-0528. E-mail: spblib@lprlibrary.org. *Br Mgr,* Charles Engle; Staff 5 (Non-MLS 5)
Founded 1975. Circ 56,613
Jul 2005-Jun 2006 Income $146,797, State $20,280, County $101,800, Other $24,717. Mats Exp $11,285, Books $7,218, Per/Ser (Incl. Access Fees) $1,801, AV Mat $2,266. Sal $65,010
Library Holdings: AV Mats 3,147; Bk Vols 29,758; Per Subs 42; Talking Bks 1,122
Open Mon, Wed, Fri & Sat 9-5, Tues & Thurs 11-7:30
Friends of the Library Group

ROSE HILL COMMUNITY, Main St, Rose Hill, 24281. (Mail add: PO Box 280, Rose Hill, 24281-0280), SAN 363-5422. Tel: 276-445-5329. FAX: 276-445-5329. E-mail: rhplib@lprlibrary.org. *Br Mgr,* Lela Johnson; Staff 1 (Non-MLS 1)
Founded 1979. Circ 9,875
Jul 2005-Jun 2006 Income $34,708, State $11,334, County $11,012, Other $12,362. Mats Exp $3,758, Books $1,806, Per/Ser (Incl. Access Fees) $867, AV Mat $1,085. Sal $8,430
Library Holdings: AV Mats 828; Bk Vols 6,200; Per Subs 20; Talking Bks 361
Open Mon & Fri 8:30-5, Tues & Thurs 11:30-8, Wed 8-Noon, Sat 10-2
SCOTT COUNTY PUBLIC, 297 W Jackson St, Gate City, 24251, SAN 363-5406. Tel: 276-386-3302. FAX: 276-386-2977. E-mail: scplib@lprlibrary.org. *Br Mgr,* Rita Walters; Staff 7 (Non-MLS 7)
Founded 1972. Circ 123,165
Jul 2005-Jun 2006 Income $242,674, State $55,715, County $102,815, Other $84,144. Mats Exp $34,544, Books $21,991, Per/Ser (Incl. Access Fees) $4,657, Micro $1,644, AV Mat $6,252. Sal $91,446
Library Holdings: AV Mats 5,627; Bk Vols 79,398; Per Subs 77; Talking Bks 2,318
Open Mon, Wed, Fri & Sat 8:30-5, Tues 8:30-8, Thurs 12-8, Sun 2-5
Friends of the Library Group
C   BASCOM SLEMP MEMORIAL, 11 Proctor St N, Big Stone Gap, 24219, SAN 363-549X. Tel: 276-523-1334. FAX: 276-523-5306. E-mail: cbslib@lprlibrary.org. *Br Mgr,* Christine Smith; Staff 6 (Non-MLS 6)
Founded 1974. Circ 71,470
Jul 2005-Jun 2006 Income $282,092, State $28,301, County $147,954, Other $105,837. Mats Exp $22,292, Books $16,247, Per/Ser (Incl. Access Fees) $3,295, Micro $110, AV Mat $2,640. Sal $101,738
Library Holdings: AV Mats 3,152; Bk Vols 53,931; Per Subs 65; Talking Bks 1,284
Open Mon, Wed, Fri & Sat 8:30-5, Tues 11:30-8, Thurs 8:30-8, Sun 2-5
Friends of the Library Group
WISE COUNTY PUBLIC, 124 Library Rd SW, 24293, SAN 363-552X. Tel: 276-328-8061. FAX: 276-328-1739. E-mail: wcplib@lprlibrary.org. *Br Mgr,* Linda Scarborough; Staff 10 (MLS 1, Non-MLS 9)
Founded 1958. Circ 145,628
Jul 2005-Jun 2006 Income $374,925, State $53,936, City $45,000, County $202,408, Other $73,581. Mats Exp $40,513, Books $26,492, Per/Ser (Incl. Access Fees) $7,586, Micro $1,680, AV Mat $4,755. Sal $193,418 (Prof $19,204)
Library Holdings: AV Mats 6,618; Bk Vols 135,430; Per Subs 158; Talking Bks 2,193
Open Mon, Tues & Thurs 8:30-8, Wed, Fri & Sat 8:30-5, Sun 2-5
Friends of the Library Group

C   UNIVERSITY OF VIRGINIA'S COLLEGE AT WISE*, John Cook Wyllie Library, One College Ave, 24293. SAN 317-4751. Tel: 276-328-0150. Circulation Tel: 276-328-0158. Interlibrary Loan Service Tel: 276-328-0160. Reference Tel: 276-328-0159. FAX: 276-328-0105. E-mail: vlf3z@uvawise.edu. Web Site: library.uvawise.edu. *Dir, Libr Serv,* Robin P Benke; Tel: 276-328-0151, E-mail: rpb@uvawise.edu; *Asst Dir, Pub Serv,* Angie Harvey; E-mail: akw2r@uvawise.edu; *Cat Librn,* Amelia C VanGundy; Tel: 276-328-0154, E-mail: acv6d@uvawise.edu; *Outreach Serv Librn,* Ann Duesing; Tel: 276-328-0168, E-mail: cad4n@uvawise.edu; *Ref Librn,* Shannon Steffey; Tel: 276-328-0157, E-mail: sb3h@uvawise.edu; Staff 14 (MLS 6, Non-MLS 8)
Founded 1954. Enrl 1,992; Fac 142; Highest Degree: Bachelor
Jul 2008-Jun 2009. Mats Exp $170,692, Books $25,109, Per/Ser (Incl. Access Fees) $73,943, Other Print Mats $9,601, Micro $21,274, AV Mat $2,818, Electronic Ref Mat (Incl. Access Fees) $34,006, Presv $3,940
Library Holdings: AV Mats 1,556; CDs 501; DVDs 298; e-books 8,525; e-journals 3,406; Microforms 68,405; Bk Titles 99,085; Bk Vols 144,919; Per Subs 720; Videos 1,498
Special Collections: Archives of Southwest Virginia Folklore Society; Beaty-Flannary Papers; Bruce Crawford Papers; Elihu Jasper Sutherland Papers; Emory L Hamilton Papers; James Taylor Adams Papers; Southwest Virginia (Archives of Southwest Virginia Historical Society; Trigg Floyd Papers; Virginia Coal Operators Coll). State Document Depository; US Document Depository
Subject Interests: Appalachian studies
Automation Activity & Vendor Info: (Acquisitions) SirsiDynix; (Cataloging) SirsiDynix; (Circulation) SirsiDynix; (Course Reserve) SirsiDynix; (ILL) OCLC; (OPAC) SirsiDynix; (Serials) SirsiDynix
Database Vendor: ABC-CLIO, ACM (Association for Computing Machinery), American Chemical Society, American Mathematical Society, BioOne, Blackwell's, Cambridge Scientific Abstracts, Cinahl Information Systems, EBSCOhost, Elsevier, Factiva.com, Facts on File, Gale Cengage Learning, H W Wilson, IEEE (Institute of Electrical & Electronics Engineers), Medline, Modern Language Association, OCLC FirstSearch, OCLC WorldCat, OVID Technologies, Project MUSE, ProQuest, PubMed, SirsiDynix, YBP Library Services
Wireless access
Publications: Guide to Archives & Special Collections; Information Guides; Periodicals & Newspaper Holdings List (Index to periodicals)

Partic in Lyrasis; OCLC Online Computer Library Center, Inc; Virtual Library of Virginia
Open Mon-Thurs 8-10, Fri 8-5, Sat 1-5, Sun 1:30-10

WOODBRIDGE

M   POTOMAC HOSPITAL*, Richard P Immerman MD Memorial Library, 2300 Opitz Blvd, 22191. Tel: 703-670-1331. FAX: 703-878-1619. E-mail: library@potomachospital.com. *Med Librn,* Pat Hammon; E-mail: phammon@sentara.com; Staff 1 (MLS 1)
Founded 1974
Library Holdings: Bk Titles 1,000; Bk Vols 1,050; Per Subs 175
Subject Interests: Allied health, Nursing
Partic in National Network of Libraries of Medicine Southeastern Atlantic Region
Restriction: Open to pub by appt only

WYTHEVILLE

J   WYTHEVILLE COMMUNITY COLLEGE LIBRARY*, 1000 E Main St, 24382. SAN 317-476X. Tel: 276-223-4743. FAX: 276-223-4745. Web Site: www.wcc.vccs.edu/library/index.php. *Dir,* Anna Ray Roberts; Tel: 276-223-4742, E-mail: wcrobea@wcc.vccs.edu; *Asst Librn,* George Mattis; Tel: 276-223-4744, E-mail: wcmattg@wcc.vccs.edu; Staff 3 (MLS 2, Non-MLS 1)
Founded 1963. Enrl 3,702; Fac 37; Highest Degree: Associate
Library Holdings: Bk Titles 26,016; Bk Vols 29,634; Per Subs 236
Special Collections: Local History & Genealogy (F B Kegley Library), bks, maps, mss, pamphlets. Oral History
Automation Activity & Vendor Info: (Cataloging) Ex Libris Group; (Circulation) Ex Libris Group; (OPAC) Ex Libris Group
Database Vendor: Gale Cengage Learning, OCLC FirstSearch, OCLC WorldCat, OVID Technologies
Partic in Virginia Commun Coll Syst; Virtual Library of Virginia
Open Mon-Thurs 8-8, Fri 8-5

YORKTOWN

S   NATIONAL PARK SERVICE*, Colonial National Historical Park Library, PO Box 210, 23690-0210. SAN 317-4778. Tel: 757-898-2410. FAX: 757-898-6346. *In Charge,* Karen G Rehm; Tel: 757-898-2416, E-mail: karen_rehm@nps.gov; *In Charge,* Jane M Sundberg; Tel: 757-898-2415, E-mail: jane_sundberg@nps.gov
Founded 1930
Library Holdings: Bk Vols 1,200
Subject Interests: Colonial hist, Revolutionary war hist
Restriction: Open by appt only

P   YORK COUNTY PUBLIC LIBRARY*, Tabb Library, 100 Long Green Blvd, 23693. SAN 317-3003. Tel: 757-890-5100. Circulation Tel: 757-890-5130. Reference Tel: 757-890-5120. FAX: 757-890-5127. Web Site: www.yorkcounty.gov/library. *Libr Dir,* Kevin W Smith; Tel: 757-890-5134, E-mail: smithk@yorkcounty.gov; *Head, Circ,* Tara Whitehead; Tel: 757-890-5135, E-mail: whitehea@yorkcounty.gov; *Head, Coll Develop,* Linda Blanchard; Tel: 757-890-5104, E-mail: linda.blanchard@yorkcounty.org; *Head, Youth Serv,* Susan Trask; Tel: 757-890-5110, E-mail: trask@yorkcounty.gov; Staff 33.5 (MLS 6, Non-MLS 27.5)
Founded 1968. Pop 65,000; Circ 576,134
Jul 2011-Jun 2012 Income (Main Library and Branch(s)) $2,525,384, State $147,983, County $2,377,401. Mats Exp $279,483, Books $181,198, Per/Ser (Incl. Access Fees) $2,000, AV Mat $68,883, Electronic Ref Mat (Incl. Access Fees) $27,402. Sal $1,623,188
Library Holdings: Bk Vols 156,000; Per Subs 160; Talking Bks 6,435; Videos 13,241
Automation Activity & Vendor Info: (Acquisitions) Horizon; (Cataloging) SirsiDynix; (ILL) OCLC WorldCat; (OPAC) Horizon; (Serials) SirsiDynix
Function: Adult bk club, Art exhibits, Audio & video playback equip for onsite use, AV serv, Bk club(s), Bks on CD, Children's prog, Computer training, Computers for patron use, Copy machines, Digital talking bks, Distance learning, e-mail serv, E-Reserves, Electronic databases & coll, Exhibits, Free DVD rentals, Handicapped accessible, Holiday prog, ILL available, Jail serv, Magnifiers for reading, Mail & tel request accepted, Music CDs, Newsp ref libr, Notary serv, Online cat, Online ref, Online searches, Orientations, Outreach serv, Photocopying/Printing, Preschool outreach, Prog for adults, Prog for children & young adult, Pub access computers, Ref & res, Ref serv available, Ref serv in person, Referrals accepted, Story hour, Summer reading prog, Teen prog, Telephone ref, Wheelchair accessible, Workshops, Writing prog
Open Mon-Thurs 10-9, Fri 10-6, Sat 10-5, Sun 1-5
Friends of the Library Group
Branches: 1
YORKTOWN BRANCH, 8500 George Washington Memorial Hwy, 23692. Tel: 757-890-3377. Circulation Tel: 757-890-5209. Reference Tel: 757-890-5207. FAX: 757-890-2956. *Libr Mgr,* Norma Colton; Tel: 757-890-3378, E-mail: coltonn@yorkcounty.gov
Founded 1968
Library Holdings: Bk Vols 60,000; Per Subs 260
Special Collections: Virginia & Local History Coll
Open Mon-Thurs 10-9, Fri 10-6, Sat 10-5, Sun 1-5
Friends of the Library Group

Date of Statistics: FY 2011
Population: 6,767,900
Population Served by Public Libraries: 6,647,030
    Unserved: 120,870
Total Volumes in Public Libraries: 17,660,434
    Volumes Per Capita: 2.66
Total Public Library Circulation: 85,794,833
Circulation Per Capita: 12.91
Total Public Library Income: $383,384,707
    Expenditures Per Capita: $55.64
    Source of Income: Over 96% from Local Jurisdiction
Number of County or Multi-county (Regional) Libraries: 26
    Counties Served: 36
Number of Mobile Units in State: 26

ABERDEEN

J   GRAYS HARBOR COLLEGE*, John Spellman Library, 1620 Edward P
Smith Dr, 98520-7599. SAN 317-4786. Tel: 360-538-4050. Reference Tel:
360-538-4054. Toll Free Tel: 800-562-4830, Ext 4050 (in state). FAX:
360-538-4294. E-mail: lib_ref@ghc.edu. Web Site: ghc.ctc.edu/library. *Asst
Dean,* Stanley W Horton; E-mail: shorton@ghc.edu; *Librn,* Adrienne
Roush; *Circ, Libr Tech,* Davis Hardee; *Circ, ILL, Libr Spec,* Valerie Busch;
Libr Tech, Media Serv, Tech Serv, Anna Patrick; *Libr Spec, Media Serv,
Tech Serv,* Cara Beth Stevenson; Staff 5 (MLS 2, Non-MLS 3)
Founded 1930. Highest Degree: Associate
Library Holdings: AV Mats 4,000; Bk Titles 33,527; Bk Vols 38,559; Per
Subs 241
Special Collections: Pacific Northwest; Small Business; Water/Fisheries
Subject Interests: Careers
Automation Activity & Vendor Info: (Acquisitions) Ex Libris Group;
(Cataloging) Ex Libris Group; (Circulation) Ex Libris Group; (OPAC) Ex
Libris Group; (Serials) Ex Libris Group
Partic in Western Libr Network
Open Mon-Wed 7:30am-8pm, Thurs 7:30-5, Fri 7:30-4:30, Sat 9-3

ANACORTES

P   ANACORTES PUBLIC LIBRARY*, 1220 Tenth St, 98221-1922. SAN
317-4794. Tel: 360-293-1910. FAX: 360-293-1929. Web Site:
library.cityofanacortes.org. *Dir,* Cynthia Harrison; Tel: 360-293-1926, Ext
23, E-mail: cynthiah@cityofanacortes.org; *Adult Serv,* Regina VanHess;
Tel: 360-293-1910, Ext 24, E-mail: ginav@cityofanacortes.org; *Ch,* Doug
Woods; *ILL,* Esther Noyes; Tel: 360-293-1910, Ext 25, E-mail:
esthern@cityofanacortes.org; Staff 3 (MLS 3)
Founded 1911. Pop 14,500; Circ 173,257
Library Holdings: Audiobooks 4,700; AV Mats 12,336; e-books 3,200;
Bk Vols 81,363; Per Subs 149
Automation Activity & Vendor Info: (Cataloging) SirsiDynix;
(Circulation) SirsiDynix; (Course Reserve) SirsiDynix; (ILL) OCLC;
(OPAC) SirsiDynix
Database Vendor: ProQuest
Partic in OCLC Online Computer Library Center, Inc
Open Mon 9-8, Tues & Wed 11-8, Thurs & Fri 11-6, Sat Noon-5, Sun 1-5
Friends of the Library Group

AUBURN

J   GREEN RIVER COMMUNITY COLLEGE*, Holman Library, 12401 SE
320th St, 98092-3699. SAN 317-4824. Tel: 253-833-9111, 253-924-0180.
Circulation Tel: 253-288-3491, Ext 2090. Reference Tel: 253-288-3491,
Ext 2091. Administration Tel: 253-833-9111, Ext 2099. Automation
Services Tel: 253-833-9111, Ext 2094. FAX: 253-288-3436, 253-288-3491.
Web Site: www.greenriver.edu/library. *Dean, Libr & Media Serv,* Kimberly
Nakano; Tel: 253-833-9111, Ext 3307, E-mail: knakano@greenriver.edu;
Libr Dir, Jennifer Dysart; E-mail: jdysart@greenriver.edu; *Instrul Serv
Librn,* Marjorie MacKenzie; Tel: 253-833-9111, Ext 2101, E-mail:
mmacken@greenriver.edu; *Circ Supvr,* Catherine Rabold; Tel:

253-833-9111, Ext 2093, E-mail: crabold@greenriver.edu; *Coll Mgt,*
Brenda Philip; Tel: 253-833-9111, Ext 2100, E-mail:
bphilip@greenriver.edu; *Media Spec,* David Prenovost; Tel: 253-833-9111,
Ext 2109, E-mail: dprenovo@greenriver.edu; *Tech Serv,* Ann Lovell; Tel:
253-833-9111, Ext 2098, E-mail: alovell@greenriver.edu; Staff 19.05 (MLS
6.7, Non-MLS 12.35)
Founded 1965. Enrl 5,400; Fac 267; Highest Degree: Associate
Jul 2005-Jun 2006 Income $1,355,000, State $804,000, Federal $26,000,
Locally Generated Income $525,000. Mats Exp $237,115, Books $92,300,
Per/Ser (Incl. Access Fees) $39,640, AV Equip $27,400, AV Mat $13,500,
Electronic Ref Mat (Incl. Access Fees) $64,275. Sal $648,000 (Prof
$338,500)
Library Holdings: Bk Titles 39,600; Bk Vols 53,000; Per Subs 285;
Videos 4,250
Automation Activity & Vendor Info: (Cataloging) Ex Libris Group;
(Circulation) Ex Libris Group; (Course Reserve) Ex Libris Group; (ILL)
OCLC; (OPAC) Ex Libris Group; (Serials) Ex Libris Group
Database Vendor: EBSCOhost, Gale Cengage Learning, ProQuest,
SerialsSolutions
Wireless access
Function: Audio & video playback equip for onsite use, Distance learning,
ILL available, Large print keyboards, Magnifiers for reading, Online
searches, Orientations, Ref serv available, Telephone ref, VHS videos
Special Services for the Blind - Assistive/Adapted tech devices, equip &
products; Closed circuit TV; Computer with voice synthesizer for visually
impaired persons; Reader equip; ZoomText magnification & reading
software
Open Mon-Thurs (Fall-Spring) 7am-9pm, Fri 7-4, Sun 1-7; Mon-Thurs
(Summer) 7:30-7:30, Sun 2-6

S   WHITE RIVER VALLEY MUSEUM LIBRARY*, 918 H St SE, 98002.
SAN 370-3215. Tel: 253-288-7433. FAX: 253-931-3098. Web Site:
www.wrvmuseum.org. *Dir,* Patricia Cosgrove; E-mail:
pcosgrove@auburnwa.gov
Founded 1959
Library Holdings: Bk Titles 2,000
Special Collections: Newpapers - Auburn & Kent 1890s-1982, photogs
Subject Interests: Local hist
Open Wed-Sun 12-4

BALLARD

S   THE SEATTLE METAPHYSICAL LIBRARY (AS-YOU-LIKE-IT
LIBRARY)*, 2220 NW Market St, Rm L-05, 98107. SAN 326-2049. Tel:
206-329-1794. E-mail: contact@SeattleMetaphysicalLibrary.org. Web Site:
www.seattlemetaphysicallibrary.org. *Exec Dir,* Margaret Bartley; E-mail:
margaret@seattlemetaphysicallibrary.org; Staff 2 (Non-MLS 2)
Founded 1961
Library Holdings: Audiobooks 100; AV Mats 400; Bks-By-Mail 11,000;
CDs 200; DVDs 400; Bk Titles 12,000; Per Subs 10; Videos 400
Special Collections: Alternative health; Alternative Science (Body-Mind
research, Tesla, W.Reich); Astrology (books and magazines); Rudolf

Steiner; UFOs; Western Esotericism - Masonic, Rosicrucian, Theosophy, Spiritualism; World Religion, mythology
Subject Interests: Alternative med, Ancient hist, Astrology, Holistic health, New Age, Occult, Relig, UFO phenomenon
Function: Archival coll, Audiobks via web, Bks on cassette, Bks on CD, CD-ROM, Free DVD rentals, Mail & tel request accepted, Mail loans to mem, Masonic res mat, Music CDs, Online cat, Spoken cassettes & CDs, Spoken cassettes & DVDs, VCDs, VHS videos, Video lending libr
Publications: News and Events (Online only)
Open Tues-Fri 4-8, Sat 1-5, Sun 1-6
Restriction: Circ to mem only, Fee for pub use, Internal circ only, Non-circulating coll, Non-circulating of rare bks, Open evenings by appt, Open to pub for ref & circ; with some limitations, Private libr, Sub libr
Friends of the Library Group

BELLEVUE

C   BELLEVUE COLLEGE*, Library Media Center, 3000 Landerholm Circle SE, 98007-6484. SAN 317-4832. Tel: 425-564-2252. Reference Tel: 425-564-6161. FAX: 425-564-6186. E-mail: reference@bellevuecollege.edu. Web Site: www.bellevuecollege.edu/lmc. *Dean,* Myra Van Vactor; E-mail: myra.vanvactor@bellevuecollege.edu; *Librn,* Kate Bradley; Tel: 425-564-2262, E-mail: kbradley@bellevuecollege.edu; *Librn,* Sayumi Irey; Tel: 425-564-2354, E-mail: sirey@bellevuecollege.edu; *Librn,* Nicole Longpre; Tel: 425-564-3071, E-mail: nlongpre@bellevuecollege.edu; *Librn,* David Oar; Tel: 425-564-3134, E-mail: doar@bellevuecollege.edu; *Librn,* Shahla Rowhani; Tel: 425-564-2260, E-mail: srowhani@bellevuecollege.edu; Staff 15 (MLS 7, Non-MLS 8)
Founded 1966. Enrl 11,000; Highest Degree: Bachelor
Jul 2009-Jun 2010 Income $1,300,000, State $1,240,000, Locally Generated Income $60,000. Mats Exp $1,300,000, Books $77,000, Per/Ser (Incl. Access Fees) $150,600, AV Equip $18,600, AV Mat $13,500, Electronic Ref Mat (Incl. Access Fees) $5,000. Sal $790,123 (Prof $441,546)
Library Holdings: High Interest/Low Vocabulary Bk Vols 200; Bk Vols 45,000; Per Subs 400
Automation Activity & Vendor Info: (Acquisitions) Ex Libris Group; (Cataloging) Ex Libris Group; (Circulation) Ex Libris Group; (ILL) OCLC FirstSearch; (OPAC) Ex Libris Group; (Serials) Ex Libris Group
Database Vendor: ARTstor, Backstage Library Works, Cinahl Information Systems, EBSCOhost, Ex Libris Group, Facts on File, Gale Cengage Learning, Hoovers, Ingram Library Services, LearningExpress, Natural Standard, netLibrary, OCLC FirstSearch, OCLC WorldCat, Oxford Online, ProQuest, ScienceDirect, SerialsSolutions, Standard & Poor's, WT Cox
Wireless access
Partic in Orbis Cascade Alliance; ORCA Consortium
Special Services for the Blind - Computer access aids
Open Mon-Thurs (Fall-Spring) 7am-8pm, Fri 7-5, Sun 1-5

C   CITY UNIVERSITY OF SEATTLE*, Vi Tasler Library, 150-120th Ave NE, 98005-3019. (Mail add: 11900 NE First St, 98005-3030), SAN 321-7191. Tel: 425-709-3444. Circulation Tel: 425-709-3440. Interlibrary Loan Service Tel: 425-709-3454. Reference Tel: 425-709-3447. Administration Tel: 425-709-3445. Toll Free Tel: 800-526-4269. FAX: 425-709-3455. E-mail: library@cityu.edu. Web Site: www.cityu.edu/library. *Dir of Libr Serv,* Mary Mara; Staff 12 (MLS 7, Non-MLS 5)
Founded 1973. Enrl 6,500; Highest Degree: Master
Jul 2009-Jun 2010. Mats Exp $287,350, Books $22,500, Micro $1,900, AV Mat $550, Electronic Ref Mat (Incl. Access Fees) $262,400. Sal $612,500
Library Holdings: AV Mats 2,970; e-books 17,340; Electronic Media & Resources 66; Microforms 551,100; Bk Vols 26,086; Per Subs 31,294; Videos 2,105
Subject Interests: Bus, Communications, Computer syst, Educ, Psychol
Automation Activity & Vendor Info: (Acquisitions) Ex Libris Group; (Cataloging) Ex Libris Group; (Circulation) Ex Libris Group; (Course Reserve) Ex Libris Group; (ILL) Clio; (OPAC) Ex Libris Group; (Serials) Ex Libris Group
Database Vendor: ACM (Association for Computing Machinery), Alexander Street Press, American Psychological Association (APA), Discovery Education, Dun & Bradstreet, EBSCOhost, IEEE (Institute of Electrical & Electronics Engineers), LexisNexis, Mergent Online, netLibrary, OCLC FirstSearch, ProQuest, PubMed, Standard & Poor's
Wireless access
Partic in OCLC Online Computer Library Center, Inc; Orbis Cascade Alliance
Open Mon-Thurs 9-9, Fri & Sat 9-5

BELLINGHAM

P   BELLINGHAM PUBLIC LIBRARY, 210 Central Ave, CS-9710, 98227-9710. SAN 363-5589. Tel: 360-778-7323. Administration Tel: 360-778-7220. Web Site: www.bellinghampubliclibrary.org. *Dir,* Pamela Nyberg Kiesner; Tel: 360-778-7221; *Asst Dir,* Christine Perkins; Tel: 360-778-7206; *Head, Tech Serv,* Madeline A Sheplor; *Pub Serv Librn,*

Katie Bray; *Ref & Coll Develop Librn,* Beth Farley; *Acq,* Cathy Coldren; *Ch,* Bethany Hoglund; *ILL,* Fay Fenske; *Ref & Teen Serv,* Jennifer Lovchik; Staff 43.12 (MLS 9, Non-MLS 34.12)
Founded 1904. Pop 81,070; Circ 1,645,360
Jan 2011-Dec 2011 Income (Main Library and Branch(s)) $3,522,326, City $3,113,099, County $139,733, Locally Generated Income $269,494. Mats Exp $408,109. Sal $2,345,192
Library Holdings: Audiobooks 5,750; CDs 12,240; DVDs 14,939; e-books 1,106; Electronic Media & Resources 7,929; Bk Titles 186,683
Special Collections: Local History Coll. State Document Depository; US Document Depository
Automation Activity & Vendor Info: (Acquisitions) Horizon; (Cataloging) OCLC Connexion; (Circulation) Horizon; (ILL) OCLC WorldCat; (OPAC) Horizon; (Serials) Horizon
Database Vendor: Baker & Taylor, Booklist Online, EBSCO Information Services, Facts on File, LearningExpress, Marcive, Inc, Newsbank, OCLC FirstSearch, OCLC WorldCat, ProQuest, ReferenceUSA, SirsiDynix, Tech Logic, ValueLine
Wireless access
Function: Adult bk club, Adult literacy prog, Children's prog, Computer training, Computers for patron use, Copy machines, Free DVD rentals, Home delivery & serv to Sr ctr & nursing homes, Homebound delivery serv, ILL available, Jazz prog, Magnifiers for reading, Music CDs, Online cat, Online ref, Online searches, Outreach serv, OverDrive digital audio bks, Photocopying/Printing, Prog for adults, Prog for children & young adult, Pub access computers, Ref serv available, Story hour, Summer reading prog, Tax forms, Teen prog, Wheelchair accessible
Partic in OCLC Online Computer Library Center, Inc
Special Services for the Deaf - Bks on deafness & sign lang; Closed caption videos; High interest/low vocabulary bks; Video relay serv
Special Services for the Blind - Accessible computers
Open Mon & Tues 10-8, Wed-Sat 10-6
Friends of the Library Group
Branches: 2
BARKLEY, 3111 Newmarket St, Ste 102, 98226. Tel: 360-778-7290. *Asst Dir,* Christine Perkins; Tel: 360-778-7206, E-mail: cperkins@cob.org; Staff 1.25 (Non-MLS 1.25)
Founded 2008
FAIRHAVEN, 1117 12th St, 98225, SAN 363-5619. Tel: 360-778-7188. FAX: 360-778-7192. *In Charge,* Donna Grasdock; Staff 1.25 (Non-MLS 1.25)
Library Holdings: Bk Vols 10,000
Open Tues-Sat 2-6
Friends of the Library Group

J   BELLINGHAM TECHNICAL COLLEGE LIBRARY, 3028 Lindbergh Ave, 98225-1599. Tel: 360-752-8383. Interlibrary Loan Service Tel: 360-752-8371. Administration Tel: 360-752-8472. FAX: 360-752-8384. Interlibrary Loan Service FAX: 360-752-7171. E-mail: library@btc.ctc.edu. Web Site: www.btc.ctc.edu/library/index.asp. *Dir,* Jane E Blume; E-mail: jblume@btc.ctc.edu; *Librn,* Traci Taylor; Tel: 360-752-8488; *Acq,* Barbara Satushek; *Cat,* Lynn Robinson; *Circ,* Sallie Davis; *Media Serv,* Craig Perry-Ollila; *Tech/eLearning,* Dawn Hawley; E-mail: dhawley@btc.ctc.edu; Staff 1.75 (MLS 1.75)
Founded 1995
Library Holdings: e-journals 2,700; Bk Titles 15,600; Per Subs 130
Automation Activity & Vendor Info: (Cataloging) Ex Libris Group; (Circulation) Ex Libris Group; (Course Reserve) Ex Libris Group; (ILL) OCLC FirstSearch; (OPAC) Ex Libris Group; (Serials) Ex Libris Group
Database Vendor: ProQuest
Wireless access
Special Services for the Blind - Audio mat
Open Mon-Thurs 7-7, Fri 7-4

C   HUXLEY COLLEGE OF THE ENVIRONMENT*, Map Library, Western Washington University, AH 101, 516 High St, 98225-9085. SAN 375-3077. Tel: 360-650-3272. FAX: 360-778-0273. Web Site: www.ac.wwu.edu/~maplib. *Interim Dir,* Evan Thornberry; E-mail: evan.thornberry@wwu.edu
Founded 1957
Library Holdings: Bk Vols 1,200
Open Mon-Fri 10-4

C   NORTHWEST INDIAN COLLEGE LIBRARY*, 2520 Kwina Rd, 98226. Tel: 360-392-4204. Toll Free Tel: 866-676-2772. FAX: 360-733-3385. E-mail: library@nwic.edu. Web Site: www.nwic.edu. *Libr Dir,* Jani Costilla; Tel: 360-392-4214
Founded 1983
Library Holdings: Bk Titles 35,000
Wireless access
Open Mon-Fri 8-5

M　ST JOSEPH HOSPITAL LIBRARY*, 2901 Squalicum Pkwy, 98225. SAN
　　317-4867. Tel: 360-738-6786. FAX: 360-715-4106. *Librn,* Beula Horak;
　　Librn, Kendra Thulin
　　Founded 1975
　　Library Holdings: Bk Vols 700; Per Subs 100
　　Subject Interests: Consumer health
　　Wireless access
　　Partic in Pacific NW Regional Health Sci Libr; Washington Medical
　　Librarians Association (WMLA)
　　Restriction: Open to others by appt, Staff & mem only

C　WESTERN WASHINGTON UNIVERSITY, Western Libraries, 516 High
　　St, MS 9103, 98225. SAN 363-5643. Tel: 360-650-3050. Circulation Tel:
　　360-650-3084. Interlibrary Loan Service Tel: 360-650-3076. Reference Tel:
　　360-650-3094. FAX: 360-650-3044. Web Site: www.library.wwu.edu.
　　Interim Dean of Libr, Rick Osen; Tel: 360-650-3051, E-mail:
　　Rick.Osen@wwu.edu; *Actg Asst Dean, Coll & Tech, Head, Info Tech,*
　　Andrea Peterson; Tel: 360-650-3894, Fax: 360-650-3954, E-mail:
　　andrea.peterson@wwu.edu; *Assoc Dean, Pub Serv,* Michael Lorenzen; Tel:
　　360-650-4449, E-mail: Michael.Lorenzen@wwu.edu; *Dir, Heritage Res,*
　　Elizabeth Joffrion; Tel: 360-650-3283, E-mail:
　　Elizabeth.Joffrion@wwu.edu; *Head, Circ,* Kimberley Marsicek; Tel:
　　360-650-7776, E-mail: kim.marsicek@wwu.edu; *Head, ILL & Assessment
　　Coordr,* Frank Haulgren; Tel: 360-650-7639, E-mail:
　　frank.haulgren@wwu.edu; *Head Music Libr,* Marian Ritter; Tel:
　　630-650-3696, E-mail: marian.ritter@wwu.edu; *Interim Head, Map Libr,
　　Ref Librn,* Rob Lopresti; Tel: 360-650-3342, E-mail:
　　rob.lopresti@wwu.edu; *Coll Develop Librn,* Jeff Purdue; Tel:
　　360-650-3079, E-mail: jeffery.purdue@wwu.edu; *Diversity & Disabilities
　　Serv Librn,* Rebecca Marrall; Tel: 360-650-4493, E-mail:
　　Rebecca.Marrall@wwu.edu; *Extended Educ Librn,* J Gabriel Gossett; Tel:
　　360-650-7555, E-mail: gabriel.gossett@wwu.edu; *Integrated Syst Librn &
　　Principal Cataloger,* Bob Thomas; Tel: 360-650-7458, E-mail:
　　bob.thomas@wwu.edu; *Librn, Col of Bus & Econ,* Elizabeth Stephan; Tel:
　　360-650-2061, E-mail: elizabeth.stephan@wwu.edu; *Librn, Woodring Col,*
　　Sylvia Tag; Tel: 360-650-7992, E-mail: sylvia.tag@wwu.edu; *Ref &
　　Digitization Librn,* Peter Smith; Tel: 360-650-3175, E-mail:
　　peter.smith@wwu.edu; *Ref Librn,* Jeanne Armstrong; Tel: 360-650-7667,
　　E-mail: jeanne.armstrong@wwu.edu; *Ref Librn,* Margaret Fast; Tel:
　　360-650-3174, E-mail: margaret.faust@wwu.edu; *Ref Librn,* Leza Madsen;
　　Tel: 360-650-7583, E-mail: leza.madsen@wwu.edu; *Ref Librn,* Paul Piper;
　　Tel: 360-650-3097, E-mail: paul.piper@wwu.edu; *Mgr, Univ Rec Ctr,* Tony
　　Kurtz; Tel: 360-650-3124, E-mail: Tony.Kurtz@wwu.edu; *Archivist, Ctr for
　　Pac NW Studies,* Ruth Steele; Tel: 360-650-7747, E-mail:
　　Ruth.Steele@wwu.edu. Subject Specialists: *Music,* Marian Ritter; Staff 60
　　(MLS 15, Non-MLS 45)
　　Founded 1899. Enrl 13,500; Highest Degree: Master
　　Library Holdings: Bk Titles 650,000; Bk Vols 800,000; Per Subs 4,900
　　Special Collections: Canadian Coll; Children's Literature Coll; Fly Fishing
　　Coll; Mongolia-Russian Far East Coll. Oral History; State Document
　　Depository; US Document Depository
　　Automation Activity & Vendor Info: (Cataloging) Innovative Interfaces,
　　Inc; (Circulation) Innovative Interfaces, Inc; (Course Reserve) Innovative
　　Interfaces, Inc; (Media Booking) Innovative Interfaces, Inc; (OPAC)
　　Innovative Interfaces, Inc; (Serials) Innovative Interfaces, Inc
　　Database Vendor: Innovative Interfaces, Inc INN - View
　　Wireless access
　　Function: ILL available
　　Partic in Wash Coop Libr Project
　　Open Mon-Thurs 7:30am-Midnight, Fri 7:30-6, Sat 10-6, Sun
　　Noon-Midnight

J　WHATCOM COMMUNITY COLLEGE LIBRARY, 237 W Kellogg Rd,
　　98226. SAN 317-4875. Tel: 360-383-3300. Interlibrary Loan Service Tel:
　　360-383-3294. Reference Tel: 360-383-3285. Administration Tel:
　　360-383-3295. Web Site: library.whatcom.ctc.edu. *Dir,* Linda Lambert; *Coll
　　Develop Librn, Instruction Librn,* Kiki Tommila; *Instruction & Ref Librn,*
　　Margaret Bikman; *Instruction & Ref Librn,* Scott Blume; *Instruction & Ref
　　Librn,* Jon McConnel; *Instruction & Ref Librn,* Ro McKernan; *Syst
　　Instruction Librn,* Sally Sheedy; *Circ,* Linda Compton-Smith; *Circ,*
　　Catherine Gundred; *Circ, Reserves,* Ara Taylor; *Circ,* Erik Wallace; *Media
　　Serv,* Jim Dodd; *ILL, Tech Serv,* Sarah Vanderpool; *Tech Serv,* Heather
　　Williams; Staff 14 (MLS 5, Non-MLS 9)
　　Founded 1972. Enrl 4,000; Fac 289; Highest Degree: Associate
　　Library Holdings: Bk Vols 38,837; Per Subs 72
　　Automation Activity & Vendor Info: (Acquisitions) Ex Libris Group;
　　(Cataloging) Ex Libris Group; (Circulation) Ex Libris Group; (Course
　　Reserve) Ex Libris Group; (ILL) OCLC FirstSearch; (OPAC) Ex Libris
　　Group
　　Database Vendor: ARTstor, Backstage Library Works, Baker & Taylor,
　　CQ Press, ebrary, EBSCOhost, Gale Cengage Learning, Medline,
　　netLibrary, Newsbank, OCLC CAMIO, OCLC FirstSearch, OCLC
　　WebJunction, OCLC WorldCat, ProQuest, Westlaw
　　Wireless access

Function: Archival coll, Audio & video playback equip for onsite use,
Audiobks via web, Computers for patron use, Copy machines, Electronic
databases & coll, Exhibits, ILL available, Music CDs, Online cat, Online
ref, Online searches, Orientations, Photocopying/Printing, Ref & res, VHS
videos
Open Mon-Thurs (Fall-Spring) 8am-9pm, Fri 8-5, Sat 10-4; Mon-Thurs
(Summer) 8-4

GL　WHATCOM COUNTY LAW LIBRARY*, Courthouse, Ste B-03, 311
　　Grand Ave, 98225. Tel: 360-676-6556. FAX: 360-676-7727. TDD:
　　360-738-4555. E-mail: lawlib@co.whatcom.wa.us. Web Site:
　　www.whatcomlawlibrary.org. *Law Librn,* Virginia Tucker; Staff 0.5 (MLS
　　0.5)
　　Library Holdings: Bk Vols 16,000
　　Database Vendor: LexisNexis, Westlaw
　　Wireless access

P　WHATCOM COUNTY LIBRARY SYSTEM*, 5205 Northwest Dr,
　　98226-9050. SAN 363-5732. Tel: 360-384-3150. Reference Tel:
　　360-354-4883. FAX: 360-384-4947. Reference FAX: 360-354-3149. Web
　　Site: www.wcls.org. *Dir,* Joan Airoldi; Tel: 360-384-3150, Ext 201, E-mail:
　　joan.airoldi@wcls.org; *Cat & Coll Librn,* Theresa Hepker; *Ch,* Theresa
　　Hadley; *Admin Serv Mgr,* Kyle Teeter; *IT Serv Mgr,* Geoff Fitzpatrick; *Pub
　　Serv Mgr,* Regan Robinson; *Ref Serv Coordr, Res Br Mgr,* Sarah Foster;
　　Syst Design/Coll Mgr, Robin Barker; *Commun Relations Coordr,* Lizz
　　Roberts; *Coordr, Teen Serv,* Aubri Keleman; *Pub Serv Coordr,* Lisa
　　Gresham; *Training & Develop Coordr,* Jeanne Fondrie; *Web Serv Coordr,*
　　Nathaniel Jenkins; *Youth Serv Coordr,* Catherine Sarette; *ILL & Circ Spec,*
　　Mary Matter; *Human Res,* Christina Read; Staff 82 (MLS 13, Non-MLS
　　69)
　　Founded 1945. Circ 1,567,130
　　Library Holdings: Audiobooks 13,147; AV Mats 50,968; CDs 13,190;
　　DVDs 19,267; Large Print Bks 5,953; Bk Vols 245,425; Per Subs 1,017;
　　Videos 4,200
　　Automation Activity & Vendor Info: (Circulation) Horizon
　　Database Vendor: BookLetters LLC, Gale Cengage Learning,
　　LearningExpress, Newsbank, ProQuest, ReferenceUSA,
　　TumbleBookLibrary, World Book Online
　　Wireless access
　　Partic in OCLC Online Computer Library Center, Inc; Washington Digital
　　Library Consortium
　　Friends of the Library Group
　　Branches: 9
　　BLAINE BRANCH, 610 Third St, Blaine, 98230, SAN 363-5767. Tel:
　　　360-332-8146. FAX: 360-332-8146. *Br Mgr,* Deborah Farmer; E-mail:
　　　debby.farmer@wcls.org
　　　Open Mon-Thurs 10-8, Fri & Sat 10-6
　　　Friends of the Library Group
　　DEMING BRANCH, 5044 Mount Baker Hwy, Deming, 98244. (Mail add:
　　　PO Box 357, Deming, 98244). Tel: 360-592-2422. FAX: 360-592-2422.
　　　Br Mgr, Katrina Carabba; E-mail: katrina.carabba@wcls.org
　　　Open Mon, Tues & Thurs 10-9, Fri & Sat 10-6
　　　Friends of the Library Group
　　EVERSON MCBEATH COMMUNITY, 104 Kirsch Dr, Everson, 98247.
　　　(Mail add: PO Box 250, Everson, 98247). Tel: 360-966-5100. FAX:
　　　360-966-5100. *Br Mgr,* Eileen Shaw; E-mail: eileen.shaw@wcls.org
　　　Open Mon-Wed 10-8, Thurs & Sun 2-6, Fri & Sat 10-6
　　　Friends of the Library Group
　　FERNDALE BRANCH, 2007 Cherry St, Ferndale, 98248. (Mail add: PO
　　　Box 1209, Ferndale, 98248-1209), SAN 363-5759. Tel: 360-384-3647.
　　　FAX: 360-384-6224. *Br Mgr,* Sarah Koehler; E-mail:
　　　sarah.koehler@wcls.org
　　　Open Mon-Thurs 10-9, Fri & Sat 10-6, Sun 1-5
　　　Friends of the Library Group
　　ISLAND BRANCH, 2144 S Nugent Rd, Lummi Island, 98262. (Mail add:
　　　PO Box 90, Lummi Island, 98262-0090). Tel: 360-758-7145. FAX:
　　　360-758-7145. *Br Mgr,* Karly Tucker; E-mail: karly.tucker@wcls.org
　　　Open Tues & Thurs 2-8, Sat 10-4
　　　Friends of the Library Group
　　LYNDEN BRANCH, 216 Fourth St, Lynden, 98264, SAN 363-5910. Tel:
　　　360-354-4883. FAX: 360-354-3149. *Br Mgr,* Sarah Foster; E-mail:
　　　sarah.foster@wcls.org
　　　Function: Ref serv available
　　　Open Mon-Thurs 10-9, Fri & Sat 10-6
　　　Friends of the Library Group
　　NORTH FORK COMMUNITY LIBRARY, 7506 Kendall Rd, Maple Falls,
　　　98266. (Mail add: PO Box 310, Maple Falls, 98266). Tel: 360-599-2020.
　　　FAX: 360-599-2020. *Br Mgr,* Georgina Furlong-Head; E-mail:
　　　georgina.furlong-head@wcls.org
　　　Open Mon & Tues 10-6, Thurs 1-8, Sat 10-5
　　　Friends of the Library Group
　　POINT ROBERTS BRANCH, Community Center, 1487 Gulf Rd, Point
　　　Roberts, 98281. (Mail add: PO Box 970, Point Roberts, 98281-0970),
　　　SAN 363-6003. Tel: 360-945-6545. FAX: 360-945-6545. *Br Mgr,* Kris
　　　Lomedico; E-mail: kris.lomedico@wcls.org

Open Tues 2-8, Wed 11-5, Sat 10-4
Friends of the Library Group
SUMAS BRANCH, 451 Second St, Sumas, 98295. (Mail add: PO Box
215, Sumas, 98295-0215). Tel: 360-988-2501. FAX: 360-988-2501. *Br
Mgr*, Karin Schulhauser; E-mail: karin.schulhauser@wcls.org
Open Mon & Wed 12-7:30, Sat 10-4
Friends of the Library Group
Bookmobiles: 1. Mobile Servs Mgr, Kathleen Neece

BREMERTON

L   HARRISON MEMORIAL HOSPITAL*, Robert S Frech Health Science
Library, 2520 Cherry Ave, 98310. SAN 327-7062. Tel: 360-792-6500. Toll
Free Tel: 800-281-4024. FAX: 360-475-8566. Web Site:
harrisonhospital.org. *Librn*, Dan Nolan; E-mail:
dannolan@hmh.westsound.net; Staff 2 (MLS 1, Non-MLS 1)
Founded 1918
Library Holdings: Bk Titles 900; Bk Vols 1,300; Per Subs 110
Automation Activity & Vendor Info: (Acquisitions) Inmagic, Inc.;
(Cataloging) Inmagic, Inc.; (Circulation) Inmagic, Inc.; (Course Reserve)
Inmagic, Inc.; (ILL) Inmagic, Inc.; (Media Booking) Inmagic, Inc.; (OPAC)
Inmagic, Inc.; (Serials) Inmagic, Inc.
Open Mon-Fri 7-3:30

S   KITSAP COUNTY HISTORICAL SOCIETY*, Museum Library, 280
Fourth St, 98337-1813. SAN 327-4292. Tel: 360-479-6226. FAX:
360-415-9294. E-mail: khsinfo@kitsaphistory.org. Web Site:
www.kitsaphistory.org. *Res Coordr*, Bonnie Chrey; E-mail:
research@kitsaphistory.org; *Archivist*, Carolyn McClurkan; Staff 3 (MLS 2,
Non-MLS 1)
Founded 1948
Library Holdings: Bk Titles 2,000
Special Collections: Kitsap County; Washington State. Oral History
Function: Res libr
Restriction: Open to pub by appt only

P   KITSAP REGIONAL LIBRARY, 1301 Sylvan Way, 98310-3498. SAN
363-6097. Tel: 360-405-9100. Interlibrary Loan Service Tel: 360-405-9109.
Administration Tel: 360-405-9158. Toll Free Tel: 877-883-9900. FAX:
360-405-9128. TDD: 360-405-9125. Web Site: www.krl.org. *Exec Dir,
Found*, Jaime Forsyth; Tel: 360-475-9039, E-mail: jforsyth@krl.org; *Chief
Financial Officer*, Robert Goldstein; Tel: 360-405-9137, E-mail:
bgoldstein@krl.org; *Libr Dir*, Jill Jean; Tel: 360-405-9136, Fax:
360-405-9156, E-mail: jjean@krl.org; *Dir, Support Serv Div*, Carol
Schuyler; Tel: 360-405-9127, E-mail: cschuyler@krl.org; *Dir, Commun
Relations*, Jeff Brody; Tel: 360-475-9032, E-mail: jbrody@krl.org; *Dir,
Human Res*, Jim Wilson; Tel: 360-475-9164, E-mail: jwilson@krl.org; *Dir,
Info Tech & Fac Div*, Susan Whitford; Tel: 360-475-9176, E-mail:
swhitford@krl.org; *Dir, Libr Serv*, Ruth Bond; Tel: 360-415-6727, E-mail:
rbond@krl.org; *Coll Mgr*, John Fossett; Tel: 360-405-9101, E-mail:
jfossett@krl.org; *Fac Mgr*, Henry Bankart; Tel: 360-405-9153, E-mail:
hbankart@krl.org; *Finance Mgr*, Linda Penovich; Tel: 360-415-6729,
E-mail: lpenovich@krl.org; *Tech Serv Mgr*, Anne Ross; Tel: 360-405-9122,
E-mail: aross@krl.org. Subject Specialists: *Media*, John Fossett; Staff 32.85
(MLS 31.85, Non-MLS 1)
Founded 1955. Pop 253,900; Circ 2,534,644
Jan 2011-Dec 2011 Income (Main Library and Branch(s)) $10,533,943,
Locally Generated Income $9,933,909, Other $600,034. Mats Exp
$1,143,999, Books $575,940, Other Print Mats $84,570, AV Mat $233,629,
Electronic Ref Mat (Incl. Access Fees) $122,880. Sal $6,216,165
Library Holdings: Audiobooks 17,862; AV Mats 55,853; CDs 14,030;
DVDs 22,734; e-books 3,327; Large Print Bks 7,639; Microforms 3,128;
Bk Vols 422,301; Per Subs 804
Special Collections: Northwest Coll
Automation Activity & Vendor Info: (Acquisitions) Polaris Library
Systems; (Cataloging) Polaris Library Systems; (Circulation) Polaris
Library Systems; (ILL) OCLC; (OPAC) Polaris Library Systems; (Serials)
Polaris Library Systems
Database Vendor: Polaris Library Systems
Wireless access
Partic in OCLC Online Computer Library Center, Inc
Friends of the Library Group
Branches: 9
BAINBRIDGE ISLAND BRANCH, 1270 Madison Ave N, Bainbridge
Island, 98110-2747, SAN 363-6127. Tel: 206-842-4162. FAX:
206-780-5310. *Br Mgr*, Rebecca Judd; Tel: 206-842-4162, Ext 9802,
E-mail: rjudd@krl.org
Founded 1963
Library Holdings: Bk Vols 81,627
Open Mon-Wed 10-8, Thurs & Fri 1-5:30, Sat 10-5
Friends of the Library Group
DOWNTOWN BREMERTON BRANCH, 612 Fifth St, 98337-1416, SAN
363-6135. Tel: 360-377-3955. FAX: 360-479-8206. *Br Mgr*, Susan Lavin;
E-mail: slavin@krl.org
Founded 1938

Library Holdings: Bk Vols 19,613
Special Collections: Adult Literacy Coll; Northwest History Coll
Open Mon & Wed 1-8, Tues 10-6, Thurs 1-5, Fri 1-6, Sat 12-4
Friends of the Library Group
KINGSTON BRANCH, Community Ctr, 11212 NE State Hwy 104,
Kingston, 98346-0519, SAN 363-6240. Tel: 360-297-3330. FAX:
360-297-2911. *Br Mgr*, Tomi Whalen; Tel: 360-297-3330, Ext 9902,
E-mail: twhalen@krl.org
Founded 1945
Library Holdings: Bk Vols 11,075
Open Mon 10-8, Tues 1-8, Wed 10-6, Thurs & Sat 1-5, Fri 1-6
Friends of the Library Group
LITTLE BOSTON, 31980 Little Boston Rd NE, Kingston, 98346-9700.
(Mail add: 31912 Little Boston Rd NE, Kingston, 98346-9700). Tel:
360-297-2670. FAX: 360-297-2011. *Br Mgr*, Tomi Whalen; Tel:
360-297-2670, Ext 9601, E-mail: twhalen@krl.org
Founded 1974
Library Holdings: Bk Vols 13,802
Special Collections: Native American Literature Coll
Open Mon & Wed 1-8, Tues 10-6, Thurs 1-5, Fri 1-6, Sat 9-1
MANCHESTER BRANCH, 8067 E Main St, Manchester, 98353. (Mail
add: PO Box 128, Manchester, 98353), SAN 363-6275. Tel:
360-871-3921. FAX: 360-871-6152. *Br Mgr*, Dee D'Haem; Tel:
360-871-3921, Ext 9201, E-mail: ddhaem@krl.org
Founded 1947
Library Holdings: Bk Vols 13,085
Open Mon & Wed 1-8, Tues 10-5, Thurs & Fri 1-5, Sat 10-4
Friends of the Library Group
PORT ORCHARD BRANCH, 87 Sidney Ave, Port Orchard, 98366-5249,
SAN 363-6151. Tel: 360-876-2224. FAX: 360-876-9588. *Br Mgr*,
Kathleen Wilson; E-mail: kwilson@krl.org
Founded 1964
Library Holdings: Bk Vols 59,201
Open Mon 1-8, Tues & Wed 10-8, Thurs 1-6, Fri 10-6, Sat 10-4
Friends of the Library Group
POULSBO BRANCH, 700 N E Lincoln St, Poulsbo, 98370-7688, SAN
363-6186. Tel: 360-779-2915. FAX: 360-779-1051. *Br Mgr*, Sharon Lee;
E-mail: sslee@krl.org
Library Holdings: Bk Vols 63,621
Special Collections: Scandinavian Coll
Open Mon 1-8, Tues & Wed 10-8, Thurs 1-5, Fri 10-6, Sat 10-5
Friends of the Library Group
SILVERDALE BRANCH, 3450 NW Carlton St, Silverdale, 98383-8325,
SAN 363-6305. Tel: 360-692-2779. FAX: 360-698-7702. *Br Mgr*,
Melody Sky Eisler
Founded 1945
Library Holdings: Bk Vols 34,438
Open Mon & Wed 10-8, Tues & Fri 10-6, Thurs & Sat 1-5
Friends of the Library Group
SYLVAN WAY BRANCH, 1301 Sylvan Way, 98310-3466. Tel:
360-405-9100. FAX: 360-405-9128. *Br Mgr*, Ruth Bond; Tel:
360-415-6727, E-mail: rbond@krl.org
Founded 1978
Library Holdings: Bk Vols 102,861
Open Mon 1-8, Tues & Wed 10-8, Thurs 1-5, Fri 10-6, Sat 10-5
Friends of the Library Group
Bookmobiles: 1. Supvr, Gwen Detweiler

J   OLYMPIC COLLEGE*, Haselwood Library, 1600 Chester Ave, 98337.
SAN 317-4891. Tel: 360-475-7250. Interlibrary Loan Service Tel:
360-475-7254. Reference Tel: 360-475-7252. Administration Tel:
360-475-7262. Toll Free Tel: 800-259-6718, Ext 7250. FAX:
360-475-7261. Web Site: www.olympic.edu. *Dean of Libr*, Ruth M Ross;
E-mail: rross@oc.ctc.edu; *Cat, Tech Serv*, Judy Cunneen; E-mail:
jcunneen@oc.ctc.edu; *ILL*, Michael Hesson; E-mail: mhesson@oc.ctc.edu;
Ref, Dianne Moore; E-mail: dmoore@oc.ctc.edu; *Ref Serv*, Kent Mercer;
E-mail: kmercer@oc.ctc.edu; Staff 6 (MLS 6)
Founded 1946. Enrl 6,480; Fac 400; Highest Degree: Associate
Library Holdings: Bk Titles 65,052; Bk Vols 70,954; Per Subs 308
Special Collections: Mountaineering & Outdoor Literature (George W
Martin Coll)
Automation Activity & Vendor Info: (Acquisitions) Ex Libris Group;
(Cataloging) Ex Libris Group; (Circulation) Ex Libris Group; (Course
Reserve) Ex Libris Group; (ILL) Ex Libris Group; (OPAC) Ex Libris
Group; (Serials) Ex Libris Group
Database Vendor: ProQuest
Open Mon-Thurs 7:30am-9pm, Fri 7:30-5, Sat 10-4, Sun 12-6
Departmental Libraries:
JOHNSON LIBRARY, 937 W Alpine Way, Shelton, 98584-1200. Tel:
360-432-5460. FAX: 360-432-5468. Web Site:
www.olympic.edu/campuses/shelton/johnsonlibrary.htm. *Lead Libr Tech*,
Sandra Reider; Tel: 360-432-5461, E-mail: sreider@oc.ctc.edu
Library Holdings: Bk Titles 1,930

POULSBO CAMPUS, 1000 Olympic College Pl NW, Poulsbo, 98370. (Mail add: 1600 Chester Ave, 98337). Tel: 360-394-2720. Toll Free Tel: 800-259-6718. FAX: 360-394-2721. Web Site: www.olympic.edu/campuses/poulsbo/library.htm. *Librn,* Judy Andersen; E-mail: jandersen@oc.ctc.edu; *Librn,* Kathy Weigert; E-mail: kweigert@oc.ctc.edu
Library Holdings: Bk Titles 355
Open Mon-Thurs 7:30am-10pm, Fri 7:30-5, Sat 8-4

UNITED STATES NAVY

A   COMMAND LIBRARY, Puget Sound Naval Shipyard & Intermediate Maintenance Facility, 1400 Farragut Ave, 98314-5001, SAN 363-6399. Tel: 360-476-2767. FAX: 360-476-1730. *Librn,* Amanda Quashnick; E-mail: psns-imf_cmd_library@navy.mil; Staff 1 (Non-MLS 1)
Founded 1936
Library Holdings: Bk Titles 1,200; Per Subs 75
Subject Interests: Bus, Eng, Leadership, Naval, Sci
Restriction: Not open to pub, Open to mil & govt employees only, Open to staff only

AM   NAVAL HOSPITAL LIBRARY*, HP01 One Boone Rd, 98312-1898, SAN 363-6429. Tel: 360-475-4316. FAX: 360-475-4324. *Head, Knowledge Mgt,* Greg Patterson; E-mail: greg.patterson@med.navy.mil; *Libr Tech,* Sheila Tacey; E-mail: sheila.tacey@med.navy.mil; Staff 2 (MLS 1, Non-MLS 1)
Founded 1947
Library Holdings: Audiobooks 300; e-books 250; e-journals 4,000; Microforms 750,000; Bk Titles 1,750; Bk Vols 1,800; Per Subs 220
Special Collections: Medical Coll
Automation Activity & Vendor Info: (Acquisitions) Ex Libris Group; (Cataloging) Ex Libris Group; (Circulation) Ex Libris Group
Database Vendor: Cinahl Information Systems, MD Consult, Micromedex, OVID Technologies, ProQuest, PubMed, UpToDate
Partic in Dialog Corp
Open Mon-Fri 6am-3:30pm
Restriction: 24-hr pass syst for students only

A   RESOURCE CENTER*, Naval Station Bremerton Base-MWR, 120 S Dewey St, Bldg 502, 98314-5000, SAN 363-6364. Tel: 360-476-3178. FAX: 360-476-2908. Web Site: www.navylifepnw.com. *In Charge,* Lela Wessner; Tel: 360-535-5932
Library Holdings: Bk Vols 5,500; Per Subs 55
Subject Interests: Naval hist
Open Mon-Thurs 10-9, Fri 10am-Midnight, Sat 11am-Midnight, Sun 11-9

BURLINGTON

P   BURLINGTON PUBLIC LIBRARY, 820 E Washington, 98233. SAN 317-4913. Tel: 360-755-0760. FAX: 360-755-0717. E-mail: blibrary@ci.burlington.wa.us. Web Site: www.burlington.lib.wa.us. *Dir,* Maggie Buckholz; E-mail: maggieb@ci.burlington.wa.us; *Ref Librn,* Karen Prasse; E-mail: karenp@ci.burlington.wa.us; *Circ, Syst Coordr,* Janet Royer; E-mail: janetr@ci.burlington.wa.us; *Adult Serv, ILL,* Mary Beth Conlee; E-mail: mconlee@ci.burlington.wa.us; *Ch,* Lisa Anderson; E-mail: landerson@ci.burlington.wa.us; *Info Res,* Janice Burwash; E-mail: jburwash@ci.burlington.wa.us; *Teen Serv,* Sarah Lunde; E-mail: sarahl@ci.burlington.wa.us; Staff 4 (MLS 3, Non-MLS 1)
Founded 1910. Pop 8,760; Circ 223,252
Library Holdings: Bk Vols 49,859; Per Subs 101
Subject Interests: NW mat
Automation Activity & Vendor Info: (Cataloging) Evergreen; (Circulation) Evergreen; (OPAC) Evergreen
Database Vendor: EBSCO Auto Repair Reference, EBSCOhost, Gale Cengage Learning, OCLC FirstSearch, ProQuest, ReferenceUSA, TumbleBookLibrary
Wireless access
Function: Adult bk club, Audio & video playback equip for onsite use, Audiobks via web, Bilingual assistance for Spanish patrons, Bks on CD, Children's prog, Citizenship assistance, Computer training, Computers for patron use, Copy machines, Digital talking bks, Electronic databases & coll, ILL available, Magnifiers for reading, Music CDs, Online ref, OverDrive digital audio bks, Preschool outreach, Prog for adults, Prog for children & young adult, Pub access computers, Ref serv available, Story hour, Teen prog, Workshops
Partic in OCLC Online Computer Library Center, Inc
Open Mon-Thurs 11-8, Fri & Sat 11-5
Restriction: Non-resident fee
Friends of the Library Group

CAMAS

P   CAMAS PUBLIC LIBRARY*, 625 NE Fourth Ave, 98607. SAN 317-4921. Tel: 360-834-4692. FAX: 360-834-0199. E-mail: library@ci.camas.wa.us. Web Site: www.ci.camas.wa.us/library. *Dir,* David Zavortink; E-mail: dzavortink@ci.camas.wa.us; *Asst Dir,* Sandy Glover;

E-mail: sglover@ci.camas.wa.us; *Youth Serv,* Ellen Good; E-mail: egood@ci.camas.wa.us; Staff 16 (MLS 3, Non-MLS 13)
Founded 1929. Pop 17,000; Circ 310,000
Jan 2009-Dec 2009 Income $1,250,000, City $1,250,000. Mats Exp $109,600. Sal $708,445
Library Holdings: AV Mats 9,518; Large Print Bks 1,500; Bk Vols 99,000; Per Subs 250
Subject Interests: Pacific Northwest
Automation Activity & Vendor Info: (Acquisitions) SirsiDynix; (Cataloging) SirsiDynix; (Circulation) SirsiDynix; (OPAC) SirsiDynix
Database Vendor: BookLetters LLC, EBSCO Auto Repair Reference, EBSCOhost, Gale Cengage Learning, McGraw-Hill, OCLC FirstSearch, OCLC WorldCat, ProQuest, SirsiDynix
Wireless access
Function: Adult bk club, Adult literacy prog, Art exhibits, Bk club(s), Bks on cassette, Bks on CD, Children's prog, Computers for patron use, Copy machines, Free DVD rentals, Handicapped accessible, ILL available, Music CDs, Online cat, Prog for adults, Prog for children & young adult, Pub access computers, Ref serv available, Story hour, Summer reading prog, Tax forms, Teen prog, Telephone ref, VHS videos, Wheelchair accessible
Partic in Metropolitan Information Exchange (MIX)
Special Services for the Deaf - Bks on deafness & sign lang
Special Services for the Blind - Bks on cassette; Bks on CD; Descriptive video serv (DVS); Large print bks; Playaways (bks on MP3)
Open Mon-Thurs 10-9, Fri & Sat 10-6
Restriction: Non-resident fee
Friends of the Library Group

CASTLE ROCK

P   CASTLE ROCK PUBLIC LIBRARY*, 137 Cowlitz St W, 98611-8998. (Mail add: PO Box 1350, 98611-1350), SAN 317-4948. Tel: 360-274-6961. FAX: 360-274-4876. E-mail: rocklibrary@hotmail.com. *City Librn, Dir,* Vicki Selander; E-mail: vicki@castlerocklibrary.org; *Asst Librn,* Rebecca Edmiston; Staff 1 (Non-MLS 1)
Founded 1922. Pop 2,100; Circ 21,000
Library Holdings: DVDs 100; Large Print Bks 600; Bk Vols 18,000; Talking Bks 200; Videos 400
Special Collections: Early Learning
Subject Interests: Genealogy, Local hist
Database Vendor: ProQuest
Wireless access
Function: Magnifiers for reading, Photocopying/Printing, Prog for children & young adult, Spoken cassettes & CDs, Summer reading prog, Tax forms, VHS videos, Video lending libr
Open Mon, Wed & Thurs 12-7, Tues & Fri 10-5, Sat 12-4
Restriction: Non-resident fee
Friends of the Library Group

CATHLAMET

P   CATHLAMET PUBLIC LIBRARY*, Blanche Bradley Memorial Library, 100 Main St, 98612. (Mail add: PO Box 335, 98612-0335), SAN 321-463X. Tel: 360-795-3254. FAX: 360-795-8500. *Librn,* Noreen G Holten; E-mail: norlib@centurytel.net; Staff 1 (Non-MLS 1)
Founded 1929. Pop 2,000; Circ 10,129
Jan 2007-Dec 2007 Income $24,000, City $21,000, County $3,000. Mats Exp $5,000, Books $4,000, AV Mat $1,000. Sal $9,300
Library Holdings: Large Print Bks 20; Bk Titles 17,000; Per Subs 14; Talking Bks 110
Wireless access
Open Mon, Thurs & Sat 1-4, Tues 2-5, Wed 6pm-7:30pm
Friends of the Library Group

CENTRALIA

J   CENTRALIA COLLEGE*, Kirk Library, 600 Centralia College Blvd, 98531. SAN 317-4956. Tel: 360-736-9391, Ext 241. Reference Tel: 360-736-9391, Ext 691. FAX: 360-330-7502. E-mail: librarian@centralia.edu. Web Site: library.centralia.edu. *Dean of Library & eLearning,* Sue Gallaway; Tel: 360-736-9391, Ext 304, E-mail: sgallaway@centralia.edu; *Librn,* Dale Carroll; Tel: 360-736-9391, Ext 259, E-mail: dcarroll@centralia.edu; *Librn,* Barret Havens; Tel: 360-736-9391, Ext 615, E-mail: bhavens@centralia.edu; *Librn,* Margaret Snyder; Tel: 360-736-9391, Ext 423, E-mail: msnyder@centralia.edu; *Circ Supvr,* Hyesoo Albright; Tel: 360-736-9391, Ext 242, E-mail: halbright@centralia.edu; *Libr Spec,* Darlene J Rahn; Tel: 360-736-9391, Ext 350, E-mail: drahn@centralia.edu; Staff 6 (MLS 4, Non-MLS 2)
Founded 1925. Enrl 2,800; Fac 63; Highest Degree: Associate
Library Holdings: CDs 700; DVDs 144; e-books 9,979; Bk Vols 37,235; Per Subs 162; Talking Bks 187; Videos 2,899
Special Collections: Centralia Massacre Coll
Automation Activity & Vendor Info: (Acquisitions) Ex Libris Group; (Cataloging) Ex Libris Group; (Circulation) Ex Libris Group; (Course Reserve) Ex Libris Group; (ILL) OCLC; (OPAC) Ex Libris Group; (Serials) Ex Libris Group

Database Vendor: EBSCOhost, Electric Library, Gale Cengage Learning, netLibrary, ProQuest, SerialsSolutions
Wireless access
Function: Doc delivery serv
Open Mon-Thurs 7:30-7:30, Fri 7:30-4

CHEHALIS

GL   LEWIS COUNTY LAW LIBRARY*, Law & Justice Ctr, 345 W Main St, 98532. (Mail add: PO Box 357, 98532-0357), SAN 317-4964. Tel: 360-740-1333.
Library Holdings: Bk Titles 15,000
Subject Interests: Legal publications
Open Mon-Fri 8-5

CHENEY

C   EASTERN WASHINGTON UNIVERSITY*, John F Kennedy Memorial Library, 816 F St, 100 LIB, 99004-2453. SAN 363-6453. Tel: 509-359-2264. Circulation Tel: 509-359-7888. Interlibrary Loan Service Tel: 509-359-2492. Reference Tel: 509-359-2263. FAX: 509-359-6456. Administration FAX: 509-359-4840. Web Site: www.ewu.edu/library. *Dean of Libr,* Richard Wilson; E-mail: richardw@ewu.edu; *Assoc Dean of Libr,* Julie L Miller; Tel: 509-359-4949, E-mail: jmiller7@ewu.edu; *Head, Coll Serv,* Carolynne Myall; Tel: 509-359-6967, Fax: 509-359-2476, E-mail: carolynne.myall@ewu.edu; *Bus Mgr,* Rose Knight; Tel: 509-359-2306, E-mail: rose.knight@mail.ewu.edu; *Coll Develop,* Theophil Otto; Tel: 509-359-7895, E-mail: theophil.otto@ewu.edu; Staff 17.63 (MLS 13.63, Non-MLS 4)
Founded 1890. Enrl 9,350; Fac 607; Highest Degree: Doctorate
Jul 2009-Jun 2010 Income (Main and Other College/University Libraries) $4,469,681. Mats Exp $1,448,699, Books $254,257, Per/Ser (Incl. Access Fees) $468,785, AV Mat $113,868, Electronic Ref Mat (Incl. Access Fees) $598,691, Presv $13,098. Sal $2,197,490 (Prof $1,209,604)
Library Holdings: AV Mats 37,875; Bks on Deafness & Sign Lang 233; CDs 3,671; DVDs 2,198; e-books 2,542; e-journals 9,610; Large Print Bks 27; Music Scores 15,343; Bk Titles 724,260; Bk Vols 795,760; Per Subs 5,653; Videos 6,882
Special Collections: EWU History Coll, archival mats; Northwest History Coll, archival mats, bks, micro. Oral History; State Document Depository; US Document Depository
Subject Interests: Applied sci, Behav sci, Bus educ, Educ, Music, Sci, Soc sci, Soc work
Automation Activity & Vendor Info: (Acquisitions) Innovative Interfaces, Inc; (Cataloging) Innovative Interfaces, Inc; (Circulation) Innovative Interfaces, Inc; (Course Reserve) Innovative Interfaces, Inc; (ILL) OCLC; (Media Booking) Innovative Interfaces, Inc; (OPAC) Innovative Interfaces, Inc; (Serials) Innovative Interfaces, Inc
Database Vendor: ABC-CLIO, ACM (Association for Computing Machinery), American Chemical Society, Bowker, Cambridge Scientific Abstracts, Career Guidance Foundation, College Source, EBSCOhost, Elsevier, Emerald, H W Wilson, Haworth Pres Inc, IEEE (Institute of Electrical & Electronics Engineers), Ingram Library Services, ISI Web of Knowledge, JSTOR, LearningExpress, LexisNexis, Mergent Online, netLibrary, Newsbank, OCLC FirstSearch, OCLC WorldCat, OVID Technologies, ProQuest, PubMed, ScienceDirect, SerialsSolutions, Wilson - Wilson Web, YBP Library Services
Wireless access
Partic in Orbis Cascade Alliance; Wash Coop Libr Project
Special Services for the Deaf - Assistive tech; Bks on deafness & sign lang; Closed caption videos; High interest/low vocabulary bks; Staff with knowledge of sign lang
Special Services for the Blind - Assistive/Adapted tech devices, equip & products; Audio mat; Bks on cassette; Bks on CD; Braille Webster's dictionary; Cassette playback machines; Closed caption display syst; Computer with voice synthesizer for visually impaired persons; Dragon Naturally Speaking software; Integrated libr/media serv; Internet workstation with adaptive software; Large screen computer & software; Magnifiers; Reader equip; Rec; Ref serv; Rental typewriters & computers; Scanner for conversion & translation of mats; Screen enlargement software for people with visual disabilities; Screen reader software; Soundproof reading booth; Text reader; Videos on blindness & phys handicaps; ZoomText magnification & reading software
Open Mon-Thurs 7:30am-10pm, Fri 7:30-6, Sat 12-5, Sun 1-9
Friends of the Library Group

CHEWELAH

P   CHEWELAH PUBLIC LIBRARY*, 307 E Clay Ave, 99109. (Mail add: PO Box 87, 99109-0087), SAN 317-4972. Tel: 509-935-6805. FAX: 509-935-4564. E-mail: chewlib@theofficenet.com. Web Site: www.scrld.org. *Librn,* Pat Thompson; *Asst Librn,* Jay Andrews; Staff 4 (Non-MLS 4)
Founded 1916. Pop 2,012; Circ 65,000

Jan 2006-Dec 2006 Income $119,959, City $84,959, County $35,000. Mats Exp $15,105, Books $13,000, Electronic Ref Mat (Incl. Access Fees) $2,105. Sal $88,000
Library Holdings: Bk Vols 39,000; Per Subs 70
Subject Interests: State hist
Automation Activity & Vendor Info: (Cataloging) TLC (The Library Corporation); (OPAC) TLC (The Library Corporation)
Open Mon & Wed 10-7, Tues & Thurs 10-6, Fri & Sat 10-5
Friends of the Library Group

CLARKSTON

P   ASOTIN COUNTY LIBRARY, 417 Sycamore St, 99403-2666. SAN 317-4980. Tel: 509-758-5454. FAX: 509-751-1460. E-mail: admin.acl@valnet.org. Web Site: www.aclib.org. *Dir,* Jennifer Ashby; E-mail: jashby.acl@valnet.org; *Youth Serv,* Mary Neuman; E-mail: mneuman.acl@valnet.org; Staff 11 (MLS 2, Non-MLS 9)
Founded 1902
Library Holdings: Bk Titles 50,000; Per Subs 111
Subject Interests: NW hist
Automation Activity & Vendor Info: (Acquisitions) ByWater Solutions; (Cataloging) ByWater Solutions; (Circulation) ByWater Solutions; (ILL) OCLC; (OPAC) ByWater Solutions; (Serials) ByWater Solutions
Database Vendor: BioPharm Insight, BookLetters LLC, EBSCO Auto Repair Reference, EBSCOhost, Gale Cengage Learning, Ingram Library Services, Newsbank, OCLC, OCLC FirstSearch, OCLC WebJunction, OCLC WorldCat, ProQuest, PubMed, World Book Online, WT Cox
Wireless access
Open Mon-Thurs 10-8, Fri & Sat 10-5
Friends of the Library Group
Branches: 1
HEIGHTS BRANCH, 2036 Fourth Ave, 99403-1322. Tel: 509-758-4601. E-mail: hts@valnet.org. *Dir,* Jennifer Ashby
  Library Holdings: Bk Titles 5,000
  Database Vendor: EBSCO Auto Repair Reference, Gale Cengage Learning, ProQuest
  Open Mon & Wed 10-5, Tues 10-7, Thurs-Sat 12-5

CLE ELUM

P   CARPENTER MEMORIAL LIBRARY*, 302 Pennsylvania Ave, 98922-1196. SAN 317-4999. Tel: 509-674-2313. FAX: 509-674-2313. E-mail: cmlibrary@cityofcleelum.com. Web Site: www.carpenter.lib.wa.us. *Librn,* Jane Agar
Founded 1978. Pop 4,500; Circ 18,400
Library Holdings: Bk Titles 12,500; Per Subs 20
Special Collections: Pacific Northwest History (Northwest Book Coll)
Subject Interests: Health, Nutrition, Wash State facts
Automation Activity & Vendor Info: (Acquisitions) Book Systems, Inc; (Cataloging) Book Systems, Inc; (Circulation) Book Systems, Inc; (Course Reserve) Book Systems, Inc; (OPAC) Book Systems, Inc; (Serials) Book Systems, Inc
Database Vendor: EBSCOhost, ProQuest
Open Tues & Thurs 9-5, Wed 10-7, Fri 10-5, Sat 10-2
Friends of the Library Group

COLFAX

P   WHITMAN COUNTY RURAL LIBRARY DISTRICT, Colfax (Main) Branch, 102 S Main St, 99111-1863. SAN 317-5006. Tel: 509-397-4366. Toll Free Tel: 877-733-3375. FAX: 509-397-6156. E-mail: info@whitco.lib.wa.us. Web Site: www.whitco.lib.wa.us. *Dir,* Kristie Kirkpatrick; E-mail: kirkpatr@colfax.com; *Assoc Dir,* Peggy Bryan; *Br Coordr,* Clancy Pool; *Syst Coordr,* James Morasch; *Ch,* Sheri Miller; *Teen Serv,* Chelsea Leachman; Staff 6 (MLS 1, Non-MLS 5)
Founded 1945. Pop 15,744; Circ 165,000
Library Holdings: Bk Titles 72,000; Bk Vols 78,000
Subject Interests: Local hist
Automation Activity & Vendor Info: (Cataloging) SirsiDynix; (Circulation) SirsiDynix; (Course Reserve) SirsiDynix; (Media Booking) SirsiDynix; (OPAC) SirsiDynix
Database Vendor: SirsiDynix
Partic in Palouse Area Library Information Services
Special Services for the Blind - Low vision equip
Open Mon-Wed 10-8, Thurs & Fri 10-6, Sat & Sun 1-5
Friends of the Library Group
Branches: 11
ALBION BRANCH, 310 F St, Albion, 99102. (Mail add: PO Box 144, Albion, 99102). Tel: 509-338-9641. *Br Mgr,* Paul Slaughter
  Library Holdings: Bk Titles 1,600
  Open Tues 3:30-7:30, Sat 12-4
  Friends of the Library Group

COLTON BRANCH, 760 Broadway Ave, Colton, 99113. (Mail add: PO Box 157, Colton, 99113). Tel: 509-229-3887. E-mail: colton@whitco.lib.wa.us. *Br Mgr,* Holly Meyer; Staff 1 (Non-MLS 1)
Library Holdings: Bk Titles 1,600
Open Mon 10-2:30, Thurs 2:30-6:30
ENDICOTT BRANCH, 324 E St, Endicott, 99125. Tel: 509-657-3429. E-mail: endicott@whitco.lib.wa.us. *Br Mgr,* Caroline Morasch
Library Holdings: Bk Titles 2,200
Open Tues 1-6, Fri 9-1
FARMINGTON BRANCH, E 203 Main St, Farmington, 99128. Tel: 509-287-2500. E-mail: farmington@whitco.lib.wa.us. *Br Mgr,* Marlee Conklin
Library Holdings: Bk Titles 1,400
Open Tues 10-2, Thurs 2-6
GARFIELD BRANCH, 109 N Third, Garfield, 99130. Tel: 509-635-1490. E-mail: garfield@whitco.lib.wa.us. *Br Mgr,* Crystal Bailey
Library Holdings: Bk Titles 2,300
Open Mon 2:30-6, Wed 10-1 & 2-5
LACROSSE BRANCH, 107 S Main, LaCrosse, 99143. Tel: 509-549-3770. FAX: 509-549-3330. E-mail: lacrosse@whitco.lib.wa.us. *Br Mgr,* Caroline Morasch
Library Holdings: Bk Titles 1,500
Open Mon 2-6, Thurs 10-2
OAKESDALE BRANCH, 101 E Steptoe, Oakesdale, 99158. Tel: 509-285-4310. E-mail: oakesdale@whitco.lib.wa.us. *Br Mgr,* Michele Wright
Library Holdings: CDs 20; DVDs 15; Large Print Bks 30; Bk Titles 1,800; Talking Bks 25; Videos 45
Open Mon 1-6, Wed 10:30-2
Friends of the Library Group
ROSALIA BRANCH, 402 S Whitman Ave, Rosalia, 99170. Tel: 509-523-3109. E-mail: rosalia@whitco.lib.wa.us. *Br Mgr,* Theresa Lautenslager
Library Holdings: Bk Titles 2,000
Open Tues 10-4, Thurs 3-7
ST JOHN BRANCH, One E Front St, Saint John, 99171. (Mail add: PO Box 5, Saint John, 99171). Tel: 509-648-3319. *Br Mgr,* Clancy Pool; E-mail: cpool@whitco.lib.wa.us
Pop 1,000; Circ 16,000
Library Holdings: Audiobooks 400; CDs 200; DVDs 200; e-books 3,000; Large Print Bks 100; Bk Titles 4,500; Bk Vols 4,500; Per Subs 10; Videos 200
Automation Activity & Vendor Info: (Cataloging) OCLC CatExpress; (ILL) OCLC WorldCat
Database Vendor: EBSCO Auto Repair Reference, EBSCOhost, Electric Library, Grolier Online, OCLC FirstSearch, OCLC WorldCat, Overdrive, Inc, ProQuest
Function: Adult bk club, After school storytime, Bks on cassette, Bks on CD, Children's prog, Computers for patron use, Copy machines, Electronic databases & coll, Exhibits, Free DVD rentals, Handicapped accessible, Home delivery & serv to Sr ctr & nursing homes, ILL available, Mail & tel request accepted, Music CDs, Outreach serv, Outside serv via phone, mail, e-mail & web, OverDrive digital audio bks, Photocopying/Printing, Preschool outreach, Prog for adults, Prog for children & young adult, Pub access computers, Ref serv available, Story hour, Summer & winter reading prog, Summer reading prog, Telephone ref, VCDs, VHS videos, Web-catalog, Wheelchair accessible
Open Mon 10:30-5, Wed 3:30-6:30, Fri 9:30-1 & 2-5
Friends of the Library Group
TEKOA BRANCH, S 139 Crosby, Tekoa, 99033. Tel: 509-284-3121. E-mail: tekoa@whitco.lib.wa.us. *Br Mgr,* Alicia Wilson
Library Holdings: Bk Titles 3,000
Open Tues 1-6, Wed 2-6, Thurs 10-4
UNIONTOWN BRANCH, 110 S Montgomery, Uniontown, 99179. Tel: 509-229-3880. E-mail: uniontown@whitco.lib.wa.us. *Br Mgr,* Angela Smeltz
Library Holdings: Bk Titles 1,500
Open Tues 3-6:30, Fri 9:30-2

COLLEGE PLACE

CR   WALLA WALLA UNIVERSITY LIBRARIES, Peterson Memorial Library, 104 S College Ave, 99324-1159. SAN 317-5014. Tel: 509-527-2134. Circulation Tel: 509-527-2191. Interlibrary Loan Service Tel: 509-527-2159, 509-527-2673. Reference Tel: 509-527-2142. Administration Tel: 509-527-2107. Automation Services Tel: 509-527-2203. Information Services Tel: 509-527-2032. FAX: 509-527-2001. Web Site: library.wallawalla.edu. *Dir of Libr,* Carolyn Gaskell; E-mail: carolyn.gaskell@wallawalla.edu; *Librn,* Bruce McClay; Tel: 503-251-7306, E-mail: bruce.mcclay@wallawalla.edu; *Electronic Res & Per Librn,* Richard W Scott; Tel: 509-527-2684, E-mail: richard.scott@wallawalla.edu; *Instrul Serv Librn & Coordr, Access Serv, Per,* Annette Melgosa; Tel: 509-527-2684, E-mail: annette.melgosa@wallawalla.edu; *Ref & ILL Librn,* Christy Scott; Fax: 509-527-2192, E-mail: christy.scott@wallawalla.edu;

Tech Serv & Syst Librn, Mark Copsey; E-mail: mark.copsey@wallawalla.edu; Staff 9.88 (MLS 5.5, Non-MLS 4.38)
Founded 1892. Enrl 1,794; Fac 138; Highest Degree: Master
Jul 2009-Jun 2010 Income (Main and Other College/University Libraries) $1,642,727. Mats Exp $561,521
Library Holdings: AV Mats 4,583; e-books 4,446; e-journals 35,179; Microforms 148,143; Bk Titles 161,603; Per Subs 807
Special Collections: Bibles, SDA History
Subject Interests: Nursing
Automation Activity & Vendor Info: (Acquisitions) Innovative Interfaces, Inc; (Cataloging) Innovative Interfaces, Inc; (Circulation) Innovative Interfaces, Inc; (Course Reserve) Innovative Interfaces, Inc; (ILL) OCLC; (OPAC) Innovative Interfaces, Inc; (Serials) Innovative Interfaces, Inc
Database Vendor: 3M Library Systems, American Mathematical Society, American Psychological Association (APA), Annual Reviews, Bowker, Cinahl Information Systems, EBSCO Information Services, EBSCOhost, Elsevier, Ex Libris Group, Gale Cengage Learning, Grolier Online, Haworth Pres Inc, Innovative Interfaces, Inc, Innovative Interfaces, Inc INN - View, JSTOR, LexisNexis, Newsbank, OCLC FirstSearch, OCLC WorldCat, Oxford Online, ProQuest, PubMed, Sage, ScienceDirect, Springer-Verlag, Springshare, LLC, STN International, Thomson - Web of Science, Wiley
Wireless access
Publications: Course Guides (Reference guide); Research Guides (Online only)
Partic in Adventist Librs Info Coop; Orbis Cascade Alliance
Open Mon-Thurs 8am-11pm, Fri 8-2:30, Sun 10am-11pm
Departmental Libraries:
SCHOOL OF NURSING LIBRARY
  See Separate Entry in Portland, OR

COLVILLE

P   COLVILLE PUBLIC LIBRARY*, 195 S Oak St, 99114-2845. SAN 317-5022. Tel: 509-684-6620. FAX: 509-684-3911. E-mail: colville.library@plix.com. Web Site: www.scrld.org. *Mgr,* Amanda McKeraghan; Staff 9 (MLS 2, Non-MLS 7)
Pop 10,000; Circ 77,531
Library Holdings: Bk Titles 36,248
Subject Interests: Genealogy, Northwest
Automation Activity & Vendor Info: (Cataloging) TLC (The Library Corporation); (Circulation) TLC (The Library Corporation); (OPAC) TLC (The Library Corporation)
Database Vendor: OCLC FirstSearch, ProQuest
Function: For res purposes, Handicapped accessible, Homebound delivery serv, ILL available, Photocopying/Printing, Prog for children & young adult, Summer reading prog, Telephone ref, Wheelchair accessible
Partic in OCLC
Open Mon-Wed 10-8, Thurs & Fri 10-6, Sat 10-5, Sun 12-4
Friends of the Library Group

CONCRETE

P   UPPER SKAGIT LIBRARY, 45770-B Main St, 98237. (Mail add: PO Box 99, 98237-0099). Tel: 360-853-7939. FAX: 360-853-7555. E-mail: info@upperskagit.lib.wa.us. Web Site: www.upperskagit.lib.wa.us. *Dir,* Aimee Hirschel; E-mail: hirschel@upperskagit.lib.wa.us; Staff 1 (MLS 1)
Pop 4,100; Circ 22,600
Jan 2011-Dec 2011 Income $285,200, County $278,800, Locally Generated Income $6,400. Mats Exp $16,100, Books $13,000, Per/Ser (Incl. Access Fees) $2,000, Electronic Ref Mat (Incl. Access Fees) $1,100. Sal $92,000 (Prof $44,000)
Library Holdings: Audiobooks 275; DVDs 400; Bk Titles 10,000; Per Subs 40
Automation Activity & Vendor Info: (Cataloging) Evergreen; (Circulation) Evergreen; (OPAC) Evergreen
Database Vendor: EBSCO Auto Repair Reference, ProQuest
Wireless access
Open Tues & Wed 11-8, Fri & Sat 11-5
Friends of the Library Group

DAVENPORT

P   DAVENPORT PUBLIC LIBRARY, 505 Seventh St, 99122. (Mail add: PO Box 1169, 99122-1169), SAN 317-5049. Tel: 509-725-4355. E-mail: davlibrary@centurytel.net. *Libr Dir,* Pike Kathryn; Staff 0.3 (MLS 0.3)
Founded 1926. Pop 1,730; Circ 6,059
Library Holdings: Bk Vols 16,000
Function: Accessibility serv available based on individual needs, Art exhibits, Bk reviews (Group), Bks on cassette, Bks on CD, Children's prog, Citizenship assistance, Computer training, Computers for patron use, Copy machines, Electronic databases & coll, Free DVD rentals, ILL available, Online cat, Photocopying/Printing, Preschool outreach, Preschool reading prog, Pub access computers, Ref serv in person, Story hour, Summer reading prog, Telephone ref, Wheelchair accessible

Special Services for the Blind - Bks on cassette; Bks on CD; Large print bks
Open Tues 3-7, Wed 9-1, Thurs 7pm-9pm, Sat 10-4
Restriction: Non-resident fee, Open to pub for ref & circ; with some limitations, Pub use on premises

DAYTON

P   COLUMBIA COUNTY RURAL LIBRARY DISTRICT*, 111 S Third St, 99328-1342. (Mail add: PO Box 74, 99328-0074). Tel: 509-382-4131. FAX: 509-382-1059. E-mail: library@daytonwa.net. Web Site: www.ccrld.lib.wa.us. *Dir,* Janet Lyon; E-mail: jlyon@daytonwa.net; *Br Mgr,* Sue Hagfeldt; *Libr Asst, Website Mgr,* Heather Stearns; *Libr Asst,* Sandra Dare; Staff 2.76 (MLS 1, Non-MLS 1.76)
Founded 1937. Pop 4,100; Circ 26,043
Library Holdings: Audiobooks 1,371; DVDs 632; Bk Titles 22,752; Per Subs 40
Wireless access
Function: Audiobks via web, Bks on cassette, Computer training, e-mail serv, Electronic databases & coll, Fax serv, Free DVD rentals, Homebound delivery serv, ILL available, Magnifiers for reading, Music CDs, Online cat, Preschool outreach, Provide serv for the mentally ill, Pub access computers, Ref serv available, Scanner, Senior computer classes, Senior outreach, Story hour, Summer reading prog, Tax forms, Telephone ref, VHS videos, Web-catalog, Workshops

DES MOINES

C   HIGHLINE COMMUNITY COLLEGE LIBRARY, 2400 S 240th St, MS 25-4, 98198. (Mail add: PO Box 98000, 98198-9800), SAN 317-5456. Tel: 206-878-3710, Ext 3234. Interlibrary Loan Service Tel: 206-878-3710, Ext 3127. Reference Tel: 206-878-3710, Ext 3232. FAX: 206-870-3776. TDD: 206-870-4853. Web Site: library.highline.edu. *Dean, Instrul Res,* Monica Luce; Tel: 206-878-3710, Ext 3230, E-mail: mluce@highline.edu; *Circ Serv Dir,* Fran Clark; Tel: 206-878-3710, Ext 3610, E-mail: fclark@highline.edu; *Dir of Tech Serv,* Position Currently Open; *Ref Librn,* Hara Brook; Tel: 206-878-3710, Ext 3248, E-mail: hbrook@highline.edu; *Ref Librn,* Karen Fernandez; Tel: 206-878-3710, Ext 3809, E-mail: kfernand@highline.edu; *Ref Librn,* Dana Franks; Tel: 206-878-3710, Ext 3240, E-mail: dfranks@highline.edu; *Ref Librn,* Jack Harton; Tel: 206-878-3710, Ext 3806, E-mail: jharton@highline.edu; *Ref Librn,* Deborah Moore; Tel: 206-878-3710, Ext 3518, E-mail: dmoore@highline.edu; *Syst Adminr,* Tom Pollard, Jr; Tel: 206-878-3710, Ext 3236, E-mail: tpollard@highline.edu. Subject Specialists: *Literacy,* Dana Franks; Staff 9 (MLS 8, Non-MLS 1)
Founded 1961. Enrl 5,600; Fac 132; Highest Degree: Associate
Library Holdings: Bks on Deafness & Sign Lang 150; High Interest/Low Vocabulary Bk Vols 500; Bk Titles 80,000; Bk Vols 96,481; Per Subs 697; Spec Interest Per Sub 30; Videos 2,873
Special Collections: State Document Depository; US Document Depository
Subject Interests: Law
Automation Activity & Vendor Info: (Acquisitions) Ex Libris Group; (Cataloging) Ex Libris Group; (Circulation) Ex Libris Group; (Course Reserve) Ex Libris Group; (OPAC) Ex Libris Group; (Serials) Ex Libris Group
Database Vendor: ARTstor, ebrary, EBSCOhost, JSTOR, LexisNexis, OCLC FirstSearch, ProQuest
Wireless access
Partic in OCLC Online Computer Library Center, Inc
Open Mon-Fri (Winter) 7am-9pm, Sat 9-5, Sun 2-9; Mon-Thurs (Summer) 8-8, Sun 2-8

EASTSOUND

P   ORCAS ISLAND LIBRARY DISTRICT*, 500 Rose St, 98245-9453. Tel: 360-376-4985. FAX: 360-376-5750. Web Site: www.orcaslibrary.org. *Dir,* Phil Heikkinen; E-mail: pheikkinen@orcaslibrary.org; Staff 8 (MLS 3, Non-MLS 5)
Founded 1988. Pop 5,100; Circ 123,229
Jan 2011-Dec 2011 Income $618,935. Mats Exp $75,682, Books $46,582, Per/Ser (Incl. Access Fees) $6,294, Micro $111, AV Mat $17,778, Electronic Ref Mat (Incl. Access Fees) $4,917. Sal $299,101 (Prof $148,160)
Library Holdings: Audiobooks 4,723; AV Mats 9,053; CDs 2,713; DVDs 2,454; e-books 1,246; Large Print Bks 450; Microforms 138; Bk Titles 35,974; Bk Vols 37,768; Per Subs 126; Talking Bks 4,723; Videos 120
Special Collections: San Juan Islands Coll
Subject Interests: Local hist, Northwestern US
Automation Activity & Vendor Info: (Acquisitions) SirsiDynix; (Cataloging) OCLC Online; (Circulation) SirsiDynix; (ILL) OCLC WorldCat; (OPAC) SirsiDynix
Database Vendor: Booklist Online, EBSCO Auto Repair Reference, Gale Cengage Learning, OCLC FirstSearch, OCLC WebJunction, OCLC WorldCat, Overdrive, Inc, Oxford Online, ProQuest, SirsiDynix
Wireless access

Function: Adult literacy prog, Audiobks via web, Bk club(s), Bks on CD, Chess club, Children's prog, Computers for patron use, Copy machines, Digital talking bks, Distance learning, e-mail & chat, Electronic databases & coll, Free DVD rentals, Handicapped accessible, Holiday prog, Home delivery & serv to Sr ctr & nursing homes, Homebound delivery serv, ILL available, Magnifiers for reading, Mail & tel request accepted, Music CDs, Online cat, Online ref, Online searches, Outreach serv, Outside serv via phone, mail, e-mail & web, OverDrive digital audio bks, Photocopying/Printing, Preschool outreach, Prog for adults, Prog for children & young adult, Pub access computers, Ref serv available, Scanner, Senior outreach, Spoken cassettes & CDs, Spoken cassettes & DVDs, Story hour, Summer reading prog, Tax forms, Teen prog, Telephone ref, VHS videos, Web-catalog, Wheelchair accessible, Writing prog
Special Services for the Deaf - Bks on deafness & sign lang
Special Services for the Blind - Audio mat; Bks on cassette; Bks on CD; Cassettes; Home delivery serv; Large print & cassettes; Large print bks; Talking bks
Open Mon-Thurs 10-7, Fri & Sat 10-5, Sun 12-3
Restriction: Non-resident fee
Friends of the Library Group

ELLENSBURG

C   CENTRAL WASHINGTON UNIVERSITY*, James E Brooks Library, 400 E University Way, 98926-7548. SAN 317-5081. Tel: 509-963-1901. Circulation Tel: 509-963-3682. Interlibrary Loan Service Tel: 509-963-1033. Reference Tel: 509-963-1021. FAX: 509-963-3684. E-mail: library@www.lib.cwu.edu. Web Site: www.lib.cwu.edu. *Dean,* Patricia Cutright; E-mail: cutright@cwu.edu; *Head, Cat,* Daniel CannCasciato; *Circ Mgr,* Kerry Slaughter; *Syst Coordr,* John Creech; *Archivist,* Position Currently Open; *Cat,* Mary Wise; *Coll Develop,* Patrick Owens; *Govt Doc,* Jan Jorgenson; *Instruction & Outreach,* Marcus Kieltyka; *ILL, Ref,* Gerard Hogan; Staff 41 (MLS 13, Non-MLS 28)
Founded 1891. Enrl 7,836; Fac 450; Highest Degree: Master
Jul 2005-Jun 2006. Mats Exp $850,396, Books $282,583, Per/Ser (Incl. Access Fees) $375,022, Manu Arch $12,564, AV Mat $13,725, Electronic Ref Mat (Incl. Access Fees) $166,502. Sal $2,012,217
Library Holdings: Bk Vols 521,548
Special Collections: State Document Depository; US Document Depository
Automation Activity & Vendor Info: (OPAC) Innovative Interfaces, Inc
Wireless access
Partic in Orbis Cascade Alliance
Friends of the Library Group

P   ELLENSBURG PUBLIC LIBRARY*, 209 N Ruby St, 98926-3397. SAN 317-509X. Tel: 509-962-7250. Circulation Tel: 509-962-7110. Reference Tel: 509-962-7228. Administration Tel: 509-962-7252. FAX: 509-962-7295. E-mail: library@ci.ellensburg.wa.us. Web Site: www.ellensburglibrary.org. *Dir,* Debby DeSoer; E-mail: desoerd@ci.ellensburg.wa.us; *Head, Ch, Ref Serv, Ch, Ref Serv, YA,* Josephine Camarillo; Tel: 509-962-7218, E-mail: camarilloj@ci.ellensburg.wa.us; *Head, Circ, ILL,* Ken Paschen; E-mail: paschenk@ci.ellensburg.wa.us; *Head, Tech Serv,* Carol Rich; Tel: 509-962-7258, E-mail: richc@cityofellensburg.org; *Hist Coll Librn, Ref Serv, Ad,* Milton L Wagy; E-mail: wagym@ci.ellensburg.wa.us; *Internet Serv, Ref,* Joan Neslund; E-mail: neslundj@cityofellensburg.org. Subject Specialists: *Local hist,* Milton L Wagy; Staff 11.7 (MLS 2, Non-MLS 9.7)
Founded 1910. Pop 17,200; Circ 185,742
Jan 2008-Dec 2008 Income $853,985, County $88,000. Mats Exp $69,525, Books $39,491, Other Print Mats $8,878, Electronic Ref Mat (Incl. Access Fees) $9,083. Sal $427,734
Library Holdings: AV Mats 9,488; e-books 10,371; Electronic Media & Resources 10; Bk Titles 54,983; Per Subs 172; Videos 5,139
Special Collections: Oral History
Subject Interests: Local hist
Automation Activity & Vendor Info: (Cataloging) Horizon; (Circulation) Horizon; (ILL) OCLC WorldCat; (OPAC) Horizon
Database Vendor: Baker & Taylor, Booklist Online, EBSCO Auto Repair Reference, LearningExpress, netLibrary, OCLC FirstSearch, OCLC WebJunction, OCLC WorldCat, ProQuest, ReferenceUSA, SirsiDynix
Wireless access
Function: Art exhibits, Audio & video playback equip for onsite use, Bilingual assistance for Spanish patrons, Bks on cassette, Bks on CD, CD-ROM, Children's prog, Citizenship assistance, Computer training, Computers for patron use, Copy machines, Digital talking bks, e-mail & chat, Electronic databases & coll, Exhibits, Free DVD rentals, Handicapped accessible, Holiday prog, Home delivery & serv to Sr ctr & nursing homes, ILL available, Magnifiers for reading, Mail & tel request accepted, Mus passes, Music CDs, Newsp ref libr, Online cat, Online ref, Online searches, Orientations, Outreach serv, Outside serv via phone, mail, e-mail & web, Photocopying/Printing, Prog for adults, Prog for children & young adult, Pub access computers, Ref & res, Ref serv in person, Scanner, Spoken cassettes & CDs, Spoken cassettes & DVDs, Story hour, Summer reading prog, Tax forms, Teen prog, Telephone ref, VHS videos, Web-catalog, Wheelchair accessible, Workshops

Special Services for the Blind - Bks on cassette; Bks on CD; Closed circuit TV; Home delivery serv; Large print bks; Magnifiers; Screen enlargement software for people with visual disabilities; Talking bks; VisualTek equip
Open Mon-Thurs 10-8, Fri 10-6, Sat & Sun 1-5
Friends of the Library Group

ENUMCLAW

P   ENUMCLAW PUBLIC LIBRARY*, 1700 First St, 98022. SAN 317-5103. Tel: 360-825-2938. FAX: 360-825-0825. E-mail: library@ci.enumclaw.wa.us. Web Site: www.enumclaw.lib.wa.us. *Dir,* Robert Baer; Staff 1 (MLS 1)
Founded 1922. Pop 11,500; Circ 165,253
Jan 2008-Dec 2008 Income $650,982. Mats Exp $53,000. Sal $375,909
Library Holdings: Bk Titles 56,450; Per Subs 147
Subject Interests: Local hist
Automation Activity & Vendor Info: (Cataloging) SirsiDynix; (Circulation) SirsiDynix; (OPAC) SirsiDynix
Database Vendor: EBSCO Auto Repair Reference, Gale Cengage Learning, Grolier Online, netLibrary, ProQuest, ReferenceUSA
Wireless access
Open Mon-Thurs 10:30-9, Sat 10:30-5, Sun 1-5
Friends of the Library Group

EVERETT

J   EVERETT COMMUNITY COLLEGE, John N Terrey Library - Media Center, 2000 Tower St, 98201-1352. SAN 317-5138. Tel: 425-388-9501. Circulation Tel: 425-388-9353. Interlibrary Loan Service Tel: 425-388-9493. Reference Tel: 425-388-9354. FAX: 425-388-9144. E-mail: library@everettcc.edu. Web Site: www.everettcc.edu/library. *Dean, Arts & Learning Res,* Jeanne Leader; Tel: 425-388-9502, E-mail: jleader@everettcc.edu; *Acq, Cat, Pub Serv,* Heather Sheppard; Tel: 425-388-9964, Ext 7345, E-mail: jwolfthal@everettcc.edu; *Circ, Pub Serv,* Robert Bertoldi; Tel: 425-388-9492, E-mail: rbertoldi@everettcc.edu; *Coll Develop, Pub Serv,* Marianne Le; Tel: 425-388-9351, E-mail: mle@everettcc.edu; *Media Spec,* Jeanie Goodhope; Tel: 425-388-9348, E-mail: jgoodhope@everettcc.edu; *Pub Serv,* David Rash; Tel: 425-388-9494, E-mail: drash@everettcc.edu; Staff 6 (MLS 6)
Founded 1948. Highest Degree: Associate
Library Holdings: AV Mats 5,914; Electronic Media & Resources 8,449; Bk Titles 48,434; Bk Vols 54,144; Per Subs 230
Automation Activity & Vendor Info: (Acquisitions) Ex Libris Group; (Cataloging) Ex Libris Group; (Circulation) Ex Libris Group; (OPAC) Ex Libris Group
Database Vendor: Dialog, OCLC FirstSearch, ProQuest
Wireless access
Publications: Bookmarks; Brochure; Search Guides
Partic in OCLC Online Computer Library Center, Inc
Special Services for the Blind - Assistive/Adapted tech devices, equip & products
Open Mon-Thurs 7:30am-8pm, Fri 7:30-4, Sat 12-4

P   EVERETT PUBLIC LIBRARY*, 2702 Hoyt Ave, 98201-3556. SAN 317-5162. Tel: 425-257-8020. Circulation Tel: 425-257-8010. Interlibrary Loan Service Tel: 425-257-7615. Reference Tel: 425-257-8000. Automation Services Tel: 425-257-8036. FAX: 425-257-8017. Reference FAX: 425-257-8016. Web Site: www.epls.org. *Dir,* Eileen D Simmons; Tel: 425-257-8001, E-mail: esimmons@ci.everett.wa.us; *Asst Dir, Head, Adult Serv, Ref,* Katherine A Mossman; Tel: 425-257-8022, E-mail: kmossman@ci.everett.wa.us; *Ch,* Dorothy Matsui; Tel: 425-257-8030, E-mail: dmatsui@ci.everett.wa.us; *Circ Supvr,* Fran Habicht; Tel: 425-257-8034, E-mail: fhabicht@ci.everett.wa.us; *ILL,* Joan Blacker; E-mail: jblacker@ci.everett.wa.us; *Tech Serv Mgr,* Pat Bennett; Tel: 425-257-8019, E-mail: pbennett@ci.everett.wa.us; Staff 19 (MLS 16, Non-MLS 3)
Founded 1894. Pop 97,500; Circ 930,710
Jan 2006-Dec 2006 Income (Main Library and Branch(s)) $4,542,318, City $4,463,318, Locally Generated Income $79,000. Mats Exp $592,784, Books $368,822, Per/Ser (Incl. Access Fees) $40,060, Other Print Mats $16,871, Micro $2,800, AV Mat $105,931, Electronic Ref Mat (Incl. Access Fees) $58,300. Sal $3,397,688
Library Holdings: AV Mats 30,317; Bks on Deafness & Sign Lang 137; CDs 6,736; DVDs 8,122; Large Print Bks 10,869; Bk Titles 175,645; Bk Vols 253,590; Per Subs 856; Talking Bks 4,274; Videos 9,999
Special Collections: City of Everett; Pacific Northwest (Northwest Coll), bks, photos, rec. Oral History; State Document Depository; US Document Depository
Automation Activity & Vendor Info: (Acquisitions) Polaris Library Systems; (Cataloging) Polaris Library Systems; (Circulation) Polaris Library Systems; (ILL) OCLC; (OPAC) Polaris Library Systems
Database Vendor: ALLDATA Online, Baker & Taylor, EBSCOhost, Gale Cengage Learning, infoUSA, LearningExpress, OCLC FirstSearch, OCLC WorldCat, ProQuest, ReferenceUSA
Wireless access

Open Mon-Wed 10-9, Thurs-Sat 10-6, Sun 1-5
Friends of the Library Group
Branches: 1
EVERGREEN, 9512 Evergreen Way, 98204, SAN 375-5916. Tel: 425-257-8260. Reference Tel: 425-257-8250. FAX: 425-257-8265. *Br Mgr,* Alan Jacobson; Tel: 425-257-8270
Founded 1985
Open Mon-Wed 10-9, Thurs-Sat 10-6, Sun 1-5
Friends of the Library Group
Bookmobiles: 1

M   PROVIDENCE REGIONAL MEDICAL CENTER EVERETT*, Sacred Heart Library, 1321 Colby Ave, 98201. (Mail add: PO Box 1147, 98206-1147), SAN 317-5197. Tel: 509-474-3094. FAX: 509-474-4475. E-mail: library.sacredheart@providence.org. Web Site: www.providence.org/everett. *Librn,* Sandy Keno; *Libr Tech,* Gail Leong; Staff 2 (Non-MLS 2)
Founded 1974
Library Holdings: Bk Titles 1,000; Per Subs 200
Subject Interests: Admin, Allied health, Med, Nursing
Partic in National Network of Libraries of Medicine
Open Mon-Fri 8-4:30

GL   SNOHOMISH COUNTY LAW LIBRARY*, M/S 703, Rm 139, 3000 Rockefeller Ave, 98201. SAN 317-5200. Tel: 425-388-3010. FAX: 425-388-3020. Web Site: www.co.snohomish.wa.us. *Librn,* Lettice Parker; E-mail: lettice.parker@co.snohomish.wa.us
Founded 1919
Library Holdings: Bk Titles 1,300; Bk Vols 20,000
Subject Interests: Case law, Statute law
Open Mon-Fri 8:30-5

R   TRINITY LUTHERAN COLLEGE*, 2802 Wetmore Ave, 98201. (Mail add: PO Box 870, 98206), SAN 317-610X. Tel: 425-392-0400, Ext 241. Toll Free Tel: 800-843-5659. FAX: 425-392-0404. E-mail: library@tlc.edu. Web Site: www.tlc.edu. *Dir,* Elliott Ohannes; E-mail: ohannes@tlc.edu
Founded 1944. Highest Degree: Bachelor
Library Holdings: Bk Vols 30,000; Per Subs 216
Special Collections: Bible Study; Bible Versions; Christian Education; Life of Christ; Theology Coll; Youth Work
Database Vendor: OCLC FirstSearch
Open Mon-Thurs 9am-10pm, Fri 9-5:30, Sat 1-5:30, Sun 6pm-10pm

FAIRCHILD AFB

A   UNITED STATES AIR FORCE*, Fairchild Base Library, Two W Castle St, 99011-8532. SAN 363-6518. Tel: 509-247-5228, 509-247-5556. FAX: 509-247-3365. *Dir,* Sherry Ann Hokanson; *Ref Librn,* Lisa M Love; E-mail: lisa.love@fairchild.af.mil; Staff 5.275 (MLS 2, Non-MLS 3.275)
Founded 1950
Library Holdings: AV Mats 3,390; Electronic Media & Resources 66; Bk Vols 28,350; Per Subs 87
Subject Interests: Mil hist, Mil sci, Northwest
Automation Activity & Vendor Info: (Cataloging) SIRSI Unicorn; (Circulation) SIRSI Unicorn; (ILL) OCLC; (OPAC) SIRSI Unicorn
Database Vendor: OCLC FirstSearch, SirsiDynix
Wireless access
Function: Accelerated reader prog, Bks on cassette, Bks on CD, CD-ROM, Children's prog, Computers for patron use, Copy machines, Doc delivery serv, Electronic databases & coll, Handicapped accessible, Online cat, Online searches, Orientations, Prog for adults, Prog for children & young adult, Pub access computers, Ref serv available, Scanner, Summer reading prog, Tax forms, Teen prog, Telephone ref
Partic in OCLC Online Computer Library Center, Inc
Open Mon-Thurs 10-8, Fri 10-5:30, Sun 10-6:30
Restriction: Authorized patrons

FEDERAL WAY

C   DEVRY UNIVERSITY, Seattle Campus Library, 3600 S 344th Way, 98001-9558. Tel: 253-943-2800. Circulation Tel: 253-943-3032. Administration Tel: 253-943-3034, 253-943-3035. Toll Free Tel: 877-923-3879. FAX: 253-943-3297. E-mail: library@sea.devry.edu. Web Site: www.sea.devry.edu/student_library.html. *Libr Dir,* Daniel Liestman; E-mail: dliestman@devry.edu; Staff 1 (MLS 1)
Founded 2001. Highest Degree: Master
Library Holdings: Bk Titles 12,000; Per Subs 45
Automation Activity & Vendor Info: (Cataloging) Ex Libris Group; (Circulation) Ex Libris Group; (OPAC) Ex Libris Group; (Serials) Ex Libris Group
Database Vendor: Agricola, EBSCOhost, Faulkner Information Services, Gale Cengage Learning, IBISWorld, IEEE (Institute of Electrical & Electronics Engineers), LexisNexis, netLibrary, ProQuest, Safari Books Online
Wireless access

Open Mon-Thurs 8-8, Fri 8-5, Sat 10-1
Restriction: Open to students, fac & staff

S   RHODODENDRON SPECIES FOUNDATION & BOTANICAL
GARDEN*, Lawrence J Pierce Library, 2525 S 336th St, 98003. (Mail
add: PO Box 3798, 98063-3798), SAN 328-087X. Tel: 253-838-4646,
253-927-6960. FAX: 253-838-4686. E-mail: rsf@rhodygarden.org. Web
Site: www.rhodygarden.org. *Librn,* Jean Cummins
Founded 1964
Library Holdings: Bk Titles 2,000; Per Subs 15

S   WEYERHAEUSER LIBRARY & INFORMATION RESOURCES*, 32901
Weyerhaeuser Way S, 98001. (Mail add: Library & Info Resources - WTC
1LIB, PO Box 9777, 98063-9777), SAN 317-5219. Tel: 253-924-3030.
FAX: 253-924-3612. *Mgr,* Susan Smith; Tel: 253-924-6262, E-mail:
susand.smith@weyerhaeuser.com
Founded 1979
Library Holdings: Bk Vols 8,000; Per Subs 300
Special Collections: Annual Reports; Trade Publications
Subject Interests: Forestry, Real estate, Wood
Automation Activity & Vendor Info: (Acquisitions) SirsiDynix;
(Cataloging) SirsiDynix; (Circulation) SirsiDynix; (OPAC) SirsiDynix;
(Serials) SirsiDynix
Wireless access
Partic in OCLC Online Computer Library Center, Inc
Restriction: Not open to pub

FRIDAY HARBOR

P   SAN JUAN ISLAND LIBRARY DISTRICT*, 1010 Guard St, 98250-9612.
SAN 317-5243. Tel: 360-378-2798. FAX: 360-378-2706. E-mail:
sjlib@sjlib.org. Web Site: www.sjlib.org. *Dir,* Marjorie Harrison; E-mail:
mharrison@sjlib.org; *Youth Serv,* Melina Lagios; E-mail:
mlagios@sjlib.org; Staff 9 (MLS 2, Non-MLS 7)
Founded 1922. Pop 7,500; Circ 160,000
Library Holdings: Bk Vols 60,000; Per Subs 170
Subject Interests: Northwest
Automation Activity & Vendor Info: (Circulation) Innovative Interfaces,
Inc
Database Vendor: BWI, Gale Cengage Learning, Ingram Library Services,
Innovative Interfaces, Inc, OCLC FirstSearch, ProQuest
Wireless access
Function: ILL available
Friends of the Library Group

S   THE WHALE MUSEUM LIBRARY, Manfred C Vernon Library, 62 First
St N, 98250-7973. (Mail add: PO Box 945, 98250-0945), SAN 329-3041.
Tel: 360-378-4710, Ext 27. FAX: 360-378-5790. Web Site:
www.whalemuseum.org. *Librn,* Amy Traxler
Founded 1979
Library Holdings: Bk Titles 600; Bk Vols 800; Videos 50
Subject Interests: Marine mammals, Pacific Northwest
Restriction: Not a lending libr

GRANDVIEW

P   BLEYHL COMMUNITY LIBRARY*, Grandview Public Library, 311
Division St, 98930-1398. SAN 317-5251. Tel: 509-882-9217. E-mail:
library@grandview.wa.us. Web Site: www.grandview.wa.us. *Librn,* Linda
Dunham; *Asst Librn,* Ruth Dirk; Staff 1 (MLS 1)
Founded 1914. Pop 8,415; Circ 42,525
Library Holdings: Bks on Deafness & Sign Lang 30; Bk Titles 42,500;
Per Subs 33
Special Collections: Blanche McLane Cook Art Coll; Local History
(Special History of Grandview), bks, pamphlets
Subject Interests: Agr, Spanish
Automation Activity & Vendor Info: (Cataloging) Follett Software;
(Circulation) Follett Software; (OPAC) Follett Software
Database Vendor: ProQuest
Open Mon-Wed 1:30-8, Thurs 10-12 & 1:30-8, Fri & Sat 1:30-5:30
Friends of the Library Group

HARRINGTON

P   HARRINGTON PUBLIC LIBRARY*, S 11 Third St, 99134. (Mail add:
PO Box 496, 99134-0496), SAN 317-5278. Tel: 509-253-4345. FAX:
509-253-4370. E-mail: library@harrington-wa.com. *Librn,* Vivienne Schultz
Pop 430; Circ 3,366
Library Holdings: Bk Titles 7,431
Open Tues 2-5, Thurs 3-6

HUNTERS

P   HUNTERS COMMUNITY LIBRARY*, 5014 Columbia River Rd, Bldg
No 11, 99157. Tel: 509-722-3877. Toll Free FAX: 877-251-3300. *Librn,*
O'Neill Nancy; E-mail: nancy@scrld.org
Library Holdings: Bk Vols 1,800
Wireless access
Open Wed & Fri 12-5

ISSAQUAH

P   KING COUNTY LIBRARY SYSTEM*, 960 Newport Way NW, 98027.
SAN 317-6061. Tel: 425-369-3200. Reference Tel: 425-462-9600.
Administration Tel: 425-369-3233. FAX: 425-369-3255. Web Site:
www.kcls.org. *Dir,* Bill Ptacek; Tel: 425-369-3232, E-mail: billp@kcls.org;
Assoc Dir, Coll Mgt, Bruce Adams; Tel: 425-369-3203, E-mail:
badams@kcls.org; *Assoc Dir-FMS,* Greg Smith; Tel: 425-369-3237, E-mail:
ggsmith@kcls.org; *Assoc Dir-ITS,* Jed Moffitt; Tel: 425-369-3433, E-mail:
jmoffitt@kcls.org; *Assoc Dir, Pub Serv,* Bruce Schauer; Tel: 425-450-1771,
E-mail: brucscha@kcls.org; *Assoc Dir, Pub Serv,* Denise Siers; Tel:
425-482-9281, E-mail: dsiers@kcls.org; *Assoc Dir, Pub Serv,* Nancy Smith;
Tel: 425-369-3309, E-mail: nsmith@kcls.org; *Mgr, Acq Serv,* Julie
Ben-Simon; Tel: 425-369-3205, E-mail: julieben@kcls.org; *Mgr, Outreach
Serv,* Holly Koelling; *Bus & Finance Mgr,* Linda Glenicki; Tel:
425-369-3260, E-mail: lglenick@kcls.org; *Cat Mgr,* Sally Smith; Tel:
425-369-3340, E-mail: ssmith@kcls.org; *Commun Relations & Mkt Mgr,*
Julie Brand Wallace; Tel: 425-369-3273, E-mail: jwallace@kcls.org;
Human Res Mgr, Charlene Richards; Tel: 425-369-3207, E-mail:
crichard@kcls.org; *Ch, YA Serv,* Joanne Vanderkooi; Tel: 425-369-3320,
E-mail: jvanderk@kcls.org; *Commun Relations Spec,* Jackie Brown; Tel:
425-369-3275, E-mail: jabrown@kcls.org; *Govt Doc,* Linda Fredericks; Tel:
425-450-1782, E-mail: lindaf@kcls.org
Founded 1942. Pop 1,800,000; Circ 1,912,200
Jan 2007-Dec 2007 Income (Main Library and Branch(s)) $82,780,945,
Locally Generated Income $81,000,000. Mats Exp $12,382,425. Sal
$50,428,185
Library Holdings: Braille Volumes 32; CDs 174,158; DVDs 131,861;
Large Print Bks 61,691; Bk Vols 916,585; Per Subs 11,000; Talking Bks
69,626; Videos 76,906
Special Collections: Nonprofit & Philanthropy Resource Center; Northwest
Coll; World Languages Coll. State Document Depository
Automation Activity & Vendor Info: (Acquisitions) Innovative Interfaces,
Inc; (Cataloging) Innovative Interfaces, Inc; (Circulation) Innovative
Interfaces, Inc; (Course Reserve) Innovative Interfaces, Inc; (ILL)
Innovative Interfaces, Inc; (Media Booking) Innovative Interfaces, Inc;
(OPAC) Innovative Interfaces, Inc; (Serials) Innovative Interfaces, Inc
Wireless access
Function: Accelerated reader prog, Adult literacy prog, After school
storytime, Art exhibits, Audio & video playback equip for onsite use,
Audiobks via web, BA reader (adult literacy), Bilingual assistance for
Spanish patrons, Bk club(s), Bks on cassette, Bks on CD, Bus archives,
CD-ROM, Children's prog, Citizenship assistance, Computer training,
Computers for patron use, Copy machines, Digital talking bks, E-Reserves,
Electronic databases & coll, Family literacy, For res purposes, Free DVD
rentals, Games & aids for the handicapped, Govt ref serv, Handicapped
accessible, Home delivery & serv to Sr ctr & nursing homes, Homebound
delivery serv, Homework prog, ILL available, Jail serv, KCLS online
newsroom (www.kcls.mediaroom.com), Music CDs, Newsp ref libr, Online
cat, Online ref, Online searches, OverDrive digital audio bks, Preschool
outreach, Prog for adults, Prog for children & young adult, Pub access
computers, Ref & res, Ref serv available, Senior computer classes, Senior
outreach, Serves mentally handicapped consumers, Spoken cassettes &
CDs, Spoken cassettes & DVDs, Summer reading prog, Tax forms, Teen
prog, Telephone ref, VHS videos, Video lending libr, Web-catalog,
Wheelchair accessible, Workshops
Publications: Inside KCLS (Newsletter)
Member Libraries: Renton Public Library
Special Services for the Blind - Large print bks
Open Mon-Fri 8-5
Friends of the Library Group
Branches: 45
ALGONA-PACIFIC LIBRARY, 255 Ellingson Rd, Pacific, 98047, SAN
328-9567. Tel: 253-833-3554. FAX: 206-296-5019.
  Open Mon-Thurs 10-9, Fri 10-6, Sat 10-5
  Friends of the Library Group
AUBURN LIBRARY, 1102 Auburn Way S, Auburn, 98002, SAN
317-4816. Tel: 253-931-3018. FAX: 253-735-5005.
  Founded 1905
  Subject Interests: Local hist, Pac NW hist
  Open Mon-Thurs 10-9, Fri 10-6, Sat 10-5, Sun 1-5
  Friends of the Library Group
BELLEVUE REGIONAL LIBRARY, 1111 110th Ave NE, Bellevue,
98004, SAN 303-528X. Tel: 425-450-1765. FAX: 425-450-2468.
  Open Mon-Thurs 9-9, Fri 10-6, Sat 10-6, Sun 12-8
  Friends of the Library Group

BLACK DIAMOND LIBRARY, 24707 Roberts Dr, Black Diamond, 98010, SAN 328-9583. Tel: 360-886-1105. FAX: 360-886-8159.
Open Mon-Thurs 10-9, Fri 10-6, Sat 10-5
Friends of the Library Group

BOTHELL REGIONAL LIBRARY, 18215 98th Ave NE, Bothell, 98011, SAN 328-0837. Tel: 425-486-7811. FAX: 206-296-5043.
Open Mon-Thurs 10-9, Fri 10-6, Sat 10-5, Sun 12-8
Friends of the Library Group

BOULEVARD PARK LIBRARY, 12015 Roseberg Ave S, Seattle, 98168, SAN 322-7138. Tel: 206-242-8662. FAX: 206-296-5044.
Founded 1927
Open Mon-Thurs 11-8:30, Fri & Sat 11-5
Friends of the Library Group

BURIEN LIBRARY, 400 SW 152nd St, Burien, 98166, SAN 328-9605. Tel: 206-243-3490. FAX: 206-433-3175.
Open Mon-Thurs 10-9, Fri 10-6, Sat 10-5, Sun 12-8
Friends of the Library Group

CARNATION LIBRARY, 4804 Tolt Ave, Carnation, 98014, SAN 328-9621. Tel: 425-333-4398. FAX: 425-333-4402.
Founded 1924
Open Mon-Thurs 10-9, Fri 10-6, Sat 10-5
Friends of the Library Group

COVINGTON LIBRARY, 27100 164th Ave SE, Covington, 98042, SAN 373-8485. Tel: 253-630-8761. FAX: 206-205-0787. Web Site: www.kcls.org.
Open Mon-Thurs 10-9, Fri 10-6, Sat 10-5, Sun 1-5
Friends of the Library Group

DES MOINES LIBRARY, 21620 11th Ave S, Des Moines, 98198, SAN 328-9648. Tel: 206-824-6066. FAX: 206-296-5047.
Open Mon-Thurs 10-9, Fri 10-6, Sat 10-5, Sun 1-5
Friends of the Library Group

DUVALL LIBRARY, 15619 Main St NE, Duvall, 98019, SAN 328-9664. Tel: 425-788-1173. FAX: 206-296-7429.
Open Tues & Sat 10-5, Wed 10-7, Thurs 1-7, Fri 10-6
Friends of the Library Group

FAIRWOOD LIBRARY, 17009 140th Ave SE, Renton, 98058, SAN 328-9680. Tel: 425-226-0522. FAX: 206-296-8115.
Open Mon-Thurs 10-9, Fri 10-6, Sat 10-5, Sun 1-5
Friends of the Library Group

FALL CITY LIBRARY, 33415 SE 42nd Pl, Fall City, 98024, SAN 328-9702. Tel: 425-222-5951. FAX: 206-296-5048.
Open Mon-Thurs 10-9, Fri 10-6, Sat 10-5
Friends of the Library Group

FEDERAL WAY REGIONAL LIBRARY, 34200 First Way S, Federal Way, 98003, SAN 372-0306. Tel: 253-838-3668. FAX: 253-661-4770.
Open Mon-Thurs 10-9, Fri 10-6, Sat 10-5, Sun 12-8
Friends of the Library Group

FEDERAL WAY 320TH LIBRARY, 848 S 320th St, Federal Way, 98003, SAN 373-8493. Tel: 253-839-0257. FAX: 206-296-5053.
Open Mon-Thurs 10-9, Fri 10-6, Sat 10-5
Friends of the Library Group

FOSTER LIBRARY, 4060 S 144th St, Tukwila, 98168, SAN 328-9214. Tel: 206-242-1640. FAX: 206-296-5055.
Open Mon-Thurs 11-9, Fri 10-6, Sat 10-5, Sun 11-5
Friends of the Library Group

GREENBRIDGE LIBRARY, 9720 Eight Ave SW, Seattle, 98106. Tel: 206-762-1682. FAX: 206-762-1684.
Open Mon-Wed 11-6, Thurs 1-8, Sat 12-4

ISSAQUAH LIBRARY, 10 W Sunset Way, 98027, SAN 328-7874. Tel: 425-392-5430. FAX: 425-392-1406.
Open Mon-Thurs 10-9, Fri 10-6, Sat 10-5, Sun 1-5
Friends of the Library Group

KENMORE LIBRARY, 18138 73rd Ave NE, Kenmore, 98028, SAN 328-9230. Tel: 425-486-8747. FAX: 206-296-5056.
Open Mon & Wed 11-9, Thurs & Fri 11-6, Sat 10-5
Friends of the Library Group

KENT REGIONAL LIBRARY, 212 Second Ave N, Kent, 98032, SAN 328-9257. Tel: 253-859-3330. FAX: 253-520-2170.
Open Mon-Thurs 10-9, Fri 10-6, Sat 10-5, Sun 1-5
Friends of the Library Group

KINGSGATE REGIONAL LIBRARY, 12315 NE 143rd St, Kirkland, 98034, SAN 328-9273. Tel: 425-821-7686. FAX: 206-296-5061.
Open Mon-Thurs 10-9, Fri 10-6, Sat 10-5, Sun 1-5
Friends of the Library Group

KIRKLAND LIBRARY, 308 Kirkland Ave, Kirkland, 98033, SAN 328-929X. Tel: 425-822-2459. FAX: 425-822-3624.
Open Mon-Thurs 10-9, Fri 10-6, Sat 10-5, Sun 1-5
Friends of the Library Group

LAKE FOREST PARK LIBRARY, 17171 Bothell Way NE, Ste A-134, Lake Forest Park, 98155, SAN 328-9192. Tel: 206-362-8860. FAX: 206-296-5054.
Open Mon-Thurs 10-9, Fri 10-6, Sat 10-5
Friends of the Library Group

LAKE HILLS LIBRARY, 15590 Lake Hills Blvd, Bellevue, 98007, SAN 328-9311. Tel: 425-747-3350. FAX: 425-643-2478.
Open Mon-Thurs 10-9, Fri 10-6, Sat 10-5, Sun 1-5
Friends of the Library Group

LIBRARY CONNECTION @ CROSSROADS, 15600 NE Eight St, Ste K-11, Bellevue, 98008. Tel: 425-644-6203. FAX: 425-644-6205.
Open Mon-Sat 10-9, Sun 11-6

LIBRARY CONNECTION @ SOUTHCENTER, 1386 Southcenter Mall, Tukwila, 98188. Tel: 206-242-6044. FAX: 206-244-2630.
Open Mon-Sat 10-9, Sun 11-7

MAPLE VALLEY LIBRARY, 21844 SE 248th St, Maple Valley, 98038, SAN 328-9338. Tel: 425-432-4620. FAX: 425-433-0837.
Open Mon-Thurs 10-9, Fri 10-6, Sat 10-5, Sun 1-5
Friends of the Library Group

MERCER ISLAND LIBRARY, 4400 88th Ave SE, Mercer Island, 98040, SAN 328-9354. Tel: 206-236-3537. FAX: 206-296-5064.
Open Mon-Thurs 10-9, Fri 10-6, Sat 10-5, Sun 1-5
Friends of the Library Group

MUCKLESHOOT LIBRARY, 39917 Auburn-Enumclaw Rd SE, Auburn, 98092, SAN 328-9370. Tel: 253-931-6779. FAX: 206-296-0215.
Open Mon-Thurs 10-9, Fri 10-6, Sat 10-5
Friends of the Library Group

NEWPORT WAY LIBRARY, 14250 SE Newport Way, Bellvue, 98006, SAN 328-9397. Tel: 425-747-2390.
Open Mon-Sat 10-8:30, Sun 11-6
Friends of the Library Group

NORTH BEND LIBRARY, 115 E Fourth St, North Bend, 98045, SAN 328-9419. Tel: 425-888-0554. FAX: 206-296-0216.
Open Mon-Thurs 10-9, Fri 10-6, Sat 10-5, Sun 1-5
Friends of the Library Group

REDMOND REGIONAL LIBRARY, 15990 NE 85th St, Redmond, 98052, SAN 328-9451. Tel: 425-885-1861. FAX: 206-296-5067.
Open Mon-Thurs 10-9, Fri 10-6, Sat 10-5, Sun 12-8
Friends of the Library Group

RICHMOND BEACH LIBRARY, 19601 21st Ave NW, Shoreline, 98177, SAN 328-9478. Tel: 206-546-3522. FAX: 206-546-6820.
Open Mon-Thurs 10-9, Fri 10-6, Sat 10-5
Friends of the Library Group

SAMMAMISH LIBRARY, 825 228th Ave SE, Sammamish, 98075, SAN 375-6041. Tel: 425-392-3130. FAX: 425-391-6707.
Founded 1998
Open Mon-Thurs 10-9, Fri 10-6, Sat 10-5, Sun 1-5
Friends of the Library Group

SHORELINE LIBRARY, 345 NE 175th St, Shoreline, 98155, SAN 328-9494. Tel: 206-362-7550. FAX: 206-296-5069.
Open Mon-Thurs 10-9, Fri 10-6, Sat 10-5, Sun 12-8
Friends of the Library Group

SKYKOMISH LIBRARY, 100 Fifth St, Skykomish, 98288, SAN 328-9516. Tel: 360-677-2660. FAX: 360-677-2096.
Open Mon & Thurs 1-7, Fri 1-5, Sat 10-2

SKYWAY LIBRARY, 7614 S 126th St, Seattle, 98178, SAN 325-1195. Tel: 206-772-5541. FAX: 206-296-5070.
Open Mon-Thurs 10-9, Fri 10-6, Sat 10-5
Friends of the Library Group

SNOQUALMIE LIBRARY, 7824 Center Blvd SE, Snoqualmie, 98065, SAN 328-9532. Tel: 425-888-1223. FAX: 206-296-0218.
Open Mon-Thurs 10-9, Fri 10-6, Sat 10-5
Friends of the Library Group

VALLEY VIEW LIBRARY, 17850 Military Rd S, SeaTac, 98188, SAN 328-9575. Tel: 206-242-6044. FAX: 206-296-5072.
Open Mon-Thurs 10-9, Fri 10-6, Sat 10-5
Friends of the Library Group

VASHON LIBRARY, 17210 Vashon Hwy SW, Vashon Island, 98070, SAN 328-0853. Tel: 206-463-2069. FAX: 206-296-5073.
Founded 1946
Open Mon-Thurs 10-8:30, Fri 10-6, Sat 10-5, Sun 1-5
Friends of the Library Group

WHITE CENTER LIBRARY, 11220 16th Ave SW, Seattle, 98146, SAN 328-9591. Tel: 206-243-0233. FAX: 206-296-5074.
Open Mon-Thurs 11-9, Fri & Sat 11-5
Friends of the Library Group

WOODINVILLE LIBRARY, 17105 Avondale Rd NE, Woodinville, 98072, SAN 373-8507. Tel: 425-788-0733. FAX: 425-788-9106.
Open Mon-Thurs 10-9, Fri 10-6, Sat 10-5, Sun 1-5
Friends of the Library Group

WOODMONT LIBRARY, 26809 Pacific Hwy S, Des Moines, 98198. Tel: 253-839-0121. FAX: 253-839-3358.
Open Mon-Thurs 10-9, Fri 10-6, Sat 10-5

YOUTH SERVICE CENTER, 1211 E Alder, Seattle, 98122, SAN 327-733X. Tel: 206-205-9641.
Restriction: Not open to pub

JOINT BASE LEWIS MCCHORD

A   UNITED STATES ARMY*, Joint Base Lewis-McChord Libraries, Bldg
     2109, 98433-9500. (Mail add: Box 339500, Fort Lewis, 98433-9500), SAN
     363-6542. Tel: 253-967-7736. Circulation Tel: 253-967-5889. Reference
     Tel: 253-966-1300. FAX: 253-967-3922. E-mail:
     lewisdmwrflls@conus.army.mil. Web Site: www.jblmmwr.com/library. *Dir,*
     Gloritha Mercer; Tel: 253-966-1312, E-mail: glo.mercer@conus.army.mil;
     Pub Serv, Jane Cherney; Tel: 253-966-1309, E-mail:
     jane.cherney@us.army.mil; *Ref,* Position Currently Open; *Tech Serv,*
     Marganne Weathers; Tel: 253-966-1321, E-mail:
     marganne.weathers@conus.army.mil; Staff 24 (MLS 7, Non-MLS 17)
     Founded 1942
     Library Holdings: Bk Vols 101,244; Per Subs 293
     Special Collections: DVD/Video Coll, children's, documentaries, how-to,
     movies; Korean, German & Spanish Language Colls, bks, mag, mat;
     Military Science Coll
     Subject Interests: Hist, Mil sci
     Automation Activity & Vendor Info: (Acquisitions) Innovative Interfaces,
     Inc - Millenium; (Cataloging) Innovative Interfaces, Inc - Millenium;
     (Circulation) Innovative Interfaces, Inc - Millenium; (OPAC) Innovative
     Interfaces, Inc - Millenium; (Serials) Innovative Interfaces, Inc - Millenium
     Database Vendor: Innovative Interfaces, Inc, SirsiDynix
     Wireless access
     Partic in Defense Digital Library Research Service (DDLRS); Fedlink;
     Merlin; OCLC Online Computer Library Center, Inc

KALAMA

P   KALAMA PUBLIC LIBRARY*, 312 First St, 98625. SAN 317-5286. Tel:
     360-673-4568. FAX: 360-673-4560. Web Site: www.kalamalibrary.org. *Dir,*
     Louise Thomas; E-mail: louise@kalamalibrary.org; *Asst Librn,* Molly
     Ciancibelli; Staff 4 (Non-MLS 4)
     Founded 1900. Circ 9,823
     Library Holdings: Bk Vols 11,000
     Special Collections: North West Coll
     Subject Interests: Classics
     Database Vendor: EBSCOhost, ProQuest
     Function: ILL available, Prog for children & young adult, Summer reading
     prog
     Open Mon-Sat 12-5
     Friends of the Library Group

KELSO

P   KELSO PUBLIC LIBRARY*, 314 Academy St, 98626-4196. SAN
     317-5294. Tel: 360-423-8110. FAX: 360-425-5195. E-mail:
     kelsopublib@kelso.gov. Web Site: www.kelso.gov/library. *Dir,* Geraldine
     De Rooy; *ILL,* Cindy Donaldson; Staff 8 (MLS 1, Non-MLS 7)
     Founded 1916. Pop 11,950; Circ 82,124
     Library Holdings: Bk Vols 35,289; Per Subs 108
     Automation Activity & Vendor Info: (Cataloging) SirsiDynix;
     (Circulation) SirsiDynix; (OPAC) SirsiDynix
     Database Vendor: ProQuest, SirsiDynix
     Open Mon-Wed 11-8, Thurs-Sat 10-5
     Friends of the Library Group

KENMORE

CM   BASTYR UNIVERSITY LIBRARY*, 14500 Juanita Dr NE, 98028. SAN
     323-7664. Tel: 425-602-3020. Interlibrary Loan Service Tel: 425-602-3021.
     FAX: 425-602-3188. E-mail: library@bastyr.edu. Web Site:
     www.bastyr.edu/library. *Dir, Libr Serv,* Jane D Saxton; Tel: 425-602-3024,
     E-mail: jsaxton@bastyr.edu; *Librn,* Susan Banks; Tel: 425-602-3022,
     E-mail: sbanks@bastyr.edu; *Librn,* Jennifer Beardsley; Tel: 425-602-3029,
     E-mail: jbeardsley@bastyr.edu; *Libr Asst,* Arlene Gillis; Tel: 425-602-3393,
     E-mail: agillis@bastyr.edu; *Libr Asst,* Margaret Holt; Tel: 425-602-3023;
     Libr Asst, Linda Tally; Staff 6 (MLS 3, Non-MLS 3)
     Founded 1980. Enrl 990; Fac 257; Highest Degree: Doctorate
     Library Holdings: CDs 1,500; DVDs 450; e-journals 3,000; Bk Titles
     19,000; Bk Vols 23,000; Per Subs 245; Videos 500
     Special Collections: Bauervic Coll of Homeopathy; Dr Jesse Mercer
     Gehman Archive, historic records, journals, prof papers; Dr John Bastyr
     Archive, historic records, journals, prof papers; Largest natural health coll
     in the PNW (Complementary & Alternative Medicine (CAM) Coll);
     Naturopathic Medicine Historical Coll
     Subject Interests: Acupuncture, Alternative med, Botanical med,
     Complementary med, Homeopathy, Natural health, Naturopathic med,
     Nutrition, Traditional Chinese med
     Automation Activity & Vendor Info: (Acquisitions) Insignia Software;
     (Cataloging) Insignia Software; (Circulation) Insignia Software; (Course
     Reserve) Insignia Software; (OPAC) Insignia Software; (Serials)
     SERHOLD
     Database Vendor: A.D.A.M. Inc, American Psychological Association
     (APA), EBSCO Information Services, EBSCOhost, Elsevier, MD Consult,
     Medline, Natural Standard, ProQuest, PubMed, Sage, ScienceDirect,
     SerialsSolutions, UpToDate, Wiley InterScience
     Wireless access
     Partic in National Network of Libraries of Medicine
     Friends of the Library Group

KENNEWICK

P   MID-COLUMBIA LIBRARIES*, 405 S Dayton, 99336. SAN 363-6577.
     Tel: 509-582-4745. FAX: 509-737-6349. Web Site:
     www.midcolumbialibraries.org. *Exec Dir,* Kyle Cox; *Coll & Merchandising
     Dir,* Michael Huff; *Finance & Bus Dir,* Anna Stroben; *Info Tech Dir,* Jon
     Stuckel; *Pub Serv Dir,* Elaine Baker; *Human Res Mgr,* Celina Bishop
     Founded 1949. Pop 182,000
     Special Collections: State Document Depository
     Subject Interests: Bus, Econ, Mexican-Am studies
     Automation Activity & Vendor Info: (Acquisitions) Polaris Library
     Systems; (Cataloging) Polaris Library Systems; (Circulation) Polaris
     Library Systems; (Course Reserve) Polaris Library Systems; (ILL) Polaris
     Library Systems; (Media Booking) Polaris Library Systems; (OPAC)
     Polaris Library Systems; (Serials) Polaris Library Systems
     Wireless access
     Function: Bk club(s), CD-ROM, Digital talking bks, Homebound delivery
     serv, ILL available, Online searches, Prog for adults, Prog for children &
     young adult, Ref serv available, Summer reading prog, VHS videos
     Partic in OCLC Online Computer Library Center, Inc
     Open Mon-Fri 8-5
     Friends of the Library Group
     Branches: 11
     BASIN CITY BRANCH, 50-A N Canal Blvd, Basin City, 99343, SAN
        373-5273. Tel: 509-269-4201. FAX: 509-269-4201. *In Charge,* Shirley
        Pattan
        Open Tues & Thurs 2-8, Wed & Sat 10-5
        Friends of the Library Group
     BENTON CITY BRANCH, 810 Horne Rd, Benton City, 99320, SAN
        326-7458. Tel: 509-588-6471. FAX: 509-588-4153. *In Charge,* Rebekah
        Kinney-Murphy
        Open Mon-Thurs 10-6, Sat 10-2
        Friends of the Library Group
     CONNELL BRANCH, 118 N Columbia, Connell, 99326. (Mail add: PO
        Box 657, Connell, 99326-0657), SAN 363-6631. Tel: 509-234-4971.
        FAX: 509-234-4902. *In Charge,* Helen Tobin
        Open Mon & Wed 3-8, Tues & Fri 12-5, Thurs 9-2, Sat 10-3
        Friends of the Library Group
     KAHLOTUS BRANCH, E 225 Weston, Kahlotus, 99335. (Mail add: PO
        Box 147, Kahlotus, 99335-0147). Tel: 509-282-3493. FAX:
        509-282-3493. Web Site: www.mcl-lib.org/kahlotus.htm. *In Charge,*
        Connie Jennings
        Open Mon & Tues 12-5, Wed 5pm-9pm, Thurs 9-2
        Friends of the Library Group
     KEEWAYDIN PARK, 405 S Dayton, 99336. Tel: 509-586-3156. *Br Supvr,*
        Candy Mendoza
        Open Mon-Wed 9-8, Thurs-Sat 9-5
        Friends of the Library Group
     KENNEWICK BRANCH, 1620 S Union, 99338, SAN 329-3343. Tel:
        509-783-7878. FAX: 509-735-2063. *Br Mgr,* Tom Moak
        Open Mon-Thurs 9-9, Fri & Sat 9-5, Sun 1-5
        Friends of the Library Group
     MERRILL'S CORNER, 5240 Eltopia W, Eltopia, 99330, SAN 370-4254.
        Tel: 509-297-4341. FAX: 509-297-4341. *In Charge,* Evangeline Mahler
        Open Mon & Wed 1-6, Fri 12-5
        Friends of the Library Group
     OTHELLO BRANCH, 101 E Main St, Othello, 99344, SAN 374-8170.
        Tel: 509-488-9683. FAX: 509-488-5321. *In Charge,* Corinne Field
        Open Mon-Wed 11-8, Thurs-Sat 11-5
        Friends of the Library Group
     PASCO BRANCH, 1320 W Hopkins, Pasco, 99301, SAN 363-6666. Tel:
        509-545-1019. FAX: 509-547-5416. *Br Mgr,* Candy Mendoza
        Open Mon-Thurs 9-9, Fri & Sat 9-5, Sun 1-5
        Friends of the Library Group
     PROSSER BRANCH, 902 Seventh St, Prosser, 99350, SAN 370-4270. Tel:
        509-786-2533. FAX: 509-786-7341. *Br Mgr,* Jessie Kovis
        Open Mon-Wed 11-8, Thurs & Fri 11-5, Sat 9-1
        Friends of the Library Group
     WEST RICHLAND BRANCH, 3803 W Van Giesen, West Richland,
        99353, SAN 363-6682. Tel: 509-967-3191. FAX: 509-967-1224. *In
        Charge,* Kayla Nield
        Open Mon-Wed 11-8, Thurs-Sat 11-5
        Friends of the Library Group
     Bookmobiles: 1

KETTLE FALLS

P   KETTLE FALLS PUBLIC LIBRARY*, 605 Meyers St, 99141. (Mail add: PO Box 478, 99141-0478), SAN 326-2995. Tel: 509-738-6817. FAX: 509-738-2787. E-mail: kfcirc@scrld.org. Web Site: www.scrld.org. *Librn,* Joan G Nullet; Staff 4 (MLS 1, Non-MLS 3)
Founded 1950. Pop 2,000; Circ 14,000
Special Collections: Old Kettle Falls Photo Coll
Automation Activity & Vendor Info: (Cataloging) TLC (The Library Corporation); (Circulation) TLC (The Library Corporation); (OPAC) TLC (The Library Corporation)
Database Vendor: ProQuest
Wireless access
Open Mon, Wed & Fri 10-6, Tues & Thurs 10-8, Sat 10-5
Friends of the Library Group

KIRKLAND

J   LAKE WASHINGTON TECHNICAL COLLEGE*, Library Media Center, 11605 132nd Ave NE, 98034-8505. Tel: 425-739-8320. FAX: 425-739-8198. E-mail: library@lwtc.edu. Web Site: www.lwtc.ctc.edu/library. *Asst Dean,* Edward Sargent; Tel: 425-739-8100, Ext 492, E-mail: edward.sargent@lwtc.edu; *Librn,* Position Currently Open; *Libr Tech,* Ellen Kinamon; Tel: 425-739-8100, Ext 503, E-mail: ellen.kinamon@lwtc.edu
Library Holdings: Bk Titles 20,000; Per Subs 230
Open Mon-Wed 7:30-4:30, Thurs 7:30-7, Fri 8-1

CR   NORTHWEST UNIVERSITY*, Hurst Library, 5520 108th Ave NE, 98083-0579. (Mail add: PO Box 579, 98083-0579), SAN 363-6720. Tel: 425-889-5266. Reference Tel: 425-889-7802. FAX: 425-889-7801. E-mail: library@northwestu.edu. Web Site: library.northwestu.edu. *Dir,* Charles Diede; Tel: 425-889-5263, E-mail: charles.diede@northwestu.edu; *Ref Librn,* Position Currently Open; *Syst Librn,* Adam Epp; Tel: 424-889-5201, E-mail: adam.epp@northwestu.edu; *Tech Serv Librn,* Leslie Engelson; Tel: 425-889-5339, E-mail: leslie.engelson@northwestu.edu; *Circ Supvr,* Dorothy Mulkey; E-mail: dorothy.mulkey@northwestu.edu; *Acq,* Gina Stocker; Tel: 425-889-5301, E-mail: gina.stocker@northwestu.edu; *Cat,* Christa Strickler; Tel: 425-889-5267; *Circ,* Emily Skolrud; E-mail: emily.skolrud@northwestu.edu; *User Serv,* David Austin; Tel: 425-889-5302, E-mail: david.austin@northwestu.edu; Staff 9 (MLS 5, Non-MLS 4)
Founded 1934. Enrl 1,260; Fac 61; Highest Degree: Master
Library Holdings: Bk Titles 75,948; Bk Vols 174,060; Per Subs 914
Special Collections: Messianic Jewish Coll; Pacific Rim; Pentecostal Movement
Subject Interests: Relig studies, Teacher educ
Automation Activity & Vendor Info: (Acquisitions) Ex Libris Group; (Cataloging) Ex Libris Group; (Circulation) Ex Libris Group; (Course Reserve) Ex Libris Group; (ILL) OCLC; (OPAC) Ex Libris Group; (Serials) Ex Libris Group
Database Vendor: Agricola, Atlas Systems, BCR: Christian Periodical Index, CQ Press, EBSCOhost, Gale Cengage Learning, H W Wilson, Hoovers, JSTOR, netLibrary, OCLC FirstSearch, OCLC WorldCat, Oxford Online, ProQuest, PubMed, RefWorks
Wireless access
Function: ILL available
Partic in Puget Sound Acad Independent Librs

LA CONNER

P   LA CONNER REGIONAL LIBRARY, 614 Morris St, 98257. (Mail add: PO Box 370, 98257-0370), SAN 317-5324. Tel: 360-466-3352. FAX: 360-466-9178. E-mail: library@lclib.lib.wa.us. Web Site: www.lclib.lib.wa.us. *Dir,* Joy C Neal; E-mail: jneal@lclib.lib.wa.us; *Libr Asst,* Amy Griffin; E-mail: agriffin@lclib.lib.wa.us; *Libr Tech,* Lane Fernando; E-mail: lfernando@lclib.lib.wa.us; *Ch Serv Spec,* K J Cooper; Staff 1.75 (MLS 1, Non-MLS 0.75)
Founded 1927. Pop 4,800; Circ 48,000
Jan 2011-Dec 2011 Income $269,000
Automation Activity & Vendor Info: (Circulation) Evergreen; (ILL) OCLC FirstSearch; (OPAC) Evergreen
Database Vendor: EBSCO Auto Repair Reference, Facts on File, OCLC FirstSearch, OCLC WorldCat, ProQuest, World Book Online
Wireless access
Function: Adult bk club, Bks on CD, Children's prog, Computer training, Computers for patron use, Copy machines, Music CDs, Online cat, OverDrive digital audio bks, Preschool outreach, Prog for children & young adult, Pub access computers, Senior computer classes, Summer reading prog, Tax forms, Teen prog, Winter reading prog
Open Mon & Thurs-Sat 11-5, Tues & Wed 11-7
Restriction: In-house use for visitors
Friends of the Library Group

S   SKAGIT COUNTY HISTORICAL MUSEUM*, Research Library, 501 S Fourth St, 98257. (Mail add: PO Box 818, 98257-0818), SAN 317-5332. Tel: 360-466-3365. FAX: 360-466-1611. E-mail: museum@co.skagit.wa.us. Web Site: www.skagitcounty.net/museum. *Curator, Interim Dir,* Pat Doran; *Bus Mgr,* Kathy Pace; *Librn,* Mari Densmore
Library Holdings: Bk Titles 1,528; Bk Vols 1,639
Special Collections: Oral History
Subject Interests: County hist, Genealogy, Local hist, State hist
Function: Archival coll
Restriction: Open by appt only

LACEY

C   SAINT MARTIN'S UNIVERSITY*, O'Grady Library, 5300 Pacific Ave SE, 98503. SAN 317-5340. Tel: 360-486-8800. Circulation Tel: 360-486-8802. Interlibrary Loan Service Tel: 360-486-8834. Reference Tel: 360-486-8803. Administration Tel: 360-486-8804. FAX: 360-486-8810. E-mail: reference@stmartin.edu. Web Site: www.stmartin.edu/library. *Dir,* Scot Harrison; Tel: 360-486-8808, E-mail: sharrison@stmartin.edu; *Spec Coll & Archives Librn,* Brother Peter Tynan; Tel: 360-486-8828, Fax: 360-486-8825, E-mail: br_peter@stmartin.edu; *Tech Serv,* Kirsti Thomas; Tel: 360-486-8827, Fax: 360-486-8825, E-mail: kthomas@stmartin.edu; Staff 12 (MLS 4, Non-MLS 8)
Founded 1895. Enrl 1,126; Fac 70; Highest Degree: Master
Library Holdings: AV Mats 1,730; e-books 7,007; Bk Titles 78,527; Bk Vols 96,936; Per Subs 633
Subject Interests: Catholic theol, Children's lit, Labor hist
Automation Activity & Vendor Info: (Acquisitions) Innovative Interfaces, Inc; (Cataloging) Innovative Interfaces, Inc; (Circulation) Innovative Interfaces, Inc; (Course Reserve) Innovative Interfaces, Inc; (ILL) OCLC ILLiad; (Media Booking) Innovative Interfaces, Inc; (OPAC) Innovative Interfaces, Inc; (Serials) Innovative Interfaces, Inc
Database Vendor: EBSCOhost, Gale Cengage Learning, JSTOR, LexisNexis, netLibrary, OCLC FirstSearch, ProQuest, Wilson - Wilson Web
Function: ILL available
Partic in Coop Libr in Olympia; Northwest Association of Private Colleges & Universities (NAPCU); OCLC Online Computer Library Center, Inc; Orbis Cascade Alliance; Puget Sound Acad Independent Librs

LAKEWOOD

J   CLOVER PARK TECHNICAL COLLEGE LIBRARY*, 4500 Steilacoom Blvd SW, Bldg 15, 98499-4098. SAN 324-5160. Tel: 253-589-5544. FAX: 253-589-5726. Web Site: www.cptc.edu/library. *Librn,* Doug Ammons; Tel: 253-589-6067, E-mail: doug.ammons@cptc.edu; *Librn,* Elaine Holster; Tel: 253-589-5628, E-mail: elaine.holster@cptc.edu; Staff 2 (MLS 2)
Highest Degree: Associate
Jul 2005-Jun 2006. Mats Exp $90,000
Library Holdings: Bk Titles 12,000; Per Subs 320
Special Collections: Technical College Materials
Subject Interests: Vocational educ
Automation Activity & Vendor Info: (Cataloging) Horizon; (Circulation) Horizon; (Course Reserve) Horizon; (ILL) Horizon; (OPAC) Horizon
Database Vendor: EBSCOhost, ProQuest, SirsiDynix
Open Mon-Thurs 7-7, Fri 7-4, Sat 9:30-2:30

J   PIERCE COLLEGE LIBRARY*, 9401 Farwest Dr SW, 98498. SAN 317-6835. Tel: 253-964-6547. Interlibrary Loan Service Tel: 253-964-7349. Reference Tel: 253-964-6555. FAX: 253-964-6713. Web Site: www.pierce.ctc.edu/library. *Dean, Libr & Institutional Effectiveness,* Debra Gilchrist; Tel: 253-964-6553, E-mail: dgilchrist@pierce.ctc.edu; *Head, Circ,* Velvet Martin; E-mail: vmartin@pierce.ctc.edu; *Head, ILL,* Barbara Perkins; E-mail: bperkins@pierce.ctc.edu; *Instrul Serv Librn, Ref,* Sarah Frye; Tel: 253-964-6303, E-mail: sfrye@pierce.ctc.edu; *Instrul Serv Librn, Ref,* Laurie Shuster; Tel: 253-964-6305, E-mail: lshuster@pierce.ctc.edu; *Instrul Serv Librn, Ref,* Emily Wood; Tel: 253-964-6302, E-mail: ewood@pierce.ctc.edu; *Ser Tech,* Kathy Gilbert; Tel: 253-964-6740, E-mail: kgilbert@pierce.ctc.edu; Staff 8 (MLS 5, Non-MLS 3)
Founded 1967. Enrl 13,500; Fac 300; Highest Degree: Associate
Library Holdings: Bk Titles 120,000; Per Subs 525
Automation Activity & Vendor Info: (Acquisitions) Ex Libris Group; (Cataloging) Ex Libris Group; (Circulation) Ex Libris Group; (Course Reserve) Ex Libris Group; (OPAC) Ex Libris Group; (Serials) Ex Libris Group
Database Vendor: EBSCOhost, ProQuest
Function: AV serv, Doc delivery serv, Handicapped accessible, ILL available, Photocopying/Printing, Ref serv available, Telephone ref, Wheelchair accessible
Partic in OCLC Online Computer Library Center, Inc; Washington Libr Network
Special Services for the Deaf - TTY equip
Restriction: Open to pub for ref & circ; with some limitations, Open to students, Open to students, fac & staff, Photo ID required for access

Departmental Libraries:
PUYALLUP CAMPUS, 1601 39th Ave SE, Puyallup, 98374. Tel:
253-840-8300. Interlibrary Loan Service Tel: 253-964-7349. Reference
Tel: 253-840-8302. Administration Tel: 253-964-6523. FAX:
253-840-8316. *Dean, Libr & Institutional Effectiveness,* Dr Debra
Gilchrist; Tel: 253-964-6553, Fax: 252-964-6713, E-mail:
dgilchrist@pierce.ctc.edu; *Dir of Libr Operations,* Christie J Flynn; Tel:
253-840-8304, E-mail: cflynn@pierce.ctc.edu; *Head, Circ,* Lori Broberg;
E-mail: lbroberg@pierce.ctc.edu; *Tech Serv & Syst Librn,* Frank Brasile;
Tel: 253-840-8306, E-mail: fbrasile@pierce.ctc.edu; *Acq, Cat Tech,*
Tamara Jordan; Tel: 253-840-8310, E-mail: tjordan@pierce.ctc.edu; *Ref
& Instruction,* Kathy Swart; Tel: 253-840-8305, E-mail:
kswart@pierce.ctc.edu; *Ref & Instruction,* Beth Thoms; Tel:
253-840-8303, E-mail: bthoms@pierce.ctc.edu; *Tech Serv,* John Jennings;
Tel: 253-840-8309, E-mail: jjennings@pierce.ctc.edu; Staff 8 (MLS 5,
Non-MLS 3)
Founded 1967. Enrl 6,300; Highest Degree: Associate
Function: AV serv, ILL available, Photocopying/Printing, Ref serv
available, Telephone ref
Restriction: Open to pub for ref & circ; with some limitations, Open to
students, Open to students, fac & staff, Photo ID required for access

LIBERTY LAKE

P   LIBERTY LAKE MUNICIPAL LIBRARY, 23123 E Mission Ave,
99019-7613. Tel: 509-232-2510, 509-232-2511. Reference Tel:
509-435-0778. Administration Tel: 509-435-0777. Toll Free Tel:
866-729-8507. FAX: 509-232-2512. E-mail: library@libertylakewa.gov.
Web Site: www.libertylakewa.gov/library. *Dir,* Pamela Mogen; E-mail:
pmogen@libertylakewa.gov; Staff 6 (MLS 2, Non-MLS 4)
Founded 2003. Pop 7,500; Circ 92,000
Jan 2012-Dec 2012 Income $410,500. Mats Exp $44,900, Books $24,000,
Per/Ser (Incl. Access Fees) $2,000, AV Equip $2,000, AV Mat $7,500,
Electronic Ref Mat (Incl. Access Fees) $9,000, Presv $400. Sal $195,249
(Prof $122,414)
Library Holdings: Audiobooks 825; AV Mats 91; CDs 28; DVDs 1,200;
e-books 12; Electronic Media & Resources 6,000; Large Print Bks 450; Bk
Titles 25,021; Per Subs 36
Automation Activity & Vendor Info: (Cataloging) ByWater Solutions;
(Circulation) ByWater Solutions; (ILL) ByWater Solutions; (OPAC)
ByWater Solutions
Database Vendor: EBSCO Information Services, Gale Cengage Learning,
Ingram Library Services, OCLC ArticleFirst, OCLC FirstSearch, OCLC
WebJunction, OCLC WorldCat, Overdrive, Inc, ProQuest, World Book
Online
Wireless access
Function: Adult bk club, Art exhibits, Audio & video playback equip for
onsite use, Audiobks via web, Bi-weekly Writer's Group, Bk club(s), Bks
on CD, Children's prog, Computer training, Computers for patron use,
Copy machines, e-mail & chat, Electronic databases & coll, Exhibits, Free
DVD rentals, Holiday prog, Home delivery & serv to Sr ctr & nursing
homes, Homebound delivery serv, ILL available, Instruction & testing,
Music CDs, Online cat, Online ref, Online searches, Outreach serv,
OverDrive digital audio bks, Photocopying/Printing, Preschool outreach,
Preschool reading prog, Prog for adults, Prog for children & young adult,
Pub access computers, Ref serv available, Ref serv in person, Senior
computer classes, Spanish lang bks, Spoken cassettes & CDs, Story hour,
Summer reading prog, Teen prog, Web-catalog, Wheelchair accessible
Partic in Cooperative Information Network; Washington Digital Library
Consortium
Open Mon 2-8, Tues, Wed & Fri 10-6, Thurs 10-8, Sat 10-4
Friends of the Library Group

LONGVIEW

P   LONGVIEW PUBLIC LIBRARY*, 1600 Louisiana St, 98632-2993. SAN
317-5375. Tel: 360-442-5300. Reference Tel: 360-442-5315. Administration
Tel: 360-442-5310. FAX: 360-442-5954. Web Site:
www.longviewlibrary.org. *Dir,* Chris Skaugset; Tel: 360-442-5309, E-mail:
chris.skaugset@ci.longview.wa.us; *Ad,* Position Currently Open; *Circ Librn,*
Position Currently Open; *Ref/Info Tech Serv Librn,* Karl Marcuson; E-mail:
karl.marcuson@ci.longview.wa.us; *Tech Serv Librn,* Karen Straube; Tel:
360-442-5316, E-mail: karen.straube@ci.longview.wa.us; *Ch, YA Serv,* Jan
Hanson; Tel: 360-442-5323, E-mail: jan.hanson@ci.longview.wa.us; Staff
21 (MLS 4, Non-MLS 17)
Founded 1926. Pop 51,000; Circ 527,000
Jan 2010-Dec 2010 Income $1,986,070
Library Holdings: AV Mats 16,676; CDs 5,960; DVDs 6,229; Bk Vols
153,456; Per Subs 250; Videos 3,878
Special Collections: '23 Club Oral History Coll, cassettes; Construction of
Longview (Long Bell Files), letters; Early Longview History (S M Morris
Coll), pictures; Longview coll (Longview Room); Fed; Rudolph Steiner
Coll. Oral History; State Document Depository
Automation Activity & Vendor Info: (Acquisitions) Horizon;
(Cataloging) Horizon; (Circulation) Horizon; (Course Reserve) Horizon;

(ILL) Horizon; (Media Booking) Horizon; (OPAC) Horizon; (Serials)
Horizon
Database Vendor: EBSCO Auto Repair Reference, Electric Library, Gale
Cengage Learning, OCLC FirstSearch, ProQuest, ReferenceUSA
Wireless access
Function: Adult bk club, Adult literacy prog, Archival coll, Art exhibits,
Audiobks via web, AV serv, BA reader (adult literacy), Bks on cassette,
Bks on CD, Children's prog, Citizenship assistance, Computers for patron
use, Copy machines, Electronic databases & coll, Equip loans & repairs,
Family literacy, Free DVD rentals, Home delivery & serv to Sr ctr &
nursing homes, Homebound delivery serv, Literacy & newcomer serv,
Music CDs, Online cat, Outreach serv, OverDrive digital audio bks,
Photocopying/Printing, Prog for adults, Prog for children & young adult,
Pub access computers, Ref & res, Ref serv in person, Story hour, Summer
reading prog, Tax forms, Teen prog, Telephone ref, VHS videos,
Wheelchair accessible
Publications: Check Us Out (Newsletter)
Special Services for the Deaf - Bks on deafness & sign lang; TDD equip
Special Services for the Blind - Bks on cassette; Bks on CD; Cassettes;
Home delivery serv; Large print bks; Talking bks
Open Mon, Tues & Thurs 10-8, Wed 10-5, Fri 10-6, Sat 12-5
Friends of the Library Group

J   LOWER COLUMBIA COLLEGE*, Alan Thompson Library, 1600 Maple
St, 98632-3907. (Mail add: PO Box 3010, 98632-3907), SAN 317-5383.
Tel: 360-442-2660. Reference Tel: 360-442-2665. Toll Free Tel:
800-850-3133. FAX: 360-442-2669. E-mail:
library.reference@lowercolumbia.edu. Web Site: lowercolumbia.edu/library.
Interim Dir, J Carmen Robinson; E-mail: crobinson@lowercolumbia.edu;
Staff 5 (MLS 1, Non-MLS 4)
Founded 1934. Enrl 2,500; Fac 90; Highest Degree: Associate
Library Holdings: Bk Titles 46,000; Bk Vols 48,000; Per Subs 150
Automation Activity & Vendor Info: (Cataloging) SirsiDynix;
(Circulation) SirsiDynix; (OPAC) SirsiDynix
Database Vendor: OCLC FirstSearch, ProQuest, SirsiDynix
Wireless access

M   SAINT JOHN MEDICAL CENTER, Minthorn Medical Library, 1615
Delaware St, 98632-2310. (Mail add: PO Box 3002, 98632-0302), SAN
317-5391. Tel: 360-414-7462. FAX: 360-414-7463. *Med Librn/CME
Coordr,* Michael Graham; Staff 1 (MLS 1)
Library Holdings: e-books 61; e-journals 6,800; Bk Vols 2,000; Per Subs
150
Subject Interests: Med, Pathology
Automation Activity & Vendor Info: (Cataloging) EOS International;
(OPAC) EOS International; (Serials) EOS International
Database Vendor: EBSCOhost, EOS International, Majors, MD Consult,
Medline, Micromedex, OVID Technologies, ProQuest, SerialsSolutions,
UpToDate
Function: Doc delivery serv, Electronic databases & coll, Health sci info
serv, ILL available, Mail & tel request accepted
Partic in Docline
Restriction: Badge access after hrs

LOPEZ ISLAND

P   LOPEZ ISLAND LIBRARY*, 2265 Fisherman Bay Rd, 98261. (Mail add:
PO Box 770, 98261-0770), SAN 326-7105. Tel: 360-468-2265. FAX:
360-468-3850. Web Site: www.lopezlibrary.org. *Dir,* Lou Pray; Staff 5
(MLS 2, Non-MLS 3)
Founded 1982. Pop 2,400; Circ 58,600
Jan 2008-Dec 2008 Income $402,300, County $386,000, Locally Generated
Income $16,300. Mats Exp $85,300, Books $75,000, Per/Ser (Incl. Access
Fees) $4,800, Electronic Ref Mat (Incl. Access Fees) $5,500. Sal $189,000
(Prof $64,000)
Library Holdings: Audiobooks 1,666; CDs 594; DVDs 3,495; e-books
153; Large Print Bks 1,500; Bk Titles 23,500; Per Subs 115; Videos 1,460
Subject Interests: Native Am art, Northwest Coast hist
Database Vendor: Gale Cengage Learning, LearningExpress, OCLC
FirstSearch, ProQuest, Wilson - Wilson Web
Wireless access
Function: ILL available, Photocopying/Printing, Prog for children & young
adult, Scanner, Summer reading prog
Open Mon & Sat 10-5, Tues, Thurs & Fri 10-6, Wed 10-9
Friends of the Library Group

LYNNWOOD

J   EDMONDS COMMUNITY COLLEGE LIBRARY, 20000 68th Ave W,
98036. SAN 317-543X. Tel: 425-640-1529. Reference Tel: 425-640-1472.
Administration Tel: 425-640-1522. Web Site: www.edcc.edu/library. *Dir,*
Lauri Kram; E-mail: lkram@edcc.edu; *Ref & Instruction Librn,* Meryl
Geffner; E-mail: meryl.geffner@edcc.edu; *Ref & Instrul Serv Librn,*
Johnetta Moore; *Tech Serv Librn,* Dale Burke; *Circ Supvr,* Nora Smith;
Tech Serv, Barbara Johnson; Staff 5 (MLS 5)

Founded 1967
Subject Interests: Hort, Legal assisting
Automation Activity & Vendor Info: (Acquisitions) Ex Libris Group; (Cataloging) Ex Libris Group; (Circulation) Ex Libris Group; (Course Reserve) Ex Libris Group; (ILL) OCLC; (OPAC) Ex Libris Group; (Serials) Ex Libris Group
Database Vendor: ARTstor, College Source, EBSCOhost, Ex Libris Group, Gale Cengage Learning, Hoovers, OCLC FirstSearch, OCLC WorldCat, ProQuest, Springshare, LLC, Westlaw
Wireless access
Partic in OCLC Online Computer Library Center, Inc
Open Mon-Thurs 7:30am-9pm, Fri 7:30-2, Sat & Sun 1-5

MONTESANO

GL GRAYS HARBOR COUNTY*, Law Library, 102 W Broadway, Rm 203, 98563. SAN 317-5472. Tel: 360-249-5311. FAX: 360-249-6391. *Librn,* Bonnie Kindle
Library Holdings: Bk Vols 5,000
Database Vendor: Westlaw
Open Mon-Fri 8-5

MOSES LAKE

J BIG BEND COMMUNITY COLLEGE LIBRARY*, 7662 Chanute St, 98837. SAN 317-5480. Tel: 509-793-2350. FAX: 509-762-2402. E-mail: librarymail@bigbend.edu. Web Site: www.bigbend.edu/library. *Dean, Info Serv,* Tim Fuhrman; E-mail: timf@bigbend.edu; *Librn,* Lance Wyman; E-mail: lancew@bigbend.edu; *Prog Coordr,* Kathy Aldrich; E-mail: kathya@bigbend.edu; *Libr Spec,* John W Anderson; E-mail: johna@bigbend.edu; *Cat,* Carolyn Riddle; E-mail: carolynr@bigbend.edu
Founded 1963. Enrl 4,622; Fac 50
Library Holdings: Bk Titles 35,731; Per Subs 150
Special Collections: Chinese Art Coll. Oral History
Subject Interests: Grant County hist, Pacific Northwest
Automation Activity & Vendor Info: (Cataloging) OCLC; (Circulation) Ex Libris Group; (OPAC) Ex Libris Group
Database Vendor: OCLC FirstSearch, ProQuest
Wireless access
Partic in Western Libr Network
Special Services for the Blind - Closed circuit TV
Open Mon-Thurs 7:30am-9pm, Fri 8-4, Sat & Sun 12-6

MOUNT VERNON

P MOUNT VERNON CITY LIBRARY*, 315 Snoqualmie St, 98273. SAN 317-5499. Tel: 360-336-6209. FAX: 360-336-6259. *Dir,* Brian M Soneda; Tel: 360-336-6249; *Dep Dir,* Sara Holahan; Staff 7 (MLS 4, Non-MLS 3)
Founded 1908. Pop 30,000; Circ 389,116
Library Holdings: AV Mats 8,964; Large Print Bks 1,559; Bk Vols 68,924; Per Subs 327; Talking Bks 1,419
Special Collections: Literacy & ESL Coll; Spanish Language Coll
Automation Activity & Vendor Info: (Acquisitions) SirsiDynix; (Cataloging) SirsiDynix; (Circulation) SirsiDynix; (OPAC) SirsiDynix
Database Vendor: EBSCOhost, ProQuest, SirsiDynix
Wireless access
Function: ILL available
Partic in OCLC Online Computer Library Center, Inc
Special Services for the Deaf - Video & TTY relay via computer
Open Mon-Thurs 10-8, Fri & Sat 10-5, Sun 1-5
Friends of the Library Group

S PACCAR, INC*, Technical Center Library, 12479 Farm to Market Rd, 98273. SAN 329-1405. Tel: 360-757-5234. FAX: 360-757-5201. Web Site: www.paccar.com. *Sr Res Spec,* Betsy Aldridge; E-mail: betsy.aldridge@paccar.com; *Doc,* Sharon Bowen
Founded 1985
Library Holdings: Bk Titles 20,000; Per Subs 200
Subject Interests: Automotive eng
Automation Activity & Vendor Info: (Cataloging) Inmagic, Inc.; (Circulation) Inmagic, Inc.; (ILL) OCLC; (OPAC) Inmagic, Inc.; (Serials) Inmagic, Inc.
Partic in OCLC Online Computer Library Center, Inc; Western Transportation Knowledge Network (WTKN)
Restriction: Staff use only

GL SKAGIT COUNTY LAW LIBRARY*, County Courthouse, 205 W Kincaid, Rm 104, 98273. SAN 375-0337. Tel: 360-336-9324. FAX: 360-336-9336. E-mail: lawlibrary@co.skagit.wa.us. Web Site: www.skagitcounty.net. *Librn,* JoAnne Giesbrecht
Library Holdings: Bk Vols 8,000
Open Mon-Fri 8:30-4:30

J SKAGIT VALLEY COLLEGE*, Norwood Cole Library, 2405 E College Way, 98273-5899. SAN 317-5510. Tel: 360-416-7850. Circulation Tel: 360-416-7837. Interlibrary Loan Service Tel: 360-416-7659. Reference Tel: 360-416-7847. Toll Free Tel: 877-385-5360. FAX: 360-416-7698. Web Site: library.skagit.edu. *Dean of Libr, Learning Res & Basic Skills,* Mindy McCormick Coslor; Tel: 360-416-7761, E-mail: mcoslor@skagit.edu; *Pub Serv,* Margret Mills; Tel: 360-416-7760, E-mail: mmills@skagit.edu; *Ref Serv,* Linda Hendrick; Tel: 360-416-7606, E-mail: lhendrick@skagit.edu; *Ref Serv,* Susan Kent; Tel: 360-416-7607, E-mail: skent@skagit.edu; *Tech Serv,* Elena Bianco; Tel: 360-416-7624, E-mail: ebianco@skagit.edu; Staff 8.2 (MLS 3.7, Non-MLS 4.5)
Founded 1926. Enrl 4,300; Fac 170; Highest Degree: Associate
Library Holdings: e-books 1,500; Bk Titles 50,255; Bk Vols 87,785; Per Subs 222
Subject Interests: Skagit County
Automation Activity & Vendor Info: (Acquisitions) Innovative Interfaces, Inc; (Cataloging) Innovative Interfaces, Inc; (Circulation) Innovative Interfaces, Inc; (Course Reserve) Innovative Interfaces, Inc; (ILL) Innovative Interfaces, Inc; (Media Booking) Innovative Interfaces, Inc; (OPAC) Innovative Interfaces, Inc
Database Vendor: ARTstor, Backstage Library Works, Checkpoint Systems, Inc, EBSCOhost, ProQuest, PubMed
Wireless access
Special Services for the Blind - Reader equip; Telesensory screen enlarger & speech synthesis interface to the OPAC
Restriction: Open to pub for ref & circ; with some limitations
Departmental Libraries:
WHIDBEY ISLAND CAMPUS LIBRARY, 1900 SE Pioneer Way, Oak Harbor, 98277-3099, SAN 376-2068. Tel: 360-679-5322. Reference Tel: 360-679-5321. FAX: 360-679-5341. *Libr Supvr-Popular Libr,* Carolyn Batchelor; Tel: 360-679-5221, E-mail: cbatchelor@skagit.edu; *Circ Librn,* Aleli Solidum; E-mail: asolidum@skagit.edu

NESPELEM

S COLVILLE CONFEDERATED TRIBE LIBRARY*, 12 Lakes, 99155. (Mail add: PO Box 150, 99155-0150), SAN 373-6881. Tel: 509-634-2791. Toll Free Tel: 888-881-7684. FAX: 509-634-2790. E-mail: alhtrc@theofficenet.com.
Founded 1983
Library Holdings: Bk Titles 6,000
Special Collections: Construction of Grand Coulee Dam & Chief Joseph Dam, 1938-1978, log, notebooks, res data, surveys
Open Mon-Fri 7:30-4
Branches:
INCHELIUM RESOURCE CENTER, 12 Community Loop Rd, Inchelium, 99138. (Mail add: PO Box 156, Inchelium, 99138-0156), SAN 373-8108. Tel: 509-722-7037. FAX: 509-533-7040. *Librn,* Adrian Holm; *Libr Assoc,* Tracy Werner; E-mail: tracy.werner@colvilletribes.com
Founded 1983
Library Holdings: Bk Vols 5,200
Open Mon-Fri 7:30-4
KELLER LIBRARY, 11673 S Hwy 21, Keller, 99140, SAN 373-8116. Tel: 509-634-2802. *Librn,* Adrian Holm
Library Holdings: Bk Vols 3,200
Open Mon-Fri 7:30-4

NEWPORT

P PEND OREILLE COUNTY LIBRARY DISTRICT, 109 S Union St, 99156. (Mail add: 116 S Washington Ave, 99156), SAN 326-1735. Tel: 509-447-2111. Toll Free Tel: 800-366-3654. FAX: 509-447-2806. E-mail: info@pocld.org. Web Site: www.pocld.org. *District Librn, Operations Mgr,* Mary Fouts; E-mail: mfouts@pocld.org; *Admin Mgr,* Colleen Auble; E-mail: cauble@pocld.org; Staff 8 (MLS 1, Non-MLS 7)
Founded 1980. Pop 12,200; Circ 83,056
Jan 2007-Dec 2007 Income (Main Library and Branch(s)) $514,339, State $59,647, Federal $23,844, County $401,132. Mats Exp $55,614, Books $39,659, Per/Ser (Incl. Access Fees) $2,898, Micro $300, AV Mat $6,307, Electronic Ref Mat (Incl. Access Fees) $6,450. Sal $269,522
Library Holdings: Audiobooks 2,573; AV Mats 4,859; CDs 650; Bk Vols 45,808; Per Subs 65; Videos 3,906
Subject Interests: Local hist
Automation Activity & Vendor Info: (Cataloging) OCLC; (Circulation) ByWater Solutions; (ILL) OCLC FirstSearch; (Media Booking) ByWater Solutions; (OPAC) ByWater Solutions
Database Vendor: EBSCOhost, Facts on File, netLibrary, ProQuest, ReferenceUSA
Wireless access
Function: Bks on CD, CD-ROM, Children's prog, Computers for patron use, Copy machines, Electronic databases & coll, Fax serv, ILL available, Music CDs, Online cat, OverDrive digital audio bks, Prog for children & young adult, Pub access computers, Ref serv in person
Partic in Cooperative Information Network

Special Services for the Deaf - Sorenson video relay syst
Friends of the Library Group
Branches: 4
CALISPEL VALLEY LIBRARY, 107 First Ave, Cusick, 99119. (Mail add:
PO Box 227, Cusick, 99119-0227), SAN 326-3754. Tel: 509-445-1215.
FAX: 509-445-1215. *Br Supvr II,* Pam Thompson; Staff 1 (Non-MLS 1)
Library Holdings: Bk Vols 7,910
Open Tues 11-8, Wed 1-5, Thurs 11-6, Sat 11-3
Friends of the Library Group
IONE PUBLIC LIBRARY, 210 Blackwell, Ste 1, Ione, 99139. (Mail add:
PO Box 605, Ione, 99139-0605), SAN 326-3770. Tel: 509-442-3030.
FAX: 509-442-3248. *Br Supvr II,* Lynn Barnes; Staff 1 (Non-MLS 1)
Library Holdings: Bk Vols 10,742
Open Tues & Thurs 10-1 & 2-6, Wed 1-5
Friends of the Library Group
METALINES COMMUNITY LIBRARY, Cutter Bldg, 302 Park St,
Metaline Falls, 99153. (Mail add: PO Box 111, Metaline Falls,
99153-0111), SAN 326-3797. Tel: 509-446-3232. FAX: 509-446-2302.
Br Supvr II, Lynn Barnes; Staff 1 (Non-MLS 1)
Library Holdings: Bk Vols 10,627
Open Mon 10-12 & 1-6, Wed 1-6, Fri 10-4, 2nd & 4th Sat 10-3
Friends of the Library Group
NEWPORT PUBLIC LIBRARY, 116 S Washington Ave, 99156. Tel:
509-447-2111. FAX: 509-447-2806. *District Librn, Operations Mgr,*
Mary Fouts; Staff 5 (Non-MLS 5)
Open Mon & Fri 10-5, Tues & Thurs 10-8, Wed 1-5, Sat 10-3
Friends of the Library Group

NINE MILE FALLS

P   LAKE SPOKANE LIBRARY*, 6176 Hwy 291, 99026-9026. Tel:
509-276-3329. FAX: 509-276-1339. Web Site:
www.librariesofstevenscounty.org. *Mgr,* Brooke Golden
Library Holdings: Bk Vols 8,000; Per Subs 20
Open Mon 10-7, Tues-Thurs 10-6, Fri 10-5, Sat 12-4

OAK HARBOR

A   UNITED STATES NAVY*, The Convergence Zone, NAS Whidbey Island,
3535 Princeton St, Bldg 2510, 98278. SAN 363-7476. Tel: 360-257-2702.
FAX: 360-257-3963. *Libr Asst,* Glenn Martin; E-mail:
glenn.martin@navy.mil
Founded 1944
Library Holdings: Bk Titles 1,600; Per Subs 23
Special Collections: Transition Assistance Management Program (TAMP);
US Navy Professional Reading Program
Subject Interests: Acad support, Recreational reading
Open Mon-Thurs 10-9, Fri & Sat 10am-Midnight, Sun 11-9

OCEAN SHORES

P   OCEAN SHORES PUBLIC LIBRARY*, 573 Point Brown Ave NW,
98569. SAN 317-5529. Tel: 360-289-3919. FAX: 360-289-4318. E-mail:
oslibrary@osgov.com. Web Site: oslibrary.info. *Dir,* Keitha Owen; Staff 4
(MLS 2, Non-MLS 2)
Founded 1972. Pop 4,860; Circ 80,650
Jan 2008-Dec 2008 Income $378,685. Mats Exp $31,960. Sal $187,469
Library Holdings: CDs 927; DVDs 804; Large Print Bks 350; Bk Vols
20,223; Per Subs 72; Talking Bks 405; Videos 373
Special Collections: Local History (Pacific Northwest Coll)
Subject Interests: Local hist
Automation Activity & Vendor Info: (Cataloging) Follett Software;
(Circulation) Follett Software
Wireless access
Function: ILL available, Photocopying/Printing, Summer reading prog,
Telephone ref, Wheelchair accessible
Publications: History of Ocean Shores
Open Tues 10-8, Wed 10-6, Thurs & Fri 10-5, Sat 10-3
Friends of the Library Group

ODESSA

P   ODESSA PUBLIC LIBRARY, 21 E First St, 99159. (Mail add: PO Box
218, 99159-0218), SAN 317-5537. Tel: 509-982-2654. FAX:
509-982-2410. *Librn,* Julie Jantz; Tel: 509-982-2903
Founded 1942. Pop 950; Circ 3,400
Library Holdings: Bk Titles 15,000
Subject Interests: US hist
Automation Activity & Vendor Info: (Acquisitions) Book Systems, Inc;
(Cataloging) Book Systems, Inc; (Circulation) Book Systems, Inc
Wireless access
Open Wed 2-5 & 7pm-9pm, Sat 12-5
Friends of the Library Group

OLYMPIA

L   ATTORNEY GENERAL'S OFFICE*, Law Library, 1101 Washington St
SE, Ste 260, 98504. (Mail add: PO Box 40115, 98504-0115), SAN
327-7046. Tel: 360-753-2681. FAX: 360-753-3490. E-mail:
library@atg.wa.gov. *Mgr,* Jane Halligan; Staff 7 (MLS 4, Non-MLS 3)
Library Holdings: Bk Titles 15,000
Automation Activity & Vendor Info: (Acquisitions) Innovative Interfaces,
Inc; (Cataloging) Innovative Interfaces, Inc; (Circulation) Innovative
Interfaces, Inc; (OPAC) Innovative Interfaces, Inc; (Serials) Innovative
Interfaces, Inc
Database Vendor: LexisNexis, Westlaw
Open Mon-Fri 8-5

C   EVERGREEN STATE COLLEGE*, Daniel J Evans Library, Library Bldg,
Rm 2300, 2700 Evergreen Pkwy NW, 98505-0002. SAN 317-5545. Tel:
360-867-6250. Circulation Tel: 360-867-6580. Interlibrary Loan Service
Tel: 360-867-6259, 360-867-6499. FAX: 360-867-6790. Interlibrary Loan
Service FAX: 360-867-6688. Web Site: www.evergreen.edu/library. *Dean,*
Libr & Media Serv, Gregg Sapp; Tel: 360-867-6607, E-mail:
sappg@evergreen.edu; *Syst Mgr,* Steve Metcalf; Tel: 360-867-6260; *Head,*
Acq, Shelley Swelland; Tel: 360-867-6127; *Head, Cat,* Tim Markus; Tel:
360-867-6124; *Head, Circ,* Mindy Muzatko; Tel: 360-867-6581; *Head, Doc*
Serv, Carlos Diaz; Tel: 360-867-6251; 360-867-6165; *Head, ILL,* Michiko
Francis; *Head, Media Serv,* Wyatt Cates; Tel: 360-867-6271; *Head, Per,*
Brian Gerheim; Tel: 360-867-6255; Staff 11 (MLS 6, Non-MLS 5)
Founded 1969. Enrl 4,102; Fac 173; Highest Degree: Master
Jul 2007-Jun 2008 Income $3,752,872, State $3,682,475, Locally
Generated Income $16,303, Other $54,094. Mats Exp $700,207, Books
$220,222, Per/Ser (Incl. Access Fees) $153,464, AV Mat $53,947,
Electronic Ref Mat (Incl. Access Fees) $272,574. Sal $1,747,651 (Prof
$98,868)
Library Holdings: AV Mats 82,023; e-journals 22,185; Bk Titles 438,736;
Bk Vols 466,564; Per Subs 459
Special Collections: Chicano & Latino Art Culture of the Pacific
Northwest, archives; Evergreen State Authors Project & Special Microfilm
Coll; Japanese Culture (Beckman Colls), rare bks; Nisqually Delta
Association Archives; TESC Archives; Washington State Folklife Council
Archives; Washington Worm Growers Assoc Archives. US Document
Depository
Automation Activity & Vendor Info: (Acquisitions) Innovative Interfaces,
Inc; (Cataloging) Innovative Interfaces, Inc; (Circulation) Innovative
Interfaces, Inc; (Course Reserve) Innovative Interfaces, Inc; (ILL)
Innovative Interfaces, Inc; (Media Booking) Innovative Interfaces, Inc;
(OPAC) Innovative Interfaces, Inc; (Serials) Innovative Interfaces, Inc
Wireless access
Partic in Coop Libr in Olympia; Orbis Cascade Alliance
Open Mon-Thurs (Winter) 8am-10:45pm, Fri 8-6:45, Sat 10:30-6:15, Sun
12-10:45; Mon-Thurs (Summer) 9-9, Fri & Sat 9-5
Friends of the Library Group

M   PROVIDENCE SAINT PETER HOSPITAL*, Library Services, 413 Lilly
Rd NE, 98506. SAN 329-4269. Tel: 360-493-7222. FAX: 360-493-5696.
E-mail: wapsphlibrary@providence.org. *Libr Mgr,* Isaac Huffman; E-mail:
isaac.huffman@providence.org
Founded 1980
Library Holdings: Bk Titles 1,500; Per Subs 350
Wireless access
Open Mon-Fri 8-4:30

J   SOUTH PUGET SOUND COMMUNITY COLLEGE LIBRARY, 2011
Mottman Rd SW, 98512. SAN 317-5553. Tel: 360-596-5271. Interlibrary
Loan Service Tel: 360-596-5426. Reference Tel: 360-596-5345.
Administration Tel: 360-596-5416. FAX: 360-596-5714. Web Site:
www.spscc.ctc.edu/library. *Dir, Libr, Media & eLearning,* Elizabeth Hill;
Librn, Sarah Kaip; *Librn,* Margaret Thomas; *Libr Supvr,* Scott Stilson;
Cataloger, Bonnie Jones; *Media Spec,* Paul Paluskas; Staff 6 (MLS 3,
Non-MLS 3)
Founded 1972. Enrl 6,000; Fac 250; Highest Degree: Associate
Jul 2011-Jun 2012 Income $744,085
Library Holdings: AV Mats 5,200; e-books 28,000; Bk Titles 35,000; Bk
Vols 41,000; Per Subs 25; Talking Bks 50; Videos 5,000
Automation Activity & Vendor Info: (Cataloging) Spydus; (Circulation)
Spydus; (Course Reserve) Spydus; (ILL) OCLC FirstSearch; (OPAC)
Spydus; (Serials) Spydus
Database Vendor: Cinahl Information Systems, CQ Press,
CredoReference, ebrary, EBSCOhost, Newsbank, OCLC FirstSearch,
ProQuest
Wireless access
Partic in OCLC Online Computer Library Center, Inc
Open Mon-Thurs 7:30am-8pm, Fri 7:30-4:30

G   WASHINGTON STATE DEPARTMENT OF NATURAL RESOURCES,
Division of Geology & Earth Resources Library, 1111 Washington St SE,
Rm 173, MS 47007, 98504-7007. SAN 317-5561. Tel: 360-902-1473.

FAX: 360-902-1785. Web Site: www.dnr.wa.gov/researchsciences/topics/geologypublicationslibrary/pages/library.aspx. *Librn,* Lee Walkling; E-mail: lee.walkling@dnr.wa.gov; Staff 2 (MLS 1, MLS 1)
Founded 1935
Library Holdings: AV Mats 50; CDs 40; DVDs 15; Bk Titles 50,000
Special Collections: Geologic & Historical Topographic Maps; Historic Coal Mine Maps; Theses Coll
Subject Interests: Geol, Maps, Mining
Function: Archival coll, Archival coll, For res purposes, For res purposes, ILL available, ILL available, Ref serv available, Ref serv available, Telephone ref, Telephone ref
Publications: Publications List (Online only)
Open Mon, Tues, Thurs & Fri 8-4:30
Restriction: Non-circulating
Friends of the Library Group

S WASHINGTON STATE HISTORICAL SOCIETY*, State Capital Museum & Outreach Center, 211 21st Ave SW, 98501. SAN 328-3259. Tel: 360-753-2580. Administration Tel: 360-586-0166. FAX: 360-586-8322.
Web Site: www.wshs.org. *Mgr,* Susan Rohrer
Founded 1941
Library Holdings: Bk Vols 300
Special Collections: Local, Regional & Washington State History
Subject Interests: Anthropology, Art, Hist, Natural hist, Wash
Function: Res libr
Partic in OCLC Eastern
Open Sat 10-4

GL WASHINGTON STATE LAW LIBRARY*, Temple of Justice, 98504.
(Mail add: PO Box 40751, 98504-0751), SAN 317-5588. Tel: 360-357-2136. FAX: 360-357-2143. E-mail: law.library@courts.wa.gov.
Web Site: www.courts.wa.gov/library. *Dir,* Kay Newman; *Ref Serv,* Dawn Kendrick; Staff 15 (MLS 4, Non-MLS 11)
Founded 1889
Library Holdings: Bk Vols 425,000; Per Subs 915
Special Collections: Legal Periodicals. US Document Depository
Subject Interests: Legal res
Automation Activity & Vendor Info: (Acquisitions) Innovative Interfaces, Inc; (Cataloging) Innovative Interfaces, Inc; (Circulation) Innovative Interfaces, Inc; (OPAC) Innovative Interfaces, Inc; (Serials) Innovative Interfaces, Inc
Database Vendor: OCLC FirstSearch
Publications: Books Recently Cataloged List (Monthly)
Open Mon-Fri 8-5

G WASHINGTON STATE OFFICE OF SECRETARY OF STATE*, Division Archives & Records Management, 1129 Washington St SE, 98504-2283.
(Mail add: PO Box 40238, 98504-0238), SAN 326-1174. Tel: 360-586-1492. Administration Tel: 360-586-2666. FAX: 360-664-8814.
E-mail: archives@secstate.wa.gov. Web Site: www.secstate.wa.gov/archives.
Acq, Terry S Badger; Tel: 360-586-1602, E-mail: tbadger@secstate.wa.gov; *State Archivist,* Jerry Handfield; *Archivist,* Tim Eckert; Tel: 509-963-2136, Fax: 509-963-1753; *Archivist,* David W Hastings; Tel: 360-753-1801, E-mail: dhastings@secstate.wa.gov; *Archivist,* Wayne Lawson; Tel: 360-753-1684, Fax: 360-664-2803, E-mail: wlawson@secstate.wa.gov; *Archivist,* Michael Saunders; Tel: 425-564-3950, Fax: 425-564-3945; *Archivist,* Diana Shenk; Tel: 360-650-2813, Fax: 360-650-3323; *Ref Serv,* Pat Hopkins; Tel: 360-586-4894, E-mail: phopkins@secstate.wa.gov; Staff 11 (MLS 11)
Special Collections: Washington State History (Washington State Archives Coll), unbound & bound recs

C WASHINGTON STATE UNIVERSITY EXTENSION*, Energy Program Library, 905 Plum St SE, 98501-1529. (Mail add: PO Box 43169, 98504-3169), SAN 374-4787. Tel: 360-956-2076. FAX: 360-236-2076.
E-mail: library@energy.wsu.edu. Web Site: www.energy.wsu.edu/library.
Mgr, Angela Santamaria; E-mail: santamariaa@energy.wsu.edu; *ILL,* Martha Parsons; E-mail: parsonsm@energy.wsu.edu; Staff 4 (MLS 3, Non-MLS 1)
Library Holdings: Bk Titles 13,000; Bk Vols 17,000; Per Subs 350
Special Collections: Building Standards
Subject Interests: Alternative energy, Bldg standards, Energy conserv, Energy policy
Automation Activity & Vendor Info: (Cataloging) Innovative Interfaces, Inc; (Circulation) Innovative Interfaces, Inc; (ILL) OCLC; (OPAC) Innovative Interfaces, Inc
Wireless access
Function: ILL available, Mail & tel request accepted, Online cat, Ref serv available, Web-catalog
Partic in OCLC Western Service Center
Open Mon-Fri 8-5
Restriction: Circ limited, Non-circulating coll, Pub use on premises

PASCO

J COLUMBIA BASIN COLLEGE LIBRARY*, 2600 N 20th Ave, 99301.
SAN 317-5618. Tel: 509-547-0511. Circulation Tel: 509-542-4458.
Reference Tel: 509-542-4890. Administration Tel: 509-542-2373.
Automation Services Tel: 509-542-4887. FAX: 509-546-0401. E-mail: library@columbiabasin.edu. Web Site: www.columbiabasin.edu/library.
Interim Dean, Libr Serv, Deborah Meadows; E-mail: dmeadows@columbiabasin.edu; *Libr Coordr, Med Librn,* Melissa McBurney; Tel: 509-544-8336, E-mail: mmcburney@columbiabasin.edu; *Cat,* Drew Proctor; Tel: 509-542-4479, E-mail: dproctor@columbiabasin.edu; *Ref Serv,* Stephen Badalamente; Tel: 509-542-4553, E-mail: sbadalamente@columbiabasin.edu; *Ref Serv,* Ying Yu; Tel: 509-542-4690, E-mail: yyu@columbiabasin.edu. Subject Specialists: *Health sci, Med,* Melissa McBurney; Staff 9 (MLS 4, Non-MLS 5)
Founded 1955. Enrl 5,158; Fac 128; Highest Degree: Bachelor
Jul 2009-Jun 2010 Income $572,428. Mats Exp $92,709, Books $14,877, Per/Ser (Incl. Access Fees) $5,649, AV Mat $863, Electronic Ref Mat (Incl. Access Fees) $71,320. Sal $343,085 (Prof $213,211)
Library Holdings: DVDs 321; e-books 31,102; e-journals 24,972; Bk Vols 60,419; Per Subs 106
Special Collections: Benton-Franklin County Regional Law Library; Medical Library Coll
Automation Activity & Vendor Info: (Acquisitions) LibLime; (Cataloging) OCLC CatExpress; (Circulation) LibLime; (ILL) OCLC; (OPAC) LibLime
Database Vendor: ABC-CLIO, Baker & Taylor, Bowker, Brodart, Checkpoint Systems, Inc, Cinahl Information Systems, CQ Press, ebrary, EBSCOhost, Elsevier, Facts on File, Gale Cengage Learning, Greenwood Publishing Group, LexisNexis, LibLime, Marquis Who's Who, McGraw-Hill, Nature Publishing Group, netLibrary, OCLC ArticleFirst, OCLC CAMIO, OCLC FirstSearch, OCLC WorldCat, OVID Technologies, Oxford Online, ProQuest, PubMed, Sage, SerialsSolutions, Westlaw, Wiley, WT Cox
Wireless access
Function: ILL available
Partic in OCLC Online Computer Library Center, Inc; Orbis Cascade Alliance
Special Services for the Blind - Assistive/Adapted tech devices, equip & products
Open Mon-Thurs 7:30-7:30, Fri 7:30-4:30, Sat 11-4

POMEROY

P DENNY ASHBY MEMORIAL LIBRARY*, Pomeroy Public Library, 856 Arlington St, 99347. (Mail add: PO Box 670, 99347-0670). Tel: 509-843-3710. E-mail: dashby@pomeroy.lib.wa.us. Web Site: www.pomeroy.lib.wa.us. *Dir,* Lillian Heytvelt; *Librn,* Phyllis Heitstuman
Library Holdings: Bk Titles 8,000; Per Subs 13
Open Mon 1-5:30, Tues 9-1, Wed & Thurs 1-7:30

PORT ANGELES

GL CLALLAM COUNTY LAW LIBRARY*, County Courthouse, 223 E Fourth St, Ste 17, 98362-3015. SAN 373-742X. Tel: 360-417-2287. *Librn,* Penny Ruby; Staff 0.19 (Non-MLS 0.19)
Library Holdings: Bk Vols 7,500
Wireless access

P NORTH OLYMPIC LIBRARY SYSTEM, 2210 S Peabody St, 98362-6536.
SAN 363-8790. Tel: 360-417-8500. Administration Tel: 360-417-8500, Ext 7702. FAX: 360-457-3125. E-mail: director@nols.org. Web Site: www.nols.org. *Dir,* Paula Simpson Barnes; Tel: 360-417-8500, Ext 7715, E-mail: pbarnes@nols.org; *Asst Dir,* Margaret Jakubcin; Tel: 360-417-8500, Ext 7714, E-mail: mjakubcin@nols.org; *Librn I/Gen Serv,* Rebecca Nugent; *Librn II,* Lorrie Kovell; Staff 7 (MLS 7)
Founded 1919. Pop 71,000; Circ 1,024,274
Library Holdings: Bk Vols 272,992; Per Subs 492
Special Collections: Clallam County History (Bert Kellogg Coll), photog, slides; Pacific Northwest History, bks, maps, oral hist
Automation Activity & Vendor Info: (Acquisitions) Polaris Library Systems; (Cataloging) Polaris Library Systems; (Circulation) Polaris Library Systems
Database Vendor: OCLC FirstSearch
Wireless access
Function: Adult bk club, Archival coll, Art exhibits, Audio & video playback equip for onsite use, Bks on CD, Children's prog, Computers for patron use, Copy machines, Electronic databases & coll, Free DVD rentals, Handicapped accessible, Homebound delivery serv, ILL available, Jail serv, Large print keyboards, Microfiche/film & reading machines, Music CDs, Newsp ref libr, Online cat, Online searches, OverDrive digital audio bks, Photocopying/Printing, Preschool outreach, Printer for laptops & handheld devices, Prog for adults, Prog for children & young adult, Pub access

computers, Story hour, Summer reading prog, Teen prog, Telephone ref, Wheelchair accessible, Winter reading prog
Partic in OCLC Online Computer Library Center, Inc
Open Mon-Thurs 10-8, Fri 10-6, Sat 10-5
Friends of the Library Group
Branches: 3
CLALLAM BAY BRANCH, 16990 Hwy 112, Clallam Bay, 98326. (Mail add: PO Box 106, Clallam Bay, 98326), SAN 363-8812. Tel: 360-963-2414. FAX: 360-963-2260. *Libr Supvr,* Theresa Tetreau; E-mail: ttetreau@nols.org; Staff 3 (Non-MLS 3)
Circ 24,790
Library Holdings: Bk Vols 17,448
Function: After school storytime, Bks on CD, Children's prog, Computers for patron use, Copy machines, Electronic databases & coll, Fax serv, Free DVD rentals, Handicapped accessible, Music CDs, Online cat, Online ref, Online searches, OverDrive digital audio bks, Photocopying/Printing, Preschool outreach, Printer for laptops & handheld devices, Prog for adults, Prog for children & young adult, Pub access computers, Ref serv in person, Summer reading prog, Wheelchair accessible
Open Mon-Wed 11-7, Thurs-Sat 10-5
Friends of the Library Group
FORKS BRANCH, 171 Forks Ave S, Forks, 98331, SAN 363-8820. Tel: 360-374-6402. FAX: 360-374-6499. E-mail: Forks@nols.org. *Libr Supvr,* Theresa Tetreau; E-mail: ttetreau@nols.org; Staff 6 (MLS 1, Non-MLS 5)
Founded 1946. Circ 69,272
Library Holdings: Bk Vols 35,044
Function: Bks on CD, Children's prog, Computers for patron use, Copy machines, Electronic databases & coll, Fax serv, Free DVD rentals, Handicapped accessible, ILL available, Music CDs, Online cat, Online ref, Online searches, OverDrive digital audio bks, Photocopying/Printing, Printer for laptops & handheld devices, Prog for adults, Prog for children & young adult, Pub access computers, Ref serv available, Spanish lang bks, Story hour, Summer reading prog, Telephone ref, Wheelchair accessible
Open Mon-Thurs 10-7, Fri & Sat 10-6
Friends of the Library Group
SEQUIM BRANCH, 630 N Sequim Ave, Sequim, 98382, SAN 363-888X. Tel: 360-683-1161. FAX: 360-681-7811. *Br Mgr,* Lauren Dahlgren; E-mail: ldahlgren@nols.org; Staff 11 (MLS 2, Non-MLS 9)
Circ 423,086
Library Holdings: Bk Vols 61,813
Function: Adult bk club, After school storytime, Art exhibits, Bks on CD, Children's prog, Computer training, Computers for patron use, Copy machines, Electronic databases & coll, Fax serv, Free DVD rentals, Handicapped accessible, Homebound delivery serv, ILL available, Music CDs, Online cat, Online ref, Online searches, OverDrive digital audio bks, Photocopying/Printing, Preschool outreach, Printer for laptops & handheld devices, Prog for adults, Prog for children & young adult, Pub access computers, Ref serv available, Story hour, Summer reading prog, Teen prog, Telephone ref
Open Mon-Thurs 10-8, Fri 10-6, Sat 10-5
Friends of the Library Group

J   PENINSULA COLLEGE LIBRARY*, John D Glann Library, 1502 E Lauridsen Blvd, 98362-6698. SAN 317-5669. Tel: 360-417-6280. Circulation Tel: 360-417-6282. Interlibrary Loan Service Tel: 360-417-6279. Reference Tel: 360-417-6281. Automation Services Tel: 360-417-6275. Toll Free Tel: 877-452-9277 (In State). FAX: 360-417-6295. Web Site: www.pc.ctc.edu. *Dir, Libr Serv,* Paula B Doherty; E-mail: paulad@pcadmin.ctc.edu; *Librn,* Gail Banwart; Tel: 360-417-6284, E-mail: gailb@pcadmin.ctc.edu; *Librn,* David Kent; Tel: 360-417-6285, E-mail: davidk@pcadmin.ctc.edu; Staff 8 (MLS 3, Non-MLS 5)
Founded 1961. Enrl 2,100; Fac 60; Highest Degree: Associate
Library Holdings: CDs 114; Music Scores 750; Bk Titles 33,310; Bk Vols 35,002; Per Subs 170; Videos 1,578
Automation Activity & Vendor Info: (Acquisitions) Ex Libris Group; (Cataloging) Ex Libris Group; (Circulation) Ex Libris Group; (Course Reserve) Ex Libris Group; (Media Booking) Ex Libris Group; (OPAC) Ex Libris Group; (Serials) Ex Libris Group
Database Vendor: ProQuest
Function: Audio & video playback equip for onsite use, AV serv, ILL available, Outside serv via phone, mail, e-mail & web, Photocopying/Printing, Ref serv available, Telephone ref
Open Mon-Thurs 8-8, Fri 8-4, Sun 5-8

PORT HADLOCK

P   JEFFERSON COUNTY RURAL LIBRARY DISTRICT, 620 Cedar Ave, 98339-9514. SAN 321-4818. Tel: 360-385-6544. FAX: 360-385-7921. Web Site: www.jclibrary.info. *Dir,* Raymond Serebrin; E-mail: rserebrin@jclibrary.info; *Assoc Dir,* Meredith Wagner; E-mail: mwagner@jclibrary.info; *Youth Serv Librn,* Martha Ashenfelter; E-mail: mashenfelter@jclibrary.info; *Circ Mgr,* Jeanne Mahan; *Mgr, Outreach Serv,*

Judith Lucia; *Mgr, Tech Serv, Syst Mgr,* Daniel Heaton; E-mail: dheaton@jclibrary.info; *Ref Serv Coordr,* Brad Collier; E-mail: bcollier@jclibrary.info; *Acq,* Shery Hart; E-mail: shart@jclibrary.info; *Info Serv, ILL,* Bonnie Glendenning; *ILL,* Meghan Gibson; Staff 19 (MLS 4, Non-MLS 15)
Founded 1980. Pop 20,000; Circ 350,000
Jan 2009-Dec 2009 Income $1,762,000, County $1,600,000, Locally Generated Income $162,000. Mats Exp $142,500, Books $84,000, Per/Ser (Incl. Access Fees) $12,500, AV Mat $40,000, Electronic Ref Mat (Incl. Access Fees) $6,000. Sal $750,000
Library Holdings: CDs 3,500; DVDs 3,000; Bk Vols 54,000; Per Subs 120; Talking Bks 2,200; Videos 2,300
Automation Activity & Vendor Info: (Acquisitions) SirsiDynix; (Cataloging) OCLC; (Circulation) SirsiDynix; (ILL) OCLC; (OPAC) SirsiDynix
Database Vendor: EBSCO Auto Repair Reference, Gale Cengage Learning, OCLC FirstSearch, OCLC WorldCat, ProQuest, ReferenceUSA, SirsiDynix
Wireless access
Open Mon-Thurs 10-8, Fri & Sat 9-5, Sun 1-5
Restriction: Circ to mem only
Friends of the Library Group
Bookmobiles: 1. Outreach Coordr, Judith Lucia

PORT ORCHARD

GL   KITSAP COUNTY LAW LIBRARY*, 614 Division St, 98366. SAN 323-6471. Tel: 360-337-5788. FAX: 360-337-5789. E-mail: library@kitsapbar.com. Web Site: www.kitsapbar.com/library. *Librn,* Paul Fjelstad; Tel: 360-613-5071
Library Holdings: Bk Vols 10,000
Open Mon-Fri 8:30-4:30

PORT TOWNSEND

P   PORT TOWNSEND PUBLIC LIBRARY*, 1220 Lawrence St, 98368-6527. SAN 317-5677. Tel: 360-385-3181. Interlibrary Loan Service Tel: 360-344-3068. Administration Tel: 360-344-3054. FAX: 360-385-5805. E-mail: ptlibrary@cityofpt.us. Web Site: www.cityofpt.us/library. *Dir,* Theresa Rini Percy; E-mail: tpercy@cityofpt.us; *Ad,* Cris Wilson; Tel: 360-379-4441, E-mail: cwilson@cityofpt.us; *Youth Serv Librn,* Jean Tarascio; Tel: 360-344-3059, E-mail: jtarascio@cityofpt.us; Staff 9 (MLS 1, Non-MLS 8)
Founded 1898. Pop 8,865; Circ 244,151
Jan 2007-Dec 2007 Income $725,546. Mats Exp $65,000, Books $40,350, Per/Ser (Incl. Access Fees) $9,650, AV Mat $7,000, Electronic Ref Mat (Incl. Access Fees) $8,000. Sal $459,905
Library Holdings: Audiobooks 1,618; CDs 990; DVDs 960; Large Print Bks 585; Bk Vols 43,624; Per Subs 160; Videos 4,125
Special Collections: Maritime Resource Center
Subject Interests: Folklore jungian psychol, Jungian psychol, Maritime, Mythology, Pac NW hist
Automation Activity & Vendor Info: (Acquisitions) Horizon; (Cataloging) SirsiDynix; (Circulation) SirsiDynix; (OPAC) SirsiDynix
Database Vendor: Dialog, ebrary, Gale Cengage Learning, OCLC FirstSearch, ProQuest, ReferenceUSA, SirsiDynix
Wireless access
Function: Adult bk club, Audiobks via web, Bk reviews (Group), Bks on cassette, Bks on CD, Children's prog, Computers for patron use, Copy machines, Electronic databases & coll, Free DVD rentals, Holiday prog, Home delivery & serv to Sr ctr & nursing homes, Homework prog, ILL available, Large print keyboards, Mail & tel request accepted, Music CDs, Online cat, Online ref, Online searches, OverDrive digital audio bks, Preschool outreach, Prog for adults, Prog for children & young adult, Pub access computers, Ref serv in person, Story hour, Summer reading prog, Tax forms, Teen prog, Telephone ref, VHS videos, Video lending libr, Web-catalog, Wheelchair accessible
Open Mon-Thurs 10-7, Fri 10-6, Sat 10-5, Sun 1-5
Friends of the Library Group

PULLMAN

P   NEILL PUBLIC LIBRARY*, Pullman Public Library, 210 N Grand Ave, 99163-2693. SAN 317-5693. Tel: 509-334-3595. Administration Tel: 509-338-3252. FAX: 509-334-6051. E-mail: library@neill-lib.org. Web Site: www.neill-lib.org. *Dir,* Joanna Bailey; Staff 4 (MLS 3, Non-MLS 1)
Founded 1921. Pop 26,590; Circ 356,836
Special Collections: English as a Second Language Coll; Local History (Palouse Region)
Automation Activity & Vendor Info: (Cataloging) Horizon; (Circulation) Horizon; (OPAC) Horizon
Database Vendor: Gale Cengage Learning, ProQuest
Open Mon 1-8, Tues & Wed 10-8, Thurs & Fri 10-6, Sat & Sun 1-5
Friends of the Library Group

C WASHINGTON STATE UNIVERSITY LIBRARIES, 100 Dairy Rd, 99164. (Mail add: PO Box 645610, 99164-5610), SAN 363-891X. Tel: 509-335-4558. Interlibrary Loan Service Tel: 509-335-9672. FAX: 509-335-6721. Interlibrary Loan Service FAX: 509-335-0934. Web Site: www.wsulibs.wsu.edu. *Dean of Libr,* Jay Starratt; E-mail: jstarratt@wsu.edu; *Assoc Dean,* Beth Blakesley; Tel: 509-335-6134, E-mail: beth.blakesley@wsu.edu; *Head, Coll,* Joel Cummings; Tel: 509-335-6493, E-mail: jcummings@wsu.edu; *Head, Ms, Archives & Spec Coll,* Trevor James Bond; Tel: 509-335-6693, E-mail: tjbond@wsu.edu; *Head, Syst,* Alan Cornish; Tel: 509-335-1895, E-mail: cornish@wsu.edu; *Head, Tech Serv,* Lihong Zhu; Tel: 509-335-7769, E-mail: lzhu2@wsu.edu; *Data Officer,* Robert Ferguson; Tel: 509-335-2520, E-mail: ferguson@wsu.edu; Staff 82 (MLS 30, Non-MLS 52)
Founded 1892. Enrl 19,443; Fac 1,650; Highest Degree: Doctorate
Jul 2011-Jun 2012. Mats Exp $6,526,298, Books $687,919, Per/Ser (Incl. Access Fees) $5,612,925. Sal $4,944,132 (Prof $1,998,697)
Library Holdings: e-books 253,398; Microforms 3,963,507; Bk Vols 2,547,082; Per Subs 48,529; Videos 32,480
Special Collections: Angling (Vern & Joan Gallup, Roy Hansberry & James C Quick Colls); Bloomsbury Coll; ERDA Coll; Ethnic History (Germans from Russia Coll); Hispanic Americana Coll; Leonard & Virginia Woolf Library; Moldenhauer Music Archives; Pacific Northwest Publishers Archives; Pierre-Jean Desmet Coll; Sitwells Coll; University Archives; Veterinary History (Smithcors Coll), archival rec, ephemera, journals, monographs & pamphlets, ms; Wildlife & Outdoor Recreation Coll, documentary rec, films, ms, photog & printed texts. Oral History; State Document Depository; UN Document Depository; US Document Depository
Automation Activity & Vendor Info: (Acquisitions) Innovative Interfaces, Inc; (Cataloging) OCLC; (Circulation) Innovative Interfaces, Inc; (OPAC) Innovative Interfaces, Inc
Database Vendor: ABC-CLIO, ACM (Association for Computing Machinery), Agricola, American Chemical Society, American Mathematical Society, American Psychological Association (APA), Annual Reviews, BioOne, Cambridge Scientific Abstracts, Cinahl Information Systems, Elsevier, Emerald, Greenwood Publishing Group, H W Wilson, IEEE (Institute of Electrical & Electronics Engineers), Innovative Interfaces, Inc, IOP, ISI Web of Knowledge, JSTOR, LexisNexis, Modern Language Association, OCLC FirstSearch, OCLC WorldCat, OVID Technologies, ProQuest, PubMed, ScienceDirect, Springer-Verlag, WestlaweCARSWELL, Wilson - Wilson Web, YBP Library Services
Wireless access
Partic in Association of Research Libraries (ARL); Greater Western Library Alliance; Orbis Cascade Alliance; Wash Coop Libr Project
Departmental Libraries:
CM ANIMAL HEALTH LIBRARY, 170 Wegner Hall, 99164. (Mail add: PO Box 646512, 99164-6512), SAN 363-9002. Tel: 509-335-9556. Administration Tel: 509-335-5544. FAX: 509-335-5158. E-mail: vetref@wsu.edu. Web Site: www.wsulibs.wsu.edu/hsl/index.htm. *Head of Libr,* Vicki F Croft; E-mail: croft@wsu.edu
Founded 1963. Highest Degree: Doctorate
Subject Interests: Pharmacology, Toxicology, Veterinary med
Database Vendor: 3M Library Systems, EBSCO Information Services, EBSCOhost, Ex Libris Group, Gale Cengage Learning, Wiley
Function: Res libr
HOLLAND & TERRELL LIBRARIES, 100 Dairy Rd, 99164. (Mail add: PO Box 645610, 99164-5610). Tel: 509-335-8516. Circulation Tel: 509-335-9672. FAX: 509-335-0934. Web Site: www.wsulibs.wsu.edu/holland/holhp.htm. *Head, Res Serv,* Beth Blakesley; Tel: 509-335-6134, E-mail: beth.blakesley@wsu.edu
Highest Degree: Doctorate
Subject Interests: Humanities, Soc sci
Open Mon-Thurs 7:30am-1:45am, Fri 7:30-5:45, Sat 9-5:45, Sun Noon-1:45am
OWEN SCIENCE & ENGINEERING, PO Box 643200, 99164-3200, SAN 363-8979. Tel: 509-335-2672, 509-335-4181. FAX: 509-335-2534. E-mail: owenref@wsu.edu. Web Site: www.wsulibs.wsu.edu/science/owen.htm. *Head, Res Serv,* Beth Blakesley; Tel: 509-335-6134, E-mail: beth.blakesley@wsu.edu
Highest Degree: Doctorate
Open Mon-Thurs 7:30am-10:45pm, Fri 7:30-5:45, Sat 12-5:45, Sun 12-10:45

PUYALLUP

M AMERICAN INSTITUTE FOR BIOSOCIAL & MEDICAL RESEARCH INC LIBRARY*, 4117 S Meridian St, 98373. (Mail add: PO Box 1174, Tacoma, 98401-1174), SAN 372-8757. Tel: 253-286-2888. FAX: 253-286-2451. Web Site: www.aibmr.com. *Dir of Tech Serv,* Jared Brodin
Library Holdings: Bk Vols 5,653; Per Subs 360
Restriction: Staff use only

S NIXON & BACCUS FAMILY ASSOCIATION CLEARINGHOUSE*, 5817 144th St E, 98375-5221. SAN 373-3009. Tel: 253-537-8288. *Mgr,* Janet G Baccus; E-mail: janetgb@comcast.net
Founded 1981
Library Holdings: Bk Vols 1,150
Subject Interests: Genealogy, Local hist

P PUYALLUP PUBLIC LIBRARY*, 324 S Meridian, 98371. SAN 317-5707. Tel: 253-841-5454. Interlibrary Loan Service Tel: 253-841-5543. Reference Tel: 253-841-5700. Administration Tel: 253-841-5452. FAX: 253-841-5483. TDD: 253-841-5544. E-mail: puylib@ci.puyallup.wa.us. Web Site: www.puyalluplibrary.org. *Dir,* Mary Jo Torgeson; E-mail: mjtorgeson@ci.puyallup.wa.us; *Mgr, Youth Serv,* Bonnie Anderson; Tel: 253-770-3334, E-mail: bonniea@ci.puyallup.wa.us; Staff 17 (MLS 6, Non-MLS 11)
Founded 1912. Pop 38,690; Circ 4
Jan 2010-Dec 2010 Income $2,419,997, City $2,393,155, Locally Generated Income $11,037, Other $15,705. Mats Exp $165,027, Books $100,676, Per/Ser (Incl. Access Fees) $7,331, Other Print Mats $1,138, AV Mat $37,538, Electronic Ref Mat (Incl. Access Fees) $18,344. Sal $827,148
Library Holdings: Audiobooks 4,784; CDs 8,581; DVDs 10,181; Electronic Media & Resources 21; Large Print Bks 3,191; Bk Vols 119,095; Per Subs 177; Videos 5,925
Subject Interests: Local hist (Puyallup Valley)
Automation Activity & Vendor Info: (Acquisitions) Horizon; (Circulation) Horizon; (ILL) OCLC FirstSearch; (OPAC) SirsiDynix
Database Vendor: Baker & Taylor, Brodart, BWI, EBSCO Auto Repair Reference, EBSCOhost, Gale Cengage Learning, Grolier Online, Ingram Library Services, LearningExpress, OCLC FirstSearch, OCLC WorldCat, Overdrive, Inc, ReferenceUSA, SirsiDynix, TumbleBookLibrary
Wireless access
Function: Bks on cassette, Bks on CD, Children's prog, Computer training, Computers for patron use, Copy machines, Digital talking bks, E-Reserves, Free DVD rentals, Home delivery & serv to Sr ctr & nursing homes, Homebound delivery serv, Homework prog, ILL available, Mus passes, Music CDs, Online cat, Online ref, Outreach serv, Photocopying/Printing, Preschool outreach, Prog for adults, Prog for children & young adult, Ref serv in person, Spoken cassettes & CDs, Spoken cassettes & DVDs, Story hour, Summer reading prog, Tax forms, Teen prog, Telephone ref, VHS videos, Wheelchair accessible
Special Services for the Deaf - Assisted listening device; Staff with knowledge of sign lang; TDD equip
Special Services for the Blind - Closed circuit TV magnifier
Open Mon-Wed 10-8, Thurs-Sat 10-5
Friends of the Library Group

REARDAN

P REARDAN MEMORIAL LIBRARY*, 120 S Oak, 99029. (Mail add: PO Box 227, 99029-0227), SAN 317-5715. Tel: 509-994-9997. E-mail: reardanlibrary@yahoo.com. *Librn,* Suzanne Schulz
Pop 450; Circ 3,395
Library Holdings: Bk Vols 9,700
Special Collections: Davenport Times Coll
Wireless access
Open Tues 2-5, Thurs 5pm-7pm, Sat 10-2
Friends of the Library Group

REDMOND

S GOLDER ASSOCIATES, INC*, Seattle Library, 18300 NE Union Hill Rd, Ste 200, 98052-3333. SAN 373-8922. Tel: 425-883-0777. FAX: 425-882-5498. Staff 1 (MLS 1)
Founded 1979
Library Holdings: Bk Titles 15,000; Per Subs 275
Automation Activity & Vendor Info: (Cataloging) Inmagic, Inc.; (Circulation) Inmagic, Inc.
Database Vendor: ProQuest
Restriction: Not open to pub

RENTON

P RENTON PUBLIC LIBRARY*, 100 Mill Ave S, 98057. SAN 363-9037. Tel: 425-430-6610. FAX: 425-430-6833. TDD: 425-430-6612. Web Site: library.rentonwa.gov. *Dir,* Bette Anderson; E-mail: banderson@rentonwa.gov; *Communications Dir,* Preeti Shridhar; Staff 6.5 (MLS 6.5)
Founded 1903. Pop 80,319; Circ 554,233
Jan 2009-Dec 2009 Income (Main Library and Branch(s)) $2,118,211. Mats Exp $281,975, Books $208,744, Per/Ser (Incl. Access Fees) $13,816, AV Mat $29,523, Electronic Ref Mat (Incl. Access Fees) $29,889. Sal $1,127,883 (Prof $491,573)
Library Holdings: Audiobooks 2,462; CDs 1,550; DVDs 9,675; Large Print Bks 2,343; Bk Vols 174,874; Per Subs 425; Videos 8,634

Special Collections: Pacific Northwest (Washington State Coll), bks, per
Automation Activity & Vendor Info: (Acquisitions) Horizon;
(Cataloging) OCLC; (Circulation) Horizon; (ILL) OCLC; (OPAC) Horizon;
(Serials) Horizon
Database Vendor: EBSCO Auto Repair Reference, Gale Cengage
Learning, ProQuest, ReferenceUSA
Wireless access
Mem of King County Library System
Special Services for the Deaf - TDD equip
Open Mon-Thurs 10-9, Fri 10-6, Sat 10-5, Sun 1-5
Friends of the Library Group
Branches: 1
HIGHLANDS, 2902 NE 12th St, 98056, SAN 363-9061. Tel:
425-430-6790. *Dir,* Bette Anderson; *Supvr,* Mary Fullerton
Library Holdings: Bk Vols 40,000
Open Mon-Thurs 10-9, Fri 10-6, Sat 10-5

J   RENTON TECHNICAL COLLEGE, Library, 3000 NE Fourth St,
98056-4195. SAN 373-6318. Tel: 425-235-2331. FAX: 425-235-7816.
E-mail: librarian@rtc.edu. Web Site: www.rtc.edu/library. *Dir,* Eric Palo;
E-mail: epalo@rtc.edu; Staff 6 (MLS 3, Non-MLS 3)
Founded 1991. Enrl 3,901; Fac 178; Highest Degree: Associate
Jul 2012-Jun 2013 Income $540,000. Sal $235,000 (Prof $121,000)
Library Holdings: Bk Vols 45,000; Per Subs 150; Videos 4,000
Special Collections: History & Culinary Education in the Pacific
Northwest (Chef Daryl Anderson Culinary Archives)
Subject Interests: Culinary
Automation Activity & Vendor Info: (Acquisitions) Ex Libris Group;
(Cataloging) Ex Libris Group; (Circulation) Ex Libris Group; (Course
Reserve) Ex Libris Group; (ILL) OCLC; (OPAC) Ex Libris Group;
(Serials) Ex Libris Group
Database Vendor: EBSCOhost, Gale Cengage Learning, Grolier Online,
ProQuest
Wireless access
Function: Archival coll, Audio & video playback equip for onsite use,
Computers for patron use, Copy machines, Electronic databases & coll,
ILL available, Online cat, Online ref, Online searches, Orientations,
Photocopying/Printing, Pub access computers, Ref & res, Ref serv
available, Scanner, VHS videos, Video lending libr, Web-catalog,
Workshops
Open Mon-Thurs 7am-8pm, Fri 7-4:30

M   VALLEY MEDICAL CENTER LIBRARY*, 400 S 43rd St, 98055. (Mail
add: PO Box 50010, 98058-5010), SAN 317-5774. Tel: 425-228-3440, Ext
3904. FAX: 425-656-5095. Web Site:
www.valleymed.org/about_vmc/departments.htm. *Librn,* Linda Drummond;
Staff 0.8 (Non-MLS 0.8)
Founded 1945
Library Holdings: Bk Titles 300; Bk Vols 675; Per Subs 30
Automation Activity & Vendor Info: (Serials) EOS International
Partic in Docline
Restriction: Staff use only

RICHLAND

S   PACIFIC NORTHWEST NATIONAL LABORATORY*, Hanford Technical
Library, 2770 University Dr, 99354. (Mail add: PO Box 999, MSIN P8-55,
99352-0999), SAN 317-5804. Tel: 509-372-7430. Circulation Tel:
509-372-7440. Interlibrary Loan Service Tel: 509-372-7456. Administration
Tel: 509-372-7450. FAX: 509-372-7431. Interlibrary Loan Service FAX:
509-372-7433. Administration FAX: 509-372-7426. E-mail:
pnl.techlib@pnl.gov. Web Site: libraryweb.pnl.gov. *Dir,* Annanaomi Sams;
Tel: 509-372-7448, Fax: 509-372-7426, E-mail: annanaomi.sams@pnl.gov;
ILL/Circ Supvr, Sarah Shoemaker; Tel: 509-372-7463, Fax: 509-372-7433,
E-mail: sarah.shoemaker@pnl.gov; Staff 27 (MLS 12, Non-MLS 15)
Founded 1948
Library Holdings: Bk Vols 41,000; Per Subs 9,000
Special Collections: Department of Energy Contractor Reports, technical
rpts; DOE Public Reading Room
Subject Interests: Eng, Environ studies, Metallurgy, Nuclear tech
Automation Activity & Vendor Info: (Cataloging) Horizon; (Circulation)
Horizon; (ILL) OCLC; (OPAC) Horizon; (Serials) Horizon
Wireless access
Function: Res libr
Open Mon-Thurs 8am-9pm, Fri 8-7, Sat 10-4

P   RICHLAND PUBLIC LIBRARY*, 955 Northgate Dr, 99352-3539. SAN
317-5839. Tel: 509-942-7454. Interlibrary Loan Service Tel: 509-942-7606.
Reference Tel: 509-942-7457. Administration Tel: 509-942-7450.
Automation Services Tel: 509-942-7408. FAX: 509-942-7442. Web Site:
www.richland.lib.wa.us. *Dir,* Ann Roseberry; E-mail:
aroseberry@ci.richland.lib.w.aus; *Circ Supvr,* Jeanette Mercier; Tel:
509-942-7456, E-mail: jmercier@richland.lib.wa.us; *Ch,* Kelly Reed; Tel:
509-942-7452, E-mail: kreed@richland.lib.wa.us; *Ref,* Connie Farr; Tel:

509-942-7446, E-mail: cfarr@richland.lib.wa.us; *Tech Serv,* Judy McMakin;
Tel: 509-942-7604, E-mail: jmcmakin@richland.lib.wa.us; Staff 21.45
(MLS 5.2, Non-MLS 16.25)
Founded 1945. Pop 48,500; Circ 528,193
Jan 2010-Dec 2010 Income City $1,733,004. Mats Exp $215,500, Books
$119,200, Per/Ser (Incl. Access Fees) $26,100, AV Mat $48,700, Electronic
Ref Mat (Incl. Access Fees) $21,500. Sal $967,895
Library Holdings: Audiobooks 8,071; AV Mats 25,238; CDs 4,723; DVDs
5,976; e-books 3,295; Electronic Media & Resources 33; Large Print Bks
5,081; Bk Vols 147,587; Per Subs 350; Videos 5,449
Special Collections: Nuclear Regulatory Commission; Repository (WPPSS
Documents), micro, print; Richland & Tri-City Area History (Local
History), bk, micro
Automation Activity & Vendor Info: (Acquisitions) SirsiDynix;
(Cataloging) SirsiDynix; (Circulation) SirsiDynix; (OPAC) SirsiDynix;
(Serials) SirsiDynix
Database Vendor: EBSCO Auto Repair Reference, EBSCOhost, Gale
Cengage Learning, infoUSA, Ingram Library Services, netLibrary,
Overdrive, Inc, ProQuest, ReferenceUSA, TumbleBookLibrary, WT Cox
Wireless access
Open Mon-Thurs 9:30-9, Fri & Sat 9:30-5, Sun (Sept-May) 1-5
Friends of the Library Group

C   WASHINGTON STATE UNIVERSITY TRI-CITIES*, Max E Benitz
Library - Consolidated Information Center, 2770 University Dr, 99354.
(Mail add: 2710 University Dr, 99354), SAN 317-5820. Tel: 509-372-7430.
Circulation Tel: 509-372-7303. FAX: 509-372-7281. E-mail:
lib-req@tricity.wsu.edu. Web Site: www.tricity.wsu.edu. *Dir,* Annanaomi
Sams; Tel: 509-372-7448, E-mail: asams@tricity.wsu.edu; *Asst Librn,*
Harvey Gover; Tel: 509-372-7204, E-mail: hgover@tricity.wsu.edu; *Circ
Supvr,* Steve Bisch; Tel: 509-372-7313, E-mail: sbisch@tricity.wsu.edu; *Ref
Serv,* Cheryl Farabee; Tel: 509-372-7387, E-mail: cherylf@tricity.wsu.edu;
Tech Serv, Kim Colvin; Staff 5 (MLS 2, Non-MLS 3)
Founded 1990. Enrl 1,250; Fac 50; Highest Degree: Master
Library Holdings: CDs 300; DVDs 110; e-books 20,000; e-journals
16,000; Bk Titles 28,000; Bk Vols 34,000; Videos 220
Special Collections: Radiation Research
Subject Interests: Health physics
Automation Activity & Vendor Info: (Cataloging) Innovative Interfaces,
Inc; (Circulation) Innovative Interfaces, Inc; (Course Reserve) Innovative
Interfaces, Inc; (ILL) OCLC; (Media Booking) Innovative Interfaces, Inc;
(OPAC) Innovative Interfaces, Inc; (Serials) Innovative Interfaces, Inc
Wireless access
Partic in OCLC Online Computer Library Center, Inc
Open Mon-Thurs 8am-9pm, Fri 8-5, Sat 10-4
Friends of the Library Group

RITZVILLE

P   RITZVILLE LIBRARY DISTRICT NO 2*, 302 W Main Ave, 99169. SAN
317-5863. Tel: 509-659-1222. FAX: 509-659-1232. E-mail:
ritzlib@ritzcom.net. Web Site: www.ritzvillelibrary.org. *Dir,* Sandra Fitch;
Staff 4 (MLS 1, Non-MLS 3)
Founded 1905. Pop 3,500; Circ 17,358
Library Holdings: AV Mats 208; e-books 278; Large Print Bks 218; Bk
Titles 17,283; Per Subs 76
Special Collections: Adams Ritzville Journal, microfilm, newsp; Burt
Kendrick Photo Coll. Municipal Document Depository
Subject Interests: Local hist
Automation Activity & Vendor Info: (ILL) OCLC
Database Vendor: ProQuest
Wireless access
Function: Home delivery & serv to Sr ctr & nursing homes, ILL available,
Photocopying/Printing, Ref serv available, Summer reading prog
Open Mon-Thurs 11-5 & 6-8, Fri 11-5, Sat 11-2
Friends of the Library Group

ROSLYN

P   ROSLYN PUBLIC LIBRARY, 201 S First, 98941. (Mail add: PO Box
451, 98941-0451), SAN 317-5871. Tel: 509-649-3420. FAX:
509-649-3420. E-mail: rpl@inlandnet.com. Web Site:
www.roslynlibrary.org. *Librn,* Erin Krake
Founded 1898. Pop 1,000; Circ 12,321
Wireless access
Function: Art exhibits, Audiobks via web, AV serv, Bk club(s), Bks on
CD, Children's prog, Computer training, Computers for patron use, Copy
machines, Digital talking bks, Electronic databases & coll, Fax serv, Free
DVD rentals, ILL available, Music CDs, OverDrive digital audio bks,
Photocopying/Printing, Preschool outreach, Preschool reading prog, Printer
for laptops & handheld devices, Prog for adults, Prog for children & young
adult, Pub access computers, Ref serv available, Story hour, Summer
reading prog, Tax forms, Telephone ref, VHS videos, Web-catalog,
Wheelchair accessible
Friends of the Library Group

ROY

P ROY CITY LIBRARY*, 122 Third St E, 98580. (Mail add: PO Box 700, 98580-0700). Tel: 253-843-2331. FAX: 253-843-0279. E-mail: roylibrary@comcast.net. Web Site: roylibrary.home.comcast.net/~roylibrary. *Dir,* Cecelia Hanson; *Asst Librn,* Kathy Fisher
Founded 1947
Library Holdings: AV Mats 157; Bk Titles 6,690; Talking Bks 80
Open Mon 10-2, Tues-Thurs 2-6, Fri 9-1
Friends of the Library Group

SEATTLE

C ANTIOCH UNIVERSITY LIBRARY*, 2326 Sixth Ave, 98121-1814. Tel: 206-268-4109. FAX: 206-441-3307. E-mail: library@antiochsea.edu. Web Site: www.antiochsea.edu. *Dir,* Dr Margaret Baldwin
Library Holdings: AV Mats 200; Bk Titles 5,500; Per Subs 110
Database Vendor: OCLC FirstSearch
Open Mon-Thurs 10-9, Fri & Sat 10-6

C ARGOSY UNIVERSITY*, Seattle Campus Library, 2601-A Elliott Ave, 98121. Tel: 206-239-2359. Toll Free Tel: 800-377-0617. FAX: 206-393-3579. Web Site: www.argosy.edu/seattle/library.aspx. *Dir, Libr Serv,* Andrew Harbison; Tel: 206-393-3576, E-mail: aharbison@edmc.edu
Founded 2001
Library Holdings: Bk Titles 2,400; Per Subs 30
Automation Activity & Vendor Info: (Cataloging) Ex Libris Group; (Circulation) Ex Libris Group; (OPAC) Ex Libris Group
Database Vendor: EBSCOhost
Wireless access
Open Mon-Thurs 7:15am-10pm, Fri 7:15am-9pm, Sat 9-5:30, Sun 9-3
Restriction: Not open to pub

S ART INSTITUTE OF SEATTLE LIBRARY*, North Campus, 5th Flr, 2323 Elliott Ave, 98121. SAN 375-4448. Tel: 206-239-2359. Toll Free Tel: 800-275-2471. FAX: 206-441-3475. E-mail: ais_library@aii.edu. Web Site: ais.aiiresources.com. *Dir,* Andrew Harbison; E-mail: aharbison@aii.edu; *Ref Serv,* Jamie Miller
Founded 1946
Library Holdings: Bk Vols 24,500; Per Subs 290
Subject Interests: Applied art, Design
Automation Activity & Vendor Info: (Cataloging) Follett Software; (Circulation) Follett Software; (OPAC) Follett Software
Database Vendor: ProQuest
Wireless access
Open Mon-Thurs 7:15am-10pm, Fri 7:15am-9pm, Sat 9-5:30, Sun 9-3

S BATTELLE SEATTLE RESEARCH CENTER*, Battelle Library Seattle, 1100 Dexter Ave N, Ste 400, 98109-3598. SAN 317-591X. Tel: 206-528-3370. FAX: 614-458-0182. E-mail: seattlelibraryservices@battelle.org. *Coordr,* Melissa Gustafson; E-mail: gustafsonm@battelle.org; Staff 1 (MLS 1)
Founded 1968
Library Holdings: Bk Titles 150; Per Subs 50
Subject Interests: Environment, Pub health, Transportation
Database Vendor: Dialog, OCLC FirstSearch, ProQuest
Partic in National Network of Libraries of Medicine; OCLC Online Computer Library Center, Inc

L CARNEY, BADLEY & SPELLMAN LIBRARY*, Law Library, 701 Fifth Ave, Ste 3600, 98104-7010. SAN 372-3313. Tel: 206-607-4149. FAX: 206-622-8983. Web Site: www.carneylaw.com. *Librn,* Melissa Miller; E-mail: miller@carneylaw.com
Library Holdings: Bk Vols 10,000; Per Subs 30
Restriction: Staff use only

C CORNISH COLLEGE OF THE ARTS LIBRARY*, 1000 Lenora St, 98121. SAN 317-5952. Tel: 206-726-5041. FAX: 206-315-5811. E-mail: libraryref@cornish.edu. Web Site: www.cornish.edu/cornish_library. *Dir, Libr Serv,* Hollis P Near; *Librn,* Heather Sheppard; *Visual Image Curator,* Bridget Nowlin; Staff 3 (MLS 2, Non-MLS 1)
Founded 1964. Enrl 750; Fac 200; Highest Degree: Bachelor
Library Holdings: CDs 4,700; e-books 2,852; Music Scores 4,300; Bk Titles 18,500; Bk Vols 20,500; Per Subs 154; Videos 2,200
Special Collections: Image Coll, digital images, 35mm slides
Subject Interests: Art, Dance, Design, Music, Performance production, Theatre
Automation Activity & Vendor Info: (Acquisitions) LibraryWorld, Inc; (Cataloging) OCLC CatExpress; (Circulation) LibraryWorld, Inc; (OPAC) LibraryWorld, Inc; (Serials) LibraryWorld, Inc
Database Vendor: ARTstor, netLibrary, OCLC FirstSearch, OCLC WorldCat, ProQuest
Wireless access

L DAVIS WRIGHT TREMAINE LLP*, Law Library, 1201 Third Ave, Ste 2200, 98101-3045. SAN 372-3631. Tel: 206-622-3150. Toll Free Tel: 877-398-8416. FAX: 206-628-7699. E-mail: info@dwt.com. Web Site: www.dwt.com. *Librn,* Christy Leith; *Assoc Librn,* Fred Hanson; Tel: 206-628-7606; *Assoc Librn,* Connelly Johnson; Tel: 206-628-7604
Library Holdings: Bk Vols 40,000
Automation Activity & Vendor Info: (Acquisitions) EOS International; (Cataloging) EOS International; (OPAC) EOS International; (Serials) EOS International
Partic in OCLC Online Computer Library Center, Inc
Restriction: Staff use only

GM DEPARTMENT OF VETERANS AFFAIRS*, Puget Sound Health Care System Seattle Division Medical Library, 1660 S Columbian Way, 98108-1597. SAN 317-6525. Tel: 206-764-2065. FAX: 206-764-2816. *Dir, Libr Serv,* Jason Oleston; E-mail: jason.oleston2@va.gov; *Librn,* Mia Hannula; Tel: 206-277-3255, E-mail: mia.hannula@va.gov; Staff 4 (MLS 2, Non-MLS 2)
Founded 1951
Library Holdings: Bk Titles 3,327; Bk Vols 4,400; Per Subs 338
Subject Interests: Alcohol abuse, Clinical med, Drug abuse, Gerontology, Metabolism, Psychol, Spinal cord injury
Automation Activity & Vendor Info: (Cataloging) EOS International; (Circulation) EOS International; (OPAC) EOS International; (Serials) EOS International
Database Vendor: EBSCOhost, Elsevier, MD Consult, OCLC FirstSearch, OVID Technologies, ProQuest
Partic in National Network of Libraries of Medicine; Vets Admin Libr Network
Open Mon-Fri 8-4:30

SR DIOCESE OF OLYMPIA*, Diocesan Resource Center, 1551 Tenth Ave E, 98102-4210. SAN 326-5277. Tel: 206-325-4200. Toll Free Tel: 800-488-4978 (WA state). FAX: 206-325-4631. *Dir,* Sue Tait; Staff 1 (MLS 1)
Library Holdings: AV Mats 960; Bk Titles 8,500; Per Subs 100
Special Collections: Episcopal Church in Western Washington
Subject Interests: Relig educ, Theol
Friends of the Library Group

G FORENSIC LABORATORY SERVICES BUREAU LIBRARY, Forensic Laboratory Library, 2203 Airport Way S, Ste 250, 98134. Tel: 206-262-6027. FAX: 206-262-6018. *Librn,* Jeff Teitelbaum; E-mail: jeff.teitelbaum@wsp.wa.gov; Staff 1 (MLS 1)
Library Holdings: DVDs 50; Bk Titles 2,000; Bk Vols 2,500; Per Subs 150; Videos 200
Subject Interests: Forensic sci
Function: ILL available
Partic in Docline
Restriction: Non-circulating to the pub

S FRYE ART MUSEUM LIBRARY*, 704 Terry Ave, 98104. SAN 317-5995. Tel: 206-622-9250. FAX: 206-223-1707. E-mail: info@fryemuseum.org. Web Site: www.fryeart.org. *Curator of Coll,* Donna L Kovalenko; E-mail: dkovalenko@fryemuseum.org
Library Holdings: Bk Vols 1,000
Special Collections: 19th & 20th Century American & German Art

L GARVEY, SCHUBERT & BARER*, Law Library, 1191 Second Ave, Ste 1800, 98101-2939. SAN 372-3968. Tel: 206-464-3939. FAX: 206-464-0125. Web Site: www.gsblaw.com. *Librn,* Jill Allyn; E-mail: jallyn@gsblaw.com
Library Holdings: Bk Vols 10,000

L GRAHAM & DUNN*, Law Library, Pier 70, 2801 Alaskan Way, Ste 300, 98121-1128. SAN 317-6010. Tel: 206-624-8300. Reference Tel: 206-903-4801. FAX: 206-340-9599. E-mail: library@grahamdunn.com. *Librn,* Katie Drake; E-mail: kdrake@grahamdunn.com; Staff 2 (MLS 1, Non-MLS 1)
Library Holdings: Bk Vols 10,000
Subject Interests: Banking, Employment law, Hospitality, Immigration, Labor law, Real estate, Securities, Tax law
Automation Activity & Vendor Info: (Cataloging) OCLC CatExpress; (Serials) Inmagic, Inc.
Database Vendor: Dialog, Infotrieve, LexisNexis, OCLC FirstSearch, OCLC WorldCat, Westlaw
Partic in OCLC Online Computer Library Center, Inc

E GROUP HEALTH COOPERATIVE*, Medical Library, 201 16th Ave E, 98112. SAN 363-924X. Tel: 206-326-3393. FAX: 206-326-2629. E-mail: medlibrary@ghc.org. *Librn,* Ryce Andrea; Tel: 206-326-3392, E-mail: ryce.a@ghc.org; *Libr Tech,* Shamus Ryan; *Web Serv,* Elisa Hoelscher; Tel: 206-326-4985, E-mail: hoelscher.e@ghc.org; Staff 3 (MLS 1, Non-MLS 2)
Founded 1969

Library Holdings: e-books 650; e-journals 8,000; Bk Titles 400; Per Subs 1
Subject Interests: Allied health care, Clinical med, Health maintenance organizations, Healthcare mgt, Nursing, Pharm
Database Vendor: EBSCOhost, EOS International, netLibrary, OVID Technologies, ProQuest, ScienceDirect, SerialsSolutions, WebFeat, Wiley
Branches:
KATHLEEN HILL LIBRARY, 320 Westlake Ave N, Ste 100, GHQ-E3S, 98109, SAN 370-7164. Tel: 206-448-2542, 206-448-2771. FAX: 206-877-0687. E-mail: library.kh@ghc.org. *Electronic Info Spec, Librn,* Patty Miller; *Libr Tech,* Aimee McAdams; Staff 2 (MLS 1, Non-MLS 1)
Founded 1987
   Library Holdings: AV Mats 130; Bk Titles 900; Per Subs 65; Videos 100
   Subject Interests: Computers, Finance, Healthcare admin, Human resources, Leadership, Mgt, Mkt, Organization
   Function: Audio & video playback equip for onsite use, Doc delivery serv, For res purposes, ILL available, Online searches, Orientations, Telephone ref, VHS videos
   Partic in Coop Libr Agency for Syst & Servs; OCLC Online Computer Library Center, Inc
   Open Mon-Fri 8-5
   Restriction: Co libr, Employees only

S   HISTORICAL SOCIETY OF SEATTLE & KING COUNTY*, Sophie Frye Bass Library of Northwest Americana, 2700 24th Ave E, 98112. SAN 317-6363. Tel: 206-324-1126. FAX: 206-324-1346. E-mail: library@seattlehistory.org. Web Site: www.seattlehistory.org. *Librn,* Carolyn Marr; *Librn,* Mary Montgomery; Staff 2 (MLS 2)
Founded 1952
Library Holdings: Bk Titles 10,000
Special Collections: Collections of the Puget Sound Maritime Historical Society & the Black Heritage Society of Washington State; PEMCO Webster & Stevens Photography Coll; PSMHS Williamson Maritime Photography Coll; Seattle Post-Intelligence Photography Coll
Subject Interests: Alaska, Hist, Maritime, Pacific Northwest, Seattle
Function: Photocopying/Printing, Res libr
Open Mon, Wed & Fri 1-5
Restriction: Non-circulating to the pub, Open to pub for ref only

M   FRED HUTCHINSON CANCER RESEARCH CENTER*, Arnold Library, 1100 Fairview Ave N, B1-010, 98109. (Mail add: PO Box 19024, B1-010, 98109-1024), SAN 317-6037. Tel: 206-667-4314. Interlibrary Loan Service Tel: 206-667-6852. FAX: 206-667-4737. E-mail: library@fhcrc.org. Web Site: www.fhcrc.org/library. *Dir,* Ann Marie Clark; Tel: 206-667-2992, E-mail: aclark@fhcrc.org; Staff 8 (MLS 3.5, Non-MLS 4.5)
Founded 1975
Subject Interests: Biochem, Biol, Biostatistics, Epidemiology, Genetics, Hematology, Immunology, Med, Molecular biol, Oncology, Pathology, Pharmacology, Pub health med, Radiology, Surgery, Virology
Automation Activity & Vendor Info: (Acquisitions) SirsiDynix; (Cataloging) Horizon; (Circulation) Horizon; (OPAC) Horizon; (Serials) SerialsSolutions
Wireless access
Function: Computers for patron use, Electronic databases & coll, ILL available, Online cat, Online searches, Pub access computers, Wheelchair accessible
Partic in Lyrasis; Nat Libr of Med/Docline; OCLC Online Computer Library Center, Inc
Restriction: Badge access after hrs, Prof mat only

L   KARR TUTTLE CAMPBELL*, Law Library, 1201 Third Ave, Ste 2900, 98101-3028. SAN 321-8163. Tel: 206-223-1313. FAX: 206-682-7100. Web Site: www.karrtuttle.com. *Head, Coll Serv,* Julie Essex-Webster; Tel: 206-224-8187, E-mail: jessex@karrtuttle.com; Staff 2 (Non-MLS 2)
Founded 1904
Library Holdings: Bk Titles 2,300; Per Subs 420
Subject Interests: Civil law, General law, Trial practice law
Partic in OCLC Online Computer Library Center, Inc

L   KELLER ROHRBACK LLP LIBRARY*, 1201 Third Ave, Ste 3200, 98101-3052. SAN 372-3623. Tel: 206-623-1900. FAX: 206-623-3384. Web Site: www.kellerrohrback.com. Staff 1 (MLS 1)
Founded 1919
Library Holdings: Bk Vols 5,600; Per Subs 18
Restriction: Staff use only

G   KING COUNTY DEPARTMENT OF NATURAL RESOURCES & PARKS*, Technical Document & Research Center, 201 S Jackson St, Ste 190, 98104. Tel: 206-684-1129. FAX: 206-296-0192. E-mail: research.center@kingcounty.gov. *Librn,* Dawn Duddleson; Staff 1 (MLS 1)
Founded 1975
Library Holdings: Bk Titles 15,000; Per Subs 50
Subject Interests: Natural res, Transportation

Automation Activity & Vendor Info: (Cataloging) LibraryWorld, Inc; (Circulation) LibraryWorld, Inc; (Serials) LibraryWorld, Inc
Function: For res purposes, Govt ref serv
Restriction: Circ limited, External users must contact libr

G   KING COUNTY HAZARDOUS WASTE LIBRARY*, 130 Nickerson St, Ste 100, 98109-1658. SAN 373-6563. Tel: 206-263-3051. FAX: 206-263-3070. E-mail: haz.waste@kingcounty.gov. Web Site: www.lhwmp.org/home/Library/index.aspx. *Librn, Web Serv,* Brian Westra; Staff 1 (MLS 1)
Founded 1992
Library Holdings: Bk Titles 3,500; Per Subs 50
Subject Interests: Environ educ, Hazardous waste mgt, Household hazardous waste, Integrated pest mgt
Automation Activity & Vendor Info: (Cataloging) EOS International; (Circulation) EOS International; (OPAC) EOS International
Database Vendor: OCLC FirstSearch

L   KING COUNTY LAW LIBRARY*, W 621 King County Courthouse, 516 Third Ave, 98104. SAN 317-6053. Tel: 206-296-0940. FAX: 206-205-0513. E-mail: kcll@metrokc.gov. Web Site: www.kcll.org. *Dir,* Marcus L Hochstetler; Tel: marcus.hochstetler@metrokc.gov; *Head, Ref,* Rita Kaiser; *Head, Tech Serv,* Rita Dermody; *Pub Serv,* Richard Stroup; *Ref,* Kim Ositis
Library Holdings: Bk Vols 90,000; Per Subs 200
Wireless access
Open Mon-Fri 8-6

L   LANE POWELL PC LIBRARY, 1420 Fifth Ave, Ste 4100, 98101-2388. SAN 321-7663. Tel: 206-223-6245. FAX: 206-223-7107. Web Site: www.lanepowell.com. *Dir of Libr,* Karen Helde; Tel: 206-223-7741, E-mail: heldek@lanepowell.com; Staff 7.6 (MLS 5.6, Non-MLS 2)
Library Holdings: Bk Vols 14,000; Per Subs 500
Subject Interests: Law
Automation Activity & Vendor Info: (Acquisitions) Inmagic, Inc.; (Cataloging) Inmagic, Inc.; (ILL) Inmagic, Inc.; (Serials) Inmagic, Inc.
Wireless access
Partic in Dialog Corp; LexisNexis; OCLC Online Computer Library Center, Inc; Westlaw

M   VIRGINIA MASON MEDICAL CENTER LIBRARY*, 925 Seneca, 98101. SAN 371-1331. Tel: 206-223-6733. FAX: 206-223-2376. *Dir,* Susan Schweinsberg Long; Staff 3 (MLS 2, Non-MLS 1)
Library Holdings: Bk Titles 1,000; Bk Vols 4,500; Per Subs 150
Special Collections: Virginia Mason Historical Archives
Automation Activity & Vendor Info: (OPAC) EOS International; (Serials) SerialsSolutions
Restriction: Staff use only

L   REED MCCLURE LAW FIRM LIBRARY*, 601 Union St, Ste 1500, 98101. SAN 373-6601. Tel: 206-292-4900. FAX: 206-223-0152. *Librn,* Ellen Hanson; E-mail: ehanson@rmlaw.com; Staff 1 (MLS 1)
Library Holdings: Bk Vols 4,000
Restriction: Staff use only

S   MOUNTAINEERS LIBRARY*, 300 Third Ave W, 98119. SAN 317-6126. Tel: 206-284-6310, Ext 3014. FAX: 206-284-4977. Web Site: www.mountaineers.org/library. *Librn,* Kathleen McCluskey; E-mail: kathleenm@mountaineers.org; Staff 1 (Non-MLS 1)
Founded 1915
Library Holdings: AV Mats 272; Electronic Media & Resources 10; Bk Vols 6,000; Per Subs 40
Special Collections: Conservation (Mountaineer Foundation Library)
Subject Interests: Climbing, Environ studies, Exploration mountaineering biog, Exploration mountaineering hist, Natural hist
Automation Activity & Vendor Info: (Cataloging) TLC (The Library Corporation)
Function: Archival coll, Doc delivery serv, Mail loans to mem, Photocopying/Printing, Ref serv available
Open Mon-Thurs (Sept-May) 5pm-9pm; Tues & Thurs (Summer) 5-8:30
Restriction: Open by appt only, Open to pub for ref & circ; with some limitations, Restricted loan policy
Friends of the Library Group

G   MUNICIPAL RESEARCH & SERVICES CENTER OF WASHINGTON LIBRARY*, 2601 Fourth Ave, Ste 800, 98121-1280. SAN 317-6134. Tel: 206-625-1300. FAX: 206-625-1220. E-mail: mrsc@mrsc.org. Web Site: www.mrsc.org. *Mgr,* Fred Ward; *Librn,* Erica Zwick; Staff 5 (MLS 2, Non-MLS 3)
Founded 1970
Library Holdings: Bk Titles 12,000; Bk Vols 15,000; Per Subs 300
Special Collections: Municipal Government Documents
Automation Activity & Vendor Info: (Cataloging) EOS International; (Circulation) EOS International; (OPAC) EOS International
Restriction: Private libr

S   MUSEUM OF FLIGHT, Harl V Brackin Library, 9404 E Marginal Way S, 98108-4097. SAN 370-6028. Tel: 206-764-5700. FAX: 206-764-5707. Web Site: www.museumofflight.org. *Head Librn,* Meredith Lowe; Tel: 206-768-7160, E-mail: mlowe@museumofflight.org; *Curator,* Daniel Hagedorn; Staff 2 (MLS 2)
Founded 1985
Library Holdings: Bk Titles 26,000; Bk Vols 40,000; Per Subs 100
Special Collections: Aviation-Aerospace (G S Williams Photographic Coll, Peter Bowers Photo Coll); D D Hatfield Aviation History Coll; E B Jeppesen Aviation History & Navigation Coll; Fighter Aces Association Archives; Lear Archives; Wright Airplane Company Coll
Subject Interests: Aerospace, Aviation
Automation Activity & Vendor Info: (Cataloging) OCLC
Function: Archival coll, For res purposes, Photocopying/Printing, Ref & res, Ref serv available, Ref serv in person, Res libr, Telephone ref
Open Mon-Fri 1-5
Restriction: Non-circulating to the pub, Open to pub for ref only

G   NATIONAL ARCHIVES & RECORDS ADMINISTRATION, The National Archives at Seattle, 6125 Sand Point Way NE, 98115-7999. Tel: 206-336-5115. FAX: 206-336-5112. E-mail: seattle.archives@nara.gov. Web Site: www.archives.gov/pacific-alaska/seattle/. *Dir,* Susan Karren; Tel: 206-336-5141
Special Collections: National Archives Documents from NARA Facilities (Microfilm Coll); Records of Federal Agencies & Federal Courts in Idaho, Oregon & Washington State
Function: Archival coll, Computers for patron use, Copy machines, Distance learning, Electronic databases & coll, Exhibits, For res purposes, Genealogy discussion group, Govt ref serv, Instruction & testing, Mail & tel request accepted, Online cat, Online ref, Online searches, Orientations, Outreach serv, Pub access computers, Ref & res, Ref serv in person, Telephone ref, Wheelchair accessible, Workshops
Open Mon-Fri 7:45-4:15
Restriction: Open to pub with supv only

G   NATIONAL ENVIRONMENTAL SATELLITE DATA & INFORMATION SERVICES*, NOAA Library Seattle, Bldg 3, 7600 Sand Point Way NE, 98115. SAN 373-8647. Tel: 206-526-6241. FAX: 206-526-4535. E-mail: seattle.library@noaa.gov. Web Site: www.wrclib.noaa.gov/. *Librn,* Brian Voss; E-mail: brian.voss@noaa.gov
Library Holdings: Bk Titles 15,000; Per Subs 200
Subject Interests: Meteorology, Oceanography
Automation Activity & Vendor Info: (Cataloging) SirsiDynix; (Circulation) SirsiDynix; (ILL) OCLC; (OPAC) SirsiDynix
Open Mon-Fri 8-4:30

G   NATIONAL MARINE FISHERIES SERVICE*, Northwest & Alaska Fisheries Science Centers Library, 2725 Montlake Blvd E, 98112. SAN 317-6568. Tel: 206-860-3210. FAX: 206-860-3442. E-mail: nwfsc.library@noaa.gov. Web Site: lib.nwfsc.noaa.gov. *Librn,* Craig Wilson
Founded 1931
Library Holdings: Bk Titles 16,000; Per Subs 250
Subject Interests: Aquatic sci, Biochem, Fisheries biol, Fisheries mgt, Food, Marine sci
Database Vendor: OCLC FirstSearch
Partic in OCLC Online Computer Library Center, Inc
Open Mon-Fri 8-5

        NORDIC HERITAGE MUSEUM
S   WALTER JOHNSON MEMORIAL LIBRARY*, 3014 NW 67th St, 98117. Tel: 206-789-5707. FAX: 206-789-3271. E-mail: nordic@nordicmuseum.org. Web Site: www.nordicmuseum.org. *Exec Dir,* Eric Nelson; Tel: 206-789-5707, Ext 14, E-mail: ericn@nordicmuseum.org; *Coll Mgr,* Lisa Hill-Festa; Tel: 206-789-5707, Ext 18; Staff 1 (Non-MLS 1)
Founded 1980
Library Holdings: Bk Vols 15,500
Special Collections: Gordon Tracie Music Library; Vanishing Generations Oral History Project. Oral History
Subject Interests: Danish (Lang), Finnish (Lang), Icelandic (Lang), Norwegian (Lang), Sound recordings, Swedish (Lang)
Function: Ref serv available
Restriction: Fee for pub use, Limited access for the pub, Non-circulating coll, Not a lending libr, Open by appt only
S   GORDON EKVALL TRACIE MUSIC LIBRARY*, 3014 NW 67th St, 98117, SAN 326-4920. Tel: 206-789-5707, Ext 13. FAX: 206-789-3271. E-mail: marym@nordicmuseum.org. Web Site: www.nordicmuseum.org.
Founded 1995
Library Holdings: AV Mats 3,000; CDs 200; DVDs 50; Music Scores 4,000; Bk Titles 2,500; Spec Interest Per Sub 40; Videos 100
Special Collections: Gordon Ekvall Tracie History Coll; Nordiska Folkdancers Coll; Skandia Folkdance Society Coll
Subject Interests: Customary life, Folk & traditional dance, Folk & traditional music, Folk art, Folk attire

Function: Archival coll, Electronic databases & coll, For res purposes, Music CDs, VHS videos
Restriction: Non-circulating coll, Not a lending libr, Open by appt only

J   NORTH SEATTLE COMMUNITY COLLEGE*, Library & Media Services, 9600 College Way N, 98103. SAN 317-6169. Tel: 206-527-3607. Reference Tel: 206-527-3609. Administration Tel: 206-527-3615. FAX: 206-527-3614. Web Site: dept.sccd.ctc.edu/nslib. *Dir,* Sharon Simes; E-mail: ssimes@sccd.ctc.edu; *Supvr, Circ,* Mary Parent; Tel: 206-526-7714, E-mail: mparent@sccd.ctc.edu; *Prog Coordr,* Alice Smith; Tel: 206-527-3610, E-mail: asmith@sccd.ctc.edu
Founded 1970. Enrl 9,000
Library Holdings: Bk Vols 54,000; Per Subs 594
Automation Activity & Vendor Info: (Cataloging) Ex Libris Group; (Circulation) Ex Libris Group; (OPAC) Ex Libris Group
Database Vendor: EBSCOhost, ProQuest
Wireless access
Open Mon-Thurs (Winter) 8am-9pm, Fri 8-4, Sat & Sun 12-5; Mon-Thurs(Summer) 9-8, Sun 12-5

M   NORTHWEST HOSPITAL & MEDICAL CENTER*, Library & Information Resources, 1550 N 115th St, D-110, 98133. SAN 317-6185. Tel: 206-368-1850. FAX: 206-368-1949. E-mail: library@nwhsea.org. *Clinical Librn, Virtual Ref,* Jessica Rieber; Staff 1 (Non-MLS 1)
Founded 1975
Library Holdings: e-books 50
Subject Interests: Med, Nursing
Database Vendor: EBSCO Information Services, Medline, Micromedex, OVID Technologies, ProQuest, PubMed, SerialsSolutions, WebMD
Wireless access
Open Mon-Fri 7-3:30

P   NORTHWEST LIBRARY ON DEAF CULTURE & HISTORY*, Community Service Center for the Deaf & Hard of Hearing, 1609 19th Ave, 98122. SAN 371-7127. Tel: 206-322-5551. FAX: 206-720-3251. E-mail: cscdhh@aol.com. Web Site: www.cscdhh.org. *Librn,* Mildred Johnson
Founded 1983
Library Holdings: Bk Titles 500
Subject Interests: Deafness
Special Services for the Deaf - Bks on deafness & sign lang; Spec interest per; Staff with knowledge of sign lang; TTY equip
Restriction: Open to pub with supv only, Open to students
Friends of the Library Group

L   FOSTER PEPPER PLLC*, Research Center, 1111 Third Ave, Ste 3400, 98101. SAN 327-4314. Tel: 206-447-6474. FAX: 206-447-9700. E-mail: researchcenter@foster.com. *Law Librn,* Barbara Rothwell; Tel: 206-447-2811, Fax: 206-749-2049, E-mail: rothb@foster.com; *Mgr, Legal & Bus Develop Res Serv,* Brenna Louzin; Tel: 206-447-6287, E-mail: louzb@foster.com; Staff 3 (MLS 2, Non-MLS 1)
Library Holdings: Bk Vols 13,000
Automation Activity & Vendor Info: (ILL) OCLC; (OPAC) EOS International
Database Vendor: Dialog, LexisNexis, Westlaw
Function: Res libr
Restriction: Not open to pub

L   PERKINS COIE LIBRARY, 1201 Third Ave, Ste 4900, 98101. SAN 317-6215. Tel: 206-359-8444. FAX: 206-359-9444. E-mail: library@perkinscoie.com. *Libr Mgr,* Amy J Eaton; E-mail: aeaton@perkinscoie.com; *Librn,* Karen Braucht; *Librn,* Robyn Hagle; *Librn,* Carol Warner; Staff 8 (MLS 4, Non-MLS 4)
Founded 1912
Library Holdings: Bk Vols 50,000; Per Subs 1,000
Subject Interests: Aviation, Corp, Environ law, Estate planning, Intellectual property, Labor law, Litigation, Probate, Pub utilities, Real estate, Securities, Taxation
Automation Activity & Vendor Info: (Cataloging) Inmagic, Inc.; (OPAC) Inmagic, Inc.; (Serials) Inmagic, Inc.
Database Vendor: Dialog, LexisNexis, OCLC FirstSearch, Westlaw
Partic in OCLC Online Computer Library Center, Inc
Restriction: Private libr

R   PLYMOUTH CONGREGATIONAL CHURCH*, Vida B Varey Library, 1217 Sixth Ave, 98101-3199. SAN 317-6223. Tel: 206-622-4865. FAX: 206-622-8726. Web Site: www.plymouthchurchseattle.org. *Librn,* Suzanne Sanderson; Staff 1 (MLS 1)
Founded 1948
Library Holdings: Bk Vols 5,300; Per Subs 6
Special Collections: Lectures & Sermons, audio cassette & CDs
Subject Interests: Relig studies
Automation Activity & Vendor Info: (Cataloging) LibraryWorld, Inc; (Circulation) LibraryWorld, Inc; (OPAC) LibraryWorld, Inc

Wireless access
Open Wed 10-1, Sun 9-Noon

SR   PROVIDENCE ARCHIVES*, Mother Joseph Province, 4800 37th Ave SW,
98126. SAN 329-5087. Tel: 206-937-4600. FAX: 206-923-4001. E-mail:
archives@providence.org. Web Site: www.providence.org/phs/archives.
Archives Dir, Loretta Zwolak Greene; Tel: 206-923-4010, E-mail:
loretta.greene@providence.org; *Visual Res Archivist, Web Coordr,* Peter F
Schmid; Tel: 206-923-4012, E-mail: peter.schmid@providence.org; *Assoc
Archivist,* Emily Hughes Dominick; Tel: 206-923-4011, E-mail:
emily.dominick@providence.org; *Asst Archivist-Tech,* Pamela Hedquist; Tel:
509-474-2319, E-mail: pamela.hedquist@providence.org; Staff 4 (MLS 1,
Non-MLS 3)
Library Holdings: Bk Titles 1,000; Videos 600
Special Collections: Mother Joseph, a Sister of Providence (1823-1902),
represents Washington State in Statuary Hall, Washington, DC
Subject Interests: Catholic Church, Educ, Healthcare, Sisters of
Providence, Soc welfare in the NW
Function: Archival coll
Publications: Past Forward (Newsletter)
Restriction: Non-circulating, Open by appt only

S   PUGET SOUND REGIONAL COUNCIL*, Information Center, 1011
Western Ave, Ste 500, 98104-1035. SAN 317-6266. Tel: 206-464-7532.
FAX: 206-587-4825. E-mail: infoctr@psrc.org. Web Site: www.psrc.org.
Mgr, Andi Markley; *Cat,* Doris Dungan; *Res,* Andi Markley; Staff 3 (MLS
3)
Founded 1967
Library Holdings: Bk Titles 3,000; Per Subs 60
Special Collections: Census; Small Area Regional Forecasts (population,
households, employment)
Subject Interests: Econ develop, Growth mgt, Transportation

L   SCHROETER, GOLDMARK & BENDER LAW LIBRARY*, 810 Third
Ave, Ste 500, 98104. SAN 323-8156. Tel: 206-622-8000. FAX:
206-682-2305. E-mail: lib@sgb-law.com. *Librn,* Mark Gardner
Library Holdings: Bk Titles 2,000; Bk Vols 3,000; Per Subs 150

SEATTLE ART MUSEUM
S   DOROTHY STIMSON BULLITT LIBRARY*, 1300 First Ave, 98101,
SAN 317-6320. Tel: 206-654-3220. FAX: 206-654-3135. Web Site:
www.seattleartmuseum.org/learn/library/default.asp. *Librn, Mgr, Libr
Serv,* Traci Timmons; E-mail: tracit@seattleartmuseum.org; Staff 1 (MLS
1)
Founded 1991
Library Holdings: Bk Vols 20,000; Per Subs 100
Special Collections: History of the Seattle Art Museum, clippings,
ephemera; Northwest Artists Files, clippings
Subject Interests: African art, Contemporary art, Decorative art,
European art, Modern art, Photog
Automation Activity & Vendor Info: (Cataloging) EOS International;
(Circulation) EOS International; (OPAC) EOS International; (Serials)
EOS International
Function: Archival coll, Photocopying/Printing, Res libr, Telephone ref
Partic in OCLC Online Computer Library Center, Inc
Open Tues-Fri 10-5
Restriction: Circulates for staff only

S   MCCAW FOUNDATION LIBRARY OF ASIAN ART, Seattle Asian Art
Museum, 1400 E Prospect St, 98112, SAN 375-538X. Tel:
206-654-3202. FAX: 206-654-3191. *Assoc Librn,* Yueh-Lin Chen;
E-mail: yueh-linc@seattleartmuseum.org; Staff 1 (MLS 1)
Founded 1933
Library Holdings: Bk Vols 15,000; Per Subs 100
Subject Interests: Asian art
Automation Activity & Vendor Info: (Cataloging) EOS International;
(Circulation) EOS International; (OPAC) EOS International; (Serials)
EOS International
Function: Archival coll, Ref serv available, Res libr, Telephone ref
Partic in OCLC Online Computer Library Center, Inc
Open Thurs & Fri 2-5, Sat 10-5
Restriction: Non-circulating to the pub

J   SEATTLE CENTRAL COMMUNITY COLLEGE*, Instructional Resource
Services Library, 1701 Broadway, 2BE2101, 98122. SAN 317-6339. Tel:
206-587-4050. Administration Tel: 206-587-5420. FAX: 206-587-3878.
Web Site: dept.sccd.ctc.edu/cclib. *Dean, Instrul Res Serv,* Wai-Fong Lee;
Tel: 206-587-4062, E-mail: wflee@sccd.ctc.edu; *Librn,* Lynn Kanne; Tel:
206-587-4072, E-mail: lkanne@sccd.ctc.edu; *Librn,* Kelley McHenry; Tel:
206-587-6336, E-mail: kmchenry@sccd.ctc.edu; *Librn,* Karen Michaelsen;
Tel: 206-587-4098, E-mail: kmicha@sccd.ctc.edu; *Librn,* Jane Shoop; Tel:
206-587-4071, E-mail: jshoop@sccd.ctc.edu; *Librn,* Sharon Spence-Wilcox;
Tel: 206-587-4069, E-mail: sspence@sccd.ctc.edu; Staff 6 (MLS 6)
Founded 1966. Enrl 7,886; Fac 174
Library Holdings: Bk Titles 60,575; Per Subs 595

Subject Interests: Archit, Art, Ethnic studies
Automation Activity & Vendor Info: (Acquisitions) Ex Libris Group;
(Cataloging) Ex Libris Group; (Circulation) Ex Libris Group; (Course
Reserve) Ex Libris Group; (OPAC) Ex Libris Group; (Serials) Ex Libris
Group
Database Vendor: OCLC FirstSearch

M   SEATTLE CHILDREN'S HOSPITAL, Library & Information Commons,
4800 Sand Point Way NE, W-6850, 98105. (Mail add: PO Box 5371,
98145-5005), SAN 317-5944. Tel: 206-987-2098. FAX: 206-987-3838.
E-mail: library@seattlechildrens.org. *Librn,* Jamie Graham; *Librn,* Sue
Groshong; *Librn,* Susan Klawansky; Staff 3 (MLS 3)
Founded 1946
Library Holdings: AV Mats 150; e-books 800; e-journals 20,000; Bk
Titles 3,500; Per Subs 250
Special Collections: Autism Coll
Subject Interests: Pediatrics
Automation Activity & Vendor Info: (Acquisitions) Ex Libris Group;
(Cataloging) Ex Libris Group; (Circulation) Ex Libris Group; (OPAC) Ex
Libris Group; (Serials) Ex Libris Group
Database Vendor: American Psychological Association (APA), Cinahl
Information Systems, Dialog, DynaMed, EBSCOhost, Elsevier, Gale
Cengage Learning, ISI Web of Knowledge, MD Consult, Micromedex,
netLibrary, OCLC FirstSearch, OVID Technologies, ProQuest, RefWorks,
ScienceDirect, SerialsSolutions, STAT!Ref (Teton Data Systems),
UpToDate
Wireless access
Open Mon-Fri 8-4:30
Restriction: Badge access after hrs

S   SEATTLE GENEALOGICAL SOCIETY LIBRARY, 6200 Sand Point Way
NE, 98115. (Mail add: PO Box 15329, 98115-0329), SAN 321-1053. Tel:
206-522-8658. E-mail: seattlegenealogicalsociety@gmail.com,
sgslibrary@gmail.com. Web Site: seattlegenealogicalsociety.org. *Libr Dir,*
Amber Brock Case. Subject Specialists: *Genealogy,* Amber Brock Case;
Staff 1 (MLS 1)
Founded 1975
Library Holdings: CDs 300; Bk Vols 8,000; Per Subs 200
Special Collections: British Isles Coll; Family Genealogies Coll; New
Jersey (George C Kent Coll); Scandinavia Coll
Subject Interests: Genealogy, Local hist
Wireless access
Function: Microfiche/film & reading machines, Online cat, Online ref,
Online searches, Orientations, Photocopying/Printing, Res libr, Res
performed for a fee, Web-catalog, Workshops
Publications: Bulletin (Bi-annually); Newsletter (Quarterly)
Open Tues-Sat 10-3, Wed 10-8
Restriction: Non-circulating

C   SEATTLE PACIFIC UNIVERSITY LIBRARY*, 3307 Third Ave W,
98119. SAN 363-9363. Tel: 206-281-2228. Interlibrary Loan Service Tel:
206-281-2154. Reference Tel: 206-281-2419. FAX: 206-281-2936. Web
Site: www.spu.edu/depts/library. *Univ Librn,* Bryce Nelson; Tel:
206-281-2414, E-mail: bnelson@spu.edu; *Electronic Res, Info Spec, Syst
Librn,* Carrie Fry; Tel: 206-281-2124, E-mail: cfry@spu.edu; *Supvr, Access
Serv,* Johanna Knudsen; Tel: 206-281-2789, E-mail: knudsen@spu.edu;
Tech Serv Coordr, Natalee Vick; Tel: 206-281-2735, E-mail:
nvick@spu.edu; *Info Spec,* Gary Fick; Tel: 206-281-2423, E-mail:
gfick@spu.edu; *Info Spec,* Stephen Perisho; Tel: 206-281-2417, E-mail:
sperisho@spu.edu; *Info Spec,* Jenifer Phelan; Tel: 206-281-2074, E-mail:
sigafoes@spu.edu. Subject Specialists: *Health sci,* Carrie Fry; *Sci tech,*
Gary Fick; *Theol,* Stephen Perisho; *Educ,* Jenifer Phelan; Staff 10 (MLS 9,
Non-MLS 1)
Founded 1891. Enrl 3,728; Fac 190; Highest Degree: Doctorate
Library Holdings: e-books 3,395; Bk Titles 163,959; Bk Vols 191,807;
Per Subs 1,230
Special Collections: Free Methodism
Subject Interests: Educ, Nursing, Psychol, Relig
Automation Activity & Vendor Info: (Acquisitions) Innovative Interfaces,
Inc; (Cataloging) Innovative Interfaces, Inc; (Circulation) Innovative
Interfaces, Inc; (Course Reserve) Innovative Interfaces, Inc; (OPAC)
Innovative Interfaces, Inc; (Serials) Innovative Interfaces, Inc
Database Vendor: Cambridge Scientific Abstracts, EBSCOhost, JSTOR,
netLibrary, OCLC FirstSearch, OCLC WorldCat, ProQuest, SerialsSolutions
Function: ILL available, Newsp ref libr, Photocopying/Printing, Ref serv
available, Telephone ref
Partic in Orbis Cascade Alliance; Puget Sound Acad Independent Librs
Open Mon-Thurs (Winter) 7:30am-11pm, Fri 7:30am-8pm, Sat 12-8, Sun
3-11; Mon-Thurs (Summer) 8-8, Fri 8-6, Sat 10-6
Restriction: Pub use on premises

M   SEATTLE PSYCHOANALYTIC SOCIETY & INSTITUTE*, Edith
Buxbaum Library, 4020 E Madison St, Ste 230, 98112. SAN 373-3025.
Tel: 206-328-5315. FAX: 206-328-5879. Web Site: www.spsi.org. *Adminr,*
Victoria Jenkins

Founded 1996
Library Holdings: e-books 30; e-journals 20; Bk Vols 5,000; Per Subs 10
Open Mon-Thurs 9-5

P   THE SEATTLE PUBLIC LIBRARY, 1000 Fourth Ave, 98104-1109. SAN
363-9398. Tel: 206-386-4636. Circulation Tel: 206-386-4190. Interlibrary
Loan Service Tel: 206-386-4601. Administration Tel: 206-386-4147.
Interlibrary Loan Service FAX: 206-386-4604. TDD: 206-386-4697.
E-mail: infospl@spl.org. Web Site: www.spl.org. *Dir of Communications,*
Andra Addison; Tel: 206-386-4103, E-mail: andra.addison@spl.org; *Human
Res Dir,* Lin Schnell; Tel: 206-733-9922, E-mail: lin.schnell@spl.org; *Info
Tech Dir,* Jim Loter; Tel: 206-386-4662, E-mail: jim.loter@spl.org; *Dir,
Prog & Serv Develop,* Chance Hunt; Tel: 206-386-4097, E-mail:
chance.hunt@spl.org; *City Librn,* Marcellus Turner; E-mail:
city.librarian@spl.org; *Circ Serv Mgr,* Megan Taylor; E-mail:
megan.taylor@spl.org
Founded 1890. Pop 608,660; Circ 11,572,778
Jan 2011-Dec 2011 Income (Main Library and Branch(s)) $50,000,000
Library Holdings: Bk Vols 926,197
Special Collections: Oral History; State Document Depository; US
Document Depository
Subject Interests: Aviation hist, Genealogy, Seattle hist
Automation Activity & Vendor Info: (Acquisitions) SirsiDynix;
(Cataloging) SirsiDynix; (Circulation) SirsiDynix; (OPAC) SirsiDynix
Database Vendor: SirsiDynix
Wireless access
Partic in OCLC Online Computer Library Center, Inc
Special Services for the Deaf - Bks on deafness & sign lang; Deaf publ;
Staff with knowledge of sign lang; Video & TTY relay via computer
Special Services for the Blind - Assistive/Adapted tech devices, equip &
products; Braille bks; Descriptive video serv (DVS); Large print bks;
Reader equip
Open Mon-Thurs 10-8, Fri & Sat 10-6, Sun 12-6
Restriction: Circ limited
Friends of the Library Group
Branches: 27
BALLARD, 5614 22nd Ave NW, 98107, SAN 363-972X. Tel:
206-684-4089. E-mail: ballard@spl.org. *Interim Br Mgr,* Dave Valencia;
Staff 14 (MLS 4.1, Non-MLS 9.9)
Founded 1907
Library Holdings: Bk Vols 62,518
Open Mon & Tues 1-8, Wed & Thurs 10-8, Fri & Sat 10-6, Sun 12-5
Friends of the Library Group
BEACON HILL, 2821 Beacon Ave S, 98144, SAN 363-9665. Tel:
206-684-4711. E-mail: beaconhill@spl.org. *Br Mgr,* Wei Cai
Founded 1945
Library Holdings: Bk Vols 28,994
Open Mon & Tues 1-8, Wed & Thurs 10-8, Fri & Sat 10-6, Sun 12-5
Friends of the Library Group
BROADVIEW, 12755 Greenwood Ave N, 98133, SAN 363-9754. Tel:
206-684-7519. *Br Mgr,* Lisa Scharnhorst; E-mail:
lisa.scharnhorst@spl.org; Staff 9.7 (MLS 3.4, Non-MLS 6.3)
Founded 1944
Library Holdings: Bk Vols 45,903
Open Mon & Tues 1-8, Wed & Thurs 10-8, Fri & Sat 10-6, Sun 12-5
Friends of the Library Group
CAPITOL HILL, 425 Harvard Ave E, 98102, SAN 363-9576. Tel:
206-684-4715. *Br Mgr,* Nancy Slote; E-mail: nancy.slote@spl.org
Founded 1954
Library Holdings: Bk Vols 37,283
Open Mon & Tues 1-8, Wed & Thurs 10-8, Fri & Sat 10-6, Sun 12-5
Friends of the Library Group
COLUMBIA, 4721 Rainier Ave S, 98118, SAN 363-9932. Tel:
206-386-1908. *Regional Mgr,* Wei Cai; Staff 9 (MLS 2.8, Non-MLS 6.2)
Founded 1909
Library Holdings: Bk Vols 38,957
Open Mon & Tues 1-8, Wed, Thurs & Sat 11-6
Friends of the Library Group
DELRIDGE, 5423 Delridge Way SW, 98106, SAN 377-7502. *Regional
Mgr,* Jane Appling
Library Holdings: Bk Vols 15,819
Friends of the Library Group
DOUGLASS-TRUTH, 2300 E Yesler Way, 98122, SAN 363-9967. Tel:
206-684-4704. *Br Mgr,* Position Currently Open
Founded 1914
Library Holdings: Bk Vols 45,231
Open Mon & Tues 1-8, Wed & Thurs 10-8, Fri & Sat 10-6, Sun 12-5
Friends of the Library Group
FREMONT, 731 N 35th St, 98103, SAN 363-9789. Tel: 206-684-4084.
Regional Mgr, Dave Valencia; Staff 4.65 (MLS 1.8, Non-MLS 2.85)
Founded 1902
Library Holdings: Bk Vols 20,557
Open Mon & Tues 1-8, Wed, Thurs & Sat 11-6
Friends of the Library Group

GREEN LAKE, 7364 E Green Lake Dr N, 98115, SAN 363-9541. Tel:
206-684-7547. *Regional Mgr,* Karen Spiel
Founded 1905
Library Holdings: Bk Vols 32,328
Open Mon & Tues 1-8, Wed, Thurs & Sat 11-6
Friends of the Library Group
GREENWOOD, 8016 Greenwood Ave N, 98103, SAN 363-9819. Tel:
206-684-4086. *Br Mgr,* Francesca Wainwright; E-mail:
francesca.wainwright@spl.org
Founded 1928
Library Holdings: Bk Vols 42,460
Open Mon & Tues 1-8, Wed & Thurs 10-8, Fri & Sat 10-6, Sun 12-5
Friends of the Library Group
HIGH POINT, 3411 SW Raymond St, 98126, SAN 323-9942. Tel:
206-684-7454. *Regional Mgr,* Jane Appling
Founded 1942
Library Holdings: Bk Vols 22,672
Open Mon & Tues 1-8, Wed, Thurs & Sat 11-6
Friends of the Library Group
INTERNATIONAL DISTRICT/CHINATOWN, 713 Eighth Ave S, 98104.
Tel: 206-386-1300. *Regional Mgr,* Wei Cai; Staff 8 (MLS 3, Non-MLS
5)
Founded 2005
Library Holdings: Bk Vols 10,047
Open Mon & Tues 1-8, Wed, Thurs & Sat 11-6
Friends of the Library Group
LAKE CITY, 12501 28th Ave NE, 98125, SAN 363-9606. Tel:
206-684-7518. *Br Mgr,* Andy Bates; E-mail: andrew.bates@spl.org; Staff
12.4 (MLS 3.8, Non-MLS 8.6)
Founded 1935
Library Holdings: Bk Vols 54,739
Open Mon & Tues 1-8, Wed & Thurs 10-8, Fri & Sat 10-6, Sun 12-5
Friends of the Library Group
MADRONA-SALLY GOLDMARK BRANCH, 1134 33rd Ave, 98122,
SAN 323-9888. Tel: 206-684-4705. *Regional Mgr,* Andy Bates
Founded 1971
Library Holdings: Bk Vols 12,623
Open Mon & Tues 1-8, Wed, Thurs & Sat 11-6
Friends of the Library Group
MAGNOLIA, 2801 34th Ave W, 98199, SAN 363-9843. Tel:
206-386-4225. *Regional Mgr,* Dave Valencia
Founded 1943
Library Holdings: Bk Vols 28,916
Open Mon & Tues 1-8, Wed, Thurs & Sat 11-6
Friends of the Library Group
MONTLAKE, 2401 24th Ave E, 98112, SAN 323-9985. Tel:
206-684-4720. *Br Mgr,* Nancy Slote; E-mail: nancy.slote@spl.org
Founded 1944
Library Holdings: Bk Vols 13,737
Open Mon & Tues 1-8, Wed & Thurs 10-8, Fri & Sat 10-6
Friends of the Library Group
NEWHOLLY, 7058 32nd Ave S, 98118, SAN 323-9969. Tel:
206-386-1905. *Regional Mgr,* Wei Cai
Founded 1943
Library Holdings: Bk Vols 15,793
Open Mon & Tues 1-8, Wed, Thurs & Sat 11-6
Friends of the Library Group
NORTH EAST, 6801 35th Ave NE, 98115, SAN 363-9630. Tel:
206-684-7539. *Regional Mgr,* Francesca Wainwright
Founded 1945
Library Holdings: Bk Vols 63,213
Open Mon & Tues 1-8, Wed, Thurs & Sat 11-6, Sun 1-5
Friends of the Library Group
NORTHGATE, 10548 Fifth Ave NE, 98125. Tel: 206-386-1980. *Regional
Mgr,* Francesca Wainwright
Founded 2003
Library Holdings: Bk Vols 25,396
Open Mon & Tues 1-8, Wed, Thurs & Sat 11-6
Friends of the Library Group
QUEEN ANNE BRANCH, 400 W Garfield St, 98119, SAN 363-9878. Tel:
206-386-4227. *Br Mgr,* Bob Hageman; E-mail: bob.hageman@spl.org
Founded 1914
Library Holdings: Bk Vols 30,202
Open Mon & Tues 1-8, Wed & Thurs 10-8, Fri & Sat 10-6
Friends of the Library Group
RAINIER BEACH, 9125 Rainier Ave S, 98118, SAN 363-9983. Tel:
206-386-1906. *Br Mgr,* Daria Cal; E-mail: daria.cal@spl.org
Founded 1912
Library Holdings: Bk Vols 47,096
Open Mon & Tues 1-8, Wed & Thurs 10-8, Fri & Sat 10-6, Sun 12-5
Friends of the Library Group
SOUTH PARK, 8604 Eighth Ave S, 98108. Tel: 206-615-1688. FAX:
206-615-0539. *Regional Mgr,* Jane Appling; Staff 1 (MLS 1)
Founded 2006
Library Holdings: Bk Vols 18,700

Automation Activity & Vendor Info: (Cataloging) Horizon; (Circulation) Horizon

Function: Adult bk club, Bilingual assistance for Spanish patrons, Bks on CD, Children's prog, Computer training, Computers for patron use, Copy machines, Electronic databases & coll, Family literacy, Homework prog, Magnifiers for reading, Music CDs, Outreach serv, Outside serv via phone, mail, e-mail & web, OverDrive digital audio bks, Photocopying/Printing, Preschool outreach, Prog for children & young adult, Pub access computers, Ref serv available, Story hour, Summer reading prog, Tax forms, Telephone ref, Web-catalog, Wheelchair accessible

Open Mon & Tues 1-8, Wed, Thurs & Sat 11-6
Friends of the Library Group

SOUTHWEST, 9010 35th Ave SW, 98126, SAN 363-9991. Tel: 206-684-7455. *Regional Mgr,* Jane Appling
Founded 1945
Library Holdings: Bk Vols 35,235
Open Mon-Thurs 10-8, Fri & Sat 10-6, Sun 1-5
Friends of the Library Group

UNIVERSITY BRANCH, 5009 Roosevelt Way NE, 98105. Tel: 206-684-4063.
Founded 1910
Library Holdings: Bk Vols 35,987
Open Mon & Tues 1-8, Wed, Thurs & Sat 11-6
Friends of the Library Group

WALLINGFORD, 1501 N 45th St, 98103, SAN 323-9926. Tel: 206-684-4088. *Regional Mgr,* Karen Spiel
Founded 1948
Library Holdings: Bk Vols 12,067
Open Mon & Tues 1-8, Wed, Thurs & Sat 11-6
Friends of the Library Group

WASHINGTON TALKING BOOK & BRAILLE
See Separate Entry under Washington Talking Book & Braille Library

WEST SEATTLE BRANCH, 2306 42nd Ave SW, 98116, SAN 364-0027. Tel: 206-684-7444. *Regional Mgr,* Jane Appling; Staff 9.8 (MLS 2.9, Non-MLS 6.9)
Founded 1910
Library Holdings: Bk Vols 38,785
Open Mon & Tues 1-8, Wed & Thurs 10-8, Fri & Sat 10-6, Sun 1-5
Friends of the Library Group

SEATTLE UNIVERSITY

C   A A LEMIEUX LIBRARY*, 901 12th Ave, 98122-4411. (Mail add: PO Box 222000, 98122-1090), SAN 317-6401. Tel: 206-296-6222. Circulation Tel: 206-296-6233. Interlibrary Loan Service Tel: 206-296-6359. Reference Tel: 206-296-6230. Automation Services Tel: 206-296-6228. FAX: 206-296-2572. Interlibrary Loan Service FAX: 206-296-6224. Web Site: www.seattleu.edu/lemlib. *Univ Librn,* John Popko; Tel: 206-296-6201, E-mail: jpopko@seattleu.edu; *Dir, Instrul & Pub Serv,* Judy Solberg; Tel: 206-296-6274, E-mail: solbergj@seattleu.edu; *Circ Mgr,* Holly Sturgeon; Tel: 206-296-6234, E-mail: sturgeon@seattleu.edu; Staff 11 (MLS 11)
Enrl 4,909; Highest Degree: Doctorate
Library Holdings: Bk Vols 216,677; Per Subs 1,604
Subject Interests: Educ, Relig studies, Software eng
Automation Activity & Vendor Info: (Acquisitions) SirsiDynix
Partic in Association of Jesuit Colleges & Universities (AJCU); Northwest Association of Private Colleges & Universities Libraries; OCLC Online Computer Library Center, Inc; Puget Sound Acad Independent Librs
Publications: Serials List

CL   SCHOOL OF LAW LIBRARY, Sullivan Hall, 901 12th Ave, 98122-4411. (Mail add: PO Box 222000, 98122-1090), SAN 364-2429. Tel: 206-398-4221. Interlibrary Loan Service Tel: 206-398-4227. Reference Tel: 206-398-4225. FAX: 206-398-4194. Web Site: law.seattleu.edu/library.xml. *Dir,* Kristin Cheney; *Coll Develop,* Kara Phillips; *Ref,* Tina Ching; *Ref,* Barbara Swatt Engstrom; *Ref,* Kerry Fitz-Gerald; *Ref,* Kelly Kunsch; *Ref,* Bob Menanteaux; *Ref,* Stephanie Wilson; *Tech Serv,* Kent Milunovich; Staff 18 (MLS 9, Non-MLS 9)
Founded 1972. Enrl 896; Fac 60; Highest Degree: Doctorate
Jul 2012-Jun 2013 Income $2,562,208. Mats Exp $1,264,756. Sal $1,297,452
Library Holdings: Microforms 109,561; Bk Titles 55,300; Bk Vols 171,896
Special Collections: US Document Depository
Automation Activity & Vendor Info: (Acquisitions) Innovative Interfaces, Inc; (Cataloging) Innovative Interfaces, Inc; (Circulation) Innovative Interfaces, Inc; (OPAC) Innovative Interfaces, Inc; (Serials) Innovative Interfaces, Inc
Partic in New England Law Library Consortium, Inc; OCLC Online Computer Library Center, Inc; Orbis Cascade Alliance

S   SHANNON & WILSON, INC*, Technical Library, 400 N 34th St, Ste 100, 98103-8636. (Mail add: PO Box 300303, 98103-9703), SAN 317-6428. Tel: 206-695-6821. FAX: 206-695-6777. *Coop Librn,* Judith Bloch; E-mail: jab@shanwil.com; Staff 1 (MLS 1)
Founded 1965
Library Holdings: Bk Titles 6,500; Bk Vols 7,000; Per Subs 170
Subject Interests: Environ eng, Geol, Geotech eng, Rock mechanics
Partic in OCLC Online Computer Library Center, Inc

L   SHORT, CRESSMAN & BURGESS*, Law Library, 999 Third Ave, Ste 3000, 98104-4008. SAN 323-5785. Tel: 206-682-3333, Ext 5555, 206-682-3333, Ext 5873. FAX: 206-340-8856. *In Charge,* Alexander Kern; E-mail: akern@scblaw.com; Staff 2 (MLS 1, Non-MLS 1)
Library Holdings: Bk Vols 6,000; Per Subs 140
Subject Interests: Real estate
Automation Activity & Vendor Info: (Cataloging) Inmagic, Inc.
Database Vendor: Dialog, LexisNexis

J   SOUTH SEATTLE COMMUNITY COLLEGE*, Library & Learning Center, 6000 16th Ave SW, 98106-1499. SAN 317-6444. Tel: 206-764-5395. Reference Tel: 206-768-6408. FAX: 206-763-5155. Web Site: dept.seattlecolleges.com/sslib. *Dean, Instrul Res,* Mary Jo White; Tel: 206-768-6400, E-mail: mwhite@sccd.ctc.edu; *Website Mgr,* Shireen Deboo; Tel: 206-768-6847, E-mail: sdeboo@sccd.ctc.edu; *Circ,* J Gorup; Tel: 206-768-6404, E-mail: jgorup@sccd.ctc.edu; *Ref,* Randy Nelson; Tel: 206-768-6405, E-mail: rnelson@sccd.ctc.edu; *Ref,* Esther Sunde; Tel: 206-768-6663, E-mail: esunde@sccd.ctc.edu; Staff 4 (MLS 4)
Founded 1971. Enrl 6,000; Fac 170
Library Holdings: Bk Vols 33,081; Per Subs 650
Special Collections: Landscape-Horticulture, bk, flm, micro & pamphlets
Subject Interests: Automotive, Aviation, Secretarial
Automation Activity & Vendor Info: (Acquisitions) Ex Libris Group; (Cataloging) Ex Libris Group; (Circulation) Ex Libris Group; (Course Reserve) Ex Libris Group; (Media Booking) Ex Libris Group; (OPAC) Ex Libris Group; (Serials) Ex Libris Group
Database Vendor: OCLC FirstSearch
Wireless access
Special Services for the Blind - Braille servs; VisualTek equip

L   STOEL, RIVES, BOLEY, JONES & GREY*, Law Library, One Union Sq, 600 University St, Ste 3600, 98101. SAN 372-3615. Tel: 206-386-7502. FAX: 206-386-7500. *Librn,* Marina Parascenzo-Brush
Library Holdings: Bk Vols 2,000
Database Vendor: OCLC FirstSearch
Restriction: Staff use only

M   SWEDISH MEDICAL CENTER LIBRARY*, First Hill Campus, 747 Broadway, 98122-4307. SAN 317-6452. Tel: 206-386-2484. FAX: 206-215-3081. Web Site: www.swedishmedical.org/library.html. *Mgr,* Sandy Norris; E-mail: sandy.norris@swedish.org; *Med Librn,* Bob Hollowell; E-mail: bob.hollowell@swedish.org; *Libr Syst Coordr,* Mike Scully; E-mail: mike.scully@swedish.org
Founded 1910
Library Holdings: Bk Vols 2,500; Per Subs 375
Special Collections: CIBA Coll, slides; Gower Coll, slides
Subject Interests: Hospital admin, Med, Nursing, Surgery
Publications: Pacific Northwest Library Identifier Codes: Directory and Key
Partic in Colorado Council of Medical Librarians; Dialog Corp
Open Mon-Fri 8-4:30

SR   TEMPLE DE HIRSCH SINAI LIBRARY*, 1511 E Pike, 98122. SAN 326-7199. Tel: 206-315-7398. FAX: 206-324-6772. E-mail: library@tdhs-nw.org. Web Site: www.tdhs-nw.org. *Head Librn,* Toby Harris. Subject Specialists: *Judaica,* Toby Harris; Staff 2 (MLS 1, Non-MLS 1)
Founded 1908
Jul 2006-Jun 2007. Mats Exp $1,500. Sal $22,500
Library Holdings: CDs 175; Large Print Bks 20; Bk Titles 8,000; Bk Vols 10,500; Per Subs 20; Talking Bks 35
Special Collections: Benjamin Zukor Children's Library; Historical Coll; Music Coll
Subject Interests: Hist, Holocaust, Judaism
Automation Activity & Vendor Info: (Cataloging) Follett Software; (Circulation) Follett Software
Open Thurs 10-6, Sun 9-12:30
Branches:
BELLEVUE BRANCH, 3850 156th Ave SE, Bellevue, 98006. Tel: 206-323-8486, Ext 7481. E-mail: library@tdhs-nw.org. Web Site: www.tdhs-nw.org/learning/special_programs.php3. *Lead Librn,* Toby Harris. Subject Specialists: *Children, Judaica,* Toby Harris; Staff 2 (MLS 1, Non-MLS 1)
Subject Interests: Hist, Holocaust, Judaism

A   UNITED STATES ARMY CORPS OF ENGINEERS*, Seattle District Library, 4735 E Marginal Way, 98134. (Mail add: PO Box 3755, 98124-3755), SAN 364-0051. Tel: 206-316-3728. FAX: 206-766-6444. E-mail: cenws.library@nws02.usace.army.mil. Web Site: www.nws.usace.army.mil. *Librn,* Shelly Trulson; E-mail: shelly.r.trulson@usace.army.mil
Founded 1940
Library Holdings: Bk Titles 12,000; Bk Vols 25,000; Per Subs 300
Subject Interests: Eng, Environment, Law
Automation Activity & Vendor Info: (Cataloging) EOS International; (Circulation) EOS International; (ILL) OCLC; (OPAC) EOS International; (Serials) EOS International
Database Vendor: OCLC FirstSearch
Partic in OCLC Online Computer Library Center, Inc
Open Mon-Fri 6:30am-3pm

GL   UNITED STATES COURTS LIBRARY, 700 Stewart St, Rm 19105, 98101. SAN 317-6460. Tel: 206-370-8975. FAX: 206-370-8976. *Librn,* Timothy Sheehy; *Asst Librn,* Sarah Griffith; *Asst Librn,* Janice Olson; *Libr Tech,* Barbara Morrison; Staff 4 (MLS 3, Non-MLS 1)
Founded 1939
Library Holdings: Bk Titles 2,400; Bk Vols 42,000; Per Subs 1,400
Special Collections: US Document Depository
Subject Interests: Law fed states, Ninth circuit states
Automation Activity & Vendor Info: (Acquisitions) SirsiDynix; (Cataloging) SirsiDynix; (OPAC) SirsiDynix
Function: ILL available
Open Mon-Fri 12:30-4:30
Restriction: Circ limited

G   UNITED STATES DEPARTMENT OF LABOR*, Occupational Safety & Health Administration Library - Region X, 1111 Third Ave, Ste 715, 98101-3212. SAN 322-709X. Tel: 206-553-5930. FAX: 206-553-6499. *Tech Info Spec,* Laura Tippetts
Founded 1971
Library Holdings: Bk Titles 1,600
Subject Interests: Eng, Safety, Toxicology
Publications: Research Resources; Standards Interpretations Index
Open Mon-Fri 8-4
Restriction: Non-circulating

G   UNITED STATES ENVIRONMENTAL PROTECTION AGENCY*, Region 10 Library, 1200 Sixth Ave, Mail-Stop OMP-104, 98101. SAN 317-5987. Tel: 206-553-1289. FAX: 206-553-6346. E-mail: library-reg10@epa.gov. Web Site: www.epa.gov/libraries/region10.html. *Supvry Librn,* Liz Doyle; Tel: 206-553-2134, E-mail: doyle.liz@epa.gov; Staff 3 (MLS 1, Non-MLS 2)
Library Holdings: Bk Vols 10,000; Per Subs 165
Special Collections: EPA reports, working papers
Subject Interests: Air pollution, Ecosystems, Environ law, Environ mgt, Hazardous mat, Solid waste mgt, Water pollution
Partic in OCLC Online Computer Library Center, Inc
Open Mon-Fri 9-12 & 1-4

S   UNIVERSITY OF WASHINGTON BOTANIC GARDENS, Elisabeth C Miller Library, 3501 NE 41st St, 98105. (Mail add: PO Box 354115, 98195-4115), SAN 328-0918. Tel: 206-543-0415. Reference Tel: 206-897-5268. FAX: 206-897-1435. E-mail: hortlib@u.washington.edu. Web Site: www.millerlibrary.org. *Curator, Mgr,* Brian Thompson; E-mail: bthomp@u.washington.edu; *Info Tech,* Tracy Mehlin; E-mail: tmehlin@u.washington.edu; Staff 2.5 (MLS 2.5)
Founded 1985
Library Holdings: Bk Vols 15,000; Per Subs 400
Special Collections: Seed Catalogs
Subject Interests: Botany, Gardening, Hort, Landscape design
Database Vendor: EBSCOhost
Wireless access
Function: Archival coll, Children's prog, Online cat, Prof lending libr, Ref serv available, Story hour
Partic in OCLC Online Computer Library Center, Inc
Open Mon Noon-8, Tues-Fri 9-5, Sat 9-3

C   UNIVERSITY OF WASHINGTON LIBRARIES*, Allen Library, 4th Flr, Rm 482, Box 352900, 98195-2900. SAN 364-0086. Tel: 206-543-1760. Interlibrary Loan Service Tel: 206-543-1878. Information Services Tel: 206-543-0242. FAX: 206-685-8727. Interlibrary Loan Service FAX: 206-685-8049. Web Site: www.lib.washington.edu. *Dean, Univ Libr,* Lizabeth A Wilson; Tel: 206-543-1763, E-mail: betsyw@u.washington.edu; *Sr Assoc Dean, Univ Libr,* Charles E Chamberlin; Tel: 206-685-1978, E-mail: cecuwa@u.washington.edu; *Head, Monographic Serv,* Joseph A Kiegel; Tel: 206-685-2298, Fax: 206-685-8782, E-mail: kiegel@u.washington.edu; *Circ Mgr,* Kirsten Spillum; Tel: 206-685-3987, Fax: 206-685-6972, E-mail: kirsten@u.washington.edu; *Head, Govt Doc,* Eleanor L Chase; Tel: 206-543-1937, E-mail: echase@u.washington.edu;

Head, Ref & Res Serv, Nancy Huling; Tel: 206-685-2211, E-mail: huling@uwashington.edu; *Ser,* James S Stickman; E-mail: stickman@uwashington.edu; *Head, Spec Coll,* Carla T Rickerson; Tel: 206-685-4480, Fax: 206-543-1931, E-mail: crick@uwashington.edu. Subject Specialists: *Slavic hist & lit,* Michael E Biggins; *SE Asia,* Judith Henchy; Staff 138 (MLS 138)
Founded 1861. Highest Degree: Doctorate
Library Holdings: Bk Vols 6,000,000; Per Subs 50,245
Special Collections: 19th Century American Literature; Architectural Drawings (Seattle & Puget Sound); Book Arts; Can & European Communities; Early Recorded Vocal Music (Eric Offenbacher Mozart Coll); Hans Christian Anderson; Historical Children's Literature; Historical Photography (particularly western Washington, Alaska & Yukon); Pacific Northwest & Alaska; Pacific Northwest Native Americans; Pacific Northwest Poets; Papers of Richard Hugo, Theodore Roethke, Anna Louise Strong, Mark Tobey, Senator Henry M Jackson, Senator Warren G Magnuson & other 20th Century Senators & Representatives from Washington State; Rowing Books; Seattle Jewish Archives; Seattle Theater Programs; Travel & Exploration; William Blake; William Butler Yeats; Wind Instrument Records (Melvin Harris Coll). Oral History; State Document Depository; UN Document Depository; US Document Depository
Automation Activity & Vendor Info: (Acquisitions) Innovative Interfaces, Inc; (Cataloging) Innovative Interfaces, Inc; (Circulation) Innovative Interfaces, Inc; (Serials) Innovative Interfaces, Inc
Database Vendor: Innovative Interfaces, Inc INN - View
Publications: Library Directions
Partic in Association of Research Libraries (ARL); OCLC Online Computer Library Center, Inc
Open Mon-Fri 8-5
Friends of the Library Group
Departmental Libraries:
ARCHITECTURE-URBAN PLANNING, 334 Gould Hall, Box 355730, 98195-5730, SAN 364-0175. Tel: 206-543-4067. E-mail: arch@lib.washington.edu. *Libr Supvr-Popular Libr,* Noreen Jacky; E-mail: noreen@u.washington.edu; *Head Librn,* Alan R Michelson; Tel: 206-543-7091, E-mail: alanmich@u.washington.edu
Library Holdings: Bk Vols 41,357
Subject Interests: Archit, Construction mgt, Landscape archit, Urban design, Urban planning
Open Mon-Thurs (Fall) 8am-9pm, Fri 8-5, Sat & Sun 1-5; Mon-Fri (Summer) 9-5
Friends of the Library Group
ART, 101 Art Bldg, Box 353440, 98195, SAN 364-0205. Tel: 206-543-0648. E-mail: art@lib.washington.edu. Web Site: www.lib.washington.edu. *Actg Head,* Angela Weaver; E-mail: aw6@u.washington.edu
Library Holdings: Bk Vols 44,000
DRAMA, Hutchinson Hall, Rm 145, Box 353950, 98195-3950, SAN 364-0299. Tel: 206-543-5148. FAX: 206-543-8512. E-mail: drama@lib.washington.edu. *Head Librn,* Angela Weaver; Tel: 206-685-3693, E-mail: aw6@u.washington.edu; *Lead Libr Tech,* Patrick Scheible; Tel: 206-685-3693, E-mail: kkt@u.washington.edu
Library Holdings: Bk Vols 29,600
Special Collections: Acting Editions of Plays
Friends of the Library Group
EAST ASIA, 322 Gowen Hall, 3rd Flr, Box 353527, 98195-3527, SAN 364-0329. Tel: 206-543-4490. FAX: 206-221-5298. E-mail: ealcirc@lib.washington.edu. *Dir,* Zhijia Shen; Tel: 206-543-5635, E-mail: zhijia@u.washington.edu; *Supvr, Circ,* Richard Carkeek; E-mail: rcarkeek@u.washington.edu; Staff 12 (MLS 6, Non-MLS 6)
Founded 1937. Highest Degree: Doctorate
Library Holdings: Bk Vols 450,811; Per Subs 2,728
Open Mon-Thurs (Fall) 8-8, Fri 8-5, Sat & Sun 1-5; Mon-Fri (Summer) 9-5, Sat & Sun 1-5
Friends of the Library Group
ENGINEERING LIBRARY, Engineering Library Bldg, Box 352170, 98195-2170, SAN 364-0353. Tel: 206-543-0740. Circulation Tel: 206-685-8324. Reference Tel: 206-543-0741. FAX: 206-543-3305. E-mail: englib@u.washington.edu. Web Site: www.lib.washington.edu/engineering. *Head Librn,* Mel DeSart; Tel: 206-685-8369, E-mail: desart@u.washington.edu; *Asst Head Librn,* Christina A Byrne; Tel: 206-685-8371, E-mail: cbyrne@u.washington.edu; *Circ Supvr,* Laura J H Leslie; E-mail: lhall@u.washington.edu; *Circ Supvr,* Steve Stockamp; E-mail: stockamp@u.washington.edu; *Lead Libr Tech,* Thomas Leahey; Tel: 206-543-5107, E-mail: tleahey@u.washington.edu
Library Holdings: Bk Vols 164,536; Per Subs 3,136
Special Collections: ACM Depository Coll; Technical Reports; United States Patent & Depository Library
Open Mon-Thurs (Fall) 8am-10pm, Fri 8-6, Sat 9-5, Sun 1-10; Mon-Thurs (Summer) 8-7, Fri 8-5, Sat & Sun 1-5
Friends of the Library Group

FISHERIES-OCEANOGRAPHY, 151 Oceanography Teaching Bldg, Box 357952, 98195-7952, SAN 364-0388. Tel: 206-543-4279. FAX: 206-543-4909. E-mail: fishlib@u.washington.edu. Web Site: www.lib.washington.edu/fish. *Head Librn,* Louise M Richards; E-mail: machung@u.washington.edu
Library Holdings: Bk Vols 66,834
Open Mon-Thurs (Fall) 8am-9pm, Fri 8-5, Sat & Sun 1-5; Mon-Fri (Summer) 8-5
Friends of the Library Group

FOSTER BUSINESS, Bank of America Exec Educ Ctr, Rm 013, Box 353224, 98195-3224, SAN 364-023X. Tel: 206-543-4360. FAX: 206-616-6430. E-mail: buslib@u.washington.edu. *Head Librn,* Gordon Aamot; Staff 8 (MLS 4, Non-MLS 4)
Library Holdings: Bk Vols 76,337

FRIDAY HARBOR, 620 University Rd, Box 352900, Friday Harbor, 98250-2900. Tel: 206-616-0758. FAX: 206-543-1273. E-mail: frihar@u.washington.edu. Web Site: www.lib.washington.edu/fhl. *Actg Head Librn,* Maureen D Nolan; Tel: 206-685-2126, Fax: 206-685-3892, E-mail: nolan@u.washington.edu; Staff 2 (MLS 1, Non-MLS 1)
Library Holdings: Bk Vols 18,000
Function: For res purposes
Open Mon-Thurs (Fall) 7:30am-10pm, Fri 7:30-6, Sat 9-5, Sun Noon-10pm; Mon-Thurs (Summer) 8am-10pm, Fri 8-5, Sat & Sun 1-5
Friends of the Library Group

CL   MARIAN GOULD GALLAGHER LAW LIBRARY, William H Gates Hall, Box 353025, 98195-3025, SAN 364-0531. Circulation Tel: 206-543-4086. Interlibrary Loan Service Tel: 206-543-4262. Reference Tel: 206-543-6794. Administration Tel: 206-543-4089. FAX: 206-685-2165. Web Site: lib.law.washington.edu. *Assoc Dean of Libr & Tech,* Penny A Hazelton; E-mail: pennyh@u.washington.edu; *Assoc Law Librn,* Jonathan Franklin; E-mail: jafrank@u.washington.edu; *Cat Librn,* Patricia Hart; Tel: 206-543-6516, E-mail: hart@u.washington.edu; *Coll Develop Librn,* Reba Turnquist; Tel: 206-543-4098, E-mail: rct@u.washington.edu; *Coll Develop/Ref Librn,* Peggy Jarrett; E-mail: pjarrett@u.washington.edu; *Ref Librn,* Sherry Leysen; Tel: 206-685-4084, E-mail: sleysen@uw.edu; *Ref Librn,* Trinie Thai-Parker; Tel: 206-685-4476, E-mail: trinie@uw.edu; *Ref Librn,* Mary Whisner; Tel: 206-543-7672, E-mail: whisner@u.washington.edu; *Ref Librn,* Alena Wolotira; Tel: 206-685-4812, E-mail: alenaw@uw.edu; *Res Sharing Librn,* Judy Ann Davis; Tel: 206-543-4262, E-mail: davisja@u.washington.edu; *Supvr, Circ,* Vickie Northington; Tel: 206-685-9459, E-mail: vcn@u.washington.edu; *Coordr, East Asian Libr Serv,* Rob Britt; Tel: 206-543-7447, E-mail: rrbritt@uw.edu; *Info Syst Coordr,* Richard Jost; Tel: 206-685-4980, E-mail: rmjost@u.washington.edu; *Coordr of Ref Serv,* Cheryl Nyberg; Tel: 206-685-4924, E-mail: cnyberg@u.washington.edu; *Coordr, Tech Serv,* Ann Nez; Tel: 206-543-6516, E-mail: acnez@u.washington.edu. Subject Specialists: *East Asian legal mat,* Rob Britt; Staff 32 (MLS 14, Non-MLS 18)
Founded 1899. Enrl 715; Fac 50; Highest Degree: Doctorate
Library Holdings: Bk Titles 179,568; Per Subs 5,273
Special Collections: East Asian Legal Materials; Washington State Legal Materials - Historical & Current. US Document Depository
Subject Interests: Indian law, Librarianship, Water law
Automation Activity & Vendor Info: (Acquisitions) Innovative Interfaces, Inc; (Cataloging) Innovative Interfaces, Inc; (Circulation) Innovative Interfaces, Inc; (OPAC) Innovative Interfaces, Inc; (Serials) Innovative Interfaces, Inc
Database Vendor: Gale Cengage Learning, LexisNexis, OCLC FirstSearch
Function: Computers for patron use, Copy machines, Doc delivery serv, Electronic databases & coll, Exhibits, ILL available, Learning ctr, Magnifiers for reading, Online cat, Online ref, Online searches, Photocopying/Printing, Pub access computers, Ref serv available, Ref serv in person
Partic in OCLC Online Computer Library Center, Inc; Orbis Cascade Alliance
Publications: Current Index to Legal Periodicals; Marian Gould Gallagher Library Publication Series
Open Mon-Thurs (Spring-Fall) 8am-11pm, Fri 8-6, Sat 11-6, Sun 11-11; Mon-Wed (Summer) 8-7, Thurs & Fri 8-5, Sun 11-6
Restriction: 24-hr pass syst for students only
Friends of the Library Group

CM   HEALTH SCIENCES LIBRARY, T-334 Health Sciences Bldg, Box 357155, 1959 NE Pacific St, 98195-7155, SAN 364-0507. Tel: 206-543-3390. Interlibrary Loan Service Tel: 206-543-1878. FAX: 206-543-3389. E-mail: hsl@u.washington.edu. Web Site: healthlinks.washington.edu. *Actg Assoc Dean, Actg Dir,* Neil Rambo; Tel: 206-543-5531, E-mail: nrambo@uw.edu; *Assoc Dir,* Nanette Welton; Tel: 206-543-5112, E-mail: nwelton@uw.edu; Staff 28 (MLS 21, Non-MLS 7)
Founded 1949
Special Collections: History of Medicine
Subject Interests: Allied health, Dentistry, Med, Nursing, Pharm, Pub health

Partic in Greater Western Library Alliance; National Network of Libraries of Medicine; OCLC Online Computer Library Center, Inc; Orbis Cascade Alliance
Friends of the Library Group

MAP COLLECTION & CARTOGRAPHIC INFORMATION SERVICES, Suzzallo/Allen Library, Basement, Universtiy of Washington, Box 352900, 98195-2900, SAN 329-3556. Tel: 206-543-9392. FAX: 206-685-8049. E-mail: maplib@u.washington.edu. *Librn,* Matthew Parsons; E-mail: parsonsm@u.washington.edu; *Librn,* Anne Zald; Tel: 206-543-2725, E-mail: zald@u.washington.edu
Library Holdings: Bk Vols 3,966
Special Collections: Aerial Photography of Washington State, 1944 to present; US Geological Survey Topographic Maps
Subject Interests: Atlases, Geog Info Systs

MATHEMATICS RESEARCH LIBRARY, C-306 Padelford Hall, 98195. (Mail add: Box 354350, 98195-4350), SAN 364-0566. Tel: 206-543-7296. E-mail: mathlib@uw.edu. Web Site: www.lib.washington.edu/math. *Head Librn,* Faye Christenberry; E-mail: fayec@uw.edu; *Lead Libr Tech,* Saundra Martin; E-mail: skmartin@u.washington.edu. Subject Specialists: *Math, Statistics,* Faye Christenberry; Staff 1.68 (MLS 0.68, Non-MLS 1)
Library Holdings: Bk Vols 61,974
Subject Interests: Math, Statistics
Open Mon-Thurs (Winter) 9-6, Fri 9-5, Sun 1-5; Mon-Fri (Summer) 9-5
Friends of the Library Group

MEDIA CENTER, Odegaard Undergraduate Library, Mezzanine Level, Box 353080, 98195-3080. Tel: 206-543-6051. Reference Tel: 206-543-2060. FAX: 206-685-8485. E-mail: medialib@u.washington.edu. Web Site: www.lib.washington.edu/media. *Libr Supvr-Popular Libr,* Amy Halligan; E-mail: apx@u.washington.edu; *Head, Distributed Media Serv,* John Vallier; Tel: 206-618-1210, E-mail: vallier@u.washington.edu; *Computer Support Analyst 1,* G Michael Milligan; E-mail: michaelm@u.washington.edu
Open Mon-Thurs (Fall) 8am-Midnight, Fri 8am-9pm, Sat 11-9, Sun 1-Midnight; Mon-Thurs (Summer) 8am-10pm, Fri 8-5, Sat 11-5, Sun 1-10
Friends of the Library Group

MUSIC, 113 Music Bldg, Box 353450, 98195-3450, SAN 364-0590. Tel: 206-543-1159, 206-543-1168. E-mail: musiclib@u.washington.edu. Web Site: www.lib.washington.edu/music. *Head Music Libr,* Judy Tsou; Tel: 206-685-3140, E-mail: jstsou@u.washington.edu; *Circ/Reserves, Supvr,* Mary Jensen; Tel: 206-685-3140, E-mail: jensen@u.washington.edu; *Music Res Librn,* Verletta Kern; E-mail: vkern@u.washington.edu; Staff 2.4 (MLS 2.4)
Library Holdings: Bk Vols 60,437
Special Collections: American Music Coll; Harris Wind Instrument Recordings Coll; Offenbacher Mozart Coll
Subject Interests: Music
Open Mon-Thurs (Fall) 8-8, Fri 8-5, Sat & Sun 1-5; Mon-Fri (Summer) 8-5
Friends of the Library Group

NATURAL SCIENCES, Allen Library S, Ground & First Flrs, Box 352900, 98195-2900, SAN 364-0620. Tel: 206-543-1243. Reference Tel: 206-543-1244. FAX: 206-685-1665. E-mail: natsci@u.washington.edu. Web Site: www.lib.washington.edu/natsci. *Actg Head Librn,* Maureen Nolan; Tel: 206-685-2126, E-mail: nolan@u.washington.edu; *Supvr,* Chery Kinnick; Tel: 206-685-2127, E-mail: kinnick@u.washington.edu; *Ref Coordr,* Kari Anderson; Tel: 206-685-2789, E-mail: karia@u.washington.edu; *Lead Libr Tech,* Kay Douglas; E-mail: kdouglas@u.washington.edu; *Lead Libr Tech,* Teresita Guerrero; Tel: 206-685-1554, E-mail: tita@u.washington.edu
Library Holdings: Bk Vols 205,847
Open Mon-Thurs (Fall) 7:30am-10pm, Fri 7:30-6, Sat 9-5, Sun Noon-10pm; Mon-Thurs (Summer) 8am-10pm, Fri 8-5, Sat & Sun 1-5

ODEGAARD UNDERGRADUATE LIBRARY, Box 353080, 98195-3080, SAN 364-0116. Tel: 206-543-2990. Administration Tel: 206-685-3752. Automation Services Tel: 206-543-1947. FAX: 206-685-8485. Web Site: www.lib.washington.edu/ougl. *Dir,* Jill M McKinstry; Tel: 206-685-3933, E-mail: jillmck@u.washington.edu; *Ref Coordr,* Kathleen Collins; Tel: 206-685-2771, E-mail: collinsk@u.washington.edu
Founded 1972
Library Holdings: Bk Vols 180,118
Open Mon-Thurs 8am-10pm, Fri 8-5, Sat 11-5, Sun 1pm-10pm
Friends of the Library Group

PHYSICS-ASTRONOMY READING ROOM, C-620 Physics Astronomy Bldg, 3910 15th Ave NE, Box 351560, 98195-1560. (Mail add: University of Washington, Box 351560, 98195-1560), SAN 364-068X. Tel: 206-543-2988. FAX: 206-685-0635. E-mail: phylib@u.washington.edu. Web Site: www.lib.washington.edu/physics. *Head Librn,* Pamela F Yorks; E-mail: yorks@u.washington.edu. Subject Specialists: *Astronomy, Physics,* Pamela F Yorks
Library Holdings: Bk Vols 29,331
Special Collections: Sky Atlases
Subject Interests: Astronomy, Astrophysics, Physics
Open Mon-Fri 10-5
Friends of the Library Group

CM K K SHERWOOD MEDICAL LIBRARY, 104 Harborview Hall, 326 Ninth Ave, Box 359902, 98104-2499, SAN 364-0779. Tel: 206-341-4124. FAX: 206-731-8673. E-mail: hmclib@u.washington.edu. Web Site: healthlinks.washington.edu. *Librn,* Amy Harper; Tel: 206-604-9876, E-mail: alharper@u.washington.edu; Staff 2 (MLS 1, Non-MLS 1)
Founded 1964
Library Holdings: Bk Titles 200; Per Subs 20
Subject Interests: Clinical med
Open Mon-Fri 8-5
Restriction: Clients only, Not a lending libr, Staff use only, Students only
Friends of the Library Group
SOCIAL WORK, 252 Social Work Bldg, Box 354900, 15th Ave NE, 98195-4900, SAN 364-0744. Tel: 206-685-2180. FAX: 206-685-7647. E-mail: swl@u.washington.edu. Web Site: healthlinks.washington.edu/hs/. *Librn,* Angela Lee; E-mail: leea@u.washington.edu; *Lead Libr Tech,* Grace Block; E-mail: gblock@u.washington.edu
Library Holdings: Bk Vols 40,000; Per Subs 247
Subject Interests: Family, Marriage, Soc policy, Soc welfare, Soc work
Open Mon-Thurs 9-8, Fri 9-5, Sat & Sun 1-5; Mon-Thurs (Summer) 10-6, Fri 10-5, Sat & Sun 1-5
Friends of the Library Group
TACOMA LIBRARY, 1900 Commerce St, Box 358460, Tacoma, 98402-3100. Tel: 253-692-4440. Reference Tel: 253-692-4442. FAX: 253-692-4445. E-mail: taclib@u.washington.edu. Web Site: www.tacoma.washington.edu/library. *Assoc Dean, Univ Libr, Dir, Learning Res,* Charles Lord; Tel: 253-692-4444, E-mail: lord@uw.edu; *Asst Dir, Head, Coll & Access Serv,* Jennifer Sundheim; Tel: 253-692-4860, E-mail: sundheim@uw.edu; *Head, Commun Outreach,* Anna Salyer; Tel: 253-692-4448, E-mail: anna3@uw.edu; *Head, Instruction Serv,* Erica Coe; Tel: 253-692-4651, E-mail: elcoe@uw.edu; *Head, Libr Info Tech,* Timothy Bostelle; Tel: 253-692-4650, E-mail: tbostell@uw.edu; *Head, Media & Visual Res,* Justin Wadland; Tel: 253-692-5741, E-mail: jwadland@uw.edu; *Head, Ref Serv,* Suzanne Klinger; Tel: 253-692-4443, E-mail: alaura@uw.edu; *Coll Develop & Admin Serv Librn,* Position Currently Open; *Supvr, Access Serv,* Marcia Monroe; Tel: 253-692-4446, E-mail: marcy@uw.edu; *Evening Circ,* Megan Saunders; Tel: 253-692-4657, E-mail: meganes0@uw.edu; *Media Tech,* Jamal Gabobe; Tel: 253-692-4643, E-mail: jamali@uw.edu; *Ser/Reserves Tech,* Gwen Lewis Kempe; Tel: 253-692-5748, E-mail: glewis@uw.edu; *Ser Tech,* Cecil Brower; Tel: 253-692-5746, E-mail: cbrower@uw.edu
Open Mon-Thurs (Winter) 7:30am-10pm, Fri 7:30-5, Sat 9-5, Sun 10-5; Mon-Thurs (Summer) 8am-9pm, Fri 8-5, Sat 10-5
Friends of the Library Group

P WASHINGTON TALKING BOOK & BRAILLE LIBRARY*, 2021 Ninth Ave, 98121-2783. SAN 317-655X. Tel: 206-615-0400. Administration Tel: 206-386-1255. Toll Free Tel: 800-542-0866. FAX: 206-615-0437. Administration FAX: 206-615-0441. TDD: 206-615-0418. E-mail: wtbbl@wtbbl.org. Web Site: www.wtbbl.org. *Coll Develop, Dir,* Gloria Leonard; Tel: 206-386-1254, E-mail: gloria.leonard@spl.org; *Asst Mgr,* Rosemary Adamski; Staff 19 (MLS 3, Non-MLS 16)
Founded 1931
Jul 2005-Jun 2006 Income $1,350,000, State $1,022,000, Federal $328,000. Sal $792,080 (Prof $203,507)
Library Holdings: Bk Vols 311,000
Special Collections: Northwest Coll; Reference Materials on Blindness & Other Disabilities; Volunteer Produced Braille & Tapes
Automation Activity & Vendor Info: (Acquisitions) Keystone Systems, Inc (KLAS); (Cataloging) Keystone Systems, Inc (KLAS); (Circulation) Keystone Systems, Inc (KLAS); (OPAC) Keystone Systems, Inc (KLAS)
Publications: Catalog of Locally Produced Titles; Large Print Calendar; Newsletters
Special Services for the Blind - Closed circuit TV; Radio reading serv
Open Mon-Fri 8:30-5

S WOODLAND PARK ZOO LIBRARY*, 601 N 59th St, 98103. SAN 328-3453. Tel: 206-684-4840. FAX: 206-233-2663. *In Charge,* Farrell Linda
Library Holdings: Bk Titles 2,000; Per Subs 33
Special Collections: audiotapes, slides, videotapes; Information on Specific Zoos in the United States & Foreign Countries; Species Vertical File
Subject Interests: Animal behavior, Birds, Endangered species, Environ, Mammals, Zoology, Zoos
Restriction: Staff use only

SEDRO-WOOLLEY

P SEDRO-WOOLLEY PUBLIC LIBRARY*, 802 Ball Ave, 98284-2008. SAN 317-6576. Tel: 360-855-1166. Web Site: www.youseemore.com/sedro-woolley. *Librn,* Debra D Peterson; E-mail: dpeters@fidalgo.net; *Asst Librn,* Teresa J Johnson; *Ch, Youth Serv,* Kathy Brewer

Pop 10,000; Circ 85,000
Library Holdings: AV Mats 2,000; Bk Vols 50,000; Per Subs 140
Automation Activity & Vendor Info: (Cataloging) TLC (The Library Corporation); (Circulation) TLC (The Library Corporation); (OPAC) TLC (The Library Corporation)
Open Mon-Thurs Noon-8, Fri & Sat Noon-4
Friends of the Library Group

SHELTON

M MASON GENERAL HOSPITAL LIBRARY*, 901 Mountain View Dr, 98584-4401. SAN 317-6614. Tel: 360-427-3609. FAX: 360-427-1921. TDD: 360-427-9593. Web Site: www.masongeneral.com. *Educ Dir,* Tom Didonna; E-mail: tdidonna@masongeneral.com
Library Holdings: Bk Vols 475; Per Subs 20
Open Mon-Fri 8-4

SHORELINE

J SHORELINE COMMUNITY COLLEGE*, Ray W Howard Library Technology Center, 16101 Greenwood Ave N, 98133-5696. SAN 317-6436. Tel: 206-546-4556. Reference Tel: 206-546-6939. Administration Tel: 206-546-4663. FAX: 206-546-4604. Web Site: www.shoreline.edu/library. *Interim Dean,* Tom J Moran; Tel: 206-546-4774, E-mail: tmoran@shoreline.edu; *Coordr, Media Serv,* Lawrence Cheng; Tel: 206-546-4592, E-mail: lcheng@shoreline.edu; *Ser,* Leslie Potter-Henderson; Tel: 206-546-4554, E-mail: lhenders@shoreline.edu; Staff 22 (MLS 6, Non-MLS 16)
Founded 1964. Enrl 5,200; Fac 150; Highest Degree: Associate
Library Holdings: AV Mats 8,261; Bks on Deafness & Sign Lang 46; Electronic Media & Resources 11,000; High Interest/Low Vocabulary Bk Vols 2,608; Large Print Bks 27; Music Scores 300; Bk Titles 48,545; Bk Vols 59,678; Per Subs 8,000
Subject Interests: Can studies, Ethnic studies, Music
Automation Activity & Vendor Info: (Acquisitions) Ex Libris Group; (Cataloging) Ex Libris Group; (Circulation) Ex Libris Group; (Course Reserve) Ex Libris Group; (ILL) OCLC; (OPAC) Ex Libris Group; (Serials) Ex Libris Group
Database Vendor: EBSCOhost, ProQuest
Partic in ORCA Consortium
Special Services for the Deaf - TTY equip; Videos & decoder
Special Services for the Blind - Copier with enlargement capabilities; Large screen computer & software; Magnifiers; Reader equip; Ref serv; Screen reader software; VisualTek equip; ZoomText magnification & reading software
Open Mon-Thurs (Winter) 7:30am-9pm, Fri 7:30-4:30, Sat & Sun 12-6; Mon-Thurs (Summer) 8-8, Sun 12-6

SPOKANE

SR CATHOLIC DIOCESAN ARCHIVES*, 1115 W Riverside Ave, 99201. SAN 328-1450. Tel: 509-358-4293. *Libr Dir,* Sister Judith Nilles; E-mail: jnilles@dioceseofspokane.org
Library Holdings: Bk Vols 2,000
Special Collections: Church; Eastern Washington Catholic Church History Coll; Western American Coll. Oral History
Restriction: Open by appt only

GM DEPARTMENT OF VETERANS AFFAIRS*, Hospital Library, 4815 N Assembly St, 99205-2697. SAN 317-6770. Tel: 509-434-7575. FAX: 509-434-7103. E-mail: spolibrary@med.va.gov. *Mgr,* Deborah Miller; *Lead Libr Tech,* Joyce Kiphart; *Libr Tech,* Mark Overman
Founded 1951
Library Holdings: Bk Titles 3,000; Per Subs 50
Subject Interests: Med, Mgt develop
Database Vendor: EBSCOhost
Partic in Vets Admin Libr Network
Open Mon-Fri 8-4:30
Restriction: Staff use only

M EMPIRE HEALTH SERVICES*, Medical Library, 910 W Fifth Ave, 99204. (Mail add: PO Box 248, 99210-0248), SAN 317-6657. Tel: 509-473-7398. FAX: 509-473-7790. E-mail: medlib@empirehealth.org. Web Site: www.deaconessmc.org/hr_medlib.asp. *Mgr,* Arleen Libertini; E-mail: liberta@empirehealth.org; Staff 1 (MLS 1)
Founded 1937
Library Holdings: Bk Titles 2,378; Per Subs 378
Subject Interests: Med
Automation Activity & Vendor Info: (Cataloging) CyberTools for Libraries; (OPAC) CyberTools for Libraries; (Serials) CyberTools for Libraries
Database Vendor: EBSCOhost, OCLC FirstSearch, OVID Technologies, ProQuest
Partic in Inland NorthWest Health Sciences Libraries
Open Mon-Fri 8-5

C   GONZAGA UNIVERSITY*, Foley Center Library, 502 E Boone Ave, 99258-0095. SAN 364-0868. Tel: 509-323-6532. Circulation Tel: 509-323-5803. Reference Tel: 509-323-5931. FAX: 509-323-5904. Web Site: www.foley.gonzaga.edu. *Dean, Libr Serv,* Eileen Bell-Garrison; Tel: 509-323-6535, E-mail: bellgarrison@gonzaga.edu; *Asst Dean, Libr Serv,* Kathleen O'Connor; Tel: 509-313-6545, E-mail: oconnor@gonzaga.edu; *Coll Develop Librn, Head, Pub Serv,* Linda Pierce; Tel: 509-323-3834, Fax: 509-323-5806, E-mail: pierce@gonzaga.edu; *Circ Supvr,* Valerie Kitt; Tel: 509-313-6540, E-mail: kitt@gonzaga.edu; *Instruction Coordr,* Kelly Jenks; Tel: 509-313-3829, E-mail: jenks@gonzaga.edu; *Ref Coordr,* John Spencer; Tel: 509-313-6110, E-mail: spencer@gonzaga.edu; *Acq Librn,* Konny Thompson; Tel: 509-313-6546, E-mail: thompson@gonzaga.edu; *Cat Librn,* Sydney Chambers; Tel: 509-313-6537, E-mail: chambers@gonzaga.edu; *Distance Learning Librn, Ref & ILL Librn,* Theresa Kappus; Tel: 509-313-6534, E-mail: kappus@gonzaga.edu; *Spec Coll Librn,* Stephanie Plowman; Tel: 509-323-3847, E-mail: plowman@gonzaga.edu; Staff 30 (MLS 10, Non-MLS 20) Founded 1992. Enrl 4,800; Fac 340; Highest Degree: Doctorate
Library Holdings: e-books 500; e-journals 18,000; Bk Titles 250,192; Bk Vols 305,517; Per Subs 1,169
Special Collections: Bing Crosby Coll, bks, memorabilia, papers & rec; Jesuitica; Labor Unions (Jay Fox Coll); Pacific Northwest History, bks & mss; Victorian Poetry (Gerard Manley Hopkins Coll)
Subject Interests: Behav sci, Philosophy, Relig studies, Soc sci
Automation Activity & Vendor Info: (Acquisitions) Ex Libris Group; (Cataloging) Ex Libris Group; (Circulation) Ex Libris Group; (Course Reserve) Ex Libris Group; (ILL) Ex Libris Group; (OPAC) Ex Libris Group; (Serials) Ex Libris Group
Wireless access
Partic in Washington Idaho Network
Open Mon-Thurs 8am-9pm, Fri 8-5, Sat & Sun 1-5

CL   GONZAGA UNIVERSITY SCHOOL OF LAW*, Chastek Library, 721 N Cincinnati St, 99202. (Mail add: PO Box 3528, 99220-3528), SAN 364-0892. Tel: 509-323-5792. Interlibrary Loan Service Tel: 509-323-3755. Reference Tel: 509-323-3758. Administration Tel: 509-323-3782. Toll Free Tel: 800-986-9585. FAX: 509-323-5733. Interlibrary Loan Service FAX: 509-323-5882. Administration FAX: 509-323-5534. E-mail: reference@lawschool.gonzaga.edu. Web Site: www.law.gonzaga.edu/library/. *Interim Dir,* Elizabeth Thweatt; E-mail: ethweatt@lawschool.gonzaga.edu; *Head, ILL,* Carolyn Hood; Tel: 509-323-3749, E-mail: chood@lawschool.gonzaga.edu; *Head, Circ,* Cecelia McMullen; Tel: 509-323-3728; *Head, Tech Serv,* Cheryl Pritchard; Tel: 509-323-3761, Fax: 509-323-3761, E-mail: cpritchard@lawschool.gonazga.edu; *Sr Ref Librn,* Buck C Sterling; Tel: 509-323-3753, E-mail: bsterling@lawschool.gonzaga.edu; *Electronic Res,* Merri Hartse; Staff 17 (MLS 5, Non-MLS 12)
Founded 1912. Enrl 626; Fac 38; Highest Degree: Doctorate
Library Holdings: Bk Titles 34,845; Bk Vols 153,433; Per Subs 2,585
Special Collections: ABA Archives; American Indian Selected Publications; Canon Law Materials; Federal Legislative Histories; Heins American Law Institution Publications; Hein's Legal Thesis & Dissertations; Karl Llewellyn Papers; Scrapbooks of the Honorable Richard Guy; Selected 19th Century Treatises. US Document Depository
Automation Activity & Vendor Info: (Acquisitions) Ex Libris Group; (Cataloging) Ex Libris Group; (Circulation) Ex Libris Group; (Course Reserve) Ex Libris Group; (ILL) OCLC; (OPAC) Ex Libris Group; (Serials) Ex Libris Group
Database Vendor: Gale Cengage Learning, LexisNexis, OCLC FirstSearch, SerialsSolutions, Westlaw
Function: AV serv, Doc delivery serv, ILL available, Photocopying/Printing, Ref serv available, Res libr, Telephone ref, Wheelchair accessible
Publications: Adjunct Faculty User Guide (Library handbook); Faculty User Guide (Library handbook); On Point (Newsletter); Pathfinders (Research guide); Student User Guide (Library handbook)
Partic in New England Law Library Consortium, Inc; OCLC Online Computer Library Center, Inc; Washington Idaho Network
Open Mon-Thurs 7am-Midnight, Fri 7am-9pm, Sat 8am-9pm, Sun 9am-Midnight
Restriction: Circ limited, In-house use for visitors

SR   JESUIT OREGON PROVINCE ARCHIVES & LIBRARY*, Gonzaga University, Special Coll, Foley Ctr, 99258-0001. SAN 326-0119. Tel: 509-323-3814. FAX: 509-324-5904. E-mail: jopa@foley.gonzaga.edu. Web Site: www.foley.gonzaga.edu/spcoll/jopa.html. *Archivist,* David Kingma; Staff 2 (MLS 1, Non-MLS 1)
Founded 1934
Library Holdings: Bk Titles 3,500; Per Subs 12
Special Collections: Indian & Eskimo Languages (Indian Language Coll), bks, mss, microfilm; Jesuit Missions of the NW (Jesuit Missions Coll), docs, letters, photogs, microfilm
Automation Activity & Vendor Info: (Acquisitions) Ex Libris Group; (Cataloging) Ex Libris Group; (Circulation) Ex Libris Group; (Course

Reserve) Ex Libris Group; (Media Booking) Ex Libris Group; (OPAC) Ex Libris Group; (Serials) Ex Libris Group
Open Mon-Fri 8:30-4:30
Friends of the Library Group

S   NORTHWEST MUSEUM OF ART & CULTURE-EASTERN WASHINGTON STATE HISTORICAL SOCIETY, Joel E Ferris Research Library & Archives, 2316 W First Ave, 99201-1099. SAN 317-6665. Tel: 509-363-5342. FAX: 509-363-5303. E-mail: archives@northwestmuseum.org. Web Site: www.northwestmuseum.org. *Coll Librn,* Jane Davey; *Curator, Spec Coll,* Rose Krause; Staff 2 (MLS 2)
Founded 1916
Library Holdings: Bk Titles 12,000; Per Subs 20
Special Collections: Manuscript Coll; Photographic Coll. Oral History
Subject Interests: Archit, Films, Hist of mining, Inland NW hist, Plateau Indian cultures, Plateau Indian hist, Women's hist
Database Vendor: OCLC WorldCat
Function: Archival coll, Photocopying/Printing
Publications: (Nolan) A Guide to the Cutter Coll 1984; (Nolan) A Night of Terror, Devastation, and Awful Woe: the Spokane Fire of 1889 (1989); (Nolan) Frank Palmer, Scenic Photographer 1987; (Nolan) Guide to Manuscript Coll 1987; Libbys' Spokane: A Visual Retrospect 1980
Partic in OCLC Online Computer Library Center, Inc
Open Wed-Fri 12-5
Restriction: Closed stack, Non-circulating coll, Open to pub for ref only

J   SPOKANE COMMUNITY COLLEGE LIBRARY*, Mailstop 2160, Learning Resources Ctr, Bldg 16, 1810 N Greene St, 99217-5399. SAN 317-6711. Tel: 509-533-7055. Circulation Tel: 509-533-8255. Reference Tel: 509-533-8821. Toll Free Tel: 800-248-5644, Ext 7055. FAX: 509-533-7276. Web Site: www.scc.spokane.edu/?library. *Dean, Instrul Serv & Telecommunications,* Mary M Carr; Tel: 509-533-7045, E-mail: mcarr@scc.spokane.edu; *Libr Supvr-Popular Libr,* Virginia L Toland; Tel: 509-533-8170, Fax: 509-533-8818, E-mail: gtoland@scc.spokane.edu; *Ref,* Timothy Aman; Tel: 509-533-7054, Fax: 509-533-8818, E-mail: taman@scc.spokane.edu; *Tech Serv,* Nancy Coffey; Tel: 509-533-8822, Fax: 509-533-8818, E-mail: ncoffey@scc.spokane.edu; Staff 22 (MLS 5, Non-MLS 17)
Founded 1963. Enrl 5,982; Fac 245
Library Holdings: Bk Titles 30,000; Bk Vols 45,000; Per Subs 245
Special Collections: Career Center
Subject Interests: Agr, Health sci, Law, Nursing
Automation Activity & Vendor Info: (Acquisitions) Ex Libris Group; (Cataloging) Ex Libris Group; (Circulation) Ex Libris Group; (OPAC) Ex Libris Group
Database Vendor: netLibrary, OCLC FirstSearch, ProQuest
Wireless access
Partic in OCLC; Washington Idaho Network
Open Mon-Thurs 7:30am-8pm, Fri 7:30-4, Sat 10-4

GL   SPOKANE COUNTY LAW LIBRARY, Gardner Center Bldg, 1033 W Gardner, 99201. SAN 317-6738. Tel: 509-477-3680. Web Site: www.spokanecounty.org/lawlibrary/content.aspx?c=1926. *Dir, Law Librn,* Cynthia Renee Lucas; E-mail: clucas@spokanecounty.org; *Libr Asst,* Tammara Bowen. Subject Specialists: *Govt, Law,* Cynthia Renee Lucas
Founded 1920
Library Holdings: Bk Vols 30,000
Automation Activity & Vendor Info: (Cataloging) LibraryWorld, Inc; (Circulation) LibraryWorld, Inc; (OPAC) LibraryWorld, Inc
Database Vendor: LexisNexis, Westlaw
Wireless access
Open Mon-Fri 8:30-5

P   SPOKANE COUNTY LIBRARY DISTRICT, Administrative Offices, 4322 N Argonne Rd, 99212-1868. SAN 364-0922. Tel: 509-893-8200. Interlibrary Loan Service Tel: 509-893-8230. FAX: 509-893-8472. E-mail: admin@scld.org. Web Site: www.scld.org. *Dir,* Nancy Ledeboer; E-mail: nledeboer@scld.org; *Adult Coll Develop Librn,* Debra Park; E-mail: dpark@scld.org; *Youth Coll Develop Librn,* Sheri Boggs; E-mail: sboggs@scld.org; *Br Serv Mgr,* Patrick Roewe; *Br Serv Mgr,* Doug Stumbough; E-mail: dstumbough@scld.org; *Bus Mgr,* William Sargent; Fax: 509-893-8471, E-mail: wsargent@scld.org; *Mgr, Coll Serv,* Andrea Sharps; E-mail: asharps@scld.org; *Communications Mgr,* Jane Baker; Tel: 509-893-8205, E-mail: jbaker@scld.org; *Mgr, Human Res,* Paul Eichenberg; E-mail: peichenberg@scld.org; *Mgr, Info Tech,* Priscilla Ice; Tel: 509-893-8450, Fax: 509-893-8478, E-mail: pice@scld.org; *Tech Serv Coordr,* Sandy Orr; E-mail: sorr@scld.org; *Data & Web Serv Adminr,* Ven Kozubenko; Tel: 509-893-8453, E-mail: vkozubenko@scld.org; Staff 32.49 (MLS 6.75, Non-MLS 25.74)
Founded 1942. Pop 252,230; Circ 2,133,916
Jan 2011-Dec 2011 Income (Main Library and Branch(s)) $10,865,892.
Mats Exp $1,468,595. Sal $5,366,379
Library Holdings: Audiobooks 36,233; CDs 17,748; DVDs 31,541; e-books 6,494; Electronic Media & Resources 2,375; Large Print Bks

14,027; Microforms 4; Bk Titles 130,820; Bk Vols 278,519; Per Subs 1,422; Videos 206

Automation Activity & Vendor Info: (Acquisitions) SirsiDynix; (Cataloging) SirsiDynix; (Circulation) SirsiDynix; (ILL) OCLC; (OPAC) SirsiDynix; (Serials) SirsiDynix

Database Vendor: Baker & Taylor, EBSCO Auto Repair Reference, EBSCOhost, Gale Cengage Learning, Grolier Online, Ingram Library Services, OCLC FirstSearch, Overdrive, Inc, ProQuest, ReferenceUSA, SirsiDynix, ValueLine, World Book Online

Wireless access

Function: Adult bk club, Art exhibits, Audiobks via web, Bks on cassette, Bks on CD, Children's prog, Computer training, Computers for patron use, Copy machines, Digital talking bks, Electronic databases & coll, Free DVD rentals, Handicapped accessible, ILL available, Magnifiers for reading, Music CDs, Online cat, Online ref, Online searches, Outreach serv, Outside serv via phone, mail, e-mail & web, OverDrive digital audio bks, Photocopying/Printing, Preschool outreach, Prog for adults, Prog for children & young adult, Pub access computers, Ref & res, Ref serv in person, Senior outreach, Story hour, Summer reading prog, Teen prog, Telephone ref, Wheelchair accessible

Partic in OCLC Online Computer Library Center, Inc

Open Mon-Fri 8-4:30

Branches: 10

AIRWAY HEIGHTS LIBRARY, 1213 S Lundstrom, Airway Heights, 99001-9000, SAN 370-1026. Tel: 509-893-8250. FAX: 509-893-8473. E-mail: ahcirc@scld.org. *Br Supvr,* Stacy Hartkorn; E-mail: pfranz@scld.org; Staff 1.68 (Non-MLS 1.68)
Circ 52,225
Open Tues & Thurs 10-8, Sat 10-6
Friends of the Library Group

ARGONNE LIBRARY, 4322 N Argonne Rd, 99212-1868, SAN 364-1074. Tel: 509-893-8260. FAX: 509-893-8474. E-mail: arcirc@scld.org. *Br Supvr,* Judy Luck; E-mail: jluck@scld.org; Staff 5.08 (Non-MLS 5.08)
Circ 146,373
Open Mon-Wed 10-8, Thurs-Sat 10-6
Friends of the Library Group

CHENEY LIBRARY, 610 First St, Cheney, 99004-1688, SAN 364-0957. Tel: 509-893-8280. FAX: 509-893-8475. E-mail: chcirc@scld.org. *Br Supvr,* Rachel Kennett; E-mail: rkennett@scld.org; Staff 4.95 (Non-MLS 4.95)
Circ 153,012
Open Mon-Wed 10-8, Thurs-Sat 10-6, Sun 1-5
Friends of the Library Group

DEER PARK LIBRARY, 208 S Forest, Deer Park, 99006. (Mail add: PO Box 729, Deer Park, 99006-0729), SAN 364-0981. Tel: 509-893-8300. FAX: 509-893-8476. E-mail: dpcirc@scld.org. *Br Supvr,* Kris Barnes; E-mail: kbarnes@scld.org; Staff 4.7 (Non-MLS 4.7)
Circ 144,862
Open Mon-Wed 10-8, Thurs-Sat 10-6, Sun 1-5
Friends of the Library Group

FAIRFIELD LIBRARY, 305 E Main, Fairfield, 99012. (Mail add: PO Box 48, Fairfield, 99012-0048), SAN 364-1015. Tel: 509-893-8320. FAX: 509-893-8477. E-mail: ffcirc@scld.org. *Br Supvr,* Bev Bergstrom; E-mail: bbergstrom@scld.org; Staff 1.83 (Non-MLS 1.83)
Circ 20,303
Open Tues 10-8, Thurs & Sat 10-6
Friends of the Library Group

MEDICAL LAKE LIBRARY, 321 E Herb, Medical Lake, 99022. (Mail add: PO Box 249, Medical Lake, 99022-0249), SAN 364-104X. Tel: 509-893-8330. FAX: 509-893-8479. E-mail: mlcirc@scld.org. *Br Supvr,* Laura Baird; E-mail: lbaird@scld.org; Staff 1.68 (Non-MLS 1.68)
Circ 51,262
Open Mon & Wed 10-8, Sat 10-6
Friends of the Library Group

MORAN PRAIRIE LIBRARY, 6004 S Regal St, 99223-6949. Tel: 509-893-8340. FAX: 509-893-8480. E-mail: mpcirc@scld.org. *Br Supvr,* Mary Kay Anderson; E-mail: manderson@scld.org; Staff 5.43 (Non-MLS 5.43)
Circ 169,897
Open Mon-Wed 10-8, Thurs-Sat 10-6, Sun 1-5
Friends of the Library Group

NORTH SPOKANE LIBRARY, 44 E Hawthorne Rd, 99218-1597, SAN 364-1104. Tel: 509-893-8350. FAX: 509-893-8481. E-mail: nscirc@scld.org. *Mgr, Br Serv,* Patrick Roewe; E-mail: proewe@scld.org; *Supvr, Ad Serv,* Position Currently Open; *Supvr, Youth Serv,* Gwendolyn Haley; E-mail: ghaley@scld.org; Staff 26.48 (MLS 8.1, Non-MLS 18.38)
Circ 514,608
Open Mon-Thurs 10-9, Fri & Sat 10-6, Sun 1-5
Friends of the Library Group

OTIS ORCHARDS LIBRARY, 22324 E Wellesley Ave, Otis Orchards, 99027-9336, SAN 371-9723. Tel: 509-893-8390. FAX: 509-893-8482. E-mail: otcirc@scld.org. *Br Supvr,* Beverly Bergstrom; E-mail: bbergstrom@scld.org; Staff 3.68 (Non-MLS 3.68)
Circ 81,348

Open Tues & Wed 10-8, Thurs & Sat 10-6
Friends of the Library Group

SPOKANE VALLEY LIBRARY, 12004 E Main Ave, Spokane Valley, 99206-5114, SAN 364-1139. Tel: 509-893-8400. FAX: 509-893-8483. E-mail: svcirc@scld.org. *Mgr, Br Serv,* Ellen Miller; E-mail: emiller@scld.org; *Adult Serv,* Stacey Goddard; E-mail: sgoddard@scld.org; *Youth Serv,* Mary Ellen Braks; E-mail: mbraks@scld.org; Staff 31.38 (MLS 9.5, Non-MLS 21.88)
Circ 535,978
Open Mon-Thurs 10-9, Fri & Sat 10-6, Sun 1-5
Friends of the Library Group

J   SPOKANE FALLS COMMUNITY COLLEGE*, Library Media Services, 3410 Ft George Wright Dr, MS 3020, 99224-5288. SAN 317-6754. Tel: 509-533-3800. Circulation Tel: 509-533-3805. Reference Tel: 509-533-3834. Administration Tel: 509-533-3204. Toll Free Tel: 800-251-1972. FAX: 509-533-3144. E-mail: refdesk@spokanefalls.edu, sfccinfo@spokanefalls.edu. Web Site: library.spokanefalls.edu. *Dean of Instruction, Libr & Distance Learning Serv,* Mary Ann Goodwin; Tel: 509-537-3820, Fax: 509-533-3820, E-mail: maryanng@spokanefalls.edu; *Instrul Serv/Ref Librn,* Janet Wingerroth; Tel: 509-533-3224, E-mail: janw@spokanefalls.edu; *Ref Librn,* Mary Nagel; Tel: 509-533-3174, E-mail: maryn@spokanefalls.edu; *Ref Librn,* Barbara Oldham; Tel: 509-533-3159, E-mail: barbarao@spokanefalls.edu; *Ref Librn,* George Suttle; Tel: 509-533-3807, E-mail: georges@spokanefalls.edu; *Circ,* Jeff Davis; Tel: 509-533-3217, E-mail: jeffd@spokanefalls.edu; *Circ, ILL,* Babs Hachey; Tel: 509-533-3818, E-mail: babsh@spokanefalls.edu; *Per,* Karen Kriberney; E-mail: karenk@spokanefalls.edu; Staff 6 (MLS 6)
Founded 1967. Enrl 4,500; Fac 150; Highest Degree: Associate
Jul 2007-Jun 2008. Mats Exp $104,000, Books $50,000, Per/Ser (Incl. Access Fees) $24,000, AV Mat $10,000, Electronic Ref Mat (Incl. Access Fees) $20,000. Sal $498,000 (Prof $274,250)
Library Holdings: Bk Titles 50,000; Bk Vols 59,000; Per Subs 170
Automation Activity & Vendor Info: (Acquisitions) Ex Libris Group; (Cataloging) Ex Libris Group; (Circulation) Ex Libris Group; (Course Reserve) Ex Libris Group; (ILL) OCLC; (OPAC) Ex Libris Group; (Serials) Ex Libris Group
Database Vendor: OCLC FirstSearch
Partic in OCLC Online Computer Library Center, Inc
Open Mon–Thurs 7:15am–9pm, Fri 7:15–4, Sat 10–4

P   SPOKANE PUBLIC LIBRARY*, 906 W Main Ave, 99201-0976. SAN 364-1163. Tel: 509-444-5300. Circulation Tel: 509-444-5333. Reference Tel: 509-444-5336. FAX: 509-444-5365. TDD: 509-444-5373. E-mail: info@spokanelibrary.org. Web Site: www.spokanelibrary.org. *Dir,* Pat Partovi; E-mail: director@spokanelibrary.org; *Neighborhood Serv Mgr,* Dennis Fredrickson; Tel: 509-444-5334, E-mail: dfredrickson@spokanelibrary.org; *Support Serv Mgr,* Rob Roose; Tel: 509-444-5320, E-mail: rroose@spokanelibrary.org; Staff 84 (MLS 20, Non-MLS 64)
Founded 1891. Pop 198,700; Circ 2,093,121
Library Holdings: Electronic Media & Resources 28; Bk Vols 527,456
Special Collections: Adult Literacy Coll; African-American Coll; Genealogy Coll, bks, clippings, mags, microfilms, microcards; History of the Book Coll; Northwest History Room. Oral History; State Document Depository; US Document Depository
Subject Interests: Genealogy
Automation Activity & Vendor Info: (Acquisitions) SirsiDynix; (Cataloging) SirsiDynix; (Circulation) SirsiDynix; (ILL) OCLC Online; (OPAC) SirsiDynix; (Serials) SirsiDynix
Database Vendor: EBSCOhost, Gale Cengage Learning, netLibrary, OCLC FirstSearch, ProQuest
Wireless access
Function: Archival coll, AV serv, Govt ref serv, Handicapped accessible, Health sci info serv, Home delivery & serv to Sr ctr & nursing homes, Homebound delivery serv, ILL available, Magnifiers for reading, Newsp ref libr, Online searches, Outside serv via phone, mail, e-mail & web, Photocopying/Printing, Prog for adults, Prog for children & young adult, Ref serv available, Summer reading prog, Telephone ref, Wheelchair accessible
Special Services for the Deaf - TDD equip; TTY equip
Special Services for the Blind - Audio mat; Bks on cassette; Bks on CD; Extensive large print coll; Home delivery serv; Large print bks; Magnifiers; Reader equip; Soundproof reading booth; Talking bks
Open Tues & Wed 10-8, Thurs-Sat 10-6
Friends of the Library Group
Branches: 5
EAST SIDE, 524 S Stone Ave, 99202, SAN 364-1228. Tel: 509-444-5375. Circulation Tel: 509-444-5378. FAX: 509-444-5369. TDD: 509-444-5383. *Br Mgr,* Dennis Bergstrom; Tel: 509-444-5376, E-mail: dbergstrom@spokanelibrary.org; *Youth Serv,* Chris LeMieux; Tel: 509-444-5377, E-mail: clemieux@spokanelibrary.org
Founded 1995. Circ 83,119
Function: Prof lending libr

Open Tues & Wed 2:30-7, Thurs 1:30-6, Fri & Sat 10-2:30
Friends of the Library Group
HILLYARD, 4005 N Cook Ave, 99207, SAN 364-1252. Tel:
509-444-5380. Circulation Tel: 509-444-5412. FAX: 509-444-5370.
TDD: 509-444-5384. *Br Mgr,* Dennis Bergstrom; Tel: 509-444-5381,
E-mail: dbergstrom@spokanelibrary.org; *Youth Serv,* Chris LeMieux; Tel:
509-444-5382, E-mail: clemieux@spokanelibrary.org
Founded 1994. Circ 133,627
Open Tues & Wed 2:30-7, Thurs 1:30-6, Fri & Sat 10-2:30
Friends of the Library Group
INDIAN TRAIL, 4909 W Barnes Rd, 99208. Tel: 509-444-5395.
Circulation Tel: 509-444-5413. FAX: 509-444-5399. TDD:
509-444-5398. *Br Mgr,* Dennis Bergstrom; Tel: 509-444-5396, E-mail:
dbergstrom@spokanelibrary.org; *Youth Serv,* Chris LeMieux; Tel:
509-444-5397, E-mail: clemieux@spokanelibrary.org
Founded 1998. Circ 134,119
Open Tues & Wed 2:30-7, Thurs 1:30-6, Fri & Sat 10-2:30
Friends of the Library Group
SHADLE, 2111 W Wellesley Ave, 99205, SAN 364-1376. Tel:
509-444-5390. Circulation Tel: 509-444-5414. FAX: 509-444-5372. *Br
Mgr,* Pat Bonner; Tel: 509-444-5391, E-mail:
pbonner@spokanelibrary.org; *Youth Serv,* Jill Bolon; Tel: 509-444-5392
Founded 1997. Circ 412,386
Open Mon & Tues 10-8, Wed-Sat 10-6
Friends of the Library Group
SOUTH HILL, 3324 S Perry Ave, 99203, SAN 364-1317. Tel:
509-444-5385. Circulation Tel: 509-444-5415. FAX: 509-444-5371.
TDD: 509-444-5389. *Br Mgr,* Louise Sullivan; Tel: 509-444-5386,
E-mail: lsullivan@spokanelibrary.org; *Youth Serv,* Susanne Miller; Tel:
509-444-5388, E-mail: smiller@spokanelibrary.org
Founded 1996. Circ 425,082
Open Mon & Tues 10-8, Wed-Sat 10-6
Friends of the Library Group
Bookmobiles: 1

S SPOKESMAN-REVIEW*, Newspaper Reference Library, 999 W Riverside
Ave, 99201. (Mail add: PO Box 2160, 99210), SAN 317-6762. Tel:
509-459-5524. Toll Free Tel: 800-789-0029, Ext 5421. FAX:
509-227-5865. E-mail: library@spokesman.com. Web Site:
www.spokesmanreview.com. *Librn,* Angie Flint; E-mail:
angief@spokesman.com
Founded 1883
Library Holdings: Bk Titles 3,000; Per Subs 15
Special Collections: Newspaper Clipping & Photographs
Restriction: Private libr

G UNITED STATES DEPARTMENT OF THE INTERIOR*, US Geological
Survey, Mineral Resources Library, W 904 Riverside Ave, Rm 202, 99201.
SAN 364-1406. Tel: 509-368-3101. FAX: 509-368-3199. *Librn,* Linda
Elmore; E-mail: lelmore@usgs.gov
Founded 1946
Library Holdings: Bk Vols 11,000; Per Subs 25
Special Collections: United States Bureau of Mines Publications; United
States Geological Survey Publications
Subject Interests: Geol, Related sci
Restriction: Open by appt only, Open to pub for ref only

CM WASHINGTON STATE UNIVERSITY, Riverpoint Campus Library, 600 N
Riverpoint Blvd, 99202. (Mail add: PO Box 1495, 99210-1495), SAN
324-6183. Tel: 509-358-7930. FAX: 509-358-7928. E-mail:
spok.lib@wsu.edu. Web Site: spokane.wsu.edu/academics/library. *Dir, Libr
Serv,* Robert M Pringle, Jr; E-mail: rpringle@wsu.edu; *Ref Librn,* Mary
Wood; E-mail: marywood@wsu.edu; *ILL,* Dee Rodgers; *ILL,* Nancy
Wagner; *Ref, Ser,* Jeanne Wagner; E-mail: wagnerj@wsu.edu; *Reserves,*
Linda Lilles; E-mail: lilles@wsu.edu; Staff 6 (MLS 2, Non-MLS 4)
Founded 1969. Enrl 1,395; Fac 70; Highest Degree: Doctorate
Library Holdings: Bk Titles 10,000; Bk Vols 11,000; Per Subs 190
Subject Interests: Health sci, Nursing, Pharm
Automation Activity & Vendor Info: (Acquisitions) Innovative Interfaces,
Inc; (Circulation) Innovative Interfaces, Inc; (Course Reserve) Docutek;
(OPAC) Innovative Interfaces, Inc; (Serials) Innovative Interfaces, Inc
Database Vendor: EBSCOhost, OCLC FirstSearch, PubMed
Wireless access
Partic in Inland NorthWest Health Sciences Libraries

C WHITWORTH UNIVERSITY*, Harriet Cheney Cowles Memorial Library,
300 W Hawthorne Rd, 99251-0001. SAN 364-1465. Tel: 509-777-3260.
Circulation Tel: 509-777-4200. Interlibrary Loan Service Tel:
509-777-4488. Reference Tel: 509-777-4491. Administration Tel:
509-777-4482. FAX: 509-777-3221. Web Site: www.whitworth.edu/library.
Dir, Dr Hans E Bynagle; E-mail: hbynagle@whitworth.edu; *Coordr of Ref
Serv,* Nancy A Bunker; Tel: 509-777-4481, E-mail:
nbunker@whitworth.edu; *Coordr, Instrul Serv,* Tami Echavarria Robinson;
Tel: 509-777-4483, E-mail: trobinson@whitworth.edu; *Coordr, Tech Syst &*

Serv, Amy C Rice; Tel: 509-777-4480, Fax: 509-777-3231, E-mail:
arice@whitworth.edu; *Prog Coordr,* Deb Fry; Tel: 509-777-3207, E-mail:
dfry@whitworth.edu; *Archivist,* Janet Hauck; Tel: 509-777-4751, E-mail:
jhauck@whitworth.edu; *Acq,* Debi Kaufman; Tel: 509-777-4485, E-mail:
dkaufman@whitworth.edu; *Circ,* Barbara Carden; Tel: 509-777-3767,
E-mail: bcarden@whitworth.edu; *ILL,* Gail Fielding; E-mail:
gfielding@whitworth.edu; *Tech Serv,* Jeanette Langston; Tel: 509-777-4226,
E-mail: jlangston@whitworth.edu. Subject Specialists: *Music, Philosophy,
Relig,* Dr Hans E Bynagle; *Bus, Econ, Hist,* Nancy A Bunker; *Natural sci,*
Tami Echavarria Robinson; *English, Polit sci, Theatre,* Amy C Rice; *Art,
Educ, Pub hist,* Janet Hauck; Staff 10.5 (MLS 5.5, Non-MLS 5)
Founded 1890. Enrl 2,886; Fac 180; Highest Degree: Master
Jul 2010-Jun 2011 Income $1,290,290, Locally Generated Income $7,135,
Parent Institution $1,281,655, Other $1,500. Mats Exp $1,268,764, Books
$150,413, Per/Ser (Incl. Access Fees) $305,556, Manu Arch $2,000, Micro
$6,000, AV Mat $13,923, Electronic Ref Mat (Incl. Access Fees) $24,239,
Presv $5,000. Sal $661,228 (Prof $415,683)
Library Holdings: Audiobooks 500; AV Mats 9,250; CDs 3,380; DVDs
1,160; e-books 75,000; e-journals 2,300; Microforms 69,850; Music Scores
6,760; Bk Vols 164,800; Per Subs 480; Videos 1,738
Special Collections: Daniel Photography Coll; Pacific Northwest Protestant
History Coll
Subject Interests: Bus, Educ, Liberal arts, Sciences
Automation Activity & Vendor Info: (Acquisitions) Ex Libris Group;
(Cataloging) Ex Libris Group; (Circulation) Ex Libris Group; (ILL) Ex
Libris Group; (OPAC) Ex Libris Group; (Serials) Ex Libris Group
Database Vendor: ACM (Association for Computing Machinery),
Alexander Street Press; American Chemical Society, American Physical
Society, Annual Reviews, ARTstor, Cambridge Scientific Abstracts, Dialog,
ebrary, EBSCOhost, Gale Cengage Learning, H W Wilson, Hoovers,
JSTOR, LexisNexis, Marquis Who's Who, McGraw-Hill, netLibrary,
OCLC ArticleFirst, OCLC FirstSearch, OCLC WorldCat, Oxford Online,
Plunkett Research, Ltd, ProQuest, RefWorks, Sage
Wireless access
Function: Archival coll, Audio & video playback equip for onsite use,
Audiobks via web, Computers for patron use, Copy machines, Electronic
databases & coll, Handicapped accessible, ILL available, Music CDs,
Online cat, Ref & res, Scanner, VCDs, VHS videos, Video lending libr,
Writing prog
Partic in OCLC Online Computer Library Center, Inc; Washington Idaho
Network
Open Mon-Thurs (Winter) 7:45am-Midnight, Fri 7:45-5:30, Sat 9-6, Sun
1pm-Midnight; Mon-Thurs (Summer) 8-8, Fri 8-5, Sat 10-5
Restriction: Circ limited, In-house use for visitors, Non-circulating of rare
bks, Open to students, fac & staff, Pub use on premises

SPRAGUE

P SPRAGUE PUBLIC LIBRARY*, 119 W Second St, 99032. (Mail add: PO
Box 264, 99032-0264). Tel: 509-257-2662. FAX: 509-257-2691. *Dir,* Judy
Boutain; E-mail: jboutain@sprague-wa.us
Library Holdings: Audiobooks 94; DVDs 15; Bk Vols 2,671; Videos 254
Special Collections: History Coll; Local History Coll
Partic in Connecticut Library Consortium
Open Mon-Fri 9-5

TACOMA

S APA - THE ENGINEERED WOOD ASSOCIATION*, Records
Department Library, 7011 S 19th St, 98466-5333. SAN 317-6797. Tel:
253-565-6600, Ext 461. FAX: 253-565-7265. E-mail: help@apawood.org.
Web Site: www.apawood.org. *Coordr,* Barbara Embrey
Library Holdings: Bk Vols 300; Per Subs 75
Subject Interests: Forestry, Wood tech
Restriction: Not a lending libr, Staff use only

J BATES TECHNICAL COLLEGE LIBRARY*, 2201 S 78th St, E201,
98409-9000. Tel: 253-680-7550. FAX: 253-680-7551. E-mail:
library@bates.ctc.edu. Web Site: library.bates.ctc.edu. *Librn,* Jennie Vano;
Tel: 253-680-7543, E-mail: jvano@bates.ctc.edu
Library Holdings: Bk Titles 8,200
Database Vendor: ProQuest
Open Mon-Thurs 8-5, Fri 10:30-4:30

CR FAITH EVANGELICAL SEMINARY LIBRARY*, 3504 N Pearl St,
98407-2607. (Mail add: PO Box 7186, 98406-0186), SAN 317-6827. Tel:
253-752-2020. Toll Free Tel: 888-777-7675. FAX: 253-759-1790. E-mail:
fsinfo@faithseminary.edu. Web Site: www.faithseminary.edu. *Pres,* Michael
Adams; *Librn,* Bebhinn Horrigan; Tel: 253-752-2020, Ext 32
Founded 1969. Enrl 400; Fac 15; Highest Degree: Doctorate
Library Holdings: Bk Vols 20,000; Per Subs 90
Wireless access
Partic in Puget Sound Area Libr Tech
Open Mon-Thurs 11-9

S   THE NEWS TRIBUNE LIBRARY*, 1950 S State St, 98405-2860. (Mail
add: PO Box 11000, 98411-0008), SAN 317-6916. Tel: 253-597-8626,
253-597-8629. Toll Free Tel: 800-289-8711. FAX: 253-597-8274. E-mail:
tntinfo@thenewstribune.com. Web Site:
www.thenewstribune.com/aboutus/contact/library. *Mgr,* Toi Britton; Staff 3
(MLS 1, Non-MLS 2)
Founded 1880
Library Holdings: Bk Vols 500; Per Subs 150
Special Collections: Newspaper clip file by subject (1955-87)
Subject Interests: Local news
Open Mon-Fri 8-3

C   PACIFIC LUTHERAN UNIVERSITY*, Robert A L Mortvedt Library,
12180 Park Ave S, 98447-0001. SAN 317-6843. Tel: 253-535-7500.
Interlibrary Loan Service Tel: 253-535-7508. Reference Tel: 253-535-7507.
Administration Tel: 253-535-7504. FAX: 253-535-7315. Interlibrary Loan
Service FAX: 253-536-5110. E-mail: libr@plu.edu. Web Site:
www.plu.edu/~libr. *Assoc Provost, Info & Tech Serv,* Chris Ferguson; *Dir,
Circ & Bldg Serv,* Diane Harris; *Dir, Digital Media Ctr,* Layne Nordgren;
Dir, Libr & Info Serv, Francesca Lane Rasmus; *Dir, Multimedia Serv,* Kirk
Isakson; *ILL Coordr,* Sue Golden; *Spec Coll, Univ Archivist,* Kerstin
Ringdahl; Staff 10 (MLS 6, Non-MLS 4)
Founded 1894. Enrl 3,661; Fac 238; Highest Degree: Master
Library Holdings: AV Mats 14,032; Bk Titles 261,291; Bk Vols 345,193;
Per Subs 4,474
Special Collections: Scandinavian Immigrant Experience Coll. Oral
History
Automation Activity & Vendor Info: (Acquisitions) Ex Libris Group;
(Cataloging) Ex Libris Group; (Circulation) Ex Libris Group; (Course
Reserve) Ex Libris Group; (ILL) OCLC; (Media Booking) Ex Libris
Group; (OPAC) Ex Libris Group; (Serials) Ex Libris Group
Database Vendor: Dialog, EBSCOhost, JSTOR, LexisNexis, OCLC
FirstSearch, ProQuest, STN International
Wireless access
Function: Archival coll, Art exhibits, Audio & video playback equip for
onsite use, AV serv, CD-ROM, Doc delivery serv, For res purposes, Health
sci info serv, ILL available, Magnifiers for reading, Music CDs, Newsp ref
libr, Online searches, Photocopying/Printing, Ref serv available, Telephone
ref, VHS videos, Web-Braille, Wheelchair accessible
Partic in Northwest Association of Private Colleges & Universities
(NAPCU); Puget Sound Acad Independent Librs
Restriction: Restricted borrowing privileges

GL   PIERCE COUNTY LAW LIBRARY*, County-City Bldg, 930 Tacoma Ave
S, Rm 1A - 105, 98402-2174. SAN 317-6851. Tel: 253-798-7494. FAX:
253-798-2989. Web Site:
www.piercecountywa.org/pc/services/lawjust/library/home.htm. *Dir,* Laurie
B Miller; Tel: 253-798-2973, E-mail: lmille2@co.pierce.wa.us; *Asst Librn,*
Tina Aure; E-mail: taure@co.pierce.wa.us; Staff 5 (MLS 2, Non-MLS 3)
Library Holdings: Bk Vols 50,000; Per Subs 20
Automation Activity & Vendor Info: (Cataloging) SirsiDynix;
(Circulation) SirsiDynix; (OPAC) SirsiDynix; (Serials) SirsiDynix
Database Vendor: LexisNexis, Westlaw
Wireless access
Function: ILL available, Photocopying/Printing
Open Mon 8:30-8, Tues-Thurs 8:30-6, Fri 8:30-5, Sun 12-5
Friends of the Library Group

P   PIERCE COUNTY LIBRARY SYSTEM*, 3005 112th St E, 98446-2215.
SAN 364-1589. Tel: 253-548-3300. Information Services Tel:
253-582-6040. FAX: 253-537-4600. TDD: 800-833-6388. Web Site:
www.piercecountylibrary.org. *Exec Dir,* Neel Parikh; Tel: 253-548-3445,
E-mail: nparikh@piercecountylibrary.org; *Dep Dir,* Georgia Lomax; Tel:
253-548-3421, E-mail: glomax@piercecountylibrary.org; *Br Experience
Dir,* Sally Porter Smith; Tel: 253-548-3422, E-mail:
sportersmith@piercecountylibrary.org; *Communications Dir,* Mary Getchell;
Tel: 253-548-3428, E-mail: mgetchell@piercecountylibrary.org; *Dir, Coll
Serv,* Lisa Bitney; Tel: 253-548-3397, E-mail:
lbitney@piercecountylibrary.org; *Dir, Libr Develop,* Lynne Hoffman; Tel:
253-548-3456, E-mail: lhoffman@piercecountylibrary.org; *Dir of Finance,*
Clifford Jo; Tel: 253-548-3453, E-mail: cjo@piercecountylibrary.org;
Human Res Dir, Holly Gorski; Tel: 253-548-3354, E-mail:
hgorski@piercecountylibrary.org; *Youth Serv Dir,* Judy Nelson; Tel:
253-548-3412, E-mail: jnelson@piercecountylibrary.org; Staff 280 (MLS
56, Non-MLS 224)
Founded 1946. Pop 559,561; Circ 8,738,850
Special Collections: Korean & Spanish. US Document Depository
Automation Activity & Vendor Info: (Circulation) Polaris Library
Systems
Wireless access
Partic in OCLC Online Computer Library Center, Inc
Special Services for the Deaf - TDD equip
Special Services for the Blind - Reader equip
Open Mon-Fri 7:30-5
Friends of the Library Group

Branches: 17
BONNEY LAKE BRANCH, 18501 90th St E, Bonney Lake, 98390, SAN
364-1643. Tel: 253-548-3308. FAX: 253-863-6016. *Managing Librn,*
Lynne Zeiher; E-mail: lzeiher@piercecountylibrary.org; *Sr Librn,* Lauren
Murphy; E-mail: lmurphy@piercecountylibrary.org
Automation Activity & Vendor Info: (Acquisitions) Polaris Library
Systems; (Cataloging) Polaris Library Systems
Database Vendor: ProQuest
Open Mon-Wed 10-9, Thurs & Fri 10-6, Sat 10-5, Sun 1-5
Friends of the Library Group
BUCKLEY BRANCH, 123 S River Ave, Buckley, 98321. (Mail add: PO
Box 167, Buckley, 98321-0167), SAN 364-1708. Tel: 360-548-3710.
FAX: 360-829-2874. *Managing Librn,* Robin Clausen; E-mail:
rclausen@piercecountylibrary.org; *Commun Br Supvr,* Kathy Norbeck;
E-mail: knorbeck@piercecountylibrary.org
Founded 1903
Library Holdings: Bk Titles 28,550
Open Mon-Wed 11-8, Thurs & Fri 11-6, Sat 11-5
Friends of the Library Group
DUPONT BRANCH, 1540 Wilmington Dr, DuPont, 98327. Tel:
253-548-3326. FAX: 253-964-4010. *Managing Librn,* Robin Clausen;
E-mail: relausen@piercecountylibrary.org; *Commun Br Supvr,* Tami
Masenhimer; E-mail: tmasenhimer@piercecountylibrary.org
Open Mon-Wed 11-8, Thurs & Fri 11-6, Sat 11-5
Friends of the Library Group
EATONVILLE BRANCH, 205 Center St W, Eatonville, 98328-9488. (Mail
add: PO Box 69, Eatonville, 98328-0069), SAN 364-1732. Tel:
253-548-3311. FAX: 360-832-7201. *Managing Librn,* Robin Clausen;
E-mail: rclausen@piercecountylibrary.org; *Commun Br Supvr,* Cindy
Dargan; E-mail: cdargan@piercecountylibrary.org
Open Mon-Wed 11-8, Thurs & Fri 11-6, Sat 11-5
Friends of the Library Group
GIG HARBOR BRANCH, 4424 Point Fosdick Dr NW, Gig Harbor, 98335,
SAN 364-1767. Tel: 253-548-3305. FAX: 253-851-8002. *Br Mgr,*
Position Currently Open
Open Mon-Thurs 10-9, Fri 10-6, Sat 10-5, Sun 1-5
Friends of the Library Group
GRAHAM BRANCH, 9202 224th St E, Graham, 98338. (Mail add: PO
Box 1267, Graham, 98338-1267), SAN 373-5656. Tel: 253-548-3322.
FAX: 253-846-5174. *Managing Librn,* Lynne Zeiher; E-mail:
lzeiher@piercecountylibrary.org; *Sr Librn,* Jane Miller; E-mail:
jmiller@piercecountylibrary.org
Founded 1992
Open Mon-Wed 10-9, Thurs & Fri 10-6, Sat 10-5, Sun 1-5
Friends of the Library Group
KEY CENTER, 8905 Key Peninsula Hwy N, Lakebay, 98349, SAN
364-1791. Tel: 253-548-3309. FAX: 253-884-3706. *Managing Librn,*
Robin Clausen; E-mail: rclausen@piercecountylibrary.org; *Commun Br
Supvr,* Rosina Vertz; E-mail: rvertz@piercecountylibrary.org
Founded 1946
Open Mon-Wed 11-8, Thurs & Fri 11-6, Sat 11-5
Friends of the Library Group
LAKEWOOD BRANCH, 6300 Wildaire Rd SW, Lakewood, 98499, SAN
364-197X. Tel: 253-548-3302. FAX: 253-589-7377. *Br Mgr,* David
Durante; E-mail: ddurante@piercecountylibrary.org
Founded 1947
Open Mon-Thurs 10-9, Fri 10-6, Sat 10-5, Sun 1-5
Friends of the Library Group
MILTON/EDGEWOOD BRANCH, 900 Meridian Ave E, Milton, 98354,
SAN 317-5464. Tel: 253-548-3725. FAX: 253-927-2581. *Managing
Librn,* Robin Clausen; E-mail: rclausen@piercecountylibrary.org;
Commun Br Supvr, Linda Case; E-mail: lcase@piercecountylibrary.org
Open Mon-Wed 11-8, Thurs & Fri 11-6, Sat 11-5
Friends of the Library Group
ORTING BRANCH, 202 Washington Ave S, Orting, 98360. (Mail add: PO
Box 1060, Orting, 98360-1060), SAN 364-1821. Tel: 253-548-3312.
FAX: 360-893-4149. *Managing Librn,* Robin Clausen; E-mail:
rclausen@piercecountylibrary.org; *Commun Br Supvr,* Susan Rigley;
E-mail: srigley@piercecountylibrary.org
Founded 1982
Open Mon-Wed 11-8, Thurs & Fri 11-6, Sat 11-5
Friends of the Library Group
PARKLAND-SPANAWAY, 13718 Pacific Ave S, 98444, SAN 364-1856.
Tel: 253-548-3304. FAX: 253-536-3789. *Managing Librn,* Keith
Knutsen; E-mail: kknutsen@piercecountylibrary.org
Open Mon-Thurs 10-9, Fri 10-6, Sat 10-5, Sun 1-5
Friends of the Library Group
SOUTH HILL, 15420 Meridian E, Puyallup, 98375, SAN 364-1880. Tel:
253-548-3303. FAX: 253-841-4692. *Br Mgr,* Rose Jetter; E-mail:
rjetter@piercecountylibrary.org
Database Vendor: Polaris Library Systems
Open Mon-Thurs 10-9, Fri 10-6, Sat 10-5, Sun 1-5
Friends of the Library Group

STEILACOOM BRANCH, 2950 Steilacoom Blvd SW, Steilacoom, 98388-5107, SAN 364-1910. Tel: 253-548-3313. FAX: 253-589-7095. *Managing Librn,* Robin Clausen; E-mail: rclausen@piercecountylibrary.org; *Commun Br Supvr,* Patti Cox; E-mail: pcox@piercecountylibrary.org
Founded 1858
Open Mon-Wed 11-8, Thurs & Fri 11-6, Sat 11-5
Friends of the Library Group
SUMMIT, 5107 112th St E, 98446, SAN 373-9090. Tel: 253-548-3321. FAX: 253-536-6009. *Managing Librn,* Lynne Zeiher; E-mail: lzeiher@piercecountylibrary.org; *Sr Librn,* Lorianne Callison; E-mail: lcallison@piercecountylibrary.org
Open Mon-Thurs 10-9, Fri 10-6, Sat 10-5, Sun 1-5
Friends of the Library Group
SUMNER BRANCH, 1116 Fryar Ave, Sumner, 98390, SAN 364-1945. Tel: 253-548-3306. FAX: 253-863-0650. *Managing Librn,* Lynne Zeiher; E-mail: lzeiher@piercecountylibrary.org; *Sr Librn,* Lisa McNamara; E-mail: lmcnamara@piercecountylibrary.org
Founded 1925
Open Mon-Thurs 10-9, Fri 10-6, Sat 10-5, Sun 1-5
Friends of the Library Group
TILLICUM BRANCH, 14916 Washington Ave SW, Lakewood, 98498, SAN 364-2003. Tel: 253-548-3314. FAX: 253-588-2095. *Managing Librn,* Robin Clausen; E-mail: rclausen@piercecountylibrary.org; *Commun Br Supvr,* Jeanine Adams; E-mail: jadams@piercecountylibrary.org
Founded 1947
Open Mon & Tues 1-5 & 6-8, Wed 12:30-5 & 6-8, Thurs 12:30-5, Fri 1-5, Sat 11-3
Friends of the Library Group
UNIVERSITY PLACE BRANCH, 3609 Market Pl W, University Place, 98466, SAN 364-2038. Tel: 253-548-3307. FAX: 253-565-2913. *Br Mgr,* Cindy Bonaro; E-mail: cbonaro@piercecountylibrary.org
Open Mon-Thurs 10-9, Fri 10-6, Sat 10-5, Sun 1-5
Friends of the Library Group

M ST JOSEPH MEDICAL CENTER LIBRARY, 1717 South J St, 98405. (Mail add: PO Box 2197, 98401-2197), SAN 317-6878. Tel: 253-426-6778. FAX: 253-426-6260. *Librn,* Brynn Beals; E-mail: brynnbeals@fhshealth.org; Staff 1 (MLS 1)
Founded 1920
Subject Interests: Hospitals, Med, Nursing, Related subj
Partic in Pacific NW Regional Health Sci Libr; Washington Libr Network

S TACOMA ART MUSEUM*, Art Resource Center, 1701 Pacific Ave, 98402. SAN 328-0497. Tel: 253-272-4258, Ext 3026. Administration Tel: 253-272-4258. FAX: 253-627-1898. Web Site: www.tacomaartmuseum.org. *Training Coordr,* Jana Wennstrom; Tel: 253-272-4258, Ext 3030, E-mail: education@tacomaartmuseum.org; *Educ Curator,* Paula McArdle; E-mail: pmcardle@tacomaartmuseum.org
Founded 1971
Library Holdings: Bk Vols 6,000; Per Subs 15
Special Collections: Japanese Prints (Lyon Coll); Tacoma & Northwest Artists
Subject Interests: Pacific Northwest
Wireless access
Publications: Exhibit Catalogues
Open Tues-Sat 10-5, Sun 12-5

J TACOMA COMMUNITY COLLEGE LIBRARY*, Pearl A Wanamaker Library, 6501 S 19th St, 98466-6100. SAN 317-6894. Tel: 253-566-5087. Interlibrary Loan Service Tel: 253-566-5088. Reference Tel: 253-566-5134. FAX: 253-566-5398. TDD: 253-566-5130. Web Site: www.tacomacc.edu/library. *Dean,* Charlie Crawford; Tel: 253-566-6005, E-mail: ccrawford@tacomacc.edu; *Mgr, Libr Operations & Tech,* Tamera Hanken; Tel: 253-566-5091, E-mail: thanken@tacomacc.edu; *Circ Supvr,* Sandra Townley; Tel: 253-566-5089, E-mail: stownley@tacomacc.edu; *Librn,* Rachel Goon; Tel: 253-566-5204, E-mail: rgoon@tacomacc.edu; *Librn,* Kendall Reid; Tel: 253-566-5102, E-mail: kreid@tacomacc.edu; *Librn,* Rebeccah Sproat; Tel: 253-566-6028, E-mail: bsproat@tacomacc.edu; *Librn,* Syd Sullivan; Tel: 253-566-5103, E-mail: sullivan@tacomacc.edu; Staff 13 (MLS 5, Non-MLS 8)
Founded 1966
Library Holdings: Bk Vols 60,000; Per Subs 1,200
Subject Interests: NW hist
Automation Activity & Vendor Info: (Acquisitions) SirsiDynix; (Cataloging) SirsiDynix; (Circulation) SirsiDynix; (Course Reserve) SirsiDynix; (ILL) SirsiDynix; (Media Booking) SirsiDynix; (OPAC) SirsiDynix; (Serials) SirsiDynix
Database Vendor: Gale Cengage Learning, ProQuest, SirsiDynix
Wireless access
Friends of the Library Group

S TACOMA FAMILY HISTORY CENTER*, 5915 S 12th, 98465. SAN 317-6819. Tel: 253-564-1103. E-mail: wa_tacoma@ldsmail.net. Web Site: www.familysearch.org. *Co-Dir,* Andy Ward; *Co-Dir,* Kay Ward
Library Holdings: Microforms 9,400; Bk Vols 3,000
Wireless access
Open Mon 9-4:30, Tues-Thurs 9-9, Fri & Sat 9-5

P TACOMA PUBLIC LIBRARY, 1102 Tacoma Ave S, 98402-2098. SAN 364-2097. Tel: 253-292-2001. Administration Tel: 253-292-2001, Ext 1111. FAX: 253-344-5584. TDD: 253-341-4712. Web Site: www.tacomapubliclibrary.org. *Libr Dir,* Odencrantz Susan; Staff 29 (MLS 11, Non-MLS 18)
Founded 1886. Pop 197,000; Circ 2,038,449
Library Holdings: AV Mats 92,779; Bk Vols 2,123,062; Per Subs 1,638
Special Collections: Geneal Coll; Historic Tacoma photos 1923-1980; Local newspapers, history and government; Northwest history, maps, docs, & bks; World War I bks & posters. Municipal Document Depository; State Document Depository; US Document Depository
Automation Activity & Vendor Info: (Acquisitions) Innovative Interfaces, Inc - Millenium; (Cataloging) Innovative Interfaces, Inc - Millenium; (Circulation) Innovative Interfaces, Inc - Millenium; (ILL) OCLC ILLiad; (OPAC) Innovative Interfaces, Inc - Millenium; (Serials) Innovative Interfaces, Inc - Millenium
Database Vendor: Baker & Taylor, BWI, Corbis, Discovery Education, Dun & Bradstreet, EBSCOhost, Electric Library, Gale Cengage Learning, Grolier Online, Marcive, Inc, Newsbank, OCLC WorldCat, Overdrive, Inc, ProQuest, ReferenceUSA, SerialsSolutions, SirsiDynix, WebFeat, World Book Online
Wireless access
Publications: Bibliographies; Pioneer
Partic in OCLC Online Computer Library Center, Inc
Special Services for the Deaf - TTY equip
Open Mon 11-8, Tues, Wed, Fri & Sat 9-6, Thurs 11-8
Branches: 8
FERN HILL, 765 S 84th St, 98444, SAN 364-2127. *Br Mgr,* Janet Myers
  Library Holdings: Bk Vols 91,434
KOBETICH, 212 Brown's Point Blvd NE, 98422, SAN 364-2151. *Br Mgr,* Ruie Miller
  Library Holdings: Bk Vols 50,518
MOORE BRANCH, 215 S 56th St, 98408, SAN 364-2216. *Br Mgr,* Vicki Armstrong
  Library Holdings: Bk Vols 103,615
MOTTET BRANCH, 3523 East G St, 98404, SAN 364-2240. *Br Mgr,* Vicki Armstrong
  Library Holdings: Bk Vols 54,715
SOUTH TACOMA, 3411 S 56th St, 98409, SAN 364-2275. *Br Mgr,* Janet Myers
  Library Holdings: Bk Vols 63,508
SWAN CREEK, 3828 Portland Ave, 98404, SAN 329-6687. *Br Mgr,* Ruie Miller
  Library Holdings: Bk Vols 42,266
SWASEY BRANCH, 7001 Sixth Ave, 98406, SAN 364-2305. *Br Mgr,* Barbara Scott
  Library Holdings: Bk Vols 96,906
WHEELOCK BRANCH, 3722 N 26th St, 98407, SAN 364-2186. *Br Mgr,* Cheryl Towne
  Library Holdings: Bk Vols 132,738

AM UNITED STATES ARMY*, Madigan Army Medical Center, Medical Library, Bldg 9040 Fitzsimmons Dr, 2nd Flr, 98431. (Mail add: Attn: MCHJ-EDML (Medical Library), 98431-1100), SAN 364-2364. Tel: 253-968-0118. FAX: 253-968-0958. E-mail: mamcmedlib@amedd.army.mil. Web Site: www.mamc.amedd.army.mil/medlib/ml_hmeinfo.htm. *Chief Librn,* Edean Berglund; E-mail: edean.berglund@us.army.mil; Staff 4 (MLS 2, Non-MLS 2)
Founded 1944
Library Holdings: Bk Titles 9,980; Bk Vols 27,101; Per Subs 450
Subject Interests: Health admin, Med, Nursing
Automation Activity & Vendor Info: (Acquisitions) Ex Libris Group; (Cataloging) Ex Libris Group; (Circulation) Ex Libris Group; (OPAC) Ex Libris Group; (Serials) Ex Libris Group
Database Vendor: Dialog, OCLC FirstSearch, OVID Technologies
Publications: Accession List
Partic in OCLC Online Computer Library Center, Inc
Restriction: Staff use only

C UNIVERSITY OF PUGET SOUND*, Collins Memorial Library, 1500 N Warner St, Campus Mail Box 1021, 98416-1021. SAN 364-2399. Tel: 253-879-3669. Interlibrary Loan Service Tel: 253-879-2879. Reference Tel: 253-879-3287. Administration Tel: 253-879-3243. Automation Services Tel: 253-879-3257. FAX: 253-879-3670. TDD: 253-879-2664. E-mail: libref@ups.edu. Web Site: www.library.ups.edu. *Dir,* Jane A Carlin; Tel: 253-879-3118, E-mail: jcarlin@ups.edu; *Assoc Dir, Coll & Tech Serv,*

Peggy Firman; Tel: 253-879-3615, E-mail: firman@ups.edu; *Assoc Dir, Info & Access Serv,* Lori Ricigliano; Tel: 253-879-3229, E-mail: ricigliano@ups.edu; *Librn,* Peggy Burge; Tel: 253-879-3512, E-mail: pburge@ups.edu; *Soc Sci Librn,* Donna Bachmann; Tel: 253-879-3619, E-mail: dbachmann@ups.edu; *Supvr, Access Serv,* Cassandra Palmore; E-mail: cpalmore@ups.edu; *Supvr, Acq,* Carmel Thompson; Tel: 253-879-3240, E-mail: cathompson@ups.edu; *Cat Supvr,* Willow Berntsen; Tel: 253-879-3107, E-mail: wberntsen@ups.edu; *Admin Coordr,* Jamie Spaine; Tel: 253-879-3243, E-mail: jspaine@ups.edu; *Archives Coordr,* Andrea Kueter; Tel: 253-879-2875, E-mail: akueter@ups.edu; *Acq,* Elin Gratton; Tel: 253-879-2668, E-mail: egratton@ups.edu; *Acq,* Nancy Piercy; Tel: 253-879-3258, E-mail: piercy@ups.edu; *Cat, Librn Tech,* Sue Boggs; Tel: 253-879-2667, E-mail: boggs@ups.edu; *Cat,* Patt Leonard; Tel: 253-879-2651, E-mail: pleonard@ups.edu; *Cat, Govt Doc,* Marlene West; Tel: 253-879-8617, E-mail: mwest@ups.edu; *Circ,* Nancy Sullivan; Tel: 253-879-2665, E-mail: nsullivan@ups.edu; *ILL Spec,* Susan Oros; Tel: 253-879-2664, E-mail: soros@ups.edu; *Reserves,* Chris Dowd; Tel: 253-879-3618, E-mail: cdowd@ups.edu; *Ser,* Wei Younts; Tel: 253-879-3617, E-mail: wyounts@ups.edu; *Webmaster,* Jeanne Kimura; Tel: 253-879-2958, E-mail: jkimura@ups.edu. Subject Specialists: *Humanities,* Peggy Burge; Staff 23 (MLS 8, Non-MLS 15)
Founded 1888. Enrl 2,576; Fac 219; Highest Degree: Doctorate
Library Holdings: AV Mats 7,865; e-books 23,819; Bk Titles 351,506; Bk Vols 475,349; Per Subs 1,426
Special Collections: Music Recordings & Scores Coll. State Document Depository; US Document Depository
Subject Interests: Liberal arts, Music
Automation Activity & Vendor Info: (Acquisitions) Innovative Interfaces, Inc; (Cataloging) Innovative Interfaces, Inc; (Circulation) Innovative Interfaces, Inc; (Course Reserve) Innovative Interfaces, Inc; (ILL) OCLC ILLiad; (Media Booking) Innovative Interfaces, Inc; (OPAC) Innovative Interfaces, Inc; (Serials) Innovative Interfaces, Inc
Database Vendor: Cambridge Scientific Abstracts, Dialog, EBSCOhost, Gale Cengage Learning, LexisNexis, OCLC FirstSearch, OCLC WorldCat, OVID Technologies, ProQuest, Swets Information Services, Wilson - Wilson Web
Wireless access
Function: Ref serv available
Publications: Acquisition List; Faculty Library Handbook
Partic in Northwest Association of Private Colleges & Universities (NAPCU); OCLC Online Computer Library Center, Inc; Puget Sound Acad Independent Librs
Open Mon-Thurs 7:30am-2am, Fri 7:30am-9pm, Sat 9-9, Sun 9am-2am

GM VA PUGET SOUND HEALTH CARE SYSTEM*, Library Service (A-142D), American Lake Div, 9600 Veterans Dr SW, Bldg 71, 98493-5000. SAN 317-6924. Tel: 253-583-1513. Interlibrary Loan Service Tel: 253-583-1509. FAX: 253-589-4029. E-mail: alvalib@va.gov. *Chief, Librn Serv,* Jason M Oleston; Tel: 253-583-1510, E-mail: jason.oleston2@va.gov; *Sr Librn Tech,* Karen S Lowman; E-mail: karen.lowman@va.gov; *Librn Tech,* Arthur James Russell, III; E-mail: arthur.russell@va.gov; Staff 3 (MLS 1, Non-MLS 2)
Founded 1924
Library Holdings: AV Mats 1,000; Large Print Bks 150; Bk Titles 5,000; Per Subs 157; Talking Bks 200
Subject Interests: Addictions, Med, Nursing, Psychiat, Psychol, Substance abuse
Automation Activity & Vendor Info: (Cataloging) EOS International; (Circulation) EOS International; (OPAC) EOS International
Database Vendor: EBSCOhost, Library Systems & Services (LSSI), OCLC FirstSearch, OVID Technologies, PubMed, STAT!Ref (Teton Data Systems), UpToDate
Function: Audio & video playback equip for onsite use, Doc delivery serv, Health sci info serv, Photocopying/Printing, Satellite serv
Partic in Docline
Special Services for the Blind - Bks on cassette; Large print bks; Talking bks
Open Mon-Fri 8-4:15
Restriction: Non-circulating to the pub

S WASHINGTON STATE HISTORICAL SOCIETY RESEARCH CENTER*, Special Collections Division, 315 N Stadium Way, 98403. SAN 317-6932. Tel: 253-798-5914. FAX: 253-597-4186. *Head, Spec Coll,* Edward W Nolan; E-mail: enolan@wshs.wa.gov; *Curator,* Elaine Miller; Tel: 253-798-5915, E-mail: emiller@wshs.wa.gov; *Curator,* Joy Werlink; Tel: 253-798-5916, E-mail: jwerlink@wshs.wa.gov; Staff 2.6 (MLS 2.6)
Founded 1891
Library Holdings: Microforms 1,200; Music Scores 900; Bk Vols 15,700
Special Collections: Washington State (Asahel Curtis Coll), mss, photos
Subject Interests: Pac NW hist
Restriction: Open by appt only

TOKELAND

S SHOALWATER BAY TRIBAL COMMUNITY LIBRARY, 2373 Old Tokeland Rd, 98590. (Mail add: PO Box 130, 98590). Tel: 360-267-8190. FAX: 360-267-6778. Web Site: www.shoalwaterbay-nsn.gov. *Mgr,* Linda Rose; E-mail: lrose@shoalwaterbay-nsn.gov
Library Holdings: Bk Titles 6,000
Special Collections: Native American
Open Mon-Fri 8:30-4:30

TOPPENISH

C HERITAGE UNIVERSITY*, Donald K C North Library, 3240 Fort Rd, 98948. SAN 324-0541. Tel: 509-865-8523. Information Services Tel: 509-865-8521. Toll Free Tel: 888-272-6190. FAX: 509-865-4144. Web Site: www.heritage.edu. *Dir,* Reesa Zuber; Tel: 509-865-8500, Ext 3436, E-mail: zuber_r@heritage.edu; *Circ, ILL,* Deborah Van Allen; Tel: 509-865-8500, Ext 3430, E-mail: vanallen_d@heritage.edu; *Ref Serv, Tech Serv,* Colleen Veomett; Tel: 509-865-8500, Ext 3427, E-mail: veomett_c@heritage.edu; Staff 2 (MLS 1, Non-MLS 1)
Founded 1982. Enrl 1,300; Fac 150; Highest Degree: Master
Library Holdings: e-books 10,000; e-journals 20,000; Bk Titles 40,000; Per Subs 160
Special Collections: Native American Coll, Cultural Diversity Emphasis
Subject Interests: Bilingual educ
Automation Activity & Vendor Info: (Acquisitions) Ex Libris Group; (Cataloging) Ex Libris Group; (Circulation) Ex Libris Group; (Course Reserve) Ex Libris Group; (ILL) OCLC; (OPAC) Ex Libris Group; (Serials) EBSCO Online
Database Vendor: Cambridge Scientific Abstracts, EBSCOhost, Gale Cengage Learning, Oxford Online, ProQuest
Wireless access
Function: Res libr
Open Mon-Thurs 8-8, Fri 8-6, Sat 9-6

P YAKAMA NATION LIBRARY*, Yakama Nation Cultural Ctr, Hwy 97 at Fort Rd, 98948. (Mail add: PO Box 151, 98948-0151), SAN 324-0312. Tel: 509-865-2800, Ext 6, 509-865-5121, Ext 4721, 509-865-5121, Ext 4747. Toll Free Tel: 800-859-5121 (WA only). FAX: 509-865-6101. *Head Librn,* Vivian Adams; E-mail: vmadams@yakama.com; *Asst Head Librn,* Jolena Tillequots; E-mail: jolena@yakama.com; *Dir, Tech & Info Serv,* Merida Kipp; E-mail: mkipp@yakama.com; *Computer Spec,* Heidi Ineguez; *Librn Tech,* Cathy Miller; E-mail: catzmeow@yakama.com; *Librn Tech,* Jolena Tillequots; Staff 4 (MLS 1, Non-MLS 3)
Founded 1980. Pop 11,440; Circ 29,720
Library Holdings: Bk Vols 17,894; Per Subs 91; Spec Interest Per Sub 88
Special Collections: American Indian Coll; Dr Helen H Schuster Coll; Strongheart Archives (Nipo Strongheart Coll); Yakama Tribal (Yakama Nation Reference Coll). Oral History
Subject Interests: Am Indian
Automation Activity & Vendor Info: (Acquisitions) SerialsSolutions; (Cataloging) Follett Software; (Circulation) Follett Software; (Course Reserve) Follett Software; (ILL) OCLC WorldCat
Database Vendor: OCLC FirstSearch, ProQuest
Partic in OCLC Online Computer Library Center, Inc
Open Mon-Fri 8-5
Restriction: Residents only, Use of others with permission of librn
Branches: 1
ENVIRONMENTAL RESTORATION WASTE MANAGEMENT, 2808 Main St, Yakima, 98903. Tel: 509-452-2502. FAX: 509-452-2503. *Mgr,* Bernice Owens
Library Holdings: Bk Vols 3,000
Open Mon-Fri 8-5

TULALIP

P SNO-ISLE LIBRARIES, 7312 35th Ave NE, 98271-7417. SAN 363-681X. Tel: 360-651-7000. Toll Free Tel: 877-766-4753. FAX: 360-651-7151. Web Site: www.sno-isle.org. *Librn Dir,* Jonalyn Woolf-Ivory; Tel: 360-651-7008, E-mail: jwoolf-ivory@sno-isle.org; *Dep Dir,* Kendra Trachta; Tel: 360-651-7066, E-mail: ktrachta@sno-isle.org; *Communications Dir,* Ken Harvey; Tel: 360-651-7030, E-mail: kharvey@sno-isle.org; Staff 463 (MLS 91, Non-MLS 372)
Founded 1945. Pop 671,143; Circ 9,578,780
Library Holdings: Bk Vols 844,484
Automation Activity & Vendor Info: (Acquisitions) TLC (The Library Corporation); (Cataloging) TLC (The Library Corporation); (Circulation) TLC (The Library Corporation)
Database Vendor: TLC (The Library Corporation)
Wireless access
Partic in OCLC Online Computer Library Center, Inc
Open Mon-Fri 8-5
Friends of the Library Group

Branches: 21

ARLINGTON COMMUNITY LIBRARY, 135 N Washington Ave, Arlington, 98223, SAN 363-6844. Tel: 360-435-3033. FAX: 360-435-3854. *Managing Librn I,* Kathy Bullene; Staff 3 (MLS 3)
Founded 1981. Pop 23,716; Circ 325,098
Library Holdings: Bk Vols 34,062
Open Mon-Thurs 10-9, Fri & Sat 10-5, Sun (Sept-June) 1-5
Friends of the Library Group

BRIER COMMUNITY LIBRARY, 23303 Brier Rd, Brier, 98036, SAN 363-6860. Tel: 425-483-0888. FAX: 425-487-1880. *Br Mgr 1,* Marlene Moodie
Founded 1996. Pop 3,832; Circ 69,694
Library Holdings: Bk Vols 10,386
Open Mon-Wed 12-8, Fri 12-6, Sat 11-5
Friends of the Library Group

CAMANO ISLAND COMMUNITY LIBRARY, 848 N Sunrise Blvd, Camano Island, 98282. Tel: 360-387-5150. FAX: 360-387-5170. *Br Mgr 1,* David Menard; E-mail: dmenard@sno-isle.org
Pop 10,353; Circ 138,468
Library Holdings: Bk Vols 2,250
Open Mon 1-5, Tues-Thurs 10-7, Fri & Sat 10-5
Friends of the Library Group

CLINTON COMMUNITY LIBRARY, 4781 Deer Lake Rd, Clinton, 98236. (Mail add: PO Box 530, Clinton, 98236). Tel: 360-341-4280. FAX: 360-341-2989. *Br Mgr 1,* Debby Colfer
Founded 2000. Pop 4,747; Circ 63,836
Library Holdings: Bk Vols 3,508
Open Tues 11-7, Wed-Sat 11-5
Friends of the Library Group

COUPEVILLE COMMUNITY LIBRARY, 788 NW Alexander St, Coupeville, 98239. (Mail add: PO Box 745, Coupeville, 98239), SAN 363-6879. Tel: 360-678-4911. FAX: 360-678-5261. *Br Mgr 1,* Leslie Franzen
Founded 1988. Pop 7,260; Circ 191,520
Library Holdings: Bk Vols 14,581
Open Mon & Wed 10-8, Tues & Thurs-Sat 10-5
Friends of the Library Group

DARRINGTON COMMUNITY LIBRARY, 1005 Cascade St, Darrington, 98241. (Mail add: PO Box 25, Darrington, 98241), SAN 363-6909. Tel: 360-436-1600. FAX: 360-436-1659. *Br Mgr 1,* Bryan Stratton
Founded 1990. Pop 1,924; Circ 54,937
Library Holdings: Bk Vols 7,136
Open Mon & Wed 11-8, Tues & Thurs-Sat 11-5
Friends of the Library Group

EDMONDS COMMUNITY LIBRARY, 650 Main St, Edmonds, 98020, SAN 363-6933. Tel: 425-771-1933. FAX: 425-771-1977. *Managing Librn I,* Lesly Kaplan; Staff 4 (MLS 4)
Founded 1982. Pop 32,214; Circ 451,262
Library Holdings: Bk Vols 63,132
Open Mon-Thurs 9-8, Fri 9-6, Sat 9-5, Sun 1-5
Friends of the Library Group

FREELAND BRANCH, 5495 Harbor Ave, Freeland, 98249. (Mail add: PO Box 1357, Freeland, 98249-1357), SAN 363-6968. Tel: 360-331-7323. FAX: 360-331-1572. *Managing Librn,* Betsy Arand; *Children & Teen Librn,* Jayanne Bixby; Staff 2 (MLS 2)
Founded 1994. Pop 4,100; Circ 192,584
Library Holdings: Bk Vols 15,900
Function: Art exhibits, Audiobks via web, Bk reviews (Group), Bks on CD, Children's prog, Citizenship assistance, Computer training, Computers for patron use, Copy machines, Digital talking bks, e-mail & chat, E-Reserves, Electronic databases & coll, Exhibits, Family literacy, Fax serv, Free DVD rentals, Handicapped accessible, Homebound delivery serv, ILL available, Mail & tel request accepted, Music CDs, Online cat, Online ref, Online searches, Outreach serv, Outside serv via phone, mail, e-mail & web, OverDrive digital audio bks, Photocopying/Printing, Preschool outreach, Prog for adults, Prog for children & young adult, Ref serv in person, Story hour, Summer & winter reading prog, Summer reading prog, Tax forms, Teen prog, Telephone ref, Wheelchair accessible
Open Mon, Tues & Thurs 11-8, Wed, Fri & Sat 10-5, Sun (Sept-June) 1-5
Friends of the Library Group

GRANITE FALLS COMMUNITY LIBRARY, 815 E Galena St, Granite Falls, 98252, SAN 363-6992. Tel: 360-691-6087. FAX: 360-691-5533. *Managing Librn I,* Jude Anderson; Staff 1 (MLS 1)
Founded 2001. Pop 6,658; Circ 127,523
Library Holdings: Bk Vols 22,559
Open Mon-Thurs 11-8, Fri & Sat 11-5
Friends of the Library Group

LAKE STEVENS COMMUNITY LIBRARY, 1804 Main St, Lake Stevens, 98258-7712. (Mail add: PO Box 217, Lake Stevens, 98258-0217), SAN 363-7026. Tel: 425-334-1900. FAX: 425-334-9487. *Managing Librn I,* Chy Ross; Staff 2 (MLS 2)
Founded 1988. Pop 16,044; Circ 179,722
Library Holdings: Bk Vols 19,338

Open Mon-Thurs 11-8, Fri & Sat 11-5
Friends of the Library Group

LANGLEY COMMUNITY LIBRARY, 104 Second St, Langley, 98260. (Mail add: PO Box 365, Langley, 98260-0365), SAN 363-7050. Tel: 360-221-4383. FAX: 360-221-3067. *Br Mgr 1,* Vicky Welfare; E-mail: vwelfare@sno-isle.org
Founded 1922. Pop 4,732; Circ 127,698
Library Holdings: Bk Vols 9,268
Function: ILL available
Open Mon-Wed 10-7, Thurs 10-5, Fri & Sat 11-5
Friends of the Library Group

LYNNWOOD COMMUNITY LIBRARY, 19200 44th Ave W, Lynnwood, 98036, SAN 363-7085. Tel: 425-778-2148. Reference Toll Free Tel: 800-645-7596. FAX: 425-774-7764. TDD: 800-647-3753. E-mail: lynnref@sno-isle.org. *Managing Librn III,* Michael Delury; Staff 9 (MLS 9)
Founded 1971. Pop 50,015; Circ 1,026,170
Library Holdings: Bk Vols 125,424
Special Services for the Deaf - TTY equip
Open Mon-Thurs 10-9, Fri 10-6, Sat 10-5, Sun 1-5
Friends of the Library Group

MARYSVILLE COMMUNITY LIBRARY, 6120 Grove St, Marysville, 98270, SAN 363-7115. Tel: 360-658-5000. FAX: 360-659-5050. *Managing Librn II,* Eric Spencer; Staff 6 (MLS 6)
Founded 1995. Pop 43,889; Circ 888,980
Library Holdings: Bk Vols 121,774
Open Mon-Thurs 10-9, Fri 10-6, Sat 10-5, Sun 1-5
Friends of the Library Group

MILL CREEK COMMUNITY LIBRARY, 15429 Bothell Everett Hwy, Mill Creek, 98012, SAN 328-9044. Tel: 425-337-4822. FAX: 425-337-3567. *Managing Librn I,* Darlene Weber; Staff 5 (MLS 5)
Founded 1987. Pop 53,453; Circ 789,106
Library Holdings: Bk Vols 51,002
Open Mon-Thurs 10-9, Fri 10-6, Sat 10-5, Sun 1-5
Friends of the Library Group

MONROE COMMUNITY LIBRARY, 1070 Village Way, Monroe, 98272, SAN 363-714X. Tel: 360-794-7851. FAX: 360-794-0292. *Managing Librn I,* Betsy Lewis; E-mail: blewis@sno-isle.org; Staff 3 (MLS 3)
Founded 2002. Pop 18,017; Circ 418,908
Library Holdings: Bk Vols 40,235
Open Mon-Thurs 10-9, Fri & Sat 10-5, Sun 1-5
Friends of the Library Group

MOUNTLAKE TERRACE COMMUNITY LIBRARY, 23300 58th Ave W, Mountlake Terrace, 98043, SAN 363-7174. Tel: 425-776-8722. FAX: 425-776-3411. *Managing Librn I,* Rosy Brewer; Staff 3 (MLS 3)
Founded 1988. Pop 12,994; Circ 205,072
Library Holdings: Bk Vols 26,824
Open Mon-Thurs 10-9, Fri 10-6, Sat 10-5, Sun 1-5
Friends of the Library Group

MUKILTEO COMMUNITY LIBRARY, 4675 Harbour Pointe Blvd, Mukilteo, 98275. Tel: 425-493-8202. FAX: 425-493-1601. *Managing Librn I,* Jane Crawford; Staff 5 (MLS 5)
Founded 1998. Pop 16,017; Circ 557,602
Library Holdings: Bk Vols 61,645
Open Mon-Thurs 10-9, Fri 10-6, Sat 10-5, Sun 1-5
Friends of the Library Group

OAK HARBOR COMMUNITY LIBRARY, 1000 SE Regatta Dr, Oak Harbor, 98277, SAN 363-7263. Tel: 360-675-5115. FAX: 360-679-3761. *Managing Librn II,* Mary Campbell; Staff 4 (MLS 4)
Pop 28,381; Circ 457,353
Library Holdings: Bk Vols 42,398
Open Mon-Thurs 9-8, Fri 9-5, Sat 10-5, Sun 1-5
Friends of the Library Group

SNOHOMISH COMMUNITY LIBRARY, 311 Maple Ave, Snohomish, 98290, SAN 363-7328. Tel: 360-568-2898. FAX: 360-568-6357. Reference FAX: 360-568-1922. *Managing Librn II,* Rebecca Loney; Staff 4 (MLS 4)
Founded 2003. Pop 35,504; Circ 617,170
Library Holdings: Bk Vols 62,556
Special Collections: Genealogy Coll; Local History Coll
Open Mon-Thurs 10-9, Fri & Sat 10-5, Sun 1-5
Friends of the Library Group

STANWOOD COMMUNITY LIBRARY, 9701 271st St NW, Stanwood, 98292-8097. (Mail add: PO Box 247, Stanwood, 98292-0247), SAN 363-7352. Tel: 360-629-3132. FAX: 360-629-3516. *Managing Librn I,* Jill Wubbenhorst; Staff 3 (MLS 3)
Founded 1970. Pop 11,425; Circ 277,964
Library Holdings: Bk Vols 23,670
Open Mon-Thurs 10-8, Fri & Sat 10-5, Sun 1-5
Friends of the Library Group

SULTAN COMMUNITY LIBRARY, 319 Main St, Ste 100, Sultan, 98294. (Mail add: PO Box 580, Sultan, 98294), SAN 363-7417. Tel: 360-793-1695. FAX: 360-793-9634. *Br Mgr 1,* Jackie Personeus
Founded 1999. Pop 7,591; Circ 142,748
Library Holdings: Bk Vols 13,361

Open Mon-Thurs 11-8, Fri & Sat 11-5
Friends of the Library Group
Bookmobiles: 2

TUMWATER

P   TIMBERLAND REGIONAL LIBRARY*, 415 Tumwater Blvd SW,
98501-5799. SAN 363-7506. Tel: 360-943-5001. Reference Tel:
360-704-4636. Toll Free Tel: 877-284-6237. FAX: 360-586-6838.
Reference FAX: 360-704-4610. Web Site: www.trlib.org. *Exec Dir,* Jodi
Reng; Tel: 360-943-5001, Ext 2501, E-mail: jreng@trlib.org; *Dir, Human
Res,* Rich Park; Tel: 360-943-5001, Ext 2513, E-mail: rpark@trlib.org;
Admin Serv Mgr, Mike Crose; Tel: 360-943-5001, Ext 2517, E-mail:
mcrose@trlib.org; *Cent Ref Mgr,* Alice Goudeaux; Tel: 360-943-5001, Ext
2620, E-mail: agoudeaux@trlib.org; *Coll Mgr,* Judy Covell; Tel:
360-943-5001, Ext 2526, E-mail: jcovell@trlib.org; *Communications Mgr,*
Jeff Kleingartner; Tel: 360-943-5001, Ext 2507, E-mail:
jkleingartner@trlib.org; *Computer Serv Mgr,* Gwen Culp; Tel:
360-943-5001, Ext 2518, E-mail: gculp@trlib.org; *Pub Serv Mgr,* Sally
Nash; Tel: 360-943-5001, Ext 2554, E-mail: snash@trlib.org; *Adult Serv
Coordr,* Tim Mallory; Tel: 360-943-5001, Ext 2502, E-mail:
tmallory@trlib.org; *Youth Serv Coordr,* Ellen Duffy; Tel: 360-943-5001,
Ext 2576, E-mail: eduffy@trlib.org. Subject Specialists: *Communications,
Pub relations,* Jeff Kleingartner; Staff 66.5 (MLS 56.125, Non-MLS
10.375)
Founded 1968. Pop 458,975; Circ 4,841,244
Library Holdings: Audiobooks 77,130; AV Mats 195,712; e-books 3,655;
Bk Vols 1,063,110; Per Subs 3,602; Talking Bks 147,748
Special Collections: State Document Depository
Subject Interests: Genealogy, Sheet music
Automation Activity & Vendor Info: (Acquisitions) SirsiDynix;
(Cataloging) SirsiDynix; (Circulation) SirsiDynix; (OPAC) SirsiDynix
Database Vendor: Gale Cengage Learning, netLibrary, OCLC FirstSearch,
ProQuest
Wireless access
Function: Audio & video playback equip for onsite use, Digital talking
bks, Handicapped accessible, Home delivery & serv to Sr ctr & nursing
homes, Homebound delivery serv, ILL available, Large print keyboards,
Libr develop, Magnifiers for reading, Online searches,
Photocopying/Printing, Prog for adults, Prog for children & young adult,
Ref serv available, Summer reading prog, Telephone ref, Wheelchair
accessible
Friends of the Library Group
Branches: 27
W H ABEL MEMORIAL LIBRARY, 125 Main St S, Montesano,
98563-3794, SAN 363-7530. Tel: 360-249-4211. FAX: 360-249-4203. *Br
Mgr,* Valerie Jester; Staff 2 (MLS 1, Non-MLS 1)
Founded 1960. Circ 88,363
Open Tues 10-7, Thurs & Fri 10-5, Sat 10-4
Friends of the Library Group
ABERDEEN BRANCH, 121 E Market St, Aberdeen, 98520-5292, SAN
363-7565. Tel: 360-533-2360. FAX: 360-533-9771. *Libr Mgr,* Christine
Peck; Staff 11 (MLS 4, Non-MLS 7)
Founded 1890. Circ 229,777
Open Mon & Tues 10-7, Wed & Thurs 10-6, Fri & Sat 10-5
Friends of the Library Group
AMANDA PARK TIMBERLAND LIBRARY, 6118 US Hwy 101,
Amanda Park, 98526-0089. (Mail add: PO Drawer K, Amanda Park,
98526-0089), SAN 363-7573. Tel: 360-288-2725. FAX: 360-288-2376.
Libr Mgr, Kathy Clayton; Staff 1 (Non-MLS 1)
Founded 1977. Circ 18,806
Open Tues 10-5, Wed 3-8, Thurs 12-7, Sat 10-3
Friends of the Library Group
CENTRALIA TIMBERLAND LIBRARY, 110 S Silver St, Centralia,
98531-4218, SAN 363-759X. Tel: 360-736-0183. FAX: 360-330-7530.
Libr Mgr, Virginia Burns; Staff 11 (MLS 5, Non-MLS 6)
Founded 1913. Circ 345,020
Open Mon & Tues 10-7, Wed & Thurs 11-7, Fri & Sat 10-5
Friends of the Library Group
ELMA BRANCH, 118 N First, Elma, 98541-0547. (Mail add: PO Box Q,
Elma, 98541-0547), SAN 363-7689. Tel: 360-482-3737. FAX:
360-482-3047. *Librn,* David Seckman; Staff 3 (MLS 1, Non-MLS 2)
Circ 81,914
Open Tues-Thurs 11-7, Fri & Sat 11-5
Friends of the Library Group
HOODSPORT BRANCH, N 40 Schoolhouse Hill Rd, Hoodsport, 98548.
(Mail add: PO Box 847, Hoodsport, 98548-0847), SAN 372-512X. Tel:
360-877-9339. FAX: 360-877-9695. *Br Mgr,* Nancy Triplett; Staff 2
(Non-MLS 2)
Founded 1989. Circ 35,541
Open Tues, Wed & Sat 11-5, Thurs 1-7
Friends of the Library Group

HOQUIAM BRANCH, 420 Seventh St, Hoquiam, 98550-3616, SAN
363-7719. Tel: 360-532-1710. FAX: 360-538-9608. *Br Mgr,* Mary
Thornton; Staff 4 (MLS 1, Non-MLS 3)
Founded 1909. Circ 92,798
Open Tues-Thurs 10-7, Fri & Sat 10-4
Friends of the Library Group
ILWACO BRANCH, 158 First Ave N, Ilwaco, 98624. (Mail add: PO Box
520, Ilwaco, 98624-0520), SAN 363-7743. Tel: 360-642-3908. FAX:
360-642-8417. *Br Mgr,* Kristine Pointer; Staff 2.1 (Non-MLS 2.1)
Circ 44,337
Function: Bks on cassette, Bks on CD, Children's prog, Computers for
patron use, Copy machines, Digital talking bks, Electronic databases &
coll, Family literacy, Free DVD rentals, Homebound delivery serv, ILL
available, Mail & tel request accepted, Mus passes, Music CDs,
Photocopying/Printing, Preschool outreach, Prog for adults, Prog for
children & young adult, Pub access computers, Ref serv available, Ref
serv in person, Story hour, Summer reading prog, Tax forms, Teen prog,
Telephone ref, Wheelchair accessible
Open Tues & Thurs 10-7, Fri 10-5, Sat 10-3
Friends of the Library Group
LACEY BRANCH, 500 College St SE, Lacey, 98503-1240, SAN
363-7778. Tel: 360-491-3860. FAX: 360-459-6714. *Sr Libr Mgr,* Selina
Gomez-Beloz; Staff 21 (MLS 5, Non-MLS 16)
Founded 1966. Circ 804,555
Open Mon & Tues 10-6, Wed & Thurs 10-7, Fri & Sat 10-5
Friends of the Library Group
MCCLEARY BRANCH, 121 S Fourth St, McCleary, 98557. (Mail add:
PO Box 660, McCleary, 98557-0660), SAN 329-6792. Tel:
360-495-3368. FAX: 360-495-4496. *Librn,* Karen Kienenberger; Staff 2
(MLS 1, Non-MLS 1)
Founded 1969
Open Tues & Wed 10-5, Thurs 1-8, Sat 10-3
Friends of the Library Group
MOUNTAIN VIEW, 210 Silverbrook Rd, Randle, 98377. (Mail add: PO
Box 340, Randle, 98377-0340), SAN 328-7114. Tel: 360-497-2665.
FAX: 360-497-7080. *Br Mgr,* Nancy Sawyer; Staff 2 (Non-MLS 2)
Founded 1988
Open Tues & Thurs 10-6, Wed 2-7, Sat 10-4
Friends of the Library Group
NASELLE BRANCH, Four Parpala Rd, Naselle, 98638. (Mail add: PO
Box 190, Naselle, 98638-0190), SAN 328-7092. Tel: 360-484-3877.
FAX: 360-484-3445. *Br Mgr,* Michelle Zilli; Staff 2 (MLS 1, Non-MLS
1)
Founded 1986. Circ 35,463
Library Holdings: Bk Vols 14,000
Open Tues & Wed 11-8, Fri 11-5, Sat 11-3
Friends of the Library Group
NORTH MASON, 23081 NE State Rte 3, Belfair, 98528-9334. (Mail add:
PO Box 1179, Belfair, 98528-1179), SAN 363-7867. Tel: 360-275-3232.
FAX: 360-275-6999. *Br Mgr,* Victoria Rexford; Staff 5 (MLS 2,
Non-MLS 3)
Founded 1950. Circ 139,054
Open Tues-Thurs 10-7, Fri & Sat 10-5
Friends of the Library Group
OAKVILLE BRANCH, 204 Main St, Oakville, 98568. (Mail add: PO Box
G, Oakville, 98568-0079), SAN 363-7891. Tel: 360-273-5305. FAX:
360-273-7446. *Br Mgr,* Deborah Baker-Receniello; Staff 1 (Non-MLS 1)
Circ 17,114
Open Tues, Wed & Sat 10-4, Thurs 2-8
Friends of the Library Group
OCEAN PARK BRANCH, 1308 256th Pl, Ocean Park, 98640. (Mail add:
PO Box 310, Ocean Park, 98640-0310), SAN 363-7905. Tel:
360-665-4184. FAX: 360-665-5983. *Br Mgr,* Iver Matheson; Staff 3
(MLS 1, Non-MLS 2)
Founded 1944. Circ 69,868
Open Tues & Thurs-Sat 10-4, Wed 10-8
Friends of the Library Group
OLYMPIA BRANCH, 313 Eighth Ave SE, Olympia, 98501-1307, SAN
363-7921. Tel: 360-352-0595. Reference Tel: 360-704-4636.
Administration Tel: 360-943-5001. FAX: 360-586-3207. *Librn,* Cheryl
Heywood; Staff 21 (MLS 6, Non-MLS 15)
Pop 40,000; Circ 873,603
Subject Interests: Genealogy, Music
Function: Adult bk club, Adult literacy prog, Audiobks via web,
Bilingual assistance for Spanish patrons, Bk club(s), Bks on cassette, Bks
on CD, Chess club, Children's prog, Computer training, Computers for
patron use, Copy machines, Digital talking bks, Distance learning,
Electronic databases & coll, Free DVD rentals, Genealogy discussion
group, Handicapped accessible, Holiday prog, Home delivery & serv to
Sr ctr & nursing homes, Homework prog, ILL available, Instruction &
testing, Music CDs, Online cat, Online ref, Orientations, Outreach serv,
Photocopying/Printing, Preschool outreach, Prog for adults, Prog for
children & young adult, Pub access computers, Ref serv available, Senior
computer classes, Senior outreach, Spoken cassettes & CDs, Spoken
cassettes & DVDs, Story hour, Summer reading prog, Tax forms, Teen

prog, Telephone ref, VHS videos, Video lending libr, Web-catalog, Wheelchair accessible, Workshops, Writing prog
Open Mon & Tues 11-8, Wed & Thurs 11-7, Fri & Sat 10-5
Friends of the Library Group
PACKWOOD BRANCH, 109 W Main St, Packwood, 98361. (Mail add: PO Box 589, Packwood, 98361-0589), SAN 363-8103. Tel: 360-494-5111. FAX: 360-494-9237. *Br Mgr,* Elizabeth Squires; Staff 2 (Non-MLS 2)
Founded 1973. Circ 32,122
Open Tues, Fri & Sat 11-3, Thurs 11-6
Friends of the Library Group
RAYMOND BRANCH, 507 Duryea St, Raymond, 98577-1829, SAN 363-7956. Tel: 360-942-2408. Toll Free Tel: 800-562-6022. FAX: 360-942-5670. *Mgr,* Emily Popovich; E-mail: epopovich@trl.org; Staff 4 (MLS 1, Non-MLS 3)
Founded 1913. Pop 10,000; Circ 49,371
Database Vendor: Factiva.com, infoUSA, LearningExpress, OneSource, Oxford Online, ReferenceUSA, SirsiDynix, Standard & Poor's, Telus, ValueLine
Function: Adult bk club, Adult literacy prog, Audiobks via web, Bks on cassette, Bks on CD, CD-ROM, Children's prog, Computer training, Computers for patron use, Copy machines, Digital talking bks, Electronic databases & coll, Handicapped accessible, ILL available, Magnifiers for reading, Mail & tel request accepted, Mus passes, Music CDs, Online cat, Online ref, Online searches, Outreach serv, Outside serv via phone, mail, e-mail & web, OverDrive digital audio bks, Preschool outreach, Prog for adults, Prog for children & young adult, Pub access computers, Ref serv available, Senior computer classes, Story hour, Summer reading prog, Tax forms, Teen prog, Telephone ref, VHS videos, Web-catalog, Wheelchair accessible
Open Tues & Thurs 11-7, Wed & Fri 11-5, Sat 11-4
Friends of the Library Group
WILLIAM G REED LIBRARY, 710 W Alder St, Shelton, 98584-2571, SAN 363-7972. Tel: 360-426-1362. FAX: 360-427-2025. Web Site: www.trlib.org/locations/shelton.aspx. *Br Mgr,* Patty Ayala Ross; Staff 12 (MLS 4, Non-MLS 8)
Founded 1974. Circ 308,304
Library Holdings: Bk Titles 100,000; Per Subs 279
Open Mon-Thurs 10-7, Fri & Sat 11-5
Friends of the Library Group
SALKUM BRANCH, 2480 US Hwy 12, Salkum, 98582. (Mail add: PO Box 120, Salkum, 98582-0120), SAN 328-7130. Tel: 360-985-2148. FAX: 360-985-7704. *Br Mgr,* Cherie Rusk; Staff 2 (MLS 1, Non-MLS 1)
Founded 1986. Circ 70,323
Open Tues & Fri 10-5, Wed & Thurs 1-8, Sat 10-4
Friends of the Library Group
VERNETTA SMITH CHEHALIS TIMBERLAND LIBRARY, 400 N Market Blvd, Chehalis, 98532. (Mail add: PO Box 419, Chehalis, 98532-0419), SAN 363-762X. Tel: 360-748-3301. FAX: 360-748-2169. *Libr Mgr,* Corine Aiken; Staff 5.875 (MLS 1, Non-MLS 4.875)
Founded 1910. Circ 130,714
Open Tues & Wed 10-8, Thurs 10-7, Fri 10-5, Sat 10-4
Friends of the Library Group
SOUTH BEND BRANCH, First & Pacific, South Bend, 98586. (Mail add: PO Box 368, South Bend, 98586-0368), SAN 363-7980. Tel: 360-875-5532. FAX: 360-875-6563. *Br Mgr,* JoAnn Rucker; Staff 1 (Non-MLS 1)
Founded 1913. Circ 23,662
Open Tues & Wed 10-5, Fri 10-4, Sat 10-3
Friends of the Library Group
TENINO BRANCH, 172 Central Ave W, Tenino, 98589. (Mail add: PO Box 4017, Tenino, 98589-4017), SAN 363-8006. Tel: 360-264-2369. FAX: 360-264-6846. *Libr Mgr,* Ryan Williams; Staff 2 (MLS 1, Non-MLS 1)
Circ 44,976
Open Tues & Wed 11-6, Thurs & Fri 11-5, Sat 11-4
Friends of the Library Group
TUMWATER BRANCH, 7023 New Market St, 98501-6563, SAN 363-8014. Tel: 360-943-7790. FAX: 360-586-9028. *Br Head,* Gail Park; Staff 15 (MLS 7, Non-MLS 8)
Circ 482,583
Open Mon & Tues 10-7, Wed & Thurs 10-6, Fri & Sat 10-5
Friends of the Library Group
WESTPORT BRANCH, 101 E Harms Ave, Westport, 98595. (Mail add: PO Box 1410, Westport, 98595-1410), SAN 363-8049. Tel: 360-268-0521. FAX: 360-268-0558. *Br Mgr,* Kathleen Ringenberg; Staff 2 (Non-MLS 2)
Founded 1963. Circ 41,756
Open Tues & Thurs 11-7, Wed & Fri 11-5, Sat 12-4
Friends of the Library Group
WINLOCK BRANCH, 322 First St, Winlock, 98596. (Mail add: PO Box 428, Winlock, 98596-0428), SAN 363-8073. Tel: 360-785-3461. FAX: 360-785-3800. *Libr Mgr,* Jamie Allwine; E-mail: jallwine@trlib.org; Staff 4 (MLS 1, Non-MLS 3)
Circ 95,421

Open Tues 12-8, Wed-Sat 10-5
Friends of the Library Group
YELM BRANCH, 210 Prairie Park St, Yelm, 98597, SAN 363-8138. Tel: 360-458-3374. FAX: 360-458-5172. *Br Mgr,* Mike Wessells; Staff 8 (MLS 2, Non-MLS 6)
Founded 1975. Circ 250,270
Open Tues-Thurs 10-8, Fri & Sat 10-5
Friends of the Library Group

P   WASHINGTON STATE LIBRARY, 6880 Capitol Blvd S, 98501-5513. (Mail add: PO Box 42460, Olympia, 98504-2460), SAN 363-8162. Tel: 360-704-5200. Circulation Tel: 360-704-5213. Interlibrary Loan Service Tel: 360-704-5252. Reference Tel: 360-704-5221. Toll Free Tel: 866-538-4996. FAX: 360-586-7575. Web Site: www.sos.wa.gov/library. *Actg State Librn,* Rand Simmons; Tel: 360-570-5585, E-mail: rand.simmons@sos.wa.gov; *Dep State Librn,* Marlys Rudeen; Tel: 360-704-7132, E-mail: mrudeen@sos.wa.gov; Staff 71.1 (MLS 33.5, Non-MLS 37.6)
Founded 1853
Library Holdings: Braille Volumes 31,824; Bk Vols 1,600,000; Per Subs 1,984; Talking Bks 298,698
Special Collections: Northwest Historical Territory Colls; Washington Newspapers; Washington State Documents. State Document Depository; US Document Depository
Subject Interests: Behav sci, Ecology, Energy, Environ studies, Health, Local govt, Med, Polit sci, Soc sci, State govt, Transportation
Automation Activity & Vendor Info: (Circulation) Innovative Interfaces, Inc
Database Vendor: OCLC FirstSearch, ProQuest
Wireless access
Function: Ref serv available
Publications: Directory of Washington Libraries; Public Administration Bibliography (Monthly); Washington Public Library Statistics; Washington State Publications (Monthly)
Special Services for the Deaf - Captioned film dep
Special Services for the Blind - Aids for in-house use; Assistive/Adapted tech devices, equip & products; Audio mat; Audiovision-a radio reading serv; Bks & mags in Braille, on rec, tape & cassette; Bks available with recordings; Bks on cassette; Braille & cassettes; Braille bks; Cassette playback machines; Cassettes; Children's Braille; Digital talking bk; Extensive large print coll; Home delivery serv; Large print & cassettes; Large print bks; Local mags & bks recorded; Machine repair; Mags & bk reproduction/duplication; Production of talking bks; Radio reading serv; Recorded bks; Sound rec; Soundproof reading booth; Talking bk & rec for the blind cat; Talking bks; Talking bks & player equip; Tel Pioneers equip repair group; Thermoform Brailon duplicator; Transcribing serv; Volunteer serv; Web-Braille
Open Mon-Fri 8-5
Friends of the Library Group
Branches: 17
AIRWAY HEIGHTS CORRECTION CENTER, 11919 W Sprague Ave, Airway Heights, 99001. (Mail add: PO Box 1899, Airway Heights, 99001-1899), SAN 378-2115. Tel: 509-244-6700, Ext 6239. FAX: 509-244-6727. E-mail: ahcc@secstate.wa.gov. *Librn,* Joyce Hanna; E-mail: jhanna@secstate.wa.gov; Staff 1 (Non-MLS 1)
Founded 1995
Library Holdings: High Interest/Low Vocabulary Bk Vols 249; Bk Vols 18,621; Per Subs 70
Open Mon 7:30am-8:30pm, Tues 12-8:30, Wed-Fri 7:30-4
CLALLAM BAY CORRECTION CENTER, 1830 Eagle Crest Way, Clallam Bay, 98326-9775, SAN 328-2287. Tel: 360-963-3216. FAX: 360-963-3293. E-mail: cbcc@sos.wa.gov. *Libr Assoc,* Valerie E Mullen; Staff 1 (Non-MLS 1)
Library Holdings: Bk Vols 13,987; Per Subs 62
Open Mon & Tues 12:30-9, Wed-Fri 7:30-4
DEPARTMENT OF LABOR & INDUSTRIES, 7273 Linderson Way SW, 98501. (Mail add: PO Box 44606, Olympia, 98504-4606), SAN 363-8359. Tel: 360-902-5498. Circulation Tel: 360-902-5421. Interlibrary Loan Service Tel: 360-902-6107. FAX: 360-902-6335. E-mail: libraryservices@lni.wa.gov. *Libr Mgr,* Lisa Engvall; E-mail: ganl235@lni.wa.gov; *Libr & Archive Prof 2,* Steve Hanson; E-mail: hasw235@lni.wa.gov; *Libr & Archives Paraprofessional 4,* Brian Frisina; E-mail: frib235@lni.wa.gov; Staff 3 (MLS 2, Non-MLS 1)
Library Holdings: Audiobooks 8; CDs 30; DVDs 75; e-journals 10; Bk Vols 7,500; Per Subs 45
Special Collections: Industry Consensus Standards
Subject Interests: Occupational health, Occupational safety, Workmen's compensation ins
Automation Activity & Vendor Info: (Circulation) Innovative Interfaces, Inc - Millenium; (OPAC) Innovative Interfaces, Inc - Millenium
Database Vendor: LexisNexis, OCLC FirstSearch, OCLC WorldCat, PubMed, Scopus, STAT!Ref (Teton Data Systems)
Open Mon-Fri 8-5

DEPARTMENT OF TRANSPORTATION, Department of Transportation, Olympia, 98504. (Mail add: PO Box 47425, Olympia, 98504-7425), SAN 363-8588. Tel: 360-705-7750. FAX: 360-705-6831. *Librn,* Kathy Szolomayer; E-mail: SzolomK@wsdot.wa.gov; *Ref Librn,* Mike Wendt; Tel: 360-705-7710, E-mail: WendtM@wsdot.wa.gov
Library Holdings: Bk Vols 2,000; Per Subs 300
Subject Interests: Hwy construction, Hwy eng, Tech innovation, Tech transfer, Transportation planning
Partic in OCLC Online Computer Library Center, Inc
Publications: Accessions List

EASTERN STATE HOSPITAL, Maple St, Medical Lake, 99022. (Mail add: PO Box 800, Medical Lake, 99022-0800). Tel: 509-299-4276, 509-299-4500. FAX: 509-299-4555. E-mail: esh@secstate.wa.gov. *Prog Mgr,* Laura Sherbo; Staff 1 (Non-MLS 1)
Library Holdings: Bk Vols 6,500; Per Subs 65
Subject Interests: Mental health
Open Tues, Thurs & Fri 7:30-4

MCNEIL ISLAND CORRECTION CENTER, PO Box 88900, MS-WT-01, Steilacoom, 98388-0900, SAN 363-8448. Tel: 253-512-6586. FAX: 253-512-6587. E-mail: micc@secstate.wa.gov. *Br Mgr,* Laura Sherbo; E-mail: lsherbo@secstate.wa.gov; *Asst Librn,* Earl Dungey; E-mail: wdungey@secstate.wa.gov; Staff 1 (Non-MLS 1)
Open Mon, Thurs & Fri 8-4, Tues & Wed 8-8

NATURAL RESOURCES BUILDING, PO Box 47000, Olympia, 98504-7000, SAN 378-2131. Tel: 360-902-2992. FAX: 360-902-2607. E-mail: nrblibrary@dfw.wa.gov. *Libr Assoc,* Ruth Keller; Staff 0.4 (Non-MLS 0.4)
Library Holdings: Bk Vols 20,000

STAFFORD CREEK CORRECTIONAL CENTER BRANCH LIBRARY, 191 Constantine Way, MS WA-39, Aberdeen, 98520, SAN 363-8197. Tel: 360-537-2258. FAX: 360-537-2501. *Libr Assoc,* Jeannie Remillard; E-mail: jremillard@secstate.wa.gov

TWIN RIVERS UNIT BRANCH LIBRARY OF THE MONROE CORRECTIONAL COMPLEX, 16774 170th Dr SE, Monroe, 98272. (Mail add: PO Box 888, MS-NM-85, Monroe, 98272-0888), SAN 363-8553. Tel: 360-794-2481. Interlibrary Loan Service Tel: 360-794-2445. FAX: 360-794-2417. E-mail: trcc@sos.wa.gov. ; Staff 1 (Non-MLS 1)
Founded 1984
Library Holdings: Bk Titles 17,000; Per Subs 25
Subject Interests: Popular fiction
Partic in OCLC Online Computer Library Center, Inc; Washington Libr Network
Open Mon, Wed & Fri 7-3:30, Tues & Thurs 12-8:30

UTILITIES & TRANSPORTATION COMMISSION, 1300 S Evergreen Pk Dr SW, Olympia, 98504. (Mail add: PO Box 47250, Olympia, 98504-7250), SAN 327-9375. Tel: 360-664-1203. Circulation Tel: 360-664-1198. Reference Tel: 360-664-1199. FAX: 360-586-1145. *Managing Librn,* Mary Lu H White; E-mail: mwhite@wutc.wa.gov; Staff 2 (MLS 1, Non-MLS 1)
Founded 1986
Library Holdings: Bk Vols 5,000; Per Subs 300
Subject Interests: Micro econ, Pipelines, RR, Transportation regulation, Trucking, Utility mgt
Function: Ref serv available

WASHINGTON CORRECTION CENTER SHELTON BRANCH, PO Box 900, MS WS-01, Shelton, 98584-0974. Tel: 360-426-4433, Ext 5505. E-mail: wcc@sos.wa.gov. *Br Librn,* Jill Merritt; Tel: 360-432-1509; Staff 2 (MLS 1, Non-MLS 1)
Open Mon & Tues 11:45-8:15, Fri 7:45-4:15

WASHINGTON CORRECTIONS CENTER FOR WOMEN, 9601 Bujacich Rd NW, MS WP-04, Gig Harbor, 98332-8300, SAN 378-2158. Tel: 253-858-4230. FAX: 253-858-4271. E-mail: wccw@secstate.wa.gov. *Librn,* Doug Andre Gelis; E-mail: dgelis@secstate.wa.gov; Staff 2 (MLS 1, Non-MLS 1)
Library Holdings: High Interest/Low Vocabulary Bk Vols 179; Bk Titles 12,000; Bk Vols 13,236; Per Subs 84
Function: ILL available
Open Mon-Fri 8-4:30

WASHINGTON STATE PENITENTIARY BRANCH LIBRARY-MAIN INSTITUTION, 1313 N 13th Ave, Walla Walla, 99362-8817. Tel: 509-525-3610, 509-526-6408. FAX: 509-526-6469. E-mail: wsp-mi@secstate.wa.gov. *Libr Assoc,* Jill Merritt
Open Mon & Tues 12-9, Wed 8-4:30, Thur & Fri 8-4

WASHINGTON STATE PENITENTIARY BRANCH LIBRARY-MEDIUM, 1313 N 13th Ave, Walla Walla, 99362-1065, SAN 363-8618. Tel: 509-525-3610, Ext 2088. FAX: 509-526-6453. E-mail: wsp-msc@secstate.wa.gov. *In Charge,* Robert Fendler; E-mail: rfendler@secstate.wa.gov
Library Holdings: High Interest/Low Vocabulary Bk Vols 75; Bk Titles 12,000; Per Subs 108
Automation Activity & Vendor Info: (ILL) OCLC
Database Vendor: EBSCOhost
Open Mon 7:30-4, Tues-Fri 7:30am-8:30pm

WASHINGTON STATE REFORMATORY, PO Box 777, MS-NM-83, Monroe, 98272-0777, SAN 363-8499. Tel: 360-794-2673, 360-794-2872. FAX: 360-794-2648. E-mail: wsr@secstate.wa.gov. *Librn,* Virginia Persak; E-mail: vpersak@secstate.wa.gov
Subject Interests: Corrections, Crime, Penology
Restriction: Not open to pub

WESTERN STATE HOSPITAL BRANCH, 9601 Steilacoom Blvd SW, WSH 08-300, W27-19, Tacoma, 98498-7213, SAN 363-8677. Tel: 253-756-2593. FAX: 253-756-3970. E-mail: wsh@sos.wa.gov. Web Site: www.sos.wa.gov/library. *Libr Assoc,* Kathleen Benoun; E-mail: kbenoun@sos.wa.gov; Staff 1 (Non-MLS 1)
Library Holdings: High Interest/Low Vocabulary Bk Vols 200; Bk Titles 7,000; Per Subs 230; Spec Interest Per Sub 200
Subject Interests: Consumer health, Dual diagnosis, Mental illness, Psychiat, Psychol, Recovery, Substance abuse
Function: ILL available
Open Mon-Wed & Fri 9-12 & 1-4, Thurs 1-4

UNION GAP

S   YAKIMA VALLEY GENEALOGICAL SOCIETY LIBRARY*, 1901 S 12th Ave, 98903. SAN 326-7830. Tel: 509-248-1328. *Librn,* Ellen Brzoska; *Asst Librn,* Irene Minicozzi; *Bibliog Instr,* Opal Myhres; *ILL,* Wilbur Helm; *Per,* Clara Yeager; *Pub Serv,* Maxine Bissell; Staff 5 (MLS 1, Non-MLS 4)
Founded 1967
Library Holdings: Bk Titles 12,000; Per Subs 300
Subject Interests: Genealogy
Wireless access
Publications: Bulletin
Open Mon-Fri 10-4, Sat (Summer) 10-4

VANCOUVER

J   CLARK COLLEGE, Lewis D Cannell Library, Mail Stop LIB 112, 1933 Fort Vancouver Way, 98663-3598. SAN 317-6975. Tel: 360-992-2151. Circulation Tel: 360-992-2504. Reference Tel: 360-992-2375. Administration Tel: 360-992-2472. FAX: 360-992-2869. Web Site: library.clark.edu. *Dean, Libr Serv, eLearning, Tutoring & Fac Develop,* Michelle Bagley; E-mail: mbagley@clark.edu; *Head, Tech Serv/Tech Serv Librn,* Radmila Ballada; Tel: 360-992-2443, E-mail: rballada@clark.edu; *Ref Librn (Info Serv),* Julie Austad; Tel: 360-992-2426, E-mail: jaustad@clark.edu; *Ref Librn (Info Serv),* Roxanne Dimyan; Tel: 360-992-2427, E-mail: rdimyan@clark.edu; *Ref Librn (Info Serv),* Zachary Grant; Tel: 360-992-2971, E-mail: zgrant@clark.edu; *Ref Librn (Info Serv),* Kitty Mackey; Tel: 360-992-2558, E-mail: kmackey@clark.edu; *Access Serv Mgr, Circ,* Amy Waite; Tel: 360-992-2152, E-mail: awaite@clark.edu; *Ref Librn (Info Serv),* Kim Read; Tel: 360-992-2826, E-mail: kread@clark.edu; Staff 20 (MLS 10, Non-MLS 10)
Founded 1933. Enrl 15,000; Fac 8; Highest Degree: Associate
Library Holdings: Bk Vols 67,000
Special Collections: Mushrooms
Automation Activity & Vendor Info: (Acquisitions) Innovative Interfaces, Inc; (Cataloging) Innovative Interfaces, Inc; (Circulation) Innovative Interfaces, Inc; (Course Reserve) Innovative Interfaces, Inc; (ILL) Innovative Interfaces, Inc; (Media Booking) Innovative Interfaces, Inc; (OPAC) Innovative Interfaces, Inc; (Serials) Innovative Interfaces, Inc
Database Vendor: EBSCOhost, Gale Cengage Learning, ProQuest, YBP Library Services
Wireless access
Partic in OCLC Online Computer Library Center, Inc; Orbis Cascade Alliance; Portland Area Library System
Open Mon-Thurs (Fall-Spring) 7am-8:30pm, Fri 7-5, Sat & Sun 1-5
Departmental Libraries:
INFORMATION COMMONS @ COLUMBIA TECH CENTER, Information Commons - CTC 245, 18700 SE Mill Plain Blvd, 98683. Tel: 360-992-6138. Circulation Tel: 360-992-6138. Reference Tel: 360-992-6113. Web Site: library.clark.edu. *Assess Serv Spec,* Connie Anderson; Tel: 360-992-6137, E-mail: clanderson@clark.edu; Staff 2 (MLS 1, Non-MLS 1)
Founded 2009. Highest Degree: Associate
Open Mon-Thurs (Fall & Spring) 7-7; Mon-Thurs (Summer) 7-6

L   CLARK COUNTY LAW LIBRARY*, 1200 Franklin St, 98660. (Mail add: PO Box 5000, 98666-5000), SAN 370-5188. Tel: 360-397-2268. E-mail: lawlibrary@clark.wa.gov. Web Site: www.clark.wa.gov/law-library/index.html. *Librn,* Maria Sosnowski; E-mail: maria.sosnowski@clark.wa.gov
Library Holdings: Bk Titles 500; Bk Vols 19,000
Special Collections: Washington Law
Open Mon-Fri 10-4

S   THE COLUMBIAN NEWSPAPER INFORMATION RESOURCE CENTER*, 415 W Sixth St, 98660. (Mail add: PO Box 180, 98666-0180), SAN 317-6983. Tel: 360-759-8036. Toll Free Tel: 800-743-3391. FAX:

360-737-6211. E-mail: archives@columbian.com. Web Site:
www.columbian.com. *Head Librn,* Diane Gibson; E-mail:
diane.gibson@columbian.com
Founded 1890
Library Holdings: Bk Titles 300
Subject Interests: Entertainers, Govt agency rpts, Hist info, Statistical data
Open Mon-Fri 8-5

P FORT VANCOUVER REGIONAL LIBRARY DISTRICT, 1007 E Mill
Plain Blvd, 98663. SAN 364-2453. Tel: 360-695-1561. Reference Tel:
360-906-5106. Automation Services Toll Free Tel: 800-750-9876. Toll Free
Tel: 888-546-2707 (toll-free from area code 509 only). FAX:
360-693-2681. E-mail: contact@fvrl.org. Web Site: www.fvrl.org. *Exec
Dir,* Nancy Tessman; *Communications Dir,* Sue Vanlaanen; Tel:
360-699-8815, E-mail: svanlaanen@fvrl.org; *Commun Libr Dir,* Jill
Rourke; *Content Mgt Dir,* Melinda Chesbro; *Operations Dir,* Patty Reyes;
Vancouver Commun Librn, Karin Ford; Staff 221 (MLS 45, Non-MLS 176)
Founded 1950. Pop 454,955; Circ 3,500,000
Library Holdings: Bk Vols 720,000
Wireless access
Friends of the Library Group
Branches: 13
BATTLE GROUND COMMUNITY LIBRARY, 1207 SE Eighth Way,
Battle Ground, 98604, SAN 364-2488. Tel: 360-687-2322. *Librn,* Jackie
Spurlock
Open Mon-Thurs 10-8, Fri & Sat 10-6
Friends of the Library Group
CASCADE PARK COMMUNITY LIBRARY, 600 NE 136th Ave, 98684,
SAN 377-0397. Tel: 360-256-7782. FAX: 360-256-7987. *Commun Librn,*
Teresa Torres
Open Tues-Thurs 9-8, Fri & Sat 9-6
Friends of the Library Group
GOLDENDALE COMMUNITY LIBRARY, 131 W Burgen, Goldendale,
98620, SAN 364-2518. Tel: 509-773-4487. *Commun Librn,* Naomi Fisher
Open Mon-Sat 10-6:30
Friends of the Library Group
LA CENTER COMMUNITY LIBRARY, 1411 NE Lockwood Creek Rd,
La Center, 98629. Tel: 360-619-1800. *Commun Librn,* Justin Keeler
Open Mon-Wed & Fri 10-6, Thurs 10-8
Friends of the Library Group
NORTH BONNEVILLE COMMUNITY LIBRARY, 214 CBD Mall (Inside
City Hall), North Bonneville, 98639, SAN 364-2542. Tel: 509-427-4439.
Commun Librn, Tina Smith
Open Tues, Wed & Thurs 1-5
RIDGEFIELD COMMUNITY LIBRARY, 210 N Main Ave, Ridgefield,
98642-9394, SAN 364-2577. Tel: 360-887-8281. *Commun Librn,* Sean
McGill
Open Tues 10-8, Wed-Fri 10-6, Sat 10-5
Friends of the Library Group
STEVENSON COMMUNITY LIBRARY, 120 NW Vancouver Ave,
Stevenson, 98648, SAN 364-2607. Tel: 509-427-5471. *Commun Librn,*
Tina Smith
Open Mon 9-5, Tues & Wed 9-8, Thurs-Sat 9-5
Friends of the Library Group
THREE CREEKS COMMUNITY LIBRARY, 800 C NE Tenney Rd,
98685. Tel: 360-517-9696. FAX: 360-574-6429. *Commun Librn,* Mike
Jansen
Open Tues-Thurs 10-8, Fri & Sat 10-6
Friends of the Library Group
VANCOUVER COMMUNITY LIBRARY (MAIN LIBRARY), 901 C St,
98660, SAN 364-2631. Tel: 360-695-1566. *Commun Librn,* Karin Ford
Open Mon-Thurs 9-8, Fri-Sat 10-6
Friends of the Library Group
VANCOUVER MALL COMMUNITY LIBRARY, 8700 NE Vancouver
Mall Dr, Ste 285, 98662, SAN 364-264X. Tel: 360-892-8256. *Commun
Librn,* Barbra Meisenheimer
Open Mon-Sat 10-9, Sun 11-6
Friends of the Library Group
WASHOUGAL COMMUNITY LIBRARY, 1661 C St, Washougal, 98671,
SAN 364-2666. Tel: 360-835-5393. FAX: 360-835-9011. *Commun Librn,*
Sean McGill
Open Tues 10-8, Wed-Sat 10-6
Friends of the Library Group
WHITE SALMON VALLEY COMMUNITY LIBRARY, 77 NE Wauna
Ave, White Salmon, 98672, SAN 364-2690. Tel: 509-493-1132. FAX:
509-493-2943. *Commun Librn,* Jennifer Hull
Open Tues 10-8, Wed-Sat 10-6
Friends of the Library Group
WOODLAND COMMUNITY LIBRARY, 770 Park St, Woodland, 98674.
Tel: 360-225-2115. FAX: 360-225-6344. *Commun Librn,* Sam Wallin
Open Mon 11-6, Tues & Wed 11-8, Thurs & Fri 10-6
Friends of the Library Group
Bookmobiles: 2

§R GOLDEN GATE BAPTIST THEOLOGICAL SEMINARY LIBRARY,
Pacific Northwest Campus, 3200 NE 109th Ave, 98682-7749. Tel:
360-882-2200. FAX: 360-882-2275. E-mail: pnwc-info@ggbts.edu. *Campus
Librn,* Patsy Yang; Tel: 360-882-2179; *Ref Asst,* Anna Cheek; Tel:
360-882-2171
Open Mon 7:45am-8pm, Tues 7:45am-6pm, Wed-Fri 9-4:30; Mon-Fri
(Summer) 9-4

M SOUTHWEST WASHINGTON MEDICAL CENTER LIBRARY*, Health
Education Ctr, 400 NE Mother Joseph Pl, 98664. (Mail add: PO Box 1600,
98668-1600), SAN 364-2720. Tel: 360-514-2045. FAX: 360-514-6466.
E-mail: library@swmedicalcenter.org. Web Site:
www.swmedctr.com/body.cfm?id=156. *Med Librn,* Madelyn Hall; Tel:
360-514-3167, E-mail: mhall@swmedicalcenter.org; Staff 1 (MLS 1)
Founded 1858
Library Holdings: Bk Vols 4,000; Per Subs 200
Wireless access
Open Mon-Fri 8-4:30

S UNITED STATES NATIONAL PARK SERVICE-FORT VANCOUVER
NATIONAL HISTORIC SITE-LIBRARY*, 1001 E Fifth St, 98661. SAN
317-6991. Tel: 360-696-7659, Ext 18. FAX: 360-696-7657. E-mail:
fova_library@nps.gov. Web Site: www.nps.gov/fova/home.htm. *Librn,* Scott
Langford
Founded 1948
Library Holdings: Bk Vols 1,300; Per Subs 4
Special Collections: Fort Vancouver National Historic Site Archaeological
Documents
Subject Interests: Hudson's Bay Co, Pac NW fur trade
Open Mon-Sun 9-5

S WASHINGTON SCHOOL FOR THE DEAF, Learning Resource Center,
McGill Library, 611 Grand Blvd, 98661-4498. SAN 317-7017. Tel:
360-696-6525, Ext 4352. FAX: 360-418-0418. Web Site: www.wsd.wa.gov.
Librn, Ginger Speranza
Founded 1886
Library Holdings: Bks on Deafness & Sign Lang 150; Bk Vols 10,978;
Per Subs 3
Special Collections: Professional Coll for Educators of the Deaf
Special Services for the Deaf - Bks on deafness & sign lang; Captioned
film dep; TTY equip; Videos & decoder
Restriction: Not open to pub

C WASHINGTON STATE UNIVERSITY LIBRARIES*, Vancouver Library,
14204 NE Salmon Creek Ave, 98686. Tel: 360-546-9680. Interlibrary Loan
Service Tel: 360-546-9683. Reference Tel: 360-546-9686. Administration
Tel: 360-546-9689. FAX: 360-546-9039. E-mail:
library@vancouver.wsu.edu. Web Site:
www.vancouver.wsu.edu/library.html. *Libr Dir,* Leslie Wykoff; Tel:
360-546-9682, E-mail: lwykoff@vancouver.wsu.edu; *Assoc Libr Dir,* Karen
Diller; Tel: 360-546-9246; *Head, Access Serv,* Linda Frederiksen; Tel:
360-546-9683, E-mail: lfrederiksen@vancouver.wsu.edu; *Head, Coll
Develop,* Kathleen C Fountain; Tel: 360-546-9694; *Head, Ref & Electronic
Serv,* Nicole Campbell; Tel: 360-546-9687, E-mail:
nmcampbell@vancouver.wsu.edu; *Ref Librn,* Marianne Bash; Tel:
360-546-9681; *Ref Librn,* Sue Phelps; Tel: 360-546-9178, E-mail:
asphelps@vancouver.wsu.edu; *Syst Instruction Librn,* Nicholas Schiller;
Tel: 360-546-9171, E-mail: schiller@vancouver.wsu.edu; *Circ & Reserves
Supvr,* Dena Keller; Tel: 360-546-9685, E-mail:
dkeller@vancouver.wsu.edu; *Acq & Ser Spec,* Kerry Hodge; Tel:
360-546-9684, E-mail: hodge@vancouver.wsu.edu; *Archive Spec,* Robert
Schimelpfenig; Tel: 360-546-9249, E-mail: schimo@vancouver.wsu.edu;
ILL Spec, Diane Manning; Tel: 360-546-9154, E-mail:
dmanning@vancouver.wsu.edu. Subject Specialists: *Nursing,* Leslie
Wykoff; *Educ, Psychol,* Linda Frederiksen; *Hist, Polit sci, Soc,* Kathleen C
Fountain; *English, Sci,* Nicole Campbell; *Bus, Sociol,* Marianne Bash;
Anthropology, Human develop, Nursing, Sue Phelps; *Computer sci,
Creative media & digital culture, Eng,* Nicholas Schiller; Staff 13.75 (MLS
8.25, Non-MLS 5.5)
Founded 1989
Library Holdings: Bk Titles 31,000; Per Subs 412
Automation Activity & Vendor Info: (ILL) OCLC
Database Vendor: Innovative Interfaces, Inc, YBP Library Services
Wireless access
Open Mon-Thurs 8am-10pm, Fri 8-5, Sat & Sun 12-5

WAITSBURG

P WELLER PUBLIC LIBRARY*, 212 Main St, 99361. (Mail add: PO Box
35, 99361-0035). Tel: 509-337-8149. *Dir,* Jan Cronkhite; Staff 1
(Non-MLS 1)
Pop 1,210; Circ 3,220
Library Holdings: CDs 35; DVDs 12; Large Print Bks 200; Bk Vols
2,000; Talking Bks 100; Videos 150
Function: Prog for children & young adult, Summer reading prog

Open Mon 3-6, Thurs 10-12 & 1-6
Friends of the Library Group

WALLA WALLA

A   UNITED STATES ARMY*, Corps of Engineers, Walla Walla District
     Technical Library, 201 N Third, 99362-1876. SAN 364-278X. Tel:
     509-527-7427. FAX: 509-527-7816. E-mail: cenww-im-sl@usace.army.mil.
     Web Site: www.nww.usace.army.mil. *Tech Serv,* Angie Camarillo
     Founded 1948
     Library Holdings: Bk Vols 19,000; Per Subs 300
     Special Collections: Law Coll
     Subject Interests: Army field law libr, Civil works constr, Eng, Fish,
     Hydrol, Water res, Wildlife
     Database Vendor: OCLC FirstSearch

GM   VETERANS AFFAIRS MEDICAL CENTER*, Jonathan M Wainwright
     Memorial Library, 77 Wainwright Dr, 99362-3994. SAN 317-7041. Tel:
     509-525-5200, Ext 22833. FAX: 509-527-6106. *Chief Librn,* Darlene
     Fleming; E-mail: darlene.fleming@va.gov; Staff 1 (MLS 1)
     Library Holdings: Audiobooks 200; DVDs 100; Bk Vols 4,000; Per Subs
     50
     Subject Interests: Med, Nursing mats
     Partic in Coop Libr Agency for Syst & Servs; National Network of
     Libraries of Medicine; Vets Admin Libr Network
     Open Mon-Fri 8:15-4:30

J   WALLA WALLA COMMUNITY COLLEGE LIBRARY*, 500 Tausick
     Way, 99362-9267. SAN 317-705X. Tel: 509-527-4294. Interlibrary Loan
     Service Tel: 509-527-4277. FAX: 509-527-4480. E-mail:
     library@wwcc.edu. Web Site: www.wwcc.edu/library. *Dir, Libr & Media,*
     Darcy Dauble; Tel: 509-527-4292, E-mail: darcy.dauble@wwcc.edu; *Instrul
     & Electronic Res Librn,* C Quill West; *Ref & Pub Serv Librn,* Jim Rice;
     Libr Supvr-Popular Libr, Stacy Prest; *Clarkston Ctr Libr Coordr,* Jackson
     Q Vance; Tel: 509-758-1714, E-mail: jackson.vance@wwcc.edu; *Cat,*
     Janelle Meier; Staff 6.5 (MLS 4, Non-MLS 2.5)
     Founded 1967
     Jul 2006-Jun 2007 Income $480,000, Parent Institution $463,000, Other
     $17,000. Mats Exp $86,000, Books $46,000, Per/Ser (Incl. Access Fees)
     $31,000, AV Mat $9,000. Sal $351,000
     Library Holdings: Bk Titles 40,000; Bk Vols 45,000; Per Subs 275;
     Videos 5,100
     Automation Activity & Vendor Info: (Cataloging) LibLime; (Circulation)
     LibLime; (Course Reserve) LibLime; (ILL) OCLC; (OPAC) LibLime;
     (Serials) LibLime
     Database Vendor: CQ Press, EBSCOhost, OCLC WorldCat, ProQuest,
     SerialsSolutions
     Wireless access
     Partic in Walla Walla Area Library Network (WALNET)
     Special Services for the Blind - Assistive/Adapted tech devices, equip &
     products
     Open Mon-Thurs 7:30-7:30, Fri 7:30-4:30, Sun 1-5

GL   WALLA WALLA COUNTY LAW LIBRARY*, County Courthouse, 315
     W Main St, 99362. SAN 317-7068. Tel: 509-527-3229. FAX:
     509-527-3214. *Librn,* Tina Driver; E-mail: tdriver@co.walla-walla.wa.us
     Library Holdings: Bk Vols 14,530
     Open Mon-Fri 9-4

P   WALLA WALLA COUNTY RURAL LIBRARY DISTRICT*, 37 Jade
     Ave, 99362-1628. SAN 373-8272. Tel: 509-527-3284. Toll Free Tel:
     800-547-7349. FAX: 509-527-3740. E-mail:
     comments@wwrurallibrary.com. Web Site: www.wwrurallibrary.com. *Exec
     Dir,* Jean H Adams; E-mail: padams@wwrurallibrary.com; *Automation Syst
     Coordr,* Josh Westbrook; E-mail: joshw@wwrurallibrary.com. Subject
     Specialists: *Computer tech,* Josh Westbrook; Staff 15 (MLS 1, Non-MLS
     14)
     Founded 1972. Pop 16,000
     Automation Activity & Vendor Info: (Cataloging) LibLime; (Circulation)
     LibLime; (ILL) OCLC
     Database Vendor: LibLime
     Wireless access
     Function: For res purposes, Handicapped accessible, Homebound delivery
     serv, ILL available, Photocopying/Printing, Prog for children & young
     adult, Ref serv available, Summer reading prog, Telephone ref, Wheelchair
     accessible
     Partic in Walla Walla Area Library Network (WALNET)
     Special Services for the Deaf - Bks on deafness & sign lang
     Friends of the Library Group
     Branches: 5
     BURBANK LIBRARY, 875 Lake Rd, Burbank, 99323. Tel: 509-545-6549.
        FAX: 509-545-6549. E-mail: burbank@wwrurallibrary.com. *Br Mgr,*
        Chris HoffmanHill
        Library Holdings: Bk Vols 30,000; Per Subs 32

Function: Photocopying/Printing, Prog for children & young adult,
        Summer reading prog
        Open Mon-Thurs 12-8, Fri 12-5, Sat 9-2
        Friends of the Library Group
     PLAZA LIBRARY, 1640 Plaza Way, 99362. Tel: 509-525-5161. FAX:
        509-525-5161. E-mail: plaza@wwrurallibrary.com. *Br Mgr,* Joel Gayton
        Open Mon-Fri 11-7, Sat & Sun 11-4
     PRESCOTT LIBRARY, 103 South D St, Prescott, 99348. (Mail add: PO
        Box 114, Prescott, 99348-0114). Tel: 509-849-2411. FAX: 509-849-2411.
        E-mail: prescott@wwrurallibrary.com. *Br Mgr,* Amy Rosenburgh
        Founded 2003
        Library Holdings: AV Mats 400; Bk Titles 8,500; Talking Bks 400
        Open Tues & Thurs Noon-8, Sat 10-3
        Friends of the Library Group
     TOUCHET COMMUNITY LIBRARY, 161 Hanson Rd, Touchet, 99360.
        (Mail add: PO Box 166, Touchet, 99360-0166). Tel: 509-394-2329.
        Administration Tel: 509-527-3284. FAX: 509-394-2329. Administration
        FAX: 509-527-3740. E-mail: touchet@wwrurallibrary.com. *Libr Mgr,*
        Carlotta Richardson; Staff 1 (Non-MLS 1)
        Founded 1987. Pop 500; Circ 15,000
        Library Holdings: Bk Vols 14,000; Per Subs 15
        Function: Accelerated reader prog, Adult bk club, Bk club(s), Bks on
        cassette, Bks on CD, Children's prog, Computer training, Computers for
        patron use, Copy machines, Fax serv, Free DVD rentals, Handicapped
        accessible, Homebound delivery serv, ILL available, Online cat, Online
        searches, Outreach serv, Photocopying/Printing, Preschool outreach, Prog
        for adults, Prog for children & young adult, Pub access computers,
        Satellite serv, Story hour, Summer reading prog, Tax forms, VHS videos,
        Video lending libr, Web-catalog, Wheelchair accessible
        Open Mon & Fri Noon-5, Wed Noon-8
        Friends of the Library Group
     VISTA HERMOSA LIBRARY, 76 Sarah Lynne Lane, Prescott, 99348.
        (Mail add: PO Box 658, Prescott, 99348). Tel: 509-749-2099. FAX:
        509-749-2099. E-mail: vista@wwrurallibrary.com. *Br Supvr,* Jose
        Mendoza
        Founded 2005
        Open Tues & Thurs 12-8

P   WALLA WALLA PUBLIC LIBRARY*, 238 E Alder, 99362. SAN
     317-7076. Tel: 509-527-4550. FAX: 509-524-7950. Web Site:
     wallawallapubliclibrary.org. *Dir, Libr Serv,* Beth Hudson; Tel:
     509-524-4433, E-mail: bhudson@ci.walla-walla.wa.us; *Young People's
     Librn,* Elizabeth George; Tel: 509-524-4431, E-mail:
     egeorge@ci.walla-walla.wa.us; *Libr Spec,* Jane Ternes; Tel: 509-524-4441,
     E-mail: jternes@ci.walla-walla.wa.us; *Pub Serv Spec,* LeeAnn Rizzuti; Tel:
     509-524-4435, E-mail: lrizzuti@ci.walla-walla.wa.us; *Pub Serv Spec,*
     Alexis Rodegerdts; Tel: 509-524-4609, E-mail:
     arodegerdts@ci.walla-walla.wa.us; Staff 11 (MLS 2, Non-MLS 9)
     Founded 1897. Pop 31,610; Circ 306,763
     Jan 2011-Dec 2011 Income $926,770, City $695,522, Locally Generated
     Income $231,248. Mats Exp $114,140, Books $73,320, Per/Ser (Incl.
     Access Fees) $9,930, AV Mat $14,690, Electronic Ref Mat (Incl. Access
     Fees) $16,200. Sal $744,490
     Library Holdings: AV Mats 4,505; DVDs 3,035; e-books 1,608; Bk Vols
     100,039; Per Subs 133; Talking Bks 2,166
     Subject Interests: Local hist
     Automation Activity & Vendor Info: (Cataloging) LibLime; (Circulation)
     LibLime; (ILL) LibLime; (OPAC) LibLime; (Serials) LibLime
     Database Vendor: EBSCO Auto Repair Reference, EBSCO Information
     Services, LibLime, OCLC WorldCat, Overdrive, Inc, ProQuest, World
     Book Online
     Wireless access
     Partic in Walla Walla Area Library Network (WALNET)
     Friends of the Library Group

C   WHITMAN COLLEGE, Penrose Library, 345 Boyer Ave, 99362. SAN
     317-7092. Tel: 509-527-5191. Circulation Tel: 509-527-5192. Interlibrary
     Loan Service Tel: 509-527-5914. Reference Tel: 509-527-5918. FAX:
     509-527-5900. Web Site: www.whitman.edu/penrose. *Col Librn,* Dalia
     Corkrum; Tel: 509-527-5193, E-mail: corkrum@whitman.edu; *Head,
     Instrul & Res Serv,* Lee P Keene; Tel: 509-527-5917, E-mail:
     keenelp@whitman.edu; *Head, Coll Mgt,* Roger Stelk; Tel: 509-527-5909,
     E-mail: stelkre@whitman.edu; *Archivist & Spec Coll Librn,* Melissa M
     Salrin; Tel: 509-526-4731, E-mail: salrinmm@whitman.edu; *Instrul &
     Access Serv Librn,* Julie Carter; Tel: 509-527-5915, E-mail:
     carterja@whitman.edu; *Instrul & Res Librn,* Lynne Vieth; Tel:
     509-527-4905, E-mail: viethls@whitman.edu; *Metadata Librn, Syst Librn,*
     Dan H Martensen; E-mail: martendh@whitman.edu; *ILL, Mgr, Access Serv,*
     Jennifer Pope; E-mail: johnsoja@whitman.edu; Staff 7 (MLS 7)
     Founded 1882. Enrl 1,596; Fac 162; Highest Degree: Bachelor
     Jul 2011-Jun 2012 Income $2,344,520. Mats Exp $1,187,150, Books
     $392,025, Per/Ser (Incl. Access Fees) $567,854, AV Mat $12,300,
     Electronic Ref Mat (Incl. Access Fees) $208,430, Presv $6,541. Sal
     $733,723 (Prof $390,212)

Library Holdings: AV Mats 8,180; e-journals 30,122; Bk Vols 560,749; Per Subs 1,849
Special Collections: Dogwood Press Coll; Early Illustrated Books (McFarlane Coll); Stuart Napoleon Coll. US Document Depository
Automation Activity & Vendor Info: (Acquisitions) Innovative Interfaces, Inc - Millenium; (Cataloging) Innovative Interfaces, Inc - Millenium; (Circulation) Innovative Interfaces, Inc - Millenium; (Course Reserve) Innovative Interfaces, Inc - Millenium; (ILL) OCLC ILLiad; (OPAC) Innovative Interfaces, Inc; (Serials) Innovative Interfaces, Inc - Millenium
Database Vendor: ABC-CLIO, Alexander Street Press, American Psychological Association (APA), Annual Reviews, ARTstor, Atlas Systems, Blackwell's, CQ Press, ebrary, EBSCO Information Services, EBSCOhost, Elsevier, Emerald, Gale Cengage Learning, H W Wilson, HeinOnline, Innovative Interfaces, Inc, ISI Web of Knowledge, JSTOR, LexisNexis, Marcive, Inc, Medline, Modern Language Association, netLibrary, Newsbank-Readex, OCLC, OCLC FirstSearch, OCLC WebJunction, OCLC WorldCat, OVID Technologies, Oxford Online, Project MUSE, ProQuest, PubMed, Sage, ScienceDirect, Scopus, Springer-Verlag, Thomson - Web of Science, Wiley, YBP Library Services
Wireless access
Function: Archival coll, Art exhibits, Audio & video playback equip for onsite use, Computers for patron use, Copy machines, e-mail & chat, E-Reserves, Electronic databases & coll, Exhibits, Fax serv, Handicapped accessible, ILL available, Magnifiers for reading, Online ref, Orientations, Photocopying/Printing, Pub access computers, Ref & res, Ref serv in person, Scanner, Telephone ref, VHS videos, Web-catalog, Workshops
Partic in Northwest Association of Private Colleges & Universities (NAPCU); Oberlin Group; OCLC Online Computer Library Center, Inc; Orbis Cascade Alliance
Open Mon-Sun 12am-12am; Mon-Sun (Summer) 9-5
Restriction: 24-hr pass syst for students only, Access at librarian's discretion, Authorized scholars by appt, Fee for pub use, Non-circulating of rare bks, Open to pub for ref & circ; with some limitations

WENATCHEE

M   CENTRAL WASHINGTON HOSPITAL*, Heminger Health Library, 1201 S Miller St, 98801. (Mail add: PO Box 1887, 98807-1887), SAN 317-7106. Tel: 509-664-3476. FAX: 509-665-6145. E-mail: cwhlibrary@cwhs.com. Web Site: www.cwhs.com. *Info Spec,* Susan Marshall; E-mail: smarshall@cwhs.com; Staff 1 (MLS 1)
Founded 1972
Library Holdings: Bk Titles 1,000; Per Subs 100
Subject Interests: Consumer health, Health, Hospital mgt, Hospital serv, Med, Nursing
Automation Activity & Vendor Info: (Acquisitions) Ex Libris Group; (Cataloging) Ex Libris Group; (Circulation) Ex Libris Group; (OPAC) Ex Libris Group; (Serials) Ex Libris Group
Database Vendor: OVID Technologies, ProQuest, PubMed, SerialsSolutions
Wireless access
Partic in Docline; National Network of Libraries of Medicine
Open Mon-Fri 8-4

P   NORTH CENTRAL REGIONAL LIBRARY*, 16 N Columbia St, 98801-8103. SAN 364-281X. Tel: 509-663-1117. Interlibrary Loan Service Tel: 509-662-5021, Ext 28. Toll Free Tel: 800-426-7323. FAX: 509-662-8060. Administration FAX: 509-662-8554. E-mail: ncrl@ncrl.org. Web Site: www.ncrl.org. *Dir,* Dean Marney; Tel: 509-663-1117, Ext 121, E-mail: dmarney@ncrl.org; *Dir, Pub Libr Support Serv,* Dan Howard; Tel: 509-663-1117, Ext 122, E-mail: dhoward@ncrl.org; *Assoc Dir,* Marilyn Neumiller; Tel: 509-663-1117, Ext 128, E-mail: mneumiller@ncrl.org; *Financial Dir,* Susan DeWitz; Tel: 509-663-1117, Ext 120, E-mail: sdewitz@ncrl.org; *Acq,* Lisa Bell; Tel: 509-663-1117, Ext 108, E-mail: lbell@ncrl.org; *Automation Syst Coordr,* Barbara Walters; Tel: 509-663-1117, Ext 129, E-mail: bwalters@ncrl.org; *Cat,* Rita Keller; Tel: 509-663-1117, Ext 110, E-mail: rkeller@ncrl.org; *Youth Serv Coordr,* Angela Morris; Tel: 509-663-1117, Ext 119, E-mail: amorris@ncrl.org; Staff 83 (MLS 3, Non-MLS 80)
Founded 1961. Pop 239,695; Circ 1,484,715
Jan 2007-Dec 2007 Income (Main Library and Branch(s)) $10,355,519, State $23,815, City $293,787, Federal $8,033, County $9,486,909, Locally Generated Income $15,958, Other $527,017. Mats Exp $1,893,893, Books $1,026,099, Other Print Mats $418,002, AV Equip $52,230, AV Mat $179,045, Electronic Ref Mat (Incl. Access Fees) $218,517. Sal $2,836,213 (Prof $310,392)
Library Holdings: Audiobooks 31,385; AV Mats 52,910; Bk Vols 526,560; Per Subs 898
Special Collections: State Document Depository
Subject Interests: Compact discs, NW hist
Automation Activity & Vendor Info: (Acquisitions) Horizon; (Cataloging) SirsiDynix
Database Vendor: EBSCOhost, ProQuest, SirsiDynix
Wireless access

Function: Bk club(s), Bks on CD, Homebound delivery serv, ILL available, Jail serv, Outreach serv, OverDrive digital audio bks, Senior outreach, Summer reading prog
Publications: Mail Order Library Catalogs (Quarterly)
Partic in OCLC Online Computer Library Center, Inc
Open Mon-Fri 8-5
Restriction: Registered patrons only
Friends of the Library Group
Branches: 28
BREWSTER PUBLIC LIBRARY, 108 S Third St, Brewster, 98812. (Mail add: PO Box 280, Brewster, 98812-0280), SAN 317-4905. Tel: 509-689-4046. FAX: 509-689-4046. E-mail: brewster@ncrl.org. *Librn,* Judy Johnston
Circ 24,825
Library Holdings: Bk Vols 9,816; Talking Bks 239; Videos 1,030
Open Mon & Tues 1-6, Wed 10-12 & 1-6, Thurs 1-6 & 7-8
Restriction: Registered patrons only
Friends of the Library Group
BRIDGEPORT COMMUNITY, 1206 Columbia Ave, Bridgeport, 98813. (Mail add: PO Box 220, Bridgeport, 98813-0220). Tel: 509-686-7281. FAX: 509-686-7281. E-mail: bridgeport@ncrl.org. *Librn,* Michelle Orosco
Circ 19,968
Library Holdings: Bk Vols 9,147; Talking Bks 243; Videos 1,475
Open Mon-Fri 10-6
Restriction: Registered patrons only
Friends of the Library Group
CASHMERE COMMUNITY, 300 Woodring, Cashmere, 98815-1061. Tel: 509-782-3314. E-mail: cashmere@ncrl.org. *Librn,* Jean Frank; E-mail: jfrank@ncrl.org
Circ 36,835
Library Holdings: Bk Vols 13,782; Talking Bks 291; Videos 1,385
Open Mon, Wed & Fri 9:30-5:30, Tues & Thurs 11-7, Sat 9:30-2:30
Restriction: Registered patrons only
Friends of the Library Group
CHELAN COMMUNITY, 417 S Bradley St, Chelan, 98816. (Mail add: PO Box 698, Chelan, 98816-0698). Tel: 509-682-5131. FAX: 509-682-5131. E-mail: chelan@ncrl.org. *Librn,* Gloria Groves; *Librn,* Lou Verellen
Circ 43,136
Library Holdings: Bk Vols 11,946; Talking Bks 366; Videos 1,360
Open Mon, Wed & Fri 10-6, Tues & Thurs 12-8, Sat 11-4
Restriction: Registered patrons only
Friends of the Library Group
COULEE CITY COMMUNITY, 405 W Main St, Coulee City, 99115. (Mail add: PO Box 387, Coulee City, 99115-0387). Tel: 509-632-8751. E-mail: couleecity@ncrl.org. *Librn,* Nancy Miller
Circ 12,403
Library Holdings: Bk Vols 5,400; Talking Bks 154; Videos 932
Open Mon & Thurs 11-5:30, Tues 11-6
Restriction: Registered patrons only
Friends of the Library Group
EAST WENATCHEE COMMUNITY, 271 Ninth St NE, East Wenatchee, 98802-4438. Tel: 509-886-7404. FAX: 509-886-7404. E-mail: eastwenatchee@ncrl.org. *Librn,* Elena Ptak
Circ 41,496
Library Holdings: Bk Vols 8,875; Talking Bks 364; Videos 1,274
Open Mon-Fri 9-5
Restriction: Registered patrons only
Friends of the Library Group
ENTIAT COMMUNITY, 14138 Kinzel St, Entiat, 98822. (Mail add: PO Box 357, Entiat, 98822-0357). Tel: 509-784-1517. FAX: 509-784-1517. E-mail: entiat@ncrl.org. *Librn,* Esther Dalgas
Circ 11,813
Library Holdings: Bk Vols 6,305; Talking Bks 156; Videos 839
Open Mon 12:30-7, Tues & Thurs 1-5:30, Wed 10-5:30
Restriction: Registered patrons only
Friends of the Library Group
EPHRATA PUBLIC LIBRARY, 45 Alder NW, Ephrata, 98823-1663, SAN 317-5111. Tel: 509-754-3971. FAX: 509-754-3971. E-mail: ephrata@ncrl.org. *Supvr,* Kay Dirks
Circ 74,419
Library Holdings: Bk Vols 25,901; Talking Bks 375; Videos 1,761
Special Collections: Grant County Genealogical Society
Open Mon-Thurs 10-8, Fri 10-5, Sat 11-4
Restriction: Registered patrons only
Friends of the Library Group
GRAND COULEE COMMUNITY, 225 Federal St, Grand Coulee, 99133. (Mail add: PO Box 62, Grand Coulee, 99133-0062). Tel: 509-633-0972. FAX: 509-633-0972. E-mail: grandcoulee@ncrl.org. *Librn,* Joette Barry
Circ 29,606
Library Holdings: Bk Vols 13,421; Per Subs 28; Talking Bks 239; Videos 1,346
Open Mon & Thurs 12:30-5:30, Tues 12:30-7:30, Wed & Fri 9:30-5:30

Restriction: Registered patrons only
Friends of the Library Group
LEAVENWORTH COMMUNITY, 700 Hwy 2, Leavenworth, 98826. (Mail
add: PO Box 308, Leavenworth, 98826-0308). Tel: 509-548-7923. FAX:
509-548-7923. E-mail: leavenworth@ncrl.org. *Librn,* Sharron Loveall
Circ 40,901
Library Holdings: Bk Vols 15,400; Talking Bks 293; Videos 1,012
Open Mon, Tues & Thurs 12-8, Wed & Fri 9:30-5:30
Restriction: Registered patrons only
Friends of the Library Group
MANSON COMMUNITY, 80 Wapato Way, Manson, 98831-9210. (Mail
add: PO Box L, Manson, 98831-0400). Tel: 509-687-3420. FAX:
509-687-3420. E-mail: manson@ncrl.org. *Librn,* Cindy Simmons
Circ 17,604
Library Holdings: Bk Vols 7,021; Talking Bks 162; Videos 1,012
Open Mon & Tues 12:30-5:30, Wed 10:30-5:30, Thurs 12:30-6:30
Restriction: Registered patrons only
Friends of the Library Group
MATTAWA COMMUNITY, 101 Manson Lane, Mattawa, 99349. (Mail
add: PO Box 967, Mattawa, 99349-0954). Tel: 509-932-5507. FAX:
509-932-5507. E-mail: mattawa@ncrl.org. *Librn,* Josie Toscano
Founded 2002. Circ 21,926
Library Holdings: Bk Vols 6,900; Talking Bks 243; Videos 1,147
Open Mon, Wed & Fri 10-5, Tues & Thurs 10-6
Restriction: Registered patrons only
Friends of the Library Group
MOSES LAKE COMMUNITY, 418 E Fifth Ave, Moses Lake,
98837-1797. Tel: 509-765-3489. FAX: 509-766-0286. E-mail:
moseslake@ncrl.org. *Regional Mgr,* Connie Kuhlmann; E-mail:
ckuhlmann@ncrl.org; *Circ Mgr,* Barbara Gallaway
Circ 135,663
Library Holdings: Bk Vols 40,860; Talking Bks 636; Videos 2,577
Open Mon-Thurs 10-8, Fri 9-6, Sat 9-5
Restriction: Registered patrons only
Friends of the Library Group
OKANOGAN COMMUNITY, 228 Pine St, Okanogan, 98840. (Mail add:
PO Box 489, Okanogan, 98840-0489). Tel: 509-422-2609. FAX:
509-422-2609. E-mail: okanogan@ncrl.org. *Librn,* Lucile Ames
Circ 15,385
Library Holdings: Bk Vols 10,256; Talking Bks 155; Videos 1,299
Open Tues, Wed & Fri 10-5:30, Thurs 12:30-8
Restriction: Registered patrons only
Friends of the Library Group
OMAK COMMUNITY, 30 S Ash, Omak, 98841. (Mail add: PO Box J,
Omak, 98841-0969). Tel: 509-826-1820. FAX: 509-826-5102. *Regional
Mgr,* Sharon Reddick; E-mail: sreddick@ncrl.org; *Circ Mgr,* Sandra
Menendez
Circ 79,832
Library Holdings: Bk Vols 25,209; Talking Bks 475; Videos 2,789
Open Mon-Thurs 10-8, Fri 10-6, Sat 10-5, Sun 1-5
Restriction: Registered patrons only
Friends of the Library Group
OROVILLE COMMUNITY, 1276 Main St, Oroville, 98844. (Mail add:
PO Box 550, Oroville, 98844-0550). Tel: 509-476-2662. FAX:
509-476-2662. E-mail: oroville@ncrl.org. *Librn,* Barbara Pollard
Circ 31,900
Library Holdings: Bk Vols 9,681; Talking Bks 245; Videos 1,342
Open Tues 11:30-7:30, Wed-Sat 9:30-5:30
Restriction: Registered patrons only
Friends of the Library Group
PATEROS COMMUNITY, 174 Pateros Mall, Pateros, 98846. (Mail add:
PO Box 306, Pateros, 98846-0306). Tel: 509-923-2298. FAX:
509-923-2298. E-mail: pateros@ncrl.org. *Librn,* Janice Darlington
Circ 16,569
Library Holdings: Bk Vols 5,886; Talking Bks 149; Videos 837
Open Tues 1-7, Wed & Thurs 12-5:30, Fri 10-12 & 1-5
Restriction: Registered patrons only
Friends of the Library Group
PESHASTIN COMMUNITY, 8396 Main St, Peshastin, 98847-9734. (Mail
add: PO Box 408, Peshastin, 98847-0408). Tel: 509-548-7821. FAX:
509-548-7821. E-mail: peshastin@ncrl.org. *Librn,* Paul Anderman
Circ 10,756
Library Holdings: Bk Vols 6,092; Talking Bks 199; Videos 770
Open Tues & Fri 1-5, Wed 11-12:30 & 1:30-5:30, Thurs 1:30-5:30 &
6-7:30, Fri 1:30-5:30
Restriction: Registered patrons only
Friends of the Library Group
QUINCY COMMUNITY, 108 B St SW, Quincy, 98848-1203. Tel:
509-787-2359. E-mail: quincy@ncrl.org. *Librn,* Schiree Ybarra; *Asst
Librn,* Cenie Appling
Circ 73,806
Library Holdings: Bk Vols 13,864; Talking Bks 487; Videos 1,946
Open Mon-Fri 9-6, Sat 12-4
Restriction: Registered patrons only
Friends of the Library Group

REPUBLIC COMMUNITY, 794 S Clark Ave, Republic, 99166-8823.
(Mail add: PO Box 601, Republic, 99166-0601). Tel: 509-775-3328.
E-mail: republic@ncrl.org. *Librn,* Gailene Hooper
Circ 47,535
Library Holdings: Bk Vols 10,110; Talking Bks 365; Videos 1,372
Open Mon-Thurs 9-6, Fri 9-5, Sat 12-5
Restriction: Registered patrons only
ROYAL CITY COMMUNITY, 136 Camelia St, Royal City, 99357. (Mail
add: PO Box 548, Royal City, 98357-0548). Tel: 509-346-9281. FAX:
509-346-9281. E-mail: royalcity@ncrl.org. *Librn,* Shannon Stewart
Circ 20,010
Library Holdings: Bk Vols 5,916; Talking Bks 240; Videos 882
Open Mon 10-11:30 & 12-7, Tues-Thurs 11-5:30
Restriction: Registered patrons only
Friends of the Library Group
SOAP LAKE COMMUNITY, 32 E Main St, Soap Lake, 98851. (Mail add:
PO Box 86, Soap Lake, 98851-0086). Tel: 509-246-1313. E-mail:
soaplake@ncrl.org. *Librn,* Jeri Hernandez
Circ 24,251
Library Holdings: Bk Vols 11,610; Talking Bks 236; Videos 990
Open Tues, Wed & Fri 9:30-5, Thurs 11:30-7, Sat 10-2
Restriction: Registered patrons only
Friends of the Library Group
TONASKET COMMUNITY, 209 A Whitcomb Ave, Tonasket,
98855-8818. Tel: 509-486-2366. FAX: 509-486-2366. E-mail:
tonasket@ncrl.org. *Librn,* Margaret Lange
Circ 44,686
Library Holdings: Bk Vols 8,856; Talking Bks 355; Videos 1,044
Open Mon & Wed-Fri 9:30-5:30, Tues 11:30-7:30
Restriction: Registered patrons only
Friends of the Library Group
TWISP COMMUNITY, 201 N Methow Valley Hwy, Twisp, 98856. (Mail
add: PO Box 237, Twisp, 98856-0237). Tel: 509-997-4681. FAX:
509-997-4681. E-mail: twisp@ncrl.org. *Librn,* Terry Dixon
Circ 30,157
Library Holdings: Bk Vols 7,769; Talking Bks 193; Videos 715
Open Mon & Wed 10:30-5:30, Tues 12:30-5:30, Thurs 12:30-8, Sat
10:30-1:30
Restriction: Registered patrons only
Friends of the Library Group
WARDEN COMMUNITY, 305 S Main St, Warden, 98857-9680. (Mail
add: PO Box 813, Warden, 98857-0813). Tel: 509-349-2226. FAX:
509-349-2226. E-mail: warden@ncrl.org. *Librn,* Phyllis Dean
Circ 21,978
Library Holdings: Bk Vols 5,736; Talking Bks 152; Videos 806
Open Mon & Wed 12:30-5:30, Tues & Thurs 12:30-7
Restriction: Registered patrons only
Friends of the Library Group
WATERVILLE COMMUNITY, 105 N Chelan St, Waterville, 98858. (Mail
add: PO Box 807, Waterville, 98858-0807). Tel: 509-745-8354. FAX:
509-745-8354. E-mail: waterville@ncrl.org. *Librn,* Sandy Bareither
Circ 16,691
Library Holdings: Bk Vols 6,758; Talking Bks 161; Videos 979
Open Mon 9:30-11:30 & 12:30-5:30, Tues & Thurs 12:30-5:30, Wed
9:30-2:30
Restriction: Registered patrons only
Friends of the Library Group
WENATCHEE PUBLIC (HEADQUARTERS), 310 Douglas St,
98801-2864. Tel: 509-662-5021. FAX: 509-663-9731. E-mail:
wenatchee@ncrl.org. *Regional Mgr,* Katy Sessions; Tel: 509-662-5021,
Ext 28, E-mail: ksessions@ncrl.org; *Circ Mgr,* Courtney Jaynes
Circ 320,993
Library Holdings: Bk Vols 83,128; Talking Bks 803; Videos 6,066
Automation Activity & Vendor Info: (Cataloging) Horizon;
(Circulation) Horizon
Open Mon-Thurs 9-8, Fri & Sat 9-6, Sun 1-5
Restriction: Registered patrons only
Friends of the Library Group
WINTHROP COMMUNITY, 49 Hwy 20, Winthrop, 98862. (Mail add: PO
Box 519, Winthrop, 99862-0519). Tel: 509-996-2685. E-mail:
winthrop@ncrl.org. *Librn,* Sally Portman
Circ 35,824
Library Holdings: Bk Vols 7,968; Talking Bks 237; Videos 907
Open Mon, Wed & Thurs 12:30-6, Tues 10-6, Fri 2:30-5:30, Sat
1:30-4:30
Restriction: Registered patrons only
Friends of the Library Group
Bookmobiles: 1. Librn, Sandi Purcell

J   WENATCHEE VALLEY COLLEGE*, John A Brown Library Media
Center, 1300 Fifth St, 98801. SAN 317-7130. Tel: 509-682-6710. FAX:
509-682-6711. Web Site: www.wvc.edu/library. *Dir,* Andrew Hersh-Tudor;
Tel: 509-682-6715, E-mail: ahershtudor@wvc.edu; *Librn,* Barbara Oldham;
Tel: 509-682-6714, E-mail: boldham@wvc.edu; *Circ,* LaiLee Daling; *ILL,*

Olivia Drakes; Tel: 509-682-6712, E-mail: odrakes@wvc.edu; *Tech Serv,* Anne Livingston; Staff 11 (MLS 3, Non-MLS 8)
Founded 1939. Enrl 6,179; Fac 73; Highest Degree: Associate
Library Holdings: CDs 304; DVDs 457; Bk Titles 35,000; Per Subs 114; Videos 3,215
Special Collections: Northwest Indian History Coll; Pacific Northwest History Coll
Subject Interests: Archit, Art, Behav sci, Nursing, Soc sci
Automation Activity & Vendor Info: (Acquisitions) Ex Libris Group; (Cataloging) Ex Libris Group; (Circulation) Ex Libris Group; (Course Reserve) Ex Libris Group; (ILL) OCLC FirstSearch; (OPAC) Ex Libris Group
Database Vendor: Ex Libris Group, OCLC FirstSearch
Wireless access
Function: Art exhibits, Audio & video playback equip for onsite use, Computers for patron use, Distance learning, e-mail serv, Electronic databases & coll, Handicapped accessible, ILL available, Online ref, Online searches, Orientations, Scanner, Tax forms, VHS videos, Video lending libr, Wheelchair accessible
Open Mon-Thurs 8-8, Fri 8-5, Sat 10-2

WILBUR

P   HESSELTINE PUBLIC LIBRARY*, 14 NW Division, 99185. (Mail add: PO Box 185, 99185-0185), SAN 317-7149. Tel: 509-647-5828. FAX: 509-647-2047. E-mail: hplwilbur@hotmail.com. *Librn,* Cathy Miller
Founded 1900. Pop 905; Circ 7,658
Jan 2005-Dec 2005 Income $16,925, City $16,700, Locally Generated Income $225. Mats Exp $3,847, Books $3,066, Per/Ser (Incl. Access Fees) $781. Sal $8,526
Library Holdings: AV Mats 643; Large Print Bks 71; Bk Vols 12,313; Per Subs 40; Talking Bks 75
Special Collections: Local Newspaper Bound 1924, 1931-32, 1934-2003
Subject Interests: NW hist
Wireless access
Open Mon, Fri & Sat 3-5, Wed 7pm-9pm
Friends of the Library Group

YACOLT

S   LARCH CORRECTIONS CENTER LIBRARY*, 15314 NE Dole Valley Rd, 98765. SAN 317-7173. Tel: 360-260-6300, Ext 215. FAX: 360-686-3892. *Commun Partnerships Coordr,* Nancy Simmons
Founded 1975
Library Holdings: Audiobooks 30; Bk Titles 1,000
Restriction: Not open to pub

YAKIMA

R   FIRST PRESBYTERIAN CHURCH LIBRARY*, Nine S Eighth Ave, 98902. SAN 317-7181. Tel: 509-248-7940. FAX: 509-248-0937. E-mail: info@firstpresyakima.com. Web Site: www.firstpresyakima.com. *Librn,* Rondi Downs
Founded 1927
Library Holdings: Bk Vols 2,000
Special Collections: Cassette tapes of sermons; Video Classes
Subject Interests: Autobiographies, Bible study, Biographies, Christian life
Partic in Pac NW Asn Church Librs
Open Mon-Fri 9-5, Sun 8-1

GL   YAKIMA COUNTY LAW LIBRARY*, Yakima County Courthouse, B33, 128 N Second St, 98901. SAN 317-7203. Tel: 509-574-2692. *Librn,* Lumi Loudon; E-mail: lumi.loudon@co.yakima.wa.us
Founded 1923
Library Holdings: Bk Vols 5,500
Database Vendor: Loislaw, Westlaw
Wireless access
Restriction: Not open to pub

J   YAKIMA VALLEY COMMUNITY COLLEGE, Raymond Library, S 16th Ave at Nob Hill Blvd, 98907. (Mail add: PO Box 22520, 98907-2520), SAN 317-7211. Tel: 509-574-4991. FAX: 509-574-4989. E-mail: reference@yvcc.edu. Web Site: www.yvcclibrary.us/yakima. *Dir, Libr & Media Serv,* Joan L Weber; Staff 7 (MLS 2, Non-MLS 5)
Founded 1929. Enrl 3,500; Fac 106
Library Holdings: AV Mats 4,300; Bk Titles 45,000; Per Subs 58; Talking Bks 40
Automation Activity & Vendor Info: (Cataloging) Ex Libris Group; (Circulation) Ex Libris Group; (Course Reserve) Ex Libris Group; (ILL) OCLC; (OPAC) Ex Libris Group
Database Vendor: 3M Library Systems, ALLDATA Online, ARTstor, CredoReference, EBSCOhost, Ex Libris Group, Facts on File, Gale Cengage Learning, McGraw-Hill, OCLC FirstSearch, ProQuest, WT Cox
Wireless access

Partic in OCLC Online Computer Library Center, Inc
Open Mon-Thurs 7:30-7:30, Fri 7:30-4:30

P   YAKIMA VALLEY LIBRARIES, 102 N Third St, 98901-2759. SAN 364-2879. Tel: 509-452-8541. FAX: 509-575-2093. Reference E-mail: reference@yvrl.org. Web Site: www.yvrl.org. *Dir,* Kim Hixson; E-mail: khixson@yvl.org; *Dep Dir,* Linda McCracken; E-mail: lmccracken@yvrl.org; *Human Res Dir,* Darline Charbonneau; E-mail: dcharbonneau@yvl.org; *Managing Librn,* Dr Francisco Garcia-Ortiz; E-mail: fgarciaortiz@yvl.org; Staff 11 (MLS 10, Non-MLS 1)
Founded 1951. Pop 247,141; Circ 874,433
Library Holdings: Electronic Media & Resources 24; Bk Vols 397,899; Per Subs 581
Special Collections: Northwest Americans & Indians of Pacific Northwest (Relander Coll), bks, clippings, letters, maps, negatives, photog & prints. State Document Depository
Subject Interests: Agr, Archit, Art, Wash hist
Automation Activity & Vendor Info: (Acquisitions) Polaris Library Systems; (Cataloging) Polaris Library Systems; (Circulation) Polaris Library Systems; (Course Reserve) Polaris Library Systems; (ILL) Polaris Library Systems; (Media Booking) Polaris Library Systems; (OPAC) Polaris Library Systems; (Serials) Polaris Library Systems
Database Vendor: OCLC FirstSearch
Wireless access
Publications: Annual Report; Large Print Book Catalogs; Local Bibliography of Yakima Valley History; Relander Collection Index; Washington State Phone Book Index
Open Mon-Wed 9-7, Thurs & Fri 9-6, Sat 10-6
Friends of the Library Group
Branches: 17
BUENA LIBRARY, 801 Buena Rd, Buena, 98921. (Mail add: PO Box 304, Buena, 98921-0304). Tel: 509-865-3390. FAX: 509-865-3390. *Commun Libr Supvr,* Kathy Garcia
Circ 6,248
Library Holdings: Electronic Media & Resources 24; Bk Vols 6,286; Per Subs 25
Open Tues-Thurs 2-7, Sat 9-2
Friends of the Library Group
GRANGER LIBRARY, 508 Sunnyside Ave, Granger, 98932. (Mail add: PO Box 797, Granger, 98932-0797). Tel: 509-854-1446. FAX: 509-854-1446. *Commun Libr Supvr,* Francisco Garcia-Ortiz; E-mail: fgarciaortiz@yvrl.org
Pop 2,859; Circ 11,008
Library Holdings: Electronic Media & Resources 24; Bk Vols 8,720; Per Subs 21
Open Mon & Wed 10-6, Tues & Thurs 2-7, Sat 2-5
HARRAH LIBRARY, 21 E Pioneer, Harrah, 98933. (Mail add: PO Box 87, Harrah, 98933-0087). Tel: 509-848-3458. FAX: 509-848-3458. *Commun Libr Supvr,* Avelina Garcia; E-mail: agarcia@yvrl.org
Pop 506; Circ 1,888
Library Holdings: Electronic Media & Resources 24; Bk Vols 4,924; Per Subs 10
Special Collections: Scrapbooks on Harrah History (dating back to the 1940's)
Open Tues & Thurs 1-6, Sat 9-2
MABTON LIBRARY, 415 B St, Mabton, 98935. (Mail add: PO Box 447, Mabton, 98935-0447). Tel: 509-894-4128. FAX: 509-894-4128. *Commun Libr Supvr,* Linda Lee Bales; E-mail: lbales@yvrl.org
Pop 2,047; Circ 5,047
Library Holdings: Electronic Media & Resources 24; Bk Vols 6,994; Per Subs 26
Open Mon-Fri 2-6
Friends of the Library Group
MOXEE LIBRARY, 255 W Seattle, Moxee, 98936. (Mail add: PO Box 458, Moxee, 98936-0458). Tel: 509-575-8854. FAX: 509-575-8854. *Commun Libr Supvr,* Elaine Perkins; E-mail: eperkins@yvrl.org
Pop 1,836; Circ 15,208
Library Holdings: Electronic Media & Resources 24; Bk Vols 8,573; Per Subs 30
Open Mon & Wed 10-6, Tues & Thurs 12-7, Fri & Sat 1-5
Friends of the Library Group
NACHES LIBRARY, 303 Naches Ave, Naches, 98937. (Mail add: PO Box 310, Naches, 98937-0310). Tel: 509-653-2005. FAX: 509-653-2005. *Commun Libr Supvr,* Katherine Ulmer; E-mail: kulmer@yvrl.org
Pop 691; Circ 9,490
Library Holdings: Electronic Media & Resources 24; Bk Vols 7,335; Per Subs 28
Open Tues-Thurs 2-7, Sat 10-3
Friends of the Library Group
RICHARD E OSTRANDER WEST VALLEY COMMUNITY LIBRARY, 223 S 72nd Ave, 98908, SAN 364-2906. Tel: 509-966-7070. FAX: 509-966-7070. *Br Mgr,* Cathy Rathbone; E-mail: crathbone@yvrl.org; Staff 3 (MLS 3)
Circ 258,845

Library Holdings: Electronic Media & Resources 24; Bk Vols 40,270; Per Subs 68
Open Mon, Fri & Sat 9-6, Tues-Thurs 9-8, Sun 10-5
Friends of the Library Group
SELAH PUBLIC LIBRARY, 106 South Second St, Selah, 98942, SAN 317-6584. Tel: 509-698-7345. FAX: 509-698-7345. *Commun Libr Supvr,* Michael Martin; E-mail: mmartin@yvrl.org
Pop 6,947; Circ 50,673
Library Holdings: Electronic Media & Resources 24; Bk Vols 23,328; Per Subs 67
Open Mon & Wed-Fri 9-6, Tues 9-8:30, Sat 10-2
Friends of the Library Group
SOUTHEAST YAKIMA LIBRARY, 1211 S Seventh St, 98901, SAN 373-1413. Tel: 509-576-0723. FAX: 509-576-0723. *Commun Libr Supvr,* Monse Vargas
Circ 4,815
Library Holdings: Electronic Media & Resources 24; Bk Vols 4,458; Per Subs 24
Open Mon-Fri 1-6, Sat 11-4
Friends of the Library Group
SUNNYSIDE LIBRARY, 621 Grant, Sunnyside, 98944. Tel: 509-837-3234. FAX: 509-837-3234. *Librn,* Francisco Garcia-Ortiz
Pop 14,828; Circ 82,710
Library Holdings: Electronic Media & Resources 24; Bk Vols 42,789; Per Subs 74
Subject Interests: Bks on cassettes
Function: Photocopying/Printing
Open Mon-Thurs 10-7, Fri & Sat 10-5, Sun 1-5
Friends of the Library Group
TERRACE HEIGHTS LIBRARY, 4011 Commonwealth Dr, 98901. Tel: 509-457-5319. FAX: 509-457-5319. *Commun Libr Supvr,* Katie Ruffcorn; E-mail: kruffcorn@yvrl.org
Circ 16,291
Library Holdings: Electronic Media & Resources 24; Bk Vols 6,823; Per Subs 26
Open Mon & Wed 12-7, Tues & Thurs 10-4, Fri 10-6, Fri & Sat 10-2
TIETON LIBRARY, 418 Maple, Tieton, 98947. (Mail add: PO Box 395, Tieton, 98947-0395). Tel: 509-673-2621. FAX: 509-673-2621. *Librn,* Position Currently Open
Pop 1,184; Circ 4,905
Library Holdings: Electronic Media & Resources 24; Bk Vols 3,602; Per Subs 18
Open Mon-Thurs 12-5
TOPPENISH LIBRARY, One South Elm, Toppenish, 98948. Tel: 509-865-3600. FAX: 509-865-3600. *Commun Libr Supvr,* Christy Troy; E-mail: ctroy@yvrl.org
Pop 9,186; Circ 25,572
Library Holdings: Electronic Media & Resources 24; Bk Vols 19,338; Per Subs 54
Function: Photocopying/Printing

Open Mon-Thurs 10-7, Fri & Sat 10-5
Friends of the Library Group
UNION GAP LIBRARY, 3104 S First St, Union Gap, 98903. Tel: 509-452-4252. FAX: 509-249-9299. *Commun Libr Supvr,* Lorinda Bowden; E-mail: lbowden@yvrl.org
Pop 5,693; Circ 26,743
Library Holdings: Electronic Media & Resources 24; Bk Vols 17,235; Per Subs 43
Open Mon-Thurs 10-7, Fri & Sat 10-5
Friends of the Library Group
WAPATO LIBRARY, 119 E Third St, Wapato, 98951. Tel: 509-877-2882. FAX: 509-877-2882. *Commun Libr Supvr,* Mickey Wittner; E-mail: mwittner@yvrl.org
Pop 4,608; Circ 25,212
Library Holdings: Electronic Media & Resources 24; Bk Vols 15,181; Per Subs 37
Function: Photocopying/Printing
Open Mon & Wed 12-8, Tues, Thurs 10-6, Fri 12-6, Sat 10-4
Friends of the Library Group
WHITE SWAN LIBRARY, 391 First St, White Swan, 98952. (Mail add: PO Box 151, White Swan, 98952-0151). Tel: 509-874-2060. FAX: 509-874-2060. *Librn,* East Cathy
Circ 3,904
Library Holdings: Electronic Media & Resources 24; Bk Vols 5,966; Per Subs 27
Open Mon-Fri 12-5
Friends of the Library Group
ZILLAH LIBRARY, 109 Seventh St, Zillah, 98953. (Mail add: PO Box 448, Zillah, 98953-0448). Tel: 509-829-6707. FAX: 509-829-6707. *Commun Libr Supvr,* Fern Greene; E-mail: fgreene@yvrl.org
Pop 2,611; Circ 15,136
Library Holdings: Electronic Media & Resources 24; Bk Vols 6,419; Per Subs 24
Open Mon-Thurs 2-7, Sat 2-5
Friends of the Library Group

S   YAKIMA VALLEY MUSEUM ARCHIVES*, Sundquist Research Library, 2105 Tieton Dr, 98902. SAN 326-4432. Tel: 509-248-0747. FAX: 509-453-4890. E-mail: info@yakimavalleymuseum.org. Web Site: www.yakimavalleymuseum.org. *Curator,* Mike Siebol
Library Holdings: Bk Vols 7,000
Special Collections: Betty Edmondson, Mayor of Yakima; Marjorie Lynch Coll (HEW State Legislator); Martha Wiley, Missionary to China 1900-1946, artifacts, correspondence; William O Douglas Coll, bks, photos, slides, stills, tapes
Subject Interests: Local hist
Publications: 100 Years 100 Women - 1889-1989
Open Tues-Fri 10-5
Restriction: Non-circulating to the pub

Date of Statistics: FY 2012
Population, 2000 Census: 1,852,994
Population Served by Public Libraries: 1,852,994
Total Volumes in Public Libraries: 5,042,543
Total Public Library Expenditures (including Grants-in-Aid):
$33,987,699
　Source of Income: Public & Private funds
　Expenditure Per Capita: $18.34
Number of Regional & Service Center Libraries: 13
Grants-in-Aid to Public Libraries: $8,212,633
　Local Income: $28,048,982
　Federal Income: $114,101
　Total Income all Sources: $36,973,959

ALDERSON

P　ALDERSON LIBRARY*, RR 1, Box 147, 24910-0147. SAN 376-7787.
Tel: 304-445-7221. FAX: 304-445-7221. Web Site: www.aldersonlib.wv.us.
Librn, Phyllis Auvil; Staff 2 (Non-MLS 2)
　Library Holdings: Bk Titles 8,000; Bk Vols 9,800; Per Subs 23
　Automation Activity & Vendor Info: (Cataloging) Innovative Interfaces,
Inc; (Circulation) Innovative Interfaces, Inc; (OPAC) Innovative Interfaces,
Inc
　Open Mon, Tues & Thurs 11-5, Wed & Fri 10-4
　Friends of the Library Group

ATHENS

C　CONCORD UNIVERSITY, J Frank Marsh Library, 1000 Vermillion St,
24712. (Mail add: PO Box 1000, 24712-1000), SAN 317-722X. Tel:
304-384-5371. Interlibrary Loan Service Tel: 304-384-5375. Reference Tel:
304-384-5374. Administration Tel: 304-384-5366. FAX: 304-384-7955.
E-mail: library@concord.edu. Web Site: library.concord.edu. *Dir,* Connie L
Shumate; E-mail: cshumate@concord.edu; *Archivist, ILL,* Charles Lilly;
E-mail: clilly@concord.edu; *Circ,* Evangeline Vaughn; E-mail:
evaughn@concord.edu; *Info Spec,* Douglas Moore; Tel: 304-384-5372,
E-mail: moore@concord.edu; *Tech Serv,* Donna Musick; Tel:
304-384-5369; Staff 5 (MLS 1, Non-MLS 4)
　Founded 1872. Enrl 2,800; Fac 100; Highest Degree: Master
　Jul 2011-Jun 2012 Income (Main Library Only) $430,284, State $356,459,
Locally Generated Income $73,825. Mats Exp $135,510, Books $50,560,
Per/Ser (Incl. Access Fees) $4,000, Manu Arch $6,750, AV Equip $14,300,
AV Mat $5,000, Electronic Ref Mat (Incl. Access Fees) $54,900. Sal
$235,799 (Prof $79,090)
　Library Holdings: CDs 1,077; DVDs 1,980; Bk Titles 130,000; Bk Vols
156,184; Per Subs 227; Videos 1,000
　Special Collections: Fred J. Lucas Audio Coll; Goodykoontz Autograph
Coll; Holographs (F Wells Goodykoontz Holograph Coll), photog; West
Virginia Coll. State Document Depository; US Document Depository
　Automation Activity & Vendor Info: (Acquisitions) Innovative Interfaces,
Inc; (Cataloging) Innovative Interfaces, Inc; (Circulation) Innovative
Interfaces, Inc; (OPAC) Innovative Interfaces, Inc; (Serials) Innovative
Interfaces, Inc
　Database Vendor: Bowker, EBSCOhost, Faulkner Information Services,
Gale Cengage Learning, ISI Web of Knowledge, JSTOR,
Newsbank-Readex, OCLC WorldCat, OVID Technologies, Westlaw
Wireless access
　Function: For res purposes
　Partic in Lyrasis; Mountain Library Network
　Open Mon-Thurs 7:45-10, Fri 7:45-4, Sat 12-4, Sun 2-10

BEAVER

G　UNITED STATES DEPARTMENT OF LABOR*, Mine Safety & Health
Administration Technical Information Center & Library, 1301 Airport Rd,
25813-9426. SAN 320-1279. Tel: 304-256-3266. FAX: 304-256-3372.
E-mail: mshalibrary@dol.gov. Web Site:

www.msha.gov/training/library/library.htm. *Dir,* Yvonne S Farley; Tel:
304-256-3531, E-mail: farley.yvonne@dol.gov; *Librn,* Michelle Lee
Kubiak; Tel: 304-256-3233, E-mail: kubiak.michelle@dol.gov; *Tech Info
Spec,* Melody Bragg; Tel: 304-256-3556, E-mail: bragg.melody@dol.gov;
Tech Info Spec, Becky Farley; Tel: 304-256-3267, E-mail:
farley.becky@dol.gov; *Tech Info Spec,* Ronald L Minor; Tel: 304-256-3229,
E-mail: minor.ronald@dol.gov; *Libr Tech,* Bonnie Carter; E-mail:
carter.bonnie@dol.gov; Staff 6 (MLS 2, Non-MLS 4)
　Founded 1976
　Library Holdings: AV Mats 1,000; Bk Titles 14,000; Bk Vols 40,000; Per
Subs 150
　Special Collections: Bureau of Mines (1910-present); Mine Accident
Reports (Middle 1800-present); Mine Disasters
　Subject Interests: Earth sci, Indust safety, Mine safety, Occupational
diseases
　Automation Activity & Vendor Info: (Acquisitions) SirsiDynix;
(Cataloging) SirsiDynix; (Circulation) SirsiDynix; (OPAC) SirsiDynix;
(Serials) SirsiDynix
　Database Vendor: OCLC FirstSearch, OCLC WorldCat, Westlaw
　Function: Archival coll, Audio & video playback equip for onsite use,
Copy machines, e-mail serv, Electronic databases & coll, Govt ref serv,
ILL available, Photocopying/Printing
　Publications: Journal holdings list; New publications; New services
Partic in Fedlink
　Open Mon-Thurs 7-6, Fri 8:30-4:30
　Restriction: Photo ID required for access

BECKLEY

GM　DEPARTMENT OF VETERANS AFFAIRS*, Medical Center Library, 200
Veterans Ave, 25801. SAN 317-7270. Tel: 304-255-2121, Ext 4342. FAX:
304-255-2431. *Librn,* Lois Watson
　Founded 1952
　Library Holdings: Bk Vols 1,000; Per Subs 50
　Open Mon-Fri 8:30-5

C　MOUNTAIN STATE UNIVERSITY LIBRARY*, 609 S Kanawha St,
25801. (Mail add: PO Box 9003, 25802), SAN 317-7246. Tel:
304-929-1368. Circulation Tel: 304-929-1367. Interlibrary Loan Service
Tel: 304-929-1528. Administration Tel: 304-929-1414. Toll Free Tel:
877-678-5427. FAX: 304-929-1665. Web Site:
www.library.mountainstate.edu. *Dir,* Judy Jean Altis; E-mail:
jaltis@mountainstate.edu; *Acad Res Librn,* Marilyn Sue Phillips; Tel:
304-929-1534, E-mail: suephil@mountainstate.edu; *Circ Librn/Ser,* Susan
Paige Hoskins; Tel: 304-929-1369, E-mail: shoskins@mountainstate.edu;
Tech Serv Librn, Valerie Ann Sellards; Tel: 304-929-1469, E-mail:
valeries@mountainstate.edu; *Ref,* Sharon Bleau; E-mail:
sharonb@mountainstate.edu; Staff 6 (MLS 5, Non-MLS 1)
　Founded 1933. Enrl 5,108; Fac 364; Highest Degree: Master
　Jul 2008-Jun 2009. Mats Exp $240,840, Books $40,715, Per/Ser (Incl.
Access Fees) $55,000, Other Print Mats $1,077, AV Equip $9,000, AV Mat
$8,748, Electronic Ref Mat (Incl. Access Fees) $126,300. Sal $369,555

Library Holdings: AV Mats 4,705; CDs 96; DVDs 370; e-books 973; Electronic Media & Resources 52; Bk Titles 72,822; Bk Vols 96,152; Per Subs 157; Videos 3,970
Subject Interests: Allied health, Appalachia, Behav sci, Bus, Computers, Econ, Interdisciplinary studies, Med, Mgt, Nursing, Soc sci, WVa
Automation Activity & Vendor Info: (Cataloging) Follett Software; (Circulation) Follett Software; (OPAC) Follett Software; (Serials) Follett Software
Database Vendor: A.D.A.M. Inc, EBSCOhost, Gale Cengage Learning, Hoovers, netLibrary, Newsbank, ProQuest, ReferenceUSA, ScienceDirect, SerialsSolutions, Standard & Poor's, STAT!Ref (Teton Data Systems), Westlaw
Function: Archival coll, Computers for patron use, Copy machines, Distance learning, Electronic databases & coll, ILL available, Magnifiers for reading, Mail & tel request accepted, Online cat, Photocopying/Printing, Scanner, Tax forms, Wheelchair accessible
Partic in Lyrasis
Special Services for the Deaf - Assistive tech; Closed caption videos
Special Services for the Blind - Aids for in-house use; Assistive/Adapted tech devices, equip & products; Computer with voice synthesizer for visually impaired persons
Open Mon-Thurs 8am-9pm, Fri 8-5, Sat 10-5, Sun 2-6
Restriction: Borrowing privileges limited to fac & registered students

P   RALEIGH COUNTY PUBLIC LIBRARY*, 221 N Kanawha St, 25801-4716. SAN 364-2933. Tel: 304-255-0511. FAX: 304-255-9161. Web Site: raleigh.lib.wv.us/. *Dir,* Amy Lilly; E-mail: amy.lilly@raleigh.lib.wv.us; Staff 2 (MLS 2)
Founded 1935. Pop 79,220
Jun 2006-May 2007 Income $1,224,301, State $321,939, City $44,000, County $414,181, Locally Generated Income $30,000, Other $414,181. Mats Exp $196,000. Sal $817,677 (Prof $50,000)
Library Holdings: AV Mats 5,359; Electronic Media & Resources 33; Bk Titles 102,890; Per Subs 92; Talking Bks 2,168
Special Collections: Business Corral; Coal Mining; History (Tams Coll); West Virginia History (West Virginia Heritage Coll)
Automation Activity & Vendor Info: (Circulation) Innovative Interfaces, Inc; (Course Reserve) Innovative Interfaces, Inc; (ILL) Innovative Interfaces, Inc; (Media Booking) Innovative Interfaces, Inc; (OPAC) Innovative Interfaces, Inc; (Serials) Innovative Interfaces, Inc
Database Vendor: Ingram Library Services, Innovative Interfaces, Inc INN - View
Wireless access
Partic in Mountain Library Network
Open Mon-Thurs 9-8, Fri & Sat 9-5, Sun 1-5
Friends of the Library Group
Branches: 3
MARSH FORK, 9802 Coal River Rd, Montcoal, 25140. (Mail add: PO Box 70, Naoma, 25140-0070), SAN 364-2968. Tel: 304-854-2677. FAX: 304-854-2666. *Librn,* Kay Daniel; Staff 3 (Non-MLS 3)
  Library Holdings: AV Mats 763; Bk Titles 10,890; Per Subs 23; Talking Bks 222
  Open Mon & Wed-Fri 9:30-4:30, Tues 11:30-6:30, Sat 10-12
  Friends of the Library Group
SHADY SPRING BRANCH, 440 Flat Top Rd, Shady Spring, 25918, SAN 322-5933. Tel: 304-763-2681. FAX: 304-763-3940. *Librn,* Carol Sponaugle; Staff 2 (Non-MLS 2)
  Library Holdings: AV Mats 1,627; Bk Titles 20,109; Per Subs 41; Talking Bks 763
  Open Mon & Wed-Fri 9-5, Tues 12-8, Sat 10-2
  Friends of the Library Group
SOPHIA BRANCH, General Delivery, 103 First St, Sophia, 25921, SAN 364-2992. Tel: 304-683-5990. FAX: 304-683-3124. *Librn,* Amanda Turner
  Library Holdings: AV Mats 867; Bk Titles 16,247; Per Subs 27; Talking Bks 222
  Open Mon & Wed-Fri 9-5, Tues 11-7, Sat 10-2
  Friends of the Library Group
Bookmobiles: 2. Bkmobiles, Amy Stover. Bk vols 33,122

BELINGTON

P   BELINGTON PUBLIC LIBRARY*, 510 Elliott Ave, 26250. (Mail add: PO Box 878, 26250-0878), SAN 325-0458. Tel: 304-823-1026. FAX: 304-823-1026. *Dir,* Tamela M Smith; Staff 1 (Non-MLS 1)
Founded 1980. Pop 6,612; Circ 9,089
Jul 2005-Jun 2006 Income $43,146, State $26,870, City $3,000, County $2,000, Locally Generated Income $7,776. Mats Exp $3,246. Sal $20,557
Library Holdings: Bk Titles 15,124
Special Collections: Genealogical Books; Language cassettes; Large Print Books
Automation Activity & Vendor Info: (Cataloging) Innovative Interfaces, Inc; (Circulation) Innovative Interfaces, Inc; (OPAC) Innovative Interfaces, Inc; (Serials) Innovative Interfaces, Inc
Partic in Northern Library Network (NorLN)

Special Services for the Deaf - Bks on deafness & sign lang; High interest/low vocabulary bks; Spec interest per
Open Mon 11-7, Tues, Thurs & Fri 12-7, Wed 9-7

BERKELEY SPRINGS

P   MORGAN COUNTY PUBLIC LIBRARY*, 105 Congress St, 25411. SAN 317-7289. Tel: 304-258-3350. FAX: 304-258-3350. Web Site: youseemore.com/morgan. *Dir,* Larry Springer; E-mail: spring_l@martin.lib.wv.us; Staff 3 (Non-MLS 3)
Pop 9,962; Circ 60,000
Jul 2006-Jun 2007 Income $85,000
Library Holdings: Bk Vols 40,000; Per Subs 32
Special Collections: West Virginia Historical & Genealogical Collection
Automation Activity & Vendor Info: (Cataloging) TLC (The Library Corporation); (Circulation) TLC (The Library Corporation); (OPAC) TLC (The Library Corporation)
Open Mon, Thurs & Fri 9-6, Tues 9-8, Wed & Sat 9-12
Friends of the Library Group

BETHANY

CR   BETHANY COLLEGE, MARY CUTLIP CENTER FOR LIBRARY & INFORMATION TECHNOLOGY, T W Phillips Memorial Library, 300 Main St, 26032. SAN 317-7297. Tel: 304-829-7321. Interlibrary Loan Service Tel: 304-829-7757. Administration Tel: 304-829-7335. FAX: 304-829-7333. E-mail: library@bethanywv.edu. Web Site: www.bethanywv.edu/library. *The Mary Cutlip Dir of Libr & Learning Res,* Heather Ricciuti; E-mail: hricciuti@bethanywv.edu; *Dir, Bethany Heritage Prog & Archivist,* Sharon Monigold; E-mail: smonigold@bethanywv.edu; *Pub Serv Librn,* Trevor Onest; E-mail: tonest@bethanywv.edu; *Tech Serv Librn,* Heather Turner; E-mail: hturner@bethanywv.edu; Staff 4 (MLS 4)
Founded 1841. Enrl 850; Fac 55; Highest Degree: Bachelor
Library Holdings: AV Mats 4,074; e-books 110,856; Electronic Media & Resources 66; Microforms 151,192; Bk Titles 127,352
Special Collections: Alexander Campbell & Christian Church - Disciples of Christ (Alexander Campbell Archives), bk, ms, per; Hazlett-Cummins Civil War Colls; James Schuyler Poetry Coll; Ornithology (Brooks Bird Club Coll), per; Upper Ohio Valley Coll, bks, ms, per
Subject Interests: Relig studies
Automation Activity & Vendor Info: (Acquisitions) Innovative Interfaces, Inc - Millenium; (Cataloging) Innovative Interfaces, Inc - Millenium; (Circulation) Innovative Interfaces, Inc - Millenium; (Course Reserve) Innovative Interfaces, Inc - Millenium; (ILL) OCLC; (OPAC) Innovative Interfaces, Inc - Millenium; (Serials) Innovative Interfaces, Inc - Millenium
Database Vendor: 3M Library Systems, ABC-CLIO, Alexander Street Press, American Chemical Society, ARTstor, EBSCOhost, Gale Cengage Learning, Greenwood Publishing Group, Grolier Online, Innovative Interfaces, Inc, JSTOR, LearningExpress, LexisNexis, Modern Language Association, netLibrary, OCLC FirstSearch, OCLC WorldCat, OVID Technologies, ProQuest, SerialsSolutions, Wiley InterScience
Wireless access
Function: Archival coll, Copy machines, e-mail & chat, Electronic databases & coll, Fax serv, Free DVD rentals, ILL available, Online cat, Photocopying/Printing, Prog for children & young adult, Pub access computers, Ref serv available
Partic in Appalachian Col Asn; Lyrasis; OCLC Online Computer Library Center, Inc
Open Mon-Thurs (Winter) 8am-Midnight, Fri 8-4, Sat 10-4, Sun 2-Midnight; Mon-Fri (Summer) 9-4
Restriction: Open to fac, students & qualified researchers, Open to pub for ref & circ; with some limitations, Open to researchers by request
Friends of the Library Group

BLUEFIELD

C   BLUEFIELD STATE COLLEGE, Wendell G Hardway Library, 219 Rock St, 24701. SAN 364-3026. Tel: 304-327-4054. Reference Tel: 304-327-4056. Administration Tel: 304-327-4050. FAX: 304-327-4203. Web Site: library.bluefieldstate.edu. *Dir, Libr Serv,* Joanna M Thompson; E-mail: jthompson@bluefieldstate.edu; *Archivist, Ref,* James Leedy; Tel: 304-327-4053, E-mail: jsleedy@bluefieldstate.edu; *Info Literacy, Ref,* Nancy Adam-Turner; Tel: 304-327-4052, E-mail: nturner@bluefieldstate.edu; Staff 3 (MLS 3)
Founded 1895. Enrl 1,556; Fac 78; Highest Degree: Bachelor
Jul 2010-Jun 2011. Mats Exp $73,713, Books $11,396, Per/Ser (Incl. Access Fees) $17,623, Other Print Mats $7,170, Electronic Ref Mat (Incl. Access Fees) $37,524. Sal $216,108 (Prof $126,720)
Library Holdings: e-journals 23; Microforms 664,020; Bk Vols 72,604; Per Subs 59
Special Collections: BSC Archives. State Document Depository; US Document Depository
Automation Activity & Vendor Info: (Cataloging) Innovative Interfaces, Inc; (Circulation) Innovative Interfaces, Inc; (Course Reserve) Innovative Interfaces, Inc; (OPAC) Innovative Interfaces, Inc; (Serials) Innovative Interfaces, Inc

Database Vendor: EBSCOhost, Gale Cengage Learning, OCLC FirstSearch, OCLC WorldCat, Westlaw, Wilson - Wilson Web
Wireless access
Function: Archival coll, Govt ref serv, ILL available, Photocopying/Printing, Ref serv available
Partic in Lyrasis; OCLC Online Computer Library Center, Inc

P   CRAFT MEMORIAL LIBRARY, 600 Commerce St, 24701. SAN 317-7319. Tel: 304-325-3943. FAX: 304-325-3702. E-mail: cml@mail.mln.lib.wv.us. Web Site: craftmemorial.lib.wv.us. *Dir,* Eva McGuire; E-mail: mcguiree@mail.mln.lib.wv.us; *Circ Mgr,* Carolina Ferrare; *Prog Serv Coordr,* Suzette S Sims; *Archivist,* Becky George; Staff 3 (MLS 3)
Founded 1972. Pop 49,805; Circ 117,351
Jul 2012-Jun 2013 Income $342,932, State $227,932, City $60,000, County $25,000, Other $30,000. Mats Exp $58,000, Books $45,000, Per/Ser (Incl. Access Fees) $3,500, Other Print Mats $3,000, Micro $3,500, AV Mat $3,000. Sal $175,456 (Prof $103,280)
Library Holdings: Audiobooks 100; CDs 840; DVDs 837; e-books 8,003; Bk Vols 52,726; Per Subs 83; Videos 115
Special Collections: Eastern Regional Coal Archives; West Virginia & Virginia History Coll
Subject Interests: Coal mining, Local hist
Automation Activity & Vendor Info: (Cataloging) Innovative Interfaces, Inc; (Circulation) Innovative Interfaces, Inc; (OPAC) Innovative Interfaces, Inc
Database Vendor: Innovative Interfaces, Inc
Wireless access
Function: Adult bk club, After school storytime, Archival coll, Bk club(s), Bks on cassette, Bks on CD, Children's prog, Computer training, Computers for patron use, Copy machines, Fax serv, Free DVD rentals, Handicapped accessible, ILL available, Magnifiers for reading, Microfiche/film & reading machines, Notary serv, Online cat, Online ref, OverDrive digital audio bks, Photocopying/Printing, Prog for adults, Prog for children & young adult, Pub access computers, Ref serv available, Ref serv in person, Res performed for a fee, Story hour, Summer reading prog, Tax forms, Teen prog, Telephone ref, VHS videos, Wheelchair accessible
Partic in Mountain Library Network
Special Services for the Blind - Large print bks
Open Mon-Thurs 9:30-7, Fri & Sat 9:30-5
Friends of the Library Group
Bookmobiles: 1. Bkmobile Assoc, Charles Jones, Bk vols 7,000

BRIDGEPORT

P   BRIDGEPORT PUBLIC LIBRARY*, 1200 Johnson Ave, 26330. SAN 317-7335. Tel: 304-842-8248. FAX: 304-842-4018. E-mail: library@bridgeportwv.com. Web Site: www.bridgeportwv.com. *Dir,* Sharon R Saye; E-mail: saye@bridgeportwv.com; Staff 19 (MLS 1, Non-MLS 18)
Founded 1956. Pop 7,306; Circ 231,000
Jul 2007-Jun 2008 Income $595,402, State $29,691, City $496,526, County $17,301, Locally Generated Income $35,000, Other $16,884. Mats Exp $108,350, Books $58,350, Per/Ser (Incl. Access Fees) $7,000, AV Mat $43,000. Sal $264,522 (Prof $59,800)
Library Holdings: AV Mats 12,117; Electronic Media & Resources 14; Bk Titles 90,000; Bk Vols 97,873; Per Subs 175
Special Collections: Michael Benedum Coll, bks, clippings, memorabilia, per, scrapbks; West Virginia Coll, bk, pamphlets. Oral History
Automation Activity & Vendor Info: (Cataloging) Follett Software; (Circulation) Follett Software; (OPAC) Follett Software
Wireless access
Publications: Bridgeport: The Town & Its People
Open Mon-Fri 10-8, Sat 12-5
Friends of the Library Group

BUCKHANNON

P   CHARLES W GIBSON PUBLIC LIBRARY*, 105 E Main St, 26201. SAN 317-7343. Tel: 304-472-2339. FAX: 304-472-2339. *Librn,* Denise Weese; Staff 2 (Non-MLS 2)
Founded 1942. Circ 28,319
Library Holdings: AV Mats 270; Bk Vols 28,500; Per Subs 15
Open Mon 9-5, Tues, Thurs & Fri 11-8, Wed 9-8, Sat 1-5

P   UPSHUR COUNTY PUBLIC LIBRARY, Rte 6, PO Box 480, Tennerton Rd, 26201. SAN 317-7351. Tel: 304-473-4219. FAX: 304-473-4222. E-mail: upshur@clark.lib.wv.us. Web Site: upshurcounty.lib.wv.us. *Dir,* Patricia Tolliver; E-mail: tolliver@clark.lib.wv.us; Staff 2 (MLS 2)
Founded 1956. Pop 23,404; Circ 102,357
Library Holdings: AV Mats 4,967; Bk Vols 68,640; Per Subs 81
Automation Activity & Vendor Info: (Cataloging) Innovative Interfaces, Inc; (Circulation) Innovative Interfaces, Inc; (OPAC) Innovative Interfaces, Inc
Partic in Northern Library Network (NorLN)

Open Mon-Thurs 10-8, Fri 10-5, Sat 10-4
Friends of the Library Group

C   WEST VIRGINIA WESLEYAN COLLEGE*, Annie Merner Pfeiffer Library, 59 College Ave, 26201. SAN 317-736X. Tel: 304-473-8059. Circulation Tel: 304-473-8013. Interlibrary Loan Service Tel: 304-473-8631. Reference Tel: 304-473-8461. FAX: 304-473-8888. E-mail: librarian@wvwc.edu. Web Site: www.wvwc.edu/lib. *Dir of Libr Serv,* Paula L McGrew; E-mail: mcgrew_p@wvwc.edu; Staff 8 (MLS 5, Non-MLS 3)
Founded 1890. Enrl 1,572; Fac 82; Highest Degree: Master
Library Holdings: AV Mats 8,524; e-books 65,400; e-journals 13,644; Bk Titles 136,598; Bk Vols 119,970; Per Subs 447
Special Collections: Jones Lincoln Coll; Manuscripts (Pearl S Buck Coll); West Virginia Historical Archives. State Document Depository
Subject Interests: Civil War hist, Relig studies, WVa Methodist Hist
Automation Activity & Vendor Info: (Acquisitions) Innovative Interfaces, Inc; (Cataloging) Innovative Interfaces, Inc; (Circulation) Innovative Interfaces, Inc; (ILL) OCLC ILLiad; (Media Booking) Innovative Interfaces, Inc; (OPAC) Innovative Interfaces, Inc; (Serials) Innovative Interfaces, Inc
Wireless access
Function: Adult bk club, Archival coll, Computers for patron use, Copy machines, e-mail & chat, Electronic databases & coll, ILL available, Online cat, Outside serv via phone, mail, e-mail & web, Prog for adults, Ref serv in person, Telephone ref, Workshops
Partic in Appalachian Col Asn; Lyrasis

BURLINGTON

P   BURLINGTON LIBRARY*, Patterson Creek Rd, 26710. (Mail add: PO Box 61, 26710-0061), SAN 376-6608. Tel: 304-289-3690. FAX: 304-289-3233. Web Site: keyser.lib.wv.us. *Librn,* Catherine Weaver; *Asst Librn,* Sandy Byram; Staff 1 (Non-MLS 1)
Library Holdings: Bk Vols 7,500; Per Subs 12
Automation Activity & Vendor Info: (Cataloging) TLC (The Library Corporation); (Circulation) TLC (The Library Corporation); (OPAC) TLC (The Library Corporation)
Open Tues & Thurs 10-5, Wed 12-5, Fri 10-2, Sat 10-3
Friends of the Library Group

BURNSVILLE

P   BURNSVILLE LIBRARY*, 235 Kanawha Ave, 26335. SAN 376-6071. Tel: 304-853-2338. Web Site: burnsville.lib.wv.us. *Librn,* Dawn D Anilao-Herron; E-mail: deedee.herron@mail.nln.lib.wv.us; Staff 2 (Non-MLS 2)
Library Holdings: AV Mats 78; Bk Vols 9,000; Per Subs 21
Automation Activity & Vendor Info: (Cataloging) Innovative Interfaces, Inc; (Circulation) Innovative Interfaces, Inc; (OPAC) Innovative Interfaces, Inc
Partic in Northern Library Network (NorLN)
Open Mon 10-7, Tues-Fri 10-5, Sat 10-2

CAPON BRIDGE

P   CAPON BRIDGE PUBLIC LIBRARY*, Rte 50, 26711. (Mail add: PO Box 88, 26711-0088), SAN 317-7378. Tel: 304-856-3777. FAX: 304-856-3777. E-mail: directorlady87@yahoo.com. *Librn,* Cathy Haines; Staff 2 (Non-MLS 2)
Founded 1969. Pop 3,545; Circ 14,200
Library Holdings: AV Mats 210; Bk Titles 20,000; Bk Vols 23,000; Per Subs 15
Automation Activity & Vendor Info: (Circulation) TLC (The Library Corporation)
Open Mon, Wed & Thurs 11-6, Tues 2-8, Fri 11-5, Sat 9-1
Friends of the Library Group

CHAPMANVILLE

P   CHAPMANVILLE PUBLIC LIBRARY*, 299 Vance St, 25508. SAN 321-0057. Tel: 304-855-3405. FAX: 304-855-8590. E-mail: chappl@hotmail.com. *Librn,* Rebecca Brock; *Asst Librn,* Thomas Artist; *Asst Librn,* Sharon Cyfers; Staff 2 (Non-MLS 2)
Founded 1977. Circ 46,521
Library Holdings: Bk Titles 21,619; Per Subs 12; Talking Bks 283; Videos 650
Special Collections: AV Coll, bks, vf; Logan County Hist Special Coll; West Virginia, bks, vf, videocassettes
Automation Activity & Vendor Info: (Cataloging) SirsiDynix; (Circulation) SirsiDynix; (OPAC) SirsiDynix
Publications: Library Paper (Newsletter)
Open Mon, Wed & Fri 10-5, Tues & Thurs 10-7

CHARLES TOWN

P   OLD CHARLES TOWN LIBRARY, INC*, 200 E Washington St, 25414. SAN 317-7386. Tel: 304-725-2208. FAX: 304-725-6618. E-mail: octl@frontiernet.net. Web Site: www.ctlibrary.org. *Dir,* Barbara Elizabeth Tinker; E-mail: octl@frontiernet.net. Subject Specialists: *Children's lit, Young adult lit,* Barbara Elizabeth Tinker; Staff 9 (MLS 2, Non-MLS 7)
Founded 1927. Pop 45,000; Circ 80,000
Library Holdings: Bk Titles 70,000; Per Subs 100
Special Collections: History & Genealogy, Civil War (Perry Coll); History & Genealogy, Local History (Locked Reference Coll); Large Type Coll, Fiction & Non-fiction; Spanish Collection
Automation Activity & Vendor Info: (Cataloging) TLC (The Library Corporation); (Circulation) TLC (The Library Corporation); (OPAC) TLC (The Library Corporation)
Wireless access
Function: Archival coll, AV serv, Handicapped accessible, Home delivery & serv to Sr ctr & nursing homes, Homebound delivery serv, Photocopying/Printing, Prog for children & young adult, Summer reading prog, Wheelchair accessible
Open Mon, Wed & Fri 9-5, Tues & Thurs 1-7, Sat 9-1
Friends of the Library Group

CHARLESTON

S   THE CLAY CENTER FOR THE ARTS & SCIENCES OF WEST VIRGINIA*, 300 Leon Sullivan Way, 25301. SAN 376-1886. Tel: 304-561-3526. Web Site: www.theclaycenter.org. *Curator, Dir,* Ric Ambrose; E-mail: rambrose@theclaycenter.org; *Coll Mgr,* Denise Deegan
Library Holdings: Bk Vols 4,000
Open Wed-Sat 10-5, Sun 12-5

R   FIRST PRESBYTERIAN CHURCH OF CHARLESTON LIBRARY*, 16 Leon Sullivan Way, 25301. Tel: 304-343-7408. FAX: 304-343-8970. E-mail: firstpresby@firstpresby.com. Web Site: www.firstpresby.com. *Librn,* Tom Daugherty; Staff 1 (MLS 1)
Library Holdings: AV Mats 250; Bk Vols 9,000; Talking Bks 175
Subject Interests: Bible, Parenting, Relig
Open Mon, Wed & Fri 9-12

L   JACKSON KELLY*, Law Library, 1600 Laidley Tower, 25322. (Mail add: PO Box 553, 25322-0553), SAN 317-7416. Tel: 304-340-1260. FAX: 304-340-1261. *Librn,* Kimberly Adkins; E-mail: ksadkins@jacksonkelly.com
Library Holdings: Bk Titles 2,000; Bk Vols 8,000
Partic in SE Asn of Law Librs

P   KANAWHA COUNTY PUBLIC LIBRARY*, 123 Capitol St, 25301. SAN 364-314X. Tel: 304-343-4646. FAX: 304-348-6530. Web Site: www.kanawhalibrary.org. *Dir,* Alan Engelbert; *Assoc Dir, Pub Serv,* Linda Miller; *Adult Serv Mgr,* Toni Blessing; *Automation & Tech Serv Mgr,* Jane Hughes; *Fac & Security Mgr,* Susanna Holstein; *Human Res Mgr,* Marsha Alford; *Ref Supvr,* Elizabeth Fraser; *Ch,* Terri McDougal; Staff 23 (MLS 23)
Founded 1909. Pop 182,000; Circ 1,158,763
Special Collections: Local History (West Virginia). Oral History; State Document Depository; US Document Depository
Wireless access
Publications: West Virginia Foundation Directory
Open Mon-Thurs 9-9, Fri & Sat 9-5, Sun (Oct-April) 1-5
Friends of the Library Group
Branches: 11
CLENDENIN, One Cardinal St, Clendenin, 25045, SAN 377-0583. Tel: 304-548-6370. FAX: 304-548-6395. *Br Mgr,* Tammy Parker
Open Tues & Thurs 10-8, Wed 12-6, Sat 10-3
CROSS LANES, 5449 Big Tyler Rd, 25313, SAN 364-3204. Tel: 304-776-5999. FAX: 304-776-6005. *Br Mgr,* Julie Spiegler
Open Tues & Thurs 10-8, Wed 10-6, Fri 10-5, Sat 10-2
DUNBAR PUBLIC, 301 12th Street Mall, Dunbar, 25064, SAN 364-3239. Tel: 304-766-7161. FAX: 304-766-7242. *Br Mgr,* Melissa Burchett
Open Mon, Tues & Thurs 10-9, Wed, Fri & Sat 10-5
ELK VALLEY, 4636 Pennsylvania Ave, 25302, SAN 364-3263. Tel: 304-965-3636. FAX: 304-965-3702. *Br Mgr,* Ellie Teaford
Open Tues & Thurs 10-8, Wed & Fri 10-5, Sat 10-3
GLASGOW BRANCH, 129 Fourth Ave, Glasgow, 25086. (Mail add: PO Box 317, Glasgow, 25086-0317), SAN 364-3298. Tel: 304-595-3131. FAX: 304-595-3148. *Br Mgr,* Cathy Pierce
Open Tues 10-8
MARMET BRANCH, 9303 Oregon Ave, Marmet, 25315, SAN 364-3301. Tel: 304-949-6628. FAX: 304-949-6639. *Br Mgr,* Cathy Pierce
Open Thurs 10-8, Fri 10-5, Sat 10-3
NITRO PUBLIC, 1700 Park Ave, Nitro, 25143, SAN 317-8110. Tel: 304-755-4432. FAX: 304-755-5130. *Mgr,* Karen Boggess; Staff 1 (Non-MLS 1)
Founded 1964

Automation Activity & Vendor Info: (Acquisitions) SirsiDynix; (Cataloging) SirsiDynix
Open Mon & Thurs 11-7, Tues & Wed 10-5
RIVERSIDE, One Warrior Way, Belle, 25015. Tel: 304-949-2400. FAX: 304-949-2509. *Br Mgr,* Cathy Pierce
SAINT ALBANS BRANCH, 602 Fourth St, Saint Albans, 25177, SAN 364-3328. Tel: 304-722-4244. FAX: 304-722-4276. *Br Mgr,* Rebecca Van Der Meer
Open Mon, Tues & Thurs 10-9, Wed, Fri & Sat 10-5, Sun (Oct-April) 1-5
SISSONVILLE, One Tinney Lane, 25312, SAN 364-3336. Tel: 304-984-2244. FAX: 304-984-2251. *Br Mgr,* Pat Abbott
Open Mon & Tues 10-8, Wed 10-5, Thurs 1-8, Sat 10-3
Bookmobiles: 1

L   ROBINSON & MCELWEE PLLC*, Law Library, 400 Fifth Third Ctr, 700 Virginia St E, Ste 400, 25301. (Mail add: PO Box 1791, 25326-1791), SAN 372-3933. Tel: 304-347-8325. FAX: 304-344-9566. Web Site: www.ramlaw.com.
Library Holdings: Bk Titles 600; Bk Vols 4,000
Automation Activity & Vendor Info: (Acquisitions) Inmagic, Inc.; (Cataloging) Inmagic, Inc.; (Circulation) Inmagic, Inc.; (Course Reserve) Inmagic, Inc.; (ILL) Inmagic, Inc.; (Media Booking) Inmagic, Inc.; (OPAC) Inmagic, Inc.; (Serials) Inmagic, Inc.
Wireless access
Restriction: Open by appt only

L   UNITED STATES COURTS LIBRARY, US Court House, 300 Virginia St E, Rm 7400, 25301. SAN 372-3488. Tel: 304-347-3420. FAX: 304-347-3423. Web Site: www.wvsd.uscourts.gov. *Librn,* Marjorie Price; E-mail: marjorie_price@ca4.uscourts.gov; Staff 2 (MLS 1, Non-MLS 1)
Library Holdings: Bk Titles 20,000; Bk Vols 25,000; Per Subs 50
Automation Activity & Vendor Info: (Cataloging) SirsiDynix
Open Mon-Fri 8:30-5
Restriction: Non-circulating

C   UNIVERSITY OF CHARLESTON*, Schoenbaum Library, 2300 MacCorkle Ave SE, 25304-1099. SAN 317-7440. Tel: 304-357-4780. Reference Tel: 304-357-4913. FAX: 304-357-4715. E-mail: librarian@ucwv.edu. Web Site: www.ucwv.edu/library. *Dir,* Lynn Sheehan; Tel: 304-357-4918, E-mail: lynnsheehan@ucwv.edu; *Ref & Instrul Serv, Instr Coordr,* John Adkins; Tel: 304-357-4779, E-mail: johnadkins@ucwv.edu; *Circ,* Rebecca Harris; E-mail: rebeccaharris@ucwv.edu; *Pub Serv, Tech Serv,* Glenda Hughes; Tel: 304-357-4917, E-mail: glendahughes@ucwv.edu; *Ser,* Lissa Adkins; E-mail: erinadkins@ucwv.edu; *Tech Spec,* Debbie Thompson; Tel: 304-357-4997, E-mail: debbiethompson@ucwv.edu; Staff 7 (MLS 3, Non-MLS 4)
Founded 1888. Enrl 1,018; Highest Degree: Master
Library Holdings: AV Mats 3,769; Bk Titles 95,792; Bk Vols 118,779; Per Subs 303
Special Collections: Appalachian Culture Coll; Civil War (Gorman Coll); Early American History (John Allen Kinnaman Circulating Coll); James Swann Etchings; Kendall Vintroux Political Cartoons; Presidential Biographies (James David Barber Coll); Rare Book Coll; West Virginia Coll
Subject Interests: Am hist, Archit, Art, Health sci, Interior design, Polit sci, Relig
Automation Activity & Vendor Info: (Cataloging) Innovative Interfaces, Inc; (Circulation) Innovative Interfaces, Inc; (Course Reserve) Innovative Interfaces, Inc; (OPAC) Innovative Interfaces, Inc; (Serials) Innovative Interfaces, Inc
Database Vendor: EBSCOhost, Gale Cengage Learning, Innovative Interfaces, Inc INN - View, JSTOR, LexisNexis, SerialsSolutions
Function: Ref serv available
Publications: Library Leaves
Partic in Appalachian Col Asn; Lyrasis
Restriction: Open to students, fac & staff, Restricted pub use

G   WEST VIRGINIA ARCHIVES & HISTORY LIBRARY, Cultural Ctr, 1900 Kanawha Blvd E, 25305-0300. SAN 317-7475. Tel: 304-558-0230. FAX: 304-558-4193. Web Site: www.wvculture.org/history. *Dir,* Joseph N Geiger, Jr; *Mgr,* Robert Taylor; E-mail: bobby.l.taylor@wv.gov; Staff 12 (MLS 1, Non-MLS 11)
Founded 1905
Library Holdings: Bk Vols 65,000; Per Subs 326
Special Collections: State Printed Documents, Manuscripts, Public Records & Photos
Subject Interests: Appalachia, Civil War, Colonial hist, Genealogy, Mid-Atlantic region, Ohio Valley, WVa hist
Automation Activity & Vendor Info: (Cataloging) Ex Libris Group; (OPAC) Ex Libris Group
Wireless access

Publications: Archives & History News (Monthly); Checklist of State Publications (Bi-annually)
Open Mon-Wed, Fri & Sat 9-5, Thurs 9-8
Restriction: Non-circulating
Friends of the Library Group

J   WEST VIRGINIA JUNIOR COLLEGE LIBRARY*, 1000 Virginia St E, 25301. SAN 375-3158. Tel: 304-345-2820, Ext 314. FAX: 304-345-1425. Web Site: www.wvjc.edu. *Asst Librn,* Debbie Minnich; Staff 1 (Non-MLS 1)
Founded 1992. Fac 20
Library Holdings: Bk Vols 4,260; Per Subs 20
Partic in WVa Network for Educ Telecomputing
Open Mon-Thurs 8am-9pm, Fri 9-4

G   WEST VIRGINIA LEGISLATIVE REFERENCE LIBRARY*, Capitol Bldg, Rm MB 27, 25305-0591. SAN 317-7505. Tel: 304-347-4830. FAX: 304-347-4901. Web Site: www.legis.state.wv.us. *Res Mgr,* Deannia Spelock; E-mail: dspelock@mail.wvnet.edu
Library Holdings: Bk Vols 3,150; Per Subs 37
Open Mon-Fri 8:30-5
Restriction: Non-circulating, Ref only

P   WEST VIRGINIA LIBRARY COMMISSION*, State Capitol Complex, 1900 Kanawha Blvd E, 25305-0620. SAN 364-3417. Tel: 304-558-2041. Circulation Tel: 304-558-2045, Ext 2066. Interlibrary Loan Service Tel: 304-558-2045, Ext 2070. Reference Tel: 304-558-2045. Toll Free Tel: 800-642-9021 (WV only). FAX: 304-558-2044. E-mail: web_one@wvlc.lib.wv.us. Web Site: www.librarycommission.wv.gov. *State Librn,* Karen E Goff; E-mail: karen.e.goff@wv.gov; *Libr Admin Serv Dir,* Denise Ash Seabolt; Tel: 304-558-2041, Ext 2087, E-mail: denise.r.seabolt@wv.gov; *Network Serv Dir,* Harlan White; Tel: 304-558-3577, Fax: 304-558-3693, E-mail: whiteh@wvlc.lib.wv.us; *Spec Serv Dir,* Donna Calvert; Tel: 304-558-4061, Fax: 304-558-6016, E-mail: donna.b.calvert@wv.gov; Staff 56 (MLS 12, Non-MLS 44)
Founded 1929. Pop 1,852,994
Jul 2008-Jun 2009 Income $16,776,971, State $13,628,970, Federal $1,950,351, Other $1,197,650. Mats Exp $2,333,795, Books $590,093, Electronic Ref Mat (Incl. Access Fees) $687,199. Sal $2,153,114
Library Holdings: Audiobooks 5,043; AV Mats 14,322; CDs 232; DVDs 2,452; e-books 2,011; e-journals 19; Electronic Media & Resources 80; Large Print Bks 11,213; Microforms 235,337; Bk Titles 126,124; Per Subs 289; Talking Bks 88,249; Videos 6,595
Special Collections: 16mm Film Coll; Government Documents
Subject Interests: Appalachia, Libr sci, Polit sci, Pub admin, W Va
Automation Activity & Vendor Info: (Acquisitions) Ex Libris Group; (Cataloging) Ex Libris Group; (Circulation) Ex Libris Group; (ILL) OCLC ILLiad; (OPAC) Ex Libris Group; (Serials) Ex Libris Group
Database Vendor: Baker & Taylor, Booklist Online, Bowker, CQ Press, CredoReference, Dun & Bradstreet, EBSCO Information Services, EBSCOhost, Foundation Center, Gale Cengage Learning, GalleryWatch, Grolier Online, H W Wilson, Hoovers, infoUSA, LearningExpress, LexisNexis, netLibrary, Newsbank, OCLC FirstSearch, OneSource, Oxford Online, ProQuest, ReferenceUSA, Wilson - Wilson Web
Wireless access
Function: Adult literacy prog, Audio & video playback equip for onsite use, Audiobks via web, AV serv, Computer training, Computers for patron use, Copy machines, Electronic databases & coll, Free DVD rentals, Govt ref serv, Handicapped accessible, ILL available, Libr develop, Newsp ref libr, Online ref, Outside serv via phone, mail, e-mail & web, Photocopying/Printing, Pub access computers, Ref serv available, Spoken cassettes & CDs, Tax forms, Telephone ref, VHS videos, Wheelchair accessible, Workshops
Publications: Annual Report; Annual Statistical Report
Partic in Lyrasis
Special Services for the Blind - Cassette playback machines; Cassettes; Descriptive video serv (DVS); Large print bks; Machine repair; Newsline for the Blind; Ref serv
Open Mon-Fri 8:30-5
Restriction: Open to pub for ref & circ; with some limitations

GL   WEST VIRGINIA SUPREME COURT OF APPEALS*, State Law Library, Bldg 1, Rm E-404, 1900 Kanawha Blvd E, 25305-0833. SAN 317-7521. Tel: 304-558-2607. FAX: 304-558-3673. Web Site: www.state.wv.us/wvsca/library/menu.htm. *Dir, Libr & Info Serv, Law Librn,* Kaye L Maerz; E-mail: kaye.maerz@courtswv.org; *Tech Serv Librn,* Janet Bosley; E-mail: janet.bosley@courtswv.org; Staff 8 (MLS 4, Non-MLS 4)
Founded 1867
Library Holdings: AV Mats 192; Bk Titles 687; Bk Vols 154,532; Per Subs 290
Special Collections: US Document Depository
Subject Interests: Govt, Law

Automation Activity & Vendor Info: (Cataloging) SirsiDynix; (Circulation) SirsiDynix; (OPAC) SirsiDynix; (Serials) SirsiDynix
Database Vendor: OCLC FirstSearch
Function: For res purposes
Partic in OCLC Online Computer Library Center, Inc
Open Mon-Thurs 8:30-7, Fri 8:30-5, Sat 10-3
Restriction: Non-circulating to the pub

CM   WEST VIRGINIA UNIVERSITY, HSC Learning Resource Center, 3110 MacCorkle Ave SE, 25304. SAN 317-753X. Tel: 304-347-1285. FAX: 304-347-1288. E-mail: chsclibrary@hsc.wvu.edu. Web Site: www.hsc.wvu.edu/charleston/library. *Dir,* Robert Cagna; Tel: 304-347-1287, E-mail: rcagna@hsc.wvu.edu; Staff 6 (MLS 1, Non-MLS 5)
Founded 1974. Highest Degree: Doctorate
Library Holdings: Bk Titles 22,000; Bk Vols 25,000; Per Subs 360
Subject Interests: Clinical med
Automation Activity & Vendor Info: (Cataloging) Ex Libris Group; (Circulation) Ex Libris Group; (OPAC) Ex Libris Group
Wireless access
Partic in Docline; National Network of Libraries of Medicine; OCLC Online Computer Library Center, Inc
Open Mon-Thurs 8am-9pm, Fri 8-4:30, Sat 9-1

CHESTER

P   LYNN MURRAY MEMORIAL LIBRARY*, 601 Railroad St, 26034. SAN 317-7548. Tel: 304-387-1010. FAX: 304-387-1010. *Dir,* Linda Clark; E-mail: linda.clark@lycos.com; *Ch,* Sue Thompson; E-mail: tsusan@lycos.com; Staff 2 (Non-MLS 2)
Founded 1971. Pop 7,409; Circ 23,380
Library Holdings: AV Mats 200; Large Print Bks 115; Bk Titles 16,081; Per Subs 42; Talking Bks 130
Partic in Northern Library Network (NorLN)
Open Mon-Thurs 10-7, Fri 10-5, Sat 10-2

CLARKSBURG

P   CLARKSBURG-HARRISON PUBLIC LIBRARY*, 404 W Pike St, 26301. SAN 317-7556. Tel: 304-627-2236. FAX: 304-627-2239. Web Site: www.clarksburglibrary.info. *Dir,* Beth Nicholson; E-mail: nicholsb@clark.lib.wv.us; *Pub Serv Dir,* Charley Hively; E-mail: hivelyc@clark.lib.wv.us; *Curator,* David Houchin; E-mail: houchin@clark.lib.wv.us; *Head, Ref,* Rebecca Lafferty; E-mail: lafferty@clark.lib.wv.us; *Commun Relations Librn,* Bill Ellifrett; E-mail: ellifrett@clark.lib.wv.us; *Ch,* Mary Loomis; E-mail: loomis@clark.lib.wv.us. Subject Specialists: *Genealogy, Local hist,* David Houchin; Staff 21 (MLS 3, Non-MLS 18)
Founded 1907. Pop 56,898; Circ 115,513
Library Holdings: Bk Titles 64,181; Bk Vols 72,090
Special Collections: UFO (Gray Barker Coll)
Subject Interests: Genealogy, Local hist
Automation Activity & Vendor Info: (Cataloging) Innovative Interfaces, Inc; (Circulation) Innovative Interfaces, Inc; (OPAC) Innovative Interfaces, Inc
Function: Handicapped accessible, ILL available, Magnifiers for reading, Photocopying/Printing, Prog for children & young adult, Ref serv available, Summer reading prog, Wheelchair accessible
Partic in Northern Library Network (NorLN)
Special Services for the Blind - Assistive/Adapted tech devices, equip & products
Open Mon-Thurs 9-8, Fri & Sat 9-6, Sun 1-6
Friends of the Library Group

GM   DEPARTMENT OF VETERANS AFFAIRS*, Louis A Johnson VA Library Service, One Medical Center Dr, 26301. SAN 317-7580. Tel: 304-623-7635. FAX: 304-623-7618. *Mgr,* Mary McCloud; E-mail: mary.mccloud@va.gov
Founded 1950
Library Holdings: AV Mats 240; Bk Vols 805; Per Subs 221
Subject Interests: Dentistry, Med, Nursing, Psychiat, Surgery
Automation Activity & Vendor Info: (Cataloging) Follett Software; (OPAC) Follett Software
Partic in National Network of Libraries of Medicine
Open Mon-Fri 7-3:30

M   UNITED HOSPITAL CENTER*, Health Science Library, Three Hospital Plaza, 26302. SAN 317-7572. Tel: 304-624-2230. FAX: 304-624-2358. *Dir,* Heather Simon; E-mail: simonh@uhcwv.org
Founded 1973
Jan 2007-Dec 2007. Mats Exp $33,510, Per/Ser (Incl. Access Fees) $28,510, AV Mat $5,000
Library Holdings: AV Mats 200; Bk Vols 2,500; Per Subs 65; Videos 1,170
Automation Activity & Vendor Info: (Cataloging) Follett Software; (Circulation) Follett Software

Function: Res libr
Partic in Docline
Open Mon, Wed & Thurs 8-4
Restriction: Non-circulating to the pub

CLAY

P CLAY COUNTY PUBLIC LIBRARY*, 614 Main St, 25043. (Mail add:
PO Box 60, 25043), SAN 317-7599. Tel: 304-587-4254. FAX:
304-587-7668. Web Site: clay.lib.wv.us. *Libr Dir,* Sheila Thorne; Staff 2
(Non-MLS 2)
Founded 1960. Pop 10,330; Circ 22,173
Library Holdings: AV Mats 1,978; Bk Vols 18,891
Automation Activity & Vendor Info: (Cataloging) Follett Software;
(Circulation) Follett Software; (OPAC) Follett Software
Open Tues-Thurs 10-6, Fri 9-5, Sat 10-2
Friends of the Library Group

COWEN

P COWEN LIBRARY*, 47 Mill St, 26206. (Mail add: PO Box 187,
26206-0187), SAN 376-7795. Tel: 304-226-5332. FAX: 304-226-5332.
Web Site: cowen.lib.wv.us. *Librn,* Randy Timm
Founded 1978. Pop 4,538
Library Holdings: Audiobooks 220; Bk Vols 19,557; Per Subs 7
Automation Activity & Vendor Info: (Cataloging) Innovative Interfaces,
Inc; (Circulation) Innovative Interfaces, Inc; (OPAC) Innovative Interfaces,
Inc
Wireless access
Partic in Northern Library Network (NorLN)
Open Mon, Tues & Thurs 8:30-4, Wed 8:30am-9pm

CRAIGSVILLE

P CRAIGSVILLE LIBRARY, 63 Library Lane, 26205. SAN 376-7809. Tel:
304-742-3532. FAX: 304-742-6904. Web Site: craigsville.lib.wv.us. *Dir,* Jo
Ann Flynn
Founded 1978. Pop 8,854; Circ 30,691
Library Holdings: AV Mats 149; Bks on Deafness & Sign Lang 12; Bk
Vols 27,324
Automation Activity & Vendor Info: (Cataloging) Innovative Interfaces,
Inc; (Circulation) Innovative Interfaces, Inc; (OPAC) Innovative Interfaces,
Inc
Wireless access
Partic in Mountain Library Network
Open Mon-Fri 9-5, Sat 9-3

DANVILLE

J SOUTHERN WEST VIRGINIA COMMUNITY & TECHNICAL
COLLEGE*, Boone/Lincoln Campus, 3505 Daniel Boone Pkwy, 25053.
Tel: 304-369-2952, Ext 18. FAX: 304-369-2954. Web Site:
www.southern.wvnet.edu. *Info Syst Tech,* Susan Ferrell; E-mail:
susief@southern.wvnet.edu
Highest Degree: Associate
Library Holdings: Bk Vols 500; Videos 10
Automation Activity & Vendor Info: (Cataloging) SirsiDynix;
(Circulation) SirsiDynix; (OPAC) SirsiDynix
Database Vendor: Gale Cengage Learning, LearningExpress
Open Mon-Thurs 10:30-7, Fri 8-4

DELBARTON

P MINGO COUNTY LIBRARY*, Main St, 25670. (Mail add: PO Box 10,
25670-0010), SAN 317-7610. Tel: 304-475-2749. FAX: 304-475-3970.
Librn, Pam Warden; E-mail: pwarden@cabell.lib.wv.us; Staff 1 (Non-MLS
1)
Founded 1972. Pop 28,296; Circ 62,987
Library Holdings: AV Mats 762; Bk Vols 45,000; Per Subs 45
Automation Activity & Vendor Info: (Cataloging) SirsiDynix;
(Circulation) SirsiDynix; (OPAC) SirsiDynix
Open Mon 10-6, Tues-Fri 8:30-4:30
Branches: 3
GILBERT BRANCH, City Hall, Gilbert, 25621. (Mail add: PO Box 266,
Gilbert, 25621-0266), SAN 324-2641. Tel: 304-664-8886. FAX:
304-664-8886. *Br Librn,* Sharon Starr; Staff 1 (Non-MLS 1)
Library Holdings: Bk Vols 4,200; Per Subs 10
Open Mon-Wed & Fri 8:30-4:30, Thurs 10-6
KERMIT BRANCH, 138-B Main St, Kermit, 25674. (Mail add: PO Box
577, Kermit, 25674-0577), SAN 324-265X. Tel: 304-393-4553. FAX:
304-393-4553. *Br Librn,* Dorothy Linville; Staff 1 (Non-MLS 1)
Library Holdings: Bk Vols 7,000; Per Subs 10
Open Mon, Wed-Fri 9-5, Tues 11-7

MATEWAN BRANCH, Warm Hollow Rd, Matewan, 25678. (Mail add: PO
Box 111, Matewan, 25678-0111), SAN 324-2668. Tel: 304-426-6306.
FAX: 304-426-6306. *Br Librn,* Donna Blankenship; Staff 2 (Non-MLS 2)
Library Holdings: Bk Vols 4,000; Per Subs 10
Open Mon-Wed & Fri 8:30-4:30, Thurs 10-6
Bookmobiles: 1

ELIZABETH

P DORA BEE WOODYARD MEMORIAL LIBRARY*, Mulberry St, 26143.
(Mail add: PO Box 340, 26143-0340), SAN 317-7629. Tel: 304-275-4295.
FAX: 304-275-4295. Web Site: dorawoodyard.lib.wv.us. *Librn,* Becky
Watson; E-mail: watsonb@mail.mln.lib.wv.us
Founded 1962. Pop 5,192; Circ 32,466
Library Holdings: Bk Vols 15,000; Per Subs 52
Special Collections: West Virginia History
Automation Activity & Vendor Info: (Cataloging) Innovative Interfaces,
Inc; (Circulation) Innovative Interfaces, Inc; (OPAC) Innovative Interfaces,
Inc
Publications: Book News
Partic in Mountain Library Network
Open Mon & Thurs 8-7, Tues, Wed & Fri 8-5

ELKINS

C DAVIS & ELKINS COLLEGE*, Booth Library, 100 Campus Dr, 26241.
SAN 317-7637. Tel: 304-637-1200. Reference Tel: 304-637-1359.
Administration Tel: 304-637-1233. FAX: 304-637-1415. E-mail:
library@davisandelkins.edu. Web Site: www.earthhome.net/library. *Asst
Dir,* Kathy Doig; Tel: 304-637-1359, E-mail: doigk@dewv.edu; *Circ Mgr,*
Paula Taylor; E-mail: taylorp@dewv.edu; *Tech Serv Coordr,* Susan
McMillon; Tel: 304-637-1336, E-mail: mcmillons@dewv.edu; Staff 5 (MLS
2, Non-MLS 3)
Founded 1904. Enrl 586; Fac 65; Highest Degree: Bachelor
Library Holdings: Bk Vols 116,000; Per Subs 459
Special Collections: Traditional Music Archives Coll. US Document
Depository
Automation Activity & Vendor Info: (Cataloging) Innovative Interfaces,
Inc; (Circulation) Innovative Interfaces, Inc; (Course Reserve) Innovative
Interfaces, Inc; (ILL) OCLC; (OPAC) Innovative Interfaces, Inc; (Serials)
Innovative Interfaces, Inc
Database Vendor: EBSCOhost, Gale Cengage Learning, Innovative
Interfaces, Inc INN - View, JSTOR, netLibrary, OCLC FirstSearch,
ProQuest, Wilson - Wilson Web
Function: Archival coll, AV serv, Handicapped accessible, ILL available,
Ref serv available
Partic in Lyrasis
Open Mon-Thurs 8am-10pm, Fri 8-4, Sat 12-4, Sun 2-10
Restriction: In-house use for visitors, Non-circulating of rare bks

P ELKINS-RANDOLPH COUNTY PUBLIC LIBRARY, 416 Davis Ave,
26241. SAN 317-7645. Tel: 304-637-0287. FAX: 304-637-0288. Web Site:
elkins.lib.wv.us. *Dir,* Audrey Taylor; *Circ,* Linda Daniels; *Circ,* Terry
Harmon; *Circ,* Pauletta Mersing-White; *Circ,* Joy Suder; *Circ,* Jane
Trimble; *Circ,* Gloria Wisbar; Staff 8 (MLS 1, Non-MLS 7)
Founded 1969. Pop 13,548; Circ 54,692
Jul 2011-Jun 2012 Income $168,708, State $61,295, City $20,000, County
$22,000, Locally Generated Income $55,413, Other $10,000. Mats Exp
$15,800, Books $12,500, Per/Ser (Incl. Access Fees) $1,800, AV Mat
$1,500. Sal $97,672 (Prof $30,500)
Library Holdings: Audiobooks 1,122; AV Mats 2,001; Bks on Deafness &
Sign Lang 6; Braille Volumes 50; CDs 135; DVDs 2,001; Large Print Bks
928; Microforms 29; Bk Vols 30,682; Per Subs 63; Videos 2,001
Automation Activity & Vendor Info: (Cataloging) Innovative Interfaces,
Inc; (Circulation) Innovative Interfaces, Inc; (OPAC) Innovative Interfaces,
Inc
Wireless access
Function: Adult literacy prog, Bks on CD, Children's prog, Citizenship
assistance, Computers for patron use, Copy machines, Digital talking bks,
Distance learning, e-mail & chat, Electronic databases & coll, Free DVD
rentals, Handicapped accessible, Holiday prog, ILL available,
Photocopying/Printing, Prog for children & young adult, Spoken cassettes
& CDs, Spoken cassettes & DVDs, Story hour, Summer reading prog,
VHS videos, Wheelchair accessible
Partic in Northern Library Network (NorLN)
Open Mon-Fri 10-9, Sat 10-5
Restriction: Non-circulating of rare bks
Friends of the Library Group

FAIRMONT

C FAIRMONT STATE UNIVERSITY*, Ruth Ann Musick Library, 1201
Locust Ave, 26554. SAN 317-767X. Tel: 304-367-4733. Interlibrary Loan
Service Tel: 304-367-4622. Reference Tel: 304-367-4121. FAX:
304-367-4677. Web Site: library.fairmontstate.edu. *Dir of Libr,* Thelma

Hutchins; E-mail: thutchins@fairmontstate.edu; *Cat Librn,* Robert
Hammonds; Tel: 304-367-4697, E-mail: rhammonds@fairmonstate.edu;
Electronic Serv Librn, Toru Chiba; Tel: 304-367-4594, E-mail:
tchiba@fairmontstate.edu; *Ref & ILL Librn,* Sharon Mazure; E-mail:
smazure@fairmontstate.edu; *Ref/Instruction Librn,* David Matthews; Tel:
304-367-4618, E-mail: dmatthews@fairmontstate.edu; *Coordr, Ref &
Instrul Serv,* Charley Hively; Tel: 304-367-4617, E-mail:
hhively@fairmontstate.edu; Staff 7 (MLS 7)
Founded 1867. Enrl 7,700; Fac 7; Highest Degree: Master
Jul 2005-Jun 2006 Income (Main and Other College/University Libraries)
$1,442,427, Parent Institution $1,442,427. Mats Exp $439,256, Books
$44,053, Per/Ser (Incl. Access Fees) $47,820, AV Mat $8,608, Electronic
Ref Mat (Incl. Access Fees) $284,924. Sal $841,970
Library Holdings: AV Mats 7,326; e-books 62,550; e-journals 27,816; Bk
Vols 217,723; Per Subs 394
Special Collections: US Document Depository
Automation Activity & Vendor Info: (Acquisitions) Innovative Interfaces,
Inc; (Cataloging) Innovative Interfaces, Inc; (Circulation) Innovative
Interfaces, Inc; (Course Reserve) Docutek; (ILL) OCLC ILLiad; (OPAC)
Innovative Interfaces, Inc; (Serials) Innovative Interfaces, Inc
Database Vendor: ARTstor, Cambridge Scientific Abstracts, EBSCOhost,
Gale Cengage Learning, JSTOR, LexisNexis, netLibrary, OCLC
FirstSearch, OVID Technologies, ProQuest, PubMed, ScienceDirect,
SerialsSolutions, STN International, Wilson - Wilson Web
Wireless access
Function: Audio & video playback equip for onsite use, Copy machines,
E-Reserves, Electronic databases & coll, Fax serv, Handicapped accessible,
ILL available, Mail & tel request accepted, Music CDs, Online info
literacy tutorials on the web & in blackboard, Online ref, Online searches,
Orientations, Photocopying/Printing, Ref & res, Ref serv available, Spoken
cassettes & CDs, Spoken cassettes & DVDs, Tax forms, Telephone ref,
VHS videos, Video lending libr, Wheelchair accessible
Partic in Lyrasis; OCLC Online Computer Library Center, Inc
Special Services for the Deaf - TTY equip
Special Services for the Blind - Assistive/Adapted tech devices, equip &
products
Open Mon-Thurs 7am-Midnight, Fri 7-7, Sat 9-6, Sun 2-Midnight

P   **MARION COUNTY PUBLIC LIBRARY***, 321 Monroe St, 26554-2952.
SAN 317-7688. Tel: 304-366-1210. FAX: 304-366-4831. Web site:
www.marioncountypubliclibrary.org. *Dir,* Erika Reed; *Acq Mgr,* Jackie
Rueger; *Ref/Outreach Coordr,* Rebecca Mayle; *Cat,* Barbara Satterfield;
Ch, Christian Cox; *Circ,* Chriss Russell; Staff 18 (MLS 1, Non-MLS 17)
Founded 1941. Pop 58,367; Circ 163,000
Jul 2006-Jun 2007 Income (Main Library and Branch(s)) $970,000, City
$20,000, County $873,000, Locally Generated Income $56,000, Other
$21,000. Mats Exp $215,000, Books $125,000, Per/Ser (Incl. Access Fees)
$17,000, AV Equip $15,000, AV Mat $35,000, Electronic Ref Mat (Incl.
Access Fees) $23,000
Library Holdings: AV Mats 3,262; Bk Vols 45,361; Per Subs 115
Special Collections: Genealogy Coll
Automation Activity & Vendor Info: (Acquisitions) Innovative Interfaces,
Inc; (Cataloging) Innovative Interfaces, Inc; (Circulation) Innovative
Interfaces, Inc; (Course Reserve) Innovative Interfaces, Inc; (OPAC)
Innovative Interfaces, Inc; (Serials) Innovative Interfaces, Inc
Database Vendor: EBSCOhost, Gale Cengage Learning, Grolier Online,
LearningExpress, ProQuest
Wireless access
Open Mon & Tues 9-8, Wed-Fri 9-6, Sat 9-4
Friends of the Library Group
Branches: 2
FAIRVIEW PUBLIC, 500 Main St, Fairview, 26570. (Mail add: PO Box
   296, Fairview, 26570-0296), SAN 324-4717. Tel: 304-449-1195. FAX:
   304-449-1021. *Dir,* Erika Reed; Tel: 304-366-1210; *Librn,* Oneita
   Opyoke; Staff 2 (Non-MLS 2)
   Library Holdings: Bk Vols 12,344; Per Subs 44
   Open Mon & Wed-Fri 9-5, Tues 9-8, Sat 9-1
   Friends of the Library Group
MANNINGTON PUBLIC, 109 Clarksburg St, Mannington, 26582, SAN
   324-4725. Tel: 304-986-2803. FAX: 304-986-3425. E-mail:
   mpl@marioncountypubliclibrary.org. *Mgr,* Alan Smith; *Ad,* Pat Koch;
   Youth Serv Librn, Cathy Pruett; Staff 2 (MLS 1, Non-MLS 1)
   Founded 1964
   Library Holdings: Bk Vols 31,186; Per Subs 56
   Open Mon 9-7, Tues-Fri 9-5, Sat 9-1
   Friends of the Library Group
Bookmobiles: 1. Bkmobile Mgr, Lynn Clough. Bk vols 2,800

FRANKLIN

P   **PENDLETON COUNTY LIBRARY***, 256 N Main St, 26807. (Mail add:
PO Box 519, 26807), SAN 364-3476. Tel: 304-358-7038. FAX:
304-358-7038. Web Site: pendleton.lib.wv.us. *Librn,* Rebecca McConnell;
Staff 1 (Non-MLS 1)
Pop 695; Circ 35,045

Library Holdings: Bk Vols 40,000; Per Subs 21
Automation Activity & Vendor Info: (Cataloging) Follett Software;
(Circulation) Follett Software; (OPAC) Follett Software
Wireless access
Open Tues-Fri 10-5, Sat 9-3
Friends of the Library Group

GASSAWAY

P   **GASSAWAY PUBLIC LIBRARY***, 536 Elk, 26624-1216. SAN 317-770X.
Tel: 304-364-8292. FAX: 304-364-8292. Web Site: gassaway.lib.wv.us. *Dir,*
Brenda Hickman; Staff 3 (Non-MLS 3)
Founded 1967. Pop 4,833; Circ 26,662
Library Holdings: Bk Vols 15,500; Per Subs 20
Database Vendor: EBSCOhost
Partic in Northern Library Network (NorLN)
Open Mon 11-6, Tues-Thurs 11-5, Fri 11-8

GLENVILLE

P   **GILMER PUBLIC LIBRARY***, 214 Walnut St, 26351. SAN 320-9822.
Tel: 304-462-5620. FAX: 304-462-5620. *Dir,* Susan Atkinson; E-mail:
atkins@clark.lib.wv.us; Staff 3 (Non-MLS 3)
Founded 1979. Pop 8,334; Circ 24,500
Library Holdings: AV Mats 400; Bk Vols 24,000; Per Subs 21
Special Collections: Local History Coll; West Virginia Coll
Automation Activity & Vendor Info: (Cataloging) Innovative Interfaces,
Inc; (Circulation) Innovative Interfaces, Inc; (OPAC) Innovative Interfaces,
Inc
Partic in Northern Library Network (NorLN)
Open Mon-Fri 10-5, Sat 10-1
Friends of the Library Group

C   **GLENVILLE STATE COLLEGE***, Robert F Kidd Library, 100 High St,
26351. SAN 317-7718. Tel: 304-462-4109. FAX: 304-462-4049. E-mail:
library.circ@glenville.edu, library@glenville.edu. Web Site:
www.glenville.edu/library.asp. *Dir,* Gail Lee Westbrook; Tel: 304-462-4109,
Ext 6161, E-mail: gail.westbrook@glenville.edu; *Ref, Staff Librn,* Virginia
Beatrice Yeager; Tel: 304-462-4109, Ext 6164, E-mail:
virginia.yeager@glenville.edu; Staff 6 (MLS 2, Non-MLS 4)
Founded 1930. Enrl 1,200; Fac 67; Highest Degree: Bachelor
Jul 2009-Jul 2010 Income $396,674. Mats Exp $113,750, Books $12,108,
Per/Ser (Incl. Access Fees) $11,334, Other Print Mats $3,738, Micro
$1,526, AV Mat $4,509, Electronic Ref Mat (Incl. Access Fees) $67,133,
Presv $7,786. Sal $203,376 (Prof $85,896)
Library Holdings: AV Mats 3,226; e-books 34,007; e-journals 25,819;
Electronic Media & Resources 41,161; Bk Titles 86,900; Bk Vols 117,024;
Per Subs 107
Special Collections: Archives & Special Collections; Berlin B Chapman
Special Coll Room. Oral History
Subject Interests: WVa
Automation Activity & Vendor Info: (Cataloging) Innovative Interfaces,
Inc - OCLC; (Circulation) Innovative Interfaces, Inc - Millenium; (Course
Reserve) Docutek; (ILL) OCLC Online; (OPAC) Innovative Interfaces, Inc
- Millenium; (Serials) Innovative Interfaces, Inc - Millenium
Database Vendor: Bowker, CQ Press, CredoReference, EBSCOhost, Gale
Cengage Learning, Innovative Interfaces, Inc, JSTOR, McGraw-Hill,
netLibrary, Overdrive, Inc, ProQuest, SerialsSolutions, SirsiDynix, Wilson -
Wilson Web
Wireless access
Function: Archival coll, Audio & video playback equip for onsite use,
Computers for patron use, Copy machines, e-mail & chat, E-Reserves,
Electronic databases & coll, Fax serv, Free DVD rentals, Handicapped
accessible, ILL available, Music CDs, Online cat, Online ref, Orientations,
OverDrive digital audio bks, Photocopying/Printing, Pub access computers,
Ref & res, Ref serv in person, Scanner, Telephone ref, VHS videos,
Wheelchair accessible
Partic in Lyrasis; Northern Library Network (NorLN)
Open Mon-Thurs 7:45am-10pm, Fri 7:45-4, Sun 2-10

GRAFTON

P   **TAYLOR COUNTY PUBLIC LIBRARY***, 200 Beech St, 26354. SAN
317-7726. Tel: 304-265-6121. FAX: 304-265-6122. E-mail:
Taylib@clark.lib.wv.us. Web Site: taylor.clark.lib.wv.us. *Dir,* Marli Jenkins;
Cat, Joyce Freeman; *Circ,* Lesley Hylton; Staff 3 (Non-MLS 3)
Founded 1979. Pop 16,089; Circ 117,892
Library Holdings: AV Mats 1,808; Large Print Bks 442; Bk Titles 27,375;
Bk Vols 35,804; Per Subs 25; Spec Interest Per Sub 30; Talking Bks 822
Special Collections: Rare West Virginia Coll
Subject Interests: Genealogy, Local hist
Automation Activity & Vendor Info: (Acquisitions) Follett Software;
(Cataloging) Follett Software; (Circulation) Follett Software; (Course
Reserve) Follett Software; (OPAC) Follett Software; (Serials) Follett
Software
Database Vendor: EBSCOhost

Wireless access
Function: Archival coll, AV serv, Handicapped accessible, Home delivery & serv to Sr ctr & nursing homes, Homebound delivery serv, ILL available, Online searches, Photocopying/Printing, Prog for children & young adult, Ref serv available, Satellite serv, Summer reading prog, Telephone ref, Wheelchair accessible
Open Mon & Thurs 9-7:30, Tues, Wed & Fri 9-5
Friends of the Library Group

GRANTSVILLE

P   CALHOUN COUNTY PUBLIC LIBRARY*, Mill St N, 26147. (Mail add: PO Box 918, 26147-0918), SAN 317-7734. Tel: 304-354-6300. FAX: 304-354-6300. Web Site: calhoun.lib.wv.us. *Librn,* Amy Cooper; Staff 2 (Non-MLS 2)
Pop 7,877; Circ 20,685
Library Holdings: AV Mats 420; Bk Vols 18,900; Per Subs 30
Open Mon-Fri 10-5

HAMLIN

P   HAMLIN-LINCOLN COUNTY PUBLIC LIBRARY*, 7999 Lynn Ave, 25523. SAN 364-3654. Tel: 304-824-5481. FAX: 304-824-7014. Web Site: www.cabell.lib.wv.us. *Dir,* Margaret Smith; Staff 3 (MLS 1, Non-MLS 2)
Founded 1972. Pop 21,382; Circ 56,986
Jul 2005-Jun 2006 Income $250,000
Library Holdings: Bk Titles 30,000; Per Subs 30
Special Collections: Genealogical Coll; West Virginia Historical Coll
Automation Activity & Vendor Info: (Cataloging) SirsiDynix; (Circulation) SirsiDynix; (OPAC) SirsiDynix
Open Mon, Wed, Thurs & Fri 8-5, Tue 8-8, Sat 9-2
Branches: 2
ALUM CREEK PUBLIC, PO Box 530, Alum Creek, 25003-0530, SAN 364-3662. Tel: 304-756-9211. FAX: 304-756-9211. *Br Librn,* Kathy Cummings; Staff 1 (Non-MLS 1)
Circ 19,807
Library Holdings: Bk Vols 16,633; Per Subs 19
Special Collections: West Virginia Coll
Open Mon & Wed-Fri 9-5, Tues 10-6
BRANCHLAND OUTPOST LIBRARY, PO Box 278, Branchland, 25506-0278, SAN 364-3689. Tel: 304-778-7315. FAX: 304-778-3840. *Br Librn,* Alice Johnston; Staff 1 (Non-MLS 1)
Circ 23,065
Library Holdings: Bk Vols 17,000; Per Subs 20
Open Tues 10-6, Wed-Fri 9-5

HARMAN

P   PIONEER MEMORIAL LIBRARY, PO Drawer 13, Rte 33E, 26270-0013. SAN 376-6020. Tel: 304-227-4788. FAX: 304-227-4788. E-mail: pioneer@clark.lib.wv.us. Web Site: www.pioneermemoriallibrary.info. *Dir,* Mary Rayme; E-mail: mary.rayme@clark.lib.wv.us; Staff 1 (Non-MLS 1)
Library Holdings: Bks on Deafness & Sign Lang 10; Bk Titles 28,000; Talking Bks 200
Automation Activity & Vendor Info: (Cataloging) Innovative Interfaces, Inc; (Circulation) Innovative Interfaces, Inc; (OPAC) Innovative Interfaces, Inc
Wireless access
Partic in Northern Library Network (NorLN)
Open Mon, Wed & Thurs 9-4, Tues 9-6
Friends of the Library Group

HARPERS FERRY

P   BOLIVAR-HARPERS FERRY PUBLIC LIBRARY*, 151 Polk St, 25425. SAN 326-3622. Tel: 304-535-2301. FAX: 304-535-2301. E-mail: bhflib@martin.lib.wv.us. Web Site: www.youseemore.com/bhf. *Dir,* Nancy Manuel; *Adult Serv,* Edie Offutt; *Cat,* Lisa Fox; *Ch,* Martha Kasmier; Staff 4 (MLS 1, Non-MLS 3)
Founded 1977. Pop 14,063; Circ 42,924
Library Holdings: Audiobooks 1,710; Bk Vols 33,428; Per Subs 16; Videos 473
Special Collections: Harpers Ferry Coll
Automation Activity & Vendor Info: (Cataloging) TLC (The Library Corporation); (Circulation) TLC (The Library Corporation); (OPAC) TLC (The Library Corporation)
Database Vendor: TLC (The Library Corporation)
Wireless access
Function: Audiobks via web, Bks on cassette, Bks on CD, Children's prog, Computers for patron use, Copy machines, e-mail & chat, e-mail serv, Electronic databases & coll, Fax serv, Free DVD rentals, Handicapped accessible, ILL available, Online cat, Online searches, OverDrive digital audio bks, Photocopying/Printing, Prog for children & young adult, Spoken cassettes & CDs, Spoken cassettes & DVDs, Story hour, Summer reading prog, Tax forms, VHS videos

Open Mon, Tues, Fri & Sat 10-5:30, Wed & Thurs 10-8
Restriction: Non-resident fee

HARRISVILLE

P   RITCHIE COUNTY PUBLIC LIBRARY*, 608 E Main St, 26362. SAN 317-7750. Tel: 304-643-2717. FAX: 304-643-4019. Web Site: ritchie.lib.wv.us. *Dir,* Emilee Seese; E-mail: seesee@mail.mln.lib.wv.us; *Asst Dir,* Thresa Prunty; *Outreach Coordr,* Diana Ritter; Staff 5 (Non-MLS 5)
Founded 1931. Pop 10,323; Circ 49,398
Library Holdings: AV Mats 500; Bks on Deafness & Sign Lang 30; Bk Titles 34,580; Per Subs 87
Special Collections: The Minnie Kendall Lowther Memorial Coll, oral hist; West Virginia History & Ritchie County History Coll, bks, rec, micro, slides, A-tapes. Oral History
Automation Activity & Vendor Info: (Cataloging) Innovative Interfaces, Inc; (Circulation) Innovative Interfaces, Inc; (OPAC) Innovative Interfaces, Inc
Partic in Northern Library Network (NorLN)
Open Mon & Thurs 9-8, Tues & Fri 9-5:30, Wed 9-12, Sat 9-2
Friends of the Library Group
Branches: 1
PENNSBORO BRANCH, 411 Main St, Pennsboro, 26415, SAN 376-897X. Tel: 304-659-2197. FAX: 304-659-2197. *Br Librn,* Jane Hearne; Staff 2 (MLS 1, Non-MLS 1)
Founded 1984. Pop 4,093; Circ 11,000
Library Holdings: Bk Vols 15,000; Per Subs 28
Open Mon & Thurs 9-8, Tues & Fri 9-5:30, Wed 9-12, Sat 9-2
Friends of the Library Group

HELVETIA

P   HELVETIA LIBRARY*, Main St, 26224. (Mail add: PO Box 15, 26224-0015), SAN 376-6128. Tel: 304-924-5063. FAX: 304-924-5063. Web Site: helvetia.lib.wv.us. *Dir,* Bruce Cressler; E-mail: bruce.cressler@clark.lib.wv.us; Staff 2 (Non-MLS 2)
Library Holdings: Bk Titles 4,500; Per Subs 20
Partic in Northern Library Network (NorLN)
Open Mon & Wed 10-6, Tues & Thurs 2-8, Fri 6-8

HILLSBORO

S   PEARL S BUCK BIRTHPLACE FOUNDATION*, Historic House Museum Library, Rt 219, 24946. (Mail add: PO Box 126, 24946-0126), SAN 377-5003. Tel: 304-653-4430. Web Site: www.pearlsbuckbirthplace.com. *Mgr,* Anita Withrow
Library Holdings: Bk Titles 400
Open Mon-Sat (May-Oct) 9-4:30
Restriction: Non-circulating to the pub

HINTON

P   SUMMERS COUNTY PUBLIC LIBRARY*, 201 Temple St, 25951. SAN 329-9384. Tel: 304-466-4490. FAX: 304-466-5260. Web Site: summers.lib.wv.us. *Dir,* Myra Ziegler; E-mail: zieglerm@mail.mln.lib.wv.us; *Asst Librn,* Sherry Gwinn; *Asst Librn,* Evelyn Phillips; Staff 3 (MLS 1, Non-MLS 2)
Founded 1977
Jul 2006-Jun 2007 Income $142,091, State $58,475, City $5,000, Locally Generated Income $10,000, Other $68,616. Mats Exp $9,205, Books $7,754, Per/Ser (Incl. Access Fees) $1,201, AV Mat $250. Sal $63,000 (Prof $27,000)
Library Holdings: Bk Titles 16,604; Per Subs 29; Talking Bks 797; Videos 1,381
Automation Activity & Vendor Info: (Acquisitions) Innovative Interfaces, Inc; (Cataloging) Innovative Interfaces, Inc; (Circulation) Innovative Interfaces, Inc; (OPAC) Innovative Interfaces, Inc
Database Vendor: Innovative Interfaces, Inc INN - View
Open Mon, Wed & Fri 9-5, Tues & Thurs 9-9, Sat 9-3
Friends of the Library Group

HUNDRED

P   HUNDRED PUBLIC LIBRARY*, Rte 250, 26575. (Mail add: PO Box 453, 26575-0453), SAN 364-4731. Tel: 304-775-5161. FAX: 304-775-5161. Web Site: hundred.lib.wv.us. *Librn,* Linnea Kumher; E-mail: kumher@hundred.lib.wv.us; Staff 1 (Non-MLS 1)
Pop 1,590; Circ 20,365
Library Holdings: Bk Vols 10,000
Automation Activity & Vendor Info: (Cataloging) Innovative Interfaces, Inc; (Circulation) Innovative Interfaces, Inc; (OPAC) Innovative Interfaces, Inc
Mem of Moundsville-Marshall County Public Library
Partic in Northern Library Network (NorLN)

Open Mon, Wed & Fri 10-5, Tues 12-7, Thurs 12-5, Sat 10-2
Friends of the Library Group

HUNTINGTON

P   CABELL COUNTY PUBLIC LIBRARY*, 455 Ninth Street Plaza, 25701.
SAN 364-3832. Tel: 304-528-5700. Information Services Tel:
304-528-5660. FAX: 304-528-5701. Circulation FAX: 304-528-5866.
Reference FAX: 304-528-5739. TDD: 304-528-5694. E-mail:
library@cabell.lib.wv.us. Web Site: www.cabell.lib.wv.us. *Dir,* Judy K
Rule; E-mail: jrule@cabell.lib.wv.us; *Dir, Info Resources & Res,* Francie
Buchanan; E-mail: fbuchanan@cabell.lib.wv.us; *Asst Dir,* Angela D Strait;
E-mail: angela.strait@cabell.lib.wv.us; *Coordr, Popular Serv,* Sara
Ramezani; E-mail: sramezan@cabell.lib.wv.us; *Coordr, Tech Serv,* Musser
Deborah; E-mail: dmusser@cabell.lib.wv.us; *Cat,* Deborah Musser; E-mail:
dmusser@cabell.lib.wv.us; *Ch,* Niza Uslan; E-mail:
nuslan@cabell.lib.wv.us; *Ref,* Mary Lou Pratt; E-mail:
mpratt@cabell.lib.wv.us; Staff 54 (MLS 11, Non-MLS 43)
Founded 1902. Pop 96,784
Jul 2010-Jun 2011 Income (Main Library and Branch(s)) $3,920,355, State
$673,906, City $15,000, Federal $203,182, County $1,386,804, Locally
Generated Income $1,361,206, Other $188,245. Mats Exp $520,340, Books
$279,988, Per/Ser (Incl. Access Fees) $42,357, Micro $10,000, AV Mat
$76,415, Electronic Ref Mat (Incl. Access Fees) $108,680, Presv $2,900.
Sal $1,662,235
Library Holdings: Audiobooks 25,769; AV Mats 19,972; DVDs 37,181;
e-books 825; Large Print Bks 20,000; Bk Titles 300,000; Bk Vols 475,796;
Per Subs 621
Special Collections: Regional History Coll
Automation Activity & Vendor Info: (Cataloging) SIRSI WorkFlows;
(Circulation) SIRSI WorkFlows; (OPAC) SIRSI WorkFlows; (Serials)
SIRSI WorkFlows
Database Vendor: EBSCO Auto Repair Reference, EBSCOhost, Facts on
File, Foundation Center, Gale Cengage Learning, Grolier Online,
LearningExpress, Newsbank, Overdrive, Inc, ProQuest, ReferenceUSA,
SirsiDynix, ValueLine
Wireless access
Function: Adult bk club, Adult literacy prog, After school storytime,
Audio & video playback equip for onsite use, Audiobks via web, AV serv,
Bk club(s), Bks on cassette, Bks on CD, Chess club, Children's prog,
Computer training, Computers for patron use, Copy machines, Digital
talking bks, e-mail serv, E-Reserves, Electronic databases & coll, Exhibits,
Fax serv, Free DVD rentals, Handicapped accessible, Home delivery &
serv to Sr ctr & nursing homes, Homework prog, ILL available, Instruction
& testing, Music CDs, Notary serv, Online cat, Online info literacy
tutorials on the web & in blackboard, Online searches, Orientations,
OverDrive digital audio bks, Photocopying/Printing, Preschool outreach,
Prog for children & young adult, Pub access computers, Ref serv available,
Ref serv in person, Senior computer classes, Spoken cassettes & CDs,
Story hour, Summer reading prog, Tax forms, Teen prog, Telephone ref,
Video lending libr, Wheelchair accessible
Publications: Library Connection (Newsletter)
Special Services for the Deaf - Bks on deafness & sign lang; TTY equip
Special Services for the Blind - Assistive/Adapted tech devices, equip &
products; Computer with voice synthesizer for visually impaired persons
Open Mon-Wed 9-8:30, Thurs & Fri 9-6, Sat 9-5, Sun 1-5
Friends of the Library Group
Branches: 8
BARBOURSVILLE BRANCH, 728 Main St, Barboursville, 25504, SAN
364-3867. Tel: 304-736-4621. FAX: 304-736-6240. Web Site:
cabell.lib.wv.us/pages/bville.htm. *Mgr,* Linda LaRue
   Library Holdings: Bk Titles 26,722; Bk Vols 32,113; Per Subs 66
   Open Mon, Tues, Wed, Fri & Sat 9-5, Thurs 9-7; Mon, Tues, Wed & Fri
   9-5, Thurs 9-7, Sat 9-1 (Summer)
COX LANDING BRANCH, Rt 1, Box 75, 6363 Cox Lane, Lesage, 25537,
SAN 376-6942. Tel: 304-733-3022. FAX: 304-733-3022. Web Site:
cabell.lib.wv.us/pages/cox.htm. *Mgr,* Marsha Childers; Staff 1 (Non-MLS
1)
   Library Holdings: Bk Titles 5,000; Bk Vols 7,615; Per Subs 15
   Open Mon-Fri 9-5
   Friends of the Library Group
GALLAHER VILLAGE, 368 Norway Ave, 25705, SAN 364-3956. Tel:
304-528-5696. FAX: 304-528-5696. Web Site:
cabell.lib.wv.us/pages/galla.htm. *Mgr,* Virginia Jaskot; Staff 4 (Non-MLS
4)
   Library Holdings: AV Mats 658; Bk Titles 28,000; Bk Vols 34,980; Per
   Subs 56
   Open Mon & Wed-Sat 9-5, Tues 9-7; Mon-Fri (Summer) 9-5
GUYANDOTTE, 203 Richmond St, 25702, SAN 364-3980. Tel:
304-528-5698. FAX: 304-528-5698. Web Site:
cabell.lib.wv.us/pages/guyan.htm. *Mgr,* Karen Fields; Staff 4 (MLS 1,
Non-MLS 3)
   Library Holdings: AV Mats 416; Bk Titles 15,283; Bk Vols 23,983; Per
   Subs 56
   Open Mon, Wed-Sat 9-5:15, Tues 9-7

MILTON BRANCH, 1140 Smith St, Milton, 25541, SAN 364-4014. Tel:
304-743-6711. FAX: 304-743-6747. Web Site:
cabell.lib.wv.us/pages/milton.htm. *Mgr,* Georgina Doss; Staff 4
(Non-MLS 4)
   Library Holdings: AV Mats 863; Bk Titles 27,342; Bk Vols 39,949; Per
   Subs 72
   Open Mon & Wed-Fri & Sat 9-5, Tues 9-7
SALT ROCK BRANCH, Salt Rock Community School, RFS No 1,
Madison Creek Rd, Salt Rock, 25559, SAN 364-4049. Tel:
304-733-2186. FAX: 304-733-2186. Web Site:
cabell.lib.wv.us/pages/saltrock.htm. *Mgr,* Beverly Harbour; Staff 2
(Non-MLS 2)
   Library Holdings: AV Mats 310; Bk Titles 5,700; Bk Vols 16,301; Per
   Subs 40
   Open Mon-Wed (Winter) 9-3, Thurs 9-7; Mon-Thurs (Summer) 9-3
P   SERVICES FOR THE BLIND & PHYSICALLY HANDICAPPED, 455
Ninth St, 25701. Tel: 304-528-5700. E-mail: tbooks@cabell.lib.wv.us.
Coordr, Vicky Woods; Staff 1 (Non-MLS 1)
   Library Holdings: Large Print Bks 13,500; Talking Bks 20,000
   Open Mon-Fri 9-5
   Friends of the Library Group
WEST HUNTINGTON, 901 W 14th St, 25704, SAN 364-4073. Tel:
304-528-5697. FAX: 304-528-5697. Web Site:
cabell.lib.wv.us/pages/westhunt.htm. *Mgr,* Delores Pyle; Staff 4
(Non-MLS 4)
   Library Holdings: AV Mats 1,512; Bk Titles 19,056; Bk Vols 31,536;
   Per Subs 46
   Open Mon- Wed & Fri- Sat 9-5, Thurs 9-7, Sat (9-1 Summer)
   Friends of the Library Group

L   HUDDLESTON BOLEN, LLP*, Law Library, 611 Third Ave, 25722-1308.
(Mail add: PO Box 2185, 25722-2185), SAN 372-3461. Tel: 304-529-6181.
FAX: 304-522-4312. Web Site: www.huddlestonbolen.com. *Librn,* Ann
Bryant; E-mail: abryant@huddlestonbolen.com; Staff 2 (Non-MLS 2)
Library Holdings: Bk Vols 35,000
Database Vendor: LexisNexis, Westlaw
Restriction: Staff use only

S   HUNTINGTON MUSEUM OF ART LIBRARY*, 2033 McCoy Rd, 25701.
SAN 317-7793. Tel: 304-529-2701, Ext 23. FAX: 304-529-7447. E-mail:
hma1@hmoa.org. Web Site: www.hmoa.org. *Librn,* Christopher Hatten
Library Holdings: Bk Titles 18,006; Bk Vols 21,000; Per Subs 55
Special Collections: Fastoria Glass Catalogs & Price Lists 1897-1980;
Fine Arts Coll; Fire Arms History & Manufacture Coll; Glass History &
Technology Coll
Subject Interests: Am glass, Antique firearms, Antique to contemporary,
Fine arts, Tapestries
Automation Activity & Vendor Info: (Cataloging) Mandarin Library
Automation
Open Tues-Fri 10-5

L   JENKINS, FENSTERMAKER, PLLC*, Law Library, PO Box 2688,
25726-2688. SAN 372-347X. Tel: 304-523-2100. FAX: 304-523-2347.
Managing Librn, Clara J Sheets; Staff 1 (Non-MLS 1)
Library Holdings: Bk Vols 5,000
Restriction: Staff use only

C   MARSHALL UNIVERSITY LIBRARIES, One John Marshall Dr,
25755-2060. SAN 317-7815. Tel: 304-696-2320. Circulation Tel:
304-696-2321. Interlibrary Loan Service Tel: 304-696-4011. Reference Tel:
304-696-2334. Administration Tel: 304-696-3095. Toll Free Tel:
800-818-9816. FAX: 304-696-5858. Administration FAX: 304-696-3229.
E-mail: library@marshall.edu. Web Site: www.marshall.edu/library. *Dir of
Libr Operations, Univ Librn,* Jingping Zhang; Tel: 304-696-2326, E-mail:
zhangj@marshall.edu; *Assoc Univ Librn, Dir, Morrow Librn,* Dr Majed
Khader; Tel: 304-696-3121, E-mail: khader@marshall.edu; *Dir, Health Sci
Libr,* Edward Dzierzak; Tel: 304-691-1753, Fax: 304-691-1766, E-mail:
dzierzak@marshall.edu; *Dir, Info Res & Serv,* Jody Perry; Tel:
304-696-3226, E-mail: jody.perry@marshall.edu; *Asst VPres for IT, Online
Learning & Libr,* Dr Monica Garcia Brooks; Tel: 304-696-6474, E-mail:
brooks@marshall.edu; *Acq Librn,* Christine Lewis; Tel: 304-696-4356,
E-mail: lewis47@marshall.edu; *Cat & Digital Serv Librn,* Gretchen Beach;
Tel: 304-696-2312, E-mail: beachgr@marshall.edu; *Digital Res & Syst
Support Librn,* Paris E Webb; Tel: 304-696-3511, E-mail:
webbp@marshall.edu; *Electronic Serv Librn,* Ron Titus; Tel: 304-696-6575,
E-mail: titus@marshall.edu; *Grad Col Librn,* Lynne Edington; Tel:
304-746-8902, E-mail: edington@marshall.edu; *Music
& Digital Serv Librn,* Thomas Walker; Tel: 304-696-2309, E-mail:
walkert@marshall.edu; *Ref Librn,* Julie Anne Robinson; Tel: 304-691-1766,
Fax: 304-691-1766, E-mail: robinsonju@marshall.edu; *Ref Serv Librn,*
Timothy Balch; Tel: 304-696-2335, E-mail: balch@marshall.edu; *Ref Serv
Librn,* Larry Sheret; Tel: 304-696-6577, E-mail: sheret@marshall.edu; *Ref
Libr Assoc,* Dorothy McGraw; Tel: 304-746-8909, E-mail:
mcgraw@marshall.edu; *Res & Instruction Librn,* Kelli Johnson; Tel:
304-696-6567, E-mail: johnson28@marshall.edu; *Res & Instruction Librn,*

Eryn Roles; Tel: 304-696-2336, E-mail: roles1@marshall.edu; *Res & Instruction Librn,* Sabrina Thomas; Tel: 304-696-3627, E-mail: tho4@marshall.edu; *Spec Coll Librn,* Kathleen Bledsoe; Tel: 304-696-3174, E-mail: bledsoek@marshall.edu; *Web Serv Librn,* Stephen Tipler; Tel: 304-696-2907, E-mail: tipler@marshall.edu; *Univ Archivist & Ms Librn,* Nathaniel DeBruin; Tel: 304-696-3525, E-mail: debruin@marshall.edu; *Bibliographer,* Jack Dickinson; Tel: 304-696-3097, E-mail: dickinson@marshall.edu; *Curator,* Lisle Brown; Tel: 304-696-2344, E-mail: brown@marshall.edu. Subject Specialists: *Health sci,* Julie Anne Robinson; Staff 44.5 (MLS 18.5, Non-MLS 26)
Founded 1929. Enrl 11,410; Fac 720; Highest Degree: Doctorate
Jul 2011-Jun 2012. Mats Exp $1,284,026. Sal $2,508,625
Library Holdings: AV Mats 43,396; CDs 212; DVDs 711; e-books 38,613; e-journals 29,053; Electronic Media & Resources 29,381; Microforms 1,014,228; Music Scores 10,205; Bk Titles 397,148; Bk Vols 485,436; Per Subs 33,622; Videos 6,055
Special Collections: Chuck Yeager Papers & Artifacts; Civil War Newspapers; Congress of Racial Equality Papers; Former West Virginia Secretary of State Ken Hechler Papers; Historic Literature (Pollard, Redgrave & Wing Books, published in England & Scotland, 1400-1700), microfilm; Hoffman History of Medicine Library; Huntington Women's Club Archives; Nelson Bond Papers; The Rosanna Blake Library of Confederate History. Oral History; State Document Depository; US Document Depository
Subject Interests: Tri-state, W Va
Automation Activity & Vendor Info: (Acquisitions) Innovative Interfaces, Inc; (Cataloging) OCLC WorldCat; (Circulation) Innovative Interfaces, Inc - Millenium; (Course Reserve) Innovative Interfaces, Inc - Millenium; (ILL) OCLC ILLiad; (Media Booking) Innovative Interfaces, Inc - Millenium; (OPAC) Innovative Interfaces, Inc - Millenium; (Serials) SerialsSolutions
Database Vendor: 3M Library Systems, ABC-CLIO, ACM (Association for Computing Machinery), Agricola, Alexander Street Press, American Chemical Society, American Mathematical Society, American Physical Society, American Psychological Association (APA), ARTstor, Atlas Systems, Baker & Taylor, Bowker, Cambridge Scientific Abstracts, Cinahl Information Systems, CISTI Source, Community of Science (COS), Corbis, CQ Press, CredoReference, Dialog, ebrary, EBSCOhost, Electric Library, Elsevier, Elsevier MDL, Emerald, Facts on File, Gale Cengage Learning, Grolier Online, H W Wilson, IEEE (Institute of Electrical & Electronics Engineers), Ingenta, Innovative Interfaces, Inc, Innovative Interfaces, Inc INN - View, IOP, JSTOR, LearningExpress, LexisNexis, Marcive, Inc, Marquis Who's Who, Medline, Modern Language Association, Nature Publishing Group, netLibrary, Newsbank, OCLC CAMIO, OCLC FirstSearch, OCLC WebJunction, OCLC WorldCat, Oxford Online, Project MUSE, ProQuest, PubMed, Sage, ScienceDirect, SerialsSolutions, Springer-Verlag, Springshare, LLC, Standard & Poor's, Thomson - Web of Science, ValueLine, Westlaw, Wiley, Wiley InterScience, Wilson - Wilson Web, YBP Library Services
Wireless access
Function: Res libr
Publications: Carlton D Weaver Transallegheny Map Collection; Guide to Local History & Genealogy; Guide to the Marshall University Libraries; James E Morrow Library Associates Brochure, Library Connection; Library Information Brochure; Marshall Messenger; WVa: Historical Guide
Partic in Lyrasis; Pennsylvania Academic Library Consortium, Inc (PALCI)
Special Services for the Blind - Braille equip; Closed circuit TV; Computer with voice synthesizer for visually impaired persons; Dragon Naturally Speaking software; Reader equip
Friends of the Library Group
Departmental Libraries:

CM   JOAN C EDWARDS SCHOOL OF MEDICINE HEALTH SCIENCE LIBRARIES, 1600 Medical Center Dr, Ste 2400, 25701-3655, SAN 322-6972. Tel: 304-691-1750. Administration Tel: 304-691-1752. FAX: 304-691-1766. Web Site: www.musom.marshall.edu. *Dir,* Edward Dzierzak; E-mail: dzierzak@marshall.edu; *Circ,* Randy Price; *Doc Delivery,* Denise Ward; E-mail: wardd@marshall.edu; *Ref,* Robert Williams; E-mail: williamr@marshall.edu; Staff 6 (MLS 2, Non-MLS 4)
Founded 1976
Library Holdings: e-books 235; e-journals 523; Bk Titles 12,545; Per Subs 251
Automation Activity & Vendor Info: (Circulation) Innovative Interfaces, Inc; (OPAC) Innovative Interfaces, Inc; (Serials) Innovative Interfaces, Inc
Database Vendor: Blackwell's, EBSCOhost
Open Mon-Thurs (Winter) 8am-11pm, Fri 8-5, Sat 10-5, Sun 1-10; Mon-Thurs (Summer) 8-8, Fri 8-5, Sat 10-5, Sun 1-5
GRADUATE COLLEGE LIBRARY, 100 Angus E Peyton Dr, South Charleston, 25303-1600, SAN 364-4227. Tel: 304-746-8900. Circulation Tel: 304-746-8910. Reference Tel: 304-746-8911. Toll Free Tel: 800-642-9842. FAX: 304-746-8905. Web Site: www.marshall.edu/library. *Assoc Dean,* Celene Seymour; E-mail: seymour@marshall.edu; *Librn,* Lynne Edington; E-mail: edington@marshall.edu; Staff 9 (MLS 3, Non-MLS 6)
Founded 1972. Enrl 2,194; Highest Degree: Master

Library Holdings: Bk Vols 8,000; Per Subs 260
Subject Interests: Educ, Leadership studies
Automation Activity & Vendor Info: (Cataloging) Innovative Interfaces, Inc; (Circulation) Innovative Interfaces, Inc; (OPAC) Innovative Interfaces, Inc
Partic in OCLC Online Computer Library Center, Inc
Open Mon-Thurs 10-9, Fri 10-5, Sat 9-4

M   SAINT MARY'S MEDICAL CENTER*, Medical Library 6-East, 2900 First Ave, 25702-1271. SAN 317-7823. Tel: 304-526-1814. FAX: 304-526-1314. Web Site: www.st-marys.org. *Librn,* Thelma Nicely; E-mail: tnicely@st-marys.org; Staff 1 (MLS 1)
Founded 1924
Library Holdings: Bk Titles 515; Bk Vols 617; Per Subs 40
Subject Interests: Clinical, Preclinical med, Surgery
Wireless access
Open Mon-Fri 8-4:30
Friends of the Library Group

HURRICANE

P   PUTNAM COUNTY LIBRARY*, 4219 State Rte 34, 25526. SAN 364-4138. Tel: 304-757-7308. FAX: 304-757-7384. E-mail: putnam@cabell.lib.wv.us. Web Site: putnam.lib.wv.us. *Dir,* Jacquelin S Chaney; E-mail: jchaney@cabell.lib.wv.us; *Head, Ref,* Linda Riffe; *Circ,* Vicki Beaver. Subject Specialists: *Early childhood develop,* Linda Riffe; Staff 9 (MLS 1, Non-MLS 8)
Founded 1960. Pop 51,588; Circ 238,455
Library Holdings: Bk Vols 93,000; Per Subs 101
Automation Activity & Vendor Info: (Circulation) SirsiDynix
Database Vendor: EBSCOhost
Publications: Friends of Putnam County Library Newsletter
Friends of the Library Group
Branches: 4
BUFFALO BRANCH, 3530 Buffalo Rd, Buffalo, 25033-9434, SAN 364-4154. Tel: 304-937-3538. FAX: 304-937-3538. *Actg Mgr,* Lu Raynes
Open Mon-Wed & Fri 9-5, Thurs 12-7
ELEANOR BRANCH, 203 Eleanor Circle, Eleanor, 25070, SAN 364-4162. Tel: 304-586-4295. FAX: 304-586-4295. *Br Mgr,* Tretha Savilla
Open Mon-Wed & Fri 9-5, Thurs 12-7
Friends of the Library Group
HURRICANE BRANCH, 410 Midland Trail, 25526, SAN 364-4197. Tel: 304-562-6711. FAX: 304-562-6711. *Br Mgr,* Becky Elliott
Open Mon, Tues & Fri 9-5, Wed 9-12:30, Thurs 1-7, Sat 10-2
POCA BRANCH, PO Box 606, Poca, 25159-0606, SAN 364-4200. Tel: 304-755-3241. FAX: 304-755-3241. *Br Mgr,* Verna Carr
Open Mon-Wed & Fri 9-5, Thurs 1-7

HUTTONSVILLE

S   HUTTONSVILLE CORRECTIONAL CENTER LIBRARY, US Rte 250, S, 26273. (Mail add: PO Box 1, 26273-0001), SAN 317-784X. Tel: 304-335-2291, Ext 244. FAX: 304-335-4256. *Librn,* Wesley Duncan; *Librn,* Aaron Collins; Staff 2 (Non-MLS 2)
Founded 1968
Library Holdings: Bks on Deafness & Sign Lang 1; High Interest/Low Vocabulary Bk Vols 25; Large Print Bks 35; Music Scores 15; Bk Titles 10,300; Per Subs 27
Special Collections: ABA Recommended Material; Huttonsville Correctional Center Coll; Law (State & Federal) Coll
Function: Computers for patron use, Copy machines, ILL available, Legal assistance to inmates, Notary serv, Photocopying/Printing
Special Services for the Blind - Large print bks & talking machines
Restriction: Inmate patrons, facility staff & vols direct access. All others through ILL only

INSTITUTE

C   WEST VIRGINIA STATE UNIVERSITY*, Drain-Jordan Library, Campus Box L17, 25112. (Mail add: PO Box 1002, 25112-1002), SAN 317-7866. Tel: 304-766-3116. Reference Tel: 304-766-3135. Administration Tel: 304-766-3117. FAX: 304-766-4103. Interlibrary Loan Service FAX: 304-766-3214. Web Site: library.wvstateu.edu. *Dir,* David Clendinning; E-mail: bdclendinning@wvstateu.edu; *Cat/Bibliog Instruction Librn,* Jean Fisher; Tel: 304-766-3158, E-mail: fisherj@wvstateu.edu; *Ref Librn,* Mary Horn; Tel: 304-766-3162, E-mail: maryhorn@wvstateu.edu; *Ser/Govt Doc Librn,* Jennifer Zuccaro; Tel: 304-766-5222, E-mail: jzuccaro@wvstateu.edu; *Syst Librn,* Deborah Jean Wells; Tel: 304-766-3150, E-mail: wells@wvstateu.edu; *Archivist,* Ellen Ressmeyer; E-mail: eressmeyer@wvstateu.edu; Staff 15 (MLS 6, Non-MLS 9)
Founded 1891. Enrl 3,190; Fac 190; Highest Degree: Master
Jul 2009-Jun 2010. Mats Exp $255,545, Books $22,551, Per/Ser (Incl. Access Fees) $194,281, Micro $35,255, AV Mat $80, Electronic Ref Mat (Incl. Access Fees) $100, Presv $3,278

Library Holdings: AV Mats 5,367; CDs 1,187; DVDs 160; e-books 3,252; e-journals 49; Microforms 78,798; Bk Titles 191,434; Bk Vols 201,517; Per Subs 319; Videos 2,062

Special Collections: College Archives, correpondence, photog, rpts; John W Davis Papers. Oral History; US Document Depository

Subject Interests: African-Am hist

Automation Activity & Vendor Info: (Acquisitions) VTLS, Inc; (Cataloging) VTLS, Inc; (Circulation) VTLS, Inc; (Course Reserve) VTLS, Inc; (OPAC) VTLS, Inc; (Serials) VTLS, Inc

Database Vendor: EBSCOhost, Gale Cengage Learning, ProQuest, ScienceDirect

Wireless access

Function: Computers for patron use, Copy machines, e-mail & chat, Handicapped accessible, Pub access computers, Scanner, Web-catalog, Wheelchair accessible

Publications: Periodical Holding List (Index to periodicals)

Partic in Lyrasis; OCLC Online Computer Library Center, Inc

Special Services for the Blind - Accessible computers; Computer with voice synthesizer for visually impaired persons; Scanner for conversion & translation of mats; ZoomText magnification & reading software

Open Mon-Thurs 8am-10pm, Fri 8-5, Sat 10-5, Sun 1-9

KEARNEYSVILLE

G   UNITED STATES GEOLOGICAL SURVEY*, Leetown Science Center Library, 11649 Leetown Rd, 25430. SAN 317-7874. Tel: 304-724-4448. FAX: 304-724-4435. Web Site: lsc-tis.library.net. *Libr Tech,* Lora McKenzie; E-mail: lmckenzie@usgs.gov
Founded 1959
Library Holdings: Bk Titles 20,000; Per Subs 38
Subject Interests: Aquatic ecology, Fish diseases, Genetics, Histology, Immunology, Nutrition, Parasitology, Physiology, Virology
Automation Activity & Vendor Info: (Cataloging) OCLC WorldCat; (ILL) OCLC FirstSearch; (OPAC) TLC (The Library Corporation)
Database Vendor: Cambridge Scientific Abstracts, EBSCOhost, Infotrieve, ISI Web of Knowledge, OCLC FirstSearch, OCLC WorldCat, ScienceDirect, TLC (The Library Corporation)
Partic in Fedlink; OCLC Online Computer Library Center, Inc
Open Mon-Fri 7:30-4

KENOVA

P   WAYNE COUNTY PUBLIC LIBRARY*, Ceredo-Kenova Memorial Public Library, 1200 Oak St, 25530-1335. SAN 317-7882. Tel: 304-453-2462. FAX: 304-453-2462. Web Site: wcpl.lib.wv.us. *Dir,* Mark Esslinger; *Cat,* Lou Ann Moore; *Ch,* Selina Huffman. Subject Specialists: *Genealogy,* Lou Ann Moore; Staff 3 (Non-MLS 3)
Pop 41,636; Circ 125,803
Library Holdings: CDs 50; DVDs 600; Bk Titles 34,697; Bk Vols 145; Per Subs 48; Videos 1,054
Automation Activity & Vendor Info: (Acquisitions) Brodart; (Cataloging) SirsiDynix; (Circulation) SirsiDynix; (OPAC) SirsiDynix; (Serials) EBSCO Online
Database Vendor: SirsiDynix
Wireless access
Special Services for the Blind - Assistive/Adapted tech devices, equip & products
Open Mon 10-6, Tues-Sat 9-5
Friends of the Library Group
Branches: 2
FORT GAY PUBLIC, 8608 Rear Broadway, Fort Gay, 25514. (Mail add: PO Box 303, Fort Gay, 25514-0303), SAN 324-2625. Tel: 304-648-5338. FAX: 304-648-5338. *Librn,* Sheila Bowen; Staff 2 (Non-MLS 2)
Circ 27,605
Library Holdings: DVDs 50; Bk Titles 10,939; Per Subs 40; Videos 700
Open Mon-Fri 9-5
Friends of the Library Group
WAYNE PUBLIC, 325 Keyser St, Wayne, 25570. (Mail add: PO Box 567, Wayne, 25570-0567), SAN 317-851X. Tel: 304-272-3756. FAX: 304-272-3756. *Librn,* Lana Smith; Staff 2 (Non-MLS 2)
Library Holdings: DVDs 200; Bk Titles 26,078; Per Subs 40; Videos 890
Open Mon & Wed-Fri 9-5, Tues 9-6, Sat 9-4:30
Friends of the Library Group

KEYSER

P   KEYSER-MINERAL COUNTY PUBLIC LIBRARY*, 105 N Main St, 26726. SAN 317-7890. Tel: 304-788-3222. FAX: 304-788-3222. Web Site: keyser.lib.wv.us. *Dir,* Connie Sutton; E-mail: sutton_c@martin.lib.wv.us; *Asst Librn,* Mary Beth Mowen; E-mail: mowen_m@martin.lib.wv.us; *Circ,* Sarah Mcguire; Staff 4 (MLS 2, Non-MLS 2)
Founded 1937. Pop 25,661; Circ 38,592
Jul 2005-Jun 2006 Income $220,314, State $135,105, City $5,000, County $40,032, Locally Generated Income $30,177, Other $10,000. Mats Exp $30,297, Books $22,583, Electronic Ref Mat (Incl. Access Fees) $5,820

Library Holdings: AV Mats 2,205; Bk Vols 22,264; Per Subs 29; Videos 740

Automation Activity & Vendor Info: (Cataloging) TLC (The Library Corporation); (Circulation) TLC (The Library Corporation); (OPAC) TLC (The Library Corporation)

Database Vendor: ProQuest

Open Mon, Wed-Fri 9-6, Tues 9-8, Sat 9-1

Friends of the Library Group

Branches: 2

BURLINGTON PUBLIC, PO Box 61, Burlington, 26710-0061. Tel: 304-289-3690. FAX: 304-289-3233. *Br Mgr,* Catherine Weaver; *Asst Librn,* Sandra Byram; Staff 2 (Non-MLS 2)
Founded 1981. Circ 10,288
Library Holdings: Bk Vols 10,164; Per Subs 10
Open Tues & Thurs 10-5, Wed 12-5, Fri 10-2, Sat 10-3
Friends of the Library Group

FORT ASHBY PUBLIC, PO Box 74, Fort Ashby, 26719-0064, SAN 329-7446. Tel: 304-298-4493. FAX: 304-298-4014. *Br Mgr,* Cindy Shanholtz; *Asst Librn,* Anne S Hyde; Staff 2 (Non-MLS 2)
Founded 1974. Circ 18,114
Library Holdings: AV Mats 173; Bk Vols 18,440; Per Subs 11; Videos 261
Open Mon & Fri 12-5, Tues-Thurs 12-5 & 6-8, Sat 9-12 & 1-4
Friends of the Library Group

J   POTOMAC STATE COLLEGE OF WEST VIRGINIA UNIVERSITY*, Mary F Shipper Library, 101 Fort Ave, 26726. SAN 317-7904. Tel: 304-788-6901. Circulation Tel: 304-788-6906. Reference Tel: 304-788-6903. Administration Tel: 304-788-6902. FAX: 304-788-6946. Web Site: www.potomacstatecollege.edu. *Dir,* Jill Gardner; E-mail: jlgardner@mail.wvu.edu; *Asst Librn,* Linda Bane; E-mail: lcbane@mail.wvu.edu; *Tech Asst II - Access Serv,* Dawn Downey; E-mail: dddowney@mail.wvu.edu; *Tech Asst II - Acq & Tech Serv,* Kathleen Weber; Tel: 304-788-6907, E-mail: ksweber@mail.wvu.edu; *Tech Asst II - Media Spec,* Patricia McGuire; Tel: 304-788-6905, E-mail: psmcguire@mail.wvu.edu; Staff 5 (MLS 2, Non-MLS 3)
Founded 1901. Enrl 1,524; Fac 32; Highest Degree: Associate
Library Holdings: Bk Vols 38,207
Subject Interests: Local hist, World War II
Automation Activity & Vendor Info: (Cataloging) Ex Libris Group; (Circulation) Ex Libris Group; (ILL) Ex Libris Group; (OPAC) Ex Libris Group
Database Vendor: EBSCOhost, LexisNexis, netLibrary
Wireless access
Function: AV serv, Distance learning, Doc delivery serv, ILL available, Photocopying/Printing, Ref serv available, Telephone ref
Partic in OCLC-LVIS; WVNET
Open Mon-Thurs 8am-9pm, Fri 8-4:30, Sat 1-4, Sun 6pm-9pm

KINGWOOD

P   KINGWOOD PUBLIC LIBRARY*, 205 W Main St, 26537-1418. SAN 317-7912. Tel: 304-329-1499. FAX: 304-329-1499. Web Site: www.kingwood.lib.wv.us. *Bibliog Instr, Coll Develop, Dir,* Joel W Beane; E-mail: beanejo@hp9k.clark.lib.wv.us; Staff 1 (MLS 1)
Founded 1941. Pop 30,000
Library Holdings: AV Mats 800; Bks on Deafness & Sign Lang 50; Bk Titles 30,751; Bk Vols 31,327; Per Subs 100
Special Collections: Preston County (Local History Coll); West Virginia Coll
Subject Interests: Relig studies
Database Vendor: Innovative Interfaces, Inc INN - View
Wireless access
Publications: Highlights (Monthly newsletter)
Partic in Northern Library Network (NorLN)
Special Services for the Deaf - Bks on deafness & sign lang; High interest/low vocabulary bks
Open Mon 9-8, Tues & Thurs 12-5, Wed & Fri 9-5, Sat 10-2
Friends of the Library Group

LEWISBURG

P   GREENBRIER COUNTY PUBLIC LIBRARY*, 152 Robert W McCormick Dr, 24901. SAN 317-7939. Tel: 304-647-7568. FAX: 304-647-7569. E-mail: greenbrier.library@mail.mln.lib.wv.us. Web Site: greenbrier.lib.wv.us. *Dir,* Ann Farr; E-mail: farrann@mail.mln.lib.wv.us; *Asst Librn,* Christy Carver; Staff 5 (MLS 2, Non-MLS 3)
Pop 8,143; Circ 64,000
Library Holdings: Bk Vols 25,000; Per Subs 53
Automation Activity & Vendor Info: (Cataloging) Innovative Interfaces, Inc; (Circulation) Innovative Interfaces, Inc; (OPAC) Innovative Interfaces, Inc
Wireless access
Partic in Mountain Library Network

Open Mon & Sun 1-5, Tues-Thurs 9-9, Fri 9-7, Sat 9-2
Friends of the Library Group

S   GREENBRIER HISTORICAL SOCIETY ARCHIVES*, 301 W
Washington St, 24901. SAN 329-0379. Tel: 304-645-3398. FAX:
304-645-5201. E-mail: archives@greenbrierhistorical.org. Web Site:
www.greenbrierhistorical.org. *Archivist,* James E Talbert
Founded 1963
Library Holdings: Bk Titles 998; Bk Vols 1,175
Special Collections: Dime Novels (Mrs Alex McVeigh Miller Coll),
autobiography, poems, stories; Marriage Bonds; West Virginia (Mrs Arthur
Dayton Coll), original drawings; West Virginia Artists (Ashton Reniers &
Naomi Hosterman Colls)
Subject Interests: Local hist
Publications: Appalachian Springs (Quarterly); GHS Annual Journal
Open Mon-Sat 10-4

J   NEW RIVER COMMUNITY & TECHNICAL COLLEGE*, Greenbrier
Valley Campus Library, 101 Church St, 24901-0151. SAN 317-7920. Tel:
304-647-6575. FAX: 304-647-6592. Web Site: gvcLibrary.nrctc.edu. *Librn,*
Robert Coston; E-mail: rcoston@newriver.edu
Library Holdings: Bk Titles 14,000; Per Subs 50
Special Collections: West Virginia Coll
Automation Activity & Vendor Info: (Cataloging) Innovative Interfaces,
Inc; (Circulation) Innovative Interfaces, Inc; (OPAC) Innovative Interfaces,
Inc
Database Vendor: Gale Cengage Learning
Partic in Mountain Library Network
Open Mon-Thurs 9-9, Fri 9-4:30

CM   WEST VIRGINIA SCHOOL OF OSTEOPATHIC MEDICINE
LIBRARY*, 400 N Lee St, 24901. SAN 317-7947. Tel: 304-647-6261.
FAX: 304-645-4443. E-mail: library@wvsom.edu. Web Site:
www.wvsom.edu/Academics/library. *Dir,* Annie McMillion; *Mgr, Libr
Serv,* Mary Essig; Staff 1 (MLS 1)
Founded 1973. Enrl 597; Fac 45; Highest Degree: Doctorate
Library Holdings: AV Mats 1,143; CDs 351; DVDs 34; e-books 15;
e-journals 1,125; Bk Titles 6,000; Bk Vols 23,588; Per Subs 231
Subject Interests: Med
Automation Activity & Vendor Info: (Cataloging) OCLC; (Circulation)
Follett Software; (ILL) OCLC; (OPAC) Follett Software; (Serials) EBSCO
Online
Database Vendor: EBSCOhost, OCLC WorldCat, PubMed, ScienceDirect
Wireless access
Function: Doc delivery serv, For res purposes, Health sci info serv, ILL
available, Online searches
Partic in Docline
Special Services for the Deaf - TTY equip
Open Mon-Thurs 7:30am-10pm, Fri 7:30-6, Sat 12-6, Sun 2-10
Restriction: Circ limited, In-house use for visitors, Non-circulating to the
pub, Restricted borrowing privileges

LOGAN

P   LOGAN AREA PUBLIC LIBRARY*, 16 Wildcat Way, 25601. Tel:
304-752-6652. FAX: 304-752-2684. *Dir,* Rebecca Blankenship
Pop 16,923
Library Holdings: AV Mats 1,540; Bk Titles 30,000; Per Subs 45; Talking
Bks 162
Automation Activity & Vendor Info: (Acquisitions) SirsiDynix;
(Cataloging) SirsiDynix; (Circulation) SirsiDynix; (ILL) SirsiDynix
Database Vendor: EBSCOhost
Open Mon-Fri 10-6

M   LOGAN REGIONAL MEDICAL CENTER*, Medical Library, 20 Hospital
Dr, 25601. SAN 317-7955. Tel: 304-831-1556. FAX: 304-831-1669. *Educ
Dir,* Cindy Fleming; E-mail: cindy.fleming@lpnt.net
Library Holdings: Bk Vols 300; Per Subs 25
Database Vendor: UpToDate
Wireless access
Publications: Abridged Index Medicus; Hospital Literature Index &
Cumulative Index to Nursing & Allied Health
Restriction: Staff use only

LOST CREEK

P   SOUTHERN AREA LIBRARY, Old Bank Bldg, Main St, 26385. (Mail
add: PO Box 282, 26385-0282), SAN 376-7760. Tel: 304-745-4865. FAX:
304-745-4865. Web Site: southernarea.lib.wv.us/. *Dir,* Mary Stenger;
E-mail: mary.stenger@clark.lib.wv.us; Staff 2 (Non-MLS 2)
Founded 1972
Library Holdings: Bk Vols 16,214; Per Subs 20; Talking Bks 207; Videos
233

Automation Activity & Vendor Info: (Cataloging) Innovative Interfaces,
Inc; (Circulation) Innovative Interfaces, Inc; (OPAC) Innovative Interfaces,
Inc
Wireless access
Partic in Northern Library Network (NorLN)
Special Services for the Blind - Large print bks
Open Tues-Fri 12-6, Sat 10-2
Friends of the Library Group

MADISON

P   BOONE-MADISON PUBLIC LIBRARY*, 375 Main St, 25130-1295.
SAN 364-4286. Tel: 304-369-7842. FAX: 304-369-2950. Web Site:
boone.lib.wv.us. *Dir,* Susan Mischler; E-mail: mischler@mail.mln.lib.wv.us;
Head, Cat, Kathy Ream; E-mail: reamk@mail.mln.lib.wv.us; *Head, Ch,*
Deanna Halstead; Staff 7 (MLS 1, Non-MLS 6)
Founded 1974. Pop 25,000; Circ 72,550
Library Holdings: Bk Vols 15,531; Per Subs 54
Special Collections: Genealogy (Boone County & Southern West Virginia
Coll)
Subject Interests: County hist
Automation Activity & Vendor Info: (Cataloging) Innovative Interfaces,
Inc; (Circulation) Innovative Interfaces, Inc; (OPAC) Innovative Interfaces,
Inc
Function: Photocopying/Printing
Partic in Mountain Library Network
Open Mon-Sat 9-5
Branches: 3
BARRETT-WHARTON BRANCH, 38487 Pond Fork Rd, Wharton, 25208.
   (Mail add: PO Box 189, Wharton, 25208-0189). Tel: 304-247-6530.
   FAX: 304-247-6530. *Br Mgr,* Janet White; E-mail:
   reamk@mail.mln.lib.wv.us; Staff 2 (Non-MLS 2)
   Library Holdings: Bk Vols 7,069
   Open Tues & Thurs 10-5, Sat 9-12
COAL RIVER, 494 John Slack Circle, Racine, 25165, SAN 364-4324. Tel:
   304-837-8437. FAX: 304-834-8437. *Br Mgr,* Bessie Barker; E-mail:
   bessieb@mail.mln.lib.wv.us; Staff 2 (Non-MLS 2)
   Library Holdings: Bk Vols 7,000
   Open Mon-Fri (Summer) 10-5; Tues-Sat (Winter) 10-5
WHITESVILLE BRANCH, 38175 Coal River Rd, Whitesville, 25209.
   (Mail add: PO Box 747, Whitesville, 25209-0747), SAN 322-5992. Tel:
   304-854-0196. FAX: 304-854-0196. *Br Mgr,* LaDonna Foster; E-mail:
   ladonna.foster@mail.mln.lib.wv.us
   Library Holdings: Bk Vols 6,250
   Function: Photocopying/Printing
   Open Tues & Fri 10-5, Sat 10-1

MAN

P   BUFFALO CREEK MEMORIAL LIBRARY*, 511 E McDonald Ave,
25635. SAN 317-7971. Tel: 304-583-7887. FAX: 304-583-0182. *Librn,*
Elizabeth Tackett; *Asst Librn,* Anna Walker; Staff 3 (Non-MLS 3)
Founded 1973. Pop 11,525; Circ 21,733; Fac 3
Library Holdings: AV Mats 238; Bk Titles 27,000; Bk Vols 33,500; Per
Subs 45
Special Collections: Cookbooks-Coal Mining Towns, photos, diet,
exercise, nutrition; West Virginia Code
Subject Interests: Diet, Exercise, Nutrition
Function: Bks on CD, Children's prog, Computers for patron use, Copy
machines, e-mail serv, Electronic databases & coll, Free DVD rentals,
Handicapped accessible, ILL available, Music CDs, Notary serv, Online
searches, Photocopying/Printing, Preschool outreach, Prog for children &
young adult, Provide serv for the mentally ill, Pub access computers,
Serves mentally handicapped consumers, Story hour, Summer reading prog,
Tax forms, Teen prog, VHS videos, Wheelchair accessible
Open Mon & Thurs 9-5, Tues, Wed & Fri 10-5
Restriction: Inmate patrons, facility staff & vols direct access. All others
through ILL only

MARLINTON

P   POCAHONTAS COUNTY FREE LIBRARIES*, 500 Eighth St,
24954-1227. SAN 364-3565. Tel: 304-799-6000. FAX: 304-799-3988. Web
Site: www.pocahontaslibrary.org. *Admin Dir,* Allen R Johnson; E-mail:
director@pocahontaslibrary.org; *Librn,* Vicky Terry; *Cat,* Pam Johnson; *Ch,*
Debora Johnson; Staff 4 (MLS 1, Non-MLS 3)
Pop 9,917; Circ 30,000
Library Holdings: AV Mats 500; Bk Vols 65,000; Per Subs 23
Automation Activity & Vendor Info: (Cataloging) Innovative Interfaces,
Inc; (Circulation) Innovative Interfaces, Inc; (OPAC) Innovative Interfaces,
Inc
Partic in Mountain Library Network
Open Mon-Thurs 10-8, Fri 10-6, Sat (Fall-Spring) 10-2

Branches: 4
DURBIN BRANCH, Main St, Durbin, 26264. (Mail add: PO Box 333, Durbin, 26264-0333), SAN 376-2416. Tel: 304-456-3142. FAX: 304-456-3142. *Librn,* Tara Bauserman; Staff 1 (Non-MLS 1)
Library Holdings: Bk Vols 6,209; Per Subs 11
Open Tues, Thurs & Fri 2-6, Wed 2-8
GREEN BANK BRANCH, Main St, Rte 28, Green Bank, 24944. (Mail add: PO Box 1, Green Bank, 24944-0001), SAN 376-2424. Tel: 304-456-4507. FAX: 304-456-4507. *Librn,* Jane Mospan; Staff 1 (Non-MLS 1)
Library Holdings: AV Mats 70; Bk Vols 20,000; Per Subs 19
Open Mon-Thurs 11-8, Fri 11-6, Sat (Sept-May) 12:30-4:30
HILLSBORO PUBLIC, Third St, Hillsboro, 24946. (Mail add: HC64, Box 398, Hillsboro, 24946-9701), SAN 364-359X. Tel: 304-653-4936. FAX: 304-653-4936. *Librn,* Elwood Groves; *Librn,* Virginia Must; Staff 2 (MLS 1, Non-MLS 1)
Circ 10,000
Library Holdings: AV Mats 300; Bk Vols 21,000; Per Subs 10
Open Mon & Fri 10-5, Tues-Thurs 10-7
Friends of the Library Group
MCCLINTIC, 500 Eighth St, 24954-1227, SAN 364-362X. Tel: 304-799-6000. FAX: 304-799-3988. E-mail: director@pocahontaslibrary.org. *Head Librn,* Vicky Terry; Staff 1 (Non-MLS 1)
Circ 5,700
Library Holdings: AV Mats 85; Bk Vols 20,000; Per Subs 20
Open Mon-Thurs 10-8, Fri 10-6, Sat 10-2
Friends of the Library Group

MARTINSBURG

M   CITY HOSPITAL, INC*, Medical Learning Resource Center, 2500 Hospital Dr, 25401. (Mail add: PO Box 1418, 25402-1418), SAN 317-798X. Tel: 304-264-1246. FAX: 304-264-1381. Web Site: www.cityhospital.org. *Librn,* Carol Joseph; E-mail: cjoseph@cityhospital.org
Library Holdings: Bk Vols 260; Per Subs 55
Open Mon-Fri 8-4:30

GM   DEPARTMENT OF VETERANS AFFAIRS*, Nursing/Education/Learning Resources Section, 510 Butler Ave, 25405-9809. SAN 317-7998. Tel: 304-263-0811, Ext 3826. FAX: 304-262-4847. *Librn,* Shannon Clever; Staff 2 (MLS 1, Non-MLS 1)
Founded 1946
Library Holdings: Bk Vols 3,977; Per Subs 200
Subject Interests: Med, Patient educ
Open Mon-Fri 8-4:30

P   MARTINSBURG-BERKELEY COUNTY PUBLIC LIBRARY*, Martinsburg Public Library, 101 W King St, 25401. SAN 364-4340. Tel: 304-267-8933. FAX: 304-267-9720. Web Site: www.youseemore.com/martinsburgberkeley. *Dir,* Pamela Coyle; E-mail: pcoyle@martin.lib.wv.us; *Financial Dir,* Carolyn Leporini; *Head, Adult Serv,* David Porterfield; *Head, Ch,* Jane Levitan; *Head, ILL,* Bernadette Whalen; *Head, Ref (Info Serv),* Keith Hammersla; *Acq,* Betty Gunnoe; *AV Coll,* Amy Cranford; *Per,* Jane Clipp; *Tech Coordr,* Brian Clark
Founded 1926. Pop 96,000; Circ 38,000
Library Holdings: CDs 300; DVDs 500; Large Print Bks 500; Bk Vols 150,000; Per Subs 310; Talking Bks 4,000; Videos 2,000
Automation Activity & Vendor Info: (Cataloging) TLC (The Library Corporation); (Circulation) TLC (The Library Corporation); (OPAC) TLC (The Library Corporation); (Serials) TLC (The Library Corporation)
Database Vendor: TLC (The Library Corporation)
Open Mon-Fri 9-9, Sat 9-5, Sun 1-5
Branches: 3
MUSSELMAN-SOUTH BERKELEY COMMUNITY LIBRARY, 126 Excellence Way, Rte 11 S, Inwood, 25428, SAN 364-443X. Tel: 304-229-2220. FAX: 304-229-7163. Web Site: www.youseemore.com/martinsburgberkeley/branch.asp?branch=3. *Dir, Br Serv,* Margaret M Demer; E-mail: demermar@martin.lib.wv.us; Staff 1 (MLS 1)
Library Holdings: AV Mats 12; Bk Titles 18,000; Bk Vols 19,250; Per Subs 65; Talking Bks 50
Special Collections: Archives Rooms
Open Mon-Thurs 7:30-6, Fri 7:30-2:30, Sun 1-4
NAYLOR MEMORIAL PUBLIC LIBRARY, 105 Potato Hill St, Hedgesville, 25427. (Mail add: PO Box 265, Hedgesville, 25427-0265), SAN 364-4375. Tel: 304-754-3949. Web Site: www.youseemore.com/martinsburgberkeley/branch.asp?branch=1. *Br Mgr,* Jacque V Seldeen; E-mail: jseldeen@martin.lib.wv.us
Library Holdings: AV Mats 700; Bk Titles 2,700; Bk Vols 2,800; Talking Bks 50
Open Mon 1-8:30, Tues-Sat 9-4:30, Sun 1-5

NORTH BERKELEY PUBLIC LIBRARY, 125 T J Jackson Dr, Falling Waters, 25419, SAN 364-4405. Tel: 304-274-3443. FAX: 304-274-3443. *Br Mgr,* Jane Sullivan
Library Holdings: AV Mats 20; Bk Titles 4,000
Open Tues & Thurs 10-7, Wed-Sat 10-5

MIDDLEBOURNE

P   TYLER COUNTY PUBLIC LIBRARY*, Main & Broad Sts, 26149. (Mail add: PO Box 124, 26149-0124), SAN 317-8005. Tel: 304-758-4304. FAX: 304-758-4304. Web Site: middlebourne.lib.wv.us. *Dir,* Rosanne Eastham
Pop 814; Circ 11,320
Library Holdings: Bk Vols 10,684
Database Vendor: EBSCOhost, Grolier Online, LearningExpress
Wireless access
Mem of Moundsville-Marshall County Public Library
Partic in Northern Library Network (NorLN)
Open Mon 11-7, Tues & Thurs 11-5:30, Wed & Fri 11-5, Sat 10-3
Friends of the Library Group

MILL CREEK

P   TYGART VALLEY COMMUNITY LIBRARY*, Rte 219-250, 26280. (Mail add: PO Box 517, 26280-0517). Tel: 304-335-6277. FAX: 304-335-6277. Web Site: tygart.lib.wv.us. *Dir,* Sharon R Mallow; *Cataloger,* Becky G Smith; Staff 4 (Non-MLS 4)
Founded 1973. Pop 4,620; Circ 18,000
Library Holdings: AV Mats 530; Bk Titles 15,000; Per Subs 8; Talking Bks 360
Automation Activity & Vendor Info: (Cataloging) Innovative Interfaces, Inc; (Circulation) Innovative Interfaces, Inc; (OPAC) Innovative Interfaces, Inc
Database Vendor: EBSCOhost, Grolier Online, LearningExpress
Wireless access
Function: Bks on cassette, Bks on CD, Children's prog, Computers for patron use, Copy machines, Electronic databases & coll, Fax serv, Free DVD rentals, Handicapped accessible, ILL available, Instruction & testing, Magnifiers for reading, Notary serv, Online cat, Online ref, Online searches, Outside serv via phone, mail, e-mail & web, Photocopying/Printing, Pub access computers, Satellite serv, Summer reading prog, Tax forms, VHS videos, Video lending libr, Wheelchair accessible
Partic in Northern Library Network (NorLN)
Open Tues-Fri 10-6, Sat 10-2

MONTGOMERY

C   WEST VIRGINIA UNIVERSITY INSTITUTE OF TECHNOLOGY, Vining Library, 405 Fayette Pike, 25136-2436. SAN 317-8013. Tel: 304-442-3230. Circulation Tel: 304-442-3495. Interlibrary Loan Service Tel: 304-442-3734. Administration Tel: 301-981-6247. FAX: 304-442-3091. E-mail: tech-library@mail.wvu.edu. Web Site: library.wvutech.edu. *Cataloger, Interim Dir,* Alena Jewel Rucker; E-mail: jewel.rucker@mail.wvu.edu; *Head, Access Serv, Staff Librn,* Mitch Casto; *Cat, Libr Assoc,* Peggy Pomeroy; Tel: 304-442-3082; *Libr Assoc, Circ & Reserves,* Prema Puttaiah; *Libr Assoc, ILL Serv,* Betty Clark; E-mail: betty.clark@mail.wvu.edu; *Acq Asst, ILL Asst,* Jane Elliott; Tel: 304-442-3816; 304-442-3324; *Per,* Anne Vinyard; Tel: 304-442-3218; Staff 7 (MLS 2, Non-MLS 5)
Founded 1897. Enrl 1,224; Fac 88; Highest Degree: Bachelor
Jul 2011-Jun 2012. Mats Exp $156,800
Library Holdings: e-journals 20; Electronic Media & Resources 48; Microforms 111,260; Bk Titles 120,100; Bk Vols 151,131; Per Subs 108
Special Collections: West Virginia Coll. State Document Depository; US Document Depository
Automation Activity & Vendor Info: (Acquisitions) Ex Libris Group; (Cataloging) Ex Libris Group; (Circulation) Ex Libris Group; (Course Reserve) Ex Libris Group; (ILL) OCLC ILLiad; (OPAC) Ex Libris Group; (Serials) Ex Libris Group
Database Vendor: American Chemical Society, American Mathematical Society, ASCE Research Library, EBSCO Information Services, EBSCOhost, Ex Libris Group, IEEE (Institute of Electrical & Electronics Engineers), IOP, JSTOR, Micromedex, OCLC, OCLC FirstSearch, OCLC WorldCat, ProQuest
Wireless access
Function: Computers for patron use, Copy machines, Doc delivery serv, Electronic databases & coll, ILL available, Instruction & testing, Microfiche/film & reading machines, Online searches, Photocopying/Printing, Ref & res, Web-catalog
Publications: Periodical Directory; Vining Library Handbook
Partic in OCLC Online Computer Library Center, Inc; WVNET
Open Mon-Thurs 7:30am-9pm, Fri 7:30-4:30, Sun 12:30-9; Mon-Fri (Summer) 8-4:30

Restriction: Borrowing privileges limited to fac & registered students, Borrowing requests are handled by ILL, Limited access for the pub, Open to pub for ref & circ; with some limitations, Open to students, fac, staff & alumni

MOOREFIELD

P   HARDY COUNTY PUBLIC LIBRARY*, 102 N Main St, 26836. SAN 364-4464. Tel: 304-538-6560. FAX: 304-538-2639. Web Site: hardycounty.martin.lib.wv.us. *Librn,* Carol See; E-mail: see_c@martin.lib.wv.us; Staff 2 (Non-MLS 2)
Founded 1939. Pop 2,400; Circ 81,482
Library Holdings: Bk Vols 55,520; Per Subs 75
Subject Interests: Local genealogy, Local hist
Automation Activity & Vendor Info: (Cataloging) Follett Software; (Circulation) Follett Software
Open Mon-Wed & Fri 9-4:30, Tues & Thurs 9-6:30, Sat 9-12:30
Friends of the Library Group
Branches: 1
    EAST HARDY, 261 Cougar Dr, Baker, 26801. (Mail add: PO Box 98, Baker, 26801-0098), SAN 364-4499. Tel: 304-897-5544. FAX: 304-897-5544. *Br Librn,* Catherine Smith; Staff 1 (Non-MLS 1)
    Library Holdings: Bk Vols 20,500; Per Subs 27
    Open Mon, Tues, Thurs & Fri 11-5, Wed 11-7

MORGANTOWN

G   CENTERS FOR DISEASE CONTROL & PREVENTION PUBLIC HEALTH LIBRARY & INFORMATION CENTER, Morgantown Branch Library, 1095 Willowdale Rd, Mailstop L-1055, 26505-2888. SAN 317-8048. Tel: 304-285-5886. FAX: 304-285-6085. E-mail: bel8@cdc.gov. *Librn,* Barbara B Landreth; Tel: 304-285-5887; Staff 2 (MLS 1, Non-MLS 1)
Founded 1972
Library Holdings: AV Mats 150; e-journals 9,369; Bk Titles 10,193; Per Subs 42
Special Collections: NIOSH Publications; NIOSHTIC Microfiche
Subject Interests: Occupational lung diseases, Worker safety
Automation Activity & Vendor Info: (Acquisitions) Ex Libris Group; (Cataloging) Ex Libris Group; (Circulation) Ex Libris Group; (ILL) OCLC ILLiad; (OPAC) Ex Libris Group; (Serials) Ex Libris Group
Database Vendor: American Psychological Association (APA), Cambridge Scientific Abstracts, Dialog, EBSCOhost, Elsevier, ISI Web of Knowledge, JSTOR, LexisNexis, OVID Technologies, ProQuest, PubMed, ScienceDirect
Partic in OCLC Online Computer Library Center, Inc
Open Mon-Fri 8-4:30
Restriction: Badge access after hrs, In-house use for visitors, Photo ID required for access

S   FEDERAL CORRECTIONAL INSTITUTION - MORGANTOWN LIBRARY*, PO Box 1000, 26507-1000. SAN 317-8021. Tel: 304-296-4416, Ext 351. FAX: 304-284-3622, 304-296-7549. *Supvr of Educ,* James Robinson; *Librn,* Lisa Luzier
Library Holdings: Bk Vols 11,000; Per Subs 62
Special Collections: Prisoner Rights

P   MORGANTOWN PUBLIC LIBRARY SYSTEM*, Morgantown Service Center, 373 Spruce St, 26505. SAN 364-4529. Tel: 304-291-7425. FAX: 304-291-7427. Web Site: morgantown.lib.wv.us. *Dir,* Sharon Turner; E-mail: turnersl@clark.lib.wv.us; *Br Mgr,* Nancy Gallagher; E-mail: gallghe@clark.lib.wv.us; *Cat,* Ellen Hathaway; E-mail: hathaway@clark.lib.wv.us; *Ch,* Ruth Godfrey; E-mail: godfreyr@clark.lib.wv.us; *Circ,* Donna Balderson; E-mail: balders@clark.lib.wv.us; *Ref Serv, Ad,* Mary Schmezer; E-mail: schmezem@clark.lib.wv.us; Staff 25 (MLS 3, Non-MLS 22)
Founded 1929. Pop 81,866; Circ 291,460
Library Holdings: AV Mats 8,500; Bk Vols 103,000; Per Subs 85; Talking Bks 10,000
Subject Interests: WVa hist
Automation Activity & Vendor Info: (Cataloging) Innovative Interfaces, Inc; (Circulation) Innovative Interfaces, Inc; (OPAC) Innovative Interfaces, Inc
Partic in Northern Library Network (NorLN)
Open Mon-Thurs (Winter) 9-8, Fri & Sat 9-4, Sun 1-4; Mon-Wed (Summer) 9-8, Thurs & Fri 9-4, Sat 10-2
Friends of the Library Group
Branches: 3
    CHEAT AREA, 121 Crosby Rd, 26508, SAN 364-4545. Tel: 304-594-1020. FAX: 304-594-1020. E-mail: cheat@clark.lib.wv.us. *Librn,* Nancy Gallagher; E-mail: gallaghe@clark.lib.wv.us; Staff 5 (MLS 1, Non-MLS 4)
    Library Holdings: AV Mats 2,000; Bk Vols 23,741; Per Subs 12; Talking Bks 600; Videos 3,113
    Partic in Northern Library Network (NorLN)

    Open Mon-Wed 9-7, Thurs 9-3, Fri 9-5, Sat 10-4
    Friends of the Library Group
    CLAY-BATTELLE PUBLIC LIBRARY, 6059 Mason Dixon Hwy, Blacksville, 26521. (Mail add: PO Box 68, Blacksville, 26521-0068), SAN 364-4561. Tel: 304-432-8531. FAX: 304-432-8288. E-mail: cheat@clark.lib.wv.us. *Librn,* Sandra Throckmorton; Staff 2 (Non-MLS 2)
    Library Holdings: Bk Vols 14,200; Per Subs 15
    Partic in Northern Library Network (NorLN)
    Open Mon & Wed-Fri 10-5, Tues 10-7
    Friends of the Library Group
    CLINTON DISTRICT LIBRARY, 2005 Grafton Rd, 26508, SAN 364-4537. Tel: 304-291-0703. FAX: 304-291-0703. E-mail: clinton@clark.lib.wv.us. *Librn,* Nancy Gallagher; *Librn,* Lynn Laughner; Staff 2 (Non-MLS 2)
    Library Holdings: AV Mats 1,933; Bk Vols 12,839; Per Subs 17
    Partic in Northern Library Network (NorLN)
    Open Mon & Wed 10-7, Tues & Thurs 10-5, Fri 10-3, Sat 11-3

G   UNITED STATES DEPARTMENT OF ENERGY*, National Energy Technology Laboratory Library, 3610 Collins Ferry Rd, 26507. (Mail add: PO Box 880, 26507-0880), SAN 317-803X. Tel: 304-285-4184. Web Site: www.netl.doe.gov. *Tech Librn,* Jo Ann Yuill; E-mail: joann.yuill@pr.netl.doe.gov
Founded 1953
Library Holdings: Bk Titles 30,000; Per Subs 150
Special Collections: DOE Fossil Energy Reports; Energy (US Dept of Energy); Mining (US Bureau of Mines Open File Reports); Mining (US Bureau of Mines, Reports of Investigations, Information Circulars)
Subject Interests: Chem, Environ mgt, Environ remediation, Fossil fuels, Geol, Petroleum
Automation Activity & Vendor Info: (Cataloging) EOS International
Partic in Dialog Corp; OCLC Online Computer Library Center, Inc
Must call for appointment for security clearance
Open Mon-Fri 8-4:30
Restriction: Non-circulating

C   WEST VIRGINIA UNIVERSITY LIBRARIES*, WVU Libraries, 1549 University Ave, 26506. (Mail add: PO Box 6069, 26506-6069), SAN 364-4588. Tel: 304-293-4040. Circulation Tel: 304-293-0355. Interlibrary Loan Service Tel: 304-293-0368. Reference Tel: 304-293-3640. Administration Tel: 304-293-5040. FAX: 304-293-6638. Web Site: www.libraries.wvu.edu. *Dean,* Frances O'Brien; *Assoc Dean,* Myra Lowe; *Dir,* Mary Strife; Tel: 904-293-4696, Ext 5112; *Dir, Info Literacy,* Carroll Wilkinson; *Head, Access & Media Serv,* Hillary Fredette; *Head, Acq,* Allyson McKee; *Head, Cat, Head, Per, Interim Head, Libr Syst,* William Rafter; *Head, Ref,* Penny Pugh; *Mgr, Libr Depository,* Randy Jenkins; *Bus Planning Officer,* Cassandra Caplan; *Curator,* John Cuthbert; Staff 112 (MLS 37, Non-MLS 75)
Founded 1867. Enrl 26,997; Fac 2,164; Highest Degree: Doctorate
Library Holdings: Bk Vols 1,616,340; Per Subs 34,855
Special Collections: Oral History; State Document Depository; US Document Depository
Subject Interests: Appalachia, Coal
Wireless access
Publications: ExLibris (Newsletter)
Partic in OCLC Online Computer Library Center, Inc; Pennsylvania Academic Library Consortium, Inc (PALCI)
Friends of the Library Group
Departmental Libraries:
EVANSDALE LIBRARY, One Evansdale Dr, 26506. Tel: 304-293-4696. Circulation Tel: 304-293-9759. Interlibrary Loan Service Tel: 304-293-9755. Reference Tel: 304-293-8286. FAX: 304-293-7330. Web Site: www.libraries.wvu.edu/evansdale. *Dir,* Mary Strife; E-mail: mstrife2@wvu.edu

CL   GEORGE R FARMER, JR COLLEGE OF LAW LIBRARY, One Law Center Dr, 26506. (Mail add: PO Box 6135, 26506-6135), SAN 364-4618. Tel: 304-293-5300. Reference Tel: 304-293-8286. FAX: 304-293-6020. Web Site: www.wvu.edu/~law/library/index.htm. *Dir,* Camille Riley; Tel: 304-293-7641, E-mail: camille.riley@mail.wvu.edu; *Electronic Serv, Ref Serv,* Susan Wolford; Tel: 304-293-6830, E-mail: susan.wolford@mail.wvu.edu; *Pub Serv,* Kevin Fredette; Tel: 304-293-7640, E-mail: kevin.fredette@mail.wvu.edu; Staff 3 (MLS 2, Non-MLS 1)
    Enrl 470
    Library Holdings: DVDs 8; Electronic Media & Resources 10; Bk Vols 339,675; Per Subs 1,070; Videos 770
    Automation Activity & Vendor Info: (Acquisitions) Ex Libris Group; (Cataloging) Ex Libris Group; (Circulation) Ex Libris Group; (Course Reserve) Ex Libris Group; (ILL) Ex Libris Group; (Media Booking) Ex Libris Group; (OPAC) Ex Libris Group; (Serials) Ex Libris Group
    Open Mon-Thurs (Sept-April) 7:30am-Midnight, Fri 8am-10pm, Sat 9-8, Sun 12-11; Mon-Fri (May-Aug) 9-8, Sat 9-6, Sun 12-6

CM   HEALTH SCIENCES LIBRARY, Robert C Byrd Health Sciences Ctr N, One Medical Center Dr, 26506. (Mail add: PO Box 9801, HSN 2000, 26506-9801), SAN 364-4642. Tel: 304-293-2113. FAX: 304-293-5995. Web Site: www.hsc.wvu.edu/library. *Dir,* Susan Arnold
      WEST VIRGINIA & REGIONAL HISTORY COLLECTION, 1549 University Ave, 26506-6069, SAN 328-8609. Tel: 304-293-3536. FAX: 304-293-3981. Web Site: www.libraries.wvu.edu/wvcollection/index.htm. *Curator,* John Cuthbert; E-mail: jcuthber@wvu.edu
      Subject Interests: Archives, Cent Appalachian hist, Coal mining hist, Culture, WVa hist

MOUNDSVILLE

P   MOUNDSVILLE-MARSHALL COUNTY PUBLIC LIBRARY*, 700 Fifth St, 26041-1993. SAN 364-4677. Tel: 304-845-6911. FAX: 304-845-6912. Web Site: moundsville.lib.wv.us. *Dir,* Susan Reilly; *Acq,* Susan Shaw; *Ch,* Vicki Howsare; *ILL,* Mildred Ulman; *Tech Serv,* Catherine Feryok; Staff 2 (MLS 2)
      Founded 1917. Pop 74,802; Circ 378,473
      Library Holdings: Bk Vols 174,989; Per Subs 170
      Special Collections: West Virginia Coll
      Automation Activity & Vendor Info: (Cataloging) Innovative Interfaces, Inc; (Circulation) Innovative Interfaces, Inc; (OPAC) Innovative Interfaces, Inc
      Wireless access
      Publications: Newsletter (Bi-monthly)
      Member Libraries: Hundred Public Library; Paden City Public Library; Pine Grove Public Library; Sistersville Public Library; Tyler County Public Library
      Partic in Northern Library Network (NorLN)
      Open Mon-Wed 10-8, Thurs-Fri 10-6, Sat 10-5
      Friends of the Library Group
      Branches: 2
      BENWOOD-MCMECHEN PUBLIC, 201 Marshall St, McMechen, 26040, SAN 364-4766. Tel: 304-232-9720. FAX: 304-232-9720. *Br Librn,* Virginia Benham
      Partic in Northern Library Network (NorLN)
      Open Mon & Tues 1-8, Wed & Thurs 11-6, Fri & Sat 10-4
      CAMERON PUBLIC, Benedum Bldg, 44 Main St, Cameron, 26033, SAN 364-4707. Tel: 304-686-2140. FAX: 304-686-2140. *Br Librn,* Mary Evelyn Garey
      Partic in Northern Library Network (NorLN)
      Open Mon & Wed 12-8, Tues 9-5, Fri & Sat 9-2

S   NORTHERN REGIONAL JAIL CORRECTIONAL FACILITY*, RD 2, Box 1, 26041-0001. SAN 317-8056. Tel: 304-843-4067, Ext 106. FAX: 304-843-4089. *Assoc Warden of Prog,* Greg Yahnke; E-mail: gregory.l.yahnke@wv.gov
      Library Holdings: Bk Vols 5,000; Per Subs 37
      Open Mon, Tues, Thurs & Fri 8:30-10:30 & 12:30-3:30, Wed 8:30-10:30, 12:30-3:30 & 5-7, Sat & Sun 8:30-10:30

MOUNT GAY

J   SOUTHERN WEST VIRGINIA COMMUNITY & TECHNICAL COLLEGE*, Harless Library, Dempsey Branch Rd, 25637. (Mail add: PO Box 2900, 25637-2900), SAN 364-4251. Tel: 304-896-7378. Interlibrary Loan Service Tel: 304-896-7306. Administration Tel: 304-896-7345. FAX: 304-752-2837. Web Site: www.southern.wvnet.edu. *Dir,* Kimberly Maynard; E-mail: kimm@southern.wvnet.edu; Staff 1 (Non-MLS 1)
      Founded 1971. Enrl 1,500; Fac 30; Highest Degree: Associate
      Library Holdings: AV Mats 2,201; CDs 258; DVDs 65; Bk Titles 32,653
      Special Collections: Local History & Genealogy (West Virginia Coll)
      Automation Activity & Vendor Info: (Acquisitions) SirsiDynix; (Cataloging) SirsiDynix; (Circulation) SirsiDynix; (Course Reserve) SirsiDynix; (ILL) OCLC Connexion; (Media Booking) SirsiDynix; (OPAC) SirsiDynix; (Serials) SirsiDynix
      Database Vendor: Gale Cengage Learning, OCLC WorldCat, SirsiDynix
      Wireless access
      Function: Electronic databases & coll, ILL available, Magnifiers for reading, Music CDs, Online cat, Pub access computers
      Partic in OCLC Online Computer Library Center, Inc
      Special Services for the Deaf - Assisted listening device; Assistive tech; TDD equip
      Special Services for the Blind - Computer with voice synthesizer for visually impaired persons; Dragon Naturally Speaking software; Reader equip
      Open Mon-Thurs 7am-8pm, Fri 7-4:30
      Friends of the Library Group

MOUNT HOPE

CR   JOHN VAN PUFFELEN LIBRARY OF THE APPALACHIAN BIBLE COLLEGE*, 161 College Dr, 25880-1040. (Mail add: PO Box ABC, Bradley, 25818-1353), SAN 317-7327. Tel: 304-877-6428, Ext 3211. FAX:

304-877-5983. E-mail: abc@abc.edu. Web Site: www.abc.edu. *Mgr, Libr Serv,* Bonita Gayle Haynes; *Librn,* Ed Arnold Chesley; Tel: 304-877-6428, Ext 3271, E-mail: ed.chesley@abc.edu. *Subject Specialists: English, Hist,* Ed Arnold Chesley; Staff 3 (MLS 1, Non-MLS 2)
      Founded 1950. Enrl 280; Fac 18; Highest Degree: Master
      Jul 2005-Jun 2006 Income $120,000. Mats Exp $118,000. Sal $55,000 (Prof $39,000)
      Library Holdings: AV Mats 70; Bk Titles 49,000; Bk Vols 50,000; Per Subs 250; Spec Interest Per Sub 175
      Special Collections: Archives Reference Coll (books 100 years old or more); Cults & Christian Counterfeits Coll; Judiaca Coll
      Subject Interests: Missions, Theol, WVa
      Automation Activity & Vendor Info: (Cataloging) Winnebago Software Co; (Circulation) Winnebago Software Co; (OPAC) Winnebago Software Co
      Database Vendor: EBSCOhost
      Function: Res libr
      Open Mon-Fri 8am-9:30pm, Sat 10am-10:30pm, Sun 2-4

MOUNT OLIVE

S   MOUNT OLIVE CORRECTIONAL COMPLEX LIBRARY*, One Mountainside Way, 25185. Tel: 304-442-7213. FAX: 304-442-7227. *Librn,* Sheila Hosey
      Library Holdings: Bk Vols 5,000; Per Subs 20

NEW CUMBERLAND

P   SWANEY MEMORIAL LIBRARY*, 100 Court St, 26047. (Mail add: PO Box 608, 26047-0608), SAN 317-8064. Tel: 304-564-3471. FAX: 304-564-3471. Web Site: www.weirton.lib.wv.us. *Librn,* Anna Raines; *Asst Librn,* Angela Skinner; Staff 2 (Non-MLS 2)
      Pop 4,666; Circ 14,098
      Library Holdings: Bk Vols 20,000; Per Subs 33
      Subject Interests: Genealogy, Local hist
      Automation Activity & Vendor Info: (Cataloging) Innovative Interfaces, Inc; (Circulation) Innovative Interfaces, Inc; (OPAC) Innovative Interfaces, Inc
      Database Vendor: EBSCOhost
      Wireless access
      Function: ILL available, Photocopying/Printing, Ref serv available
      Partic in Northern Library Network (NorLN)
      Open Mon-Thurs 11-7, Fri 9-4

NEW MARTINSVILLE

P   NEW MARTINSVILLE PUBLIC LIBRARY, 160 Washington Ave, 26155. SAN 317-8080. Tel: 304-455-4545. FAX: 304-455-4545. E-mail: nmplibrary@hotmail.com. Web Site: www.newmartinsville.lib.wv.us. *Dir,* Janet Witten Conn; Staff 5 (MLS 1, Non-MLS 4)
      Founded 1946. Pop 8,300
      Library Holdings: AV Mats 625; Bk Vols 30,000; Per Subs 40
      Special Collections: Genealogy; West Virginia materials
      Function: Audiobks via web, Bk reviews (Group), Children's prog, Computers for patron use, e-mail & chat, Fax serv, Handicapped accessible, ILL available, Mail & tel request accepted, Microfiche/film & reading machines, Music CDs, Online cat, OverDrive digital audio bks, Photocopying/Printing, Preschool reading prog, Pub access computers, Scanner, Story hour, Summer reading prog, Tax forms, VHS videos, Web-catalog
      Partic in Northern Library Network (NorLN)
      Open Mon-Wed 10-8, Fri & Sat 10-5
      Friends of the Library Group

NUTTER FORT

P   NUTTER FORT LIBRARY*, 1300 Buckhannon Pike, 26301-4406. SAN 376-7779. Tel: 304-622-7563. FAX: 304-622-7563. *Dir,* Dottie White; E-mail: dottie.white@clark.lib.wv.us; Staff 1 (Non-MLS 1)
      Library Holdings: Bk Titles 12,000; Bk Vols 25,000; Per Subs 15
      Partic in Northern Library Network (NorLN)
      Open Mon-Fri (Winter) 10-5:30, Sat 10-1; Mon 10-5:30, Tues-Fri (Summer) 10-4
      Friends of the Library Group

OAK HILL

P   FAYETTE COUNTY PUBLIC LIBRARIES*, 531 Summit St, 25901. SAN 364-4820. Tel: 304-465-0121. FAX: 304-465-5306. Web Site: www.fayette.lib.wv.us. *Dir,* Judy Gunsaulis; E-mail: gunsaulj@raleigh.lib.wv.us; Staff 6 (MLS 1, Non-MLS 5)
      Founded 1959. Pop 47,952; Circ 213,170
      Library Holdings: Bk Vols 83,000; Per Subs 26
      Special Collections: Books About West Virginia & by West Virginia Authors (West Virginia Room Coll); Books-by-Mail Coll

Automation Activity & Vendor Info: (Cataloging) Innovative Interfaces, Inc; (Circulation) Innovative Interfaces, Inc; (OPAC) Innovative Interfaces, Inc

Open Mon-Fri 9-5

Branches: 7

ANSTED PUBLIC, 102 Oak St, Ansted, 25812. (Mail add: PO Box 428, Ansted, 25812-0428), SAN 364-4944. Tel: 304-658-5472. FAX: 304-658-5472. *Librn,* Carla Lucas; *Librn,* Janice Woods; Staff 2 (Non-MLS 2)

> **Library Holdings:** Bk Titles 9,000; Per Subs 15
> Open Tues & Thurs 2-8, Wed 9-4, Fri 10-5, Sat 9-1

FAYETTEVILLE BRANCH, 200 W Maple Ave, Fayetteville, 25840, SAN 364-4855. Tel: 304-574-0070. FAX: 304-574-0070. *Librn,* Linda Stewart; Staff 2 (Non-MLS 2)

> **Library Holdings:** Bk Vols 23,318; Per Subs 31
> **Special Collections:** West Virginia Coll
> Open Mon 12-8, Tues-Fri 10-5, Sat 9-1

GAULEY BRIDGE BRANCH, 286 Railroad St, Gauley Bridge, 25085. (Mail add: PO Box 487, Gauley Bridge, 25085-0487), SAN 364-4898. Tel: 304-632-2172. FAX: 304-632-2172. *Librn,* Tammy Cooper; Staff 1 (Non-MLS 1)

> **Library Holdings:** Bk Vols 4,000; Per Subs 17
> Open Tues 1-7, Wed-Fri 11-5

PATRICK C GRANEY JR LIBRARY, 500 Main St, Mount Hope, 25880, SAN 364-488X. Tel: 304-877-3260. FAX: 304-877-3260. *Br Librn,* Randall Ballard; Staff 1 (Non-MLS 1)

> **Library Holdings:** Bk Vols 6,800; Per Subs 19
> Open Mon-Fri 9-3

MEADOW BRIDGE BRANCH, 53 Montrado St, Meadow Bridge, 25976, SAN 326-8314. Tel: 304-484-7942. FAX: 304-484-7942. *Librn,* Janet Kincaid; Staff 2 (Non-MLS 2)

> **Library Holdings:** Bk Vols 3,113; Per Subs 11
> Open Mon, Wed & Thurs 10-4, Tues 12-7

MONTGOMERY BRANCH, 507 Ferry St, Montgomery, 25136, SAN 364-4979. Tel: 304-442-5665. FAX: 304-442-5665. *Librn,* Linda Beal; Staff 2 (Non-MLS 2)

> **Library Holdings:** Bk Vols 9,506; Per Subs 28
> Partic in Mountain Library Network
> Open Mon, Tues, Thurs & Fri 10-5, Wed 12-7

OAK HILL BRANCH, 611 Main St, 25901, SAN 364-491X. Tel: 304-469-9890. FAX: 304-469-9890. *Br Mgr,* Paula Carter; E-mail: carterpa@mail.mln.lib.wv.us; Staff 4 (Non-MLS 4)

> **Library Holdings:** Bk Vols 17,982; Per Subs 39
> Open Mon, Wed & Fri 10-5, Tues & Thurs 10-7, Sat 10-2

PADEN CITY

P   PADEN CITY PUBLIC LIBRARY*, 114 S Fourth Ave, 26159. SAN 317-8129. Tel: 304-337-9333. FAX: 304-337-9333. Web Site: padencity.lib.wv.us. *Dir,* Joanna Casto; E-mail: casto@weirton.lib.wv.us; *Asst Librn,* Judy Giles; Staff 3 (Non-MLS 3)
Founded 1947. Pop 4,989; Circ 9,754
Library Holdings: Bk Titles 11,821; Per Subs 30
Automation Activity & Vendor Info: (Cataloging) Innovative Interfaces, Inc; (Circulation) Innovative Interfaces, Inc; (OPAC) Innovative Interfaces, Inc
Wireless access
Mem of Moundsville-Marshall County Public Library
Partic in Northern Library Network (NorLN)
Open Mon, Tues & Thurs 1-8, Wed 10-5, Fri 1-5, Sat 10-1

PARKERSBURG

M   CAMDEN-CLARK MEMORIAL HOSPITAL*, Medical Library, 800 Garfield Ave, 26101. SAN 317-8137. Tel: 304-424-2450. FAX: 304-424-2861. *Librn,* Shauna Harper; E-mail: slharper@ccmh.org; Staff 1 (Non-MLS 1)
Founded 1900
Library Holdings: Bk Titles 2,700; Per Subs 200
Subject Interests: Allied health, Med, Nursing
Partic in National Network of Libraries of Medicine
Open Mon-Fri 7-3:30

P   PARKERSBURG & WOOD COUNTY PUBLIC LIBRARY*, Wood County Service Center, 3100 Emerson Ave, 26104-2414. SAN 364-5002. Tel: 304-420-4587. Circulation Tel: 304-420-4587, Ext 17. Interlibrary Loan Service Tel: 304-420-4587, Ext 27. Reference Tel: 304-420-4587, Ext 21. Administration Tel: 304-420-4587, Ext 11. FAX: 304-420-4589. E-mail: library@park.lib.wv.us. Web Site: parkersburg.lib.wv.us. *Dir,* Brian E Raitz; E-mail: raitzb@park.lib.wv.us; *Ch,* Brenda Gellner; Tel: 304-420-4587, Ext 20, E-mail: taylorb@park.lib.wv.us; *ILL,* Harriet Collins; E-mail: parkwoodill@gmail.com; *Ref,* Jamie Fabian; E-mail: fabianj@park.lib.wv.us; *Tech Serv,* Hazel Stewart; Tel: 304-420-4587, Ext 23, E-mail: stewarth@park.lib.wv.us; *Media Spec,* Lynn Roberts; Tel:

304-420-4587, Ext 18, E-mail: robertsl@park.lib.wv.us; Staff 24 (MLS 3, Non-MLS 21)
Founded 1905. Pop 77,125; Circ 337,620
Jul 2011-Jun 2012 Income (Main Library and Branch(s)) $1,278,613, State $386,732, City $210,348, County $234,618, Locally Generated Income $70,000, Other $376,915. Mats Exp $221,650, Books $140,950, Per/Ser (Incl. Access Fees) $16,000, AV Mat $38,700, Electronic Ref Mat (Incl. Access Fees) $26,000. Sal $824,936
Library Holdings: Audiobooks 6,265; AV Mats 233; CDs 1,911; DVDs 5,654; Bk Vols 179,915; Per Subs 182; Videos 4,138
Special Collections: West Virginia History & Genealogical Coll, bks & microfilm
Automation Activity & Vendor Info: (Acquisitions) Innovative Interfaces, Inc; (Cataloging) Innovative Interfaces, Inc; (Circulation) Innovative Interfaces, Inc; (OPAC) Innovative Interfaces, Inc
Database Vendor: Baker & Taylor, EBSCOhost, Gale Cengage Learning, ProQuest
Wireless access
Function: AV serv, For res purposes, Govt ref serv, Handicapped accessible, Homebound delivery serv, ILL available, Magnifiers for reading, Prog for children & young adult, Ref serv available, Res libr, Satellite serv, Summer reading prog, Wheelchair accessible
Partic in Mountain Library Network
Open Mon-Thurs 9-9, Fri & Sat 9-5, Sun (Fall & Spring) 1-5
Friends of the Library Group
Branches: 4

P   SERVICES FOR THE BLIND & PHYSICALLY HANDICAPPED, 3100 Emerson Ave, 26104. Tel: 304-420-4587, Ext 13. FAX: 304-420-4589. *Librn for Blind & Physically Handicapped,* Lindsay Place; E-mail: lindsay.place@park.lib.wv.us
Founded 1970
Special Services for the Blind - Braille equip; Braille paper; Home delivery serv; Magnifiers; Volunteer serv
Open Mon-Sat 9-5

SOUTH PARKERSBURG, 1713 Blizzard Dr, 26101, SAN 364-5061. Tel: 304-428-7041. FAX: 304-428-7041. *Librn,* Rachel Hyde; E-mail: rachel.hyde@mail.mln.lib.wv.us; Staff 1 (Non-MLS 1)
Founded 1973
Open Mon-Thurs 12-7, Fri 10-5
Friends of the Library Group

WAVERLY, 450 Virginia St, Waverly, 26184, SAN 377-8215. Tel: 304-464-5668. FAX: 304-464-5668. *Librn,* Amy Sandy; E-mail: amy.sandy@mail.mln.lib.wv.us
Open Tues & Thurs 3-7
Friends of the Library Group

WILLIAMSTOWN BRANCH, 201 W Fifth St, Williamstown, 26187, SAN 364-5096. Tel: 304-375-6052. FAX: 304-375-6052. *Librn,* Matt Emrick; E-mail: matt.emrick@park.lib.wv.us
Founded 1977
Library Holdings: Large Print Bks 300; Bk Vols 10,500
Open Mon-Thurs 12-7, Fri 10-5
Friends of the Library Group
Bookmobiles: 1

M   SAINT JOSEPH'S HOSPITAL*, Educational Resources Center, 1824 Murdoch Ave, 26102. SAN 317-8188. Tel: 304-424-4607. FAX: 304-424-4635. *Librn,* Deana Wolfe; E-mail: deana.wolfe@lpht.net
Founded 1967
Library Holdings: Bk Titles 3,000; Per Subs 190
Subject Interests: Hospital admin, Med, Nursing
Partic in WVa Health Sci Asn
Open Mon-Fri 8:30-4

R   TEMPLE B'NAI ISRAEL LIBRARY*, 1703 20th St, 26101. SAN 317-8196. Tel: 304-428-1192. Web Site: www.templebnaisrael.org. *Pres,* Doug Kreinik; Tel: 304-485-6729; Staff 2 (MLS 1, Non-MLS 1)
Founded 1949
Library Holdings: Bk Titles 1,030; Bk Vols 1,530
Special Collections: Jewish Authors
Subject Interests: Judaica

C   WEST VIRGINIA UNIVERSITY*, 300 Campus Dr, 26104. SAN 317-8161. Tel: 304-424-8260. FAX: 304-424-8349. Web Site: www.wvup.edu/library/index.htm. *Dir,* Stephen Hupp; E-mail: stephen.hupp@mail.wvu.edu; *Assoc Librn,* Lisa Gianettino; Staff 6 (MLS 3, Non-MLS 3)
Founded 1971. Enrl 3,329; Fac 119
Library Holdings: e-books 3,000; Bk Vols 55,000; Per Subs 100
Subject Interests: Children's lit
Automation Activity & Vendor Info: (Acquisitions) Ex Libris Group; (Cataloging) Ex Libris Group; (Circulation) Ex Libris Group; (ILL) Ex Libris Group; (OPAC) Ex Libris Group; (Serials) Ex Libris Group
Database Vendor: EBSCOhost, LexisNexis
Wireless access

Partic in Lyrasis; OCLC Online Computer Library Center, Inc
Friends of the Library Group

PARSONS

P   FIVE RIVERS PUBLIC LIBRARY*, 301 Walnut St, 26287. SAN
317-820X. Tel: 304-478-3880. FAX: 304-478-3880. E-mail:
parsons@clark.lib.wv.us. Web Site: fiverivers.lib.wv.us. *Dir*, Nancy Moore;
Librn, Ellouise Smith; *Asst Librn*, Kathy Phillips; E-mail:
phillipk@clark.lib.wv.us
Founded 1974. Pop 4,136; Circ 12,918
Library Holdings: Bk Vols 17,733; Per Subs 11; Talking Bks 378; Videos
398
Automation Activity & Vendor Info: (Cataloging) Innovative Interfaces,
Inc; (Circulation) Innovative Interfaces, Inc; (OPAC) Innovative Interfaces,
Inc
Partic in Northern Library Network (NorLN)
Open Mon (June-Aug) 9-7, Tues-Fri 9-4, Sat 9-1; Mon (Sept-May) 9-7,
Tues-Fri 9-5, Sat 9-1

PAW PAW

P   PAW PAW PUBLIC LIBRARY*, 250 Moser Ave, 25434-9500. (Mail add:
PO Box 9, 25434-0009), SAN 317-8218. Tel: 304-947-7013. FAX:
304-947-7013. E-mail: info@pawpawpubliclibrary.com. Web Site:
www.youseemore.com/pawpaw. *Dir*, Nellie Leach; E-mail:
nellie@pawpawpubliclibrary.com; Staff 1 (Non-MLS 1)
Founded 1971. Pop 4,043; Circ 10,000
Library Holdings: Bk Vols 18,000; Per Subs 31; Talking Bks 300
Automation Activity & Vendor Info: (Cataloging) TLC (The Library
Corporation); (Circulation) TLC (The Library Corporation); (OPAC) TLC
(The Library Corporation)
Wireless access
Special Services for the Blind - Audio mat; Large print bks
Open Mon-Wed 9-12 & 1-5, Thurs 11-7, Fri 9-12 & 1-4
Friends of the Library Group

PETERSBURG

P   GRANT COUNTY LIBRARY*, 18 Mountain View St, 26847-1524. SAN
317-8226. Tel: 304-257-4122. FAX: 304-257-4122. Web Site:
www.youseemore.com/grant. *Librn*, Barbara Carr; *Asst Librn*, Christine
Cook; Staff 2 (Non-MLS 2)
Founded 1963. Pop 11,299; Circ 36,988
Library Holdings: Bk Vols 36,000; Per Subs 44; Talking Bks 767
Automation Activity & Vendor Info: (Cataloging) TLC (The Library
Corporation); (Circulation) TLC (The Library Corporation); (OPAC) TLC
(The Library Corporation)
Open Mon, Tues, Thurs & Fri 9-5, Wed 9-8, Sat 9-12
Friends of the Library Group
Branches: 1
ALLEGHENY-MOUNTAIN TOP, PO Box 161, Mount Storm,
26739-0161, SAN 324-2544. Tel: 304-693-7504. FAX: 304-693-7504.
Web Site: youseemore.com/allegheny. *Br Librn*, Dana Carr; Staff 1
(Non-MLS 1)
Library Holdings: Bk Vols 15,500; Per Subs 20
Open Mon 12-6, Tues-Fri 11-5
Friends of the Library Group

PETERSTOWN

P   PETERSTOWN PUBLIC LIBRARY*, 23 College Ave, 24963. (Mail add:
PO Box 698, 24963-0698). Tel: 304-753-9568. FAX: 304-753-9684. Web
Site: peterstown.lib.wv.us. *Dir*, Cindy Laws; E-mail:
lawsc@mail.mln.lib.wv.us
Pop 5,665; Circ 25,200
Library Holdings: AV Mats 330; Bk Titles 28,220; Per Subs 21; Talking
Bks 160
Automation Activity & Vendor Info: (Cataloging) Innovative Interfaces,
Inc; (Circulation) Innovative Interfaces, Inc; (OPAC) Innovative Interfaces,
Inc
Function: Distance learning
Partic in Mountain Library Network
Open Mon & Thurs 9-5, Wed 9-1, Fri 9-4, Sat 9-12

PHILIPPI

C   ALDERSON-BROADDUS COLLEGE*, Pickett Library, College Hill Rd,
26416. SAN 317-8234. Tel: 304-457-6229. FAX: 304-457-6239. Web Site:
www.ab.edu. *Dir*, David E Hoxie; Staff 1.5 (MLS 1.5)
Enrl 750; Fac 58; Highest Degree: Master
Library Holdings: e-books 50,000; Electronic Media & Resources 11,000;
Bk Vols 60,000; Per Subs 89
Special Collections: Baptist Archives Coll; Civil War Coll
Subject Interests: Educ

Automation Activity & Vendor Info: (Cataloging) Innovative Interfaces,
Inc; (Circulation) Innovative Interfaces, Inc; (Course Reserve) Innovative
Interfaces, Inc; (ILL) OCLC; (OPAC) Innovative Interfaces, Inc
Database Vendor: EBSCOhost, JSTOR, ProQuest, Wilson - Wilson Web
Wireless access
Partic in OCLC Online Computer Library Center, Inc
Open Mon-Thurs (Winter) 8am-10pm, Fri 8-5, Sat 1-5, Sun 1-10; Mon-Fri
(Summer) 8-4:30

P   PHILIPPI PUBLIC LIBRARY, 102 S Main St, 26416-1317. SAN
317-8242. Tel: 304-457-3495. FAX: 304-457-5569. Web Site:
philippi.lib.wv.us. *Dir*, Judy Larry; Staff 1 (Non-MLS 1)
Founded 1966. Pop 9,539; Circ 20,260
Jul 2012-Jun 2013 Income $89,923, State $47,695, City $27,035, County
$2,500, Other $12,693. Mats Exp $7,241, Books $5,400, Per/Ser (Incl.
Access Fees) $1,100, AV Mat $741. Sal $56,341
Library Holdings: Audiobooks 313; Bks on Deafness & Sign Lang 20;
Braille Volumes 3; DVDs 769; Large Print Bks 288; Bk Titles 20,834; Per
Subs 46
Special Collections: Civil War Coll; Genealogy Coll; Library of America;
Local History Coll; West Virginia Coll
Automation Activity & Vendor Info: (Cataloging) Innovative Interfaces,
Inc; (Circulation) Innovative Interfaces, Inc; (OPAC) Innovative Interfaces,
Inc
Wireless access
Function: Bks on CD, CD-ROM, Children's prog, Computer training,
Computers for patron use, Copy machines, e-mail serv, Electronic
databases & coll, Fax serv, Genealogy discussion group, Handicapped
accessible, ILL available, Notary serv, Online cat, Photocopying/Printing,
Prog for children & young adult, Ref & res, Scanner, Story hour, Summer
reading prog, Tax forms, Video lending libr, Web-catalog, Wheelchair
accessible
Partic in Northern Library Network (NorLN)
Open Mon-Thurs 10-6, Fri 10-5, Sat 10-2

PIEDMONT

P   PIEDMONT PUBLIC LIBRARY*, One Child Ave, 26750. SAN 317-8250.
Tel: 304-355-2757. FAX: 304-355-2757. *Librn*, Paula Boggs; E-mail:
pboggs@martin.lib.wv.us; Staff 1 (Non-MLS 1)
Founded 1960. Pop 1,417; Circ 9,048
Jul 2011-Jun 2012 Income $24,042, State $6,542, City $800, County
$5,000, Locally Generated Income $8,700, Other $3,000
Library Holdings: Audiobooks 118; Bk Vols 19,609; Per Subs 7; Videos
48
Wireless access
Function: Accelerated reader prog, Bks on cassette, Computers for patron
use, Copy machines, Fax serv, Handicapped accessible, Holiday prog,
Home delivery & serv to Sr ctr & nursing homes, Summer reading prog,
Tax forms, Wheelchair accessible
Open Mon-Fri 12-6, Sat 11-3

PINE GROVE

P   PINE GROVE PUBLIC LIBRARY*, Main St, 26419. (Mail add: PO Box
416, 26419-0416), SAN 317-8269. Tel: 304-889-3288. FAX:
304-889-3288. Web Site: nwvlc.clark.lib.wv.us. *Co-Dir*, Donna Goontz;
Co-Dir, Carma Wyatt; Staff 1 (Non-MLS 1)
Founded 1975. Pop 3,386; Circ 7,607
Library Holdings: AV Mats 50; Bk Vols 3,000; Per Subs 15
Automation Activity & Vendor Info: (Circulation) Innovative Interfaces,
Inc; (OPAC) Innovative Interfaces, Inc
Wireless access
Mem of Moundsville-Marshall County Public Library
Partic in Northern Library Network (NorLN)
Open Mon, Tues & Wed 12-5, Thurs 11-6, Fri 10-2

PINEVILLE

P   WYOMING COUNTY PUBLIC LIBRARY*, Castle Rock Ave, 24874.
(Mail add: PO Box 130, 24874-0130), SAN 364-5126. Tel: 304-732-6228.
Administration Tel: 304-732-6800. Web Site: wyoming.lib.wv.us. *Dir*,
Carolyn M Gaddis
Founded 1966. Pop 28,990; Circ 86,523
Library Holdings: AV Mats 310; Bks on Deafness & Sign Lang 15; High
Interest/Low Vocabulary Bk Vols 425; Bk Titles 63,065; Bk Vols 65,220;
Per Subs 95
Special Collections: West Virginia History & Literature; Wyoming County,
WV Genealogy & History
Automation Activity & Vendor Info: (Cataloging) VTLS, Inc;
(Circulation) VTLS, Inc
Open Mon & Wed-Fri 9-5, Tues 9-6
Friends of the Library Group

Branches: 4

HANOVER PUBLIC, 5556 Interstate Hwy, Hanover, 24839. (Mail add: PO Box 9, Hanover, 24839-0009). Tel: 304-664-5580. FAX: 304-664-5580. *Br Mgr,* Rachel Beavers
Open Wed & Fri 9-5, Thurs 9-6, Sat 9-3
Friends of the Library Group

MULLENS AREA PUBLIC, 102 Fourth St, Mullens, 25882, SAN 364-5215. Tel: 304-294-6687. FAX: 304-294-6687. *Br Mgr,* Cindy Nuckolls
Open Mon 9-6, Tues, Thurs & Fri 9-5, Wed 9-3, Sat 10-3
Friends of the Library Group

OCEANA PUBLIC, 101 Cook Pkwy, Oceana, 24870. (Mail add: PO Box 1768, Oceana, 24870-1768). Tel: 304-682-6784. FAX: 304-682-6784. *Br Mgr,* Glenna Brown
Open Mon, Tues & Fri 9-5, Wed 9-3, Thurs 9-6, Sat 9-1
Friends of the Library Group

PINEVILLE BRANCH, Corner of Costle Rock & Bank St, 24874. (Mail add: PO Box 130, 24874-0130), SAN 364-5150. Tel: 304-732-6228. FAX: 304-732-6899. *Br Mgr,* Laura Mellon; Staff 2 (Non-MLS 2)
Pop 28,990
Library Holdings: Bk Titles 20,280; Bk Vols 21,190; Per Subs 37
Open Mon, Thurs & Fri 9-5, Tues 9-6, Wed 9-3, Sat 9-12
Friends of the Library Group

POINT PLEASANT

P   MASON COUNTY LIBRARY SYSTEM*, 508 Viand St, 25550-1199. SAN 364-524X. Tel: 304-675-0894. FAX: 304-675-0895. Web Site: masoncounty.lib.wv.us. *Mgr,* Debbie Hopson; E-mail: hopsond@mail.mln.lib.wv.us; Staff 9 (MLS 1, Non-MLS 8)
Founded 1930. Pop 25,178; Circ 151,613
Library Holdings: Bk Vols 52,000; Per Subs 50
Special Collections: Local History Coll
Automation Activity & Vendor Info: (Cataloging) Innovative Interfaces, Inc; (Circulation) Innovative Interfaces, Inc; (OPAC) Innovative Interfaces, Inc
Partic in Mountain Library Network
Open Mon 1-5, Tues-Sat 10-6
Friends of the Library Group
Branches: 3

HANNAN, 6760 Ashton-Upland Rd, Ashton, 25503, SAN 326-7539. Tel: 304-743-6200. FAX: 304-743-6200. *Librn,* Teresa Perry; Staff 2 (Non-MLS 2)
Library Holdings: Bk Vols 7,232; Per Subs 10
Open Mon & Tues 12-5, Wed & Thurs 11-4

MASON CITY PUBLIC, Eight Brown St, Mason, 25260, SAN 364-5274. Tel: 304-773-5580. FAX: 304-773-5580. *Librn,* Pamela Thompson; Staff 2 (Non-MLS 2)
Library Holdings: Bk Vols 10,006; Per Subs 15
Open Wed-Fri 9-5
Friends of the Library Group

NEW HAVEN PUBLIC, 106 Main St, New Haven, 25265, SAN 364-5304. Tel: 304-882-3252. FAX: 304-882-3252. *Librn,* Pamela Thompson; Staff 3 (Non-MLS 3)
Library Holdings: Bk Vols 10,970; Per Subs 15
Open Mon-Thurs 11-6
Friends of the Library Group

PRINCETON

M   PRINCETON COMMUNITY HOSPITAL LIBRARY, 122 12th St, 24740-2352. (Mail add: PO Box 1369, 24740-1369), SAN 317-8277. Tel: 304-487-7000, 304-487-7714. Administration Tel: 304-487-7242. Information Services Tel: 304-487-7256. FAX: 304-487-7524. Administration FAX: 304-487-2161. Information Services FAX: 304-487-7146. Web Site: www.pchonline.org. *Librn,* Lynn P Pendleton; E-mail: lpendleton@pchonline.org; Staff 1 (Non-MLS 1)
Founded 1970
Library Holdings: Bk Titles 283; Per Subs 12
Database Vendor: UpToDate, WT Cox
Wireless access

P   PRINCETON PUBLIC LIBRARY*, 205 Center St, 24740-2932. SAN 317-8285. Tel: 304-487-5045. FAX: 304-487-5046. E-mail: ppl@mail.mln.lib.wv.us. Web Site: princeton.lib.wv.us. *Dir,* Connie L Shumate
Founded 1922. Pop 12,000; Circ 223,000
Library Holdings: Bk Titles 99,000; Per Subs 160
Special Collections: Genealogy Coll; Local History Coll; Print Coll; West Virginia Coll
Wireless access
Partic in Lyrasis
Open Mon, Tues & Thurs 9-8, Wed, Fri & Sat 9-5
Friends of the Library Group

RAINELLE

P   RAINELLE MUNICIPAL PUBLIC LIBRARY*, 312 Seventh St, 25962-1649. SAN 328-0675. Tel: 304-438-3008. FAX: 304-438-3008. *Dir,* Debra Goddard; E-mail: dgoddard@mail.mln.lib.wv.us; Staff 3 (Non-MLS 3)
Founded 1973. Pop 7,334; Circ 48,083
Library Holdings: Bk Titles 14,000; Per Subs 12
Automation Activity & Vendor Info: (Cataloging) Innovative Interfaces, Inc; (Circulation) Innovative Interfaces, Inc; (OPAC) Innovative Interfaces, Inc
Partic in Mountain Library Network
Open Mon & Fri 10-5, Tues-Thurs 10-6, Sat 10-2
Friends of the Library Group

RICHWOOD

P   RICHWOOD PUBLIC LIBRARY*, Eight White Ave, 26261. SAN 317-8307. Tel: 304-846-6099. FAX: 304-846-9290. Web Site: www.richwood.lib.wv.us. *Dir,* Robin Bartlett; E-mail: bartlettr@mail.mln.lib.wv.us; *Asst Librn,* Judy Davis; Staff 5 (Non-MLS 5)
Founded 1942. Circ 40,503
Library Holdings: Bk Vols 35,000; Per Subs 95
Automation Activity & Vendor Info: (Cataloging) Innovative Interfaces, Inc; (Circulation) Innovative Interfaces, Inc; (OPAC) Innovative Interfaces, Inc
Open Mon 10-7, Tues, Thurs & Fri 10-5, Sat 10-1

RIPLEY

P   JACKSON COUNTY LIBRARY*, 208 N Church St, 25271-1204. SAN 364-5339. Tel: 304-372-5343. FAX: 304-372-7935. Web Site: jackson.park.lib.wv.us. *Dir,* Suzette Lowe; E-mail: lowesuz@mail.mln.lib.wv.us; Staff 1 (MLS 1)
Founded 1949. Pop 25,938; Circ 121,630
Library Holdings: Bk Vols 34,266; Per Subs 65
Subject Interests: Genealogy, Local hist
Automation Activity & Vendor Info: (Cataloging) Innovative Interfaces, Inc; (Circulation) Innovative Interfaces, Inc; (OPAC) Innovative Interfaces, Inc
Database Vendor: EBSCOhost
Wireless access
Open Mon & Fri (Winter) 9-5, Tues-Thurs 9-8, Sat 9-3; Mon-Wed & Fri (Summer) 9-5, Thurs 9-8, Sat 9-3
Branches: 1

RAVENSWOOD BRANCH, 323 Virginia St, Ravenswood, 26164, SAN 364-5363. Tel: 304-273-5343. FAX: 304-273-5395. *Dir,* Lynn Pauley; Staff 2 (Non-MLS 2)
Library Holdings: Bk Vols 23,586; Per Subs 40
Open Mon & Fri (Winter) 9-5, Tues & Thurs 9-8, Sat 9-3; Mon, Tues & Fri (Summer) 9-5, Thurs 9-8, Sat 9-3

ROMNEY

P   HAMPSHIRE COUNTY PUBLIC LIBRARY*, 153 W Main St, 26757. SAN 317-8315. Tel: 304-822-3185. FAX: 304-822-3955. TDD: 711-304-822-3185. E-mail: hampshire.library@martin.lib.wv.us. Web Site: www.hampshirecopubliclib.com. *Dir,* Amanda Snyder
Founded 1942
Jul 2005-Jun 2006 Income $190,309
Library Holdings: Bk Vols 51,709; Per Subs 63
Special Collections: Census of the County 1810-1920, micro; Local History Coll; Local Newspaper Coll (1884-present), micro
Automation Activity & Vendor Info: (Cataloging) Follett Software; (Circulation) Follett Software; (OPAC) Follett Software
Open Mon & Fri 10-8, Tues-Fri 10-6, Sat 10-4
Friends of the Library Group

P   WEST VIRGINIA SCHOOL FOR THE BLIND LIBRARY, 301 E Main St, 26757. SAN 317-8323. Tel: 304-822-4656, 304-822-4894. FAX: 304-822-4896. E-mail: mchilds@access.k12.wv.us. *Librn,* Mona Childs
Library Holdings: Bk Vols 200; Talking Bks 10,000
Special Collections: Visual Impairment & Blindness Coll
Open Mon-Fri 8-4

S   WEST VIRGINIA SCHOOL FOR THE DEAF & BLIND LIBRARY*, 301 E Main St, 26757. SAN 317-8331. Tel: 304-822-4860. FAX: 304-822-4870. TDD: 304-822-4860. *Librn,* Position Currently Open; Staff 1 (MLS 1)
Founded 1870
Library Holdings: High Interest/Low Vocabulary Bk Vols 1,000; Bk Vols 10,000; Per Subs 40
Special Collections: Deaf & Deafness
Subject Interests: Educ of the deaf, WVa

Special Services for the Deaf - Captioned film dep; High interest/low vocabulary bks; Staff with knowledge of sign lang; TDD equip
Restriction: Open to students, Ref only to non-staff, Staff & mem only

RONCEVERTE

P   RONCEVERTE PUBLIC LIBRARY*, 712 W Main St, 24970. SAN 376-7345. Tel: 304-647-7400. FAX: 304-647-7651. Web Site: ronceverte.lib.wv.us. *Dir,* Cherie Davis; E-mail: davis_cl@mail.mln.lib.wv.us; Staff 2 (Non-MLS 2)
Library Holdings: Bk Vols 22,000; Per Subs 32
Automation Activity & Vendor Info: (Cataloging) Innovative Interfaces, Inc; (Circulation) Innovative Interfaces, Inc; (OPAC) Innovative Interfaces, Inc
Open Mon & Wed-Fri 11-5, Tues 11-7, Sat 10-3
Friends of the Library Group

RUPERT

P   RUPERT COMMUNITY PUBLIC LIBRARY*, 602 Nicholas St, 25984. (Mail add: PO Box 578, 25984-0578), SAN 328-0659. Tel: 304-392-6158. FAX: 304-392-5460. Web Site: rupert.lib.wv.us. *Dir,* Carol McClung; Staff 3 (Non-MLS 3)
Founded 1977. Pop 4,185; Circ 8,113
Library Holdings: AV Mats 229; Large Print Bks 100; Bk Titles 14,740; Per Subs 19; Talking Bks 239
Automation Activity & Vendor Info: (Cataloging) Innovative Interfaces, Inc; (Circulation) Innovative Interfaces, Inc; (OPAC) Innovative Interfaces, Inc
Partic in Mountain Library Network
Open Tues, Wed & Fri 10-5, Thurs 11-6, Sat 10-3

SAINT MARYS

P   PLEASANTS COUNTY PUBLIC LIBRARY*, 101 Lafayette St, 26170-1025. SAN 317-834X. Tel: 304-684-7494. FAX: 304-684-7495. Web Site: pleasants.lib.wv.us. *Dir,* Eleanor Poling; E-mail: polinge@mail.mln.lib.wv.us
Founded 1935. Pop 7,514
Library Holdings: AV Mats 75; Bk Vols 26,023; Per Subs 25
Automation Activity & Vendor Info: (Cataloging) Innovative Interfaces, Inc; (Circulation) Innovative Interfaces, Inc; (OPAC) Innovative Interfaces, Inc
Function: Adult literacy prog, AV serv, Handicapped accessible, ILL available, Photocopying/Printing, Prog for adults, Prog for children & young adult, Summer reading prog, VHS videos, Wheelchair accessible
Special Services for the Blind - Talking bks
Open Mon-Wed 10-8, Thurs 5-8, Fri 10-5, Sat 10-3

SAINT MARY'S

S   ST MARY'S CORRECTIONAL CENTER LIBRARY*, 2880 N Pleasants Hwy, 26170. Tel: 304-684-5500. FAX: 304-684-4000. *Librn,* Barbara Renner
Library Holdings: Bk Vols 4,000; Per Subs 14
Open Mon-Fri 8:15am-8:45pm, Sat 8:15-2:30

SALEM

C   SALEM INTERNATIONAL UNIVERSITY BENEDUM LIBRARY, KD Hurley Blvd, 26426. (Mail add: PO Box 500, 26426-0500), SAN 364-5398. Tel: 304-326-1390. FAX: 304-326-1240. E-mail: library@salemu.edu. Web Site: www.salemu.edu/library. *Dean, Learning Res,* Dr Phyllis D Freedman; Tel: 304-326-1238, E-mail: pfreedman@salemu.edu; *Govt Doc,* James Rogers; E-mail: jrogers@salemu.edu; Staff 2 (MLS 1, Non-MLS 1)
Founded 1888. Enrl 789; Fac 19; Highest Degree: Master
Jan 2011-Dec 2011. Mats Exp $16,129, Books $5,960, Micro $2,700, Electronic Ref Mat (Incl. Access Fees) $5,000. Sal $100,000
Library Holdings: Bk Titles 66,000; Bk Vols 70,000; Per Subs 25; Spec Interest Per Sub 2
Special Collections: Seventh Day Baptist. US Document Depository
Subject Interests: Educ, Local hist
Automation Activity & Vendor Info: (Cataloging) SirsiDynix; (Circulation) SirsiDynix; (Course Reserve) SirsiDynix; (ILL) OCLC; (OPAC) SirsiDynix
Database Vendor: EBSCOhost, LearningExpress, OVID Technologies, SirsiDynix
Wireless access
Function: Archival coll, Computers for patron use, Copy machines, Electronic databases & coll, Govt ref serv, Handicapped accessible, ILL available, Microfiche/film & reading machines, Online cat, Online ref, Online searches, Photocopying/Printing, Pub access computers, Ref serv available, Ref serv in person, Tax forms, Wheelchair accessible
Partic in Lyrasis; OCLC Online Computer Library Center, Inc

Open Mon-Thurs 8-8, Fri 1-5, Sat & Sun 4-8
Restriction: Limited access for the pub

SAULSVILLE

J   SOUTHERN WEST VIRGINIA COMMUNITY & TECHNICAL COLLEGE*, Wyoming/McDowell Campus, Rte 97, 25876. (Mail add: PO Box 638, Pineville, 24874-0638). Tel: 304-294-8346. FAX: 304-294-8534. Web Site: www.southern.wvnet.edu. *Info Syst Tech,* Michael Hunter; E-mail: michaelh@southern.wvnet.edu
Highest Degree: Associate
Library Holdings: Bk Vols 350
Automation Activity & Vendor Info: (Cataloging) SirsiDynix; (Circulation) SirsiDynix; (OPAC) SirsiDynix
Database Vendor: Gale Cengage Learning, LearningExpress
Open Mon, Thurs & Fri 8-4:30, Tues & Wed 12:30-9

SHEPHERDSTOWN

C   SHEPHERD UNIVERSITY, Scarborough Library, 301 N King St, 25443. (Mail add: PO Box 5001, 25443-5001), SAN 317-8358. Circulation Tel: 304-876-5421, 304-876-5696. Interlibrary Loan Service Tel: 304-876-5691. Reference Tel: 304-876-5420. FAX: 304-876-0731. Web Site: www.shepherd.edu/libweb. *Dean,* Ann Watson; *Electronic Res/Coll Develop Coordr,* Rhonda Donaldson; *Instruction Coordr,* Laura A Neal; *Ref Coordr,* Ann W Henriksson; *Syst Coordr,* Yanhong Wang; Staff 15.25 (MLS 5.5, Non-MLS 9.75)
Founded 1871. Enrl 4,388; Fac 323; Highest Degree: Master
Jul 2011-Jun 2012 Income (Main Library Only) $1,308,235, Locally Generated Income $25,273, Parent Institution $1,282,962. Mats Exp $359,461, Books $73,344, Per/Ser (Incl. Access Fees) $34,315, Micro $11,017, AV Mat $5,299, Electronic Ref Mat (Incl. Access Fees) $235,486. Sal $680,023 (Prof $331,978)
Library Holdings: AV Mats 11,232; e-books 6,212; Microforms 86,009; Bk Vols 158,967; Per Subs 48,188
Special Collections: Folk Coll; Rare Book Coll; Shepherd Univ Archives; West Virginia Coll. State Document Depository; US Document Depository
Automation Activity & Vendor Info: (Acquisitions) Ex Libris Group; (Cataloging) Ex Libris Group; (Circulation) Ex Libris Group; (ILL) OCLC WorldCat; (OPAC) Ex Libris Group
Database Vendor: Agricola, American Chemical Society, CQ Press, EBSCOhost, Ex Libris Group, Foundation Center, Gale Cengage Learning, Grolier Online, IEEE (Institute of Electrical & Electronics Engineers), JSTOR, LexisNexis, netLibrary, OCLC FirstSearch, OCLC WorldCat, Project MUSE, ProQuest, PubMed
Wireless access
Partic in Lyrasis; OCLC Online Computer Library Center, Inc
Open Mon-Thurs 8-11, Fri 8-5, Sat 10-5, Sun 12-11
Friends of the Library Group

P   SHEPHERDSTOWN PUBLIC LIBRARY*, German & King Sts, 25443. (Mail add: PO Box 278, 25443-0278), SAN 329-7012. Tel: 304-876-2783. FAX: 304-876-6213. Web Site: www.lib.shepherdstown.wv.us. *Dir,* Hali Taylor; Staff 4 (MLS 1, Non-MLS 3)
Founded 1922
Library Holdings: Bk Titles 18,000; Per Subs 30
Automation Activity & Vendor Info: (Cataloging) TLC (The Library Corporation); (Circulation) TLC (The Library Corporation); (OPAC) TLC (The Library Corporation)
Partic in WV Libr Comm
Open Mon-Thurs 10-7, Sat 9-1
Friends of the Library Group

G   UNITED STATES FISH & WILDLIFE SERVICE*, National Conservation Training Center Library, 698 Conservation Way, 25443. Tel: 304-876-7304. Administration Tel: 304-876-7399. FAX: 304-876-7213. E-mail: library@fws.gov. Web Site: library.fws.gov. *Chief Librn,* Anne Post; E-mail: anne_post@fws.gov; *Tech Info Spec,* Eileen Hornbaker; Tel: 304-876-7687, E-mail: eileen_hornbaker@fws.gov; Staff 2 (MLS 1, Non-MLS 1)
Founded 1997
Oct 2011-Sept 2012. Mats Exp $650,000, Books $50,000, Per/Ser (Incl. Access Fees) $400,000, Electronic Ref Mat (Incl. Access Fees) $200,000
Library Holdings: e-journals 2,600; Electronic Media & Resources 105; Bk Titles 13,000; Bk Vols 15,000; Per Subs 120; Videos 200
Special Collections: Classic Conservation Coll; Environmental Education Coll; FWS National Digital Library. Oral History
Subject Interests: Ecology, Environ educ, Fisheries, Leadership, Natural res mgt, Training, Wildlife conserv
Automation Activity & Vendor Info: (Cataloging) OCLC; (ILL) OCLC; (OPAC) SirsiDynix
Database Vendor: Amigos Library Services, BioOne, Blackwell's, Cambridge Scientific Abstracts, EBSCOhost, Elsevier, HeinOnline, JSTOR, Nature Publishing Group, OCLC FirstSearch, OCLC WorldCat, ProQuest,

RefWorks, ScienceDirect, SerialsSolutions, SirsiDynix, Thomson - Web of Science, Wiley InterScience, WT Cox
Publications: Journal of Fish & Wildlife Management (Quarterly); North American Fauna (Annually)
Partic in Fedlink
Special Services for the Blind - Accessible computers
Open Mon, Tues & Thurs 6:30am-8pm, Tues & Fri 6:30-5

SHINNSTON

P   LOWE PUBLIC LIBRARY*, 40 Bridge St, 26431. SAN 317-8366. Tel: 304-592-1700. FAX: 304-592-1700. *Librn,* Deborah Starkey; E-mail: starkeyd@clark.lib.wv.us; Staff 1 (Non-MLS 1)
Pop 3,059; Circ 20,850
Library Holdings: Bk Vols 32,000; Per Subs 10
Automation Activity & Vendor Info: (Cataloging) Innovative Interfaces, Inc; (Circulation) Innovative Interfaces, Inc; (OPAC) Innovative Interfaces, Inc
Partic in Northern Library Network (NorLN)
Open Mon-Fri 12-5:30
Friends of the Library Group

SISTERSVILLE

P   SISTERSVILLE PUBLIC LIBRARY*, 518 Wells St, 26175. SAN 317-8374. Tel: 304-652-6701. FAX: 304-652-6701. Web Site: sistersville.lib.wv.us. *Dir,* Heather Diane Weekley; *Librn,* Sabrina Kyle; *Librn,* Margaret Arianne Roberts; Staff 2 (Non-MLS 2)
Founded 1907. Pop 11,320; Circ 13,101
Library Holdings: Bk Vols 18,000; Per Subs 37
Automation Activity & Vendor Info: (Cataloging) Innovative Interfaces, Inc; (Circulation) Innovative Interfaces, Inc; (OPAC) Innovative Interfaces, Inc
Wireless access
Mem of Moundsville-Marshall County Public Library
Partic in Northern Library Network (NorLN)
Open Mon & Fri 1-5, Tues & Thurs 1-8, Wed 10-3, Sat 10-2

SOUTH CHARLESTON

P   SOUTH CHARLESTON PUBLIC LIBRARY*, 312 Fourth Ave, 25303-1297. SAN 317-8382. Tel: 304-744-6561. FAX: 304-744-8808. E-mail: reference@scpl.wvnet.edu. Web Site: www.infospot.org. *Dir,* Jennifer Soule; *Asst Dir,* Linda Heddinger; Staff 6 (MLS 4, Non-MLS 2)
Founded 1943. Circ 172,383
Library Holdings: Bk Vols 71,733; Per Subs 70; Talking Bks 4,680; Videos 6,126
Subject Interests: WVa hist
Wireless access
Open Mon-Thurs 9-9, Fri 9-6, Sat 9-5, Sun (Oct-March) 1-5
Friends of the Library Group

M   THOMAS MEMORIAL HOSPITAL LIBRARY*, 4605 MacCorkle Ave SW, 25309. SAN 317-8390. Tel: 304-766-5377. FAX: 304-766-5925. Web Site: www.thomaswv.org. *Dir of Educ,* Stephanie Posey; E-mail: stephanie.posey@thomaswv.org
Library Holdings: Per Subs 10
Wireless access
Restriction: Staff use only
Friends of the Library Group

G   WEST VIRGINIA DEPARTMENT OF HEALTH & HUMAN RESOURCES*, Office of Laboratory Services, 167 11th Ave, 25303. SAN 327-6716. Tel: 304-558-3530. FAX: 304-558-2006.
Library Holdings: Bk Vols 325
Restriction: Staff use only

SPENCER

P   ROANE COUNTY PUBLIC LIBRARY*, 110 Parking Plaza, 25276. SAN 317-8420. Tel: 304-927-1130. FAX: 304-927-1196. Web Site: roanecountylibrary.org. *Dir,* Cindy Castle; Staff 6 (MLS 2, Non-MLS 4)
Founded 1952. Pop 15,952; Circ 48,968
Library Holdings: Bk Vols 39,000; Per Subs 35
Special Collections: West Virginia History, bks, per, memorabilia
Automation Activity & Vendor Info: (Cataloging) Innovative Interfaces, Inc; (Circulation) Innovative Interfaces, Inc; (OPAC) Innovative Interfaces, Inc
Partic in Mountain Library Network
Open Mon 9-6, Tues-Fri 9-5, Sat 9-12
Friends of the Library Group
Branches: 2
    GEARY LIBRARY-HEALTH CARE FACILITY, 98 Library Lane, Ste 1, Left Hand, 25251-9744. (Mail add: PO Box 90, Left Hand, 25251-0090). Tel: 304-565-4608. FAX: 304-565-4608. *Br Librn,* Sandra Morton; Staff 2 (Non-MLS 2)

Founded 1993. Pop 3,000; Circ 10,000
Library Holdings: DVDs 150; e-books 500; Large Print Bks 100; Bk Vols 10,000; Per Subs 25
Automation Activity & Vendor Info: (Cataloging) Innovative Interfaces, Inc - Millenium; (Circulation) Innovative Interfaces, Inc - Millenium; (ILL) Innovative Interfaces, Inc - Millenium; (OPAC) Innovative Interfaces, Inc - Millenium
Database Vendor: EBSCOhost
Function: Children's prog, Computer training, Computers for patron use, ILL available, Notary serv, Photocopying/Printing, Prog for children & young adult, Pub access computers, Senior computer classes, Summer reading prog, Web-catalog
Open Mon-Wed 9-5
Friends of the Library Group
    WALTON PUBLIC LIBRARY, Two Cunningham Lane, Walton, 25286, SAN 376-6101. Tel: 304-577-6071. FAX: 304-577-6071. *Br Librn,* Debbie Greathouse; Staff 3 (MLS 1, Non-MLS 2)
Library Holdings: Bk Vols 10,000; Per Subs 30
Database Vendor: EBSCOhost
Open Mon & Tues 12-6, Thurs 4-8, Sat 12-2
Friends of the Library Group

SUGAR GROVE

A   UNITED STATES NAVY*, NIOC Sugar Grove, WV Base Library, Bldg 63, Rm 208 NIOC, 26815. Tel: 304-249-6321. FAX: 304-249-6385. E-mail: library@mwrsugargrove.com. Web Site: www.mwrsugargrove.com. *Actg Mgr,* Dudley James Gregory; Staff 1 (Non-MLS 1)
Founded 1977
Library Holdings: Bk Titles 5,000
Subject Interests: Mil hist
Database Vendor: EBSCOhost

SUMMERSVILLE

P   SUMMERSVILLE PUBLIC LIBRARY*, 6201 Webster Rd, 26651. SAN 317-8447. Tel: 304-872-0844. FAX: 304-872-0845. E-mail: spl@mail.mln.lib.wv.us. *Dir,* Sarah Cranstoun
Pop 8,845; Circ 41,000
Library Holdings: AV Mats 500; Bk Vols 32,000; Per Subs 89; Talking Bks 275
Automation Activity & Vendor Info: (Cataloging) Innovative Interfaces, Inc; (Circulation) Innovative Interfaces, Inc; (OPAC) Innovative Interfaces, Inc
Wireless access
Partic in Mountain Library Network
Open Mon-Thurs 9-8, Fri 9-6, Sat 9-2

SUMMIT POINT

P   SOUTH JEFFERSON PUBLIC LIBRARY*, 49 Church St, 25446. (Mail add: PO Box 17, 25446-0017), SAN 328-1205. Tel: 304-725-6227. FAX: 304-728-2586. Web Site: www.youseemore.com/southjefferson. *Dir,* Dana S Jenkins; E-mail: jenkinsd@martin.lib.wv.us; Staff 1 (Non-MLS 1)
Founded 1984. Pop 14,063
Library Holdings: Bk Titles 10,000; Per Subs 16
Automation Activity & Vendor Info: (Cataloging) TLC (The Library Corporation); (Circulation) TLC (The Library Corporation); (OPAC) TLC (The Library Corporation)
Open Mon & Wed 10-6, Tues & Thurs 10-8, Sat 10-3, Sun 1-5

SUTTON

P   SUTTON PUBLIC LIBRARY*, 450 Fourth St, No C, 26601. SAN 317-8455. Tel: 304-765-7224. FAX: 304-765-7224. E-mail: splnot@clark.lib.wv.us. Web Site: www.sutton.lib.wv.us. *Dir,* Mary Jane Stewart; *Asst Librn,* Karen Bush; Staff 2 (Non-MLS 2)
Founded 1968. Pop 5,467; Circ 13,000
Library Holdings: High Interest/Low Vocabulary Bk Vols 50; Bk Vols 15,000; Per Subs 20; Talking Bks 300
Automation Activity & Vendor Info: (Cataloging) Innovative Interfaces, Inc; (Circulation) Innovative Interfaces, Inc; (OPAC) Innovative Interfaces, Inc
Partic in Northern Library Network (NorLN)
Open Mon-Fri 10-5, Sat 10-3
Friends of the Library Group

TERRA ALTA

P   TERRA ALTA PUBLIC LIBRARY, 701-B E State Ave, 26764-1204. SAN 317-8463. Tel: 304-789-2724. FAX: 304-789-2724. *Librn,* Ima Thomas; *Asst Librn,* Sharon Haskiell; *Asst Librn,* Linda Kope; *Asst Librn,* LaDonna Ringer
Founded 1972. Pop 11,734; Circ 96,595
Library Holdings: AV Mats 159; Bks on Deafness & Sign Lang 8; Large Print Bks 557; Bk Vols 67,994; Per Subs 86; Videos 1,136

Special Collections: Barbour, Marion & Taylor Counties & Census, microfilm; Grafton Sentinel, Preston County Journal, Preston County News & West Virginia Argus, microfilm; Obituaries
Subject Interests: Genealogy, Local hist
Wireless access
Function: ILL available, Newsp ref libr, Photocopying/Printing, Ref serv available, Telephone ref
Partic in Northern Library Network (NorLN)
Special Services for the Blind - Talking bks
Open Mon 4-8, Tues-Fri 8:30-5:30

THOMAS

P   MOUNTAINTOP LIBRARY*, Grant St, 26292. (Mail add: PO Box 217, 26292-0217), SAN 376-611X. Tel: 304-463-4582. FAX: 304-463-4582. Web Site: mountaintop.lib.wv.us. *Librn,* Inza E Wilcox; E-mail: wilcox_i@clark.lib.wv.us; Staff 1 (Non-MLS 1)
Library Holdings: Bk Vols 40,000; Per Subs 32
Automation Activity & Vendor Info: (Cataloging) Innovative Interfaces, Inc; (Circulation) Innovative Interfaces, Inc
Partic in Northern Library Network (NorLN)
Open Mon & Wed 8-5, Tues & Thurs 11-7, Fri 10-4

UNION

P   MONROE COUNTY PUBLIC LIBRARY*, 103 South St, 24983. (Mail add: PO Box 558, 24983-0558), SAN 317-8471. Tel: 304-772-3038. FAX: 304-772-4052. Web Site: www.monroe.lib.wv.us. *Librn,* Doris McCurdy; E-mail: mccurdy@mail.mln.lib.wv.us; *Asst Librn,* Ted Davis; Staff 2 (Non-MLS 2)
Founded 1947. Pop 11,272; Circ 22,125
Library Holdings: Bk Titles 25,000; Per Subs 16
Automation Activity & Vendor Info: (Cataloging) Innovative Interfaces, Inc; (Circulation) Innovative Interfaces, Inc; (OPAC) Innovative Interfaces, Inc
Open Mon-Wed & Fri 8:30-5:30, Sat 8:30-12
Friends of the Library Group

VALLEY HEAD

P   VALLEY HEAD PUBLIC LIBRARY*, US Rt 219 S, 26294. (Mail add: PO Box 98, 26294-0098), SAN 317-848X. Tel: 304-339-6071. FAX: 304-339-6071. *Dir,* Edna Mae Wood; E-mail: wood_mae@clark.lib.wv.us; Staff 4 (MLS 1, Non-MLS 3)
Founded 1975. Pop 2,000; Circ 5,987
Library Holdings: Bk Vols 10,000; Per Subs 32
Partic in Northern Library Network (NorLN)
Open Mon 1:30-9, Tues-Thurs 9:30-5
Friends of the Library Group

VIENNA

C   OHIO VALLEY UNIVERSITY LIBRARY*, One Campus View Dr, 26105-8000. SAN 317-8153. Tel: 304-865-6112. FAX: 304-865-6001. Web Site: www.ovu.edu/library. Staff 1 (MLS 1)
Founded 1960. Enrl 574; Fac 86; Highest Degree: Master
Jun 2005-May 2006. Mats Exp $64,774
Library Holdings: AV Mats 6,779; e-books 93,763; Bk Vols 34,000; Per Subs 142
Special Collections: Oral History
Subject Interests: Relig studies
Automation Activity & Vendor Info: (Cataloging) Innovative Interfaces, Inc; (Circulation) Innovative Interfaces, Inc - OCLC; (ILL) OCLC WorldCat; (OPAC) Innovative Interfaces, Inc
Database Vendor: EBSCOhost, Gale Cengage Learning, JSTOR, netLibrary, Wilson - Wilson Web
Wireless access
Partic in Appalachian Col Asn; Christian Col Libr; Midwest Libr Consortium; WV Libr Comm
Open Mon, Tues & Thurs 8am-11:30pm, Wed 8-5 & 8:30-11:30, Fri 8-5, Sat 1-5, Sun 2-5 & 8-11:30

P   VIENNA PUBLIC LIBRARY*, 2300 River Rd, 26105. SAN 317-8498. Tel: 304-295-7771. FAX: 304-295-7776. E-mail: info@viennapubliclibrary.org. Web Site: www.viennapubliclibrary.org. *Dir,* Alice C Thomas; *Ch,* Holly Van Camp; *Tech Serv,* Terry Mullins; Staff 4 (MLS 2, Non-MLS 2)
Founded 1959. Pop 10,862; Circ 115,000
Jul 2009-Jun 2010 Income $515,315, State $61,744, City $298,084, County $55,306, Locally Generated Income $41,054, Other $57,958. Mats Exp $62,165, Books $49,689, Per/Ser (Incl. Access Fees) $3,955, AV Mat $8,521. Sal $200,235 (Prof $132,887)
Library Holdings: Audiobooks 300; Braille Volumes 10; CDs 1,756; DVDs 1,600; Large Print Bks 17,773; Bk Titles 58,000; Bk Vols 58,295; Per Subs 80; Videos 1,200
Special Collections: West Virginia History Coll

Subject Interests: Local hist
Automation Activity & Vendor Info: (Cataloging) Innovative Interfaces, Inc; (Circulation) Innovative Interfaces, Inc; (OPAC) Innovative Interfaces, Inc; (Serials) Innovative Interfaces, Inc
Wireless access
Function: Web-catalog
Publications: Check It Out (Newsletter)
Partic in Mountain Library Network
Open Mon-Thurs 10-8, Fri & Sat 10-5
Friends of the Library Group

WAR

P   WAR PUBLIC LIBRARY*, Bldg 701, Berwind Lake Rd, 24892. (Mail add: PO Box 68, 24892-0068), SAN 320-4278. Tel: 304-875-4622. FAX: 304-875-4622. Web Site: war.lib.wv.us. *Dir,* Frances Blankenship; E-mail: francis_b@raleigh.lib.wv.us; Staff 2 (Non-MLS 2)
Library Holdings: Bk Vols 34,000
Partic in Mountain Library Network
Open Tues-Fri 10-6, Sat 11-4

WEBSTER SPRINGS

P   WEBSTER-ADDISON PUBLIC LIBRARY*, 331 S Main St, 26288. SAN 317-8528. Tel: 304-847-5764. FAX: 304-847-5764. *Dir,* Angela Powers
Founded 1972. Pop 9,000
Library Holdings: Bk Vols 21,000; Per Subs 10
Special Collections: West Virginia Coll
Automation Activity & Vendor Info: (Cataloging) Innovative Interfaces, Inc; (Circulation) Innovative Interfaces, Inc; (OPAC) Innovative Interfaces, Inc
Partic in Northern Library Network (NorLN)
Open Mon-Wed & Fri 8:30-4:30, Thurs 8:30-6, Sat 10-2
Friends of the Library Group

WEIRTON

P   MARY H WEIR PUBLIC LIBRARY*, 3442 Main St, 26062. SAN 317-8544. Tel: 304-797-8510. FAX: 304-797-8526. Web Site: weirton.lib.wv.us. *Dir,* Richard G Rekowski; *Asst Dir,* Pat Barnett; *Ref,* Lois Aleta Fundis; E-mail: fundisl@weirton.lib.wv.us; Staff 19 (MLS 3, Non-MLS 16)
Founded 1958. Pop 38,000
Library Holdings: Bk Vols 113,012; Per Subs 110
Special Collections: State Document Depository; US Document Depository
Subject Interests: Local hist
Automation Activity & Vendor Info: (Acquisitions) Innovative Interfaces, Inc; (Cataloging) Innovative Interfaces, Inc; (Circulation) Innovative Interfaces, Inc; (OPAC) Innovative Interfaces, Inc
Database Vendor: EBSCOhost
Wireless access
Publications: The Way Toward Literacy
Partic in Northern Library Network (NorLN)
Special Services for the Deaf - High interest/low vocabulary bks
Open Mon-Thurs 10-8, Fri & Sat 10-5
Friends of the Library Group

WELCH

P   MCDOWELL PUBLIC LIBRARY*, Welch Library, 90 Howard St, 24801. SAN 364-5517. Tel: 304-436-3070. FAX: 304-436-8079. Web Site: mcdowell.lib.wv.us. *Dir,* Donna Morgan; E-mail: ldonna@mail.mln.lib.wv.us; *Ch,* Judy Long; Staff 7 (MLS 1, Non-MLS 6)
Founded 1954. Pop 35,233
Library Holdings: Bk Vols 48,226; Per Subs 57
Special Collections: Medical Coll; Southern Appalachian Culture Coll; West Virginiana Coal Mining Coll
Automation Activity & Vendor Info: (Cataloging) Innovative Interfaces, Inc; (Circulation) Innovative Interfaces, Inc; (OPAC) Innovative Interfaces, Inc
Partic in Mountain Library Network
Open Mon-Fri 9-5
Friends of the Library Group
Branches: 3
BRADSHAW BRANCH, City Hall Bldg, Main St, Bradshaw, 24817. (Mail add: PO Box 498, Bradshaw, 24817-0498), SAN 364-5541. Tel: 304-967-5140. FAX: 304-967-5140. *Br Librn,* Iris Shelton; Staff 2 (Non-MLS 2)
Library Holdings: AV Mats 227; Bk Vols 19,005; Per Subs 16; Videos 149
Open Mon-Fri 9-5
Friends of the Library Group

IAEGER BRANCH, West Virginia Ave, Iaeger, 24844. (Mail add: PO Box 149, Iaeger, 24844-0149). Tel: 304-938-3825. FAX: 304-938-3825. *Br Librn,* Marilyn Fain; E-mail: fainm@raleigh.lib.wv.us; Staff 1 (Non-MLS 1)
   Library Holdings: AV Mats 50; Bk Vols 15,810; Per Subs 16; Videos 130
   Open Mon-Fri 10-5
   Friends of the Library Group
NORTHFORK BRANCH, Rte 52, Northfork, 24868. (Mail add: PO Box 229, Northfork, 24868-0229), SAN 364-572X. Tel: 304-862-4541. FAX: 304-862-4541. *Br Librn,* Donna Carter; Staff 1 (Non-MLS 1)
   Library Holdings: AV Mats 63; Bk Vols 11,001; Per Subs 10; Videos 152
   Open Mon-Fri 10-5
   Friends of the Library Group

WELLSBURG

P   BROOKE COUNTY PUBLIC LIBRARY*, 945 Main St, 26070. SAN 364-5754. Tel: 304-737-1551. FAX: 304-737-1010. E-mail: bcpl@lycos.com. Web Site: www.wellsburg.lib.wv.us/. *Dir,* Mary Kay Wallace; Staff 3 (Non-MLS 3)
   Founded 1898. Pop 24,000; Circ 64,000
   Jul 2009-Jun 2010 Income (Main Library Only) $207,996, State $100,056, City $7,440, County $98,500, Locally Generated Income $2,000. Mats Exp $58,600, Books $32,000, Per/Ser (Incl. Access Fees) $1,500, Manu Arch $9,000, Other Print Mats $1,000, AV Equip $9,000, AV Mat $4,000, Electronic Ref Mat (Incl. Access Fees) $2,100. Sal $180,190
   Library Holdings: Audiobooks 575; AV Mats 25; Bks on Deafness & Sign Lang 20; Braille Volumes 6; CDs 200; DVDs 350; Large Print Bks 1,000; Bk Titles 34,000; Per Subs 12; Talking Bks 700; Videos 250
   Special Collections: American Defenders of Bataan & Corregidor POW's, WWII, 1941-1945
   Subject Interests: Genealogy, Local hist, Tourism, World War II
   Automation Activity & Vendor Info: (Cataloging) Innovative Interfaces, Inc; (Circulation) Innovative Interfaces, Inc; (OPAC) Innovative Interfaces, Inc
   Wireless access
   Partic in Northern Library Network (NorLN)
   Open Mon-Thurs 10-7, Fri & Sat 9-5
   Friends of the Library Group
   Branches: 1
   FOLLANSBEE BRANCH, 844 Main St, Follansbee, 26037. (Mail add: PO Box 664, Follansbee, 26037-0664), SAN 364-5789. Tel: 304-527-0860. Information Services FAX: 304-527-3039. *Dir,* Mary Kay Wallace
   Pop 3,900
      Library Holdings: Bk Vols 15,500; Per Subs 12
      Open Mon-Thurs 11-7, Fri & Sat 9-1
      Friends of the Library Group

WEST LIBERTY

C   WEST LIBERTY UNIVERSITY*, Paul N Elbin Library, CSC No 135, 26074. (Mail add: PO Box 295, 26074-0295), SAN 317-8579. Tel: 304-336-8035. Circulation Tel: 304-336-8369. Interlibrary Loan Service Tel: 304-336-8352. Reference Tel: 304-336-8261. Toll Free Tel: 866-937-8542. FAX: 304-336-8186. Web Site: www.westliberty.edu. *Dir,* Cheryl Harshman; E-mail: harshmac@westliberty.edu; *Cat,* Jennifer D Cross; *Computer Serv,* Luann P Johnson; Staff 6 (MLS 3, Non-MLS 3)
   Founded 1932. Enrl 2,200; Highest Degree: Bachelor
   Library Holdings: Bk Titles 190,000; Bk Vols 195,000; Per Subs 125
   Special Collections: Nelle Krise Rare Book Room
   Subject Interests: Criminal justice, Educ, Music, Nursing
   Automation Activity & Vendor Info: (Cataloging) Ex Libris Group; (Circulation) Ex Libris Group; (ILL) OCLC; (OPAC) Ex Libris Group
   Database Vendor: Gale Cengage Learning, LexisNexis, OCLC FirstSearch, ProQuest
   Wireless access
   Partic in OCLC Online Computer Library Center, Inc
   Open Mon-Thurs 8am-11pm, Fri 8-4, Sat 12-4, Sun 5-11
   Friends of the Library Group

WEST UNION

P   DODDRIDGE COUNTY PUBLIC LIBRARY, 117 Court St, 26456. SAN 364-5819. Tel: 304-873-1941. FAX: 304-873-1324. *Librn,* Cathy J Ash; *Asst Librn,* Sheila McCutchan; Staff 2 (Non-MLS 2)
   Founded 1952. Pop 6,994; Circ 61,678
   Library Holdings: Bk Titles 29,818; Per Subs 54
   Special Collections: Doddridge County History; Farm Women Reading Coll; Local Genealogy; West Virginia History. Oral History
   Publications: Booklines (Newsletter)
   Partic in Northern Library Network (NorLN)
   Open Mon 8:30-7, Tues, Thurs & Fri 8:30-5, Sat 9-12

Branches: 1
CENTER POINT BRANCH, General Delivery, Center Point, 26339, SAN 364-5843. Tel: 304-782-2461. FAX: 304-782-2461. *Librn,* Cathy Ash; E-mail: ashcathy@clark.lib.wv.us; Staff 2 (Non-MLS 2)
   Founded 1978
   Library Holdings: Bk Titles 5,146; Per Subs 10
   Open Mon, Tues & Fri 8:30-4, Thurs 12-7, Sat 9-12

WESTON

P   LOUIS BENNETT PUBLIC LIBRARY*, 148 Court Ave, 26452. SAN 317-8587. Tel: 304-269-5151. FAX: 304-269-7332. E-mail: lbpl148@yahoo.com. Web Site: louisbennett.lib.wv.us. *Dir,* Karen H Enderle
   Founded 1923. Pop 17,223; Circ 32,390
   Library Holdings: Bk Vols 18,000; Per Subs 26
   Special Collections: Bennett Family Archive; West Virginia Coll
   Automation Activity & Vendor Info: (Cataloging) Follett Software; (Circulation) Follett Software; (OPAC) Follett Software
   Wireless access
   Open Mon-Fri 10-6, Sat 10-2
   Friends of the Library Group

S   WILLIAM SHARPE JR HOSPITAL*, Patients' Library, 936 Sharpe Hospital Rd, 26452. SAN 317-8595. Tel: 304-269-1210, Ext 399. FAX: 304-269-6235. *Mgr,* Heather Lovett
   Founded 1969
   Library Holdings: Bk Vols 4,600; Per Subs 25
   Open Mon-Fri 9-5

WHEELING

S   THE MUSEUMS OF OGLEBAY INSTITUTE LIBRARY*, Mansion Museum & Glass Museum, Oglebay Institute, The Burton Center, 26003. SAN 317-8617. Tel: 304-242-7272. FAX: 304-242-7287. Web Site: www.oionline.com. *Dir,* Christin L Stein; E-mail: cstein@oionline.com; *Asst Dir,* Mary Coffman; *Curator,* Holly H McCluskey; E-mail: hmccluskey@oionline.com; *Curator,* Travis Zeik; E-mail: tzeik@oionline.com. Subject Specialists: *Glass,* Holly H McCluskey
   Founded 1934
   Library Holdings: Bk Titles 750
   Special Collections: Brown Coll of Wheeling History, photogs; Wheeling & Belmont Bridge Company Papers; Wheeling City Directories
   Subject Interests: Decorative art, Local hist
   Function: Archival coll, For res purposes, ILL available, Photocopying/Printing
   Open Mon-Sat 10-5, Sun 12-5
   Restriction: Non-circulating, Not a lending libr, Open by appt only

GL   OHIO COUNTY LAW LIBRARY*, City-County Bldg, Rm 406, 1500 Chapline St, 26003. SAN 317-8625. Tel: 304-234-3780. FAX: 304-234-6437. Web Site: www.state.wv.us/wvsca. *Librn,* Nancy Chatlak; E-mail: nancychatlak@courtswv.org
   Founded 1919
   Library Holdings: Bk Vols 37,000
   Special Collections: Supreme Court Records & Briefs
   Open Mon-Fri 8:30-4
   Restriction: Non-circulating to the pub, Open to pub for ref only

P   OHIO COUNTY PUBLIC LIBRARY*, 52 16th St, 26003-3696. SAN 364-5878. Tel: 304-232-0244. FAX: 304-232-6848. E-mail: ocplweb@weirton.lib.wv.us. Web Site: wheeling.weirton.lib.wv.us. *Dir,* Dottie Thomas; *Asst Dir, Head, Tech Serv,* Louis Horacek; *Adult Serv, Head, Ref,* Amy Kastigar; Staff 21 (MLS 3, Non-MLS 18)
   Founded 1882. Pop 47,427; Circ 269,630
   Jul 2005-Jun 2006 Income $1,067,422, State $192,761, County $736,369, Other $138,292. Mats Exp $189,372, Books $126,944, Per/Ser (Incl. Access Fees) $18,271, AV Mat $34,347, Electronic Ref Mat (Incl. Access Fees) $9,810. Sal $612,926 (Prof $171,582)
   Library Holdings: AV Mats 8,315; Large Print Bks 6,980; Bk Titles 110,262; Bk Vols 128,097; Per Subs 304
   Special Collections: Wheeling-Ohio County History (Wheeling Coll)
   Automation Activity & Vendor Info: (Cataloging) Follett Software; (Circulation) Follett Software; (ILL) OCLC; (OPAC) Follett Software
   Database Vendor: Gale Cengage Learning, ProQuest
   Wireless access
   Publications: First Look at Books (Newsletter)
   Partic in Northern Library Network (NorLN)
   Open Mon-Thurs 9-9, Fri 10-5, Sat 9-5, Sun 1-5
   Bookmobiles: 1

M   OHIO VALLEY MEDICAL CENTER*, Hupp Medical Library, 2000 Eoff St, 26003. SAN 317-8633. Tel: 304-234-8771. FAX: 304-234-8330. Web Site: www.ohiovalleymedicalcenter.com. *Dir,* Harriet Kelly; E-mail: hkelly@ovrh.org; Staff 1 (MLS 1)

Founded 1955
Library Holdings: Bk Vols 6,500; Per Subs 95
Special Collections: Medical Classics; Osterman Psychiatric Coll
Subject Interests: Med, Med hist, Nursing, Psychiat
Automation Activity & Vendor Info: (Cataloging) TLC (The Library
Corporation); (Circulation) TLC (The Library Corporation); (OPAC) TLC
(The Library Corporation)
Open Mon-Fri 8:30-4:30
Restriction: Non-circulating to the pub

J   WEST VIRGINIA NORTHERN COMMUNITY COLLEGE LIBRARY*,
Learning Resource Center, 1704 Market St, 26003-3699. SAN 364-5932.
Tel: 304-233-5900, Ext 4252. FAX: 304-232-0965. Web Site:
www.northern.wvnet.edu/~library. *Dir,* Patricia Stroud; Tel: 304-723-2210,
Ext 5621, E-mail: pstroud@northern.wvnet.edu; Staff 2 (MLS 2)
Founded 1972. Enrl 1,856; Fac 55; Highest Degree: Associate
Jul 2006-Jun 2007 Income (Main Library and Branch(s)) $493,235. Mats
Exp $81,209, Books $10,511, Per/Ser (Incl. Access Fees) $22,433, Micro
$1,107, AV Mat $6,395, Electronic Ref Mat (Incl. Access Fees) $40,763.
Sal $312,277 (Prof $126,071)
Library Holdings: AV Mats 3,617; Bk Titles 30,626; Bk Vols 33,818; Per
Subs 151
Database Vendor: EBSCOhost, OCLC WorldCat, OVID Technologies,
ProQuest, Wilson - Wilson Web
Wireless access
Departmental Libraries:
NEW MARTINSVILLE CAMPUS, 141 Main St, New Martinsville, 26155,
SAN 317-8102. Tel: 304-455-4684, Ext 4727. *Dir,* Pat Stroud; E-mail:
pstroud@northern.wvnet.edu; *Librn,* Janet Corbitt; Tel: 304-455-4684,
Ext 4701, E-mail: jcorbitt@northern.wvnet.edu
Open Mon-Thurs 9-7, Fri 8:30-4:30

M   WHEELING HOSPITAL, INC*, Henry G Jepson Memorial Library, One
Medical Park, 26003. SAN 317-865X. Tel: 304-243-3308. FAX:
304-243-3329. *Librn,* Karen Leach; E-mail: kleach@wheelinghosp.com
Founded 1966
Library Holdings: Bk Titles 700; Per Subs 75
Open Mon-Fri 7:30-4

C   WHEELING JESUIT UNIVERSITY*, Bishop Hodges Library, 316
Washington Ave, 26003-6295. SAN 317-8641. Tel: 304-243-2226. FAX:
304-243-2466. E-mail: library@wju.edu. Web Site: www.wju.edu/library.
Assoc Librn, Libr Dir, Kelly Mummert; E-mail: kmummert@wju.edu; *Asst
Librn,* Paula Lestini; *ILL,* Barbara Julian; Staff 4.3 (MLS 2, Non-MLS 2.3)
Founded 1955. Enrl 1,258; Fac 73; Highest Degree: Doctorate
Jul 2009-Jun 2010. Mats Exp $178,950, Books $19,037, Per/Ser (Incl.
Access Fees) $65,713, Micro $5,565, AV Mat $4,803, Electronic Ref Mat
(Incl. Access Fees) $83,832
Library Holdings: AV Mats 830; e-books 144,698; e-journals 25,733;
Microforms 133,355; Bk Vols 148,383; Per Subs 311
Subject Interests: Local hist
Automation Activity & Vendor Info: (Acquisitions) Innovative Interfaces,
Inc - Millenium; (Cataloging) Innovative Interfaces, Inc - Millenium;
(Circulation) SirsiDynix; (Course Reserve) Innovative Interfaces, Inc -
Millenium; (ILL) OCLC; (OPAC) Innovative Interfaces, Inc - Millenium;
(Serials) Innovative Interfaces, Inc - Millenium
Database Vendor: ABC-CLIO, Alexander Street Press, Annual Reviews,
ARTstor, BioOne, CountryWatch, CQ Press, EBSCOhost, Facts on File,
Foundation Center, Gale Cengage Learning, H W Wilson, Innovative
Interfaces, Inc, JSTOR, LexisNexis, netLibrary, OHIONET, Project MUSE,
ProQuest, Wiley
Wireless access
Partic in Appalachian Col Asn; OCLC Online Computer Library Center,
Inc; OHIONET; Westchester Academic Library Directors Organization
(WALDO)

WHITE SULPHUR SPRINGS

P   WHITE SULPHUR SPRINGS PUBLIC LIBRARY*, 203 W Main St,
24986-2411. SAN 317-8676. Tel: 304-536-1171. FAX: 304-536-3801. Web
Site: whitesulphursprings.lib.wv.us. *Dir,* Julia Gillilan; E-mail:
julia.gillilan@mail.mln.lib.wv.us; Staff 2 (Non-MLS 2)
Founded 1917. Pop 6,689; Circ 24,000
Library Holdings: CDs 42; Large Print Bks 85; Bk Titles 18,000; Bk Vols
22,000; Per Subs 44; Talking Bks 100; Videos 80
Automation Activity & Vendor Info: (Cataloging) Innovative Interfaces,
Inc; (Circulation) Innovative Interfaces, Inc; (OPAC) Innovative Interfaces,
Inc
Function: Photocopying/Printing
Partic in Mountain Library Network
Open Mon-Fri 10-6, Sat 10-2
Friends of the Library Group

WILLIAMSON

J   SOUTHERN WEST VIRGINIA COMMUNITY & TECHNICAL
COLLEGE*, Williamson Campus Library, 1601 Armory Dr, 25661. SAN
364-5967. Tel: 304-236-7616. Interlibrary Loan Service Tel: 304-236-7638.
Administration Tel: 304-896-7345. FAX: 304-235-6043. Web Site:
www.southern.wvnet.edu. *Dir,* Kim Maynard; E-mail:
kimm@southern.wvnet.edu; Staff 1 (MLS 1)
Founded 1971. Enrl 365; Fac 17; Highest Degree: Associate
Library Holdings: AV Mats 2,744; Bk Vols 25,638; Per Subs 102
Special Collections: Appalachian Coll; Children's Coll. State Document
Depository
Automation Activity & Vendor Info: (Acquisitions) SirsiDynix;
(Cataloging) SirsiDynix; (Circulation) SirsiDynix; (ILL) OCLC Connexion;
(OPAC) SirsiDynix
Database Vendor: Gale Cengage Learning, OCLC WorldCat, SirsiDynix
Wireless access
Function: Computers for patron use, Copy machines, Electronic databases
& coll, ILL available, Magnifiers for reading, Online cat, Orientations, Pub
access computers
Partic in OCLC Online Computer Library Center, Inc
Special Services for the Deaf - Assisted listening device; Assistive tech
Special Services for the Blind - Accessible computers; Dragon Naturally
Speaking software; Networked computers with assistive software; Screen
reader software; ZoomText magnification & reading software
Open Mon-Thurs 7am-8pm, Fri 7-4:30, Sat 9-1
Restriction: Open to students, fac & staff

P   WILLIAMSON PUBLIC LIBRARY*, 101 Logan St, 25661. SAN
317-8684. Tel: 304-235-6029. FAX: 304-235-6029. Web Site:
williamsonlibrary.lib.wv.us. *Dir,* Position Currently Open; *Financial Dir,*
Larry Brown; E-mail: lbrown@cabell.lib.wv.us; *Librn,* Lola Henry; E-mail:
william@cabell.lib.wv.us; *Librn,* Elizabeth Lovett; E-mail:
william@cabell.lib.wv.us; Staff 4 (Non-MLS 4)
Pop 4,558; Circ 27,818
Jul 2005-Jun 2006 Income $43,191, State $18,523, City $11,823, Locally
Generated Income $2,845, Other $10,000. Mats Exp $39,723, Books
$4,503, Per/Ser (Incl. Access Fees) $316, Other Print Mats $86, Micro
$310, AV Mat $103, Electronic Ref Mat (Incl. Access Fees) $265. Sal
$23,276
Library Holdings: AV Mats 85; CDs 15; DVDs 25; Large Print Bks 150;
Bk Titles 17,000; Bk Vols 26,000; Per Subs 21; Videos 130
Automation Activity & Vendor Info: (Acquisitions) SIRSI-DRA;
(Cataloging) SIRSI-DRA; (Circulation) SIRSI-DRA; (Course Reserve)
SIRSI-DRA; (ILL) SIRSI-DRA; (Media Booking) SIRSI-DRA; (OPAC)
SIRSI-DRA; (Serials) SIRSI-DRA
Database Vendor: EBSCOhost
Wireless access
Open Mon-Fri 10-5

Date of Statistics: FY 2009
Population, 2004 Census: 5,688,040
Population Served by Public Libraries: 5,688,040
Total Volumes in Public Libraries: 20,056,755
    Volumes Per Capita: 3.53
Total Public Library Circulation: 65,478,078
    Circulation Per Capita: 11.51
Total Public Library Income (including Grants-in-Aid):
    $230,021,878
    Average Income: $594,370
    Source of Income: Local 63.8%; county 23.7%; state 2.6%;
    federal .4%; other 9.5%

Expenditures Per Capita: $37.95 (Includes public library
expenditures only)
Number of Bookmobiles in State: 10
Grants and Services to Public Libraries:
    Federal (LSTA): $3,162,937
    State Aid:
        Public Library Systems: $16,783,500
        Services to Blind & Physically Handicapped (through
        contract with the Milwaukee Public Library): $921,000
    Milwaukee Public Library (Interlibrary Loan Contract):
    $52,000
    Wisconsin Interlibrary Loan Service: $99,000. This and the
    Milwaukee Public Library contract above augment the ability of
    the State Reference & Loan Library to serve the needs of its
    statewide clientele.

ABBOTSFORD

P   ABBOTSFORD PUBLIC LIBRARY*, 203 Birch St, 54405. (Mail add: PO
Box 506, 54405-0506), SAN 317-8692. Tel: 715-223-3920. FAX:
715-223-4979. *Dir,* Erica Grunseth; E-mail: egrunseth@wvls.lib.wi.us
Founded 1903. Pop 1,900; Circ 15,500
Library Holdings: Bk Vols 12,000; Per Subs 40
Automation Activity & Vendor Info: (Acquisitions) SirsiDynix;
(Cataloging) SirsiDynix; (Circulation) SirsiDynix; (OPAC) SirsiDynix
Mem of Wisconsin Valley Library Service
Open Mon-Thurs 10-8, Fri 10-5, Sat 10-2

ADAMS

P   ADAMS COUNTY LIBRARY*, 569 N Cedar St, Ste 1, 53910-9800. SAN
317-8706. Tel: 608-339-4250. FAX: 608-339-4575. Web Site:
www.scls.lib.wi.us/acl/index.html. *Dir,* Dan C Calef; E-mail:
calef@scls.lib.wi.us; *Asst Dir,* Rene Elkington; E-mail:
renelk@scls.lib.wi.us; Staff 1 (MLS 1)
Founded 1974. Pop 18,000; Circ 53,165
Library Holdings: AV Mats 3,078; Large Print Bks 500; Bk Titles 23,400;
Bk Vols 23,560; Per Subs 107; Talking Bks 1,150
Automation Activity & Vendor Info: (Cataloging) SirsiDynix;
(Circulation) SirsiDynix; (OPAC) SirsiDynix
Wireless access
Partic in Wis Libr Consortium
Open Mon-Wed (Winter) 9-7, Thurs 1-7, Fri 9-5, Sat 10-2; Mon, Wed, Fri
(Summer) 9-5, Thurs 1-7, Sat 10-2
Friends of the Library Group

ALBANY

P   ALBANY PUBLIC LIBRARY*, 200 N Water St, 53502. (Mail add: PO
Box 329, 53502-0329), SAN 317-8714. Tel: 608-862-3491. E-mail:
albanypl@tds.net. Web Site: www.albanylibrary.org. *Dir,* Jacci Baker;
E-mail: jaccibakeralb@tds.net; Staff 5 (MLS 1, Non-MLS 4)
Founded 1964. Pop 1,360
Library Holdings: Bk Vols 17,000; Per Subs 80
Automation Activity & Vendor Info: (Cataloging) Follett Software;
(Circulation) Follett Software; (OPAC) Follett Software
Open Mon-Fri 1-7, Sat 9-12
Friends of the Library Group

ALGOMA

P   ALGOMA PUBLIC LIBRARY*, 406 Fremont St, 54201. SAN 317-8722.
Tel: 920-487-2295. FAX: 920-487-3941. E-mail: alg@mail.nfls.lib.wi.us.
Dir, Rita Schiesser; E-mail: rschiess@mail.nfls.lib.wi.us; Staff 4 (Non-MLS
4)
Founded 1922. Pop 3,348; Circ 100,145
Jan 2007-Dec 2007 Income $267,119, State $2,157, City $134,813, County
$96,118, Locally Generated Income $34,031. Mats Exp $31,712, Books

$23,812, Per/Ser (Incl. Access Fees) $3,400, AV Mat $4,300, Presv $200.
Sal $112,427 (Prof $105,667)
Library Holdings: AV Mats 6,270; Bk Vols 29,312; Per Subs 98; Videos
4,707
Subject Interests: Local hist
Automation Activity & Vendor Info: (Acquisitions) Infor Library &
Information Solutions; (Cataloging) Infor Library & Information Solutions;
(Circulation) Infor Library & Information Solutions; (ILL) Infor Library &
Information Solutions; (OPAC) Infor Library & Information Solutions
Mem of Nicolet Federated Library System
Partic in OWLSnet
Open Mon-Fri 10-7, Sat 10-3
Friends of the Library Group

ALMA

P   ALMA PUBLIC LIBRARY*, 312 Main St N, 54610-0277. SAN
325-3775. Tel: 608-685-3823. FAX: 608-685-4935. E-mail:
almapl@wrlsweb.org. *Librn,* Marie Marquardt
Pop 896
Library Holdings: Bk Vols 12,000; Per Subs 60
Automation Activity & Vendor Info: (Acquisitions) Follett Software;
(Cataloging) Follett Software; (Circulation) Follett Software
Mem of Winding Rivers Library System
Open Mon, Wed & Fri 10:30-7

ALTOONA

P   ALTOONA PUBLIC LIBRARY*, 1303 Lynn Ave, 54720-0278. SAN
324-7198. Tel: 715-839-5029. FAX: 715-830-5119. E-mail:
altoonapl@ifls.lib.wi.us. Web Site: www.altoonapubliclibrary.org. *Dir,* Mary
Vernau; E-mail: maryvernau@ifls.lib.wi.us; *Asst Dir,* Carol Hillman;
E-mail: carolh@ifls.lib.wi.us; *Asst Librn,* Dianne Dunn; E-mail:
diannedunn@ifls.lib.wi.us; *Youth Serv,* Regina Arndt; E-mail:
reginaarndt@ifls.lib.wi.us; Staff 4 (MLS 1, Non-MLS 3)
Pop 8,691; Circ 34,764
Library Holdings: Audiobooks 3,090; DVDs 5,310; Bk Vols 45,000; Per
Subs 135
Open Mon-Thurs 9-8, Fri 9-6, Sat 9-5
Friends of the Library Group

AMERY

P   AMERY PUBLIC LIBRARY*, 801 Keller Ave S, 54001-1096. SAN
376-673X. Tel: 715-268-9340. FAX: 715-268-8659. E-mail:
amerypl@spacestar.net. *Librn,* Barbara Sorenson
Library Holdings: Bk Vols 62,000; Per Subs 65
Automation Activity & Vendor Info: (Acquisitions) Follett Software;
(Cataloging) Follett Software; (Circulation) Follett Software
Mem of Indianhead Federated Library System
Open Mon & Fri 10-8, Tues & Wed 10-6, Thurs 10-2, Sat 9-1
Friends of the Library Group

AMHERST

P   LETTIE W JENSEN PUBLIC LIBRARY*, 278 N Main St, 54406-9101. Tel: 715-824-5510. E-mail: amherstlibrary@amherst.k12.wi.us. *Dir,* Kristi Pennebecker
Pop 964; Circ 22,367
Library Holdings: AV Mats 1,839; Bk Titles 19,421; Per Subs 106; Talking Bks 483
Automation Activity & Vendor Info: (Cataloging) Follett Software; (Circulation) Follett Software; (OPAC) Follett Software
Mem of South Central Library System
Open Mon 9-12 & 2-5, Tues & Thurs 2-5, Wed 2-8, Sat 9-1
Friends of the Library Group

ANTIGO

P   ANTIGO PUBLIC LIBRARY*, 617 Clermont St, 54409-1894. SAN 317-8749. Tel: 715-623-3724. FAX: 715-627-2317. E-mail: antigopl@wvls.lib.wi.us. Web Site: www.antigopl.org. *Dir,* Cynthia Taylor; E-mail: ctaylor@wvls.lib.wi.us; *Outreach Librn,* Vicky Marx; E-mail: vmarx@antigopl.org; *ILL,* Elizabeth Merry; E-mail: emerry@antigopl.org; Staff 1 (MLS 1)
Founded 1900. Pop 20,618; Circ 169,420
Library Holdings: Bk Vols 72,000; Per Subs 180
Automation Activity & Vendor Info: (Circulation) Horizon; (Course Reserve) Horizon
Database Vendor: EBSCO Information Services
Mem of Wisconsin Valley Library Service
Partic in Wisconsin Valley Library Service
Open Mon-Thurs 9-8, Fri 9-5, Sat 9-4
Friends of the Library Group
Branches: 3
ELCHO BRANCH, Hwy 45 N, Elcho, 54428. (Mail add: PO Box 800, Elcho, 54428-0800). Tel: 715-275-3225. *Librn,* Pat Brunner; E-mail: pbrunner@antigopl.org
   Library Holdings: Bk Titles 1,500
   Open Mon 12-4, Wed 10-6, Thurs 3-6
ELTON BRANCH, W4904, Hwy 64, Elton, 54430-0046. Tel: 715-882-3881. *Br Mgr,* Kristy Heistad
   Library Holdings: Bk Titles 1,500
   Open Mon 11-7, Tues 1-6, Wed 10-6, Fri 9-5
WHITE LAKE BRANCH, White Lake Village Hall, 615 School St, White Lake, 54491. (Mail add: PO Box 8, White Lake, 54491-0008). Tel: 715-882-8501. *Br Mgr,* Vicki Wallace
   Library Holdings: Bk Titles 1,500
   Open Tues 10:30-5:30, Wed 3-7

APPLETON

P   APPLETON PUBLIC LIBRARY*, 225 N Oneida St, 54911-4780. SAN 317-8765. Tel: 920-832-6170. Circulation Tel: 920-832-6179. Reference Tel: 920-832-6173. FAX: 920-832-6182. Web Site: www.apl.org. *Dir,* Terry P Dawson; E-mail: tdawson@apl.org; *Asst Dir,* Colleen T Rortvedt; Tel: 920-832-6168, E-mail: crortvedt@apl.org; *Bus Mgr,* Tony Wieczorek; E-mail: twieczorek@apl.org; *Tech Coordr,* Kurt Riechers; E-mail: kriechers@apl.org; *Ch,* Carole De Jardin; Tel: 920-832-6187, E-mail: cdejardin@apl.org; *Circ,* Vicki Lenz; E-mail: vienz@apl.org; *ILL,* Karen Probst; Tel: 920-832-6175, E-mail: kprobst@apl.org; *Ref,* Margaret Shriver; E-mail: mshriver@apl.org; *Tech Serv,* Michael Nitz; Tel: 920-832-6184, E-mail: mnitz@apl.org; Staff 17 (MLS 17)
Founded 1897. Pop 110,000; Circ 1,387,981
Jan 2008-Dec 2008 Income $4,303,161, City $3,627,257, County $675,904. Mats Exp $528,335, Books $340,284, Per/Ser (Incl. Access Fees) $29,903, Micro $8,432, AV Mat $122,139, Electronic Ref Mat (Incl. Access Fees) $27,577. Sal $2,341,985 (Prof $435,282)
Library Holdings: Bk Titles 307,600; Bk Vols 402,883; Per Subs 600
Special Collections: State Document Depository
Subject Interests: Local hist
Automation Activity & Vendor Info: (Acquisitions) Innovative Interfaces, Inc - OCLC; (Cataloging) Innovative Interfaces, Inc; (Circulation) Innovative Interfaces, Inc; (ILL) OCLC WorldCat; (OPAC) Innovative Interfaces, Inc
Database Vendor: Baker & Taylor, BWI, Gale Cengage Learning, netLibrary, Newsbank, OCLC FirstSearch, OCLC WorldCat
Wireless access
Function: Art exhibits, Audio & video playback equip for onsite use, AV serv, CD-ROM, Digital talking bks, Games & aids for the handicapped, Govt ref serv, Handicapped accessible, Home delivery & serv to Sr ctr & nursing homes, Homebound delivery serv, ILL available, Magnifiers for reading, Orientations, Outside serv via phone, mail, e-mail & web, Photocopying/Printing, Prog for adults, Prog for children & young adult, Ref serv available, Serves mentally handicapped consumers, Spoken cassettes & CDs, Summer reading prog, Telephone ref, VHS videos, Wheelchair accessible
Mem of Outagamie Waupaca Library System
Partic in OCLC Online Computer Library Center, Inc; OWLSnet

Special Services for the Deaf - TDD equip; TTY equip
Special Services for the Blind - Aids for in-house use; Assistive/Adapted tech devices, equip & products; Audio mat; Bks & mags in Braille, on rec, tape & cassette; Bks on cassette; Bks on CD; Braille bks; Children's Braille; Computer with voice synthesizer for visually impaired persons; Large print bks; Low vision equip; Magnifiers; Reader equip; Talking bk & rec for the blind cat; Talking bks; Volunteer serv
Open Mon-Thurs 9-9, Fri 9-6, Sat 9-5, Sun 1-5
Friends of the Library Group

J   FOX VALLEY TECHNICAL COLLEGE*, William M Sirek Educational Resource Center, 1825 N Bluemound Dr, 54914. (Mail add: PO Box 2277, 54912-2277), SAN 317-8773. Tel: 920-735-5600, 920-735-5746. Reference Tel: 920-735-2416. FAX: 920-735-4870. E-mail: library@fvtc.edu. Web Site: www.fvtc.edu/library. *Dir,* Karen Parson; Tel: 920-735-4762, E-mail: parson@fvtc.edu; *Res,* Henry Beno; Tel: 920-735-5747; *Tech Serv,* Mary Beth Kelley; Tel: 920-735-4836
Founded 1967. Enrl 4,405; Fac 285
Library Holdings: Bk Vols 50,000; Per Subs 303
Subject Interests: Agr, Environ studies, Med
Automation Activity & Vendor Info: (Acquisitions) Ex Libris Group; (Cataloging) Ex Libris Group; (Circulation) Ex Libris Group; (Course Reserve) Ex Libris Group; (ILL) Ex Libris Group; (Media Booking) Ex Libris Group; (OPAC) Ex Libris Group; (Serials) Ex Libris Group
Database Vendor: EBSCOhost, ProQuest
Open Mon-Thurs (Winter) 7:15am-10pm, Fri 7:15-4:30, Sat 10-2; Mon-Thurs (Summer) 7:30-9, Fri 7:30-1:30

C   LAWRENCE UNIVERSITY, Seeley G Mudd Library, 113 S Lawe St, 54911-5683. SAN 364-5991. Circulation Tel: 920-832-6750. Interlibrary Loan Service Tel: 920-832-6758. Reference Tel: 920-832-6752. FAX: 920-832-6967. E-mail: reference@lawrence.edu. Web Site: www.lawrence.edu/library. *Dir,* Peter J Gilbert; Tel: 920-832-7353, E-mail: peter.j.gilbert@lawrence.edu; *Dir of Tech Serv,* Jill Thomas; *Music Librn, Ref Librn,* Antoinette Powell; Tel: 920-832-6995; *Ref Librn,* Gretchen Revie; *Ref Librn, Web Librn,* Julie Fricke; *Supvr, Circ,* Cynthia Patterson; *Syst Coordr,* Kathy Isaacson; *Visual Res,* Colette Brautigam; Staff 15 (MLS 6, Non-MLS 9)
Founded 1847. Enrl 1,441; Fac 140; Highest Degree: Bachelor
Library Holdings: Bk Vols 395,032; Per Subs 1,787
Special Collections: Lincoln Coll. State Document Depository; US Document Depository
Automation Activity & Vendor Info: (Acquisitions) Ex Libris Group; (Cataloging) Ex Libris Group; (Circulation) Ex Libris Group; (Course Reserve) Ex Libris Group; (OPAC) Ex Libris Group; (Serials) Ex Libris Group
Database Vendor: EBSCOhost, Gale Cengage Learning, ISI Web of Knowledge, JSTOR, LexisNexis, Marquis Who's Who, Modern Language Association, Nature Publishing Group, Newsbank-Readex, OCLC FirstSearch, OCLC WorldCat, Oxford Online, Project MUSE, ProQuest, PubMed, RefWorks
Wireless access
Partic in Fox Valley Library Council; NE Wis Intertype Librs, Inc; OCLC Online Computer Library Center, Inc; Wisconsin Library Services

L   OUTAGAMIE COUNTY LAW LIBRARY*, 320 S Walnut St, 54911. SAN 327-8360. Tel: 920-832-5149. FAX: 920-832-5115. *Librn,* Lynn Driessen
Library Holdings: Bk Vols 4,000
Open Mon-Fri 8-4:30

P   OUTAGAMIE WAUPACA LIBRARY SYSTEM*, 225 N Oneida, 54911-4780. SAN 317-879X. Tel: 920-832-6190. FAX: 920-832-6422. Web Site: www.infosoup.org, www.owlsnet.info, www.owlsweb.info. *Dir,* Richard Krumwiede; E-mail: rick@mail.owls.lib.wi.us; *Automation Syst Coordr,* Gerri Moeller; *Cat Librn,* Holly Ledvina; *Continuing Education & Consulting Librn,* Leslie Farrell; *Electronic Res Librn,* Evan Bend; *Web Coordr,* Beth Carpenter; Staff 9 (MLS 7, Non-MLS 2)
Founded 1975
Jan 2007-Dec 2007 Income $3,462,842, State $628,075, Federal $14,500, County $2,012,866, Locally Generated Income $807,401. Mats Exp $110,328, Books $1,000, Per/Ser (Incl. Access Fees) $2,250, Electronic Ref Mat (Incl. Access Fees) $107,078. Sal $549,658
Automation Activity & Vendor Info: (Acquisitions) Innovative Interfaces, Inc; (Cataloging) Innovative Interfaces, Inc; (Circulation) Innovative Interfaces, Inc; (ILL) Innovative Interfaces, Inc; (OPAC) Innovative Interfaces, Inc; (Serials) Innovative Interfaces, Inc
Database Vendor: BookLetters LLC, Gale Cengage Learning, LearningExpress, netLibrary, Newsbank, OCLC WorldCat, Overdrive, Inc, ProQuest
Member Libraries: Appleton Public Library; Black Creek Village Library; Clintonville Public Library; Hortonville Public Library; Iola Village Library; Kaukauna Public Library; Kimberly Public Library; Marion Public Library; Muehl Public Library; Neuschafer Community Library; New London Public Library; Scandinavia Public Library; Shiocton Public

Library; Sturm Memorial Library; Waùpaca Area Public Library; Weyauwega Public Library
Partic in OWLSnet

M　SAINT ELIZABETH HOSPITAL*, Health Science Library, 1506 S Oneida St, 54915. SAN 317-8803. Tel: 920-738-2324. Administration Tel: 920-738-2325. FAX: 920-831-1265. *Dir, Libr Serv,* Mary M Bayorgeon; E-mail: mbayorgeon@affinityhealth.org; Staff 3 (MLS 2, Non-MLS 1)
Founded 1968
Library Holdings: e-books 300; e-journals 7,000; Bk Titles 3,000; Bk Vols 3,150; Per Subs 350
Subject Interests: Consumer health, Hospital admin, Med, Nursing
Automation Activity & Vendor Info: (Cataloging) EOS International; (Circulation) EOS International; (OPAC) EOS International; (Serials) EOS International
Database Vendor: Blackwell's, EBSCOhost, Gale Cengage Learning, OVID Technologies, PubMed, SerialsSolutions, STAT!Ref (Teton Data Systems)
Partic in Docline; Fox River Valley Area Library Consortium; Fox Valley Library Council; National Network of Libraries of Medicine
Open Mon-Fri 8-4:30

ARCADIA

P　ARCADIA FREE PUBLIC LIBRARY*, 406 E Main St, 54612-1396. SAN 317-8811. Tel: 608-323-7505. FAX: 608-323-7505. E-mail: rkdpubli@wrlsweb.org. *Dir,* Carol Krett; *Asst Librn,* Jennifer Losinski
Founded 1899. Pop 2,159; Circ 38,035
Library Holdings: Bk Vols 17,000; Per Subs 88
Automation Activity & Vendor Info: (Cataloging) Horizon; (Circulation) Horizon; (OPAC) Horizon
Wireless access
Mem of Winding Rivers Library System
Open Mon & Thurs 12-8, Tues, Wed & Fri 9-5, Sat 9-12

ARGYLE

P　ARGYLE PUBLIC LIBRARY*, 401 E Milwaukee, 53504. (Mail add: PO Box 250, 53504-0250), SAN 317-882X. Tel: 608-543-3113. E-mail: arglibr@mhtc.net. Web Site: www.swls.org/member.ar.html. *Dir,* Jacqueline A Whitmar; Tel: 608-543-3193, E-mail: jwhitmar@swls.org
Pop 479; Circ 4,726
Library Holdings: Bk Vols 6,703; Per Subs 20
Special Collections: Argyle Atlas Newspaper Coll (bound issues beginning in 1887)
Mem of Southwest Wisconsin Library System
Open Tues 2-8, Wed 4-8, Thurs 6-8, Fri 9:30-11:30 & 2-5, Sat 9:30-11:30

ARPIN

P　LESTER PUBLIC LIBRARY OF ARPIN*, 8091 County Rd E, 54410-9602. (Mail add: PO Box 36, 54410-0036), SAN 317-8838. Tel: 715-652-2273. FAX: 715-652-6262. E-mail: arpinpl@tds.net. Web Site: www.arpinpl.org.
Founded 1951
Library Holdings: Bk Vols 9,000; Per Subs 40
Wireless access
Mem of South Central Library System
Open Mon & Wed 4-8, Tues 12-8, Thurs & Sat 9-12, Fri 9-5

ASHLAND

L　ASHLAND COUNTY LAW LIBRARY, Courthouse, Rm 304, 201 W Main St, 54806. Tel: 715-682-7016. FAX: 715-682-7919. *In Charge,* Kathleen Colgrove
Jan 2012-Dec 2012 Income $5,000
Library Holdings: Bk Vols 6,500; Per Subs 15
Open Mon-Fri 8-4

P　NORTHERN WATERS LIBRARY SERVICE*, 3200 E Lakeshore Dr, 54806-2510. SAN 317-8854. Tel: 715-682-2365. Toll Free Tel: 800-228-5684. FAX: 715-685-2704. E-mail: nwls@nwls.lib.wi.us. Web Site: www.nwls.wislib.org. *Dir,* Jim Trojanowski; Tel: 715-682-2365, Ext 11, E-mail: jtrojanowski@nwls.lib.wi.us; *Asst Dir,* Michael Sheehan; Tel: 715-682-2365, Ext 12, E-mail: msheehan@nwls.lib.wi.us; *Bus Mgr,* Linda Stobbe; Tel: 715-682-2365, Ext 14, E-mail: lstobbe@nwls.lib.wi.us; *ILL,* Linda Bailen; E-mail: lbailen@nwls.lib.wi.us; *Network Adminr,* Michael Sauvola; E-mail: msauvola@nwls.lib.wi.us
Founded 1972. Pop 140,000; Circ 65,081
Automation Activity & Vendor Info: (Acquisitions) Innovative Interfaces, Inc - Millenium; (Cataloging) Innovative Interfaces, Inc - Millenium; (Circulation) Innovative Interfaces, Inc - Millenium; (ILL) Innovative Interfaces, Inc - Millenium; (OPAC) Innovative Interfaces, Inc - Millenium; (Serials) Innovative Interfaces, Inc - Millenium
Database Vendor: Innovative Interfaces, Inc INN - View, Marcive, Inc

Wireless access
Publications: Streams (Online only)
Member Libraries: Bad River Public Tribal Library; Bayfield Carnegie Library; Ben Guthrie-Lac Du Flambeau Public Library; Boulder Junction Public Library; Drummond Public Library; Evelyn Goldberg Briggs Memorial Library; Forest Lodge Library; Frank B Koller Memorial Library; Grantsburg Public Library; Hurley Public Library; Lac Courte Oreilles Ojibwa Community College Library; Land O'Lakes Public Library; Larsen Family Public Library; Legion Memorial Library; Madeline Island Public Library; Mercer Public Library; Phelps Public Library; Plum Lake Public Library; Presque Isle Community Library; Shell Lake Public Library; Sherman & Ruth Weiss Community Library; Spooner Memorial Library; Superior Public Library; Walter E Olson Memorial Library; Washburn Public Library; Winter Public Library

C　NORTHLAND COLLEGE*, Dexter Library, 1411 Ellis Ave, 54806-3999. SAN 317-8846. Tel: 715-682-1279. Interlibrary Loan Service Tel: 715-682-1297. Administration Tel: 715-682-1302. FAX: 715-682-1693. Web Site: library.northland.edu. *Dir, Instrul Serv Librn, Ref Serv,* Julia Trojanowski; E-mail: jtrojan@northland.edu; *Acq Librn, ILL, Ser Librn,* Elizabeth Madsen-Genszler; E-mail: emadsen-genszler@northland.edu; *Cat Librn, Syst Adminr,* Sharon Youngberg; Tel: 715-682-1298, E-mail: syoungberg@northland.edu; Staff 3 (MLS 2, Non-MLS 1)
Founded 1892. Enrl 600; Fac 54; Highest Degree: Bachelor
Jul 2009-Jun 2010 Income $414,281, Parent Institution $359,281, Other $55,000. Mats Exp $158,000, Books $55,000, Per/Ser (Incl. Access Fees) $51,000, Micro $12,000, AV Mat $10,000, Electronic Ref Mat (Incl. Access Fees) $30,000. Sal $117,000 (Prof $89,000)
Library Holdings: DVDs 200; Bk Titles 64,000; Bk Vols 74,000; Per Subs 240; Videos 1,200
Subject Interests: Environ studies, Native Am studies
Automation Activity & Vendor Info: (Acquisitions) Ex Libris Group; (Cataloging) Ex Libris Group; (Circulation) Ex Libris Group; (Course Reserve) Ex Libris Group; (ILL) OCLC; (OPAC) Ex Libris Group; (Serials) Ex Libris Group
Database Vendor: Alexander Street Press, Annual Reviews, Bowker, Checkpoint Systems, Inc, EBSCOhost, Ex Libris Group, ISI Web of Knowledge, JSTOR, LexisNexis, McGraw-Hill, OCLC FirstSearch, OCLC WorldCat, ProQuest
Wireless access
Partic in Wisconsin Library Services
Open Mon-Thurs 8am-11pm, Fri 8-5, Sat Noon-4, Sun Noon-11

P　VAUGHN PUBLIC LIBRARY*, 502 W Main St, 54806. SAN 317-8862. Tel: 715-682-7060. FAX: 715-682-7185. Web Site: nwls.wislib.org/about/libas.htm, vpl.coawi.org. *Dir,* Shirley Miller; Tel: 715-682-7060, Ext 22, E-mail: smiller@coawi.org; Staff 6 (MLS 1, Non-MLS 5)
Founded 1888. Pop 13,109; Circ 137,210
Library Holdings: AV Mats 4,807; CDs 1,050; DVDs 1,475; Bk Titles 27,450; Bk Vols 31,132; Per Subs 111; Videos 1,072
Automation Activity & Vendor Info: (Cataloging) Innovative Interfaces, Inc; (Circulation) Innovative Interfaces, Inc; (OPAC) Innovative Interfaces, Inc
Wireless access
Partic in Merlin
Open Mon-Thurs 9-8, Fri 9-5, Sat 9-1
Friends of the Library Group

CM　WISCONSIN INDIANHEAD TECHNICAL COLLEGE*, Ashland Campus Learning Resource Center, 2100 Beaser Ave, 54806. Tel: 715-682-4591, Ext 3108. Toll Free Tel: 800-243-9482, Ext 3108. FAX: 715-682-8040. Web Site: www.witc.edu. *Libr Tech,* Dee Barabe; E-mail: dee.barabe@witc.edu; *Libr Tech,* Melissa Weber
Library Holdings: AV Mats 2,000; Bk Titles 6,300; Per Subs 78
Automation Activity & Vendor Info: (Cataloging) Gateway; (Circulation) Gateway; (OPAC) Gateway
Open Mon-Thurs 7:30-7, Fri 7:30-4

AUGUSTA

P　AUGUSTA MEMORIAL PUBLIC LIBRARY*, 113 N Stone St, 54722-6000. (Mail add: PO Box 474, 54722-0474), SAN 326-1204. Tel: 715-286-2070. FAX: 715-286-5367. E-mail: augustalibrary@ifls.lib.wi.us. Web Site: augustalibrary.org. *Dir,* Leslie LaRose; *Asst Librn,* David Fleiger; *Asst Librn,* Eileen Stensen; Staff 1 (Non-MLS 1)
Pop 1,550; Circ 28,750
Library Holdings: Large Print Bks 582; Bk Vols 16,433; Per Subs 101; Talking Bks 976; Videos 1,374
Automation Activity & Vendor Info: (Acquisitions) Innovative Interfaces, Inc; (Cataloging) Innovative Interfaces, Inc; (Circulation) Innovative Interfaces, Inc; (Course Reserve) Innovative Interfaces, Inc; (ILL) Innovative Interfaces, Inc; (Media Booking) Innovative Interfaces, Inc; (OPAC) Innovative Interfaces, Inc; (Serials) Innovative Interfaces, Inc
Mem of Indianhead Federated Library System

Open Tues-Wed 9-7, Thurs-Sat 11-5
Friends of the Library Group

BALDWIN

P   BALDWIN PUBLIC LIBRARY*, 400 Cedar St, 54002-0475. (Mail add:
PO Box 475, 54002-0475), SAN 317-8870. Tel: 715-684-3813. FAX:
715-684-5115. E-mail: baldwinlibrary@ifls.lib.wi.us. Web Site:
www.baldwinlibrary.org. *Dir,* Rebecca Dixen; E-mail: dixen@ifls.lib.wi.us;
ILL, Marna Grafenstein; E-mail: baldwinill@ifls.lib.wi.us; *Youth Serv,* Judy
Jensen; E-mail: judyj@ifls.lib.wi.us; Staff 3.3 (MLS 1, Non-MLS 2.3)
Founded 1941. Pop 7,000; Circ 90,000
Library Holdings: Bk Titles 25,000; Per Subs 80
Automation Activity & Vendor Info: (Acquisitions) Innovative Interfaces,
Inc; (Cataloging) Innovative Interfaces, Inc; (Circulation) Innovative
Interfaces, Inc
Database Vendor: EBSCOhost, ProQuest
Wireless access
Function: Adult bk club, Audiobks via web, Bilingual assistance for
Spanish patrons, Bk club(s), Bks on cassette, Bks on CD, Children's prog,
Computers for patron use, Copy machines, e-mail serv, Electronic
databases & coll, Equip loans & repairs, Fax serv, Free DVD rentals,
Games & aids for the handicapped, Handicapped accessible, Holiday prog,
ILL available, Instruction & testing, Large print keyboards, Magnifiers for
reading, Mail & tel request accepted, Music CDs, Newsp ref libr, Online
cat, Online ref, Outside serv via phone, mail, e-mail & web, OverDrive
digital audio bks, Photocopying/Printing, Preschool outreach, Prof lending
libr, Prog for adults, Prog for children & young adult, Pub access
computers, Ref & res, Senior outreach, Spoken cassettes & CDs, Spoken
cassettes & DVDs, Story hour, Summer reading prog, Tax forms, Teen
prog, Telephone ref, VHS videos, Web-catalog, Wheelchair accessible
Mem of Indianhead Federated Library System
Special Services for the Deaf - Assistive tech; Closed caption videos
Special Services for the Blind - Assistive/Adapted tech devices, equip &
products; Bks available with recordings; Bks on cassette; Bks on CD;
Cassette playback machines; Cassettes; Computer with voice synthesizer
for visually impaired persons; Copier with enlargement capabilities; Large
print & cassettes; Large print bks; Large screen computer & software;
Magnifiers; PC for handicapped; Recorded bks; Screen reader software;
ZoomText magnification & reading software
Open Mon & Fri 1-5, Tues-Thurs 10-8, Sat 10-1
Friends of the Library Group

BALSAM LAKE

P   BALSAM LAKE PUBLIC LIBRARY*, 404 Main St, 54810-7261. (Mail
add: PO Box 340, 54810-0340), SAN 317-8889. Tel: 715-485-3215. FAX:
715-485-3215. E-mail: balsamlakepl@ifls.lib.wi.us. *Dir,* Patricia Olson;
Asst Dir, Jeanne Kahl
Founded 1946. Pop 1,000; Circ 12,779
Library Holdings: Bk Vols 18,000; Per Subs 40
Special Collections: Native American Materials Coll; Wisconsin Coll
Mem of Indianhead Federated Library System
Open Mon 12-8, Tues, Fri & Sat 10-2, Wed 10-8

BARABOO

P   BARABOO PUBLIC LIBRARY*, 230 Fourth Ave, 53913. SAN 317-8897.
Tel: 608-356-6166. FAX: 608-355-2779. Web Site: www.scls.lib.wi.us/bar.
Dir, Richard MacDonald; E-mail: rmacdonald@scls.lib.wi.us; *Ch,* Miriam
Thompson; *Circ,* Meg Allen; *ILL,* Nathan Rybarczyk; *Tech Serv,* Ruth Ann
Anderson; Staff 15 (MLS 2, Non-MLS 13)
Founded 1903. Pop 20,599; Circ 230,625
Library Holdings: AV Mats 2,925; Large Print Bks 1,827; Bk Vols
60,910; Per Subs 198; Talking Bks 2,896
Automation Activity & Vendor Info: (Acquisitions) SirsiDynix;
(Cataloging) SirsiDynix; (Circulation) SirsiDynix; (ILL) SirsiDynix;
(OPAC) SirsiDynix; (Serials) SirsiDynix
Database Vendor: SirsiDynix
Mem of South Central Library System
Open Mon-Thurs 9-8:30, Fri 9-5, Sat 9-1
Friends of the Library Group

S   CIRCUS WORLD MUSEUM*, Robert L Parkinson Library & Research
Center, 415 Lynn St, 53913. (Mail add: 550 Water St, 53913-2597), SAN
317-8900. Tel: 608-356-8342, Ext 3281. FAX: 608-355-7959. *Archivist,*
Erin Elizabeth Foley; Tel: 608-356-8342, Ext 3283, E-mail:
efoley.cwm@baraboo.com; Staff 3 (MLS 1, Non-MLS 2)
Founded 1966
Library Holdings: Bk Titles 3,259; Bk Vols 4,834; Per Subs 29
Subject Interests: Circus, Wild West
Function: Archival coll
Publications: Current Circus Activity; loan lists for books, serials, films &
videos; USA & Canada List
Open Thurs 8:30-Noon & 1-4:30

S   INTERNATIONAL CRANE'FOUNDATION*, Ron Sauey Memorial
Library for Bird Conservation, E-11376 Shady Lane Rd, 53913-9778.
(Mail add: PO Box 447, 53913-0447), SAN 321-902X. Tel: 608-356-9462,
Ext 124. FAX: 608-356-9465. E-mail: library@savingcranes.org. Web Site:
www.savingcranes.org. *Librn,* Betsy Didrickson
Founded 1973
Library Holdings: Bk Titles 4,000; Per Subs 150
Subject Interests: Biol, Conserv, Ornithology, Wetlands
Partic in Wisconsin Library Services
Restriction: Open by appt only

GL   SAUK COUNTY LAW LIBRARY*, 515 Oak St, 53913. SAN 377-9874.
Tel: 608-355-3287. FAX: 608-355-3480. *In Charge,* Donna Mueller
Library Holdings: Bk Vols 3,000
Open Mon-Fri 8-4:30

C   UNIVERSITY OF WISCONSIN BARABOO-SAUK COUNTY*, T N
Savides Library, 1006 Connie Rd, 53913. SAN 317-8927. Tel:
608-355-5251. FAX: 608-355-5291. Web Site:
www.baraboo.uwc.edu/library/libraryinfo.htm. *Dir,* Mark L
Rozmarynowski; Tel: 608-355-5249, E-mail:
mark.rozmarynowski@uwc.edu; *Assoc Librn,* Ann Vogl; E-mail:
ann.vogl@uwc.edu; Staff 3 (MLS 3)
Founded 1968. Enrl 400; Fac 42; Highest Degree: Associate
Jul 2005-Jun 2006 Income $118,920. Mats Exp $22,567. Sal $91,860 (Prof
$90,376)
Library Holdings: Bk Vols 37,357; Per Subs 110
Automation Activity & Vendor Info: (Acquisitions) Ex Libris Group;
(Cataloging) Ex Libris Group; (Circulation) Ex Libris Group; (ILL) OCLC
ILLiad
Partic in OCLC Online Computer Library Center, Inc; S Cent Libr Syst;
Wisconsin Library Services
Open Mon, Tues & Thurs 8:30-7, Wed 8:30-5, Fri 8:30-4

BARNEVELD

P   BARNEVELD PUBLIC LIBRARY*, 107 W Orbison St, 53507-9400.
(Mail add: PO Box 92, 53507-0092), SAN 317-8935. Tel: 608-924-3711.
FAX: 608-924-3711. Web Site: www.swls.org/member.ba.html. *Dir,* Debra
Kabler; E-mail: dkabler@swls.org
Founded 1955. Pop 1,088; Circ 2,856
Library Holdings: AV Mats 543; Bk Vols 7,749; Per Subs 14; Talking
Bks 189
Subject Interests: Local hist
Automation Activity & Vendor Info: (OPAC) Horizon
Database Vendor: SirsiDynix
Mem of Southwest Wisconsin Library System
Open Mon & Wed 10-8, Tues & Fri 10-5, Thurs 1-8, Sat 10-1

BARRON

P   BARRON PUBLIC LIBRARY*, Ten N Third St, 54812-1119. SAN
317-8943. Tel: 715-537-3881. FAX: 715-537-5080. E-mail:
barronpl@yahoo.com. *Dir,* Nancy Ausman-Dhatt; E-mail:
ndhatt@ifls.lib.wi.us; Staff 7 (MLS 1, Non-MLS 6)
Founded 1909
Library Holdings: Bk Vols 30,000; Per Subs 80
Automation Activity & Vendor Info: (Cataloging) SirsiDynix;
(Circulation) SirsiDynix
Mem of Indianhead Federated Library System
Partic in Barron County Libr Servs (BCLS)
Open Mon-Thurs 10-7, Fri 10-5, Sat 9-12
Friends of the Library Group

BAYFIELD

P   BAYFIELD CARNEGIE LIBRARY*, 37 N Broad St, 54814-9620. (Mail
add: PO Box 727, 54814-0727), SAN 317-8951. Tel: 715-779-3953. FAX:
715-779-5094. Web Site:
www.nwls.lib.wi.us/memberlibraries/bayfieldcarnegielibrary.html. *Dir,*
Roberta Baggerley; E-mail: robertab@bayfield.nwls.lib.wi.us
Founded 1903. Pop 786; Circ 12,000
Library Holdings: Bk Vols 14,000; Per Subs 28
Mem of Northern Waters Library Service
Open Mon, Tues & Thurs 1-7:30, Wed & Fri 9:30-5, Sat 9:30-3

P   MAZINAIGAN WAAKAAIGANT - RED CLIFF PUBLIC LIBRARY*,
88850 Church Rd, 54814-4604. Tel: 715-779-3764. FAX: 715-779-5093.
Web Site: nwls.wislib.org/about/librc.htm. *Dir,* Gina LaGrew; E-mail:
glagrew@redcliff.nwls.lib.wi.us; Staff 1 (Non-MLS 1)
Pop 1,700
Oct 2005-Sept 2006 Income $36,000
Library Holdings: AV Mats 2,000; Bk Vols 8,000; Per Subs 20
Special Collections: Native American Coll

Automation Activity & Vendor Info: (Cataloging) Innovative Interfaces, Inc; (Circulation) Innovative Interfaces, Inc; (OPAC) Innovative Interfaces, Inc
Open Mon-Fri 10-5

S NATIONAL PARK SERVICE*, Apostle Islands National Lakeshore Library, 415 Washington Ave, Rte 1, 54814. (Mail add: PO Box 4, 54814-0004), SAN 328-1779. Tel: 715-779-3397. FAX: 715-779-3049. *Head, Info Serv,* Myra Dec; Tel: 715-779-3397, Ext 301
Founded 1975
Library Holdings: Bk Vols 1,500; Per Subs 30
Special Collections: Oral History
Subject Interests: Local hist
Restriction: Staff use only

BEAVER DAM

M BEAVER DAM COMMUNITY HOSPITALS, INC LIBRARY*, 707 S University Ave, 53916. Tel: 920-887-4124. FAX: 920-887-4187. *Librn,* Dianne Fashun; E-mail: dfashun@bdch.org. Subject Specialists: *Consumer health & wellness,* Dianne Fashun
Library Holdings: Bks on Deafness & Sign Lang 1; CDs 7; DVDs 54; e-books 79; e-journals 340; Large Print Bks 4; Bk Titles 850; Per Subs 10; Spec Interest Per Sub 10
Subject Interests: Health, Med, Wellness
Database Vendor: EBSCOhost, Medline, OVID Technologies, PubMed, UpToDate
Restriction: Med staff only

P BEAVER DAM COMMUNITY LIBRARY*, 311 N Spring St, 53916-2043. SAN 317-8978. Tel: 920-887-4631. FAX: 920-887-4633. Web Site: www.beaverdam.lib.wi.us. *Dir,* Susan Mary Mevis; Tel: 920-887-4631, Ext 12, E-mail: mevis@mwfls.org; Staff 12 (MLS 4, Non-MLS 8)
Founded 1884. Circ 288,894
Library Holdings: Bk Vols 105,000; Per Subs 195
Automation Activity & Vendor Info: (Acquisitions) SirsiDynix; (Cataloging) SirsiDynix; (Circulation) SirsiDynix; (Course Reserve) SirsiDynix; (ILL) SirsiDynix; (Media Booking) SirsiDynix; (OPAC) SirsiDynix; (Serials) SirsiDynix
Database Vendor: EBSCOhost, Gale Cengage Learning, SirsiDynix, Wilson - Wilson Web
Mem of Mid-Wisconsin Federated Library System
Open Mon-Fri 9-8:30, Sat 9-5
Friends of the Library Group

J MORAINE PARK TECHNICAL COLLEGE LIBRARY*, Beaver Dam Campus, 700 Gould St, 53916-1994. SAN 317-896X. Tel: 920-887-4406. FAX: 920-887-4473. Web Site: www.morainepark.edu. *Librn,* Mary Janice Powers; Staff 3 (Non-MLS 3)
Library Holdings: Bk Vols 4,000; Per Subs 50
Automation Activity & Vendor Info: (Acquisitions) Ex Libris Group; (Cataloging) Ex Libris Group; (Circulation) Ex Libris Group; (Course Reserve) Ex Libris Group; (ILL) Ex Libris Group; (Media Booking) Ex Libris Group; (OPAC) Ex Libris Group; (Serials) Ex Libris Group
Partic in WISPALS Library Consortium
Open Mon-Thurs 8am-9:30pm, Fri 8-4

BELLEVILLE

P BELLEVILLE PUBLIC LIBRARY*, 130 S Vine St, 53508-9102. (Mail add: PO Box 140, 53508-0140), SAN 317-8986. Tel: 608-424-1812. FAX: 608-424-3545. E-mail: jcblvlib@scls.lib.wi.us. Web Site: www.scls.lib.wi.us/blv. *Dir,* Jean Christensen; E-mail: jcblvlib@scls.lib.wi.us; *Ch,* Denise Mussehl
Founded 1878
Library Holdings: Bk Vols 22,000; Per Subs 65
Subject Interests: Local hist
Open Mon-Thurs 9-1 & 2-7, Fri 9-1 & 2-5, Sat 9-12
Friends of the Library Group

BELMONT

P JOHN TURGESON PUBLIC LIBRARY*, Belmont Public, 220 S Mound Ave, 53510. SAN 317-8994. Tel: 608-762-5137. FAX: 608-762-5525. *Dir,* Sylvia Henry
Pop 1,335; Circ 5,504
Library Holdings: Bk Vols 18,000
Automation Activity & Vendor Info: (Cataloging) SirsiDynix; (Circulation) SirsiDynix
Mem of Southwest Wisconsin Library System
Open Mon, Wed & Fri (Winter) 1-6:30, Sat 8:30-12; Mon & Fri (Summer) 1-6:30, Wed 8:30-12 & 1-6:30

BELOIT

C BELOIT COLLEGE*, Colonel Robert H Morse Library & Richard Black Information Center, 731 College St, 53511-5595. SAN 364-6238. Tel: 608-363-2483. Circulation Tel: 608-363-2230. Interlibrary Loan Service Tel: 608-363-2567. Reference Tel: 608-363-2544. Administration Tel: 608-363-2481. FAX: 608-363-2487. Web Site: www.beloit.edu/library. *Asst Dir, Libr Serv,* Lisa Viezbicke; Tel: 608-363-2486, E-mail: viezbick@beloit.edu; *Digital Res Librn,* Josh Hickman; Tel: 608-363-2246, E-mail: hickmanj@beloit.edu; Staff 6 (MLS 5, Non-MLS 1)
Founded 1849. Enrl 1,344; Fac 104
Library Holdings: Bk Titles 239,654; Bk Vols 257,417; Per Subs 1,859
Special Collections: Beloit Poetry Journal Coll; Cullister International Coll; Pacifism & Nonviolence (M L King Coll), mat by & about Presidents F D Roosevelt, Woodrow Wilson, Abraham Lincoln. State Document Depository; US Document Depository
Automation Activity & Vendor Info: (Acquisitions) SirsiDynix; (Cataloging) SirsiDynix; (Circulation) SirsiDynix; (Course Reserve) SirsiDynix; (OPAC) SirsiDynix; (Serials) SirsiDynix
Wireless access
Mem of Arrowhead Library System
Partic in OCLC Online Computer Library Center, Inc; The Oberlin Group; Wis Asn of Independent Cols & Univs; Wisconsin Library Services
Open Mon-Thurs (Winter) 8:30am-Midnight, Fri 8:30am-10pm, Sat 11-10, Sun 11am-Midnight; Mon-Fri (Summer) 9-5

P BELOIT HISTORICAL SOCIETY*, Arthur L Luebke Memorial Library, Lincoln Ctr, 845 Hackett St, 53511. SAN 371-1641. Tel: 608-365-7835. FAX: 608-365-5999. E-mail: beloiths@ticon.net. Web Site: www.ticon.net/~beloiths. *Dir,* Paul Kerr; E-mail: pkerr@beloithistoricalsociety.com
Library Holdings: Bk Vols 500; Per Subs 12
Subject Interests: Local hist, Old books

P BELOIT PUBLIC LIBRARY, 605 Eclipse Blvd, 53511. SAN 317-9001. Tel: 608-364-2905. Circulation Tel: 608-364-2911. Interlibrary Loan Service Tel: 608-364-2914. Administration Tel: 608-364-2908. FAX: 608-364-2907. E-mail: reference@beloitlibrary.info. Web Site: www.beloitlibrary.info. *Libr Dir,* Kristi Howe; Tel: 608-364-2917, E-mail: khowe@beloitlibrary.info; *Head, Adult Serv,* Joan Nicholas; Tel: 608-364-2909, E-mail: jnicholoas@beloitlibrary.info; *Head, Tech Serv,* Roger Dutcher; Tel: 608-364-2897, E-mail: rdutcher@beloitlibrary.info; *Head, Youth Serv,* Jeni Schomber; Tel: 608-364-5754, E-mail: jschomber@beloitlibrary.info; *Circ Mgr,* Tina Kakuske; Tel: 608-364-5766, E-mail: tkakuske@beloitlibrary.info; *Computer Serv Mgr,* Wyatt Ditzler; Tel: 608-364-5755, E-mail: wditzler@beloitlibrary.info; Staff 30 (MLS 4, Non-MLS 26)
Founded 1902. Pop 37,625; Circ 529,803
Subject Interests: Genealogy, Local hist
Automation Activity & Vendor Info: (Cataloging) Innovative Interfaces, Inc; (Circulation) Innovative Interfaces, Inc; (OPAC) Innovative Interfaces, Inc
Wireless access
Function: Bks on CD, Children's prog, Computer training, Computers for patron use, Copy machines, e-mail serv, E-Reserves, Electronic databases & coll, Exhibits, Fax serv, Free DVD rentals, Genealogy discussion group, Handicapped accessible, Home delivery & serv to Sr ctr & nursing homes, Homebound delivery serv, ILL available, Large print keyboards, Magnifiers for reading, Mail & tel request accepted, Microfiche/film & reading machines, Music CDs, Online cat, Outreach serv, OverDrive digital audio bks, Photocopying/Printing, Prog for adults, Prog for children & young adult, Provide serv for the mentally ill, Ref serv available, Ref serv in person, Scanner, Spanish lang bks, Spoken cassettes & CDs, Story hour, Summer reading prog, Tax forms, Teen prog, Telephone ref, Web-catalog, Wheelchair accessible
Mem of Arrowhead Library System
Open Mon-Thurs 9:30-9, Fri & Sat 9:30-5:30
Friends of the Library Group

BENTON

P BENTON PUBLIC LIBRARY*, 48 W Main St, 53803-0026. (Mail add: PO Box 26, 53803-0026), SAN 317-9052. Tel: 608-759-2665. Web Site: www.ci.benton.wi.us/web.bpl.htm. *Dir,* Janet Johnson; E-mail: jjohnson@swls.org; Staff 1 (MLS 1)
Founded 1922. Pop 1,400; Circ 6,000
Library Holdings: AV Mats 500; Large Print Bks 40; Bk Titles 6,000; Per Subs 20; Talking Bks 100
Special Collections: Local history
Automation Activity & Vendor Info: (Circulation) SirsiDynix
Function: ILL available
Mem of Southwest Wisconsin Library System
Open Mon 11:30-6:30, Tues-Fri 4-6:30, Sat 9-12

BERLIN

P   BERLIN PUBLIC LIBRARY*, 121 W Park Ave, 54923. SAN 317-9060.
Tel: 920-361-5420. FAX: 920-361-5424. E-mail: director@berlinlibrary.org.
Web Site: www.berlinlibrary.org. *Ch, Co-Dir,* Christine Carroll; E-mail:
carroll@berlinlibrary.org; *Co-Dir, Ref Serv,* Diane Disterhaft; E-mail:
disterhaft@berlinlibrary.org; Staff 3 (Non-MLS 3)
Founded 1903. Pop 9,000; Circ 120,000
Library Holdings: Bks on Deafness & Sign Lang 35; High Interest/Low
Vocabulary Bk Vols 500; Bk Vols 50,000; Per Subs 101
Special Collections: Literacy Coll; Spanish Language Materials Coll
Subject Interests: Literacy, Local hist
Automation Activity & Vendor Info: (Cataloging) SirsiDynix;
(Circulation) SirsiDynix; (OPAC) SirsiDynix
Special Services for the Deaf - TTY equip
Special Services for the Blind - Magnifiers
Open Mon-Thurs 9-8, Fri 9-6, Sat 9-5 (Summer 9-1)
Friends of the Library Group

BIG BEND

P   BIG BEND VILLAGE LIBRARY*, W230 S90175 Nevins St, 53103-9722.
(Mail add: PO Box 40, 53103-0040), SAN 324-7880. Tel: 262-662-3571.
FAX: 262-662-3459, 262-662-3751. Web Site:
www.wcfls.lib.wi.us/bigbend. *Coll Develop, Dir,* Sadie Soneberg; E-mail:
soneberg@wcfls.lib.wi.us; Staff 4 (MLS 1, Non-MLS 3)
Founded 1964. Pop 1,299; Circ 11,799
Library Holdings: Bk Vols 10,000; Per Subs 29
Subject Interests: Local hist
Mem of Waukesha County Federated Library System
Open Mon & Thurs 3-9, Tues & Wed 9:30-12 & 6pm-9pm, Fri 3-6, Sat
9-1

BLACK CREEK

P   BLACK CREEK VILLAGE LIBRARY*, 507 S Maple St, 54106-9304.
SAN 317-9087. Tel: 920-984-3094. Automation Services Tel:
920-984-3472. FAX: 920-984-3559. E-mail: bcl@mail.owls.lib.wi.us. Web
Site: www.blackcreeklibrary.org. *Dir of Libr,* Valerie J Husom; E-mail:
vhusom@mail.owls.lib.wi.us; *Circ Librn,* Kelly Oskey; *Youth Serv Librn,*
Melanie Waldron; Staff 1 (Non-MLS 1)
Founded 1975. Pop 3,000; Circ 42,000
Jan 2007-Dec 2007 Income $101,807, City $47,580, County $50,227,
Locally Generated Income $3,500, Other $500. Mats Exp $13,300, Books
$6,000, Per/Ser (Incl. Access Fees) $1,700, AV Mat $5,600. Sal $60,000
(Prof $33,100)
Library Holdings: AV Mats 1,950; CDs 300; DVDs 1,500; e-books
10,000; Electronic Media & Resources 10,000; Large Print Bks 1,500; Bk
Titles 19,000; Bk Vols 19,000; Per Subs 75; Talking Bks 1,500; Videos
1,700
Automation Activity & Vendor Info: (Acquisitions) Innovative Interfaces,
Inc - OCLC; (Cataloging) Innovative Interfaces, Inc - OCLC; (Circulation)
Innovative Interfaces, Inc; (ILL) OCLC FirstSearch; (OPAC) Innovative
Interfaces, Inc - OCLC
Wireless access
Function: Accelerated reader prog, Archival coll, Audio & video playback
equip for onsite use, Audiobks via web, AV serv, Bk reviews (Group), Bks
on cassette, Bks on CD, Children's prog, Computer training, Computers for
patron use, Copy machines, E-Reserves, Electronic databases & coll, Fax
serv, Home delivery & serv to Sr ctr & nursing homes, Homebound
delivery serv, ILL available, Mail & tel request accepted, Music CDs,
Notary serv, Online searches, Photocopying/Printing, Prog for adults, Prog
for children & young adult, Summer reading prog, Tax forms, Teen prog,
VHS videos, Web-catalog
Mem of Outagamie Waupaca Library System
Partic in OWLSnet
Open Mon-Thurs 9-6, Fri 9-5, Sat (Sept-May) 9-12

BLACK EARTH

P   BLACK EARTH PUBLIC LIBRARY*, 1210 Mills St, 53515. (Mail add:
PO Box 347, 53515-0347), SAN 317-9095. Tel: 608-767-2400, Ext 3.
FAX: 608-767-2064. E-mail: berstaff@scls.lib.wi.us. *Libr Dir,* Carolyn
Shaffer; Staff 3 (MLS 1, Non-MLS 2)
Founded 1938. Pop 1,400; Circ 32,445
Library Holdings: AV Mats 1,663; Bk Titles 16,056; Per Subs 54
Mem of South Central Library System
Open Mon-Thurs 10-1 & 2-7, Fri 10-5, Sat 10-2
Friends of the Library Group

BLACK RIVER FALLS

P   BLACK RIVER FALLS PUBLIC LIBRARY*, 222 Fillmore St, 54615.
SAN 364-6386. Tel: 715-284-4112. FAX: 715-284-5369. Web Site:
www.blackriverfallslibrary.org. *Dir,* Muriel Gunderson; E-mail:
m.gunderson@wrlsweb.org; *Youth Serv,* Nancy Oldham

Founded 1872. Pop 16,000; Circ 83,847
Library Holdings: AV Mats 1,362; Large Print Bks 104; Bk Titles 25,481;
Per Subs 71; Talking Bks 1,144
Subject Interests: County hist, Genealogy, Indians, Local hist
Automation Activity & Vendor Info: (Circulation) Horizon; (OPAC)
Horizon; (Serials) Horizon
Wireless access
Mem of Winding Rivers Library System
Open Mon-Thurs 10-8, Fri 10-5, Sat 10-4 (May-Sept 10-2)
Branches: 1
CHILDRENS ROOM, 222 Fillmore St, 54615. Tel: 715-284-4112. FAX:
715-284-5369. *Librn,* Nancy Oldham
Open Mon 12-8, Tues & Thurs 10-5, Fri 12-5

BLAIR

P   BLAIR-PRESTON PUBLIC LIBRARY*, 122 S Urberg Ave, 54616-0165.
(Mail add: PO Box 165, 54616-0165), SAN 317-9109. Tel: 608-989-2502.
E-mail: blairpl@wrlsweb.org. *Librn,* Kristine McNamer
Founded 1916. Pop 2,500; Circ 15,000
Library Holdings: Bk Vols 8,500
Subject Interests: Rural
Automation Activity & Vendor Info: (Cataloging) Horizon; (Circulation)
Horizon; (OPAC) Horizon
Wireless access
Publications: Book List
Mem of Winding Rivers Library System
Open Mon-Fri 12:30-6, Sat 9-12

BLANCHARDVILLE

P   BLANCHARDVILLE PUBLIC LIBRARY*, 208 Mason St, 53506. SAN
317-9117. Tel: 608-523-2055. FAX: 608-523-4321. Web Site:
www.blanchardville.com/village/library.html. *Dir,* Gretchen Dieterich;
E-mail: gdieterich@swls.org
Pop 806; Circ 8,176
Library Holdings: Bk Vols 10,000; Per Subs 60
Subject Interests: Local hist
Automation Activity & Vendor Info: (Cataloging) Horizon; (Circulation)
Horizon; (OPAC) Horizon
Mem of Southwest Wisconsin Library System
Open Mon 9-2 & 4:30-7:30, Wed 9-5, Thurs 12-7:30, Sat 9-2

BLOOMER

P   G E BLESKACEK MEMORIAL LIBRARY*, Bloomer Public Library,
1519 17th Ave, 54724. SAN 317-9125. Tel: 715-568-2384. FAX:
715-568-2387. E-mail: bloomerlibrary@ifls.lib.wi.us. Web Site:
www.ifls.lib.wi.us. *Dir,* Mary Cummings; Staff 3 (Non-MLS 3)
Founded 1917. Pop 4,711; Circ 44,468
Library Holdings: Bk Titles 18,975; Bk Vols 25,153; Per Subs 75
Automation Activity & Vendor Info: (Cataloging) Follett Software;
(Circulation) Follett Software
Mem of Indianhead Federated Library System
Open Mon, Wed & Fri 10-6, Tues & Thurs 10-8, Sat 9-12
Friends of the Library Group

BLOOMINGTON

P   BLOOMINGTON PUBLIC LIBRARY*, 453 Canal St, 53804. (Mail add:
PO Box 38, 53804-0038), SAN 317-9133. Tel: 608-994-2531. Web Site:
www.swls.org/member.bt.html. *Dir,* Jim Warczak; E-mail:
jwarczak@swls.org
Founded 1905. Pop 701; Circ 6,457
Library Holdings: Bk Vols 6,929; Per Subs 10
Automation Activity & Vendor Info: (Acquisitions) SirsiDynix;
(Cataloging) SirsiDynix; (Circulation) SirsiDynix
Wireless access
Mem of Southwest Wisconsin Library System
Open Mon 3:30-6:30, Wed 9-12 & 2-5, Fri 1-5 & Sat 9-12

BOSCOBEL

P   HILDEBRAND MEMORIAL LIBRARY*, Boscobel Public, 1033
Wisconsin Ave, 53805-1597. SAN 317-9141. Tel: 608-375-5723. FAX:
608-375-4750. Web Site: www.swls.org/member.bw.html. *Dir,* Robin
Orlandi; E-mail: rorlandi@swls.org
Founded 1906. Pop 3,047; Circ 32,353
Library Holdings: Bk Vols 21,500; Per Subs 36
Special Collections: Boscobel Dial Newspaper Coll, micro
Automation Activity & Vendor Info: (Circulation) SirsiDynix
Mem of Southwest Wisconsin Library System
Partic in OCLC Online Computer Library Center, Inc
Open Mon & Wed 10-8, Tues & Thurs 1-8, Fri 10-5, Sat 1-4

S   WISCONSIN SECURE PROGRAM FACILITY LIBRARY*, 1101
     Morrison Dr, 53805. (Mail add: PO Box 1000, 53805-1000), SAN
     378-3774. Tel: 608-375-5656. FAX: 608-375-5434. *Sr Librn,* Linda
     Oatman; E-mail: linda.oatman@wisconsin.gov; Staff 1 (MLS 1)
     Library Holdings: Bk Titles 26,000; Bk Vols 43,000; Per Subs 20
     Automation Activity & Vendor Info: (Circulation) Follett Software
     Open Mon-Fri 7:30-4

BOULDER JUNCTION

P   BOULDER JUNCTION PUBLIC LIBRARY*, 5386 Park St, 54512-9605.
     (Mail add: PO Box 9, 54512-0009), SAN 324-7414. Tel: 715-385-2050.
     E-mail: info@boulder.nwls.lib.wi.us. Web Site: boulderjunction.wislib.org.
     Dir, Cherie Sanderson; E-mail: csanderson@boulder.nwls.lib.wi.us; Staff 3
     (Non-MLS 3)
     Founded 1976. Pop 1,200
     Function: ILL available, Photocopying/Printing, Prog for adults, Prog for
     children & young adult, Summer reading prog
     Mem of Northern Waters Library Service
     Open Mon, Wed, Fri & Sat 10-1, Tues & Thurs 10-7
     Friends of the Library Group

BOYCEVILLE

P   BOYCEVILLE PUBLIC LIBRARY*, 903 Main St, 54725-9595. (Mail
     add: PO Box 129, 54725-0129), SAN 317-915X. Tel: 715-643-2106.
     E-mail: boycevillepl@ifls.lib.wi.us. Web Site: www.boycevillelibrary.org.
     Dir, Ginny Julson; E-mail: ginnyjulson@ifls.lib.wi.us; Staff 4 (Non-MLS 4)
     Founded 1900. Pop 2,100; Circ 27,000
     Library Holdings: Bk Vols 9,030; Per Subs 34
     Automation Activity & Vendor Info: (Circulation) Innovative Interfaces,
     Inc
     Wireless access
     Mem of Indianhead Federated Library System
     Open Tues & Thurs 11-6, Wed & Fri 11-7, Sat 10-12:30
     Friends of the Library Group

BRANDON

P   BRANDON PUBLIC LIBRARY*, 117 E Main St, 53919. (Mail add: PO
     Box 208, 53919-0208), SAN 317-9168. Tel: 920-346-2350. FAX:
     920-346-5895. E-mail: director@brandonlibrary.net. Web Site:
     www.brandonlibrary.net. *Dir,* Tylor S Loest; Staff 2 (MLS 1, Non-MLS 1)
     Founded 1913. Pop 1,263; Circ 8,975
     Library Holdings: AV Mats 429; Bks on Deafness & Sign Lang 13; High
     Interest/Low Vocabulary Bk Vols 143; Large Print Bks 142; Bk Titles
     8,200; Per Subs 68; Talking Bks 353
     Automation Activity & Vendor Info: (Circulation) Follett Software;
     (OPAC) Follett Software
     Open Mon-Thurs 2-6, Fri 11-5, Sat 9-12

BRILLION

P   BRILLION PUBLIC LIBRARY*, 326 N Main St, 54110. SAN 317-9176.
     Tel: 920-756-3215. FAX: 920-756-3874. Web Site:
     www.ci.brillion.wi.us/library_home.html. *Dir,* Christine Moede; E-mail:
     cmoede@mcls.lib.wi.us
     Founded 1928. Pop 3,000; Circ 7,800
     Library Holdings: AV Mats 3,453; Bk Titles 31,359; Per Subs 151
     Automation Activity & Vendor Info: (Cataloging) SIRSI Unicorn;
     (Circulation) SIRSI Unicorn; (OPAC) SIRSI-iBistro; (Serials) SIRSI
     Unicorn
     Wireless access
     Mem of Manitowoc-Calumet Library System
     Special Services for the Blind - Bks on CD
     Open Mon (Sept-June) 8-8, Tues 9-8, Wed & Thurs 12-8, Fri 12-6, Sat
     9-12; Mon (June-Sept) 8-8, Tues & Wed 9-8, Thurs 12-8, Fri 12-6
     Restriction: Access for corporate affiliates
     Friends of the Library Group

BRODHEAD

P   BRODHEAD MEMORIAL PUBLIC LIBRARY*, 902 W Second Ave,
     53520-1308. SAN 317-9184. Tel: 608-897-4070. E-mail: library@wekz.net.
     Web Site: www.brodheadlibrary.org. *Dir,* Gloria Rosa
     Founded 1909. Pop 3,153; Circ 32,122
     Library Holdings: Bk Titles 37,000; Per Subs 67
     Mem of South Central Library System
     Open Mon-Thurs (Winter) 9-8, Fri 9-6, Sat 9-1; Mon-Thurs (Summer) 9-7,
     Fri 9-6, Sat 9-1

BROOKFIELD

P   BROOKFIELD PUBLIC LIBRARY, 1900 N Calhoun Rd, 53005. SAN
     317-9192. Tel: 262-782-4140. FAX: 262-796-6670. TDD: 262-796-6714.
     E-mail: brookfieldpubliclibrary@ci.brookfield.wi.us. Web Site:

www.brookfieldlibrary.com. *Dir,* Edell Schaefer; E-mail:
schaefer@ci.brookfield.wi.us; *Pub Serv Mgr,* Cathy Tuttrup; *Tech Serv
Mgr,* Sue Brown; *Children's Serv Supvr,* Vicki Brostrom; *Circ Supvr,* Kim
Sagan; Staff 32.46 (MLS 8, Non-MLS 24.46)
Founded 1960. Pop 42,482; Circ 721,613
Library Holdings: AV Mats 20,815; Bk Vols 342,600; Per Subs 414
Special Collections: Frank Urban Coll (Railroad History and Sherlock
Holmes). Oral History
Subject Interests: Fine arts, Home improvement, Travel
Automation Activity & Vendor Info: (Serials) SirsiDynix
Wireless access
Publications: BrookBytes (Newsletter)
Open Mon-Thurs 9-9, Fri & Sat 9-5, Sun (Oct-May) 1-4
Friends of the Library Group

S   INTERNATIONAL FOUNDATION OF EMPLOYEE BENEFIT PLANS,
     Information Center, 18700 W Bluemound Rd, 53045-2936. SAN 317-9214.
     Tel: 262-786-6710, Ext 5. Toll Free Tel: 888-334-3327, Ext 5. FAX:
     262-786-8780. E-mail: infocenter@ifebp.org. Web Site: www.ifebp.org.
     Dir, Info Serv/Publ, Kelli Kolsrud; E-mail: kellik@ifebp.org; *Dir, Res &
     Ref Serv,* Patricia Krajnak; E-mail: patk@ifebp.org; *Dir of Tech Serv,* Julia
     E Miller; E-mail: juliem@ifebp.org; *Employee Benefits Info Spec,* Lois
     Mathis-Gleason; E-mail: loismg@ifebp.org; *Info Spec,* Sharon Olecheck;
     E-mail: sharono@ifebp.org; *Info Spec,* Mary G. Sanchez; E-mail:
     marys@ifebp.org; Staff 7 (MLS 5, Non-MLS 2)
     Founded 1970
     Jan 2009-Dec 2009. Mats Exp $127,000, Books $10,000, Per/Ser (Incl.
     Access Fees) $74,000, Electronic Ref Mat (Incl. Access Fees) $43,000. Sal
     $550,000
     Library Holdings: e-journals 50; Bk Vols 8,000; Per Subs 250
     Subject Interests: Employee benefits, Ins, Pensions
     Automation Activity & Vendor Info: (Acquisitions) Inmagic, Inc.;
     (Cataloging) Inmagic, Inc.; (Circulation) Inmagic, Inc.; (OPAC) Inmagic,
     Inc.; (Serials) Inmagic, Inc.
     Database Vendor: Dialog, EBSCOhost, LexisNexis
     Function: Doc delivery serv, Ref serv available, Res libr
     Open Mon-Fri 8-5
     Restriction: Lending to staff only, Mem only, Open to others by appt

S   HOWARD C RAETHER LIBRARY*, 13625 Bishop's Dr, 53005-6607.
     SAN 328-3062. Tel: 262-814-1556. Toll Free Tel: 800-228-6332. FAX:
     262-789-6977. E-mail: nfda@nfda.org. *Mgr,* Kathleen Ann Walczak;
     E-mail: kwalczak@nfda.org; Staff 1 (MLS 1)
     Founded 1998
     Library Holdings: Bk Vols 2,000
     Special Collections: Books on Dying, Death & Grief (1400's-1900's)
     Subject Interests: Death
     Database Vendor: OCLC FirstSearch
     Function: Res libr
     Restriction: Not a lending libr

BROWN DEER

P   BROWN DEER PUBLIC LIBRARY*, 5600 W Bradley Rd, 53223-3510.
     SAN 317-9230. Tel: 414-357-0106. FAX: 414-354-8081. Web Site:
     www.browndeerwi.org/brown-deer-services.cfm?id=27. *Dir,* Joseph Rice;
     E-mail: joseph.rice@mcfls.org; *Ch,* Dana Andersen-Kopczyk; E-mail:
     dana.andersen@mcfls.org; Staff 4 (MLS 4)
     Founded 1969. Pop 14,000; Circ 311,563
     Library Holdings: Bk Vols 78,500; Per Subs 200
     Automation Activity & Vendor Info: (Acquisitions) Innovative Interfaces,
     Inc - Millenium; (Cataloging) Innovative Interfaces, Inc - Millenium;
     (Circulation) Innovative Interfaces, Inc - Millenium; (OPAC) Innovative
     Interfaces, Inc - Millenium; (Serials) Innovative Interfaces, Inc - Millenium
     Wireless access
     Mem of Milwaukee County Federated Library System
     Friends of the Library Group

BROWNSVILLE

P   BROWNSVILLE PUBLIC LIBRARY*, 379 Main St, 53006-0248. (Mail
     add: PO Box 248, 53006-0248), SAN 317-9249. Tel: 920-583-4325. FAX:
     920-583-4325. E-mail: brownlib@mwfls.org. Web Site:
     www.brownsville.lib.wi.us. *Dir,* Sue Kinyon; E-mail: bplsue@mwfls.org
     Founded 1949. Pop 2,800; Circ 36,160
     Library Holdings: Bk Vols 23,200; Per Subs 67
     Automation Activity & Vendor Info: (Cataloging) SirsiDynix;
     (Circulation) SirsiDynix; (OPAC) SirsiDynix
     Wireless access
     Mem of Mid-Wisconsin Federated Library System
     Open Mon, Tues & Thurs 1-7, Wed & Fri 3-6, Sat (Sept-May) 10-12

BRUCE

P   BRUCE AREA LIBRARY*, 102 W River Ave, 54819. (Mail add: PO Box 277, 54819), SAN 376-6721. Tel: 715-868-2005. *Dir,* Kathleen Voss; E-mail: voss@ifls.lib.wi.us; Staff 1 (Non-MLS 1)
Pop 2,700; Circ 8,181
Library Holdings: AV Mats 1,000; Bks on Deafness & Sign Lang 10; Large Print Bks 671; Bk Titles 15,000; Per Subs 20; Talking Bks 357
Automation Activity & Vendor Info: (Cataloging) Horizon; (Circulation) Horizon
Mem of Indianhead Federated Library System
Open Mon-Wed & Fri 10-5, Thurs 10-7, Sat 10-12
Friends of the Library Group

BURLINGTON

P   BURLINGTON PUBLIC LIBRARY*, 166 E Jefferson St, 53105. SAN 317-9257. Tel: 262-763-7623. Reference Tel: 262-342-1142. FAX: 262-763-1938. E-mail: director@burlington.lib.wi.us. Web Site: www.burlington.lib.wi.us. *Dir,* Gayle A Falk; E-mail: gafalk@burlington.lib.wi.us; *Head, Ref,* Judy Rockwell; E-mail: jrockwel@burlington.lib.wi.us; *Automation Syst Coordr,* Tammy McCarthy; Tel: 262-342-1134; *Ch,* Joy Schnupp; E-mail: jschnupp@burlington.lib.wi.us; Staff 6 (MLS 4, Non-MLS 2)
Founded 1908. Pop 18,859; Circ 206,517
Jan 2009-Dec 2009 Income $707,689, City $329,254, County $302,322, Locally Generated Income $30,300, Other $45,813. Mats Exp $74,230. Sal $392,659
Library Holdings: Bk Vols 60,865; Per Subs 184
Special Collections: Church of the Latter Day Saints - Strangite (Strangite Mormon Newspapers & Chronicles)
Automation Activity & Vendor Info: (Acquisitions) SirsiDynix; (Cataloging) SirsiDynix; (Circulation) SirsiDynix; (OPAC) SirsiDynix; (Serials) SirsiDynix
Database Vendor: EBSCOhost
Friends of the Library Group

BUTLER

P   BUTLER PUBLIC LIBRARY*, 12621 W Hampton Ave, 53007-1705. SAN 317-9273. Tel: 262-783-2535. FAX: 262-783-9900. E-mail: buill@wcfls.lib.wi.us. Web Site: www.wcfls.lib.wi.us/butler. *Dir,* Jo Reitman
Founded 1964. Pop 2,055
Library Holdings: Bk Vols 22,000; Per Subs 95
Open Mon-Thurs 12-8, Fri 12-6, Sat (Sept-May) 10-1
Friends of the Library Group

CABLE

P   FOREST LODGE LIBRARY*, 13450 County Hwy M, 54821. (Mail add: PO Box 176, 54821-0176), SAN 317-9281. Tel: 715-798-3189. Web Site: cable.wislib.org. *Dir,* Karlan E K Williams; E-mail: karlan@cable.nwls.lib.wi.us
Pop 1,000; Circ 7,500
Library Holdings: Bk Titles 8,000; Per Subs 30
Subject Interests: Local hist, Natural hist
Mem of Northern Waters Library Service
Open Mon, Tues, Thurs, Fri 10-6, Wed 10-8 & Sat 10-4
Friends of the Library Group

CADOTT

P   CADOTT COMMUNITY LIBRARY*, 331 N Main St, 54727. (Mail add: PO Box 68, 54727-0068), SAN 317-929X. Tel: 715-289-4950. FAX: 715-289-3149. E-mail: cadottpl@ifls.lib.wi.us. Web Site: www.cadottlibrary.org. *Dir,* Jennifer Smith; E-mail: jsmith@ifls.lib.wi.us; Staff 1 (Non-MLS 1)
Founded 1955. Pop 2,500; Circ 27,500
Jan 2005-Dec 2005 Income $83,500, City $49,000, County $26,500, Locally Generated Income $2,000, Other $6,000. Mats Exp $25,852, Books $16,132, Per/Ser (Incl. Access Fees) $2,175, AV Equip $3,000, AV Mat $4,000, Electronic Ref Mat (Incl. Access Fees) $545. Sal $40,000
Library Holdings: AV Mats 968; Bk Titles 29,530; Per Subs 75; Talking Bks 877
Special Collections: Oral History
Automation Activity & Vendor Info: (Acquisitions) Innovative Interfaces, Inc; (Cataloging) Innovative Interfaces, Inc; (Circulation) Innovative Interfaces, Inc; (OPAC) Innovative Interfaces, Inc
Function: Adult bk club, ILL available, Photocopying/Printing, Prog for children & young adult, Summer reading prog, VHS videos
Mem of Indianhead Federated Library System
Open Mon 11-5, Tues, Thurs & Fri 1-5, Wed 9-7, Sat 9-12
Friends of the Library Group

CAMBRIA

P   JANE MORGAN MEMORIAL LIBRARY*, 109 W Edgewater St, 53923. (Mail add: PO Box 477, 53923-0477), SAN 324-7902. Tel: 920-348-4030. *Dir,* Jennifer Tallman
Pop 680
Library Holdings: Bk Vols 6,000; Per Subs 25
Subject Interests: Local community, Welsh
Mem of South Central Library System
Open Mon & Wed 10-8, Tues & Thurs-Fri 10-5, Sat 9-Noon

CAMBRIDGE

P   CAMBRIDGE COMMUNITY LIBRARY*, 200 Spring St, 53523-9218. (Mail add: PO Box 490, 53523-0490), SAN 325-1934. Tel: 608-423-3900. FAX: 608-423-7330. E-mail: jmbdirlb@scls.lib.wi.us. *Dir,* Joan Behm; Staff 5 (MLS 1, Non-MLS 4)
Founded 1978. Pop 4,800; Circ 37,000
Library Holdings: AV Mats 1,696; Bk Titles 18,795; Per Subs 1,218
Subject Interests: Local hist
Automation Activity & Vendor Info: (Cataloging) SirsiDynix; (Circulation) SirsiDynix; (ILL) SirsiDynix
Wireless access
Partic in Library Interchange Network (LINK)
Open Mon & Wed 1-6, Tues & Thurs 9-8, Fri 1-5, Sat 9-1
Friends of the Library Group

CAMERON

P   CAMERON PUBLIC LIBRARY*, 506 Main St, 54822. (Mail add: PO Box 343, 54822-0343), SAN 377-9300. Tel: 715-458-2267. FAX: 715-458-2267. E-mail: cameronpl@cameronpl.org. *Dir,* Dawn Ayers
Pop 1,425
Library Holdings: Audiobooks 500; Bks on Deafness & Sign Lang 12; Braille Volumes 33; CDs 50; DVDs 300; Large Print Bks 300; Bk Titles 10,000; Per Subs 24; Videos 600
Automation Activity & Vendor Info: (Acquisitions) Innovative Interfaces, Inc - Millenium; (Cataloging) Innovative Interfaces, Inc - Millenium; (Circulation) Innovative Interfaces, Inc - Millenium; (OPAC) Innovative Interfaces, Inc - Millenium; (Serials) Innovative Interfaces, Inc - Millenium
Database Vendor: EBSCOhost, SirsiDynix
Wireless access
Mem of Indianhead Federated Library System
Open Mon-Fri 11-6, Sat 10-12
Friends of the Library Group

CAMPBELLSPORT

P   CAMPBELLSPORT PUBLIC LIBRARY*, 220 N Helena St, 53010-0405. (Mail add: PO Box 405, 53010-0405), SAN 317-9303. Tel: 920-533-8534. FAX: 920-533-8712. E-mail: director@campbellsportlibrary.org. Web Site: www.campbellsportlibrary.org. *Dir,* Stephanie Remillard; E-mail: remillard@campbellsportlibrary.org
Founded 1929. Pop 1,700; Circ 19,421
Library Holdings: Bk Vols 12,000; Per Subs 30
Wireless access
Mem of Winnefox Library System
Open Mon & Tues 12-8, Wed 10-6, Thurs 12-5, Fri 10-5, Sat 9-12

CASHTON

P   CASHTON MEMORIAL LIBRARY*, 809 Main St, 54619. (Mail add: PO Box 234, 54619-0234), SAN 377-9610. Tel: 608-654-5465. FAX: 608-654-7383. E-mail: torklib@wrlsweb.org. Web Site: www.wrlsweb.org/cashton/. *Librn,* Jill Bjornstad
Library Holdings: Bk Titles 7,000; Per Subs 15
Automation Activity & Vendor Info: (Cataloging) Follett Software; (Circulation) Follett Software
Mem of Winding Rivers Library System
Open Mon & Fri 12:30-5:30, Tues 12:30-7, Wed 9-1:30
Friends of the Library Group

CASSVILLE

P   ECKSTEIN MEMORIAL LIBRARY*, Cassville Public Library, 1034 E Dewey St, 53806. (Mail add: PO Box 450, 53806), SAN 317-9311. Tel: 608-725-5838. FAX: 608-725-5152. Web Site: www.cassville.org/cl-library.html. *Dir,* Susan Uppena; E-mail: suppena@swls.org; *Asst Librn,* Bae Ruth Kirschbaum
Pop 1,085; Circ 10,082
Library Holdings: AV Mats 296; Large Print Bks 174; Bk Vols 12,940; Per Subs 32; Talking Bks 168
Automation Activity & Vendor Info: (Cataloging) Horizon; (Circulation) Horizon; (OPAC) Horizon
Wireless access

Mem of Southwest Wisconsin Library System
Open Mon & Thurs 10-5, Wed 12-8, Sat 9-12

CEDAR GROVE

P   CEDAR GROVE PUBLIC LIBRARY*, 131 Van Altena Ave, 53013. (Mail add: PO Box 287, 53013-0287), SAN 317-932X. Tel: 920-668-6834. FAX: 920-668-8744. Web Site: www.cedargrove.lib.wi.us. *Dir,* Connie Acker; E-mail: cpacker@esls.lib.wi.us; *Webmaster,* Peter DeHaai
Founded 1944
Library Holdings: AV Mats 1,214; Bk Vols 24,529; Per Subs 192; Talking Bks 734
Special Collections: Small Dutch Heritage Coll
Automation Activity & Vendor Info: (Cataloging) SirsiDynix; (Circulation) SirsiDynix; (OPAC) SirsiDynix
Wireless access
Mem of Eastern Shores Library System
Open Mon-Thurs 10-8, Fri 10-5, Sat 10-12
Friends of the Library Group

CEDARBURG

P   CEDARBURG PUBLIC LIBRARY*, W63 N583 Hanover Ave, 53012. SAN 317-9338. Tel: 262-375-7640. FAX: 262-375-7618. *Dir,* Mary Marquardt; E-mail: mmarqrdt@esls.lib.wi.us; Staff 13 (MLS 4, Non-MLS 9)
Founded 1911. Pop 17,075; Circ 205,144
Jan 2006-Dec 2006 Income $653,965, City $408,888, County $4,367, Locally Generated Income $28,500, Other $212,210. Mats Exp $90,668. Sal $334,156
Library Holdings: CDs 1,177; DVDs 1,084; Large Print Bks 1,621; Bk Titles 73,000; Bk Vols 75,872; Per Subs 205; Talking Bks 1,852; Videos 3,594
Subject Interests: Civil War, Popular fiction
Automation Activity & Vendor Info: (Circulation) SirsiDynix; (OPAC) SirsiDynix
Publications: Informational Brochure
Mem of Eastern Shores Library System
Open Mon-Thurs 9-9, Fri & Sat 10-5, Sun (Sept-May) 1-5
Friends of the Library Group

CENTURIA

P   CENTURIA PUBLIC LIBRARY*, 409 Fourth St, 54824-7468. (Mail add: PO Box 370, 54824-0370), SAN 376-6713. Tel: 715-646-2630. FAX: 715-646-2630. E-mail: centuriapl@ifls.lib.wi.us. Web Site: www.centurialibrary.org. *Dir,* Lynne M Schauls
Library Holdings: Bk Vols 7,300; Per Subs 20
Mem of Indianhead Federated Library System
Open Mon 12-5, Tues & Wed 12-8, Sat 10-12

CHETEK

P   CALHOUN MEMORIAL LIBRARY, Chetek Library, 321 Moore St, 54728. (Mail add: PO Box 25, 54728-0025), SAN 317-9346. Tel: 715-924-3195. FAX: 715-925-2052. Web Site: www.calhounmemoriallibrary.org. *Dir,* Carol Burnham; E-mail: burnham@calhounmemoriallibrary.org
Founded 1888. Pop 4,000; Circ 45,000
Library Holdings: AV Mats 1,500; Braille Volumes 46; Bk Titles 15,764; Per Subs 40; Talking Bks 1,003
Special Collections: Children's Books in Braille
Automation Activity & Vendor Info: (Acquisitions) Innovative Interfaces, Inc; (Cataloging) Innovative Interfaces, Inc; (ILL) Innovative Interfaces, Inc; (OPAC) Innovative Interfaces, Inc
Mem of Indianhead Federated Library System
Open Mon, Wed & Fri 9-6, Tues & Thurs 1-6, Sat 9-12
Friends of the Library Group

CHILTON

P   CHILTON PUBLIC LIBRARY*, 221 Park St, 53014. SAN 317-9354. Tel: 920-849-4414. FAX: 920-849-2370. Web Site: www.chilton.lib.wi.us. *Dir,* Kathy Garton; E-mail: kgarton@esls.lib.wi.us; *Asst Librn,* Carol Kupsky; *Asst Librn,* Mary Riesterer; *Asst Librn,* Patti Sabo; *Asst Librn,* Joyce Sell
Founded 1933. Pop 6,859; Circ 116,294
Library Holdings: Bk Vols 41,204; Per Subs 170
Special Collections: Parent/Teachers Coll; Wis Coll
Automation Activity & Vendor Info: (Cataloging) SirsiDynix; (Circulation) SirsiDynix; (OPAC) SirsiDynix
Wireless access
Mem of Manitowoc-Calumet Library System
Open Mon-Thurs 10-8, Fri 10-6, Sat 10-1, Sun Noon-3
Friends of the Library Group

CHIPPEWA FALLS

P   CHIPPEWA FALLS PUBLIC LIBRARY*, 105 W Central, 54729-2397. SAN 317-9362. Tel: 715-723-1146. Reference Tel: 715-723-1146, Ext 206. FAX: 715-720-6922. E-mail: cflib@ifls.lib.wi.us. Web Site: www.chippewafallslibrary.org. *Dir,* Rosemary Kilbridge; E-mail: kilbriro@ifls.lib.wi.us; *Bus Mgr,* Karen Grothe; E-mail: kagrothe@ifls.lib.wi.us; *Ch,* Colleen Crowley; E-mail: ccrowley@ifls.lib.wi.us; *Circ,* Lynn Kuechenmeister; E-mail: lykuchen@ifls.lib.wi.us; *ILL, Ref,* Terri Anderson; E-mail: terran@ifls.lib.wi.us; *Tech Serv,* Julie Woodruff; E-mail: jwoodruf@ifls.lib.wi.us; Staff 5 (MLS 5)
Founded 1893. Pop 39,943; Circ 411,365
Library Holdings: AV Mats 7,348; e-books 13,385; High Interest/Low Vocabulary Bk Vols 200; Bk Titles 6,074; Bk Vols 94,558; Per Subs 215; Videos 4,192
Special Collections: Wisconsin Historical Coll, bks, fs, microfilm
Automation Activity & Vendor Info: (Acquisitions) Innovative Interfaces, Inc; (Cataloging) Innovative Interfaces, Inc; (Circulation) Innovative Interfaces, Inc; (OPAC) Innovative Interfaces, Inc; (Serials) Innovative Interfaces, Inc
Function: Adult bk club
Mem of Indianhead Federated Library System
Special Services for the Blind - Aids for in-house use
Open Mon-Thurs (Winter) 10-8, Fri 10-5:30, Sat 10-4:30; Mon & Thurs (Summer) 10-8, Tues, Wed & Fri 10-5:30, Sat 10-12:30
Friends of the Library Group

CLEAR LAKE

P   CLEAR LAKE PUBLIC LIBRARY*, 350 Fourth Ave, 54005. (Mail add: PO Box 365, 54005-0365), SAN 376-6705. Tel: 715-263-2802. E-mail: clearlakelib@clearlakelibrary.org. Web Site: www.clearlakelibrary.org. *Librn,* Christine LaFond; Staff 1 (MLS 1)
Pop 142,536
Library Holdings: AV Mats 1,669; e-books 6,763; Bk Vols 12,894; Per Subs 68
Automation Activity & Vendor Info: (Acquisitions) Innovative Interfaces, Inc; (Cataloging) Innovative Interfaces, Inc; (Circulation) Innovative Interfaces, Inc; (Course Reserve) Innovative Interfaces, Inc; (ILL) Innovative Interfaces, Inc; (Media Booking) Innovative Interfaces, Inc; (OPAC) Innovative Interfaces, Inc; (Serials) Innovative Interfaces, Inc
Wireless access
Mem of Indianhead Federated Library System
Open Mon & Tues 11-7, Wed 2-8, Thurs 9-2, Fri 11-5, Sat 9:30-1:30
Friends of the Library Group

CLEVELAND

J   LAKESHORE TECHNICAL COLLEGE LIBRARY*, 1290 North Ave, 53015. SAN 317-9389. Tel: 920-458-4183, Ext 130. FAX: 920-693-8966. E-mail: library@gotoltc.edu. Web Site: gotoltc.edu/library. *Mgr,* Linda McCabe; *Info Spec,* Barbara Kussman; Tel: 920-693-1149, E-mail: barbara.kussman@gotoltc.com; Staff 4 (MLS 1, Non-MLS 3)
Founded 1965. Enrl 2,000; Fac 85; Highest Degree: Associate
Jul 2008-Jun 2009. Mats Exp $30,000, Books $11,000, Per/Ser (Incl. Access Fees) $13,000, Other Print Mats $2,000, Electronic Ref Mat (Incl. Access Fees) $4,000. Sal $106,000 (Prof $67,000)
Library Holdings: Bk Vols 16,000; Per Subs 220
Subject Interests: Nursing
Automation Activity & Vendor Info: (Cataloging) Ex Libris Group; (Circulation) Ex Libris Group; (Course Reserve) Ex Libris Group; (Serials) Ex Libris Group
Function: Computers for patron use, Copy machines, E-Reserves, Electronic databases & coll, Online cat
Partic in OCLC Online Computer Library Center, Inc; WISPALS Library Consortium
Open Mon-Thurs 7:30-7:30, Fri 7:30-3:30

CLINTON

P   CLINTON PUBLIC LIBRARY*, 214 Mill St, 53525-9459. (Mail add: PO Box 487, 53525-0487), SAN 317-9397. Tel: 608-676-5569. Web Site: als.lib.wi.us/CPL. *Dir,* Michelle Dennis; E-mail: dennis.michelle@als.lib.wi.us
Founded 1913
Library Holdings: Bk Vols 29,000; Per Subs 50
Automation Activity & Vendor Info: (Acquisitions) Innovative Interfaces, Inc; (Cataloging) Innovative Interfaces, Inc; (Circulation) Innovative Interfaces, Inc
Mem of Arrowhead Library System
Open Mon-Thurs 9-8, Fri 9-5, Sat 9-3
Friends of the Library Group

CLINTONVILLE

P   CLINTONVILLE PUBLIC LIBRARY, 75 Hemlock St, 54929-1461. SAN
      317-9400. Tel: 715-823-4563. FAX: 715-823-7134. E-mail:
      cpl@mail.owls.lib.wi.us. Web Site: www.clintonvillelibrary.org. *Dir,*
      Kathleen Mitchell; E-mail: kmitchel@mail.owls.lib.wi.us; *Ch,* Diane
      Raschke; *Libr Asst,* Jamison Hein; Staff 3 (MLS 2, Non-MLS 1)
      Founded 1905. Pop 4,543; Circ 125,223
      Jan 2011-Dec 2011 Income $421,620, City $267,794, Federal $1,765,
      County $120,919, Locally Generated Income $17,038, Other $14,104. Mats
      Exp $57,603, Books $43,886, Per/Ser (Incl. Access Fees) $6,064, AV Mat
      $7,653. Sal $204,212 (Prof $114,238)
      Library Holdings: Audiobooks 3,197; AV Mats 874; e-books 17,194;
      Electronic Media & Resources 11,139; Bk Vols 63,007; Per Subs 149;
      Videos 4,960
      Automation Activity & Vendor Info: (Cataloging) Innovative Interfaces,
      Inc - Millenium; (Circulation) Innovative Interfaces, Inc - Millenium;
      (OPAC) Innovative Interfaces, Inc; (Serials) Innovative Interfaces, Inc -
      Millenium
      Database Vendor: EBSCOhost, Medline, netLibrary, Newsbank, OCLC
      WorldCat, ProQuest, PubMed
      Wireless access
      Function: Adult bk club, After school storytime, Audio & video playback
      equip for onsite use, Audiobks via web, Bks on cassette, Bks on CD,
      Children's prog, Computers for patron use, Copy machines, E-Reserves,
      Electronic databases & coll, Free DVD rentals, Handicapped accessible,
      Homebound delivery serv, ILL available, Large print keyboards, Magnifiers
      for reading, Microfiche/film & reading machines, Music CDs, Online cat,
      Online searches, OverDrive digital audio bks, Photocopying/Printing,
      Preschool reading prog, Prog for adults, Prog for children & young adult,
      Pub access computers, Ref & res, Scanner, Spanish lang bks, Spoken
      cassettes & CDs, Story hour, Summer reading prog, Tax forms, Teen prog,
      Telephone ref, VHS videos, Video lending libr, Wheelchair accessible
      Mem of Outagamie Waupaca Library System
      Partic in OWLSnet
      Open Mon-Thurs 10-8, Fri 10-5, Sat 10-1:30
      Friends of the Library Group

COBB

P   COBB PUBLIC LIBRARY*, 109 Mifflin St, 53526. SAN 317-9419. Tel:
      608-623-2554. FAX: 608-623-2554. Web Site:
      www.swls.org/member.co.html. *Dir,* Sherry Nagel; E-mail:
      snagel@swls.org; Staff 0.5 (Non-MLS 0.5)
      Founded 1931. Pop 442; Circ 7,972
      Jan 2006-Dec 2006 Income $24,566, City $19,936, County $4,630. Mats
      Exp $1,800
      Library Holdings: Bk Vols 5,833; Talking Bks 284; Videos 511
      Automation Activity & Vendor Info: (Acquisitions) SirsiDynix;
      (Cataloging) SirsiDynix; (Circulation) SirsiDynix
      Mem of Southwest Wisconsin Library System
      Open Mon 4pm-7pm, Tues & Thurs 9:30-5:30, Sat 9:30-12:30
      Friends of the Library Group

COLBY

P   COLBY PUBLIC LIBRARY*, 211 W Spence St, 54421. (Mail add: PO
      Box 318, 54421-0318), SAN 317-9427. Tel: 715-223-2000. *Dir,* Vicky
      Calmes; E-mail: calmes@wvls.lib.wi.us; Staff 3 (Non-MLS 3)
      Founded 1879. Pop 1,706
      Library Holdings: AV Mats 1,360; Bk Vols 15,087; Per Subs 66; Talking
      Bks 1,359
      Database Vendor: EBSCOhost, Gale Cengage Learning, ProQuest,
      SirsiDynix
      Mem of Wisconsin Valley Library Service
      Open Mon & Thurs 1-5, Tues 10-8, Wed & Fri 10-5, Sat 9-12
      Friends of the Library Group

COLFAX

P   COLFAX PUBLIC LIBRARY*, 613 Main St, 54730. (Mail add: PO Box
      525, 54730-0525), SAN 317-9435. Tel: 715-962-4334. E-mail:
      colfaxpl@ifls.lib.wi.us. *Dir,* Lisa L Ludwig
      Founded 1901. Pop 1,166; Circ 26,069
      Library Holdings: Bk Vols 10,000; Per Subs 41
      Mem of Indianhead Federated Library System
      Open Mon & Thurs 1-8, Tues & Fri 1-5, Wed 10-5
      Friends of the Library Group

COLOMA

P   COLOMA PUBLIC LIBRARY*, 155 Front St, 54930-9670. (Mail add: PO
      Box 99, 54930-0099). Tel: 715-228-2530. FAX: 715-228-2532. Web Site:
      www.colomalibrary.org. *Dir,* Sandy Zuehlke; E-mail:
      zuehlke@colomalibrary.org; Staff 3 (Non-MLS 3)
      Pop 1,200; Circ 28,183

Library Holdings: Bk Vols 12,000; Per Subs 50
Open Mon, Wed & Fri 10-5, Thurs 10-7, Sat 10-1
Friends of the Library Group

COLUMBUS

P   COLUMBUS PUBLIC LIBRARY, 223 W James St, 53925-1572. SAN
      317-9443. Tel: 920-623-5910. FAX: 920-623-5928. E-mail:
      colpl@scls.lib.wi.us. Web Site: www.columbuspubliclibrary.info. *Dir,*
      Cindy Fesemyer; E-mail: cfesemyer@scls.lib.wi.us; Staff 8 (MLS 1,
      Non-MLS 7)
      Founded 1877. Pop 9,076; Circ 116,547
      Jan 2011-Dec 2011 Income $369,810, City $257,231, County $110,694,
      Locally Generated Income $75, Other $1,810. Mats Exp $46,125, Books
      $31,290, Per/Ser (Incl. Access Fees) $4,399, Other Print Mats $3,518, AV
      Mat $3,955, Electronic Ref Mat (Incl. Access Fees) $2,963. Sal $102,056
      (Prof $47,088)
      Library Holdings: AV Mats 7,870; e-books 11,965; Electronic Media &
      Resources 4,160; Bk Vols 46,200; Per Subs 88; Videos 2,918
      Special Collections: Local History (Richard Stare Coll), articles; Local
      Newspapers Coll 1850-present, microfilm
      Subject Interests: Local hist
      Automation Activity & Vendor Info: (Cataloging) OpenAccess Software,
      Inc; (Circulation) OpenAccess Software, Inc
      Database Vendor: EBSCO Auto Repair Reference, EBSCOhost, infoUSA,
      LearningExpress, Overdrive, Inc, ProQuest, Telus
      Wireless access
      Function: Accessibility serv available based on individual needs, Adult bk
      club, Adult literacy prog, After school storytime, Archival coll, Audio &
      video playback equip for onsite use, Audiobks via web, Bilingual
      assistance for Spanish patrons, Bk club(s), Bks on cassette, Bks on CD,
      CD-ROM, Children's prog, Computer training, Computers for patron use,
      Copy machines, Digital talking bks, e-mail serv, E-Reserves, Electronic
      databases & coll, Family literacy, Fax serv, Free DVD rentals, Games &
      aids for the handicapped, Handicapped accessible, Home delivery & serv to
      Sr ctr & nursing homes, Homebound delivery serv, ILL available,
      Instruction & testing, Large print keyboards, Literacy & newcomer serv,
      Mail & tel request accepted, Mail loans to mem, Microfiche/film & reading
      machines, Music CDs, Notary serv, Online cat, Online ref, Online searches,
      Orientations, Outreach serv, Outside serv via phone, mail, e-mail & web,
      OverDrive digital audio bks, Photocopying/Printing, Preschool outreach,
      Prog for adults, Prog for children & young adult, Pub access computers,
      Ref & res, Ref serv available, Ref serv in person, Scanner, Senior
      computer classes, Senior outreach, Spanish lang bks, Story hour, Summer
      reading prog, Tax forms, Teen prog, Telephone ref, VHS videos, Video
      lending libr, Web-catalog, Wheelchair accessible
      Partic in Library Interchange Network (LINK)
      Special Services for the Deaf - Sign lang interpreter upon request for prog
      Special Services for the Blind - Bks on cassette; Bks on CD; Home
      delivery serv; Large print bks; Magnifiers; ZoomText magnification &
      reading software
      Open Mon-Thurs 9-8:30, Fri 9-5:30, Sat 9-1
      Friends of the Library Group

COON VALLEY

P   KNUTSON MEMORIAL LIBRARY*, 500 Central Ave, 54623. (Mail add:
      PO Box 99, 54623-0099). Tel: 608-452-3757. FAX: 608-452-2090. *Dir,*
      Karen Bernau; E-mail: k.bernau@wrlsweb.org
      Pop 1,727
      Library Holdings: Bk Titles 9,000; Per Subs 50
      Automation Activity & Vendor Info: (Cataloging) Horizon; (Circulation)
      Horizon; (OPAC) Horizon
      Mem of Winding Rivers Library System
      Open Mon & Thurs 1-5, Tues 5-9, Fri 10-2, Sat 10-1

CORNELL

P   CORNELL PUBLIC LIBRARY*, 117 N Third St, 54732. (Mail add: PO
      Box 796, 54732-0796), SAN 317-9451. Tel: 715-239-3709. FAX:
      715-239-3704. E-mail: cornellpl@ifls.lib.wi.us. *Dir,* Sharon Shepard
      Founded 1928. Pop 3,500; Circ 26,000
      Library Holdings: AV Mats 1,191; CDs 300; DVDs 270; Large Print Bks
      676; Bk Titles 10,297; Per Subs 36; Talking Bks 300; Videos 917
      Special Collections: Local History Coll
      Automation Activity & Vendor Info: (Circulation) Winnebago Software
      Co
      Mem of Indianhead Federated Library System
      Partic in Wiscat
      Open Mon 1-7, Tues 1-5, Wed 3-8, Thurs 10-5, Fri & Sat 10-2
      Friends of the Library Group

CRANDON

P CRANDON PUBLIC LIBRARY*, 110 W Polk St, 54520-1458. SAN 317-946X. Tel: 715-478-3784. FAX: 715-478-3784. Web Site: www.crandonpl.org. *Dir,* Michelle Gobart; E-mail: mgobart@wvls.lib.wi.us; *Asst Dir,* Laurie Renel-Faledas; E-mail: lrenel@wvls.lib.wi.us
Founded 1910. Pop 9,044; Circ 18,364
Library Holdings: Bk Vols 17,000; Per Subs 27
Mem of Wisconsin Valley Library Service
Open Mon-Wed & Fri 9-5, Thurs 9-7, Sat 9-Noon
Friends of the Library Group

CROSS PLAINS

P ROSEMARY GARFOOT PUBLIC LIBRARY*, 2107 Julius St, 53528-9499. SAN 317-9478. Tel: 608-798-3881. FAX: 608-798-0196. *Dir,* Pam Bosben; E-mail: pbosben@scls.lib.wi.us; *Asst Dir,* Sue Freedman; *Youth Serv Coordr,* Catherine Baer; *Circ Supvr,* Kris Loman
Founded 1964. Pop 2,840
Library Holdings: Bk Titles 25,389; Per Subs 125
Special Collections: State Document Depository
Mem of South Central Library System
Friends of the Library Group

CUDAHY

P CUDAHY FAMILY LIBRARY*, 3500 Library Dr, 53110. (Mail add: PO Box 100450, 53110-6107), SAN 317-9494. Tel: 414-769-2244. FAX: 414-769-2252. E-mail: cpl.reference@mcfls.org. Web Site: www.cudahyfamilylibrary.org. *Dir, Libr Serv,* Rebecca Roepke; Tel: 414-769-2246, E-mail: rebecca.roepke@mcfls.org; Staff 4 (MLS 4)
Founded 1906. Pop 18,429; Circ 239,562
Library Holdings: AV Mats 14,863; Bk Vols 100,000; Per Subs 200
Subject Interests: Local hist
Automation Activity & Vendor Info: (Cataloging) Innovative Interfaces, Inc; (Circulation) Innovative Interfaces, Inc; (OPAC) Innovative Interfaces, Inc; (Serials) Innovative Interfaces, Inc
Database Vendor: ALLDATA Online, Baker & Taylor, Checkpoint Systems, Inc, EBSCO Auto Repair Reference, EBSCOhost, LearningExpress, Standard & Poor's
Wireless access
Mem of Milwaukee County Federated Library System
Partic in Library Council of Southeastern Wisconsin, Inc
Open Mon-Thurs (Winter) 10-8, Fri & Sat 9-5, Sun 12-4; Mon-Thurs (Summer) 10-8, Fri 9-5, Sat & Sun 12-4
Friends of the Library Group

S LADISH CO*, Technical Information Center, 5481 S Packard Ave, 53110. (Mail add: PO Box 8902, 53110-8902), SAN 373-305X. Tel: 414-747-3063. FAX: 414-747-3036. *Mgr,* Dave Furrer
Library Holdings: Bk Vols 2,000; Per Subs 12
Restriction: Co libr

CUMBERLAND

P CUMBERLAND PUBLIC LIBRARY*, 1305 Second Ave, 54829. (Mail add: PO Box 97, 54829-0097), SAN 317-9524. Tel: 715-822-2767. E-mail: cumberlandpl@ifls.lib.wi.us. *Dir,* Diana Ostness; *Asst Dir,* Julie Anderson
Founded 1898. Pop 2,000; Circ 45,506
Library Holdings: Bk Vols 21,000; Per Subs 61
Automation Activity & Vendor Info: (Cataloging) SirsiDynix; (Circulation) SirsiDynix; (ILL) SirsiDynix; (OPAC) SirsiDynix
Open Mon, Wed & Fri 10-6, Tues & Thurs 10-8, Sat 9-1
Friends of the Library Group

DALLAS

P DALLAS PUBLIC LIBRARY*, Main St, 54733. (Mail add: PO Box 84, 54733-0084). Tel: 715-837-1186. E-mail: dlibrary@chibardun.net. *Librn,* Beatrice Andel
Founded 1969. Pop 400; Circ 4,200
Library Holdings: Bk Titles 4,937; Bk Vols 5,012
Friends of the Library Group

DARIEN

P DARIEN PUBLIC LIBRARY*, 47 Park St, 53114-0465. (Mail add: PO Box 490, 53114-0490), SAN 317-9540. Tel: 262-882-5155. FAX: 262-882-5157. *Librn,* Jeannine Heskett; E-mail: heskett@darien.lib.wi.us
Founded 1922. Pop 2,000
Library Holdings: Bk Vols 10,000
Automation Activity & Vendor Info: (Acquisitions) SirsiDynix; (Cataloging) SirsiDynix; (Circulation) SirsiDynix
Mem of Lakeshores Library System

Open Mon-Thurs 10-8, Fri & Sat 10-3
Friends of the Library Group

DARLINGTON

P JOHNSON PUBLIC LIBRARY*, 131 E Catherine St, 53530. SAN 317-9559. Tel: 608-776-4171. Web Site: www.swls.org/darlingtonlibrary. *Libr Dir,* Nita Burke; E-mail: nburke@swls.org; *Ch,* Janis Schlappi; E-mail: jschlappi@swls.org; Staff 1 (MLS 1)
Pop 2,400; Circ 46,600
Library Holdings: Bk Titles 25,000; Bk Vols 30,000; Per Subs 95
Special Collections: Darlington Newspapers (1865-present), micro; Lafayette County Newspaper on micro; Parenting Coll in Parent's Place area in library
Automation Activity & Vendor Info: (Acquisitions) SirsiDynix; (Cataloging) SirsiDynix; (Circulation) SirsiDynix; (OPAC) SirsiDynix
Database Vendor: ProQuest
Wireless access
Mem of Southwest Wisconsin Library System
Open Mon 10-8, Tues 1:30-5:30, Wed & Thurs 1:30-8:30, Fri 10-5, Sat 8:30-3:30
Friends of the Library Group

DE PERE

SR SAINT NORBERT ABBEY, Augustine Library, 1016 N Broadway, 54115-2697. SAN 317-9575. Tel: 920-337-4354. *Librn,* Karen E Mand; E-mail: karen.mand@snc.edu; Staff 1 (Non-MLS 1)
Founded 1898
Jul 2011-Jun 2012 Income $7,600. Mats Exp $1,500, Books $1,300. Sal $4,100
Library Holdings: Bk Titles 8,000; Bk Vols 11,200
Subject Interests: Archives, Bible, Canon law, Church hist, Monasticism, Philosophy, Premonstratensian hist, Relig orders, Theol
Automation Activity & Vendor Info: (Cataloging) Innovative Interfaces, Inc; (OPAC) Innovative Interfaces, Inc
Function: Archival coll
Restriction: Open by appt only

CR TODD WEHR LIBRARY, ST NORBERT COLLEGE*, 301 Third St, 54115. (Mail add: 100 Grant St, 54115-2002), SAN 317-9583. Tel: 920-403-3280. Circulation Tel: 920-403-3466. Interlibrary Loan Service Tel: 920-403-3283. Reference Tel: 920-403-3160. Administration Tel: 920-403-3290. FAX: 920-403-4064. Interlibrary Loan Service FAX: 920-403-4079. E-mail: library@snc.edu, refdesk@snc.edu. Web Site: www.snc.edu/library. *Dir,* Felice Maciejewski; E-mail: felice.maciejewski@snc.edu; *Head, Circ,* David Bosco; Tel: 920-403-3293, E-mail: david.bosco@snc.edu; *Head, Pub Serv,* Sally L Hansen; Tel: 920-403-3453, E-mail: sally.hansen@snc.edu; *Head, Tech Serv,* Sally V Cubitt; Fax: 920-403-4067, E-mail: sally.cubitt@snc.edu; *Info Literacy Librn,* Paul Waelchli; Tel: 920-403-3291, E-mail: paul.waelchli@snc.edu; *Syst Librn,* Kimberly M Boldt; Tel: 920-403-3282, E-mail: kimberly.boldt@snc.edu; *Acq,* Kerrie Chang; Tel: 920-403-3271, E-mail: kerrie.chang@snc.edu; *Cat,* Karen Mand; Tel: 920-403-3269, E-mail: karen.mand@snc.edu; *Circ,* Candy Klos; E-mail: candace.klos@snc.edu; *Circ,* Tony Laluzerne; E-mail: tony.laluzerne@snc.edu; *Circ,* Jenny Phillip; E-mail: jenny.phillip@snc.edu; *Circ,* Jessica Vargas Robinson; E-mail: jess.vargas@snc.edu; *ILL,* Connie Meulemans; E-mail: connie.meulemans@snc.edu; *Libr Operations,* Olivia Dart; Tel: 920-403-3061, E-mail: olivia.dart@snc.edu; *Ser,* Rochelle Van Erem; Tel: 920-403-3270, E-mail: rochelle.vanerem@snc.edu; Staff 5 (MLS 5)
Founded 1898. Enrl 2,169; Fac 175; Highest Degree: Master
Jun 2006-May 2007. Mats Exp $347,817, Books $107,858, Per/Ser (Incl. Access Fees) $134,129, Micro $10,663, Electronic Ref Mat (Incl. Access Fees) $95,167. Sal $409,706 (Prof $198,876)
Library Holdings: AV Mats 6,831; Microforms 30,299; Bk Vols 212,012; Per Subs 24,766
Special Collections: Papers of John F Bennett
Subject Interests: Humanities, Norbertine studies, Relig, Theol
Automation Activity & Vendor Info: (Acquisitions) Innovative Interfaces, Inc; (Cataloging) Innovative Interfaces, Inc; (Circulation) Innovative Interfaces, Inc; (Course Reserve) Innovative Interfaces, Inc; (ILL) OCLC ILLiad; (Media Booking) Innovative Interfaces, Inc; (OPAC) Innovative Interfaces, Inc; (Serials) Innovative Interfaces, Inc
Database Vendor: Cambridge Scientific Abstracts, EBSCOhost, Gale Cengage Learning, JSTOR, LexisNexis, netLibrary, OCLC FirstSearch, OCLC WorldCat, ProQuest, ScienceDirect
Wireless access
Open Mon-Thurs 7am-1am, Fri 7am-9pm, Sat Noon-9pm, Sun Noon-1am

DE SOTO

P   DE SOTO PUBLIC LIBRARY*, 111 S Houghton St, 54624. (Mail add: PO Box 187, 54624-0187), SAN 376-6632. Tel: 608-648-3593. E-mail: despl@mwt.net. Web Site: www.mwt.net/~despl. *Dir,* Will Fryer
Library Holdings: Bk Titles 12,000; Bk Vols 13,000; Per Subs 40
Open Tues & Wed 12:30-8, Sat 8-1

DEER PARK

P   DEER PARK PUBLIC LIBRARY*, 112 Front St W, 54007. SAN 377-9882. Tel: 715-269-5464. FAX: 715-269-5464. E-mail: deerparkpl@ifls.lib.wi.us. Web Site: www.deerparkwi.org/library. *Dir,* Brenda J Kaczmarski; E-mail: brendak@ifls.lib.wi.us; Staff 1 (Non-MLS 1)
Library Holdings: Bk Vols 9,500; Per Subs 42
Automation Activity & Vendor Info: (Acquisitions) Innovative Interfaces, Inc; (Cataloging) Innovative Interfaces, Inc; (Circulation) Innovative Interfaces, Inc; (OPAC) Innovative Interfaces, Inc; (Serials) Innovative Interfaces, Inc
Partic in Wis Libr Asn
Open Tues 2-8, Wed 10-1, Thurs 1-6, Sat 9-12

DEERFIELD

P   DEERFIELD PUBLIC LIBRARY*, 12 W Nelson St, 53531-9669. (Mail add: PO Box 408, 53531-0408), SAN 317-9591. Tel: 608-764-8102. Web Site: www.scls.lib.wi.us/deerfield. *Dir,* Kaia Fry; E-mail: kaiafry@scls.lib.wi.us; *Ch,* Gail Moynihan; E-mail: gamoynihan@scls.lib.wi.us
Founded 1974. Pop 2,073; Circ 59,210
Library Holdings: Bk Vols 19,456; Per Subs 86
Automation Activity & Vendor Info: (Cataloging) SirsiDynix; (Circulation) SirsiDynix
Wireless access
Open Mon & Thurs 12-8, Tues, Wed & Fri 9-5, Sat 9-12
Friends of the Library Group

DEFOREST

P   DEFOREST AREA PUBLIC LIBRARY*, 203 Library St, 53532. SAN 317-9567. Tel: 608-846-5482. FAX: 608-846-6875. E-mail: dft@scls.lib.wi.us. Web Site: www.deforest.lib.wi.us. *Dir,* Jan Berg; E-mail: bergjd@scls.lib.wi.us; *Asst Dir, Head, Circ,* Gisela Newbegin; E-mail: giselan@scls.lib.wi.us; *Ch,* Louise Valdovinos; *Tech Serv Librn,* LuAnn Norton; *Youth Serv Librn,* Robert Fourie; *Circ Mgr,* Traci Lerum; Staff 6 (MLS 2, Non-MLS 4)
Founded 1964. Pop 7,997; Circ 286,760
Library Holdings: AV Mats 11,437; Bk Titles 56,655; Per Subs 183
Subject Interests: Popular mat
Automation Activity & Vendor Info: (Cataloging) SirsiDynix; (Circulation) SirsiDynix; (OPAC) SirsiDynix
Function: Adult bk club, Audiobks via web, Bk club(s), Bks on cassette, Bks on CD, CD-ROM, Computers for patron use, Copy machines, Digital talking bks, e-mail serv, Electronic databases & coll, Equip loans & repairs, Exhibits, Free DVD rentals, Holiday prog, Home delivery & serv to Sr ctr & nursing homes, ILL available, Notary serv, Online cat, Prog for adults, Prog for children & young adult, Pub access computers, Senior computer classes, Senior outreach, Story hour, Summer & winter reading prog, Tax forms, Teen prog, Winter reading prog, Workshops
Mem of South Central Library System
Open Mon-Thurs 9-8, Fri & Sat 9-5
Friends of the Library Group

DELAFIELD

P   DELAFIELD PUBLIC LIBRARY*, 500 Genessee St, 53018-1895. SAN 317-9605. Tel: 262-646-6230. FAX: 262-646-6232. Web Site: delafieldlibrary.org. *Dir,* Terry Zignego
Founded 1907. Circ 145,000
Library Holdings: Bk Vols 60,000; Per Subs 90
Subject Interests: Art, Cooking, Detective fiction, Needlecrafts, Parenting
Automation Activity & Vendor Info: (Cataloging) SirsiDynix; (Circulation) SirsiDynix; (OPAC) SirsiDynix
Mem of Waukesha County Federated Library System
Open Mon-Thurs 10-8:30, Fri 10-5, Sat 10-2, Sun 1-4
Friends of the Library Group

DELAVAN

P   ARAM PUBLIC LIBRARY*, 404 E Walworth Ave, 53115-1208. SAN 317-9613. Tel: 262-728-3111. FAX: 262-728-3111. TDD: 262-728-2620. E-mail: interlib@delavan.lib.wi.us. Web Site: www.delavan.lib.wi.us. *Dir,* Amber McCrea; Staff 13 (MLS 2, Non-MLS 11)
Founded 1908. Pop 17,000; Circ 101,000
Library Holdings: Bk Titles 60,000

Automation Activity & Vendor Info: (Cataloging) SirsiDynix; (Circulation) SirsiDynix; (OPAC) SirsiDynix
Database Vendor: Baker & Taylor, EBSCOhost, Gale Cengage Learning, ProQuest
Wireless access
Mem of Lakeshores Library System
Special Services for the Deaf - Bks on deafness & sign lang; Closed caption videos; Deaf publ; TDD equip
Open Mon-Thurs (Winter) 9-8:30, Fri 9-5, Sat 9-3; Mon & Wed 9-8:30, Tues, Thurs & Fri 9-5, Sat (Summer) 9-Noon
Friends of the Library Group

S   WISCONSIN SCHOOL FOR THE DEAF*, John R Gant Library, 309 W Walworth Ave, 53115. SAN 317-9621. Tel: 262-728-7127, Ext 7133. FAX: 262-728-7129. Web Site: www.wsd.k12.wi.us/. *Librn,* Nell Fleming; E-mail: nell.fleming@wsd.k12.wi.us; *Libr Asst,* Patricia Kostechka; E-mail: patricia.kostechka@wsd.k12.wi.us; Staff 1 (MLS 1)
Founded 1930
Library Holdings: Bk Vols 11,250
Special Services for the Deaf - Coll on deaf educ; Deaf publ
Open Mon-Fri 7:30-4:30

DODGEVILLE

P   DODGEVILLE PUBLIC LIBRARY*, 139 S Iowa St, 53533. SAN 317-963X. Tel: 608-935-3728. FAX: 608-935-9405. Web Site: dodgevillelibrary.com. *Dir,* Vickie Stangel; E-mail: vstangel@swls.org; *Ch,* Carol Gleichauf; E-mail: cgleichauf@swls.org; Staff 7 (MLS 1, Non-MLS 6)
Founded 1900. Pop 4,200; Circ 133,645
Library Holdings: Bk Vols 23,131; Per Subs 56
Automation Activity & Vendor Info: (Cataloging) SirsiDynix; (Circulation) SirsiDynix
Function: Homebound delivery serv, ILL available, Photocopying/Printing, Prog for children & young adult, Summer reading prog, Wheelchair accessible
Mem of Southwest Wisconsin Library System
Open Mon, Wed & Fri 10-6, Tues & Thurs 10-7, Sat 9-1
Friends of the Library Group

S   LANDS END*, Corporate Library, One Lands End Lane, 53595. SAN 378-0902. Tel: 608-935-4175. Toll Free Tel: 800-963-4816. FAX: 608-935-4260. Toll Free FAX: 800-332-0103. Web Site: www.landsend.com. *Librn,* Kimberly Boughton; E-mail: kmbough@landsend.com
Library Holdings: Bk Titles 2,000; Per Subs 60

DORCHESTER

P   DORCHESTER PUBLIC LIBRARY*, 155 N Second St, 54425-9700. (Mail add: PO Box 198, 54425-0198), SAN 317-9648. Tel: 715-654-5959. FAX: 715-654-5802. *Dir,* Susan Wild; E-mail: swild@wvls.lib.wi.us
Pop 698; Circ 10,671
Library Holdings: Bk Vols 12,000; Per Subs 45
Automation Activity & Vendor Info: (Acquisitions) Horizon; (Cataloging) Horizon; (Circulation) Horizon; (OPAC) Horizon
Mem of Wisconsin Valley Library Service
Open Mon 11-7, Tues 1-6, Wed 10-6, Fri 9-5
Friends of the Library Group

DRUMMOND

P   DRUMMOND PUBLIC LIBRARY*, 14990 Superior St, 54832. (Mail add: PO Box 23, 54832-0023), SAN 317-9656. Tel: 715-739-6290. E-mail: drumlib@drummond.nwls.lib.wi.us. *Dir,* Suzanne Widmar
Library Holdings: Bk Vols 7,200
Mem of Northern Waters Library Service
Open Mon & Sat 9-1, Tues, Wed & Fri 10-5, Thurs 10-6

DUNBAR

SR   NORTHLAND INTERNATIONAL UNIVERSITY LIBRARY*, W10085 Pike Plains Rd, 54119. Tel: 715-324-6999, Ext 5500. Circulation Tel: 715-324-6900, Ext 5501. Reference Tel: 715-324-6900, Ext 5500. FAX: 715-324-6133. E-mail: library@ni.edu. *Dir,* Van Carpenter; Staff 24 (MLS 1, Non-MLS 23)
Founded 1967. Enrl 606; Highest Degree: Master
Library Holdings: AV Mats 4,100; CDs 130; Bk Titles 42,400; Bk Vols 46,700; Per Subs 220; Videos 1,070
Special Collections: Rare Theological Books
Subject Interests: Bible, Theol
Automation Activity & Vendor Info: (Cataloging) OCLC; (Circulation) LibLime; (Course Reserve) LibLime; (ILL) OCLC; (OPAC) LibLime; (Serials) EBSCO Online
Wireless access

Function: Archival coll, Audio & video playback equip for onsite use, AV serv, CD-ROM, ILL available, Outside serv via phone, mail, e-mail & web, Photocopying/Printing, Spoken cassettes & CDs, VHS videos
Open Mon, Tues, Thurs & Fri 7:30am-10pm, Wed 7:30-5 & 8-10, Sat 11-5
Restriction: Fee for pub use, Open to students, fac & staff

DURAND

P   DURAND PUBLIC LIBRARY, 604 Seventh Ave E, 54736. SAN 317-9664. Tel: 715-672-8730. *Adult Serv, Dir,* Patti Blount; E-mail: pblount@durand.k12.wi.us; *Ch,* Avonelle Lamphere
Founded 1886. Circ 40,536
Library Holdings: Bk Vols 47,000; Per Subs 51
Special Collections: Local Newspaper, 1889-present
Subject Interests: Local hist
Automation Activity & Vendor Info: (Cataloging) Follett Software; (Circulation) Follett Software
Mem of Indianhead Federated Library System
Open Mon-Fri (Winter) 8-7, Sat 9-12; Tues-Fri (Summer) 9-6

EAGLE

P   ALICE BAKER MEMORIAL PUBLIC LIBRARY*, 820 E Main, 53119. (Mail add: PO Box 520, 53119-0520), SAN 376-6640. Tel: 262-594-2800. FAX: 262-594-5126. Web Site: www.wcfls.lib.wi.us/eagle. *Dir,* Allison Chase; E-mail: chase@eagle.lib.wi.us; *ILL,* K Boucher; E-mail: kboucher@eagle.lib.wi.us
Library Holdings: Bk Titles 17,000; Bk Vols 20,000; Per Subs 80
Mem of Waukesha County Federated Library System
Open Mon-Wed 10-8, Thurs & Fri 10-5, Sat 10-12
Friends of the Library Group

EAGLE RIVER

P   WALTER E OLSON MEMORIAL LIBRARY*, 203 N Main St, 54521. (Mail add: PO Box 69, 54521-0069), SAN 317-9672. Tel: 715-479-8070. FAX: 715-479-2435. Web Site: olson.wislib.org. *Dir,* Diana B Anderson; Tel: 715-479-8070, Ext 21, E-mail: danderson@olson.nwls.lib.wi.us; *Ch, Tech Serv,* Patricia Lamon; Tel: 715-479-8070, Ext 22, E-mail: plamon@olson.nwls.lib.wi.us; *ILL,* Mickee Stuckemeyer; Tel: 715-479-8070, Ext 23, E-mail: mickee@olson.nwls.lib.wi.us; Staff 3 (Non-MLS 3)
Founded 1915. Pop 8,000; Circ 56,427
Jan 2009-Dec 2009 Income $205,331, City $148,226, Federal $828, County $16,800, Locally Generated Income $32,200, Other $7,277. Mats Exp $30,780, Books $22,000, Per/Ser (Incl. Access Fees) $4,500, AV Equip $1,300, AV Mat $2,980. Sal $125,343 (Prof $44,488)
Library Holdings: AV Mats 4,624; e-books 11,545; Electronic Media & Resources 1,217; Bk Titles 40,758; Per Subs 161
Special Collections: Harvard Classics; Library of America; Literacy Coll (GED, High interest/low vocabulary, ESL)
Automation Activity & Vendor Info: (Acquisitions) Innovative Interfaces, Inc; (Cataloging) Innovative Interfaces, Inc - OCLC; (Circulation) Innovative Interfaces, Inc; (ILL) Innovative Interfaces, Inc; (OPAC) Innovative Interfaces, Inc
Wireless access
Function: AV serv, Handicapped accessible, Homebound delivery serv, ILL available, Magnifiers for reading, Photocopying/Printing, Prog for adults, Prog for children & young adult, Ref serv available, Serves mentally handicapped consumers, Summer reading prog, Telephone ref, Wheelchair accessible
Publications: Annual Report (Annually)
Mem of Northern Waters Library Service
Partic in Merlin
Special Services for the Deaf - Bks on deafness & sign lang; High interest/low vocabulary bks
Special Services for the Blind - Aids for in-house use; Assistive/Adapted tech devices, equip & products; Audio mat; Bks available with recordings; Bks on cassette; Bks on CD; Cassette playback machines; Copier with enlargement capabilities; Extensive large print coll; Home delivery serv; Internet workstation with adaptive software; Magnifiers
Open Mon 9-7, Tues-Thurs 9-6, Fri 9-5, Sat 9-3
Friends of the Library Group

L   VILAS COUNTY LAW LIBRARY*, 330 Court St, 54521. SAN 377-9653. Tel: 715-479-3638. FAX: 715-479-3740.
Library Holdings: Bk Vols 1,000; Per Subs 5
Open Mon-Fri 8-4

EAST TROY

P   EAST TROY LIONS PUBLIC LIBRARY*, 3094 Graydon Ave, 53120. SAN 317-9680. Tel: 262-642-6262. E-mail: illet@easttroy.lib.wi.us. Web Site: www.easttroy.lib.wi.us. *Dir,* Jackie Gotz; E-mail: gotz@easttroy.lib.wi.us

Founded 1895. Pop 3,300; Circ 46,000
Library Holdings: Bk Titles 20,000; Bk Vols 24,000; Per Subs 85
Special Collections: State Document Depository; UN Document Depository; US Document Depository
Automation Activity & Vendor Info: (Acquisitions) SirsiDynix; (Cataloging) SirsiDynix; (Circulation) SirsiDynix; (OPAC) SIRSI-iBistro
Mem of Lakeshores Library System
Open Mon-Thurs 10-7, Fri 10-5, Sat 10-1

EAU CLAIRE

S   CHIPPEWA VALLEY MUSEUM, INC*, 1204 Carson Park Dr, 54702. (Mail add: PO Box 1204, 54702-1204), SAN 327-8425. Tel: 715-834-7871. FAX: 715-834-6624. E-mail: info@cvmuseum.com. Web Site: www.cvmuseum.com. *Librn,* Eldbjorg Tobin; E-mail: history@cvmuseum.com
Library Holdings: Bk Vols 3,000
Open Tues-Fri 1-5

J   CHIPPEWA VALLEY TECHNICAL COLLEGE LIBRARY*, 620 W Clairemont Ave, 54701-6162. SAN 317-9699. Tel: 715-833-6285. Reference Tel: 715-833-6461. FAX: 715-833-6470. E-mail: reference@cvtc.edu. Web Site: www.cvtc.edu/library. *In Charge,* Philip Palser; Tel: 715-833-6364, E-mail: ppalser@cvtc.edu; Staff 3 (Non-MLS 3)
Founded 1965. Enrl 4,003; Fac 212; Highest Degree: Associate
Library Holdings: AV Mats 1,337; e-books 13,807; Bk Titles 15,800; Bk Vols 19,613; Per Subs 395; Videos 4,075
Subject Interests: Allied health, Nursing, Paralegal
Automation Activity & Vendor Info: (Acquisitions) Ex Libris Group; (Cataloging) Ex Libris Group; (Circulation) Ex Libris Group; (Course Reserve) Ex Libris Group; (Media Booking) Ex Libris Group; (OPAC) Ex Libris Group; (Serials) Ex Libris Group
Database Vendor: EBSCOhost, netLibrary, ProQuest, Westlaw
Partic in OCLC Online Computer Library Center, Inc; Wisconsin Library Services
Open Mon-Fri 7:30am-8pm, Sat (Winter) 9-3; Mon-Fri (Summer) 7:30-4

CR   CHURCH OF THE LUTHERAN CONFERENCE*, Immanuel Lutheran College Library, 501 Grover Rd, 54701. SAN 377-9505. Tel: 715-836-6636. FAX: 715-836-6634. *Librn,* Aaron Gullerid; E-mail: aaron.gullerid@ilc.edu
Founded 1959. Enrl 180; Fac 14
Library Holdings: Braille Volumes 6; CDs 50; DVDs 12; Large Print Bks 50; Music Scores 100; Bk Titles 11,000; Per Subs 60; Videos 100
Subject Interests: Relig
Automation Activity & Vendor Info: (Acquisitions) Library Concepts; (Cataloging) Library Concepts; (Circulation) Library Concepts
Wireless access
Mem of Indianhead Federated Library System
Restriction: Not open to pub

S   EAU CLAIRE LEADER-TELEGRAM NEWSROOM LIBRARY*, 701 S Farwell St, 54702. (Mail add: PO Box 570, 54702-0570), SAN 377-9327. Tel: 715-833-9200. FAX: 715-858-7308. *Librn,* Laura Heyde
Library Holdings: Bk Vols 70
Special Collections: News Archival Coll, 1879-present

P   INDIANHEAD FEDERATED LIBRARY SYSTEM*, 1538 Truax Blvd, 54703. SAN 317-9729. Tel: 715-839-5082. Interlibrary Loan Service Tel: 715-839-5077. FAX: 715-839-5151. Web Site: www.ifls.lib.wi.us. *Dir,* John Thompson; E-mail: thompson@ifls.lib.wi.us; Staff 9 (MLS 4, Non-MLS 5)
Founded 1978. Pop 437,000
Automation Activity & Vendor Info: (Cataloging) Innovative Interfaces, Inc; (Circulation) Innovative Interfaces, Inc; (ILL) Innovative Interfaces, Inc; (OPAC) Innovative Interfaces, Inc
Function: Doc delivery serv, ILL available, Online ref, Prof lending libr, Ref & res, Workshops
Publications: Roundabout IFLS (Newsletter)
Member Libraries: Amery Public Library; Augusta Memorial Public Library; Baldwin Public Library; Balsam Lake Public Library; Barron Public Library; Boyceville Public Library; Bruce Area Library; Cadott Community Library; Calhoun Memorial Library; Cameron Public Library; Carleton A Friday Memorial Library; Centuria Public Library; Chippewa Falls Public Library; Church of the Lutheran Conference; Clarella Hackett Johnson Library; Clear Lake Public Library; Colfax Public Library; Cornell Public Library; Cumberland Public Library; D R Moon Memorial Library; Durand Public Library; Ellsworth Public Library; Elmwood Public Library; Fairchild Public Library; Fall Creek Public Library; Frederic Public Library; G E Bleskacek Memorial Library; Glenwood City Public Library; Hammond Community Library; Hawkins Area Library; Hazel Mackin Community Library; Hudson Area Joint Library; L E Phillips Memorial Public Library; Luck Public Library; Menomonie Public Library; Milltown Public Library; Ogema Public Library; Park Falls Public Library; Pepin Public Library; Plum City Public Library; Polk County Library Federation;

Rice Lake Public Library; River Falls Public Library; Rusk County Community Library; Somerset Public Library; Spring Valley Public Library; St Croix Falls Public Library; Turtle Lake Public Library; Woodville Community Library
Restriction: Circulates for staff only, Not open to pub

M MAYO CLINIC HEALTH SYSTEM*, Eau Claire Medical Library, 1221 Whipple St, 54702-4105. SAN 317-9737. Tel: 715-838-3248. FAX: 715-838-3289. E-mail: library.eauclaire@mayo.edu. *Supvr,* Matt Hoy; Staff 5 (MLS 2, Non-MLS 3)
Founded 1930
Library Holdings: Bk Vols 4,260; Per Subs 300
Special Collections: Consumer Health Information Center Coll
Subject Interests: Allied health, Hospital admin, Med, Nursing
Automation Activity & Vendor Info: (Cataloging) Innovative Interfaces, Inc; (Circulation) Innovative Interfaces, Inc
Publications: Newsletter
Open Mon-Fri 8-4:30

P L E PHILLIPS MEMORIAL PUBLIC LIBRARY*, 400 Eau Claire St, 54701. SAN 317-9710. Tel: 715-839-1648, 715-839-5004. Circulation Tel: 715-839-5003. Interlibrary Loan Service Tel: 715-839-3877. Administration Tel: 715-839-5002. Toll Free Tel: 800-525-7787. FAX: 715-839-5310. Administration FAX: 715-839-3822. TDD: 715-839-1689. E-mail: librarian@eauclaire.lib.wi.us. Web Site: www.ecpubliclibrary.info. *Dir,* John Stoneberg; Tel: 715-839-5001, E-mail: johns@eauclaire.lib.wi.us; *Asst Dir,* Mark Troendle; Tel: 715-839-6225, E-mail: markt@eauclaire.lib.wi.us; *Bus Mgr,* Julie Gast; Tel: 715-839-5063, E-mail: julieg@eauclaire.lib.wi.us; *Circ Serv Mgr,* Laura Miller; Tel: 715-839-5098, E-mail: lauram@eauclaire.lib.wi.us; *Pub Relations & Prog Serv Mgr,* Bess Arneson; Tel: 715-839-5094, E-mail: bessa@eauclaire.lib.wi.us; *Mgr, Ref Serv,* Renee Ponzio; Tel: 715-839-1683, E-mail: reneep@eauclaire.lib.wi.us; *Tech Serv Mgr,* Sharon Price; Tel: 715-839-1647, E-mail: sharonp@eauclaire.lib.wi.us; *Youth Serv Mgr,* Shelly Collins-Fuerbringer; Tel: 715-839-2898, E-mail: shellyc@eauclaire.lib.wi.us; *YA Serv,* Dayna Myers; Tel: 715-839-2897, E-mail: daynam@eauclaire.lib.wi.us; Staff 6 (MLS 5, Non-MLS 1)
Founded 1875. Pop 98,286; Circ 1,321,985
Library Holdings: Audiobooks 7,153; CDs 14,516; DVDs 10,953; Large Print Bks 15,034; Microforms 1,401; Bk Vols 207,145; Videos 10,255
Special Collections: Municipal Document Depository; State Document Depository
Automation Activity & Vendor Info: (Acquisitions) Innovative Interfaces, Inc; (Cataloging) Innovative Interfaces, Inc; (Circulation) Innovative Interfaces, Inc; (Course Reserve) Innovative Interfaces, Inc; (ILL) Innovative Interfaces, Inc; (Media Booking) Innovative Interfaces, Inc; (OPAC) Innovative Interfaces, Inc; (Serials) Innovative Interfaces, Inc
Database Vendor: Innovative Interfaces, Inc, Innovative Interfaces, Inc INN - View
Wireless access
Mem of Indianhead Federated Library System
Partic in OCLC Online Computer Library Center, Inc
Special Services for the Deaf - High interest/low vocabulary bks; Spec interest per; TDD equip
Open Mon-Thurs 10-9, Fri 10-6, Sat 10-5, Sun 1-5
Friends of the Library Group

M SACRED HEART HOSPITAL*, St Francis Resource Center, 900 W Clairemont Ave, 54701. SAN 317-9745. Tel: 715-717-4330. FAX: 715-717-6576. *In Charge,* Evie Warns
Founded 1964
Library Holdings: Bk Titles 150; Per Subs 9
Subject Interests: General med
Partic in Greater Midwest Regional Medical Libr Network

C UNIVERSITY OF WISCONSIN-EAU CLAIRE*, William D McIntyre Library, 105 Garfield Ave, 54702-4004. SAN 317-9761. Tel: 715-836-3715. Circulation Tel: 715-836-3856. Interlibrary Loan Service Tel: 715-836-5377. Reference Tel: 715-836-3858. FAX: 715-836-2949. Web Site: www.uwec.edu/library. *Dir of Libr,* John Pollitz; Tel: pollitjh@uwec.edu; *Educ Librn, Head, Access Serv,* Kathryn Tvaruzka; Tel: 715-836-4522, E-mail: tvaruzke@uwec.edu; *Distance Educ Coordr, Head, Res & Instruction, Ref Librn,* Jill Markgraf; E-mail: markgrjs@uwec.edu; *Head, Syst,* Bryan Vogh; Tel: 715-836-4962, E-mail: voyhbs@uwec.edu; *Head, Tech Serv,* Dr Janice Bogstad; Tel: 715-836-6032, E-mail: bogstajm@uwec.edu; *Electronic Res Librn,* Stephanie Wical; Tel: 715-836-3508, E-mail: wicalsh@uwec.edu; *Ref Librn,* Eric Jennings; *Ref Librn,* Hans Kishel; *Ref Librn & Govt Publ,* Robin Miller; *Spec Coll Librn,* Position Currently Open; *Archivist, Rec Mgr,* Greg Kocken; Tel: 715-834-3873, E-mail: kockeng@uwec.edu; *Circ Serv Supvr,* BebeAnna Buck; *Reserves Supvr,* Janet Peterson; *Coordr, Cat,* Randy Olson; Tel: 715-836-4335, E-mail: olsonran@uwec.edu; *ILL Coordr,* John McCrackin; E-mail: mccracjm@uwec.edu; *Archives,* Lark Keating-Hadlock; Staff 30 (MLS 12, Non-MLS 18)

Founded 1916. Enrl 10,566; Fac 508; Highest Degree: Master
Library Holdings: Bk Titles 416,587; Bk Vols 491,129; Per Subs 1,369
Special Collections: Area Research Center; Campus Evolution Records (reflecting change from normal school to university); Chippewa Valley Historical Manuscripts & Local Government Records; Early Settlement, Lumbering, Labor, Genealogy & Politics; Uniroyal Management & Labor Union Records; Wood Family Farm Diaries. Oral History; State Document Depository; US Document Depository
Subject Interests: Educ, Nursing
Automation Activity & Vendor Info: (Acquisitions) Ex Libris Group; (Cataloging) Ex Libris Group; (Circulation) Ex Libris Group; (Course Reserve) Ex Libris Group; (ILL) OCLC; (Media Booking) Ex Libris Group; (OPAC) Ex Libris Group; (Serials) Ex Libris Group
Wireless access
Publications: Off the Shelf (Newsletter)
Partic in OCLC Online Computer Library Center, Inc; Wisconsin Library Services
Open Mon-Thurs 7am-1am, Fri 7am-9pm, Sat 9-9, Sun 11am-1am

EDGERTON

P EDGERTON PUBLIC LIBRARY*, 101 Albion St, 53534-1836. SAN 317-977X. Tel: 608-884-4511. FAX: 608-884-7575. E-mail: edgertonlibrary@als.lib.wi.us. Web Site: www.als.lib.wi.us/EPL. *Librn,* Sherry Machones; E-mail: machones.sherry@als.lib.wi.us; Staff 1 (MLS 1)
Founded 1866. Pop 8,049; Circ 72,449
Library Holdings: AV Mats 3,040; Large Print Bks 1,410; Bk Titles 26,500; Bk Vols 26,546; Per Subs 100
Subject Interests: Local hist
Automation Activity & Vendor Info: (Circulation) Innovative Interfaces, Inc; (OPAC) Innovative Interfaces, Inc
Wireless access
Mem of Arrowhead Library System
Open Mon-Thurs (Winter) 10-8, Fri 10-5, Sat 10-3, Sun 1-4; Mon & Wed (Summer) 10-6, Tues & Thurs 10-8, Fri 10-5, Sat 10-3
Friends of the Library Group

ELKHART LAKE

P ELKHART LAKE PUBLIC LIBRARY*, 40 Pine St, PO Box R, 53020-0367. SAN 376-6624. Tel: 920-876-2554.
Library Holdings: Bk Titles 5,000; Bk Vols 16,626; Per Subs 24
Mem of Eastern Shores Library System
Friends of the Library Group

ELKHORN

J GATEWAY TECHNICAL COLLEGE*, Elkhorn Campus Library, 400 County Rd H, 53121. SAN 317-9788. Tel: 262-741-8042, 262-741-8438. FAX: 262-741-8585. E-mail: elkhornlrc@gtc.edu. Web Site: www.gtc.edu/library. *Libr Instruction & Ref Spec,* Sylvia Linton; Fax: 262-741-8201; Staff 2 (MLS 1, Non-MLS 1)
Highest Degree: Associate
Library Holdings: Bks on Deafness & Sign Lang 800; CDs 30; DVDs 30; e-books 1,500; e-journals 1,000; Bk Vols 5,900; Per Subs 35; Videos 150
Special Collections: Interpreter for Deaf, bks, v-tapes
Subject Interests: Acctg, Allied health, Bus, Deaf interpreting, Graphic Communications, Info tech, Nursing
Automation Activity & Vendor Info: (Acquisitions) Ex Libris Group; (Cataloging) Ex Libris Group; (Circulation) Ex Libris Group; (Course Reserve) Ex Libris Group; (ILL) OCLC; (OPAC) Ex Libris Group; (Serials) Ex Libris Group
Database Vendor: EBSCO Auto Repair Reference, EBSCOhost, LearningExpress, Micromedex, Wilson - Wilson Web
Wireless access
Function: Online ref, Online searches, Orientations
Partic in Wis PALS Libr Consortium
Open Mon-Thurs 8-8, Fri 8-4

P MATHESON MEMORIAL LIBRARY, 101 N Wisconsin, 53121. SAN 317-9818. Tel: 262-723-2678. FAX: 262-723-2870. E-mail: mmlinfo@elkhorn.lib.wi.us. Web Site: www.elkhorn.lib.wi.us. *Dir,* Lisa Selje; *Ad,* Angela Meyers; E-mail: ameyers@elkhorn.lib.wi.us; *Youth Serv Librn,* Jennifer Wharton; E-mail: jwharton@lakeshores.lib.wi.us; Staff 9 (MLS 3, Non-MLS 6)
Founded 1901. Pop 23,241; Circ 208,606
Jan 2012-Dec 2012 Income $696,521; City $355,111, County $304,910, Locally Generated Income $26,000, Other $9,000. Mats Exp $76,700, Books $48,100, Per/Ser (Incl. Access Fees) $6,600, AV Mat $22,000
Library Holdings: AV Mats 8,128; CDs 1,464; DVDs 3,600; High Interest/Low Vocabulary Bk Vols 400; Large Print Bks 1,000; Bk Titles 60,624; Per Subs 98
Special Collections: Robert Burns (Matheson Coll)
Subject Interests: Cookery

Automation Activity & Vendor Info: (Acquisitions) SirsiDynix; (Cataloging) SirsiDynix; (Circulation) SirsiDynix; (OPAC) SirsiDynix; (Serials) SirsiDynix
Database Vendor: Baker & Taylor, BWI, EBSCOhost, Gale Cengage Learning, Overdrive, Inc, ReferenceUSA, SirsiDynix
Wireless access
Function: Adult bk club, Audiobks via web, AV serv, Bk club(s), Bks on CD, Children's prog, Computer training, Computers for patron use, Copy machines, Doc delivery serv, e-mail & chat, Electronic databases & coll, Fax serv, Free DVD rentals, Handicapped accessible, Homebound delivery serv, ILL available, Music CDs, Online cat, OverDrive digital audio bks, Prog for adults, Prog for children & young adult, Pub access computers, Scanner, Story hour, Tax forms
Mem of Lakeshores Library System
Open Mon-Thurs 9-8, Fri 9-6, Sat 10-2
Friends of the Library Group

ELLSWORTH

P   ELLSWORTH PUBLIC LIBRARY*, 312 W Main, 54011. SAN 317-9826. Tel: 715-273-3209. FAX: 715-273-3209. E-mail: ellsworthpl@ifls.lib.wi.us. Web Site: www.ellsworthlibrary.org. *Dir,* Shelley Anderson; E-mail: sanderson@ifls.lib.wi.us; Staff 1 (Non-MLS 1)
Founded 1924. Pop 3,100; Circ 76,670
Library Holdings: Bk Vols 19,000; Per Subs 66
Wireless access
Mem of Indianhead Federated Library System
Open Mon, Wed & Fri 10-6, Tues & Thurs 10-8, Sat 9-1

ELM GROVE

P   ELM GROVE PUBLIC LIBRARY*, 13600 W Juneau Blvd, 53122-1679. SAN 317-9834. Tel: 262-782-6717. FAX: 262-780-4827. E-mail: egill@elmgrove.lib.wi.us. Web Site: www.elmgrovelibrary.org. *Dir,* Robert Trunley; E-mail: rtrunley@elmgrove.lib.wi.us; *Ad,* Paulette Brooks; *Ad, ILL Librn,* Susan Freitag; E-mail: sdfreita@elmgrove.lib.wi.us; *Ad,* Lori Kuban; *Ad, Cat Librn,* Sarah Muench; E-mail: muench@elmgrove.lib.wi.us; *Youth Serv Librn,* Sue Daniels; E-mail: sdaniels@elmgrove.lib.wi.us; Staff 8 (MLS 5, Non-MLS 3)
Founded 1962. Pop 6,261; Circ 110,000
Library Holdings: AV Mats 3,460; Large Print Bks 531; Bk Titles 49,414; Per Subs 115; Talking Bks 1,776
Subject Interests: Gen popular
Automation Activity & Vendor Info: (Circulation) SirsiDynix; (OPAC) SIRSI-iBistro
Wireless access
Mem of Waukesha County Federated Library System
Open Mon-Thurs 10-8:30, Fri & Sat 10-5
Friends of the Library Group

ELMWOOD

P   ELMWOOD PUBLIC LIBRARY*, 111 N Main St, 54740. (Mail add: PO Box 55, 54740-0055). Tel: 715-639-2615. FAX: 715-639-2615. E-mail: elmwoodpl@ifls.lib.wi.us. Web Site: www.elmwoodlibrary.org. *Head Librn,* Jayne Geraets; *Asst Librn,* Linda Weber
Library Holdings: Bk Titles 11,349; Per Subs 49
Automation Activity & Vendor Info: (Cataloging) Innovative Interfaces, Inc; (Circulation) Innovative Interfaces, Inc
Mem of Indianhead Federated Library System
Special Services for the Deaf - Assistive tech
Open Mon 10-5, Tues, Thurs & Fri 11-5, Wed 10-7
Friends of the Library Group

ELROY

P   ELROY PUBLIC LIBRARY*, 501 Second Main St, 53929-1255. SAN 317-9842. Tel: 608-462-2407. FAX: 608-462-2407. E-mail: elroypl2@wrlsweb.org. Web Site: www.elroywi.com/library.htm. *Dir,* Mary Waarvik
Founded 1908. Pop 1,500; Circ 27,760
Library Holdings: Bk Vols 20,000; Per Subs 80
Automation Activity & Vendor Info: (Acquisitions) Horizon; (Cataloging) Horizon; (Circulation) Horizon
Mem of Winding Rivers Library System
Open Mon-Fri 11-6, Sat 10-2
Friends of the Library Group

ENDEAVOR

P   ENDEAVOR PUBLIC LIBRARY*, 125 Park S, 53930. (Mail add: PO Box 80, 53930-0080), SAN 322-8525. Tel: 608-587-2902. FAX: 608-587-2902. Web Site: www.endeavorlibrary.org. *Dir,* Roxie Novak; E-mail: novak@endeavorlibrary.org; *Librn,* Scharron Lake; Staff 2 (Non-MLS 2)
Founded 1962. Pop 500
Library Holdings: Bk Vols 10,000; Per Subs 38

Automation Activity & Vendor Info: (Cataloging) SirsiDynix; (Circulation) SirsiDynix; (OPAC) SirsiDynix
Mem of Winnefox Library System
Open Mon, Wed & Thurs 10-6, Fri 12-5, Sat 10-1
Friends of the Library Group

ETTRICK

P   ETTRICK PUBLIC LIBRARY*, 15570 School St, 54627. (Mail add: PO Box 147, 54627-0147). Tel: 608-525-3408. E-mail: ettrickpl@wrlsweb.org. *Librn,* Karyn Schmidt; E-mail: k.schmidt@wrlsweb.org
Founded 1999. Pop 525
Jan 2008-Dec 2008 Income $21,000
Library Holdings: CDs 25; Bk Vols 8,000; Talking Bks 500; Videos 400
Special Collections: Ettrick Advance Newspaper, 1919-1956, microfilm
Automation Activity & Vendor Info: (Cataloging) SirsiDynix; (Circulation) SirsiDynix; (OPAC) SirsiDynix
Mem of Winding Rivers Library System

EVANSVILLE

P   EAGER FREE PUBLIC LIBRARY*, 39 W Main St, 53536. SAN 317-9850. Tel: 608-882-2260, 608-882-2275. FAX: 608-882-2261. E-mail: eagerfree@als.lib.wi.us. Web Site: als.lib.wi.us/EFPL. *Dir,* Kathi Lee Kemp; Tel: 608-882-2278, E-mail: kemp.kathi@als.lib.wi.us; *Adult Serv,* Tina Kakuske
Founded 1898. Circ 50,167
Library Holdings: Bk Titles 29,000; Per Subs 125
Special Collections: Evansville Historical Materials Coll; Wisconsin Writers Coll. Oral History
Wireless access
Mem of Arrowhead Library System
Open Mon-Thurs 9:30-8, Fri 9:30-6, Sat 9:30-1
Friends of the Library Group

FAIRCHILD

P   FAIRCHILD PUBLIC LIBRARY*, 208 Huron St, 54741. (Mail add: PO Box 149, 54741-0149), SAN 377-9904. Tel: 715-334-4007. E-mail: fairchildlibrary@centurylink.net. *Librn,* Rozanne Traczek
Library Holdings: Bk Vols 11,813; Per Subs 20
Mem of Indianhead Federated Library System
Open Mon-Fri 1-5

FALL CREEK

P   FALL CREEK PUBLIC LIBRARY*, 122 E Lincoln Ave, 54742-9425. (Mail add: PO Box 426, 54742-0426), SAN 324-1548. Tel: 715-877-3334. FAX: 715-877-2392. E-mail: fallcreek@ifls.lib.wi.us. Web Site: www.fallcreekpubliclibrary.org. *Dir,* Patty Braden; E-mail: braden@ifls.lib.wi.us
Library Holdings: Bk Vols 15,000; Per Subs 21
Automation Activity & Vendor Info: (Acquisitions) Innovative Interfaces, Inc; (Cataloging) Innovative Interfaces, Inc; (Circulation) Innovative Interfaces, Inc
Mem of Indianhead Federated Library System
Open Tues-Thurs 10-7, Fri 10-4, Sat 9-1
Friends of the Library Group

FENNIMORE

P   DWIGHT T PARKER PUBLIC LIBRARY*, 925 Lincoln Ave, 53809-1743. SAN 317-9877. Tel: 608-822-6294. E-mail: parker9@grant.tds.net. *Dir,* Trudi Freymiller
Pop 2,387; Circ 72,000
Library Holdings: Bk Vols 31,000
Automation Activity & Vendor Info: (Acquisitions) Follett Software; (Cataloging) Follett Software; (Circulation) Follett Software
Function: Prog for children & young adult, Summer reading prog
Publications: A History of Fennimore
Mem of Southwest Wisconsin Library System
Open Mon-Thurs 10-7, Fri 10-4, Sat 10-2

P   SOUTHWEST WISCONSIN LIBRARY SYSTEM*, 1775 Fourth St, 53809-1137. SAN 317-9885. Tel: 608-822-3393. Toll Free Tel: 866-866-3393. FAX: 608-822-6251. Web Site: www.swls.org. *Dir, Spec Needs,* Krista Ross; E-mail: kross@swls.org; *Cat,* Kim F Streif; Tel: 608-822-2055, E-mail: kstreif@swis.org; *Circ, ILL,* Peggy S Freymiller; Tel: 608-822-2052, E-mail: pfrymllr@swls.org; *Mkt,* Leah W Herrling; Tel: 608-822-2054, E-mail: lherr@swls.org; *Tech Serv,* Betty Sautter; E-mail: bsautter@swls.org. Subject Specialists: *Pub relations,* Leah W Herrling; Staff 8 (MLS 2, Non-MLS 6)
Founded 1959. Pop 123,000
Library Holdings: Bk Titles 3,500; Bk Vols 4,000; Per Subs 15
Subject Interests: Regional hist

Automation Activity & Vendor Info: (Cataloging) SirsiDynix; (Circulation) SirsiDynix
Wireless access
Publications: Stepping Stones, Stepping Stones for Children (Newsletter)
Member Libraries: Allen Dietzman Library; Argyle Public Library; Barneveld Public Library; Benton Public Library; Blanchardville Public Library; Bloomington Public Library; Brewer Public Library; Cobb Public Library; Cuba City Public Library; Dodgeville Public Library; Dwight T Parker Public Library; Eckstein Memorial Library; Gays Mills Public Library; Hazel Green Public Library; Hildebrand Memorial Library; John Turgeson Public Library; Johnson Public Library; Lone Rock Public Library; McCoy Public Library; Mineral Point Public Library; Montfort Public Library; Muscoda Public Library; Platteville Public Library; Prairie du Chien Memorial Library; Schreiner Memorial Library; Soldiers Grove Public Library; The Mound Center Library; Viola Public Library
Partic in Wisconsin Library Services
Open Mon-Fri 8-4:30

FLORENCE

P   FLORENCE COUNTY LIBRARY*, 400 Olive Ave, 54121. (Mail add: PO Box 440, 54121-0440), SAN 376-6616. Tel: 715-528-3094. FAX: 715-528-5338. E-mail: flo@mail.nfls.lib.wi.us. *Dir,* Mary Seggelink
Library Holdings: e-books 10,000; Bk Vols 18,000; Per Subs 12; Talking Bks 700; Videos 2,000
Automation Activity & Vendor Info: (Acquisitions) Innovative Interfaces, Inc; (Cataloging) Innovative Interfaces, Inc; (Circulation) Innovative Interfaces, Inc; (OPAC) Innovative Interfaces, Inc
Mem of Nicolet Federated Library System
Open Mon & Wed 9-12 & 3:30-7:30, Tues & Thurs 3:30-7:30, Fri 9-12, Sat 9-1
Friends of the Library Group

FOND DU LAC

GL   FOND DU LAC CIRCUIT COURT*, Law Library, PO Box 1355, 54935-1355. SAN 317-9907. Tel: 920-929-3040. FAX: 920-929-3933.
Library Holdings: Bk Vols 1,500
Function: Res libr
Open Mon-Fri 8-4:30

S   FOND DU LAC COUNTY HISTORICAL SOCIETY*, Library/Archives, Blakely Museum, 336 Old Pioneer Rd, 54935-6126. (Mail add: PO Box 1284, 54936-1284). Tel: 920-922-0991. E-mail: fdlhistory1@yahoo.com. Web Site: www.fdlhistory.com. *Dir,* Sally Albertz; Staff 3 (MLS 1, Non-MLS 2)
Founded 1990
Library Holdings: Bk Vols 10,000
Subject Interests: Genealogy, Local hist
Open Mon 9-11, Wed 1-6, Sat 9-2

P   FOND DU LAC PUBLIC LIBRARY, 32 Sheboygon St, 54935. SAN 317-9915. Tel: 920-929-7080. FAX: 920-929-7082. E-mail: reference@fdlpl.org. Web Site: www.fdlpl.org. *Dir,* Jon-Mark Bolthouse; E-mail: bolthouse@fdlpl.org; Staff 32 (MLS 10, Non-MLS 22)
Founded 1876. Pop 71,541; Circ 859,012
Library Holdings: Bk Vols 175,668; Per Subs 372
Special Collections: Municipal, State Document Depository
Automation Activity & Vendor Info: (Acquisitions) SirsiDynix; (Cataloging) SirsiDynix; (Circulation) SirsiDynix; (OPAC) SirsiDynix
Database Vendor: EBSCO Auto Repair Reference, EBSCO Information Services, Newsbank, ProQuest, ReferenceUSA
Wireless access
Mem of Winnefox Library System
Partic in Wisconsin Library Services
Open Mon-Thurs (Winter) 9-8, Fri 9-6, Sat 9-5, Sun 12-4; Mon-Thurs (Summer) 9-8, Fri 9-6, Sat 9-1
Friends of the Library Group

C   MARIAN UNIVERSITY*, Cardinal Meyer Library, 45 S National Ave, 54935. SAN 317-9923. Tel: 920-923-7641, 920-923-8725. FAX: 920-923-7154. E-mail: refdesk@mariancollege.edu. Web Site: www.mariancollege.edu. *Dir,* Mary Ellen Gormican; E-mail: mgormican@mariancollege.edu; *Archivist,* Melissa Adler; Tel: 920-923-8747; *Cat, Syst Coordr,* Paul Koch; *Circ,* Connie Conrad; E-mail: cconrad@mariancollege.edu; *Circ,* Jane McGovern; *Ref,* Sarah Thibodeau; Tel: 920-923-8096, E-mail: srthibodeau64@mariancollege.edu; Staff 9 (MLS 6, Non-MLS 3)
Founded 1936. Enrl 1,794; Highest Degree: Master
Library Holdings: Bk Vols 91,000; Per Subs 551
Subject Interests: Educ, Nursing
Automation Activity & Vendor Info: (Cataloging) Innovative Interfaces, Inc; (Circulation) Innovative Interfaces, Inc; (OPAC) Innovative Interfaces, Inc

Partic in Fox River Valley Area Library Consortium; Fox Valley Library Council; OCLC Online Computer Library Center, Inc; Wisconsin Library Services
Open Mon-Thurs 7:30am-11pm, Fri 7:30-4:30, Sat 12-4, Sun 3-11

J   MORAINE PARK TECHNICAL COLLEGE LIBRARY, 235 N National Ave, 54936. (Mail add: PO Box 1940, 54936-1940), SAN 364-6440. Tel: 920-929-2470. Interlibrary Loan Service Tel: 920-924-3118. Reference Tel: 920-924-3108. FAX: 920-924-3117. Web Site: www.morainepark.edu/library.
Founded 1965. Enrl 3,200; Fac 150
Library Holdings: Bk Titles 22,000; Bk Vols 35,000; Per Subs 436
Automation Activity & Vendor Info: (Acquisitions) Ex Libris Group; (Cataloging) Ex Libris Group; (Circulation) Ex Libris Group; (Course Reserve) Ex Libris Group; (ILL) OCLC; (Media Booking) Ex Libris Group; (OPAC) Ex Libris Group; (Serials) Ex Libris Group
Database Vendor: EBSCOhost, Facts on File, Gale Cengage Learning, OVID Technologies, ProQuest, ReferenceUSA, Westlaw
Wireless access
Partic in Fox River Valley Area Library Consortium; Wis PALS Libr Consortium
Open Mon-Thurs 7:30am-9:30pm, Fri 7:30-4, Sat 8-4

S   TAYCHEEDAH CORRECTIONAL INSTITUTION LIBRARY*, 751 Hwy K, 54935-9099. SAN 318-4110. Tel: 920-929-3800, Ext 3899. FAX: 920-929-7899. *Librn,* Mary Wood
Founded 1967
Library Holdings: Bk Vols 14,000; Per Subs 45
Special Collections: Legal Coll - Women's Issues
Automation Activity & Vendor Info: (Acquisitions) Follett Software; (Cataloging) Follett Software; (Circulation) Follett Software
Open Mon & Tues 1-8:45, Wed-Fri 8-4

C   UNIVERSITY OF WISCONSIN-FOND DU LAC LIBRARY*, 400 University Dr, 54935-2950. Tel: 920-929-3616. FAX: 920-929-7640. Web Site: www.fdl.uwc.edu/library. *Dir,* Kathryn Johnston; Tel: 920-929-3617
Library Holdings: Bk Titles 40,000; Per Subs 80
Open Mon-Thurs 8-7, Fri 8-4:30

FONTANA

P   FONTANA PUBLIC LIBRARY*, 166 Second Ave, 53125. (Mail add: PO Box 437, 53125-0437), SAN 317-9966. Tel: 262-275-5107. FAX: 262-275-2179. E-mail: fontana@fontana.lib.wi.us. Web Site: www.lakeshores.lib.wi.us/fontana/fontana.htm. *Dir,* Nancy Krei; E-mail: krei@fontana.lib.wi.us
Founded 1931
Library Holdings: Bk Vols 30,000; Per Subs 50
Subject Interests: Circus, Craft, Gardening, Local hist, Med
Automation Activity & Vendor Info: (Cataloging) SirsiDynix; (Circulation) SirsiDynix
Mem of Lakeshores Library System
Open Mon, Wed & Fri 9:30-5, Tues & Thurs 9:30-8, Sat 9-1

FORT ATKINSON

M   FORT ATKINSON MEMORIAL HOSPITAL*, Medical Library, 611 E Sherman Ave, 53538. Tel: 920-568-5194. FAX: 920-568-5195. *Coordr,* Carrie Garity
Library Holdings: Bk Vols 75; Per Subs 55
Open Mon-Fri 8-4:30

P   DWIGHT FOSTER PUBLIC LIBRARY*, 102 E Milwaukee Ave, 53538-2049. SAN 317-9974. Tel: 920-563-7790. FAX: 920-563-7774. Web Site: www.fortlibrary.org. *Dir,* Connie Meyer; E-mail: cmeyer@fortlibrary.org; *Asst Dir,* Amy Lutzke; E-mail: alutzke@fortlibrary.org; *Ch,* Shelly Menzer; E-mail: smenzer@fortlibrary.org; Staff 3 (MLS 2, Non-MLS 1)
Founded 1890. Pop 16,236; Circ 226,488
Library Holdings: Bk Titles 85,000; Bk Vols 100,000; Per Subs 237
Special Collections: Local History, bks & clippings; Lorine Niedecker Coll
Automation Activity & Vendor Info: (Cataloging) SIRSI Unicorn; (Circulation) SIRSI Unicorn; (OPAC) SIRSI Unicorn
Database Vendor: EBSCO Information Services, Gale Cengage Learning, ProQuest
Wireless access
Mem of Mid-Wisconsin Federated Library System
Open Mon-Thurs (Winter) 9-9, Fri & Sat 9-5; Mon-Thurs (Summer) 9-8, Fri 9-5, Sat 9-1
Friends of the Library Group

S HOARD HISTORICAL MUSEUM LIBRARY*, 401 Whitewater Ave, 53538. SAN 373-3068. Tel: 920-563-7769. FAX: 920-568-3203. E-mail: info@hoardmuseum.org. Web Site: www.hoardmuseum.org. *Dir,* Sue Hartwick; E-mail: hartwick@hoardmuseum.org
Library Holdings: Bk Vols 5,000
Subject Interests: Civil War, Local hist
Open Tues-Sat (Winter) 9:30-3:30; Tues-Sat 9:30-4:30, Sun (Summer) 11-3
Restriction: Not a lending libr

FORT MCCOY

A UNITED STATES ARMY*, Fort McCoy Post Library, Bldg 2000, S 11th Ave, 54656-5000. SAN 320-5223. Tel: 608-388-2410. FAX: 608-388-2690. *Dir,* David Onstad; *Librn,* Tom Schmidt
Library Holdings: Bk Vols 10,000; Per Subs 20
Special Collections: Encyclopaedia Britannica Coll, ninth ed circa 1892; Military Insignia & Memorabilia & Patch Coll
Subject Interests: Mil hist, World War I, World War II
Automation Activity & Vendor Info: (Cataloging) SydneyPlus; (Circulation) SydneyPlus
Open Mon-Sun 8am-11pm

FOX LAKE

S FOX LAKE CORRECTIONAL INSTITUTION LIBRARY*, PO Box 147, 53933-0147. SAN 364-6475. Tel: 920-928-3151, Ext 6240. FAX: 920-928-6229. *Sr Librn,* Bob Zabkowicz; Staff 1 (MLS 1)
Founded 1962
Library Holdings: Bk Vols 15,000; Per Subs 50
Subject Interests: Fiction, Legal
Automation Activity & Vendor Info: (Cataloging) Follett Software; (Circulation) Follett Software; (Course Reserve) Follett Software; (ILL) Follett Software; (Media Booking) Follett Software; (OPAC) Follett Software; (Serials) Follett Software

P FOX LAKE PUBLIC LIBRARY*, 117 W State St, 53933-9505. (Mail add: PO Box 47, 53933-0047), SAN 317-9982. Tel: 920-928-3223. FAX: 920-928-3810. Web Site: www.foxlake.lib.wi.us. *Dir,* Julie Flemming; E-mail: julieflemming@mwfls.org
Founded 1910. Pop 3,000; Circ 30,000
Library Holdings: Bk Titles 12,000; Per Subs 100
Automation Activity & Vendor Info: (Circulation) SirsiDynix
Mem of Mid-Wisconsin Federated Library System
Open Mon-Thurs 11-8, Fri 11-5, Sat 11-3
Friends of the Library Group

FRANKLIN

P FRANKLIN PUBLIC LIBRARY*, 9151 W Loomis Rd, 53132. SAN 324-0916. Tel: 414-425-8214. FAX: 414-425-9498. Web Site: www.mcfls.org/franklin. *Dir,* Barbara Roark; E-mail: barbara.roark@mcfls.org; *Circ Supvr,* Lydia Robotewskyj; *Adult Serv,* Jennifer Loeffel; *Ref Serv,* Beverly Polaski; *Ref Serv,* Andy Scott; *Youth Serv,* Debbie Olguin; *Ref Serv, YA,* Keri Whitmore; Staff 7 (MLS 6, Non-MLS 1)
Founded 1980. Pop 35,000
Jan 2010-Dec 2010. Mats Exp $104,000, Books $95,000, Per/Ser (Incl. Access Fees) $9,000. Sal $568,766 (Prof $316,940)
Library Holdings: Bk Titles 117,000; Per Subs 180
Automation Activity & Vendor Info: (Acquisitions) Innovative Interfaces, Inc - Millenium; (Cataloging) Innovative Interfaces, Inc - Millenium; (Circulation) Innovative Interfaces, Inc; (OPAC) Innovative Interfaces, Inc - Millenium; (Serials) Innovative Interfaces, Inc - Millenium
Database Vendor: EBSCO Auto Repair Reference, EBSCOhost, Evanced Solutions, Inc, Gale Cengage Learning, netLibrary, Overdrive, Inc, ProQuest, ReferenceUSA, Standard & Poor's
Wireless access
Mem of Milwaukee County Federated Library System
Open Mon-Thurs 10-8:30, Fri & Sat 10-5, Sun (Sept-May) 1-4
Friends of the Library Group

R SACRED HEART SCHOOL OF THEOLOGY*, Leo Dehon Library, 7335 S Hwy 100, 53132. (Mail add: PO Box 429, Hales Corners, 53130-0429), SAN 318-0212. Tel: 414-425-8300, Ext 7278. Administration Tel: 414-425-8300, Ext 6990. Information Services Tel: 414-425-8300, Ext 7280. FAX: 414-529-6992. E-mail: library@shst.edu. Web Site: www.shst.edu/leodehon-library/index.htm. *Dir, Libr & Acad Info Serv,* Gene Engeldinger; E-mail: eengeldinger@shst.edu; *Acad Info Serv,* Kathleen Harty; E-mail: kharty@shst.edu; *Tech Serv,* Ann Owen; E-mail: aowen@shst.edu; Staff 3 (MLS 3)
Founded 1932. Enrl 137; Fac 21; Highest Degree: Master
Library Holdings: Audiobooks 27; AV Mats 19,648; Bks on Deafness & Sign Lang 18; CDs 188; DVDs 132; e-books 2,100; e-journals 2,369; Electronic Media & Resources 175; Microforms 1,405; Bk Vols 94,258; Per Subs 460; Spec Interest Per Sub 425; Videos 1,269

Special Collections: Lux Center for Jewish-Cathoilc Dialogue; Religious Americana; Sacred Heart Coll
Subject Interests: Canon law, Church hist, Liturgy, Sacred scripture
Automation Activity & Vendor Info: (Acquisitions) Innovative Interfaces, Inc; (Cataloging) Innovative Interfaces, Inc; (Circulation) Innovative Interfaces, Inc; (Course Reserve) Innovative Interfaces, Inc; (ILL) OCLC; (OPAC) Innovative Interfaces, Inc; (Serials) Innovative Interfaces, Inc
Database Vendor: Bowker, EBSCO Information Services, EBSCOhost, OCLC WorldCat, Oxford Online, SerialsSolutions, YBP Library Services
Wireless access
Function: Computers for patron use, Copy machines, E-Reserves, Electronic databases & coll, ILL available, Music CDs, Online cat, Photocopying/Printing, Spoken cassettes & CDs, VHS videos, Web-catalog
Publications: Introduction to Theological Studies - Seminar (Research guide); Library Policies & Procedures (Library handbook); New Library Acquisitions (Quarterly)
Partic in Southeastern Wisconsin Information Technology Exchange, Inc; WILS
Special Services for the Blind - Braille equip
Restriction: 24-hr pass syst for students only, Authorized patrons, Borrowing requests are handled by ILL, Open to pub for ref & circ; with some limitations

FREDERIC

P FREDERIC PUBLIC LIBRARY*, 127 Oak St W, 54837. (Mail add: PO Box 700, 54837-0700), SAN 377-9920. Tel: 715-327-4979. FAX: 715-327-4455. E-mail: fredericpl@ifls.lib.wi.us. Web Site: www.fredericlibrary.org. *Librn,* Christine Byerly; E-mail: byerly@ifls.lib.wi.us
Wireless access
Mem of Indianhead Federated Library System
Open Mon-Fri 10-6, Sat 10-1
Friends of the Library Group

FREMONT

P NEUSCHAFER COMMUNITY LIBRARY*, 317 Wolf River Dr, 54940-9054. (Mail add: PO Box 498, 54940-0498), SAN 375-0469. Tel: 920-446-2474. FAX: 920-446-2480. E-mail: fpl@mail.owls.lib.wi.us. Web Site: www.owls.lib.wi.us/fpl. *Dir,* Susan O'Leary-Frick; E-mail: soleary@mail.owls.lib.wi.us; *Asst Librn,* Jill Kocovsky
Pop 735; Circ 1,829
Library Holdings: Bk Vols 4,000; Per Subs 44
Mem of Outagamie Waupaca Library System
Open Mon, Wed & Fri 9-6, Tues 1-6, Sat (May-Sept) 9-12
Friends of the Library Group

FRIENDSHIP

M MOUNDVIEW MEMORIAL HOSPITAL*, Medical Library, 402 W Lake St, 53934. (Mail add: PO Box 40, 53934-0040). Tel: 608-339-3331. FAX: 608-339-9385. Web Site: www.moundview.org. *Mgr,* Maureen Bruce
Library Holdings: Bk Vols 400; Per Subs 20

GALESVILLE

P GALESVILLE PUBLIC LIBRARY*, 16787 S Main St, 54630. (Mail add: PO Box 697, 54630-0697), SAN 317-9990. Tel: 608-582-2552. E-mail: galepublib@gmail.com, galepuyouth@gmail.com. Web Site: www.wrlsweb.org/galesville. *Dir,* Meredith Houge; *Asst Librn,* Cindi Schein; *Youth Serv,* Wina Mortenson; Staff 1.6 (Non-MLS 1.6)
Founded 1911. Pop 1,600; Circ 27,737
Library Holdings: Large Print Bks 1,020; Bk Vols 13,700; Per Subs 45; Videos 563
Wireless access
Function: Adult bk club, Audio & video playback equip for onsite use, Audiobks via web, Bks on cassette, Bks on CD, Children's prog, Computers for patron use, Copy machines, Digital talking bks, Distance learning, e-mail & chat, Exhibits, Handicapped accessible, Home delivery & serv to Sr ctr & nursing homes, Homebound delivery serv, ILL available, Large print keyboards, Magnifiers for reading, Music CDs, OverDrive digital audio bks, Photocopying/Printing, Prog for adults, Prog for children & young adult, Pub access computers, Story hour, Summer reading prog, Tax forms, Telephone ref, VHS videos, Wheelchair accessible
Mem of Winding Rivers Library System
Open Mon & Fri 10-7, Tues-Thurs 2-8, Sat 9-2
Friends of the Library Group

GAYS MILLS

P GAYS MILLS PUBLIC LIBRARY*, 205 Main St, 54631-8158. (Mail add: PO Box 215, 54631-0215), SAN 318-000X. Tel: 608-735-4331. *Dir,* Maura Jean Otis; E-mail: motis@swls.org
Founded 1941. Pop 625; Circ 6,829

Library Holdings: Bk Vols 6,700; Per Subs 31
Automation Activity & Vendor Info: (Circulation) Horizon
Mem of Southwest Wisconsin Library System
Open Mon 1-5 & 5:30-8:30, Tues & Thurs 5:30-8:30, Wed & Sat 9-1, Fri 1-5
Friends of the Library Group

GENOA CITY

P　GENOA CITY PUBLIC LIBRARY*, 126 Freeman St, 53128-2073. (Mail add: PO Box 727, 53128-0727), SAN 318-0018. Tel: 262-279-6188. FAX: 262-279-3665. E-mail: genoa@genoacity.lib.wi.us. Web Site: www.genoacity.lib.wi.us. *Dir,* Lisa Ahler
Founded 1900. Pop 1,356; Circ 15,280
Library Holdings: Bk Vols 10,000; Per Subs 45
Automation Activity & Vendor Info: (Cataloging) SirsiDynix; (Circulation) SirsiDynix
Mem of Lakeshores Library System
Open Mon & Wed 10-7, Tues & Fri 9-5, Sat 9-3
Friends of the Library Group

GERMANTOWN

P　GERMANTOWN COMMUNITY LIBRARY*, N112W16957 Mequon Rd, 53022. (Mail add: PO Box 670, 53022-0670), SAN 318-0026. Tel: 262-253-7760. FAX: 262-253-7763. Web Site: www.germantownlibrarywi.org. *Dir,* Roberta M Olson; Tel: 262-253-7762, E-mail: rolson@germantownlibrarywi.org; *Ch,* Stephanie Reister; E-mail: sreister@germantownlibrarywi.org; Staff 15 (MLS 4, Non-MLS 11)
Founded 1963. Pop 33,000; Circ 333,000
Library Holdings: AV Mats 20,000; e-books 8,825; Electronic Media & Resources 3,700; Bk Vols 119,000; Per Subs 250
Automation Activity & Vendor Info: (Cataloging) SirsiDynix; (Circulation) SirsiDynix; (OPAC) SirsiDynix
Database Vendor: EBSCOhost, SirsiDynix
Wireless access
Mem of Mid-Wisconsin Federated Library System
Open Mon-Thurs 9-8, Fri 9-5, Sat 9-4 (9-3 Summer)
Friends of the Library Group

GILLETT

P　GILLETT PUBLIC LIBRARY*, 200 E Main St, 54124-9386. (Mail add: PO Box 109, 54124-0109), SAN 318-0034. Tel: 920-855-6224. FAX: 920-855-6533. E-mail: gil@mail.nfls.lib.wi.us. *Librn,* Kaye Rankel; E-mail: krankel@mail.nfls.lib.wi.us
Founded 1927. Pop 3,000; Circ 8,858
Library Holdings: Bk Vols 8,700; Per Subs 25
Automation Activity & Vendor Info: (Acquisitions) Infor Library & Information Solutions; (Cataloging) Infor Library & Information Solutions; (Circulation) Infor Library & Information Solutions
Mem of Nicolet Federated Library System
Open Tues-Fri 9-7, Sat 9-12
Friends of the Library Group

GILMAN

P　WESTERN TAYLOR COUNTY PUBLIC LIBRARY*, 380 E Main St, 54433. (Mail add: PO Box 87, 54433-0087), SAN 318-0042. Tel: 715-447-5486. FAX: 715-447-8134. Web Site: www.wvls.lib.wi.us/westtaylorcopl/. *Dir,* Denise Korenuk; E-mail: dkorenuk@wvls.lib.wi.us
Library Holdings: Bk Vols 7,800; Per Subs 55
Automation Activity & Vendor Info: (Cataloging) Horizon; (Circulation) Horizon; (OPAC) Horizon
Mem of Wisconsin Valley Library Service
Open Mon-Wed 12-6, thurs 2-6, Fri 11-7

GLENDALE

CM　COLUMBIA COLLEGE OF NURSING LIBRARY*, 4425 N Port Washington Rd, 53212. SAN 364-9563. Tel: 414-326-2330. FAX: 414-326-2331. Web Site: www.ccon.edu. *Mgr, Libr Serv,* Sharon Wochos; Tel: 414-291-1626
Founded 1901
Library Holdings: Bk Vols 9,400; Per Subs 275
Special Collections: ANA Monograph Series; History of Nursing Coll; NLN Publications
Publications: Audiovisual Software List; New Materials List (monthly); Serials List
Partic in Library Council of Southeastern Wisconsin, Inc; Southeastern Wisconsin Health Science Library Consortium; Wis Health Sci Libr Asn
Restriction: Open by appt only

P　NORTH SHORE LIBRARY, 6800 N Port Washington Rd, 53217. SAN 324-7201. Tel: 414-351-3461. FAX: 414-351-3528. Web Site: www.mcfls.org/northshorelibrary. *Dir,* Richard Nelson; E-mail: dick.nelson@mcfls.org; *Ch,* Beth Henika; *Ref/Tech Proc,* Mitch Hahn; Staff 6 (MLS 6)
Founded 1979. Pop 25,600; Circ 350,227
Library Holdings: Audiobooks 5,712; e-books 27,088; Bk Vols 127,000; Per Subs 260; Videos 9,082
Automation Activity & Vendor Info: (Acquisitions) Innovative Interfaces, Inc; (Cataloging) Innovative Interfaces, Inc; (Circulation) Innovative Interfaces, Inc; (Course Reserve) Innovative Interfaces, Inc; (ILL) Innovative Interfaces, Inc; (Media Booking) Innovative Interfaces, Inc; (OPAC) Innovative Interfaces, Inc; (Serials) Innovative Interfaces, Inc
Wireless access
Mem of Milwaukee County Federated Library System
Joint library - operated by 4 municipalities
Open Mon-Thurs 10-8:30, Fri & Sat 10-5, Sun 1-5
Friends of the Library Group

GLENWOOD CITY

P　GLENWOOD CITY PUBLIC LIBRARY, 127 Pine St, 54013-8554. (Mail add: PO Box 247, 54013-0247), SAN 318-0050. Tel: 715-265-7443. FAX: 715-265-7307. E-mail: gcpublib@ifls.lib.wi.us. Web Site: www.glenwoodcitylibrary.org. *Dir,* Shaleen Culbert; E-mail: gclibrary@glenwoodcitylibrary.org; Staff 1 (Non-MLS 1)
Founded 1900. Pop 2,867; Circ 29,641
Jan 2012-Dec 2012 Income $94,200, City $48,000, County $45,000, Locally Generated Income $1,200. Mats Exp $11,700, Books $8,100, Per/Ser (Incl. Access Fees) $900, AV Mat $1,200, Electronic Ref Mat (Incl. Access Fees) $1,500. Sal $45,000 (Prof $22,000)
Library Holdings: AV Mats 1,200; e-books 8,805; Large Print Bks 300; Bk Titles 8,259; Per Subs 45
Automation Activity & Vendor Info: (Cataloging) Innovative Interfaces, Inc; (Circulation) Innovative Interfaces, Inc; (OPAC) Innovative Interfaces, Inc
Database Vendor: Ebooks Corporation, EBSCO Information Services, EBSCOhost, Innovative Interfaces, Inc, Medline, ProQuest
Wireless access
Function: Adult bk club, After school storytime, Audiobks via web, Bks on cassette, Bks on CD, CD-ROM, Children's prog, Computers for patron use, Copy machines, Electronic databases & coll, Fax serv, Free DVD rentals, Handicapped accessible, Holiday prog, ILL available, Large print keyboards, Mail & tel request accepted, Music CDs, Online cat, Online ref, Prog for adults, Pub access computers, Ref serv available, Summer reading prog, Tax forms, VHS videos, Wheelchair accessible
Mem of Indianhead Federated Library System
Special Services for the Blind - Audio mat; Bks on cassette; Bks on CD; Computer access aids; Internet workstation with adaptive software; Large print bks; ZoomText magnification & reading software
Open Mon 3-7:30, Tues & Wed 10-6, Thurs 10-7:30, Fri 10-5, Sat 10-1
Restriction: Circ to mem only, Non-circulating coll, Non-circulating of rare bks, Non-resident fee

GRAFTON

P　USS LIBERTY MEMORIAL PUBLIC LIBRARY*, 1620 11th Ave, 53024-2404. SAN 318-0069. Tel: 262-375-5315. FAX: 262-375-5317. E-mail: grafton@esls.lib.wi.us. Web Site: www.grafton.lib.wi.us. *Dir,* John Hanson; E-mail: jhanson4@esls.lib.wi.us; Staff 11 (MLS 2, Non-MLS 9)
Founded 1956. Pop 15,000; Circ 193,000
Jan 2006-Dec 2006 Income $520,000, County $10,000, Locally Generated Income $510,000. Mats Exp $50,000, Books $34,000, Per/Ser (Incl. Access Fees) $8,000, AV Mat $8,000. Sal $270,000
Library Holdings: AV Mats 7,000; Bks on Deafness & Sign Lang 20; e-books 7,700; High Interest/Low Vocabulary Bk Vols 60; Large Print Bks 1,500; Bk Titles 69,000; Bk Vols 70,000; Per Subs 165; Talking Bks 1,600
Automation Activity & Vendor Info: (Cataloging) Horizon; (Circulation) Horizon; (OPAC) Horizon
Publications: Library Letter (Quarterly)
Mem of Eastern Shores Library System
Open Mon-Thurs 10-8, Fri 10-5, Sat 10-2
Friends of the Library Group

GRANTON

P　SAMSON MEMORIAL LIBRARY*, 107 Second St, 54436. (Mail add: PO Box 70, 54436-0070), SAN 318-0077. Tel: 715-238-5250. FAX: 715-238-8605. *Dir,* Becky Short; E-mail: bshort@wvls.lib.wi.us; *Asst Librn, ILL,* Missy Walz; E-mail: mwalz@wvls.lib.wi.us
Pop 425; Circ 4,772
Library Holdings: Bk Vols 7,542; Per Subs 24
Mem of Wisconsin Valley Library Service
Open Mon & Fri 1-4, Tues 1-3, Wed 9:30-12 & 1-5, Fri 1-5, Sat 9:30-11:30

GRANTSBURG

P GRANTSBURG PUBLIC LIBRARY*, 415 S Robert St, 54840-7423. SAN 318-0085. Tel: 715-463-2244. FAX: 715-463-5555. Web Site: www.nwls.wislib.org/about/libgr.htm. *Dir,* Judy Pearson; E-mail: judy@grantsburg.nwls.lib.wi.us
Pop 1,200; Circ 14,510
Library Holdings: Bk Vols 16,000; Per Subs 37
Subject Interests: Local authors, Local hist
Automation Activity & Vendor Info: (Cataloging) Innovative Interfaces, Inc; (Circulation) Innovative Interfaces, Inc; (OPAC) Innovative Interfaces, Inc
Mem of Northern Waters Library Service
Open Mon, Tues & Thurs 1-6, Wed 10:30-6, Fri 10-2, Sat (Sept-May) 9-12

GREEN BAY

M BELLIN HOSPITAL*, Health Science Library, 744 S Webster Ave, 54301-3581. (Mail add: PO Box 23400, 54305-3400), SAN 318-0093. Tel: 920-433-3693. FAX: 920-433-7498. E-mail: roselibr@bellin.org. Web Site: www.bellin.org. *Librn,* Cynthia Reinl; Staff 2 (MLS 1, Non-MLS 1)
Founded 1910
Library Holdings: Bk Vols 2,800; Per Subs 250
Subject Interests: Allied health, Med, Nursing
Partic in Fox River Valley Area Library Consortium; National Network of Libraries of Medicine; NE Wis Intertype Librs, Inc
Open Mon-Fri 8-4:30

P BROWN COUNTY LIBRARY, 515 Pine St, 54301. SAN 364-653X. Tel: 920-448-4400. Circulation Tel: 920-448-5832. Interlibrary Loan Service Tel: 920-448-4417. FAX: 920-448-4376. E-mail: bc_library@co.brown.wi.us. Web Site: www.browncountylibrary.org. *Dir,* Lynn M Stainbrook; Tel: 920-448-5810, E-mail: stainbrook_lm@co.brown.wi.us; *Automation & Financial Serv Mgr,* Lori J Denault; Fax: 920-448-5802, E-mail: denault_lj@co.brown.wi.us; *Coll Develop Mgr,* Dale V Cropper; Tel: 920-448-5801, E-mail: cropper_dv@co.brown.wi.us.; *Communications & Libr Prog Mgr,* Susan M Lagerman; Tel: 920-448-5806, E-mail: lagerman_sm@co.brown.wi.us; *Operations Mgr,* Lynn M Hoffman; Tel: 920-448-5808, E-mail: hoffman_lm@co.brown.wi.us; *Supvr, Pub Serv,* Sandy J Kallunki; Tel: 920-448-5844, Fax: 920-448-6253, E-mail: kallunki_sj@co.brown.wi.us; *Tech Serv & Circ Supvr,* Otnie L Dechert; Tel: 920-448-5831, Fax: 920-448-6254, E-mail: dechert_ol@co.brown.wi.us; Staff 22 (MLS 7, Non-MLS 15)
Founded 1968. Pop 240,404; Circ 2,443,834
Library Holdings: AV Mats 41,281; Bk Vols 468,451; Per Subs 1,128
Special Collections: Brown County History Coll; Wisconsin History Coll
Subject Interests: Genealogy
Automation Activity & Vendor Info: (Acquisitions) SirsiDynix; (Cataloging) SirsiDynix; (Circulation) SirsiDynix; (OPAC) SIRSI-iBistro
Database Vendor: 3M Library Systems, Baker & Taylor, BWI, EBSCOhost, Evanced Solutions, Inc, Gale Cengage Learning, Ingram Library Services, LearningExpress, Newsbank, OCLC WorldCat, Overdrive, Inc, ProQuest, SirsiDynix, TumbleBookLibrary, ValueLine
Wireless access
Function: Adult bk club, Art exhibits, Audiobks via web, Bilingual assistance for Spanish patrons, Bk club(s), Bks on cassette, Bks on CD, Bus archives, CD-ROM, Children's prog, Computer training, Computers for patron use, Copy machines, e-mail serv, E-Reserves, Electronic databases & coll, Exhibits, Fax serv, Free DVD rentals, Handicapped accessible, Holiday prog, Home delivery & serv to Sr ctr & nursing homes, Homebound delivery serv, ILL available, Jail serv, Magnifiers for reading, Mail & tel request accepted, Monthly prog for perceptually impaired adults, Music CDs, Notary serv, Online cat, Online ref, Online searches, Orientations, Outreach serv, Outside serv via phone, mail, e-mail & web, OverDrive digital audio bks, Photocopying/Printing, Preschool outreach, Prog for adults, Prog for children & young adult, Pub access computers, Ref & res, Ref serv available, Referrals accepted, Scanner, Senior outreach, Story hour, Summer & winter reading prog, Summer reading prog, Tax forms, Teen prog, Telephone ref, Wheelchair accessible, Workshops
Mem of Nicolet Federated Library System
Partic in NE Wis Intertype Librs, Inc
Special Services for the Deaf - Assisted listening device; Assistive tech; Bks on deafness & sign lang; Closed caption videos; High interest/low vocabulary bks; Spec interest per
Special Services for the Blind - Audio mat; BiFolkal kits; Bks on cassette; Bks on CD; Cassettes; Home delivery serv; Internet workstation with adaptive software; Large print & cassettes; Large print bks; Magnifiers; Student ref mat taped; Videos on blindness & phys handicaps
Open Mon-Thurs (Winter) 9-9, Fri & Sat 9-5, Sun 12-4; Mon-Thurs (Summer) 9-8, Fri 9-5, Sat 9-1
Friends of the Library Group

Branches: 8
ASHWAUBENON BRANCH, 1060 Orlando Dr, 54304, SAN 364-6599. Tel: 920-492-4913. FAX: 920-492-4914. E-mail: bc_library_ashwaubenon@co.brown.wi.us. *Supvr,* Anne Mead
Open Mon-Thurs (Winter) 10-8, Fri & Sat 10-5; Mon (Summer) 10-8, Tues-Fri 10-5, Sat 10-1
Friends of the Library Group
DENMARK BRANCH, 450 N Wall St, Denmark, 54208. (Mail add: PO Box 667, Denmark, 54208), SAN 364-6629. Tel: 920-863-6613. FAX: 920-863-3001. E-mail: bc_library_denmark@co.brown.wi.us. *Libr Assoc,* Charlotte Franke; *Libr Assoc,* Deneen Schweiner
Open Mon & Tues (Winter) 1-8, Wed 10-5, Thurs & Fri 1-5; Mon & Wed (Summer) 10-12 & 1-5, Tues 1-5 & 6-8, Thurs & Fri 1-5
Friends of the Library Group
EAST BRANCH, 2255 Main St, 54302-3743, SAN 364-6742. Tel: 920-391-4600. FAX: 920-391-4601. E-mail: bc_library_east@co.brown.wi.us. *Supvr,* Bobbie Kuehn; Staff 6 (MLS 1, Non-MLS 5)
Circ 220,000
Open Mon-Thurs (Winter) 10-8, Fri & Sat 10-5; Mon-Wed (Summer) 10-8, Thurs & Fri 10-5, Sat 10-1
Friends of the Library Group
KRESS FAMILY BRANCH, 333 N Broadway, De Pere, 54115, SAN 364-6653. Tel: 920-448-4407. FAX: 920-448-4406. E-mail: bc_library_depere@co.brown.wi.us. *Libr Supvr,* Clare Kindt; Staff 7 (MLS 1, Non-MLS 6)
Open Mon-Thurs 10-8, Fri & Sat 10-5
Friends of the Library Group
PULASKI BRANCH, 222 W Pulaski St, Pulaski, 54162, SAN 364-6777. Tel: 920-822-3220. FAX: 920-822-5589. E-mail: bc_library_pulaski@co.brown.wi.us. *Br Mgr,* Position Currently Open; Staff 3 (MLS 1, Non-MLS 2)
Open Mon 1-8, Tues 10-8, Wed & Thurs 10-5, Fri 1-5, Sat 10-1
Friends of the Library Group
SOUTHWEST BRANCH, 974 Ninth St, 54304, SAN 364-6807. Tel: 920-492-4910. FAX: 920-492-4911. E-mail: bc_library_southwest@co.brown.wi.us. *Supvr,* Karla Giraldez
Open Mon-Wed 9-8, Thurs-Sat 10-5
Friends of the Library Group
WEYERS-HILLIARD BRANCH, 2680 Riverview Dr, 54313, SAN 364-6718. Tel: 920-448-4405. FAX: 920-448-4404. E-mail: bc_library_howard@co.brown.wi.us. *Libr Supvr,* Eileen Below
Open Mon-Thurs 10-8, Fri & Sat 10-5
Friends of the Library Group
WRIGHTSTOWN BRANCH, 615 Main St, Wrightstown, 54180, SAN 364-6831. Tel: 920-532-4011. FAX: 920-532-4199. E-mail: bc_library_wrightstown@co.brown.wi.us. *Libr Assoc,* Penny Barta
Open Mon, Tues & Thurs 10-12 & 1-5, Wed 1-4 & 5-8
Friends of the Library Group
Bookmobiles: 1

R FIRST UNITED METHODIST CHURCH LIBRARY*, 501 Howe St, 54301. SAN 318-0107. Tel: 920-437-9252. FAX: 920-437-0991. E-mail: office@fumcgb.org. Web Site: www.fumcgb.org. *Ch,* Barbara Hayes; E-mail: bhayes@fumcgb.org
Founded 1959
Library Holdings: Bk Titles 1,500; Bk Vols 1,550; Per Subs 10
Open Mon-Fri 8-5, Sun 7-Noon

S GREEN BAY CORRECTIONAL INSTITUTION LIBRARY, PO Box 19033, 54307-9033. SAN 318-0115. Tel: 920-432-4877, Ext 3457. FAX: 920-432-5388. *Librn,* Mark Kulieke
Founded 1898
Library Holdings: Bk Vols 8,000; Per Subs 30
Subject Interests: Law
Restriction: Not open to pub

S NEVILLE PUBLIC MUSEUM OF BROWN COUNTY LIBRARY*, 210 Museum Pl, 54303-2760. SAN 329-2568. Tel: 920-448-4460. FAX: 920-448-4458. Web Site: www.nevillepublicmuseum.org. *Librn,* Jeanine Mead; Tel: 920-448-7844, E-mail: mead_jm@co.brown.wi.us; Staff 1 (Non-MLS 1)
Founded 1915
Library Holdings: Bk Titles 4,500; Per Subs 20
Subject Interests: Art, Dolls, Local hist, Mus practice, Nat sci, Textiles
Function: Photocopying/Printing
Restriction: Not a lending libr, Open by appt only

P NICOLET FEDERATED LIBRARY SYSTEM*, 515 Pine St, 3rd Flr, 54301-5194. SAN 318-0123. Tel: 920-448-4410. Interlibrary Loan Service Tel: 920-448-4417. FAX: 920-448-4420. Web Site: www.nfls.lib.wi.us. *Dir,* Mark D Merrifield; E-mail: mmerrifi@mail.nfls.lib.wi.us; Staff 8 (MLS 2, Non-MLS 6)
Founded 1976. Pop 431,057

Jan 2011-Dec 2011 Income $1,105,000
Automation Activity & Vendor Info: (Acquisitions) Innovative Interfaces, Inc; (Cataloging) Innovative Interfaces, Inc; (Circulation) Innovative Interfaces, Inc; (Course Reserve) Innovative Interfaces, Inc; (ILL) Innovative Interfaces, Inc - OCLC; (Media Booking) Innovative Interfaces, Inc; (OPAC) Innovative Interfaces, Inc; (Serials) Innovative Interfaces, Inc
Wireless access
Publications: NicBits (Newsletter)
Member Libraries: Algoma Public Library; Brown County Library; Door County Library; Farnsworth Public Library; Florence County Library; Gillett Public Library; Kewaunee Public Library; Lakes Country Public Library; Lena Public Library; Marinette County Library System; Menominee Tribal County Library; Oconto Falls Community Library; Oneida Community Library; Shawano City-County Library; Suring Area Public Library
Partic in NE Wis Intertype Librs, Inc; OWLSnet
Open Mon-Fri 9-5

S NORTHEAST WISCONSIN MASONIC LIBRARY & MUSEUM*, 525 N Taylor St, 54303. Tel: 920-491-8374. E-mail: newmlm@netnet.net. *Dir of Libr Serv,* Alice Byrns
Library Holdings: Bk Titles 1,400
Open Mon-Fri 8am-11am

J NORTHEAST WISCONSIN TECHNICAL COLLEGE LIBRARY*, 2740 W Mason St, 54303-4966. (Mail add: PO Box 19042, 54307-9042), SAN 318-0131. Tel: 920-498-5487. Interlibrary Loan Service Tel: 920-498-5493. Reference Tel: 920-498-5490. FAX: 920-498-6910. E-mail: interlibrary.loan@nwtc.edu. Web Site: www.nwtc.edu/services/library. *Mgr, Product Res & Libr Serv,* Kim LaPlante; E-mail: kim.laplante@nwtc.edu; *Coordr, Libr Instruction,* Julie Chapman; E-mail: julie.chapman@nwtc.edu; *Circ,* Ellen Bricco; Tel: 920-498-6812, E-mail: ellen.bricco@nwtc.edu; *Circ,* Suzanne Holvenstot; Tel: 920-498-5732, E-mail: suzanne.holvenstot@nwtc.edu; Staff 7 (MLS 3, Non-MLS 4)
Founded 1966. Enrl 7,400; Highest Degree: Associate
Jul 2009-Jun 2010 Income $839,844. Mats Exp $311,206, Books $158,327, Per/Ser (Incl. Access Fees) $96,198, AV Mat $24,468, Electronic Ref Mat (Incl. Access Fees) $32,213. Sal $344,565 (Prof $139,989)
Library Holdings: Audiobooks 990; DVDs 9,000; e-books 18,747; e-journals 25,000; Microforms 410; Bk Titles 25,000; Bk Vols 27,676; Per Subs 483; Videos 2,121
Special Collections: Correspondence Course Videos; Developmental Education (Student Study Success Coll); Renewable Energy, Recycling, Sustainable Agriculture & Green Architecture (Sustainability Coll)
Automation Activity & Vendor Info: (Acquisitions) Ex Libris Group; (Cataloging) Ex Libris Group; (Circulation) Ex Libris Group; (Course Reserve) SirsiDynix; (ILL) Auto-Graphics, Inc; (OPAC) Ex Libris Group; (Serials) Ex Libris Group
Database Vendor: CredoReference, Dun & Bradstreet, ebrary, EBSCO Auto Repair Reference, EBSCOhost, Fastcase, Gale Cengage Learning, LearningExpress, netLibrary, OCLC FirstSearch, OCLC WorldCat, ProQuest, Safari Books Online, SerialsSolutions, SirsiDynix, Springshare, LLC, Westlaw, Wilson - Wilson Web
Wireless access
Function: Art exhibits, Audio & video playback equip for onsite use, Bks on cassette, Bks on CD, Computer training, Computers for patron use, Copy machines, Distance learning, Doc delivery serv, E-Reserves, Electronic databases & coll, Equip loans & repairs, Handicapped accessible, ILL available, Learning ctr, Online cat, Online info literacy tutorials on the web & in blackboard, Online ref, Online searches, Orientations, Outside serv via phone, mail, e-mail & web, Photocopying/Printing, Pub access computers, Scanner, Telephone ref, Wheelchair accessible
Publications: Copyright Policy & Handbooks (Documents); Library Guides (Research guide); Online Catalog & Database Instruction Handbook (Reference guide); Wisconsin Technical College ILL Directory (Library handbook)
Partic in Fox River Valley Area Library Consortium; NE Wis Intertype Librs, Inc; Northeast Wisconsin Education Resource Alliance (New ERA); Wisconsin Library Services
Special Services for the Deaf - Closed caption videos
Open Mon-Thurs (Fall-Spring) 7am-10pm, Fri 7-4:30, Sat 8-4; Mon-Thurs (Summer) 7-6, Fri 7-4:30

C UNIVERSITY OF WISCONSIN-GREEN BAY, David A Cofrin Library, 2420 Nicolet Dr, 54311-7001. SAN 318-0158. Tel: 920-465-2333. Interlibrary Loan Service Tel: 920-465-2385. Reference Tel: 920-465-2303. Administration Tel: 920-465-2537. Automation Services Tel: 920-465-2893. Information Services Tel: 920-465-2540. FAX: 920-465-2136. E-mail: refdesk@uwgb.edu. Web Site: www.uwgb.edu/library. *Dir,* Paula M Ganyard; E-mail: ganyardp@uwgb.edu; *Univ Archivist,* Debra Anderson; Tel: 920-465-2539, E-mail: andersod@uwgb.edu; *Distance Educ Librn,* Anne Kasuboski; Tel: 920-465-2543, E-mail: kasubosa@uwgb.edu; *Electronic Res Mgt Librn,* Melissa Platkowski; Tel: 920-465-2764; E-mail:

platkowm@uwgb.edu; *Instruction & Ref Librn,* Joe Hardenbrook; Tel: 920-465-2666, E-mail: hardenbj@uwgb.edu; *Automation Coordr,* Marlys Brunsting; E-mail: brunstim@uwgb.edu; *Coordr, Cat,* Debra Strelka; Tel: 920-465-2154, E-mail: strelkad@uwgb.edu; *Coll Develop, Govt Doc Coordr,* Joan Robb; Tel: 920-465-2384, E-mail: robbj@uwgb.edu; *Coordr, Pub Serv,* Emily Rogers; Tel: 920-465-2304, E-mail: rogerse@uwgb.edu; *Ref Coordr,* Renee Ettinger; Tel: 920-465-2542, E-mail: ettinger@uwgb.edu; *Evening Supvr,* Lindsay Simmenson; E-mail: simmensl@uwgb.edu; *Acq, Govt Doc,* Leah Leibergen; Tel: 920-465-2382, E-mail: leibergl@uwgb.edu; *Cataloger,* Tony LaLuzerne; Tel: 920-465-2785, E-mail: laluzera@uwgb.edu; *Ser,* Jeanette Skwor; Tel: 920-465-2670, E-mail: skworj@uwgb.edu; *Archives Asst,* Jean Wentz; Tel: 920-465-2539, E-mail: wentzj@uwgb.edu; Staff 16 (MLS 11, Non-MLS 5)
Founded 1967. Enrl 6,600; Fac 168; Highest Degree: Master
Jul 2009-Jun 2010 Income $1,418,770. Mats Exp $466,115, Books $58,942, Per/Ser (Incl. Access Fees) $284,074, Other Print Mats $244, Micro $1,274, AV Mat $9,593, Electronic Ref Mat (Incl. Access Fees) $107,297, Presv $4,691. Sal $836,741 (Prof $503,505)
Library Holdings: Bk Titles 245,961; Bk Vols 287,330; Per Subs 571
Special Collections: Belgian-American Ethnic Coll; Fort Howard Business Archives; Local History (Area Research Center), bks, micro, ms; University Archives. State Document Depository; US Document Depository
Subject Interests: Environ studies, Humanities, Music, Natural sci
Automation Activity & Vendor Info: (Acquisitions) Ex Libris Group; (Cataloging) Ex Libris Group; (Circulation) Ex Libris Group; (Course Reserve) Ex Libris Group; (ILL) OCLC; (Media Booking) Ex Libris Group; (OPAC) Ex Libris Group; (Serials) Ex Libris Group
Database Vendor: ARTstor, CQ Press, EBSCOhost, H W Wilson, IEEE (Institute of Electrical & Electronics Engineers), JSTOR, LexisNexis, Marcive, Inc, netLibrary, OCLC WorldCat, OVID Technologies, Project MUSE, ProQuest, PubMed, Thomson - Web of Science, Westlaw, Wilson - Wilson Web
Wireless access
Partic in NE Wis Intertype Librs, Inc; OCLC Online Computer Library Center, Inc; Wisconsin Library Services

GREEN LAKE

P CAESTECKER PUBLIC LIBRARY*, 518 Hill St, 54941-8828. (Mail add: PO Box 278, 54941-0278), SAN 318-0166. Tel: 920-294-3572. FAX: 920-294-6055. Web Site: www.greenlakelibrary.org. *Dir,* Linda DeNell; E-mail: denell@greenlakelibrary.org; *Asst Dir,* Mary Kay Carroll; E-mail: mcarroll@greenlakelibrary.org; Staff 1 (MLS 1)
Pop 2,523; Circ 68,264
Library Holdings: Bk Vols 21,800; Per Subs 95
Wireless access
Mem of Winnefox Library System
Open Mon, Wed & Fri 9:30-6, Tues & Thurs 9:30-7, Sat 9:30-12:30, Sun 1-4
Friends of the Library Group

GREENDALE

P GREENDALE PUBLIC LIBRARY*, 5647 Broad St, 53129-1887. SAN 318-0174. Tel: 414-423-2136. FAX: 414-423-2139. Web Site: www.greendale.org/library/l-admin.htm. *Dir,* Gary Warren Niebuhr; E-mail: gary.niebuhr@mcfls.org; *Librn,* Sandra Grams; E-mail: sandra.grams@mcfls.org; *Librn,* Betty Grypp; E-mail: betty.grypp@mcfls.org
Founded 1938. Pop 15,500; Circ 183,251
Library Holdings: AV Mats 2,500; CDs 2,200; DVDs 1,500; Bk Vols 55,540; Per Subs 80
Subject Interests: Local hist
Automation Activity & Vendor Info: (Acquisitions) Innovative Interfaces, Inc; (Cataloging) Innovative Interfaces, Inc; (Circulation) Innovative Interfaces, Inc
Mem of Milwaukee County Federated Library System
Partic in Library Council of Southeastern Wisconsin, Inc
Open Mon-Thurs 10-8, Fri & Sat 10-5, Sun 1-4
Friends of the Library Group

GREENFIELD

P GREENFIELD PUBLIC LIBRARY*, 7215 W Coldspring, 53220. SAN 325-1578. Tel: 414-321-9595. FAX: 414-321-8595. E-mail: librarian@greenfieldpubliclibrary.org. Web Site: www.greenfieldlibrary.org. *Dir,* Sheila O'Brien; E-mail: sheilao@greenfieldwi.us; Staff 11 (MLS 3, Non-MLS 8)
Circ 419,982
Library Holdings: AV Mats 16,283; Bk Vols 99,024; Per Subs 120
Automation Activity & Vendor Info: (Acquisitions) Innovative Interfaces, Inc; (Cataloging) Innovative Interfaces, Inc; (Circulation) Innovative Interfaces, Inc; (Course Reserve) Innovative Interfaces, Inc; (ILL) Innovative Interfaces, Inc; (Media Booking) Innovative Interfaces, Inc; (OPAC) Innovative Interfaces, Inc; (Serials) Innovative Interfaces, Inc

Wireless access
Open Mon-Wed 9:30-8, Thurs & Fri 9:30-5, Sat 9:30-2

GREENWOOD

P   GREENWOOD PUBLIC LIBRARY*, 102 N Main St, 54437. (Mail add: PO Box 100, 54437-0100), SAN 318-0190. Tel: 715-267-7103. FAX: 715-267-6636. *Librn,* Pat Braun; E-mail: pbraun@wvls.lib.wi.us
Founded 1913. Pop 3,400; Circ 54,164
Library Holdings: AV Mats 855; Bk Titles 19,682; Per Subs 87; Talking Bks 726
Special Collections: National Geographic, 1916-1987
Subject Interests: Hist
Automation Activity & Vendor Info: (Cataloging) SirsiDynix; (Circulation) SirsiDynix
Publications: Booklist; CCBC; Library Journal
Mem of Wisconsin Valley Library Service
Partic in Midwest Collaborative for Library Services (MCLS)
Open Mon & Wed 3-9, Tues, Thurs & Fri 8:30-5, Sat 9am-11:30am

HALES CORNERS

P   HALES CORNERS LIBRARY*, 5885 S 116th St, 53130-1707. SAN 318-0204. Tel: 414-529-6150. FAX: 414-529-6154. Web Site: www.mcfls.org/halescorners. *Dir,* Patricia Laughlin; E-mail: pat.laughlin@mcfls.org; Staff 20 (MLS 3, Non-MLS 17)
Founded 1976. Pop 7,640; Circ 157,040
Library Holdings: Audiobooks 1,609; CDs 2,085; DVDs 3,447; Bk Titles 37,658; Per Subs 117
Automation Activity & Vendor Info: (Acquisitions) Innovative Interfaces, Inc; (Cataloging) Innovative Interfaces, Inc; (Circulation) Innovative Interfaces, Inc; (OPAC) Innovative Interfaces, Inc
Wireless access
Mem of Milwaukee County Federated Library System
Open Mon-Thurs 10-8, Fri 10-6, Sat 10-5, Sun (Winter) 1-5
Friends of the Library Group

S   LIBRARY OF THE FRIENDS OF BOERNER BOTANICAL GARDENS*, Boerner Botanical Library, 9400 Boerner Dr, 53130. Tel: 414-525-5637. E-mail: library@fbbg.org. *Librn,* Dennis Sampson; Staff 0.25 (MLS 0.15, Non-MLS 0.1)
Library Holdings: Bk Titles 3,000
Subject Interests: Botany
Open Tues & Thurs 1:30-4:30, Sat 10:30-1:30
Restriction: Circ to mem only

HAMMOND

P   HAMMOND COMMUNITY LIBRARY*, 850 Davis St, 54015. (Mail add: PO Box 120, 54015-0120), SAN 318-0220. Tel: 715-796-2281. FAX: 715-796-2332. E-mail: hammondpl@ifls.lib.wi.us. Web Site: www.hammondpubliclibrary.org. *Dir,* Michelle Johnson
Founded 1968. Pop 1,800; Circ 55,000
Library Holdings: Bk Vols 15,000; Per Subs 80
Automation Activity & Vendor Info: (Acquisitions) Innovative Interfaces, Inc; (Cataloging) Innovative Interfaces, Inc; (Circulation) Innovative Interfaces, Inc
Mem of Indianhead Federated Library System
Open Mon-Thurs 10-8, Fri 10-6

HANCOCK

P   HANCOCK PUBLIC LIBRARY*, 114 S Main St, 54943. (Mail add: PO Box 217, 54943-0217), SAN 318-0239. Tel: 715-249-5817. FAX: 715-249-5815. E-mail: director@hancocklibrary.org. Web Site: www.hancocklibrary.org. *Dir,* Lisa Eisch; E-mail: eisch@hancocklibrary.org
Pop 1,664; Circ 26,551
Library Holdings: Bk Vols 6,000; Per Subs 50
Special Collections: Census, microfilm; Hancock-Coloma News; Plainfield Sun Newsp; Waushara Argus
Subject Interests: Local hist
Wireless access
Mem of Winnefox Library System
Open Mon, Thurs & Fri 12-6, Wed 10-6, Sat 10-1
Friends of the Library Group

HARTFORD

P   HARTFORD PUBLIC LIBRARY*, 115 N Main St, 53027-1596. SAN 318-0255. Tel: 262-673-8240. FAX: 262-673-8300. Web Site: www.hartfordlibrary.org/. *Dir,* Michael J Gelhausen; Tel: 262-673-8241, E-mail: mikeg@hartfordlibrary.org; *Ch,* Audrey Wolter; Tel: 262-673-8242, E-mail: awol@hartfordlibrary.org; Staff 11 (MLS 2, Non-MLS 9)
Founded 1904. Pop 20,000; Circ 176,685
Jan 2005-Dec 2005 Income $762,049, State $1,458, City $475,071, Federal $400, County $184,080, Locally Generated Income $57,085, Other

$43,955. Mats Exp $123,418, Books $91,446, Per/Ser (Incl. Access Fees) $7,843, Other Print Mats $775, AV Mat $21,413, Electronic Ref Mat (Incl. Access Fees) $1,941. Sal $283,891 (Prof $98,200)
Library Holdings: AV Mats 11,461; Large Print Bks 2,143; Bk Vols 102,271; Per Subs 200; Talking Bks 3,381
Special Collections: All US Census Records for Wisconsin-Washington & Dodge County, micro; History Room Coll; Local History, micro; Local Papers (1864-2005), micro
Automation Activity & Vendor Info: (Cataloging) SirsiDynix; (Circulation) SirsiDynix; (OPAC) SirsiDynix
Function: Homebound delivery serv
Partic in Library Council of Southeastern Wisconsin, Inc
Open Mon-Fri 9-8:30, Sat 9-5 (9-12 Summer)

HARTLAND

P   HARTLAND PUBLIC LIBRARY*, 110 E Park Ave, 53029. SAN 318-0263. Tel: 262-367-3350. FAX: 262-369-2251. E-mail: info@hartland.lib.wi.us. Web Site: www.hartlandlibrary.org. *Dir,* Nancy Massnick; E-mail: massnick@hartland.lib.wi.us; *Ch,* Sue Bannon; *Ref Serv,* Barb Svoboda; *Tech Serv,* Sandra Salzman; Staff 16 (MLS 4, Non-MLS 12)
Founded 1897. Pop 12,000; Circ 210,000
Jan 2006-Dec 2006. Mats Exp $100,000
Library Holdings: Bk Titles 70,000; Per Subs 100
Special Collections: Art Prints
Subject Interests: City hist
Automation Activity & Vendor Info: (Cataloging) SirsiDynix; (Circulation) SirsiDynix; (OPAC) SirsiDynix
Database Vendor: Baker & Taylor, Checkpoint Systems, Inc, EBSCOhost, Grolier Online, netLibrary, Newsbank, ProQuest, ReferenceUSA
Wireless access
Function: Bk club(s), Copy machines, Electronic databases & coll, Handicapped accessible, Homebound delivery serv, ILL available, Online ref, Prog for children & young adult, Spoken cassettes & CDs, Summer reading prog, Tax forms, Telephone ref, VHS videos
Open Mon-Thurs (Winter) 9-8, Fri 9-5, Sat 9-4; Mon-Thurs (Summer) 9-8, Fri 9-5, Sat 9-12
Friends of the Library Group

HAWKINS

P   HAWKINS AREA LIBRARY*, 709 Main St, 54530-9557. (Mail add: PO Box 17, 54530-0017), SAN 324-1246. Tel: 715-585-2311. FAX: 715-585-2311. E-mail: hawkinslibrary@ifls.lib.wi.us. *Dir, Librn,* Arlene Mabie
Founded 1979. Pop 800; Circ 5,600
Library Holdings: Audiobooks 97; AV Mats 397; CDs 245; DVDs 180; Electronic Media & Resources 8; Large Print Bks 187; Bk Titles 9,200; Per Subs 12; Videos 400
Automation Activity & Vendor Info: (Circulation) Winnebago Software Co
Wireless access
Mem of Indianhead Federated Library System
Partic in OCLC Online Computer Library Center, Inc
Open Mon-Fri 9-5, Sat 10-12
Friends of the Library Group

HAYWARD

J   LAC COURTE OREILLES OJIBWA COMMUNITY COLLEGE LIBRARY*, 13466 W Trepania Rd, 54843-2181. SAN 377-967X. Tel: 715-634-4790, Ext 108. Toll Free Tel: 888-526-6221. FAX: 715-634-5049. Web Site: www.lco.edu/library/index.html. *Head Librn,* Caryl Pfaff; E-mail: pfaff@lco.edu
Founded 1990. Enrl 450; Fac 35; Highest Degree: Associate
Library Holdings: Bk Vols 19,000; Per Subs 100
Special Collections: American Indian Coll, audio bks, bks, videos. State Document Depository
Subject Interests: Native Am
Automation Activity & Vendor Info: (Acquisitions) Follett Software; (Cataloging) Follett Software; (Circulation) Follett Software; (Course Reserve) Follett Software
Function: ILL available
Mem of Northern Waters Library Service
Partic in Am Indian Libr Asn; American Indian Higher Education Consortium; Wis Libr Asn
Open Mon-Thurs (Winter) 8-5:30, Fri 8-4:30; Mon-Fri (Summer) 8-4:30
Bookmobiles: 1

P   SHERMAN & RUTH WEISS COMMUNITY LIBRARY*, 10788 State Hwy 77 W, 54843. (Mail add: PO Box 917, 54843-0917), SAN 318-0271. Tel: 715-634-2161. FAX: 715-634-5257. E-mail: hlibrary@hayward.nwls.lib.wi.us. Web Site: www.weisscommunitylibrary.com. *Dir,* Molly Lank Jones; E-mail:

mlank-jones@hayward.nwls.lib.wi.us; *Librn,* Carol Martin; E-mail: cmartin@hayward.nwls.lib.wi.us; Staff 5 (Non-MLS 5)
Founded 1904. Circ 67,723
Library Holdings: Bk Vols 28,372; Per Subs 61
Subject Interests: Wis hist
Automation Activity & Vendor Info: (Acquisitions) Innovative Interfaces, Inc; (Cataloging) Innovative Interfaces, Inc; (Circulation) Innovative Interfaces, Inc
Wireless access
Function: Bk club(s), CD-ROM, ILL available, Magnifiers for reading, Music CDs, Online searches, Photocopying/Printing, Prog for children & young adult, Ref serv available, Spoken cassettes & CDs, Summer reading prog, VHS videos
Mem of Northern Waters Library Service
Open Mon, Wed & Fri 10-5, Tues & Thurs 10-8, Sat 10-3
Friends of the Library Group

HAZEL GREEN

P   HAZEL GREEN PUBLIC LIBRARY*, 1610 Fairplay, 53811. (Mail add: PO Box 367, 53811-0367). Tel: 608-854-2952. FAX: 608-854-2417. *Dir,* Melissa Reiff; E-mail: mreiff@swls.org
Pop 1,183; Circ 7,090
Library Holdings: Bk Vols 6,500; Per Subs 10
Automation Activity & Vendor Info: (Cataloging) Horizon; (Circulation) Horizon; (OPAC) Horizon
Mem of Southwest Wisconsin Library System
Open Mon, Tues, Thurs, Fri 2:20-5:30, Wed 2:20-8, Sat 8:30-12:30

HILLSBORO

P   HILLSBORO PUBLIC LIBRARY*, 819 High Ave, 54634. (Mail add: PO Box 468, 54634-0468), SAN 318-0298. Tel: 608-489-2192. E-mail: hlibrary@wrlsweb.org. *Dir,* Debra K Lambert
Pop 1,273; Circ 35,100
Library Holdings: Bk Vols 24,000; Per Subs 45
Automation Activity & Vendor Info: (Acquisitions) Follett Software; (Cataloging) Follett Software; (Circulation) Follett Software
Open Tues & Thurs 9-5, Wed & Fri 11-5 & 6-8, Sat 9-12

HOLMEN

P   LA CROSSE COUNTY LIBRARY*, Administration Ctr, 103 State St, 54636. (Mail add: Administration Ctr, PO Box 220, 54636-0220), SAN 364-7196. Tel: 608-526-9600. FAX: 608-526-3299. Web Site: www.lacrossecountylibrary.com. *Dir,* Christine McArdle Rojo; E-mail: mcardle-rojo.chris@lacrossecounty.org; *Cat Librn,* Christine Bradshaw; E-mail: bradshaw.chris@lacrossecounty.org; *Ch,* Carol Knapmiller; Tel: 608-526-4641, E-mail: knapmiller.carol@lacrossecounty.org; *Ch,* Karen Kroll; E-mail: kroll.karen@lacrossecounty.org; *Ch,* Katherine Sandy; E-mail: sandy.katherine@lacrossecounty.org; *Ch,* Megan Shaw; E-mail: shaw.megan@lacrossecounty.org; Staff 7.47 (MLS 1, Non-MLS 6.47)
Founded 1898. Pop 56,059; Circ 349,863
Library Holdings: AV Mats 7,888; Bk Titles 137,556; Per Subs 336; Videos 7,030
Automation Activity & Vendor Info: (Cataloging) Horizon; (Circulation) Horizon; (OPAC) Horizon; (Serials) Horizon
Database Vendor: SirsiDynix
Mem of Winding Rivers Library System
Friends of the Library Group
Branches: 5
JOHN BOSSHARD MEMORIAL, 1720 Henry Johns Blvd, Bangor, 54614, SAN 364-7226. Tel: 608-486-4408. FAX: 608-486-4408. E-mail: bangorlibrary@lacrossecounty.org. *Libr Assoc,* Shari Axelsen; E-mail: axelsen.shari@lacrossecounty.org; Staff 1.53 (Non-MLS 1.53)
Automation Activity & Vendor Info: (Acquisitions) SirsiDynix; (Cataloging) SirsiDynix; (Circulation) SirsiDynix
Open Mon & Wed 10-8, Tues & Thurs 3-6, Fri 10-5, Sat 9-1
Friends of the Library Group
CAMPBELL, Campbell Town Hall, 2219 Bainbridge St, LaCrosse, 54603, SAN 364-7250. Tel: 608-783-0052. Administration Tel: 608-526-9600. Administration FAX: 608-526-3299. E-mail: campbelllibrary@lacrossecounty.org. *Libr Assoc,* Sarah Stuber; E-mail: stuber.sarah@lacrossecounty.org; Staff 0.6 (Non-MLS 0.6)
Automation Activity & Vendor Info: (OPAC) SirsiDynix
Friends of the Library Group
HOLMEN AREA, 103 State St, 54636. (Mail add: PO Box 220, 54636-0220). Tel: 608-526-4198. Reference Tel: 608-526-3311. FAX: 608-526-3299. E-mail: holmenlibrary@lacrossecounty.org. *Br Mgr,* Deen Layland; E-mail: layland.deen@lacrossecounty.org; *Automation Syst Coordr, Ref,* Susanne Stranc; E-mail: stranc.sue@lacrossecounty.org; Staff 3.7 (MLS 0.94, Non-MLS 2.76)
Open Mon, Wed & Thurs 10-8, Tues 1-8, Fri 10-5, Sat 9-2
HAZEL BROWN LEICHT MEMORIAL LIBRARY, 201 Neshonoc Rd, West Salem, 54669, SAN 364-734X. Tel: 608-786-1505. FAX: 608-786-0036. E-mail: westsalemlibrary@lacrossecounty.org. *Br Mgr,*

Sharon Aldahl; E-mail: aldahl.sharon@lacrossecounty.org; Staff 2.75 (Non-MLS 2.75)
Open Mon & Wed 10-8, Tues & Thurs 1-8, Fri 12-6, Sat 10-1
ONALASKA PUBLIC, 741 Oak Ave S, Onalaska, 54650, SAN 364-7315. Tel: 608-781-9568. Reference Tel: 608-781-9599. FAX: 608-781-9594. E-mail: onalaskalibrary@lacrossecounty.org. *Br Mgr,* Katewin Peterson; *Ref Librn,* Carol Petrowski; E-mail: petrowski.carol@lacrossecounty.org; *Ref Librn,* Vickie Wally; E-mail: walley.vickie@lacrossecounty.org; Staff 7.19 (MLS 0.47, Non-MLS 6.72)
Open Mon, Wed & Thus 9-9, Tues 12-9, Fri 9-5, Sat 9-2
Friends of the Library Group

HORICON

P   HORICON PUBLIC LIBRARY*, 404 E Lake St, 53032-1297. SAN 318-0301. Tel: 920-485-3535. FAX: 920-485-3536. E-mail: horiconlibrary@mwfls.org. Web Site: www.horicon.lib.wi.us. *Dir,* Geri Feucht; E-mail: gfeucht@mwfls.org; *Asst Dir,* Deb Antony; E-mail: antony@mwfls.org; *Youth Serv Librn,* Shannon Barniskis; E-mail: shannonb@mwfls.org
Founded 1899. Pop 3,782; Circ 60,000
Library Holdings: Bk Vols 28,500; Per Subs 65
Automation Activity & Vendor Info: (Cataloging) SirsiDynix; (Circulation) SirsiDynix
Mem of Mid-Wisconsin Federated Library System
Open Mon-Thurs 11-8, Fri 11-6, Sat 10-2
Friends of the Library Group

P   MID-WISCONSIN FEDERATED LIBRARY SYSTEM*, 112 Clinton St, 53032. SAN 317-9931. Tel: 920-485-0833. Toll Free Tel: 800-660-6899. FAX: 920-485-0899. Web Site: www.mwfls.org. *Dir,* Walter Burkhalter; E-mail: wburkh@mwfls.org; *Automation Serv,* Steven Platteter; E-mail: sepp@mwfls.org; Staff 5 (MLS 2, Non-MLS 3)
Founded 1974. Pop 300,000
Member Libraries: Beaver Dam Community Library; Brownsville Public Library; Dwight Foster Public Library; Fox Lake Public Library; Germantown Community Library; Horicon Public Library; Hustisford Community Library; Hutchinson Memorial Library; Iron Ridge Public Library; Irvin L Young Memorial Library; Jefferson Public Library; Johnson Creek Public Library; Juneau Public Library; Karl Junginger Memorial Library; Kewaskum Public Library; L D Fargo Public Library; Lomira Public Library; Lowell Public Library; Mayville Public Library; Powers Memorial Library; Reeseville Public Library; Slinger Community Library; Theresa Public Library; Watertown Public Library; Waupun Public Library; West Bend Community Memorial Library
Partic in OCLC Online Computer Library Center, Inc; Wisconsin Library Services

HORTONVILLE

P   HORTONVILLE PUBLIC LIBRARY*, 102 W Main St, 54944. SAN 318-031X. Tel: 920-779-4279. FAX: 920-779-4279. E-mail: hpl@mail.owls.lib.wi.us. Web Site: www.hortonvillelibrary.org. *Dir,* Carolyn R Habeck; E-mail: chabeck@mail.owls.lib.wi.us; Staff 1 (Non-MLS 1)
Founded 1920. Pop 2,596; Circ 8,636
Library Holdings: Bks on Deafness & Sign Lang 50; CDs 235; DVDs 254; e-books 9,887; Large Print Bks 453; Bk Vols 17,000; Per Subs 113; Talking Bks 784; Videos 1,208
Automation Activity & Vendor Info: (Acquisitions) Innovative Interfaces, Inc; (Cataloging) Innovative Interfaces, Inc; (Circulation) Innovative Interfaces, Inc; (OPAC) Innovative Interfaces, Inc
Mem of Outagamie Waupaca Library System
Open Mon-Thurs 9-6, Fri 9-5, Sat (Winter) 9-12
Friends of the Library Group

HUDSON

P   HUDSON AREA JOINT LIBRARY, 700 First St, 54016. SAN 318-0336. Tel: 715-386-3101. Reference Tel: 715-386-3101, Ext 101. Administration Tel: 715-386-3101, Ext 105. FAX: 715-381-0468. E-mail: hudsonpl@hudsonpubliclibrary.org. Web Site: www.hudsonpubliclibrary.org. *In Charge,* Matthew Winkler; Staff 3 (MLS 1, Non-MLS 2)
Founded 1904. Pop 29,131
Jan 2011-Dec 2011 Income $688,589, City $629,026, County $55,328, Other $4,235. Mats Exp $102,943, Books $77,762, Per/Ser (Incl. Access Fees) $9,030, AV Mat $16,151. Sal $279,710 (Prof $61,225)
Library Holdings: AV Mats 2,356; Bk Vols 59,680; Per Subs 126; Videos 3,006
Automation Activity & Vendor Info: (Cataloging) Innovative Interfaces, Inc; (Circulation) Innovative Interfaces, Inc; (OPAC) Innovative Interfaces, Inc; (Serials) Innovative Interfaces, Inc
Database Vendor: 3M Library Systems, Baker & Taylor, BWI, EBSCOhost, Gale Cengage Learning, MITINET, Inc, netLibrary, ProQuest
Wireless access

Function: Art exhibits, Audiobks via web, Bk club(s), Bks on CD, Children's prog, Computer training, Computers for patron use, Copy machines, Digital talking bks, ILL available, OverDrive digital audio bks, Photocopying/Printing, Story hour, Tax forms, Web-catalog, Wheelchair accessible
Mem of Indianhead Federated Library System
Open Mon-Thurs 10-8, Fri 10-6, Sat 10-3
Restriction: 24-hr pass syst for students only
Friends of the Library Group

HURLEY

P   HURLEY PUBLIC LIBRARY*, 405 Fifth Ave N, 54534-1170. SAN 318-0344. Tel: 715-561-5707. FAX: 715-561-3222. *Dir,* Lynne Pedri
Pop 4,664; Circ 18,300
Library Holdings: Bk Vols 9,500; Per Subs 24
Publications: Booklist
Mem of Northern Waters Library Service
Open Mon (Winter) 9-7, Tues-Fri 9-5; Mon-Fri (Summer) 9-5

HUSTISFORD

P   HUSTISFORD COMMUNITY LIBRARY*, 609 W Juneau St, 53034. SAN 370-6591. Tel: 920-349-3463. FAX: 920-349-4540. E-mail: hustipl@mwfls.org. Web Site: www.hustisford.lib.wi.us. *Dir,* Candace Graulich; E-mail: graulich@mwfls.org; *Ch,* Monica Wasemiller; E-mail: monicaw@mwfls.org; Staff 4 (Non-MLS 4)
Founded 1986. Pop 2,615; Circ 45,011
Library Holdings: Audiobooks 621; AV Mats 3,802; CDs 387; DVDs 2,211; e-books 8,825; Large Print Bks 218; Bk Vols 21,101; Per Subs 77; Talking Bks 964; Videos 583
Automation Activity & Vendor Info: (Acquisitions) SirsiDynix; (Cataloging) SirsiDynix; (Circulation) SirsiDynix; (ILL) Auto-Graphics, Inc; (OPAC) SirsiDynix; (Serials) SirsiDynix
Wireless access
Function: Adult bk club, AV serv, Bks on CD, CD-ROM, Children's prog, Computers for patron use, Copy machines, Fax serv, Free DVD rentals, Holiday prog, ILL available, Music CDs, Online cat, Online ref, Online searches, OverDrive digital audio bks, Photocopying/Printing, Prog for children & young adult, Story hour, Summer reading prog, Tax forms, Wheelchair accessible
Mem of Mid-Wisconsin Federated Library System
Open Mon-Thurs 12-7:30, Fri 12-6, Sat 9-1
Friends of the Library Group

INDEPENDENCE

P   INDEPENDENCE PUBLIC LIBRARY*, 23688 Adams St, 54747. (Mail add: PO Box 99, 54747-0099), SAN 318-0352. Tel: 715-985-3616. FAX: 715-985-2530. E-mail: indplbry@triwest.net. *Dir,* Cathy Kruckenberg
Founded 1908. Pop 1,244; Circ 12,949
Library Holdings: Bk Vols 14,000; Per Subs 65
Automation Activity & Vendor Info: (Cataloging) Follett Software; (Circulation) Follett Software
Open Mon 12-8, Tues-Thurs 12-6, Fri 9-5, Sat 9-12

IOLA

P   IOLA VILLAGE LIBRARY*, 180 S Main St, 54945-9689. (Mail add: PO Box 336, 54945-0336), SAN 324-6965. Tel: 715-445-4330. FAX: 715-445-2917. Web Site: www.owls.lib.wi.us/ivl. *Dir,* Robyn Grove; E-mail: regrove@mail.owls.lib.wi.us; *Asst Dir,* Lisa Bauer; E-mail: lbauer@mail.owls.lib.wi.us
Pop 1,109; Circ 17,976
Library Holdings: Bk Vols 18,000; Per Subs 58
Automation Activity & Vendor Info: (Cataloging) Infor Library & Information Solutions; (Circulation) Infor Library & Information Solutions
Mem of Outagamie Waupaca Library System
Open Mon & Wed-Fri 9-5:30, Tues 9-8
Friends of the Library Group

IRON RIDGE

P   IRON RIDGE PUBLIC LIBRARY*, 205 Park St, 53035. (Mail add: PO Box 247, 53035-0247), SAN 364-6114. Tel: 920-387-3637. FAX: 920-387-3637. E-mail: iridge@mwfls.org. Web Site: www.ironridge.lib.wi.us. *Dir,* Jerilyn Papenfuss
Founded 1991. Pop 1,025; Circ 22,850
Jul 2005-Jun 2006 Income $25,000
Library Holdings: Bk Vols 18,750; Per Subs 30
Database Vendor: SirsiDynix
Mem of Mid-Wisconsin Federated Library System
Open Mon-Thurs 3-8, Sat 8-1

IRON RIVER

P   EVELYN GOLDBERG BRIGGS MEMORIAL LIBRARY*, 68235 S Main St, 54847. (Mail add: PO Box 145, 54847-0145). Tel: 715-372-5451. FAX: 715-372-5451. Web Site: ironriver.wislib.org. *Dir,* Courtney Dietsche; E-mail: cdietsche@ir.nwls.lib.wi.us; Staff 1 (MLS 1)
Library Holdings: Bk Titles 9,000
Wireless access
Mem of Northern Waters Library Service
Open Mon & Tues 12-8, Wed & Thurs 10-6, Fri 9-5, Sat 9-12
Friends of the Library Group

JANESVILLE

P   ARROWHEAD LIBRARY SYSTEM*, 210 Dodge St, 53545-3809. SAN 318-0360. Tel: 608-758-6690. FAX: 608-758-6689. Web Site: als.lib.wi.us. *Dir,* Ruth Ann Montgomery; Tel: 608-758-6693, E-mail: montgomery.ruthann@als.lib.wi.us; Staff 2 (MLS 2)
Founded 1974. Pop 154,588
Jan 2005-Dec 2005 Income $1,370,109, State $414,754, Federal $13,603, County $929,752, Other $12,000. Mats Exp $3,160, Books $2,000, Per/Ser (Incl. Access Fees) $1,160. Sal $154,525 (Prof $49,103)
Library Holdings: AV Mats 1,020; Large Print Bks 9,893; Bk Vols 9,893; Per Subs 39; Talking Bks 1,020
Member Libraries: Aurora Public Library; Beloit College; Beloit Public Library; Blackhawk Technical College Library; Buhl Public Library; Clinton Public Library; Duluth Public Library; Eager Free Public Library; Edgerton Public Library; Grand Marais Public Library; Hedberg Public Library; Hibbing Public Library; International Falls Public Library; McKinley Public Library; Milton Public Library; Moose Lake Public Library; Orfordville Public Library; Two Harbors Public Library; Wisconsin Center for the Blind & Visually Impaired
Partic in North Country Library Cooperative; OCLC Online Computer Library Center, Inc
Special Services for the Blind - Bks on cassette; Large print bks
Open Mon-Fri 8-5

J   BLACKHAWK TECHNICAL COLLEGE LIBRARY, 6004 S County Rd G, 53547. (Mail add: PO Box 5009, 53547-5009), SAN 318-0379. Tel: 608-757-7671. FAX: 608-743-4518. Web Site: www.blackhawk.edu/library/library.htm. *Librn,* Janet Laura White; Tel: 608-757-7705, E-mail: jwhite@blackhawk.edu; *Cat,* Tara Kilby; Tel: 608-743-4515, E-mail: tkilby@blackhawk.edu; Staff 3 (MLS 1, Non-MLS 2)
Founded 1966. Enrl 1,527; Fac 100; Highest Degree: Associate
Jul 2005-Jun 2006. Mats Exp $84,585, Books $16,987, Per/Ser (Incl. Access Fees) $23,827, Micro $3,000, AV Mat $20,265, Electronic Ref Mat (Incl. Access Fees) $20,506. Sal $125,813 (Prof $67,347)
Library Holdings: Bks on Deafness & Sign Lang 15; CDs 46; DVDs 95; e-books 20,845; e-journals 11; High Interest/Low Vocabulary Bk Vols 800; Bk Titles 18,800; Bk Vols 19,000; Per Subs 290; Talking Bks 438; Videos 5,128
Special Collections: Child Care Coll; High/Low Coll; Professional Coll
Automation Activity & Vendor Info: (Cataloging) OCLC Connexion; (Circulation) Auto-Graphics, Inc; (OPAC) Auto-Graphics, Inc
Database Vendor: Baker & Taylor, EBSCOhost, Gale Cengage Learning, LexisNexis, OCLC WorldCat, OVID Technologies, ProQuest, World Book Online
Wireless access
Mem of Arrowhead Library System
Partic in South Central Wisconsin Health Science Library Consortium; WILS
Open Mon-Thurs 7:30am-9pm, Fri 7:30-4, Sat 9-1
Departmental Libraries:
AVIATION CENTER, 4618 S Columbia Dr, 53546. Tel: 608-757-7743. Toll Free Tel: 800-498-1282. FAX: 608-758-6950. Web Site: www.blackhawk.edu/gi/facilities/facavi.htm. *Mgr, Libr Serv,* Janet Laura White; E-mail: jwhite@blackhawk.edu
  Library Holdings: Bk Titles 250
  Open Mon-Fri 8-4

P   HEDBERG PUBLIC LIBRARY, 316 S Main St, 53545. SAN 318-0387. Tel: 608-758-6600. Circulation Tel: 608-758-6582. Interlibrary Loan Service Tel: 608-758-6598. Reference Tel: 608-758-6581. Information Services Tel: 608-758-6588. FAX: 608-758-6583. E-mail: referencedesk@hedbergpubliclibrary.org. Web Site: www.hedbergpubliclibrary.org. *Dir,* Bryan J McCormick; Tel: 608-758-6594, E-mail: bmccormick@hedbergpubliclibrary.org; *Head, Circ,* Michelle Dennis; Tel: 608-758-6610, E-mail: mdennis@hedbergpubliclibrary.org; *Head, Coll Develop, Tech Serv,* Carol Kuntzelman; Tel: 608-758-6607, E-mail: ckuntzelman@hedbergpubliclibrary.org; *Head, Info Serv,* Mary Buelow; Tel: 608-758-5808, Fax: 608-758-6615, E-mail: mbuelow@hedbergpubliclibrary.org; *Head, Youth Serv,* Sharon Grover; Tel: 608-758-6584, E-mail: sgrover@hedbergpubliclibrary.org; *Computer Syst*

Mgr, Emrick Gunderson; Tel: 608-758-6599, E-mail: egundersojn@hedbergpubliclibrary.org; *Pub Relations Mgr,* Elizabeth Hough; Tel: 608-758-6607, E-mail: ehough@hedbergpubliclibrary.org; *YA Serv,* Laurie Bartz; E-mail: lbartz@hedbergpubliclibrary.org; Staff 52 (MLS 13, Non-MLS 39)
Founded 1884. Pop 82,411; Circ 1,153,991
Library Holdings: AV Mats 45,812; Bk Vols 228,038; Per Subs 579
Special Collections: Job Resource Center; Local History (Janesville Room)
Automation Activity & Vendor Info: (Acquisitions) Innovative Interfaces, Inc - Millenium; (Cataloging) Innovative Interfaces, Inc - Millenium; (Circulation) Innovative Interfaces, Inc - Millenium; (ILL) Auto-Graphics, Inc; (OPAC) Innovative Interfaces, Inc - Millenium; (Serials) Innovative Interfaces, Inc - Millenium
Database Vendor: Baker & Taylor, BookLetters LLC, BWI, Children's Literature Comprehensive Database Company (CLCD), EBSCOhost, Gale Cengage Learning, infoUSA, LearningExpress, Mergent Online, OCLC FirstSearch, ProQuest, ReferenceUSA, ValueLine, World Book Online
Wireless access
Publications: Library Matters (Newsletter)
Mem of Arrowhead Library System
Partic in OCLC Online Computer Library Center, Inc; WILS
Special Services for the Deaf - TDD equip
Special Services for the Blind - Assistive/Adapted tech devices, equip & products
Open Mon-Fri 9-9, Sat 9-5, Sun 1-5
Friends of the Library Group

S   ROCK COUNTY HISTORICAL SOCIETY*, Archives of Rock County History, 933 Mineral Point Ave, 53545. (Mail add: PO Box 8096, 53547-8096), SAN 318-0425. Tel: 608-756-4509. Toll Free Tel: 800-577-1859. FAX: 608-741-9596. E-mail: rchs@rchs.us. Web Site: www.rchs.us. *Dir,* Joel Haaften; *Coll Mgr,* Laurel Fant; *Archivist,* Ruth Anderson
Founded 1948
Library Holdings: Bk Titles 8,385; Per Subs 19
Special Collections: Carrie Jacobs Bond Coll; Frances Willard Coll; Historic Materials (Samson Tractor Company), papers; Land Speculation (Tallman Family), papers; Local History, diaries & family papers; Local Organizations Coll; Rock County Industrial Development Coll; Women's Christian Temperance Union Coll
Subject Interests: Archit studies of local hist sites, Hist of Rock county, Survey of all hist sites
Open Mon-Fri 9-3
Restriction: Not a lending libr

R   SEVENTH DAY BAPTIST HISTORICAL SOCIETY LIBRARY, 3120 Kennedy Rd, 53545-0225. (Mail add: PO Box 1678, 53547-1678), SAN 310-4311. Tel: 608-752-5055. FAX: 608-752-7711. E-mail: sdbhist@seventhdaybaptist.org. Web Site: www.sdbhistory.org, www.seventhdaybaptist.org. *Dir, Librarian-Historian,* Nicholas J Kersten; Staff 2 (Non-MLS 2)
Founded 1916
Library Holdings: Bk Titles 2,600; Bk Vols 4,500; Per Subs 25
Special Collections: 17th-20th Century English Seventh Day Baptist Churches (Mill Yard Church & Sabbatarian Literature Coll), bks & ms; Archives of Seventh Day Baptist General Conference, USA & Canada; China Mission Coll, 1847-1945, ms & ephemera; Early African Seventh Day Baptist Missions (Nyasaland Missions Coll), 1895-1914; Ephrata, PA Cloister (Julius F Sachse Coll), bks, ms, ephemera, realia
Subject Interests: Hist of the Sabbath, Seventh Day Baptists
Automation Activity & Vendor Info: (Acquisitions) Cuadra Associates; (Cataloging) Cuadra Associates; (OPAC) Cuadra Associates; (Serials) Cuadra Associates
Wireless access
Function: Res libr
Publications: Annual Report; Books & Pamphlets on Seventh Day Baptist History; Occasional Newsletter
Restriction: Not a lending libr, Open by appt only

C   UNIVERSITY OF WISCONSIN-ROCK COUNTY LIBRARY*, Gary J Lenox Library, 2909 Kellogg Ave, 53546-5606. SAN 318-0433. Tel: 608-758-6531. FAX: 608-758-6560. Web Site: rock.uwc.edu/library. *Dir,* Brian Beecher; E-mail: brian.beecher@uwc.edu; *Assoc Librn,* Lynn Gilman; E-mail: lynn.gilman@uwc.edu; *Asst Librn,* Julie Orvis; E-mail: julie.orvis@uwc.edu; Staff 3 (MLS 2, Non-MLS 1)
Founded 1966. Enrl 990; Fac 50; Highest Degree: Associate
Library Holdings: AV Mats 2,129; Bk Titles 54,886; Per Subs 220
Special Collections: State Document Depository
Automation Activity & Vendor Info: (Acquisitions) Ex Libris Group; (Cataloging) Ex Libris Group; (Circulation) Ex Libris Group; (Course Reserve) Ex Libris Group; (ILL) Ex Libris Group; (OPAC) Ex Libris Group; (Serials) Ex Libris Group
Database Vendor: EBSCOhost, Gale Cengage Learning, JSTOR, LexisNexis, netLibrary, OCLC FirstSearch, ProQuest, Wilson - Wilson Web

Wireless access
Partic in OCLC Online Computer Library Center, Inc
Open Mon-Thurs (Winter) 8am-8:30pm, Fri 8-5; Mon-Thurs (Summer) 8-4:30, Fri 8-Noon

S   WISCONSIN CENTER FOR THE BLIND & VISUALLY IMPAIRED*, Wisconsin School for the Visually Handicapped Library, 1700 W State St, 53546. SAN 318-0441. Tel: 608-758-6118. Toll Free Tel: 866-284-1107. FAX: 608-758-6161. *In Charge,* Michelle Rueckert; Staff 1 (Non-MLS 1)
Library Holdings: Bk Vols 12,000; Per Subs 90
Automation Activity & Vendor Info: (Circulation) SirsiDynix
Mem of Arrowhead Library System

JEFFERSON

P   JEFFERSON PUBLIC LIBRARY*, 321 S Main St, 53549-1772. SAN 324-2161. Tel: 920-674-7733. FAX: 920-674-7735. Web Site: www.jefferson.lib.wi.us. *Dir,* Jocelyn Bubolz; E-mail: jbubolz@mwfls.org; *Automation Syst Coordr, ILL,* Sue McKechnie; *Ch,* Sharon Weber; *Ref Serv,* Leann Schwandt-Lehner; *Tech Serv,* Hazel Rooker; Staff 7.3 (MLS 1.9, Non-MLS 5.4)
Founded 1871. Pop 11,647; Circ 102,395
Jan 2007-Dec 2007 Income $443,792, City $298,135, County $116,032, Locally Generated Income $6,920, Other $21,090. Mats Exp $37,721, Books $23,252, Per/Ser (Incl. Access Fees) $2,000, AV Mat $9,954, Electronic Ref Mat (Incl. Access Fees) $375. Sal $227,927
Library Holdings: Audiobooks 1,788; DVDs 2,184; e-books 8,825; Electronic Media & Resources 2,745; Bk Titles 51,699; Per Subs 120
Automation Activity & Vendor Info: (Acquisitions) SirsiDynix; (Cataloging) SirsiDynix; (Circulation) SirsiDynix; (Course Reserve) SirsiDynix; (ILL) SirsiDynix; (Media Booking) SirsiDynix; (OPAC) SirsiDynix; (Serials) SirsiDynix
Database Vendor: EBSCOhost, ProQuest
Wireless access
Function: Accelerated reader prog
Mem of Mid-Wisconsin Federated Library System
Open Mon-Thurs (Winter) 10-9, Fri & Sat 10-5; Mon-Thurs (Summer) 10-7, Fri 10-5, Sat 10-1
Restriction: Access at librarian's discretion

JOHNSON CREEK

P   JOHNSON CREEK PUBLIC LIBRARY*, 125 Lincoln St, 53038. (Mail add: PO Box 130, 53038-0130), SAN 324-1254. Tel: 920-699-3741. FAX: 920-699-3741. E-mail: Help@johnsoncreeklibrary.org. *Dir,* Luci Bledsoe; E-mail: luci@johnsoncreeklibrary.org; Staff 2 (MLS 1, Non-MLS 1)
Founded 1902. Pop 2,153; Circ 20,648
Library Holdings: Bk Titles 19,000; Per Subs 50
Automation Activity & Vendor Info: (Acquisitions) SirsiDynix; (Cataloging) SirsiDynix; (Circulation) SirsiDynix; (OPAC) SirsiDynix
Mem of Mid-Wisconsin Federated Library System
Open Mon-Thurs 10-7, Fri 10-6, Sat 10-1
Friends of the Library Group

JUNEAU

P   JUNEAU PUBLIC LIBRARY*, 250 N Fairfield Ave, 53039-1323. SAN 318-045X. Tel: 920-386-4805. FAX: 920-386-4806. E-mail: juneau@mwfls.org. Web Site: www.juneau.lib.wi.us. *Dir,* Barbara Smith
Founded 1949
Library Holdings: Bk Vols 30,000; Per Subs 51
Automation Activity & Vendor Info: (Acquisitions) SirsiDynix; (Cataloging) SirsiDynix; (Circulation) SirsiDynix
Mem of Mid-Wisconsin Federated Library System
Open Mon-Thurs 11-8, Fri 11-4, Sat 9-12
Friends of the Library Group

KAUKAUNA

P   KAUKAUNA PUBLIC LIBRARY*, 111 Main Ave, 54130-2436. SAN 318-0468. Tel: 920-766-6340. FAX: 920-766-6343. E-mail: kau@mail.owls.lib.wi.us. Web Site: www.kaukaunalibrary.org. *Dir,* Margaret J Waggoner; E-mail: mwaggone@mail.owls.lib.wi.us; *Asst Dir,* Diane Wittman; E-mail: dwittman@mail.owls.lib.wi.us; *Youth Serv Librn,* Rose Selle; E-mail: rselle@mail.owls.lib.wi.us; Staff 4 (MLS 2, Non-MLS 2)
Founded 1899. Pop 19,757; Circ 239,550
Library Holdings: Bk Vols 59,756; Per Subs 200
Special Collections: State Document Depository
Subject Interests: Wis hist
Automation Activity & Vendor Info: (Acquisitions) Innovative Interfaces, Inc; (Cataloging) Innovative Interfaces, Inc - OCLC; (Circulation) Innovative Interfaces, Inc; (Course Reserve) Innovative Interfaces, Inc; (OPAC) Innovative Interfaces, Inc
Database Vendor: EBSCOhost, OCLC WorldCat

Wireless access
Mem of Outagamie Waupaca Library System
Partic in OWLSnet
Open Mon-Thurs 9-8, Fri 9-5, Sat 9-4

KENDALL

P KENDALL PUBLIC LIBRARY*, 110 E South Railroad St, 54638-9999.
SAN 318-0476. Tel: 608-463-7103. E-mail: klibrary@wrlsweb.org. *Dir,*
Helen Zuhlke
Founded 1946. Pop 468
Library Holdings: Bk Vols 10,000; Per Subs 25
Automation Activity & Vendor Info: (Acquisitions) SirsiDynix;
(Cataloging) SirsiDynix; (Circulation) SirsiDynix; (OPAC) SirsiDynix
Mem of Winding Rivers Library System
Open Tues & Fri 10-6, Thurs 1-6
Friends of the Library Group

KENOSHA

C CARTHAGE COLLEGE*, Hedberg Library, 2001 Alford Park Dr,
53140-1900. SAN 318-0492. Tel: 262-551-5900. Interlibrary Loan Service
Tel: 262-551-5907. FAX: 262-551-5904. Web Site: www.carthage.edu. *Dir,*
VPres for Acad Info Serv, Eugene A Engeldinger; *Dir of Computer Ctr,*
Carol Sabbar; *Head, Media Serv,* Mike Love; *Head, Pub Serv,* Dennis
Unterholzner; *Head, Tech Serv,* Richard Hren; *Access Serv Librn,* Kathy
Myers; *Ref/Media Serv Librn,* Chris Grugel; *Ref/User Instruction Librn,*
Tina Eger; *Asst Cat Librn,* Bobbi-Jean Ludwig; *Network Adminr,* James
Walsh; Staff 7 (MLS 7)
Founded 1847. Enrl 2,250; Fac 125; Highest Degree: Master
Jul 2008-Jun 2009. Mats Exp $320,000, Books $61,000, Per/Ser (Incl.
Access Fees) $115,000, Micro $6,000, AV Equip $21,000, AV Mat
$14,000, Electronic Ref Mat (Incl. Access Fees) $97,000, Presv $6,000
Library Holdings: AV Mats 6,500; e-books 12,000; Bk Titles 125,000; Bk
Vols 145,000; Per Subs 415
Special Collections: Center for Children's Literature Coll; Civil War
(Palumbo Coll)
Automation Activity & Vendor Info: (Acquisitions) LibLime;
(Cataloging) LibLime; (Circulation) LibLime; (Course Reserve) LibLime;
(ILL) LibLime; (Media Booking) LibLime; (OPAC) LibLime; (Serials)
LibLime
Wireless access
Partic in Coun of Wis Librs, Inc; OCLC Online Computer Library Center,
Inc; Wis Libr Consortium; Wisconsin Library Services

C GATEWAY TECHNICAL COLLEGE*, Learning Resources Center
Library, 3520 30th Ave, 53144-1690. SAN 364-7013. Tel: 262-564-2786.
Interlibrary Loan Service Tel: 262-564-2378. FAX: 262-564-2787. E-mail:
kenoshalrc@gtc.edu. Web Site: www.gtc.edu/library. *Mgr, Libr Serv,* Gary
Flynn; E-mail: flynng@gtc.edu; *Acq, Cat,* Judy Quinn; Tel: 262-564-2604,
564-2654, E-mail: quinnj@gtc.edu; *Circ,* April Lindquist; Tel:
262-564-2540, E-mail: lindquista@gtc.edu; *ILL,* Linda Cate; E-mail:
catel@gtc.edu; *Ref Serv,* Ellen Pedraza; E-mail: pedraza@gtc.edu; *Ser,*
Mary Chartier; Tel: 262-564-2380, E-mail: chartierm@gtc.edu; Staff 7
(MLS 2, Non-MLS 5)
Founded 1964. Fac 201
Library Holdings: Bks on Deafness & Sign Lang 417; Bk Titles 35,000;
Bk Vols 90,000; Per Subs 365
Subject Interests: Aviation, Computer sci, Hort, Interior design, Law
enforcement, Nursing, Phys therapy
Automation Activity & Vendor Info: (Acquisitions) Ex Libris Group;
(Cataloging) Ex Libris Group; (Circulation) Ex Libris Group; (Course
Reserve) Ex Libris Group; (OPAC) Ex Libris Group; (Serials) Ex Libris
Group
Database Vendor: EBSCOhost, Gale Cengage Learning, ProQuest, Wilson
- Wilson Web
Partic in Library Council of Southeastern Wisconsin, Inc; Wis PALS Libr
Consortium
Special Services for the Deaf - Videos & decoder
Open Mon-Thurs 7:45am-8:30pm, Fri 7:45-4, Sat 9-Noon

S KENOSHA COUNTY HISTORICAL SOCIETY*, Kenosha History Center
Archives, 220 51st Pl, 53140. SAN 318-0530. Tel: 262-654-5770. FAX:
262-654-1730. E-mail: kchs@acronet.net. Web Site:
www.kenoshahistorycenter.org. *Exec Dir,* Tom Schleif; *Curator,* Cynthia
Nelson; Staff 1 (Non-MLS 1)
Founded 1878
Library Holdings: Bk Titles 3,000
Subject Interests: City of Kenosha, Kenosha county, Local hist, State of
Wisc
Function: Archival coll
Open Tues-Fri 2-4:30
Restriction: Non-circulating, Open to pub for ref only

P KENOSHA PUBLIC LIBRARY*, 812 56th St, 53140-3735. (Mail add: PO
Box 1414, 53141-1414), SAN 364-7048. Tel: 262-564-6100. Circulation
Tel: 262-564-6101. Interlibrary Loan Service Tel: 262-564-6312. Reference
Tel: 262-564-6130. Administration Tel: 262-564-6300. FAX: 262-564-6370.
Web Site: www.mykpl.info. *Dir,* Douglas Baker; Tel: 262-564-6324,
E-mail: dbaker@kenosha.lib.wi.us; *Asst Libr Dir,* Lin Swartz-Truesdell;
Tel: 262-564-6326, E-mail: lswartzt@kenosha.lib.wi.us; *Head, Admin Serv,*
Kris Neiman; Tel: 262-564-6325, E-mail: kneiman@kenosha.lib.wi.us;
Head, Ch, Roxane Bartelt; Tel: 262-564-6151, E-mail:
rbartelt@kenosha.lib.wi.us; *Head, Circ,* Linda Anderson; Tel:
262-564-6134, E-mail: landerso@kenosha.lib.wi.us; *Head, Ref Serv,* Tom J
Carson; Tel: 262-564-6132, E-mail: tcarson@kenosha.lib.wi.us; *Coll
Develop,* Ellen Melyon; Tel: 262-564-6327, E-mail:
emelyon@kenosha.lib.wi.us; Staff 36 (MLS 24, Non-MLS 12)
Founded 1895. Pop 164,465; Circ 1,157,686
Jan 2009-Dec 2009 Income $6,634,593, City $4,578,890, Federal $20,705,
County $1,521,395, Locally Generated Income $187,815. Mats Exp
$602,490. Sal $4,855,726
Library Holdings: Bk Vols 401,800
Special Collections: Developmental Coll; Kenosha Author Coll; Kenosha
History Coll
Subject Interests: Local hist
Automation Activity & Vendor Info: (Acquisitions) Infor Library &
Information Solutions; (Cataloging) Infor Library & Information Solutions;
(Circulation) Infor Library & Information Solutions; (OPAC) Infor Library
& Information Solutions
Wireless access
Function: Adult bk club, Adult literacy prog, After school storytime,
Audio & video playback equip for onsite use, Audiobks via web, Bk
club(s), Bk reviews (Group), Bks on cassette, Bks on CD, Bus archives,
CD-ROM, Children's prog, Computer training, Computers for patron use,
Copy machines, Digital talking bks, E-Reserves, Electronic databases &
coll, Exhibits, Family literacy, Games & aids for the handicapped,
Handicapped accessible, Holiday prog, Home delivery & serv to Sr ctr &
nursing homes, Homebound delivery serv, ILL available, Instruction &
testing, Jail serv, Large print keyboards, Magnifiers for reading, Music
CDs, Online cat, Online ref, Outreach serv, OverDrive digital audio bks,
Photocopying/Printing, Preschool outreach, Prog for adults, Prog for
children & young adult, Provide serv for the mentally ill, Pub access
computers, Ref & res, Ref serv available, Ref serv in person, Serves
mentally handicapped consumers, Spoken cassettes & CDs, Story hour,
Summer reading prog, Teen prog, VHS videos, Wheelchair accessible,
Workshops
Publications: Guide to Genealogy; Job Search Information; Kenosha
Organization Directory; Local Historical Resources; Newsnotes
Partic in OCLC Online Computer Library Center, Inc; Wisconsin Library
Services
Open Mon-Thurs 9-9, Fri 9-6, Sat 9-5, Sun (Sept-May) 12-4
Friends of the Library Group
Bookmobiles: 1. Librn, Therese O'Halloran. Bk vols 11,706

S KENOSHA PUBLIC MUSEUMS LIBRARY*, 5500 First Ave, 53140.
SAN 318-0557. Tel: 262-653-4140, 262-653-4426. FAX: 262-653-4437.
Web Site: www.kenoshapublicmuseum.org. *Dir,* Dan Joyce; Tel:
262-653-4427, E-mail: djoyce@kenosha.org; *Curator,* Nancy Mathews;
E-mail: mnancym@kenosha.org. Subject Specialists: *Anthropology,* Nancy
Mathews; Staff 6 (Non-MLS 6)
Founded 1936
Library Holdings: AV Mats 300; Bk Vols 10,000; Per Subs 21
Special Collections: Art Reference; Civil War Archives; Natural Sciences
Reference
Subject Interests: Anthropology, Art, Civil War, Mus, Paleontology
Function: Ref & res
Restriction: Open by appt only, Open to pub for ref only

M UNITED HOSPITAL SYSTEM*, Kenosha Medical Center Library, 6308
Eighth Ave, 53143. SAN 318-0549. Tel: 262-656-2120. FAX:
262-653-5780. *Librn,* Patty Westrich; E-mail: patty.westrich@uhsi.org
Founded 1970
Library Holdings: Bk Vols 250; Per Subs 100
Subject Interests: Cardiology, Med, Nursing, Oncology
Partic in Southeastern Wisconsin Health Science Library Consortium
Open Mon-Fri 7-5
Restriction: Med staff only

C UNIVERSITY OF WISCONSIN-PARKSIDE LIBRARY*, 900 Wood Rd,
53141. (Mail add: PO Box 2000, 53141-2000), SAN 318-0573. Tel:
262-595-2356. Circulation Tel: 262-595-2238. Interlibrary Loan Service
Tel: 262-595-2595. Reference Tel: 262-595-2360. FAX: 262-595-2545.
Web Site: www.uwp.edu/departments/library/. *Dir,* Vanaja Menon; E-mail:
vanaja.menon@uwp.edu; *Access Serv Librn,* Marilyn Pinzger; Tel:
262-595-2166, E-mail: pinzger@uwp.edu; *Automation Librn,* Luellen
Breed; Tel: 262-595-2274, E-mail: breed@uwp.edu; *Instrul Serv Librn,*
Erika Behling; Tel: 262-595-2642, E-mail: erika.behling@uwp.edu;
Archivist, Ref & Instruction Librn, Nicholas Weber; Tel: 262-595-2077,

E-mail: webern@uwp.edu; *Coordr, Electronic Res,* Rick Krause; E-mail: Richard.Krause@uwp.edu; *Ref Serv Coordr,* Kimberly Bartosz; E-mail: bartosz@uwp.edu; *Cataloger, Coll Develop, Webmaster,* Dina Kaye; Tel: 262-595-2215, E-mail: kaye@uwp.edu; *Circ,* Heather Spencer; E-mail: heather.spencer@uwp.edu; *ILL,* Tricia Steele; Tel: 262-595-2168, E-mail: tricia.steele@uwp.edu; Staff 16 (MLS 9, Non-MLS 7)
Founded 1967. Enrl 5,500; Fac 190; Highest Degree: Master
Library Holdings: AV Mats 22,800; CDs 4,820; DVDs 1,090; Bk Titles 268,200; Bk Vols 390,400; Per Subs 825; Videos 5,820
Special Collections: 18th & 19th Century American Drama (Teisberg & Perishable Press Coll); Irving Wallace Papers. State Document Depository
Automation Activity & Vendor Info: (Acquisitions) Ex Libris Group; (Cataloging) Ex Libris Group; (Circulation) Ex Libris Group; (Course Reserve) Docutek; (ILL) OCLC; (Media Booking) Ex Libris Group; (OPAC) Ex Libris Group; (Serials) Ex Libris Group
Partic in Coun of Wis Librs, Inc; OCLC Online Computer Library Center, Inc; Wisconsin Library Services
Open Mon-Thurs (Winter) 7:45am-11:30pm, Fri 7:45am-7pm, Sat 10-6, Sun Noon-10:30pm; Mon-Thurs (Summer) 7:45am-9:30pm, Fri 7:45am-4:30pm, Sat 10-6
Friends of the Library Group

KESHENA

J COLLEGE OF MENOMINEE NATION LIBRARY*, N 172 Hwy 47/55, 54135. (Mail add: PO Box 1179, 54135-1179). Tel: 715-799-5600, Ext 3003. FAX: 715-799-5605. Web Site: www.menominee.edu/library/home.htm. *Dir,* Maria Escalante; E-mail: mescalante@menominee.edu; Staff 4 (MLS 1, Non-MLS 3)
Enrl 503; Fac 33; Highest Degree: Bachelor
Jul 2010-Jun 2011 Income $142,000
Library Holdings: AV Mats 1,814; Bk Titles 16,854; Per Subs 30
Special Collections: Native American Coll, incl Menominee Tribe & Tribal Enterprise
Subject Interests: Computer sci, Natural res, Sustainable develop, Tribal legal studies
Automation Activity & Vendor Info: (Cataloging) LibLime; (Circulation) LibLime; (OPAC) LibLime
Wireless access
Function: Archival coll, Bks on cassette, Bks on CD, Computers for patron use, Copy machines, Electronic databases & coll, Exhibits, Fax serv, ILL available, Music CDs, Outreach serv, Photocopying/Printing, Prog for adults, Pub access computers, Ref & res, Scanner
Open Mon-Thurs (Winter) 8-8, Fri 8-4:30; Mon-Fri (Summer) 8-4:30

P MENOMINEE TRIBAL COUNTY LIBRARY*, W2760 Chief Little Wave Rd, 54135. (Mail add: PO Box 1090, 54135-1090), SAN 318-0581. Tel: 715-799-5212. FAX: 715-799-6516. E-mail: kes@mail.nfls.lib.wi.us. *Dir,* Michael Wilber; E-mail: mwilber@mail.nfls.lib.wi.us
Founded 1964. Pop 450; Circ 5,000
Library Holdings: Bk Vols 10,000; Per Subs 44
Mem of Nicolet Federated Library System
Open Mon-Thurs (Winter) 9-6, Fri 9-4:30, Mon-Fri (Summer) 9-5

KEWASKUM

P KEWASKUM PUBLIC LIBRARY*, 206 First St, 53040-8929. (Mail add: PO Box 38, 53040-0038), SAN 318-059X. Tel: 262-626-4312. FAX: 262-626-4861. E-mail: kewaskum@mwfls.org. Web Site: www.kewaskum.lib.wi.us. *Dir,* Steven Baker; E-mail: bakers@mwfls.org
Founded 1913. Pop 2,600; Circ 30,863
Library Holdings: Bk Vols 27,000; Per Subs 75
Automation Activity & Vendor Info: (Acquisitions) SirsiDynix; (Cataloging) SirsiDynix; (Circulation) SirsiDynix
Mem of Mid-Wisconsin Federated Library System
Open Mon-Wed 10-8, Thurs & Fri 10-5, Sat 10-1

KEWAUNEE

P KEWAUNEE PUBLIC LIBRARY*, 822 Juneau St, 54216-1200. SAN 318-0603. Tel: 920-388-5015. FAX: 920-388-5016. E-mail: kew@mail.nfls.lib.wi.us. Web Site: www.nfls.lib.wi.us/kew/. *Dir,* Susan Grosshuesch; E-mail: sgrosshu@mail.nfls.lib.wi.us
Founded 1906. Pop 20,103; Circ 63,931
Library Holdings: Bk Vols 31,000; Per Subs 130
Automation Activity & Vendor Info: (Cataloging) Infor Library & Information Solutions; (Circulation) Infor Library & Information Solutions
Mem of Nicolet Federated Library System
Open Mon-Thurs 10-8, Fri 10-6, Sat 10-4
Friends of the Library Group

KIEL

P KIEL PUBLIC LIBRARY*, 511 Third St, 53042. SAN 318-0611. Tel: 920-894-7122. FAX: 920-894-4023. E-mail: kielpl@mcls.lib.wi.us. Web Site: www.kiel.lib.wi.us. *Dir,* Julia Davis; E-mail: jdavis@mcls.lib.wi.us;

Youth Serv Dir, Joie Baldock; E-mail: jbaldock@mcls.lib.wi.us; *Coordr, Tech Serv, ILL,* Terry Kuske; Staff 3 (MLS 1, Non-MLS 2)
Founded 1925. Pop 7,500; Circ 80,000
Jul 2005-Jun 2006. Mats Exp $31,400, Books $22,800, Per/Ser (Incl. Access Fees) $3,000, AV Mat $3,800, Electronic Ref Mat (Incl. Access Fees) $300, Presv $1,500
Library Holdings: Bk Vols 40,000; Per Subs 120
Subject Interests: Career, Wis
Automation Activity & Vendor Info: (Cataloging) SirsiDynix; (Circulation) SirsiDynix; (OPAC) SirsiDynix
Wireless access
Mem of Manitowoc-Calumet Library System
Open Mon-Thurs 9-8, Fri 9-6, Sat 9-1
Friends of the Library Group

KIMBERLY

P KIMBERLY PUBLIC LIBRARY*, James J Siebers Memorial Library, 515 W Kimberly Ave, 54136. SAN 318-062X. Tel: 920-788-7515. FAX: 920-788-7516. E-mail: KIM@mail.owls.lib.wi.us. Web Site: www.kimlit.org. *Dir,* Beth Carpenter; E-mail: bcarpent@mail.owls.lib.wi.us
Founded 1907. Pop 16,500; Circ 300,000
Library Holdings: Bk Titles 100,000; Bk Vols 105,000; Per Subs 150
Automation Activity & Vendor Info: (Cataloging) Innovative Interfaces, Inc; (Circulation) Innovative Interfaces, Inc; (OPAC) Innovative Interfaces, Inc
Mem of Outagamie Waupaca Library System
Partic in Fox River Valley Area Library Consortium
Open Mon-Thurs 10-8, Fri 10-5, Sat (Winter) 10-2
Branches: 1
GERARD H VAN HOOF LIBRARY, 625 Grand Ave, Little Chute, 54140. Tel: 920-788-7825. FAX: 920-788-7827. E-mail: lit@mail.owls.lib.wi.us. *Dir,* Barbara Wentzel
Library Holdings: Bk Vols 50,000; Per Subs 150
Open Mon-Thurs (Winter) 9-8, Fri 9-5, Sat 10am-Noon; Mon & Wed (Summer) 9-8, Tues, Thurs & Fri 9-5

KING

S WISCONSIN VETERANS' HOME LIBRARY*, Hwy QQ, 54946. SAN 377-9696. Tel: 715-258-5586, Ext 2366. FAX: 715-258-5736. *Librn,* Linda Hager
Library Holdings: Bk Titles 10,000; Per Subs 20
Special Collections: War History Coll, Civil War to Present
Subject Interests: Civil War, Wars

KINGSTON

P MILL POND PUBLIC LIBRARY*, 140 N South St, 53939. (Mail add: PO Box 98, 53939-0098), SAN 318-0638. Tel: 920-394-3281. FAX: 920-394-3281. Web Site: www.millpondlibrary.org. *Dir,* Sara Wilson; E-mail: wilson@millpondlibrary.org
Founded 1964. Circ 10,531
Library Holdings: Bk Vols 7,900
Automation Activity & Vendor Info: (Cataloging) SirsiDynix; (Circulation) SirsiDynix
Mem of Winnefox Library System
Open Mon, Tues & Thurs 1-6, Wed 9-11 & 1-6, Sat 9-11
Friends of the Library Group

KOHLER

P KOHLER PUBLIC LIBRARY*, 333 Upper Rd, 53044. SAN 318-0646. Tel: 920-459-2923. FAX: 920-459-2930. Web Site: www.esls.lib.wi.us/kohler.html, www.kohler.lib.wi.us. *Librn,* Erin Coppersmith; E-mail: ecoppers@esls.lib.wi.us; Staff 1 (MLS 1)
Pop 1,800; Circ 35,400
Library Holdings: Bk Vols 10,000; Per Subs 60
Automation Activity & Vendor Info: (Acquisitions) Horizon; (Cataloging) Horizon; (Circulation) Horizon
Mem of Eastern Shores Library System
Open Mon-Thurs (Winter) 8am-8:30pm, Fri 8-5, Sun 1-4; Mon-Thurs 9-8:30, Fri 12-5, Sun (Summer) 1-4
Friends of the Library Group

LA CROSSE

SR DIOCESE OF LA CROSSE ARCHIVES*, PO Box 4004, 54602-4004. SAN 373-3076. Tel: 608-788-7700. FAX: 608-788-8413. E-mail: archives@dioceseoflacrosse.com. Web Site: www.dioceseoflacrosse.com. *Archivist,* Robert Altmann; Staff 1 (Non-MLS 1)
Library Holdings: Bk Vols 100
Special Collections: Local Church history (Catholic)
Subject Interests: Canon law, Church hist

R   ENGLISH LUTHERAN CHURCH LIBRARY*, 1509 King St, 54601.
SAN 318-0662. Tel: 608-784-9335. FAX: 608-784-8936. Web Site:
www.englishlutheran.org. *Librn,* Nancy Mills
Founded 1953
Library Holdings: Bk Titles 3,500
Subject Interests: Bible ref, Children's relig studies, Christian novels,
Relig studies
Partic in La Crosse Libr

M   GUNDERSEN LUTHERAN HEALTH SYSTEM*, Adolf Gundersen, MD
Health Sciences Library, 1900 South Ave, H01-011, 54601-9980. SAN
318-0689. Tel: 608-775-5410. FAX: 608-775-6343. E-mail:
library@gundluth.org. *Dir,* Melinda Orebaugh; Staff 5 (MLS 5)
Founded 1965
Library Holdings: e-books 150; e-journals 5,800; Bk Titles 6,000; Bk
Vols 8,000; Per Subs 650
Subject Interests: Consumer health, Hospital health sci, Nursing

P   LA CROSSE PUBLIC LIBRARY*, 800 Main St, 54601. SAN 364-7374.
Tel: 608-789-7100. Circulation Tel: 608-789-7124. Reference Tel:
608-789-7122. Administration Tel: 608-789-7123. FAX: 608-789-7106.
Circulation FAX: 608-789-7109. TDD: 608-789-7073. E-mail:
refdesk@lacross.lib.wi.us. Web Site: www.lacrosselibrary.org. *Dir,* Kelly
Kreig-Sigman; E-mail: k.krieg-sigman@lacrosse.lib.wi.us; *Head, Ref (Info
Serv)* Rochelle Hartman; Tel: 608-789-8191, Fax: 608-789-7161, E-mail:
r.hartman@lacrosse.lib.wi.us; *Bus & Finance Mgr,* Loretta Kilmer; Tel:
608-789-7147, E-mail: l.kilmer@lacrosse.lib.wi.us; *Automation Syst
Coordr,* David Goldfein; Tel: 608-789-7142, E-mail:
d.goldfein@lacrosse.lib.wi.us; *Commun Relations Coordr,* Patricia Boge;
Archivist, Anita T Doering; Tel: 608-789-7156, E-mail:
ad@lacrosse.lib.wi.us; Staff 22.88 (MLS 8.5, Non-MLS 14.38)
Founded 1888. Pop 51,426; Circ 948,342
Jan 2007-Dec 2007 Income (Main Library and Branch(s)) $5,102,141,
State $136,195, City $4,155,048, Locally Generated Income $337,866,
Other $378,439. Mats Exp $519,476, Books $328,292, AV Mat $156,184,
Electronic Ref Mat (Incl. Access Fees) $35,000. Sal $2,349,705
Library Holdings: AV Mats 23,697; Electronic Media & Resources
10,688; Bk Vols 213,486; Per Subs 552; Videos 16,559
Special Collections: State Document Depository; US Document
Depository
Subject Interests: Local hist
Automation Activity & Vendor Info: (Acquisitions) Horizon;
(Cataloging) Horizon; (Circulation) Horizon; (Serials) Horizon
Database Vendor: EBSCOhost, Gale Cengage Learning, LexisNexis,
netLibrary, OCLC FirstSearch, OVID Technologies, SirsiDynix
Wireless access
Function: Archival coll, CD-ROM, Handicapped accessible, Home
delivery & serv to Sr ctr & nursing homes, Homebound delivery serv, ILL
available, Magnifiers for reading, Music CDs, Photocopying/Printing, Prof
lending libr, Prog for children & young adult, Ref serv available, Spoken
cassettes & CDs, Summer reading prog, VHS videos, Wheelchair
accessible
Mem of Winding Rivers Library System
Partic in WILS
Special Services for the Deaf - Assistive tech; Closed caption videos; TTY
equip
Special Services for the Blind - Assistive/Adapted tech devices, equip &
products; BiFolkal kits; Bks on cassette; Bks on CD; Large print bks;
Magnifiers; Reader equip; Talking bks
Open Mon-Thurs 9-9, Fri & Sat 9-5, Sun 1-5
Friends of the Library Group
Branches: 2
   NORTH COMMUNITY, 1552 Kane St, 54603, SAN 364-7404. Tel:
     608-789-7102. FAX: 608-789-7104. *Br Coordr,* Lois Gilbert; Tel:
     608-789-7189, E-mail: l.gilbert@lacrosse.lib.wi.us
     Open Mon-Wed 12-8, Thurs-Sat 10-5
     Friends of the Library Group
   SOUTH COMMUNITY, 1307 S 16th St, 54601, SAN 364-7439. Tel:
     608-789-7103. FAX: 608-789-7105. *Br Coordr,* Lois Gilbert; Tel:
     608-789-7189, E-mail: l.gilbert@lacrosse.lib.wi.us
     Open Mon-Wed 12-8, Thurs-Sat 10-5
     Friends of the Library Group

S   LA CROSSE TRIBUNE LIBRARY*, 401 N Third St, 54601. SAN
325-058X. Tel: 608-791-8256. FAX: 608-782-9723. Web Site:
www.lacrossetribune.com. *Librn,* Chris Zobin
Special Collections: Newspaper Story & Photo Archives
Open Mon-Fri 8-5

S   MAYO CLINIC HEALTH SYSTEM - LA CROSSE, Health Sciences
Library, (Formerly Franciscan Skemp Healthcare - Mayo Health System),
700 West Ave S, 54601. SAN 318-0697. Tel: 608-785-0940, Ext 2685.
FAX: 608-392-9495. *Health Sci Librn,* Leah Osterhaus
Founded 1945

Library Holdings: Bk Titles 1,280; Per Subs 91
Subject Interests: Dentistry, Med, Nursing
Open Mon-Fri 7:30-4

R   OUR SAVIOR'S LUTHERAN CHURCH LIBRARY*, 612 Division St,
54601. SAN 328-5928. Tel: 608-782-3468. FAX: 608-782-3468. Web Site:
www.oursaviorslutheranchurch.net.
Library Holdings: Bk Vols 300
Restriction: Mem only

C   UNIVERSITY OF WISCONSIN-LA CROSSE*, Murphy Library Resource
Center, 1631 Pine St, 54601-3748. SAN 318-0727. Tel: 608-785-8505.
Circulation Tel: 608-785-8507. Interlibrary Loan Service Tel:
608-785-8636. Reference Tel: 608-785-8508. Administration Tel:
608-785-8520. Automation Services Tel: 608-785-8399. FAX:
608-785-8639. Interlibrary Loan Service FAX: 608-785-8806. Web Site:
www.uwlax.edu/murphylibrary. *Dir,* Anita Evans; Tel: 608-785-8805,
E-mail: evans.anit@uwlax.edu; *Automation Librn, Cat,* William Doering;
Tel: 608-785-8399, E-mail: doering.will@uwlax.edu; *Acq,* Jenifer Holman;
Tel: 608-785-8395, Fax: 608-785-8634, E-mail: holman.jeni@uwlax.edu;
Circ, Michele Strange; Tel: 608-785-8943, E-mail:
strange.mich@uwlax.edu; *Coll Develop,* John Jax; Tel: 608-785-8567,
E-mail: jax.john@uwlax.edu; *Doc Delivery, ILL, Ref Serv,* Randall
Hoelzen; Tel: 608-785-8398, E-mail: hoelzen.rand@uwlax.edu; *Electronic
Res,* Galadriel Chilton; Tel: 608-785-8738, E-mail:
chilton.gala@uwlax.edu; *Govt Doc,* Michael Current; Tel: 608-785-8739,
E-mail: current.mich@uwlax.edu; *Info Serv,* Cris Prucha; Tel:
608-785-8637, E-mail: prucha.cris@uwlax.edu; *Outreach Serv Librn,*
Stefan Smith; Tel: 608-785-8396, E-mail: smith.stef@uwlax.edu; *Spec Coll
& Archives Librn,* Paul Beck; Tel: 608-785-8511, E-mail:
beck.paul@uwlax.edu; Staff 24 (MLS 11, Non-MLS 13)
Founded 1909. Enrl 9,975; Fac 443; Highest Degree: Master
Library Holdings: e-books 8,308; Electronic Media & Resources 192; Bk
Titles 325,525; Bk Vols 410,736; Per Subs 1,052
Special Collections: Contemporary Poetry; Gothic Literature (Arkham
House & Skeeters Coll); Inland River Steamboats, photog; Regional
History Coll, photographs; Small Presses Coll. Oral History; State
Document Depository; US Document Depository
Subject Interests: Allied health, Educ, Phys educ
Automation Activity & Vendor Info: (Acquisitions) Ex Libris Group;
(Cataloging) Ex Libris Group; (Circulation) Ex Libris Group; (Course
Reserve) Ex Libris Group; (ILL) OCLC; (OPAC) Ex Libris Group;
(Serials) Ex Libris Group
Wireless access
Publications: Fine Print (Newsletter)
Partic in OCLC Online Computer Library Center, Inc; Wisconsin Library
Services
Special Services for the Blind - Assistive/Adapted tech devices, equip &
products
Open Mon-Thurs 7:30am-Midnight, Fri 7:30-6, Sat 11-6, Sun
Noon-Midnight
Friends of the Library Group

G   USGS*, Upper Midwest Environmental Sciences Center, 2630 Fanta Reed
Rd, 54603-1223. SAN 318-0719. Tel: 608-781-6215. FAX: 608-783-6066.
Librn, Kathy Mannstedt
Founded 1959
Library Holdings: Bk Titles 5,000; Per Subs 60
Special Collections: Bulletin of United States Fish Commission
Subject Interests: Chem, Chem registration, Ecology of large river systs,
Fish culture, Limnology
Automation Activity & Vendor Info: (Cataloging) EOS International;
(OPAC) EOS International

C   VITERBO UNIVERSITY*, Todd Wehr Memorial Library, 900 Viterbo Dr,
54601. SAN 318-0743. Tel: 608-796-3270. FAX: 608-796-3275. E-mail:
reference@viterbo.edu. Web Site: www.viterbo.edu/library. *Dir,* Position
Currently Open; *Asst Dir,* Nancy Steinhoff; Tel: 608-796-3278, E-mail:
ncsteinhoff@viterbo.edu; *Info Serv Librn,* Susan Spiker; Tel: 608-796-3267,
E-mail: saspiker@viterbo.edu; *Outreach Librn, Tech Coordr, Webmaster,*
Kim Olson-Kopp; Tel: 608-796-3263, E-mail: kmolsonkopp@viterbo.edu;
Ser Librn, Marilyn Adam; Tel: 608-796-3268, E-mail:
msadam@viterbo.edu; *Archivist, Ser Librn,* Jonathan Hinck; Tel:
608-796-3262, E-mail: jhhinck@viterbo.edu; *Tech Serv Librn,* Elizabeth
Ehr; Tel: 608-796-3265, E-mail: esehr@viterbo.edu; *Acq, Cat Tech, Info
Serv Supvr,* Polly Forsell; Tel: 608-796-3271, E-mail:
pkforsell@viterbo.edu; *Info Serv Supvr,* Gregg Ruston; Tel: 608-796-3277,
E-mail: gruston@viterbo.edu; Staff 9 (MLS 5, Non-MLS 4)
Founded 1890. Enrl 2,470; Fac 120; Highest Degree: Master
Library Holdings: CDs 1,132; e-books 11,884; Bk Titles 69,384; Per Subs
549; Videos 1,974
Special Collections: Catholic History Coll; Music Scores
Subject Interests: Educ, Fine arts, Liberal arts, Nursing, Relig studies
Automation Activity & Vendor Info: (Acquisitions) Innovative Interfaces,
Inc; (Cataloging) Innovative Interfaces, Inc; (Circulation) Innovative

Interfaces, Inc; (Course Reserve) Innovative Interfaces, Inc; (ILL) OCLC; (OPAC) Innovative Interfaces, Inc; (Serials) Innovative Interfaces, Inc
Database Vendor: Innovative Interfaces, Inc INN - View
Partic in Wis Libr Consortium
Open Mon-Thurs 7am-1am, Fri 7am-8pm, Sat 11-6, Sun Noon-1am
Restriction: Open to fac, students & qualified researchers, Open to pub for ref & circ; with some limitations
Friends of the Library Group

R WESLEY UNITED METHODIST CHURCH LIBRARY*, 721 King St, 54601. SAN 318-0751. Tel: 608-782-3018. FAX: 608-782-3018. *Chair,* Marion Boyle; Staff 8 (MLS 1, Non-MLS 7)
Founded 1965
Library Holdings: Bk Titles 2,500
Subject Interests: Behav sci, Biog, Fiction, Relig studies, Soc sci
Friends of the Library Group

J WESTERN TECHNICAL COLLEGE LIBRARY*, 400 Seventh St N, R201, 54601. SAN 318-076X. Tel: 608-785-9142. Reference Tel: 608-785-9406. E-mail: library@westerntc.edu. Web Site: www.westerntc.edu/library. *Dir,* Ronald G Edwards; Staff 6 (MLS 2, Non-MLS 4)
Founded 1967. Enrl 3,700; Fac 185; Highest Degree: Associate
Jul 2006-Jun 2007. Mats Exp $52,750, Books $28,850, Per/Ser (Incl. Access Fees) $15,000, Electronic Ref Mat (Incl. Access Fees) $8,900
Library Holdings: High Interest/Low Vocabulary Bk Vols 600; Bk Titles 33,000; Per Subs 260
Automation Activity & Vendor Info: (Cataloging) Follett Software; (Circulation) Follett Software; (OPAC) Follett Software
Partic in Wisconsin Library Services
Open Mon-Thurs 7:30am-8pm, Fri 7:30-4, Sat 9-1

P WINDING RIVERS LIBRARY SYSTEM*, 800 Main St, 54601-4122. SAN 318-0778. Tel: 608-789-7151. FAX: 608-789-7106. Web Site: www.wrlsweb.com, www.wrlsweb.org. *Dir,* David Polodna; E-mail: dlp@wrlsweb.org; Staff 4 (MLS 3, Non-MLS 1)
Founded 1967. Pop 272,732
Jan 2010-Dec 2010 Income $916,924, State $826,624, Federal $30,900, County $48,500, Locally Generated Income $8,200, Other $2,700. Mats Exp $2,200. Sal $557,000
Automation Activity & Vendor Info: (Cataloging) Horizon; (Circulation) Horizon; (ILL) Auto-Graphics, Inc; (OPAC) Horizon
Database Vendor: netLibrary, Overdrive, Inc
Wireless access
Publications: Whirlpools (Newsletter)
Member Libraries: Alma Public Library; Arcadia Free Public Library; Bekkum Memorial Library; Black River Falls Public Library; Blair-Preston Public Library; Cashton Memorial Library; Elroy Public Library; Ettrick Public Library; Galesville Public Library; Hatch Public Library; Hauge Memorial Library; Hillsboro Public Library; Independence Public Library; Kendall Public Library; Knutson Memorial Library; La Crosse County Library; La Crosse Public Library; Lawton Memorial Library; McIntosh Memorial Library; Mondovi Public Library; Necedah Memorial Library; New Lisbon Memorial Library; Norwalk Public Library; Ontario Public Library; Readstown Public Library; Shirley M Wright Memorial Library; Sparta Free Library; Strum Public Library; Taylor Memorial Library; Tomah Public Library; Whitehall Public Library; Wilton Public Library; Wonewoc Public Library
Partic in Wisconsin Public Library Consortium
Open Mon-Fri 8-4:30
Restriction: Limited access for the pub

LA FARGE

P LAWTON MEMORIAL LIBRARY*, 118 N Bird St, 54639. (Mail add: PO Box 38, 54639-0038), SAN 318-0786. Tel: 608-625-2015. FAX: 608-625-2329. E-mail: lafargepl@wrlsweb.org. *Dir,* Rita Wachuta-Breckel
Founded 1923. Pop 829; Circ 17,361
Library Holdings: Bk Titles 13,000; Per Subs 53
Special Collections: Arrowheads. Oral History
Automation Activity & Vendor Info: (Cataloging) Horizon; (Circulation) Horizon
Wireless access
Mem of Winding Rivers Library System
Open Mon 12-5, Tues & Fri 9:30-12 & 12:30-5, Wed 1-8, Sat 9-1
Friends of the Library Group

LA POINTE

P MADELINE ISLAND PUBLIC LIBRARY*, One Library St, 54850. (Mail add: PO Box 65, 54850-0065), SAN 318-0794. Tel: 715-747-3662. FAX: 715-747-3661. E-mail: madlib4@yahoo.com. Web Site: madisland.wislib.org. *Dir,* Constance Ross; *Librn,* Seri Demorest; E-mail: seri@madeline.nwls.lib.wi.us
Founded 1960. Pop 180; Circ 4,636

Library Holdings: Bk Vols 6,500; Per Subs 50
Mem of Northern Waters Library Service
Open Mon & Wed (Winter) 4-8, Tues, Thurs & Fri 10-5, Sat 10-12; Mon & Wed (Summer) 10-8, Tues, Thurs & Fri 10-5, Sat 10-12

LA VALLE

P LA VALLE PUBLIC LIBRARY*, 101 W Main, 53941-9564. (Mail add: PO Box 7, 53941-0007), SAN 318-0808. Tel: 608-985-8383. FAX: 608-985-8382. E-mail: lavlib@mwt.net. Web Site: www.scls.lib.wi.us/lav. *Dir,* David Doering
Pop 414; Circ 3,000
Library Holdings: Bk Vols 7,100
Automation Activity & Vendor Info: (Acquisitions) SirsiDynix; (Cataloging) SirsiDynix; (Circulation) SirsiDynix
Mem of South Central Library System
Open Mon-Wed 3-5, Thurs 5-7, Sat 2-5

LAC DU FLAMBEAU

P BEN GUTHRIE-LAC DU FLAMBEAU PUBLIC LIBRARY*, 622 Peace Pipe Rd, 54538. (Mail add: PO Box 368, 54538-0368), SAN 376-6586. Tel: 715-588-7001. E-mail: ldflib@ldf.nwls.lib.wi.us. Web Site: www.nwls.lib.wi.us/. *Librn,* Mary M Mann
Library Holdings: Bk Titles 6,000; Bk Vols 15,000; Per Subs 24
Mem of Northern Waters Library Service
Open Mon 10-12:30 & 1:30-4, Tues 10-12:30 & 1:30-8:30, Wed & Thurs 10-12:30 & 1:30-5, Fri 10-4 & Sat 10-2

LADYSMITH

P RUSK COUNTY COMMUNITY LIBRARY*, Ladysmith Public Library, 418 Corbett Ave, 54848-1396. SAN 318-0816. Tel: 715-532-2604. FAX: 715-532-2658. E-mail: ladysmithpl@ifls.lib.wi.us. Web Site: www.ladysmithpl.org/. *Librn,* Carolyn Forde; *Ch,* Nancy Reidner; *ILL,* Jane Schimka; Staff 1 (MLS 1)
Founded 1907. Pop 15,047; Circ 64,171
Library Holdings: Bk Titles 45,000; Per Subs 121
Automation Activity & Vendor Info: (Cataloging) SirsiDynix; (Circulation) SirsiDynix
Mem of Indianhead Federated Library System
Open Mon & Wed-Fri 10-6, Tues 10-8, Sat 10-3
Friends of the Library Group

LAKE GENEVA

P LAKE GENEVA PUBLIC LIBRARY*, 918 W Main St, 53147-1890. SAN 318-0840. Tel: 262-249-5299. FAX: 262-249-5284. E-mail: lakegene@lakegeneva.lib.wi.us. Web Site: www.lakegeneva.lib.wi.us. *Dir,* Andrea Peterson; E-mail: andreap@lakegeneva.lib.wi.us; *Youth Serv,* Sara Soukup; E-mail: soukup@lakegeneva.lib.wi.us; Staff 3 (MLS 2, Non-MLS 1)
Founded 1895. Pop 18,954; Circ 102,722
Library Holdings: Bk Vols 46,356; Per Subs 179
Subject Interests: Local hist
Automation Activity & Vendor Info: (Cataloging) SirsiDynix; (Circulation) SirsiDynix; (OPAC) SirsiDynix
Publications: Lakeside Reader (Newsletter)
Mem of Lakeshores Library System
Open Mon-Thurs 9-8, Fri 9-6, Sat 9-1
Friends of the Library Group

LAKE MILLS

P L D FARGO PUBLIC LIBRARY*, 120 E Madison St, 53551-1644. SAN 318-0867. Tel: 920-648-2166. FAX: 920-648-5561. E-mail: lmill@mwfls.org. Web Site: www.lakemills.lib.wi.us. *Dir,* Gerard Saylor; E-mail: lmdir@mwfls.org; *Youth Serv Librn,* Carolyn Wey; *ILL,* Jim Braughler; Staff 5 (MLS 1, Non-MLS 4)
Founded 1902. Pop 5,400; Circ 92,500
Library Holdings: Bk Titles 30,000; Per Subs 111
Special Collections: Aztalan Historical Society (Lake Mills) Print & Picture Coll; Local History (Lake Mills Leader 1902-present)
Automation Activity & Vendor Info: (Circulation) SirsiDynix
Mem of Mid-Wisconsin Federated Library System
Open Mon-Thurs 9-9, Fri & Sat 9-5
Friends of the Library Group

LAKEWOOD

P LAKES COUNTRY PUBLIC LIBRARY*, 15235 Hwy 32, 54138. (Mail add: PO Box 220, 54138-0220), SAN 377-9947. Tel: 715-276-9020. FAX: 715-276-7151. E-mail: lak@mail.nfls.lib.wi.us. Web Site: www.nfls.lib.wi.us/lak/. *Dir,* Pamela F Ellingson; E-mail: pellings@mail.nfls.lib.wi.us
Library Holdings: Bk Titles 11,000; Per Subs 60

Automation Activity & Vendor Info: (Cataloging) Infor Library & Information Solutions; (Circulation) Infor Library & Information Solutions
Mem of Nicolet Federated Library System
Open Mon, Tues & Thurs 9-5, Wed & Fri 2-8, Sat 9-2

LANCASTER

P   SCHREINER MEMORIAL LIBRARY, Lancaster Public Library, 113 W Elm St, 53813-1202. SAN 318-0875. Tel: 608-723-7304. FAX: 608-723-7304. Web Site: www.swls.org/member.la.html. *Dir,* Alan M Tollefson; E-mail: atollefson@swls.org; *Ch & Youth Librn,* Tara Brimmer; E-mail: tbrimmer@swls.org; Staff 2 (MLS 1, Non-MLS 1)
Founded 1901. Pop 3,868; Circ 87,907
Jan 2011-Dec 2011 Income (Main Library and Branch(s)) $431,815, City $232,500, County $87,531, Other $111,784. Mats Exp $71,205, Books $48,703, Per/Ser (Incl. Access Fees) $3,712, AV Mat $18,790. Sal $164,475 (Prof $48,000)
Library Holdings: Audiobooks 719; CDs 1,202; DVDs 1,796; Bk Vols 34,949; Per Subs 114; Videos 210
Automation Activity & Vendor Info: (Circulation) Auto-Graphics, Inc; (OPAC) Auto-Graphics, Inc
Database Vendor: EBSCOhost, netLibrary, Overdrive, Inc, SirsiDynix
Wireless access
Mem of Southwest Wisconsin Library System
Open Mon-Thurs 9-8, Fri 9-5, Sat 9-1, Sun (Oct-April) 1-4
Branches: 1
POTOSI BRANCH, 103 N Main St, Potosi, 53820. (Mail add: PO Box 97, Potosi, 53820-0097). Tel: 608-763-2115. *In Charge,* Susan Ackland; E-mail: sackland@swls.org
Founded 2007. Pop 1,912
Jan 2011-Dec 2011 Income $22,689, City $19,055, County $2,480, Other $1,154. Mats Exp $9,757, Books $8,507, Per/Ser (Incl. Access Fees) $750, AV Mat $500. Sal $13,446
Library Holdings: Audiobooks 84; CDs 45; DVDs 335; Bk Vols 4,554; Per Subs 30; Videos 188
Automation Activity & Vendor Info: (Circulation) Auto-Graphics, Inc
Database Vendor: EBSCOhost, netLibrary, Overdrive, Inc
Open Tues & Thurs 3-8, Wed 10-1, Sat 9-1

LAND O'LAKES

P   LAND O'LAKES PUBLIC LIBRARY*, 4242 County Hwy B, 54540. (Mail add: PO Box 450, 54540-0450), SAN 318-0883. Tel: 715-547-6006. FAX: 715-547-6004. Web Site: landolakeslibrary.com. *Dir,* Julie Zelten; E-mail: zelten@lol.nwls.lib.wi.us; *Cataloger,* Frisk Miller; *Youth Serv,* Karen Weber-Mendham
Pop 794; Circ 3,866
Library Holdings: Bk Vols 17,530
Automation Activity & Vendor Info: (Cataloging) Innovative Interfaces, Inc; (Circulation) Innovative Interfaces, Inc; (OPAC) Innovative Interfaces, Inc
Mem of Northern Waters Library Service
Open Mon, Thurs & Sat 9-12, Tues, Wed & Fri 9-5
Friends of the Library Group

LAONA

P   EDITH EVANS COMMUNITY LIBRARY*, 5216 Forest Ave, 54541. (Mail add: PO Box 127, 54541-0127), SAN 318-0891. Tel: 715-674-4751. FAX: 715-674-5904. *Librn,* Cynthia M Lemerande; E-mail: clemer@wvls.lib.wi.us
Founded 1917. Pop 2,000
Library Holdings: Bk Vols 12,000; Per Subs 95
Automation Activity & Vendor Info: (Cataloging) Horizon; (Circulation) Horizon
Mem of Wisconsin Valley Library Service
Open Mon & Wed-Fri (Winter) 8-3, Tues 8-3 & 5pm-7pm; Mon & Wed-Fri(Summer) 8-2, Tues 8-2 & 5pm-7pm

LENA

P   LENA PUBLIC LIBRARY, 200 E Main St, 54139. SAN 377-9963. Tel: 920-829-5335. FAX: 920-829-5335. E-mail: LEN@mail.nfls.lib.wi.us. *Dir,* Becky DeCloux; Staff 1 (Non-MLS 1)
Library Holdings: Bk Titles 10,971; Per Subs 55
Automation Activity & Vendor Info: (Cataloging) Innovative Interfaces, Inc; (Circulation) Innovative Interfaces, Inc; (OPAC) Innovative Interfaces, Inc
Wireless access
Mem of Nicolet Federated Library System
Open Mon-Thurs 10-6, Fri 10-4
Friends of the Library Group

LIVINGSTON

P   ALLEN DIETZMAN LIBRARY*, Livingston Public Library, 220 W Barber Ave, 53554. (Mail add: PO Box 216, 53554-0216), SAN 318-0905. Tel: 608-943-6801. FAX: 608-943-6800. Web Site: www.swls.org/member.li.html. *Dir,* Betty Schambow; E-mail: bschambow@swls.org
Pop 597; Circ 3,380
Library Holdings: AV Mats 230; Bk Vols 4,462; Per Subs 10; Videos 60
Automation Activity & Vendor Info: (Acquisitions) Horizon; (Cataloging) Horizon; (Circulation) Horizon; (OPAC) Horizon
Wireless access
Mem of Southwest Wisconsin Library System
Open Mon 1-6, Wed 12:30-7:30, Thurs & Sat 9-12
Friends of the Library Group

LODI

P   LODI WOMAN'S CLUB PUBLIC LIBRARY*, 130 Lodi St, 53555-1217. SAN 318-0913. Tel: 608-592-4130. FAX: 608-592-2327. Web Site: www.lodipubliclibrary.org. *Co-Dir,* Trisha Frankland; E-mail: trish.lodi@scls.lib.wi.us; *Co-Dir,* Kristine Millard
Pop 9,000; Circ 99,455
Library Holdings: e-books 8,277; Bk Vols 26,757; Per Subs 144; Talking Bks 1,580
Automation Activity & Vendor Info: (Acquisitions) Horizon; (Course Reserve) Horizon; (OPAC) Horizon
Wireless access
Mem of South Central Library System
Open Mon-Thurs 9-8, Fri 9-5, Sat 9:30-2
Friends of the Library Group

LOMIRA

P   LOMIRA PUBLIC LIBRARY*, 1038 Main St, 53048-9515. (Mail add: PO Box 1108, 53048-1108), SAN 318-0921. Tel: 920-269-4115. FAX: 920-269-4115. Web Site: www.lomira.lib.wi.us. *Dir,* Jane Kietzer; E-mail: lpljane@mwfls.org; *Librn,* Ann Kohli; *Librn,* Andrea Stallman
Founded 1938. Pop 1,732; Circ 18,996
Library Holdings: Bk Titles 17,255; Bk Vols 17,675; Per Subs 52
Special Collections: Commemorative Stamps Coll, 1972-1988; Local Genealogy Coll, church & cemetary rec; Local Newspaper, micro
Automation Activity & Vendor Info: (Cataloging) SIRSI WorkFlows; (Circulation) SIRSI WorkFlows; (OPAC) SIRSI WorkFlows
Mem of Mid-Wisconsin Federated Library System
Open Mon-Thurs 1:30-7:30, Fri 1:30-5, Sat (Sept-May) 9-11
Friends of the Library Group

LONE ROCK

P   LONE ROCK PUBLIC LIBRARY*, 234 N Broadway, 53556. (Mail add: PO Box 7, 53556-0007), SAN 318-093X. Tel: 608-583-2034. FAX: 608-583-2034. Web Site: www.swls.org/member.lr.html. *Libr Dir,* Rita Magno; E-mail: rmagno@swls.org
Founded 1972. Pop 929; Circ 4,250
Library Holdings: Bk Vols 5,400; Per Subs 10
Automation Activity & Vendor Info: (Cataloging) Horizon; (Circulation) Horizon; (OPAC) Horizon
Wireless access
Mem of Southwest Wisconsin Library System
Open Tues-Thurs 11-7, Fri 9-5

LOWELL

P   LOWELL PUBLIC LIBRARY*, 105 N River St, 53557. (Mail add: PO Box 15, 53557-0015), SAN 364-6149. Tel: 920-927-5700. FAX: 920-927-5700. E-mail: lowell@mwfls.org. Web Site: www.villageoflowell.com. *Dir,* Shirley Rhode
Library Holdings: AV Mats 225; CDs 75; Large Print Bks 134; Bk Vols 5,808; Per Subs 34; Talking Bks 93; Videos 225
Mem of Mid-Wisconsin Federated Library System
Open Mon & Sat 8-12, Tues-Thurs 2-6

LOYAL

P   LOYAL PUBLIC LIBRARY*, 214 N Main St, 54446. (Mail add: PO Box 337, 54446-0337), SAN 318-0948. Tel: 715-255-8189. FAX: 715-255-8348. Web Site: wvls.lib.wi.us/loyalpl. *Dir,* Judith Bobrofsky; E-mail: jbobrofs@wvls.lib.wi.us; *Asst Librn,* Kathleen Lyons; Staff 2 (Non-MLS 2)
Founded 1901. Pop 4,184; Circ 29,073
Jan 2006-Dec 2006 Income $80,000, Other $5,312. Mats Exp $14,000. Sal $33,000
Library Holdings: AV Mats 700; Bk Titles 16,665; Per Subs 76; Talking Bks 240
Automation Activity & Vendor Info: (Circulation) SirsiDynix

Mem of Wisconsin Valley Library Service
Open Mon, Tues, Thurs & Fri 10-12 & 1-5:30, Wed 10-6

LUCK

P   LUCK PUBLIC LIBRARY*, 21 Second Ave W, 54853. (Mail add: PO Box 500, 54853-0500), SAN 318-0956. Tel: 715-472-2770. FAX: 715-472-4312. E-mail: luckpl@ifls.lib.wi.us. *Dir,* Jill Gover; Staff 2 (Non-MLS 2)
Founded 1938. Pop 1,025; Circ 21,000
Library Holdings: Bk Titles 9,000; Per Subs 13
Special Collections: Oral History
Subject Interests: County hist, Local hist, Wis
Mem of Indianhead Federated Library System
Open Mon, Wed & Fri 1-5, Tues & Thurs 1-8, Sat 10-12

S   PROGRESSIVE FOUNDATION*, Nukewatch Library, 740 Round Lake Rd, 54853. (Mail add: PO Box 649, 54853-0649), SAN 370-1980. Tel: 715-472-4185. FAX: 715-472-4184. E-mail: nukewatch@lakeland.ws. Web Site: www.nukewatch.com. *Dir,* John LaForge; *Dir,* Bonnie Urfer
Founded 1979
Library Holdings: DVDs 20; Bk Titles 300; Per Subs 10; Videos 100
Special Collections: State Document Depository
Subject Interests: Cancer, Nuclear waste, Nuclear weapons, Radiation, Radioactive waste, Uranium
Publications: Nukewatch (Quarterly)

MADISON

P   DANE COUNTY LIBRARY SERVICE*, 201 W Mifflin St, 53703-2597. SAN 318-1014. Tel: 608-266-6388. E-mail: dcljac@scls.lib.wi.us. Web Site: www.dcls.info. *Dir,* Julie Anne Chase; Staff 8 (MLS 2, Non-MLS 6)
Founded 1966. Pop 110,500; Circ 174,281
Jan 2007-Dec 2007 Income $3,976,956, County $3,955,794, Other $21,162. Mats Exp $71,209, Books $49,967, AV Mat $19,973, Electronic Ref Mat (Incl. Access Fees) $1,269. Sal $390,098
Library Holdings: AV Mats 8,684; e-books 8,291; Electronic Media & Resources 2,012; Bk Vols 39,375; Per Subs 48
Automation Activity & Vendor Info: (Acquisitions) SirsiDynix; (Cataloging) SirsiDynix; (Circulation) SirsiDynix; (OPAC) SirsiDynix; (Serials) SirsiDynix
Function: Home delivery & serv to Sr ctr & nursing homes, Homebound delivery serv, ILL available, Prog for children & young adult, Summer reading prog
Mem of South Central Library System
Partic in Library Interchange Network (LINK)
Special Services for the Blind - Home delivery serv
Friends of the Library Group
Bookmobiles: 1

S   DANE COUNTY REGIONAL PLANNING COMMISSION LIBRARY*, 30 W Mifflin St, Ste 402, 53703. SAN 318-1030. Tel: 608-266-4137. FAX: 608-266-9117. E-mail: info@danecorpc.org. Web Site: www.danecorpc.org. *In Charge,* Chris Gjestson
Founded 1968
Library Holdings: Bk Vols 3,900; Per Subs 30
Subject Interests: Census, Environ studies, Housing, Land use planning, Master plans, Pop, Transportation, Water res mgt

GM   DEPARTMENT OF VETERANS AFFAIRS*, Hospital Library, 2500 Overlook Terrace, 53705-2286. SAN 318-1286. Tel: 608-256-1901, 608-280-7173. FAX: 608-280-7108. *Mgr,* Jill Everson; E-mail: jill.everson@med.va.gov; Staff 1 (Non-MLS 1)
Founded 1951
Library Holdings: Bk Vols 285; Per Subs 34
Special Collections: General Medicine, AV
Partic in National Network of Libraries of Medicine; South Central Wisconsin Health Science Library Consortium
Open Mon-Fri 7:30-4

L   DEWITT, ROSS & STEVENS SC*, Law Library, Two E Mifflin St, Ste 600, 53703. SAN 372-3593. Tel: 608-283-5504. FAX: 608-252-9243. Web Site: www.dewittross.com. *Dir,* Richard D Hendricks; E-mail: rdh@dewittross.com; Staff 2 (MLS 1, Non-MLS 1)
Library Holdings: Bk Vols 17,000; Per Subs 50
Wireless access
Restriction: Staff use only

C   EDGEWOOD COLLEGE LIBRARY*, Oscar Rennebohm Library, 1000 Edgewood College Dr, 53711-1997. SAN 364-7463. Tel: 608-663-3300. Circulation Tel: 608-663-3278. Interlibrary Loan Service Tel: 608-663-3302. Administration Tel: 608-663-3306. Automation Services Tel: 608-663-3284. FAX: 608-663-6778. Web Site: library.edgewood.edu. *Dir,* Sylvia Contreras; *Circ Supvr,* Julie Wendt; *Head, Pub Serv,* Andrea Kenny;

Head, Tech Serv, John Elliott; *Coordr, Acq,* Mary Ann Smith; *Coordr, ILL,* Rod Lysenko; *Archivist,* Sarah Naughton; *Ref/Electronic Serv Librn,* Carolyn De Luna; *Web Librn,* Jonathan Bloy; Staff 6 (MLS 6)
Founded 1941. Enrl 1,935; Fac 223; Highest Degree: Doctorate
Library Holdings: e-books 8,731; Bk Titles 100,460; Bk Vols 119,884; Per Subs 331
Subject Interests: Bus, Educ, Nursing
Automation Activity & Vendor Info: (Acquisitions) Innovative Interfaces, Inc; (Cataloging) Innovative Interfaces, Inc; (Circulation) Innovative Interfaces, Inc; (Course Reserve) Docutek; (ILL) OCLC; (OPAC) Innovative Interfaces, Inc; (Serials) Innovative Interfaces, Inc
Database Vendor: EBSCOhost, Gale Cengage Learning, LexisNexis, netLibrary, OCLC FirstSearch, ProQuest
Partic in WILS
Open Mon-Thurs 7:30am-11pm, Fri 7:30-6, Sat 10-6, Sun 11-11

C   HERZING COLLEGE LIBRARY*, 5218 E Terrace Dr, 53718-8340. SAN 378-0597. Tel: 608-249-6611. Circulation Tel: 608-663-0825. FAX: 608-249-8593. *Librn,* Beth Huwe; Tel: 608-663-0816, E-mail: bethhuwe@msn.herzing.edu; Staff 1 (MLS 1)
Library Holdings: Bk Vols 10,000
Automation Activity & Vendor Info: (Cataloging) Ex Libris Group; (Circulation) Ex Libris Group
Open Mon-Thurs 8-8, Fri 8-4:30

S   KRAFT FOODS/OSCAR MAYER FOODS*, Research Information Center, 910 Mayer Ave, 53704. SAN 318-1170. Tel: 608-285-4025. FAX: 608-285-6010. *Info Scientist,* Diane Gurtner; Staff 0.5 (MLS 0.5)
Library Holdings: Bk Vols 2,000; Per Subs 120
Subject Interests: Food sci, Meat, Poultry proc
Restriction: Staff use only

J   MADISON AREA TECHNICAL COLLEGE*, Truax Library, 3550 Anderson St, Rm 230, 53704. SAN 318-1073. Tel: 608-246-6640. Reference Tel: 608-243-4264. FAX: 608-246-6644. Web Site: matcmadison.edu/library/library/about.shtm. *Dir,* Julie Gores; Tel: 608-246-6633, E-mail: jgores@matcmadison.edu; *Assoc Librn,* Cecily Lehman; Tel: 608-246-6634, E-mail: calehman@matcmadison.edu; *ILL Librn,* Mark Luetkehoelter; Tel: 608-246-6638, E-mail: mluetkehoelt@matcmadison.edu; *Outreach Serv Librn, Ser,* Terry Ross; Tel: 608-246-6635, E-mail: tdross@matcmadison.edu; *Tech Coordr,* Nathan Dowd; Tel: 608-246-6637, E-mail: ndowd@matcmadison.edu; *Circ Supvr,* Erika Linzner; Tel: 608-246-6659, E-mail: elinzner@matcmadison.edu; *Acq, Cat,* Mark Perkins; Tel: 608-246-6923, E-mail: mcperkins@matcmadison.edu; *Cat,* Kelley Minica; Tel: 608-243-4086, E-mail: kminica@matcmadison.edu; *Instr,* Donna Marconnet; Tel: 608-243-4085, E-mail: dmarconnet@matcmadison.edu; *Ref Serv,* Claire Rasmussen; Tel: 608-246-6085, E-mail: rasmussen@matcmadison.edu; Staff 32 (MLS 5, Non-MLS 27)
Founded 1965. Enrl 7,600; Fac 360
Library Holdings: Bk Titles 55,000; Bk Vols 62,000; Per Subs 900
Automation Activity & Vendor Info: (Acquisitions) SirsiDynix; (Cataloging) SirsiDynix; (Circulation) SirsiDynix; (Course Reserve) SirsiDynix; (ILL) SirsiDynix; (Media Booking) SirsiDynix; (OPAC) SirsiDynix; (Serials) SirsiDynix
Publications: Bibliographies; Library Guide
Open Mon-Thurs (Fall & Spring) 7:30am-9pm, Fri 7:30-4:30, Sat 9-1; Mon-Thurs (Summer) 7:30-7, Fri 7:30-4:30

P   MADISON PUBLIC LIBRARY, 201 W Mifflin St, 53703. SAN 364-7617. Tel: 608-266-6300. Circulation Tel: 608-266-6357. Interlibrary Loan Service Tel: 608-266-6302. Reference Tel: 608-266-6350. Administration Tel: 608-266-6363. FAX: 608-266-4338. Reference FAX: 608-266-4230. E-mail: madcirc@scls.lib.wi.us. Web Site: www.madisonpubliclibrary.org. *Dir,* Greg Mickells; E-mail: LibraryAdministration@cityofmadison.com; Staff 45.43 (MLS 42.14, Non-MLS 3.29)
Founded 1875. Pop 221,735; Circ 4,398,343
Library Holdings: AV Mats 115,621; Bks on Deafness & Sign Lang 103; Braille Volumes 25; CDs 38,995; DVDs 19,634; e-books 6,821; Electronic Media & Resources 1,701; High Interest/Low Vocabulary Bk Vols 1,669; Large Print Bks 21,221; Music Scores 4,024; Bk Titles 356,562; Bk Vols 785,674; Per Subs 2,647; Talking Bks 20,911; Videos 38,660
Special Collections: Local Materials; Music. US Document Depository
Automation Activity & Vendor Info: (Acquisitions) SirsiDynix; (Cataloging) SirsiDynix; (Circulation) SirsiDynix; (OPAC) SirsiDynix; (Serials) SirsiDynix
Database Vendor: EBSCOhost, Gale Cengage Learning, ProQuest
Wireless access
Partic in Multitype Libr Coun
Special Services for the Deaf - Bks on deafness & sign lang; Spec interest per; TDD equip
Open Mon-Thurs 9-9, Fri 9-6, Sat 9-5, Sun (Oct-April) 1-5
Friends of the Library Group

Branches: 8

ALICIA ASHMAN BRANCH, 733 N High Point Rd, 53717. Tel: 608-824-1780. FAX: 608-824-1790. *Br Supvr,* Alice Oakey; Tel: 608-824-1785, E-mail: aoakey@scls.lib.wi.us
Library Holdings: AV Mats 16,031; High Interest/Low Vocabulary Bk Vols 60; Large Print Bks 858; Bk Titles 59,289; Bk Vols 72,336; Per Subs 199; Talking Bks 3,227
Open Mon-Fri 9-9, Sat 9-5
Friends of the Library Group

HAWTHORNE BRANCH, 2707 E Washington Ave, 53704, SAN 364-7641. Tel: 608-246-4548. FAX: 608-246-4549. E-mail: mplhawthorne@gmail.com. *Br Supvr,* Marc Gartler; E-mail: mgartler@cityofmadison.com
Library Holdings: AV Mats 7,438; High Interest/Low Vocabulary Bk Vols 108; Large Print Bks 395; Bk Titles 37,433; Bk Vols 41,345; Per Subs 143; Talking Bks 953
Open Mon-Fri 10-8, Sat 9-5
Friends of the Library Group

LAKEVIEW, 2845 N Sherman Ave, 53704, SAN 364-7706. Tel: 608-246-4547. FAX: 608-246-4699. E-mail: lakeviewlib@gmail.com. *Br Supvr,* Marc Gartler; E-mail: mgartler@cityofmadison.com
Library Holdings: AV Mats 8,352; High Interest/Low Vocabulary Bk Vols 112; Large Print Bks 455; Bk Titles 37,713; Bk Vols 43,723; Per Subs 168; Talking Bks 1,351
Open Mon-Fri 10-8, Sat 9-5
Friends of the Library Group

MEADOWRIDGE, 5740 Raymond Rd, 53711, SAN 364-7730. Tel: 608-288-6160. FAX: 608-288-6162. *Br Supvr,* Alice Oakey; E-mail: aokey@scls.lib.wi.us
Library Holdings: AV Mats 8,716; High Interest/Low Vocabulary Bk Vols 107; Large Print Bks 337; Bk Titles 39,606; Bk Vols 46,901; Per Subs 161; Talking Bks 1,353
Open Mon-Fri 10-8, Sat 9-5
Friends of the Library Group

MONROE, 1705 Monroe St, 53711, SAN 364-7765. Tel: 608-266-6390. FAX: 608-266-6396. *Supv Librn,* Mary Burton; Tel: 608-224-7103, Fax: 608-224-7102, E-mail: mburton2@cityofmadison.com
Library Holdings: AV Mats 5,860; High Interest/Low Vocabulary Bk Vols 47; Large Print Bks 274; Bk Titles 18,809; Bk Vols 24,267; Per Subs 97; Talking Bks 948
Open Mon, Wed & Fri 1-9, Tues 10-6, Thurs 12-6, Sat 9:30-5
Friends of the Library Group

PINNEY BRANCH, 204 Cottage Grove Rd, 53716, SAN 364-782X. Tel: 608-224-7100. FAX: 608-224-7102. *Supv Librn,* Mary Burton; Tel: 608-224-7103, E-mail: mburton2@cityofmadison.com
Library Holdings: AV Mats 12,820; Bks on Deafness & Sign Lang 16; CDs 4,434; DVDs 1,905; Electronic Media & Resources 217; High Interest/Low Vocabulary Bk Vols 109; Large Print Bks 435; Music Scores 58; Bk Titles 73,964; Bk Vols 89,709; Per Subs 223; Talking Bks 2,625; Videos 3,610
Open Mon-Fri 9-9, Sat 9-5
Friends of the Library Group

SEQUOYA BRANCH, 4340 Tokay Blvd, 53711, SAN 364-7854. Tel: 608-266-6385. FAX: 608-266-7353. *Br Supvr,* Jane Roughen; E-mail: jroughen@cityofmadison.com
Library Holdings: AV Mats 18,482; High Interest/Low Vocabulary Bk Vols 148; Large Print Bks 744; Bk Titles 83,099; Bk Vols 109,044; Per Subs 246; Talking Bks 3,798
Open Mon-Fri 9-9, Sat 9-5, Sun (Sept-May) 1-5
Friends of the Library Group

SOUTH MADISON BRANCH, 2222 S Park St, 53713, SAN 364-7889. Tel: 608-266-6395. FAX: 608-266-6303. *Br Supvr,* Michael Spelman; E-mail: mspelman@scls.lib.wi.us
Library Holdings: AV Mats 6,260; High Interest/Low Vocabulary Bk Vols 210; Large Print Bks 369; Bk Titles 25,625; Bk Vols 29,140; Per Subs 103; Talking Bks 1,227
Open Mon-Fri 10-8, Sat 9-5
Friends of the Library Group

G   MENDOTA MENTAL HEALTH INSTITUTE*, Patients Library, 301 Troy Dr, 53704-1599. SAN 318-1146. Tel: 608-301-1196. FAX: 608-301-1169. *Librn,* Jennifer Friedman; E-mail: jennifer.friedman@wisconsin.gov; Staff 1 (MLS 1)
Founded 1955
Library Holdings: AV Mats 2,200; Bks on Deafness & Sign Lang 10; Braille Volumes 10; CDs 1,100; DVDs 125; High Interest/Low Vocabulary Bk Vols 150; Large Print Bks 30; Bk Vols 16,000; Per Subs 30; Videos 600
Subject Interests: Mental health, Organizational hist, Self help
Automation Activity & Vendor Info: (Cataloging) Follett Software; (Circulation) Follett Software
Partic in Wiscat
Special Services for the Blind - Bks on CD
Restriction: Not open to pub

M   MERITER HOSPITAL*, Health Resource Library, Two Atrium, 202 S Park St, 53715. SAN 364-7587. Tel: 608-417-5900. FAX: 608-267-6007. E-mail: library@meriter.com. Web Site: www.meriter.com/mhs/hospital/library.htm. *Librn,* Robert Koehler; E-mail: rkoehler@meriter.com
Library Holdings: Bk Titles 2,000; Per Subs 285
Subject Interests: Dentistry, Hospital admin, Med, Nursing
Partic in Regional Med Libr - Region 3
Open Mon 10-6, Tues-Thurs 10-7, Fri 10-3
Restriction: Non-circulating, Open to pub for ref only

S   NORWEGIAN AMERICAN GENEALOGICAL CENTER & NAESETH LIBRARY, 415 W Main St, 53703-3116. SAN 326-0038. Tel: 608-255-2224. FAX: 608-255-6842. E-mail: genealogy@nagcnl.org. Web Site: www.nagcnl.org. *Exec Dir,* Jeanne Wright; E-mail: jwright@nagcnl.org
Founded 1974
Library Holdings: AV Mats 4,000; Bk Titles 4,810; Bk Vols 4,920
Subject Interests: Genealogy, Norwegian (Lang), Norwegian hist
Wireless access
Function: Res libr
Publications: Norwegian Tracks (Bi-annually)
Restriction: Circ to mem only, Open by appt only, Open to researchers by request

S   PROMEGA CORP*, Information Resource Center, 2800 Woods Hollow Rd, 53711. Tel: 608-274-4330. FAX: 608-277-2601. E-mail: library@promega.com. Web Site: www.promega.com. *Dir,* Bob Koechley
Library Holdings: Bk Vols 5,000; Per Subs 300

S   RAYOVAC*, Technology Center Library, 601 Rayovac Dr, 53711. SAN 318-1049. Tel: 608-275-4714. FAX: 608-275-4992. *Librn,* Betsy Vogel; E-mail: betsy.vogel@spectrumbrands.com
Founded 1967
Library Holdings: Bk Titles 3,000; Per Subs 100
Special Collections: Company & Government Reports (Uniterm Coll), paper & micro
Subject Interests: Batteries, Chem, Electrochem, Eng, Flashlights, Patents
Automation Activity & Vendor Info: (Acquisitions) Inmagic, Inc.; (Cataloging) Inmagic, Inc.; (Circulation) Inmagic, Inc.
Partic in Madison Area Libr Coun
Open Mon-Fri 8:30-5

M   ST MARY'S HOSPITAL MEDICAL CENTER*, Medical Library, 700 S Park St, 53715. SAN 318-1219. Tel: 608-258-6533. FAX: 608-258-6119. E-mail: smhmc_medical_library@ssmhc.com. *Head of Libr,* Leslie A Christensen; Tel: 608-258-6532, E-mail: leslie_christensen@ssmhc.com; *Consumer Health Librn,* Casey Petersen; Tel: 608-512-4000, E-mail: casey_petersen@ssmhc.com; *Tech Serv Librn,* Kari Zelinka; Tel: 608-258-6161, E-mail: kari_zelinka@ssmhc.com; *ILL,* Jodi Burgess; Tel: 608-258-6535, E-mail: jodi_burgess@ssmhc.com; Staff 3 (MLS 2, Non-MLS 1)
Founded 1974
Library Holdings: e-books 275; e-journals 1,500; Bk Titles 1,200; Per Subs 50
Subject Interests: Hospital admin, Med, Nursing
Database Vendor: Dialog, EBSCOhost, Lexi-Comp, Micromedex, Natural Standard, OVID Technologies, PubMed
Partic in Docline; Greater Midwest Regional Medical Libr Network; Wis Health Sci Libr Asn
Restriction: Badge access after hrs

P   SOUTH CENTRAL LIBRARY SYSTEM, 4610 S Biltmore Lane, Ste 101, 53718-2153. SAN 364-7919. Tel: 608-246-7970. FAX: 608-246-7958. Web Site: www.scls.info. *Dir,* Martha Van Pelt; Tel: 608-246-7975, E-mail: mvanpelt@scls.lib.wi.us; *ILS Project Mgr,* Victoria Teal Lovely; Tel: 608-242-4713, E-mail: vtl@scls.lib.wi.us; *Support Serv Mgr,* Kerrie Goeden; Tel: 608-246-7972, E-mail: kgoeden@scls.lib.wi.us; *Delivery Coordr,* Bruce Smith; Tel: 608-266-4695, E-mail: bsmith@scls.lib.wi.us; Staff 57 (MLS 8, Non-MLS 49)
Founded 1975. Pop 786,103
Jan 2012-Dec 2012 Income $8,973,009, State $2,057,367
Library Holdings: Bk Vols 917; Per Subs 38
Subject Interests: Libr, Librarianship
Automation Activity & Vendor Info: (Acquisitions) LibLime; (Cataloging) LibLime; (Circulation) LibLime; (ILL) LibLime; (OPAC) LibLime; (Serials) LibLime
Database Vendor: Bowker, EBSCOhost, Gale Cengage Learning, LibLime, netLibrary, OCLC, OCLC FirstSearch, OCLC WorldCat, Overdrive, Inc, Progressive Technology Federal Systems, Inc (PTFS), ProQuest, ReferenceUSA, Safari Books Online, SerialsSolutions
Wireless access
Member Libraries: Adams County Library; Albany Public Library; Angie Williams Cox Public Library; Baraboo Public Library; Belleville Public

Library; Black Earth Public Library; Brodhead Memorial Public Library; Cambridge Public Library; Columbus Public Library; Dane County Library Service; Deerfield Public Library; DeForest Area Public Library; Fitchburg Public Library; Hutchinson Community College; Jane Morgan Memorial Library; Kilbourn Public Library; Kraemer Library & Community Center; La Valle Public Library; Lester Public Library of Arpin; Lester Public Library of Rome; Lester Public Library of Vesper; Lettie W Jensen Public Library; Lodi Woman's Club Public Library; Madison Public Library; Marshall Community Library; Marshfield Public Library; Mazomanie Free Library; McFarland Public Library; McMillan Memorial Library; Middleton Public Library; Monona Public Library; Monroe Public Library; Monticello Public Library; Mount Horeb Public Library; New Glarus Public Library; North Freedom Public Library; Oregon Public Library; Pittsville Community Library; Portage County Public Library; Portage Public Library; Poynette Public Library; Prairie du Sac Public Library; Reedsburg Public Library; Rio Community Library; Rock Springs Public Library; Rosemary Garfoot Public Library; Sauk City Public Library; Spring Green Community Library; Stoughton Public Library; Sun Prairie Public Library; Verona Public Library; Waunakee Public Library; Wyocena Public Library

R TRINITY LUTHERAN CHURCH LIBRARY*, 1904 Winnebago St, 53704. SAN 318-1251. Tel: 608-249-8527. FAX: 608-249-9070. E-mail: tlcmsn@merr.com. Web Site: www.merr.com/users/tlcmsn. *Librn,* Sharon Kenyon
Founded 1944
Library Holdings: Bk Vols 4,500
Subject Interests: Relig studies
Open Mon-Fri 8-4:30, Sun 8:30-10:30

G UNITED STATES FOREST SERVICE, Forest Products Laboratory Library, One Gifford Pinchot Dr, 53726-2398. SAN 318-126X. Tel: 608-231-9313. Interlibrary Loan Service Tel: 608-231-9498. Reference Tel: 608-231-9491. FAX: 608-231-9311. TDD: 608-231-9544. E-mail: pdl_fpl_library@fs.fed.us. Web Site: www.fpl.fs.fed.us/products/library/index.php. *Cat, Head of Libr, Ref Serv,* Julie Blankenburg; E-mail: jblankenburg@fs.fed.us; *Acq,* Shelley Bishop; Tel: 608-231-9312, E-mail: sdbishop@fs.fed.us; *Cat,* David C Smith; Tel: 608-231-9415, E-mail: davidcsmith@fs.fed.us; *ILL Spec,* Mary Funmaker; E-mail: mfunmaker@fs.fed.us; Staff 4 (MLS 2, Non-MLS 2)
Founded 1910
Library Holdings: Bk Titles 44,000; Bk Vols 99,000; Per Subs 340
Special Collections: Oral History
Subject Interests: Adhesives, Drying, Energy from wood, Fire sci, Mycology, Paint & coatings, Pulp & paper, Recycling, Solid wood products, Tech, Wood eng
Automation Activity & Vendor Info: (Cataloging) OCLC; (OPAC) CyberTools for Libraries
Function: ILL available
Partic in FS-Info; OCLC Online Computer Library Center, Inc; Wisconsin Library Services
Open Mon-Fri 8-4
Restriction: In-house use for visitors, Non-circulating to the pub, Open to pub for ref only

C UNIVERSITY OF WISCONSIN-MADISON*, General Library System & Memorial Library, 728 State St, 53706. SAN 364-8036. Tel: 608-262-3193. Circulation Tel: 608-263-7360. Interlibrary Loan Service Tel: 608-262-2571. Reference Tel: 608-263-3242. FAX: 608-265-2754. Web Site: www.library.wisc.edu. *Dir,* Kenneth Frazier; Tel: 608-262-2600; *Dep Dir,* Edward Van Gemert; Tel: 608-262-0950; *Spec Coll Librn,* Robin Rider; *Automation Syst Coordr,* Nolan Pope; *ILL,* Heather Weltin; *Ref,* Nancy McClements; *Tech Serv,* Richard Reeb. Subject Specialists: *Hist of sci,* Robin Rider; *SE Asia,* Larry Ashumn; *Latin Am,* Paloma Celis Carbajal; *Europe,* John Dillon; *Africa,* David Henige; *Educ, Psychol,* Marilyn Hicks; *Soc sci & issues,* Emile Ngo Nguidjol; *European hist,* Barbara Walden; *Women studies,* Phyllis Weisbard
Founded 1850. Enrl 40,793; Fac 2,054; Highest Degree: Doctorate Jul 2005-Jun 2006. Mats Exp $11,582,710. Sal $22,380,731 (Prof $13,380,066)
Library Holdings: Bk Vols 6,057,201; Per Subs 39,802
Special Collections: 17th & 18th Century European Theology (Chwalibog Coll); 20th Century English & American Literature Coll; Alchemy (Duveen Coll); American Gift Books & Annuals; American Music (Tams-Witmark Coll); Balcanica Coll; Belgian Congo Archival Materials (Deryck Coll); Book Plates; Brazilian Positivism Coll; Brodhead Manuscripts; Buddhism Coll; C S Lewis Letters; Calvinist Theology & Dutch History (Tank Coll); Carol von Linee Coll; Chess (Peter G Toepfer Coll); Children's Literature (Burgess Coll); Civil War Band Books; Classical & 19th Century German Literature (George B Wild Coll); Cossack Coll; Dalton Trumbo Coll; Dutch Pamphlets; Early American Women Authors (William Cairns Coll); English 19th Century Free Thought Coll; English 19th Century Social & Economic Pamphlets; English Grammars (Berry Coll); English Manor Rolls; English Romantic Poetry

(Arthur Beatty Coll); English Temperance (Guy Hayler Coll); Eugene O'Neill Coll; European & American Student Publications; European Socialism (Herman Schlueter Library & William English Walling Coll); Ferber Coll; French 18th Century Literature & Culture (Tucker Coll); French Political Pamphlets, 1560-1648; French Protestantism (Montauban Coll); French Revolutionary Pamphlets; French Socialist Congresses Coll; French Student Revolt, 1968; German 18th Century Theater Coll; German Expressionism Coll; German Philology Coll; Grotius Coll; Herald Coll (Leon Srabian Herald, Poet & Philosopher); History of Chemistry (Cole Duveen Coll); History of Science Coll; Icelandic History & Literature Coll; Irish History & Literature Coll; Italian 16th Century Imprints (Giolito Coll); Joseph Priestly Coll; Judaica (Joseph L Baron Coll); Juridical Materials, 15th & 16th Century; Latimer Coll (Matthias Collection of the Letters of Marjorie Latimer); Lithuanian History & Literature (Alfred Senn Coll); Little Magazines (Marvin Sukov Coll); Lutheran Theology (Hoyer Coll); Madras History Sources; Mark Twain (George H Brownell & Norman Bassett Coll); Mazarinades Coll; Medieval History Coll; Medieval Spanish Literature Coll; Mesmer Coll; Mexican Pamphlets; Mottey Coll; National Socialism Coll; Natural History & English Literature (Chester H Thordarson Coll); Norwegian Local History Coll; O Henry Coll; Papyri Coll; Polish Literature & History Coll; Private Press Coll; Renaissance Epic Coll; Robert Boyle Coll; Rousseau Coll; Russian Culture (Romanovskii Coll); Russian Revolutionary Movement (Russian Free Press Coll); Russian Satirical Journals; Saint Simon Coll; Scandinavian Literature & Language (Olson Coll); Scandinavian Literature (Mimers Coll); Swift (Teerink Coll); Swiss Literature Romande; The Lost Dauphin (William W Wight Coll); Theater (Thomas H Dickinson Coll); Tibetan Coll; Welsh Theology (Jones-Roberts Coll). UN Document Depository; US Document Depository
Automation Activity & Vendor Info: (Acquisitions) Ex Libris Group; (Cataloging) Ex Libris Group; (Circulation) Ex Libris Group; (Course Reserve) Ex Libris Group; (OPAC) Ex Libris Group; (Serials) Ex Libris Group
Database Vendor: EBSCOhost, LexisNexis, OCLC FirstSearch, OVID Technologies, ProQuest, TLC (The Library Corporation)
Friends of the Library Group
Departmental Libraries:
BIOLOGY LIBRARY, 430 Lincoln Dr, 53706, SAN 364-815X. Tel: 608-262-2740. FAX: 608-262-9003. E-mail: biolib@library.wisc.edu. Web Site: biology.library@wisc.edu. *Interim Librn,* Amanda Werhane; E-mail: awerhane@library.wisc.edu; Staff 1 (MLS 1)
Library Holdings: Bk Vols 50,000
Subject Interests: Botany, Conserv biol, Natural hist, Zoology
Open Mon-Thurs (Winter) 9-8:45, Fri 9-4:45, Sat & Sun 1-4:45; Mon-Fri (Summer) 9-4:45
BUSINESS LIBRARY, Grainger Hall, Rm 2200, 975 University Ave, 53706, SAN 364-8184. Tel: 608-262-5935. Reference Tel: 608-265-6202. FAX: 608-262-9001. E-mail: askbusiness@library.wisc.edu. Web Site: business.library.wisc.edu. *Head Librn,* Michael G Enyart; Tel: 608-263-3902, E-mail: menyart@library.wisc.edu; *Data Librn,* Peggy Smith; Tel: 608-890-1901, E-mail: psmith@library.wisc.edu; *Ref/Instruction Librn,* Eunice Gandt; *Access Serv,* Debra Ahrens; E-mail: dahrens@library.wisc.edu; *Tech Serv,* Gail Glaze; Tel: 608-262-4007, E-mail: gglaze@library.wisc.edu; Staff 7 (MLS 5, Non-MLS 2)
Library Holdings: Bk Vols 53,000
Open Mon-Thurs 8am-11pm, Fri 8-8, Sat 10-5, Sun 10am-11pm
CENTER FOR DEMOGRAPHY & ECOLOGY LIBRARY, 4471 Social Science Bldg, 1180 Observatory Dr, 53706-1393, SAN 323-9993. Tel: 608-263-6372. FAX: 608-262-8400. E-mail: library@ssc.wisc.edu. *Dir,* John Carlson; Tel: 608-262-4879, E-mail: jcarlson@ssc.wisc.edu; Staff 1 (MLS 1)
Founded 1970
Library Holdings: Bk Titles 15,000; Bk Vols 18,000; Per Subs 68
Subject Interests: Pop studies
Function: Doc delivery serv, Ref serv available, Res libr
Open Mon, Wed & Thurs 8:30-4:30, Tues 12-4:30, Fri 8:30-11:30
Restriction: Circ limited
CHEMISTRY LIBRARY, 1101 University Ave, 53706, SAN 364-8214. Tel: 608-262-2942. FAX: 608-262-9002. Web Site: chemistry.library.wisc.edu. *Co-Dir,* Sharon Mulvey; *Co-Dir,* Emily Wixson; Staff 2 (MLS 2)
Library Holdings: Bk Vols 50,722
Open Mon-Fri 8-5
COLLEGE (UNDERGRADUATE) LIBRARY, 600 N Park St, 53706, SAN 364-8060. Tel: 608-262-3245. FAX: 608-262-4631. E-mail: helenc@library.wisc.edu. Web Site: college.library.wisc.edu. *Dir,* Carrie Kruse; Staff 12.5 (MLS 12.5)
Library Holdings: Bk Vols 96,565
Open Mon-Sun 10am-11:45pm
COOPERATIVE CHILDREN'S BOOK CENTER, 4290 Helen C White Hall, 600 N Park St, 53706, SAN 323-9977. Tel: 608-263-3720. FAX: 608-262-4933. E-mail: ccbcinfo@education.wisc.edu. Web Site: www.education.wisc.edu/ccbc/. *Dir,* Kathleen T Horning; Tel: 608-263-3721, E-mail: horning@education.wisc.edu; Staff 3 (MLS 3)
Founded 1963

Library Holdings: Bk Vols 25,000
Open Mon-Thurs (Winter) 9-7, Fri 9-4, Sat & Sun 12:30-4; Mon-Fri (Summer) 9-4

CM   EBLING LIBRARY, 750 Highland Ave, 53705, SAN 364-8540. Tel: 608-262-2020. FAX: 608-262-4732. E-mail: eblinghelp@library.wisc.edu. Web Site: ebling.library.wisc.edu. *Dir,* Julie Schneider; Tel: 608-263-5755; Staff 18 (MLS 18)
      Library Holdings: Bk Titles 168,328; Bk Vols 371,687
      Special Collections: History of Medicine, especially Anatomical Works
      Subject Interests: Allied health, Cancer res, Hospital admin, Neuroscience, Nursing
      Function: Archival coll, Doc delivery serv, Health sci info serv, ILL available, Photocopying/Printing
      Open Mon-Thurs 7:30am-11:45pm, Fri 7:30-5:45, Sat 10-5:45, Sun 10am-11:45pm
      GEOGRAPHY, 280 Science Hall, 550 N Park St, 53706, SAN 364-8249. Tel: 608-262-1706. E-mail: geoglib@library.wisc.edu. Web Site: geography.library.wisc.edu/. *Librn,* Thomas Tews; E-mail: ttews@library.wisc.edu; Staff 2 (MLS 1, Non-MLS 1)
      Library Holdings: Bk Vols 70,000
      Open Mon-Thurs 9-8, Fri 9-4:30, Sun 1-5; Mon-Fri (Summer) 9-4:30
      NIEMAN GRANT JOURNALISM READING ROOM, 2130 Vilas Hall, 821 University Ave, 53706, SAN 364-8516. Tel: 608-263-3387. E-mail: jrrlib@library.wisc.edu.
      Library Holdings: Bk Vols 1,000; Per Subs 30
      Subject Interests: Journalism, Mass communications
      STEPHEN COLE KLEENE MATHEMATICS LIBRARY, 480 Lincoln Dr, 53706, SAN 364-8486. Tel: 608-262-3596. FAX: 608-263-8891. E-mail: mathlib@library.wisc.edu. Web Site: math.library.wisc.edu. *Head of Librn,* Travis Warwick; Tel: 608-263-2274, E-mail: twarwick@library.wisc.edu; Staff 1 (MLS 1)
      Founded 1963
      Library Holdings: Bk Vols 56,000
      Subject Interests: Computer sci, Math, Physics, Statistics
      Function: Res libr
      Open Mon-Thurs (Winter) 8:30-8, Fri 8:30-5, Sun 3-6; Mon-Fri (Summer) 8:30-5
      KOHLER ART LIBRARY, 800 University Ave, 53706, SAN 364-8338. Tel: 608-263-2258. FAX: 608-263-2255. E-mail: askart@library.wisc.edu. *Dir,* Lynette Korenic; Tel: 608-263-2256, E-mail: lkorenic@library.wisc.edu; Staff 4 (MLS 2, Non-MLS 2)
      Library Holdings: Bk Vols 183,000; Per Subs 460
      Special Collections: Artists' Books; Frank Lloyd Wright Coll; Illuminated Manuscript Facsimiles; Toy & Movable Books
      Subject Interests: African art, Decorative art, Medieval art, Photog
      Open Mon-Thurs (Winter) 8am-9:45pm, Fri 8-4:45, Sat & Sun 11-4:45; Mon-Fri (Summer) 9-4:45
      L & S LEARNING SUPPORT SERVICES, Van Hise Hall, 1220 Linden Dr, 53706. Tel: 608-262-1408. FAX: 608-262-7579. Web Site: babel.lss.wisc.edu. *Dir,* Bruno Browning; *Head Librn,* Mary Prochniak; E-mail: mary@lss.wisc.edu; *AV,* Dennis Rinzel; *AV,* Doug Worsham; *Network Serv,* Karen Tusack
      Library Holdings: AV Mats 5,000
      Open Mon-Thurs 8:30-8:30, Fri 8:30-5:30

CL   LAW SCHOOL, 975 Bascom Mall, 53706, SAN 364-8397. Tel: 608-262-1128. Administration Tel: 608-263-7822. FAX: 608-262-2775. Web Site: library.law.wisc.edu/. *Dir,* Steven Barkan; Tel: 608-262-1151; Staff 24 (MLS 13, Non-MLS 11)
      Library Holdings: Bk Titles 168,851; Bk Vols 404,061; Per Subs 6,073
      Special Collections: US Document Depository
      Subject Interests: Criminal justice, Environ law
      C K LEITH LIBRARY OF GEOLOGY & GEOPHYSICS, 1215 W Dayton St, 53706-1692, SAN 364-8273. Tel: 608-262-8956. FAX: 608-262-0693. E-mail: geolib@library.wisc.edu. Web Site: www.geology.wisc.edu/library. *Librn,* Marie Dvorzak; E-mail: mdvorzak@library.wisc.edu; Staff 2 (MLS 1, Non-MLS 1)
      Founded 1974
      Library Holdings: Bk Vols 80,000
      Special Collections: Map Coll
      Subject Interests: Geol, Geophysics
      Open Mon-Thurs (Fall-Spring) 8:30-8, Fri 8:30-5, Sun 1-5; Mon-Fri (Summer) 8:30-5
      MERIT LIBRARY (MEDIA, EDUCATION RESOURCES & INFORMATION TECHNOLOGY), 225 N Mills St, 53706, SAN 364-8303. Tel: 608-263-4750. Administration Tel: 608-263-8199. Information Services Tel: 608-263-4751. FAX: 608-262-6050. E-mail: meritlibrary@education.wisc.edu. Web Site: merit.education.wisc.edu. *Chief Info Officer, Dir,* Dan Jacobsohn; Tel: 608-263-4755, E-mail: jacobsohn@wisc.edu; *Asst Dir,* Anna Lewis; E-mail: alewis@education.wisc.edu; *Electronic Res, Info Serv,* James Jonas; Tel: 608-263-4934, E-mail: jjonas@education.wisc.edu; *Tech Serv,* Vince Jenkins; Tel: 608-262-7301, E-mail: vjenkins@education.wisc.edu; Staff 8 (MLS 4, Non-MLS 4)
      Founded 1848. Highest Degree: Doctorate
      Library Holdings: Bk Vols 65,463; Per Subs 386

Special Collections: US Document Depository
Subject Interests: Teacher educ
Function: Prof lending libr
Partic in WILS
Open Mon-Thurs (Sept-May) 8am-10pm, Fri 8-5, Sun 12-10
MILLS MUSIC LIBRARY, 728 State St, 53706, SAN 364-8575. Tel: 608-263-1884. FAX: 608-265-2754. E-mail: askmusic@library.wisc.edu. Web Site: music.library.wisc.edu. *Dir,* Jeanette Casey; Staff 3 (MLS 3)
Library Holdings: Bk Vols 71,500
Special Collections: 19th Century American Music Imprints; Civil War Band Books
Open Mon-Thurs 8:30am-10pm, Fri 8:30-5, Sat 12-5, Sun 1-10
PHYSICS LIBRARY, 4220 Chamberlin Hall, 1150 University Ave, 53706, SAN 364-863X. Tel: 608-262-9500. FAX: 608-265-2754. E-mail: physlib@library.wisc.edu. Web Site: physics.library.wisc.edu. *Dir, Physics & Astronomy Librn,* Kerry L Kresse; Tel: 608-262-8696, E-mail: kkresse@library.wisc.edu; Staff 2 (MLS 1, Non-MLS 1)
Founded 1972
Library Holdings: Bk Vols 56,205
Automation Activity & Vendor Info: (ILL) OCLC ILLiad
Function: Res libr
Partic in Council of Independent Colleges (CIC); WILS
Open Mon-Thurs 8-7, Fri 8-5, Sun 1-5
PLANT PATHOLOGY MEMORIAL, 1630 Linden Dr, Rm 584, 53706, SAN 328-8277. Tel: 608-262-8698. FAX: 608-263-2626. Web Site: www.plantpath.wisc.edu/library/. *Librn,* Steve Cloyd; E-mail: scloyd@library.wisc.edu; Staff 1 (MLS 1)
Library Holdings: Bk Vols 13,630; Per Subs 75
Special Collections: Virus Literature (Johnson-Hoggan-Fulton Virus Coll), abstracts on cards, bks
Subject Interests: Plant pathology, Plant virology
Function: For res purposes, Ref serv available
Open Mon-Fri 9am-12:45pm
PRIMATE CENTER - LAWRENCE JACOBSEN LIBRARY, 1220 Capitol Ct, 53715, SAN 364-8664. Tel: 608-263-3512. FAX: 608-263-4031. E-mail: library@primate.wisc.edu. Web Site: pin.primate.wisc.edu. *Dir,* Ray Hamel; E-mail: hamel@primate.wisc.edu; *Spec Coll & AV,* Ryan Engel; *Tech Serv,* Joanne Brown; E-mail: brown@primate.wisc.edu; Staff 4 (MLS 4)
Founded 1973
Library Holdings: AV Mats 15,500; Bk Vols 22,500; Per Subs 12; Videos 1,055
Special Collections: Archives; Digital Primate Images Coll; Primatology Coll, audiovisuals, bks, per
Subject Interests: Aging, Animal welfare, Neurobiol, Primatology, Reproductive biol, Veterinary med, Virology
Function: Archival coll, Computers for patron use, Copy machines, Electronic databases & coll, Online cat, Online ref, Pub access computers, Ref serv available, Ref serv in person, Scanner, VHS videos, Video lending libr
Open Mon-Fri 8-5
Friends of the Library Group
ARTHUR H ROBINSON MAP LIBRARY, 310 Science Hall, 550 N Park St, 53706-1491, SAN 364-8451. Tel: 608-262-1471. FAX: 608-265-3991. *Librn,* Jaime Stoltenberg; E-mail: jstoltenberg@wisc.edu; Staff 1 (MLS 1)
Library Holdings: Bk Vols 1,000
Special Collections: Wisconsin Aerial Photographs
Subject Interests: Aerial photog, Maps
SCHOOL OF LIBRARY & INFORMATION STUDIES LIBRARY, 600 N Park St, Rm 4191, 53706, SAN 364-8427. Tel: 608-263-2960. FAX: 608-263-4849. E-mail: slislib@library.wisc.edu. Web Site: slislib.library.wisc.edu. *Dir,* Michele Besant; Tel: 608-263-2963, E-mail: mbesant@library.wisc.edu; Staff 1 (MLS 1)
Highest Degree: Doctorate
Library Holdings: Bk Vols 66,000
Subject Interests: Children's lit, Info sci, Libr
Friends of the Library Group
SOCIAL SCIENCE REFERENCE LIBRARY, 1180 Observatory Drl, Rm 8432, 53706, SAN 364-8729. Tel: 608-262-6195. *Head of Librn,* Tom Durkin; Tel: 608-263-4072, E-mail: tdurkin@library.wisc.edu; Staff 1 (MLS 1)
Library Holdings: Bk Vols 14,618
Special Collections: Industrial Relations; Poverty; Social Systems
Subject Interests: Econ, Ind relig
SOCIAL WORK LIBRARY, 1350 University Ave, Rm 236, 53706, SAN 364-8753. Tel: 608-263-3840. FAX: 608-265-2754. E-mail: socworklib@mail.library.wisc.edu. *Dir,* Jane Linzmeyer; Staff 1 (MLS 1)
Library Holdings: Bk Vols 26,000
Subject Interests: Child welfare, Family issues, Gerontology
Open Mon-Thurs 8:30-6:30, Fri 8:30-4:30, Sat & Sun 12:30-4:30
SPACE SCIENCE & ENGINEERING CENTER - SCHWERDTFEGER LIBRARY, 1225 W Dayton St, 53706, SAN 323-9845. Tel: 608-262-0987. FAX: 608-262-5974. E-mail: library@ssec.wisc.edu. Web

Site: library.ssec.wisc.edu. *Librn,* Jean M Phillips; Tel: 608-262-8164,
E-mail: jean.phillips@ssec.wisc.edu; Staff 2 (MLS 2)
Library Holdings: Bk Vols 40,000
Subject Interests: Atmospheric sci, Space sci
Open Mon-Fri 8:30-5

STEENBOCK MEMORIAL AGRICULTURAL LIBRARY, 550 Babcock
Dr, 53706, SAN 364-8095. Tel: 608-262-9635. Circulation Tel:
608-262-1371. FAX: 608-263-3221. E-mail:
asksteenbock@library.wisc.edu. Web Site: steenbock.library.wisc.edu.
Interim Head of Libr, Lisa Wettleson; Tel: 608-263-7574; *Head, Coll,
Access & Tech Serv,* James Buckett; E-mail: jbuckett@library.wisc.edu;
Head, Info Serv, Beverly R Phillips; Tel: 608-263-2411, E-mail:
bphillips@library.wisc.edu; Staff 12 (MLS 12)
Library Holdings: Bk Vols 225,000
Subject Interests: Agr, Human ecology, Natural res, Veterinary med

KURT WENDT ENGINEERING LIBRARY, 215 N Randall Ave, 53706,
SAN 364-8788. Tel: 608-262-3493. Reference Tel: 608-262-0696.
Information Services Tel: 608-262-3536. FAX: 608-262-4739,
608-265-8751. E-mail: askwendt@engr.wisc.edu. Web Site:
wendt.library.wisc.edu. *Dir,* Deborah Helman; Tel: 608-262-7980,
E-mail: dhelman@engr.wisc.edu; *Head, Digital & Computer Serv,* Eric
Larson; *Head, Fac & Student Serv,* Amy Kindschi; *Circ & Info Serv
Librn,* Anne Glorioso; *Coll & Scholarly Communications, Librn,* Jody
Hoesly; *Info Serv Librn,* Anne Rauh; *Periodicals Librn,* Rolf Rodefeld;
Patents & Tech Rpt Librn, Nancy Spitzer; *Reserves & Info Serv Librn,*
Ryan Schryver; *Res Sharing Librn,* Christy Henrickson; *Res Sharing
Librn,* Karen Wagner; *Res Sharing Librn,* Richard West; *Ser Tech Serv
Librn,* Richard West; *Instruction Coordr,* Diana Wheeler. Subject
Specialists: *Patents, Tech rpts,* Nancy Spitzer
Library Holdings: Bk Vols 304,609
Subject Interests: Atmospheric, Computer sci, Eng, Oceanic sci

WISCONSIN CENTER FOR FILM & THEATER RESEARCH, 816 State
St, 53706, SAN 323-9861. Tel: 608-264-6466. FAX: 608-264-6472.
E-mail: askmovies@wisconsinhistory.org. Web Site:
wcftr.commarts.wisc.edu/, www.wisconsinhistory.org/wcftr. *Dir,* Vance
Kepley; E-mail: vikepley@wisc.edu; *Librn,* Maxine Fleckner Ducey; Tel:
608-264-6467
Open Mon-Fri 8-5, Sat 9-4

WISCONSIN'S WATER LIBRARY, 1975 Willow Dr, 2nd Flr,
53706-1177, SAN 321-981X. Tel: 608-262-3069. FAX: 608-262-0591.
E-mail: askwater@aqua.wisc.edu. Web Site: aqua.wisc.edu/waterlibrary.
Founded 1966
Library Holdings: Bk Titles 24,000; Bk Vols 30,000; Per Subs 60
Special Collections: Water-Related Children's Books
Subject Interests: Great Lakes, Water, Water res, Wis
Automation Activity & Vendor Info: (Cataloging) Ex Libris Group;
(Circulation) Ex Libris Group; (OPAC) Ex Libris Group
Function: Homebound delivery serv, ILL available, Ref serv available
Partic in Univ of Wis Spec Campus Libr Group
Publications: Recent Acquisitions & Web Sites of Interest (Monthly)
Open Mon-Fri 9-4:30

WOODMAN ASTRONOMICAL LIBRARY, 6515 Sterling Hall, 475 N
Charter St, 53706, SAN 364-8842. Tel: 608-262-1320. FAX:
608-236-6386. E-mail: astrolib@library.wisc.edu. Web Site:
astronomy.library.wisc.edu/. *Dir, Physics & Astronomy Libr,* Kerry
Kresse; Tel: 608-262-8696, E-mail: kkresse@library.wisc.edu; Staff 2
(MLS 1, Non-MLS 1)
Founded 1881
Library Holdings: Bk Vols 18,537

G WISCONSIN DEPARTMENT OF EMPLOYEE TRUST FUNDS
LIBRARY, 801 W Badger Rd, 53713-2526. (Mail add: PO Box 7931,
53707-7931), SAN 324-7376. Tel: 608-267-2926. FAX: 608-267-4549.
Web Site: etf.wi.gov. *Librn,* Margery Katz; E-mail:
margery.katz@etf.wi.gov; Staff 1 (MLS 1)
Founded 1972
Library Holdings: Bk Titles 3,500; Per Subs 200
Subject Interests: Acctg, Employee benefits, Health ins, Pensions, Pub
employee retirement

GL WISCONSIN DEPARTMENT OF JUSTICE, Law Library, 17 W Main St,
53703. (Mail add: PO Box 7857, 53707-7857), SAN 318-1324. Tel:
608-266-1546. *Law Librn,* Amy J Thornton; Staff 1.5 (MLS 1, Non-MLS
0.5)
Founded 1969
Library Holdings: Bk Titles 16,000; Bk Vols 40,000; Per Subs 30
Special Collections: Wisconsin Attorney General Material
Subject Interests: Wis law
Database Vendor: Westlaw
Publications: Index Digest to Opinions of the Attorney General of the
State of Wisconsin, 1845-1972, 1973-current
Restriction: Open to staff only

P WISCONSIN DEPARTMENT OF PUBLIC INSTRUCTION*, Division for
Libraries, Technology & Community Learning, 125 S Webster St, 53707.
(Mail add: PO Box 7841, 53707-7841), SAN 364-8877. Tel: 608-266-2205.
FAX: 608-266-8770. Web Site: dpi.wi.gov/dltcl. *Asst State Superintendent,*
Kurt Kiefer; E-mail: kurt.kiefer@dpi.wi.gov; Staff 1 (Non-MLS 1)
Open Mon-Fri 7:30-4:30
Branches: 4

DPI PROFESSIONAL LIBRARY, GEF 3 Bldg, 3rd Flr, 125 S Webster St,
53703. (Mail add: PO Box 7841, 53707-7841), SAN 364-8990. Tel:
608-266-3108. FAX: 608-266-2529. Web Site: dpi.wi.gov/lbstat/lib2.html.
Librn, Kay Ihlenfeldt; E-mail: kay.ihlenfeldt@dpi.state.wi.us; Staff 3
(MLS 1, Non-MLS 2)
Founded 1968
Library Holdings: Bk Vols 3,000; Per Subs 150
Subject Interests: Educ, Educ statistics, Libr sci
Partic in S Cent Libr Syst
Open Mon-Fri 8-4

INSTRUCTIONAL MEDIA & TECHNOLOGY TEAM, 125 S Webster St,
53707. (Mail add: PO Box 7841, 53707-7841), SAN 364-8931. Tel:
608-266-3856. Toll Free Tel: 800-441-4563. FAX: 608-267-1052. Web
Site: www.dpi.wi.gov/imt/index.html. *Dir,* Stephen Sanders; E-mail:
stephen.sanders@dpi.wi.gov
Open Mon-Fri 7:30-4:30

PUBLIC LIBRARY DEVELOPMENT TEAM, 125 S Webster St, 53702.
(Mail add: PO Box 7841, 53707-7841), SAN 364-9024. Tel:
608-267-9225. FAX: 608-266-2529. Web Site: dpi.wi.gov/pld/index.html,
www.dpi.state.wi.us/dltcl/pld. *Dir,* Michael Cross; E-mail:
michael.cross@dpi.state.wi.us; Staff 6 (MLS 6)
Founded 1968

REFERENCE & LOAN LIBRARY, 2109 S Stoughton Rd, 53716-2899,
SAN 364-9059. Tel: 608-224-6167. Toll Free Tel: 888-542-5543. FAX:
608-224-6178. Web Site: dpi.wi.gov/rll/index.html. *Dir,* Sally Drew; Tel:
608-224-6161, E-mail: sally.drew@dpi.state.wi.us; *Wis Doc Dep
Prog/Wis Digital Archives,* Abby Swanton; *Supvr, ILL & Ref Serv,*
Martha Berninger; Tel: 608-224-6168; Fax: 608-224-6168, E-mail:
martha.berninger; *Supvr, Res Sharing Tech,* David Sleasman; Tel:
608-224-6179, E-mail: david.sleasman@dpi.wi.gov; Staff 12 (MLS 11,
Non-MLS 1)
Library Holdings: Bk Titles 140,000; Bk Vols 151,096; Per Subs 60
Automation Activity & Vendor Info: (Acquisitions) Baker & Taylor;
(Cataloging) OCLC; (Circulation) AmLib Library Management System;
(ILL) Auto-Graphics, Inc; (OPAC) Auto-Graphics, Inc
Database Vendor: Dialog, EBSCOhost, Gale Cengage Learning, OCLC
FirstSearch, OCLC WorldCat
Function: Online ref, Online searches
Partic in Dialog Corp; OCLC Online Computer Library Center, Inc
Special Services for the Blind - Newsline for the Blind
Open Mon-Fri 8-4

S WISCONSIN DEPARTMENT OF VETERANS AFFAIRS*, Wisconsin
Veterans Museum Research Center, 30 W Mifflin St, Ste 300, 53703. SAN
325-4992. Tel: 608-267-1790. FAX: 608-264-7615. E-mail:
reference.desk@dva.state.wi.us. Web Site:
museum.dva.state.wi.us/researchcenter.asp. *Dir,* Richard H Zeitlin; *Librn,*
Amy O'Shea; Tel: 608-261-5408, E-mail: amy.oshea@dva.state.wi.us;
Archives Coll Mgr, Gayle J Martinson; Tel: 608-261-0536, E-mail:
gayle.martinson@dva.state.wi.us; *Ref & Outreach Archivist,* Russell P
Horton; E-mail: russell.horton@dva.state.wi.us; Staff 4 (MLS 4)
Founded 1901
Library Holdings: AV Mats 1,200; Music Scores 60; Bk Titles 15,000;
Per Subs 40; Videos 200
Special Collections: Manuscript Coll; Veteran Group Organizational
Records; Wisconsin National Guard Coll, photogs, rec; Wisconsin Veterans
Oral History Project. Oral History
Subject Interests: Mil hist, Wis hist
Automation Activity & Vendor Info: (Cataloging) OCLC
Function: Archival coll
Partic in Wiscat
Open Mon-Fri 9-3:30
Restriction: Non-circulating
Friends of the Library Group

S WISCONSIN HISTORICAL SOCIETY LIBRARY*, 816 State St, 53706.
SAN 318-1227. Tel: 608-264-6534. FAX: 608-264-6520. Web Site:
www.wisconsinhistory.org/libraryarchives. *Dir,* Peter Gottlieb; *Dep Dir,*
Michael Edmonds; *Pub Serv, Ref Serv,* Richard Pifer; Staff 34 (MLS 19,
Non-MLS 15)
Founded 1847
Library Holdings: Bk Vols 4,100,000
Subject Interests: Ethnic hist, Labor hist, Mil hist, Minority hist,
Numismatics, Philately, Reform movements, Relig, Relig hist, Women's
hist
Automation Activity & Vendor Info: (Cataloging) Ex Libris Group;
(OPAC) Ex Libris Group
Wireless access

Partic in Center for Research Libraries; Coun of Wis Librs, Inc; OCLC Online Computer Library Center, Inc
Special Services for the Deaf - TTY equip
Open Mon-Thurs 8am-9pm, Fri & Sat 8-5

G   WISCONSIN LEGISLATIVE REFERENCE BUREAU, Research and Library Services, One E Main St, 53703-3373. (Mail add: PO Box 2037, 53701-2037), SAN 318-1332. Reference Tel: 608-266-0341. FAX: 608-266-5648. Web Site: lrbcat.legis.wisconsin.gov/. *Mgr, Libr & Res Serv,* Julie Pohlman; *Sr Legis Librn,* Patricia Reichert; *Legis Librn,* Eileen Snyder. Subject Specialists: *Cataloging,* Patricia Reichert; *Electronic resources, Govt doc,* Eileen Snyder; Staff 7 (MLS 6, Non-MLS 1)
Founded 1901
Library Holdings: Bk Titles 100,000
Special Collections: Bill Drafting Records, files, micro; Bill Index, 1897-present; Clipping Coll, 1900-present; Wisconsin Bills, 1897-present; Wisconsin State Government Documents. State Document Depository
Subject Interests: Conserv, Constitutional revision, Crime, Educ, Energy, Fed govt relating to state legislation, Judiciary, Labor relations, Legislation, Local govt relating to state legislation, Pollution control, State finance, State govt legislative proc, Taxation, Transportation, Welfare
Automation Activity & Vendor Info: (Cataloging) Innovative Interfaces, Inc - Millenium; (Circulation) Innovative Interfaces, Inc - Millenium; (ILL) OCLC; (OPAC) Innovative Interfaces, Inc - Millenium; (Serials) Innovative Interfaces, Inc - Millenium
Database Vendor: OCLC
Wireless access
Publications: Index to Bulletin of Proceedings; Informational Bulletins, Wisconsin Briefs (on assorted topics relating to state government & state legislation); Tap the Power: annotated bibliographies (Acquisition list); Wisconsin Blue Book (biennial)
Open Mon-Fri 7:45-5

M   WISCONSIN MEDICAL SOCIETY LIBRARY*, 330 E Lakeside St, 53715-2074. (Mail add: PO Box 1109, 53701-1109), SAN 318-1235. Tel: 608-442-3800. Toll Free Tel: 866-442-3800. FAX: 608-442-3802. Web Site: www.wisconsinmedicalsociety.org. *In Charge,* Kendi Parvin; E-mail: kendip@wismed.org
Founded 1841
Library Holdings: Bk Vols 100; Per Subs 50
Restriction: Not open to pub

G   WISCONSIN STATE DEPARTMENT OF TRANSPORTATION LIBRARY*, 4802 Sheboygan Ave, Rm 100A, 53707. (Mail add: PO Box 7957, 53707-7957), SAN 364-9296. Tel: 608-264-8142. FAX: 608-261-6306. E-mail: library@dot.wi.gov. Web Site: dot.wi.gov/library. *Head Librn, Webmaster,* John Cherney; E-mail: john.cherney@dot.wi.gov; Staff 2 (MLS 1.5, Non-MLS 0.5)
Founded 1967
Library Holdings: Bk Vols 43,000; Per Subs 350
Special Collections: Regional Planning Commission Reports; Traffic Accident Facts from the 50 States; Transportation (Transportation Research Board)
Subject Interests: Air transportation, Construction, Eng, Evaluation, Hwy transportation, Rail transportation, Transportation
Automation Activity & Vendor Info: (Cataloging) OCLC
Database Vendor: TLC (The Library Corporation)
Partic in OCLC Online Computer Library Center, Inc; Wiscat
Open Mon-Fri 8:30-5

S   WISCONSIN STATE JOURNAL - CAPITAL TIMES LIBRARY*, 1901 Fish Hatchery Rd, 53713. (Mail add: PO Box 8060, 53708), SAN 318-1367. Tel: 608-252-6412. FAX: 608-252-6119. E-mail: lybrary@madison.com. Web Site: www.madison.com. *Dir,* Ronald J Larson; E-mail: rlarson@madison.com; Staff 4 (MLS 1, Non-MLS 3)
Library Holdings: Bk Vols 700
Subject Interests: Current events
Function: Archival coll, Res libr
Partic in Dialog Corp; Dow Jones News Retrieval; LexisNexis; News Bank; News Libr; ProQuest
Special Services for the Blind - Newsline for the Blind
Restriction: Open by appt only

GL   WISCONSIN STATE LAW LIBRARY, 120 Martin Luther King Jr Blvd, 2nd Flr, 53703. (Mail add: PO Box 7881, 53707-7881). Tel: 608-266-1600. Reference Tel: 608-267-9696. Toll Free Tel: 800-322-9755. FAX: 608-267-2319. E-mail: wsll.ref@wicourts.gov. Web Site: wilawlibrary.gov. *State Law Librn,* Julie A Tessmer; Tel: 608-261-2340, E-mail: julie.tessmer@wicourts.gov; *Dep Law Librn,* Amy Witt Crowder; Tel: 608-267-2253, E-mail: amy.crowder@wicourts.gov; *Dir of Ref & Outreach Serv,* Connie Von Der Heide; Tel: 608-267-2202, E-mail: connie.vonderheide@wicourts.gov; Staff 12.5 (MLS 8, Non-MLS 4.5)
Founded 1836
Library Holdings: e-journals 8,000; Bk Vols 150,000; Per Subs 500

Special Collections: Prose & Cons Legal Fiction Coll; Wisconsin Administrative Code Replaced Pages, 1950-Present; Wisconsin Appendices & Briefs, 1836-Present; Wisconsin Court of Appeals Unpublished Opinions, 1978-Present; Wisconsin Judicial Council Coll. US Document Depository
Subject Interests: Court decisions, Fed govt, Govt doc, Legal per, Legal texts, State govt, Statutes
Automation Activity & Vendor Info: (Acquisitions) Innovative Interfaces, Inc; (Cataloging) Innovative Interfaces, Inc; (Circulation) Innovative Interfaces, Inc; (ILL) OCLC Online; (OPAC) Innovative Interfaces, Inc; (Serials) Innovative Interfaces, Inc
Database Vendor: Gale Cengage Learning, HeinOnline, LexisNexis, OCLC FirstSearch, OCLC WorldCat, SerialsSolutions, Westlaw
Wireless access
Function: Audio & video playback equip for onsite use, Computer training, Doc delivery serv, e-mail serv, Fax serv, ILL available, Mail & tel request accepted, Online searches, Orientations, Ref serv available, Referrals accepted, Telephone ref
Publications: WSLL @ Your Service (Monthly newsletter); WSLL Manual, 2008 (Library handbook)
Partic in OCLC Online Computer Library Center, Inc; Westlaw
Open Mon-Fri 8-5
Restriction: Circ limited
Branches:
DANE COUNTY LEGAL RESOURCE CENTER, Courthouse Rm L1007, 215 S Hamilton St, 53703, SAN 321-9941. Tel: 608-266-6316. FAX: 608-266-5988. E-mail: dclrc.ref@wicourts.gov. Web Site: wilawlibrary.gov. *Br Librn,* Lisa Winkler; E-mail: lisa.winkler@wicourts.gov; Staff 1.5 (MLS 1, Non-MLS 0.5)
  Function: Copy machines, Electronic databases & coll, Mail & tel request accepted, Ref serv available, Referrals accepted, Telephone ref
  Publications: Dane County Landlord/Tenant Legal Resource Guide (Reference guide); Directory of Wisconsin Law Libraries Open to the Public (Reference guide); Guide to Low-Cost Legal Assistance in Dane County (Reference guide)
  Open Mon-Fri 8:30-4:30
  Restriction: Circ limited, Non-circulating to the pub
MILWAUKEE LEGAL RESOURCE CENTER, Courthouse, Rm 307A, 901 N Ninth St, Milwaukee, 53233. Tel: 414-278-4900. FAX: 414-223-1818. *Br Librn,* Lynne Gehrke; E-mail: lynne.gehrke@wicourts.gov; Staff 2.5 (MLS 1, Non-MLS 1.5)
  Function: Copy machines, Handicapped accessible, Mail & tel request accepted, Ref serv available, Referrals accepted, Telephone ref
  Open Mon-Fri 8-4:30
  Restriction: Circ limited, Non-circulating to the pub

MANAWA

P   STURM MEMORIAL LIBRARY*, 130 N Bridge St, 54949-9517. (Mail add: PO Box 20, 54949-0020), SAN 318-1405. Tel: 920-596-2252. FAX: 920-596-2234. E-mail: man@mail.owls.lib.wi.us. *Dir,* Ellen L Connor; E-mail: econnor@mail.owls.lib.wi.us
Founded 1910. Pop 2,582; Circ 29,000
Library Holdings: Bk Vols 22,000; Per Subs 60
Subject Interests: Fishing, Hunting, Rodeos, Wis, World War II
Database Vendor: netLibrary
Mem of Outagamie Waupaca Library System
Open Mon, Tues, Thurs & Fri 9:30-5:30, Wed 9:30-8, Sat (Winter) 9-12

MANITOWISH WATERS

P   FRANK B KOLLER MEMORIAL LIBRARY*, 51S02 Hwy 51, 54545. (Mail add: PO Box 100, 54545-0100), SAN 376-6659. Tel: 715-543-2700. FAX: 715-543-2700. Web Site: koller.wislib.org. *Dir,* Janelle M Kohl; E-mail: jkohl@koller.nwls.lib.wi.us
Pop 2,000; Circ 23,079
Jul 2005-Jun 2006 Income $120,170, State $422, City $50,105, Federal $839, County $2,600. Mats Exp $9,382, Books $7,699, AV Mat $1,650. Sal $35,000 (Prof $18,054)
Library Holdings: AV Mats 3,272; Large Print Bks 130; Bk Vols 24,400; Per Subs 69; Talking Bks 1,384
Subject Interests: Arts & crafts, Cooking, Popular fiction, World War II
Automation Activity & Vendor Info: (Cataloging) Innovative Interfaces, Inc; (Circulation) Innovative Interfaces, Inc; (ILL) Brodart; (OPAC) Innovative Interfaces, Inc
Database Vendor: EBSCOhost
Wireless access
Mem of Northern Waters Library Service
Partic in Merlin
Open Mon, Wed & Fri (Winter) 9-3, Tues & Thurs 3-7, Sat 9-12; Mon, Wed & Fri (Summer) 9-3, Tues & Thurs 3-8, Sat 9-1
Friends of the Library Group

MANITOWOC

M HOLY FAMILY MEMORIAL*, Health Sciences Library, 2300 Western Ave, 54220-3712. (Mail add: PO Box 1450, 54221-1450), SAN 318-1413. Tel: 920-684-2260. FAX: 920-684-2009. *Librn,* Dan Eckert; E-mail: deckert@hfmhealth.org; Staff 2 (MLS 1, Non-MLS 1)
Founded 1975. Pop 80,000
Library Holdings: AV Mats 200; Bk Titles 2,500; Bk Vols 3,000; Per Subs 200
Subject Interests: Clinical med, Hospital admin, Nursing
Publications: Newsletter
Partic in Docline; Fox River Valley Area Library Consortium; Wiscat

P MANITOWOC PUBLIC LIBRARY*, 707 Quay St, 54220. SAN 318-143X. Tel: 920-686-3000. E-mail: mplref@manitowoc.org. Web Site: www.manitowoclibrary.org. *Dir,* Cherilyn Stewart; *Youth Serv Mgr,* Ann Herrmann; *Coll Develop Coordr,* David J Ellison; *Coordr, Pub Serv,* Rachel Muchin Young; *Coordr, Tech Serv,* Cheryl Nessman; Staff 5 (MLS 5)
Founded 1900. Pop 58,213; Circ 674,092
Library Holdings: Bk Vols 200,185; Per Subs 359
Special Collections: Art & Gardening (Ruth West Library of Beauty); Behnke Historic Photo Coll; World War II Personal Narratives. Oral History; State Document Depository
Subject Interests: Submarines
Automation Activity & Vendor Info: (Acquisitions) SirsiDynix; (Circulation) SirsiDynix; (Serials) SirsiDynix
Database Vendor: EBSCO Information Services, ProQuest, ReferenceUSA
Wireless access
Publications: Newsletter
Mem of Manitowoc-Calumet Library System
Partic in OCLC Online Computer Library Center, Inc
Open Mon-Thurs 9-8, Fri 9-6, Sat 9-5, Sun 12-4
Friends of the Library Group

CR SILVER LAKE COLLEGE, Erma M & Theodore M Zigmunt Library, 2406 S Alverno Rd, 54220. SAN 318-1448. Tel: 920-686-6174. Interlibrary Loan Service Tel: 920-686-6212. FAX: 920-684-7082. E-mail: slclibrary@silver.sl.edu. Web Site: www.sl.edu/library. *Dir, Libr Serv,* Sister Ritarose Stahl; Tel: 920-686-6134, E-mail: ritarose.stahl@sl.edu; *Dir, Access Serv, ILL,* Lisa Kliment; E-mail: lisa.kliment@sl.edu; *Tech Serv Mgr,* Sister Helen Marie Paul; Tel: 920-686-6171, E-mail: helenmarie.paul@sl.edu; *Pub Serv Asst,* Shawn Linsmeier; Tel: 920-686-6145, E-mail: shawn.linsmeier@sl.edu. Subject Specialists: *Children's lit,* Sister Ritarose Stahl; Staff 4 (MLS 2, Non-MLS 2)
Founded 1935. Enrl 690; Fac 110; Highest Degree: Master
Jul 2012-Jun 2013 Income $177,884, Federal $6,525, Parent Institution $171,359. Mats Exp $59,000, Books $11,980, Per/Ser (Incl. Access Fees) $12,000, Other Print Mats $1,720, AV Mat $1,050, Electronic Ref Mat (Incl. Access Fees) $32,250. Sal $107,978 (Prof $62,989)
Library Holdings: AV Mats 13,149; CDs 1,043; DVDs 573; Large Print Bks 28; Music Scores 945; Bk Vols 61,393; Per Subs 184; Videos 1,467
Special Collections: Kodaly Music
Subject Interests: Educ, Juv lit, Music, Rare bks
Automation Activity & Vendor Info: (Acquisitions) Innovative Interfaces, Inc; (Cataloging) Innovative Interfaces, Inc; (Circulation) Innovative Interfaces, Inc; (Course Reserve) Innovative Interfaces, Inc; (ILL) OCLC; (OPAC) Innovative Interfaces, Inc; (Serials) Innovative Interfaces, Inc
Database Vendor: Cinahl Information Systems, EBSCOhost, Innovative Interfaces, Inc INN - View, JSTOR, ProQuest
Wireless access
Function: Bks on cassette, Computers for patron use, Copy machines, Fax serv, Free DVD rentals, Handicapped accessible, ILL available, Music CDs, Online cat, Online info literacy tutorials on the web & in blackboard, Orientations, Photocopying/Printing, Ref serv available, Scanner, VHS videos, Video lending libr, Wheelchair accessible
Publications: Acquisition List
Partic in Wiscat
Open Mon-Thurs (Winter) 8am-8:30pm, Fri 8-4, Sat 12-4; Mon-Fri (Summer) 9-4
Restriction: Non-circulating coll, Non-circulating of rare bks

S WISCONSIN MARITIME MUSEUM*, Library & Archives, 75 Maritime Dr, 54220. SAN 326-5129. Tel: 920-684-0218. Toll Free Tel: 1-866-724-2356. FAX: 920-684-0219. E-mail: museum@wisconsinmaritime.org. Web Site: www.wisconsinmaritime.org. *Coll Mgr,* Cristin J Waterbury; E-mail: museum@wisconsinmaritime.org
Founded 1969
Special Collections: 20th Century Great Lakes Ship Construction (Burger Boat Company Coll), blueprints, mss, photos; Captain Timothy Kelley Family Coll, 1870-1943, diaries; Early Great Lakes Shipping (Carus Section of Henry N Barkhausen Coll), mss, photos; Great Lakes Maritime History (Henry N Barkhausen Coll), art, bks, photos; Great Lakes Ship Logs, 19th-20th Centuries; Kahlenberg Coll, affidavits, cats, photos, sales

bulletins; Manitowoc Company Coll, blueprints, mss, photos; Maritime History Rare Book Coll, Early 19th-Early 20th Centuries; Wooden Shipbuilding Coll, art, plans, vessel lists; World War II Ship Construction (Berns Photographic Coll); World War II Submarine USS Cobia Coll, blueprints, manuals, tech guides
Subject Interests: Great Lakes maritime hist
By appointment only

MARINETTE

L MARINETTE COUNTY LAW LIBRARY*, 1926 Hall Ave, 54143-1717. SAN 327-6724. Tel: 715-732-7449, 715-732-7450. *Dir,* Tim Duket
Library Holdings: Bk Vols 1,000
Open Mon-Fri 8:30-4:30

P MARINETTE COUNTY LIBRARY SYSTEM*, Stephenson Public Library, 1700 Hall Ave, 54143-1799. SAN 318-1480. Tel: 715-732-7570. FAX: 715-732-7575. E-mail: mrt@mail.nfls.lib.wi.us. Web Site: www.marinettecountylibraries.org. *Dir,* Jennifer Thiele; Tel: 715-732-7572, E-mail: jthiele@mail.nfls.lib.wi.us
Pop 42,000; Circ 378,319
Library Holdings: Bk Vols 200,000; Per Subs 550
Special Collections: Marinette history
Automation Activity & Vendor Info: (Cataloging) Innovative Interfaces, Inc; (Circulation) Innovative Interfaces, Inc; (OPAC) Innovative Interfaces, Inc; (Serials) Innovative Interfaces, Inc
Mem of Nicolet Federated Library System
Open Mon-Thurs (Winter) 9-9, Fri 9-6, Sat 9-5; Mon-Wed (Summer) 9-6, Thurs 9-8, Fri 9-5, Sat 9-Noon
Friends of the Library Group
Branches: 6
COLEMAN PUBLIC LIBRARY, 123 W Main St, Coleman, 54112, SAN 329-6466. Tel: 920-897-2400. FAX: 920-897-2400. E-mail: col@mail.nfls.lib.wi.us. *Librn,* Dorothy Kaminsk; E-mail: dkaminsk@mail.nfls.lib.wi.us
Open Mon, Wed & Fri 9-5:30
Friends of the Library Group
CRIVITZ PUBLIC LIBRARY, 606 Louisa St, Crivitz, 54114. (Mail add: PO Box 100, Crivitz, 54114-0100), SAN 324-038X. Tel: 715-854-7562. FAX: 715-854-7562. E-mail: cri@mail.nfls.lib.wi.us. *Librn,* Cyndie Shaffer; E-mail: cshaffer@mail.nfls.lib.wi.us
Open Mon & Wed-Fri 9-5
GOODMAN LIBRARY STATION, One Falcon Crest, Goodman, 54125. (Mail add: PO Box 160, Goodman, 54125-0160), SAN 323-5637. Tel: 715-336-2575. FAX: 715-336-2576. E-mail: goo@mail.nfls.lib.wi.us. *Librn,* Bruce Darne; E-mail: bdarne@mail.nfls.lib.wi.us
Open Thurs 3:30-6:30
NIAGARA PUBLIC LIBRARY, 1029 Roosevelt Rd, Niagara, 54151-1205. (Mail add: PO Box 108, Niagara, 54151-0108), SAN 318-2940. Tel: 715-251-3236. FAX: 715-251-3236. E-mail: nia@mail.nfls.lib.wi.us. Web Site: www.nfls.lib.wi.us/mrt/nia.htm. *Librn,* Bruce Darne
Open Mon 11-6, Tues 1-6, Wed 9-12 & 1-5, Fri 1-5
Friends of the Library Group
PESHTIGO PUBLIC LIBRARY, 331 French St, Peshtigo, 54157-1219. (Mail add: PO Box 155, Peshtigo, 54157-0155), SAN 318-3203. Tel: 715-582-4905. FAX: 715-582-4905. E-mail: pes@mail.nfls.lib.wi.us. *Librn,* Jenny Hipke; E-mail: jhipke@mail.nfls.lib.wi.us
Open Mon, Wed & Fri 9-6
WAUSAUKEE PUBLIC LIBRARY, 911 Cedar St, Wausaukee, 54177. (Mail add: PO Box 139, Wausaukee, 54177-0139), SAN 324-0398. Tel: 715-856-5995. FAX: 715-856-5995. E-mail: was@mail.nfls.lib.wi.us. *Librn,* Karen Kortbein; E-mail: kkortbein@mail.nfls.lib.wi.us
Open Mon, Wed & Fri 9-6
Friends of the Library Group

J UNIVERSITY OF WISCONSIN*, Marinette Library, 750 W Bay Shore, 54141-1299. SAN 318-1502. Tel: 715-735-4306. FAX: 715-735-4307. *Dir,* Constance V Scofield; E-mail: cscofiel@uwc.edu; Staff 1 (MLS 1)
Founded 1965. Enrl 551; Fac 30; Highest Degree: Associate
Library Holdings: Bk Titles 24,697; Bk Vols 29,000; Per Subs 189
Special Collections: Naval Architecture & Boating (Clinton F DeWitt Coll)
Automation Activity & Vendor Info: (Acquisitions) Ex Libris Group; (Cataloging) Ex Libris Group; (Circulation) Ex Libris Group; (Course Reserve) Ex Libris Group; (OPAC) Ex Libris Group; (Serials) Ex Libris Group
Database Vendor: EBSCOhost, LexisNexis, ProQuest, Wilson - Wilson Web
Partic in OCLC Online Computer Library Center, Inc
Open Mon-Thurs 8am-10pm, Fri 8-5, Sat 11:30-4, Sun 1-5

MARION

P　MARION PUBLIC LIBRARY*, 120 N Main, 54950. (Mail add: PO Box 267, 54950-0267), SAN 318-1510. Tel: 715-754-5368. FAX: 715-754-4610. Web Site: www.marionpubliclibrary.info/. *Dir,* Trinitie Wilke; *Asst Dir,* Bob Tomczyk; *Librn,* Gail Klemann; E-mail: gklemann@mail.owls.lib.wi.us; *Asst Librn,* Sharon Stuhr; E-mail: sstuhr@mail.owls.lib.wi.us
Founded 1924. Pop 1,300; Circ 35,000
Library Holdings: Bk Titles 23,000; Per Subs 30
Automation Activity & Vendor Info: (Cataloging) Infor Library & Information Solutions; (Circulation) Infor Library & Information Solutions; (OPAC) Infor Library & Information Solutions
Wireless access
Mem of Outagamie Waupaca Library System
Open Mon-Fri 9-5
Friends of the Library Group

MARSHALL

P　MARSHALL COMMUNITY LIBRARY*, 605 Waterloo Rd, 53559. SAN 318-1537. Tel: 608-655-3123. E-mail: marstf@scls.lib.wi.us. Web Site: www.marlib.org/. *Dir,* Diana Skalitzky; E-mail: dianas@scls.lib.wi.us; Staff 2 (MLS 1, Non-MLS 1)
Founded 1956. Pop 3,450; Circ 45,000
Library Holdings: Bks on Deafness & Sign Lang 20; Bk Vols 29,000; Per Subs 80
Subject Interests: Local hist
Automation Activity & Vendor Info: (Acquisitions) SirsiDynix; (Cataloging) SirsiDynix; (Circulation) SirsiDynix
Mem of South Central Library System
Open Mon-Wed 9-7, Thurs & Fri 9-5, Sat 9-3
Friends of the Library Group

MARSHFIELD

M　MARSHFIELD CLINIC*, George E Magnin Medical Library, 1000 N Oak Ave, 54449-5777. SAN 318-1545. Tel: 715-387-5183. FAX: 715-389-5366. Web Site: www.marshfieldclinic.kramesonline.com. *Mgr,* Alana Ziaya; Tel: 715-387-5184, E-mail: ziaya.alana@marshfieldclinic.org; *Ref Librn,* Barbara Bartkowiak; Tel: 715-389-4285; *Ref Librn,* Brian Finnegan; Tel: 715-389-5272; Staff 5 (MLS 2, Non-MLS 3)
Founded 1916
Library Holdings: e-books 100; Bk Vols 3,200; Per Subs 449
Special Collections: Biostatistics; Technical Writing
Subject Interests: Clinical med, Supporting sci
Partic in Regional Med Libr - Region 3
Open Mon-Fri 8-5

P　MARSHFIELD PUBLIC LIBRARY*, 211 E Second St, 54449. SAN 318-1553. Tel: 715-387-8494. FAX: 715-387-6909. E-mail: busoff@marshfieldlibrary.org. Web Site: www.marshfieldlibrary.org. *Dir,* Lori Belongia; Tel: 715-387-8494, Ext 214, E-mail: lbelongia@marshfieldlibrary.org; *Asst Dir, Head, Tech Serv,* Kathy Baker; Tel: 715-387-8494, Ext 213, E-mail: kbaker@marshfieldlibrary.org; *Head, Adult Serv,* Mary Adler; Tel: 715-387-8494, Ext 217, E-mail: madler@marshfieldlibrary.org; *Head, Ch,* Kim Ropson; Tel: 715-387-8494, Ext 218, E-mail: kropson@marshfieldlibrary.org; *Circ,* Rob Schultz; Tel: 715-387-8494, Ext 230, E-mail: rschultz@marshfieldlibrary.org; *Info Tech,* Rob Mader; Tel: 715-387-8494, Ext 232, E-mail: rmader@marshfieldlibrary.org; *ILL,* Patty Steele; Tel: 715-387-8494, Ext 233, E-mail: psteele@marshfieldlibrary.org; Staff 5 (MLS 4, Non-MLS 1)
Founded 1901. Pop 28,021; Circ 441,154
Jan 2010-Dec 2010 Income $1,591,672, City $1,268,744, Federal $1,300, County $197,134, Locally Generated Income $50,418, Other $74,076. Mats Exp $154,418, Books $120,629, AV Mat $27,334, Electronic Ref Mat (Incl. Access Fees) $6,455. Sal $726,283 (Prof $500,970)
Library Holdings: Audiobooks 3,406; CDs 5,141; DVDs 9,761; e-books 6,811; Electronic Media & Resources 95; High Interest/Low Vocabulary Bk Vols 336; Large Print Bks 3,295; Microforms 2,212; Music Scores 349; Bk Vols 116,199; Per Subs 233; Videos 5,948
Special Collections: Foreign Language (Spanish Coll)
Subject Interests: Genealogy, Local hist
Automation Activity & Vendor Info: (Acquisitions) Polaris Library Systems; (Cataloging) Polaris Library Systems; (Circulation) Polaris Library Systems; (ILL) Polaris Library Systems; (OPAC) Polaris Library Systems; (Serials) Polaris Library Systems
Database Vendor: ABC-CLIO, EBSCOhost, Gale Cengage Learning, netLibrary, OCLC FirstSearch, Overdrive, Inc, Polaris Library Systems, ProQuest, ReferenceUSA, SirsiDynix
Wireless access
Mem of South Central Library System
Partic in OCLC Online Computer Library Center, Inc; WILS
Special Services for the Deaf - Assistive tech; Closed caption videos; TTY equip; Videos & decoder
Special Services for the Blind - Assistive/Adapted tech devices, equip & products; Audio mat; Bks on CD; Cassette playback machines; Cassettes; Closed circuit TV magnifier; Copier with enlargement capabilities; Descriptive video serv (DVS); Home delivery serv; Internet workstation with adaptive software; Large print & cassettes; Large print bks; Low vision equip; Magnifiers; Talking bks; Videos on blindness & phys handicaps
Open Mon-Fri 9-8, Sat 9-5
Friends of the Library Group

J　MID-STATE TECHNICAL COLLEGE*, 2600 W Fifth St, 54449. SAN 318-1561. Tel: 715-389-7020. FAX: 715-389-2864. E-mail: librarymfcampus@mstc.edu. Web Site: www.mstc.edu/academics/library.htm. *Libr Serv Mgr,* Maria Hernandez; Tel: 715-422-5469, Fax: 715-422-5466, E-mail: maria.hernandez@mstc.edu
Library Holdings: Bk Titles 4,500; Per Subs 80
Automation Activity & Vendor Info: (Acquisitions) Ex Libris Group; (Cataloging) Ex Libris Group; (Circulation) Ex Libris Group; (Course Reserve) Docutek; (OPAC) Ex Libris Group
Database Vendor: Agricola, EBSCOhost, Facts on File, Grolier Online, H W Wilson, ProQuest, ReferenceUSA, Wilson - Wilson Web
Wireless access
Open Mon-Thurs 7:30-7:30, Fri 7:30-4

M　SAINT JOSEPH'S HOSPITAL*, Learning Resource Center, 611 Saint Joseph Ave, 54449. SAN 318-157X. Tel: 715-387-7374. FAX: 715-387-7107. *Asst Librn,* Patricia Ottelien; E-mail: patricia.ottelien@ministryhealth.org; *Syst Librn,* Marie Janz; Tel: 715-346-5090, Fax: 715-343-3246, E-mail: marie.janz@ministryhealth.org; Staff 2 (MLS 1, Non-MLS 1)
Founded 1918
Library Holdings: Bk Titles 7,300; Bk Vols 7,889; Per Subs 161
Special Collections: Nursing (Historical Coll)
Subject Interests: Consumer health, Nursing
Partic in Greater Midwest Regional Medical Libr Network; Medical Library Association (MLA); Wisconsin Valley Library Service

J　UNIVERSITY OF WISCONSIN*, Marshfield-Wood County Library, 2000 W Fifth St, 54449-3310. SAN 318-1588. Tel: 715-389-6512, 715-389-6531. FAX: 715-389-6539. Web Site: www.marshfield.uwc.edu. *Dir,* Ruth V Elberbrook; E-mail: relderbr@uwc.edu; *Assoc Librn,* Laurie Petri; E-mail: lpetri@uwc.edu; *Circ, ILL,* Judy Polege; E-mail: jpolege@uwc.edu; Staff 2 (MLS 2)
Founded 1964. Enrl 600; Highest Degree: Associate
Library Holdings: Bk Titles 29,156; Bk Vols 31,954; Per Subs 145
Automation Activity & Vendor Info: (Acquisitions) Ex Libris Group; (Cataloging) Ex Libris Group; (Circulation) Ex Libris Group; (Course Reserve) Ex Libris Group; (ILL) Ex Libris Group; (Media Booking) Ex Libris Group; (OPAC) Ex Libris Group; (Serials) Ex Libris Group
Database Vendor: EBSCOhost, netLibrary, OCLC FirstSearch, ProQuest, TLC (The Library Corporation), Wilson - Wilson Web
Partic in OCLC Online Computer Library Center, Inc; Wisconsin Library Services
Open Mon-Thurs 8-7, Fri 8-4

MAUSTON

P　HATCH PUBLIC LIBRARY*, 111 W State St, 53948-1344. SAN 318-1596. Tel: 608-847-4454. FAX: 608-847-2306. E-mail: maustonpl@wrlsweb.org. Web Site: www.hatchpubliclibrary.org. *Dir,* Bridget Christenson; E-mail: b.christenson@wrlsweb.org; *Youth Serv,* Debby Brooks; Staff 9 (Non-MLS 9)
Founded 1897. Pop 3,600; Circ 108,812
Library Holdings: Bks on Deafness & Sign Lang 25; High Interest/Low Vocabulary Bk Vols 600; Bk Vols 32,000; Per Subs 106
Subject Interests: Juneau County hist
Automation Activity & Vendor Info: (Cataloging) SirsiDynix; (Circulation) SirsiDynix
Mem of Winding Rivers Library System
Open Mon-Thurs 9-8, Fri 9-5, Sat 9-3
Friends of the Library Group

M　MILE BLUFF MEDICAL CENTER*, 1050 Division St, 53948. Tel: 608-847-6161. FAX: 608-847-6017. *Librn,* Martha Airth-Kindree; E-mail: mairth-kindree@milebluff.com
Library Holdings: Bk Titles 50; Bk Vols 300; Per Subs 150

MAYVILLE

P　MAYVILLE PUBLIC LIBRARY*, 111 N Main St, 53050. SAN 318-160X. Tel: 920-387-7910. FAX: 920-387-7917. E-mail: maylib@mwfls.org. Web Site: www.mayville.lib.wi.us. *Dir,* Alixe M Bielot; E-mail: alixe@mwfls.org; *Cataloger,* Rhonda Klemme; *Ch, ILL,* Sheila Steger; *Circ,* Linda Bath; *Circ,* Cindy Giese; *Circ, Tech Serv,* Yvonne Paulsen; Staff 6 (MLS 1, Non-MLS 5)

Founded 1904. Pop 5,240; Circ 71,138
Library Holdings: Bk Vols 57,000; Per Subs 120
Special Collections: Mayville News, 1906-Present
Automation Activity & Vendor Info: (Acquisitions) SirsiDynix;
(Cataloging) SirsiDynix; (Circulation) SirsiDynix
Database Vendor: SirsiDynix
Wireless access
Function: Copy machines, Homebound delivery serv, ILL available, Music
CDs, Newsp ref libr, Photocopying/Printing, Prog for children & young
adult, Spoken cassettes & CDs, Summer reading prog, Tax forms, Video
lending libr
Open Mon-Thurs (Winter) 11-8, Fri 11-6, Sat 9-3; Mon-Thurs (Summer)
11-8, Fri 11-6

MAZOMANIE

P   MAZOMANIE FREE LIBRARY*, 102 Brodhead St, 53560. (Mail add:
PO Box 458, 53560-0458), SAN 318-1618. Tel: 608-795-2104. FAX:
608-795-2102. E-mail: mazlib@scls.lib.wi.us. Web Site:
www.scls.lib.wi.us/maz. *Dir,* Audrey Johnson; E-mail:
ajohnson@scls.lib.wi.us; Staff 3 (MLS 1, Non-MLS 2)
Founded 1899
Library Holdings: Bk Vols 18,000; Per Subs 59
Subject Interests: Genealogy, Local hist
Automation Activity & Vendor Info: (Cataloging) SirsiDynix;
(Circulation) SirsiDynix
Mem of South Central Library System
Open Mon-Thurs 10-12 & 2-7, Fri 10-5, Sat 10-1
Friends of the Library Group

MCFARLAND

P   MCFARLAND PUBLIC LIBRARY*, E D Locke Public Library, 5920
Milwaukee St, 53558-8962. SAN 337-9343. Tel: 608-838-9243. E-mail:
mcflib@scls.lib.wi.us. Web Site: www.scls.lib.wi.us/mcf/index.html. *Dir,*
Shelley Selle; E-mail: shelley@scls.lib.wi.us
Founded 1997
Library Holdings: Bk Vols 30,900; Per Subs 118
Mem of South Central Library System
Open Mon-Thurs 9-9, Fri & Sat 9-5:30, Sun 12-3
Friends of the Library Group

MEDFORD

P   FRANCES L SIMEK MEMORIAL LIBRARY-MEDFORD*, 400 N Main,
54451. SAN 318-1626. Tel: 715-748-2505. FAX: 715-748-4160. E-mail:
medref@wvls.lib.wi.us. Web Site: www.sws-wis.com/medfordpubliclibrary.
Dir, Ann Harris; E-mail: harris@wvls.lib.wi.us; *Librn,* Marlene Klemm;
E-mail: mklemm@wvls.lib.wi.us; *Tech Support Analyst,* Jenny Rundquist
Founded 1916. Pop 13,900; Circ 115,000
Library Holdings: Bk Titles 43,000; Per Subs 110
Automation Activity & Vendor Info: (Cataloging) SirsiDynix;
(Circulation) SirsiDynix
Mem of Wisconsin Valley Library Service
Open Mon-Thurs 9-8, Fri 9-6, Sat (Winter) 9-2:30
Friends of the Library Group

MELLEN

P   LEGION MEMORIAL LIBRARY*, 102 E Bennett Ave, 54546. (Mail add:
PO Box 47, 54546-0047), SAN 318-1642. Tel: 715-274-8331. FAX:
715-274-3707. Web Site: nwls.wislib.org/about/libme.htm. *Dir,* Jennifer
Thewis; E-mail: jennie@legionmem.nwls.lib.wi.us
Founded 1929. Pop 2,000; Circ 11,000
Library Holdings: Bk Titles 8,000; Per Subs 40
Automation Activity & Vendor Info: (Cataloging) Innovative Interfaces,
Inc; (Circulation) Innovative Interfaces, Inc; (OPAC) Innovative Interfaces,
Inc
Publications: Booklist
Mem of Northern Waters Library Service
Open Mon-Thurs 9-12 & 2-6, Fri & Sat 9-12
Friends of the Library Group

MENASHA

P   MENASHA PUBLIC LIBRARY*, Elisha D Smith Public Library, 440
First St, 54952-3191. SAN 318-1650. Tel: 920-967-3660. Circulation Tel:
920-967-3680. Reference Tel: 920-967-3690. FAX: 920-967-5159. E-mail:
reference@menashalibrary.org. Web Site: www.menashalibrary.org. *Dir,*
Tasha Saecker; Tel: 920-967-3661, E-mail: tasha@menashalibrary.org; *Acq,
Head, Adult Serv, Ref Serv,* Joe Bongers; E-mail:
bongers@menashalibrary.org; *Head, Circ,* Catherine Brandt; E-mail:
brandt@menashalibrary.org; *Head, Ch,* Kathy Beson; Tel: 920-967-3671,
E-mail: kbeson@menashalibrary.org; *Ref Serv Coordr,* Kathleen Hannah;
Tel: 920-967-3692, E-mail: hannah@menashalibrary.org; *Adult Ref,* Ana

Acosta; *Ref,* Patricia Stanislowski; *YA Serv,* Vanessa Taylir; Staff 34 (MLS
6, Non-MLS 28)
Founded 1896. Pop 25,000; Circ 290,000
Library Holdings: Bks on Deafness & Sign Lang 35; High Interest/Low
Vocabulary Bk Vols 50; Bk Vols 140,000; Per Subs 200
Subject Interests: Local hist
Automation Activity & Vendor Info: (Acquisitions) SirsiDynix;
(Cataloging) SirsiDynix; (Circulation) SirsiDynix; (Course Reserve)
SirsiDynix; (ILL) SirsiDynix; (Media Booking) SirsiDynix; (OPAC)
SirsiDynix; (Serials) SirsiDynix
Database Vendor: Gale Cengage Learning, SirsiDynix
Wireless access
Function: Archival coll
Mem of Winnefox Library System
Open Mon-Thurs 8:30-8:30, Fri 8:30-6, Sat 8:30-4:30, Sun 1-5
Friends of the Library Group

J   UNIVERSITY OF WISCONSIN-FOX VALLEY LIBRARY*, 1478
Midway Rd, 54952-1297. SAN 318-1669. Tel: 920-832-2672. Interlibrary
Loan Service Tel: 920-832-2673. Reference Tel: 920-832-2676. FAX:
920-832-2874. Web Site: www.uwfoxvalley.uwc.edu. *Dir,* April
Kain-Breese; Tel: 920-832-2675, E-mail: april.kain-breese@uwc.edu; *Circ,*
Marketta Helen; E-mail: marketta.helen@uwc.edu; *Circ,* John Wisneski;
E-mail: john.wisneski@uwc.edu; *ILL, Ref Serv,* Christine Chamness;
E-mail: chris.chamness@uwc.edu; Staff 4 (MLS 2, Non-MLS 2)
Founded 1937. Enrl 1,700; Fac 63; Highest Degree: Associate
Library Holdings: Bks on Deafness & Sign Lang 13; Bk Titles 30,188;
Bk Vols 34,716; Per Subs 178
Automation Activity & Vendor Info: (Acquisitions) Ex Libris Group;
(Cataloging) Ex Libris Group; (Circulation) Ex Libris Group; (Course
Reserve) Ex Libris Group; (ILL) Ex Libris Group; (Media Booking) Ex
Libris Group; (OPAC) Ex Libris Group
Partic in Fox Valley Library Council; OCLC Online Computer Library
Center, Inc; Wisconsin Library Services
Special Services for the Blind - Magnifiers
Open Mon-Thurs (Winter) 8am-9pm, Fri 8-4, Sun 5-9; Mon-Thurs
(Summer) 8-6, Fri 8-4

MENOMONEE FALLS

M   COMMUNITY MEMORIAL HOSPITAL*, McKay Memorial Library,
W180 N8085 Town Hall Rd, 53051-3558. (Mail add: PO Box 408,
53052-0408), SAN 324-721X. Tel: 262-257-3440. FAX: 262-257-3311.
Librn, Bea Keppel; E-mail: bkeppel@communitymemorial.com
Library Holdings: Bk Titles 360; Per Subs 200
Subject Interests: Hospital admin, Med, Nursing
Publications: Acquisitions list (annual); serial holdings list; VC list
Partic in Greater Midwest Regional Medical Libr Network; Southeastern
Wisconsin Health Science Library Consortium
Restriction: Staff use only

P   MENOMONEE FALLS PUBLIC LIBRARY*, W156 N8436 Pilgrim Rd,
53051. SAN 318-1677. Tel: 262-532-8900. FAX: 262-532-8939. Web Site:
www.mf.lib.wi.us. *Dir,* Jane Schall; E-mail: jaschall@mf.lib.wi.us; *Asst
Dir/Bus Mgr,* Mari Schmidt; *Pub Serv Mgr, Teen Librn,* Kifflie Scott; *Info
Tech Mgr,* Robert Rapp; *Ch, Youth Serv,* Kris Stabo; *ILL,* Sandy Stein; *Ref
Serv, Ad,* Karen Esvang; Staff 7 (MLS 5, Non-MLS 2)
Founded 1906. Pop 32,000; Circ 372,000
Library Holdings: Bk Vols 140,000; Per Subs 362
Special Collections: Historical Photograph Coll; Menomonee Falls Local
History
Automation Activity & Vendor Info: (Acquisitions) Innovative Interfaces,
Inc; (Cataloging) Innovative Interfaces, Inc; (Circulation) Innovative
Interfaces, Inc; (Course Reserve) Innovative Interfaces, Inc; (ILL)
Innovative Interfaces, Inc; (Media Booking) Innovative Interfaces, Inc;
(OPAC) Innovative Interfaces, Inc; (Serials) Innovative Interfaces, Inc
Wireless access
Mem of Waukesha County Federated Library System
Partic in OCLC Online Computer Library Center, Inc
Open Mon-Thurs 9-9, Fri & Sat 9-5
Friends of the Library Group

MENOMONIE

P   MENOMONIE PUBLIC LIBRARY, 600 Wolske Bay Rd, 54751. SAN
318-1685. Tel: 715-232-2164. FAX: 715-232-2324. E-mail:
info@menomonielibrary.org, starkt@menomonielibrary.org. Web Site:
www.menomonielibrary.org. *Dir,* Ted Stark; E-mail:
starkt@menomonielibrary.org; *Asst Dir,* Helen Hullberg; Staff 15.5 (MLS
2, Non-MLS 13.5)
Founded 1874. Pop 35,000; Circ 399,000
Jan 2011-Dec 2011 Income $1,002,321, City $438,700, County $445,734,
Locally Generated Income $117,887. Mats Exp $110,000, Books $80,000,
AV Mat $30,000. Sal $70,000
Library Holdings: Bk Vols 54,000; Per Subs 120

Automation Activity & Vendor Info: (Acquisitions) Innovative Interfaces, Inc - Millenium; (Cataloging) Innovative Interfaces, Inc - Millenium; (Circulation) Innovative Interfaces, Inc - Millenium; (ILL) Innovative Interfaces, Inc - Millenium; (OPAC) Innovative Interfaces, Inc - Millenium; (Serials) Innovative Interfaces, Inc - Millenium
Database Vendor: BookLetters LLC, EBSCOhost
Wireless access
Function: Adult bk club, Adult literacy prog, After school storytime, Audiobks via web, Bk club(s), Bks on CD, Children's prog, Computer training, Computers for patron use, Copy machines, Digital talking bks, E-Reserves, Family literacy, Free DVD rentals, Handicapped accessible, ILL available, Magnifiers for reading, Microfiche/film & reading machines, Music CDs, Prog for adults, Prog for children & young adult, Pub access computers, Ref serv available, Senior computer classes, Spoken cassettes & CDs, Spoken cassettes & DVDs, Summer reading prog, Tax forms, Teen prog, Telephone ref, Video lending libr, Web-catalog, Wheelchair accessible, Workshops
Mem of Indianhead Federated Library System
Special Services for the Deaf - Adult & family literacy prog; Assisted listening device; Assistive tech; TDD equip
Special Services for the Blind - Bks on CD; Copier with enlargement capabilities; Large print bks & talking machines; Large screen computer & software; Magnifiers; Playaways (bks on MP3); Recorded bks; Ref serv; Talking bks
Open Mon-Thurs 10-9ï¿½ Fri 10-6ï¿½ Sat 10-5ï¿½ Sun 1-5
Friends of the Library Group

C   UNIVERSITY OF WISCONSIN-STOUT LIBRARY*, 315 Tenth Ave, 54751-0790. Tel: 715-232-1215. Interlibrary Loan Service Tel: 715-232-1112. Reference Tel: 715-232-1353. FAX: 715-232-1783. Interlibrary Loan Service FAX: 715-232-2618. TDD: 715-232-1333. E-mail: library@uwstout.edu. Web Site: www.uwstout.edu/lib. *Interim Dir,* William L Johnston; Tel: 715-232-1184, E-mail: johnstonw@uwstout.edu; *Dir, Instrul Res Serv,* Robert Butterfield; Tel: 715 232-2617, Fax: 715-232-1783, E-mail: butterfieldr@uwstout.edu; *Coll Develop/Educ Mat Ctr/Instruction Librn,* Cory Mitchell; Tel: 715 232-2363, E-mail: mitchellc@uwstout.edu; *Instrul Serv Librn, Ref Serv,* Jessica Polzer; Tel: 715-232-2141, E-mail: polzerj@uwstout.edu; *Libr Syst/Access Serv Mgr,* Susan Lindahl; Tel: 715-232-3382, E-mail: lindahls@uwstout.edu; *Interim Archivist,* Paul Roberts; Tel: 715-232-2300, E-mail: robertsp@uwstout.edu; *Cat,* Rebecca Peters; Tel: 715-232-2094; *Electronic Res,* Lelah Lugo; Tel: 715-232-1552, E-mail: lugola@uwstout.edu; *ILL,* Josh Steans; E-mail: steansj@uwstout.edu; *Ref Serv,* Carol Hagness; Tel: 715-232-1892, E-mail: hagnessc@uwstout.edu; *Ref Serv,* Jana Reeg-Steidinger; Tel: 715-232-1553, E-mail: reegj@uwstout.edu; Staff 23.25 (MLS 10.75, Non-MLS 12.5)
Founded 1891. Enrl 9,339; Fac 470; Highest Degree: Master
Jul 2010-Jul 2011. Mats Exp $703,000, Books $175,000, Per/Ser (Incl. Access Fees) $230,000, Micro $28,000, AV Mat $20,000, Electronic Ref Mat (Incl. Access Fees) $250,000
Library Holdings: AV Mats 14,533; e-books 203,504; e-journals 100,796; Microforms 1,292,457; Bk Vols 234,344; Per Subs 891
Special Collections: Oral History
Subject Interests: Consumer studies, Early childhood educ, Family studies, Hospitality, Indust tech, Manufacturing eng, Tourism, Vocational rehabilitation
Automation Activity & Vendor Info: (Acquisitions) Ex Libris Group; (Cataloging) Ex Libris Group; (Circulation) Ex Libris Group; (Course Reserve) Ex Libris Group; (ILL) Ex Libris Group; (Media Booking) Ex Libris Group; (OPAC) Ex Libris Group; (Serials) Ex Libris Group
Wireless access
Function: Art exhibits, Audio & video playback equip for onsite use, Bks on cassette, Bks on CD, Computers for patron use, Distance learning, e-mail & chat, E-Reserves, Electronic databases & coll, Free DVD rentals, ILL available, Large print keyboards, Magnifiers for reading, Mail & tel request accepted, Online cat, Online ref, Online searches, Ref & res, Ref serv available, Ref serv in person, Res libr, Telephone ref, VHS videos, Video lending libr, Wheelchair accessible
Partic in OCLC Online Computer Library Center, Inc
Special Services for the Deaf - TDD equip
Special Services for the Blind - Computer with voice synthesizer for visually impaired persons; Large screen computer & software; Reader equip

MEQUON

M   COLUMBIA ST MARY'S OZAUKEE CAMPUS*, Kacmarcik Education Resource Center, 13111 N Port Washington Rd, 53097. SAN 324-6981. Tel: 262-243-7448. E-mail: kacmarcik-library@columbia-stmarys.org. Web Site: www.stmarysfoundation-ozaukee.org/kacmarcik/index.cfm. *Librn,* Position Currently Open; Staff 1 (MLS 1)
Founded 2003
Library Holdings: AV Mats 100; Bk Titles 900; Per Subs 30
Subject Interests: Consumer health

Wireless access
Partic in Greater Midwest Regional Medical Libr Network; Southeastern Wisconsin Health Science Library Consortium

CR   CONCORDIA UNIVERSITY WISCONSIN*, Rincker Memorial Library, 12800 N Lake Shore Dr, 53097-2402. SAN 318-1901. Tel: 262-243-4330, 262-243-4403. Circulation Tel: 262-243-4420. Reference Tel: 262-243-4408. FAX: 262-243-4424. Web Site: www.cuw.edu/tools/library.html. *Dir,* Richard L Wohlers; E-mail: richard.wohlers@cuw.edu; *Instrul Serv Librn, Ref,* Christian Himsel; Tel: 262-243-4534; *Access Serv, ILL, Ref Serv,* Carol Mittag; E-mail: carol.mittag@cuw.edu; *Cat, Ref Serv,* Gae Kelly; Tel: 262-243-4402, E-mail: gae.kelly@cuw.edu; *Distance Educ, Ref Serv,* Karen Nowak; *Ref Serv, Ser,* Kathy Malland; Staff 11 (MLS 6, Non-MLS 5)
Founded 1881. Enrl 5,412; Highest Degree: Master
Library Holdings: Bk Vols 114,000; Per Subs 600
Special Collections: 16th & 17th Century Lutheran Theology; German Hymnals
Subject Interests: Church music, Educ, Nursing, Phys therapy, Theol
Automation Activity & Vendor Info: (OPAC) Innovative Interfaces, Inc
Database Vendor: EBSCOhost, Gale Cengage Learning, Innovative Interfaces, Inc INN - View, LexisNexis, OCLC FirstSearch, OVID Technologies, ProQuest, SirsiDynix
Function: Doc delivery serv, ILL available, Outside serv via phone, mail, e-mail & web, Ref serv available, Telephone ref
Publications: Library Communique (Newsletter)
Partic in Southeastern Wisconsin Information Technology Exchange, Inc; Wis Asn of Independent Cols & Univs; Wisconsin Library Services
Open Mon-Thurs (Fall & Spring) 7:30am-Midnight, Fri 7:30-6, Sat 9-5, Sun 12:30-Midnight; Mon-Thurs (Summer) 8-8, Fri 8-4:30, Sat 9-5

J   MILWAUKEE AREA TECHNICAL COLLEGE*, Mequon Campus Library, 5555 W Highland Rd, Rm A282, 53092-1199. SAN 318-1707. Tel: 262-238-2301. Web Site: library.matc.edu. *Head Librn,* Nick Jones; Tel: 262-238-2212, E-mail: jonesnc@matc.edu; *Circ, Ref Serv,* Matt Kawa; Tel: 262-238-2391; *Ref Serv,* Alexandra Koroscik; E-mail: koroscia@matc.edu; *Ref Serv,* Martha Starck; E-mail: starckm@matc.edu; Staff 4 (MLS 3, Non-MLS 1)
Founded 1977
Library Holdings: Bk Titles 16,500; Bk Vols 18,051; Per Subs 175
Subject Interests: Bus, Hort, Interior design, Landscape archit, Nursing, Philosophy, Sociol
Database Vendor: EBSCOhost, Gale Cengage Learning, ProQuest, SirsiDynix, Westlaw
Open Mon-Thurs 7:45am-9pm, Fri 7:45-4:30, Sat (Fall & Spring) 9-1
Restriction: Non-circulating to the pub

R   HORACE J & IDABELL ROSEN LIBRARY*, Beth El Ner Tamid Synagogue, 2909 W Mequon Rd, 53092. SAN 318-1863. Tel: 262-242-6900. FAX: 262-242-3952. *Librn,* Maggi Treager
Library Holdings: Bk Titles 3,000; Per Subs 15
Special Collections: Jewish Music Coll
Subject Interests: Jewish hist, Jewish lit, Judaism
Special Services for the Blind - Bks on cassette; Braille bks
Open Mon-Fri 8-5, Sun 10-12

P   FRANK L WEYENBERG LIBRARY OF MEQUON-THIENSVILLE, 11345 N Cedarburg Rd, 53092-1998. SAN 318-1715. Tel: 262-242-2593. FAX: 262-478-3200. E-mail: admin@flwlib.org. Web Site: www.flwlib.org. *Dir,* Linda Bendix; E-mail: director@flwlib.org; *Patron Serv Mgr,* Nyama Marsh; *Access Serv,* Pat Bluhm; E-mail: access@flwlib.org; Staff 4 (MLS 4)
Founded 1954. Pop 25,000; Circ 325,000
Library Holdings: Bk Vols 140,000; Per Subs 170
Special Collections: Local History of Mequon & Thiensville
Automation Activity & Vendor Info: (Acquisitions) Polaris Library Systems; (Cataloging) Polaris Library Systems; (Circulation) Polaris Library Systems; (OPAC) Polaris Library Systems; (Serials) Polaris Library Systems
Mem of Eastern Shores Library System
Open Mon-Thurs 10-8, Fri & Sat 10-6

R   WISCONSIN LUTHERAN SEMINARY LIBRARY, 6633 W Wartburg Circle, 53092-1530. SAN 318-1723. Tel: 262-242-8113. FAX: 262-242-8118. E-mail: library@wls.wels.net. Web Site: www.wls.wels.net. *Dir,* John P Hartwig; Staff 2 (MLS 2)
Founded 1878. Enrl 133; Fac 16; Highest Degree: Master
Library Holdings: Bk Vols 78,000; Per Subs 200
Subject Interests: Bible, Church hist, Doctrinal, Lutheran church, Practical theol, Relig studies
Wireless access

MERCER

P   MERCER PUBLIC LIBRARY*, 2648 W Margaret St, 54547. (Mail add: PO Box 561, 54547-0561). Tel: 715-476-2366. FAX: 715-476-2366. Web Site: www.nwls.lib.wi.us. *Dir,* Debbie Hohner; E-mail: dhohner@mercer.nwls.lib.wi.us
Founded 1940. Pop 3,000; Circ 10,300
Library Holdings: Bk Vols 6,756; Per Subs 26
Mem of Northern Waters Library Service
Open Mon, Wed & Fri (Winter) 9-5, Tues & Thurs 9-6, Sat 9-12; Mon-Thurs (Summer) 9-7, Fri 9-5, Sat 9-12
Friends of the Library Group

MERRILL

SR   OUR SAVIOUR'S LUTHERAN CHURCH LIBRARY*, 300 Logan, 54452. SAN 324-7228. Tel: 715-536-5813. FAX: 715-536-3658. *Librn,* Brenda Mueller
Library Holdings: Bk Titles 753; Bk Vols 763
Restriction: Mem only

P   T B SCOTT LIBRARY*, Merrill Public Library, 106 W First St, 54452-2398. SAN 318-174X. Tel: 715-536-7191. FAX: 715-536-1705. Web Site: wvls.lib.wi.us/merrillpl. *Dir,* Stacy Stevens; E-mail: stevens@wvls.lib.wi.us; *Asst Libr Dir, Head, Adult Serv,* Don Litzer; E-mail: dlitzer@wvls.lib.wi.us; *Head, Youth Serv,* Linda Schuster; E-mail: schuster@wvls.lib.wi.us; *Circ Coordr, Syst Adminr,* Eleanor Schwartz; E-mail: schwartz@wvls.lib.wi.us; Staff 21 (MLS 3, Non-MLS 18)
Founded 1891. Pop 21,000; Circ 297,563
Jan 2007-Dec 2007 Income $933,483, City $512,432, Federal $1,432, County $371,561, Locally Generated Income $21,500, Other $26,558. Mats Exp $102,199, Books $73,222, Per/Ser (Incl. Access Fees) $9,064, Micro $688, AV Mat $19,225. Sal $510,960
Library Holdings: Audiobooks 2,877; AV Mats 11,863; CDs 2,693; DVDs 1,713; Large Print Bks 4,657; Microforms 765; Bk Vols 95,500; Per Subs 177; Videos 3,939
Special Collections: Wisconsin & Local History
Automation Activity & Vendor Info: (Acquisitions) Horizon; (Circulation) Fretwell-Downing; (ILL) Auto-Graphics, Inc; (OPAC) SirsiDynix
Database Vendor: EBSCOhost, Gale Cengage Learning, netLibrary, OCLC WebJunction, Overdrive, Inc, P4 Performance Management, Inc, ProQuest, SirsiDynix
Wireless access
Function: Children's prog, Computer training, Computers for patron use, Copy machines, Digital talking bks, E-Reserves, Electronic databases & coll, Free DVD rentals, Games & aids for the handicapped, Genealogy discussion group, Handicapped accessible, Holiday prog, Home delivery & serv to Sr ctr & nursing homes, Homebound delivery serv, ILL available, Magnifiers for reading, Music CDs, Newsp ref libr, Online cat, Online searches, Orientations, Outreach serv, Outside serv via phone, mail, e-mail & web, OverDrive digital audio bks, Photocopying/Printing, Preschool outreach, Prof lending libr, Prog for adults, Prog for children & young adult, Pub access computers, Ref serv available, Senior computer classes, Senior outreach, Spoken cassettes & CDs, Spoken cassettes & DVDs, Story hour, Summer reading prog, Tax forms, Teen prog, Telephone ref, VHS videos, Video lending libr, Web-catalog, Wheelchair accessible
Special Services for the Deaf - ADA equip; Assistive tech; Bks on deafness & sign lang; Closed caption videos; High interest/low vocabulary bks; Sign lang interpreter upon request for prog; TDD equip
Special Services for the Blind - Braille music coll; Copier with enlargement capabilities; Large print bks; Low vision equip; Screen enlargement software for people with visual disabilities; Screen reader software; Talking bk serv referral; ZoomText magnification & reading software
Open Mon-Thurs (Winter) 9:30-8, Fri 9:30-6, Sat 9:30-4; Mon-Thurs (Summer) 9:30-8, Fri 9:30-5
Friends of the Library Group

R   TRINITY CHURCH LIBRARY*, 107 N State St, 54452. SAN 325-111X. Tel: 715-536-5482. FAX: 715-539-2911. E-mail: trinluth@dwave.net. Web Site: trinitymerrill.com.
Library Holdings: Bk Vols 200

MIDDLETON

P   MIDDLETON PUBLIC LIBRARY*, 7425 Hubbard Ave, 53562-3117. SAN 318-1758. Tel: 608-831-5564. Circulation Tel: 608-827-7401. Interlibrary Loan Service Tel: 608-827-7421. Reference Tel: 608-827-7403. Administration Tel: 608-827-7425. FAX: 608-836-5724. E-mail: mid@scls.lib.wi.us. Web Site: www.midlibrary.org. *Dir,* Pamela Wesby; E-mail: pamela@scls.lib.wi.us; *Circ Supvr,* Elizabeth Bauer; Tel: 608-827-7404, E-mail: eibauer@scls.lib.wi.us; *Head, Info Tech,* Patrick Williams; Tel: 608-827-7422, E-mail: williams@scls.lib.wi.us; *Adult Serv,* Jim Ramsey; Tel: 608-827-7423, E-mail: jramsey@scls.lib.wi.us; *Ch,*

Svetha Hetzler; Tel: 608-827-7411, E-mail: hetzlers@scls.lib.wi.us; *Tech Serv,* Sarah Hartman; Tel: 608-827-7421, E-mail: hartmans@scls.lib.wi.us; *YA Serv,* Rebecca Van Dan; Tel: 608-827-7410, E-mail: rvandan@scls.lib.wi.us; *Youth Serv,* Amanda Struckmeyer; Tel: 608-827-7407, E-mail: astruckmeyer@scls.lib.wi.us; Staff 18 (MLS 7, Non-MLS 11)
Founded 1926. Pop 26,393; Circ 670,000
Jan 2007-Dec 2007 Income $1,499,660, State $1,237, City $926,218, County $512,205, Locally Generated Income $60,000. Mats Exp $274,237, Books $179,237, Per/Ser (Incl. Access Fees) $18,000, AV Mat $72,000, Electronic Ref Mat (Incl. Access Fees) $5,000. Sal $738,652 (Prof $401,040)
Library Holdings: AV Mats 18,307; CDs 4,207; DVDs 7,341; Large Print Bks 1,912; Bk Vols 83,157; Per Subs 293; Talking Bks 2,807; Videos 3,008
Automation Activity & Vendor Info: (Acquisitions) SirsiDynix; (Cataloging) SirsiDynix; (Circulation) SirsiDynix; (OPAC) SirsiDynix; (Serials) SirsiDynix
Wireless access
Function: AV serv, Handicapped accessible, Homebound delivery serv, ILL available, Magnifiers for reading, Online searches, Outside serv via phone, mail, e-mail & web, Photocopying/Printing, Prog for adults, Prog for children & young adult, Ref serv available, Referrals accepted, Summer reading prog, Telephone ref, Wheelchair accessible, Workshops
Publications: The Bookworm (Bi-monthly)
Mem of South Central Library System
Partic in Library Interchange Network (LINK)
Special Services for the Blind - Large print bks; Lending of low vision aids; Low vision equip; Magnifiers
Open Mon-Thurs 9-9, Fri 9-6, Sat 9-5, Sun (Sept-May) 1-5
Friends of the Library Group

MILLTOWN

P   MILLTOWN PUBLIC LIBRARY, 61 W Main St, 54858. (Mail add: PO Box 69, 54858-0068), SAN 318-1766. Tel: 715-825-2313. FAX: 715-825-4422. E-mail: milltownpl@ifls.lib.wi.us. Web Site: www.ifls.lib.wi.us. *Dir,* Deanna Wheeler; E-mail: dwheeler@milltownpubliclibrary.org; *Youth Serv,* Cole Zrostlik; E-mail: czrostlik@milltownpubliclibrary.org; *Libr Asst,* Kris Brooks; E-mail: kbrooks@milltownpubliclibrary.org; *Libr Asst,* Krista Schwartz; E-mail: kschwartz@milltownpubliclibrary.org
Pop 900
Automation Activity & Vendor Info: (Acquisitions) Innovative Interfaces, Inc; (Cataloging) Innovative Interfaces, Inc; (Circulation) Innovative Interfaces, Inc
Mem of Indianhead Federated Library System
Open Mon-Thurs 10-7, Fri 10-5, Sat 10-2
Friends of the Library Group

MILTON

P   MILTON PUBLIC LIBRARY*, 430 E High St, 53563. SAN 318-1782. Tel: 608-868-7462. FAX: 608-868-6926. Web Site: www.als.lib.wi.us/MPL. *Dir,* Lisa Brooks; E-mail: brooks.lisa@als.lib.wi.us; Staff 5 (MLS 1, Non-MLS 4)
Founded 1967. Pop 7,577; Circ 79,948
Library Holdings: AV Mats 3,308; Large Print Bks 179; Bk Titles 28,016; Per Subs 42
Automation Activity & Vendor Info: (Acquisitions) Follett Software; (Cataloging) Follett Software; (Circulation) Follett Software
Mem of Arrowhead Library System
Open Mon-Thurs 9-8, Fri 9-5, Sat 9-4, Sun 1-4
Friends of the Library Group

MILWAUKEE

S   ALDRICH CHEMICAL CO, INC LIBRARY*, 6000 N Teutonia Ave, 53209-3645. SAN 318-1790. Tel: 414-273-3850. FAX: 414-298-7960. *Pub Relations,* Toby McGuire; Tel: 414-273-3850, Ext 5462
Founded 1950
Library Holdings: Bk Vols 3,500; Per Subs 92
Subject Interests: Chem
Restriction: Staff use only

S   THE ALLIANCE FOR CHILDREN & FAMILIES*, Severson National Information Center, 11700 W Lake Park Dr, 53224. SAN 311-757X. Tel: 414-359-1040, Ext 3615. Toll Free Tel: 800-221-3726, Ext 3615. FAX: 414-359-1074. E-mail: severson@alliance1.org. Web Site: www.alliance1.org. *Librn,* Liz Caldwell; *Librn,* Mary Kaczmarek; *Tech Serv,* Mary Jo Gehrking; Staff 5 (MLS 3, Non-MLS 2)
Founded 1945
Library Holdings: Bk Vols 3,100; Per Subs 200
Special Collections: Administration & Programs of Family Service Agencies & child residential care institutions, ephemeral material

Subject Interests: Behav sci, Family studies, Nonprofit mgt, Psychol, Soc sci, Soc work
Partic in Library Council of Southeastern Wisconsin, Inc; Wis Health Sci Libr Asn
Restriction: Staff & mem only

C   ALVERNO COLLEGE LIBRARY, 3401 S 39th St, 53215. SAN 318-1820. Tel: 414-382-6052. Circulation Tel: 414-382-6060. Interlibrary Loan Service Tel: 414-382-6397. Reference Tel: 414-382-6062. Information Services Tel: 414-382-6433. FAX: 414-382-6354. Web Site: www.depts.alverno.edu/library. *Dir,* Carol Brill; Tel: 414-382-6054, E-mail: carol.brill@alverno.edu; *Asst Dir,* Larry Duerr; Tel: 414-382-6173, E-mail: larry.duerr@alverno.edu; *Spec Coll & Archives Librn, Tech Serv,* Debra Butz; Tel: 414-382-6202, Ext 2080, E-mail: debra.butz@alverno.edu; *Ref Librn,* Jeffrey Desannoy; Tel: 414-382-6355, E-mail: jeffrey.desannoy@alverno.edu; *Ref Librn,* Dolores Skowronek; Tel: 414-382-6184, E-mail: dolores.skowronek@alverno.edu; *Webmaster/Ref Librn,* Maureen Schinner; Tel: 414-382-6058, E-mail: maureen.schinner@alverno.edu; *Archivist, Rec Mgr, Ref Serv,* Sara Shutkin; Tel: 414-382-6202, Ext 2079, E-mail: sara.shutkin@alverno.edu; *ILL/Circ Supvr,* Kathy Bailey; Tel: 414-382-6397, E-mail: kathy.bailey@alverno.edu; *Acq/Res Mgt Asst,* Diane Klajbor; Tel: 414-382-6056, E-mail: diane.klajbor@alverno.edu; *Cataloger,* Sister MaryAnn Schmidt; Tel: 414-382-6063, E-mail: maryann.schmidt@alverno.edu; *Cat, Ref Serv, Ser,* Cathy Carey; Tel: 414-382-6180, E-mail: catherine.carey@alverno.edu; *Info Spec,* Jill Nell; E-mail: jill.nell@alverno.edu. Subject Specialists: *Hist, Humanities,* Larry Duerr; *Bus, Educ,* Jeffrey Desannoy; *Health sci,* Dolores Skowronek; Staff 13 (MLS 9, Non-MLS 4)
Founded 1887. Enrl 2,815; Fac 118; Highest Degree: Master
Library Holdings: e-books 75,179; Music Scores 2,465; Bk Titles 71,771; Per Subs 429; Videos 2,474
Special Collections: Children's Literature Coll; Corporate Annual Reports; Fine Arts Coll; Teaching Materials Coll
Subject Interests: Educ, Ethnicity, Music, Nursing, Women studies
Automation Activity & Vendor Info: (Acquisitions) Innovative Interfaces, Inc; (Cataloging) Innovative Interfaces, Inc; (Circulation) Innovative Interfaces, Inc; (Course Reserve) Innovative Interfaces, Inc; (ILL) Innovative Interfaces, Inc; (Media Booking) Innovative Interfaces, Inc; (OPAC) Innovative Interfaces, Inc; (Serials) Innovative Interfaces, Inc
Database Vendor: Alexander Street Press, ARTstor, CredoReference, ebrary, EBSCOhost, Gale Cengage Learning, Innovative Interfaces, Inc INN - View, JSTOR, Medline, Mergent Online, netLibrary, Newsbank, OCLC FirstSearch, OCLC WorldCat, ProQuest, PubMed, ScienceDirect, SerialsSolutions, ValueLine, Wiley
Wireless access
Partic in OCLC Online Computer Library Center, Inc; Southeastern Wisconsin Information Technology Exchange, Inc; Wis Asn of Independent Cols & Univs; Wisconsin Library Services
Special Services for the Blind - Reader equip
Open Mon-Thurs (Winter) 7:30am-10pm, Fri 7:30-8, Sat 9-6, Sun 12-5; Mon-Thurs (Summer) 8:30-8, Fri 8:30-5, Sat 10-3

S   AMERICAN SOCIETY FOR QUALITY*, Quality Information Center, 600 N Plankinton Ave, 53203-2914. (Mail add: PO Box 3005, 53203-3005), SAN 328-5944. Tel: 414-272-8575. Toll Free Tel: 800-248-1946, Ext 8693. FAX: 414-765-8660. E-mail: qic@asq.org. Web Site: www.asq.org/info/library/. *Res Librn,* Alice Haley; Tel: 414-298-8789, E-mail: ahaley@asq.org; Staff 2 (MLS 1, Non-MLS 1)
Founded 1994
Library Holdings: Bk Vols 3,700; Per Subs 20; Spec Interest Per Sub 15
Special Collections: ANSI/ISO/ASQ Standards; ASQ & Quality Press Publications
Subject Interests: Auditing, Quality assurance, Quality control, Quality mgt
Automation Activity & Vendor Info: (Cataloging) Inmagic, Inc.; (Circulation) Inmagic, Inc.; (OPAC) Inmagic, Inc.
Database Vendor: Dialog
Function: Res libr
Restriction: Not a lending libr, Staff & mem only

M   AURORA HEALTH CARE LIBRARIES*, 2900 W Oklahoma Ave, 53215-4330. (Mail add: PO Box 2901, 53201-2901), SAN 318-2452. Tel: 414-649-7356. FAX: 414-649-7037. E-mail: aurora.libraries@aurora.org. Web Site: www.aurora.org. *Dir,* Kathleen Strube; E-mail: kathy.strube@aurora.org; Staff 13 (MLS 9, Non-MLS 4)
Founded 1967
Library Holdings: e-books 330; e-journals 6,000; Bk Vols 14,000; Per Subs 255
Automation Activity & Vendor Info: (Acquisitions) EOS International; (Cataloging) EOS International; (Circulation) EOS International; (OPAC) EOS International; (Serials) Ex Libris Group
Database Vendor: CredoReference, Dialog, EBSCOhost, Elsevier, EOS International, Ex Libris Group, Gale Cengage Learning, MD Consult, Medline, Micromedex, Nature Publishing Group, OVID Technologies, PubMed, ScienceDirect, Swets Information Services, UpToDate, Wiley

Wireless access
Partic in Fox River Valley Area Library Consortium; Southeastern Wisconsin Health Science Library Consortium

M   BLOOD CENTER OF WISCONSIN*, Benz Oil Library, 638 N 18th St, 53233-2121. (Mail add: PO Box 2178, 53201-2178), SAN 318-210X. Tel: 414-937-6112. FAX: 414-937-6332. *Librn,* Mary Lou Rice
Founded 1951
Library Holdings: e-journals 97; Bk Vols 925; Per Subs 97
Subject Interests: Hematology, Immunology
Function: ILL available, Res libr
Partic in Southeastern Wisconsin Health Science Library Consortium
Restriction: Staff use only

C   BRYANT & STRATTON COLLEGE LIBRARY-MILWAUKEE*, 310 W Wisconsin Ave, Ste 500, 53203-2200. SAN 377-936X. Tel: 414-276-5200. FAX: 414-276-3930. Web Site: www.bryantstratton.edu. *Dir,* Lloyd G Daub; E-mail: lgdaub@bryantstratton.edu
Library Holdings: Bk Titles 2,000; Per Subs 100
Partic in Library Council of Southeastern Wisconsin, Inc; Wis Libr Asn

C   CARDINAL STRITCH UNIVERSITY LIBRARY, 6801 N Yates Rd, 53207-3985. SAN 364-9326. Tel: 414-410-4263. Interlibrary Loan Service Tel: 414-410-4264. Reference Tel: 414-410-4257. Administration Tel: 414-410-4261. Automation Services Tel: 414-410-4256. Toll Free Tel: 800-347-8822. FAX: 414-410-4268. E-mail: reference@stritch.edu. Web Site: library.stritch.edu. *Dir,* David Weinberg-Kinsey; E-mail: dwweinberg-kins@stritch.edu; *Cat Librn, Metadata Librn,* Elizabeth Schroeder; Tel: 414-410-4258, E-mail: eeschroeder2@stritch.edu; *Digital Res Librn, Web Librn,* Neal Bogda; E-mail: npbogda@stritch.edu; *Electronic Res Librn,* Louise Diodato; Tel: 414-410-4265, Fax: lwdiodato@stritch.edu; *Info Literacy Librn,* Rita Mitchell; Tel: 414-410-4118, E-mail: rmmitchell@stritch.edu; *User Experience Librn,* Rosalia Ballinger; Tel: 414-410-4272, E-mail: raballinger@stritch.edu; *Circ Supvr,* Jodi Bennett; Tel: 414-410-4262, E-mail: jlbennett@stritch.edu; *Asst Circ Supvr,* Nathan Mundell; Tel: 414-410-4607, E-mail: ndmundell@stritch.edu; *Curator, Operations Mgr,* Laurie Swartwout; E-mail: lgswartwout@stritch.edu; *Instrul Designer,* Christine Dereberry; Tel: 414-410-4455, E-mail: cldereberry@stritch.edu; *Instructional Technologist,* Hope Liu; Tel: 414-410-4454, E-mail: hqliu@stritch.edu. Subject Specialists: *Arts & Sci,* Rita Mitchell; *Educ, Juv lit,* Laurie Swartwout; Staff 10 (MLS 7, Non-MLS 3)
Founded 1937. Enrl 7,125; Fac 248; Highest Degree: Doctorate
Library Holdings: AV Mats 6,280; e-books 11,750; Microforms 121,312; Bk Titles 99,904; Bk Vols 138,740; Per Subs 4,215
Special Collections: Cianciolo Children's & YA Literature Research Center (books, rare books, art work); Franciscan Library (books, rare books, periodicals)
Subject Interests: Bus, Educ, Nursing
Automation Activity & Vendor Info: (Acquisitions) Innovative Interfaces, Inc; (Cataloging) Innovative Interfaces, Inc; (Circulation) Innovative Interfaces, Inc; (Course Reserve) Innovative Interfaces, Inc; (ILL) OCLC ILLiad; (Media Booking) Innovative Interfaces, Inc; (OPAC) Innovative Interfaces, Inc; (Serials) Innovative Interfaces, Inc
Database Vendor: ARTstor, Blackwell's, Cambridge Scientific Abstracts, Cinahl Information Systems, CountryWatch, CQ Press, ebrary, EBSCOhost, Gale Cengage Learning, Greenwood Publishing Group, Innovative Interfaces, Inc, JSTOR, Medline, netLibrary, OCLC FirstSearch, OCLC WorldCat, Oxford Online, ProQuest, PubMed, Sage, SerialsSolutions, Springshare, LLC, Standard & Poor's, YBP Library Services
Wireless access
Function: Audio & video playback equip for onsite use, Copy machines, Distance learning, E-Reserves, Electronic databases & coll, Exhibits, Handicapped accessible, ILL available, Instruction & testing, Online cat, Online ref, Outside serv via phone, mail, e-mail & web, Photocopying/Printing, Pub access computers, VHS videos, Wheelchair accessible
Partic in OCLC Online Computer Library Center, Inc; Southeastern Wisconsin Information Technology Exchange, Inc; Wis Asn of Independent Cols & Univs
Open Mon-Thurs 7:30am-11pm, Fri 7:30am-8pm, Sat 9:30-4:30, Sun Noon-11pm

R   CONGREGATION EMANU-EL B'NE JESHURUN LIBRARY, Rabbi Dudley Weinberg Library, 2020 W Brown Deer Rd, 53217. SAN 318-191X. Tel: 414-228-7545. FAX: 414-228-7884. E-mail: librarian@ceebj.org. Web Site: www.ceebj.org. Staff 1 (MLS 1)
Founded 1929
Library Holdings: Bk Vols 8,500; Per Subs 10
Subject Interests: Judaica
Automation Activity & Vendor Info: (Cataloging) Follett Software; (Circulation) Follett Software
Wireless access

R CONGREGATION SHALOM*, Sherman Pastor Memorial Library, 7630 N
Santa Monica Blvd, 53217. SAN 318-1928. Tel: 414-352-9288. FAX:
414-352-9280. Web Site: www.cong-shalom.org. *Librn,* Elaine Friedman;
E-mail: elaine@cong-shalom.org
Founded 1970
Library Holdings: Bk Titles 6,000; Per Subs 10
Subject Interests: Children's fiction, Holocaust, Israel, Jewish fiction,
Judaica, Non-fiction
Partic in Library Council of Southeastern Wisconsin, Inc
Open Mon & Wed 12:30-3:45, Tues 9am-12:30pm, Sun 9-1
Friends of the Library Group

M DEPARTMENT OF VETERANS AFFAIRS*, Medical Library, VA
Medical Ctr, 5000 W National Ave, 53295. SAN 365-0375. Tel:
414-384-2000. FAX: 414-382-5334. *Librn,* Janice Curnes; Tel:
414-384-2000, Ext 42342; Staff 3 (MLS 3)
Library Holdings: Bk Titles 5,392; Per Subs 428
Subject Interests: Allied health, Dentistry, Med, Nursing, Psychol,
Rehabilitation, Surgery
Automation Activity & Vendor Info: (Cataloging) EOS International;
(Circulation) EOS International; (OPAC) EOS International; (Serials) EOS
International
Database Vendor: OVID Technologies, PubMed
Partic in National Network of Libraries of Medicine; Southeastern
Wisconsin Health Science Library Consortium
Open Mon-Fri 8-4:30

M ENDOMETRIOSIS ASSOCIATION LIBRARY & READING ROOM*,
8585 N 76th Pl, 53223-2692. SAN 374-5104. Tel: 414-355-2200. Toll Free
Tel: 800-992-3636. FAX: 414-355-6065. E-mail:
endo@endometriosisassn.org. Web Site: www.endometriosisassn.org. *Librn,*
Cassandra Hurtado
Library Holdings: Bk Vols 300
Function: Res libr
Open Mon-Fri 8:30-5
Restriction: Circ to mem only, Circulates for staff only, Non-circulating to
the pub

L FOLEY & LARDNER*, Law Library, 777 E Wisconsin Ave, 53202-5306.
SAN 318-1960. Tel: 414-271-2400. Reference Tel: 414-297-5406. FAX:
414-297-4900. Web Site: www.foley.com. *Dir,* Susan O'Toole; E-mail:
sotoole@foleylaw.com; *Acq, Coll Develop,* Linda A Mariske; Staff 7 (MLS
2, Non-MLS 5)
Founded 1842
Library Holdings: Bk Vols 32,000; Per Subs 450
Subject Interests: Corporate finance, Employment law, Intellectual
property, Securities, Tax
Automation Activity & Vendor Info: (Cataloging) Inmagic, Inc.;
(Circulation) Inmagic, Inc.
Restriction: Staff use only

R HOPE LUTHERAN CHURCH LIBRARY*, 1115 N 35th St, 53208. SAN
327-4586. Tel: 414-342-0471. *Librn,* Beverly Bischoff
Library Holdings: Bk Titles 3,246
Subject Interests: Relig
Publications: Lutheran Church Library mazazine; Media magazine
Open Sun 9-11

G LEGISLATIVE REFERENCE BUREAU*, City Hall, Rm B-11, 200 E
Wells St, 53202-3567. SAN 318-2177. Tel: 414-286-2297. FAX:
414-286-3004. Web Site: www.ci.mil.wi.us/legislativereference1136.htm.
Libr Mgr, Eileen Lipinski; Tel: 414-286-8818, E-mail:
elipin@milwaukee.gov; *Librn,* Mary Lohmeier; Tel: 414-286-2280, E-mail:
mlohme@milwaukee.gov; *Librn,* Kathleen Williams; Tel: 414-286-2299,
E-mail: kwilli@milwaukee.gov; Staff 4 (MLS 3, Non-MLS 1)
Founded 1908
Library Holdings: Bk Vols 50,000; Per Subs 180
Special Collections: Census Reports; City of Milwaukee Documents;
Milwaukee Code of Ordinances. Municipal Document Depository
Subject Interests: Urban affairs
Automation Activity & Vendor Info: (Acquisitions) EOS International;
(Cataloging) EOS International; (OPAC) EOS International; (Serials) EOS
International
Database Vendor: Dialog, EBSCOhost, Factiva.com, Newsbank, ProQuest
Function: Govt ref serv, ILL available, Photocopying/Printing, Res libr,
Telephone ref
Partic in Library Council of Southeastern Wisconsin, Inc
Open Mon-Fri 8-4:45
Restriction: Circ limited, Closed stack, Lending to staff only, Pub use on
premises

CL MARQUETTE UNIVERSITY*, Law Library, Sensenbrenner Hall, 1103 W
Wisconsin Ave, 53233-2313. (Mail add: PO Box 3137, 53201-3137), SAN
364-9687. Tel: 414-288-7092. FAX: 414-288-5914. Web Site:

www.mu.edu/law/library/research.html. *Dir,* Patricia Cervenka; E-mail:
patricia.cervenka@marquette.edu; *Assoc Dir,* Theodore Potter; *Circ Supvr,*
Robin Cork; E-mail: robin.cork@marquette.edu; *Acq, Supvr, Ser,* Linda
Keys; E-mail: linda.keys@marquette.edu; *Head, Acq, Head, Ser,* James A
Mumm; E-mail: jim.mumm@marquette.edu; *Head, Cat,* Angelina G
Joseph; E-mail: angelina.joseph@marquette.edu; *Computer Serv, Tech Mgr,*
Stephen Nelson; E-mail: stephen.nelson@marquette.edu; *Govt Doc, Libr
Serv Coordr,* Lois A O'Brien; E-mail: lois.o'brien@marquette.edu; *Instrul
Serv/Ref Librn,* Leslie Behroozi; E-mail: leslie.behroozi@marquette.edu;
Instrul Serv/Ref Librn, Julie Norton; E-mail: julie.norton@marquette.edu;
Ref Serv, Julia Jaet; E-mail: julia.jaet@marquette.edu; Staff 17 (MLS 8,
Non-MLS 9)
Founded 1908
Library Holdings: Bk Titles 150,134; Bk Vols 308,104; Per Subs 3,231
Automation Activity & Vendor Info: (Acquisitions) Innovative Interfaces,
Inc; (Cataloging) Innovative Interfaces, Inc; (Circulation) Innovative
Interfaces, Inc; (Course Reserve) Innovative Interfaces, Inc; (ILL)
Innovative Interfaces, Inc; (Media Booking) Innovative Interfaces, Inc;
(OPAC) Innovative Interfaces, Inc; (Serials) Innovative Interfaces, Inc
Database Vendor: Innovative Interfaces, Inc INN - View
Publications: Monthly Acquisitions List; Weekly Contents Pages Service
Open Mon-Sun (Spring) 7am-Midnight; Mon-Thurs (Summer) 7am-10pm,
Fri 7-6, Sat & Sun 9-5

C MARQUETTE UNIVERSITY LIBRARIES*, Raynor Memorial Libraries,
1355 W Wisconsin Ave, 53233. (Mail add: PO Box 3141, 53201-3141),
SAN 364-9652. Tel: 414-288-7214. Circulation Tel: 414-288-7555.
Interlibrary Loan Service Tel: 414-288-7257. Reference Tel: 414-288-7556.
FAX: 414-288-7813. Interlibrary Loan Service FAX: 414-288-5324.
E-mail: memref@marquette.edu. Web Site: www.marquette.edu/library.
Dean, Univ Libr, Janice Welburn; E-mail: janice.welburn@marquette.edu;
Assoc Dean, Jean Zanoni; Tel: 414-288-5979, E-mail:
jean.zanoni@marquette.edu; *Head, Access Serv,* Joan Sommer; Tel:
414-288-3606, E-mail: joan.sommer@marquette.edu; *Head, Acq,* Position
Currently Open; *Head, Libr Info Tech,* Edward Sanchez; Tel:
414-288-6043, E-mail: edward.sanchez@marquette.edu; *Head, Res &
Instrul Serv,* Heather James; *Head, Ser,* Alice Gormley; Tel: 414-288-7252,
Fax: 414-288-8740, E-mail: alice.gormley@marquette.edu; *Head, Spec Coll
& Archives,* Matt Blessing; Tel: 414-288-5901, Fax: 414-288-6709, E-mail:
matt.blessing@marquette.edu; *Head, Tech Serv,* Judith Carter; *Acq Librn,*
Kristina Starkus; Tel: 414-288-1985, Fax: 414-288-3123, E-mail:
kristina.starkus@marquette.edu; *Coll Develop Librn,* Jay Kirk; Tel:
414-288-5213, E-mail: jay.kirk@marquette.edu; *Diversity Serv Librn,*
Alberto Herrera; Tel: 414-288-2140, Fax: 414-288-8821, E-mail:
alberto.herrera@marquette.edu; *Outreach Librn,* Susan Hopwood; Tel:
414-288-5995, E-mail: susan.hopwood@marquette.edu. Subject Specialists:
Educ, Joan Sommer; *Lit in English,* Susan Hopwood; Staff 32 (MLS 30,
Non-MLS 2)
Founded 1881. Enrl 10,283; Fac 609; Highest Degree: Doctorate
Jul 2007-Jun 2008 Income $10,569,173, Federal $175,783, Parent
Institution $10,306,060, Other $87,330. Mats Exp $6,189,058, Books
$1,780,572, Per/Ser (Incl. Access Fees) $4,371,868, Presv $36,618. Sal
$3,574,395 (Prof $1,909,926)
Library Holdings: AV Mats 18,356; e-books 247,109; e-journals 20,189;
Bk Titles 892,336; Bk Vols 1,015,443; Per Subs 3,145
Special Collections: Bureau of Catholic Indian Mission, Records of (Holy
Rosary Mission/Red Cloud Indian School; St Francis Mission; St Stephen's
Mission; Tekakwitha Conference); Catholic Broadcasters Association;
Citizens for Educational Freedom; Council on Urban Life (Milwaukee);
Dorothy Day & the Catholic Worker Movement; Elizabeth W Houghton
Coll, mss; H Herman Rauch Labor Arbitration Files; Industrial Problems;
Jesuitica; JRR Tolkien Coll, mss; Justice & Peace Center; Madonna Center
(Chicago); National Black Sisters Conference; National Catholic
Conference for Interracial Justice; National Catholic Rural Life
Conference; National Coalition of American Nuns; National Sisters
Vocation Conference; Personal Papers (Charles J Kersten, Msgr Luigi G
Ligutti, Don McNeill, George New, Jessica Powers (Sister Miriam), Karl J
Priebe, John O Riedl, Brother Leo V Ryan CSV, Tommy G Thompson, Sr
Margaret Ellen Traxler SSND, Clement J Zablocki); Philanthropy &
Fundraising (Foundation Center Regional Reference Coll), bks, current per,
microfiche, pamphlets; President's Committee on Employment of the
Handicapped; Project Equality, Inc (National Office); Sister
Formation/Religious Formation Conference; Social Justice Papers-Catholic
Association for International Peace
Subject Interests: Dentistry, Math, Nursing, Philosophy, Theol
Automation Activity & Vendor Info: (Acquisitions) Innovative Interfaces,
Inc; (Cataloging) Innovative Interfaces, Inc; (Circulation) Innovative
Interfaces, Inc; (Course Reserve) Innovative Interfaces, Inc; (ILL) OCLC;
(Media Booking) Innovative Interfaces, Inc; (OPAC) Innovative Interfaces,
Inc; (Serials) Innovative Interfaces, Inc
Database Vendor: 3M Library Systems, ACM (Association for Computing
Machinery), Alexander Street Press, American Chemical Society, American
Mathematical Society, American Physical Society, American Psychological
Association (APA), Annual Reviews, Atlas Systems, Blackwell's, Bowker,
Cambridge Scientific Abstracts, CQ Press, Dun & Bradstreet, EBSCOhost,

Elsevier, Elsevier MDL, Emerald, Facts on File, Gale Cengage Learning, H W Wilson, Haworth Pres Inc, Hoovers, IEEE (Institute of Electrical & Electronics Engineers), infoUSA, Ingenta, Innovative Interfaces, Inc, IOP, ISI Web of Knowledge, JSTOR, Lexi-Comp, LexisNexis, Marquis Who's Who, MD Consult, Medline, Mergent Online, Modern Language Association, Nature Publishing Group, netLibrary, OCLC FirstSearch, OCLC WorldCat, OCLC-RLG, OVID Technologies, Oxford Online, Paratext, ProQuest, PubMed, ReferenceUSA, RefWorks, Safari Books Online, Sage, ScienceDirect, Springer-Verlag, Standard & Poor's, STAT!Ref (Teton Data Systems), Thomson - Web of Science, UpToDate, Wiley, Wiley InterScience, Wilson - Wilson Web
Wireless access
Publications: Foundations in Wisconsin: A Directory (Annually)
Partic in Association of Jesuit Colleges & Universities (AJCU); Center for Research Libraries; Library Council of Southeastern Wisconsin, Inc; Midwest Health Sci Libr Network; OCLC Online Computer Library Center, Inc
Open Mon-Thurs 7:45am-11:45pm, Fri 7:45am-10pm, Sat 10-10, Sun 10am-11:45pm
Restriction: Res pass required for non-affiliated visitors

CM   MEDICAL COLLEGE OF WISCONSIN LIBRARIES, Todd Wehr Library, Health Research Ctr, 3rd Flr, 8701 Watertown Plank Rd, 53226-0509. SAN 320-541X. Tel: 414-955-8323. Circulation Tel: 414-955-8300. Interlibrary Loan Service Tel: 414-955-8310. Reference Tel: 414-955-8302. FAX: 414-955-6532. Web Site: www.lib.mcw.edu. *Dir,* Mary B Blackwelder; E-mail: blackwel@mcw.edu; *Asst Dir,* Karen L Hanus; Tel: 414-955-8329, E-mail: khanus@mcw.edu; *Outreach Serv Librn,* Emily Merkt; Tel: 414-955-8427; *Syst Mgr,* Jeff Hagedorn; Tel: 414-955-8515; *Coll Mgt/Res Sharing,* Tatiana Miller; Tel: 414-955-8140; *Info Res,* Deborah Ruck; Tel: 414-955-8522; *Pub Serv,* Michelle Washington; Tel: 414-955-8305; *Ref,* Rita Sieracki; Tel: 414-955-8327; Staff 29 (MLS 14, Non-MLS 15)
Founded 1913. Enrl 1,200; Highest Degree: Doctorate
Library Holdings: e-books 3,380; e-journals 9,040; Bk Vols 252,969; Per Subs 9,076
Special Collections: Medical History (Horace Manchester Brown Coll)
Subject Interests: Clinical med, Nursing
Automation Activity & Vendor Info: (OPAC) Innovative Interfaces, Inc
Database Vendor: OVID Technologies
Wireless access
Partic in National Network of Libraries of Medicine
Departmental Libraries:
CHILDREN'S HOSPITAL OF WISCONSIN LIBRARY, 9000 W Wisconsin Ave, 53226. (Mail add: PO Box 1997, 53226-1997). Tel: 414-266-2340. E-mail: askchw@mcw.edu. *Clinical Serv Librn,* Barbara Ruggeri; Staff 2 (MLS 1, Non-MLS 1)
    Library Holdings: Bk Titles 986; Per Subs 9,076
    Subject Interests: Pediatrics
    Open Mon-Fri 8-4:30
FROEDTERT HOSPITAL LIBRARY, Froedtert Specialty Clinics Bldg, 2nd Flr, 9200 W Wisconsin Ave, 53226, SAN 318-2142. Tel: 414-805-4311. FAX: 414-805-4313. *Librn,* Linda Backus; Staff 1 (MLS 1)
    Founded 1958
    Library Holdings: Bk Vols 1,148; Per Subs 9,030
    Subject Interests: Clinical med, Consumer health, Hospital admin, Nursing
    Partic in OCLC Online Computer Library Center, Inc
    Open Mon-Fri 8-4:30

G   METROPOLITAN MILWAUKEE FAIR HOUSING COUNCIL LIBRARY*, 600 E Mason St, Ste 200, 53202. SAN 324-1599. Tel: 414-278-1240. FAX: 414-278-8033. E-mail: mmfhc@aol.com. Web Site: www.mhawauk.org/html/ki0wmo6n.htm. *Tech Serv Dir,* Margaret Bowitz
Founded 1977
Library Holdings: Bk Titles 2,500; Per Subs 32
Subject Interests: Civil rights, Fair housing, Landlord-tenant relations
Publications: Brochures in English & Spanish; Case Study Reports; Fair Housing Keys (Newsletter); Your Move, Your Choice (Milwaukee Neighborhoods)
Partic in Library Council of Southeastern Wisconsin, Inc
Open Mon-Fri 8-4:30

L   MICHAEL BEST & FRIEDRICH LLP, Information Services Department, 100 E Wisconsin Ave, 53202-4108. SAN 318-2088. Tel: 414-271-6560. FAX: 414-277-0656, *Dir, Info Serv,* Jane B Moberg; E-mail: jbmoberg@michaelbest.com; *Sr Info Spec,* Candace Hall Slaminski; E-mail: chslaminski@michaelbest.com; *Info Spec,* Sarah E Bolgert; E-mail: sebolgert@michaelbest.com; Staff 3 (MLS 3)
Founded 1848
Library Holdings: Bk Vols 25,000
Subject Interests: Antitrust law, Copyright law, Corporate law, Labor law, Patent law, Taxation law, Trademark law, Wis law
Automation Activity & Vendor Info: (Acquisitions) Inmagic, Inc.; (Cataloging) Inmagic, Inc.; (OPAC) Inmagic, Inc.; (Serials) Inmagic, Inc.

Database Vendor: Dialog, LexisNexis, Westlaw
Wireless access
Restriction: Co libr

M   MILWAUKEE ACADEMY OF MEDICINE LIBRARY*, 8701 Watertown Plank Rd, 53226. SAN 327-408X. Tel: 414-456-8249. FAX: 414-456-6537. *In Charge,* Amy John; E-mail: amyjohn@execpc.com
Library Holdings: Bk Vols 1,500
Restriction: Open by appt only

J   MILWAUKEE AREA TECHNICAL COLLEGE*, Rasche Memorial Library, 700 W State St, 53233-1443. (Mail add: 1015 N Sixth St, 53233), SAN 364-9717. Tel: 414-297-7030. Reference Tel: 414-297-7559. FAX: 414-297-6798. E-mail: library@matc.edu. Web Site: www.matc.edu. *Dir,* Jeff Jackson; Tel: 414-297-6946; *ILL,* Mark Zera; Staff 12 (MLS 12)
Founded 1935. Enrl 70,000; Fac 811
Library Holdings: Bk Titles 52,000; Bk Vols 70,000; Per Subs 380
Automation Activity & Vendor Info: (Acquisitions) SirsiDynix; (Cataloging) SirsiDynix; (Circulation) SirsiDynix; (Course Reserve) SirsiDynix; (OPAC) SirsiDynix; (Serials) SirsiDynix
Database Vendor: EBSCOhost, ProQuest
Partic in Library Council of Southeastern Wisconsin, Inc
Open Mon-Thurs 7:30am-9:30pm, Fri 7:30-4

S   MILWAUKEE ART MUSEUM LIBRARY*, Art Research Library, Milwaukee Art Museum, 700 N Art Museum Dr, 53202. SAN 318-2096. Tel: 414-224-3270. FAX: 414-271-7588. E-mail: library@mam.org. *Archivist, Art Librn,* Heather Lynn Winter. Subject Specialists: *Archit,* Heather Lynn Winter; Staff 2 (MLS 1, Non-MLS 1)
Founded 1916
Subject Interests: Archit
Restriction: Open by appt only

P   MILWAUKEE COUNTY FEDERATED LIBRARY SYSTEM*, 709 N Eighth St, 53233-2414. SAN 318-2118. Tel: 414-286-3210. FAX: 414-286-3209. Web Site: www.mcfls.org. *Dir,* James Gingery; Tel: 414-286-8149, E-mail: jim.gingery@mcfls.org; *Adminr,* Steve Heser; Tel: 414-286-5934, E-mail: steve.heser@mcfls.org; *Network Adminr,* Hieu Tran; Tel: 414-286-8684, E-mail: hieu.tran@mcfls.org; Staff 3 (MLS 2, Non-MLS 1)
Founded 1973. Pop 933,067
Library Holdings: Bk Vols 4,750,000
Automation Activity & Vendor Info: (Acquisitions) Innovative Interfaces, Inc; (Circulation) Innovative Interfaces, Inc; (OPAC) Innovative Interfaces, Inc; (Serials) Innovative Interfaces, Inc
Database Vendor: Innovative Interfaces, Inc INN - View
Member Libraries: Brown Deer Public Library; Cudahy Family Library; Franklin Public Library; Greendale Public Library; Hales Corners Library; Milwaukee Public Library; North Shore Library; Oak Creek Public Library; Shorewood Public Library; South Milwaukee Public Library; St Francis Public Library; Wauwatosa Public Library; West Allis Public Library; Whitefish Bay Public Library
Partic in Coun of Wis Librs, Inc; Library Council of Southeastern Wisconsin, Inc
Open Mon-Thurs 8:30-8:30, Fri & Sat 8:30-5:30, Sun 1-5

S   MILWAUKEE COUNTY HISTORICAL SOCIETY*, Library & Archives, 910 N Old World Third St, 53203. SAN 318-2126. Tel: 414-273-8288. FAX: 414-273-3268. E-mail: mchs@prodigy.net. Web Site: www.milwaukeecountyhistsoc.org. *Curator,* Steven Daily; *Asst Curator,* Kevin Abing; Staff 2 (MLS 2)
Founded 1935
Library Holdings: Bk Vols 12,000
Subject Interests: Ethnic hist, Milwaukee, Socialism, Wis
Open Mon-Fri 9:30-4:30, Sat 10-4:30

C   MILWAUKEE INSTITUTE OF ART & DESIGN LIBRARY*, 273 E Erie St, 53202-6003. SAN 318-2215. Tel: 414-847-3342. FAX: 414-291-8077. Web Site: www.miad.edu/content/view/146/215. *Dir, Libr Serv,* Cynthia D Lynch; Tel: 414-847-3340, E-mail: clynch@miad.edu; *Asst Libr Dir,* Nancy A Siker; E-mail: nsiker@miad.edu; Staff 3 (MLS 1, Non-MLS 2)
Founded 1977. Enrl 650; Highest Degree: Bachelor
Jun 2006-May 2007 Income $241,000
Library Holdings: AV Mats 1,000; Bk Titles 23,000; Per Subs 125
Special Collections: Art slides
Subject Interests: Advertising, Aesthetics, Art hist, Artists' monographs, Decorative art, Graphic design, Interior design, Painting, Photog, Sculpture, Typography
Automation Activity & Vendor Info: (Cataloging) Innovative Interfaces, Inc; (Circulation) Innovative Interfaces, Inc; (Course Reserve) Innovative Interfaces, Inc; (OPAC) Innovative Interfaces, Inc; (Serials) Innovative Interfaces, Inc

Database Vendor: ARTstor, EBSCOhost, Innovative Interfaces, Inc INN - View, ProQuest, Wilson - Wilson Web
Partic in Library Council of Southeastern Wisconsin, Inc; Southeastern Wisconsin Information Technology Exchange, Inc
Open Mon-Thurs 7:30am-9pm, Fri 7:30-5, Sun (Fall & Spring) 3-9

R   MILWAUKEE JEWISH COUNCIL FOR COMMUNITY RELATIONS LIBRARY*, 1360 N Prospect Ave, 2nd Flr, 53202-3091. SAN 371-7925. Tel: 414-390-5777. FAX: 414-390-5787. E-mail: info@mjccr.org. Web Site: www.mjccr.org. *Asst Dir,* Kathy Heilbronner; Tel: 414-390-5736; Staff 2 (MLS 1, Non-MLS 1)
Library Holdings: Bk Vols 500; Per Subs 10
Subject Interests: Holocaust, Israel, Relig
Partic in Library Council of Southeastern Wisconsin, Inc
Open Mon-Fri 8:30-5

S   MILWAUKEE JOURNAL SENTINEL*, News Information Center, PO Box 661, 53201-0661. SAN 318-2169. Tel: 414-224-2171. Web Site: www.jsonline.com. *Mgr,* Alan King
Founded 1922
Library Holdings: Bk Vols 5,000
Special Collections: Milwaukee Journal & Milwaukee Sentinel, micro, newsp clippings, photos; Milwaukee Journal Sentinel, micro, newsp clippings, photogs
Subject Interests: Milwaukee, Wis
Database Vendor: LexisNexis
Partic in News Bank
Special Services for the Blind - Newsline for the Blind
Restriction: Not open to pub

P   MILWAUKEE PUBLIC LIBRARY*, 814 W Wisconsin Ave, 53233-2385. SAN 364-9741. Tel: 414-286-3000. Interlibrary Loan Service Tel: 414-286-3082. Reference Tel: 414-286-3011. FAX: 414-286-2794. E-mail: mailbox@mpl.org. Web Site: www.mpl.org. *Libr Dir,* Paula Kiely; *Dep Dir, Pub Serv,* Joan Johnson; *Head, Tech Serv,* Bruce Gay; *Bus Mgr,* Taj Schoening; *Pub Serv Mgr,* Christine Arkenberg; *Circ Coordr,* Kathryn Mlsna; *Youth Serv Coordr,* Kelly Hughbanks. Subject Specialists: *Bus,* Christine Arkenberg; Staff 90 (MLS 90)
Founded 1878. Pop 595,598; Circ 2,944,880
Jan 2006-Dec 2006 Income (Main Library and Branch(s)) $26,248,818, State $852,889, City $23,930,159, Federal $610,803, Other $854,967. Mats Exp $2,042,452, Books $842,876, Other Print Mats $913, AV Mat $196,000, Electronic Ref Mat (Incl. Access Fees) $280,000. Sal $14,189,419
Library Holdings: AV Mats 247,358; Bk Vols 2,556,562; Per Subs 8,519
Special Collections: Alexander Mitchell Coll; American Maps; Art & Motion Picture Posters; Charles King Coll; City Archives, bk & pamphlet; Cookery (Breta Greim Coll); Current Trade Books for Children (Historical Reference Coll 1976 to date); Early American Imprints, microfiche; Eastman Fairy Tale Coll; Great Lakes Ships & Shipping (Runge Marine Memorial), pamphlets & photog bk; H G Wells Coll; Historical Popular Children's Literature Coll (1850-1940); Historical Recordings; Literature (Definitive Editions of British & American Writers); Milwaukee Artists; Milwaukee Road Railroad Archives; Rare Bird Prints (Audubon Folio Prints), pictures; Significant Publishers Series; United States, British & Canadian Patents; Wisconsin Architectural Archives. State Document Depository; US Document Depository
Subject Interests: Railroad hist
Wireless access
Publications: Milwaukee Reader; Miscellaneous Booklists & Brochures; Staff News (Staff newsletter); Weekly Accessions List
Mem of Milwaukee County Federated Library System
Partic in HQ-WIS Reg Libr for Blind & Physically Handicapped; Library Council of Southeastern Wisconsin, Inc; OCLC Online Computer Library Center, Inc
Special Services for the Deaf - Staff with knowledge of sign lang; TTY equip
Friends of the Library Group
Branches: 12
ATKINSON, 1960 W Atkinson Ave, 53209, SAN 364-9806. Tel: 414-286-3068. FAX: 414-286-8469. *Br Head,* David Allen Sikora; Staff 6 (MLS 4, Non-MLS 2)
Library Holdings: Bk Vols 73,078
Function: Adult bk club, Art exhibits, Audiobks via web, Bks on cassette, Bks on CD, CD-ROM, Children's prog, Computer training, Computers for patron use, Copy machines, e-mail serv, E-Reserves, Electronic databases & coll, Free DVD rentals, Holiday prog, Homework prog, ILL available, Large print keyboards, Magnifiers for reading, Music CDs, Online cat, Online ref, OverDrive digital audio bks, Preschool outreach, Prog for adults, Prog for children & young adult, Pub access computers, Ref & res, Spoken cassettes & CDs, Spoken cassettes & DVDs, Summer reading prog, Tax forms, Teen prog, VHS videos, Web-catalog, Wheelchair accessible
Open Mon-Wed 1-8:30, Thurs-Sat 10-5
Friends of the Library Group

BAY VIEW, 2566 S Kinnickinnic Ave, 53207, SAN 373-9244. Tel: 414-286-3019. FAX: 414-286-8459. *Br Mgr,* Christopher Gawronski
Library Holdings: Bk Vols 76,932
Open Mon-Thurs 10-8:30, Fri & Sat 10-5
Friends of the Library Group
CAPITOL, 3969 N 74th St, 53216, SAN 364-9830. Tel: 414-286-3006. FAX: 414-286-8432. *Br Mgr,* Acklen J Banks, Jr
Library Holdings: Bk Vols 115,705
Open Mon-Thurs 10-8:30, Fri & Sat 10-5, Sun (Oct-April) 1-5
Friends of the Library Group
CENTER STREET, 2727 W Fond du Lac Ave, 53210, SAN 364-9865. Tel: 414-286-3090. FAX: 414-286-8467. *Br Mgr,* Kirsten Thompson
Library Holdings: Bk Vols 72,926
Open Mon & Wed 12-8:30, Tues & Thurs 10:30-8:30, Fri 10-5, Sat (Sept-May) 10-5
Friends of the Library Group
EAST, 1910 E North Ave, 53202, SAN 364-989X. Tel: 414-286-3058. FAX: 414-286-8431. *Br Mgr,* Nancy Torphy
Library Holdings: Bk Vols 100,409
Open Mon-Thurs 10-8:30, Fri & Sat 10-5
Friends of the Library Group
FOREST HOME, 1432 W Forest Home Ave, 53204, SAN 364-9954. Tel: 414-286-3083. FAX: 414-286-8461. *Br Mgr,* Position Currently Open
Library Holdings: Bk Vols 78,926
Open Mon-Wed 1-8:30, Thurs & Fri 10-5
Friends of the Library Group
MARTIN LUTHER KING BRANCH, 310 W Locust St, 53212, SAN 365-0014. Tel: 414-286-3098. FAX: 414-286-8465. TDD: 414-286-2419. *Br Mgr,* Rachel Collins; Staff 8 (MLS 4, Non-MLS 4)
Library Holdings: Bk Vols 92,833
Open Mon-Wed 1-8:30, Thurs & Fri 10-5, Sat (Sept-May) 10-5
Friends of the Library Group
MILL ROAD, 6431 N 76th St, 53223, SAN 365-0049. Tel: 414-286-3088. FAX: 414-286-8454. *Br Mgr,* Joy Kilimann
Library Holdings: Bk Vols 89,644
Open Mon-Thurs 10-8:30, Fri & Sat 10-5
Friends of the Library Group
TIPPECANOE, 3912 S Howell Ave, 53207, SAN 365-0138. Tel: 414-286-3085. FAX: 414-286-8405. *Br Mgr,* Neal Kaluzny
Library Holdings: Bk Vols 93,326
Open Mon-Wed 1-8:30, Thurs & Fri 10-5, Sat (Sept-May) 10-5
Friends of the Library Group
VILLARD AVENUE, 3310 W Villard Ave, 53209, SAN 365-0073: Tel: 414-286-3079. FAX: 414-286-8473. *Br Mgr,* Brian Williams-Vanklooster
Library Holdings: Bk Vols 77,337
Open Mon-Wed 1-8:30, Thurs & Fri 10-5, Sat (Sept-May) 10-5
Friends of the Library Group
WASHINGTON PARK, 2121 N Sherman Blvd, 53208, SAN 364-992X. Tel: 414-286-3066. FAX: 414-286-8471. *Br Mgr,* Enid Gruszka
Library Holdings: Bk Vols 61,151
Open Mon-Thurs 10-8:30 Fri & Sat 10-5
Friends of the Library Group
ZABLOCKI, 3501 W Oklahoma Ave, 53215, SAN 365-0103. Tel: 414-286-3055. FAX: 414-286-8430. *Br Mgr,* Linda Vincent
Library Holdings: Bk Vols 78,072
Open Mon-Thurs 10-8:30, Fri & Sat 10-5, Sun (Oct-April) 1-5
Friends of the Library Group

S   MILWAUKEE PUBLIC MUSEUM*, Library & Archives, 800 W Wells St, 53233. SAN 318-2193. Tel: 414-278-2736. FAX: 414-278-6100. Web Site: www.mpm.edu/collections/dept/library.php. *In Charge,* Claudia Jacobson; E-mail: jacobson@mpm.edu; Staff 2 (MLS 2)
Founded 1883
Library Holdings: Bk Titles 30,000; Bk Vols 130,000; Per Subs 1,200
Special Collections: Milwaukee Public Museum Archives
Subject Interests: Anthropology, Archaeology, Botany, Decorative art, Ecology, Geol, Museology, Paleontology, Zoology
Partic in Library Council of Southeastern Wisconsin, Inc; OCLC Online Computer Library Center, Inc; Wisconsin Library Services
Restriction: Non-circulating to the pub, Open by appt only

C   MILWAUKEE SCHOOL OF ENGINEERING*, Walter Schroeder Library, 500 E Kilbourn Ave, 53202. SAN 318-2207. Tel: 414-277-7180. FAX: 414-277-7186. E-mail: library@msoe.edu. Web Site: www.msoe.edu/library. *Dir,* Gary S Shimek; Tel: 414-277-7181, E-mail: shimek@msoe.edu; *ILL Librn,* Elizabeth Suelzer; Tel: 414-277-7182, E-mail: suelzer@msoe.edu; *Ref, Cat & Med Librn,* Pam Gorzalski; Tel: 414-277-7141, E-mail: gorzalsk@msoe.edu; *Ref & Ser Librn,* Karen Bolton; Tel: 414-277-7183, E-mail: bolton@msoe.edu; *Sr Circ & Reserves Coordr,* Sarah Rowell; E-mail: rowell@msoe.edu; Staff 5 (MLS 4, Non-MLS 1)
Founded 1903. Enrl 2,434; Fac 183; Highest Degree: Master
Library Holdings: AV Mats 1,518; e-books 25,000; e-journals 70,000; Bk Titles 49,527; Per Subs 389

Special Collections: Fred Portz Special Chemistry Coll; MSOE Biomolecular Models Lending Library; MSOE-MMAC Business & Management Multimedia Coll, CDs, tapes, videos
Subject Interests: Archit eng, Biomed eng, Computer eng, Electrical eng, Fluid power, Indust mgt, Mechanical eng, Nursing
Automation Activity & Vendor Info: (Acquisitions) SirsiDynix; (Cataloging) SirsiDynix; (Circulation) SirsiDynix; (Course Reserve) SirsiDynix; (ILL) Clio; (OPAC) SirsiDynix; (Serials) SirsiDynix
Database Vendor: Annual Reviews, ASCE Research Library, Backstage Library Works, Cambridge Scientific Abstracts, College Source, EBSCOhost, Elsevier, Gale Cengage Learning, H W Wilson, IEEE (Institute of Electrical & Electronics Engineers), Knovel, Medline, OCLC FirstSearch, OCLC WorldCat, OVID Technologies, ProQuest, ReferenceUSA, ScienceDirect, SirsiDynix, ValueLine, Wiley InterScience
Function: ILL available
Partic in Library Council of Southeastern Wisconsin, Inc; OCLC Online Computer Library Center, Inc; Wisconsin Library Services
Open Mon-Thurs 7:30am-11pm, Fri 7:30-6, Sat 10-6, Sun 1-9
Restriction: Circ limited, In-house use for visitors, Non-circulating to the pub

S　　MILWAUKEE SECURE DETENTION FACILITY LIBRARY*, 1015 N Tenth St, 53233. (Mail add: PO Box 05740, 53212-5740). Tel: 414-225-5685. FAX: 414-225-5681. *Librn,* Karen Nimz; E-mail: karen.nimz@doc.state.wi.us
Library Holdings: Bk Vols 7,000; Per Subs 56
Automation Activity & Vendor Info: (Cataloging) Follett Software; (Circulation) Follett Software
Open Mon-Fri 7:45-4:30

GL　　MMSD LAW LIBRARY*, 260 W Seeboth St, 53204. Tel: 414-225-2098. FAX: 414-225-0167. *Paralegal Adminr/Law Librn,* Linda Mooney; E-mail: lmooney@mmsd.com; Staff 1 (MLS 1)
Founded 1977
Jan 2010-Dec 2010. Mats Exp $81,000, Books $45,000, Electronic Ref Mat (Incl. Access Fees) $36,000
Library Holdings: Bk Vols 10,000
Function: Electronic databases & coll, Govt ref serv
Restriction: Govt use only

R　　MOUNT CARMEL LUTHERAN CHURCH LIBRARY*, 8424 W Center St, 53222. SAN 318-2231. Tel: 414-771-1270. FAX: 414-771-1616. E-mail: office@mountcarmelchurch.org. Web Site: www.execpc.com/~mcarmel/. *Librn,* Wendy Nielson
Founded 1947
Library Holdings: Bk Vols 4,500; Per Subs 10
Special Collections: Bibles; Norwegian Heritage
Subject Interests: Relig

CR　　MOUNT MARY COLLEGE*, Patrick & Beatrice Haggerty Library, 2900 N Menomonee River Pkwy, 53222-4597. SAN 318-224X. Tel: 414-258-4810, Ext 190. Reference Tel: 414-256-0190. Administration Tel: 414-258-4810, Ext 337. FAX: 414-256-1205. Web Site: topcat.switchinc.org, www.mtmary.edu/library.htm. *Dir,* Julie Kamikawa; Staff 10 (MLS 8, Non-MLS 2)
Founded 1913. Enrl 1,732; Fac 112; Highest Degree: Master
Subject Interests: Art, Art therapy, Behav sci, Communication, Dietetics, Educ, Fashion design, Fashion merchandising, Occupational therapy, Soc work
Partic in OCLC Online Computer Library Center, Inc; Southeastern Wisconsin Information Technology Exchange, Inc
Restriction: Authorized patrons

S　　PLANNED PARENTHOOD OF WISCONSIN, INC*, Maurice Ritz Resource Center, 302 N Jackson St, 53202. SAN 318-2355. Tel: 414-289-3704. Administration Tel: 414-271-8045. Toll Free Tel: 800-472-2703, Ext 3704. FAX: 414-271-1935. Web Site: www.ppwi.org. *Librn,* Anne K Brosowsky; Staff 1 (Non-MLS 1)
Founded 1972
Library Holdings: AV Mats 50; Bk Titles 3,000; Per Subs 100; Spec Interest Per Sub 20
Subject Interests: Family planning, Human sexuality, Reproductive health, Sex educ
Function: ILL available, Photocopying/Printing, Prof lending libr, Ref serv available, Referrals accepted, Res libr, Telephone ref
Publications: Audiovisual Bibliography (Bibliographies); Check It Out (Acquisition list); Health News Alert (Newsletter); Literature Bibliography (Bibliographies); The Educator's Report (Newsletter)
Partic in Association of Population/Family Planning Libraries & Information Centers-International (APLIC-I); Library Council of Southeastern Wisconsin, Inc; Southeastern Wisconsin Health Science Library Consortium
Restriction: Open by appt only

R　　PRINCE OF PEACE LUTHERAN CHURCH LIBRARY*, 4419 S Howell Ave, 53207. SAN 318-2363. Tel: 414-483-3828. E-mail: popchurch@sbcglobal.net. Web Site: princeofpeace-elca.org. *Librn,* Mrs Robert Heinritz
Founded 1963
Library Holdings: Bk Vols 2,600
Special Collections: Martin Luther Coll

G　　PUBLIC POLICY FORUM*, Researching Community Issues, 633 W Wisconsin Ave, Ste 406, 53203. Tel: 414-276-8240. FAX: 414-276-9962. E-mail: forum@publicpolicyforum.org. Web Site: www.publicpolicyforum.org. *Dir, Res,* Anneliese Dickman; E-mail: adickman@publicpolicyforum.org; *Res,* Ryan Horton; E-mail: rhorton@publicpolicyforum.org; Staff 2 (MLS 2)
Founded 1913
Library Holdings: Bk Titles 3,000; Per Subs 100
Publications: Bulletin (Monthly); Special Reports
Restriction: Open by appt only
Friends of the Library Group

L　　QUARLES & BRADY*, Law Library, 411 E Wisconsin Ave, 53202-4491. SAN 318-2371. Tel: 414-277-5000. FAX: 414-271-3552. Web Site: www.quarles.com. *Mgr,* Tony Chan; Staff 6 (MLS 4, Non-MLS 2)
Founded 1910
Library Holdings: Bk Vols 10,000; Per Subs 100
Subject Interests: Banking, Bankruptcy, Environ law, Estate planning, Hospital, Immigration, Labor, Litigation, Patents, Pensions, Real estate, Sch law, Securities, Taxation, Trademarks
Open Mon-Fri 8-5

L　　REINHART BOERNER VAN DEUREN SC*, Information Resource Center, 1000 N Water St, Ste 2100, 53203-3400. SAN 324-0177. Tel: 414-298-8253. FAX: 414-298-8097. Web Site: www.reinhartlaw.com. *Dir,* Carol Bannen; Staff 6 (MLS 5, Non-MLS 1)
Founded 1975
Library Holdings: Bk Titles 6,000; Bk Vols 20,000; Per Subs 460
Subject Interests: Employee benefits
Automation Activity & Vendor Info: (Acquisitions) EOS International; (Cataloging) EOS International; (Circulation) EOS International; (OPAC) EOS International; (Serials) EOS International
Partic in Library Council of Southeastern Wisconsin, Inc

S　　ROCKWELL AUTOMATION LIBRARY*, 1201 S Second St, 53204. SAN 318-1804. Tel: 414-382-2342. FAX: 414-382-2462. *Head of Libr,* Shannon Urban
Founded 1942
Library Holdings: Bk Titles 10,000; Per Subs 425
Special Collections: Military standards & specifications
Subject Interests: Electrical, Electronic eng, Indust automation, Mechanical eng, Physics
Database Vendor: Factiva.com, LexisNexis
Partic in Library Council of Southeastern Wisconsin, Inc
Restriction: Not open to pub

M　　SAINT FRANCIS HOSPITAL*, Health Sciences Library, 3237 S 16th St, 53215. SAN 318-2428. Tel: 414-647-5156. FAX: 414-647-5195. Web Site: www.wflibraries.org. *Librn,* June Regis; E-mail: june.regis@wfhc.org
Founded 1974
Library Holdings: Bk Titles 2,500; Per Subs 25
Subject Interests: Allied health, Med, Nursing
Partic in Library Council of Southeastern Wisconsin, Inc; Southeastern Wisconsin Health Science Library Consortium
Open Wed-Fri 7:30-4

M　　SAINT MARY'S HOSPITAL*, Health Sciences Library, 2323 N Lake Dr, 53201. (Mail add: PO Box 503, 53201-0503), SAN 318-2460. Tel: 414-291-1278. FAX: 414-291-1281. *Librn,* Sharon Wochos; Staff 1 (MLS 1)
Founded 1959
Library Holdings: Bk Vols 2,900; Per Subs 275
Subject Interests: Nursing, Rehabilitation
Open Mon-Fri 8-4:30

GL　　UNITED STATES COURTS LIBRARY*, 517 E Wisconsin Ave, Rm 516, 53202. SAN 372-364X. Tel: 414-297-1698. FAX: 414-297-1695. Web Site: www.lb7.uscourts.gov. *Librn,* Mary B Jones
Library Holdings: Bk Vols 20,000
Open Mon-Fri 8:30-5

C　　UNIVERSITY OF WISCONSIN-MILWAUKEE LIBRARIES*, Golda Meir Library, 2311 E Hartford Ave, 53211. (Mail add: PO Box 604, 53201-0604), SAN 365-0227. Tel: 414-229-4785, 414-229-6202. Circulation Tel: 414-229-4132. Interlibrary Loan Service Tel:

414-229-4493. Reference Tel: 414-229-4659. FAX: 414-229-6766. TDD: 800-947-3529. Web Site: www4.uwm.edu/libraries. *Dir,* Ewa Barczyk; *Assoc Dir,* Susanna Pathak; *Dir, Libr Develop,* Susan Modder; *Interim Asst Dir, User Serv Div,* Michael Doylen; *Music Librn,* Rebecca Littman; *Coordr, Learning Commons,* Molly Mathias; *Access Serv,* Lisa Weikel; *Coll Develop, Tech Serv,* Janet Padway; *Doc Delivery, ILL,* Leigh Dorsey; *Res & Instrul Serv,* Linda Kopecky; *Ser, E-Res,* Karen Jander; *Spec Coll,* Max Yela; *Syst,* Jim Lowrey; Staff 74 (MLS 40, Non-MLS 34)
Founded 1956. Enrl 30,455; Fac 1,269; Highest Degree: Doctorate
Library Holdings: Bk Titles 1,670,813; Bk Vols 2,213,354; Per Subs 57,270
Special Collections: 17th Century Literature Coll; Area Research Center of the State Historical Society of Wisconsin, bks, ms; Blatz Brewing Company Records; Camus Bibliography Research Coll; Education, Children's Literature (Curriculum Coll), bks & non-print media; Franklin Delano Roosevelt (Jagodzinski Coll); George Hardie Aerospace Coll; Harrison Forman Photograph Coll; Institutional History (University of Wisconsin-Milwaukee Archives), ms; Layton School of Art Library Coll; Little Review Papers, ms; Milwaukee Polish & the Roman Kwasniewski Photo Archive; Milwaukee Press Club Records; Shakespeare Research Coll; Social Justice (Fromkin Memorial Coll); Wisconsin Legislation Reference Bureau Clippings File, micro. State Document Depository; US Document Depository
Subject Interests: Archit, Art, Behav sci, Cartography, Econ, Educ, Eng, Geog, Geol sci, Hist, Related fields, Soc sci, Urban studies
Wireless access
Publications: AGS Collection Special Publications Series; Current Geographical Publications; UWM Libraries Newsletter
Partic in Dialog Corp; Library Council of Southeastern Wisconsin, Inc; National Network of Libraries of Medicine; OCLC Online Computer Library Center, Inc; SDC Info Servs; Wisconsin Library Services
Special Services for the Deaf - TDD equip
Special Services for the Blind - Assistive/Adapted tech devices, equip & products; Braille bks; Braille Webster's dictionary; Reader equip; ZoomText magnification & reading software
Open Sun Noon-Fri 7pm, Sat 9am-8pm
Friends of the Library Group

Departmental Libraries:

AMERICAN GEOGRAPHICAL SOCIETY LIBRARY, Golda Meir Library, 2311 E Hartford Ave, 53211. (Mail add: PO Box 399, 53201-0399), SAN 365-0251. Tel: 414-229-3984, 414-229-6282. Toll Free Tel: 800-558-8993. FAX: 414-229-3624. E-mail: agsl@uwm.edu. Web Site: www4.uwm.edu/Libraries/AGSL. *Librn,* Cristina Miller; E-mail: crmiller@uwm.edu; *Digital Spacial Data Librn,* Lisa Schelling; E-mail: schelil@uwm.edu; *Adminr, Curator,* Christopher Baruth, PhD; E-mail: cmb@uwm.edu; *Photog Curator/Photographic Serv Adminr,* Susan Peschel; E-mail: sqp@uwm.edu; *Cat,* Angie Cope; E-mail: acope@uwm.edu; *Digital Serv,* Position Currently Open; *Presv Spec,* Ann Barnish; E-mail: barnisha@uwm.edu; *Ref Serv,* Jovanka Ristic; E-mail: ristic@uwm.edu; *Support Serv,* Kay Guildner; E-mail: guildner@uwm.edu. Subject Specialists: *Cartography,* Angie Cope; *Digital spatial data, GIS,* Position Currently Open; Staff 8 (MLS 6, Non-MLS 2)
Founded 1851
Subject Interests: Cartography, Exploration, Geog
Function: Res libr
Publications: AGS Library Special Publications; Current Geographical Publications: Contents (Online only); Online Geographical Bibliography (GEOBIB)
Open Mon-Fri 8-4:30
Friends of the Library Group

S   WISCONSIN CONSERVATORY MUSIC LIBRARY*, 1584 N Prospect Ave, 53202. SAN 318-2576. Tel: 414-276-5760. FAX: 414-276-6076. Web Site: www.wcmusic.org. *Chief Librn,* Raymond Mueller; E-mail: raymueller@wcmusic.org
Founded 1969
Library Holdings: CDs 15,000; Music Scores 10,000; Bk Titles 10,000
Special Collections: Late 19th & Early 20th Century Music; Music for Classical Guitar; Music for the Violin (Hatzi Coll)
Publications: Twelve Landler for Two Guitars (facsimile reprint of 19th-century music)
Partic in Library Council of Southeastern Wisconsin, Inc
Open Mon-Wed 12-6, Thurs & Fri 12-5, Sat 9-1

C   WISCONSIN LUTHERAN COLLEGE LIBRARY, Marvin M Schwan Library, 8800 W Bluemound Rd, 53226. SAN 324-7236. Tel: 414-443-8864. FAX: 414-443-8505. E-mail: library@wlc.edu. Web Site: www.wlc.edu/library. *Dir of Libr Serv,* Starla Siegmann; *Info Literacy Librn, Res Asst,* Jenny Baker
Founded 1978. Enrl 700; Fac 50; Highest Degree: Bachelor
Library Holdings: Bk Vols 75,000
Subject Interests: Liberal arts, Lutheran theol
Automation Activity & Vendor Info: (Acquisitions) Innovative Interfaces, Inc; (Cataloging) Innovative Interfaces, Inc; (Circulation) Innovative

Interfaces, Inc; (Course Reserve) Innovative Interfaces, Inc; (ILL) OCLC FirstSearch; (Media Booking) Innovative Interfaces, Inc; (OPAC) Innovative Interfaces, Inc; (Serials) Innovative Interfaces, Inc
Database Vendor: American Chemical Society, American Psychological Association (APA), Baker & Taylor, BioOne, Checkpoint Systems, Inc, EBSCOhost, Elsevier, Gale Cengage Learning, Innovative Interfaces, Inc, ISI Web of Knowledge, JSTOR, netLibrary, Newsbank-Readex, OCLC FirstSearch, OCLC WorldCat, Project MUSE, ProQuest, PubMed, ScienceDirect, SerialsSolutions, STN International, Thomson - Web of Science
Wireless access
Partic in OCLC Online Computer Library Center, Inc; Southeastern Wisconsin Information Technology Exchange, Inc; Wisconsin Library Services

P   WISCONSIN TALKING BOOK & BRAILLE LIBRARY, 813 W Wells St, 53233-1436. SAN 318-2614. Tel: 414-286-3045. Toll Free Tel: 800-242-8822. FAX: 414-286-3102. E-mail: wtbbl@milwaukee.gov. Web Site: dpi.wi.gov/rll/wrlbph/, talkingbooks.wi.gov. *Mgt Librn,* Linda S Vincent; Tel: 414-286-3010, E-mail: lvince@milwaukee.gov; *Outreach Librn,* Roxanne Staveness; Tel: 414-286-6918, E-mail: RoStave@milwaukee.gov; *Ref Librn,* Kimberly Tomlinson; E-mail: kstomli@milwaukee.gov; Staff 15 (MLS 3, Non-MLS 12)
Founded 1960
Library Holdings: Audiobooks 74,000; Braille Volumes 1,845; DVDs 558; Bk Titles 74,000; Per Subs 70
Special Collections: Wisconsin Subjects & Authors, braille & digital cartridges
Automation Activity & Vendor Info: (Acquisitions) Keystone Systems, Inc (KLAS); (Cataloging) Keystone Systems, Inc (KLAS); (Circulation) Keystone Systems, Inc (KLAS); (Course Reserve) Keystone Systems, Inc (KLAS); (ILL) Keystone Systems, Inc (KLAS); (OPAC) Keystone Systems, Inc (KLAS); (Serials) Keystone Systems, Inc (KLAS)
Wireless access
Function: Accessibility serv available based on individual needs, Bks on cassette, Digital talking bks, e-mail serv, Mail & tel request accepted, Mail loans to mem, Online cat, Outreach serv, Spoken cassettes & DVDs, Summer reading prog, Web-Braille, Web-catalog, Wheelchair accessible
Publications: Bulletin Board (Newsletter)
Special Services for the Blind - Mags & bk reproduction/duplication; Newsletter (in large print, Braille or on cassette); Newsline for the Blind; Recorded bks; Talking bk & rec for the blind cat; Talking bks; Talking bks & player equip; Web-Braille
Open Mon-Fri 9-5
Restriction: Restricted borrowing privileges, Visually impaired students & their teachers, Visually impaired students, teachers & their parents

MINERAL POINT

P   MINERAL POINT PUBLIC LIBRARY*, 137 High St, 53565. SAN 318-2622. Tel: 608-987-2447. FAX: 608-987-2447. Web Site: www.swls.org/member.mi.html. *Dir,* Barbara Polizzi; E-mail: bpolizzi@swls.org; *Curator,* Mary Alice Moore; E-mail: minptroom@hotmail.com; *Asst Curator,* Mary Faith Angall; Staff 1 (Non-MLS 1)
Founded 1895. Pop 2,617; Circ 30,022
Library Holdings: Bks on Deafness & Sign Lang 55; Bk Titles 16,971; Bk Vols 17,034; Per Subs 55
Special Collections: Mineral Point Room of Local History; Natural History (Loraine Nohr Memorial Library of Natural History)
Automation Activity & Vendor Info: (Cataloging) SirsiDynix; (Circulation) SirsiDynix; (ILL) SirsiDynix; (OPAC) SirsiDynix
Mem of Southwest Wisconsin Library System
Open Mon-Wed & Fri 10-5:30, Thurs 10-5:30 & 7-8:30, Sat 12-4
Friends of the Library Group

MINOCQUA

P   MINOCQUA PUBLIC LIBRARY*, 415 Menominee St, 54548. (Mail add: PO Box 1087, 54548-1087), SAN 318-2630. Tel: 715-356-4437. FAX: 715-358-2873. E-mail: minlibra@wvls.lib.wi.us. Web Site: www.minocqualibrary.org. *Dir,* Mary Taylor; E-mail: mtaylor1@wvls.lib.wi.us; *Adult Serv,* Cindy Hultman; E-mail: chultman@wvls.lib.wi.us
Founded 1933
Library Holdings: Bk Vols 28,000; Per Subs 100
Automation Activity & Vendor Info: (Cataloging) SirsiDynix; (Circulation) SirsiDynix; (OPAC) SirsiDynix
Mem of Wisconsin Valley Library Service
Open Mon-Wed 9:30-8, Thurs & Fri 9-5, Sat 9:30-Noon
Friends of the Library Group

MONDOVI

P　MONDOVI PUBLIC LIBRARY, 146 W Hudson St, 54755. SAN
318-2649. Tel: 715-926-4403. E-mail: mondovipl@wrlsweb.org. Web Site:
www.wrlsweb.org/mondovi. *Dir,* Arin Christopher Wilken; Staff 5
(Non-MLS 5)
Founded 1902. Pop 5,000; Circ 36,000
Jan 2013-Dec 2013 Income $71,489, State $3,500, City $55,204, County
$12,785. Mats Exp $18,300, Books $14,750, Per/Ser (Incl. Access Fees)
$1,800, AV Mat $1,750. Sal $44,969 (Prof $21,778)
Library Holdings: AV Mats 825; CDs 172; Large Print Bks 423; Bk Vols
22,825; Per Subs 55; Talking Bks 317; Videos 507
Automation Activity & Vendor Info: (Cataloging) Follett Software;
(Circulation) Follett Software; (OPAC) Follett Software
Database Vendor: EBSCOhost
Mem of Winding Rivers Library System
Open Mon & Wed 9-6, Tues & Thurs 2-8, Fri 1-3, Sat 9-12
Friends of the Library Group

MONONA

P　MONONA PUBLIC LIBRARY*, 1000 Nichols Rd, 53716-2531. SAN
318-2657. Tel: 608-222-6127. FAX: 608-222-8590. E-mail:
monona@scls.lib.wi.us. Web Site: www.mononalibrary.info. *Dir,* Demita
Gerber; E-mail: dgerber@scls.lib.wi.us; *Librn,* Rob Klecker; *Pub Serv
Librn,* Erick Plumb; *Youth Serv Coordr,* Karen Wendt
Founded 1964. Pop 11,000; Circ 280,100
Library Holdings: Bk Vols 60,672; Per Subs 80
Special Collections: Living History of Historic Blooming Grove. Oral
History
Automation Activity & Vendor Info: (Acquisitions) SirsiDynix;
(Cataloging) SirsiDynix; (Circulation) SirsiDynix
Mem of South Central Library System
Open Mon-Thurs 10-8, Fri 10-6, Sat 9-5, Sun 1-4
Friends of the Library Group

MONROE

M　MONROE CLINIC, Medical Library, 515 22nd Ave, 53566. SAN
322-7634. Tel: 608-324-1164. FAX: 608-324-2499. E-mail:
library@monroeclinic.org. *Libr Coordr,* Marcia Kaiser; Tel: 608-324-1590;
Staff 0.5 (MLS 0.5)
Founded 1973
Library Holdings: Bk Titles 700; Per Subs 100
Subject Interests: Med, Nursing
Database Vendor: Micromedex, OVID Technologies, UpToDate
Wireless access
Partic in South Central Wisconsin Health Science Library Consortium
Restriction: Non-circulating to the pub

P　MONROE PUBLIC LIBRARY*, 925 16th Ave, 53566-1497. SAN
318-2665. Tel: 608-328-7010. FAX: 608-329-4657. E-mail:
ludemail@scls.lib.wi.us. Web Site: www.monroepubliclibrary.org. *Dir,*
Barbara Brewer; E-mail: bbrewer@scls.lib.wi.us; *Acq,* Ann Mueller; Staff 1
(MLS 1)
Founded 1904. Pop 18,515; Circ 224,034
Library Holdings: Bk Vols 80,721; Per Subs 177
Subject Interests: Green County, Wis hist
Automation Activity & Vendor Info: (Circulation) SirsiDynix
Open Mon-Thurs 9-9, Fri 9-6, Sat 9-4
Friends of the Library Group

MONTELLO

P　MONTELLO PUBLIC LIBRARY*, 128 Lake Ct, 53949-9204. (Mail add:
PO Box 457, 53949-0457), SAN 325-2892. Tel: 608-297-7544. FAX:
608-297-2673. Web Site: www.montellolibrary.org. *Dir,* Sharon McDowell;
E-mail: mcdowell@montellolibrary.org; Staff 1 (MLS 1)
Founded 1936. Pop 1,500; Circ 24,591
Library Holdings: Bk Titles 12,000; Per Subs 40
Special Collections: John Muir Coll, bks & magazines
Automation Activity & Vendor Info: (Cataloging) SirsiDynix;
(Circulation) SirsiDynix
Wireless access
Mem of Winnefox Library System
Open Mon & Thurs 10-7:30, Tues & Wed 10-5, Fri 9-5, Sat 10-1
Friends of the Library Group

MONTFORT

P　MONTFORT PUBLIC LIBRARY*, 102 E Park St, 53569. (Mail add: PO
Box 8, 53569-0008), SAN 318-2673. Tel: 608-943-6265. FAX:
608-943-6265. E-mail: montlibr@mhtc.net. *Dir,* Marcie Harwick
Founded 1885. Pop 663; Circ 429,000
Jan 2005-Dec 2005 Income $25,189, City $20,589, County $4,600. Mats
Exp $4,032, Books $3,200, AV Mat $832. Sal $9,059 (Prof $8,459)

Library Holdings: AV Mats 210; Large Print Bks 85; Bk Vols 6,049;
Talking Bks 125
Mem of Southwest Wisconsin Library System
Open Mon 2-8:30, Tues 10-6, Wed 2-8:30, Thurs & Fri 2-5:30, Sat 9-11

MONTICELLO

P　MONTICELLO PUBLIC LIBRARY*, 512 E Lake Ave, 53570-9658. (Mail
add: PO Box 149, 53570-0149), SAN 377-998X. Tel: 608-938-4011. FAX:
608-938-1772. E-mail: mntlibr7@tds.net. *Dir,* Sharon Briggs
Library Holdings: Bk Titles 14,000; Per Subs 50
Automation Activity & Vendor Info: (Cataloging) Follett Software;
(Circulation) Follett Software
Mem of South Central Library System
Open Mon 1-5:30, Tues & Thurs 1-7:30, Wed 9-12 & 1-7:30, Fri 9-12 &
1-5:30, Sat 9-12
Friends of the Library Group

MOUNT HOREB

P　MOUNT HOREB PUBLIC LIBRARY*, 105 Perimeter Rd, 53572. SAN
318-2711. Tel: 608-437-5021. FAX: 608-437-6264. E-mail:
mhpl@scls.lib.wi.us. Web Site: www.scls.lib.wi.us/mounthoreb. *Dir,*
Lysianne Unruh; E-mail: lunruh@scls.lib.wi.us; *Circ Supvr,* Brendan
Faherty; E-mail: bfaherty@scls.lib.wi.us; *Tech Serv,* Pam Cairney; *Tech
Serv,* Carol Cullen; *Youth Serv,* Linda Colby; Staff 16 (MLS 2, Non-MLS
14)
Founded 1877. Pop 7,000; Circ 166,125
Library Holdings: AV Mats 1,993; Bk Vols 32,753; Per Subs 166; Talking
Bks 1,552
Special Collections: Girl & Boy Scout Coll; Mount Horeb Mail
Newspaper, July 17, 1883-1992
Wireless access
Function: Homebound delivery serv, ILL available, Magnifiers for reading,
Photocopying/Printing, Prog for children & young adult, Ref serv available,
Summer reading prog, Telephone ref, Wheelchair accessible
Publications: The Mount Horeb Reader (Newsletter)
Mem of South Central Library System
Partic in Library Interchange Network (LINK)
Special Services for the Blind - Bks on cassette; Bks on CD; Home
delivery serv; Low vision equip; Magnifiers
Mon-Thurs 9:30-8:30, Fri 9:30-5:30, Sat 9:30-3:30
Friends of the Library Group

MUKWONAGO

P　MUKWONAGO COMMUNITY LIBRARY*, 300 Washington Ave,
53149-1909. SAN 318-272X. Tel: 262-363-6411. Reference Tel:
262-363-6456. FAX: 262-363-6457. Web Site:
www.wcfls.lib.wi.us/mukcom/. *Dir,* Kathleen McBride; E-mail:
kmcbride@mukcom.lib.wi.us
Library Holdings: Bk Vols 69,000; Per Subs 152
Subject Interests: Hist
Automation Activity & Vendor Info: (Cataloging) SirsiDynix;
(Circulation) SirsiDynix; (OPAC) SirsiDynix
Mem of Waukesha County Federated Library System
Open Mon-Thurs 9-8:30, Fri 9-5, Sat 9-4 (Summer 9-2)
Friends of the Library Group

MUSCODA

P　MUSCODA PUBLIC LIBRARY*, 206 N Wisconsin Ave, 53569. SAN
318-2738. Tel: 608-739-3182. FAX: 608-739-3183. Web Site:
www.muscodapubliclibrary.wordpress.com. *Dir,* Lorna Aigner; E-mail:
laigner@swls.org; *Asst Librn,* Lynn Meister
Founded 1926. Pop 1,453; Circ 15,915
Library Holdings: Bk Titles 8,000; Bk Vols 10,541; Per Subs 25
Subject Interests: Local hist
Automation Activity & Vendor Info: (Cataloging) Horizon; (Circulation)
Horizon; (OPAC) Horizon
Mem of Southwest Wisconsin Library System
Open Mon-Wed 10-8, Fri 10-5, Sat 9-Noon

MUSKEGO

P　MUSKEGO PUBLIC LIBRARY*, S73 W16663 Janesville Rd, 53150.
(Mail add: PO Box 810, 53150-0810), SAN 318-2746. Tel: 262-971-2100.
Circulation Tel: 262-971-2111. Interlibrary Loan Service Tel:
262-971-2112. Reference Tel: 262-971-2101. Administration Tel:
262-971-2119. Automation Services Tel: 262-971-2108. Information
Services Tel: 262-971-2105. FAX: 262-971-2115. Web Site:
www.ci.muskego.wi.us/library. *Dir,* Pete Loeffel; *Interim Dir,* Bernie
Bellin; *Asst Dir,* Jane Genzel; E-mail: jgenzel@ci.muskego.wi.us; *Head,
Info Serv,* Paula House; Tel: 262-971-2109, E-mail:
phouse@ci.muskego.wi.us; *Head, Pub Serv,* Penny Halle; Tel:
262-971-2106, E-mail: phalle@ci.muskego.wi.us; *Head, Support Serv,*

Linda Brown; E-mail: lbrown@ci.muskego.wi.us; Staff 8 (MLS 2, Non-MLS 6)
Founded 1960. Pop 26,000; Circ 193,522
Jan 2006-Dec 2006 Income $1,281,745, State $1,670, Provincial $21,220, City $1,045,382, County $28,342, Locally Generated Income $22,964, Parent Institution $92,540, Other $69,627. Mats Exp $132,421, Books $73,776, Per/Ser (Incl. Access Fees) $13,670, AV Mat $38,630, Electronic Ref Mat (Incl. Access Fees) $5,345, Presv $1,000. Sal $506,529 (Prof $205,385)
Library Holdings: AV Mats 9,016; Bks on Deafness & Sign Lang 100; High Interest/Low Vocabulary Bk Vols 200; Large Print Bks 2,500; Bk Titles 98,000; Bk Vols 110,670; Per Subs 300
Automation Activity & Vendor Info: (Acquisitions) SirsiDynix; (Cataloging) SirsiDynix; (Circulation) SirsiDynix; (ILL) SirsiDynix; (Media Booking) SirsiDynix; (OPAC) SirsiDynix; (Serials) SirsiDynix
Wireless access
Function: Adult bk club, Art exhibits, Bk club(s), Bks on cassette, Bks on CD, CD-ROM, Children's prog, Computer training, Computers for patron use, Copy machines, E-Reserves, Electronic databases & coll, Free DVD rentals, Handicapped accessible, Holiday prog, ILL available, Magnifiers for reading, Mail & tel request accepted, Music CDs, Online cat, Online ref, Online searches, OverDrive digital audio bks, Photocopying/Printing, Preschool outreach, Prof lending libr, Prog for adults, Prog for children & young adult, Ref & res, Ref serv available, Senior computer classes, Spoken cassettes & CDs, Spoken cassettes & DVDs, Summer reading prog, Tax forms, Teen prog, Telephone ref, VHS videos, Video lending libr, Wheelchair accessible, Workshops, Writing prog
Mem of Waukesha County Federated Library System
Partic in OCLC Online Computer Library Center, Inc; Wiscat
Open Mon-Thurs 9-9, Fri & Sat 9-5
Restriction: Authorized patrons
Friends of the Library Group

NASHOTAH

SR　NASHOTAH HOUSE LIBRARY*, 2777 Mission Rd, 53058-9793. SAN 318-2754. Tel: 262-646-6535. FAX: 262-646-6504. Web Site: www.nashotah.edu/library. *Dir,* David Sherwood; Tel: 262-646-6534, E-mail: librarian@nashotah.edu; *ILL, Ser,* Laura Hummer; E-mail: loan@nashotah.edu. Subject Specialists: *Ascetic theol,* David Sherwood; Staff 4 (MLS 1, Non-MLS 3)
Founded 1842
Library Holdings: Bk Vols 100,000; Per Subs 300
Special Collections: Archives of Nashotah House; National Altar Guild Coll; Prayer Books (Underwood Coll)
Subject Interests: Anglicana, Bks of common prayer, Especially Bibles, Pre-1800 imprints
Automation Activity & Vendor Info: (Acquisitions) EOS International; (Cataloging) EOS International; (Circulation) EOS International; (ILL) OCLC; (OPAC) EOS International; (Serials) EOS International
Database Vendor: ebrary, EBSCOhost, OCLC FirstSearch, Oxford Online, ProQuest, YBP Library Services
Wireless access
Partic in Library Council of Southeastern Wisconsin, Inc; OCLC Online Computer Library Center, Inc; Wisconsin Library Services
Open Mon-Fri 8:30-4:20

NECEDAH

P　NECEDAH MEMORIAL LIBRARY*, 216 S Main St, 54646. (Mail add: PO Box 279, 54646-0279), SAN 318-2762. Tel: 608-565-7979. E-mail: necmem@wrls.org. *Dir,* Jim Eliason; Staff 1 (MLS 1)
Founded 1914. Pop 3,000
Library Holdings: Bk Vols 10,329; Per Subs 26
Mem of Winding Rivers Library System
Open Mon-Wed & Fri 12:30-5, Sat 9-1

NEENAH

M　THEDA CLARK MEDICAL CENTER*, ThedaCare Library, 130 Second St, 54956-2883. (Mail add: PO Box 2021, 54957-2021), SAN 318-2789. Tel: 920-729-2190. FAX: 920-729-2321. *Librn,* Mary Horan; Staff 2 (MLS 1, Non-MLS 1)
Founded 1970
Library Holdings: Bk Titles 1,300; Bk Vols 1,800; Per Subs 300
Subject Interests: Critical care, Maternal fetal med, Neonatal intensive care, Trauma
Partic in Fox River Valley Area Library Consortium; Fox Valley Library Council
Open Mon-Fri 7:30-3:30

S　J J KELLER & ASSOCIATES, INC*, Research & Technical Library, 3003 W Breezewood Lane, 54956-9611. (Mail add: PO Box 368, 54957-0368), SAN 318-2797. Tel: 920-722-2848. FAX: 920-720-7741. Web Site: www.jjkeller.com. *Sr Coll Adminr,* Janice Laubenstein; Tel: 920-722-7271

Founded 1958
Subject Interests: Distribution, Hazardous waste, Human resources, Occupational safety, Regulatory law, Safety, Security, Transportation, Trucking
Wireless access
Partic in Fox Valley Library Council
Restriction: Staff use only

S　KIMBERLY-CLARK CORP LIBRARY*, 2100 Winchester Rd, 54957. (Mail add: PO Box 999, 54957-0999), SAN 318-2800. Tel: 920-721-5262. FAX: 920-721-6394. *Mgr, Libr Serv,* Cheryl R Nelson; E-mail: crnelson@kcc.com; Staff 4 (MLS 2, Non-MLS 2)
Library Holdings: Bk Vols 20,000; Per Subs 450
Subject Interests: Chem, Paper, Pulp sci, Textiles
Database Vendor: SirsiDynix

P　NEENAH PUBLIC LIBRARY, 240 E Wisconsin Ave, 54956-3010. (Mail add: PO Box 569, 54957-0569), SAN 318-2819. Tel: 920-886-6315. Circulation Tel: 920-886-6320. Interlibrary Loan Service Tel: 920-886-6313. Administration Tel: 920-886-6300. FAX: 920-886-6324. Circulation FAX: 920-886-6323. Web Site: www.neenahlibrary.org. *Dir,* Stephen Lewis Proces; *Asst Dir,* Gretchen Raab; Tel: 920-886-6310; *Adult Serv,* Nicole Hardina-Wilhelm; Tel: 920-886-6312; *Adult Serv,* Melissa Kazmer; *Adult Serv,* Cheryl Kraft; Tel: 920-886-6314; *Adult Serv,* Michael Thomas; Tel: 920-886-6311; *Circ,* Nancy Britten; *Youth Serv,* Katrina Collins; Tel: 920-886-6330; Staff 8 (MLS 8)
Founded 1884. Pop 50,000; Circ 950,000
Library Holdings: Audiobooks 8,000; CDs 12,000; DVDs 25,000; e-books 15,000; Electronic Media & Resources 800; High Interest/Low Vocabulary Bk Vols 300; Large Print Bks 3,000; Bk Vols 200,000; Per Subs 375; Videos 6,000
Subject Interests: Local hist, Naval hist
Automation Activity & Vendor Info: (Acquisitions) SirsiDynix; (Cataloging) SirsiDynix; (Circulation) SirsiDynix; (OPAC) SirsiDynix; (Serials) SirsiDynix
Database Vendor: SirsiDynix
Wireless access
Function: AV serv, Handicapped accessible, Home delivery & serv to Sr ctr & nursing homes, Homebound delivery serv, ILL available, Online searches, Photocopying/Printing, Prog for adults, Prog for children & young adult, Ref serv available, Serves mentally handicapped consumers, Summer reading prog, Telephone ref, Wheelchair accessible
Publications: Newsletters (Bi-monthly)
Mem of Winnefox Library System
Open Mon-Thurs (Winter) 9-9, Fri 9-6, Sat 9-5, Sun 1-5; Mon-Thurs (Summer) 9-9, Fri 9-6, Sat 9-1
Friends of the Library Group

NEILLSVILLE

P　NEILLSVILLE PUBLIC LIBRARY*, 409 Hewett St, 54456-1923. SAN 318-2827. Tel: 715-743-2558. FAX: 715-743-6213. Web Site: wvls.lib.wi.us/NeillsvillePublicLibrary. *Dir,* Jo Ann Gustavson; E-mail: gustav@wvls.lib.wi.us
Pop 6,900; Circ 79,358
Library Holdings: Bk Vols 28,000; Per Subs 97
Automation Activity & Vendor Info: (Cataloging) Follett Software; (Circulation) Follett Software; (OPAC) Follett Software
Mem of Wisconsin Valley Library Service
Open Mon & Wed 10-8, Tues, Thurs & Fri 9-5, Sat 9-12
Friends of the Library Group

NEKOOSA

P　CHARLES & JOANN LESTER LIBRARY*, 100 Park St, 54457. SAN 318-2835. Tel: 715-886-7879. E-mail: nkpl@charter.net. Web Site: www.scls.lib.wi.us/nek. *Dir,* Darla Allen
Founded 1939. Pop 2,794; Circ 48,340
Library Holdings: Bk Vols 40,000; Per Subs 70
Open Mon, Tues & Thurs 9-7, Wed 9-8, Fri 9-5, Sat 9-12
Friends of the Library Group

P　LESTER PUBLIC LIBRARY OF ROME*, 1157 Rome Center Dr, 54457. Tel: 715-325-8990. FAX: 715-325-8993. E-mail: romelib@wctc.net. Web Site: www.romepubliclibrary.org. *Dir,* Lore Ponshock; *Asst Dir,* Marilyn Bailey; *Librn,* Jim Keith
Library Holdings: AV Mats 800; Bk Titles 14,000; Per Subs 31; Talking Bks 400
Automation Activity & Vendor Info: (Cataloging) Follett Software; (Circulation) Follett Software
Wireless access
Mem of South Central Library System
Open Mon, Wed & Fri 10-5, Tues & Thurs 10-7, Sat 9-12

NEOSHO

P   NEOSHO PUBLIC LIBRARY*, Hwy 67, 53059. SAN 328-736X. Tel:
920-625-3086. E-mail: nplibrary11a@charter.net. *Librn,* Linda Albertson
Library Holdings: Bk Vols 1,500
Open Tues & Thurs 10-2

NESHKORO

P   NESHKORO PUBLIC LIBRARY*, 132 S Main St, 54960. (Mail add: PO
Box 196, 54960-0196), SAN 378-0007. Tel: 920-293-4026. FAX:
920-293-4026. E-mail: director@neshkorolibrary.org. Web Site:
www.neshkorolibrary.org. *Dir,* Cheryl Milbrandt; Staff 2 (Non-MLS 2)
Founded 1975. Pop 484
Library Holdings: Bk Titles 10,000; Per Subs 20
Mem of Winnefox Library System
Open Mon & Tues (Winter) 9-5, Fri 12-5; Tues-Thurs (Summer) 10-5
Friends of the Library Group

NEW BERLIN

P   NEW BERLIN PUBLIC LIBRARY, 15105 Library Lane, 53151. SAN
318-2851. Tel: 262-785-4980. FAX: 262-785-4984. E-mail:
nbinfo@newberlinlibrary.org. Web Site: www.newberlinlibrary.org. *Dir,*
Dennis Sampson; E-mail: dsampson@newberlinlibrary.org; *Asst Dir, Ch,*
Melissa Schneider; *Head, Adult Serv,* Barbara Draeger; *Adult & Children's
Ref,* Michelle Plunkett; *Adult Ref,* Natalie Beacom; *Adult Ref,* Jerry
Dombraski; *Adult Ref,* Marnie Schmidt; *Ch,* Mary Flagg; *Ch, Ref,* Michelle
Neubauer; Staff 22 (MLS 9, Non-MLS 13)
Founded 1969. Pop 38,000; Circ 378,000
Library Holdings: Bk Vols 150,000; Per Subs 253
Special Collections: State Selected Depository Library. State Document
Depository
Subject Interests: Cookery, Hist, Indust
Automation Activity & Vendor Info: (Cataloging) Polaris Library
Systems; (Circulation) Polaris Library Systems; (OPAC) Polaris Library
Systems
Database Vendor: SirsiDynix
Wireless access
Publications: Annotated Bibliographies for Young Readers & Their
Parents; Annotated Bibliographies of Business Resources; Library Info
Brochure
Mem of Waukesha County Federated Library System
Open Mon-Thurs 9-9, Fri & Sat 9-5, Sun (Sept-May) 1-4
Friends of the Library Group

NEW GLARUS

P   NEW GLARUS PUBLIC LIBRARY*, 319 Second St, 53574. (Mail add:
PO Box 35, 53574-0035), SAN 318-286X. Tel: 608-527-2003. FAX:
608-527-5126. E-mail: ngpl@scls.lib.wi.us. Web Site: www.scls.lib.wi.us.
Dir, Denise Anton Wright; E-mail: dawright@scls.lib.wi.us; *Asst Dir,* Janis
Merkle; *Ch,* Ignacia Boersma
Founded 1934. Pop 2,731; Circ 67,487
Library Holdings: Bk Vols 22,179; Per Subs 104
Mem of South Central Library System
Open Mon-Fri 10-7, Sat 10-1
Friends of the Library Group

NEW HOLSTEIN

P   NEW HOLSTEIN PUBLIC LIBRARY*, 2115 Washington St, 53061-1098.
SAN 318-2878. Tel: 920-898-5165. FAX: 920-898-9022. Web Site:
www.newholsteinlibrary.org. *Dir,* Barbara A Weber; E-mail:
bweber@mcls.lib.wi.us
Founded 1929. Pop 7,300; Circ 63,900
Library Holdings: Bk Vols 40,462; Per Subs 111
Automation Activity & Vendor Info: (Cataloging) SirsiDynix;
(Circulation) SirsiDynix; (OPAC) SirsiDynix
Wireless access
Mem of Manitowoc-Calumet Library System
Open Mon & Wed (Winter) 9-7:30, Tues & Thurs 10-7:30, Fri 10-6, Sat
10-2; Mon & Wed (Summer) 9-7:30, Tues, Thurs & Fri 10-6

NEW LISBON

S   NEW LISBON CORRECTIONAL INSTITUTION LIBRARY*, 2000
Progress Rd, 53950. Tel: 608-562-7375. FAX: 608-562-6410. *Librn,* Lynn
Martin; Staff 1 (MLS 1)
Founded 2003
Library Holdings: Bk Vols 10,000; Per Subs 30
Automation Activity & Vendor Info: (Cataloging) Follett Software;
(Circulation) Follett Software; (ILL) Auto-Graphics, Inc; (OPAC) Follett
Software
Open Mon-Sun 7:50am-8:50pm

P   NEW LISBON MEMORIAL LIBRARY*, 115 W Park St, 53950-1250.
SAN 318-2886. Tel: 608-562-3213. FAX: 608-562-3213. E-mail:
nlploff@wrlsweb.org. Web Site: www.wrlsweb.org/newlisbon/. *Dir,* Mary
Crawford
Founded 1931
Library Holdings: Bk Vols 29,765; Per Subs 97
Special Collections: Indian Artifacts (Harry Mortenson Coll), bks
Automation Activity & Vendor Info: (Acquisitions) SirsiDynix;
(Cataloging) SirsiDynix; (Circulation) SirsiDynix
Mem of Winding Rivers Library System
Open Mon 12-8, Tues 9-12 & 1-5:30, Wed 9-5:30, Thurs 9-12, 1-5 & 6-8,
Fri 12-5

NEW LONDON

P   NEW LONDON PUBLIC LIBRARY, 406 S Pearl St, 54961-1441. SAN
318-2908. Tel: 920-982-8519. FAX: 920-982-8617. E-mail:
nlp@mail.owls.lib.wi.us. Web Site: www.newlondonlibrary.org. *Dir,* Ann
Hunt; E-mail: ahunt@mail.owls.lib.wi.us; *Ch,* Stacy Mueller; *Adult Serv,*
Mehta Hess; Staff 7 (MLS 2, Non-MLS 5)
Founded 1895. Pop 12,000; Circ 148,000
Jan 2012-Dec 2012 Income $463,278. Mats Exp $59,130, Books $38,513,
Per/Ser (Incl. Access Fees) $3,100, Other Print Mats $5,000, AV Mat
$11,940, Electronic Ref Mat (Incl. Access Fees) $577. Sal $219,615 (Prof
$169,615)
Library Holdings: Bk Titles 49,900; Bk Vols 54,900; Per Subs 119
Special Collections: Historical Coll
Automation Activity & Vendor Info: (Acquisitions) Innovative Interfaces,
Inc; (Cataloging) Innovative Interfaces, Inc; (Circulation) Innovative
Interfaces, Inc; (ILL) OCLC WorldCat; (OPAC) Innovative Interfaces, Inc
Database Vendor: EBSCOhost, Gale Cengage Learning
Wireless access
Mem of Outagamie Waupaca Library System
Open Mon-Thurs (Winter) 9-8, Fri 9-6, Sat 9-2, Sun 1-5; Mon-Thurs
(Summer) 9-8, Fri 9-6
Friends of the Library Group

NEW RICHMOND

P   CARLETON A FRIDAY MEMORIAL LIBRARY*, New Richmond Public
Library, 155 E First St, 54017. SAN 318-2916. Tel: 715-243-0431. FAX:
715-246-2691. E-mail: nrpublib@ifls.lib.wi.us. Web Site:
www.fridaylibrary.org. *Dir,* Scott Vrieze; *Ch,* Georgia Jones; *ILL,* Sandra
Venhor; *Pub Serv,* Bev Jacobs; *Pub Serv,* Leanne A Koepke; *Tech Serv,*
Jennifer Rickard; Staff 9 (MLS 2, Non-MLS 7)
Founded 1883. Pop 17,553; Circ 190,404
Library Holdings: AV Mats 2,951; Bk Vols 42,395; Per Subs 120
Special Collections: New Richmond Historical Coll. Oral History
Automation Activity & Vendor Info: (Acquisitions) Innovative Interfaces,
Inc; (Cataloging) Innovative Interfaces, Inc; (Circulation) Innovative
Interfaces, Inc; (OPAC) Innovative Interfaces, Inc
Database Vendor: EBSCOhost, ProQuest
Wireless access
Function: Bk club(s), Bks on cassette, Bks on CD, Children's prog,
Computers for patron use, Electronic databases & coll, Free DVD rentals
Mem of Indianhead Federated Library System
Open Mon-Thurs 9-8, Fri 9-6, Sat 9-3
Friends of the Library Group

J   WISCONSIN INDIANHEAD TECHNICAL COLLEGE*, New Richmond
Campus Learning Resources Center, 1019 S Knowles Ave, 54017. SAN
318-2924. Tel: 715-246-6561, Ext 4222. Toll Free Tel: 800-243-9482, Ext
4222. FAX: 715-246-2777. Web Site: www.witc.edu/library/index.htm. *Libr
Tech,* Cheri Croft; *Libr Tech,* Adam Nelson; Staff 2 (MLS 1, Non-MLS 1)
Founded 1968. Enrl 1,000; Fac 52
Library Holdings: Bk Titles 11,351; Per Subs 160
Subject Interests: Agr, Allied health, Bus, Indust, Nursing, Trade
Automation Activity & Vendor Info: (Cataloging) Gateway; (Circulation)
Gateway; (Course Reserve) Docutek; (OPAC) Gateway
Database Vendor: Cinahl Information Systems, CredoReference, EBSCO
Information Services, EBSCOhost, Facts on File, Gale Cengage Learning,
H W Wilson, Hoovers, infoUSA, Medline, netLibrary, ProQuest, PubMed,
ReferenceUSA, SerialsSolutions, WebFeat, Wilson - Wilson Web
Open Mon-Thurs 7:30-7, Fri 7:30-4

NORTH FOND DU LAC

P   SPILLMAN LIBRARY*, 719 Wisconsin Ave, 54937-1335. SAN 318-2959.
Tel: 920-929-3771. FAX: 920-929-3669. Web Site:
www.northfonddulaclibrary.org. *Dir,* Lois Potratz; E-mail:
director@northfonddulaclibrary.org
Library Holdings: Bk Vols 25,000; Per Subs 50
Automation Activity & Vendor Info: (Cataloging) SirsiDynix;
(Circulation) SirsiDynix; (OPAC) SirsiDynix
Mem of Winnefox Library System
Open Mon & Thurs 8-8, Tues, Wed & Fri 10-5, Sat 10-1

NORTH FREEDOM

P   NORTH FREEDOM PUBLIC LIBRARY*, 105 N Maple St, 53951. (Mail add: PO Box 60, 53951), SAN 318-2967. Tel: 608-522-4571. FAX: 608-522-4574. E-mail: caboose@scls.lib.wi.us. Web Site: www.scls.lib.wi.us/nof. *Dir,* Katie Conway
    Founded 1898. Pop 649; Circ 9,000
    Library Holdings: Bk Titles 4,500; Bk Vols 4,600; Per Subs 30
    Subject Interests: Hist, Natural sci
    Mem of South Central Library System
    Open Mon-Thurs 3-7, Fri & Sat 9-2

NORTH LAKE

P   TOWN HALL LIBRARY*, N 76 W 31429 Hwy VV, 53064. (Mail add: PO Box 158, 53064-0158), SAN 318-2975. Tel: 262-966-2933. FAX: 262-966-3365. Web Site: www.wcfls.lib.wi.us/townhall. *Dir,* Heidi Cox; E-mail: hcox@wcfls.lib.wi.us; Staff 10 (MLS 1, Non-MLS 9)
    Founded 1964. Pop 8,500
    Library Holdings: AV Mats 6,200; e-books 7,951; Bk Titles 38,000; Bk Vols 40,000; Per Subs 110; Talking Bks 2,984
    Automation Activity & Vendor Info: (Cataloging) SirsiDynix; (Circulation) SirsiDynix; (Course Reserve) SirsiDynix; (ILL) SirsiDynix; (Media Booking) SirsiDynix; (OPAC) SirsiDynix; (Serials) SirsiDynix
    Database Vendor: EBSCOhost, Gale Cengage Learning, netLibrary, Newsbank, OCLC FirstSearch
    Wireless access
    Function: Homebound delivery serv, ILL available, Music CDs, Online searches, Photocopying/Printing, Prog for children & young adult, Ref serv available, Spoken cassettes & CDs, Summer reading prog, Telephone ref, VHS videos
    Mem of Waukesha County Federated Library System
    Open Mon-Thurs 9-8, Fri 9-5, Sat 9-1, Sun 12-4
    Friends of the Library Group

NORWALK

P   NORWALK PUBLIC LIBRARY*, 101 Railroad St, 54648. (Mail add: PO Box 132, 54648-0132). Tel: 608-823-7473. E-mail: norwalkpl@wrlsweb.org. *Dir,* Jeanne Rice; Staff 0.75 (MLS 0.75)
    Founded 1995. Pop 945; Circ 6,674
    Library Holdings: AV Mats 400; Bk Titles 8,000; Per Subs 20; Talking Bks 200
    Automation Activity & Vendor Info: (Cataloging) Follett Software; (Circulation) Follett Software
    Mem of Winding Rivers Library System
    Partic in Connecticut Library Consortium
    Open Mon & Wed 11-7, Tues 2-7, Fri 9-5
    Friends of the Library Group

OAK CREEK

J   MILWAUKEE AREA TECHNICAL COLLEGE*, South Campus Library, 6665 S Howell Ave, 53154. SAN 318-2991. Circulation Tel: 414-571-4601. Reference Tel: 414-571-4720. FAX: 414-571-4747. *Campus Librn,* Jenn Medved; Tel: 414-571-4602; *Ref Librn,* Patrick Mundt; E-mail: mundtp@matc.edu; Staff 3 (MLS 2, Non-MLS 1)
    Library Holdings: Bk Titles 14,100; Bk Vols 16,500; Per Subs 90
    Subject Interests: Air conditioning, Computer sci, Fire, Police sci
    Automation Activity & Vendor Info: (Acquisitions) SirsiDynix; (Cataloging) SirsiDynix; (Circulation) SirsiDynix; (Course Reserve) SirsiDynix; (OPAC) SirsiDynix; (Serials) SirsiDynix
    Database Vendor: EBSCOhost, Gale Cengage Learning, ProQuest
    Partic in Library Council of Southeastern Wisconsin, Inc
    Open Mon-Thurs 7:45am-9:30pm, Fri 7:45-4

P   OAK CREEK PUBLIC LIBRARY*, 8620 S Howell Ave, 53154. SAN 318-3009. Tel: 414-764-4400. FAX: 414-768-6583. Web Site: www.mcfls.org/ocpl. *City Librn,* Jill Leninger; Tel: 414-768-6580, E-mail: jill.lininger@mcfls.org; *Asst City Librn,* Susan Kaczmarek; *Children's & YA Librn,* Karen Doro; *Ref Librn,* John Huffstetter; *Ref Librn,* Richmond Kinney; Staff 4.5 (MLS 4.5)
    Founded 1972. Pop 32,341; Circ 264,672
    Jan 2008-Dec 2008 Income $795,240. Mats Exp $96,800, Books $65,200, Per/Ser (Incl. Access Fees) $10,600, AV Mat $21,000. Sal $463,380 (Prof $246,010)
    Library Holdings: AV Mats 11,467; CDs 4,392; DVDs 2,654; e-books 11,956; Large Print Bks 1,950; Bk Vols 65,112; Per Subs 195; Videos 3,585
    Subject Interests: Popular mat
    Automation Activity & Vendor Info: (Cataloging) Innovative Interfaces, Inc; (Circulation) Innovative Interfaces, Inc; (Media Booking) Innovative Interfaces, Inc; (OPAC) Innovative Interfaces, Inc; (Serials) Innovative Interfaces, Inc
    Wireless access
    Publications: Bookmark; Calendar (Monthly)

Mem of Milwaukee County Federated Library System
Partic in Library Council of Southeastern Wisconsin, Inc
Open Mon-Wed 10-8:30, Thurs 12-8:30, Fri 10-5, Sat 10-4, Sun (Sept-May) 1-4
Friends of the Library Group

OAKFIELD

P   OAKFIELD PUBLIC LIBRARY, 130 N Main St, 53065-9563. SAN 318-3017. Tel: 920-583-4552. FAX: 920-583-2544. Web Site: www.oakfieldlibrary.org. *Dir,* Sharon Belling; E-mail: director@oakfieldlibrary.org; *Librn,* Lori DeHaan; Staff 1.13 (Non-MLS 1.13)
    Founded 1898. Pop 2,250; Circ 27,560
    Jan 2011-Dec 2011 Income $71,072, City $45,040, County $26,032
    Library Holdings: Audiobooks 75; CDs 110; DVDs 1,000; e-books 13,452; Bk Titles 15,543; Per Subs 42
    Automation Activity & Vendor Info: (Cataloging) SirsiDynix; (Circulation) SIRSI WorkFlows; (OPAC) SirsiDynix
    Database Vendor: EBSCO Auto Repair Reference, EBSCOhost, ProQuest
    Wireless access
    Mem of Winnefox Library System
    Open Mon, Wed & Thurs 1-7, Tues 10-5, Fri 12-5

OCONOMOWOC

P   OCONOMOWOC PUBLIC LIBRARY*, 200 South St, 53066-5213. SAN 318-3033. Tel: 262-569-2193. Administration Tel: 262-569-2194. FAX: 262-569-2176. *Dir,* Ray McKenna; E-mail: rmckenna@cooney.lib.wi.us; Staff 30 (MLS 3, Non-MLS 27)
    Founded 1893. Pop 27,000; Circ 248,907
    Library Holdings: Bk Vols 99,920; Per Subs 240
    Subject Interests: Art, Biog
    Automation Activity & Vendor Info: (Cataloging) SirsiDynix; (Circulation) SirsiDynix; (ILL) SirsiDynix; (OPAC) SirsiDynix
    Database Vendor: Baker & Taylor, BWI
    Wireless access
    Mem of Waukesha County Federated Library System
    Open Mon-Thurs (Winter) 10-9, Fri 10-5, Sat 9-5, Sun 1-4; Mon-Thurs (Summer) 9-8, Fri 9-5, Sat 9-1
    Friends of the Library Group

OCONTO

P   FARNSWORTH PUBLIC LIBRARY*, 715 Main St, 54153-1795. SAN 318-3041. Tel: 920-834-7730. E-mail: oco@mail.nfls.lib.wi.us. Web Site: www.nfls.lib.wi.us/oco. *Dir,* Margaret Murphy; E-mail: pmurphy@mail.nfls.lib.wi.us
    Founded 1903. Pop 4,446; Circ 50,000
    Library Holdings: Bk Vols 28,000; Per Subs 36
    Subject Interests: Local hist
    Automation Activity & Vendor Info: (Cataloging) Innovative Interfaces, Inc; (Circulation) Innovative Interfaces, Inc; (OPAC) Innovative Interfaces, Inc
    Mem of Nicolet Federated Library System
    Partic in Wiscat
    Open Tues & Wed 11-7, Thurs & Fri 9-5, Sat 9-12
    Friends of the Library Group

OCONTO FALLS

P   OCONTO FALLS COMMUNITY LIBRARY*, 251 N Main St, 54154-1048. SAN 318-305X. Tel: 920-846-2673. FAX: 920-846-9946. E-mail: ocf@mail.nfls.lib.wi.us. *Dir,* Joan Denis; E-mail: jdenis@mail.nfls.lib.wi.us
    Pop 4,500; Circ 43,110
    Library Holdings: AV Mats 1,874; Bk Vols 14,371; Per Subs 108; Talking Bks 761
    Automation Activity & Vendor Info: (Cataloging) Innovative Interfaces, Inc; (Circulation) Innovative Interfaces, Inc; (OPAC) Innovative Interfaces, Inc
    Mem of Nicolet Federated Library System
    Open Mon-Thurs 10-7, Fri 10-5, Sat 9-12
    Friends of the Library Group

ODANAH

P   BAD RIVER PUBLIC TRIBAL LIBRARY, 72682 Maple St, 54861. (Mail add: PO Box 39, 54861), SAN 377-9386. Tel: 715-682-7111, Ext 1532. FAX: 715-682-7118. E-mail: brlibrary@maaskii.nwls.lib.wi.us. *Librn,* Norma J Soulier
    Library Holdings: Audiobooks 112; DVDs 260; Bk Titles 13,500; Per Subs 31; Videos 1,086
    Subject Interests: Native Am
    Mem of Northern Waters Library Service
    Partic in Wis Libr Asn

Open Mon-Fri (Winter) 10-6; Mon-Thurs (Summer) 11-6, Fri 11-5
Friends of the Library Group

OGEMA

P   OGEMA PUBLIC LIBRARY*, W 5005 State Rd 86, 54459. (Mail add:
PO Box 603, 54459-0603), SAN 322-838X. Tel: 715-767-5130. FAX:
715-767-5130. E-mail: ogemapl@centurytel.net. Web Site:
www.ogemalibrary.org. *Librn,* LaVonne Mattson
Founded 1973. Pop 1,000; Circ 7,673
Library Holdings: Bk Titles 16,000
Automation Activity & Vendor Info: (Cataloging) Follett Software;
(Circulation) Follett Software
Mem of Indianhead Federated Library System
Open Tues & Thurs 9-12 & 1-7, Wed 9-12 & 1-6, Fri 9-12, Sat 10-12

OMRO

P   OMRO PUBLIC LIBRARY*, Carter Memorial Library, 405 E Huron St,
54963-1405. SAN 324-7244. Tel: 920-685-7016. FAX: 920-685-7017.
E-mail: director@omrolibrary.org. Web Site: www.omrolibrary.org. *Dir,*
Julie Stobbe; E-mail: stobbe@omrolibrary.org; Staff 5 (MLS 1, Non-MLS
4)
Pop 3,600; Circ 39,357
Library Holdings: Bk Vols 21,500; Per Subs 70
Special Collections: Local History Coll
Automation Activity & Vendor Info: (Cataloging) SirsiDynix;
(Circulation) SirsiDynix; (OPAC) SirsiDynix
Database Vendor: EBSCOhost, netLibrary
Wireless access
Mem of Winnefox Library System
Open Mon & Thurs 10-7, Tues, Wed & Fri 10-5, Sat 9-12
Friends of the Library Group

ONALASKA

S   UPPER MISSISSIPPI RIVER CONSERVATION COMMITTEE
LIBRARY*, 555 Lester Ave, 54650. SAN 371-7917. Tel: 608-783-8432.
FAX: 608-783-8450. Web Site: www.mississippi-river.com/umrcc. *Coordr,*
Scott Yess; E-mail: scott_yess@fws.gov
Library Holdings: Bk Vols 5,000; Per Subs 100
Restriction: Non-circulating to the pub

ONEIDA

P   ONEIDA COMMUNITY LIBRARY*, 201 Elm St, 54155. (Mail add: PO
Box 365, 54155-0365), SAN 324-7791. Tel: 920-869-2210. FAX:
920-869-1299. E-mail: one@mail.nfls.lib.wi.us. *Dir,* Lou Williams; E-mail:
lwilliam@oneidanation.org; *Ch,* Kymberley Pelky
Founded 1968. Pop 4,232; Circ 10,000
Library Holdings: Bk Titles 16,000; Per Subs 42
Special Collections: Iroquois-Oneida Indian Coll, bks, flms; Native
American Coll, bks, flms, reels, fiche
Mem of Nicolet Federated Library System
Open Mon (Winter) 10-6, Tues-Thurs 10-8, Fri 1-5, Sat 10-3, Sun 2-4;
Mon 10-6 (Summer) Tues-Thurs 10-8, Fri 1-5, Sat 10-3
Branches: 1
GREEN EARTH BRANCH LIBRARY, W1273 Redtail Dr, De Pere,
  54155-9423, SAN 375-4766. Tel: 920-833-7226. E-mail:
  on2@mail.nfls.lib.wi.us. *Librn,* Eleanore Danforth
  Founded 1996. Pop 4,232
  Library Holdings: Bk Titles 4,940
  Open Mon-Thurs 9-5, Fri 1-5

ONTARIO

P   ONTARIO PUBLIC LIBRARY*, 313 Main St, 54651. (Mail add: PO Box
69, 54651-0069), SAN 318-3068. Tel: 608-337-4651. FAX: 608-337-4814.
E-mail: ontlibr@wrlsweb.org. *Dir,* Laurie Erickson
Circ 18,000
Library Holdings: AV Mats 424; Bk Vols 11,843; Per Subs 66; Videos
275
Mem of Pioneer Library System; Winding Rivers Library System
Open Mon & Wed (Winter) 10-5, Fri 10-7, Sat 9-12; Mon & Wed
(Summer) 9-5, Fri 10-7

OOSTBURG

P   OOSTBURG PUBLIC LIBRARY*, 213 N Eighth St, 53070. SAN
318-3076. Tel: 920-564-2934. E-mail: oostburgref@esls.lib.wi.us. Web Site:
www.oostburg.org/library. *Ch, Dir,* Trixine Tahtinen; E-mail:
tahtinen@esls.lib.wi.us; *Asst Dir,* Colleen Swart; E-mail:
cswart@esls.lib.wi.us; *Librn,* Phyllis Parrish; *ILL, Tech Serv,* Laurie Schuh;
E-mail: lschuh@esls.lib.wi.us
Founded 1941. Pop 3,500
Library Holdings: Bk Vols 26,000; Per Subs 70

Automation Activity & Vendor Info: (Acquisitions) SirsiDynix;
(Cataloging) SirsiDynix; (Circulation) SirsiDynix; (OPAC) SirsiDynix
Mem of Eastern Shores Library System
Open Mon-Thurs 10-8, Fri 10-5, Sat 10-1
Friends of the Library Group

OREGON

P   OREGON PUBLIC LIBRARY*, 256 Brook St, 53575. SAN 318-3084.
Tel: 608-835-3656. FAX: 608-835-2856. E-mail: orelib@scls.lib.wi.us. Web
Site: www.oregonpubliclibrary.org. *Dir,* Susan Santer; E-mail:
sbsanter@scls.lib.wi.us; *Ad, Ref Librn,* Susan Kosharek; E-mail:
@scls.lib.wi.us; *Youth Serv Librn,* Kelly Allen; E-mail: kpa@scls.lib.wi.us;
Circ Supvr, Judy Collison; E-mail: judyc@scls.lib.wi.us; *Tech Serv Supvr,*
Mary Davidson; E-mail: maryd@scls.lib.wi.us; Staff 9 (MLS 3, Non-MLS
6)
Jan 2007-Dec 2007 Income $514,878, City $362,162, County $152,716.
Mats Exp $58,137, Books $43,658, AV Mat $13,585, Electronic Ref Mat
(Incl. Access Fees) $894
Library Holdings: AV Mats 7,773; Bk Titles 55,000; Per Subs 147
Automation Activity & Vendor Info: (Acquisitions) SirsiDynix;
(Cataloging) SirsiDynix; (Circulation) SirsiDynix; (OPAC) SirsiDynix;
(Serials) SirsiDynix
Wireless access
Open Mon-Thurs 9-8:30, Fri 9-6, Sat 10-2
Friends of the Library Group

ORFORDVILLE

P   ORFORDVILLE PUBLIC LIBRARY*, 203 W Beloit St, 53576-8749.
(Mail add: PO Box 249, 53576-0249), SAN 318-3092. Tel: 608-879-9229.
FAX: 608-879-2031. *Dir,* Sarah Strunz; E-mail: strunz.sarah@als.lib.wi.us;
Staff 2 (Non-MLS 2)
Founded 1905. Pop 1,136; Circ 6,149
Library Holdings: Bk Vols 12,295
Automation Activity & Vendor Info: (Cataloging) Follett Software;
(Circulation) Follett Software; (OPAC) Follett Software
Mem of Arrowhead Library System
Open Mon-Fri 12-7

OSCEOLA

P   OSCEOLA PUBLIC LIBRARY*, 102 Chieftain St, 54020. (Mail add: PO
Box 816, 54020), SAN 376-608X. Tel: 715-294-2310. FAX: 715-755-3510.
E-mail: osceolapl@ifls.lib.wi.us. *Dir,* Nate Deprey; E-mail:
deprey@ifls.lib.wi.us
Library Holdings: Bk Vols 19,000; Per Subs 79
Automation Activity & Vendor Info: (Acquisitions) Innovative Interfaces,
Inc; (Cataloging) Innovative Interfaces, Inc; (Circulation) Innovative
Interfaces, Inc; (Course Reserve) Innovative Interfaces, Inc; (ILL)
Innovative Interfaces, Inc; (Media Booking) Innovative Interfaces, Inc;
(OPAC) Innovative Interfaces, Inc; (Serials) Innovative Interfaces, Inc
Open Mon 10-5, Tues-Thurs 10-7, Fri 12-5, Sat 10-3
Friends of the Library Group

OSHKOSH

S   EAA LIBRARY*, Boeing Aeronautical, 3000 Poberezny Rd, 54904. (Mail
add: PO Box 3086, 54903-3086), SAN 324-7252. Tel: 920-426-4848. FAX:
920-426-4828. E-mail: library@eaa.org. Web Site: www.eaa.org/museum.
Mgr, Libr Serv, Susan A Lurvey; E-mail: slurvey@eaa.org. Subject
Specialists: *Aviation hist,* Susan A Lurvey; Staff 1 (Non-MLS 1)
Founded 1972
Library Holdings: Bk Titles 10,000; Per Subs 30
Special Collections: Don Dwiggins Coll; Max Conrad Coll
Subject Interests: Aircraft, Amateur construction, Aviation, Aviation hist
Function: ILL available
Open Mon-Fri 8:30-5
Restriction: Not a lending libr

J   FOX VALLEY TECHNICAL COLLEGE*, Oshkosh Campus Library, 150
N Campbell Rd, 54903. (Mail add: PO Box 2217, 54903-2217). Tel:
920-236-6113. FAX: 920-236-6160. E-mail: library@fvtc.edu. Web Site:
www.fvtc.edu. *Mgr, Libr Serv,* Karen Parson; Tel: 920-735-4762
Library Holdings: Bk Titles 4,768
Open Mon-Thurs (Sept-May) 7:30-3:30 & 5-8, Fri 7:15-2; Mon-Thurs
(June-Aug) 7:30-3:30 & 4:30-7:30, Fri 7:30-11:30 & 4:30-7:30

M   MERCY MEDICAL CENTER*, The Clark Family Health Science Library,
500 S Oakwood Rd, 54903. (Mail add: PO Box 3370, 54903-3370), SAN
318-3106. Tel: 920-223-0342. FAX: 920-223-0343. Web Site:
www.affinityhealth.org/object/library.html. *Librn,* Michele Matucheski; Tel:
920-223-0340; Staff 1.5 (MLS 1, Non-MLS 0.5)
Founded 1906
Library Holdings: e-books 300; Bk Vols 5,000; Per Subs 250
Subject Interests: Consumer health, Med, Nursing, Surgery

Automation Activity & Vendor Info: (Cataloging) EOS International; (OPAC) EOS International; (Serials) EOS International
Database Vendor: EBSCOhost, Gale Cengage Learning, OVID Technologies, ProQuest
Partic in Fox River Valley Area Library Consortium; Fox Valley Library Council; Greater Midwest Regional Medical Libr Network
Open Mon-Fri 8-4:30

S   OSHKOSH CORRECTIONAL INSTITUTION LIBRARY*, 1730 W Snell Rd, 54903. (Mail add: PO Box 3530, 54903-3530). Tel: 920-231-4010, Ext 2220. FAX: 920-236-2626. *Librn,* Cassandra Chaney
Library Holdings: Bk Vols 30,000; Per Subs 40
Open Mon-Fri 7:45-4:30

P   OSHKOSH PUBLIC LIBRARY*, 106 Washington Ave, 54901-4985. SAN 365-0405. Tel: 920-236-5201, 920-236-5205. Circulation Tel: 920-236-5203. Administration Tel: 920-236-5210. Information Services Tel: 920-236-5202. FAX: 920-236-5228. TDD: 920-236-5204. Web Site: www.oshkoshpubliclibrary.org. *Dir,* Jeff Gilderson-Duwe; E-mail: gilderson-duwe@oshkoshpubliclibrary.org; *Asst Dir,* Joan Mueller; Tel: 920-236-5231, E-mail: mueller@oshkoshpubliclibrary.org; *Acq,* Kathleen Grace; Tel: 920-236-5232, E-mail: grace@oshkoshpubliclibrary.org; *Automation Syst Coordr,* Karen Boehning; E-mail: boehring@winnefox.org; *Ch,* Laurie Magee; E-mail: magee@oshkoshpubliclibrary.org; *Circ,* Victoria Vandenberg; E-mail: vandenberg@oshkoshpubliclibrary.org; *Ref Serv, Ad,* Janice Dibble; Fax: 920-236-5227, E-mail: dibble@oshkoshpubliclibrary.org; Staff 17 (MLS 13, Non-MLS 4)
Founded 1895. Pop 87,358; Circ 1,109,915
Library Holdings: AV Mats 47,471; Bk Vols 270,178; Per Subs 560
Subject Interests: Genealogy, Local hist
Automation Activity & Vendor Info: (Acquisitions) SirsiDynix; (Cataloging) SirsiDynix; (Circulation) SirsiDynix; (OPAC) SirsiDynix
Wireless access
Publications: Library Lines (Newsletter)
Mem of Winnefox Library System
Partic in Fox Valley Library Council; OCLC Online Computer Library Center, Inc; Wisconsin Library Services
Special Services for the Deaf - TDD equip
Special Services for the Blind - Assistive/Adapted tech devices, equip & products; BiFolkal kits; Bks on cassette; Bks on CD; Computer with voice synthesizer for visually impaired persons; Large print & cassettes; Large print bks; Talking bks; ZoomText magnification & reading software
Open Mon-Thurs (Fall) 9-9, Fri 9-6, Sat 9-5, Sun 1-5; Mon-Thurs (Summer) 9-9, Fri 9-6, Sat 9-1
Friends of the Library Group

S   OSHKOSH PUBLIC MUSEUM LIBRARY*, 1331 Algoma Blvd, 54901-2799. SAN 318-3114. Tel: 920-236-5773. FAX: 920-424-4738. Web Site: www.oshkoshmuseum.org, www.oshkoshmuseum.org/virtual. *Archivist,* Scott Cross; E-mail: scross@ci.oshkosh.wi.us
Founded 1924
Library Holdings: Bk Titles 6,000
Special Collections: Local History (Oshkosh Pioneers), bks, doc, photog. Oral History
Subject Interests: Archaeology, Archit, Art, Local hist, Logging, Lumbering, Meteorites, Natural hist
Function: Archival coll
Restriction: Open by appt only

C   UNIVERSITY OF WISCONSIN OSHKOSH, Polk Library, 801 Elmwood Ave, 54901. SAN 365-0529. Tel: 920-424-4333. Circulation Tel: 920-424-3320. FAX: 920-424-7338. E-mail: infodesk@uwosh.edu. Web Site: www.uwosh.edu/library. *Dir,* Patrick J Wilkinson; Tel: 920-424-2147, E-mail: wilkinso@uwosh.edu; *Head, Coll & Tech Serv,* Ronald Hardy; Tel: 920-424-2097, E-mail: hardyr@uwosh.edu; *Head, Govt Info,* Michael Watkins; Tel: 920-424-7305, E-mail: watkins@uwosh.edu; *Head, Pub Serv,* Sarah Neises; Tel: 920-424-0401, E-mail: neises@uwosh.edu; *Archivist & Communications Librn,* Joshua Ranger; Tel: 920-424-0828, E-mail: ranger@uwosh.edu; *Circ Serv Librn,* Crystal Buss; Tel: 920-424-7315, E-mail: buss@uwosh.edu; *Distance Educ Librn,* Erin Mischak; Tel: 920-424-1361, Fax: 920-424-7334, E-mail: mischake@uwosh.edu; *Educ Mat Ctr Librn,* Stephen Katz; Tel: 920-424-2320; *Electronic Res Librn,* Jeffery Brunner; Tel: 920-424-0371, Fax: 920-424-7734, E-mail: brunnerj@uwosh.edu; *Info Literacy Librn,* Theodore Mulvey; Tel: 920-424-7329, E-mail: mulveyt@uwosh.edu; *Ref Librn,* Cynthia Huebschen; Tel: 920-424-7327, E-mail: huebschc@uwosh.edu; *Syst Librn,* Craig Thomas; Tel: 920-424-7323, E-mail: thomascr@uwosh.edu; *Coordr, Info Literacy,* Marisa Finkey; Tel: 920-424-3436, E-mail: finkey@uwosh.edu; *ILL,* Sara Stichert; Tel: 920-424-3348, E-mail: stichert@uwosh.edu; Staff 25.5 (MLS 13, Non-MLS 12.5)
Founded 1871. Enrl 13,513; Fac 628; Highest Degree: Master
Library Holdings: e-journals 52,718; Bk Vols 620,114; Per Subs 883
Special Collections: University Archives Coll; Wisconsin Area Research Center Coll. State Document Depository; US Document Depository

Subject Interests: Bus, Educ, Nursing, Undergrad studies
Automation Activity & Vendor Info: (Acquisitions) Ex Libris Group; (Cataloging) Ex Libris Group; (Circulation) Ex Libris Group; (Course Reserve) SirsiDynix; (ILL) OCLC ILLiad; (OPAC) Ex Libris Group; (Serials) Ex Libris Group
Database Vendor: 3M Library Systems, Agricola, Alexander Street Press, American Chemical Society, American Geophysical Union, American Mathematical Society, American Physical Society, ARTstor, Atlas Systems, Baker & Taylor, BioOne, Bowker, Children's Literature Comprehensive Database Company (CLCD), CQ Press, ebrary, EBSCOhost, Elsevier, Ex Libris Group, Gale Cengage Learning, IEEE (Institute of Electrical & Electronics Engineers), Ingenta, IOP, ISI Web of Knowledge, JSTOR, LexisNexis, MD Consult, Mergent Online, Modern Language Association, Nature Publishing Group, Newsbank, OCLC FirstSearch, OCLC WorldCat, OVID Technologies, Oxford Online, Project MUSE, ProQuest, RefWorks, Sage, ScienceDirect, SerialsSolutions, Springer-Verlag, UpToDate, ValueLine, Wiley, YBP Library Services
Wireless access
Publications: Polk Library News (Newsletter)
Partic in Fox Valley Library Council; OCLC Online Computer Library Center, Inc
Open Mon-Thurs 7am-1am, Fri 7-6, Sat 10-6, Sun 10am-1am

GL   WINNEBAGO COUNTY COURT HOUSE*, Law Library, Court House, 415 Jackson St, 54903-4794. (Mail add: PO Box 2808, 54903-2808), SAN 318-3130. Tel: 920-236-4808. FAX: 920-303-4783. *In Charge,* Thomas Gritton
Library Holdings: Bk Vols 12,000
Open Mon-Fri 8-4:30

P   WINNEFOX LIBRARY SYSTEM, 106 Washington Ave, 54901-4985. SAN 318-3149. Tel: 920-236-5220. FAX: 920-236-5228. Web Site: www.winnefox.org. *Dir,* Jeff Gilderson-Duwe; *Asst Dir,* Mark Arend; E-mail: arend@winnefox.org; *Tech Coordr,* Karen Boehning; *ILL,* Joy Schwarz; Staff 10 (MLS 4, Non-MLS 6)
Founded 1977. Pop 205,522
Library Holdings: Bk Vols 10,685; Per Subs 31
Publications: Trustee Tales Newsletter; Winnefox Library System Directory; Winnefox Library System Interlibrary Loan Manual
Member Libraries: Berlin Public Library; Brandon Public Library; Caestecker Public Library; Campbellsport Public Library; Endeavor Public Library; Fond Du Lac Public Library; Hancock Public Library; Leon-Saxeville Township Library; Menasha Public Library; Mill Pond Public Library; Montello Public Library; Neenah Public Library; Neshkoro Public Library; Oakfield Public Library; Omro Public Library; Oshkosh Public Library; Packwaukee Public Library; Patterson Memorial Library; Poy Sippi Public Library; Redgranite Public Library; Ripon Public Library; Spillman Library; Wautoma Public Library; Westfield Public Library; Winneconne Public Library
Partic in Fox Valley Library Council

OSSEO

P   HAUGE MEMORIAL LIBRARY*, 50655 Charles St, 54758. (Mail add: PO Box 659, 54758-0659), SAN 318-3157. Tel: 715-597-3444. E-mail: haugeml@triwest.net. *Dir,* Arlie J Schwoch
Pop 1,500; Circ 25,000
Library Holdings: Bk Vols 16,000; Per Subs 38
Automation Activity & Vendor Info: (Cataloging) Winnebago Software Co; (Circulation) Winnebago Software Co
Mem of Winding Rivers Library System
Open Mon, Wed & Thurs 9-12 & 1-7, Fri 9-12 & 1-4, Sat 9-12
Friends of the Library Group

OWEN

P   OWEN PUBLIC LIBRARY*, 414 Central Ave, 54460-9777. (Mail add: PO Box 130, 54460-0130), SAN 318-3165. Tel: 715-229-2939. FAX: 715-229-2939. Web Site: wvls.lib.wi.us/owenpl. *Dir,* Shirley Lehr; E-mail: slehr@wvls.lib.wi.us
Pop 1,000; Circ 29,000
Library Holdings: Bk Vols 19,000; Per Subs 45
Automation Activity & Vendor Info: (Acquisitions) SirsiDynix; (Cataloging) SirsiDynix; (Circulation) SirsiDynix; (OPAC) SirsiDynix
Mem of Wisconsin Valley Library Service
Open Mon-Fri 1-8

OXFORD

P   OXFORD PUBLIC LIBRARY*, 129 S Franklin St, 53952. (Mail add: PO Box 32, 53952-0032), SAN 376-6594. Tel: 608-586-4458. FAX: 608-586-4459. E-mail: director@oxfordlibrary.org. Web Site: www.oxfordlibrary.org. *Dir,* Jim Walker; E-mail: walker@oxfordlibrary.org
Library Holdings: AV Mats 1,100; Bk Vols 10,700; Per Subs 30
Open Mon & Thurs 10-12 & 2-5:30, Tues & Wed 2-7, Fri 2-5:30, Sat 9-12

PACKWAUKEE

P   PACKWAUKEE PUBLIC LIBRARY*, N3511 State St, 53953. (Mail add: PO Box 406, 53953-0403), SAN 377-9734. Tel: 608-589-5202. FAX: 608-589-5202. E-mail: director@packwaukeelibrary.org. Web Site: www.packwaukeelibrary.org. *Dir,* Candace Covinton; E-mail: covington@packwaukeelibrary.org
     Library Holdings: Bk Titles 7,500; Per Subs 30
     Mem of Winnefox Library System
     Partic in Fox Valley Library Council
     Open Mon & Thurs 12-7, Tues, Wed & Fri 12-5, Sat 10-2

PALMYRA

P   POWERS MEMORIAL LIBRARY*, 115 Main St, 53156. (Mail add: PO Box O, 53156-0924), SAN 318-3173. Tel: 262-495-4605. FAX: 262-495-8617. Web Site: www.palmyra.lib.wi.us. *Dir,* Kathleen Hookham; E-mail: khook@mwfls.org; Staff 1 (MLS 1)
     Founded 1927. Pop 2,500; Circ 44,431
     Library Holdings: Bk Vols 27,686; Per Subs 90
     Special Collections: Local Newspaper-Palmyra Enterprise, 1874-present, bd vols & micro
     Automation Activity & Vendor Info: (Acquisitions) SirsiDynix; (Cataloging) SirsiDynix; (Circulation) SirsiDynix; (ILL) Auto-Graphics, Inc
     Mem of Mid-Wisconsin Federated Library System
     Open Mon 10-7, Tues & Thurs 1-7, Wed & Fri 10-5, Sat 10-2
     Friends of the Library Group

PARDEEVILLE

P   ANGIE WILLIAMS COX PUBLIC LIBRARY*, 119 N Main St, 53954-0370. (Mail add: PO Box 370, 53954-0370), SAN 318-3181. Tel: 608-429-2354. FAX: 608-429-4308. E-mail: parstaff@scls.lib.wi.us. Web Site: www.scls.lib.wi.us/par. *Dir,* Alyssa Cleland; *Libr Asst,* Linda Glasgow
     Founded 1925
     Jan 2005-Dec 2005 Income $113,098, City $53,674, County $46,688, Locally Generated Income $5,236, Other $7,500. Mats Exp $14,478, Books $11,178, Per/Ser (Incl. Access Fees) $1,900, AV Mat $1,400. Sal $61,875 (Prof $29,952)
     Library Holdings: AV Mats 1,137; Bk Vols 19,293; Per Subs 69; Talking Bks 556
     Automation Activity & Vendor Info: (Cataloging) SirsiDynix; (Circulation) SirsiDynix; (OPAC) SirsiDynix; (Serials) SirsiDynix
     Function: Handicapped accessible, ILL available, Prog for children & young adult, Summer reading prog
     Mem of South Central Library System
     Open Mon-Thurs 10-7:30, Fri 10-5, Sat 10-1
     Friends of the Library Group

PARK FALLS

P   PARK FALLS PUBLIC LIBRARY*, 121 N Fourth Ave, 54552. SAN 318-319X. Tel: 715-762-3121. FAX: 715-762-2286. E-mail: pfpl@ifls.lib.wi.us. Web Site: www.parkfallslibrary.org. *Dir,* Gary Olson; *Adult Serv,* Debra Hyde; *Ch,* Sherry Ryther; Staff 3 (MLS 3)
     Founded 1906. Pop 15,000; Circ 60,080
     Library Holdings: Bk Titles 36,000; Per Subs 130
     Subject Interests: Local hist, Lumber, Lumbering
     Mem of Indianhead Federated Library System
     Open Mon-Fri 10-8, Sat 10-2
     Friends of the Library Group

PEPIN

P   PEPIN PUBLIC LIBRARY*, 510 Second St, 54759. (Mail add: PO Box 277, 54759-0277), SAN 374-5465. Tel: 715-442-4932. E-mail: pepinlib@ifls.lib.wi.us. *Dir,* Christy Rundquist; Staff 3 (Non-MLS 3)
     Library Holdings: Bk Titles 12,323; Per Subs 38
     Automation Activity & Vendor Info: (Cataloging) Innovative Interfaces, Inc; (Circulation) Innovative Interfaces, Inc; (OPAC) Innovative Interfaces, Inc
     Mem of Indianhead Federated Library System
     Open Tues-Thurs 10-7, Sat 9-12
     Friends of the Library Group

PEWAUKEE

P   PEWAUKEE PUBLIC LIBRARY*, 210 Main St, 53072-3596. SAN 318-3211. Tel: 262-691-5670. FAX: 262-691-5673. E-mail: pwlib@pewaukee.lib.wi.us. Web Site: www.pewaukeelibrary.org. *Dir,* Jennie Stoltz; E-mail: jstoltz@pewaukee.lib.wi.us; Staff 13 (MLS 7, Non-MLS 6)
     Founded 2005. Pop 20,000; Circ 344,000
     Jan 2009-Dec 2009 Income $983,712, City $886,701, County $64,986, Locally Generated Income $26,000, Other $6,025. Mats Exp $117,300,

Books $82,000, Per/Ser (Incl. Access Fees) $6,300, AV Mat $29,000. Sal $483,284
     Library Holdings: Audiobooks 3,273; CDs 2,109; DVDs 5,347; e-books 3,024; Bk Vols 92,677; Per Subs 196; Videos 965
     Automation Activity & Vendor Info: (Acquisitions) SIRSI WorkFlows; (Cataloging) SIRSI WorkFlows; (Circulation) SIRSI WorkFlows; (ILL) SIRSI WorkFlows; (OPAC) SIRSI-iBistro; (Serials) SIRSI WorkFlows
     Wireless access
     Function: Adult bk club, After school storytime, Archival coll, Art exhibits, Bks on cassette, Bks on CD, Children's prog, Computer training, Computers for patron use, Copy machines, Digital talking bks, E-Reserves, Free DVD rentals, Handicapped accessible, Holiday prog, Home delivery & serv to Sr ctr & nursing homes, Homebound delivery serv, ILL available, Music CDs, Newsp ref libr, Online cat, Online ref, Online searches, Outreach serv, Outside serv via phone, mail, e-mail & web, OverDrive digital audio bks, Photocopying/Printing, Preschool outreach, Prog for adults, Prog for children & young adult, Provide serv for the mentally ill, Pub access computers, Ref serv in person, Senior computer classes, Senior outreach, Serves mentally handicapped consumers, Spoken cassettes & CDs, Spoken cassettes & DVDs, Story hour, Summer reading prog, Tax forms, Teen prog, Telephone ref, VHS videos, Wheelchair accessible
     Mem of Waukesha County Federated Library System
     Open Mon-Thurs 9:30-8:30, Fri & Sat 9:30-5
     Friends of the Library Group

J   WAUKESHA COUNTY TECHNICAL COLLEGE LIBRARY, 800 Main St, 53072. SAN 318-322X. Tel: 262-691-5316. Interlibrary Loan Service Tel: 262-691-5108. Reference Tel: 262-691-7896. FAX: 262-695-3402. Circulation FAX: 262-695-3448. Web Site: www.wctc.edu/library. *Dir of Libr Serv,* Terry Kemper; Tel: 262-695-3459, E-mail: tkemper1@wctc.edu; *Ref & Instrul Serv, Instr Coordr,* Colleen Cullen; Tel: 262-691-7877, E-mail: ccullen@wctc.edu; Staff 7.5 (MLS 2, Non-MLS 5.5)
     Founded 1965. Enrl 3,936; Fac 235; Highest Degree: Associate
     Library Holdings: Bks on Deafness & Sign Lang 41; e-books 77,000; Bk Titles 32,719; Per Subs 412
     Special Collections: Career Coll; Educational Resources Information Center Coll (ERIC); International Trade
     Subject Interests: Electronics, Financial planning, Fire sci, Intl trade, Mkt, Nursing, Police, Printing, Publ, Retail mgt, Sci
     Automation Activity & Vendor Info: (Acquisitions) Ex Libris Group; (Cataloging) Ex Libris Group; (Circulation) Ex Libris Group; (Course Reserve) Ex Libris Group; (OPAC) Ex Libris Group; (Serials) Ex Libris Group
     Database Vendor: CountryWatch, EBSCOhost, Facts on File, Gale Cengage Learning, LearningExpress, LexisNexis, Newsbank, OCLC WorldCat, ProQuest, ReferenceUSA
     Wireless access
     Function: Archival coll, Distance learning, Doc delivery serv, Homebound delivery serv, ILL available, Online searches, Orientations
     Partic in Wis PALS Libr Consortium; Wisconsin Library Services
     Open Mon-Thurs 7:30am-8pm, Fri 7:30-4:30, Sat 9-1
     Restriction: Open to pub for ref & circ; with some limitations

PHELPS

P   PHELPS PUBLIC LIBRARY*, Eleanor Ellis Public Library, 4495 Town Hall Rd, 54554. SAN 318-3238. Tel: 715-545-2887. FAX: 715-545-2887. Web Site: nwls.wislib.org/about/libph.htm. *Dir,* June Franzen; E-mail: jfranzen@phelps.nwls.lib.wi.us
     Founded 1934
     Library Holdings: Bk Vols 10,916; Per Subs 19
     Subject Interests: Wis
     Automation Activity & Vendor Info: (Cataloging) Innovative Interfaces, Inc; (Circulation) Innovative Interfaces, Inc
     Mem of Northern Waters Library Service
     Open Mon, Tues, Thurs & Fri 10-4, Sat 10-12

PHILLIPS

P   PHILLIPS PUBLIC LIBRARY*, 286 Cherry St, 54555-1240. SAN 374-6046. Tel: 715-339-2868. *Dir,* John F Hendricks; E-mail: johnhendricks@ifls.lib.wi.us; *Cat,* Dawn Seeger; *Ch,* Jo Hick; *Circ,* Nancy Genisio; *Circ, ILL,* Barb Schaumberg; *Circ,* Denise Stanke; Staff 1 (MLS 1)
     Founded 1917. Pop 8,500; Circ 93,482
     Jan 2007-Dec 2007 Income $311,352, City $129,756, County $135,474, Locally Generated Income $46,122. Mats Exp $31,850, Books $24,000, Per/Ser (Incl. Access Fees) $1,800, Micro $800, AV Mat $4,050, Electronic Ref Mat (Incl. Access Fees) $1,200. Sal $149,166 (Prof $45,700)
     Library Holdings: AV Mats 856; CDs 1,716; DVDs 1,059; e-books 8,805; Large Print Bks 377; Bk Titles 25,000; Per Subs 78; Talking Bks 500; Videos 800

Automation Activity & Vendor Info: (Cataloging) Innovative Interfaces, Inc; (Circulation) Innovative Interfaces, Inc; (ILL) Innovative Interfaces, Inc; (OPAC) Innovative Interfaces, Inc; (Serials) Innovative Interfaces, Inc
Open Mon-Fri 9-8, Sat 9-1
Friends of the Library Group

PINE RIVER

P   LEON-SAXEVILLE TOWNSHIP LIBRARY*, Pine River Public Library, N4715 Main St, 54965. (Mail add: PO Box 247, 54965-0247), SAN 318-3246. Tel: 920-987-5110. FAX: 920-987-5110. Web Site: www.pineriverlibrary.org. *Dir,* Jeanne Williamson; E-mail: director@pineriverlibrary.org
Founded 1965. Pop 2,300
Library Holdings: CDs 250; Large Print Bks 125; Bk Titles 14,200; Per Subs 70; Talking Bks 600; Videos 1,600
Special Collections: Wisconsin - Homeschooling
Subject Interests: Pine river hist
Automation Activity & Vendor Info: (Cataloging) SirsiDynix; (Circulation) SirsiDynix; (ILL) OCLC WorldCat
Wireless access
Mem of Winnefox Library System
Open Mon 4-7, Tues, Thurs & Fri 2-7, Wed 10-7, Sat 10-1
Friends of the Library Group

PITTSVILLE

P   PITTSVILLE COMMUNITY LIBRARY*, 5291 Third Ave, 54466-0911. SAN 318-3254. Tel: 715-884-6500. *Librn,* Position Currently Open
Founded 1975. Pop 2,000; Circ 11,163
Library Holdings: Bk Vols 14,000; Per Subs 80
Automation Activity & Vendor Info: (Acquisitions) Follett Software; (Cataloging) Follett Software; (Circulation) Follett Software
Mem of South Central Library System
Open Tues & Fri 9-7, Wed 12-5, Thurs 12-6, Sat 9-2
Friends of the Library Group

PLAIN

P   KRAEMER LIBRARY & COMMUNITY CENTER*, 910 Main St, 53577. SAN 318-3262. Tel: 608-546-4201. FAX: 608-546-4201. E-mail: plalib@scls.lib.wi.us. *Dir,* Jeffrey C Harrison; E-mail: jcharrison@scls.lib.wi.us; *Asst Librn,* Kathy Kieler
Founded 1964. Pop 815
Library Holdings: Bk Vols 10,820; Per Subs 40
Automation Activity & Vendor Info: (Cataloging) SirsiDynix; (Circulation) SirsiDynix
Wireless access
Mem of South Central Library System
Open Mon-Thurs 1-7:30, Fri 9-5, Sat 9-1

PLAINFIELD

P   PLAINFIELD PUBLIC LIBRARY*, 126 S Main St, 54966-0305. (Mail add: PO Box 305, 54966-0305), SAN 318-3270. Tel: 715-335-4523. FAX: 715-335-6712. E-mail: director@plainfieldlibrary.org. Web Site: www.plainfieldlibrary.org. *Dir,* Linda Helmrick; E-mail: helmrick@plainfieldlibrary.org
Founded 1915. Pop 902; Circ 16,558
Library Holdings: Bk Vols 10,000
Special Collections: Oral History
Subject Interests: Local hist
Open Mon 12-5, Tues & Fri 10-5, Wed 10-5 & 7-8, Sat 9-Noon
Friends of the Library Group

PLATTEVILLE

P   PLATTEVILLE PUBLIC LIBRARY*, 65 S Elm, 53818. SAN 318-3289. Tel: 608-348-7441. FAX: 608-348-9923. *Dir,* Rose Frost; Tel: 608-348-7441, Ext 5, E-mail: rfrost@plattevillepubliclibrary.org; *Ch,* Erin Isabell; *Info Serv,* Daniel Ellingson; *Outreach Serv Librn,* Debra Burkholder; Staff 4 (MLS 1, Non-MLS 3)
Founded 1906. Pop 10,035; Circ 114,009
Library Holdings: Bk Vols 40,000; Per Subs 150
Automation Activity & Vendor Info: (Acquisitions) Horizon; (Cataloging) Horizon; (Circulation) Horizon; (OPAC) Horizon
Function: Homebound delivery serv
Mem of Southwest Wisconsin Library System
Open Mon-Thurs 9-8, Fri 9-6, Sat 9-5, Sun 1-6

M   SOUTHWEST HEALTH CENTER*, Health Resource Center & Medical Library, 1400 E Side Rd, 53818. Tel: 608-831-4444. FAX: 608-831-3334. E-mail: library@southwesthealth.org. Web Site: www.southwesthealth.org/healthresourcecenter. *In Charge,* Gwen Kirchof
Library Holdings: e-journals 10; Bk Titles 350

Automation Activity & Vendor Info: (Cataloging) LibraryWorld, Inc; (Circulation) LibraryWorld, Inc
Database Vendor: UpToDate
Open Mon-Fri 8-8, Sat 10-2

C   UNIVERSITY OF WISCONSIN - PLATTEVILLE, Elton S Karrmann Library, One University Plaza, 53818. SAN 318-3297. Circulation Tel: 608-342-1679. Interlibrary Loan Service Tel: 608-342-1648. Reference Tel: 608-342-1668. Administration Tel: 608-342-1688. Automation Services Tel: 608-342-1210. Information Services Tel: 608-342-1421. Toll Free Tel: 888-450-4632. FAX: 608-342-1645. E-mail: reference@uwplatt.edu. Web Site: www.uwplatt.edu/library. *Dir,* Zora Sampson; E-mail: sampsonz@uwplatt.edu; *Head, Circ & Ref,* John Berg; Tel: 608-342-1355, E-mail: bergjo@uwplatt.edu; *Head, Acq & Coll Develop,* Judith Wurtzler; Tel: 608-342-1077, E-mail: wurtzler@uwplatt.edu; *Head, Archives,* James Hibbard; Tel: 608-342-1229, E-mail: hibbardj@uwplatt.edu; *Head, Cat, Webmaster,* Jessica Donahoe; Tel: 608-342-1348, E-mail: donahoej@uwplatt.edu; *Head, Instrul Mat Lab,* Regina Pauly; Tel: 608-342-1099, E-mail: paulyr@uwplatt.edu; *Head, Syst,* Jon Musselman; Tel: 608-342-1649, E-mail: musselmj@uwplatt.edu; *ILL,* Lori Wedig; *Ref,* Kay Young; Tel: 608-342-1134, E-mail: young@uwplatt.edu; Staff 9 (MLS 8, Non-MLS 1)
Founded 1866. Enrl 7,124; Fac 365; Highest Degree: Master
Jul 2007-Jun 2008 Income $1,640,502, State $1,500,774, Federal $39,093, Locally Generated Income $41,172, Other $59,463. Mats Exp $465,036, Books $119,308, Per/Ser (Incl. Access Fees) $246,092, Micro $23,689, AV Mat $20,818, Electronic Ref Mat (Incl. Access Fees) $50,146, Presv $4,983. Sal $864,321 (Prof $411,145)
Library Holdings: Audiobooks 69; AV Mats 15,555; CDs 784; DVDs 1,887; e-books 13; e-journals 20; Electronic Media & Resources 93; Microforms 1,023,415; Bk Titles 209,239; Bk Vols 240,625; Per Subs 927; Videos 12,060
Special Collections: Archives (Area Research Center), ms; Regional History. State Document Depository; US Document Depository
Subject Interests: Computer sci, Eng, Indust tech mgt, Middle-level educ, Project mgt
Automation Activity & Vendor Info: (Acquisitions) Ex Libris Group; (Cataloging) Ex Libris Group; (Circulation) Ex Libris Group; (ILL) OCLC; (Media Booking) Ex Libris Group; (OPAC) Ex Libris Group; (Serials) Ex Libris Group
Database Vendor: Alexander Street Press, American Chemical Society, American Mathematical Society, American Psychological Association (APA), ASCE Research Library, Baker & Taylor, BioOne, Cinahl Information Systems, College Source, Community of Science (COS), Coutts Information Service, CQ Press, EBSCO Information Services, EBSCOhost, Gale Cengage Learning, H W Wilson, IOP, ISI Web of Knowledge, JSTOR, Knovel, LexisNexis, MD Consult, Modern Language Association, Nature Publishing Group, netLibrary, Newsbank-Readex, OCLC FirstSearch, OCLC WorldCat, Oxford Online, Project MUSE, ProQuest, RefWorks, Thomson - Web of Science, Westlaw, Wilson - Wilson Web, YBP Library Services
Wireless access
Open Mon-Thurs 7:45am-Midnight, Fri 7:45am-8pm, Sat 11-8, Sun 1-Midnight

PLUM CITY

P   PLUM CITY PUBLIC LIBRARY*, 611 Main St, 54761-9044. (Mail add: PO Box 203, 54761-9044), SAN 378-0023. Tel: 715-647-2373. FAX: 715-647-2373. E-mail: plumcitylib@ifls.lib.wi.us. Web Site: www.plumcitylibrary.org/. *Dir,* Jacquie Pool
Library Holdings: Bk Titles 13,700; Per Subs 48
Subject Interests: Local hist
Mem of Indianhead Federated Library System
Open Tues & Fri 12:30-5, Wed 12:30-9, Thurs 10-5, Sat 10-1

PLYMOUTH

S   KETTLE MORAINE CORRECTIONAL INSTITUTION LIBRARY*, W9071 Forest Dr, 53073. (Mail add: PO Box 31, 53073-0031), SAN 324-1734. Tel: 920-526-3244, Ext 309. FAX: 920-526-3989. *Librn,* Conrad Reedy
Library Holdings: Bk Titles 20,000; Per Subs 45
Automation Activity & Vendor Info: (Acquisitions) Follett Software; (Cataloging) Follett Software; (Circulation) Follett Software
Open Mon-Sat 8-4:30 & 5-9

C   LAKELAND COLLEGE, John Esch Library, W3718 South Dr, 53073. (Mail add: PO Box 359, Sheboygan, 53082-0359), SAN 318-3807. Tel: 920-565-1238. FAX: 920-565-1206. *Dir,* Ann Penke; Tel: 920-565-1242, E-mail: penkea@lakeland.edu; *Distance Educ Librn,* Teresa Grimm; E-mail: grimmtm@lakeland.edu; *ILL,* Joseph Pirillo; E-mail: pirillojm@lakeland.edu; *Per,* Robert Schuricht; E-mail: schurichtbe@lakeland.edu; Staff 4 (MLS 4)
Founded 1940. Enrl 835; Fac 59; Highest Degree: Master

Jul 2011-Jun 2012. Mats Exp $154,334, Books $30,439, Per/Ser (Incl. Access Fees) $70,315, AV Mat $444, Electronic Ref Mat (Incl. Access Fees) $53,136

Library Holdings: AV Mats 2,881; CDs 1,481; DVDs 188; e-books 27,105; e-journals 2,634; Microforms 5,011; Music Scores 953; Bk Titles 58,767; Bk Vols 69,593; Per Subs 270; Videos 869

Subject Interests: Jewish holocaust, Modern Am poetry

Automation Activity & Vendor Info: (Circulation) Polaris Library Systems; (OPAC) Polaris Library Systems

Database Vendor: EBSCOhost, JSTOR, LexisNexis, OCLC WorldCat, ProQuest, Sage

Wireless access

Partic in WILS

Open Mon-Thurs 7:30am-11pm, Fri 7:30-5, Sat 10-5, Sun Noon-11

P   PLYMOUTH PUBLIC LIBRARY*, 130 Division St, 53073-1802. SAN 318-3300. Tel: 920-892-4416. FAX: 920-892-6295. *Dir,* Martha Suhfras; E-mail: msuhfras@esls.lib.wi.us; *Adult Serv,* Rachel Stoyke; *Ch,* Carol Langkabel; Staff 2 (MLS 2)
Founded 1909. Pop 12,600; Circ 112,000
Jan 2007-Dec 2007 Income $501,707, City $379,000, County $122,707. Mats Exp $89,600, Books $68,000, Per/Ser (Incl. Access Fees) $5,600, AV Mat $11,000, Electronic Ref Mat (Incl. Access Fees) $5,000. Sal $179,000
Library Holdings: AV Mats 4,000; Bks on Deafness & Sign Lang 100; e-books 7,000; High Interest/Low Vocabulary Bk Vols 50; Large Print Bks 1,500; Bk Vols 71,000; Per Subs 180; Talking Bks 500
Subject Interests: Local city (Plymouth) hist
Automation Activity & Vendor Info: (Cataloging) SirsiDynix; (Circulation) SirsiDynix; (ILL) SirsiDynix; (OPAC) SirsiDynix; (Serials) SirsiDynix
Database Vendor: Gale Cengage Learning, infoUSA, P4 Performance Management, Inc, ProQuest
Mem of Eastern Shores Library System
Open Mon-Thurs 9-8, Fri 9-5, Sat 9-3
Friends of the Library Group

PORT WASHINGTON

P   W J NIEDERKORN LIBRARY*, Port Washington Public, 316 W Grand Ave, 53074-2293. SAN 318-3319. Tel: 262-284-5031. FAX: 262-284-7680. Web Site: www.ci.port-washington.wi.us/library/library.htm, www.portwashington.lib.wi.us. *Dir,* David Nimmer; E-mail: dnimmer@esls.lib.wi.us; *Adult Serv,* Annie Bahringer; *Ch,* Cindy Beyer; *ILL, Tech Serv,* Nina Ryer
Pop 10,617; Circ 222,094
Library Holdings: AV Mats 3,478; e-books 7,583; Bk Vols 55,000; Per Subs 202; Talking Bks 2,417
Wireless access
Mem of Eastern Shores Library System
Open Mon-Thurs (Winter) 9-8, Fri 9-6, Sat 9-4, Sun 1-4; Mon-Thurs (Summer) 9-8, Fri 9-6, Sat 9-1
Friends of the Library Group

PORTAGE

S   COLUMBIA CORRECTIONAL INSTITUTION LIBRARY, 2925 Columbia Dr, 53901. (Mail add: PO Box 950, 53901-0950), SAN 370-7407. Tel: 608-742-9100, Ext 9247. FAX: 608-742-9111. *Librn,* Position Currently Open
Founded 1986. Pop 880
Library Holdings: High Interest/Low Vocabulary Bk Vols 100; Bk Titles 16,500; Bk Vols 20,000; Per Subs 25
Automation Activity & Vendor Info: (Acquisitions) Follett Software; (Cataloging) Follett Software; (Circulation) Follett Software
Function: Legal assistance to inmates, Photocopying/Printing, Tax forms
Partic in Wisconsin Library Services
Special Services for the Blind - Large print bks
Restriction: Circ limited, Internal circ only

P   PORTAGE PUBLIC LIBRARY*, 253 W Edgewater St, 53901. SAN 318-3335. Tel: 608-742-4959. FAX: 608-742-3819. E-mail: porill@scls.lib.wi.us. Web Site: www.portagelibrary.us. *Dir,* Shannon M Schultz; E-mail: shannons@scls.lib.wi.us; Staff 4 (MLS 2, Non-MLS 2)
Founded 1902. Pop 19,560; Circ 209,257
Jan 2010-Dec 2010 Income $633,220, State $625, City $374,027, Federal $1,300, County $167,857, Other $89,411. Mats Exp $95,149, Books $67,464, Per/Ser (Incl. Access Fees) $6,897, AV Mat $11,980, Electronic Ref Mat (Incl. Access Fees) $8,808. Sal $247,471 (Prof $174,142)
Library Holdings: AV Mats 5,394; e-books 7,494; Electronic Media & Resources 5,260; Bk Vols 66,674; Per Subs 145
Special Collections: Zona Gale Coll. State Document Depository
Automation Activity & Vendor Info: (Circulation) LibLime
Wireless access
Open Mon-Thurs 9-8:30, Fri 9-6, Sat 10-4
Friends of the Library Group

POY SIPPI

P   POY SIPPI PUBLIC LIBRARY*, W2251 Commercial St, 54967-8423. (Mail add: PO Box 345, 54967-0345), SAN 318-3343. Tel: 920-987-5737. FAX: 920-987-5737. Web Site: www.poysippilibrary.org. *Dir,* Carol Cate; E-mail: director@poysippilibrary.org
Founded 1963. Pop 2,734
Library Holdings: Bks on Deafness & Sign Lang 15; DVDs 86; e-books 7,951; High Interest/Low Vocabulary Bk Vols 72; Large Print Bks 58; Music Scores 72; Bk Titles 10,727; Talking Bks 82; Videos 1,647
Automation Activity & Vendor Info: (Cataloging) SirsiDynix; (Circulation) SirsiDynix; (OPAC) SirsiDynix
Mem of Winnefox Library System
Open Mon 10-7, Wed 12-7, Thurs & Fri 3-7, Sat 9-12
Friends of the Library Group

POYNETTE

P   POYNETTE PUBLIC LIBRARY*, 118 N Main, 53955. (Mail add: PO Box 368, 53955-0368), SAN 318-3351. Tel: 608-635-7577. FAX: 608-635-7577. E-mail: poylib@scls.lib.wi.us. Web Site: www.scls.lib.wi.us/poy. *Dir,* Gary Yurgil
Founded 1941. Pop 5,000; Circ 10,000
Library Holdings: Bk Titles 17,100; Per Subs 35
Automation Activity & Vendor Info: (Acquisitions) SirsiDynix; (Cataloging) SirsiDynix; (Circulation) SirsiDynix; (OPAC) SirsiDynix
Wireless access
Mem of South Central Library System
Open Mon-Thurs 9:30-8, Fri 9:30-5:30, Sat 9:30-1
Friends of the Library Group

PRAIRIE DU CHIEN

P   PRAIRIE DU CHIEN MEMORIAL LIBRARY*, Joseph W & Emma L Wachute Memorial, 125 S Wacouta Ave, 53821-1632. SAN 318-336X. Tel: 608-326-6211. FAX: 608-326-7069. Web Site: www.swls.org. *Dir,* Nancy K Ashmore; E-mail: nashmore@swls.org; Staff 4 (MLS 1, Non-MLS 3)
Founded 1897. Pop 6,018; Circ 52,120
Library Holdings: Bk Vols 32,000; Per Subs 49
Special Collections: Local Newspapers 1864-2001, microfilm
Subject Interests: Local hist, Wis
Automation Activity & Vendor Info: (Cataloging) Horizon; (Circulation) Horizon; (OPAC) Horizon
Function: Photocopying/Printing
Mem of Southwest Wisconsin Library System
Open Mon-Thurs 9-8, Fri 9-5, Sat 9-1
Friends of the Library Group

PRAIRIE DU SAC

P   PRAIRIE DU SAC PUBLIC LIBRARY*, 560 Park Ave, 53578-1199. SAN 318-3378. Tel: 608-643-8318. FAX: 608-643-4897. Web Site: www.scls.lib.wi.us/pds. *Dir,* Jennifer E Endres; E-mail: jepds@scls.lib.wi.us; *Ad,* Meagan Statz; *Youth Serv Librn,* Beth Hays
Founded 1900
Library Holdings: Bk Vols 36,000; Per Subs 134
Subject Interests: Local hist
Mem of South Central Library System
Open Mon-Fri 9-8, Sat 9-4
Friends of the Library Group

PRESCOTT

P   PRESCOTT PUBLIC LIBRARY*, 800 Borner St N, 54021-1703. SAN 318-3394. Tel: 715-262-5555. FAX: 715-262-4229. E-mail: prescottlib@ifls.lib.wi.us. Web Site: prescottpubliclibrary.org. *Dir,* Jane E Enright; E-mail: enright@ifls.lib.wi.us; *Tech Serv Mgr,* Jane Miller; E-mail: jmiller@ifls.lib.wi.us; *Programming Spec,* Becky Arenivar; E-mail: arenivar@ifls.lib.wi.us
Founded 1900. Pop 3,900; Circ 51,000
Library Holdings: Bk Vols 22,000; Per Subs 35
Subject Interests: Local hist, Wis hist
Automation Activity & Vendor Info: (Circulation) Innovative Interfaces, Inc
Open Mon-Thurs 10-8, Fri 10-6, Sat 10-3

PRESQUE ISLE

P   PRESQUE ISLE COMMUNITY LIBRARY*, 8306 School Loop Rd, 54557. (Mail add: PO Box 115, 54557-0115), SAN 376-6667. Tel: 715-686-7613. FAX: 715-686-2588. Web Site: presqueisle.wislib.org. *Dir,* Pam Eschenbauch; E-mail: pam@irmastein.nwls.lib.wi.us
Library Holdings: AV Mats 2,500; Bk Vols 12,000; Per Subs 26
Automation Activity & Vendor Info: (Acquisitions) Innovative Interfaces, Inc; (Cataloging) Innovative Interfaces, Inc; (Circulation) Innovative Interfaces, Inc; (OPAC) Innovative Interfaces, Inc

Mem of Northern Waters Library Service
Open Mon, Wed & Fri 10-4, Tues & Thurs 4-9, Sat 10-12

PRINCETON

P   PRINCETON PUBLIC LIBRARY*, 424 W Water St, 54968-9147. SAN
318-3416. Tel: 920-295-6777. FAX: 920-295-3303. E-mail:
director@princetonpublib.org. Web Site: www.princetonpublib.org. *Dir,*
Vicki Duhr; E-mail: duhr@princetonpublib.org
Founded 1933
Library Holdings: Bk Titles 17,000; Per Subs 46
Automation Activity & Vendor Info: (Cataloging) SirsiDynix;
(Circulation) SirsiDynix; (Course Reserve) SirsiDynix; (OPAC) SirsiDynix;
(Serials) SirsiDynix
Wireless access
Open Mon 9-6, Tues-Thurs 10-8, Fri 9-5, Sat 9-1
Friends of the Library Group

RACINE

ALL SAINTS HEALTHCARE
M   LIBRARY & COMMUNITY RESOURCE CENTER*, c/o Saint Mary's
Medical Ctr, 3801 Spring St, 53405, SAN 318-3483. Tel: 262-636-4300.
Founded 1932
Library Holdings: Bk Titles 175; Per Subs 175
Subject Interests: Med, Nursing
Partic in Docline; Regional Med Libr - Region 3
Open Mon-Fri 8-4:30
M   SAINT MARY'S MEDICAL CENTER LIBRARY*, 3801 Spring St,
53405, SAN 328-3429. Tel: 262-687-4011. FAX: 262-687-4175. E-mail:
library@allsaintshealthcare.org. *Dir, Libr Serv,* Carrie Papa
Library Holdings: Bk Titles 575
Subject Interests: Cardiology, Nursing, Orthopedics, Pediatrics, Surgery
Open Mon-Fri 8-4:30

S   DEKOVEN FOUNDATION*, DeKoven Center Library, 600 21st St,
53403. SAN 374-6194. Tel: 262-633-6401. FAX: 262-633-6401. E-mail:
dekoven.center@juno.com. Web Site: www.dekovencenter.pair.com. *Librn,*
Kathleen Cloyd
Founded 1852
Library Holdings: Bk Vols 5,000
Special Collections: History of Racine & The DeKoven Foundation, 1852-
(Walker Archives), docs
Publications: Reflections (Newsletter); To Hear Celestial Harmonies:
Essays on James DeKoven & The DeKoven Center (Local historical
information)
Open Mon-Fri 9-5

C   GATEWAY TECHNICAL COLLEGE*, Learning Resources
Center/Library, 1001 S Main St, 53403-1582. SAN 324-3362. Tel:
262-619-6220. FAX: 262-619-6221. E-mail: racinelrc@gtc.edu. Web Site:
www.gtc.edu/library. *Librn,* Linda M Pulera; *Circ, Ref Serv,* Robert A
Domes; Tel: 262-619-6370, E-mail: domesr@gtc.edu; *Circ,* April Gandy;
Tel: 262-619-6414, E-mail: gandya@gtc.edu; Staff 3 (MLS 2, Non-MLS 1)
Enrl 2,200; Fac 85; Highest Degree: Associate
Library Holdings: Bk Vols 15,000; Per Subs 150
Subject Interests: Culinary arts, Electronics, Fire sci, Gen educ,
Wordprocessing
Automation Activity & Vendor Info: (Acquisitions) Ex Libris Group;
(Cataloging) Ex Libris Group; (Circulation) Ex Libris Group; (Course
Reserve) Ex Libris Group; (OPAC) Ex Libris Group; (Serials) Ex Libris
Group
Database Vendor: EBSCOhost, Gale Cengage Learning, ProQuest, Wilson
- Wilson Web
Function: ILL available, Online searches, Orientations
Partic in Library Council of Southeastern Wisconsin, Inc; WISPALS
Library Consortium
Open Mon-Thurs 7:45-8:30, Fri 7:45-4
Restriction: Open to pub for ref & circ; with some limitations, Open to
students, fac & staff, Photo ID required for access

S   RACINE ART MUSEUM LIBRARY*, 441 Main St, 53403. (Mail add: PO
Box 187, 53401-0187), SAN 318-3505. Tel: 262-638-8300. FAX:
262-898-1045. E-mail: raminfo@ramart.org. Web Site: www.ramart.org.
Curator of Coll, Exec Dir, Bruce W Pepich; Tel: 262-638-8300, Ext 106,
E-mail: bpepich@ramart.org
Founded 1941
Library Holdings: Per Subs 12
Special Collections: Exhibition Catalogues
Subject Interests: Art, Art hist, Out-of-print
Function: For res purposes
Partic in Tri County Libr Consortium
Restriction: Open by appt only

GL   RACINE COUNTY LAW LIBRARY*, 730 Wisconsin Ave, 53403-1247.
SAN 318-3475. Tel: 262-636-3773. FAX: 262-636-3341. *In Charge,* Rose
Lee; E-mail: rose.lee@wicourts.gov
Library Holdings: Bk Vols 16,000
Open Mon-Fri 8:30-5

S   RACINE HERITAGE MUSEUM*, Archives-Research Center, 701 S Main
St, 53403-1211. SAN 318-3467. Tel: 262-636-3926. FAX: 262-636-3940.
E-mail: inquire@clmail.com. Web Site: www.racineheritagemuseum.org.
Archivist, Mary Nelson; *Curator,* Karen Brown; Staff 1 (Non-MLS 1)
Founded 1969
Library Holdings: Bk Titles 500
Special Collections: Racine County Histories, City & County Directories,
Photographs, Corporate Historical Documents, Maps & Atlases, Obituaries,
Family History Documents & Genealogies, Indexes to Cemeteries,
Naturalizations, Censuses, Surnames & Subjects
Subject Interests: Corporate hist, Local family hist, Mil hist, Racine Co
hist
Function: Res libr
Publications: Museum Newsletter
Open Tues 1-4:30, Sat 10-1
Restriction: Non-circulating

P   RACINE PUBLIC LIBRARY*, 75 Seventh St, 53403. SAN 365-0588. Tel:
262-636-9241. Interlibrary Loan Service Tel: 262-636-9299. Reference Tel:
262-636-9217. Automation Services Tel: 262-636-9249. FAX:
262-636-9260. Web Site: www.racinelibrary.info/. *Libr Dir,* Jessica
MacPhail; Tel: 262-636-9252, E-mail: director@racinelibrary.info; Staff 16
(MLS 16)
Founded 1897. Pop 142,112; Circ 971,175
Library Holdings: AV Mats 29,279; Bks on Deafness & Sign Lang 211;
e-books 8,869; High Interest/Low Vocabulary Bk Vols 160; Large Print
Bks 4,637; Bk Titles 198,710; Bk Vols 267,447; Per Subs 465; Spec
Interest Per Sub 299; Talking Bks 8,367
Special Collections: Early Childhood Resource Coll; Racine City &
County Historical Material, bks, pamphlets & clippings. Oral History; State
Document Depository; US Document Depository
Automation Activity & Vendor Info: (Acquisitions) SirsiDynix;
(Cataloging) SirsiDynix; (Circulation) SirsiDynix; (Course Reserve)
SirsiDynix; (ILL) SirsiDynix; (Media Booking) SirsiDynix; (OPAC)
SirsiDynix; (Serials) SirsiDynix
Mem of Lakeshores Library System
Partic in OCLC Online Computer Library Center, Inc
Special Services for the Deaf - Assisted listening device; Bks on deafness
& sign lang; Captioned film dep; Closed caption videos; TTY equip
Special Services for the Blind - Accessible computers; Audio mat; Bks &
mags in Braille, on rec, tape & cassette; Bks on CD; Computer with voice
synthesizer for visually impaired persons; Copier with enlargement
capabilities; Descriptive video serv (DVS); Extensive large print coll;
Home delivery serv; Internet workstation with adaptive software; Large
print bks; Large screen computer & software; Ref serv; Screen enlargement
software for people with visual disabilities; Talking bks
Open Mon-Wed 9-9, Thurs 9-5:30, Fri 1-5:30, Sat 1-5, Sun (Oct-Apr) 2-5
Friends of the Library Group
Bookmobiles: 1. Head of Extn/Adult Servs, Jill Hartmann. Bk titles 4,570

RANDOLPH

P   HUTCHINSON MEMORIAL LIBRARY*, 228 N High St, 53956. SAN
318-3521. Tel: 920-326-4640. FAX: 920-326-4642. Web Site:
www.randolph.lib.wi.us. *Dir,* Ione Deich; E-mail: ione@randolph.lib.wi.us;
Asst Librn, Paulette Miller; *Asst Librn,* Darlene Missall
Founded 1906. Pop 1,869
Library Holdings: Bk Vols 23,000; Per Subs 40
Special Collections: Randolph Advance Newspapers (1890-present), micro
Automation Activity & Vendor Info: (Cataloging) SirsiDynix;
(Circulation) SirsiDynix; (OPAC) SirsiDynix; (Serials) SirsiDynix
Mem of Mid-Wisconsin Federated Library System
Open Mon-Thurs 9-8, Fri 1-6, Sat 9-3 (Summer 9-12)
Friends of the Library Group

RANDOM LAKE

P   LAKEVIEW COMMUNITY LIBRARY*, 112 Butler St, 53075-1708.
(Mail add: PO Box 326, 53075-0326), SAN 318-353X. Tel: 920-994-4825.
FAX: 920-994-2230. E-mail: raref@esls.lib.wi.us. Web Site:
randomlake.lib.wi.us. *Dir,* Darla Jean Kraus; E-mail: dkraus@esls.lib.wi.us;
Staff 6 (Non-MLS 6)
Founded 1957. Pop 5,000; Circ 59,188
Jan 2005-Dec 2005 Income $234,141, Federal $1,039, County $32,359,
Locally Generated Income $145,636, Other $55,107. Mats Exp $24,059,
Books $18,137, Per/Ser (Incl. Access Fees) $1,812, Other Print Mats $105,
AV Mat $4,005. Sal $147,795
Library Holdings: AV Mats 2,978; Bk Titles 33,377; Per Subs 72
Special Collections: Local Newspapers 1918-1998, micro

Automation Activity & Vendor Info: (Acquisitions) SirsiDynix; (Cataloging) SirsiDynix; (Circulation) SirsiDynix; (Course Reserve) SirsiDynix; (ILL) SirsiDynix; (Media Booking) SirsiDynix; (OPAC) SirsiDynix; (Serials) SirsiDynix
Mem of Eastern Shores Library System
Open Mon-Thurs 9:30-8, Fri 9:30-5:30, Sat 9:30-12:30
Friends of the Library Group

READSTOWN

P   READSTOWN PUBLIC LIBRARY*, 129 W Wisconsin, 54652. Tel: 608-629-5465. FAX: 608-629-5465. E-mail: readslib@yahoo.com. *Dir,* Helen Jane Fortney
Library Holdings: Bk Titles 18,000; Per Subs 100; Talking Bks 250
Mem of Winding Rivers Library System
Open Mon-Fri 1-6

REDGRANITE

P   REDGRANITE PUBLIC LIBRARY, 135 W Bannerman Ave, 54970. (Mail add: PO Box 291, 54970-0291), SAN 318-3548. Tel: 920-566-0176. E-mail: director@redgranitelibrary.org. Web Site: www.redgranitelibrary.org. *Dir,* Jean Nelson; E-mail: jnelson@redgranitelibrary.org; Staff 2 (MLS 1, Non-MLS 1)
Library Holdings: AV Mats 700; Large Print Bks 100; Bk Vols 10,000; Per Subs 30; Talking Bks 50
Special Collections: Local History
Automation Activity & Vendor Info: (Cataloging) SirsiDynix; (Circulation) SirsiDynix; (OPAC) SirsiDynix
Mem of Winnefox Library System
Open Mon 11-6, Wed 11-7, Fri 11-5, Sat 9-12
Friends of the Library Group

REEDSBURG

P   REEDSBURG PUBLIC LIBRARY*, 370 Vine St, 53959-1917. SAN 318-3556. Tel: 608-524-3316, 608-768-7323. FAX: 608-524-9024. Web Site: www.reedsburglibrary.org. *Dir,* Susan J Steiner; E-mail: sjs@scls.lib.wi.us; *Asst Dir,* Sue Ann Kucher; E-mail: kuchers@scls.lib.wi.us; *Youth Serv Librn,* Kris Houtler; E-mail: khoutler@scls.lib.wi.us; *Circ Supvr,* Maureen Palmer; E-mail: maureenp@scls.lib.wi.us; *Tech Serv,* Wendy Collins; E-mail: wcollins@scls.lib.wi.us; Staff 12 (MLS 2, Non-MLS 10)
Founded 1898. Pop 18,000; Circ 289,365
Jan 2009-Dec 2009 Income $575,110, City $334,273, County $217,541, Locally Generated Income $1,400, Other $21,896. Mats Exp $143,306, Books $50,000, Per/Ser (Incl. Access Fees) $3,550, Other Print Mats $66,376, AV Mat $22,550, Electronic Ref Mat (Incl. Access Fees) $830. Sal $385,084
Library Holdings: Bk Titles 70,555; Per Subs 137
Automation Activity & Vendor Info: (Circulation) SirsiDynix; (Serials) SirsiDynix
Wireless access
Mem of South Central Library System
Friends of the Library Group

REESEVILLE

P   REESEVILLE PUBLIC LIBRARY*, 216 S Main St, 53579. (Mail add: PO Box 279, 53579-0279), SAN 364-6173. Tel: 920-927-7390. FAX: 920-927-7390. E-mail: reesevillelibrary@mwfls.org. Web Site: www.reeseville.lib.wi.us. *Dir,* Ann M Powers; E-mail: apowers@mwfls.org
Founded 1964
Library Holdings: Bk Vols 9,675
Mem of Mid-Wisconsin Federated Library System
Open Mon & Wed 9-noon & 1-4, Tues & Thurs 1-7, Fri 1-4, Sat 9-noon

RHINELANDER

J   NICOLET AREA TECHNICAL COLLEGE*, Richard J Brown Library, 5364 College Dr, 54501. (Mail add: PO Box 518, 54501), SAN 318-3572. Tel: 715-365-4479. Circulation Tel: 715-365-4576. Reference Tel: 715-365-4606. Administration Tel: 715-365-4489. Toll Free Tel: 800-544-3039. FAX: 715-365-4404. Web Site: www.nicoletcollege.edu. *Dir,* Marc Boucher; Tel: 715-365-4489, E-mail: mboucher@nicoletcollege.edu; *Automation Librn, Cat,* Barbara Heiffner; Tel: 715-365-4486, E-mail: heiffner@nicoletcollege.edu; *Br Librn,* Jeff Siemers; Tel: 715-356-6753, E-mail: jsiemers@nicoletcollege.edu; *Access Serv, ILL,* Maureen McCloskey; Tel: 715-365-4606, E-mail: mmcclosk@nicoletcollege.edu; *Acq,* Terri Cable; Tel: 715-365-4436, Fax: 715-365-4551, E-mail: tcable@nicoletcollege.edu; *AV Coordr,* Roger Davis; Tel: 715-365-4428, E-mail: rdavis1@nicoletcollege.edu; *Circ,* Barbara Hackbarth; Tel: 715-365-4691, E-mail: bhackbarth@nicoletcollege.edu; *Circ,* Sharon Johnson; E-mail: sjjohnso@nicoletcollege.edu; *Circ,* Kathleen Tromp; E-mail: ktromp@nicoletcollege.edu; *Online Serv,* Karen

Quattrocchi; Tel: 715-365-4409, E-mail: kquattro@nicoletcollege.edu; Staff 4 (MLS 1, Non-MLS 3)
Founded 1969. Enrl 1,500; Fac 75; Highest Degree: Associate
Library Holdings: Bk Vols 45,000; Per Subs 350
Special Collections: State Document Depository
Subject Interests: Art, Native Am, Nursing
Automation Activity & Vendor Info: (Cataloging) Follett Software; (Circulation) Follett Software; (ILL) OCLC WorldCat; (OPAC) Follett Software
Database Vendor: EBSCOhost, OCLC FirstSearch, ProQuest, ReferenceUSA, SerialsSolutions, SirsiDynix
Wireless access
Publications: Handbook; Subject Bibliographies & Pathfinders
Partic in OCLC Online Computer Library Center, Inc; Wisconsin Library Services
Open Mon-Thurs (Fall & Winter) 8-8, Fri & Sat 8-4; Mon & Wed (Summer) 8-6, Tues & Thurs 8-8, Fri 8-4

P   RHINELANDER DISTRICT LIBRARY*, 106 N Stevens St, 54501-3193. SAN 318-3580. Tel: 715-365-1070. FAX: 715-365-1076. Web Site: www.rhinelanderlibrary.org. *Dir,* Ed Hughes; E-mail: EHughes@rhinelanderlibrary.org; *Assoc Dir, Ch,* Thomas Hurlburt; Tel: 715-365-1073, E-mail: hurlburt@wvls.lib.wi.us; *Tech Coordr,* John Moxon; *Outreach Serv,* Catherine Parker; *Syst Adminr,* Nilla Sjoberg; Staff 13 (MLS 2, Non-MLS 11)
Founded 1898. Pop 18,511; Circ 190,605
Library Holdings: Bk Vols 72,807; Per Subs 149; Videos 3,542
Special Collections: Art (Ruth Smith Bump Coll)
Subject Interests: Archit, Art, Genealogy, Local hist, State hist
Automation Activity & Vendor Info: (Acquisitions) Horizon; (Cataloging) Horizon; (Circulation) SirsiDynix
Database Vendor: EBSCOhost, ProQuest
Function: Adult bk club, Copy machines, Genealogy discussion group, Handicapped accessible, Home delivery & serv to Sr ctr & nursing homes, ILL available, Mail & tel request accepted, Music CDs, Preschool outreach, Prog for adults, Prog for children & young adult, Ref serv available, Serves mentally handicapped consumers, Spoken cassettes & CDs, Summer reading prog, Tax forms, VCDs, VHS videos, Wheelchair accessible
Mem of Wisconsin Valley Library Service
Open Mon & Tues (Winter) 9-8, Wed, Thurs, Fri 9-6, Sat 9-4; Mon (Summer) 9-8, Tues, Wed, Thurs, Fri 9-6, Sat 9-1
Friends of the Library Group

G   UNITED STATES DEPARTMENT OF AGRICULTURE*, North Central Research Station, Forestry Sciences Laboratory Library, 5985 Hwy K, 54501. SAN 327-9952. Tel: 715-362-7474. FAX: 715-362-1166. *Librn,* Penny Kluetz
Founded 1960
Library Holdings: Bk Vols 3,010
Subject Interests: Biol, Botany, Ecology, Genetics, Physiology
Open Mon-Fri 8-4:30

RIB LAKE

P   RIB LAKE PUBLIC LIBRARY*, 645 Pearl St, 54470. (Mail add: PO Box 188, 54470-0188), SAN 318-3599. Tel: 715-427-5769. Interlibrary Loan Service Tel: 715-847-5549. FAX: 715-427-5368. E-mail: blomberg@wvls.lib.wi.us. Web Site: www.riblakepl.org. *Dir,* David Judell; E-mail: djudell@wvls.lib.wi.us
Founded 1900. Pop 19,000
Library Holdings: Bk Titles 14,000; Per Subs 83
Subject Interests: Arts, Wis
Automation Activity & Vendor Info: (Cataloging) SirsiDynix; (Circulation) SirsiDynix; (OPAC) SirsiDynix
Mem of Wisconsin Valley Library Service
Open Mon, Tues & Fri 10-6, Wed & Thurs Noon-8, Fri 10-6, Sat 10-1

RICE LAKE

P   RICE LAKE PUBLIC LIBRARY*, Two E Marshall St, 54868. SAN 318-3602. Tel: 715-234-4861. FAX: 715-234-5026. E-mail: www.ricelakelibrary.org. Web Site: www.ricelakelibrary.org. *Dir,* Dawn Wacek; *Adult Serv Mgr,* Tami Richardson; *Youth Serv Mgr,* Ashley Bieber; *Tech Serv Supvr,* Linda Mullin; *Coordr, ILL,* Mark Drkula; *Circ,* Laura Anderson; Staff 14.12 (MLS 3, Non-MLS 11.12)
Founded 1896. Pop 8,580; Circ 204,000
Library Holdings: AV Mats 1,661; DVDs 1,000; e-books 15,845; Bk Vols 40,224; Per Subs 189; Videos 760
Subject Interests: Local hist
Automation Activity & Vendor Info: (Cataloging) Innovative Interfaces, Inc; (Circulation) Innovative Interfaces, Inc; (OPAC) Innovative Interfaces, Inc; (Serials) Innovative Interfaces, Inc
Database Vendor: EBSCOhost
Wireless access

Function: Adult bk club, Audio & video playback equip for onsite use, Audiobks via web, Bi-weekly Writer's Group, Bks on cassette, Bks on CD, Children's prog, Computers for patron use, Copy machines, Fax serv, Handicapped accessible, Home delivery & serv to Sr ctr & nursing homes, ILL available, Large print keyboards, Magnifiers for reading, Music CDs, Notary serv, Online cat, Online ref, OverDrive digital audio bks, Prog for adults, Prog for children & young adult, Scanner, Story hour, Summer reading prog, Tax forms, Teen prog
Mem of Indianhead Federated Library System
Special Services for the Blind - Assistive/Adapted tech devices, equip & products; Bks on cassette; Bks on CD; Computer with voice synthesizer for visually impaired persons; Large print bks; Open bk software on pub access PC
Open Mon-Thurs 9-8, Fri & Sat 9-5, Sun (Winter) 1-5
Restriction: 24-hr pass syst for students only
Friends of the Library Group

J UNIVERSITY OF WISCONSIN*, Barron County Library, 1800 College Dr, 54868-2497. SAN 318-3610. Tel: 715-234-8369. Toll Free Tel: 888-893-9892. FAX: 715-234-1975. Web Site: barron.uwc.edu/library. *Dir,* Zora J Sampson; E-mail: zsampson@uwc.edu; *Circ,* Linda L Snider; Tel: 715-234-1876, Ext 5461, E-mail: lsnider@uwc.edu; Staff 3 (MLS 1, Non-MLS 2)
Founded 1968. Enrl 434; Fac 26; Highest Degree: Associate
Library Holdings: Bk Titles 27,269; Bk Vols 32,168; Per Subs 460
Automation Activity & Vendor Info: (Acquisitions) Ex Libris Group; (Cataloging) Ex Libris Group; (Circulation) Ex Libris Group; (ILL) Ex Libris Group
Database Vendor: EBSCOhost, LexisNexis, OCLC FirstSearch, ProQuest, SirsiDynix, TLC (The Library Corporation), Wilson - Wilson Web
Function: For res purposes
Open Mon-Thurs (Winter) 8am-9pm, Fri 8-5, Sun 9-5; Mon-Thurs (Summer) 9-4

J WISCONSIN INDIANHEAD TECHNICAL COLLEGE*, Learning Resource Center, 1900 College Dr, 54868. SAN 318-3629. Tel: 715-234-7082, Ext 5424. Toll Free Tel: 800-243-9482, Ext 5424. FAX: 715-234-5172. Web Site: www.witc.edu. *Libr Tech,* Mary Alice Larson; *Libr Tech,* Jennifer McNicholas; *Libr Tech,* Gladys Prytz
Library Holdings: Bk Titles 6,844
Automation Activity & Vendor Info: (Cataloging) Gateway; (Circulation) Gateway; (OPAC) Gateway
Database Vendor: Gale Cengage Learning, Wilson - Wilson Web
Open Mon-Thurs 7:30-7, Fri 7:30-4

RICHLAND CENTER

P BREWER PUBLIC LIBRARY*, Richland Center Public Library, 325 N Central Ave, 53581-1802. SAN 318-3637. Tel: 608-647-6444. FAX: 608-647-6797. E-mail: richlandcenterpl@yahoo.com. Web Site: www.rc.swls.org. *Dir,* Michele Nolen-Karras; *Ch,* Ed Tiegs
Founded 1900. Pop 5,114; Circ 104,233
Library Holdings: Bk Vols 52,119; Per Subs 111
Special Collections: Richland County History Coll. Oral History
Mem of Southwest Wisconsin Library System
Open Mon-Thurs 10-8, Fri 10-5, Sat 10-2
Friends of the Library Group

C UNIVERSITY OF WISCONSIN-RICHLAND*, Miller Memorial Library, 1200 US Hwy 14 W, 53581-1399. SAN 318-3645. Tel: 608-647-6186, Ext 220. Circulation Tel: 608-647-6186, Ext 293. FAX: 608-647-6225. E-mail: rlnlibrary@uwc.edu. Web Site: www.richland.uwc.edu/academic/library. *Dir,* James A Gollata; E-mail: james.gollata@uwc.edu; *Assoc Librn,* Lisa Killips; E-mail: lisa.killips@uwc.edu
Founded 1967. Enrl 400
Library Holdings: Bk Vols 45,000
Automation Activity & Vendor Info: (Acquisitions) Ex Libris Group; (Cataloging) Ex Libris Group; (Circulation) Ex Libris Group; (Course Reserve) Ex Libris Group; (ILL) Ex Libris Group; (Media Booking) Ex Libris Group; (OPAC) Ex Libris Group; (Serials) Ex Libris Group
Partic in OCLC Online Computer Library Center, Inc; Wisconsin Library Services
Open Mon-Thurs 8:30-7, Fri 8:30-4, Sun 4-8

RIO

P RIO COMMUNITY LIBRARY*, 324 W Lyons St, 53960. (Mail add: PO Box 306, 53960-0306), SAN 318-3653. Tel: 920-992-3206. FAX: 920-992-3983. E-mail: riolib@yahoo.com. *Dir,* Erin Elizabeth Foley; *Asst Dir,* Jon Pribbenow; *Circ,* Dawn Golliher; *Circ,* Jackie Nachreiner; Staff 2 (MLS 1, Non-MLS 1)
Founded 1917. Pop 2,683; Circ 35,000
Jan 2011-Dec 2011 Income $130,942, City $76,305, County $49,137, Locally Generated Income $5,500. Mats Exp $9,400, Books $7,700,

Per/Ser (Incl. Access Fees) $1,200, AV Mat $500. Sal $74,331 (Prof $56,878)
Library Holdings: Audiobooks 439; CDs 575; DVDs 887; High Interest/Low Vocabulary Bk Vols 441; Large Print Bks 866; Microforms 1; Bk Vols 20,708; Per Subs 60; Videos 1,142
Automation Activity & Vendor Info: (Cataloging) Book Systems, Inc; (Circulation) Book Systems, Inc; (OPAC) Book Systems, Inc
Wireless access
Function: Bk club(s), Bks on cassette, Bks on CD, Children's prog, Computers for patron use, Copy machines, e-mail serv, Electronic databases & coll, Exhibits, Fax serv, Free DVD rentals, Handicapped accessible, Holiday prog, ILL available, Mail & tel request accepted, Music CDs, Notary serv, Online cat, Online ref, Online searches, OverDrive digital audio bks, Photocopying/Printing, Prog for children & young adult, Ref & res, Ref serv available, Ref serv in person, Spoken cassettes & CDs, Spoken cassettes & DVDs, Story hour, Summer reading prog, Tax forms, Telephone ref, VHS videos, Wheelchair accessible
Mem of South Central Library System
Open Mon & Wed 10-8, Tues, Thurs & Fri 10-5, Sat 10-3
Friends of the Library Group

RIPON

C RIPON COLLEGE*, Lane Library, 300 Seward St, 54971. (Mail add: PO Box 248, 54971-0248), SAN 318-3661. Tel: 920-748-8175. Interlibrary Loan Service Tel: 920-748-8747. Administration Tel: 920-748-8750. FAX: 920-748-7243. Web Site: www.ripon.edu/library. *Dean, VPres,* Christophor M Ogle; E-mail: OgleC@ripon.edu; *Asst Librn, Chair, Libr Serv, User Serv,* Andrew R Prellwitz; E-mail: PrellwitzA@ripon.edu; *Acq,* Sharon Wielgus; Tel: 920-748-8330, E-mail: wielguss@ripon.edu; *Archivist, Ref Serv,* Valerie Viers; Tel: 920-748-8752, E-mail: viersv@ripon.edu; *Cat, ILL,* Carl Ziebell; Tel: 920-748-8746, E-mail: ziebellc@ripon.edu; *Circ,* Jeanne Chaney; Tel: 920-748-8747, E-mail: chaneyj@ripon.edu; *Ser, Syst Coordr,* Ane Carriveau; Tel: 920-748-8750, E-mail: carriveaua@ripon.edu; Staff 4.75 (MLS 3, Non-MLS 1.75)
Founded 1851. Enrl 988; Fac 74; Highest Degree: Bachelor
Library Holdings: Bk Titles 125,742; Bk Vols 164,610; Per Subs 794
Special Collections: ColisLotory; Local History (Pedrick Coll); Wisconsin Authors (Wisconsin's Own Library). State Document Depository; US Document Depository
Subject Interests: Liberal arts
Automation Activity & Vendor Info: (Acquisitions) Innovative Interfaces, Inc; (Cataloging) Innovative Interfaces, Inc; (Circulation) Innovative Interfaces, Inc; (Course Reserve) Innovative Interfaces, Inc; (ILL) Clio; (OPAC) Innovative Interfaces, Inc; (Serials) Innovative Interfaces, Inc
Database Vendor: American Chemical Society, American Psychological Association (APA), BioOne, Cambridge Scientific Abstracts, EBSCOhost, LexisNexis, OCLC FirstSearch, OCLC WorldCat, ProQuest, PubMed
Wireless access
Function: ILL available
Publications: Bibliographic guides
Partic in Fox Valley Library Council; OCLC Online Computer Library Center, Inc; Wisconsin Library Services
Open Mon-Thurs 7:30-Midnight, Fri 7:30am-8pm, Sat 10-8, Sun Noon-Midnight
Friends of the Library Group

P RIPON PUBLIC LIBRARY*, 120 Jefferson St, 54971-1395. SAN 318-367X. Tel: 920-748-6160. FAX: 920-748-6298. Web Site: www.riponlibrary.org. *Dir,* Desiree M Bongers; E-mail: dbongers@riponlibrary.org; *Adult Serv,* Shannon Stiller; E-mail: stiller@riponlibrary.org; *Ch,* Linda DeCramer; E-mail: decramer@riponlibrary.org; Staff 5 (MLS 2, Non-MLS 3)
Founded 1885. Pop 11,500
Library Holdings: AV Mats 5,772; Bk Titles 56,837; Per Subs 152
Automation Activity & Vendor Info: (Cataloging) SirsiDynix; (Circulation) SirsiDynix; (OPAC) SirsiDynix
Database Vendor: EBSCOhost, Gale Cengage Learning, ProQuest, SirsiDynix
Publications: Ripon Public Library (Newsletter)
Mem of Winnefox Library System
Open Mon-Fri (Winter) 9:30-8, Sat 10-4, Sun 1-4; Mon-Thurs (Summer) 9:30-8, Fri 9:30-6, Sat 10-1
Friends of the Library Group

RIVER FALLS

P RIVER FALLS PUBLIC LIBRARY*, 140 Union St, 54022. SAN 318-3688. Tel: 715-425-0905. FAX: 715-425-0914. Web Site: www.rfcity.org/library. *Dir,* Nancy Y Miller; Tel: 715-425-0905, Ext 101, E-mail: nancymiller@ifls.lib.wi.us; *Ch,* Susan Pesheck; Tel: 715-425-0905, Ext 105, E-mail: susanpesheck@ifls.lib.wi.us; *Ref Serv, Ad,* Kim Kiiskinen; Tel: 715-425-0905, Ext 104, E-mail: kiiski@ifls.lib.wi.us; *Tech Serv,* Jon George; Tel: 715-425-0905, Ext 120, E-mail: jongeorge@ifls.lib.wi.us; Staff 14 (MLS 4, Non-MLS 10)

Circ 347,000
Library Holdings: Bk Titles 70,000; Per Subs 200
Subject Interests: Hist of River Falls
Automation Activity & Vendor Info: (Cataloging) Innovative Interfaces, Inc; (Circulation) Innovative Interfaces, Inc; (OPAC) Innovative Interfaces, Inc; (Serials) Innovative Interfaces, Inc
Database Vendor: EBSCOhost, Innovative Interfaces, Inc INN - View Wireless access
Function: Art exhibits, Audiobks via web, Bk club(s), Bks on cassette, Bks on CD, Computers for patron use, Copy machines, Equip loans & repairs, Fax serv, Handicapped accessible, Home delivery & serv to Sr ctr & nursing homes, ILL available, Magnifiers for reading, Music CDs, Online cat, Online ref, Outreach serv, Prog for adults, Prog for children & young adult, Scanner, Senior outreach, Story hour, Summer reading prog, Tax forms, Teen prog, Telephone ref
Mem of Indianhead Federated Library System
Special Services for the Deaf - Closed caption videos
Special Services for the Blind - Accessible computers; Bks on cassette; Bks on CD
Open Mon-Thurs 9-8, Fri 9-6, Sat 10-4, Sun (Sept-May) 1-4

C   UNIVERSITY OF WISCONSIN-RIVER FALLS*, Chalmer Davee Library, 410 S Third St, 54022. SAN 318-3696. Tel: 715-425-3321. Interlibrary Loan Service Tel: 715-425-4286. Reference Tel: 715-425-3343. Administration Tel: 715-425-3222. FAX: 715-425-0609. Web Site: www.uwrf.edu/library. *Dir,* Valerie I Malzacher; E-mail: valerie.i.malzacher@uwrf.edu; *Head, Circ, Head, Libr Syst,* Maureen Olle-LaJoie; Tel: 715-425-3799, E-mail: maureen.olle-lajoie@uwrf.edu; *Govt Doc, Head, Tech Serv,* Michele McKnelly; Tel: 715-425-4482, E-mail: michele.mcknelly@uwrf.edu; *Head, Univ Archives & Area Res Ctr,* Kathie Otto; Tel: 715-425-3567, E-mail: kathryn.otto@uwrf.edu; *Cat/Metadata Librn,* Heidi Southworth; Tel: 715-425-3924, E-mail: heidi.southworth@uwrf.edu; *Coll Develop Librn,* Lisa Pillow; Tel: 715-425-3360, E-mail: lisa.pillow@uwrf.edu; *Ref & Instrul Serv Librn,* Tom Smisek; Tel: 715-425-3312, E-mail: thomas.smisek@uwrf.edu; *Ref & Instrul Serv Librn,* Anne Tuveson; Tel: 715-425-3312, E-mail: anne.tuveson@uwrf.edu; *Coordr, Ref & Instrul Serv,* Brad Gee; Tel: 715-425-3552, E-mail: brad.gee@uwrf.edu; Staff 22 (MLS 9, Non-MLS 13)
Founded 1875. Enrl 6,900; Fac 276; Highest Degree: Master
Jul 2009-Jun 2010 Income $1,423,705, State $1,276,497, Federal $13,725, Locally Generated Income $5,000, Other $128,483. Mats Exp $479,522, Books $46,994, Per/Ser (Incl. Access Fees) $215,232, Manu Arch $2,000, Micro $5,947, AV Mat $17,015, Electronic Ref Mat (Incl. Access Fees) $192,334. Sal $833,111 (Prof $407,583)
Library Holdings: AV Mats 11,187; e-books 58,247; e-journals 4,805; Electronic Media & Resources 126; Microforms 1,129,863; Music Scores 4,068; Bk Vols 226,809; Per Subs 500
Special Collections: Northwestern Wisconsin History; University History. Oral History; State Document Depository; US Document Depository
Subject Interests: Agr, Educ, Hist
Automation Activity & Vendor Info: (Acquisitions) Ex Libris Group; (Cataloging) Ex Libris Group; (Circulation) Ex Libris Group; (Course Reserve) Ex Libris Group; (ILL) OCLC ILLiad; (OPAC) Ex Libris Group; (Serials) Ex Libris Group
Database Vendor: ABC-CLIO, Agricola, Alexander Street Press, American Chemical Society, American Mathematical Society, American Physical Society, American Psychological Association (APA), BioOne, Cambridge Scientific Abstracts, Cinahl Information Systems, Community of Science (COS), CQ Press, EBSCOhost, Elsevier, Emerald, Gale Cengage Learning, H W Wilson, IEEE (Institute of Electrical & Electronics Engineers), infoUSA, IOP, ISI Web of Knowledge, JSTOR, Knovel, LexisNexis, Modern Language Association, netLibrary, OCLC WorldCat, OVID Technologies, Oxford Online, Project MUSE, ProQuest, PubMed, ReferenceUSA, Sage, ScienceDirect, Springshare, LLC, Thomson - Web of Science, Wilson - Wilson Web, YBP Library Services Wireless access
Publications: UW-RF Library News
Partic in OCLC Online Computer Library Center, Inc; Wisconsin Library Services
Special Services for the Blind - Accessible computers; Magnifiers

ROBERTS

P   HAZEL MACKIN COMMUNITY LIBRARY*, 107 W Main St, 54023. (Mail add: PO Box 88, 54023-0088), SAN 318-370X. Tel: 715-749-3849. E-mail: robertslibrary@ifls.lib.wi.us. Web Site: www.robertspubliclibrary.org. *Dir,* Beverly Jacobson; *Asst Librn,* Kathy Miller; Staff 1 (Non-MLS 1)
Founded 1975. Pop 1,500; Circ 21,429
Library Holdings: AV Mats 759; Bks on Deafness & Sign Lang 25; e-books 15,845; Large Print Bks 390; Bk Titles 12,206; Per Subs 47; Talking Bks 670; Videos 740
Automation Activity & Vendor Info: (Cataloging) Innovative Interfaces, Inc; (Circulation) Innovative Interfaces, Inc; (ILL) Innovative Interfaces, Inc; (OPAC) Innovative Interfaces, Inc

Database Vendor: Innovative Interfaces, Inc INN - View
Mem of Indianhead Federated Library System
Open Tues, Wed & Fri (Winter) 10-5, Thurs 1-7:30, Sat 9-12; Tues, Wed & Fri (Summer) 10-5, Thurs 10-7:30

ROCHESTER

P   ROCHESTER PUBLIC LIBRARY*, 208 W Spring St, 53167. (Mail add: PO Box 245, 53167-0245), SAN 318-3718. Tel: 262-534-3533. FAX: 262-534-3531. Web Site: www.rochester.lib.wi.us. *Dir,* Mary Stapleton; E-mail: stapleto@rochester.lib.wi.us
Founded 1890
Library Holdings: Bk Vols 15,000; Per Subs 56
Automation Activity & Vendor Info: (Acquisitions) SirsiDynix; (Cataloging) SirsiDynix; (Circulation) SirsiDynix; (OPAC) SirsiDynix
Open Mon-Thurs 10-8:30, Sat 10-4, Sun 1-4
Friends of the Library Group

ROCK SPRINGS

P   ROCK SPRINGS PUBLIC LIBRARY*, 101 First St, 53961-8011. (Mail add: PO Box 56, 53961-0056), SAN 318-3726. Tel: 608-522-5050. FAX: 608-522-5050. Interlibrary Loan Service E-mail: rkslib@scls.lib.wi.us. Web Site: www.scls.lib.wi.us/rks. *Libr Dir,* Norma Jean LeMoine; *Youth Serv,* Marie Finley
Founded 1957. Pop 1,500; Circ 9,300
Jul 2005-Jun 2006. Mats Exp $2,700. Sal $19,554
Library Holdings: Bk Titles 6,638
Subject Interests: Local hist
Automation Activity & Vendor Info: (Cataloging) SirsiDynix; (Circulation) SirsiDynix; (ILL) OCLC WorldCat
Mem of South Central Library System
Open Mon 9-12, Tues & Thurs 3-7, Wed 9-12 & 3-7, Sat 10-12

SAINT CROIX FALLS

P   ST CROIX FALLS PUBLIC LIBRARY*, 230 S Washington St, 54024. (Mail add: 710 Hwy 35 S, St Croix Falls, 54024), SAN 378-004X. Tel: 715-483-1777. FAX: 715-483-1777. E-mail: scflibrary@ifls.lib.wi.us. *Dir,* Sarah Adams; *Asst Librn,* Eloise Anderson; *Asst Librn,* Su Leslie; *IT & Network Syst,* Kris Schwartz
Library Holdings: Bk Titles 15,000; Per Subs 32
Special Collections: Wisconsin History Coll; Wisconsin Newspapers 1872-
Wireless access
Mem of Indianhead Federated Library System
Open Mon-Fri 10-7, Sat 10-1

SAINT FRANCIS

R   SAINT FRANCIS SEMINARY*, Salzmann Library, 3257 S Lake Dr, 53235-0905. SAN 318-2436. Tel: 414-747-6479. Interlibrary Loan Service Tel: 414-747-6478. Reference Tel: 414-747-6476. FAX: 414-747-6483. Web Site: www.sfs.edu/salzmann.html. *Dir,* Kathy Frymark; kfrymark@sfs.edu; *Tech Serv,* Kate Ganski; E-mail: kganski@sfs.edu; Staff 4 (MLS 3, Non-MLS 1)
Founded 1845. Enrl 152; Fac 18; Highest Degree: Master
Library Holdings: Bk Titles 80,000; Bk Vols 84,120; Per Subs 508
Special Collections: Rembert G Weakland Coll
Subject Interests: Biblical works, Bioethics, Canon law, Church hist, Milwaukee, Patristics, Scripture, Theol, Wis, Women's studies
Automation Activity & Vendor Info: (Acquisitions) Innovative Interfaces, Inc; (Cataloging) Innovative Interfaces, Inc; (Circulation) Innovative Interfaces, Inc; (Course Reserve) Innovative Interfaces, Inc; (ILL) OCLC Online; (Media Booking) Innovative Interfaces, Inc; (OPAC) Innovative Interfaces, Inc; (Serials) Innovative Interfaces, Inc
Database Vendor: EBSCOhost, OCLC FirstSearch
Function: ILL available, Photocopying/Printing, Ref serv available, Telephone ref
Partic in OCLC Online Computer Library Center, Inc; Southeastern Wisconsin Information Technology Exchange, Inc; Wisconsin Library Services
Open Tues-Thurs 10-6, Fri 10-4, Sat 12-4
Friends of the Library Group

P   ST FRANCIS PUBLIC LIBRARY*, 4230 S Nicholson Ave, 53235. SAN 323-4738. Tel: 414-481-7323. FAX: 414-481-8949. *Dir,* Maggie Luczywko; E-mail: maggie.luczywko@mcfls.org; *Ch,* Suzanne Doyle; *Ref,* Constance Sheehan; Staff 4 (MLS 3, Non-MLS 1)
Pop 9,893; Circ 109,442
Library Holdings: Bk Vols 46,326; Per Subs 118
Automation Activity & Vendor Info: (Cataloging) Innovative Interfaces, Inc; (Circulation) Innovative Interfaces, Inc
Publications: Annual Report
Mem of Milwaukee County Federated Library System; Northwest Kansas Library System
Special Services for the Deaf - TDD equip

Open Mon-Thurs 10-8, Fri 10-5, Sat 9-4, Sun 1-4
Friends of the Library Group

SALEM

P   COMMUNITY LIBRARY, 24615 89th St, 53168. SAN 377-9521. Tel:
262-843-3348. FAX: 262-843-3144. Web Site: www.communitylib.org. *Dir,*
LeeAnn Briese; E-mail: lbriese@community.lib.wi.us; *Head, Circ Serv,*
Sharon Welsh; E-mail: swelsh@community.lib.wi.us; *Head, Info Serv,* Irene
Scherer; E-mail: ischerer@community.lib.wi.us; *Head, Tech Serv,* Danijela
Djurdjevic; E-mail: ddjurdje@community.lib.wi.us; *Head, Youth Serv,* Katie
Kiekhaefer; E-mail: kkiekhae@community.lib.wi.us
Founded 1977
Library Holdings: Bk Titles 48,000; Per Subs 275
Automation Activity & Vendor Info: (Acquisitions) Infor Library &
Information Solutions; (Cataloging) Infor Library & Information Solutions;
(Circulation) Infor Library & Information Solutions
Wireless access
Mem of Mohawk Valley Library System
Open Mon-Thurs 9-8, Fri & Sat 9-4
Branches: 2
SILVER LAKE COMMUNITY, 729 S Cogswell Dr, Silver Lake, 53170,
    SAN 377-9777. Tel: 262-889-4606. FAX: 262-889-8505.
    Open Mon, Tues & Thurs 3:30-7, Wed 1:30-5, Sat 9-1
TWIN LAKES BRANCH, 110 S Lake Ave, Twin Lakes, 53181, SAN
    377-9815. Tel: 262-877-4281. FAX: 262-877-2682. *Ref Serv,* Danijela
    Djurdjevic
    Open Mon-Thurs 10-8, Sat 10-4, Sun 12-5

SAND CREEK

P   CLARELLA HACKETT JOHNSON LIBRARY*, E 9311 County Rd I,
54765. (Mail add: PO Box 156, 54765-0156), SAN 378-0066. Tel:
715-658-1269. E-mail: sandcreeklib@ifls.lib.wi.us. *Librn,* Cathy LeFevre
Pop 500
Library Holdings: Bk Titles 8,000; Per Subs 20
Mem of Indianhead Federated Library System
Open Mon & Fri 10-12 & 1-5, Sat 8-12

SAUK CITY

P   SAUK CITY PUBLIC LIBRARY, 515 Water St, 53583-1159. SAN
318-3750. Tel: 608-643-8346. E-mail: skclibrary@scls.lib.wi.us. Web Site:
www.saukcitylibrary.org. *Dir,* Ben Miller; E-mail: skcben@scls.lib.wi.us;
Asst Dir, Peggy Heidenreich; E-mail: skcpeggy@scls.lib.wi.us; *Youth Serv,*
Mary Zenker
Founded 1924
Library Holdings: Bk Vols 28,000; Per Subs 96
Special Collections: Oral History
Database Vendor: LearningExpress
Wireless access
Function: Homebound delivery serv
Mem of South Central Library System
Special Services for the Blind - Audio mat; Large print bks
Open Mon-Thurs 9-8, Fri 9-5:30, Sat 9-2

SAUKVILLE

P   OSCAR GRADY PUBLIC LIBRARY*, 151 S Main St, 53080-1930. SAN
324-7988. Tel: 262-284-6022. FAX: 262-284-1933. E-mail:
maher@esls.lib.wi.us. Web Site: www.saukville.lib.wi.us. *Dir,* Linda A
Pierschalla; E-mail: lpiersch@esls.lib.wi.us; Staff 10 (MLS 1, Non-MLS 9)
Founded 1972. Pop 4,100; Circ 87,600
Jan 2006-Dec 2006 Income $310,300, City $252,500, County $57,800.
Mats Exp $39,000. Sal $140,000
Library Holdings: Bk Vols 40,000; Per Subs 100
Special Collections: Saukville history
Automation Activity & Vendor Info: (Cataloging) SirsiDynix;
(Circulation) SirsiDynix; (OPAC) SirsiDynix; (Serials) SirsiDynix
Database Vendor: netLibrary, OCLC WorldCat
Function: Prog for children & young adult, Summer reading prog,
Telephone ref
Mem of Eastern Shores Library System
Special Services for the Deaf - Bks on deafness & sign lang
Special Services for the Blind - BiFolkal kits; Bks on CD; Talking bks
Open Mon-Thurs 9-8, Fri 9-5, Sat 9-3
Friends of the Library Group

SAYNER

P   PLUM LAKE PUBLIC LIBRARY*, 8789 Peterson St, 54560. (Mail add:
PO Box 229, 54560-0229), SAN 318-3769. Tel: 715-542-2020. FAX:
715-542-2627. Web Site: sayner.wislib.org. *Dir,* Ida Nemec; E-mail:
ida@plumlib.nwls.lib.wi.us; Staff 1.125 (Non-MLS 1.125)
Founded 1939. Pop 800; Circ 27,475

Library Holdings: AV Mats 2,218; CDs 1,405; DVDs 200; e-books
11,409; Large Print Bks 550; Bk Titles 21,174; Bk Vols 21,724; Per Subs
118; Talking Bks 1,056
Special Collections: Memorial Coll
Subject Interests: Local hist
Automation Activity & Vendor Info: (Acquisitions) Innovative Interfaces,
Inc; (Cataloging) Innovative Interfaces, Inc; (Circulation) Innovative
Interfaces, Inc; (ILL) Brodart; (OPAC) Innovative Interfaces, Inc
Database Vendor: Innovative Interfaces, Inc INN - View
Wireless access
Mem of Northern Waters Library Service
Partic in Merlin
Open Mon & Wed 10-7, Tues & Thurs-Sat 10-1
Friends of the Library Group

SCANDINAVIA

P   SCANDINAVIA PUBLIC LIBRARY*, 349 N Main St, 54977. (Mail add:
PO Box 157, 54977-0157), SAN 377-9750. Tel: 715-467-4636. E-mail:
sca@mail.owls.lib.wi.us. Web Site: www.owls.lib.wi.us/sca. *Librn,* Susan
Vater-Olsen; E-mail: svater@mail.owls.lib.wi.us; Staff 1 (Non-MLS 1)
Pop 642
Library Holdings: AV Mats 1,500; Bk Titles 6,300; Per Subs 20
Mem of Outagamie Waupaca Library System
Partic in OWLSnet
Open Mon, Tues & Fri 2-6, Thurs 9-1 & 2-6

SEYMOUR

P   MUEHL PUBLIC LIBRARY, 436 N Main, 54165-1021. SAN 318-3777.
Tel: 920-833-2725. FAX: 920-833-9804. E-mail: sey@mail.owls.lib.wi.us.
Web Site: www.muehlpubliclibrary.org. *Libr Dir, Programmer,* Elizabeth M
Timmins; E-mail: etimmins@mail.owls.lib.wi.us; Staff 3 (MLS 1,
Non-MLS 2)
Founded 1901. Pop 6,000; Circ 80,146
Jan 2011-Dec 2011 Income $212,897, City $131,567, County $69,931,
Locally Generated Income $10,947, Other $452. Mats Exp $33,886, Books
$27,426, Per/Ser (Incl. Access Fees) $270, AV Mat $6,190. Sal $119,356
(Prof $40,004)
Library Holdings: Audiobooks 1,133; Bks on Deafness & Sign Lang 10;
CDs 89; DVDs 1,882; e-books 17,194; Electronic Media & Resources
11,139; Large Print Bks 756; Bk Titles 27,407; Per Subs 9; Videos 871
Automation Activity & Vendor Info: (Circulation) Innovative Interfaces,
Inc; (OPAC) Innovative Interfaces, Inc
Wireless access
Function: Adult bk club, Art exhibits, Audiobks via web, Children's prog,
Computers for patron use, Copy machines, Doc delivery serv, Family
literacy, Free DVD rentals, Holiday prog, ILL available, Learning ctr,
Magnifiers for reading, Music CDs, Online cat, Online ref, Orientations,
Outreach serv, OverDrive digital audio bks, Photocopying/Printing,
Preschool outreach, Preschool reading prog, Prog for adults, Prog for
children & young adult, Pub access computers, Scanner, Spoken cassettes
& CDs, Story hour, Summer reading prog, Telephone ref, VHS videos,
Workshops
Mem of Outagamie Waupaca Library System
Open Mon-Thurs (Winter) 10-8, Fri 10-6, Sat 10-2; Mon-Thurs (Summer)
10-8, Fri 10-5
Friends of the Library Group

SHARON

P   BRIGHAM MEMORIAL LIBRARY*, 131 Plain St, 53585. SAN
318-3785. Tel: 262-736-4249. FAX: 262-736-3239. *Librn,* Elizabeth Fraser;
E-mail: fraser@sharon.lib.wi.us
Founded 1927. Pop 1,280; Circ 21,000
Library Holdings: Bk Vols 14,000; Per Subs 35
Mem of Lakeshores Library System
Open Mon & Thurs 10-6, Tues 12-8, Wed & Fri 9-5, Sat 9-12
Friends of the Library Group

SHAWANO

P   SHAWANO CITY-COUNTY LIBRARY*, 128 S Sawyer St, 54166-2496.
SAN 365-0642. Tel: 715-526-3829. FAX: 715-526-6772. E-mail:
sha@mail.nfls.lib.wi.us. Web Site: www.shawanolibrary.org. *Dir,* Kristie
Wilson; Tel: 715-526-3829, Ext 123, E-mail: kwilson@mail.nfls.lib.wi.us;
Adult Coll Develop Librn, Position Currently Open; *Ch,* Julie Dassler;
Digital Librn, Penny Habeck; *ILL & Children's Coll Develop Librn,* Sue
Porath; Staff 11.5 (MLS 1, Non-MLS 10.5)
Founded 1899. Pop 42,000; Circ 356,500
Jan 2009-Dec 2009 Income (Main Library Only) $581,387, City $111,918,
County $447,674, Locally Generated Income $21,795. Mats Exp $107,577,
Books $84,643, Per/Ser (Incl. Access Fees) $7,400, Other Print Mats $143,
Micro $1,972, AV Mat $13,419. Sal $286,889
Library Holdings: AV Mats 15,466; Electronic Media & Resources
16,553; Bk Vols 131,333; Per Subs 40

Special Collections: Christmas Coll; Native American Coll

Automation Activity & Vendor Info: (Acquisitions) Innovative Interfaces, Inc; (Cataloging) Innovative Interfaces, Inc; (Circulation) Innovative Interfaces, Inc; (ILL) Innovative Interfaces, Inc; (Media Booking) Innovative Interfaces, Inc; (OPAC) Innovative Interfaces, Inc

Function: After school storytime, Audiobks via web, AV serv, Bks on cassette, Bks on CD, Children's prog, Computers for patron use, Copy machines, Digital talking bks, e-mail & chat, e-mail serv, E-Reserves, Electronic databases & coll, Equip loans & repairs, Family literacy, Fax serv, Free DVD rentals, Handicapped accessible, Holiday prog, Home delivery & serv to Sr ctr & nursing homes, ILL available, Music CDs, OverDrive digital audio bks, Photocopying/Printing, Preschool outreach, Prof lending libr, Prog for adults, Prog for children & young adult, Pub access computers, Ref serv available, Ref serv in person, Scanner, Story hour, Summer & winter reading prog, Summer reading prog, Tax forms, Teen prog, Telephone ref, VHS videos, Web-catalog, Wheelchair accessible

Mem of Nicolet Federated Library System

Partic in OWLSnet

Open Mon & Wed 8-8, Tues, Thurs & Fri 8-5, Sat 9-1

Friends of the Library Group

Branches: 5

BIRNAMWOOD PUBLIC, 337 S Main St, Birnamwood, 54414-9259, SAN 365-0669. Tel: 715-449-3120. *Librn,* Jan Atkinson
Library Holdings: Bk Vols 25,897
Open Mon-Thurs 2-8, Sat 9-12
Friends of the Library Group

BONDUEL PUBLIC, 117 1/2 W Green Bay St, Bonduel, 54107-8302. (Mail add: PO Box 687, Bonduel, 54107-0687), SAN 365-0677. Tel: 715-758-2267. FAX: 715-758-6841. E-mail: bon@mail.nfls.lib.wi.us. *Librn,* Carol Luepke; E-mail: cluepke@mail.nfls.lib.wi.us
Library Holdings: Bk Vols 13,963
Open Mon & Wed 3-7, Tues & Thurs 9-2, Sat 9-12
Friends of the Library Group

MATTOON-HUTCHINS COMMUNITY LIBRARY, 311 Slate Ave, Mattoon, 54450-0266. (Mail add: PO Box 266, Mattoon, 54450-0266), SAN 329-3505. Tel: 715-489-3333. E-mail: mat@mail.nfls.lib.wi.us. *Librn,* Joyce Reichert; E-mail: jreicher@mail.nfls.lib.wi.us
Library Holdings: Bk Vols 5,971
Open Tues & Thurs 12-6, Wed 9-3
Friends of the Library Group

TIGERTON PUBLIC, 221 Birch St, Tigerton, 54486. (Mail add: PO Box 166, Tigerton, 54486-0166), SAN 365-0707. Tel: 715-535-2194. FAX: 715-535-2666. E-mail: tig@mail.nfls.lib.wi.us. *Librn,* Peggy Slicer; E-mail: pslicer@mail.nfls.lib.wi.us
Library Holdings: Bk Vols 12,570
Open Wed & Thurs 10-6, Fri 2-8, Sat 2-5
Friends of the Library Group

WITTENBERG PUBLIC, 302 S Cherry St, Wittenberg, 54499. (Mail add: PO Box 295, Wittenberg, 54499-0295), SAN 365-0715. Tel: 715-253-2936. E-mail: wit@mail.nfls.lib.wi.us. *Librn,* Leslie Hill; E-mail: lhill@mail.nfls.lib.wi.us
Library Holdings: Bk Vols 15,020
Open Mon, Tues & Thurs (Fall-Spring) 2-7, Wed & Fri 10-5, Sat 9-Noon; Mon-Thurs (Summer) 2-7, Fri 10-5
Friends of the Library Group

Bookmobiles: 1

SHEBOYGAN

P EASTERN SHORES LIBRARY SYSTEM*, 4632 S Taylor Dr, 53081-1107. SAN 318-3831. Tel: 920-208-4900. FAX: 920-208-4901. Web Site: www.esls.lib.wi.us. *Dir,* David J Weinhold; E-mail: weinhold@esls.lib.wi.us; *Automation Librn,* Paul Onufrak; E-mail: ponufrak@esls.lib.wi.us; *Cat Librn,* Alison Ross; Staff 9.85 (MLS 3.75, Non-MLS 6.1)
Founded 1979. Pop 201,092; Circ 80,568
Jan 2010-Dec 2010 Income $2,541,410, State $622,950, Federal $39,982, County $1,614,833, Locally Generated Income $195,443, Other $68,202. Mats Exp $28,898, Books $17,713, Electronic Ref Mat (Incl. Access Fees) $11,185. Sal $468,993 (Prof $241,377)
Library Holdings: Audiobooks 449; e-books 12,071; Electronic Media & Resources 4,748; Bk Vols 26,658; Per Subs 56; Videos 1,303
Automation Activity & Vendor Info: (Acquisitions) Polaris Library Systems; (Cataloging) Polaris Library Systems; (Circulation) Polaris Library Systems; (ILL) Auto-Graphics, Inc; (Media Booking) Polaris Library Systems; (OPAC) Polaris Library Systems; (Serials) Polaris Library Systems
Database Vendor: CredoReference, EBSCOhost, LearningExpress, netLibrary, OCLC FirstSearch, OCLC WorldCat, Overdrive, Inc, TumbleBookLibrary
Wireless access
Function: Doc delivery serv, e-mail serv, Electronic databases & coll, Jail serv, Libr develop, Online cat, Outreach serv, OverDrive digital audio bks, Summer reading prog, Web-catalog, Workshops
Publications: The Library Connection (Newsletter)

Member Libraries: Cedar Grove Public Library; Cedarburg Public Library; Elkhart Lake Public Library; Frank L Weyenberg Library of Mequon-Thiensville; Kohler Public Library; Lakeview Community Library; Mead Public Library; Oostburg Public Library; Oscar Grady Public Library; Plymouth Public Library; Sheboygan Falls Memorial Library; USS Liberty Memorial Public Library; W J Niederkorn Library
Partic in Wisconsin Library Services; Wisconsin Public Library Consortium Special Services for the Blind - BiFolkal kits
Bookmobiles: 1. Bk titles 24,970

S JOHN MICHAEL KOHLER ARTS CENTER*, Resource Center, 608 New York Ave, 53081-4507. (Mail add: PO Box 489, 53082-0489), SAN 318-3793. Tel: 920-458-6144. FAX: 920-458-4473. E-mail: resourcecenter@jmkac.org. Web Site: www.jmkac.org/resource/resourcecenter.html. *Dir,* Ruth DeYoung Kohler; Staff 1 (MLS 1)
Founded 1967
Library Holdings: Bk Titles 4,000; Bk Vols 5,500; Per Subs 65
Subject Interests: Contemporary Am crafts, Contemporary art, Self taught artists
Automation Activity & Vendor Info: (Cataloging) Follett Software; (Circulation) Follett Software; (OPAC) Follett Software
Function: Res libr
Publications: Exhibition Catalogs & Related Publications
Restriction: Non-circulating

P MEAD PUBLIC LIBRARY, 710 N Eighth St, 53081-4563. SAN 318-3815. Tel: 920-459-3400. Circulation Tel: 920-459-3400, Ext 3401. Interlibrary Loan Service Tel: 920-459-3400, Ext 3430. Reference Tel: 920-459-3400, Ext 3422. Administration Tel: 920-459-3400, Ext 3416. FAX: 920-459-0204. Web Site: www.meadpubliclibrary.org. *Dir, Libr Serv,* Sharon L Winkle; Tel: 920-459-3400, Ext 3414, E-mail: sharon.winkle@meadpubliclibrary.org; *Dep Dir,* Mark J Zehfus; Tel: 920-459-3400, Ext 3410, E-mail: mark.zehfus@meadpubliclibrary.org; *Mgr, Ad Serv, Ref,* Debbra L Voss; Tel: 920-459-3400, Ext 3420, E-mail: deb.voss@meadpubliclibrary.org; *Mgr, Ch Serv,* Karin A Menzer; Tel: 920-459-3400, Ext 3433, E-mail: karin.menzer@meadpubliclibrary.org; *Circ Mgr, Tech Serv Mgr,* Diane L Kallas; Tel: 920-459-3400, Ext 3403, E-mail: diane.kallas@meadpubliclibrary.org; *Info Tech Spec,* Dale D Gort; Tel: 920-459-3400, Ext 3415, E-mail: dale.gort@meadpubliclibrary.org; Staff 43.2 (MLS 8.63, Non-MLS 34.57)
Founded 1897. Circ 841,853
Library Holdings: Audiobooks 16,453; AV Mats 23,503; e-books 27,679; Bk Vols 312,745; Per Subs 419
Special Collections: United States & State Census Coll
Subject Interests: Furniture, Local hist
Automation Activity & Vendor Info: (Acquisitions) Polaris Library Systems; (Cataloging) Polaris Library Systems; (Circulation) Polaris Library Systems; (Media Booking) Polaris Library Systems; (OPAC) Polaris Library Systems; (Serials) Polaris Library Systems
Database Vendor: OCLC FirstSearch, Polaris Library Systems, ProQuest
Wireless access
Publications: Annual Report; Footnotes (Bi-monthly); Mead Sheet (Monthly)
Mem of Eastern Shores Library System
Open Mon-Thurs (Oct-April) 9-8, Fri & Sat 9-5, Sun 1-5; Mon & Wed (May-Sept) 9-8, Tues, Thurs & Fri 9-5, Sat 9-1
Friends of the Library Group

S SHEBOYGAN PRESS LIBRARY*, 632 Center Ave, 53081. (Mail add: PO Box 358, 53081-0358), SAN 375-0760. Tel: 920-457-7711. Toll Free Tel: 800-686-3900 (WI only). FAX: 920-457-3573. E-mail: info@HTLinc.com. Web Site: www.sheboygan-press.com. *Librn,* Heather Heberlein; Tel: 920-453-5110, E-mail: hheberle@sheboygan-press.com
Library Holdings: Bk Vols 500
Special Collections: Sheboygan Press (1856-present)

J UNIVERSITY OF WISCONSIN SHEBOYGAN*, University Library, One University Dr, 53081-4789. SAN 318-3858. Tel: 920-459-6625. Interlibrary Loan Service Tel: 920-459-6681. Reference Tel: 920-459-4410. Administration Tel: 920-459-6679. FAX: 920-459-6602. Web Site: sheboygan.uwc.edu/library. *Dir,* Jeffrey A Ellair; E-mail: jeffrey.ellair@uwc.edu; *ILL,* Karen L McArdle; E-mail: karen.mcardle@uwc.edu; *Ref,* Amy M Mussell; E-mail: amy.mussell@uwc.edu; Staff 3 (MLS 2, Non-MLS 1)
Founded 1965. Enrl 690; Fac 29; Highest Degree: Associate
Jul 2006-Jun 2007 Income $512,327, Federal $3,103, Parent Institution $504,224, Other $5,000. Mats Exp $36,054, Books $22,372, Per/Ser (Incl. Access Fees) $13,267, AV Mat $415. Sal $120,244 (Prof $101,849)
Library Holdings: AV Mats 2,066; Bk Titles 37,137; Bk Vols 42,136; Per Subs 115
Automation Activity & Vendor Info: (Acquisitions) Ex Libris Group; (Cataloging) Ex Libris Group; (Circulation) Ex Libris Group; (Course Reserve) Ex Libris Group; (ILL) OCLC ILLiad; (OPAC) Ex Libris Group

Database Vendor: Alexander Street Press, ARTstor, EBSCOhost, Gale
Cengage Learning, JSTOR, LexisNexis, netLibrary, OCLC WorldCat,
Project MUSE, ProQuest, Wilson - Wilson Web
Wireless access
Partic in OCLC Online Computer Library Center, Inc; Wisconsin Library
Services
Open Mon-Thurs 8am-9pm, Fri 8-4:30, Sun 5-9

SHEBOYGAN FALLS

S   SHEBOYGAN COUNTY HISTORICAL RESEARCH CENTER
LIBRARY*, 518 Water St, 53085. SAN 325-5557. Tel: 920-467-4667.
FAX: 920-467-1395. E-mail: schrc@execpc.com. Web Site: www.schrc.org.
Dir, Beth Dipple; *Librn,* Janice Hildebrand; *Librn,* Carol Shaffer; Staff 21
(Non-MLS 21)
Founded 1983
Library Holdings: Bk Vols 5,000
Special Collections: Sheboygan County. Oral History
Subject Interests: Sheboygan County hist
Publications: The Researcher
Open Tues-Sat 9-4
Friends of the Library Group

P   SHEBOYGAN FALLS MEMORIAL LIBRARY*, 330 Buffalo St,
53085-1399. (Mail add: PO Box 140, 53085-0140), SAN 318-3866. Tel:
920-467-7908. *Dir,* J Scott Gehrig; E-mail: sgehrig@esls.lib.wi.us
Founded 1924. Pop 10,000; Circ 126,000
Jan 2009-Dec 2009 Income $300,000, City $216,000, County $84,000.
Mats Exp $63,000, Books $39,000, Per/Ser (Incl. Access Fees) $6,750, AV
Mat $18,500, Electronic Ref Mat (Incl. Access Fees) $2,000. Sal
$1,535,000
Library Holdings: AV Mats 24,500; Bk Vols 46,000; Per Subs 137
Subject Interests: Biog, Hist
Automation Activity & Vendor Info: (Acquisitions) Polaris Library
Systems; (Cataloging) Polaris Library Systems; (Circulation) Polaris
Library Systems; (OPAC) Polaris Library Systems
Wireless access
Mem of Eastern Shores Library System
Open Mon-Fri 9-8, Sat 9-3
Friends of the Library Group

SHELL LAKE

P   SHELL LAKE PUBLIC LIBRARY*, 501 First St, 54871. (Mail add: PO
Box 318, 54871-0318), SAN 318-3874. Tel: 715-468-2074. FAX:
715-468-7638. E-mail: slplibrary@gmail.com. *Dir,* Beth Carlson
Circ 11,194
Library Holdings: Bk Vols 17,000
Special Collections: Holiday Coll; Hunting Fishing Coll; Wisconsin Coll
Automation Activity & Vendor Info: (Acquisitions) Follett Software;
(Cataloging) Follett Software; (Circulation) Follett Software
Mem of Northern Waters Library Service
Open Mon & Wed 12-8, Tues, Thurs & Fri 10-5, Sat 10-1
Friends of the Library Group

G   WASHBURN COUNTY LAW LIBRARY, Courthouse, 54871. (Mail add:
PO Box 339, 54871-0339), SAN 328-3569. Tel: 715-468-4688. FAX:
715-468-4678. *In Charge,* Karen Nord
Library Holdings: Bk Vols 150
Open Mon-Fri 8-4:30

SHIOCTON

P   SHIOCTON PUBLIC LIBRARY*, W7740 Pine St, 54170. SAN 378-0082.
Tel: 920-986-3933. FAX: 920-986-3743. *Libr Dir,* Becky Rickel; E-mail:
brickel@mail.owls.lib.wi.us
Library Holdings: Bk Titles 10,000; Per Subs 20
Automation Activity & Vendor Info: (Cataloging) Innovative Interfaces,
Inc; (Circulation) Innovative Interfaces, Inc; (OPAC) Innovative Interfaces,
Inc
Wireless access
Mem of Outagamie Waupaca Library System
Open Mon & Wed 12-7, Tues, Thurs & Fri 12-5

SHOREWOOD

P   SHOREWOOD PUBLIC LIBRARY*, 3920 N Murray Ave, 53211-2385.
SAN 318-3882. Tel: 414-847-2670. Web Site: www.shorewoodlibrary.org.
Dir, Elizabeth Carey; E-mail: beth.carey@mcfls.org; *Adult Serv,* Pete
Loeffel; *Ch,* Heide Piehler; *Tech Serv,* Nancy Shimon; *YA Serv,* Tiffany
Wait; Staff 5 (MLS 5)
Founded 1903. Pop 13,000; Circ 320,000
Library Holdings: Bk Vols 51,000; Per Subs 110
Automation Activity & Vendor Info: (Acquisitions) Innovative Interfaces,
Inc; (Cataloging) Innovative Interfaces, Inc; (Circulation) Innovative

Interfaces, Inc; (OPAC) Innovative Interfaces, Inc; (Serials) Innovative
Interfaces, Inc
Database Vendor: Baker & Taylor, BookLetters LLC, Checkpoint
Systems, Inc, Comprise Technologies, Inc, EBSCOhost, Gale Cengage
Learning, Innovative Interfaces, Inc, netLibrary, ProQuest, ReferenceUSA,
Standard & Poor's, ValueLine, World Book Online
Wireless access
Mem of Milwaukee County Federated Library System
Open Mon-Wed 9:30-8:30, Thurs & Fri 9:30-5:30, Sat 9-4, Sun 1-4
Friends of the Library Group

SHULLSBURG

P   MCCOY PUBLIC LIBRARY*, Shullsburg Public, 190 N Judgement St,
53586. SAN 318-3890. Tel: 608-965-4424, Ext 5. FAX: 608-965-4809.
E-mail: shpublib@mwt.net. Web Site:
www.shullsburgwisconsin.org/shullsburgmcoylibrary.html. *Dir,* Carol
Stoudt; E-mail: cstoudt@swls.org
Pop 1,246; Circ 10,144
Library Holdings: Bk Vols 5,740; Per Subs 12
Mem of Southwest Wisconsin Library System
Open Tues 12-8, Wed 4-8, Thurs 10-6, Fri 2-6, Sat 9-12
Friends of the Library Group
Branches: 1
GRATIOT ANNEX, 3895 Main St, Gratiot, 53541. Tel: 608-922-3803. *Dir,*
Carol Stoudt; E-mail: cstoudt@swls.org
Founded 2003
Library Holdings: Bk Vols 1,200; Per Subs 10
Open Tues 9-11am, Wed 1:30-4, Thurs 5-8, Sat 9-Noon
Friends of the Library Group

SINSINAWA

P   THE MOUND CENTER LIBRARY*, 585 County Rd Z, 53824. Tel:
608-748-4411. FAX: 608-748-4491. E-mail: center@sinsinawa.org. *Librn,*
Sister Janette Wicker
Library Holdings: Bk Titles 11,876
Automation Activity & Vendor Info: (Cataloging) Follett Software
Wireless access
Mem of Southwest Wisconsin Library System
Open Mon-Fri 8:30-11

SLINGER

P   SLINGER COMMUNITY LIBRARY*, 220 Slinger Rd, 53086-9586. SAN
378-0104. Tel: 262-644-6171. FAX: 262-644-8061. Web Site:
www.slinger.lib.wi.us. *Dir,* Jennifer Einwalter; E-mail: jeinwalt@mwfls.org;
Staff 8 (MLS 1, Non-MLS 7)
Pop 12,645; Circ 126,524
Library Holdings: CDs 500; DVDs 2,673; Large Print Bks 1,200; Bk
Titles 33,158; Per Subs 60; Talking Bks 1,000
Automation Activity & Vendor Info: (Acquisitions) SirsiDynix;
(Cataloging) SirsiDynix; (Circulation) SirsiDynix; (OPAC) SirsiDynix
Wireless access
Mem of Mid-Wisconsin Federated Library System
Partic in Wis Libr Asn
Open Mon, Tues & Thurs 9-8, Wed 9-6, Fri 9-5, Sat 9-12
Friends of the Library Group

SOLDIERS GROVE

P   SOLDIERS GROVE PUBLIC LIBRARY*, Solar Town Ctr, 102 Passive
Sun Dr, 54655. (Mail add: PO Box 6, Solar Town Ctr, 54655-0006), SAN
318-3912. Tel: 608-624-5815. E-mail: sglibry@swls.org. Web Site:
www.swls.org/member.so.html. *Dir,* Cele Wolf; E-mail: cwolf@swls.org;
Staff 2 (MLS 1, Non-MLS 1)
Founded 1970. Pop 653; Circ 7,051
Library Holdings: Bk Vols 12,427
Automation Activity & Vendor Info: (Cataloging) SirsiDynix;
(Circulation) SirsiDynix; (OPAC) SirsiDynix
Wireless access
Mem of Southwest Wisconsin Library System
Open Mon, Wed & Fri 1:30-5:30, Tues & Thurs 10-12, 1:30-5:30 & 7-9,
Sat 9-12
Restriction: Borrowing requests are handled by ILL

SOMERSET

P   SOMERSET PUBLIC LIBRARY*, 208 Hud St, 54025. (Mail add: PO Box
129, 54025-0129), SAN 318-3920. Tel: 715-247-5228. FAX:
715-247-5141. E-mail: somersetpl@ifls.lib.wi.us. Web Site:
www.somersetlibrary.org. *Dir,* Norma Scott
Founded 1974. Pop 2,972; Circ 27,933
Library Holdings: Bk Vols 12,000; Per Subs 60
Special Collections: Somerset History

Automation Activity & Vendor Info: (Cataloging) Innovative Interfaces, Inc; (Circulation) Innovative Interfaces, Inc
Mem of Indianhead Federated Library System
Open Mon & Fri 11-6, Tues-Thurs 11-8, Sat 9-12
Friends of the Library Group

SOUTH MILWAUKEE

P　SOUTH MILWAUKEE PUBLIC LIBRARY*, 1907 Tenth Ave, 53172. SAN 318-3939. Tel: 414-768-8195. FAX: 414-768-8072. Web Site: www.southmilwaukee.org/library. *Dir,* Bob Pfeiffer; E-mail: bob.pfeiffer@mcfls.org; *Youth Serv Librn,* Denise Herr; E-mail: denise.herr@mcfls.org; Staff 8 (MLS 3, Non-MLS 5)
Founded 1899. Pop 21,310; Circ 211,013
Jan 2009-Dec 2009 Income $850,423, City $816,928, Locally Generated Income $33,495. Mats Exp $80,217, Books $54,492, Per/Ser (Incl. Access Fees) $9,004, AV Mat $8,946, Electronic Ref Mat (Incl. Access Fees) $7,775. Sal $424,592 (Prof $157,643)
Library Holdings: Audiobooks 2,986; AV Mats 7,827; CDs 13,049; DVDs 2,804; e-books 361; Large Print Bks 2,144; Bk Vols 127,564; Per Subs 106; Videos 7,273
Special Collections: Cookbooks; Local History-South Milwaukee
Automation Activity & Vendor Info: (Acquisitions) Baker & Taylor; (Cataloging) Innovative Interfaces, Inc; (Circulation) Innovative Interfaces, Inc; (ILL) Innovative Interfaces, Inc; (OPAC) Innovative Interfaces, Inc; (Serials) Innovative Interfaces, Inc
Database Vendor: Baker & Taylor, EBSCO Auto Repair Reference, EBSCOhost, Innovative Interfaces, Inc, OCLC WorldCat, ProQuest, ReferenceUSA, ValueLine
Wireless access
Mem of Milwaukee County Federated Library System
Special Services for the Deaf - ADA equip; Bks on deafness & sign lang; Closed caption videos
Special Services for the Blind - Audio mat; Bks on cassette; Bks on CD; Large print & cassettes; Large print bks; Magnifiers
Open Mon-Wed 9-8, Thurs 9-6:30, Fri 9-5, Sat 9-4
Friends of the Library Group

SPARTA

S　MONROE COUNTY LOCAL HISTORY ROOM & LIBRARY*, 200 W Main St, 54656-2141. SAN 326-6192. Tel: 608-269-8680. FAX: 608-269-8921. E-mail: mclhr@centurytel.net. Web Site: www.monroecountyhistory.org. *Dir,* Jarrod Roll
Library Holdings: Bk Vols 2,000; Per Subs 30
Special Collections: Municipal Document Depository

P　SPARTA FREE LIBRARY*, 124 W Main St, 54656. (Mail add: PO Box 347, 54656-0347), SAN 318-3947. Tel: 608-269-2010. FAX: 608-269-1542. E-mail: spartalibrary@wrlsweb.org. Web Site: www.spartalibrary.org. *Dir,* Pamela Westby
Founded 1861. Pop 15,000
Jan 2005-Dec 2005 Income $360,352, City $252,000, County $85,701, Locally Generated Income $14,351, Parent Institution $8,300. Mats Exp $47,038, Books $35,553, Per/Ser (Incl. Access Fees) $5,559, AV Equip $2,025, AV Mat $3,901. Sal $190,465 (Prof $50,000)
Library Holdings: Bks on Deafness & Sign Lang 10; Bk Vols 50,800; Per Subs 150; Spec Interest Per Sub 20
Subject Interests: Best sellers, Bicycles, Bicycling, Local hist
Automation Activity & Vendor Info: (Cataloging) Horizon; (Circulation) Horizon; (OPAC) Horizon
Database Vendor: ProQuest
Publications: Sparta Free Library Newsletter (printed 6 times a year)
Mem of Winding Rivers Library System
Open Mon-Thurs 10-9, Fri 10-5, Sat 10-4

SPOONER

P　SPOONER MEMORIAL LIBRARY*, 421 High St, 54801-1431. SAN 318-3955. Tel: 715-635-2792. FAX: 715-635-2147. *Dir,* Jane Frankiewicz; E-mail: janef@spooner.nwls.lib.wi.us; *Acq, Cat,* Sharlene Parish; E-mail: sharp@spooner.nwls.lib.wi.us; *Ch,* Katie Johnson; E-mail: katiej@spooner.nwls.lib.wi.us; *ILL,* Sharon Tarr; E-mail: starr@spooner.nwls.lib.wi.us; *Tech Serv,* Jill Fredrickson; E-mail: jillf@spooner.nwls.lib.wi.us
Founded 1915. Pop 2,500; Circ 42,640
Library Holdings: Bk Vols 33,000; Per Subs 160
Subject Interests: Archit, Art
Automation Activity & Vendor Info: (Cataloging) Follett Software; (Circulation) Follett Software
Mem of Northern Waters Library Service
Open Mon-Thurs 9-8, Fri 9-5, Sat 9-1
Friends of the Library Group

SPRING GREEN

P　SPRING GREEN COMMUNITY LIBRARY*, 230 E Monroe St, 53588-8035. (Mail add: PO Box 520, 53588-8035), SAN 318-3971. Tel: 608-588-2276. E-mail: sgrlib@scls.lib.wi.us. Web Site: www.scls.lib.wi.us/sgr. *Dir,* Carol Anderson; E-mail: canderson@scls.lib.wi.us; *Ch, Youth Serv Coordr,* Brenda Francis; E-mail: bfrancis@scls.lib.wi.us; *Circ Serv, ILL,* Jean Porter; *Circ Serv,* Bridget Roberts; *Tech Serv,* Mary Brey
Founded 1905. Pop 1,441; Circ 50,000
Library Holdings: Bks on Deafness & Sign Lang 50; Bk Vols 21,965; Per Subs 91
Special Collections: Frank Lloyd Wright Coll; Wisconsin Authors Coll; Wisconsin History Coll
Automation Activity & Vendor Info: (Acquisitions) SirsiDynix; (Cataloging) SirsiDynix; (Circulation) SirsiDynix; (Course Reserve) SirsiDynix; (ILL) SirsiDynix; (Media Booking) SirsiDynix; (OPAC) SirsiDynix; (Serials) SirsiDynix
Mem of South Central Library System
Open Mon-Thurs 12:30-8, Fri 9-5:30, Sat 9-12:30
Friends of the Library Group

SPRING VALLEY

P　SPRING VALLEY PUBLIC LIBRARY*, E 121 S Second St, 54767. (Mail add: PO Box 217, 54767-0217), SAN 376-6675. Tel: 715-778-4590. FAX: 715-778-4590. E-mail: svpl@ifls.lib.wi.us. *Librn,* Doris Ronnander
Library Holdings: Bk Titles 14,000; Per Subs 33
Automation Activity & Vendor Info: (Acquisitions) Innovative Interfaces, Inc; (Cataloging) Innovative Interfaces, Inc; (Circulation) Innovative Interfaces, Inc; (Course Reserve) Innovative Interfaces, Inc; (ILL) Innovative Interfaces, Inc; (Media Booking) Innovative Interfaces, Inc; (OPAC) Innovative Interfaces, Inc; (Serials) Innovative Interfaces, Inc
Open Mon & Sat 9-12, Tues-Thurs 11-7

STANLEY

P　D R MOON MEMORIAL LIBRARY*, 154 Fourth Ave, 54768. SAN 318-398X. Tel: 715-644-2004. FAX: 715-644-2941. E-mail: librarypl@yahoo.com. *Dir,* Susan Anderson
Founded 1901. Pop 4,004; Circ 33,682
Library Holdings: DVDs 130; Bk Vols 25,902; Per Subs 82; Talking Bks 1,065; Videos 800
Automation Activity & Vendor Info: (Cataloging) Mandarin Library Automation; (Circulation) Mandarin Library Automation
Mem of Indianhead Federated Library System
Open Mon-Wed 1-8, Thurs 10-5, Fri 10-3, Sat 10-12
Friends of the Library Group

S　STANLEY CORRECTIONAL INSTITUTION LIBRARY*, 100 Corrections Dr, 54768. Tel: 715-644-2960, Ext 3446. FAX: 715-644-3777. *Librn,* Position Currently Open
Library Holdings: Bk Vols 14,000; Per Subs 95
Automation Activity & Vendor Info: (Cataloging) Follett Software; (Circulation) Follett Software
Open Mon-Sun 8am-8:30pm

STETSONVILLE

P　JEAN M THOMSEN MEMORIAL LIBRARY*, 105 N Gershwin St, 54480. (Mail add: PO Box 99, 54480-0099), SAN 318-3998. Tel: 715-678-2892. FAX: 715-678-2892. *Dir,* Patricia Reich; E-mail: preich@wvls.lib.wi.us
Pop 715; Circ 14,850
Library Holdings: AV Mats 1,132; Bk Titles 15,114; Per Subs 53
Subject Interests: Cookery, Handicrafts
Automation Activity & Vendor Info: (Cataloging) SirsiDynix; (Circulation) SirsiDynix; (OPAC) SirsiDynix
Publications: Booklist; Library Journal
Mem of Wisconsin Valley Library Service
Open Mon, Tues & Thurs 2-8, Wed 9-12 & 2-8, Fri 2-6:30, Sat (Sept-May) 9-12

STEVENS POINT

J　MID-STATE TECHNICAL COLLEGE*, Stevens Point Campus Library, 933 Michigan Ave, 54481. SAN 318-4005. Tel: 715-342-3129, 715-344-3063. FAX: 715-342-3134. *Dir,* Sharon Peters; E-mail: sharon.peters@mstc.edu
Founded 1974. Enrl 200; Fac 15
Library Holdings: Bk Titles 3,000; Per Subs 50
Automation Activity & Vendor Info: (Cataloging) Ex Libris Group; (Circulation) Ex Libris Group
Open Mon-Thurs 8-8, Fri 8-3

P   PORTAGE COUNTY PUBLIC LIBRARY, Charles M White Library Bldg,
     1001 Main St, 54481-2860. SAN 318-403X. Tel: 715-346-1544.
     Administration Tel: 715-346-1545. Toll Free Tel: 800-264-0766. FAX:
     715-346-1239. Web Site: www.pcpl.lib.wi.us. *Dir,* Robert J Stack; E-mail:
     bstack@uwsp.edu; *Asst Dir,* Deborah M McCabe; E-mail:
     deborah.mccabe@uwsp.edu; *Br & Extn Librn,* Pamela Hill; E-mail:
     pam.hill@uwsp.edu; *Ref/Tech Support Librn,* Charles A Danner; Tel:
     715-345-5360, E-mail: charles.danner@uwsp.edu; *Youth Serv Librn,* Nicole
     E Ozanich; E-mail: nicole.ozanich@uwsp.edu; *Tech Serv,* Victoria A
     Billings; E-mail: vicky.billings@uwsp.edu; Staff 46 (MLS 6, Non-MLS 40)
     Founded 1895. Pop 70,785; Circ 506,079
     Jan 2010-Dec 2010 Income (Main Library and Branch(s)) $1,868,186
     Library Holdings: Bk Vols 157,918; Per Subs 391
     Automation Activity & Vendor Info: (Acquisitions) Ex Libris Group;
     (Cataloging) Ex Libris Group; (Circulation) Ex Libris Group; (OPAC) Ex
     Libris Group; (Serials) Ex Libris Group
     Database Vendor: EBSCOhost, ProQuest
     Wireless access
     Mem of South Central Library System
     Open Mon-Thurs (Winter) 9:30-9, Fri 9:30-6, Sat 9:30-5, Sun 1-5; Mon &
     Thurs (Summer) 9:30-8, Tues, Wed & Fri 9:30-5, Sat 9-12
     Friends of the Library Group
     Branches: 3
     ALMOND BRANCH, Village Hall, 122 Main St, Almond, 54909. Tel:
        715-366-2151. FAX: 715-366-2151. Web Site:
        library.uwsp.edu/pcl/almond.htm. *Br & Extn Librn,* Pam Hill; E-mail:
        pam.hill@uwsp.edu
        Open Tues 1-5 & 5:30-7:30, Thurs 10-12 & 1-5, Sat 9-12
     PLOVER BRANCH, 2151 Roosevelt Dr, Plover, 54467. Tel:
        715-341-4007. FAX: 715-346-1601. Web Site:
        library.uwsp.edu/pcl/plover.htm. *Br & Extn Librn,* Pam Hill; E-mail:
        pam.hill@uwsp.edu
        Open Tues-Thurs 10-8, Fri 10-5, Sat 9-1
     ROSHOLT BRANCH, Village Hall, 137 N Main St, Rosholt, 54473. Tel:
        715-677-4512. FAX: 715-677-4512. Web Site:
        library.uwsp.edu/pcl/rosholt.htm.
        Open Mon & Fri 1-5, Wed 1-5 & 5:30-7:30

M   SAINT MICHAEL'S HOSPITAL*, Health Science Library, 900 Illinois
     Ave, 54481. SAN 328-5553. Tel: 715-346-5091. FAX: 715-343-3246. Web
     Site: library@ministryhealth.org. *Asst Librn,* Deb Knippel; Staff 1
     (Non-MLS 1)
     Library Holdings: Bk Vols 450
     Subject Interests: Leadership, Med, Nursing
     Partic in Greater Midwest Regional Medical Libr Network; Health Science
     Information Consortium of Toronto; Maine School & Library Network;
     NW Hospital Consortium
     Open Mon-Fri 8-4:30

C   UNIVERSITY OF WISCONSIN-STEVENS POINT*, University Library,
     900 Reserve St, 54481-1985. SAN 318-4021. Tel: 715-346-3038.
     Circulation Tel: 715-346-2540. Reference Tel: 715-346-2836. FAX:
     715-346-3857. E-mail: lrcsec@uwsp.edu. Web Site: library.uwsp.edu. *Dir,*
     Dr Kathy Davis; Tel: 715-346-4193, Fax: 715-346-2367, E-mail:
     kdavis@uwsp.edu; *Head, Ref,* Dr Patti Becker; Tel: 715-346-4443, E-mail:
     p2becker@uwsp.edu; *Tech Librn,* Terri Muraski; Tel: 715-346-3349,
     E-mail: tmuraski@uwsp.edu; *Access Serv,* Aaron Nichols; *Archivist,* Ruth
     Wachter-Nelson; Tel: 715-346-2586, E-mail: rwachter@uwsp.edu; *Bibliog
     Instr, Media Spec,* Dr Axel Schmetzke; Tel: 715-346-4658, E-mail:
     aschmetz@uwsp.edu; *Doc,* Marg Whalen; Tel: 715-346-3726, E-mail:
     m2whalen@uwsp.edu; *Ref Serv,* Cathy Palmini; Tel: 715-346-4725, E-mail:
     cpalmini@uwsp.edu. Subject Specialists: *Hist,* Ruth Wachter-Nelson; Staff
     33 (MLS 15, Non-MLS 18)
     Founded 1894. Enrl 8,800; Highest Degree: Master
     Library Holdings: Bk Titles 244,441; Bk Vols 321,226; Per Subs 8,470
     Special Collections: John F Kennedy Assassination. State Document
     Depository; US Document Depository
     Subject Interests: Censorship, Educ, Environ studies, Ethnic studies, Hist
     Automation Activity & Vendor Info: (Acquisitions) Ex Libris Group;
     (Cataloging) Ex Libris Group; (Circulation) Ex Libris Group; (ILL) Ex
     Libris Group; (OPAC) Ex Libris Group; (Serials) Ex Libris Group
     Database Vendor: EBSCOhost, LexisNexis, OCLC FirstSearch, OVID
     Technologies, Wilson - Wilson Web
     Partic in Wisconsin Library Services
     Open Mon-Thurs 7:45am-11pm, Fri 7:45am-9pm, Sat 9-9, Sun Noon-1am

STOUGHTON

S   CUMMINS FILTRATION*, Corporate Technical Library, 1801 Hwy
     51-138, 53589. (Mail add: PO Box 428, 53589-0428), SAN 374-5015. Tel:
     608-873-4370. FAX: 608-873-1550. *Tech Leader-Eng Standards,* Jayne
     Fischer; E-mail: jayne.fischer@cummins.com; Staff 1 (Non-MLS 1)
     Library Holdings: Bk Titles 900; Per Subs 15
     Subject Interests: Acoustics, Automotive filtration

P   STOUGHTON PUBLIC LIBRARY*, 304 S Fourth St, 53589-0191. SAN
     318-4048. Tel: 608-873-6281. FAX: 608-873-0108. E-mail:
     storef@scls.lib.wi.us. Web Site: www.stoughtonpubliclibrary.org. *Libr Dir,*
     Jaime Vache; *Ch,* Cathie Burns; *Circ,* Sarah Bukrey; *Pub Serv,* Sarah
     Carlson; *Tech Serv,* Marilyn Granrud; Staff 2 (MLS 2)
     Founded 1901
     Library Holdings: Bk Vols 58,042; Per Subs 175
     Automation Activity & Vendor Info: (Acquisitions) SirsiDynix;
     (Cataloging) SirsiDynix; (Circulation) SirsiDynix; (OPAC) SirsiDynix;
     (Serials) SirsiDynix
     Database Vendor: OCLC FirstSearch
     Wireless access
     Mem of South Central Library System
     Special Services for the Blind - Accessible computers; Bks on cassette;
     Bks on CD; Computer access aids
     Open Mon-Thurs 9-9, Fri & Sat 9-5
     Friends of the Library Group

STRUM

P   STRUM PUBLIC LIBRARY*, 114 Fifth Ave, 54770. (Mail add: PO Box
     10, 54770-0010), SAN 318-4056. Tel: 715-695-3848. FAX: 715-695-3510.
     E-mail: strumpl@wrlsweb.org. *Dir,* Dawn Hering
     Pop 6,000; Circ 9,000
     Library Holdings: Bk Titles 10,000; Per Subs 24
     Automation Activity & Vendor Info: (Acquisitions) Follett Software;
     (Cataloging) Follett Software; (Circulation) Follett Software
     Mem of Winding Rivers Library System
     Open Mon & Fri 9:30-3:30, Tues & Wed 9:30-7:30, Sat 9-12
     Friends of the Library Group

STURGEON BAY

P   DOOR COUNTY LIBRARY*, 107 S Fourth Ave, 54235. SAN 318-4064.
     Tel: 920-743-6578. FAX: 920-743-6697. E-mail: dcl@mail.nfls.lib.wi.us.
     Web Site: www.doorcountylibrary.org. *Dir,* Rebecca N Berger; E-mail:
     rberger@mail.nfls.lib.wi.us; *Acq,* Chris Milton; Tel: 920-746-2491, E-mail:
     cmilton@mail.nfls.lib.wi.us; *Ad,* Laura Kayacan; Tel: 920-746-7121,
     E-mail: lkayacan@mail.nfls.lib.wi.us; *Cataloger, Tech Serv,* Tracy Vreeke;
     Tel: 920-746-7116, E-mail: tvreeke@mail.nfls.lib.wi.us
     Founded 1950. Circ 283,143
     Library Holdings: Bk Vols 154,066; Per Subs 466
     Special Collections: Door County Authors
     Subject Interests: Local hist
     Wireless access
     Publications: Friends of Door County Libraries
     Mem of Nicolet Federated Library System
     Partic in OWLSnet
     Open Mon-Thurs 9-9, Fri 9-6, Sat 9-5
     Friends of the Library Group
     Branches: 8
     BAILEYS HARBOR BRANCH, 2392 Hwy F, Baileys Harbor, 54202.
        (Mail add: PO Box 307, Baileys Harbor, 54202-0307), SAN 324-3095.
        Tel: 920-839-2210. E-mail: bai@mail.nfls.lib.wi.us. *Br Mgr,* Jeanne
        Majeski
        Library Holdings: Bk Vols 9,161
        Open Mon & Fri 10-4, Wed 1-7, Sat 9-2
     CENTRAL LIBRARY, 107 S Fourth Ave, 54235. *Adult Serv,* Laura
        Kayacan; *Ch, YA Serv,* Beth Lokken; *Circ,* Linda Streyle
        Library Holdings: Bk Vols 75,940
        Subject Interests: Door County hist, Local hist
        Open Mon-Thurs 9-9, Fri 9-6, Sat 9-5
        Friends of the Library Group
     EGG HARBOR BRANCH, 7860 Hwy 42, Egg Harbor, 54209. (Mail add:
        PO Box 207, Egg Harbor, 54209-0207), SAN 324-3109. Tel:
        920-868-2664. E-mail: egg@mail.nfls.lib.wi.us. *Br Mgr,* Dixie Jorns
        Library Holdings: Bk Vols 8,413
        Open Tues (Winter) 3-6, Wed & Thurs 10-2, Sat 10-12; Tues (Summer)
        1-7, Wed & Thurs 10-4, Sat 10-2
        Friends of the Library Group
     EPHRAIM BRANCH, 9996 Water St, Ephraim, 54211. (Mail add: PO Box
        150, Ephraim, 54211-0150), SAN 324-3117. Tel: 920-854-2014. E-mail:
        eph@mail.nfls.lib.wi.us. *Br Mgr,* Linda Malmgren; E-mail:
        lmalmgre@mail.nfls.lib.wi.us
        Library Holdings: Bk Vols 8,200
        Subject Interests: Ephraim hist
        Friends of the Library Group
     FISH CREEK BRANCH, 4097 Hwy 42, Fish Creek, 54212. (Mail add: PO
        Box 7, Fish Creek, 54212-0007), SAN 324-3125. Tel: 920-868-3471.
        FAX: 920-868-3072. E-mail: fis@mail.nfls.lib.wi.us. *Br Mgr,* Holly
        Somerhalder
        Library Holdings: Bk Vols 11,261
        Friends of the Library Group

FORESTVILLE BRANCH, 123 Hwy 42 S, Forestville, 54213. (Mail add: PO Box 308, Forestville, 54213-0308), SAN 324-3133. Tel: 920-856-6886. E-mail: for@mail.nfls.lib.wi.us. *Br Mgr,* Barbara Husch
Library Holdings: Bk Vols 10,586
Open Mon & Wed 1-7, Tues 9-2, Fri 9-5
Friends of the Library Group

SISTER BAY-LIBERTY GROVE BRANCH, 301 Mill Rd, Sister Bay, 54234. (Mail add: PO Box 347, Sister Bay, 54234-0347), SAN 324-3141. Tel: 920-854-2721. E-mail: sis@mail.nfls.lib.wi.us. *Br Mgr,* Betty Ann Curzon
Library Holdings: Bk Vols 13,715
Open Mon (Winter) 10-7, Tues 1-7, Wed 10-5, Fri 10-4, Sat 10-2; Mon-Wed (Summer) 10-8, Thurs & Fri 10-5, Sat 10-2
Friends of the Library Group

WASHINGTON ISLAND BRANCH, Main & Lakeview Rds, Washington Island, 54246, SAN 324-315X. Tel: 920-847-2323. E-mail: wsh@mail.nfls.lib.wi.us. *Br Mgr,* Marcia Carr
Library Holdings: Bk Vols 15,715
Open Mon & Wed 1-4, Tues 9-1 & 6-8, Thurs 9-1, Fri 1-5

STURTEVANT

S   RACINE CORRECTIONAL INSTITUTION LIBRARY*, 2019 Wisconsin St, 53177. (Mail add: PO Box 900, 53177-0900). Tel: 262-886-3214, Ext 3800. FAX: 262-886-3514. *Librn,* Kim Graba
Library Holdings: Bk Vols 12,472; Per Subs 96
Automation Activity & Vendor Info: (Cataloging) Follett Software; (Circulation) Follett Software

SUN PRAIRIE

P   SUN PRAIRIE PUBLIC LIBRARY*, 1350 Linnerud Dr, 53590-2631. SAN 318-4072. Tel: 608-825-7323. Information Services Tel: 608-825-0702. FAX: 608-825-3936. E-mail: sun@scls.lib.wi.us. Web Site: www.sunprairiepubliclibrary.org. *Dir,* Tracy Herold; E-mail: therold@scls.lib.wi.us; *Adult Serv,* Carol Iwanowski; E-mail: caroli@scls.lib.wi.us; *Circ,* Pearl Mosier; E-mail: pmosier@scls.lib.wi.us; *Tech Serv,* Debra Bird; E-mail: bird@scls.lib.wi.us; *Youth Serv,* Lynn Montague; E-mail: lmontague@scls.lib.wi.us; Staff 21 (MLS 6, Non-MLS 15)
Founded 1901. Pop 30,000; Circ 625,000
Library Holdings: AV Mats 13,275; Large Print Bks 1,381; Bk Vols 92,271; Per Subs 278
Wireless access
Mem of South Central Library System
Partic in Library Interchange Network (LINK)
Special Services for the Blind - Talking bks
Open Mon-Thurs (Sept-May) 9-9, Fri & Sat 9-5, Sun 1-5
Friends of the Library Group

SR   WISCONSIN CONFERENCE UNITED METHODIST CHURCH*, Historical Library, 750 Windsor St, 53590. (Mail add: PO Box 620, 53590-0620), SAN 323-6358. Tel: 608-837-7328, Ext 243. FAX: 608-837-8547. E-mail: archives@wisconsinumc.org. *Archivist,* Lynn Lubkeman
Library Holdings: Bk Titles 2,000
Special Collections: Diaries of William Ames 1857-98, Michael Benson 1832-1919 & Joseph Austin 1838-85
Restriction: Open by appt only

SUPERIOR

P   SUPERIOR PUBLIC LIBRARY*, 1530 Tower Ave, 54880-2532. SAN 365-0731. Tel: 715-394-8860. Circulation Tel: 715-394-8863. Interlibrary Loan Service Tel: 715-394-8875. Administration Tel: 715-394-8877. FAX: 715-394-8870. TDD: 715-394-8878. Web Site: www.ci.superior.wi.us. *Dir,* Janet I Jennings; E-mail: jenningsj@ci.superior.wi.us; *Circ Mgr,* Kyle Hawley; E-mail: hawleyk@superior.nwls.lib.wi.us; *Ch,* Nora B Fie; E-mail: fien@superior.nwls.lib.wi.us; *Tech Serv,* Linda M Olson; E-mail: olsonl@superior.nwls.lib.wi.us; Staff 4 (MLS 4)
Founded 1888. Pop 27,638; Circ 399,368
Library Holdings: Audiobooks 6,759; AV Mats 10,690; Bk Vols 132,140; Per Subs 234
Special Collections: Art (Anna B Butler Coll), photogs; City of Superior & Douglas County, Wisconsin, archives (State Historical Society of Wisconsin Area Research Center); Learning Disabilities (Burton Ansell Memorial Coll), bks, pamphlets, film; Rare Books (Henry S Butler Coll); Superior, Wisconsin, Newspapers from 1855; Wisconsin History (Henry E Legler Coll), bks, docs, micro, mss, film, photogs, A-tapes, V-tapes, pamphlets. State Document Depository
Subject Interests: Archit, Art, Genealogy, Heraldry, Hist, Labor hist, Music
Automation Activity & Vendor Info: (Cataloging) Innovative Interfaces, Inc; (Circulation) Innovative Interfaces, Inc; (OPAC) Innovative Interfaces, Inc

Wireless access
Publications: "Remembering the Globe" Video (Local historical information)
Partic in Merlin
Special Services for the Blind - Reader equip
Open Mon-Thurs 9-8:30, Fri 9-5, Sat 10-2
Friends of the Library Group
Branches: 1
JOAN SALMEN MEMORIAL, Village Hall, 9240 E Main St, Solon Springs, 54873-8051. (Mail add: PO Box 295, Solon Springs, 54873-0295). Tel: 715-378-4452. *Librn,* Linda Moe; E-mail: moel@superior.nwls.lib.wi.us
Library Holdings: Bk Titles 3,000
Open Mon 2-7, Thurs 9:30-2:30

CR   UNIVERSITY OF WISCONSIN-SUPERIOR*, Jim Dan Hill Library, PO Box 2000, Belknap & Catlin, 54880-2000. SAN 318-4099. Tel: 715-394-8343. Interlibrary Loan Service Tel: 715-394-8130. Reference Tel: 715-394-8341. FAX: 715-394-8462. Web Site: www.uwsuper.edu. *Dir,* Deb Nordgren; Tel: 715-394-8233, E-mail: dnordgre@uwsuper.edu; *Instruction & Ref Librn,* Carolyn Caffrey; *Ref/Govt Doc Librn,* Ella Cross; Tel: 715-394-8512, E-mail: ecross@uwsuper.edu; *Archivist/Librn, Ref & Info Literacy Librn,* Laura Jacobs; Tel: 715-394-8359, E-mail: ljacobs@uwsuper.edu; *Ref/Distance Learning Librn, Tech Librn,* Kristen Lindquist; *Assoc Librn,* Connie Moeller; *Circ,* Lori Hughes; *ILL,* Colleen Knettel; *Cat, Tech Serv,* Janet Baltes; Tel: 715-394-8136, E-mail: jbaltes@uwsuper.edu; *Tech Serv,* Jody Johnson; Staff 11 (MLS 5, Non-MLS 6)
Founded 1896. Enrl 2,350; Fac 135; Highest Degree: Master
Library Holdings: Bk Titles 198,569; Bk Vols 250,468; Per Subs 1,894
Special Collections: Lake Superior Marine Museum Association Coll; Literature (John W R Beecroft); Regional History Coll. State Document Depository; US Document Depository
Subject Interests: Educ, Govt
Automation Activity & Vendor Info: (Acquisitions) Ex Libris Group; (Cataloging) Ex Libris Group; (Circulation) Ex Libris Group; (Course Reserve) Ex Libris Group; (OPAC) Ex Libris Group; (Serials) Ex Libris Group
Database Vendor: Dialog, EBSCOhost, Gale Cengage Learning, LexisNexis, OCLC FirstSearch, OVID Technologies, Westlaw, Wilson - Wilson Web
Publications: IITC Connections
Partic in Coun of Wis Librs, Inc; ISI; OCLC Online Computer Library Center, Inc; Wisconsin Library Services
Special Services for the Blind - Computer with voice synthesizer for visually impaired persons
Open Mon-Thurs 7:45am-10pm, Fri 7:45-4:30, Sat 10-4, Sun 2-10

J   WISCONSIN INDIANHEAD TECHNICAL COLLEGE*, Superior Campus Learning Resource Center, 600 N 21st St, 54880-5296. SAN 318-4102. Tel: 715-394-6677, Ext 6276. Toll Free Tel: 800-243-9484. FAX: 715-394-3771. Web Site: www.witc.edu. *Dir,* Matthew D Rosendahl; *Libr Tech,* Adam Brisk; *Libr Tech,* Dianne Mencel; *Libr Tech,* Alison Stucke
Founded 1965
Library Holdings: Bk Titles 10,548; Per Subs 190
Automation Activity & Vendor Info: (Cataloging) Gateway; (Circulation) Gateway; (OPAC) Gateway
Database Vendor: Gale Cengage Learning, Wilson - Wilson Web
Open Mon-Thurs 7:30-7, Fri 7:30-4

SURING

P   SURING AREA PUBLIC LIBRARY, 604 E Main St, 54174. (Mail add: PO Box 74, 54174-0074). Tel: 920-842-4451. E-mail: sur@mail.nfls.lib.wi.us. Web Site: www.nfls.lib.wi.us/sur. *Dir,* Amanda Burns; E-mail: aburns@mail.nfls.lib.wi.us; *Ch,* Jill Trochta; E-mail: jtrochta@mail.nfls.lib.wi.us; *Libr Asst,* Mary Langhoff; E-mail: mlanghof@mail.nfls.lib.wi.us; Staff 1.5 (MLS 1, Non-MLS 0.5)
Founded 1986. Pop 3,000
Library Holdings: Bk Titles 15,000; Per Subs 68
Automation Activity & Vendor Info: (Acquisitions) Innovative Interfaces, Inc - OCLC; (Cataloging) Innovative Interfaces, Inc - OCLC; (Circulation) Innovative Interfaces, Inc - OCLC; (ILL) Innovative Interfaces, Inc - OCLC; (OPAC) Innovative Interfaces, Inc - OCLC; (Serials) Innovative Interfaces, Inc - OCLC
Function: Adult bk club, Audiobks via web, Bk club(s), Bks on cassette, Bks on CD, Children's prog, e-mail & chat, Electronic databases & coll, Handicapped accessible, Holiday prog, Homework prog, ILL available, Music CDs, Online cat, OverDrive digital audio bks, Photocopying/Printing, Prog for adults, Prog for children & young adult, Provide serv for the mentally ill, Pub access computers, Ref serv available, Story hour, Summer reading prog, Tax forms, Teen prog, VHS videos, Wheelchair accessible
Mem of Nicolet Federated Library System

Partic in OWLSnet
Open Mon & Wed 10-6, Tues, Thurs & Fri 1-5, Sat 10-12
Friends of the Library Group

SUSSEX

P   PAULINE HAASS PUBLIC LIBRARY*, N64 W23820 Main St,
53089-3120. SAN 324-1300. Tel: 262-246-5180. Reference Tel:
262-246-5181. FAX: 262-246-5236. Web Site: www.wcfls.lib.wi.us/phpl.
Dir, Kathy B Klager; E-mail: kbklager@phpl.lib.wi.us; *Ch,* Kerry Pinkner;
Tel: 262-246-5182, E-mail: kpinkner@phpl.lib.wi.us; *Ref Serv, Ad,* E Ralph
Illick; E-mail: rillick@phpl.lib.wi.us; *Ref Serv, Ad,* Becky Sorenson;
E-mail: sorenson@phpl.lib.wi.us; *Tech Serv,* Janet Soofi; E-mail:
jsoofi@phpl.lib.wi.us; Staff 27 (MLS 8, Non-MLS 19)
Founded 1988. Pop 19,722; Circ 302,000
Library Holdings: Bk Vols 75,857; Per Subs 161
Automation Activity & Vendor Info: (Cataloging) SirsiDynix;
(Circulation) SirsiDynix; (OPAC) SirsiDynix
Database Vendor: SirsiDynix
Wireless access
Publications: Checking In: News from the Pauline Haass Public Library
(Newsletter)
Mem of Waukesha County Federated Library System
Open Mon-Thurs 9:30-8, Fri 9:30-5, Sat 9:30-4 (9:30-1 Summer), Sun 1-4
Friends of the Library Group

TAYLOR

P   TAYLOR MEMORIAL LIBRARY*, 402 Second St, 54659. (Mail add: PO
Box 130, 54659-0130). Tel: 715-662-2310. FAX: 715-662-2034. E-mail:
taylorlibrary@wrlsweb.org. *Dir,* Karyn Schmidt; E-mail:
tk.schmidt@wrlsweb.org
Founded 1999. Pop 519
Library Holdings: Bk Titles 7,000; Talking Bks 20; Videos 200
Mem of Winding Rivers Library System
Open Tues & Thurs 2-7, Fri 9-5

THERESA

P   THERESA PUBLIC LIBRARY*, 290 Mayville St, 53091-0307. (Mail add:
PO Box 307, 53091-0307), SAN 364-6203. Tel: 920-488-2342. FAX:
920-488-2342. E-mail: tpl@mwfls.org. *Dir,* Mary Alice Bodden; *Librn,*
Candace Dennis; *Ch,* Elizabeth Bodden; *Ref Serv,* Laura Harron
Pop 2,300
Library Holdings: Bk Titles 23,000; Per Subs 50
Subject Interests: Collectibles, Local hist
Automation Activity & Vendor Info: (Cataloging) SirsiDynix;
(Circulation) SirsiDynix
Mem of Mid-Wisconsin Federated Library System
Open Mon-Thurs 1-8, Fri 1-5, Sat (Oct-May) 10-12
Friends of the Library Group

THIENSVILLE

S   EDUCATIONAL LEADERSHIP INSTITUTE LIBRARY*, 424 Susan
Lane, 53092. SAN 373-3084. Tel: 262-512-2875. *Dir,* Dr Jeremy Lietz
Library Holdings: Bk Vols 1,087
Special Collections: Regional Demographic Data; School Law; School
Organization & Routines; Special Education Adminstration
Restriction: Open by appt only

THORP

P   THORP PUBLIC LIBRARY*, 401 S Conway Dr, 54771. (Mail add: PO
Box 407, 54771-0407), SAN 318-4129. Tel: 715-669-5953. FAX:
715-669-7319. Web Site: www.thorppubliclibrary.org. *Dir,* Julie Beloungy;
E-mail: beloungy@wvls.lib.wi.us; *Asst Dir,* April Gentz; E-mail:
gentz@wvls.lib.wi.us
Founded 1898. Pop 1,650; Circ 43,540
Library Holdings: CDs 170; DVDs 545; Large Print Bks 350; Bk Vols
25,000; Per Subs 72; Talking Bks 150; Videos 352
Automation Activity & Vendor Info: (Cataloging) Horizon; (Circulation)
Horizon; (OPAC) Horizon
Wireless access
Mem of Wisconsin Valley Library Service
Open Mon & Wed 12-8, Tues & Thurs 10-5:30, Fri 9-3, Sat 9-12
Friends of the Library Group

THREE LAKES

P   EDWARD U DEMMER MEMORIAL LIBRARY*, 6961 W School St,
54562. SAN 318-4137. Tel: 715-546-3391. FAX: 715-546-2930. Web Site:
www.demmerlibrary.org. *Dir,* Janet Dixon; E-mail: jdixon@wvls.lib.wi.us;
Asst Dir, Nancy Brewster; E-mail: nbrewste@wvls.lib.wi.us; *Adult Serv,*
Stacey Orr; *ILL,* Carolyn Eaglesham; *Youth Serv,* Kelly Strauss
Founded 1949. Pop 2,000; Circ 40,892

Library Holdings: Bk Titles 27,279; Per Subs 72
Automation Activity & Vendor Info: (Cataloging) Horizon; (Circulation)
Horizon; (OPAC) Horizon
Publications: Demmer Library Newsletter (Monthly)
Mem of Wisconsin Valley Library Service
Open Mon & Wed 9-8, Tues, Thurs & Fri 9-5, Sat 9-2
Friends of the Library Group

TOMAH

GM   DEPARTMENT OF VETERAN AFFAIRS*, VA Medical Center Library,
500 E Veterans St, 54660. SAN 318-4153. Tel: 608-372-1716. FAX:
608-372-1670. *Coordr,* Kathy Sasbender; Tel: 608-372-1270, E-mail:
kathy.sasbender@med.va.gov; Staff 2 (MLS 1, Non-MLS 1)
Founded 1947
Library Holdings: Bk Titles 7,800; Per Subs 316
Subject Interests: Clinical med, Nursing, Patient health educ, Psychiat,
Psychol
Automation Activity & Vendor Info: (Acquisitions) Follett Software;
(Cataloging) Follett Software; (Circulation) Follett Software; (Course
Reserve) Follett Software; (ILL) Follett Software; (Media Booking) Follett
Software; (OPAC) Follett Software
Partic in Greater Midwest Regional Medical Libr Network; Northwestern
Wisconsin Health Science Library Consortium; Vets Admin Libr Network
Open Mon-Fri 7:30-4

P   TOMAH PUBLIC LIBRARY*, 716 Superior Ave, 54660-2098. SAN
318-4145. Tel: 608-374-7470. FAX: 608-374-7471. E-mail:
tomah_public_library@yahoo.com. Web Site: www.tomah.com/tomahpl.
Dir, Cathy W Peterson; *Ch,* Geraldine Wells; *ILL,* Irma Keller; Staff 6
(MLS 1, Non-MLS 5)
Founded 1876. Pop 16,547; Circ 116,368
Library Holdings: Bk Vols 50,722
Automation Activity & Vendor Info: (Cataloging) Follett Software;
(Circulation) Follett Software; (ILL) Brodart; (OPAC) Follett Software
Function: Ref serv available
Mem of Winding Rivers Library System
Friends of the Library Group

TOMAHAWK

P   TOMAHAWK PUBLIC LIBRARY, 300 W Lincoln Ave, 54487. SAN
318-4161. Tel: 715-453-2455. FAX: 715-453-1630. *Dir,* Mary E Dunn;
E-mail: dunn@wvls.lib.wi.us; *Ch,* Annette Miller; E-mail:
amiller@wvls.lib.wi.us; Staff 8 (Non-MLS 8)
Pop 8,088; Circ 101,257
Jan 2011-Dec 2011 Income $413,173, City $180,399, County $170,019,
Other $62,755. Mats Exp $49,963. Sal $154,840
Library Holdings: Audiobooks 3,467; Bk Titles 51,579
Automation Activity & Vendor Info: (Acquisitions) SirsiDynix;
(Cataloging) SirsiDynix; (Circulation) SirsiDynix; (OPAC) SirsiDynix;
(Serials) SirsiDynix
Database Vendor: Gale Cengage Learning, SirsiDynix
Wireless access
Function: Telephone ref
Open Mon-Thurs (Winter) 10-8, Fri 10-6, Sat 10-1; Mon-Thurs (Summer)
10-7, Fri 10-6, Sat 10-1
Friends of the Library Group

TREMPEALEAU

P   SHIRLEY M WRIGHT MEMORIAL LIBRARY*, 11455 Fremont St,
54661-9247. SAN 318-417X. Tel: 608-534-6197. FAX: 608-534-6197. Web
Site: www.wrlsweb.org/trempealeau. *Adminr, Dir,* Judy Grant; E-mail:
ja.grant@wrlsweb.org
Founded 1913. Pop 1,519; Circ 28,000
Library Holdings: Bk Vols 16,000; Per Subs 42
Automation Activity & Vendor Info: (Acquisitions) Horizon;
(Cataloging) Horizon; (Circulation) Horizon; (OPAC) Horizon
Wireless access
Mem of Winding Rivers Library System
Open Mon-Thurs 11-7, Fri 11-6, Sat 9-12
Friends of the Library Group

TURTLE LAKE

P   TURTLE LAKE PUBLIC LIBRARY*, 114 E Martin Ave, 54889. (Mail
add: PO Box 272, 54889-0272), SAN 376-6748. Tel: 715-986-6418. FAX:
715-986-4618. E-mail: turtlelakepl@ifls.lib.wi.us. Web Site:
www.turtlelakepubliclibrary.org. *Dir,* Adam Zens; E-mail:
zens@ifls.lib.wi.us
Library Holdings: e-books 5,000; Bk Titles 14,818; Per Subs 30
Automation Activity & Vendor Info: (Cataloging) SirsiDynix;
(Circulation) SirsiDynix; (OPAC) SirsiDynix
Mem of Indianhead Federated Library System
Partic in Barron County Libr Servs (BCLS)

Special Services for the Blind - Braille bks
Open Mon, Tues, Thurs & Fri 10-6, Wed 12-8, Sat 10-12

TWO RIVERS

P   LESTER PUBLIC LIBRARY*, 1001 Adams St, 54241. SAN 318-4188.
Tel: 920-793-8888. Interlibrary Loan Service Tel: 920-793-7105. Reference
Tel: 920-793-7114. FAX: 920-793-7150. E-mail: lesref@esls.lib.wi.us. Web
Site: www.tworivers.lib.wi.us. *Dir,* Jeff Dawson; Tel: 920-793-7104,
E-mail: jdawson@esls.lib.wi.us; *Circ,* Betty Kuhn; Staff 4 (MLS 1,
Non-MLS 3)
Founded 1891. Pop 19,045; Circ 186,636
Library Holdings: Bk Vols 55,000; Per Subs 215
Subject Interests: Genealogy, Local hist
Automation Activity & Vendor Info: (Acquisitions) SirsiDynix;
(Cataloging) SirsiDynix; (Circulation) SirsiDynix; (Course Reserve)
SirsiDynix; (ILL) SirsiDynix; (Media Booking) SirsiDynix; (OPAC)
SirsiDynix; (Serials) SirsiDynix
Wireless access
Mem of Manitowoc-Calumet Library System
Open Mon-Thurs 9-8:30, Fri 9-5:30, Sat 10-2
Friends of the Library Group

P   MANITOWOC-CALUMET LIBRARY SYSTEM, 4519 Lincoln Ave,
54241. SAN 318-1421. Tel: 920-553-6257. FAX: 920-553-6259. Web Site:
www.mclsweb.org/mclsweb. *Dir,* Rebecca Petersen; Staff 1 (MLS 1)
Founded 1977
Automation Activity & Vendor Info: (Circulation) SirsiDynix; (ILL)
Auto-Graphics, Inc
Database Vendor: SirsiDynix
Publications: What's New? (Monthly Bibliography)
Member Libraries: Brillion Public Library; Chilton Public Library; Kiel
Public Library; Lester Public Library; Manitowoc Public Library; New
Holstein Public Library
Open Mon-Fri 8-4:30

UNION GROVE

P   GRAHAM PUBLIC LIBRARY*, 1215 Main St, 53182-1303. SAN
318-4196. Tel: 262-878-2910. FAX: 262-878-0213. Web Site:
www.uniongrove.lib.wi.us/. *Dir,* Kathryn A Hanson; E-mail:
khanson3@uniongrove.lib.wi.us; Staff 2 (Non-MLS 2)
Pop 8,291; Circ 70,092
Library Holdings: CDs 1,258; DVDs 1,012; e-books 8,948; Electronic
Media & Resources 4,307; Bk Titles 36,084; Per Subs 102
Subject Interests: Local genealogy, Local hist
Automation Activity & Vendor Info: (Cataloging) SirsiDynix;
(Circulation) SirsiDynix; (OPAC) SirsiDynix
Wireless access
Mem of Lakeshores Library System
Partic in OCLC Online Computer Library Center, Inc
Open Mon-Thurs 9-8, Fri 9-5, Sat 9-3

VERONA

P   VERONA PUBLIC LIBRARY*, 500 Silent St, 53593. SAN 318-4218. Tel:
608-845-7180. FAX: 608-845-8917. Web Site:
www.veronapubliclibrary.org. *Dir,* Brian Simons; E-mail:
bsimons@scls.lib.wi.us; *Head, Ch,* Stacy Burkart; *Ref Librn,* Maggie
Kenaley; *Ch,* Tiffany Thiede; Staff 22 (MLS 5, Non-MLS 17)
Founded 1959. Pop 19,678; Circ 499,380
Jan 2007-Dec 2007 Income $1,009,777, State $574, City $604,523, County
$185,529, Other $219,151. Mats Exp $93,454, Books $66,903, Per/Ser
(Incl. Access Fees) $5,500, AV Mat $18,851, Electronic Ref Mat (Incl.
Access Fees) $2,200. Sal $410,886 (Prof $182,990)
Library Holdings: Audiobooks 2,480; Bks on Deafness & Sign Lang 39;
Braille Volumes 28; CDs 3,543; DVDs 2,899; e-books 8,276; Electronic
Media & Resources 2,012; Large Print Bks 1,087; Bk Vols 499,350; Per
Subs 139; Videos 2,097
Automation Activity & Vendor Info: (Acquisitions) Baker & Taylor;
(Cataloging) SirsiDynix; (Circulation) SirsiDynix; (ILL) ADLiB; (OPAC)
SirsiDynix
Wireless access
Function: Adult bk club, Bks on cassette, Bks on CD, Children's prog,
Computers for patron use, Copy machines, E-Reserves, Electronic
databases & coll, Fax serv, Handicapped accessible, ILL available,
Magnifiers for reading, Music CDs, Online cat, Outreach serv,
Photocopying/Printing, Preschool outreach, Prog for adults, Prog for
children & young adult, Ref serv available, Scanner, Story hour, Summer
reading prog, Tax forms, Teen prog, Telephone ref, VHS videos,
Wheelchair accessible, Workshops
Mem of South Central Library System
Special Services for the Deaf - Bks on deafness & sign lang; Closed
caption videos; Sign lang interpreter upon request for prog

Special Services for the Blind - Assistive/Adapted tech devices, equip &
products; Bks on cassette; Bks on CD; Braille bks; Large print bks;
Magnifiers; Recorded bks
Open Mon-Thurs 9-9, Fri 9-5, Sat 9-4
Friends of the Library Group

VESPER

P   LESTER PUBLIC LIBRARY OF VESPER, 6550 Virginia St, 54489-9999.
SAN 318-4226. Tel: 715-569-4669. E-mail: vespl@tds.net. *Dir,* Andrea L
Halbersma; Staff 1 (Non-MLS 1)
Founded 1950. Circ 12,500
Library Holdings: Bk Vols 15,000; Per Subs 16
Special Collections: World War II
Subject Interests: Christian bks
Database Vendor: EBSCOhost, ProQuest
Wireless access
Mem of South Central Library System
Open Mon 10-5, Tues 10:30-5, Wed 12-7, Thurs 12-6, Fri 9-1, Sat 9-12
Friends of the Library Group

VIOLA

P   VIOLA PUBLIC LIBRARY*, 137 S Main St, 54664-7037. SAN
318-4234. Tel: 608-627-1850. FAX: 608-627-1850. Web Site:
www.swls.org/member.vi.html. *Dir,* Lynette Owens; E-mail:
lowens@swls.org; Staff 1 (Non-MLS 1)
Founded 1918. Pop 422; Circ 6,759
Library Holdings: Bk Vols 15,000; Per Subs 70
Special Collections: Issues of Local Newspaper, 1891-1996, microfilm
Automation Activity & Vendor Info: (Cataloging) SirsiDynix;
(Circulation) SirsiDynix; (ILL) SirsiDynix; (OPAC) SirsiDynix
Mem of Southwest Wisconsin Library System
Open Tues & Thurs 9:30-5, Wed & Fri 2-7, Sat 9:30-12:30

VIROQUA

P   MCINTOSH MEMORIAL LIBRARY*, Viroqua Public Library, 118 E
Jefferson St, 54665. SAN 318-4242. Tel: 608-637-7151. Interlibrary Loan
Service Tel: 608-637-7151, Ext 3. Administration Tel: 608-637-7151, Ext
5. FAX: 608-637-8608. Web Site: www.wrlsweb.org/viroqua. *Dir,* Trina
Erickson; E-mail: t.erickson@wrlsweb.org; *Asst Dir, ILL,* Lucille Jacobson;
E-mail: l.jacobson@wrlsweb.org; *Ch,* Shirley Creager; Tel: 608-637-7151,
Ext 4, E-mail: s.creager@wrlsweb.org; Staff 5 (MLS 1, Non-MLS 4)
Founded 1898. Pop 10,000; Circ 68,000
Library Holdings: AV Mats 1,361; Bks on Deafness & Sign Lang 12;
Large Print Bks 1,200; Bk Titles 35,000; Bk Vols 35,478; Per Subs 100;
Talking Bks 789
Automation Activity & Vendor Info: (Circulation) Horizon; (OPAC)
Horizon
Function: ILL available, Photocopying/Printing, Prog for children & young
adult, Summer reading prog, Telephone ref
Mem of Winding Rivers Library System
Partic in Wisconsin Library Services
Open Mon-Thurs 10-8, Fri 10-6, Sat 9-3
Friends of the Library Group

WABENO

P   WABENO PUBLIC LIBRARY*, 4556 N Branch St, 54566. (Mail add: PO
Box 340, 54566-0340), SAN 318-4250. Tel: 715-473-4131. FAX:
715-473-4131. E-mail: wabenopl@ez-net.com. *Dir,* Carollee
Saffioti-Hughes; E-mail: carollee@wvls.lib.wi.us
Founded 1910. Pop 1,200; Circ 16,799
Library Holdings: Bk Titles 7,150; Per Subs 21
Mem of Wisconsin Valley Library Service
Open Mon, Tues, Thurs, Fri Noon-4:30, Wed Noon-6, Sat 9am-11:30am
Friends of the Library Group

WALWORTH

P   WALWORTH MEMORIAL LIBRARY*, 101 Maple Ave, 53184-9530.
(Mail add: PO Box 280, 53184-0280), SAN 318-4277. Tel: 262-275-6322.
FAX: 262-275-5315. *Librn,* Bobbi Sorrentino; E-mail:
sorrenti@walworth.lib.wi.us
Pop 1,750; Circ 35,000
Library Holdings: Bk Vols 14,500; Per Subs 33
Automation Activity & Vendor Info: (Cataloging) SirsiDynix;
(Circulation) SirsiDynix
Mem of Lakeshores Library System
Open Mon & Wed 10-8, Tues, Thurs, Fri & Sat 10-5
Friends of the Library Group

WASHBURN

P   WASHBURN PUBLIC LIBRARY*, 307 Washington Ave, 54891-1165.
(Mail add: PO Box 248, 54891-0248), SAN 318-4285. Tel: 715-373-6172.
FAX: 715-373-6186. Web Site: nwls.wislib.org/about/libwa.htm. *Dir,*
Darrell Pendergrass; E-mail: dpendergrass@washburn.nwls.lib.wi.us
Founded 1904. Pop 6,000; Circ 45,000
Library Holdings: Bk Titles 30,000; Per Subs 60
Automation Activity & Vendor Info: (OPAC) Innovative Interfaces, Inc
Database Vendor: Innovative Interfaces, Inc INN - View
Function: ILL available
Mem of Northern Waters Library Service
Partic in Merlin
Open Mon-Thurs 10-8, Fri 10-5, Sat 10-2
Friends of the Library Group

WATERFORD

P   LAKESHORES LIBRARY SYSTEM*, 725 Cornerstone Crossing, Ste C,
53185. SAN 318-3459. Tel: 262-514-4500. Toll Free Tel: 800-435-2537.
FAX: 262-514-4544. Web Site: www.lakeshores.lib.wi.us. *Adminr,* Hewitt
Kristen; Tel: 262-514-4500, Ext 66, E-mail: khewitt@lakeshores.lib.wi.us;
Libr Develop Coordr, Peggy Shaffer; Tel: 262-514-4500, Ext 68; *ILL Spec,*
Vicki Keith; Tel: 262-514-4500, Ext 64; *Syst Serv,* Jim Novy; Tel:
262-514-4500, Ext 65; *Youth Serv,* Rhonda Puntney; Tel: 262-514-4500,
Ext 67; Staff 6 (MLS 3, Non-MLS 3)
Founded 1983. Pop 281,000
Automation Activity & Vendor Info: (Acquisitions) SirsiDynix;
(Cataloging) SirsiDynix; (Circulation) SirsiDynix; (ILL) SirsiDynix;
(OPAC) SirsiDynix; (Serials) SirsiDynix
Database Vendor: SirsiDynix
Wireless access
Publications: Lake Shore Lines
Member Libraries: Aram Public Library; Barrett Memorial Library;
Brigham Memorial Library; Burlington Public Library; Darien Public
Library; East Troy Lions Public Library; Fontana Public Library; Genoa
City Public Library; Graham Public Library; Lake Geneva Public Library;
Matheson Memorial Library; Racine Public Library; Walworth Memorial
Library
Partic in OCLC Online Computer Library Center, Inc

P   WATERFORD PUBLIC LIBRARY*, 101 N River St, 53185-4149. SAN
318-4307. Tel: 262-534-3988. Administration Tel: 262-534-3988, Ext 30.
FAX: 262-534-9624. Web Site: www.waterford.lib.wi.us. *Dir,* Pam Belden;
E-mail: psbelden@waterford.lib.wi.us; Staff 8 (MLS 1, Non-MLS 7)
Founded 1967. Pop 25,000; Circ 226,877
Library Holdings: Bk Vols 45,000; Per Subs 192
Automation Activity & Vendor Info: (Cataloging) SirsiDynix;
(Circulation) SirsiDynix; (Course Reserve) SirsiDynix; (ILL) SirsiDynix;
(Media Booking) SirsiDynix; (OPAC) SirsiDynix; (Serials) SirsiDynix
Open Mon-Thurs 9-8, Fri 9-5, Sat 9-3
Friends of the Library Group

WATERLOO

P   KARL JUNGINGER MEMORIAL LIBRARY, 625 N Monroe St,
53594-1183. SAN 318-4315. Tel: 920-478-3344. FAX: 920-478-2351. Web
Site: www.waterloo.lib.wi.us. *Dir,* Cecilia Wiltzius; E-mail:
cwiltzius@mwfls.org; *Assoc Dir,* Joel Zibell; *Ch,* Amanda Brueckner; Staff
4 (MLS 3, Non-MLS 1)
Founded 1901. Pop 3,300; Circ 50,000
Library Holdings: CDs 400; DVDs 1,600; Bk Vols 29,000; Talking Bks
1,200
Special Collections: American Wood Carvings (Leon Wood Coll)
Subject Interests: Children's lit, Genealogy, Local hist
Automation Activity & Vendor Info: (Acquisitions) SirsiDynix;
(Cataloging) SirsiDynix; (Circulation) SirsiDynix; (OPAC) SirsiDynix;
(Serials) SirsiDynix
Wireless access
Mem of Mid-Wisconsin Federated Library System
Open Mon-Thurs 10-7, Fri 12-5, Sat 10-3

WATERTOWN

CR   MARANATHA BAPTIST BIBLE COLLEGE, Cedarholm Library &
Resource Center, 745 W Main St, 53094. SAN 370-6206. Tel:
920-206-2375. FAX: 920-261-9109. E-mail: library@mbbc.edu. Web Site:
library.mbbc.edu. *Dir,* Lois Oetken; E-mail: lois.oetken@mbbc.edu. Subject
Specialists: *Theol,* Lois Oetken; Staff 4.5 (MLS 1, Non-MLS 3.5)
Founded 1968. Enrl 736; Fac 59; Highest Degree: Master
Jul 2012-Jun 2013 Income (Main Library Only) $104,375. Mats Exp
$76,280, Books $35,567, Per/Ser (Incl. Access Fees) $13,424, AV Equip
$560, AV Mat $500, Electronic Ref Mat (Incl. Access Fees) $25,359, Presv
$870. Sal $219,676

Library Holdings: Bks on Deafness & Sign Lang 90; CDs 1,628; DVDs
562; e-books 11,935; Electronic Media & Resources 1,155; Microforms
227; Music Scores 239; Bk Titles 89,167; Bk Vols 114,126; Per Subs 298
Special Collections: Weeks Coll
Automation Activity & Vendor Info: (Acquisitions) EOS International;
(Cataloging) EOS International; (Circulation) EOS International; (OPAC)
EOS International; (Serials) EOS International
Database Vendor: EBSCOhost, EOS International, Facts on File, JSTOR,
netLibrary, WebFeat
Wireless access
Function: Archival coll, Audiobks via web, Bks on CD, Computers for
patron use, Copy machines, Distance learning, e-mail & chat, Electronic
databases & coll, Free DVD rentals, Instruction & testing, Learning ctr,
Online cat, Online ref, Online searches, Orientations, Outside serv via
phone, mail, e-mail & web, Photocopying/Printing, Pub access computers,
Ref & res, Ref serv available, Ref serv in person, Scanner
Partic in Christian Libr Network; WILS; Wiscat
Open (Winter) Mon, Tues & Thurs 7am-9:30pm, Wed & Fri 7-5, Sat 9-9;
Mon-Fri (Summer) 8-4:30
Restriction: 24-hr pass syst for students only, ID required to use
computers (Ltd hrs), In-house use for visitors, Non-circulating of rare bks,
Non-resident fee, Open to pub for ref & circ; with some limitations, Open
to students, fac & staff, Restricted borrowing privileges

M   WATERTOWN MEMORIAL HOSPITAL*, C J Quirk Health Sciences
Library, 125 Hospital Dr, 53098-3384. SAN 374-4841. Tel: 920-262-4278.
FAX: 920-262-4266. E-mail: librarian@wahs.com. Web Site:
www.wahs.com. *In Charge,* Mike Strasser
Founded 1988
Library Holdings: Bk Titles 300; Per Subs 100
Subject Interests: Allied health, Consumer health, Med, Nursing

P   WATERTOWN PUBLIC LIBRARY*, 100 S Water St, 53094-4320. SAN
318-4331. Tel: 920-262-4090. FAX: 920-261-8943. E-mail:
askrefwt@mwfls.org. Web Site: www.watertown.lib.wi.us. *Dir,* Diane
Jaroch; E-mail: jarochd@mwfls.org; *Asst Dir, Ch,* Peg Checkai; Tel:
920-262-4090, Ext 24, E-mail: libraryyouth@mwfls.org; *Ad, Ref Coordr,
Tech Coordr,* Dan Malosh; E-mail: dmalosh@mwfls.org; *Circ Librn, Syst
Adminr,* Sharry Lueck; Tel: 920-262-4090, Ext 18, E-mail:
luecks@mwfls.org; Staff 4 (MLS 4)
Founded 1907
Library Holdings: Bk Vols 99,000
Subject Interests: Local hist
Mem of Mid-Wisconsin Federated Library System
Open Mon-Thurs 9-8, Fri 9-6, Sat 9-1
Friends of the Library Group

WAUKESHA

CR   CARROLL COLLEGE*, Todd Wehr Memorial Library, 100 N East Ave,
53186. SAN 318-434X. Tel: 262-524-7175. Interlibrary Loan Service Tel:
262-524-7674. Reference Tel: 262-650-4892. FAX: 262-524-7377. Web
Site: divisions.cc.edu/library/. *Dir,* Dr Lelan McLemore; Tel:
262-524-7177, E-mail: lmclemor@cc.edu; *Assoc Dir,* Allison Reeves; Tel:
262-524-7180, E-mail: areeves@cc.edu; *Instrul Serv Librn,* Susan Heffron;
Tel: 262-524-7674, E-mail: sheffron@cc.edu; *Archivist, Database Mgr, Ser,*
Catherine Sanders; Tel: 262-951-3016, E-mail: csanders@cc.edu; *Mgr, ILL,*
Meg Rein; Tel: 262-650-4889, E-mail: mrein@cc.edu; *Access Serv,* Amelia
Osterud; Tel: 262-650-4888, E-mail: aosterud@cc.edu; *Circ,* Carole
Winrich; Tel: 262-524-7307, E-mail: cwinrich@cc.edu; *Pub Serv, Tech
Serv,* Susan Riehl; Tel: 262-650-4832, E-mail: sriehl@cc.edu; *Ref,* Dr
Linda Hartig; Tel: 262-524-7179, E-mail: lhartig@cc.edu. Subject
Specialists: *Educ,* Allison Reeves; *Health sci,* Susan Heffron; *Copyright,
Politics, Pub hist,* Catherine Sanders; *Hist, Math, Relig,* Susan Riehl;
English, Music, Psychol, Dr Linda Hartig; Staff 8 (MLS 5, Non-MLS 3)
Founded 1846. Enrl 2,546; Fac 94; Highest Degree: Master
Library Holdings: e-books 7,343; e-journals 14,000; Bk Vols 150,000; Per
Subs 341
Special Collections: English & Scottish 19th Century Literature Coll;
Welsh Literature & Language Coll
Subject Interests: Hist, Relig studies
Automation Activity & Vendor Info: (Acquisitions) Innovative Interfaces,
Inc; (Cataloging) Innovative Interfaces, Inc; (Circulation) Innovative
Interfaces, Inc; (Course Reserve) Innovative Interfaces, Inc; (ILL)
Innovative Interfaces, Inc; (OPAC) Innovative Interfaces, Inc; (Serials)
Innovative Interfaces, Inc
Database Vendor: EBSCOhost, Gale Cengage Learning, JSTOR,
LexisNexis, netLibrary, OCLC FirstSearch, ProQuest, SerialsSolutions
Partic in Library Council of Southeastern Wisconsin, Inc; Wis Asn of
Independent Cols & Univs
Open Mon-Thurs (Winter) 7:30am-Midnight, Fri 7:30am-8pm, Sat 9-8, Sun
Noon-Midnight; Mon-Thurs (Summer) 8-7, Fri 8-4:30
Restriction: Private libr
Friends of the Library Group

R FIRST BAPTIST CHURCH LIBRARY-WAUKESHA, 247 Wisconsin Ave,
53186. SAN 318-4358. Tel: 262-542-7233. FAX: 262-542-1367. E-mail:
office@firstbaptistwaukesha.com. Web Site: www.firstbaptistwaukesha.com.
Librn, Sandra Cope; Tel: 262-549-9711, E-mail: scope@wi.rr.com; Staff 1
(MLS 1)
Library Holdings: Bk Vols 3,000
Special Collections: Christian Education Materials
Subject Interests: Relig

S KALMBACH PUBLISHING CO LIBRARY, David P Morgan Memorial
Library, 21027 Crossroads Circle, 53186. (Mail add: PO Box 1612,
53187-1612), SAN 318-2002. Tel: 262-796-8776, Ext 423. FAX:
262-796-6468. *Librn,* Thomas E Hoffmann
Founded 1949
Library Holdings: Bk Titles 19,000; Per Subs 140; Videos 500
Special Collections: Digital Photo Library
Subject Interests: Mil hist, Railroads, Sciences, Transportation

J UNIVERSITY OF WISCONSIN COLLEGES*, Waukesha Library &
Media Services, 1500 University Dr, 53188. SAN 318-4382. Tel:
262-521-5473. Interlibrary Loan Service Tel: 262-521-5531. FAX:
262-521-5116. E-mail: waklib@uwc.edu, wakmedia@uwc.edu. Web Site:
www.waukesha.uwc.edu. *Dir, Libr & Media Serv,* Scott Silet; E-mail:
scott.silet@uwc.edu; *Sr Acad Librn,* Jane Cavanaugh; *Admin Prog Mgr II,*
Denise Spleas; *Media/IT Mgr,* Cheryl Schoenhaar
Founded 1966. Enrl 2,200; Fac 85; Highest Degree: Bachelor
Library Holdings: AV Mats 1,500; e-journals 7,000; Electronic Media &
Resources 250; Bk Vols 60,000; Per Subs 125
Automation Activity & Vendor Info: (Acquisitions) Ex Libris Group;
(Cataloging) Ex Libris Group; (Circulation) Ex Libris Group; (Course
Reserve) Ex Libris Group; (ILL) Ex Libris Group; (Media Booking) Ex
Libris Group; (OPAC) Ex Libris Group; (Serials) Ex Libris Group
Partic in Library Council of Southeastern Wisconsin, Inc; Wisconsin
Library Services
Open Mon-Thurs 7:30am-8pm, Fri 7:30-5

P WAUKESHA COUNTY FEDERATED LIBRARY SYSTEM*, 831 N
Grand Ave, Ste 220, 53186-4822. SAN 321-1061. Tel: 262-896-8080.
Reference Tel: 262-896-8083. FAX: 262-896-8086. TDD: 262-896-8089.
E-mail: wcfls@wcfls.lib.wi.us. Web Site: www.wcfls.lib.wi.us. *Dir,* Thomas
J Hennen, Jr; E-mail: thennen@wcfls.lib.wi.us; *Automation Syst Coordr,*
Mellanie Mercier; E-mail: mmercier@wcfls.lib.wi.us; *ILL, Ref,* Laurie
Freund; E-mail: ljfreund@wcfls.lib.wi.us; Staff 5 (MLS 5)
Founded 1981. Pop 373,372
Member Libraries: Alice Baker Memorial Public Library; Big Bend
Village Library; Brookfield Public Library; Delafield Public Library; Elm
Grove Public Library; Menomonee Falls Public Library; Mukwonago
Community Library; Muskego Public Library; New Berlin Public Library;
Oconomowoc Public Library; Pauline Haass Public Library; Pewaukee
Public Library; Town Hall Library; Waukesha Public Library
Special Services for the Deaf - Assisted listening device; Assistive tech;
Closed caption videos; High interest/low vocabulary bks; Pocket talkers;
Sign lang interpreter upon request for prog; TDD equip
Special Services for the Blind - BiFolkal kits; Bks on CD; Extensive large
print coll; Home delivery serv; Large print bks; Low vision equip;
Magnifiers; Playaways (bks on MP3); Talking bks
Open Mon-Fri 8-5

S WAUKESHA COUNTY HISTORICAL SOCIETY & MUSEUM*,
Research Center, 101 W Main St, 53186. SAN 318-4390. Tel:
262-521-2859. FAX: 262-521-2865. Web Site:
www.waukeshacountymuseum.org/. *Archivist,* Eric Vanden Heuvel; E-mail:
evandenheuvel@wchsm.org; *Curator,* Elisabeth Engel; Staff 1 (MLS 1)
Founded 1914
Library Holdings: Bk Titles 4,500; Per Subs 49
Special Collections: Waukesha County Family & Local History Coll
Function: Ref serv available
Publications: Landmark (Quarterly oral history magazine)
Open Tues, Fri & Sat 10-12 & 12:30-4:30, Thurs 12:30-4:30
Restriction: Non-circulating

M WAUKESHA MEMORIAL HOSPITAL*, ProHealth Care Library, 725
American Ave, 53188-9982. SAN 318-4404. Tel: 262-928-2150. FAX:
262-928-2514. *Med Librn,* Vicki Kuenzi; E-mail: vicki.kuenzi@phci.org;
Staff 0.6 (MLS 0.6)
Founded 1959
Library Holdings: e-books 140; e-journals 1,525; Bk Vols 2,036; Per Subs
148
Subject Interests: Hospital admin, Med, Nursing
Database Vendor: EBSCOhost, MD Consult, OVID Technologies,
PubMed, STAT!Ref (Teton Data Systems)
Wireless access

Function: Copy machines, Doc delivery serv, Electronic databases & coll,
Health sci info serv, ILL available, Online cat, Online searches,
Orientations, Photocopying/Printing, Scanner
Partic in Midwest Health Sci Libr Network; Southeastern Wisconsin Health
Science Library Consortium
Open Mon-Fri 8-4:30
Restriction: Hospital staff & commun, Med & nursing staff, patients &
families, Open to pub for ref only, Open to students, fac & staff

P WAUKESHA PUBLIC LIBRARY, 321 Wisconsin Ave, 53186-4786. SAN
318-4412. Tel: 262-524-3680. Circulation Tel: 262-524-3684. Reference
Tel: 262-524-3682. FAX: 262-524-3677. TDD: 262-524-3696. Web Site:
www.waukesha.lib.wi.us. *Dir,* Grant C Lynch; Tel: 262-524-3681, E-mail:
glynch@waukesha.lib.wi.us; *Dep Libr Dir,* Karol Kennedy; Tel:
262-524-3746, E-mail: kkennedy@waukesha.lib.su; *Asst Libr Dir,* John
Klima; Tel: 262-524-3688, E-mail: jklima@waukesha.lib.wi.us; *Ch Mgr,*
Kerry Pinkner; Tel: 262-524-3695, E-mail: kpinkner@waukesha.lib.wi.us;
Info Serv Mgr, Kori Hall; Tel: 262-524-3904, E-mail:
khall@waukesha.lib.wi.us; *Tech Serv Mgr,* Beth Bechtel; Tel:
262-522-7283, E-mail: bbechtel@waukesha.lib.wi.us; *Circ Supvr,* Nancy
McGuire; Tel: 262-524-3693; Staff 44 (MLS 14, Non-MLS 30)
Founded 1896. Pop 93,237; Circ 1,409,738
Jan 2011-Dec 2011 Income $4,147,261, State $78,300, City $2,314,492,
Federal $4,327, County $1,131,054, Locally Generated Income $23,749,
Other $144,809. Mats Exp $419,055, Books $274,296, Other Print Mats
$2,146, AV Mat $121,299, Electronic Ref Mat (Incl. Access Fees) $21,314.
Sal $1,949,827
Library Holdings: AV Mats 20,606; e-books 9,733; Bk Vols 270,617; Per
Subs 419; Videos 22,170
Special Collections: State Document Depository; US Document
Depository
Automation Activity & Vendor Info: (Acquisitions) SirsiDynix;
(Cataloging) SirsiDynix; (Circulation) SirsiDynix; (OPAC) SirsiDynix;
(Serials) SirsiDynix
Database Vendor: EBSCOhost, Gale Cengage Learning, OCLC
FirstSearch, ProQuest, Wilson - Wilson Web
Wireless access
Function: Adult bk club, Adult literacy prog, Art exhibits, Audiobks via
web, AV serv, Bk club(s), Bks on cassette, Bks on CD, Bus archives,
CD-ROM, Children's prog, Computer training, Computers for patron use,
Copy machines, Digital talking bks, E-Reserves, Electronic databases &
coll, Free DVD rentals, Home delivery & serv to Sr ctr & nursing homes,
Homebound delivery serv, ILL available, Magnifiers for reading, Music
CDs, Newsp ref libr, Online cat, Online ref, Online searches, Outreach
serv, OverDrive digital audio bks, Photocopying/Printing, Prog for adults,
Prog for children & young adult, Senior computer classes, Story hour,
Summer reading prog, Teen prog, Telephone ref, VHS videos, Wheelchair
accessible
Mem of Waukesha County Federated Library System
Special Services for the Deaf - TTY equip
Restriction: ID required to use computers (Ltd hrs)
Friends of the Library Group

WAUNAKEE

P WAUNAKEE PUBLIC LIBRARY*, 710 South St, 53597-1638. SAN
318-4420. Tel: 608-849-4217. FAX: 608-849-7817. E-mail:
waupl@scls.lib.wi.us. Web Site: www.waunakeepubliclibrary.org. *Dir,*
Susan Hedrick; E-mail: shedrick@scls.lib.wi.us; *Youth Serv Dir,* Lisa
Wegner; E-mail: lwegner@scls.lib.wi.us
Pop 10,755; Circ 234,252
Library Holdings: AV Mats 7,963; CDs 4,382; DVDs 3,581; e-books
8,153; Bk Titles 60,578; Per Subs 368; Talking Bks 3,896
Special Collections: Oral History
Automation Activity & Vendor Info: (Acquisitions) SirsiDynix;
(Cataloging) SirsiDynix; (Circulation) SirsiDynix; (OPAC) SirsiDynix;
(Serials) SirsiDynix
Mem of South Central Library System
Open Mon-Thurs 9-9, Fri 9-5, Sat 10-5
Friends of the Library Group

WAUPACA

P WAUPACA AREA PUBLIC LIBRARY, 107 S Main St, 54981-1521. SAN
318-4447. Tel: 715-258-4414. Reference Tel: 715-258-4416. E-mail:
wau@mail.owls.lib.wi.us. Web Site: www.waupacalibrary.org. *Dir,* Peg
Burington; E-mail: pburingt@mail.owls.lib.wi.us; *Asst Libr Dir,* Dominic
Frandrup; E-mail: dfrandru@mail.owls.lib.wi.us; *ILL Librn,* Patsy Servey;
Teen Librn, Position Currently Open; *Youth Serv Librn,* Sue Abrahamson;
Staff 4 (MLS 2, Non-MLS 2)
Founded 1900. Pop 17,000; Circ 305,000
Library Holdings: Audiobooks 1,500; CDs 3,000; DVDs 4,000; Large
Print Bks 2,500; Bk Vols 64,000; Per Subs 120
Special Collections: Wisconsin History Collection

Automation Activity & Vendor Info: (Cataloging) Innovative Interfaces, Inc; (Circulation) Innovative Interfaces, Inc
Wireless access
Mem of Outagamie Waupaca Library System
Open Mon-Thurs 9-8, Fri 9-5, Sat 10-2
Friends of the Library Group

WAUPUN

S DODGE CORRECTIONAL INSTITUTION LIBRARY*, One W Lincoln St, 53963. (Mail add: PO Box 661, 53963-0661), SAN 365-0855. Tel: 920-324-5577, Ext 6570. FAX: 920-324-6297. *Librn,* Sara Krause; *Librn,* John Lungren; E-mail: john.lungren@wisconsin.gov; Staff 8 (MLS 2, Non-MLS 6)
Library Holdings: Bk Titles 8,700; Per Subs 67
Subject Interests: Criminal justice, Law
Automation Activity & Vendor Info: (Cataloging) Follett Software; (Circulation) Follett Software; (OPAC) Follett Software
Open Mon-Fri 7-4:30

S WAUPUN CORRECTIONAL INSTITUTION LIBRARY*, 200 S Madison St, 53963-2069. (Mail add: PO Box 351, 53963-0351), SAN 318-4463. Tel: 920-324-5571. FAX: 920-324-7250. *Librn,* Nevin B Webster; E-mail: nevin.webster@doc.state.wi.us; Staff 1 (Non-MLS 1)
Founded 1890
Library Holdings: Bk Vols 13,000; Per Subs 90
Automation Activity & Vendor Info: (Circulation) Follett Software; (OPAC) Follett Software
Open Mon-Fri 7:30-10:30, 12:30-3:30 & 5:45-8:45

P WAUPUN PUBLIC LIBRARY, 123 S Forest St, 53963. (Mail add: PO Box 391, 53963-0391), SAN 318-4455. Tel: 920-324-7925. E-mail: wpl@mwfls.org. Web Site: www.waupunpubliclibrary.org. *Dir,* Bret Jaeger; E-mail: bret@mwfls.org; *Asst Dir,* Pam Garcia; E-mail: pgarcia@mwfls.org; *Youth Serv Librn,* Kay Hansen; E-mail: kmhlib@mwfls.org; *Circ,* Kathy Jensen; E-mail: kathyj@mwfls.org; *ILL,* Donna Maxwell; E-mail: dmaxwell@mwfls.org; Staff 8.4 (MLS 2, Non-MLS 6.4)
Founded 1858. Pop 14,000; Circ 129,711
Jan 2010-Dec 2010 Income $626,071, State $799, City $540,774, County $78,738, Locally Generated Income $5,760. Mats Exp $85,907, Books $60,515, Per/Ser (Incl. Access Fees) $10,469, AV Mat $7,501, Electronic Ref Mat (Incl. Access Fees) $7,422. Sal $312,343 (Prof $114,110)
Library Holdings: AV Mats 4,197; DVDs 2,927; Electronic Media & Resources 318; Bk Vols 62,334; Per Subs 153
Subject Interests: Wis hist
Automation Activity & Vendor Info: (Cataloging) SIRSI WorkFlows; (Circulation) SIRSI WorkFlows; (OPAC) SIRSI-iBistro; (Serials) SIRSI WorkFlows
Database Vendor: SirsiDynix
Wireless access
Mem of Mid-Wisconsin Federated Library System
Open Mon-Thurs 9-8, Fri 9-5:30, Sat 10-4:30
Friends of the Library Group

WAUSAU

M ASPIRUS WAUSAU HOSPITAL*, Dr Joseph F Smith Medical Library, 333 Pine Ridge Blvd, 54401. SAN 328-3038. Tel: 715-847-2184. FAX: 715-847-2183. Web Site: www.aspiruslibrary.org. *Dir,* Jan Kraus; E-mail: jank@aspirus.org; Staff 4 (MLS 1, Non-MLS 3)
Library Holdings: e-journals 300; Bk Vols 1,400; Per Subs 200
Partic in Northern Wis Health Sci Libr Coop
Open Mon-Fri 8-4:30

S MARATHON COUNTY HISTORICAL SOCIETY LIBRARY*, 410 McIndoe St, 54403. SAN 324-1572. Tel: 715-848-0378. FAX: 715-848-0576. E-mail: research@marathoncountyhistory.com. Web Site: www.marathoncountyhistory.com. *Dir,* Mary Jane Uecker-Hettinga; *Librn,* Mary Forer; Staff 2 (MLS 1, Non-MLS 1)
Founded 1980
Library Holdings: Bk Vols 7,500; Per Subs 20
Special Collections: Marathon County Plat Maps & City Directories
Subject Interests: County hist, Genealogy, Logging
Function: Res libr
Open Tues-Thurs 9-3:30

P MARATHON COUNTY PUBLIC LIBRARY*, 300 N First St, 54403-5405. SAN 365-0944. Tel: 715-261-7200. Interlibrary Loan Service Tel: 715-261-7244. Reference Tel: 715-261-7230. Information Services Tel: 715-261-7240. FAX: 715-261-7204. E-mail: info@mcpl.us, ref@mcpl.us. Web Site: www.mcpl.us. *Dir,* Ralph Illick; Tel: 715-261-7211, E-mail: ralph.illick@co.marathon.wi.us; Staff 47 (MLS 4, Non-MLS 43)
Founded 1974. Pop 134,063; Circ 1,125,370

Library Holdings: AV Mats 31,677; e-books 8,240; Microforms 66,082; Bk Vols 328,306; Per Subs 608
Special Collections: Old Popular Sheet Music; Wisconsin History. Oral History; State Document Depository; US Document Depository
Automation Activity & Vendor Info: (Acquisitions) SirsiDynix; (Cataloging) SirsiDynix; (Circulation) SirsiDynix; (OPAC) SirsiDynix
Database Vendor: SirsiDynix
Wireless access
Mem of Wisconsin Valley Library Service
Partic in OCLC Online Computer Library Center, Inc; WILS; Wisconsin Valley Library Service
Open Mon-Thurs 9-8:30, Fri 9-5, Sat 9-1
Friends of the Library Group
Branches: 8
ATHENS BRANCH, 221 Caroline St, Athens, 54411-0910, SAN 365-0979. Tel: 715-257-7292. FAX: 715-257-7292. *Br Coordr,* Deborah Balz; E-mail: debabalz@yahoo.com
Founded 1926
Library Holdings: Bk Vols 19,206
Open Mon & Thurs 1-8, Tues 9-5, Wed & Fri 1-5
Friends of the Library Group
JOSEPH DESSERT BRANCH, 123 Main St, Mosinee, 54455-1441, SAN 365-1037. Tel: 715-693-2144. FAX: 715-693-2144. *Br Coordr,* Nancy Dahlke; E-mail: Nancy.Dahlke@co.marathon.wi.us
Founded 1899
Library Holdings: Bk Vols 18,353
Open Mon & Thurs 12-8, Tues & Wed 9-5, Fri 12-4
Friends of the Library Group
EDGAR BRANCH, 224 S Third Ave, Edgar, 54426. (Mail add: PO Box 228, Edgar, 54426-0228), SAN 365-1061. Tel: 715-352-3155. FAX: 715-352-3155. *Br Coordr,* Debbie Gauerke; E-mail: dgauerke@co.marathon.wi.us
Founded 1928
Library Holdings: Bk Vols 13,351
Open Mon & Wed 1-7, Tues & Thurs 9-4, Fri 1-5
Friends of the Library Group
HATLEY BRANCH, 435 Curtis Ave, Hatley, 54440. (Mail add: PO Box 129, Hatley, 54440-0129). Tel: 715-446-3537. FAX: 715-446-3537. *Br Supvr,* Sharon Luebbe; E-mail: sharon.luebbe@co.marathon.wi.us; *Br Asst,* Kristy Balliett; *Br Asst,* Karen Jacobson
Founded 2005
Open Mon & Wed 10-6, Tues & Thurs 10-8, Fri 1-5, Sat (Winter) 10-2
MARATHON CITY BRANCH, 515 Washington St, Marathon, 54448, SAN 365-1126. Tel: 715-443-2775. FAX: 715-443-2775. *Br Coordr,* Lavone Runge; E-mail: Lavone.Runge@co.marathon.wi.us
Founded 1954
Library Holdings: Bk Vols 11,406
Open Mon & Wed 10-7, Tues, Thurs & Fri 10-5, Sat (Winter) 10-2
Friends of the Library Group
ROTHSCHILD BRANCH, 211 Grand Ave, Rothschild, 54474-1122, SAN 365-1150. Tel: 715-359-6208. FAX: 715-359-6208. *Br Coordr,* Laura L Headrick
Founded 1949
Library Holdings: Bk Vols 29,775
Open Mon-Thurs 10-8, Fri 10-5, Sat (Winter) 10-2
Friends of the Library Group
SPENCER BRANCH, 105 Park St, Spencer, 54479-0398. (Mail add: PO Box 398, Spencer, 54479-0398), SAN 365-1215. Tel: 715-659-3996. FAX: 715-659-3996. *Br Coordr,* Judy Berger; E-mail: judy.berger@co.marathon.wi.us
Founded 1875
Library Holdings: Bk Vols 15,694
Open Mon & Thurs 3-8, Tues & Wed 9-5, Fri 1-5
Friends of the Library Group
STRATFORD BRANCH, 400 N Fourth Ave, Stratford, 54484. (Mail add: PO Box 74, Stratford, 54484-0074), SAN 365-124X. Tel: 715-687-4420. FAX: 715-687-4420. *Br Coordr,* Janice Pankratz; E-mail: janice.pankratz@co.marathon.wi.us
Library Holdings: Bk Vols 18,093
Open Mon 10-5, Tues 1-7, Wed 10-7, Thurs & Fri 1-5
Friends of the Library Group

C NORTHCENTRAL TECHNICAL COLLEGE LIBRARY*, 1000 W Campus Dr, 54401. SAN 318-448X. Tel: 715-803-1115. Administration Tel: 715-803-1216. FAX: 715-675-9776. E-mail: lib@ntc.edu. Web Site: www.ntc.edu/library.html. *Libr Serv Tech,* Linda Gau; Tel: 715-803-1056, E-mail: gau@ntc.edu; Staff 3.34 (MLS 1.67, Non-MLS 1.67)
Founded 1969. Enrl 3,800; Fac 159; Highest Degree: Associate
Library Holdings: Bks on Deafness & Sign Lang 200; e-books 350; Bk Vols 29,902; Per Subs 75
Special Collections: American Sign Language
Subject Interests: Computer sci, Nursing, Police sci
Automation Activity & Vendor Info: (Acquisitions) Ex Libris Group; (Cataloging) Ex Libris Group; (Circulation) Ex Libris Group; (OPAC) Ex Libris Group; (Serials) Ex Libris Group

Database Vendor: ALLDATA Online, EBSCOhost, Elsevier, Ex Libris Group, Facts on File, Gale Cengage Learning, H W Wilson, netLibrary, Newsbank, OCLC FirstSearch, OVID Technologies, ProQuest, PubMed, SerialsSolutions, Springer-Verlag
Wireless access
Function: Telephone ref
Partic in WISPALS Library Consortium
Special Services for the Deaf - Am sign lang & deaf culture; Bks on deafness & sign lang; Closed caption videos; Coll on deaf educ
Special Services for the Blind - Accessible computers; Bks on cassette; Bks on CD; Blind students ctr; Copier with enlargement capabilities; PC for handicapped; ZoomText magnification & reading software
Open Mon-Thurs 7:30am-8pm, Fri 7:30-6, Sat 9am-12:45pm

C   UNIVERSITY OF WISCONSIN CENTER-MARATHON COUNTY LIBRARY*, 518 S Seventh Ave, 54401-5396. SAN 318-4498. Tel: 715-261-6220. Reference Tel: 715-261-6218. FAX: 715-261-6330. Web Site: www.uwmc.uwc.edu. *Dir,* Judy Palmateer; Tel: 715-261-6219, E-mail: judy.palmateer@uwc.edu; *Circ,* Justeen Vollrath; Tel: 715-261-6202, E-mail: justeen.vollrath@uwc.edu; *Ref,* Todd Roll; E-mail: todd.roll@uwc.edu; *Tech Coordr,* Paul Henfer; Tel: 715-261-6208, E-mail: paul.henfer@uwc.edu; Staff 4 (MLS 2, Non-MLS 2)
Founded 1938. Enrl 1,300; Fac 45; Highest Degree: Associate
Library Holdings: Bk Titles 40,000; Bk Vols 42,000; Per Subs 101
Automation Activity & Vendor Info: (Cataloging) Ex Libris Group; (Circulation) Ex Libris Group; (Course Reserve) Ex Libris Group; (Media Booking) Ex Libris Group; (OPAC) Ex Libris Group; (Serials) Ex Libris Group
Database Vendor: EBSCOhost, Gale Cengage Learning, OCLC FirstSearch, ProQuest, Wilson - Wilson Web
Partic in OCLC Online Computer Library Center, Inc; Wisconsin Library Services
Open Mon-Thurs 7:45am-9pm, Fri 7:45-4, Sun 6pm-9pm

P   WISCONSIN VALLEY LIBRARY SERVICE*, 300 N First St, 54403. SAN 318-4501. Tel: 715-261-7250. Interlibrary Loan Service Tel: 715-261-7258. Reference Tel: 715-261-7255. Administration Tel: 715-261-7256. FAX: 715-261-7259. Web Site: wvls.lib.wi.us. *Dir,* Marla Sepnafski; E-mail: msepnafs@wvls.lib.wi.us; *Dir, Info Tech,* Joshua Klingbeil; E-mail: jklingbeil@wvls.lib.wi.us; *ILS Adminr,* Inese Christman; E-mail: ichristman@wvls.lib.wi.us; *ILL,* Juanita Thomas; E-mail: jathomas@wvls.lib.wi.us; *Pub Libr Consult,* Kris Adams Wendt; E-mail: kawendt@wvls.lib.wi.us; Staff 4 (MLS 3, Non-MLS 1)
Founded 1961. Pop 283,913
Jan 2011-Dec 2011 Income $1,697,881, State $946,603, Federal $89,200, County $41,184, Locally Generated Income $20,000, Other $600,894. Mats Exp $54,937, Books $6,900, Per/Ser (Incl. Access Fees) $1,700, Other Print Mats $1,287, AV Mat $12,000, Electronic Ref Mat (Incl. Access Fees) $33,050. Sal $483,242 (Prof $234,952)
Automation Activity & Vendor Info: (Acquisitions) SirsiDynix; (Cataloging) SirsiDynix; (Circulation) SirsiDynix; (ILL) OCLC WorldCat; (OPAC) SirsiDynix; (Serials) SirsiDynix
Database Vendor: EBSCO Information Services, Gale Cengage Learning, SirsiDynix
Wireless access
Member Libraries: Abbotsford Public Library; Antigo Public Library; Colby Public Library; Crandon Public Library; Dorchester Public Library; Edith Evans Community Library; Edward U Demmer Memorial Library; Frances L Simek Memorial Library-Medford; Greenwood Public Library; Jean M Thomsen Memorial Library; Loyal Public Library; Marathon County Public Library; Minocqua Public Library; Neillsville Public Library; Owen Public Library; Rhinelander District Library; Rib Lake Public Library; Samson Memorial Library; Thorp Public Library; Tomahawk Public Library; Wabeno Public Library; Westboro Public Library; Western Taylor County Public Library; Withee Public Library
Partic in OCLC Online Computer Library Center, Inc; Wisconsin Public Library Consortium
Special Services for the Blind - Audio mat; Bks on CD; Large print bks; Talking bks
Open Mon-Fri 8-5

S   LEIGH YAWKEY WOODSON ART MUSEUM LIBRARY*, 700 N 12th St, 54403-5007. SAN 326-5161. Tel: 715-845-7010. FAX: 715-845-7103. E-mail: museum@lywam.org. Web Site: www.lywam.org. *Librn,* Kathryn Piffl
Library Holdings: Bk Titles 1,800; Per Subs 30
Subject Interests: Birds, Decorative art
Restriction: Open by appt only

WAUTOMA

P   WAUTOMA PUBLIC LIBRARY*, 410 W Main St, 54982-5415. (Mail add: PO Box 269, 54982-0269), SAN 318-451X. Tel: 920-787-2988. FAX: 920-787-7786. Web Site: www.wautomalibrary.org. *Dir,* Mary Elizabeth Knuth; E-mail: knuth@wautomalibrary.org; Staff 3.2 (Non-MLS 3.2)
Pop 9,200; Circ 109,446
Library Holdings: Bk Vols 25,000; Per Subs 78
Automation Activity & Vendor Info: (OPAC) SirsiDynix
Database Vendor: SirsiDynix
Wireless access
Mem of Winnefox Library System
Open Mon-Fri 9-6, Sat 10-3
Friends of the Library Group

WAUWATOSA

R   BETHANY-CALVARY UNITED METHODIST CHURCH LIBRARY*, 7265 W Center St, 53210-1129. SAN 318-4528. Tel: 414-258-2868. FAX: 414-258-4171. *Librn,* Leslie Karabon
Library Holdings: Bk Titles 500
Subject Interests: Relig studies
Open Mon-Fri 8-3, Sun 8-12

P   WAUWATOSA PUBLIC LIBRARY*, 7635 W North Ave, 53213-1718. SAN 318-4544. Tel: 414-471-8484. Reference Tel: 414-471-8485. Administration Tel: 414-471-8487. FAX: 414-479-8984. E-mail: tosa.mail@mcfls.org. Web Site: tpublib.fp.execpc.com. *Dir,* Mary Murphy; E-mail: mary.murphy@mcfls.org; *Asst Dir,* Shawn Duffy; *Ch,* Ann Kriegisch; *Ref,* Jess Brown; Staff 12 (MLS 9, Non-MLS 3)
Founded 1886. Pop 49,300; Circ 834,000
Library Holdings: AV Mats 22,000; Bk Vols 227,000; Per Subs 302
Special Collections: Oral History
Automation Activity & Vendor Info: (Acquisitions) Innovative Interfaces, Inc; (Cataloging) Innovative Interfaces, Inc; (Circulation) Innovative Interfaces, Inc; (OPAC) Innovative Interfaces, Inc
Database Vendor: Alexander Street Press, EBSCO Auto Repair Reference, EBSCO Information Services, EBSCOhost, ProQuest, Standard & Poor's, ValueLine, Wilson - Wilson Web, World Book Online
Wireless access
Function: Homebound delivery serv, Prog for children & young adult, Ref serv available
Mem of Milwaukee County Federated Library System
Partic in Wisconsin Library Services
Open Mon-Thurs 9-9, Fri & Sat 9-5 (Summer 9-1), Sun 1-4 (Oct-Apr)

WEBSTER

P   LARSEN FAMILY PUBLIC LIBRARY*, Burnett Community Library, 7401 W Main St, 54893-8209. (Mail add: PO Box 510, 54893-0510), SAN 376-6136. Tel: 715-866-7697. FAX: 715-866-8842. Web Site: webster.wislib.org. *Dir,* Patti Meyer; E-mail: pmeyer@webster.nwls.lib.wi.us; *Librn,* Desiree Steinberg; E-mail: dsteinberg@webster.nwls.lib.wi.us
Founded 1992. Pop 5,250; Circ 15,000
Library Holdings: Bk Vols 20,193; Per Subs 68
Automation Activity & Vendor Info: (Acquisitions) Innovative Interfaces, Inc; (Cataloging) Innovative Interfaces, Inc; (Circulation) Innovative Interfaces, Inc; (OPAC) Innovative Interfaces, Inc
Mem of Northern Waters Library Service
Open Mon & Wed 10-7, Tues & Thurs 12-6, Fri 10-4, Sat 10-1
Friends of the Library Group

WEST ALLIS

M   AURORA WEST ALLIS MEDICAL CENTER*, Ziebert Medical Library, 8901 W Lincoln Ave, 53227-0901. SAN 318-4579. Tel: 414-328-7910. FAX: 414-328-7912. E-mail: ziebert.library@aurora.org. Web Site: www.aurorahealthcare.org. *Lead Librn,* Sandra Karnold; E-mail: sandra.karnold@aurora.org; Staff 2 (MLS 1, Non-MLS 1)
Library Holdings: Bk Titles 600; Per Subs 100
Wireless access
Partic in Southeastern Wisconsin Health Science Library Consortium

R   HOLY TRINITY LUTHERAN CHURCH LIBRARY*, 11709 W Cleveland Ave, 53227-2901. SAN 318-4552. Tel: 414-321-0700. FAX: 414-321-5530. *Librn,* Janice Blaney
Founded 1960
Library Holdings: Bk Titles 5,016; Videos 235
Subject Interests: Lutheran church statements on social issues, Teaching pictures
Open Sun 9-12

J   MILWAUKEE AREA TECHNICAL COLLEGE*, West Allis Campus Library, 1200 S 71st St, Rm 213, 53214-3110. SAN 318-4560. Tel: 414-456-5392. Reference Tel: 414-456-5214. FAX: 414-456-5413. Web

Site: www.library.matc.edu. *Campus Librn*, Martin Liddy; E-mail: liddym@matc.edu; *Circ, Tech Serv*, Carol Henschel; Tel: 414-456-5393, E-mail: henschec@matc.edu; Staff 2 (Non-MLS 2)
Library Holdings: Bk Vols 16,000
Subject Interests: Design, Electronic systs, Funeral serv, Hotel, Interior design, Liberal arts, Motel mgt, Sci
Automation Activity & Vendor Info: (Cataloging) Innovative Interfaces, Inc; (Circulation) Innovative Interfaces, Inc; (OPAC) Innovative Interfaces, Inc
Partic in Library Council of Southeastern Wisconsin, Inc
Open Mon-Thurs 7:45am-8:30pm, Fri 7:45-4, Sat 10-2

P   WEST ALLIS PUBLIC LIBRARY*, 7421 W National Ave, 53214-4699. SAN 365-1304. Tel: 414-302-8503. Reference Tel: 414-302-8500. Administration Tel: 414-302-8501. FAX: 414-302-8545. TDD: 414-302-8540. Web Site: www.ci.west-allis.wi.us/library. *Dir*, Michael Koszalka; E-mail: mkoszalka@ci.west-allis.wi.us; Staff 8 (MLS 8)
Founded 1898. Pop 60,607; Circ 747,463
Library Holdings: AV Mats 25,627; Electronic Media & Resources 38; Bk Vols 215,767; Per Subs 372
Automation Activity & Vendor Info: (Acquisitions) Innovative Interfaces, Inc; (Cataloging) Innovative Interfaces, Inc; (Circulation) Innovative Interfaces, Inc; (OPAC) Innovative Interfaces, Inc; (Serials) Innovative Interfaces, Inc
Database Vendor: EBSCOhost, Gale Cengage Learning
Mem of Milwaukee County Federated Library System
Partic in OCLC Online Computer Library Center, Inc
Special Services for the Deaf - TTY equip
Special Services for the Blind - Assistive/Adapted tech devices, equip & products
Open Mon & Wed 9-9, Tues & Thurs 12-9, Fri & Sat 9-6, Sun (Oct-April) 1-5
Friends of the Library Group

WEST BEND

J   MORAINE PARK TECHNICAL COLLEGE*, West Bend Campus Library, 2151 N Main St, 53090-1598. SAN 318-4587. Tel: 262-334-3413, Ext 5759. FAX: 262-335-5829. *Ref Librn*, Richard Huebschman; E-mail: rhuebschman@morainepark.edu
Founded 1969
Library Holdings: Bk Titles 5,000; Bk Vols 12,000; Per Subs 150
Subject Interests: Adult basic educ, Computer sci, Indust, Mkt, Nursing, Trade
Automation Activity & Vendor Info: (Acquisitions) Ex Libris Group; (Cataloging) Ex Libris Group; (Circulation) Ex Libris Group; (Course Reserve) Ex Libris Group; (ILL) Ex Libris Group; (Media Booking) Ex Libris Group; (OPAC) Ex Libris Group; (Serials) Ex Libris Group
Partic in Fox River Valley Area Library Consortium; Mid-Wis Multi-type Libr
Open Mon-Thurs 8-9:30, Fri 8-4, Sat 9-Noon

J   UNIVERSITY OF WISCONSIN*, Washington County Library, 400 University Dr, 53095-3619. SAN 318-4595. Tel: 262-335-5206. FAX: 262-335-5220. Web Site: washington.uwc.edu/library/. *Dir*, Marc Boucher; Tel: 262-335-5214, E-mail: marc.boucher@uwc.edu; *Assoc Librn*, Ruth Maschmeier; E-mail: ruth.mashmeier@uwc.edu; *Assoc Librn*, Renee Sikma; Tel: 262-335-5248, E-mail: renee.sikma@uwc.edu; Staff 2 (MLS 2)
Founded 1968. Enrl 900; Fac 29; Highest Degree: Associate
Library Holdings: Bk Titles 43,124; Per Subs 150
Special Collections: Indians of North America Coll; International Folk Music Coll
Automation Activity & Vendor Info: (Acquisitions) Ex Libris Group; (Cataloging) Ex Libris Group; (Circulation) Ex Libris Group; (Course Reserve) Ex Libris Group; (OPAC) Ex Libris Group
Database Vendor: EBSCOhost, LexisNexis, ProQuest, Wilson - Wilson Web
Partic in Coun of Univ of Wis Librs; OCLC Online Computer Library Center, Inc
Open Mon-Thurs (Winter) 8am-10pm, Fri 8-4:30, Sun 12:30-4:30; Mon-Thurs (Summer) 10-6

P   WEST BEND COMMUNITY MEMORIAL LIBRARY*, 630 Poplar St, 53095-3380. SAN 318-4617. Tel: 262-335-5151. Reference Tel: 262-335-5152. FAX: 262-335-5150. Reference FAX: 262-335-5169. E-mail: libref@west-bendlibrary.org. Web Site: www.west-bendlibrary.org. *Dir*, John Reid; Tel: 262-335-5151, Ext 125; Staff 29 (MLS 8, Non-MLS 21)
Founded 1901. Pop 50,000; Circ 555,531
Library Holdings: Bk Titles 103,500; Bk Vols 125,251; Per Subs 360
Database Vendor: SirsiDynix
Wireless access
Mem of Mid-Wisconsin Federated Library System
Open Mon-Thurs (Winter) 9-9, Fri 9-7, Sat 9-4; Mon-Thurs (Summer) 9-9, Fri 9-6, Sat 9-1

WESTBORO

P   WESTBORO PUBLIC LIBRARY*, W4941 Center St, 54490. (Mail add: PO Box 100, 54490), SAN 318-4641. Tel: 715-427-5864. FAX: 715-427-5354. *Dir*, Debbie Meier; E-mail: dmeier@wvls.lib.wi.us
Founded 1947. Pop 900; Circ 9,000
Library Holdings: Bk Titles 7,000; Per Subs 40
Automation Activity & Vendor Info: (Cataloging) Horizon; (Circulation) Horizon; (OPAC) Horizon
Database Vendor: netLibrary, ProQuest
Mem of Wisconsin Valley Library Service
Open Tues-Thurs 11-7, Sat 9-12

WESTBY

P   BEKKUM MEMORIAL LIBRARY*, 206 N Main St, 54667-1108. SAN 318-465X. Tel: 608-634-4419. FAX: 608-634-6429. E-mail: bekkuml@wrlsweb.org. Web Site: www.wrlsweb.org. *Dir*, Cindy Brown
Pop 3,000; Circ 35,000
Library Holdings: Bk Vols 15,000; Per Subs 98
Automation Activity & Vendor Info: (Cataloging) Horizon; (Circulation) Horizon
Mem of Winding Rivers Library System
Open Mon-Fri 11-8, Sat & Sun 1-4

WESTFIELD

P   WESTFIELD PUBLIC LIBRARY*, Ethel Everhard Memorial Library, 117 E Third St, 53964-9107. (Mail add: PO Box 355, 53964-0355), SAN 318-4668. Tel: 608-296-2544. FAX: 608-296-2622. Web Site: www.westfieldlibrary.org. *Dir*, Marie Boleman; E-mail: boleman@westfieldlibrary.org
Pop 3,948; Circ 25,451
Library Holdings: Bk Vols 13,000; Per Subs 38
Subject Interests: Wis
Automation Activity & Vendor Info: (Cataloging) SirsiDynix; (Circulation) SirsiDynix; (OPAC) SirsiDynix
Mem of Winnefox Library System
Partic in Midwest Collaborative for Library Services (MCLS)
Open Mon-Thurs 9-6, Fri & Sat 9-12
Friends of the Library Group

WEYAUWEGA

P   WEYAUWEGA PUBLIC LIBRARY*, 301 S Mill St, 54983. (Mail add: PO Box 6, 54983-0006), SAN 318-4676. Tel: 920-867-3742. FAX: 920-867-3741. E-mail: wey@mail.owls.lib.wi.us. Web Site: www.wegalibrary.org. *Dir*, Kristi E Pennebecker; E-mail: kpennebe@mail.owls.lib.wi.us; *Ch*, Kelly Kneisler; Staff 1 (Non-MLS 1)
Founded 1912. Pop 3,500; Circ 48,000
Jan 2009-Dec 2009 Income $133,707, City $99,915, County $33,792. Mats Exp $16,095, Books $10,000, Per/Ser (Incl. Access Fees) $1,100, AV Equip $150, AV Mat $4,000, Electronic Ref Mat (Incl. Access Fees) $845. Sal $65,000
Library Holdings: Bk Vols 20,000; Per Subs 70
Wireless access
Mem of Outagamie Waupaca Library System
Open Mon-Thurs 9:30-6, Fri 9:30-5, Sat 9:30-3

WHITEFISH BAY

P   WHITEFISH BAY PUBLIC LIBRARY*, 5420 N Marlborough Dr, 53217. SAN 318-2568. Tel: 414-964-4380. FAX: 414-964-5733. Web Site: www.wfblibrary.org. *Dir*, Kristen Hewitt; E-mail: k.hewitt@wfblibrary.org; *Librn*, Amy Krahn; *Ch*, Ann Piehl; *Circ*, Jennifer Williams; E-mail: jwilliams@wfblibrary.org; *Reader Serv*, Elke Saylor; E-mail: elkes@wfblibrary.org; Staff 9 (MLS 4, Non-MLS 5)
Founded 1936. Pop 13,999; Circ 262,158
Library Holdings: Bk Vols 72,000; Per Subs 144
Subject Interests: Local hist
Automation Activity & Vendor Info: (Cataloging) Innovative Interfaces, Inc; (Circulation) Innovative Interfaces, Inc; (OPAC) Innovative Interfaces, Inc
Wireless access
Function: Ref serv available
Publications: Newsletter
Mem of Milwaukee County Federated Library System
Open Mon-Thurs 10-8:30, Fri 10-5:30, Sat 10-4, Sun (Fall-Spring) 1-4
Friends of the Library Group

WHITEHALL

P   WHITEHALL PUBLIC LIBRARY*, 36245 Park St, 54773. (Mail add: PO Box 36, 54773-0036), SAN 318-4684. Tel: 715-538-4107. FAX: 715-538-2301. E-mail: whitehallpl@tcc.coop, whtlpl@wrlsweb.org. *Dir*, Fred Nehring

Pop 3,415; Circ 14,243
Library Holdings: Bk Vols 15,437
Mem of Winding Rivers Library System
Open Mon-Fri 12-7, Sat 9:30-12

WHITEWATER

C UNIVERSITY OF WISCONSIN-WHITEWATER LIBRARY*, 800 W
Main St, 53190. (Mail add: PO Box 900, 53190-0900), SAN 365-1398.
Tel: 262-472-5511. Reference Tel: 262-472-1032. FAX: 262-472-5727.
E-mail: library@uww.edu. Web Site: library.uww.edu. *Dir,* Joyce Huang;
Tel: 262-472-5516, E-mail: huangj@uww.edu; *Head, Circ,* Patricia Fragola;
Tel: 262-472-5673, E-mail: fragolap@uww.edu; *Head, Doc Serv, Head,
Ref,* Barbara Bren; Tel: 262-472-5521, E-mail: brenb@uww.edu; *Head,
Tech Serv,* Dianne Witte; Tel: 262-472-1022, E-mail: witted@uww.edu;
Coll Develop Mgr, Instrul Serv Librn, Ref Serv, Carol Elsen; Tel:
262-472-5751, E-mail: elsenc@uww.edu; *Instrul Serv Librn, Ref Serv,*
Kelly Hafermann; Tel: 262-472-5525, E-mail: hafermak@uww.edu; *Instrul
Serv Librn, Ref Serv,* Ronna Hoeper; Tel: 262-472-5522, E-mail:
hoeperr@uww.edu; *Instrul Serv Librn, Ref Serv,* Kyle Naff; Tel:
262-472-5519, E-mail: naffk@uww.edu; *Instrul Serv Librn, Ref Serv,*
Martha Stephenson; Tel: 262-472-4366, E-mail: stephenm@uww.edu;
Automation Syst Coordr, Allan Davis; Tel: 262-472-5011, E-mail:
davisa@uww.edu; *Archivist,* Karen Weston; Tel: 262-472-5520, E-mail:
westonk@uww.edu; *ILL,* Joe Jaquess; Tel: 262-472-1881, E-mail:
jaquessj@uww.edu; *Ser,* Sharon Knight; Tel: 262-472-5515, E-mail:
knights@uww.edu. Subject Specialists: *Dance, Music, Performing arts,*
Patricia Fragola; *Communication, Law, Polit sci,* Barbara Bren;
Anthropology, Philosophy, Relig, Dianne Witte; *Chem, Fine arts, Geog,*
Carol Elsen; *Educ,* Kelly Hafermann; *Hist,* Ronna Hoeper; *Bus, Economics,*
Kyle Naff; *Lit, Physics,* Martha Stephenson; *Computer sci, Math,* Allan
Davis; Staff 12.5 (MLS 11.5, Non-MLS 1)
Founded 1868. Enrl 10,502; Fac 502; Highest Degree: Master
Jul 2006-Jun 2007 Income $2,214,188, State $2,174,386, Federal $29,797,
Other $10,005. Mats Exp $863,153, Books $147,074, Per/Ser (Incl. Access
Fees) $379,897, Other Print Mats $3,129, Micro $20,902, AV Equip
$2,009, AV Mat $38,318, Electronic Ref Mat (Incl. Access Fees) $259,389,
Presv $12,435. Sal $1,145,593 (Prof $603,076)
Library Holdings: AV Mats 19,732; e-books 30,629; e-journals 3,270;
Electronic Media & Resources 187; Bk Titles 488,070; Bk Vols 671,633;
Per Subs 4,816
Special Collections: Criminology (Steinmetz Coll); George A Custer
(Kenneth Hammer Coll); Local History (Area Research Center Coll): bks,
mss & archives. State Document Depository; US Document Depository
Subject Interests: Educ, Finance
Automation Activity & Vendor Info: (Acquisitions) Ex Libris Group;
(Cataloging) Ex Libris Group; (Circulation) Ex Libris Group; (Course
Reserve) Ex Libris Group; (ILL) OCLC ILLiad; (OPAC) Ex Libris Group;
(Serials) Ex Libris Group
Database Vendor: 3M Library Systems, Alexander Street Press,
Blackwell's, Cambridge Scientific Abstracts, EBSCOhost, Gale Cengage
Learning, ISI Web of Knowledge, JSTOR, LexisNexis, netLibrary, OCLC
FirstSearch, OCLC WorldCat, ProQuest, PubMed, ScienceDirect, STN
International, Westlaw, Wilson - Wilson Web
Wireless access
Function: Audio & video playback equip for onsite use, Copy machines,
Distance learning, E-Reserves, Electronic databases & coll, ILL available,
Magnifiers for reading, Music CDs, Online ref, Photocopying/Printing, Pub
access computers, Ref serv available, Scanner, Spoken cassettes & CDs,
Spoken cassettes & DVDs, VHS videos, Wheelchair accessible
Publications: Resource (Newsletter)
Partic in Coun of Wis Librs, Inc; CUWL; Wisconsin Library Services
Special Services for the Blind - Computer with voice synthesizer for
visually impaired persons; Reader equip; ZoomText magnification &
reading software
Open Mon-Thurs (Fall) 7:30am-Midnight, Fri 7:30am-8pm, Sat 9-8, Sun
1-Midnight; Mon-Thurs (Summer) 7am-9pm, Fri 7-4:30, Sat 12-4, Sun 4-8
Restriction: Authorized patrons, In-house use for visitors, Open to
students, fac & staff
Friends of the Library Group

P IRVIN L YOUNG MEMORIAL LIBRARY*, 431 W Center St,
53190-1915. SAN 318-4692. Tel: 262-473-0530. FAX: 262-473-0539. Web
Site: www.whitewater.lib.wi.us. *Dir,* Stacey L Lunsford; E-mail:
lunsford@mwfls.org; *Adult Serv, Asst Dir, Ref,* Sally Mason; E-mail:
smason@mwfls.org; *Ch,* Cathy Bloom; E-mail: cbloom@mwfls.org; Staff 3
(MLS 2, Non-MLS 1)
Founded 1899. Pop 19,000; Circ 171,639
Library Holdings: Bks on Deafness & Sign Lang 20; High Interest/Low
Vocabulary Bk Vols 100; Bk Titles 63,000; Bk Vols 65,500; Per Subs 287
Special Collections: Achen Photographs; Whitewater history
Subject Interests: Local hist, Spanish
Automation Activity & Vendor Info: (Cataloging) SirsiDynix;
(Circulation) SirsiDynix; (OPAC) SirsiDynix
Database Vendor: Gale Cengage Learning

Mem of Mid-Wisconsin Federated Library System
Open Mon-Thurs 9-8:30, Fri & Sat 9-5:30
Friends of the Library Group

WILD ROSE

P PATTERSON MEMORIAL LIBRARY*, 500 Division St, 54984-6857.
(Mail add: PO Box 305, 54984-0305), SAN 318-4706. Tel: 920-622-3835.
FAX: 920-622-5140. Web Site: www.wildroselibrary.org. *Dir,* Linda R
Steffen; E-mail: director@wildroselibrary.org; Staff 4 (Non-MLS 4)
Founded 1930. Pop 3,500; Circ 56,500
Library Holdings: Bks on Deafness & Sign Lang 10; High Interest/Low
Vocabulary Bk Vols 200; Bk Titles 15,500; Per Subs 50
Special Collections: Local Oral History on Audio Cassette & CD. Oral
History
Automation Activity & Vendor Info: (Cataloging) SirsiDynix;
(Circulation) SirsiDynix; (OPAC) SirsiDynix
Wireless access
Mem of Winnefox Library System
Open Mon-Wed 10-6, Thurs & Fri 10-8
Friends of the Library Group

WILLIAMS BAY

P BARRETT MEMORIAL LIBRARY*, 65 W Geneva St, 53191-0190. SAN
318-4714. Tel: 262-245-2709. E-mail: wmsbay@williamsbay.lib.wi.us. Web
Site: www.williamsbay.lib.wi.us/. *Dir,* Ann Becker; E-mail:
becker@williamsbay.lib.wi.us; Staff 4 (MLS 1, Non-MLS 3)
Founded 1903. Pop 2,415; Circ 70,210
Library Holdings: Bk Titles 18,006; Bk Vols 18,350; Per Subs 64
Automation Activity & Vendor Info: (Cataloging) SirsiDynix;
(Circulation) SirsiDynix; (OPAC) SirsiDynix
Mem of Lakeshores Library System
Open Mon & Wed 9-7, Tues, Thurs, Fri 9-6, Sat 10-2
Friends of the Library Group

WILTON

P WILTON PUBLIC LIBRARY*, 400 East St, 54670. (Mail add: PO Box
280, 54670-0280), SAN 318-4730. Tel: 608-435-6710. FAX:
608-435-6190. E-mail: wiltonlibrary@wrlsweb.org. Web Site:
www.wrlsweb.org/wilton. *Dir,* Karen Carr
Circ 10,130
Library Holdings: Bk Titles 14,000; Per Subs 55
Automation Activity & Vendor Info: (Cataloging) Horizon; (Circulation)
Horizon; (OPAC) Horizon
Wireless access
Mem of Winding Rivers Library System
Partic in Wiscat
Open Mon 10-6, Tues 3:30-6, Fri 11:30-6, Sat 9-11:30

WINCHESTER

P WINCHESTER PUBLIC LIBRARY*, 2117 Lake St, 54557-9104. SAN
370-7008. Tel: 715-686-2926. FAX: 715-686-2926. Web Site:
www.nwls.wislib.org. *Dir,* Cela McGinnis; E-mail:
cmcginnis@winchester.nwls.lib.wi.us; Staff 1 (Non-MLS 1)
Founded 1986. Pop 400; Circ 4,392
Jan 2007-Dec 2007 Income $28,000. Sal $16,000
Library Holdings: AV Mats 1,100; Bks on Deafness & Sign Lang 20;
CDs 25; Large Print Bks 550; Bk Titles 13,400; Per Subs 39; Talking Bks
400
Wireless access
Partic in Wiscat
Open Mon & Thurs 11-7, Sat 9-1
Friends of the Library Group

WINNECONNE

P WINNECONNE PUBLIC LIBRARY*, 31 S Second St, 54986. (Mail add:
PO Box 518, 54986-0518). Tel: 920-582-7091. FAX: 920-582-9426.
E-mail: director@winneconnelibrary.org. Web Site:
www.winneconnelibrary.org. *Adminr,* Edith Phillips; E-mail:
phillips@winneconnelibrary.org; Staff 3 (MLS 1, Non-MLS 2)
Founded 1913. Pop 2,500; Circ 68,000
Jan 2005-Dec 2005 Income $165,000, City $78,000, County $87,000. Mats
Exp $38,800, Books $24,000, Per/Ser (Incl. Access Fees) $2,800, AV Mat
$12,000. Sal $38,000 (Prof $53,000)
Library Holdings: AV Mats 1,190; Bks on Deafness & Sign Lang 50;
CDs 815; DVDs 1,680; e-books 7,270; Large Print Bks 1,000; Bk Vols
25,740; Per Subs 94; Videos 1,910
Subject Interests: Local hist
Automation Activity & Vendor Info: (Acquisitions) SirsiDynix;
(Cataloging) SirsiDynix; (Circulation) SirsiDynix; (ILL) SirsiDynix;
(Media Booking) SirsiDynix; (OPAC) SirsiDynix; (Serials) SirsiDynix

Database Vendor: EBSCOhost, Grolier Online, netLibrary, OCLC WorldCat, ProQuest, SirsiDynix
Mem of Winnefox Library System
Open Mon-Fri 10-6, Sat 10-1
Friends of the Library Group

WINTER

P   WINTER PUBLIC LIBRARY*, 5129 N Main St, 54896. (Mail add: PO Box 340, 54896-0340), SAN 318-4757. Tel: 715-266-2144. *Dir,* Susan Johnson
Pop 2,300; Circ 28,000
Library Holdings: Bk Vols 10,000; Per Subs 35
Automation Activity & Vendor Info: (Cataloging) Innovative Interfaces, Inc; (Circulation) Innovative Interfaces, Inc
Wireless access
Mem of Northern Waters Library Service
Open Mon-Fri 9-5, Sat 9-Noon

WISCONSIN DELLS

P   KILBOURN PUBLIC LIBRARY*, 620 Elm St, 53965. SAN 318-4765. Tel: 608-254-2146. E-mail: dells@scls.lib.wi.us. Web Site: www.scls.lib.wi.us/wid. *Dir,* Cathy Jean Borck; E-mail: ckborck@scls.lib.wi.us; *Youth Serv,* Charlotte Walch Davies; Staff 4 (MLS 1, Non-MLS 3)
Founded 1897. Pop 2,500; Circ 52,463
Library Holdings: Bk Titles 40,000; Per Subs 95
Special Collections: Local Newspapers from 1856 to Date, micro
Subject Interests: Hist
Automation Activity & Vendor Info: (Acquisitions) SirsiDynix; (Cataloging) SirsiDynix; (Circulation) SirsiDynix; (OPAC) SirsiDynix; (Serials) SirsiDynix
Mem of South Central Library System
Partic in S Cent Libr Syst
Open Mon-Thurs (Winter) 10-8, Fri 10-5, Sat 10-2; Mon-Thurs (Summer)10-7, Fri 10-5, Sat 10-2
Friends of the Library Group

WISCONSIN RAPIDS

P   MCMILLAN MEMORIAL LIBRARY*, 490 E Grand Ave, 54494-4898. SAN 318-4781. Tel: 715-423-1040. Circulation Tel: 715-422-5133. Reference Tel: 715-422-5136. Administration Tel: 715-422-5129. FAX: 715-423-2665. TDD: 715-422-5138. E-mail: askmcm@scls.lib.wi.us. Web Site: www.mcmillanlibrary.org. *Dir,* Ronald McCabe; E-mail: rmccabe@wctc.net; *Asst Dir,* Andrew Barnett; *Head, Adult Serv,* Eric Norton; *Head, Support Serv,* Janet Smith; *Head, Youth Serv,* Kerry Preece; Staff 8 (MLS 6, Non-MLS 2)
Founded 1889. Pop 40,000; Circ 489,554
Library Holdings: AV Mats 16,000; Bk Vols 90,000; Per Subs 250
Subject Interests: Genealogy, Local hist, Paper indust
Automation Activity & Vendor Info: (Circulation) SirsiDynix
Wireless access
Mem of South Central Library System
Special Services for the Deaf - TDD equip
Open Mon-Thurs 9-8, Fri 9-6, Sat 9-5

J   MID-STATE TECHNICAL COLLEGE LIBRARY*, 500 32nd St N, 54494. SAN 365-1576. Tel: 715-422-5470. Interlibrary Loan Service Tel: 715-422-5468. Administration Tel: 715-422-5469. Automation Services Tel: 715-422-5467. FAX: 715-422-5466. E-mail: librarywrcampus@mstc.edu. Web Site: www.mstc.edu/academics/library.htm. *Libr Serv Mgr,* Maria Hernandez; E-mail: maria.hernandez@mstc.edu; Staff 1 (MLS 1)
Founded 1967. Enrl 2,400; Fac 104; Highest Degree: Associate
Library Holdings: Bk Titles 20,500; Per Subs 348
Subject Interests: Nursing
Automation Activity & Vendor Info: (Acquisitions) Ex Libris Group; (Cataloging) Ex Libris Group; (Circulation) Ex Libris Group; (OPAC) Ex Libris Group; (Serials) Ex Libris Group
Database Vendor: Agricola, Cinahl Information Systems, EBSCOhost, Facts on File, Newsbank, ProQuest, ReferenceUSA
Partic in Wisconsin Library Services; WISPALS Library Consortium
Open Mon-Thurs (Winter) 7:30-6, Fri 7:30-4; Mon-Thurs (Summer) 7:30-5:30

S   NEW PAGE CORP*, Research Library, 300 N Biron Dr, 54494. SAN 318-4773. Tel: 715-422-2368. FAX: 715-422-2227. Web Site: www.newpagecorp.com. *Librn,* Cindy Van Ert; E-mail: cindy.vanert@newpagecorp.com
Library Holdings: Bk Vols 10,000; Per Subs 700
Subject Interests: Computer sci, Eng, Graphic arts, Paper sci, Pulp
Automation Activity & Vendor Info: (Cataloging) EOS International; (Circulation) EOS International; (OPAC) EOS International; (Serials) EOS International
Publications: From the Stacks (quarterly newsletter)
Partic in Dialog Corp; Sci & Tech Info Network
Restriction: Open by appt only, Staff use only

WITHEE

P   WITHEE PUBLIC LIBRARY*, 511 Division St, 54498. (Mail add: PO Box 147, 54498-0147), SAN 318-479X. Tel: 715-229-2010. FAX: 715-229-2010. Web Site: wvls.lib.wi.us/witheepl/. *Dir,* Loralee Petersen; E-mail: petersen@wvls.lib.wi.us; Staff 1.2 (Non-MLS 1.2)
Pop 1,590; Circ 11,000
Library Holdings: AV Mats 1,000; Large Print Bks 50; Bk Titles 9,600; Per Subs 23
Special Collections: Oral History
Mem of Wisconsin Valley Library Service
Open Mon & Thurs 12-5, Tues 12-7, Fri 10-7, Sat 10-2

WONEWOC

P   WONEWOC PUBLIC LIBRARY*, 305 Center St, 53968-9398. (Mail add: PO Box 116, 53968-0116), SAN 318-4803. Tel: 608-464-7625. E-mail: wonewoc@wrlsweb.org. Web Site: www.wrlsweb.org/wonewoc. *Dir,* Kim Dearth
Founded 1910. Pop 1,500; Circ 24,357
Library Holdings: Bk Titles 15,000; Per Subs 40
Special Collections: Wonewoc Genealogy; Wonewoc History
Automation Activity & Vendor Info: (Cataloging) Horizon; (Circulation) Horizon; (OPAC) Horizon
Mem of Winding Rivers Library System
Open Mon & Wed 9-7, Tues, Thurs & Fri 9-5

WOODRUFF

M   HOWARD YOUNG MEDICAL CENTER*, Health Science Library, 240 Maple St, 54568. (Mail add: PO Box 470, 54568-0470), SAN 327-4926. Tel: 715-356-8070. FAX: 715-356-8561. E-mail: hylib@hyhc.com.
Library Holdings: Bk Titles 1,200; Per Subs 75
Subject Interests: Orthopedics, Surgery
Partic in Greater Midwest Regional Medical Libr Network; Northwestern Wisconsin Health Science Library Consortium

WOODVILLE

P   WOODVILLE COMMUNITY LIBRARY*, 124 Main St, 54028. (Mail add: PO Box 204, 54028-0204), SAN 318-4811. Tel: 715-698-2430. FAX: 715-698-2441. E-mail: woodpl@ifls.lib.wi.us. Web Site: www.woodvillelibrary.org. *Dir,* Karen Furo-Bonnstetter
Founded 1963. Pop 3,000
Library Holdings: Bk Titles 10,000; Per Subs 20
Automation Activity & Vendor Info: (Cataloging) Innovative Interfaces, Inc; (Circulation) Innovative Interfaces, Inc; (OPAC) Innovative Interfaces, Inc
Mem of Indianhead Federated Library System
Open Mon, Wed & Fri 12-5, Tues & Thurs 10-7, Sat 9-Noon

WYOCENA

P   WYOCENA PUBLIC LIBRARY*, 165 E Dodge St, 53969. (Mail add: PO Box 913, 53969-0913). Tel: 608-429-4899. FAX: 608-429-4902. *Dir,* Mary Friesen; E-mail: mfriesen@slcs.lib.wi.us; Staff 1 (Non-MLS 1)
Founded 2005. Pop 713
Jan 2006-Dec 2006 Income $59,803
Library Holdings: AV Mats 300; CDs 130; Bk Vols 5,000; Per Subs 21
Automation Activity & Vendor Info: (Cataloging) SirsiDynix; (Circulation) SirsiDynix; (OPAC) SirsiDynix
Wireless access
Mem of South Central Library System
Partic in Library Interchange Network (LINK)
Open Mon-Thurs 9:30-12 & 3-7, Sat 9:30-12:30
Friends of the Library Group

Date of Statistics: FY 2011
Population, 2009 (est): 563,626
Population Served by Public Libraries: 544,270
Total Volumes in Public Libraries: 2,449,702
    Volumes Per Capita: 4.3
Total Public Library Circulation: 5,181,007
    Circulation Per Capita: 9.2
Total Public Library Income: $29,479,653
Source of Income:
    Local Public Funds: $27,960,519
    State Funds: $30,095
    Other sources: $1,474,569 (does not include Federal - reported below)
    Expenditures Per Capita: $52.09
Number of County Libraries: 23
Federal: $14,470

BASIN

P   BIG HORN COUNTY LIBRARY*, 430 West C St, 82410. (Mail add: PO Box 231, 82410), SAN 365-1606. Tel: 307-568-2388. Toll Free Tel: 877-768-2388 (WY only). FAX: 307-568-2011. E-mail: director@bhclibrary.org. Web Site: bhclibrary.org/. *Dir,* Julia Kelso; *Asst Dir,* Cindy Wood; E-mail: wcindy@will.state.wy.us; *Ch,* Lisa Chestnut; *ILL,* Christina Greenfield; Staff 8 (MLS 2, Non-MLS 6)
Founded 1903. Pop 12,301; Circ 71,113
Library Holdings: CDs 57; Large Print Bks 201; Bk Titles 98,304; Bk Vols 99,111; Per Subs 147; Talking Bks 802; Videos 701
Subject Interests: Wyo
Automation Activity & Vendor Info: (Cataloging) SirsiDynix; (Circulation) SirsiDynix; (ILL) SirsiDynix; (Serials) SirsiDynix
Function: Bus archives
Partic in WYLD Network
Open Mon, Thurs & Fri 10-5, Tues 10-7, Wed 10-6, Sat 9-Noon
Friends of the Library Group
Branches: 5
DEAVER BRANCH, 180 W First St, Deaver, 82421. (Mail add: PO Box 202, Deaver, 82421-0202), SAN 365-169X. *Librn,* Molly Yates; Tel: 307-664-2736; Staff 1 (MLS 1)
Pop 150
Library Holdings: Bk Titles 5,860; Bk Vols 6,000
Open Wed 4:30-6:30, Fri 3-5
FRANNIE BRANCH, 311 Fourth St, Frannie, 82423. (Mail add: PO Box 23, Frannie, 82423-0023), SAN 365-172X. Tel: 307-664-2323. E-mail: frannielibrary@yahoo.com. *Librn,* Molly Yates; Staff 1 (MLS 1)
Pop 150
Library Holdings: Bk Titles 7,610; Bk Vols 8,000
Open Tues & Thurs 4:30-6:30
GREYBULL BRANCH, PO Box 226, Greybull, 82426-0226, SAN 365-1754. Tel: 307-765-2551. Web Site: www.greybullpubliclibrary.org/. *Head Librn,* Betty Koller; Staff 2 (Non-MLS 2)
Pop 1,800
Library Holdings: Bk Titles 16,181; Bk Vols 17,012; Per Subs 20
Open Mon, Tues & Thurs 11-5, Wed 11-6, Fri Noon-4
Friends of the Library Group
HYATTVILLE LIBRARY, 2045 Hwy 31, Hyattville, 82428, SAN 373-9252. Tel: 307-469-2444. *Librn,* Cecelia Sylvester; E-mail: cwsyl@tctwest.net; Staff 1 (Non-MLS 1)
Pop 100
Library Holdings: Bk Titles 1,500
Open Fri 2-6
LOVELL BRANCH LIBRARY, 300 Oregon Ave, Lovell, 82431. Tel: 307-548-7228. FAX: 307-548-7228. E-mail: lovell@lovellwylibrary.org. Web Site: lovellwylibrary.org. *Librn,* Donna Capellen; Staff 2 (Non-MLS 2)
Pop 2,000
Library Holdings: Bk Titles 17,800; Bk Vols 18,900; Per Subs 37
Open Mon-Thurs 11-6, Fri 11-5
Friends of the Library Group

BUFFALO

P   JOHNSON COUNTY LIBRARY, 171 N Adams Ave, 82834. SAN 318-4846. Tel: 307-684-5546. FAX: 307-684-7888. Web Site: www.jclwyo.org. *Dir,* Cynthia R Twing; E-mail: ctwing@johnsoncountylibraries.org; *Asst Dir, Ch,* Mary Rhoads; Staff 9.9 (MLS 1, Non-MLS 8.9)
Founded 1909. Pop 8,600; Circ 77,993
Jul 2011-Jun 2012 Income (Main Library and Branch(s)) $701,848, City $10,000, County $685,055, Locally Generated Income $685,055, Parent Institution $6,793. Mats Exp $47,512, Books $42,803, Per/Ser (Incl. Access Fees) $4,710, AV Mat $9,290. Sal $340,232
Library Holdings: AV Mats 5,000; CDs 2,523; DVDs 2,487; e-books 20,000; Large Print Bks 1,000; Bk Vols 63,037; Per Subs 168
Special Collections: Local History Coll; Western History Coll. Oral History
Subject Interests: Wyo hist
Automation Activity & Vendor Info: (Circulation) SirsiDynix; (ILL) SirsiDynix; (OPAC) SirsiDynix; (Serials) SirsiDynix
Database Vendor: EBSCOhost, OCLC FirstSearch, SirsiDynix, Wilson - Wilson Web
Wireless access
Partic in Wyo Libr Database
Open Mon-Thurs 10-8, Fri & Sat 10-5, Sun (Sept-May) 1-4
Friends of the Library Group
Branches: 2
KAYCEE BRANCH, 231 Ritter Ave, Kaycee, 82639. (Mail add: PO Box 226, Kaycee, 82639-0226), SAN 325-3198. Tel: 307-738-2473. FAX: 307-738-2473. *Br Mgr,* Bonnie Ross; E-mail: bross@johnsoncountylibraries.org; *Librn,* Monica Brock
Library Holdings: AV Mats 796; Bk Vols 5,788; Per Subs 26
Database Vendor: 3M Library Systems, EBSCOhost, Medline, OCLC, ProQuest, PubMed, SirsiDynix, WebMD, Wilson - Wilson Web
Open Tues 1-8, Wed 1-5:30, Fri 10-12 & 1-4, Sat 2-5
Friends of the Library Group
LINCH BRANCH, PO Box 160, Linch, 82640-0160, SAN 323-8059. Tel: 307-437-6424. *Librn,* Cathy Andreen
Library Holdings: AV Mats 113; Bk Vols 7,240; Per Subs 12
Open Tues 1-5, Thurs 1-4
Friends of the Library Group

CASPER

J   CASPER COLLEGE*, Goodstein Foundation Library, 125 College Dr, 82601. SAN 318-4870. Tel: 307-268-2269. FAX: 307-268-2682. Web Site: caspercollege.edu/library. *Librn,* Michelle DeSalvo; E-mail: mdesalvo@caspercollege.edu; Staff 10 (MLS 4, Non-MLS 6)
Founded 1945. Enrl 3,460; Fac 169; Highest Degree: Associate
Library Holdings: Bk Vols 125,000
Automation Activity & Vendor Info: (Acquisitions) SirsiDynix; (Cataloging) SirsiDynix; (Circulation) SirsiDynix; (Course Reserve) SirsiDynix; (ILL) SirsiDynix; (OPAC) SirsiDynix; (Serials) SirsiDynix

Wireless access
Partic in OCLC Online Computer Library Center, Inc; Wyo Libr Database

P   NATRONA COUNTY PUBLIC LIBRARY*, 307 E Second St, 82601.
SAN 365-1843. Tel: 307-237-4935. FAX: 307-266-3734. E-mail:
reference@natronacountylibrary.org. Web Site:
www.natronacountylibrary.org. *Dir,* Bill Nelson; Tel: 307-237-4935, Ext
115, E-mail: bnelson@natronacountylibrary.org; *Pub Serv Librn,* Kate
Mutch; *Ref Librn,* Nicholle Gerharter; *Bus Mgr,* Greta Lehnerz; *Circ Mgr,*
Shelly Padilla; E-mail: spadilla@will.state.wy.us; *Commun Relations
Coordr,* Brenda Thomson; *Tech Serv Coordr,* Susan Stanton; Tel:
307-237-4935, Ext 120, E-mail: sstanton@will.state.wy.us; *Young Adult
Serv Coordr,* Jenn Beckstead; *Youth Serv Coordr,* Jerry Jones; Tel:
307-237-4935, Ext 129, E-mail: jjones@will.state.wy.us; *ILL,* Lida Vollin;
Tel: 307-237-4935, Ext 121, E-mail: natrill@will.state.wy.us; Staff 32
(MLS 8, Non-MLS 24)
Founded 1910. Pop 69,010; Circ 570,538
Jul 2005-Jun 2006 Income (Main Library and Branch(s)) $1,853,566. Mats
Exp $240,000. Sal $957,327
Library Holdings: AV Mats 19,923; Bk Vols 129,541; Per Subs 200
Special Collections: Selective Government Documents. State Document
Depository; US Document Depository
Subject Interests: Literacy, Literacy for adults, Local hist
Automation Activity & Vendor Info: (Cataloging) SirsiDynix;
(Circulation) SirsiDynix; (ILL) SirsiDynix; (OPAC) SirsiDynix; (Serials)
SirsiDynix
Database Vendor: EBSCOhost, OCLC FirstSearch, TLC (The Library
Corporation), Wilson - Wilson Web
Publications: Monthly Calendar of Events; Newsletter (Quarterly)
Partic in Wyo Libr Network
Open Mon-Thurs (Sept-May) 10-9, Fri & Sat 10-5, Sun 1-5; Mon-Thurs
(Jun-Aug) 10-7, Fri & Sat 10-5
Friends of the Library Group
Branches: 2
MARK J DAVIS JR MEMORIAL - EDGERTON BRANCH, 935
    Cottonwood, Edgerton, 82635. (Mail add: PO Box 269, Edgerton,
    82635), SAN 365-1878. Tel: 307-437-6617. FAX: 307-437-6617. *Librn,*
    Michelle Butler; Staff 2 (Non-MLS 2)
    Pop 708; Circ 2,140
    Library Holdings: Bk Vols 6,000; Per Subs 10; Videos 51
    Open Mon & Fri 11-5, Wed 1-7
BOB GOFF-MILLS BRANCH, 717 Fifth St, Mills, 82644. Tel:
    307-265-6017. FAX: 307-265-6017.
    Founded 1998. Pop 2,590
    Library Holdings: Bk Vols 4,600
    Function: ILL available, Prog for children & young adult, Summer
    reading prog
    Open Mon-Thurs 10-5, Fri 1-5
Bookmobiles: 1. Coordr, Tonya Newsome

M   UNIVERSITY OF WYOMING FAMILY MEDICINE RESIDENCY
PROGRAM*, Lange Library, 1522 East A St, 82601. SAN 370-517X. Tel:
307-233-6055. FAX: 307-473-1284. *Med Librn,* Mary V Humphrey;
E-mail: maryhum@uwyo.edu; Staff 1 (Non-MLS 1)
Founded 1978
Library Holdings: Bk Titles 232; Bk Vols 280; Per Subs 15
Special Collections: Geriatric Coll; Obstetrics & Gynecology Coll;
Pediatrics Coll; Sports Medicine Coll
Subject Interests: Family med, Geriatric, Obgyn, Pediatrics, Primary
health care, Sports med
Automation Activity & Vendor Info: (ILL) Gateway
Database Vendor: EBSCOhost
Function: Doc delivery serv
Partic in Colorado Council of Medical Librarians; National Network of
Libraries of Medicine Midcontinental Region
Open Mon-Fri 8-5
Restriction: Restricted borrowing privileges

G   WYOMING GAME & FISH DEPARTMENT LIBRARY*, 3030 Energy
Lane, 82604. Tel: 307-473-3400. Toll Free Tel: 800-233-8544 (Wyoming
only). FAX: 307-473-3433. *Mgr,* Linda Lembeck; Tel: 307-473-3402; Staff
1 (Non-MLS 1)
Library Holdings: Bk Titles 158; Bk Vols 259; Per Subs 40
Special Collections: Wyoming Game & Fish Publications; Wyoming
Wildlife Magazine
Subject Interests: Conserv, Fisheries, Wildlife
Function: ILL available
Special Services for the Deaf - Spec interest per
Special Services for the Blind - Bks on cassette
Open Mon-Fri 8-5

CENTENNIAL

S   LARAMIE SOILS SERVICE INC LIBRARY*, 26 Six Bar E Rd, 82055.
(Mail add: PO Box 7, 82055-0007). Tel: 307-742-4185. E-mail:
laramiesoilsservice@msn.com. *Librn,* Mike McFaul; Staff 1 (Non-MLS 1)
Founded 1979
Library Holdings: Bk Titles 525; Bk Vols 600; Per Subs 19
Special Collections: Geoarchaeological Reports & Related Materials,
maps, photos; Soil Samples; Volcanic Ash
Partic in Colorado Alliance of Research Libraries
Open Mon-Fri 9-5

CHEYENNE

GM   DEPARTMENT OF VETERANS AFFAIRS*, Learning Resources Service,
2360 E Pershing Blvd, 82001. SAN 318-4927. Tel: 307-778-7321. FAX:
307-778-7356. *Librn,* Kerry Skidmore; E-mail:
kerry.skidmore@med.va.gov; Staff 2 (MLS 1, Non-MLS 1)
Library Holdings: Bk Vols 1,500; Per Subs 216
Automation Activity & Vendor Info: (Circulation) SirsiDynix; (OPAC)
SirsiDynix
Open Mon-Fri 8-4:30

S   GRAND LODGE OF ANCIENT FREE & ACCEPTED MASONS OF
WYOMING LIBRARY*, 1820 Capitol Ave, 82001. SAN 327-7690. Tel:
307-630-5933. *Librn,* William Teter; Staff 1 (Non-MLS 1)
Founded 1875
Library Holdings: Bk Titles 3,680; Bk Vols 3,791
Special Collections: American History; Masonic Related Subjects;
Masonic Subjects
Function: For res purposes, ILL available
Restriction: Open by appt only, Open to pub upon request, Registered
patrons only

J   LARAMIE COUNTY COMMUNITY COLLEGE LIBRARY*, 1400 E
College Dr, 82007-3204. SAN 318-4900. Tel: 307-778-1205. Interlibrary
Loan Service Tel: 307-778-1202. Reference Tel: 307-778-1206.
Administration Tel: 307-778-1377. Toll Free Tel: 800-522-2993, Ext 1205.
FAX: 307-778-1399. TDD: 307-778-1266. Web Site:
www.lccc.wy.edu/library. *Dir,* Karen Lange; Tel: 307-778-1204, E-mail:
klange@lccc.wy.edu; *Circ,* Carolyn Cuestas; E-mail: ccuestas@lccc.wy.edu;
Ref, Paula Munoz; Tel: 307-778-1378, E-mail: pmunoz@lccc.wy.edu; *Ref,*
Maggie Swanger; Tel: 307-778-1283, E-mail: mswanger@lccc.wy.edu; *Tech
Serv,* Meghan Kelly; Tel: 307-778-1201, E-mail: mkelly@lccc.wy.edu;
Staff 11 (MLS 4, Non-MLS 7)
Founded 1969. Enrl 3,292; Fac 90
Jul 2005-Jun 2006 Income $710,000. Mats Exp $135,803. Sal $307,881
(Prof $109,577)
Library Holdings: AV Mats 31,428; e-journals 30; Bk Titles 45,078; Bk
Vols 53,075; Per Subs 240
Special Collections: Foundation Center Coll; Higher Education Prof Coll
Subject Interests: Equine, Nursing, Radiography
Automation Activity & Vendor Info: (Acquisitions) SirsiDynix;
(Cataloging) SirsiDynix; (Circulation) SirsiDynix; (ILL) Fretwell-Downing;
(OPAC) SirsiDynix; (Serials) SirsiDynix
Database Vendor: Baker & Taylor, EBSCOhost, Gale Cengage Learning,
JSTOR, LexisNexis, OCLC WorldCat, ProQuest, SirsiDynix
Wireless access
Publications: Wyoming Foundation Directory
Partic in Wyo Libr Network
Special Services for the Deaf - TDD equip
Open Mon-Thurs 8am-9pm, Fri 8-4:30, Sat 10-4, Sun 2:30-7:30

P   LARAMIE COUNTY LIBRARY SYSTEM, 2200 Pioneer Ave,
82001-3610. SAN 365-1908. Tel: 307-634-3561. FAX: 307-634-2082.
Interlibrary Loan Service E-mail: ill@lclsonline.org. Web Site:
www.laramiecountylibrary.org, www.lclsonline.org. *County Librn,* Lucie P
Osborn; Tel: 307-773-7220, E-mail: losborn@lclsonline.org; *Dep County
Librn,* Carey Hartmann; Tel: 307-773-7222, E-mail:
chartmann@lclsonline.org; *Chief Operations Officer,* Laura Block; Tel:
307-773-7223, E-mail: lblock@lclsonline.org; *Outreach Serv Librn,* Susan
Parkins; Tel: 307-773-7228, E-mail: sparkins@lclsonline.org; *Spec Coll
Librn,* Elaine Jones Hayes; Tel: 307-773-7232, E-mail:
ehayes@lclsonline.org; *Info Tech Serv Mgr,* Sue Hollingshead; Tel:
307-773-7234, E-mail: shollingshead@lclsonline.org; *Mgr, Circ & Br Serv,*
Kashawna White; Tel: 307-773-7210, E-mail: kwhite@lclsonline.org; *Mgr,
Commun & Media Relations,* Melinda Brazzale; Tel: 307-773-7225,
E-mail: mbrazzale@lclsonline.org; *Mgr, Computer Ctr & Cat Serv,* Cara
Nett; Tel: 307-773-7231, E-mail: cnett@lclsonline.org; *Mgr, Ref & Coll
Serv,* Elizabeth Thorson; Tel: 307-773-7230, E-mail:
ethorson@lclsonline.org; *Mgr, Youth & Outreach Serv,* Beth Cook; Tel:
307-773-7227, E-mail: bcook@lclsonline.org; *AV Coordr,* Kim West; Tel:
307-773-7212, E-mail: kwest@lclsonline.org; *ILL Spec,* Katie Rahman; Tel:
307-773-7233, E-mail: ill@lclsonline.org; Staff 47 (MLS 11, Non-MLS 36)
Founded 1886. Pop 86,353; Circ 887,881

Jul 2009-Jun 2010 Income $4,397,385. Mats Exp $341,500
Library Holdings: AV Mats 41,878; Large Print Bks 5,849; Bk Vols
334,464; Per Subs 416
Special Collections: Trails Coll; Western Hist Coll; Wyoming Hist Coll
Subject Interests: Genealogy
Automation Activity & Vendor Info: (Acquisitions) SirsiDynix;
(Cataloging) SirsiDynix; (Circulation) SirsiDynix; (ILL) SirsiDynix;
(OPAC) SirsiDynix; (Serials) SirsiDynix
Database Vendor: SirsiDynix
Wireless access
Publications: Annual Report; Library Newsletter
Special Services for the Deaf - Assisted listening device; Closed caption
videos
Special Services for the Blind - BiFolkal kits; Computer with voice
synthesizer for visually impaired persons; Copier with enlargement
capabilities; Large print bks; Low vision equip; Magnifiers; Recorded bks;
Screen enlargement software for people with visual disabilities; Sound rec
Open Mon-Thurs 10-9, Fri & Sat 10-6, Sun 1-5
Restriction: 24-hr pass syst for students only
Friends of the Library Group
Branches: 2
BURNS BRANCH, 112 Main St, Burns, 82053. (Mail add: PO Box 220,
Burns, 82053-0220), SAN 365-1932. Tel: 307-547-2249. FAX:
307-547-9253. *Br Mgr,* Sharon Mikesell; Staff 2 (Non-MLS 2)
Pop 2,110; Circ 10,287
Library Holdings: CDs 41; Bk Titles 7,639; Bk Vols 7,740; Per Subs 21
Open Mon, Tues & Fri 9-12:30 & 1-5:30, Thurs 9:30-7, Sat 9:30-1:30
PINE BLUFFS BRANCH, 110 E Second St, Pine Bluffs, 82082. (Mail
add: PO Box 639, Pine Bluffs, 82082-0639), SAN 365-1967. Tel:
307-245-3646. FAX: 307-245-3029. *Br Mgr,* Sharon Mikesell; Staff 2
(Non-MLS 2)
Library Holdings: CDs 42; Bk Titles 18,911; Bk Vols 19,791; Per Subs
52; Videos 119
Open Tues 8:30-7, Wed-Fri 8:30-5, Sat 8:30am-12:30pm
Bookmobiles: 1

M   UNIVERSITY OF WYOMING AT CHEYENNE*, Family Practice
Residency Program Library, 821 E 18th St, 82001-4775. SAN 321-7922.
Tel: 307-777-7911, Ext 116. FAX: 307-638-3616. Web Site:
www.uwyo.edu/chyfamprac/cheyfpr.htm. *Librn,* Valerie Vasquez; Staff 1
(MLS 1)
Founded 1950
Library Holdings: Bk Titles 601; Bk Vols 790; Per Subs 70
Special Collections: Medical Society
Subject Interests: Clinical med
Open Mon-Fri 8-5

G   WYOMING STATE ARCHIVES*, Historical Research Library, Barrett
Bldg, 2301 Central Ave, 82002. SAN 365-2025. Tel: 307-777-7826. FAX:
307-777-7044. E-mail: wyarchive@state.wy.us. Web Site:
wyoarchives.state.wy.us. *Dir,* Tony Adams, CRM
Library Holdings: Bk Vols 15,000
Special Collections: WPA Federal Writers Project, maps, newspapers, oral
histories, photographs, state & local government records. Municipal
Document Depository; Oral History; State Document Depository

P   WYOMING STATE LIBRARY*, 2800 Central Ave, 82002. SAN
365-2084. Tel: 307-777-6333. Automation Services Tel: 307-777-6339.
FAX: 307-777-6289. E-mail: refdesk@state.wy.us. Web Site:
will.state.wy.us. *State Librn,* Lesley Boughton; Tel: 307-777-5911, E-mail:
lesley.boughton@wyo.gov; *Digital Initiatives Librn,* Erin Kinney;
Intellectual Property Librn, Karen Kitchens; Tel: 307-777-7281; *Outreach
Librn,* Sara Francis; *Outreach Librn,* Chris Van Burgh; *Spec Projects Librn,*
Venice Beske; *Statistics Librn,* Susan Mark; *Bus Mgr,* Jack Willmarth; Tel:
307-777-5917; *Mgr, Libr Develop,* Jamie Markus; Tel: 307-777-5914,
E-mail: jamie.markus@wyo.gov; *Mgr, Publ & Mkt,* Tina Lyles; Tel:
307-777-6338, E-mail: tina.lyles@wyo.gov; *State Govt Info Coordr, Tech
Serv Librn,* Trish Palluck; Tel: 307-777-5913, E-mail:
tirsh.palluck@wyo.gov. Subject Specialists: *Patents, Trademarks,* Karen
Kitchens; Staff 19 (MLS 15, Non-MLS 4)
Founded 1871
Jul 2009-Jun 2010 Income $6,002,259, State $3,253,908, Federal $751,832,
Locally Generated Income $1,996,519. Mats Exp $51,000, Books $30,000,
Per/Ser (Incl. Access Fees) $15,000, AV Equip $6,000. Sal $1,635,983
Library Holdings: CDs 190; Large Print Bks 415; Bk Titles 496,850; Bk
Vols 500,000; Per Subs 348; Videos 1,470
Special Collections: State Document Depository; US Document
Depository
Subject Interests: Govt info, Libr sci, Patents, Trademarks, Wyo
Automation Activity & Vendor Info: (Acquisitions) SirsiDynix;
(Cataloging) SirsiDynix; (Circulation) SirsiDynix; (Course Reserve)
SirsiDynix; (ILL) Fretwell-Downing; (Media Booking) SirsiDynix; (OPAC)
SirsiDynix; (Serials) SirsiDynix
Database Vendor: Agricola, Baker & Taylor, CQ Press, Dialog, ebrary,
EBSCOhost, Electric Library, Gale Cengage Learning, H W Wilson,

HeinOnline, Ingram Library Services, LearningExpress, LexisNexis,
Medline, netLibrary, OCLC FirstSearch, OCLC WorldCat, Progressive
Technology Federal Systems, Inc (PTFS), ProQuest, PubMed,
SerialsSolutions, SirsiDynix, Wiley, Wilson - Wilson Web
Wireless access
Publications: Catalog of Wyoming State Grants; Outrider (Newsletter);
Wyoming Annual Report (Annual report); Wyoming Library Directory
(Annually); Wyoming Library Laws (Local historical information);
Wyoming Library Roundup (Quarterly)
Partic in WYLD Network
Open Mon-Fri 8-5

GL   WYOMING SUPREME COURT*, Wyoming State Law Library, Supreme
Court Bldg, 2301 Capitol Ave, 82002-0450. SAN 320-4286. Tel:
307-777-7509. FAX: 307-777-7240. Web Site:
www.courts.state.wy.us/lawlibrary. *Dir,* Kathleen Carlson; E-mail:
kcarlson@courts.state.wy.us; *Electronic Serv,* Kristin Karr; Tel:
307-777-6487, E-mail: kkarr@courts.state.wy.us; *Pub Serv,* Diane
Bauersfeld; Tel: 307-777-8564, E-mail: dbauersfeld@courts.state.wy.us;
Staff 4 (MLS 3, Non-MLS 1)
Founded 1871
Library Holdings: Bk Titles 3,000; Bk Vols 113,000; Per Subs 240
Special Collections: US Document Depository
Automation Activity & Vendor Info: (Acquisitions) SirsiDynix;
(Cataloging) SirsiDynix; (OPAC) SirsiDynix; (Serials) SirsiDynix
Publications: Quick Index to Wyoming Statutes Annotated
Partic in OCLC Online Computer Library Center, Inc

CODY

S   BUFFALO BILL HISTORICAL CENTER*, McCracken Research Library,
720 Sheridan Ave, 82414. SAN 318-4943. Tel: 307-578-4059. FAX:
307-527-6042. E-mail: hmrl@bbhc.org. Web Site: www.bbhc.org/hmrl.
Librn, Mary M Robinson; E-mail: maryr@bbhc.org; *Curator,* Kurt
Graham; E-mail: kurtg@bbhc.org; *Cat,* Karling Abernathy; E-mail:
karlinga@bbhc.org; Staff 4 (MLS 4)
Founded 1927
Library Holdings: Bk Vols 20,000; Per Subs 96
Special Collections: Archives, photogs; Buffalo Bill Coll, mss; Dude
Ranching; W H D Koerner Coll; William F Cody; Winchester Repeating
Arms Company Archives; Wyoming Territorial Imprints, 1866-1890;
Yellowstone National Park Coll
Subject Interests: Firearms, Mus ref mat, Native Am studies, Western Am
natural hist, Western art, Western hist, Western lit
Automation Activity & Vendor Info: (Cataloging) SirsiDynix;
(Circulation) SirsiDynix; (ILL) OCLC Online; (OPAC) SirsiDynix
Database Vendor: Dialog, EBSCOhost, OCLC FirstSearch, SirsiDynix,
Wilson - Wilson Web
Function: Archival coll, ILL available, Photocopying/Printing, Res libr,
Telephone ref
Publications: Annotated Bibliographies
Partic in OCLC Online Computer Library Center, Inc; WYLD Network
Open Mon-Fri (Apr-Oct) 8-12 & 1-5 ; Tues-Fri (Nov-Mar) 10-12 & 1-3
Restriction: Closed stack, In-house use for visitors, Internal circ only,
Non-circulating coll, Not a lending libr
Friends of the Library Group

L   PARK COUNTY BAR ASSOCIATION*, Law Library, Court House, 1002
Sheridan Ave, 82414. SAN 370-1867. Tel: 307-754-2254. FAX:
307-527-8687. *Pres,* Joseph Darrah; Staff 2 (Non-MLS 2)
Library Holdings: Bk Titles 11,800; Bk Vols 12,600; Per Subs 41
Open Mon-Fri 8:30-4:30

P   PARK COUNTY PUBLIC LIBRARY*, 1500 Heart Mountain St, 82414.
SAN 365-2149. Tel: 307-527-1880. Administration Tel: 307-527-1882.
FAX: 307-527-1888. E-mail: cody@parkcountylibrary.org. Web Site:
www.parkcountylibrary.org. *Dir,* Frances Backus Clymer; Tel:
307-527-1881, E-mail: fclymer@parkcountylibrary.org; *Librn,* Marjorie
Buchholz; Tel: 307-527-1883, E-mail: mbuchholz@parkcountylibrary.org;
ILL, Ref Librn, Carmela Conning; E-mail: parkill@parkcountylibrary.org;
Youth Serv Librn, Jessica Neiweem; E-mail:
jneiweem@parkcountylibrary.org; *Circ Mgr,* Pam Smith; E-mail:
psmith@parkcountylibrary.org; *Tech Serv Mgr,* Edie Phillips; E-mail:
ephillips@parkcountylibrary.org; *Ch,* Holly Baker; Tel: 307-527-1884,
E-mail: hbaker@parkcountylibrary.org. Subject Specialists: *Young adult lit,*
Jessica Neiweem; *Children's lit,* Holly Baker; Staff 24 (MLS 4, Non-MLS
20)
Founded 1906. Pop 27,500; Circ 293,000
Jul 2005-Jun 2006 Income (Main Library and Branch(s)) $1,029,000. Mats
Exp $94,500. Sal $608,000
Library Holdings: AV Mats 17,367; Bk Titles 148,369; Per Subs 187
Special Collections: Planetree Health Resource Center
Subject Interests: County hist, Wyo authors, Yellowstone National Park

Automation Activity & Vendor Info: (Acquisitions) SirsiDynix; (Cataloging) SirsiDynix; (Circulation) SirsiDynix; (ILL) OCLC; (OPAC) SirsiDynix; (Serials) SirsiDynix
Database Vendor: EBSCOhost, Gale Cengage Learning, OCLC FirstSearch, Wilson - Wilson Web
Wireless access
Function: Art exhibits, Audiobks via web, Bk club(s), Bks on cassette, Bks on CD, CD-ROM, Children's prog, Computers for patron use, Copy machines, Digital talking bks, e-mail serv, Electronic databases & coll, Exhibits, Family literacy, Free DVD rentals, Govt ref serv, Handicapped accessible, Health sci info serv, Holiday prog, Home delivery & serv to Sr ctr & nursing homes, Homework prog, ILL available, Instruction & testing, Mail & tel request accepted, Music CDs, Newsp ref libr, Online cat, Online searches, Orientations, Outreach serv, Outside serv via phone, mail, e-mail & web, Photocopying/Printing, Preschool outreach, Prof lending libr, Prog for adults, Prog for children & young adult, Pub access computers, Ref & res, Ref serv in person, Senior outreach, Spoken cassettes & CDs, Spoken cassettes & DVDs, Story hour, Summer reading prog, Tax forms, Teen prog, Telephone ref, VHS videos, Video lending libr, Web-catalog, Wheelchair accessible
Partic in WYLD Network
Open Mon-Thurs 9-8, Fri 9-5:30, Sat 9-5, Sun 1-4
Friends of the Library Group
Branches: 2
MEETEETSE BRANCH, 2107 Idaho, Meeteetse, 82433. (Mail add: PO Box 252, Meeteetse, 82433-0129), SAN 365-2173. Tel: 307-868-2248. FAX: 307-868-2248. E-mail: meeteetse@parkcountylibrary.org. *Br Mgr,* Laura Crossett; *Asst Librn,* Beth Roberson; Staff 4 (MLS 1, Non-MLS 3)
Founded 1927. Pop 390; Circ 23,495
Function: Adult bk club, AV serv, Bk club(s), Bks on cassette, Bks on CD, CD-ROM, Children's prog, Computers for patron use, Copy machines, e-mail serv, Electronic databases & coll, Free DVD rentals, Handicapped accessible, Holiday prog, ILL available, Mail & tel request accepted, Music CDs, Online cat, Online info literacy tutorials on the web & in blackboard, Online searches, Orientations, Photocopying/Printing, Prog for adults, Prog for children & young adult, Pub access computers, Ref & res, Ref serv in person, Spoken cassettes & CDs, Spoken cassettes & DVDs, Story hour, Summer reading prog, Tax forms, Teen prog, Telephone ref, VHS videos, Web-catalog, Wheelchair accessible
Open Mon, Tues, Thurs & Fri 7:45-4:15, Wed 7:45-4:15 & 6-8; Mon-Fri (Summer) 8-4
Friends of the Library Group
POWELL BRANCH, 217 E Third, Powell, 82435-1903, SAN 365-2203. Tel: 307-754-8828. FAX: 307-754-8824. E-mail: powell@parkcountylibrary.org; *Br Librn,* Lisa Printz; E-mail: lprintz@parkcountylibrary.org; *Adult Serv, ILL,* Maggie Sullivan; E-mail: msullivan@parkcountylibrary.org; *AV,* Jo Ann Norlin; E-mail: jnorlin@parkcountylibrary.org; *Ch,* Position Currently Open; Staff 8 (MLS 1, Non-MLS 7)
Founded 1911. Pop 4,500; Circ 67,130
Automation Activity & Vendor Info: (Acquisitions) OCLC
Database Vendor: LexisNexis, Medline, netLibrary, OCLC WorldCat, ProQuest, PubMed, SirsiDynix
Function: Accelerated reader prog, Adult bk club, Art exhibits, Audio & video playback equip for onsite use, Audiobks via web, AV serv, Bks on cassette, Bks on CD, Children's prog, Computer training, Computers for patron use, Copy machines, e-mail & chat, Electronic databases & coll, Equip loans & repairs, Exhibits, Free DVD rentals, Genealogy discussion group, Handicapped accessible, Holiday prog, Home delivery & serv to Sr ctr & nursing homes, ILL available, Instruction & testing, Magnifiers for reading, Music CDs, Online cat, Online ref, Online searches, Outreach serv, Outside serv via phone, mail, e-mail & web, Photocopying/Printing, Preschool outreach, Prog for adults, Prog for children & young adult, Pub access computers, Ref serv available, Ref serv in person, Referrals accepted, Res performed for a fee, Senior outreach, Serves mentally handicapped consumers, Story hour, Summer reading prog, Tax forms, Teen prog, VHS videos, Wheelchair accessible
Special Services for the Deaf - Bks on deafness & sign lang; Sign lang interpreter upon request for prog
Special Services for the Blind - Audio mat; Bks available with recordings; Bks on cassette; Bks on CD; Large print bks; Magnifiers; Playaways (bks on MP3)
Open Mon & Thurs 9-8, Tues, Wed & Fri 9-5:30, Sat 9-1
Friends of the Library Group

CROWHEART

P   CROWHEART PUBLIC LIBRARY*, 33 Old Yellowstone Hwy, 82512. (Mail add: PO Box 606, 82512-0606). Tel: 307-486-2280. E-mail: crowheartlibrary@wyoming.com. *Mgr,* Kaye Stoll; *Asst Librn,* Jane Maller; *Asst Librn,* Alicia Rux
Library Holdings: Bk Titles 500
Open Mon & Fri 5:30pm-8:30pm, Wed 10-2

DOUGLAS

P   CONVERSE COUNTY LIBRARY*, 300 Walnut St, 82633. SAN 365-2238. Tel: 307-358-3644. FAX: 307-358-6743. Web Site: conversecountylibrary.com, www.conversecountylibrary.org. *Dir,* Karen Hopkins; E-mail: khopkins@conversecountylibrary.org; *Ch,* Erika Mariner; E-mail: emariner@conversecountylibrary.org; *YA Librn,* Ian Lindeman; E-mail: ilindeman@conversecountylibrary.org; *Circ, ILL,* Cinnamon Hopkins; E-mail: cinnamon@conversecountylibrary.org; *Tech Serv,* Donna Rusk; E-mail: drusk@conversecountylibrary.org; Staff 13 (Non-MLS 13)
Founded 1905. Pop 13,578; Circ 88,883
Jul 2009-Jun 2010 Income (Main Library and Branch(s)) $787,049. Mats Exp $111,029, Books $52,355, Per/Ser (Incl. Access Fees) $6,650, Micro $40, AV Mat $40,096, Electronic Ref Mat (Incl. Access Fees) $11,888. Sal $334,390
Library Holdings: Audiobooks 4,268; DVDs 3,294; e-books 5,135; Bk Vols 56,218; Per Subs 174
Special Collections: Doris Shannon Garst Coll; Wyoming & Surrounding States (Western American Coll)
Subject Interests: Quilting, Vietnam conflict, Western Americana
Automation Activity & Vendor Info: (Cataloging) SirsiDynix; (Circulation) SirsiDynix; (ILL) SirsiDynix; (OPAC) SirsiDynix; (Serials) SirsiDynix
Database Vendor: Baker & Taylor, EBSCOhost, Facts on File, H W Wilson, HeinOnline, infoUSA, OCLC FirstSearch, ProQuest, ReferenceUSA, SirsiDynix, Thomson Carswell, TLC (The Library Corporation), Wilson - Wilson Web
Wireless access
Function: Adult bk club, Audiobks via web, Bk club(s), Bks on cassette, Bks on CD, Children's prog, Computers for patron use, Copy machines, Distance learning, Doc delivery serv, e-mail & chat, e-mail serv, E-Reserves, Electronic databases & coll, Exhibits, Fax serv, Free DVD rentals, Handicapped accessible, Holiday prog, Home delivery & serv to Sr ctr & nursing homes, ILL available, Music CDs, Online cat, Online ref, Online searches, Outreach serv, Photocopying/Printing, Preschool outreach, Prog for adults, Prog for children & young adult, Pub access computers, Ref serv available, Scanner, Senior outreach, Spoken cassettes & CDs, Spoken cassettes & DVDs, Story hour, Summer reading prog, Tax forms, Teen prog, Telephone ref, VHS videos, Video lending libr, Web-catalog
Publications: Bridges (Newsletter)
Open Mon & Fri 9-6, Tues & Thurs 9-8, Sat 9-2
Branches: 1
GLENROCK BRANCH, 518 S Fourth St, Glenrock, 82637. (Mail add: PO Box 1000, Glenrock, 82637-1000), SAN 365-2262. Tel: 307-436-2573. FAX: 307-436-8525. *Br Mgr,* Paul Pidde; *Ch,* Rita Heath; E-mail: rheath@will.state.wy.us; *Circ,* Trudy Martinez; E-mail: tmartinez@will.state.wy.us; Staff 3 (Non-MLS 3)
Founded 1939. Pop 2,234
Library Holdings: Bk Vols 16,348; Per Subs 55
Function: ILL available
Open Mon, Wed & Fri 10-5, Tues & Thurs 10-8, Sat 10-1

ENCAMPMENT

S   GRAND ENCAMPMENT MUSEUM, INC LIBRARY*, 807 Barnett Ave, 82325. (Mail add: PO Box 43, 82325-0043), SAN 373-3092. Tel: 307-327-5308. E-mail: gemuseum@aol.com. Web Site: www.grandencampmentmuseum.org. *In Charge,* Candy Moulton; Staff 19 (MLS 1, Non-MLS 18)
Founded 1964
Library Holdings: Bk Titles 300
Subject Interests: Hist, Wyo
Function: For res purposes, Photocopying/Printing, Res libr
Open Mon-Sat 10-5, Sun (Summer) 1-5
Restriction: In-house use for visitors, Open to pub for ref only

ETHETE

J   WIND RIVER TRIBAL COLLEGE LIBRARY*, 533 Ethete Rd, 82520. (Mail add: PO Box 8300, 82520). Tel: 307-335-8243. Toll Free Tel: 866-701-8385. FAX: 307-335-8148. Web Site: www.wrtribalcollege.com. *Librn,* Helen Knudsen; E-mail: hknudsen@windrivertc.org; Staff 1 (MLS 1)
Founded 2002. Enrl 65; Fac 18; Highest Degree: Associate
Library Holdings: AV Mats 35; Bk Titles 4,500; Bk Vols 5,000; Talking Bks 12
Special Collections: Biography Coll; English Language Coll-Rhetoric & Grammar; History Coll; US Government Coll
Automation Activity & Vendor Info: (OPAC) Surpass
Partic in WYLD Network
Open Mon-Fri 8am-9pm

EVANSTON

P UINTA COUNTY LIBRARY*, 701 Main St, 82930. SAN 365-2297. Tel: 307-789-2770. Reference Tel: 307-789-1328. FAX: 307-789-0148. Web Site: www.uintalibrary.org. *Dir,* Dale E Collum; Tel: 307-789-5227, E-mail: dcollum@uintalibrary.org; *Adult Serv,* Claire Francis; E-mail: cfrancis@uintalibrary.org; *Ch,* Michelle Kallas; Tel: 307-789-1329, E-mail: mkallas@uintalibrary.org; *Circ,* Kathy Kallas; E-mail: kkallas@uintalibrary.org; Staff 28 (MLS 3, Non-MLS 25)
Founded 1904. Pop 21,285; Circ 147,488
Library Holdings: Bk Vols 89,536; Per Subs 249
Subject Interests: Nat parks of western US, Western Americana
Automation Activity & Vendor Info: (Cataloging) SirsiDynix; (Circulation) SirsiDynix; (OPAC) SirsiDynix; (Serials) SirsiDynix
Database Vendor: EBSCOhost, OCLC FirstSearch, SirsiDynix, Wilson - Wilson Web
Wireless access
Partic in WYLD Network
Open Mon-Thurs 9-7, Fri & Sat 9-5
Branches: 2
LYMAN BRANCH, 204 E Sage, Lyman, 82937. (Mail add: PO Box 839, Lyman, 82937-0839). Tel: 307-787-6556. FAX: 307-787-6339. E-mail: lymanlib@bvea.net. *Br Mgr,* Susan Worthen; E-mail: sworthen@uintalibrary.org; Staff 2 (Non-MLS 2)
Founded 1916. Pop 1,700; Circ 36,470
Library Holdings: Bk Vols 15,583; Per Subs 62
Automation Activity & Vendor Info: (Acquisitions) SirsiDynix
Open Mon-Thurs 10-7, Fri 10-4, Sat 10-2
MOUNTAIN VIEW BRANCH, Second & Cedar St, Mountain View, 82939. (Mail add: PO Box 530, Mountain View, 82939-0530), SAN 365-2351. Tel: 307-782-3161. FAX: 307-782-6640. E-mail: mtviewlib@bvea.net. *Br Mgr,* Nita Duncan; E-mail: nduncan@uintalibrary.org; Staff 2 (Non-MLS 2)
Founded 1940. Pop 1,182; Circ 44,388
Library Holdings: Bk Vols 16,943; Per Subs 46
Open Mon-Thurs 10-7, Fri 10-5, Sat 10-2

M WYOMING STATE HOSPITAL LIBRARY*, 831 Hwy 150 S, 82930-5340. (Mail add: PO Box 177, 82931-0177), SAN 318-496X. Tel: 307-789-3464, Ext 785. FAX: 307-789-7373. *Librn,* William L Matchinski; Staff 2 (MLS 2)
Founded 1890
Library Holdings: Bk Vols 4,500; Per Subs 40
Subject Interests: Med, Psychiat, Psychol
Open Mon-Fri 8-5

F E WARREN AFB

A UNITED STATES AIR FORCE*, Francis E Warren Air Force Base Library, Bldg 214, 7205 Randall Ave, 82005-2988. SAN 365-2386. Tel: 307-773-3416. FAX: 307-773-4515. *Supvr, Libr Ref,* Nicole Bejcek; Staff 2 (MLS 1, Non-MLS 1)
Library Holdings: Bk Titles 46,154; Bk Vols 47,164; Per Subs 75; Videos 2,500
Automation Activity & Vendor Info: (Cataloging) Softlink America; (Circulation) Softlink America
Wireless access
Open Mon, Wed & Fri 10-7, Tues & Thurs 10-8, Sat 10-6

GILLETTE

M CAMPBELL COUNTY MEMORIAL HOSPITAL LIBRARY*, 501 S Burma, 82716-3426. (Mail add: PO Box 3011, 82717-3011), SAN 371-8239. Tel: 307-688-1380. FAX: 307-688-1390. *Librn,* Michlene D Mankin; E-mail: michlene.mankin@ccmh.net; Staff 1 (Non-MLS 1)
Jul 2006-Jun 2007. Mats Exp $23,520, Books $2,000, Per/Ser (Incl. Access Fees) $16,000, Electronic Ref Mat (Incl. Access Fees) $5,520. Sal $52,000
Library Holdings: Bk Titles 2,000; Per Subs 150
Subject Interests: Mental health
Wireless access
Restriction: Staff use only

P CAMPBELL COUNTY PUBLIC LIBRARY SYSTEM*, 2101 S 4-J Rd, 82718-5205. SAN 365-2416. Tel: 307-687-0009. Reference Tel: 307-687-0115. Information Services Tel: 307-682-3223. FAX: 307-686-4009. Web Site: www.ccpls.org. *Exec Dir,* Patricia Myers; E-mail: pmyers@will.state.wy.us; *Bus Mgr,* Terri Lesley; E-mail: tlesley@will.state.wy.us; *Ch,* Marcia Cheney; Tel: 307-687-9225, E-mail: mcheney@will.state.wy.us; *Circ,* Jackie Darnall; E-mail: jdarnall@will.state.wy.us; *Extn Serv,* Pat Brose; Tel: 307-687-9228, E-mail: pbrose@will.state.wy.us; *Ref,* Ara Anderson; E-mail: aanderso@will.state.wy.us; *Tech Serv,* Lori Kirchoff; E-mail: lkirchoff@will.state.wy.us; *YA Serv,* Susan Knesel; Tel: 307-687-9227, E-mail: sknesel@will.state.wy.us; Staff 8 (MLS 1, Non-MLS 7)
Founded 1928. Pop 33,698; Circ 351,371

Library Holdings: AV Mats 27,149; Bk Vols 129,247; Per Subs 358
Special Collections: US Geological Survey Map Depository; Western Art. US Document Depository
Automation Activity & Vendor Info: (Acquisitions) SirsiDynix; (Cataloging) SirsiDynix; (Circulation) SirsiDynix; (OPAC) SirsiDynix; (Serials) SirsiDynix
Publications: Among the Stacks (Newsletter); Among the Stacks (Monthly)
Partic in OCLC Online Computer Library Center, Inc; WYLD Network
Special Services for the Deaf - High interest/low vocabulary bks
Open Mon-Thurs 9-9, Fri & Sat 9-5
Branches: 1
WRIGHT BRANCH, 305 Wright Blvd, Wright, 82732. (Mail add: PO Box 600, Wright, 82732-0600), SAN 365-2475. Tel: 307-464-0500. FAX: 307-464-0502. *Br Mgr,* Mandy Quarders; E-mail: MJQ71@ccgov.net
Founded 1978
Library Holdings: Bk Vols 8,000; Per Subs 30
Open Mon, Tues & Thurs 10-8, Wed & Fri 10-5, Sat 10-2

J NORTHERN WYOMING COMMUNITY COLLEGE DISTRICT - GILLETTE COLLEGE*, Elizabeth Kerns Daly Library, 300 W Sinclair, 82718. Tel: 307-686-0254. FAX: 307-686-0339. *Dir,* Diana Oedekoven; Tel: 307-686-0254, Ext 1453, E-mail: diana@sheridan.edu; *Info Spec,* Linda Buus; E-mail: lbuus@sheridan.edu; Staff 2 (MLS 1, Non-MLS 1)
Library Holdings: Bk Titles 6,500; Per Subs 25
Wireless access
Open Mon-Thurs (Winter) 8am-9pm, Fri 8-5, Sun 10-6; Mon-Fri (Summer) 8-5

GREEN RIVER

P SWEETWATER COUNTY LIBRARY SYSTEM, Sweetwater County Library, 300 N First East, 82935. SAN 365-2505. Tel: 307-875-3615. Administration Tel: 307-872-3200. FAX: 307-872-3203. Administration FAX: 307-872-3249. Web Site: www.sweetwaterlibraries.com. *Libr Dir,* Kinney Scott; Tel: 307-875-3615, Ext 5130, E-mail: skinney@sweetwaterlibraries.com; *Libr Mgr,* Carla Hardy; Tel: 307-875-3615, Ext 1410, E-mail: chardy@sweetwaterlibraries.com; *Acq Librn,* Janet Maez; Tel: 307-352-6660, E-mail: jmaez@sweetwaterlibraries.com; *Outreach Librn,* Barbara Killpack; Tel: 307-875-3615, Ext 1440, E-mail: outreach@sweetwaterlibraries.com; *Bus Mgr,* Barbara Kendall; E-mail: bkendall@sweetwaterlibraries.com; *Circ Mgr, Ref Mgr,* Jacqueline Kramer; Tel: 307-875-3615, Ext 1120, E-mail: jkramer@sweetwaterlibraries.com; *Mgr, Youth Serv,* Ellie Davis; Tel: 307-875-3615, Ext 1300, E-mail: eeaton@sweetwaterlibraries.com; *Cat, Tech Serv,* Carla Perez; *Pub Relations,* Brittany Wells; Tel: 307-875-3615, Ext 5300, E-mail: bwells@sweetwaterlibraries.com. Subject Specialists: *Pub relations,* Brittany Wells
Founded 1907. Pop 42,000
Subject Interests: Spanish, Western
Automation Activity & Vendor Info: (Acquisitions) SirsiDynix; (Cataloging) SirsiDynix; (Circulation) SirsiDynix; (Serials) SirsiDynix
Wireless access
Publications: The Library Link (Newsletter)
Open Mon-Thurs 9-8, Fri & Sat 10-5
Friends of the Library Group
Branches: 8
BAIROIL BRANCH LIBRARY, 101 Blue Bell St, Bairoil, 82322. (Mail add: PO Box 40, Bairoil, 82322-0040), SAN 365-253X. Tel: 307-328-0239. FAX: 307-328-0239. E-mail: bairoil@sweetwaterlibraries.com. *Br Librn,* Miles Barbara
Open Mon & Wed 3-5:30, Tues 6pm-8:30pm, Sat 9am-11:30am
FARSON BRANCH LIBRARY, Farson Eden School Bldg, 30 Hwy 28, Farson, 82932. (Mail add: PO Box 400, Farson, 82932-0400), SAN 365-2564. Tel: 307-273-9301. FAX: 307-273-9313. E-mail: farson@sweetwaterlibraries.com. *Br Librn,* Anna Smith
Open Mon-Thurs 4pm-7pm
GRANGER BRANCH LIBRARY, 60 Spruce, Granger, 82934. (Mail add: PO Box 38, Granger, 82934-0038), SAN 365-2572. Tel: 307-875-8038. FAX: 307-875-8038. E-mail: granger@sweetwaterlibraries.com. *Br Librn,* Felicia Smith
Open Tues Noon-3, Wed 4-7, Thurs 3-6
RELIANCE BRANCH LIBRARY, 1329 Main St, Reliance, 82943. (Mail add: PO Box 460, Reliance, 82943-0460), SAN 365-2610. Tel: 307-352-6670. FAX: 307-352-6670. E-mail: reliance@sweetwaterlibraries.com. *Br Librn,* Pat Moreno
Open Mon & Tues 2-6, Wed & Thurs 2:30-5:30
ROCK SPRINGS LIBRARY, 400 C St, Rock Springs, 82901-6221, SAN 365-2629. Tel: 307-352-6667. FAX: 307-352-6657. Web Site: www.sweetwaterlibraries.com/libraries/rslindex.php. *Libr Mgr,* Dan Amsberry; Tel: 307-352-6667, Ext 2410, E-mail: damsberry@sweetwaterlibraries.com; *Circ Mgr, Ref Mgr,* Kris Klute; Tel: 307-352-6667, Ext 2220, E-mail: kklute@sweetwaterlibraries.com; *Mgr, Youth Serv,* Anne Parady; Tel: 307-352-6667, Ext 2300
Open Mon-Thurs 9-8, Fri & Sat 10-5

SUPERIOR BRANCH LIBRARY, Three N Main, Superior, 82945. (Mail add: PO Box 99, Superior, 82945-0099), SAN 365-2653. Tel: 307-352-6671. FAX: 307-352-6671. E-mail: superior@sweetwaterlibraries.com. *Br Librn,* Amber George
Open Tues 8-Noon, Thurs 2-6

WAMSUTTER BRANCH LIBRARY, 230 Tierney, Lot 44, Wamsutter, 82336. (Mail add: PO Box 189, Wamsutter, 82336-0189). Tel: 307-324-9121. FAX: 307-324-9121. E-mail: wamsutter@sweetwaterlibraries.com. *Br Librn,* Joan Harris
Open Mon-Thurs 2:30-6

WHITE MOUNTAIN LIBRARY, 2935 Sweetwater Dr, Rock Springs, 82901-4331, SAN 329-6814. Tel: 307-362-2665. FAX: 307-352-6655. *Libr Mgr,* Jason Grubb; Tel: 307-362-2665, Ext 3410, E-mail: jgrubb@sweetwaterlibraries.com; *Circ Mgr, Ref Mgr,* Michelle Maser; Tel: 307-362-2665, Ext 3220, E-mail: mmaser@sweetwaterlibraries.com; *Mgr, Youth Serv,* Vicki Riley; Tel: 307-362-2665, Ext 3310, E-mail: vriley@sweetwaterlibraries.com
Open Mon-Thurs 9-8, Fri & Sat 10-5
Friends of the Library Group

HUDSON

P   HUDSON YABLONSKI COMMUNITY LIBRARY*, 208 Illinois St, 82515. (Mail add: PO Box 56, 82515-0056). Tel: 307-332-3605. FAX: 307-332-3625. E-mail: thudson@tcinc.net. *Mgr,* Mary Anne Robeson
Library Holdings: Bk Titles 11,000
Open Wed-Sat 12-5

JACKSON

GM   ST JOHN'S MEDICAL CENTER*, Medical Library, PO Box 428, 83001-0428. SAN 323-6145. Tel: 307-739-7371. FAX: 307-739-7372. *Librn,* Maureen O'Leary; *Librn,* Doreen Ward; E-mail: dvward@teton.hospital.org; Staff 3 (MLS 2, Non-MLS 1)
Library Holdings: Bk Titles 825; Bk Vols 1,112; Per Subs 101
Open Mon-Fri 8:30-4:30

P   TETON COUNTY LIBRARY, 125 Virginian Lane, 83001. (Mail add: PO Box 1629, 83001-1629), SAN 365-2688. Tel: 307-733-2164. FAX: 307-733-4568. E-mail: tetnadm@tclib.org. Web Site: tclib.org. *Dir,* Debra Adams; Tel: 307-733-2164, Ext 128, E-mail: dadams@tclib.org; *Asst Dir,* Isabel Zumel; Tel: 307-733-2164, Ext 101, E-mail: izumel@tclib.org; *Coll Develop Mgr,* Christy Smirl; Tel: 307-733-2164, Ext 260, E-mail: csmirl@tclib.org; *Communications Mgr,* Margaret Thompson; Tel: 307-733-2164, Ext 112, E-mail: mthompson@tclib.org; *Educ & Prog Mgr,* Dimmie Zeigler; Tel: 307-733-2164, Ext 229, E-mail: dzeigler@tclib.org; *Info Mgr,* Tony Goymerac; Tel: 307-733-2164, Ext 131, E-mail: tgoymerac@tclib.org; *IT Mgr,* Madeleine Mundt; Tel: 307-733-2164, Ext 143, E-mail: mmundt@tclib.org; *Patron Serv Mgr,* Adam Van Sickle; Tel: 307-733-2164, Ext 257, E-mail: avansickle@tclib.org; *Youth Serv Mgr,* D Gifford; Tel: 307-733-2164, Ext 221, E-mail: dgifford@tclib.org; *Webmaster,* Jason Lewis; Tel: 307-733-2164, Ext 109, E-mail: jlewis@tclib.org; Staff 38.5 (MLS 5, Non-MLS 33.5)
Founded 1937. Pop 21,294; Circ 321,169
Jul 2011-Jun 2012 Income (Main Library and Branch(s)) $2,939,289, County $2,665,126, Locally Generated Income $53,300
Library Holdings: AV Mats 15,754; DVDs 7,357; Large Print Bks 398; Bk Titles 96,756; Per Subs 266
Special Collections: American Alpine Club; Grant Writing (Foundation Center); Western Americana
Automation Activity & Vendor Info: (Acquisitions) FileMaker; (Cataloging) SirsiDynix; (Circulation) SirsiDynix; (OPAC) SirsiDynix; (Serials) FileMaker
Database Vendor: ALLDATA Online, Bowker, College Source, CQ Press, ebrary, EBSCOhost, Facts on File, Gale Cengage Learning, H W Wilson, HeinOnline, infoUSA, LearningExpress, netLibrary, OCLC WorldCat, Oxford Online, P4 Performance Management, Inc, ProQuest, ReferenceUSA, SirsiDynix, STAT!Ref (Teton Data Systems), Wilson - Wilson Web
Wireless access
Function: Art exhibits, Audio & video playback equip for onsite use, Audiobks via web, Bilingual assistance for Spanish patrons, Bks on cassette, Bks on CD, CD-ROM, Children's prog, Computer training, Computers for patron use, Copy machines, Distance learning, e-mail serv, Electronic databases & coll, Free DVD rentals, Handicapped accessible, Health sci info serv, Home delivery & serv to Sr ctr & nursing homes, Homebound delivery serv, ILL available, Music CDs, Notary serv, Online cat, Online ref, Online searches, Photocopying/Printing, Prog for adults, Prog for children & young adult, Senior computer classes, Spoken cassettes & CDs, Summer reading prog, Tax forms, Teen prog, Telephone ref, VHS videos, Web-catalog, Wheelchair accessible
Partic in WYLD Network
Open Mon-Thurs 10-8, Fri 10-5:30, Sat & Sun 1-5
Restriction: Non-circulating coll, Non-resident fee
Friends of the Library Group

Branches: 1
ALTA BRANCH, 50 Alta School Rd, Alta, 83414. Tel: 307-353-2505. FAX: 307-353-2473. *Br Mgr,* Gretchen Ann Notzold; E-mail: gnotzold@tclib.org; Staff 1 (Non-MLS 1)
Founded 1962. Pop 544
Library Holdings: AV Mats 280; CDs 60; DVDs 70; Large Print Bks 10; Bk Titles 4,000; Per Subs 1; Videos 150
Automation Activity & Vendor Info: (Circulation) SIRSI-iBistro; (ILL) Fretwell-Downing; (OPAC) SIRSI-iBistro
Open Tues-Thurs 12-6, Sat 10-4
Friends of the Library Group

KELLY

S   TETON SCIENCE SCHOOL LIBRARY*, One Ditch Creek Rd, 83011. (Mail add: PO Box 68, 83011-0068), SAN 327-8379. Tel: 307-733-4765. FAX: 307-739-9388. E-mail: info@tetonscience.org. Web Site: www.tetonscience.org. *Dir,* Jack Shea; Staff 1 (Non-MLS 1)
Library Holdings: Bk Titles 2,111; Bk Vols 2,290; Per Subs 23; Videos 49
Open Mon-Fri 8:30-4:30
Restriction: Non-circulating to the pub

KEMMERER

P   LINCOLN COUNTY LIBRARY*, 519 Emerald, 83101. SAN 365-2742. Tel: 307-877-6961. FAX: 307-877-4147. Web Site: linclib.org. *Dir,* Brenda McGinnis; E-mail: bmcginnis@linclib.org; *Ch,* Lora Sanchez; E-mail: lsanchez@linclib.org; *Tech Serv,* Sheryl Alleman; Staff 18.27 (Non-MLS 18.27)
Founded 1983. Pop 16,383; Circ 192,362
Jul 2006-Jun 2007 Income (Main Library and Branch(s)) $1,109,746, State $113,815, County $969,573, Locally Generated Income $1,400, Other $24,958. Mats Exp $179,128, Books $154,518, Per/Ser (Incl. Access Fees) $9,817, Micro $15, AV Mat $9,778, Electronic Ref Mat (Incl. Access Fees) $5,000. Sal $587,435
Library Holdings: AV Mats 9,478; Bk Vols 111,473; Per Subs 243
Automation Activity & Vendor Info: (Circulation) SirsiDynix
Database Vendor: EBSCOhost, OCLC FirstSearch
Wireless access
Function: ILL available
Special Services for the Blind - Large print bks
Open Mon-Wed 10-8, Thurs & Fri 10-6, Sat 10-2
Branches: 5
ALPINE BRANCH, 243 River Circle, Alpine, 83126. (Mail add: PO Box 3168, Alpine, 83126). Tel: 307-654-7323. FAX: 307-654-2158. Web Site: linclib.org/alpine. *Br Mgr,* Wendi Walton; E-mail: wwalton@linclib.org; *Ch,* Rachelle Draney; E-mail: rdraney@linclib.org
Open Mon, Wed, Fri 10-6, Tues, Thurs 10-8, Sat 10-2
COKEVILLE BRANCH, 240 E Main St, Cokeville, 83114. (Mail add: PO Box 69, Cokeville, 83114-0069), SAN 365-2807. Tel: 307-279-3213. FAX: 307-279-3263. Web Site: linclib.org/cokeville. *Br Librn,* Gayle Chadwick; E-mail: gchadwick@linclib.org; *Ch,* Lynette Nate
Open Mon 11-8, Tues-Thurs 11-6, Fri 11-4, Sat 10-2
LABARGE BRANCH, 262 Main St, LaBarge, 83123. (Mail add: PO Box 57, LaBarge, 83123-0057), SAN 365-2815. Tel: 307-386-2571. FAX: 307-386-2569. Web Site: will.state.wy.us/labarge. *Br Librn,* Marika Thayer; E-mail: mthayer@linclib.org; *Ch,* Sunny Craig
Founded 1981
Open Mon & Tues 1-8, Wed & Thurs 10-5, Fri 1-6, Sat 10-2
STAR VALLEY, 261 Washington, Afton, 83110. (Mail add: PO Box 849, Afton, 83110-0849), SAN 365-2777. Tel: 307-885-3158. FAX: 307-885-9651. Web Site: linclib.org/star. *Librn,* Marilyn Heiner; E-mail: mheiner@linclib.org; *Ch,* Teresa Newton
Open Mon, Wed & Fri 10-6, Tues & Thurs 10-8, Sat 10-2
Friends of the Library Group
THAYNE BRANCH, 117 Peterson Pkwy, Thayne, 83127. (Mail add: PO Box 660, Thayne, 83127-0660). Tel: 307-883-7323. FAX: 307-883-7324. Web Site: linclib.org/thayne. *Br Librn,* Holly Parker; E-mail: hparker@linclib.org; *Ch,* Sherry Skinner
Library Holdings: Bk Vols 3,000
Open Mon, Wed & Fri 11-6, Tues & Thurs 11-8

LANDER

P   FREMONT COUNTY LIBRARY SYSTEM*, 451 N Second St, 82520-2316. SAN 365-2831. Tel: 307-332-5194. Administration Tel: 307-332-1600. FAX: 307-332-1504, 307-332-3909. E-mail: fremontstaff@fclsonline.org. Web Site: fclsonline.org. *Dir,* Jill Rourke; E-mail: jrourke@fclsonline.org; *Libr Mgr, Mgr, Ad Serv,* Barbara Oakleaf; E-mail: boakleaf@fclsonline.org; *Ch,* Linda Willenbrecht; *ILL,* Becky Packer; Staff 1 (MLS 1)
Founded 1907. Pop 36,000; Circ 165,677
Jul 2005-Jun 2006 Income (Main Library and Branch(s)) $1,280,000. Mats Exp $101,000. Sal $556,350
Library Holdings: AV Mats 14,510; Bk Vols 187,690; Per Subs 228

Special Collections: Western Americana Coll
Subject Interests: Art, Fishing
Automation Activity & Vendor Info: (Acquisitions) SirsiDynix; (Cataloging) SirsiDynix; (Circulation) SirsiDynix; (OPAC) SirsiDynix; (Serials) SirsiDynix
Database Vendor: EBSCOhost, Wilson - Wilson Web
Wireless access
Partic in WYLD Network
Open Mon-Thurs 10-9, Fri & Sat 10-4
Friends of the Library Group
Branches: 2
DUBOIS BRANCH, 202 N First, Dubois, 82513. (Mail add: PO Box 787, Dubois, 82513-0787), SAN 365-2866. Tel: 307-455-2992. FAX: 307-455-2032. *Br Mgr, Head Librn,* Paula Sabatka; E-mail: psabatka@fclsonline.org; *Ch,* Darci Stafford; E-mail: dstafford@fclsonline.org; *ILL & Ser,* Lisa Wetmore; E-mail: lwetmore@fclsonline.org; Staff 5 (Non-MLS 5)
Pop 3,000; Circ 12,000
Library Holdings: AV Mats 1,100; Bk Vols 14,000
Special Collections: Big Horn Sheep Center Coll; Lucius Burch Local History Coll
Open Mon, Tues & Thurs 10-7, Wed 10-8, Fri & Sat 10-4
Friends of the Library Group
RIVERTON BRANCH, 1330 W Park, Riverton, 82501, SAN 365-3048. Tel: 307-856-3556. FAX: 307-857-3722. E-mail: riverton@will.state.wy.us. *Adult Serv, Br Mgr,* Gloria Brodle; *Ch,* Katy Jost; *ILL, YA Serv,* Shari Haskins; *Ser,* Sara Davis
Circ 76,019
Library Holdings: AV Mats 5,000; Bk Vols 74,979; Per Subs 150
Special Collections: Western Americana Coll
Subject Interests: Genealogy, Small bus
Open Mon-Thurs 10-9, Fri & Sat 10-4
Friends of the Library Group

G   WYOMING STATE TRAINING SCHOOL MEDICAL LIBRARY*, 8204 State Hwy 789, 82520-9499. SAN 329-0646. Tel: 307-335-6804. FAX: 307-335-6990. *Librn,* Shirley Townsend
Library Holdings: Bk Titles 500; Per Subs 11
Subject Interests: Pediatrics
Special Services for the Deaf - Bks on deafness & sign lang; High interest/low vocabulary bks; Spec interest per; Staff with knowledge of sign lang
Open Mon-Fri 7-3:30
Restriction: Staff use only

LARAMIE

P   ALBANY COUNTY PUBLIC LIBRARY, Laramie Main Library, 310 S Eighth St, 82070-3969. SAN 365-3102. Tel: 307-721-2580. Interlibrary Loan Service Tel: 307-721-2580, Ext 5422. Reference Tel: 307-721-2580, Ext 5462. FAX: 307-721-2584. Web Site: albanycountylibrary .org. *County Librn,* Susan M Simpson; Tel: 307-721-2580, Ext 5565, E-mail: ssimpson@albanycountylibrary.org; *Br Librn,* Deb Shogren; E-mail: dshogren@albanycountylibrary.org; *Br Librn,* Shirley Smith; E-mail: ssmith@albanycountylibrary.org; *Pub Serv Librn,* Kathy Marquis; 307-721-2580, Ext 5438, E-mail: kmarquis@albanycountylibrary.org; *Tech Serv Librn,* Nathan E Bender; E-mail: nbender@albanycountylibrary.org; *Youth Serv Librn,* Ruth Hitchcock; E-mail: rhitchcock@albanycountylibrary.org; *Admin Serv Mgr,* Sam Farstad; E-mail: sfarstad@albanycountylibrary.org; *Circ Supvr,* Nicole Maxwell; E-mail: nmaxwell@albanycountylibrary.org; *Pub Relations Coordr,* Caitlin White; Tel: 307-721-2580, Ext 5456, E-mail: cwhite@albanycountylibrary.org; *ILL,* Bernie Burr-Wilken; E-mail: bburrwilken@albanycountylibrary.org; *Pub Serv,* Miranda Webster; E-mail: mwebster@albanycountylibrary.org; *Tech Serv,* Rekha Agarwal; E-mail: ragarwal@albanycountylibrary.org; *Tech Serv,* Tracy Pulley; E-mail: tpulley@albanycountylibrary.org; *YA Spec,* Bailey Murray; Tel: 307-721-5459, E-mail: bmurray@albanycountylibrary.org; *YA Spec,* Laura Prestia; *Youth Serv,* Brenda Barton; E-mail: bbarton@albanycountylibrary.org; *Youth Serv,* Deborah Kassner; E-mail: dkassner@albanycountylibrary.org; Staff 4.73 (MLS 4.23, Non-MLS 0.5)
Founded 1887. Pop 32,758; Circ 190,042
Jul 2011-Jun 2012 Income (Main Library and Branch(s)) $875,430, City $17,515, Federal $2,113, County $719,063, Other $136,739. Mats Exp $57,345. Sal $503,067
Library Holdings: Audiobooks 4,529; AV Mats 4,047; Electronic Media & Resources 20,000; Bk Vols 121,719; Per Subs 396; Videos 4,111
Subject Interests: Local hist, Oral hist
Automation Activity & Vendor Info: (Acquisitions) SirsiDynix; (Cataloging) SirsiDynix; (Circulation) SirsiDynix; (ILL) Fretwell-Downing; (OPAC) SirsiDynix; (Serials) SirsiDynix
Database Vendor: Agricola, CQ Press, EBSCOhost, LearningExpress, LexisNexis, Medline, netLibrary, OCLC FirstSearch, OCLC WorldCat, ProQuest, PubMed, Wilson - Wilson Web
Wireless access

Function: Adult bk club, Audiobks via web, Bk club(s), Bks on CD, Children's prog, Computer training, Computers for patron use, Copy machines, Electronic databases & coll, Fax serv, Free DVD rentals, Home delivery & serv to Sr ctr & nursing homes, Homebound delivery serv, ILL available, Mail & tel request accepted, Music CDs, Online cat, Photocopying/Printing, Preschool outreach, Prog for adults, Prog for children & young adult, Pub access computers, Ref serv available, Scanner, Spoken cassettes & CDs, Story hour, Summer reading prog, Tax forms, Telephone ref
Publications: The Newsletter of the Albany County Public Library (Monthly newsletter)
Partic in WYLD Network
Special Services for the Deaf - TTY equip
Open Tues-Thurs 10-8, Fri-Sun 1-5
Restriction: 24-hr pass syst for students only
Friends of the Library Group
Branches: 2
CENTENNIAL VALLEY BRANCH, PO Box 188, Centennial, 82055-0188, SAN 365-3137. Tel: 307-745-8393. Web Site: www.centenniallibrary.net/. *Br Librn,* Deb Shogren; Staff 0.15 (Non-MLS 0.15)
Founded 1978
Library Holdings: AV Mats 165; Large Print Bks 17; Bk Vols 3,280
Database Vendor: ebrary, Wiley
Open Mon-Fri 11-3, Thurs 5pm-7pm
Friends of the Library Group
ROCK RIVER BRANCH, 386 Ave D, Rock River, 82083. (Mail add: PO Box 213, Rock River, 82083-0213), SAN 365-3161. *Br Librn,* Shirley Smith; Staff 0.15 (Non-MLS 0.15)
Pop 202
Library Holdings: AV Mats 315; Large Print Bks 39; Bk Vols 3,889
Automation Activity & Vendor Info: (ILL) Gateway
Database Vendor: Wiley
Function: Adult bk club
Open Wed 9:30-12:30 & 1:30-4:30

S   AMERICAN HERITAGE CENTER*, Toppan Rare Books Library, Centennial Complex, Dept 3924, 1000 E University Ave, 82071. SAN 377-0591. Tel: 307-766-2565. FAX: 307-766-5511. Web Site: ahc.uwyo.edu/about/departments/toppan.htm. *Librn,* Ann Marie Lane; E-mail: amlane@uwyo.edu; Staff 1 (MLS 1)
Library Holdings: Bk Titles 30,000
Automation Activity & Vendor Info: (Cataloging) OCLC
Open Mon-Fri (Winter) 8-5; Mon-Fri (Summer) 7:30-4:30

M   IVINSON MEMORIAL HOSPITAL LIBRARY*, 255 N 30th St, 82072. SAN 324-377X. Tel: 307-742-2141, Ext 5288. FAX: 307-721-9804. E-mail: imhlib@vcn.com. *In Charge,* Chanda Dougherty
Founded 1964
Library Holdings: Bk Titles 510; Bk Vols 690; Per Subs 42
Subject Interests: Nursing
Open Mon-Fri 8:30-6
Restriction: Staff use only

S   LARAMIE PLAINS MUSEUM ASSOCIATION INC LIBRARY*, 603 Ivinson Ave, 82070-3299. SAN 326-1220. Tel: 307-742-4448. E-mail: laramiemuseum@bresnan.net. Web Site: www.laramiemuseum.org. *Exec Dir,* Mary Mountain; E-mail: lpmdirector@bresnan.net; *Curator,* Connie Lindmier; *Curator,* Joney Wilmot
Founded 1972
Library Holdings: Bk Vols 1,000
Special Collections: Oral History
Open Tues-Sat 1-4

CL   UNIVERSITY OF WYOMING*, George W Hopper Law Library, Dept 3035, 1000 E University Ave, 82071. SAN 365-3374. Tel: 307-766-2210. Reference Tel: 307-766-5737. FAX: 307-766-4044. Web Site: uwadmnweb.uwyo.edu/lawlib. *Librn,* Tim Kearley; *Admin Librn,* Debora Person; E-mail: dperson@uwyo.edu; *Electronic Serv,* Tawnya Plumb; E-mail: tplumb@uwyo.edu; Staff 8 (MLS 3, Non-MLS 5)
Founded 1920. Enrl 235; Highest Degree: Doctorate
Library Holdings: Bk Vols 143,000; Per Subs 1,850; Videos 328
Special Collections: Roman Law (Blume Coll). US Document Depository
Subject Interests: US law
Automation Activity & Vendor Info: (Acquisitions) Ex Libris Group; (Cataloging) Ex Libris Group; (Circulation) Ex Libris Group; (ILL) OCLC; (OPAC) Ex Libris Group; (Serials) Ex Libris Group
Partic in OCLC Online Computer Library Center, Inc
Open Mon-Thurs 7:30am-Midnight, Fri 7:30am-9pm, Sat 9-9, Sun 9am-Midnight

C   UNIVERSITY OF WYOMING LIBRARIES, 13th & Ivinson, 82071. (Mail add: Dept 3334, 1000 E University Ave, 82071), SAN 365-3196. Tel: 307-766-3279. Circulation Tel: 307-766-3190. Interlibrary Loan Service

Tel: 307-766-5168. Reference Tel: 307-766-2070. FAX: 307-766-2510. Interlibrary Loan Service FAX: 307-766-3062. Web Site: www-lib.uwyo.edu. *Dean,* Maggie Farrell; E-mail: farrell@uwyo.edu; *Assoc Dean,* Lori Phillips; Tel: 307-766-3859, E-mail: lphil@uwyo.edu; *Head, Access Serv,* William Van Arsdale; E-mail: arsdale@uwyo.edu; *Head, Coll Develop,* Sandra Barstow; Tel: 307-766-5621, E-mail: sbarstow@uwyo.edu; *Head, Res & Instruction,* Jamie Kearley; Tel: 307-766-3425, E-mail: jkearley@uwyo.edu; *Head, Tech Serv,* Deborah McCarthy; Tel: 307-766-4228, Fax: 307-766-5588, E-mail: mccarthy@uwyo.edu; Staff 91 (MLS 30, Non-MLS 61)
Founded 1887. Enrl 10,538; Fac 624; Highest Degree: Doctorate
Jul 2008-Jun 2009. Mats Exp $7,261,106, Books $3,435,937, Per/Ser (Incl. Access Fees) $2,201,321, Electronic Ref Mat (Incl. Access Fees) $856,081. Sal $3,612,028
Library Holdings: e-books 56,924; Bk Vols 1,483,791; Per Subs 14,006
Special Collections: Grace Raymond Hebard Coll, maps, published mat. US Document Depository
Subject Interests: State hist
Automation Activity & Vendor Info: (Acquisitions) Innovative Interfaces, Inc - Millenium; (Cataloging) Innovative Interfaces, Inc - Millenium; (Circulation) Innovative Interfaces, Inc - Millenium; (Course Reserve) Innovative Interfaces, Inc - Millenium; (ILL) OCLC ILLiad; (Media Booking) Innovative Interfaces, Inc - Millenium; (OPAC) Innovative Interfaces, Inc - Millenium; (Serials) Innovative Interfaces, Inc - Millenium
Database Vendor: ABC-CLIO, ACM (Association for Computing Machinery), Agricola, Alexander Street Press, ARTstor, BioOne, Children's Literature Comprehensive Database Company (CLCD), Cinahl Information Systems, CQ Press, ebrary, EBSCOhost, Elsevier, Greenwood Publishing Group, H W Wilson, HeinOnline, IEEE (Institute of Electrical & Electronics Engineers), ISI Web of Knowledge, JSTOR, LearningExpress, Lexi-Comp, LexisNexis, Marcive, Inc, Medline, Modern Language Association, netLibrary, OCLC FirstSearch, OVID Technologies, PubMed, Sage, ScienceDirect, UpToDate, ValueLine, Wiley InterScience, Wilson - Wilson Web
Wireless access
Function: Archival coll, AV serv, Distance learning, Doc delivery serv, Handicapped accessible, Health sci info serv, ILL available, Online searches, Ref serv available
Publications: Check It Out (Newsletter); The Library Associate (Quarterly)
Partic in Center for Research Libraries; Colorado Alliance of Research Libraries; Lyrasis; Mid-Continental Regional Med Librs Asn; OCLC Online Computer Library Center, Inc
Restriction: Open to pub for ref & circ; with some limitations, Open to students, fac & staff
Departmental Libraries:
BRINKERHOFF EARTH RESOURCES INFORMATION CENTER, 1000 E University Ave, 82071, SAN 365-3250. Tel: 307-766-3374. Reference Tel: 307-766-3328. FAX: 307-766-6679. Web Site: www-lib.uwyo.edu/libgeo. *Interim Head of Libr,* Larry Schmidt; Tel: 307-766-2844, E-mail: lschmidt@uwyo.edu
   Subject Interests: Geochemistry, Geol, Geomorphology, Geophysics, Paleontology, Remote sensing, Sedimentology
LEARNING RESOURCE CENTER, Dept 3374, 1000 E University Ave, 82071, SAN 328-7270. Tel: 307-766-2527. Web Site: uwyo.edu. *Interim Head of Libr,* Cass Kvenild; Tel: 307-766-5119, E-mail: ckvenild@uwyo.edu
   Special Collections: NASA Regional Teachers Resource Center
   Subject Interests: Practical educ
   Open Mon-Fri 8-5
LIBRARY ANNEX, Dept 3262, 1000 E University Ave, 82071, SAN 365-3285. Tel: 307-766-6539. *Access Serv,* Toni Boughton; Tel: 307-766-6535, E-mail: tlhb@uwyo.edu; *Access Serv,* William Van Arsdale; Tel: 307-766-2499, E-mail: arsdale@uwyo.edu
ROCKY MOUNTAIN HERBARIUM REFERENCE COLLECTION, Dept 3262, 1000 E University Ave, 82071, SAN 328-7297. Tel: 307-766-2236. *Librn,* Janis Leath; Fax: 307-766-5588, E-mail: leath@uwyo.edu

LUSK

P   NIOBRARA COUNTY LIBRARY*, 425 S Main, 82225. (Mail add: PO Box 510, 82225-0510), SAN 318-4994. Tel: 307-334-3490. FAX: 307-334-3490. Web Site: niobraracountylibrary.org. *Dir,* Debbie Sturman; Staff 2.62 (Non-MLS 2.62)
Founded 1913. Pop 2,428; Circ 42,077
Library Holdings: AV Mats 5,161; Bk Titles 29,732; Per Subs 81
Open Mon, Tues, Thurs & Fri 10-6, Wed 12-7, Sun (Sept-May) 12-4
Friends of the Library Group

S   WYOMING WOMEN'S CENTER LIBRARY*, 1000 W Griffith, 82225. (Mail add: PO Box 300, 82225-0020), SAN 320-9881. Tel: 307-334-3693, Ext 244. FAX: 307-334-2254. *Librn,* Virginia Pullen; Staff 1 (Non-MLS 1)
Founded 1980
Library Holdings: Bk Titles 4,121; Bk Vols 4,280; Per Subs 10
Open Mon-Fri 5-8

MOOSE

S   NATIONAL PARK SERVICE, Grand Teton National Park Library, PO Box Drawer 170, 83012-0170. SAN 321-0189. Tel: 307-739-3592. FAX: 307-739-3443. Web Site: www.nps.gov/grte. *In Charge,* Elizabeth Maki; Staff 1 (Non-MLS 1)
Founded 1929
Library Holdings: Bk Titles 3,110; Bk Vols 3,340; Per Subs 29; Videos 11
Subject Interests: Botany, Geol, Local hist, Natural hist, Zoology
Restriction: Not a lending libr, Open by appt only

NEWCASTLE

S   ANNA MILLER MUSEUM LIBRARY*, 401 Delaware, 82701. (Mail add: PO Box 698, 82701), SAN 326-5757. Tel: 307-746-4188. FAX: 307-746-4629. *Dir,* Bobbie Jo Stith; Staff 1 (Non-MLS 1)
Library Holdings: Bk Titles 6,120; Bk Vols 6,360; Per Subs 12
Special Collections: Newcastle History; Newsletter Journal, newsp. Oral History
Wireless access
Open Mon-Fri 9-5
Friends of the Library Group

P   WESTON COUNTY PUBLIC LIBRARY*, 23 W Main St, 82701. SAN 365-3404. Tel: 307-746-2206. FAX: 307-746-2218. Web Site: will.state.wy.us/weston/. *Dir,* Brenda Mahoney-Ayres; E-mail: bmahoneyayres@westongov.com; *Adult Serv,* Judy Ann Scott; E-mail: jscott@westongov.com; *Ch,* Barrett Rich; E-mail: brich@westongov.com; *Circ Serv,* Lisa Thomas; Staff 4 (MLS 0, Non-MLS 4)
Founded 1911. Pop 6,659; Circ 57,022
Jul 2009-Jun 2010 Income $231,328. Mats Exp $17,340, Books $11,240, Per/Ser (Incl. Access Fees) $4,400, AV Mat $1,700
Library Holdings: Audiobooks 599; CDs 660; DVDs 950; Large Print Bks 835; Bk Vols 30,135; Per Subs 65; Videos 999
Special Collections: Wyoming Coll
Automation Activity & Vendor Info: (Cataloging) SirsiDynix; (Circulation) SirsiDynix; (ILL) SirsiDynix; (OPAC) SirsiDynix; (Serials) SirsiDynix
Database Vendor: Baker & Taylor, EBSCOhost, HeinOnline, LearningExpress, OCLC WorldCat, ProQuest, SirsiDynix, Wilson - Wilson Web
Wireless access
Function: Audio & video playback equip for onsite use, Bks on cassette, Bks on CD, Children's prog, Copy machines, Electronic databases & coll, Free DVD rentals, Handicapped accessible, ILL available, Instruction & testing, Music CDs, Photocopying/Printing, Prog for adults, Prog for children & young adult, Summer reading prog, Tax forms, Telephone ref, VHS videos, Wheelchair accessible
Partic in WYLD Network
Open Mon-Fri 9-6
Restriction: Non-circulating coll
Branches: 1
UPTON BRANCH, 722 Fourth St, Upton, 82730. (Mail add: PO Box 605, Upton, 82730-0605), SAN 365-3439. Tel: 307-468-2324. FAX: 307-468-2324. *Br Mgr,* Sherri Randall; E-mail: srandall@westongov.com; Staff 1 (Non-MLS 1)
Founded 1968. Pop 950; Circ 8,650
Library Holdings: DVDs 915; Bk Titles 9,250; Bk Vols 9,410; Per Subs 26
Function: Bks on cassette, Bks on CD, Computers for patron use, Fax serv, Free DVD rentals, ILL available, Photocopying/Printing, Prog for children & young adult, Pub access computers, Summer reading prog
Partic in WYLD Network
Open Mon-Fri 12-5:30

PAVILLION

P   PAVILLION PUBLIC LIBRARY*, 203 N Main, 82523. (Mail add: PO Box 278, 82523-0278). Tel: 307-856-0151; 307-857-7440. FAX: 307-857-7440. Web Site: fremontcountylibraries.org. *Mgr,* Joyce Raymond
Library Holdings: Bk Titles 1,000
Open Mon-Thurs 10-7, Fri-Sat 10-4

PINEDALE

P   SUBLETTE COUNTY LIBRARY*, 155 S Tyler Ave, 82941. (Mail add: PO Box 489, 82941-0489), SAN 318-5001. Tel: 307-367-4115. FAX: 307-367-6722. Web Site: pinedaleonline.com/library, www.sublettecountylibrary.org. *Dir,* Daphne Platts; E-mail: daphneplatts@hotmail.com; *Asst Dir,* Sukey Hohl; E-mail: sukeybook@yahoo.com; Staff 10 (MLS 2, Non-MLS 8)
Founded 1967. Pop 6,100; Circ 87,910
Library Holdings: DVDs 1,750; Large Print Bks 170; Bk Titles 63,981; Bk Vols 65,710; Per Subs 236; Talking Bks 2,200; Videos 3,000
Special Collections: Film books; Rocky Mountain Fur Trade, photogs

Automation Activity & Vendor Info: (Cataloging) SirsiDynix; (Circulation) SirsiDynix
Open Mon-Fri 10-5:30 & 7-9, Sat 10-5
Friends of the Library Group
Branches: 1
BIG PINEY BRANCH, 106 Fish St, Big Piney, 83113. (Mail add: PO Box 489, Big Piney, 83113), SAN 321-7396. Tel: 307-276-3515. FAX: 307-276-3516. E-mail: BPBranch@sublettecountylibrary.org. Web Site: sublettecountylibrary.org/BigPineyBranch.htm. *Dir,* Debi Morley; Staff 3 (MLS 1, Non-MLS 2)
　Library Holdings: CDs 22; Bk Titles 20,879; Bk Vols 22,163; Per Subs 37; Videos 57
　Open Mon & Wed 10-5 & 7-9, Tues, Thurs & Fri 10-5, Sat 10-2
　Friends of the Library Group

POWELL

J　NORTHWEST COLLEGE*, Hinckley Library, 231 W Sixth St, 82435. SAN 318-501X. Tel: 307-754-6207. FAX: 307-754-6010. Web Site: www.northwestcollege.edu/library. *Dir,* Susan Richards; E-mail: susan.richards@northwestcollege.edu; Staff 5 (MLS 3, Non-MLS 2)
Founded 1948. Enrl 1,600; Fac 102; Highest Degree: Associate
Library Holdings: Bk Titles 47,190; Bk Vols 48,351; Per Subs 396; Videos 121
Special Collections: State Document Depository; US Document Depository
Subject Interests: Country music, Heart Mountain
Database Vendor: SirsiDynix
Wireless access
Partic in Wyo Libr Database
Open Mon-Thurs 7:45am-11pm, Fri 7:45-5, Sat 11-6, Sun 2-10

RAWLINS

P　CARBON COUNTY LIBRARY SYSTEM*, 215 W Buffalo St, 82301. SAN 365-3463. Tel: 307-328-2618. FAX: 307-328-2615. Web Site: www.carboncolibrary.state.wy.us. *Dir,* Vicki Hitchcock; E-mail: vhitchcock@will.state.wy.us; *Coll Develop, Tech Serv,* Vicky Baunach; Staff 3 (MLS 1, Non-MLS 2)
Founded 1925. Pop 15,690; Circ 81,750
Library Holdings: AV Mats 3,054; CDs 90; Large Print Bks 300; Bk Vols 93,355; Per Subs 75; Videos 3,764
Automation Activity & Vendor Info: (Cataloging) SirsiDynix; (Circulation) SirsiDynix
Open Mon, Tues & Thurs 10-8, Wed 10-6, Fri 10-5, Sat 10-3
Friends of the Library Group
Branches: 7
ELK MOUNTAIN BRANCH, 105 Bridge St, Elk Mountain, 82324. (Mail add: PO Box 156, Elk Mountain, 82324-0156), SAN 365-351X. Tel: 307-348-7421. FAX: 307-348-7421. *Mgr,* Linda Runyan; Staff 2 (Non-MLS 2)
　Library Holdings: Bk Titles 15,166; Bk Vols 17,198; Per Subs 10
　Open Tues 9-11 & 2:30-6:30, Thurs 2:30-6:30
ENCAMPMENT BRANCH, 202 Rankin St, Encampment, 82325. (Mail add: PO Box 495, Encampment, 82325), SAN 365-3528. Tel: 307-327-5775. FAX: 307-327-5775. *Br Mgr,* Dawna Martin; Staff 1 (Non-MLS 1)
　Library Holdings: Bk Titles 18,191; Bk Vols 19,430; Per Subs 21; Videos 30
　Open Mon, Tues & Thurs 11-4, Wed 1-6
　Friends of the Library Group
HANNA BRANCH, 303 Third St, Hanna, 82327. (Mail add: PO Box 297, Hanna, 82327-0297), SAN 365-3552. Tel: 307-325-9357. FAX: 307-325-9357. *Mgr,* Linda Runyan; Staff 1 (Non-MLS 1)
　Library Holdings: Bk Titles 21,210; Bk Vols 22,100; Per Subs 19; Videos 51
　Open Mon 2:30-6:30, Wed 12-4, Fri 9:30-11
LITTLE SNAKE RIVER VALLEY BRANCH, 105 Second St, Baggs, 82321. (Mail add: PO Box 370, Baggs, 82321-0370), SAN 365-3498. Tel: 307-383-7323. FAX: 307-383-7323. *Mgr,* Cherl Fisher; Staff 1 (Non-MLS 1)
　Library Holdings: Bk Titles 17,177; Bk Vols 18,490; Per Subs 19; Videos 27
　Open Mon 2:30-5:30, Tues & Thurs 10-12:30 & 1:30-5:30, Wed 1:30-4 & 6-8
　Friends of the Library Group
MEDICINE BOW BRANCH, 314 Sage St, Medicine Bow, 82329. (Mail add: PO Box 279, Medicine Bow, 82329-0279), SAN 365-3587. Tel: 307-379-2888. FAX: 307-379-2888. *Br Mgr,* Bonnie Culver
　Library Holdings: Bk Titles 12,160; Bk Vols 14,292; Per Subs 11; Videos 21
　Open Tues 9:30-Noon, Thurs 9:30-12 & 1-6

SARATOGA BRANCH, 503 W Elm St, Saratoga, 82331. (Mail add: PO Box 27, Saratoga, 82331-0027), SAN 365-3617. Tel: 307-326-8209. FAX: 307-326-8209. E-mail: sarabl@union-tel.com. *Mgr,* Ruth Hackett; Staff 1 (Non-MLS 1)
　Library Holdings: Bk Titles 15,191; Bk Vols 16,811; Per Subs 16
　Open Mon, Tues & Thurs 11-7, Wed & Fri 11-2
　Friends of the Library Group
SINCLAIR BRANCH, 100 E Lincoln, Sinclair, 82334. (Mail add: PO Box 8, Sinclair, 82334-0008), SAN 365-3633. Tel: 307-324-6231. FAX: 307-324-6231. *Mgr,* Patty McCulloch; Staff 1 (Non-MLS 1)
　Library Holdings: Bk Titles 12,191; Bk Vols 13,480; Per Subs 11; Videos 16
　Open Tues 1-5, Thurs 1-5 & 6-8

S　WYOMING STATE PENITENTIARY LIBRARY, 2900 S Higley Blvd, 82301. (Mail add: PO Box 400, 82301-0400), SAN 318-5036. Tel: 307-328-1441. FAX: 307-328-7471. *Educ Mgr,* Dr Bill Schnackenberg; *Librn,* Amber Craig; E-mail: amber.craig@wyo.gov; Staff 1 (Non-MLS 1)
Founded 1924
Library Holdings: Bk Titles 4,100; Bk Vols 4,300
Subject Interests: Adventure, Sci fict, Western stories
Open Mon-Fri 7:30-4

RIVERTON

J　CENTRAL WYOMING COLLEGE LIBRARY*, 2660 Peck Ave, 82501. SAN 318-5044. Tel: 307-855-2141. Interlibrary Loan Service Tel: 307-855-2178. Toll Free Tel: 800-735-8418, Ext 2141 (Instate only). FAX: 307-855-2094. Web Site: www.cwc.edu/student_services/library/index. *Dir,* Coralina Daly; E-mail: cdaly@cwc.edu; *Tech Serv,* Kristy Hardtke; Tel: 307-855-2109, E-mail: khardtke@cwc.edu; Staff 2 (MLS 2)
Founded 1967
Library Holdings: Bk Titles 44,291; Bk Vols 45,067; Per Subs 110; Videos 239
Special Collections: American Indian Coll; Wyoming Coll. Oral History; US Document Depository
Subject Interests: Geol, Wyo
Database Vendor: ARTstor, EBSCOhost, JSTOR, ScienceDirect, Wilson - Wilson Web
Wireless access
Publications: Specialized Subject Bibliographies
Open Mon-Fri 8-5

M　RIVERTON MEMORIAL HOSPITAL*, Reference Library, 2100 W Sunset, 82501. SAN 370-890X. Tel: 307-856-4161. FAX: 307-857-3586. Web Site: www.riverton-hospital.com. *Staff Educ Coordr,* Nancy Wright
Library Holdings: Bk Titles 305; Bk Vols 390
Wireless access
Open Mon-Fri 8-4:30
Restriction: Staff use only

S　WYOMING DEPARTMENT OF CORRECTIONS*, Wyoming Honor Farm Library, 40 Honor Farm Rd, 82501-8400. Tel: 307-856-9578. FAX: 307-856-2505. *Librn,* Charlene Delaunay
Library Holdings: CDs 200; DVDs 150; Bk Vols 5,000; Per Subs 40
Restriction: Not open to pub, Staff & inmates only

ROCK SPRINGS

S　MEMORIAL HOSPITAL OF SWEETWATER COUNTY*, Media & Resource Center, 1200 College Dr, 82901-5868. (Mail add: PO Box 1359, 82902-1359), SAN 377-0575. Tel: 307-352-8433. FAX: 307-352-8173. Web Site: www.minershospital.com. *Media & Res Spec,* Kathy Tacke; Staff 1 (Non-MLS 1)
Library Holdings: Bk Titles 1,500; Bk Vols 1,750; Per Subs 160
Subject Interests: Nursing
Partic in Medical Library Association (MLA)
Open Mon-Fri 8-4:30

J　WESTERN WYOMING COMMUNITY COLLEGE*, Hay Library, 2500 College Dr, 82902. SAN 318-5079. Tel: 307-382-1700. FAX: 307-382-7665. Web Site: www.wwcc.wy.edu/library. *Dir,* Carol Brown; Tel: 307-382-1701, E-mail: cabrown@wwcc.wy.edu; *Assoc Librn, Tech Serv,* Connie Hollin; Tel: 307-382-1702, E-mail: chollin@wwcc.wy.edu; *Pub Serv,* Fern Stringham; E-mail: fstringh@wwcc.wy.edu; *Tech Serv,* Linda Halter; Tel: 307-382-1703, E-mail: lhalter@wwcc.wy.edu; Staff 4 (MLS 2, Non-MLS 2)
Founded 1959. Enrl 3,147; Fac 250; Highest Degree: Associate
Library Holdings: e-books 600; Bk Vols 65,000; Per Subs 150; Videos 330
Special Collections: Local Newspapers (Rock Springs Rocket & Green River Star), micro. Oral History; State Document Depository; US Document Depository

Automation Activity & Vendor Info: (Acquisitions) Baker & Taylor; (Cataloging) SirsiDynix; (Circulation) SirsiDynix; (ILL) SirsiDynix; (OPAC) SirsiDynix; (Serials) SirsiDynix
Database Vendor: Agricola, ALLDATA Online, American Psychological Association (APA), ARTstor, Baker & Taylor, Cinahl Information Systems, CQ Press, EBSCO Auto Repair Reference, EBSCOhost, Elsevier, Gale Cengage Learning, Gallup, H W Wilson, JSTOR, LearningExpress, LexisNexis, Medline, Micromedex, OCLC FirstSearch, ProQuest, PubMed, Safari Books Online, ScienceDirect, SerialsSolutions, SirsiDynix, Wilson - Wilson Web
Wireless access
Open Mon-Thurs 7:15am-11pm, Fri 7:15-5, Sat 1-5, Sun 5-10

SHERIDAN

GM DEPARTMENT OF VETERANS AFFAIRS*, Medical Center Library, 1898 Fort Rd, 82801. SAN 318-5095. Tel: 307-672-1661. FAX: 307-672-1652. *Librn,* Pat Carlson; Staff 1 (MLS 1)
Founded 1922
Library Holdings: Bk Titles 7,000; Bk Vols 7,500; Per Subs 200
Subject Interests: Med, Nursing, Psychiat, Psychol, Substance abuse
Automation Activity & Vendor Info: (Circulation) SirsiDynix; (OPAC) SirsiDynix
Database Vendor: EBSCOhost, ProQuest, UpToDate
Partic in Vets Admin Libr Network; Wyo Libr Database
Open Mon-Fri 7:30-4

J NORTHERN WYOMING COMMUNITY COLLEGE DISTRICT*, 3059 Coffeen Ave, 82801-1500. (Mail add: Griffith Memorial Library, PO Box 1500, 82801-1500), SAN 318-5087. Tel: 307-674-6446. Circulation Tel: 307-674-6446, Ext 2500. FAX: 307-674-3350. E-mail: library@sheridan.edu. Web Site: www.sheridan.edu/library. *Dir,* Katrina Brown; E-mail: kbrown@sheridan.edu; *Acq,* Virginia Brown; E-mail: vbrown@sheridan.edu; *Circ, Per,* Peg Parkison; E-mail: parkison@sheridan.edu; *Circ,* Janice Wetherington; *Circ, Tech Serv,* Judith Garber; E-mail: jgarber@sheridan.edu; Staff 6 (MLS 1, Non-MLS 5)
Founded 1948. Enrl 3,200; Fac 87; Highest Degree: Associate
Jul 2008-Jun 2009. Mats Exp $83,400, Books $23,000, AV Mat $13,200, Electronic Ref Mat (Incl. Access Fees) $7,400. Sal $168,000 (Prof $56,000)
Library Holdings: Bk Titles 19,000; Bk Vols 29,000; Per Subs 124
Automation Activity & Vendor Info: (Acquisitions) SIRSI-iLink; (Cataloging) SirsiDynix; (Circulation) SirsiDynix; (Course Reserve) SIRSI-iLink; (ILL) OCLC; (OPAC) SIRSI-iLink; (Serials) SIRSI-iLink
Database Vendor: ALLDATA Online, ARTstor, Bowker, College Source, CQ Press, ebrary, EBSCOhost, Elsevier, Facts on File, Gale Cengage Learning, H W Wilson, JSTOR, LexisNexis, netLibrary, OCLC WorldCat, Oxford Online, ProQuest, ScienceDirect, SerialsSolutions, SirsiDynix, Wiley, Wilson - Wilson Web
Wireless access
Partic in WYLD Network
Special Services for the Blind - Computer with voice synthesizer for visually impaired persons
Open Mon-Thurs 8am-10pm, Fri 8-Noon, Sat 12-5, Sun 3-10

P SHERIDAN COUNTY PUBLIC LIBRARY SYSTEM, Sheridan County Fulmer Public Library, 335 W Alger St, 82801-3899. SAN 365-3676. Tel: 307-674-8585, Ext 5. Circulation Tel: 307-674-8585, Ext 3. Reference Tel: 307-674-8585, Ext 15. Administration FAX: 307-674-7374. Web Site: www.sheridanwyolibrary.org. *Dir,* Cameron Duff; Tel: 307-674-8585, Ext 12, E-mail: cduff@sheridanwyolibrary.org; *Ch,* Michelle Havenga; E-mail: mhavenga@sheridanwyolibrary.org; *Circ Librn,* Marci Mock; E-mail: mmock@sheridanwyolibrary.org; *Info Serv Librn,* Anita Weisheit; E-mail: aweisheit@sheridanwyolibrary.org; *Spec Coll Librn,* Judy Slack; E-mail: jslack@sheridanwyolibrary.org; *Tech Serv Librn,* Linda Hossfeld; E-mail: lhossfeld@sheridanwyolibrary.org; *Fac Mgr,* Kip Bethurem; E-mail: kbethurem@sheridanwyolibrary.org; *Prog Coordr, Young Adult Serv Coordr,* Debbie Iverson; E-mail: diverson@sheridanwyolibrary.org; *Homebound Serv,* Judy Armstrong; E-mail: jarmstrong@sheridanwyolibrary.org; *ILL,* Chris Gonzales; E-mail: cgonzales@sheridanwyolibrary.org; *Network Adminr,* David Hartschuh; E-mail: dhartschuh@sheridanwyolibrary.org; Staff 13 (MLS 3, Non-MLS 10)
Founded 1905. Pop 29,239; Circ 323,238
Library Holdings: AV Mats 15,794; CDs 5,257; DVDs 10,537; Electronic Media & Resources 157; Large Print Bks 5,000; Bk Titles 133,351; Per Subs 191
Special Collections: Folklore & Storytelling (Spell-Spinner Coll). Oral History
Subject Interests: Genealogy, Local hist
Automation Activity & Vendor Info: (Acquisitions) SirsiDynix; (Cataloging) SirsiDynix; (Circulation) SirsiDynix; (ILL) Fretwell-Downing; (OPAC) SirsiDynix; (Serials) SirsiDynix
Database Vendor: EBSCOhost, SirsiDynix, Wilson - Wilson Web

Function: Bk club(s), Computer training, Copy machines, Digital talking bks, e-mail serv, Electronic databases & coll, Handicapped accessible, Home delivery & serv to Sr ctr & nursing homes, Homebound delivery serv, Homework prog, ILL available, Magnifiers for reading, Mail & tel request accepted, Music CDs, Online ref, Online searches, Orientations, Photocopying/Printing, Preschool outreach, Prog for adults, Prog for children & young adult, Ref serv available, Senior computer classes, Summer reading prog, Tax forms, Telephone ref, VHS videos
Partic in WYLD Network
Special Services for the Deaf - TTY equip
Open Mon-Thurs 9-9, Fri & Sat 9-5, Sun (Sept-May) 1-5
Friends of the Library Group
Branches: 3
CLEARMONT BRANCH, 1254 Front St, Clearmont, 82835. (Mail add: PO Box 26, Clearmont, 82835-0026), SAN 365-3706. Tel: 307-758-4331. FAX: 307-758-4331. E-mail: cbl@sheridanwyolibrary.org. *Mgr,* Barbara Carlock; Staff 1 (Non-MLS 1)
Library Holdings: AV Mats 916; Bk Titles 8,193; Per Subs 13
Database Vendor: ebrary, netLibrary, OCLC WorldCat, ProQuest
Open Mon, Tues & Thurs 2-6:30, Wed & Fri 9-1
STORY BRANCH, 20 N Piney, Story, 82842. (Mail add: PO Box 188, Story, 82842-0188), SAN 365-3730. Tel: 307-683-2922. FAX: 307-683-2922. E-mail: sbl@sheridanwyolibrary.org. *Mgr,* Jo Elliott; Staff 1 (Non-MLS 1)
Library Holdings: AV Mats 868; Bk Titles 9,823
Database Vendor: ebrary, netLibrary, OCLC WorldCat
Open Mon-Fri 12:30-5:30, Sat 9-1
TONGUE RIVER BRANCH, 145 Coffeen, Ranchester, 82839. (Mail add: PO Box 909, Ranchester, 82839-0909), SAN 365-3765. Tel: 307-655-9726. FAX: 307-655-9384. E-mail: trbl@sheridanwyolibrary.org. *Mgr,* Connie Fiedor; Staff 1 (Non-MLS 1)
Pop 2,000; Circ 12,089
Library Holdings: Audiobooks 471; AV Mats 1,296; CDs 889; DVDs 324; e-books 3; Electronic Media & Resources 65; Large Print Bks 284; Bk Titles 13,958; Per Subs 25; Videos 955
Database Vendor: ebrary, OCLC WorldCat
Function: Adult bk club, Art exhibits, Copy machines, e-mail serv, Electronic databases & coll, Fax serv, ILL available, Photocopying/Printing, Prog for children & young adult, Pub access computers, Summer reading prog, Tax forms
Special Services for the Blind - Home delivery serv
Open Mon-Fri 10-12 & 1-6

M WHEDON CANCER FOUNDATION LIBRARY*, 30 S Scott St, 82801-6308. (Mail add: PO Box 683, 82801-0683), SAN 328-1299. Tel: 307-672-2941. FAX: 307-672-7273. E-mail: whedoncancer@fiberpipe.net. Web Site: www.uwyo.edu/~whedon. *Mgr,* Bethany Lawrence; Staff 2 (Non-MLS 2)
Founded 1981
Library Holdings: Bk Titles 761; Bk Vols 830; Per Subs 50
Special Collections: Breast Cancer Coll, Hospice & ACS (lending library of videos)
Partic in Docline; Midcontinental Regional Med Libr Program
Open Mon-Fri 9-5

SHOSHONI

P SHOSHONI PUBLIC LIBRARY*, 216 Idaho St, 82649. Tel: 307-876-2777. FAX: 307-876-2777. E-mail: shoshol@shoshone.lili.org. Web Site: shoshone.lili.org. *Librn,* Sabrina Lawson
Library Holdings: AV Mats 1,100; Bk Vols 8,700
Special Collections: Canvas-Back 1940's Children's Book Coll
Automation Activity & Vendor Info: (Cataloging) JayWil Software Development, Inc; (Circulation) JayWil Software Development, Inc
Open Mon-Thurs (Winter) 9:30-6, Fri 9:30-4, Sat 10-2; Mon-Thurs (Summer) 9:30-6, Fri 9:30-5

SUNDANCE

P CROOK COUNTY LIBRARY*, 414 Main St, 82729. (Mail add: PO Box 910, 82729-0910), SAN 365-379X. Tel: 307-283-1006, 307-283-1008. FAX: 307-283-1006. E-mail: crookcountylib@rangeweb.net. Web Site: will.state.wy.us/crook. *Dir,* Jill A Mackey; *Adult Serv,* Violet Smith; *Tech Serv,* Tanya Brekke; *Youth Serv,* Bonnie Stahla; Staff 4 (Non-MLS 4)
Founded 1937. Pop 6,000; Circ 35,890
Library Holdings: Large Print Bks 238; Bk Titles 75,861; Bk Vols 77,490; Per Subs 278; Talking Bks 1,090; Videos 1,816
Special Collections: Wyomingana
Automation Activity & Vendor Info: (Acquisitions) SirsiDynix; (Cataloging) SirsiDynix; (Circulation) SirsiDynix; (ILL) SirsiDynix
Database Vendor: EBSCOhost
Function: Adult bk club, Audio & video playback equip for onsite use, Audiobks via web, AV serv, Bi-weekly Writer's Group, Bks on cassette, Bks on CD, Children's prog, Computers for patron use, Copy machines, e-mail serv, E-Reserves, Electronic databases & coll, Fax serv, Free DVD

rentals, Govt ref serv, Health sci info serv, Holiday prog, ILL available, Notary serv, Online cat, Outreach serv, Photocopying/Printing, Preschool outreach, Prog for adults, Prog for children & young adult, Pub access computers, Spoken cassettes & CDs, Story hour, Summer reading prog, Tax forms, Teen prog, Telephone ref, VHS videos, Video lending libr, Wheelchair accessible
Partic in Wyo Libr Database
Open Mon 9-8, Tues-Fri 9-5:30
Friends of the Library Group
Branches: 2
HULETT BRANCH, 115 N Hwy 24, Hulett, 82720. (Mail add: PO Box 219, Hulett, 82720-0219), SAN 365-382X. Tel: 307-467-5676. FAX: 307-467-5250. E-mail: library467@rpconnect.net. *Br Librn,* Elizabeth Gaines; *Asst Br Librn,* Michelle Gillam; Staff 2 (Non-MLS 2)
   Library Holdings: CDs 33; Large Print Bks 60; Bk Titles 31,195; Bk Vols 32,410; Per Subs 57; Videos 90
   Open Mon-Thurs 9-4:30
   Friends of the Library Group
MOORCROFT BRANCH, 105 E Converse, Moorcroft, 82721. (Mail add: PO Box 10, Moorcroft, 82721-0010), SAN 365-3854. Tel: 307-756-3232. FAX: 307-756-3232. *Br Librn,* Maureen Farrier; *Adult Serv,* Pamela Jespersen; *Youth Serv,* Judy Stenbak
   Library Holdings: CDs 31; Large Print Bks 57; Bk Titles 27,017; Bk Vols 28,194; Per Subs 63; Videos 88
   Open Mon-Fri 10-5:30

THERMOPOLIS

P   HOT SPRINGS COUNTY LIBRARY*, 344 Arapahoe, 82443-0951. (Mail add: PO Box 951, 82443-0951), SAN 318-5109. Tel: 307-864-3104. FAX: 307-864-5416. *Dir,* Chrissy Bendlin; E-mail: cbendlin@will.state.wy.us; *Ch, ILL,* Tracey A Kinnaman; E-mail: kinnaman@will.state.wy.us; *Adult Serv, Circ, ILL,* Nancy Barton; E-mail: nbarton@will.state.wy.us; *Circ,* Sue Hurd; Staff 2 (Non-MLS 2)
   Founded 1918. Pop 4,665; Circ 35,050
   Jul 2009-Jun 2010 Income $201,500, County $200,000, Locally Generated Income $1,500. Mats Exp $35,000. Sal $136,232
   Library Holdings: AV Mats 568; Bks on Deafness & Sign Lang 50; Electronic Media & Resources 21; Large Print Bks 2,470; Bk Vols 54,900; Per Subs 80; Talking Bks 1,399; Videos 208
   Special Collections: Local Newspapers from 1905, micro; Wyoming History Coll
   Subject Interests: Behav sci, Natural sci, Soc sci
   Automation Activity & Vendor Info: (Cataloging) SirsiDynix; (Circulation) SirsiDynix; (OPAC) SirsiDynix; (Serials) SirsiDynix
   Database Vendor: SirsiDynix
   Function: Distance learning, ILL available, Online searches, Photocopying/Printing, Prog for children & young adult, Spoken cassettes & CDs, Summer reading prog, Telephone ref, VHS videos
   Open Mon, Wed-Fri (Sept-May) 9-6, Tues 9-7; Mon-Fri (June-Aug) 9-6
   Friends of the Library Group

S   WYOMING PIONEER HOME LIBRARY*, 141 Pioneer Home Dr, 82443-2451. SAN 372-8781. Tel: 307-864-3151. FAX: 307-864-2934. E-mail: wphactco@yahoo.com. *Librn,* Julie Geiser
   Library Holdings: Bk Vols 900; Per Subs 30
   Subject Interests: Fiction, Hist
   Restriction: Residents only, Staff use only

TORRINGTON

C   EASTERN WYOMING COLLEGE LIBRARY*, 3200 West C, 82240. SAN 318-5117. Tel: 307-532-8210. FAX: 307-532-8225. Web Site: www.ewc.wy.edu. *Dir,* Marilyn Miller; E-mail: mmiller@ewc.wy.edu; *Asst Dir,* Becky Lorenz; E-mail: blorenz@ewc.wy.edu; Staff 2 (MLS 1, Non-MLS 1)
   Founded 1948. Enrl 1,040; Fac 60; Highest Degree: Associate
   Library Holdings: Bk Titles 29,000; Bk Vols 34,000; Per Subs 121
   Special Collections: Oral History
   Subject Interests: Agr, Criminal justice, Educ, Hist, Veterinary tech
   Open Mon-Thurs 7:30am-9pm, Fri 7:30-5, Sun 2-9

P   GOSHEN COUNTY LIBRARY, 2001 East A St, 82240-2898. SAN 318-5125. Tel: 307-532-3411. FAX: 307-532-2169. *Dir,* Isabel M Hoy; Staff 5.5 (Non-MLS 5.5)
   Founded 1922. Pop 13,249; Circ 67,473
   Jul 2012-Jun 2013 Income $308,211. Mats Exp $61,512, Books $55,075, AV Mat $6,437. Sal $194,601
   Library Holdings: Electronic Media & Resources 4,047; Bk Vols 42,868; Per Subs 101; Talking Bks 946; Videos 290

Automation Activity & Vendor Info: (Circulation) SirsiDynix; (OPAC) SirsiDynix
Database Vendor: EBSCOhost, Gale Cengage Learning, OCLC FirstSearch, SirsiDynix, Wilson - Wilson Web
Wireless access
Function: ILL available
Partic in Wyo Libr Database
Open Mon 8-8, Tues-Fri 10-6, Sat 10-3

WHEATLAND

P   PLATTE COUNTY PUBLIC LIBRARY*, 904 Ninth St, 82201-2699. SAN 365-3889. Tel: 307-322-2689. Toll Free Tel: 888-841-0964. FAX: 307-322-3540. E-mail: platcircmgr@will.state.wy.us. Web Site: www-wsl.state.wy.us/platte/. *Dir,* Julie Henion; *Circ Mgr,* Ruth Vaughn; *Tech Serv Mgr,* Lee Miller; Staff 8 (MLS 2, Non-MLS 6)
   Founded 1894. Pop 9,012; Circ 73,441
   Library Holdings: CDs 110; Bk Titles 61,112; Bk Vols 63,491; Per Subs 94; Videos 542
   Special Collections: Oral History
   Subject Interests: County hist, Wyo hist
   Automation Activity & Vendor Info: (Cataloging) TLC (The Library Corporation); (Circulation) TLC (The Library Corporation)
   Database Vendor: EBSCOhost
   Open Mon-Thurs 10-8, Fri 10-5, Sat 10-2
   Friends of the Library Group
   Branches: 3
   CHUGWATER BRANCH, 301 Second St, Chugwater, 82210. (Mail add: PO Box 215, Chugwater, 82210), SAN 365-3919. Tel: 307-422-3275. E-mail: chuglibrary@yahoo.com. Web Site: www-wsl.state.wy.us/platte/chugwater.htm. *Librn,* Darla Teter; Staff 1 (MLS 1)
      Pop 244; Circ 908
      Library Holdings: Bk Titles 4,031; Bk Vols 5,100; Per Subs 11
      Open Mon & Fri 2-5, Wed 11-2
      Friends of the Library Group
   GLENDO BRANCH, 213 Second St, Glendo, 82213. (Mail add: PO Box 295, Glendo, 82213), SAN 365-3943. Tel: 307-735-4480. *Librn,* Betty Amick
      Pop 231; Circ 840
      Library Holdings: Large Print Bks 12; Bk Titles 4,062; Bk Vols 5,281; Per Subs 16; Talking Bks 103; Videos 178
      Open Tues & Thurs 1:30-5, Sat 1-4
   GUERNSEY BRANCH, 108 S Wyoming Ave, Guernsey, 82214. (Mail add: PO Box 607, Guernsey, 82214), SAN 365-3978. Tel: 307-836-2816. E-mail: guercircmgr@will.state.wy.us. *Librn,* Pat Carpenter
      Pop 1,147; Circ 3,020
      Library Holdings: Bk Titles 9,142; Bk Vols 10,111; Per Subs 23
      Open Mon & Wed 12-7, Tues & Thurs 12-5, Fri 12-4

WORLAND

P   WASHAKIE COUNTY LIBRARY SYSTEM, 1019 Coburn Ave, 82401. SAN 365-4001. Tel: 307-347-2231. FAX: 307-347-2248. E-mail: director@washakiecountylibrary.com. Web Site: www.washakiecountylibrary.com. *Dir,* Karen Funk; Staff 2 (Non-MLS 2)
   Founded 1914. Pop 8,290; Circ 4,950
   Library Holdings: AV Mats 2,000; Bk Vols 61,000; Per Subs 44
   Automation Activity & Vendor Info: (Circulation) SirsiDynix
   Database Vendor: EBSCOhost, Gale Cengage Learning, OCLC FirstSearch, SirsiDynix, TLC (The Library Corporation), Wilson - Wilson Web
   Wireless access
   Function: Scanner, Spanish lang bks, Story hour, VHS videos, Winter reading prog
   Partic in WYLD Network
   Open Mon, Wed & Fri 8-5, Tues & Thurs 8-8, Sat 9-1
   Friends of the Library Group
   Branches: 1
   TEN SLEEP BRANCH, 200 N Fir St, Ten Sleep, 82442. (Mail add: PO Box 107, Ten Sleep, 82442), SAN 365-4036. Tel: 307-366-2348. E-mail: tensleep@washakiecountylibrary.com. *Libr Dir,* Karen Funk
      Pop 300
      Function: Bks on cassette, Bks on CD, Children's prog, Copy machines, Equip loans & repairs, ILL available, Online cat, Online ref, Photocopying/Printing, Preschool reading prog, Spanish lang bks, Spoken cassettes & CDs, Spoken cassettes & DVDs, Story hour, VHS videos, Workshops
      Open Mon-Fri 8-5, Sat 9-1
      Friends of the Library Group

LIBRARIES IN PUERTO RICO AND REGIONS ADMINISTERED BY THE UNITED STATES

AMERICAN SAMOA

MAPUSAGA

J   AMERICAN SAMOA COMMUNITY COLLEGE LIBRARY*, Learning Resource Center, Malaeimi Village, Malaeimi Rd, 96799. (Mail add: PO Box 2609, Pago Pago, 96799-2609), SAN 365-4605. Tel: 684-699-5728. Circulation Tel: 684-699-9155, Ext 418. Reference Tel: 684-699-9155, Ext 419, 684-699-9155, Ext 420. FAX: 684-699-5732. *Dir,* Emma F C Pen; *Ref,* Reupena Lesa; Staff 8 (MLS 1, Non-MLS 7)
Founded 1974. Enrl 1,000; Fac 50; Highest Degree: Associate
Library Holdings: AV Mats 1,640; Bk Titles 32,861; Bk Vols 35,941; Per Subs 108
Special Collections: Govt & Territory; Pacific & Samoa Coll. US Document Depository
Subject Interests: Anthropology, Archaeology, Creative writing, Ethnography, Forests, Geog, Geol, Indigenous art, Lang, Marine biol, Meteorology, Natural marine resources, Oceanography, Pac lit, Samoan hist
Automation Activity & Vendor Info: (Cataloging) Follett Software; (Circulation) Follett Software; (OPAC) Follett Software
Publications: Library Handbook (Library handbook)
Open Mon-Fri 7:30-7:30

PAGO PAGO

P   AMERICAN SAMOA OFFICE OF LIBRARY SERVICES*, American Library Bldg, 96799. (Mail add: PO Box 1329, 96799-1329), SAN 365-463X. Tel: 684-699-2170. FAX: 684-633-4240, 684-699-2193. *Asst Dir,* Bessie Manase; *Rare Bks, Spec Coll Librn,* Arieta Thompson; Staff 5 (MLS 1, Non-MLS 4)
Founded 1913. Pop 35,000; Circ 201,000
Library Holdings: AV Mats 1,384; Bk Titles 127,691; Bk Vols 129,414; Per Subs 108
Special Collections: Pacific Islands, bks, flm, recs, & VF; Territory. UN Document Depository
Open Mon-Fri 7:30-4
Branches: 12
ALATAUA LUA SCHOOL LIBRARY, 96799, SAN 326-8276. Tel: 684-688-7516. FAX: 684-633-4240. ; Staff 2 (Non-MLS 2)
  Library Holdings: Bk Titles 1,090; Bk Vols 1,290; Per Subs 16
  Open Mon-Fri 7:30-4
FAGA'ITUA BRANCH, Faga'itua Village, 96799, SAN 365-4699. Tel: 684-622-7504. FAX: 684-633-4240. *Librn,* Mata Peters; Staff 2 (Non-MLS 2)
  Library Holdings: AV Mats 790; Bk Titles 5,650; Bk Vols 6,200; Per Subs 23
  Open Mon-Fri 7:30-4
LEONE SCHOOL - COMMUNITY, Vailoa Village, 96799, SAN 365-4753. Tel: 684-688-7458. FAX: 684-633-4240. *Librn,* Debbie Duilefano; Staff 2 (Non-MLS 2)
  Library Holdings: Bk Titles 7,091; Bk Vols 7,350; Per Subs 18
  Open Mon-Fri 7:30-4
LUPELELE, Iliili Village, 96799, SAN 322-6395. Tel: 684-688-7832. FAX: 684-633-4240. *Librn,* Mata Tilito; Staff 2 (Non-MLS 2)
  Library Holdings: AV Mats 680; Bk Titles 6,140; Bk Vols 6,490; Per Subs 22
  Open Mon-Fri 7:30-4
MANU'A, Tau Community School, Manu'a Island, 96799, SAN 365-4818. Tel: 684-732-3512. FAX: 684-633-4240. *Librn,* Alofa Veligitone; Staff 1 (Non-MLS 1)
  Library Holdings: AV Mats 780; Bk Titles 5,120; Bk Vols 5,461; Per Subs 21
  Open Mon-Fri 7:30-4
MANULELE, Nuiuuli Village, 96799, SAN 322-6409. Tel: 684-699-9617. FAX: 684-633-4240. *Librn,* Agapapalagi Malofie; Staff 2 (Non-MLS 2)
  Library Holdings: AV Mats 890; Bk Titles 8,190; Bk Vols 84,610; Per Subs 33
  Open Mon-Fri 7:30-4
MATAFAO SCHOOL COMMUNITY LIBRARY, Fagaalu Village, 96799, SAN 365-4796. Tel: 684-633-2401. FAX: 684-633-2401. *Librn,* Matavaine O'Brien; Staff 1 (MLS 1)
  Library Holdings: Bk Titles 4,290; Bk Vols 5,160; Per Subs 29
  Open Mon-Fri 7:30-4
LEONE MIDKIFF BRANCH, Leone Village, 96799, SAN 365-480X. Tel: 684-688-7458. FAX: 684-633-4240. *Librn,* Florentine Peo
  Library Holdings: AV Mats 560; Bk Titles 6,280; Bk Vols 6,491; Per Subs 42
  Open Mon-Fri 7:30-4
OLOSEGA SCHOOL LIBRARY, 96799, SAN 326-825X. Tel: 684-655-1206. FAX: 684-633-4240. *Librn,* Evelini Puletasi; Staff 1 (Non-MLS 1)
  Library Holdings: AV Mats 340; Bk Titles 1,940; Bk Vols 2,060; Per Subs 18
  Open Mon-Fri 7:30-4
PAGO PAGO BRANCH, PO Box 272, 96799. Tel: 684-633-5651. FAX: 684-633-4240. *Librn,* Lomi Bali; Staff 1 (Non-MLS 1)
  Library Holdings: Bk Titles 4,980; Bk Vols 5,160; Per Subs 21
  Open Mon-Fri 7:30-4
PAVAIAI BRANCH, Pavaiai Village, 96799, SAN 365-4834. Tel: 684-639-9605. FAX: 684-633-4240. *Librn,* Kopa Siatunuu; Staff 1 (Non-MLS 1)
  Library Holdings: AV Mats 560; Bk Titles 4,690; Bk Vols 4,810; Per Subs 19
  Open Mon-Fri 7:30-4
TAUFUNA HIGH SCHOOL - COMMUNITY, Taufuna Village, 96799, SAN 365-4842. Tel: 684-699-1303. FAX: 684-633-4240. *Librn,* Ruth Apulu; Staff 1 (Non-MLS 1)
  Library Holdings: AV Mats 670; Bk Titles 2,184; Bk Vols 2,370; Per Subs 26
  Open Mon-Fri 7:30-4

P   FELETI BARSTOW PUBLIC LIBRARY*, PO Box 997687, 96799. Tel: 684-633-5816. FAX: 684-633-5823. E-mail: barstow@americansamoa.gov. Web Site: www.fbpl.org. *Territorial Librn,* Cheryl Morales Polataivao; *Asst*

Librn, Betty Herdrich; *Asst Librn,* Mary Tiumalu; *Cataloger,* Tamara
Zielinski; *Circ Serv Coordr,* Lily Tunai; *Syst Adminr,* Loring Faiivae
Founded 2000
Library Holdings: Bk Titles 37,865
Automation Activity & Vendor Info: (Cataloging) Follett Software;
(Circulation) Follett Software
Database Vendor: Gale Cengage Learning
Open Mon, Wed & Fri 9-5, Tues & Thurs (Winter) 9-7, Sat 10-2; Mon-Fri
(Summer) 9-5, Sat 10-2

APO AP

A   UNITED STATES AIR FORCE*, Andersen Air Force Base Library, 36 FSS/FSDL (FL 5240), Unit 14004, Box 28, 96543-4004. SAN 365-4575. Tel: 671-366-4291. FAX: 671-366-2728. E-mail: andersen.library@andersen.af.mil. *Dir*, M Taitano; *Info Tech Spec*, R Fernandez; Staff 2 (MLS 1, Non-MLS 1)
Library Holdings: Bk Vols 33,500; Per Subs 125
Subject Interests: Air War College, Micronesia, Project warrior, SE Asia, The Pacific
Partic in Guam Libr Asn

HAGATNA

L   GUAM LAW LIBRARY, 141 San Ramon St, 96910-4333. SAN 324-8011. Tel: 671-472-8062, 671-477-7623. FAX: 671-472-1246. E-mail: gll@teleguam.net. Web Site: www.guamlawlibrary.org. *Exec Dir/Librn*, Geraldine Amparo Cepeda; E-mail: gllexecdir@teleguam.net
Founded 1978
Jan 2011-Dec 2011 Income $407,143, County $395,213, Locally Generated Income $5,708, Other $6,221. Mats Exp $275,773. Sal $98,261
Library Holdings: Bk Titles 5,911; Bk Vols 55,862
Special Collections: Guam; Law; Pacific Islands
Database Vendor: HeinOnline, LexisNexis, Westlaw
Wireless access
Open Mon-Fri 8-6, Sat 9-1

P   GUAM PUBLIC LIBRARY*, Nieves M Flores Memorial Library, 254 Martyr St, 96910. Tel: 671-475-4753, 671-475-4754. FAX: 671-477-9777. Web Site: gpls.guam.gov. *Actg Dir*, Christina N M Watson; E-mail: cwatson@gpls.guam.gov
Library Holdings: AV Mats 1,200; Bk Vols 236,960; Per Subs 100
Special Collections: Guam History; Local Docs; Western Pacific Coll
Subject Interests: Classical lit, Gen ref, Western lit
Automation Activity & Vendor Info: (Acquisitions) Horizon; (Cataloging) Horizon; (Circulation) Horizon
Function: ILL available, Telephone ref
Publications: 1977 Pacific Daily News Index; Guam Newsletter (Newsletter); Index to Vital Statistics; Life of San Vitores; Union Catalog of Guam & Pacific Area Materials; Union List of Serials
Open Mon-Thurs 10-6, Sat 9-1

MANGILAO

J   GUAM COMMUNITY COLLEGE, Learning Resource Center Library, One Sesame St, 96921. (Mail add: PO Box 23069, Barrigada, 96921). Tel: 671-735-0228, 671-735-0229. E-mail: gcc.library@guamcc.edu. Web Site: www.guamcc.edu. *Ref & Instruction Librn*, Christine Matson; Tel: 671-735-0231, E-mail: christine.matson@guamcc.edu; *Tech Serv Librn*, B Robert Neff; E-mail: bernard.neff@guamcc.edu; Staff 6 (MLS 2, Non-MLS 4)
Founded 1967. Enrl 2,500; Fac 186; Highest Degree: Associate
Library Holdings: Bk Vols 20,000; Per Subs 120

Special Collections: Pacific Coll
Subject Interests: Guam, Micronesia
Automation Activity & Vendor Info: (Cataloging) SirsiDynix; (Circulation) SirsiDynix; (Course Reserve) SirsiDynix; (OPAC) SirsiDynix
Database Vendor: EBSCOhost, SirsiDynix
Wireless access

C   UNIVERSITY OF GUAM, Richard F Taitano Micronesian Area Research Center, Guam & Micronesia Collection, UOG Sta, 96923. SAN 321-9887. Tel: 671-735-2157, 671-735-2160. Reference Tel: 671-735-2162. Administration Tel: 671-735-2750. FAX: 671-734-7403. Web Site: www.uog.edu/marc. *Spanish Doc Coll*, Omaira Brunal-Perry; E-mail: obrunal@uguam.uog.edu; *Ref*, Monique Storie; *Ref Serv*, Perry J Panguelinan; *Tech Serv*, Lourdes Nededog; E-mail: louann@uguam.uog.edu; *Tech Serv*, Carmen F Quintanilla; Tel: 671-735-2161, E-mail: cquintan@uguam.uog.edu; Staff 5 (MLS 2, Non-MLS 3)
Founded 1967. Enrl 4,200; Highest Degree: Master
Library Holdings: Bk Titles 25,000; Bk Vols 40,000
Special Collections: Manuscripts Coll; Reference Coll; Spanish Documents Coll
Subject Interests: Micronesia, Oceania
Automation Activity & Vendor Info: (Cataloging) SirsiDynix; (Circulation) SirsiDynix; (OPAC) SirsiDynix; (Serials) SirsiDynix
Database Vendor: SirsiDynix
Function: For res purposes
Partic in National Network of Libraries of Medicine; National Network of Libraries of Medicine Pacific Southwest Region
Open Mon-Fri 9-5
Restriction: Non-circulating
Friends of the Library Group

C   UNIVERSITY OF GUAM*, Robert F Kennedy Memorial Library, UOG Sta, 96923. SAN 318-5281. Tel: 671-735-2331, 671-735-2332. Interlibrary Loan Service Tel: 671-735-2311. Reference Tel: 671-735-2341. Automation Services Tel: 671-735-2321, 671-735-2322. FAX: 671-734-6882. Web Site: www.uog.edu/library. *Dir*, Christine Ku Scott-Smith; Tel: 671-735-2333, E-mail: csctsmth@uguam.uog.edu; *Acq/Coll Develop Librn*, Dr Nick J Goetzfridt; Tel: 671-735-2300, E-mail: ngoetzfr@uguam.uog.edu; *Cat & Tech Serv Librn*, Rick L Castro; Tel: 671-735-2307, E-mail: rcastro@uguam.uog.edu; *Circ/ILL Librn*, Paul B Drake; Tel: 671-735-2345, E-mail: pdrake@uguam.uog.edu; *Govt Doc Librn*, Suzanne T Bell; Tel: 671-735-2316, E-mail: stbell@uguam.uog.edu; *Asst Librn, Per & Reserve Serv Librn*, Kevin Latham; Tel: 671-735-2335, E-mail: klatham@uguam.uog.edu; *Syst & Network Librn*, Maria B Ovalles; E-mail: ovallmar@uguam.uog.edu; *Ref & Info Literacy Instruction*, Mark C Goniwiecha; Tel: 671-735-2340, E-mail: markg@uguam.uog.edu; Staff 27 (MLS 9, Non-MLS 18)
Founded 1952. Enrl 3,500; Highest Degree: Master
Library Holdings: AV Mats 4,946; e-journals 24,190; Microforms 185,111; Bk Titles 94,795; Bk Vols 120,999; Per Subs 1,379

Special Collections: East Asian Coll; Juvenile Coll; Theses & Special Project Coll. US Document Depository
Subject Interests: Agr, Arts, Educ, Humanities, Libr sci, Lit, Mil sci, Sci, Soc sci
Automation Activity & Vendor Info: (Acquisitions) SirsiDynix; (Cataloging) SirsiDynix; (Circulation) SirsiDynix; (Course Reserve) SirsiDynix; (ILL) SirsiDynix; (Media Booking) SirsiDynix; (OPAC) SirsiDynix; (Serials) SirsiDynix
Database Vendor: 3M Library Systems, Agricola, American Mathematical Society, ARTstor, EBSCO Information Services, EBSCOhost, H W Wilson,

JSTOR, Newsbank, OCLC FirstSearch, OCLC WorldCat, OVID Technologies, ProQuest, PubMed, SirsiDynix, Wilson - Wilson Web
Wireless access
Partic in Midwest Collaborative for Library Services (MCLS); OCLC Online Computer Library Center, Inc
Special Services for the Deaf - Adult & family literacy prog
Open Mon-Thurs 8-8, Fri 9-5, Sat 8-4
Friends of the Library Group

SAIPAN

P JOETEN-KIYU PUBLIC LIBRARY*, Beach Rd, Susupe, 96950. (Mail add: PO Box 501092, 96950), SAN 377-0419. Tel: 670-235-7322, 670-235-7324. Administration Tel: 670-235-7318. FAX: 670-235-7550. E-mail: adminlib@cnmilibrary.com, saipanlib@cnmilibrary.com. Web Site: www.cnmilibrary.com. *Exec Dir, State Libr Info Ctr,* John O DLR Gonzales; Tel: 670-235-7315, Fax: 670-235-7550, E-mail: saipanlib@cnmilibrary.com; *Ch,* Erlinda Naputi; Staff 9 (MLS 1, Non-MLS 8)
Founded 1992. Pop 78,252; Circ 68,977
Library Holdings: AV Mats 3,088; Bk Titles 36,735; Bk Vols 40,540; Per Subs 101; Talking Bks 100
Special Collections: Pacific Area & World War II Pacific (Pacific Reference Coll); Saipan, Tinian & Rota History, 1972-1994
Automation Activity & Vendor Info: (Cataloging) SirsiDynix; (Circulation) SirsiDynix
Function: AV serv, Handicapped accessible, Homebound delivery serv, Online searches, Prog for adults, Prog for children & young adult, Summer reading prog, Workshops
Open Tues-Fri 10-6, Sat 9-4
Friends of the Library Group

Branches: 1
TINIAN PUBLIC, PO Box 520704, Tinian, 96952, SAN 376-8368. Tel: 670-433-0504. E-mail: tinianpubliclibrary.staff2010@hotmail.com. *Libr Supvr,* Lorna Cruz; Staff 1 (MLS 1)
   Library Holdings: Bk Vols 3,200; Per Subs 10
Bookmobiles: Swain D Cangco, Bookmobile Asst

J NORTHERN MARIANAS COLLEGE*, Olympio T Borja Memorial Library, Fina Sisu Lane, Bldg O, 96950. (Mail add: PO Box 501250, 96950-9999), SAN 378-0848. Tel: 670-234-3690, Ext 1122. FAX: 670-234-0759. Web Site: www.nmcnet.edu/library.cfm. *Dir,* Matthew Pastula; E-mail: matthewp@nmcnet.edu; *Academy Librn,* Van Rider; E-mail: vanr@nmcnet.edu; *Pub Serv,* Smith Magiel; E-mail: magiels@nmcnet.edu; *Tech Serv,* Greg Sablan; E-mail: gregs@nmcnet.edu. Subject Specialists: *Oceania,* Smith Magiel; Staff 8 (MLS 4, Non-MLS 4)
Founded 1981. Enrl 1,239; Fac 91; Highest Degree: Bachelor
Library Holdings: AV Mats 850; Bk Titles 30,000; Bk Vols 44,000; Per Subs 520
Special Collections: Asian Develop Bank
Departmental Libraries:
PACIFIC COLLECTION, PO Box 501250, 96950, SAN 378-1860. Tel: 670-234-5498, Ext 1111. FAX: 670-234-0759. *Archivist Tech,* Tonny Goobaad
   Library Holdings: Bk Vols 7,500; Per Subs 350
   Open Mon-Fri 8-5

PUERTO RICO

AGUADILLA

C INTER-AMERICAN UNIVERSITY OF PUERTO RICO*, Aguadilla
Campus Library, PO Box 20000, 00905. SAN 318-5346. Tel:
787-891-0925. FAX: 787-882-3020. E-mail: inter@edu.nyulfo. Web Site:
www.aguadilla.inter.edu. *Dir,* Monserrate Yulfososa; *Librn,* Mildred Lopez;
Staff 14 (MLS 3, Non-MLS 11)
Founded 1968. Fac 138
Library Holdings: Bk Vols 57,000; Per Subs 397
Special Collections: Manuel Mendez Ballister Coll
Database Vendor: OCLC FirstSearch
Publications: Faculty catalog; Periodical catalog; Student catalog
Partic in Davis-Louven
Open Mon-Fri 7am-9pm, Sat 7-3:30

ARECIBO

J INTER-AMERICAN UNIVERSITY OF PUERTO RICO*, Center for
Access to Information-Biblioteca Rene Marques, Barrio San Daniel, Sector
Las Canelas, 00614-4050. (Mail add: PO Box 4050, 00614-4050), SAN
318-5362. Tel: 787-878-5475, Ext 2321. FAX: 787-880-1624. Web Site:
www.arecibo.inter.edu. *Dir,* Sara Abreu; E-mail: sabreu@arecibo.inter.edu;
Staff 14 (MLS 2, Non-MLS 12)
Founded 1958. Enrl 3,500; Fac 100; Highest Degree: Master
Library Holdings: Bk Titles 57,389; Bk Vols 67,960; Per Subs 315
Subject Interests: Anesthesia, Biol, Census, Criminal justice, Doc, Educ,
Microbiology, Nursing
Automation Activity & Vendor Info: (Acquisitions) SirsiDynix;
(Cataloging) SirsiDynix; (Circulation) SirsiDynix; (Course Reserve)
SirsiDynix; (ILL) SirsiDynix; (Media Booking) SirsiDynix; (OPAC)
SirsiDynix; (Serials) SirsiDynix
Database Vendor: Gale Cengage Learning

S NATIONAL ASTRONOMY & IONOSPHERE CENTER*, Arecibo
Observatory Library, Carretera 625 Final, 00612. (Mail add: HC3 Box
53995, 00612), SAN 352-583X. Tel: 787-878-2612, Ext 215.
Administration Tel: 787-879-3007. FAX: 787-878-1861. Web Site:
www.naic.edu. *In Charge,* Carmen Rosario
Founded 1963
Library Holdings: Bk Titles 2,530; Bk Vols 2,580; Per Subs 45
Special Collections: Arecibo Observatory Reports; Palomar Sky Atlas;
Theses Coll
Subject Interests: Astronomy, Astrophysics, Computer sci, Electronics,
Eng, Physics
Database Vendor: Dialog

C PONTIFICIA CATHOLIC UNIVERSITY OF PUERTO RICO,
ARECIBO*, PO Box 144045, 00614-4045. SAN 318-5354. Tel:
787-881-1212, Ext 6028. FAX: 787-881-0777. *Librn,* Nora Garcia; *Asst
Librn, Ref,* Lydia Ortega; Staff 8 (MLS 2, Non-MLS 6)
Founded 1973. Enrl 1,300
Library Holdings: Bk Titles 42,000; Bk Vols 50,000; Per Subs 642

Special Collections: Puerto Rican Coll, bks & printed mat
Automation Activity & Vendor Info: (Acquisitions) SirsiDynix;
(Cataloging) SirsiDynix; (Circulation) SirsiDynix; (Course Reserve)
SirsiDynix; (ILL) SirsiDynix; (Media Booking) SirsiDynix; (OPAC)
SirsiDynix; (Serials) SirsiDynix
Database Vendor: EBSCOhost, ProQuest
Wireless access
Open Mon-Thurs 8am-10pm, Fri 8am-9pm, Sat 8-4

C UNIVERSITY OF PUERTO RICO*, Arecibo University College Library,
130 Ave Universidad, 00612-3145. (Mail add: PO Box 4010, 00614-4010),
SAN 318-5370. Tel: 787-815-0000, Ext 3151. Circulation Tel:
787-815-0000, Ext 3155. Interlibrary Loan Service Tel: 787-815-0000, Ext
3172. Reference Tel: 787-815-0000, Ext 3175. Administration Tel:
787-815-0000, Ext 5000. Automation Services Tel: 787-815-0000, Ext
3153. FAX: 787-878-9363. Web Site: upra.edu. *Dir,* Luis Concepcion;
Bibliog Instr, Jadira Maldonado; *Coll Develop,* Aixa Morales; *Media Spec,*
Marinilda Fuentes; *Ref,* Luis Rios; Staff 10 (MLS 10)
Founded 1967. Enrl 3,537; Fac 225; Highest Degree: Bachelor
Library Holdings: Bk Titles 62,906; Bk Vols 79,845; Per Subs 2,460
Special Collections: Arecibo Region Historical Coll; Francisco Matos
Paoli Private Library; Juvenile Coll
Subject Interests: Biol, Computer sci, Educ, Nursing
Open Mon-Thurs 7am-10pm, Fri 7-4:30, Sat 8-4:30, Sun 5-9

BARRANQUITAS

C INTER-AMERICAN UNIVERSITY OF PUERTO RICO*, Barranquitas
Campus Library, Bo Helechal, Carr 156 Intersiccion 719, 00794. (Mail
add: PO Box 517, 00794), SAN 318-5389. Tel: 787-857-2585,
787-857-3600, Ext 2063. Reference Tel: 787-857-3600, Ext 2075. FAX:
787-857-2244. Web Site: www.br.inter.edu. *Dir,* Maribel Lopez; E-mail:
mlopez@br.inter.edu; Staff 2 (MLS 1, Non-MLS 1)
Founded 1959. Enrl 1,502
Library Holdings: Bk Titles 27,246; Bk Vols 33,024; Per Subs 223
Automation Activity & Vendor Info: (Circulation) SirsiDynix; (Course
Reserve) SirsiDynix
Database Vendor: Gale Cengage Learning, Innovative Interfaces, Inc INN
- View, ProQuest
Partic in OCLC Online Computer Library Center, Inc
Open Mon-Thurs 7:30am-9pm, Fri 7:30-6, Sat 7:30-4

BAYAMON

C INTER-AMERICAN UNIVERSITY OF PUERTO RICO*, Recinto de
Bayamon, 500 Carretera Dr, 00957-6257. SAN 318-5400. Tel:
787-279-1912. FAX: 787-279-2205. Web Site:
www.inter.edu/bayamoni.html. *Dir,* Carmen Ortega; Tel: 787-257-7373, Ext
2501; *Ref,* Maria E Villamil; Staff 4 (MLS 4)
Founded 1967. Enrl 4,701
Library Holdings: Bk Vols 57,880; Per Subs 1,228
Special Collections: Interamerican Press; Puerto Rico

Subject Interests: Sci
Database Vendor: OCLC FirstSearch

C UNIVERSIDAD CENTRAL DE BAYAMON LIBRARY*, Learning
Resources Center, PO Box 1725, 00960-1725. SAN 318-5427. Tel:
787-786-3030, Ext 2136. FAX: 787-740-2200. E-mail:
annettevalentin@ucb.edu.pr. Web Site: www.ucb.edu.pr/. *Dir,* Annette
Valentin
Founded 1961. Enrl 2,700; Fac 127; Highest Degree: Master
Library Holdings: Bk Vols 45,000
Special Collections: Cesareo Rosa Nieves Coll; Puerto Rican Literature
Coll
Subject Interests: Catholic theol, Philosophy
Open Mon-Thurs 7am-10pm, Fri & Sat 8-5

CM UNIVERSIDAD CENTRAL DEL CARIBE*, Biblioteca Arturo L Carrion
Pacheco, Avenida Laurel, Santa Juanita, 00956. (Mail add: PO Box 60327,
00960-6032), SAN 370-7288. Tel: 787-785-6039, 787-798-3001, Ext 2304.
Information Services Tel: 787-798-3001, Ext 2309. FAX: 787-785-3425.
Web Site: www.uccaribe.edu. *Dir, Med Libr,* Mildred I Rivera; Tel:
787-798-3001, Ext 2305, E-mail: mildred.rivera@uccaribe.edu; *Librn,*
Maria Isabel Chevere; Tel: 787-798-3001, Ext 2306, E-mail:
maria.chevere@uccaribe.edu; *Libr Tech,* Juanita Lopez; Tel: 787-798-3001,
Ext 2307, E-mail: jlopez@uccaribe.edu; *Libr Tech,* Santos Rafael; Tel:
787-798-3001, Ext 2308, E-mail: rafael.santos@uccaribe.edu; *Libr Tech,*
Rosa Sanchez; Tel: 787-798-3001, Ext 2308, E-mail:
rsanchez@uccaribe.edu; Staff 6 (MLS 2, Non-MLS 4)
Founded 1976. Enrl 380; Highest Degree: Doctorate
Library Holdings: e-books 20; e-journals 140; Bk Titles 2,816; Bk Vols
33,112; Per Subs 619
Automation Activity & Vendor Info: (Acquisitions) EOS International;
(Cataloging) EOS International; (Circulation) EOS International; (OPAC)
EOS International; (Serials) EOS International
Database Vendor: EBSCOhost, OVID Technologies
Function: AV serv, Doc delivery serv, Health sci info serv, ILL available,
Online searches, Photocopying/Printing, Res libr
Open Mon-Thurs 7am-Midnight, Fri 7am-10pm, Sat & Sun 12-8:30,
Holidays 8-4:30
Restriction: Open to pub for ref & circ; with some limitations, Photo ID
required for access, Prof mat only

C UNIVERSITY OF PUERTO RICO*, Learning Resources Center, Minillas
Park, 170, 174 Rd, 00959-1919. SAN 318-5435. Tel: 787-993-0000, Ext
3222, 787-993-8857. FAX: 787-993-8914. E-mail: biblioteca@uprb.edu.
Web Site: www.uprb.edu/cra. *Libr Dir,* Maria de los Angeles Zavala-Colon;
E-mail: maria.zavala@upr.edu; *Head, Circ, ILL,* Delia Colon; E-mail:
delia.colon@upr.edu; *Head, Puerto Rican Coll,* Alba Osorio; E-mail:
alba.osorio@upr.edu; *Instruction Librn,* Ivette Maldonado; E-mail:
ivette.maldonado1@upr.edu; *Librn, Patent & Trademark,* Raul
Pagan-Falcon; E-mail: raul.pagan@upr.edu; *Ref Librn,* Myrna Torres;
E-mail: myrna.torres@upr.edu; *Ser Librn,* Loida Correa; E-mail:
loida.correa@upr.edu; *Coordr, Tech Serv,* David Negron; E-mail:
david.negron3@uprb.edu; *Cataloger,* Iraida Rios; E-mail:
iraida.rios1@upr.edu. Subject Specialists: *Cataloging,* David Negron; Staff
24 (MLS 9, Non-MLS 15)
Founded 1971. Enrl 4,916; Fac 309; Highest Degree: Bachelor
Library Holdings: AV Mats 1,810; CDs 5; DVDs 10; e-books 18; Bk
Titles 56,325; Bk Vols 541; Videos 100
Special Collections: Children's Literature; Patent Room, US Patent &
Trademark Depository; Puerto Rican Coll. US Document Depository
Subject Interests: Biol, Bus, Educ, Eng
Automation Activity & Vendor Info: (Acquisitions) Horizon;
(Cataloging) Horizon; (Circulation) Horizon; (OPAC) Horizon
Database Vendor: American Chemical Society, American Psychological
Association (APA), CRC Press/Taylor & Francis CRCnetBASE, EBSCO
Information Services, EBSCOhost, Elsevier, Gale Cengage Learning, H W
Wilson, ProQuest, PubMed, ScienceDirect
Wireless access
Function: Handicapped accessible, ILL available
Open Mon-Thurs 7am-10pm, Fri 7-4:30, Sat 8-4, Sun 12-4
Restriction: Borrowing privileges limited to fac & registered students,
In-house use for visitors, Open to pub for ref only

CAROLINA

C UNIVERSIDAD DEL ESTE LIBRARY*, Calle 190, Esquina 220 Bo
Sabana Abajo, 00984-2010. (Mail add: PO Box 2010, 00984-2010), SAN
320-0515. Tel: 787-257-7373, Ext 2504. Circulation Tel: 787-257-7373,
Ext 2507. Reference Tel: 787-257-7373. FAX: 787-257-7373, Ext 2516.
Web Site: www.une.suagm.edu. *Actg Dean,* Carmen Ortega; Tel:
787-257-7373, Ext 2501; *Actg Dir,* Elsa Mariani; *Head Librn,* Victor
Rodriguez; Staff 28 (MLS 13, Non-MLS 15)
Founded 1949. Enrl 8,998; Fac 84; Highest Degree: Master
Library Holdings: Bk Titles 45,046; Bk Vols 53,485; Per Subs 423

Special Collections: Ana G Mendez; Jesus T Pinero Numismatica
Subject Interests: Bus admin, Computers, Criminal justice, Educ,
Radiology, Sciences
Automation Activity & Vendor Info: (Acquisitions) Ex Libris Group;
(Cataloging) Ex Libris Group; (Circulation) Ex Libris Group; (OPAC) Ex
Libris Group; (Serials) Ex Libris Group
Database Vendor: EBSCOhost, OCLC FirstSearch, OVID Technologies,
Wilson - Wilson Web
Function: AV serv, Newsp ref libr, Photocopying/Printing, Ref serv
available, Referrals accepted
Publications: Biblio-Notas; La Revista Informa; Lista de nuevas
Adquisiciones (Acquisition list); Manual del CRA para la Facultad; Manual
del CRA para los Estudiantes
Partic in Lyrasis
Open Mon-Fri 7am-10pm, Sat 8-5, Sun 12-5

CAYEY

C UNIVERSITY OF PUERTO RICO LIBRARY, CAYEY CAMPUS*,
Biblioteca Victor M Pons Gil, 205 Ave Antonio R Barcelo, 00736. SAN
318-5443. Tel: 787-738-2161, Ext 2021, 787-738-5651. Reference Tel:
787-738-2161, Ext 2131. FAX: 787-263-2108. E-mail:
biblioteca@cayey.upr.edu. Web Site: www.cayey.upr.edu. *Dir,* Sonia de la
Cruz Davila; *Dir, Commun & Tech Serv,* Juan Jose Berrios; Tel:
787-738-2161, Ext 2447, E-mail: jberrios@cayey.upr.edu; *Dir, Info
Literacy,* Magda Perez; Tel: 787-738-2161, Ext 2453, E-mail:
mperez@cayey.upr.edu; *Dir, Ref & Libr Info Serv,* Michelle Rivera; E-mail:
mirivera@cayey.upr.edu; *Ser Coll Dir,* David Castro; Tel: 787-738-5651,
Ext 2024, E-mail: davidcastroquiles@yahoo.com; *Coordr, Circ,* Mariano
Guetierrez; E-mail: mgutierrez@cayey.upr.edu; *Tech Coordr,* Eddie Burgos;
E-mail: eburgos@cayey.upr.edu; *Ch,* Noemi Martinez; Tel: 787-738-2161,
Ext 2069, E-mail: nmartinez@cayey.upr.edu; *Music & Media Librn, Per,*
Gustavo Salvarrey; Tel: 787-738-2161, Ext 2138, E-mail:
gsalvarrey@cayey.upr.edu; *Spec Coll Librn,* Aixa Leon; Tel: 787-738-2161,
Ext 2226, E-mail: aleon@cayey.upr.edu; *Spec Coll & Archives Librn,*
Wanda Pabellon; Tel: 787-738-2161, Ext 2026, E-mail:
wpabellon@cayey.upr.edu; Staff 28 (MLS 7, Non-MLS 21)
Founded 1967. Enrl 3,202; Fac 240; Highest Degree: Bachelor
Jul 2007-Jun 2008 Income $164,351,650. Mats Exp $216,622, Books
$50,000, Per/Ser (Incl. Access Fees) $88,000, AV Equip $9,227, AV Mat
$8,000, Electronic Ref Mat (Incl. Access Fees) $54,000, Presv $5,000. Sal
$1,141,203 (Prof $34,581)
Library Holdings: Bk Vols 192,757; Per Subs 1,706
Special Collections: Gender Coll; Juvenile Coll; Miguel Melendez Munoz
Coll; Music & Media Coll; Puerto Rican Coll
Subject Interests: Bus admin, Educ, Humanities, Natural sci, Soc sci,
Women
Automation Activity & Vendor Info: (Cataloging) Horizon; (Circulation)
Horizon; (OPAC) Horizon; (Serials) EBSCO Online
Database Vendor: EBSCOhost, Gale Cengage Learning, ProQuest, Wilson
- Wilson Web
Publications: Acquisition List; Bibliographies
Special Services for the Deaf - Assistive tech
Special Services for the Blind - Assistive/Adapted tech devices, equip &
products
Open Mon-Thurs 7:30am-11pm, Fri 7:30-4:30, Sat 11-3, Sun 3-8

FAJARDO

C INTER-AMERICAN UNIVERSITY-FAJARDO CAMPUS*, Centro de
Acceso a la Informacion, Calle Union, Batey Central, 00738. (Mail add:
Call Box 70003, 00738-7003), SAN 365-4966. Tel: 787-863-2390.
Interlibrary Loan Service Tel: 787-863-2390, Ext 2226. FAX:
787-860-3470. Web Site: cai.inter.edu, fajardo.inter.edu/cai. *Dir,* Angie E
Colon; Tel: 787-863-2390, Ext 2213, E-mail:
angie.colon@fajardo.inter.edu; Staff 9 (MLS 3, Non-MLS 6)
Founded 1961. Enrl 1,860; Fac 35; Highest Degree: Bachelor
Library Holdings: Bk Titles 27,000; Bk Vols 34,000; Per Subs 675
Special Collections: Puerto Rico Data Census Center
Subject Interests: Recycling
Database Vendor: Gale Cengage Learning, OVID Technologies

FORT BUCHANAN

A UNITED STATES ARMY, Fort Buchanan Post Library, Post Library, Bldg
518, 518 Depot Rd, 00934-4559. SAN 365-5024. Tel: 787-707-3208.
Administration Tel: 787-707-3812. FAX: 787-707-3480. Web Site:
mylibraryus.fmwr.net/search~S20, www.buchananmwr.com. *Supvry Librn,*
Eva Cabanas -Malave; E-mail: eva.j.cabanas-malave.naf@mail.mil; Staff 6
(MLS 2, Non-MLS 4)
Library Holdings: Bk Titles 28,787; Bk Vols 29,888; Per Subs 200
Special Collections: Children's Coll
Database Vendor: OCLC FirstSearch
Partic in Fedlink; OCLC Online Computer Library Center, Inc
Open Mon-Fri 10-8, Sat 10-5

GUAYAMA

C   INTER-AMERICAN UNIVERSITY OF PUERTO RICO*, Guayama
     Campus Library, Call Box 10004, 00785-0004. SAN 318-5478. Tel:
     787-864-2222. FAX: 787-864-8232. Web Site: www.guayama.inter.edu.
     Librn, Myrna Rosario Santiago; Staff 10 (MLS 3, Non-MLS 7)
     Founded 1958. Fac 46
     Library Holdings: Bk Vols 21,000; Per Subs 130
     Special Collections: Afro-antillian Poetry Coll; Luis Palis Matos Coll
     Subject Interests: Educ, Humanities, Nursing, Sci
     Automation Activity & Vendor Info: (Cataloging) SirsiDynix;
     (Circulation) SirsiDynix
     Database Vendor: Gale Cengage Learning, OVID Technologies
     Publications: Infocai Bulletin
     Friends of the Library Group

GURABO

C   UNIVERSIDAD DEL TURABO*, Learning Center, PO Box 3030,
     00778-3030. SAN 321-611X. Tel: 787-743-7979, Ext 4501. Circulation
     Tel: 787-743-7979, Ext 4522. Reference Tel: 787-743-7979, Ext 4515.
     FAX: 787-743-7924. Web Site: ut.suagm.edu. *Dir,* Luisa Torres; E-mail:
     ut_lutorres@suagm.edu; *Vice Chancellor of Info Serv,* Sarai Lastra; *Eng
     Librn,* Jolanda Lopez; *Info Literacy Librn,* Maria Gomez; *Info Literacy
     Librn,* Miriam Martinez; *Cat,* Melva Rivera; E-mail:
     ut_mrivera@suagm.edu; *Cat,* Marjorie Torres; E-mail:
     ut_mtorres@suagm.edu; *Ref, Ser,* Aida Medina; E-mail:
     ut_amedina@suagm.edu; *Ref Serv, Ser,* Ruy W Monroe; E-mail:
     ut_rmonroe@suagm.edu; Staff 17 (MLS 7, Non-MLS 10)
     Founded 1969. Enrl 15,000; Highest Degree: Master
     Library Holdings: e-books 6,000; e-journals 30,000; Bk Titles 94,000; Bk
     Vols 150,000; Per Subs 450
     Automation Activity & Vendor Info: (Acquisitions) Ex Libris Group;
     (Cataloging) Ex Libris Group; (Circulation) Ex Libris Group; (Course
     Reserve) Ex Libris Group; (OPAC) Ex Libris Group; (Serials) Ex Libris
     Group
     Database Vendor: EBSCOhost, ProQuest
     Wireless access
     Publications: Acquisitions List
     Open Mon-Fri 7am-10pm, Sat 7:30-6, Sun 10-4

HATO REY

C   AMAURY VERAY MUSIC LIBRARY*, 350 Rafael Lamar, 00918. SAN
     318-5672. Tel: 787-751-0160, Ext 256. FAX: 787-754-5934. Web Site:
     www.cmpr.edu/biblioteca. *Coll Develop, Dir,* Damaris Cordero; E-mail:
     dcordero@cmpr.gobierno.pr; *Acq, Asst Librn,* Orlando Toro; Tel:
     787-751-0160, Ext 225, E-mail: otoro@cmpr.gobierno.pr; *Coordr, AV,*
     Rafael Sustache; Tel: 787-751-0160, Ext 279, E-mail:
     rsustache@cmpr.gobierno.pr; *Ref & Instrul Serv Librn,* Milagros Escalera;
     E-mail: mescalera@cmpr.gobierno.pr; *Tech Coordr,* Sigfredo López; Tel:
     787-751-0160, Ext 252, E-mail: slopez@cmpr.gobierno.pr; *Cat,* María del
     Carmen Maldonado; Tel: 787-751-0160, Ext 247, E-mail:
     mcmaldon@cmpr.gobierno.pr
     Founded 1962. Enrl 330; Fac 60; Highest Degree: Master
     Library Holdings: AV Mats 135; Braille Volumes 17; CDs 1,597; DVDs
     168; e-journals 108; Electronic Media & Resources 102; Music Scores
     26,450; Bk Titles 4,685; Bk Vols 4,889; Per Subs 120; Videos 567
     Special Collections: Music (Puerto Rican & Latin American Composers)
     Subject Interests: Music
     Automation Activity & Vendor Info: (Acquisitions) Ex Libris Group;
     (Cataloging) Ex Libris Group; (Circulation) Ex Libris Group; (OPAC) Ex
     Libris Group
     Database Vendor: EBSCOhost, OCLC FirstSearch, ProQuest
     Function: Audio & video playback equip for onsite use, AV serv,
     CD-ROM, Electronic databases & coll, Music CDs, Online searches,
     Orientations, Ref serv available, Res libr, Spoken cassettes & CDs, Spoken
     cassettes & DVDs, Telephone ref, VHS videos
     Open Mon-Thurs 7:30am-9pm, Fri 7:30-6:30, Sat 9-6
     Restriction: In-house use for visitors

     INTER-AMERICAN UNIVERSITY OF PUERTO RICO
C   INFORMATION ACCESS CENTER*, Carr PR 1, Esq Calle Francisco
     Sein, 00919. (Mail add: PO Box 191293, 00919-1293), SAN 365-5059.
     Tel: 787-250-1912, Ext 2160, 787-250-1912, Ext 2514. Circulation Tel:
     787-250-1912, Ext 2295. Interlibrary Loan Service Tel: 787-250-1913,
     Ext 2309. FAX: 787-751-3915. Web Site:
     www.metro.inter.edu/servacad/cai. *Dir,* Rosa M Pimentel; E-mail:
     rpimente@inter.edu; *ILL,* Pilar Ortiz Del Valle; E-mail:
     pilarortiz@hotmail.com; Staff 16 (MLS 5, Non-MLS 11)
     Founded 1961. Enrl 10,500; Fac 693; Highest Degree: Doctorate
     Jul 2005-Jun 2006. Mats Exp $390,000, Books $100,000, Per/Ser (Incl.
     Access Fees) $140,000, AV Equip $15,000, AV Mat $10,000, Electronic
     Ref Mat (Incl. Access Fees) $120,000. Sal $541,920
     Library Holdings: Bk Vols 113,200; Per Subs 2,771

Special Collections: Juvenile Coll; Puerto Rican Coll. Oral History
Subject Interests: Criminal justice, Educ, Liberal arts, Med tech,
Nursing, Psychol, Sci tech, Theol
Automation Activity & Vendor Info: (Acquisitions) SirsiDynix;
(Cataloging) SirsiDynix; (Circulation) SirsiDynix; (Course Reserve)
SirsiDynix; (ILL) SirsiDynix; (Media Booking) SirsiDynix; (OPAC)
SirsiDynix; (Serials) SirsiDynix
Database Vendor: Cambridge Scientific Abstracts, EBSCOhost, Gale
Cengage Learning, netLibrary, OCLC WorldCat, OVID Technologies,
OVID Technologies, ProQuest, SirsiDynix, Wilson - Wilson Web
Function: Govt ref serv, ILL available, Large print keyboards, Newsp ref
libr, Online searches, Orientations, Photocopying/Printing, Ref serv
available, VCDs, VHS videos, Wheelchair accessible, Workshops
Special Services for the Deaf - Assistive tech; Staff with knowledge of
sign lang
Special Services for the Blind - Assistive/Adapted tech devices, equip &
products; Computer with voice synthesizer for visually impaired persons;
Scanner for conversion & translation of mats
Open Mon-Thurs 7am-11pm, Fri 7am-8pm, Sat 8-5, Sun 12:30-4:30
Restriction: Open to pub for ref only, Open to students, fac & staff,
Photo ID required for access, Restricted pub use, Visually impaired
students & their teachers

CL   SCHOOL OF LAW LIBRARY, PO Box 70351, 00936, SAN 318-5818.
     Tel: 787-751-1912. Circulation Tel: 787-751-1912, Ext 2075. Interlibrary
     Loan Service Tel: 787-751-1912, Ext 2027. Reference Tel:
     787-751-1912, Ext 2029. Administration Tel: 787-751-1912, Ext 2042.
     Automation Services Tel: 787-751-1912, Ext 2066. FAX: 787-753-6851.
     Web Site: www.inter.edu. *Dir,* Ruben Sanchez; *Spec Coll Librn,* Lillian E
     Santiago; *Acq,* Noelia Rendon; E-mail: nrendon@inter.edu; *Cat,* Maria
     Cardona; *Ref Serv,* Alberto Guzman; *Ref Serv,* Luz Pizarro; Staff 18
     (MLS 7, Non-MLS 11)
     Founded 1961. Enrl 504; Fac 24; Highest Degree: Doctorate
     Library Holdings: Bk Vols 205,000; Per Subs 200
     Special Collections: Domingo Toledo Alamo Coll; Fernos Coll; Jose
     Echeverria Coll
     Subject Interests: Civil law
     Automation Activity & Vendor Info: (Acquisitions) SirsiDynix;
     (Cataloging) SirsiDynix; (Circulation) SirsiDynix; (Course Reserve)
     SirsiDynix; (Media Booking) SirsiDynix; (OPAC) SirsiDynix; (Serials)
     SirsiDynix
     Database Vendor: Gale Cengage Learning, LexisNexis, Westlaw
     Publications: Acquisitions List; Bibliographies
     Open Mon-Fri 8am-11pm, Sat & Sun 9-9

L   MCCONNELL VALDES*, 270 Munoz Rivera Ave, 00918. SAN 371-9316.
     Tel: 787-250-5147, 787-759-9292. FAX: 787-759-9225. *Dir,* Betsaida
     Velez-Natal; E-mail: bv@mcvpr.com; Staff 5 (MLS 1, Non-MLS 4)
     Founded 1947
     Library Holdings: Bk Titles 40,000; Bk Vols 58,000; Per Subs 124
     Subject Interests: Corporate law, Taxes
     Automation Activity & Vendor Info: (Cataloging) Follett Software;
     (OPAC) Follett Software; (Serials) Follett Software
     Database Vendor: Dialog, LexisNexis, Westlaw
     Partic in Dialog Corp; Westlaw
     Restriction: Staff use only

L   UNITED STATES COURT OF APPEALS*, First Circuit Satellite Library,
     Federal Bldg, Rm 121, 150 Chardon Ave, 00918. SAN 372-3585. Tel:
     787-772-3096. FAX: 787-766-5747. *Librn,* Ana Milagros Rodriguez; *Tech
     Serv,* Jose Garcia
     Library Holdings: Bk Vols 30,000; Per Subs 50
     Partic in Lexis, OCLC Online Computer Libr Ctr, Inc; Westlaw

MAYAGUEZ

C   PONTIFICAL CATHOLIC UNIVERSITY OF PUERTO RICO*,
     Mayaguez Branch Library, Ramon Emeterio Betances St 482, 00680. (Mail
     add: PO Box 1326, 00681-1326), SAN 318-5540. Tel: 787-834-5151, Ext
     5008. Reference Tel: 787-834-5151, Ext 5010. Administration Tel:
     787-834-5151, Ext 5009. Information Services Tel: 787-834-5151, Ext
     5011. FAX: 787-831-7155. Web Site: mayaguez.pucpr.edu/biblioteca. *Head
     Librn,* Edwin Ramos; E-mail: edramos@email.pucpr.edu; *Ref Serv,*
     Gerinaldo Camacho; E-mail: gcamacho@email.pucpr.edu; *Ref Serv,* Arlene
     Concepcion; E-mail: arlene_concepcion@email.pucpr.edu; *Cat,* Elisa I
     Gonzalez; E-mail: elisa.gonzalez@email.pucpr.edu; Staff 5 (MLS 3,
     Non-MLS 2)
     Founded 50. Enrl 1,800; Fac 100; Highest Degree: Master
     Jul 2010-Jun 2011. Mats Exp $87,500, Books $37,000, Per/Ser (Incl.
     Access Fees) $38,000, Manu Arch $5,000, Other Print Mats $1,000, AV
     Equip $2,000, AV Mat $1,500, Electronic Ref Mat (Incl. Access Fees)
     $1,000, Presv $2,000. Sal $137,362 (Prof $102,875)
     Library Holdings: AV Mats 1,150; DVDs 45; e-books 47,000; Bk Titles
     35,774; Bk Vols 37,987; Per Subs 78; Videos 889
     Subject Interests: Gen (encyclopedias), Relig, Sci

Automation Activity & Vendor Info: (Acquisitions) Horizon; (Cataloging) Horizon; (Circulation) Horizon; (ILL) Horizon; (Media Booking) Horizon; (OPAC) Horizon; (Serials) Horizon
Database Vendor: EBSCOhost, ProQuest, SirsiDynix, Wilson - Wilson Web
Wireless access
Open Mon-Thurs 8am-10pm, Fri & Sat 8-4

C   UNIVERSIDAD ADVENTISTA DE LAS ANTILLAS*, Biblioteca Dennis Soto, Carr 106 Km 2 Interior, Bo La Quinta, 00680. (Mail add: PO Box 118, 00681). Tel: 787-834-9595, Ext 2216. FAX: 787-834-6015. Web Site: library.uaa.edu. *Dir,* Aixa Vega; Tel: 787-834-9595, Ext 2314, E-mail: avega@uaa.edu; *Acq,* Nydia Martinez; Tel: 787-834-9595, Ext 2311, E-mail: nortiz@uaa.edu; *Circ,* Gladys Rodriguez; Tel: 787-834-9595, Ext 2313, E-mail: gsoto@uaa.edu; *Ref Serv,* Maribel Cedeno; Tel: 787-834-9595, Ext 2274, E-mail: mcedeno@uaa.edu; *Tech Serv,* Marlene Escandon; E-mail: mescandon@uaa.edu; Staff 5 (MLS 3, Non-MLS 2)
Founded 1961. Enrl 767; Fac 72; Highest Degree: Master
Library Holdings: Bk Vols 87,706; Per Subs 353
Special Collections: Puerto Rico; Theology
Subject Interests: Theol
Automation Activity & Vendor Info: (Cataloging) TLC (The Library Corporation); (Circulation) TLC (The Library Corporation)
Database Vendor: EBSCOhost
Partic in Lyrasis
Open Mon-Thurs 7:30am-9:30pm, Fri 7:30-1, Sun 5pm-9:30pm

C   UNIVERSITY OF PUERTO RICO*, Mayaguez Campus General Library, Alfonso Valdes Ave, No 259 N, 00681. (Mail add: PO Box 9022, 00681-9022), SAN 365-5172. Tel: 787-265-3810, 787-832-4040. Circulation Tel: 787-832-4040, Ext 2159. Interlibrary Loan Service Tel: 787-832-4040, Ext 2205, 787-832-4040, Ext 3752. Reference Tel: 787-832-4040, Ext 2023, 787-832-4040, Ext 2259. Automation Services Tel: 787-832-4040, Ext 5456. FAX: 787-265-5483. Interlibrary Loan Service FAX: 787-831-4890. Automation Services FAX: 787-265-5456. E-mail: library@uprm.edu. Web Site: www.uprm.edu/library. *Dir,* Dr Jose A Mari-Mutt, PhD; E-mail: jmari@uprm.edu; *Coordr, Pub Serv Librn III,* Sara Ruiz; E-mail: ruizs@uprm.edu; Staff 68 (MLS 25, Non-MLS 43)
Founded 1911. Enrl 12,311; Fac 1,100; Highest Degree: Doctorate
Jul 2007-Jun 2008. Mats Exp $2,000,800, Books $94,421, Per/Ser (Incl. Access Fees) $1,810,666, AV Equip $2,000, AV Mat $3,138, Electronic Ref Mat (Incl. Access Fees) $88,075, Presv $2,500. Sal $2,918,108 (Prof $1,267,104)
Library Holdings: CDs 2,036; DVDs 132; e-books 5,294; e-journals 38,875; Microforms 284,007; Music Scores 422; Bk Titles 164,303; Bk Vols 215,861; Per Subs 1,046; Videos 4,729
Special Collections: Marine Sciences Coll; Sala Manuel Maria Sama (Puerto Rican Coll). State Document Depository; US Document Depository
Subject Interests: Applied tech, Bus, Census data, Chem eng, Civil eng, Computer eng, Electrical eng, Electronic resources, Indust eng, Marine sci, Mechanical eng, Natural sci, Patents trademarks, Soc sci, Visually impaired
Automation Activity & Vendor Info: (Acquisitions) SirsiDynix; (Cataloging) SirsiDynix; (Circulation) SirsiDynix; (OPAC) SirsiDynix; (Serials) SirsiDynix
Database Vendor: Cambridge Scientific Abstracts, CRC Press/Taylor & Francis CRCnetBASE, EBSCOhost, Gale Cengage Learning, LexisNexis, Marcive, Inc, OCLC FirstSearch, ProQuest, ScienceDirect, SirsiDynix, Wilson - Wilson Web
Wireless access
Function: Art exhibits, Audio & video playback equip for onsite use, AV serv, Computers for patron use, Copy machines, e-mail serv, E-Reserves, Electronic databases & coll, Govt ref serv, ILL available, Instruction & testing, Large print keyboards, Literacy & newcomer serv, Magnifiers for reading, Mail & tel request accepted, Music CDs, Online cat, Online info literacy tutorials on the web & in blackboard, Online ref, Online searches, Orientations, Outside serv via phone, mail, e-mail & web, Photocopying/Printing, Pub access computers, Ref & res, Ref serv available, Telephone ref, VHS videos, Web-catalog, Workshops
Partic in Associated Colleges of the Midwest; Lyrasis; OCLC Online Computer Library Center, Inc
Special Services for the Deaf - Assistive tech
Special Services for the Blind - Accessible computers; Assistive/Adapted tech devices, equip & products; Compressed speech equip; Computer with voice synthesizer for visually impaired persons; Internet workstation with adaptive software; Large screen computer & software; Magnifiers; Networked computers with assistive software
Open Mon-Thurs 6am-2am, Fri 6-4:30, Sat 12-5, Sun 2-Midnight
Restriction: Non-circulating of rare bks
Departmental Libraries:
MARINE SCIENCE, PO Box 9022, 00681-9022. Tel: 787-832-4040, Ext 2513. Web Site: www.uprm.edu/library. *In Charge,* Deixter Mendez; Staff 2 (MLS 1, Non-MLS 1)
    Library Holdings: Bk Titles 4,741; Bk Vols 5,449; Per Subs 42

Subject Interests: Aquaculture, Chem oceanography, Fisheries biol, Marine biol
Open Mon-Fri 7:30-4:00

MERCEDITA

C   INTER-AMERICAN UNIVERSITY OF PUERTO RICO*, Ponce Campus Library, 104 Parque Industrial Turpeaux, Rd 1, 00715-1602. SAN 318-5575. Tel: 787-284-1912. Interlibrary Loan Service Tel: 787-284-1912, Ext 2119. Administration Tel: 787-284-1912, Ext 2287. FAX: 787-841-0103. E-mail: webcai@ponce.inter.edu. Web Site: ponce.inter.edu/cai. *Info Access Ctr Dir,* Brunilda Figueroa-Marrero; Tel: 787-284-2127, E-mail: bfiguero@ponce.inter.edu; *Coll Develop Librn,* Ana Matos-Cabrera; E-mail: amatos@ponce.inter.edu; *Info Literacy Librn,* Maria M Silvestrini-Ruiz; E-mail: msilvest@ponce.inter.edu; *Ref Librn,* María Musalem-Michelem; E-mail: mmusalem@ponce.inter.edu; Staff 10 (MLS 2, Non-MLS 8)
Founded 1966. Enrl 4,200; Fac 76; Highest Degree: Bachelor
Library Holdings: Bk Titles 44,153; Bk Vols 50,767; Per Subs 576
Special Collections: Puerto Rican Coll
Subject Interests: Applied sci, Computers, Econ, Educ
Automation Activity & Vendor Info: (Acquisitions) SirsiDynix; (Cataloging) SirsiDynix; (Circulation) SirsiDynix; (Course Reserve) SirsiDynix; (ILL) SirsiDynix; (Media Booking) SirsiDynix; (OPAC) SirsiDynix
Database Vendor: Gale Cengage Learning, OVID Technologies, ProQuest
Function: Ref serv available
Partic in Dobis-Leuven
Restriction: Not open to pub, Open to students

PONCE

M   PONCE SCHOOL OF MEDICINE LIBRARY*, Fundacion Angel Ramos Library, 395 Zona Industrial Reparada 2, Calle Dr Luis F Sala, 00716-2348. (Mail add: PO Box 7004, 00732), SAN 371-425X. Tel: 787-840-2575. Circulation Tel: 787-840-2575, Ext 2225. Interlibrary Loan Service Tel: 787-840-2575, Ext 2228. Reference Tel: 787-840-2575, Ext 2223. FAX: 787-844-3865. E-mail: library@psm.edu. Web Site: library.psm.edu, psm.edu. *Actg Dir,* Carmen G Malavet; E-mail: cmalavet@psm.edu; Staff 8 (MLS 2, Non-MLS 6)
Founded 1977. Enrl 590; Fac 250; Highest Degree: Doctorate
Jul 2010-Jun 2011 Income $462,054. Mats Exp $260,374, Books $10,595, Per/Ser (Incl. Access Fees) $74,426, AV Mat $1,500, Electronic Ref Mat (Incl. Access Fees) $164,853, Presv $9,000. Sal $78,377 (Prof $64,000)
Library Holdings: CDs 403; DVDs 57; e-books 3,792; e-journals 26,839; Microforms 11,760; Bk Titles 12,754; Bk Vols 45,852; Per Subs 914; Videos 252
Special Collections: Puerto Rican Publications, bks, journals
Automation Activity & Vendor Info: (Cataloging) TLC (The Library Corporation); (Circulation) TLC (The Library Corporation); (OPAC) TLC (The Library Corporation); (Serials) TLC (The Library Corporation)
Database Vendor: American Psychological Association (APA), EBSCOhost, Elsevier, McGraw-Hill, MD Consult, Medline, Nature Publishing Group, OVID Technologies, PubMed, ScienceDirect, TLC (The Library Corporation)
Wireless access
Function: Computer training, Computers for patron use, Copy machines, Doc delivery serv, e-mail serv, E-Reserves, Fax serv, Handicapped accessible, Health sci info serv, Holiday prog, ILL available, Mail & tel request accepted, Online cat, Online searches, Orientations, Outside serv via phone, mail, e-mail & web, Photocopying/Printing, Ref serv available, Ref serv in person, Referrals accepted, Res libr, Scanner, Telephone ref, Web-catalog, Wheelchair accessible, Workshops
Partic in Docline; National Network of Libraries of Medicine
Open Mon-Fri 7am-11:30pm, Sat Noon-8:30, Sun 3pm-11:30pm
Restriction: In-house use for visitors

PONTIFICAL CATHOLIC UNIVERSITY OF PUERTO RICO
C   ENCARNACION VALDES LIBRARY*, 2250 Avenida Las Americas, Ste 509, 00717-0777, SAN 365-5261. Tel: 787-841-2000, Ext 1801, 787-841-2000, Ext 1802. Circulation Tel: 787-841-2000, Ext 1810. Interlibrary Loan Service Tel: 787-841-2000, Ext 1815. Reference Tel: 787-841-2000, Ext 1818. FAX: 787-284-0235. E-mail: library@pucpr.edu. Web Site: www.pucpr.edu. *Dir,* Esther Irizarry-Vazquez; *Asst Dir,* Ana Aurelia Torres; Tel: 787-841-2000, Ext 1811, E-mail: antorres@email.pucpr.edu; *Asst Librn,* Arleyn D Jusino; E-mail: ajusino@email.pucpr.edu; *Music & Media Librn,* Migdalia Ramos; Tel: 787-841-2000, Ext 1807, E-mail: mramos@email.pucpr.edu; *Adminr,* Cecilia Lugo; E-mail: clugo@email.pucpr.edu; *Automation Syst Coordr,* Edna Amalia Ramirez; Tel: 787-841-2000, Ext 1813, E-mail: eramirez@pucpr.edu; *Acq,* Maria de los Angeles Rivera; Tel: 787-841-2000, Ext 1817, E-mail: marivera@email.pucpr.edu; *Acq,* Magda Vargas; Tel: 787-841-2000, Ext 1816, E-mail: mvargas@pucpr.edu; *Bibliog Instr, ILL,* Madeline Nazario; E-mail: mnazario@pucpr.edu; *Cat,* Mildred Lopez; Tel: 787-841-2000, Ext 1821, E-mail:

milopez@email.pucpr.edu; *Cat,* Pedro L Rivera; E-mail:
privera@email.pucpr.edu; *Circ,* Ruth Arzola; E-mail: rarzola@email.pucpr.edu;
Circ, Marlyn Santiago; E-mail: masantiago@email.pucpr.edu; *Govt Doc,*
Maria M Bonet; Tel: 787-841-2000, Ext 1806, E-mail:
mbonet@email.pucpr.edu; *Info Literacy,* Cirilo Toro; Tel: 787-841-2000,
Ext 1814, E-mail: ctoro@email.pucpr.edu; *Info Serv,* Kenia Nazario; Tel:
787-841-2000, Ext 1809, E-mail: knazario@email.pucpr.edu; *Per,*
Francisco Plata; Tel: 787-841-2000, Ext 1809, E-mail:
fplata@email.pucpr.edu; *Per,* Rosaura Romero; Tel: 787-841-2000, Ext
1809, E-mail: rromero@pucpr.edu; *Libr Tech,* Alexis Rivera; Tel:
787-841-2000, Ext 1809, E-mail: arivera@email.pucpr.edu; *Ref,* Ileana
Amill; E-mail: iamill@pucpr.edu; *Ref Serv,* Jose Santos; E-mail:
jsantos@email.pucpr.edu; *Spec Coll & Archives Librn,* Vidalina
Rodriguez; Tel: 787-841-2000, Ext 1808, E-mail: vrodriguez@pucpr.edu;
Spec Coll & Archives Librn, Blanca Valentin; Tel: 787-841-2000, Ext
1808, E-mail: balentin@email.pucpr.edu; Staff 23 (MLS 12, Non-MLS
11)
Founded 1950. Enrl 10,045; Fac 311; Highest Degree: Doctorate
Library Holdings: CDs 4,668; e-books 23,525; e-journals 24,163; Bk
Vols 270,453; Per Subs 12,798
Special Collections: Education (ERIC Documents); Monsignor Vincent
Murga Coll; Puerto Rican Coll; Strategic Publications Center of the
PAHO. US Document Depository
Subject Interests: Bus, Educ, Nursing, Relig, Sciences
Automation Activity & Vendor Info: (Acquisitions) SirsiDynix;
(Cataloging) SirsiDynix; (Circulation) SirsiDynix; (Course Reserve)
SirsiDynix; (OPAC) SirsiDynix; (Serials) SirsiDynix
Database Vendor: EBSCOhost, Gale Cengage Learning, OCLC
FirstSearch, OVID Technologies, ProQuest, SirsiDynix, Wilson - Wilson
Web
Function: For res purposes
Partic in OCLC Online Computer Library Center, Inc
Publications: Annual Report; Faculty handbook; Student handbook
Special Services for the Deaf - Assistive tech
Special Services for the Blind - Computer with voice synthesizer for
visually impaired persons
Open Mon-Thurs 7:30am-10pm, Fri 7:30-4, Sat 8-8

CL MONSEIGNOR FREMIOT TORRES OLIVER LEGAL INFORMATION
& RESEARCH CENTER*, 2250 Avenida Las Americas, Ste 544,
00717-9997, SAN 365-5296. Tel: 787-841-2000, Ext 1850, 1851.
Reference Tel: 787-841-2000, Ext 1853. FAX: 787-841-5354. E-mail:
bib_derecho@email.pucpr.edu. Web Site: www.pucpr.edu. *Dir,* Noelia
Padua; Tel: 787-841-2000 Ext 1852, E-mail: npadua@email.pucpr.edu;
Automation Syst Coordr, Cat, Tammy Martinez; Tel: 787-841-2000, Ext
1858, E-mail: tmartinez@email.pucpr.edu; *Circ, Ref,* Miguel Alvarez;
E-mail: malvarez@email.pucpr.edu; *Circ, Ref,* Teresita Colon; E-mail:
tguillemard@email.pucpr.edu; *Acq,* Maria del C Gonzalez; Tel:
787-841-2000 Ext.1857, E-mail: mcgonzalez@email.pucpr.edu; Staff 11
(MLS 5, Non-MLS 6)
Founded 1961. Enrl 585; Fac 48
Library Holdings: Bk Titles 28,878; Bk Vols 227,926; Per Subs 2,505
Special Collections: Puerto Rico Coll. UN Document Depository; US
Document Depository
Subject Interests: Civil, Constitutional, Criminal, Law, Roman
Partic in Lyrasis; OCLC Online Computer Library Center, Inc
Publications: Boletin Informativo (Publicacion Trimestral); Sumario de
Revistas en Espanol
Open Mon-Thurs 7:30-12, Fri 7:30-11, Sat 9-8, Sun 1-9

SAN GERMAN

C INTER-AMERICAN UNIVERSITY OF PUERTO RICO, Juan Cancio
Ortiz Library, San German Campus, Ave Inter-American University, Rd
102, K 30 6, 00683-9801. (Mail add: PO Box 5100, 00683-9801), SAN
318-5648. Tel: 787-264-1912, Ext 7521. Circulation Tel: 787-264-1912,
Ext 7534. Reference Tel: 787-264-1912, Ext 7535. Administration Tel:
787-264-1912, Ext 7520. FAX: 787-264-2544. E-mail:
presinterbiblio@sg.inter.edu. Web Site: cai.sg.inter.edu. *Libr Dir,* Doris
Asencio-Toro; Tel: 787-892-5115, E-mail: dasencio@sg.inter.edu; *Asst Libr
Dir,* Carlos Garcia-Hernandez; Tel: 787-264-1912, Ext 7523, E-mail:
cgarcia@sg.inter.edu; *Puerto Rican Coll Librn,* María Juárez-Ponce; Tel:
787-264-1912, Ext 7536, E-mail: maria_juarez@alpha.sg.inter.edu; *Ref
Librn,* Magdalena Torres-Aveillez; E-mail: magtorres@sg.inter.edu; *Ser
Librn,* Jenny Salazar-Mallorquin; Tel: 787-264-1912, Ext 7537, E-mail:
jsmallor@sg.inter.edu; Staff 19 (MLS 5, Non-MLS 14)
Founded 1923. Enrl 5,389; Fac 326; Highest Degree: Doctorate
Jul 2011-Jun 2012. Mats Exp $150,502, Books $30,087, Per/Ser (Incl.
Access Fees) $54,602, AV Equip $1,263, AV Mat $2,302, Electronic Ref
Mat (Incl. Access Fees) $61,948, Presv $300. Sal $563,560 (Prof
$211,088)
Library Holdings: AV Mats 23,670; Braille Volumes 12; CDs 3,849;
DVDs 469; e-books 21,686; e-journals 118; Large Print Bks 17;
Microforms 571,242; Music Scores 1,205; Bk Titles 124,052; Bk Vols
159,118; Per Subs 2,294; Videos 2,214

Special Collections: Centro de Documentación Histórica Arturo Morales
Carrión (Personal Library & Documents (books, pamphlets, periodicals)
print); Museo y Archivo Histórico (Manuscripts, rarebooks, books,
pamphlets, periodicals & photographs about the history & development of
the Interamerican University of Puerto Rico – 1912 to present (print,
online)); Sala de Puerto Rico Angel R. González (Books, pamphlets, CD's
written by Puerto Rican authors & about Puerto Rican topics (print &
electronic))
Subject Interests: Applied sci, Art, Bio, Bus, Chem, Educ, Environ sci,
Liberal arts, Linguistics, Lit, Math, Med tech, Music, Nursing, Phys educ,
Psychol, Radiology, Recreation, Soc sci
Automation Activity & Vendor Info: (Acquisitions) SirsiDynix;
(Cataloging) SirsiDynix; (Circulation) SirsiDynix; (Media Booking)
SirsiDynix; (Serials) SirsiDynix
Database Vendor: Bowker, EBSCO Information Services, EBSCOhost,
Emerald, Gale Cengage Learning, netLibrary, OCLC, OVID Technologies,
ProQuest, RefWorks, SirsiDynix, Wilson - Wilson Web
Wireless access
Function: AV serv, Computers for patron use, Copy machines, Doc
delivery serv, e-mail serv, Electronic databases & coll, Exhibits, Fax serv,
Handicapped accessible, ILL available, Mail & tel request accepted,
Microfiche/film & reading machines, Online cat, Online info literacy
tutorials on the web & in blackboard, Online ref, Online searches,
Orientations, Outside serv via phone, mail, e-mail & web,
Photocopying/Printing, Ref & res, Ref serv available, Ref serv in person,
Telephone ref, VHS videos, Web-catalog, Wheelchair accessible
Publications: Bibliographic Instruction Series (Online only); Clases de
Informes; Informes Orales; Análisis crítico de un artículo, Informe de
investigación o tesis; Propuesta de investigación por C. García (Reference
guide); Cómo acceder remotamente a las bases de datos (Reference guide);
Cómo renovar libros desde su hogar (Reference guide); Derechos de autor
por RUrrego (Reference guide); Guides (Online only); Listado de revistas
en el CAI (Online only); Recent Acquisitions Lists Online (Online only);
Recorrido virtual (Online only)
Partic in Lyrasis
Special Services for the Blind - Accessible computers; Assistive/Adapted
tech devices, equip & products; Braille equip; Computer with voice
synthesizer for visually impaired persons; PC for handicapped; Text reader;
ZoomText magnification & reading software
Open Mon-Thurs 7:30am-10pm, Fri 7:30-5, Sat 8-5, Sun 1-10
Restriction: Non-circulating of rare bks

SAN JUAN

C CARLOS ALBIZU MIRANDA LIBRARY, San Francisco Corner, 151
Tanca St, 00902. (Mail add: PO Box 9023711, 00902-3711). Tel:
787-725-6500, Ext 1567, 787-725-6500, Ext 1568. Circulation Tel:
787-725-6500, Ext 1525. Web Site: www.sju.albizu.edu. *Dir,* Yolanda
Rosario; Staff 5 (MLS 1, Non-MLS 4)
Founded 1966. Enrl 950; Fac 80; Highest Degree: Doctorate
Jul 2012-Jun 2013 Income $132,410. Mats Exp $177,360, Books $34,260,
Per/Ser (Incl. Access Fees) $58,100, Electronic Ref Mat (Incl. Access
Fees) $85,000. Sal $73,000 (Prof $35,000)
Library Holdings: e-books 22,425; e-books 22,425; e-journals 49,830;
e-journals 49,830; Bk Titles 17,451; Per Subs 194
Special Collections: Dissertations
Subject Interests: Behav sci, Psychol, Speech disorders
Automation Activity & Vendor Info: (Cataloging) Follett Software;
(Circulation) Follett Software; (OPAC) Follett Software
Database Vendor: American Psychological Association (APA),
Blackwell's, ebrary, EBSCOhost, Gale Cengage Learning, OCLC
FirstSearch, ProQuest, Wilson - Wilson Web
Wireless access
Open Mon-Thurs 7am-10:30pm, Fri 7-4, Sat 8-5, Sun 1-6
Restriction: Circulates for staff only

G COMMONWEALTH OF PUERTO RICO*, Office of Management &
Budget, 254 Tetuan & Cruz Sts, 00902. (Mail add: PO Box 9023228,
00902-3328), SAN 365-5776. Tel: 787-725-9420, Ext 2139. FAX:
787-721-8329. Web Site: www.ogp.govierno.pr. *Librn,* Isaias Pecho
Founded 1942
Library Holdings: Bk Vols 4,600; Per Subs 140
Special Collections: Public Documents; Puerto Rican Budget
Subject Interests: Econ, Law, Polit sci, Pub admin
Restriction: Restricted pub use

P COMMONWEALTH OF PUERTO RICO*, Library & Information
Services Program, Cesar Gonzalez Ave, 00919. (Mail add: PO Box
190759, 00919-0759), SAN 318-5494. Tel: 787-759-2000, Ext 2822. FAX:
787-753-6945. *Dir,* Sandra Castro; E-mail: castroas@de.gobierno.pr
Library Holdings: Bk Vols 920,213
Special Collections: Blind & Physically Handicapped Coll (856 titles);
Puerto Rican Authors & Themes About Puerto Rican Culture
Publications: Union Catalogue of Puerto Rican Materials
Open Mon-Fri 8-4:30

GM DEPARTMENT OF VETERANS AFFAIRS*, Library Service, Library Service 142D, Ten Calle Casia, 00921-3201. SAN 318-5745. Tel: 787-641-7582, Ext 12165, 787-641-7582, Ext 12226. Reference Tel: 787-641-7582, Ext 12163, 787-641-7582, Ext 12392. Administration Tel: 787-641-7582, Ext 12227. FAX: 787-641-4550. *Chief,* Dr Elsa M Lopez, PhD; Tel: 787-641-3639, E-mail: elsa.lopez@med.va.gov; *Admin Serv,* Hilaria Soto, II; Tel: 787-641-7582, Ext 12227, E-mail: hilaria.soto@med.va.gov; *Libr Tech,* Rosa I Castro; E-mail: rosa.castro@med.va.gov; *Libr Tech,* Sonia Rosario; E-mail: sonia.rosario-franco@med.va.gov; *Ref Serv,* Jose Quinones-Figueroa; Tel: 787-641-7582, Ext 12392, E-mail: jose.quinones@med.va.gov; *Ref Serv,* Carmen J Sierra; Tel: 787-641-7582, Ext 12163, Fax: 787-641-7582, E-mail: carmen.sierra-ramirez@med.va.gov. Subject Specialists: *Educ, Med libr,* Dr Elsa M Lopez, PhD; *Patient info,* Carmen J Sierra; Staff 6 (MLS 3, Non-MLS 3)
Founded 1946
Library Holdings: AV Mats 2,125; Braille Volumes 125; e-books 40; e-journals 182; Large Print Bks 100; Bk Titles 19,500; Bk Vols 31,973; Per Subs 544; Talking Bks 250
Special Collections: Medical Information; Patient Education
Subject Interests: Allied health, Dentistry, Med, Nursing
Function: Handicapped accessible, Health sci info serv, ILL available, Online searches, Orientations, Ref serv available, Res libr, Satellite serv, Wheelchair accessible
Special Services for the Blind - Large print bks
Restriction: Clients only, In-house use for visitors, Staff & patient use

R EVANGELICAL SEMINARY OF PUERTO RICO*, Juan Valdes Library, 776 Ponce de Leon Ave, 00925-9907. SAN 328-5162. Tel: 787-763-6700, Ext 231. FAX: 787-751-0847. *Dir,* Myrna E Perez Lopez; E-mail: meperez@se-pr.edu; Staff 3 (MLS 2, Non-MLS 1)
Founded 1919. Enrl 225; Fac 8; Highest Degree: Doctorate
Library Holdings: Bk Titles 70,667; Bk Vols 75,000
Special Collections: Historical Archives of Protestantism in Puerto Rico; Puerto Rican Coll of Protestantism; Spanish Reformers
Subject Interests: Relig, Theol
Automation Activity & Vendor Info: (Acquisitions) Mandarin Library Automation; (Cataloging) Mandarin Library Automation; (Circulation) Mandarin Library Automation; (Course Reserve) Mandarin Library Automation; (ILL) Mandarin Library Automation; (Media Booking) Mandarin Library Automation; (OPAC) Mandarin Library Automation; (Serials) Mandarin Library Automation
Wireless access
Open Mon-Thurs 9-9, Fri 8:30-5, Sat 9-4

P PUERTO RICO REGIONAL LIBRARY FOR THE BLIND & PHYSICALLY HANDICAPPED*, Biblioteca Regional para Ciegos y Fisicamente Impedidos de Puerto Rico, 520 Ponce De Leon Ave, Ste 2, 00901. SAN 320-4294. Tel: 787-723-2519. Toll Free Tel: 800-981-8008. FAX: 787-721-8177. *Dir,* Igri S Enriquez; E-mail: enriquezri@de.gobierno.pr; Staff 8 (MLS 1, Non-MLS 7)
Founded 1975. Pop 1,849; Circ 71,128
Library Holdings: Talking Bks 36,522
Special Collections: Braille Books & Magazines in Spanish; Cassette Books & Magazines in English & Spanish
Subject Interests: Braille mat in Spanish incl rec, Cassettes
Function: Equip loans & repairs, Handicapped accessible, ILL available, Mail & tel request accepted, Mail loans to mem, Orientations, Spoken cassettes & CDs, Web-Braille
Publications: Carta Informativa (Bi-monthly)
Special Services for the Blind - Bks & mags in Braille, on rec, tape & cassette; Braille alphabet card; Braille equip; Braille servs; Cassette playback machines; Computer with voice synthesizer for visually impaired persons; Internet workstation with adaptive software; Large print bks & talking machines; Multimedia ref serv (large print, Braille using CD-ROM tech); Musical scores in Braille & large print; Newsletter (in large print, Braille or on cassette); Newsline for the Blind; PC for handicapped; Reader equip; Scanner for conversion & translation of mats; Spanish Braille mags & bks; Talking machines; Text reader; Transcribing serv; Variable speed audiotape players; VisualTek equip; Web-Braille
Open Mon-Fri 8-4:30
Restriction: Registered patrons only
Friends of the Library Group

GL SUPREME COURT LIBRARY OF PUERTO RICO*, Munoz Rivera Ave, Puerta de Tierra, 00902. (Mail add: PO Box 9022392, 00902-2392), SAN 365-5806. Tel: 787-289-0179, 787-723-3550. Circulation Tel: 787-723-6033, Ext 2153, 787-723-6033, Ext 2155. FAX: 787-724-5090. Web Site: www.tribunalpr.org. *Dir,* Ivette Torres-Alvarez; *Circ, Head, Pub Serv,* Evelyn N Ortiz-Hernandez; E-mail: evelyno@tribunales.gobierno.pr; *Cat,* Luis Bonilla-Mangual; Tel: 787-723-6033, Ext 2163, E-mail: luisb@tribunales.gobierno.pr. Subject Specialists: *Puerto Rican law,* Evelyn N Ortiz-Hernandez; Staff 11 (MLS 4, Non-MLS 7)
Founded 1832. Highest Degree: Master

Special Collections: Rare Books Coll
Subject Interests: Civil law, Common law
Automation Activity & Vendor Info: (Cataloging) Ex Libris Group; (Circulation) Ex Libris Group; (OPAC) Ex Libris Group
Database Vendor: LexisNexis
Function: For res purposes, Govt ref serv, ILL available, Photocopying/Printing
Publications: InfoJuris (Monthly bulletin)
Restriction: Circ to mem only

UNIVERSITY OF PUERTO RICO

CM CONRADO F ASENJO LIBRARY (MEDICAL SCIENCES CAMPUS)*, Medical Sciences Campus, Main Bldg, Unit C, 00935. (Mail add: PO Box 365067, 00936-5067), SAN 318-5737. Tel: 787-751-8199, 758-2525, Ext 1200. Circulation Tel: 787-758-2526. Interlibrary Loan Service Tel: 787-758-2525, Ext 2923. Reference Tel: 787-758-2525, Ext 1369. Administration Tel: 787-758-2525, Ext 2083. FAX: 787-759-6713, 282-6438. Web Site: www.rcm-library.rcm.upr.edu. *Dir,* Dr Irma Quinones-Mauras; *Tech Serv Dir,* Nilca Parrilla; Tel: 787-758-2525, Ext 1346, E-mail: nparrilla@rcm.upr.edu; *Head, Ref,* Margarita Gonzalez; E-mail: mgonzalez@rcm.upr.edu; *Spec Coll Librn,* Carmen Santos; Tel: 787-758-2525, Ext 1224, E-mail: csantos@rcm.upr.edu; Staff 39 (MLS 12, Non-MLS 27)
Founded 1950. Enrl 2,480; Pop 165,000; Circ 22,552; Highest Degree: Doctorate
Library Holdings: AV Mats 2,207; Electronic Media & Resources 20; Bk Titles 42,906; Bk Vols 46,304; Per Subs 1,162
Special Collections: Dr Bailey K Ashford; History of Medicine; Puerto Rican Coll
Subject Interests: Health sci professions
Database Vendor: EBSCOhost, OVID Technologies
Function: AV serv, Handicapped accessible, ILL available, Libr develop, Online searches, Prof lending libr, Ref serv available, Wheelchair accessible, Workshops
Partic in Greater NE Regional Med Libr Program; SE-Atlantic Regional Med Libr Servs
Open Mon-Thurs 7am-11pm, Sat 8am-10pm, Sun 9am-10pm
Restriction: Non-circulating coll

CL LAW SCHOOL LIBRARY, Avenidas Ponce de Leon & Gandara, 00931. (Mail add: PO Box 23310, 00931-3310), SAN 365-5474. Tel: 787-999-9684, 787-999-9702. Circulation Tel: 787-999-9702. Interlibrary Loan Service Tel: 787-999-9690. Reference Tel: 787-999-9688. Administration Tel: 787-999-9683, 787-999-9685. Information Services Tel: 787-999-9698. FAX: 787-999-9680. Web Site: www.law.upr.edu/biblioteca. *Dir,* Maria M Otero; E-mail: motero@law.upr.edu; *Head, Acq,* Lizette Lopez; Tel: 787-999-9703, E-mail: llopez@law.upr.edu; *Head, Cat,* Esther Villarino; Tel: 787-999-9709, E-mail: evillarino@law.upr.edu; *Head, Circ,* Samuel Serrano; Tel: 787-999-9898, E-mail: sserrano@law.upr.edu; *Head, Ser,* Josefina Ortiz; Tel: 787-999-9691, E-mail: jortiz@law.upr.edu; Staff 36 (MLS 8, Non-MLS 28)
Founded 1913. Enrl 710
Library Holdings: Per Subs 4,800
Special Collections: US Document Depository
Subject Interests: Rare bks
Automation Activity & Vendor Info: (Cataloging) Horizon; (Circulation) Horizon; (OPAC) Horizon; (Serials) Horizon
Partic in Lyrasis; OCLC Online Computer Library Center, Inc
Special Services for the Blind - Computer with voice synthesizer for visually impaired persons

C UNIVERSITY OF PUERTO RICO LIBRARY*, Natural Sciences Library, Rio Piedras Campus, 00931. (Mail add: PO Box 70377, 00936-8377), SAN 365-5539. Tel: 787-764-0000, Ext 2359. FAX: 787-764-2890. *Dir,* Julia Y Velez; Tel: 787-764-0000, Ext 5983, E-mail: julia.velez@upr.edu; *Asst Librn,* Nivia Santiago; *Coordr, Info Serv,* Zulma Quiles-Miranda; Staff 13 (MLS 5, Non-MLS 8)
Founded 1954. Highest Degree: Doctorate
Library Holdings: Bk Titles 40,000; Bk Vols 186,000; Per Subs 1,200
Special Collections: Puerto Rico Science Coll
Subject Interests: Astronomy, Biol, Botany, Chem, Geol, Math, Physics, Pure sci, Zoology
Wireless access
Function: Ref serv available
Open Mon-Thurs 8am-10pm, Fri 8-5, Sat & Sun 9-5

C UNIVERSITY OF PUERTO RICO LIBRARY SYSTEM*, University of Puerto Rico, Rio Piedras Campus, 00931. (Mail add: PO Box 23302, 00931-3302), SAN 365-5385. Tel: 787-764-0000, Ext 5085. Circulation Tel: 787-764-0000, Ext 7850. Reference Tel: 787-764-0000, Ext 5242. Automation Services Tel: 787-764-0000, Ext 5088. Information Services Tel: 787-764-0000, Ext 3335. FAX: 787-772-1479. Web Site: biblioteca.uprrp.edu. *Dir,* Snejanka Penkova; Tel: 787-764-0000, Ext 5085, E-mail: snejanka.penkova@uprrp.edu; *Asst Dir,* Amílcar Tirado; Tel: 787-764-0000, Ext 5090, E-mail: atirado@uprrp.edu; *Ast Dir, Libr Dept,*

Aracelis Sosa; Tel: 787-764-0000, Ext 2790, E-mail: asosa@uprrp.edu; *Asst Dir, Pub Serv,* José Pagán; Tel: 787-764-0000, Ext 2789, E-mail: jlpagan@uprrp.edu; *Asst Dir, Tech Serv,* Ana Rosa Cordero; Tel: 787-764-0000, Ext 5222, E-mail: arcordero@uprrp.edu; Staff 113 (MLS 40, Non-MLS 73)

Founded 1903. Highest Degree: Doctorate

Jul 2007-Jun 2008. Mats Exp $3,296,316, Books $447,700, Per/Ser (Incl. Access Fees) $2,472,456, AV Mat $20,000, Electronic Ref Mat (Incl. Access Fees) $356,160

Library Holdings: e-books 35; e-journals 3,000; Bk Titles 4,076,000; Per Subs 3,012

Special Collections: Arts & Dance (Arts Coll); Caribbean & Latin American Studies Coll; El Mundo Newspaper Photographs; History, Literature & Social Science (Puerto Rican Coll); Josefina del Toro Fulladosa Coll, rare bks; Services for the Blind Coll; Zenobia & Juan Ramon Jimenez Literature Coll. Oral History; UN Document Depository; US Document Depository

Automation Activity & Vendor Info: (Acquisitions) Horizon; (Circulation) Horizon

Database Vendor: ABC-CLIO, American Chemical Society, American Mathematical Society, Annual Reviews, Baker & Taylor, BioOne, Blackwell's, Bloomberg, Bowker, Checkpoint Systems, Inc, CRC Press/Taylor & Francis CRCnetBASE, Dun & Bradstreet, EBSCO Information Services, EBSCOhost, Elsevier, Facts on File, Gale Cengage Learning, Greenwood Publishing Group, H W Wilson, ISI Web of Knowledge, JSTOR, LexisNexis, Marcive, Inc, OCLC WorldCat, Project MUSE, ProQuest, Sage, Springer-Verlag, Standard & Poor's, Wiley, Wilson - Wilson Web, YBP Library Services

Publications: Al Dia (newsletter); Collections description brochures; Lumbre (newsletter); Perspectiva (journal); Services description brochures; Subject bibliographies

Partic in OCLC Online Computer Library Center, Inc

Special Services for the Deaf - Assistive tech; Coll on deaf educ; Deaf publ; FullTalk; Spec interest per; Staff with knowledge of sign lang; Video & TTY relay via computer

Special Services for the Blind - Assistive/Adapted tech devices, equip & products; Audio mat; Braille equip; Braille servs; Computer with voice synthesizer for visually impaired persons; Talking bks

Restriction: Open to pub with supv only

Departmental Libraries:

ANGEL QUINTERO ALFARO LIBRARY (GENERAL STUDIES), Rio Piedras Campus, Faculta de Estudios Generales, 00931. (Mail add: PO Box 23302, 00931-3302), SAN 365-5490. Tel: 787-764-0000, Ext 2223. FAX: 787-773-1729. Administration FAX: 787-763-5685. *Head Librn,* Aurea E Maisonet-Rodriguez; Tel: 787-764-0000, Ext 5196, Fax: 787-772-1479, E-mail: aurmaisonet@uprrp.edu; Staff 6 (MLS 2, Non-MLS 4)

Founded 1971. Enrl 3,096; Fac 260; Highest Degree: Bachelor

Library Holdings: AV Mats 215; Bk Titles 9,783; Per Subs 19

Open Mon-Thurs 8-8, Fri & Sat 8-4:30

ARTS COLLECTION, Recinto de Rio Piedras, 00931. (Mail add: PO Box 23302, 00931-3302), SAN 327-9871. Tel: 787-764-0000, Ext 3492. FAX: 787-763-5685. E-mail: artes@uprrp.edu. *Head Librn,* Iris D Rodriguez-Parrilla; Tel: 787-764-0000, Ext 5156, E-mail: idrodriguez@uprrp.edu; Staff 4 (MLS 1, Non-MLS 3)

Founded 1953

Library Holdings: Bk Vols 34,667

Special Collections: Artist Illustrated Books; Arts Exhibition Catalogs; Catalogos de Expos de Arte Sebastian Gonzalez Garcia; Dance Archives Collection; Rare Art Books

Subject Interests: Graphic, Visual arts

Function: Res libr

Publications: Lista anotada de recursos de la Coleccion de las Artes, Serie: indices; Manual de Instruccion Bibliotecaria: Las artes sus recursos y serv ARTES (information sheet of organized exhibitions)

BUSINESS ADMINISTRATION LIBRARY, Rio Piedras Campus, 00931. (Mail add: PO Box 23302, 00931-3302), SAN 365-5466. Tel: 787-764-0000, Ext 3150, 787-764-0000, Ext 5175. FAX: 787-772-1479. Web Site: biblioteca.uprrp.edu/baebib.htm. *Chief Librn,* Lourdes Cadiz Ocasio; E-mail: loucadiz@uprrp.edu

Enrl 2,862

Library Holdings: AV Mats 89; Bk Vols 35,882

Subject Interests: Acctg, Computer sci, Finance, Human resources, Mgt, Mkt, Statistics

Open Mon-Thurs (Winter) 7:30am-10pm, Fri 7:30-4:30, Sat 8:30-4:30; Mon-Thurs (Summer) 8-6, Fri 8-4:30, Sat 8:30-4:30

CARIBBEAN & LATIN AMERICAN STUDIES COLLECTION, Rio Piedras Campus, 00931. (Mail add: PO Box 23302, 00931-3302), SAN 327-9855. Tel: 787-764-0000, Ext 3319. *Librn,* Almaluces Figueroa-Ortiz; Tel: 787-764-0000, Ext 3339, Fax: 787-772-1479, E-mail: afigueroa@uprrp.edu

Library Holdings: Bk Vols 142,004

Special Collections: Latin American Pamphlets from the Yale University Library Coll; Peron's Documents Coll; Rare Books and Carribean

Organizations Documents; The Latin American Documents Project A & B

Subject Interests: Caribbean-demography, Economics, Educ, Statistics, Tourism, Trade

Publications: ACURIL (Newsletter)

CIRCULATION & RESERVE COLLECTION, Rio Piedras Campus, 00931. (Mail add: PO Box 23302, 00931-3302), SAN 376-2327. Tel: 787-764-0000, Ext 3335, 787-764-0000, Ext 5116. Circulation Tel: 787-764-0000, Ext 5159. Interlibrary Loan Service Tel: 787-764-0000, Ext 5119. FAX: 787-764-0000, Ext 3335. Web Site: biblioteca.uprrp.edu/circ-reserva.htm. *Actg Circ Supvr,* Nancy Abreu-Baez; Fax: 787-772-1479, E-mail: nabreu@uprrp.edu. Subject Specialists: *Humanities, Lit,* Nancy Abreu-Baez

Library Holdings: Bk Titles 278,686; Bk Vols 391,954

Subject Interests: Humanities, Soc sci

Open Mon & Thurs 8am-10pm, Fri & Sat 8-6, Sun 10-6

JOSEFINA DEL TORO FULLADOSA COLLECTION, RARE BOOKS & MANUSCRIPTS, Rio Piedras Campus, 00931. (Mail add: PO Box 23302, 00931-3302), SAN 327-9898. Tel: 787-764-0000, Ext 7845. Administration Tel: 787-764-0000, Ext 5085. Web Site: biblioteca.uprrp.edu/bib-col/jtf.html. *Head Librn, Rare Bks,* Aura Diaz Lopez; Tel: 787-764-0000, Ext 7920, Fax: 787-763-5685, E-mail: aura.diaz1@upr.edu. Subject Specialists: *Latin Am studies, Rare bks,* Aura Diaz Lopez; Staff 1 (MLS 1)

Highest Degree: Doctorate

Library Holdings: Bk Vols 9,594

Special Collections: Genaro Cautino Coll; Nemours Coll, (Haiti)

Subject Interests: Hist (Americana), Lit, Relig

Database Vendor: ScienceDirect

Function: Archival coll, Art exhibits, Computers for patron use, e-mail & chat, Electronic databases & coll, Exhibits, ILL available, Ref serv in person, Wheelchair accessible

Restriction: Closed stack, Internal use only, Non-circulating of rare bks

DOCUMENTS & MAPS COLLECTION, Rio Piedras Campus, 00931. (Mail add: PO Box 23302, 00931-3302), SAN 376-2335. Tel: 787-764-0000, Ext 3514. FAX: 787-763-5410. *Librn,* Jose Pagan; Fax: 787-772-1479, E-mail: jlpagan@uprrp.edu

Library Holdings: AV Mats 125; CDs 509; Microforms 800,553; Bk Vols 896; Per Subs 618

Special Collections: UN Document Depository; US Document Depository

Subject Interests: Caribbean area, Econ, Latin area

ZENOBIA & JUAN RAMON JIMENEZ ROOM, Rio Piedras Campus, Edif Jose M Lazaro, 00931. (Mail add: PO Box 23302, 00931-3302), SAN 327-9936. Tel: 787-764-0000, Ext 3475. *Librn,* Carmen L Busquets; Tel: 787-764-0000, Ext 5170, Fax: 787-772-1479, E-mail: lilybusquets@hotmail.com

Library Holdings: Bk Vols 104,937

Special Collections: Bernardo G Candamo Coll; Juan Guerrero Ruiz Personal Library; Rafael Cansinos Assens Coll; Zenobia & Juan R Jimenez Personal Library & Documents

Subject Interests: Spanish lit

Open Mon-Thurs 7:45am-9:45pm, Fri 7:45-4:15, Sat 8:45-4:15

LIBRARY & INFORMATION SCIENCES, Rio Piedras Campus, Edif Jose M Lazaro, 00931. (Mail add: PO Box 23302, 00931-3302), SAN 365-5504. Tel: 787-764-0000, Ext 3482. *Head Librn,* Dr Luis O Casiano-Torres; Tel: 787-764-0000, Ext 5112, Fax: 787-772-1479, E-mail: locasiano@uprrp.edu

Enrl 131; Highest Degree: Master

Library Holdings: Bk Vols 111,553

Special Collections: Juvenile Coll

Subject Interests: Info, Libr sci

Publications: Egebiana (Journal); Servicio de alerta

Open Mon-Thurs 8am-9pm, Fri 8-5, Sat 8-6, Sun 11-5

LIBRARY SERVICES FOR THE PHYSICALLY HANDICAPPED, Rio Piedras Campus, Edif Jose M Lazaro, 00931. (Mail add: PO Box 23302, 00931-3302), SAN 327-9790. Tel: 787-764-0000, Ext 5173. FAX: 787-764-0000, Ext 5120. E-mail: atecno@uprrp.edu, biblioteca@uprrp.edu. *Head Librn,* Yarelis Torres; Fax: 787-772-1479, E-mail: yatorres@uprrp.edu

Library Holdings: AV Mats 28; Bk Titles 590; Per Subs 21

Special Collections: Books in Braille; Large Print; Talking Books

Subject Interests: Blind-educ, Hist, Lang, Lit, Printing, Rehabilitation, Writing systs

Special Services for the Blind - Assistive/Adapted tech devices, equip & products

Open Mon-Thurs 8am-9pm, Fri 8-4:30, Sat 8-4

MONSERRATE SANTANA DE PALES LIBRARY, Rio Piedras Campus, Facultad de Ciencias Sociales, 00931. (Mail add: PO Box 23302, 00931-3302), SAN 365-5652. Tel: 787-764-0000, Ext 4262, 787-764-0000, Ext 5635. *Librn,* Elsa E Rodriguez-Gonzalez; Fax: 787-772-1479, E-mail: eerodriguez@uprrp.edu

Enrl 595; Highest Degree: Doctorate

Library Holdings: AV Mats 16; Bk Titles 12,265; Bk Vols 13,235; Per Subs 202

Subject Interests: Child abuse, Counseling, Family relations, Med soc work, Psychopathology, Rehabilitation, Soc serv, Soc work

MUSIC LIBRARY, Agustin Stahl Bldg, Rio Piedras Campus, 00931. (Mail add: PO Box 23302, Estacion Universidad, 00931-3302), SAN 327-9812. Tel: 787-764-0000, Ext 5204, 787-764-0000, Ext 5205. *Head Librn,* Doris E Rivera-Marrero; Tel: 787-764-0000, Ext 5202, Fax: 787-772-1479, E-mail: derivera@uprrp.edu

Founded 1953. Enrl 109

Library Holdings: AV Mats 23,839; Music Scores 8,543; Bk Titles 9,250; Bk Vols 12,420; Per Subs 231

PERIODICALS COLLECTION, Rio Piedras Campus, Edif Jose M Lazaro, 00931. (Mail add: PO Box 23302, Estacion Universidad, 00931-3302), SAN 376-2343. Tel: 787-764-0000, Ext 3487. FAX: 787-763-4611. *Head Librn,* Sylvia Sola-Fernandez; Tel: 787-764-0000, Ext 5133, Fax: 787-772-1479, E-mail: ssola@uprrp.edu

Library Holdings: CDs 56; Microforms 681,686; Bk Vols 93,929; Per Subs 120,559

Subject Interests: Humanities, Soc sci

PLANNING LIBRARY, Rio Piedras Campus, Plaza Universitaria, 00931. (Mail add: PO Box 23302, 00931-3302), SAN 365-5563. Tel: 787-764-0000, Ext 3186. FAX: 787-763-5605. *Head Librn,* Lourdes Ramirez-Rivera; Tel: 787-764-0000, Ext 85524, Fax: 787-772-1479, E-mail: lramirez@uprrp.edu

Enrl 118

Library Holdings: AV Mats 89; Bk Titles 17,274; Bk Vols 19,088; Per Subs 360

Subject Interests: Environ, Planning econ, Regional, Soc urban

PUBLIC ADMINISTRATION LIBRARY, Rio Piedras Campus, 00931. (Mail add: PO Box 23302, Estacion Universidad, 00931-3302), SAN 365-5598. Tel: 787-764-0000, Ext 5181, 787-764-0000, Ext 5182. *Head Librn,* Aracelis Sosa-Arzuaga; Fax: 787-772-1479, E-mail: asosa@uprrp.edu

Enrl 189

Library Holdings: AV Mats 1; Bk Titles 12,664; Bk Vols 17,155; Per Subs 153

Subject Interests: Admin law, Labor legislation, Organization theory, Personnel admin

PUERTO RICAN COLLECTION, Rio Piedras Campus, Edif Jose M Lazaro, 00931. (Mail add: PO Box 23302, Estacion Universidad, 00931-3302), SAN 327-991X. Tel: 787-764-0000, Ext 3463, 787-764-0000, Ext 3471. *Head Librn,* Maria E Ordonez-Mercado; Tel: 787-764-0000, Ext 5160, Fax: 787-772-1479, E-mail: mordonez@uprrp.edu

Library Holdings: Bk Titles 40,624; Bk Vols 1,147,000; Per Subs 4,665

Special Collections: Antonio S Pedreira Coll; Emilio J Pasarell Coll; Gerardo Selles Sola Coll; Miguel Guerra Mondragon Coll; Sociedad Economica de Amigos del Pais

Subject Interests: Puerto Ricans, Puerto Rico

REFERENCE COLLECTION, Rio Piedras Campus, Edif Jose M Lazaro, 00931. (Mail add: PO Box 23302, Estacion Universidad, 00931-3302), SAN 376-2351. Tel: 787-764-0000, Ext 3327. *Head Librn,* Sylvia Sola-Fernandez; Tel: 787-764-0000, Ext 5133, Fax: 787-772-1479, E-mail: ssola@uprrp.edu

Library Holdings: Microforms 681,688; Bk Titles 93,929; Bk Vols 120,559

Subject Interests: Humanities, Soc sci

SOCIAL SCIENCES RESERVE ROOM, Rio Piedras Campus, 00931. (Mail add: PO Box 23302, Estacion Universidad, 00931-3302), SAN 365-544X. Tel: 787-764-0000, Ext 2483, 787-764-0000, Ext 5219. *Head*

Librn, Myrna I Nieves-Ortiz; Fax: 787-772-1479, E-mail: mnieves@uprrp.edu

Library Holdings: Bk Vols 13,582

Subject Interests: Soc sci

GERARDO SELLES SOLA LIBRARY (EDUCATION LIBRARY), Eugenio Maria de Hostos Bldg, Rio Piedras Campus, 00931. (Mail add: UPR Sta, PO Box 23302, 00931-3302), SAN 365-5482. Tel: 787-764-0000, Ext 4149. Reference Tel: 787-764-0000, Ext 7733. E-mail: bibeduca@rrpac.upr.clu.edu. Web Site: biblioteca.rrp.upr.edu. *Dir,* Snejanka Penkova; E-mail: snejanka.penkova@uprrp.edu. Subject Specialists: *Bus admin, Psychol,* Snejanka Penkova; Staff 7 (MLS 3, Non-MLS 4)

Founded 1946. Pop 4,200; Circ 87,900; Fac 230; Highest Degree: Doctorate

Library Holdings: AV Mats 733; Bk Titles 34,333; Bk Vols 40,665; Per Subs 224

Special Collections: Theses & Dissertations

Subject Interests: Counseling, Curric, Educ, Educ philos, Educ sociol, Guidance, Juv, Psychol

Function: Res libr

Special Services for the Blind - Computer with voice synthesizer for visually impaired persons

Open Mon-Thurs 8am-9pm, Fri 8-4:30, Sat 8-4

Restriction: Secured area only open to authorized personnel

G USDA FOREST SERVICE*, International Institute of Tropical Forestry Library, Jardin Botanico Sur, 1201 Calle Ceiba, 00926-1119. SAN 322-7944. Tel: 787-766-5335. FAX: 787-766-6302. Web Site: www.fs.fed.us/global/iitf. *Info Spec,* Gisel Reyes; Tel: 787-766-5335, Ext 350, E-mail: greyes@fs.fed.us; Staff 4 (MLS 1, Non-MLS 3)

Founded 1939

Library Holdings: Bk Titles 6,000; Per Subs 50

Special Collections: Tropical Forestry

Subject Interests: Tropical ecology, Tropical forestry

Publications: General Technical Reports; IITF Annual Letter; Research Papers; Resource Bulletins

Open Mon, Wed & Fri 11-4, Tues & Thurs 8-1

SANTURCE

CR UNIVERSITY OF THE SACRED HEART*, Madre Maria Teresa Guevara Library, Rosales St, PO Box 12383, 00914-0383. SAN 318-5788. Tel: 787-728-1515, Ext 4353. FAX: 787-268-8868. Web Site: www.sagrado.edu. *Dir,* Sonia Diaz-Latorre; Tel: 787-728-1515, Ext 4356, E-mail: sdiaz@sagrado.edu; *Cat,* Carmen L Aponte; *Media Spec,* Carlos Perez; *Ref,* Holanda Rendon; *Spec Coll Librn,* Carlos M Gonzalez; *Spec Coll Librn,* Andres Lopez; *Tech Serv Librn,* Francisco Solis; Tel: 787-728-1515, Ext 4364, E-mail: fsolis@sagrado.edu; Staff 24 (MLS 11, Non-MLS 13)

Founded 1936. Enrl 5,000; Fac 417; Highest Degree: Master

Library Holdings: Bk Titles 120,563; Bk Vols 204,296; Per Subs 1,500

Special Collections: Historical Archives of the Institution

Automation Activity & Vendor Info: (Cataloging) SirsiDynix; (Circulation) SirsiDynix; (Course Reserve) SirsiDynix; (OPAC) SirsiDynix; (Serials) SirsiDynix

Database Vendor: Dialog, EBSCOhost, Foundation Center, ProQuest, YBP Library Services

Publications: Delfilinea (quarterly); Guia para la presentacion y aprobacionde una Tesis de Grado; Library Guides; Manual para la Preparacion de un Trabajo de Invesitgacion; Tapia Ayer y Hoy

Partic in Dialog Corp

Friends of the Library Group

KINGSHILL

C   UNIVERSITY OF THE VIRGIN ISLANDS*, Saint Croix Campus Library-Melvin H Evans Center for Learning, RR 2, Box 10000, 00850-9781. SAN 318-5842. Tel: 340-692-4130. Reference Tel: 340-692-4138. FAX: 340-692-4135. Web Site: library.uvi.edu. *Dir, Libr Serv,* Jennifer Jackson; Tel: 340-692-4000, Fax: 340-692-4005, E-mail: jjackso@uvi.edu; *Adminr, Ref & Info Serv, Team Leader,* Judith V Rogers; Tel: 340-692-4132, E-mail: jrogers@uvi.edu; *Instrul Serv Librn,* Eva Maddox; Tel: 340-692-4137, E-mail: emaddox@uvi.edu; *Head, Cat,* Wenda Stephenson; Tel: 340-692-4136, E-mail: wstephe@uvi.edu; Staff 8 (MLS 4, Non-MLS 4)
Founded 1969. Enrl 1,200; Fac 85; Highest Degree: Master
Library Holdings: AV Mats 799; Bk Vols 55,809; Per Subs 171
Special Collections: Caribbean materials; VI documents
Automation Activity & Vendor Info: (Cataloging) SirsiDynix; (Circulation) SirsiDynix; (Course Reserve) SirsiDynix; (OPAC) SirsiDynix
Database Vendor: Gale Cengage Learning, OCLC FirstSearch, OVID Technologies, SirsiDynix
Function: For res purposes, ILL available, Photocopying/Printing
Publications: Acquisitions List; Library Handbook; Library Newsletter
Partic in Lyrasis; Virgin Islands Libr & Info Network
Open Mon-Thurs 8am-10pm, Fri 8-8, Sat 9-5, Sun 1-6
Restriction: Open to pub for ref & circ; with some limitations

SAINT CROIX

P   THE FLORENCE A S WILLIAMS PUBLIC LIBRARY*, 1122 King St Christiansted, 00820-4951. SAN 318-5885. Tel: 340-773-5715. FAX: 340-773-5327. Web Site: www.virginislandspubliclibraries.org. *Librn,* Letitia Gittens; Staff 2 (MLS 1, Non-MLS 1)
Founded 1920
Library Holdings: Bk Titles 22,180; Bk Vols 24,690; Per Subs 27
Special Collections: Virgin Islands & Caribbean Materials. State Document Depository; US Document Depository
Subject Interests: Hist
Open Mon-Fri 9-5

SAINT JOHN

P   ELAINE IONE SPRAUVE LIBRARY, Enighed Estate, Cruz Bay, 00831. (Mail add: PO Box 30, 00831), SAN 318-5893. Tel: 340-776-6359. FAX: 340-776-6901. Web Site: www.virginislandspubliclibraries.org. *Librn IV,* Carol McGuinness; E-mail: carol.mcguinness@dpnr.gov.vi; Staff 2 (MLS 1, Non-MLS 1)
Founded 1959. Pop 5,000
Library Holdings: DVDs 900; Large Print Bks 5; Bk Titles 16,400; Bk Vols 17,900; Per Subs 15
Special Collections: West Indies. State Document Depository
Automation Activity & Vendor Info: (Cataloging) SirsiDynix; (Circulation) SirsiDynix
Database Vendor: SirsiDynix

Open Mon-Fri 9-5
Friends of the Library Group

SAINT THOMAS

P   ENID M BAA LIBRARY & ARCHIVES*, 20 Dronningens Gade, 00802. SAN 365-5954. Tel: 340-774-0630. FAX: 340-775-1887. E-mail: dlamdir@vipowernet.net. Staff 2 (MLS 1, Non-MLS 1)
Founded 1924. Pop 51,000; Circ 102,416
Library Holdings: Bk Titles 48,911; Bk Vols 51,113; Per Subs 37
Special Collections: Building Houses Von Scholten; Caribbeana; UN & VI Documents Coll
Open Mon & Fri 9-5, Tues-Thurs 9-8, Sat 10-2
Friends of the Library Group

C   UNIVERSITY OF THE VIRGIN ISLANDS*, Ralph M Paiewonsky Library, Two John Brewers Bay, 00802-9990. SAN 365-6012. Tel: 340-693-1361, 340-693-1367. FAX: 340-693-1365. Web Site: library.uvi.edu. *Managing Librn,* Linda Robinson Barr; E-mail: lbarr@uvi.edu; *Pub Serv,* Cynthia Richards; Tel: 340-693-1369, E-mail: crichar@uvi.edu; *Syst Coordr,* Sharlene Harris; Tel: 340-693-1368, E-mail: sharris@uvi.edu; Staff 10 (MLS 5, Non-MLS 5)
Founded 1963. Enrl 2,719; Fac 89; Highest Degree: Master
Library Holdings: AV Mats 1,240; Bk Titles 93,450; Bk Vols 96,810; Per Subs 717; Videos 390
Special Collections: Caribbean Area Coll, VF; Melchior Center for Recent Virgin Islands History. US Document Depository
Subject Interests: Caribbean hist, Caribbean lit, Caribbean politics, Govt
Automation Activity & Vendor Info: (Cataloging) SirsiDynix; (Circulation) SirsiDynix; (ILL) SirsiDynix; (OPAC) SirsiDynix
Database Vendor: Gale Cengage Learning, OCLC FirstSearch, OVID Technologies, SirsiDynix
Publications: Acquisitions list; Library handbooks; Periodical List
Partic in Lyrasis; Virgin Islands Libr & Info Network
Open Mon-Thurs 8am-10pm, Fri 8-8, Sat 10-5, Sun 1-10

P   VIRGIN ISLANDS DIVISION OF LIBRARIES, ARCHIVES & MUSEUMS*, 23 Dronningens Gade, 00802. SAN 365-592X. Tel: 340-774-3407. FAX: 340-775-1887. *Territorial Dir of Libr, Archives & Mus,* Ingrid Bough; *Spec Coll Librn,* Beverly Smith; *Syst Mgr,* Christian Doute; Staff 4 (MLS 2, Non-MLS 2)
Founded 1920. Pop 100,000; Circ 156,915
Library Holdings: AV Mats 2,117; Large Print Bks 190; Bk Vols 168,724; Per Subs 180; Videos 310
Special Collections: Virgin Islands; Von Scholten Coll, Founded 1920: Danish West Indies, Virgin Islands & Caribbean, bks, doc, local newsp, mss, maps, pamphlets, per, photogs, VF. UN Document Depository
Publications: Annual Report; Caribbeana: Recent Acquisitions of Caribbean Materials in Virgin Islands Libraries; Checklist of Virgin Islands Government Documents; Information (Newsletter); Occasional Papers Series; Union Catalog of 16mm Motion Pictures; Union List of Periodicals

and Newspapers; Virgin Islands Govt Blou bks; Virgin Islands Govt Calendar for 1985; Virgin Islands Newspaper Index
Partic in Vilinet
Open Mon & Fri 9-5, Tues-Thurs 9-8, Sat 10-4
Branches: 4

P   REGIONAL LIBRARY FOR THE BLIND & PHYSICALLY HANDICAPPED, 3012 Golden Rock, Christiansted, Saint Croix, 00820, SAN 365-5989. Tel: 340-772-2250. FAX: 340-772-3545. E-mail: reglib@viaccess.net. *Head Librn,* Letitia G Gittens; Tel: 340-773-5715; *Librn Tech I,* Dorothea Vivican; *Librn Tech III,* Sandra Solomon; Staff 3 (MLS 1, Non-MLS 2)
Founded 1968

Library Holdings: Talking Bks 15,000
Publications: Regional Newsletter
Special Services for the Blind - Newsletter (in large print, Braille or on cassette)
Open Mon-Fri 9-5
Restriction: Authorized patrons

ENID M BAA LIBRARY & ARCHIVES
    See Separate Entry
ELAINE IONE SPRAUVE LIBRARY
    See Separate Entry in Saint John
THE FLORENCE A S WILLIAMS PUBLIC LIBRARY
    See Separate Entry in Saint Croix

LIBRARIES IN CANADA

ALBERTA

Date of Statistics: FY 2010
Population, 2012: 3,699,939
Population Served by Public Libraries: 3,529,214 (99.6%)
   Unserved: 14,583 (0.4%)
Total Volumes Held by Public Libraries: 10,447,312
   Volumes Per Capita: 2.96
Total Public Library Circulation: 42,480,340
Circulation Per Capita: 12.04
Total Local Support for Public Libraries: $113,133,285
Total Provincial Support for Public Libraries: $24,729,402
   Provincial Support Per Capita: $7.01

ACADIA VALLEY

P   ACADIA MUNICIPAL LIBRARY*, PO Box 6, T0J 0A0. Tel:
403-972-3744. FAX: 403-972-2000. E-mail: aavalibrary@marigold.ab.ca.
Librn, Brandi Smith
Wireless access
Mem of Marigold Library System
Open Mon 9-3, Tues 9-3:30, Thurs 9-2

ACME

P   ACME MUNICIPAL LIBRARY*, 610 Walsh Ave, T0M 0A0. (Mail add:
PO Box 326, T0M 0A0), SAN 318-5915. Tel: 403-546-3845. FAX:
403-546-2248. E-mail: aamlibrary@marigold.ab.ca. *Mgr,* Jonquil Thiessen
Founded 1955. Pop 648; Circ 11,798
Library Holdings: Bk Vols 12,000; Per Subs 40
Special Collections: Can & Prov
Mem of Marigold Library System
Open Mon 12-3, Tues & Thurs 5-9, Wed 1-4

AIRDRIE

P   AIRDRIE PUBLIC LIBRARY*, 111-304 Main St SE, T4B 3C3. SAN
325-1993. Tel: 403-948-0600. FAX: 403-912-4002. E-mail:
library.staff@airdriepubliclibrary.ca. Web Site: www.airdriepubliclibrary.ca.
Dir, Janine Jevine
Founded 1971. Pop 42,000; Circ 200,000
Library Holdings: Bk Vols 55,000; Per Subs 100
Subject Interests: Airdrie hist, District hist
Database Vendor: Gale Cengage Learning
Mem of Marigold Library System
Partic in The Alberta Library
Open Mon-Thurs 9-8:30, Fri 9-5, Sat 10-5, Sun 1-5
Friends of the Library Group

ALBERTA BEACH

P   ALBERTA BEACH MUNICIPAL LIBRARY*, PO Box 186, T0E 0A0.
Tel: 780-924-3491. FAX: 780-924-3491. E-mail: ablibrary@yrl.ab.ca.
Librn, Cathy Brennan
Pop 762
Library Holdings: Bk Titles 10,000; Per Subs 10
Automation Activity & Vendor Info: (Acquisitions) SirsiDynix
Wireless access
Mem of Yellowhead Regional Library
Open Tues & Thurs 2:30-8, Wed 9:30-4:30, Sat 11-3
Friends of the Library Group

ALDER FLATS

P   ALDER FLATS PUBLIC LIBRARY*, PO Box 148, T0C 0A0. Tel:
780-388-3881. FAX: 780-388-3887. E-mail: af@wrps.ab.ca. Web Site:
www.alderflatslibrary.ab.ca. *Libr Dir,* Judy Miners
Library Holdings: Bk Titles 10,000
Automation Activity & Vendor Info: (Acquisitions) SirsiDynix
Mem of Yellowhead Regional Library
Open Tues 1-4 (1-5 Summer), Thurs, 7pm-9-pm

ALIX

P   ALIX PUBLIC LIBRARY*, PO Box 69, T0C 0B0. Tel: 403-747-3233.
E-mail: alixpublic@libs.prl.ab.ca. Web Site: alixpublic.prl.ab.ca. *Libr Mgr,*
Beth Richardson
Pop 825
Library Holdings: Bk Titles 10,000; Per Subs 12
Automation Activity & Vendor Info: (Acquisitions) Horizon;
(Circulation) Horizon; (ILL) Horizon; (OPAC) Horizon
Mem of Parkland Regional Library
Open Tues 9:30-4:30, Wed 4-8, Thurs 10:30-4:30, Sat 10-2

ALLIANCE

P   ALLIANCE PUBLIC LIBRARY*, PO Box 185, T0B 0A0. Tel:
780-879-3733. E-mail: alliancelibrary@prl.ab.ca. Web Site:
www.alliance.prl.ab.ca. *Libr Mgr,* Tracy Rombouth
Pop 171
Library Holdings: Bk Titles 6,000
Automation Activity & Vendor Info: (Acquisitions) Horizon;
(Cataloging) Horizon; (Circulation) Horizon; (ILL) Horizon; (Media
Booking) Horizon; (OPAC) Horizon; (Serials) Horizon
Mem of Parkland Regional Library
Open Tues 2-6, Fri 9-1

AMISK

P   AMISK PUBLIC LIBRARY*, 5005 50 St, T0B 0B0. Tel: 780-628-5457.
FAX: 780-856-3980. E-mail: amiskpubliclibrary@libs.prl.ab.ca. Web Site:
amisklibrary.prl.ab.ca. *Libr Mgr,* Carmen Toma
Pop 181
Library Holdings: Bk Titles 7,200
Mem of Parkland Regional Library
Open Tues & Thurs 9-12 & 1-5, Wed 1-5 & 7-9

ANDREW

P   ANDREW PUBLIC LIBRARY*, PO Box 180, T0B 0C0. Tel:
780-365-3501, Ext 225. FAX: 780-365-3734. E-mail: public@mcsnet.ca.
Librn, Denise Dorland
Pop 490
Library Holdings: Bk Titles 15,000; Per Subs 20

Automation Activity & Vendor Info: (Acquisitions) Follett Software; (Cataloging) Follett Software; (Circulation) Follett Software; (Media Booking) Follett Software; (OPAC) Follett Software; (Serials) Follett Software
Database Vendor: EBSCOhost
Open Mon & Wed-Fri 8:45-3:45, Tues 8:45-3:45 & 7-9

ASHMONT

P   ASHMONT COMMUNITY LIBRARY*, PO Box 330, T0A 0C0. SAN 329-255X. Tel: 780-726-3793, 780-726-3877. FAX: 780-726-3777. E-mail: librarian@ashmontlibrary.ab.ca. Web Site: www.ashmontlibrary.ab.ca. *Librn,* Karen Duperron; *Asst Librn,* Tonya Hlushko
Founded 1984. Pop 746; Circ 21,656
Library Holdings: Bk Titles 16,000; Per Subs 31
Mem of Northern Lights Library System
Special Services for the Deaf - Bks on deafness & sign lang; High interest/low vocabulary bks
Open Mon & Tues 8-3:30 & 4:30-8, Wed 8-3:30 & 4:30-7:30, Thurs & Fri 8-3:30

ATHABASCA

P   ATHABASCA MUNICIPAL LIBRARY, Alice B Donahue Library & Archives, 4716 48th St, T9S 2B6. (Mail add: PO Box 2099, T9S 2B6). Tel: 780-675-2735. FAX: 780-675-2735. E-mail: librarian@athabascalibrary.ab.ca. Web Site: athabascalibrary.ab.ca. *Librn,* Cynthia Graefe
Pop 29,000; Circ 40,000
Library Holdings: Audiobooks 200; AV Mats 100; DVDs 500; Large Print Bks 481; Bk Vols 23,000; Per Subs 38
Special Collections: Local History Archive Coll
Mem of Northern Lights Library System
Open Tues, Wed & Fri 10-5:30, Thurs 10-8, Sat 10-4

C   ATHABASCA UNIVERSITY LIBRARY*, One University Dr, T9S 3A3. SAN 321-3781. Tel: 780-675-6254. FAX: 780-675-6478. E-mail: library@athabascau.ca. Web Site: library.athabascau.ca. *Dir, Libr Serv,* Steve Schafer; Tel: 780-675-6259, E-mail: steves@athabascau.ca; *Head, Digital Initiatives & Electronic Res,* Tony Tin; Tel: 780-675-6486, E-mail: tonyt@athabascau.ca; *Head, Info Literacy & Pub Serv,* Elaine Fabbro; *Head, Tech Serv & Syst,* Douglas Kariel; Tel: 780-675-6261, E-mail: dougk@athabascau.ca; Staff 15 (MLS 5, Non-MLS 10)
Founded 1970. Enrl 7,200; Highest Degree: Doctorate
Library Holdings: e-books 185,000; e-journals 60,000; Bk Titles 155,000; Per Subs 500
Special Collections: Can; Distance Education (Reverend Edward Checkland Coll)
Automation Activity & Vendor Info: (Acquisitions) Innovative Interfaces, Inc; (Cataloging) Innovative Interfaces, Inc; (Circulation) Innovative Interfaces, Inc; (Course Reserve) Innovative Interfaces, Inc; (ILL) Innovative Interfaces, Inc; (OPAC) Innovative Interfaces, Inc; (Serials) Innovative Interfaces, Inc
Database Vendor: EBSCOhost, Gale Cengage Learning, OCLC FirstSearch, OVID Technologies, ProQuest, Wilson - Wilson Web
Partic in The Alberta Library
Open Mon-Fri 8:30-4:30

BANFF

S   BANFF CENTRE*, Paul D Fleck Library & Archives, 107 Tunnel Mountain Dr, T1L 1H5. (Mail add: PO Box 1020, T1L 1H5), SAN 320-8826. Tel: 403-762-6265. FAX: 403-762-6266. E-mail: archives@banffcentre.ca, library@banffcentre.ca. Web Site: www.banffcentre.ca/library. *Music Librn,* Kyla Jemison; Tel: 403-762-6221, E-mail: kyla_jemison@banffcentre.ca; *Archivist,* Jane Parkinson; Tel: 403-762-6440, E-mail: jane_parkinson@banffcentre.ca; Staff 3 (MLS 3)
Founded 1979
Library Holdings: Music Scores 18,000; Bk Vols 38,000; Per Subs 170; Videos 3,500
Special Collections: Artist Book Coll
Subject Interests: Mgt arts, Performing arts, Visual arts
Automation Activity & Vendor Info: (Cataloging) SirsiDynix; (Circulation) SirsiDynix; (OPAC) SirsiDynix
Database Vendor: SirsiDynix
Wireless access
Partic in The Alberta Library
Open Mon-Thurs 9-7, Fri 9-5, Sun 11-7

P   BANFF PUBLIC LIBRARY*, 101 Bear St, T1L 1H3. (Mail add: PO Box 996, T1H 1H3), SAN 318-5931. Tel: 403-762-2661. FAX: 403-762-3805. E-mail: info@bannflibrary.ab.ca. Web Site: www.bannflibrary.ab.ca. *Librn,* Denise Drury; Staff 8 (MLS 1, Non-MLS 7)
Pop 8,352; Circ 100,000
Library Holdings: Bk Vols 39,000

Subject Interests: Mountaineering
Open Mon 10-8, Tues-Thurs & Fri 10-6, Sat 11-6, Sun 1-4:30

M   MINERAL SPRINGS HOSPITAL*, Medical Library, 305 Lynx St, T1L 1H7. (Mail add: PO Box 1050, T1L 1H7), SAN 329-904X. Tel: 403-762-2222. FAX: 403-762-4193. *Supv Librn,* Maureen Wotherspoon; E-mail: maureen.wotherspoon@covenanthealth.ca
Library Holdings: CDs 50; Bk Titles 100; Per Subs 10

S   WHYTE MUSEUM OF THE CANADIAN ROCKIES*, Archives & Library, 111 Bear St, T1L 1A3. (Mail add: PO Box 160, T1L 1A3), SAN 318-594X. Tel: 403-762-2291, Ext 335. FAX: 403-762-2339. E-mail: archives@whyte.org. Web Site: www.whyte.org. *Librn,* Elizabeth Kundert-Cameron; *Archivist,* Jennifer Rutkair; Staff 3 (MLS 2, Non-MLS 1)
Founded 1967
Library Holdings: Bk Titles 5,000; Bk Vols 6,500; Per Subs 128
Special Collections: Local Newspaper, 1900 to present, micro to 1983; Map Coll
Subject Interests: Can Rocky Mountains, Environ, Hist of Can Rockies, Hist of Western Can
Publications: The Cairn (Newsletter)
Open Mon-Fri 10-5
Restriction: Closed stack, In-house use for visitors, Non-circulating coll, Not a lending libr

BARNWELL

P   BARNWELL PUBLIC LIBRARY, 500 Second St W, T0K 0B0. (Mail add: PO Box 261, T0K 0B0). Tel: 403-223-3626. E-mail: libbar@chinookarch.ab.ca. *Libr Mgr,* Susan Torrie; *Libr Asst,* Helen Dyck
Pop 875
Library Holdings: Bk Titles 3,500; Per Subs 20
Wireless access
Special Services for the Blind - Daisy reader
Open Tues, Wed & Fri 12-5, Thurs 10:30-5, Sat 10-1

BARRHEAD

S   ALBERTA DISTANCE LEARNING CENTRE BUILDING LIBRARY*, Distributed Learning Branch, 4601 63rd Ave, T7N 1P4. (Mail add: PO Box 4000, T7N 1P4), SAN 326-6664. Tel: 780-674-8756. FAX: 780-674-6561. *Librn,* Suzanne P Williams
Library Holdings: Bk Titles 14,000; Per Subs 10
Special Collections: Distance Education Coll
Publications: Courses; Directories; Handbooks
Restriction: Co libr, Not open to pub

P   BARRHEAD PUBLIC LIBRARY*, 5103 53rd Ave, T7N 1N9. SAN 318-5958. Tel: 780-674-8519. FAX: 780-674-8520. E-mail: plibrary@phrd.ab.ca. Web Site: www.barrheadpubliclibrary.ca. *Dir,* Elaine Dickie; Staff 6 (MLS 1, Non-MLS 5)
Founded 1950. Pop 9,981; Circ 218,272
Library Holdings: Bk Titles 46,000; Bk Vols 51,000; Per Subs 135
Subject Interests: Local hist
Mem of Yellowhead Regional Library
Open Mon & Fri (Nov-Apr) 10-5:30, Tues-Thurs 10-8, Sat 12-4; Mon-Wed & Fri (May-Oct) 10-5:30, Thurs 10-8, Sat 12-4
Friends of the Library Group

BASHAW

P   BASHAW PUBLIC LIBRARY*, 5020 52 St, T0B 0H0. (Mail add: PO Box 669, T0B 0H0). Tel: 780-372-4055. FAX: 780-372-4055. E-mail: bashawlibrary@libs.prl.ab.ca. Web Site: www.bashawlibrary.prl.ab.ca. *Librn,* Cindy Hunter
Pop 880; Circ 10,267
Library Holdings: Large Print Bks 9,258; Bk Titles 15,000; Per Subs 10
Automation Activity & Vendor Info: (Acquisitions) SirsiDynix
Mem of Parkland Regional Library
Open Mon 1:30-4:30, Tues-Fri 10-4:30, Sat 10-Noon

BAWLF

P   BAWLF PUBLIC LIBRARY, David Knipe Memorial Library, 203 Hanson St, T0B 0J0. (Mail add: Box 116, T0B 0J0). Tel: 780-373-3882. FAX: 780-373-3882. E-mail: bawlflibrary@prl.ab.ca. Web Site: www.bawlflibrary.prl.ab.ca. *Librn,* Fern Reinke
Pop 500
Library Holdings: AV Mats 740; Bk Titles 6,092
Wireless access
Mem of Parkland Regional Library
Open Mon, Wed & Fri 11-7, Thurs 3-7
Friends of the Library Group

BEAR CANYON

P   BEAR POINT COMMUNITY LIBRARY*, PO Box 43, T0H 0B0. SAN 372-719X. Tel: 780-595-3771. FAX: 780-595-3762. Web Site: www.bearpointlibrary.ab.ca. *Librn,* Barb Evans-Conrad; E-mail: barbi002@hotmail.com
Founded 1979. Pop 300
Library Holdings: Bk Titles 5,000; Bk Vols 5,200
Automation Activity & Vendor Info: (Cataloging) SirsiDynix; (OPAC) SirsiDynix
Mem of Peace Library System
Open Mon 10-3
Friends of the Library Group

BEAUMONT

P   BIBLIOTHEQUE DE BEAUMONT LIBRARY*, 5700 49 St, T4X 1S7. Tel: 780-929-2665. FAX: 780-929-1291. E-mail: library@beaumontlibrary.com. Web Site: www.beaumontlibrary.com. *Dir,* Christina Wilson; E-mail: christina@beaumontlibrary.com
Pop 13,287
Library Holdings: Audiobooks 361; AV Mats 1,094; Bks on Deafness & Sign Lang 50; Large Print Bks 300; Bk Vols 26,453; Per Subs 47; Talking Bks 50
Special Collections: French Reading Materials
Subject Interests: Early literacy, Graphic novels, Parenting
Automation Activity & Vendor Info: (Acquisitions) Polaris Library Systems; (Cataloging) Polaris Library Systems; (Circulation) Polaris Library Systems; (ILL) Polaris Library Systems; (OPAC) Polaris Library Systems
Mem of Yellowhead Regional Library
Open Mon-Thurs 9-8, Fri 9-4, Sat 10-4, Sun 12-4

BEAVERLODGE

G   AGRICULTURE & AGRI-FOOD CANADA*, BeaverLodge Research Farm Library, PO Box 29, T0H 0C0. SAN 318-5966. Tel: 780-354-2212. FAX: 780-354-5150, 780-354-8171. *Adminr,* Shelly Maingille
Library Holdings: Bk Titles 1,500; Per Subs 20
Subject Interests: Apiculture, Environ, Northern agr
Publications: Research Highlights (Annually)
Partic in Agr Can Librs
Open Mon-Fri 8-4:30
Restriction: Open to pub with supv only

P   BEAVERLODGE PUBLIC LIBRARY, 406 Tenth St, T0H 0C0. (Mail add: PO Box 119, T0H 0C0), SAN 318-5974. Tel: 780-354-2569. FAX: 780-354-3078. E-mail: librarian@beaverlodgelibrary.ab.ca. Web Site: www.beaverlodgelibrary.ab.ca. *Librn,* Shelly Longson; Staff 5 (Non-MLS 5)
Founded 1945. Pop 5,800; Circ 34,783
Library Holdings: Bk Titles 28,000; Per Subs 50
Mem of Peace Library System
Open Mon, Tues, Thurs & Fri 10-6, Wed 10-8, Sat 12-4
Friends of the Library Group

BEISEKER

P   BEISEKER MUNICIPAL LIBRARY*, 700 First St, T0M 0G0. (Mail add: PO Box 8, T0M 0G0). Tel: 403-947-3230. FAX: 403-947-2146. E-mail: abemlibrary@marigold.ab.ca. *Librn,* Shauna Sox
Pop 828
Library Holdings: Bk Titles 6,500
Subject Interests: Local hist
Automation Activity & Vendor Info: (Acquisitions) SirsiDynix; (Cataloging) SirsiDynix; (Circulation) SirsiDynix; (ILL) SirsiDynix; (Serials) SirsiDynix
Database Vendor: EBSCOhost, SirsiDynix
Mem of Marigold Library System
Open Mon, Wed & Thurs 3-7, Tues & Sat 10-2

BENTLEY

P   BENTLEY MUNICIPAL LIBRARY, 5014 - 49 Ave, T0C 0J0. (Mail add: Box 361, T0C 0J0). Tel: 403-748-4626. FAX: 403-748-4627. E-mail: bentleylibrary@libs.prl.ab.ca. Web Site: bentleylibrary.prl.ab.ca. *Libr Mgr,* Suzanne Moore
Pop 1,134
Library Holdings: Bk Titles 10,000; Talking Bks 114; Videos 99
Automation Activity & Vendor Info: (Acquisitions) SirsiDynix
Mem of Parkland Regional Library
Open Tues, Wed & Fri 10-5:30, Thurs 12-7:30, Sat 11-4
Friends of the Library Group

BERWYN

S   BERWYN MUNICIPAL LIBRARY*, 5105 51st St, T0H 0E0. (Mail add: PO Box 89, T0H 0E0), SAN 318-5990. Tel: 780-338-3616. FAX: 780-338-3616. Web Site: www.berwynlibrary.ab.ca. *Librn,* Kim Byard
Pop 546
Library Holdings: Large Print Bks 150; Bk Titles 8,200
Special Collections: Children's Circle Video Coll
Automation Activity & Vendor Info: (Acquisitions) SirsiDynix; (Circulation) SirsiDynix
Mem of Peace Library System
Open Mon & Sat 11-5, Thurs 11-7

BIG VALLEY

P   BIG VALLEY MUNICIPAL LIBRARY*, 29 First Ave S, T0J 0G0. (Mail add: PO Box 205, T0J 0G0). Tel: 403-876-2642. FAX: 403-876-2401. E-mail: bigvalleylibrary@libs.prl.ab.ca. Web Site: www.bvlibrary.prl.ab.ca. *Libr Mgr,* Linda Stillinger; Staff 1 (Non-MLS 1)
Pop 365; Circ 1,200
Library Holdings: Bk Titles 12,600; Per Subs 12
Wireless access
Mem of Parkland Regional Library
Open Tues-Thurs 9-12 & 2-5, Fri 9-Noon
Friends of the Library Group

BLACKFALDS

P   BLACKFALDS PUBLIC LIBRARY*, 5018 Waghorn St, T0M 0J0. (Mail add: PO Box 70, T0M 0J0). Tel: 403-885-2343. Administration Tel: 403-885-4386. FAX: 403-885-4353. E-mail: library@blackfaldslibrary.ca. Web Site: www.blackfaldslibrary.ca. *Libr Mgr,* Carley Binder
Pop 6,400; Circ 48,364
Library Holdings: Bk Titles 18,167; Per Subs 67; Talking Bks 359; Videos 1,677
Automation Activity & Vendor Info: (Acquisitions) SirsiDynix; (Circulation) Horizon
Wireless access
Function: Archival coll, Art exhibits, Handicapped accessible, Homebound delivery serv, ILL available, Mail loans to mem, Photocopying/Printing, Prog for adults, Prog for children & young adult, Ref serv available, Summer reading prog, VHS videos, Wheelchair accessible
Mem of Parkland Regional Library
Open Mon & Wed 10-8:30, Tues, Thurs & Sat 2-5, Fri 10-5
Friends of the Library Group

BLAIRMORE

P   CROWSNEST PASS MUNICIPAL LIBRARY*, PO Box 1177, T0K 0E0. SAN 320-4464. Tel: 403-562-8393. FAX: 403-562-8397. E-mail: libbla@chinookarch.ab.ca. *Librn,* Diane Delauw
Pop 5,000; Circ 28,000
Library Holdings: Bk Vols 25,000
Wireless access
Open Mon, Wed, & Fri 9-6, Tues-Thurs 9-8, Sat (Winter) 12-4

BLUE RIDGE

P   BLUE RIDGE COMMUNITY LIBRARY*, PO Box 264, T0E 0B0. Tel: 780-648-7323. E-mail: blueridgelibrary@yrl.ab.ca. Web Site: www.blueridgelibrary.ab.ca. *Libr Mgr,* Sue Curtis; E-mail: sucurtis@telusplanet.net
Library Holdings: AV Mats 500; DVDs 500; Bk Titles 8,000; Per Subs 18; Talking Bks 75
Automation Activity & Vendor Info: (Acquisitions) SirsiDynix
Mem of Yellowhead Regional Library
Open Tues 12-8, Wed 10-4, Fri 12-6
Friends of the Library Group

BODO

P   BODO PUBLIC LIBRARY*, PO Box 93, T0B 0M0. Tel: 780-753-6323. FAX: 780-753-8195. E-mail: bodolibrary@libs.prl.ab.ca. Web Site: bodolibrary.prl.ab.ca. *Libr Mgr,* Roxanna Wotschell
Library Holdings: CDs 20; Large Print Bks 10; Bk Titles 3,500; Per Subs 10
Wireless access
Mem of Parkland Regional Library
Open Mon & Tues 9:30-12:30, Wed 8-4

BON ACCORD

P   BON ACCORD PUBLIC LIBRARY, PO Box 749, T0A 0K0. SAN 372-7947. Tel: 780-921-2540. FAX: 780-921-2580. E-mail: librarian@bonaccordlibrary.ab.ca. Web Site: www.bonaccordlibrary.ab.ca. *Libr Mgr,* Peggy Teneycke; *ILL,* Joyce Curtis-Bonardi; Staff 1 (Non-MLS 1)

Founded 1982. Pop 1,532; Circ 32,000
Database Vendor: Polaris Library Systems
Wireless access
Function: Adult bk club
Mem of Northern Lights Library System
Open Mon & Sat 10-2, Tues & Thurs 10-8, Wed & Fri 10-4:30
Friends of the Library Group

BONNYVILLE

P   BONNYVILLE MUNICIPAL LIBRARY*, 4804 49th Ave, T9N 2J3. (Mail add: PO Box 8058, T9N 2J3), SAN 318-6016. Tel: 780-826-3071. FAX: 780-826-2058. E-mail: librarian@bonnyvillelibrary.ab.ca. Web Site: www.bonnyvillelibrary.ab.ca. *Chairperson,* Brian Wood; *Dir,* Ina Smith; *Asst Librn,* Linda Smiley; Staff 1 (MLS 1)
Pop 12,168; Circ 60,000
Library Holdings: Bk Vols 24,000
Special Collections: Audio Books Coll; French Easy Read Coll; Large Print Book Coll
Automation Activity & Vendor Info: (Acquisitions) Polaris Library Systems; (Cataloging) Polaris Library Systems; (Circulation) Polaris Library Systems; (OPAC) Polaris Library Systems; (Serials) Polaris Library Systems
Database Vendor: Polaris Library Systems
Wireless access
Function: Adult bk club, Children's prog, Computers for patron use, Copy machines, e-mail & chat, Fax serv, Home delivery & serv to Sr ctr & nursing homes, ILL available, Online cat, Online ref, Online searches, Scanner
Mem of Northern Lights Library System
Partic in The Regional Automation Consortium (TRAC)
Special Services for the Deaf - Assistive tech
Special Services for the Blind - Accessible computers; Assistive/Adapted tech devices, equip & products; Audio mat; Bks on cassette; Bks on CD; Large print bks
Open Mon-Thurs 9-8, Fri 9-5, Sat 11-5

BOW ISLAND

P   BOW ISLAND MUNICIPAL LIBRARY*, 510 Centre St, T0K 0G0. (Mail add: PO Box 608, T0K 0G0). Tel: 403-545-2828. FAX: 403-545-6642. E-mail: bowlib@shortgrass.ca. Web Site: www.shortgrass.ca/bowisland. *Chairperson,* Cindy Orr; *Mgr,* Susan Andersen; Staff 1 (Non-MLS 1)
Founded 1975. Pop 1,704; Circ 40,000
Library Holdings: AV Mats 2,000; Bk Vols 18,000; Per Subs 50
Mem of Shortgrass Libr Syst
Friends of the Library Group

BOWDEN

P   BOWDEN PUBLIC LIBRARY*, PO Box 218, T0M 0K0. Tel: 403-224-3688. FAX: 403-224-3735. E-mail: bowdenlibrary@prl.ab.ca. Web Site: www.bowdenlibrary.prl.ab.ca. *Libr Mgr,* Julie Brown
Library Holdings: Bk Vols 17,000; Per Subs 20
Wireless access
Mem of Parkland Regional Library
Open Tues-Thurs 12-8, Sat 10-4

BOYLE

P   BOYLE PUBLIC LIBRARY, PO Box 450, T0A 0M0. SAN 321-0170. Tel: 780-689-4161. FAX: 780-689-5660. E-mail: librarian@boylepublib.ab.ca. Web Site: www.boylepublib.ab.ca. *Chmn,* Arlene Walker; *Librn,* Kathy Bulmer
Founded 1980. Pop 862
Library Holdings: Bk Titles 10,000
Wireless access
Mem of Northern Lights Library System
Open Tues-Sat 12:30-5
Friends of the Library Group

BRETON

P   BRETON MUNICIPAL LIBRARY*, 4916-50 Ave, T0C 0P0. (Mail add: Box 447, T0C 0P0). Tel: 780-696-3740. FAX: 780-696-3590. Web Site: www.bretonlibrary.ab.ca. *Libr Dir,* Diane Shave; Staff 3 (Non-MLS 3)
Founded 1972. Pop 573
Library Holdings: AV Mats 191; Large Print Bks 135; Bk Titles 8,000; Talking Bks 70
Automation Activity & Vendor Info: (Acquisitions) Polaris Library Systems; (Cataloging) Polaris Library Systems; (Circulation) Polaris Library Systems; (ILL) Polaris Library Systems; (OPAC) Polaris Library Systems
Wireless access
Function: Bks on cassette, Bks on CD, Computer training, Computers for patron use, Electronic databases & coll, Free DVD rentals, Handicapped

accessible, ILL available, Large print keyboards, Music CDs, Online cat, OverDrive digital audio bks, Pub access computers, Ref & res, Scanner, Spoken cassettes & CDs, Story hour, Summer reading prog, Telephone ref, VHS videos, Wheelchair accessible
Mem of Yellowhead Regional Library
Open Mon-Thurs 10-5, Fri 10-8, Sat 9-2

BROOKS

P   BERRY CREEK COMMUNITY LIBRARY*, RR 2, T1R 1E2. Tel: 403-566-3743. FAX: 403-566-3736. E-mail: acclibrary@marigold.ab.ca, bccslibrary@plrd.ab.ca. *Librn,* Susan Connors
Library Holdings: CDs 30; Large Print Bks 70; Bk Titles 14,000; Bk Vols 20,000; Per Subs 20; Talking Bks 30; Videos 50
Automation Activity & Vendor Info: (Cataloging) Follett Software; (Circulation) Follett Software; (ILL) SirsiDynix; (OPAC) Follett Software
Database Vendor: EBSCOhost
Mem of Marigold Library System
Partic in Chinook Arch Regional Libr Syst
Open Mon-Thurs 8:30-3:30

P   BROOKS PUBLIC LIBRARY*, 420 First Ave W, T1R 1B9. (Mail add: PO Box 1149, T1R 1B9), SAN 318-6024. Tel: 403-362-2947. FAX: 403-362-8111. E-mail: brolib@shortgrass.ca. Web Site: www.shortgrass.ca/bpl. *Head Librn,* Sarah McCormack; Staff 9 (MLS 1, Non-MLS 8)
Founded 1951. Pop 13,000; Circ 130,000
Library Holdings: Audiobooks 1,052; Bks on Deafness & Sign Lang 20; High Interest/Low Vocabulary Bk Vols 2,000; Bk Titles 44,000; Bk Vols 43,000; Per Subs 197
Special Collections: Scammell (Wild Life & Hunting Coll)
Subject Interests: Gardening, Genealogical, Local hist
Automation Activity & Vendor Info: (Acquisitions) SirsiDynix; (Cataloging) SirsiDynix; (Circulation) SirsiDynix; (OPAC) SirsiDynix; (Serials) SirsiDynix
Database Vendor: EBSCOhost, Gale Cengage Learning, SirsiDynix
Mem of Shortgrass Libr Syst
Special Services for the Blind - Bks on cassette; Bks on CD; Braille bks; Reader equip
Open Mon, Fri & Sat 10-5, Tues-Thurs 10-8, Sun 1-5

S   CROP DIVERSIFICATION CENTRE SOUTH LIBRARY*, 301 Horticultural Sta Rd E, T1R 1E6. SAN 377-1024. Tel: 403-362-1350. FAX: 403-362-1306. Web Site: www.agric.gov.ab.ca. *Librn,* Shelley Barkley; E-mail: shelley.barkley@gov.ab.ca
Library Holdings: Bk Titles 1,500; Per Subs 20
Restriction: Staff use only

S   EASTERN IRRIGATION DISTRICT, Archives & Library, 550 Industrial Rd W, T1R 1B2. (Mail add: PO Bag 8, T1R 1B2), SAN 373-675X. Tel: 403-362-1400. FAX: 403-362-6206. E-mail: archive@eid.ca. Web Site: www.eid.ca. *Librn,* Darlene Fisher
Library Holdings: Bk Titles 1,200
Special Collections: Irrigation (CPR Eastern Section Coll), bks, linens, ms, maps
Automation Activity & Vendor Info: (Acquisitions) Inmagic, Inc.
Restriction: Open by appt only

BROWNFIELD

P   BROWNFIELD PUBLIC LIBRARY*, Box 63, T0C 0R0. Tel: 403-578-2247. FAX: 403-578-4208. E-mail: brownfieldlibrary@libs.prl.ab.ca. Web Site: www.brownfieldlibrary.prl.ab.ca. *Libr Mgr,* Darvy Gilbertson
Founded 1992. Pop 200
Library Holdings: Bk Titles 29,000; Videos 350
Automation Activity & Vendor Info: (Acquisitions) Horizon; (Cataloging) Horizon; (Circulation) Horizon; (Course Reserve) Horizon; (ILL) Horizon; (Media Booking) Horizon; (OPAC) Horizon; (Serials) Horizon
Function: Adult bk club, Audiobks via web, Bks on CD, Computers for patron use, Electronic databases & coll, Free DVD rentals, Mail loans to mem, Online cat, Online ref, Online searches, Outside serv via phone, mail, e-mail & web, Photocopying/Printing, Pub access computers, Res libr, Summer reading prog, VHS videos, Video lending libr, Wheelchair accessible
Mem of Parkland Regional Library
Open Tues 12-6, Thurs 12-4
Friends of the Library Group

BRUDERHEIM

P   METRO KALYN COMMUNITY LIBRARY, 5017-49 St, Bag 250, T0B 0S0. Tel: 780-796-3032. FAX: 780-796-3032. E-mail: librarian@bruderheimpl.ab.ca. Web Site: www.bruderheimpl.ab.ca. *Librn,* Diana Mack

Pop 1,202
Automation Activity & Vendor Info: (Acquisitions) Polaris Library
Systems
Mem of Northern Lights Library System
Open Tues & Thurs 3-8, Wed 11-4, Sat 10-3

CALGARY

S AEROSPACE MUSEUM ASSOCIATION OF CALGARY LIBRARY,
Library & Archives, 4629 McCall Way NE, T2E 8A5. SAN 327-5027. Tel:
403-250-3752. FAX: 403-250-8399. E-mail: info@asmac.ab.ca. Web Site:
www.asmac.ab.ca. Staff 1 (MLS 1)
Library Holdings: Bk Vols 15,000; Per Subs 25
Special Collections: Original Aviation Log Books
Subject Interests: Hist of aircraft, Hist of aviation
Function: For res purposes
Restriction: Open to pub by appt only

CR ALBERTA BIBLE COLLEGE LEARNING RESOURCE CENTRE, 635
Northmount Dr NW, T2K 3J6. SAN 326-5005. Tel: 403-282-2994. FAX:
403-282-3084. E-mail: library@abccampus.ca. Web Site:
www.abccampus.ca. *Learning Res Ctr Coordr,* Lisa Cutforth-Anderson;
Tel: 403-282-2994, Ext 242, E-mail: lcanderson@abccampus.ca; Staff 1.5
(Non-MLS 1.5)
Founded 1937. Enrl 63; Fac 6; Highest Degree: Bachelor
Library Holdings: Bk Titles 26,000; Per Subs 400
Special Collections: Churches of Christ & Christian Churches in Western
Canada
Subject Interests: Biblical studies, Restoration hist
Automation Activity & Vendor Info: (Acquisitions) LibLime;
(Cataloging) LibLime; (Circulation) LibLime; (OPAC) LibLime; (Serials)
LibLime
Database Vendor: EBSCOhost
Wireless access
Function: Archival coll, Computers for patron use, Copy machines, Doc
delivery serv, e-mail serv, E-Reserves, Electronic databases & coll, Free
DVD rentals, Handicapped accessible, ILL available, Mail & tel request
accepted, Mail loans to mem, Online cat, Online ref, Online searches,
Orientations, Outside serv via phone, mail, e-mail & web,
Photocopying/Printing, Printer for laptops & handheld devices, Prof lending
libr, Pub access computers, Ref serv in person, Spoken cassettes & CDs,
Telephone ref, VHS videos, Web-catalog, Wheelchair accessible,
Workshops
Special Services for the Deaf - Bks on deafness & sign lang; Staff with
knowledge of sign lang
Special Services for the Blind - Cassettes; Free checkout of audio mat
Open Mon-Thurs 9:15-9, Fri 9:15-5, Sat Noon-4

M ALBERTA CHILDREN'S HOSPITAL KNOWLEDGE CENTRE*, 2888
Shaganappi Trail NW, A2-908, 2nd Flr, T3B 6AB. SAN 322-7766. Tel:
403-955-7077. FAX: 403-955-2799. E-mail: achinfo@ucalgary.ca. *Librn,*
Taryn Lenders; Tel: 403-955-2722; *Info Serv Spec,* Spencer Stevens; Staff 3
(MLS 1, Non-MLS 2)
Founded 1982
Library Holdings: Bk Titles 3,000; Bk Vols 4,000; Per Subs 220
Automation Activity & Vendor Info: (Cataloging) SirsiDynix
Open Mon-Fri 8-4

C ALBERTA COLLEGE OF ART & DESIGN, Luke Lindoe Library, 1407
14th Ave NW, T2N 4R3. SAN 320-2798. Tel: 403-284-7631. FAX:
403-289-6682. E-mail: library@acad.ca. Web Site:
www.acad.ab.ca/library.html. *Dir,* Christine E Sammon; Tel: 403-284-7630,
E-mail: christine.sammon@acad.ca; Staff 7 (MLS 2, Non-MLS 5)
Founded 1926. Enrl 999; Fac 97; Highest Degree: Bachelor
Library Holdings: AV Mats 40,000; DVDs 1,052; e-books 67,000;
Electronic Media & Resources 32; Bk Titles 35,645; Per Subs 111
Special Collections: Visual Art Images
Automation Activity & Vendor Info: (Acquisitions) SirsiDynix;
(Cataloging) SirsiDynix; (Circulation) SirsiDynix; (Course Reserve)
SirsiDynix; (OPAC) SirsiDynix
Database Vendor: ARTstor, Cambridge Scientific Abstracts, EBSCOhost,
Gale Cengage Learning, H W Wilson, JSTOR, ProQuest, Wilson - Wilson
Web
Wireless access
Function: Doc delivery serv, ILL available, Online searches,
Photocopying/Printing, Res libr, Telephone ref
Publications: Film Holdings List; Periodical Holdings List
Special Services for the Deaf - Closed caption videos
Restriction: Open to pub for ref & circ; with some limitations, Open to
students, fac & staff

G ALBERTA HUMAN SERVICES*, Alberta Work Centre, 855 Eighth Ave
SW, 5th Flr, T2P 3P1. SAN 373-7594. Tel: 403-297-6344. FAX:
403-297-6235. E-mail: el.ds-calgary@gov.ab.ca. Web Site:

employment.alberta.ca/ces/2957.html. *Libr Tech,* Elaine Peters; E-mail:
elaine.peters@gov.ab.ca; Staff 1 (Non-MLS 1)
Founded 1990
Library Holdings: Bk Titles 1,000; Per Subs 20
Subject Interests: Careers, Employment, Entrepreneurship, Job search,
Training
Automation Activity & Vendor Info: (Acquisitions) Inmagic, Inc.;
(Cataloging) Inmagic, Inc.
Open Mon-Fri 8:15-4:30
Restriction: Not a lending libr

ALBERTA LAW LIBRARIES
GL CALGARY BRANCH*, Calgary Court Centre, 601 Fifth St SW, T2P 5P7,
SAN 318-6032. Tel: 403-297-6148. Toll Free Tel: 866-448-6148. FAX:
403-297-5171. E-mail: all.ca@gov.ab.ca. Web Site: www.lawlibrary.ab.ca.
Dir, Sonia Poulin; Tel: 4780-422-1011; Staff 6 (MLS 2, Non-MLS 4)
Founded 1905
Library Holdings: Bk Vols 50,000; Per Subs 400
Special Collections: Alberta Legal Archives Program; Historical Index
& Biographical File to Superior Court Judges of Southern Alberta
(1883-present); Unreported Decisions for Supreme Court, Federal Court
& all levels of Courts of Alberta
Subject Interests: Computer law, Energy law, Law off mgt, Pacific Rim
Automation Activity & Vendor Info: (Cataloging) Ex Libris Group;
(Circulation) Ex Libris Group; (OPAC) Ex Libris Group; (Serials) Ex
Libris Group
Database Vendor: LexisNexis
Publications: A Selected Checklist of Legal Publications for the Alberta
Practitioner; Energy Law Bibliography; Sample Jury Charges
Open Mon-Fri 8:15-4:30
GL OFFICE OF THE CHIEF MEDICAL EXAMINER INFORMATION
CENTRE, 4070 Bowness Rd NW, T3B 3R7, SAN 374-6615. Tel:
403-297-8123, Ext 224. FAX: 403-297-3429. *Librn,* Karen McManus;
E-mail: karen.mcmanus@gov.ab.ca; Staff 0.2 (MLS 0.2)
Founded 1983
Library Holdings: Bk Titles 1,010; Bk Vols 1,250
Subject Interests: Forensic medicine, Pathology
Automation Activity & Vendor Info: (Acquisitions) Inmagic, Inc.;
(Cataloging) Inmagic, Inc.
Restriction: Staff use only
GL JUDICIAL*, Calgary Courts Ctr, 2001-N, 601 - 5 St SW, T2P 5P7. Tel:
403-297-3118. FAX: 403-297-2981. E-mail:
judicial-south.libraries@gov.ab.ca. *Asst Dir,* Rhonda O'Neill; Tel:
403-297-3958, E-mail: rhonda.oneill@gov.ab.ca; *Law Librn,* Rachel
Appleby; Tel: 403-592-4796, E-mail: rachel.appleby@gov.ab.ca; *Law
Librn,* Lyn Beattie; Tel: 403-297-8234, E-mail: lyn.beattie@gov.ab.ca;
Law Librn, Lola Salami; Tel: 403-297-3231, E-mail:
lola.salami@gov.ab.ca; *Br Mgr,* Carolyn Walker; Tel: 403-297-3959,
E-mail: carolyn.walker@gov.ab.ca; *Info & Res Mgr,* Susan Platt; Tel:
403-297-7355, E-mail: susan.e.platt@gov.ab.aca; Staff 2 (MLS 2)
Library Holdings: Bk Vols 9,200
Subject Interests: Civil, Criminal, Family law, Youth law
Function: For res purposes
Restriction: Not open to pub

S ALBERTA WILDERNESS ASSOCIATION*, Alberta Wilderness Resource
Centre, 455 12th St NW, T2N 1Y9. (Mail add: PO Box 6398, Sta D, T2P
2E1), SAN 323-830X. Tel: 403-283-2025. FAX: 403-270-2743. E-mail:
awa@shaw.ca. Web Site: www.albertawilderness.ca. *In Charge,* Sean
Nichols
Library Holdings: Bk Titles 15,000; Per Subs 50
Subject Interests: Conserv
Restriction: Open to pub for ref only

C AMBROSE LIBRARY*, 150 Ambrose Circle SW, T3H 0L5. SAN
320-7870. Tel: 403-410-2000. FAX: 403-571-2556. E-mail:
library@ambrose.edu. Web Site: www.ambrose.edu. *Dir of Libr Serv,* H D
Ayer; Tel: 403-310-2947; Staff 2 (MLS 1, Non-MLS 1)
Founded 1925. Enrl 800; Fac 39; Highest Degree: Master
Library Holdings: CDs 1,651; DVDs 628; e-journals 61,567; Electronic
Media & Resources 50; Microforms 28,833; Bk Titles 93,360; Bk Vols
114,401; Per Subs 200; Videos 560
Special Collections: Christian & Missionary Alliance
Subject Interests: Christian studies, Hist, Music
Automation Activity & Vendor Info: (Acquisitions) SirsiDynix;
(Cataloging) SirsiDynix; (Circulation) SirsiDynix; (Course Reserve)
SirsiDynix; (OPAC) SirsiDynix; (Serials) SirsiDynix
Database Vendor: BioOne, Canadian Reference Centre, Coutts
Information Service, EBSCOhost, Gale Cengage Learning, OCLC
WorldCat, ProQuest, Wilson - Wilson Web, World Book Online, YBP
Library Services
Wireless access
Function: Res libr
Partic in The Alberta Library
Open Mon-Thurs 8am-10pm, Fri 8-6, Sat 10-5

S   AMEC AMERICAS*, Information Resource Centre, 801 Sixth Ave SW, Ste 900, T2P 3W3. SAN 318-6172. Tel: 403-298-4518. FAX: 403-298-4125. *Coordr,* Anne-Marie Gazsi; E-mail: anne-marie.gazsi@amec.com; Staff 1 (Non-MLS 1)
Founded 1975
Library Holdings: Bk Titles 10,000; Bk Vols 12,000; Per Subs 40; Spec Interest Per Sub 40
Special Collections: Proprietary Technical Reports; Specifications & Standards
Subject Interests: Civil eng, Electrical eng, Environ, Mechanical eng
Automation Activity & Vendor Info: (Cataloging) SydneyPlus; (Circulation) SydneyPlus; (OPAC) SydneyPlus; (Serials) EBSCO Online
Database Vendor: IHS, Knovel
Function: ILL available
Restriction: Staff use only

S   ARUSHA CENTRE SOCIETY*, Community Development Resource Centre, 233 12th Ave, Ste 207, T2R 0G5. SAN 371-0483. Tel: 403-270-3200. FAX: 403-270-8832. E-mail: library@arusha.org. Web Site: www.arusha.org.
Library Holdings: Bk Vols 1,000
Subject Interests: Educ, Intl develop, Multicultural educ, Race relations
Open Tues-Thurs 10:30-3:30

L   BENNETT JONES LLP LIBRARY, 4500 Bankers Hall E, 855 Second St SW, T2P 4K7. SAN 327-5000. Tel: 403-298-3165. FAX: 403-265-7219. Web Site: www.bennettjones.com. *Natl Dir, Libr & Info Serv,* Christy MacKinnon
Library Holdings: Bk Vols 30,000; Per Subs 900
Subject Interests: Law
Automation Activity & Vendor Info: (Acquisitions) SirsiDynix; (Cataloging) SirsiDynix; (Circulation) SirsiDynix; (OPAC) SirsiDynix; (Serials) SirsiDynix
Database Vendor: SirsiDynix
Restriction: Staff use only

L   BORDEN LADNER GERVAIS LLP LIBRARY*, Centennial Place, East Tower, 1900, 530-Third Ave SW, T2P 0R3. SAN 328-0683. Tel: 403-232-9500. FAX: 403-266-1395. Web Site: www.blg.com. *Mgr,* Joan Seally; Staff 2 (MLS 1, Non-MLS 1)
Library Holdings: Bk Titles 2,500; Per Subs 350
Automation Activity & Vendor Info: (Cataloging) Horizon; (Serials) Horizon
Partic in Westlaw
Open Mon-Fri 8-5:30
Friends of the Library Group

L   BURNET, DUCKWORTH & PALMER, LLP*, Information & Research Services, 2400, 525-Eighth Ave SW, T2P 1G1. SAN 327-7623. Tel: 403-260-0100. FAX: 403-260-0332. Web Site: www.bdplaw.com. *Dir,* Jackelyn Degrees; Staff 1 (MLS 1)
Library Holdings: Bk Vols 10,000
Subject Interests: Law
Restriction: Open to staff only

CR   CALGARY ACADEMY LIBRARY, 1677 93rd St SW, T3H 0R3. SAN 320-7617. Tel: 403-686-6444, Ext 258. FAX: 403-240-3427. Web Site: www.calgaryacademy.com. *Librn,* Darcie Tate; Staff 1 (MLS 1)
Founded 1981. Enrl 550; Fac 100; Highest Degree: Master
Library Holdings: Bk Vols 20,000
Special Collections: Learning Disabilities, Special Needs
Subject Interests: Theol
Restriction: Not open to pub

S   CALGARY BOARD OF EDUCATION*, Innovation & Learning Commons, Second Flr Safran N, 1221 Eighth St SW, T2R 0L4. SAN 318-6083. Tel: 403-817-7814. FAX: 403-777-6027. Web Site: www.cbe.ab.ca. *Head Librn,* Renee Martin
Founded 1973
Library Holdings: Bk Titles 30,000
Subject Interests: Budgeting, Curric planning, Educ planning, Evaluation, Prof develop mat in educ, Programming, Special aspects of educ
Open Mon, Wed & Fri 8:30-4:30, Thurs 10-6

M   CALGARY HEALTH REGION*, Rockyview General Hospital Knowledge Centre, 7007 14th St SW, T2V 1P9. SAN 373-6512. Tel: 403-943-3373. FAX: 403-943-3486. E-mail: rghinfo@ucalgary.ca. Web Site: www.hinc.ucalgary.ca. *Librn,* Elizabeth Aitken; E-mail: eaitken@ucalgary.ca; Staff 3 (MLS 1, Non-MLS 2)
Founded 1986
Library Holdings: e-journals 8,000; Electronic Media & Resources 2,000; Bk Titles 4,000; Per Subs 3
Subject Interests: Allied health, Consumer health, Med, Nursing
Open Mon-Fri 8-4

S   CALGARY HERALD LIBRARY*, 215 16th St SE, T2P 0W8. (Mail add: PO Box 2400, Sta M, T2P 0W8), SAN 318-6105. FAX: 403-235-7361. FAX: 403-235-7379. Web Site: www.calgaryherald.com. *Librn,* Karen Crosby; E-mail: kcrosby@theherald.canwest.com; *Librn,* Norma Marr
Founded 1949
Library Holdings: Bk Titles 2,000; Per Subs 100
Special Collections: Newsclippings, microfiche
Database Vendor: EBSCOhost
Open Mon-Fri 9-6
Restriction: Not open to pub

P   CALGARY PUBLIC LIBRARY*, 616 Macleod Trail SE, T2G 2M2. SAN 365-6047. Tel: 403-260-2600. FAX: 403-237-5393. TDD: 403-264-8021. E-mail: dearlibrary@calgarypubliclibrary.com. Web Site: www.calgarypubliclibrary.com. *Dep Chief Exec Officer,* Ellen Humphrey; E-mail: ellen.humphrey@calgarypubliclibrary.com; *Chief Exec Officer,* Position Currently Open; Staff 80 (MLS 80)
Founded 1912. Pop 1,042,000; Circ 14,310,227
Library Holdings: Bk Vols 3,029,921; Per Subs 5,208
Special Collections: Canada Coll; Government Documents; Telephone Directories. Can & Prov; Municipal Document Depository
Subject Interests: Directories, Law, Maps, Multilingual
Automation Activity & Vendor Info: (Acquisitions) SirsiDynix; (Cataloging) SirsiDynix; (Circulation) SirsiDynix; (ILL) SirsiDynix; (OPAC) SirsiDynix
Database Vendor: Agricola, ALLDATA Online, Canadian Reference Centre, EBSCO Information Services, EBSCOhost, Gale Cengage Learning, LearningExpress, Marquis Who's Who, Mergent Online, netLibrary, Overdrive, Inc, ProQuest, ReferenceUSA, SirsiDynix, TLC (The Library Corporation), Wilson - Wilson Web, World Book Online Wireless access
Function: Adult bk club, Adult literacy prog, After school storytime, Archival coll, Art exhibits, Audio & video playback equip for onsite use, Audiobks via web, AV serv, Bilingual assistance for Spanish patrons, Bk club(s), Bks on CD, Bus archives, CD-ROM, Children's prog, Citizenship assistance, Computer training, Computers for patron use, Copy machines, Digital talking bks, Doc delivery serv, e-mail & chat, E-Reserves, Electronic databases & coll, Equip loans & repairs, Exhibits, Family literacy, Free DVD rentals, Games & aids for the handicapped, Genealogy discussion group, Govt ref serv, Handicapped accessible, Health sci info serv, Holiday prog, Home delivery & serv to Sr ctr & nursing homes, Homebound delivery serv, Homework prog, ILL available, Jail serv, Large print keyboards, Learning ctr, Literacy & newcomer serv, Magnifiers for reading, Mail & tel request accepted, Music CDs, Newsp ref libr, Online cat, Online ref, Online searches, Orientations, Outreach serv, Photocopying/Printing, Preschool outreach, Prog for adults, Prog for children & young adult, Provide serv for the mentally ill, Pub access computers, Ref & res, Ref serv available, Ref serv in person, Res libr, Res performed for a fee, Scanner, Senior computer classes, Senior outreach, Serves mentally handicapped consumers, Spoken cassettes & CDs, Spoken cassettes & DVDs, Story hour, Summer reading prog, Teen prog, Telephone ref, VCDs, Video lending libr, Web-Braille, Web-catalog, Wheelchair accessible, Workshops, Writing prog
Publications: At Your Library (Quarterly)
Partic in Utlas
Special Services for the Deaf - Adult & family literacy prog; Assisted listening device; Assistive tech; Bks on deafness & sign lang; Closed caption videos; TDD equip; TTY equip
Special Services for the Blind - Accessible computers; Aids for in-house use; Assistive/Adapted tech devices, equip & products; Audio mat; Bks & mags in Braille, on rec, tape & cassette; Bks available with recordings; Bks on cassette; Bks on CD; Braille bks; Computer access aids; Daisy reader; Descriptive video serv (DVS); Digital talking bk; Dragon Naturally Speaking software; Extensive large print coll; Home delivery serv; Large print & cassettes; Large print bks; Large print bks & talking machines; Magnifiers; PC for handicapped; Reader equip; Recorded bks; Talking bks; Volunteer serv
Open Mon-Thurs 9-8, Fri 9-5, Sat 10-5, Sun (Fall-Spring) 12-5
Restriction: Circ to mem only, Fee for pub use, Non-circulating coll, Non-circulating to the pub, Non-resident fee, Open to pub for ref & circ; with some limitations, Open to students, Pub ref by request, Pub use on premises, Restricted loan policy, Visually impaired students & their teachers
Branches: 18
BOWNESS, 7930 Bowness Rd NW, T3B 0H3, SAN 365-6071. *Mgr,* Allison Thomson
Founded 1979. Pop 14,128; Circ 144,644
Library Holdings: CDs 3,521; Bk Vols 32,748; Per Subs 1,592; Talking Bks 1,670; Videos 1,530
Special Collections: Travelling Coll in Spanish & Dutch
Automation Activity & Vendor Info: (Acquisitions) ARIS-Atlantic Rim Information Systems

Function: Adult bk club, Adult literacy prog, After school storytime, Bk club(s), Bks on CD, Children's prog, Computer training, Computers for patron use, Copy machines, Digital talking bks, Electronic databases & coll, Family literacy, Free DVD rentals, Govt ref serv, Home delivery & serv to Sr ctr & nursing homes, Homebound delivery serv, Homework prog, ILL available, Music CDs, Online cat, Online ref, Online searches, Outreach serv, Photocopying/Printing, Preschool outreach, Prog for adults, Prog for children & young adult, Pub access computers, Ref serv available, Res performed for a fee, Senior computer classes, Senior outreach, Summer reading prog

Special Services for the Deaf - Adult & family literacy prog; Assistive tech; Bks on deafness & sign lang; Closed caption videos; TDD equip; TTY equip

Special Services for the Blind - Accessible computers; Aids for in-house use; Assistive/Adapted tech devices, equip & products; Audio mat; Bks on cassette; Bks on CD; Braille bks

Open Mon & Wed 1-9, Tues 10-9, Thurs-Sat 10-5, Sun (Fall-Spring) 12-5

ALEXANDER CALHOUN BRANCH, 3223 14th St SW, T2T 3V8, SAN 365-6101. *Mgr,* Marje Wing

Founded 1954. Pop 37,744; Circ 423,840

Library Holdings: CDs 8,218; DVDs 2,365; Bk Vols 70,546; Per Subs 2,561; Talking Bks 3,074

Function: Adult bk club, Adult literacy prog, Bk club(s), Bks on CD, Children's prog, Computer training, Computers for patron use, Copy machines, Digital talking bks, E-Reserves, Family literacy, Free DVD rentals, Handicapped accessible, Home delivery & serv to Sr ctr & nursing homes, Homebound delivery serv, Music CDs, Online searches, Outreach serv, Photocopying/Printing, Pub access computers, Senior computer classes, Senior outreach, Summer reading prog, Wheelchair accessible

Special Services for the Deaf - Assistive tech

Special Services for the Blind - Assistive/Adapted tech devices, equip & products; Bks on cassette; Bks on CD

Open Mon-Thurs 10-9, Fri & Sat 10-5, Sun (Fall-Spring) 12-5

Restriction: Non-resident fee

W R CASTELL CENTRAL LIBRARY, 616 Macleod Trail SE, T2G 2M2, SAN 365-6055. Tel: 403-260-2600. FAX: 403-237-5393. *Cent Libr Mgr,* Gerry Burger-Martindale; *Sr Mgr,* Nancy MacKenzie; *Mgr,* Jeri Maitland; *Mgr, Diversity Serv,* Umashanie Reddy; Tel: 403-260-2702, Fax: 403-260-2737; *Mgr, Vols Serv,* Azmin Poonja; *Mgr, Youth Serv,* Jean Ludlum; *Circ,* Evette Berry

Founded 1963. Pop 51,624; Circ 928,333

Library Holdings: CDs 41,665; DVDs 12,339; Bk Vols 454,656; Per Subs 8,430; Talking Bks 22,461

Special Collections: Archival Coll; Local History Coll. Can & Prov

Function: Adult bk club, Adult literacy prog, Audio & video playback equip for onsite use, Audiobks via web, Bk club(s), Bks on cassette, Bks on CD, CD-ROM, Children's prog, Computer training, Computers for patron use, Copy machines, Digital talking bks, e-mail serv, E-Reserves, Electronic databases & coll, Family literacy, Free DVD rentals, Govt ref serv, Handicapped accessible, Home delivery & serv to Sr ctr & nursing homes, Homebound delivery serv, Homework prog, ILL available, Large print keyboards, Magnifiers for reading, Music CDs, Newsp ref libr, Online cat, Online searches, Orientations, Outreach serv, Photocopying/Printing, Preschool outreach, Prog for adults, Prog for children & young adult, Pub access computers, Ref & res, Ref serv available, Ref serv in person, Res libr, Res performed for a fee, Senior computer classes, Senior outreach, Serves mentally handicapped consumers, Spoken cassettes & CDs, Summer reading prog, Teen prog, Telephone ref, VHS videos, Wheelchair accessible

Special Services for the Deaf - Adult & family literacy prog; Assisted listening device; Bks on deafness & sign lang; Closed caption videos; TDD equip; TTY equip

Special Services for the Blind - Accessible computers; Assistive/Adapted tech devices, equip & products; Bks available with recordings; Bks on CD; Braille bks; Daisy reader; Digital talking bk; Extensive large print coll; Home delivery serv; Large print bks; PC for handicapped; Talking bks; Volunteer serv

Open Mon-Thurs 9-8, Fri 9-5, Sat 10-5, Sun (Fall-Spring) 12-5

Restriction: Circ to mem only, Non-circulating coll, Non-circulating of rare bks, Non-resident fee

COUNTRY HILLS, 11950 Country Village Link NE, T3K 6E3. *Mgr,* Susan Anderson

Founded 2004. Pop 60,788; Circ 832,048

Library Holdings: Audiobooks 3,863; CDs 14,363; DVDs 6,272; Bk Vols 104,025; Per Subs 3,996; Talking Bks 3,863

Function: Bk club(s), Bks on CD, Children's prog, Computer training, Computers for patron use, Copy machines, E-Reserves, Electronic databases & coll, Family literacy, Free DVD rentals, Games & aids for the handicapped, Handicapped accessible, Home delivery & serv to Sr ctr & nursing homes, Homebound delivery serv, Homework prog, ILL available, Literacy & newcomer serv, Music CDs, Online cat, Online searches, Outreach serv, Preschool outreach, Prog for adults, Prog for children & young adult, Pub access computers, Senior computer classes,

Senior outreach, Story hour, Summer reading prog, Teen prog, Wheelchair accessible

Open Mon-Thurs 10-9, Fri & Sat 10-5, Sun (Sept-May) 12-5

Restriction: Circ to mem only, Non-circulating coll, Non-resident fee

CROWFOOT, 8665 Nose Hill Dr, T3G 5T3. *Mgr,* Allison Thomson

Founded 2003. Pop 104,492; Circ 1,442,474

Library Holdings: Audiobooks 7,383; CDs 22,960; DVDs 9,662; Bk Vols 171,614; Per Subs 6,592; Talking Bks 7,383

Function: Adult bk club, Bk club(s), Bks on CD, Children's prog, Computer training, Copy machines, E-Reserves, Electronic databases & coll, Family literacy, Free DVD rentals, Handicapped accessible, Home delivery & serv to Sr ctr & nursing homes, Homebound delivery serv, Homework prog, ILL available, Literacy & newcomer serv, Music CDs, Online cat, Outreach serv, Preschool outreach, Prog for adults, Prog for children & young adult, Pub access computers, Senior computer classes, Story hour, Summer reading prog, Teen prog

Special Services for the Deaf - Assistive tech; Bks on deafness & sign lang; Captioned film dep; Closed caption videos; TDD equip; TTY equip

Special Services for the Blind - Accessible computers; Assistive/Adapted tech devices, equip & products; Audio mat; Bks available with recordings; Bks on CD

Open Mon-Thurs 10-9, Fri & Sat 10-5, Sun (Sept-May) 12-5

Restriction: Circ to mem only, Non-resident fee

FISH CREEK, 11161 Bonaventure Dr SE, T2J 6S1, SAN 365-6225. *Mgr,* Donna Bedry

Founded 1985. Pop 98,383; Circ 1,059,232

Library Holdings: CDs 23,369; DVDs 6,431; Bk Titles 285,158; Per Subs 7,729; Talking Bks 6,121

Subject Interests: Literacy, Multilingual

Function: Adult literacy prog, Audio & video playback equip for onsite use, Audiobks via web, Bk club(s), Bks on cassette, Bks on CD, Children's prog, Computer training, Computers for patron use, Copy machines, Digital talking bks, E-Reserves, Electronic databases & coll, Family literacy, Homebound delivery serv, Music CDs, Online ref, Orientations, Photocopying/Printing, Preschool outreach, Prog for adults, Prog for children & young adult, Summer reading prog, VHS videos, Wheelchair accessible

Special Services for the Deaf - Adult & family literacy prog; Assistive tech; Bks on deafness & sign lang; TDD equip; TTY equip

Special Services for the Blind - Accessible computers; Aids for in-house use; Assistive/Adapted tech devices, equip & products; Bks available with recordings; Bks on CD; Braille bks; Daisy reader; Digital talking bk; Large print bks; PC for handicapped; Recorded bks; Talking bks

Open Mon-Thurs 10-9, Fri & Sat 10-5, Sun (Sept-May) 12-5

Restriction: Circ to mem only, In-house use for visitors, Mem only, Non-circulating coll, Non-resident fee

FOREST LAWN, 4807 Eighth Ave SE, T2A 4M1, SAN 365-6195. *Mgr,* Carole Marion

Pop 63,849; Circ 455,855

Library Holdings: CDs 7,545; DVDs 3,792; Bk Titles 64,471; Per Subs 3,404; Talking Bks 3,295

Special Collections: Multi-languages Coll

Function: Adult literacy prog, Audio & video playback equip for onsite use, Bk club(s), Bks on CD, Children's prog, Computer training, Computers for patron use, Copy machines, E-Reserves, Electronic databases & coll, Family literacy, Free DVD rentals, Handicapped accessible, Homebound delivery serv, Learning ctr, Music CDs, Newsp ref libr, Online cat, Online searches, Outreach serv, Photocopying/Printing, Preschool outreach, Prog for adults, Prog for children & young adult, Pub access computers, Senior computer classes, Senior outreach, Story hour, Summer reading prog, Teen prog, VHS videos, Wheelchair accessible

Special Services for the Deaf - Adult & family literacy prog; Assistive tech; Closed caption videos; TDD equip; TTY equip

Special Services for the Blind - Accessible computers; Aids for in-house use; Assistive/Adapted tech devices, equip & products; Bks available with recordings; Bks on cassette; Bks on CD; Braille bks; Computer access aids; Computer with voice synthesizer for visually impaired persons; Daisy reader; Digital talking bk; Extensive large print coll; Home delivery serv; Large print bks; PC for handicapped; Recorded bks; Talking bks

Open Mon-Thurs 10-9, Fri & Sat 10-5, Sun (Fall-Spring) 12-5

Restriction: Non-resident fee

GLENMORE SQUARE, Glenmore Sq Shopping Ctr, 7740 18th St SE, T2C 2N5, SAN 378-1631. *Mgr,* Donna Bedry

Pop 19,002; Circ 193,701

Library Holdings: CDs 3,731; DVDs 2,784; Bk Titles 41,221; Per Subs 1,540; Talking Bks 2,337

Function: Adult bk club, Adult literacy prog, Audiobks via web, Bk club(s), Bks on cassette, Bks on CD, CD-ROM, Children's prog, Computer training, Computers for patron use, Copy machines, e-mail serv, E-Reserves, Electronic databases & coll, Family literacy, Free DVD rentals, Handicapped accessible, Homebound delivery serv, ILL available, Music CDs, Online ref, Online searches, Orientations, Preschool outreach, Prog for adults, Prog for children & young adult, Summer

reading prog, Teen prog, VHS videos, Video lending libr, Wheelchair accessible
Special Services for the Deaf - Accessible learning ctr; Adult & family literacy prog; Assisted listening device; Assistive tech; Closed caption videos; TDD equip; TTY equip
Special Services for the Blind - Accessible computers; Aids for in-house use; Bks available with recordings; Bks on CD; Braille bks; Computer access aids; Daisy reader; Digital talking bk; Extensive large print coll; Large print bks; PC for handicapped; Talking bks
Open Mon, Tues & Thurs 10-9, Wed 1-9, Fri & Sat 10-5, Sun (Fall-Spring) 12-5
Restriction: Circ to mem only, In-house use for visitors, Non-circulating coll, Non-resident fee
MEMORIAL PARK, 1221 Second St SW, T2R 0W5, SAN 365-625X.
Mgr, Marje Wing
Founded 1912. Pop 11,217; Circ 144,856
Library Holdings: CDs 4,405; DVDs 1,601; Bk Vols 20,996; Per Subs 1,190; Talking Bks 2,141
Subject Interests: Multilingual
Function: Adult bk club, Adult literacy prog, Audiobks via web, Bk club(s), Bks on cassette, Bks on CD, CD-ROM, Children's prog, Computer training, Computers for patron use, Copy machines, e-mail serv, E-Reserves, Electronic databases & coll, Family literacy, Free DVD rentals, Handicapped accessible, Home delivery & serv to Sr ctr & nursing homes, Homebound delivery serv, Homework prog, ILL available, Music CDs, Online searches, Orientations, Photocopying/Printing, Preschool outreach, Prog for adults, Prog for children & young adult, Senior computer classes, Senior outreach, Summer reading prog, VHS videos, Wheelchair accessible
Special Services for the Deaf - Adult & family literacy prog; Assisted listening device; Assistive tech; Closed caption videos; TDD equip; TTY equip
Special Services for the Blind - Aids for in-house use; Assistive/Adapted tech devices, equip & products; Bks on cassette; Bks on CD; Daisy reader; Large print bks; PC for handicapped; Recorded bks; Talking bks
Open Mon, Fri & Sat 10-5, Tues & Thurs 12-8, Sun (Fall-Spring) 12-5
Restriction: Circ to mem only, In-house use for visitors, Non-resident fee
NOSE HILL, 1530 Northmount Dr NW, T2L 0G6, SAN 365-6438. *Mgr,* Ann Lidgren
Founded 1976. Pop 46,959; Circ 866,877
Library Holdings: CDs 15,949; DVDs 6,388; Bk Vols 115,474; Per Subs 6,088; Talking Bks 4,667
Special Collections: Multi-languages Coll
Function: Adult bk club, Adult literacy prog, Audiobks via web, Bk club(s), Bks on cassette, Bks on CD, CD-ROM, Children's prog, Computer training, Computers for patron use, Copy machines, Digital talking bks, e-mail serv, E-Reserves, Electronic databases & coll, Family literacy, Free DVD rentals, Handicapped accessible, Home delivery & serv to Sr ctr & nursing homes, Homebound delivery serv, Homework prog, ILL available, Music CDs, Orientations, Photocopying/Printing, Preschool outreach, Prog for adults, Prog for children & young adult, Senior computer classes, Senior outreach, Spoken cassettes & CDs, Spoken cassettes & DVDs, Summer reading prog, Teen prog, VHS videos, Wheelchair accessible
Special Services for the Deaf - Accessible learning ctr; Adult & family literacy prog; Assisted listening device; Assistive tech; Deaf publ; TDD equip; TTY equip
Special Services for the Blind - Accessible computers; Aids for in-house use; Assistive/Adapted tech devices, equip & products; Audio mat; Bks available with recordings; Bks on CD; Braille bks; Daisy reader; Digital talking bk; Extensive large print coll; Large print bks; PC for handicapped; Talking bks
Open Mon-Thurs 10-9, Fri & Sat 10-5, Sun (Fall-Spring) 12-5
Restriction: Circ to mem only, In-house use for visitors, Non-resident fee
LOUISE RILEY BRANCH, 1904 14th Ave NW, T2N 1M5, SAN 365-6284. *Mgr,* Kari Brawn
Founded 1959. Pop 45,927; Circ 602,120
Library Holdings: CDs 12,206; DVDs 5,202; Bk Vols 79,345; Per Subs 4,530; Talking Bks 4,690
Special Collections: French & Vientamese bks; Travelling Collection of Adult & Children's Chinese & Spanish Books
Function: Adult bk club, Adult literacy prog, Audiobks via web, Bk club(s), Bks on cassette, Bks on CD, CD-ROM, Children's prog, Computer training, Computers for patron use, Copy machines, e-mail serv, E-Reserves, Electronic databases & coll, Family literacy, Free DVD rentals, Handicapped accessible, Homebound delivery serv, Homework prog, ILL available, Learning ctr, Music CDs, Online cat, Online searches, Photocopying/Printing, Preschool outreach, Prog for adults, Prog for children & young adult, Pub access computers, Senior computer classes, Summer reading prog, Teen prog, VHS videos, Wheelchair accessible

Special Services for the Deaf - Accessible learning ctr; Adult & family literacy prog; Assisted listening device; Assistive tech; Bks on deafness & sign lang; TDD equip; TTY equip
Special Services for the Blind - Accessible computers; Aids for in-house use; Assistive/Adapted tech devices, equip & products; Audio mat; Bks on CD; Braille bks; Daisy reader; Digital talking bk; Home delivery serv; Large print & cassettes; Large print bks; PC for handicapped; Talking bks; Volunteer serv
Open Mon-Thurs 10-9, Fri & Sat 10-5, Sun (Fall-Spring) 12-5
Restriction: Circ to mem only, In-house use for visitors, Non-resident fee
SADDLETOWNE LIBRARY, 7556 Falconridge Blvd NE, T3J 0C9.
Open Mon-Thurs 10-9, Fri & Sat 10-5, Sun (May-Sept) 12-5
SHAGANAPPI, Multi-Service Ctr, 3415 Eighth Ave SW, T3C 0E8, SAN 365-6314. *Mgr,* Janet MacKinnon
Founded 1964. Pop 14,373; Circ 232,786
Library Holdings: CDs 5,992; DVDs 3,182; Bk Vols 50,695; Per Subs 3,621; Talking Bks 2,970
Special Collections: Vietnamese Cass
Subject Interests: Fr (Lang), Multilingual
Function: Adult bk club, Adult literacy prog, Audio & video playback equip for onsite use, Audiobks via web, Bk club(s), Bks on cassette, Bks on CD, CD-ROM, Children's prog, Computer training, Computers for patron use, Copy machines, Digital talking bks, e-mail serv, E-Reserves, Electronic databases & coll, Family literacy, Free DVD rentals, Handicapped accessible, Home delivery & serv to Sr ctr & nursing homes, Homebound delivery serv, Homework prog, ILL available, Music CDs, Orientations, Photocopying/Printing, Preschool outreach, Prog for adults, Prog for children & young adult, Senior computer classes, Senior outreach, Spoken cassettes & CDs, Summer reading prog, VHS videos, Wheelchair accessible
Open Mon & Wed 1-9, Tues 10-9, Thurs & Sat 10-5, Sun (Fall-Spring) 12-5
Restriction: Fee for pub use, Mem only, Non-resident fee
SHAWNESSY, South Fish Creek Complex, 333 Shawville Blvd SE, T2Y 4H3, SAN 328-8048. *Mgr,* Sara House
Founded 2001. Pop 96,936; Circ 941,836
Library Holdings: CDs 13,248; DVDs 6,355; Bk Vols 119,940; Per Subs 3,661; Talking Bks 5,153
Function: Adult bk club, Adult literacy prog, Audio & video playback equip for onsite use, Audiobks via web, Bk club(s), Bks on cassette, Bks on CD, CD-ROM, Children's prog, Computer training, Computers for patron use, Copy machines, Digital talking bks, e-mail serv, E-Reserves, Equip loans & repairs, Family literacy, Free DVD rentals, Handicapped accessible, Homebound delivery serv, Homework prog, ILL available, Music CDs, Online searches, Orientations, Photocopying/Printing, Preschool outreach, Prog for adults, Prog for children & young adult, Senior computer classes, Senior outreach, Spoken cassettes & CDs, Teen prog, VHS videos, Wheelchair accessible
Special Services for the Deaf - Adult & family literacy prog; Assisted listening device; Assistive tech; TDD equip; TTY equip
Special Services for the Blind - Accessible computers; Aids for in-house use; Bks on CD; Braille bks; Daisy reader; Digital talking bk; Home delivery serv; Large print bks; PC for handicapped; Recorded bks; Talking bks
Open Mon-Thurs 10-9, Fri & Sat 10-6, Sun (Fall-Spring) 12-5
Restriction: Circ to mem only, In-house use for visitors, Non-resident fee
SIGNAL HILL, 5994 Signal Hill Centre SW, T3H 3P8, SAN 378-1658.
Mgr, Sharon Wirzba
Founded 1998. Pop 77,053; Circ 812,236
Library Holdings: CDs 10,469; DVDs 4,697; Bk Vols 84,579; Per Subs 3,676; Talking Bks 4,007
Function: Adult bk club, Adult literacy prog, Audio & video playback equip for onsite use, Bk club(s), Bks on cassette, Bks on CD, CD-ROM, Children's prog, Computer training, Computers for patron use, Copy machines, Digital talking bks, e-mail serv, E-Reserves, Electronic databases & coll, Family literacy, Free DVD rentals, Handicapped accessible, Home delivery & serv to Sr ctr & nursing homes, Homebound delivery serv, Homework prog, ILL available, Music CDs, Online cat, Online ref, Online searches, Orientations, Outreach serv, Photocopying/Printing, Preschool outreach, Prog for adults, Prog for children & young adult, Pub access computers, Senior computer classes, Senior outreach, Teen prog, VHS videos, Wheelchair accessible
Special Services for the Deaf - Adult & family literacy prog; Assistive tech; TDD equip; TTY equip
Special Services for the Blind - Accessible computers; Aids for in-house use; Assistive/Adapted tech devices, equip & products; Audio mat; Bks on CD; Braille bks; Daisy reader; Large print bks; Talking bks; Volunteer serv
Open Mon-Thurs 10-9, Fri & Sat 10-5, Sun (Fall-Spring) 12-5
Restriction: Circ to mem only, Non-resident fee
SOUTHWOOD, 924 Southland Dr SW, T2W 0J9, SAN 365-6349. *Mgr,* Elena Doebele
Founded 1966. Pop 49,153; Circ 472,879

Library Holdings: CDs 7,850; DVDs 2,274; Bk Vols 64,351; Per Subs 2,864; Talking Bks 2,935
Function: Bk club(s), Bks on CD, Children's prog, Computer training, Computers for patron use, Copy machines, E-Reserves, Electronic databases & coll, Family literacy, Free DVD rentals, Handicapped accessible, Home delivery & serv to Sr ctr & nursing homes, Homebound delivery serv, ILL available, Literacy & newcomer serv, Music CDs, Online cat, Online searches, Outreach serv, Photocopying/Printing, Preschool outreach, Prog for adults, Prog for children & young adult, Pub access computers, Senior computer classes, Senior outreach, Story hour, Summer reading prog, Teen prog
Special Services for the Deaf - Assisted listening device; Assistive tech; TDD equip; TTY equip
Special Services for the Blind - Accessible computers; Aids for in-house use; Bks on CD; Digital talking bk; Large print bks; Talking bks
Open Mon-Thurs 10-9, Fri & Sat 10-5, Sun (Fall-Spring) 12-5
Restriction: Circ to mem only, Non-resident fee
THORN-HILL, 6617 Centre St N, T2K 4Y5, SAN 365-6403. *Mgr,* Janet MacKinnon
Founded 1974. Pop 47,299; Circ 544,636
Library Holdings: CDs 7,488; DVDs 4,013; Bk Vols 66,924; Per Subs 3,519; Talking Bks 3,361
Special Collections: Travelling Deposit Colls in Chinese, Vietnamese & Spanish
Function: Adult bk club, Adult literacy prog, Bk club(s), Bks on cassette, Bks on CD, CD-ROM, Children's prog, Computer training, Computers for patron use, Copy machines, Digital talking bks, e-mail serv, E-Reserves, Electronic databases & coll, Family literacy, Free DVD rentals, Handicapped accessible, Home delivery & serv to Sr ctr & nursing homes, Homebound delivery serv, Homework prog, ILL available, Literacy & newcomer serv, Music CDs, Online cat, Online searches, Orientations, Outreach serv, Preschool outreach, Prog for adults, Prog for children & young adult, Pub access computers, Senior computer classes, Senior outreach, Spoken cassettes & CDs, Story hour, Summer reading prog, Teen prog, VHS videos, Wheelchair accessible
Open Mon-Thurs 10-9, Fri & Sat 10-5, Sun (Fall-Spring) 12-5
Restriction: Circ to mem only, Non-resident fee
VILLAGE SQUARE, 2623 56th St NE, T1Y 6E7, SAN 365-6276. *Mgr,* Jody Crilly
Founded 1983. Pop 137,000; Circ 1,003,493
Library Holdings: CDs 14,694; DVDs 5,613; Bk Vols 131,121; Per Subs 8,678; Talking Bks 5,703
Function: Adult bk club, Adult literacy prog, Audio & video playback equip for onsite use, Audiobks via web, Bk club(s), Bks on cassette, Bks on CD, CD-ROM, Children's prog, Computer training, Computers for patron use, Copy machines, Digital talking bks, e-mail serv, E-Reserves, Electronic databases & coll, Family literacy, Free DVD rentals, Handicapped accessible, Home delivery & serv to Sr ctr & nursing homes, Homebound delivery serv, Homework prog, ILL available, Music CDs, Orientations, Photocopying/Printing, Preschool outreach, Prog for adults, Prog for children & young adult, Senior computer classes, Senior outreach, Spoken cassettes & CDs, Summer reading prog, Teen prog, VHS videos, Wheelchair accessible
Open Mon-Thurs 10-9, Fri & Sat 10-5, Sun (Fall-Spring) 12-5
Restriction: Circ to mem only, Non-resident fee

S　CANADIAN INSTITUTE OF RESOURCES LAW, University of Calgary, Murray Fraser Hall, Rm 3353, T2N 1N4. SAN 326-4378. Tel: 403-220-3200. FAX: 403-282-6182. E-mail: cirl@ucalgary.ca. Web Site: www.cirl.ca. *Exec Dir,* Allan Ingelson; *Admin,* Nancy Money; *Info Res,* Sue Parsons
Founded 1979
Library Holdings: Bk Titles 500
Restriction: Open by appt only

S　CANADIAN PACIFIC RAILWAY*, Business Information Services, 401 Ninth Ave SW, 7th Flr, T2P 4Z4. SAN 319-7174. Tel: 403-319-3794. FAX: 403-319-6257. Web Site: www.cpr.ca. *Info Spec,* G Fraser; Tel: 403-319-6193, E-mail: gail_fraser@cpr.ca; *Info Spec,* Gary Pon; *Info Spec,* J Smart; Tel: 403-319-6189, E-mail: jennifer_smart@cpr.ca; Staff 3 (MLS 3)
Founded 1972
Library Holdings: Bk Vols 12,500; Per Subs 500
Subject Interests: Rail, Transportation
Restriction: Co libr

G　CENTRE FOR SUICIDE PREVENTION, 2005*, SIEC Library, 105 12 Ave SE, Ste 320, T2G 1A1. SAN 326-5390. Tel: 403-245-3900. FAX: 403-245-0299. E-mail: siec@suicideinfo.ca. Web Site: www.suicideinfo.ca. *Librn,* Robert Olson; Staff 2 (MLS 2)
Founded 1982
Library Holdings: DVDs 2,000; Bk Titles 35,000
Special Collections: Suicide Database (SIEC Coll)
Subject Interests: Suicide

Publications: Facing the Facts: Suicide in Canada; Information Kits; SIEC Alert (Bi-monthly); Suicide Attempts; Youth Suicide & You
Open Mon-Fri 9-4:30

G　THE CITY OF CALGARY, CORPORATE RECORDS, ARCHIVES, 313 Seventh Ave SE, T2G 0J1. (Mail add: City Clerk's Office, No 8007, PO Box 2100, Sta M, T2P 2M5), SAN 373-3610. Tel: 403-268-8180. FAX: 403-268-6731. E-mail: archives@calgary.ca. Web Site: www.calgary.ca. *Archivist,* Janice Brum; *Archivist,* Lynn Bullock; *Archivist,* Glennda Leslie; *Archivist,* Carol Stokes
Special Collections: Records of OCO '88, the organizing committee for the staging of the XV Olympic Winter Games. Municipal Document Depository

GL　CITY OF CALGARY LAW DEPARTMENT LIBRARY*, 800 Mecleod Trail SE, 12th Flr, No 8053, T2P 2M5. SAN 371-6775. Tel: 403-268-2441. FAX: 403-268-4634. *In Charge,* Ela Figueria; Tel: 403-268-2429; Staff 1 (MLS 1)
Library Holdings: Bk Titles 1,100; Bk Vols 6,500; Per Subs 125
Restriction: Staff use only

S　DEVON CANADA CORP*, Corporate Library, 2000, 400 - Third Ave SW, T2P 4H2. SAN 377-578X. Tel: 403-232-5581. E-mail: library@dvn.com. *Coop Librn,* Mariela Parra; Staff 1 (Non-MLS 1)
Library Holdings: Bk Vols 6,000; Per Subs 50
Database Vendor: EBSCOhost, LexisNexis
Wireless access
Open Mon-Fri 8-5

C　DEVRY CALGARY LIBRARY, 2700, 3rd Ave SE, T2A 7W4. Tel: 403-207-3100. Toll Free Tel: 800-363-5558, Ext 3100. FAX: 403-207-6226. E-mail: cal-library@devry.edu. Web Site: www.cal.devry.edu/library.html. *Libr Coordr,* Patricia Ranger; E-mail: pranger@devry.edu; Staff 1 (Non-MLS 1)
Enrl 500; Highest Degree: Bachelor
Library Holdings: e-books 15,552; Bk Titles 18,000
Database Vendor: CredoReference, EBSCOhost, Faulkner Information Services, Hoovers, LexisNexis, Plunkett Research, Ltd, ProQuest, Safari Books Online
Wireless access
Function: Free DVD rentals, ILL available, Instruction & testing, Mail loans to mem, Online cat, Online ref, Online searches, Orientations
Open Mon & Wed 10-6, Tues & Thurs 10-8, Fri 10-4

S　ENCANA CORPORATION*, Information & Records Centre, 150 Ninth Ave SW, T2P 2S5. (Mail add: PO Box 2850, T2P 2S5), SAN 326-4653. Tel: 403-645-7645. FAX: 403-645-7649. E-mail: information.centre@encana.com. Web Site: www.encana.com. *In Charge,* Jeanne Kimber; Tel: 403-645-7644, E-mail: jeanne.kimber@encana.com; Staff 4 (MLS 1, Non-MLS 3)
Library Holdings: Bk Vols 25,000; Per Subs 400
Subject Interests: Geol, Petroleum eng
Automation Activity & Vendor Info: (Cataloging) SirsiDynix; (Circulation) SirsiDynix; (OPAC) SirsiDynix; (Serials) SirsiDynix
Function: Doc delivery serv, Electronic databases & coll, ILL available, Online cat, Online ref, Online searches, Ref & res
Partic in Can Asn of Spec Librs Info Servs; Can Libr Asn
Restriction: Authorized personnel only, Circulates for staff only, Co libr, Not open to pub

L　FRASER MILNER CASGRAIN LLP*, Bankers Ct, 15th Flr, 850 Second St SW, T2P 0R8. SAN 371-7755. Tel: 403-268-7000. FAX: 403-268-3100. Web Site: www.frasermilnercasgrain.com. *Cat Spec,* Elaine Weich; *Info Analyst,* Terry Colborne; Staff 2 (MLS 1, Non-MLS 1)
Founded 1956
Library Holdings: Bk Titles 12,000; Bk Vols 25,000; Per Subs 1,800
Restriction: Not open to pub

S　GLENBOW MUSEUM LIBRARY*, 130 Ninth Ave SE, T2G 0P3. SAN 318-613X. Tel: 403-268-4197. FAX: 403-232-6569. Web Site: www.glenbow.org. *Sr Librn,* Lindsay Moir; Tel: 403-268-4198, E-mail: lmoir@glenbow.org; *Ref Serv,* Jennifer Hanblin; Staff 1 (MLS 1)
Founded 1956
Library Holdings: Bk Vols 100,000; Per Subs 80
Special Collections: Equestrian
Subject Interests: Art exhibits catalogs, Artic Can, Can art, Museology, NW Coast Indians, Plains Indians, Western Can
Publications: Canadian West Discovered
Open Tues-Fri 10-5
Restriction: Non-circulating

S　HATCH ENERGY LIBRARY*, 840 Seventh Ave SW, Ste 700, T2P 3G2. SAN 328-0357. Tel: 403-920-3101. FAX: 403-266-5730. *Librn,* Annaliese Dalmoro; E-mail: adalmoro@hatch.ca
Founded 1981

Library Holdings: Bk Titles 1,600; Per Subs 60
Subject Interests: Civil eng
Restriction: Staff use only

S HUSKY ENERGY CORPORATE LIBRARY*, 707 Eighth Ave SW, 19 Flr, T2P 3G7. SAN 327-5043. Tel: 403-298-6111. Circulation Tel: 403-298-7065. FAX: 403-298-6263. *Head Librn,* Wanda Oleszkiewicz; Staff 2 (MLS 1, Non-MLS 1)
Library Holdings: Bk Vols 200,000; Per Subs 450
Subject Interests: Computers, Eng, Geol, Petroleum exploration
Restriction: Staff use only

S JACOBS CANADA INC*, 205 Quarry Park Blvd SE, T2C 3E7. SAN 373-3629. Tel: 403-258-6411. FAX: 403-255-1421. *Librn,* Carol Seebruch; E-mail: carol.seebruch@jacobs.com
Founded 1978
Library Holdings: Bk Vols 1,260; Per Subs 30
Restriction: Employee & client use only

S KLOHN CRIPPEN BERGER LTD, Library & Records Centre, 500 2618 Hopewell Pl NE, T1Y 7J7. Tel: 403-731-6880. Web Site: www.klohn.com. *Librn,* Sarah Gustafson; E-mail: sgustafson@klohn.com; Staff 1 (MLS 1)

S LEARNINGLINKS RESOURCE CENTRE*, 3930 20th St SW, T2T 4Z9. SAN 326-7857. Tel: 403-249-4606, 403-686-9300. Toll Free Tel: 877-686-9300. FAX: 403-686-0627. E-mail: learninglinks@calgarylearningcentre.com, library@literacyalberta.ca. Web Site: learninglinkslibrary.ca. *Librn,* Laura Godfrey; Staff 2 (Non-MLS 2)
Founded 1984
Library Holdings: Bk Titles 17,000; Per Subs 5; Videos 324
Subject Interests: ADHD (Attention deficit hyperactivity disorder), Adult literacy, Attention deficit disorder, Family literacy, Learning difficulties, Spec educ
Open Mon-Fri 8:30-4:30

S MATRIX SOLUTIONS LIBRARY*, 150-13 Ave SW, Ste 200, T2R 0V2. SAN 371-7526. Tel: 403-237-0606. FAX: 403-263-2493. E-mail: matrix.recordsmanagement@matrix-solutions.com. Web Site: www.matrix-solutions.com. *Librn,* Dawn Catena
Founded 1984
Library Holdings: Bk Titles 800; Per Subs 15
Special Collections: Soil Science & Reclamation, bks, papers, proceedings; Sulphur & the Environment (Sour Gas Effects Coll), bks, papers, proceedings
Restriction: Not open to pub, Staff use only

L MCCARTHY TETRAULT LLP LIBRARY*, 421 Seventh Ave SW, Ste 3300, T2P 4K9. SAN 372-882X. Tel: 403-260-3503. FAX: 403-260-3501. *Dir, Libr Serv,* Phyllis Thornton; Tel: 403-260-3670, E-mail: pthornton@mccarthy.ca; Staff 2.5 (Non-MLS 2.5)
Library Holdings: Bk Titles 2,300; Bk Vols 30,000; Per Subs 125
Subject Interests: Law
Automation Activity & Vendor Info: (Acquisitions) SydneyPlus; (Cataloging) SydneyPlus; (Circulation) SydneyPlus; (OPAC) SydneyPlus; (Serials) SydneyPlus
Database Vendor: HeinOnline, Infomart, LexisNexis, Westlaw, Westlaw Business, WestlaweCARSWELL
Wireless access
Function: ILL available
Restriction: Staff use only

L MILES DAVISON LIBRARY*, 205 Fifth Ave SW, Ste 1600, T2P 2V7. SAN 321-5539. Tel: 403-298-0325. FAX: 403-263-6840. E-mail: thefirm@milesdavison.com. Web Site: www.milesdavison.com.
Library Holdings: Bk Titles 12,300; Per Subs 62
Subject Interests: Bankruptcy, Insolvency, Law, Native law
Automation Activity & Vendor Info: (Acquisitions) Inmagic, Inc.; (Cataloging) Inmagic, Inc.; (Serials) Inmagic, Inc.
Database Vendor: LexisNexis, Westlaw
Restriction: Staff use only
Friends of the Library Group

C MOUNT ROYAL UNIVERSITY LIBRARY*, 4825 Mount Royal Gate SW, T3E 6K6. SAN 318-6180. Tel: 403-440-6140. Circulation Tel: 403-440-6019. Interlibrary Loan Service Tel: 403-440-6133. Administration Tel: 403-440-6124. Information Services Tel: 403-440-6088. FAX: 403-440-6758. Web Site: library.mtroyal.ca. *Chair,* Pearl Herscovitch; Tel: 403-440-6022; *Univ Librn,* Carol Shepstone; Tel: 403-440-6134; *Coll Coordr,* Meagan Bowler; Tel: 403-440-6126; *Syst Coordr,* Kalen Gibb; Tel: 403-440-8516; *Access Serv,* Cari Merkley; Tel: 403-440-5068; *Access Serv,* Geoff Owens; Tel: 403-440-7737; *Info Serv,* Michelle Sinotte; Tel: 403-440-5683; *Tech Serv,* Francine May; Tel: 403-440-6128; Staff 64 (MLS 16, Non-MLS 48)

Highest Degree: Bachelor
Library Holdings: Bk Vols 185,000; Per Subs 8,000
Automation Activity & Vendor Info: (Acquisitions) Ex Libris Group; (Cataloging) Ex Libris Group; (Circulation) Ex Libris Group; (Course Reserve) Ex Libris Group; (ILL) Relais International; (Media Booking) Ex Libris Group; (OPAC) Ex Libris Group; (Serials) Ex Libris Group
Database Vendor: EBSCOhost, OCLC FirstSearch, ProQuest
Publications: Faculty & Staff Guide; Library Film & Video; Library Handbook; Policy Handbooks; Student Guide
Partic in The Alberta Library
Open Mon-Thurs 7:45am-10pm, Fri 7:45am-8pm, Sat & Sun 10-8

G NATIONAL ENERGY BOARD LIBRARY, 444 Seventh Ave SW, T2P 0X8. SAN 368-0134. Tel: 403-299-3561. FAX: 403-292-5576. E-mail: library@neb-one.gc.ca. *Acq & Cat,* Courtney Walker; *Ref,* Andrea Caza
Founded 1959
Library Holdings: CDs 220; DVDs 70; Microforms 1,260; Bk Titles 18,500; Per Subs 125; Videos 145
Subject Interests: Electricity, Energy, Natural gas, Oil, Petroleum indust, Trade
Publications: Current Periodicals List
Partic in Council of Federal Libraries Consortium
Open Mon-Fri 9-4

G NATURAL RESOURCES CANADA LIBRARY, Geological Survey of Canada Calgary Library, 3303 33rd St NW, 2nd Flr, T2L 2A7. SAN 318-6121. Tel: 403-292-7165. FAX: 403-292-5377. E-mail: calgary.ref@nrcan.gc.ca. Web Site: www.nrcan.gc.ca/library/6259. *Librn,* Edward Hau; Staff 2 (MLS 1, Non-MLS 1)
Library Holdings: Bk Vols 100,000; Per Subs 150
Subject Interests: Can arctic, Energy, Gas, Geol, Oil, Paleontology, Sedimentary geol
Automation Activity & Vendor Info: (Cataloging) Evergreen; (Circulation) Evergreen; (OPAC) Evergreen
Database Vendor: EBSCOhost
Open Mon-Thurs 8-4, Fri 8-3:15

S NEXEN INC LIBRARY, 801 Seventh Ave SW, T2P 3P7. SAN 371-8956. Tel: 403-699-5425. FAX: 403-232-1826. Web Site: www.nexeninc.com. *Librn,* Marlene Robertson; E-mail: marlene_robertson@nexeninc.com; Staff 1 (Non-MLS 1)
Library Holdings: Bk Titles 4,000; Bk Vols 6,000; Per Subs 200
Subject Interests: Gas, Oil
Automation Activity & Vendor Info: (Cataloging) Inmagic, Inc.
Open Mon-Fri 7:30-4:30
Restriction: Staff use only

L NORTON ROSE CANADA LLP*, Law Library, Devon Tower, 400 Third Ave SW, Ste 3700, T2P 4H2. SAN 372-395X. Tel: 403-267-9466. FAX: 403-264-5973. Web Site: www.nortonrose.com. *Mgr, Libr Serv,* Judy Harvie; E-mail: judy.harvie@nortonrose.com; *Ref Librn,* Julia Millar; Tel: 403-267-8384, E-mail: julia.millar@nortonrose.com
Library Holdings: Bk Vols 10,000
Subject Interests: Corporate law
Automation Activity & Vendor Info: (Cataloging) SirsiDynix
Database Vendor: Infomart, LexisNexis, Westlaw
Wireless access

CR ROCKY MOUNTAIN COLLEGE LIBRARY, 4039 Brentwood Rd NW, T2L 1L1. SAN 321-1231. Tel: 403-284-5100. Circulation Tel: 403-284-5100, Ext 253. FAX: 403-220-9567. E-mail: library@rockymountaincollege.ca. Web Site: www.rockymountaincollege.ca/pages/library.php. *Head Librn,* Darcy Gullacher; E-mail: dgullacher@rockymountaincollege.ca; Staff 1 (MLS 1)
Founded 1992. Enrl 155; Fac 9; Highest Degree: Bachelor
Library Holdings: e-books 1,500; e-journals 600; Bk Vols 41,000; Per Subs 100
Subject Interests: Biblical studies, Christian educ, Church music, Relig studies, Theol
Automation Activity & Vendor Info: (Acquisitions) LibLime; (Cataloging) LibLime; (Circulation) LibLime; (Course Reserve) LibLime; (ILL) LibLime; (Media Booking) LibLime; (OPAC) LibLime; (Serials) LibLime
Database Vendor: ebrary, EBSCOhost, Gale Cengage Learning, netLibrary, ProQuest
Wireless access

S ST VLADIMIR'S LIBRARY & ARCHIVES*, 404 Meredith Rd NE, T2E 5A6. SAN 326-4750. Tel: 403-264-3437. FAX: 403-264-3438. E-mail: stvladim@telus.net. Web Site: www.stvlads.com. *Librn,* Mykola Woron; *Asst Librn,* Orest Skibinsky; *Asst Librn,* Wasyl Swityk; *Asst Librn,* Nick Topolnyski
Founded 1958

Library Holdings: Bk Titles 16,200; Bk Vols 17,618; Per Subs 13,882; Videos 357
Special Collections: Children & Youth Coll; Periodicals; Theatrical Coll; Ukrainian Events in Canada & Abroad, progs

J   SOUTHERN ALBERTA INSTITUTE OF TECHNOLOGY LIBRARY*, 1301 16th Ave NW, T2M 0L4. SAN 318-6229. Tel: 403-210-4477. Interlibrary Loan Service Tel: 403-284-8411. FAX: 403-284-8619. E-mail: library@sait.ca. Web Site: library.sait.ca. *Mgr,* Susan Brayford; Staff 20 (MLS 6, Non-MLS 14)
Founded 1921. Enrl 12,780; Fac 575
Library Holdings: e-books 123,000; Bk Vols 99,000; Per Subs 430
Subject Interests: Bus admin, Culinary, Electronics, Info tech, Petroleum, Trades & apprentices
Automation Activity & Vendor Info: (Acquisitions) SirsiDynix; (Cataloging) SirsiDynix; (OPAC) SirsiDynix
Wireless access
Partic in The Alberta Library

S   SUNCOR ENERGY LIBRARY*, 150-Sixth Ave SW, T2P 3E3. (Mail add: PO Box 2844, T2P 3E3), SAN 371-4640. Tel: 403-296-8000. FAX: 403-296-3030. *In Charge,* Shellie Streeton; Tel: 403-296-4413; Staff 1 (MLS 1)
Library Holdings: e-books 2,000; e-journals 3,000
Restriction: Open to staff only

S   TALISMAN ENERGY INC*, Information Resources Centre, 2000, 888 Third St SW, T2P 5C5. SAN 323-8717. Tel: 403-237-1429. FAX: 403-231-2823. E-mail: irc@talisman-energy.com. Web Site: www.talisman-energy.com. *Supvr,* Cathy Ross; *Info Res,* Margo Price; *Info Res Spec,* Barbara Lane
Subject Interests: Bus pub, Eng, Petroleum geol
Automation Activity & Vendor Info: (Acquisitions) Inmagic, Inc.; (Cataloging) Inmagic, Inc.; (Circulation) Inmagic, Inc.; (OPAC) Inmagic, Inc.; (Serials) Inmagic, Inc.
Database Vendor: Dialog, EBSCOhost, Factiva.com
Partic in Special Libraries Association
Open Mon-Fri 7:30-5

C   UNIVERSITY OF CALGARY LIBRARY*, 2500 University Dr NW, T2N 1N4. SAN 365-6705. Tel: 403-220-5953. Circulation Tel: 403-220-5963. Interlibrary Loan Service Tel: 403-220-5967. Reference Tel: 403-220-8895. FAX: 403-282-1218. E-mail: libinfo@ucalgary.ca. Web Site: library.ucalgary.ca, www.ucalgary.ca/library. *Vice Provost for Libr,* Thomas Hickerson; E-mail: tom.hickerson@ucalgary.ca; *Asst Vice-Provost - Coll/Librn,* Helen Clarke; Tel: 403-220-3796, E-mail: hclarke@ucalgary.ca; *Assoc Vice-Provost - Learning/Librn,* Claudette Cloutier; Tel: 403-220-3447, E-mail: ccloutier@ucalgary.ca; *Assoc Vice-Provost - Res/Librarian,* Kim Clarke; *Assoc Univ Librn,* Mary McConnell; Tel: 403-220-3725, E-mail: mmcconne@ucalgary.ca; *Head, Doc Delivery/ILL,* Maureen McDonald; Tel: 403-220-7819, E-mail: dmmcdona@ucalgary.ca; *Metadata Librn,* Heather D'Amour; Tel: 403-220-3591, E-mail: damour@ucalgary.ca; *Assoc Librn, Info Tech Serv,* Shawna Sadler; Tel: 403-220-3739, E-mail: ssadler@ucalgary.ca; *Circ Mgr,* Lucille Wallace; Tel: 403-220-3758, E-mail: lewallac@ucalgary.ca; Staff 49 (MLS 43, Non-MLS 6)
Founded 1964. Enrl 28,306; Fac 2,209; Highest Degree: Doctorate
Library Holdings: Bk Titles 1,595,184; Bk Vols 2,535,714; Per Subs 24,928
Special Collections: Arctic Institute of North America Coll; Books & the Book Arts (Evelyn de Mille Coll); Canadian Architectural Archive Coll; Canadian Literature Coll, bks & authors' mss; Canadian Prairies & Arctic (Margaret Hess Coll), bks & govt publications; Contemporary British Poets (Eric W White Coll); Music Archives; Recreational Mathematics (Strens)
Subject Interests: Archit, Educ, Eng, Environ design, Geol, Humanities, Kinesiology, Law, Med, Nursing, Soc work
Automation Activity & Vendor Info: (Acquisitions) SirsiDynix; (Cataloging) SirsiDynix; (Circulation) SirsiDynix; (Course Reserve) SirsiDynix; (ILL) Relais International; (OPAC) SirsiDynix; (Serials) SirsiDynix
Database Vendor: Dialog, EBSCOhost, Gale Cengage Learning, OCLC FirstSearch, OVID Technologies, ProQuest
Function: Archival coll, Doc delivery serv, ILL available, Photocopying/Printing, Ref serv available, Res libr, Telephone ref
Partic in Canadian Association of Research Libraries; Council of Prairie & Pacific University Libraries; The Alberta Library
Special Services for the Blind - Large screen computer & software; Magnifiers
Departmental Libraries:
BUSINESS LIBRARY, Haskayne School of Business, Scurfield Hall, Rm 301, T2N 1N4, SAN 376-995X. Circulation Tel: 403-220-7236. Reference Tel: 403-220-6113. FAX: 403-220-0120. Web Site: library.ucalgary.ca/business. *Libr Dir,* Justine Wheeler; Tel: 403-220-5084, E-mail: justine.wheeler@haskayne.ucalgary.ca; *Bus Librn,*

Rhinnon Jessup; Tel: 403-220-4410; *Bus Librn,* Elizabeth Watson; Tel: 403-220-7223, E-mail: liz.watson@haskayne.ucalgary.ca; Staff 6 (MLS 3, Non-MLS 3)
Enrl 3,000; Fac 90; Highest Degree: Doctorate
Library Holdings: e-journals 6,000; Bk Vols 9,000; Per Subs 250
Subject Interests: Bus, Energy, Mgt
Open Mon-Fri 8:30-4:30, Sat & Sun 12-4
DOUCETTE LIBRARY OF TEACHING RESOURCES, 370 Education Block, 2500 University Dr NW, T2N 1N4. Tel: 403-220-5637. Reference Tel: 403-220-3848. FAX: 403-220-8211. Web Site: www.educ1.ucalgary.ca/doucette. *Actg Dir,* Laura Koltutsky; Tel: 403-220-6295, E-mail: ljkoltut@ucalgary.ca; *Head, Circ,* Linda Johnson; Tel: 403-220-3982, E-mail: johnson@ucalgary.ca; *Ref Serv,* Tammy Flanders; Tel: 403-220-3984, E-mail: tflander@ucalgary.ca; Staff 10 (MLS 1, Non-MLS 9)
Enrl 1,000; Highest Degree: Bachelor
Library Holdings: AV Mats 11,800; Bk Titles 59,000; Per Subs 35
Subject Interests: Curric, Educ
Open Mon-Thurs 8:30-6, Fri 8:30-4:30
GALLAGHER LIBRARY, 180 Earth Sciences Bldg, 2500 University Dr NW, T2N 1N4, SAN 365-673X. Reference Tel: 403-220-6042. FAX: 403-282-6075. E-mail: gallagher.library@ucalgary.ca. Web Site: library.ucalgary.ca/branches/gallagherlibrary.
Founded 1973. Highest Degree: Doctorate
Library Holdings: Bk Titles 50,740; Bk Vols 87,439; Per Subs 306
Special Collections: University of Calgary Geology & Geophysics Theses
Database Vendor: SirsiDynix
Function: Res libr
Open Mon-Thurs (Winter) 8am-9pm, Fri 8:30-4:30, Sat & Sun 12-4; Mon-Fri (Summer) 8:30-4:30
CM   HEALTH SCIENCES LIBRARY, Health Sci Ctr, 3330 Hospital Dr NW, T2N 4N1, SAN 365-6799. Tel: 403-220-6857. Circulation Tel: 403-220-6855. Interlibrary Loan Service Tel: 403-220-7419. Administration Tel: 403-220-6859. FAX: 403-210-9847. E-mail: hslibr@ucalgary.ca. Web Site: library.ucalgary.ca/branches/hsl. *Dir, Health Sci Libr,* Susan Powelson; Tel: 403-220-6858, E-mail: susan.powelson@ucalgary.ca; *Head, Health Info Network,* Renee Reaume; Tel: 403-220-5573, E-mail: rreaume@ucalgary.ca; *Librn, Peter Lougheed Ctr Knowledge Ctr,* Taryn Lenders; Tel: 403-943-4737, E-mail: tlenders@ucalgary.ca; *Librn, Peter Lougheed Ctr Knowledge Ctr,* Kathryn Ranjit; Tel: 403-943-4736, E-mail: kathryn.ranjit@ucalgary.ca; *Librn, Rock View Gen Hospital Knowlege Ctr,* Elizabeth Aitken; Tel: 403-943-3488, E-mail: eaitken@ucalgary.ca; *Librn, Tom Baker Cancer Ctr Knowledge Ctr, Holy Cross Site,* Yongtao Lin; Tel: 403-521-3285, E-mail: yolin@ucalgary.ca; *Librn, Tom Baker Cancer Ctr Knowledge Ctr, Holy Cross Site,* Marcus Vaska; Tel: 403-698-8016, E-mail: mmvaska@ucalgary.ca; *Veterinary Med Librn,* Lorraine Toews; Tel: 403-220-3750, E-mail: ltoews@ucalgary.ca; *Gen Mgr, Health Knowledge Network,* Pat Sandercock; Tel: 403-220-8250, E-mail: pasander@ucalgary.ca; *Operations Mgr,* Mary Grant; Tel: 403-220-5035, E-mail: grantm@ucalgary.ca; Staff 28.5 (MLS 11, Non-MLS 17.5)
Founded 1968. Highest Degree: Doctorate
Special Collections: Mackie Family History of Neuroscience Coll, 16th-20th century hist bks, autographs, journal articles, off-prints, pamphlets
Subject Interests: Med, Med hist, Nursing, Veterinary med
CL   LAW LIBRARY, 2500 University Dr NW, T2N 1N4, SAN 365-6764. Circulation Tel: 403-220-3727. Reference Tel: 403-220-7274. Administration Tel: 403-220-5091. FAX: 403-282-3000. Web Site: library.ucalgary.ca/branches/law. *Dir,* Kim Clarke; Tel: 403-220-6702, E-mail: kim.clarke@ucalgary.ca; *Law Librn,* Nadine Hoffman; Tel: 403-220-8392, E-mail: nadine.hoffman@ucalgary.ca; Staff 7 (MLS 2, Non-MLS 5)
Founded 1976
Special Collections: 18th-19th Century English; pre 1900 Canadian
Subject Interests: Environ law, Natural res
Automation Activity & Vendor Info: (OPAC) SirsiDynix

CALLING LAKE

P   CALLING LAKE PUBLIC LIBRARY*, PO Box 129, T0G 0K0. Tel: 780-331-3027. FAX: 780-891-3029. E-mail: librarian@callinglakelibrary.ab.ca. Web Site: www.callinglakelibrary.ab.ca. *Librn,* Diane Collyer
Library Holdings: Bk Vols 2,000; Per Subs 10
Mem of Peace Library System
Open Tues & Fri 10-3, Wed & Thurs 12-5

CALMAR

P   CALMAR PUBLIC LIBRARY*, 4705 50th Ave, T0C 0V0. (Mail add: PO Box 328, T0C 0V0), SAN 318-6245. Tel: 780-985-3472. FAX: 780-985-2859. E-mail: calmarlibrary@yrl.ab.ca. Web Site:

www.calmarpubliclibrary.ca. *Chairperson,* Joan Wynne; *Libr Mgr,* Kim Johnson
Pop 2,000; Circ 7,365
Library Holdings: Bk Vols 11,000; Per Subs 25
Open Mon & Wed 11-8, Tues, Thurs & Fri 11-5, Sat 11-3

CAMROSE

GL ALBERTA LAW LIBRARIES - CAMROSE*, Courthouse, 5210 - 49th Ave, T4V 3Y2. SAN 377-4090. Tel: 780-980-7592. FAX: 780-679-1253.
Library Holdings: Bk Vols 6,000

P CAMROSE PUBLIC LIBRARY*, 4710 50th Ave, T4V 0R8. SAN 318-6253. Tel: 780-672-4214. FAX: 780-672-9165. E-mail: cpl.library@prl.ab.ca. Web Site: www.cpl.prl.ab.ca. *Chairperson,* Anjah Howard; *Librn,* Deborah Cryderman
Founded 1919. Pop 17,000; Circ 192,000
Library Holdings: Bk Vols 45,000; Per Subs 65
Subject Interests: Recreational reading
Automation Activity & Vendor Info: (Acquisitions) Horizon; (Cataloging) Horizon; (Circulation) Horizon; (ILL) Horizon; (OPAC) Horizon
Database Vendor: SirsiDynix
Publications: By the Book (Quarterly)
Mem of Parkland Regional Library
Open Mon-Thurs 10-8, Fri & Sat 10-6

SR CANADIAN LUTHERAN BIBLE INSTITUTE LIBRARY*, 4837 52A St, T4V 1W5. SAN 375-0256. Tel: 780-672-4454. FAX: 780-672-4455. E-mail: clbi@clbi.edu. Web Site: clbi.edu. *Librn,* Carolyn Olson
Library Holdings: Bk Vols 11,000; Per Subs 21
Open Mon-Sun 7:30am-11pm

C UNIVERSITY OF ALBERTA, Augustana Faculty Library, 4901 46th Ave, T4V 2R3. SAN 320-281X. Tel: 780-679-1189. Circulation Tel: 780-679-1156. Reference Tel: 780-679-1592. FAX: 780-679-1594. E-mail: augustana.library@ualberta.ca. Web Site: www.library.ualberta.ca/augustana. *Head Librn,* Nancy Goebel; E-mail: nancy.goebel@ualberta.ca; *Ref,* Paul Neff; E-mail: paul.neff@ualberta.ca; Staff 9 (MLS 3, Non-MLS 6)
Founded 1911. Enrl 1,000; Fac 65
Library Holdings: Bk Titles 150,000; Per Subs 300
Special Collections: Scandinavia, artifacts, bks
Subject Interests: English, Lang, Music, Relig studies, Soc sci
Automation Activity & Vendor Info: (Acquisitions) SirsiDynix; (Cataloging) SirsiDynix; (Circulation) SirsiDynix; (Course Reserve) SirsiDynix; (ILL) Relais International; (OPAC) SirsiDynix; (Serials) SirsiDynix

CANMORE

GL ALBERTA LAW LIBRARIES - CANMORE*, Provincial Bldg, 314, 800 Railway Ave, T1W 1P1. SAN 377-4074. Tel: 403-678-5915. FAX: 403-678-4936. *Libr Coordr,* Marianne Wasch; E-mail: marianne.wasch@gov.ab.ca; Staff 1 (Non-MLS 1)
Open Wed 9-2:30

P CANMORE PUBLIC LIBRARY*, 950 Eighth Ave, T1W 2T1. SAN 321-0642. Tel: 403-678-2468. FAX: 403-678-2165. E-mail: info@canmorelibrary.ab.ca. Web Site: canmorelibrary.ab.ca. *Dir,* Michelle Preston; E-mail: mpreston@canmorelibrary.ab.ca; *AV,* Brenda Baerg; *Cat,* Cherill Shannon; *ILL,* Tina Fong; Staff 9 (MLS 2, Non-MLS 7)
Founded 1971. Pop 12,317; Circ 180,000
Library Holdings: Bk Titles 60,173; Per Subs 123
Automation Activity & Vendor Info: (Circulation) SirsiDynix; (OPAC) SirsiDynix
Database Vendor: SirsiDynix
Mem of Marigold Library System
Open Mon-Thurs 11-8, Fri-Sun 11-5
Friends of the Library Group

CARBON

P CARBON MUNICIPAL LIBRARY*, 401 Bruce Ave, T0M 0L0. (Mail add: PO Box 70, T0M 0L0), SAN 322-8312. Tel: 403-572-3440. E-mail: acarmlibrary@marigold.ab.ca. *Librn,* Jay-Lynn Boutin
Founded 1981. Pop 538
Library Holdings: Bk Titles 8,500; Per Subs 10
Automation Activity & Vendor Info: (Acquisitions) SirsiDynix
Mem of Marigold Library System
Special Services for the Deaf - Assisted listening device
Special Services for the Blind - Bks on CD
Open Tues & Wed 6pm-9pm, Thurs 9-4:30, Sat 9-2
Friends of the Library Group

CARDSTON

P JIM & MARY KEARL LIBRARY OF CARDSTON*, 25 Third Ave W, T0K 0K0. (Mail add: PO Box 1560, T0K 0K0), SAN 318-6261. Tel: 403-653-4775. Administration Tel: 403-653-4707. FAX: 403-653-4716. Web Site: www.cardstonlibrary.ca. *Libr Mgr,* Donna Beazer; Staff 7 (Non-MLS 7)
Founded 1931. Pop 3,475; Circ 90,000
Library Holdings: CDs 860; DVDs 800; Bk Vols 29,000; Per Subs 65; Talking Bks 805; Videos 300
Subject Interests: Biographies, LDS fiction & non-fiction, Local hist
Automation Activity & Vendor Info: (Cataloging) SirsiDynix; (Circulation) SirsiDynix; (OPAC) SirsiDynix
Database Vendor: SirsiDynix
Wireless access
Function: After school storytime, CD-ROM, Electronic databases & coll, Fax serv, Handicapped accessible, ILL available, Magnifiers for reading, Online searches, Photocopying/Printing, Prog for children & young adult, Summer reading prog, VHS videos
Special Services for the Blind - Audio mat; Bks on CD; Extensive large print coll
Open Mon, Wed & Fri 10-6, Thurs 10-8, Sat 12-5

CARMANGAY

P CARMANGAY MUNICIPAL LIBRARY*, 416 Grand Ave, T0L 0N0. (Mail add: PO Box 67, T0L 0N0). Tel: 403-643-3777. FAX: 403-643-3777. E-mail: help@carmangaylibrary.ca. Web Site: www.carmangaylibrary.ca. *Librn,* Joanne DeGroot
Pop 300
Library Holdings: Bk Titles 10,000
Automation Activity & Vendor Info: (Acquisitions) SirsiDynix
Open Tues & Thurs 1:30-5, Wed 6:30pm-8:30pm, Fri 9:15-12 & 1:30-3:30, Sat 9:30-12

CAROLINE

P CAROLINE MUNICIPAL LIBRARY*, 5023 50th Ave, T0M 0M0. (Mail add: Box 339, T0M 0M0). Tel: 403-722-4060. FAX: 403-722-4070. E-mail: carolinelibrary@libs.prl.ab.ca. Web Site: carolinelibrary.prl.ab.ca. *Libr Mgr,* Rita Collins; *Libr Mgr,* Allison Hewitt
Library Holdings: Bk Vols 16,000; Per Subs 25
Wireless access
Mem of Parkland Regional Library
Open Tues-Fri 11-6, Sat 11-3
Friends of the Library Group

CARSTAIRS

P CARSTAIRS PUBLIC LIBRARY*, 1402 Scarlett Ranch Blvd, T0M 0N0. (Mail add: PO Box 941, T0M 0N0). Tel: 403-337-3943. FAX: 403-337-3943. E-mail: carstairs@libs.prl.ab.ca. Web Site: carstairspublic.prl.ab.ca. *Head Librn,* Joanne Merrick; *Asst Head Librn,* Marg Reid
Pop 3,459; Circ 24,824
Library Holdings: Audiobooks 453; DVDs 679; Music Scores 61; Bk Vols 12,861; Per Subs 25
Automation Activity & Vendor Info: (Acquisitions) SirsiDynix; (Cataloging) SirsiDynix; (Circulation) SirsiDynix; (ILL) SirsiDynix
Mem of Parkland Regional Library
Open Tues 10-6, Wed & Thurs 10-8, Fri 10-5, Sat 10-3
Friends of the Library Group

CASTOR

P CASTOR MUNICIPAL LIBRARY*, 5103 51 St, T0C 0X0. (Mail add: Box 699, T0C 0X0), SAN 318-627X. Tel: 403-882-3999. FAX: 403-882-3915. E-mail: castorlibrary@libs.prl.ab.ca. Web Site: castorlibrary.prl.ab.ca. *Chairperson,* Fran Cox; *Librn,* Wendy Bozek
Pop 1,000; Circ 8,806
Library Holdings: DVDs 400; Bk Titles 7,000
Mem of Parkland Regional Library
Open Mon & Fri 1:30-5, Wed 10-12 & 1:30-5

CEREAL

P CEREAL & DISTRICT MUNICIPAL LIBRARY*, 415 Main St, T0J 0N0. (Mail add: PO Box 218, T0J 0N0). Tel: 403-326-3853. E-mail: acermlibrary@marigold.ab.ca. *Librn,* Denise Stief
Pop 160
Library Holdings: Bk Vols 8,000
Mem of Marigold Library System
Open Mon, Wed & Thurs 11:30-5, Tues 2-6:30

CHAMPION

P   CHAMPION MUNICIPAL LIBRARY*, Two Ave South, T0L 0R0. (Mail add: PO Box 177, T0L 0R0). Tel: 403-897-3099. FAX: 403-897-3099. E-mail: help@championlibrary.ca. Web Site: www.championlibrary.ca. *Librn,* Patty Abel
Founded 1951. Pop 378
Library Holdings: Bk Vols 10,000
Wireless access
Open Tues 2-5, Wed 10-12 & 5-8, Thurs 10-12 & 2-5, Fri 10-1

CHAUVIN

P   CHAUVIN MUNICIPAL LIBRARY*, 5200 Fourth Ave N, T0B 0V0. (Mail add: PO Box 129, T0B 0V0). Tel: 780-858-3746. FAX: 780-858-2392. E-mail: librarian@chauvinmunicipallibrary.ab.ca. Web Site: www.chauvinmunicipallibrary.ab.ca. *Librn,* Linda Russnak
Pop 378
Library Holdings: Bk Vols 12,000
Mem of Northern Lights Library System
Open Tues, Wed & Fri 9-3:30, Thurs 9-6:30

CHESTERMERE

P   CHESTERMERE PUBLIC LIBRARY*, Chestermere Town Hall, 105B Marina Rd, T1X 1V7. Tel: 403-272-9025. FAX: 403-272-9036. E-mail: acheslibrary@marigold.ab.ca. Web Site: www.chestermerepubliclibrary.com. *Dir,* Position Currently Open; *Asst Dir,* Debbi Weber
Pop 13,760
Library Holdings: AV Mats 1,204; Bk Vols 34,257; Per Subs 120; Talking Bks 1,058
Wireless access
Mem of Marigold Library System
Partic in The Regional Automation Consortium (TRAC)
Open Tues-Thurs 10-8:30, Fri & Sat 10-5
Friends of the Library Group

CLARESHOLM

P   CLARESHOLM PUBLIC LIBRARY*, 211 49th Ave W, T0L 0T0. (Mail add: PO Box 548, T0L 0T0), Tel: 403-625-6296. FAX: 403-625-2939. Web Site: www.claresholmlibrary.ca. *Libr Mgr,* Kathy Davies; E-mail: kdavies@claresholmlibrary.ca; *Asst Libr Mgr,* Betty Hoare; Staff 3 (Non-MLS 3)
Founded 1938. Pop 5,000; Circ 53,000
Library Holdings: Audiobooks 1,282; Bks on Deafness & Sign Lang 10; CDs 328; DVDs 641; Large Print Bks 607; Bk Vols 27,252; Per Subs 70; Videos 1,135
Special Collections: Multilingual Book Coll; Newspaper Coll (1907-present), microfilm
Automation Activity & Vendor Info: (Acquisitions) SIRSI WorkFlows; (Cataloging) SIRSI WorkFlows; (Circulation) SIRSI WorkFlows; (Course Reserve) SIRSI WorkFlows; (Media Booking) SIRSI WorkFlows; (OPAC) SIRSI WorkFlows; (Serials) SIRSI WorkFlows
Database Vendor: Gale Cengage Learning
Wireless access
Function: ILL available, Photocopying/Printing
Special Services for the Blind - Assistive/Adapted tech devices, equip & products; Audio mat; Bks on cassette; Bks on CD; Computer access aids; Computer with voice synthesizer for visually impaired persons; Copier with enlargement capabilities; Daisy reader; Large print bks; Large print bks & talking machines; Large screen computer & software; Low vision equip; Magnifiers
Open Mon-Wed & Fri 10-5:30, Thurs 10-8, Sat 10-3
Friends of the Library Group

CLIVE

P   CLIVE PUBLIC LIBRARY*, 5115 50th St, T0C 0Y0. (Mail add: PO Box 209, T0C 0Y0). Tel: 403-784-3131. FAX: 403-784-3131. E-mail: clivelibrary@libs.prl.ab.ca. Web Site: clivepublib.prl.ab.ca. *Chairperson,* Wanda Wagner; *Librn,* Sandra Ward; *Asst Librn,* Cathryn Ogoby
Pop 675
Library Holdings: CDs 30; DVDs 400; Bk Titles 7,000
Automation Activity & Vendor Info: (Acquisitions) SirsiDynix
Mem of Parkland Regional Library
Open Tues-Thurs 11-6, Fri 11-4

COALDALE

P   COALDALE PUBLIC LIBRARY*, 2014 18th St, T1M 1M1. (Mail add: PO Box 1207, T1M 1N1), SAN 318-630X. Tel: 403-345-1340. Interlibrary Loan Service Tel: 403-380-1512. FAX: 403-345-1342. E-mail: help@coaldalelibrary.ca. Web Site: www.coaldalelibrary.ca. *Librn,* Heather Nicholson; *Asst Librn,* Lorraine Mackie
Founded 1945. Pop 10,000; Circ 90,000

Library Holdings: Bk Vols 32,000; Per Subs 100
Subject Interests: Dutch lang, German lang
Wireless access
Publications: Monthly newsletter
Partic in Chinook Arch Regional Libr Syst
Open Mon-Thurs 11-9, Fri & Sat 11-5
Friends of the Library Group

COCHRANE

P   COCHRANE PUBLIC LIBRARY*, Nan Boothby Memorial Library, 405 Railway St W, T4C 2E2. SAN 318-6318. Tel: 403-932-4353. FAX: 403-932-4385. Web Site: www.cochranepubliclibrary.ca. *Librn,* David Larson; E-mail: d.larson@cochranepubliclibrary.ca
Pop 15,000; Circ 120,000
Library Holdings: Bk Vols 40,000; Per Subs 93
Automation Activity & Vendor Info: (Cataloging) Follett Software; (Circulation) Follett Software; (OPAC) Follett Software
Mem of Marigold Library System
Special Services for the Blind - Bks on cassette
Open Mon, Fri & Sat 10-5, Tues-Thurs 10-8, Sun 12-5
Friends of the Library Group

S   STOCKMEN'S MEMORIAL FOUNDATION LIBRARY*, 101 RancheHouse Rd, T4C 1A7. (Mail add: Box 459, T4C 1A7), SAN 372-5499. Tel: 403-932-3782. FAX: 403-851-1324. E-mail: library@smflibrary.ca. Web Site: www.smflibrary.ca. *Librn,* Jana Wilson; Staff 1 (Non-MLS 1)
Founded 1980
Library Holdings: Bk Vols 13,000; Per Subs 40; Spec Interest Per Sub 40
Special Collections: Cattle Ranching History, bks, doc; Oral-Video History, V-tapes. Oral History
Automation Activity & Vendor Info: (Cataloging) Inmagic, Inc.
Open Mon-Fri 9-12 & 1-4
Restriction: Non-circulating to the pub

COLD LAKE

P   COLD LAKE PUBLIC LIBRARY*, Grand Centre, 5513-B 48th Ave, T9M 1X9. SAN 320-5231. Tel: 780-594-5101. Interlibrary Loan Service Tel: 780-594-7425. Administration Tel: 780-594-8828. FAX: 780-594-7787. Web Site: www.library.coldlake.ab.ca. *Dir,* Mary Anne Penner; E-mail: director@library.coldlake.ab.ca; *Librn,* Leslie Price
Founded 1975. Pop 14,000; Circ 21,600
Library Holdings: AV Mats 3,219; Bk Titles 24,367; Per Subs 49
Mem of Northern Lights Library System
Open Mon & Wed 10-6, Tues & Thurs 10-8, Fri 10-5, Sat 10-4
Friends of the Library Group
Branches: 1
HARBOR VIEW, 1301 Eighth Ave, T9M 1J7. (Mail add: 5513B 48 Ave, T9M 1X9). Tel: 780-639-3967. FAX: 780-639-3963. *Dir,* Mary Anne Penner; E-mail: director@library.coldlake.ab.ca; *Librn,* Tanya Boudreau
Library Holdings: AV Mats 2,585; Bk Titles 24,934; Per Subs 47
Open Mon & Wed 12-8, Tues & Thurs 10-6, Fri 10-5, Sat 10-3

CONSORT

P   CONSORT MUNICIPAL LIBRARY*, Box 456, T0C 1B0. SAN 318-6342. Tel: 403-577-2501. E-mail: aconmlibrary@marigold.ab.ca. *Libr Mgr,* Marian Walsh
Pop 739; Circ 17,706
Library Holdings: Bk Vols 20,300
Mem of Marigold Library System
Open Mon 3-8:30, Tues & Thurs 2-8:30, Wed 1-6; Mon (Summer) 3-8:30, Tues & Thurs 12-6, Wed 1-6

CORONATION

P   CORONATION MEMORIAL LIBRARY*, 5001 Royal St, T0C 1C0. (Mail add: PO Box 453, T0C 1C0), SAN 318-6350. Tel: 403-578-3445. E-mail: coronationlibrary@libs.prl.ab.ca. Web Site: coronationlib.prl.ab.ca. *Librn,* Margo McPhail; *Asst Librn,* Azusa Watson
Pop 1,074; Circ 9,329
Library Holdings: Audiobooks 50; CDs 60; DVDs 200; Large Print Bks 500; Bk Titles 9,000; Per Subs 10; Talking Bks 20
Wireless access
Mem of Parkland Regional Library
Open Mon, Wed & Fri 1:30-4:30, Tues & Thurs 9-12 & 1-4:30

COUTTS

P   COUTTS MUNICIPAL LIBRARY*, 218 First Ave S, T0K 0N0. (Mail add: Box 216, T0K 0N0). Tel: 403-344-3804. E-mail: libcou@chinookarch.ab.ca. *Librn,* Sharon Wollersheim; E-mail: sharon.wollersheim@gmail.com
Pop 364

Library Holdings: Bk Titles 7,500
Wireless access
Open Tues 2:30-8:30, Wed 9:30-1:30, Thurs 9:30-1:30 & 6:30-8:30

CREMONA

P   CREMONA MUNICIPAL LIBRARY*, 205 First St E, T0M 0R0. (Mail
add: General Delivery, T0M 0R0). Tel: 403-637-3762. FAX: 403-637-2101.
E-mail: cremonalibrary@libs.prl.ab.ca. Web Site:
www.village.cremona.ab.ca. *Librn,* Sandra Herbert
Library Holdings: Bk Titles 5,000
Automation Activity & Vendor Info: (Acquisitions) SirsiDynix
Mem of Parkland Regional Library
Open Mon 10am-11:30am, Wed 3-4:30, Thurs 7pm-8:30pm, Fri 1:30-4

CROSSFIELD

P   CROSSFIELD MUNICIPAL LIBRARY*, 1026 Chisholm Ave, T0M 0S0.
(Mail add: PO Box 355, T0M 0S0), SAN 318-6377. Tel: 403-946-4232.
FAX: 403-946-4212. E-mail: crossfield.library@telus.net. Web Site:
www.crossfieldlibrary.org. *Chairperson,* Myrna Worthington; *Mgr,* Lorea
Anderson
Pop 2,800; Circ 20,508
Library Holdings: Bk Vols 25,000; Per Subs 54
Wireless access
Function: Photocopying/Printing
Open Mon-Thurs 10-8, Fri 10-6, Sat 10-2
Friends of the Library Group

CZAR

P   CZAR MUNICIPAL LIBRARY*, PO Box 127, T0B 0Z0. Tel:
780-857-3740. FAX: 780-857-2223. E-mail: czarlibrary@libs.prl.ab.ca.
Chairperson, Sandy Klassen; *Librn,* Jackie Almberg
Pop 175
Library Holdings: Bk Titles 3,500
Mem of Parkland Regional Library
Open Mon & Wed 11-5

DARWELL

P   DARWELL PUBLIC LIBRARY*, 54225B Hwy 765, T0E 0L0. (Mail add:
Box 206, T0E 0L0). Tel: 780-892-3746. FAX: 780-892-3743. E-mail:
adarlibrary@yrl.ab.ca. *Librn,* Sandra Stepaniuk
Founded 1985. Pop 1,500
Library Holdings: Bk Vols 7,300
Wireless access
Mem of Yellowhead Regional Library
Open Mon, Tues & Thurs 10-3, Wed & Fri 5-8
Friends of the Library Group

DAYSLAND

P   DAYSLAND PUBLIC LIBRARY, 5130 50th St, T0B 1A0. (Mail add: PO
Box 700, T0B 1A0). Tel: 780-679-7263. FAX: 780-374-2455. E-mail:
dayslandlibrary@libs.prl.ab.ca. *Libr Mgr,* Tara Mazur
Pop 779
Library Holdings: Bk Vols 6,000
Mem of Parkland Regional Library
Open Tues & Thurs 1-8, Fri 10-12 & 1-5

DEBOLT

P   DEBOLT PUBLIC LIBRARY, PO Box 480, T0H 1B0. Tel: 780-957-3770.
E-mail: librarian@deboltlibrary.ab.ca. *Libr Mgr,* Rachel Stoesz
Library Holdings: Bk Vols 12,000; Per Subs 12
Automation Activity & Vendor Info: (Acquisitions) Polaris Library
Systems; (Cataloging) Polaris Library Systems; (Circulation) Polaris
Library Systems
Wireless access
Mem of Peace Library System
Open Mon 3-9, Thurs & Sat 10-5; Mon (Summer) 3-9, Tues-Thurs & Sat
10-5

DELBURNE

P   DELBURNE MUNICIPAL LIBRARY*, 2210 Main St, T0M 0V0. (Mail
add: PO Box 405, T0M 0V0), SAN 321-5792. Tel: 403-749-3848. FAX:
403-749-2800. E-mail: delburnelibrary@libs.prl.ab.ca. Web Site:
delburnelibrary.prl.ab.ca. *Libr Mgr,* Mattie Jensen; Staff 1 (Non-MLS 1)
Founded 1928. Pop 719; Circ 7,493
Library Holdings: Bk Vols 7,116
Automation Activity & Vendor Info: (Acquisitions) SirsiDynix;
(Cataloging) SirsiDynix; (Circulation) SirsiDynix; (ILL) SirsiDynix;
(Serials) SirsiDynix
Mem of Parkland Regional Library

Open Tues-Fri 11-5, Sat 11-2
Friends of the Library Group

DELIA

P   DELIA MUNICIPAL LIBRARY*, 205 Third Ave N, T0J 0W0. (Mail add:
PO Box 236, T0J 0W0). Tel: 403-364-3777. FAX: 403-364-3805. E-mail:
adm.library@plrd.ab.ca. Web Site: www.delialibrary.ca. *Librn,* Leah Hunter
Pop 232; Circ 17,644
Library Holdings: Bk Vols 20,016; Per Subs 43
Wireless access
Mem of Marigold Library System
Open Mon 10-12 & 1-6, Tues 4-6, Wed 2-8, Thurs 2-5, Fri 10-12 & 1-3
Friends of the Library Group

DEVON

P   DEVON PUBLIC LIBRARY*, 101, 17 Athabasca Ave, T9G 1G5. SAN
318-6407. Tel: 780-987-3720. E-mail: devon@devonpubliclibrary.ca. Web
Site: www.devonpubliclibrary.ca. *Dir,* Audrey Benjamin; E-mail:
audrey@devonpubliclibrary.ca; *Chairperson,* Aaron Van Beers; Staff 1
(Non-MLS 1)
Founded 1955. Pop 6,534; Circ 69,177
Library Holdings: Audiobooks 1,413; DVDs 1,497; Bk Vols 26,418; Per
Subs 52
Wireless access
Function: Adult bk club, Bks on CD, Children's prog, Electronic databases
& coll, ILL available, Online cat, OverDrive digital audio bks,
Photocopying/Printing, Prog for adults, Prog for children & young adult,
Pub access computers, Summer reading prog, Wheelchair accessible
Mem of Yellowhead Regional Library
Open Mon-Thurs 9-8, Fri 9-6, Sat 10-4
Friends of the Library Group

DIDSBURY

P   DIDSBURY MUNICIPAL LIBRARY*, 2033 19th Ave, T0M 0W0. (Mail
add: PO Box 10, T0M 0W0). Tel: 403-335-3142. FAX: 403-335-3141.
E-mail: didsburylibrary@libs.prl.ab.ca. Web Site: dml.prl.ab.ca.
Chairperson, Paula Harris; *Librn,* Inez Kosinski
Founded 1908. Pop 5,000
Library Holdings: Bk Titles 27,000
Wireless access
Mem of Parkland Regional Library
Open Mon 12-5, Tues, Fri & Sat 9-5, Wed & Thurs 9-8
Friends of the Library Group

DONALDA

P   DONALDA PUBLIC LIBRARY*, 5001 Main St, T0B 1H0. (Mail add: PO
Box 40, T0B 1H0). Tel: 403-883-2345. FAX: 403-883-2022. E-mail:
donaldalibrary@libs.prl.ab.ca. Web Site: donaldalibrary.prl.ab.ca. *Librn,*
Kelly Andres
Library Holdings: Bk Vols 4,000
Automation Activity & Vendor Info: (Cataloging) Horizon; (Circulation)
Horizon; (OPAC) Horizon
Wireless access
Mem of Parkland Regional Library
Open Mon-Wed 3-6, Thurs 6-9

DRAYTON VALLEY

P   DRAYTON VALLEY MUNICIPAL LIBRARY, 5120 - 52 St, T7A 1A1.
(Mail add: PO Box 6240, T7A 1R7). Tel: 780-514-2228. FAX:
780-514-2532. E-mail: dvml@incentre.net. Web Site:
www.draytonvalleylibrary.ca. *Dir,* Nesan Naidoo; *Librn,* Sandy Faunt;
E-mail: sfaunt@draytonvalley.ca; Staff 1 (Non-MLS 1)
Founded 1957. Pop 7,000; Circ 64,000
Jan 2006-Dec 2006 Income (CAN) $274,298, Provincial (CAN) $26,641,
City (CAN) $106,967, County (CAN) $122,690, Locally Generated Income
(CAN) $12,000, Other (CAN) $6,000. Mats Exp (CAN) $28,000. Sal
(CAN) $204,794
Library Holdings: Bk Titles 25,840; Per Subs 52
Automation Activity & Vendor Info: (Circulation) Polaris Library
Systems; (OPAC) Polaris Library Systems
Wireless access
Function: Bks on cassette, Bks on CD, CD-ROM, Computers for patron
use, Copy machines, ILL available, Music CDs, Online searches, Prog for
children & young adult, Summer reading prog
Mem of Yellowhead Regional Library
Partic in The Regional Automation Consortium (TRAC)
Open Mon-Thurs 10-8, Fri 10-5, Sat 12-4

DRUMHELLER

P   DRUMHELLER PUBLIC LIBRARY*, 224 Centre St, T0J 0Y2. (Mail add:
     PO Box 1599, T0J 0Y0), SAN 318-6423. Tel: 403-823-1371. FAX:
     403-823-3651. E-mail: drumlib@magtech.ca. Web Site:
     www.drumhellerlibrary.ca. *Dir of Libr Serv,* Mellissa D'Onofrio-Jones;
     E-mail: mellissa@magtech.ca; *Asst Librn,* Debbie LaPlante; Staff 6 (MLS
     1, Non-MLS 5)
     Founded 1922. Pop 7,833
     Jan 2006-Dec 2006 Income (CAN) $233,054, Provincial (CAN) $50,510,
     City (CAN) $105,925, Federal (CAN) $4,221, Locally Generated Income
     (CAN) $72,398. Mats Exp (CAN) $222,499, Books (CAN) $4,000, Per/Ser
     (Incl. Access Fees) (CAN) $1,500, Manu Arch (CAN) $300, Micro (CAN)
     $1,039, AV Mat (CAN) $1,300. Sal (CAN) $150,000
     Library Holdings: AV Mats 387; Bks on Deafness & Sign Lang 12; CDs
     25; DVDs 30; High Interest/Low Vocabulary Bk Vols 700; Large Print Bks
     463; Bk Titles 29,170; Bk Vols 29,178; Per Subs 71; Talking Bks 367;
     Videos 1,027
     Special Collections: Area Newspapers from 1914, microfilm; Audios;
     Early Drumheller Records; Large Print Books; Literacy & ESL, Family
     Resource Library
     Subject Interests: Dinosauria, Employment, Literacy, Local area hist bks
     Automation Activity & Vendor Info: (Cataloging) Polaris Library
     Systems; (Circulation) Polaris Library Systems; (OPAC) Polaris Library
     Systems
     Wireless access
     Publications: Library Information Pamphlets; Weekly Newspaper Column
     Mem of Marigold Library System
     Partic in The Alberta Library; The Regional Automation Consortium
     (TRAC)
     Open Mon, Fri & Sat 9-5, Tues-Thurs 9-8
     Restriction: Pub use on premises
     Friends of the Library Group

S   ROYAL TYRRELL MUSEUM OF PALAEONTOLOGY LIBRARY*,
     Midland Provincial Park, Hwy 838 N Dinosaur Trail, Box 7500, T0J 0Y0.
     SAN 371-750X. Tel: 403-823-7707, Ext 6213. FAX: 403-823-7131.
     E-mail: tyrrell.library@gov.ab.ca. *Head of Libr,* Amanda Green
     Founded 1985
     Library Holdings: Bk Titles 20,000; Bk Vols 60,000; Per Subs 100
     Subject Interests: Geol, Museology, Paleontology

DUCHESS

P   DUCHESS & DISTRICT PUBLIC LIBRARY*, 256A Louise Ave, Box
     88, T0J 0Z0. Tel: 403-378-4369. FAX: 403-378-4369. E-mail:
     duclib@shortgrass.ca. Web Site: www.duchesspubliclibrary.ca. *Mgr,*
     Shannon Vanderloh
     Pop 836
     Library Holdings: Bk Vols 6,000
     Wireless access
     Open Tues & Thurs 10-4, Wed 3-8

DUFFIELD

P   DUFFIELD PUBLIC LIBRARY*, PO Box 479, T0E 0N0. Tel:
     780-892-2644. FAX: 780-892-3344. *Librn,* Brenda Baron; E-mail:
     bbrenda@psd70.ab.ca
     Library Holdings: Bk Vols 13,000
     Wireless access
     Mem of Yellowhead Regional Library
     Open Mon 9-5, Tues & Thurs 9-3, Wed 9-7, Fri 9-4

P   KEEPHILLS PUBLIC LIBRARY*, 51515 Range Rd 32A, T0E 0N0. (Mail
     add: RR 1, T0E 0N0). Tel: 780-731-0000, 780-731-3965. FAX:
     780-731-2433. E-mail: keephillslibrary@yrl.ab.ca. Web Site:
     www.pcmlibraries.ab.ca/content/keephills-public-library. *Librn,* Debbie
     Ramsey; *Libr Mgr,* Kathy Conn
     Library Holdings: Bk Vols 7,000
     Wireless access
     Mem of Yellowhead Regional Library
     Open (Winter) Tues & Fri 10-6, Wed 12-8; Tues (Summer) 9-4, Wed 12-8

EAGLESHAM

P   EAGLESHAM PUBLIC LIBRARY*, PO Box 206, T0H 1H0. SAN
     320-9873. Tel: 780-359-3792. FAX: 780-359-3745. *Chief Librn,* Norma
     Bolster; E-mail: normabolster@pwsd76.ab.ca
     Pop 300; Circ 2,000
     Library Holdings: Bk Titles 5,000; Per Subs 10
     Wireless access
     Open Mon, Wed, Fri 9-11:30 & 12:30-3:30, Tues, Thurs 9-11:30 &
     12:30-4:30

ECKVILLE

P   ECKVILLE MUNICIPAL LIBRARY*, 4855-51 Ave, T0M 0X0. (Mail
     add: PO Box 492, T0M 0X0). Tel: 403-746-3240. FAX: 403-746-5348.
     E-mail: eckvillelibrary@libs.prl.ab.ca. Web Site: eckvillelibrary.prl.ab.ca.
     Libr Mgr, Carol Griner
     Pop 1,019
     Library Holdings: Bk Vols 7,500
     Wireless access
     Mem of Parkland Regional Library
     Open Tues 10-12 & 1-7, Wed 10-6, Fri 10-12 & 1-6, Sat 10-1
     Friends of the Library Group

EDBERG

P   EDBERG MUNICIPAL LIBRARY, 48 First Ave W, T0B 1J0. (Mail add:
     PO Box 93, T0B 1J0). Tel: 780-678-5606. FAX: 780-877-2562. E-mail:
     edberglibrary@prl.ab.ca. Web Site: edberglibrary.prl.ab.ca. *Libr Mgr,*
     Colleen Wack
     Pop 150
     Library Holdings: Bk Vols 4,500
     Automation Activity & Vendor Info: (Circulation) Horizon
     Wireless access
     Mem of Parkland Regional Library
     Special Services for the Blind - Bks on CD; Daisy reader; Large print bks
     Open Mon 9:30-11:30 & 7-9, Wed & Thurs 7pm-9pm, Tues 2-4, Fri 4-6

EDGERTON

P   EDGERTON PUBLIC LIBRARY*, PO Box 180, T0B 'IK0. Tel:
     780-755-2666. FAX: 780-755-2666. E-mail:
     librarian@edgertonlibrary.ab.ca. Web Site: edgertonlibrary.ab.ca. *Libr Mgr,*
     Mary Ann Sparks
     Pop 403
     Library Holdings: Bk Vols 10,500
     Automation Activity & Vendor Info: (Acquisitions) SirsiDynix;
     (Cataloging) SirsiDynix; (Circulation) SirsiDynix; (ILL) SirsiDynix
     Wireless access
     Open Mon & Fri 4-6, Tues 5-9, Wed & Thurs 2:30-4:30, Sat 1-3

EDMONTON

S   ACUREN GROUP, INC*, 7450 18th St, T6P 1N8. SAN 326-3843. Tel:
     780-440-2131. FAX: 780-440-1167. Web Site: www.acuren.com. *Librn,*
     Susan Lim
     Founded 1978
     Library Holdings: Bk Titles 2,500; Per Subs 50
     Subject Interests: Corrosion, Failure analysis, Metallurgy, Non-destructive
     testing, Ultrasonic flaw detection, Visual inspection, Welding
     Publications: Newsletter (monthly)
     Open Mon-Fri 8-5
     Restriction: Internal circ only

S   ALBERTA ASSOCIATION FOR COMMUNITY LIVING*, Reg Peters
     Resource Centre, 11724 Kingsway Ave, T5G 0X5. SAN 374-8936. Tel:
     780-451-3055, Ext 225. FAX: 780-453-5779. E-mail: library@aacl.org.
     Web Site: www.aacl.org. *Libr Tech,* Lisa Snyder; Staff 1 (Non-MLS 1)
     Library Holdings: AV Mats 100; DVDs 32; Bk Titles 3,700; Per Subs 75;
     Videos 469
     Subject Interests: Deinstitutionalization, Integrated educ
     Automation Activity & Vendor Info: (Acquisitions) L4U Library
     Software; (Cataloging) L4U Library Software; (Circulation) L4U Library
     Software; (Course Reserve) L4U Library Software; (ILL) L4U Library
     Software; (Media Booking) L4U Library Software; (OPAC) L4U Library
     Software; (Serials) L4U Library Software
     Database Vendor: L4U Library Software
     Open Mon-Fri 8:30-4:30

S   ALBERTA COMMITTEE OF CITIZENS WITH DISABILITIES
     LIBRARY*, Resource Centre, 106-10423 178 St NW, T5S 1R5. SAN
     377-4023. Tel: 780-488-9088. Toll Free Tel: 800-387-2514. FAX:
     780-488-3757. E-mail: accd@accd.net. Web Site: www.accd.net. *Adminr,*
     Trudy Huget; E-mail: trudy@accd.net
     Library Holdings: Bk Titles 1,200; Per Subs 10
     Special Services for the Deaf - TTY equip
     Open Mon-Fri 8:30-4:30

G   ALBERTA CULTURE, Provincial Archives of Alberta, Reference Library,
     8555 Roper Rd, T6E 5W1. SAN 365-6853. Tel: 780-427-1750. Reference
     Tel: 780-427-1056. FAX: 780-427-4646. E-mail: paa@gov.ab.ca. Web Site:
     culture.alberta.ca/archives/default.aspx, provincialarchives.alberta.ca. *Exec
     Dir,* Leslie Latta-Guthrie; *Dir, Access & Presv Serv,* Susan Stanton; *Ref
     Archivist/Librn,* Robin H Wallace; Tel: 780-415-8451, E-mail:
     robin.wallace@gov.ab.ca; Staff 1 (MLS 1)
     Founded 1967
     Library Holdings: Bk Vols 12,000

Special Collections: Alberta Local History; Alberta Pioneer Railway
Association; Archives & Record Management; Government of Alberta
(annual reports)
Subject Interests: Alberta hist, Conserv, Local hist, Western Canadiana
Database Vendor: Gallery Systems
Function: Archival coll, Computers for patron use, Online cat,
Photocopying/Printing, Ref serv available
Open Tues-Sat 9-4:30, Wed 9-9
Restriction: Closed stack, Non-circulating, Non-circulating of rare bks,
Not a lending libr, Pub use on premises, Registered patrons only
Friends of the Library Group

G   ALBERTA DEPARTMENT OF ENVIRONMENT LIBRARY*, Alberta
       Government Library-Great West Life Site, 9920 108th St, 6th Flr, T5K
       2M4. SAN 318-6504. Tel: 780-427-5870. FAX: 780-422-0170. E-mail:
       library.gwl@gov.ab.ca. Web Site: www.environment.alberta.ca/01393.html.
       Head Librn, Laura Lemmens; E-mail: laura.lemmens@gov.ab.ca; *Acq, ILL,*
       Sharon Van Bruggen; Tel: 780-422-7549, E-mail:
       sharon.vanbruggen@gov.ab.ca; *Cat,* Cindy Ingram; Tel: 780-427-3920,
       E-mail: cindy.ingram@gov.ab.ca; *Ser,* Bonnie Kendall; Tel: 780-422-7214,
       E-mail: bonnie.kendell@gov.ab.ca; Staff 6 (MLS 1, Non-MLS 5)
       Founded 1972
       Library Holdings: Bk Titles 95,000; Per Subs 350
       Special Collections: Alberta Environmental Impact Assessments;
       Athabasca Oil Sands Materials, bks & reports; EPA Reports on microfiche
       1972-1990; Peace-Athabasca Delta, tech reports
       Subject Interests: Air quality, Conserv, Ecology, Environ impact
       assessment, Fish, Forestry, Oil sands, Waste mgt, Water, Water resources
       planning, Wildlife
       Automation Activity & Vendor Info: (Acquisitions) SirsiDynix;
       (Cataloging) SirsiDynix; (Circulation) SirsiDynix; (Serials) SirsiDynix
       Database Vendor: Agricola, Cambridge Scientific Abstracts, EBSCOhost,
       Gale Cengage Learning
       Partic in NEOS Library Consortium
       Open Mon-Fri 8:15-4:30

S   ALBERTA GENEALOGICAL SOCIETY LIBRARY & RESEARCH
       CENTRE*, No 162-14315-118 Ave, T5L 4S6. SAN 373-8949. Tel:
       780-424-4429. FAX: 780-423-8980. E-mail: agsoffice@interbaun.com. Web
       Site: www.agsedm.edmonton.ab.ca. *Libr Dir,* Arlene Borgstede
       Founded 1982
       Library Holdings: Bk Titles 4,000; Per Subs 20
       Special Collections: Research & Genealogy Coll
       Publications: Relatively Speaking (Quarterly)
       Open Tues-Thurs 10-3

G   ALBERTA GOVERNMENT LIBRARY, 107th Street Site, South Tower,
       3rd Flr, 10030 107th St, T5J 3E4. SAN 322-7367. Tel: 780-427-7272.
       FAX: 780-422-3980. E-mail: library.107st@gov.ab.ca. *Head Librn,* Teresa
       Bendall; E-mail: teresa.bendall@gov.ab.ca; Staff 7 (MLS 2, Non-MLS 5)
       Founded 1972
       Library Holdings: e-journals 38; Bk Vols 15,000; Per Subs 99
       Special Collections: Employment Standards & Labour Relations; Human
       Services & Social Policy. Can & Prov; State Document Depository
       Automation Activity & Vendor Info: (Acquisitions) SIRSI WorkFlows;
       (Cataloging) SIRSI WorkFlows; (Circulation) SIRSI WorkFlows; (Media
       Booking) SIRSI WorkFlows; (OPAC) SirsiDynix; (Serials) SIRSI
       WorkFlows
       Database Vendor: Dialog, EBSCOhost, Gale Cengage Learning,
       SirsiDynix
       Wireless access
       Open Mon-Fri 8:15-4:30

GM   ALBERTA GOVERNMENT LIBRARY*, Telus Plaza North Tower Site,
       10025 Jasper Ave, 15th Flr, T5J 2N3. (Mail add: PO Box 1360, Sta Main,
       T5J 2N3), SAN 326-2286. Tel: 780-427-8720. Interlibrary Loan Service
       Tel: 780-644-1375. FAX: 780-422-9694. E-mail: library.tpn@gov.ab.ca,
       libraryill.tpn@gov.ab.ca. Web Site: www.neoslibraries.ca/node/221. *Head
       Librn,* Peggy Yeh; Tel: 780-415-0228, E-mail: peggy.yeh@gov.ab.ca; *Librn
       & Ref Supvr,* Linda Bumstead; Tel: 780-415-0224, E-mail:
       linda.bumstead@gov.ab.ca; *Acq & ILL Tech,* Kathy Elson; Tel:
       780-415-0223, E-mail: kathy.elson@gov.ab.ca; *Cat Tech,* Brenda Kinnee;
       Tel: 780-415-0226, E-mail: brenda.kinnee@gov.ab.ca; *ILL Tech,* Blanka
       Kaiser; E-mail: blanka.kaiser@gov.ab.ca; *Libr Tech,* Jadwiga Windyga; Tel:
       780-427-0403, E-mail: jadwiga.windyga@gov.ab.ca; *Ser Tech,* Andrea
       Wilson; Tel: 780-415-0222, E-mail: andrea.m.wilson@gov.ab.ca; Staff 6
       (MLS 2, Non-MLS 4)
       Founded 1974
       Library Holdings: e-journals 200; Electronic Media & Resources 30; Bk
       Titles 15,000; Bk Vols 16,000; Per Subs 250
       Special Collections: AIDS Coll; Department Reports
       Subject Interests: Addictions, Health econ, Health planning, Health policy,
       Mental health
       Automation Activity & Vendor Info: (Serials) EBSCO Online

Publications: Health and Addictions (Online only); Legislative Awareness
(Online only); Subject Bibliographies (Online only)
Open Mon-Fri 8:15-4:30

G   ALBERTA GOVERNMENT LIBRARY, Capital Boulevard Site, Capital
       Blvd, 11th Flr, 10044 - 108 St, T5J 5E6. SAN 365-6977. Tel:
       780-427-2985. FAX: 780-427-5927. E-mail: library.cap@gov.ab.ca. *Head
       Librn,* Gary Weber; E-mail: gary.weber@gov.ab.ca; *Ref Librn,* Ikram
       Cheikhi; Tel: 780-427-6249, E-mail: ikram.cheikhi@gov.ab.ca; *Ref Librn,*
       Mica Wickramasekara; E-mail: mica.wickramasekara@gov.ab.ca. *Web Serv
       Librn,* Ann Schiebelbein; E-mail: ann.schiebelbein@gov.ab.ca. Subject
       Specialists: *Educ, Fr lang,* Ikram Cheikhi; *Adult educ,* Ann Schiebelbein;
       Staff 4 (MLS 4)
       Founded 1940
       Library Holdings: Bk Titles 46,000; Per Subs 300
       Special Collections: Archival Annual Reports & Publications of the
       Departments of Aboriginal Relations, Culture, Education, Enterprise &
       Advanced Education, International & Intergovernmental Relations,
       Municipal Affairs, Service Alberta, Tourism, Parks & Recreation and
       Treasury Board & Finance; Collection of resources authorized for use in
       Alberta schools by Alberta Education
       Subject Interests: Educ
       Automation Activity & Vendor Info: (Acquisitions) SirsiDynix;
       (Cataloging) SirsiDynix; (Circulation) SirsiDynix; (ILL) A-G Canada Ltd;
       (OPAC) SirsiDynix; (Serials) SirsiDynix
       Database Vendor: Canadian Reference Centre, Dun & Bradstreet,
       EBSCOhost, Factiva.com, Gale Cengage Learning, Infomart, ProQuest,
       SirsiDynix, Springer-Verlag
       Wireless access
       Function: Ref serv available
       Partic in NEOS Library Consortium; The Alberta Library
       Open Mon-Fri 8:15-4:30
       Restriction: Circ limited

S   ALBERTA HISTORICAL RESOURCES FOUNDATION LIBRARY*,
       8820 112th St, T6G 2P8. SAN 327-4969. Tel: 780-431-2305. FAX:
       780-427-5598. *In Charge,* Carina Naranjilla; E-mail:
       carina.naranjilla@gov.ab.ca
       Library Holdings: Bk Titles 9,000; Bk Vols 12,000
       Special Collections: Alberta History; Archaeology
       Open Mon-Fri 8:15-12 & 1-4:30

S   ALBERTA INNOVATES-TECHNOLOGY FUTURES*, Library &
       Information Centre, 250 Karl Clark Rd, T6N 134. SAN 365-7035. Tel:
       780-450-5229. FAX: 780-450-8996. E-mail:
       millwoods_library@albertainnovates.ca. Web Site:
       www.albertatechfutures.ca. *Librn,* Renee Morrissey; E-mail:
       renee.morrissey@albertainnovates.ca; *Acq of New Ser, Circ, Ref,* Lucy
       Heintz; Tel: 780-450-5064, E-mail: heintz@albertainnovates.ca; *ILL,*
       Roberto Pellegrino; Tel: 780-450-5057, E-mail:
       pellegrino@albertainnovates.ca; Staff 3 (MLS 1, Non-MLS 2)
       Founded 1950
       Library Holdings: Bk Titles 40,000; Per Subs 300
       Subject Interests: Chem, Chem eng, Environ eng, Environ res, Forest res,
       Heavy oil, Indust eng, Manufacturing tech, Oil sands, Pharmaceuticals,
       Pulp & paper
       Partic in NEOS Library Consortium
       Open Mon-Fri 8:30-12 & 1-4:30
       Branches:
       VEGREVILLE BRANCH, Hwy 16A 75th St, Vegreville, T9C 1T4. (Mail
          add: PO Box 4000, Vegreville, T9C 1T4), SAN 378-1453. Tel:
          780-632-8417. Interlibrary Loan Service Tel: 780-632-8419. FAX:
          780-632-8300. *Libr Asst,* Audrey Lyons; E-mail:
          audrey.lyons@albertainnovates.ca
          Founded 1979
          Subject Interests: Air emissions, Environ health, Environ tech, Land
          reclamation econ, Plant ecology, Solid waste mgt, Toxicology, Waste
          water treatment, Weed control, Wildlife
          Automation Activity & Vendor Info: (Cataloging) SIRSI WorkFlows;
          (Circulation) SIRSI WorkFlows; (ILL) SIRSI WorkFlows; (OPAC) SIRSI
          Unicorn; (Serials) SIRSI WorkFlows
          Database Vendor: Knovel, SirsiDynix
          Open Mon-Fri 8:15-12 & 1-4:30
       CALGARY BRANCH, 3608 33rd St NW, Calgary, T2L 2A6, SAN
          328-0330. Tel: 403-210-5292. FAX: 403-210-5380. E-mail:
          calgary_library@arc.ab.ca. *ILL, Online Serv, Ref,* Guy Trott; E-mail:
          trott@arc.ab.ca; Staff 1 (MLS 1)
          Open Mon-Fri 8:15-4:30

       ALBERTA LAW LIBRARIES
GL   , Law Courts North, 5th Flr, 1A Sir Winston Churchill Sq, T5J 0R2, SAN
       321-3641. Tel: 780-427-3327. FAX: 780-427-0481. E-mail:
       judicial-north.libraries@gov.ab.ca. *Dir,* Sonia Poulin; *Asst Dir,* Rhonda
       O'Neill; *Info, Res & Training Serv Mgr,* Position Currently Open; *Info,
       Res & Access Mgr,* Michael Decore; *Info Tech Serv Mgr,* Sophie Song

Founded 1976
Library Holdings: Bk Vols 15,000
Subject Interests: Civil, Criminal, Family law, Youth law
Automation Activity & Vendor Info: (Acquisitions) Ex Libris Group; (Cataloging) Ex Libris Group; (Circulation) Ex Libris Group; (ILL) Ex Libris Group; (OPAC) Ex Libris Group; (Serials) Ex Libris Group
Function: For res purposes
Publications: Alberta Provincial Court Decisions (Annually)
Restriction: Not open to pub

GL DEPARTMENTAL LIBRARY*, 400A Bowker Bldg, North, 9833 - 109 St, T5K 2E8, SAN 318-6474. Tel: 780-422-6264. Information Services Tel: 780-422-4946. FAX: 780-422-5912. *Librn,* Linda Harmata; E-mail: linda.harmata@gov.ab.ca; Staff 2 (MLS 1, Non-MLS 1)
Founded 1912
Library Holdings: Bk Vols 23,350
Special Collections: Classical English, Canadian & American Texts (16th-19th Centuries)
Subject Interests: Can civil law, Constitutional law, Criminal law, Intl law
Restriction: Not open to pub

GL EDMONTON*, Law Courts Bldg, 2nd Flr, 1A Sir Winston Churchill Sq, T5J 0R2, SAN 372-3569. Tel: 780-422-2342. Toll Free Tel: 866-230-8068. FAX: 780-427-0397. E-mail: all.edm@gov.ab.ca. Web Site: www.lawlibrary.ab.ca. *Libr Dir,* Sonia Poulin; Tel: 780-422-1011, E-mail: sonia.poulin@gov.ab.ca; *Asst Libr Dir,* Rhonda O'Neill; Tel: 403-297-3958, E-mail: rhonda.o'neill@gov.ab.ca; *Calgary Librn,* Dale Barrie; Tel: 403-297-7355, E-mail: dale.barrie@gov.ab.ca; *Edmonton Librn,* Jane Cavanagh; Tel: 780-415-8584, E-mail: jane.cavanagh@gov.ab.ca
Library Holdings: Bk Vols 58,000; Per Subs 200
Automation Activity & Vendor Info: (Acquisitions) Ex Libris Group; (Cataloging) Ex Libris Group; (Circulation) Ex Libris Group; (OPAC) Ex Libris Group; (Serials) Ex Libris Group
Database Vendor: LexisNexis, Westlaw
Open Mon-Fri 8:15-4:30

GM OFFICE OF THE CHIEF MEDICAL EXAMINER INFORMATION CENTRE, 7007 116th St, T6H 5R8, SAN 374-5643. Tel: 780-427-4987. FAX: 780-422-1265. *Librn,* Michelle Whaley; E-mail: michelle.whaley@gov.ab.ca; Staff 1 (MLS 1)
Library Holdings: Bk Titles 1,300; Per Subs 111
Subject Interests: Forensic sci, Pathology, Pharmacology, Toxicology
Restriction: Staff use only

G ALBERTA LEGISLATURE LIBRARY, 216 Legislature Bldg, 10800-97 Ave, T5K 2B6. SAN 318-6679. Tel: 780-427-2473. FAX: 780-427-6016. E-mail: library.requests@assembly.ab.ca. Web Site: www.assembly.ab.ca. *Bibliog Serv Librn,* Vivianne Fagnan; Tel: 780-427-5893, E-mail: vivianne.fagan@assembly.ab.ca; *Govt Doc Librn,* Louise England; Tel: 780-415-4502, E-mail: louise.england@assembly.ab.ca; *Legis Librn,* Valerie Footz; Tel: 780-427-0202, E-mail: val.footz@assembly.ab.ca; *Presv Librn, Res Librn,* Leanne Thompson; Tel: 780-422-9316, E-mail: leanne.thompson@assembly.ab.ca; *Ser Librn,* Warren Maynes; Tel: 780-427-0201, E-mail: warren.maynes@assembly.ab.ca; *Syst Librn,* Paul Pype; Tel: 780-644-5015, E-mail: paul.pype@assembly.ab.ca; *Coordr, Coll Serv,* Selva Suppiah; Tel: 780-644-5605, E-mail: selva.suppiah@assembly.ab.ca; *Ref & Res Coordr,* Heather Close; Tel: 780-427-0204, E-mail: heather.close@assembly.ab.ca; Staff 19 (MLS 9, Non-MLS 10)
Founded 1906
Library Holdings: Bk Vols 432,000; Per Subs 450
Special Collections: Government Publication Coll; Provincial Weekly Newspaper Coll. Can & Prov
Subject Interests: Can hist, Econ, Law, Polit sci, Pub admin, Soc
Automation Activity & Vendor Info: (Acquisitions) SirsiDynix; (Cataloging) SirsiDynix; (Circulation) SirsiDynix; (OPAC) SirsiDynix; (Serials) SirsiDynix
Publications: New Books in the Library; Selected Periodical Articles in the Library
Open Mon-Fri 8:15-4:30

S ALBERTA SCHOOL FOR THE DEAF LIBRARY*, 6240 113 St, T6H 3L2. SAN 324-5241. Tel: 780-436-0465. FAX: 780-436-5863. Web Site: www.asd.epsb.ca. *Librn,* Kathy Myitrai; Fax: 780-436-0385; *Asst Librn,* Heather Haw
Founded 1966
Library Holdings: Bk Titles 16,000; Per Subs 60
Special Collections: Alberta Curriculum
Subject Interests: Deaf, Spec educ
Special Services for the Deaf - Bks on deafness & sign lang; Captioned film dep; High interest/low vocabulary bks; Spec interest per; Staff with knowledge of sign lang; TTY equip
Restriction: Not open to pub

S ALBERTA TEACHERS' ASSOCIATION LIBRARY*, 11010 142 St, T5N 2R1. SAN 318-6547. Tel: 780-447-9442. FAX: 780-455-6481. E-mail: library@ata.ab.ca. Web Site: www.teachers.ab.ca. *Librn,* Sandra Anderson; *Archivist, Info & Rec Mgr,* Margaret Shane; Tel: 780-447-9429; Staff 2 (Non-MLS 2)
Founded 1939
Library Holdings: Bk Vols 13,000; Per Subs 500; Videos 500
Special Collections: Canadian Teachers Associations Publications
Subject Interests: Educ, Wellness
Wireless access
Function: AV serv, Computers for patron use, Copy machines, e-mail serv, Electronic databases & coll, For res purposes, Online cat, Online searches, Ref serv available
Open Mon-Fri (Winter) 8-5; Mon-Fri (Summer) 8-4:30

S AMEC*, 5681-70 St, T6B 3P6. SAN 372-8846. Tel: 780-436-2152. FAX: 780-435-8425. Web Site: www.amec.com. *In Charge,* Angela Kepper; E-mail: angela.kepper@amec.com
Founded 1950
Library Holdings: Bk Vols 1,500; Per Subs 18
Restriction: Staff use only

L BISHOP & MCKENZIE LLP, BARRISTERS & SOLICITORS LIBRARY*, 10104 103rd Ave, Ste 2500, T5J 1V3. SAN 371-0262. Tel: 780-426-5550. FAX: 780-426-1305. Web Site: www.bishopmckenzie.com. *Mgr, Libr & Res Serv,* Judy Oberg; Staff 1 (MLS 1)
Library Holdings: Bk Titles 1,600; Per Subs 212
Automation Activity & Vendor Info: (Cataloging) Inmagic, Inc.

S CAMERON SCIENCE & TECHNOLOGY LIBRARY*, University of Alberta, Science & Technology Library (Cameron), T6G 2J8. Tel: 780-492-8440. Web Site: www.library.ualberta.ca/scitech. *Head of Libr,* Tim Klassen; Tel: 780-492-7918, E-mail: tim.klassen@ualberta.ca
Founded 1960
Library Holdings: Bk Vols 10,000
Special Collections: Circumpolar Studies Coll; Northern Aboriginal Studies Coll; William C Wonders Map Coll
Subject Interests: Alaska, Antarctic, Can arctic, Childrens' bks, Pipelines, Scandinavia, Travel info
Automation Activity & Vendor Info: (Cataloging) SirsiDynix
Function: ILL available, Ref serv available
Open Mon-Thurs 8am-10pm, Fri 8-6, Sat 11-6, Sun 11-10

GL CANADA DEPARTMENT OF JUSTICE*, Law Library, Epcort Tower, 300 10423 101 St, T5J 3Y4. SAN 371-7828. Tel: 780-495-2973. Interlibrary Loan Service Tel: 780-495-5539. FAX: 780-495-2854. E-mail: edmlawlib@justice.gc.ca. *Regional Librn,* Cathy Woodside; Staff 5 (MLS 2, Non-MLS 3)
Library Holdings: Bk Titles 2,500; Bk Vols 14,000; Per Subs 75
Subject Interests: Aboriginal law, Can law, Constitutional, Criminal law, Litigation, Tax law
Automation Activity & Vendor Info: (Cataloging) SirsiDynix; (Circulation) SirsiDynix; (OPAC) SirsiDynix; (Serials) SirsiDynix
Database Vendor: LexisNexis, WestlaweCARSWELL
Function: ILL available, Photocopying/Printing
Restriction: Open to staff only

CITY OF EDMONTON

G ARCHIVES*, 10440 - 108 Ave, 2nd Flr, Prince of Wales Armouries Heritage Centre, T5H 3Z9, SAN 321-0065. Tel: 780-496-8711. FAX: 780-496-8732. E-mail: cms.archives@edmonton.ca. Web Site: archivesphotos.edmonton.ca. *Archivist,* Paula Aurini-Onderwater; Tel: 780-496-8723, E-mail: paulaaurini.onderwater@edmonton.ca; *Archivist,* D Kim Christie-Milley; Tel: 780-496-8716, E-mail: kim.christie-milley@edmonton.ca; *Archivist,* Kathryn Ivany; Tel: 780-496-8721, E-mail: kathryn.ivany@edmonton.ca; *Archivist,* Tim O'Grady; E-mail: tim.o-grady@edmonton.ca; *Archivist,* Elizabeth Walker; Tel: 780-496-8714, E-mail: elizabeth.walker@edmonton.ca; *Asst Archivist,* TJ Lewis; Tel: 780-496-8722, E-mail: tj.lewis@edmonton.ca; *Ref Archivist,* Sherry Bell; E-mail: sharon.bell@edmonton.ca. Subject Specialists: *Photog,* Paula Aurini-Onderwater; *Architectural drawings,* D Kim Christie-Milley; *Local hist,* Kathryn Ivany; *Genealogy,* Sherry Bell; Staff 6 (MLS 3, Non-MLS 3)
Founded 1971
Library Holdings: Bk Titles 4,000
Special Collections: Can & Prov; Municipal Document Depository; Oral History
Function: Archival coll, e-mail serv, Electronic databases & coll, Exhibits, Handicapped accessible, Photocopying/Printing, Ref serv available, Res performed for a fee, Scanner
Publications: Inventories & Indexes to Specific Collections (Archives guide)
Open Mon, Tues, Thurs & Fri 8:30-4:30, Wed 8:30-8
Restriction: In-house use for visitors, Non-circulating, Not a lending libr, Open to pub for ref only

G   SUSTAINABLE DEVELOPMENT LIBRARY*, HSBC, 5th Flr, 10250 101
St, T5J 3P4, SAN 320-2976. Tel: 780-496-6165. FAX: 780-496-6054.
Web Site: www.edmonton.ca. *Librn,* Katherina Hui; Staff 2 (Non-MLS 2)
Founded 1962
Library Holdings: Bk Titles 7,000; Per Subs 100
Subject Interests: Regional planning, Urban design, Urban planning
Restriction: Open by appt only
Friends of the Library Group

C   CONCORDIA UNIVERSITY COLLEGE OF ALBERTA*, Arnold Guebert
Library, 7128 Ada Blvd, T5B 4E4. SAN 318-658X. Tel: 780-479-9338.
Administration Tel: 780-479-9334. FAX: 780-471-6796. E-mail:
circle@concordia.ab.ca. Web Site: library.concordia.ab.ca. *Dir,* Dan Mirau;
E-mail: dan.mirau@concordia.ab.ca; *Info Serv Coordr,* Lynette
Toews-Neufeldt; Tel: 780-479-9339, E-mail:
lynette.toews-neufeldt@concordia.ab.ca; Staff 11 (MLS 3, Non-MLS 8)
Founded 1921. Enrl 1,300; Fac 100; Highest Degree: Master
Library Holdings: Bk Vols 85,000; Per Subs 20,000
Subject Interests: Applied psychol, English lit, Math, Relig studies
Wireless access
Partic in NEOS Library Consortium
Open Mon-Thurs 7:45am-9pm, Fri 7:45am-5pm, Sat 10-5, Sun 12-7

M   CROSS CANCER INSTITUTE LIBRARY*, Abdul Khaliq Library, 11560
University Ave, T6G 1Z2. SAN 320-7714. Tel: 780-432-8593. FAX:
780-432-8886. E-mail: ccilibra@albertahealthservices.ca. Web Site:
www.albertahealthservices.ca. *Librn,* Linda Harris; E-mail:
linda.harris2@albertahealthservices.ca; Staff 1 (MLS 1)
Library Holdings: Bk Titles 2,000; Bk Vols 4,000; Per Subs 61
Subject Interests: Cancer
Database Vendor: SirsiDynix
Partic in NEOS Library Consortium
Open Mon-Fri 8-4:30

S   EDMONTON AUTISM SOCIETY LIBRARY*, 11720 Kingsway Ave, No
101, T5G 0X5. SAN 329-9821. Tel: 780-453-3971. FAX: 780-447-4948.
E-mail: autism@autismedmonton.org. Web Site: www.autismedmonton.org.
Exec Dir, Freda Badry
Founded 1971
Library Holdings: Bk Titles 300
Publications: Autism Now (Newsletter)
Open Mon-Fri 9-5
Restriction: Mem only

S   EDMONTON HUMANE SOCIETY*, Education Resource Library,
13620-163 St NW, T5V 0B2. SAN 375-7595. Tel: 780-471-1774. FAX:
780-479-8946. E-mail: education@edmontonhumanesociety.com. Web Site:
www.edmontonhumanesociety.com. *Educ Coordr,* Kristen McKenna
Library Holdings: Bk Titles 350

S   EDMONTON POLICE*, Robert F Lunney Library, 9620 103A Ave, 2nd
flr, T5H 0H7. SAN 375-1163. Tel: 780-421-3459. E-mail: epslib@telus.net.
Web Site: www.police.edmonton.ab.ca/library.htm. *Librn,* Janice Broverman
Library Holdings: AV Mats 200; Bk Titles 15,000; Per Subs 140
Automation Activity & Vendor Info: (Cataloging) Insignia Software;
(Circulation) Insignia Software; (Serials) EBSCO Online
Restriction: Open by appt only

P   EDMONTON PUBLIC LIBRARY*, Stanley A Milner Library, Seven Sir
Winston Churchill Sq, T5J 2V4. SAN 365-7159. Tel: 780-496-7070.
Reference Tel: 780-496-7020. FAX: 780-496-1885. Information Services
FAX: 780-496-7001. Web Site: www.epl.ca. *Chief Exec Officer,* Linda
Cook; Tel: 780-496-7050, Fax: 780-496-7097, E-mail: lcook@epl.ca; *Exec
Dir, Mgt Serv,* Joanne Griener; Tel: 780-496-6822, E-mail: jgriener@epl.ca;
Exec Dir, Pub Serv, Pilar Martinez; Tel: 780-496-5522, E-mail:
pmartinez@epl.ca
Founded 1913. Pop 812,201; Circ 13,402,504
Special Collections: Western Canadiana. Can & Prov
Automation Activity & Vendor Info: (Acquisitions) SirsiDynix;
(Cataloging) SirsiDynix; (Circulation) SirsiDynix
Wireless access
Partic in The Alberta Library
Special Services for the Deaf - Staff with knowledge of sign lang
Open Mon-Fri 9-9, Sat 9-6, Sun 1-5
Friends of the Library Group
Branches: 15
    ABBOTTSFIELD-PENNY MCKEE BRANCH, 3410 118th Ave, T5W
0Z4, SAN 377-8045. Tel: 780-496-7839. FAX: 780-496-8397. *Mgr,*
Valerie McNiven; E-mail: vmcniven@epl.ca
Open Mon-Thurs 10-9, Fri 10-5, Sat 10-6, Sun 1-5
Friends of the Library Group

    CALDER, 12522 132nd Ave, T5L 3P9, SAN 365-7183. Tel:
780-496-7090. FAX: 780-496-1453. *Mgr,* Gail Walker; E-mail:
gwalker@epl.ca
Open Mon-Thurs 10-9, Fri & Sat 10-6, Sun 1-5
Friends of the Library Group
    CAPILANO, 201 Capilano Mall, 5004-98 Ave, T6A 0A1, SAN 365-7213.
Tel: 780-496-1802. FAX: 780-496-7009. *Mgr,* Paula Benson; E-mail:
pbenson@epl.ca; *Asst Librn,* Melanie Morck
Open Mon-Thurs 10-9, Fri 10-6, Sat 9:30-5:30, Sun 1-5
Friends of the Library Group
    CASTLE DOWNS, 106 Lakeside Landing, 15379 Castle Downs Rd, T5X
3Y7, SAN 365-7221. Tel: 780-496-1804. FAX: 780-496-7005. *Mgr,*
Edith Parsons; Tel: 780-496-2708, E-mail: eparsons@epl.ca
Open Mon-Thurs 10-9, Fri & Sat 10-6, Sun 1-5
Friends of the Library Group
    HIGHLANDS, 6516 118th Ave, T5W 1G6, SAN 365-7272. Tel:
780-496-1806. FAX: 780-496-7012. *Mgr,* Melanie Johnson; *Asst Mgr,*
Bernice Linkewich; E-mail: blinkewich@epl.ca
Open Mon, Fri & Sat 10-6, Tues-Thurs 10-8
Friends of the Library Group
    LOIS HOLE LIBRARY, 17650-69 Ave NW, T5T 3X9, SAN 376-9534.
Tel: 780-442-0885. FAX: 780-442-0887. *Mgr,* Myra Skaronski; E-mail:
mskaronski@epl.ca; *Assoc Mgr,* Yvonne Footz; *Membership Serv Supvr,*
Heather Chartier
Open Mon-Thurs 10-9, Fri & Sat 10-6, Sun 1-5
Friends of the Library Group
    IDYLWYLDE, 8310 88th Ave NW, T6C 1L1, SAN 365-7302. Tel:
780-496-1808. FAX: 780-496-7092. *Mgr,* Richard Thornley; E-mail:
rthornley@epl.ca
Open Mon-Thurs 10-9, Fri & Sat 10-6, Sun 1-5
    JASPER PLACE, 9010 156th St, T5R 5X7, SAN 365-7337. Tel:
780-496-1810. FAX: 780-496-7004. *Mgr,* Edith Parsons; Tel:
780-496-2708, Fax: 780-496-7005, E-mail: eparsons@epl.ca
Open Mon-Thurs 10-9, Fri & Sat 10-6, Sun 1-5
Friends of the Library Group
    LONDONDERRY, 110 Londonderry Mall, 137th Ave & 66th St, T5C
3C8, SAN 365-7248. Tel: 780-496-1814. FAX: 780-496-1452. *Mgr,*
Carla Palichuk; E-mail: cpalichuk@epl.ca; *Asst Mgr,* Rhonda Rowe;
Staff 24 (MLS 3, Non-MLS 21)
Founded 1979
Open Mon-Thurs 10-9, Fri 10-6, Sat 9:30-5:30, Sun 1-5
Friends of the Library Group
    MILL WOODS, 601 Mill Woods Town Centre, 2331 66 St, T6K 4B5,
SAN 365-7345. Tel: 780-496-1818. FAX: 780-496-1450. *Mgr,* Sharon
Karr; Tel: 780-496-7077; *Assoc Mgr,* Heather Santes; Tel: 780-496-7842;
Ch, Susan Mikytyshyn; Tel: 780-496-7276; *Commun Librn,* Bronwyn
Burlingham; Tel: 780-442-4534; *Membership Serv Supvr,* Gail Petryk;
Tel: 780-496-1821
Open Mon-Thurs 10-9, Fri & Sat 10-5:30, Sun 1-5
Friends of the Library Group
    RIVERBEND, 460 Riverbend Sq, Rabbit Hill Rd & Terwillegar Dr, T6R
2X2. Tel: 780-944-5311. FAX: 780-944-5327. *Mgr,* Hazel Spratt;
Commun Librn, Kim Bates
Open Mon-Thurs 10-9, Fri & Sat 10-6, Sun 1-5
Friends of the Library Group
    SPRUCEWOOD, 11555 95th St, T5G 1L5, SAN 365-7396. Tel:
780-496-7099. FAX: 780-496-7010. *Mgr,* Connie Hargreaves; Tel:
780-496-1054
Open Mon-Thurs 10-9, Fri & Sat 10-6, Sun 1-5
Friends of the Library Group
    STRATHCONA, 8331 104th St, T6E 4E9, SAN 365-7426. Tel:
780-496-1828. FAX: 780-496-1451. *Mgr,* Mary Jane Bilsland; E-mail:
mbilsland@epl.ca; *Asst Mgr,* Janice Sabourin; *Libr Asst,* Megan Wilson
Open Mon-Thurs 10-9, Fri & Sat 10-6, Sun 1-5
Friends of the Library Group
    WHITEMUD CROSSING, 145 Whitemud Crossing Shopping Ctr,
4211-106 St, T6J 6L7, SAN 365-7361. Tel: 780-496-1822. FAX:
780-496-7007. *Mgr,* Jason Openo; E-mail: jopeno@epl.ca
Open Mon-Thurs 10-9, Fri & Sat 10-6, Sun 1-5
Friends of the Library Group
    WOODCROFT, 13420 114th Ave, T5M 2Y5, SAN 365-7450. Tel:
780-496-1830. FAX: 780-496-7089. *Mgr,* Tiina Payson; Tel:
780-496-6894; *Asst Mgr,* Margo DeMoor; Tel: 780-496-6891
Founded 1956
Open Mon-Thurs 10-9, Fri & Sat 10-6, Sun 1-5
Friends of the Library Group

L   FRASER MILNER CASGRAIN LLP*, Barristers & Solicitors Library,
2900 Manulife Pl, 10180 - 101 St, Ste 2900, T5J 3V5. SAN 328-1620. Tel:
780-423-7371. Circulation Tel: 780-423-7370. FAX: 780-423-7276. Web
Site: www.fmc-law.com. *Info Res Mgr,* Josette McEachern; E-mail:
josette.mceachern@fmc-law.com; Staff 2.5 (Non-MLS 2.5)
Founded 1887
Library Holdings: CDs 3; e-books 5; e-journals 1; Electronic Media &
Resources 14; Bk Titles 3,327; Bk Vols 18,000; Per Subs 41; Videos 5

Subject Interests: Law
Automation Activity & Vendor Info: (Cataloging) EOS International; (Circulation) Inmagic, Inc.; (OPAC) EOS International; (Serials) EOS International
Database Vendor: H W Wilson, HeinOnline, Infomart, Ingenta, JSTOR, LexisNexis, Quicklaw, ScienceDirect, Thomson Carswell, WestlaweCARSWELL
Wireless access
Publications: Acquisitions List
Restriction: By permission only

M   GLENROSE REHABILITATION HOSPITAL*, Library Services, 10230 111 Ave NW, T5G 0B7. SAN 320-7722. Tel: 780-735-8823. FAX: 780-735-8863. E-mail: glenroselibrary@albertahealthservices.ca.
Library Holdings: Bk Vols 10,000; Per Subs 150
Subject Interests: Geriatrics, Rehabilitation
Partic in NEOS Library Consortium

M   GREY NUNS COMMUNITY HOSPITAL-CARITAS HEALTH GROUP*, Health Sciences Library, 1100 Youville Dr W, T6L 5X8. SAN 318-6601. Tel: 780-735-7300. FAX: 780-735-7202. E-mail: GNHLibrary@covenanthealth.ca. *Librn,* Connie Winther; Tel: 780-735-7251; Staff 3 (MLS 1, Non-MLS 2)
Founded 1986
Library Holdings: Bk Titles 1,800; Per Subs 93
Subject Interests: Allied health, Med, Nursing, Palliative care
Automation Activity & Vendor Info: (Acquisitions) SirsiDynix; (Cataloging) SirsiDynix; (Circulation) SirsiDynix; (Course Reserve) SirsiDynix; (ILL) SirsiDynix; (Media Booking) SirsiDynix; (OPAC) SirsiDynix; (Serials) SirsiDynix
Database Vendor: SirsiDynix
Function: Doc delivery serv, ILL available
Partic in NEOS Library Consortium
Restriction: Staff use only

CL   HEALTH LAW INSTITUTE LIBRARY*, University of Alberta, Law Centre, T6G 2H5. SAN 326-7644. Tel: 780-248-1175. FAX: 780-492-9575. E-mail: hli@law.ualberta.ca. Web Site: www.law.ualberta.ca/centres/hli. *Exec Dir,* Tracey Bailey; E-mail: nmhawkins@law.ualberta.ca
Library Holdings: Bk Titles 100; Per Subs 30
Special Collections: Canadian Reported & Unreported Cases Dealing with Health Law, 1950 to present; Canadian, Commonwealth & American Journals & Articles on Medical Legal Issues; English & Commonwealth Health Law Cases, 1975 to present; Law Reform Commission of Canada Reports; Selected United States Health Law Court Cases
Open Mon-Fri 8-4

S   HEMISPHERE ENGINEERING INC LIBRARY*, 10950 119th St, T5H 3P5. SAN 323-875X. Tel: 780-452-1800. FAX: 780-453-5205.
Library Holdings: Bk Vols 300
Restriction: Staff use only

C   THE KING'S UNIVERSITY COLLEGE*, Simona Maaskant Library, 9125 50th St, T6B 2H3. SAN 325-2345. Tel: 780-465-8304. Interlibrary Loan Service Tel: 780-465-3500, Ext 8054. Reference Tel: 780-465-3500, Ext 8052. Administration Tel: 780-465-3500, Ext 8053. FAX: 780-465-3534. E-mail: library@kingsu.ca. Web Site: www.kingsu.ca. *Dir of Libr Serv,* Tim Janewski; E-mail: tim.janewski@kingsu.ca; *ILL, Ser,* Bonita Bjornson; E-mail: bonita.bjornson@kingsu.ca; Staff 5 (MLS 2, Non-MLS 3)
Founded 1979. Enrl 650; Fac 50; Highest Degree: Bachelor
Library Holdings: Bk Vols 100,000; Per Subs 300
Subject Interests: Curric, Liberal arts
Automation Activity & Vendor Info: (Acquisitions) SirsiDynix; (Cataloging) SirsiDynix; (Circulation) SirsiDynix; (OPAC) SirsiDynix; (Serials) SirsiDynix
Database Vendor: EBSCOhost, Gale Cengage Learning, OCLC FirstSearch, OVID Technologies, ProQuest, SirsiDynix
Wireless access
Function: ILL available
Partic in Council of Prairie & Pacific University Libraries; NEOS Library Consortium
Open Mon-Thurs 8am-9pm, Fri 8-5, Sat 10-5
Restriction: Pub use on premises

J   GRANT MACEWAN UNIVERSITY LIBRARY*, 10700 104th Ave, T5J 4S2. (Mail add: PO Box 1796, T5J 2P2), SAN 320-0787. Tel: 780-497-5850. Interlibrary Loan Service Tel: 780-497-5857. Reference Tel: 780-497-5882. Administration Tel: 780-497-5892. FAX: 780-497-5895. Circulation FAX: 780-497-4566. Web Site: www.library.macewan.ca. *Chief Librn,* Debbie McGugan; Tel: 780-497-5894, E-mail: mcgugand@macewan.ca; *Chair, Ref & Res Serv,* Yvonne Rezek; *Ref Librn,* Richard Hayman; *Ref Librn,* Karen Hering; *Ref Librn,* Brian Jackson; *Ref Librn,* Jessica Knoch; *Ref Librn,* Nicolle Lemay; *Ref Librn,* Valla McLean;

Ref Librn, Lisa Shamchuk; *Ref Librn,* Tara Stieglitz; *Tech Librn,* Roxy Garstad; *Admin Mgr,* Glenna Helm; Tel: 780-497-5893; *Acq & Cat Mgr,* Jill Day; *Mgr, Borrower Serv,* Nick Ursulak; *Coordr of Libr Tech,* Gordon Bertrand; *Info Syst Spec,* Susan Jones; Staff 10 (MLS 10)
Founded 1971. Enrl 11,000; Fac 658
Library Holdings: AV Mats 31,803; Bk Vols 400,000; Per Subs 30,000
Subject Interests: Commun studies, Fine arts, Health, Univ transfer
Database Vendor: EBSCOhost, Gale Cengage Learning, Wilson - Wilson Web
Function: Telephone ref
Partic in NEOS Library Consortium; The Alberta Library
Departmental Libraries:
ALBERTA COLLEGE CAMPUS LIBRARY, 10050 MacDonald Dr, T5J 2B7. SAN 320-7692. Tel: 780-423-3738. FAX: 780-424-6371. Web Site: library.macewan.ca. *Mgr,* Lana Thompson; E-mail: thompsonl48@macewan.ca; Staff 3 (Non-MLS 3)
Founded 1903. Enrl 1,000
    Library Holdings: Bks on Deafness & Sign Lang 20; Bk Titles 8,000; Bk Vols 10,000; Per Subs 20
    Subject Interests: English, Music
    Automation Activity & Vendor Info: (Acquisitions) SirsiDynix; (Cataloging) SirsiDynix; (OPAC) SirsiDynix
CENTER FOR THE ARTS & COMMUNICATIONS LIBRARY, 10045 156th St, T5P 2P7, SAN 321-9410. Tel: 780-497-4346. FAX: 780-497-4367. *Campus Librn,* Robert Zylstra; Tel: 780-633-3036, E-mail: zylstrar@macewan.ca; *Tech Spec,* Jason Nalenko
Founded 1971
SOUTH CAMPUS LIBRARY, 7319 29th Ave, T6K 2P1, SAN 318-6644. Tel: 780-497-4054. FAX: 780-497-4184. *Librn,* Melinda Spears; *Libr Tech,* Marge Gray; Tel: 780-497-4052, E-mail: graym@macewan.ca
Founded 1971
    Database Vendor: SirsiDynix

M   MISERICORDIA COMMUNITY HOSPITAL - CARITAS HEALTH GROUP*, Weinlos Library, 16940 87th Ave, T5R 4H5. SAN 318-6687. Tel: 780-735-2708. FAX: 780-735-2509. E-mail: mislibrary@covenanthealth.ca. Web Site: www.covenanthealth.ca. *Libr Mgr,* Sharna Polard; Tel: 780-735-7251; Staff 3 (MLS 1, Non-MLS 2)
Founded 1971
Library Holdings: Bk Titles 1,500; Bk Vols 2,075; Per Subs 111
Special Collections: History of Medicine
Subject Interests: Allied health, Med, Nursing
Automation Activity & Vendor Info: (Cataloging) SirsiDynix; (Circulation) SirsiDynix; (OPAC) SirsiDynix; (Serials) SirsiDynix
Database Vendor: EBSCOhost
Function: Doc delivery serv, ILL available
Partic in NEOS Library Consortium
Open Mon-Fri 7:30-3:45
Restriction: Non-circulating to the pub

C   NEWMAN THEOLOGICAL COLLEGE LIBRARY*, 10012 84 St NW, T6A 0B2. SAN 373-2851. Tel: 780-392-2450. FAX: 780-462-4013. E-mail: ntc.library@newman.edu. Web Site: www.newman.edu/library.aspx. *Librn,* James Derksen; Staff 3 (MLS 1, Non-MLS 2)
Founded 1917. Enrl 100; Fac 20; Highest Degree: Master
Library Holdings: Bk Titles 36,000; Per Subs 230
Automation Activity & Vendor Info: (Cataloging) SirsiDynix; (Circulation) SirsiDynix; (Course Reserve) SirsiDynix; (OPAC) SirsiDynix
Partic in NEOS Library Consortium
Open Mon-Fri 9-4

J   NORQUEST COLLEGE, Learner Center - Library, 10215-108th St, 5th Flr, T5J 1L6. SAN 371-0491. Tel: 708-644-6070. FAX: 780-644-6082. E-mail: library@norquest.ca. Web Site: library.norquest.ca. *Head Librn,* Eve Poirier; *Coordr, Libr Instruction,* Liz Fulton-Lyne; E-mail: liz.Fulton-Lyne@norquest.ca; *Libr Syst Coordr,* Kathy Zarft; E-mail: kathy.zarft@norquest.ca; Staff 11 (MLS 2, Non-MLS 9)
Founded 1965. Enrl 4,023; Fac 255
Library Holdings: AV Mats 5,725; e-books 40,000; Bk Titles 42,460; Per Subs 250
Subject Interests: Acad upgrading, Career educ, English as a second lang
Partic in The Alberta Library

S   NORTHERN ALBERTA INSTITUTE OF TECHNOLOGY*, McNally Library, 11762 106th St NW, T5G 3H3. SAN 318-6709. Tel: 780-471-8844. FAX: 780-471-8813. Web Site: www.nait.ca/library.
Founded 1963
Library Holdings: Bk Titles 53,000; Per Subs 250
Special Collections: Automotive Manuals; Small Business
Subject Interests: Applied arts, Computer tech, Eng tech, Paramedical, Trades
Automation Activity & Vendor Info: (Acquisitions) Ex Libris Group; (Cataloging) Ex Libris Group; (Circulation) Ex Libris Group; (Course

Reserve) Ex Libris Group; (Media Booking) Ex Libris Group; (OPAC) Ex Libris Group; (Serials) Ex Libris Group
Database Vendor: Dialog, EBSCOhost, OVID Technologies, Wilson - Wilson Web
Publications: Staff Handbook; Student Brochure
Partic in The Alberta Library
Open Mon-Thurs 7:45am-9pm, Fri 7:45-5, Sat & Sun 12-5

G   NORTHERN FORESTRY CENTRE*, Woodlot Extension Library, 5320 122nd St, Rm 052, T6H 3S5. SAN 318-6563. Tel: 780-735-7324. FAX: 780-435-7356, 780-435-7359. Web Site: www.nrcan.gc.ca/library/6261. *Libr Mgr,* Denise Leroy; E-mail: dleroy@nrcan.gc.ca; Staff 1 (MLS 1)
Founded 1948
Subject Interests: Climate change, Ecology, Entomology, Fire, Forest health, Forest mgt, Soils
Automation Activity & Vendor Info: (Cataloging) SIRSI Unicorn; (Circulation) SIRSI Unicorn; (Serials) SIRSI Unicorn
Database Vendor: Agricola, BioOne, EBSCOhost, netLibrary, OCLC FirstSearch, OVID Technologies, ScienceDirect, SirsiDynix, Springer-Verlag
Partic in Council of Federal Libraries Consortium; Natural Resources Can Libr Network
Open Mon-Fri 8:30-4:30

M   ROYAL ALEXANDRA HOSPITAL*, Library Services, 10240 Kingsway, T5H 3V9. SAN 365-7485. Tel: 780-735-5832. FAX: 780-735-4136. E-mail: rahlibrary@albertahealthservices.ca. *Librn,* Morgan Truax; E-mail: morgan.truax@albertahealthservices.ca; *Libr Tech,* Fazia Baksh; E-mail: fazia.baksh@albertahealthservices.ca; Staff 2 (Non-MLS 2)
Founded 1963
Library Holdings: Bk Titles 4,000; Per Subs 50
Subject Interests: Health, Med
Partic in NEOS Library Consortium
Open Mon-Fri 8-4:15

JR   SAINT JOSEPH'S COLLEGE LIBRARY*, University of Alberta, 11325 89th Ave, T6G 2J5. SAN 318-6717. Tel: 780-492-7681, Ext 238. FAX: 780-492-8145. E-mail: librsjc@ualberta.ca. Web Site: www.library.ualberta.ca, www.stjosephs.ualberta.ca/library.aspx. *Dir, Libr Serv,* Donna Meen; E-mail: donna.meen@ualberta.ca; Staff 3 (MLS 1, Non-MLS 2)
Founded 1964. Enrl 1,700; Fac 13
Library Holdings: AV Mats 150; Bk Vols 40,000; Per Subs 80
Special Collections: St Joseph's Ethics Library
Subject Interests: Bible studies, Catholic Church, Ethics, Philosophy, Theol
Partic in NEOS Library Consortium

UNIVERSITY OF ALBERTA
C   ARCHIVES*, Books & Records Depository, 100 8170 50th St, T6B 1E6. Tel: 780-466-6118, 780-466-6123. FAX: 780-466-5210. E-mail: archives@ualberta.ca. Web Site: www.ualberta.ca/archives. *Archivist,* Bryan Corbett; E-mail: bryan.corbett@ualberta.ca; *Assoc Archivist,* James Franks; *Assoc Archivist,* Raymond Frogner; Staff 4 (MLS 1, Non-MLS 3)
Founded 1968
Library Holdings: AV Mats 300,000; Bk Vols 100; Per Subs 10
Open Mon, Wed & Fri 8:30-4:30

C   BIBLIOTHEQUE SAINT-JEAN*, 8406 rue Marie-Anne Gaboury (91 St), T6C 4G9, SAN 365-7876. Tel: 780-465-8711. FAX: 780-468-2550. E-mail: bsjref@library.ualberta.ca. Web Site: www.library.ualberta.ca/francais. *Librn,* Tatiana Usova; Tel: 780-465-8710, E-mail: usova@ualberta.ca; Staff 11 (MLS 4, Non-MLS 7)
Founded 1910. Enrl 680; Highest Degree: Master
Apr 2007-Mar 2008. Mats Exp $218,000, Books (CAN) $145,000, Per/Ser (Incl. Access Fees) (CAN) $60,000, Other Print Mats (CAN) $10,000, Electronic Ref Mat (Incl. Access Fees) (CAN) $3,000
Library Holdings: Bk Vols 200,000; Per Subs 400
Special Collections: Canadiana, particularly French Canadian & Western Canadian Literature & History Coll; Eduq Microfiche; French Federal Documents
Subject Interests: Arts, Educ, Soc sci
Automation Activity & Vendor Info: (Cataloging) SirsiDynix; (Circulation) SirsiDynix; (Course Reserve) SirsiDynix; (OPAC) SirsiDynix
Partic in Association of Research Libraries (ARL)
Publications: Library Guides & Bibliographies in the French Language

C   HERBERT T COUTTS EDUCATION & PHYSICAL EDUCATION LIBRARY*, Educations Bldg, T6G 2G5, SAN 365-7663. Tel: 780-492-3770. Circulation Tel: 780-492-4566. Toll Free Tel: 800-207-0172. FAX: 780-492-8367. E-mail: educref@library.ualberta.ca. Web Site: www.library.ualberta.ca. *Head of Libr,* Katherine Koch; Tel: 780-492-1460; Staff 28 (MLS 6, Non-MLS 22)

Founded 1948. Enrl 5,000; Highest Degree: Doctorate
Library Holdings: Bk Titles 250,000; Per Subs 800
Special Collections: Children's Literature (Historical Coll), curriculum mats, textbks; Research Coll on Reading (William S Gray Coll)
Subject Interests: Curric, Educ, Health promotion
Database Vendor: EBSCOhost, Gale Cengage Learning, OCLC FirstSearch, OVID Technologies, ProQuest, SirsiDynix, TLC (The Library Corporation), Wilson - Wilson Web
Partic in Association of Research Libraries (ARL); Canadian Association of Research Libraries; Canadian Research Knowledge Network; Computer Sciences Corporation; Council of Prairie & Pacific University Libraries; NEOS Library Consortium; Spires; The Alberta Library; Utlas

C   RUTHERFORD (HUMANITIES & SOCIAL SCIENCES) LIBRARY*, 1-01 Rutherford South, T6G 2J8, SAN 365-7698. Tel: 780-492-3794. FAX: 780-492-5083. E-mail: hssref2@ualberta.ca. Web Site: www.guides.library.ualberta.ca/rutherford. *Head of Libr,* Christine Brown; Tel: 780-492-1405, E-mail: christine.brown@ualberta.ca; *Pub Serv Mgr,* Lindsay Johnston; Tel: 780-492-0598. Subject Specialists: *Sociol,* Christine Brown; Staff 16 (MLS 16)
Founded 1973. Enrl 39,000; Fac 3,094; Highest Degree: Doctorate
Library Holdings: Bk Vols 2,100,000; Per Subs 5,000
Special Collections: Bunyan Coll; Milton Coll; Romanticism Coll. Can & Prov
Subject Interests: Canadiana, Slavic
Automation Activity & Vendor Info: (Acquisitions) SirsiDynix; (Cataloging) SirsiDynix; (Circulation) SirsiDynix; (Course Reserve) SirsiDynix; (ILL) Relais International; (OPAC) SirsiDynix; (Serials) SirsiDynix
Database Vendor: Cambridge Scientific Abstracts, EBSCOhost, Factiva.com, Gale Cengage Learning, JSTOR, netLibrary, OCLC FirstSearch, OCLC WorldCat, OVID Technologies, SirsiDynix
Function: Doc delivery serv, Govt ref serv, ILL available, Ref serv available, Res libr, Wheelchair accessible
Partic in Coun of Atlantic Univ Librns; CREPUQ; Ontario Council of University Libraries
Special Services for the Deaf - Assistive tech
Special Services for the Blind - Assistive/Adapted tech devices, equip & products; Reader equip; Ref serv

C   SCIENCE & TECHNOLOGY LIBRARY*, Cameron Library, T6G 2J8, SAN 365-7728. Tel: 780-492-7912, 780-492-8440. FAX: 780-492-2721. E-mail: sciref@ualberta.ca. Web Site: www.library.ualberta.ca. *Actg Head Librn,* Tim Klassen; Tel: 780-492-7918, E-mail: tim.klassen@ualberta.ca
Highest Degree: Doctorate
Special Collections: Can & Prov
Subject Interests: Agr, Eng, Forestry, Human ecology, Maps, Northern studies

CM   JOHN W SCOTT HEALTH SCIENCES LIBRARY*, Walter C Mackenzie Health Sciences Ctr 2K3 28, T6G 2R7, SAN 365-7752. Tel: 780-492-3899. Reference Tel: 780-492-7947. FAX: 780-492-6960. E-mail: jwsinfo@library.ualberta.ca. Web Site: www.library.ualberta.ca. *Head of Libr,* Marlene Dorgan; Tel: 780-492-7945, E-mail: marlene.dorgan@ualberta.ca; *Coll Mgr,* Trish Chatterley; Tel: 780-492-7933, E-mail: trish.chatterley@ualberta.ca; *Pub Serv Mgr,* Linda Slater; Tel: 780-492-7948, E-mail: linda.slater@ualberta.ca; Staff 10 (MLS 10)
Founded 1925. Enrl 47,000; Fac 468; Highest Degree: Doctorate
Special Collections: Historical (Rawlinson)
Subject Interests: Dentistry, Med, Nursing, Pharmaceutical sci, Rehabilitation med
Automation Activity & Vendor Info: (Acquisitions) SirsiDynix; (Cataloging) SirsiDynix; (Circulation) SirsiDynix; (Course Reserve) SirsiDynix; (OPAC) SirsiDynix; (Serials) SirsiDynix
Partic in Association of Research Libraries (ARL); Canadian Research Knowledge Network; Council of Prairie & Pacific University Libraries
Open Mon-Thurs (Fall/Winter) 8am-10pm, Fri 8-6, Sat 11-6, Sun 11-10, Mon-Thurs (Spring/Summer) 8-7, Fri 8-5, Sat & Sun 11-6

C   UNIVERSITY LIBRARY*, 5-02 Cameron Libr, T6G 2J8, SAN 365-7604. Tel: 780-492-3790. FAX: 780-492-8302. *Interim Chief Librn,* Katheryn Arbuckle; *Assoc Univ Librn,* Kathleen DeLong; *Assoc Univ Librn,* Merrill Distad; Staff 85 (MLS 85)
Founded 1909. Enrl 36,562; Fac 2,055; Highest Degree: Doctorate
Apr 2006-Mar 2007. Mats Exp (CAN) $18,490,704. Sal (CAN) $17,694,883 (Prof (CAN) $6,635,702)
Library Holdings: Bk Vols 6,720,775; Per Subs 45,110
Special Collections: Alberta Folklore Coll; Canadian Fine Printing Coll; Contemporary Bookworks Coll; Literature (Bunyan, Milton, Yeats, Lawrence, Cuala Press, Curwen Press, Grabhorn Press & Wordsworth Colls), Javitch Coll of South & North American Indian Material; Salzburg Coll (Theology & Canon Law); Victorian Book Arts, Rutherford Coll of Western Canadiana. Can & Prov; UN Document Depository
Subject Interests: Agr, Legal, Med, Sci, Sociol, Sports
Automation Activity & Vendor Info: (Circulation) SirsiDynix
Partic in Association of Research Libraries (ARL)

CL   JOHN ALEXANDER WEIR MEMORIAL LAW LIBRARY*, Law Centre, 111 St & 89 Ave, T6G 2H5, SAN 365-7787. Tel: 780-492-3371. FAX: 780-492-7546. E-mail: lawref@library.ualberta.ca. Web Site: guides.library.ualberta.ca. *Librn,* Quoika-Stanka Wanda; E-mail: wanda.quoika-stanka@ualberta.ca; *Circ,* Shelley Brown; Tel: 780-492-1445, E-mail: shelley.brown@ualberta.ca; *Pub Serv,* Grant Kayler; Staff 6.75 (MLS 1.75, Non-MLS 5)
Founded 1951
Library Holdings: Bk Vols 375,000; Per Subs 4,900
Subject Interests: Common law, Health, Tax
Partic in Association of Research Libraries (ARL); Dialog Corp; Westlaw
Publications: Courtroom Decorum; Law Library Guides; Legal Bibliography & Research Manual
Open Mon-Fri (Summer) 9-5; Mon-Thurs (Winter) 8am-10pm, Fri 8-6, Sat & Sun 11-10

C   WILLIAM C WONDERS MAP COLLECTION*, 1-55 Cameron Library, T6G 2J8, SAN 365-7841. Tel: 780-492-8440. FAX: 780-492-2721. Web Site: guides.library.ualberta.ca/maps. *Librn,* Virginia Pow; Tel: 780-492-7919, E-mail: virginia.pow@ualberta.ca; *Cataloger,* David L Jones; Tel: 780-492-3433, E-mail: david.jones@ualberta.ca; Staff 2 (MLS 1, Non-MLS 1)
Founded 1967. Enrl 34,000; Highest Degree: Doctorate
Library Holdings: Bk Vols 6,000; Per Subs 15
Special Collections: Map Sheets & Air Photographs
Subject Interests: Cartography, Exploration, Geog, Geol, Topography
Automation Activity & Vendor Info: (Cataloging) SirsiDynix; (Circulation) SirsiDynix; (OPAC) SirsiDynix
Publications: Maps in the Service of Administration

CR   VANGUARD COLLEGE LIBRARY, Schalm Memorial Collection, 12140 103 St, T5G 2J9. SAN 320-3018. Tel: 780-452-0808. Circulation Tel: 780-452-0801, Ext 225. FAX: 780-452-5803. E-mail: library@vanguardcollege.com. Web Site: www.vanguardcollege.com. *Libr Dir,* Brad Fawcett; E-mail: brad.fawcett@vanguardcollege.com; Staff 2 (MLS 1, Non-MLS 1)
Founded 1947. Enrl 180; Highest Degree: Bachelor
Library Holdings: Bk Titles 55,000; Per Subs 65
Subject Interests: Biblical studies, Christian educ, Counseling, Pastoral theol, Relig studies
Automation Activity & Vendor Info: (Cataloging) SirsiDynix; (Circulation) SIRSI WorkFlows; (Course Reserve) SIRSI WorkFlows
Database Vendor: EBSCOhost
Wireless access
Partic in NEOS Library Consortium

EDSON

GL   ALBERTA LAW LIBRARIES - EDSON*, Provincial Bldg, 205, 111-54th St, T7E 1T2. SAN 377-4848. Tel: 780-723-8283. FAX: 780-723-8909. *Libr Coordr,* Judy Chin; E-mail: judy.chin@gov.ab.ca; Staff 1 (Non-MLS 1)
Open Tues 8-1

P   EDSON PUBLIC LIBRARY*, 4726-8 Avenue, T7E 1S8. SAN 318-6741. Tel: 780-723-6691. FAX: 780-723-9728. E-mail: archives@edsonlibrary.ca, info@edsonlibrary.ca. Web Site: www.edsonlibrary.ca. *Chairperson,* Barbara Prescott; *Head Librn,* JoAnn Hooper; E-mail: hooperj@edsonlibrary.ca
Founded 1940. Pop 13,000; Circ 65,000
Library Holdings: Bk Vols 31,361; Per Subs 39
Special Collections: Can & Prov; Edson Newspapers (Edson Archives)
Automation Activity & Vendor Info: (Cataloging) Polaris Library Systems; (Circulation) Polaris Library Systems; (OPAC) Polaris Library Systems
Database Vendor: EBSCOhost, Gale Cengage Learning
Mem of Yellowhead Regional Library
Open Mon-Fri 10-8, Sat 10-3

ELK POINT

P   ELK POINT PUBLIC LIBRARY*, 5123 - 50 Ave, T0A 1A0. (Mail add: PO Box 750, T0A 1A0), SAN 318-675X. Tel: 780-724-3737. FAX: 780-724-3739. E-mail: librarian@elkpointlibrary.ab.ca. Web Site: www.elkpointlibrary.ab.ca. *Chairperson,* Laverne Wilson; *Librn,* Daphne Schnurer
Founded 1950. Pop 1,440; Circ 24,685
Library Holdings: Bk Titles 13,000; Bk Vols 14,000; Per Subs 30
Mem of Northern Lights Library System
Open Mon, Tues & Thurs 1-5, Wed 1-8, Fri 10-5; Mon & Wed (Summer) 12-8, Tues, Thurs & Fri 9-5, Sat 10-5
Friends of the Library Group

P   NORTHERN LIGHTS LIBRARY SYSTEM*, 5650 48th St, T0A 1A0. (Mail add: Postal Bag 8, T0A 1A0). Tel: 780-724-2596. Toll Free Tel: 800-232-7290. Web Site: www.nlls.ab.ca. *Exec Dir,* Mircea Panciuk; E-mail: mpanciuk@nlls.ab.ca

Library Holdings: Bk Titles 12,500
Member Libraries: Alice Melnyk Public Library; Anne Chorney Public Library; Ashmont Community Library; Athabasca Municipal Library; Bibliotheque Mallaig Library; Bon Accord Public Library; Bonnyville Municipal Library; Boyle Public Library; Chauvin Municipal Library; Cold Lake Public Library; Elk Point Public Library; Gibbons Municipal Library; Grassland Public Library; Holden Municipal Library; Irma Municipal Library; Kitscoty Public Library; Lac La Biche County Library Board; Mannville Centenial Public Library; Marwayne Public Library; McPherson Municipal Library; Metro Kalyn Community Library; Morinville Public Library; Mundare Municipal Library; Myrnam Community Library; Newbrook Public Library; Paradise Valley Municipal Library; Radway & District Municipal Library; Redwater Public Library; Rochester Community Library; Saint Paul Municipal Library; Smoky Lake Municipal Library; Thorhild Library; Vegreville Centennial Library; Vermilion Public Library; Viking Municipal Library; Vilna Municipal Library; Wainwright Public Library
Open Mon-Fri 8:30-4:30

ELMWORTH

P   ELMWORTH COMMUNITY LIBRARY*, Box 23, T0H 1J0. Tel: 780-354-2930. FAX: 780-354-3639. E-mail: librarian@elmworthlibrary.ab.ca. *Librn,* Doreen Dunbar
Library Holdings: Bk Vols 9,000; Per Subs 30
Mem of Peace Library System
Open Wed 2-7, Thurs & Fri 12-5

EMPRESS

P   EMPRESS MUNICIPAL LIBRARY*, 613 Third Ave, T0J 1E0. (Mail add: PO Box 188, T0J 1E0). Tel: 403-565-3936. FAX: 403-565-2010. E-mail: aemlibrary@marigold.ab.ca. Web Site: www.marigold.ab.ca/about/memberlibs/empress.html. *Chairperson,* Hank Liphuysen; *Libr Mgr,* Charl Vincent
Pop 181
Wireless access
Mem of Marigold Library System
Open Tues-Fri 11:30-5

ENCHANT

P   ENCHANT COMMUNITY LIBRARY*, 234 Center St, T0K 0V0. (Mail add: PO Box 3000, T0K 0V0). Tel: 403-739-3835. E-mail: help@enchantlibrary.ca. Web Site: www.enchantlibrary.ca. *Librn,* Sharon Hagen
Library Holdings: Bk Vols 10,000
Open Mon 9am-11am, Tues 9-7, Wed 9am-12:30pm, Thurs 9-7, Sat 9-2

ENTWISTLE

P   ENTWISTLE PUBLIC LIBRARY*, 5232 - 50 St, T0E 0S0. (Mail add: PO Box 128, T0E 0S0). Tel: 780-727-3811. FAX: 780-727-2440. *Librn,* Karen Gibb; E-mail: kgibb@psd70.ab.ca
Library Holdings: Bk Vols 10,000
Mem of Yellowhead Regional Library
Open Mon & Tues 9-5, Wed & Thurs 9-7, Fri 11-5

EVANSBURG

P   EVANSBURG PUBLIC LIBRARY*, 4707 46th Ave, T0E 0T0. Tel: 780-727-2030, 780-727-3925. FAX: 780-727-2060. Web Site: www.evansburglibrary.ab.ca. *Libr Mgr,* Heather Nutbrown; E-mail: heatnutb@gypsd.ca
Library Holdings: DVDs 1,000; Bk Vols 10,000; Per Subs 26
Mem of Yellowhead Regional Library
Open Mon 9-12, Tues-Thurs 9-8

EXSHAW

P   BIGHORN LIBRARY*, Two Heart Mountain Dr, T0L 2C0. (Mail add: PO Box 157, T0L 2C0). Tel: 403-673-3571. FAX: 403-673-3571. E-mail: aexclibrary@marigold.ab.ca. Web Site: www.bighornlibrary.ca. *Librn,* Rose Reid
Library Holdings: Audiobooks 96; DVDs 404; Bk Vols 8,907; Per Subs 16; Talking Bks 8
Automation Activity & Vendor Info: (Cataloging) Polaris Library Systems
Wireless access
Mem of Marigold Library System
Special Services for the Blind - Daisy reader
Open Mon 9-3, Tues 9-3 & 6:30-9, Wed 3:30-5 & 6:30-9, Thurs 3-9, Fri 2-6
Friends of the Library Group

FAIRVIEW

P   FAIRVIEW PUBLIC LIBRARY*, 10209 109th St, T0H 1L0. (Mail add:
     PO Box 248, T0H 1L0), SAN 318-6768. Tel: 780-835-6768. FAX:
     780-835-2613. E-mail: librarian@fairviewlibrary.ab.ca. Web Site:
     www.fairviewlibrary.ab.ca. *Libr Mgr,* Chris Burkholder
     Founded 1938. Pop 5,100; Circ 31,000
     Library Holdings: Bk Titles 29,000; Circ 31,000
     Automation Activity & Vendor Info: (ILL) Polaris Library Systems
     Wireless access
     Open Tues & Thurs 10-8, Wed & Fri 10-5:30, Sat 10-4

FALHER

P   BIBLIOTHEQUE DENTINGER*, Falher Municipal Library, Central Ave
     SE, No 027, T0H 1M0. (Mail add: PO Box 60, T0H 1M0), SAN
     373-8531. Tel: 780-837-2776. FAX: 780-837-8755. E-mail:
     library@falherlibrary.ab.ca. Web Site:
     www.peacelibrarysystem.ab.ca/falher.html. *Librn,* Jocelyne Glerzaif; *Librn,*
     Joyce Goran
     Pop 4,041
     Library Holdings: Bk Titles 13,157
     Special Collections: French Coll, bks
     Mem of Peace Library System
     Open Tues 9-5, Wed-Fri 12-5

FAWCETT

P   M ALICE FROSE LIBRARY*, PO Box 150, T0G 0Y0. SAN 318-6776.
     Tel: 780-954-3827. FAX: 780-954-3934. *Dir,* Marie Meyn; E-mail:
     mmeyn@phrd.ab.ca
     Founded 1963. Pop 500; Circ 10,000
     Library Holdings: Bk Vols 9,000; Per Subs 60
     Database Vendor: Polaris Library Systems
     Wireless access
     Mem of Yellowhead Regional Library
     Open Mon, Tues, Thurs & Fri 9-4, Wed 9-8

FLATBUSH

P   FLATBUSH COMMUNITY LIBRARY*, General Delivery, T0G 0Z0. Tel:
     780-681-3756. E-mail: librarian@flatbushlibrary.ab.ca. Web Site:
     www.flatbushlibrary.ab.ca. *Librn,* Rose Herdman
     Library Holdings: Bk Vols 6,000
     Mem of Peace Library System
     Open Tues 10-1 & 6-9, Thurs 10-1

FOREMOST

P   FOREMOST MUNICIPAL LIBRARY*, 103 First Ave E, T0K 0X0. (Mail
     add: Box 397, T0K 0X0). Tel: 403-867-3855. FAX: 403-867-3856. E-mail:
     forlib@shortgrass.ca. Web Site: www.shortgrass.ca. *Mgr,* Joan Beutler;
     Staff 2 (Non-MLS 2)
     Founded 1987. Pop 531
     Library Holdings: Bk Vols 12,000; Per Subs 25; Talking Bks 150; Videos
     300
     Automation Activity & Vendor Info: (Acquisitions) SirsiDynix
     Wireless access
     Mem of Shortgrass Libr Syst
     Open Tues & Thurs (Sept-June) 10:30-5:30 & 6:30-8, Wed 10:30-5, Fri
     10:30-3; Mon-Fri (July & Aug) 10-4
     Friends of the Library Group

FORESTBURG

P   FORESTBURG MUNICIPAL LIBRARY*, 4901 50th St, T0B 1N0. (Mail
     add: PO Box 579, T0B 1N0), SAN 318-6784. Tel: 780-582-4110. FAX:
     780-582-4127. E-mail: forestburglibrary@libs.prl.ab.ca. *Libr Mgr,* Christine
     Callihoe; Staff 1 (MLS 1)
     Founded 1955. Pop 863; Circ 8,000
     Library Holdings: Bk Titles 8,000
     Mem of Parkland Regional Library
     Open Tues, Wed & Fri 10-6, Thurs 10-8, Sat 10-1
     Friends of the Library Group

FORT ASSINIBOINE

P   FORT ASSINIBOINE PUBLIC LIBRARY*, 35 State Ave, T0G 1A0.
     (Mail add: General Delivery, T0G 1A0). Tel: 780-584-2227. FAX:
     780-674-8575. *Librn,* Louise Davison; E-mail: ldavison@phrd.ab.ca
     Pop 4,100
     Library Holdings: Bk Vols 17,500
     Automation Activity & Vendor Info: (Acquisitions) Polaris Library
     Systems; (Cataloging) Polaris Library Systems; (Circulation) Polaris
     Library Systems; (ILL) Polaris Library Systems
     Mem of Yellowhead Regional Library
     Open Mon 8:30-4 & 7-9, Tues-Fri (Winter & Spring) 8:30-4

FORT MACLEOD

P   RCMP CENTENNIAL LIBRARY*, Fort Macleod Municipal Library, 264
     24th St, T0L 0Z0. (Mail add: PO Box 1479, T0L 0Z0), SAN 321-0022.
     Tel: 403-553-3880. E-mail: libmac@chinookarch.ab.ca. *Chairperson,*
     Marilyn Roemer; *Librn,* Laurie Huestis
     Pop 3,072; Circ 36,000
     Library Holdings: Bk Titles 29,000; Bk Vols 32,000; Per Subs 43
     Automation Activity & Vendor Info: (Acquisitions) SirsiDynix;
     (Cataloging) SirsiDynix; (Circulation) SirsiDynix; (OPAC) SirsiDynix
     Open Mon-Wed 9-5, Thurs 1-9, Fri & Sat 1-5

FORT MCMURRAY

P   FORT MCMURRAY PUBLIC LIBRARY*, 151 MacDonald Dr, T9H 5C5.
     SAN 318-6792. Tel: 780-743-7800. FAX: 780-743-7938. Web Site:
     www.fmpl.ca. *Dir,* Richard Salmons; *Ad,* Nicole Greville; *Adult Serv, Ref
     Serv,* Miranda Maguire; E-mail: miranda.maguire@fmpl.ca; *Ch,* Jennifer
     Mason; *Circ Serv,* Angela Gallant; E-mail: angela.gallant@fmpl.ca; *Mkt,*
     Carolyn Murray; E-mail: carolyn.murray@fmpl.ca; *Tech Serv,* Mark
     Anthony; E-mail: mark.anthony@fmpl.ca; Staff 3 (MLS 2, Non-MLS 1)
     Founded 1965. Pop 95,000; Circ 212,000
     Jan 2008-Dec 2008 Income (CAN) $2,880,601, Provincial (CAN)
     $331,086, City (CAN) $2,366,015, Locally Generated Income (CAN)
     $87,000, Other (CAN) $96,500. Mats Exp (CAN) $300,000, Books (CAN)
     $187,500, Per/Ser (Incl. Access Fees) (CAN) $22,500, Micro (CAN)
     $2,000, AV Mat (CAN) $60,000, Electronic Ref Mat (Incl. Access Fees)
     (CAN) $28,000. Sal (CAN) $1,730,000 (Prof (CAN) $215,000)
     Library Holdings: AV Mats 2,042; High Interest/Low Vocabulary Bk Vols
     374; Bk Titles 80,000; Bk Vols 88,352; Per Subs 130
     Subject Interests: Local hist
     Automation Activity & Vendor Info: (Acquisitions) SirsiDynix;
     (Cataloging) SirsiDynix; (Circulation) SirsiDynix; (ILL) SirsiDynix;
     (OPAC) SirsiDynix
     Database Vendor: SirsiDynix
     Open Mon-Fri 9-9, Sat 9-5, Sun 1-5

J   KEYANO COLLEGE LIBRARY*, 8115 Franklin Ave, T9H 2H7. SAN
     321-3986. Tel: 780-791-4917. FAX: 780-791-1555. E-mail:
     circulation@keyano.ca. Web Site: www.keyano.ca/library. *Dir, Libr & Educ
     Res,* John Burgess; Tel: 780-791-8927, E-mail: john.burgess@keyano.ca;
     Info Librn, Kimberly Kerr; Tel: 780-791-8911, E-mail:
     kimberly.kerr@keyano.ca; *Per,* Evelyn Graham; Tel: 780-791-4916, E-mail:
     evelyn.graham@keyano.ca; Staff 6 (MLS 2, Non-MLS 4)
     Founded 1965. Enrl 1,300; Fac 129
     Library Holdings: Bk Titles 36,743; Per Subs 260
     Subject Interests: Art, Educ, Local hist, Tech educ, Trades
     Automation Activity & Vendor Info: (Acquisitions) SirsiDynix;
     (Cataloging) SirsiDynix; (Circulation) SirsiDynix; (Course Reserve)
     SirsiDynix; (OPAC) SirsiDynix; (Serials) SirsiDynix
     Wireless access
     Publications: Annual Report; Serials Holding List; Staff Handbook;
     Student Handbook

FORT SASKATCHEWAN

GL   ALBERTA LAW LIBRARIES - FORT SASKATCHEWAN*, Courthouse,
     10504-100th Ave, T8L 3S9. SAN 371-0238. Tel: 780-998-1200. FAX:
     780-998-7222. *Libr Coordr,* Elaine Mayer; E-mail:
     elaine.mayer@gov.ab.ca; Staff 1 (Non-MLS 1)
     Open Wed & Thurs 8:30-1:30

P   FORT SASKATCHEWAN PUBLIC LIBRARY*, 10011 102nd St, T8L
     2C5. SAN 325-2450. Tel: 780-998-4275. FAX: 780-992-3255. Web Site:
     www.fspl.ca. *Libr Dir,* Angela Kubik; Tel: 780-998-4288, E-mail:
     akublik@fspl.ca
     Founded 1953. Pop 17,000; Circ 159,000
     Library Holdings: Bk Vols 60,000; Per Subs 85
     Open Mon-Thurs 10-9, Fri 10-6, Sat 10-5, Sun 1-5

FORT VERMILION

P   FORT VERMILION COMMUNITY LIBRARY*, 5103 River Rd, T0H
     1N0. (Mail add: Bag 4000, T0H 1N0), SAN 318-6806. Tel: 780-927-4279.
     FAX: 780-927-4746. E-mail: afvclibrary@platinum.ca. Web Site:
     www.fvclibrary.com. *Librn/Mgr,* Debbie Bueckert
     Pop 3,000; Circ 5,000
     Library Holdings: Bk Vols 16,000; Per Subs 10
     Wireless access
     Open Mon, Wed, Fri & Sat 12:30-5:30, Tues & Thurs 12:30-8

FOX CREEK

P　FOX CREEK MUNICIPAL LIBRARY, 501 Eighth St, T0H 1P0. (Mail
add: PO Box 1078, T0H 1P0). Tel: 780-622-2343. FAX: 780-622-4160.
Web Site: www.foxcreeklibrary.ca. *Head Librn*, Leslie Ann Sharkey
Pop 2,400
Library Holdings: Bk Vols 22,000
Automation Activity & Vendor Info: (Acquisitions) Polaris Library
Systems; (Cataloging) Polaris Library Systems; (Circulation) Polaris
Library Systems; (ILL) Polaris Library Systems; (Media Booking) Polaris
Library Systems; (OPAC) Polaris Library Systems; (Serials) Polaris Library
Systems
Mem of Peace Library System
Open Mon, Wed & Fri (Winter) 8:15-4, Tues & Thurs 8:15-4 & 6-9, Sat
11-1; Tues & Thurs (Summer) 6-9, Wed 1-4, Sat 11-1

GALAHAD

P　GALAHAD PUBLIC LIBRARY*, PO Box 58, T0B 1R0. Tel:
780-583-3917. FAX: 780-583-3917. E-mail: gallib@libs.prl.ab.ca. Web
Site: galahadpublic.prl.ab.ca. *Chairperson*, Penny Lindballe-Vincett; *Libr
Mgr*, Christine Callihoe
Pop 161
Library Holdings: Bk Vols 5,500
Mem of Parkland Regional Library
Open Tues 7pm-9pm, Wed 9-5

GEM

P　GEM JUBILEE LIBRARY*, PO Box 6, T0J 1M0. Tel: 403-641-3245.
FAX: 403-641-3245. *Librn*, Esther Hiebert
Library Holdings: Bk Vols 8,000
Open Wed 7-9, Fri 2-4:30

GIBBONS

P　GIBBONS MUNICIPAL LIBRARY*, 4807 50th Ave, T0A 1N0. (Mail
add: PO Box 510, T0A 1N0), SAN 372-7734. Tel: 780-923-2004. FAX:
780-923-2015. E-mail: librarian@gibbonslibrary.ab.ca. *Chairperson*, Ingrid
Franchuk; *Librn*, Grail Rubin
Founded 1973. Pop 2,828; Circ 15,523
Library Holdings: Bk Titles 12,200; Per Subs 20
Automation Activity & Vendor Info: (Acquisitions) Polaris Library
Systems; (Cataloging) Polaris Library Systems; (Circulation) Polaris
Library Systems; (ILL) Polaris Library Systems
Wireless access
Function: Free DVD rentals
Mem of Northern Lights Library System
Open Mon, Wed & Fri 11-5, Tues & Thurs 11-8

GLEICHEN

P　GLEICHEN & DISTRICT LIBRARY*, 404 Main St, T0J 1N0. (Mail add:
PO Box 160, T0J 1N0), SAN 322-7685. Tel: 403-734-2390. FAX:
403-734-2390. E-mail: agmlibrary@marigold.ab.ca. Web Site:
www.gleichenlibrary.ca. *Libr Mgr*, Faydra Beard
Founded 1979. Pop 400; Circ 1,500
Library Holdings: Bk Vols 10,000
Mem of Marigold Library System
Open Tues 12-8, Thurs 12-6, Fri 10-4

GLENWOOD

P　GLENWOOD MUNICIPAL LIBRARY*, 59 Main Ave, T0K 2R0. (Mail
add: PO Box 1156, T0K 2R0). Tel: 403-393-7260. E-mail:
help@glenwoodlibrary.ca. Web Site: www.glenwoodlibrary.ca. *Chairperson*,
April Demes
Pop 500; Circ 32,000
Library Holdings: DVDs 1,500; Large Print Bks 126; Bk Titles 22,000;
Per Subs 20; Talking Bks 200
Open Mon & Wed 3-6, Tues & Thurs 5-8, Fri 9-Noon

GRANDE CACHE

P　GRANDE CACHE MUNICIPAL LIBRARY*, 10601 Shand Ave, T0E
0Y0. (Mail add: PO Box 809, T0E 0Y0), SAN 325-0342. Tel:
780-827-2081. FAX: 780-827-3112. *Chairperson*, Janis Franklin; *Librn*,
Laurel A Kelsch; Staff 1 (MLS 1)
Founded 1970. Pop 5,000; Circ 22,000
Library Holdings: Bk Vols 20,000; Per Subs 21
Mem of Yellowhead Regional Library
Open Mon-Thurs 11-8, Fri 11-5, Sat & Sun 12-3

GRANDE PRAIRIE

P　GRANDE PRAIRIE PUBLIC LIBRARY, 101-9839 103 Ave, T8V 6M7.
SAN 318-6814. Tel: 780-532-3580. Interlibrary Loan Service Tel:
780-357-7468. Reference Tel: 780-357-7455. FAX: 780-538-4983. E-mail:
gplib@gppl.ab.ca. Web Site: www.gppl.ab.ca. *Chair*, Wade Nellis; *Adult
Serv, Dep Dir, Head, Info Serv*, Pam Chislett; Tel: 780-357-7474, E-mail:
pchislett@gppl.ab.ca; *Head, Children's/Youth Serv*, Serena
Boyte-Hawryluk; Tel: 780-357-7454, E-mail: sboyte@gppl.ab.ca; *Circ*,
Heather Willner; E-mail: hwillner@gppl.ab.ca; *Tech Serv*, Belinda
Blackbourn; Tel: 780-357-7460, E-mail: bblackbourn@gppl.ab.ca; Staff 30
(MLS 3, Non-MLS 27)
Founded 1939. Pop 55,032; Circ 500,000
Library Holdings: Bk Vols 149,000; Per Subs 183
Special Collections: Hauge Coll; Isabel Campbell Photo Coll; Peace
Country Histories
Subject Interests: Genealogy, Local hist
Automation Activity & Vendor Info: (Circulation) Polaris Library
Systems; (ILL) Polaris Library Systems; (OPAC) Polaris Library Systems
Database Vendor: Gale Cengage Learning
Wireless access
Publications: In Touch (Newsletter)
Mem of Peace Library System
Partic in The Alberta Library; The Regional Automation Consortium
(TRAC)
Open Mon-Thurs 10-9, Fri 10-6, Sat 10-5, Sun 1-5

J　GRANDE PRAIRIE REGIONAL COLLEGE*, Library & Media Services,
10726 106th Ave, T8V 4C4. SAN 318-6822. Tel: 780-539-2939.
Interlibrary Loan Service Tel: 780-539-2899. Reference Tel: 780-539-2822.
FAX: 780-539-2730. Web Site: library.gprc.ab.ca. *Chair*, Jennifer Thomas;
E-mail: jthomas@gprc.ab.ca; *Librn*, Ann Gish; Tel: 780-539-2940, E-mail:
agish@gprc.ab.ca; Staff 16 (MLS 2, Non-MLS 14)
Founded 1966
Library Holdings: Bk Vols 87,422; Per Subs 350
Automation Activity & Vendor Info: (Circulation) SirsiDynix
Database Vendor: EBSCOhost, Gale Cengage Learning, OVID
Technologies, ProQuest
Function: Archival coll
Partic in NEOS Library Consortium
Open Mon-Fri (Sept-Apr) 8am-9pm, Sat & Sun 12-6; Mon-Fri (May-Aug)
8:30-4:30

P　HIV NORTH SOCIETY*, 3039804 100 Ave, Ste 303, T8V 0T8. SAN
375-9024. Tel: 780-538-3388. FAX: 780-538-3368. E-mail:
info@hivnorth.org. Web Site: www.hivnorth.org. *Exec Dir*, Brenda
Yamkowy
Library Holdings: CDs 10; DVDs 55; Large Print Bks 15; Music Scores
25; Bk Vols 572; Per Subs 10; Videos 72
Wireless access
Open Mon-Thurs 9-4:30, Fri 9-4

P　PEACE LIBRARY SYSTEM*, 8301 110 St, T8W 6T2. SAN 373-8221.
Tel: 780-538-4656. FAX: 780-539-5285. E-mail:
peacelib@peacelibrarysystem.ab.ca. Web Site:
www.peacelibrarysystem.ab.ca. *Dir*, Linda Duplessis; E-mail:
ldupless@peacelibrarysystem.ab.ca; *Head, Tech Serv*, Carol Downing;
E-mail: cdowning@peacelibrarysystem.ab.ca; Staff 16 (MLS 3, Non-MLS
13)
Founded 1986. Pop 124,000
Library Holdings: Bk Vols 32,275; Per Subs 10
Automation Activity & Vendor Info: (Acquisitions) Polaris Library
Systems; (Cataloging) Polaris Library Systems; (Circulation) Polaris
Library Systems; (ILL) Polaris Library Systems; (OPAC) Polaris Library
Systems
Database Vendor: EBSCOhost, Gale Cengage Learning
Publications: Peace Library System News 'n' Notes (Newsletter)
Member Libraries: Bear Point Community Library; Beaverlodge Public
Library; Berwyn Municipal Library; Bibliotheque de St Isidore;
Bibliotheque Dentinger; Brownvale Community Library; Calling Lake
Public Library; DeBolt Public Library; Elmworth Community Library;
Fairview Public Library; Flatbush Community Library; Fox Creek
Municipal Library; Grande Prairie Public Library; Grimshaw Municipal
Library; High Level Municipal Library; High Prairie Municipal Library;
Hines Creek Municipal Library; Hythe Public Library; Keg River
Community Library; Kinuso Municipal Library; La Glace Community
Library; Manning Municipal & District Library; McLennan Municipal
Library; Nampa Municipal Library; Peace River Municipal Library;
Rainbow Lake Municipal Library; Rotary Club of Slave Lake Public
Library; Rycroft Municipal Library; Sexsmith Shannon Municipal Library;
Smith Community Library; Spirit River Municipal Library; Tangent
Community Library; Valhalla Public Library; Valleyview Municipal
Library; Wabasca Public Library; Worsley & District Public Library
Partic in The Alberta Library

Restriction: Not open to pub
Friends of the Library Group

M   QUEEN ELIZABETH II HOSPITAL*, Regional Library, 10409 98th St,
T8V 2E8. SAN 320-3042. Tel: 780-538-7124. FAX: 780-538-7507.
Founded 1984
Library Holdings: Bk Titles 8,167; Per Subs 156
Subject Interests: Anesthesiology, Emergency med, Geriatrics, Med,
Oncology, Orthopedics, Pathology, Pediatrics, Radiology, Surgery

GRASSLAND

P   GRASSLAND PUBLIC LIBRARY*, PO Box 150, T0A 1V0. Tel:
780-525-3733. FAX: 780-525-3750. E-mail:
librarian@grasslandlibrary.ab.ca. Web Site: www.grasslandlibrary.ab.ca.
Librn, Barb Cholach; *Librn,* Lori Zachkrewich
Library Holdings: Bk Vols 10,000; Per Subs 40
Function: Photocopying/Printing, Pub access computers, Summer reading
prog
Mem of Northern Lights Library System
Open Mon, Wed & Fri 8:30-3:30, Tues & Thurs 8:30-6:30

GRASSY LAKE

P   GRASSY LAKE PUBLIC LIBRARY*, PO Box 690, T0K 0Z0. Tel:
403-655-2232. FAX: 403-655-2259. *Librn,* Nancy Nelson; E-mail:
nancy.nelson@horizon.ab.ca
Library Holdings: Bk Vols 6,000
Open Mon-Fri 8:30-3:30

GRIMSHAW

P   BROWNVALE COMMUNITY LIBRARY*, PO Box 407, T0H 0L0. Tel:
780-597-2250. *Libr Mgr,* Maureen Osowetski
Library Holdings: Bk Titles 3,200
Mem of Peace Library System
Open Mon 7pm-8pm, Thurs 3:30-5

P   GRIMSHAW MUNICIPAL LIBRARY*, Grimshaw Public Library, 5007
47th Ave, T0H 1W0. (Mail add: PO Box 588, T0H 1W0), SAN 318-6849.
Tel: 780-332-4553. FAX: 780-332-1250. E-mail:
read@grimshawlibrary.ab.ca. Web Site: www.grimshawlibrary.ab.ca. *Libr
Mgr,* Linda Chmilar; E-mail: librarian@grimshawlibrary.ab.ca; *Asst Librn,*
Kim Byard
Pop 2,500; Circ 3,500
Library Holdings: Bk Titles 24,000; Per Subs 12
Automation Activity & Vendor Info: (Acquisitions) Polaris Library
Systems; (Cataloging) Polaris Library Systems
Wireless access
Mem of Peace Library System
Open Tues, Wed & Fri 9-5, Thurs 9-5 & 6-8:30, Sat 12-5

GROUARD

C   NORTHERN LAKES COLLEGE LIBRARY*, Mission St, T0G 1C0.
(Mail add: Bag 3000, T0G 1C0), SAN 323-8164. Tel: 780-849-8671. FAX:
780-751-3386. Web Site: www.northernlakescollege.ca. *Libr Dir,* Deborah
Kendze; Staff 1 (MLS 1)
Founded 1975. Enrl 1,000
Library Holdings: Audiobooks 749; Bks on Deafness & Sign Lang 37;
CDs 151; DVDs 565; e-books 370; e-journals 4; Bk Vols 59,370; Per Subs
204; Talking Bks 4,139
Subject Interests: Native Can people
Automation Activity & Vendor Info: (Acquisitions) SirsiDynix;
(Cataloging) SirsiDynix; (Circulation) SirsiDynix; (Course Reserve)
SirsiDynix; (Media Booking) SirsiDynix; (OPAC) SirsiDynix; (Serials)
SirsiDynix
Database Vendor: EBSCOhost, Gale Cengage Learning
Partic in The Alberta Library
Open Mon-Fri 8:15-4:30

GUNN

P   RICH VALLEY PUBLIC LIBRARY, RR 1, T0E 1A0. Tel: 780-967-3525.
E-mail: rvpublib@yrl.ab.ca. Web Site: www.richvalleylibrary.ab.ca. *Librn,*
Betty Ann Laporte; Tel: 780-967-0502, E-mail: laporte@gardener.com
Library Holdings: Bk Vols 10,000
Wireless access
Mem of Yellowhead Regional Library
Open Tues 5-8, Wed 10-2:30, Thurs 2-6:30

HANNA

P   HANNA MUNICIPAL LIBRARY*, PO Box 878, T0J 1P0. SAN
318-6865. Tel: 403-854-3865. FAX: 403-854-2772. E-mail:
library@hanna.ca. Web Site: www.hanna.ca/library, www.hannalibrary.ca.
Dir, Cheryl A Johnson; *Chmn of Libr Board,* Evangeline Lamson
Founded 1953. Pop 3,003; Circ 31,000
Library Holdings: Bk Vols 26,000
Subject Interests: Local hist
Automation Activity & Vendor Info: (Circulation) SirsiDynix
Wireless access
Mem of Marigold Library System
Partic in The Regional Automation Consortium (TRAC)
Special Services for the Blind - VISTA low vision equip loan prog
Open Mon-Wed & Fri 9-5, Thurs 9-8, Sat 2-4

HARDISTY

P   HARDISTY & DISTRICT PUBLIC LIBRARY*, 5027 - 50 St, T0B 1V0.
(Mail add: Box 539, T0B 1V0). Tel: 780-888-3947. FAX: 780-888-3947.
E-mail: hardistylibrary@libs.prl.ab.ca. Web Site: hardistylib.prl.ab.ca. *Librn,*
Billi-Jo Wildeboer; Staff 2 (Non-MLS 2)
Founded 1982. Pop 743
Library Holdings: Bk Vols 8,000
Function: Copy machines, Fax serv, ILL available, Mail loans to mem,
Photocopying/Printing, Summer reading prog, Wheelchair accessible
Mem of Parkland Regional Library
Open Tues & Thurs 11am-5pm, Wed 1-9, Sat 1-5
Friends of the Library Group

HAY LAKES

P   HAY LAKES MUNICIPAL LIBRARY*, PO Box 69, T0B 1W0. SAN
318-6873. Tel: 780-878-2665. *Librn,* Melissa Korth; *Asst Librn,* Cara
Arbour
Founded 1956. Pop 2,000; Circ 5,500
Library Holdings: Bk Titles 6,000; Per Subs 12
Special Collections: Enbridge Environmental Coll
Subject Interests: Alternative agr, Alternative health, Children's fiction,
Local hist
Mem of Parkland Regional Library
Partic in The Alberta Library
Open Tues-Thurs 9-8
Friends of the Library Group

HAYS

P   HAYS PUBLIC LIBRARY*, Box 36, T0K 1B0. Tel: 403-725-3744. FAX:
403-725-3744. E-mail: help@hayslibrary.ca, libhay@chinook.ca. Web Site:
www.hayslibrary.ca. *Librn,* Diane Wickenheiser
Library Holdings: Bk Vols 11,000
Open Mon 12-5, Wed 12-7, Fri 11-7

HEISLER

P   HEISLER MUNICIPAL LIBRARY*, 100 Haultain Ave, T0B 2A0. (Mail
add: Box 111, T0B 2A0). Tel: 780-889-3925. FAX: 780-889-3925. E-mail:
heislerlibrary@libs.prl.ab.ca. Web Site: heislerlibrary.prl.ab.ca. *Librn,*
Marvis Zimmer
Founded 1992. Pop 151
Library Holdings: Bk Vols 11,000
Mem of Parkland Regional Library
Open Wed 9-12 & 1-6

HIGH LEVEL

P   HIGH LEVEL MUNICIPAL LIBRARY*, 10601 103 St, T0H 1Z0. Tel:
780-926-2097. FAX: 780-926-4268. E-mail:
librarian@highlevellibrary.ab.ca. *Chairperson,* Monica Longard; *Librn,*
Jennilyn Boire; Staff 4 (Non-MLS 4)
Pop 3,887
Library Holdings: Bk Vols 20,300; Per Subs 51
Automation Activity & Vendor Info: (Acquisitions) Polaris Library
Systems; (Cataloging) Polaris Library Systems; (Circulation) Polaris
Library Systems; (ILL) Polaris Library Systems; (OPAC) Polaris Library
Systems; (Serials) Polaris Library Systems
Wireless access
Mem of Peace Library System
Open Tues & Thurs 10-8, Wed & Fri 10-6, Sat 12-5

HIGH PRAIRIE

GL   ALBERTA LAW LIBRARIES - HIGH PRAIRIE*, Courthouse, 4911-53
Ave, T0G 1E0. (Mail add: PO Box 1470, T0G 1E0), SAN 377-4864. Tel:
780-523-6600. FAX: 780-523-6643. *Libr Coordr,* Heather Pratt; E-mail:
heather.pratt@gov.ab.ca; Staff 1 (Non-MLS 1)
Open Mon 9-12 & 1-3, Wed 9-1

P HIGH PRAIRIE MUNICIPAL LIBRARY, 4723 53rd Ave, T0G 1E0. (Mail add: PO Box 890, T0G 1E0), SAN 318-6881. Tel: 780-523-3838. FAX: 780-523-3838. E-mail: librarian@highprairielibrary.ab.ca. *Chairperson,* Ann Stewart; *Libr Mgr,* Janet G Lemay; Staff 1 (Non-MLS 1)
Founded 1953. Pop 2,820; Circ 28,189
Library Holdings: Bk Titles 22,496; Per Subs 124
Mem of Peace Library System
Open Mon 1-9, Tues & Fri 9:30-5:30, Wed & Thurs 9:30-9, Sat 10:30-5:30, Sun 1-5

HIGH RIVER

P HIGH RIVER CENTENNIAL LIBRARY, 909 First St SW, T1V 1A5. SAN 318-689X. Tel: 403-652-2917. FAX: 403-652-7203. Web Site: www.highriverlibrary.ca. *Dir,* Deb Gardiner; E-mail: director@highriverlibrary.ca; *Asst Librn,* Cheryl Taylor-Smith
Founded 1939. Pop 12,000; Circ 155,555
Library Holdings: Bk Vols 50,000; Per Subs 110
Special Collections: Complementary & Alternative Medicine Coll; High River Times, micro; Local Alberta History Coll. Can & Prov
Wireless access
Mem of Marigold Library System
Partic in The Regional Automation Consortium (TRAC)
Special Services for the Blind - Visunet prog (Canada)
Open Mon-Fri 10-8, Sat 10-4
Friends of the Library Group

HINES CREEK

P HINES CREEK MUNICIPAL LIBRARY, 212-10 St, T0H 2A0. (Mail add: PO Box 750, T0H 2A0). Tel: 780-494-3879. FAX: 780-494-3605. E-mail: librarian@hinescreeklibrary.ab.ca. Web Site: www.hinescreeklibrary.ab.ca. *Chairperson,* Lorraine Brauer; *Librn,* Sharon Nezarko
Pop 396
Library Holdings: Bk Titles 8,500
Wireless access
Mem of Peace Library System
Open Tues 12-8, Wed & Thurs 10-6

HINTON

GL ALBERTA LAW LIBRARIES - HINTON*, Courthouse, 237 Jasper St, West & Pembina Ave, T7V 1X7. Tel: 780-865-8268. FAX: 780-865-8253. *Libr Coordr,* Judy Waymark; E-mail: judy.waymark@gov.ab.ca
Open Mon & Wed 8:30-Noon & 1-3:30

P HINTON MUNICIPAL LIBRARY*, 803 Switzer Dr, T7V 1V1. SAN 318-6903. Tel: 780-865-2363. Administration Tel: 780-865-6051. FAX: 780-865-4292. E-mail: hettwild@hintonlibrary.org. Web Site: www.hintonlibrary.org. *Chairperson,* Don Podlubny; *Librn,* Hetty Wilderdijk; E-mail: hettwild@hintonlibrary.org; Staff 2 (MLS 2)
Founded 1969. Pop 9,405; Circ 88,000
Library Holdings: Bk Titles 38,000; Per Subs 150
Special Collections: Can & Prov
Subject Interests: Local hist
Automation Activity & Vendor Info: (Circulation) SirsiDynix; (OPAC) SirsiDynix
Wireless access
Publications: History of Hinton
Mem of Yellowhead Regional Library
Open Mon-Thurs 10-8, Fri 10-5, Sat 10-3

HOLDEN

P HOLDEN MUNICIPAL LIBRARY*, 4912-50 St, T0B 2C0. (Mail add: Box 26, T0B 2C0). Tel: 780-688-3838. FAX: 780-688-3838. E-mail: librarian@holdenlibrary.ab.ca. Web Site: www.holdenlibrary.ab.ca. *Chairperson,* Julianne Foster; *Librn,* Annette Chrystian
Pop 374
Library Holdings: Bk Vols 2,000
Database Vendor: Overdrive, Inc
Wireless access
Mem of Northern Lights Library System
Partic in The Alberta Library; The Regional Automation Consortium (TRAC)
Open Mon (Summer) 12:30-5, Tues 10-6, Wed & Fri 9:30-5, Thurs 9:30-9, Sat 10-1; Tues (Winter) 10-6, Thurs 5-9, Sat 10-1

HUGHENDEN

P HUGHENDEN PUBLIC LIBRARY*, Seven McKenzie Ave, T0B 2E0. (Mail add: PO Box 36, T0B 2E0). Tel: 780-856-2435. FAX: 780-856-2435. E-mail: hughendenlibrary@libs.prl.ab.ca. Web Site: hughendenlibrary.prl.ab.ca. *Mgr,* Patricia Mackie
Library Holdings: Bk Vols 8,000
Automation Activity & Vendor Info: (OPAC) Horizon

Wireless access
Mem of Parkland Regional Library
Open Tues 11-6:30, Thurs 9-12:30 & 1:30-5, Sat 11-3

HUSSAR

P HUSSAR MUNICIPAL LIBRARY, Hussar School, T0J 1S0. (Mail add: General Delivery, T0J 1S0). Tel: 403-787-3781. FAX: 403-787-3922. E-mail: ahumlibrary@marigold.ab.ca. Web Site: www.marigold.ab.ca/content/member-library-directory. *Chairperson,* Tim Frank; Tel: 403-787-3781, Ext 4813; *Mgr,* Gay V Harms
Pop 245
Wireless access
Mem of Marigold Library System
Open Tues (Winter) 12-7:30, Thurs 12-4:30; Tues (Summer) 12-6:30, Thurs 12-4

HYTHE

P HYTHE PUBLIC LIBRARY*, PO Box 601, T0H 2C0. Tel: 780-356-3014. FAX: 780-356-2009. E-mail: staff@hythelibrary.ab.ca. Web Site: www.hythelibrary.ab.ca. *Librn,* Charlene McCoy
Founded 1984
Library Holdings: Bk Vols 15,000
Wireless access
Mem of Peace Library System
Open Tues & Fri 10-5, Wed 7-9, Thurs 10-5 & 7-9

INNISFAIL

P INNISFAIL PUBLIC LIBRARY*, 5300A 55th St Close, T4G 1R6. SAN 377-4740. Tel: 403-227-4407. FAX: 403-227-3122. E-mail: innisfail@libs.prl.ab.ca. Web Site: ipl.prl.ab.ca. *Chairperson,* Jack Zenert; *Librn,* Laurie Hodges-Humble
Pop 7,248
Library Holdings: Bk Titles 40,000; Bk Vols 52,000
Wireless access
Mem of Parkland Regional Library
Open Mon, Wed & Fri 9:30-5:30, Tues & Thurs 12-8, Sat 10-3
Friends of the Library Group

IRMA

P IRMA MUNICIPAL LIBRARY*, 5012 51st Ave, T0B 2H0. (Mail add: PO Box 340, T0B 2H0). Tel: 780-754-3746. FAX: 780-754-3802. *Chairperson,* Ruth Jamison; *Librn,* Leah Larson
Pop 444
Library Holdings: Bk Vols 11,000
Mem of Northern Lights Library System
Open Mon 7pm-9pm, Tues & Thurs 8:45-3:30, Wed 8:45-3:30 & 7-9

IRRICANA

P IRRICANA LIBRARY*, Curling Rink, West Side, 302-3 St, T0M 1B0. (Mail add: PO Box 299, T0M 1B0). Tel: 403-935-4818. FAX: 403-935-4818. E-mail: ailibrary@marigold.ab.ca. Web Site: www.irricanalibrary.ca. *Libr Mgr,* Elysse Reicheneder
Pop 1,162
Library Holdings: Bk Vols 12,000
Wireless access
Mem of Marigold Library System
Open Mon 4-8, Tues & Thurs 11-5, Wed 11-8, Sat 11-4
Friends of the Library Group

JARVIE

P JARVIE PUBLIC LIBRARY*, PO Box 119, T0G 1H0. Tel: 780-954-3935. FAX: 780-954-3885. E-mail: choule@phrd.ad.ca. *Librn,* Eileen Lea
Library Holdings: Bk Vols 9,000
Automation Activity & Vendor Info: (Acquisitions) SirsiDynix; (Cataloging) SirsiDynix; (Circulation) SirsiDynix; (Course Reserve) SirsiDynix; (ILL) SirsiDynix; (Media Booking) SirsiDynix; (OPAC) SirsiDynix; (Serials) SirsiDynix
Wireless access
Mem of Yellowhead Regional Library
Open Tues 4-8

JASPER

P JASPER MUNICIPAL LIBRARY*, 500 Robson St, T0E 1E0. Tel: 780-852-3652. FAX: 780-852-5841. E-mail: jasperlibrary@town.jasper.ab.ca. Web Site: jasperlibrary.ab.ca. *Librn,* Judy Krefting; Staff 4 (Non-MLS 4)
Founded 1942. Pop 5,200; Circ 43,000
Library Holdings: AV Mats 5,000; Bk Vols 18,000; Per Subs 60
Automation Activity & Vendor Info: (Acquisitions) Polaris Library Systems; (Cataloging) Polaris Library Systems; (Circulation) Polaris

Library Systems; (Course Reserve) Polaris Library Systems; (ILL) Polaris Library Systems; (Media Booking) Polaris Library Systems; (OPAC) Polaris Library Systems; (Serials) Polaris Library Systems
Wireless access
Function: ILL available
Mem of Yellowhead Regional Library
Open Mon-Thurs 10-8, Fri & Sat 10-5
Friends of the Library Group

KEG RIVER

P   KEG RIVER COMMUNITY LIBRARY*, NE 21-101-24-W5, T0H 2G0. (Mail add: PO Box 68, T0H 2G0), SAN 326-498X. Tel: 780-981-2090. *Librn,* Betty Hasenack; *Asst Librn,* Susan MacDougall
Founded 1967. Pop 100; Circ 1,000
Library Holdings: Audiobooks 177; CDs 31; DVDs 300; Large Print Bks 25; Bk Titles 14,000; Per Subs 17; Videos 1,000
Mem of Peace Library System

KILLAM

P   KILLAM MUNICIPAL LIBRARY, PO Box 329, T0B 2L0. Tel: 780-385-3032. E-mail: killamlibrary@prl.ab.ca. Web Site: killamlibrary.prl.ab.ca. *Libr Mgr,* Norm Savage; Staff 1 (Non-MLS 1)
Founded 1938. Pop 1,019
Library Holdings: DVDs 350; Large Print Bks 5; Bk Vols 5,853; Per Subs 14; Talking Bks 5
Automation Activity & Vendor Info: (Acquisitions) Horizon; (Cataloging) Horizon; (Circulation) Horizon; (Course Reserve) Horizon; (ILL) Horizon; (Media Booking) Horizon; (OPAC) Horizon; (Serials) Horizon
Database Vendor: SirsiDynix
Wireless access
Mem of Parkland Regional Library
Open Mon 10-8:30, Tues-Thurs 2:30-5:30
Friends of the Library Group

KINUSO

P   KINUSO MUNICIPAL LIBRARY*, PO Box 60, T0G 1K0. Tel: 780-775-3694. FAX: 780-775-3560. E-mail: librarian@kinusolibrary.ab.ca. Web Site: www.peacelibrarysystem.ab.ca/kinuso.html. *Chairperson,* Lorrie Shelp; *Libr Mgr,* Susan Moody
Pop 231
Library Holdings: Bk Titles 9,000
Wireless access
Mem of Peace Library System
Open Mon, Wed & Fri 8:45-3:15, Tues & Thurs 8:45-5:15

KITSCOTY

P   KITSCOTY PUBLIC LIBRARY, 4910 51 St, T0B 2P0. (Mail add: PO Box 39, T0B 2P0), SAN 326-6451. Tel: 780-846-2822. FAX: 780-846-2215. E-mail: librarian@kitscotypubliclibrary.ab.ca. *Chairperson - Pub Libr Board,* Ellen Frank; *Librn,* Colleen Tabish
Pop 810
Library Holdings: Bk Titles 12,000; Per Subs 20
Automation Activity & Vendor Info: (Cataloging) Polaris Library Systems; (Circulation) Polaris Library Systems
Wireless access
Mem of Northern Lights Library System
Open Mon, Tues, Thurs & Fri 1-4:30, Wed 1-8

LA CRETE

P   LA CRETE COMMUNITY LIBRARY*, 10001 99th Ave, T0H 2H0. (Mail add: PO Box 609, T0H 2H0), SAN 318-692X. Tel: 780-928-3166. FAX: 780-928-3166. *Librn,* Helen Wiebe; E-mail: helenw@fvsd.ab.ca; Staff 1 (Non-MLS 1)
Pop 9,000
Library Holdings: Bk Titles 25,000; Per Subs 40
Subject Interests: Christian fiction, Quilting
Automation Activity & Vendor Info: (Cataloging) Insignia Software; (Circulation) Insignia Software
Open Mon & Fri 8:30-4, Tues-Thurs 8:30am-9pm, Sat 12-4
Bookmobiles: 1

LA GLACE

P   LA GLACE COMMUNITY LIBRARY, 9924 97 Ave, T0H 2J0. (Mail add: PO Box 209, T0H 2J0). Tel: 780-568-4696. FAX: 780-568-4707. E-mail: librarian@laglacelibrary.ab.ca. *Libr Mgr,* Evelyn Siebert
Library Holdings: Bk Vols 15,000; Bk Vols 15,000
Automation Activity & Vendor Info: (Acquisitions) Polaris Library Systems; (Cataloging) Polaris Library Systems; (Circulation) Polaris

Library Systems; (ILL) Polaris Library Systems; (Serials) Polaris Library Systems
Database Vendor: EBSCO Auto Repair Reference, EBSCOhost
Wireless access
Mem of Peace Library System
Partic in The Regional Automation Consortium (TRAC)
Open Mon, Wed & Thurs 1-5, Tues 1-5 & 7-9, Sat 10-12
Friends of the Library Group

LAC LA BICHE

P   LAC LA BICHE COUNTY LIBRARY BOARD, Stuart MacPherson Public Library, 8702 91st Ave, T0A 2C0. (Mail add: Box 2039, T0A 2C0), SAN 325-2914. Tel: 780-623-7467. FAX: 780-623-7497. E-mail: headlibrarian@stuartmacphersonlibrary.ca. *Dir, Libr Serv,* Maureen Penn; Staff 7 (MLS 1, Non-MLS 6)
Founded 1946. Pop 9,123; Circ 45,604
Library Holdings: DVDs 1,308; Bk Vols 42,507; Per Subs 192; Talking Bks 550
Automation Activity & Vendor Info: (Acquisitions) Polaris Library Systems; (Cataloging) Polaris Library Systems; (Circulation) Polaris Library Systems; (ILL) Polaris Library Systems; (Media Booking) Polaris Library Systems; (OPAC) Polaris Library Systems; (Serials) Polaris Library Systems
Database Vendor: EBSCOhost
Wireless access
Mem of Northern Lights Library System
Partic in The Regional Automation Consortium (TRAC)
Open Mon-Thurs 10-8, Fri 10-6, Sat (Winter) 10-4
Friends of the Library Group
Branches: 1
PLAMONDON MUNICIPAL LIBRARY, Ecole Plamondon, Plamondon, T0A 2T0. (Mail add: Box 630, Plamondon, T0A 2T0). Tel: 780-798-3852. E-mail: headlibrarian@stuartmacphersonlibrary.ca. *Dir, Libr Serv,* Maureen Penn; Tel: 780-623-7467; *Sch Librn,* Pam Lien
Founded 1959
Subject Interests: Local hist
Open Mon, Tues, Thurs & Fri 8:30-4, Wed 8:30-8
Friends of the Library Group

C   PORTAGE COLLEGE LIBRARY*, 9531 94th Ave, T0A 2C0. (Mail add: PO Box 417, T0A 2C0). Tel: 780-623-5650. Interlibrary Loan Service Tel: 780-623-5755. Toll Free Tel: 866-623-5551. FAX: 780-623-5656. E-mail: library@portagecollege.ca. Web Site: www.portagecollege.ca. *Pub Serv Librn,* Terry Donovan; E-mail: terry.donovan@portagecollege.ca; Staff 4 (MLS 1, Non-MLS 3)
Founded 1977. Enrl 990; Fac 87
Library Holdings: AV Mats 3,207; e-books 979; Bk Vols 15,341; Per Subs 73
Subject Interests: Col educ, College
Automation Activity & Vendor Info: (Cataloging) SirsiDynix; (Circulation) SirsiDynix; (OPAC) SirsiDynix
Database Vendor: CredoReference, EBSCOhost, Gale Cengage Learning, Oxford Online, ProQuest, Wilson - Wilson Web
Wireless access
Function: Computers for patron use, Copy machines, Electronic databases & coll, Handicapped accessible, ILL available, Instruction & testing, Orientations, Ref serv available, Scanner, VHS videos, Wheelchair accessible
Partic in The Alberta Library
Open Mon-Thurs 8am-9pm, Fri 8-4:30, Sat 1-4, Sun 1-7
Restriction: Open to pub for ref & circ; with some limitations

LACOMBE

S   CANADIAN AGRICULTURE LIBRARY*, Lacombe Research Centre, 6000 C&E Trail, T4L 1W1. SAN 327-9367. Tel: 403-782-8136. FAX: 403-782-6120. *Librn,* Kathryn Moore; Staff 1 (MLS 1)
Library Holdings: Bk Vols 1,000; Per Subs 6
Special Collections: Historical Photographs
Partic in Council of Federal Libraries Consortium
Open Tues-Thurs 9-5

CR   CANADIAN UNIVERSITY COLLEGE LIBRARY*, 5410 Ramona Ave, T4L 2B7. SAN 318-6334. Tel: 403-782-3381, Ext 4101. Reference Tel: 403-782-3381, Ext 4102. FAX: 403-782-3977. E-mail: library@cauc.ca. Web Site: www.neoslibraries.ca. *Ref & Circ Librn,* Sheila Clark; E-mail: sclark@cauc.ca; *Asst Librn,* Carol Nicks; Tel: 403-782-3381, Ext 4105, E-mail: cnicks@cauc.ca; Staff 5 (MLS 2, Non-MLS 3)
Founded 1907. Enrl 500; Fac 37; Highest Degree: Bachelor
May 2005-Apr 2006 Income (CAN) $324,430, Locally Generated Income (CAN) $13,824, Parent Institution (CAN) $310,606. Mats Exp (CAN) $119,475, Books (CAN) $72,855, Per/Ser (Incl. Access Fees) (CAN) $27,433, Electronic Ref Mat (Incl. Access Fees) (CAN) $19,187. Sal (CAN) $187,034 (Prof (CAN) $156,327)

Library Holdings: AV Mats 2,406; e-books 1,000; e-journals 9,759; Bk Vols 68,705; Per Subs 200
Special Collections: Seventh-day Adventist Church in Canada
Subject Interests: Liberal arts
Automation Activity & Vendor Info: (Acquisitions) SirsiDynix; (Cataloging) SirsiDynix; (Circulation) SirsiDynix; (Course Reserve) SirsiDynix; (ILL) SirsiDynix; (OPAC) SirsiDynix; (Serials) SirsiDynix
Database Vendor: Baker & Taylor, EBSCOhost, Gale Cengage Learning, OCLC FirstSearch, ProQuest, SirsiDynix
Wireless access
Publications: Framework of Learning Resources (1988)
Partic in NEOS Library Consortium
Open Mon-Thurs 8am-10:30pm, Fri 8-3, Sun 1-10

P   LACOMBE PUBLIC LIBRARY*, Mary C Moore Public Library, 101-5214 50 Ave, T4L 0B6. Tel: 403-782-3433. FAX: 403-782-3329. E-mail: mcmpl@libs.prl.ab.ca. Web Site: www.lacombelibrary.org. *Head Librn,* Christina Petrisor; E-mail: christinap@libs.prl.ab.ca; Staff 4.5 (MLS 1, Non-MLS 3.5)
Founded 1931. Pop 11,733; Circ 129,273
Library Holdings: Bk Vols 25,000; Per Subs 65
Automation Activity & Vendor Info: (Acquisitions) Horizon; (Cataloging) Horizon; (Circulation) Horizon; (ILL) Horizon; (Media Booking) Horizon; (OPAC) Horizon; (Serials) Horizon
Database Vendor: SirsiDynix
Wireless access
Function: Bks on CD
Mem of Parkland Regional Library
Open Mon, Wed, Fri & Sat 10-5, Tues & Thurs 10-8:30
Friends of the Library Group

P   PARKLAND REGIONAL LIBRARY*, 5404 56th Ave, T4L 1G1. SAN 318-6946. Tel: 403-782-3850. FAX: 403-782-4650. Web Site: www.prl.ab.ca. *Dir,* Ronald Sheppard; *Librn,* Susan Grieshaber-Otto; *Tech Serv,* Marquita Bevans; Staff 5 (MLS 5)
Founded 1959
Special Collections: Can
Database Vendor: SirsiDynix
Publications: Annual Report
Member Libraries: Alix Public Library; Alliance Public Library; Amisk Public Library; Bashaw Public Library; Bawlf Public Library; Bentley Municipal Library; Big Valley Municipal Library; Blackfalds Public Library; Bodo Public Library; Bowden Public Library; Brownfield Public Library; Camrose Public Library; Caroline Municipal Library; Carstairs Public Library; Castor Municipal Library; Clive Public Library; Coronation Memorial Library; Cremona Municipal Library; Czar Municipal Library; Daysland Public Library; Delburne Municipal Library; Didsbury Municipal Library; Donalda Public Library; Eckville Municipal Library; Edberg Municipal Library; Elnora Public Library; Forestburg Municipal Library; Galahad Public Library; Hardisty & District Public Library; Hay Lakes Municipal Library; Heisler Municipal Library; Hughenden Public Library; Innisfail Public Library; Killam Municipal Library; Lacombe Public Library; Lougheed Public Library; Nordegg Public Library; Olds & District Municipal Library; Penhold & District Public Library; Ponoka Public Library; Provost Municipal Library; Rimbey Municipal Library; Rocky Mountain House Public Library; Sedgewick Municipal Library; Spruce View Public Library; Stettler Public Library; Sundre Municipal Library; Sylvan Lake Municipal Library; Water Valley Public Library

LAMONT

P   LAMONT PUBLIC LIBRARY*, 4811 50 Ave, T0B 2R0. (Mail add: PO Box 180, T0B 2R0), SAN 318-6954. Tel: 780-895-2299. FAX: 780-895-2600. E-mail: lamontpublib@hotmail.com. *Chairperson,* Pat Purschke; *Librn,* Rose Konsorada; Staff 1 (Non-MLS 1)
Founded 1955. Pop 1,800; Circ 5,000
Library Holdings: Bk Titles 16,000
Wireless access
Open Mon, Wed & Fri 8:30-3:30, Tues & Thurs 8:30-3:30 & 6-9, Sat 10-1

LEDUC

GL   ALBERTA LAW LIBRARIES - LEDUC*, Courthouse, 4612-50th St, T9E 6L1. Tel: 780-980-7592. FAX: 780-986-0345. *Libr Coordr,* Judy Rembish; E-mail: judy.rembish@gov.ab.ca; Staff 1 (Non-MLS 1)
Open Thurs 8-4:30

P   LEDUC PUBLIC LIBRARY*, Two Alexandra Park, T9E 4C4. SAN 318-6962. Tel: 780-986-2637. Administration Tel: 780-986-2638. FAX: 780-986-3462. Web Site: www.leduclibrary.ca. *Libr Dir,* Carla Frybort; *Pub Serv Coordr,* Sharon McAmmond; *Adult Prog & Serv,* Holly Lovatt; Staff 15 (MLS 2, Non-MLS 13)
Pop 24,000; Circ 140,000
Jan 2012-Dec 2012 Income (CAN) $904,025, Provincial (CAN) $67,053, City (CAN) $802,140, County (CAN) $9,838, Locally Generated Income

(CAN) $18,718, Other (CAN) $6,276. Mats Exp (CAN) $136,539, Books (CAN) $112,239, Per/Ser (Incl. Access Fees) (CAN) $5,000, AV Mat (CAN) $18,400, Electronic Ref Mat (Incl. Access Fees) (CAN) $900. Sal (CAN) $524,921
Library Holdings: AV Mats 1,093; CDs 2,211; DVDs 670; Electronic Media & Resources 43; Large Print Bks 776; Bk Vols 47,852; Per Subs 102; Videos 1,233
Special Collections: Local Newspaper 1907-1988, microfilm
Automation Activity & Vendor Info: (Cataloging) Polaris Library Systems
Database Vendor: EBSCO Information Services
Wireless access
Function: Adult bk club, Adult literacy prog, After school storytime, Art exhibits, Audio & video playback equip for onsite use, AV serv, Bk club(s), Bks on CD, Computer training, Copy machines, Digital talking bks, e-mail serv, Electronic databases & coll, Family literacy, Fax serv, Handicapped accessible, ILL available, Large print keyboards, Monthly prog for perceptually impaired adults, Music CDs, Online cat, Outside serv via phone, mail, e-mail & web, Photocopying/Printing, Preschool outreach, Prog for adults, Prog for children & young adult, Ref serv available, Scanner, Senior computer classes, Spoken cassettes & DVDs, Summer reading prog, Telephone ref, VHS videos, Wheelchair accessible, Workshops
Mem of Yellowhead Regional Library
Open Mon-Thurs 10-9, Fri & Sat 10-5, Sun (Winter) 12-4
Friends of the Library Group

LETHBRIDGE

G   AGRICULTURE & AGRI-FOOD CANADA, Canadian Agriculture Library-Lethbridge, 5403 First Ave S, T1J 4B1. (Mail add: PO Box 3000, T1J 4B1), SAN 318-6970. Tel: 403-317-3392. FAX: 403-382-3156. *Head, Info Ctr,* Karen Mah; Tel: 403-327-4561; Staff 1.7 (MLS 1, Non-MLS 0.7)
Founded 1950
Special Collections: Archives (Research Station Historical Material); Publications Reprints, 1906-present; Research Station Slides; Resident Scientists' Reprints
Subject Interests: Agr, Animal nutrition, Climate, Livestock, Plant sci, Soil sci
Database Vendor: OVID Technologies
Function: Res libr
Partic in Can Agr Libr Network; Council of Federal Libraries Consortium
Open Mon-Fri 8:30-12 & 1-4

GL   ALBERTA LAW LIBRARIES*, Court House, 320 Fourth St S, T1J 1Z8. SAN 320-7757. Tel: 403-381-5639. FAX: 403-381-5703. Web Site: www.lawlibrary.ab.ca. *Coordr,* Grant Janzen
Library Holdings: Bk Titles 16,000
Open Mon-Fri 8:15-4:30

J   LETHBRIDGE COLLEGE*, Buchanan Library, 3000 College Dr S, T1K 1L6. SAN 318-6989. Tel: 403-320-3352. Interlibrary Loan Service Tel: 403-320-3352. E-mail: buchanan.library@lethbridgecollege.ca. Web Site: www.lethbridgecollege.ca. *Mgr,* Fiona Dyer; E-mail: dyer.fiona@lethbridgecollege.ca; *Circ,* Anneliese Klassen; *Info Serv,* Corene Kozey; Staff 2 (MLS 2)
Founded 1967
Library Holdings: Bk Vols 65,000; Per Subs 200
Special Collections: Buchanan Art Coll
Subject Interests: Criminal justice, Environ studies, Nursing
Automation Activity & Vendor Info: (Acquisitions) Ex Libris Group; (Cataloging) Ex Libris Group; (Circulation) Ex Libris Group; (Course Reserve) Ex Libris Group; (Media Booking) Ex Libris Group; (OPAC) Ex Libris Group; (Serials) Ex Libris Group
Database Vendor: EBSCOhost, Gale Cengage Learning, ProQuest
Wireless access
Publications: Buchanan Resource Center Pathfinders; Canadian Perspectives; Library Guide; Library of Congress Classification System Brochure; Student Library Handbook
Open Mon-Thurs 7:30am-10pm

P   LETHBRIDGE PUBLIC LIBRARY*, 810 Fifth Ave S, T1J 4C4. SAN 318-6997. Tel: 403-380-7310. FAX: 403-329-1478. E-mail: questions@lethlib.ca. Web Site: www.lethlib.ca. *Dir,* Todd Gnissios; Tel: 403-380-7340, E-mail: todd.gnissios@lethlib.ca; *Assoc Dir, Pub Serv,* Elisabeth Hegerat; Tel: 403-320-4187, E-mail: elisabeth.hegerat@lethlib.ca; *Coord, Ad Serv,* Pat Schieman; Tel: 403-380-7325, E-mail: pat.schieman@lethlib.ca; *Customer Serv Coordr,* Natalie Pavlis; Tel: 403-380-7343, E-mail: natalie.pavlis@lethlib.ca; *Coordr, Youth Serv,* Barbara Ramp; Tel: 403-380-7312, E-mail: barbara.ramp@lethlib.ca; Staff 13 (MLS 10, Non-MLS 3)
Founded 1919. Pop 87,882; Circ 675,050
Special Collections: Southern Alberta History (Senator Buchanan Coll). Can & Prov
Wireless access

Function: Art exhibits, Audiobks via web, Bk club(s), Bks on CD, Computers for patron use, Copy machines, Electronic databases & coll, Home delivery & serv to Sr ctr & nursing homes, Homebound delivery serv, ILL available, Magnifiers for reading, Mus passes, Music CDs, Online cat, OverDrive digital audio bks, Prog for adults, Prog for children & young adult, Pub access computers, Ref serv available, Story hour, Summer reading prog, Telephone ref
Publications: Annual Report; Happening (brochure)
Partic in Chinook Arch Regional Libr Syst
Open Mon-Fri 9:30-9, Sat 9:30-5:30, Sun 1:30-5:30
Friends of the Library Group
Bookmobiles: 1

S   SIR ALEXANDER GALT MUSEUM & ARCHIVES*, West End of Fifth Ave S, T1J 0P6. (Mail add: 910 - 4 Ave S, T1J 0P6), SAN 327-442X. Tel: 403-329-7302. FAX: 403-329-4958. E-mail: archives@galtmuseum.com. Web Site: www.galtmuseum.com. *Archivist,* Andrew Chernevych; E-mail: andrew.chernevych@galtmuseum.com; *Asst Archivist,* Trish Purkis
Library Holdings: Bk Titles 575; Bk Vols 800
Special Collections: Lethbridge News 1901-1906 & Lethbridge Herald 1905-1918: A Subject & Biographical Index (1987)
Open Mon-Fri 10-4:30
Friends of the Library Group

S   SOUTHERN ALBERTA ART GALLERY LIBRARY*, Turcotte Library, 601 Third Ave S, T1J 0H4. SAN 321-6225. Tel: 403-327-8770. FAX: 403-328-3913. E-mail: info@saag.ca. Web Site: saag.ca. *Operations Dir,* Marilyn Smith; *Librn,* Elspeth Nickle; *Librn,* Glenna Westwood; *Curator,* Ryan Doherty
Founded 1975
Library Holdings: Bk Titles 6,000; Per Subs 17
Special Collections: Artists' Films, Videos & Slides
Wireless access
Open Tues-Sat 10-5, Sun 1-5

C   UNIVERSITY OF LETHBRIDGE LIBRARY*, 4401 University Dr, T1K 3M4. SAN 318-7004. Tel: 403-329-2261, 403-329-2263. FAX: 403-329-2234. Web Site: www.uleth.ca/lib. *Assoc Univ Librn, Client Serv & Fac,* Brenda Mathenia; *Assoc Univ Librn, Info Syst & Tech Serv,* Wendy Merkley; Staff 47 (MLS 14, Non-MLS 33)
Founded 1967. Enrl 8,380; Fac 483; Highest Degree: Doctorate
Library Holdings: Bk Vols 533,154; Per Subs 1,296
Special Collections: Can; Canadiana (Woodworth Coll); University Archives
Subject Interests: Educ, Fine arts, Humanities, Native Am studies, Nursing
Automation Activity & Vendor Info: (Acquisitions) Innovative Interfaces, Inc; (Cataloging) Innovative Interfaces, Inc; (Circulation) Innovative Interfaces, Inc; (Course Reserve) Innovative Interfaces, Inc; (ILL) Relais International; (Media Booking) Innovative Interfaces, Inc; (OPAC) Innovative Interfaces, Inc; (Serials) Innovative Interfaces, Inc
Database Vendor: EBSCOhost, Gale Cengage Learning, JSTOR, ProQuest
Open Mon-Thurs (Winter) 8am-11pm, Fri 8-6, Sat 10-6, Sun 1-9; Mon-Thurs (Summer) 8-8, Fri 8-4:30

LINDEN

P   LINDEN MUNICIPAL LIBRARY*, 215-One St SE, T0M 1J0. (Mail add: PO Box 120, T0M 1J0). Tel: 403-546-3757. FAX: 403-546-4220. E-mail: almlibrary@marigold.ab.ca. Web Site: www.marigold.ab.ca.about/memberlibs/linden.html. *Managing Dir,* Debbie Martin; Staff 1.8 (Non-MLS 1.8)
Pop 741
Library Holdings: Bk Vols 8,900
Database Vendor: Polaris Library Systems
Mem of Marigold Library System
Open Tues & Thurs 4-9, Wed 11-9

LLOYDMINSTER

P   LLOYDMINSTER PUBLIC LIBRARY, 5010 49th St, T9V 0K2. SAN 319-9509. Tel: 780-875-0850. Reference Tel: 780-875-0877. FAX: 780-875-6523. E-mail: info@lloydminster.info. Interlibrary Loan Service E-mail: ill@lloydminster.info. Web Site: www.lloydminster.info. *Chairperson,* Tony Knowler; *Dir,* Ronald J Gillies; E-mail: hlib@lloydminster.info; *Coll Mgt, Outreach Serv Librn,* Sherlane Phillips; E-mail: sphillips@lloydminster.info; *Ref Serv,* Michele Duczek; E-mail: mduczek@lloydminster.info; Staff 11 (MLS 2, Non-MLS 9)
Pop 27,804; Circ 160,000
Jan 2011-Dec 2011 Income (CAN) $1,026,103, Provincial (CAN) $94,734, City (CAN) $736,020, County (CAN) $1,500, Locally Generated Income (CAN) $25,000, Other (CAN) $167,847. Mats Exp (CAN) $123,000, Books (CAN) $99,000, Per/Ser (Incl. Access Fees) (CAN) $12,000, AV Mat (CAN) $12,000. Sal (CAN) $488,029

Library Holdings: Large Print Bks 2,200; Bk Titles 72,156; Bk Vols 79,155; Per Subs 186; Talking Bks 966; Videos 1,927
Subject Interests: Local hist
Automation Activity & Vendor Info: (Cataloging) Mandarin Library Automation; (Circulation) Mandarin Library Automation; (ILL) Innovative Interfaces, Inc - Millenium; (OPAC) Mandarin Library Automation; (Serials) Mandarin Library Automation
Database Vendor: EBSCOhost, Gale Cengage Learning
Wireless access
Function: Handicapped accessible, Home delivery & serv to Sr ctr & nursing homes, Homebound delivery serv, ILL available, Magnifiers for reading, Prog for children & young adult, Ref serv available, Summer reading prog, Telephone ref
Mem of Lakeland Library Region
Open Mon-Thurs 10-9, Fri 10-6, Sat 10-5
Friends of the Library Group

LOMOND

P   LOMOND MUNICIPAL LIBRARY*, Two Railway Ave N, T0L 1G0. (Mail add: PO Box 290, T0L 1G0). Tel: 403-792-3934. FAX: 403-792-3934. E-mail: liblom@chinookarch.ab.ca. Web Site: lomondlibrary.ca. *Chairperson,* Robert Donnelly; *Librn,* Kate Koch; Staff 1 (Non-MLS 1)
Pop 171
Library Holdings: Bk Vols 11,534
Wireless access
Special Services for the Blind - Bks on cassette
Open Mon 5-8, Tues & Thurs 10-5, Wed 10-2
Friends of the Library Group

LONGVIEW

P   LONGVIEW MUNICIPAL LIBRARY*, 128 Morrison Pl, T0L 1H0. (Mail add: PO Box 189, T0L 1H0). Tel: 403-558-3927. FAX: 403-558-3927. E-mail: alomlibrary@marigold.ab.ca. *Libr Mgr,* Joan Maxwell
Pop 307
Library Holdings: Bk Titles 6,000
Wireless access
Mem of Marigold Library System
Open Tues & Thurs 10-5, Wed 12-7

LOUGHEED

P   LOUGHEED PUBLIC LIBRARY*, 5004 50 St, T0B 2V0. Tel: 780-386-2498. FAX: 780-386-2136. E-mail: lougheedlibrary@libs.prl.ab.ca. Web Site: lougheed.prl.ab.ca. *Librn,* Barb McConnell
Pop 400
Library Holdings: Audiobooks 10; AV Mats 300; CDs 25; Large Print Bks 50; Bk Titles 8,500; Talking Bks 105; Videos 120
Wireless access
Mem of Parkland Regional Library
Open Mon, Wed, & Thurs 12-5
Friends of the Library Group

MAGRATH

P   MAGRATH PUBLIC LIBRARY, Six N First St W, T0K 1J0. (Mail add: Box 295, T0K 1J0), SAN 318-7012. Tel: 403-758-6498. FAX: 403-758-6442. E-mail: help@mcgrathlibrary.ca. *Coord Librn, Fac/Staff/Circ/Mat Handling & Libr Mgt,* Ann Pilling; *Head Librn,* Charlotte Lester
Founded 1937. Pop 2,081; Circ 32,173
Library Holdings: Bk Vols 31,521
Wireless access
Open Mon 5pm-8pm, Tues 1:30-8, Wed 12-8, Thurs 1:30-6, Fri 1-5
Friends of the Library Group

MALLAIG

P   BIBLIOTHEQUE MALLAIG LIBRARY, Mallaig Public Library, 3110 First St E, T0A 2K0. (Mail add: PO Box 90, T0A 2K0). Tel: 780-635-3858. FAX: 780-635-3938. E-mail: mcs@sperd.net. Web Site: www.mallaiglibrary.ab.ca. *Librn,* Louise Jodoin; Staff 1.13 (Non-MLS 1.13)
Library Holdings: Bk Vols 15,000
Wireless access
Mem of Northern Lights Library System
Open Mon-Wed 8:30-7, Thurs & Fri 8:30-4

MA-ME-O BEACH

P   PIGEON LAKE PUBLIC LIBRARY*, 603-2 Second Ave, T0C 1X0. SAN 325-2272. Tel: 780-586-3778. Toll Free FAX: 888-452-0989. E-mail: pigeonlakelibrary@yrl.ab.ca. Web Site: www.pigeonlakepubliclibrary.ab.ca. *Librn,* Opal Taylor; Staff 1 (Non-MLS 1)

Founded 1967. Pop 800; Circ 3,219
Library Holdings: Bk Titles 9,700; Videos 250
Mem of Yellowhead Regional Library
Open Mon & Wed 11-7, Thurs 11-4

MANNING

P   MANNING MUNICIPAL & DISTRICT LIBRARY*, 311 Fourth Ave SE,
T0H 2M0. (Mail add: PO Box 810, T0H 2M0). Tel: 780-836-3054. E-mail:
librarian@manninglibrary.ab.ca. Web Site: manninglibrary.ab.ca. *Head
Librn,* Lori Jackson
Library Holdings: Bk Vols 10,000
Wireless access
Mem of Peace Library System
Special Services for the Deaf - Adult & family literacy prog; Bks on
deafness & sign lang; High interest/low vocabulary bks
Special Services for the Blind - Audio mat; Bks available with recordings;
Bks on CD; Copier with enlargement capabilities; Large print bks
Open Tues-Thurs 11-7, Fri & Sat 11-5:30
Friends of the Library Group
Bookmobiles: 1. Diane Hyslop

MANNVILLE

P   MANNVILLE CENTENIAL PUBLIC LIBRARY*, PO Box 186, T0B
2W0. SAN 318-7020. Tel: 780-763-3611. FAX: 780-763-3688. E-mail:
librarian@mannvillelibrary.ab.ca. Web Site: www.mannvillelibrary.ab.ca/.
Librn, Theresa Myroniuk; *Libr Mgr,* Clara Grouwstra
Pop 722; Circ 10,000
Library Holdings: Large Print Bks 200; Bk Titles 10,000; Per Subs 15
Subject Interests: Local hist
Automation Activity & Vendor Info: (Cataloging) SirsiDynix;
(Circulation) SirsiDynix; (ILL) SirsiDynix
Database Vendor: SirsiDynix
Wireless access
Mem of Northern Lights Library System
Open Tues & Fri 10-5, Thurs 11-6
Friends of the Library Group

MARWAYNE

P   MARWAYNE PUBLIC LIBRARY*, PO Box 174, T0B 2X0. Tel:
780-847-3930. FAX: 780-847-3796. E-mail:
librarian@marwaynelibrary.ab.ca. Web Site: www.marwaynelibrary.ab.ca.
Libr Mgr, Carmen Smart
Pop 830
Library Holdings: Bk Vols 15,000; Per Subs 30
Wireless access
Mem of Northern Lights Library System
Open Mon-Fri 9-3:30, Sat 10-3

MAYERTHORPE

P   MAYERTHORPE PUBLIC LIBRARY*, 4911 52nd St, T0E 1N0. (Mail
add: PO Box 810, T0E 1N0), SAN 318-7039. Tel: 780-786-2404. FAX:
780-786-4590. E-mail: mayerthorpepl@yahoo.ca. *Librn,* Gloria Wilson;
Asst Librn, Ruth Anderson
Founded 1972. Pop 3,000; Circ 10,000
Library Holdings: Bk Vols 10,000
Wireless access
Mem of Yellowhead Regional Library
Open Mon, Thurs & Fri 10-5, Tues 2-7, Wed 10-7
Friends of the Library Group

MCLENNAN

P   MCLENNAN MUNICIPAL LIBRARY*, 019 First Ave NW, T0H 2L0.
(Mail add: Box 298, T0H 2L0). Tel: 780-324-3767. FAX: 780-324-2288.
E-mail: librarian@mclennanlibrary.ab.ca. Web Site: mclennanlibrary.ab.ca.
Pop 900
Library Holdings: Audiobooks 63; DVDs 13; Bk Titles 11,342; Per Subs
12
Automation Activity & Vendor Info: (Acquisitions) Polaris Library
Systems; (Cataloging) Polaris Library Systems; (Circulation) Polaris
Library Systems; (ILL) Polaris Library Systems
Wireless access
Mem of Peace Library System
Open Mon 1-5, Tues & Thurs 10-12 & 1-5:30, Wed & Fri 1-5:30,

MEDICINE HAT

C   MEDICINE HAT COLLEGE LIBRARY, Vera Braken Library, 299 College
Dr SE, T1A 3Y6. SAN 318-7047. Tel: 403-529-3867. FAX: 403-504-3634.
Web Site: www.mhc.ab.ca/library. *Dir of Libr Serv,* Keith Walker; Tel:
403-504-3539, E-mail: kwalker@mhc.ab.ca; *Coll & Instruction Librn,*
Leigh Cunningham; E-mail: lcunningham@mhc.ab.ca; *Info & Tech Librn,*

Lilian Li; Tel: 403-529-3869, E-mail: lli@mbc.ab.ca; Staff 20 (MLS 3,
Non-MLS 17)
Founded 1965. Enrl 3,000; Fac 170; Highest Degree: Bachelor
Library Holdings: AV Mats 9,000; e-books 85,000; Music Scores 4,000;
Bk Vols 95,000; Per Subs 550
Automation Activity & Vendor Info: (Acquisitions) Innovative Interfaces,
Inc; (Cataloging) Innovative Interfaces, Inc; (Circulation) Innovative
Interfaces, Inc; (Course Reserve) Innovative Interfaces, Inc; (ILL) Relais
International; (Media Booking) Innovative Interfaces, Inc; (OPAC)
Innovative Interfaces, Inc; (Serials) Innovative Interfaces, Inc
Database Vendor: 3M Library Systems, Agricola, ARTstor, Bowker,
CEDROM-SNi, CredoReference, Discovery Education, EBSCOhost,
Elsevier, Gale Cengage Learning, H W Wilson, Innovative Interfaces, Inc,
McGraw-Hill, Modern Language Association, OCLC WorldCat, Project
MUSE, ProQuest, Thomson Carswell, World Book Online
Wireless access
Partic in The Alberta Library
Open Mon-Thurs 7:30am-10pm, Fri 7:30-6, Sat 10-6, Sun 1-8

P   MEDICINE HAT PUBLIC LIBRARY*, 414 First St SE, T1A 0A8. SAN
318-7055. Tel: 403-502-8527. Circulation Tel: 403-502-8525. Reference
Tel: 403-502-8538. FAX: 403-502-8529. E-mail: library@medicinehat.ca.
Web Site: www.mhpl.info. *Chief Librn,* Shelley Ross; Tel: 403-502-8528,
E-mail: shelleyr@shortgrass.ca; *Head, Adult Serv,* Hilary Munro; E-mail:
hilarym@shortgrass.ca; *Head, Ch,* Carol Ann Cross-Roen; E-mail:
carolann@shortgrass.ca; *Head, Ref Serv,* Sheila Drummond; E-mail:
sheilad@shortgrass.ca; *Circ Mgr,* Annette Ziegler; E-mail:
annettez@shortgrass.ca; Staff 42 (MLS 4, Non-MLS 38)
Founded 1915. Pop 61,097; Circ 523,538
Library Holdings: Bk Titles 143,826; Per Subs 324
Special Collections: Can
Database Vendor: SirsiDynix
Wireless access
Publications: Library Connection
Mem of Shortgrass Libr Syst
Partic in The Alberta Library
Open Mon-Thurs 10-9, Fri & Sat 10-5:30, Sun 1-5:30
Friends of the Library Group

MILK RIVER

P   MILK RIVER MUNICIPAL LIBRARY*, PO Box 579, T0K 1M0. Tel:
403-647-3793. E-mail: mkrlib@chinookarch.ab.ca. *Libr Mgr,* Kathleen
Irving
Pop 568
Library Holdings: Bk Vols 10,000; Videos 900
Open Wed-Fri 11-6

MILLET

P   MILLET PUBLIC LIBRARY*, 5031 49th Ave, T0C 1Z0. (Mail add: PO
Box 30, T0C 1Z0). Tel: 780-387-5222. E-mail: millet@yrl.ab.ca. *Libr Mgr,*
Margaret Blackstock
Pop 2,125
Library Holdings: Bk Vols 14,207
Mem of Yellowhead Regional Library
Open Tues-Thurs 10-8, Fri & Sat 12-5

MILO

P   MILO MUNICIPAL LIBRARY, 116 Center St, T0L 1L0. (Mail add: PO
Box 30, T0L 1L0). Tel: 403-599-3850. FAX: 403-599-3850. E-mail:
libmil@milolibrary.ca. Web Site: www.milolibrary.ca. *Librn,* Joanne
Monner
Pop 115
Library Holdings: Audiobooks 205; Bks on Deafness & Sign Lang 15;
CDs 40; DVDs 1,000; Large Print Bks 200; Music Scores 75; Bk Vols
13,568; Per Subs 18
Wireless access
Open Tues 10-5 & 7-9, Thurs & Fri 10-5
Friends of the Library Group

MORINVILLE

P   MORINVILLE PUBLIC LIBRARY, 10119 100th Ave, T8R 1P8. SAN
325-1586. Tel: 780-939-3292. FAX: 780-939-2757. E-mail:
info@morinvillelibrary.ca. Web Site: www.morinvillelibrary.ca. *Libr Mgr,*
Isabelle Cramp
Pop 6,540; Circ 66,525
Library Holdings: Bk Vols 30,000
Wireless access
Mem of Northern Lights Library System
Open Mon-Thurs 10-8, Fri 12-6, Sat 10-2
Friends of the Library Group

MORRIN

P   MORRIN MUNICIPAL LIBRARY*, 113 Main St, T0J 2B0. (Mail add: PO Box 284, T0J 2B0). Tel: 403-772-3922. FAX: 403-772-3922. E-mail: amomlibrary@marigold.ab.ca. Web Site: www.marigold.ab.ca.about/memberlibs/morrin.html. *Librn*, Carla Mieller; Staff 0.7 (Non-MLS 0.7)
Founded 1983. Pop 500
Automation Activity & Vendor Info: (Cataloging) Polaris Library Systems; (Circulation) Polaris Library Systems; (ILL) Polaris Library Systems; (OPAC) Polaris Library Systems
Database Vendor: Polaris Library Systems
Wireless access
Mem of Marigold Library System
Open Tues-Thurs 12-6
Friends of the Library Group

MUNDARE

P   MUNDARE MUNICIPAL LIBRARY*, 5128 50th St, T0B 3H0. (Mail add: PO Box 3, T0B 3H0). Tel: 780-764-3929. FAX: 780-764-2003. *Librn*, Miranda Peyton
Pop 715
Library Holdings: Bk Vols 6,000
Mem of Northern Lights Library System
Open Mon & Wed 1-7, Thurs 10-5

MYRNAM

P   MYRNAM COMMUNITY LIBRARY*, New Myrnam School, 5105-50 St, T0B 3K0. Tel: 780-366-3801. FAX: 780-366-2332. E-mail: librarian@myrnamlibrary.ab.ca. Web Site: www.myrnamlibrary.ab.ca. *Libr Mgr*, Ann Godzuik
Library Holdings: Bk Vols 4,000
Automation Activity & Vendor Info: (Cataloging) Polaris Library Systems; (Circulation) Polaris Library Systems; (OPAC) Polaris Library Systems
Wireless access
Mem of Northern Lights Library System
Open Mon & Fri 9-4, Tues & Thurs 9-5, Wed 9-4 & 5:30-8:30

NAMPA

P   NAMPA MUNICIPAL LIBRARY*, 10203 99th Ave, T0H 2R0. (Mail add: PO Box 509, T0H 2R0), SAN 318-7063. Tel: 780-322-3805. FAX: 780-322-3955. E-mail: nlibrary@nampalibrary.ab.ca. Web Site: www.nampalibrary.ab.ca. *Librn*, Cathy Rasmussen
Founded 1963. Pop 1,535; Circ 3,948
Library Holdings: Bk Vols 18,200; Per Subs 1
Subject Interests: Area hist
Mem of Peace Library System
Open Mon 1-4 & 7-9, Tues-Fri 10-5

NANTON

P   THELMA FANNING MEMORIAL LIBRARY*, 1907 21 Ave, T0L 1R0. (Mail add: PO Box 310, T0L 1R0), SAN 318-7071. Tel: 403-646-5535. E-mail: nantlibr@chinookarch.ab.ca. *Libr Mgr*, Malcolm Stick; Staff 4 (Non-MLS 4)
Pop 2,055; Circ 14,323
Library Holdings: Bk Vols 19,821; Per Subs 26
Wireless access
Function: Homebound delivery serv
Special Services for the Blind - Audio mat; Bks on cassette; Bks on CD
Open Tues-Thurs 11-8, Fri 1-6, Sat 11-4

NEERLANDIA

P   NEERLANDIA PUBLIC LIBRARY*, PO Box 10, T0G 1R0. SAN 318-708X. Tel: 780-674-5384. FAX: 780-674-2927. *Librn*, Dagmar Visser; E-mail: dvisser@phrd.ab.ca
Founded 1973. Pop 1,000; Circ 28,000
Library Holdings: Bk Vols 12,865; Per Subs 33
Special Collections: Historical Books
Mem of Yellowhead Regional Library
Open Mon, Tues, Thurs & Fri 8:30-12 & 1-4:30, Wed 8:30-12, 1-4:30 & 7-9

NEW SAREPTA

P   NEW SAREPTA PUBLIC LIBRARY*, 5150 Centre St, T0B 3M0. (Mail add: PO Box 147, T0B 3M0). Tel: 780-975-7513. FAX: 780-941-2224. *Libr Mgr*, Willow Schnell
Founded 1976. Pop 3,700
Library Holdings: Bk Vols 8,000
Automation Activity & Vendor Info: (Acquisitions) Polaris Library Systems; (Cataloging) Polaris Library Systems; (Circulation) Polaris

Library Systems; (ILL) Polaris Library Systems; (OPAC) Polaris Library Systems; (Serials) Polaris Library Systems
Wireless access
Mem of Yellowhead Regional Library
Partic in The Alberta Library; The Regional Automation Consortium (TRAC)
Special Services for the Blind - Daisy reader
Open Tues & Thurs 8:30am-9pm, Wed 8:30-2, Sat 11-3
Friends of the Library Group

NEWBROOK

P   NEWBROOK PUBLIC LIBRARY*, PO Box 208, T0A 2P0. SAN 318-7098. Tel: 780-576-3772. FAX: 780-576-3773. E-mail: librarian@newbrooklibrary.ab.ca. *Libr Mgr*, Rachel Oehlerking
Pop 1,080; Circ 4,000
Library Holdings: Bk Vols 9,500
Mem of Northern Lights Library System
Open Mon 1-4, Tues & Thurs 4-8

NITON JUNCTION

P   GREEN GROVE PUBLIC LIBRARY*, PO Box 219, T0E 1S0. Tel: 780-795-2474. FAX: 780-795-3933. Web Site: www.greengrovelibrary.ab.ca. *Libr Mgr*, Toni Smigelski; E-mail: toniice@ggpsd.ab.ca
Library Holdings: DVDs 600; Bk Vols 15,500; Talking Bks 100; Videos 100
Automation Activity & Vendor Info: (Acquisitions) Polaris Library Systems; (Cataloging) Polaris Library Systems; (Circulation) Polaris Library Systems; (Course Reserve) Polaris Library Systems; (ILL) Polaris Library Systems; (Serials) Polaris Library Systems
Mem of Yellowhead Regional Library
Open Mon-Wed 10-4:30, Thurs 12:30-8

NORDEGG

P   NORDEGG PUBLIC LIBRARY*, General Delivery, T0M 2H0. Tel: 403-800-3667. FAX: 403-721-3930. Web Site: nordegglibrary.prl.ab.ca. *Librn*, Heather Clement
Library Holdings: DVDs 25; Bk Vols 4,000; Talking Bks 50; Videos 300
Mem of Parkland Regional Library
Open Wed-Fri 7pm-9:30pm, Sat 12-3

OKOTOKS

P   OKOTOKS PUBLIC LIBRARY, 7 Riverside Dr, T1S 1A6. (Mail add: PO Box 310, T1S 1A6), SAN 372-7130. Tel: 403-938-2220. Toll Free FAX: 403-938-4317. E-mail: aomlibrary@marigold.ab.ca, librarian@okotokslibrary.ca. Web Site: www.okotokslibrary.ca. *Dir*, Tessa Nettleton; Staff 8 (MLS 1, Non-MLS 7)
Founded 1979. Pop 24,500; Circ 350,000
Library Holdings: Audiobooks 1,507; AV Mats 6,421; CDs 2,021; DVDs 3,335; Large Print Bks 721; Bk Vols 50,243; Per Subs 92
Automation Activity & Vendor Info: (Acquisitions) Polaris Library Systems; (Cataloging) Polaris Library Systems; (Circulation) Polaris Library Systems; (OPAC) Polaris Library Systems; (Serials) Polaris Library Systems
Database Vendor: 3M Library Systems, Canadian Reference Centre, EBSCO Auto Repair Reference, Ex Libris Group, Gale Cengage Learning, McGraw-Hill, OCLC WorldCat, Polaris Library Systems, ProQuest, SirsiDynix, World Book Online
Wireless access
Mem of Marigold Library System
Open Mon-Thurs 9:30-8:30, Fri & Sat 10-5, Sun 1-5
Restriction: 24-hr pass syst for students only, Access at librarian's discretion, Access for corporate affiliates, Authorized patrons, Authorized personnel only, Authorized scholars by appt, Badge access after hrs, Borrowing privileges limited to anthropology fac & libr staff, Borrowing privileges limited to fac & registered students, Borrowing requests are handled by ILL, By permission only, Circ limited, Circ privileges for students & alumni only, Circ to mem only, Circ to mil employees only, Circulates for staff only, Clients only, Closed stack, Co libr, Congregants only, Employee & client use only, Employee & their associates, Employees only, Fed grantees by appt only, Govt use only, Hospital staff & commun, In-house use for visitors, Internal circ only, Lending libr only via mail, Lending to staff only, Limited access for the pub, Med & nursing staff, patients & families, Med staff only, Mem only, Mem organizations only, Mil only, Mil, family mem, retirees, Civil Serv personnel NAF only, Non-circulating, Non-circulating of rare bks, Non-circulating to the pub, Non-resident fee, Not a lending libr, Not open to pub, Off-site coll in storage - retrieval as requested, Open by appt only, Open evenings by appt, Open only to librarians, Open to dept staff only, Open to employees & special libr, Open to fac, students & qualified researchers, Open to govt employees only, Open to hospital affiliates only, Open to mil & govt employees only, Open to others by appt, Open to pub by appt only, Open

to pub for ref & circ; with some limitations, Open to pub for ref only, Open to pub upon request, Open to pub with supv only, Open to qualified scholars, Open to researchers by request, Open to staff only, Open to staff, patients & family mem, Open to staff, students & ancillary prof, Open to students, Open to students, fac & staff, Open to students, fac & staff of Classics Dept only, Open to students, fac, staff & alumni, Open to tribal commun mem only, Photo ID required for access, Prof mat only, Pub access for legal res only, Pub ref by request, Ref only, Registered patrons only, Researchers by appt only, Residents only, Restricted borrowing privileges, Restricted pub use, Serves prof staff, students & interns only, Staff & inmates only, Staff & patient use, Staff use by sub only, Staff use, pub by appt, Use of others with permission of librn, Visitors must make appt to use bks in the libr, Visually impaired students & their teachers, Visually impaired students, teachers & their parents
Friends of the Library Group

OLDS

P   OLDS & DISTRICT MUNICIPAL LIBRARY*, 5217 52nd St, T4H 1S8. SAN 372-686X. Tel: 403-556-6460. FAX: 403-556-6692. E-mail: oml2@libs.prl.ab.ca. Web Site: www.oml.prl.ab.ca. *Libr Mgr,* Lesley Winfield
Pop 7,248
Library Holdings: Bk Titles 38,000; Per Subs 60
Mem of Parkland Regional Library
Open Mon & Thurs 9:30-8, Tues, Wed & Fri 9:30-5, Sat 12-5
Friends of the Library Group

J   OLDS COLLEGE LIBRARY*, 4500 50th St, T4H 1R6. SAN 318-7101. Tel: 403-556-4600. Interlibrary Loan Service Tel: 403-556-4601. FAX: 403-556-4705. Web Site: www.oldscollege.ca/library. *Dir,* Robin Minion
Founded 1968. Enrl 1,200; Fac 126
Library Holdings: Bk Vols 60,000; Per Subs 275
Special Collections: Can & Prov
Subject Interests: Agr, Agr bus, Environ, Hort
Automation Activity & Vendor Info: (Acquisitions) SirsiDynix; (Cataloging) SirsiDynix; (Circulation) SirsiDynix; (OPAC) SirsiDynix
Database Vendor: SirsiDynix
Partic in NEOS Library Consortium
Open Mon-Thurs 7:45am-11pm, Fri 7:45-6, Sat 11-5, Sun 2-10

ONOWAY

P   ONOWAY PUBLIC LIBRARY*, 4708 Lac Sainte Anne Trail, T0E 1V0. (Mail add: Box 484, T0E 1V0). Tel: 780-967-2445. FAX: 888-467-1309. E-mail: onowaylibrary@yrl.ab.ca. Web Site: www.onowaylibrary.ab.ca. *Librn,* Kelly L Huxley
Pop 1,036
Library Holdings: Bk Vols 15,127
Automation Activity & Vendor Info: (Acquisitions) Polaris Library Systems; (Cataloging) Polaris Library Systems; (Circulation) Polaris Library Systems; (ILL) Polaris Library Systems
Mem of Yellowhead Regional Library
Open Tues 1:30-7:30, Wed-Sat 10:30-4:30

OYEN

P   OYEN MUNICIPAL LIBRARY*, 105 Third Ave W, T0J 2J0. (Mail add: Box 328, T0J 2J0), SAN 318-711X. Tel: 403-664-3580. FAX: 403-664-2520. E-mail: aoymlibrary@marigold.ab.ca. Web Site: www.marigold.ab.ca.about/memberlibs/oyen.html. *Libr Mgr,* Trish Fischbuch; *Librn,* Lois Bedwell
Pop 1,101; Circ 4,337
Library Holdings: Bk Vols 11,525; Per Subs 25
Wireless access
Mem of Marigold Library System
Partic in Marigold Regional Libr
Open Mon & Wed 12-5, Tues & Thurs 3-8

PARADISE VALLEY

P   PARADISE VALLEY MUNICIPAL LIBRARY*, PO Box 60, T0B 3R0. Tel: 780-745-2277. FAX: 780-745-2641. Web Site: www.paradisevalleylibrary.ab.ca. *Librn,* Sandra Babcock; E-mail: sandra.babcock@btps.ca
Pop 152
Library Holdings: Bk Vols 10,000
Database Vendor: Overdrive, Inc
Mem of Northern Lights Library System
Partic in The Alberta Library; The Regional Automation Consortium (TRAC)
Open Mon, Tues, Thurs & Fri 9-3:30, Wed 9-8; Tues (Summer) 9-4:30, Wed Noon-8

PEACE RIVER

L   ALBERTA LAW LIBRARIES*, Peace River Branch, Courthouse, 9905 - 97 Avenue, T8S 1S4. (Mail add: Bag 900, PO Box 34, T8S 1S4), SAN 372-8862. Tel: 780-624-6418. FAX: 780-624-7101. Web Site: www.lawlibrary.ab.ca.
Library Holdings: Bk Vols 10,500; Per Subs 50
Automation Activity & Vendor Info: (Acquisitions) Ex Libris Group; (Cataloging) Ex Libris Group; (Circulation) Ex Libris Group; (ILL) Ex Libris Group; (OPAC) Ex Libris Group; (Serials) Ex Libris Group
Database Vendor: LexisNexis
Function: ILL available
Open Mon-Wed 8:15-4
Restriction: Non-circulating to the pub

P   PEACE RIVER MUNICIPAL LIBRARY*, 9807 97th Ave, T8S 1H6. SAN 318-7128. Tel: 780-624-4076. FAX: 780-624-4086. E-mail: ill@prmlibrary.ab.ca. Web Site: www.prmlibrary.ab.ca. *Libr Mgr,* Linda Prudholme-Wardor
Pop 6,240; Circ 70,000
Library Holdings: Bk Vols 30,000
Mem of Peace Library System
Open Tues & Wed 11-6, Thurs & Fri 10-8, Sat 10-5
Friends of the Library Group

S   PEACE RIVER MUSEUM, ARCHIVES & MACKENZIE CENTRE*, 10302 99th St, T8S 1K1. SAN 374-8847. Tel: 780-624-4261. FAX: 780-624-4270. E-mail: info@peaceriver.net. Web Site: www.peaceriver.ca/visitors/101-museum. *Dir,* Laura Gloor; Staff 2 (Non-MLS 2)
Founded 1967
Library Holdings: Bk Titles 500
Open Mon-Fri 10-5
Friends of the Library Group

PENHOLD

P   PENHOLD & DISTRICT PUBLIC LIBRARY, Penhold Regional Multi-Plex, One Waskasoo Ave, T0M 1R0. (Mail add: PO Box 675, T0M 1R0), SAN 324-3788. Tel: 403-886-2636. FAX: 403-886-2638. E-mail: penholdlibrary@prl.ab.ca. Web Site: www.penholdlibrary.prl.ab.ca. *Libr Mgr,* Myra Binnendyk; *Asst Librn,* Karen Thomson
Founded 1981. Circ 24,209
Library Holdings: Audiobooks 294; AV Mats 692; CDs 187; Bk Titles 11,382
Wireless access
Mem of Parkland Regional Library
Open Tues & Wed 10-8, Thurs & Fri 10-5, Sat 10-3

PICTURE BUTTE

P   PICTURE BUTTE MUNICIPAL LIBRARY*, 120 Fourth St, T0K 1V0. (Mail add: PO Box 1130, T0K 1V0), SAN 318-7136. Tel: 403-732-4141. E-mail: help@picturebuttelibrary.ca. Web Site: www.picturebuttelibrary.ca. Founded 1962. Pop 1,701; Circ 40,000
Library Holdings: Bk Vols 26,000; Per Subs 38
Special Collections: Dutch Book Coll
Open Tues & Thurs-Sat 10-5, Wed 10-7

PINCHER CREEK

P   PINCHER CREEK MUNICIPAL LIBRARY*, 899 Main St, T0K 1W0. (Mail add: PO Box 2020, T0K 1W0), SAN 318-7144. Tel: 403-627-3813. FAX: 403-627-2847. E-mail: help@pinchercreeklibrary.ca. *Actg Chief Librn,* Janice Day; Staff 1 (Non-MLS 1)
Pop 7,000; Circ 47,556
Library Holdings: Bk Vols 32,000; Per Subs 25
Special Services for the Blind - Audio mat; Bks available with recordings; Bks on cassette; Bks on CD; Cassette playback machines; Cassettes; Talking bks
Open Tues & Thurs 10-8, Wed & Fri 10-6, Sat 10-4:30
Friends of the Library Group

PONOKA

M   ALBERTA HEALTH SERVICES*, Centennial Centre for Mental Health & Brain Injury Learning Resource Center, PO Box 1000, T4J 1R8. SAN 324-5454. Tel: 403-783-7691. FAX: 403-783-7695. E-mail: ccmhbi@albertahealthservices.ca. Web Site: www.albertahealthservices.ca. *Mgr, Libr Serv,* Position Currently Open; *Circ,* Phyllis Chadderton; *Doc Delivery, Tech Serv,* Lori Maisey; E-mail: lori.maisey@albertahealthservices.ca. Subject Specialists: *Psychiat,* Position Currently Open; Staff 2 (Non-MLS 2)
Founded 1971
Library Holdings: Bk Titles 4,500; Bk Vols 7,300; Per Subs 275

Subject Interests: Geriatric psychiatry, Mental health, Mental health of children, Psychiat
Automation Activity & Vendor Info: (Circulation) Inmagic, Inc.; (Serials) EBSCO Online
Database Vendor: EBSCOhost, OVID Technologies
Partic in Docline
Open Mon-Fri 8-4:15
Branches:
ALBERTA HOSPITAL-EDMONTON LIBRARY, 17480 Fort Rd, Edmonton, T5J 2J7, SAN 320-7684. Tel: 780-342-5268. FAX: 780-342-5608. E-mail: ahelibrary@albertahealthservices.ca. *Med Libr Tech,* Eileen Cardy
Library Holdings: Bk Vols 5,000
Restriction: Staff use only
RED DEER REGIONAL HOSPITAL CENTRE MEDICAL LIBRARY SERVICES, 3942 50A Ave, Red Deer, T4N 4E7, SAN 324-4121. Tel: 403-343-4557. FAX: 403-343-4910. E-mail: library@dthr.ab.ca. Web Site: www.dthr.ab.ca. *Dir, Libr Serv,* Dixie Anderson; E-mail: dixie.anderson@albertahealthservices.ca; Staff 4 (Non-MLS 4)
Founded 1980
Library Holdings: AV Mats 244; Bk Titles 863; Bk Vols 4,701; Per Subs 355
Special Collections: Consumer Health Coll; Personal Resource Coll
Subject Interests: Allied health, Med, Nursing
Open Mon-Fri 8-4:15
Friends of the Library Group

P   PONOKA PUBLIC LIBRARY*, PO Box 4160, T4J 1R6. Tel: 403-783-3843. FAX: 403-783-3973. E-mail: ponokalibrary@libs.prl.ab.ca. Web Site: ponokalibrary.prl.ab.ca. *Librn,* Norma-Jean Colquhoun
Library Holdings: Bk Vols 30,000
Automation Activity & Vendor Info: (Cataloging) Horizon; (Circulation) Horizon; (OPAC) Horizon
Wireless access
Mem of Parkland Regional Library
Open Mon, Tues & Fri 10-5:30, Wed & Thurs 10-8, Sat 11-4

PROVOST

P   PROVOST MUNICIPAL LIBRARY*, PO Box 120, T0B 3S0. SAN 318-7160. Tel: 780-753-2801. FAX: 780-753-2801. E-mail: provostlibrary@libs.prl.ab.ca. *Librn,* Colleen Vaughan
Founded 1950. Pop 1,800; Circ 7,072
Library Holdings: Bk Vols 8,473
Mem of Parkland Regional Library
Open Mon-Thurs 1-8, Fri & Sat 1-5

RADWAY

P   RADWAY & DISTRICT MUNICIPAL LIBRARY*, PO Box 220, T0A 2V0. Tel: 780-736-3548. FAX: 780-736-3858. E-mail: librarian@radwaylibrary.ab.ca. *Libr Mgr,* Morgan Johnstone
Library Holdings: Bk Vols 12,000
Special Collections: Books in Ukrainian
Wireless access
Mem of Northern Lights Library System
Special Services for the Deaf - Adult & family literacy prog; Bks on deafness & sign lang
Special Services for the Blind - Accessible computers; Aids for in-house use; Audio mat; Bks on CD; Compressed speech equip; Computer access aids; Daisy reader; Screen enlargement software for people with visual disabilities; Screen reader software; ZoomText magnification & reading software
Open Mon, Wed & Fri 9-4, Tues & Thurs 9-8
Friends of the Library Group

RAINBOW LAKE

P   RAINBOW LAKE MUNICIPAL LIBRARY*, PO Box 266, T0H 2Y0. Tel: 780-956-3656. FAX: 780-956-3858. E-mail: librarian@rainbowlakelibrary.ab.ca. *Libr Mgr,* Chloe Laptich
Library Holdings: Bk Vols 10,000
Automation Activity & Vendor Info: (Acquisitions) Polaris Library Systems; (Cataloging) Polaris Library Systems; (Circulation) Polaris Library Systems; (ILL) Polaris Library Systems
Database Vendor: EBSCO - WebFeat, EBSCO Auto Repair Reference, EBSCO Information Services, EBSCOhost
Wireless access
Mem of Peace Library System
Open Tues-Fri 4-8, Sat 11-3

RALSTON

P   GRAHAM COMMUNITY LIBRARY, Ralston Community Centre, R35 Dugway Dr, T0J 2N0. (Mail add: PO Box 40, T0J 2N0), SAN 318-7187. Tel: 403-544-3670. FAX: 403-544-3814. E-mail: grahamlib@yahoo.ca.

Web Site: graham.shortgrass.ca. *Librn,* Stefanie Schranz; Staff 3 (Non-MLS 3)
Founded 1954. Pop 1,500; Circ 15,000
Library Holdings: Bk Vols 20,000; Per Subs 10
Special Collections: Military History Coll
Subject Interests: British authors
Database Vendor: EBSCO Auto Repair Reference, EBSCO Information Services, EBSCOhost, World Book Online
Wireless access
Mem of Shortgrass Libr Syst
Open Mon & Wed 10-8, Tues & Thurs 10-4, Fri 9-4

RAYMOND

P   RAYMOND PUBLIC LIBRARY*, 15 Broadway S, T0K 2S0. (Mail add: PO Box 258, T0K 2S0). Tel: 403-752-4785. FAX: 587-271-4710. E-mail: rlibrary@raymondlibrary.ca. *Head Librn,* Faye Geddes; E-mail: fgeddes@raymondlibrary.ca
Pop 3,200; Circ 17,894
Library Holdings: Bk Vols 26,000
Special Services for the Blind - Reader equip
Open Mon-Thurs 10-6, Fri 10-7:30, Sat 1:30-4:30
Friends of the Library Group

RED DEER

L   ALBERTA LAW LIBRARIES - RED DEER*, Courthouse, 4909 - 48 Ave, T4N 3T5. SAN 375-0329. Tel: 403-340-5499. FAX: 403-340-7194. Web Site: www.lawlibrary.ab.ca. *Libr Coordr,* Beth Ernst; E-mail: beth.ernst@gov.ab.ca; Staff 2 (Non-MLS 2)
Automation Activity & Vendor Info: (Acquisitions) Ex Libris Group; (Cataloging) Ex Libris Group; (Circulation) Ex Libris Group; (ILL) Ex Libris Group; (OPAC) Ex Libris Group; (Serials) Ex Libris Group
Database Vendor: LexisNexis
Open Mon-Fri 8:15-4:30

G   RED DEER & DISTRICT ARCHIVES*, 4525 47 A Ave, T4N 3T4. (Mail add: PO Box 5008, T4N 3T4), SAN 373-8280. Tel: 403-309-8403. FAX: 403-340-8728. E-mail: archives@reddeer.ca. Web Site: www.reddeer.ca/archives. *Archivist,* Jillian Staniec; Staff 4 (Non-MLS 4)
Founded 1964
Library Holdings: Bk Titles 2,000; Per Subs 10
Special Collections: Alberta Genealogical Society; City of Red Deer Coll. Oral History
Subject Interests: Genealogy, Local hist
Open Mon-Fri 9-5

J   RED DEER COLLEGE LIBRARY*, 100 College Blvd, T4N 5H5. (Mail add: PO Box 5005, T4N 5H5), SAN 318-7209. Tel: 403-342-3344. Reference Tel: 403-342-3152. FAX: 403-346-8500. E-mail: rdclibrary@rdc.ab.ca, reference@rdc.ab.ca. Web Site: library.rdc.ab.ca/. *Dean,* Alice McNair; E-mail: alice.mcnair@rdc.ab.ca; *Chair,* Kristine Plaston; Tel: 403-342-3578; *Bibliog Instr,* Michelle Edwards; E-mail: michelle.edwards@rdc.ab.ca; *Circ,* Barb Mahoney; E-mail: barb.mahoney@rdc.ab.ca; *Coll Mgt,* Tencil Vuori; E-mail: tencil.vuori@rdc.ab.ca; *Info Tech,* Michelle Edwards; E-mail: michelle.edwards@rdc.ab.ca; *Media Spec,* Lillian Teh-Frenette; E-mail: lillian.tehfrenette@rdc.ab.ca; *Web Coordr,* Yvonne Phillips; E-mail: yvonne.phillips@rdc.ab.ca; Staff 30 (MLS 11, Non-MLS 19)
Founded 1964. Enrl 3,570; Fac 210
Library Holdings: Bk Vols 150,000
Special Collections: Can & Prov
Automation Activity & Vendor Info: (OPAC) Bibliomation Inc
Database Vendor: EBSCOhost, Gale Cengage Learning, OVID Technologies, ProQuest, Wilson - Wilson Web
Wireless access
Partic in NEOS Library Consortium; The Alberta Library

P   RED DEER PUBLIC LIBRARY*, 4818 49th St, T4N 1T9. SAN 318-7217. Tel: 403-346-4576. FAX: 403-341-3110. Web Site: www.rdpl.org. *Librn,* Dean Frey; E-mail: dfrey@rdpl.org; *Adult Serv,* Cynthia Belanger; *Ch,* Jill Griffith; Staff 4 (MLS 4)
Founded 1914. Circ 813,000
Library Holdings: Bk Vols 185,000; Per Subs 180
Publications: LINK (Bi-monthly)
Open Mon-Thurs 9:30-8:30, Fri & Sat 9:30-5:30, Sun 1:30-5
Friends of the Library Group
Branches: 1
DAWE, 56 Holt St, T4N 6A6. Tel: 403-341-3822. FAX: 403-343-2120. *Librn,* Tatyana Poliakevitch
Library Holdings: Bk Vols 50,000
Automation Activity & Vendor Info: (Acquisitions) BiblioCommons; (Cataloging) BiblioCommons; (Circulation) BiblioCommons; (Serials) BiblioCommons
Open Mon-Thurs 9:30-8:30, Fri 9:30-5:30, Sat 12-4

REDCLIFF

P   REDCLIFF PUBLIC LIBRARY, 131 Main St S, T0J 2P0. (Mail add: PO Box 280, T0J 2P0), SAN 320-5258. Tel: 403-548-3335. FAX: 403-548-6295. E-mail: redlib@shortgrass.ca. *Libr Mgr,* Tracy Weinrauch
Founded 1967. Pop 5,500; Circ 51,826
Library Holdings: CDs 529; DVDs 1,248; e-books 828; Electronic Media & Resources 236; Bk Vols 16,601; Per Subs 85; Talking Bks 676
Wireless access
Mem of Shortgrass Libr Syst
Special Services for the Deaf - Bks on deafness & sign lang; Closed caption videos
Special Services for the Blind - Bks & mags in Braille, on rec, tape & cassette; Bks on CD; Daisy reader; Large print bks; Talking bks
Open Mon-Thurs 10-8, Fri & Sat 10-5, Sun 1-4

REDWATER

S   AGRIUM, INC*, Redwater-Library Services, Bag 20, T0A 2W0. SAN 374-7875. Tel: 780-998-6130. FAX: 780-998-5916. Staff 1 (Non-MLS 1)
Founded 1981
Library Holdings: Bk Vols 7,500; Per Subs 180
Restriction: Open to staff only

P   REDWATER PUBLIC LIBRARY*, 4915 48th St, T0A 2W0. (Mail add: PO Box 384, T0A 2W0), SAN 318-7225. Tel: 780-942-3464. Web Site: www.redwaterlibrary.ab.ca. *Dir of Libr Serv,* Judy Dewald; E-mail: director@redwaterlibrary.ab.ca
Pop 2,172; Circ 40,000
Automation Activity & Vendor Info: (Acquisitions) Polaris Library Systems; (Cataloging) Polaris Library Systems; (Circulation) Polaris Library Systems; (ILL) Polaris Library Systems; (OPAC) Polaris Library Systems; (Serials) Polaris Library Systems
Database Vendor: EBSCOhost
Wireless access
Mem of Northern Lights Library System
Special Services for the Blind - Accessible computers; Assistive/Adapted tech devices, equip & products; Bks on cassette; Bks on CD; Daisy reader; Large print bks; Mags & bk reproduction/duplication; Talking bks
Open Tues-Thurs 12-8, Fri 10-6, Sat 10-4
Friends of the Library Group

RIMBEY

P   RIMBEY MUNICIPAL LIBRARY*, 4938 50th Ave, T0C 2J0. (Mail add: Box 1130, T0C 2J0). Tel: 403-843-2841. E-mail: rimbeylibrarian@libs.prl.ab.ca. Web Site: rimbeylibrary.prl.ab.ca. *Librn,* Jean Keetch
Pop 2,500
Library Holdings: Bk Vols 19,000
Wireless access
Mem of Parkland Regional Library
Open Tues, Wed, Fri & Sat 10-5, Thurs 10-8
Friends of the Library Group

ROCHESTER

P   ROCHESTER COMMUNITY LIBRARY*, PO Box 309, T0G 1Z0. Tel: 780-698-3970. FAX: 780-698-2290. E-mail: librarian@rochesterlibrary.ab.ca. *Librn,* Tammy Morey
Founded 1986. Pop 600
Library Holdings: AV Mats 300; Bks on Deafness & Sign Lang 50; High Interest/Low Vocabulary Bk Vols 300; Large Print Bks 60; Bk Titles 13,000; Bk Vols 11,200; Per Subs 12; Talking Bks 20
Special Collections: Railroads. Oral History
Publications: Rochester Library Newsletter (Monthly)
Mem of Northern Lights Library System
Open Mon, Tues, Thurs & Fri 9-3:30, Wed 4-7:30
Friends of the Library Group

ROCKY MOUNTAIN HOUSE

P   ROCKY MOUNTAIN HOUSE PUBLIC LIBRARY*, 4922 52nd St, T4T 1B1. (Mail add: Box 1497, T4T 1B1). Tel: 403-845-2042, 403-845-5775. FAX: 403-845-5633. E-mail: armh@libs.prl.ab.ca. Web Site: rmhlibrary.prl.ab.ca. *Libr Mgr,* Cathie MacDonald
Pop 7,231; Circ 87,028
Library Holdings: Bk Vols 36,197; Per Subs 79
Automation Activity & Vendor Info: (Acquisitions) Horizon; (Cataloging) Horizon; (Circulation) Horizon; (ILL) Horizon; (Serials) Horizon
Wireless access
Mem of Parkland Regional Library
Open Mon, Wed & Fri 10-6, Tues & Thurs 10-8, Sat 11-5
Friends of the Library Group

ROCKYFORD

P   ROCKYFORD MUNICIPAL LIBRARY, Community Centre, 412 Serviceberry Trail, T0J 2R0. (Mail add: PO Box 277, T0J 2R0), SAN 321-0162. Tel: 403-533-3964. E-mail: armlibrary@marigold.ab.ca. Web Site: www.rockyfordlibrary.ca. *Libr Mgr,* Jocelyne Kisko; Staff 2 (Non-MLS 2)
Founded 1963. Pop 1,196; Circ 3,485
Library Holdings: Bk Titles 5,000
Subject Interests: Local hist
Wireless access
Mem of Marigold Library System
Special Services for the Blind - Daisy reader
Open Tues-Thurs 2-8

ROLLING HILLS

P   ROLLING HILLS PUBLIC LIBRARY*, 302 Fourth St, T0J 2S0. Tel: 403-964-2186. FAX: 403-964-3659. E-mail: rhlcapic@eidnet.org. Web Site: www.shortgrass.ca. *Librn,* Johnene Amulung
Library Holdings: Bk Vols 15,000
Automation Activity & Vendor Info: (Cataloging) BiblioCommons; (Circulation) BiblioCommons
Mem of Shortgrass Libr Syst
Open Mon 7pm-9pm, Wed 9-Noon, Thurs 10:30-3; Mon-Thurs (Summer) 9-4:30

ROSEMARY

P   ROSEMARY COMMUNITY LIBRARY*, 622 Dahlia St, T0J 2W0. (Mail add: PO Box 210, T0J 2W0), SAN 318-7233. Tel: 403-378-4493, Ext 150. FAX: 403-378-4388. Web Site: www.shortgrass.ca/rml. *Chairperson,* Donna Janzen; *Libr Mgr,* Vanessa Plett; E-mail: vanessa.plett@grasslands.ab.ca
Pop 366; Circ 7,000
Library Holdings: Bk Vols 11,000
Database Vendor: BiblioCommons, SirsiDynix
Wireless access
Mem of Shortgrass Libr Syst
Open Mon, Wed & Fri 9-3, Tues 9-8, Thurs 9-8 (10-6 Summer)

RUMSEY

P   RUMSEY COMMUNITY LIBRARY*, PO Box 113, T0J 2Y0. SAN 321-0928. Tel: 403-368-3939. FAX: 403-368-3939. E-mail: arumlibrary@marigold.ab.ca. Web Site: www.rumseylibrary.ca. *Libr Mgr,* Patty Steen
Founded 1978. Pop 300
Library Holdings: Audiobooks 150; AV Mats 50; DVDs 50; Large Print Bks 15; Bk Titles 4,734; Bk Vols 5,000; Per Subs 10
Subject Interests: Gardening
Wireless access
Mem of Marigold Library System
Open Tues & Wed 10-6

RYCROFT

P   RYCROFT MUNICIPAL LIBRARY*, 4732 50th St, T0H 3A0. (Mail add: PO Box 248, T0H 3A0). Tel: 780-765-3973. FAX: 780-765-2002. E-mail: rycroft@telusplanet.net. Web Site: www.rycroftlibrary.ab.ca. *Librn,* Christina Otterstrom-Cedar
Pop 609
Library Holdings: Bk Vols 7,000
Wireless access
Mem of Peace Library System
Open Mon-Fri (Summer) 10-6; Tues-Thurs (Winter) 2-6, Sat 10-1

RYLEY

P   MCPHERSON MUNICIPAL LIBRARY*, 5113 50 St, T0B 4A0. (Mail add: PO Box 139, T0B 4A0). Tel: 780-663-3999. FAX: 780-663-3909. E-mail: librarian@mcphersonlibrary.ab.ca. Web Site: www.mcphersonlibrary.ab.ca. *Libr Mgr,* Laura Hill; Staff 1 (Non-MLS 1)
Pop 437
Library Holdings: Bk Vols 10,000
Wireless access
Function: Fax serv, Photocopying/Printing, Prog for children & young adult
Mem of Northern Lights Library System
Special Services for the Blind - Large print bks; Reader equip
Open Tues & Fri 10-7, Wed 1-9, Thurs 1-8, Sat 10-2
Friends of the Library Group

SANGUDO

P   SANGUDO PUBLIC LIBRARY*, 5131 53rd Ave, T0E 2A0. (Mail add: PO Box 524, T0E 2A0), SAN 318-725X. Tel: 780-785-3431. FAX: 780-785-3179. E-mail: sangudolibrary@yrl.ab.ca. Web Site: www.sangudolibrary.ca. *Librn,* Monica Grove; *Asst Librn,* Cathy Ciphery
    Pop 422
    Library Holdings: DVDs 120; Large Print Bks 70; Bk Vols 9,900; Per Subs 22; Talking Bks 30
    Wireless access
    Mem of Yellowhead Regional Library
    Open Tues & Wed 4-7, Thurs 6-9
    Friends of the Library Group

SEBA BEACH

P   SEBA BEACH PUBLIC LIBRARY*, 140 3rd St, T0E 2B0. Tel: 780-797-3940. FAX: 780-797-3800. E-mail: sebabeachlibrary@yrl.ab.ca. Web Site: www.sebabeachlibrary.ab.ca. *Libr Mgr,* Judy Mott
    Pop 137
    Library Holdings: Bk Vols 11,000
    Automation Activity & Vendor Info: (Acquisitions) SirsiDynix; (Cataloging) SirsiDynix; (Circulation) SirsiDynix; (Course Reserve) SirsiDynix; (ILL) SirsiDynix; (Media Booking) SirsiDynix; (OPAC) SirsiDynix; (Serials) SirsiDynix
    Database Vendor: SirsiDynix
    Wireless access
    Mem of Yellowhead Regional Library
    Partic in The Regional Automation Consortium (TRAC)
    Open Tues-Sat 10-5

SEDGEWICK

P   SEDGEWICK MUNICIPAL LIBRARY*, 5301 51st Ave, T0B 4C0. (Mail add: PO Box 569, T0B 4C0). Tel: 780-384-3003. FAX: 780-384-3003. E-mail: sedgewicklibrary@libs.prl.ab.ca. Web Site: sedgpublib.prl.ab.ca. *Librn,* Judy Ferrier
    Library Holdings: Bk Vols 10,000
    Wireless access
    Mem of Parkland Regional Library
    Open Mon & Wed 5:30-8:30, Tues, Thurs & Sat 1:30-5:30
    Friends of the Library Group

SEXSMITH

CR   PEACE RIVER BIBLE INSTITUTE LIBRARY, 9601 100th St, T0H 3C0. (Mail add: Box 99, T0H 3C0), SAN 323-7648. Tel: 780-568-3962. FAX: 780-568-4431. E-mail: library@prbi.edu. Web Site: prbi.edu. *Librn,* Wanda Penner; Tel: 780-568-3962, Ext 240
    Founded 1933. Fac 15; Highest Degree: Bachelor
    Library Holdings: Bk Vols 19,000; Per Subs 90
    Subject Interests: Theol
    Open Mon-Fri 7am-11pm, Sat 9-5
    Restriction: Non-circulating

P   SEXSMITH SHANNON MUNICIPAL LIBRARY*, 9917 99th Ave, T0H 3C0. (Mail add: Box 266, T0H 3C0), SAN 318-7268. Tel: 780-568-4333. FAX: 780-568-7249. E-mail: librarian@shannonlibrary.ab.ca. Web Site: www.shannonlibrary.ab.ca. *Libr Mgr,* Sheryl Pelletier; Staff 2 (Non-MLS 2)
    Founded 1946. Pop 2,418; Circ 30,000
    Library Holdings: CDs 550; DVDs 800; Bk Vols 18,553; Per Subs 22
    Automation Activity & Vendor Info: (Cataloging) Polaris Library Systems; (Circulation) Polaris Library Systems; (Course Reserve) Polaris Library Systems; (OPAC) Polaris Library Systems
    Wireless access
    Mem of Peace Library System
    Partic in The Alberta Library; The Regional Automation Consortium (TRAC)
    Open Mon 1-5:30, Tues, Wed & Fri 10-5:30, Thurs 10-8, Sat 12-4
    Friends of the Library Group

SHERWOOD PARK

GL   ALBERTA LAW LIBRARIES - SHERWOOD PARK*, Courthouse, 190 Chippewa Rd, T8A 4H5. Tel: 780-416-4087. FAX: 780-449-1490. *Libr Coordr,* Judy Rembish; E-mail: judy.rembish@gov.ab.ca; Staff 1 (Non-MLS 1)
    Open Wed 8:15-12 & 1-4:30

P   STRATHCONA COUNTY LIBRARY, 401 Festival Lane, T8A 5P7. SAN 318-7276. Tel: 780-410-8600. Administration Tel: 780-410-8603. FAX: 780-467-6861. E-mail: info@sclibrary.ab.ca. Web Site: www.sclibrary.ab.ca. *Dir,* Sharon Siga; E-mail: ssiga@sclibrary.ab.ca; *Adult Serv Mgr,* Heide Blackmore; E-mail: hblackmore@sclibrary.ab.ca; *Youth Serv Mgr,* Donna Riehl; E-mail: driehl@sclibrary.ab.ca; Staff 24 (MLS 13, Non-MLS 11)
    Founded 1974. Pop 94,802; Circ 1,357,118

Jan 2011-Dec 2011 Income (CAN) \$8,441,969, Provincial (CAN) \$475,189, Federal (CAN) \$9,637, County (CAN) \$7,168,000, Locally Generated Income (CAN) \$690,970, Other (CAN) \$98,173. Mats Exp (CAN) \$578,512, Books (CAN) \$387,658, Per/Ser (Incl. Access Fees) (CAN) \$31,597, AV Mat (CAN) \$121,566, Electronic Ref Mat (Incl. Access Fees) (CAN) \$37,691. Sal (CAN) \$4,423,385
    Library Holdings: AV Mats 33,704; Bk Titles 148,102; Bk Vols 183,865; Per Subs 527
    Subject Interests: Local hist
    Automation Activity & Vendor Info: (Acquisitions) SirsiDynix; (Cataloging) SirsiDynix; (Circulation) SirsiDynix; (ILL) SirsiDynix; (OPAC) BiblioCommons
    Database Vendor: ALLDATA Online, Baker & Taylor, BiblioCommons, BookLetters LLC, Booklist Online, Canadian Reference Centre, CredoReference, EBSCOhost, Grolier Online, Overdrive, Inc, ProQuest, SirsiDynix, TumbleBookLibrary, World Book Online
    Wireless access
    Function: Accessibility serv available based on individual needs, Adult bk club, Adult literacy prog, After school storytime, Audio & video playback equip for onsite use, AV serv, Bk club(s), Bks on CD, Chess club, Children's prog, Computer training, Computers for patron use, Copy machines, Digital talking bks, e-mail serv, Electronic databases & coll, Exhibits, Family literacy, Fax serv, Free DVD rentals, Games & aids for the handicapped, Handicapped accessible, Home delivery & serv to Sr ctr & nursing homes, Homebound delivery serv, Homework prog, ILL available, Instruction & testing, Large print keyboards, Literacy & newcomer serv, Magnifiers for reading, Mail & tel request accepted, Microfiche/film & reading machines, Music CDs, Online cat, Online ref, Online searches, Orientations, Outreach serv, Outside serv via phone, mail, e-mail & web, Photocopying/Printing, Preschool outreach, Preschool reading prog, Printer for laptops & handheld devices, Prog for adults, Prog for children & young adult, Pub access computers, Ref serv available, Ref serv in person, Scanner, Senior outreach, Serves mentally handicapped consumers, Story hour, Summer reading prog, Teen prog, Telephone ref, Wheelchair accessible, Workshops, Writing prog
    Publications: Strathcona County Library Program Guide (Quarterly)
    Partic in The Alberta Library
    Special Services for the Deaf - Assistive tech; Bks on deafness & sign lang; Captioned film dep
    Special Services for the Blind - Accessible computers; Assistive/Adapted tech devices, equip & products; Audio mat; Bks on CD; Braille bks; Club for the blind; Computer access aids; Copier with enlargement capabilities; Daisy reader; Digital talking bk; Digital talking bk machines; Extensive large print coll; Free checkout of audio mat; Home delivery serv; Internet workstation with adaptive software; Large print bks; Large screen computer & software; Magnifiers; Playaways (bks on MP3); Reader equip; Screen enlargement software for people with visual disabilities; Screen reader software; Talking bks; Talking machines; Visunet prog (Canada); ZoomText magnification & reading software
    Open Mon-Fri 9:30-9, Sat 9:30-5, Sun (Sept-July) 1-5
    Friends of the Library Group
    Bookmobiles: 1. Coordr, Diana Balbar. Titles 14,883

SLAVE LAKE

J   NORTHERN LAKES COLLEGE LIBRARY*, 1201 Main St SE, T0G 2A3. SAN 370-6613. Tel: 780-849-8670. FAX: 780-849-2570. Web Site: www.northernlakescollege.ca. *Dir, Libr Serv,* Deborah Kendze; Staff 3 (MLS 2, Non-MLS 1)
    Founded 1989. Enrl 1,000; Fac 104
    Library Holdings: AV Mats 4,000; Bk Vols 37,500; Per Subs 300
    Special Collections: Native Canadians Coll
    Automation Activity & Vendor Info: (Acquisitions) SirsiDynix; (Cataloging) SirsiDynix; (Circulation) SirsiDynix; (Course Reserve) SirsiDynix; (Media Booking) SirsiDynix; (OPAC) SirsiDynix; (Serials) SirsiDynix
    Wireless access
    Open Mon-Fri 8:15-4:30

P   ROTARY CLUB OF SLAVE LAKE PUBLIC LIBRARY*, 101 Main St SE, T0G 2A0. (Mail add: PO Box 540, T0G 2A0), SAN 372-669X. Tel: 780-849-5250. FAX: 780-849-3275. E-mail: librarian@slavelakelibrary.ab.ca. Web Site: www.slavelakelibrary.ab.ca. *Libr Mgr,* Shane Palmar; *Asst Librn,* Pat Mcleod; *Prog Coordr,* Robin-Lee Vance; Staff 6 (MLS 1, Non-MLS 5)
    Founded 1972. Pop 10,000; Circ 36,000
    Library Holdings: Bk Titles 25,000; Per Subs 50
    Wireless access
    Mem of Peace Library System
    Open Mon-Thurs 10-8, Fri & Sat 10-5

SMITH

P   SMITH COMMUNITY LIBRARY*, PO Box 134, T0G 2B0. Tel: 780-829-2389. FAX: 780-829-2389. E-mail: librarian@smithlibrary.ab.ca. Web Site: www.smithlibrary.ab.ca. *Head Librn,* Mary Hastie; *Librn,* Sheri Neuman
Library Holdings: Bk Vols 25,000; Per Subs 10
Mem of Peace Library System
Partic in The Regional Automation Consortium (TRAC)
Open Tues & Thurs 12-6, Sat 10-2

SMOKY LAKE

P   SMOKY LAKE MUNICIPAL LIBRARY, 5010-50 St, T0A 3C0. (Mail add: PO Box 490, TOA 3CO), SAN 318-7284. Tel: 780-656-4212. FAX: 780-656-4212. E-mail: librarian@smokylakelibrary.ab.ca. Web Site: www.smokylakelibrary.ab.ca. *Libr Mgr,* Melody Kaban; Staff 1 (Non-MLS 1)
Founded 1941. Pop 1,011
Library Holdings: DVDs 620; Bk Vols 12,140; Per Subs 16; Talking Bks 50
Wireless access
Function: ILL available
Mem of Northern Lights Library System
Open Mon 3-7:30, Tues, Thurs & Fri 2-6, Wed 10-12 & 2-6

SPIRIT RIVER

P   SPIRIT RIVER MUNICIPAL LIBRARY*, PO Box 490, T0H 3G0. SAN 318-7292. Tel: 780-864-4038. *Librn,* Tracy Skoworodko; E-mail: librarian@spiritriverlibrary.ab.ca
Pop 1,104; Circ 5,504
Library Holdings: Bk Vols 8,500
Wireless access
Mem of Peace Library System
Open Tues 10-6, Thurs 1-8, Sat 12-5

SPRUCE GROVE

P   SPRUCE GROVE PUBLIC LIBRARY*, 35 Fifth Ave, T7X 2C5. SAN 318-7306. Tel: 780-962-4423, Ext 107. FAX: 780-962-4826. E-mail: library@sgpl.ca. Web Site: www.spgl.ca. *Dir,* Tammy Svenningsen; E-mail: tammy@sgpl.ca; *Pub Serv Mgr,* Byron Walker; E-mail: byron@sgpl.ca; Staff 24 (MLS 3, Non-MLS 21)
Founded 1961. Pop 30,000; Circ 250,000
Library Holdings: AV Mats 8,164; Bk Vols 47,037; Per Subs 91
Database Vendor: EBSCOhost, Gale Cengage Learning
Wireless access
Function: Adult literacy prog, Audio & video playback equip for onsite use, Games & aids for the handicapped, Govt ref serv, Handicapped accessible, Home delivery & serv to Sr ctr & nursing homes, Homebound delivery serv, ILL available, Music CDs, Online searches, Orientations, Photocopying/Printing, Prog for adults, Prog for children & young adult, Ref serv available, Spoken cassettes & CDs, Summer reading prog, Telephone ref, Wheelchair accessible, Workshops
Mem of Yellowhead Regional Library
Partic in The Alberta Library
Open Tues-Fri 9-8, Sat 12-5, Sun 12-4
Friends of the Library Group

P   YELLOWHEAD REGIONAL LIBRARY, 433 King St, T7X 2Y1. (Mail add: Box 4270, T7X 2Y1), SAN 318-7314. Tel: 780-962-2003. Interlibrary Loan Service Tel: 780-962-2003, Ext 222. Administration Tel: 780-962-2003, Ext 221. FAX: 780-962-2770. E-mail: info@yrl.ab.ca. Web Site: www.yrl.ab.ca. *Dir,* Kevin Dodds; Tel: 780-962-2003, Ext 226, E-mail: kdodds@yrl.ab.ca; *Asst Dir, Mgr, Bibliog Serv,* Wendy Sears Ilnicki; Tel: 780-962-2003, Ext 225, E-mail: wsears@yrl.ab.ca; *Client Serv Mgr,* Stephanie Thero; Tel: 780-962-2003, Ext 224, E-mail: sthero@yrl.ab.ca; Staff 24 (MLS 5, Non-MLS 19)
Founded 1971
Automation Activity & Vendor Info: (Acquisitions) Polaris Library Systems; (Cataloging) Polaris Library Systems; (Circulation) Polaris Library Systems; (ILL) Polaris Library Systems; (OPAC) Polaris Library Systems
Database Vendor: Baker & Taylor, Brodart, EBSCO Auto Repair Reference, EBSCOhost, Gale Cengage Learning, OCLC WorldCat, Overdrive, Inc, Polaris Library Systems
Publications: YRL Annual Report; YRL Focus (Newsletter)
Member Libraries: Alberta Beach Municipal Library; Alder Flats Public Library; Barrhead Public Library; Bibliotheque de Beaumont Library; Blue Ridge Community Library; Breton Municipal Library; Calmar Public Library; Darwell Public Library; Devon Public Library; Drayton Valley Municipal Library; Duffield Public Library; Edson Public Library; Entwistle Public Library; Evansburg Public Library; Fort Assiniboine Public Library; Grande Cache Municipal Library; Green Grove Public Library; Hinton Municipal Library; Jarvie Public Library; Jasper Municipal

Library; Keephills Public Library; Leduc Public Library; M Alice Frose Library; Mayerthorpe Public Library; Millet Public Library; Neerlandia Public Library; New Sarepta Public Library; Onoway Public Library; Pigeon Lake Public Library; Rich Valley Public Library; Sangudo Public Library; Seba Beach Public Library; Spruce Grove Public Library; Stony Plain Public Library; Swan Hills Municipal Library; Thorsby Municipal Library; Tomahawk Public Library; Wabamun Public Library; Warburg Public Library; Westlock Municipal Library; Wetaskiwin Public Library; Wildwood Public Library
Partic in The Regional Automation Consortium (TRAC)
Open Mon-Fri 8:30-4:30

SPRUCE VIEW

P   SPRUCE VIEW PUBLIC LIBRARY*, Hwy 54, T0M 1V0. (Mail add: PO Box 130, T0M 1V0). Tel: 403-728-0012. FAX: 403-728-3155. E-mail: svlibrary@libs.prl.ab.ca. Web Site: svlibrary.prl.ab.ca. *Libr Mgr,* Paddy Birkeland
Library Holdings: Bk Vols 22,000
Automation Activity & Vendor Info: (Cataloging) SirsiDynix; (Circulation) SirsiDynix; (OPAC) SirsiDynix
Wireless access
Mem of Parkland Regional Library
Open Mon, Tues & Thurs 11-4, Wed 11-8

ST. ALBERT

GL   ALBERTA LAW LIBRARIES - ST ALBERT*, Courthouse, Three Saint Anne St, T8N 2E8. Tel: 780-458-7300. FAX: 780-460-2963. *Libr Coordr,* Louise Byrne; E-mail: louise.byrne@gov.ab.ca; Staff 1 (Non-MLS 1)
Open Mon 8:15-12:15, Tues 8:30-3

S   MUSEE HERITAGE MUSEUM*, Museum & Archives, Five Saint Anne St, T8N 3Z9. SAN 373-6245. Tel: 780-459-1528. FAX: 780-459-1232. E-mail: museum@artsheritage.ca. Web Site: www.museeheritage.com. *Dir,* Ann Ramsden
Founded 1984
Library Holdings: Bk Titles 1,000
Special Collections: Oral History
Subject Interests: Museology
Function: Res libr
Restriction: Not a lending libr, Open by appt only
Friends of the Library Group

P   ST ALBERT PUBLIC LIBRARY, Five Saint Anne St, T8N 3Z9. SAN 321-5784. Tel: 780-459-1530. FAX: 780-458-5772. E-mail: sapl@sapl.ab.ca. Web Site: www.sapl.ab.ca. *Libr Dir,* Peter Bailey; E-mail: pbailey@sapl.ab.ca; *Pub Serv Mgr,* Heather Dolman; E-mail: hdolman@sapl.ab.ca; *Tech & Support Mgr,* Pat Fader; E-mail: pfader@sapl.ab.ca; *Ch,* Barbara Moreau; E-mail: bmoreau@sapl.ab.ca; *Circ,* Kathleen Troppmann; E-mail: ktroppmann@sapl.ab.ca; Staff 32.5 (MLS 5, Non-MLS 27.5)
Founded 1961. Pop 60,994; Circ 885,363
Library Holdings: Audiobooks 5,096; AV Mats 24,526; Bks on Deafness & Sign Lang 208; Braille Volumes 11; CDs 8,491; DVDs 9,670; e-books 15,199; e-journals 36,000; High Interest/Low Vocabulary Bk Vols 84; Large Print Bks 3,929; Microforms 171; Bk Titles 151,845; Bk Vols 155,349; Per Subs 375
Special Collections: Can
Automation Activity & Vendor Info: (Acquisitions) SirsiDynix; (Cataloging) SirsiDynix; (Circulation) SirsiDynix; (ILL) SirsiDynix; (OPAC) BiblioCommons
Database Vendor: Alexander Street Press, BiblioCommons, EBSCOhost, Gale Cengage Learning, ProQuest, World Book Online
Wireless access
Partic in The Alberta Library
Open Mon-Thurs 9-9, Fri 9-6, Sat 9-5, Sun 1-5
Friends of the Library Group

ST. ISIDORE

P   BIBLIOTHEQUE DE ST ISIDORE*, PO Box 1168, T0H 3B0. Tel: 780-624-8192. FAX: 780-624-8192. *Librn,* Marie Lavoie; E-mail: marielavoie@bibliothequestisidore.ab.ca
Library Holdings: Bk Vols 3,000
Mem of Peace Library System
Open Mon-Fri 9-12 & 1-4:30

ST. PAUL

P   SAINT PAUL MUNICIPAL LIBRARY*, 4802-53 St, T0A 3A0. SAN 318-7241. Tel: 780-645-4904. FAX: 780-645-5198. E-mail: librarian@stpaullibrary.ab.ca. Web Site: www.stpaullibrary.ab.ca. *Libr Mgr,* Kerry Trottier; Staff 3 (Non-MLS 3)
Founded 1935. Pop 5,114; Circ 44,000

Library Holdings: CDs 290; DVDs 50; Bk Titles 24,000; Per Subs 35; Videos 1,200
Wireless access
Function: Computers for patron use, Handicapped accessible, Homebound delivery serv, ILL available, Large print keyboards, Music CDs, Online searches, Orientations, Photocopying/Printing, Prog for adults, Prog for children & young adult, Serves mentally handicapped consumers, Spoken cassettes & CDs, Spoken cassettes & DVDs, Summer reading prog, Telephone ref, VHS videos, Workshops
Mem of Northern Lights Library System
Open Tues-Thurs (Sept-June) 10-8, Fri & Sat 10-5; Mon, Wed & Fri (July & Aug) 10-5, Tues & Thurs 10-8
Friends of the Library Group

STANDARD

P   STANDARD MUNICIPAL LIBRARY*, PO Box 305, T0J 3G0. SAN 324-0401. Tel: 403-644-3995. E-mail: astmlibrary@marigold.ab.ca. *Libr Mgr,* Adreena Harder
Founded 1982. Pop 375; Circ 2,275
Library Holdings: Bk Titles 10,000; Per Subs 15
Wireless access
Mem of Marigold Library System
Open Mon & Tues 3-7, Wed & Sat 10-3
Friends of the Library Group

STAVELY

P   STAVELY MUNICIPAL LIBRARY, 4823 49th St, T0L 1Z0. (Mail add: PO Box 100, T0L 1Z0). Tel: 403-549-2190. FAX: 403-549-2190. E-mail: libsta@chinookarch.ab.ca. Web Site: www.stavely.ca/municipal-library.htm. *Librn,* Bev Olsen
Pop 455
Library Holdings: Bk Vols 5,000
Automation Activity & Vendor Info: (Acquisitions) SirsiDynix; (Cataloging) SirsiDynix; (Circulation) SirsiDynix; (ILL) SirsiDynix
Database Vendor: Gale Cengage Learning
Wireless access
Open Mon 1:30-6, Tues 9-5, Wed 1:30-7, Thurs 1:30-5

STETTLER

P   STETTLER PUBLIC LIBRARY*, 6202 44th Ave, 2nd Flr, T0C 2L1. SAN 318-7322. Tel: 403-742-2292. FAX: 403-742-5481. E-mail: spl@libs.prl.ab.ca. Web Site: spl.prl.ab.ca. *Head Librn,* Mary Zazelenchuk; *Asst Librn,* Crystal Friars; Staff 2 (MLS 1, Non-MLS 1)
Pop 10,583; Circ 56,000
Library Holdings: AV Mats 1,169; Bk Vols 30,000; Per Subs 60
Automation Activity & Vendor Info: (Circulation) Horizon; (OPAC) Horizon; (Serials) Horizon
Wireless access
Mem of Parkland Regional Library
Open Mon, Tues, Fri & Sat 10-6, Wed & Thurs 10-8
Friends of the Library Group

STIRLING

P   STIRLING MUNICIPAL LIBRARY*, Theodore Brandley Library, PO Box 100, T0K 2E0. Tel: 403-756-3665. E-mail: libstir@chinookarch.ab.ca. Web Site: www.stirlinglibrary.ca. *Dir, Libr Serv,* Laura Quinton; *Librn,* Sheila Cooper-Bikman
Pop 1,041
Library Holdings: Bk Titles 10,000; Bk Vols 13,000
Automation Activity & Vendor Info: (Acquisitions) SirsiDynix; (Cataloging) SirsiDynix; (Circulation) SirsiDynix; (Course Reserve) SirsiDynix; (ILL) SirsiDynix; (Media Booking) SirsiDynix; (OPAC) SirsiDynix; (Serials) SirsiDynix
Database Vendor: Gale Cengage Learning
Wireless access
Open Mon 2-5, Tues & Thurs 1-7, Wed 2-7, Fri 5-8; Mon-Wed & Fri (Summer) 10-5, Thurs 10-7

STONY PLAIN

GL   ALBERTA LAW LIBRARIES - STONY PLAIN*, Courthouse, 4711-44th Ave, T7Z 1N5. Tel: 780-458-7300, Ext 240. FAX: 780-963-6402.

P   STONY PLAIN PUBLIC LIBRARY*, 4613-52 Ave, No 112, T7Z 1E7. SAN 373-7268. Tel: 780-963-5440. FAX: 780-963-1746. E-mail: info@stonyplainlibrary.org. Web Site: www.stonyplainlibrary.org. *Dir,* Tamara Van Biert; Staff 7 (Non-MLS 7)
Founded 1945. Pop 10,544
Library Holdings: CDs 342; Bk Titles 40,000; Per Subs 86; Talking Bks 1,025; Videos 1,296
Special Collections: Parkland Adult Literacy Coll
Subject Interests: Parenting

Automation Activity & Vendor Info: (Acquisitions) SirsiDynix; (Cataloging) SirsiDynix; (Circulation) SirsiDynix; (Course Reserve) SirsiDynix; (ILL) SirsiDynix; (Media Booking) SirsiDynix; (OPAC) SirsiDynix; (Serials) SirsiDynix
Database Vendor: SirsiDynix
Mem of Yellowhead Regional Library
Open Mon-Fri 10-8, Sat 10-5
Friends of the Library Group

STRATHMORE

P   MARIGOLD LIBRARY SYSTEM*, 710-Second St, T1P 1K4. SAN 321-3447. Tel: 403-934-5334. Toll Free Tel: 1-855-934-5334. FAX: 403-934-5331. E-mail: admin@marigold.ab.ca. Web Site: www.marigold.ab.ca. *Dir,* Michelle Toombs; Tel: 403-934-5334, Ext 224, E-mail: michelle@marigold.ab.ca; *Asst Dir,* Laura Taylor; Tel: 403-934-5334, Ext 242, E-mail: laura@marigold.ab.ca; *Mgr, Bibliog Serv,* Margaret Newton; Tel: 403-934-5334, Ext 233, E-mail: margaret@marigold.ab.ca; *Communications & Info,* Carlee Pilikowski; Tel: 403-934-5334, Ext 237, E-mail: carlee@marigold.ab.ca; Staff 9 (MLS 7, Non-MLS 2)
Founded 1981. Pop 238,827; Circ 1,047,084
Jan 2007-Dec 2007 Income (CAN) $3,111,305, Provincial (CAN) $719,832, City (CAN) $1,404,582, Locally Generated Income (CAN) $68,176, Other (CAN) $918,715. Mats Exp (CAN) $526,437, Books (CAN) $485,086, Electronic Ref Mat (Incl. Access Fees) (CAN) $41,351. Sal (CAN) $918,403
Library Holdings: Electronic Media & Resources 43; Bk Vols 496,494; Per Subs 15
Special Collections: Complementary & Alternative Medicine Coll; Professional Literature Coll
Database Vendor: SirsiDynix
Wireless access
Publications: Advocacy!@your Library (Bi-monthly); Annual Report; Marigold Report (Monthly); Member Library Newsletter (Monthly)
Member Libraries: Acadia Municipal Library; Acme Municipal Library; Airdrie Public Library; Beiseker Municipal Library; Berry Creek Community Library; Bighorn Library; Canmore Public Library; Carbon Municipal Library; Carseland Public Library; Cereal & District Municipal Library; Chestermere Public Library; Cochrane Public Library; Consort Municipal Library; Delia Municipal Library; Drumheller Public Library; Empress Municipal Library; Gleichen & District Library; Hanna Municipal Library; High River Centennial Library; Hussar Municipal Library; Irricana Library; Linden Municipal Library; Longview Municipal Library; Millarville Community Library; Morrin Municipal Library; Okotoks Public Library; Oyen Municipal Library; Rockyford Municipal Library; Rumsey Community Library; Sheep River Library; Standard Municipal Library; Strathmore Municipal Library; Three Hills Municipal Library; Trochu Municipal Library; Youngstown Municipal Library
Partic in The Alberta Library; The Regional Automation Consortium (TRAC)
Special Services for the Blind - Daisy reader

P   STRATHMORE MUNICIPAL LIBRARY*, 85 Lakeside Blvd, T1P 1A1. SAN 318-7330. Tel: 403-934-5440. FAX: 403-934-1908. E-mail: asmlibrary@marigold.ab.ca. Web Site: www.strathmorelibrary.ca. *Libr Mgr,* Jesse Traquair; E-mail: asmlibmgr@marigold.ab.ca; Staff 6 (MLS 1, Non-MLS 5)
Pop 12,139; Circ 101,000
Library Holdings: Bk Vols 36,000; Per Subs 35
Wireless access
Mem of Marigold Library System
Open Mon-Fri 10-7, Sat 10-5

SUNDRE

P   SUNDRE MUNICIPAL LIBRARY, 310 Center St N, T0M 1X0. (Mail add: PO Box 539, T0M 1X0). Tel: 403-638-4000. FAX: 403-638-5755. E-mail: sundrelibrary@libs.prl.ab.ca. Web Site: sundre.prl.ab.ca. *Libr Dir,* Jennifer MacKinnon; Staff 1 (MLS 1)
Founded 1947. Pop 5,600
Library Holdings: Bk Vols 25,000
Automation Activity & Vendor Info: (Acquisitions) SirsiDynix; (Cataloging) SirsiDynix; (Circulation) SirsiDynix; (Serials) SirsiDynix
Wireless access
Mem of Parkland Regional Library
Partic in The Alberta Library
Special Services for the Blind - Daisy reader
Open Tues & Fri 12-5, Wed 12-8, Thurs 9-5, Sat 11-3
Friends of the Library Group

SWAN HILLS

P   SWAN HILLS MUNICIPAL LIBRARY*, 5536 Main St, T0G 2C0. (Mail add: PO Box 386, TOG 2CO), SAN 325-240X. Tel: 780-333-4505. FAX: 780-333-4551. Web Site: swanhillslibrary.ab.ca. *Librn*, Nancy Keough; E-mail: nkeough@yrl.ab.ca

Founded 1970. Pop 1,807; Circ 15,097

Library Holdings: AV Mats 500; Bk Titles 14,216; Per Subs 21; Talking Bks 100

Database Vendor: SirsiDynix

Wireless access

Mem of Yellowhead Regional Library

Partic in The Alberta Library; The Regional Automation Consortium (TRAC)

Open Mon 1-5, Tues & Thurs 1-5 & 7-9, Wed 10-5, Sat 1-4

Friends of the Library Group

SYLVAN LAKE

P   SYLVAN LAKE MUNICIPAL LIBRARY*, 4715-50 Ave, T4S 1A2. Tel: 403-887-2130. FAX: 403-887-0537. E-mail: sylvan.library@libs.prl.ab.ca. Web Site: sylvanlibrary.prl.ab.ca. *Dir*, Shannan Sword

Pop 13,000

Library Holdings: Bk Vols 35,000

Database Vendor: SirsiDynix

Wireless access

Function: ILL available, Photocopying/Printing, Ref serv available

Mem of Parkland Regional Library

Open Mon 1-8, Tues-Thurs 10-8, Fri & Sat 10-5, Sun 1-5

TABER

P   TABER PUBLIC LIBRARY, 5415 50 Ave, T1G 1V2. SAN 318-7349. Tel: 403-223-4343. FAX: 403-223-4314. E-mail: libtab@chinookarch.ab.ca. Web Site: www.taberlibrary.ca. *Libr Mgr*, Diane Zelenka

Pop 8,100; Circ 75,873

Library Holdings: Bk Vols 40,000; Per Subs 51

Special Collections: CNIB Daisy Books

Database Vendor: SirsiDynix

Wireless access

Publications: Newsletter (Quarterly)

Open Tues, Wed & Sat 10-5:30, Thurs & Fri 10-9

TANGENT

P   TANGENT COMMUNITY LIBRARY*, PO Box 63, T0H 3J0. Tel: 780-837-6443. *Librn*, Janice Brassard

Library Holdings: Bk Vols 8,000

Mem of Peace Library System

Open Tues 1-5, Thurs 12-4

THORHILD

P   THORHILD LIBRARY, 210 Seventh Ave, T0A 3J0. (Mail add: PO Box 658, T0A 3J0). Tel: 780-398-3502. FAX: 780-398-3504. E-mail: librarian@thorhildlibrary.ab.ca. Web Site: www.thorhildlibrary.ab.ca. *Libr Mgr*, Rose Alexander

Library Holdings: Audiobooks 200; CDs 500; DVDs 450; Bk Vols 10,000; Per Subs 20; Talking Bks 100; Videos 500

Automation Activity & Vendor Info: (Acquisitions) Polaris Library Systems; (Cataloging) Polaris Library Systems; (Circulation) Polaris Library Systems

Database Vendor: Polaris Library Systems, SirsiDynix

Wireless access

Mem of Northern Lights Library System

Open Tues-Thurs (Winter) 10-1 & 2-7, Fri & Sat 10-1; Mon & Fri (Summer) 8:30-4:30, Tues-Thurs 9-7, Sat 9-1

Friends of the Library Group

THORSBY

P   THORSBY MUNICIPAL LIBRARY, 4901 - 48 Ave, T0C 2P0. (Mail add: Box 680, T0C 2P0). Tel: 780-789-3808. FAX: 780-789-3805. E-mail: thorsbypublib@yrl.ab.ca. Web Site: www.thorsbymunicipallibrary.ab.ca. *Libr Dir*, Louise Normandeau

Pop 799

Library Holdings: Bk Vols 8,000

Automation Activity & Vendor Info: (Acquisitions) SirsiDynix; (Cataloging) SirsiDynix; (Circulation) SirsiDynix; (ILL) SirsiDynix

Mem of Yellowhead Regional Library

Open Tues & Thurs (Winter) 12:30-7, Wed 12:30-8; Tues-Thurs (Summer) 12-7

THREE HILLS

CR   PRAIRIE BIBLE INSTITUTE*, T S Rendall Library, 330 Fourth Ave N, T0M 2N0. (Mail add: Box 4000, T0M 2N0), SAN 320-3050. Tel: 403-443-8029. FAX: 403-443-5540. E-mail: library@prairie.edu. Web Site: www.prairie.edu/library. *Libr Dir*, Veronica Lewis; Tel: 403-443-5511, Ext 3343, E-mail: veronica.lewis@prairie.edu; Staff 2 (MLS 2)

Founded 1922. Enrl 300; Highest Degree: Bachelor

Library Holdings: AV Mats 550; Music Scores 71,600; Bk Titles 56,000; Bk Vols 68,000; Per Subs 125; Videos 400

Subject Interests: Relig studies

Automation Activity & Vendor Info: (Acquisitions) SirsiDynix; (Cataloging) SirsiDynix; (Circulation) SirsiDynix; (Course Reserve) SirsiDynix; (OPAC) SirsiDynix; (Serials) SirsiDynix

Database Vendor: EBSCOhost

Wireless access

Open Mon-Thurs 8am-10pm, Fri 8-7

P   THREE HILLS MUNICIPAL LIBRARY*, 160 Third Ave S, T0M 2A0. (Mail add: PO Box 207, T0M 2A0), SAN 318-7357. Tel: 403-443-2360. E-mail: athmlibrary@marigold.ab.ca. Web Site: www.3hillslibrary.com. *Libr Mgr*, Karen Nickel; *Libr Mgr*, Cathy Rendall

Pop 3,322; Circ 30,869

Library Holdings: Bk Vols 16,000; Per Subs 65

Automation Activity & Vendor Info: (Acquisitions) Polaris Library Systems; (Cataloging) Polaris Library Systems; (Circulation) Polaris Library Systems; (Course Reserve) Polaris Library Systems; (ILL) Polaris Library Systems; (Media Booking) Polaris Library Systems; (OPAC) Polaris Library Systems; (Serials) Polaris Library Systems

Database Vendor: Polaris Library Systems

Wireless access

Mem of Marigold Library System

Special Services for the Blind - Talking bks

Open Tues-Fri 10-8, Sat 10-3

TILLEY

P   TILLEY DISTRICT & PUBLIC LIBRARY*, 148 First St E, T0J 3K0. (Mail add: PO Box 177, T0J 3K0). Tel: 403-377-2233, Ext 150. FAX: 403-377-2097. Web Site: www.shortgrass-lib.ab.ca/tpl. *Libr Mgr*, Brenda Arnold

Pop 422

Library Holdings: Bk Vols 11,000

Open Mon (Sept-June) 7pm-9pm, Wed 9-11 & 7-9, Sat 10-Noon; Mon & Sat (July-Aug) 10-Noon, Wed 1-4 & 7-9

TOMAHAWK

P   TOMAHAWK PUBLIC LIBRARY*, PO Box 69, T0E 2H0. Tel: 780-339-3935. FAX: 780-339-2121. *Librn*, Chris Goerz; E-mail: cgoerz@psd70.ab.ca

Library Holdings: Bk Vols 5,000; Per Subs 25

Automation Activity & Vendor Info: (Acquisitions) SirsiDynix; (Cataloging) SirsiDynix; (Circulation) SirsiDynix; (Course Reserve) SirsiDynix; (ILL) SirsiDynix; (Media Booking) SirsiDynix; (OPAC) SirsiDynix

Mem of Wisconsin Valley Library Service; Yellowhead Regional Library

Open Tues & Thurs 8:30-4, Wed 11-7, Fri 11-5

TROCHU

P   TROCHU MUNICIPAL LIBRARY*, 317 Main St, T0M 2C0. (Mail add: PO Box 396, T0M 2C0), SAN 372-6657. Tel: 403-442-2458. E-mail: atrmlibrary@marigold.ab.ca, atrmlibrary@telusplanet.net. *Libr Mgr*, Sherie Campbell; Staff 1 (Non-MLS 1)

Founded 1958. Pop 1,113; Circ 5,073

Library Holdings: Bk Titles 10,000; Per Subs 10

Subject Interests: Local hist, Music

Automation Activity & Vendor Info: (Circulation) SirsiDynix

Mem of Marigold Library System

Open Wed-Fri 10:30-5:30

TURNER VALLEY

P   SHEEP RIVER LIBRARY, 129 Main St NE, T0L 2A0. (Mail add: PO Bag 10, T0L 2A0), SAN 325-2485. Tel: 403-933-3278. FAX: 403-933-3298. E-mail: abdsrclibrary@marigold.ab.ca. Web Site: www.sheepriverlibrary.ca. *Libr Mgr*, Jan Burney; *Libr Tech*, Gita Grahame; Staff 4 (Non-MLS 4)

Founded 1981. Pop 4,500; Circ 38,554

Library Holdings: CDs 222; DVDs 683; Large Print Bks 500; Bk Titles 18,532; Per Subs 69; Talking Bks 808

Wireless access

Function: Adult bk club, Bk club(s), Fax serv, Handicapped accessible, ILL available, Photocopying/Printing, Prog for adults, Prog for children & young adult, Scanner

Mem of Marigold Library System
Partic in The Alberta Library
Open Mon, Fri & Sat 10-5, Tues-Thurs 10-8
Friends of the Library Group

TWO HILLS

P   ALICE MELNYK PUBLIC LIBRARY*, Two Hills Public Library, 5009
     50th Ave, T0B 4K0. (Mail add: PO Box 460, T0B 4K0), SAN 318-7373.
     Tel: 780-657-3553. FAX: 780-657-3553. E-mail:
     librarian@twohillslibrary.ab.ca. Web Site: www.twohillslibrary.ab.ca. *Libr
     Mgr,* Cheryl Paulichuk
     Pop 1,250; Circ 14,000
     Library Holdings: Audiobooks 30; CDs 230; DVDs 800; Large Print Bks
     30; Bk Titles 8,000; Bk Vols 12,000; Talking Bks 12; Videos 470
     Automation Activity & Vendor Info: (Circulation) Polaris Library
     Systems; (ILL) Polaris Library Systems
     Database Vendor: EBSCO Information Services, Overdrive, Inc, Polaris
     Library Systems
     Wireless access
     Mem of Northern Lights Library System
     Open Mon, Tues, Thurs & Fri (Sept-June) 9:30-4, Wed 11-6; Mon-Fri
     (July & Aug) 9-5:30

VALHALLA CENTRE

P   VALHALLA PUBLIC LIBRARY*, PO Box 68, T0H 3M0. Tel:
     780-356-3834. FAX: 780-356-3834. E-mail: librarian@valhallalibrary.ab.ca.
     Librn, Gail Perry
     Library Holdings: Bk Vols 8,000
     Automation Activity & Vendor Info: (Circulation) Polaris Library
     Systems; (OPAC) Polaris Library Systems
     Mem of Peace Library System
     Open Mon & Thurs 11-4, Wed 11-5

VALLEYVIEW

P   VALLEYVIEW MUNICIPAL LIBRARY*, 4804 50th Ave, T0H 3N0.
     (Mail add: PO Box 897, T0H 3N0), SAN 321-3595. Tel: 780-524-3033.
     FAX: 780-524-4563. E-mail: librarian@valleyviewlibrary.ab.ca. Web Site:
     www.valleyviewlibrary.ab.ca. *Libr Mgr,* Susanne Tremblay; *Asst Mgr,* Pat
     Mabley; E-mail: pat@valleyviewlibrary.ab.ca; Staff 1 (Non-MLS 1)
     Founded 1970. Pop 7,000; Circ 28,000
     Library Holdings: Bks on Deafness & Sign Lang 10; CDs 150; DVDs
     500; Bk Titles 27,000; Per Subs 40; Videos 450
     Special Collections: Art Gallery Featuring Local Exhibitors; Pictorial
     History of Valleyview & District
     Automation Activity & Vendor Info: (Cataloging) Polaris Library
     Systems; (Circulation) Polaris Library Systems; (OPAC) Polaris Library
     Systems
     Database Vendor: EBSCOhost, Gale Cengage Learning
     Function: Adult bk club, Adult literacy prog, Art exhibits, Bks on cassette,
     Bks on CD, CD-ROM, Chess club, Computers for patron use, Copy
     machines, e-mail serv, Family literacy, Fax serv, Govt ref serv,
     Handicapped accessible, ILL available, Music CDs, Online cat, Online info
     literacy tutorials on the web & in blackboard, Online searches,
     Photocopying/Printing, Prog for children & young adult, Pub access
     computers, Scanner, Spoken cassettes & CDs, Summer reading prog, VHS
     videos, Wheelchair accessible
     Mem of Peace Library System
     Partic in The Regional Automation Consortium (TRAC)
     Special Services for the Deaf - Bks on deafness & sign lang; Closed
     caption videos
     Special Services for the Blind - Bks on cassette; Bks on CD; Daisy reader;
     Large print bks; Recorded bks; Talking bk serv referral; Talking bks
     Open Tues-Thurs 11-7, Fri & Sat 11-5

VAUXHALL

P   VAUXHALL PUBLIC LIBRARY*, PO Box 265, T0K 2K0. Tel:
     403-654-2370. FAX: 403-654-2370. E-mail: libvau@chinookarch.ab.ca.
     Librn, Sarah Fehr
     Pop 1,112
     Library Holdings: Bk Vols 1,100
     Open Tues & Wed 10-1 & 2-6, Thurs 2-8, Fri 2-6, Sat 10-1
     Friends of the Library Group

VEGREVILLE

P   VEGREVILLE CENTENNIAL LIBRARY*, 4709 50th St, T9C 1R1. (Mail
     add: PO Box 129, T9C 1R1), SAN 318-7381. Tel: 780-632-3491. FAX:
     780-603-2338. E-mail: library@vegreville.com. Web Site:
     www.vegrevillelibrary.ab.ca. *Mgr, Libr Serv,* Kenneth Allan; Staff 10 (MLS
     1, Non-MLS 9)
     Founded 1920. Pop 6,000
     Library Holdings: Bk Vols 40,000; Per Subs 50

Wireless access
Function: Adult bk club, Art exhibits, Bks on cassette, Bks on CD,
Children's prog, Computers for patron use, E-Reserves, Free DVD rentals,
Home delivery & serv to Sr ctr & nursing homes, Homebound delivery
serv, ILL available, Music CDs, Online cat, Photocopying/Printing, Prog
for children & young adult, Ref serv available, Serves mentally
handicapped consumers, Story hour, Summer reading prog
Mem of Northern Lights Library System
Partic in The Alberta Library
Special Services for the Blind - Bks on cassette; Bks on CD; Large print
bks; Talking bks
Open Mon-Thurs (Nov-May) 10-9, Fri 10-6, Sat & Sun 12-4; Mon, Wed &
Fri (June-Oct) 10-6, Tues & Thurs 10-9

VERMILION

GL   ALBERTA LAW LIBRARIES - VERMILION*, Provincial Bldg,
     4701-42nd St, T9X 1J9. Tel: 780-853-8249. FAX: 780-853-8200. *Libr
     Coordr,* Crystal Gilbertson; E-mail: dawn.newberry@gov.ab.ca; Staff 1
     (Non-MLS 1)
     Library Holdings: Bk Vols 6,400
     Open Mon 8:30-2

C   LAKELAND COLLEGE LIBRARY*, 5707 College Dr, T9X 1K5. SAN
     320-3115. Tel: 780-853-8460. Interlibrary Loan Service Tel: 780-871-5796.
     FAX: 780-853-8662. Web Site: www.lakelandcollege.ca/library. *Chair,*
     Angela Wilm; Staff 8 (MLS 3, Non-MLS 5)
     Founded 1913
     Library Holdings: Bk Vols 90,000
     Subject Interests: Agr, Arts, Environ, Life sci, Soc sci
     Wireless access
     Partic in NEOS Library Consortium
     Open Mon-Thurs 8:15am-10pm, Fri 8:15-4:30, Sat & Sun 12-6

P   VERMILION PUBLIC LIBRARY, 5001 49th Ave, T9X 1B8. SAN
     318-739X. Tel: 780-853-4288. FAX: 780-853-1783. E-mail:
     admin@vermilionpubliclibrary.ca. Web Site: www.vplibrary.ca. *Libr Mgr,*
     Stuart Pauls; Staff 3.32 (Non-MLS 3.32)
     Founded 1932. Pop 4,435; Circ 58,000
     Library Holdings: AV Mats 67; CDs 306; Large Print Bks 1,500; Bk Vols
     20,000; Per Subs 70; Talking Bks 415; Videos 1,500
     Special Collections: Local Newspaper 1900-present, micro
     Subject Interests: Bus, Local hist
     Function: Computer training, Copy machines, Electronic databases & coll,
     Fax serv, Genealogy discussion group, Handicapped accessible, Home
     delivery & serv to Sr ctr & nursing homes, Homebound delivery serv, ILL
     available, Photocopying/Printing, Prog for adults, Prog for children &
     young adult, Ref serv available, Spoken cassettes & CDs, Summer reading
     prog, VHS videos, Wheelchair accessible
     Mem of Northern Lights Library System
     Partic in The Regional Automation Consortium (TRAC)
     Open Tues-Thurs 10-7, Fri & Sat 10-5
     Friends of the Library Group

VETERAN

P   VETERAN MUNICIPAL LIBRARY*, 201 Lucknow St, T0C 2S0. (Mail
     add: Box 527, T0C 2S0). Tel: 403-575-3915. FAX: 403-575-3870. *Librn,*
     Nicole Larson; E-mail: nicole.larson@plrd.ab.ca
     Pop 293
     Library Holdings: Bk Vols 8,000
     Open Mon, Wed & Fri 12:15-4:15, Tues & Thurs 12:15-4:15 & 7-9

VIKING

P   VIKING MUNICIPAL LIBRARY*, PO Box 300, T0B 4N0. SAN
     318-7403. Tel: 780-336-4992. FAX: 780-336-4992. E-mail:
     librarian@vikinglibrary.ab.ca. *Librn,* Maryann Wolosinka
     Pop 1,800; Circ 8,336
     Library Holdings: Bk Vols 8,813
     Mem of Northern Lights Library System
     Partic in Northern Lights Library Network
     Open Tues 3-8, Wed 10-5, Thurs 10-8
     Friends of the Library Group

VILNA

P   VILNA MUNICIPAL LIBRARY*, 5431-50th St, T0A 3L0. (Mail add: PO
     Box 119, T0A 3L0). Tel: 780-636-2077. FAX: 780-636-3243. E-mail:
     librarian@vilnapubliclibrary.ab.ca. Web Site: www.vilnapubliclibrary.ab.ca.
     Libr Mgr, Roxanne Long
     Library Holdings: Bk Vols 7,000
     Automation Activity & Vendor Info: (Cataloging) SirsiDynix;
     (Circulation) SirsiDynix; (OPAC) SirsiDynix
     Mem of Northern Lights Library System
     Open Tues & Thurs 3:30-7:30, Sat 12-4

VULCAN

P   VULCAN MUNICIPAL LIBRARY*, 303 Centre St, T0L 2B0. (Mail add: PO Box 1120, T0L 2B0), SAN 318-7411. Tel: 403-485-2571. FAX: 403-485-2571. E-mail: libvul@chinookarch.ca. Web Site: www.vulcanlibrary.ca. *Mgr,* Penny Allen; E-mail: pallen@vulcanlibrary.ca
Pop 1,800; Circ 20,000
Library Holdings: Audiobooks 321; CDs 150; DVDs 200; Bk Titles 13,314; Per Subs 4; Videos 800
Automation Activity & Vendor Info: (Cataloging) SirsiDynix; (Circulation) SirsiDynix; (OPAC) SirsiDynix
Wireless access
Function: Adult bk club, Art exhibits, Audio & video playback equip for onsite use, Bks on cassette, Bks on CD, Children's prog, Computer training, Computers for patron use, Copy machines, e-mail & chat, e-mail serv, Electronic databases & coll, Fax serv, Free DVD rentals, Home delivery & serv to Sr ctr & nursing homes, ILL available, Music CDs, Online cat, Online ref, Photocopying/Printing, Prog for children & young adult, Pub access computers, Story hour, Summer reading prog, Wheelchair accessible
Open Mon, Wed & Fri 11-5, Tues 10-5, Thurs 10-6, Sat 11-3
Friends of the Library Group

WABAMUN

P   WABAMUN PUBLIC LIBRARY*, 5132 53rd Ave, T0E 2K0. (Mail add: PO Box 89, T0E 2K0). Tel: 780-892-2713. FAX: 780-892-7294. Web Site: www.wabamunlibrary.ca. *Librn,* Betty Lalonde; E-mail: bettyl@wabamunlibrary.ca
Pop 664
Library Holdings: AV Mats 1,500; Bk Vols 15,000; Per Subs 45; Talking Bks 172
Automation Activity & Vendor Info: (Cataloging) Polaris Library Systems; (Circulation) Polaris Library Systems; (OPAC) Polaris Library Systems
Mem of Yellowhead Regional Library
Open Tues & Wed 11-8:30, Thurs & Fri 11-5, Sat 11-2
Friends of the Library Group

WABASCA

P   WABASCA PUBLIC LIBRARY*, PO Box 638, T0G 2K0. Tel: 780-891-2203. FAX: 780-891-2402. E-mail: wabpl@telus.net. Web Site: www.wabasca.com/library. *Libr Mgr,* Joy Grant
Library Holdings: Bk Vols 20,000
Automation Activity & Vendor Info: (Cataloging) Polaris Library Systems; (Circulation) Polaris Library Systems; (OPAC) Polaris Library Systems
Wireless access
Mem of Peace Library System
Open Tues 12-7, Wed & Thurs 12-8, Fri & Sat 10-4

WAINWRIGHT

P   WAINWRIGHT PUBLIC LIBRARY*, 921 Third Ave, T9W 1C5. SAN 325-2051. Tel: 780-842-2673. FAX: 780-842-2340. E-mail: librarian@wainwrightlibrary.ab.ca. Web Site: www.wainwrightlibrary.ab.ca. *Libr Mgr,* Jodi Dahlgren; *Asst Librn,* Ginette Crandall
Pop 5,365; Circ 50,000
Library Holdings: Bk Titles 21,500; Bk Vols 27,000; Per Subs 44
Automation Activity & Vendor Info: (Cataloging) SirsiDynix; (Circulation) SirsiDynix
Mem of Northern Lights Library System
Partic in Northern Lights Library Network
Open Mon, Wed & Fri 10-6, Tues & Thurs 10-8, Sat (Sept-June) 12-4

WARBURG

P   WARBURG PUBLIC LIBRARY, 5212 50 Ave, T0C 2T0. (Mail add: PO Box 299, T0C 2T0). Tel: 780-848-2391. FAX: 780-848-2296. E-mail: warburglibrary@yrl.ab.ca. *Librn,* Gail O'Neil
Pop 721
Library Holdings: Bk Vols 9,000; Per Subs 15
Automation Activity & Vendor Info: (Acquisitions) Polaris Library Systems; (Cataloging) Polaris Library Systems; (Circulation) Polaris Library Systems; (ILL) Polaris Library Systems; (Serials) Polaris Library Systems
Database Vendor: Gale Cengage Learning
Mem of Yellowhead Regional Library
Open Tues-Thurs 10-6, Sat 12-4

WARNER

P   WARNER MEMORIAL LIBRARY*, PO Box 270, T0K 2L0. SAN 318-7438. Tel: 403-642-3988. E-mail: wml@chinookarch.ab.ca. *Librn,* Andrea Tapp; *Asst Librn,* Penny Pittman
Pop 379; Circ 3,576
Library Holdings: Bk Vols 18,000; Per Subs 10
Automation Activity & Vendor Info: (Cataloging) SirsiDynix; (Circulation) SirsiDynix
Wireless access
Open Tues & Thurs 11-6, Wed 2-8

WASKATENAU

P   ANNE CHORNEY PUBLIC LIBRARY*, 5125-51 St, T0A 3P0. (Mail add: PO Box 130, T0A 3P0). Tel: 780-358-2777. FAX: 780-358-2777. E-mail: librarian@waskatenaulibrary.ab.ca. Web Site: www.waskatenaulibrary.ab.ca. *Librn,* Goedele Kerckhof
Pop 252
Library Holdings: Bk Vols 15,000
Wireless access
Mem of Northern Lights Library System
Open Tues & Thurs (Sept-June) 12-7, Tues (July & Aug) 1:30-5

WATER VALLEY

P   WATER VALLEY PUBLIC LIBRARY*, PO Box 250, T0M 2E0. Tel: 403-637-3899. E-mail: watervalleylibrary@libs.prl.ab.ca. Web Site: watervalleycommunity.ca/library.html. *Libr Mgr,* Jaymee Shea
Founded 1950
Library Holdings: Bk Vols 8,000
Function: Children's prog, ILL available, Photocopying/Printing
Mem of Parkland Regional Library
Open Wed 9:30am-11:30am, Thurs 9:30-11:30 & 6:30-8:30, Sat 10-1
Friends of the Library Group

WESTLOCK

P   WESTLOCK MUNICIPAL LIBRARY*, 10007 100 Ave, No 1, T7P 2H5. SAN 318-7446. Tel: 780-349-3060. FAX: 780-349-5291. E-mail: info@westlocklibrary.ca. *Dir,* Doug Whistance-Smith
Founded 1945. Pop 17,000; Circ 75,000
Jan 2005-Dec 2005 Income (CAN) $135,953, Provincial (CAN) $50,103, City (CAN) $30,000, County (CAN) $30,000, Locally Generated Income (CAN) $25,850. Mats Exp (CAN) $14,000. Sal (CAN) $88,871
Library Holdings: Per Subs 52
Automation Activity & Vendor Info: (Cataloging) Polaris Library Systems; (Circulation) Polaris Library Systems; (OPAC) Polaris Library Systems
Mem of Yellowhead Regional Library
Partic in The Regional Automation Consortium (TRAC)
Special Services for the Blind - Talking bks
Open Mon-Fri 9:30-6, Sat 10-4
Friends of the Library Group

WETASKIWIN

S   REYNOLDS-ALBERTA MUSEUM REFERENCE CENTRE*, Two KMS W Hwy 13, T9A 2G1. (Mail add: PO Box 6360 Stn Main, T9A 2G1), SAN 318-7454. Tel: 780-361-1351, Ext 254, 780-361-1351, Ext 255. FAX: 780-361-1239. E-mail: refctr.ram@gov.ab.ca. Web Site: www.reynoldsalbertamuseum.com. *Curator,* Randy Kvill; E-mail: randy.kvill@gov.ab.ca; Staff 4 (MLS 1, Non-MLS 3)
Founded 1992
Library Holdings: Bk Titles 3,000; Per Subs 60; Spec Interest Per Sub 50
Special Collections: Original Trade Publications, manuals, sales literature, subject & advertising files
Subject Interests: Agr, Aviation, Hist of transportation, Indust, Motor vehicles
Automation Activity & Vendor Info: (Cataloging) SirsiDynix
Restriction: Non-circulating

P   WETASKIWIN PUBLIC LIBRARY*, 5002 51st Ave, T9A 0V1. SAN 318-7462. Tel: 780-361-4446. FAX: 780-352-3266. E-mail: library@wetaskiwin.ca. Web Site: www.westaskiwinpubliclibrary@ab.ca. *Mgr, Libr Serv,* Rachelle Kuzyk; E-mail: rkuzyk@wetaskiwin.ca; Staff 7 (MLS 1, Non-MLS 6)
Founded 1928. Pop 12,000; Circ 150,000
Library Holdings: Bk Titles 37,000; Per Subs 115
Special Collections: International Fiction Coll
Automation Activity & Vendor Info: (Cataloging) Polaris Library Systems; (Circulation) Polaris Library Systems
Database Vendor: EBSCOhost, Gale Cengage Learning
Mem of Yellowhead Regional Library
Open Mon-Thurs 10-8, Fri & Sat 10-5
Friends of the Library Group

WILDWOOD

P   WILDWOOD PUBLIC LIBRARY, 5215-50th St, T0E 2M0. (Mail add: PO Box 118, T0E 2M0). Tel: 780-325-3882. FAX: 780-325-3880. E-mail: wildwoodlibrary@yrl.ab.ca. Web Site: www.wildwoodlibrary.ab.ca. *Libr Mgr,* Terrie Stone
     Library Holdings: Bk Vols 18,000; Per Subs 52
     Automation Activity & Vendor Info: (Acquisitions) Polaris Library Systems; (Cataloging) Polaris Library Systems; (Circulation) Polaris Library Systems; (Course Reserve) Polaris Library Systems; (ILL) Polaris Library Systems; (Media Booking) Polaris Library Systems; (OPAC) Polaris Library Systems
     Wireless access
     Special Services for the Deaf - Bks on deafness & sign lang
     Special Services for the Blind - Accessible computers; Assistive/Adapted tech devices, equip & products; Bks & mags in Braille, on rec, tape & cassette; Bks available with recordings
     Open Mon-Wed & Fri 10-5, Thurs 10-8
     Friends of the Library Group

WILLINGDON

P   WILLINGDON PUBLIC LIBRARY*, 4911-52 Ave, T0B 4R0. (Mail add: PO Box 270, T0B 4R0), SAN 318-7489. Tel: 780-367-2146, 780-367-2642. E-mail: willingdonl.bry@digitalweb.net. *Chairperson,* Darlene Ezio; *Libr Mgr,* Frances Hols
     Pop 295
     Library Holdings: Bk Vols 13,302
     Open Tues 5-7

WINFIELD

P   WINFIELD PUBLIC LIBRARY*, PO Box 360, T0C 2X0. Tel: 780-682-2498. FAX: 780-682-2490. *Librn,* Lorna Smith
     Library Holdings: Large Print Bks 90; Bk Vols 20,000
     Open Tues 11-4 & 7-9

WORSLEY

P   WORSLEY & DISTRICT PUBLIC LIBRARY*, PO Box 246, T0H 3W0. Tel: 780-685-3842. FAX: 780-685-3766. E-mail: awdlib@hotmail.com. Web Site: www.worsleylibrary.ab.ca. *Librn,* Colleen Rook; E-mail: rookc@prsd.ab.ca
     Library Holdings: Bk Titles 3,000; Per Subs 15
     Automation Activity & Vendor Info: (Acquisitions) SirsiDynix
     Mem of Peace Library System
     Open Tues & Fri (Sept-July) 8-4; Wed & Thurs (August) 10-3

YOUNGSTOWN

P   YOUNGSTOWN MUNICIPAL LIBRARY*, PO Box 39, T0J 3P0. Tel: 403-779-3864. FAX: 403-779-3828. E-mail: aymlibrary@marigold.ab.ca. Web Site: www.marigold.ab.ca/about/memberlibs/youngstown.html. *Librn,* Nicky Armstrong
     Pop 184
     Library Holdings: Bk Vols 6,500
     Automation Activity & Vendor Info: (Acquisitions) SirsiDynix; (Cataloging) SirsiDynix; (Circulation) SirsiDynix; (Course Reserve) SirsiDynix; (ILL) SirsiDynix
     Mem of Marigold Library System
     Open Mon, Wed & Thurs 9:30-5, Tues 12-8
     Friends of the Library Group

ZAMA CITY

P   ZAMA COMMUNITY LIBRARY*, PO Box 14, T0H 4E0. Tel: 780-683-2888. E-mail: library@zamacity.ca. *Chairperson,* Lisa Wardley; *Librn,* Janet Forrest
     Library Holdings: Bk Vols 300,000
     Open Mon-Thurs (Summer) 7pm-9pm, Sun 1-4; Mon-Thurs (Winter) 1-4 & 7-9, Sun 1-4

Date of Statistics: CY 2010
Population, 2008 (est.): 4,455,207
Population Served by Public Libraries: 4,404,212
  Unserved: 50,995
Total Volumes in Public Libraries: 13,725,698
  Volumes Per Capita: 3.1
Total Public Library Circulation: 56,729,462
  Circulation Per Capita: 12.9
Total Public Library Income: $203,377,559
  Expenditures Per Capita: $46.18
Number of Bookmobiles in Province: 2

ABBOTSFORD

CR   COLUMBIA BIBLE COLLEGE LIBRARY, Columbia Resource Centre, 2940 Clearbrook Rd, V2T 2Z8. SAN 328-0489. Tel: 604-853-3567. FAX: 604-853-3063. E-mail: cbclibrary@columbiabc.edu. Web Site: www.columbiabc.edu/library. *Dir, Libr Serv,* Richard Thiessen; Tel: 604-853-3358, E-mail: richard.thiessen@columbiabc.edu; *Assoc Librn,* Anne Andres; E-mail: anne.andres@columbiabc.edu; Staff 4 (MLS 2, Non-MLS 2)
Enrl 408; Fac 17; Highest Degree: Bachelor
May 2012-Apr 2013. Mats Exp (CAN) $259,230, Books (CAN) $14,800, Per/Ser (Incl. Access Fees) (CAN) $17,562. Sal (CAN) $187,136
Library Holdings: CDs 754; DVDs 750; e-books 71,886; e-journals 5,833; Microforms 2,426; Bk Titles 42,491; Bk Vols 51,154; Per Subs 139; Videos 1,250
Subject Interests: Anabaptists, Church hist, Mennonite, Theol
Automation Activity & Vendor Info: (Acquisitions) Evergreen; (Cataloging) Evergreen; (Circulation) Evergreen; (Course Reserve) Evergreen; (OPAC) Evergreen; (Serials) Evergreen
Database Vendor: EBSCOhost, ProQuest, WebClarity Software Inc
Wireless access
Partic in BC Electronic Library Network; BC Libraries Cooperative
Open Mon, Wed & Fri 8:45am-9:15pm, Tues & Thurs 8:15am-9:15pm, Sat 11-4:45

P   FRASER VALLEY REGIONAL LIBRARY*, Administrative Centre, 34589 Delair Rd, V2S 5Y1. SAN 318-7500. Tel: 604-859-7141. Interlibrary Loan Service Tel: 604-859-7141, Ext 315. Toll Free Tel: 888-668-4141 (BC only). FAX: 604-859-5701. E-mail: info@fvrl.bc.ca. Web Site: www.fvrl.bc.ca. *Chief Exec Officer,* Robert O'Brennan; E-mail: robert.obrennan@fvrl.bc.ca; *Dir, Corporate Serv,* Mary O'Callaghan; E-mail: mary.ocallaghan@fvrl.bc.ca; *Dir, Client Serv,* Rita Penco; E-mail: rita.penco@fvrl.bc.ca; *Dir, Info Tech & Support Serv,* Scott Hargrove; E-mail: shargrove@fvrl.bc.ca; *Mgr, Info Tech,* Brad Fenrick; E-mail: brad.fenrick@fvrl.bc.ca; *Mgr, Support Serv,* Mary Kierans; E-mail: mary.kierans@fvrl.bc.ca; Staff 336 (MLS 31, Non-MLS 305)
Founded 1930. Pop 600,000
Library Holdings: Bk Vols 973,453
Special Collections: British Columbiana
Automation Activity & Vendor Info: (Circulation) Innovative Interfaces, Inc; (ILL) Innovative Interfaces, Inc; (OPAC) Innovative Interfaces, Inc
Database Vendor: Innovative Interfaces, Inc INN - View
Publications: Annual Report, brochures, booklists
Partic in Public Library InterLINK
Friends of the Library Group
Branches: 24
AGASSIZ LIBRARY, 7140 Cheam Ave, Agassiz, V0M 1A0. (Mail add: PO Box 7, Agassiz, V0M 1A0), SAN 321-1916. Tel: 604-796-9510. FAX: 604-796-9517. *Libr Mgr,* Nicole Glentworth; E-mail: nicole.glentworth@fvrl.bc.ca
  Open Tues-Thurs 10-8, Fri & Sat 10-5

ALDERGROVE BRANCH, 26770 - 29th Ave, Aldergrove, V4W 3B8, SAN 321-1924. Tel: 604-856-6415. FAX: 604-856-6816. *Libr Mgr,* David Thiessen; E-mail: david.thiessen@fvrl.bc.ca
  Open Mon-Thurs 10-9, Fri & Sat 10-5
  Friends of the Library Group
MURIEL ARNASON LIBRARY (WILLOWBROOK), Township of Langley Civic Centre, 130 - 20338 65 Ave, Langley, V2Y 2X3. Tel: 604-532-3590. FAX: 604-534-3141. *Libr Mgr,* David Thiessen; E-mail: david.thiessen@fvrl.bc.ca
  Open Mon-Thurs 10-9, Fri & Sat 10-5, Sun 1-5
BOSTON BAR LIBRARY, Box 400, Boston Bar Elementary School, 47643 Old Boston Bar Rd, Boston Bar, V0K 1C0, SAN 321-1932. Tel: 604-867-8847. FAX: 604-867-9549. *Libr Mgr,* Nicole Glentworth; E-mail: nicole.glentworth@fvrl.bc.ca
  Open Wed 2:30-5 & 5:30-9, Fri 12:30-5 & 5:30-7
BROOKSWOOD LIBRARY, 20045 - 40th Ave, Langley, V3A 2W2, SAN 321-1940. Tel: 604-534-7055. FAX: 604-532-7432. *Libr Mgr,* David Thiessen; E-mail: david.thiessen@fvrl.bc.ca
  Open Tues & Wed 12-8, Thurs-Sat 10-5
  Friends of the Library Group
CHILLIWACK LIBRARY, 45860 First Ave, Chilliwack, V2P 7K1, SAN 321-1959. Tel: 604-792-1941. FAX: 604-532-7483. *Libr Mgr,* Nicole Glentworth; E-mail: nicole.glentworth@fvrl.bc.ca
  Open Mon-Thurs 10-9, Fri 10-6, Sat 10-5, Sun 1-5
  Friends of the Library Group
CITY OF LANGLEY LIBRARY, 20399 Douglas Crescent, Langley, V3A 4B3, SAN 321-2033. Tel: 604-514-2850. FAX: 604-534-2985. *Libr Mgr,* Pat Dawson; E-mail: pat.dawson@fvrl.bc.ca
  Open Mon-Thurs 9-9, Fri 9-5, Sat 10-5, Sun 1-5
  Friends of the Library Group
CLEARBROOK LIBRARY, 32320 George Ferguson Way, V2T 6N4, SAN 321-1967. Tel: 604-859-7814. FAX: 604-859-7329. *Libr Mgr,* Hilary Russell; E-mail: hilary.russell@fvrl.bc.ca
  Open Mon-Thurs 10-9, Fri-Sun 10-5
  Friends of the Library Group
FORT LANGLEY LIBRARY, Box 312, 9167 Glover Rd, Fort Langley, V1M 2R6, SAN 321-1991. Tel: 604-888-0722. FAX: 604-882-0729. *Libr Mgr,* David Thiessen; E-mail: david.thiessen@fvrl.bc.ca
  Open Tues & Wed 1-8, Thurs-Sat 10-12:30 & 1-5
TERRY FOX LIBRARY, 2470 Mary Hill Rd, Port Coquitlam, V3C 3B1, SAN 321-2106. Tel: 604-927-7999. FAX: 604-941-8365. *Libr Mgr,* Pat Dawson; E-mail: pat.dawson@fvrl.bc.ca
  Open Mon-Thurs 10-9, Fri & Sat 10-5, Sun (September-June) 1-5
  Friends of the Library Group
HOPE LIBRARY, 1005A - Sixth Ave, Hope, V0X 1L0, SAN 321-2025. Tel: 604-869-2313. FAX: 604-869-2472. *Libr Mgr,* Nicole Glentworth; Fax: nicole.glenwor@fvrl.bc.ca
  Open Tues 10-8, Wed 1-8, Thurs & Fri 10-5, Sat 1-5, Sun (Sept-June) 1-5

LADNER PIONEER LIBRARY, 4683 - 51st St, Delta, V4K 2V8, SAN 321-1983. Tel: 604-946-6215. FAX: 604-946-7821. *Libr Mgr,* Gillian McLeod; E-mail: gillian.mcleod@fvrl.bc.ca
Open Mon-Thurs 10-9, Fri & Sat 10-5, Sun 11-5
Friends of the Library Group

GEORGE MACKIE LIBRARY, 8440 - 112th St, Delta, V4C 4W9, SAN 321-2009. Tel: 604-594-8155. FAX: 604-594-9364. *Libr Mgr,* Gillian McLeod; E-mail: gillian.mcleod@fvrl.bc.ca
Open Mon-Thurs 10-9, Fri & Sat 10-5, Sun 11-5
Friends of the Library Group

MAPLE RIDGE PUBLIC LIBRARY, 130 - 22470 Dewdney Trunk Rd, Maple Ridge, V2X 5Z6, SAN 321-2017. Tel: 604-467-7417. FAX: 604-467-7404. *Libr Mgr,* Caro O'Kennedy; E-mail: caro.okennedy@fvrl.bc.ca; Staff 14 (MLS 1, Non-MLS 13)
Pop 60,000; Circ 450,000
Open Mon-Fri 10-9, Sat 10-5, Sun (September-June) 1-5
Friends of the Library Group

MISSION LIBRARY, 33247 Second Ave, Mission, V2V 1J9, SAN 321-205X. Tel: 604-826-6610. FAX: 604-826-6614. *Libr Mgr,* Teresa MacLeod; E-mail: teresa.macleod@fvrl.bc.ca
Open Mon-Thurs 10-9, Fri & Sat 10-5, Sun 1-5
Friends of the Library Group

MOUNT LEHMAN LIBRARY, 5875 Mount Lehman Rd, V4X 1VS, SAN 321-2068. Tel: 604-856-4988. FAX: 604-856-4908. Web Site: www.fvrl.bc.ca. *Libr Mgr,* Hillary Russell; E-mail: hillary.russell@fvrl.bc.ca
Open Tues-Fri 1:30-5:30

MSA CENTENNIAL LIBRARY, 33660 S Fraser Way, V2S 2B9, SAN 321-1908. Tel: 604-853-1753. FAX: 604-853-7861. *Libr Mgr,* Hillary Russell; E-mail: hilary.russell@fvrl.bc.ca
Open Mon-Thurs 10-9, Fri & Sat 10-5
Friends of the Library Group

MURRAYVILLE LIBRARY, Unit 100 - 22071 48 Ave, Langley, V3A 3N1. Tel: 604-533-0339. FAX: 604-514-7260. *Libr Mgr,* David Thiessen; E-mail: david.thiessen@fvrl.bc.ca
Open Mon-Thurs 10-9, Fri & Sat 10-5, Sun 1-5

PITT MEADOWS PUBLIC LIBRARY, 12047 Harris Rd, Pitt Meadows, V3Y 1Z2, SAN 321-2092. Tel: 604-465-4113. FAX: 604-465-9732. *Libr Mgr,* Caro O'Kennedy; E-mail: caro.okennedy@fvrl.bc.ca
Open Mon-Thurs 10-9, Fri & Sat 10-5, Sun (September-June) 12-4

TSAWWASSEN LIBRARY, 1321A - 56th St, Delta, V4L 2A6, SAN 321-2122. Tel: 604-943-2271. FAX: 604-943-6941. *Libr Mgr,* Gillian McLeod; E-mail: gillian.mcleod@fvrl.bc.ca; Staff 8 (MLS 1, Non-MLS 7)
Open Mon-Thurs 10-9, Fri & Sat 10-5, Sun 11-5
Friends of the Library Group

WALNUT GROVE LIBRARY, Walnut Grove Community Centre, 8889 Walnut Grove Dr, Langley, V1M 2N7, SAN 375-2917. Tel: 604-882-0410. FAX: 604-882-3754. *Libr Mgr,* David Thiessen; E-mail: david.thiessen@fvrl.bc.ca
Open Mon-Fri 10-9, Sat 10-5, Sun 1-5

WHITE ROCK LIBRARY, 15342 Buena Vista Ave, White Rock, V4B 1Y6, SAN 321-2157. Tel: 604-541-2201. FAX: 604-541-2209. *Libr Mgr,* David Thiessen; E-mail: david.thiessen@fvrl.bc.ca
Open Mon-Wed 10-9, Thurs-Sat 10-5, Sun (Thanksgiving-Easter) 1-5

YALE LIBRARY, Box 17, Yale Elementary School, 65050 Albert St, Yale, V0K 2S0, SAN 321-2165. Tel: 604-863-2279. FAX: 604-863-0138. *Libr Mgr,* Nicole Glentworth; E-mail: nicole.glenworth@fvrl.bc.ca
Open Tues & Thurs 4-8, Sat 1-5

YARROW LIBRARY, 4670 Community St, Yarrow, V2R 5E1, SAN 324-2730. Tel: 604-823-4664. FAX: 604-823-4686. *Libr Mgr,* Nicole Glentworth; E-mail: nicole.glenworth@fvrl.bc.ca
Open Tues 10-8, Wed 10-12:30 & 1-4:30, Thurs 1:30-5:30 & 6-8, Sat 10-3

S   REGIONAL TREATMENT CENTRE/PACIFIC INSTITUTION LIBRARY*, 33344 King Rd, V2S 4P4. (Mail add: PO Box 3000, V2S 4P4), SAN 370-6303. Tel: 604-870-7700, Ext 3399. FAX: 604-870-7746. *Librn,* J Joslin
Library Holdings: Bk Titles 12,000

CR   SUMMIT PACIFIC COLLEGE*, Lorne Philip Hudson Memorial Library, 35235 Straiton Rd, V2S 7Z1. (Mail add: PO Box 1700, V2S 7E7), SAN 320-3069. Tel: 604-851-7230. FAX: 604-853-8951. E-mail: librarian@summitpacific.ca. *Librn,* Laurence M Van Kleek; *Libr Tech,* Bonnie Brauer; Staff 1.83 (MLS 1, Non-MLS 0.83)
Founded 1941. Enrl 196; Highest Degree: Bachelor
Jul 2008-Jun 2009. Mats Exp (CAN) $131,631, Books (CAN) $12,735, Per/Ser (Incl. Access Fees) (CAN) $14,864, Manu Arch (CAN) $500. Sal (CAN) $76,828
Library Holdings: AV Mats 682; Bks on Deafness & Sign Lang 15; Braille Volumes 3; CDs 111; DVDs 28; e-journals 235; Microforms 2,059; Music Scores 112; Bk Titles 56,545; Bk Vols 62,828; Per Subs 142; Videos 248

Special Collections: Pentecostal Church History (The Pentecostal Testimony Coll), per
Subject Interests: Relig studies
Automation Activity & Vendor Info: (Acquisitions) LibraryWorld, Inc; (Cataloging) LibraryWorld, Inc; (Circulation) LibraryWorld, Inc; (OPAC) LibraryWorld, Inc; (Serials) LibraryWorld, Inc
Database Vendor: EBSCOhost
Wireless access
Function: Archival coll, Audio & video playback equip for onsite use, CD-ROM, Computers for patron use, Copy machines, ILL available, Mail loans to mem, Music CDs, Online cat, Photocopying/Printing, Pub access computers, Ref & res, Res libr, Scanner, VHS videos
Open Mon, Tues & Thurs 8am-10pm, Wed & Fri 8-5, Sat 9-5
Restriction: Authorized patrons, Borrowing privileges limited to fac & registered students, Borrowing requests are handled by ILL, External users must contact libr, In-house use for visitors, Open to pub upon request, Open to students, fac & staff, Restricted borrowing privileges, Secured area only open to authorized personnel

C   UNIVERSITY OF THE FRASER VALLEY, Abbotsford Campus Library, 33844 King Rd, V2S 7M8. SAN 318-7497. Tel: 604-504-7441. Circulation Tel: 604-854-4545. Interlibrary Loan Service Tel: 604-864-4678. Reference Tel: 604-504-7441, Ext 4221. Administration Tel: 604-864-4696. FAX: 604-853-8055. Reference FAX: 604-853-0796. Web Site: www.ufv.ca/library. *Univ Librn,* Kim Isaac; E-mail: kim.isaac@ufv.ca; *Coll Librn,* Patti Wilson; Tel: 604-504-7441, Ext 4277, E-mail: patti.wilson@ufv.ca; Staff 23 (MLS 5, Non-MLS 18)
Founded 1974. Enrl 10,000; Highest Degree: Master
Special Collections: Fraser Valley Heritage Coll
Wireless access
Partic in BC Electronic Library Network; Canadian Research Knowledge Network; Council of Prairie & Pacific University Libraries; Electronic Health Library of British Columbia
Open Mon-Thurs 8am-10pm, Fri 8-6, Sat 10-6, Sun 12-6
Departmental Libraries:
CHILLIWACK CAMPUS, Library, Bldg A, 45190 Caen Ave, Chilliwack, V2R 0N3. Tel: 604-792-0025, 604-795-2824. Circulation Tel: 604-792-0025, Ext 2824. FAX: 604-792-8550. *Univ Librn,* Kim Isaac
Open Mon-Thurs 8am-9pm, Fri 8-4:30, Sat 10-6
HERITAGE PARK (MISSION) CAMPUS, 33700 Prentis Ave, Mission, V2V 7B1. Tel: 604-820-6009. Administration Tel: 604-820-6000. Administration FAX: 604-826-0681. E-mail: circmiss@ucfv.ca. *Libr Tech,* Shawnna Pierce
Open Mon-Thurs 8:30am-10pm, Fri 8-6, Sat 10-6, Sun 12-6

AGASSIZ

G   CORRECTIONAL SERVICE OF CANADA-PACIFIC REGION*, Kent Institution Library, 4732 Cemetery Rd, V0M 1A0. (Mail add: PO Box 1500, V0M 1A0), SAN 375-4820. Tel: 604-796-2121, Ext 4329. FAX: 604-796-4500. *Librn,* Catherine Ings; E-mail: ingsca@csc-scc.gc.ca; Staff 0.8 (Non-MLS 0.8)
Jul 2005-Jun 2006. Mats Exp $5,000
Library Holdings: Bk Titles 12,000
Open Mon-Thurs 5am-7:15pm

ALERT BAY

P   ALERT BAY PUBLIC LIBRARY & MUSEUM, 118 Fir St, V0N 1A0. (Mail add: PO Box 440, V0N 1A0). Tel: 250-974-5721. FAX: 250-974-5026. E-mail: abplb@island.net. Web Site: www.alertbay.com/library/, www.island.net/~abplb. *Commun Librn,* Steven Wong; *Archivist,* Joyce Wilby; E-mail: jwilby@island.net
Founded 1959
Library Holdings: Audiobooks 5; CDs 9; DVDs 22; Large Print Bks 171; Bk Titles 9,240; Bk Vols 9,326; Per Subs 1
Open Mon, Fri & Sat 1-4, Wed 1-5

ATLIN

C   NORTHERN LIGHTS COLLEGE*, Atlin Learning Centre Library, PO Box 29, V0W 1A0. Tel: 250-651-7762. FAX: 250-651-7730. *Continuing Educ Coordr,* Position Currently Open
Library Holdings: Bk Titles 1,000
Open Mon-Fri 9-12

BAMFIELD

C   WESTERN CANADIAN UNIVERSITIES MARINE SCIENCES SOCIETY*, Bamfield Marine Sciences Centre Library, 100 Pachena Rd, V0R 1B0. SAN 322-8665. Tel: 250-728-3301, Ext 213. FAX: 250-728-3452. E-mail: library@bms.bc.ca. Web Site: www.bms.bc.ca/library/index.html. *Info & Communications Officer,* Sarah Gellard Tyne; E-mail: library@bms.bc.ca. Subject Specialists: *Marine sci,* Sarah Gellard Tyne; Staff 1 (Non-MLS 1)
Founded 1972

Library Holdings: Bk Titles 4,350; Per Subs 54
Subject Interests: Marine & coastal sci
Automation Activity & Vendor Info: (OPAC) Inmagic, Inc.
Wireless access
Function: Archival coll, Audio & video playback equip for onsite use, AV serv, Doc delivery serv, For res purposes, Handicapped accessible, ILL available, Photocopying/Printing, Ref serv available, Res libr
Open Mon-Fri 9-5
Restriction: Circ limited, Not a lending libr

BARKERVILLE

S   BARKERVILLE HISTORIC TOWN LIBRARY & ARCHIVES, 14301 Hwy 26 E, V0K 1B0. (Mail add: Box 19, V0K 1B0), SAN 326-1360. Tel: 250-994-3332. Toll Free Tel: 1-888-994-3332. FAX: 250-994-3435. E-mail: barkerville@barkerville.ca. Web Site: www.barkerville.ca. *Archivist, Librn,* M Kilsby; Tel: 250-994-3332, Ext 26
Library Holdings: Bk Vols 15,000
Special Collections: Barkerville & Cariboo Records; Chinese Coll, doc, photog; Euro-Canadian Records; Photographs Cross Indexed Database
Subject Interests: Genealogy, Mining
Wireless access
Function: Archival coll, Audio & video playback equip for onsite use, Bus archives, Electronic databases & coll, For res purposes, Microfiche/film & reading machines, Online searches, Photocopying/Printing, Ref & res, Res libr, Res performed for a fee, Web-catalog
Restriction: Access at librarian's discretion, Non-circulating coll, Open by appt only, Open to pub for ref only, Open to pub upon request, Open to researchers by request

BOWEN ISLAND

P   BOWEN ISLAND PUBLIC LIBRARY*, 430 Bowen Island Trunk Rd, V0N 1G0. (Mail add: PO Box 10, V0N 1G0). Tel: 604-947-9788. FAX: 604-947-9788. E-mail: bbi@bowenlibrary.ca. Web Site: www.bowenlibrary.ca. *Chief Librn,* Tina Nielsen
Library Holdings: Bk Vols 19,000; Per Subs 40
Automation Activity & Vendor Info: (Cataloging) Horizon; (Circulation) Horizon; (OPAC) Horizon
Database Vendor: EBSCOhost, World Book Online
Wireless access
Open Tues & Thurs-Sat 10-5:30, Wed 10-8

BURNABY

S   AUTISM SOCIETY OF BRITISH COLUMBIA LIBRARY*, 3701 E Hastings, Ste 303, V5C 2H6. SAN 372-6975. Tel: 604-434-0880. Toll Free Tel: 888-437-0880. FAX: 604-434-0801. E-mail: librarian@autismbc.ca. Web Site: www.autismbc.ca. *Librn,* Stella Hui
Library Holdings: Bk Titles 1,800; Bk Vols 2,100
Subject Interests: Autism, Learning disabilities
Automation Activity & Vendor Info: (Acquisitions) Inmagic, Inc.; (Cataloging) Inmagic, Inc.; (Circulation) Inmagic, Inc.; (Serials) Inmagic, Inc.
Open Mon-Fri 9:30-4:30

C   BRITISH COLUMBIA INSTITUTE OF TECHNOLOGY LIBRARY*, 3700 Willingdon Ave, SE14, V5G 3H2. SAN 318-7519. Tel: 604-432-8370. Interlibrary Loan Service Tel: 604-432-8619. Administration Tel: 604-432-8827. FAX: 604-430-5443. Circulation FAX: 604-434-5148. Interlibrary Loan Service FAX: 604-435-9641. Administration FAX: 604-434-1585. Web Site: www.bcit.ca/library. *Head of Libr,* Brigitte Peter-Cherneff; Tel: 604-432-8360; Staff 35 (MLS 10, Non-MLS 25)
Founded 1964. Enrl 47,969; Fac 1,590; Highest Degree: Master
Apr 2005-Mar 2006 Income (CAN) $3,010,000. Mats Exp (CAN) $754,549, Books (CAN) $280,050, Per/Ser (Incl. Access Fees) (CAN) $150,980, Other Print Mats (CAN) $17,519, AV Mat (CAN) $31,500, Electronic Ref Mat (Incl. Access Fees) (CAN) $274,500. Sal (CAN) $1,986,750
Library Holdings: AV Mats 6,551; e-books 9,269; Bk Titles 186,820; Per Subs 978
Special Collections: ANSI Standards; Census; Company Annual Reports; CSA Standards; Government and law; Micro Software; NTIS Reports; SAE Reports; Statistics Canada publications
Subject Interests: Computer sci, Eng, Forestry
Wireless access
Function: Archival coll, AV serv, Bus archives, Distance learning, Doc delivery serv, For res purposes, Govt ref serv, Handicapped accessible, Health sci info serv, ILL available, Libr develop, Online searches, Outside serv via phone, mail, e-mail & web, Photocopying/Printing, Ref serv available, Res libr, Satellite serv, Wheelchair accessible
Partic in BC Electronic Library Network
Special Services for the Deaf - TTY equip
Includes Burnaby, Marine & Aerospace & Technology Campus Libraries
Restriction: Open to pub upon request, Open to students, fac & staff

P   BURNABY PUBLIC LIBRARY, 6100 Willingdon Ave, V5H 4N5. SAN 365-7965. Tel: 604-436-5427. FAX: 604-436-2961. Web Site: www.bpl.bc.ca. *Chief Librn,* Edel Toner-Rogala; E-mail: edel.toner-rogala@bpl.bc.ca; Staff 135.8 (MLS 33.4, Non-MLS 102.4)
Founded 1954. Pop 227,389; Circ 3,797,307
Jan 2011-Dec 2011. Mats Exp (CAN) $1,445,394
Library Holdings: Bk Titles 298,660; Bk Vols 584,466; Per Subs 979
Automation Activity & Vendor Info: (Acquisitions) SirsiDynix; (Cataloging) SirsiDynix; (Circulation) SirsiDynix; (OPAC) SirsiDynix; (Serials) SirsiDynix
Database Vendor: SirsiDynix
Wireless access
Partic in Public Library InterLINK
Open Mon-Fri 9-9, Sat 9-6, Sun 1-5
Branches: 4
CAMERON BRANCH, 9523 Cameron St, V3J 1L6, SAN 365-7973. Tel: 604-421-5454. *Br Mgr,* Elizabeth Davies; Staff 11.52 (MLS 2.87, Non-MLS 8.65)
Circ 521,027
Open Mon-Thurs 10-9, Fri & Sat 10-6, Sun 1-5
TOMMY DOUGLAS BRANCH, 7311 Kingsway, V5E 1G8, SAN 365-8023. Tel: 604-522-3971. *Br Mgr,* Roberta Summersgill; Staff 17.86 (MLS 4.56, Non-MLS 13.3)
Circ 666,102
Open Mon-Fri 10-9, Sat 10-6, Sun 1-5
MCGILL BRANCH, 4595 Albert St, V5C 2G6, SAN 365-8058. Tel: 604-299-8955. FAX: 604-299-7000. *Br Mgr,* Linda Shineton; Staff 24.35 (MLS 6.97, Non-MLS 17.38)
Circ 963,907
Open Mon-Fri 10-9, Sat 10-6, Sun 1-5
BOB PRITTIE METROTOWN BRANCH, 6100 Willingdon Ave, V5H 4N5, SAN 372-5170. Tel: 604-436-5400. FAX: 604-436-9087. *Br Mgr,* Deb Thomas; Tel: 604-436-5432, Fax: 604-436-2961; Staff 82.07 (MLS 19, Non-MLS 63.07)
Circ 1,611,975
Special Collections: British Columbia Coll
Open Mon-Fri 9-9, Sat 9-6, Sun 1-5
Bookmobiles: 1

M   FRASER HEALTH AUTHORITY*, Burnaby Hospital Library, 3935 Kincaid St, V5G 2X6. SAN 324-4431. Tel: 604-412-6255. FAX: 604-412-6177. *Librn,* Hoong Lim; E-mail: hoong.lim@fraserhealth.ca
Founded 1960
Aug 2005-Jul 2006. Mats Exp (CAN) $20,000
Library Holdings: e-journals 250; Bk Titles 800; Per Subs 45
Subject Interests: Healthcare, Med, Nursing
Database Vendor: OVID Technologies, Swets Information Services

S   GOLDER ASSOCIATES, LTD*, 4260 Still Creek Dr, 5th Flr, V5C 6C6. SAN 323-8245. Tel: 604-298-6623, Ext 4349. FAX: 604-298-5253. E-mail: solutions@golder.com.. Web Site: www.golder.com. *Librn,* Fareeza Karimushan
Library Holdings: Bk Titles 3,700; Per Subs 100
Special Collections: Oil Sands
Open Mon-Fri 8:30-5
Restriction: Restricted pub use

G   GREATER VANCOUVER REGIONAL DISTRICT LIBRARY*, 4330 Kingsway, V5H 4G8. SAN 321-4591. Tel: 604-432-6335. FAX: 604-432-6445. Web Site: www.gvrd.bc.ca. *Librn,* Annette Dignan; E-mail: annette.dignan@gvrd.bc.ca; Staff 2 (MLS 1, Non-MLS 1)
Founded 1970
Library Holdings: Bk Titles 34,000; Per Subs 500
Special Collections: Greater Vancouver Regional District Reports; Member Municipality Reports
Subject Interests: Air quality, Eng, Housing, Planning, Pollution control, Recreation, Transportation, Waste mgt, Wastewater
Automation Activity & Vendor Info: (Cataloging) SirsiDynix; (Circulation) SirsiDynix; (OPAC) SirsiDynix; (Serials) SirsiDynix
Open Mon-Fri 8-4

C   SIMON FRASER UNIVERSITY LIBRARY*, W A C Bennett Library, 8888 University Dr, V5A 1S6. SAN 318-7578. Tel: 778-782-4084. Circulation Tel: 778-782-4345. Interlibrary Loan Service Tel: 778-782-3625. Reference Tel: 778-782-5735. FAX: 778-782-3023. Interlibrary Loan Service FAX: 778-782-4908. Reference FAX: 778-782-6926. E-mail: libask@sfu.ca. Web Site: www.lib.sfu.ca. *Univ Librn,* Chuck Eckman; Tel: 778-782-3265, E-mail: ceckman@sfu.ca; *Assoc Univ Librn, Admin Serv,* Position Currently Open; *Assoc Univ Librn, Coll & Scholarly Communication,* Position Currently Open; *Assoc Univ Librn, Learning & Res Serv,* Elaine Fairey; Tel: 778-782-3252, E-mail: efairey@sfu.ca; *Assoc Univ Librn, Tech Serv & Spec Coll,* Brian Owen; Tel: 778-782-7095, E-mail: gwbowen@sfu.ca; *Head, Access Serv,* Scott Mackenzie; Tel: 778-782-4081, E-mail: smackena@sfu.ca; *Head, Acq,*

Head, Ser, Patty Gallilee; Tel: 778-782-3916, E-mail: plg@sfu.ca; *Head, Cat,* Penny Swanson; Tel: 778-782-3184, Fax: 604-291-6579, E-mail: pswanson@sfu.ca; *Head, Info & Instrul Serv,* Janis McKenzie; Tel: 778-782-6865, E-mail: jlm15@sfu.ca; *Head, Syst,* Mark Jordan; Tel: 778-782-5753, E-mail: mjordan@sfu.ca; *Spec Coll Librn,* Eric Swanick; Tel: 778-782-4626, E-mail: eswanick@sfu.ca; Staff 49 (MLS 38, Non-MLS 11)
Founded 1965. Enrl 26,670; Highest Degree: Doctorate
Apr 2007-Mar 2008. Mats Exp (CAN) $9,117,090. Sal (CAN) $9,242,486
Library Holdings: AV Mats 983,117; e-books 405,222; e-journals 41,898; Bk Vols 2,369,049; Per Subs 48,558; Videos 9,250
Special Collections: Aldus Pius Manutius (Aldine Coll); Canadian Newspaper Editorial Cartoons, 1952-present (Len Norris, Roy Peterson, Graham Harrop, Bob Krieger & Dan Murphy); Contemporary Literature (20th Century Avant Garde & Innovative Literature Coll); Harrison Brown Coll, photogs; History of Canada & Western Canada (CCF Holdings, Labour & Doukhobor Materials); Special Manuscripts Coll (Bill Bissett, Anne Cameron, Betty Lambert, Ezra Pound, Papers of "Open Letter" magazine, Papers of BP Nichol & Archival Material from Talonbooks); Wordsworth Coll
Automation Activity & Vendor Info: (Acquisitions) Innovative Interfaces, Inc; (Cataloging) Innovative Interfaces, Inc; (Circulation) Innovative Interfaces, Inc; (Course Reserve) Innovative Interfaces, Inc; (ILL) Relais International; (OPAC) Innovative Interfaces, Inc; (Serials) Innovative Interfaces, Inc
Database Vendor: ACM (Association for Computing Machinery), Alexander Street Press, American Chemical Society, American Mathematical Society, Annual Reviews, ARTstor, BioOne, Blackwell's, Bowker, Cambridge Scientific Abstracts, Coutts Information Service, ebrary, EBSCOhost, Gale Cengage Learning, IEEE (Institute of Electrical & Electronics Engineers), ISI Web of Knowledge, JSTOR, LexisNexis, Nature Publishing Group, netLibrary, OCLC FirstSearch, OVID Technologies, ProQuest, PubMed, Repere, Safari Books Online, ScienceDirect, Wilson - Wilson Web
Wireless access
Function: Audio & video playback equip for onsite use, Distance learning, Doc delivery serv, For res purposes, Handicapped accessible, ILL available, Photocopying/Printing, Ref serv available, Res libr, Telephone ref, Wheelchair accessible, Workshops
Partic in BC Electronic Library Network; Canadian Research Knowledge Network; Council of Prairie & Pacific University Libraries
Special Services for the Blind - Assistive/Adapted tech devices, equip & products; Talking bks; ZoomText magnification & reading software
Open Mon-Thurs 8am-11:45pm, Fri 8-8, Sat & Sun 10-10
Friends of the Library Group

S   TELUS*, Knowledge Center, 3777 Kingsway, 5th Flr, V5H 3Z7. SAN 318-7535. Tel: 604-432-2671. FAX: 604-435-0510. *Librn,* Todd Colin; E-mail: colin.todd@telus.com; Staff 2 (MLS 1, Non-MLS 1)
Founded 1948
Library Holdings: Bk Titles 1,500; Per Subs 55
Open Mon-Fri 9-5

BURNS LAKE

P   BURNS LAKE PUBLIC LIBRARY*, 585 Government St, V0J 1E0. (Mail add: PO Box 449, V0J 1E0). Tel: 250-692-3192. FAX: 250-692-7488. E-mail: blplib@telus.net. Web Site: www.sandercott.com/burnslakelibrary. *Chief Librn,* Linda Palmer; *Asst Librn,* Elaine Wiebe; *Ch,* Jenny Harms
Founded 1944. Pop 1,415; Circ 56,648
Jan 2005-Dec 2005 Income (CAN) $133,698, Provincial $22,150, County $111,548. Mats Exp (CAN) $31,400. Sal (CAN) $90,000
Library Holdings: CDs 106; DVDs 30; Large Print Bks 300; Bk Titles 30,251; Per Subs 45; Talking Bks 500; Videos 204
Automation Activity & Vendor Info: (Cataloging) Follett Software; (Circulation) Follett Software; (ILL) Auto-Graphics, Inc; (OPAC) Follett Software
Database Vendor: EBSCOhost
Function: Adult bk club, CD-ROM, Home delivery & serv to Sr ctr & nursing homes, Homebound delivery serv, ILL available, Music CDs, Newsp ref libr, Online searches, Photocopying/Printing, Prog for children & young adult, Serves mentally handicapped consumers, Spoken cassettes & CDs, Spoken cassettes & DVDs, Summer reading prog, VHS videos, Wheelchair accessible
Open Tues-Thurs 10-7, Fri & Sat 10-5
Restriction: Authorized patrons, Circ to mem only, Non-circulating coll, Non-resident fee

J   COLLEGE OF NEW CALEDONIA*, Lakes District Library, 545 Hwy 16, V0J 1E0. (Mail add: PO Box 5000, V0J 1E0), SAN 326-5722. Tel: 250-692-1700. Administration Tel: 250-692-1714. FAX: 250-692-1750. Web Site: www.cnc.bc.ca. *Librn,* Sue Waddle; E-mail: waddle@cnc.bc.ca
Founded 1974
Library Holdings: Bk Vols 5,000; Per Subs 10

CAMPBELL RIVER

S   CAMPBELL RIVER MUSEUM & ARCHIVES*, Reference Library, 470 Island Hwy, V9W 4Z9. (Mail add: PO Box 70, Sta A, V9W 4Z9), SAN 323-5246. Tel: 250-287-3103. FAX: 250-286-0109. E-mail: general.inquiries@crmuseum.ca. Web Site: www.crmuseum.ca. *Dir,* Lesia Davis; *Coll Develop,* Sandra Parrish
Library Holdings: Bk Vols 1,400
Subject Interests: Ethnology, Musicology

J   NORTH ISLAND COLLEGE*, Campbell River Campus Library, 1685 S Dogwood St, V9W 8C1. Tel: 250-923-9787. FAX: 250-923-9786. Web Site: library.nic.bc.ca. *Libr Tech,* Diane Newman
Library Holdings: Bk Titles 8,000
Automation Activity & Vendor Info: (Acquisitions) SirsiDynix; (Cataloging) SirsiDynix; (Circulation) SirsiDynix; (Course Reserve) SirsiDynix; (OPAC) SirsiDynix
Wireless access
Open Mon-Thurs 8-6, Fri (Fall & Spring) 8-4

CASTLEGAR

P   CASTLEGAR & DISTRICT PUBLIC LIBRARY*, 1005 Third St, V1N 2A2. SAN 365-8112. Tel: 250-365-6611. FAX: 250-365-7765. Web Site: www.castlegarlibrary.com. *Dir,* Heather Maisel; Staff 5 (MLS 1, Non-MLS 4)
Founded 1947. Pop 13,427
Library Holdings: Bk Titles 60,000; Per Subs 110
Automation Activity & Vendor Info: (Acquisitions) Evergreen; (Cataloging) Evergreen; (Circulation) Evergreen; (OPAC) Evergreen
Function: ILL available
Special Services for the Blind - Bks on cassette
Open Mon-Thurs 10-8, Fri-Sun 10-5

J   SELKIRK COLLEGE LIBRARY*, 301 Frank Beinder Way, V1N 3J1. SAN 318-7594. Tel: 250-365-1229, 250-365-7292, Ext 229. Administration Toll Free Tel: 888-953-1133, Ext 229. FAX: 250-365-7259. E-mail: bcs@selkirk.bc.ca.. Web Site: www.library.selkirk.bc.ca. *Col Librn,* Gregg Currie; Tel: 250-365-1263, E-mail: gcurrie@selkirk.ca; *Ref Librn,* Judy Deon; Tel: 250-365-1382, E-mail: jdeon@selkirk.ca; Staff 10 (MLS 2, Non-MLS 8)
Founded 1966
Library Holdings: Bk Vols 76,000; Per Subs 500
Special Collections: Kootenay Materials
Automation Activity & Vendor Info: (Circulation) SirsiDynix; (OPAC) SIRSI-iLink
Database Vendor: EBSCOhost, OVID Technologies, ProQuest, Wilson - Wilson Web
Wireless access
Function: ILL available
Publications: Kootenaiana
Partic in BC Electronic Library Network
Open Mon & Fri 7:30-5, Tues-Thurs 7:30-7, Sat & Sun Noon-4

CHETWYND

P   CHETWYND PUBLIC LIBRARY*, 5012 46th St, V0C 1J0. (Mail add: PO Box 1420, V0C 1J0), SAN 318-7608. Tel: 250-788-2559. FAX: 250-788-2186. Web Site: chetwynd.bclibrary.ca/. *Head Librn,* Fay Asleson; E-mail: fasleson@pris.ca; *Asst Librn,* Brenda Lukey
Founded 1967. Pop 7,000; Circ 44,355
Library Holdings: Bk Vols 22,000; Per Subs 35
Automation Activity & Vendor Info: (Cataloging) Mandarin Library Automation; (Circulation) Mandarin Library Automation; (OPAC) Mandarin Library Automation
Partic in North East Library Federation (NELF)
Open Mon & Wed 8-9, Tues & Thurs 8-4:30, Fri 8-7, Sat & Sun 12-4

CHILLIWACK

S   CHILLIWACK MUSEUM & HISTORICAL SOCIETY*, 45820 Spadina Ave, V2P 1T3. SAN 326-5218. Tel: 604-795-5210, 604-795-9255. FAX: 604-795-5291. E-mail: info@chilliwackmuseum.ca. Web Site: www.chilliwackmuseum.ca. *Dir,* Ron Denman; *Archivist,* Shannon Anderson; *Curator,* Paul Ferguson
Library Holdings: Bk Titles 2,000; Per Subs 12
Special Collections: Local municipal govt
Partic in Can Museums Asn
Open Mon-Fri 9-4:30

COQUITLAM

P   COQUITLAM PUBLIC LIBRARY*, 575 Poirier St, V3J 6A9. SAN 365-8171. Tel: 604-931-2416. Circulation Tel: 604-937-4141. Reference Tel: 604-937-4144. FAX: 604-931-6739. Web Site: www.library.coquitlam.bc.ca. *Dir,* Maureen Woods; Tel: 604-937-4131,

E-mail: mwoods@library.coquitlam.bc.ca; *Dep Dir,* Rhian Piprell; Tel: 604-937-4132; *Adult Serv, ILL,* Leslie Utsunomiya; Tel: 604-937-4140, E-mail: lutsunom@library.coquitlam.bc.ca; *Ch,* Deborah Duncan; Tel: 604-937-4142, E-mail: dduncan@library.coquitlam.bc.ca; *Circ,* Mary Beth Folino; Tel: 604-937-4141, Fax: 604-927-3570, E-mail: mfolino@library.coquitlam.bc.ca; *Commun Serv,* Barbara Weston; Tel: 604-937-4140, E-mail: bweston@library.coquitlam.bc.ca; *Ref,* Gillian Campbell; Tel: 604-937-4147, Fax: 604-931-1460, E-mail: gcampbel@library.coquitlam.bc.ca; *Syst Coordr,* Nancy Collins; Tel: 604-937-4151, E-mail: systems@library.coquitlam.bc.ca; *Tech Serv,* Jocelan Litton; Tel: 604-937-4150, E-mail: jlitton@library.coquitlam.bc.ca; *YA Serv,* Chris Miller; Tel: 604-937-4140, E-mail: cmiller@library.coquitlam.bc.ca
Founded 1978. Pop 111,514; Circ 998,216
Library Holdings: Bk Titles 122,000; Per Subs 417
Special Collections: National Film Board of Canada, video
Subject Interests: Auto manuals, Local hist
Partic in Public Library InterLINK
Open Mon-Thurs 10-9, Fri & Sat 10-5, Sun (Sept-May) 12-5
Branches: 1
CITY CENTRE, 3001 Burlington Dr, V3B 6X1, SAN 365-8228. Tel: 604-927-3560. Circulation Tel: 604-627-3562. FAX: 604-927-3570. *Dir,* Rhian Piprell; Tel: 604-937-4132, E-mail: rpiprell@library.coquitlam.bc.ca; *Ch,* Barbara Weston; Tel: 604-927-3561, E-mail: bweston@library.coquitlam.bc.ca; *Br Supvr,* Brenda Meade Husain; Tel: 604-927-3566, E-mail: bmeadehusain@library.coquitlam.bc.ca
Open Mon-Thurs 10-9, Fri & Sat 10-5, Sun (Sept-April) 12-5

S　　INTERTEK TESTING SERVICES*, Warnock Hersey Library, 1500 Brigantine Dr, V3K 7C1. SAN 374-6208. Tel: 604-520-3321. FAX: 604-524-9186. Web Site: www.intertek-etlsemko.com. *Mgr,* Simon Knight
Library Holdings: Bk Titles 600; Bk Vols 800; Per Subs 500
Open Mon-Fri 7:30-5

M　　RIVERVIEW HOSPITAL*, Library Services, 2601 Lougheed Hwy, V3C 4J2. SAN 318-7934. Tel: 604-524-7000, 604-524-7386. FAX: 604-524-7021. E-mail: library@bcmhs.bc.ca. Web Site: www.bcmhs.bc.ca/library. *Librn,* Greg Rowell; Staff 3 (MLS 1, Non-MLS 2)
Library Holdings: Bk Titles 8,000; Bk Vols 10,000; Per Subs 150
Subject Interests: Psychiat
Function: Ref serv available
Publications: Acquisitions List; In The Journals; Serials Holdings List

COURTENAY

J　　NORTH ISLAND COLLEGE*, Comox Valley Campus Library, 2300 Ryan Rd, V9N 8N6. Tel: 250-334-5001. FAX: 250-334-5291. Web Site: library.nic.bc.ca. *Coordr, Libr Serv,* Mary Anne Guenther; *Coll Develop,* Amanda Pitchford; Tel: 250-334-5097
Library Holdings: Bk Titles 30,000
Automation Activity & Vendor Info: (Acquisitions) SirsiDynix; (Cataloging) SirsiDynix; (Circulation) SirsiDynix; (Course Reserve) SirsiDynix; (OPAC) SirsiDynix
Database Vendor: EBSCOhost, Wilson - Wilson Web
Open Mon-Fri (Summer) 8-4; Mon-Thurs (Spring & Fall) 8-7:30, Fri 8-4

CRANBROOK

J　　COLLEGE OF THE ROCKIES*, Learning Resource Centre, 2700 College Way, V1C 5L7. (Mail add: PO Box 8500, V1C 5L7). Tel: 250-489-8294. Interlibrary Loan Service Tel: 250-489-2751 local 3410. Reference Tel: 250-489-8292. FAX: 250-489-8256. E-mail: circdesk@cotr.bc.ca, library@cotr.bc.ca. Interlibrary Loan Service E-mail: ill@cotr.bc.ca. Web Site: library.cotr.bc.ca. *Libr Mgr/Coordr,* Position Currently Open
Founded 1976. Enrl 1,500; Fac 60
Wireless access
Partic in BC Electronic Library Network
Special Services for the Deaf - Closed caption videos
Special Services for the Blind - Computer access aids; Copier with enlargement capabilities; Dragon Naturally Speaking software
Open Mon-Thurs (Sept-April) 8am-9:30pm, Fri 8-5, Sat 10-4, Sun 12-4; Mon-Fri (May-Aug) 8-5

P　　CRANBROOK PUBLIC LIBRARY*, 1212 Second St N, V1C 4T6. SAN 318-7616. Tel: 250-426-4063. FAX: 250-426-2098. Web Site: www.cranbrookpubliclibrary.ca.ca. *Chief Librn,* Ursula Brigl; Staff 8.7 (MLS 1.4, Non-MLS 7.3)
Founded 1925. Pop 2,500; Circ 224,000
Jan 2008-Dec 2008 Income (CAN) $745,911, Provincial (CAN) $110,265, City (CAN) $441,055, County (CAN) $110,265, Locally Generated Income (CAN) $84,326. Mats Exp (CAN) $90,129, Books (CAN) $67,288, Per/Ser (Incl. Access Fees) (CAN) $8,101, AV Mat (CAN) $10,756, Electronic Ref Mat (Incl. Access Fees) (CAN) $3,984. Sal (CAN) $472,881

Library Holdings: Audiobooks 1,509; Bks on Deafness & Sign Lang 40; CDs 1,479; DVDs 1,506; e-books 5,508; Electronic Media & Resources 35; High Interest/Low Vocabulary Bk Vols 35; Large Print Bks 1,082; Music Scores 300; Bk Titles 58,135; Bk Vols 65,863; Per Subs 180; Videos 1,207
Automation Activity & Vendor Info: (Acquisitions) SirsiDynix; (Cataloging) SirsiDynix; (Circulation) SirsiDynix; (ILL) Auto-Graphics, Inc; (OPAC) SirsiDynix; (Serials) SirsiDynix
Database Vendor: EBSCOhost, SirsiDynix
Wireless access
Function: After school storytime, Audiobks via web, AV serv, Bk club(s), Bks on cassette, Bks on CD, CD-ROM, Children's prog, Computers for patron use, Copy machines, Digital talking bks, e-mail & chat, e-mail serv, E-Reserves, Electronic databases & coll, Equip loans & repairs, Family literacy, Free DVD rentals, Holiday prog, Home delivery & serv to Sr ctr & nursing homes, Homebound delivery serv, Homework prog, ILL available, Large print keyboards, Online cat, Online ref, Online searches, Outside serv via phone, mail, e-mail & web, OverDrive digital audio bks, Photocopying/Printing, Preschool outreach, Prog for adults, Prog for children & young adult, Pub access computers, Ref serv available, Spoken cassettes & CDs, Spoken cassettes & DVDs, Story hour, Summer reading prog, Teen prog, VHS videos, Web-catalog, Wheelchair accessible
Publications: Annual Report; Inhouse Publications (Documents)
Special Services for the Blind - Bks on cassette; Bks on CD; Copier with enlargement capabilities; Home delivery serv; Large print bks; PC for handicapped
Open Tues-Thurs 9-9, Fri & Sat 10-6, Sun 12-6
Friends of the Library Group

CRESTON

P　　CRESTON PUBLIC LIBRARY ASSOCIATION*, 531-16th Ave S, V0B 1G5. SAN 318-7632. Tel: 250-428-4141. FAX: 250-428-4703. E-mail: info@crestonlibrary.com. Web Site: www.crestonlibrary.com. *Chief Librn,* Ann Day; E-mail: ann.day@crestonlibrary.com; Staff 1 (MLS 1)
Founded 1921. Pop 11,574; Circ 229,282
Library Holdings: AV Mats 2,748; Large Print Bks 152; Bk Titles 35,039; Bk Vols 38,581; Per Subs 65; Talking Bks 112
Automation Activity & Vendor Info: (Cataloging) Mandarin Library Automation; (Circulation) Mandarin Library Automation; (OPAC) Mandarin Library Automation
Special Services for the Blind - Home delivery serv; Large print bks; Talking bks
Open Tues, Thurs & Sat 10-5, Wed & Fri 10-8
Friends of the Library Group

DAWSON CREEK

P　　DAWSON CREEK MUNICIPAL PUBLIC LIBRARY*, 1001 McKellar Ave, V1G 4W7. SAN 318-7640. Tel: 250-782-4661. FAX: 250-782-4667. E-mail: dclib@pris.bc.ca. Web Site: www.dcpl.dawson-creek.bc.ca/. *Librn,* Jenny Snyder; Staff 6 (Non-MLS 6)
Founded 1948. Pop 18,326; Circ 121,907
Library Holdings: CDs 771; DVDs 183; Large Print Bks 1,575; Bk Vols 72,715; Per Subs 96; Talking Bks 1,291; Videos 1,091
Special Collections: Peace River History (Dorthea Calverley Coll)
Subject Interests: Compact discs
Automation Activity & Vendor Info: (Acquisitions) Mandarin Library Automation; (Cataloging) Mandarin Library Automation; (Circulation) Mandarin Library Automation; (ILL) Auto-Graphics, Inc; (Media Booking) Mandarin Library Automation; (OPAC) Mandarin Library Automation; (Serials) Mandarin Library Automation
Wireless access
Special Services for the Blind - Home delivery serv
Open Mon, Sat & Sun 1:30-5:30, Tues-Thurs 9:30-8, Fri 9:30-5:30
Friends of the Library Group

C　　NORTHERN LIGHTS COLLEGE LIBRARY*, Dawson Creek Campus Library, 11401 Eighth St, V1G 4G2. SAN 324-2129. Tel: 250-784-7533. FAX: 250-784-7567. *Librn,* Janet H Beavers; E-mail: jbeavers@nlc.bc.ca; Staff 2 (MLS 2)
Founded 1975. Enrl 1,319; Fac 100; Highest Degree: Associate
Library Holdings: Bk Vols 50,000; Per Subs 374
Automation Activity & Vendor Info: (Acquisitions) SirsiDynix; (Cataloging) SirsiDynix; (Circulation) SirsiDynix; (OPAC) SirsiDynix; (Serials) SirsiDynix
Database Vendor: EBSCOhost
Partic in BC Electronic Library Network
Open Mon-Thurs 8:30-8, Fri 8:30-4:30, Sat 1-5

ELKFORD

P　　ELKFORD PUBLIC LIBRARY*, 816 Michele Rd, V0B 1H0. (Mail add: PO Box 280, V0B 1H0), SAN 318-7659. Tel: 250-865-2912. FAX: 250-865-2460. E-mail: elklib1@telus.net. Web Site:

www3.telus.net/public/rlklib1/home. *Librn,* Sharon Gumowsky; *Asst Librn,*
Diane Andrews
Founded 1974. Pop 2,854; Circ 27,913
Library Holdings: Bk Vols 24,000
Open Tues-Thurs 10-7, Fri 12-7, Sat 12-5

FERNIE

S   FERNIE CHAMBER OF COMMERCE*, Business Information Library,
102 Commerce Rd, V0B 1M5. SAN 373-7454. Tel: 250-423-6868. FAX:
250-423-3811. E-mail: info@ferniechamber.com. Web Site:
www.ferniechamber.com. *Mgr,* Beth Dennahower
Library Holdings: Bk Titles 170

P   FERNIE HERITAGE LIBRARY*, 492 Third Ave, V0B 1M0. (Mail add:
PO Box 448, V0B 1M0), SAN 318-7667. Tel: 250-423-4458.
Administration Tel: 250-423-7135. FAX: 250-423-7906. E-mail:
library@elkvalley.net. Web Site: www.fernieheritagelibrary.com. *Libr Dir,*
Emma Dressler; *Asst Librn,* Marilyn Razzo
Founded 1920. Pop 7,909; Circ 54,328
Library Holdings: Bk Titles 30,000
Special Collections: Foreign/Independent Films; Language Learning,
cassettes. Oral History
Automation Activity & Vendor Info: (Cataloging) Mandarin Library
Automation; (Circulation) Mandarin Library Automation; (OPAC)
Mandarin Library Automation
Open Tues-Fri 11-8, Sat 12-5

FORT NELSON

P   FORT NELSON PUBLIC LIBRARY*, 5315-50th Ave S, Box 330, V0C
1R0. SAN 318-7675. Tel: 250-774-6777. FAX: 250-774-6777. E-mail:
fnpl@fortnelson.bclibrary.ca. Web Site: fortnelson.bclibrary.ca. *Commun
Librn,* Nola Newman; *Asst Librn,* Joan Davidson; *Asst Librn, ILL,* Sylvia
Bramhill; E-mail: bfn.ill@fortnelson.bclibrary.ca; *Asst Librn, Tech Support,*
Linda Novotny; E-mail: lnovotny@fortnelson.bclibrary.ca
Pop 5,000; Circ 26,809
Library Holdings: Bk Vols 30,000
Partic in North East Library Federation (NELF)
Open Mon-Wed Noon-5 & 7pm-9pm, Thurs & Fri 10-5, Sat & Sun
Noon-4

FORT SAINT JOHN

P   FORT ST JOHN PUBLIC LIBRARY ASSOCIATION*, 10015-100th Ave,
V1J 1Y7. SAN 318-7691. Tel: 250-785-3731. FAX: 250-785-7982. E-mail:
fsjlibrary@fsjlibrary.ca. Web Site: fortstjohn.bclibrary.ca. *Dir,* Kimberly
Partanen; Staff 7 (Non-MLS 7)
Founded 1950. Pop 28,000
Library Holdings: Bk Vols 60,000
Automation Activity & Vendor Info: (Acquisitions) Mandarin Library
Automation
Wireless access
Partic in North East Library Federation (NELF)
Friends of the Library Group

C   NORTHERN LIGHTS COLLEGE*, Fort St John Campus Library, 9820
120 Ave, V1J 6K1. (Mail add: PO Box 1000, V1J 6K1), SAN 324-2137.
Tel: 250-787-6213. Toll Free Tel: 866-463-6652, Ext 6213. FAX:
250-785-1294. E-mail: fsj-lib@nlc.bc.ca. Web Site: library.nlc.bc.ca. *Librn,*
Dawna Turcotte; Staff 2.5 (MLS 1, Non-MLS 1.5)
Highest Degree: Associate
Library Holdings: Bk Titles 16,000; Per Subs 30
Automation Activity & Vendor Info: (Circulation) SirsiDynix
Database Vendor: Canadian Reference Centre, Cinahl Information
Systems, EBSCO Auto Repair Reference, EBSCOhost, Medline, OVID
Technologies, ProQuest, Wilson - Wilson Web
Wireless access
Open Mon-Thurs (Sept-May) 8-8, Fri 8:30-4:30, Sat 12-4

FORT ST. JAMES

P   FORT ST JAMES PUBLIC LIBRARY, Fort St James Bicentennial Library,
425 Manson St, V0J 1P0. (Mail add: PO Box 729, V0J 1P0), SAN
318-7683. Tel: 250-996-7431. FAX: 250-996-7484. E-mail:
fortlib@fsjames.com. Web Site: fortstjames.bclibrary.ca. *Head Librn,*
Wayne Briscoe
Pop 4,068; Circ 20,094
Library Holdings: Bk Vols 14,200; Per Subs 27
Function: Adult bk club, Bk club(s), Bks on cassette, Children's prog,
Computer training, Computers for patron use, Copy machines, Digital
talking bks, e-mail & chat, Electronic databases & coll, Family literacy,
Fax serv, Games & aids for the handicapped, Handicapped accessible,
Holiday prog, Home delivery & serv to Sr ctr & nursing homes,
Homebound delivery serv, ILL available, Instruction & testing, Large print

keyboards, Magnifiers for reading, Orientations, Outreach serv, OverDrive
digital audio bks, Photocopying/Printing, Preschool outreach, Prog for
children & young adult, Pub access computers, Ref & res, Ref serv in
person, Senior computer classes, Senior outreach, Spoken cassettes & CDs,
Story hour, Summer reading prog, Teen prog, Telephone ref, Wheelchair
accessible
Open Tues & Fri 11:30-8, Wed & Thurs 11:30-4:30, Sat 11-3

FORT STEELE

S   FORT STEELE HERITAGE TOWN LIBRARY*, 9851 Hwy 93-95, V0B
1N0. SAN 328-0594. Tel: 250-417-6000. FAX: 250-489-2624. E-mail:
ftsteele@cyberlink.bc.ca. Web Site: www.fortsteele.bc.ca. *Curator,* Georgia
Roller; Tel: 250-417-6000, Ext 108
Founded 1965
Library Holdings: Bk Vols 10,000; Per Subs 35
Special Collections: 19-20th Century Material History; East Kootenay
History; Heritage Restoration, photogs & archives; Region
Open Mon-Fri 8-3:30

FRASER LAKE

P   FRASER LAKE PUBLIC LIBRARY*, 228 Endako Ave, V0J 1S0. (Mail
add: PO Box 520, V0J 1S0), SAN 377-2128. Tel: 250-699-8888. FAX:
250-699-8899. E-mail: fllibrarian@bcgroup.net. Web Site:
www.fraserlake.ca/library. *Chief Librn,* Audrey Fennema; Staff 3
(Non-MLS 3)
Library Holdings: Bk Vols 17,214; Per Subs 72; Talking Bks 150
Automation Activity & Vendor Info: (Acquisitions) Follett Software;
(Cataloging) Follett Software; (Circulation) Follett Software; (ILL) Follett
Software; (OPAC) Follett Software
Database Vendor: EBSCOhost, World Book Online
Open Tues & Fri 10-4, Wed & Thurs 3-8, Sat 10-2
Friends of the Library Group

FRUITVALE

P   BEAVER VALLEY PUBLIC LIBRARY*, 1847 First St, V0G 1L0. (Mail
add: PO Box 429, V0G 1L0), SAN 324-1742. Tel: 250-367-7114. FAX:
250-367-7130. E-mail: bvpublic@telus.net. Web Site: www.bvpl.kics.bc.ca.
Librn, Marie Zettl; *Asst Librn,* Monique Mudie; *Asst Librn,* Susan
Vellutini; *Asst Librn,* April Wilmot; Staff 1 (Non-MLS 1)
Pop 5,777; Circ 69,202
Library Holdings: Bk Titles 32,000; Per Subs 82
Automation Activity & Vendor Info: (Cataloging) Mandarin Library
Automation; (Circulation) Mandarin Library Automation; (OPAC)
Mandarin Library Automation
Wireless access
Mem of Kootenay Library Federation
Special Services for the Blind - Digital talking bk; Reader equip
Open Mon-Wed 11-8, Thurs & Fri 11-5, Sat 1-5
Friends of the Library Group

GIBSONS

P   GIBSONS & DISTRICT PUBLIC LIBRARY*, 470 S Fletcher Rd, V0N
1V0. (Mail add: PO Box 109, V0N 1V0), SAN 318-7705. Tel:
604-886-2130. FAX: 604-886-2689. Web Site: www.gdpl.scrd.bc.ca. *Chief
Librn,* Position Currently Open; *Ch,* Heather Evans-Cullen; Staff 8 (MLS
4, Non-MLS 4)
Founded 1914. Pop 9,302
Library Holdings: Large Print Bks 500; Bk Vols 40,000; Per Subs 80;
Talking Bks 600
Automation Activity & Vendor Info: (Acquisitions) Horizon;
(Cataloging) Horizon; (Media Booking) Horizon; (OPAC) Horizon
Function: Govt ref serv, Handicapped accessible, Home delivery & serv to
Sr ctr & nursing homes, ILL available, Prog for children & young adult,
Ref serv available, Summer reading prog
Open Tues, Fri & Sat 10-5, Wed & Thurs 10-8:30
Friends of the Library Group

GRAND FORKS

P   GRAND FORKS & DISTRICT PUBLIC LIBRARY*, 7342 Fifth St, V0H
1H0. (Mail add: PO Box 1539, V0H 1H0), SAN 377-063X. Tel:
250-442-3944. FAX: 250-442-2645. E-mail: library@gfpl.ca. Web Site:
www.grandforkslibrary.com. *Dir,* Heather Buzzell; Staff 1 (MLS 1)
Pop 9,000
Library Holdings: Bk Titles 33,000; Per Subs 103; Talking Bks 1,004
Automation Activity & Vendor Info: (Cataloging) Mandarin Library
Automation; (Circulation) Mandarin Library Automation; (OPAC)
Mandarin Library Automation
Open Tues & Thurs 10-8, Wed, Fri & Sat 10-5
Friends of the Library Group

GRANISLE

P GRANISLE PUBLIC LIBRARY, Two Village Sq, McDonald Ave, V0J 1W0. (Mail add: PO Box 550, V0J 1W0), SAN 377-2241. Tel: 250-697-2713. *Chief Librn,* Sherry Smith
Pop 600
Library Holdings: Bk Titles 9,200; Bk Vols 9,500; Per Subs 40; Talking Bks 270
Partic in N Cent Libr Asn
Open Mon & Wed 6:30pm-9pm, Tues, Thurs & Fri 12-4
Friends of the Library Group

GREENWOOD

P GREENWOOD PUBLIC LIBRARY, 346 S Copper St, V0H 1J0. (Mail add: PO Box 279, V0H 1J0), SAN 324-1181. Tel: 250-445-6111. FAX: 250-445-6111. E-mail: greenlib@shaw.ca. Web Site: greenwood.bclibrary.ca. *Head Librn,* Judy M Foucher; *Asst Librn,* Clare Folvik; Staff 2 (Non-MLS 2)
Founded 1945. Pop 912; Circ 5,084
Library Holdings: Bk Titles 8,833; Bk Vols 9,165; Per Subs 20
Function: ILL available, Magnifiers for reading, Photocopying/Printing, Ref serv available, Summer reading prog
Open Mon-Wed 12-7:30, Fri 12-5, Sat 12-3

HAZELTON

P HAZELTON DISTRICT PUBLIC LIBRARY*, 4255 Government St, V0J 1Y0. (Mail add: PO Box 323, V0J 1Y0), SAN 318-7721. Tel: 250-842-5961. FAX: 250-842-2176. E-mail: hazlib@bulkley.net. Web Site: www.hazeltonlibrary.bc.ca. *Chief Librn,* Eve Hope
Founded 1948. Pop 6,537; Circ 24,321
Library Holdings: Bk Titles 27,439; Bk Vols 28,854; Per Subs 92
Subject Interests: Local hist
Automation Activity & Vendor Info: (Circulation) Follett Software
Open Mon 7:30pm-9pm, Tues 11-5 & 7:30pm-9pm, Wed 11-9, Thurs & Fri 11-5, Sat 12-4

HOUSTON

P HOUSTON PUBLIC LIBRARY*, 3150 14th St, V0J 1Z0. (Mail add: PO Box 840, V0J 1Z0). Tel: 250-845-2256. FAX: 250-845-2088. *Chief Librn,* Karen Filipkowski; *Asst Librn,* Videe Davies; *Asst Librn,* Rebekah Huston; *Asst Librn,* Erna Vander Heide; Staff 4 (Non-MLS 4)
Founded 1964. Pop 3,800; Circ 40,000
Library Holdings: Bk Vols 24,692; Per Subs 40
Automation Activity & Vendor Info: (Acquisitions) Follett Software; (Cataloging) Follett Software; (Circulation) Follett Software; (ILL) Auto-Graphics, Inc; (OPAC) Follett Software
Database Vendor: EBSCOhost
Function: ILL available, Photocopying/Printing, Prog for children & young adult, Summer reading prog, Telephone ref, Wheelchair accessible
Open Tues & Fri 10-5 & 7pm-9pm, Wed & Thurs 10-5, Sat 10-4

HUDSON'S HOPE

P HUDSON'S HOPE PUBLIC LIBRARY*, 9905 Dudley Dr, V0C 1V0. (Mail add: PO Box 269, V0C 1V0), SAN 318-773X. Tel: 250-783-9414. FAX: 250-783-5272. E-mail: hh.ill@pris.ca. Web Site: hp.bccna.bc.ca/Library/HudsonsHope/, hudsonshope.bclibrary.ca. *Librn,* Karen Anderson; *Asst Librn,* Rosaleen Ward
Pop 1,600
Library Holdings: Bk Titles 17,000; Bk Vols 18,000; Per Subs 15
Function: Fax serv, Homebound delivery serv, ILL available, Photocopying/Printing, Ref serv available
Partic in DRAL Libr; North East Library Federation (NELF)
Open Mon & Thurs 1:30-4 & 6:30pm-9pm, Wed & Sun 1:30-4
Friends of the Library Group

C NORTHERN LIGHTS COLLEGE*, Hudson's Hope Learning Centre Library, 9471 Beattie Dr, V0C 1V0. (Mail add: PO Box 268, V0C 1V0). Tel: 250-783-5711. FAX: 250-783-5788. Web Site: www.nlc.bc.ca. *Librn,* Steve Metzger
Library Holdings: Bk Titles 500
Open Mon-Fri 9-4

INVERMERE

P INVERMERE PUBLIC LIBRARY*, 201 Seventh Ave, V0A 1K0. (Mail add: PO Box 989, V0A 1K0), SAN 318-7748. Tel: 250-342-6416. FAX: 250-342-6416. E-mail: invlibrary@cyberlink.bc.ca. Web Site: hp.bccna.bc.ca/library/invermere. *Librn,* Elizabeth A Robinson; *Asst Librn,* Virginia Walker
Founded 1963. Pop 6,235; Circ 23,007
Library Holdings: Bk Titles 15,000; Bk Vols 15,500; Per Subs 25

Function: ILL available
Open Tues & Fri 10-5:30, Wed 12-8, Thurs 12-5:30, Sat 10-4

KAMLOOPS

M THOMPSON CARIBOO SHUSWAP HEALTH SCIENCES LIBRARY*, 311 Columbia St, V2C 2T1. SAN 375-4855. Tel: 250-314-2234. FAX: 250-314-2189. E-mail: tcslibrary@interiorhealth.ca. Web Site: www.interiorhealth.ca. *Librn,* Lisa D Gysel; E-mail: lisa.gysel@interiorhealth.ca; *Libr Tech,* Paula Hardy; Tel: 250-314-2342, E-mail: paula.hardy@interiorhealth.ca; Staff 2 (MLS 1, Non-MLS 1)
Library Holdings: Bk Titles 1,500; Per Subs 80
Wireless access

P THOMPSON-NICOLA REGIONAL DISTRICT LIBRARY SYSTEM*, 300-465 Victoria St, V2C 2A9. SAN 365-8503. Tel: 250-374-8866. FAX: 250-372-5614. E-mail: postmaster@tnrdlib.bc.ca. Web Site: www.tnrdlib.bc.ca.
Founded 1974. Pop 160,000; Circ 1,007,624
Library Holdings: Bk Vols 303,357; Per Subs 200
Special Collections: Canadiana. Can & Prov
Publications: "Tattler" (Newsletter); Annual Reports
Member Libraries: Thompson-Nicola Regional District Library System
Branches: 13
ASHCROFT BRANCH, 201 Brink St, Ashcroft, V0K 1A0. (Mail add: PO Box 789, Ashcroft, V0K 1A0). Tel: 250-453-9042. Web Site: www.tnrdlib.bc.ca/LibrarySystem/Branches/ash.shtml. *Br Mgr,* Jane Flaherty
Open Tues & Thurs 1:30-5, Wed & Fri 1:30-5 & 6:30pm-8:30pm
BARRIERE BRANCH, 4511 Barriere Town Rd, Barriere, V0E 1E0. (Mail add: PO Box 100, Barriere, V0E 1E0), SAN 325-2612. Tel: 250-672-5811. FAX: 250-672-5811. Web Site: www.tnrdlib.bc.ca/LibrarySystem/Branches/bar.shtml. *Librn,* Linda Kelley
Founded 1974. Pop 5,000
Library Holdings: Bk Titles 7,592; Bk Vols 12,000; Per Subs 19
Special Collections: Local History (Barriere District Coll), notes, files, newsp clippings. Oral History
Mem of Thompson-Nicola Regional District Library System
Special Services for the Deaf - Bks on deafness & sign lang
Open Tues & Thurs 10:30-5, Wed & Fri 10:30-1 & 6:30pm-8:30pm
BLUE RIVER BRANCH, 829 Cedar St, Blue River, V0E 1J0. (Mail add: PO Box 47, Blue River, V0E 1J0). Tel: 250-673-8235. FAX: 250-673-8235. Web Site: www.tnrdlib.bc.ca/LibrarySystem/Branches/blu.shtml. *Br Mgr,* Rebecca Beaton
Open Tues & Sat 1-5, Wed & Thurs 6pm-8pm, Fri 1-4
CACHE CREEK BRANCH, 1390 Quartz Rd, Cache Creek, V0K 1H0. (Mail add: PO Box 429, Cache Creek, V0K 1H0). Tel: 250-457-9953. Web Site: www.tnrdlib.bc.ca/LibrarySystem/Branches/ccr.shtml. *Br Mgr,* Jane Flaherty
Open Tues & Thurs 2:30-5 & 6:30pm-8:30pm, Wed 2-5, Sat 1-4
CHASE BRANCH, 614 Shuswap Ave, Chase, V0E 1M0. (Mail add: PO Box 590, Chase, V0E 1M0). Tel: 250-679-3331. Web Site: www.tnrdlib.bc.ca/LibrarySystem/Branches/cha.shtml. *Br Mgr,* Jo-Anne Becker
Open Tues 10-4, Wed & Fri 12-4, Thurs 12-4 & 6pm-8pm, Sat 10-3
CLEARWATER BRANCH, 422 Murtle Crescent, Clearwater, V0E 1N1. Tel: 250-674-2543. *Br Mgr,* Darlene Cowie
Open Tues-Thurs & Sat 10-4, Fri 1-7
CLINTON BRANCH, 1506 Tingley St, Clinton, V0K 1K0. (Mail add: PO Box 550, Clinton, V0K 1K0). Tel: 250-459-7752. FAX: 250-459-7752. Web Site: www.tnrdlib.bc.ca/LibrarySystem/Branches/cli.shtml. *Br Mgr,* Catheryn Munro
Open Tues 1-7:30, Thurs 3-7:30, Sat 10-2
KAMLOOPS BRANCH, 100-465 Victoria St, V2C 2A9. Tel: 250-372-5145. Web Site: www.tnrdlib.bc.ca/LibrarySystem/Branches/kam.shtml. *Br Mgr,* Alex MacDonald
Open Mon, Fri & Sat 10-5, Tues-Thurs 10-9, Sun (Oct-Apr) 12-4
LOGAN LAKE BRANCH, 70-150 Opal Dr, Logan Lake, V0K 1W0. (Mail add: PO Box 310, Logan Lake, V0K 1W0). Tel: 250-523-6745. FAX: 250-523-6745. Web Site: www.tnrdlib.bc.ca/LibrarySystem/Branches/log.shtml. *Br Mgr,* Seiko Niven
Open Tues 10-2 & 6pm-8pm, Wed 12-4, Thurs 10-3, Fri 11-4
LYTTON BRANCH, 121 Fourth St, Lytton, V0K 1Z0. (Mail add: PO Box 220, Lytton, V0K 1Z0). Tel: 250-455-2521. FAX: 250-455-2521. Web Site: www.tnrdlib.bc.ca/LibrarySystem/Branches/lyt.shtml. *Br Mgr,* Georgia Lesley
Open Tues 3-8, Wed 10-1, Thurs 2-6, Sat 1-4
MERRITT BRANCH, 1691 Garcia St, Merritt, V1K 1B8. (Mail add: PO Box 1510, Merritt, V1K 1B8). Tel: 250-378-4737. Web Site: www.tnrdlib.bc.ca/LibrarySystem/Branches/mer.shtml. *Br Mgr,* Deborha Merrick
Open Tues & Wed 10-8, Thurs-Sat 10-5

NORTH KAMLOOPS BRANCH, 795 Tranquille Rd, V2B 3J3. Tel: 250-554-1124. FAX: 250-376-3825. Web Site: www.tnrdlib.bc.ca/LibrarySystem/Branches/nkm.shtml. *Br Mgr,* Michael Killick
Open Mon, Fri & Sat 10-5, Tues-Thurs 10-9
SAVONA BRANCH, 60 Savona St, Savona, V0K 2J0. (Mail add: PO Box 169, Savona, V0K 2J0). Tel: 250-373-2666. Web Site: www.tnrdlib.bc.ca/LibrarySystem/Branches/svn.shtml. *Br Mgr,* Sandra Rawson
Open Wed 12-6, Thurs 3-7, Fri 10-3
Bookmobiles: 1

C THOMPSON RIVERS UNIVERSITY*, Kamloops Campus Library, 900 McGill Rd, V2C 5N3. (Mail add: Box 3010, V2C 5 N3), SAN 328-7815. Tel: 250-828-5300. FAX: 250-828-5313. Web Site: www.tru.ca/library. *Univ Librn,* Nancy Levesque; Tel: 250-828-5305, E-mail: levesque@tru.ca; *Acq Librn,* Penny Haggarty; *Distance Learning Librn, Doc Delivery,* Brenda Smith; *Info Serv Librn,* Kathy Gaynor; *Instruction Librn, Outreach Librn,* Elizabeth Rennie; E-mail: erennie@tru.ca; *Syst Librn,* Michael Coyne
Library Holdings: Bk Vols 200,000
Function: ILL available
Partic in BC Electronic Library Network
Open Mon-Thurs 8am-9pm, Fri 8-5, Sat 9-5, Sun 9-9

KASLO

P KASLO & DISTRICT PUBLIC LIBRARY*, 413 Fourth St, V0G 1M0. (Mail add: PO Box 760, V0G 1M0). Tel: 250-353-2942. E-mail: kaslo.bclibrary.ca, librarian@pop.kin.bc.ca. Web Site: www.kin.bc.ca/kin/library/librarylinks.html. *Librn,* Annie Reynolds
Pop 1,750; Circ 16,762
Library Holdings: Bk Titles 13,800; Per Subs 22
Open Tues 12-5, Thurs 12-8, Fri 3-6, Sat 10:30-4

KELOWNA

C OKANAGAN COLLEGE LIBRARY, 1000 KLO Rd, V1Y 4X8. SAN 365-9739. Administration Tel: 250-862-5477. Administration FAX: 250-862-5609. Web Site: www.okanagan.bc.ca/library. *Libr Dir,* Ross Tyner; E-mail: rhtyner@okanagan.bc.ca; *Cat & Acq,* Eva Engman; E-mail: eengman@okanagan.bc.ca; *Syst Librn,* Gilbert Bede; E-mail: gbede@okanagan.bc.ca; *Web Serv Librn,* Roen Janyk; E-mail: rjanyk@okanagan.bc.ca; *Pub Serv,* Anne Cossentine; E-mail: acossentine@okanagan.bc.ca; *Pub Serv,* Leanna Jantzi; E-mail: ljantzi@okanagan.bc.ca; *Pub Serv,* Taryn Schmid; E-mail: tschmid@okanagan.bc.ca; *Pub Serv,* Jennifer Sigalet; E-mail: jsigalet@okanagan.bc.ca; *Pub Serv,* Michelle Ward; E-mail: mward@okanagan.bc.ca
Founded 2005. Highest Degree: Bachelor
Automation Activity & Vendor Info: (Acquisitions) Ex Libris Group; (Cataloging) Ex Libris Group; (Circulation) Ex Libris Group; (OPAC) Ex Libris Group; (Serials) Ex Libris Group
Wireless access
Partic in BC Electronic Library Network; Council of Prairie & Pacific University Libraries

P OKANAGAN REGIONAL LIBRARY*, 1430 KLO Rd, V1W 3P6. SAN 365-9763. Tel: 250-860-4033. FAX: 250-861-8696. E-mail: admin@orl.bc.ca. Web Site: www.orl.bc.ca. *Exec Dir,* Lesley Dieno; Tel: 250-860-4033, Ext 1111; *Br Head Librn,* Maureen Curry; *Br Head Librn,* Roswitha Klawitter; *Br Head Librn,* Fern Teleglow; *IT Mgr,* Jeff Campbell; *Pub Serv Mgr,* Pam Medland; *Adult Serv, Coll Develop,* Barbara Jo May; *Ch, Coll Develop,* Linda Youmans; *Tech Serv,* Paula Trout; Staff 21 (MLS 18, Non-MLS 3)
Founded 1936. Pop 359,952
Library Holdings: Microforms 3,113; Bk Titles 173,322; Bk Vols 725,129; Per Subs 1,816; Talking Bks 5,544; Videos 24,423
Automation Activity & Vendor Info: (Acquisitions) SirsiDynix; (Cataloging) SirsiDynix; (Circulation) SirsiDynix; (OPAC) SirsiDynix; (Serials) SirsiDynix
Database Vendor: ALLDATA Online, Baker & Taylor, EBSCO Auto Repair Reference, EBSCOhost, ProQuest, World Book Online
Wireless access
Publications: Annual report
Open Mon-Fri 8-4:30
Friends of the Library Group
Branches: 29
ARMSTRONG BRANCH, 10-3305 Smith Dr, Armstrong, V0E 1B1. Tel: 250-546-8311.
Open Tues, Thurs & Sat 10-5, Wed 1-5, Fri 10-8
Friends of the Library Group
CHERRYVILLE BRANCH, 1114 Hwy 6, Cherryville, V0E 2G3. Tel: 250-547-9776.
Open Wed & Thurs 4-8

ENDERBY BRANCH, 514 Cliff Ave, Enderby, V0E 1V0. (Mail add: PO Box 226, Enderby, V0E 1V0). Tel: 250-838-6488.
Founded 1865
Open Tues & Wed 10-5, Fri 10-8, Sat 11-5
Friends of the Library Group
FALKLAND BRANCH, 5771 Hwy 97, Falkland, V0E 1W0. (Mail add: PO Box 33, Falkland, V0E 1W0). Tel: 250-379-2705. *Commun Librn,* Diana McCarthy
Open Tues 2-5 & 6-8, Wed & Thurs 1-6
GOLDEN BRANCH, 819 Park Ave, Golden, V0A 1H0. (Mail add: PO Box 750, Golden, V0A 1H0). Tel: 250-344-6516.
Open Tues, Fri & Sat 10-5, Thurs 10-8
HEDLEY BRANCH, Old Age Pensioner's Hall, Corner of Scott St & Irene, Hedley, V0X 1K0. (Mail add: PO Box 190, Hedley, V0X 1K0). Tel: 250-292-8209.
Open Thurs 2-7
KALEDEN BRANCH, Kaleden Community Hall, 101 Linden Ave, Kaleden, V0H 1K0. (Mail add: PO Box 370, Kaleden, V0H 1K0). Tel: 250-497-8066.
Open Tues 1-8, Thurs & Sat 1-5
KELOWNA BRANCH, 1380 Ellis St, V1Y 2A2. Tel: 250-762-2800.
Open Mon, Fri & Sat 10-5:30, Tues-Thurs 10-9, Sun (Oct-Mar) 1-5
Friends of the Library Group
KEREMEOS BRANCH, 638 Seventh Ave, Keremeos, V0X 1N3. (Mail add: PO Box 330, Keremeos, V0X 1N0). Tel: 250-499-2313.
Open Tues 10-5, Wed 1-7, Thurs & Fri 1-5, Sat 10-2
Friends of the Library Group
LAKE COUNTRY BRANCH, 2-10150 Bottom Wood Lake Rd, Lake Country, V4V 2M1. Tel: 250-766-3141.
Open Tues & Thurs 10-6, Wed 10-8, Fri & Sat 10-5
LUMBY BRANCH, 2250 Shields Ave, Lumby, V0E 2G0. (Mail add: PO Box 116, Lumby, V0E 2G0). Tel: 250-547-9528. *Br Head,* Mitzi Fortin
Open Tues 11-7, Wed, Thurs & Sat 11-3, Fri 11-4
MISSION, Capital News Centre, 4105 Gordon Dr, V1W 4Z1. Tel: 250-764-2254.
Open Mon, Wed, Fri & Sat 10-5, Tues & Thurs 10-8
NARAMATA BRANCH, Community Hall, 3580 Third St, Naramata, V0H 1N0. (Mail add: PO Box 190, Naramata, V0H 1N0). Tel: 250-496-5679.
Open Tues 1-5, Thurs 1-8, Fri 12-4
Friends of the Library Group
NORTH SHUSWAP, 3867 Squilax Anglemont Hwy, Scotch Creek, V0E 1M5. Tel: 250-955-8198. E-mail: NorthShuswap@orl.bc.ca.
Open Tues 12-7, Wed & Fri 11-3, Sat 11-4
OKANAGAN FALLS BRANCH, 101-850 Railway Lane, Okanagan Falls, V0H 1R4. Tel: 250-497-5886. E-mail: OkanaganFalls@orl.bc.ca.
Open Tues 12-8, Wed 10-4, Fri 10-5, Sat 10-2
Friends of the Library Group
OLIVER BRANCH, 6239 Station St, Oliver, V0H 1T0. (Mail add: PO Box 758, Oliver, V0H 1T0). Tel: 250-498-2242.
Open Tues & Thurs 10-6, Wed 12-8, Fri 12-6, Sat 10-3
Friends of the Library Group
OSOYOOS BRANCH, Sonora Centre, 8505 68th Ave, Osoyoos, V0H 1V7. (Mail add: PO Box 1038, Osoyoos, V0H 1V0). Tel: 250-495-7637.
Open Tues 12-8, Wed & Thurs 12-5, Fri 10-5, Sat 10-3
Friends of the Library Group
OYAMA BRANCH, 15718 Oyama Rd, Oyama, V4V 2E1. Tel: 250-548-3377.
Open Tues & Thurs 2-4 & 6pm-8pm
PEACHLAND BRANCH, Peachland Village Mall, 40-5500 Clements Crescent, Peachland, V0H 1X5. Tel: 250-767-9111.
Open Tues 12-5 & 6pm-8pm, Wed 12-5, Thurs-Sat 11-5
Friends of the Library Group
PRINCETON BRANCH, 107 Vermilion Ave, Princeton, V0X 1W0. (Mail add: PO Box 958, Princeton, V0X 1W0). Tel: 250-295-6495.
Open Tues 12-5 & 6pm-8pm, Wed & Fri 12-5, Sat 10-1
REVELSTOKE BRANCH, Recreation Centre, 605 Campbell Ave, Revelstoke, V0E 2S0. (Mail add: PO Box 1289, Revelstoke, V0E 2S0). Tel: 250-837-5095.
Open Tues 12-8, Wed 12-7, Thurs 10-4, Fri & Sat 10-5
RUTLAND, Plaza 33 Mall, 20-301 Hwy 33 West, V1X 1X8. Tel: 250-765-8165.
Open Mon & Thurs-Sat 10-5, Tues & Wed 10-8
SALMON ARM BRANCH, 285 Piccadilly Place Mall, 1151 Tenth Ave SW, Salmon Arm, V1E 1T3. Tel: 250-832-6161.
Open Mon, Wed, Thurs & Sat 10-5, Tues & Fri 10-8, Sun (Oct-Mar) 12-4
Friends of the Library Group
SICAMOUS BRANCH, 2-446 Main St, Sicamous, V0E 2V1. (Mail add: PO Box 15, Sicamous, V0E 2V0). Tel: 250-836-4845.
Open Tues 10-5, Wed 12-5, Fri 12-7, Sat 10-4
SILVER CREEK, 921 Salmon River Rd, Salmon Arm, V1E 3G3. Tel: 250-832-4719.
Open Tues 1-7, Wed & Thurs 1-5:30

SOUTH SHUSWAP BRANCH, Blind Bay Market, 1-2676 Fairway Hills Rd, Blind Bay, V0E 1H2. Tel: 250-675-4818. E-mail: southshuswap@orl.bc.ca.
Open Tues & Sat 10-5, Wed & Fri 10-6
Friends of the Library Group
SUMMERLAND BRANCH, 9525 Wharton St, Summerland, V0H 1Z0. (Mail add: Box 1198, Summerland, V0H 1Z0). Tel: 250-494-5591.
Open Tues & Thurs 11-8:30, Wed, Fri & Sat 10-5
Friends of the Library Group
VERNON BRANCH, 3001 32nd Ave, Vernon, V1T 2L8. Tel: 250-542-7610.
Open Mon, Fri & Sat 10-5:30, Tues-Thurs 10-9, Sun (Oct-Mar) 12-4
Friends of the Library Group
WESTBANK BRANCH, Westridge Mall, 31-2484 Main St, Hwy 97S, West Kelowna, V4T 2G2. Tel: 250-768-4369.
Open Mon & Sat 10-5, Tues, Thurs & Fri 10-6, Wed 10-8
Friends of the Library Group

KIMBERLEY

P   KIMBERLEY PUBLIC LIBRARY*, 115 Spokane St, V1A 2E5. Tel: 250-427-3112. FAX: 250-427-7157. Web Site: kimberley.bclibrary.ca. *Dir,* Karin Von Wittgenstein
Pop 7,000
Library Holdings: AV Mats 696; Large Print Bks 220; Bk Titles 35,000; Per Subs 110; Talking Bks 739
Automation Activity & Vendor Info: (Acquisitions) Mandarin Library Automation; (Cataloging) Mandarin Library Automation; (Circulation) Mandarin Library Automation; (Course Reserve) Mandarin Library Automation; (ILL) Mandarin Library Automation; (Media Booking) Mandarin Library Automation; (OPAC) Mandarin Library Automation; (Serials) Mandarin Library Automation
Database Vendor: EBSCOhost
Wireless access
Function: Homebound delivery serv
Special Services for the Blind - Bks on cassette
Open Mon-Wed, Fri & Sat 10-5, Thurs 10-8

KITIMAT

S   KITIMAT MUSEUM & ARCHIVES*, 293 City Centre, V8C 1T6. SAN 329-2193. Tel: 250-632-8950. FAX: 250-632-7429. E-mail: kitimatmuseum@telus.net. Web Site: www.kitimatmuseum.ca, www.livinglandscapes.bc.ca. *Curator,* Louise Avery
Founded 1969
Library Holdings: Bk Titles 400
Special Collections: Alcan Aluminum Smelters & Chemicals Ltd (1950s); Northern Sentinel Press Ltd Coll. Oral History
Subject Interests: NW native studies
Open Mon-Sat (June-Aug) 10-5; Mon-Fri (Sept-May)10-5, Sat 12-5

P   KITIMAT PUBLIC LIBRARY ASSOCIATION, 940 Wakashan Ave, V8C 2G3. SAN 318-7780. Tel: 250-632-8985. FAX: 250-632-2630. E-mail: kitimatlibrary@telus.net. Web Site: www.kitimatpubliclibrary.org. *Libr Dir,* Virginia Charron; Staff 8 (MLS 1, Non-MLS 7)
Founded 1955. Pop 10,000
Library Holdings: Bk Vols 50,000
Special Collections: Large Print Coll; Multilingual Coll
Subject Interests: Local hist
Friends of the Library Group

LANGLEY

S   SOCIETY OF CHRISTIAN SCHOOLS IN BRITISH COLUMBIA LIBRARY, 7600 Glover Rd, V2Y 1Y1. SAN 375-0353. Tel: 604-888-6366. FAX: 604-888-2791. E-mail: scsbc@twu.ca. Web Site: www.scsbc.ca. *Exec Dir,* H Contant
Library Holdings: Bk Vols 3,500

C   TRINITY WESTERN UNIVERSITY*, Norma Marion Alloway Library, 7600 Glover Rd, V2Y 1Y1. SAN 320-3077. Tel: 604-513-2023. Interlibrary Loan Service Tel: 604-513-2121, Ext 3914. Reference Tel: 604-513-2121, Ext 3903. Administration Tel: 604-513-2121, Ext 3902. FAX: 604-513-2063. E-mail: library@twu.ca. Web Site: www.twu.ca/library. *Univ Librn,* Ted Goshulak; Tel: 604-513-2121, Ext 3905, E-mail: tgosh@twu.ca; Staff 15 (MLS 7, Non-MLS 8)
Founded 1962. Enrl 2,350; Fac 150; Highest Degree: Master
Library Holdings: CDs 1,182; DVDs 1,000; e-books 11,402; e-journals 12,929; Microforms 333,489; Bk Vols 225,000; Per Subs 813; Videos 3,000
Special Collections: Mel Smith Papers; Robert N Thompson Papers
Automation Activity & Vendor Info: (Acquisitions) SirsiDynix; (Cataloging) SirsiDynix; (Circulation) SirsiDynix; (Course Reserve) SirsiDynix; (OPAC) SirsiDynix

Database Vendor: Cambridge Scientific Abstracts, EBSCOhost, Elsevier MDL, Gale Cengage Learning, ISI Web of Knowledge, JSTOR, ProQuest, PubMed, ScienceDirect, SirsiDynix, Wilson - Wilson Web
Wireless access
Partic in BC Electronic Library Network; Canadian Research Knowledge Network; Council of Prairie & Pacific University Libraries
Open Mon & Thurs 7:45am-11pm, Fri 7:45-6, Sat 6-6, Sun 1:30-5

LILLOOET

P   LILLOOET AREA LIBRARY ASSOCIATION*, Lillooet Public Library, 930 Main St, V0K 1V0. (Mail add: PO Box 939, V0K 1V0). Tel: 250-256-7944. FAX: 250-256-7924. E-mail: lala@lillooet.bclibrary.ca. Web Site: www.lillooetlibrary.bc.ca/capp/information.html. *Chief Librn,* Betty Weaver; Staff 2 (Non-MLS 2)
Library Holdings: Bk Titles 12,000; Per Subs 25
Automation Activity & Vendor Info: (Acquisitions) Evergreen; (Circulation) Evergreen; (OPAC) Evergreen
Wireless access
Function: Adult literacy prog, Audiobks via web, Bks on cassette, Bks on CD, Children's prog, Computer training, Computers for patron use, Copy machines, Digital talking bks, e-mail & chat, Electronic databases & coll, Family literacy, Free DVD rentals, Home delivery & serv to Sr ctr & nursing homes, Homebound delivery serv, ILL available, Music CDs, Online cat, Online ref, Online searches, OverDrive digital audio bks, Preschool outreach, Pub access computers, Ref serv in person, Story hour, Summer reading prog, VHS videos, Video lending libr, Wheelchair accessible
Open Tues-Thurs 11-7, Fri & Sat 11-2
Branches: 2
BRIDGE RIVER BRANCH, Box 19, Shalaith, V0N 3C0. Tel: 250-259-8242. *Librn,* Roberta Miller
Library Holdings: Bk Titles 6,000
Open Tues 4-8, Wed 1-5
GOLD BRIDGE BRANCH, General Delivery, Gold Bridge, V0K 1P0. Tel: 250-238-2521. FAX: 250-238-2521. E-mail: goldbridge@lillooetlibrary.bc.ca. *Librn,* Jean Shaw; E-mail: jean@lillooet.bclibrary.ca
Library Holdings: Bk Titles 4,698
Open Mon 1-3, Thurs 1-5, Sat 11-1

MACKENZIE

P   MACKENZIE PUBLIC LIBRARY*, 400 Skeena Dr, V0J 2C0. (Mail add: Bag Delivery 750, V0J 2C0). Tel: 250-997-6343. FAX: 250-997-5792. E-mail: mackenziepubliclibrary@gmail.com. Web Site: mackenzie.bclibrary.ca. *Librn,* Wanda Davis
Library Holdings: Bk Titles 40,000; Per Subs 93
Open Mon-Thurs 9:30-8, Fri 9:30-4, Sat & Sun 11-4

MCBRIDE

P   MCBRIDE & DISTRICT PUBLIC LIBRARY, 241 Dominion St, V0J 2E0. (Mail add: PO Box 489, V0J 2E0). Tel: 250-569-2411. FAX: 250-569-2411. E-mail: library@mcbridebc.org. Web Site: www.library.mcbride.bc.ca. *Libr Dir,* Naomi Balla-Boudreau
Library Holdings: Bk Titles 25,000
Automation Activity & Vendor Info: (Circulation) Evergreen; (OPAC) Evergreen
Wireless access
Open Tues 10-5 & 7-9, Wed & Thurs 10-5, Fri 2-9, Sat 2-5

MERRITT

C   NICOLA VALLEY INSTITUTE OF TECHNOLOGY LIBRARY*, 4155 Belshaw St, V1K 1R1. Tel: 250-378-3303. Administration Tel: 250-378-3345. Toll Free Tel: 877-682-3300 (BC only). FAX: 250-378-3332. E-mail: info@nvit.bc.ca. Web Site: www.nvit.bc.ca. *Librn,* Jim Bruce; *Coordr,* Sherry Garcia
Library Holdings: AV Mats 683; Bk Titles 14,000; Per Subs 150
Automation Activity & Vendor Info: (Cataloging) LEX Systems Inc; (Circulation) LEX Systems Inc; (Course Reserve) LEX Systems Inc; (OPAC) LEX Systems Inc
Open Mon-Thurs (Sept-Apr) 8:30-8:30, Fri 8:30-4:30, Sat & Sun 12-4; Mon-Fri (May-Aug) 8-4:30

MIDWAY

P   MIDWAY PUBLIC LIBRARY*, 612 Sixth Ave, V0H 1M0. (Mail add: PO Box 268, V0H 1M0). Tel: 250-449-2620. FAX: 250-449-2389. E-mail: office@midwaylibrary.bc.ca. Web Site: www.midwaylibrary.bc.ca. *Librn,* Stephanie Bolt; Staff 1 (Non-MLS 1)
Circ 1,000
Library Holdings: Bk Titles 10,000; Per Subs 12
Automation Activity & Vendor Info: (Acquisitions) L4U Library Software; (Cataloging) L4U Library Software; (Circulation) L4U Library

Software; (Course Reserve) L4U Library Software; (ILL) L4U Library Software; (Media Booking) L4U Library Software; (OPAC) L4U Library Software; (Serials) L4U Library Software
Function: Handicapped accessible, Home delivery & serv to Sr ctr & nursing homes, Homebound delivery serv, ILL available, Online searches, Photocopying/Printing, Prog for children & young adult, Ref & res, Ref serv available, Serves mentally handicapped consumers, Spoken cassettes & CDs, Spoken cassettes & DVDs, Summer reading prog, VHS videos, Wheelchair accessible
Open Tues-Fri 11-5

MISSION

S   MISSION COMMUNITY ARCHIVES*, 33215 Second Ave, V2V 4L1. (Mail add: PO Box 3522, V2V 4L1), SAN 328-462X. Tel: 604-820-2621. E-mail: mca@missionarchives.com. Web Site: www.missionarchives.com. *Archivist,* Valerie Billesberger
Library Holdings: Bk Titles 300
Special Collections: Reference Coll
Subject Interests: Genealogy, Local hist

R   WESTMINSTER ABBEY LIBRARY, SEMINARY OF CHRIST THE KING*, V2V 4J2. SAN 324-0460. Tel: 604-826-8975. *Librn,* Boniface Aicher; E-mail: bonifaceaicher@yahoo.ca
Founded 1940. Enrl 60; Fac 20; Highest Degree: Doctorate
Library Holdings: Bk Vols 50,000; Per Subs 100
Subject Interests: Bible, Canon law, Church hist, Theol

NAKUSP

P   NAKUSP PUBLIC LIBRARY ASSOCIATION*, 92 W Sixth Ave, V0G 1R0. (Mail add: PO Box 297, V0G 1R0), SAN 318-7802. Tel: 250-265-3363. FAX: 250-265-3363. E-mail: bna@netidea.com. Web Site: www.nakusplibrary.bc.ca. *Librn,* Evelyn Goodell; *Asst Librn,* Susan Rogers; Staff 2 (Non-MLS 2)
Founded 1920. Pop 2,750; Circ 37,500
Library Holdings: Bk Titles 12,390; Bk Vols 12,418; Per Subs 39; Talking Bks 345
Special Collections: Computer Disk Coll; Literacy Coll
Automation Activity & Vendor Info: (Acquisitions) Evergreen; (Cataloging) Evergreen; (ILL) Evergreen; (OPAC) Evergreen
Wireless access
Special Services for the Blind - Talking bks
Open Mon & Wed 12-4:30 & 7pm-9pm, Fri 12-4:30, Sat 10-4:30
Friends of the Library Group

NANAIMO

J   MALASPINA UNIVERSITY-COLLEGE LIBRARY*, 900 Fifth St, V9R 5S5. SAN 318-7829. Tel: 250-753-3245. Circulation Tel: 250-740-6330. Reference Tel: 250-740-6151. Administration Tel: 250-740-6331. FAX: 250-740-6473. Web Site: www.mala.ca/www.discover/library/index.htm. *Dir,* Bob Foley; E-mail: foleyb@mala.bc.ca; *Regional Librn,* Eileen Edmunds; Tel: 250-753-3245, Ext 2272, E-mail: edmundse@mala.bc.ca; *Syst Librn,* Gwen Bailey; Tel: 250-753-3245, Ext 2444, E-mail: baileyg@mala.bc.ca; *Ref,* Jean Blackburn; Tel: 250-753-3245, Ext 2091, E-mail: blackbuj@mala.bc.ca; *Ref,* Jennifer Brownlow; Tel: 250-740-6335, E-mail: brownlow@mala.bc.ca; *Ref,* Linda Leger; Tel: 250-753-3245, Ext 2347, E-mail: legerl@mala.bc.ca; *Ref,* Lyn Makepeace; Tel: 250-753-3245, Ext 2271, E-mail: makepel@mala.bc.ca; *Ref,* Faith Takishita; Tel: 250-753-3245, Ext 2268, E-mail: takishif@mala.bc.ca; *Tech Serv,* Hans Fadum; Tel: 250-753-3245, Ext 2270, E-mail: fadum@mala.bc.ca
Founded 1969. Fac 352
Special Collections: Oral History
Automation Activity & Vendor Info: (Acquisitions) SirsiDynix; (Cataloging) SirsiDynix; (Circulation) SirsiDynix; (Course Reserve) SirsiDynix; (Media Booking) SirsiDynix; (OPAC) SirsiDynix; (Serials) SirsiDynix
Partic in BC Electronic Library Network

P   VANCOUVER ISLAND REGIONAL LIBRARY, 6250 Hammond Bay Rd, V9R 5N3. (Mail add: PO Box 3333, V9R 5N3), SAN 366-0729. Tel: 250-758-4697. FAX: 250-758-2482. E-mail: ill@virl.bc.ca, info@virl.bc.ca. Web Site: www.virl.bc.ca. *Exec Dir,* Rosemary Bonanno; Tel: 250-729-2313, E-mail: rbonanno@virl.bc.ca; *Dir of Finance,* Adrian Maas; Tel: 250-729-2319, E-mail: amaas@virl.bc.ca; *Dir, Human Res,* Harold Kamikawaji; Tel: 250-729-2306, E-mail: hkamikawaji@virl.bc.ca; *Dir of Libr Serv,* Fiona Anderson; Tel: 250-753-1154, Ext 243, E-mail: fanderson@virl.bc.ca; Staff 180 (MLS 34, Non-MLS 146)
Founded 1936. Pop 430,000; Circ 4,533,001
Library Holdings: AV Mats 89,413; Bk Titles 246,407; Bk Vols 1,394,347; Per Subs 3,099; Talking Bks 24,628; Videos 48,090
Special Collections: British Columbia History (British Columbia & Northwest Coll)

Automation Activity & Vendor Info: (Acquisitions) SirsiDynix; (Cataloging) SirsiDynix; (Circulation) SirsiDynix; (OPAC) SirsiDynix; (Serials) SirsiDynix
Database Vendor: SirsiDynix
Wireless access
Function: Accelerated reader prog
Publications: NewsBrief
Friends of the Library Group
Branches: 37
BELLA COOLA BRANCH, 450 MacKenzie St, Bella Coola, V0T 1C0, SAN 366-0745. Tel: 250-799-5330. FAX: 250-799-5330. E-mail: bellacoola@virl.bc.ca. *Libr Mgr,* Stephen Warren
   Library Holdings: Bk Vols 17,875
   Open Wed 10-1:30, Thurs-Sat 10-12 & 1-5
CAMPBELL RIVER BRANCH, 1240 Shopper's Row, Campbell River, V9W 2C8, SAN 366-0788. Tel: 250-287-3655. FAX: 250-287-2119. *Libr Mgr,* Elaine Julian; E-mail: ejulian@virl.bc.ca
   Library Holdings: Bk Vols 84,678
   Open Mon-Fri 10-8, Sat 10-5
CHEMAINUS BRANCH, 2592 Legion St, Chemainus, V0R 1K0. (Mail add: PO Box 72, Chemainus, V0R 1K0), SAN 366-0818. Tel: 250-246-9471. FAX: 250-246-9411. *Libr Mgr,* Barbara Kerfoot; E-mail: bkerfoot@virl.bc.ca
   Library Holdings: Bk Vols 22,745
   Open Mon, Tues & Thurs-Sat 10-12 & 1-5, Wed 1-8
COMOX BRANCH, 1729 Comox Ave, Comox, V9M 3M2, SAN 366-0877. Tel: 250-339-2971. FAX: 250-339-2940. *Libr Mgr,* Abbas Saffari; E-mail: asaffari@virl.bc.ca
   Library Holdings: Bk Vols 30,637
   Open Mon-Wed, Fri & Sat 10-5:30, Thurs 10-8
CORTES ISLAND, Sutil Point Rd, Mansons Landing, V0P 1K0. Tel: 250-935-6566. FAX: 250-935-6522. *Libr Mgr,* Susan Yates; E-mail: syates@virl.bc.ca
   Library Holdings: Bk Vols 9,424
   Open Mon, Wed & Fri 1-4:30
COURTENAY BRANCH, 300 Sixth St, Courtenay, V9N 9V9, SAN 366-0907. Tel: 250-334-3369. FAX: 250-334-0910. *Libr Mgr,* Elizabeth Johnson; E-mail: ejohnson@virl.bc.ca
   Library Holdings: Bk Vols 103,324
   Open Mon-Fri 10-8, Sat 10-5, Sun 12:30-4
COWICHAN, 2687 James St, Duncan, V9L 2X5, SAN 366-0966. Tel: 250-746-7661. FAX: 250-746-5595. *Libr Mgr,* Melanie Reaveley; E-mail: mreaveley@virl.bc.ca
   Library Holdings: Bk Vols 97,800
   Open Mon-Fri 10-8, Sat 10-5, Sun 12:30-4
COWICHAN LAKE, 38 King George, Lake Cowichan, V0R 2G0. (Mail add: PO Box 918, Lake Cowichan, V0R 2G0), SAN 366-1059. Tel: 250-749-3431. FAX: 250-749-3401. *Libr Mgr,* Barbara Kerfoot; E-mail: bkerfoot@virl.bc.ca
   Library Holdings: Bk Vols 29,000
   Open Tues, Wed & Fri 10-8, Thurs & Sat 10-5
CUMBERLAND BRANCH, 2724 Dunsmuir Ave, Cumberland, V0R 1S0. (Mail add: PO Box 378, Cumberland, V0R 1S0), SAN 366-0931. Tel: 250-336-8121. FAX: 250-336-8100. *Libr Mgr,* Barbara Kerfoot; E-mail: bkerfoot@virl.bc.ca
   Library Holdings: Bk Vols 24,039
   Open Tues & Fri 10-12 & 1-5, Thurs 10-12 & 1-6, Sat 1-5
GABRIOLA ISLAND BRANCH, Folklife Village, 5-575 North Rd, Gabriola Island, V0R 1X5. Tel: 250-247-7878. FAX: 250-247-7892. *Libr Mgr,* Susan Yates; E-mail: syates@virl.bc.ca
   Circ 59,884
   Library Holdings: Bk Vols 22,251
   Open Tues, Fri & Sat 10-5, Wed & Thurs 10-8
GOLD RIVER BRANCH, 396 Nimpkish Dr, Gold River, V0P 1G0. (Mail add: PO Box 309, Gold River, V0P 1G0), SAN 366-0990. Tel: 250-283-2502. FAX: 250-283-2552. *Libr Mgr,* Laura Beswick; E-mail: lbeswick@virl.bc.ca
   Library Holdings: Bk Vols 15,579
   Open Tues 1-5 & 6:30-8:30, Wed & Fri 1:30-5 & 6:30-8:30, Sat 1:30-5
HORNBY ISLAND BRANCH, New Horizons Ctr, 1765 Sollans Rd, Hornby Island, V0R 1Z0. (Mail add: PO Box 37, Hornby Island, V0R 1Z0), SAN 329-5990. Tel: 250-335-0044. FAX: 250-335-0134. *Libr Mgr,* Susan Yates; E-mail: syates@virl.bc.ca
   Library Holdings: Bk Vols 11,888
   Open Tues, Fri & Sat 10-12 & 1-5, Thurs 11-7
LADYSMITH BRANCH, 740 First Ave, No 3, Ladysmith, V9G 1A3. (Mail add: PO Box 389, Ladysmith, V9G 1A3), SAN 366-1024. Tel: 250-245-2322. FAX: 250-245-2393. *Libr Mgr,* Stephen Warren; E-mail: swarren@virl.bc.ca
   Library Holdings: Bk Vols 55,718
   Open Mon, Wed & Sat 10-5, Tues, Thurs & Fri 10-8

MASSET BRANCH, 2123 Collison, Masset, V0T 1M0. (Mail add: PO Box 710, Masset, V0T 1M0), SAN 366-1105. Tel: 250-626-3663. FAX: 250-626-3663. *Libr Mgr,* Rand Flem-Ath; E-mail: rflemath@virl.bc.ca
Library Holdings: Bk Vols 14,114
Open Tues 2-6, Thurs 2-5 & 6-8, Sat 12-5

NANAIMO HARBOURFRONT BRANCH, 90 Commercial St, V9R 5G4, SAN 366-1113. Tel: 250-753-1154. FAX: 250-754-1483. *Libr Mgr,* Judy Wilson; E-mail: jwilson@virl.bc.ca
Library Holdings: Bk Vols 117,242
Open Mon-Fri 10-8, Sat 10-5, Sun 12-4

NANAIMO WELLINGTON, 3032 Barons Rd, V9T 4B5, SAN 366-1571. Tel: 250-758-5544. FAX: 250-758-7513. *Libr Mgr,* Gloria Novak; E-mail: gnovak@virl.bc.ca
Library Holdings: Bk Vols 69,494
Open Mon-Fri 10-8, Sat 10-5

PARKSVILLE BRANCH, 100 Jensen Ave E, Parksville, V9P 2G6. (Mail add: PO Box 508, Parksville, V9P 2G6), SAN 366-1148. Tel: 250-248-3841. FAX: 250-248-0170. *Libr Mgr,* Lynda Colbeck; E-mail: lcolbeck@virl.bc.ca
Library Holdings: Bk Vols 62,981
Open Mon-Thurs 10-8, Fri & Sat 10-5, Sun 12:30-4

PORT ALBERNI BRANCH, 4245 Wallace St, Port Alberni, V9Y 3Y6, SAN 366-1172. Tel: 250-723-9511. FAX: 250-723-5366. *Libr Mgr,* Michael De Leur; E-mail: mdeleur@virl.bc.ca; Staff 7 (MLS 1, Non-MLS 6)
Founded 1936
Library Holdings: Bk Vols 50,612
Open Mon, Tues & Thurs 10-8, Wed, Fri & Sat 10-5

PORT ALICE BRANCH, Marine Dr, Port Alice, V0N 2N0. (Mail add: PO Box 190, Port Alice, V0N 2N0), SAN 366-1202. Tel: 250-284-3554. FAX: 250-284-3557. *Libr Mgr,* Beswick Laura; E-mail: lbeswick@virl.bc.ca
Library Holdings: Bk Vols 15,886
Open Tues-Thurs 2-4 & 7pm-9pm

PORT CLEMENTS BRANCH, 35 Cedar Ave W, Port Clements, V0T 1R0. (Mail add: PO Box 283, Port Clements, V0T 1R0), SAN 366-1180. Tel: 250-557-4402. FAX: 250-557-4402. *Libr Mgr,* Rand Flem-Ath; E-mail: rflemath@virl.bc.ca
Library Holdings: Bk Vols 8,882
Open Wed 3-5 & 7pm-9pm, Fri 3-6

PORT HARDY BRANCH, 7110 Market, Port Hardy, V0N 2P0. (Mail add: PO Box 251, Port Hardy, V0N 2P0), SAN 366-1237. Tel: 250-949-6661. FAX: 250-949-6600. *Libr Mgr,* Laura Beswick; E-mail: lbeswick@virl.bc.ca
Library Holdings: Bk Vols 21,454
Open Tues 10-6, Wed & Fri 12-5, Thurs 12-5 & 6pm-8pm, Sat 10-2

PORT MCNEILL BRANCH, Broughton Plaza, No 4, Port McNeill, V0N 2R0. (Mail add: PO Box 786, Port McNeill, V0N 2R0), SAN 366-1261. Tel: 250-956-3669. FAX: 250-956-3669. *Libr Mgr,* Laura Beswick; E-mail: lbeswick@virl.bc.ca
Library Holdings: Bk Vols 20,804
Open Tues & Wed 1-5 & 6pm-8pm, Thurs 10-12 & 1-5, Sat 10-3

PORT RENFREW BRANCH, General Delivery, Elementary School, Port Renfrew, V0S 1K0, SAN 366-1296. Tel: 250-647-5423. FAX: 250-647-5400. *Libr Mgr,* Rand Flem-Ath; E-mail: rflemath@virl.bc.ca
Library Holdings: Bk Vols 7,379
Open Tues & Thurs 2-4 & 6pm-8pm

QUADRA ISLAND, 712 Cramer Rd, Heriot Bay, V0P 1H0. (Mail add: PO Box 310, Heriot Bay, V0P 1H0), SAN 329-6016. Tel: 250-285-2216. FAX: 250-285-2248. *Libr Mgr,* Susan Yates; E-mail: syates@virl.bc.ca
Library Holdings: Bk Vols 13,543
Open Tues, Fri & Sat 10-12 & 1-5, Wed 12-5 & 6:30pm-8:30pm

QUALICUM BEACH BRANCH, 101-660 Primrose St, Qualicum Beach, V9K 1S9, SAN 366-1326. Tel: 250-752-6121. FAX: 250-752-6630. *Libr Mgr,* Candy Ashbridge
Library Holdings: Bk Vols 43,841
Open Mon-Thurs 10-8, Fri & Sat 10-5

QUEEN CHARLOTTE CITY BRANCH, Community Hall, 138 Bay, Queen Charlotte City, V0T 1S0. (Mail add: PO Box 339, Queen Charlotte City, V0T 1S0), SAN 366-1334. Tel: 250-559-4518. FAX: 250-559-4518. *Libr Mgr,* Rand Flem-Ath; E-mail: rflemath@virl.bc.ca
Library Holdings: Bk Vols 18,780
Open Mon & Wed 10:30-12:30, 1:30-5:30 & 6:30pm-8:30pm, Sat 10:30-12:30 & 1:30-5:30

SANDSPIT BRANCH, Seabreeze Plaza, Sandspit, V0T 1T0. (Mail add: PO Box 228, Sandspit, V0T 1T0), SAN 326-5714. Tel: 250-637-2247. FAX: 250-637-2247. *Libr Mgr,* Rand Flem-Ath; E-mail: rflemath@virl.bc.ca
Library Holdings: Bk Vols 8,914
Open Tues 3-6:30, Thurs 3-5 & 7pm-8:30pm

SAYWARD BRANCH, Sayward Centre Mall, 641C Kelsey Way, Sayward, V0P 1R0. (Mail add: PO Box 310, Sayward, V0P 1R0), SAN 366-1350. Tel: 250-282-5551. FAX: 250-282-5533. *Libr Mgr,* Laura Beswick; E-mail: lbeswick@virl.bc.ca

Library Holdings: Bk Vols 10,988
Open Tues & Thurs 2-5 & 6-8

SIDNEY BRANCH, 10091 Resthaven Dr, Sidney, V8L 3G3, SAN 366-1415. Tel: 250-656-0944. FAX: 250-656-6400. *Libr Mgr,* Sharon Walker; E-mail: swalker@virl.bc.ca
Library Holdings: Bk Vols 72,376
Open Mon-Fri 10-8, Sat 10-5, Sun 1-4:30

SOINTULA BRANCH, 280 First St, Sointula, V0N 3E0. (Mail add: PO Box 187, Sointula, V0N 3E0), SAN 371-9863. Tel: 250-973-6493. FAX: 250-973-6493. *Libr Mgr,* Laura Beswick; E-mail: lbeswick@virl.bc.ca
Library Holdings: Bk Vols 13,442
Open Mon 2-5 & 6pm-9pm, Wed 2-4 & 6pm-9pm, Thurs 2pm-9pm

SOOKE BRANCH, 2065 Anna Marie Rd, Sooke, V0S 1N0. (Mail add: PO Box 468, Sooke, V0S 1N0), SAN 366-144X. Tel: 250-642-3022. FAX: 250-642-3994. *Libr Mgr,* Rusi Jokhi; E-mail: rjokhi@virl.bc.ca
Library Holdings: Bk Vols 38,712
Open Mon 1-5, Tues & Wed 10-8, Thurs-Sat 10-5

SOUTH COWICHAN, 310-2720 Mill Bay Rd, Mill Bay, V0R 2P0. (Mail add: PO Box 2000, Mill Bay, V0R 2P0), SAN 366-1385. Tel: 250-743-5436. FAX: 250-743-5506. *Libr Mgr,* Judy Baxter; E-mail: jbaxter@virl.bc.ca
Library Holdings: Bk Vols 38,745
Open Mon, Tues, Fri & Sat 10-5, Wed & Thurs 10-8

TAHSIS BRANCH, 977 S Maquinna, Tahsis, V0P 1X0. (Mail add: PO Box 458, Tahsis, V0P 1X0), SAN 366-1474. Tel: 250-934-6621. FAX: 250-934-6621. *Libr Mgr,* Laura Beswick; E-mail: lbeswick@virl.bc.ca
Library Holdings: Bk Vols 11,216
Open Tues & Thurs 2-4:30 & 6pm-8pm, Wed 2-5

TOFINO BRANCH, 331 Main St, Tofino, V0R 2Z0. (Mail add: PO Box 97, Tofino, V0R 2Z0), SAN 366-1504. Tel: 250-725-3713. FAX: 250-725-3743. *Libr Mgr,* Rand Flem-Ath; E-mail: rflemath@virl.bc.ca
Library Holdings: Bk Vols 9,197
Open Wed-Fri 3-7, Sat 10-12 & 1-5

UCLUELET BRANCH, 1768 Peninsula, Ucluelet, V0R 3A0. (Mail add: PO Box 247, Ucluelet, V0R 3A0), SAN 366-1563. Tel: 250-726-4642. FAX: 250-726-4622. *Libr Mgr,* Rand Flem-Ath; E-mail: rflemath@virl.bc.ca
Library Holdings: Bk Vols 14,651
Open Tues & Wed 1-6, Fri 3-7, Sat 10-2

UNION BAY BRANCH, 5527 Island Hwy, Union Bay, V0R 3B0. (Mail add: PO Box 81, Union Bay, V0R 3B0), SAN 366-1539. Tel: 250-335-2433. FAX: 250-335-2492. *Libr Mgr,* Barbara Kerfoot; E-mail: bkerfoot@virl.bc.ca
Library Holdings: Bk Vols 7,965
Open Tues & Fri 10-1:30 & 2-5:30

WOSS BRANCH, PO Box 5280, Woss, V0N 3P0, SAN 366-158X. Tel: 250-281-2263. FAX: 250-281-2273. E-mail: woss@virl.bc.ca. *Libr Mgr,* Janet Delgatty
Library Holdings: Bk Vols 5,896
Open Tues & Thurs 3-4:30 & 6-8

NELSON

P   NELSON PUBLIC LIBRARY, 602 Stanley St, V1L 1N4. SAN 318-7845. Tel: 250-352-6333. FAX: 250-354-1799. E-mail: library@nelson.ca. Web Site: nelson.bclibrary.ca. *Chief Librn,* June Stockdale; Staff 7 (MLS 1, Non-MLS 6)
Founded 1920. Pop 9,515; Circ 127,000
Jan 2005-Dec 2005 Income (CAN) $564,701, Provincial (CAN) $45,735, City (CAN) $437,120, Federal (CAN) $2,376, Locally Generated Income (CAN) $77,200, Other (CAN) $2,270. Mats Exp (CAN) $51,231, Books (CAN) $41,450, Per/Ser (Incl. Access Fees) (CAN) $4,200, AV Mat (CAN) $4,430, Electronic Ref Mat (Incl. Access Fees) (CAN) $1,151. Sal (CAN) $293,700 (Prof (CAN) $84,000)
Library Holdings: Bk Vols 60,000
Special Collections: Kootenay Archives
Automation Activity & Vendor Info: (Acquisitions) Evergreen; (Cataloging) Evergreen; (Circulation) Evergreen; (OPAC) L4U Library Software; (Serials) L4U Library Software
Open Mon & Wed 11-8, Tues & Thurs-Sat 11-6
Friends of the Library Group

NEW WESTMINSTER

C   DOUGLAS COLLEGE LIBRARY*, Bill Hughes Family Library, 700 Royal Ave, V3M 5Z5. (Mail add: PO Box 2503, V3L 5B2), SAN 320-7781. Tel: 604-527-5182. Circulation Tel: 604-527-5568. Reference Tel: 604-527-5176. FAX: 604-527-5193. E-mail: infodesk@douglas.bc.ca. Web Site: library.douglas.bc.ca. *Dir,* Carole Compton-Smith; E-mail: compton-smithc@douglas.bc.ca; *Instrul Serv Librn,* Patti Romanko; Tel: 604-527-5183, E-mail: romankop@douglas.bc.ca; *Ref Librn,* Julie Grellier; Tel: 604-527-5183, E-mail: grellierj@douglas.bc.ca; *Ref Serv Librn,* Mary Matthews; Tel: 604-527-5438, E-mail: matthewsm@douglas.bc.ca; *Circ, Syst, Tech Serv,* Gretchen Goertz; Tel: 604-527-5259, E-mail: goertzg@douglas.bc.ca; *Coll Develop,* Susan Ashcroft; Tel: 604-527-5189,

E-mail: ashcrofts@douglas.bc.ca; *Info Literacy,* Sandra Hochstein; Tel: 604-777-6135, E-mail: hochsteins@douglas.bc.ca; *Microcomputers & AV Equip Librn,* Sam Catherine Cheng; Tel: 604-527-5181, E-mail: chengs@douglas.bc.ca; *Online Serv,* Jean Cockburn; Tel: 604-527-5184, E-mail: cockburnj@douglas.bc.ca; *Ser & Microcomputers,* Christian Guillou; Tel: 604-527-5184, E-mail: guillouc@douglas.bc.ca; *Tech Coordr,* Debra Flewelling; Tel: 604-527-5190, E-mail: flewellingd@douglas.bc.ca; *Web Serv,* Dianne Hewitt; E-mail: hewittd@douglas.bc.ca; Staff 34 (MLS 12, Non-MLS 22)
Founded 1970. Enrl 5,700; Fac 375
Library Holdings: AV Mats 956; Bks on Deafness & Sign Lang 383; e-journals 14,817; Music Scores 7,161; Bk Titles 144,076; Per Subs 956; Videos 9,038
Automation Activity & Vendor Info: (Acquisitions) Innovative Interfaces, Inc; (Cataloging) Innovative Interfaces, Inc; (Circulation) Innovative Interfaces, Inc; (Course Reserve) Innovative Interfaces, Inc; (Media Booking) Innovative Interfaces, Inc; (OPAC) Innovative Interfaces, Inc; (Serials) Innovative Interfaces, Inc
Database Vendor: EBSCOhost, Gale Cengage Learning, OVID Technologies, ProQuest
Partic in BC Electronic Library Network

C　　JUSTICE INSTITUTE OF BRITISH COLUMBIA LIBRARY, 715 McBride Blvd, V3L 5T4. SAN 318-8299. Tel: 604-528-5599. FAX: 604-528-5593. TDD: 604-528-5626. E-mail: library@jibc.ca. Interlibrary Loan Service E-mail: ill@jibc.bc.ca. Web Site: www.jibc.ca. *Inst Librn,* April Haddad; Tel: 604-528-5594, E-mail: ahaddad@jibc.ca; *Assoc Librn,* Christine Babec; Tel: 604-528-5595, E-mail: cbabec@jibc.ca; *Electronic Res & Ref Librn,* Christine-Louise Dujmovich; Tel: 604-528-5597, E-mail: cdujmovich@jibc.ca; *Librn, Ref & Copyright,* Farrah Little; Tel: 604-528-5893, E-mail: flittle@jibc.ca; *Ref & Instruction Librn,* Marjory Jardine; Tel: 604-528-5592, E-mail: mjardine@jibc.ca; *Ser & Acq Tech,* Eileen Brosnan; E-mail: ebrosnan@jibc.ca; *Libr Asst,* Elizabeth Fletcher; Tel: 604-528-5596, E-mail: efletcher@jibc.ca; *Video Bookings, ILL & Overdues,* Robert Hooft; Tel: 604-528-5598, E-mail: rhooft@jibc.ca; Staff 8 (MLS 5, Non-MLS 3)
Founded 1978
Library Holdings: AV Mats 4,160; e-books 863; e-journals 24; Bk Vols 23,475; Per Subs 171
Special Collections: Justice Institute Photographs
Subject Interests: Adult educ, Criminology, Disaster planning, Emergency med, Forensic sci, Law mgt, Psychol
Automation Activity & Vendor Info: (Acquisitions) SirsiDynix; (Cataloging) SirsiDynix; (Circulation) SirsiDynix; (Course Reserve) SirsiDynix; (ILL) Auto-Graphics, Inc; (Media Booking) SirsiDynix; (OPAC) SirsiDynix; (Serials) SerialsSolutions
Database Vendor: Bowker, Cambridge Scientific Abstracts, Canadian Reference Centre, CRC Press/Taylor & Francis CRCnetBASE, EBSCOhost, Gale Cengage Learning, LexisNexis, OVID Technologies, ProQuest, PubMed, SerialsSolutions, Springshare, LLC, STAT!Ref (Teton Data Systems)
Wireless access
Publications: Bibliographies
Partic in BC Electronic Library Network; Council of Prairie & Pacific University Libraries
Special Services for the Deaf - TDD equip
Open Mon-Fri 8-5, Sat (Sept-June) 9-4

P　　NEW WESTMINSTER PUBLIC LIBRARY*, 716 Sixth Ave, V3M 2B3. SAN 318-787X. Tel: 604-527-4660. Circulation Tel: 604-527-4667. Reference Tel: 604-527-4665. FAX: 604-527-4674. TDD: 604-527-4679. Web Site: www.nwpl.ca. *Chief Librn,* Julie Spurrell; Tel: 604-527-4675; *Dep Librn,* Maureen Allen; Tel: 604-527-4669, E-mail: mallen@nwpl.ca; *Supvr, Circ,* Obrand Joanne; *Ch, Head, Ref,* Ann Lunghamer; Tel: 604-527-4678, E-mail: alung@nwpl.ca; *Head, Tech Serv,* Jean Simpson; Tel: 604-527-4671, E-mail: ajsimp@nwpl.ca; Staff 55 (MLS 19, Non-MLS 36)
Founded 1865. Pop 57,602; Circ 762,663
Library Holdings: AV Mats 23,880; Bk Titles 191,736; Per Subs 574
Subject Interests: Local hist
Automation Activity & Vendor Info: (Cataloging) SirsiDynix; (Circulation) SirsiDynix; (OPAC) SirsiDynix
Database Vendor: EBSCOhost
Function: Photocopying/Printing
Partic in Public Library InterLINK
Special Services for the Deaf - Closed caption videos; TDD equip
Special Services for the Blind - Closed circuit TV magnifier; Large print bks
Open Mon-Fri 9:30-9, Sat 9:30-5:30, Sun 1-5

M　　ROYAL COLUMBIAN HOSPITAL*, Fraser Health Authority, 330 E Columbia St, V3L 3W7. SAN 324-4628. Tel: 604-520-4755. FAX: 604-520-4804. *Librn,* Sue Abzinger
Library Holdings: Bk Titles 5,500; Per Subs 130

Subject Interests: Allied health, Med, Nursing
Restriction: Staff use only

NORTH VANCOUVER

C　　CAPILANO COLLEGE LIBRARY*, 2055 Purcell Way, V7J 3H5. SAN 318-7888. Tel: 604-984-4944. Reference Tel: 604-984-1769. FAX: 604-984-1728. Web Site: www.capilanou.ca. *Univ Librn,* Grace Makarewicz; *Circ,* David Lambert; Tel: 604-986-1911, Ext 2108, E-mail: dlambert@capcollege.bc.ca; *Coll Develop,* Karin Hall; Tel: 604-986-1911, Ext 2164, E-mail: khall@capcollege.bc.ca; *Tech Serv,* Sidney Myers; Tel: 604-986-1911, Ext 2129, E-mail: smyers@capcollege.bc.ca; Staff 26 (MLS 6, Non-MLS 20)
Founded 1968. Enrl 5,350; Fac 367
Library Holdings: AV Mats 4,825; e-books 800; Bk Vols 113,044; Per Subs 440
Special Collections: Can
Subject Interests: Arts, Asia-Pacific progs, Legal careers, Tech careers
Automation Activity & Vendor Info: (Acquisitions) Innovative Interfaces, Inc; (Cataloging) Innovative Interfaces, Inc; (Circulation) Innovative Interfaces, Inc; (Course Reserve) Innovative Interfaces, Inc; (ILL) Innovative Interfaces, Inc; (Media Booking) Innovative Interfaces, Inc; (OPAC) Innovative Interfaces, Inc; (Serials) Innovative Interfaces, Inc
Database Vendor: EBSCOhost, ProQuest, Wilson - Wilson Web
Wireless access
Partic in BC Electronic Library Network
Open Mon-Thurs 8am-9:30pm, Fri 8-4:30, Sat & Sun 1-5

P　　NORTH VANCOUVER CITY LIBRARY, 120 West 14th St, V7M 1N9. SAN 318-790X. Tel: 604-998-3450. Reference Tel: 604-998-3490. FAX: 604-983-3624. E-mail: nvcl@cnv.org. Web Site: www.cnv.org/nvcl. *Chief Librn,* Jane Watkins; E-mail: jwatkins@cnv.org; Staff 40 (MLS 10, Non-MLS 30)
Founded 1924. Pop 48,858; Circ 624,759
Library Holdings: AV Mats 17,707; CDs 3,801; DVDs 7,262; Electronic Media & Resources 14; Large Print Bks 3,561; Bk Titles 93,314; Bk Vols 130,939; Per Subs 184; Talking Bks 3,277; Videos 2,600
Automation Activity & Vendor Info: (Acquisitions) Horizon; (Cataloging) Horizon; (Circulation) Horizon; (ILL) A-G Canada Ltd; (OPAC) Horizon
Database Vendor: SirsiDynix
Wireless access
Partic in Public Library InterLINK
Open Mon-Fri 9-9, Sat 9-5, Sun 1-5
Friends of the Library Group

P　　NORTH VANCOUVER DISTRICT PUBLIC LIBRARY*, Administration, 1277 Lynn Valley Rd, V7J 2A1. SAN 366-1652. Tel: 604-990-5800. FAX: 604-984-7600. Web Site: www.nvdpl.ca. *Dir, Libr Serv,* Gerry Collver; E-mail: collverg@nvdpl.ca; *Mgr, Pub Serv,* Louise Broadley; E-mail: broadleyl@nvdpl.ca; *Support Serv Mgr,* Michael DeKoven; E-mail: dekovenm@nvdpl.ca; *Tech Serv Mgr,* Corinne McConchie; *Coordr, Ch & Youth Serv,* Allison Taylor McBryde; Staff 21.3 (MLS 9, Non-MLS 12.3)
Founded 1964. Pop 89,132; Circ 1,697,462
Jan 2008-Dec 2008 Income (Main Library and Branch(s)) (CAN) $5,048,460, Provincial (CAN) $215,000, City (CAN) $4,570,310, Locally Generated Income (CAN) $263,150. Mats Exp (CAN) $588,847. Sal (CAN) $3,758,455
Library Holdings: AV Mats 54,259; Bk Vols 231,367
Automation Activity & Vendor Info: (Acquisitions) Horizon; (Cataloging) Horizon; (Circulation) Horizon; (Course Reserve) Horizon; (ILL) Horizon; (Media Booking) Horizon; (OPAC) Horizon; (Serials) Horizon
Database Vendor: SirsiDynix
Wireless access
Partic in Public Library InterLINK
Special Services for the Blind - Bks on cassette; Bks on CD
Open Mon-Fri 9-5
Friends of the Library Group
Branches: 3
CAPILANO, 3045 Highland Blvd, V7R 2X4, SAN 366-1687. Tel: 604-987-4471. FAX: 604-987-0956. *Br Mgr,* Susan Larsen; Staff 13.3 (MLS 3.8, Non-MLS 9.5)
　Open Mon-Fri 10-9, Sat 10-5, Sun 12-5
LYNN VALLEY MAIN, 1277 Lynn Valley Rd, V7J 2A1, SAN 366-1741. Tel: 604-984-0286. FAX: 604-984-7600. *Br Mgr, Main Libr,* Penny Forsyth Manchester; Staff 15.2 (MLS 4.5, Non-MLS 10.7)
　Open Mon-Fri 9-9, Sat 9-5, Sun 12-5
　Friends of the Library Group
PARKGATE, 3675 Banff Ct, V7G 2A6, SAN 366-1717. Tel: 604-929-3727. FAX: 604-929-0758. *Br Mgr,* Helen Kaiser; Staff 13.4 (MLS 4, Non-MLS 9.4)
　Open Mon-Fri 10-9, Sat 10-5, Sun 12-5
　Friends of the Library Group

M   VANCOUVER COASTAL HEALTH*, Lions Gate Hospital Library, 231 E
     15th St, V7L 2L7. SAN 318-7896. Tel: 604-988-3131. FAX:
     604-984-5838. Web Site: www.vch.ca. *Librn,* Position Currently Open
     Founded 1961
     Library Holdings: Bk Titles 1,500; Per Subs 66
     Open Mon 7:30-3:30, Tues-Fri 8:30-4:30

PEMBERTON

P   PEMBERTON & DISTRICT PUBLIC LIBRARY*, 7390 Cottonwood St,
     V0N 2L0. (Mail add: PO Box 430, V0N 2L0). Tel: 604-894-6916. FAX:
     604-894-6916. E-mail: library@pembertonlibrary.bc.ca. Web Site:
     www.pembertonlibrary.bc.ca. *Librn,* Janet Naylor; *Asst Librn,* Shannon
     Ellis; *Asst Librn,* Marilyn Marinus
     Library Holdings: Bk Titles 12,000; Per Subs 20
     Automation Activity & Vendor Info: (Acquisitions) Follett Software;
     (Cataloging) Follett Software; (Circulation) Follett Software; (Course
     Reserve) Follett Software; (ILL) Follett Software; (Media Booking) Follett
     Software; (OPAC) Follett Software; (Serials) Follett Software
     Open Tues 11-5:30, Wed 12:30-5:30, Thurs 2-8, Fri 10:30-5:30, Sat 1-5

PENDER ISLAND

P   PENDER ISLAND PUBLIC LIBRARY*, 4407 Bedwell Harbour Rd, V0N
     2M0. (Mail add: PO Box 12, V0N 2M0). Tel: 250-629-3722. FAX:
     250-629-3788. E-mail: pilibrary@shaw.ca. *Chief Librn,* Jean MacDonald
     Library Holdings: Bk Vols 18,000; Per Subs 15
     Wireless access
     Function: Computers for patron use
     Open Tues & Thurs-Sat 10-4

PENTICTON

SR   BIBLE HOLINESS MOVEMENT LIBRARY, 311 Falcon Pl, V2A 8K6.
     (Mail add: PO Box 223, Postal Sta A, Vancouver, V6C 2M3), SAN
     374-4264. Tel: 250-492-3376. *Pres,* Wesley H Wakefield
     Founded 1949
     Library Holdings: AV Mats 80; CDs 14; DVDs 16; Bk Titles 4,160; Bk
     Vols 4,264; Spec Interest Per Sub 9; Videos 42
     Special Collections: Salvationist/Holiness History (mission directories,
     multi-lang copies of the Bible & original hymn composites); Wesleyan
     Christian Theology (Wesley's Works Coll)
     Subject Interests: Anti-slavery, Evangelism, Missions & missionaries,
     Substance abuse
     Restriction: Open by appt only

G   CANADA INSTITUTE FOR SCIENTIFIC & TECHNICAL
     INFORMATION, NATIONAL RESEARCH COUNCIL OF CANADA*,
     Herzberg Institute of Astrophysics, 717 White Lake Rd, V2A 6J9. (Mail
     add: PO Box 248, V2A 6J9), SAN 328-2066. Tel: 250-490-4311. FAX:
     250-493-7767. Web Site: cisti-icist.nrc-cnrc.gc.ca/nis/victoria_e.shtml. *Info
     Serv,* Mary Ferguson; Tel: 250-497-2311, E-mail:
     mary.ferguson@nrc-cnrc.gc.ca; Staff 1 (MLS 1)
     Founded 1979
     Subject Interests: Astronomy, Astrophysics, Eng
     Function: Wheelchair accessible
     Open Mon & Wed 9-5
     Restriction: Pub use on premises

P   PENTICTON PUBLIC LIBRARY*, 785 Main St, V2A 5E3. SAN
     318-7926. Tel: 250-770-7781. Reference Tel: 250-770-7782. Administration
     Tel: 250-770-7784. FAX: 250-770-7787. E-mail: library@summer.com.
     Web Site: www.library.penticton.bc.ca. *Chief Librn,* Larry R Little; E-mail:
     llittle@summer.com; *Ch,* Julia Cox; Tel: 250-770-7783; *Pub Serv,* Karen
     Kellerman; Tel: 250-770-7786; *Syst Librn,* Shelley Murphy; Tel:
     250-770-7785; Staff 22 (MLS 4, Non-MLS 18)
     Founded 1909. Pop 34,014; Circ 317,978
     Jan 2007-Dec 2007 Income (CAN) $1,139,073, Provincial (CAN)
     $123,834, City (CAN) $893,934, Locally Generated Income (CAN)
     $111,139. Mats Exp (CAN) $1,148,635, Books (CAN) $123,441, Per/Ser
     (Incl. Access Fees) (CAN) $20,001, AV Mat (CAN) $9,524, Presv (CAN)
     $1,392. Sal (CAN) $684,540
     Library Holdings: CDs 952; DVDs 1,100; Large Print Bks 2,500; Bk
     Titles 121,952; Per Subs 221; Talking Bks 1,830
     Subject Interests: Agr, Local hist, Wine
     Automation Activity & Vendor Info: (Cataloging) SirsiDynix;
     (Circulation) SirsiDynix; (OPAC) SirsiDynix
     Database Vendor: Baker & Taylor, EBSCO Auto Repair Reference,
     EBSCOhost, SirsiDynix, World Book Online
     Wireless access
     Special Services for the Blind - Audio mat
     Open Mon, Wed, Fri & Sat 9:30-5:30, Tues & Thurs 9:30-9, Sun
     (Oct-Apr) 1-5

PORT ALBERNI

J   NORTH ISLAND COLLEGE*, Port Alberni Campus Library, 3699 Roger
     St, V9Y 8E3. Tel: 250-724-8717, 250-724-8760. Circulation Tel:
     250-724-8733. Toll Free Tel: 800-715-0914, Ext 5097. FAX:
     250-724-8700. Web Site: library.nic.bc.ca. *Circ, ILL, Ref,* Hannah Leprette;
     Circ, Coll Develop, Ref, Sherry Kropninski; Tel: 250-724-8717, E-mail:
     sherry.kropninski@nic.bc.ca; Staff 2 (Non-MLS 2)
     Library Holdings: Bk Titles 8,000
     Automation Activity & Vendor Info: (Acquisitions) SirsiDynix;
     (Cataloging) SirsiDynix; (Circulation) SirsiDynix; (Course Reserve)
     SirsiDynix; (ILL) SirsiDynix; (Media Booking) SirsiDynix; (OPAC)
     SirsiDynix; (Serials) SirsiDynix
     Database Vendor: EBSCOhost, Infotrieve, netLibrary, OVID Technologies,
     ProQuest, PubMed, Wilson - Wilson Web
     Wireless access
     Function: CD-ROM, Copy machines, Electronic databases & coll, ILL
     available, Online ref, Orientations, Ref serv available, VHS videos
     Partic in BC Electronic Library Network
     Special Services for the Deaf - High interest/low vocabulary bks
     Special Services for the Blind - Closed circuit TV
     Open Mon-Thurs (Fall & Winter) 8:30-8, Fri 8:30-4:30
     Restriction: In-house use for visitors, Open to students, fac & staff, Pub
     use on premises

PORT MOODY

P   PORT MOODY PUBLIC LIBRARY*, 100 Newport Dr, V3H 3E1. (Mail
     add: PO Box 37, V3H 3E1), SAN 318-7950. Tel: 604-469-4575,
     604-469-4577. Administration Tel: 604-469-4686. FAX: 604-469-4576.
     E-mail: askthelibrary@cityofportmoody.com. Web Site:
     library.portmoody.ca. *Actg Dir, Dep Dir,* Andree Duval; E-mail:
     andree.duval@cityofportmoody.com; *Actg Dep Dir,* Maryn Ashdown;
     E-mail: maryn.ashdown@cityofportmoody.com; *Head, Adult Serv,* Barbara
     Buxton; E-mail: barbara.buxton@cityofportmoody.com; *Head, Syst, Head,
     Tech Serv,* Martin Boughner; E-mail:
     martin.boughner@cityofportmoody.com; *Circ Supvr,* Renelle Acres; *Circ
     Supvr,* Carolyn Bond; Staff 14 (MLS 6, Non-MLS 8)
     Founded 1943. Pop 30,000; Circ 513,516
     Library Holdings: AV Mats 10,259; Bk Titles 96,182; Per Subs 160
     Automation Activity & Vendor Info: (Acquisitions) Horizon;
     (Cataloging) Horizon; (Circulation) Horizon; (OPAC) Horizon
     Partic in Public Library InterLINK
     Open Mon-Fri 9-9, Sat 9-5, Sun 1-5

POUCE COUPE

P   POUCE COUPE PUBLIC LIBRARY*, 5000-49th Ave, V0C 2C0. (Mail
     add: PO Box 75, V0C 2C0), SAN 318-7969. Tel: 250-786-5765. FAX:
     250-786-5765. E-mail: bpoc.ill@pris.bc.ca. Web Site:
     www.pris.bc.ca/pouce-lib/. *Librn,* Courtenay Johnston; *Librn,* Patricia
     MacDonald
     Founded 1940. Pop 813; Circ 11,000
     Library Holdings: Bk Vols 15,000
     Partic in North East Library Federation (NELF)
     Friends of the Library Group

POWELL RIVER

P   POWELL RIVER PUBLIC LIBRARY*, 4411 Michigan Ave, V8A 2S3.
     SAN 366-1776. Tel: 604-485-4796. FAX: 604-485-5320. E-mail:
     powellriverlibrary@shaw.ca. Web Site: www.powellriverlibrary.ca, *Chief
     Librn,* Charlie Kregel; Tel: 604-485-8661, E-mail:
     ckregel@powellriverlibrary.ca; *Asst Chief Librn,* Jomichele Seidl; Tel:
     604-485-8664, E-mail: jseidl@powellriverlibrary.ca; *Children's Serv
     Coordr, Libr Tech,* Jeannette Jones; Tel: 604-485-8625, E-mail:
     jjones@powellriverlibrary.ca; *Libr Tech, Network Adminr,* Valerie McKeen;
     Tel: 604-485-8663, E-mail: vmckeen@powellriverlibrary.ca; Staff 11 (MLS
     2, Non-MLS 9)
     Founded 1973. Pop 20,000; Circ 176,000
     Library Holdings: AV Mats 4,655; High Interest/Low Vocabulary Bk Vols
     50; Large Print Bks 1,152; Bk Titles 48,700; Bk Vols 50,719; Per Subs
     155; Talking Bks 1,000
     Automation Activity & Vendor Info: (Acquisitions) Evergreen;
     (Cataloging) MITINET, Inc; (Circulation) Evergreen; (ILL) Auto-Graphics,
     Inc; (OPAC) Evergreen
     Database Vendor: EBSCO Auto Repair Reference, EBSCOhost,
     Overdrive, Inc, ProQuest, World Book Online
     Wireless access
     Function: Bk club(s), Bks on cassette, Children's prog, Computer training,
     Computers for patron use, Copy machines, Digital talking bks, Electronic
     databases & coll, Free DVD rentals, Handicapped accessible, Homebound
     delivery serv, ILL available, Online cat, Online ref, Outreach serv,
     OverDrive digital audio bks, Photocopying/Printing, Preschool outreach,
     Prof lending libr, Pub access computers, Ref & res, Ref serv in person,
     Scanner, Story hour, Summer reading prog, VHS videos, Web-catalog

Open Mon & Thurs 10-6, Tues, Wed & Fri 10-8:30, Sat 10-5
Friends of the Library Group

PRINCE GEORGE

L   BRITISH COLUMBIA COURTHOUSE LIBRARY SOCIETY*, Court
     House, 250 George St, V2L 5S2. SAN 328-249X. Tel: 250-614-2763.
     FAX: 250-614-2788. *Librn,* Julie Loerke
     Library Holdings: Bk Vols 15,000
     Open Mon-Fri 8-12 & 1-4

J   COLLEGE OF NEW CALEDONIA LIBRARY, 3330 22nd Ave, V2N 1P8.
     SAN 318-7977. Tel: 250-562-2131, Ext 298. FAX: 250-561-5845. TDD:
     250-561-5852. E-mail: cnclibrary@cnc.bc.ca. Web Site: www.cnc.bc.ca.
     Dir, Katherine Plett; *Bibliog Instr,* Sandra Chulka; *Pub Serv,* Jennifer
     Sauve; *Tech Serv,* B Yee; Staff 12 (MLS 4, Non-MLS 8)
     Founded 1969. Enrl 3,113; Fac 240; Highest Degree: Associate
     Library Holdings: AV Mats 7,135; e-books 6,000; Bk Titles 166,634; Per
     Subs 336
     Special Collections: Can & Prov
     Automation Activity & Vendor Info: (Acquisitions) SirsiDynix;
     (Cataloging) SirsiDynix; (Circulation) SirsiDynix; (Course Reserve)
     SirsiDynix; (ILL) SirsiDynix; (OPAC) SirsiDynix
     Partic in BC Electronic Library Network

P   PRINCE GEORGE PUBLIC LIBRARY*, Bob Harkins Branch, 887
     Dominion St, V2L 5L1. SAN 318-8000. Tel: 250-563-9251. FAX:
     250-563-0892. E-mail: ask@lib.pg.bc.ca. Web Site: www.lib.pg.bc.ca. *Chief
     Librn,* Allan Wilson; *Pub Serv Mgr,* Marc Saunders; *Support Serv Coordr,*
     Paul Burry; Staff 19 (MLS 8, Non-MLS 11)
     Founded 1955. Pop 88,054; Circ 758,139
     Library Holdings: Audiobooks 2,808; CDs 4,168; DVDs 3,033; Bk Titles
     129,208; Bk Vols 151,880; Per Subs 303
     Special Collections: Local History Coll
     Automation Activity & Vendor Info: (Circulation) SirsiDynix; (ILL)
     Amicus; (Media Booking) Baker & Taylor; (OPAC) SirsiDynix
     Database Vendor: Baker & Taylor, EBSCO Auto Repair Reference,
     EBSCOhost, netLibrary, ProQuest, SirsiDynix
     Wireless access
     Function: Adult bk club, Audiobks via web, Bk club(s), Bks on CD,
     Children's prog, Computer training, Computers for patron use, Copy
     machines, e-mail & chat, Electronic databases & coll, Exhibits, Family
     literacy, Free DVD rentals, ILL available, Music CDs, Online cat, Online
     ref, Outreach serv, OverDrive digital audio bks, Prog for adults, Senior
     outreach, Teen prog, Telephone ref, Wheelchair accessible
     Open Mon-Thurs 10-9, Fri & Sat 10-5:30, Sun (Sept-April) 1-5
     Friends of the Library Group
     Branches: 1
     NECHAKO BRANCH, 6547 Hart Hwy, V2K 3A4, SAN 321-7434. Tel:
        250-962-9710. FAX: 250-962-7394. *Br Supvr,* Catherine Checkley;
        E-mail: ccheckley@lib.pg.bc.ca; Staff 1 (Non-MLS 1)
        Founded 1980
        Library Holdings: Audiobooks 284; CDs 1,258; DVDs 876; Bk Titles
        21,818; Bk Vols 27,569; Per Subs 33
        Open Mon & Fri 10-9, Tues-Thurs & Sat 10-6
        Friends of the Library Group

M   PRINCE GEORGE REGIONAL HOSPITAL*, Medical Library, 1475
     Edmonton St, V2M 1S2. SAN 323-8202. Tel: 250-565-2219. FAX:
     250-565-2787. *Librn,* Anne Allgaier; E-mail:
     anne.allgaier@northernhealth.ca
     Library Holdings: Bk Titles 1,200; Per Subs 190
     Subject Interests: Allied health, Med
     Publications: Newsletter for Staff
     Open Mon-Fri 8-4
     Restriction: Staff use only

C   UNIVERSITY OF NORTHERN BRITISH COLUMBIA LIBRARY*,
     Geoffrey R Weller Library, 333 University Way, V2N 4Z9. Tel:
     250-960-6600, 250-960-6612. Interlibrary Loan Service Tel: 250-960-5231.
     Reference Tel: 250-960-6475. FAX: 250-960-6610. E-mail:
     libcirc@unbc.ca. Web Site: www.library.unbc.ca. *Univ Librn,* Position
     Currently Open; *Assoc Univ Librn,* JoAnn Murphy; Tel: 250-960-6654,
     E-mail: murphy1@unbc.ca; *Head Archivist,* Rose Ramona; Tel:
     250-960-6603, E-mail: roserm@unbc.ca; *Acq Librn,* Joanne Matthews; Tel:
     250-960-6615, E-mail: matthews@unbc.ca; *Cat Librn,* Eleanor Annis; Tel:
     250-960-6617, E-mail: eleanora@unbc.ca
     Founded 1989
     Library Holdings: e-journals 29,206; Bk Vols 220,489; Per Subs 1,005
     Function: Computers for patron use
     Open Mon-Wed & Fri (Winter) 8-6, Thurs 8am-9pm, Sat & Sun Noon-5
     Mon-Fri (Summer) 10-5

PRINCE RUPERT

P   PRINCE RUPERT LIBRARY*, 101 Sixth Ave W, V8J 1Y9. SAN
     318-8019. Tel: 250-627-1345. FAX: 250-627-7743. E-mail:
     info@princerupertlibrary.ca. Web Site: www.princerupertlibrary.ca. *Chief
     Librn,* Denise St Arnaud; E-mail: chieflib@citytel.net; *Dep Librn,* Joe
     Zelwietro; Staff 10 (MLS 4, Non-MLS 6)
     Pop 17,500; Circ 103,919
     Library Holdings: Bk Vols 70,000
     Special Collections: Northwest History Coll
     Subject Interests: Boating, Fisheries
     Automation Activity & Vendor Info: (Cataloging) Evergreen;
     (Circulation) Evergreen; (OPAC) Evergreen
     Wireless access
     Publications: Annual Report
     Special Services for the Blind - Home delivery serv
     Open Mon-Thurs 10-9, Fri 10-5, Sat & Sun 1-5
     Friends of the Library Group

QUESNEL

P   QUESNEL LIBRARY*, 101 410 Kinchant St, V2J 7J5. SAN 325-2140.
     Tel: 250-992-7912. FAX: 250-992-9882. E-mail:
     quesnelib@cariboord.bc.ca. Web Site: www.cln.bc.ca. *Librn,* Barbara
     Mackenzie; Staff 2 (MLS 1, Non-MLS 1)
     Founded 1926. Pop 21,000; Circ 120,000
     Library Holdings: High Interest/Low Vocabulary Bk Vols 100; Bk Titles
     45,000; Per Subs 100
     Automation Activity & Vendor Info: (Acquisitions) Infor Library &
     Information Solutions; (Cataloging) Infor Library & Information Solutions;
     (Circulation) Infor Library & Information Solutions; (Course Reserve)
     Infor Library & Information Solutions; (ILL) Infor Library & Information
     Solutions; (Media Booking) Infor Library & Information Solutions;
     (OPAC) Infor Library & Information Solutions; (Serials) Infor Library &
     Information Solutions
     Special Services for the Deaf - Bks on deafness & sign lang; High
     interest/low vocabulary bks; Staff with knowledge of sign lang
     Special Services for the Blind - Talking bks
     Open Tues-Thurs 10-8, Fri & Sat 10-5

RADIUM HOT SPRINGS

P   RADIUM HOT SPRINGS PUBLIC LIBRARY*, PO Box 293, V0A 1M0.
     Tel: 250-347-9131. E-mail: radiumpubliclibrary@telus.net. Web Site:
     www.radiumhotsprings.org. *Chief Librn,* Jane Jones
     Library Holdings: Bk Vols 10,000
     Open Tues & Thurs 2-4 & 7-9, Sat 10-Noon, Sun 2-4

RICHMOND

S   MACDONALD, DETTWILER & ASSOCIATES LIBRARY*, 13800
     Commerce Pkwy, V6V 2J3. SAN 323-9632. Tel: 604-278-3411, Ext 2447.
     FAX: 604-278-2117. Web Site: www.mda.ca. *Librn,* Julie Jarvis; Staff 2
     (MLS 1, Non-MLS 1)
     Founded 1979
     Library Holdings: Bk Titles 2,200; Bk Vols 2,500; Per Subs 275
     Partic in Dialog Corp
     Open Mon-Fri 7:30-5
     Restriction: Staff use only

P   RICHMOND PUBLIC LIBRARY*, Brighouse, 100-7700 Minoru Gate,
     V6Y 1R9. SAN 318-8035. Tel: 604-231-6422. Circulation Tel:
     604-231-6404. Reference Tel: 604-231-6413. FAX: 604-273-0459. E-mail:
     admin@yourlibrary.ca. Web Site: www.yourlibrary.ca. *Dep Dir,* Cate V
     McNeely; Tel: 604-231-6420, E-mail: cate.mcneely@yourlibrary.ca; *Chief
     Librn,* Greg Buss; Tel: 604-231-6418, E-Mail: greg.buss@yourlibrary.ca;
     Pub Serv Mgr, Beryl Jeffrey; Tel: 604-231-6417, E-mail:
     beryl.jeffrey@yourlibrary.ca; *Mgr, Ref & Info Serv,* Mark Ellis; Tel:
     604-231-6410, E-mail: mark.ellis@yourlibrary.ca; Staff 23 (MLS 23)
     Founded 1976. Pop 172,714; Circ 3,580,000
     Library Holdings: Bk Titles 165,692; Bk Vols 421,867
     Automation Activity & Vendor Info: (Circulation) VTLS, Inc; (OPAC)
     VTLS, Inc
     Wireless access
     Publications: Annual Report
     Open Mon-Fri 9am-9:30pm, Sat & Sun 10-5
     Friends of the Library Group
     Branches: 2
     IRONWOOD BRANCH, Ironwood Plaza, 8200-11688 Steveston Hwy,
        V7A 1N6. Tel: 604-231-6468. FAX: 604-274-0454. *Br Mgr,* Dace Beggs
        Library Holdings: Bk Titles 75,000
        Open Mon-Fri 10-10, Sat & Sun 10-5
     STEVESTON BRANCH, 4111 Moncton St, V7E 3A8. Tel: 604-274-2012.
        Br Mgr, Susan Walters
        Library Holdings: Bk Titles 6,000
        Open Mon-Fri 10-9, Sat & Sun 10-5

S   TRITON ENVIRONMENTAL CONSULTANTS LTD LIBRARY*, 8971 Beckwith Rd, V6X 1V4. SAN 328-0268. Tel: 604-279-2093. FAX: 604-279-2047. Web Site: www.triton-env.com. *Mgr, Libr Serv,* Position Currently Open
Library Holdings: Bk Titles 3,000; Per Subs 10
Subject Interests: Aquatic studies, Eng, Fisheries res, Water res
Restriction: Circulates for staff only, Co libr, Restricted pub use

S   WORKERS' COMPENSATION BOARD OF BRITISH COLUMBIA LIBRARY*, WorkSafeBC Library, 6951 Westminster Hwy, V7C 1C6. SAN 318-8426. Tel: 604-231-8450. FAX: 604-279-7608. E-mail: library@worksafebc.com. Web Site: www.worksafebc.com. *Librn,* Lance Nordstrom; *Acq,* Shirley Gawne; *Per,* Helena Rutkowski; *Ref Serv,* Ana Rosa Blue; *Tech Serv,* Marci Gibson; Staff 6 (MLS 3, Non-MLS 3) Founded 1970
Library Holdings: Bk Titles 10,000; Bk Vols 18,000; Per Subs 850
Subject Interests: Accident prevention, Compensation law, Compensation med, Occupational health, Occupational safety, Vocational rehabilitation
Automation Activity & Vendor Info: (Acquisitions) Inmagic, Inc.; (Cataloging) Inmagic, Inc.; (Circulation) Inmagic, Inc.; (OPAC) Inmagic, Inc.

ROSSLAND

S   ROSSLAND HISTORICAL MUSEUM ASSOCIATION ARCHIVES*, PO Box 26, V0G 1Y0. SAN 375-667X. Tel: 250-362-7722. FAX: 250-362-5379. E-mail: museum@rossland.com. Web Site: www.rosslandmuseum.ca. *Pres,* Jack McDonald; *Archivist,* Joyce Austin
Subject Interests: Mining
Partic in British Columbia Mus Asns

P   ROSSLAND PUBLIC LIBRARY ASSOCIATION, 2180 Columbia Ave, V0G 1Y0. (Mail add: PO Box 190, V0G 1Y0), SAN 318-8043. Tel: 250-362-7611. FAX: 250-362-7138. E-mail: info@rossland.bclibrary.ca. Web Site: rossland.bclibrary.ca. *Libr Dir,* Katie Albright; E-mail: director@rossland.bclibrary.ca
Pop 3,800; Circ 41,000
Library Holdings: Bk Titles 18,000; Bk Vols 19,000; Per Subs 54
Wireless access
Open Mon-Wed 1-8, Thurs 10-8, Fri 10-6, Sat & Sun 1-5

SALMO

P   SALMO PUBLIC LIBRARY*, 106 Fourth St, V0G 1Z0. (Mail add: PO Box 458, V0G 1Z0). Tel: 250-357-2312. FAX: 250-357-2312. E-mail: salmolibrary@netidea.com. Web Site: salmo.bclibrary.ca. *Actg Libr Dir,* Marianne Hansen; E-mail: splhansen@telus.net
Pop 2,600; Circ 24,789
Library Holdings: AV Mats 2,000; Bk Vols 14,121
Automation Activity & Vendor Info: (Cataloging) Mandarin Library Automation; (Circulation) Mandarin Library Automation; (OPAC) Mandarin Library Automation
Open Mon & Fri 10-5, Tues & Thurs 3-8, Sat 10-2

SALT SPRING ISLAND

P   SALT SPRING ISLAND PUBLIC LIBRARY, 129 McPhillips Ave, V8K 2T6. Tel: 250-537-4666. Interlibrary Loan Service Tel: 250-537-5532. Automation Services Tel: 250-931-2665. FAX: 250-537-4666. E-mail: info@saltspringlibrary.com. Web Site: www.saltspringlibrary.com. *Chief Librn,* Brigitte Peter-Cherneff; E-mail: librarian@saltspringlibrary.com; *Librn,* Karen Hudson; Staff 2 (MLS 2)
Founded 1964. Pop 10,000; Circ 120,000
Library Holdings: Audiobooks 3,500; AV Mats 3,140; CDs 1,158; DVDs 3,000; e-books 3,500; Large Print Bks 881; Bk Titles 46,000; Bk Vols 50,000; Per Subs 65; Talking Bks 20
Automation Activity & Vendor Info: (Cataloging) Evergreen; (Circulation) Evergreen; (ILL) Auto-Graphics, Inc; (OPAC) Evergreen
Database Vendor: EBSCOhost
Wireless access
Function: BA reader (adult literacy), Bks on cassette, Bks on CD, CD-ROM, Computer training, Computers for patron use, Copy machines, Digital talking bks, E-Reserves, Electronic databases & coll, Home delivery & serv to Sr ctr & nursing homes, Homebound delivery serv, ILL available, Magnifiers for reading, Mail & tel request accepted, Music CDs, Online cat, Online ref, Online searches, OverDrive digital audio bks, Photocopying/Printing, Prog for children & young adult, Pub access computers, Ref & res, Ref serv available, Spoken cassettes & CDs, Spoken cassettes & DVDs, Story hour, Summer reading prog, Telephone ref, VHS videos, Web-catalog, Wheelchair accessible
Open Mon-Sat 10-5

SECHELT

P   SECHELT PUBLIC LIBRARY*, 5797 Cowrie St, V0N 3A0. (Mail add: PO Box 2104, V0N 3A0). Tel: 604-885-3260. FAX: 604-885-5183. E-mail: inquiries@secpl.scrd.bc.ca. Web Site: www.secpl.scrd.bc.ca. *Chief Librn,* Iris Loewen; Staff 8 (MLS 2, Non-MLS 6)
Founded 1981
Jan 2005-Dec 2005 Income (CAN) $587,000. Mats Exp (CAN) $64,200, Books (CAN) $50,000, Per/Ser (Incl. Access Fees) (CAN) $4,000, AV Mat (CAN) $7,500, Electronic Ref Mat (Incl. Access Fees) (CAN) $2,700. Sal (CAN) $263,000
Library Holdings: Bk Vols 40,000; Per Subs 107
Automation Activity & Vendor Info: (Acquisitions) Horizon; (Cataloging) Horizon; (Circulation) Horizon; (OPAC) Horizon
Database Vendor: ProQuest
Function: Archival coll, ILL available, Online searches, Photocopying/Printing, Prog for children & young adult, Ref serv available, Spoken cassettes & CDs, Summer reading prog, Telephone ref, VHS videos, Wheelchair accessible
Open Tues, Fri & Sat 10-5, Wed & Thurs 10-8
Friends of the Library Group

SIDNEY

S   BRITISH COLUMBIA LAND SURVEYORS FOUNDATION*, Anna Papove Memorial Library, No 301-2400 Bevan Ave, V8L 1W1. SAN 375-832X. Tel: 250-655-7222. FAX: 250-655-7223. E-mail: office@abcls.ca. Web Site: www.abcls.ca. *Exec Dir,* Janice Henshaw
Founded 1989
Library Holdings: Bk Titles 900
Special Collections: BC Land Surveyors Annual Reports, 1914-2005
Open Mon-Fri 8:30-4

S   FISHERIES & OCEANS CANADA*, Institute of Ocean Sciences Library, 9860 W Saanich Rd, V8L 3S1. (Mail add: PO Box 6000, V8L 4B2), SAN 327-2818. Tel: 250-363-6392. FAX: 250-363-6749. E-mail: paclibraryios@pac.dfo-mpo.gc.ca. Web Site: www.pac.dfo-mpo.gc.ca/english/libraries/ios.htm. *Librn,* Pamela Wilkins; Staff 1 (MLS 1)
Friends of the Library Group

SMITHERS

P   SMITHERS PUBLIC LIBRARY, 3817 Alfred Ave, Box 55, V0J 2N0. SAN 318-8078. Tel: 250-847-3043. FAX: 250-847-1533. E-mail: contact@smitherslibrary.ca. Web Site: smithers.bclibrary.ca. *Dir,* Tracey Therrien; E-mail: ttherrien@smitherslibrary.ca; *Libr Asst,* Wendy Banta; *Libr Asst,* Michael Hurwitz; *Libr Asst,* Lynnda McDougall; *Libr Asst,* Kathy Spiro; *Libr Asst,* Katherine Wilford; Staff 5 (Non-MLS 5)
Pop 9,069
Library Holdings: Bk Vols 30,000; Per Subs 65
Subject Interests: Forestry, Local hist, Mining
Automation Activity & Vendor Info: (Cataloging) Follett Software; (OPAC) Follett Software
Function: ILL available, Photocopying/Printing, Ref serv available, Telephone ref
Open Mon, Wed & Fri 12-5, Tues & Thurs 12-9, Sat 10:30-5
Friends of the Library Group

SPARWOOD

P   SPARWOOD PUBLIC LIBRARY*, 110 Pine Ave, V0B 2G0. (Mail add: PO Box 1060, V0B 2G0), SAN 318-8086. Tel: 250-425-2299. FAX: 250-425-0229. E-mail: sparwoodlibrary@elkvalley.net. Web Site: www.elkvalley.net/sparwoodlibrary/, www.sparwoodlibrary.ca. *Librn,* James Bertoia; E-mail: bertoiaj@telus.net
Founded 1974. Pop 5,000
Jan 2005-Dec 2005 Income (CAN) $188,000, Provincial (CAN) $20,000, City (CAN) $120,000, County (CAN) $18,000, Locally Generated Income (CAN) $30,000. Mats Exp (CAN) $33,000, Books (CAN) $24,000, Per/Ser (Incl. Access Fees) (CAN) $5,500, AV Mat (CAN) $2,500, Electronic Ref Mat (Incl. Access Fees) (CAN) $1,000. Sal (CAN) $80,000
Library Holdings: AV Mats 300; Bks on Deafness & Sign Lang 10; CDs 200; DVDs 50; Large Print Bks 300; Bk Titles 30,000; Bk Vols 32,000; Per Subs 50; Talking Bks 300; Videos 500
Subject Interests: Local hist
Automation Activity & Vendor Info: (Cataloging) Mandarin Library Automation; (Circulation) Mandarin Library Automation; (ILL) Auto-Graphics, Inc; (OPAC) Mandarin Library Automation
Wireless access
Open Tues & Thurs 10-8, Wed, Fri & Sat 10-5

SQUAMISH

P   SQUAMISH PUBLIC LIBRARY*, 37907 Second Ave, V8B 0A7. (Mail add: PO Box 1039, V8B 0A7), SAN 318-8094. Tel: 604-892-3110. FAX: 604-892-9376. Web Site: www.squamish.bclibrary.ca. *Dir,* Maureen Painter; Staff 7.7 (MLS 1, Non-MLS 6.7)
Founded 1956. Pop 16,417; Circ 120,582
Jan 2009-Dec 2009 Income (CAN) \$902,137, Provincial (CAN) \$102,211, City (CAN) \$728,918, Federal (CAN) \$4,766, Other \$66,242. Mats Exp (CAN) \$123,949, Books (CAN) \$94,019, Per/Ser (Incl. Access Fees) (CAN) \$8,000, AV Mat (CAN) \$12,000, Electronic Ref Mat (Incl. Access Fees) (CAN) \$9,930. Sal (CAN) \$577,046
Library Holdings: Audiobooks 2,176; DVDs 4,451; Bk Vols 66,124; Per Subs 203
Special Collections: Oral Coll; Squasm Area Historical Files (part 1) Basic History & (part 2) Historical Photographs
Automation Activity & Vendor Info: (Acquisitions) Horizon; (Cataloging) Horizon; (Circulation) Horizon; (OPAC) Horizon; (Serials) Horizon
Partic in Public Library InterLINK
Open Mon-Thurs 1-8, Fri-Sun 10-4
Friends of the Library Group

STEWART

P   STEWART PUBLIC LIBRARY*, 824 A Main St, V0T 1W0. (Mail add: PO Box 546, V0T 1W0). Tel: 250-636-2380. FAX: 250-636-2380. E-mail: bsp_ill@mountainharbour.ca. Web Site: www.stewartpubliclibrary.com. *Librn,* Galina Durant
Library Holdings: Bk Vols 16,000; Per Subs 36
Automation Activity & Vendor Info: (Cataloging) LibraryWorld, Inc; (Circulation) LibraryWorld, Inc
Database Vendor: EBSCOhost
Open Mon-Thurs 10-12 & 2-3

SUMMERLAND

G   CANADIAN AGRICULTURE LIBRARY - SUMMERLAND, (Formerly Agriculture & Agri-Food Canada), 4200 Hwy 97, V0H 1Z0. (Mail add: PO Box 5000, V0H 1Z0), SAN 318-8108. Tel: 250-494-2100. FAX: 250-494-0755. *Managing Librn,* Lynne Boyd; E-mail: lynne.boyd@agr.gc.ca
Subject Interests: Agr eng, Entomology, Food sci, Fruit processing, Microbiology, Plant pathology, Pomology, Soil sci, Viticulture, Wine chem
Restriction: Open by appt only

SURREY

S   BRITISH COLUMBIA GENEALOGICAL SOCIETY*, Resource Centre, 12837 76th Ave, No 211, V3W 2V3. (Mail add: Lansdowne Mall, PO Box 88054, Richmond, V6X 3T6), SAN 328-011X. Tel: 604-502-9119. E-mail: bcgs@bcgs.ca. Web Site: www.bcgs.ca. *Adminr,* Betty Allen; Tel: 604-888-7870, E-mail: allenbb@lynx.net; Staff 30 (Non-MLS 30)
Founded 1979
Library Holdings: Bk Titles 10,000
Special Collections: British Columbia Cemetery Recordings; British Columbia Research Master Card File & Clipping File; Canadian Census Films
Subject Interests: Genealogy
Wireless access
Function: Res libr
Publications: Catalogue
Open Tues, Thurs & Sat 10-3

C   KWANTLEN POLYTECHNIC UNIVERSITY LIBRARY, Coast Capital Savings Library, 12666 72 Ave., V3W 2M8. SAN 321-3714. Tel: 604-599-3178. Circulation Tel: 604-599-2103. Interlibrary Loan Service Tel: 604-599-2959. Reference Tel: 604-599-3434. FAX: 604-599-2106. Reference FAX: 604-599-2532. Web Site: www.kwantlen.ca/library. *Univ Librn,* Todd Mundle; Tel: 604-599-3400, E-mail: Todd.Mundle@kwantlen.ca; *AV Coll & Instrul Librn,* Sigrid Kargut; Tel: 604-599-2378, E-mail: Sigrid.Kargut@kwantlen.ca; *Circ & AV Serv Librn,* Colleen van de Voort; Tel: 604-599-2090, E-mail: Colleen.vandeVoort@kwantlen.ca; *Coll Develop Librn,* Linda Rogers; Tel: 604-599-2942, E-mail: Linda.Rogers@kwantlen.ca; *Coll Develop Librn,* Elaine Samwald; Tel: 604-599-3066, E-mail: Elaine.Samwald@kwantlen.ca; *Pub Relations Librn,* Lisa Hubick; Tel: 604-599-3404, Fax: 604-599-3202, E-mail: Lisa.Hubick@kwantlen.ca; *Pub Serv Librn,* Celia Brinkerhoff; Tel: 604-599-3235, E-mail: Celia.Brinkerhoff@kwantlen.ca; *Pub Serv Librn,* Mirela Djokic; Tel: 604-599-3389, E-mail: Mirela.Djokic@kwantlen.ca; *Pub Serv Librn,* Ulrike Kestler; Tel: 604-599-3199, E-mail: Ulrike.Kestler@kwantlen.ca; *Pub Serv Librn,* Jean McKendry; Tel: 604-599-3486, E-mail: Jean.McKendry@kwantlen.ca; *Pub Serv Librn,* Jan Penhorwood; Tel: 604-599-3236, E-mail: Jan.Penhorwood@kwantlen.ca; *Res Support & Data*

Serv Librn, Chris Burns; Tel: 604-599-3198, E-mail: Chris.Burns@kwantlen.ca; *Ser & Pub Serv Librn,* Margaret Brown; Tel: 604-599-2087, E-mail: Margaret.Brown@kwantlen.ca; *Syst, Web & ILL Librn,* Caroline Daniels; Tel: 604-599-2701, E-mail: Caroline.Daniels@kwantlen.ca; *Tech Serv & Pub Serv Librn,* Linda Woodcock; Tel: 604-599-2591, E-mail: Linda.Woodcock@kwantlen.ca; *Trades & Electronic Res Librn,* Angela Ryan; Tel: 604-598-6040, Fax: 604-598-6035, E-mail: Angela.Ryan@kwantlen.ca; *Operations Mgr,* Ann McBurnie; Tel: 604-599-3415, E-mail: Ann.McBurnie@kwantlen.ca; *Ref Serv Coordr,* Denise Dale; Tel: 604-599-2999, E-mail: Denise.Dale@kwantlen.ca. Subject Specialists: *Polit sci, Sociol,* Sigrid Kargut; *Math, Sci,* Colleen van de Voort; *Asian & cultural studies, Hist, Policy,* Linda Rogers; *Arts, Bus,* Elaine Samwald; *Computer sci, Info tech,* Lisa Hubick; *Biol, Chem, Hort,* Celia Brinkerhoff; *Eng, Philosophy,* Mirela Djokic; *Lang, Linguistics,* Ulrike Kestler; *Anthropology, Geog, Geol,* Jean McKendry; *Psychol,* Jan Penhorwood; *Criminology,* Chris Burns; *Counseling, Health sci, Spec educ,* Margaret Brown; *Music, Trades,* Angela Ryan; *Creative writing, Econ, Pub relations,* Denise Dale; Staff 54.8 (MLS 16.5, Non-MLS 38.3)
Founded 1981. Enrl 9,329; Fac 652; Highest Degree: Bachelor
Apr 2011-Mar 2012. Mats Exp (CAN) \$4,938,667, Books (CAN) \$419,634, Per/Ser (Incl. Access Fees) (CAN) \$91,022, AV Equip (CAN) \$22,405, AV Mat (CAN) \$35,199, Electronic Ref Mat (Incl. Access Fees) (CAN) \$449,337. Sal (CAN) \$3,696,233
Library Holdings: AV Mats 2,719; e-books 36,155; e-journals 36,617; Electronic Media & Resources 4,862; Bk Vols 236,893; Per Subs 664; Videos 8,840
Automation Activity & Vendor Info: (Acquisitions) SirsiDynix; (Cataloging) SirsiDynix; (Circulation) SirsiDynix; (Course Reserve) SirsiDynix; (ILL) Relais International; (Media Booking) SirsiDynix; (OPAC) SirsiDynix; (Serials) SirsiDynix
Database Vendor: ABC-CLIO, ACM (Association for Computing Machinery), Agricola, ALLDATA Online, American Psychological Association (APA), ARTstor, Auto-Graphics, Inc, Cambridge Scientific Abstracts, Dun & Bradstreet, EBSCOhost, Elsevier, Gale Cengage Learning, H W Wilson, HeinOnline, Hoovers, JSTOR, LexisNexis, netLibrary, OCLC, OVID Technologies, Oxford Online, Project MUSE, ProQuest, Quicklaw, Sage, ScienceDirect, SerialsSolutions, Wiley, Wilson - Wilson Web
Wireless access
Partic in BC Electronic Library Network; Council of Prairie & Pacific University Libraries
Special Services for the Deaf - Bks on deafness & sign lang; Closed caption videos; High interest/low vocabulary bks
Special Services for the Blind - Accessible computers; BC CILS; Telesensory screen enlarger; ZoomText magnification & reading software
Open Mon-Thurs 7:30am-11pm, Fri 7:30-9, Sat 10-4, Sun 1-5

M   BOHDAN LESACK MEMORIAL LIBRARY, 13750 96th Ave, V3V 1Z2. SAN 373-6628. Tel: 604-585-5666, Ext 772467. FAX: 604-585-5540. E-mail: library@fraserhealth.ca. Web Site: library.fraserhealth.ca. *Librn,* Linda May Howard; E-mail: linda.howard@fraserhealth.ca. Subject Specialists: *Allied health, Clinical med, Nursing,* Linda May Howard; Staff 1.4 (MLS 1, Non-MLS 0.4)
Founded 1987
Library Holdings: DVDs 50; e-books 20; e-journals 5,000; Bk Titles 1,500; Bk Vols 2,000; Per Subs 40; Videos 100
Subject Interests: Allied health, Health serv admin, Med, Nursing
Automation Activity & Vendor Info: (Cataloging) Inmagic, Inc.; (OPAC) Inmagic, Inc.
Database Vendor: EBSCO Information Services, EBSCOhost, Lexi-Comp, Medline, OVID Technologies, ScienceDirect, UpToDate
Function: For res purposes
Publications: Library RX (Monthly newsletter); Residential Services Journal Watch (Current awareness service)
Partic in Docline; Health Libr Asn of BC (HLABC); US National Library of Medicine
Open Mon-Fri 9-5

S   MUSLIM EDUCATION & WELFARE FOUNDATION OF CANADA, Jannat Bibi Library, 14175 Kindersley Dr, V3R 5P6. (Mail add: 2580 McGill St, Vancouver, V5K 1H1), SAN 373-8256. Tel: 604-255-9941. FAX: 604-255-9941. *Librn,* Basil Ahmad
Founded 1987
Library Holdings: Bk Titles 3,000; Bk Vols 60,000
Special Collections: Religion of Islam
Subject Interests: Arabic lang, Biol, Chem, English (Lang), Geog, Geol, Math, Physics
Publications: Arabic Language; Islaamic English; Islaamic Geography; Islaamic Geography Map Book; Islaamic Mathematics; Learning Arabic Writing

M   SEMIAHMOO HOUSE SOCIETY LIBRARY*, 15310 24th Ave, V4A 2J1. SAN 375-1910. Tel: 604-536-1242. FAX: 604-536-9507. E-mail: shs@shsbc.ca. Web Site: www.semi-house-society.com.
Library Holdings: Bk Vols 500
Restriction: Mem only, Private libr

P   SURREY PUBLIC LIBRARY, 10350 University Dr, V3T 4B8. SAN 324-3486. Tel: 604-598-7300. Interlibrary Loan Service Tel: 604-598-7380. Reference Tel: 604-598-7366. FAX: 604-598-7310. Interlibrary Loan Service FAX: 604-598-7361. E-mail: libraryinfo@surrey.ca. Web Site: www.surreylibraries.ca. *Chief Librn,* Melanie G Houlden; Tel: 604-598-7305, E-mail: mghoulden@surrey.ca; *Dep Chief Librn,* Surinder Bhogal; Tel: 604-598-7304, E-mail: sbhogal@surrey.ca; *Mrg, Admin Serv,* Michael Ho; Tel: 604-598-7303, E-mail: mho@surrey.ca; *Mgr, Info Tech,* Jim Walsh; Tel: 604-598-7309, E-mail: wjwalsh@surrey.ca; Staff 40.46 (MLS 40.46)
Founded 1983. Pop 462,454; Circ 3,699,925
Jan 2011-Dec 2011 Income (Main Library and Branch(s)) (CAN) $14,208,442, Provincial (CAN) $1,060,000, City (CAN) $12,538,759, Locally Generated Income (CAN) $609,683, Sal (CAN) $10,851,856
Library Holdings: Bk Vols 680,309; Per Subs 2,811
Special Collections: Automotive & Genealogy (Surrey Genealogical Coll), bks, fiche, flm, pamphlets. Can & Prov
Automation Activity & Vendor Info: (Acquisitions) Horizon; (Cataloging) Horizon; (Circulation) Horizon; (OPAC) Horizon; (Serials) Horizon
Database Vendor: EBSCOhost, netLibrary
Wireless access
Publications: Canadian Genealogical Handbook (Research guide); Planning a Genealogy Trip to the Vancouver Area (Union list of serials)
Special Services for the Blind - Closed circuit TV; Home delivery serv; Large print bks; Screen enlargement software for people with visual disabilities; Talking bks
Open Mon-Thurs 9:30-9, Fri 9:30-5, Sat 10-5, Sun 1-5
Branches: 9
CITY CENTRE, 10350 University Dr, V3T 4B8, SAN 324-475X. Tel: 604-598-7420. FAX: 604-598-7421. *Br Mgr,* April L Cox; Tel: 604-598-7430, E-mail: alcox@surrey.ca
CLOVERDALE, 5642 176A St, V3S 4G9, SAN 324-4784. Tel: 604-598-7320. FAX: 604-598-7321. *Br Mgr,* Carol De Boeck; Tel: 604-598-7330, E-mail: cjdeboeck@surrey.ca
FLEETWOOD, 15996 84th Ave, V3S 2N7, SAN 376-1177. Tel: 604-598-7340. FAX: 604-598-7321. *Br Mgr,* Carol De Boeck; E-mail: cjdeboeck@surrey.ca
GUILDFORD, 15105 105th Ave, V3R 7G8, SAN 324-4741. Tel: 604-598-7360. FAX: 604-598-7361. *Br Mgr,* Jane Knight; Tel: 604-598-7370, E-mail: jknight@surrey.ca
NEWTON, 13795 70th Ave, V3W 0E1, SAN 324-4768. Tel: 604-598-7400. FAX: 604-598-7401. *Mgr,* Jennifer Brajcich; E-mail: jbrajcich@surrey.ca
   Open Mon-Fri 9:30-9, Sat 10-5, Sun 1-5
OCEAN PARK, 12854 17th Ave, V4A 1T5, SAN 324-4776. Tel: 604-502-6304. FAX: 604-502-6468. *Br Mgr,* Jennifer Brajcich; Tel: 604-502-6448, E-mail: jbrajcich@surrey.ca
   Open Mon-Fri 9:30-9, Sat 10-5, Sun 1-5
PORT KELLS, 18885 88th Ave, V4N 3G5, SAN 324-4792. Tel: 604-598-7440. FAX: 604-598-7441. *Br Mgr,* Jane Knight; E-mail: jknight@surrey.ca
SEMIAHMOO LIBRARY, 1815-152 St, V4A 9Y9. Tel: 604-592-6900. FAX: 604-502-5751. *Br Mgr,* Trish Miller; Tel: 604-592-6911, E-mail: temiller@city.surrey.bc.ca
STRAWBERRY HILL, 7399- 122nd St, V3W 5J2. Tel: 604-501-5836. FAX: 604-501-5846. *Br Mgr,* Surinder Bhogal; Tel: 604-501-5841, E-mail: sbhogal@city.surrey.bc.ca
   Open Mon-Fri 9:30-9, Sat 10-5, Sun 1-5

TERRACE

J   NORTHWEST COMMUNITY COLLEGE LIBRARY*, 5331 McConnell Ave, V8G 4X2. SAN 322-8487. Tel: 250-638-5407. FAX: 250-635-1594. Interlibrary Loan Service E-mail: ill@nwcc.bc.ca. Web Site: www.nwcc.bc.ca. *Regional Librn, Syst Librn,* Michele Cook; *Librn,* Tim MacDonald; *Coordr,* Melanie Wilke; *Cat,* Karen Westbay; *Pub Serv,* Louise Chaput; *Pub Serv,* Jan Currie; *Pub Serv,* Penny Llewellyn; *Pub Serv,* Lawrie McArthur; *Pub Serv,* Julia Moore; *Pub Serv,* Mike Rauschenberger; Staff 8 (MLS 5, Non-MLS 3)
Founded 1975. Enrl 1,800; Fac 300; Highest Degree: Associate
Library Holdings: Bk Titles 68,000; Per Subs 200; Videos 7,000
Special Collections: Local History (Archives of Northwest BC Coll)
Subject Interests: Arts, Culinary arts, Early childhood educ, Natural res, Nursing, Sciences, Tourism, Trades
Database Vendor: SirsiDynix
Wireless access
Partic in BC Electronic Library Network

Special Services for the Deaf - High interest/low vocabulary bks; Spec interest per
Open Mon-Thurs 8am-9pm, Fri 8-5, Sat & Sun 1-5

P   TERRACE PUBLIC LIBRARY*, 4610 Park Ave, V8G 1V6. SAN 318-8116. Tel: 250-638-8177. FAX: 250-635-6207. E-mail: library@terracelibrary.ca. Web Site: www.terracelibrary.ca. *Librn,* Ed Curell; *Ch,* Melanie Wilke; Staff 14 (MLS 1, Non-MLS 13)
Founded 1929. Pop 19,917; Circ 213,716
Jan 2005-Dec 2005 Income (CAN) $636,702, Provincial (CAN) $71,394, City (CAN) $497,850, Locally Generated Income (CAN) $39,511, Other (CAN) $27,947. Mats Exp (CAN) $100,719, Books (CAN) $78,719, Per/Ser (Incl. Access Fees) (CAN) $12,000, AV Mat (CAN) $5,000, Electronic Ref Mat (Incl. Access Fees) (CAN) $5,000. Sal (CAN) $273,734 (Prof (CAN) $65,000)
Library Holdings: AV Mats 6,581; Bk Titles 69,352; Bk Vols 70,551; Per Subs 202
Special Collections: History of the Northwest of British Columbia; Indian Culture of Northwest British Columbia; Terrace Coll. Oral History
Publications: History of Terrace
Open Mon 1-9, Tues-Fri 10-9, Sat 10-5, Sun 1-5

TRAIL

S   TECK COMINCO METALS LTD*, Information Resources, Cominco Research, V1R 4S4. (Mail add: PO Box 2000, V1R 4S4), SAN 318-8124. Tel: 250-364-4432. FAX: 250-364-4456. Web Site: www.teckcominco.com. *In Charge,* Fran Noone
Founded 1925
Library Holdings: Bk Vols 10,000; Per Subs 110
Special Collections: Metals Abstracts; US & Canadian Patent Abstracts
Subject Interests: Chem, Chem eng, Metallurgy, Mining

P   TRAIL & DISTRICT PUBLIC LIBRARY, 1051 Victoria St, V1R 3T3. SAN 318-8132. Tel: 250-364-1731. FAX: 250-364-2176. E-mail: director@traillibrary.com. Web Site: www.traillibrary.com. *Dir,* Belinda Wilkinson; Staff 5 (MLS 1, Non-MLS 4)
Pop 9,050; Circ 54,442
Library Holdings: Bk Vols 45,000
Special Collections: Local History
Automation Activity & Vendor Info: (Acquisitions) L4U Library Software; (Cataloging) L4U Library Software; (Circulation) L4U Library Software; (ILL) Auto-Graphics, Inc; (OPAC) L4U Library Software; (Serials) L4U Library Software
Database Vendor: Auto-Graphics, Inc, EBSCO Auto Repair Reference, EBSCOhost, Gale Cengage Learning, L4U Library Software, Overdrive, Inc, TumbleBookLibrary
Wireless access
Open Mon-Fri 9-8, Sat 9-3:30
Friends of the Library Group

TUMBLER RIDGE

P   TUMBLER RIDGE PUBLIC LIBRARY*, 340 Front St, V0C 2W0. (Mail add: PO Box 70, VOC 2WO). Tel: 250-242-4778. FAX: 250-242-4707. E-mail: tr-lib@pris.bc.ca. Web Site: tumblerridge.bclibrary.ca. *Libr Dir,* Michele Burton; E-mail: mburton@tumblerridgelibrary.org; *Ch,* Sharon Bray; *Head, Tech Serv,* Jacob Fehr; Staff 4 (Non-MLS 4)
Pop 4,000; Circ 20,375
Library Holdings: Audiobooks 26; CDs 253; DVDs 208; Large Print Bks 317; Bk Titles 33,790; Per Subs 40; Videos 1,324
Automation Activity & Vendor Info: (Acquisitions) Mandarin Library Automation; (Cataloging) Mandarin Library Automation; (Circulation) Mandarin Library Automation; (ILL) A-G Canada Ltd; (OPAC) Mandarin Library Automation; (Serials) Mandarin Library Automation
Database Vendor: EBSCO Auto Repair Reference, EBSCOhost, H W Wilson, Overdrive, Inc, ProQuest, World Book Online
Wireless access
Function: Adult bk club, After school storytime, Art exhibits, Bk club(s), Bks on cassette, Bks on CD, Children's prog, Computer training, Computers for patron use, Copy machines, Distance learning, e-mail & chat, E-Reserves, Electronic databases & coll, Equip loans & repairs, Fax serv, Free DVD rentals, Govt ref serv, Handicapped accessible, Holiday prog, Homebound delivery serv, ILL available, Literacy & newcomer serv, Music CDs, Online cat, Online ref, Online searches, Orientations, Outreach serv, OverDrive digital audio bks, Photocopying/Printing, Prog for adults, Prog for children & young adult, Pub access computers, Ref & res, Ref serv available, Ref serv in person, Scanner, Story hour, Summer reading prog, VHS videos, Video lending libr, Wheelchair accessible
Partic in North East Library Federation (NELF)
Open Tues-Thurs 10-8, Fri & Sat 10-5, Sun 1-5

VALEMOUNT

P   VALEMOUNT PUBLIC LIBRARY*, 1090A Main St, V0E 2Z0. (Mail
add: PO Box 368, V0E 2Z0), SAN 318-8140. Tel: 250-566-4367. FAX:
250-566-4278. E-mail: library@valemount.com. Web Site:
www.library.valemount.com. *Librn,* Wendy Cinnamon; *Circ,* Hollie
Blanchette; *ILL,* Elli Haag
Founded 1964. Pop 2,007; Circ 18,480
Library Holdings: Bk Vols 15,803; Per Subs 40
Open Tues, Thurs & Fri 10-5, Wed 10-9, Sat 11-3

VANCOUVER

M   ALS SOCIETY OF BRITISH COLUMBIA*, British Columbia Library,
1600 W Sixth Ave, Ste 208, V6J 1R3. SAN 373-6482. Tel: 604-685-0737.
Toll Free Tel: 800-708-3228. FAX: 604-685-0725. E-mail:
volunteer@alsbc.ca. Web Site: www.alsbc.ca. *Exec Dir,* Paul Hiller; Staff 1
(Non-MLS 1)
Founded 1981
Library Holdings: Bk Titles 50; Bk Vols 300; Per Subs 10
Special Collections: Amyotrophic Lateral Sclerosis, AV, bks, pamphlets &
v-tapes
Publications: Communique (Newsletter)

S   ASSOCIATION OF BOOK PUBLISHERS OF BRITISH COLUMBIA
LIBRARY*, 107-100 W Pender St, V6B 1R8. SAN 370-8160. Tel:
604-684-0228. FAX: 604-684-5788. E-mail: admin@books.bc.ca. Web Site:
www.books.bc.ca. *Exec Dir,* Margaret Reynolds
Founded 1974
Library Holdings: Bk Titles 200; Bk Vols 250

M   BC CANCER AGENCY*, Rix Family Discovery Centre Library, 675 W
Tenth Ave, V5Z 1L3. SAN 318-8213. Tel: 604-675-8001. FAX:
604-675-8009. E-mail: library@bccancer.bc.ca. Web Site:
bcca.andornot.com (Catalog), www.bccancer.bc.ca. *Prov Libr Leader,*
Cathy Rayment; Tel: 604-675-8004, E-mail: crayment@bccancer.bc.ca;
Staff 7 (MLS 3, Non-MLS 4)
Founded 1975
Library Holdings: Bk Titles 3,800; Per Subs 213
Special Collections: Patient Cancer Library, AV, bks
Subject Interests: Cancer nursing, Cancer treatment, Psychol of cancer,
Radiation biol
Partic in Electronic Health Library of British Columbia
Open Mon-Fri 9-5

L   BORDEN LADNER GERVAIS LLP LIBRARY*, 1200 Waterfront Centre,
200 Burrard St, V7X 1T2. (Mail add: PO Box 48600, V7X 1T2). Tel:
604-640-4012. FAX: 604-662-5347. *Mgr,* Jean Chong; Staff 4 (MLS 2,
Non-MLS 2)
Founded 1970
Library Holdings: Bk Vols 10,000; Per Subs 50
Restriction: Not open to pub

S   BRITISH COLUMBIA SECURITIES COMMISSION*, Knowledge
Centre, 701 W Georgia St, V7Y 1L2. (Mail add: Pacific Ctr, PO Box
10142, V7Y 1L2), SAN 370-9663. Tel: 604-899-6524. Toll Free Tel:
800-373-6393 (AB & BC only). FAX: 604-899-6506. Web Site:
www.bcsc.bc.ca. *Mgr,* Karen Barratt; E-mail: kbarratt@bcsc.bc.ca; Staff 3
(MLS 2, Non-MLS 1)
Library Holdings: Bk Vols 1,500; Per Subs 100
Subject Interests: Securities
Automation Activity & Vendor Info: (Acquisitions) Inmagic, Inc.;
(Cataloging) Inmagic, Inc.; (OPAC) Inmagic, Inc.; (Serials) Inmagic, Inc.
Open Mon-Fri 8:30-4:30

L   BULL, HOUSSER & TUPPER LIBRARY*, 3000 Royal Centre, 1055 W
Georgia St, V6E 3R3. SAN 327-2753. Tel: 604-641-4878. FAX:
604-646-2535. Web Site: www.bht.com. *Mgr, Libr Serv,* Lynda Roberts;
E-mail: ljr@bht.com; *Ref,* Joanne Jensen; Tel: 604-641-4965, Fax:
604-646-2643, E-mail: jcj@bht.com; Staff 3 (MLS 2, Non-MLS 1)
Library Holdings: Bk Titles 20,000
Database Vendor: Dialog, LexisNexis, TLC (The Library Corporation)
Restriction: Staff use only

G   CANADA DEPARTMENT OF JUSTICE*, Law Library, 900-840 Howe
St, V6Z 2S9. SAN 329-2355. Tel: 604-666-0549. FAX: 604-666-3038.
Mgr, Libr Serv, Judy Deavy; E-mail: judy.deavy@justice.gc.ca; Staff 6
(MLS 2, Non-MLS 4)
Founded 1967
Library Holdings: Bk Vols 19,000
Automation Activity & Vendor Info: (Acquisitions) Inmagic, Inc.;
(Cataloging) Inmagic, Inc.; (Circulation) Inmagic, Inc.; (Course Reserve)
Inmagic, Inc.; (ILL) Inmagic, Inc.; (Media Booking) Inmagic, Inc.; (OPAC)
Inmagic, Inc.; (Serials) Inmagic, Inc.

Open Mon-Fri 9-5
Restriction: 24-hr pass syst for students only, Access at librarian's
discretion

S   EMILY CARR INSTITUTE OF ART & DESIGN LIBRARY*, 1399
Johnston St, Granville Island, V6H 3R9. SAN 318-8256. Tel:
604-844-3840. FAX: 604-844-3801. Web Site: www.eciad.bc.ca. *Dir,*
Sheila Wallace; E-mail: sheilaw@eciad.bc.ca; Staff 9 (MLS 2, Non-MLS
7)
Founded 1927
Library Holdings: AV Mats 2,700; Bk Titles 23,500; Per Subs 160
Subject Interests: Art, Design
Automation Activity & Vendor Info: (Acquisitions) SirsiDynix;
(Cataloging) SirsiDynix; (Circulation) SirsiDynix; (Course Reserve)
SirsiDynix; (OPAC) SirsiDynix; (Serials) SirsiDynix
Database Vendor: SirsiDynix
Partic in BC Electronic Library Network

S   CENTRAL 1 CREDIT UNION CORPORATE INFORMATION
CENTRE*, 1441 Creekside Dr, V6J 4S7. SAN 321-4362. Tel:
604-737-5971. Toll Free Tel: 800-661-6813. E-mail:
infocentre@central1.com. Web Site: infocentre.central1.com. *Coordr,* Linda
Dmytryshyn; Staff 1 (Non-MLS 1)
Founded 1975
Library Holdings: Bk Titles 500; Per Subs 50
Special Collections: Cooperatives; Credit Unions
Subject Interests: Finance
Open Mon-Fri 8:30-4:30

M   COLLEGE OF PHYSICIANS & SURGEONS OF BRITISH
COLUMBIA*, Medical Library Service, 100-1383 W Eighth Ave, V6H
4C4. SAN 318-8221. Tel: 604-733-6671. FAX: 604-737-8582. E-mail:
medlib@mls.cpsbc.ca. Web Site: www.mls.cpsbc.bc.ca. *ILL,* Christine
Adams; E-mail: cadams@mls.cpsbc.ca; *Ref,* Judy Neill; E-mail:
jneill@mls.cpsbc.ca; *Doc Delivery,* Linda Einblau; E-mail:
leinblau@mls.cpsbc.ca; *Ser,* Elizabeth Barratt; *Acq of Monographs,* Marcia
Bilinsky; E-mail: marciab@mls.cpsbc.ca; *Cat,* Karen MacDonell; E-mail:
kare@telus.net; *Syst Coordr,* Ida Bradd; Staff 13 (MLS 5, Non-MLS 8)
Founded 1906
Library Holdings: Bk Vols 12,000; Per Subs 600
Special Collections: Oral History
Subject Interests: Behav sci, Hist, Med, Psychol, Sexology, Soc sci
Database Vendor: OVID Technologies
Publications: Recent & Recommended Books for Hospital Medical
Libraries (annual)
Partic in Nat Libr of Med, MEDLARS
Open Mon 8:30am-9pm, Tues-Fri 8:30-4:30

M   COLLEGE OF REGISTERED NURSES OF BRITISH COLUMBIA
LIBRARY, Helen Randal Library, 2855 Arbutus St, V6J 3Y8. SAN
320-3107. Tel: 604-736-7331. FAX: 604-738-2272. Web Site:
www.crnbc.ca. *Mgr,* Joan Andrews; E-mail: andrews@crnbc.ca; Staff 4
(MLS 2, Non-MLS 2)
Founded 1966
Library Holdings: AV Mats 250; Bks-By-Mail 3,000; e-books 200;
e-journals 150; Bk Titles 3,000; Per Subs 400
Special Collections: Nursing Biographical Files British Columbia; Oral
History Coll on British Columbia Nursing. Can & Prov; Oral History
Subject Interests: Nursing
Wireless access
Partic in Health Libr Asn of BC (HLABC)
Open Mon-Fri 8:30-4:30

J   COLUMBIA COLLEGE LIBRARY*, 500-555 Seymour St, V6B 6J9.
SAN 318-823X. Tel: 604-683-8360. FAX: 604-682-7191. Web Site:
www.columbia-college.org. *Head Librn,* Yvonne De Souza; Tel:
604-683-8360, Ext 325, E-mail: ydesouza@columbiacollege.bc.ca; Staff 2
(MLS 2)
Founded 1965. Enrl 600; Fac 70; Highest Degree: Doctorate
Library Holdings: Bk Titles 26,000
Subject Interests: Acad
Automation Activity & Vendor Info: (Acquisitions) Follett Software;
(Cataloging) Follett Software; (Circulation) Follett Software; (Course
Reserve) Follett Software; (ILL) Follett Software; (Media Booking) Follett
Software; (OPAC) Follett Software; (Serials) Follett Software
Database Vendor: EBSCOhost
Publications: Booking or Borrowing? A Faculty Guide to the Library;
How to Write a Footnote; Welcome to the Columbia College Library
Open Mon-Thurs 9-7, Fri 9-5

L   DAVIS & CO*, Law Library, 666 Burrard St, Ste 2800, V6C 2Z7. SAN
327-5515. Tel: 604-643-6425. FAX: 604-605-3598. Web Site:
www.davis.ca. *Librn,* Joan Mulholland; E-mail: jmulholland@davis.ca; *Ref
Serv,* Wendy Holmes; *Tech Serv,* Betty Rexin

Library Holdings: Bk Vols 14,000
Open Mon-Fri 8-5

S   DELOITTE & TOUCHE*, Library Information Center, 2800-1055
Dunsmuir St, Ste 2200, V7X 1P4. SAN 327-277X. Tel: 604-669-4466.
Information Services Tel: 604-640-3026. FAX: 604-685-0458. Web Site:
www.deloitte.ca. *Librn,* Nada Djurovic; E-mail: ndjurovic@deloitte.ca
Library Holdings: e-journals 10; Bk Vols 2,000; Per Subs 35
Open Mon-Fri 7:30-4

G   ENVIRONMENT CANADA*, Pacific & Yukon Region Library, 201 - 401
Burrard St, V6C 3S5. SAN 375-3700. Tel: 604-666-5914. FAX:
604-666-1788. E-mail: nvan.library@ec.gc.ca. *Head Librn,* Andrew Fabro;
Librn, Adele Cohen
Library Holdings: Bk Vols 16,500; Per Subs 85

L   FARRIS MANAGEMENT LTD*, Law Library, 700 W Georgia St, 26th
Flr, V7Y 1B3. (Mail add: PO Box 10026, V7Y 1B3), SAN 321-5083. Tel:
604-684-9151. FAX: 604-661-9349. Web Site: www.farris.com. *Librn,*
Wilma MacFarlane; E-mail: wmacfarlane@farris.com; Staff 2 (MLS 1,
Non-MLS 1)
Library Holdings: Bk Titles 2,000; Per Subs 300

S   FASKEN MARTINEAU DUMOULIN LLP LIBRARY*, 2900-550 Burrard
St, V6C 0A3. SAN 321-9038. Tel: 604-631-3131. Reference Tel:
604-631-4716. FAX: 604-631-3232. Reference FAX: 604-632-4716.
E-mail: ref@fasken.com. *Dir, Libr & Info Serv,* Teresa Gleave; Tel:
604-631-4804, E-mail: tgleave@fasken.com; *Librn,* Marnie Bailey. Subject
Specialists: *Bus, Can law,* Teresa Gleave; *Bus, Can law,* Marnie Bailey;
Staff 3.6 (MLS 2, Non-MLS 1.6)
Library Holdings: Bk Vols 15,000
Special Collections: Canadian & British law; Canadian Labour Law;
Limited American Material
Automation Activity & Vendor Info: (Cataloging) Inmagic, Inc.; (Serials)
Inmagic, Inc.
Database Vendor: Factiva.com, HeinOnline, Infomart, LexisNexis,
Quicklaw, WestlaweCARSWELL
Wireless access
Restriction: Staff use only

G   FISHERIES & OCEANS CANADA*, Pacific Region Headquarters
Library, 401 Burrard St, Ste 200, V6C 3S4. SAN 326-5633. Tel:
604-666-3851. FAX: 604-666-3145. E-mail: paclibrary@pac.dfo-mpo.gc.ca.
Web Site: inter01.dfo-mpo.gc.ca/wavesdocs/waves_mainmenu.html. *Head,
Libr Serv,* Marcia Heather Croy-Vanwely; Tel: 604-666-6371, E-mail:
croyvanwelym@pac.dfo-mpo.gc.ca; *Asst Librn,* Louise Archibald; Staff 2
(MLS 1, Non-MLS 1)
Founded 1969
Library Holdings: Bk Titles 2,150; Per Subs 68
Function: ILL available

G   FORINTEK CANADA CORP*, 2665 East Mall, V6T 1W5. SAN
318-8264. Tel: 604-224-3221, Ext 668. FAX: 604-222-5690. Web Site:
www.forintek.ca. *Librn,* Barbara Holder; E-mail: holder@van.forintek.ca;
Staff 2 (MLS 1, Non-MLS 1)
Founded 1927
Library Holdings: Bk Titles 5,500; Per Subs 250
Subject Interests: Composite products, Plywood, Presv, Saw milling,
Timber mechanics, Wood anatomy, Wood chem, Wood pathology
Automation Activity & Vendor Info: (Cataloging) Inmagic, Inc.
Publications: Bibliographies
Open Mon-Fri 8-4

S   THE FRASER INSTITUTE LIBRARY*, 1770 Burrard St, 4th Flr, V6J
3G7. SAN 325-2418. Tel: 604-688-0221. FAX: 604-688-8539. *Librn,*
Marie Morris
Founded 1974
Library Holdings: Bk Titles 6,000; Per Subs 200
Subject Interests: Govt, Pub policy
Restriction: Staff use only

L   HARPER GREY LLP LIBRARY*, 3200-650 W Georgia St, V6B 4P7.
Tel: 604-895-2861. FAX: 604-669-9385. *Librn,* Liisa Tella; E-mail:
ltella@hgelaw.com; Staff 2 (MLS 1, Non-MLS 1)
Library Holdings: Bk Titles 2,000; Bk Vols 8,000; Per Subs 175
Subject Interests: Law
Automation Activity & Vendor Info: (Cataloging) Inmagic, Inc.
Restriction: Staff use only

S   AUDREY & HARRY HAWTHORN LIBRARY & ARCHIVES AT THE
UBC MUSEUM OF ANTHROPOLOGY*, 6393 NW Marine Dr, V6T
1Z2. SAN 373-7624. Tel: 604-822-4834. FAX: 604-822-2974. E-mail:
archives@moa.ubc.ca, library@moa.ubc.ca. Web Site:

www.moa.ubc.ca/collections/archives.php,
www.moa.ubc.ca/collections/library.php. *Libr Res Serv Mgr,* Shannon
LaBelle; *Dept Head, Info Mgr,* Ann Stevenson; *Coordr, Oral Hist Lang
Lab,* Gerry Lawson; *Archivist,* Krisztina Laszlo; Staff 3.2 (MLS 2.2,
Non-MLS 1)
Founded 1990
Library Holdings: Bk Titles 12,000; Per Subs 15
Subject Interests: Mat culture, Mus studies, Northwest Coast hist
Wireless access
Function: Archival coll, Computers for patron use, Electronic databases &
coll, Online cat, Photocopying/Printing, Ref serv available
Open Mon-Thurs 10-4
Restriction: Circulates for staff only

S   KLOHN CRIPPEN BERGER LTD, Library & Records Centre, 2955
Virtual Way, Ste 500, V5M 4X6. SAN 323-8261. Tel: 604-251-8435. FAX:
604-669-3835. Web Site: www.klohn.com. *Info & Libr Mgr,* Kim Feltham;
E-mail: kfeltham@klohn.com; *Libr Tech,* Heather Duff; E-mail:
hduff@klohn.com; Staff 2 (MLS 1, Non-MLS 1)
Founded 1971
Library Holdings: e-journals 10; Bk Titles 14,000; Bk Vols 15,000; Per
Subs 75
Subject Interests: Environ eng, Geotechnical, Hydroelectric, Mining eng,
Power eng, Transportation eng, Water res
Automation Activity & Vendor Info: (Acquisitions) Inmagic, Inc.;
(Cataloging) Inmagic, Inc.; (Circulation) Inmagic, Inc.; (Serials) Inmagic,
Inc.
Open Mon-Fri 9-5

L   LANG MICHENER LLP LIBRARY*, 1500-1055 W Georgia St, V6E
4N7. (Mail add: PO Box 11117, V6E 4N7), SAN 328-2279. Tel:
604-689-9111. FAX: 604-685-7084. E-mail: library@lmls.com. *Mgr,* Anne
Ikeda
Library Holdings: Bk Vols 14,000; Per Subs 180
Subject Interests: Law

C   LANGARA COLLEGE LIBRARY*, 100 W 49th Ave, V5Y 2Z6. Tel:
604-323-5462. Circulation Tel: 604-323-5250. Interlibrary Loan Service
Tel: 604-323-5422, Reference Tel: 604-323-5388. FAX: 604-323-5577.
Interlibrary Loan Service FAX: 604-323-5512. Web Site:
www.langara.bc.ca. *Dir,* Grace Makarawicz; E-mail:
gmakarewicz@langara.bc.ca
Library Holdings: Bk Titles 157,350
Open Mon-Thurs (Winter) 8am-9pm, Fri 8-5, Sat 12-5; Mon-Fri (Summer)
9-4:30, Tues & Wed 9-9

S   LEARNING DISABILITIES ASSOCIATION OF BRITISH
COLUMBIA-VANCOUVER CHAPTER*, Resource Centre, 3292 E
Broadway, V5M 1Z8. SAN 377-2543. Tel: 604-873-8139. FAX:
604-873-8140. E-mail: info@ldav.ca. Web Site: www.ldav.ca. *Commun
Serv Coordr,* Anita Kwan
Founded 1970
Library Holdings: Bk Titles 375; Bk Vols 900

L   MCCARTHY TETRAULT LIBRARY*, 777 Dunsmuir St, No 1300, V7Y
1K2. (Mail add: PO Box 10424, Pacific Centre, V7Y 1K2), SAN
323-9810. Tel: 604-643-7100. FAX: 604-643-7900. Web Site:
www.mccarthy.ca. *Libr Dir,* Joanne Lecky; *Librn,* Elena Barreiro; Tel:
604-643-7178, E-mail: ebarreiro@mccarthy.ca; *Libr Tech,* Bethany
Webster; Tel: 604-643-7112, E-mail: bwebster@mccarthy.ca; Staff 4 (MLS
2, Non-MLS 2)
Library Holdings: Bk Vols 14,000
Restriction: Private libr

G   MINISTRY OF THE ATTORNEY GENERAL*, Judge's Library, Superior
Law Courts, 800 Smithe St, V6Z 2E1. SAN 366-1954. Tel: 604-660-2799.
FAX: 604-660-1723. Web Site: www.courts.gov.bc.ca. *Librn,* Diane
LeMieux
Founded 1945
Library Holdings: Bk Titles 2,000; Bk Vols 15,000; Per Subs 20
Partic in Can Libr Asn
Restriction: Staff use only

G   NATURAL RESOURCES CANADA*, Geological Survey of Canada
Geoscience Research Library, 625 Robson St, V6B 5J3. SAN 320-779X.
Tel: 604-666-3812. Reference Tel: 604-666-1147. FAX: 604-666-7186.
E-mail: libvan@nrcan.gc.ca. *Head Librn,* Diane Thompson; Staff 2 (MLS
1, Non-MLS 1)
Founded 1973
Library Holdings: Bk Vols 125,000; Per Subs 900
Special Collections: Cordillera & Pacific Continental Shelf
Subject Interests: Biostratigraphy, Earth sci, Geohazards, Geophysics,
Marine geol, Micropaleontology, Paleontology, Urban geol
Automation Activity & Vendor Info: (Serials) EBSCO Online

Database Vendor: Innovative Interfaces, Inc INN - View
Open Mon-Fri 8:30-4:30
Restriction: Restricted borrowing privileges

S   PACIFIC NEWSPAPER GROUP LIBRARY*, PNG News Research
    Library, 200 Granville St, V6C 3N3. SAN 318-8310. Tel: 604-605-2605.
    Administration Tel: 604-605-2933. FAX: 604-605-2353. E-mail:
    infoline@sunprovince.com, library@sunprovince.com. Web Site:
    www.theprovince.com/about-the-province/library.html,
    www.vancouversun.com/about-vancouver-sun/library.html. *Mgr,* Debbie L
    Millward; E-mail: dmillward@sunprovince.com; *Librn,* Kathryn Bird; Tel:
    604-605-2699, E-mail: kbird@sunprovince.com; *Librn,* Sandra Boutilier;
    Tel: 604-605-2653, E-mail: sboutilier@sunprovince.com; *Librn,* Carolyn
    Soltau; Tel: 604-605-2584, E-mail: csoltau@sunprovince.com. Subject
    Specialists: *Info mgt, Libr admin, News,* Debbie L Millward; *Graphics,
    News,* Kathryn Bird; *Graphics, News,* Sandra Boutilier; *News,* Carolyn
    Soltau; Staff 6 (MLS 4, Non-MLS 2)
    Founded 1965
    Special Collections: Newspaper Clippings of Vancouver Province;
    Newspaper Clippings of Vancouver Sun
    Subject Interests: Investigative reporting, Media, Newsmedia
    Database Vendor: Dialog, Factiva.com, LexisNexis
    Function: Newsp ref libr
    Restriction: Access at librarian's discretion, Authorized patrons,
    Authorized personnel only, By permission only, Circulates for staff only,
    Clients only, Co libr, Employees only, External users must contact libr, Fee
    for pub use, Not a lending libr, Not open to pub, Private libr

S   PACIFIC SALMON COMMISSION LIBRARY*, 1155 Robson St, Ste
    600, V6E 1B5. SAN 318-7861. Tel: 604-684-8081. FAX: 604-666-8707.
    Web Site: www.psc.org. *Librn,* Teri Tarita; E-mail: tarita@psc.org
    Library Holdings: Bk Vols 13,000; Per Subs 500
    Special Collections: Salmon Fishery Coll, mss, data rpt
    Subject Interests: Fish biol, Fish pop dynamics, Fishery mgt, Salmon biol
    Automation Activity & Vendor Info: (Cataloging) Inmagic, Inc.
    Publications: Annual Report; Annual Report of Fraser River Sockeye
    Fishing Season; News release; Technical report

S   PRICEWATERHOUSECOOPERS LIBRARY*, 200-250 Howe St, V6C
    3S7. SAN 326-1549. Tel: 604-806-7087. FAX: 604-806-7806. Web Site:
    www.pwc.com. *Librn,* Jane Moxon
    Founded 1979
    Library Holdings: Bk Titles 1,000; Per Subs 150
    Subject Interests: Acctg
    Restriction: Staff use only

CR REGENT COLLEGE, John Richard Allison Library, 5800 University Blvd,
    V6T 2E4. Tel: 604-221-3340. Toll Free Tel: 800-663-8664. FAX:
    604-224-3097. E-mail: library@regent-college.edu. Web Site:
    www.regent-college.edu. *Interim Dir,* Craig Gay; Tel: 604-224-3245, Ext
    322, E-mail: cgay@regent-college.edu; *Circ Coordr,* Winnie Kan; Tel:
    604-221-3369, E-mail: wkan@regent-college.edu; *Pub Serv,* Richard
    Matiachuk; Tel: 604-221-3341, E-mail: rmatiachuk@regent-college.edu;
    Ser, Melodie Rae Storey; Tel: 604-221-3397, E-mail:
    mstorey@regent-college.edu; *Tech Serv,* Audrey Williams; Tel:
    604-221-3364, E-mail: audrey@regent-college.edu
    Library Holdings: AV Mats 10,191; Bk Vols 163,287; Per Subs 357;
    Videos 621
    Special Collections: 19th Century Pamphlets on Religious, Cultural &
    Political Topics (Wilberforce Coll); Holocaust Nazi Germany (John S
    Conway Research Coll); Jacques Ellul Coll; Puritan & Anglican Colls, rare
    bks
    Automation Activity & Vendor Info: (Acquisitions) Innovative Interfaces,
    Inc; (Cataloging) Innovative Interfaces, Inc; (Circulation) Innovative
    Interfaces, Inc; (OPAC) Innovative Interfaces, Inc; (Serials) Innovative
    Interfaces, Inc
    Wireless access
    Open Mon-Thurs 8am-10pm, Fri 8-5, Sat 9-5

C   SIMON FRASER UNIVERSITY VANCOUVER LIBRARY*, Samuel &
    Frances Belzberg Library, 515 W Hastings St, V6B 5K3. Tel:
    778-782-5050. Reference Tel: 778-782-5051. FAX: 778-782-5052. Web
    Site: www.lib.sfu.ca/belzberg. *Head Librn,* Karen Marotz; E-mail:
    marotz@sfu.ca; *Circ,* Daniel Jans; *Ref Serv,* Mike McIntosh; E-mail:
    mmcintosh@sfu.ca; *Ref Serv,* Nina Smart; E-mail: nsmart@sfu.ca
    Library Holdings: Bk Vols 10,000; Per Subs 100
    Wireless access
    Open Mon-Thurs 10-9, Fri 10-7, Sat 10-5

S   SOCIETY PROMOTING ENVIRONMENTAL CONSERVATION*, Lille
    d'Easum Memorial Library, 2150 Maple St, V6J 3T3. Tel:
    604-736-7732. FAX: 604-736-7115. Web Site: www.spec.bc.ca. *Info Spec,*
    Joni Sherman
    Founded 1969

Library Holdings: Bk Titles 250; Per Subs 100
Publications: Spectrum (Quarterly)
Open Mon-Fri 10-4

S   TECK RESOURCES LIMITED, Corporate Library, 3300-550 Burrard St,
    V6C 0B3. SAN 326-4971. Tel: 604-699-4263. Interlibrary Loan Service
    Tel: 604-699-4111. FAX: 604-699-4711. Web Site: www.teck.com. *Coordr,*
    Keith Low; E-mail: keith.low@teck.com; Staff 3 (MLS 2, Non-MLS 1)
    Library Holdings: Per Subs 200
    Special Collections: Centre for Resource Studies Publications; Resource
    Company Annual Reports
    Subject Interests: Bus, Coal, Geol, Metals, Mgt, Mining
    Automation Activity & Vendor Info: (Cataloging) Inmagic, Inc.; (OPAC)
    Inmagic, Inc.
    Database Vendor: Bloomberg, Dialog, Factiva.com, Infomart, LexisNexis,
    Quicklaw, STN International, WestlaweCARSWELL
    Function: ILL available
    Open Mon-Fri 8-5
    Restriction: Access at librarian's discretion

S   THURBER ENGINEERING LIBRARY*, 1281 W Georgia St, Ste 900,
    V6E 3J7. SAN 328-0284. Tel: 604-684-4384. FAX: 604-684-5124. Web
    Site: www.thurber.ca. *Librn,* A Keller; E-mail: akeller@thurber.ca
    Founded 1957
    Library Holdings: Bk Titles 2,300; Bk Vols 4,450; Per Subs 52
    Special Collections: British Columbia (Air Photos Coll)
    Restriction: Staff use only

S   UNION OF BRITISH COLUMBIA INDIAN CHIEFS*, Resource Centre,
    342 Water St, 4th Flr, V6B 1B6. SAN 373-6644. Tel: 604-684-0231. FAX:
    604-684-5726. E-mail: library@ubcic.bc.ca. Web Site: www.ubcic.bc.ca.
    Dir, Alissa Cherry; E-mail: acherry@ubcic.bc.ca; *Archivist,* Nadine Hafner;
    E-mail: nhafner@ubcic.bc.ca; *Digital Librn,* Mimi Lam; E-mail:
    mlam@ubcic.bc.ca; Staff 3 (MLS 3)
    Founded 1972
    Library Holdings: Bk Vols 12,000; Per Subs 75
    Special Collections: Colonial Correspondence; McKenna-McBride
    Transcripts; Paul Chartrand Coll; RG-10; Union of BC Indian Chiefs fonds
    Wireless access
    Function: Archival coll, For res purposes, ILL available,
    Photocopying/Printing, Ref serv available, Res libr, Telephone ref
    Partic in Archives Association of British Columbia (AABC); BC Electronic
    Library Network
    Restriction: Access at librarian's discretion, Circ limited, Non-circulating
    to the pub, Not open to pub, Open by appt only, Private libr

C   UNIVERSITY OF BRITISH COLUMBIA LIBRARY, 1961 East Mall,
    V6T 1Z1. SAN 366-1989. Tel: 604-827-3434. Interlibrary Loan Service
    Tel: 604-822-6596. Web Site: www.library.ubc.ca. *Univ Librn,* Ingrid
    Parent; Tel: 604-827-3486, Fax: 604-822-3242, E-mail:
    ingrid.parent@ubc.ca; *Assoc Univ Librn, Client Serv & Prog,* Leonora
    Crema; Tel: 604-282-8473, E-mail: leonora.crema@ubc.ca; *Assoc Univ
    Librn, Coll & Scholarly Communication,* Jo Anne Newyear-Ramirez; Tel:
    604-822-2740, E-mail: joanne.newyear-ramirez@ubc.ca; *Assoc Univ Librn,
    Librn Syst & Info Tech,* Rue Ramirez; Tel: 604-822-5241, E-mail:
    rue.ramirez@ubc.ca; *Assoc Univ Librn, Res Serv,* Lea Starr; Tel:
    604-822-2826, E-mail: lea.starr@ubc.ca; *Dir, Finance & Fac,* Jean-Paul
    Eidsvik; Tel: 604-822-5903, E-mail: jean-paul.eidsvik@ubc.ca; *Assessment
    Librn,* Jeremy Buhler; Tel: 604-827-3510, E-mail: jeremy.buhler@ubc.ca;
    ILL, David Winter; Tel: 604-822-6721, Fax: 604-822-6465, E-mail:
    david.winter@ubc.ca; Staff 285 (MLS 86, Non-MLS 199)
    Founded 1915. Enrl 54,677; Fac 2,678; Highest Degree: Doctorate
    Apr 2010-Mar 2011. Mats Exp (CAN) $16,211,415. Sal (CAN)
    $18,376,937
    Library Holdings: Bk Vols 6,478,708
    Special Collections: A J T Taylor Coll; A M Donaldson Burns Coll;
    Chung Coll; Dictionaries & Related Works (H Rocke Robertson Coll);
    Douglas Coupland Archives; Doukhobor Coll; Early & Historical
    Children's Literature (Arkley Coll); Harry Hawthorne Angling Coll;
    History of Medicine & Science; Howay-Reid Coll; Japanese Maps of the
    Edo Period (George H Beans Coll); Malcolm Lowry Coll; Norman
    Colbeck Coll; Philip J Thomas Popular Song Coll; P'u-pan Coll; Stockett
    Thomas J Wise Coll; Stravinsky Coll; Thomas Murray Coll; University
    Archives. Can & Prov; Municipal Document Depository; UN Document
    Depository
    Automation Activity & Vendor Info: (Acquisitions) Ex Libris Group;
    (Cataloging) Ex Libris Group; (Circulation) Ex Libris Group; (Course
    Reserve) Ex Libris Group; (Media Booking) Ex Libris Group; (OPAC) Ex
    Libris Group; (Serials) Ex Libris Group
    Wireless access
    Function: Res libr
    Publications: Connects (Irving K Barber Learning Centre); Friends of the
    Library; Guide for Students; Insight (Newsletter); Report to the Senate
    Friends of the Library Group

Departmental Libraries:

ART, ARCHITECTURE & PLANNING, Irving K Barber Learning Ctr, 1961 East Mall, V6T 1Z1, SAN 320-104X. Tel: 604-822-3943. FAX: 604-822-3779. Web Site: aarp.library.ubc.ca. *Actg Head,* Paula Farrar; E-mail: paula.farrar@ubc.ca
　Special Collections: Rare Book Coll
　Subject Interests: Can art

ASIAN, 1871 West Mall, V6T 1Z2, SAN 366-1997. Tel: 604-822-2427. Reference Tel: 604-822-2023. FAX: 604-822-0650. Web Site: asian.library.ubc.ca. *Head Librn,* Eleanor Yuen; Tel: 604-822-5905, E-mail: eleanor.yuen@ubc.ca
　Founded 1960
　Special Collections: Canadian-Japanese Studies; Chinese-Canadian Settlement in British Columbia, Canada; Ching-I Chai Coll; Illegal Chinese Immigrants Virtual Photo Coll; Japanese Government Publications; Pearl Delta Area Research Materials; P'u-pan Coll; Sung Hsueh-Peng Coll; Swann Coll
　Subject Interests: Arts, Chinese hist, Culture, Economics, Indonesia, Japanese culture, Korea, Lit, Politics, Relig, S Asia
　Partic in Coun on East Asian Librs

IRVING K BARBER LEARNING CENTRE, 1961 East Mall, V6T 1Z1. Web Site: www.ikebarberlearningcentre.ubc.ca. *Dir,* Simon Neame; Tel: 604-822-3096, E-mail: simon.neame@ubc.ca

CM　BIOMEDICAL, Gordon & Leslie Diamond Health Care Ctr, 2775 Laurel St, 2nd Flr, V5Z 1M9, SAN 366-2373. Tel: 604-875-4505. FAX: 604-875-4689. Web Site: www.library.ubc.ca/bmb. *Librn,* Dean Giustini; Tel: 604-875-4111, Ext 6-2392, E-mail: dean.giustini@ubc.ca

EDUCATION, 2125 Main Mall, V6T 1Z4, SAN 366-2136. Tel: 604-822-5381. Reference Tel: 604-822-3767. FAX: 604-822-5378. Web Site: education.library.ubc.ca. *Actg Head Librn,* Jo-Anne Naslund; Tel: 604-822-0940, E-mail: jo-anne.naslund@ubc.ca

ERIC HAMBER LIBRARY, Children's & Women's Health Ctr, 4480 Oak St, V6H 3V4, SAN 318-8353. Circulation Tel: 604-875-2155. Reference Tel: 604-875-2154. FAX: 604-875-2195. Web Site: www.library.ubc.ca/hamber. *Librn,* Tricia Yu; E-mail: tricia.yu@ubc.ca

HUMANITIES & SOCIAL SCIENCES, KOERNER LIBRARY, 1958 Main Mall, V6T 1Z2, SAN 366-2012. Tel: 604-822-6363. Reference Tel: 604-822-2725. FAX: 604-822-9122. Web Site: hss.library.ubc.ca. *Interim Head Librn,* Trish Rosseel; Tel: 604-822-8667, E-mail: trish.rosseel@ubc.ca

DAVID LAM MANAGEMENT RESEARCH LIBRARY, 2033 Main Mall, V6T 1Z2, SAN 374-7492. Tel: 604-822-9400. FAX: 604-822-9398. Web Site: lam.library.ubc.ca. *Head Librn,* Jan Wallace; Tel: 604-822-9392, E-mail: jan.wallace@ubc.ca
　Founded 1985. Highest Degree: Doctorate
　Subject Interests: Bus admin, Commerce

CL　LAW, 1822 East Mall, V6T 1Z1, SAN 366-2160. Tel: 604-822-4238. Reference Tel: 604-822-9379. FAX: 604-822-6864. Web Site: law.library.ubc.ca. *Head of Libr,* Sandra Wilkins; Tel: 604-822-2396, E-mail: sandra.wilkins@ubc.ca; *Assoc Librn,* Mary Mitchell; Tel: 604-822-4203, E-mail: mary.mitchell@ubc.ca

MUSIC, 6361 Memorial Rd, V6T 1Z2, SAN 366-225X. Tel: 604-822-3589. Reference Tel: 604-822-6835. FAX: 604-822-1966. Web Site: music.library.ubc.ca. *Head of Libr,* Kirsten Walsh; Tel: 604-822-1408, E-mail: kirsten.walsh@ubc.ca
　Founded 1967. Highest Degree: Doctorate

OKANAGAN LIBRARY, 3333 University Way, Kelowna, V1V 1V7. *Chief Librn,* Melody Burton; E-mail: melody.burton@ubc.ca

RARE BOOKS & SPECIAL COLLECTIONS, Irving K Barber Learning Ctr, 1961 East Mall, V6T 1Z1, SAN 376-9208. Tel: 604-822-2521. FAX: 604-822-9587. Web Site: www.library.ubc.ca/spcoll. *Librn,* Ralph Stanton; Tel: 604-822-4879, E-mail: ralph.stanton@ubc.ca

CM　SAINT PAUL'S HOSPITAL LIBRARY, 1081 Burrard St, V6Z 1Y6, SAN 318-8345. Tel: 604-806-8425. FAX: 604-806-8013. Web Site: www.library.ubc.ca/stpauls. *Librn,* Barbara Saint; Tel: 604-682-2344, Ext 62090, E-mail: barbara.saint@ubc.ca

SCIENCE & ENGINEERING, Irving K Barber Learning Ctr, 1961 East Mall, V6T 1Z1, SAN 376-9194. Reference Tel: 604-822-3295. FAX: 604-822-5366. Web Site: scieng.library.ubc.ca. *Head, Sci & Eng,* Aleteia Greenwood; Tel: 604-822-0689, E-mail: aleteia.greenwood@ubc.ca.
　Subject Specialists: *Civil eng, Mechanical eng,* Aleteia Greenwood

UNIVERSITY ARCHIVES, Irving K Barber Learning Centre, 1961 East Mall, V6T 1Z1. Tel: 604-822-5877. Web Site: www.library.ubc.ca/archives. *Archivist,* Chris Hives; Tel: 604-827-3951, E-mail: chris.hives@ubc.ca

CM　WOODWARD BIOMEDICAL LIBRARY, 2198 Health Sciences Mall, V6T 1Z3, SAN 366-2349. Tel: 604-822-4440. FAX: 604-822-5596. Web Site: www.library.ubc.ca/woodward. *Interim Head Librn,* Kathryn Hornby; Tel: 604-822-4970, E-mail: kathy.hornby@ubc.ca
　Friends of the Library Group

XWI7XWA LIBRARY-FIRST NATIONS HOUSE OF LEARNING, 1985 West Mall, V6T 1Z2. Reference Tel: 604-822-8738. Web Site: xwi7xwa.library.ubc.ca. *Br Head,* Ann Doyle; Tel: 604-822-2385, E-mail: ann.doyle@ubc.ca. Subject Specialists: *First Nations,* Ann Doyle

S　VANCOUVER AQUARIUM MARINE SCIENCE CENTRE*, Robin Best Library, 845 Avison Way, Stanley Park, V6G 3E2. (Mail add: PO Box 3232, V6B 3X8), SAN 321-0901. Tel: 604-659-3404. FAX: 604-659-3515. *Mgr, Libr & Info Serv,* Ann Breolini; E-mail: ann.breolini@vanaqua.org; Staff 1 (MLS 1)
Founded 1967
Library Holdings: DVDs 30; e-journals 84; Bk Vols 5,500; Per Subs 40
Publications: Waters
Open Mon-Fri 8-3

S　VANCOUVER ART GALLERY LIBRARY*, 750 Hornby St, V6Z 2H7. SAN 318-8388. Tel: 604-662-4709. FAX: 604-682-1086. E-mail: library@vanartgallery.bc.ca. Web Site: www.vanartgallery.bc.ca. *Librn,* Cheryl A Siegel; E-mail: casiegel@vanartgallery.bc.ca; Staff 2 (MLS 1, Non-MLS 1)
Founded 1962
Jan 2006-Dec 2006 Income (Main Library Only) (CAN) $92,000. Mats Exp (CAN) $25,000. Sal (CAN) $82,000 (Prof (CAN) $50,000)
Library Holdings: AV Mats 40,000; CDs 40; DVDs 10; Bk Titles 47,500; Per Subs 122
Special Collections: Artistic Biographical Files
Subject Interests: Can fine art, Related subj
Automation Activity & Vendor Info: (Cataloging) LibraryWorld, Inc; (Serials) LibraryWorld, Inc
Open Mon-Fri 1-5
Restriction: Non-circulating to the pub

J　VANCOUVER COMMUNITY COLLEGE*, King Edward & City Centre Campus Libraries, 250 W Pender St, V6B 1S9. Tel: 604-443-8566. Circulation Tel: 604-443-8340, 604-871-7322. Interlibrary Loan Service Tel: 604-871-7119. Reference Tel: 604-443-8339, 604-871-7326. Administration Tel: 604-443-8567. FAX: 604-443-8588. TDD: 604-443-8549, 604-871-7325. E-mail: library@vcc.ca. Web Site: library.vcc.ca. *Dir, Libr & Media,* Lila Heilbrunn; E-mail: lheilbrunn@vcc.ca; *Head, Libr & Info Serv,* Melinda Baranieski; Tel: 604-871-7319, E-mail: mbaranieski@vcc.ca; *Head, Syst,* Jacqueline Van Dyk; Tel: 604-871-7157, E-mail: jvandyk@vcc.ca; *Instrul Serv Librn,* Irene King; Tel: 604-871-7225; *Instrul Serv Librn,* Cathie Perry; Tel: 604-443-8349, E-mail: cperry@vcc.bc.ca; *Circ Mgr,* Virginia Adams; Tel: 604-871-7497, E-mail: vadams@vcc.ca; *Coordr, Tech Serv,* Ella-Fay Zalezsak; Tel: 604-871-7385, Fax: 604-871-7446, E-mail: efzalezsak@vcc.ca; *Coll Develop,* Brenda Appleton; Tel: 604-443-8641, E-mail: bappleton@vcc.ca; *Coll Mgt, Libr Instruction,* Mark Goertz; *Libr Tech,* Tom Lazar; E-mail: tlazar@vcc.ca. Subject Specialists: *Spec needs,* Irene King; *Health,* Cathie Perry; *Bus,* Brenda Appleton; Staff 33.88 (MLS 9.11, Non-MLS 24.77)
Founded 1971. Enrl 7,969; Fac 451; Highest Degree: Associate
Library Holdings: AV Mats 8,518; e-books 769; Bk Vols 81,228; Per Subs 753
Subject Interests: Adult educ, Bus, Computer sci, Health sci, Hospitality, Vocational training
Automation Activity & Vendor Info: (Acquisitions) VTLS, Inc; (Cataloging) VTLS, Inc; (Circulation) VTLS, Inc; (Course Reserve) VTLS, Inc; (Media Booking) VTLS, Inc; (OPAC) VTLS, Inc; (Serials) VTLS, Inc
Database Vendor: Baker & Taylor, EBSCOhost, Gale Cengage Learning, OVID Technologies, ProQuest, PubMed
Function: Copy machines, Doc delivery serv, Electronic databases & coll, Handicapped accessible, ILL available, Learning ctr, Music CDs, Online ref
Publications: English as a Second Language Bibliographic (Reference guide)
Partic in BC Electronic Library Network; NET
Special Services for the Deaf - TDD equip; TTY equip; Videos & decoder
Special Services for the Blind - Closed circuit TV magnifier; Computer with voice synthesizer for visually impaired persons; Low vision equip
Open Mon-Fri 9-8
Restriction: Circ to mem only, In-house use for visitors, Open to students, fac & staff, Photo ID required for access, Registered patrons only

S　VANCOUVER HOLOCAUST EDUCATION CENTRE LIBRARY & ARCHIVES, 50-950 W 41st Ave, V5Z 2N7. SAN 373-7934. Tel: 604-264-0499. FAX: 604-264-0497. E-mail: library@vhec.org. Web Site: www.vhec.org. *Librn,* S LaBelle; *Archivist,* E Shaffer; E-mail: archives@vhec.org; Staff 1.4 (MLS 1.4)
Founded 1988
Library Holdings: AV Mats 495; CDs 45; DVDs 60; Bk Titles 2,400; Videos 450
Special Collections: Holocaust Studies Coll, archival, audio, AV, bks. Oral History
Function: Archival coll, Art exhibits, Audio & video playback equip for onsite use, CD-ROM, Handicapped accessible, Music CDs, Ref serv available, VHS videos, Wheelchair accessible
Restriction: Circ to mem only

P   VANCOUVER PUBLIC LIBRARY*, 350 W Georgia St, V6B 6B1. SAN
     366-2527. Tel: 604-331-3600. FAX: 604-331-3800. E-mail: info@vpl.ca.
     Web Site: www.vpl.ca. *City Librn*, Sandra Singh
     Founded 1887. Pop 587,891; Circ 10,115,900
     Library Holdings: AV Mats 164,416; Bk Titles 991,191; Bk Vols
     2,491,206; Per Subs 11,662; Talking Bks 11,267
     Special Collections: Early Children's Books (Marion Thompson Coll);
     Historical Photographs; North West History
     Subject Interests: Econ, Fine arts, Govt, Hist, Lang, Lit, Multicultural,
     Multilingual, Sci, Soc sci, Sports
     Automation Activity & Vendor Info: (Acquisitions) SirsiDynix;
     (Cataloging) SirsiDynix; (Circulation) SirsiDynix; (ILL) SirsiDynix;
     (OPAC) SirsiDynix; (Serials) SirsiDynix
     Wireless access
     Partic in Public Library InterLINK
     Open Mon-Thurs 10-9, Fri & Sat 10-6, Sun 12-5
     Friends of the Library Group
     Branches: 21
     BRITANNIA, 1661 Napier St, V5L 4X4, SAN 366-2551. Tel:
       604-665-2222. FAX: 604-665-3523. *Br Head,* Cathy Wang
       Open Mon, Thurs & Fri 8:30-5, Tues & Wed 8:30am-9pm, Sat 9:30-5,
       Sun 1-5
     CARNEGIE READING ROOM, 401 Main St, V6A 2T7, SAN 366-256X.
       Tel: 604-665-3010. FAX: 604-665-3016. *Br Head,* Beth Davies
       Open Mon-Sun 10-10
       Friends of the Library Group
     CHAMPLAIN HEIGHTS, 7110 Kerr St, V5S 4W2, SAN 366-2578. Tel:
       604-665-3955. FAX: 604-665-3929. *Br Head,* Susan Watson
       Open Tues, Wed & Sat 10-6, Thurs & Fri 10-9
       Friends of the Library Group
     COLLINGWOOD, 2985 Kingsway, V5R 5J4, SAN 366-2586. Tel:
       604-665-3953. FAX: 604-665-3403. *Br Head,* Anne Martin
       Open Tues 10-9, Wed & Thurs 10-6, Fri & Sat 10-5
       Friends of the Library Group
     DUNBAR, 4515 Dunbar St, V6S 2G7, SAN 366-2616. Tel: 604-665-3968.
       FAX: 604-665-3550. *Br Head,* Susan Bridgman
       Open Tues & Wed 10-9, Thurs-Sat 10-6
       Friends of the Library Group
     FIREHALL, 1455 W Tenth Ave, V6H 1J8, SAN 366-2918. Tel:
       604-665-3970. FAX: 604-665-3401. *Br Head,* Noni Mildenberger
       Open Tues & Wed 12-9, Thurs-Sat 10-6
       Friends of the Library Group
     FRASERVIEW, 1950 Argyle Dr, V5P 2A8, SAN 366-2640. Tel:
       604-665-3957. FAX: 604-665-3431. *Br Head,* Jinder Johal
       Open Tues & Wed 12-9, Thurs-Sat 10-6
       Friends of the Library Group
     HASTINGS, 2674 E Hastings St, V5K 1Z6, SAN 366-2675. Tel:
       604-665-3959. FAX: 604-665-3930. *Br Head,* Kirsty Elsmlie
       Open Tues & Wed 10-9, Thurs-Sat 10-6
       Friends of the Library Group
     JOE FORTES BRANCH, 870 Denman St, V6G 2L8, SAN 366-2705. Tel:
       604-665-3972. FAX: 604-665-3524. *Br Head,* Thomas Quigley
       Open Mon, Tues & Thurs 10-9, Wed & Fri 10-6, Sat 10-5, Sun 1-5
       Friends of the Library Group
     KENSINGTON COMMUNITY, 3927 Knight St, V5N 3L8, SAN
       366-2721. Tel: 604-665-3961. FAX: 604-665-3385. *Librn,* Yukiko Tosa
       Open Tues, Wed, Fri & Sat 10-6, Thurs 12-8
       Friends of the Library Group
     KERRISDALE, 2112 W 42nd Ave, V6M 2B6, SAN 366-273X. Tel:
       604-665-3974. FAX: 604-606-2788. Web Site:
       www.vpl.ca/branches/details/kerrisdale_branch. *Br Head,* Desiree Baron;
       Staff 2 (MLS 2)
       Founded 1943
       Open Tues & Thurs 9:30-8, Wed & Fri 9:30-6, Sat 9:30-5:30
     KITSILANO, 2425 Macdonald St, V6K 3Y9, SAN 366-2799. Tel:
       604-665-3976. FAX: 604-665-3931. *Br Head,* Daniela Esparo
       Open Mon-Thurs 10-9, Fri & Sat 10-6, Sun 1-5
       Friends of the Library Group
     MARPOLE BRANCH, 8386 Granville St, V6P 4Z7, SAN 366-2888. Tel:
       604-665-3978. FAX: 604-665-3552. *Br Head,* Jane Curry
       Open Tues & Wed 12-9, Thurs-Sat 10-6
       Friends of the Library Group
     MOUNT PLEASANT, One Kingsway, V5T 3H7, SAN 366-2829. Tel:
       604-665-3962. FAX: 604-665-3495. *Br Head,* Judi Walker
       Open Mon-Fri 9-9, Sat & Sun 9-6
       Friends of the Library Group
     OAKRIDGE, 650 W 41st Ave, No 191, V5Z 2M9, SAN 366-2853. Tel:
       604-665-3980. FAX: 604-665-3932. *Br Head,* Dawn Ibey
       Open Mon & Wed-Fri 10-9, Tues & Sat 10-6, Sun 1-5
       Friends of the Library Group
     OUTREACH SERVICES, 345 Robson St, Ste 302, V6B 6B3. Tel:
       604-331-4100. FAX: 604-331-4101. *Br Head,* Pauline Preston; Staff 6
       (MLS 1, Non-MLS 5)
       Open Tues-Thurs 10-5:30, Fri & Sat 10-5
       Friends of the Library Group

RENFREW, 2969 E 22nd Ave, V5M 2Y3, SAN 374-8146. Tel:
       604-257-8705. FAX: 604-257-8704. *Br Head,* Ross Bliss
       Library Holdings: Bk Vols 52,000
       Open Mon-Thurs 10-9, Fri & Sat 10-6, Sun 1-5
       Friends of the Library Group
     RILEY PARK COMMUNITY, Little Mountain Neighbourhood House,
       3981 Main St, V5V 3P3, SAN 366-2896. Tel: 604-665-3964. FAX:
       604-665-3553. *Librn,* Lindsay Pagnucco
       Open Tues, Wed, Fri & Sat 10-6, Thurs 12-8
       Friends of the Library Group
     SOUTH HILL, 6076 Fraser St, V5W 2Z7, SAN 366-2942. Tel:
       604-665-3965. FAX: 604-665-3440. *Br Head,* Lysanne Fox
       Open Tues & Thurs 12-9, Wed, Fri & Sat 10-6
       Friends of the Library Group
     STRATHCONA, 592 E Pender St, V6A 1V5, SAN 366-2977. Tel:
       604-665-3967. FAX: 604-665-3549. *Br Head,* Megan Langley
       Open Mon-Fri 9-5, Sat 11-4
       Friends of the Library Group
     WEST POINT GREY, 4480 W Tenth Ave, V6R 2H9, SAN 366-2993. Tel:
       604-665-3982. FAX: 604-665-3551. *Br Head,* Pearl Perehudoff
       Open Tues 12-9, Wed 10-9, Thurs-Sat 10-6
       Friends of the Library Group

R   VANCOUVER SCHOOL OF THEOLOGY, H R MacMillan Library, 6000
     Iona Dr, V6T 1L4. SAN 318-840X. Tel: 604-822-9430. Toll Free Tel:
     888-858-7715. FAX: 604-822-9212. Web Site: www.vst.edu. *Dir,* Patricia
     Dutcher-Walls; *Circ,* Faye Chisholm; *Tech Serv,* Kirsty Dickson; Staff 2.5
     (MLS 1.5, Non-MLS 1)
     Founded 1971. Enrl 250; Highest Degree: Master
     Library Holdings: Bk Vols 96,000; Per Subs 330
     Subject Interests: Anglican Church, Church hist, Methodist histl mat,
     Presbyterian churches, Theol
     Automation Activity & Vendor Info: (Cataloging) Innovative Interfaces,
     Inc; (Circulation) Innovative Interfaces, Inc; (Course Reserve) Innovative
     Interfaces, Inc; (ILL) Innovative Interfaces, Inc; (Media Booking)
     Innovative Interfaces, Inc; (OPAC) Innovative Interfaces, Inc; (Serials)
     Innovative Interfaces, Inc
     Wireless access
     Function: Res libr
     Publications: Accessions List
     Open Mon-Thurs (Sept-April) 8-6, Fri 8-5, Sat 12-6; Mon-Fri (May-Aug)
     8:30-4:30

S   VANDUSEN BOTANICAL GARDENS ASSOCIATION*, VanDusen
     Gardens Library, 5251 Oak St, V6M 4H1. SAN 326-5021. Tel:
     604-257-8668. FAX: 604-266-4236. E-mail: library@vandusen.org. Web
     Site: www.vandusen.org. *Librn,* Marina Princz; E-mail:
     library@vandusen.org; Staff 1 (MLS 1)
     Founded 1977
     Library Holdings: Bk Titles 5,800; Per Subs 50
     Special Collections: Gardening (Special Collecting Area: Plant
     Exploration); Horticulture & Botany
     Subject Interests: Botany, Hort
     Open Tues-Fri 9:30-3, Wed 7am-9pm, Sun 1-4

S   VIDEO OUTT*, Video Media Library, 1965 Main St, V5T 3C1. SAN
     324-6620. Tel: 604-872-8449. FAX: 604-876-1185. E-mail:
     videoout@telus.net. Web Site: www.videoinstudios.com. *In Charge,*
     Jennifer Fisher
     Library Holdings: Bk Titles 700; Per Subs 250
     Special Collections: Metro Media
     Subject Interests: Soc documentary, Video art
     Publications: Video Guide (Quarterly)
     Open Mon-Wed & Fri 8-4, Thurs 11-10

VANDERHOOF

P   VANDERHOOF PUBLIC LIBRARY*, 230 E Stuart St, Bag 6000, V0J
     3A0. SAN 318-8434. Tel: 250-567-4060. FAX: 250-567-4458. E-mail:
     vhlp@telus.net. Web Site: www.vanderhoofpubliclibrary.com. *Librn,* Jane
     Gray; E-mail: 250-567-6651
     Pop 3,906; Circ 43,000
     Library Holdings: Bk Titles 14,909; Bk Vols 14,952
     Function: Homebound delivery serv, ILL available, Meeting rooms,
     Photocopying/Printing
     Open Tues, Thurs & Sat 10-5, Wed 12-5 & 6:30-8:30, Fri 12-7

VICTORIA

GL   BRITISH COLUMBIA LEGISLATIVE LIBRARY*, Parliament Bldgs,
     V8V 1X4. SAN 318-8450. Tel: 250-387-6510. FAX: 250-356-1373. Web
     Site: www.llbc.leg.bc.ca. *Dir,* Jane Taylor; Tel: 250-387-6500, E-mail:
     jane.taylor@leg.bc.ca; *Syst Librn,* Sheila Gann; Tel: 250-387-1051, E-mail:
     sheila.gann@leg.bc.ca; *ILL,* Pat Somerton; E-mail: pat.somerton@leg.bc.ca;
     Tech Serv, Wendy Carmichael; Tel: 250-356-9186, Fax: 250-356-7216,

E-mail: wendy.carmichael@leg.bc.ca; *Coll Develop,* Cindy Tanner; Tel: 250-953-4718, E-mail: cindy.tanner@leg.bc.ca; Staff 15 (MLS 15)
Founded 1863
Library Holdings: Per Subs 708
Special Collections: British Columbia & Canadian Government Publications
Subject Interests: Hist, Law, Parliamentary procedure, Polit sci
Automation Activity & Vendor Info: (Acquisitions) SirsiDynix; (Cataloging) SirsiDynix; (Circulation) SirsiDynix; (OPAC) SirsiDynix; (Serials) SirsiDynix
Open Mon-Fri 8:30-5

G   BRITISH COLUMBIA MINISTRY OF EDUCATION*, Libraries & Literacy, 620 Superior St, 5th Flr, V8V 1V2. (Mail add: PO Box 9831, Stn Prov Govt, V8W 9T1), SAN 366-3213. Tel: 250-356-1791. FAX: 250-953-3225. E-mail: plsb@gov.bc.ca. Web Site: www.bced.gov.bc.ca/pls. *Dir,* Jacqueline van Dyk
Publications: British Columbia Public Libraries: Statistics

G   BRITISH COLUMBIA MINISTRY OF ENERGY & MINES*, James T Fyles Library, 1810 Blanshard St, V8W 9N3. (Mail add: PO Box 9321, Stn Provincial Government, V8W 9N3), SAN 318-8485. Tel: 250-952-0660. FAX: 250-952-0581. Web Site: www.em.gov.bc.ca/publicinfo/library/default.htm. *Adminr,* Jennifer Lu; E-mail: jennifer.lu@gov.bc.ca; *Libr Tech,* Janice M Brisson; Tel: 250-952-0583, E-mail: janice.m.brisson@gov.bc.ca; Staff 2 (Non-MLS 2)
Founded 1917
Library Holdings: Bk Titles 32,000; Bk Vols 45,000; Per Subs 500
Special Collections: Coal Industry Coll; Community Studies; Corporation Annual Reports; Energy Studies; Fed/Prov; Mine Studies; Regional Studies; Tourism Studies
Subject Interests: Energy, Geol, Mining, Petroleum eng, Tourism
Automation Activity & Vendor Info: (Acquisitions) BiblioMondo; (Cataloging) BiblioMondo; (Circulation) BiblioMondo; (Serials) BiblioMondo
Database Vendor: TLC (The Library Corporation)
Function: ILL available, Ref serv available
Open by appointment only
Restriction: Lending to staff only

G   BRITISH COLUMBIA MINISTRY OF FORESTS LIBRARY*, 722 Johnson St, 4th Flr, V8W 9C2. (Mail add: PO Box 9523, V8W 9C2), SAN 320-3093. Tel: 250-387-3628. FAX: 250-953-3079. Web Site: www.for.gov.bc.ca/hfd/library. *Librn,* Susanne Barker; E-mail: susanne.barker@gems7.gov.bc.ca; *Libr Tech,* Roxanne Smith
Founded 1959
Library Holdings: Bk Titles 100,000; Per Subs 200
Subject Interests: Environ studies, Forest mgt, Forestry
Publications: Accession list
Open Mon-Fri 8-4:30

C   CAMOSUN COLLEGE LIBRARY*, 3100 Foul Bay Rd, V8P 5J2. SAN 318-8477. Tel: 250-370-3619. Reference Tel: 250-370-3622. FAX: 250-370-3624. E-mail: library@camosun.bc.ca. Web Site: www.camosun.bc.ca/library. *Chair,* Richard Baer; Tel: 250-370-3604, E-mail: baer@camosun.bc.ca; Staff 18 (MLS 5, Non-MLS 13)
Founded 1971. Enrl 5,973; Fac 413; Highest Degree: Associate
Library Holdings: Bk Titles 56,517; Bk Vols 108,359; Per Subs 390
Automation Activity & Vendor Info: (Acquisitions) SirsiDynix; (Cataloging) SirsiDynix; (Circulation) SirsiDynix; (Course Reserve) SirsiDynix; (ILL) SirsiDynix; (Media Booking) SirsiDynix; (OPAC) SirsiDynix; (Serials) SirsiDynix
Database Vendor: EBSCOhost, ProQuest, Wilson - Wilson Web
Function: Res libr
Partic in BC Electronic Library Network
Open Mon-Thurs 9-9, Fri 9-5, Sat 10-6, Sun 2-6

P   GREATER VICTORIA PUBLIC LIBRARY BOARD*, 735 Broughton St, V8W 3H2. SAN 366-306X. Tel: 250-382-7241. Circulation Tel: 250-413-0361. Administration Tel: 250-384-5222. FAX: 250-382-7125. Administration FAX: 250-385-5971. TDD: 250-413-0364. Web Site: www.gvpl.ca. *Chief Exec Officer,* Barry Holmes; E-mail: bholmes@gvpl.ca; Staff 38 (MLS 37, Non-MLS 1)
Founded 1864. Pop 294,773; Circ 4,872,496
Library Holdings: AV Mats 88,646; Bk Titles 314,483; Bk Vols 838,096; Per Subs 2,269; Talking Bks 23,436
Subject Interests: Local hist
Automation Activity & Vendor Info: (Acquisitions) Innovative Interfaces, Inc; (Cataloging) Innovative Interfaces, Inc; (Circulation) Innovative Interfaces, Inc; (OPAC) Innovative Interfaces, Inc; (Serials) Innovative Interfaces, Inc
Wireless access
Publications: Check it Out at the Library
Friends of the Library Group

Branches: 7
EMILY CARR BRANCH, 3500 Blanshard St, V8X 1W3, SAN 366-3183. Tel: 250-475-6100. FAX: 250-475-6102. *Br Head,* Anne Parker; E-mail: aparker@gvpl.ca
Friends of the Library Group
CENTRAL SAANICH, 1209 Clarke Rd, V8M 1P8. Tel: 250-652-2013. FAX: 250-652-6224. *Br Head,* Olivia Anderson; Tel: 250-727-0104, E-mail: oanderso@gvpl.ca
ESQUIMALT, 1231 Esquimalt Rd, V9A 3P1, SAN 366-3094. Tel: 250-414-7198. FAX: 250-412-8542. *Br Head,* Cheryl Osborn
Friends of the Library Group
BRUCE HUTCHISON BRANCH, 4636 Elk Lake Dr, V9Z 7K2, SAN 374-5228. Tel: 250-727-0104. *Br Head,* Olivia Anderson; E-mail: oanderso@gvpl.ca
Friends of the Library Group
JUAN DE FUCA BRANCH, 1759 Island Hwy, V9B 1J1, SAN 376-2238. Tel: 250-391-0653. FAX: 250-391-0879. *Br Head,* Rina Hadziev; E-mail: rhadziev@gvpl.ca
Friends of the Library Group
NELLIE MCCLUNG BRANCH, 3950 Cedar Hill Rd, V8P 3Z9, SAN 366-3124. Tel: 250-477-7111. FAX: 250-477-4257. *Br Head,* Joyce Josephson; E-mail: jjosephs@gvpl.ca
Friends of the Library Group
OAK BAY, 1442 Monterey Ave, V8S 4W1, SAN 366-3159. Tel: 250-592-2489. FAX: 250-370-0837. *Br Head,* Neil McAllister; E-mail: nmcallis@gvpl.ca
Library Holdings: Bk Vols 89,745
Friends of the Library Group

GM   HEALTH & HUMAN SERVICES LIBRARY, BRITISH COLUMBIA MINISTRY OF HEALTH, 1515 Blanshard St, Main Flr, V8W 3C8. SAN 366-3000. Tel: 250-952-2196. FAX: 250-952-2180. E-mail: hlth.library@gov.bc.ca. Web Site: www.health.gov.bc.ca/library. *Head Librn,* Antje Helmuth; Staff 7 (MLS 4, Non-MLS 3)
Founded 2002
Library Holdings: Bk Titles 22,000; Per Subs 500; Videos 2,000
Subject Interests: Aboriginal issues, Alcohol abuse, Child welfare, Dentistry, Drug abuse, Epidemiology, Gerontology, Health educ, Hospital admin, Learning disorders, Long term care, Mental health, Nursing, Pub health admin, Pub health inspection, Pub sector mgt, Soc work, Speech disorders
Automation Activity & Vendor Info: (Cataloging) SIRSI Unicorn; (Circulation) SIRSI Unicorn; (Media Booking) SIRSI Unicorn; (OPAC) SIRSI-iLink; (Serials) SIRSI Unicorn
Database Vendor: EBSCOhost, Medline, OVID Technologies, PubMed, RefWorks
Partic in Electronic Health Library of British Columbia; Govt Libr Asn of BC; Health Libr Asn of BC (HLABC)
Open Mon-Fri 8:30-4:30

C   LESTER B PEARSON COLLEGE OF THE PACIFIC*, Norman McKee Lang Library, 650 Pearson College Dr, V9C 4H7. SAN 328-1825. Tel: 250-391-2423. FAX: 250-391-2412. Web Site: www.pearsoncollege.ca. *Chief Librn,* Sherry Crowther; Staff 1 (MLS 1)
Founded 1974. Enrl 200; Fac 25
Library Holdings: DVDs 240; Electronic Media & Resources 30; Bk Vols 18,000; Per Subs 90; Videos 400
Special Collections: International Affairs (Giovanni Costigan Lectures Coll); Lester B Pearson Bk Coll; Pearson College Archive
Database Vendor: EBSCOhost, H W Wilson, PubMed, World Book Online
Wireless access
Partic in BC Electronic Library Network
Open Mon-Fri 8:30am-Midnight, Sat & Sun 9am-Midnight

S   MARITIME MUSEUM OF BRITISH COLUMBIA LIBRARY*, 28 Bastion Sq, V8W 1H9. SAN 322-7073. Tel: 250-385-4222, Ext 105. Administration Tel: 250-385-4222, Ext 107. FAX: 250-382-2869. Web Site: www.mmbc.bc.ca. *Coll Mgt,* Richard MacKenzie; E-mail: richardmackenzie@mmbc.bc.ca; Staff 6 (MLS 1, Non-MLS 5)
Founded 1954
Library Holdings: Bk Titles 7,000; Per Subs 25
Special Collections: Maritime Hist (NW Coast & British Columbia)
Open Mon-Fri 1-4
Restriction: Not a lending libr

G   NATURAL RESOURCES CANADA-CANADIAN FOREST SERVICE*, Pacific Forestry Centre Library, 506 W Burnside Rd, V8Z 1M5. SAN 318-8507. Tel: 250-363-0680. FAX: 250-363-6035. E-mail: interlibraryloans@nrcan.gc.ca. Web Site: www.metafore2.nrcan-rncan.gc.ca. *Mgr, Libr Serv,* Alice Solyma; E-mail: asolyma@pfc.cfs.nrcan.gc.ca; Staff 3 (MLS 2, Non-MLS 1)
Founded 1940
Library Holdings: Bk Titles 90,000; Bk Vols 137,000; Per Subs 250

Special Collections: Entomological Society of British Columbia Library; Pacific Forestry Centre Library
Subject Interests: Forest health, Forest products
Automation Activity & Vendor Info: (Acquisitions) SirsiDynix; (Cataloging) SirsiDynix; (Circulation) SirsiDynix; (OPAC) SirsiDynix; (Serials) SirsiDynix
Database Vendor: Agricola, Annual Reviews, Blackwell's, Dialog, ISI Web of Knowledge, JSTOR, Nature Publishing Group, netLibrary, OCLC FirstSearch, OVID Technologies, ScienceDirect, SirsiDynix, Springer-Verlag
Partic in Coun of Canadian Forest Serv Librs; Federal Librs Consortium (Canada)

UNIVERSITY OF VICTORIA LIBRARIES
C   MCPHERSON LIBRARY*, PO Box 1800, V8W 3H5, SAN 366-3450. Tel: 250-721-8211. Circulation Tel: 250-721-6673. Interlibrary Loan Service Tel: 250-721-8236. Reference Tel: 250-721-8274. FAX: 250-721-8215. Interlibrary Loan Service FAX: 250-721-8243. Reference FAX: 250-721-8235. Web Site: gateway.uvic.ca. *Univ Librn,* Marnie Swanson; E-mail: mswanson@uvic.ca; *Asst Univ Librn,* Wendie McHenry; E-mail: wmchenry@uvic.ca; *Dir, Pub Serv,* Shailoo Bedi; E-mail: shailoo@uvic.ca; *Assoc Univ Librn, Coll Serv, Assoc Univ Librn, Info Serv,* Joanne Henning; E-mail: jhenning@uvic.ca; *Assoc Univ Librn, Info Tech, Assoc Univ Librn, Tech Serv,* Ken Cooley; E-mail: kcooley@uvic.ca; *Spec Coll Librn,* Chris Petter; E-mail: cpetter@uvic.ca; *Coordr, Cat,* Sam Aquila; E-mail: saquila@uvic.ca; *Coordr, Ser,* Elena Romaniuk; E-mail: eromaniu@uvic.ca; *Develop Officer,* Jane Buzza; E-mail: jbuzza@uvic.ca; *Coordr, ILL,* Nancy Stuart; E-mail: nstuart@uvic.ca; *Univ Archivist,* Jane Turner; E-mail: jturner@uvic.ca; Staff 40 (MLS 31, Non-MLS 9)
Founded 1902. Highest Degree: Doctorate
Library Holdings: CDs 64,515; e-journals 11,000; Music Scores 34,704; Bk Vols 1,856,987; Per Subs 14,473; Videos 7,904
Special Collections: English Literature (Anglo-Irish Renaissance); English Literature (John Betjeman Coll), bks, mss; English Literature (Robert Graves Coll), bks & mss; Literature, Art History (Herbert Read Coll), bks, mss. Can & Prov
Subject Interests: Behav sci, Econ, Educ, Environ studies, Hist, Lang, Law, Lit, Music, Natural sci, Soc sci
Automation Activity & Vendor Info: (Acquisitions) Ex Libris Group; (Cataloging) Ex Libris Group; (Circulation) Ex Libris Group; (OPAC) Ex Libris Group
Partic in AG Canada; BC Electronic Library Network; Canadian Association of Research Libraries; Council of Prairie & Pacific University Libraries; OCLC Online Computer Library Center, Inc
Friends of the Library Group
CL   DIANA M PRIESTLY LAW LIBRARY*, PO Box 2300, STN CSC, V8W 3B1, SAN 366-3485. Tel: 250-721-8565. FAX: 250-472-4174. E-mail: lawill@uvic.ca. *Assoc Prof, Assoc Univ Librn,* Neil A Campbell; *Acq,* I Godfrey
Founded 1974
Library Holdings: Bk Vols 413,000; Per Subs 1,935
Special Collections: Common Law; English Language
Partic in AG Canada; OCLC Online Computer Library Center, Inc
Publications: Constitution Act, 1982 - Canadian Charter of Rights & Freedoms; Law Library Occasional Paper No 1: Judges of British Columbia to 1957; Law Reporting in BC - Out of The West; The Writings of D M Gordon, Esq, QC - A List

M   VANCOUVER ISLAND HEALTH AUTHORITY MEDICAL LIBRARIES*, Royal Jubilee Hospital, 1952 Bay St, V8R 1J8. SAN 318-8574. Tel: 250-370-8612, 250-370-8723. FAX: 250-370-8274. E-mail: libsvs@viha.ca. Web Site: www.viha.ca/library/south. *Mgr,* Cliff Cornish; E-mail: cliff.cornish@viha.ca; *Asst Librn,* Joyce Constantine; E-mail: joyce.constantine@viha.ca
Library Holdings: Per Subs 550
Special Collections: Medical History & Biography
Subject Interests: Geriatrics, Hospital mgt
Publications: GVHS Library Newsletter (Quarterly)
Open Mon-Fri 8:30-4:30

S   VICTORIA CONSERVATORY OF MUSIC*, Leon & Thea Koerner Foundation Library, 907 Pandora Ave, V8V 3P4. SAN 323-441X. Tel: 250-386-5311, Ext 234. FAX: 250-386-6602. E-mail: info@vcm.bc.ca. Web Site: www.vcm.bc.ca. *Librn,* John Johnston
Library Holdings: Bk Titles 5,000; Per Subs 15
Open Tues-Fri 9-5

S   VIEW ROYAL READING CENTRE*, View Royal Community Library, 103B-1497 Admirals Rd, V9A 2P8. Tel: 250-479-2723. FAX: 250-479-2723. E-mail: vivr.ill@shaw.ca. Web Site: viewroyal.bclibrary.ca. *Libr Mgr,* Doreen Jackman; Staff 0.25 (MLS 0.25)

Founded 1971. Pop 9,300
Library Holdings: Bk Vols 16,500
Function: Family literacy
Open Mon 10-4 & 7pm-9pm, Tues 1-4 & 7pm-9pm, Wed & Thurs 1-7, Fri 1-4, Sat 10-4
Restriction: Circ to mem only

WEST VANCOUVER

P   WEST VANCOUVER MEMORIAL LIBRARY*, 1950 Marine Dr, V7V 1J8. SAN 318-8582. Tel: 604-925-7400. FAX: 604-925-5933. E-mail: info@westvanlibrary.ca. Web Site: www.westvanlibrary.ca. *Chief Librn,* Ann Goodhart
Founded 1950. Pop 46,022; Circ 970,050
Jan 2006-Dec 2006 Income (CAN) $3,612,130, Provincial (CAN) $135,937, City (CAN) $3,018,762, Locally Generated Income (CAN) $209,328, Other (CAN) $248,103. Mats Exp (CAN) $424,567. Sal (CAN) $2,454,992
Library Holdings: AV Mats 27,349; Bk Vols 247,561; Per Subs 356
Special Collections: History & Literature of Persia (Persian Language Coll)
Subject Interests: Fine arts, Music
Automation Activity & Vendor Info: (Acquisitions) Innovative Interfaces, Inc; (Cataloging) Innovative Interfaces, Inc; (Circulation) Innovative Interfaces, Inc; (OPAC) Innovative Interfaces, Inc; (Serials) Innovative Interfaces, Inc
Wireless access
Function: Art exhibits, Audio & video playback equip for onsite use, Computer training, Home delivery & serv to Sr ctr & nursing homes, Homebound delivery serv, ILL available, Prog for adults, Prog for children & young adult, Summer reading prog, Wheelchair accessible
Publications: Annual Report; Fulfilling a Dream: West Vancouver Memorial Library, 1919-1990; Inquiring Mind (Newsletter)
Partic in Public Library InterLINK
Special Services for the Blind - Large print bks & talking machines; Magnifiers
Friends of the Library Group
Bookmobiles: 1

WHISTLER

P   WHISTLER PUBLIC LIBRARY*, 4329 Main St, V0N 1B4. Tel: 604-935-8433. FAX: 604-935-8434. E-mail: info@whistlerlibrary.ca. Web Site: www.whistlerlibrary.ca. *Dir,* Lauren Stara; E-mail: lstara@whistlerlibrary.ca; *Pub Serv Librn,* Nadine White; E-mail: nwhite@whistlerlibrary.ca; *Youth Serv Librn,* Libby McKeever; E-mail: lmckeever@whistlerlibrary.ca; *Circ Supvr,* Danusia Smit; E-mail: dsmit@whistlerlibrary.ca; Staff 6 (MLS 2, Non-MLS 4)
Founded 1986. Pop 10,000; Circ 140,000
Library Holdings: Bk Titles 45,000; Per Subs 129
Automation Activity & Vendor Info: (Cataloging) OCLC CatExpress; (Circulation) Evergreen; (OPAC) Evergreen
Database Vendor: ProQuest
Wireless access
Open Mon-Sat 11-7, Sun 11-4
Restriction: Authorized patrons
Friends of the Library Group

WILLIAMS LAKE

C   THOMPSON RIVERS UNIVERSITY*, Williams Lake Campus Library, 1250 Western Ave, V2G 1H7. Tel: 250-392-8030. FAX: 250-392-4984. E-mail: wlmain@tru.ca. Web Site: www.tru.ca/williamslake. *Librn,* Elizabeth Rennie; E-mail: erennie@tru.ca
Library Holdings: AV Mats 800; Bk Vols 10,000
Automation Activity & Vendor Info: (Acquisitions) SirsiDynix; (Cataloging) SirsiDynix; (Circulation) SirsiDynix; (Course Reserve) SirsiDynix; (ILL) SirsiDynix; (Media Booking) SirsiDynix; (OPAC) SirsiDynix; (Serials) SirsiDynix
Open Mon-Thurs 8:30-8, Fri 8:30-4:30

P   WILLIAMS LAKE LIBRARY*, 180 N Third Ave, Ste A, V2G 2A4. SAN 318-8590. Tel: 250-392-3630. Toll Free Tel: 800-665-1636, Ext 210. FAX: 250-392-3518. E-mail: wlake@Cariboord.bc.ca. Web Site: www.cariboard.bc.ca/network.htm, www.cln.bc.ca. *Dir,* Colleen Swift; Staff 2 (MLS 1, Non-MLS 1)
Founded 1976. Pop 25,000; Circ 125,000
Library Holdings: Bk Titles 93,000; Bk Vols 160,000; Per Subs 150
Special Collections: Oral History
Subject Interests: Local hist
Publications: A Brief History of Williams Lake
Open Tues-Thurs 10-8, Fri & Sat 10-5
Friends of the Library Group

BALDUR

P RURAL MUNICIPALITY OF ARGYLE PUBLIC LIBRARY*, 627
Elizabeth Ave, R0K 0B0. (Mail add: PO Box 10, R0K 0B0), SAN
378-0120. Tel: 204-535-2314. FAX: 204-535-2242. E-mail:
argyle@prairiespirit.mb.ca. *Chairperson,* Susan Kentner; *Librn,* Cheri
McLaren
Founded 1982. Pop 1,200
Library Holdings: Bk Titles 10,000; Per Subs 25
Special Services for the Blind - Audio mat; Large print bks
Open Mon & Wed 7pm-9pm, Tues-Thurs 1-4

BEAUSEJOUR

P BROKENHEAD RIVER REGIONAL LIBRARY*, 427 Park Ave, R0E
0C0. (Mail add: PO Box 1087, R0E 0C0), SAN 377-9831. Tel:
204-268-7570. FAX: 204-268-7570. Web Site:
www.brokenheadriverregionallibrary.ca. *Librn,* Debbie Winnicki; E-mail:
debbiewinnickibrrl@mts.net
Pop 6,763
Library Holdings: Bk Titles 30,998; Per Subs 80
Database Vendor: EBSCOhost
Wireless access
Function: ILL available
Partic in Can Libr Asn; Manitoba Libr Asn; Manitoba Libr Trustees Asn
Open Tues & Thurs 9-5, Wed 11-8, Fri 9-8, Sat 11-3

BOISSEVAIN

P BOISSEVAIN & MORTON REGIONAL LIBRARY*, 436 S Railway, R0K
0E0. (Mail add: PO Box 340, R0K 0E0), SAN 318-8612. Tel:
204-534-6478. FAX: 204-534-3710. E-mail: mbom@mts.net. Web Site:
www.bmlibrary.ca. *Head Librn,* Michelle Scott
Founded 1959. Pop 2,800; Circ 39,000
Library Holdings: Bk Titles 24,000; Per Subs 40
Special Collections: Local History (Boissevain Community Archives), ms,
photog. Oral History
Wireless access
Publications: Annual Report
Open Tues 9-8, Wed-Sat 9-5

BRANDON

J ASSINIBOINE COMMUNITY COLLEGE LIBRARY, 1430 Victoria Ave
E, R7A 2A9. SAN 320-7811. Tel: 204-725-8727. Toll Free Tel:
800-862-6307, Ext 6638. FAX: 204-725-8740. E-mail:
library@assiniboine.net. Web Site: www.assiniboine.net,
www.assiniboine.net/library. *Mgr, Libr Serv,* Susan Gatin; Tel:
204-725-8727, Ext 6637, E-mail: gatins@assiniboine.net
Founded 1968
Library Holdings: AV Mats 2,070; Bks on Deafness & Sign Lang 80;
CDs 270; DVDs 1,250; e-books 1,055; e-journals 15; Electronic Media &

Resources 10; Bk Titles 15,150; Bk Vols 19,200; Per Subs 290; Videos
2,920
Automation Activity & Vendor Info: (Cataloging) Insignia Software;
(Circulation) Insignia Software; (OPAC) Insignia Software; (Serials)
Insignia Software
Database Vendor: ALLDATA Online, CredoReference, EBSCOhost,
Elsevier, netLibrary, ScienceDirect, Springshare, LLC
Wireless access
Partic in Can Libr Asn; Manitoba Libr Asn; Manitoba Library Consortium,
Inc
Open Mon-Thurs 8-7:30, Fri 8-4:30, Sat 12-4

M BRANDON REGIONAL HEALTH AUTHORITY*, Health Resource
Center, 150 McTavish Ave E, R7A 2B3. SAN 320-782X. Tel:
204-578-4080. Interlibrary Loan Service Tel: 204-578-4081. FAX:
204-578-4984. E-mail: library@brandonrha.mb.ca. *Mgr, Libr Serv,* Wendy
Wareham; Staff 4 (Non-MLS 4)
Founded 1950
Library Holdings: Bk Vols 6,000; Per Subs 150
Special Collections: Consumer Health; Hospital Administrative Archives
Database Vendor: EBSCOhost
Partic in Manitoba Health Libr Asn
Open Mon-Fri 8-4:30

C BRANDON UNIVERSITY*, John E Robbins Library, 270 18th St, R7A
6A9. SAN 318-8639. Tel: 204-727-9688. Circulation Tel: 204-727-9646.
Interlibrary Loan Service Tel: 204-727-7316. Reference Tel: 204-727-9702.
Administration Tel: 204-727-9767. FAX: 204-727-1072. Administration
FAX: 204-727-8571. Web Site: www.brandonu.ca/library. *Actg Univ Librn,
Automation Syst Coordr,* Chris Hurst; Tel: 204-727-9687, E-mail:
hurst@brandonu.ca; *Archivist,* Position Currently Open; *Cat,* Marianne
Reid; Tel: 204-727-7384, E-mail: reidm@brandonu.ca; *Electronic Res, Ref,*
Rainer Schira; Tel: 204-727-7463, E-mail: schirar@brandonu.ca; *Extn Serv,*
Carmen Kazakoff-Lane; Tel: 204-727-7483, E-mail:
kazakoff@barndonu.ca; Staff 23 (MLS 5, Non-MLS 18)
Founded 1899. Enrl 2,700; Fac 186; Highest Degree: Master
Library Holdings: Bk Titles 350,000; Bk Vols 450,000; Per Subs 800
Special Collections: Aboriginal Literature Coll; Great Plains Coll; Musical
Theatre Coll
Subject Interests: Music, Native studies
Automation Activity & Vendor Info: (Cataloging) Ex Libris Group;
(Circulation) Ex Libris Group; (Course Reserve) Ex Libris Group; (OPAC)
Ex Libris Group; (Serials) Ex Libris Group
Wireless access
Partic in Canadian Research Knowledge Network; Council of Prairie &
Pacific University Libraries; Manitoba Library Consortium, Inc
Open Mon-Thurs 8:30am-10pm, Fri 8:30-5, Sat 1-6, Sun 1-8

G CANADA AGRICULTURE & AGRI-FOOD CANADA*, Library &
Information Centre, RR 3, Box 1000A, R7A 5Y3. SAN 322-7618. Tel:
204-726-7650. FAX: 204-728-3858. E-mail: libbrandon@agr.gc.ca. Web

Site: res2.agr.ca/brandon/welcome.htm. *Librn,* Carol Enns; Tel:
204-578-3595, E-mail: cenns@agr.gc.ca
Library Holdings: Bk Titles 2,000; Per Subs 170
Special Collections: Agriculture Canada Publications; Reprints of
Scientists' Research Articles & Technology Transfer Reports
Subject Interests: Agronomy, Animal sci, Plant sci, Soil sci
Automation Activity & Vendor Info: (Cataloging) Infor Library &
Information Solutions
Database Vendor: EBSCOhost
Publications: Library Newsletter
Open Mon-Fri 8-4:30
Restriction: Non-circulating

P   WESTERN MANITOBA REGIONAL LIBRARY*, 710 Rosser Ave, Unit
1, R7A 0K9. SAN 366-354X. Tel: 204-727-6648. FAX: 204-727-4447.
E-mail: brandon@wmrl.ca. Web Site: www.wmrl.ca. *Chief Librn,* Kathy
Thornborough; *Asst Librn,* Shelley Mortensen; Staff 2 (MLS 1, Non-MLS
1)
Founded 1967. Pop 49,610; Circ 275,776
Library Holdings: AV Mats 5,145; Bk Vols 126,687; Per Subs 314;
Talking Bks 1,334; Videos 2,533
Automation Activity & Vendor Info: (Cataloging) SirsiDynix;
(Circulation) SirsiDynix; (OPAC) SirsiDynix
Database Vendor: EBSCOhost
Partic in Manitoba Library Consortium, Inc
Open Mon & Thurs 10-9, Tues, Wed, Fri & Sat 10-6
Branches: 5
BRANDON BRANCH, 710 Rosser Ave, Unit 1, R7A 0K9, SAN
366-3566. Tel: 204-727-6648. FAX: 204-727-4447. *Chief Librn,* Kathy
Thornborough; Staff 2 (MLS 1, Non-MLS 1)
Founded 1946. Pop 39,716; Circ 204,605
Library Holdings: AV Mats 4,354; Bk Vols 89,705; Per Subs 178;
Talking Bks 628; Videos 1,665
Special Collections: Oral History
Open Mon & Thurs 10-9, Tues, Wed, Fri & Sat 10-6
CARBERRY-NORTH CYPRESS BRANCH, 115 Main St, Carberry, R0K
0H0. (Mail add: PO Box 382, Carberry, R0K 0H0), SAN 366-3574. Tel:
204-834-3043. E-mail: carberry@wmrlibrary.mb.ca. *Br Supvr,* Diane
Gawel
Founded 1967. Pop 3,366
Library Holdings: AV Mats 920; Bk Vols 14,877; Per Subs 48; Talking
Bks 33; Videos 535
Special Collections: School District Records
Open Tues-Fri 9-11 & 12-5, Sat 9-12 & 1-5
Friends of the Library Group
GLENBORO/SOUTH CYPRESS LIBRARY BRANCH, 105 Broadway St,
Glenboro, R0K 0X0. (Mail add: PO Box 429, Glenboro, R0K 0X0),
SAN 366-3582. Tel: 204-827-2874. *Br Supvr,* Jackie Steele; E-mail:
jackie@wmrl.ca
Pop 1,477
Library Holdings: Audiobooks 15; AV Mats 329; Bks-By-Mail 50; Bks
on Deafness & Sign Lang 3; CDs 11; DVDs 178; e-books 500;
e-journals 3; Electronic Media & Resources 3; High Interest/Low
Vocabulary Bk Vols 42; Large Print Bks 101; Microforms 48; Bk Titles
10,158; Per Subs 39
Special Collections: Local Archives
Automation Activity & Vendor Info: (Acquisitions) Horizon;
(Cataloging) Horizon; (Circulation) Horizon
Open Tues-Fri 9-12 & 1-5
HARTNEY/CAMERON BRANCH, 209 Airdrie St, Hartney, R0M 0X0.
(Mail add: Box 121, Hartney, R0M 0X0). Tel: 204-858-2101. E-mail:
hartney@wmrlibrary.mb.ca. *Br Supvr,* Brenda Hicks
Pop 942
Open Tues-Fri 1-5
Friends of the Library Group
NEEPAWA BRANCH, 280 Davidson St, Neepawa, R0J 1H0. (Mail add:
PO Box 759, Neepawa, R0J 1H0), SAN 366-3604. Tel: 204-476-5648.
E-mail: neepawa@wmrlibrary.mb.ca. *Br Supvr,* Liana Kaiser
Pop 4,109
Library Holdings: AV Mats 344; Bk Vols 17,892; Per Subs 49; Videos
217
Open Mon, Wed & Fri 10-5, Tues & Thurs 10-5 & 7pm-9pm
Friends of the Library Group

CARMAN

P   BOYNE REGIONAL LIBRARY*, 15 First Ave SW, R0G 0J0. (Mail add:
PO Box 788, R0G 0J0), SAN 318-8647. Tel: 204-745-3504. E-mail:
boynereg@mts.net. *Librn,* Sandra Yeo
Founded 1969. Pop 5,478
Library Holdings: Bk Vols 30,000
Database Vendor: EBSCOhost
Wireless access
Open Tues, Wed, Fri & Sat 9-5, Thurs 9-8

CHURCHILL

P   CHURCHILL PUBLIC LIBRARY*, 181 Laverendrye Ave, R0B 0E0.
(Mail add: PO Box 730, R0B 0E0), SAN 320-989X. Tel: 204-675-2731.
E-mail: mchlibrary@yahoo.ca. *Librn,* Bonnie Allen
Founded 1975. Pop 1,089; Circ 20,295
Library Holdings: Bk Vols 24,000; Per Subs 20
Special Collections: Canada North Coll
Automation Activity & Vendor Info: (Cataloging) LibraryWorld, Inc;
(Circulation) LibraryWorld, Inc; (OPAC) LibraryWorld, Inc
Wireless access
Partic in Man Libr Asn
Open Mon-Fri 1-4:45, Tues & Thurs 7pm-9pm, Sat 1-5

DAUPHIN

P   PARKLAND REGIONAL LIBRARY, 504 Main St N, R7N 1C9. SAN
318-8663. Tel: 204-638-6410. FAX: 204-638-9483. E-mail:
prlhq@parklandlib.mb.ca. Web Site: www.parklandlib.mb.ca. *Dir,*
Jean-Louis Guillas; E-mail: jguillas@parklandlib.mb.ca; Staff 1 (MLS 1)
Founded 1976. Pop 41,800
Library Holdings: Bk Vols 132,000; Per Subs 134
Automation Activity & Vendor Info: (Cataloging) TLC (The Library
Corporation); (Circulation) TLC (The Library Corporation); (OPAC) TLC
(The Library Corporation)
Database Vendor: EBSCOhost
Wireless access
Function: ILL available
Open Mon-Fri 8:30-4:30
Bookmobiles: 1

DELORAINE

P   BREN DEL WIN CENTENNIAL LIBRARY*, 211 N Railway W, R0M
0M0. (Mail add: PO Box 584, R0M 0M0), SAN 321-351X. Tel:
204-747-2415. E-mail: bdwlib@mts.net. *Librn,* Lorraine Stovin; Staff 1
(MLS 1)
Founded 1979. Pop 2,392
Library Holdings: Bk Vols 13,800; Per Subs 35
Wireless access
Open Tues-Sat 9-5

ERIKSDALE

P   ERIKSDALE PUBLIC LIBRARY*, PO Box 219, R0C 0W0. SAN
377-8991. Tel: 204-739-2668. E-mail: epl1@mts.net. Web Site:
www.eriksdalepl.org. *Librn,* Linda Lee
Founded 1997
Library Holdings: Bk Titles 6,000; Per Subs 10
Database Vendor: EBSCOhost
Wireless access
Partic in Manitoba Libr Asn; Pub Libr Servs
Open Tues & Thurs 11-5, Sat 11-1

FLIN FLON

P   FLIN FLON PUBLIC LIBRARY*, 58 Main St, R8A 1J8. SAN 318-8671.
Tel: 204-687-3397. FAX: 204-687-4233. E-mail: ffpl@mts.net. Web Site:
flinflonpubliclibrary.ca. *Adminr,* Phyllis Stadnick
Founded 1957. Pop 8,261; Circ 48,102
Library Holdings: Bk Vols 24,504; Per Subs 62
Database Vendor: EBSCOhost
Open Mon-Thurs (Winter) 10-7, Fri 10-5, Sat 10-4 ; Mon-Thurs (Summer)
10-7, Fri 10-5

GILLAM

P   BETTE WINNER PUBLIC LIBRARY*, Recreation Ctr, R0B 0L0. (Mail
add: PO Box 400, R0B 0L0), SAN 321-1789. Tel: 204-652-2617. FAX:
204-652-2617. E-mail: bwinner@gillamnet.com. Web Site:
townofgillam.com. *Head Librn,* Ricci Bangle; *Asst Librn,* Dawna Gray
McDonald
Pop 1,200
Library Holdings: Bk Titles 8,789; Bk Vols 9,537; Per Subs 45
Automation Activity & Vendor Info: (Acquisitions) Keystone Systems,
Inc (KLAS); (Cataloging) L4U Library Software; (Circulation) L4U
Library Software
Database Vendor: EBSCOhost
Wireless access
Partic in Pub Libr Servs
Open Mon 6pm-8:30pm, Tues 1-8:30, Wed 9:30-1:30 & 6pm-8:30pm,
Thurs 1-5, Sat 2-5

GIMLI

P   EVERGREEN REGIONAL LIBRARY*, 65 First Ave, R0C 1B0. (Mail
add: PO Box 1140, R0C 1B0), SAN 366-3639. Tel: 204-642-7912. FAX:
204-642-8319. E-mail: gimlilibrary@mts.net. Web Site: erlibrary.ca. *Librn,*
Valerie Eyolfson
Founded 1965. Pop 10,097; Circ 72,615
Library Holdings: AV Mats 1,582; Bks on Deafness & Sign Lang 51; Bk
Titles 67,241; Per Subs 86; Talking Bks 779
Special Collections: French, German, Icelandic, Norwegian, Polish &
Ukrainian Books
Subject Interests: Icelandic local hist, Ukrainian local hist
Wireless access
Special Services for the Blind - Braille bks; Talking bks
Open Tues, Thurs & Fri 9-5, Wed 9-8, Sat 10-5
Branches: 2
ARBORG BRANCH, Box 4053, Arborg, R0C 0A0, SAN 366-3663. Tel:
204-376-5388. E-mail: arborglibrary@mts.net. *Librn,* Rachel Plett
    Library Holdings: Bk Titles 17,500
    Open Mon & Thurs 11-5, Tues 1-8, Wed 12-5
RIVERTON BRANCH, 56 Laura Ave, Riverton, R0C 2R0. (Mail add: Box
310, Riverton, R0C 2R0), SAN 366-3698. Tel: 204-378-2988. E-mail:
rilibrary@mts.net. *Librn,* Kelly Deneka
    Library Holdings: Bk Titles 18,000
    Open Tues & Wed 11-5, Thurs 11-7, Fri 10-5

HEADINGLEY

P   HEADINGLEY MUNICIPAL LIBRARY*, 49 Alboro St, R4J 1A3. SAN
377-9408. Tel: 204-888-5410. FAX: 204-831-7207. E-mail:
hml@mymts.net. Web Site: www.headingleylibrary.ca. *Head Librn,* Joan
Spice
Library Holdings: Bk Titles 10,000; Per Subs 25
Database Vendor: EBSCOhost
Wireless access
Partic in Manitoba Libr Asn; Manitoba Libr Trustees Asn
Open Mon & Fri 9:30-12:30 & 6pm-8pm, Tues & Thurs 9:30-3, Wed
9:30-8, Sat 9:30-12:30

HOLLAND

P   VICTORIA MUNICIPAL LIBRARY*, 102 Stewart Ave, R0G 0X0. (Mail
add: PO Box 371, R0G 0X0), SAN 378-0228. Tel: 204-526-2011. E-mail:
victlib@goinet.ca. *Librn,* Linda Clark; *Asst Librn,* Barb Grift
Library Holdings: Bk Titles 8,000; Bk Vols 12,000
Database Vendor: EBSCOhost
Partic in Manitoba Libr Asn
Open Tues 10-12 & 2-5:30, Wed 2-5:30 & 6:30pm-8pm, Thurs & Fri
2-5:30, Sat 10-12 & 2-5

KILLARNEY

P   LAKELAND REGIONAL LIBRARY*, 318 Williams Ave, R0K 1G0.
(Mail add: PO Box 970, R0K 1G0), SAN 366-3728. Tel: 204-523-4949.
FAX: 204-523-7460. E-mail: lrl@mts.net. Web Site:
lakelandregionallibrary.ca. *Chief Librn,* Carol Chapman
Founded 1959. Pop 5,600; Circ 85,500
Library Holdings: Bk Titles 29,000; Per Subs 60
Database Vendor: EBSCOhost
Wireless access
Open Tues & Thurs 9-5, Wed 9-9, Sat 9-12 & 1-5
Branches: 1
CARTWRIGHT BRANCH, 483 N Railway Ave, Cartwright, R0K 0L0.
(Mail add: Box 235, Cartwright, R0K 0L0), SAN 366-3752. Tel:
204-529-2261. E-mail: cartlib@hotmail.com. *Librn,* Andrea Trembath
    Database Vendor: EBSCOhost
    Open Tues-Fri 9-5

LA BROQUERIE

P   BIBLIOTHEQUE SAINT-JOACHIM LIBRARY*, 29 Normandeau Bay,
R0A 0W0. (Mail add: Box 39, R0A 0W0), SAN 377-8819. Tel:
204-424-9533. FAX: 204-424-5610. E-mail: bsjl@bsjl.ca. Web Site:
www.bsjl.ca. *Librn,* Rolande Durand
Pop 3,659; Circ 30,605
Library Holdings: CDs 917; DVDs 703; Bk Titles 17,913; Per Subs 60;
Videos 710
Database Vendor: EBSCOhost
Wireless access
Partic in Manitoba Libr Asn; Manitoba Libr Trustees Asn
Open Mon-Fri (Fall & Winter) 3:30-8:30; Mon & Tues (Summer) 2-7,
Wed-Fri 10-3

LAC DU BONNET

P   LAC DU BONNET REGIONAL LIBRARY*, 84 Third St, R0E 1A0.
(Mail add: PO Box 216, R0E 1A0), SAN 377-8835. Tel: 204-345-2653.
FAX: 204-345-6827. E-mail: mldb@mts.net. Web Site:
www.library.lacdubonnet.info. *Head Librn,* Vickie Short
Library Holdings: Bk Titles 21,450; Per Subs 72
Database Vendor: EBSCOhost
Wireless access
Partic in Manitoba Libr Asn; Manitoba Libr Trustees Asn
Special Services for the Blind - Talking bks
Open Tues & Thurs 10:30-5 & 7-8:30, Wed & Fri 12-5, Sat 10:30-2:30

LEAF RAPIDS

P   LEAF RAPIDS PUBLIC LIBRARY*, Town Center Complex, R0B 1W0.
(Mail add: Box 190, R0B 1W0), SAN 321-3544. Tel: 204-473-2742. *Librn,*
Craig Butler
Founded 1972. Pop 550; Circ 2,500
Library Holdings: Bk Vols 19,600
Database Vendor: EBSCOhost
Wireless access
Function: ILL available
Partic in Manitoba Libr Trustees Asn
Open Tues, Thurs & Fri 12-4, Wed 2-6, Sat 11-3

LUNDAR

P   PAULINE JOHNSON LIBRARY*, 23 Main St, R0C 1Y0. (Mail add: PO
Box 698, R0C 1Y0), SAN 377-9424. Tel: 204-762-5367. FAX:
204-762-5367. E-mail: mlpj@mymts.net. Web Site: www.mplj.mb.ca.
Librn, Laurie Arnason
Founded 1996. Pop 1,339
Library Holdings: Bk Titles 12,500; Per Subs 14
Database Vendor: EBSCOhost
Wireless access
Partic in Can Libr Asn
Open Tues & Thurs 10-6, Wed & Fri 10-5, Sat 10-2

LYNN LAKE

P   LYNN LAKE LIBRARY*, PO Box 1127, R0B 0W0. SAN 377-8959. Tel:
204-356-8222. *In Charge,* David Campbell
Pop 1,038
Library Holdings: Bk Titles 8,700
Partic in Pub Libr Servs
Open Mon-Fri 10-3

MACGREGOR

P   NORTH NORFOLK MACGREGOR REGIONAL LIBRARY, 35 Hampton
E, R0H 0R0. (Mail add: PO Box 760, R0H 0R0), SAN 377-9629. Tel:
204-685-2796. FAX: 204-685-2478. E-mail: maclib@mts.net. Web Site:
www.nnmrl.net. *Librn,* Antoinette Blankvoort; Staff 2 (Non-MLS 2)
Founded 1992. Pop 3,900; Circ 20,000
Library Holdings: Bk Vols 12,000; Per Subs 70
Database Vendor: EBSCOhost
Wireless access
Partic in Manitoba Libr Asn; Manitoba Libr Trustees Asn; Pub Libr Servs
Open Tues 10-8, Wed & Fri 10-5, Sat 10-3

MANITOU

P   MANITOU REGIONAL LIBRARY*, 418 Main St, R0G 1G0. (Mail add:
PO Box 432, R0G 1G0), SAN 378-0244. Tel: 204-242-3134. FAX:
204-242-3184. E-mail: manitoulibrary@mts.net. Web Site:
manitouregionallibrary.ca. *Head Librn,* Beverley Boote; Staff 2 (Non-MLS
2)
Pop 2,500
Jan 2005-Dec 2005 Income $22,905, Provincial $12,088, County $7,000,
Other $3,817. Mats Exp $5,500, Books $4,500, AV Mat $1,000. Sal
$10,000
Library Holdings: AV Mats 463; DVDs 16; Large Print Bks 50; Music
Scores 500; Bk Titles 10,833; Per Subs 10; Talking Bks 69; Videos 378
Special Collections: Nellie McClung Coll
Wireless access
Open Tues 10-12 & 1-5:30, Thurs & Fri 1-5:30, Sat 10-12 & 1-4:30

MELITA

P   SOUTHWESTERN MANITOBA REGIONAL LIBRARY*, Melita Library,
149 Main St, R0M 1L0. (Mail add: PO Box 670, R0M 1L0), SAN
318-868X. Tel: 204-522-3923. FAX: 204-522-3923. E-mail:
swmblib@mts.net. *Librn,* Valorie A Wray; *Asst Librn,* Bev Johnson; Staff
2 (Non-MLS 2)
Founded 1959. Pop 3,100; Circ 21,673
Library Holdings: Bk Vols 18,021; Per Subs 113

Automation Activity & Vendor Info: (Cataloging) Insignia Software; (Circulation) Insignia Software; (ILL) Insignia Software
Wireless access
Function: ILL available
Open Tues-Sat 9:30-12:30 & 1:30-5:30
Branches: 2
NAPINKA BRANCH, 57 Souris St, Napinka, R0M 1N0. (Mail add: Box 275, R0M 1L0). Tel: 204-665-2282. *Librn,* Trevor Mclughlin
Open Tues 9:30-2:30, Thurs 1-6
PIERSON BRANCH, 58 Railway Ave, Pierson, R0M 1S0. (Mail add: PO Box 39, Pierson, R0M 1S0), SAN 320-0523. Tel: 204-634-2215. FAX: 204-634-2479. E-mail: pclibrary@goinet.ca. Web Site: www.wix.com/swmblib/library-page. *Librn,* Mary-Anne Minshull
Founded 1978
Library Holdings: Bk Vols 4,000; Per Subs 30
Open Mon, Wed & Fri 10-5

MINNEDOSA

P   MINNEDOSA REGIONAL LIBRARY*, 45 First Ave, R0J 1E0. (Mail add: Box 1226, R0J 1E0), SAN 318-8698. Tel: 204-867-2585. FAX: 204-867-6140. E-mail: mmr@mts.net. *Head of Libr,* Linda Cook
Founded 1976. Pop 3,657; Circ 46,166
Library Holdings: AV Mats 881; Large Print Bks 637; Bk Vols 19,600; Per Subs 25; Talking Bks 106
Wireless access
Open Tues 9:30-8, Wed-Sat 9:30-5:30

NORWAY HOUSE

P   UNIVERSITY COLLEGE OF THE NORTH*, Norway House Public Library, Box 880, R0B 1B0. SAN 377-9645. Tel: 204-359-6296. FAX: 204-359-6262. *Librn,* Samantha Duncan; E-mail: sduncan@ucn.ca
Pop 5,000
Library Holdings: DVDs 280; Large Print Bks 40; Bk Titles 10,000; Talking Bks 35; Videos 50
Function: ILL available
Partic in Pub Libr Servs
Open Mon-Thurs 8:30-8, Fri 8:30-4:30, Sat & Sun 1-5

NOTRE DAME DE LOURDES

P   BIBLIOTHEQUE PERE CHAMPAGNE*, 44 Rue Rogers, R0G 1M0. (Mail add: CP 399, R0G 1M0), SAN 377-9890. Tel: 204-248-2386. E-mail: ndbiblio@yahoo.ca. *Librn,* Gisele Theroux
Founded 1988. Pop 620
Library Holdings: Per Subs 12; Videos 500
Wireless access
Function: ILL available
Partic in Manitoba Libr Asn
Open Tues-Fri 9:30-12:30 & 1:30-4:30
Bookmobiles: 1

OTTERBURNE

CR   PROVIDENCE UNIVERSITY COLLEGE & SEMINARY LIBRARY, Ten College Crescent, R0A 1G0. SAN 318-8701. Tel: 204-433-7488. FAX: 204-433-7158. Web Site: www.providenceuc.ca/college/library/. *Dir,* Terry Kennedy; E-mail: terry.kennedy@prov.ca; *Tech Serv,* Martha Loeppky; E-mail: martha.loeppky@prov.ca; Staff 3 (MLS 1, Non-MLS 2)
Founded 1925. Enrl 400; Fac 50; Highest Degree: Doctorate
Library Holdings: AV Mats 3,300; Bk Vols 88,000; Per Subs 311
Special Collections: Contemporary Religious Movements, VF; ESL; Rare Books
Subject Interests: Bible, Counsel, Missions, Theol
Automation Activity & Vendor Info: (Acquisitions) Ex Libris Group; (Cataloging) Ex Libris Group; (Circulation) Ex Libris Group; (Course Reserve) Ex Libris Group; (OPAC) Ex Libris Group; (Serials) Ex Libris Group
Database Vendor: EBSCOhost, JSTOR, ProQuest
Wireless access
Partic in Association of Christian Librarians; Manitoba Library Consortium, Inc; OCLC Online Computer Library Center, Inc
Open Mon-Fri 8:15am-10pm, Sat 10-10

PINAWA

P   PINAWA PUBLIC LIBRARY, Vanier Rd, R0E 1L0. (Mail add: General Delivery, R0E 1L0), SAN 318-8736. Tel: 204-753-2496. FAX: 204-753-2770. E-mail: email@pinawapubliclibrary.com. Web Site: www.pinawapubliclibrary.com. *Head Librn,* Marg Stokes; *Asst Librn,* Audrey Miller; *Asst Librn,* Donna Schofield
Founded 1966. Pop 1,485; Circ 16,479
Jan 2011-Dec 2011 Income (CAN) $55,286, Provincial (CAN) $19,546, City (CAN) $31,500, Locally Generated Income (CAN) $3,590, Other (CAN) $650. Mats Exp (CAN) $13,843, Books (CAN) $10,478, Per/Ser

(Incl. Access Fees) (CAN) $1,501, AV Mat (CAN) $1,864. Sal (CAN) $34,950
Library Holdings: Audiobooks 180; Bks on Deafness & Sign Lang 5; DVDs 617; Bk Titles 23,951; Per Subs 62; Videos 274
Automation Activity & Vendor Info: (Cataloging) Insignia Software; (Circulation) Insignia Software; (OPAC) Insignia Software
Wireless access
Function: Audiobks via web, Bks on CD, Computers for patron use, Copy machines, E-Reserves, Electronic databases & coll, Equip loans & repairs, Free DVD rentals, Handicapped accessible, Home delivery & serv to Sr ctr & nursing homes, Homebound delivery serv, ILL available, Online cat, OverDrive digital audio bks, Photocopying/Printing, Printer for laptops & handheld devices, Pub access computers, Scanner, Story hour, VHS videos, Web-catalog, Wheelchair accessible
Open Mon 6:30pm-9pm, Tues-Fri 1:30-4:30 & 6:30-9, Sat 1-3
Friends of the Library Group

PORTAGE LA PRAIRIE

G   MANITOBA AGRICULTURE, FOOD & RURAL INITIATIVES*, Food Development Centre Library, 810 Phillips St, R1N 3J9. (Mail add: PO Box 1240, R1N 3J9), SAN 322-7960. Tel: 204-239-3465. Toll Free Tel: 800-870-1044 (Canada only). FAX: 204-239-3180. Web Site: www.gov.mb.ca/agriculture/fdc/services/library/fdc10s00.html, www.manitoba.ca/fdc. *Info Officer,* Alana Henuset. Subject Specialists: *Agr, Food sci,* Alana Henuset; Staff 1 (MLS 1)
Founded 1978
Library Holdings: AV Mats 100; Bk Titles 2,775; Bk Vols 2,900; Per Subs 80
Special Collections: HACCP Coll; Nutraceuticals & Functional Foods Coll
Subject Interests: Food chem, Food safety, Food sci, Food tech
Database Vendor: Dialog, OVID Technologies
Wireless access
Function: Doc delivery serv, For res purposes, Govt ref serv, Homebound delivery serv, ILL available, Online searches, Photocopying/Printing, Prof lending libr, Ref serv available, Res libr, Telephone ref, Wheelchair accessible
Restriction: Open to pub by appt only

M   MANITOBA DEVELOPMENTAL CENTRE MEMORIAL LIBRARY, 840 3rd St NE, R1N 3C6. (Mail add: PO Box 1190, R1N 3C6), SAN 327-8670. Tel: 204-856-4230. FAX: 204-856-4221. *Staff Develop Coordr,* Lavone Lesperance-Caron; E-mail: lavone.lesperance-caron@gov.mb.ca; Staff 1 (Non-MLS 1)
Library Holdings: Bk Vols 2,500
Open Mon-Fri 9-4

P   PORTAGE LA PRAIRIE REGIONAL LIBRARY*, 40-B Royal Rd N, R1N 1V1. SAN 318-8752. Tel: 204-857-4271. FAX: 204-239-4387. E-mail: portlib@portagelibrary.com. Web Site: www.portagelibrary.com. *Librn,* Percy Gregoire-Voskamp
Founded 1968. Pop 21,756; Circ 177,902
Jan 2010-Dec 2010 Income $565,060, City $238,749, County $79,094. Mats Exp $74,051, Books $60,063, Per/Ser (Incl. Access Fees) $3,068, AV Mat $10,920. Sal $337,453
Library Holdings: AV Mats 6,154; CDs 696; DVDs 3,561; Bk Titles 61,011; Per Subs 74; Talking Bks 3,561
Subject Interests: Local hist, Native studies
Wireless access
Open Tues-Fri 10-8, Sat 9:30-5:30

RAPID CITY

P   RAPID CITY REGIONAL LIBRARY*, 425 Third Ave, R0K 1W0. SAN 321-3552. Tel: 204-826-2732. E-mail: rcreglib@mts.net. *Librn,* Shirley Martin
Founded 1974. Pop 1,283
Library Holdings: Bk Vols 15,018; Per Subs 27
Database Vendor: EBSCOhost
Open Mon 7pm-9pm, Tues & Thurs 2-5 & 7pm-9pm, Fri & Sat 2-5
Friends of the Library Group

RESTON

P   RESTON DISTRICT LIBRARY*, 220 Fourth St, R0M 1X0. SAN 321-3560. Tel: 204-877-3673. *Librn,* Onagh Williamson
Founded 1975. Pop 2,200; Circ 17,500
Library Holdings: Bk Vols 11,800; Per Subs 734
Automation Activity & Vendor Info: (Acquisitions) Auto-Graphics, Inc; (Cataloging) Auto-Graphics, Inc; (Circulation) Auto-Graphics, Inc; (Course Reserve) Auto-Graphics, Inc; (ILL) Auto-Graphics, Inc
Database Vendor: EBSCOhost
Wireless access
Partic in Pub Libr Servs
Open Tues-Fri 9:30-5:30, Sat 9:30-5

RIVERS

P   PRAIRIE CROCUS REGIONAL LIBRARY*, 137 Main St, R0K 1X0.
SAN 318-8779. Tel: 204-328-7613. E-mail: pcrl@mts.net. Web Site:
www.prairiecrocuslibrary.ca. *Librn,* Dora Irvine
Pop 2,034
Library Holdings: Bk Vols 15,000
Database Vendor: EBSCOhost
Wireless access
Open Wed 2-8, Thurs 1-4, Fri 9:30-12 & 1-5:30, Sat 10-2

ROSSBURN

P   ROSSBURN REGIONAL LIBRARY*, 57 High St, R0J 1V0. (Mail add:
PO Box 87, R0J 1V0), SAN 321-1797. Tel: 204-859-2687. FAX:
204-859-2687. E-mail: rrl@mts.net. *Librn,* Stephanie Parkinson
Founded 1975. Pop 1,350; Circ 7,000
Library Holdings: Bk Titles 11,000; Per Subs 19
Database Vendor: EBSCOhost
Open Tues & Fri 9:30-5:30, Wed 12:30-8, Thurs 12:30-5:30

RUSSELL

P   RUSSELL & DISTRICT REGIONAL LIBRARY*, PO Box 340, R0J
1W0. SAN 366-3906. Tel: 204-773-3127. FAX: 204-773-3127. E-mail:
ruslib@mts.net. *Librn,* Ruth Ellingsworth
Founded 1958. Pop 3,188; Circ 27,450
Library Holdings: Bk Titles 14,973; Bk Vols 27,445; Per Subs 25
Automation Activity & Vendor Info: (Cataloging) New Generation
Technologies Inc. (LiBRARYSOFT); (Circulation) New Generation
Technologies Inc. (LiBRARYSOFT); (OPAC) New Generation
Technologies Inc. (LiBRARYSOFT)
Database Vendor: EBSCOhost
Function: ILL available
Open Wed & Fri 12-5, Sat 11-3
Friends of the Library Group
Branches: 1
BINSCARTH BRANCH, 106 Russell St, Binscarth, R0J 0G0. (Mail add:
PO Box 379, Binscarth, R0J 0G0), SAN 366-3930. Tel: 204-532-2447.
Librn, Ruth Ellingsworth
Library Holdings: Bk Vols 1,000
Open Wed & Fri 12-5

SAINT BONIFACE

C   DIRECTION DES RESSOURCES EDUCATIVES FRANCAISES, Library
& Materials Production Branch, Dept of Educ, 0140-200 Ave de la
Cathedrale, R2H 0H7. SAN 320-7846. Tel: 204-945-8594. FAX:
204-945-0092. E-mail: dref@gov.mb.ca. Web Site: www.dref.mb.ca. *Dir,*
Lynette Chartier
Library Holdings: Bk Titles 40,000; Bk Vols 60,000
Subject Interests: Educ curricula, Interest ctr
Automation Activity & Vendor Info: (Acquisitions) BiblioMondo;
(Cataloging) BiblioMondo; (Circulation) BiblioMondo; (Course Reserve)
BiblioMondo; (ILL) BiblioMondo; (OPAC) BiblioMondo; (Serials)
BiblioMondo
Database Vendor: EBSCOhost
Wireless access
Publications: Bulletin (Annually)
Open Mon-Thurs 9-6, Fri 9-5, Sat 9-4

S   LA SOCIETE HISTORIQUE DE SAINT-BONIFACE BIBLIOTHEQUE*,
340 Provencher Blvd, R2H 0G7. SAN 329-2282. Tel: 204-233-4888. FAX:
204-231-2562. E-mail: shsb@shsb.mb.ca. Web Site: www.shsb.mb.ca. *Exec
Dir,* Gilles Lesage
Founded 1902
Library Holdings: Bk Titles 40,000; Per Subs 40
Special Collections: Oral History
Open Mon-Fri 9-4:30, Sat 9-Noon

SAINT CLAUDE

P   BIBLIOTHEQUE SAINT CLAUDE LIBRARY*, 50 First St, R0G 1Z0.
(Mail add: PO Box 203, R0G 1Z0), SAN 377-9912. Tel: 204-379-2524.
Librn, Lynn Gobin
Pop 609
Library Holdings: Bk Titles 10,000; Per Subs 15
Wireless access
Function: ILL available
Partic in Manitoba Libr Servs
Open Tues & Wed 1-5, Thurs 10-1 & 6:30-8:30

SAINT GEORGES

P   BIBLIOTHEQUE ALLARD REGIONAL LIBRARY*, 104086 PTH 11,
R0E 1V0. (Mail add: PO Box 157, R0E 1V0), SAN 377-9661. Tel:
204-367-8443. FAX: 204-367-1780. E-mail: info@allardlibrary.com. Web
Site: www.allardlibrary.com. *Adminr,* Élise Zolinski; *Librn,* Madeleine
Boisjoli; *Librn,* Julie Lavoie; *Asst Librn,* Kelly Murray; *Student Serv Librn,*
Shanise Powell; Staff 5 (Non-MLS 5)
Founded 1983. Pop 2,600
Library Holdings: Bk Titles 20,600; Per Subs 81
Automation Activity & Vendor Info: (Cataloging) Follett Software;
(Circulation) Follett Software
Database Vendor: EBSCOhost
Wireless access
Open Tues 10:30-5, Wed & Thurs 12-8, Fri 12-5, Sat 10-2
Friends of the Library Group

SAINT PIERRE JOLYS

P   JOLYS REGIONAL LIBRARY*, 505 Herbert Ave N, R0A 1V0. (Mail
add: PO Box 118, R0A 1V0), SAN 366-3965. Tel: 204-433-7729. FAX:
204-433-7412. E-mail: stplibrary@jrlibrary.mb.ca. Web Site:
www.jrlibrary.mb.ca. *Dir,* Claudette Baldwin
Founded 1962. Pop 4,300
Library Holdings: AV Mats 500; Bk Titles 36,719; Per Subs 21; Talking
Bks 114
Database Vendor: EBSCOhost
Wireless access
Open Mon, Wed & Fri 9-5, Tues & Thurs 9-8, Sat 10-1
Branches: 1
SAINT MALO, PO Box 593, Saint Malo, R0A 1T0, SAN 366-399X. Tel:
204-347-5606. E-mail: stmlibrary@ratrivercomm.ca. *Librn,* Alime Pilotte
Library Holdings: Bk Titles 7,000; Per Subs 15
Open Tues & Thurs 2:30-8, Wed & Fri 2:30-5, Sat 10-1

SAINTE ANNE

P   BIBLIOTHEQUE STE ANNE*, 16 Rue de l'Eglise, R5H 1H8. SAN
377-9440. Tel: 204-422-9958. FAX: 204-422-9958. E-mail:
steannelib@steannemb.ca. Web Site: www.bibliosteannelib.8m.com. *Librn,*
Mona Gauthier
Founded 1990
Library Holdings: Audiobooks 49; CDs 120; DVDs 80; Large Print Bks
287; Bk Titles 21,500; Per Subs 29; Talking Bks 64
Database Vendor: EBSCOhost
Wireless access
Partic in Pub Libr Systs
Open Tues & Wed 2-8, Thurs & Sat 10-2

SAINT-JEAN-BAPTISTE

P   BIBLIOTHEQUE MONTCALM LIBRARY*, 113 B, Second Ave, R0G
2B0. (Mail add: PO Box 345, R0G 2B0), SAN 377-9564. Tel:
204-758-3137. FAX: 204-758-3574. E-mail: biblio@atrium.ca. *Librn,*
Danielle Vincent
Founded 1995. Pop 1,600
Library Holdings: Bk Vols 20,000; Per Subs 20
Function: ILL available
Partic in Pub Libr Servs
Open Mon & Fri 9-4, Tues-Thurs 9-4 & 5-8

SELKIRK

P   RED RIVER NORTH REGIONAL LIBRARY*, 303 Main St, R1A 1S7.
SAN 321-3587. Tel: 204-482-3522. FAX: 204-482-6166. E-mail:
library@ssarl.org. Web Site: www.ssarl.org. *Librn,* Ken Kuryliw
Founded 1976. Pop 30,000
Library Holdings: Bk Vols 61,000; Per Subs 150
Automation Activity & Vendor Info: (Cataloging) Follett Software;
(Circulation) Follett Software; (ILL) Follett Software; (OPAC) Follett
Software
Database Vendor: EBSCOhost
Wireless access
Open Tues-Fri 9:30-9, Sat 9:30-5, Sun 1-5

SHILO

S   ROYAL CANADIAN ARTILLERY MUSEUM LIBRARY*, CFB Shilo,
R0K 2A0. SAN 327-5418. Tel: 204-765-3000, Ext 4066. FAX:
204-765-5289. E-mail: rcamuse@mts.net. Web Site: www.artillery.net,
www.rcamuseum.com. *Curator,* Clive Prothero-Brooks
Library Holdings: Bk Vols 15,000; Per Subs 10
Open Mon-Fri 10-5

S   SHILO COMMUNITY LIBRARY*, PO Box 177, R0K 2A0. SAN 318-8809. E-mail: shilocommunitylibrary@yahoo.ca. *Librn,* Patricia Wells; *Asst Librn,* Tracy Gerbasi-Askeland
Library Holdings: Bk Titles 17,500
Open Mon 6pm-8:30pm, Tues & Thurs 9:30-4 & 6pm-8:30pm

SNOW LAKE

P   SNOW LAKE COMMUNITY LIBRARY*, PO Box 760, R0B 1M0. SAN 377-9688. Tel: 204-358-2322. FAX: 204-358-2116. E-mail: dslibrary@hotmail.com. *Librn,* Vivian Bennett
Library Holdings: Bk Titles 12,927; Per Subs 15
Automation Activity & Vendor Info: (Cataloging) LibraryWorld, Inc; (Circulation) LibraryWorld, Inc; (OPAC) LibraryWorld, Inc
Database Vendor: EBSCOhost
Partic in Manitoba Libr Asn; Manitoba Libr Trustees Asn
Open Tues & Thurs 1-4 & 6:30pm-8:30pm, Sat 1-4

SOMERSET

P   BIBLIOTHEQUE SOMERSET LIBRARY*, 289 Carlton Ave, R0G 2L0. (Mail add: PO Box 279, R0G 2L0), SAN 377-9580. Tel: 204-744-2170. FAX: 204-744-2170. E-mail: somlib@mts.net. *Chairperson,* Dr Michel Bruneau; *Librn,* Audrey Bessette
Jan 2005-Dec 2005 Income $18,000
Library Holdings: Bk Titles 9,500; Per Subs 30
Automation Activity & Vendor Info: (Acquisitions) New Generation Technologies Inc. (LiBRARYSOFT); (Cataloging) New Generation Technologies Inc. (LiBRARYSOFT); (Circulation) New Generation Technologies Inc. (LiBRARYSOFT); (Course Reserve) New Generation Technologies Inc. (LiBRARYSOFT); (ILL) New Generation Technologies Inc. (LiBRARYSOFT); (OPAC) New Generation Technologies Inc. (LiBRARYSOFT); (Serials) New Generation Technologies Inc. (LiBRARYSOFT)
Database Vendor: EBSCOhost
Partic in Manitoba Libr Asn; Pub Libr Servs
Open Mon, Wed & Fri 9-1, Tues & Thurs 1-6, Sat 10-1

SOURIS

P   GLENWOOD & SOURIS REGIONAL LIBRARY*, 18-114 Second St S, R0K 2C0. (Mail add: PO Box 760, R0K 2C0), SAN 318-8817. Tel: 204-483-2757. E-mail: frontdesk@sourislibrary.mb.ca. Web Site: www.sourislibrary.mb.ca. *Dir,* Connie Bradshaw
Founded 1958. Pop 2,572; Circ 18,745
Library Holdings: Bk Vols 18,543; Per Subs 40
Wireless access
Open Tues 12-6 & 7pm-9pm, Wed 11-1, Thurs & Fri 12-6, Sat 10-3

SOUTH MORRIS

P   VALLEY REGIONAL LIBRARY*, 141 Main St S, R0G 1K0. (Mail add: PO Box 397, Morris, R0G 1K0), SAN 377-9548. Tel: 204-746-2136. FAX: 204-746-6953. E-mail: valleylib@mts.net. Web Site: www.town.morris.mb.ca/morris/library. *Librn,* Dianne DeKezel; *Librn,* Claudia Schmidt; Staff 3 (Non-MLS 3)
Founded 1993
Library Holdings: Bk Titles 16,828; Per Subs 10
Database Vendor: EBSCOhost
Partic in Can Libr Asn; Manitoba Libr Asn
Open Tues-Thurs 11-8, Sat 11-3

STE ROSE DU LAC

P   STE ROSE REGIONAL LIBRARY*, 580 Central Ave, R0L 1S0. SAN 318-8787. Tel: 204-447-2527. FAX: 204-447-2527. E-mail: sroselib@mts.net. Web Site: www.steroseregionallibrary.info. *Librn,* Elaine Marie Chaput
Founded 1962. Pop 2,163; Circ 32,988
Library Holdings: Bk Vols 19,300; Per Subs 25
Database Vendor: EBSCOhost
Open Mon-Fri 11-5

STEINBACH

P   JAKE EPP LIBRARY*, 255 Elmdale Dr, R5G 1N6. (Mail add: PO Box 2050, R5G 1N6), SAN 318-8825. Tel: 204-326-6841. FAX: 204-326-6859. E-mail: jakeepplibrary@yahoo.com. Web Site: www.jakeepplibrary.com. *Head Librn,* Loraine M Trudeau; *Asst Librn,* Carolyn Graham; *ILL,* Agnes Foth
Founded 1973. Pop 10,000
Library Holdings: Bk Titles 79,000; Per Subs 125
Automation Activity & Vendor Info: (Circulation) Insignia Software
Database Vendor: EBSCOhost
Wireless access
Partic in Manitoba Libr Asn

Open Mon-Fri 10-9, Sat 10-5
Friends of the Library Group

CR   STEINBACH BIBLE COLLEGE LIBRARY*, 50 PTH 12 N, R5G 1T4. SAN 324-4636. Tel: 204-326-6451. FAX: 204-326-6908. E-mail: library@sbcollege.ca. Web Site: www.sbcollege.ca/library. *Librn,* LeRoy Barkman; E-mail: lbarkman@sbcollege.ca; *Asst Librn,* Chrystie Boggs; Staff 1 (MLS 1)
Founded 1937. Enrl 125; Fac 13; Highest Degree: Bachelor
Library Holdings: CDs 200; DVDs 500; Bk Titles 32,000; Bk Vols 37,500; Per Subs 97
Subject Interests: Biblical studies, Hist, Mennonites, Theol
Automation Activity & Vendor Info: (Cataloging) Follett Software; (Circulation) Follett Software; (OPAC) Follett Software
Wireless access
Function: ILL available
Open Mon-Fri 8:30-12 & 1-4:30

STONEWALL

S   INSTITUTE FOR WETLAND & WATERFOWL RESEARCH LIBRARY, Ducks Unlimited Canada Library, One Mallard Bay at Hwy 220, R0C 2Z0. (Mail add: PO Box 1160, R0C 2Z0), SAN 327-4365. Tel: 204-467-3276. Toll Free Tel: 800-665-3825. FAX: 204-467-9028. E-mail: library@ducks.ca. Web Site: www.ducks.ca/our-science/research-library. *Librn,* Ian Glass; E-mail: i_glass@ducks.ca; Staff 1 (MLS 1)
Library Holdings: e-journals 150; Bk Titles 6,000; Per Subs 10
Subject Interests: Biol, Conserv, Ecology, Waterfowl, Wetlands, Wildlife biol
Database Vendor: EBSCO Information Services, EBSCOhost, JSTOR
Wireless access
Function: ILL available
Restriction: Open to pub by appt only

P   SOUTH INTERLAKE REGIONAL LIBRARY*, 419 Main St, R0C 2Z0. SAN 318-8833. Tel: 204-467-8415. FAX: 204-467-9809. E-mail: sirl@mts.net. Web Site: www.sirlibrary.com. *Head Librn,* Darlene Dallman; *Circ,* Sharon Scott; E-mail: circ@sirlibrary.com
Founded 1967. Circ 178,211
Library Holdings: Bk Titles 55,000; Per Subs 34
Subject Interests: Agr, Econ, Natural sci
Database Vendor: EBSCOhost
Open Tues & Wed (Fall & Spring) 10-8, Thurs 3-8, Fri 10-6, Sat 10-5, Sun 11-3; Tues & Wed (Summer) 10-6, Thurs 3-8, Fri & Sat 10-4
Friends of the Library Group
Branches: 1
TEULON BRANCH, 19 Beach Rd E, Teulon, R0C 3B0. (Mail add: PO Box 68, Teulon, R0C 3B0), SAN 372-4980. Tel: 204-886-3648. FAX: 204-886-3661. E-mail: teulonbranchlibrary@yahoo.com. *Br Librn,* Linda Rogers
Library Holdings: Bk Vols 8,000
Open Tues, Wed & Fri 10-5:30, Thurs 12-8, Sat 10-1
Bookmobiles: 1

SWAN RIVER

P   NORTH-WEST REGIONAL LIBRARY*, 610 First St N, R0L 1Z0. (Mail add: PO Box 999, R0L 1Z0), SAN 366-4023. Tel: 204-734-3880. FAX: 204-734-3880. E-mail: nwrl@mymts.net. Web Site: www.swanriverlibrary.ca. *Head Librn,* Kathy Sterma
Founded 1966. Pop 7,291; Circ 84,235
Library Holdings: Bk Titles 21,810; Per Subs 25
Database Vendor: EBSCOhost, L4U Library Software, Overdrive, Inc
Wireless access
Special Services for the Blind - Bks available with recordings; Bks on cassette; Bks on CD; Cassettes; Daisy reader; Large print bks; Visunet prog (Canada)
Open Mon, Wed & Fri 10-5, Tues & Thurs 10-5 & 7pm-9pm, Sat 10:30-5
Branches: 1
BENITO BRANCH, 141 Main St, Benito, R0L 0C0. (Mail add: PO Box 220, Benito, R0L 0C0), SAN 366-4058. Tel: 204-539-2446. FAX: 204-539-2446. E-mail: benlib@mymts.net. *Librn,* Gloria Stesenko
Founded 1965
Library Holdings: Bk Titles 9,355; Per Subs 19; Talking Bks 29
Open Tues 1-5, Thurs 1-5 & 7-9, Fri 12-5, Sat 10-5

THE PAS

P   THE PAS REGIONAL LIBRARY*, 53 Edwards Ave, R9A 1R2. (Mail add: PO Box 4100, R9A 1R2), SAN 318-871X. Tel: 204-623-2023. FAX: 204-623-4594. E-mail: library@mts.net. Web Site: www.mts.net/~library. *Adminr,* Lauren Wadelius
Founded 1961. Pop 8,315
Library Holdings: Bk Vols 33,500; Per Subs 90
Special Collections: Northern Canada History Coll

Automation Activity & Vendor Info: (Acquisitions) L4U Library Software; (Cataloging) L4U Library Software; (Circulation) L4U Library Software; (Course Reserve) L4U Library Software; (ILL) L4U Library Software; (Media Booking) L4U Library Software; (OPAC) L4U Library Software; (Serials) L4U Library Software
Wireless access
Function: Adult bk club, BA reader (adult literacy), Digital talking bks, Handicapped accessible, Homebound delivery serv, ILL available, Orientations, Photocopying/Printing, Prog for children & young adult, Ref serv available, Spoken cassettes & CDs, Spoken cassettes & DVDs, Summer reading prog, VHS videos, Wheelchair accessible
Open Mon-Fri 10-6, Sat 1-5
Restriction: Circ to mem only, Non-resident fee

C UNIVERSITY COLLEGE OF THE NORTH LIBRARIES, Seventh & Charlebois, R9A 1M7. (Mail add: PO Box 3000, R9A 1M7), SAN 320-7838. Tel: 204-627-8561. FAX: 204-623-4597. E-mail: library@ucn.ca. Web Site: www.ucn.ca. *Coll Develop, Info Literacy, Librn,* Heather Smith; Staff 8 (MLS 3, Non-MLS 5)
Founded 1968. Enrl 900; Highest Degree: Bachelor
Library Holdings: Bk Vols 36,000; Per Subs 120
Special Collections: Aboriginal Languages & Research Coll
Subject Interests: Bus admin, Dentistry, Med nursing, Trades
Automation Activity & Vendor Info: (Cataloging) SIRSI WorkFlows; (OPAC) SIRSI WorkFlows
Database Vendor: SirsiDynix
Function: Audio & video playback equip for onsite use, CD-ROM, Computers for patron use, Copy machines, e-mail serv, Electronic databases & coll, Equip loans & repairs, Exhibits, Fax serv, Govt ref serv, ILL available, Music CDs, Online cat, Orientations, Photocopying/Printing, Pub access computers, Res libr, Scanner, VHS videos, Workshops
Partic in Manitoba Library Consortium, Inc
Open Mon-Thurs (Winter) 8am-10pm, Fri 8-5, Sun 5-9; Mon-Fri (Summer) 8-5
Restriction: Circ privileges for students & alumni only
Departmental Libraries:
THOMPSON CAMPUS, 504 Princeton Dr, Thompson, R8N 0A5, SAN 377-8851. Tel: 204-677-6408. FAX: 204-677-6416. *In Charge,* Shelly Doman; E-mail: sdoman@ucn.ca
  Library Holdings: Bk Vols 3,000; Per Subs 10
  Partic in Manitoba Libr Asn
  Open Mon-Thurs 8am-10pm, Fri 8-6, Sun 6pm-10pm

S SAM WALLER MUSEUM LIBRARY*, 306 Fischer Ave, R9A 1K4. (Mail add: PO Box 185, R9A 1K4), SAN 377-9726. Tel: 204-623-3802. FAX: 204-623-5506. E-mail: samwallermuseum@mymts.net. Web Site: www.samwallermuseum.ca. *Dir,* Sharain Jones; *Curator,* Laurel Neustaedter
Library Holdings: Bk Titles 800; Per Subs 3
Function: Ref serv available
Partic in Asn of Manitoba Museums; Can Museums Asn; Manitoba Hist Soc
Open Mon-Sun 1-5

THOMPSON

P THOMPSON PUBLIC LIBRARY*, 81 Thompson Dr N, R8N 0C3. SAN 318-8841. Tel: 204-677-3717. FAX: 204-778-5844. E-mail: info@thompsonlibrary.com. Web Site: www.thompsonlibrary.com. *Chief Librn,* Cheryl Davies
Founded 1967. Pop 15,000
Library Holdings: Audiobooks 764; CDs 1,047; DVDs 2,123; e-books 10,015; Large Print Bks 660; Bk Vols 40,237; Per Subs 50
Special Collections: Inter-Universities (North); Native People (The North)
Subject Interests: Native issues, Northern issues
Automation Activity & Vendor Info: (Acquisitions) Insignia Software; (Cataloging) Insignia Software; (Circulation) Insignia Software; (Course Reserve) Insignia Software; (ILL) Insignia Software; (Media Booking) Insignia Software; (OPAC) Insignia Software; (Serials) Insignia Software
Database Vendor: EBSCOhost
Wireless access
Function: Audiobks via web, Bks on CD, Children's prog, Computers for patron use, Copy machines, Electronic databases & coll, Exhibits, Fax serv, Free DVD rentals, ILL available, Music CDs, OverDrive digital audio bks, Pub access computers, Senior outreach, Spoken cassettes & CDs, Spoken cassettes & DVDs, Story hour, Summer reading prog
Open Tues & Wed 12-8, Thurs-Sat 10-6
Restriction: Circ to mem only, Open to pub for ref & circ; with some limitations
Friends of the Library Group

C UNIVERSITY OF MANITOBA FACULTY OF SOCIAL WORK*, Ann Charter Resource Centre, Three Station Rd, R8N 0N3. Tel: 204-677-1462. FAX: 204-677-4110. Web Site: www.mla.mb.ca/libdir.html. *Librn,* Eleanor Welton; E-mail: weltone@cc.umanitoba.ca

Library Holdings: Bk Titles 3,000; Per Subs 20
Wireless access
Function: ILL available
Open Mon-Fri 8:30-4:30

VIRDEN

P BORDER REGIONAL LIBRARY, Virden Branch, 312 Seventh Ave, R0M 2C0. (Mail add: PO Box 970, R0M 2C0). Tel: 204-748-3862. FAX: 204-748-3862. E-mail: borderlibraryvirden@rfnow.com. Web Site: www.borderregionallibrary.ca. *Librn,* Linda Grant-Braybrook; *Coordr,* Mary Anne Lamy; E-mail: brlcoord@rfnow.com; Staff 3 (Non-MLS 3)
Founded 1959. Pop 5,346; Circ 32,500
Library Holdings: Bk Titles 35,000; Per Subs 42
Special Collections: Can & Prov
Subject Interests: Local hist
Database Vendor: EBSCOhost
Wireless access
Function: Handicapped accessible, ILL available, Prog for adults, Prog for children & young adult, Spoken cassettes & CDs, Summer reading prog, VHS videos, Wheelchair accessible
Partic in Manitoba Pub Libr Servs
Special Services for the Deaf - Assistive tech
Special Services for the Blind - Assistive/Adapted tech devices, equip & products; Talking bks
Open Tues, Wed, Fri & Sat 10-5:30, Thurs 10-8
Branches: 2
ELKHORN BRANCH, 110 Richhill Ave, Elkhorn, R0M 0N0. (Mail add: PO Box 370, Elkhorn, R0M 0N0), SAN 366-4112. Tel: 204-845-2292. *Librn,* Tamara Bajus; Staff 2 (Non-MLS 2)
  Founded 1959. Pop 1,000; Circ 12,000
  Library Holdings: Bk Vols 10,979
  Special Collections: Elkhorn Mercury Newspaper Coll
  Function: Art exhibits, Handicapped accessible, Home delivery & serv to Sr ctr & nursing homes, ILL available, Newsp ref libr, Prog for children & young adult, Summer reading prog, VHS videos
  Open Tues, Thurs & Sat 10-5:30, Wed 6-8
MCAULEY BRANCH, 207 Qu'Appelle St, McAuley, R0M 1H0. (Mail add: PO Box 234, McAuley, R0M 1H0), SAN 370-5781. Tel: 204-722-2221. *Librn,* Diane Webb; Staff 2 (Non-MLS 2)
  Founded 1990. Pop 325; Circ 5,000
  Library Holdings: Bk Vols 5,135
  Function: Art exhibits, ILL available, Summer reading prog, VHS videos
  Open Tues & Fri 9-12 & 1-5

WINKLER

P SOUTH CENTRAL REGIONAL LIBRARY*, 160 Main St, R6W 4B4. SAN 366-3817. Tel: 204-325-5864. FAX: 204-331-1847. E-mail: scrlheadlib@mts.net. Interlibrary Loan Service E-mail: scrlillm@mts.net. Web Site: www.scrlibrary.mb.ca. *Head Librn,* Mary Toma; Staff 5 (Non-MLS 5)
Founded 1965. Pop 32,481
Library Holdings: Bk Vols 80,000; Per Subs 102
Database Vendor: EBSCOhost
Open Tues & Thurs 10-8:30, Wed, Fri & Sat 10-5:30
Branches: 4
ALTONA BRANCH, PO Box 650, Altona, R0G 0B0, SAN 370-4599. Tel: 204-324-1503. E-mail: alib@scrlibrary.nb.ca. *Br Librn,* Liz Forrester
  Open Tues & Thurs 10-8:30, Wed, Fri & Sat 10-5:30
MIAMI BRANCH, 423 Norton Ave, Miami, R0G 1H0. (Mail add: PO Box 431, Miami, R0G 1H0). Tel: 204-435-2032. E-mail: thlib@scrlibrary.mb.ca.
  Open Mon 2-5, Tues 10-1 & 1:30-4:30, Thurs 2-6 & 6:30-8:30
MORDEN BRANCH, 514 Stephen St, Morden, R6M 1T7, SAN 373-7020. Tel: 204-822-4092. E-mail: mlib@scrlibrary.mb.ca. *Br Librn,* Cathy Ching
  Open Tues & Thurs 10-8:30, Wed, Fri & Sat 10-5:30
WINKLER BRANCH, 160 Main St, R6W 4B4, SAN 366-3841. Tel: 204-325-7174. E-mail: wlib@scrlibrary.mb.ca. *Br Librn,* Elaine Dyck
  Open Tues & Thurs 10-8:30, Wed, Fri & Sat 10-5:30

WINNIPEG

S ADDICTIONS FOUNDATION OF MANITOBA*, William Potoroka Memorial Library, 1031 Portage Ave, R3G 0R8. SAN 327-5396. Tel: 204-944-6279. Toll Free Tel: 866-638-2561. FAX: 204-772-0225. E-mail: library@afm.mb.ca. Web Site: www.afm.mb.ca. *Libr Coordr,* Jackie Massey; Tel: 204-944-6367; *Cat & Ref,* Alina Trocaru; Tel: 204-944-6275, E-mail: atrocaru@afm.mb.ca; *Circ & Ref,* Melissa Mascus; E-mail: mmascu@afm.mb.ca
Library Holdings: Bk Titles 5,600; Bk Vols 6,750; Per Subs 32
Special Collections: Fetal Alcohol Syndrome/Effects; Harm Reduction; Sex Trade & Sexual Exploitation

Automation Activity & Vendor Info: (Cataloging) Sydney; (Circulation) Sydney; (Media Booking) Sydney
Open Mon, Tues & Fri (Winter) 8:30-4:30, Wed & Thurs 10-6; Mon-Fri (Summer) 8:30-4:30

S   AECOM CANADA LTD*, 99 Commerce Dr, R3T 0Y7. Tel: 204-477-5381. FAX: 204-475-3646. Web Site: aecom.com.
Function: ILL available
Restriction: Restricted pub use, Staff use only

SR   AHMADIYYA MUSLIM ASSOCIATION LIBRARY*, Islamic Ahmadiyya Library, 525 Kylemore Ave, R3L 1B5. SAN 370-5501. Tel: 204-475-2642. FAX: 204-452-2455. *In Charge,* Masef Dawood
Library Holdings: AV Mats 300; Bk Vols 2,000; Per Subs 10
Subject Interests: Comparative relig

L   AMT MANAGEMENT SERVICES LIBRARY*, 360 Main St, 30th Flr, R3C 4G1. SAN 323-6056. Tel: 204-957-0050. FAX: 204-957-0840.
Founded 1973
Library Holdings: Bk Titles 4,000; Bk Vols 10,000; Per Subs 400
Automation Activity & Vendor Info: (Acquisitions) Inmagic, Inc.; (Cataloging) Inmagic, Inc.; (ILL) Inmagic, Inc.; (OPAC) Inmagic, Inc.; (Serials) Inmagic, Inc.
Restriction: Staff use only

G   ARCHIVES OF MANITOBA*, 130-200 Vaughan St, R3C 1T5. SAN 328-5316. Tel: 204-945-3971. Toll Free Tel: 800-617-3588. FAX: 204-948-2008. E-mail: archives@gov.mb.ca. Web Site: www.gov.mb.ca/chc/archives/. *Archivist,* Maureen Dolyniuk; *Archivist,* Scott Goodine; *Archivist,* Jocelyn McKillop; *Archivist,* Ala Rekrut; Staff 47 (MLS 27, Non-MLS 20)
Special Collections: Hudson's Bay Company Archives, maps, photos; Manitoba Government & Private Records
Open Mon-Fri 9-4

CR   BOOTH UNIVERSITY COLLEGE*, John Fairbank Memorial Library, 300-290 Vaughan St, R3B 2L9. SAN 324-2900. Tel: 204-924-4858. Toll Free Tel: 877-924-6684. FAX: 204-924-4873. E-mail: library@boothuc.ca. Web Site: www.boothuc.ca/library. *Dir, Libr Serv,* Meagan Morash; Tel: 204-924-4857; Staff 3 (MLS 1, Non-MLS 2)
Founded 1982. Enrl 254; Fac 6; Highest Degree: Bachelor
Library Holdings: AV Mats 1,500; Bk Titles 45,000; Bk Vols 55,000; Per Subs 150
Special Collections: Salvation Army Publications
Subject Interests: Ethics, Soc work, Theol
Automation Activity & Vendor Info: (Cataloging) Innovative Interfaces, Inc; (Circulation) Innovative Interfaces, Inc; (Course Reserve) Innovative Interfaces, Inc; (OPAC) Innovative Interfaces, Inc
Database Vendor: EBSCOhost, ProQuest
Function: Archival coll, Audio & video playback equip for onsite use, Distance learning, Doc delivery serv, Electronic databases & coll, For res purposes, ILL available, Mail & tel request accepted, Online cat, Photocopying/Printing, Ref serv available, Telephone ref
Partic in ALA; Can Libr Asn; Manitoba Libr Asn; Manitoba Library Consortium, Inc
Open Mon-Thurs (Winter & Spring) 8am-9pm, Fri 8-6, Sat 10-5; Mon-Fri (Summer) 8-4

S   CANADA/MANITOBA BUSINESS SERVICE CENTRE LIBRARY, 240 Graham Ave, Ste 250, R3C 0J7. SAN 318-8981. Tel: 204-984-2272. Toll Free Tel: 800-665-2019. FAX: 204-983-3852. TDD: 800-457-8466. E-mail: manitoba@canadabusiness.mb.ca. Web Site: www.canadabusiness.mb.ca. *Client Serv Spec/Librn,* Peggy Neal; *Info Spec/Librn,* Oliver D Bernuetz; Tel: 204-983-6182, E-mail: oliver.bernuetz@canadabusiness.ca; *Circ Media,* Debbie Rind; *Tech Serv,* Jane Bullied; Staff 4 (MLS 2, Non-MLS 2)
Founded 1999
Library Holdings: Audiobooks 562; AV Mats 2,323; DVDs 1,249; e-books 2,068; Bk Titles 12,356; Per Subs 252; Videos 527
Special Collections: ARMA Library
Subject Interests: Bus, Human resource mgt, Intellectual property, Intl trading, Mgt, Tourism, Worker safety
Automation Activity & Vendor Info: (Acquisitions) LibLime; (Cataloging) LibLime; (Circulation) LibLime; (Course Reserve) LibLime; (ILL) LibLime; (OPAC) LibLime; (Serials) LibLime
Database Vendor: EBSCOhost, Gale Cengage Learning
Partic in Manitoba Library Consortium, Inc
Special Services for the Deaf - TDD equip; TTY equip
Special Services for the Blind - Audio mat; Bks & mags in Braille, on rec, tape & cassette; Bks on CD; Large print bks; Magnifiers
Open Mon-Fri 8-4:30
Restriction: Not a lending libr

G   CANADIAN AGRICULTURE LIBRARY - WINNIPEG*, Cereal Research Center Library, Agriculture & Agri-Food Canada, 195 Dafoe Rd, R3T 2M9. SAN 366-4147. Tel: 204-983-0721, 204-983-0755. Reference Tel: 204-983-0755. FAX: 204-983-4604. E-mail: info@agr.gc.ca. Web Site: agr.gc.ca. *Librn,* Sean O'Hara; E-mail: sean.ohara@agr.gc.ca; *Libr Tech,* Tim Verry
Founded 1957
Library Holdings: e-books 6,000; e-journals 10,000; Bk Vols 3,000; Per Subs 25
Subject Interests: Plant breeding, Plant pathology, Plant physiology, Stored products entomology, Stored products mycology
Automation Activity & Vendor Info: (Cataloging) Innovative Interfaces, Inc - Millenium; (Circulation) Innovative Interfaces, Inc - Millenium; (ILL) OCLC; (OPAC) Innovative Interfaces, Inc - Millenium; (Serials) Innovative Interfaces, Inc - Millenium
Database Vendor: CRC Press/Taylor & Francis CRCnetBASE, EBSCOhost, Knovel, netLibrary, OVID Technologies, ScienceDirect, Scopus
Partic in Federal Librs Consortium (Canada)
Open Mon-Fri 8-4

G   CANADIAN GRAIN COMMISSION LIBRARY*, 801-303 Main St, R3C 3G8. SAN 366-4171. Tel: 204-984-6336. Reference Tel: 204-983-0878. FAX: 204-983-6098. E-mail: library-bibliotheque@grainscanada.gc.ca. Web Site: www.grainscanada.gc.ca. *Coordr, Libr Serv,* Dawn Bassett; *Libr Tech,* Christine Wallmann; E-mail: cwallman@grainscanada.gc.ca; Staff 2 (MLS 1, Non-MLS 1)
Founded 1913
Library Holdings: AV Mats 25; e-books 1,200; e-journals 175; Bk Titles 7,500; Per Subs 250
Special Collections: Canadian International Grains Institute - Bound Series of Lectures
Subject Interests: Cereal & oilseed chem, Grain handling
Automation Activity & Vendor Info: (Cataloging) EOS International; (Circulation) EOS International; (OPAC) EOS International; (Serials) EOS International
Database Vendor: EBSCOhost, netLibrary, OCLC FirstSearch, OCLC WorldCat, OVID Technologies, ScienceDirect
Function: Res libr
Partic in Can Agr Libr Network; Council of Federal Libraries Consortium
Restriction: Staff use only

CR   CANADIAN MENNONITE UNIVERSITY LIBRARY, 500 Shaftesbury Blvd, R3P 2N2. SAN 320-7862. Tel: 204-487-3300. Interlibrary Loan Service Tel: 204-487-3300, Ext 394. Reference Tel: 204-594-0514. FAX: 204-837-7415. E-mail: library@cmu.ca. Web Site: www.cmu.ca/library. *Libr Dir,* Vic Froese, PhD; Tel: 204-487-3300, Ext 393, E-mail: vfroese@cmu.ca; *Assoc Librn,* Paul Friesen; Tel: 204-487-3300, Ext 319, E-mail: pfriesen@cmu.ca. Subject Specialists: *Theol,* Vic Froese, PhD; *Mennonite,* Paul Friesen; Staff 5.83 (MLS 2, Non-MLS 3.83)
Founded 2000. Enrl 540; Fac 42; Highest Degree: Master
Library Holdings: Bks on Deafness & Sign Lang 37; CDs 2,272; DVDs 343; e-books 75,565; Music Scores 709; Bk Titles 119,344; Bk Vols 161,869; Per Subs 250; Videos 274
Special Collections: Mennonite Historical Library
Subject Interests: Arts, Mennonitica, Music, Relig studies
Automation Activity & Vendor Info: (Acquisitions) Innovative Interfaces, Inc; (Cataloging) Innovative Interfaces, Inc; (Circulation) Innovative Interfaces, Inc; (Course Reserve) Innovative Interfaces, Inc; (Media Booking) Innovative Interfaces, Inc - Millenium; (OPAC) Innovative Interfaces, Inc; (Serials) Innovative Interfaces, Inc
Database Vendor: EBSCOhost, Gale Cengage Learning, JSTOR, Oxford Online, ProQuest
Wireless access
Function: Audio & video playback equip for onsite use, Computers for patron use, Copy machines, Doc delivery serv, Electronic databases & coll, Free DVD rentals, ILL available, Music CDs, Online cat, Online ref, Photocopying/Printing, Ref & res, Ref serv available, Ref serv in person, Telephone ref, VHS videos, Web-catalog, Wheelchair accessible
Partic in Council of Prairie & Pacific University Libraries; Manitoba Library Consortium, Inc
Open Mon-Thurs (Fall & Winter) 8am-9pm, Fri 8-5, Sat 11-5; Mon-Fri (Summer) 8:30-5

M   CANADIAN PARAPLEGIC ASSOCIATION*, Manitoba Incorporated Library-Tony Mann, 211-825 Sherbrook St, R3A 1M5. SAN 373-3130. Tel: 204-786-4753. FAX: 204-786-1140. E-mail: winnipeg@canparaplegic.org. Web Site: www.cpamanitoba.ca.
Library Holdings: Bk Vols 350; Per Subs 50
Open Mon-Fri 8:30-4:30
Restriction: Non-circulating, Ref only

M   CANCERCARE MANITOBA LIBRARY*, 4005 675 McDermot Ave, R3E 0V9. SAN 320-7900. Tel: 204-787-2136. FAX: 204-787-4761. *Librn,* Ruth Holmberg; E-mail: ruth.holmberg@cancercare.mb.ca
Founded 1962
Library Holdings: Bk Vols 2,500; Per Subs 100
Publications: Annual Report
Partic in Docline
Restriction: Staff use only

CR   CENTRE FOR CHRISTIAN STUDIES LIBRARY, Woodsworth House, 60 Maryland St, R3G 1K7. SAN 326-4238. Tel: 204-783-4490, Ext 26. FAX: 204-786-3012. E-mail: info@ccsonline.ca. Web Site: www.ccsonline.ca/Resources/library.html. *In Charge,* Scott Douglas
Founded 1892. Enrl 50
Library Holdings: Bk Vols 4,000; Per Subs 8
Special Collections: Diaconal History Coll
Automation Activity & Vendor Info: (Cataloging) Innovative Interfaces, Inc; (Circulation) Innovative Interfaces, Inc; (OPAC) Innovative Interfaces, Inc
Wireless access
Function: Distance learning, Doc delivery serv, ILL available, Mail loans to mem, Online cat, Outside serv via phone, mail, e-mail & web
Restriction: In-house use for visitors, Open to fac, students & qualified researchers, Open to students, fac & staff

S   CENTRE FOR INDIGENOUS ENVIRONMENTAL RESOURCES*, 245 McDermot Ave, 3rd Flr, R3B 0456. SAN 377-8894. Tel: 204-956-0660. FAX: 204-956-1895. E-mail: earth@cier.ca. Web Site: www.cier.ca/information-and-resources/cier-library.aspx.
Founded 1996
Library Holdings: Electronic Media & Resources 1,700; Bk Titles 2,200; Per Subs 25
Subject Interests: Aboriginal studies, Biodiversity, Climate change, Environment, First Nations, Sustainability, Water
Function: Electronic databases & coll
Restriction: Open to pub by appt only

SR   CENTRE FOR MENNONITE BRETHREN STUDIES ARCHIVE*, 1310 Taylor Ave, R3M 3Z6. SAN R3M 3Z6. Tel: 204-669-6575. FAX: 204-654-1865. Web Site: www.mbconf.ca/mb/cmbs.htm. *Archivist,* Conrad Stoesz
Founded 1979
Library Holdings: Bk Titles 3,000; Bk Vols 4,000; Per Subs 300
Special Collections: Mennonite (JA Toews Coll). Oral History
Automation Activity & Vendor Info: (Acquisitions) Innovative Interfaces, Inc - Millenium; (Cataloging) Innovative Interfaces, Inc - Millenium; (Circulation) Innovative Interfaces, Inc - Millenium; (ILL) Innovative Interfaces, Inc - Millenium; (Media Booking) Innovative Interfaces, Inc - Millenium; (OPAC) Innovative Interfaces, Inc - Millenium; (Serials) Innovative Interfaces, Inc - Millenium
Wireless access
Open Mon-Fri 8:30-4:30

S   CITY OF WINNIPEG WATER & WASTE DEPARTMENT*, Resource Centre, 1199 Pacific Ave, R3E 3S8. (Mail add: City of Winnipeg, Water & Waste Dept, Resource Centre, R3E 3S8), SAN 377-9467. Tel: 204-986-3250. FAX: 204-224-0032. *Libr Tech,* Joann Da Silva; E-mail: jdasilva@winnipeg.ca; *Libr Tech,* Glen Ellis; E-mail: gellis@winnipeg.ca; *Tech Support,* Doug Bogaski; Tel: 204-986-3880, E-mail: dbogaski@winnipeg.ca. Subject Specialists: *Civil eng, Municipal water & waste disposal,* Joann Da Silva; Staff 3 (Non-MLS 3)
Founded 1985
Library Holdings: Bk Titles 15,000; Per Subs 425
Special Collections: AWWA & WACE Standards
Subject Interests: Flood control, Recycling, Solid waste, Solid waste disposal, Waste water treatment, Water supply
Automation Activity & Vendor Info: (Acquisitions) EOS International; (Cataloging) EOS International; (Circulation) EOS International; (OPAC) EOS International; (Serials) EOS International
Function: ILL available, Ref serv available
Partic in Manitoba Asn of Libr Technicians; Manitoba Libr Asn
Restriction: Open by appt only
Friends of the Library Group

C   COLLEGE UNIVERSITAIRE DE SAINT-BONIFACE*, Bibliotheque Alfred-Monnin, 200 Ave de la Cathedrale, R2H 0H7. SAN 318-8892. Tel: 204-233-0210, Ext 403. Circulation Tel: 204-235-4403. Reference Tel: 204-237-1818, Ext 308. Administration Tel: 204-233-0210, Ext 331. FAX: 204-233-9472. E-mail: biblio@ustboniface.mb.ca. Web Site: biblio.cusb.ca. *Dir,* Louise Ayotte-Zarelski; E-mail: layottez@ustboniface.mb.ca; *Dir, Pub Serv,* Daniel Beaulieu; E-mail: dbeaulie@ustboniface.mb.ca; Staff 8 (MLS 2, Non-MLS 6)
Founded 1818. Enrl 995; Fac 155; Highest Degree: Master

Apr 2007-Mar 2008 Income (CAN) $626,648. Mats Exp (CAN) $166,500, Books (CAN) $40,400, Per/Ser (Incl. Access Fees) (CAN) $75,000. Sal (CAN) $456,000
Library Holdings: Bk Titles 96,000; Bk Vols 133,000; Per Subs 492
Special Collections: French & French Canadian Literature Coll
Subject Interests: Arts, Bus admin, Can studies, Educ, Fr Can studies, Humanities, Sci
Automation Activity & Vendor Info: (Acquisitions) SirsiDynix; (Cataloging) SirsiDynix; (Circulation) SirsiDynix; (Course Reserve) SirsiDynix; (Media Booking) SirsiDynix; (OPAC) SirsiDynix; (Serials) SirsiDynix
Database Vendor: SirsiDynix
Wireless access
Function: Ref serv available
Partic in Manitoba Library Consortium, Inc
Open Mon-Thurs (Fall & Winter) 8am-11pm, Fri 8-6, Sat 10-7, Sun 1-5; Mon-Thurs (Summer) 8:30-8:30, Fri 8:30-4:30

G   DEPARTMENT OF FISHERIES & OCEANS CANADA, CENTRAL & ARCTIC REGION*, Eric Marshall Aquatic Research Library, 501 University Crescent, R3T 2N6. SAN 318-8868. Tel: 204-983-5170. Interlibrary Loan Service Tel: 204-983-5169. FAX: 204-984-4668. E-mail: library-fwi@dfo-mpo.gc.ca. Web Site: www.dfo-mpo.gc.ca. *Libr Tech,* Margaret Dyck; E-mail: margaret.dyck@dfo-mpo.gc.ca; *Libr Tech,* Jane Martin; E-mail: jane.martin@dfo-mpo.gc.ca. Subject Specialists: *Cataloging,* Margaret Dyck; Staff 2.5 (MLS 1, Non-MLS 1.5)
Founded 1966
Library Holdings: Bk Titles 20,000; Bk Vols 22,500; Per Subs 200
Special Collections: Algae (Fritsch Coll of Illustrations of Freshwater Algae); Arctic Petroleum Operators Association Reports, microfiche
Subject Interests: Arctic ecol, Freshwater fish, Limnology
Database Vendor: BioOne, Brodart, Cambridge Scientific Abstracts, CISTI Source, EBSCO Information Services, Elsevier, Infotrieve, ISI Web of Knowledge, JSTOR, netLibrary, OCLC WorldCat
Function: Online cat, Orientations, Photocopying/Printing
Partic in Council of Federal Libraries Consortium
Open Mon-Fri 8:30-3:30
Restriction: Restricted pub use

L   FILLMORE RILEY*, Law Library, 1700-360 Main St, R3C 3Z3. SAN 328-0616. Tel: 204-956-2970. FAX: 204-957-0516. E-mail: frinfo@fillmoreriley.com. *Librn,* Allan Chan; Staff 2 (MLS 1, Non-MLS 1)
Library Holdings: Bk Titles 6,000; Bk Vols 10,000; Per Subs 30
Database Vendor: LexisNexis
Wireless access
Restriction: Staff use only

S   GRAND LODGE OF MANITOBA, Masonic Resource Centre, Grand Lodge of Manitoba, 420 Corydon Ave, R3L 0N8. SAN 318-9066. Tel: 204-453-7410. Toll Free Tel: 800-665-2712. FAX: 204-284-3527. E-mail: mrc@grandlodge.mb.ca. Web Site: www.glmb.ca/masonic-resource-centre.html. *Librn,* Brother Brian Rountree; Staff 1 (MLS 1)
Founded 1878
Library Holdings: AV Mats 150; Bk Vols 2,500
Subject Interests: Freemasonry
Database Vendor: LibraryWorld, Inc
Wireless access
Restriction: Circ to mem only

S   HERITAGE WINNIPEG CORP LIBRARY*, 63 Albert St, Ste 509, R3B 1G4. SAN 374-8316. Tel: 204-942-2663. FAX: 204-942-2094. E-mail: info@heritagewinnipeg.com. Web Site: www.heritagewinnipeg.com. *Exec Dir,* Cindy Tugwell
Library Holdings: Bk Vols 980; Per Subs 3
Wireless access
Open Mon-Fri 9:30-5

S   HUMAN RESOURCES DEVELOPMENT-LABOUR PROGRAM*, Central Region Resource Centre, 201-391 York Ave, R3C 0P4. SAN 375-8079. Tel: 204-983-7223. FAX: 204-983-2117.
Library Holdings: Bk Titles 1,000

G   INDUSTRIAL TECHNOLOGY CENTRE, Library & Technical Information Services, 200-78 Innovation Dr, R3T 6C2. SAN 327-2877. Tel: 204-480-0336. Toll Free Tel: 800-728-7933. FAX: 204-480-0345. E-mail: library@itc.mb.ca. Web Site: www.itc.mb.ca. *Librn,* Betty Dearth; E-mail: bdearth@itc.mb.ca; Staff 1 (MLS 1)
Founded 1980
Library Holdings: Bk Vols 5,000; Per Subs 100
Subject Interests: Eng, Indust standards, Manufacturing
Database Vendor: Dialog, EBSCOhost, OCLC WorldCat
Function: ILL available

Partic in Manitoba Government Libraries Council; Manitoba Library Consortium, Inc
Open Mon-Fri 8:30-4:30

G INNOVATION, ENERGY & MINES, Mineral Resources Library, 1395 Ellice Ave, Ste 360, R3G 3P2. SAN 322-6808. Tel: 204-945-6569. Toll Free Tel: 800-223-5215. FAX: 204-945-8427. E-mail: minesinfo@gov.mb.ca. Web Site: www.gov.mb.ca/stem/mrd/info/library/index.html. *Libr Serv Coordr,* Lori Janower; E-mail: lori.janower@gov.mb.ca; *Acq,* Elaine Hunter; Tel: 204-945-4154, E-mail: elaine.hunter@gov.mb.ca; Staff 2 (Non-MLS 2)
Founded 1975
Library Holdings: Bk Titles 29,580; Bk Vols 30,000; Per Subs 350
Special Collections: Geological Survey of Canada Reports; Manitoba Geological Survey; US Geological Survey. Can & Prov; US Document Depository
Subject Interests: Mining, Petroleum
Automation Activity & Vendor Info: (Acquisitions) Inmagic, Inc.; (Cataloging) Inmagic, Inc.; (Circulation) Inmagic, Inc.; (ILL) Inmagic, Inc.; (Media Booking) Inmagic, Inc.; (OPAC) Inmagic, Inc.; (Serials) Inmagic, Inc.
Database Vendor: EBSCOhost
Wireless access
Publications: Bibliography of Rockhounding; Serials Holdings List (Monthly)
Partic in Manitoba Library Consortium, Inc
Open Mon-Fri 8:30-4:30

C INTERNATIONAL INSTITUTE FOR SUSTAINABLE DEVELOPMENT*, Information Centre, 161 Portage Ave E 6th flr, R3B 0Y4. SAN 377-9602. Tel: 204-958-7724. Interlibrary Loan Service Tel: 204-958-7755. FAX: 204-958-7710. Web Site: www.iisd.org/ic/. *Res & Learning Resources Mgr,* Marlene Roy; E-mail: mroy@iisd.ca; Staff 1 (Non-MLS 1)
Founded 1993. Highest Degree: Master
Library Holdings: e-books 16,000; e-journals 75; Bk Titles 24,000
Subject Interests: Sustainable develop
Database Vendor: Dialog, EBSCOhost
Wireless access
Function: Online searches
Restriction: Open by appt only

S LEGISLATIVE ASSEMBLY*, Elections Manitoba Library, 200 Vaughan St, Main Flr, R3C 1T5. SAN 374-616X. Tel: 204-945-3225. FAX: 204-945-6011. E-mail: election@elections.mb.ca. Web Site: www.electionsmanitoba.ca. *In Charge,* Susie Mapue
Library Holdings: Bk Titles 2,000; Per Subs 10
Special Collections: Electoral Reform & Party Financing (Royal Commission Coll)
Open Mon-Fri 8:30-4:30

G LEGISLATIVE LIBRARY OF MANITOBA*, 200 Vaughan St, Rm 100, R3C 1T5. SAN 318-8965. Tel: 204-945-4330. FAX: 204-948-1312. E-mail: legislative_library@gov.mb.ca. Web Site: www.gov.mb.ca/chc/leg-lib/index.html. *Legis Librn,* Tannis Gretzinger; E-mail: tannis.gretzinger@gov.mb.ca; *Head, Coll Develop,* Jason Woloski; Tel: 204-945-1582, E-mail: jason.woloski@gov.mb.ca; *Head, Govt Doc & Libr Syst,* Dorryce Smelts; Tel: 204-945-1069, E-mail: dorryce.smelts@gov.mb.ca; *Head, Ref (Info Serv),* Louise Ayotte-Zaretski; E-mail: louise.ayotte@gov.mb.ca
Founded 1870
Library Holdings: Bk Vols 120,000
Special Collections: Manitoba Newspapers Coll (Manitoba Government Publications). Can & Prov
Subject Interests: Can hist, Economics, Manitoba hist, Rural
Automation Activity & Vendor Info: (Acquisitions) SirsiDynix; (Cataloging) SirsiDynix; (Circulation) SirsiDynix; (Course Reserve) SirsiDynix; (OPAC) SirsiDynix
Database Vendor: EBSCOhost, Factiva.com, Infomart
Publications: Manitoba Government Publications Checklist (Monthly); Selected New Titles (Monthly)
Partic in Manitoba Government Libraries Council; Manitoba Library Consortium, Inc
Open Mon-Fri 10-5

S MANITOBA ASSOCIATION OF PLAYWRIGHTS LIBRARY*, 100 Arthur St, Ste 503, R3B 1H3. SAN 327-487X. Tel: 204-942-8941. FAX: 204-942-1555. *Coordr,* Rory Runnells; *Librn,* Carolyn Gray
Library Holdings: Bk Vols 4,000
Special Collections: Manitoba Plays; Theater Archives
Open Fri 9-5

S MANITOBA CRAFTS MUSEUM & LIBRARY*, 1B-183 Kennedy St, R3C 1S6. SAN 327-4349. Tel: 204-487-6117. FAX: 204-487-6117. E-mail: mcml@mts.net. Web Site: www.mts.net/~mcml/. *Curator,* Andrea Reichert
Founded 1932
Library Holdings: Bk Titles 3,500
Special Collections: Rare Books
Open Tues & Wed (Winter) 10-4, Sat 12-4; Tues-Sat (Summer) 10-4

G MANITOBA DEPARTMENT OF CULTURE, HERITAGE & TOURISM*, Legislative Reading Room, 450 Broadway Ave, Rm 260, R3C 0V8. SAN 377-3078. Tel: 204-945-4243. FAX: 204-948-2167. E-mail: reading@leg.gov.mb.ca. *Mem Serv Librn,* Margaret Wilson; *Libr Tech,* Janina Smithson
Library Holdings: Bk Titles 57,500
Automation Activity & Vendor Info: (Acquisitions) SirsiDynix; (Cataloging) SirsiDynix; (Circulation) SirsiDynix; (Course Reserve) SirsiDynix; (ILL) SirsiDynix; (Media Booking) SirsiDynix; (OPAC) SirsiDynix; (Serials) SirsiDynix
Open Mon-Fri 8:30-4:30

G MANITOBA DEPARTMENT OF EDUCATION*, Instructional Resources Unit Library, 1181 Portage Ave, R3G 0T3. SAN 318-899X. Tel: 204-945-5371. Interlibrary Loan Service Tel: 204-945-2271. FAX: 204-945-8756. E-mail: irucirc@gov.mb.ca. Web Site: libinfo.merlin.mb.ca. *Coordr,* John Tooth; Tel: 204-945-7833, E-mail: jtooth@gov.mb.ca; Staff 27 (MLS 7, Non-MLS 20)
Founded 1916
Apr 2005-Mar 2006. Mats Exp $123,400. Sal $1,000,000
Library Holdings: Bk Titles 100,000; Bk Vols 170,000; Per Subs 650
Special Collections: Education in Manitoba, doc; Manitoba Government Publications; Manitoba Recommended Textbooks
Automation Activity & Vendor Info: (Acquisitions) BiblioMondo; (Cataloging) BiblioMondo; (Circulation) BiblioMondo; (Media Booking) BiblioMondo; (OPAC) BiblioMondo; (Serials) BiblioMondo
Database Vendor: Gale Cengage Learning, ProQuest
Publications: Bibliographies Online; Catalogs
Open Mon-Sat 8:30-5

G MANITOBA DEPARTMENT OF FINANCE*, Fiscal Research Division Library, 910-386 Broadway, R3C 3R6. SAN 326-5765. Tel: 204-945-3757, 204-945-8329. FAX: 204-945-5051. *Librn,* Cheryl Hutchinson; E-mail: chutchinso@gov.mb.ca; Staff 1 (MLS 1)
Library Holdings: Bk Titles 3,200; Per Subs 88
Subject Interests: Economics, Finance, Taxation
Publications: Manitoba Budget Address
Restriction: Staff use only

GL MANITOBA DEPARTMENT OF JUSTICE, Legal Aid Library, 100-287 Broadway Ave, R3C 0R9. SAN 373-3149. Tel: 204-985-8500. FAX: 204-944-8582.
Library Holdings: Bk Vols 600
Restriction: Staff use only

S MANITOBA GENEALOGICAL SOCIETY INC LIBRARY*, 1045 St James St, Unit E, R3H 1B1. SAN 328-1728. Tel: 204-783-9139. E-mail: contact@mbgenealogy.com. Web Site: www.mbgenealogy.com. *Librn,* Mary Bole
Founded 1976
Library Holdings: AV Mats 600; Bk Titles 10,000; Per Subs 70
Special Collections: Manitoba Records, incl Cemetery Transcriptions, Church Records, Newspaper Indexes & Local History Books
Subject Interests: Genealogy, Local family hist
Open Tues & Thurs 10:30-3:30, Wed 10:30-3:30 & 7-9, Sun 12-4

S MANITOBA HYDRO LIBRARY*, 360 Portage Ave, R3C 30G8. (Mail add: PO Box 815, R3C 2P4), SAN 318-9031. Tel: 204-360-3212. Interlibrary Loan Service Tel: 204-360-4708. FAX: 204-360-6104. Web Site: www.hydro.mb.ca. *Coop Librn,* Rhona Lapierre; E-mail: rlapierre@hydro.mb.ca; *Ref Librn,* Ruth Epp; Staff 6 (MLS 2, Non-MLS 4)
Subject Interests: Energy, Eng, Manitoba hydro hist
Automation Activity & Vendor Info: (Acquisitions) SydneyPlus; (Cataloging) SydneyPlus; (Circulation) SydneyPlus; (Course Reserve) SydneyPlus; (ILL) SydneyPlus; (Media Booking) SydneyPlus; (OPAC) SydneyPlus; (Serials) SydneyPlus
Open Mon-Fri 8-4:30

S MANITOBA INDIGENOUS CULTURE-EDUCATIONAL CENTER*, Peoples Library, 119 Sutherland Ave, R2W 3C9. SAN 327-4381. Tel: 204-942-0228. FAX: 204-947-6564. *Librn,* Cindy LaVallee
Library Holdings: Bk Titles 20,000; Bk Vols 22,000; Per Subs 250
Wireless access
Open Mon-Fri 8:30-4:30

G   MANITOBA LABOUR BOARD LIBRARY, 175 Hargrave St, 5th Flr, R3C 3R8. SAN 371-8484. Tel: 204-945-5046. FAX: 204-945-1296. E-mail: mlb@gov.mb.ca. Web Site: www.gov.mb.ca/labour/labbrd. *Res,* Jodi Gilmore
Founded 1985
Library Holdings: Bk Titles 50; Per Subs 3
Special Collections: Board Written Reasons for Decision (Substantive Orders); Collective Agreements; Grievance Arbitration Awards
Open Mon-Fri 8:30-4:30
Restriction: Non-circulating, Restricted access

L   MANITOBA LAW LIBRARY, INC, Great Library, Law Courts Bldg, Rm 331, 408 York Ave, R3C 0P9. SAN 318-8957. Tel: 204-945-1958. FAX: 204-948-2138. Web Site: www.lawsociety.mb.ca. *Chief Librn,* R Garth Niven; Tel: 204-945-1959, E-mail: gniven@gov.mb.ca; *Tech Serv,* Wilf Scharbach; E-mail: wscharbach@jus.gov.mb.ca
Founded 1877
Library Holdings: Bk Vols 50,000; Per Subs 400
Special Collections: Manitoba Judgments, 1970 to present
Database Vendor: LexisNexis
Function: Res libr
Restriction: Mem only

S   THE MANITOBA MUSEUM*, Library & Archives, 190 Rupert Ave, R3B 0N2. SAN 318-904X. Tel: 204-988-0692. FAX: 204-942-3679. Web Site: www.manitobamuseum.ca. *Mgr,* Cindi Steffan; Tel: 204-988-0662, E-mail: csteffan@manitobamuseum.ca; Staff 1 (MLS 1)
Founded 1967
Library Holdings: Bk Titles 22,000; Bk Vols 30,000; Per Subs 100
Special Collections: Oral History
Subject Interests: Applied arts, Astronomy, Fundraising, Human hist, Museology, Natural hist
Restriction: Open by appt only, Open to pub for ref only

S   MANITOBA SCHOOL FOR THE DEAF MULTIMEDIA CENTER*, 242 Stradford St, R2Y 2C9. SAN 327-4322. Tel: 204-945-8934. FAX: 204-945-1767. *Coordr,* Diane Bilyj
Library Holdings: Bk Vols 10,000
Automation Activity & Vendor Info: (Acquisitions) SydneyPlus; (Cataloging) SydneyPlus; (Circulation) SydneyPlus; (Course Reserve) SydneyPlus; (ILL) SydneyPlus; (Media Booking) SydneyPlus; (OPAC) SydneyPlus; (Serials) SydneyPlus
Database Vendor: EBSCOhost
Open Mon-Fri 8:30-3:30

S   MFL OCCUPATIONAL HEALTH CENTRE*, Resource Centre, 275 Broadway, Ste 102, R3C 4M6. SAN 328-0632. Tel: 204-949-0811. Toll Free Tel: 888-843-1229 (Manitoba only). FAX: 204-956-0848. Web Site: www.mflohc.mb.ca.
Library Holdings: Bk Titles 1,000; Per Subs 20
Special Collections: NIOSH
Open Mon-Fri 9-5
Restriction: Circulates for staff only, Non-circulating to the pub

L   MYERS, WEINBERG LLP*, Law Library, 724-240 Graham Ave, R3C 0J7. SAN 324-1912. Tel: 204-942-0501. FAX: 204-956-0625. *Librn,* Suzanne Crowe
Library Holdings: Bk Titles 520; Bk Vols 600; Per Subs 40
Subject Interests: Admin law, Civil litigation, Crim law, Family law, Labor law
Wireless access
Open Mon-Fri 8:30-5

L   PITBLADO LAW LIBRARY*, 2500-360 Main St, R3C 4H6. SAN 370-7202. Tel: 204-956-0560. FAX: 204-957-0227. Web Site: www.pitblado.com. *Librn,* Christina Lopez; E-mail: lopez@pitblado.com
Library Holdings: Bk Titles 800; Per Subs 20
Database Vendor: LexisNexis
Wireless access
Restriction: Not open to pub

S   RAINBOW RESOURCE CENTRE LIBRARY*, 170 Scott St, R3C 2Z6. (Mail add: PO Box 1661, R3C 2Z6), SAN 326-2278. Tel: 204-474-0212. FAX: 204-478-1160. E-mail: info@rainbowresourcecentre.org. Web Site: www.rainbowresourcecentre.org. *Pub Serv,* Chris Vogel
Founded 1973
Library Holdings: Bk Titles 3,500; Bk Vols 4,000; Per Subs 37
Special Collections: Oral History
Subject Interests: Gay & lesbian, Sexuality
Function: Orientations, Photocopying/Printing, Prog for adults, Prog for children & young adult, Ref serv available
Open Tues 1-7, Wed & Thurs 1-6, Fri 1-5
Restriction: Mem only, Open to pub for ref & circ; with some limitations, Open to researchers by request, Pub use on premises

C   RED RIVER COLLEGE LIBRARY*, 2055 Notre Dame Ave, R3H 0J9. SAN 318-9090. Tel: 204-632-2322. Reference Tel: 204-632-2233. Toll Free Tel: 888-445-0312. FAX: 204-697-4791. E-mail: library@rrc.mb.ca. Web Site: www.rrc.mb.ca/library. *Dir,* Patricia Burt; Tel: 204-632-2382, E-mail: pburt@rrc.mb.ca; *Coll Develop & Off-Campus Serv Coordr,* Phyllis Barich; Tel: 204-949-8372, Fax: 204-949-9173, E-mail: pbarich@rrc.mb.ca; *Pub Serv Coordr,* Norman Beattie; Tel: 204-632-2470, E-mail: nbeattie@rrc.mb.ca; *Libr Syst & Serv Tech,* Mark Nelson; Tel: 204-632-2417, E-mail: mnelson@rrc.mb.ca; Staff 19 (MLS 4, Non-MLS 15)
Founded 1963. Enrl 8,596; Fac 750
Library Holdings: Bk Vols 69,856; Per Subs 567
Subject Interests: Applied arts, Educ, Health
Automation Activity & Vendor Info: (Acquisitions) Ex Libris Group; (Cataloging) Ex Libris Group; (Circulation) Ex Libris Group; (Course Reserve) Ex Libris Group; (Media Booking) Ex Libris Group; (OPAC) Ex Libris Group; (Serials) Ex Libris Group
Database Vendor: ACM (Association for Computing Machinery), Blackwell's, Canadian Reference Centre, Cinahl Information Systems, Coutts Information Service, ebrary, EBSCO Auto Repair Reference, EBSCOhost, Ex Libris Group, OCLC FirstSearch, OVID Technologies, Oxford Online, PubMed, Repere
Wireless access
Function: ILL available
Partic in Consortia Canada; Manitoba Library Consortium, Inc
Open Mon-Thurs 7:45am-9pm, Fri 7:45-4:30, Sat 8:30-4

S   SEXUALITY EDUCATION RESOURCE CENTRE*, 200-226 Osborne St N, R3C 1V4. SAN 374-5902. Tel: 204-982-7800. FAX: 204-982-7819. E-mail: info@serc.mb.ca. Web Site: www.serc.mb.ca. *In Charge,* Gwen Crawley; E-mail: gwenc@serc.mb.ca
Library Holdings: AV Mats 25; Bk Titles 1,500; Per Subs 20
Special Collections: Sexuality & Reproductive (Health Coll)
Subject Interests: Parenting, Spec needs
Open Mon-Fri 9-4
Restriction: Fee for pub use

G   STATISTICS CANADA*, Advisory Services, 200-123 Main St, R3C 1A3. SAN 320-9644. Tel: 204-983-5883. Toll Free Tel: 800-263-1136. FAX: 204-983-7543. E-mail: infostats@statcan.gc.ca. Web Site: www.statcan.gc.ca. *In Charge,* Raimi Osseni; E-mail: raimi.osseni@statcan.gc.ca; Staff 2 (MLS 2)
Library Holdings: Bk Titles 10,000; Bk Vols 13,500; Per Subs 25
Restriction: Not open to pub

L   TAYLOR MCCAFFREY*, Law Library, 400 St Mary Ave, 9th Flr, R3C 4K5. SAN 373-6156. Tel: 204-988-0463. FAX: 204-957-0945. *Librn,* Patrick Fawcett
Library Holdings: Bk Vols 5,000; Per Subs 40
Automation Activity & Vendor Info: (Acquisitions) Inmagic, Inc.; (Cataloging) Inmagic, Inc.; (Serials) Inmagic, Inc.
Restriction: Staff use only

S   TRANSPORT CANADA*, Technical Reference Centre, 344 Edmonton St, 2nd Flr, R3C 0P6. (Mail add: PO Box 8550, R3C 0P6). Tel: 204-984-1886. FAX: 204-984-4874. E-mail: trc-pnr@tc.gc.ca. *Tech Spec,* Kirsten Rytter
Library Holdings: Bk Titles 3,000; Per Subs 50
Special Collections: Aviation Coll; Marine, Rail & Grain Transportation Coll; Non-Transport Related Materials
Function: ILL available
Restriction: Staff use only

S   UKRAINIAN NATIONAL HOME ASSOCIATION LIBRARY*, 582 Burrows Ave, R2W 2A6. SAN 323-9659. Tel: 204-582-4528. *Pres,* Fred Mykytyshyn
Library Holdings: Bk Vols 2,000
Special Collections: Ukrainian History, Art, Music & Biographies
Function: Res libr
Restriction: Open by appt only

G   UNITED NATIONS ASSOCIATION IN CANADA, WINNIPEG BRANCH*, Nan Florence Library, c/o The University of Winnipeg Library, 515 Portage Ave, R3B 2E9. SAN 372-7165. Tel: 204-586-0173. FAX: 204-783-8910. E-mail: unac@merlin.mb.ca. Web Site: www.unacwinnipeg.ca. *In Charge,* Muriel Smith
Founded 1972
Library Holdings: Bk Titles 1,000; Per Subs 86
Open Mon-Wed 9:30-1:30

UNIVERSITY OF MANITOBA

M   MISERICORDIA HEALTH CENTRE LIBRARY*, 99 Cornish Ave, R3C 1A2, SAN 326-3428. Tel: 204-788-8109. FAX: 204-889-4174. E-mail: maclibrary@umanitoba.ca. Web Site: www.umanitoba.ca/libraries. *Librn,* Lesley Mackie; *Libr Tech,* Kathy Finlayson; Staff 2 (Non-MLS 2)
>
> **Library Holdings:** Bk Titles 3,000; Per Subs 10
> **Subject Interests:** Med, Nursing, Ophthalmology
> **Function:** Res libr
> Open Mon-Fri 8:30-4:30
> **Restriction:** Non-circulating

C   ST ANDREW'S COLLEGE LIBRARY*, 29 Dysart Rd, R3T 2M7, SAN 322-7324. Tel: 204-474-8901. FAX: 204-474-7624. *Librn,* Halia Teterenko; Staff 2 (Non-MLS 2)
>
> Founded 1946. Enrl 80; Fac 8; Highest Degree: Master
> **Library Holdings:** Bk Vols 37,000; Per Subs 20; Spec Interest Per Sub 12
> **Special Collections:** Old Cyrillic Manuscripts & Printed Books
> **Subject Interests:** Eastern Christianity, Soviet studies, Theol, Ukrainian church, Ukrainian culture, Ukrainian hist, Ukrainian lit
> **Function:** Ref serv available
> **Publications:** Selected Guide to the Rare Book Collection of St Andrew's College Library; Ukranian Serials: A Checklist of Ukranian Periodicals & Newspapers at St Andrew's College
> Open Mon-Fri 8:30-4:30

M   SEVEN OAKS GENERAL HOSPITAL LIBRARY, 2300 McPhillips St, R2V 3M3, SAN 324-119X. Tel: 204-632-3107. Circulation Tel: 204-632-3124. FAX: 204-694-8240. E-mail: soghlibrary@umanitoba.ca. *Librn,* Kerry Macdonald; E-mail: kerry.macdonald@ad.umanitoba.ca; Staff 1 (MLS 1)
>
> Founded 1980
> **Library Holdings:** Bk Titles 1,500; Per Subs 70
> **Subject Interests:** Educ, Med, Nursing
> **Automation Activity & Vendor Info:** (Acquisitions) SirsiDynix; (Cataloging) SirsiDynix; (Circulation) SirsiDynix; (Course Reserve) SirsiDynix; (ILL) SirsiDynix; (OPAC) SirsiDynix; (Serials) SirsiDynix
> Open Mon-Fri 8:30-4:30

C   UNIVERSITY OF MANITOBA LIBRARIES*, Elizabeth Dafoe Libr, Rm 156, R3T 2N2. SAN 366-435X. Tel: 204-474-9881. FAX: 204-474-7583. Web Site: www.umanitoba.ca/libraries. *Dir,* K Adams; *Assoc Dir, Coll,* D Breyfogle; *Archivist, Spec Coll Librn,* S Sweeney; *Ref,* J Blanchard; Staff 55 (MLS 55)
>
> Founded 1885. Enrl 23,000; Fac 2,274; Highest Degree: Doctorate
> **Library Holdings:** e-books 199,390; e-journals 36,906; Bk Vols 2,000,000; Per Subs 6,876
> **Special Collections:** Andrew Suknaski Coll, ms, typescripts; Bertram Brooker Coll, bks, ms, typescripts; Canadiana (H Gerald Wade Coll), bks, ms; Charles M Gordon (Ralph Connor) Coll, ms, typescripts; Dorothy Livesay Coll, bks, ms, typescripts; Dysart Coll, rare bks & ms; Eli Mandel Coll, ms, typescripts; Food & Agriculture Organization Document Depository; Frederick Philip Grove Coll, ms, typescripts; Henry Kreisel Coll, ms, typescripts; History & Religion (Vatican Letters & Documents Concerning North America, 1688-1908), micro, photocopy; Icelandic & Slavic Coll, bks, journals; J W Dafoe Coll, ms, typescripts; John Newlove Coll, ms, typescripts; M Charles Cohen Coll, bks, ms; Marshall J Gauvin Coll; Medicine (Ross Mitchell Coll), classic & rare bks, journals; Oscar Brand Coll, ms, music scores; P H T Thorlakson Coll, ms, speeches, typescripts; Rt Hon Edward Schreyer Papers; T G Hamilton Coll, affidavits, ms, photogs; University Archives; Winnipeg Tribune, archives, photogs. Can & Prov; UN Document Depository
> **Subject Interests:** Agr, Archit, Dentistry, Educ, Eng, Humanities, Law, Med, Mus, Sci, Soc sci
> **Automation Activity & Vendor Info:** (Acquisitions) SirsiDynix; (Cataloging) SirsiDynix; (Circulation) SirsiDynix; (Course Reserve) SirsiDynix; (ILL) SirsiDynix; (Media Booking) SirsiDynix; (OPAC) SirsiDynix; (Serials) SirsiDynix
> **Database Vendor:** Agricola, American Chemical Society, American Physical Society, Annual Reviews, ARTstor, ASCE Research Library, BioOne, Blackwell's, Canadian Reference Centre, Cinahl Information Systems, CredoReference, EBSCOhost, Emerald, IEEE (Institute of Electrical & Electronics Engineers), IOP, JSTOR, Knovel, MD Consult, Nature Publishing Group, netLibrary, OCLC FirstSearch, OVID Technologies, Oxford Online, ProQuest, PubMed, RefWorks, Sage, ScienceDirect, Scopus, UpToDate, Wiley InterScience
> Wireless access
> **Publications:** Catalogues of Archival Collections; Papers of Charles William Gordon; The Dysart Memorial Collection of Rare Books & Manuscripts Catalogue; The Papers of Dorothy Livesay, For God, King, Pen & Country
> Partic in Association of Research Libraries (ARL); BRS; Can-Ole; Dialog Corp; IDRC; Info-globe; Knowledge Index; SDC Info Servs; Westlaw
> Open Mon-Fri 8am-11pm

Departmental Libraries:

ARCHITECTURE & FINE ARTS LIBRARY, 206 Russell Bldg, 84 Curry Pl, R3T 2N2. Tel: 204-474-9216. Reference Tel: 204-474-8447. FAX: 204-474-7539. *Head Librn,* Mary Lochhead; Tel: 204-474-9217, E-mail: mary_lochhead@umanitoba.ca
> **Library Holdings:** Per Subs 475
> **Special Collections:** Slide Coll
> **Subject Interests:** Archit, City planning, Design, Environ studies, Fine arts, Interior design, Landscape archit, Regional planning
> Open Mon-Thurs 8:30am-9pm, Fri 8:30-5, Sat & Sun 12:30-5

ALBERT D COHEN MANAGEMENT LIBRARY, 208 Drake Centre, 181 Freedman Crescent, R3T 5V4. Tel: 204-474-8440. FAX: 204-474-7542. *Librn,* Dennis Felbel; Tel: 202-474-9064; *Ref Serv,* Ganga Dakshinamurti; Tel: 204-474-8441
> **Library Holdings:** Per Subs 450
> **Subject Interests:** Acctg, Bus admin, Finance, Mkt
> Open Mon-Thurs 8:30-7, Fri 8:30-5, Sat 10-1

CONCORDIA HOSPITAL LIBRARY, 1095 Concordia Ave, R2K 3S8. Tel: 204-661-7163. FAX: 204-661-7282. E-mail: chlibrary@umanitoba.ca. Web Site: www.umanitoba.ca/libraries/health/concordia. *Librn,* Melissa Raynard; Tel: 204-661-7440

DONALD W CRAIK ENGINEERING LIBRARY, 351 Engineering Bldg, R3T 2N2. Tel: 204-474-6360. Reference Tel: 204-474-6850. FAX: 204-474-7520. *Librn,* N Godavari; *Circ,* Paula Meyer
> **Subject Interests:** Agr, Civil, Electrical, Geol eng, Mechanical eng
> Open Mon-Thurs 8:30am-9pm, Fri 8:30-5, Sat & Sun 1-5

CM   J W CRANE MEMORIAL LIBRARY, 2109 Portage Ave, R3J 0L3, SAN 318-8906. Tel: 204-831-2152. Administration Tel: 204-831-2107. FAX: 204-888-1805. E-mail: dlclibrary@umanitoba.ca. Web Site: www.umanitoba.ca/libraries/health/deerlodge. *Head, Libr & Info Serv,* Angela Osterreicher; E-mail: angela_osterreicher@umanitoba.ca; *Sr Libr Tech,* Diana Stojanovic-Lewis; *Libr Tech,* Pamela Southam; *Long Term Care Librn,* Laurie Blanchard; Tel: 204-831-2943, E-mail: laurie_blanchard@umanitoba.ca; Staff 4 (MLS 1.5, Non-MLS 2.5)
> **Library Holdings:** Bk Titles 10,000; Per Subs 250
> **Special Collections:** Gerontology & Geriatrics (UMI Coll), microfiche
> **Subject Interests:** Geriatrics, Gerontology, Long term care
> **Database Vendor:** EBSCOhost, SirsiDynix
> **Publications:** Agelit (Quarterly); Current Perspectives Series; Video Catalogue; Web Pick of the Week
> Open Mon-Fri 8:30-4:30

ELIZABETH DAFOE LIBRARY, 25 Chancellor's Circle, R3T 2N2. Tel: 204-474-9544. FAX: 204-474-7577. *Head, Archives & Spec Coll,* Shelley Sweeney; Tel: 204-474-6350, E-mail: shelley_sweeney@umanitoba.ca; *Head, Ref,* Jim Blanchard; Tel: 204-474-6846, E-mail: jim_blanchard@umanitoba.ca; *Head Librn,* Nicole Michaud-Oystryk; Tel: 204-474-9211, E-mail: nicole_michaud-oystryk@umanitoba.ca; *Librn,* Sigrid Johnson; *Coll Develop,* James Kominowski; *Ref Serv,* Emma Popowich. Subject Specialists: *Iceland,* Sigrid Johnson; *Slavic hist & lit,* James Kominowski
> **Special Collections:** Icelandic & Slavic Coll, archives, ms, rare bks
> **Subject Interests:** Human ecology, Humanities, Nursing
> Open Mon-Thurs (Summer) 8:15am-9pm, Fri 8:15-5, Sat 10-5; Mon-Fri (Winter) 9-5

ECKHARDT-GRAMATTE MUSIC LIBRARY, 223-4 Music Bldg, 65 Dafoe Rd, R3T 2N2. Tel: 204-474-9567. FAX: 204-474-7253. Web Site: www.umanitoba.ca/libraries/units/music. *Head Librn,* Janneka Guise; Staff 4 (MLS 1, Non-MLS 3)
> Enrl 300; Highest Degree: Master
> **Library Holdings:** AV Mats 8,000; CDs 6,000; DVDs 128; e-journals 300; Music Scores 21,000; Bk Vols 13,000; Per Subs 145; Videos 350
> Open Mon-Thurs 8:30-8, Fri 8:30-5, Sat & Sun 12-5

FATHER HAROLD DRAKE LIBRARY - ST PAULS COLLEGE, 70 Dysart Rd, R3T 2M6, SAN 366-4686. Tel: 204-474-8585. FAX: 204-474-7615. *Head Librn,* Jim Blanchard; Tel: 204-474-6882; *Circ Supvr,* Bill Wsiaki; *Libr Tech,* Barbara Unger
> **Library Holdings:** Bk Titles 75,000; Per Subs 240
> **Subject Interests:** Catholic studies, Peace & conflict studies
> **Database Vendor:** EBSCOhost
> Open Mon-Fri (Summer) 8:30-4:30

CM   BILL LARSON LIBRARY (GRACE HOSPITAL), 300 Booth Dr, R3J 3M7, SAN 320-7889. Tel: 204-837-0127. FAX: 204-897-9486. E-mail: gghlibrary@umanitoba.ca. *Librn,* Lori Giles-Smith; E-mail: lori_giles-smith@umanitoba.ca; *Libr Asst,* Lenore Finlay; Tel: 204-837-0518, E-mail: lenore_finlay@umanitoba.ca; Staff 2 (MLS 1, Non-MLS 1)
> Founded 1974
> **Subject Interests:** Allied health, Consumer health, Med, Nursing
> Open Mon-Fri 8:30-4:30

CM   NEIL JOHN MACLEAN HEALTH SCIENCES LIBRARY, 223 Brodie Centre, 727 McDermot Ave, R3E 3P5. (Mail add: 770 Bannatyne Ave, R3E 0W3), SAN 366-4597. Tel: 204-789-3342, 204-789-3464. Interlibrary Loan Service Tel: 204-789-3707. Administration Tel: 204-789-3821. Automation Services Tel: 204-789-3461. FAX:

204-789-3922. Automation Services FAX: 204-789-3923. E-mail:
njm_ref@umanitoba.ca. Web Site: www.umanitoba.ca/libraries/health.
Head, Health Sci Libr, Ada Ducas; E-mail: ada_ducas@umanitoba.ca;
Doc Delivery, Libr Supvr-Popular Libr, Candice Lewis; Tel:
204-789-3345, E-mail: candice_lewis@umanitoba.ca; *Res Support Serv,*
Carol Cooke; Staff 9.24 (MLS 9.24)
Highest Degree: Doctorate
Library Holdings: AV Mats 5,657; e-books 144,768; e-journals 4,500;
Bk Titles 103,977; Per Subs 130
Special Collections: Aboriginal Health Coll; Consumer Health Coll;
History of Medicine Coll; Manitoba Authors (Medical Field); Rare Book
Coll
Subject Interests: Allied health, Dental, Dental hygiene, Med, Nursing,
Occupational therapy, Pediatrics, Phys therapy
Automation Activity & Vendor Info: (Acquisitions) SirsiDynix;
(Cataloging) SirsiDynix; (Circulation) SirsiDynix; (Course Reserve)
SirsiDynix; (ILL) Relais International; (Media Booking) SirsiDynix;
(OPAC) SirsiDynix; (Serials) SirsiDynix
Database Vendor: Cambridge Scientific Abstracts, EBSCOhost, Elsevier,
OVID Technologies
Function: Archival coll, AV serv, Doc delivery serv, Health sci info serv,
ILL available, Online cat, Orientations, Outreach serv,
Photocopying/Printing, Pub access computers, Ref & res, Ref serv
available, Satellite serv, Wheelchair accessible
Partic in Association of Faculties of Medicine of Canada (AFMC)
Publications: InfoRx, InfoRn (Newsletter)
Open Mon-Thurs 8am-11pm, Sat 9am-11pm, Sun 10am-9pm
MISERICORDIA HEALTH CARE LIBRARY, 99 Cornish Ave, R3C 1A2.
Tel: 204-788-8109. FAX: 204-889-4174. E-mail:
library@miseri.winnipeg.mb.ca. Web Site: www.umanitoba.ca/libraries.
Librn, Lesley Mackie; E-mail: lesley_mackie@umanitoba.ca
WILLIAM R NEWMAN LIBRARY (AGRICULTURE), 66 Dafoe Rd,
R3T 2N2. Tel: 204-474-8382. FAX: 204-474-7527. E-mail:
agrref@ms.umanitoba.ca. Web Site:
www.umanitoba.ca/libraries/units/agriculture. *Head Librn,* Sharida
Hosein; Tel: 204-474-6334, E-mail: sherida_hosein@umanitoba.ca
Function: ILL available, Photocopying/Printing
Open Mon-Thurs (Fall & Winter) 8:30-5:30, Fri 8:30-4:30; Mon-Fri
(Summer) 8:30-12 & 1-4:30
Restriction: Staff use only
RIVERVIEW HEALTH CENTRE VIRTUAL LIBRARY, One Morley St,
R3L 2P4. Tel: 204-478-6873. FAX: 204-478-6121. E-mail:
dlclibrary@umanitoba.ca. *Outreach Librn,* Laurie Blanchard; Staff 1
(MLS 0.5, Non-MLS 0.5)
ST JOHN'S COLLEGE LIBRARY, 92 Dysart Rd, R3T 2M5, SAN
366-4651. Tel: 204-474-8542. FAX: 204-474-7614. *Head of Libr,* Jim
Blanchard; *Circ Supvr,* Cathy Mudry; E-mail:
cathy_mudry@umanitoba.ca; *Libr Asst,* Amrit Chhina; E-mail:
amrit_chhina@umanitoba.ca
Special Collections: Dead Sea Scrolls; King James Bible
Subject Interests: Can studies, Early christianity, English lit, Fr lit,
Relig
Database Vendor: EBSCOhost
Open Mon-Fri 8:15-8 (8:15-4:30 Summer)
SCIENCES & TECHNOLOGY LIBRARY, 211 Machray Hall, R3T 2N2.
Tel: 204-474-9281. FAX: 204-474-7627. *Librn,* Vera Keown; Tel:
204-474-8302
Library Holdings: Bk Vols 220,000; Per Subs 1,900
Subject Interests: Agr, Eng
Database Vendor: EBSCOhost
Open Mon-Sat 9-5
Friends of the Library Group
SEVEN OAKS GENERAL HOSPITAL LIBRARY, 2300 McPhillips St,
R2V 3M3. Tel: 204-632-3107. FAX: 204-694-8240. E-mail:
soghlibrary@umanitoba.ca. *Librn,* Kerry Macdonald; E-mail:
kerry_macdonald@umanitoba.ca
CAROLYN SIFTON-HELENE FULD LIBRARY, St Boniface Hospital,
409 Tache Ave, R2H 2A6, SAN 377-0648. Tel: 204-237-2807. FAX:
204-235-3339. E-mail: sbghlib@cc.umanitoba.ca. Web Site:
www.umanitoba.ca/libraries/health/sbgh. *Librn,* Christine Shaw-Daigle;
Tel: 204-237-2808, E-mail: christine_shaw-daigle@umanitoba.ca;
Clinical Librn, Andrea Szwajcer; Tel: 204-237-2991, E-mail:
andrea_szwajcer@umanitoba.ca; Staff 4.5 (MLS 2, Non-MLS 2.5)
Founded 1998
Subject Interests: Cardiovascular res, Clinical med, Nursing
Open Mon-Fri 8:30-4:30

CM VICTORIA GENERAL HOSPITAL LIBRARY, 2340 Pembina Hwy, R3T
2E8. Tel: 204-477-3307. FAX: 204-269-7936. E-mail:
vghlibrary@umanitoba.ca. *Librn,* Lisa Demczuk; Tel: 204-477-3284; *Libr
Tech,* Jan Mcleod; Staff 2 (MLS 1, Non-MLS 1)
Database Vendor: EBSCOhost
Open Mon-Fri 8:30-4:30

CL E K WILLIAMS LAW LIBRARY, 401 Robson Hall, 224 Dysart Rd, R3T
2N2. Tel: 204-474-9995. FAX: 204-474-7582. *Law Librn,* J Eaton; Tel:
204-474-9996; *Circ Supvr,* Gail Mackisey; *Coll Develop,* Ariana Sirko;
Tel: 204-474-6371, E-mail: ariana_sirko@umanitoba.ca
Library Holdings: Per Subs 1,900
Special Collections: KWIC Index to Unreported Manitoba Case Laws
Partic in Manitoba Library Consortium, Inc
Open Mon-Thurs 8:30am-10pm, Fri 8:30-6, Sat & Sun 1-5

C UNIVERSITY OF WINNIPEG LIBRARY*, 515 Portage Ave, R3B 2E9.
SAN 318-9171. Tel: 204-786-9801. Circulation Tel: 204-786-9808.
Interlibrary Loan Service Tel: 204-786-9814. Reference Tel: 204-786-9815.
Automation Services Tel: 204-786-9812. Toll Free Tel: 888-393-1830.
FAX: 204-783-8910. Interlibrary Loan Service FAX: 204-786-1824.
E-mail: reference@uwinnipeg.ca. Web Site: cybrary.uwinnipeg.ca. *Dean,*
Univ Libr, Jane Duffy; *Univ Librn,* Mark Leggott; *ILL Supvr,* Heather
Mathieson; E-mail: he.mathieson@uwinnipeg.ca; *Ref Supvr,* Jackie
Mikolash; Tel: 204-786-9871; *Coordr, Coll Serv,* Megan Anderson; Tel:
204-786-9124; *Coordr, Info Tech,* Michael Hohner; E-mail:
m.hohner@uwinnipeg.ca; *Archivist,* Gabrielle Prefontaine; Tel:
204-786-9914; *Circ,* Laura Buttler; *Circ,* Alan Gershuny; *Circ,* Pat Russell.
Subject Specialists: *Biol, Chem, Physics,* Mark Leggott; *Admin studies,*
Math, Statistics, Michael Hohner; *Hist, Philosophy,* Gabrielle Prefontaine;
Staff 38 (MLS 8, Non-MLS 30)
Founded 1871. Enrl 9,800; Fac 325; Highest Degree: Master
Library Holdings: AV Mats 3,934; e-books 1,081; Bk Titles 406,067; Bk
Vols 509,106; Per Subs 1,541
Special Collections: Asian Development Bank; Canadiana (Ashdown);
Children's Literature; Conference of Manitoba & Northwestern Ontario
Archives; Drache Legal Coll; Eastern European Genealogical Society Coll;
Rare Book Coll; Rutherford (British History Coll); Science Fiction
Winnipeg & Manitoba
Subject Interests: Liberal arts
Automation Activity & Vendor Info: (Acquisitions) Innovative Interfaces,
Inc; (Cataloging) Innovative Interfaces, Inc; (Circulation) Innovative
Interfaces, Inc; (Course Reserve) Innovative Interfaces, Inc; (Media
Booking) Innovative Interfaces, Inc; (OPAC) Innovative Interfaces, Inc;
(Serials) Innovative Interfaces, Inc
Database Vendor: EBSCOhost, JSTOR, LexisNexis, OCLC FirstSearch,
OCLC WorldCat, OVID Technologies, ProQuest, PubMed, ScienceDirect
Partic in Canadian Research Knowledge Network; Council of Prairie &
Pacific University Libraries; MLC
Special Services for the Deaf - Assistive tech
Special Services for the Blind - Closed circuit TV; Computer with voice
synthesizer for visually impaired persons; ZoomText magnification &
reading software
Open Mon-Thurs 8am-10:45pm, Fri 8-4:45, Sat & Sun 11-5:45

S VOLUNTEER MANITOBA*, Five Donald St S, 4th Flr, R3L 2T4. SAN
378-0295. Tel: 204-477-5180. FAX: 204-453-6198. E-mail:
vmresource@mts.net. Web Site: www.volunteermanitoba.ca. *Res Coordr,*
Linda Horodecki; Tel: 204-477-5180, Ext 223
Library Holdings: Bk Titles 5,000; Per Subs 15; Videos 110
Special Collections: Canada Volunteerism Initiative Coll; Leadership
Winnipeg Coll; MVSI Coll
Subject Interests: Fundraising, Volunteer mgt, Volunteerism
Function: ILL available
Open Mon-Fri 9-4:30

S WESTERN CANADA AVIATION MUSEUM LIBRARY-ARCHIVES*,
Hangar T-2, 958 Ferry Rd, R3H 0Y8. SAN 328-3747. Tel: 204-786-5503.
FAX: 204-775-4761. E-mail: info@wcam.mb.ca. Web Site:
www.wcam.mb.ca. *In Charge,* Brian Watson
Library Holdings: Bk Titles 300; Per Subs 30
Special Collections: Aeronautical maps; Aircraft Blueprints; TCA
Engineering & Overhaul Dept Records; Technical & Overhaul Manuals
Subject Interests: Metallurgy
Publications: WCAM Aviation Reveu (Quarterly)
Open Mon & Wed 9-2

S WINNIPEG ART GALLERY*, Clara Lander Library, 300 Memorial Blvd,
R3C 1V1. SAN 318-9198. Tel: 204-786-6641. FAX: 204-788-4998. E-mail:
librarian@wag.ca. Web Site: www.wag.ca. *Librn,* Kenlyn Collins; E-mail:
kcollins@wag.ca; Staff 1 (MLS 1)
Founded 1950
Library Holdings: Bk Vols 30,000; Per Subs 100
Special Collections: Institutional Archives; Inuit Art Coll
Subject Interests: Can art
Automation Activity & Vendor Info: (Cataloging) Follett Software;
(OPAC) Winnebago Software Co
Wireless access
Open Tues-Fri 11-4:30
Restriction: Open to pub for ref only

S   WINNIPEG FREE PRESS LIBRARY*, 1135 Mountain Ave, R2X 3B6.
     SAN 318-9201. Tel: 204-697-7291. FAX: 204-697-7412. Web Site:
     www.winnipegfreepress.com. *Librn,* Margaret MacMillan
     Founded 1927
     Library Holdings: Bk Titles 700; Per Subs 10
     Wireless access
     Restriction: Open to pub by appt only, Staff use only

P   WINNIPEG PUBLIC LIBRARY*, 251 Donald St, R3C 3P5. SAN
     366-4740. Tel: 204-986-6462. FAX: 204-942-5671. Web Site:
     www.winnipeg.ca/library. *Mgr, Libr Serv,* Rick Walker
     Founded 1885. Circ 5,723,951
     Library Holdings: Bk Vols 1,558,909; Per Subs 1,484
     Automation Activity & Vendor Info: (Acquisitions) SirsiDynix;
     (Cataloging) SirsiDynix; (Circulation) SirsiDynix; (Course Reserve)
     SirsiDynix; (ILL) SirsiDynix; (Media Booking) SirsiDynix; (OPAC)
     SirsiDynix; (Serials) SirsiDynix
     Database Vendor: EBSCOhost
     Open Mon-Thurs 10-9, Fri & Sat 10-5, Sun 1-5
     Friends of the Library Group
     Branches: 20
     CHARLESWOOD, 5014 Roblin Blvd, R3R 0G7, SAN 366-4775. Tel:
        204-986-3072. FAX: 204-986-3545. *Br Head,* Liv Thorseth
        Open Mon, Tues & Thurs 10-8:30, Fri & Sat 10-5
        Friends of the Library Group
     CORNISH, 20 West Gate, R3C 2E1, SAN 366-4791. Tel: 204-986-4679.
        FAX: 204-986-7126. *Br Head,* Rick Watkins
        Open Mon, Tues & Thurs 1-8:30, Fri & Sat 10-5
        Friends of the Library Group
     FORT GARRY, 1360 Pembina Hwy, R3T 2B4, SAN 366-483X. Tel:
        204-986-4910. FAX: 204-986-3399. *Br Head,* Jane Bridle
        Open Mon, Tues & Thurs 10-8:30, Wed, Fri & Sat 10-5
        Friends of the Library Group
     HENDERSON, 1-1050 Henderson Hwy, R2K 2M5, SAN 366-4848. Tel:
        204-986-4314. FAX: 204-986-3065. *Br Head,* Ed Cuddy
        Open Mon, Tues & Thurs 10-8:30, Wed, Fri & Sat 10-5, Sun 1-5
        Friends of the Library Group
     MILLENNIUM, 251 Donald St, R3C 3P5, SAN 328-7386. Tel:
        204-986-6440. FAX: 204-942-5671. *Admin Coordr, Cent Libr Serv,* Vera
        Andrysiak
        Open Mon-Thurs 10-9, Fri & Sat 10-5, Sun 1-5
        Friends of the Library Group
     MUNROE, 489 London St, R2K 2Z4, SAN 366-4880. Tel: 204-986-3736.
        FAX: 204-986-7125. *Br Head,* Randy Plant
        Open Mon, Tues & Thurs 1-8:30, Fri & Sat 10-5
        Friends of the Library Group
     OSBORNE, 625 Osborne St S, R3L 2B3, SAN 366-4899. Tel:
        204-986-4775. FAX: 204-986-7124. *Br Head,* Carole Reeve
        Open Mon, Tues & Thurs 1-8:30, Fri & Sat 10-5
        Friends of the Library Group
     PEMBINA TRAIL, 2724 Pembina Hwy, R3T 2H7, SAN 328-9095. Tel:
        204-986-4370. FAX: 204-986-3290. *Br Head,* Kamini Madansingh; Staff
        12 (MLS 1, Non-MLS 11)
        Open Mon, Tues & Thurs 10-8:30, Fri & Sat 10-5, Sun 1-5
        Friends of the Library Group
     LOUIS RIEL BRANCH, 1168 Dakota St, R2N 3T8, SAN 370-4556. Tel:
        204-986-4568. FAX: 204-986-3274. *Br Head,* Trevor Lockhart
        Open Mon, Tues & Thurs 10-8:30, Fri & Sat 10-5
        Friends of the Library Group
     RIVER HEIGHTS, 1520 Corydon Ave, R3N 0J6, SAN 366-4953. Tel:
        204-986-4934. FAX: 204-986-3544. *Br Head,* Sally Stephens
        Open Mon, Tues & Thurs 10-8:30, Fri & Sat 10-5
        Friends of the Library Group

ST BONIFACE, 100-131 Provencher Blvd, R2H 0G2, SAN 366-4929. Tel:
   204-986-4331. FAX: 204-986-6827. *Br Head,* Edith Boulet
   Open Mon-Thurs 10-9, Fri & Sat 10-5, Sun 1-5
   Friends of the Library Group
ST JAMES-ASSINIBOIA, 1910 Portage Ave, R3J 0J2, SAN 366-497X.
   Tel: 204-986-5583. FAX: 204-986-3798. *Br Head,* Phil Bravo
   Open Mon, Tues & Thurs 10-8:30, Wed, Fri & Sat 10-5
   Friends of the Library Group
ST JOHN'S, 500 Salter St, R2W 4M5, SAN 366-4988. Tel: 204-986-4689.
   FAX: 204-986-7123. *Br Head,* David Jacobson
   Open Mon, Tues & Thurs 1-8:30, Fri & Sat 10-5
   Friends of the Library Group
ST VITAL, 6 Fermor Ave, R2M 0Y2, SAN 366-4996. Tel: 204-986-5625.
   FAX: 204-986-3173. *Br Head,* Stephanie Graham
   Open Mon, Tues & Thurs 10-8:30, Wed, Fri & Sat 10-5
   Friends of the Library Group
SIR WILLIAM STEPHENSON, 765 Keewatin St, R2X 3B9, SAN
   377-8061. Tel: 204-986-7070. FAX: 204-986-7201. *Br Head,* Andrew
   McCulloch; Tel: 204-986-7156, E-mail: amcculloch@winnipeg.ca
   Open Tues-Thurs 10-9, Fri & Sat 10-5, Sun 1-5
   Friends of the Library Group
TRANSCONA, 111 Victoria Ave W, R2C 1S6, SAN 366-5003. Tel:
   204-986-3950. FAX: 204-986-3172. *Br Head,* Angela Mehmel
   Open Mon, Tues & Thurs 10-8:30, Fri & Sat 10-5
   Friends of the Library Group
WEST END, 999 Sargent Ave, R3E 3K6, SAN 366-5011. Tel:
   204-986-4677. FAX: 204-986-7129. *Br Head,* Joey Olafsson
   Open Mon & Sat 10-5, Tues-Thurs 1-8:30, Fri 10-6
   Friends of the Library Group
WEST KILDONAN, 365 Jefferson Ave, R2V 0N3, SAN 366-502X. Tel:
   204-986-4384. FAX: 204-986-3373. *Br Head,* Evelyn Piush
   Open Mon, Tues & Thurs 10-8:30, Wed, Fri & Sat 10-5
   Friends of the Library Group
WESTWOOD, 66 Allard Ave, R3K 0T3, SAN 366-5038. Tel:
   204-986-4742. FAX: 204-986-3799. *Br Head,* Jill Johnston
   Open Mon, Tues & Thurs 10-8:30, Fri & Sat 10-5, Sun 1-5
   Friends of the Library Group
WINDSOR PARK, 955 Cottonwood Rd, R2J 1G3, SAN 366-5046. Tel:
   204-986-4945. FAX: 204-986-7122. *Br Head,* Debbie Clague
   Open Mon, Tues & Thurs 1-8:30, Fri & Sat 10-5
   Friends of the Library Group

S   WINNIPEG SCHOOL DIVISION*, Library Support Services, 1075
     Wellington Ave, R3E 0J7. SAN 324-5225. Tel: 204-788-0203. Circulation
     Tel: 204-788-0203, Ext 143. Administration Tel: 204-788-0203, Ext 146.
     FAX: 204-783-9628. E-mail: wlsslibrary@wsd1.org. Web Site:
     www.wsd1.org/pc_lms. *Mgr,* Laura Cowie; E-mail: lcowie@wsd1.org; *Ref
     Libr Tech,* Marsha Bowyer; E-mail: mbowyer@wsd1.org. Subject
     Specialists: *Children's & young adult res, Prof res for teachers,* Laura
     Cowie; *Prof res for teachers,* Marsha Bowyer; Staff 1 (MLS 1)
     Founded 1965. Enrl 32,900; Fac 5,417
     Library Holdings: AV Mats 4,208; Bk Vols 8,488; Per Subs 110
     Special Collections: Local Archives for School Division
     Subject Interests: Educ
     Automation Activity & Vendor Info: (Cataloging) TLC (The Library
     Corporation); (Media Booking) TLC (The Library Corporation); (OPAC)
     TLC (The Library Corporation)
     Database Vendor: EBSCOhost, TLC (The Library Corporation)
     Function: Art exhibits, Computers for patron use, Electronic databases &
     coll, Equip loans & repairs, Online cat, Online ref, Online searches,
     Orientations, Prof lending libr, Pub access computers, Ref & res, Scanner,
     Workshops
     Partic in Manitoba Libr Asn; Manitoba Library Consortium, Inc
     Open Mon-Fri 8:30-4:30
     Restriction: Employees only, In-house use for visitors

Date of Statistics: FY 2011-2012
Population, 2011 Census: 751,171
Population Served by Regional Libraries: 582,387
Total Volumes in Public Libraries: 1,942,611*
Total Public Library Circulation: 2,717,615*
Total Public Library Income: $18,241,079.26
   Provincial Grant: $14,803,873.00
   Municipal Funding: $7,335,655.90
   Provincial & Municipal: $22,139,528,90
Number of Bookmobiles in Province: 3 *Includes physical
   materials as well as electronic materials available for download
   through Overdrive.

BATHURST

P   CHALEUR LIBRARY REGION*, Smurfit-Stone Public Library, 150 St
     George St, Ste 1, E2Q 1B5. Tel: 506-548-0706. FAX: 506-548-0708.
     E-mail: bibliocn@gnb.ca. *Actg Libr Dir,* Dayna DeBenedet; Staff 4 (MLS
     1, Non-MLS 3)
     Founded 1967
     Wireless access
     Open Tues & Thurs (Winter) 10-8, Wed, Fri & Sat 10-5; Mon, Wed & Fri
     (Summer) 10-5, Tues & Thurs 10-8

M   CHALEUR REGIONAL HOSPITAL*, Dr D A Thompson Memorial
     Library, 1750 Sunset Dr, E2A 4L7. SAN 324-394X. Tel: 506-544-2446.
     FAX: 506-544-2017. *Librn,* Suzanne Doucet; E-mail:
     suzanne.doucet2@vitalitenb.ca
     Library Holdings: Bk Titles 1,488; Per Subs 100
     Open Mon-Fri 8-4

CAMPBELLTON

P   CHALEUR LIBRARY REGION*, 113A Roseberry St, E3N 2G6. SAN
     366-5070. Tel: 506-789-6599. FAX: 506-789-7318. Web Site:
     www.gnb.ca/0003/regions/chaleur-e.asp. *Regional Dir,* Sarah Kilfoil; Staff
     40 (MLS 11, Non-MLS 29)
     Founded 1964. Pop 92,947; Circ 334,517
     Apr 2007-Mar 2008 Income (CAN) $2,029,170. Mats Exp (CAN)
     $229,395, Books (CAN) $219,020, Per/Ser (Incl. Access Fees) (CAN)
     $10,375. Sal (CAN) $1,656,577
     Library Holdings: Bk Vols 255,345; Per Subs 281
     Branches: 10
     ATHOLVILLE PUBLIC LIBRARY, 275 rue Notre-Dame, Atholville, E3N
     4T1, SAN 372-0160. Tel: 506-789-2914. FAX: 506-789-2056. E-mail:
     biblioda@gnb.ca. *Libr Mgr,* Nicole Richard; E-mail:
     nicole.r.richard@gnb.ca; Staff 1 (Non-MLS 1)
     Founded 1967
     Open Tues, Wed, Fri & Sat (Winter) 9:30-12 & 1-5, Thurs 1-5 &
     6pm-8:30pm; Mon-Wed & Fri (Summer) 9:30-12 & 1-5, Thurs 1-5 &
     6pm-8:30pm
     BAS-CARAQUET PUBLIC LIBRARY, 8185-2 rue Saint Paul,
     Bas-Caraquet, E1W 6C4, SAN 366-5100. Tel: 506-726-2775. FAX:
     506-726-2770. E-mail: bibliobc@gnb.ca. *Libr Mgr,* Mylene May Gionet;
     Staff 1.5 (Non-MLS 1.5)
     Founded 1989
     Open Tues (Winter) 1-5 & 6pm-8:30pm, Wed-Sat 9:30-12 & 1-5; Mon &
     Wed-Fri (Summer) 9:30-12 & 1-5, Tues 1-5 & 6pm-8:30pm
     CAMPBELLTON CENTENNIAL LIBRARY, 19 Aberdeen St, Ste 100,
     E3N 2J4, SAN 366-5135. Tel: 506-753-5253. FAX: 506-753-3803.
     E-mail: bibliocc@gnb.ca. *Libr Dir,* Jocelyn Paquette; E-mail:
     jocelyn.paquette@gnb.ca; Staff 8.5 (MLS 4, Non-MLS 4.5)
     Founded 1966
     Open Tues & Wed (Winter) 10-8:30, Thurs-Sat 10-5; Mon, Thurs & Fri
     (Summer) 10-5, Tues & Wed 10-8:30

DALHOUSIE CENTENNIAL LIBRARY, 403 rue Adelaïde, Dalhousie,
     E8C 1B6, SAN 372-0179. Tel: 506-684-7370. FAX: 506-684-7374.
     E-mail: bibliocd@gnb.ca. *Libr Mgr,* Sandra B Carter; Staff 2.5
     (Non-MLS 2.5)
     Founded 1967
     Open Tues & Wed (Winter) 1-5 & 6pm-8:30pm, Thurs-Sat 9:30-12 &
     1-5; Mon, Thurs & Fri (Summer) 9:30-12 & 1-5, Tues & Wed 1-5 &
     6pm-8:30pm
LAMEQUE PUBLIC LIBRARY, 46 du Pêcheur Nord St, Lameque, E8T
     1J3, SAN 366-516X. Tel: 506-344-3262. FAX: 506-344-3263. E-mail:
     bibliopl@gnb.ca. *Libr Mgr,* Jeanne-Mance Noël; E-mail:
     jeanne-mance.noel@gnb.ca; Staff 1.5 (Non-MLS 1.5)
     Founded 1989
     Open Tues (Winter) 1-5 & 6-8:30, Wed-Sat 9:30-12 & 1-5; Mon &
     Wed-Fri (Summer) 9:30-12 & 1-5, Tues 1-5 & 6pm-8:30pm
LAVAL-GOUPIL PUBLIC LIBRARY, 128 Mgr Chiasson St, Shippagan,
     E8S 1X7, SAN 366-5240. Tel: 506-336-3920. FAX: 506-336-3921. *Libr
     Mgr,* Pauline Godin; E-mail: pauline.godin@gnb.ca; Staff 2 (Non-MLS
     2)
     Founded 1980
     Open Tues (Winter) 1-5 & 6pm-8:30pm, Wed-Sat 9:30-12 & 1-5; Mon &
     Wed-Fri (Summer) 9:30-12 & 1-5, Tues 1-5 & 6pm-8:30pm
MGR PAQUET PUBLIC LIBRARY, 10A du Colisée St, Caraquet, E1W
     1A5, SAN 366-5224. Tel: 506-726-2681. FAX: 506-726-2685. E-mail:
     bibliock@gnb.ca. *Libr Mgr,* Carole Hébert; E-mail:
     carole.hebert@gnb.ca; Staff 2 (Non-MLS 2)
     Founded 1973
     Open Tues (Winter) 1-5 & 6pm-8:30pm, Wed-Sat 9:30-12 & 1-5; Mon &
     Wed-Fri (Summer) 9:30-12 & 1-5, Tues 1-5 & 6pm-8:30pm
MGR ROBICHAUD PUBLIC LIBRARY, 855 Principale St, Local 3,
     Beresford, E8K 1T3, SAN 372-0187. Tel: 506-542-2704. FAX:
     506-542-2714. E-mail: bibliomr@gnb.ca. *Libr Dir,* Araya-Yohannes
     Bekele; Staff 2 (MLS 1, Non-MLS 1)
     Founded 1983
     Open Tues & Thurs (Winter) 1-5 & 6pm-8:30pm, Wed, Fri & Sat
     9:30-12 & 1-5; Mon, Wed & Fri (Summer) 9:30-12 & 1-5, Tues & Thurs
     1-5 & 6pm-8:30pm
PETIT-ROCHER PUBLIC LIBRARY, 702 Principale St, Office 110,
     Petit-Rocher, E8J 1V1, SAN 366-5119. Tel: 506-542-2744. FAX:
     506-542-2745. E-mail: bibliopr@gnb.ca. *Actg Libr Mgr,* Jennifer
     Iannuzzelli; Staff 2 (Non-MLS 2)
     Founded 1987
     Open Tues & Thurs-Sat (Winter) 9:30-12 & 1-5, Wed 1-5 &
     6pm-8:30pm; Mon, Tues, Thurs & Fri (Summer) 9:30-12 & 1-5, Wed
     1-5 & 6pm-8:30pm
     Friends of the Library Group
TRACADIE-SHEILA PUBLIC LIBRARY, 3620 Main St, Tracadie-Sheila,
     E1X 1C9. (Mail add: CP 3654, Main Postal Office, Tracadie-Sheila, E1X
     1G5), SAN 366-5259. Tel: 506-393-4005. FAX: 506-394-4009. E-mail:
     bibliots@gnb.ca. *Actg Libr Dir,* Amanda Halfpenny; Staff 2 (MLS 1,
     Non-MLS 1)
     Founded 1975

Open Tues (Winter) 1:30-5 & 6pm-8:30pm, Wed-Sat 9:30-12:30 & 1:30-5; Mon & Wed-Fri (Summer) 9:30-12:30 & 1:30-5, Tues 1:30-5 & 6pm-8:30pm
Bookmobiles: 1. Supvr, Darlene MacLean

CARAQUET

S   FEDERATION DES CAISSES POPULAIRES ACADIENNES*, Bibliotheque Mgr-J-L-Chiasson, Place de l'Arcadie 295 boul Saint Pierre ouest, E1W 1B7. (Mail add: PO Box 5554, E1W 1B7), SAN 370-6214. Tel: 506-726-4000, 506-726-4500. FAX: 506-726-4001. *Archivist,* Jacqueline Dujas; Tel: 506-726-4510
Library Holdings: Bk Titles 2,500; Per Subs 45
Open Mon-Fri 9-5

DORCHESTER

S   CORRECTIONAL SERVICES OF CANADA*, Westmoreland Institution Library, 4902 A Main St, E4K 2Y9. SAN 329-2363. Tel: 506-379-4502, 506-379-4550. FAX: 506-379-4616. *In Charge,* Danny Smith; *Coordr,* Frank Landry; E-mail: landryfg@csc-scc.gc.ca; Staff 1 (MLS 1)
Founded 1984
Library Holdings: Bk Vols 6,000; Per Subs 40
Subject Interests: Art
Publications: Hill-Top Journal
Open Mon-Sat 1-4 & 6pm-8pm, Sun 1-4
Friends of the Library Group

EDMUNDSTON

S   FRASER PAPERS INC LIBRARY*, Central Tech Dept, 27 Rice St, E3V 1S9. SAN 318-9236. Tel: 506-737-2252. FAX: 506-737-2137. *Librn,* Linda Smyth
Founded 1940
Library Holdings: Bk Titles 2,100
Subject Interests: Lumber, Paper, Paperboard, Pulp
Open Mon-Fri 8-4:30
Restriction: Co libr

P   HAUT-SAINT-JEAN REGIONAL LIBRARY, Region de Bibliotheques du Haut-Saint-Jean, 15, rue de l'Église St, Ste 102, E3V 1J3. SAN 366-5283. Tel: 506-735-2074. FAX: 506-735-2193. Web Site: www.gnb.ca/0003/nbpls.htm. *Regional Dir,* Joanne Jacob; *Asst Regional Dir,* Patrick Provencher; *Pub Serv Librn,* Michelle Bourque; *Tech Serv Librn,* Rachel Lavoie; Staff 4 (MLS 4)
Founded 1971
Library Holdings: Bk Vols 302,882; Per Subs 538
Special Collections: Professional Coll (libr sci)
Database Vendor: EBSCOhost
Wireless access
Publications: Jalons historiques: la Bibliotheque Regionale du Haut-Saint-Jean au nord-ouest du Nouveau-Brunswick, Bulletin du Haut-Saint-Jean
Special Services for the Blind - Talking bks
Friends of the Library Group
Branches: 12
DR WALTER CHESTNUT PUBLIC LIBRARY, 395 Main St., Unit 1, Hartland, E7P 2N3. Tel: 506-375-4876. FAX: 506-375-6816. *Libr Mgr,* Jean Haywood
L P FISHER PUBLIC LIBRARY, 679 Main St, Woodstock, E7M 2E1. Tel: 506-325-4777. FAX: 506-325-4811. *Libr Mgr,* Jonathan Tait
GRAND SAULT PUBLIC, 131 Rue Pleasant, Ste 201, Grand Sault, E3Z 1G6, SAN 366-5348. Tel: 506-475-7781. FAX: 506-475-7783. E-mail: gfplib@gnb.ca. *Libr Dir,* Danielle Chafetz
Founded 1972
Library Holdings: Bk Vols 21,691; Per Subs 38
Subject Interests: Genealogy
Open Tues & Thurs 12-8, Wed & Fri 10-5, Sat 11-4
KEDGWICK PUBLIC, 116 Notre-Dame St, Unit P, Kedgwick, E8B 1H8, SAN 366-5356. Tel: 506-284-2757. FAX: 506-284-4557. E-mail: bibliopk@gnb.ca. *Libr Mgr,* Diane Thompson
Founded 1983
Library Holdings: Bk Vols 8,500; Per Subs 20
Open Mon, Tues, Thurs & Fri 10-12 & 1-5, Wed 1-5 & 6pm-8pm
LA MOISSON PUBLIC, 206 Canada St, Saint Quentin, E8A 1H1, SAN 366-5380. Tel: 506-235-1955. FAX: 506-235-1957. E-mail: bibliolm@gnb.ca. *Mgr,* Helene DuRepos Theriault
Founded 1969
Library Holdings: Bk Vols 19,997; Per Subs 24
Open Tues & Thurs 9-12, 1-5 & 7pm-9pm, Wed & Fri 9-12 & 1-5, Sat 10-12 & 1-4
ANDREW & LAURA MCCAIN PUBLIC LIBRARY, 8 McCain St, Florenceville-Bristol, E7L 3H6. Tel: 506-392-5294. FAX: 506-392-8108. *Libr Mgr,* Julie Craig

MONSEIGNEUR PLOURDE PUBLIC, 15 Bellevue St, Saint Francois, E7A 1A4, SAN 366-5364. Tel: 506-992-6052. FAX: 506-992-6047. E-mail: stfplib@gnb.ca. *Mgr,* Bertin Nadeau
Founded 1983
Library Holdings: Bk Vols 13,500; Per Subs 15
Open Tues, Wed & Fri 10-12 & 1-5, Thurs 1-5 & 6:30pm-8:30pm, Sat 12:30-4:30
MONSEIGNEUR W J CONWAY PUBLIC, 33 rue Irene, E3V 1B7, SAN 366-5313. Tel: 506-735-4713. FAX: 506-737-6848. E-mail: biblioed@gnb.ca. *Chief Librn,* Emilie Lefrancois
Founded 1972
Library Holdings: Bk Vols 43,361; Per Subs 96
Open Tues & Thurs 10-9, Wed, Fri & Sat 10-5
NACKAWIC PUBLIC-SCHOOL LIBRARY, 30 Landegger Dr, Nackawic, E6G 1E9. Tel: 506-575-2136. FAX: 506-575-2336. *Libr Mgr,* Paulette Tonner
PERTH-ANDOVER PUBLIC LIBRARY, 642 E Riverside Dr, Perth-Andover, E7H 1Z6. Tel: 506-273-2843. FAX: 506-273-1913. *Libr Mgr,* Tammie Wright
PLASTER ROCK PUBLIC-SCHOOL LIBRARY, 290-A Main St, Plaster Rock, E7G 2C6. Tel: 506-356-6018. FAX: 506-356-6019. *Libr Mgr,* Carolyn Knowlton
DR LORNE J VIOLETTE PUBLIC LIBRARY, 180 Rue St-Jean, Saint Leonard, E7E 2B9, SAN 366-5372. Tel: 506-423-3025. FAX: 506-423-3026. E-mail: stlplib@gnb.ca. *Mgr,* Lise Poitras
Founded 1972
Library Holdings: Audiobooks 50; AV Mats 50; Bks on Deafness & Sign Lang 10; CDs 400; DVDs 200; High Interest/Low Vocabulary Bk Vols 125; Large Print Bks 300; Bk Vols 22,057; Per Subs 12
Database Vendor: ProQuest
Open Tues 12-5 & 6pm-8pm, Wed & Sat 10-12 & 1-5

C   UNIVERSITY DE MONCTON*, Bibliotheque Rhea-Larose, 165 boul Hebert, E3V 2S8. SAN 318-9228. Tel: 506-737-5058. FAX: 506-737-5373. Web Site: www.umce.ca. *Dir,* Guy Lefrancois; Tel: 506-737-5266; *Ref,* Claire Charest; Staff 9 (MLS 1, Non-MLS 8)
Founded 1972. Enrl 600; Highest Degree: Master
Library Holdings: Bk Vols 70,000; Per Subs 325
Special Collections: State Document Depository
Subject Interests: Forestry sci, Local hist
Automation Activity & Vendor Info: (Acquisitions) Infor Library & Information Solutions; (Cataloging) Infor Library & Information Solutions; (Circulation) Infor Library & Information Solutions; (OPAC) Infor Library & Information Solutions
Database Vendor: Gale Cengage Learning, OCLC FirstSearch, OVID Technologies, ProQuest
Publications: Bibliographies
Partic in Coun of Atlantic Univ Librns
Open Mon-Fri 8:30am-9pm, Sat & Sun 12:30-4:30

FREDERICTON

S   ADI LTD LIBRARY*, 1133 Regent St, Ste 300, E3B 3Z2. SAN 377-2497. Tel: 506-454-8000. FAX: 506-459-3954. *Librn,* Debra E Edmondson; E-mail: dee@adi.ca
Library Holdings: Bk Vols 600; Per Subs 30
Restriction: Not open to pub

S   BEAVERBROOK ART GALLERY LIBRARY*, 703 Queen St, E3B 5A6. (Mail add: PO Box 605, Sta A, E3B 5A6), SAN 371-7569. Tel: 506-458-2028. FAX: 506-459-7450. Web Site: www.beaverbrookartgallery.org. *Curator, Dep Dir,* Terry Graff; E-mail: tgraff@beaverbrookartgallery.org
Founded 1959
Library Holdings: DVDs 40; Bk Titles 3,500; Per Subs 35; Videos 350
Special Collections: Contemporary Art of Atlantic Canada; Graham Sutherland; Modern British Painting; Modern Canadian Art; Victorian Painting
Restriction: Open by appt only

G   CANADIAN AGRICULTURE LIBRARY-FREDERICTON*, Agriculture & Agri-Food Canada, 850 Lincoln Rd, E3B 4Z7. SAN 318-9244. Tel: 506-452-4810. FAX: 506-452-3316. E-mail: nbfag@agr.gc.ca. Web Site: www.agr.gc.ca/cal. *Head Librn,* André Gionet; E-mail: andre.gionet@agr.gc.ca; Staff 1 (MLS 1)
Founded 1952
Library Holdings: Bk Titles 4,200; Per Subs 30
Subject Interests: Agr, Entomology, Plant breeding, Plant pathology, Potatoes, Soil sci
Restriction: Staff use only

M   DR EVERETT CHALMERS HOSPITAL*, Dr G Moffatt Health Sciences Library, 700 Priestman St, E3B 5N5. (Mail add: PO Box 9000, E3B 5N5), SAN 327-4055. Tel: 506-452-5432. FAX: 506-452-5585. Web Site:

www.rvhlibrary.nb.ca. *Mgr, Libr Serv,* Paul Clark; E-mail:
Paul.Clark@horizonnb.ca
Library Holdings: Bk Vols 5,000; Per Subs 200
Special Collections: Classics of Medicine Series
Subject Interests: Allied health, Med, Nursing
Wireless access
Publications: Info Pulse
Open Mon-Fri 8-6

SR   DIOCESAN SYNOD OF FREDERICTON*, Anglican Diocesan Archives
     & Medley Library, c/o Provincial Archives of New Brunswick, PO Box
     6000, E3B 5H1. SAN 327-3024. Tel: 506-453-2122. FAX: 506-453-3288.
     Archivist, Frank Morehouse
     Founded 1963
     Library Holdings: Bk Vols 4,000
     Subject Interests: Church hist, Music, Theol
     Restriction: Open by appt only

L   LAW SOCIETY OF NEW BRUNSWICK LIBRARY, Justice Bldg, E3B
     5H1. (Mail add: PO Box 6000, E3B 5H1), SAN 318-9252. Tel:
     506-453-2500. FAX: 506-453-9438. E-mail: lawlibry@nbnet.nb.ca. *Law
     Librn,* Tanya Davis; *Asst Librn,* Judy Lane; Staff 1 (MLS 1)
     Founded 1846
     Library Holdings: Electronic Media & Resources 15; Bk Vols 25,000
     Restriction: Not open to pub, Staff & mem only

G   NATURAL RESOURCES CANADA LIBRARY*, Hugh John Flemming
     Forestry Centre, 1350 Regent St S, E3B 5P7. (Mail add: PO Box 4000,
     E3B 5P7), SAN 318-9260. Tel: 506-452-3541, 506-452-3614. FAX:
     506-452-3525. E-mail: afclib@nrcan-rncan.gc.ca. Web Site:
     metafore2.nrcan-rncan.gc.ca. *Libr Mgr,* Sandra Lowman; *Libr Tech,* Kelly
     Dickson
     Founded 1921
     Library Holdings: Bk Vols 15,000; Per Subs 100
     Special Collections: Canadian Provincial Forestry Publications
     Subject Interests: Biodiversity, Ecology, Entomology, Forestry incl
     develop, Genetics, Pathology, Silviculture, Theses
     Automation Activity & Vendor Info: (Cataloging) SirsiDynix;
     (Circulation) SirsiDynix; (OPAC) SirsiDynix
     Open Mon-Fri 8:30-4:30

C   NEW BRUNSWICK COLLEGE OF CRAFT & DESIGN LIBRARY*, 457
     Queen St, 3rd Flr, E3B 5H1. (Mail add: PO Box 6000, E3B 5H1), SAN
     374-5775. Tel: 506-453-5938. Administration Tel: 506-453-2305. FAX:
     506-457-7352. Web Site:
     www.nbccd.ca/en/home/currentstudents/library.aspx. *Coordr, Libr Serv,*
     Julieta Lumbria McDonald; E-mail: julie.mcdonald@gnb.ca; Staff 1
     (Non-MLS 1)
     Founded 1987. Enrl 184; Fac 34
     Library Holdings: AV Mats 11; CDs 10; DVDs 115; Bk Titles 7,000; Per
     Subs 110; Videos 445
     Subject Interests: Art educ, Arts, Clay, Communications, Design, Fashion
     design, Jewelry, N Am Indian art, Photog, Pottery, Textiles design, Visual
     arts
     Automation Activity & Vendor Info: (Acquisitions) Follett Software;
     (Cataloging) Follett Software; (Circulation) Follett Software; (Course
     Reserve) Follett Software; (ILL) Follett Software; (Media Booking) Follett
     Software; (OPAC) Follett Software
     Database Vendor: EBSCOhost
     Wireless access
     Function: Electronic databases & coll, Instruction & testing, Online
     searches, Orientations, Photocopying/Printing, Ref serv in person
     Restriction: Open to students, fac, staff & alumni
     Friends of the Library Group

G   NEW BRUNSWICK DEPARTMENT OF POST-SECONDARY
     EDUCATION, TRAINING & LABOUR LIBRARY*, 470 York St, E3B
     5H1. SAN 318-9279. Tel: 506-453-8247. FAX: 506-453-3618. *Librn,* Mary
     Comeau; E-mail: mary.comeau@gnb.ca; Staff 1 (Non-MLS 1)
     Library Holdings: Bk Titles 4,242; Bk Vols 5,225; Per Subs 50
     Special Collections: Govt Docs
     Subject Interests: Adult educ
     Automation Activity & Vendor Info: (Cataloging) Follett Software;
     (Circulation) Follett Software
     Open Mon-Fri 8:15-4:30
     Restriction: Employee & client use only, External users must contact libr

S   NEW BRUNSWICK EMERGENCY MEASURES ORGANIZATION
     LIBRARY*, Victoria Health Ctr, Ground Flr, 65 Brunswick St, E3B 5H1.
     SAN 377-4058. Tel: 506-453-2133. FAX: 506-453-5513. *Mgr,* Lisa Munn
     Library Holdings: Bk Vols 20,580
     Open Mon-Fri 8:15-4:30

G   NEW BRUNSWICK LEGISLATIVE LIBRARY*, Legislative Bldg, 706
     Queen St, E3B 1C5. (Mail add: PO Box 6000, E3B 5H1), SAN 318-9295.
     Tel: 506-453-2338. Interlibrary Loan Service Tel: 506-444-5039.
     Administration Tel: 506-453-8346. FAX: 506-444-5889. E-mail:
     library.biblio-info@gnb.ca. Web Site: www.gnb.ca/legis/leglibbib. *Govt Doc
     Librn,* Janet McNeil; Tel: 506-453-8348, E-mail: janet.mcneil@gnb.ca;
     Legis Librn, Kenda Clark-Gorey; E-mail: kenda.clark.gorey@gnb.ca;
     Outreach Librn, Kathleen Jeffries; Tel: 506-453-8345, E-mail:
     kathleen.jeffries@gnb.ca; *Automation Spec,* Anthony Lovesey; Tel:
     506-444-4997, E-mail: anthony.lovesey@gnb.ca; Staff 7 (MLS 2, Non-MLS
     5)
     Founded 1841
     Library Holdings: Bk Titles 63,000; Per Subs 300
     Special Collections: Government Documents; New Brunswickana. Can &
     Prov
     Subject Interests: Behav sci, Soc sci
     Automation Activity & Vendor Info: (Cataloging) Horizon; (Circulation)
     Horizon; (OPAC) Horizon
     Publications: New Brunswick Government Documents (Annually);
     Periodical Contents; Selected Accessions List (Quarterly)
     Open Mon-Fri 8-5
     Restriction: Circ limited

G   NEW BRUNSWICK PUBLIC LIBRARY SERVICE*, 250 King St, E3B
     9M9. (Mail add: PO Box 6000, E3B 5H1), SAN 318-9309. Tel:
     506-453-2354. FAX: 506-444-4064. Web Site: www.gnb.ca/0003/who.asp.
     Exec Dir, Sylvie Madeau; *Asst Dir,* Ella Nason; *Cat,* Lorraine Morehouse;
     Syst Librn, David Campbell; Staff 14 (MLS 7, Non-MLS 7)
     Founded 1954
     Library Holdings: Bk Titles 1,000; Per Subs 80
     Subject Interests: Libr sci, Mgt
     Automation Activity & Vendor Info: (Acquisitions) SirsiDynix;
     (Cataloging) SirsiDynix; (Circulation) SirsiDynix; (OPAC) SirsiDynix
     Database Vendor: EBSCOhost, ProQuest, SirsiDynix
     Function: Prof lending libr
     Publications: Regional & Public Library Statistics
     Open Mon-Fri 8-5

G   THE OMBUDSMAN LIBRARY*, 548 York St, E3B 3R2. (Mail add: PO
     Box 6000, E3B 5H1), SAN 373-4919. Tel: 506-453-2789. FAX:
     506-453-5599. E-mail: nbombud@gnb.ca. *In Charge,* Julie Dickison
     Library Holdings: Bk Vols 100
     Open Mon-Fri 8:30-4:30

S   PROVINCIAL ARCHIVES OF NEW BRUNSWICK*, 23 Dineen Dr, E3B
     5A3. (Mail add: PO Box 6000, E3B 5H1), SAN 318-9317. Tel:
     506-453-2122. FAX: 506-453-3288. E-mail: provincial.archives@gnb.ca.
     Web Site: www.gnb.ca/archives. *Dir,* Marion Beyea; E-mail:
     marion.beyea@gnb.ca; *Mgr,* Fred Farrell; E-mail: fred.farrell@gnb.ca;
     Conserv Librn, Dean Lund; E-mail: dean.lund@gnb.ca; *AV,* Allen Doiron;
     E-mail: allen.doiron@gnb.ca; *Govt Doc,* Diana Moore; E-mail:
     diana.moore@gnb.ca; *Pub Serv,* Heather Lyons; E-mail:
     heather.lyons@gnb.ca; Staff 25 (Non-MLS 25)
     Founded 1968
     Library Holdings: Bk Vols 4,000
     Special Collections: New Brunswick, broadcast rec, bus & family papers,
     flm & videos, govt rec, maps, photogs, plans
     Publications: County Census (Archives guide)
     Open Mon-Fri 10-5, Sat 8:30-5
     Friends of the Library Group

C   UNIVERSITY OF NEW BRUNSWICK LIBRARIES*, Five Macaulay Dr,
     E3B 5H5. (Mail add: PO Box 7500, E3B 5H5), SAN 366-5402. Tel:
     506-453-4740. Interlibrary Loan Service Tel: 506-453-4743. FAX:
     506-453-4595. Interlibrary Loan Service FAX: 506-453-4596. E-mail:
     library@unb.ca. Web Site: www.lib.unb.ca/. *Dir,* John Teskey; Tel:
     506-458-7958, E-mail: jteskey@unb.ca; *Assoc Dir of Libr/Coll Serv,*
     Jocelyne Thompson; Tel: 506-458-7053, E-mail: jlt@unb.ca; *Assoc Dir of
     Libr/Learning & Res Serv,* Lesley Balcom; Tel: 506-458-7056, E-mail:
     lbalcom@unb.ca; *Dept Head, Archives,* Francesca Holyoke; Tel:
     506-453-4965, E-mail: holyoke@unb.ca; *Dept Head, Ref,* James Mckenzie;
     Tel: 506-458-7056, E-mail: jmackenz@unb.ca; *Head, Cat,* Barbara
     Wheeler; Tel: 506-458-7412, E-mail: barbw@unb.ca; *Acq,* Diane Budaker;
     Tel: 506-453-3529, E-mail: dbudaker@unb.ca. Subject Specialists: *English,*
     James Mckenzie; Staff 24 (MLS 22, Non-MLS 2)
     Founded 1829. Enrl 8,333; Fac 460; Highest Degree: Doctorate
     Library Holdings: Bk Vols 1,185,417; Per Subs 3,011
     Special Collections: Beaverbrook bks, pamphlets, per, newspapers from
     1785-date, mss; Canadian Literature (Rufus Hathaway Coll), bks,
     pamphlets, per & mss; Canadian Loyalists (Loyalists Studies Programme,
     Canadian depository), mss, microflm; Children's Literature Coll; His
     Times, bks, memorabilia & mss; New Brunswick History & Literature;
     New Brunswick School Textbooks Coll; Political (R B Bennett, Prime
     Minister), mss. Oral History; State Document Depository; UN Document
     Depository; US Document Depository

Automation Activity & Vendor Info: (Acquisitions) SirsiDynix; (Cataloging) SirsiDynix; (Circulation) SirsiDynix; (Course Reserve) SirsiDynix; (ILL) Relais International; (OPAC) SirsiDynix; (Serials) SirsiDynix

Database Vendor: ABC-CLIO, ACM (Association for Computing Machinery), Agricola, Alexander Street Press, American Chemical Society, American Mathematical Society, American Physical Society, American Psychological Association (APA), Annual Reviews, ARTstor, BioOne, Cambridge Scientific Abstracts, CEDROM-SNi, Children's Literature Comprehensive Database Company (CLCD), Cinahl Information Systems, Coutts Information Service, CRC Press/Taylor & Francis CRCnetBASE, CredoReference, Dialog, ebrary, EBSCOhost, Elsevier, Emerald, Faulkner Information Services, Gale Cengage Learning, H W Wilson, Haworth Pres Inc, HeinOnline, IBISWorld, IEEE (Institute of Electrical & Electronics Engineers), Infomart, Ingenta, Ingram Library Services, IOP, ISI Web of Knowledge, JSTOR, LexisNexis, Marcive, Inc, McGraw-Hill, Medline, Modern Language Association, Nature Publishing Group, netLibrary, OCLC FirstSearch, OCLC WorldCat, Oxford Online, Paratext, Project MUSE, ProQuest, PubMed, Quicklaw, RefWorks, Sage, ScienceDirect, Scopus, Springer-Verlag, Swets Information Services, Thomson - Web of Science, Wiley InterScience
Wireless access

Publications: Maritime Pamphlets Coll annotated list; Quest Users Guide Partic in Canadian Association of Research Libraries; Consortia Canada; Council of Atlantic University Libraries (CAUL)
Special Services for the Deaf - Accessible learning ctr; Assistive tech
Special Services for the Blind - Accessible computers; Aids for in-house use; Assistive/Adapted tech devices, equip & products; Bks on CD; Computer with voice synthesizer for visually impaired persons

Departmental Libraries:
ENGINEERING, Sir Edmund Head Hall, Rm C-15, 15 Dineen Dr, E3B 5A3. (Mail add: PO Box 7500, E3B 5H5). Tel: 506-453-4747. FAX: 506-453-4829. Web Site: www.lib.unb.ca/engineering/enggpage.htm. *Head, Eng Libr,* Steve Lelievre; *Circ,* Neil Toner
  Library Holdings: Bk Vols 47,000; Per Subs 600
GERARD V LA FOREST LAW LIBRARY, Ludlow Hall, 2nd Flr, 41 Dineen Dr, E3B 5A3. (Mail add: Bag Service No 44999, E3B 6C9), SAN 366-553X. Tel: 506-453-4734. FAX: 506-451-6948, 506-453-5186. E-mail: lawlib@unb.ca. Web Site: www.unb.ca/law/library. *Head Law Librn,* Janet Moss; Tel: 506-442-3266, E-mail: jmoss@unb.ca; *Ref/Instruction Librn,* Catherine Cotter; E-mail: cacotter@unb.ca; *Tech Serv Librn,* Darren Furey; *Acq, Cat, ILL,* Margaret Forster; *Cat, Reserves,* Heather Doherty; *Circ, Ser,* Yolande Gagnon; Staff 6.4 (MLS 3, Non-MLS 3.4)
  Founded 1892
  Subject Interests: Common law
SCIENCE & FORESTRY, Four Bailey Dr, E3B 5H5. (Mail add: PO Box 7500, E3B 5H5). Tel: 506-453-4601, 506-458-7759. FAX: 506-453-3518. E-mail: scilib@unb.ca. Web Site: www.lib.unb.ca/science. *Head Librn,* Stephen Sloan; E-mail: sloan@unb.ca. Subject Specialists: *Biol, Chem, Math,* Stephen Sloan
  Open Mon-Fri 8am-11pm (8-6 May-Aug), Sat 8am-9pm, Sun 10am-11pm

P   YORK LIBRARY REGION*, Four Carleton St, E3B 5P4. SAN 366-5550. Tel: 506-453-5380. Reference Tel: 506-460-2812. FAX: 506-457-4878. E-mail: dpetlinfo@gnb.ca. Web Site: www.gnb.ca/publiclibraries. *Regional Dir,* Jill Katherine Foster; *Asst Regional Dir,* Bill Mitchell; Tel: 506-457-7271, E-mail: bill.mitchell@gnb.ca; *Head, Ref Serv,* Stephanie Furrow; Tel: 506-460-2807, Fax: 506-460-2801, E-mail: stephanie.furrow@gnb.ca; *Pub Serv Librn,* Christan Sheridan; Tel: 506-444-2603, E-mail: christan.sheridan@gnb.ca; Staff 58 (MLS 14, Non-MLS 44)
Founded 1958. Pop 154,953; Circ 788,100
Apr 2006-Mar 2007 Income (CAN) $3,084,657, Provincial (CAN) $3,075,353, Locally Generated Income (CAN) $9,304. Mats Exp (CAN) $129,461, Books (CAN) $91,165, Per/Ser (Incl. Access Fees) (CAN) $12,725, Micro (CAN) $4,706, AV Mat (CAN) $20,146, Presv (CAN) $719. Sal (CAN) $1,905,626
Library Holdings: AV Mats 49,216; DVDs 1,420; Bk Vols 452,317; Per Subs 453; Talking Bks 3,050; Videos 12,295
Special Collections: New Brunswick Local History Coll; Talking Book Coll. Can & Prov; Oral History
Automation Activity & Vendor Info: (Acquisitions) SirsiDynix; (Cataloging) SirsiDynix; (Circulation) SirsiDynix; (ILL) Anacortes Software Inc; (OPAC) SirsiDynix
Database Vendor: SirsiDynix
Special Services for the Blind - Talking bks
Open Mon-Fri 8-5
Restriction: Not a lending libr
Branches: 14
BIBLIOTHEQUE DRE-MARGUERITE-MICHAUD, 715 Priestman St, E3B 5W7, SAN 366-5585. Tel: 506-453-7100. FAX: 506-453-3958. E-mail: bibliodmm@gnb.ca. *Librn,* Francoise Caron; E-mail: francoise.caron@gnb.ca; Staff 3 (MLS 1, Non-MLS 2)

Founded 1978. Pop 47,560; Circ 76,204
Library Holdings: AV Mats 4,125; DVDs 173; Bk Vols 32,955; Per Subs 50; Videos 1,582
Open Mon, Wed & Fri 9-5, Tues & Thurs 9-8, Sat 1-5
CHATHAM PUBLIC LIBRARY, 24 King St, Miramichi, E1N 2N1, SAN 366-5615. Tel: 506-773-6274. FAX: 506-773-6963. E-mail: chathmpl@gnb.ca. *Actg Libr Dir,* Jennifer Wilcox; Staff 2 (MLS 1, Non-MLS 1)
Founded 1975. Pop 18,508; Circ 41,077
Library Holdings: AV Mats 727; Bk Vols 20,025; Per Subs 27; Videos 880
Open Tues & Thurs 1-8, Wed, Fri & Sat 10-5
CHIPMAN BRANCH, Eight King St, Chipman, E4A 2H3, SAN 366-564X. Tel: 506-339-5852. FAX: 506-339-9804. E-mail: chipman.publiclibrary@gnb.ca. *Libr Mgr,* Krista Blyth; E-mail: krista.blyth@gnb.ca; Staff 1.5 (Non-MLS 1.5)
Founded 1975. Pop 1,432; Circ 18,730
Library Holdings: AV Mats 527; Bk Vols 15,495; Per Subs 20; Videos 391
Open Tues, Wed, Fri & Sat 10-12:30 & 1:30-5, Thurs 1:30-5 & 6pm-8:30pm
Friends of the Library Group
DOAKTOWN COMMUNITY LIBRARY, 430 Main St, Doaktown, E9C 1E8, SAN 370-131X. Tel: 506-365-2018. FAX: 506-365-2019. E-mail: dtcslib@gnb.ca. *Libr Mgr,* Belva Brown; E-mail: belva.brown@gnb.ca; Staff 2 (Non-MLS 2)
Founded 1986. Pop 955; Circ 23,495
Apr 2006-Mar 2007 Income $27,667, City (CAN) $13,000, Locally Generated Income (CAN) $7,881, Other (CAN) $6,786
Library Holdings: AV Mats 1,010; Bk Vols 18,863; Per Subs 33; Videos 826
Open Mon-Wed & Fri 9-12:30 & 1:30-5, Thurs 12-5 & 6-8
FREDERICTON PUBLIC LIBRARY, 12 Carleton St, E3B 5P4, SAN 366-5739. Tel: 506-460-2800. FAX: 506-460-2801. E-mail: ftonpub@gnb.ca. *Libr Dir,* Brian Steeves; Tel: 506-460-2809, E-mail: brian.steeves@gnb.ca; *Head, Ref Serv,* Stephanie Furrow; Tel: 506-460-2807, E-mail: stephanie.furrow@gnb.ca; *Ch,* Nancy Edgar; Tel: 506-460-2900, E-mail: nancy.edgar@gnb.ca; *Circ Supvr,* Sheila Grondin-Lyons; Tel: 506-460-2804, E-mail: sheila.grondin-lyons@gnb.ca; *Young Adult & Adult Serv Coordr,* Leslie Cockburn; Tel: 506-460-2482, E-mail: leslie.cockburn@gnb.ca; Staff 16 (MLS 4, Non-MLS 12)
Founded 1959. Pop 47,560; Circ 342,282
Apr 2006-Mar 2007 Income $388,144, City (CAN) $337,332, Locally Generated Income (CAN) $50,812
Library Holdings: AV Mats 26,396; DVDs 598; Bk Titles 126,119; Per Subs 103; Talking Bks 3,049; Videos 4,257
Special Services for the Blind - Bks on cassette; Cassette playback machines
Open Mon, Tues, Thurs & Sat 10-5, Wed & Fri 10-9
Friends of the Library Group
HARVEY COMMUNITY LIBRARY, 2055 Rte 3, Harvey Station, E6K 3W9. (Mail add: PO Box 258, Harvey Station, E6K 3W9), SAN 370-1328. Tel: 506-366-2206. FAX: 506-366-2210. E-mail: harvey.library@gnb.ca. *Libr Mgr,* Joanne M Cole; E-mail: joanne.m.cole@gnb.ca; Staff 1 (Non-MLS 1)
Founded 1986. Enrl 350; Pop 349; Circ 19,014
Apr 2006-Mar 2007 Income (CAN) $23,169, City (CAN) $1,935, Locally Generated Income (CAN) $12,237, Other $6,396
Library Holdings: AV Mats 1,231; DVDs 32; Bk Vols 14,532; Per Subs 52; Videos 556
Database Vendor: EBSCOhost
Open Mon & Fri 11:30-4 & 7pm-9pm, Tues-Thurs 9:30-12:30 & 1:15-4
MCADAM PUBLIC LIBRARY, 146 Saunders Rd, McAdam, E6J 1L2, SAN 366-5763. Tel: 506-784-1403. E-mail: mcadam.library@gnb.ca. *Actg Libr Serv Mgr,* Julian Christie; Staff 2 (Non-MLS 2)
Founded 1962. Pop 1,513; Circ 9,234
Library Holdings: AV Mats 733; DVDs 70; Bk Vols 14,532; Videos 354
Open Tues & Thurs 10:30-12, 12:45-5 & 6:30pm-8pm, Wed, Fri & Sat 9-12 & 12:45-5
MEDIATHEQUE PERE LOUIS LAMONTAGNE, Carrefour-Beausoleil, 300 Chemin Beaverbrook, Miramichi, E1V 1A1, SAN 328-7785. Tel: 506-627-4084. FAX: 506-627-4592. E-mail: mediathequep@gnb.ca. *Libr Dir,* Geneviève Thériault; E-mail: genevieve.theriault@gnb.ca; Staff 2 (MLS 1, Non-MLS 1)
Founded 1986. Pop 18,508; Circ 20,132
Library Holdings: AV Mats 1,421; DVDs 42; Bk Vols 18,267; Per Subs 23; Videos 464
Unilingual French Library located in a French cultural centre
Open Mon, Tues, Thurs & Fri 9-1 & 2-5, Wed 12-5 & 6pm-8pm
MINTO PUBLIC LIBRARY, 420 Pleasant Dr, Unit 2, Minto, E4B 2T3, SAN 373-5095. Tel: 506-327-3220. FAX: 506-327-3041. E-mail: minto.publiclibrary@gnb.ca. *Libr Mgr,* Mary Lambropoulos; E-mail: mary.lambropoulos@gnb.ca; Staff 2 (Non-MLS 2)
Founded 1992. Pop 2,776; Circ 10,270

Apr 2008-Mar 2009 Income $30,408, City $27,191, Locally Generated Income $3,217

Open Tues, Thurs & Fri 10-12 & 1-5, Wed 12-8, Sat 10-12 & 1-3

NASHWAAKSIS PUBLIC SCHOOL LIBRARY, 324 Fulton Ave, E3A 5J4, SAN 373-5109. Tel: 506-453-3241. FAX: 506-444-4129. E-mail: nashwaaksis.library@gnb.ca. Web Site: www.gnb.ca. *Libr Dir,* Candace Hare; Staff 4 (MLS 1, Non-MLS 3)

Founded 1963. Circ 37,951

Library Holdings: AV Mats 1,023; Bk Vols 31,964; Per Subs 42; Videos 810

Open Mon, Wed, Fri & Sat (Fall, Winter & Spring) 10-5, Tues & Thurs 10-9; Mon, Wed, Fri (Summer) 10-5, Tues & Thurs 10-9

Friends of the Library Group

NEWCASTLE BRANCH, 100 Fountain Head Lane, Miramichi, E1V 4A1. (Mail add: PO Box 599, Miramichi, E1V 3T7), SAN 370-1336. Tel: 506-623-2450. FAX: 506-623-2335. E-mail: npublib@gnb.ca. *Librn,* Catherine Reid; E-mail: catherine.reid@gnb.ca; Staff 2 (MLS 1, Non-MLS 1)

Founded 1989. Pop 18,508; Circ 48,778

Apr 2006-Mar 2007 Income $122,803, City (CAN) $114,800, Locally Generated Income (CAN) $8,003

Library Holdings: AV Mats 1,126; Bk Vols 34,021; Per Subs 14; Videos 819

Open Tues & Wed 1-8, Thurs-Sat 10-5

OROMOCTO BRANCH, 54 Miramichi Rd, Oromocto, E2V 1S2, SAN 366-5887. Tel: 506-357-3329. FAX: 506-357-5161. E-mail: oromocto.publiclibrary@gnb.ca. *Librn,* Muriel Morton; E-mail: muriel.morton@gnb.ca; Staff 5 (MLS 1, Non-MLS 4)

Founded 1960. Pop 8,843; Circ 68,715

Library Holdings: AV Mats 1,488; Bk Vols 70,212; Per Subs 27; Videos 1,203

Open Mon 12:30-8:30, Tues & Wed 10-8:30, Thurs 10-6, Fri & Sat 10-5

STANLEY COMMUNITY LIBRARY, 28 Bridge St, Unit 2, Stanley, E6B 1B2, SAN 366-5976. Tel: 506-367-2492. FAX: 506-367-7699. *Libr Mgr,* Sarah Richard; Fax: 506-367-2764; Staff 1 (Non-MLS 1)

Founded 1968. Pop 460; Circ 13,474

Library Holdings: AV Mats 565; DVDs 30; Bk Vols 13,660; Videos 404

Open Mon, Tues, Thurs & Fri 9-12:30 & 1:30-4:30, Wed 12-5 & 6pm-8pm

UPPER MIRAMICHI COMMUNITY LIBRARY, Central New Brunswick Academy Bldg, 7263 Rte 8, New Bandon, E9C 2A7, SAN 372-5278. Tel: 506-369-2022. FAX: 506-369-2023. *Libr Mgr,* Gail Ross; E-mail: gail.ross@gnb.ca; Staff 2 (Non-MLS 2)

Founded 1990. Pop 906; Circ 16,296

Library Holdings: AV Mats 606; Bk Titles 13,492; Per Subs 12; Videos 519

Open Mon, Tues, Thurs & Fri 9-12:30 & 1:30-5, Wed 12-5 & 6-8

Bookmobiles: 1. Supvr, Maria Whitlock

MIRAMICHI

M   HORIZON HEALTH NETWORK*, Library Services, 500 Water St, E1V 3G5. SAN 327-4268. Tel: 506-623-3215. FAX: 506-623-3280. E-mail: library.miramichi@horizon.nb.ca. Staff 2 (MLS 1, Non-MLS 1)

Founded 1974

Library Holdings: Bk Titles 2,000; Per Subs 150

Subject Interests: Allied health, Med, Nursing

Automation Activity & Vendor Info: (Cataloging) Inmagic, Inc.

Database Vendor: EBSCOhost, OVID Technologies

Restriction: Staff use only

MONCTON

P   ALBERT-WESTMORLAND-KENT REGIONAL LIBRARY*, 644 Main St, Ste 201, E1C 1E2. SAN 366-600X. Tel: 506-869-6032. FAX: 506-869-6022. *Dir,* Tina Bourgeois; E-mail: tina.bourgeois@gnb.ca; *Ref,* Nora Kennedy; E-mail: nora.kennedy@gnb.ca; Staff 6 (MLS 6)

Founded 1957. Pop 187,768

Library Holdings: Bk Titles 154,503; Bk Vols 387,037; Per Subs 372

Subject Interests: Culture, Local hist

Automation Activity & Vendor Info: (Acquisitions) Inlex; (Cataloging) Inlex; (Circulation) Inlex; (ILL) Inlex; (OPAC) Inlex

Publications: Panorama (Newsletter)

Open Mon-Fri 8:30-5

Branches: 16

BIBLIOTHEQUE PUBLIQUE DE CAP-PELE, 2638, Chemin Acadie, Cap-Pele, E4N 1E3. Tel: 506-577-2090. FAX: 506-577-2094. E-mail: bibliothequepublique.cap-pele@gnb.ca. *Libr Mgr,* Goguen Michele-Ann

BIBLIOTHEQUE PUBLIQUE DE ROGERSVILLE, 65, rue de l'Ecole, Unit 1, Rogersville, E4Y 1V4. Tel: 506-775-2102. FAX: 506-775-2087. E-mail: bibliotheque.publiquederogersville@gnb.ca. *Actg Libr Mgr,* Annick Goguen

BIBLIOTHEQUE PUBLIQUE GERALD-LEBLANC DE BOUCTOUCHE, 84 boul Irving, Unite 100, Bouctouche, E4S 3L4, SAN 373-1847. Tel: 506-743-7263. FAX: 506-743-7263. E-mail: bibliothequepublique.gerald-leblanc@gnb.ca. *Libr Mgr,* Sylvie LeBlanc

Open Mon-Fri 8:30-5

DIEPPE PUBLIC, 333 Acadie Ave, Dieppe, E1A 1G9, SAN 366-6034. Tel: 506-877-5015, 506-877-7945. FAX: 506-877-7897. E-mail: bibliothequepublique.dedieppe@gnb.ca. *Libr Dir,* Nathalie Brun

Open Mon-Fri 8:30-5

DORCHESTER PUBLIC, 3516 Cape Rd, Dorchester, E4K 2X5, SAN 366-6069. Tel: 506-379-3032. FAX: 506-379-3033. E-mail: dorchester.publiclibrary@gnb.ca. *Libr Mgr,* Krista Johansen

HILLSBOROUGH PUBLIC, 2849 Main St, Unit 2, Hillsborough, E4H 2X7, SAN 366-6093. Tel: 506-734-3722. FAX: 506-734-3711. Web Site: hillsborough.publiclibrary@gnb.ca. *Libr Mgr,* Barbara Alcorn; E-mail: barbara.alcorn@gnb.ca

Open Tues, Wed, Fri & Sat 10-12 & 1-5, Thurs 1-5 & 6-8

MEMRAMCOOK PUBLIC, 540 Centrale St, Unit 1, Memramcook, E4K 3S6, SAN 366-6271. Tel: 506-758-4029. FAX: 506-758-4079. E-mail: bibliotheque.publiquedememramcook@gnb.ca. *Libr Mgr,* Jocelyne LeBlanc; E-mail: jocelyne.leblanc@gnb.ca

MONCTON PUBLIC, 644 Main St, Ste 101, E1C 1E2, SAN 366-6158. Tel: 506-869-6000. FAX: 506-869-6040. E-mail: moncton.publiclibrary@gnb.ca. *City Librn,* Chantale Bellemare; E-mail: chantale.bellemare@gnb.ca

Open Mon-Fri 8:30-5

PETITCODIAC PUBLIC, Six Kay St, Ste 101, Petitcodiac, E4Z 4K6, SAN 366-6166. Tel: 506-756-3144. FAX: 506-756-3142. E-mail: petitcodiac.publiclibrary@gnb.ca. *Libr Mgr,* Cathy MacDonald; E-mail: cathy.macdonald@gnb.ca

RICHIBOUCTOU PUBLIC, 9376 Main St, Richibouctou, E4W 4C9, SAN 366-6190. Tel: 506-523-7851. FAX: 506-523-7851. E-mail: bibliothequepublique.derichibouctou@gnb.ca. *Actg Libr Mgr,* Sylvie Bourque

Open Mon-Fri 8:30-5

RIVERVIEW PUBLIC, 34 Honour House Ct, Riverview, E1B 3Y9, SAN 366-6212. Tel: 506-387-2108. FAX: 506-387-4970. E-mail: riverview.publiclibrary@gnb.ca. *Libr Dir,* Lynn Cormier; E-mail: lynn.cormier@gnb.ca

Database Vendor: EBSCOhost, Electric Library, ProQuest

SACKVILLE PUBLIC, 66 Main St, Sackville, E4L 4A7, SAN 366-6247. Tel: 506-364-4915. FAX: 506-364-4915. E-mail: sackville.publiclibrary@gnb.ca. *Libr Mgr,* Allan Alward; E-mail: allan.alward@gnb.ca

Open Tues, Wed, Fri & Sat 10-12 & 1-5, Thurs 1-5 & 6-8

SAINT-ANTOINE PUBLIC, 11 Ave Jeanne d'Arc, Saint Antoine, E4V 1H2, SAN 366-6263. Tel: 506-525-4028. FAX: 506-525-4199. E-mail: bibliotheque.publiquedesaint-antoine@gnb.ca. *Libr Mgr,* Paulette Leger; E-mail: paulette.leger@gnb.ca

Open Wed, Fri & Sat 9-5, Tues & Thurs 1-8

SALISBURY PUBLIC, 3215 Main St, Salisbury, E4J 2K7, SAN 366-628X. Tel: 506-372-3240. FAX: 506-372-3261. E-mail: salisbury.publiclibrary@gnb.ca. *Libr Mgr,* Margaret Crosthwaite

Library Holdings: Bk Vols 10,000

Open Tues, Thurs-Sat (Winter) 10-12 & 1-5, Wed 1-5 & 6-8; Mon, Tues, Thurs & Fri (Summer) 10-12 & 1-5, Wed 1-5 & 6-8

SHEDIAC PUBLIC, 337 Main St, Unit 100, Shediac, E4P 2B1, SAN 366-6301. Tel: 506-532-7000, Ext 244. FAX: 506-532-8400. E-mail: bibliothequepublique.deshediac@gnb.ca. *Libr Mgr,* Gabrielle Leblanc; E-mail: gabrielle.leblanc@gnb.ca

Open Mon-Fri 8:30-5

Bookmobiles: 1

C   ATLANTIC BAPTIST UNIVERSITY*, George A Rawlyk Library, 333 Gorge Rd, E1C 3H9. (Mail add: Box 6004, E1C 9L7), SAN 324-1203. Tel: 506-863-6443. FAX: 506-858-9694. Web Site: www.abu.nb.ca. *Librn,* Ivan W Douthwright; *Asst Librn,* Irene Ferguson

Founded 1949. Enrl 735; Fac 65; Highest Degree: Bachelor

Library Holdings: Bk Vols 57,000; Per Subs 155

Subject Interests: Art, Lit, Maritime Can hist, Music, Relig

G   CANADA DEPARTMENT OF FISHERIES & OCEANS*, Gulf Fisheries Centre-Library, 343 Ave Universite, E1C 9B6. (Mail add: PO Box 5030, E1C 9B6), SAN 370-6230. Tel: 506-851-6264. FAX: 506-851-2766. Web Site: www.dfo-mpo.gc.ca/libraries-bibliotheques/glf-eng.htm. *Regional Librn,* Lynne Post; E-mail: lynne.post@dfo-mpo.gc.ca; *Asst Librn,* Gisele Richard; Tel: 506-851-6254, E-mail: gisele.m.richard@dfo-mpo.gc.ca; Staff 1.5 (MLS 1, Non-MLS 0.5)

Founded 1982

Library Holdings: Bk Titles 21,000; Per Subs 5

Open Mon-Fri 8:30-12 & 1-4:30

M   HORIZON HEALTH NETWORK, Library Services Horizon Health Network - Moncton, (Formerly South-East Regional Health Authority), 135 MacBeath Ave, E1C 6Z8. SAN 318-9341. Tel: 506-857-5447. FAX:

506-857-5785. *Librn,* Lori Leger; Tel: 506-870-2546; Staff 3 (MLS 1, Non-MLS 2)
Library Holdings: Bk Vols 10,000; Per Subs 300
Partic in Dialog Corp; Docline; National Network of Libraries of Medicine
Open Mon-Fri 9-4

L   MONCTON AREA LAWYERS' ASSOCIATION, Barristers' Law Library, 145 Assomption Blvd, E1C 0R2. SAN 373-1316. Tel: 506-389-1649. FAX: 506-856-6031. *Librn,* Jacqueline A Cormier; Staff 1 (Non-MLS 1)
Library Holdings: Bk Titles 700; Bk Vols 3,000
Open Mon-Fri 8:30-12 & 1-4:30

C   NEW BRUNSWICK COMMUNITY COLLEGE*, Moncton Campus Library, 1234 Mountain Rd, E1C 8H9. SAN 329-7322. Tel: 506-856-2226. FAX: 506-856-3180. *Libr Coordr,* Elizabeth Crawford; E-mail: elizabeth.crawford@gnb.ca
Founded 1965. Enrl 1,200; Fac 200
Library Holdings: Bk Titles 13,000; Per Subs 50
Special Collections: Disability Information Coll, bks, mag, pamphlets. Can & Prov
Subject Interests: Civil eng, Electronics
Automation Activity & Vendor Info: (Cataloging) Follett Software; (Circulation) Follett Software; (OPAC) Follett Software
Database Vendor: EBSCOhost
Wireless access
Special Services for the Deaf - Spec interest per
Open Mon-Thurs 8am-10pm, Fri 8-4:30, Sun 10-6

C   UNIVERSITE DE MONCTON*, Bibliotheque Champlain, 415 Ave de l'Universite, E1A 3E9. (Mail add: 18 Ave Antonine-Maillet, E1A 3E9), SAN 366-6336. Tel: 506-858-4012. Interlibrary Loan Service Tel: 506-858-4185. Reference Tel: 506-858-4998. FAX: 506-858-4086. E-mail: bichamp@umoncton.ca. Web Site: www.umoncton.ca/umcm-bibliotheque-champlain. *Chief Librn,* Alain Roberge; *Head, ILL,* Denise M Savoie; *Pub Serv Librn,* Julie Marcoux; *Ref Librn,* Pierre Goguen; *Ref Librn,* Nathalie Richard; Staff 9 (MLS 5, Non-MLS 4)
Founded 1965. Enrl 5,200; Fac 280; Highest Degree: Doctorate
Library Holdings: Bk Vols 434,000; Per Subs 1,595
Special Collections: Acadian Literature & History; Can; French Canadian Literature
Automation Activity & Vendor Info: (Acquisitions) Infor Library & Information Solutions; (Cataloging) Infor Library & Information Solutions; (Circulation) Infor Library & Information Solutions; (OPAC) Infor Library & Information Solutions; (Serials) Infor Library & Information Solutions
Database Vendor: Dialog, EBSCOhost, OCLC FirstSearch, OVID Technologies, ProQuest
Partic in Coun of Atlantic Univ Librns; Utlas
Departmental Libraries:
CENTRE D'ETUDES ACADIENNES, 18, Ave Antonine-Maillet, E1A 3E9. Tel: 506-858-4085. FAX: 506-858-4530. Web Site: www.umoncton.ca. *Mgr,* Kenneth Breau
Library Holdings: Bk Vols 13,000; Per Subs 100
Special Collections: Acadian History. Oral History
Publications: Contact-Acadie
Open Mon-Wed & Fri 8:30-4:30, Thurs 8:30-4:30 & 7-10
CENTRE DE RESSOURCES PEDAGOGIQUES, 68, rue Notre-Dame-du-Sacré-Coeur, Pavillon Jeanne-de-Valois, local B-010, E1A 3E9. Tel: 506-858-4356. FAX: 506-858-4317. E-mail: crp@umoncton.ca. *In Charge,* Julie Boudreau; *Pub Serv,* Marie-Josée Robichaud
Founded 1973. Fac 35; Highest Degree: Doctorate
Library Holdings: Bk Vols 32,000
Subject Interests: Educ
Open Mon-Fri 8-5, Sun 12-5

CL   LAW LIBRARY, E1A 3E9. Tel: 506-858-4547. FAX: 506-858-4518. *Dir,* Jeanne Maddix; Staff 6 (MLS 2, Non-MLS 4)
Founded 1978. Enrl 106; Highest Degree: Master
Library Holdings: Electronic Media & Resources 40; Bk Vols 150,000; Per Subs 350
Subject Interests: Common law
Automation Activity & Vendor Info: (Acquisitions) Infor Library & Information Solutions; (Cataloging) Infor Library & Information Solutions; (Circulation) Infor Library & Information Solutions; (Course Reserve) Infor Library & Information Solutions; (ILL) Infor Library & Information Solutions; (Media Booking) Infor Library & Information Solutions; (OPAC) Infor Library & Information Solutions; (Serials) Infor Library & Information Solutions
Database Vendor: 3M Library Systems, Brodart, CEDROM-SNi, Coutts Information Service, CredoReference, EBSCOhost, Elsevier, HeinOnline, LexisNexis, OCLC FirstSearch, OCLC WorldCat, Oxford Online, ProQuest, Quicklaw, Repere, Sage, SerialsSolutions, Thomson Carswell, Westlaw, WestlaweCARSWELL, Wiley InterScience
Open Mon-Fri 8:30am-10pm

PRINCE WILLIAM

S   KINGS LANDING LIBRARY*, 5804 Rte 102, E6K 0A5. SAN 377-077X. Tel: 506-363-4999. FAX: 506-363-4989. Web Site: www.kingslanding.nb.ca. *Curator,* Darryl Butler; E-mail: dbutler@kingslanding.nb.ca
Library Holdings: Bk Titles 5,000
Open Mon-Fri 9-4

SACKVILLE

C   MOUNT ALLISON UNIVERSITY LIBRARIES & ARCHIVES*, Ralph Pickard Bell Library, 49 York St, E4L 1C6. SAN 366-645X. Tel: 506-364-2562. FAX: 506-364-2617. Web Site: www.mta.ca/library. *Univ Librn,* Bruno Gnassi; Tel: 506-364-2567, E-mail: bgnassi@mta.ca; *Univ Archivist,* David Mawhinney; Tel: 506-364-2691, E-mail: dmawhinney@mta.ca; *Head, Acq,* Filis Fahey; Tel: 506-364-2566, E-mail: ffahey@mta.ca; *Head, Circ,* Anne McLeod; Tel: 506-364-3569, E-mail: amacleod@mta.ca; *Head, Tech Serv,* Ruthmary MacPherson; Tel: 506-364-2691, E-mail: rmacpherson@mta.ca; *Pub Serv Librn,* Anita Cannon; Tel: 506-364-2572, E-mail: acannon@mta.ca; *Syst Librn,* Brian McNally; Tel: 506-364-2237, E-mail: bmcnally@mta.ca; *Coll Develop,* Margaret Fancy; Tel: 506-364-2585, E-mail: mfancy@mta.ca; Staff 29 (MLS 9, Non-MLS 20)
Founded 1862. Enrl 2,200; Fac 140; Highest Degree: Master
Library Holdings: Bk Titles 450,000; Bk Vols 500,000; Per Subs 1,250
Special Collections: Folklore, Ballads & Poetry (Mary Mellish Archibald Coll), a-tapes, bks, per & rec; Local History Archives; Maritime Provinces (Winthrop Pickard Bell Coll), bks, maps, micro & per
Automation Activity & Vendor Info: (Acquisitions) SirsiDynix; (Cataloging) SirsiDynix; (OPAC) SirsiDynix
Wireless access
Publications: Bell Catalogue of Acadiana; Bibliography of George Frances Gilman Stanley; Catalogue of Canadian Folk Music; Classified Catalogue of Canadian Music; Lawren Phillips Harris: A Bibliography; Maritime Literature Reprint Series; Scores & Recordings
Partic in Utlas
Open Mon-Fri 8:30-4
Departmental Libraries:
ALFRED WHITEHEAD MUSIC LIBRARY, 134 Main St, E4L 1A6. Tel: 506-364-2561. Administration Tel: 506-364-2214. E-mail: musiclibrary@mta.ca. Web Site: www.mta.ca/library/music. *Music Librn,* Peter Higham; E-mail: phigham@mta.ca; Staff 2 (MLS 1, Non-MLS 1)
Enrl 2,000; Fac 16; Highest Degree: Master
Special Collections: Canadian Music Coll
Automation Activity & Vendor Info: (Acquisitions) SirsiDynix; (Cataloging) SirsiDynix; (Circulation) SirsiDynix; (Course Reserve) SirsiDynix; (ILL) Relais International; (OPAC) SirsiDynix; (Serials) SirsiDynix
Partic in Council of Atlantic University Libraries (CAUL)
Open Mon-Thurs (Winter) 8:30-4:30 & 7-10, Fri 8:30-4:30, Sat 11-5, Sun 1:15-4:15 & 7pm-10pm; Mon-Thurs (Spring & Summer) 8:30-4, Fri 10:30-4
Restriction: Limited access for the pub, Open to fac, students & qualified researchers, Open to students, fac & staff

SAINT ANDREWS

G   FISHERIES & OCEANS CANADA*, Biological Station Library, 531 Brandy Cove Rd, E5B 2L9. SAN 318-9376. Tel: 506-529-5909. Administration Tel: 506-529-5748. FAX: 506-529-5862. E-mail: standrews.library-bibliotheque@dfo-mpo.gc.ca. Web Site: www.dfo-mpo.gc.ca/libraries-bibliotheques/maritimes-eng.htm#andrews. *Head, Libr Serv,* Charlotte McAdam; *ILL,* Joanne Cleghorn; Staff 2 (MLS 1, Non-MLS 1)
Founded 1908
Library Holdings: Bk Vols 6,000
Special Collections: Department of Fisheries & Oceans Series
Subject Interests: Aquaculture, Chem, Fisheries, Marine biol
Automation Activity & Vendor Info: (Cataloging) Livelink for Libraries; (Circulation) Livelink for Libraries; (OPAC) Livelink for Libraries; (Serials) Livelink for Libraries
Function: Photocopying/Printing
Partic in Council of Federal Libraries Consortium
Open Mon-Fri 8-4:30
Restriction: Non-circulating, Ref only

S   SUNBURY SHORES ARTS & NATURE CENTRE, INC LIBRARY*, 139 Water St, E5B 1A7. SAN 320-3190. Tel: 506-529-3386. FAX: 506-529-4779. E-mail: info@sunburyshores.org. Web Site: www.sunburyshores.org. *Dir,* Jamie Steel
Founded 1964
Library Holdings: Bk Titles 1,000; Per Subs 10
Special Collections: Kronenburg Memorial Art Coll
Subject Interests: Art educ, Conserv, Ecology, Natural hist

Wireless access
Open Mon-Sat 8:30-4:30, Sun (July & Aug) 12-4

SAINT JOHN

R ANGLICAN CHURCH OF CANADA, CHURCH ARMY IN CANADA
TAYLOR COLLEGE*, Cowan Memorial Library, 105 Mountianview Dr,
E2J 5B5. SAN 321-7108. Tel: 506-693-8975. FAX: 506-657-8217. *Librn,*
Edith Boyles
Founded 1975
Library Holdings: Bk Vols 9,000; Per Subs 20
Publications: Anglican Crusader (Quarterly)
Open Mon-Fri 8-5

J NEW BRUNSWICK COMMUNITY COLLEGE*, L R Fulton Library &
Audiovisual Center, 950 Grandview Ave, E2L 3V1. (Mail add: PO Box
2270, E2L 3V1). Tel: 506-658-6726. FAX: 506-643-2853. *Librn,* Jennifer
Edgar; Tel: 506-658-6727, E-mail: jennifer.edgar@gnb.ca; *Asst Librn,*
Elizabeth Weaver; E-mail: elizabeth.weaver@gnb.ca; Staff 3 (MLS 1,
Non-MLS 2)
Library Holdings: Bk Vols 15,000; Per Subs 300
Automation Activity & Vendor Info: (Cataloging) Follett Software;
(Circulation) Follett Software; (OPAC) Follett Software; (Serials) Surpass
Database Vendor: EBSCOhost
Wireless access
Open Mon-Thurs 8am-9pm, Fri 8-4:30

S NEW BRUNSWICK MUSEUM ARCHIVES & RESEARCH LIBRARY,
277 Douglas Ave, E2K 1E5. SAN 318-9406. Tel: 506-643-2322. FAX:
506-643-2360. E-mail: archives@nbm-mnb.ca. Web Site:
www.nbm-mnb.ca. *Head Librn,* Felicity Osepchook; Tel: 506-643-2324,
E-mail: felicity.osepchook@nbm-mnb.ca; Staff 3 (Non-MLS 3)
Founded 1931
Library Holdings: Bk Titles 45,000; Per Subs 500
Special Collections: Art & Canadiana (Webster Coll); New Brunswickana
(Ganong Coll)
Subject Interests: Botany, Decorative art, Fine arts, Geol, Shipping,
Zoology
Open Tues-Fri 10-4:30

L PATTERSON, PALMER, HUNT & MURPHY LAW LIBRARY*, One
Brunswick Sq, Ste 1500, E2L 4H8. (Mail add: PO Box 1324, E2L 4H8),
SAN 326-4696. Tel: 506-632-8900. FAX: 506-632-8809. *In Charge,*
Rodney Larsen
Library Holdings: Bk Titles 4,000
Restriction: Not open to pub, Private libr

L SAINT JOHN LAW SOCIETY LIBRARY*, 110 Charlotte St, E2L 4Y9.
(Mail add: PO Box 5001, E2L 4Y9), SAN 373-8302. Tel: 506-658-2542.
FAX: 506-634-7556. E-mail: sjlaw@nbnet.nb.ca. *Librn,* Marilyn Brown;
Staff 1 (Non-MLS 1)
Library Holdings: Bk Vols 12,000; Per Subs 23

M SAINT JOHN REGIONAL HOSPITAL, Library Services, (Formerly
Horizon Health Network), 400 University Ave, E2L 4L2. SAN 326-002X.
Tel: 506-648-6763. FAX: 506-648-6859. E-mail:
library.saintjohn@horizonnb.ca. Staff 3 (MLS 1, Non-MLS 2)
Library Holdings: Bk Titles 2,000; Per Subs 500
Open Mon-Fri 8-4

C UNIVERSITY OF NEW BRUNSWICK, SAINT JOHN CAMPUS, Hans
W Klohn Commons, 100 Tucker Park Rd, E2L 4L5. (Mail add: PO Box
5050, E2L 4L5), SAN 318-9422. Tel: 506-648-5710. Interlibrary Loan
Service Tel: 506-648-5705. Reference Tel: 506-648-5888. Administration
Tel: 506-648-5700. FAX: 506-648-5701. E-mail: hwkcommons@unb.ca.
Web Site: www.lib.unb.ca. *Head, Access & Res Serv,* Diane Buhay; *Head,
Bibliog & Coll Serv,* Janet Fraser; *Electronic Serv Librn,* Linda Hansen;
Staff 16 (MLS 4, Non-MLS 12)
Founded 1965. Enrl 2,650; Fac 125
Library Holdings: e-books 23,000; e-journals 13,000; Electronic Media &
Resources 80; Bk Titles 159,072; Bk Vols 218,336; Per Subs 550; Videos
511
Special Collections: Beat Generation; Governors-General of Canada;
Science Fiction & Fantasy
Subject Interests: Bahav sci, Hist, Marine biol, Nursing, Soc sci
Database Vendor: EBSCOhost
Wireless access
Function: Archival coll, Copy machines, Distance learning, Doc delivery
serv, e-mail serv, Equip loans & repairs, ILL available, Mail & tel request
accepted, Online info literacy tutorials on the web & in blackboard,
Outside serv via phone, mail, e-mail & web, Ref serv available, VHS
videos, Video lending libr
Open Mon-Thurs 8am-11pm, Fri 8-5, Sat 10-6, Sun 1-9

SHIPPAGAN

C UNIVERSITE DE MONCTON*, Bibliotheque du Campus de Shippagan,
218 Blvd J-D-Gauthier, E8S 1P6. SAN 370-6478. Tel: 506-336-3418,
506-336-3420. Toll Free Tel: 800-363-8336. FAX: 506-336-3434. *Mgr,*
Hélène McLaughlin
Library Holdings: Bk Titles 40,000; Per Subs 325
Wireless access
Open Mon-Thurs 8:30am-10:45pm, Fri 8:30-6

SUSSEX

CR KINGSWOOD UNIVERSITY*, Earle & Marion Trouten Library, 26
Western St, E4E 1E6. (Mail add: PO Box 5125, E4E 5L2), SAN 370-5625.
Tel: 506-432-4400. Circulation Tel: 506-432-4437. FAX: 506-432-4425.
E-mail: library@kingswood.edu. Web Site: www.kingswood.edu. *Dir, Libr
Serv,* Jane Higle; E-mail: higlej@kingswood.edu; *Libr Asst,* Virnna Sabine;
Staff 2 (MLS 1, Non-MLS 1)
Founded 1945. Enrl 210; Fac 10; Highest Degree: Bachelor
Library Holdings: Bk Titles 30,000; Bk Vols 36,000
Subject Interests: Biblical studies, Theol
Automation Activity & Vendor Info: (Cataloging) TLC (The Library
Corporation); (Circulation) TLC (The Library Corporation); (OPAC) TLC
(The Library Corporation)
Wireless access
Open Mon-Thurs (Fall & Winter) 9am-10pm, Fri 9-5, Sat 1-5

WATERVILLE

M UPPER RIVER VALLEY HOSPITAL LIBRARY*, 11300 Rte 130, E7P
0A4. SAN 328-2309. Tel: 506-375-2740. FAX: 506-375-2680. Web Site:
www.rvhlibrary.nb.ca. *Libr Tech,* Marilyn A Sherman, Jr; E-mail:
marilyn.sherman@rvh.nb.ca
Library Holdings: Bk Titles 500; Per Subs 40
Partic in Maritimes Health Libraries Association
Open Mon-Fri 10-3:30

Date of Statistics: FY 2011-2012
Population, 2011 (Demography est.): 514,536
Population Served by Public Libraries: 442,409 (with direct access) remainder serviced through outreach
Total Volumes in Public Libraries: 1,305,647
Total Public Library Circulation: 1,595,918

ARNOLD'S COVE

P   ARNOLD'S COVE PUBLIC LIBRARY*, Five Highliner Dr, AoB 1A0. (Mail add: PO Box 239, A0B 1A0). Tel: 709-463-8707. Web Site: www.nlpubliclibraries.ca. *Librn,* Gwen Smith
Library Holdings: Bk Vols 11,000; Per Subs 22
Automation Activity & Vendor Info: (Cataloging) SirsiDynix; (Circulation) SirsiDynix; (OPAC) SirsiDynix
Wireless access
Open Mon & Wed 6-9, Tues 1-4, Thurs 10-1, Sat 12-3

BAY ROBERTS

P   BAY ROBERTS PUBLIC LIBRARY, PO Box 610, A0A 1G0. Tel: 709-786-9629. FAX: 709-786-9674. Web Site: www.nlpl.ca. *Librn,* Marilyn Clarke
Wireless access
Open Tues-Thurs 10:30-5 & 7-9, Fri 11-5, Sat 12-4

BELL ISLAND

P   BELL ISLAND PUBLIC LIBRARY*, 20 Bennett St, A0A 4H0. (Mail add: PO Box 760, A0A 4H0). Tel: 709-488-2413. FAX: 709-488-2413. Web Site: www.nlpubliclibraries.ca. *Librn,* Lois Clarke; E-mail: loisclarke@nlpubliclibraries.ca
Library Holdings: Per Subs 24
Open Tues-Fri 1-5, Sat 9-1

BONAVISTA

P   BONAVISTA PUBLIC LIBRARY, Church St, A0C 1B0. (Mail add: PO Box 400, A0C 1B0). Tel: 709-468-2185. Web Site: www.nlpl.ca. *Librn,* Brenda Wilton
Founded 1945. Pop 3,800; Circ 10,000
Library Holdings: Bk Vols 14,000; Per Subs 25
Wireless access
Open Mon-Wed & Sat 2-5 & 7pm-9pm

BRIGUS

P   BRIGUS PUBLIC LIBRARY*, General Delivery, A0A 1K0. Tel: 709-528-3156. Web Site: www.nlpubliclibraries.ca. *Librn,* Elsie Percy
Library Holdings: Bk Titles 25,000; Per Subs 20
Open Mon, Tues & Sat 2-5, Wed 9-1

BURIN BAY ARM

P   BURIN PUBLIC LIBRARY*, Rte 220, A0E 1G0. (Mail add: PO Box 219, A0E 1G0). Tel: 709-891-1924. FAX: 709-891-1924. Web Site: www.nlpubliclibraries.ca. *Librn,* Patricia Peddle; E-mail: patriciapeddle@nlpubliclibraries.ca
Library Holdings: Bk Vols 10,000; Per Subs 40
Open Tues & Thurs 2-5:30 & 7pm-9pm, Wed 10-12 & 2-5:30, Sat 11-4

CARBONEAR

P   CARBONEAR PUBLIC LIBRARY*, 256 Water St, A1Y 1C4. (Mail add: PO Box 928, A1Y 1C4). Tel: 709-596-3382. Web Site: www.nlpubliclibraries.ca. *Librn,* Maureen Snow
Library Holdings: Bk Vols 15,000; Per Subs 24
Wireless access
Open Mon 12-4, Tues & Fri 10:30-4:30, Wed & Thurs 12:30-4:30 & 6:30-8:30

CATALINA

P   CATALINA PUBLIC LIBRARY*, Joseph E Clouter Memorial Public Library, PO Box 69, A0C 1J0. Tel: 709-469-3045. FAX: 709-469-3045. E-mail: www.nlpubliclibraries.ca/. *Librn,* Kim Johnson; E-mail: kimjohnson@nlpubliclibraries.ca
Founded 1937
Library Holdings: Bk Vols 9,157
Open Tues & Thurs 2-5 & 7pm-9pm, Wed 2-5, Sat 2-4
Friends of the Library Group

CLARENVILLE

P   CLARENVILLE PUBLIC LIBRARY*, 98 Manitoba Dr, A5A 1K7. Tel: 709-466-7634. FAX: 709-466-7634. Web Site: www.nlpubliclibraries.ca. *Librn,* Tanya MacLean
Library Holdings: Bk Vols 21,560
Wireless access
Open Mon 10-12 & 1-5, Tues & Wed 10-5 & 6:30-8:30, Thurs & Fri 10-5, Sat 11-3

CONCEPTION BAY SOUTH

P   CONCEPTION BAY SOUTH PUBLIC LIBRARY, 110 Conception Bay Hwy, A1W 1N1. Tel: 709-834-4241. Web Site: www.nlpubliclibraries.ca. *Librn,* Rebecca Stone
Library Holdings: Bk Titles 14,000; Per Subs 44
Wireless access
Open Mon & Fri (Winter) 12:30-4:45, Tues & Wed 10-5 & 7-8:45, Thurs 12:30-5 & 7-8:45, Sat 10-3:45; Mon (Summer) 12-4:15, Tues-Thurs 9:30-4:30 & 6:30-8:15, Fri 9:30-4:15

CORNER BROOK

G   NATURAL RESOURCES CANADA LIBRARY*, PO Box 960, A2H 6J3. SAN 366-6549. Tel: 709-637-4900. Reference Tel: 506-452-3541, 506-452-3614. FAX: 709-637-4910. E-mail: afclib@nrcan-rncan.gc.ca. *Libr Mgr,* Emmanuel Bayo Aregbesola; Staff 2 (MLS 1, Non-MLS 1)
Founded 1966
Library Holdings: Bk Vols 4,000; Per Subs 50
Subject Interests: Ecology, Entomology, Forestry
Automation Activity & Vendor Info: (OPAC) SirsiDynix
Open Mon-Fri 9-4:30

G   NEWFOUNDLAND DEPARTMENT OF NATURAL RESOURCES
LIBRARY*, Herald Bldg, Four Herald Ave, A2H 6J8. (Mail add: PO Box
2006, A2H 6J8) SAN 323-9128. Tel: 709-637-2307. FAX: 709-637-2403.
Librn, Bruce Boland; E-mail: bboland@gov.nl.ca
Founded 1984
Library Holdings: Bk Titles 10,000; Per Subs 100
Special Collections: Newfoundland Forestry
Subject Interests: Forestry
Publications: Accession List (Monthly)
Open Mon-Fri (Sept-May) 8:30-4:30, (8:30-4 June-Aug)

M   WESTERN MEMORIAL REGIONAL HOSPITAL*, Health Sciences
Library, West Valley Rd, A2H 6J7. (Mail add: PO Box 2005, A2H 6J7),
SAN 329-9759. Tel: 709-637-5000, Ext 5395, 709-637-5395. FAX:
709-637-5268. *Dir, Libr Serv,* Kim Hancock; Staff 2 (MLS 2)
Library Holdings: Bk Titles 11,000; Per Subs 250
Subject Interests: Allied health, Med, Nursing
Open Mon-Thurs 8am-10pm, Fri 8-5, Sat 1-5, Sun 1-10
Restriction: Restricted borrowing privileges

FORTUNE

P   FORTUNE PUBLIC LIBRARY*, Temple St, A0E 1P0. (Mail add: PO Box
400, A0E 1P0). Tel: 709-832-0232. FAX: 709-832-2210. Web Site:
www.nlpubliclibraries.ca. *Librn,* Fay Herridge
Library Holdings: Bk Vols 7,350; Per Subs 20
Open Mon, Tues, Thurs & Fri 2-5, Wed 2-5 & 6pm-9pm

FOX HARBOUR

P   FOX HARBOUR PUBLIC LIBRARY*, PO Box 74, A0B 1V0. Tel:
709-227-2135. FAX: 709-227-2135. Web Site: www.nlpubliclibraries.ca.
Librn, Catherine Murray
Library Holdings: Bk Vols 5,280; Per Subs 14
Wireless access
Open Mon-Wed 1-4, Thurs 1-3

GANDER

M   CENTRAL REGIONAL INTEGRATED HEALTH AUTHORITY*, James
Paton Memorial Hospital Health Services Library, 125 Trans Canada Hwy,
A1V 1P7. SAN 329-8736. Tel: 709-256-5760. FAX: 709-256-4308. *Tech
Serv,* Marion Brake; E-mail: brakem@cehcib.nf.ca; Staff 1 (Non-MLS 1)
Library Holdings: Bk Vols 350; Per Subs 110
Automation Activity & Vendor Info: (Acquisitions) Nicholas;
(Cataloging) Nicholas; (Circulation) Nicholas; (Serials) Nicholas

GARNISH

P   GARNISH PUBLIC LIBRARY*, Sunset Dr, A0E 1T0. (Mail add: PO Box
40, A0E 1T0). Tel: 709-826-2371. *Librn,* Linda Nolan
Library Holdings: Bk Vols 6,600; Per Subs 21
Open Mon & Wed 6:30pm-8:30pm, Tues & Thurs 6:30pm-9pm, Sat 3-5 &
6:30pm-8:30pm

GRAND BANK

P   GRAND BANK PUBLIC LIBRARY*, Church St, A0E 1W0. (Mail add:
PO Box 1000, A0E 1W0). Tel: 709-832-0310. FAX: 709-832-0310. Web
Site: www.nlpubliclibraries.ca. *Librn,* Jane Fox; E-mail:
janefox@nlpubliclibraries.ca
Library Holdings: Bk Vols 12,000; Per Subs 27
Wireless access
Open Tues 9-12 & 1:30-5, Wed 1-5 & 6pm-9pm, Thurs-Sat 2-5

HARBOUR GRACE

P   HARBOUR GRACE PUBLIC LIBRARY*, Harvey St, A0A 2M0. (Mail
add: PO Box 40, A0A 2M0). Tel: 709-596-3894. Web Site:
www.nlpubliclibraries.ca. *Librn,* Doreen Quinn; E-mail:
doreenquinn@nlpubliclibraries.ca
Library Holdings: Bk Vols 11,000; Per Subs 25
Wireless access
Open Mon, Fri & Sat 1-4, Tues & Wed 10:30-4, Thurs 1-4 & 7-9

HARE BAY

P   HARE BAY-DOVER PUBLIC LIBRARY*, Jane Collins Academy, 12
Anstey's Rd, A0G 2P0. (Mail add: PO Box 117, A0G 2P0). Tel:
709-537-2391. FAX: 709-537-2374. Web Site: www.nlpubliclibraries.ca.
Librn, Jane Rogers-Willis
Founded 1972. Pop 1,580
Library Holdings: Bk Vols 6,200; Per Subs 17
Automation Activity & Vendor Info: (Cataloging) Follett Software;
(Circulation) Follett Software; (ILL) Horizon
Open Mon & Tues 3-8:30, Wed & Thurs 11:30-5

HOLYROOD

P   HOLYROOD PUBLIC LIBRARY*, Witless Bay Access Rd, A0A 2R0.
(Mail add: PO Box 263, A0A 2R0). Tel: 709-229-7852. Administration
Tel: 709-737-3508. FAX: 709-229-7852. Administration FAX:
709-737-3571. Web Site: www.nlpubliclibraries.ca. *Br Librn,* Marianne
King
Library Holdings: Large Print Bks 300; Bk Titles 15,200; Per Subs 27
Special Collections: Local Geanealogy (Harbour Main/Holyrood Coll)
Wireless access
Open Tues 2-5 & 7pm-9pm, Wed 2:30-5, Thurs 2:30-5 & 7-9, Fri & Sat
12-4

MARYSTOWN

P   MARYSTOWN PUBLIC LIBRARY*, Columbia Dr, A0E 2M0. (Mail add:
PO Box 1270, A0E 2M0). Tel: 709-279-1507. FAX: 709-279-1507. Web
Site: www.nlpubliclibraries.ca. *Librn,* Patricia Mayo; E-mail:
patsymayo@nlpubliclibraries.ca
Library Holdings: Bk Vols 6,000; Per Subs 20
Wireless access
Open Mon & Thurs 12-5, Tues & Fri 12-5 & 7pm-9pm, Sat 2-4

MOUNT PEARL

G   DEPARTMENT OF GOVERNMENT SERVICES, GOVERNMENT OF
NEWFOUNDLAND & LABRADOR*, Occupational Health & Safety
Library & Information Services, Donovans Industrial Park, 15 Dundee Ave,
A1N 4R6. (Mail add: PO Box 8700, St John's, A1B 4J6), SAN 377-0796.
Tel: 709-729-5264. FAX: 709-729-3445. *Coordr, Libr Serv,* Position
Currently Open
Founded 1992
Library Holdings: Bk Titles 2,000; Bk Vols 2,500; Per Subs 50
Subject Interests: Environ health, Occupational health, Occupational
safety, Pub health
Automation Activity & Vendor Info: (Cataloging) Inmagic, Inc.;
(Circulation) Inmagic, Inc.; (Serials) Inmagic, Inc.
Function: Res libr
Open Mon-Fri 8:30-4
Restriction: Ref only to non-staff

P   ROSS KING MEMORIAL PUBLIC LIBRARY*, 65 Olympic Dr, A1N
5H6. Tel: 709-368-3603, 709-368-7338. FAX: 709-368-0758. Web Site:
www.nlpl.ca. *Libr Tech,* Y Gillard
Pop 26,000
Library Holdings: Bk Vols 28,500
Automation Activity & Vendor Info: (Cataloging) SirsiDynix;
(Circulation) SirsiDynix; (OPAC) SirsiDynix
Wireless access
Function: Photocopying/Printing
Open Mon & Wed 10-8:45, Tues, Thurs & Fri 10-4:45, Sat (Winter)
10-4:45

OLD PERLICAN

P   OLD PERLICAN PUBLIC LIBRARY*, PO Box 265, A0A 3G0. Tel:
709-587-2028. Web Site: www.nlpubliclibraries.ca. *Librn,* Cathy Hatch
Library Holdings: Bk Vols 8,757; Per Subs 23
Open Tues 11-12 & 2-5, Wed 2-6, Thurs 1-5, Fri 6pm-9pm

PLACENTIA

P   PLACENTIA RESOURCE CENTER*, 14 Atlantic Ave, A0B 2Y0. (Mail
add: PO Box 119, A0B 2Y0). Tel: 709-227-3621. FAX: 709-227-3621.
Web Site: www.nlpubliclibraries.ca. *Librn,* Doris Bowering
Library Holdings: Bk Titles 2,000; Per Subs 65
Automation Activity & Vendor Info: (Cataloging) SirsiDynix;
(Circulation) SirsiDynix
Wireless access
Open Tues & Thurs 9:30-12:30, 1:30-4:30 & 6pm-8pm, Wed 9:30-12:30 &
1:30-4:30, Fri & Sat 10-12 & 12-2

POUCH COVE

P   POUCH COVE PUBLIC LIBRARY*, PO Box 40, A0A 3L0. Tel:
709-335-2652. FAX: 709-335-2652. Web Site: www.nlpubliclibraries.ca.
Librn, Laura Bragg; E-mail: lauranoseworthy@nlpubliclibraries.ca
Library Holdings: Per Subs 29
Wireless access
Open Mon & Wed 6pm-8pm, Tues & Thurs 1:30-4:30, Fri 10-12

SOUTHERN HARBOUR

P   SOUTHERN HARBOUR PUBLIC LIBRARY*, One Municipal Dr, A0B
3H0. (Mail add: PO Box 167, A0B 3H0). Tel: 709-463-8814. FAX:
709-463-8814. Web Site: www.nlpubliclibraries.ca. *Librn,* Bride Whiffen
Library Holdings: Bk Vols 7,006; Per Subs 23

Wireless access
Open Mon 9:30-1, Tues-Fri 1:30-5, Sat 1-5

ST. BRIDE'S

P   CAPE SHORE PUBLIC LIBRARY*, General Delivery, A0B 2Z0. Tel:
709-337-2360. FAX: 709-337-2360. Web Site: www.nlpubliclibraries.ca.
Librn, Jacqueline Nash
Library Holdings: Bk Vols 5,000
Open Mon 9-12 & 12:30-5, Tues & Thurs 12:30-5 & 6pm-8pm, Wed
12:30-5

ST. JOHN'S

G   CANADA-NEWFOUNDLAND OFFSHORE PETROLEUM BOARD
LIBRARY*, TD Pl, 3rd Flr, 140 Water St, A1C 6H6. SAN 323-9268. Tel:
709-778-1400. FAX: 709-778-1473. Web Site: www.cnlopb.nl.ca. *Librn,*
Judy Ryall; Tel: 709-778-1449, E-mail: jryall@cnlopb.nl.ca; Staff 1 (MLS
1)
Library Holdings: Bk Titles 5,000; Per Subs 50
Automation Activity & Vendor Info: (Acquisitions) Inmagic, Inc.;
(Cataloging) Inmagic, Inc.
Open Mon-Fri 8:30-5

C   COLLEGE OF THE NORTH ATLANTIC*, Prince Philip Drive Campus
Library, One Prince Philip Dr, A1C 5P7. (Mail add: PO Box 1693, A1C
5P7), SAN 366-6573. Tel: 709-758-7274. Interlibrary Loan Service Tel:
709-758-7447. FAX: 709-758-7448. *Librn,* Susan Prior; Tel: 709-758-7448,
E-mail: susan.prior@cna.nl.ca; *Prov Coordr,* Lynn Cuff; Tel:
709-643-7762; Staff 1 (MLS 1)
Founded 1963. Enrl 1,800; Fac 100
Library Holdings: Bk Titles 14,000; Bk Vols 16,000; Per Subs 200
Special Collections: Can & Prov
Departmental Libraries:
BAIE VERTE CAMPUS, One Terranova Rd, Baie Verte, A0K 1B0, SAN
377-8460. Tel: 709-532-8066. FAX: 709-532-4624. Web Site:
www.cna.nl.ca. *Libr Tech II,* Michael Power
Library Holdings: Bk Vols 5,000
Open Mon-Thurs 8-4:30, Fri 8-1
BAY ST GEORGE, 432 Massachusetts Dr, Stephenville, A2N 2Z6. (Mail
add: PO Box 5400, Stephenville, A2N 2Z6), SAN 377-8487. Tel:
709-643-7752. Administration Tel: 709-643-7762. FAX: 709-643-7786.
Web Site: www.cna.nl.ca. *Librn,* Lynn Cuff; Staff 4 (MLS 1, Non-MLS
3)
Enrl 900; Fac 90
Library Holdings: Bk Vols 14,000; Per Subs 150
Subject Interests: Archives, Folklore, Nfld & Labrador, Rare bks
Open Mon-Thurs 8-8, Fri 8-4, Sat 2-5, Sun 6pm-9pm
BONAVISTA CAMPUS, PO Box 670, Bonavista, A0C 1B0, SAN
377-8509. Tel: 709-468-1716. FAX: 709-468-2004. *Tech Serv,* Tracy
Mouland; E-mail: tracy.mouland@cna.nl.ca; Staff 1 (Non-MLS 1)
Library Holdings: Bk Titles 3,500
Function: Res libr
BURIN CAMPUS, PO Box 370, Burin Bay Arm, A0E 1G0, SAN
377-8525. Tel: 709-891-5622. FAX: 709-891-2256. *Libr Tech,* Sandra
Shallow; E-mail: sandra.shallow@cna.nl.ca
Library Holdings: Bk Titles 8,000; Per Subs 25
Open Mon-Fri 8:30-4
CARBONEAR CAMPUS RESOURCE CENTER, Four Pikes Lane,
Carbonear, A1Y 1A7, SAN 377-8541. Tel: 709-596-6139, 709-596-8925.
FAX: 709-596-2688. Web Site: www.cna.nl.ca. *Librn,* Stephen Nolan;
Tech Serv, Brenda Peach; Tel: 709-596-8940
Library Holdings: Bk Titles 4,000; Per Subs 20
Automation Activity & Vendor Info: (Serials) EBSCO Online
Open Mon-Thurs 8:30-5, Fri 8:30-4
CLARENVILLE CAMPUS, 69 Pleasant St, Clarenville, A5A 1V9, SAN
377-8568. Tel: 709-466-6940. FAX: 709-466-2771. *Librn,* Joanne
Deluney
Enrl 700; Fac 27
Library Holdings: Bk Vols 7,000; Per Subs 40
Open Mon-Fri 8:30-4:30
RAYMOND J CONDON MEMORIAL LIBRARY, Labrador West
Campus, One Campbell Dr, Labrador City, A2V 2Y1, SAN 377-8665.
Tel: 709-944-6862. FAX: 709-944-6581. *Librn,* Gary Peschell; Staff 2
(MLS 1, Non-MLS 1)
Founded 1989
Library Holdings: DVDs 12; Bk Vols 5,000; Per Subs 60; Videos 700
Special Collections: Newfoundland Coll
Subject Interests: Mining tech
Open Mon-Thurs (Winter) 8:30-4:30 & 5:30-9, Fri 8:30-4:30, Sun
12-4:30; Mon-Fri (Summer) 8:30-4
CORNER BROOK CAMPUS, PO Box 822, Corner Brook, A2H 6H6,
SAN 377-8584. Tel: 709-637-8528. FAX: 709-634-2126. *Librn,* Marian
Burnett; E-mail: marian.burnett@cna.nl.ca; Staff 4 (MLS 1, Non-MLS 3)
Library Holdings: Bk Vols 10,000

Subject Interests: Natural res
Open Mon-Thurs 8-5 & 6pm-9pm, Fri 8-4:30, Sun 1-5 & 6pm-9pm
GANDER CAMPUS, One Magee Rd, Gander, A1V 1W8. (Mail add: PO
Box 395, Gander, A1V 1W8), SAN 377-8606. Tel: 709-651-4815. FAX:
709-651-4854. E-mail: libga@cna.nl.ca. Web Site:
www.cna.nl.ca/campus/ga/library.asp. *Col Librn,* Karen Patzold; Staff 1
(MLS 1)
Subject Interests: Adult basic educ, Aircraft maintenance & eng,
Electronics, Engine repair
Function: Audio & video playback equip for onsite use, CD-ROM,
Computers for patron use, Copy machines, Electronic databases & coll,
ILL available, Instruction & testing, Learning ctr, Online cat, Online
searches, Orientations, Outside serv via phone, mail, e-mail & web,
Photocopying/Printing, Pub access computers, Ref & res, Ref serv
available, Telephone ref, VHS videos, Web-catalog, Wheelchair
accessible
Open Mon-Thurs 8-12 & 12:30-4, Fri 8-1
GRAND FALLS-WINDSOR CAMPUS, Five Cromer Ave, Grand
Falls-Windsor, A2A 1X3, SAN 377-8622. Tel: 709-292-5637. FAX:
709-489-5765. E-mail: libgf@cna.nl.ca. Web Site:
www.cna.nl.ca/bottomtoolbar/library. *Col Librn,* John L Whelan; E-mail:
john.whelan@cna.nl.ca; *Libr Tech,* Andrew Barker; E-mail:
andrew.barker@cna.nl.ca; *Libr Tech,* Susan Hamilton; E-mail:
susan.hamilton@cna.nl.ca; Staff 2 (MLS 1, Non-MLS 1)
Library Holdings: Bk Vols 5,000
Special Collections: Grand Falls-Windsor Campus Archive
Function: Archival coll, Audio & video playback equip for onsite use,
AV serv, CD-ROM, Computers for patron use, Copy machines, Distance
learning, Doc delivery serv, e-mail serv, Electronic databases & coll, ILL
available, Libr develop, Mail & tel request accepted, Mail loans to mem,
Newsp ref libr, Online cat, Online ref, Online searches, Orientations,
Outside serv via phone, mail, e-mail & web, Photocopying/Printing, Prof
lending libr, Pub access computers, Ref & res, Ref serv available,
Referrals accepted, Res libr, Spoken cassettes & CDs, Spoken cassettes
& DVDs, Telephone ref, VHS videos, Video lending libr, Web-catalog,
Wheelchair accessible
Open Mon-Thurs (Fall & Winter) 8am-9:30pm, Fri 8-4:30, Sat Noon-4;
Mon-Wed (Summer) 9-4, Thurs 9-12 & 2-4, Fri 9-3:30
Restriction: Open to pub for ref & circ; with some limitations, Open to
students, fac, staff & alumni
HAPPY VALLEY-GOOSE BAY CAMPUS, 219 Hamilton River Rd,
Happy Valley-Goose Bay, A0P 1E0. (Mail add: PO Box 1720, Sta B,
Happy Valley-Goose Bay, A0P 1E0), SAN 377-8649. Tel: 709-896-6307.
FAX: 709-896-3733. E-mail: libhv@cna.nl.ca. Web Site:
www.cna.nl.ca/campus/hvgb/library.asp. *Librn,* Shannon McAlorum; Tel:
709-896-6772, E-mail: shannon.mcalorum@cna.nl.ca
Special Collections: Labrador Coll, texts; Labrador Institute Archives,
photog, original mat. Can & Prov; Oral History
PLACENTIA CAMPUS, PO Box 190, Placentia, A0B 2Y0, SAN
377-8681. Tel: 709-227-6264. FAX: 709-227-7185. *Libr Tech,* Linda
Reddigan
PORT AUX BASQUES CAMPUS, 59 Grand Bay Rd, Port aux Basques,
A0M 1C0. (Mail add: PO Box 760, Port aux Basques, A0M 1C0), SAN
377-8703. Tel: 709-695-3343. FAX: 709-695-2963. E-mail:
libpab@cna.nl.ca. Web Site: www.cna.nl.ca/Campus/pab/library.asp. *Libr
Tech II,* Tanya Wells; E-mail: tanya.wells@cna.nl.ca
Open Mon-Fri 8:30-4:30
SEAL COVE CAMPUS LEARNING RESOURCE CENTRE, 1670
Conception Bay Hwy, Conception Bay South, A0A 3T0. (Mail add: PO
Box 19003, Station Seal Cove, Conception Bay South, A1X 5C7), SAN
373-5354. Tel: 709-744-6829. FAX: 709-744-3929. *Librn,* Bonnie
Morgan; Staff 1 (MLS 1)
Founded 1992. Enrl 200; Fac 23; Highest Degree: Certificate
Library Holdings: CDs 50; High Interest/Low Vocabulary Bk Vols 30;
Bk Titles 2,700; Bk Vols 3,000; Per Subs 50; Videos 300
Special Collections: Newfoundland
Subject Interests: Adult educ, Culinary arts, Electrical trades, Heating
syst, Petroleum
Automation Activity & Vendor Info: (Acquisitions) SirsiDynix;
(Cataloging) SirsiDynix; (Circulation) SirsiDynix; (Course Reserve)
SirsiDynix; (ILL) SirsiDynix; (Media Booking) SirsiDynix; (OPAC)
SirsiDynix
Database Vendor: ProQuest
Special Services for the Deaf - Assistive tech
Special Services for the Blind - Assistive/Adapted tech devices, equip &
products
Open Mon-Fri 8:30-4:30
ANNA TEMPLETON CAMPUS, 278 Duckworth St, A1C 1H3. (Mail add:
PO Box 1693, A1C 5P7), SAN 377-872X. Tel: 709-739-5894. FAX:
709-739-7624. E-mail: atcprintdye@hotmail.com. *Librn,* Susan Prior;
Tel: 709-758-7448, Fax: 709-758-7231, E-mail: susan.prior@cna.nl.ca
Founded 1994. Enrl 50; Fac 3
Subject Interests: Art hist, Costume, Craft hist, Design, Handicraft,
Quilting, Textile design, Weaving

L DEPARTMENT OF JUSTICE*, Law Library, East Block, Confederation Bldg, 5th Flr, 100 Prince Philip Dr, A1B 4J6. (Mail add: PO Box 8700, A1B 4J6), SAN 372-3577. Tel: 709-729-0285. FAX: 709-729-1370. Web Site: www.gov.nl.ca/just. *Dir*, Sean Dawe; Tel: 709-729-2861, E-mail: seand@gov.nl.ca; *Librn*, Brenda Blundon; E-mail: brendab@gov.nl.ca; *Libr Tech*, Anita Power Taylor; Tel: 709-729-2912, E-mail: anitapowertaylor@gov.nl.ca; Staff 2 (MLS 1, Non-MLS 1)
Library Holdings: Bk Vols 22,000; Per Subs 100
Subject Interests: Govt
Function: Govt ref serv
Restriction: Access at librarian's discretion, Open to govt employees only, Open to others by appt, Open to researchers by request, Restricted access, Restricted borrowing privileges

G DEPARTMENT OF NATURAL RESOURCES, GOVERNMENT OF NEWFOUNDLAND & LABRADOR*, Geological Survey Library, 50 Elizabeth Ave, A1B 1W5. (Mail add: PO Box 8700, A1B 4J6), SAN 318-9503. Tel: 709-729-3159. FAX: 709-729-4491. Web Site: www.nr.gov.nl.ca/mines&en/geosurvey. *In Charge*, Cindy Saunders; E-mail: cindysaunders@gov.nl.ca
Library Holdings: Bk Vols 1,000; Per Subs 20
Special Collections: Mineral Resources & Geology Technical Library, publs, rpts; Mineral Resources, Geology & Mineral Exploration - Newfoundland & Labrador, co & govt rpts
Subject Interests: Geol, Mineral exploration
Open Mon-Fri 8:30-4:30
Restriction: Restricted pub use

P MICHAEL DONOVAN LIBRARY*, 655 Topsail Rd, A1E 2E3. Tel: 709-737-2621. FAX: 709-737-2621. Web Site: www.nlpubliclibraries.ca. *Librn*, Rita Roberts
Library Holdings: Bk Vols 23,400
Open Tues 10-8:30, Wed-Sat 10-5:30

EASTERN HEALTH
S ADDICTIONS SERVICES LIBRARY, Mount Pearl Sq, 760 Topsail Rd, A1B 4A4. (Mail add: PO Box 13122, A1B 4A4), SAN 373-3157. Tel: 709-752-4120, 709-752-4121. FAX: 709-752-4412. E-mail: ads.library@easternhealth.ca. *Librn*, Cooke Heather; E-mail: heather.cooke@easternhealth.ca; *Tech Support*, Leslie Stafford; E-mail: leslie.noftallstafford@easternhealth.ca
Library Holdings: CDs 170; DVDs 50; Bk Vols 5,200; Per Subs 10; Videos 1,000
Function: AV serv, For res purposes, Handicapped accessible, Libr develop, Photocopying/Printing, Wheelchair accessible
Open Mon-Fri 8:30-4:30
Restriction: Access at librarian's discretion, Clients only, Lending to staff only, Open to pub for ref & circ; with some limitations
CM CENTRE FOR NURSING STUDIES LEARNING RESOURCE CENTRE*, 100 Forest Rd, A1A 1E5, SAN 318-9465. Tel: 709-777-8192. Interlibrary Loan Service Tel: 709-777-8194. Reference Tel: 709-777-8189. FAX: 709-777-8193. Web Site: www.cns.nf.ca. *Librn*, Karen Hutchens; Tel: 709-777-8189; Staff 3 (MLS 1, Non-MLS 2)
Founded 1996. Enrl 550; Fac 50; Highest Degree: Bachelor
Library Holdings: AV Mats 420; Bk Vols 9,400; Per Subs 65
Automation Activity & Vendor Info: (Cataloging) LibraryWorld, Inc; (Circulation) LibraryWorld, Inc
Open Mon-Thurs 8:30am-10pm, Fri 8:30-4:30, Sat 12-5, Sun 12-10
Restriction: Open to students, fac & staff
M ST CLAIRE'S MERCY HOSPITAL LIBRARY*, 154 Le Marchant Rd, A1C 5B8, SAN 327-5434. Tel: 709-777-5414. FAX: 709-777-5812. *Librn*, Jordan Pike; Staff 1 (MLS 1)
Founded 1954
Library Holdings: Bk Titles 1,500; Per Subs 90
Automation Activity & Vendor Info: (Cataloging) BiblioMondo; (Circulation) BiblioMondo
Database Vendor: EBSCOhost
Function: ILL available
Partic in Docline
Open Mon-Fri 8-4
M WATERFORD HOSPITAL LIBRARY & INFORMATION SERVICES*, Waterford Bridge Rd, A1E 4J8, SAN 318-952X. Tel: 709-777-3368. FAX: 709-777-3319. Web Site: www.hccsj.nf.ca. *Librn*, Debra Kearsey; E-mail: debra.kearsey@easternhealth.ca
Founded 1969
Library Holdings: Bk Titles 300; Per Subs 80
Subject Interests: Geriatrics, Mental health, Psychiat
Open Mon-Fri 8:30-4:30

G FISHERIES & OCEANS CANADA*, Regional Library, 80 E White Hills Rd, A1C 5X1. (Mail add: PO Box 5667, A1C 5X1), SAN 366-6514. Tel: 709-772-2020, 709-772-2022. FAX: 709-772-2575. E-mail: nafclibrary@dfo-mpo.gc.ca. Web Site: waves-vagues.dfo-mpo.gc.ca/waves-vagues. *Regional Librn*, Annette

Anthony; E-mail: annette.anthony@dfo-mpo.gc.ca; *Libr Tech*, Maria Belanger; Staff 3 (MLS 1, Non-MLS 2)
Founded 1933
Library Holdings: Bk Titles 12,000; Bk Vols 45,000; Per Subs 245
Subject Interests: Biochem, Biol, Fisheries, Fisheries econ, Limnology, Oceanography
Function: Res libr
Publications: Waves
Open Mon-Fri 8-4
Restriction: Photo ID required for access

G GOVERNMENT OF NEWFOUNDLAND & LABRADOR*, Women's Policy Office Resource Centre Library, PO Box 8700, A1B 4J6. SAN 374-6186. Tel: 709-729-0934. FAX: 709-729-2331. *Libr Tech*, Marie Oneil; Staff 2 (MLS 1, Non-MLS 1)
Founded 1985
Library Holdings: Bk Titles 3,907
Publications: New Acquisitions List (Monthly)
Open Mon-Fri 8:30-4:30

L LAW SOCIETY OF NEWFOUNDLAND LIBRARY*, 196-198 Water St, A1C 1A9. (Mail add: PO Box 1028, A1C 5M3), SAN 318-9481. Tel: 709-753-7770. FAX: 709-753-0054. E-mail: lawlibrary@lawsociety.nf.ca. Web Site: www.lawsociety.nf.ca/library. *Librn*, Gail Hogan; *Librn*, Harriet Mercer
Library Holdings: Bk Vols 10,000
Subject Interests: British law, Can
Restriction: Open by appt only

P MARJORIE MEWS PUBLIC LIBRARY*, 12 Highland Dr, A1A 3C4. Tel: 709-737-3020. Web Site: www.nlpubliclibraries.ca. *Librn*, Paul Williams
Library Holdings: Bk Titles 28,000
Automation Activity & Vendor Info: (Acquisitions) SirsiDynix
Open Tues 10-8:30, Wed-Sat 10-5:30

MEMORIAL UNIVERSITY OF NEWFOUNDLAND
C FISHERIES & MARINE INSTITUTE - DR C R BARRETT LIBRARY*, 155 Ridge Rd, A1C 5R3. (Mail add: PO Box 4920, A1C 5R3), SAN 318-9449. Tel: 709-778-0662. Reference Tel: 709-778-0615. FAX: 709-778-0316. E-mail: barrett@mi.mun.ca. Web Site: www.mi.mun.ca/library. *Head, Pub Serv*, Catherine Lawton; E-mail: catherine.lawton@mi.mun.ca; Staff 8 (MLS 1, Non-MLS 7)
Founded 1985. Enrl 1,500; Highest Degree: Master
Library Holdings: AV Mats 1,600; Bk Vols 44,000; Per Subs 495
Subject Interests: Architectural eng tech, Electrical, Environ eng, Fisheries tech, Food tech, Geomatics, Marine eng, Nautical sci, Naval archit, Ocean environ, Petroleum eng, Shipbuilding
Automation Activity & Vendor Info: (Acquisitions) SirsiDynix; (Cataloging) SirsiDynix; (Circulation) SirsiDynix; (Course Reserve) SirsiDynix; (ILL) SirsiDynix; (Media Booking) SirsiDynix; (OPAC) SirsiDynix; (Serials) SirsiDynix
Function: Res libr
Open Mon-Fri 8:30-5
CM HEALTH SCIENCES LIBRARY*, Memorial University, 300 Prince Philip Dr, A1B 3V6, SAN 366-6727. Circulation Tel: 709-777-6671. Reference Tel: 709-777-6672. Administration Tel: 709-777-7036. FAX: 709-777-6866. E-mail: hslinfo@mun.ca. Web Site: www.library.mun.ca/hsl/. *Assoc Univ Librn*, George Beckett; Tel: 709-777-6670, E-mail: georger@mun.ca; *Head, Pub Serv*, Linda Barnett; Tel: 709-777-6676, E-mail: lbarnett@mun.ca; Staff 23 (MLS 7, Non-MLS 16)
Founded 1967
Special Collections: History of Medicine
Subject Interests: Allied health, Med, Nursing
Automation Activity & Vendor Info: (Acquisitions) SIRSI Unicorn; (Cataloging) SIRSI Unicorn; (Circulation) SIRSI Unicorn; (Course Reserve) SIRSI Unicorn; (ILL) Relais International; (OPAC) SIRSI-iBistro; (Serials) SIRSI Unicorn
Database Vendor: Dialog, OVID Technologies
Partic in Association of Faculties of Medicine of Canada (AFMC); Canadian Research Knowledge Network; Council of Atlantic University Libraries (CAUL)
Publications: Library Guides; Library Links (Newsletter)
C FERRISS HODGETT LIBRARY*, University Dr, Corner Brook, A2H 6P9, SAN 366-6662. Tel: 709-637-6267. Interlibrary Loan Service Tel: 709-637-6271. FAX: 709-637-6273, 709-639-8125. Web Site: www.library.mun.ca, www.swgc.mun.ca. *Assoc Univ Librn*, Elizabeth Behrens; E-mail: ebehrens@swgc.mun.ca; *Circ*, Beverly Greene; *Ref Serv*, Louise McGillis; Tel: 709-637-6200, Ext 6122
Founded 1975. Enrl 1,124; Fac 60
Library Holdings: Bk Vols 125,000; Per Subs 550
Automation Activity & Vendor Info: (Acquisitions) SirsiDynix; (Cataloging) SirsiDynix; (Circulation) SirsiDynix; (Course Reserve) SirsiDynix; (ILL) SirsiDynix; (Media Booking) SirsiDynix; (OPAC) SirsiDynix; (Serials) SirsiDynix

Database Vendor: EBSCOhost
Open Mon-Thurs 8am-11pm, Fri 8-5, Sat 1-5, Sun 2-10

C LABRADOR INSTITUTE OF NORTHERN STUDIES INFORMATION
CENTRE LIBRARY*, Sta B, PO Box 490, Labrador, A0P 1E0, SAN
326-8144. Tel: 709-896-6210. FAX: 709-896-2970. *In Charge,* Beatrice
Dickers; E-mail: beatrice.dickers@mun.ca
Founded 1983
Library Holdings: Bk Titles 3,000; Per Subs 10
Special Collections: Labrador-Arctic Reference Materials - 1919-present
Subject Interests: Environ issues, Labrador mats, Northern studies
Automation Activity & Vendor Info: (Acquisitions) SirsiDynix;
(Cataloging) SirsiDynix; (Circulation) SirsiDynix; (Course Reserve)
SirsiDynix; (ILL) SirsiDynix; (Media Booking) SirsiDynix; (OPAC)
SirsiDynix; (Serials) SirsiDynix
Open Mon-Fri 8:30-4:30

C QUEEN ELIZABETH II LIBRARY*, 234 Elizabeth Ave, A1B 3Y1, SAN
366-6638. Tel: 709-737-7428. Circulation Tel: 709-737-7423. Interlibrary
Loan Service Tel: 709-737-7424. Administration Tel: 709-737-3862.
Information Services Tel: 709-737-7427. FAX: 709-737-2153. Web Site:
www.library.mun.ca. *Univ Librn,* Lorraine A Busby; E-mail:
lbusby@mun.ca; *Div Head, Syst Coordr,* Lisa Goddard; Tel:
709-737-2124, E-mail: lgoddard@mun.ca; *Head, Coll Develop,*
Christopher Dennis; Tel: 709-737-3214, E-mail: cdennis@mun.ca; *Head,
Info Serv, Ref,* Karen Lippold; Staff 139.5 (MLS 29.5, Non-MLS 110)
Founded 1925. Fac 925; Highest Degree: Doctorate
Library Holdings: Bk Vols 1,542,859; Per Subs 37,532
Special Collections: Newfoundlandia Coll, AV & maps. Can & Prov
Automation Activity & Vendor Info: (Acquisitions) SirsiDynix;
(Cataloging) SirsiDynix; (Circulation) SirsiDynix; (Course Reserve)
SirsiDynix; (ILL) SirsiDynix; (OPAC) SirsiDynix; (Serials) SirsiDynix
Open Mon-Fri 8:30-5

S NEWFOUNDLAND & LABRADOR OIL & GAS INDUSTRIES
ASSOCIATION, Atlantic Pl, Ste 602, 215 Water St, Box 44, A1C 6C9.
SAN 371-9081. Tel: 709-758-6610. FAX: 709-758-6611. E-mail:
noia@noia.ca. Web Site: www.noia.ca. *Librn,* Marilyn Buckingham; Staff 1
(MLS 1)
Founded 1977
Library Holdings: Bk Titles 2,000
Subject Interests: Gas, Oil
Publications: NOIA News (Quarterly)
Restriction: Internal use only

S NEWFOUNDLAND & LABRADOR TEACHERS' ASSOCIATION
LIBRARY*, Three Kenmount Rd, A1B 1W1. SAN 377-3302. Tel:
709-726-3223. FAX: 709-726-4302. Web Site: www.nlta.nl.ca. *In Charge,*
Joann Russell; E-mail: jrussell@nlta.nl.ca
Library Holdings: Bk Titles 5,000
Open Mon-Fri 8:30-4:30

G NEWFOUNDLAND DEPARTMENT OF MUNICIPAL & PROVINCIAL
AFFAIRS*, Urban & Rural Planning Division Library, Confederation Bldg,
W Block, A1B 4J6. (Mail add: PO Box 8700, A1B 4J6), SAN 323-9225.
Tel: 709-729-3088, 709-729-3090. FAX: 709-729-0477. *Librn,* Robert
Cotter; E-mail: rcotter@gov.nl.ca
Library Holdings: Bk Titles 3,000; Per Subs 14
Special Collections: Municipal Plans for Communities of Newfoundland &
Labrador
Subject Interests: Housing
Open Mon-Fri 8:30-4:30
Restriction: Staff use only

S NEWFOUNDLAND HISTORICAL SOCIETY LIBRARY*, Colonial Bldg,
Military Rd, A1C 2C9. (Mail add: Churchill Sq, PO Box 23154, A1B 4J9),
SAN 377-2411. Tel: 709-722-3191. FAX: 709-729-0578. E-mail:
nhs@nf.aibn.com. Web Site: www.infonet.st-johns.nf.ca/providers/nfldhist.
In Charge, Allan Byrne; Staff 1 (Non-MLS 1)

Founded 1905
Library Holdings: Bk Titles 600; Bk Vols 650; Per Subs 11
Special Collections: Archival Coll
Subject Interests: Hist, Labrador, Nfld & Labrador
Function: ILL available
Open Wed & Thurs 9:30-4
Restriction: Not a lending libr

CR QUEEN'S COLLEGE LIBRARY*, 210 Prince Philip Dr, Ste 3000, A1B
3R6. SAN 371-7550. Tel: 709-753-0116. FAX: 709-753-1214. E-mail:
queens@mun.ca. Web Site: www.mun.ca/queens. *In Charge,* John Mellis;
Staff 1 (MLS 1)
Founded 1841. Enrl 35; Fac 4; Highest Degree: Master
Library Holdings: Bk Titles 17,000; Bk Vols 17,800; Per Subs 60
Subject Interests: Theol

ST. LAWRENCE

P ST LAWRENCE PUBLIC LIBRARY*, PO Box 366, A0E 2V0. Tel:
709-873-2650. E-mail: bsl@ill.nlpubliclibraries.ca. *Librn,* Vicki Lockyer;
E-mail: vickilockyer@nlpubliclibraries.ca
Library Holdings: Bk Vols 8,500
Open Mon 5pm-9pm, Tues & Thurs 1pm-6:30pm, Wed & Fri 12-3, Sat 2-5

TORBAY

P TORBAY PUBLIC LIBRARY, 1288A Torbay Rd, A1K 1B2. Tel:
709-437-6571. FAX: 709-437-6571. Web Site: www.nlpubliclibraries.ca.
Librn, Marcia Deibel
Library Holdings: Bk Vols 12,000; Per Subs 30
Wireless access
Open Mon 6:30pm-8:30pm, Tues 10-12, 1:30-4:30 & 6:30-8:30, Wed 9-12
& 1:30-4:30, Thurs 1:30-4:30 & 6:30-8:30

TREPASSEY

P TREPASSEY PUBLIC LIBRARY*, Molloy's Rd, A0A 4B0. (Mail add:
PO Box 183, A0A 4B0). Tel: 709-438-2224. FAX: 709-438-2224. Web
Site: www.nlpubliclibraries.ca. *Librn,* Patsy McCormack
Library Holdings: Bk Vols 6,000; Per Subs 18
Wireless access
Open Mon, Wed & Thurs 3-7, Tues 10-12, Fri 9-12

VICTORIA

P VICTORIA PUBLIC LIBRARY*, PO Box 190, A0A 4G0. Tel:
709-596-3682. Web Site: www.nlpubliclibraries.ca. *Librn,* Shona Colbourne
Library Holdings: Bk Vols 3,500; Per Subs 16
Open Mon, Wed & Fri 1-5

WHITBOURNE

P WHITBOURNE PUBLIC LIBRARY*, Main St, A0B 3K0. (Mail add: PO
Box 400, A0B 3K0). Tel: 709-759-2461. FAX: 709-759-2461. Web Site:
www.nlpubliclibraries.ca. *Librn,* Gloria Somerton
Library Holdings: Bk Vols 6,291
Wireless access
Open Tues 1-5 & 6-8, Thurs 12:30-4:30, Fri 11-4

WINTERTON

P WINTERTON PUBLIC LIBRARY*, Main St, A0B 3M0. (Mail add: PO
Box 119, A0B 3M0). Tel: 709-583-2119. FAX: 709-583-2119. Web Site:
www.nlpubliclibraries.ca. *Librn,* Betty Pitcher
Library Holdings: Bk Vols 4,388; Per Subs 21
Wireless access
Open Mon-Wed 2-5, Thurs 2-8

NORTHWEST TERRITORIES

Date of Statistics: FY 2004-2005
Population: 42,083
Population Served by Public Libraries: 42,083
Total Volumes in Public Libraries: 186,755 (approximate, including headquarters holdings)
Total Public Library Circulation: 130,000
Total Public Library Budget: (Includes Territorial and Municipal Funding): $1,425,000

FORT SMITH

J   AURORA COLLEGE*, Thebacha Campus Library, 50 Conibear St, X0E 0P0. (Mail add: Bag Service No 2, X0E 0P0), SAN 324-5330. Tel: 867-872-7544. Circulation Tel: 867-872-7549. FAX: 867-872-4511. E-mail: tclibrary@auroracollege.nt.ca. Web Site: www.auroracollege.nt.ca/thebacha_opener.asp. *Librn,* Alexandra Hook; E-mail: ahook@auroracollege.nt.ca; Staff 1 (MLS 1)
Founded 1982. Fac 60
Library Holdings: AV Mats 1,000; Bk Vols 16,000; Per Subs 300
Subject Interests: N, Native studies
Automation Activity & Vendor Info: (Cataloging) SirsiDynix; (Circulation) SirsiDynix; (OPAC) SirsiDynix
Database Vendor: Gale Cengage Learning, ProQuest, Wilson - Wilson Web
Special Services for the Blind - Closed circuit TV magnifier; Reader equip
Open Mon-Thurs 8:30am-9pm, Fri 8:30-5, Sat 1-5, Sun 1-9

INUVIK

G   AURORA COLLEGE*, Aurora Research Institute Library, 191 Mackenzie Rd, X0E 0T0. (Mail add: PO Box 1450, X0E 0T0), SAN 324-1629. Tel: 867-777-3298, Ext 207. Administration Tel: 867-777-3298. FAX: 867-777-4264. E-mail: library@nwtresearch.com. Web Site: www.nwtresearch.com/resources/library.aspx. *Librn,* Annika Trimble; E-mail: atrimble@auroracollege.nt.ca; Staff 1 (Non-MLS 1)
Founded 1965
Library Holdings: Bk Titles 20,000; Per Subs 72; Spec Interest Per Sub 35; Videos 210
Special Collections: Arctic Research (Thesis Coll); Northern Material & Arctic Research (Rare Books Coll)
Subject Interests: Agr res, Arctic geol, Arctic res, Botany, Fisheries res, Native studies, Natural sci, Oral hist, Permafrost, Wildlife res
Wireless access
Function: Alaskana res, For res purposes, ILL available, Online searches, Prof lending libr, Res libr, VHS videos, Video lending libr
Open Mon-Fri 8:30-12 & 1-5

P   INUVIK CENTENNIAL LIBRARY*, 100 Mackenzie Rd, X0E 0T0. (Mail add: PO Box 1640, X0E 0T0), SAN 318-9694. Tel: 867-777-8620. FAX: 867-777-8621. E-mail: IK_Library@gov.nt.ca. Web Site: www.inuvik.net/icl. *Head Librn,* Beverly Garven; *Asst Librn, Head, ILL,* Valerie Townsend; E-mail: inuvik_interlibrary-loans@gov.nt.ca; *Libr Tech,* Wendy Mead; Staff 10 (Non-MLS 10)
Founded 1967. Pop 3,600
Jan 2005-Dec 2005 Income (CAN) $327,000, Provincial (CAN) $40,000, City (CAN) $267,000, Other (CAN) $20,000. Sal (CAN) $155,000
Library Holdings: Bk Vols 30,000; Per Subs 72
Special Collections: Dick Hill/Northern Coll
Automation Activity & Vendor Info: (Acquisitions) SirsiDynix; (Cataloging) SirsiDynix; (Circulation) SirsiDynix; (Course Reserve) SirsiDynix; (ILL) SirsiDynix; (OPAC) SirsiDynix; (Serials) SirsiDynix

Database Vendor: OCLC WorldCat, SirsiDynix
Special Services for the Blind - Bks on cassette; Large print bks
Open Mon-Thurs 10-6 & 7pm-9pm, Fri 10-6, Sat & Sun 1-5

NORMAN WELLS

P   NORMAN WELLS COMMUNITY LIBRARY*, PO Box 97, X0E 0V0. SAN 318-9716. Tel: 867-587-3714. FAX: 867-587-3714. E-mail: normanwells_library@govt.nt.ca. *Librn,* Lori Shapansky
Library Holdings: Bk Titles 10,000; Per Subs 15
Open Tues & Thurs 6:30pm-9pm, Wed & Fri 3:30pm-6pm, Sat 1pm-4:30pm
Friends of the Library Group

YELLOWKNIFE

G   GOVERNMENT OF THE NORTHWEST TERRITORIES*, Department of Environment & Natural Resources/Industry, Tourism & Investment (ENR-ITI), 600, 5102 50th Ave, X1A 3S8. SAN 370-1255. Tel: 867-920-8606. FAX: 867-873-0293. E-mail: enriti_library@gov.nt.ca. Web Site: www.enr.gov.nt.ca/_live/pages/wppages/enr_library.aspx. *Info Coordr,* Aingeal Stone; E-mail: aingeal_stone@gov.nt.ca; Staff 2 (MLS 1, Non-MLS 1)
Founded 1980
Library Holdings: Bk Titles 22,000; Per Subs 120
Special Collections: Traditional Knowledge. Can & Prov
Subject Interests: Biodiversity, Climate change, Conserv, Environment, Forestry, Mining, Wildlife
Automation Activity & Vendor Info: (Cataloging) Follett Software; (Circulation) Follett Software; (OPAC) EOS International
Database Vendor: EBSCOhost, ISI Web of Knowledge
Function: CD-ROM, Computers for patron use, Doc delivery serv, e-mail serv, Electronic databases & coll, Govt ref serv, ILL available, Mail & tel request accepted, Mail loans to mem, Online cat, Ref serv available, VHS videos
Publications: Recent Acquisitions (Acquisition list)
Restriction: Circ limited, Closed stack, Open to others by appt

G   LEGISLATIVE LIBRARY OF THE NORTHWEST TERRITORIES, Legislative Assembly Bldg, 4570 - 48th St, X1A 2L9. (Mail add: PO Box 1320, X1A 2L9), SAN 318-9783. Tel: 867-669-2202. FAX: 867-873-0207. Web Site: www.assembly.gov.nt.ca. *Librn,* Vera Raschke; Staff 3 (MLS 2, Non-MLS 1)
Founded 1973
Library Holdings: Bk Vols 45,000; Per Subs 200
Subject Interests: Native issues, Northern issues, Polit sci
Automation Activity & Vendor Info: (Acquisitions) SirsiDynix; (Cataloging) SirsiDynix; (Circulation) SirsiDynix; (OPAC) SirsiDynix
Open Mon-Fri 8:30-5

P   YELLOWKNIFE PUBLIC LIBRARY*, Centre Square Mall, 5022 49th St,
      2nd Flr, X1A 2N5. (Mail add: PO Box 694, X1A 2N5), SAN 318-9791.
      Tel: 867-920-5642. Information Services Tel: 867-669-3403. FAX:
      867-920-5671. E-mail: library@yellowknife.ca. *Mgr,* Deborah Bruser; Tel:
      867-669-3401, E-mail: dbruser@yellowknife.ca; *Pub Serv,* Shad Turner;
      Tech Serv, Kris Solowy; Tel: 867-669-3402; Staff 7 (MLS 2, Non-MLS 5)
      Founded 1949. Pop 18,500; Circ 87,000
      Library Holdings: High Interest/Low Vocabulary Bk Vols 400; Bk Titles
      70,000; Per Subs 127
      Special Collections: Northern Collection

Subject Interests: Can arctic
Automation Activity & Vendor Info: (Cataloging) SirsiDynix;
(Circulation) SirsiDynix; (OPAC) SirsiDynix
Database Vendor: EBSCOhost, OCLC FirstSearch, SirsiDynix
Function: ILL available
Open Mon-Thurs 10-9, Fri & Sat 10-6, Sun (Oct-Apr) 1-5
Restriction: Circ limited
Friends of the Library Group

NOVA SCOTIA

Date of Statistics: FY 2011-2012
Population, NS (est.): 945,437
Population Served by Public Libraries 945,437
Total Volumes in Public Libraries: 2,245,289
Circulation Per Capita: 7.8
Municipalities: 55
Service Points: 83

AMHERST

P   CUMBERLAND PUBLIC LIBRARIES, 21 Acadia St, 2nd Flr, B4H 4W3. (Mail add: PO Box 220, B4H 3Z2), SAN 366-7057. Tel: 902-667-2135. FAX: 902-667-1360. E-mail: information@cumberlandpubliclibraries.ca. Web Site: www.cumberlandpubliclibraries.ca. *Chief Librn,* Beth Clinton; Tel: 902-667-1767, E-mail: beth.clinton@cumberlandpubliclibraries.ca; *Dep Chief Librn,* Denise Corey; E-mail: denise.corey@cumberlandpubliclibraries.ca; *Youth Serv Librn,* Chantelle Taylor; E-mail: chantelle.taylor@cumberlandpubliclibraries.ca; Staff 3 (MLS 3)
Founded 1967. Pop 32,045; Circ 130,857
Library Holdings: Bk Vols 80,830; Per Subs 96
Wireless access
Friends of the Library Group
Branches: 7
ADVOCATE LIBRARY, Fundy Tides Recreation Ctr, 93 Mills Rd, Advocate Harbour, B0M 1A0. (Mail add: PO Box 1, Advocate Harbour, B0M 1A0), SAN 325-4259. Tel: 902-392-2214.
   Function: ILL available, Photocopying/Printing
FOUR FATHERS MEMORIAL, 21 Acadia St, B4H 3L5. (Mail add: PO Box 220, B4H 3Z2), SAN 366-7081. Tel: 902-667-2549. FAX: 902-667-1360.
   Function: ILL available, Photocopying/Printing
   Open Mon, Fri & Sat 10-5, Tues & Wed 10-8
   Friends of the Library Group
OXFORD LIBRARY, 22 Water St, Oxford, B0M 1P0, SAN 366-7111. Tel: 902-447-2440.
   Function: ILL available, Photocopying/Printing
   Open Wed 11-2 & 2-5, Thurs 2-5 & 6-8, Fri 11-1 & 2-5, Sat 10-3
PARRSBORO LIBRARY, 91 Queen St, Parrsboro, B0M 1S0, SAN 366-7146. Tel: 902-254-2046.
   Function: ILL available, Photocopying/Printing
   Open Tues & Wed 1-4 & 6-8, Thurs & Fri 10-1 & 2-5, Sat 10-3
PUGWASH LIBRARY, 10222 Durham St, Pugwash, B0K 1L0, SAN 329-5591. Tel: 902-243-3331.
   Function: ILL available, Photocopying/Printing
   Open Tues & Fri 12-5, Wed & Thurs 2-7, Sat 9-2
   Friends of the Library Group
RIVER HEBERT LIBRARY, 2730 Barronsfield Rd, River Hebert, B0L 1G0, SAN 329-563X. Tel: 902-251-2324.
   Function: ILL available, Photocopying/Printing
   Open Wed & Fri 10-1 & 2-4, Thurs 2-7, Sat 10-3
SPRINGHILL MINERS MEMORIAL LIBRARY, 85 Main St, Springhill, B0M 1X0, SAN 366-7170. Tel: 902-597-2211.
   Function: ILL available, Photocopying/Printing
   Open Tues 11-1 & 2-8, Wed & Thurs 10-1 & 2-6, Fri 11-1 & 2-5, Sat 10-1

ANTIGONISH

C   SAINT FRANCIS XAVIER UNIVERSITY*, Angus L MacDonald Library, West St, B2G 2W5. (Mail add: PO Box 5000, B2G 2W5), SAN 366-7596. Tel: 902-867-2267. Circulation Tel: 902-867-2228. Interlibrary Loan Service Tel: 902-867-2421. Reference Tel: 902-867-2242. FAX: 902-867-5153. Web Site: libmain.stfx.ca/newlib/. *Librn,* Lynne Murphy; E-mail: lmurphy@stfx.ca; *Spec Coll Librn,* Maureen Williams; Tel: 902-867-5328, E-mail: mwilliam@stfx.ca; *Syst Coordr,* Gord Bertrand; Tel: 902-867-2334, E-mail: gbertran@stfx.ca; *Cat,* Grace MacPherson; E-mail: gmacpher@stfx.ca; *Coll Develop,* Glenna Quinn; Tel: 902-867-2168, E-mail: gquinn@stfx.ca; *ILL,* Angela Hagar; E-mail: illoan@stfx.ca; *Ref,* Barbara Phillips; E-mail: bphillip@stfx.ca; *Tech Serv,* Elaine MacLean; Tel: 902-867-2221, E-mail: emaclean@stfx.ca; Staff 38 (MLS 8, Non-MLS 30)
Founded 1852. Enrl 3,251; Fac 170; Highest Degree: Master
Library Holdings: Bk Vols 498,741; Per Subs 1,604
Special Collections: Can; Celtic Coll; Nova Scotiana (Shell Coll)
Publications: Forward (Newsletter)
Partic in Novanet
Open Mon-Fri 8:15am-midnight, Sat 10-10, Sun 11-11
Departmental Libraries:
MARIE MICHAEL LIBRARY, Coady International Institute, PO Box 5000, B2G 2W5, SAN 366-7626. Tel: 902-867-3964. FAX: 902-867-3907. Web Site: www.coady.stfx.ca/library. *Libr Spec,* Catherine Irving; E-mail: cirving@stfx.ca; Staff 1 (Non-MLS 1)
Founded 1959
Library Holdings: CDs 100; e-journals 20; Bk Vols 12,500; Per Subs 95; Videos 900
Special Collections: Antigonish Movement Coll
Subject Interests: Adult educ, Credit unions, Develop studies
Automation Activity & Vendor Info: (Cataloging) Ex Libris Group; (OPAC) Ex Libris Group
Function: Audio & video playback equip for onsite use, CD-ROM, Doc delivery serv, ILL available, Music CDs, Ref serv available, Telephone ref, VCDs, VHS videos, Workshops
Publications: Gender & Sustainable Rural Development: A Resource Directory (1996); Toward Total Wellness: Women in the Caribbean (1994)
Open Mon-Fri 9-5

BADDECK

S   ALEXANDER GRAHAM BELL NATIONAL HISTORIC SITE OF CANADA, Reference Library & Archives, 559 Chebucto St, B0E 1B0. (Mail add: PO Box 159, B0E 1B0), SAN 370-775X. Tel: 902-295-2069. FAX: 902-295-3496. Web Site: www.parkscanada.gc.ca. *Mgr,* Eddie Kennedy; E-mail: eddy.kennedy@pc.gc.ca
Founded 1977
Library Holdings: Bk Titles 450; Bk Vols 620
Special Collections: Alexander Graham Bell Coll, incl AEA bulletins, Beinn Bhreagh recorder, dictated, home & lab notes, letter bks, secondary res mat

Wireless access
Restriction: Open by appt only

BARRINGTON

S   CAPE SABLE HISTORICAL SOCIETY ARCHIVES & LIBRARY*, 2402
     Hwy 3, B0W 1E0. SAN 370-7253. Tel: 902-637-2185. FAX:
     902-637-2185. *Mgr,* Brenda Maxwell; E-mail: maxwelbm@gov.ns.ca
     Founded 1933
     Library Holdings: Bk Vols 750
     Subject Interests: Local hist
     Open Mon-Sat 9:30-5, Sun 1-5

BRIDGETOWN

P   ANNAPOLIS VALLEY REGIONAL LIBRARY*, PO Box 640, B0S 1C0.
     SAN 366-7235. Tel: 902-665-2995. FAX: 902-665-4899. E-mail:
     insar@nsar.library.ns.ca. Web Site: www.valleylibrary.ca. *In Charge,* Wendy
     Trimper; E-mail: wtrimper@nsar.library.ns.ca; Staff 27 (MLS 3, Non-MLS
     24)
     Founded 1949. Pop 103,836; Circ 573,720
     Library Holdings: Bk Vols 283,899; Per Subs 260
     Restriction: Not open to pub
     Branches: 11
     ANNAPOLIS ROYAL BRANCH, 285 Saint George St, Annapolis Royal,
       B0S 1A0. (Mail add: PO Box 579, Annapolis Royal, B0S 1A0), SAN
       366-726X. Tel: 902-532-2226. *Librn,* Dorothy McDonald
       Library Holdings: Bk Vols 10,869
       Open Mon 2-5 & 6:30pm-8:30pm, Wed & Fri 10-5, Thurs 10-5 &
       6:30pm-8:30pm, Sat 10-2
       Friends of the Library Group
     BERWICK BRANCH, 210 Commercial St, Berwick, B0P 1E0, SAN
       366-7294. Tel: 902-538-4030. E-mail: berwick@nsar.library.ns.ca. *Librn,*
       Alissa Thorne
       Library Holdings: Bk Vols 8,597
       Open Mon & Fri 2-5 & 6:30pm-8:30pm, Wed 10-5, Fri 2-5, Sat 10-2
     HANTSPORT BRANCH, 11 School St, Hantsport, B0P 1P0. (Mail add:
       PO Box 542, Hantsport, B0P 1P0), SAN 366-7359. Tel: 902-684-4005.
       E-mail: hantspor@nsar.library.ns.ca. *Librn,* Diana Thompson
       Library Holdings: Bk Vols 11,552
       Open Mon 6:30pm-8:30pm, Tues & Thurs 1:30-4:30 & 6:30pm-8:30pm,
       Wed 1:30-4:30
     KENTVILLE BRANCH, 95 Cornwallis St, Kentville, B4N 3X7. (Mail
       add: PO Box 625, Kentville, B4N 3X7), SAN 366-7383. Tel:
       902-679-2544. FAX: 902-679-2544. E-mail: kentvill@nsar.library.ns.ca.
       Librn, Julie Johnson
       Library Holdings: Bk Vols 12,740
       Open Mon & Wed 10-5, Tues 2-5, Thurs & Fri 10-5 & 6:30pm-8:30pm,
       Sat 10-2
       Friends of the Library Group
     KINGSTON BRANCH, 671 Main St, Kingston, B0P 1R0. (Mail add: PO
       Box 430, Kingston, B0P 1R0), SAN 366-7413. Tel: 902-765-3631.
       E-mail: kingston@nsar.library.ns.ca. *Librn,* Andrea Leeson
       Library Holdings: Bk Vols 10,222
       Open Tues & Thurs 2-5 & 6:30pm-8:30pm, Fri 6:30pm-8:30pm, Sat
       10-2
     LAWRENCETOWN BRANCH, 50 Elliot Rd, Lawrencetown, B0S 1M0,
       SAN 366-7448. Tel: 902-584-2102. FAX: 902-584-2085. E-mail:
       library.avlawrencetown@nscc.ca. *Regional Librn,* Lana Kamennof-Sine;
       E-mail: lana.kamennof-sine@nscc.ca; *Campus Librn,* Peggy Weatherson;
       E-mail: peggy.weatherson@nscc.ca
       Library Holdings: Bk Vols 5,000
       Open Mon-Wed 8-4, Thurs-Fri 1-4
     MIDDLETON BRANCH, 45 Gates Ave, Middleton, B0S 1P0. (Mail add:
       PO Box 667, Middleton, B0S 1P0), SAN 366-7472. Tel: 902-825-4835.
       E-mail: middleto@nsar.library.ns.ca. *Librn,* Susan Aldred
       Library Holdings: Bk Vols 12,004
       Open Tues & Fri 2-5 & 6:30pm-8:30pm, Wed 2-5, Thurs 10-5, Sat 10-2
       Friends of the Library Group
     ROBERT MILLER MEMORIAL - BRIDGETOWN BRANCH, 271
       Granville St, B0S 1C0. (Mail add: PO Box 39, B0S 1C0), SAN
       366-7324. Tel: 902-665-2758. E-mail: bridgeto@nsar.library.ns.ca. *In
       Charge,* Amy Mcdonald
       Library Holdings: Bk Vols 6,956
       Open Tues & Fri 2-5 & 6:30-8:30, Thurs 2-5, Sat 10-1
     PORT WILLIAMS BRANCH, Community Centre, 131 Main St, Port
       Williams, B0P 1T0. (Mail add: PO Box 70, Port Williams, B0P 1T0),
       SAN 366-7502. Tel: 902-542-3005. FAX: 902-542-3005. E-mail:
       portwill@nsar.library.ns.ca. *Librn,* Susan Mullen
       Library Holdings: Bk Vols 10,271
       Open Mon & Fri 2-5 & 6:30pm-8:30pm, Wed 10-5, Sat 10-2
       Friends of the Library Group

WINDSOR BRANCH, 195 Albert St, Windsor, B0N 2T0. (Mail add: PO
  Box 106, Windsor, B0N 2T0), SAN 366-7537. Tel: 902-798-5424. Toll
  Free Tel: 866-922-0229. FAX: 902-798-0634. E-mail:
  windsor@nsar.library.ns.ca. *Librn,* Katherine McCoubrey
  Library Holdings: Bk Vols 13,426
  Open Tues-Thurs 10-5 & 6:30pm-8:30pm, Fri & Sat 10-5, Sun 2-5
  Friends of the Library Group
WOLFVILLE BRANCH, 21 Elm Ave, Wolfville, B4P 2A1, SAN
  366-7561. Tel: 902-542-5760. FAX: 902-542-5780. E-mail:
  wolfvill@nsar.library.ns.ca. *Librn,* Lisa Rice
  Library Holdings: Bk Vols 16,604
  Open Tues-Thurs 11-5 & 6:30pm-8:30pm, Fri & Sat 11-5, Sun 1-5
  Friends of the Library Group
Bookmobiles: 2

BRIDGEWATER

J   NOVA SCOTIA COMMUNITY COLLEGE*, Lunenburg Campus Library,
     75 High St, B4V 1V8. Tel: 902-543-0684. FAX: 902-543-0652. Web Site:
     www.library.nscc.ca. *Regional Librn,* Mary Jane Pittman; Tel:
     902-543-0690, E-mail: maryjane.pittman@nscc.ca; *Libr Tech,* Margareta
     Schirra; E-mail: Margareta.Schirra@nscc.ca
     Library Holdings: Bk Titles 2,801

CHURCH POINT

C   UNIVERSITE SAINTE-ANNE*, Bibliotheque Louis-R-Comeau, 1695, Rte
     1, B0W 1M0. (Mail add: PO Box 40, B0W 1M0), SAN 318-9813. Tel:
     902-769-2114, Ext 161. Circulation Tel: 902-769-2114, Ext 158.
     Interlibrary Loan Service Tel: 902-769-2114, Ext 163. Reference Tel:
     902-769-2114, Ext 162. FAX: 902-769-0137. E-mail:
     claire.robicheau@usainteanne.ca. Web Site: www.usainteanne.ca/biblio. *Dir,*
     Janice Boudreau; E-mail: janice.boudreau@usaintanne.ca; *Ref Librn,* Cecile
     Pothier-Comeau; E-mail: cecile.pothiercomeau@usainteanne.ca; *ILL,*
     Corinne Arsenault; E-mail: corinne.arsenault@usainteanne.ca; Staff 2 (MLS
     2)
     Founded 1870. Enrl 407; Fac 45; Highest Degree: Master
     Apr 2006-Mar 2007. Mats Exp (CAN) $100,000, Books (CAN) $50,000,
     Per/Ser (Incl. Access Fees) (CAN) $50,000. Sal (CAN) $214,000
     Library Holdings: Bk Titles 78,000; Bk Vols 80,000; Per Subs 204
     Special Collections: History & Folklore (Acadiana), bks, micro, newsp
     Subject Interests: Children's lit
     Automation Activity & Vendor Info: (Acquisitions) BiblioMondo;
     (Cataloging) BiblioMondo; (Circulation) BiblioMondo; (Course Reserve)
     BiblioMondo; (ILL) BiblioMondo; (Media Booking) BiblioMondo; (OPAC)
     BiblioMondo; (Serials) BiblioMondo
     Database Vendor: EBSCOhost, Gale Cengage Learning, OCLC
     FirstSearch, ProQuest, ScienceDirect
     Function: Doc delivery serv, Handicapped accessible, ILL available,
     Photocopying/Printing, Wheelchair accessible
     Partic in Canadian Research Knowledge Network; Coun of Atlantic Univ
     Librns
     Open Mon-Fri 9am-10:30pm, Sat 1-4:30, Sun 1-4:30 & 6pm-10:30pm
     Restriction: Clients only, Fee for pub use

DARTMOUTH

S   BLACK CULTURAL CENTRE FOR NOVA SCOTIA LIBRARY*, No 7
     Hwy at Cherry Brook Rd, 1149 Main St, B2Z 1A8. SAN 374-6178. Tel:
     902-434-6223. Toll Free Tel: 800-465-0765. FAX: 902-434-2306. E-mail:
     mail@bccns.com. Web Site: www.bccns.com. *Curator,* Henry Bishop
     Founded 1983
     Library Holdings: Bk Titles 3,000
     Special Collections: Black Culture. Oral History
     Publications: Out of the Past Into the Future; Out of the Past Into the
     Future, Vol 1; Publications List; Traditional Lifetime Stories, Vol 1;
     Traditional Lifetime Stories, Vol 2
     Open Mon-Fri 9-5

G   CANADA DEPARTMENT OF FISHERIES & OCEANS*, Bedford
     Institute of Oceanography Library, One Challenger Dr, B2Y 4A2. (Mail
     add: PO Box 1006, B2Y 4A2), SAN 318-983X. Tel: 902-426-3683.
     Administration Tel: 902-426-6266. FAX: 902-496-1544. E-mail:
     Dartmouth.Library-Bibliotheque@dfo-mpo.gc.ca. Web Site:
     www.dfo-mpo.gc.ca/libraries-bibliotheques/maritimes-eng.htm#bedford,
     www.dfo-mpo.gc.ca/libraries-bibliotheques/maritimes-fra.htm. *Archivist,
     Librn,* Marilynn Rudi; E-mail: marilynn.rudi@dfo-mpo.gc.ca; *Libr Mgr,*
     Anna Fiander; E-mail: anna.fiander@dfo-mpo.gc.ca; *Info Officer,* Anne
     Mazerall; E-mail: anne.mazerall@dfo-mpo.gc.ca; *ILL,* Rhonda Coll;
     E-mail: rhonda.coll@dfo-mpo.gc.ca; Staff 5 (MLS 2, Non-MLS 3)
     Founded 1962
     Library Holdings: Bk Titles 18,000; Bk Vols 125,000; Per Subs 1,100
     Special Collections: Arctic & Eastern Canadian Projects (Environmental
     Assessment Document Coll); Marine Sciences Coll
     Subject Interests: Marine sci, Oceanography

Function: ILL available
Open Mon-Fri 8-5
Restriction: Lending to staff only, Open to pub for ref only

G   CANADA DEPARTMENT OF NATIONAL DEFENCE*, Defence
Research & Development Canada-Atlantic Library, Nine Grove St, B3A
3C5. (Mail add: PO Box 1012, B2Y 3Z7), SAN 318-9821. Tel:
902-426-3100, Ext 135. FAX: 902-426-9654. E-mail:
atl.library@drdc-rddc.gc.ca. *Libr Serv Mgr,* Iris Jane Ouellette; E-mail:
iris.ouellette@drdc-rddc.gc.ca; Staff 2 (MLS 1, Non-MLS 1)
Founded 1946
Special Collections: Reference Related Technical Reports (25,000)
Subject Interests: Acoustics, Analytical chem, Computer sci, Electrical
eng, Hydronautics, Math, Metallurgy, Naval sci, Oceanography, Physics
Automation Activity & Vendor Info: (Acquisitions) BiblioMondo;
(Cataloging) BiblioMondo; (Circulation) BiblioMondo; (Serials)
BiblioMondo
Open Mon-Fri 7:30-4:30
Restriction: Restricted access

M   CAPITAL HEALTH/NOVA SCOTIA HOSPITAL, W James Meredith
Health Sciences Library, Hugh Bell Bldg, Rm 200, 300 Pleasant St, B2Y
3Z9. (Mail add: PO Box 1004, B2Y 3Z9), SAN 324-5861. Tel:
902-464-3254. FAX: 902-464-4804. E-mail: cdhalib@cdha.nshealth.ca.
Mgr, Libr Serv, Penny A Logan; Tel: 902-473-4383; *Libr Tech,* MacKenzie
Rob; Tel: 902-464-3255; *Libr Tech,* Heather Zinn; Tel: 902-464-3254; Staff
2 (Non-MLS 2)
Founded 1860
Library Holdings: Bk Titles 3,330; Per Subs 114
Subject Interests: Mental illness, Psychiat, Psychol
Automation Activity & Vendor Info: (Cataloging) Inmagic, Inc.; (OPAC)
Inmagic, Inc.
Database Vendor: Blackwell's, Cinahl Information Systems, Community
of Science (COS), EBSCOhost, McGraw-Hill, MD Consult, Micromedex,
Natural Standard, Nature Publishing Group, OVID Technologies, Oxford
Online, ProQuest, PubMed, RefWorks, ScienceDirect, Springer-Verlag,
STAT!Ref (Teton Data Systems), Wiley InterScience
Wireless access
Partic in Atlantic Health Knowledge Partnership (AHKP); Docline;
National Network of Libraries of Medicine
Open Mon-Fri 8:30-4:30

S   DARTMOUTH HERITAGE MUSEUM LIBRARY, Evergreen house, 26
Newcastle St, B2Y 3M5. SAN 377-3353. Tel: 902-464-2300. FAX:
902-464-8210. E-mail: museum@bellaliant.com. Web Site:
www.dartmouthheritagemuseum.ns.ca. *Interim Dir,* Bonnie Elliott; Staff 2
(Non-MLS 2)
Library Holdings: Bk Titles 400; Bk Vols 500; Per Subs 20
Mem of Halifax Public Libraries
Open Mon-Sat 9-4
Friends of the Library Group

G   ENVIRONMENT CANADA*, Atlantic Region Library, Queen Sq, 5th Flr,
45 Alderny Dr, B2Y 2N6. SAN 327-5450. Tel: 902-426-7232. FAX:
902-426-6143. E-mail: librarybiblio.dartmouth@ec.gc.ca. *Librn,* Angela
Ward-Smith; E-mail: angela.wardsmith@ec.gc.ca; Staff 1 (MLS 1)
Library Holdings: Bk Vols 3,000
Wireless access
Partic in Council of Federal Libraries Consortium
Restriction: Open by appt only

P   HALIFAX PUBLIC LIBRARIES, 60 Alderney Dr, B2Y 4P8. SAN
366-7928. Tel: 902-490-5744. Interlibrary Loan Service Tel: 902-490-5821.
FAX: 902-490-5762. Web Site: www.halifaxpubliclibraries.ca. *Chief Exec
Officer,* Judith Hare; E-mail: harej@halifaxpubliclibraries.ca; *Dep Exec Dir,*
Bruce Gorman; E-mail: gormanb@halifax.ca; Staff 316 (MLS 50,
Non-MLS 266)
Pop 372,858; Circ 4,875,328
Apr 2011-Mar 2012 Income (Main Library and Branch(s)) (CAN)
$22,226,229, Provincial (CAN) $4,835,200, County (CAN) $16,825,162,
Locally Generated Income (CAN) $561,894, Other (CAN) $3,973. Mats
Exp (CAN) $1,778,880, Books (CAN) $1,142,380, Per/Ser (Incl. Access
Fees) (CAN) $137,300, AV Mat (CAN) $364,700, Electronic Ref Mat
(Incl. Access Fees) (CAN) $134,500. Sal (CAN) $15,482,232
Library Holdings: CDs 36,037; DVDs 79,662; Bk Titles 340,491
Special Collections: Reference Halifax Coll
Subject Interests: Archit, Art, Hist
Database Vendor: SirsiDynix
Wireless access
Function: Handicapped accessible, Homebound delivery serv, ILL
available, Prog for adults, Prog for children & young adult, Ref serv
available, Summer reading prog, Wheelchair accessible

Publications: Bibliographies; Branch Profiles (Library statistics & report);
Community Directories, Library Guide, Resource Lists; Halifax Public
Libraries Library Guide (Library handbook)
Member Libraries: Dartmouth Heritage Museum Library
Restriction: Non-circulating coll
Branches: 14
ALDERNEY GATE, 60 Alderney Dr, B3H 3C3. Tel: 902-490-5840. FAX:
902-490-5842. TDD: 902-490-5770. *Br Mgr,* Helen Thexton; Staff 22
(MLS 5, Non-MLS 17)
Founded 1989. Pop 28,572; Circ 474,455
Special Services for the Deaf - TDD equip
BEDFORD BRANCH, Wardour Centre, 15 Dartmouth Rd, Bedford, B4A
3X6, SAN 376-8597. Tel: 902-490-5740. FAX: 902-490-5752. *Mgr,*
Hannah Colville; Staff 7 (MLS 2, Non-MLS 5)
Founded 1990. Pop 18,271; Circ 316,602
  Library Holdings: CDs 2,420; DVDs 2,998; Videos 868
CAPTAIN WILLIAM SPRY BRANCH, Ten Kidston Rd, Halifax, B3R
2J7, SAN 366-7960. Tel: 902-490-5734. FAX: 902-490-5741. *Mgr,*
Matthew McCarthy; Staff 10 (MLS 2, Non-MLS 8)
Founded 1986. Pop 27,746; Circ 202,919
COLE HARBOUR BRANCH, 51 Forest Hills Pkwy, Cole Harbour, B2W
6C6, SAN 376-8619. Tel: 902-434-7228. FAX: 902-434-7448. *Mgr,*
Janice Fiander; Staff 11 (MLS 2, Non-MLS 9)
Founded 1989. Pop 50,785; Circ 397,838
DARTMOUTH NORTH BRANCH, 134 Pinecrest Dr, B3A 2J9, SAN
376-8627. Tel: 902-490-5840. FAX: 902-490-5842. *Br Mgr,* Darla
Muzzerall; Staff 4 (MLS 1, Non-MLS 3)
Founded 1996. Pop 7,025; Circ 69,204
KESHEN GOODMAN BRANCH, 330 Lacewood Dr, Halifax, B3M 4G2,
SAN 370-0208. Tel: 902-490-5738. FAX: 902-490-5739. *Mgr,* Sarah
Wenning; Staff 29 (MLS 5, Non-MLS 24)
Founded 1989. Pop 54,492; Circ 948,496
HALIFAX NORTH MEMORIAL, 2285 Gottingen St, Halifax, B3K 3B6,
SAN 366-7952. Tel: 902-490-5723. FAX: 902-490-5737. *Mgr,* Darla
Muzzerall; Staff 10 (MLS 2, Non-MLS 8)
Founded 1966. Pop 8,316; Circ 126,688
MUSQUODOBOIT HARBOUR BRANCH, Village Plaza, 7900 No 7
Hwy, Musquodoboit Harbour, B0J 1L0, SAN 376-8651. Tel:
902-889-2227. FAX: 902-889-3799. *Mgr,* Denise Somers; Staff 3 (MLS
1, Non-MLS 2)
Founded 1997. Pop 5,985; Circ 82,829
SACKVILLE BRANCH, 636 Sackville Dr, Lower Sackville, B4C 2S4,
SAN 376-866X. Tel: 902-865-8653. FAX: 902-865-2370. *Mgr,* Kathleen
Peverill; Staff 14 (MLS 3, Non-MLS 11)
Founded 1996. Pop 42,473; Circ 447,037
J D SHATFORD MEMORIAL, 10353 St Margaret Bay Rd, No 3 Hwy,
Hubbards, B0J 1T0, SAN 376-8635. Tel: 902-857-9176. FAX:
902-857-1397. *Mgr,* Elaine Murray; Staff 2 (Non-MLS 2)
Founded 1969. Pop 1,059; Circ 57,196
SHEET HARBOUR BRANCH, Blue Water Business Ctr, 22756 Hwy No
7, Sheet Harbour, B0J 3B0, SAN 376-8678. Tel: 902-885-2391. FAX:
902-885-2749. *Mgr,* Denise Somers; Staff 3 (MLS 1, Non-MLS 2)
Founded 1992. Pop 3,141; Circ 37,913
SPRING GARDEN ROAD MEMORIAL, 5381 Spring Garden Rd, Halifax,
B3J 1E9, SAN 376-8686. Tel: 902-490-5821. FAX: 902-490-5747. *Mgr,*
Darlene Beck; Tel: 902-490-5804; Staff 35 (MLS 8, Non-MLS 27)
Founded 1951. Pop 51,730; Circ 717,856
Function: Prog for adults, Prog for children & young adult, Ref serv
available, Summer reading prog
Restriction: Non-circulating coll
TANTALLON PUBLIC, 3646 Hammonds Plains Rd, Upper Tantallon, B0J
3J0. Tel: 902-826-3330. FAX: 902-826-3328. *Br Mgr,* Elaine D Murray;
Tel: 902-826-3331; Staff 12 (MLS 2, Non-MLS 10)
Founded 2001. Pop 19,825; Circ 304,654
Function: Prog for children & young adult
Open Tues-Thurs 10-9, Fri & Sat 10-5, Sun (Sept-May) 2-5
WOODLAWN PUBLIC, 31 Eisener Blvd, B2W 0J1, SAN 376-8708. Tel:
902-435-8352. FAX: 902-435-8380. *Br Mgr,* Charby Slemin; Staff 21
(MLS 4, Non-MLS 17)
Founded 1975. Pop 26,795; Circ 425,350
Function: Prog for adults, Prog for children & young adult, Summer
reading prog
Open Tues-Thurs 10-9, Fri & Sat 10-5, Sun (Sept-May) 2-5
Bookmobiles: 1

S   NORTHWEST ATLANTIC FISHERIES ORGANIZATION LIBRARY,
Two Morris Dr, Ste 100, B3B 1K8. (Mail add: PO Box 638, B2Y 3Y9),
SAN 373-3165. Tel: 902-468-5590. FAX: 902-468-5538. E-mail:
info@nafo.int. Web Site: www.nafo.int. *In Charge,* Lisa Pelzmann; E-mail:
lpelzmann@nafo.int
Library Holdings: Bk Titles 50; Bk Vols 100
Function: Ref & res
Restriction: Access at librarian's discretion

J   NOVA SCOTIA COMMUNITY COLLEGE*, Waterfront Campus Library, 80 Mawiomi Pl, B2Y 0A5. Tel: 902-491-1035. FAX: 902-491-1037. E-mail: library.waterfront@nscc.ca. Web Site: www.library.nscc.ca. *Regional Librn,* Ann Roman; E-mail: ann.roman@nscc.ca; *Libr Tech,* Rodney Tucker; E-mail: rodney.tucker@nscc.ca; Staff 4 (MLS 2, Non-MLS 2)
Founded 2007. Enrl 1,900
Open Mon-Thurs 8-5, Fri 8-4

S   SCHIZOPHRENIA SOCIETY OF NOVA SCOTIA LIBRARY*, E C Purdy Bldg, Rm B23, 300 Pleasant St, B2Y 3Z9. SAN 373-6105. Tel: 902-465-2601. Toll Free Tel: 800-465-2601. FAX: 902-465-5479. Web Site: www.ssns.ca. *Librn,* Cindy Crowell
Library Holdings: Bk Vols 70
Open Mon-Fri 8:30-4:30

GLACE BAY

S   MINERS' MUSEUM LIBRARY*, 17 Museum St, B1A 5T8. (Mail add: PO Box 310, B1A 5T8), SAN 324-0029. Tel: 902-849-4522. FAX: 902-849-8022. E-mail: info@minersmuseum.com. Web Site: www.minersmuseum.com. *Dir,* Tom Miller
Founded 1967
Library Holdings: Bk Titles 1,000; Per Subs 600
Special Collections: Technical Information on Coal Mining Pre-1965

GUYSBOROUGH

S   GUYSBOROUGH HISTORICAL SOCIETY*, Old Court House Museum & Information Centre, 106 Church St, B0H 1N0. (Mail add: PO Box 232, B0H 1N0), SAN 377-0931. Tel: 902-533-4008. FAX: 902-533-2258. Web Site: www.guysboroughcountyheritage.ca. *Curator,* Kim Avery
Founded 1973
Library Holdings: Bk Titles 100; Bk Vols 125
Subject Interests: Genealogy
Open Mon-Fri (June-Oct) 9-5

HALIFAX

M   AIDS COALITION OF NOVA SCOTIA LIBRARY, 1668 Barrington St, B3J 2A2. SAN 374-8871. Tel: 902-425-4882. Toll Free Tel: 800-566-2437. FAX: 902-422-6200. E-mail: acns@acns.ns.ca. Web Site: www.acns.ns.ca. *Exec Dir,* Maria MacIntosh
Library Holdings: CDs 50; Bk Titles 800; Per Subs 10; Videos 140
Special Collections: Pamphlets/Brochures dating from 1979, on AIDS/HIV & Related Topics
Open Mon-Fri 10-4

S   ALZHEIMER SOCIETY OF NOVA SCOTIA RESOURCE CENTRE*, 5954 Spring Garden Rd, B3H 1Y7. SAN 377-2187. Tel: 902-422-7961. Toll Free Tel: 800-611-6345 (Nova Scotia only). FAX: 902-422-7971. E-mail: info@alzheimer.ns.ca. Web Site: www.alzheimer.ns.ca.
Library Holdings: Bk Titles 460
Open Mon-Thurs 8:30-4:30, Fri 8:30-4 (July & Aug 8:30-1)
Restriction: Restricted loan policy

S   ART GALLERY OF NOVA SCOTIA LIBRARY*, 1723 Hollis St, B3J 3C8. (Mail add: PO Box 2262, B3J 3C8), SAN 377-4899. Tel: 902-424-7542. FAX: 902-424-7359. Web Site: www.artgalleryofnovascotia.ca. *Chief Exec Officer, Dir,* Ray Cronin; *Curator of Coll,* Shannon Parker; E-mail: parkers@gov.ns.ca
Library Holdings: Bk Titles 1,400
Open Mon (April-Oct) 10-5, Tues-Sun 10-5, Thurs 10-9

S   ATLANTIC PROVINCES ECONOMIC COUNCIL LIBRARY*, 5121 Sackville St, Ste 500, B3J 1K1. SAN 329-9473. Tel: 902-422-6516. FAX: 902-429-6803. E-mail: info@apec-econ.ca. *Pres,* Elizabeth Beale
Library Holdings: Bk Vols 1,000; Per Subs 12
Subject Interests: Atlantic region economy, Can
Open Mon-Fri 8:30-4:30

S   ATLANTIC PROVINCES SPECIAL EDUCATION AUTHORITY LIBRARY, 5940 South St, B3H 1S6. Tel: 902-424-5639, 902-424-8524. FAX: 902-424-3808. E-mail: library@apsea.ca. Web Site: www.apsea.ca/library. *Librn,* Lynn MacGregor; E-mail: lynn_macgregor@apsea.ca; *Libr Tech,* Corinne Gilroy; E-mail: corinne_gilroy@apsea.ca; *Libr Tech,* Samantha Neukom; Tel: 902-424-8525, E-mail: samantha_neukom@apsea.ca; *Libr Tech,* Gail Simms; Tel: 902-424-4614, E-mail: gail_simms@apsea.ca
Wireless access
Open Mon-Fri 8-5:30

R   ATLANTIC SCHOOL OF THEOLOGY LIBRARY*, 624 Francklyn St, B3H 3B5. SAN 318-9899. Tel: 902-423-7986. FAX: 902-423-7941. E-mail: astcirc@astheology.ns.ca, astref@astheology.ns.ca. Web Site:

astheology.ns.ca/library. *Dir,* Joyce Thomson; Tel: 902-496-7948, E-mail: jthomson@astheology.ns.ca; *Electronic Serv Librn,* Keith Noseworthy; E-mail: knoseworthy@astheology.ns.ca; Staff 6 (MLS 4, Non-MLS 2)
Founded 1971. Highest Degree: Master
Library Holdings: AV Mats 1,667; Bk Vols 71,547; Per Subs 350; Videos 384
Special Collections: Church History; Ecumenical; J B Hardie Arabic & Islamic Library; Presbyterian Canadian Missionary
Subject Interests: Relig, Theol
Automation Activity & Vendor Info: (Acquisitions) Infor Library & Information Solutions; (Cataloging) Infor Library & Information Solutions; (Circulation) Infor Library & Information Solutions; (Course Reserve) Infor Library & Information Solutions
Database Vendor: OCLC FirstSearch
Publications: John B Hardie Arabic & Islamic Coll, catalogue
Partic in Novanet
Open Mon-Thurs 8:30am-9pm, Fri 8:30-4:30, Sat 11-4:30, Sun 1:30-4:30

S   CANADA DEPARTMENT OF NATIONAL DEFENCE*, Cambridge Military Library, Royal Artillery Park, Bldg No 3, 5460 Royal Artillery Court, B3J 0A8. SAN 325-2604. Tel: 902-427-4494. FAX: 902-427-4495. E-mail: clibrary@ns.aliantzinc.ca. *Librn,* Jeanne Howell; Staff 1 (MLS 1)
Founded 1817
Library Holdings: Bk Vols 30,000
Special Collections: Corfu Coll
Subject Interests: Local hist, Mil
Open Mon & Tues 8-3

C   DALHOUSIE UNIVERSITY, Killam Memorial Library, 6225 University Ave, B3H 4H8. (Mail add: PO Box 15000, B3H 4R2), SAN 366-7804. Administration Tel: 902-494-3621. Web Site: libraries.dal.ca/locations_services/locations/killam_memorial_library.html. *Actg Head, Libr,* Joyline Makani; E-mail: joyline.makani@dal.ca
Founded 1867. Highest Degree: Doctorate
Special Collections: Australian Literature; Early Imprints & Fine Bindings (Douglas Cockerell Coll); Francis Bacon Coll; J J Stewart Maritime Coll; K G T Webster Castle Coll; Oscar Wilde Coll; Rudyard Kipling (James MacGregor Stewart Coll); Thomas Chandler Haliburton Coll; Thomas Raddall Manuscripts & Papers; William Gilpin Coll
Subject Interests: Arts, Bus & mgt, Computer sci, Humanities, Sci, Soc sci
Automation Activity & Vendor Info: (Acquisitions) Ex Libris Group; (Cataloging) Ex Libris Group; (Circulation) Ex Libris Group; (ILL) Relais International; (OPAC) Ex Libris Group
Wireless access
Partic in Canadian Research Knowledge Network; Coun of Atlantic Univ Librns; Novanet
Departmental Libraries:

CL   SIR JAMES DUNN LAW LIBRARY, Weldon Law Bldg, 6061 University Ave, B3H 4H9, SAN 366-7863. Tel: 902-494-2640. FAX: 902-494-6669. E-mail: lawill@dal.ca. Web Site: www.library.dal.ca/~law/index.html. *Law Librn,* Ann Morrison; E-mail: ann.morrison@dal.ca; *Pub Serv Librn,* David Michels; E-mail: david.michels.dal.ca; *ILL,* Brenda Cook; Tel: 902-494-8858
Founded 1883
Library Holdings: Bk Vols 275,408; Per Subs 600
Subject Interests: Intl law, Law of the sea
Publications: Marine Affairs Bibliography
Open Mon-Thurs 8am-10:45pm, Fri 8am-9pm, Sat 9-6, Sun 11-10:45

CM   W K KELLOGG HEALTH SCIENCES LIBRARY, Tupper Medical Bldg, 5850 College St, B3H 1X5. Circulation Tel: 902-494-2479. Interlibrary Loan Service Tel: 902-494-2469. Reference Tel: 902-494-2482. Administration Tel: 902-494-2458. Interlibrary Loan Service FAX: 902-494-3750. Administration FAX: 902-494-3798. E-mail: kellogg@dal.ca. Web Site: www.library.dal.ca/kellogg. *Head of Libr,* Patrick Ellis; E-mail: pellis@dal.ca; *Head of Doc Delivery,* Joe Wickens; E-mail: illnshdm@dal.ca; *Head, Tech Serv,* Judith Coughlan-Lambly; *Coordr, Ref (Info Serv),* Ann Barrett; Tel: 902-494-1649, E-mail: ann.barrett@dal.ca; *Cat,* Tim Ruggles
Founded 1890
Library Holdings: Bk Vols 208,000
Subject Interests: Dentistry, Health serv admin, Human communication disorders, Med, Nursing, Occupational therapy, Pharm, Physiotherapy
Automation Activity & Vendor Info: (Cataloging) Ex Libris Group; (Circulation) Ex Libris Group; (OPAC) Ex Libris Group; (Serials) EBSCO Online
Partic in Docline
Open Mon-Thurs 8am-11pm, Fri 8-7, Sat 10-6, Sun 11-11

SEXTON DESIGN & TECHNOLOGY LIBRARY, 1360 Barrington St, B3J 2X4. (Mail add: PO Box 1000, B3J 2X4), SAN 319-0102. Tel: 902-494-3240. FAX: 902-494-6089. E-mail: sexton.library@dal.ca. *Chief Librn,* Donna Richardson; Tel: 902-494-3979, E-mail: donna.richardson@dal.ca; *Asst Librn, Ref Serv,* Helen Powell; E-mail:

helen.powell@dal.ca; *ILL,* Christine Whynot; E-mail:
christine.whynot@dal.ca; Staff 5 (MLS 5)
Founded 1949. Enrl 1,250; Fac 110; Highest Degree: Doctorate
Library Holdings: Bk Titles 45,000; Bk Vols 141,000; Per Subs 740
Subject Interests: Agr eng, Applied math, Archit, Chem eng, Civil eng,
Computer sci, Electrical eng, Eng, Environ, Food sci, Metallurgical,
Mining eng, Rural planning, Urban
Publications: Tuns Library Newsletter
Open Mon-Thurs 8am-Midnight, Fri 8am-9pm, Sat 9-9, Sun
10am-Midnight

M   IWK HEALTH CENTRE FOR CHILDREN, WOMEN & FAMILIES*,
Health Sciences Library, 5980 University Ave, B3H 4N1. SAN 325-5913.
Tel: 902-470-7058. FAX: 902-470-7122. Web Site:
www.iwk.nshealth.ca/resources/. *Librn,* Darlene Chapman; Tel: 902-
470-6729, E-mail: darlene.chapman@iwk.nshealth.ca; *ILL,* Pam Parker;
E-mail: pam.parker@iwk.nshealth.ca; Staff 3 (MLS 1, Non-MLS 2)
Library Holdings: Bk Titles 1,000; Bk Vols 32,170; Per Subs 170
Subject Interests: Neonatology, Obstetrics, Pediatrics, Women's health
Publications: Newsletter
Open Mon-Fri 9-5

L   LEGAL INFORMATION SOCIETY OF NOVA SCOTIA LIBRARY*,
5523 B Young St, B3K 1Z7. SAN 373-644X. Tel: 902-454-2198. FAX:
902-455-3105. E-mail: lisns@legalinfo.org. *Dir,* Maria Franks
Library Holdings: Bk Titles 2,500; Bk Vols 3,000; Per Subs 20
Partic in Novanet
Restriction: Not open to pub

G   LEGISLATIVE LIBRARY OF NOVA SCOTIA*, Province House, 2nd Flr,
B3J 2P8. (Mail add: PO Box 396, B3J 2P8), SAN 318-9961. Tel:
902-424-5932. FAX: 902-424-0220. E-mail: leglib@gov.ns.ca. Web Site:
nslegislature.ca/index.php/library. *Mgr, Info Serv,* Anne Van Iderstine;
E-mail: vanideal@gov.ns.ca; *Info & Libr Tech Mgr,* David McDonald;
E-mail: mcdonads@gov.ns.ca; *Librn,* Margaret Murphy; E-mail:
murphymf@gov.ns.ca; *Info Serv Librn,* Heather Ludlow; E-mail:
ludlowh@gov.ns.ca; Staff 7 (MLS 4, Non-MLS 3)
Founded 1862
Library Holdings: Bk Vols 200,000
Special Collections: Novascotiana Coll
Subject Interests: Can hist, Fed, Nova Scotiana, Polit sci, Prov govt doc
Database Vendor: Innovative Interfaces, Inc INN - View
Publications: A History of Province House; Nova Scotia Book of Days;
Publications of the Province of Nova Scotia (Annual & Monthly)
Open Mon-Fri 8:30-4:30

S   MARITIME MUSEUM OF THE ATLANTIC*, Nils Jannasch Library,
1675 Lower Water St, B3J 1S3. SAN 325-6294. Tel: 902-424-7890. FAX:
902-424-0612. E-mail: mmalibry@gov.ns.ca.
Library Holdings: Bk Titles 6,000; Per Subs 39
Special Collections: Nautical Charts; Photographs Coll; Vessel Plans
Restriction: Open by appt only

L   MCINNES COOPER LIBRARY*, 1300-1969 Upper Water St, B3J 2V1.
(Mail add: PO Box 730, B3J 2V1), SAN 328-0861. Tel: 902-444-8468.
FAX: 902-425-6350, 902-425-6386. Web Site: www.mcinnescooper.com.
Regional Mgr, Libr Serv, Kate Green Stanhope; E-mail:
kate.stanhope@mcinnescooper.com; Staff 4 (MLS 2, Non-MLS 2)
Automation Activity & Vendor Info: (Acquisitions) Inmagic, Inc.;
(Cataloging) Inmagic, Inc.; (Serials) Inmagic, Inc.
Partic in Can Asn of Law Librs

L   STEWART MCKELVEY, Law Library, 1959 Upper Water St, Ste 900, B3J
3N2. (Mail add: PO Box 997, B3J 2X2), SAN 322-7014. Tel:
902-420-3200. Interlibrary Loan Service Tel: 902-490-8541. Administration
Tel: 902-490-8573. FAX: 902-420-1417. E-mail:
library@stewartmckelvey.com, *Knowledge Mgr,* Cynthia Murphy; E-mail:
cmurphy@stewartmckelvey.com; *Sr Libr Tech,* Christine Eidt; E-mail:
cmeidt@stewartmckelvey.com; *Libr Tech,* Victoria Nicoll; Tel:
902-420-3200, Ext 109; Staff 2.5 (MLS 1, Non-MLS 1.5)
Founded 1867
Library Holdings: Bk Vols 15,000; Per Subs 250
Restriction: Access for corporate affiliates, Co libr, Employee & client use
only, Not a lending libr

C   MOUNT SAINT VINCENT UNIVERSITY LIBRARY, 166 Bedford Hwy,
B3M 2J6. SAN 318-9988. Tel: 902-457-6250. Reference Tel:
902-457-6525. FAX: 902-457-6445. E-mail: library@msvu.ca. Web Site:
www.msvu.ca/library. *Univ Librn,* Tanja Harrison; Tel: 902-457-6108,
E-mail: tanja.harrison@msvu.ca; *Coordr, Pub Serv, Librn,* Meg Raven; Tel:
902-457-6403; E-mail: meg.raven@msvu.ca; *Coll & Archives Librn,*
Terrence Paris; Tel: 902-457-6526, E-mail: terrence.paris@msvu.ca;
E-Learning Librn, Denyse Rodrigues; Tel: 902-457-6200, E-mail:

denyse.rodrigues@msvu.ca; *Syst Librn,* Stanislav Orlov; E-mail:
stan.orlov@msvu.ca; *Mgr, Access Serv,* Shelagh Legere; Tel: 902-457-6204,
E-mail: shelagh.legere@msvu.ca; *Archivist,* Roger Gillis; Tel:
902-457-6401, E-mail: roger.gillis@msvu.ca; *Doc Delivery,* Katie Puxley;
Tel: 902-457-6435, E-mail: katie.puxley@msvu.ca; Staff 21 (MLS 5,
Non-MLS 16)
Founded 1873. Enrl 4,030; Fac 330; Highest Degree: Doctorate
Apr 2012-Mar 2013 Income (CAN) $1,929,628. Mats Exp (CAN)
$569,177, Books (CAN) $19,891, Per/Ser (Incl. Access Fees) (CAN)
$52,727, AV Mat (CAN) $4,516, Electronic Ref Mat (Incl. Access Fees)
(CAN) $491,260, Presv (CAN) $783. Sal (CAN) $1,200,889 (Prof (CAN)
$455,983)
Library Holdings: AV Mats 1,692; e-books 391,196; e-journals 33,872;
Bk Titles 223,483; Bk Vols 240,542; Per Subs 10,510
Special Collections: Canadian Drama Coll; English Literature (MacDonald
Coll); Lesbian Pulp Fiction Coll; Women & Peace Coll; Women's Studies
(Centennial, Gerritsen & Women's History), bks, micro. Can & Prov
Subject Interests: Child & youth study, Cultural studies, Educ, Family
studies, Gerontology, Human nutrition, Info tech, Pub relations, Tourism,
Women's studies
Automation Activity & Vendor Info: (Acquisitions) Ex Libris Group;
(Cataloging) Ex Libris Group; (Circulation) Ex Libris Group; (Course
Reserve) Ex Libris Group; (ILL) Relais International; (OPAC) Ex Libris
Group; (Serials) Ex Libris Group
Database Vendor: ABC-CLIO, Agricola, Alexander Street Press,
American Chemical Society, American Mathematical Society, American
Psychological Association (APA), Blackwell's, Cambridge Scientific
Abstracts, CEDROM-SNi, Coutts Information Service, Ebooks Corporation,
ebrary, EBSCO Information Services, EBSCOhost, Elsevier, Emerald, Ex
Libris Group, Gale Cengage Learning, Ingram Library Services, ISI Web
of Knowledge, JSTOR, Medline, netLibrary, OCLC Openly Informatics,
OCLC WorldCat, Oxford Online, Paratext, Project MUSE, ProQuest,
PubMed, RefWorks, Sage, ScienceDirect, Springer-Verlag, Swets
Information Services, Thomson - Web of Science, Wiley InterScience
Wireless access
Function: Archival coll, CD-ROM, Distance learning, Doc delivery serv,
E-Reserves, ILL available, Magnifiers for reading, Online info literacy
tutorials on the web & in blackboard, Online ref, Orientations, Ref serv
available, Spoken cassettes & CDs, Telephone ref, VHS videos, Workshops
Publications: Guide to Resources in Women's Studies (Research guide)
Partic in Coun of Atlantic Univ Librns; Novanet
Open Mon-Thurs 8am-11pm, Fri 8-6, Sat 9-6, Sun 12-9

S   MULTICULTURAL ASSOCIATION OF NOVA SCOTIA LIBRARY*,
1113 Marginal Rd, B3H 4P7. SAN 376-1800. Tel: 902-423-6534. FAX:
902-422-0881. E-mail: admin@mans.ns.ca. Web Site: www.mans.ns.ca.
Admin Senior Librn, Patty Ha-Tran
Library Holdings: Bk Vols 1,000
Subject Interests: Multicultural
Open Mon-Fri 9-5

L   NOVA SCOTIA BARRISTERS' SOCIETY*, Library & Information
Services, 1815 Upper Water St, 7th Flr, B3J 1S7. SAN 319-0005. Tel:
902-425-2665. FAX: 902-422-1697. E-mail: nsbslib@nsbs.org. Web Site:
www.nsbs.org/library.php. *Dir, Libr & Info Serv,* Barbara Campbell;
E-mail: bcampbel@nsbs.org; *Electronic Serv Librn,* Deborah Copeman;
E-mail: dcopeman@nsbs.org; *Info Serv Librn,* Susan Jones; E-mail:
sjones@nsbs.org; Staff 3 (MLS 3)
Founded 1797
Library Holdings: Bk Vols 15,000
Special Collections: Unreported Nova Scotia Decisions
Subject Interests: Can law
Automation Activity & Vendor Info: (Serials) Inmagic, Inc.
Database Vendor: HeinOnline, WestlaweCARSWELL
Wireless access
Publications: Nova Scotia Current Law (Monthly); Nova Scotia Law News
(Quarterly)
Restriction: Mem only

C   NOVA SCOTIA COLLEGE OF ART & DESIGN LIBRARY*, 5163 Duke
St, B3J 3J6. SAN 319-0013. Tel: 902-494-8196. Interlibrary Loan Service
Tel: 902-494-8255. Administration Tel: 902-494-8181. FAX: 902-425-1978.
Web Site: www.nscad.ns.ca/library.html. *Dir,* Ilga Leja; E-mail:
ilga@nscad.ns.ca; Staff 6 (MLS 2, Non-MLS 4)
Founded 1887. Enrl 730; Fac 45; Highest Degree: Master
Library Holdings: Bk Titles 37,000; Per Subs 225
Subject Interests: 20th Century art hist, Contemporary art, Environ
planning, Graphic design, Photog
Automation Activity & Vendor Info: (Acquisitions) Infor Library &
Information Solutions; (Cataloging) Infor Library & Information Solutions;
(Circulation) Infor Library & Information Solutions; (OPAC) Infor Library
& Information Solutions; (Serials) Infor Library & Information Solutions
Partic in Novanet
Open Mon-Thurs 8:30-10, Fri 8:30-7, Sat & Sun 1-5

J NOVA SCOTIA COMMUNITY COLLEGE*, Institute of Technology Library, 5685 Leeds St, B3J 3C4. (Mail add: PO Box 2210, B3J 3C4), SAN 319-0072. Tel: 902-491-4694. FAX: 902-491-2015. E-mail: library.institute@nscc.ca. Web Site: www.library.nscc.ca. *Campus Librn,* Position Currently Open; *Libr Tech,* Jeanette Macdonald; E-mail: jeanette.macdonald@nscc.ca; Staff 1 (MLS 1)
Founded 1972. Enrl 1,100
Library Holdings: Bk Vols 7,809
Special Collections: Student Technical Reports
Subject Interests: Trades
Open Mon & Wed 8-5, Tues & Thurs 8-7, Fri 8-4

G NOVA SCOTIA DEPARTMENT OF EDUCATION LIBRARY*, 2021 Brunswick St, B3J 2S9. (Mail add: PO Box 578, B3J 2S9), SAN 329-2371. Tel: 902-424-4920. Reference Tel: 902-424-5264. FAX: 902-424-0519. E-mail: educlib@gov.ns.ca. Web Site: www.ednet.ns.ca. *Librn,* Lynn Duquette; *Libr Tech,* Kristina Holman; E-mail: holmank@gov.ns.ca; Staff 2 (MLS 1, Non-MLS 1)
Founded 1986
Library Holdings: Bk Vols 12,000; Per Subs 75
Special Collections: Nova Scotia Educational System (Departmental Archives)
Open Mon-Fri 8:30-4:30

G NOVA SCOTIA DEPARTMENT OF NATURAL RESOURCES LIBRARY, Founders Sq, 1701 Hollis St, 3rd Flr, B3J 3M8. (Mail add: PO Box 698, B3J 2T9), SAN 324-7465. Tel: 902-424-8633. FAX: 902-424-7735. E-mail: nsdnrlib@gov.ns.ca. *Librn,* Tracy Lenfesty; E-mail: lenfestl@gov.ns.ca; *Libr Asst,* Janelle Brenton; Tel: 902 424 3179, E-mail: brentojl@gov.ns.ca; Staff 2 (MLS 1, Non-MLS 1)
Founded 1960
Library Holdings: Microforms 20,000; Bk Titles 35,000; Per Subs 200
Special Collections: Annual Reports (Geological Survey of Canada, Nova Scotia Department of Mines, Nova Scotia Department of Lands & Forests); Company Exploration Reports Coll; GSC Publications & Maps on Nova Scotia; NSDNR Publications & Maps
Subject Interests: Forestry, Geoscience, Land use, Mining eng, Recreation, Resource mgt, Wildlife
Automation Activity & Vendor Info: (Cataloging) SirsiDynix; (OPAC) SirsiDynix
Function: Archival coll, ILL available, Online cat, Ref serv available, Wheelchair accessible
Open Mon-Fri 8.30-4
Restriction: Open to pub for ref & circ; with some limitations

G NOVA SCOTIA DEPARTMENT OF TRANSPORTATION & PUBLIC WORKS*, Technical Services Library, 107 Parent Dr, B2T 1J6. SAN 325-1004. Tel: 902-860-2999. *Librn,* Margaret Reed
Founded 1978
Library Holdings: Bk Titles 2,000; Per Subs 15
Subject Interests: Civil, Eng, Transportation
Open Mon-Fri 8:30-4

G NOVA SCOTIA DEPARTMENT OF TRANSPORTATION & PUBLIC WORKS*, Head Office Library, PO Box 186, B3J 2N2. SAN 372-610X. Tel: 902-424-6720. FAX: 902-425-3994. *Librn,* Margaret E Reid
Library Holdings: Bk Titles 2,000; Per Subs 20
Open Mon-Fri 8:30-4

G NOVA SCOTIA ENVIRONMENT LIBRARY*, 5151 Terminal Rd, 5th Flr, B3J 1A1. (Mail add: PO Box 442, B3J 2P8), SAN 319-0056. Tel: 902-722-1330. FAX: 902-424-0503. E-mail: envirolibrary@gov.ns.ca. Web Site: www.gov.ns.ca/nse. *Info Res, Librn,* Natalie MacPherson; E-mail: macphend@gov.ns.ca; Staff 1 (MLS 1)
Founded 1975
Special Collections: Environmental Assessments; Nova Scotia Reports
Subject Interests: Air quality, Protected areas, Sewage, Sustainable develop, Water, Water studies
Automation Activity & Vendor Info: (Cataloging) Inmagic, Inc.; (Serials) Inmagic, Inc.
Database Vendor: EBSCOhost
Function: ILL available
Restriction: Open by appt only, Restricted loan policy

G NOVA SCOTIA GOVERNMENT*, Department of Justice Library, 5151 Terminal Rd, B3J 2L7. (Mail add: PO Box 7, B3J 2L7), SAN 366-810X. Tel: 902-424-7699. FAX: 902-424-1730. *Mgr, Info Serv,* Therese Lamie; E-mail: lamietm@gov.ns.ca
Founded 1972
Library Holdings: Bk Titles 4,500; Bk Vols 9,000; Per Subs 30
Special Collections: Law
Subject Interests: Can, Criminology, English law, Police sci
Restriction: Staff use only

L NOVA SCOTIA LEGAL AID LIBRARY*, 5475 Spring Garden Rd, Ste 401, B3J 3T2. SAN 375-345X. Tel: 902-420-6590. FAX: 902-428-5736. *Res Coordr,* Peter D Lambly; E-mail: peter.lambly@nslegalaid.ca; Staff 1 (MLS 1)
Library Holdings: Bk Titles 680; Per Subs 12
Restriction: Staff use only

S NOVA SCOTIA MUSEUM LIBRARY*, 1747 Summer St, B3H 3A6. SAN 319-0080. Tel: 902-424-7198. FAX: 902-424-0560. E-mail: mnhlibry@gov.ns.ca.
Founded 1884
Library Holdings: Bk Vols 13,000; Per Subs 100
Subject Interests: Decorative art, Early tech, Museology, Natural hist, NS soc hist
Restriction: Open by appt only, Open to pub for ref only

G NOVA SCOTIA PROVINCIAL LIBRARY*, 2021 Brunswick St, 2nd Flr, B3K 2Y5. (Mail add: Box 578, B3J 2S9), SAN 366-8223. Tel: 902-424-2457. FAX: 902-424-0633. E-mail: nspl@gov.ns.ca. Web Site: www.library.ns.ca. *Prov Librn,* Jennifer Evans; Tel: 902-424-2455, E-mail: admin@nshpl.library.ns.ca; *Mgr, Syst & Coll Access,* Denise Parrott; Tel: 902-424-2458, E-mail: parrotdf@gov.ns.ca; *Coordr, Pub Serv,* Michael Colborne; Tel: 902-424-4852, E-mail: colbormb@gov.ns.ca; Staff 22 (MLS 10, Non-MLS 12)
Founded 1952
Apr 2008-Mar 2009 Income (CAN) $1,707,000. Mats Exp (CAN) $11,262. Sal (CAN) $1,172,666
Library Holdings: Bk Titles 1,800; Per Subs 50
Subject Interests: Libr sci
Automation Activity & Vendor Info: (Acquisitions) SirsiDynix; (Cataloging) SirsiDynix; (Circulation) SirsiDynix; (OPAC) SirsiDynix
Database Vendor: Bowker, CEDROM-SNi, Gale Cengage Learning, ProQuest, World Book Online
Publications: Nova Scotia Provincial-Regional Libraries Annual Report
Restriction: Not open to pub

G PARKS CANADA*, Atlantic Service Centre Library, Historic Properties, 1869 Upper Water St, B3J 1S9. SAN 325-0679. Tel: 902-426-7266. FAX: 902-426-7012. E-mail: asc.library@pc.gc.ca. *Info Mgt Spec, Librn,* Hedy Armour; Staff 2 (MLS 1, Non-MLS 1)
Library Holdings: Bk Vols 20,000; Per Subs 100
Subject Interests: Atlantic Canada hist & archaeol, Nat parks & historic sites, Natural res conservation & mgt
Open Mon-Fri 8:30-4:30

S PUBLIC ARCHIVES OF NOVA SCOTIA, Nova Scotia Archives, 6016 University Ave, B3H 1W4. SAN 319-0110. Tel: 902-424-6060. Reference Tel: 902-424-6055. FAX: 902-424-0628. E-mail: nsarm@gov.ns.ca. Web Site: www.gov.ns.ca/nsarm. *Archivist, Dir,* Lois K Yorke; E-mail: yorkelk@gov.ns.ca; *Mgr,* Position Currently Open
Founded 1931
Library Holdings: Bk Vols 50,000
Special Collections: Akins Library Coll (static); Genealogical Research Resources; NS Historical Newspaper Coll (static); Provincial Heritage Newspaper Coll. Can & Prov
Subject Interests: Govt doc, Nova Scotiana
Wireless access
Open Mon, Tues, Thurs & Fri 8:30-4:30, Wed 4:30pm-9pm, Sat 9-5
Restriction: Non-circulating to the pub

C SAINT MARY'S UNIVERSITY, Patrick Power Library, 5429 Inglis St, B3H 3C3. SAN 366-8401. Tel: 902-420-5547. Interlibrary Loan Service Tel: 902-420-5542. Reference Tel: 902-420-5544. Administration Tel: 902-420-5534. FAX: 902-420-5561. Web Site: www.smu.ca/library. *Univ Librn,* Marie DeYoung; Tel: 902-420-5532, E-mail: marie.deyoung@smu.ca; *Assoc Univ Librn, Info Syst,* Peter Webster; Tel: 902-420-5507, E-mail: peter.webster@smu.ca; *Mgr, Access Serv,* Susan Cannon; Tel: 902-420-5656, E-mail: susan.cannon@smu.ca; *Mgr, Acq Serv,* Terri Winchcombe; Tel: 902-420-5535, E-mail: terri.winchcombe@smu.ca; *Archivist,* Hansel Cook; Tel: 902-420-5508, E-mail: hansel.cook@smu.ca; *Acq of New Ser,* Megan McCarthy; Tel: 902-491-6320; *Govt Doc,* Brenda Potter; Tel: 902-420-5548, E-mail: govdoc@smu.ca; *ILL,* Sandra Hamm; E-mail: sandra.hamm@smu.ca; *Ref,* Position Currently Open; Staff 43 (MLS 9, Non-MLS 34)
Founded 1802. Enrl 8,541; Fac 237; Highest Degree: Doctorate
Special Collections: Atlantic Canada; Eric; Irish Studies; Latin America
Subject Interests: Educ, Relig studies
Automation Activity & Vendor Info: (Acquisitions) Ex Libris Group; (Cataloging) Ex Libris Group; (Circulation) Ex Libris Group; (Course Reserve) Ex Libris Group; (ILL) Relais International; (OPAC) Ex Libris Group; (Serials) Ex Libris Group
Database Vendor: Blackwell's, Dialog, EBSCOhost, Elsevier MDL, LexisNexis, OCLC FirstSearch, ProQuest, ScienceDirect, Wiley
Wireless access

Publications: A Guide to the Patrick Power Library; Annual Report; Patrick Power Library Workbook; Psychology Workbook; Research Works; Sociology Workbook; The Perfect Term Paper
Partic in Can On-Line Enquiry; Dialog Corp; Univ of Toronto Libr Automation Syst
Departmental Libraries:

P   FERGUSON LIBRARY FOR PRINT HANDICAPPED STUDENTS, 923 Robie, B3H 3C3. Tel: 902-420-5553. FAX: 902-420-5561. E-mail: ferguson1@stmarys.ca. Web Site: www.stmarys.ca/administration/library. *Coordr,* Walt Tanner; E-mail: walt.tanner@stmarys.ca
Founded 1975
Library Holdings: e-books 200; Talking Bks 1,000
Open Mon-Fri (Winter) 9-5 Mon-Fri (Summer) 9-4:30

C   UNIVERSITY OF KING'S COLLEGE LIBRARY*, 6350 Coburg Rd, B3H 2A1. SAN 319-0129. Tel: 902-422-1271. FAX: 902-423-3357. E-mail: library@ukings.ns.ca. Web Site: www.ukings.ns.ca/kings/library. *Librn,* Drake Petersen; E-mail: drake.petersen@ukings.ns.ca; *Asst Librn, Ref Serv,* Patricia L Chalmers; E-mail: patricia.chalmers@ukings.ns.ca; *ILL,* Elaine MacInnis; E-mail: illnshk@admin.ukings.ns.ca; *Acq, Ser,* Paulette Lambert
Founded 1789. Fac 24; Highest Degree: Bachelor
Library Holdings: Bk Vols 80,000
Special Collections: Dr Bray Associates Libraries; Tractarian Theology (Bishop Kingdon Coll); University Archives; Weldon Loyalist China Coll
Subject Interests: Classics, Hist, Journalism, Lit, Philosophy, Theol
Partic in Novanet
Open Mon-Thurs 9am-11pm, Fri 9-5, Sat & Sun 1-6

HEBBVILLE

P   SOUTH SHORE PUBLIC LIBRARIES, 15442 Hwy Three, B4V 6X6. (Mail add: PO Box 34, Bridgewater, B4V 2W6). Tel: 902-543-2548. Administration Tel: 877-455-2548. E-mail: info@southshorepubliclibraries.ca. Web Site: www.southshorepubliclibraries.ca. *Chief Exec Officer,* Troy Myers; *Librn,* Cathy MacDonald; *Librn,* Jeff Mercer; Staff 3 (MLS 3)
Founded 1972
Automation Activity & Vendor Info: (Cataloging) SirsiDynix; (Circulation) SirsiDynix
Branches: 3
BRIDGEWATER BRANCH, 547 King St, Bridgewater, B4V 1B3. (Mail add: PO Box 34, Bridgewater, B4V 2W6), SAN 366-7685. Tel: 902-543-2548. FAX: 902-543-0819.
LUNENBURG BRANCH, 19 Pelham St, Lunenburg, B0J 2C0, SAN 366-7715. Tel: 902-634-8008. E-mail: lunenbur@southshorepubliclibraries.ca.
Open Mon-Wed, Fri & Sat 10-5, Thurs 10-8, Sun Noon-4
THOMAS H RADDALL LIBRARY, 145 Old Bridge St, Liverpool, B0T 1K0, SAN 366-7707. Tel: 902-354-5270.
Open Tues, Wed & Fri 10-5, Thurs 10-8, Sat & Sun 12-4
Bookmobiles: 1

KENTVILLE

G   AGRICULTURE & AGRI-FOOD CANADA, CANADIAN AGRICULTURE LIBRARY*, Atlantic Food & Horticulture Research Centre, 32 Main St, B4N 1J5. SAN 322-8290. Tel: 902-679-5508. Interlibrary Loan Service Tel: 902-679-5343. FAX: 902-679-5784. E-mail: library-kent@agr.gc.ca. Web Site: www.agr.ca/progser/cal_e.phtml. *Librn,* Jerry Miner; E-mail: minerj@agr.gc.ca; *ILL,* Pat Melanson; Staff 2 (MLS 1, Non-MLS 1)
Founded 1952
Library Holdings: Bk Titles 3,500; Bk Vols 10,000; Per Subs 350
Subject Interests: Food, Hort, Pesticides, Residues
Automation Activity & Vendor Info: (Cataloging) Infor Library & Information Solutions
Partic in Dialog Corp
Open Mon-Fri 8-4:30

S   DESTINATION SOUTHWEST NOVA SCOTIA ASSOCIATION LIBRARY*, PO Box 416, B4N 3X1. SAN 375-3735. Tel: 902-697-3500. Toll Free Tel: 866-260-3882. FAX: 902-697-3505. E-mail: info@destinationsouthwestnova.com. Web Site: www.destinationsouthwestnova.com. *Gen Mgr,* Madonna Spinazola
Special Collections: Oral History
Subject Interests: Tourism
Open Mon-Fri 8:30-4:30

J   NOVA SCOTIA COMMUNITY COLLEGE, Kingstec Campus Library, 236 Belcher St, B4N 0A6. SAN 371-7151. Tel: 902-679-7380. Reference Tel: 902-679-7379. FAX: 902-679-5187. E-mail: library.kingstec@nscc.ca. Web Site: www.library.nscc.ca. *Campus Librn,* Lana Kamennof-Sine; E-mail: lana.kamennof-sine@nscc.ca; *Libr Tech,* Carolyn Armstrong; *Libr Tech,* Paula J Coldwell; E-mail: paula.coldwell@nscc.ca. Subject

Specialists: *Addictions, Allied health, Hort,* Lana Kamennof-Sine; Staff 3 (MLS 1, Non-MLS 2)
Founded 1964. Enrl 1,000; Fac 75
Library Holdings: Bk Titles 14,000; Bk Vols 19,000; Per Subs 30
Special Collections: Local Radio Station Record Coll, 45 & 33 1/3; Self-Esteem Coll
Subject Interests: Bus, Entrepreneurship, Health serv, Trades
Automation Activity & Vendor Info: (Cataloging) Ex Libris Group; (Circulation) Ex Libris Group
Database Vendor: EBSCOhost, Gale Cengage Learning, ProQuest
Wireless access
Function: Computers for patron use, Copy machines, Doc delivery serv, Electronic databases & coll, Handicapped accessible, Health sci info serv, ILL available, Learning ctr, Mail & tel request accepted, Online cat, Online ref, Online searches, Orientations, Outside serv via phone, mail, e-mail & web, Photocopying/Printing, Pub access computers, Ref serv available, Scanner, Telephone ref, VHS videos, Web-catalog, Wheelchair accessible, Workshops
Special Services for the Deaf - Bks on deafness & sign lang
Open Mon-Thurs (Sept-May) 8-8, Fri 8-5, Sat 12-3; Mon-Fri (June-Sept) 8-5

LOUISBOURG

G   FORTRESS OF LOUISBOURG LIBRARY*, Parks Canada, 259 Park Service Rd, B1C 2L2. SAN 319-0153. Tel: 902-733-3534. FAX: 902-733-2423. E-mail: lhs.library@pc.gc.ca. *Librn,* Judith Poulain Romard
Founded 1963
Library Holdings: Microforms 1,335; Bk Vols 18,770; Per Subs 82
Special Collections: French Colonial History (18th century); Reconstruction
Open Mon-Fri 8-4:40

MULGRAVE

P   EASTERN COUNTIES REGIONAL LIBRARY*, 390 Murray St, B0E 2G0. (Mail add: PO Bag 2500, B0E 2G0), SAN 366-8460. Tel: 902-747-2597. FAX: 902-747-2500. E-mail: info@nsme.library.ns.ca. Web Site: ecrl.library.ns.ca. *Chief Librn,* Petra Mauerhoff; E-mail: pmauerhoff@nsme.library.ns.ca; *Pub Serv, Ref Librn,* Mary Landry; E-mail: mlandry@nsme.library.ns.ca; *ILL,* Mildred Carrigan; E-mail: insme@nsme.library.ns.ca
Founded 1969. Pop 41,830; Circ 145,513
Library Holdings: Bk Vols 104,800; Per Subs 200
Special Collections: Acadian Culture Coll
Subject Interests: Genealogy, Local hist
Open Mon-Fri 8-5
Branches: 6
CANSO BRANCH, 130 School St, Canso, B0H 1H0. (Mail add: PO Box 44, Canso, B0H 1H0). Tel: 902-366-2955. FAX: 902-366-2955. E-mail: canso@nsme.library.ns.ca. *In Charge,* Sandra Dixon
Founded 1969
Library Holdings: Bk Vols 6,500
Open Mon & Thurs 1-4 & 6pm-8pm, Tues & Fri 10-12 & 1-4, Sat 11-2
COADY & TOMPKINS MEMORIAL, 7972 Cabot Trail Hwy, General Delivery, Margaree Forks, B0E 2A0. Tel: 902-248-2821. FAX: 902-248-2821. E-mail: margaree@nsme.library.ns.ca. *In Charge,* Anne LeBlanc
Founded 1978
Library Holdings: Bk Vols 8,000
Open Mon 1:30-4:30 & 6:30pm-8:30pm, Tues & Wed 6:30pm-8:30pm, Thurs 10-12, 1:30-4:30 & 6:30pm-8:30pm, Fri & Sat 1:30-4:30
PETIT DE GRAT BRANCH, 3435 Hwy, No 206, Petit de Grat, B0E 2L0. (Mail add: PO Box 151, Petit de Grat, B0E 2L0). Tel: 902-226-3534. FAX: 902-226-3534. E-mail: petitdeg@nsme.library.ns.ca. *In Charge,* Kenneth David
Founded 1982
Library Holdings: Bk Vols 12,000
Open Mon, Tues & Thurs 2-8, Wed & Sat 10-4
PORT HAWKESBURY BRANCH, 304 Pitt St (SAERC), Unit 3, Port Hawkesbury, B9A 2T9. Tel: 902-625-2729. FAX: 902-625-2729. E-mail: porthawk@nsme.library.ns.ca. *In Charge,* Ann Campbell
Founded 1969
Library Holdings: Bk Vols 10,000
Special Services for the Blind - Closed circuit TV
Open Mon-Fri 3pm-8pm, Sat 11-2
SHERBROOKE BRANCH, 11 Main St, Sherbrooke, B0J 3C0. (Mail add: PO Box 177, Sherbrooke, B0J 3C0). Tel: 902-522-2180. FAX: 902-522-2180. E-mail: sherbroo@nsme.library.ns.ca. *In Charge,* Lesley Brothers
Founded 1969
Library Holdings: Bk Vols 6,500
Open Mon-Wed 2-5 & 6pm-8pm, Thurs 2-5, Fri 10:30-4, Sat 11-2

CYRIL WARD MEMORIAL, 27 Pleasant St, Guysborough, B0H 1N0. (Mail add: PO Box 191, Guysborough, B0H 1N0). Tel: 902-533-3586. E-mail: cyrilwar@nsme.library.ns.ca. *In Charge,* Annemarie Bieber
Founded 1986
Library Holdings: Bk Vols 8,300
Open Mon, Tues & Thurs 2-7, Fri & Sat 10-2

NEW GLASGOW

M ABERDEEN HOSPITAL*, Dr G R Douglas Memorial Library, 835 E River Rd, B2H 3S6. SAN 371-9960. Tel: 902-752-7600, Ext 2130. FAX: 902-752-2507. *Libr Tech,* Summer-Lee Burns; Staff 1 (Non-MLS 1)
Library Holdings: DVDs 35; e-books 50; e-journals 86; Bk Titles 500; Per Subs 20; Videos 89
Subject Interests: Allied health, Med, Nursing
Function: Ref & res, Res libr
Open Mon-Fri 8-4
Restriction: Badge access after hrs, Circulates for staff only, Hospital employees & physicians only, Open to others by appt

P PICTOU - ANTIGONISH REGIONAL LIBRARY*, 182 Dalhousie, B2H 5E3. (Mail add: PO Box 276, B2H 5E3), SAN 366-8649. Tel: 902-755-6031. FAX: 902-755-6775. TDD: 902-755-8233. E-mail: info@parl.ns.ca. Web Site: www.parl.ns.ca. *Dep Chief Librn,* Fred Popowich; *Chief Librn,* Eric Stackhouse; Staff 48 (MLS 3, Non-MLS 45)
Founded 1951. Pop 68,272; Circ 380,294
Library Holdings: Bk Vols 142,071; Per Subs 359
Automation Activity & Vendor Info: (Acquisitions) MultiLIS; (Circulation) MultiLIS
Database Vendor: Gale Cengage Learning, SirsiDynix
Open Mon-Fri 8-4:30
Friends of the Library Group
Branches: 7
ANTIGONISH LIBRARY, College St, Antigonish, B2G 2M5. (Mail add: PO Box 1741, Antigonish, B2G 2M5), SAN 366-8673. Tel: 902-863-4276. E-mail: antigoni@nsngp.library.ns.ca. *In Charge,* Rhynda Tudor
Library Holdings: Bk Vols 30,123
Open Wed, Fri & Sat 10-5, Tues & Thurs 10-9
NEW GLASGOW LIBRARY, 182 Dalhousie St, B2H 5E3. (Mail add: PO Box 276, B2H 5E3), SAN 366-8703. Tel: 902-752-8233. FAX: 902-755-6775. E-mail: newglasg@nsngp.library.ns.ca. *Managing Librn,* Carol MacMillan
Library Holdings: Bk Vols 146,220
Open Tues-Fri 10-9, Sat 10-5, Sun (Winter) 2-5
PICTOU LIBRARY, Water St, Pictou, B0K 1H0. (Mail add: PO Box 622, Pictou, B0K 1H0), SAN 366-8738. Tel: 902-485-5021. E-mail: pictou@nsngp.library.ns.ca. *In Charge,* Bonnie Allan
Library Holdings: Bk Vols 20,288
Open Tues-Thurs 12-9, Wed, Fri & Sat 10-5
RIVER JOHN LIBRARY, Main St, River John, B0K 1N0. (Mail add: PO Box 104, River John, B0K 1N0), SAN 374-3519. Tel: 902-351-2599. E-mail: riverjoh@nsngp.library.ns.ca. *In Charge,* Margaret Maclean
Library Holdings: Bk Vols 14,201
Open Tues & Thurs 2-5 & 7pm-9pm, Wed & Fri 10-1 & 2-5, Sat 10-12 & 1-4
STELLARTON LIBRARY, Ford St, Stellarton, B0K 1S0. (Mail add: PO Box 1372, Stellarton, B0K 1S0), SAN 366-8762. Tel: 902-755-1638. E-mail: stellart@nsngp.library.ns.ca. *In Charge,* Peggy Dennis
Library Holdings: Bk Vols 14,542
Open Tues & Thurs 2-5 & 7pm-9pm, Wed & Fri 9-12 & 2-5, Sat 10-12 & 1-4
TRENTON LIBRARY, 122 Main St, Trenton, B0K 1X0. (Mail add: PO Box 612, Trenton, B0K 1X0), SAN 366-8797. Tel: 902-752-5181. E-mail: trenton@nsngp.library.ns.ca. *In Charge,* Shelley MacLean
Library Holdings: Bk Vols 6,827
Open Tues & Thurs 2-5 & 7pm-9pm, Wed & Fri 9-12 & 2-5, Sat 10-12 & 1-4
WESTVILLE LIBRARY, 2020 Queen St, Westville, B0K 2A0. (Mail add: PO Box 627, Westville, B0K 2A0), SAN 366-8827. Tel: 902-396-5022. E-mail: westvill@nsngp.library.ns.ca. *In Charge,* Gina Snell
Library Holdings: Bk Vols 11,514
Open Tues & Thurs 2-5 & 7pm-9pm, Wed & Fri 9-12 & 2-5, Sat 10-12 & 1-4

PORT HAWKESBURY

J NOVA SCOTIA COMMUNITY COLLEGE*, Strait Area Campus Library, 226 Reeves St, B9A 2W2. SAN 372-7327. Tel: 902-625-2380, 902-625-4364. FAX: 902-625-0193. E-mail: library.straitarea@nscc.ca. Web Site: www.nscc.ns.ca/About_NSCC/Locations/Strait.asp. *Librn,* Lana MacLean; Tel: 902-625-4075, E-mail: lana.maclean@nscc.ca; *Libr Tech,* Margaret Eager; E-mail: margie.eager@nscc.ca; Staff 1 (MLS 1)
Library Holdings: Bk Titles 6,000; Bk Vols 10,091; Per Subs 80

Special Collections: Marine Engineering & Navigation
Open Mon-Thurs 8-5, Fri 8-4

SHELBURNE

J NOVA SCOTIA COMMUNITY COLLEGE*, Shelburne Campus Library, 1575 Lake Rd, B0T 1W0. (Mail add: PO Box 760, B0T 1W0). Tel: 902-875-8640. FAX: 902-875-8669. E-mail: library.shelburne@nscc.ca. Web Site: www.library.nscc.ca. *Libr Tech,* Susan Balkam; Tel: 902-543-0690, E-mail: susan.balkam@nscc.ca
Library Holdings: Bk Vols 1,045
Automation Activity & Vendor Info: (Cataloging) Ex Libris Group; (Circulation) Ex Libris Group; (OPAC) Ex Libris Group; (Serials) Ex Libris Group
Open Mon-Fri 8-12:30

S SHELBURNE COUNTY ARCHIVES & GENEALOGICAL SOCIETY LIBRARY*, 168 Water St, B0T 1W0. (Mail add: PO Box 248, B0T 1W0), SAN 377-1245. Tel: 902-875-4299. FAX: 902-875-3267. E-mail: gencentre@ns.sympatico.ca. Web Site: nsgna.ednet.ns.ca/shelburne. *Archives Mgr,* Kim Walker
Founded 1987
May 2007-Apr 2008 Income (CAN) $15,000
Library Holdings: CDs 10; Bk Titles 3,600; Per Subs 10
Restriction: Not a lending libr

SPRINGHILL

J NOVA SCOTIA COMMUNITY COLLEGE*, Cumberland Campus Library, One Main St, B0M 1X0. (Mail add: PO Box 550, B0M 1X0). Tel: 902-597-4109. FAX: 902-597-8548. E-mail: library.cumberland@nscc.ca. Web Site: www.nscc.ns.ca/lrc/access/cumberland.htm. *Libr Tech,* Jo-Ann Potter; E-mail: jo-ann.potter@nscc.ca
Library Holdings: Bk Titles 2,000; Bk Vols 2,106

STELLARTON

J NOVA SCOTIA COMMUNITY COLLEGE*, Pictou Campus Library, 39 Acadia Ave, B0K 1S0. (Mail add: PO Box 820, B0K 1S0). Tel: 902-755-7201. FAX: 902-755-7289. E-mail: library.pictou@nscc.ca. *Regional Librn,* Charmaine Borden; E-mail: charmaine.borden@nscc.ca; *Campus Librn,* Debbie Kaleva; E-mail: debbie.kaleva@nscc.ca
Library Holdings: Bk Vols 4,665; Per Subs 50
Subject Interests: Local Celtic hist
Function: Computer training, Computers for patron use, Copy machines, Distance learning, Doc delivery serv, e-mail serv, E-Reserves, Electronic databases & coll, Equip loans & repairs, Free DVD rentals, Handicapped accessible, ILL available, Instruction & testing, Online cat, Online ref, Online searches, Orientations, Photocopying/Printing, Pub access computers, Ref & res, Ref serv available, Scanner, Story hour, Wheelchair accessible, Workshops
Partic in Novanet
Open Mon-Thurs 8-6, Fri 8-4, Sat (Sept-April) 10-2

S NOVA SCOTIA MUSEUM OF INDUSTRY LIBRARY*, 147 N Foord St, B0K 1S0. (Mail add: PO Box 2590, B0K 1S0), SAN 375-0361. Tel: 902-755-5425. FAX: 902-755-7045. E-mail: industry@gov.ns.ca. *Acq, Actg Librn, Curator,* Mary Guildford
Founded 1986
Library Holdings: Bk Vols 3,200; Per Subs 35
Restriction: Non-circulating to the pub

SYDNEY

G CANADA DEPARTMENT OF FISHERIES & OCEANS*, Canadian Coast Guard College Library, 1190 Westmount Rd, B1P 6L1. (Mail add: PO Box 4500, B1P 6L1), SAN 319-017X. Tel: 902-564-3660, Ext 1164. FAX: 902-564-3672. E-mail: cgclibrary@dfo-mpo.gc.ca. Web Site: www.cgc.ns.ca/library. *Librn,* Danielle McKinley; *Tech Serv,* Bruce Barnaby; Staff 3 (MLS 1, Non-MLS 2)
Founded 1965. Enrl 100
Library Holdings: Bk Titles 28,000; Bk Vols 36,000; Per Subs 250
Special Collections: Ships Magnetism
Subject Interests: Marine eng, Mechanical eng, Navigation
Partic in OCLC Online Computer Library Center, Inc
Open Mon-Thurs 8:30-4 & 6pm-9pm, Fri 8:30-4

M CAPE BRETON DISTRICT HEALTH AUTHORITY*, Cape Breton Healthcare Complex Health Sciences Library, 1482 George St, B1P 1P3. SAN 373-3181. Tel: 902-567-8000, Ext 2738. Circulation Tel: 902-567-8000, Ext 2739. FAX: 902-567-7878. *Chief Librn,* Patricia Colford Foley; E-mail: foleyp@cbdha.nshealth.ca; Staff 2 (MLS 1, Non-MLS 1)
Library Holdings: Bk Vols 6,000; Per Subs 230
Subject Interests: Allied health, Family med, Geriatrics, Med, Nursing, Obstetrics, Oncology, Pediatrics, Psychiat

Function: Res libr
Open Mon-Fri 8:30-4:30

P　CAPE BRETON REGIONAL LIBRARY, James McConnell Memorial Library, 50 Falmouth St, B1P 6X9. SAN 319-0188. Tel: 902-562-3279. FAX: 902-564-0765. E-mail: inssc@nssc.library.ns.ca. Web Site: www.cbrl.ca. *Regional Librn,* S Faye MacDougall; E-mail: fmacdoug@nssc.library.ns.ca; *Coll Librn,* Ian MacIntosh; *Br Mgr,* Lisa Mulak; Tel: 902-562-3161, E-mail: lmulak@nssc.library.ns.ca; *ILL,* Barbara MacLean; Staff 51 (MLS 8, Non-MLS 43)
Founded 1950. Pop 113,559; Circ 457,888
Apr 2011-Mar 2012 Income (Main Library and Branch(s)) (CAN) $2,747,419, Provincial (CAN) $1,900,800, County (CAN) $696,100, Locally Generated Income (CAN) $123,757, Other (CAN) $26,762. Mats Exp (CAN) $285,647, Books (CAN) $262,490, AV Mat (CAN) $23,157. Sal (CAN) $1,752,852
Library Holdings: Audiobooks 1,165; DVDs 7,322; e-books 3,520; e-journals 4,469; Microforms 1,102; Bk Vols 220,954; Per Subs 301; Talking Bks 3,183
Special Collections: Local History (Nova Scotia), bks, micro, playscripts. Can & Prov
Subject Interests: Local hist
Automation Activity & Vendor Info: (Acquisitions) SirsiDynix; (Cataloging) SirsiDynix; (Circulation) SirsiDynix; (ILL) SirsiDynix; (OPAC) SirsiDynix
Database Vendor: SirsiDynix
Wireless access
Function: Adult bk club, Archival coll, Bk club(s), Bks on cassette, Bks on CD, Children's prog, Free DVD rentals, ILL available, Online cat, Orientations, OverDrive digital audio bks, Prog for adults, Prog for children & young adult, Pub access computers, Ref serv available, Ref serv in person, Senior computer classes, Story hour, Summer reading prog
Publications: Annual Report
Special Services for the Deaf - Assistive tech
Special Services for the Blind - Accessible computers
Open Tues-Fri 10-9, Sat 10-5:30
Friends of the Library Group
Branches: 12
FLORENCE PUBLIC, 676 Bras d'or Florence Rd, Florence, B1Y 1E4. Tel: 902-736-7583. E-mail: florence@nssc.library.ns.ca. *Br Supvr,* Clare MacKillop
　Open Tues & Thurs 1-5 & 7pm-9pm, Wed & Fri 1-5, Sat 10-1
BADDECK PUBLIC, 526 Chebucto St, Baddeck, B0E 1B0. (Mail add: PO Box 88, Baddeck, B0E 1B0). Tel: 902-295-2055. E-mail: baddeck@nssc.library.ns.ca. *Librn,* Karen MacNeil
　Open Mon 1-5, Tues & Fri 1-5 & 6pm-8pm, Thurs 5-8pm, Sat 10-12 & 1-5
DOMINION PUBLIC, 78 Commercial St, Unit A, Dominion, B1G 1B4. Tel: 902-849-3590. E-mail: dominion@nscc.library.ns.ca. *Br Supvr,* Clare MacKillop; Tel: 902-562-3279, E-mail: cmackill@nssc.library.ns.ca
　Open Mon & Tues 1-5:30 & 7pm-9pm, Wed 1-5:30, Thurs & Fri 10-12, 1-5:30 & 7-9, Sat 10-12 & 1-5:30
DONKIN PUBLIC, 81 Centre Ave, Donkin, B1A 6N4. Tel: 902-737-1154. E-mail: donkin@nssc.library.ns.ca. *Br Supvr,* Clare MacKillop
　Open Mon, Tues & Fri 3-5:30, Wed & Thurs 3-5:30 & 6:30pm-9pm
GLACE BAY PUBLIC, 121 Union St, Glace Bay, B1A 2P8. Tel: 902-849-8657. E-mail: glacebay@nssc.library.ns.ca. *Librn,* Cynthia McIntyre
　Open Mon 2-9, Tues-Fri 10-9, Sat 10-5:30
MARTHA HOLLETT MEMORIAL, One Fraser Ave, Sydney Mines, B1V 2B8. Tel: 902-736-3219. E-mail: sydneymi@nssc.library.ns.ca. *Br Supvr,* Clare MacKillop
　Open Mon 1:30-5:30 & 7pm-9pm, Tues-Thurs 10-5:30 & 7pm-9pm, Fri 10-5:30, Sat 10-12 & 1-5:30
W W LEWIS MEMORIAL, Ten Upper Warren St, Louisbourg, B1C 1M6. Tel: 902-733-3608. E-mail: louisbou@nssc.library.ns.ca. *Br Supvr,* Clare MacKillop
　Open Tues 2-5 & 7pm-9pm, Wed 2-5, Thurs 2-5 & 7pm-9pm, Fri 10-11:30 & 2-5:30, Sat 2-5
MAIN-A-DIEU PUBLIC, 2886 Louisbourg-Main-a-Dieu Rd, Main-a-Dieu, B1C 1X5. Tel: 902-733-5708. E-mail: mainadie@nssc.library.ns.ca. *Br Supvr,* Clare MacKillop; Tel: 902-562-3279, E-mail: cmackill@nssc.library.ns.ca
　Open Mon & Wed 7pm-9pm, Tues 1-5, Thurs 12-4, Sat 2-5
NEW WATERFORD BRANCH, 3390 Plummer Ave, New Waterford, B1H 4K4. (Mail add: PO Box 12, New Waterford, B1H 4K4). Tel: 902-862-2892. E-mail: newwater@nssc.library.ns.ca. *Br Supvr,* Clare MacKillop
　Open Mon 1:30-5:30 & 7-9, Tues-Thurs 10-9, Fri 10-5:30 & 7-9, Sat 10-5:30
WILFRED ORAM CENTENNIAL, 299 Commercial St, North Sydney, B2A 1B9. Tel: 902-794-3272. E-mail: northsyd@nssc.library.ns.ca. *Br Supvr,* Clare MacKillop
　Open Mon 1:30-5:30 & 7pm-9pm, Tues-Thurs 10-9, Fri 10-5:30 & 7pm-9pm, Sat 10-5:30

TOMPKINS MEMORIAL, Tompkins Pl, 2249 Sydney Rd, Unit 3, Reserve Mines, B1E 1J9. Tel: 902-849-6685. E-mail: reservem@nssc.library.ns.ca. *Br Supvr,* Clare MacKillop; Tel: 902-562-3279, E-mail: cmackill@nssc.library.ns.ca
　Open Mon, Tues & Fri 2-5:30, Wed & Thurs 2-5:30 & 6:30pm-8:30pm
VICTORIA NORTH REGIONAL, 36243 Cabot Trail, Ingonish, B0C 1K0. Tel: 902-285-2544. E-mail: ingonish@nssc.library.ns.ca. *Librn,* Karen MacNeil
　Open Tues-Thurs 12-5 & 6pm-8pm, Fri 9-Noon & 1-5, Sat 10-Noon & 1-5
Bookmobiles: 2. Br Supvr, Clare MacKillop & Supvr, Victoria County Libr Serv, Erin Phillips

C　CAPE BRETON UNIVERSITY LIBRARY*, 1250 Grand Lake Rd, B1P 6L2. (Mail add: PO Box 5300, B1P 6L2), SAN 366-8851. Tel: 902-563-1421. Circulation Tel: 902-563-1320. Interlibrary Loan Service Tel: 902-563-1995. Reference Tel: 902-563-1387. Administration Tel: 902-563-1698. FAX: 902-563-1826. Administration FAX: 902-563-1177. Web Site: www.capebreton.ca/library. *Dir,* Robert Campbell; Tel: 902-563-1698, Fax: 902-563-1177, E-mail: robert_campbell@cbu.ca; *Librn,* Cathy Chisholm; Tel: 902-563-1993, E-mail: cathy_chisholm@cbu.ca; *Librn,* Mary Dobson; E-mail: mary_dobson@cbu.ca; *Librn,* Lenard Lawless; E-mail: lenard_lawless@cbu.ca; *Librn,* Ron Rooth; E-mail: ron_rooth@cbu.ca; *Librn,* Laura Syms; E-mail: laura_syms@cbu.ca; Staff 17 (MLS 6, Non-MLS 11)
Founded 1951. Enrl 3,600; Fac 160; Highest Degree: Master
Library Holdings: Bk Titles 250,000; Bk Vols 296,000; Per Subs 700
Special Collections: Bras d'Or Studies; Economic & Social History of Cape Breton Island, pamphlets, rpts, etc; Folklore; Scottish Coll (Gaelic & English)
Subject Interests: Local hist
Automation Activity & Vendor Info: (Acquisitions) Ex Libris Group; (Cataloging) Ex Libris Group; (Circulation) Ex Libris Group; (Course Reserve) Ex Libris Group; (OPAC) Ex Libris Group; (Serials) Ex Libris Group
Database Vendor: Agricola, EBSCOhost, JSTOR, OCLC WorldCat, ScienceDirect, STN International
Wireless access
Partic in Novanet
Special Services for the Blind - Assistive/Adapted tech devices, equip & products
Open Mon-Thurs 8:30am-10pm, Fri 8:30-5, Sat 11-4, Sun 12-9
Friends of the Library Group
Departmental Libraries:
BEATON INSTITUTE, 1250 Grand Lake Rd, B1P 6L2. (Mail add: PO Box 5300, B1P 6L2), SAN 366-8886. Tel: 902-563-1329. Automation Services FAX: 902 562-8899. E-mail: beaton@capebretonu.ca. Web Site: beaton.capebretonu.ca. *Mgr,* Catherine Arseneau; Tel: 902-563-1326, Fax: 902-562-8899, E-mail: catherine_arseneau@cbu.ca; *Archivist,* Jodi McDavid; Tel: 902-563-1690, Fax: 902-562-8899, E-mail: jodi_mcdavid@cbu.ca
Founded 1957
Library Holdings: AV Mats 3,500; Bk Titles 1,700; Bk Vols 1,800; Per Subs 15
Special Collections: Cape Breton, bks, mss, micro, newsp, pamphlets; Gaelic & Scottish Coll, rare bks & mss. Oral History
Subject Interests: Local hist
Function: Archival coll, Res libr
Publications: Guide to the Genealogical Holdings; Guide to the Manuscript Holdings
Open Mon, Tues, Thurs & Fri 10-4, Wed 10-7
Restriction: Non-circulating

J　NOVA SCOTIA COMMUNITY COLLEGE*, Marconi Campus Library, 1240 Grand Lake Rd, B1P 6J7. (Mail add: PO Box 1042, B1P 6J7). Tel: 902-563-2102. FAX: 902-563-0511. E-mail: library.marconi@nscc.ca. Web Site: www.library.nscc.ca. *Regional Librn,* Lana MacLean; E-mail: lana.maclean@nscc.ca; *Libr Tech,* Joanne Coombs; E-mail: joanne.coombs@nscc.ca; Staff 3 (MLS 2, Non-MLS 1)
Library Holdings: Bk Titles 3,000
Automation Activity & Vendor Info: (Cataloging) Ex Libris Group; (Circulation) Ex Libris Group; (Course Reserve) Ex Libris Group; (ILL) Ex Libris Group; (OPAC) Ex Libris Group
Database Vendor: EBSCOhost, ProQuest, PubMed
Wireless access
Open Mon-Fri 8-4

TRURO

P　COLCHESTER - EAST HANTS REGIONAL LIBRARY*, 754 Prince St, B2N 1G9. SAN 366-8916. Tel: 902-895-0235, 902-895-1625, 902-895-4183. FAX: 902-895-7149. E-mail: anstc@nstc.library.ns.ca. Web Site: cehlibrary.ednet.ns.ca. *Regional Dir,* Janet Pelley; E-mail: jpelley@nstc.library.ns.ca; *ILL,* Estelle Grajczyk; E-mail:

instc@nstc.library.ns.ca; *Ref Serv,* Lesley Brann; E-mail: lbrann@nstc.library.ns.ca
Founded 1950. Pop 69,975; Circ 326,487
Library Holdings: Bk Vols 142,896; Per Subs 271
Open Mon-Fri 9-5
Friends of the Library Group
Branches: 4
ELMSDALE BRANCH, 753 Hwy 2, Elmsdale, B2S 1A8. Tel: 902-883-9838. E-mail: elmsdale@nstc.library.ns.ca. *In Charge,* Rosalind Morrison
Founded 1989. Pop 10,000; Circ 37,717
Library Holdings: Bk Vols 14,700
Open Tues 10-8, Thurs & Fri 1-8, Sat 1-5
MOUNT UNIACKE BRANCH, 555 Hwy One, Mount Uniacke, B0N 1Z0. Tel: 902-866-0124. FAX: 902-866-0519. E-mail: mtuniack@nstc.library.ns.ca. *Br Mgr,* Jean Murphy
Founded 2004. Pop 3,500
Library Holdings: Bk Vols 4,400
Automation Activity & Vendor Info: (Circulation) SirsiDynix; (OPAC) SirsiDynix
Open Tues 1-8, Thurs 3-8, Fri 2-5, Sat 10-1
STEWIACKE BRANCH, Town Hall Bldg, Stewiacke, B0N 2J0. Tel: 902-639-2481. E-mail: stewiack@nstc.library.ns.ca.
Founded 1951. Pop 4,305; Circ 42,958
Library Holdings: Bk Vols 17,200
Open Tues 1-5, Thurs 10-12, 1-5 & 6:30pm-8:30pm, Fri 1-5 & 7pm-9pm, Sat 12-4
TATAMAGOUCHE BRANCH, Main St, Tatamagouche, B0N 2J0. Tel: 902-657-3064. E-mail: tatamago@nstc.library.ns.ca.
Founded 1951. Pop 3,150; Circ 16,178
Library Holdings: Bk Vols 11,000
Open Tues 11-5 & 7pm-9pm, Thurs 11-5, Fri 1-5 & 7pm-9pm, Sat 9-12
Bookmobiles: 1. Librns, Marilyn MacWha and Patricia Thorsen

S COLCHESTER HISTORICAL SOCIETY ARCHIVES, 29 Young St, B2N 5C5. (Mail add: PO Box 412, B2N 5C5), SAN 375-7501. Tel: 902-895-6284. FAX: 902-895-9530. E-mail: archivist@colchesterhistoreum.ca. Web Site: colchesterhistoreum.ca. *Archivist,* Nan Harvey; Staff 1 (MLS 1)
Library Holdings: Bk Titles 3,000
Subject Interests: Genealogies, Hist
Open Tues-Fri (Sept-June) 10-12 & 2-4, Sat 1-4; Mon-Fri (July-Aug) 10-5, Sat & Sun 2-5

S INSTITUTE FOR HUMAN SERVICES EDUCATION*, Russell Resource Library, 60 Lorne St, Ste 1, B2N 3K3. Tel: 902-893-3342. FAX: 902-895-4487. Web Site: www.inst.hse.ca. *Libr Coordr,* Denise MacKinnon
Library Holdings: Bk Titles 8,000; Bk Vols 10,000; Per Subs 25; Videos 700
Subject Interests: Early childhood, Spec educ
Automation Activity & Vendor Info: (Cataloging) Chancery SMS; (Circulation) Chancery SMS; (OPAC) Chancery SMS
Open Mon-Thurs 8:30-4:30, Fri 8:30-12, Sat 8:30-1

C NOVA SCOTIA AGRICULTURAL COLLEGE LIBRARY*, MacRae Library, 135 College Rd, B2N 5E3. (Mail add: PO Box 550, B2N 5E3), SAN 319-0196. Tel: 902-893-6669. Circulation Tel: 902-893-4576. Interlibrary Loan Service Tel: 902-893-4578. Reference Tel: 902-893-4595. Administration Tel: 902-893-6670. FAX: 902-895-0934. E-mail: library@nsac.ca. Web Site: www.nsac.ca/library. *Univ Librn,* Elaine McInnis; *Head, Acq & Ser,* Verna Mingo; *Cat,* Jennifer MacIsaac; Tel: 902-893-4578, E-mail: j2macisaac@nsac.ca; *Circ,* Sherree Miller; *ILL,* Jolene Reid; *Ref,* Erin MacPherson; Staff 3 (Non-MLS 3)
Founded 1905. Enrl 793; Fac 70; Highest Degree: Master
Apr 2007-Mar 2008 Income (CAN) $713,200. Mats Exp (CAN) $350,000, Books (CAN) $34,600, Per/Ser (Incl. Access Fees) (CAN) $127,800, Manu Arch (CAN) $1,200, Electronic Ref Mat (Incl. Access Fees) (CAN) $186,400. Sal (CAN) $327,100
Library Holdings: AV Mats 457; CDs 256; e-books 500; e-journals 23,000; Bk Titles 36,500; Bk Vols 49,859; Per Subs 535; Videos 291
Special Collections: Agricola Archives; Can & Prov
Subject Interests: Agr, Agr eng, Animal sci, Environ sci, Hort, Plant sci, Rural entrepreneurship
Automation Activity & Vendor Info: (Acquisitions) Ex Libris Group; (Cataloging) Ex Libris Group; (Circulation) Ex Libris Group; (Course Reserve) Ex Libris Group; (ILL) Ex Libris Group; (OPAC) Ex Libris Group; (Serials) Ex Libris Group
Database Vendor: Agricola, American Chemical Society, CISTI Source, Coutts Information Service, EBSCOhost, Ex Libris Group, ISI Web of Knowledge, JSTOR, Knovel, netLibrary, OCLC FirstSearch, OCLC WorldCat, ProQuest, PubMed, RefWorks, ScienceDirect, Springer-Verlag, Wiley
Wireless access

Publications: Agricola Archives Fact Sheets (Archives guide); Library Trust Fund Update (Newsletter); MacRae Library Handbook; NSAC Style Manual (Annually)
Partic in Council of Atlantic University Libraries (CAUL); Novanet
Open Mon-Thurs 8:30am-10:30pm, Fri 8:30-5, Sat 10-5, Sun 10am-10:30pm

J NOVA SCOTIA COMMUNITY COLLEGE*, Truro Campus Library, 36 Arthur St, B2N 1X5. SAN 319-020X. Tel: 902-893-5326. FAX: 902-893-6693. E-mail: library.truro@nscc.ca. Web Site: www.library.nscc.ca. *Regional Librn,* Charmaine Borden; E-mail: charmaine.borden@nscc.ca; Staff 3 (MLS 1, Non-MLS 2)
Founded 1995. Enrl 1,000
Library Holdings: Bk Vols 30,000; Per Subs 150
Special Collections: Community Economic Development
Subject Interests: Acad upgrading, Commun develop, Corrections
Wireless access
Publications: Handbook; Periodical Holdings list
Open Mon-Thurs 8-6, Fri (Oct-April) 8-4:30

L PATTERSON PALMER LIBRARY*, PO Box 1068, B2N 5B9. SAN 321-7000. Tel: 902-897-2000. FAX: 902-893-3071. *Librn,* Patti Sharpe; E-mail: psharpe@pattersonlaw.ca
Founded 1932
Library Holdings: Bk Titles 2,500; Bk Vols 6,500; Per Subs 15
Subject Interests: Commercial, Family, Income tax, Ins, Probate law, Real estate
Open Mon-Fri 9-5

WOLFVILLE

C ACADIA UNIVERSITY*, Vaughan Memorial Library, 50 Acadia St, B4P 2R6. (Mail add: PO Box 4, B4P 2R6), SAN 366-8975. Tel: 902-585-1249. Reference Tel: 902-585-1170. FAX: 902-585-1748. E-mail: libweb@acadiau.ca. Web Site: library.acadiau.ca. *Univ Librn,* Sara Lochhead; Tel: 902-585-1510, Fax: 902-585-1094, E-mail: sara.lochhead@acadiau.ca; *Head, Res Serv,* Jennifer Richard; *Acad Librn,* Mike Beazley; *Acad Librn,* Patricia Gallant; *Acad Librn,* Anthony Pash; *Acad Librn,* Erin Patterson; *Acad Librn,* Ann Smith; Staff 34 (MLS 8, Non-MLS 26)
Founded 1841. Highest Degree: Master
Library Holdings: Bk Vols 700,000; Per Subs 1,900
Special Collections: Atlantic Baptist Archives; Esther Clark Wright Archives
Subject Interests: Med
Function: For res purposes
Partic in Can-Ole; Dialog Corp; Infoline; NY Times Info Bank; SDC Search Serv; Wilsonline
Restriction: Pub use on premises

YARMOUTH

S FIREFIGHTERS' MUSEUM OF NOVA SCOTIA LIBRARY*, 451 Main St, B5A 1G9. SAN 326-1867. Tel: 902-742-5525. FAX: 902-742-5525. *Curator,* David Darby; E-mail: darbydl@gov.ns.ca
Founded 1974
Library Holdings: Bk Vols 500; Per Subs 15
Open Mon-Fri (Oct-May) 9-4, Sat 1-4; Mon-Sat (June-Sept) 9-5, Sun 10-5

J NOVA SCOTIA COMMUNITY COLLEGE*, Burridge Campus Library, 372 Pleasant St, B5A 2L2. Tel: 902-742-3416. FAX: 902-742-0519. E-mail: library.burridge@nscc.ca. Web Site: www.library.nscc.ca. *Libr Tech,* Terri Noble; E-mail: terri.noble@nscc.ca
Library Holdings: Bk Vols 3,128
Automation Activity & Vendor Info: (Cataloging) Infor Library & Information Solutions; (Circulation) Infor Library & Information Solutions; (Course Reserve) Infor Library & Information Solutions; (ILL) Infor Library & Information Solutions; (Media Booking) Infor Library & Information Solutions; (OPAC) Infor Library & Information Solutions
Open Mon-Fri 8-5

P WESTERN COUNTIES REGIONAL LIBRARY*, 405 Main St, B5A 1G3. SAN 366-9092. Tel: 902-742-2486. FAX: 902-742-6920. E-mail: ansy@nsy.library.ns.ca. Web Site: www.westerncounties.ca. *Dir,* Erin Comeau; E-mail: ecomeau@nsy.library.ns.ca; *Dep Dir,* Joanne Head; E-mail: jhead@nsy.library.ns.ca; *Coordr,* Rick Beharriell; E-mail: rick@wcrl.library.ns.ca; *Coordr,* Deborah Duke; E-mail: dduke@nsy.library.ns.ca; *Syst Coordr,* Scott MacMullen; E-mail: smacmull@nsy.library.ns.ca; Staff 5 (MLS 4, Non-MLS 1)
Founded 1969. Pop 65,135; Circ 258,228
Apr 2005-Mar 2006 Income (Main Library and Branch(s)) (CAN) $1,451,931, Provincial (CAN) $969,400, County (CAN) $322,700, Other (CAN) $159,719. Mats Exp (CAN) $214,632. Sal (CAN) $901,747
Library Holdings: Bk Vols 149,044

Special Collections: H R Banks Nova Scotiana Coll, bks, per, pamphlets; Nova Scotia History, bks, micro
Automation Activity & Vendor Info: (Acquisitions) SirsiDynix; (Cataloging) SirsiDynix; (Circulation) SirsiDynix; (OPAC) SirsiDynix
Database Vendor: Gale Cengage Learning, SirsiDynix
Wireless access
Open Mon-Fri 8:30-4:30
Friends of the Library Group
Branches: 10
BARRINGTON MUNICIPAL, 3533 Hwy No 3, Barrington Passage, B0W 1G0. (Mail add: PO Box 310, Barrington Passage, B0W 1G0), SAN 366-9106. Tel: 902-637-3348. E-mail: barringt@nsy.library.ns.ca. *In Charge,* Margo Chetwynd
Open Tues 10-5, Wed-Fri 12:30-5 & 6-8, Sat 10-2
Friends of the Library Group
CLARE, No 8196 Hwy One, Meteghan, B0W 2J0. (Mail add: PO Box 265, Meteghan, B0W 2J0), SAN 366-9114. Tel: 902-645-3350. E-mail: clare@nsy.library.ns.ca. *In Charge,* Glenda Comeau
Open Tues & Thurs 10-4 & 6-8, Wed & Fri 10-4, Sat 10-12
CLARK'S HARBOUR BRANCH, 2642 Main St, Clark's Harbour, B0W 1P0. (Mail add: PO Box 189, Clark's Harbour, B0W 1P0), SAN 366-9122. Tel: 902-745-2885. E-mail: clarksha@nsy.library.ns.ca. *In Charge,* Shelley Smith
Open Tues & Thurs 3:30-8, Wed & Fri 2-5, Sat 10-12:30
Friends of the Library Group
LOCKEPORT BRANCH, 35 North St, Lockeport, B0T 1L0. (Mail add: PO Box 265, Lockeport, B0T 1L0), SAN 366-9181. Tel: 902-656-2817. E-mail: lockepor@nsy.library.ns.ca. *In Charge,* Heather Suttle
Open Tues & Thurs 2:30-5 & 6-7:30, Wed 10:30-1 & 2:30-5, Fri 2:30-5, Sat 10-12
Friends of the Library Group
MCKAY MEMORIAL LIBRARY, 254 Water St, Shelburne, B0T 1W0. (Mail add: PO Box 158, Shelburne, B0T 1W0), SAN 366-9246. Tel: 902-875-3615. FAX: 902-875-1015. E-mail: shelburn@nsy.library.ns.ca. *In Charge,* Edith Bower
Open Tues-Thurs 12:30-5 & 6-8, Fri 10-5, Sat 10-2
Restriction: Restricted pub use
Friends of the Library Group
PUBNICO BRANCH, 35 Hwy, No 335, Pubnico Head, B0W 2W0. (Mail add: PO Box 22, Pubnico, B0W 2W0), SAN 366-9211. Tel: 902-762-2204. FAX: 902-762-3208. E-mail: pubnico@nsy.library.ns.ca. *In Charge,* Beatrice Adams

Open Tues-Thurs 3-5:30 & 6-8, Fri 3-5, Sat 10-12
Friends of the Library Group
WESTPORT BRANCH, 17 Second St, Westport, B0V 1H0. (Mail add: PO Box 1194, Westport, B0V 1H0), SAN 322-6328. Tel: 902-839-2955. E-mail: westport@nsy.library.ns.ca. *In Charge,* June Swift
Open Mon, Tues, Thurs & Sun 2-5, Wed 5-8
Friends of the Library Group
WEYMOUTH BRANCH, No 4609, Hwy One, Weymouth, B0W 3T0. (Mail add: PO Box 340, Weymouth, B0W 3T0), SAN 366-9254. Tel: 902-837-4596. E-mail: weymouth@nsy.library.ns.ca. *In Charge,* Marguerite Thibault
Open Tues & Fri 1:30-4:30 & 6-8, Wed 1:30-4:30, Thurs 12:30-4:30, Sat 10-1
Friends of the Library Group
ISAIAH W WILSON MEMORIAL, 84 Warwick St, Digby, B0V 1A0. (Mail add: PO Box 730, Digby, B0V 1A0), SAN 366-9157. Tel: 902-245-2163. E-mail: digby@nsy.library.ns.ca. *In Charge,* Thelma Pulsifer
Open Tues-Thurs 12:30-5 & 6-8, Fri 10-5, Sat 10-2
YARMOUTH BRANCH, 405 Main St, B5A 1G3, SAN 366-9262. Tel: 902-742-5040. FAX: 902-742-6920. E-mail: yarmouth@nsy.library.ns.ca. *Librn,* Debby Little; Staff 8 (MLS 1, Non-MLS 7)
Open Mon-Thurs 10-8, Fri 10-5, Sat 10-4, Sun (Sept-May) 1-4

S   YARMOUTH COUNTY MUSEUM & ARCHIVES*, 22 Collins St, B5A 3C8. SAN 319-0218. Tel: 902-742-5539. FAX: 902-749-1120. E-mail: ycarchives@eastlink.ca. Web Site: yarmouthcountymuseum.ednet.ns.ca. *Librn,* J Stuart McLean; Staff 1 (MLS 1)
Founded 1935
Library Holdings: Bk Titles 3,000
Special Collections: Bob Brooks Photo Coll; Dominion Textiles Coll; RCAF Station Yarmouth, 1940-1945
Subject Interests: Local photog, Marine hist, Mus artifacts, NS hist, Yarmouth County genealogies, Yarmouth County hist, Yarmouth newsps
Publications: Butter the Size of an Egg 2001; Historic Yarmouth 1997; Historigram (Monthly newsletter); Index to Yarmouth Shipping; Surname Index of Births, Marriages, Deaths to the Yarmouth County Newspapers Vol 1 (1830-1839), Vol 2 (1840-1849), Vol 3 (1850-1859), Vol 4 (1860-1869) (Index to newspapers); Vital Records of Township of Yarmouth 1792-1811; Yarmouth 1821; Yarmouth 1918; Yarmouth Past & Present 1902
Restriction: Non-circulating

CAMBRIDGE BAY

J   NUNAVUT ARCTIC COLLEGE*, Kitikmeot Campus Library, PO Box 54, X0B 0C0. Web Site: www.nac.nu.ca. *Librn,* Leigh Ann Cumming

IGLOOLIK

S   NUNAVUT RESEARCH INSTITUTE*, Igloolik Research Centre Library, PO Box 210, X0A 0L0. SAN 323-8547. Tel: 867-934-2069. Toll Free Tel: 866-988-4636. FAX: 867-934-2058. *Operations Dir,* Leah Otak; *Coordr,* John MacDonald
Founded 1975
Library Holdings: Bk Titles 3,000
Special Collections: Arctic Research, bks & micro; Inuit (Eskimo) Oral History
Restriction: Non-circulating to the pub

IQALUIT

P   IQALUIT CENTENNIAL LIBRARY*, Bag 189A, X0A 0H0. SAN 318-9651. Tel: 867-979-5400. FAX: 867-979-1373. E-mail: nuic@gov.nu.ca. *Head Librn,* Grant Karcich; E-mail: gkarcich@gov.nu.ca; *Librn,* Diane Corbeil; E-mail: dcorbeil@gov.nu.ca
Library Holdings: Bk Vols 32,000; Per Subs 80
Special Collections: T H Manning Coll (Arctica & Antarctica)

Automation Activity & Vendor Info: (Cataloging) VTLS, Inc; (Circulation) VTLS, Inc; (OPAC) VTLS, Inc
Open Mon, Wed & Fri 1-6, Tues & Thurs 3-8, Sat 1-4

J   NUNAVUT ARCTIC COLLEGE*, Nunatta Campus Library (Main), Tunnganaqsarvik Bldg, 1st Flr, X0A 0H0. (Mail add: PO Box 600, X0A 0H0), SAN 372-7203. Tel: 867-979-7220. FAX: 867-979-7102. E-mail: librarian@nac.nu.ca. Web Site: www.nac.nu.ca. *Mgr, Libr Serv,* Position Currently Open; *Libr Tech,* Katharine Tagak-Devries; Staff 2 (MLS 1, Non-MLS 1)
Founded 1986. Enrl 1,000; Fac 23
Library Holdings: Bk Titles 12,000; Bk Vols 14,000; Per Subs 140
Special Collections: Arctic Discovery - Exploration (Pilot Coll); Northern - Arctic Studies (Cooke Coll)
Open Mon-Fri 8:45-4:45

GL   NUNAVUT COURT OF JUSTICE LIBRARY*, PO Box 297, X0A 0H0. Tel: 867-975-6134. FAX: 867-975-6168. E-mail: courtlibary@gov.nu.ca. Web Site: www.nunavutcourtofjustice.ca. *Librn,* Elisa Chandler
Open Mon-Fri 8:30-5

RANKIN INLET

J   NUNAVUT ARCTIC COLLEGE*, Kivalliq Campus Library, Bag 002, X0C 0G0. Tel: 867-645-5500. FAX: 867-645-2387. E-mail: librarian@nac.nu.ca. Web Site: www.nac.nu.ca/library.
Open Mon-Thurs 6pm-8pm, Sat 3-5

ONTARIO

ADDISON

P ELIZABETHTOWN-KITLEY TOWNSHIP PUBLIC LIBRARY, New Dublin, 6544 New Dublin Rd, K0E 1A0. SAN 319-0226. Tel: 613-498-3338. E-mail: elizndub@elizabethtown-kitley.on.ca. Web Site: www.elizabethtown-kitley.on.ca. *Chairperson,* Jill Yeatman; E-mail: jillelspeth@hotmail.com; *Chief Exec Officer, Head Librn,* Ruth Blanchard
Pop 9,724; Circ 17,689
Library Holdings: Bk Vols 25,000; Per Subs 10
Wireless access
Partic in Southern Ontario Libr Serv
Open Mon 1-5:30, Thurs 1-8:30
Branches: 2
KITLEY BRANCH, 424 Hwy 29, Toledo, K0E 1Y0. FAX: 613-345-7235. *Librn,* Charlotte Hoy
Open Mon & Fri 9-4:30, Tues 9-8
LYN BRANCH, 14 Main St, Lyn, K0E 1M0. (Mail add: Box 158, Lyn, K0E 1M0). Tel: 613-345-0033. *Br Mgr,* Beverley LaBrash
Open Tues 1-8, Fri 1-6

AJAX

P AJAX PUBLIC LIBRARY, 55 Harwood Ave S, L1S 2H8. SAN 366-9270. Tel: 905-683-4000. FAX: 905-683-6960. E-mail: libraryinfo@ajaxlibrary.ca. Web Site: www.ajaxlibrary.ca. *Chief Exec Officer,* Donna Bright; Tel: 905-683-4000, Ext 8825, E-mail: donna.bright@ajaxlibrary.ca; *Mgr, Access Serv,* Dan Gioiosa; Tel: 905-683-4000, Ext 8824, E-mail: dan.gioiosa@ajaxlibrary.ca; *Mgr, Coop Serv,* Susan Burrill; Tel: 905-683-4000, Ext 8822, E-mail: susan.burrill@ajaxlibrary.ca; *Pub Serv Mgr,* Cindy Poon; Tel: 905-683-4000, Ext 8801, E-mail: cindy.poon@ajaxlibrary.ca; *Br Serv Coordr,* Cindy Kimber; Tel: 905-683-4000, Ext 8902, E-mail: cindy.kimber@ajaxlibrary.ca; *Coordr, Info Serv,* Sarah Dodge; Tel: 905-683-4000, Ext 8802, E-mail: sarah.dodge@ajaxlibrary.ca; *Circ Serv,* Eleanor May; Tel: 905-683-4000, Ext 8821, E-mail: eleanor.may@ajaxlibrary.ca; Staff 8 (MLS 4, Non-MLS 4)
Founded 1952. Pop 109,000; Circ 850,000
Library Holdings: Bk Titles 156,506; Per Subs 252
Special Collections: Local History Coll; Multilingual Coll. Can & Prov
Automation Activity & Vendor Info: (Acquisitions) SirsiDynix; (Cataloging) SIRSI WorkFlows; (Circulation) SIRSI WorkFlows; (OPAC) SirsiDynix
Database Vendor: EBSCOhost, Gale Cengage Learning, netLibrary, Overdrive, Inc
Wireless access
Function: Adult bk club, Art exhibits, Bk club(s), Bks on CD, CD-ROM, Children's prog, Citizenship assistance, Computer training, Computers for patron use, Copy machines, Digital talking bks, Electronic databases & coll, Exhibits, Free DVD rentals, Handicapped accessible, Holiday prog, Home delivery & serv to Sr ctr & nursing homes, ILL available, Large print keyboards, Literacy & newcomer serv, Magnifiers for reading, Microfiche/film & reading machines, Music CDs, Online cat, Online ref, Online searches, Outreach serv, OverDrive digital audio bks, Photocopying/Printing, Printer for laptops & handheld devices, Prog for adults, Prog for children & young adult, Pub access computers, Senior computer classes, Spanish lang bks, Summer & winter reading prog, Teen prog, Telephone ref, Web-Braille, Wheelchair accessible
Publications: Pages (Bi-monthly)
Partic in Southern Ontario Libr Serv
Open Mon-Thurs 10-9, Fri & Sat 10-5, Sun (Sept-July) 1-5
Friends of the Library Group
Branches: 2
MCLEAN BRANCH, 95 Magill Dr, L1T 4M5, SAN 374-8154. Tel: 905-428-8489. FAX: 905-428-3743. *Br Serv Coordr,* Cindy Kimber; Tel: 905-683-4000, Ext 8902, E-mail: cindy.kimber@ajaxlbrary.ca
  Library Holdings: Bk Titles 38,000
  Open Mon & Fri 1-9, Tues-Thurs 10-9, Sat 10-5, Sun (Oct-April) 1-5
  Friends of the Library Group
VILLAGE BRANCH, 58 Church St N, L1T 2W6, SAN 366-9300. Tel: 905-683-1140. FAX: 905-683-1140. *Br Serv Coordr,* Cindy Kimber; Tel: 905-619-2529, Ext 8902, E-mail: cindy.kimber@ajax.ca
  Library Holdings: Bk Titles 17,000
  Open Mon-Thurs 3:30-7:30, Fri & Sat 11-3:30

ALFRED

C UNIVERSITE DE GUELPH-CAMPUS D'ALFRED, BIBLIOTHEQUE*, 31 Saint Paul St, K0B 1A0. SAN 326-7741. Tel: 613-679-2218. FAX: 613-679-2423. Web Site: www.collegedalfred.ca. *Libr Assoc,* Lyne Gagné Lalonde; E-mail: lgagne@alfredc.uoguelph.ca; Staff 1 (Non-MLS 1)
Founded 1981. Enrl 150; Fac 22
Library Holdings: Bk Vols 22,000; Per Subs 125; Videos 2,000
Special Collections: Agriculture Coll; Food Science Coll; French Video Coll; Horticulture Coll; International Development in Agriculture; Veterinary Technology Coll
Subject Interests: Agr
Automation Activity & Vendor Info: (Cataloging) Ex Libris Group; (Circulation) Ex Libris Group
Wireless access
Open Mon-Thurs 8:30-7, Fri 8:30-4:30

ALLISTON

P NEW TECUMSETH PUBLIC LIBRARY*, 17 Victoria St E, L9R 1V6. (Mail add: PO Box 399, L9R 1V6), SAN 372-4034. Tel: 705-435-0250. FAX: 705-435-0750. Web Site: www.ntpl.ca. *Chief Exec Officer,* Mark Gagnon; E-mail: mgagnon@ntpl.ca
Founded 1924. Pop 28,000; Circ 326,643
Library Holdings: AV Mats 6,757; Large Print Bks 1,277; Bk Titles 90,668; Bk Vols 118,667; Per Subs 115
Special Collections: New Tecumseth Digital History; Sir Frederick Banting Digital Library
Subject Interests: Govt doc, Local hist
Automation Activity & Vendor Info: (Cataloging) SirsiDynix; (Circulation) SirsiDynix; (OPAC) SirsiDynix
Database Vendor: SirsiDynix

Wireless access
Friends of the Library Group
Branches: 3
D A JONES BRANCH, 42 Main St W, Beeton, L0G 1A0. (Mail add: PO Box 399, L9R 1V6), SAN 319-0455. Tel: 905-729-3726. *Br Mgr,* Lori Whittemore; Staff 3 (Non-MLS 3)
   Library Holdings: Bk Vols 20,000
   Open Tues-Thurs 10-8, Fri & Sat 10-5
PAM KIRKPATRICK BRANCH, Tottenham Mall, 5-55 Queen St S, Tottenham, L0G 1W0. (Mail add: PO Box 399, L9R 1V6), SAN 319-5791. Tel: 905-936-2291. *Br Mgr,* Lori Whittemore
   Library Holdings: Bk Vols 20,000
   Open Tues-Thurs 10-8, Fri 10-5, Sat 10-3
MEMORIAL BRANCH, 17 Victoria St E, L9R 1V6. (Mail add: PO Box 399, L9R 1V6), SAN 319-0250. Tel: 705-435-5651. FAX: 705-435-0750. *Br Mgr,* Vaughn Thurman; *Tech Serv,* Patti Worden; Staff 6 (Non-MLS 6)
   Library Holdings: Bk Vols 33,000
   Open Mon 10-6, Tues-Thurs 10-8, Fri & Sat 10-5

ALMONTE

P   MISSISSIPPI MILLS LIBRARIES*, Almonte Library, 155 High St, K0A 1A0. (Mail add: PO Box 820, K0A 1A0), SAN 319-0269. Tel: 613-256-1037. FAX: 613-256-4887. *Chief Librn,* Peter Nelson; E-mail: pnelson@mississippimills.ca; *Ch, Dep Chief Librn,* Monica Blackburn; Staff 1 (MLS 1)
   Pop 12,000
   Library Holdings: Bk Vols 49,000; Per Subs 32
   Subject Interests: Local hist
   Partic in Ont Pub Libr Info Network; Southern Ontario Libr Serv
   Open Mon, Tues & Thurs 2pm-8:30pm, Wed 10-8:30, Fri 10-6

AMELIASBURGH

P   COUNTY OF PRINCE EDWARD LIBRARIES*, Al Purdy Branch, 809 Whitney Rd, K0K 1A0. Tel: 613-968-9327. FAX: 613-961-7992. E-mail: ameliasburgh@peclibrary.org.
   Founded 2001
   Library Holdings: Bk Vols 15,000; Per Subs 10
   Open Tues 2-7, Thurs 1-5, Sat 10-3

AMHERSTBURG

S   FORT MALDEN NATIONAL HISTORIC SITE OF CANADA RESOURCE CENTRE*, 100 Laird Ave, N9V 2Z2. (Mail add: PO Box 38, N9V 2Z2), SAN 319-0277. Tel: 519-736-5416. FAX: 519-736-6603. Web Site: www.parkscanada.gc.ca/malden. *Spec Coll & Archives Librn,* John MacLeod; E-mail: john.macleod@pc.gc.ca; Staff 1 (MLS 1)
   Founded 1939
   Library Holdings: Bk Titles 3,950; Per Subs 12
   Special Collections: Archival Documents Relating to Fort's History
   Subject Interests: British mil to 1860, Hist of Fort Malden, Local hist to 1860, Local Indian groups, Pioneer life, Rebellion of 1837, War of 1812
   Function: Res libr
   Restriction: Open by appt only, Open to pub for ref only

ANCASTER

C   REDEEMER COLLEGE LIBRARY*, 777 Garner Rd E, L9K 1J4. SAN 324-010X. Tel: 905-648-2131. FAX: 905-648-2134. Web Site: www.redeemer.ca. *Assoc VPres, Libr Info Tech,* Janny Eikelboom; E-mail: jeikelboom@redeemer.ca; *Pub Serv Librn,* Marlene Power; *Circ Serv Supvr,* Jolene Veenstra; *Acq, ILL,* Patrick Kok; *Cat & Ref,* Helen Reitsma; Staff 3 (MLS 3)
   Enrl 900; Fac 46
   Library Holdings: Bk Titles 75,000; Bk Vols 90,000; Per Subs 330
   Special Collections: Dutch Reformed Theology Coll; Science & Christian Faith Coll
   Subject Interests: Educ, English, Faith, Hist, Lit, Philosophy, Psychol, Sci, Theol
   Publications: Annual Report
   Partic in OCLC Online Computer Library Center, Inc
   Open Mon-Fri (Fall & Winter) 8am-Midnight, Sat 8-8; Mon-Fri (Summer) 8:30-4:30

ANGUS

P   ESSA PUBLIC LIBRARY, 8505 County Rd 10, Unit 1, L0M 1B1. SAN 319-0285. Tel: 705-424-6531. Administration Tel: 705-424-2679. FAX: 705-424-5521. E-mail: admin@essa.library.on.ca, essalib@essa.library.on.ca. Web Site: www.essa.library.on.ca. *Chief Exec Officer,* Janine Harris-Wheatley; E-mail: ceoadmin@essa.library.on.ca; *Mgr, Pub Serv,* Laura Wark; E-mail: lwark@essa.library.on.ca; *Coordr, Support Serv,* Angie Wishart; Staff 2 (MLS 2)
   Founded 1967. Pop 18,500; Circ 140,000

Jan 2010-Dec 2011 Income (CAN) $500,000, Other (CAN) $90,000
Library Holdings: Audiobooks 10,000; Large Print Bks 300; Bk Vols 65,000; Per Subs 350
Automation Activity & Vendor Info: (Acquisitions) SirsiDynix; (Cataloging) SirsiDynix; (Circulation) SirsiDynix; (OPAC) SirsiDynix; (Serials) SirsiDynix
Database Vendor: SirsiDynix
Wireless access
Function: Children's prog, Copy machines, Digital talking bks, Exhibits, Fax serv, Free DVD rentals, Handicapped accessible, Homebound delivery serv, Homework prog, ILL available, Magnifiers for reading, Mail & tel request accepted, Music CDs, Online cat, OverDrive digital audio bks, Photocopying/Printing, Preschool outreach, Preschool reading prog, Prog for adults, Prog for children & young adult, Pub access computers, Scanner, Spoken cassettes & CDs, Story hour, Summer reading prog, Wheelchair accessible
Partic in County of Simcoe Libr Coop; Southern Ontario Libr Serv
Special Services for the Deaf - High interest/low vocabulary bks
Special Services for the Blind - Aids for in-house use; Bks on CD; Home delivery serv; Large print bks; Magnifiers; PC for handicapped
Open Mon-Thurs 10-8, Fri & Sat 10-5
Restriction: Circ to mem only, Open to fac, students & qualified researchers
Branches: 1
THORNTON BRANCH, 34 Robert St, Thornton, L0L 2N0. Tel: 705-458-2549. FAX: 705-458-1820. *Chief Exec Officer,* Janine Harris-Wheatley; Tel: 705-424-6531, E-mail: ceoadmin@essa.library.on.ca
   Automation Activity & Vendor Info: (Acquisitions) Horizon; (Cataloging) Horizon; (Circulation) Horizon; (OPAC) Horizon
   Open Mon 9-Noon & 6pm-9pm, Tues 9-Noon, Wed 2pm-9pm, Sat 9-2

APSLEY

P   NORTH KAWARTHA PUBLIC LIBRARY, 175 Burleigh St, K0L 1A0. (Mail add: PO Box 335, K0L 1A0), SAN 319-0293. Tel: 705-656-4333. FAX: 705-656-2538. E-mail: info@northkawarthalibrary.com. Web Site: www.northkawarthalibrary.com. *Chief Exec Officer,* Shannon Hunter; E-mail: s.hunter@northkawartha.on.ca; *Librn,* Debbie Hall; E-mail: dhall@northkawarthalibrary.com; *Tech Serv Coordr,* Susan Suhr; E-mail: s.suhr@northkawarthalibrary.com
   Founded 1971. Pop 2,200; Circ 22,000
   Jan 2012-Dec 2012 Income (CAN) $151,140, Provincial (CAN) $80,300, City (CAN) $57,000, Locally Generated Income (CAN) $13,840. Mats Exp (CAN) $10,024, Books (CAN) $7,274, Other Print Mats (CAN) $2,000, AV Mat (CAN) $750. Sal (CAN) $50,163
   Library Holdings: Large Print Bks 150; Bk Titles 15,500; Bk Vols 16,600; Per Subs 18; Talking Bks 150
   Wireless access
   Partic in Southern Ontario Libr Serv
   Open Tues-Fri 9:30-5, Sat 9-2

ARNPRIOR

P   ARNPRIOR PUBLIC LIBRARY*, 21 Madawaska St, K7S 1R6. SAN 319-0307. Tel: 613-623-2279. FAX: 613-623-0281. E-mail: library@arncap.com. Web Site: www.arnprior.library.on.ca. *Chief Librn,* Karen DeLuca; Staff 2 (Non-MLS 2)
   Pop 15,000
   Library Holdings: Bk Vols 54,000; Per Subs 60
   Automation Activity & Vendor Info: (Acquisitions) Follett Software
   Function: AV serv, ILL available
   Partic in Southern Ontario Libr Serv
   Open Mon-Thurs 12-8, Fri 9-5, Sat 10-5

ATHENS

P   TOWNSHIP OF ATHENS PUBLIC LIBRARY*, Five Central St, K0E 1B0. (Mail add: PO Box 309, K0E 1B0), SAN 319-0315. Tel: 613-924-2048. E-mail: athenspl@bellnet.ca. *Librn,* Freda Schaafsma; *Ch,* Hennie Janssens
   Pop 2,800; Circ 9,435
   Library Holdings: Audiobooks 78; Bk Titles 10,606; Per Subs 24; Videos 114
   Automation Activity & Vendor Info: (Acquisitions) Duncan Systems Specialists Inc; (Cataloging) Duncan Systems Specialists Inc; (Circulation) Duncan Systems Specialists Inc
   Wireless access
   Partic in Southern Ontario Libr Serv
   Open Tues & Thurs 2-4:30, Wed 6-8, Fri 3:30-8:30, Sat 9:30-11:30
   Friends of the Library Group

ATIKOKAN

S   QUETICO PARK*, John B Ridley Research Library, Quetico Park, P0T 1C0. SAN 373-7926. Tel: 807-929-2571, Ext 224. FAX: 807-929-2123. *Librn,* Andrea Allison; E-mail: andrea.allison@ontario.ca; Staff 1 (MLS 1) Founded 1986
Library Holdings: Bk Titles 5,000; Per Subs 15
Special Collections: Quetico Park Coll, bks, photog, slides. Oral History
Automation Activity & Vendor Info: (Cataloging) Inmagic, Inc.
Restriction: Open to pub for ref only

AURORA

P   AURORA PUBLIC LIBRARY*, 15145 Young St, L4G 1M1. SAN 319-0331. Tel: 905-727-9493. FAX: 905-727-9374. E-mail: apl@library.on.ca. Web Site: www.library.aurora.on.ca. *Chief Librn/CEO,* Louise Procter Maio; *Head, Adult Serv,* P Damphouse; *Head, Ch,* J Jordan; Staff 14 (MLS 4, Non-MLS 10)
Founded 1855. Pop 49,000; Circ 550,000
Special Collections: Can
Database Vendor: Canadian Reference Centre, EBSCO Auto Repair Reference, EBSCOhost, Electric Library, Gale Cengage Learning, netLibrary, ProQuest, World Book Online
Wireless access
Open Mon 1-9, Tues-Thurs 9:30-9, Fri & Sat 9:30-5, Sun 1-5

AYLMER

S   ONTARIO POLICE COLLEGE LIBRARY*, 10716 Hacienda Rd, N5H 2T2. (Mail add: PO Box 1190, N5H 2T2), SAN 325-6197. Tel: 519-773-4264, 519-773-4266. FAX: 519-773-8225. *Librn,* Eileen Wereley; E-mail: eileen.wereley@ontario.ca; Staff 2 (MLS 1, Non-MLS 1)
Library Holdings: Bk Vols 14,000; Per Subs 100
Wireless access
Function: Archival coll, Computers for patron use, Copy machines, Electronic databases & coll, Govt ref serv, Newsp ref libr, Orientations, Photocopying/Printing, Prof lending libr
Publications: Acquisitions List; User Guides
Restriction: Open to govt employees only, Open to others by appt, Open to researchers by request, Visitors must make appt to use bks in the libr

BADEN

P   REGION OF WATERLOO LIBRARY, 2017 Nafziger Rd, N3A 3H4. (Mail add: 150 Frederick St, 2nd Flr, Kitchener, N2G 4J3), SAN 368-8119. Tel: 519-575-4590. FAX: 519-634-5371. E-mail: libhq@regionofwaterloo.ca. Web Site: www.rwl.library.on.ca. *Dir,* Lucille Bish; Tel: 519-575-4570, E-mail: lbish@regionofwaterloo.ca; *Mgr, Info Serv,* Kelly Bernstein; E-mail: kbernstein@regionofwaterloo.ca; *Mgr, Pub Serv,* Katherine Seredynska; E-mail: kseredynska@regionofwaterloo.ca; Staff 4 (MLS 2, Non-MLS 2)
Founded 1968. Pop 55,491; Circ 368,787
Library Holdings: AV Mats 3,830; Bks on Deafness & Sign Lang 68; High Interest/Low Vocabulary Bk Vols 189; Large Print Bks 1,495; Bk Titles 109,126; Bk Vols 168,316; Per Subs 258; Talking Bks 1,944
Automation Activity & Vendor Info: (Cataloging) SirsiDynix; (Circulation) SirsiDynix; (OPAC) SirsiDynix
Database Vendor: SirsiDynix
Function: ILL available, Photocopying/Printing, Telephone ref
Partic in Ontario Library Consortium; Southern Ontario Libr Serv
Friends of the Library Group
Branches: 10
AYR BRANCH, 137 Stanley St, Ayr, N0B 1E0. (Mail add: PO Box 1179, Ayr, N0B 1E0), SAN 368-8143. Tel: 519-632-7298. E-mail: ayrlib@regionofwaterloo.ca. *Br Mgr,* Michele Hopkins; Staff 1 (MLS 1)
Friends of the Library Group
BADEN BRANCH, 115 Snyder's Rd E, N3A 2V4, SAN 368-8178. Tel: 519-634-8933. E-mail: badenlib@regionofwaterloo.ca. *Mgr, Pub Serv,* Katherine Seredynska; *Asst Br Supvr,* Christine Baechler; Staff 1 (Non-MLS 1)
BLOOMINGDALE BRANCH, 860 Sawmill Rd, Bloomingdale, N0B 1K0, SAN 368-8208. Tel: 519-745-3151. E-mail: bloomlib@regionofwaterloo.ca. *Asst Br Supvr,* Susan O'Toole
ELMIRA BRANCH, 65 Arthur St S, Elmira, N3B 2M6, SAN 368-8216. Tel: 519-669-5477. E-mail: elmlib@regionofwaterloo.ca. *Br Mgr,* Sheryl Tilley; Staff 1 (MLS 1)
Founded 1888
Function: Handicapped accessible, Home delivery & serv to Sr ctr & nursing homes, Homebound delivery serv, ILL available, Photocopying/Printing, Prog for children & young adult, Summer reading prog, Telephone ref
LINWOOD BRANCH, 5279 Ament Line, Linwood, N0B 2A0, SAN 368-8224. Tel: 519-698-2700. E-mail: linwdlib@regionofwaterloo.ca. *Asst Br Supvr,* Gayna McGarrity

NEW DUNDEE BRANCH, 136 Main St, New Dundee, N0B 2E0. (Mail add: PO Box 269, New Dundee, N0B 2E0), SAN 368-8232. Tel: 519-696-3041. E-mail: ndlib@regionofwaterloo.ca. *Asst Br Supvr,* Lynn Weiss
NEW HAMBURG BRANCH, 145 Huron St, New Hamburg, N3A 1K1, SAN 368-8240. Tel: 519-662-1112. E-mail: nhlib@regionofwaterloo.ca. *Br Mgr,* Yvonne Zyma
ST CLEMENTS BRANCH, 3605 Lobsinger Line, St. Clements, N0B 2M0, SAN 368-8259. Tel: 519-699-4341. E-mail: stclemlib@regionofwaterloo.ca. *Asst Br Supvr,* Lois Johnson
ST JACOBS BRANCH, 29 Queensway Dr, St. Jacobs, N0B 2N0. (Mail add: PO Box 507, St. Jacobs, N0B 2N0), SAN 368-8267. Tel: 519-664-3443. E-mail: stjaclib@regionofwaterloo.ca. *Asst Br Supvr,* Susan Letkeman
WELLESLEY BRANCH, 1137 Henry St, Wellesley, N0B 2T0. (Mail add: PO Box 190, Wellesley, N0B 2T0), SAN 368-8291. Tel: 519-656-2001. E-mail: wellslib@regionofwaterloo.ca. *Br Mgr,* Twyla Knight

BALA

S   WAHTA MOHAWKS*, First Nation Library, 2664 Meskoa Rd 38, P0C 1A0. (Mail add: PO Box 260, P0C 1A0), SAN 377-4716. Tel: 705-756-2354. FAX: 705-756-2376. Web Site: www.wahta.ca. *Librn,* Shirley Sahanatien
Library Holdings: Bk Vols 8,000; Per Subs 10
Open Mon-Fri 8:30-4:30

BALMERTOWN

P   BALMERTOWN PUBLIC LIBRARY*, 12 Fifth St, P0V 1C0. (Mail add: PO Box 280, P0V 1C0), SAN 319-034X. Tel: 807-735-2110. FAX: 807-735-2110. E-mail: rllib212@yahoo.com. *Librn,* Lisa Johnson; Staff 1 (Non-MLS 1)
Founded 1970. Pop 2,113
Jan 2011-Dec 2011 Income $243,806, Provincial $22,772, City $202,000, Federal $6,000, Locally Generated Income $13,034. Mats Exp $20,700, Books $19,000, AV Mat $1,700
Library Holdings: DVDs 500; Large Print Bks 97; Bk Titles 13,101; Bk Vols 13,500; Per Subs 10; Talking Bks 200
Mem of Ontario Library Service North
Open Mon-Fri 11-8

BANCROFT

P   BANCROFT PUBLIC LIBRARY*, 14 Flint Ave, K0L 1C0. (Mail add: PO Box 127, K0L 1C0), SAN 319-0358. Tel: 613-332-3380. FAX: 613-332-5473. E-mail: info@bancroftpubliclibrary.ca. Web Site: bancroftpubliclibrary.ca. *Chief Exec Officer,* Vanessa Holm
Founded 1901
Library Holdings: Bk Vols 20,000; Per Subs 40
Mem of Southern Adirondack Library System
Partic in Southern Ontario Libr Serv
Open Tues & Wed 12-7, Thurs-Sat 10-3

P   CARLOW-MAYO PUBLIC LIBRARY, c/o Hermon Public School, 124 Fort Stewart Rd, RR 4, K0L 1C0. SAN 319-0366. Tel: 613-332-2544. FAX: 613-223-2544. E-mail: carlowmayopl@gmail.com. Web Site: www.carlowmayopubliclibrary.ca. *Librn,* Laurie Cannon
Founded 1970. Circ 5,700
Library Holdings: Bk Titles 9,410; Bk Vols 10,410; Per Subs 20; Videos 500
Open Tues 10-1 & 5-8, Thurs 5-8, Sat 10-1
Friends of the Library Group

BARRIE

P   BARRIE PUBLIC LIBRARY*, 60 Worsley St, L4M 1L6. SAN 319-0374. Tel: 705-728-1010. FAX: 705-728-4322. E-mail: barlib@city.barrie.on.ca. Web Site: www.library.barrie.on.ca. *Dir,* Al Davis; Tel: 705-728-1010, Ext 7500, E-mail: adavis@barrie.ca; *Mgr, Ad Serv,* Shonna Froebel; Tel: 705-728-1010, Ext 7014, E-mail: sfroebel@barrie.ca; *Mgr, Ch Serv,* Jane Salmon; Tel: 705-728-1010, Ext 7017, E-mail: jsalmon@barrie.ca; *Mgr, Pub & Br Serv,* Jaime Griffis; Tel: 705-728-1010, Ext 7009, E-mail: jgriffis@barrie.ca; *Tech Mgr,* Khuan Seow; Tel: 705-728-1010, Ext 7010, E-mail: kseow@barrie.ca; Staff 27 (MLS 11, Non-MLS 16)
Founded 1862. Pop 135,000; Circ 1,541,729
Library Holdings: Audiobooks 7,286; Braille Volumes 94; CDs 7,582; DVDs 21,571; e-books 13,569; Large Print Bks 10,825; Microforms 669; Bk Titles 310,729; Per Subs 296; Talking Bks 1,286
Special Collections: Local History (Fred Grant Coll & Montagu Leeds Coll), microfilm; Ontario Genealogical Society, Simcoe County Branch. Can & Prov
Automation Activity & Vendor Info: (Acquisitions) SirsiDynix; (Cataloging) SirsiDynix; (Circulation) SirsiDynix; (OPAC) SirsiDynix; (Serials) SirsiDynix

Database Vendor: Canadian Reference Centre, CEDROM-SNi, Dun & Bradstreet, EBSCOhost, Gale Cengage Learning, netLibrary, Overdrive, Inc, ProQuest, TumbleBookLibrary, World Book Online
Wireless access
Function: Adult bk club, Audiobks via web, Bks on CD, Children's prog, Computers for patron use, Copy machines, Digital talking bks, e-mail serv, Electronic databases & coll, Free DVD rentals, Handicapped accessible, Home delivery & serv to Sr ctr & nursing homes, Homebound delivery serv, ILL available, Jazz prog, Magnifiers for reading, Music CDs, Online cat, Online ref, Online searches, Outreach serv, OverDrive digital audio bks, Prog for adults, Prog for children & young adult, Pub access computers, Senior computer classes, Senior outreach, Summer reading prog, Teen prog, Telephone ref, Wheelchair accessible
Publications: @your library (Newsletter); Information Barrie Community Directory (Business & organization papers & directories)
Partic in Southern Ontario Libr Serv
Special Services for the Blind - Bks on cassette; Bks on CD; Children's Braille; Daisy reader; Digital talking bk; Home delivery serv; Large print bks; Magnifiers; Talking bks
Open Mon-Thurs 10-9, Fri & Sat 10-5, Sun 12-5
Branches: 1
PAINSWICK BRANCH, 48 Dean Ave, L4N 0C2. (Mail add: 60 Worsley St, L4M 1L6). Tel: 705-728-1010. FAX: 705-728-4322. E-mail: barlib@barrie.ca. *Mgr, Br & Pub Serv,* Jaime Griffis; Tel: 705-728-1010, Ext 7009, E-mail: jgriffis@barrie.ca; Staff 6.5 (MLS 3, Non-MLS 3.5)
Founded 2012
Automation Activity & Vendor Info: (Circulation) Horizon; (OPAC) BiblioCommons
Function: Adult bk club, Audiobks via web, Bks on CD, Children's prog, Computer training, Computers for patron use, Copy machines, e-mail serv, Free DVD rentals, Handicapped accessible, ILL available, Online cat, Online ref, OverDrive digital audio bks, Prog for adults, Prog for children & young adult, Pub access computers, Summer reading prog, Wheelchair accessible, Workshops
Special Services for the Blind - Audio mat; Bks on CD; Digital talking bk; Extensive large print coll; Home delivery serv; Large print bks; Talking bks from Braille Inst
Open Mon 10-5, Tues-Fri 10-9, Sat 10-5, Sun 12-5
Restriction: ID required to use computers (Ltd hrs), In-house use for visitors, Non-resident fee

J   GEORGIAN COLLEGE, Library Commons, One Georgian Dr, L4M 3X9. SAN 319-0390. Tel: 705-728-1968. Circulation Tel: 705-722-5139. Interlibrary Loan Service Tel: 705-728-1968, Ext 1682. FAX: 705-722-1584. Reference FAX: 705-722-1508. E-mail: library@georgiancollege.ca. Web Site: library.georgianc.on.ca. *Dir,* Katherine Wallis; Tel: 705-728-1968, Ext 1684, E-mail: katherine.wallis@georgiancollege.ca
Founded 1967. Enrl 8,200
Library Holdings: AV Mats 8,000; Bk Vols 75,000; Per Subs 600
Automation Activity & Vendor Info: (Acquisitions) SirsiDynix; (Cataloging) SirsiDynix; (Circulation) SirsiDynix; (Media Booking) SirsiDynix; (OPAC) SirsiDynix; (Serials) SirsiDynix
Database Vendor: CredoReference, ebrary, EBSCOhost, Elsevier, Gale Cengage Learning, Infomart, Infotrieve, Ingenta, LexisNexis, OVID Technologies, Oxford Online, ProQuest, PubMed, Quicklaw, ScienceDirect, SerialsSolutions, SirsiDynix, Springshare, LLC, WebClarity Software Inc, WestlaweCARSWELL
Wireless access
Partic in Ontario Colleges Library Service (OCLS)
Open Mon-Thurs 7:30am-11pm, Fri 7:30-5, Sat 10-5, Sun 1-8

M   ROYAL VICTORIA REGIONAL HEALTH CENTER*, Health Library, 201 Georgian Dr, L4M 6M2. SAN 373-6725. Tel: 705-728-9090, Ext 42631. FAX: 705-739-5693. E-mail: healthlibrary@rvh.on.ca. Web Site: www.rvh.on.ca.
Library Holdings: Bk Vols 2,695; Per Subs 50
Special Collections: Biomedical Coll; Nursing & Allied Health Coll
Subject Interests: Consumer health, Med, Nursing
Automation Activity & Vendor Info: (Acquisitions) Eloquent Systems Inc; (Cataloging) Eloquent Systems Inc; (Circulation) Eloquent Systems Inc; (Course Reserve) Eloquent Systems Inc; (OPAC) Eloquent Systems Inc
Database Vendor: EBSCOhost
Partic in Canadian Health Libraries Association
Open Mon-Fri 8:30-4:30

M   STROKE RECOVERY ASSOCIATION*, Research Library, 80 Bradford St, Unit 239A, L4N 6S7. SAN 329-1545. Tel: 416-425-4209. Toll Free Tel: 888-540-6666. FAX: 705-737-9982. *Chair,* Clay Outwater
Founded 1975
Publications: Monthly Magazine

BARRY'S BAY

P   BARRY'S BAY & AREA PUBLIC LIBRARY, Opeongo Line, No 19474, K0J 1B0. (Mail add: PO Box 970, K0J 1B0), SAN 319-0404. Tel: 613-756-2000. FAX: 613-756-2000. E-mail: bblibry@bellnet.ca. *Chief Exec Officer,* Karen Filipkowski
Founded 1960. Pop 5,000; Circ 28,000
Library Holdings: Bk Vols 21,000; Per Subs 32
Wireless access
Partic in Southern Ontario Libr Serv
Open Mon & Wed 1-5, Tues 1-5 & 6:30-8:30, Thurs 11-5, Fri 1-6, Sat 11-4

BATH

G   CORRECTIONAL SERVICE OF CANADA*, Millhaven Institution Inmate Library, Hwy 33, K0H 1G0. (Mail add: PO Box 280, K0H 1G0), SAN 329-0840. Tel: 613-351-8000. Administration Tel: 613-351-8219. FAX: 613-351-8136. *Librn,* Amy Pianosi; Staff 5 (MLS 1, Non-MLS 4)
Library Holdings: Bk Titles 10,000
Special Collections: Multilingual (Asian); Native
Open Mon-Fri 8-4

BEACHBURG

P   WHITEWATER REGION*, Beachburg Branch, 20 Cameron St, K0J 1C0. (Mail add: PO Box 159, K0J 1C0), SAN 319-0439. Tel: 613-582-7090. *Librn,* Marilyn Labow; E-mail: mlabow@nrtco.net; Staff 1 (Non-MLS 1)
Pop 693; Circ 1,687
Library Holdings: Large Print Bks 200; Bk Titles 4,600; Bk Vols 5,000; Per Subs 20; Talking Bks 300
Partic in Southern Ontario Libr Serv
Open Mon & Thurs 6:30pm-8:30pm, Tues 10-5, Sat 9-Noon

BEAMSVILLE

P   LINCOLN PUBLIC LIBRARY*, 4996 Beam St, L0R 1B0. (Mail add: Box 460, L0R 1B0), SAN 367-0058. Tel: 905-563-7014. FAX: 905-563-1810. E-mail: info@lincoln.library.on.ca. Web Site: www.lincoln.library.on.ca. *Chief Exec Officer,* Jill Nickolsen
Founded 1886. Pop 22,000; Circ 240,000
Library Holdings: Bks on Deafness & Sign Lang 15; High Interest/Low Vocabulary Bk Vols 25; Bk Vols 69,000; Per Subs 46
Special Collections: Adult Basic Education; Canadian Federal Documents (partial depository); Local History Coll; Provincial Government Documents (partial depository). Oral History
Automation Activity & Vendor Info: (Cataloging) MultiLIS; (Circulation) MultiLIS; (OPAC) MultiLIS; (Serials) MultiLIS
Database Vendor: Gale Cengage Learning
Partic in Southern Ontario Libr Serv
Special Services for the Blind - Bks on CD
Open Mon-Thurs 9-8, Fri 9-5, Sat 10-5
Branches: 1
MOSES F RITTENHOUSE BRANCH, 4080 John Charles Blvd, Vineland, L0R 2C0, SAN 367-0082. Tel: 905-562-5711. FAX: 905-562-3454. *Chief Exec Officer,* Jill Nicholson
Library Holdings: Bk Titles 57,000

BEAVERTON

P   BROCK TOWNSHIP PUBLIC LIBRARY, 401 Simcoe St, L0K 1A0. (Mail add: PO Box 310, L0K 1A0). Tel: 705-426-9283. FAX: 705-426-9353. E-mail: info@brocklibraries.ca. Web Site: www.brocklibraries.ca. *Chief Exec Officer,* Susan Dalton; E-mail: susan.dalton@brocklibraries.ca; Staff 2 (MLS 2)
Founded 1853. Pop 11,797; Circ 68,684
Special Collections: Local history items
Automation Activity & Vendor Info: (Acquisitions) SirsiDynix; (Cataloging) SirsiDynix; (Circulation) SirsiDynix; (OPAC) SirsiDynix
Database Vendor: EBSCOhost, Gale Cengage Learning, Overdrive, Inc, ProQuest, SirsiDynix, World Book Online
Wireless access
Function: Computers for patron use
Friends of the Library Group
Branches: 2
TIMOTHY FINDLEY MEMORIAL LIBRARY - CANNINGTON, 38 Laidlaw St, Cannington, L0E 1E0. (Mail add: PO Box 89, Cannington, L0E 1E0). Tel: 705-432-2867. FAX: 705-432-3282. E-mail: canningtonbranch@brocklibraries.ca. *Chief Exec Officer,* Susan Dalton; Tel: 705-426-9283, E-mail: susandalton@brocklibraries.ca
Founded 1889
Library Holdings: DVDs 300; Large Print Bks 300; Bk Titles 8,000; Per Subs 120
Open Tues & Fri 2-7:30, Wed & Thurs 10-3, Sat 10-2
Friends of the Library Group

SUNDERLAND PUBLIC LIBRARY, 41 Albert St, Sunderland, L0C 1H0. (Mail add: PO Box 208, Sunderland, L0C 1H0). Tel: 705-357-3109. FAX: 705-357-3109. E-mail: sunderlandbranch@brocklibraries.ca. *Chief Exec Officer,* Susan Dalton; Tel: 613-426-9283, E-mail: susandalton@brocklibraries.ca
Founded 1900
Open Tues & Thurs 2-8, Wed 2-5, Sat 10-2
Friends of the Library Group

BELLEVILLE

P   BELLEVILLE PUBLIC LIBRARY*, 254 Pinnacle St, K8N 3B1. SAN 367-0147. Tel: 613-968-6731. FAX: 613-968-6841. E-mail: infoserv@bellevillelibrary.com. Web Site: www.bellevillelibrary.com. *Chief Exec Officer,* Trevor Pross; E-mail: tpross@bellevillelibrary.com; Staff 36 (MLS 5, Non-MLS 31)
Founded 1876. Pop 48,000; Circ 345,000
Jan 2012-Dec 2012 Income (CAN) $2,000,000, Provincial (CAN) $84,357, City (CAN) $1,123,178, Locally Generated Income (CAN) $82,250, Other (CAN) $148,029. Mats Exp (CAN) $189,490. Sal (CAN) $840,452
Library Holdings: High Interest/Low Vocabulary Bk Vols 600; Large Print Bks 5,300; Bk Titles 100,000; Bk Vols 140,000; Per Subs 125; Talking Bks 3,000; Videos 5,000
Special Collections: Canadiana; Local Authors (Canadiana Room). Can & Prov
Subject Interests: Genealogy
Automation Activity & Vendor Info: (Acquisitions) SirsiDynix; (Cataloging) SirsiDynix; (Circulation) SirsiDynix; (OPAC) SirsiDynix
Partic in Southern Ontario Libr Serv
Open Mon-Thurs 9:30-8, Fri 9:30-5, Sat 9:30-5:30
Friends of the Library Group

J   THE PARROTT CENTRE, Loyalist College Library, 376 Wallbridge-Loyalist Rd, K8N 5B9. (Mail add: PO Box 4200, K8N 5B9), SAN 319-0463. Tel: 613-969-1913, Ext 2339. Circulation Tel: 613-969-1913, Ext 2141, 613-969-1913, Ext 2696. Interlibrary Loan Service Tel: 613-969-1913, Ext 2175. Administration Tel: 613-969-1913, Ext 2249. Automation Services Tel: 613-969-1913, Ext 2183, 613-969-1913, Ext 2216. Information Services Tel: 613-969-1913, Ext 2317. Toll Free Tel: 888-569-2547. FAX: 613-969-5183. E-mail: library@loyalistc.on.ca. Web Site: www.loyalistlibrary.com. *Dir, Libr & Res Serv,* Ross W Danaher; E-mail: rdanaher@loyalistc.on.ca; *Archives Mgr, Info Serv, ILL,* Lynn McCracken; E-mail: lmccrack@loyalistc.on.ca; *Acq, Electronic Res, Libr Tech,* Mrs Dayle Gorsline; E-mail: dgorslin@loyalistc.on.ca; *AV Coll, Info Serv, Libr Tech,* Position Currently Open; *Cat, Libr Tech, Tech Serv,* Danielle Emon; Tel: 613-969-1913, Ext 2183, E-mail: emon@loyalistc.on.ca; *Circ,* Cheryl Steele; E-mail: csteele@loyalistc.on.ca; *Circ,* Carla Williamson; E-mail: cwilliam@loyalistc.on.ca; *Libr Tech,* Cindy Fort; Tel: 613-969-1913, Ext 2595, E-mail: cfort@loyalistc.on.ca; *Libr Tech,* Barbara Harvey; Tel: 613-969-1913, Ext 2595, E-mail: bharvey@loyalistc.on.ca; *Libr Tech, Copyright,* Denise Galloway; Tel: 613-969-1913, Ext 2595, E-mail: dgalloway@loyalistc.on.ca; *Res Analyst,* Julie Rivers; Tel: 613-969-1913, Ext 2363, E-mail: jrivers@loyalistc.on.ca; Staff 10 (MLS 1, Non-MLS 9)
Founded 1967. Enrl 3,000; Fac 145
Library Holdings: AV Mats 10,025; e-books 28,348; e-journals 14,000; Bk Titles 30,674; Bk Vols 55,000; Per Subs 292
Special Collections: John Peterson Photography Coll; Lorraine Monk Coll; Loyalist College Archives
Automation Activity & Vendor Info: (Acquisitions) Mandarin Library Automation; (Cataloging) Mandarin Library Automation; (Circulation) Mandarin Library Automation; (Course Reserve) Mandarin Library Automation; (Media Booking) Mandarin Library Automation; (OPAC) Mandarin Library Automation
Database Vendor: Canadian Reference Centre, Cinahl Information Systems, ebrary, EBSCO Information Services, EBSCOhost, Gale Cengage Learning, H W Wilson, Hoovers, LexisNexis, McGraw-Hill, Medline, netLibrary, OCLC WorldCat, Oxford Online, ProQuest, Quicklaw, RefWorks, WebClarity Software Inc
Wireless access
Function: Audiobks via web, Computers for patron use, Copy machines, Digital talking bks, Distance learning, Electronic databases & coll, Handicapped accessible, Microfiche/film & reading machines, Online cat, Orientations, Photocopying/Printing, Pub access computers, Web-catalog
Open Mon-Thurs 8am-9pm, Fri 8-4:30, Sat 9-4, Sun 12-4
Restriction: Borrowing privileges limited to fac & registered students, ID required to use computers (Ltd hrs), In-house use for visitors, Open to fac, students & qualified researchers, Open to students, fac & staff, Pub use on premises

BLIND RIVER

P   BLIND RIVER PUBLIC LIBRARY*, Eight Woodward Ave, P0R 1B0. (Mail add: PO Box 880, P0R 1B0), SAN 319-0471. Tel: 705-356-7616. FAX: 705-356-7343. E-mail: brpl@onlink.net. Web Site: olsn.ca/blindriverlibrary. *Librn,* Rhea Marcellus
Founded 1926. Pop 4,471
Library Holdings: Bk Vols 15,000; Per Subs 15
Function: ILL available, Ref serv available
Open Mon-Thurs 10-4:30 & 6-8, Fri 10-4:30, Sat 10-1
Friends of the Library Group

BLOOMFIELD

P   COUNTY OF PRINCE EDWARD LIBRARIES*, Bloomfield Branch, 300 Main St, K0K 1G0. (Mail add: PO Box 9, K0K 1G0), SAN 319-048X. Tel: 613-393-3400. FAX: 613-393-1887. E-mail: bloomfield@peclibrary.org. *Librn,* Patricia Dubyk
Library Holdings: Bk Vols 9,000
Mem of Ontario Library Service North
Open Tues 3-7, Thurs 10-5, Sat 10-4
Friends of the Library Group

BOLTON

P   CALEDON PUBLIC LIBRARY*, Albion Bolton Branch, 150 Queen St S, L7E 1E3. SAN 319-0498. Tel: 905-857-1400. FAX: 905-857-8280. E-mail: bolton@caledon.library.on.ca. Web Site: www.caledon.library.on.ca. *Chief Exec Officer,* Bill Manson; Tel: 905-584-1456. E-mail: bmanson@caledon.library.on.ca; *Dir, Communications,* Mary Maw; E-mail: mmaw@caledon.library.on.ca; *Br Mgr,* Sharon Wilson; E-mail: swilson@caledon.library.on.ca; *Mgr, Lending Serv,* Kelley Potter; *Ch,* Laura Luopa; *Info Tech,* Mojgan Schmalenberg; E-mail: mschmale@caledon.library.on.ca
Founded 1974. Pop 53,000; Circ 333,000
Automation Activity & Vendor Info: (Cataloging) SirsiDynix; (Circulation) SirsiDynix; (OPAC) SirsiDynix
Database Vendor: EBSCOhost, SirsiDynix
Partic in Ontario Library Consortium; Southern Ontario Libr Serv
Friends of the Library Group
Branches: 6
ALTON BRANCH, 35 Station Rd, Alton, L7K 0E2, SAN 320-0655. Tel: 519-941-5480. E-mail: alton@caledon.library.on.ca. *Br Mgr,* Nancy Early
   Open Tues & Wed 2-8:30, Thurs 10-5, Sat 10-4
   Friends of the Library Group
BELFOUNTAIN BRANCH, 17247 Shaw's Creek Rd, Caledon, L7K 0E8, SAN 320-0663. Tel: 519-927-5701. E-mail: belftn@caledon.library.on.ca. *Br Supvr,* Sue Hamilton
   Open Tues-Thurs 4-8, Sat 10-4; Tues & Wed (Summer) 2-8, Thurs 10-2, Sat 10-4
   Friends of the Library Group
CALEDON EAST BRANCH, 6500 Old Church Rd, Caledon East, L0N 1E0, SAN 320-068X. Tel: 905-584-1456. E-mail: ceast@caledon.library.on.ca. *Br Mgr,* Penny Ridler; *Tech Serv,* Gillian Booth-Moyle; E-mail: mfleetwood@caledon.library.on.ca
   Open Mon & Fri 9-3, Tues-Thurs 9-8:30, Sat 10-4; Tues & Thurs (Summer) 2-8:30, Wed 10-5, Sun 10-4
   Friends of the Library Group
CALEDON VILLAGE, 18313 Hurontario St, Caledon Village, L7K 0X7, SAN 320-0671. Tel: 519-927-5800. E-mail: village@caledon.library.on.ca. *Br Mgr,* Theresa Borehan
   Open Tues & Thurs 2-8:30, Wed & Fri 10-5, Sat 10-4
   Friends of the Library Group
MARGARET DUNN BRANCH, 20 Snellcrest Dr, Mayfield, L7C 1B5, SAN 320-1682. Tel: 905-843-0457. E-mail: dunn@caledon.library.on.ca. *Br Supvr,* Heather Ryall
   Open Mon 4-8:30, Tues, Thurs & Fri 2-8:30, Wed 10-5, Sat 10-4
INGLEWOOD BRANCH, 15825 McLaughlin Rd, Inglewood, L7C 1H4, SAN 320-0698. Tel: 905-838-3324. E-mail: inglewd@caledon.library.on.ca. *Br Mgr,* Sheila Howlett-Soltysiak
   Open Tues & Thurs 2-8:30, Wed 10-5, Sat 10-4
   Friends of the Library Group

BONFIELD

P   BONFIELD PUBLIC LIBRARY, 365 Hwy 531, P0H 1E0. SAN 319-0501. Tel: 705-776-2396. FAX: 705-776-1154. E-mail: bpl@ontera.net. Web Site: www.onlink.net/~bpl. *Chief Librn,* Jeannette Shields; *Asst Librn,* Andree Gagne; Staff 2 (Non-MLS 2)
Founded 1974. Pop 2,081; Circ 10,235
Library Holdings: Bk Vols 12,500; Per Subs 23
Automation Activity & Vendor Info: (Circulation) Follett Software
Wireless access
Function: ILL available
Open Mon 10-6, Tues & Thurs 4-8, Wed 10-8, Sat 10-1
Friends of the Library Group

BORDEN

CANADA DEPARTMENT OF NATIONAL DEFENCE
G   BASE BORDEN PUBLIC & MILITARY LIBRARY*, CFB BORDEN, 41
Kapyong Rd, L0M 1C0, SAN 367-0201. Tel: 705-424-1200, Ext 2273.
Chief Librn, Don Allen; E-mail: don.allen@forces.gc.ca
Library Holdings: Bk Vols 45,000; Per Subs 20
Subject Interests: Mil
Partic in County of Simcoe Libr Coop
Open Tues-Fri 12-8, Sat 12-4
Friends of the Library Group

GM   CANADIAN FORCES HEALTH SERVICES TRAINING CENTRE*, CFB
Borden, 0-166, 30 Ortona Rd, Rm 1113, L0M 1C0. (Mail add: PO Box
1000, Sta Main, L0M 1C0), SAN 367-0236. Tel: 705-424-1200, Ext
3627. FAX: 705-423-2613.
Library Holdings: AV Mats 660; Bk Vols 15,000; Per Subs 40
Subject Interests: Emergency med, Mil med, Nursing, Preventive med

BOWMANVILLE

P   CLARINGTON PUBLIC LIBRARY*, Bowmanville Branch, 163 Church
St, L1C 1T7. SAN 367-0295. Tel: 905-623-7322. FAX: 905-623-9905.
Administration FAX: 905-623-8608. E-mail: info@clarington.library.on.ca.
Web Site: www.clarington-library.on.ca. *Libr Dir,* Edith Hopkins
Founded 1974. Pop 80,000
Jan 2007-Dec 2007 Income (Main Library and Branch(s)) (CAN)
$2,257,962, Provincial (CAN) $78,370, City (CAN) $2,050,988, Federal
(CAN) $9,947. Mats Exp (CAN) $242,540. Sal (CAN) $155,252
Library Holdings: Bk Vols 164,000; Per Subs 132
Automation Activity & Vendor Info: (Acquisitions) Library Systems &
Services (LSSI); (Circulation) SirsiDynix
Partic in Southern Ontario Libr Serv
Open Mon & Fri 10-9, Sat 10-5, Sun 12-5
Branches: 3
COURTICE BRANCH, 2950 Courtice Rd, Courtice, L1E 2H8. Tel:
905-404-0707. Administration Tel: 905-623-7322, Ext 722.
Administration FAX: 905-623-8608. *Coordr, Br Serv,* Janet Vanderveen
Open Mon-Thurs 10-8, Fri 10-6, Sat 10-5, Sun 12-5
NEWCASTLE VILLAGE BRANCH, 150 King Ave E, Newcastle, L1B
1L5, SAN 367-035X. Tel: 905-987-4844. Administration Tel:
905-623-7322. Administration FAX: 905-623-8608. *Coordr, Br Serv,* Paul
Axford
Open Mon-Wed 1-8, Tues & Thurs 10-6, Fri 1-6, Sat 10-5, Sun 12-5
ORONO BRANCH, 127 Church St, Orono, L0B 1M0, SAN 367-0325. Tel:
905-983-5507. Administration Tel: 905-623-7322. Administration FAX:
905-623-8608. *Coordr, Br Serv,* Darlene McCann
Open Mon, Tues, Thurs & Fri 1-6, Wed 1-8, Sat 10-2

BRACEBRIDGE

P   BRACEBRIDGE PUBLIC LIBRARY*, 94 Manitoba St, P1L 2B5. SAN
319-051X. Tel: 705-645-4171. FAX: 705-645-6551. E-mail:
bracelib@vianet.on.ca. Interlibrary Loan Service E-mail: illo@vianet.ca.
Web Site: www.bracebridge.library.on.ca. *Chief Librn,* Cathryn Rodney;
E-mail: crodney@vianet.ca; *Ch, Youth Serv,* Cindy Buhne; E-mail:
cbuhne@vianet.ca; *ILL,* Nancy Beasley; E-mail: nbeasley@vianet.ca; *Ref,*
Mary Armstrong; *Ref,* Ruth Holtz; E-mail: holtzr@vianet.on.ca; *Ref,*
Evelyn Payton; E-mail: epayton@vianet.on.ca; Staff 4 (MLS 4)
Founded 1906. Pop 15,652; Circ 137,516
Library Holdings: e-books 14,865; Bk Titles 42,226; Bk Vols 52,986; Per
Subs 128
Special Collections: Muskoka Coll; Prov; Rene Caisse Coll
Automation Activity & Vendor Info: (Cataloging) SirsiDynix;
(Circulation) SirsiDynix; (OPAC) SirsiDynix
Database Vendor: SirsiDynix
Wireless access
Open Mon & Fri 9-6, Tues-Thurs 9-8, Sat 9-4

BRADFORD

P   BRADFORD-WEST GWILLIMBURY PUBLIC LIBRARY*, 425 Holland
St W, L3Z 0J2. SAN 319-0528. Tel: 905-775-3328. FAX: 905-775-1236.
E-mail: bwgmailbox@bradford.library.on.ca. Web Site:
www.bradford.library.on.ca. *Chief Exec Officer,* Elizabeth Fenwick; *Dep
Chief Exec Officer,* Nina Cunniff; *Circ Mgr,* Kim Perry
Founded 1879
Library Holdings: Bk Vols 90,000; Per Subs 120
Subject Interests: Local hist
Wireless access
Partic in Southern Ontario Libr Serv
Open Mon-Thurs 9:30-9, Fri & Sat 9:30-5:30
Friends of the Library Group

BRAMPTON

P   BRAMPTON LIBRARY*, 65 Queen St E, L6W 3L6. SAN 367-0384. Tel:
905-793-4636. FAX: 905-453-0810. TDD: 866-959-9994. E-mail:
info@bramlib.on.ca. Web Site: www.BramptonLibrary.ca. *Chief Exec
Officer,* Cathy Matyas; Tel: 905-793-4636, Ext 4311, E-mail:
cmatyas@bramlib.on.ca; Staff 168 (MLS 23, Non-MLS 145)
Founded 1974. Pop 500,000; Circ 1,000,000
Library Holdings: Bk Titles 235,129; Bk Vols 578,475
Special Collections: Can & Prov; Community Information (Multilingual
Literary French, large print, talking books)
Subject Interests: Archit, Art, Behav sci, Law, Local hist, Soc sci
Automation Activity & Vendor Info: (Acquisitions) SirsiDynix;
(Cataloging) SirsiDynix; (Circulation) SirsiDynix; (OPAC) SirsiDynix
Database Vendor: SirsiDynix
Wireless access
Open Mon-Thurs 10-9, Fri 10-6, Sat 10-5, Sun 1-5
Branches: 5
CHINGUACOUSY BRANCH, 150 Central Park Dr, L6T 1B4, SAN
367-0449. Tel: 905-793-4636, Ext 4120. FAX: 905-793-0506. *Br Mgr,*
David Hill; E-mail: dhill@bramlib.on.ca
Special Collections: Community Information Centre
Subject Interests: Genealogy, Law, Literacy, Multilingual
Open Mon-Thurs 10-9, Fri 10-6, Sat 10-5, Sun 1-5
CYRIL CLARK BRANCH, 20 Loafers Lake Lane, L6Z 1X9, SAN
322-6034. Tel: 905-793-4636, Ext 4404. FAX: 905-846-4278. *Br Mgr,*
Young Lark Jin; E-mail: yljin@bramlib.on.ca
Subject Interests: Literacy, Multilingual
Branch is temporarily closed for renovations
Friends of the Library Group
FOUR CORNERS BRANCH, 65 Queen St E, L6W 3L6, SAN 367-0414.
Tel: 905-793-4636, Ext 4318. FAX: 905-453-4602. *Br Mgr,* Emma
Duncan; E-mail: eduncan@bramlib.on.ca
Subject Interests: Literacy, Multilingual
Open Mon-Thurs 10-9, Fri 10-6, Sat 10-5, Sun 1-5
MOUNT PLEASANT VILLAGE BRANCH, 100 Commuter Dr, L7A 0G2.
Tel: 905-793-4636.
Pop 500,000; Circ 100,000
Open Mon-Thurs 2-9, Fri 2-6, Sat 10-5, Sun 1-5
SOUTH FLETCHER'S BRANCH, 500 Ray Lawson Blvd, L6Y 5B3, SAN
376-9658. Tel: 905-793-4636, Ext 4505. FAX: 905-453-8425. *Br Mgr,*
Julie Andrews-Jotham
Open Mon-Thurs 10-9, Fri 10-6, Sat 10-5, Sun 1-5

BRANTFORD

S   BRANT HISTORICAL SOCIETY LIBRARY*, 57 Charlotte St, N3T 2W6.
SAN 320-8788. Tel: 519-752-2483. FAX: 519-752-1931. *Exec Dir,* Joan
Kanigan-Fairen
Founded 1908
Library Holdings: Bk Titles 800
Special Collections: Brant County History Coll
Open Wed-Fri 10-4, Sat 1-4, Sun (July & Aug) 1-4

P   BRANTFORD PUBLIC LIBRARY, 173 Colborne St, N3T 2G8. SAN
319-0544. Tel: 519-756-2220. FAX: 519-756-4979. E-mail:
info@brantford.library.on.ca. Web Site: brantford.library.on.ca. *Chief Exec
Officer,* Rose Vespa; Tel: 519-756-2220, Ext 319, E-mail:
rvespa@brantford.library.on.ca; *Mgr, Access & Mat Mgt,* Alaa El-Talmas;
Tel: 519-756-2220, Ext 314, E-mail: aeltalmas@brantford.library.on.ca;
Mgr, Bus Serv, Ken Symons; Tel: 519-756-2220, Ext 320, E-mail:
ksymons@brantford.library.on.ca; *Mgr, Info & Partnership Serv,* Kathryn
Drury; Tel: 519-756-2220, Ext 309, E-mail: kdrury@brantford.library.on.ca;
Mgr, Mkt, Communications & Develop, Paula Thomlison; Tel:
519-756-2220, Ext 343, E-mail: pthomlison@brantford.library.on.ca; *Mgr,
Br & Popular Serv,* Genevieve Kwant; Tel: 519-756-2220, Ext 324, E-mail:
gkwant@brantford.library.on.ca; Staff 64 (MLS 8, Non-MLS 56)
Founded 1884. Pop 92,000; Circ 1,000,000
Library Holdings: Bk Titles 153,923; Bk Vols 189,727; Per Subs 255
Special Collections: Can & Prov
Subject Interests: Adult literacy, Local hist
Automation Activity & Vendor Info: (Acquisitions) SirsiDynix;
(Cataloging) SirsiDynix; (Circulation) SirsiDynix; (Serials) SirsiDynix
Partic in Southern Ontario Libr Serv
Open Mon-Thurs 9-9, Fri 9-6, Sat 9-5, Sun 1:30-5
Branches: 1
ST PAUL AVENUE BRANCH, 441 St Paul Ave, N3R 4N8, SAN
324-0258. Tel: 519-753-2179. FAX: 519-753-3557. *Librn,* Genevieve
Kwant
Library Holdings: Bk Titles 42,398; Bk Vols 46,379; Per Subs 65
Open Tues-Thurs 9-8, Fri & Sat 9-5

BRIDGENORTH

P SMITH-ENNISMORE-LAKEFIELD LIBRARY*, 836 Charles St, K0L 1H0. (Mail add: PO Box 2200, Lakefield, K0L 2H0), SAN 367-6021. Tel: 705-652-8623. FAX: 705-652-8878. Web Site: www.mypubliclibrary.ca. *Librn,* Jill Warren; E-mail: jwarren@mypubliclibrary.ca
Founded 1897. Pop 17,000; Circ 135,000
Library Holdings: Bk Vols 70,000
Special Collections: Local History Coll
Open Mon 1-5, Tues, Wed & Fri 10-5, Thurs 10-8, Sat 10-4

P SMITH-ENNISMORE-LAKEFIELD PUBLIC LIBRARY, Bridgenorth Library, 836 Charles St, K0L 1H0. (Mail add: PO Box 500, K0L 1H0), SAN 373-7373. Tel: 705-292-5065. FAX: 705-292-6695. *Chief Librn,* Joan MacDonald; E-mail: jmacdonald@mypubliclibrary.ca; Staff 4 (Non-MLS 4)
Founded 1972. Pop 16,420; Circ 170,000
Jan 2011-Dec 2011 Income (CAN) \$426,806, Provincial (CAN) \$37,113, Federal (CAN) \$2,155, County (CAN) \$299,014, Locally Generated Income (CAN) \$88,524. Mats Exp (CAN) \$66,473, Books (CAN) \$50,131, Per/Ser (Incl. Access Fees) (CAN) \$3,398, AV Mat (CAN) \$12,559, Electronic Ref Mat (Incl. Access Fees) (CAN) \$385. Sal (CAN) \$169,000
Library Holdings: Bk Titles 60,000; Bk Vols 69,000; Per Subs 75
Automation Activity & Vendor Info: (Acquisitions) Mandarin Library Automation; (Cataloging) Mandarin Library Automation; (Circulation) Mandarin Library Automation; (OPAC) Mandarin Library Automation
Wireless access
Partic in Southern Ontario Libr Serv
Open Mon 1-5, Tues & Thurs 1-8, Wed & Fri 10-5, Sat 10-4

BRIGHTON

P BRIGHTON PUBLIC LIBRARY*, 35 Alice St, K0K 1H0. (Mail add: PO Box 3008, K0K 1H0), SAN 319-0579. Tel: 613-475-2511. E-mail: brightonpl@gmail.com. Web Site: www.brighton.library.on.ca. *Chief Librn,* Maureen Venton; *Asst Librn,* Sharon Bugg; *Ch,* Jeni Dyment; Staff 3 (MLS 3)
Pop 10,500; Circ 140,000
Library Holdings: Bk Titles 30,000; Per Subs 72
Database Vendor: EBSCOhost
Partic in Southern Ontario Libr Serv
Open Mon-Wed & Fri 9:30-4:30, Thurs 9:30-7:30, Sat 9:30-3

BRITT

P BRITT AREA LIBRARY*, 841 Riverside Dr, P0G 1A0. (Mail add: PO Box 2, P0G 1A0), SAN 324-1211. Tel: 705-383-2292. FAX: 705-383-0077. E-mail: britt.lib@hotmail.com. Web Site: www.olsn.ca/BrittPL. *Chief Librn,* Barbara Wohleber; *Asst Librn,* Carole Laframboise; *Asst Librn,* Ann Palamar; *Computer Librn,* Alyson Marrin; *Coll Develop,* Anette Niffin; Staff 5 (Non-MLS 5)
Founded 1979. Pop 600
Library Holdings: Bk Vols 10,000; Per Subs 25
Special Collections: Canadian Aviation History
Subject Interests: Can aviation, Folk tales
Wireless access
Publications: Brochure
Open Mon-Wed & Fri 9-3, Thurs 9-3 & 7-8:30
Friends of the Library Group

P MAGNETAWAN FIRST NATION PUBLIC LIBRARY*, Ten Regional Rd & Hwy 529, P0G 1A0. SAN 372-6630. Tel: 705-383-2477. FAX: 705-383-2566. E-mail: mfnlibrary@hotmail.com. *Chief Librn,* Lee Ann Pitawanakwat; E-mail: leeann45@hotmail.com
Founded 1985. Pop 90; Circ 12,500
Library Holdings: High Interest/Low Vocabulary Bk Vols 200; Large Print Bks 100; Bk Titles 5,000; Bk Vols 7,000
Special Collections: First Nations Coll. Can & Prov; Municipal Document Depository
Subject Interests: Local hist
Automation Activity & Vendor Info: (Cataloging) Follett Software; (Circulation) Follett Software
Wireless access
Publications: Magnetawan First Nation Newsletter
Special Services for the Deaf - Bks on deafness & sign lang; Closed caption videos; Staff with knowledge of sign lang
Special Services for the Blind - Large print bks
Open Mon & Wed 12-5, Tues & Thurs 11-5

BROCKVILLE

P AUGUSTA TOWNSHIP PUBLIC LIBRARY, 4500 County Rd 15, RR 2, K6V 5T2. Tel: 613-926-2449. FAX: 613-702-0441. E-mail: augusta@augustalibrary.com. Web Site: www.augustalibrary.com. *Librn,* Angie Knights; *Librn,* Linda Parrott; Staff 1 (Non-MLS 1)
Pop 7,600; Circ 20,170

Library Holdings: Bk Vols 24,000
Wireless access
Open Mon, Tues & Thurs 1:30-5:30 & 6-8, Wed & Sat 9-1

P BROCKVILLE PUBLIC LIBRARY*, 23 Buell St, K6V 5T7. (Mail add: Box 100, K6V 5T7), SAN 319-0587. Tel: 613-342-3936. FAX: 613-342-9598. E-mail: info@brockvillelibrary.ca. Web Site: www.brockvillelibrary.ca. *Chief Librn,* Linda Chadwick; *Access Serv,* Amanda Robinson; *Pub Serv,* Maureen Wharton; Staff 11 (MLS 3, Non-MLS 8)
Founded 1903. Pop 22,000
Library Holdings: Bk Vols 70,000; Per Subs 50
Automation Activity & Vendor Info: (Acquisitions) SirsiDynix
Publications: Newsletter
Open Mon 10-1, Tues-Thurs 10-8, Fri & Sat 10-5, Sun (Sept-June) 1-5
Friends of the Library Group

J ST LAWRENCE COLLEGE LIBRARY*, Brockville Campus, 2288 Parkedale Ave, K6V 5X3. SAN 367-0473. Tel: 613-345-0660, Ext 3104. E-mail: illbrock@sl.on.ca. Web Site: home.sl.on.ca/library. *Libr Tech,* Carrie Lanigan; Staff 1 (Non-MLS 1)
Founded 1970. Enrl 500; Fac 50; Highest Degree: Doctorate
Library Holdings: AV Mats 5,000; Bk Vols 10,000; Per Subs 5,000
Subject Interests: Health sci, Law, Musical theatre
Automation Activity & Vendor Info: (Acquisitions) SirsiDynix; (Cataloging) SirsiDynix; (Circulation) SirsiDynix; (Media Booking) SirsiDynix; (OPAC) SirsiDynix
Database Vendor: EBSCOhost, OVID Technologies, ProQuest
Wireless access

BRUCE MINES

P BRUCE MINES & PLUMMER ADDITIONAL UNION PUBLIC LIBRARY*, 33 Desbarats St, P0R 1C0. (Mail add: PO Box 249, P0R 1C0), SAN 319-0609. Tel: 705-785-3370. FAX: 705-785-3370. E-mail: bmpa@ontera.net. Web Site: www.bruceminesandplummerlibrary.ca. *Chief Librn/CEO,* Lorelee Gordon
Pop 1,130; Circ 12,197
Library Holdings: AV Mats 350; Bk Titles 9,327; Talking Bks 225
Automation Activity & Vendor Info: (Cataloging) SIRSI WorkFlows; (Circulation) SIRSI WorkFlows; (OPAC) SIRSI-iBistro; (Serials) SIRSI WorkFlows
Database Vendor: Canadian Reference Centre, EBSCO Auto Repair Reference, EBSCOhost, Gale Cengage Learning, netLibrary, Overdrive, Inc
Wireless access
Function: Handicapped accessible, Homebound delivery serv, ILL available, Online searches, Photocopying/Printing, Prog for children & young adult, Summer reading prog, Telephone ref, Wheelchair accessible, Workshops
Mem of Ontario Library Service North
Open Tues & Thurs 10-7:30, Wed & Fri 11-6, Sat 10-12
Friends of the Library Group

BURK'S FALLS

P BURK'S FALLS, ARMOUR & RYERSON UNION PUBLIC LIBRARY, 39 Copeland St, P0A 1C0. (Mail add: PO Box 620, P0A 1C0), SAN 319-0617. Tel: 705-382-3327. FAX: 705-382-3327. E-mail: info@burksfallslibrary.com. Web Site: www.burksfallslibrary.com. *Chief Librn,* Nieves Guijarro; Staff 3 (Non-MLS 3)
Founded 1896. Pop 3,752
Library Holdings: Bk Vols 11,000; Per Subs 23
Special Collections: History of Burk's Falls Ontario & District
Wireless access
Open Tues & Thurs 10-8, Wed & Sat 10-3, Fri 10-5
Friends of the Library Group

BURLINGTON

P BURLINGTON PUBLIC LIBRARY*, 2331 New St, L7R 1J4. SAN 367-0538. Tel: 905-639-3611. FAX: 905-681-7277. Web Site: www.bpl.on.ca. *Chief Exec Officer,* Maureen Barry; Tel: 905-639-3611, Ext 100, E-mail: barrym@bpl.on.ca; *Dir, Serv Develop,* Andrea Gordon; *Dir, Serv Delivery,* Judy Hyland; *Mgr, Ch Serv,* Laura Williams; Tel: 905-639-3611, Ext 135, E-mail: williamsl@bpl.on.ca; *Media Spec,* Debbie Sumpter; E-mail: sumpterd@bpl.on.ca; Staff 23 (MLS 21, Non-MLS 2)
Founded 1872. Pop 170,000; Circ 1,700,000
Jan 2007-Dec 2007 Income (Main Library and Branch(s)) (CAN) \$8,588,311, Provincial (CAN) \$229,380, City (CAN) \$8,063,131, Locally Generated Income (CAN) \$295,800. Mats Exp (CAN) \$842,417. Sal (CAN) \$4,991,996
Library Holdings: Bk Titles 170,000; Bk Vols 315,000; Per Subs 285
Special Collections: Can & Prov
Automation Activity & Vendor Info: (Acquisitions) SirsiDynix; (Cataloging) SirsiDynix; (Circulation) SirsiDynix; (OPAC) BiblioCommons; (Serials) SirsiDynix

Database Vendor: Canadian Reference Centre, EBSCOhost, Electric Library, Gale Cengage Learning, netLibrary, Overdrive, Inc, SirsiDynix
Wireless access
Partic in Southern Ontario Libr Serv
Special Services for the Deaf - Bks on deafness & sign lang
Special Services for the Blind - Assistive/Adapted tech devices, equip & products; Audio mat; Bks on CD; Daisy reader; Extensive large print coll; Home delivery serv; Info on spec aids & appliances; Internet workstation with adaptive software; Large print & cassettes; Large print bks; Large screen computer & software; Low vision equip; Magnifiers; Networked computers with assistive software; Screen enlargement software for people with visual disabilities; Screen reader software; Sound rec; Talking bks; Talking bks & player equip; Text reader; Vera Arkenstone; VisualTek equip; ZoomText magnification & reading software
Open Mon-Thurs 9-9, Fri 9-6, Sat 9-5, Sun (Nov-April) 1-5
Branches: 5
ALDERSHOT, 550 Plains Rd E, L7T 2E3, SAN 367-0562. Tel: 905-333-9995. *Br Mgr,* Susan Fitzgerald-Bell
Open Tues, Wed & Fri 10-6, Thurs 10-9, Sat 9-5; Mon-Wed & Fri (Summer) 10-6, Thurs 10-9
BRANT HILLS, 2255 Brant St, L7P 5C8, SAN 367-0651. Tel: 905-335-2209. *Br Supvr,* Rosemary Minnella; E-mail: minnellar@bpl.on.ca
Open Mon-Thurs 9-9, Fri 9-6, Sat 9-5
KILBRIDE, 6611 Panton St, L0P 1G0, SAN 367-0597. Tel: 905-335-4011. *Br Supvr,* Dianne Warrick; E-mail: warrick@bpl.on.ca
Open Mon & Wed 6pm-9pm, Sat 9-Noon
NEW APPLEBY, 676 Appleby Line, L7L 5Y1, SAN 367-0627. Tel: 905-639-6373. *Br Supvr,* Dianne Warrick; E-mail: warrickd@bpl.on.ca
Open Tues, Wed & Fri 10-6, Thurs 10-9, Sat 9-5; Mon-Wed & Fri (Summer) 10-6, Thurs 10-9
TANSLEY WOODS, 1996 Itabashi Way, L7M 4J8, SAN 377-6948. Tel: 905-336-5583. FAX: 905-336-4266. *Br Mgr,* Christine Dalgetty; E-mail: dalgettyc@bpl.on.ca
Open Mon-Thurs 9-9, Fri 9-6, Sat 9-5, Sun (Nov-April) 1-5

G   CORPORATION OF THE CITY OF BURLINGTON*, Municipal Reference Centre, 426 Brant St, L7R 3Z6. (Mail add: PO Box 5013, L7R 3Z6), SAN 373-6288. Tel: 905-335-7777. FAX: 905-335-7881. E-mail: cob@burlington.ca. Web Site: www.burlington.ca. *Librn,* Wes Roberts
Founded 1986
Library Holdings: Bk Titles 250
Special Collections: Municipal Government
Restriction: Staff use only

S   ENVIRONMENT CANADA LIBRARY, BURLINGTON*, Canada Centre for Inland Waters Library, 867 Lakeshore Rd, L7R 4A6. (Mail add: PO Box 5050, L7R 4A6), SAN 319-0625. Tel: 905-336-4982. FAX: 905-336-4428. E-mail: librarybiblioburlington@ec.gc.ca. *Head of Libr,* Francesco Lai; E-mail: francesco.lai@ec.gc.ca; *Asst Librn,* Mary Orlik; Staff 3 (MLS 1, Non-MLS 2)
Founded 1967
Library Holdings: Bk Vols 3,000
Subject Interests: Fisheries, Great Lakes, Hydraulics, Hydrographic surveying, Limnology, Wastewater tech, Water pollution
Automation Activity & Vendor Info: (Cataloging) BiblioMondo; (Circulation) BiblioMondo; (OPAC) BiblioMondo; (Serials) BiblioMondo
Partic in Council of Federal Libraries Consortium; Dialog Corp
Open Mon-Fri 8-4
Restriction: Non-circulating to the pub, Open to fac, students & qualified researchers

S   HALTON DISTRICT SCHOOL BOARD, J W Singleton Education Library, 2050 Guelph Line, L7P 5A8. SAN 373-7411. Tel: 905-335-3665. FAX: 905-335-9802. Web Site: www.hdsb.ca/library. *Mgr, Instrul Media,* Lynn Wisniewski; E-mail: wisniewskil@hdsb.ca; Staff 4 (MLS 1, Non-MLS 3)
Founded 1984
Library Holdings: Electronic Media & Resources 3,500; Bk Titles 500
Automation Activity & Vendor Info: (Cataloging) Horizon; (Circulation) Horizon; (Media Booking) Horizon; (OPAC) Horizon
Database Vendor: EBSCOhost, Grolier Online
Wireless access
Function: Prof lending libr, Video lending libr
Partic in Halinet
Open Mon-Fri 8-4
Restriction: Circ limited, Circulates for staff only

S   ROYAL BOTANICAL GARDENS LIBRARY*, 680 Plains Rd W, L7T 4H4. (Mail add: PO Box 399, Hamilton, L8N 3H8), SAN 319-0633. Tel: 905-527-1158. FAX: 905-577-0375.
Founded 1946
Library Holdings: Bk Titles 14,000; Per Subs 90

Special Collections: Checklists & Registration Lists; Nursery & Seed Trade Catalogs
Subject Interests: Botany, Conserv, Natural hist, Ornamental hort

CALABOGIE

P   GREATER MADAWASKA PUBLIC LIBRARY*, 4984 Calabogie Rd, K0J 1H0. (Mail add: PO Box 160, K0J 1H0), SAN 325-0326. Tel: 613-752-2317. FAX: 613-752-2617. E-mail: library@greatermadawaska.com. Web Site: www.townshipofgreatermadawska.com/library.htm. *Chief Exec Officer, Librn,* Meriah Caswell
Founded 1978
Library Holdings: Bk Titles 9,500
Partic in Southern Ontario Libr Serv
Open Tues 1-7, Wed-Sat 9am-12:30pm

CAMBRIDGE

P   CAMBRIDGE LIBRARIES & GALLERIES, One North Sq, N1S 2K6. SAN 367-0686. Tel: 519-621-0460. FAX: 519-621-2080. Web Site: www.cambridgelibraries.ca. *Chief Librn,* Greg Hayton; E-mail: ghayton@cambridgelibraries.ca; *Ch,* Helen Kelly; E-mail: hkelly@cambridgelibraries.ca; *Ref,* Cathy Kiedrowski; E-mail: ckiedrowski@cambridgelibraries.ca
Founded 1973. Pop 132,300; Circ 1,237,088
Library Holdings: Bk Vols 135,548; Per Subs 235
Subject Interests: Local hist
Automation Activity & Vendor Info: (Acquisitions) Innovative Interfaces, Inc
Wireless access
Function: Art exhibits, Audiobks via web, AV serv, Bk reviews (Group), Bks on CD, CD-ROM, Children's prog, Citizenship assistance, Computer training, Computers for patron use, Copy machines, e-mail & chat, Electronic databases & coll, Family literacy, Free DVD rentals, Handicapped accessible, Holiday prog, Home delivery & serv to Sr ctr & nursing homes, Homebound delivery serv, ILL available, Large print keyboards, Literacy & newcomer serv, Magnifiers for reading, Mail & tel request accepted, Music CDs, Online cat, Online ref, Outreach serv, OverDrive digital audio bks, Photocopying/Printing, Prog for children & young adult, Pub access computers, Ref serv available, Senior outreach, Spoken cassettes & CDs, Spoken cassettes & DVDs, Story hour, Summer reading prog, Telephone ref, Web-catalog, Wheelchair accessible
Special Services for the Blind - Reader equip
Open Mon-Thurs 9:30-8:30, Fri & Sat 9:30-5:30, Sun 1-5
Branches: 3
CLEMENS MILL, 50 Saginaw Pkwy, N1T 1W2. (Mail add: PO Box 546, N1R 5W1), SAN 377-6778. Tel: 519-740-6294. FAX: 519-621-2080. *Br Mgr,* Greg Bester; E-mail: gbester@cambridgelibraries.ca
Library Holdings: Bk Vols 59,000
Open Mon-Thurs 12-8:30, Fri 12-5:30, Sat 9:30-5:30, Sun (Sept-June) 1-5
HESPELER, Five Tannery St E, N3C 2C1, SAN 367-0716. Tel: 519-658-4412. FAX: 519-621-2080. *Br Mgr,* Angela Caretta; E-mail: acaretta@cambridgelibraries.ca
Library Holdings: Bk Vols 50,000
Open Mon-Thurs 12-8:30, Fri 12-5:30, Sat 9:30-5:30, Sun (Sept-May) 1-5
PRESTON, 435 King St E, N3H 3N1, SAN 367-0740. Tel: 519-653-3632. FAX: 519-621-2080. *Br Mgr,* Ruth Germann; E-mail: rgermann@cambridgelibraries.ca
Library Holdings: Bk Vols 60,000
Open Mon-Thurs 12-8:30, Fri 12-5:30, Sat 9:30-5:30, Sun (Sept-May) 1-5

R   HERITAGE COLLEGE & SEMINARY LIBRARY, 175 Holiday Inn Dr, N3C 3T2. SAN 322-6468. Tel: 519-651-2869. Interlibrary Loan Service Tel: 519-651-2869, Ext 216. Reference Tel: 519-651-2869, Ext 215. FAX: 519-651-2870. E-mail: library@heritage-theo.edu. *Librn,* Jenny A Griffin; E-mail: jgriffin@heritage-theo.edu; Staff 3 (MLS 1, Non-MLS 2)
Founded 1976. Enrl 350; Fac 32; Highest Degree: Master
Library Holdings: Bk Titles 43,000; Per Subs 175
Special Collections: Old Elementary; Pre-1900 Baptist Periodicals; Works by & about John Bunyan
Subject Interests: Anabaptists, Baptist hist, Puritans
Automation Activity & Vendor Info: (Cataloging) SirsiDynix; (Circulation) SirsiDynix; (OPAC) SirsiDynix

CARDINAL

P   EDWARDSBURGH/CARDINAL PUBLIC LIBRARY, Cardinal Branch, 618 County Rd 2, K0E 1E0. Tel: 613-657-3822. E-mail: cardinallibrary@bellnet.ca. Web Site: cardinallibrary.ca. *Head Librn,* Margaret Ann Gaylord

Library Holdings: CDs 300; DVDs 50; Large Print Bks 200; Bk Titles 20,000; Per Subs 15
Database Vendor: Brodart, Canadian Reference Centre, EBSCOhost, Sage
Wireless access
Function: Wheelchair accessible
Open Mon & Wed 6:30pm-9pm, Tues & Thurs 1:30-4:30, Sat 9:30-Noon
Friends of the Library Group
Branches: 1
SPENCERVILLE BRANCH, Five Henderson St, Spencerville, K0E 1X0. (Mail add: Box 130, Spencerville, K0E 1X0), SAN 319-4264. Tel: 613-658-5575. FAX: 613-658-5575. E-mail: library@spencerville.ca. Web Site: www.spencervillelibrary.ca. *Head Librn,* Kathy Colwell
Pop 4,397; Circ 9,706
Library Holdings: Bk Vols 10,000; Per Subs 24
Partic in Southern Ontario Libr Serv
Open Tues-Thurs 2-5 & 7-9, Sat 9:30-1
Friends of the Library Group

CARLETON PLACE

P   CARLETON PLACE PUBLIC LIBRARY*, 101 Beckwith St, K7C 2T3. SAN 319-0706. Tel: 613-257-2702. E-mail: carletonlibdsl@vianet.ca. *Librn,* Janet French-Baril; Staff 5 (Non-MLS 5)
Founded 1846. Pop 9,000
Library Holdings: Bk Vols 52,000; Per Subs 70
Partic in Southern Ontario Libr Serv
Open Mon-Thurs 2:30pm-9pm, Fri 9:30-5:30, Sat 10-5

CHAPLEAU

P   CHAPLEAU PUBLIC LIBRARY*, 20 Pine St, P0M 1K0. (Mail add: PO Box 910, P0M 1K0), SAN 319-0757. Tel: 705-864-0852. FAX: 705-864-0295. E-mail: plchapleau@post.library.on.ca. Web Site: www.chapleaucapsite.zoomshare.com. *Chief Librn,* Maureen Travis
Pop 2,800; Circ 35,104
Library Holdings: DVDs 400; Bk Titles 16,944; Per Subs 35; Talking Bks 85; Videos 200
Wireless access
Function: Bks on cassette, Bks on CD, Computer training, Computers for patron use, Copy machines, e-mail serv, Fax serv, Handicapped accessible, ILL available, VHS videos
Open Mon, Tues & Thurs 12-8, Wed & Fri 1-5
Friends of the Library Group

CHATHAM

P   CHATHAM-KENT PUBLIC LIBRARY, 120 Queen St, N7M 2G6. SAN 319-0765. Tel: 519-354-2940. Administration Tel: 519-354-7352. FAX: 519-354-7366. Administration FAX: 519-354-2602. E-mail: cklibrary@chatham-kent.ca. Web Site: chatham-kent.ca/library. *Dir of Libr,* Kathryn Goodhue; E-mail: kathryng@chatham-kent.ca; *Coll Develop Librn,* Arlene Maris; E-mail: arlenem@chatham-kent.ca; *Mgr, Pub Serv,* Tania Sharpe; E-mail: tanias@chatham-kent.ca; *Admin Serv,* Kim Lachine-Caron; E-mail: kiml@chatham-kent.ca; *ILL,* Barbara Lyszak; E-mail: barbaral@chatham-kent.ca; Staff 9 (MLS 9)
Founded 1890. Pop 104,000; Circ 803,767
Library Holdings: Bk Vols 304,638
Special Collections: Local Hist (Hist of City of Chatham & Kent County & the Underground Railway), bks, microflm
Automation Activity & Vendor Info: (Acquisitions) SirsiDynix; (Cataloging) SirsiDynix; (Circulation) SirsiDynix; (OPAC) SirsiDynix
Database Vendor: SirsiDynix
Wireless access
Open Mon-Thurs 9:30-8:30, Fri 9:30-6, Sat 9:30-5
Friends of the Library Group
Branches: 11
BLENHEIM BRANCH, 16 George St, Blenheim, N0P 1A0. (Mail add: PO Box 1979, Blenheim, N0P 1A0), SAN 367-0805. Tel: 519-676-3174. FAX: 519-676-2304.
Open Tues & Thurs 12-8, Wed & Fri 10-3, Sat 12-4
BOTHWELL BRANCH, 320 Main St, Bothwell, N0P 1C0, SAN 367-083X. Tel: 519-695-2844. FAX: 519-695-5079. *Br Head,* Nell Evans; Staff 1 (Non-MLS 1)
Open Tues & Thurs 3-8, Fri & Sat 10-1
DRESDEN BRANCH, 187 Brown St, Dresden, N0P 1M0, SAN 367-0864. Tel: 519-683-4922. FAX: 519-683-1857. *Br Head,* Tamar Malic; Staff 2 (Non-MLS 2)
Open Tues & Thurs 12-8, Wed 12-5, Fri 10-3, Sat 10-2
Friends of the Library Group
, 780 Ross Line, Erieau, N0P 1N0, SAN 376-1061. Tel: 519-676-3945. *Br Coordr,* MaryAnn Wright
Open Mon & Tues 10-3, Thurs 1-7
HIGHGATE BRANCH, 291 King St, Highgate, N0P 1T0, SAN 367-0899. Tel: 519-678-3313. FAX: 519-678-3313. *Br Head,* Cathy Hill; Staff 1 (Non-MLS 1)
Open Mon & Wed 3-8, Fri 10-3

MERLIN BRANCH, 13 Aberdeen St, Merlin, N0P 1W0, SAN 367-0929. Tel: 519-689-4944. *Br Head,* Tracy Morton; Staff 1 (Non-MLS 1)
Open Tues 2-5 & 6-8, Thurs 3-5 & 6-8, Fri 2-5, Sat 10-2
RIDGETOWN BRANCH, 54 Main St, Ridgetown, N0P 2C0, SAN 367-0953. Tel: 519-674-3121. *Br Head,* Vera Todd-Roberts; Staff 3 (Non-MLS 3)
Open Mon & Fri 12-5, Tues & Thurs 12-8, Sat 10-2
Friends of the Library Group
THAMESVILLE BRANCH, Three London Rd, Thamesville, N0P 2K0, SAN 367-0988. Tel: 519-692-4251. FAX: 519-692-5915. *Br Head,* Deborah Kennedy; Staff 1 (Non-MLS 1)
Open Tues & Thurs 1-5, Wed 4-8, Sat 10-2
TILBURY BRANCH, Two Queen St, Tilbury, N0P 2L0. (Mail add: PO Box 999, Tilbury, N0P 2L0), SAN 367-1011. Tel: 519-682-0100. *Br Head,* Jone Dalgleish; Staff 3 (Non-MLS 3)
Open Mon & Fri 12-5, Tues & Thurs 12-8, Sat 10-2
WALLACEBURG BRANCH, 209 James St, Wallaceburg, N8A 2N4, SAN 367-1046. Tel: 519-627-5292. FAX: 519-627-3039. *Br Head,* Susan Handsor; Staff 4 (Non-MLS 4)
Subject Interests: Genealogy, Local hist
Open Mon & Wed 10-6, Tues & Thurs 12-8, Fri & Sat 10-5
WHEATLEY BRANCH, 35 Talbot St W, Wheatley, N0P 2P0, SAN 367-1070. Tel: 519-825-7131. FAX: 519-825-7537. *Br Head,* Claudette Sykes; Staff 1 (Non-MLS 1)
Open Tues & Thurs 4-8, Wed & Sat 10-2

J   ST CLAIR COLLEGE*, Thames Campus Library Resource Centre, 1001 Grand Ave W, N7M 5W4. SAN 324-167X. Tel: 519-354-9100, Ext 3232, 519-354-9100, Ext 3273. FAX: 519-354-5496. Web Site: www.stclaircollege.ca. *Tech Serv,* Jeanette Giroux; E-mail: jgiroux@stclaircollege.ca; *Tech Serv,* Cheryl Smith; E-mail: csmith@stclaircollege.ca
Library Holdings: Bk Vols 10,000; Per Subs 90
Wireless access
Open Mon-Thurs 7:30am-9pm, Fri 7:30-4, Sat 9-3

CLINTON

P   HURON COUNTY LIBRARY*, Administration Office, 77722B London Rd, N0M 1L0. (Mail add: RR 5, N0M 1L0), SAN 367-2638. Tel: 519-482-5457. FAX: 519-482-7820. E-mail: admin@huroncounty.ca. Web Site: www.huroncounty.ca. *County Librn,* Meighan Wark; *Dep Librn,* Sharon Cox; *ILL,* Katie Schedlich; Staff 2 (MLS 2)
Founded 1967. Pop 59,068; Circ 358,327
Library Holdings: Bk Titles 148,225; Bk Vols 250,462; Per Subs 2,694
Special Collections: Canadiana. Can & Prov
Automation Activity & Vendor Info: (Acquisitions) SirsiDynix; (Cataloging) SirsiDynix; (Circulation) SirsiDynix; (OPAC) SirsiDynix
Database Vendor: EBSCOhost
Wireless access
Partic in Southern Ontario Libr Serv
Open Mon-Fri 8:30-4:30
Friends of the Library Group
Branches: 11
BAYFIELD BRANCH, 20 Main St, Bayfield, N0M 1G0. (Mail add: PO Box 2090, Bayfield, N0M 1G0), SAN 367-2697. Tel: 519-565-2886. E-mail: bayfieldlibrary@huroncounty.ca. *Br Mgr,* Helen Gianoulis; Tel: 519-524-9261; *Br Asst,* Anny Johnston; E-mail: ajohnston@huroncounty.ca
Special Collections: Local History
Open Mon & Fri 1-5, Tues 10-12 & 1-5, Wed & Thurs 1-5 & 6-8, Sat 10-2
Friends of the Library Group
BLYTH BRANCH, 435 Queen St, Blyth, N0M 1H0. (Mail add: PO Box 388, Blyth, N0M 1H0), SAN 367-2816. Tel: 519-523-4400. E-mail: blythlibrary@huroncounty.ca. *Br Mgr,* Paula Mackie
Library Holdings: Bk Vols 3,000
Open Tues & Thurs 1-5 & 6pm-8pm, Fri & Sat 10-2
Friends of the Library Group
BRUSSELS BRANCH, 402 Turnberry St, Brussels, N0G 1H0. (Mail add: PO Box 80, Brussels, N0G 1H0), SAN 367-2875. Tel: 519-887-6448. E-mail: brusselslibrary@huroncounty.ca. *Br Mgr,* Anne Dodington
Open Tues & Thurs 1-5 & 6pm-8pm, Fri & Sat 10-2
CLINTON BRANCH, 27 Albert St, N0M 1L0. (Mail add: PO Box 370, N0M 1L0), SAN 367-2905. Tel: 519-482-3673. E-mail: clintonlibrary@huroncounty.ca. *Br Mgr,* Michelle Carter; *Asst Br Mgr,* Sally Van Doornik
Open Mon, Tues & Thurs 1-8, Fri 10-5, Wed & Sat 10-2, Sun (Winter) 1-5
EXETER BRANCH, 330 Main St, Exeter, N0M 1S6. (Mail add: PO Box 609, Exeter, N0M 1S6), SAN 367-3081. Tel: 519-235-1890. E-mail: exeterlibrary@huroncounty.ca. *Br Mgr,* Jane Hundey
Open Mon, Tues & Thurs 1-8, Wed, Fri & Sat 10-5, Sun (Winter) 1-5
Friends of the Library Group

GODERICH BRANCH, 52 Montreal St, Goderich, N7A 2G4, SAN 367-3146. Tel: 519-524-9261. E-mail: goderichlibrary@huroncounty.ca. *Br Mgr,* Helen Gianoulis
Open Mon-Fri 10-8, Sat 10-5, Sun (Winter) 1-5
Friends of the Library Group

HENSALL BRANCH, 108 King St, Hensall, N0M 1X0. (Mail add: PO Box 249, Hensall, N0M 1X0), SAN 367-3200. Tel: 519-262-2445. E-mail: hensalllibrary@huroncounty.ca. *Br Mgr,* Anne Dodington
Open Tues & Thurs 1-5 & 6pm-8pm, Wed & Sat 10-2
Friends of the Library Group

KIRKTON BRANCH, 70497 Perth Rd 164, Kirkton, N0K 1K0. (Mail add: RR 1, Kirkton, N0K 1X0), SAN 367-326X. Tel: 519-229-8854. E-mail: kirktonlibrary@huroncounty.ca. *Br Mgr,* Jane Hundey; *Br Asst,* Cheryl Rau
Open Tues 10-12 & 1-5, Thurs 1-5 & 6pm-8pm, Sat 9-Noon
Friends of the Library Group

SEAFORTH BRANCH, 108 Main St S, Seaforth, N0K 1W0. (Mail add: PO Box 490, Seaforth, N0K 1W0), SAN 367-3383. Tel: 519-527-1430. E-mail: seaforthlibrary@huroncounty.ca. *Br Mgr,* Anne Dodington
Open Mon, Tues & Thurs 1-8, Wed & Sat 10-2, Fri 10-5, Sun (Winter) 1-5

WINGHAM BRANCH, 281 Edward St, Wingham, N0G 2W0. (Mail add: PO Box 280, Wingham, N0G 2W0), SAN 367-3448. Tel: 519-357-3312. E-mail: winghamlibrary@huroncounty.ca. *Br Mgr,* Paula Mackie
Open Tues-Thurs 10-8, Fri 10-5, Sat 10-3, Sun (Winter) 1-5
Friends of the Library Group

ZURICH BRANCH, 50 Main St, Zurich, N0M 2T0. (Mail add: PO Box 201, Zurich, N0M 2T0), SAN 367-3472. Tel: 519-236-4965. E-mail: zurichlibrary@huroncounty.ca. *Br Mgr,* Michelle Carter
Open Tues & Thurs 1-5 & 6-8, Fri & Sat 10-2
Friends of the Library Group

COBALT

P   COBALT PUBLIC LIBRARY*, 30 Lang St, P0J 1C0. (Mail add: PO Box 170, P0J 1C0), SAN 319-0803. Tel: 705-679-8120. FAX: 705-679-8120. E-mail: cobaltlibrary@ontera.net. Web Site: www.cobaltlibrary.com. *Chief Exec Officer,* Margaret Leaper
Founded 1961. Pop 1,200; Circ 13,000
Library Holdings: DVDs 500; Large Print Bks 1,500; Bk Vols 12,000; Per Subs 32; Talking Bks 80; Videos 500
Automation Activity & Vendor Info: (Acquisitions) LiBRARYSOFT; (Cataloging) LiBRARYSOFT; (Circulation) LiBRARYSOFT; (OPAC) LiBRARYSOFT
Wireless access
Function: Audio & video playback equip for onsite use, Bks on cassette, Bks on CD, Computers for patron use, Copy machines, e-mail & chat, Fax serv, Free DVD rentals, Govt ref serv, Homebound delivery serv, ILL available, Mail & tel request accepted, Online ref, Online searches, Photocopying/Printing, Ref serv available, Scanner, VHS videos
Mem of Ontario Library Service North
Open Mon-Fri (Summer) 12:30-5:30, Sat 2-5; Mon, Wed & Fri (Winter) 12:30-5:30, Tues & Thurs 2-8, Sat 2-5

COBOURG

P   COBOURG PUBLIC LIBRARY, 200 Ontario St, K9A 5P4. SAN 319-0811. Tel: 905-372-9271. FAX: 905-372-4538. E-mail: info@cobourg.library.on.ca. Web Site: www.cobourg.library.on.ca. *Chief Exec Officer,* Charmaine Lindsay; Tel: 905-372-9271, Ext 6200, E-mail: clindsay@cobourg.library.on.ca; *Youth Serv Coordr,* Rhonda Perry; *Access Serv,* Heather Viscount; Staff 5 (MLS 2, Non-MLS 3)
Founded 1886. Pop 28,000; Circ 261,969
Jan 2011-Dec 2011 Income (CAN) $1,001,561. Mats Exp (CAN) $129,129. Sal (CAN) $572,314
Library Holdings: Bk Titles 61,948; Bk Vols 67,762; Per Subs 104
Subject Interests: Local hist
Automation Activity & Vendor Info: (Acquisitions) Horizon
Database Vendor: EBSCOhost, LearningExpress, World Book Online
Wireless access
Partic in Southern Ontario Libr Serv
Open Mon-Wed 10-8, Thurs-Sat 10-5, Sun 1-5

COCHRANE

P   COCHRANE PUBLIC LIBRARY*, 178 Fourth Ave, P0L 1C0. (Mail add: PO Box 700, P0L 1C0), SAN 319-082X. Tel: 705-272-4178. FAX: 705-272-4165. E-mail: library@town.cochrane.on.ca. Web Site: www.olsn.ca/cochrane. *Chief Exec Officer,* Christina Blazecka; Staff 1 (Non-MLS 1)
Founded 1921. Pop 5,500; Circ 38,415
Library Holdings: CDs 20; DVDs 230; Large Print Bks 497; Bk Vols 28,326; Per Subs 89; Talking Bks 202; Videos 465
Special Collections: Local History & Genealogy Coll
Automation Activity & Vendor Info: (Acquisitions) Follett Software; (Cataloging) Follett Software; (OPAC) Follett Software

Function: Archival coll, Art exhibits, Bks on cassette, Bks on CD, CD-ROM, Children's prog, Computer training, Computers for patron use, Copy machines, E-Reserves, Electronic databases & coll, Exhibits, Family literacy, Fax serv, Free DVD rentals, Handicapped accessible, Holiday prog, Home delivery & serv to Sr ctr & nursing homes, Homebound delivery serv, Homework prog, ILL available, Large print keyboards, Magnifiers for reading, Music CDs, Online cat, Photocopying/Printing, Pub access computers, Ref & res, Ref serv in person, Senior computer classes, Serves mentally handicapped consumers, Story hour, Summer reading prog, Teen prog, VHS videos, Wheelchair accessible, Winter reading prog
Partic in Ont Libr Serv-North
Open Mon (Summer) 1-8, Tues & Thurs 10-4:30, Wed & Fri 10-8, Sat 9-3; Mon (Winter) 1-8, Tues, Thurs & Sat 10-5, Wed & Fri 10-8
Friends of the Library Group

COE HILL

P   WOLLASTON & LIMERICK PUBLIC LIBRARY*, Main St, K0L 1P0. (Mail add: PO Box 280, K0L 1P0), SAN 319-0838. Tel: 613-337-5183. FAX: 613-337-5183. E-mail: coehilllibrary@bellnet.ca. Web Site: www.wollaston-limericklibrary.ca. *Librn,* Bonnie Weise
Pop 1,487; Circ 10,599
Library Holdings: Bk Vols 6,000
Partic in Southern Ontario Libr Serv
Open Tues-Fri 1-6

COLBORNE

P   TOWNSHIP OF CRAMAHE PUBLIC LIBRARY*, Colborne Branch, Six King St, K0K 1S0. (Mail add: PO Box 190, K0K 1S0), SAN 319-0846. Tel: 905-355-3722. FAX: 905-355-3430. E-mail: colblib@cramahetownship.ca. Web Site: www.colbornecap.com. *Chief Librn,* Lorna Houston
Founded 1914. Pop 3,200; Circ 15,029
Library Holdings: Bk Vols 10,000
Subject Interests: Local hist of Colborne
Function: Homebound delivery serv
Publications: History of Colborne

COLDWATER

P   COLDWATER MEMORIAL PUBLIC LIBRARY*, 31 Coldwater Rd, L0K 1E0. (Mail add: PO Box 278, L0K 1E0), SAN 319-0854. Tel: 705-686-3601. FAX: 705-686-3741. E-mail: library@coldwater.library.on.ca. Web Site: www.coldwater.library.on.ca. *Librn,* Heather Walker
Pop 11,000; Circ 9,319
Library Holdings: Bk Vols 19,000; Per Subs 20
Partic in Southern Ontario Libr Serv
Open Mon 1-5, Tues & Thurs 10-12, 1-5 & 7-9, Fri & Sat 9-Noon

COLLINGWOOD

P   COLLINGWOOD PUBLIC LIBRARY, 55 St Marie St, L9Y 0W6. SAN 319-0862. Tel: 705-445-1571. FAX: 705-445-3704. Web Site: www.collingwoodpubliclibrary.ca. *Dir of Libr Serv,* Lynda Reid; Tel: 705-445-1571, Ext 6223, E-mail: lried@collingwoodpubliclibrary.ca; *Supvr, Ch Serv,* Ashley Kulchycki; Tel: 705-445-1571, Ext 6234, E-mail: akulchycki@collingwoodpubliclibrary.ca; *AV,* Ruth Branget; Tel: 705-445-1571, Ext 6224, E-mail: rbranget@collingwoodpubliclibrary.ca; *Pub Relations,* Position Currently Open; *Ref,* Keith Tippin; Tel: 705-445-1571, Ext 6227, E-mail: ktippin@collingwoodpubliclibrary.ca; *Tech Serv,* Karen Berry; Tel: 705-445-1571, Ext 6231, E-mail: kberry@collingwoodpubliclibrary.ca; Staff 13 (MLS 1, Non-MLS 12)
Pop 18,000; Circ 162,066
Library Holdings: CDs 2,471; DVDs 673; Large Print Bks 1,977; Bk Titles 65,352; Bk Vols 74,999; Per Subs 128; Talking Bks 324; Videos 3,199
Special Collections: Municipal Document Depository
Subject Interests: Genealogy, Local hist
Automation Activity & Vendor Info: (Acquisitions) SirsiDynix; (Cataloging) SirsiDynix; (Circulation) SirsiDynix; (OPAC) SirsiDynix
Wireless access
Partic in Southern Ontario Libr Serv
Open Mon-Thurs 10-9, Fri 10-8, Sat 10-5, Sun 1-4
Friends of the Library Group

CONSECON

P   COUNTY OF PRINCE EDWARD LIBRARIES*, Consecon Branch, 211 County Rd 29, K0K 1T0. (Mail add: PO Box 130, K0K 1T0). Tel: 613-392-1106. FAX: 613-392-4461. E-mail: consecon@peclibrary.org. *Librn,* Dianne Cranshaw
Founded 1926
Library Holdings: Bk Vols 10,000
Open Wed 12-7, Fri-Sat 10-3

COOKSTOWN

P   INNISFIL PUBLIC LIBRARY*, Cookstown Branch, 20 Church St, L0L
1L0. SAN 319-0870. Tel: 705-458-1273. Interlibrary Loan Service Tel:
705-436-1681. FAX: 705-458-1294. E-mail:
cookstown.branch@innisfil.library.on.ca. Web Site:
www.innisfil.library.on.ca. *Librn,* Susan Baues
Pop 1,500; Circ 45,000
Library Holdings: Bk Vols 15,000; Per Subs 25
Open Tues & Thurs 1-8, Wed 10-8, Fri 10-5, Sat 10-3
Friends of the Library Group

CORNWALL

P   CORNWALL PUBLIC LIBRARY, 45 Second St E, K6H 1Y2. (Mail add:
PO Box 939, K6H 5V1), SAN 319-0889. Tel: 613-932-4796. FAX:
613-932-2715. E-mail: generalmail@library.cornwall.on.ca. Web Site:
www.library.cornwall.on.ca. *Chief Exec Officer, Chief Librn,* Dawn Kiddell;
Staff 30 (MLS 4, Non-MLS 26)
Founded 1895. Pop 46,349; Circ 275,590
Library Holdings: Bk Titles 114,000; Bk Vols 140,000; Per Subs 196
Automation Activity & Vendor Info: (Acquisitions) Polaris Library
Systems; (Circulation) Polaris Library Systems; (ILL) Fretwell-Downing;
(OPAC) Polaris Library Systems; (Serials) Polaris Library Systems
Database Vendor: Baker & Taylor, EBSCOhost, Gale Cengage Learning,
Overdrive, Inc, TumbleBookLibrary, World Book Online
Wireless access
Function: Accessibility serv available based on individual needs, Adult bk
club, After school storytime, Audiobks via web, Bk club(s), Bks on
cassette, Bks on CD, Chess club, Children's prog, Computer training, Copy
machines, Digital talking bks, e-mail & chat, e-mail serv, Electronic
databases & coll, Family literacy, Fax serv, Free DVD rentals, Handicapped
accessible, Homebound delivery serv, Homework prog, ILL available,
Large print keyboards, Magnifiers for reading, Mail & tel request accepted,
Microfiche/film & reading machines, Music CDs, Newsp ref libr, Online
ref, Orientations, OverDrive digital audio bks, Photocopying/Printing,
Preschool outreach, Preschool reading prog, Prog for adults, Prog for
children & young adult, Pub access computers, Ref serv available,
Telephone ref
Special Services for the Deaf - Bks on deafness & sign lang; High
interest/low vocabulary bks
Special Services for the Blind - Accessible computers; Daisy reader; Large
print & cassettes; Large print bks; Magnifiers; Talking bk serv referral;
ZoomText magnification & reading software
Open Mon-Thurs 9-8:30, Fri & Sat 9:30-5, Sun (Sept-May) 12-4
Friends of the Library Group

G   PARKS CANADA - ONTARIO SERVICE CENTRE LIBRARY*, 111
Water St E, K6H 6S3. SAN 321-1274. Tel: 613-938-5786. FAX:
613-938-5766. E-mail: biblio-cso.library-osc@pc.gc.ca. *Librn,* Joan M
Lipscombe; Tel: 613-938-5787; Staff 1 (MLS 1)
Founded 1972
Subject Interests: Archaeology, Can hist, Can mil hist, Ecology, Glass,
Historic sites pottery, Nat parks, Natural hist

C   ST LAWRENCE COLLEGE LIBRARY*, Cornwall Campus, Two Saint
Lawrence Dr, K6H 4Z1. SAN 319-0897. Tel: 613-933-6080, Ext 2701.
Web Site: www.sl.on.ca/services/library/links.htm. *Librn,* Jill Baker; *Libr
Tech,* Jessica Dubois; Staff 1 (MLS 1)
Founded 1967
Library Holdings: Bk Vols 10,000; Per Subs 51; Videos 600
Subject Interests: Behav sci, Soc sci
Automation Activity & Vendor Info: (Circulation) SirsiDynix; (OPAC)
SirsiDynix
Wireless access
Open Mon-Thurs 8am-9pm, Fri 8-6, Sat 10-2

P   STORMONT, DUNDAS & GLENGARRY COUNTY LIBRARY*, 26 Pitt
St, K6J 3P2. SAN 367-1100. Tel: 613-936-8777. Administration Tel:
613-936-8777, Ext 226. FAX: 613-936-2532. E-mail:
generalinfo@sdglibrary.ca. Web Site: www.sdglibrary.ca. *Mgr, Libr Serv,*
Pamela Haley; E-mail: phaley@sdglibrary.ca; *Serv Delivery Librn,* Karen
Franklin; Tel: 613-936-8777, Ext 211, E-mail: kfranklin@sdglibrary.ca;
Cat/Acq Tech, Bernice Gauthier; Tel: 613-936-8777, Ext 213, E-mail:
bgauthier@sdglibrary.ca; *Cat/Acq Tech,* Maureen Stephens; Tel:
613-936-8777, Ext 225, E-mail: mstephens@sdglibrary.ca; Staff 52 (MLS
2, Non-MLS 50)
Founded 1971. Pop 64,000; Circ 210,614
Jan 2010-Dec 2010 Income (Main Library and Branch(s)) (CAN)
$1,761,946, Provincial (CAN) $132,000, County (CAN) $1,365,596,
Locally Generated Income (CAN) $264,350. Mats Exp (CAN) $280,000,
Books (CAN) $102,000, Per/Ser (Incl. Access Fees) (CAN) $28,000, AV
Mat (CAN) $15,000, Electronic Ref Mat (Incl. Access Fees) (CAN)
$35,000. Sal (CAN) $1,149,636 (Prof (CAN) $80,943)

Library Holdings: Audiobooks 317; AV Mats 2,050; CDs 845; DVDs
1,046; e-books 50; Electronic Media & Resources 21; Large Print Bks
3,193; Bk Titles 110,000; Bk Vols 172,000; Per Subs 390
Special Collections: Local History Coll. Can & Prov
Automation Activity & Vendor Info: (Acquisitions) Polaris Library
Systems; (Cataloging) Polaris Library Systems; (Circulation) Polaris
Library Systems; (OPAC) Polaris Library Systems; (Serials) EBSCO
Online
Database Vendor: Booklist Online, Canadian Reference Centre,
CEDROM-SNi, EBSCO Auto Repair Reference, EBSCOhost, Gale
Cengage Learning, Overdrive, Inc, ProQuest, SerialsSolutions
Wireless access
Function: Adult bk club, After school storytime, Audio & video playback
equip for onsite use, Audiobks via web, Bk club(s), Bks on CD, CD-ROM,
Children's prog, Computer training, Computers for patron use, Copy
machines, Digital talking bks, e-mail & chat, Electronic databases & coll,
Equip loans & repairs, Exhibits, Family literacy, Fax serv, Games & aids
for the handicapped, Holiday prog, Home delivery & serv to Sr ctr &
nursing homes, Homebound delivery serv, Homework prog, ILL available,
Large print keyboards, Mail & tel request accepted, Mail loans to mem,
Mus passes, Online cat, Online ref, Online searches, Orientations, Outreach
serv, Outside serv via phone, mail, e-mail & web, OverDrive digital audio
bks, Photocopying/Printing, Prog for adults, Prog for children & young
adult, Pub access computers, Ref serv available, Ref serv in person,
Scanner, Senior computer classes, Senior outreach, Serves mentally
handicapped consumers, Spoken cassettes & CDs, Spoken cassettes &
DVDs, Story hour, Summer reading prog, Teen prog, Telephone ref, Video
lending libr
Publications: Assorted Subject/Services (Consumer guide); SDG Navigator
(Quarterly)
Partic in Knowledge Ontario
Special Services for the Deaf - Accessible learning ctr; Bks on deafness &
sign lang; Closed caption videos
Special Services for the Blind - Accessible computers; Assistive/Adapted
tech devices, equip & products; Audio mat; Bks on CD; Computer access
aids; Computer with voice synthesizer for visually impaired persons;
Copier with enlargement capabilities; Daisy reader; Digital talking bk;
Extensive large print coll; Home delivery serv; Internet workstation with
adaptive software; Playaways (bks on MP3); Recorded bks; Screen
enlargement software for people with visual disabilities; Screen reader
software; Sub-lending agent for Braille Inst Libr; Talking bks; Talking bks
& player equip; Text reader
Restriction: Circ to mem only, Lending limited to county residents,
Non-resident fee
Friends of the Library Group
Branches: 18
ALEXANDRIA BRANCH, 170A MacDonald Blvd, Alexandria, K0C 1A0,
SAN 377-6913. Tel: 613-525-3241. FAX: 613-525-2034. *Serv Delivery
Tech,* Darlene Atkins; Staff 3 (Non-MLS 3)
Open Tues-Thurs 10-8, Fri 1-4, Sat 10-1
Friends of the Library Group
AVONMORE BRANCH, 16301 Fairview Dr, Avonmore, K0C 1C0, SAN
377-693X. Tel: 613-346-2137.
Open Tues 3-8, Wed & Sat 10-1, Thurs 4-8
CHESTERVILLE BRANCH, One Mill St, Chesterville, K0C 1H0, SAN
377-6972. Tel: 613-448-2616. *Br Support,* Kelly DeJong
Open Tues 3-8, Wed 10-2, Thurs 5-8, Sat 10-1
CRYSLER BRANCH, 16 Third St, Crysler, K0C 1G0, SAN 377-6999. Tel:
613-987-2090. *Br Support,* Jenna LaMarche
Open Tues 3-8, Wed & Sat 10-1, Thurs 4-8
DALKEITH BRANCH, 1835 County Rd No 23, Dalkeith, K0B 1E0, SAN
377-7006. Tel: 613-874-2337. *Br Support,* Helen Kaufmann
Open Tues & Thurs 4-8, Wed 10-2, Sat 10-1
FINCH BRANCH, 17A George St, Finch, K0C 1K0, SAN 377-7022. Tel:
613-984-2807. *Br Support,* Peggy Pollock
Open Mon & Wed 9-1, Tues & Thurs 10-8, Fri 1-4, Sat 10-1
INGLESIDE BRANCH, Ten Memorial Sq, Ingleside, K0C 1M0, SAN
377-7065. Tel: 613-537-2592. *Br Support,* Linda Prieur
Open Mon 4-9, Tues 9-7, Wed 10-8, Thurs 4-8, Fri 1-4, Sat 10-1
IROQUOIS BRANCH, One Dundas St & Elizabeth St, Iroquois, K0E 1K0.
Tel: 613-652-4377. *Br Support,* Catherine Francis; *Br Support,* Eleanor
Piertsma
Open Tues & Thurs 3-8, Wed 10-2, Fri 1-4, Sat 10-1
LANCASTER BRANCH, (Main St) 195 Military St, Lancaster, K0C 1N0,
SAN 377-7081. Tel: 613-347-2311. FAX: 613-347-9088. *Br Support,*
Tara Anderson; *Br Support,* Leni Kraska
Open Mon 9-1, Tues 10-8, Wed 4-9, Thurs 3-8, Fri 1-4, Sat 10-1
LONG SAULT BRANCH, 50 Milles Roches Rd (Fire Hall), Long Sault,
K0C 1P0, SAN 377-712X. Tel: 613-534-2605. FAX: 613-534-4641. *Br
Support,* Mrs Chris Denis
Open Tues & Thurs 10-8, Wed 4-8, Fri 1-4, Sat 10-1
Friends of the Library Group

MAXVILLE BRANCH, Two Spring St, Maxville, K0C 1T0, SAN 377-7146. Tel: 613-527-2235. *Br Support,* Position Currently Open
Open Tues 3-8, Wed & Sat 10-1, Thurs 4-8
Friends of the Library Group
MOREWOOD BRANCH, 21 Russel St, Morewood, K0A 2R0, SAN 377-7189. Tel: 613-448-3822. *Br Support,* Ruth Gilwood
Open Tues 3-8, Wed & Sat 10-1, Thurs 4-8
MORRISBURG BRANCH, 28 Ottawa St (Arena SE), Morrisburg, K0C 1X0, SAN 377-7200. Tel: 613-543-3384. FAX: 613-543-2427. *Br Support,* Catherine Francis; *Br Support,* Peggy Hawn; *Br Support,* Beverley Richmire
Open Mon 4-9, Tues-Thurs 10-8, Wed 9-1, Fri 1-4, Sat 10-1
ST ANDREWS BRANCH, 17283 Raisin River Heritage Centre, County Rd 18, Saint Andrews, K0C 2A0, SAN 377-7014. Tel: 613-932-6012. *Br Support,* Millie Wheeler
Open Tues & Thurs 4-8, Wed 10-2, Sat 10-1
SOUTH MOUNTAIN BRANCH, Main St, South Mountain, K0E 1W0, SAN 377-7057. Tel: 613-989-2199. *Br Support,* Peggy Hawn
Open Tues 5-8, Wed 10-2, Thurs 3-8, Sat 10-1
Friends of the Library Group
WILLIAMSBURG BRANCH, 4296 Main St (Hwy 31), Williamsburg, K0C 2H0, SAN 377-7073. Tel: 613-535-2185. *Br Support,* Beverley Richmire
Open Tues-Thurs 4-8, Sat 10-1
WILLIAMSTOWN BRANCH, 19692 William St, Williamstown, K0C 2J0, SAN 377-709X. Tel: 613-347-3397. *Br Support,* Position Currently Open
Open Tues & Thurs 3-8, Wed 10-3, Sat 10-1
WINCHESTER BRANCH, 547 St Lawrence St, Winchester, K0C 2K0, SAN 377-7111. Tel: 613-774-2612. FAX: 613-774-5866. *Br Support,* Ruth Gatenby; *Br Support,* Peggy Pollock; *Br Support,* Gail Storring
Open Mon 9-1, Tues & Thurs 10-8, Wed 4-9, Fri 1-4, Sat 10-1

DEEP RIVER

P   W B LEWIS PUBLIC LIBRARY*, 55 Ridge Rd, K0J 1P0. (Mail add: PO Box 278, K0J 1P0), SAN 319-0943. Tel: 613-584-4244. FAX: 613-584-1405. *Librn,* Jill Foster; Staff 6 (MLS 1, Non-MLS 5)
Founded 1947. Pop 4,200
Library Holdings: Bk Titles 35,000; Bk Vols 38,000; Per Subs 110
Automation Activity & Vendor Info: (Cataloging) Follett Software; (Circulation) Follett Software; (OPAC) Follett Software
Publications: Seasons (newsletter)
Friends of the Library Group

P   THE TOWN OF LAURENTIAN HILLS PUBLIC LIBRARY*, 34465 Hwy 17, RR 1, Hwy 17, K0J 1P0. SAN 319-0951. Tel: 613-584-2714. FAX: 613-584-9145. *Librn,* Maureen Bakewell
Founded 1974. Pop 2,800
Library Holdings: Large Print Bks 386; Bk Vols 21,900; Per Subs 45; Talking Bks 496; Videos 415
Automation Activity & Vendor Info: (Acquisitions) Insignia Software; (Cataloging) Insignia Software; (Circulation) Insignia Software; (OPAC) Insignia Software
Wireless access
Partic in Southern Ontario Libr Serv
Open Mon 6:30pm-8:30pm, Tues & Thurs 10-12 & 1-3, Wed 10-12 & 6:30-8:30, Sat 10-12
Friends of the Library Group

DESERONTO

P   DESERONTO PUBLIC LIBRARY*, 358 Main St W, K0K 1X0. (Mail add: PO Box 302, K0K 1X0), SAN 319-0978. Tel: 613-396-2744. FAX: 613-396-3466. E-mail: info@deserontopubliclibrary.ca. Web Site: www.deserontopubliclibrary.org. *Librn,* Frances Smith; *Libr Asst,* Ruth Sager; Staff 1 (Non-MLS 1)
Founded 1896. Pop 2,853; Circ 2,000
Library Holdings: Bk Titles 20,000; Per Subs 20
Special Collections: North American Indian Coll
Subject Interests: Local hist
Publications: In Review-Canadian Books for Children; Ontario Library Review
Open Mon 1-8, Tues 4-8, Wed 10-8, Fri & Sat 10-2

DON MILLS

S   TORONTO REAL ESTATE BOARD LIBRARY*, 1400 Don Mills Rd, M3B 3N1. SAN 323-6293. Tel: 416-443-8152. FAX: 416-443-0797, 416-443-9703. Web Site: www.trebnet.com. *Mgr, Res,* Michael J Murphy
Library Holdings: Bk Titles 4,000
Open Mon-Fri 8:30-4:15

DORION

P   DORION PUBLIC LIBRARY*, 170 Dorion Loop Rd, P0T 1K0. SAN 319-1036. Tel: 807-857-2289. FAX: 807-857-2203. E-mail: dorlib@tbaytel.net. Web Site: www.dorionpubliclibrary.ca. *Librn,* Betty Chambers; *Asst Librn,* Paulette Forsythe; *Asst Librn,* Lee Harris
Founded 1961. Pop 700; Circ 6,000
Library Holdings: Bk Vols 10,000
Mem of Ontario Library Service North
Open Mon & Fri 4:15-6:15 & 7-9, Tues & Thurs 4:15-6:15, Wed 12:30-3, 4:15-6:15 & 7-9, Sat 10-4

DOWNSVIEW

M   HUMBER RIVER REGIONAL HOSPITAL*, Thomas J Malcho Memorial Library, 2111 Finch Ave W, M3N 1N1. SAN 324-671X. Tel: 416-744-2500, Ext 2583. FAX: 416-747-3819. E-mail: healthscienceslibrary@hrrh.on.ca. Web Site: www.hrrh.on.ca. *Health Sci Librn,* Abdul Pullattayil; Staff 1 (MLS 1)
Library Holdings: Bk Titles 1,300; Per Subs 200
Subject Interests: Allied health, Hospital admin, Med, Nursing
Restriction: Staff use only

DRYDEN

P   DRYDEN PUBLIC LIBRARY*, 36 Van Horne Ave, P8N 2A7. SAN 319-1095. Tel: 807-223-1475. FAX: 807-223-4312. E-mail: library@dryden.ca. Web Site: www.dryden.ca. *Chief Exec Officer,* Sandra Weitzel; Staff 4 (MLS 1, Non-MLS 3)
Founded 1925. Pop 7,800; Circ 95,000
Library Holdings: Bk Vols 40,000; Per Subs 32
Subject Interests: Local hist
Mem of Ontario Library Service North
Open Mon-Thurs 10-8, Fri & Sun 10-5, Sat 1-4

DUBREUILVILLE

P   DUBREUILVILLE PUBLIC LIBRARY*, 120 Magpie St, P0S 1B0. (Mail add: PO Box 39, P0S 1B0), SAN 319-1109. Tel: 705-884-1435. Toll Free Tel: 877-637-8010. FAX: 705-884-1437. E-mail: dpl@dubreuilville.ca. Web Site: www.dubreuilville.ca. *Chief Exec Officer,* Brigitte Tremblay; *Librn,* Brigitte Tremblay
Founded 1969. Pop 900
Library Holdings: DVDs 400; Bk Vols 6,500; Per Subs 25; Videos 350
Wireless access
Open Mon-Fri 1-7, Sat & Sun 12-4

DUNDALK

P   SOUTHGATE PUBLIC LIBRARY*, 80 Proton St, N0C 1B0. (Mail add: PO Box 190, N0C 1B0), SAN 319-1117. Tel: 519-923-3248. FAX: 519-923-3248. E-mail: southgatepl@bmts.com. Web Site: www.southgate-library.com. *Librn,* Dianne Dean
Pop 4,000; Circ 19,615
Library Holdings: Bk Vols 12,500; Per Subs 23
Special Collections: Dundalk Herald Weekly Newspaper, microfilm; Local Area Genealogy Records, digitized
Wireless access
Open Tues-Thurs 11-8, Fri 11-3, Sat 10-2
Friends of the Library Group

DUNNVILLE

P   HALDIMAND COUNTY PUBLIC LIBRARY*, 111 Broad St E, N1A 2X5. (Mail add: Box 187, N1A 2X5), SAN 319-0668. Tel: 905-318-3272. Information Services Tel: 905-318-3272, Ext 6111. FAX: 905-774-4294. E-mail: library@haldimandcounty.on.ca. Web Site: library.haldimandcounty.on.ca. *Chief Exec Officer,* Debra Jackson; Tel: 905-318-3272, E-mail: djackson@haldimandcounty.on.ca; *Acq Mgr, Dep Chief Exec Officer,* Paul Diette; Staff 4 (MLS 1, Non-MLS 3)
Founded 2001. Pop 41,000; Circ 369,000
Jan 2005-Dec 2005 Income (Main Library and Branch(s)) (CAN) $1,309,150, Provincial (CAN) $80,000, City (CAN) $1,099,150, Federal (CAN) $51,000, Locally Generated Income (CAN) $79,000. Mats Exp (CAN) $186,500, Books (CAN) $145,000, Per/Ser (Incl. Access Fees) (CAN) $15,000, AV Mat (CAN) $20,000, Electronic Ref Mat (Incl. Access Fees) (CAN) $6,500. Sal (CAN) $800,000 (Prof (CAN) $80,000)
Library Holdings: Bk Vols 190,000; Per Subs 278
Automation Activity & Vendor Info: (Acquisitions) SirsiDynix; (Cataloging) SirsiDynix; (Circulation) SirsiDynix; (OPAC) SirsiDynix
Branches: 6
CALEDONIA BRANCH, 100 Haddington St, Unit 2, Caledonia, N3W 2N4, SAN 377-6573. Tel: 905-765-2634. FAX: 905-765-2634. *Mgr,* Teresa Thompson; *Br Coordr,* Roberta Chapman; Tel: 905-768-5941
Library Holdings: Bk Vols 53,000; Per Subs 55
Open Mon 3-8, Tues & Thurs 1-8, Wed 10-8, Fri & Sat 10-5, Sun 12-4

CAYUGA BRANCH, 28 Cayuga St N, Cayuga, N0A 1E0. (Mail add: PO Box 550, Cayuga, N0A 1E0), SAN 329-3386. Tel: 905-772-5726. FAX: 905-772-5726. *Br Coordr,* Paul Diette; E-mail: pdiette@haldimandcounty.on.ca
Library Holdings: Bk Vols 16,000; Per Subs 31
Open Tues 10-8, Thurs 2-8, Fri & Sat 10-2

DUNNVILLE BRANCH, 317 Chestnut St, N1A 2H4, SAN 319-1133. Tel: 905-774-4240. FAX: 905-774-2530. *Sr Asst Librn,* Lynn Harrison; *Br Coordr,* Paul Diette; Tel: 905-772-5726, E-mail: pdiette@haldimandcounty.on.ca
Founded 1854. Pop 11,460; Circ 170,000
Library Holdings: Bk Vols 55,000; Per Subs 58
Open Tues & Wed 10-8, Thurs & Fri 10-6, Sat 10-5, Sun 12-4
Friends of the Library Group

HAGERSVILLE BRANCH, 13 Alma St N, Hagersville, N0A 1H0. (Mail add: PO Box 219, Hagersville, N0A 1H0), SAN 329-336X. Tel: 905-768-5941. FAX: 905-768-5941. *Sr Librn, Pub,* Teresa Thompson; *Br Coordr,* Roberta Chapman
Library Holdings: Bk Vols 22,000; Per Subs 30
Open Tues 10-8, Wed, Fri & Sat 10-2, Thurs 12-8

JARVIS BRANCH, Two Monson St, Jarvis, N0A 1J0. Tel: 519-587-4746. FAX: 519-587-3470. *Sr Asst Librn,* Cathie Rounce; *Br Coordr,* Roberta Chapman; Tel: 519-587-4746
Library Holdings: Bk Vols 21,000; Per Subs 20
Open Mon 1-5, Tues 10-8, Thurs 1-8, Fri 10-1, Sat 10-4
Friends of the Library Group

SELKIRK BRANCH, 34 Main St W, Selkirk, N0A 1P0. (Mail add: PO Box 130, Selkirk, N0A 1P0), SAN 319-4140. Tel: 905-776-2127. FAX: 905-776-3116. *Br Coordr,* Paul Diette; E-mail: pdiette@haldimandcounty.on.ca; Staff 2 (MLS 1, Non-MLS 1)
Founded 1890. Pop 19,000; Circ 26,800
Library Holdings: Bk Titles 21,000; Bk Vols 22,000; Per Subs 40
Subject Interests: Local hist
Open Mon 1-5, Tues 10-8, Thurs 3-8, Sat 10-4
Friends of the Library Group

DURHAM

P　WEST GREY PUBLIC LIBRARY*, 240 Garafraxa St N, N0G 1R0. (Mail add: PO Box 706, N0G 1R0), SAN 319-1141. Tel: 519-369-2107. FAX: 519-369-9966. E-mail: westgreylibrary@yahoo.ca. Web Site: www.westgreylibraries.com. *Head of Libr,* Marlaine Elvidge; Staff 2 (MLS 1, Non-MLS 1)
Founded 1859. Pop 11,000; Circ 44,000
Library Holdings: Bk Vols 30,000; Per Subs 20
Special Collections: Durham Newspapers, dating back to 1859, 1985-present on microfiche; Federal & Provincial Publications; Genealogy Coll
Subject Interests: Local hist
Function: ILL available, Photocopying/Printing
Partic in Southern Ontario Libr Serv
Open Tues-Fri 11-8, Sat 12-4
Friends of the Library Group
Branches: 3

ELMWOOD BRANCH, 25 Main St S, Elmwood, N0G 1S0. (Mail add: PO Box 160, Elmwood, N0G 1S0). Tel: 519-363-3321. FAX: 519-363-3321. E-mail: elmwoodbranchlibrary@yahoo.ca. *Librn,* Marye Smith
Founded 1905
Open Tues & Fri 2-8

NEUSTADT PUBLIC, 511 Mill St, Neustadt, N0G 2M0, SAN 328-1043. Tel: 519-799-5830. FAX: 519-799-5830. Web Site: www.westgreylibrary.com. *Librn,* Kathleen Scott; E-mail: kathleen@westgreylibrary.com; Staff 1 (MLS 1)
Founded 1985. Pop 546; Circ 1,687
Library Holdings: Bk Titles 4,597
Mem of Ontario Library Service North
Open Thurs 11-7, Sat 11-3
Friends of the Library Group

NORMANBY TOWNSHIP PUBLIC, 574 Louisa St, Ayton, N0G 1C0. (Mail add: PO Box 70, Ayton, N0G 1C0). Tel: 519-665-7784. *Librn,* Agnes Rivers-Moore
Open Tues & Fri 3:30-8

EAR FALLS

P　EAR FALLS TOWNSHIP LIBRARY*, Two Willow Crescent, P0V 1T0. (Mail add: PO Box 369, P0V 1T0), SAN 319-115X. Tel: 807-222-3209. FAX: 807-222-3432. E-mail: efpl@goearfalls.com. Web Site: www.olsn.ca/earfallspl. *Coordr, Libr Serv,* Becky Bergman
Pop 1,150; Circ 20,000
Library Holdings: Bk Titles 15,591; Per Subs 9
Mem of Ontario Library Service North
Open Mon & Thurs 10:30-1:30, 2-4:30 & 6-8, Tues & Wed 10:30-1:30 & 2-4:30, Fri 9-1

EARLTON

P　ARMSTRONG TOWNSHIP PUBLIC LIBRARY*, 35 Tenth St, P0J 1E0. (Mail add: PO Box 39, P0J 1E0), SAN 319-1168. Tel: 705-563-2717. FAX: 705-563-2093. E-mail: earltonlibrary@ntl.sympatico.ca. Web Site: www.olsn.ca/armstrong. *Head Librn,* Ghislaine Gravel
Founded 1977. Pop 1,334; Circ 15,036
Library Holdings: Bk Vols 10,300; Per Subs 12
Open Mon 9-5, Tues & Thurs 9-4 & 6pm-8pm, Fri 9-4

EGANVILLE

P　BONNECHERE UNION PUBLIC LIBRARY*, 74 A Maple St, K0J 1T0. (Mail add: PO Box 39, K0J 1T0), SAN 319-1176. Tel: 613-628-2400. FAX: 613-628-5377. E-mail: bonncherepl@renc.igs.net. Web Site: www.bonnechereupl.com. *Chief Exec Officer,* Jennifer Coleman-Davidson; Staff 3 (MLS 1, Non-MLS 2)
Pop 6,500; Circ 30,000
Library Holdings: Bk Titles 20,000; Per Subs 30
Partic in Southern Ontario Libr Serv
Open Mon & Sat 10:30am-1:30pm, Tues & Fri 10-6, Wed & Thurs 10:30-7:30

ELGIN

P　RIDEAU LAKES PUBLIC LIBRARY*, Halladay St, K0G 1E0. (Mail add: PO Box 189, K0G 1E0), SAN 367-1283. Tel: 613-359-5334. FAX: 613-359-5418. E-mail: admin@rideaulakeslibrary.ca. Web Site: www.rideaulakeslibrary.ca. *Coordr,* Sue Warren
Library Holdings: Bk Titles 37,000; Per Subs 60
Special Collections: Large Print Coll; Local History Coll, bks, doc; Talking Books Coll
Wireless access
Publications: Walking & Driving Tours of North Leeds
Open Mon 5-8, Tues & Thurs 1-8, Wed 10-4, Fri 1-4, Sat 9:30-12:30
Branches: 5

DELTA BRANCH, 18 King St, Unit 2, Delta, K0E 1G0, SAN 367-1348. Tel: 613-928-2991. FAX: 613-928-2991. E-mail: delta@rideaulakeslibrary.ca. *Librn,* Joan Cochrane; *Librn,* Liz Pribe
Open Tues 5-8, Wed & Sat 9:30-12:30, Thurs 1-4

ELGIN/ADMINISTRATION BRANCH, PO Box 189, K0G 1E0, SAN 367-1313. Tel: 613-359-5315. E-mail: elgin@rideaulakeslibrary.ca.
Open Mon 5-8, Tues & Thurs 1-8, Wed 10-4, Fri 1-4, Sat 9:30-12:30

NEWBORO, Ten Brock St, Newboro, K0G 1P0, SAN 378-1895. Tel: 613-272-0241. FAX: 613-272-0241. E-mail: newboro@rideaulakeslibrary.ca. *Librn,* Elva McCann
Open Tues 5-8, Thurs 1-5, Fri 9-Noon, Sat 1-4

PORTLAND BRANCH, Hwy 15, Portland, K0G 1V0, SAN 367-1437. Tel: 613-272-2832. FAX: 613-272-2832. E-mail: portland@rideaulakeslibrary.ca. *Librn,* Joan Cochrane
Open Mon 5-8, Wed 2-5, Fri 9:30-Noon, Sat 1-4

SOUTH ELMSLEY, c/o Lombardy Public School RR 1, 596 Hwy 15, Lombardy, K0G 1L0. Tel: 613-284-9827. FAX: 613-284-1523. E-mail: southelmsley@rideaulakeslibrary.ca. *Librn,* Joan Cochrane
Open Tues & Wed 4-8, Thurs 4-8 (9-1 Summer), Sat 9:30-1

ELK LAKE

P　ELK LAKE PUBLIC LIBRARY, First St, P0J 1G0. (Mail add: PO Box 218, P0J 1G0), SAN 322-8037. Tel: 705-678-2340. FAX: 705-678-2340. E-mail: elklake@onlink.net. Web Site: www.elklake.ca. *Librn,* Cyndi Stockman
Founded 1970. Pop 522; Circ 603
Library Holdings: Bk Titles 10,000; Per Subs 15
Special Services for the Blind - Assistive/Adapted tech devices, equip & products
Open Tues & Thurs 7pm-9pm, Wed & Sat 12:30-4:30

ELLIOT LAKE

P　ELLIOT LAKE PUBLIC LIBRARY*, Algo Centre Mall, 151 Ontario Ave, P5A 2T2. SAN 319-1192. Tel: 705-848-2287, Ext 2800. FAX: 705-461-9464. Web Site: www.cityofelliotlake.com/library.html. *Chief Librn,* Pat McGurk; E-mail: pat.mcgurk@city.elliotlake.on.ca
Founded 1959. Pop 11,549; Circ 101,332
Library Holdings: Bk Vols 60,000; Per Subs 40
Subject Interests: Local hist, Mine decommissioning, Nuclear develop
Automation Activity & Vendor Info: (Acquisitions) Follett Software; (Cataloging) Follett Software; (Circulation) Follett Software; (OPAC) Follett Software
Wireless access
Function: Art exhibits, AV serv, Bks on cassette, Bks on CD, CD-ROM, Children's prog, Computers for patron use, Copy machines, Electronic databases & coll, Equip loans & repairs, Fax serv, Handicapped accessible, ILL available, Online searches, Orientations, Photocopying/Printing, Prog for children & young adult, Referrals accepted, Serves mentally

handicapped consumers, Spoken cassettes & CDs, Summer reading prog, Telephone ref, VHS videos, Wheelchair accessible
Open Mon-Wed & Fri 9:30-5, Thurs 9:30-8, Sat 10-5
Restriction: Access for corporate affiliates

EMO

P EMO PUBLIC LIBRARY*, Jesse St, P0W 1E0. (Mail add: PO Box 490, P0W 1E0), SAN 319-1230. Tel: 807-482-2575. FAX: 807-482-2575. E-mail: emolib@bellnet.ca. Web Site: www.twspemo.on.ca/library. *Chief Librn,* Shirley Sheppard; *Asst Librn,* Kathy Leek
Founded 1940. Pop 2,500; Circ 28,000
Library Holdings: Bk Vols 24,904; Per Subs 12
Automation Activity & Vendor Info: (Acquisitions) SirsiDynix; (Cataloging) SirsiDynix; (Circulation) SirsiDynix; (Course Reserve) SirsiDynix; (ILL) SirsiDynix; (Media Booking) SirsiDynix; (OPAC) SirsiDynix; (Serials) SirsiDynix
Database Vendor: SirsiDynix
Wireless access
Mem of Ontario Library Service North
Open Mon, Wed & Fri 1-5, Tues 10-7, Thurs 1-7, Sat 10-2
Friends of the Library Group

ENGLEHART

P ENGLEHART PUBLIC LIBRARY*, 71 Fourth Ave, P0J 1H0. (Mail add: PO Box 809, P0J 1H0), SAN 319-1249. Tel: 705-544-2100. FAX: 705-544-2238. E-mail: techepl@onlink.net. Web Site: www.englehartpubliclibrary.ca. *Chief Exec Officer,* Sharon Williams; *Librn,* Liz Robitaille
Founded 1961. Pop 3,700; Circ 21,300
Library Holdings: AV Mats 1,000; Large Print Bks 908; Bk Titles 22,168; Bk Vols 22,477; Per Subs 32; Talking Bks 455
Special Collections: Can & Prov; Municipal Document Depository
Subject Interests: Local hist
Automation Activity & Vendor Info: (Cataloging) Follett Software; (Circulation) Follett Software
Partic in Ont Libr Serv-North
Special Services for the Blind - Braille bks
Open Tues & Thurs 12-5, Wed 12-9, Fri 10-1, Sat 10-3
Friends of the Library Group

ENNISMORE

P SMITH-ENNISMORE-LAKEFIELD PUBLIC LIBRARY*, Ennismore Branch, 551 Ennis Rd, K0L 1T0. SAN 319-1257. Tel: 705-292-8022. FAX: 705-292-8022. Web Site: www.mypubliclibrary.ca. *Librn,* Carol Crough
Founded 1971
Library Holdings: Bk Vols 18,500; Per Subs 20
Open Mon, Wed & Fri 1-5, Tues & Thurs 9-1 & 7pm-9pm, Sat 9-3
Friends of the Library Group

ESPANOLA

P ESPANOLA PUBLIC LIBRARY*, 245 Avery Dr, P5E 1S4. SAN 319-1265. Tel: 705-869-2940. FAX: 705-869-6463. E-mail: library@town.espanola.on.ca. Web Site: www.espanola.library.on.ca. *Chief Librn/CEO,* Charles Grayson; Staff 1 (MLS 1)
Founded 1958. Pop 5,500; Circ 65,000
Jan 2010-Dec 2010. Mats Exp (CAN) $43,000
Library Holdings: Bk Titles 45,000; Bk Vols 46,000; Per Subs 100
Subject Interests: Local hist
Automation Activity & Vendor Info: (Cataloging) Follett Software; (Circulation) Follett Software; (OPAC) Follett Software
Function: Copy machines, Fax serv, Homebound delivery serv, ILL available, Music CDs, Photocopying/Printing, Prog for children & young adult, Spoken cassettes & CDs, Summer reading prog, VHS videos, Wheelchair accessible
Open Mon-Thurs (Winter) 9-8, Fri 9-5, Sat & Sun 10-2; Mon-Thurs (Summer) 9-8, Fri 9-5
Friends of the Library Group

ESSEX

P ESSEX COUNTY LIBRARY, 360 Fairview Ave W, Ste 101, N8M 1Y3. SAN 367-1496. Tel: 519-776-5241. FAX: 519-776-6851. E-mail: digitalmedia@essexcountylibrary.ca. Web Site: www.essexcountylibrary.ca. *Chief Exec Officer, Chief Librn,* Janet A Woodbridge; *Dep Chief Librn, Mgr, Br,* Jennifer Franklin-McInnis; *Mgr, Tech Serv,* Patricia Knight; Staff 109 (MLS 6, Non-MLS 103)
Founded 1966. Pop 177,891; Circ 978,496
Library Holdings: CDs 21,561; DVDs 9,863; e-books 8,007; e-journals 7,355; Bk Titles 157,696; Bk Vols 321,969; Per Subs 159
Automation Activity & Vendor Info: (Acquisitions) SirsiDynix; (Cataloging) SirsiDynix; (Circulation) SirsiDynix; (OPAC) SirsiDynix
Special Services for the Deaf - Bks on deafness & sign lang

Branches: 14

AMHERSTBURG BRANCH, 232 Sandwich St S, Amherstburg, N9V 2A4, SAN 367-1526. Tel: 226-946-1549, Ext 240. *Supvr,* Christina Richert
Open Mon & Tues 1-8, Wed & Thurs 10-8, Fri 10-6, Sat 10-5

COMBER BRANCH, 6400 Main St, Comber, N0P 1J0. (Mail add: PO Box 250, Comber, N0P 1J0), SAN 367-1550. Tel: 226-946-1529, Ext 222. *Supvr,* Gisele Levesque
Open Mon & Thurs 5-8, Tues 2:30-5:30, Sat 10-1

COTTAM BRANCH, 122 Fox St, Cottam, N0R 1B0. (Mail add: Box 159, Cottam, N0R 1B0), SAN 367-1585. Tel: 226-946-1529, Ext 212. *Supvr,* Darlene Baker
Open Mon & Thurs 5-8, Tues 2:30-5:30, Sat 10-1

ESSEX BRANCH, 35 Gosfield Townline W, N8M 0A1, SAN 367-164X. Tel: 226-946-1529, Ext 250. *Supvr,* Mary Mastronardi; Tel: 226-946-1529, Ext 250
Open Mon & Tues 1-8, Wed & Thurs 10-8, Fri 10-6, Sat 10-5

HARROW BRANCH, 140 King St W, Harrow, N0R 1G0. (Mail add: PO Box 550, Harrow, N0R 1G0), SAN 367-1674. Tel: 226-946-1529, Ext 260. *Supvr,* Cathy Humphrey
Automation Activity & Vendor Info: (Circulation) SIRSI WorkFlows
Open Mon-Thurs 1:30-8, Sat 10-4

KINGSVILLE BRANCH, 40 Main W, Kingsville, N9Y 1H3, SAN 367-1704. Tel: 226-946-1529, Ext 270. *Supvr,* Eileen Bushman
Open Mon & Tues 1-8, Wed & Thurs 10-8, Fri 10-6, Sat 10-5

LAKESHORE, 304 Rourke Line Rd, RR No 3, Belle River, N0R 1A0, SAN 367-1615. Tel: 226-946-1529, Ext 280. *Supvr,* Ruth Sylvestre
Open Mon-Thurs 1-8, Fri 10-6, Sat 10-4

LASALLE BRANCH, 1555 Talbot Rd, Unit 400, LaSalle, N9H 2N2, SAN 367-1739. Tel: 226-946-1529, Ext 210. *Supvr,* Donna Spickett
Open Mon-Thurs 10-8, Fri 10-6, Sat 10-5, Sun (Oct-May) 12-5

LEAMINGTON BRANCH, One John St, Leamington, N8H 1H1, SAN 378-0600. Tel: 226-946-1529, Ext 220. *Supvr,* Sue Tuck
Open Mon-Thurs 10-8, Fri 10-6, Sat 10-5

MCGREGOR BRANCH, 9571 Walker Rd, McGregor, N0R 1J0. (Mail add: PO Box 1044, McGregor, N0R 1J0), SAN 367-1798. Tel: 226-946-1529, Ext 211. *Supvr,* Kattie Neels
Open Mon, Wed & Thurs 5-8, Tues 2:30-5:30, Sat 10-3

RUTHVEN BRANCH, 1695 Elgin St, Ruthven, N0P 2G0. (Mail add: PO Box 279, Ruthven, N0P 2G0), SAN 367-1828. Tel: 226-946-1529, Ext 221. *Supvr,* Adam Craig
Open Mon & Thurs 5-8, Tues 2:30-5:30, Sat 10-1

STONEY POINT BRANCH, 6720 Tecumseh Rd, Stoney Point, N0R 1N0. (Mail add: PO Box 14, Stoney Point, N0R 1N0), SAN 367-1887. Tel: 226-946-1529, Ext 232. *Supvr,* Vanessa Chiller
Open Mon, Wed & Thurs 5-8, Tues 2:30-5:30, Sat 10-3

TECUMSEH BRANCH, 13675 St Gregory's Rd, Tecumseh, N8N 3E4, SAN 367-1852. Tel: 226-946-1529, Ext 230. *Supvr,* Anita Johnson
Open Mon-Thurs 10-8, Fri 10-6, Sat 10-5, Sun (Oct-May) 12-5

WOODSLEE BRANCH, 100 S Middle Rd, Woodslee, N0R 1V0. (Mail add: PO Box 158, Woodslee, N0R 1V0), SAN 367-1925. Tel: 226-946-1529, Ext 231. *Supvr,* Colette Currie
Open Mon, Wed & Thurs 5-8, Tues 2:30-5:30, Sat 10-3

S PROVERBS HERITAGE ORGANIZATION*, John Freeman Walls Historic Site & Underground Railroad Museum Library, 932 Lakeshore Rd 107, RR 3, N8M 2X7. SAN 376-0782. Tel: 519-727-6555. FAX: 519-727-5793. Web Site: www.undergroundrailroadmuseum.org. *Curator,* Anna Walls; E-mail: adaywalls@aol.com; *Curator,* Dr Bryan Walls; Tel: 519-727-4866, E-mail: bryanugrr@aol.com
Library Holdings: Bk Vols 100
Restriction: Open by appt only

ETOBICOKE

S INFRASTRUCTURE HEALTH & SAFETY ASSOCIATION LIBRARY*, 21 Voyager Ct S, M9W 5M7. SAN 373-3270. Tel: 416-679-4065. FAX: 416-674-8866. Web Site: www.ihsa.ca. *Info Coordr,* Patricia Dean; E-mail: pdean@ihsa.ca; Staff 1 (MLS 1)
Library Holdings: Bk Vols 3,000; Per Subs 60
Subject Interests: Construction safety, Occupational health, Occupational safety
Database Vendor: Dialog, EBSCOhost, WestlaweCARSWELL
Function: Res libr
Open Mon-Fri 8:30-3:30
Restriction: Circulates for staff only, Open to others by appt

M WILLIAM OSLER HEALTH CENTRE - ETOBICOKE HOSPITAL CAMPUS*, Medical Library, 101 Humber College Blvd, M9V 1R8. SAN 326-954X. Tel: 416-747-3400, Ext 33334. FAX: 416-747-3484. Web Site: www.williamoslerhc.on.ca. *Librn,* Darren Hamilton; E-mail: darren_hamilton@oslerhc.org; Staff 1 (MLS 1)
Library Holdings: Bk Vols 1,000; Per Subs 100
Automation Activity & Vendor Info: (Acquisitions) Inmagic, Inc.; (Cataloging) Inmagic, Inc.; (Circulation) Inmagic, Inc.; (Serials) Inmagic, Inc.

Database Vendor: OVID Technologies, ProQuest
Open Mon-Fri 8-6
Restriction: By permission only

FERGUS

P   WELLINGTON COUNTY LIBRARY*, Headquarters, 552 Wellington Rd
     18, RR1, N1M 2W3. SAN 367-2271. Tel: 519-846-0918. FAX:
     519-846-2066. Web Site: www.wclib.ca. *Chief Librn,* Murray McCabe;
     E-mail: murraym@wellington.ca; *Cat,* Elaine Salter; Tel: 519-846-0918,
     Ext 223, E-mail: elaines@wellington.ca; *Libr Tech-ILLO,* Deanna Stevens;
     Tel: 519-846-0918, Ext 225, E-mail: deannas@wellington.ca; Staff 15
     (MLS 1, Non-MLS 14)
     Founded 1974
     Library Holdings: Bk Vols 100,000; Per Subs 250
     Mem of Ontario Library Service North
     Open Mon-Fri 8:30-4:30
     Branches: 14
     ABOYNE, 552 Wellington Rd 18, RR 1, N1M 2W3, SAN 367-2336. Tel:
       519-846-0918, Ext 222. E-mail: aboynelib@county.wellington,on.ca. *Br
       Mgr,* Joyce Tenhage; E-mail: joycet@county.wellington.on.ca
       Open Mon-Fri 10-8, Sat 10-5
     ARTHUR BRANCH, 183 George St, Arthur, N0G 1A0. (Mail add: PO
       Box 550, Arthur, N0G 1A0), SAN 367-2301. Tel: 519-848-3999. E-mail:
       arthurlib@county.wellington.on.ca. *Br Mgr,* Lynn Rawlins; E-mail:
       lynnr@county.wellington.on.ca
       Open Tues & Wed 1-5 & 7pm-9pm, Thurs 1-5, Fri 10-5, Sat 10-2
     CLIFFORD BRANCH, Seven Brown St N, Box 14, Clifford, N0G 1M0,
       SAN 367-2360. Tel: 519-327-8328. E-mail: cliffordlib@wellington.ca. *Br
       Mgr,* Henny Derbecker; E-mail: hennyd@wellington.ca
       Open Tues 10-8, Wed & Thurs 2-8, Fri 10-6, Sat 10-3
     DRAYTON BRANCH, 24 Wood St, Drayton, N0G 1P0, SAN 319-1087.
       Tel: 519-638-3788. E-mail: draytonlib@county.wellington.on.ca. *Br Mgr,*
       Bertha Van Soest; E-mail: berthav@county.wellington.on.ca
       Open Tues & Wed 2-8, Fri 2-5, Sat 10-1
     ELORA BRANCH, 144 Geddes St, Elora, N0B 1S0, SAN 319-1214. Tel:
       519-846-0190. FAX: 519-846-0344. E-mail:
       eloralib@county.wellington.ca. *Br Mgr,* Bonnie Moebus; E-mail:
       bonniem@county.wellington.ca
       Open Mon, Wed & Fri 10-5, Tues & Thurs 2-9, Sat 10-3
     ERIN BRANCH, 14 Boland Dr, Erin, N0B 1T0, SAN 367-2395. Tel:
       519-833-9762. E-mail: erinlib@county.wellington.on.ca. *Br Mgr,* Beverly
       Picken; E-mail: bevp@county.wellington.on.ca
       Open Mon, Wed & Fri 10-5, Tues & Thurs 10-5 & 7-9, Sat 10-3
     FERGUS BRANCH, 190 St Andrew St W, N1M 1N5. Tel: 519-843-1180.
       FAX: 519-843-5743. E-mail: ferguslib@county.wellington.on.ca. *Br Mgr,*
       Judy Howard; E-mail: judyh@county.wellington.on.ca
       Open Mon-Thurs 10-8, Fri 10-5, Sat 10-3
     HARRISTON BRANCH, 88 Mill St, Harriston, N0G 1Z0, SAN 319-163X.
       Tel: 519-338-2396. E-mail: harristonlib@county.wellington.on.ca. *Br
       Mgr,* Dorothy Pike; E-mail: dorothyp@county.wellington.on.ca
       Open Mon & Thurs 10-9, Tues & Fri 1:30-9, Sat 10-3
     HILLSBURGH BRANCH, 98B Main St, Hillsburgh, N0B 1Z0, SAN
       319-1702. Tel: 519-855-4010. FAX: 519-855-4873. E-mail:
       hillsburglib@county.wellington.on.ca. *Br Mgr,* Donna Revell; E-mail:
       donnar@county.wellington.on.ca
       Pop 7,651; Circ 65,056
       Library Holdings: Bk Vols 23,000; Per Subs 48
       Partic in Southern Ontario Libr Serv
       Open Mon & Fri 2-5, Tues-Thurs 10-8, Sat 10-4
       Friends of the Library Group
     MARDEN BRANCH, 7368 Wellington Rd 30, RR 5, Guelph, N1H 6J2.
       Tel: 519-763-7445. FAX: 519-763-0706. E-mail:
       mardenlib@county.wellington.on.ca. *Br Mgr,* Trudy Gohn; E-mail:
       trudyg@county.wellington.on.ca
       Open Mon & Wed 10-8, Tues & Thurs 2-8, Sat 10-5, Sun 1-5
     MOUNT FOREST BRANCH, 118 Main St, Mount Forest, N0G 2L0, SAN
       319-2695. Tel: 519-323-4541. E-mail:
       mtforestlib@county.wellington.on.ca. *Br Mgr,* Gwynne Smith; E-mail:
       gwynnes@county.wellington.on.ca
       Open Mon, Tues, Thurs & Fri 1-5 & 6:30-9, Sat 10-2
     PALMERSTON BRANCH, 265 Bell St, Palmerston, N0G 2P0, SAN
       367-2425. Tel: 519-343-2142. E-mail:
       palmerstolib@county.wellington.on.ca. *Br Mgr,* Barbara Burrows; E-mail:
       barbb@county.wellington.on.ca
       Open Tues-Thurs 10-8, Fri 2-6, Sat 10-3
     PUSLINCH TOWNSHIP, 29 Wellington Rd 46S, RR3, Guelph, N1H 6H9,
       SAN 328-9850. Tel: 519-763-8026. FAX: 519-763-4122. E-mail:
       puslinchlib@county.wellington.on.ca. *Br Mgr,* Frankie Shaw; E-mail:
       frankies@county.wellington.on.ca
       Open Tues & Thurs 2-9, Fri 2-5, Sat 10-5
     ROCKWOOD BRANCH, 85 Christie St, Rockwood, N0B 2K0, SAN
       319-3853. Tel: 519-856-4851. FAX: 519-856-2990. E-mail:
       rockwoodlib@county.wellington.on.ca. *Br Mgr,* Linda Hornick; E-mail:
       lindah@county.wellington.on.ca

Pop 5,800; Circ 21,543
Library Holdings: Bk Vols 22,000; Per Subs 35
Open Mon-Thurs 10-8, Fri & Sat 10-4

S   WELLINGTON COUNTY MUSEUM & ARCHIVES, 0536 Wellington Rd
     18, RR 1, N1M 2W3. SAN 370-5579. Tel: 519-846-0916, Ext 5225. FAX:
     519-846-9630. E-mail: archivist@wcm.on.ca. Web Site:
     www.wellington.ca/museum. *Archivist,* Karen Wagner; Tel: 519-846-0916;
     Staff 3 (MLS 2, Non-MLS 1)
     Founded 1976
     Library Holdings: Bk Vols 2,300
     Special Collections: Architecture (Couling Coll) slides; Genealogy Coll;
     Municipal Records, County of Wellington, bks, ledgers, film
     Wireless access
     Function: Archival coll, Photocopying/Printing
     Publications: CIRCA (Newsletter)
     Restriction: Pub use on premises

FLESHERTON

P   GREY HIGHLANDS PUBLIC LIBRARY*, Flesherton Public Library, 101
     Highland Dr, N0C 1E0. (Mail add: Box 280, N0C 1E0), SAN 319-1303.
     Tel: 519-924-2241. FAX: 519-924-2562. E-mail: flepub@bmts.com. Web
     Site: www.greyhighlandspubliclibrary.com. *Chief Exec Officer,* Wilda
     Allen; *Asst Librn,* Jan Moore
     Founded 1908. Pop 11,000; Circ 21,000
     Library Holdings: AV Mats 500; Large Print Bks 300; Bk Vols 14,000;
     Per Subs 50; Talking Bks 200
     Subject Interests: Local hist
     Automation Activity & Vendor Info: (Circulation) Follett Software
     Open Tues 10-8:30, Wed & Fri 1-5, Thurs 1-5 & 6:30pm-8:30pm, Sat 9-2
     Friends of the Library Group
     Branches: 2
     WALTER HARRIS MEMORIAL LIBRARY, 75 Walker St, Markdale,
       N0C 1H0. (Mail add: PO Box 499, Markdale, N0C 1H0), SAN
       319-2385. Tel: 519-986-3436. FAX: 519-986-4799. E-mail:
       whml@bmts.com. Web Site:
       www.greyhighlandspubliclibrary.com/Markdale. *Br Head,* Beth Kennedy;
       E-mail: bkennedy@bmts.com
       Founded 1915
       Library Holdings: Bk Titles 22,000; Per Subs 47
       Subject Interests: Local hist
       Open Tues, Wed & Fri 10-5:30, Thurs 1-8:30, Sat 10-3:30
       Friends of the Library Group
     KIMBERLEY LIBRARY, Kimberley Memorial Hall, Grey Rd 13,
       Kimberley, N0C 1G0, SAN 319-1877. Tel: 519-599-6146. FAX:
       519-599-6990. E-mail: kimberleylibrary@hotmail.com. Web Site:
       www.greyhighlandspubliclibrary.com/Kimberley. *Mgr,* Linda Weatheral
       Library Holdings: Bk Titles 7,000; Bk Vols 7,200
       Open Tues 12-5, Thurs 10-2:30 & 6:30-8:30, Sat 10-2
       Friends of the Library Group

FONTHILL

P   PELHAM PUBLIC LIBRARY*, 43 Pelham Town Sq, L0S 1E0. (Mail add:
     PO Box 830, L0S 1E0), SAN 319-132X. Tel: 905-892-6443. FAX:
     905-892-3392. E-mail: admin@pelhamlibrary.on.ca. Web Site:
     www.pelhamlibrary.on.ca. *Chief Librn/CEO,* Stephanie Stowe; E-mail:
     sstowe@pelhamlibrary.on.ca; *Dep Chief Exec Officer,* Marsha Hunt;
     E-mail: mhunt@pelhamlibrary.on.ca
     Founded 1852. Pop 16,598; Circ 171,372
     Library Holdings: Bk Vols 58,000
     Automation Activity & Vendor Info: (Cataloging) Evergreen;
     (Circulation) Evergreen; (OPAC) Evergreen
     Wireless access
     Open Mon-Thurs 9:30-8, Fri 9:30-6, Sat 9:30-5
     Friends of the Library Group
     Branches: 1
     MAPLE ACRE, 781 Canboro Rd, Fenwick, L0S 1C0. (Mail add: PO Box
       294, Fenwick, L0S 1C0), SAN 376-8171. Tel: 905-892-5226.
       Open Mon-Thurs 1-7, Fri 1-6, Sat 10-2
       Friends of the Library Group

FORESTER'S FALLS

P   WHITEWATER REGION PUBLIC LIBRARY*, Foresters Falls Branch,
     2022 Foresters Fall Rd, K0J 1V0. (Mail add: PO Box 69, K0J 1V0), SAN
     319-1338. Tel: 613-646-2543. *Librn,* Debbie Byce; E-mail:
     dbyce2247@yahoo.com
     Pop 1,700; Circ 2,450
     Library Holdings: Bk Vols 6,000; Per Subs 13
     Open Tues 1-5 & 7pm-9pm, Thurs 9-12 & 7pm-9pm, Sat 9-Noon

FORT ERIE

P   FORT ERIE PUBLIC LIBRARY*, Centennial Library, 136 Gilmore Rd, L2A 2M1. SAN 367-245X. Tel: 905-871-2546. FAX: 905-871-2191. Web Site: www.forterie.library.on.ca. *Chief Exec Officer,* Gordon Thomson; Fax: 905-871-9884, E-mail: gthomson@forterie.library.on.ca; *Bus Mgr,* Maria Brigantino; Tel: 905-871-2546, Ext 307, Fax: 905-871-9884, E-mail: mbrigantino@forterie.library.on.ca; *Syst Adminr,* Michael Schell; E-mail: mschell@forterie.library.on.ca; Staff 22 (MLS 3, Non-MLS 19)
Founded 1891. Pop 28,300; Circ 20,000
Library Holdings: Bk Vols 56,000; Per Subs 71
Subject Interests: Local hist
Database Vendor: SirsiDynix
Open Mon-Thurs & Sat 10-5, Fri 10-6
Branches: 2
CRYSTAL RIDGE, 89 Ridge Rd, Ridgeway, L0S 1N0, SAN 367-2484. Tel: 905-894-1281. FAX: 905-894-9248. *Br Mgr,* Jean Christie; E-mail: jchristie@forterie.library.on.ca
    Library Holdings: Bk Vols 28,000; Per Subs 36
    Open Mon-Thurs 10-9, Fri 10-5, Sat 10-3
    Friends of the Library Group
STEVENSVILLE BRANCH, 2508 Stevensville Rd, Stevensville, L0S 1S0, SAN 367-2549. Tel: 905-382-2051. FAX: 905-382-4683. *Br Head,* Deborah Ashworth; E-mail: dashworth@forterie.library.on.ca
    Library Holdings: Bk Vols 11,000; Per Subs 23
    Open Mon & Wed 3-7:30, Tues, Thurs & Fri 12:30-5, Sat 10-2:30
    Friends of the Library Group

FORT FRANCES

P   FORT FRANCES PUBLIC LIBRARY*, 601 Reid Ave, P9A 0A2. SAN 319-1354. Tel: 807-274-9879. FAX: 807-274-4496. Web Site: www.fort-frances.com/library.
Founded 1914. Pop 8,200; Circ 157,000
Library Holdings: Bk Vols 54,000; Per Subs 143
Automation Activity & Vendor Info: (Acquisitions) SirsiDynix
Mem of Ontario Library Service North
Open Mon-Fri (Sept-May) 9-9, Sat 10-5, Sun 1-4
Friends of the Library Group

S   UNITED NATIVE FRIENDSHIP CENTRE*, Literacy Department Library, 516 Portage Ave, P9A 3N1. (Mail add: PO Box 752, P9A 3N1), SAN 373-7578. Tel: 807-274-8541. FAX: 807-274-4110. *Librn,* Dean McMahon; Staff 2 (MLS 2)
Library Holdings: Bk Titles 400; Per Subs 50
Special Services for the Deaf - High interest/low vocabulary bks
Open Mon-Fri 8:30-4:30

GANANOQUE

P   GANANOQUE PUBLIC LIBRARY*, 100 Park St, K7G 2Y5. SAN 319-1370. Tel: 613-382-2436. E-mail: gplp@bellnet.ca. *Librn,* John Love
Pop 5,000; Circ 39,400
Library Holdings: Bk Titles 19,000; Bk Vols 19,500; Per Subs 40
Special Collections: Gananoque History Coll
Open Mon-Fri 1-5, Sat 10-3

GEORGETOWN

S   CPI CANADA, INC*, Technical Library, 45 River Dr, L7G 2J4. SAN 325-6685. Tel: 905-877-0161. FAX: 905-877-5327. Web Site: www.cpii.com/cmp. *Tech Support,* Liz Robb
Library Holdings: Bk Vols 1,015
Subject Interests: Eng
Open Mon-Fri 8:30-5

P   HALTON HILLS PUBLIC LIBRARY, Nine Church St, L7G 2A3. SAN 367-2573. Tel: 905-873-2681. FAX: 905-873-6118. Web Site: www.hhpl.on.ca. *Dir,* Jane Diamanti; E-mail: jane.diamanti@haltonhills.ca; *Dep Dir,* Geoffrey Cannon; E-mail: geoff.cannon@haltonhills.ca; Staff 6 (MLS 6)
Founded 1880. Pop 60,000; Circ 490,000
Special Collections: Local Hist
Automation Activity & Vendor Info: (Acquisitions) SirsiDynix; (Cataloging) SirsiDynix; (Circulation) SirsiDynix; (OPAC) SirsiDynix
Database Vendor: SirsiDynix
Wireless access
Publications: Index to Births, Marriage, Deaths for Georgetown Herald, Acton Free Press, Canadian Champion Newspapers
Partic in Halinet
Open Tues & Thurs 9:30-8:30, Fri & Sat 9:30-5, Sun (Oct-May) 1-5
Friends of the Library Group

Branches: 1
ACTON BRANCH, 17 River St, Acton, L7J 1C2, SAN 367-2603. Tel: 519-853-0301. FAX: 519-853-3110. *Br Librn,* Mary Land; E-mail: mary.land@haltonhills.ca
    Open Tues-Thurs 9:30-8:30, Fri & Sat 9:30-5
    Friends of the Library Group

GODERICH

L   HURON LAW ASSOCIATION*, Huron County Courthouse Library, One The Square, N7A 1M2. SAN 325-1373. Tel: 519-524-7962. FAX: 519-524-1065. E-mail: huronlaw@hurontel.on.ca. *Librn,* Barb Alcook
Library Holdings: Bk Vols 7,800
Special Collections: Canadian Statutes back to 1852
Restriction: Staff & mem only

GORE BAY

P   GORE BAY UNION PUBLIC LIBRARY*, 15 Water St, P0P 1H0. (Mail add: PO Box 225, P0P 1H0), SAN 319-1419. Tel: 705-282-2221. FAX: 705-282-3076. E-mail: gorebaylibrary@gorebaycable.com. *Librn,* Johanna Allison
Pop 1,466; Circ 18,269
Library Holdings: Bk Titles 48,000; Per Subs 9
Mem of Ontario Library Service North
Open Mon & Tues 2-5, Thurs & Fri 2-8, Sat 10-1

GRAND VALLEY

P   GRAND VALLEY PUBLIC LIBRARY*, Four Amaranth St E, L0N 1G0. (Mail add: PO Box 129, L0N 1G0), SAN 319-1435. Tel: 519-928-5622. FAX: 519-928-2586. Web Site: www.grandvalley.org. *Librn,* Shann Leighton; E-mail: shannleighton@primus.ca
Founded 1913. Pop 2,537; Circ 59,323
Jan 2005-Dec 2005 Income $181,955, Provincial (CAN) $4,298, City (CAN) $153,238, Federal (CAN) $6,011, Locally Generated Income (CAN) $18,408. Mats Exp $27,213, Books (CAN) $22,326, Per/Ser (Incl. Access Fees) (CAN) $1,800, AV Mat (CAN) $2,339, Electronic Ref Mat (Incl. Access Fees) (CAN) $748
Library Holdings: CDs 343; DVDs 1,200; Large Print Bks 456; Bk Vols 21,546; Per Subs 53; Talking Bks 329
Automation Activity & Vendor Info: (Cataloging) ByWater Solutions; (Circulation) ByWater Solutions; (OPAC) ByWater Solutions
Wireless access
Partic in Southern Ontario Libr Serv
Open Mon, Wed & Fri 10-6, Tues & Thurs 2-8, Sat 10-4
Friends of the Library Group

GRAVENHURST

P   GRAVENHURST PUBLIC LIBRARY*, 180 Sharpe St W, P1P 1J1. SAN 319-1443. Tel: 705-687-3382. FAX: 705-687-7016. Web Site: www.gravenhurst.ca/library. *Chief Librn,* Robena Kirton
Pop 10,500; Circ 82,000
Library Holdings: Bk Vols 37,000; Per Subs 50
Automation Activity & Vendor Info: (Cataloging) SirsiDynix; (Circulation) SirsiDynix; (OPAC) SirsiDynix
Database Vendor: SirsiDynix
Partic in Southern Ontario Libr Serv
Open Mon & Fri 10-5, Tues-Thurs 10-8, Sat 10-3

GRIMSBY

P   GRIMSBY PUBLIC LIBRARY, 18 Carnegie Lane, L3M 1Y1. SAN 319-1451. Tel: 905-945-5142. FAX: 905-945-4442. Web Site: library.grimsby.ca. *Chief Librn,* Lita Barry; Staff 2 (MLS 2)
Founded 1871. Pop 25,000; Circ 236,000
Library Holdings: Bk Vols 50,000; Per Subs 100
Wireless access
Open Mon-Thurs 9-9, Fri & Sat 9-5, Sun (Sept-Apr) 1-5

GUELPH

S   FARM & FOOD CARE ONTARIO LIBRARY*, 100 Stone Rd W, Ste 106, N1G 5L3. SAN 373-6792. Tel: 519-837-1326. FAX: 519-837-3209. E-mail: info@farmfoodcare.org. Web Site: www.farmfoodcare.org. *Exec Dir,* Crystal MacKay
Founded 1988
Library Holdings: Bk Titles 50; Per Subs 20
Wireless access
Publications: Food for Thought (Booklet & Video)

M   GUELPH GENERAL HOSPITAL, Dr William Howitt Memorial Learning Centre, 115 Delhi St, N1E 4J4. SAN 325-0466. Tel: 519-837-6440, Ext 2215. FAX: 519-837-6467. *Libr & Info Spec,* Tracy Morgan; E-mail: tmorgan@gghorg.ca; Staff 1 (Non-MLS 1)

Founded 1979
Partic in Canadian Health Libraries Association; Ont Libr Asn; Ontario
Health Libraries Association; Wellington-Waterloo-Dufferin Health Library
Network
Open Tues-Thurs 7:30-3:30
Restriction: Restricted access

P　　GUELPH PUBLIC LIBRARY*, 100 Norfolk St, N1H 4J6. SAN
319-146X. Tel: 519-824-6220. FAX: 519-824-8342. Web Site:
www.library.guelph.on.ca. *Chief Exec Officer,* Kitty Pope; E-mail:
kpope@library.guelph; *Adult Info Serv Mgr, Circ,* Steve Kraft; E-mail:
skraft@libray.guelph.on.ca; *Adult Serv,* Cathy McInnis; E-mail:
cmcinnis@library.guelph.on.ca; *Archives,* Darcy Hiltz; *Ch,* Andrea Curtis;
Extn Serv, Glenda Duffin; E-mail: gduffin@library.guelph.on.ca; *Info Serv,*
Karen Cafarella; *ILL,* Mary Ellen Cann; Staff 42 (MLS 13, Non-MLS 29)
Founded 1883. Pop 100,000; Circ 1,200,000
Library Holdings: AV Mats 16,400; e-books 3,400; High Interest/Low
Vocabulary Bk Vols 120; Large Print Bks 7,000; Bk Titles 195,700; Bk
Vols 300,650; Per Subs 185; Talking Bks 1,500
Special Collections: Can & Prov
Subject Interests: Local hist
Automation Activity & Vendor Info: (Acquisitions) SirsiDynix;
(Cataloging) SirsiDynix; (Circulation) SirsiDynix
Database Vendor: SirsiDynix
Wireless access
Special Services for the Blind - Bks on cassette; Bks on CD; Braille bks;
Talking bks
Open Mon-Fri 10-9, Sat 9-5, Sun 1-5 (May-Sept)
Friends of the Library Group
Branches: 5
BULL FROG MALL BRANCH, 380 Eramosa Rd, N1E 6R2. Tel:
　519-829-4401. *Br Supvr,* Dan Atkins
　Open Mon-Fri 10-8, Sat 9-5, Sun (Winter) 1-5
EAST SIDE BRANCH, One Starwood Dr, N1E 0H5. Tel: 519-829-4405.
　Br Supvr, Nancy Clarke
　Open Mon-Fri 10-8, Sat 9-5, Sun (Winter) 1-5
SCOTTSDALE CENTRE BRANCH, 650 Scottsdale Dr, N1G 3M2. Tel:
　519-829-4402. *Br Dir,* Robin Tunney
　Open Mon-Fri 10-8, Sun (Winter) 1-5
WEST END BRANCH, 21 Imperial Rd S, N1K 1X3. Tel: 519-829-4403.
　Br Supvr, Sharon Turner
　Open Mon-Fri 10-9, Sat 9-5, Sun 1-5
WESTMINSTER SQUARE BRANCH, 100-31 Farley Dr, N1L 0B7. Tel:
　519-829-4404. *Br Supvr,* Cathy Taylor
　Open Mon-Fri 10-8, Sat 9-5, Sun (Winter) 1-5
Bookmobiles: 1

S　　OPIRG GUELPH LIBRARY, University of Guelph, One Trent Lane, N1G
2W1. SAN 325-6014. Tel: 519-824-2091. FAX: 519-824-8990. E-mail:
opirg@uoguelph.ca. Web Site: www.opirgguelph.org. *In Charge,* Caroline
Ayer; Staff 0.5 (Non-MLS 0.5)
Founded 1976
Library Holdings: AV Mats 50; Bk Titles 1,500; Per Subs 20; Spec
Interest Per Sub 10
Wireless access
Function: AV serv, Copy machines, Orientations, Workshops
Open Mon-Thurs 11-5
Restriction: Circ to mem only, Limited access for the pub, Mem only,
Open to pub for ref & circ; with some limitations

C　　UNIVERSITY OF GUELPH*, McLaughlin Library, 50 Stone Rd E, N1G
2W1. SAN 319-1508. Tel: 519-824-4120, Ext 52075, 519-824-4120, Ext
52181. Interlibrary Loan Service Tel: 519-824-4120, Ext 52301. Reference
Tel: 519-824-4120, Ext 54255. Administration Tel: 519-824-4120, Ext
52073. Information Services Tel: 519-824-4120, Ext 56802. FAX:
519-824-6931. Web Site: www.lib.uoguelph.ca/. *Chief Librn,* Michael
Ridley; E-mail: mridley@uoguelph.ca; *Circ, Mgr, ILL,* Donna Sartori;
E-mail: dsartori@uoguelph.ca; *Acq,* Linda DaMaren; Tel: 519-824-4120,
Ext 53623, E-mail: linda@uoguelph.ca; *E-Learning & Reserves,* Heather
Martin; Tel: 519-824-4120, Ext 54701, E-mail: martin@uoguelph.ca; *Info
Res,* Helen Salmon; Tel: 519-824-4120, Ext 52121, E-mail:
hsalmon@uoguelph.ca; *Res Serv,* Janet Kaufman; E-mail:
jkaufman@uoguelph.ca; *Spec Coll & Archives Librn,* Lorne Bruce; Tel:
519-824-4120, Ext 52089, E-mail: lbruce@uoguelph.ca; Staff 36 (MLS 28,
Non-MLS 8)
Founded 1968. Enrl 14,300; Fac 939; Highest Degree: Doctorate
Library Holdings: Bk Vols 1,000,250; Per Subs 7,609
Special Collections: Agricultural Government Publications from many
countries; Agricultural History; Apiculture; Early Canadian Travel Coll;
Family Studies; FAO, Can & Prov, ERIC; Guelph Spring Festival;
Landscape Architecture; Literary & Theatre Archives (Blyth Festival, Black
Theatre Canada, Factory Theatre, NDWT, LM Montgomery, Pheonix
Theatre, Shaw Festival Theatre, Theatre Columbus, Theatre Francais de
Toronto, Le Theatre du P'tit Bonheur, Theatre Passe Maraille, Tarragon

Theatre, Theatre of Toronto, Toronto Free Theatre, Toronto Workshop
Production, Young People's & Open Circle Theatre of Toronto); National
Board Archives; Scottish Studies; Upper Canada History
Subject Interests: Agr, Biological sci, Consumer studies, Environ sci,
Family studies, Food admin, Hotel, Veterinary med
Automation Activity & Vendor Info: (Acquisitions) Ex Libris Group;
(Cataloging) Ex Libris Group; (Circulation) Ex Libris Group; (Course
Reserve) Ex Libris Group; (ILL) Ex Libris Group; (Media Booking) Ex
Libris Group; (OPAC) Ex Libris Group; (Serials) Ex Libris Group
Publications: Bernard Shaw on Stage; Bibliography Series; Collection
Update; Shaw Festival Production Record; Technical Report Series; Theater
Archives
Partic in Association of Research Libraries (ARL)
Departmental Libraries:
LIBRARY CENTRE FOR STUDENTS WITH DISABILITIES, 50 Stone
　Rd E, N1G 2W1. Tel: 519-824-4120, Ext 52312. *Mgr,* Athel Gow
　Open Mon-Fri 8:30-4:30

S　　UPPER GRAND DISTRICT SCHOOL BOARD, Terry James Resource
Library, 500 Victoria Rd N, N1E 6K2. SAN 329-9732. Tel: 519-822-4420.
FAX: 519-763-6870. E-mail: terryjames.library@ugdsb.on.ca. Web Site:
library.ugdsb.on.ca. *Mgr, Libr Serv,* Michelle Campbell; E-mail:
michelle.campbell@ugdsb.on.ca. Subject Specialists: *Educ,* Michelle
Campbell; Staff 13.5 (MLS 1, Non-MLS 12.5)
Founded 1972
Library Holdings: Audiobooks 100; DVDs 2,000; Bk Titles 15,000; Per
Subs 25; Videos 5,000
Subject Interests: Spec educ
Automation Activity & Vendor Info: (Cataloging) SirsiDynix;
(Circulation) SirsiDynix; (Media Booking) SirsiDynix; (OPAC) SirsiDynix
Database Vendor: SirsiDynix
Wireless access
Publications: Bibliographies

L　　WELLINGTON LAW ASSOCIATION LIBRARY*, Court House, 74
Woolwich St, N1H 3T9. SAN 328-0160. Tel: 519-763-6365. FAX:
519-763-6847. E-mail: wellington@on.aibn.com. *Librn,* John Eddie Kerr
Library Holdings: Bk Vols 6,000

HAILEYBURY

C　　NORTHERN COLLEGE LIBRARY*, 640 Latchford St, P0J 1K0. (Mail
add: PO Box 2060, P0J 1K0), SAN 367-3502. Tel: 705-672-3376, Ext
8806. FAX: 705-672-5404. E-mail: libraryh@northern.on.ca. Web Site:
www.northernc.on.ca. *Libr Tech,* Brenda Morissette; E-mail:
morissetteb@northern.on.ca
Enrl 450; Fac 25
Library Holdings: Bk Titles 4,000; Per Subs 30
Wireless access
Partic in Ontario Colleges Library Service (OCLS)
Open Mon-Fri (Summer) 8-1 & 2-4; Mon-Fri (Winter) 8am-9pm, Sat 10-3

HALIBURTON

P　　HALIBURTON COUNTY PUBLIC LIBRARY*, Administrative Centre, 78
Maple Ave, K0M 1S0. (Mail add: PO Box 119, K0M 1S0), SAN
319-1524. Tel: 705-457-2241. FAX: 705-457-9586. E-mail:
info@haliburtonlibrary.ca. Web Site: www.haliburtonlibrary.ca. *Chief Exec
Officer, County Librn,* Bessie Sullivan; *Br Serv Librn,* Catherine Coles;
Coll Develop, Mkt, Sherrill Sherwood; Staff 5 (MLS 2, Non-MLS 3)
Founded 1965. Pop 16,000; Circ 100,746
Jan 2010-Dec 2010 Income (CAN) $715,355, Provincial (CAN) $120,355,
County (CAN) $595,000. Mats Exp $99,589, Books $78,862, Per/Ser (Incl.
Access Fees) $5,727, AV Mat $12,000, Presv $3,000. Sal (CAN) $496,061
Library Holdings: Audiobooks 1,149; DVDs 2,814; Large Print Bks
2,214; Bk Vols 474,811; Per Subs 42
Automation Activity & Vendor Info: (Acquisitions) SIRSI WorkFlows;
(Cataloging) SIRSI WorkFlows; (Circulation) SIRSI WorkFlows; (ILL)
SIRSI WorkFlows; (OPAC) SIRSI WorkFlows
Wireless access
Partic in Ontario Library Consortium; Southern Ontario Libr Serv
Open Mon-Fri 8:30-4:30
Friends of the Library Group
Branches: 8
CARDIFF BRANCH, 2778 Monck Rd, Cardiff, K0L 1M0. Tel:
　613-339-2712. *Supvr,* Cathy Passaretti
　Open Tues 2-6, Wed 6:30pm-8:30pm, Fri & Sat 10-Noon
DORSET BRANCH, 1051 Main St, Dorset, P0A 1E0. Tel: 705-766-9969.
　Supvr, Ruth Lynch
　Open Tues & Sat 10am-12:30pm, Wed 2-4:30, Thurs 6pm-8pm
DYSART BRANCH, 78 Maple Ave, K0M 1S0. Tel: 705-457-1791. *Supvr,*
　Victoria Fraser
　Open Tues-Thurs 10-8, Fri 10-5

GOODERHAM BRANCH, 1032 Gooderham St, Gooderham, K0M 1R0. Tel: 705-447-3163. *Supvr,* Marilyn Billings
Open Tues 6pm-8pm, Wed & Thurs 1-4, Sat 10-Noon

HIGHLAND GROVE BRANCH, 5373 Loop Rd, Highland Grove, K0L 2A0. Tel: 705-448-2652. *Supvr,* Joanne Burroughs
Open Tues & Sat 12-3:30, Thurs 6:30pm-8:30pm

MINDEN BRANCH, 176 Bobcaygeon Rd, Minden, K0M 2K0. Tel: 705-286-2491. *Supvr,* Diane Peacock
Open Tues-Thurs 10-8, Fri & Sat 10-5

STANHOPE BRANCH, 1109 N Shore Rd, Algonquin Highlands, K0M 1J1. Tel: 705-489-2402. *Supvr,* Gayle Wetmore
Open Tues 12-2 & 6-9, Wed 10-2, Thurs & Sat 10-Noon

WILBERFORCE BRANCH, 2307 Loop Rd, Wilberforce, K0L 3C0. Tel: 705-448-2510. *Supvr,* Donna Atkinson
Open Tues 6pm-8pm, Thurs & Fri 12:30-4, Sat 10-12:30

HAMILTON

S ARCELORMITTAL DOFASCO, Library Resource Centre, 1390 Burlington St E, L8N 3J5. (Mail add: PO Box 2460, L8N 3J5), SAN 373-143X. Tel: 905-548-7200, Ext 6223. FAX: 905-548-4653. E-mail: libraryresourcecentre@arcelormittal.com. *Mgr,* Carolyne Darimont; *Asst Librn,* Alice Desrocher; Staff 2 (MLS 2)
Library Holdings: Bk Vols 5,000; Per Subs 200
Subject Interests: Metallurgy
Automation Activity & Vendor Info: (Acquisitions) SydneyPlus; (Cataloging) SydneyPlus; (Circulation) SydneyPlus; (OPAC) SydneyPlus
Database Vendor: American Chemical Society, Dialog, EBSCO Information Services, EBSCOhost, Elsevier, Factiva.com, Infotrieve, Knovel, ScienceDirect
Restriction: Access at librarian's discretion, Authorized personnel only, Circulates for staff only, Not open to pub

S MURIEL ISABEL BOSTWICK LIBRARY*, Art Gallery of Hamilton, 123 King St W, L8P 4S8. SAN 325-6359. Tel: 905-527-6610. FAX: 905-577-6940. Web Site: www.artgalleryofhamilton.on.ca. *Pres,* Louise Dompierre; *Librn,* Helen Hadden
Library Holdings: Bk Vols 1,200; Per Subs 57

R CANADIAN BAPTIST ARCHIVES*, McMaster Divinity Col, 1280 Main St W, L8S 4K1. SAN 319-1532. Tel: 905-525-9140, Ext 23511. FAX: 905-577-4782. E-mail: cbarch@mcmaster.ca. Web Site: www.macdiv.ca/students/baptistarchives.php. *Archives Dir,* Dr Gord Heath; Tel: 905-525-9140, Ext 26409, E-mail: gheath@mcmaster.ca; *Archivist,* Adam McCulloch
Founded 1865
Special Collections: Brethren Coll; C H Spurgeon Coll; French Canadian Protestant Coll; John Milton Society for the Blind in Canada Coll; McMaster University Coll (to 1957)
Subject Interests: Biographies of ministers, Bks about Baptists, Bks by Baptists, Can Baptist church life, Doctrine, Educ work, Hist, Lay leaders
Restriction: Open by appt only

G CANADIAN CENTRE FOR OCCUPATIONAL HEALTH & SAFETY, Resource Centre, 135 Hunter St E, L8N 1M5. SAN 321-9054. Tel: 905-572-2981, Ext 4454. FAX: 905-572-4500. E-mail: docdel@ccohs.ca. Web Site: www.ccohs.ca. *Supvr,* Janice Carey; Staff 1 (Non-MLS 1)
Founded 1981
Library Holdings: AV Mats 250; CDs 186; DVDs 53; e-journals 14; Electronic Media & Resources 150; Microforms 245,000; Bk Titles 35,000; Bk Vols 67,000; Per Subs 418; Spec Interest Per Sub 48; Videos 185
Special Collections: CIS Occupational Health & Safety Coll, 1969-2011, microfiche; NIOSHtic, 1971-1998, microfiche; OSHline, 1999-present
Subject Interests: Occupational health, Occupational safety
Automation Activity & Vendor Info: (Acquisitions) EBSCO Online; (ILL) Amicus; (Serials) Inmagic, Inc.
Database Vendor: FileMaker
Publications: Canadiana; CIS; OSHline
Open Mon-Fri 8:30-4:30
Restriction: Restricted loan policy

M HAMILTON HEALTH SCIENCES*, Juravinski Cancer Centre Library, 699 Concession St, L8V 5C2. SAN 324-6663. Tel: 905-387-9711, Ext 65100. FAX: 905-575-6317. E-mail: librarian@jcc.hhsc.ca. Web Site: www.hrcc.on.ca/. *Librn,* Mike Fraumeni
Library Holdings: Bk Vols 1,000; Per Subs 60
Subject Interests: Oncology
Restriction: Open by appt only

M HAMILTON HEALTH SCIENCES*, General Medical Library, 286 Victoria Ave N, L8L 5G4. SAN 319-1559. Tel: 905-527-4322, Ext 44247, 905-527-4322, Ext 44248. FAX: 905-577-1453. E-mail: libraryg@hhsc.ca. Web Site: www.hamiltonhealthsciences.ca. *Librn,* Victoria Chambers; *Mgr,*

Debra Wingfield; E-mail: wingfdeb@hhsc.ca; *Libr Tech,* Karen Murray; Staff 4 (MLS 1, Non-MLS 3)
Founded 1931
Library Holdings: Bk Vols 3,500; Per Subs 135
Subject Interests: Cardiology, Neurology, Nursing, Nutrition, Rehabilitation, Trauma
Restriction: Staff use only

L HAMILTON LAW ASSOCIATION LIBRARY*, Anthony Pepe Memorial Law Library, 45 Main St E, Ste 500, L8N 2B7. SAN 319-1567. Tel: 905-522-1563. FAX: 905-572-1188. Web Site: www.hamiltonlaw.on.ca. *Librn,* Mary Jane Kearns-Padgett; Staff 3 (MLS 1, Non-MLS 2)
Founded 1879
Library Holdings: Bk Vols 28,000
Database Vendor: LexisNexis
Wireless access
Publications: Members' Handbook; News Magazine; The HLA Journal (Bi-monthly)
Restriction: Mem only

P HAMILTON PUBLIC LIBRARY, 55 York Blvd, L8R 3K1. (Mail add: PO Box 2700, L8N 4E4), SAN 367-3537. Tel: 905-546-3200. FAX: 905-546-3202. Web Site: www.myhamilton.ca/public-library. *Chief Librn,* Paul Takala; Tel: 905-546-3215, E-mail: ptakala@hpl.ca; *Dir of Coll,* Michael Ciccone; E-mail: mciccone@hpl.ca; *Dir, Pub Serv,* Karen Anderson; Tel: 905-546-3200, Ext 3497, E-mail: kjanders@hpl.ca; *Dir, Pub Serv,* Rebecca Raven; Tel: 905-546-3200, Ext 3455, E-mail: rraven@hpl.ca; *Dir, Finance & Fac,* Robin Hewitt; E-mail: rhewitt@hpl.ca; *Dir, Human Res,* Lisa Dupelle; Fax: 905-546-3204, E-mail: ldupelle@hpl.ca; Staff 294 (MLS 46, Non-MLS 248)
Founded 1889. Pop 531,057; Circ 6,906,628
Special Collections: Canadiana, bks, micro; Local History (Hamilton), bks, micro; Rare Books (incl Cummer, Lyle, Mullin & Witton Colls); Resource Center for Disabled Persons; War of 1812, bks & maps
Subject Interests: Fiction, Fine arts, Soc sci
Automation Activity & Vendor Info: (Circulation) Horizon
Wireless access
Function: Adult bk club, Adult literacy prog, Archival coll, Art exhibits, Audiobks via web, Bk club(s), Bk reviews (Group), Bks on CD, Children's prog, Computer training, Computers for patron use, Digital talking bks, e-mail serv, E-Reserves, Electronic databases & coll, Exhibits, Free DVD rentals, Handicapped accessible, Homebound delivery serv, Homework prog, ILL available, Learning ctr, Literacy & newcomer serv, Magnifiers for reading, Music CDs, Online cat, Online ref, Online searches, Orientations, Outreach serv, OverDrive digital audio bks, Photocopying/Printing, Prog for adults, Prog for children & young adult, Pub access computers, Ref serv in person, Senior computer classes, Senior outreach, Story hour, Summer reading prog, Teen prog, Telephone ref, Web-catalog, Wheelchair accessible
Publications: What's Happening (Newsletter)
Partic in Southern Ontario Libr Serv
Open Mon-Thurs 9-9, Fri 9-6, Sat 9-5, Sun (Sept-April) 1-5
Restriction: Authorized scholars by appt
Friends of the Library Group
Branches: 23
ANCASTER, 300 Wilson St E, Ancaster, L9G 2B9, SAN 367-4258. Tel: 905-648-6911. *Mgr,* Amy Hunter; Tel: 905-546-3200, Ext 3463, E-mail: ahunter@hpl.ca
Circ 369,223
Function: Children's prog, Computers for patron use, Electronic databases & coll, OverDrive digital audio bks, Photocopying/Printing, Preschool outreach, Prog for adults, Prog for children & young adult, Pub access computers, Story hour, Summer reading prog, Wheelchair accessible
Open Mon-Thurs 10-9, Sat 10-5
Friends of the Library Group
BARTON, 571 Barton St E, L8L 2Z4, SAN 367-3561. Tel: 905-546-3450. *Br Mgr,* Meg Uttangi-Matsos; Tel: 905-546-3200, Ext 3452, E-mail: muttangi@hpl.ca
Circ 137,776
Function: Children's prog, Computers for patron use, OverDrive digital audio bks, Photocopying/Printing, Pub access computers, Story hour, Summer reading prog, Wheelchair accessible
Open Mon & Wed 1-8, Tues, Thurs & Sat 10-5
Friends of the Library Group
BINBROOK BRANCH, 2641 Hwy 56, Binbrook, L0R 1C0. (Mail add: PO Box 89, Binbrook, L0R 1C0), SAN 367-4282. Tel: 905-692-3323. *Br Mgr,* Rita Bozz; Tel: 905-546-3200, Ext 1046, E-mail: rbozz@hpl.ca
Circ 91,471
Function: Children's prog, Computers for patron use, Prog for children & young adult, Story hour, Summer reading prog
Open Mon & Wed 1-8, Tues, Thurs & Sat 10-5
Friends of the Library Group

CARLISLE BRANCH, 1496 Centre Rd, Carlisle, L0R 1H0. (Mail add: PO Box 320, Carlisle, L0R 1H0), SAN 367-4312. Tel: 905-689-8769. *Br Mgr,* Ania Van Minnen; Tel: 905-546-3200, Ext 6603, E-mail: avanminn@hpl.ca
Circ 43,131
Function: Computers for patron use, Photocopying/Printing, Pub access computers, Story hour, Summer reading prog, Wheelchair accessible
Open Mon-Wed 2-8, Thurs & Sat 10-5
Friends of the Library Group

CONCESSION, 565 Concession St, L8V 1A8, SAN 367-3650. Tel: 905-546-3200, Ext 3415. *Br Mgr,* Rita Bozz; Tel: 905-546-3200, Ext 1046, E-mail: rbozz@hpl.ca
Circ 198,473
Function: Children's prog, Computers for patron use, OverDrive digital audio bks, Photocopying/Printing, Pub access computers, Story hour, Summer reading prog, Wheelchair accessible
Open Tues & Thurs 10-8, Wed & Fri 10-6, Sat 10-5
Friends of the Library Group

DUNDAS BRANCH, 18 Ogilvie St, Dundas, L9H 2S2, SAN 319-1125. Tel: 905-627-3507. *Br Mgr,* Leslie Muirhead; Tel: 905-627-3507, Ext 1404, E-mail: lmuirhea@hpl.ca
Founded 1883. Circ 411,865
Special Collections: Arts & Crafts Coll; Children's French Coll; Dundas History Coll
Subject Interests: Can poetry
Function: Children's prog, Computers for patron use, OverDrive digital audio bks, Photocopying/Printing, Pub access computers, Story hour, Summer reading prog, Wheelchair accessible
Open Tues-Thurs 10-9, Fri 10-6, Sat 10-5, Sun (Sept-April) 1-5
Friends of the Library Group

FREELTON BRANCH, 1803 Brock Rd, Freelton, L0R 1K0. (Mail add: PO Box 15, Freelton, L0R 1K0), SAN 367-4347. Tel: 905-659-7639. *Br Mgr,* Ania Van Minnen; Tel: 905-546-3200, Ext 6603, E-mail: avanminn@hpl.ca
Circ 29,048
Function: Children's prog, OverDrive digital audio bks, Photocopying/Printing, Pub access computers, Story hour, Summer reading prog, Wheelchair accessible
Open Mon & Wed 4-8, Tues, Thurs & Sat 2-5
Friends of the Library Group

GREENSVILLE, 59 Kirby Ave, Unit 5, Greensville, L9H 4H6, SAN 367-4401. Tel: 905-627-4951. *Br Mgr,* Leslie Muirhead; Tel: 905-546-3200, Ext 1404, E-mail: lmuirhea@hpl.ca
Circ 33,417
Function: Children's prog, OverDrive digital audio bks, Photocopying/Printing, Pub access computers, Story hour, Summer reading prog, Wheelchair accessible
Open Mon & Wed 4-8, Tues, Thurs & Sat 2-5
Friends of the Library Group

KENILWORTH, 103 Kenilworth Ave N, L8H 4R6, SAN 367-3596. Tel: 905-546-3960. *Br Mgr,* Meg Uttangi-Matsos; Tel: 905-546-3200, Ext 3473, E-mail: muttangi@hpl.ca
Circ 192,032
Function: Children's prog, Computers for patron use, OverDrive digital audio bks, Photocopying/Printing, Pub access computers, Story hour, Summer reading prog, Wheelchair accessible
Open Mon & Wed 10-6, Tues & Thurs 10-8, Sat 10-5
Friends of the Library Group

LOCKE, 285 Locke St S, L8P 4C2, SAN 367-3626. Tel: 905-546-3492. *Br Mgr,* Caitlin Fralick; Tel: 905-546-3200, Ext 3400, E-mail: cfralick@hpl.ca
Circ 171,343
Function: Children's prog, Computers for patron use, OverDrive digital audio bks, Photocopying/Printing, Pub access computers, Story hour, Summer reading prog, Wheelchair accessible
Open Mon, Wed & Sat 10-5, Tues & Thurs 1-8
Friends of the Library Group

LYNDEN BRANCH, 79 Lynden Rd, Lynden, L0R 1T0. (Mail add: PO Box 9, Lynden, L0R 1T0), SAN 367-4436. Tel: 519-647-2571. *Br Mgr,* Ania Van Minnen; Tel: 905-546-3200, Ext 6603, E-mail: avanminn@hpl.ca
Circ 52,182
Function: Children's prog, Computers for patron use, Photocopying/Printing, Pub access computers, Summer reading prog
Open Mon-Wed 2-8, Thurs 2-5, Sat 10-4
Friends of the Library Group

MILLGROVE BRANCH, 857 Millgrove Side Rd, Millgrove, L0R 1V0. (Mail add: PO Box 220, Millgrove, L0R 1V0), SAN 367-4460. Tel: 905-689-6582. *Br Mgr,* Ania Van Minnen; Tel: 905-546-3200, Ext 6603, E-mail: avanminn@hpl.ca
Circ 21,980
Function: Children's prog, Computers for patron use, OverDrive digital audio bks, Photocopying/Printing, Pub access computers, Story hour, Summer reading prog, Wheelchair accessible

Open Mon & Wed 2-5, Tues & Thurs 4-8, Sat 10-1
Friends of the Library Group

MOUNT HOPE, 3027 Homestead Dr, Mount Hope, L0R 1W0, SAN 367-4371. Tel: 905-679-6445. *Br Mgr,* Rita Bozz; Tel: 905-546-3200, Ext 1046, E-mail: rbozz@hpl.ca
Circ 31,599
Function: Children's prog, Computers for patron use, OverDrive digital audio bks, Photocopying/Printing, Story hour, Summer reading prog, Wheelchair accessible
Open Mon & Wed 2-5, Tues & Thurs 2-8
Friends of the Library Group

RED HILL, 695 Queenston Rd, L8G 1A1, SAN 367-3715. Tel: 905-546-2069. *Br Mgr,* Jennifer Gal; Tel: 905-546-3200, Ext 2976, E-mail: jgal@hpl.ca
Circ 343,423
Function: Children's prog, Computers for patron use, OverDrive digital audio bks, Photocopying/Printing, Pub access computers, Story hour, Summer reading prog, Wheelchair accessible
Open Tues-Thurs 10-9, Fri 10-6, Sat 10-5, Sun (Sept-April) 1-5
Friends of the Library Group

ROCKTON BRANCH, 795 Old Hwy 8, Rockton, L0R 1X0. (Mail add: Rockton Post Office, Rockton, L0R 1X0), SAN 367-4525. Tel: 519-647-2272. *Br Mgr,* Ania Van Minnen; Tel: 905-546-3200, Ext 6603, E-mail: avanminn@hpl.ca
Circ 23,105
Function: Children's prog, Computers for patron use, OverDrive digital audio bks, Photocopying/Printing, Pub access computers, Story hour, Summer reading prog
Open Mon & Wed 2-5, Tues & Thurs 4-8, Sat 10-1
Friends of the Library Group

SALTFLEET, 131 Gray Rd, Stoney Creek, L8G 3V3, SAN 367-455X. Tel: 905-662-8611. *Br Mgr,* Simona Dinu; Tel: 905-546-3200, Ext 3417, E-mail: sdinu@hpl.ca
Circ 266,839
Function: Children's prog, Computers for patron use, OverDrive digital audio bks, Photocopying/Printing, Pub access computers, Story hour, Summer reading prog, Wheelchair accessible
Open Mon-Wed 10-9, Thurs 10-6, Sat 10-5
Friends of the Library Group

SHERWOOD, 467 Upper Ottawa St, L8T 3T3, SAN 367-374X. Tel: 905-546-3249. *Br Mgr,* Yvonne Patch; Tel: 905-546-3200, Ext 3436, E-mail: ypatch@hpl.ca
Circ 299,677
Function: Children's prog, Computers for patron use, OverDrive digital audio bks, Photocopying/Printing, Story hour, Summer reading prog, Wheelchair accessible
Open Mon, Wed & Thurs 10-9, Tues 10-6, Sat 10-5
Friends of the Library Group

STONEY CREEK BRANCH, 777 Hwy 8, Stoney Creek, L8E 5J4, SAN 367-4614. Tel: 905-643-2912. *Br Mgr,* Simona Dinu; Tel: 905-546-3200, Ext 1046, E-mail: sdinu@hpl.ca
Circ 113,135
Function: Children's prog, Computers for patron use, OverDrive digital audio bks, Photocopying/Printing, Pub access computers, Story hour, Summer reading prog, Wheelchair accessible
Open Mon & Wed 1-8, Tues, Thurs & Sat 10-5
Friends of the Library Group

TERRYBERRY, 100 Mohawk Rd W, L9C 1W1, SAN 367-3774. Tel: 905-546-3921. *Br Mgr,* Karen Peter; Tel: 905-546-3200, Ext 7065, E-mail: kpeter@hpl.ca
Circ 658,896
Function: Adult bk club, Children's prog, Photocopying/Printing, Prog for adults, Prog for children & young adult, Story hour, Summer reading prog, Wheelchair accessible
Open Mon-Thurs 10-9, Sat 10-5
Friends of the Library Group

TURNER PARK, 352 Rymal Rd E, L9B 1C2, SAN 367-3685. Tel: 905-546-4790. *Br Mgr,* Carol Wilkinson; Tel: 905-546-3200, Ext 4224, E-mail: cwilkins@hpl.ca
Circ 492,989
Function: Children's prog, Computers for patron use, OverDrive digital audio bks, Photocopying/Printing, Pub access computers, Story hour, Summer reading prog, Wheelchair accessible
Open Mon-Thurs 10-9, Sat 10-5; Sun (Sept-April) 1-5
Friends of the Library Group

VALLEY PARK, 970 Paramount Dr, L8J 1Y2, SAN 367-4495. Tel: 905-573-3141. *Br Mgr,* Yvonne Patch; Tel: 905-546-3200, Ext 3436, E-mail: ypatch@hpl.ca
Circ 172,104
Function: Story hour, Summer reading prog, Wheelchair accessible
Open Mon-Thurs 10-8, Sat 10-5
Friends of the Library Group

WATERDOWN BRANCH, 25 Mill St N, Waterdown, L0R 2H0. (Mail
add: PO Box 550, Waterdown, L0R 2H0), SAN 367-4649. Tel:
905-689-6269. *Br Mgr,* Ania Van Minnen; Tel: 905-546-3200, Ext 6603,
E-mail: avanminn@hpl.ca
Circ 192,140
Function: Children's prog, Computers for patron use, OverDrive digital
audio bks, Photocopying/Printing, Pub access computers, Story hour,
Summer reading prog, Wheelchair accessible
Open Mon-Thurs 10-8, Sat 10-5
Friends of the Library Group
WESTDALE, 955 King St W, L8S 1K9, SAN 367-3804. Tel:
905-546-3456. *Br Mgr,* Caitlin Fralick; Tel: 905-546-3200, Ext 3400,
E-mail: cfralick@hpl.ca
Circ 303,268
Function: Children's prog, Computers for patron use, OverDrive digital
audio bks, Photocopying/Printing, Prog for adults, Prog for children &
young adult, Story hour, Summer reading prog, Wheelchair accessible
Open Mon 10-6, Tues-Thurs 10-9, Sat 10-5
Friends of the Library Group
Bookmobiles: 2. Mgr, Susan Beattie

S   HAMILTON SPECTATOR LIBRARY*, 44 Frid St, L8N 3G3. SAN
319-1605. Tel: 905-526-3315. Web Site: www.thespec.com. *Sr Info Spec,*
Tammie Danciu; E-mail: tdanciu@thespec.com; *Info Tech,* Marilyn
McGrory
Founded 1846
Library Holdings: Bk Vols 4,500
Special Collections: Spectator Issues (1846 to present), Clippings (1972 to
present)
Subject Interests: Current events, News
Open Mon-Fri 8:30-4:30

R   HAMILTON WENTWORTH CATHOLIC DISTRICT SCHOOL BOARD*,
Nicholas Mancini Library Information Center, 44 Hunt St, L8R 3R1. SAN
322-8649. Tel: 905-525-2930. FAX: 905-523-0247. Web Site:
www.hwcdsb.ca. *Mgr,* Phillip Jeffrey; E-mail: jeffreyp@fc.hwcdsb.ca; Staff
10 (MLS 1, Non-MLS 9)
Library Holdings: Bk Titles 7,000; Per Subs 150
Special Collections: Language Arts (Primary & Literature Loan Service
Coll)
Publications: Learning Materials Catalogue; New at the Professional
Library; Professional Bks List
Special Services for the Deaf - Spec interest per
Open Mon-Fri 8-4:30

C   MCMASTER UNIVERSITY LIBRARY, Mills Memorial Library, 1280
Main St W, L8S 4L6. SAN 367-3863. Tel: 905-525-9140, Ext 22077.
Reference Tel: 905-525-9140, Ext 22533. FAX: 905-524-9850. E-mail:
library@mcmaster.ca. Web Site: library.mcmaster.ca. *Actg Univ Librn,*
Vivian Lewis; Tel: 905-524-9140, Ext 23883, E-mail:
lewisvm@mcmaster.ca; *Assoc Univ Librn,* Dale Askey; Tel: 905-525-9140,
Ext 21880, E-mail: askeyd@mcmaster.ca; *Assoc Univ Librn,* Anne Pottier;
Tel: 905-524-9140, Ext 22410, E-mail: pottier@mcmaster.ca; *Assoc Univ
Librn,* Wade Wyckoff; Tel: 905-524-9140, Ext 26557, E-mail:
wyckoff@mcmaster.ca; *Adminr,* Marlene Mastragostino; Tel:
905-525-9140, Ext 24355, E-mail: mastrag@mcmaster.ca; *Libr Develop,*
Anne Plessl; Tel: 905-525-9140, Ext 24865, E-mail: plessla@mcmaster.ca;
Staff 43 (MLS 43)
Founded 1887. Enrl 28,482; Fac 1,330; Highest Degree: Doctorate
May 2010-Apr 2011 Income (Main and Other College/University Libraries)
$17,333,032
Library Holdings: Bk Vols 1,925,459; Per Subs 73,267
Special Collections: Bertrand Russell Archives, bks, ms, flms, tapes;
British Literature (18th Century Coll); Canadian Literary Papers (eg Pierre
Berton, Farley Mowat); Canadian Publishing Papers (Macmillan of Canada,
McClelland & Stewart, Clarke Irwin, etc); Fed & Prov; Holocaust &
Underground Resistance Movements; War & Peace (Vera Brittain Archives,
Canadian Participation in the World Wars)
Subject Interests: British hist, English lit, Geol, Nuclear physics, Relig
studies
Automation Activity & Vendor Info: (Acqusitions) SirsiDynix;
(Circulation) SirsiDynix
Database Vendor: SirsiDynix
Wireless access
Function: Telephone ref
Publications: McMaster University Library Research News
Partic in Canadian Research Knowledge Network; Ontario Council of
University Libraries
Open Mon-Thurs 8am-11pm, Fri 8-6, Sat 10:30-6, Sun 10:30am-11pm
Departmental Libraries:
H G THODE LIBRARY OF SCIENCE & ENGINEERING, 1280 Main St
W, L8S 4P5. Tel: 905-525-9140, Ext 22000. FAX: 905-777-1110.
  E-mail: thoderef@mcmaster.ca. *Assoc Univ Librn,* Anne Pottier; Tel:

905-524-9140, Ext 22410, E-mail: pottier@mcmaster.ca; *Libr Serv Mgr,*
Position Currently Open
Open Mon-Thurs 8am-11pm, Fri 8-6, Sat 10:30-6, Sun 10:30am-11pm

CM HEALTH SCIENCES LIBRARY, 1280 Main St W, L8S 4K1, SAN
367-3898. Tel: 905-525-9140, Ext 22320. FAX: 905-528-3733. E-mail:
hslib@mcmaster.ca. *Dir,* Liz Bayley; Tel: 905-525-9140, Ext 22545,
E-mail: bayleyl@mcmaster.ca; Staff 26 (MLS 8, Non-MLS 18)
Founded 1971
Library Holdings: Bk Titles 57,350; Per Subs 4,430
Special Collections: History of Health & Medicine Coll
Partic in Canadian Research Knowledge Network; Hamilton & District
Health Library Network; Ontario Council of University Libraries; Ontario
Learning Resources for Nursing (OLRN) Consortium
Open Mon-Thurs (Spring) 8am-9:45pm, Fri 8-7:45, Sat & Sun 10-5:45;
Mon-Thurs (Summer) 8-7:45, Fri 8-5:45, Sat & Sun 10-5:45; Mon-Thurs
(Fall & Winter) 8am-11:15pm, Fri 8am-9:45pm, Sat 10-5:45, Sun
10am-10:45pm
INNIS BUSINESS LIBRARY, Kenneth Taylor Hall, 1280 Main St W, Rm
108, L8S 4M4, SAN 367-3928. Tel: 905-525-9140, Ext 22081. FAX:
905-524-0816. E-mail: innisref@mcmaster.ca. *Libr Serv Mgr,* Ann
Pearce; E-mail: apearce@mcmaster.ca
Open Mon-Thurs 8:30am-11pm, Fri 8:30-6, Sun 1-8

J   MOHAWK COLLEGE LIBRARY, Cummings Library, 135 Fennell Ave W,
L9C 1E9. (Mail add: PO Box 2034, L8N 3T2), SAN 367-4010. Tel:
905-575-2077. Information Services Tel: 905-575-2274. FAX:
905-575-2011. E-mail: braintogo@mohawkcollege.ca. Web Site:
www.mohawkcollege.ca/brain. *Assoc Dean, Libr & Learning,* Anna
Johnston; Tel: 905-540-1212, Ext 2737, E-mail:
anna.johnston@mohawkcollege.ca; *Coll & Access Mgt Librn,* Cynthia
Williamson; Tel: 905-575-1212, Ext 3129, E-mail:
cynthia.williamson@mohawkcollege.ca; *Digital Serv Librn,* Jenn Horwath;
Tel: 905-575-1212, Ext 3194, E-mail: jenn.horwath@mohawkcollege.ca;
Digital Syst Librn, Robert Soulliere; Tel: 905-575-1212, Ext 3936, E-mail:
robert.soulliere@mohawkcollege.ca; *Outreach & Instruction Librn,* Marilyn
McDermott; Tel: 905-540-4247, Ext 26720, Fax: 905-528-5307, E-mail:
marilyn.mcdermott@mohawkcollege.ca; Staff 20 (MLS 5, Non-MLS 15)
Founded 1967. Enrl 11,000; Fac 525; Highest Degree: Bachelor
Library Holdings: Bk Vols 50,400; Per Subs 800
Subject Interests: Chem, Computers
Automation Activity & Vendor Info: (Acquisitions) Evergreen;
(Cataloging) Evergreen; (Circulation) Evergreen; (OPAC) Evergreen;
(Serials) Evergreen
Wireless access
Publications: Educational Technology at Mohawk
Open Mon-Thurs 8-7, Fri 8-4:30, Sat 8:30-4:30
Departmental Libraries:
BIZHUB, 135 Fennell Ave W, L9C 1E9. (Mail add: PO Box 2034, L8N
3T2). Tel: 905-575-1212. FAX: 905-575-2011. Web Site:
www.brain.mohawkcollege.ca.
Founded 1967. Enrl 13,000; Fac 525
Automation Activity & Vendor Info: (Course Reserve) Evergreen;
(Media Booking) Evergreen
Database Vendor: Canadian Reference Centre, Cinahl Information
Systems, ebrary, EBSCOhost, Gale Cengage Learning, McGraw-Hill,
OVID Technologies, ProQuest, PubMed, Quicklaw, Safari Books Online,
STAT!Ref (Teton Data Systems), World Book Online, YBP Library
Services
Open Mon-Fri 8am-10pm
BRANTFORD LIBRARY, 411 Elgin St, Brantford, N3T 5V2, SAN
320-5436. Tel: 519-758-6019. Information Services Tel: 519-758-6020.
FAX: 519-758-6008. *In Charge,* Christine Chiasson; Tel: 519-759-7200,
Ext 6020; Staff 1 (Non-MLS 1)
Library Holdings: Bk Vols 9,771; Per Subs 70
Open Mon-Fri 8:30-4:30
IAHS (INSTITUTE FOR APPLIED HEALTH SCIENCES) LIBRARY,
1400 Main St W, L8S 1C7. (Mail add: PO Box 2034, L8N 3T2). Tel:
905-540-4247, Ext 26835. Information Services Tel: 905-540-4247, Ext
26834. FAX: 905-528-5307. *Outreach & Instruction Librn,* Marilyn
McDermott; Tel: 905-540-4247, Ext 26720, E-mail:
marilyn.mcdermott@mohawkcollege.ca; Staff 5 (MLS 1, Non-MLS 4)
Founded 1978. Enrl 1,500; Fac 120; Highest Degree: Bachelor
Library Holdings: Bk Vols 10,978; Per Subs 140
Subject Interests: Allied health, Nursing
Function: ILL available, Ref serv available
Partic in Hamilton & District Health Library Network
Open Mon-Thurs 8:30-7, Fri 8:30-4:30, Sat 11-3
STARRT (SKILLED TRADES & APPRENTICESHIP RESEARCH,
RESOURCES & TRAINING) LIBRARY, 481 Barton St E, Stoney
Creek, L8E 2L7, SAN 320-5452. Tel: 905-575-2504. Information
Services Tel: 905-575-1212, Ext 5038. FAX: 905-575-2549. *Libr Serv
Tech,* April Speare; Tel: 905-575-2504, Ext 5028, E-mail:
april.speare@mohawkcollege.ca; Staff 1 (Non-MLS 1)
Library Holdings: Bk Vols 7,600; Per Subs 45
Open Mon-Thurs 8-7, Fri 8-4

M   ST JOSEPH HEALTHCARE CENTRE FOR MOUNTAIN HEALTH SERVICES*, Library Resource Centre, 100 W Fifth St, L8N 3K7. (Mail add: PO Box 585, L8N 3K7), SAN 324-6604. Tel: 905-388-2511, Ext 36322. FAX: 905-388-7141. Web Site: www.stjosephham.on.ca. *Librn,* Anne Devries
Library Holdings: Bk Titles 1,500; Per Subs 75
Subject Interests: Psychiat disciplines, Related disciplines
Restriction: Open to students, fac & staff

M   SAINT JOSEPH'S HOSPITAL*, Sherman Library, 50 Charlton Ave E, L8N 4A6. SAN 319-1583. Tel: 905-522-4941, Ext 33410. FAX: 905-540-6504. E-mail: library@stjosham.on.ca. *Librn,* Jean Maragno; E-mail: jmaragno@stjosham.on.ca
Founded 1964
Library Holdings: Bk Vols 2,500; Per Subs 180
Special Collections: History of Medicine; Osler Coll
Automation Activity & Vendor Info: (Cataloging) Eloquent Systems Inc
Database Vendor: EBSCOhost, Micromedex, OVID Technologies, PubMed, UpToDate
Wireless access
Open Mon, Wed & Fri 8-6, Tues & Thurs 8-8

S   STELCO, INC*, Information Centre, 386 Wilcox St, L8P 1A2. (Mail add: PO Box 2030, L8N 3T1), SAN 373-1537. Tel: 905-528-2511, Ext 2076. FAX: 905-308-7012. *Librn,* Carol Cernile; E-mail: carol.cernile@stelco.ca
Library Holdings: Bk Vols 6,000; Per Subs 50
Open Mon-Fri 8-5

CR   THEOLOGICAL COLLEGE OF THE CANADIAN REFORMED CHURCHES LIBRARY*, Canadian Reformed Theological Seminary Library, 110 W 27th St, L9C 5A1. Tel: 905-575-3688. FAX: 905-575-0799. Web Site: www.theologicalcollege.ca. *Librn,* Margaret Van der Velde; E-mail: mvandervelde@seminary.canrc.org; Staff 1 (MLS 1)
Founded 1969. Enrl 15; Fac 4
Library Holdings: Bk Vols 27,000
Special Collections: 16th Century Books
Subject Interests: Calvinism, Church hist
Automation Activity & Vendor Info: (Acquisitions) Inmagic, Inc.
Database Vendor: EBSCOhost
Wireless access
Partic in Christian Library Consortium
Open Mon-Fri 8:30-4:30

HANOVER

P   HANOVER PUBLIC LIBRARY, 451 Tenth Ave, N4N 2P1. SAN 319-1621. Tel: 519-364-1420. FAX: 519-364-1747. E-mail: hanpub@hanover.ca. *Chief Exec Officer, Chief Librn,* Agnes Rivers-Moore; E-mail: arm@hanover.ca; Staff 5 (MLS 1, Non-MLS 4)
Founded 1906. Pop 7,500; Circ 75,000
Library Holdings: Audiobooks 1,300; DVDs 2,600; e-books 35,000; e-journals 21,000; High Interest/Low Vocabulary Bk Vols 30; Large Print Bks 2,200; Bk Vols 30,000; Per Subs 100
Special Collections: Can & Prov
Subject Interests: Local hist
Automation Activity & Vendor Info: (Acquisitions) LibLime; (Cataloging) LibLime; (Circulation) LibLime; (OPAC) LibLime; (Serials) LibLime
Wireless access
Function: Adult bk club, Chess club, Computer training, Copy machines, Digital talking bks, e-mail serv, Electronic databases & coll, Handicapped accessible, Home delivery & serv to Sr ctr & nursing homes, Homebound delivery serv, ILL available, Magnifiers for reading, Mail & tel request accepted, Newsp ref libr, Photocopying/Printing, Preschool outreach, Prog for adults, Prog for children & young adult, Senior computer classes, Spoken cassettes & CDs, Spoken cassettes & DVDs, Summer reading prog, Telephone ref, Video lending libr
Partic in OLA; Southern Ontario Libr Serv
Open Mon-Fri 10-8, Sat 10-5, Sun 1-5
Friends of the Library Group

HARROW

G   CANADIAN AGRICULTURE LIBRARY-HARROW*, 2585 County Rd 20 E, RR No 2, N0R 1G0. SAN 319-1648. Tel: 519-738-1204. FAX: 519-738-2929. E-mail: oharag@agr.gc.ca. *Head of Libr,* Lorraine Smith; Staff 1 (MLS 1)
Founded 1940
Library Holdings: Bk Titles 6,000; Per Subs 25
Subject Interests: Agr res, Clonal genebank, Greenhouse res, Soils
Open Mon-Fri 8:30-4:30

HAWKESBURY

P   HAWKESBURY PUBLIC LIBRARY*, 550 Higginson St, K6A 1H1. SAN 319-1680. Tel: 613-632-0106, Ext 2253. FAX: 613-636-2097. Web Site: www.bibliotheque.hawkesbury.on.ca. *Chief Exec Officer,* Lynn Belle-Isle; Staff 10 (MLS 1, Non-MLS 9)
Founded 1963. Pop 10,300
Library Holdings: Bk Vols 70,000; Per Subs 80
Special Collections: Genealogy (French)
Automation Activity & Vendor Info: (Cataloging) Mandarin Library Automation; (Circulation) Mandarin Library Automation; (OPAC) Mandarin Library Automation
Wireless access
Partic in Mandarin; Southern Ontario Libr Serv
Open Mon-Fri 9-8:30, Sat 9-4, Sun 12-4
Friends of the Library Group
Bookmobiles: 1

HEARST

P   HEARST PUBLIC LIBRARY*, 801 George St, P0L 1N0. (Mail add: PO Box 15000, P0L 1N0), SAN 319-1699. Tel: 705-372-2843. FAX: 705-372-2833. E-mail: hearstpl@ontera.net, ohe@ontera.net. Web Site: www.bibliohearst.on.ca. *Chief Librn,* Francine Daigle; *Asst Librn,* Julie Portelance
Founded 1975. Pop 6,000
Library Holdings: Bk Vols 26,000; Per Subs 60
Automation Activity & Vendor Info: (Cataloging) SirsiDynix; (Circulation) MultiLIS
Database Vendor: SirsiDynix
Wireless access
Open Mon-Thurs 9:30-6, Fri 9:30-9, Sat 9:30-4
Friends of the Library Group

HILTON BEACH

P   HILTON UNION PUBLIC LIBRARY*, 3085 Marks St, P0R 1G0. (Mail add: RR 1, P0R 1G0), SAN 319-1710. Tel: 705-255-3520. E-mail: hiltonlibrary@xplornet.ca. *Librn,* Melanie Dorscht
Founded 1920. Pop 370; Circ 5,500
Library Holdings: Bk Vols 8,550
Special Collections: St Joseph's Island (Pioneer to Present)
Open Mon 3-5 & 7pm-9pm, Wed & Sat 1-5
Friends of the Library Group

HONEY HARBOUR

P   GEORGIAN BAY TOWNSHIP LIBRARY, 2587 Honey Harbour Rd, P0E 1H0. (Mail add: PO Box 220, P0E 1E0), SAN 319-2318. Tel: 705-756-8851. FAX: 705-756-8851. E-mail: info@gbpl.ca. *Librn,* Barbara Swyers
Pop 1,000
Library Holdings: Bk Vols 9,183
Automation Activity & Vendor Info: (Cataloging) SIRSI WorkFlows; (Circulation) SirsiDynix
Database Vendor: SirsiDynix
Wireless access

HORNEPAYNE

P   HORNEPAYNE PUBLIC LIBRARY, 68 Front St, P0M 1Z0. (Mail add: PO Box 539, P0M 1Z0), SAN 319-1729. Tel: 807-868-2332. FAX: 807-868-3111. E-mail: hpl1@ontera.net. Web Site: www.olsn.ca/hornepayne. *Chief Exec Officer,* Darnelle Hill; E-mail: dhill@ontera.net; *Circ,* Margarita LeFort
Founded 1967. Pop 1,041; Circ 12,000
Library Holdings: Bk Vols 15,000; Per Subs 15
Wireless access
Open Wed & Thurs 1-6, Fri 1-5 & 7-9, Sat 1-5

HUNTSVILLE

P   HUNTSVILLE PUBLIC LIBRARY*, Seven Minerva St E, P1H 1W4. SAN 319-1737. Tel: 705-789-5232. Web Site: www.huntsvillelibrary.net. *Chief Librn,* Debra Duce; E-mail: dduce@huntsvillelibrary.net
Founded 1885. Pop 20,000; Circ 234,231
Library Holdings: Bk Vols 52,000; Per Subs 143
Special Collections: Muskoka Coll. Can & Prov
Wireless access
Partic in Southern Ontario Libr Serv
Open Mon & Fri 10:30-6, Tues-Thurs 10:30-7:30, Sat 10:30-4, Sun 1-4
Friends of the Library Group

IGNACE

P   IGNACE PUBLIC LIBRARY*, 36 Main St, P0T 1T0. (Mail add: PO Box 480, P0T 1T0), SAN 319-1745. Tel: 807-934-2280. FAX: 807-934-6452. Web Site: www.olfn.ca/ignace. *Chief Exec Officer,* Pamela Greenwood; E-mail: ceoignacelibrary@gmail.com
Pop 1,300; Circ 14,174
Automation Activity & Vendor Info: (OPAC) SIRSI Unicorn
Wireless access
Function: Children's prog, Computers for patron use, Copy machines, Digital talking bks, Free DVD rentals, Handicapped accessible, Holiday prog, ILL available, Music CDs, Online cat, OverDrive digital audio bks, Scanner
Open Tues-Thurs 12-6, Fri & Sat 12-4
Friends of the Library Group

IRON BRIDGE

P   HURON SHORES PUBLIC LIBRARY, Ten John St, P0R 1H0. (Mail add: PO Box 339, P0R 1H0), SAN 319-1753. Tel: 705-843-2192. FAX: 705-843-2035. E-mail: huronshores@ontera.net. Web Site: www.olsn.ca/huronshores. *Chief Librn,* Terri Beharriell
Pop 1,794; Circ 1,798
Library Holdings: Bk Titles 4,424; Bk Vols 4,956
Restriction: Access at librarian's discretion

KAGAWONG

P   BILLINGS TOWNSHIP PUBLIC LIBRARY*, 18 Upper St, P0P 1J0. (Mail add: PO Box 37, P0P 1J0), SAN 319-1788. Tel: 705-282-2944. E-mail: billings@xplornet.com. Web Site: olsn.ca/billingslibrary. *Chief Exec Officer, Librn,* Susan Hart
Founded 1968. Pop 500; Circ 5,548
Library Holdings: CDs 400; DVDs 400; Bk Titles 7,137; Bk Vols 4,522; Per Subs 10; Videos 200
Wireless access
Open Tues & Thurs 4-7, Sat 10-1

KANATA

S   CANADIAN WILDLIFE FEDERATION*, 350 Michael Cowpland Dr, K2M 2W1. SAN 326-8632. Tel: 613-599-9594. Toll Free Tel: 800-563-9453. FAX: 613-599-4428. E-mail: info@cwf-fcf.org. Web Site: www.cwf-fcf.org. *In Charge,* Colleen Hyslop
Library Holdings: e-books 7,000
Special Collections: Canadian Wildlife Federation Archives
Publications: Annual Report of the Canadian Wildlife Federation; Biosphere; Canadian Wildlife; Endangered Species Fact Sheet; Habitat 2000 Wildlife Habitat Improvement Series for Youth; Poaching Report; Project Wild; Wild; Your Big Backyard

KAPUSKASING

P   KAPUSKASING PUBLIC LIBRARY, 24 Mundy Ave, P5N 1P9. SAN 319-180X. Tel: 705-335-3363. FAX: 705-335-2464. E-mail: kaplibrary@ntl.sympatico.ca. Web Site: www.kapuskasinglibrary.ca. *Chief Exec Officer,* Nicole Audet; *Mgr, Libr Serv,* Mrs Johane Kosowan; Staff 1 (MLS 1)
Founded 1964. Pop 9,501; Circ 42,391
Library Holdings: Bk Titles 29,447; Bk Vols 36,397; Per Subs 50
Wireless access
Mem of Ontario Library Service North
Open Mon, Tues & Thurs 10-8, Wed 4-8, Fri 10-5, Sat 12-4
Friends of the Library Group

KEARNEY

P   KEARNEY & AREA PUBLIC LIBRARY*, Eight Main St, P0A 1M0. (Mail add: PO Box 220, P0A 1M0), SAN 319-1818. Tel: 705-636-5849. E-mail: kearneylibrary@hotmail.ca. *Librn,* Brandi Nolan
Pop 800; Circ 7,000
Library Holdings: Bk Vols 9,290; Per Subs 13
Function: Homebound delivery serv, ILL available, Prog for children & young adult, Ref serv available, Summer reading prog, Wheelchair accessible
Mem of Ontario Library Service North
Open Tues 10-12 & 1-4:30, Wed-Fri 12:30-4:30, Sat 1-3:30

KEENE

P   OTONABEE-SOUTH MONAGHAN TOWNSHIP PUBLIC LIBRARY*, Gayle Nelson Keene Public Library, 3252 CR 2, K0L 2G0. (Mail add: PO Box 9, K0L 2G0), SAN 319-1826. Tel: 705-295-6814. E-mail: keene_library@nexicom.net. Web Site: www.otosoumon.library.on.ca. *Chief Exec Officer,* Carolanne Nadeau; Staff 7 (Non-MLS 7)
Pop 6,200; Circ 46,000
Library Holdings: Bk Vols 32,000; Per Subs 100

Open Tues-Thurs 12-8, Sat 11-4
Friends of the Library Group
Branches: 2
BAILIEBORO BRANCH, 199 CR 28, Bailieboro, K0L 1B0. Tel: 705-939-6510. FAX: 705-939-6510. *Chief Exec Officer,* Carolanne Nadeau
Open Tues-Thurs 11:30-4 & 6-8, Sat 10-3
STEWART HALL, 1490 Matchett Line, Peterborough, K9J 6Y3. (Mail add: Box 9, K0L 2G0). Tel: 705-749-5642. E-mail: keene_library@nexicom.net. *Chief Exec Officer,* Carolanne Nadeau
Open Mon (May-Oct) 3-7, Wed 3-8, Sat 11-2:30

KEMPTVILLE

P   NORTH GRENVILLE PUBLIC LIBRARY, Norenberg Bldg, One Water St, K0G 1J0. (Mail add: PO Box 538, K0G 1J0), SAN 319-1850. Tel: 613-258-5577. FAX: 613-258-4134. E-mail: info@ngpl.ca. Web Site: www.ngpl.ca. *Chief Exec Officer,* Susan Higgins; Tel: 613-258-4711, Ext 6, E-mail: shiggins@ngpl.ca; *Info Serv Librn,* Patsy Brooks; Tel: 613-258-4711; *Tech Serv Librn,* Patricia Evans; Tel: 613-258-4711, Ext 5, E-mail: pevans@ngpl.ca; *Children's & Teen Programmer,* Sue Bergeron; Tel: 613-258-4711, Ext 4, E-mail: kids@ngpl.ca; Staff 3 (MLS 1, Non-MLS 2)
Founded 1998. Pop 15,085; Circ 78,000
Automation Activity & Vendor Info: (Cataloging) SirsiDynix; (Circulation) SirsiDynix; (ILL) Fretwell-Downing; (OPAC) SirsiDynix
Database Vendor: netLibrary, ProQuest, SirsiDynix
Wireless access
Partic in Ontario Library Consortium; Southern Ontario Libr Serv
Special Services for the Blind - Talking bks
Open Mon, Tues & Thurs 10-9, Wed 1-9, Fri & Sat 10-5
Friends of the Library Group
Branches: 1
BURRITTS RAPIDS BRANCH, One Grenville St, Burritts Rapids, K0G 1B0. (Mail add: PO Box 538, K0G 1J0). Tel: 613-269-3636. E-mail: burritts@ngpl.ca. Web Site: www.ngpl.ca. *Br Head,* Liz Dwyer
Open Tues 1-5, Wed 6pm-9pm, Sat 10-3
Friends of the Library Group

J   UNIVERSITY OF GUELPH, KEMPTVILLE CAMPUS*, Purvis Library, PO Box 2003, K0G 1J0. SAN 319-1842. Tel: 613-258-8336, Ext 634. FAX: 613-258-8294. Web Site: www.kemptvillec.uoguelph.ca. *Librn,* Debra Simpson; E-mail: dsimpson@kemptvillec.uoguelph.ca
Founded 1946
Library Holdings: Bk Titles 13,000; Per Subs 170
Subject Interests: Agr, Equine, Food safety, Nutrition
Open Mon-Thurs (Sept-April) 9-9, Fri 9-5, Sat & Sun 12-5

KENORA

P   KENORA PUBLIC LIBRARY*, 24 Main St S, P9N 1S7. SAN 319-1869. Tel: 807-467-2081. FAX: 807-467-2085. Web Site: www.kenorapubliclibrary.org. *Head Librn,* Erin Roussin; E-mail: eroussin@kenora.ca; *Asst Librn,* Cathy Peacock; E-mail: cpeacock@kenora.ca; *Ch,* Crystal Alcock; E-mail: cralcock@kenora.ca; *ILL,* M A Eisler; E-mail: maeisler@kenora.ca; *Ref,* Lori Jackson; E-mail: ljackson@kenora.ca; Staff 3 (Non-MLS 3)
Founded 1885. Pop 15,000; Circ 214,582
Library Holdings: Bk Vols 64,000; Per Subs 140
Subject Interests: Local hist
Mem of Ontario Library Service North
Open Mon & Fri 9-5, Tues-Thurs 9-8, Sat 10-4
Branches: 1
KEEWATIN BRANCH, 221 Main St, Keewatin, P0X 1C0. Tel: 807-547-2145. FAX: 807-547-3145. *Head Librn,* Erin Roussin; E-mail: eroussin@kenora.ca; Staff 3 (Non-MLS 3)
Founded 1973
Open Mon, Tues & Fri 11:30-4:30, Thurs 3-8

KING CITY

P   KING TOWNSHIP PUBLIC LIBRARY*, 1970 King Rd, L7B 1A6. (Mail add: PO Box 399, L7B 1A6), SAN 319-1885. Tel: 905-833-5101. FAX: 905-833-0824. Web Site: www.king-library.on.ca. *Chief Exec Officer, Chief Librn,* Rona O'Banion; Staff 6 (MLS 4, Non-MLS 2)
Founded 1893. Pop 19,800; Circ 159,319
Jan 2007-Dec 2007 Income $1,014,057, Provincial (CAN) $29,000, City (CAN) $985,057. Mats Exp $114,169, Books (CAN) $79,000, Per/Ser (Incl. Access Fees) (CAN) $8,060, AV Mat (CAN) $17,033, Electronic Ref Mat (Incl. Access Fees) (CAN) $10,076
Library Holdings: CDs 1,800; DVDs 4,000; e-books 1,000; e-journals 2,000; Bk Titles 67,252; Per Subs 80; Talking Bks 3,000
Special Collections: Archives (Local History); Can & Prov
Automation Activity & Vendor Info: (Acquisitions) SirsiDynix; (Cataloging) SirsiDynix; (Circulation) SirsiDynix; (Course Reserve) SirsiDynix; (OPAC) SirsiDynix

Database Vendor: EBSCOhost, netLibrary, SirsiDynix
Partic in Ontario Library Consortium
Special Services for the Blind - Assistive/Adapted tech devices, equip &
products; Bks on cassette; Bks on CD; Computer with voice synthesizer
for visually impaired persons; Copier with enlargement capabilities; Home
delivery serv; PC for handicapped; Ref serv; Spec prog; Talking bks;
Volunteer serv

J   SENECA COLLEGE OF APPLIED ARTS & TECHNOLOGY*, King
Campus, Suddick Resource Centre, 13990 Dufferin St N, L7B 1B3. SAN
368-9212. Tel: 416-491-5050. FAX: 905-833-1106. Web Site:
learningcommons.senecacollege.ca. *Dir,* Tanis Fink; *Mgr,* Cynthia McKeich
Subject Interests: Diving, Early childhood educ, Golf course landscaping,
Golf course maintenance, Law enforcement, Nursing, Recreation, Tourism,
Veterinary sci
Wireless access
Partic in Dobis
Open Mon-Thurs 7:30-7:30, Fri 7:30-5
Departmental Libraries:
NEWNHAM CAMPUS (MAIN), 1750 Finch Ave E, North York, M2J
2X5, SAN 368-9204. Tel: 416-491-5050, Ext 22100. Circulation Tel:
416-491-5050, Ext 22099. Interlibrary Loan Service Tel: 416-491-5050,
Ext 22094. Administration Tel: 416-491-5050, Ext 22097. FAX:
416-491-3349. Information Services FAX: 416-492-7184. Web Site:
library.senecacollege.ca. *Dir,* Tanis Fink; Tel: 416-491-5050, Ext 77526,
E-mail: tanis.fink@senecacollege.ca; *Assoc Dir, Mgr,* Carolyn Lam;
E-mail: carolyn.lam@senecacollege.ca; *Coll Develop, Info Serv, Librn,*
Kelly Donaldson; Tel: 416-491-5050, Ext 26139, Fax: 416-492-7184,
E-mail: kelly.donaldson@senecacollege.ca; *Librn, Pub Serv,* Daniel
Michniewicz; Tel: 416-491-5050, Ext 22761, Fax: 416-492-7184, E-mail:
daniel.michniewicz@senecacollege.ca; *Info Serv Librn, Mkt,* Rhonda
Roth; Tel: 416-491-5050, Ext 22093, Fax: 416-492-7184, E-mail:
rhonda.roth@senecacollege.ca; *Metadata Librn/Spec,* Jennifer Peters; Tel:
416-491-5050, Ext 22070, E-mail: jennifer.peters@senecacollege.ca; *Tech
Serv Librn,* Rosina Leung; Tel: 416-491-5050, Ext 22391, E-mail:
rosina.leung@senecacollege.ca; *Mgr, Libr Syst & Support Serv,* Jane Foo;
Tel: 416-491-5050, Ext 22011, E-mail: jane.foo@senecacollege.ca; *Info
Serv, Libr Instruction,* Rosalie Waller; Tel: 416-491-5050, Ext 22072,
Fax: 416-492-7184, E-mail: rosalie.waller@senecacollege.ca
Library Holdings: Bk Vols 50,000; Per Subs 472
Special Collections: Women in Canada
Partic in Dobis
Open Mon-Thurs 7:30am-11pm, Fri 7:30am-10pm, Sat 8:30-5, Sun 9-5
SENECA @ YORK, 70 The Pond Rd, North York, M3J 3M6. Tel:
416-491-5050, Ext 33040. *Librn,* Pamela Bolan; *Mgr,* Joy Muller; Tel:
416-491-5050, Ext 30042; Staff 10 (MLS 4, Non-MLS 6)
Enrl 4,000; Highest Degree: Bachelor
Library Holdings: Bk Titles 15,000
Open Mon-Fri 8am-10:30pm, Sat & Sun 9-5

KINGSTON

L   THE FRONTENAC LAW ASSOCIATION LIBRARY*, Frontenac County
Court House, Five Court St, K7L 2N4. SAN 370-7776. Tel: 613-542-0034.
FAX: 613-531-9764. E-mail: library@cfla.on.ca. Web Site: www.cfla.on.ca.
Libr Tech, Jackie Hassefras; *Libr Asst,* Nicolette Okrunlicova
Library Holdings: Bk Vols 9,000

P   KINGSTON FRONTENAC PUBLIC LIBRARY, 130 Johnson St, K7L
1X8. SAN 367-4827. Tel: 613-549-8888. FAX: 613-549-8476. Web Site:
www.kfpl.ca. *Chief Librn,* Patricia Enright; Tel: 613-549-8888, Ext 1230,
E-mail: penright@kfpl.ca; *Dir, Br Operations,* Barbara Love; Tel:
613-549-8888, Ext 1180, E-mail: blove@kfpl.ca; *Dir, Human Res,* Shelagh
Quigley; Tel: 613-549-8888, Ext 1515, E-mail: squigley@kfpl.ca; *Dir,
Outreach & Tech,* Lester Webb; Tel: 613-549-8888, Ext 1290, E-mail:
lwebb@kfpl.ca; *Br Operations Mgr,* Laura Carter; Tel: 613-549-8888, Ext
1330, E-mail: lcarter@kfpl.ca; *Mgr, Prog & Outreach,* Kimberly
Sutherland Mills; Tel: 613-549-8888, Ext 1520, E-mail: kmills@kfpl.ca;
Staff 60 (MLS 15, Non-MLS 45)
Founded 1834. Pop 150,000
Library Holdings: Bk Titles 270,000; Bk Vols 425,000; Per Subs 400
Special Collections: Local History (Grant Allen Coll); Local Newspaper
Coll, 1810-present, micro
Subject Interests: Genealogy, Local hist
Automation Activity & Vendor Info: (Acquisitions) Infor Library &
Information Solutions; (Cataloging) Infor Library & Information Solutions;
(Circulation) Infor Library & Information Solutions; (Course Reserve)
Infor Library & Information Solutions; (ILL) Infor Library & Information
Solutions; (Media Booking) Infor Library & Information Solutions;
(OPAC) Infor Library & Information Solutions; (Serials) Infor Library &
Information Solutions
Wireless access
Open Mon-Thurs 9-9, Fri & Sat 9-5, Sun (Oct-April) 1-5
Friends of the Library Group

Branches: 15
ARDEN BRANCH, 5998 Arden Rd, Arden, K0H 1B0. (Mail add: 130
Johnson St, K7L 1X8), SAN 367-4851. Tel: 613-335-2570. *Br Mgr,*
Laura Carter
Library Holdings: Bk Vols 3,000
Open Tues 2-6, Thurs 5-8, Sat 10-1
CALVIN PARK BRANCH, 88 Wright Crescent, K7L 4T9. (Mail add: 130
Johnson St, K7L 1X8), SAN 370-355X. Tel: 613-546-2582. *Br Mgr,*
Laura Carter
Library Holdings: Bk Vols 48,000
Open Mon-Wed 9-9, Fri & Sat 9-5
Friends of the Library Group
CLOYNE BRANCH, 1011 Little Pond Rd, Cloyne, K0H 1K0. (Mail add:
130 Johnson St, K7L 1X8), SAN 367-4916. Tel: 613-336-8744. *Br Mgr,*
Laura Carter
Library Holdings: Bk Vols 11,000
Open Tues 10-3, Wed 5-8, Fri 12-4, Sat 9-12
Friends of the Library Group
HARTINGTON BRANCH, 5597 Hwy 38, Hartington, K0H 1W0. (Mail
add: 130 Johnson, K7L 1X8), SAN 367-4940. Tel: 613-372-2524. *Br
Mgr,* Laura Carter
Library Holdings: Bk Vols 6,000
Open Mon & Wed 1-5 & 6-8, Sat 1-4
Friends of the Library Group
HOWE ISLAND BRANCH, 50 Baseline Rd, Howe Island, K7G 2V6.
(Mail add: 130 Johnson St, K7L 1X8), SAN 325-4003. Tel:
613-549-7972. *Br Mgr,* Laura Carter
Library Holdings: Bk Vols 2,800
Open Tues 3-5, Thurs 6-8, Sat 10-12
Friends of the Library Group
KINGSCOURT BRANCH, 115 Kirkpatrick St, K7K 2P4. (Mail add: 130
Johnson St, K7L 1X8), SAN 370-3541. Tel: 613-546-0698. *Br Mgr,*
Laura Carter
Library Holdings: Bk Vols 29,000
Open Tues & Thurs 10-8, Sat 9-5
MOUNTAIN GROVE BRANCH, 1455 Mountain Grove Rd, Mountain
Grove, K0H 2E0. (Mail add: 130 Johnson St, K7L 1X8), SAN 367-5033.
Tel: 613-335-5360. *Br Mgr,* Laura Carter
Library Holdings: Bk Vols 2,600
Open Tues & Fri 2-5, Wed 5:30-7:30, Sat 12:30-2:30
Friends of the Library Group
PARHAM BRANCH, 1021 Long Lake Rd, Parham, K0H 2K0. (Mail add:
130 Johnson St, K7L 1X8), SAN 367-5076. Tel: 613-375-6400. *Br Mgr,*
Laura Carter
Library Holdings: Bk Vols 2,000
Open Tues 4-6, Thurs 6-8, Sat 10-Noon
Friends of the Library Group
PITTSBURGH BRANCH, 80 Gore Rd, K7K 6X6. (Mail add: 130 Johnson
St, K7L 1X8), SAN 367-4886. Tel: 613-542-8222. *Br Mgr,* Laura Carter
Library Holdings: Bk Vols 27,000
Open Tues-Thurs 10-8, Sat 9-5
Friends of the Library Group
PLEVNA BRANCH, 6638 Buckshot Lake Rd, Plevna, K0H 2M0. (Mail
add: 130 Johnson St, K7L 1XB), SAN 377-7510. Tel: 613-479-2542. *Br
Mgr,* Laura Carter
Library Holdings: Bk Vols 1,800
Open Tues & Thurs 2-4 & 5-7, Fri & Sat 10-1
SHARBOT LAKE BRANCH, 1037 Robert St, Sharbot Lake, K0H 2P0.
(Mail add: 130 Johnson St, K7L 1X8), SAN 367-5092. Tel:
613-279-2583. *Br Mgr,* Laura Carter
Library Holdings: Bk Vols 6,000
Open Tues & Thurs 1-5 & 6-8, Fri 2-5, Sat 10-2
Friends of the Library Group
STORRINGTON BRANCH, 3910 Battersea Rd, Battersea, K0H 1H0.
(Mail add: 130 Johnson St, K7L 1X8), SAN 367-4975. Tel:
613-353-6333. *Br Mgr,* Laura Carter
Library Holdings: Bk Vols 3,700
Open Tues & Thurs 1-5 & 6-8, Sat 1-4
Friends of the Library Group
SYDENHAM BRANCH, 4432 George St, Sydenham, K0H 2TO. (Mail
add: 130 Johnson St, K7L 1X8), SAN 367-5122. Tel: 613-376-3437. *Br
Mgr,* Laura Carter
Library Holdings: Bk Vols 11,000
Open Mon 10-6, Tues & Thurs 1-8, Fri 10-5, Sat 10-2
Friends of the Library Group
ISABEL TURNER BRANCH, 935 Gardiners Rd, K7M 9A9. (Mail add:
130 Johnson St, K7L 1X8), SAN 367-5009. Tel: 613-389-2611. *Br Mgr,*
Laura Carter
Library Holdings: Bk Vols 102,000
Open Mon-Thurs 9-9, Fri & Sat 9-5, Sun (Oct-April) 1-5
WOLFE ISLAND BRANCH, Ten Hwy 95, Wolfe Island, K0H 2Y0. (Mail
add: 130 Jonson st, K7L 1X8), SAN 322-5925. Tel: 613-385-2112. *Br
Mgr,* Laura Carter
Library Holdings: Bk Vols 5,700

Open Tues & Thurs 1-5 & 6-8, Fri (July & Aug) 2-5, Sat 10-1
Friends of the Library Group

S   LAND FORCE CONCEPTS & DESIGN*, Fort Frontenac Army Library,
317 Ontario St, K7K 7B4. (Mail add: PO Box 17000, Sta Forces, K7K
7B4), SAN 319-1907. Tel: 613-541-5010, Ext 5829. Interlibrary Loan
Service Tel: 613-541-5010, Ext 5815. FAX: 613-546-0589. *Chief Librn,*
David Willis; Staff 4 (MLS 1, Non-MLS 3)
Founded 1947. Circ 12,000
Apr 2007-Mar 2008. Mats Exp (CAN) $110,000
Library Holdings: Bk Titles 100,000; Bk Vols 90,000; Per Subs 250
Special Collections: The Study of Conflict & Land Warfare in the
Canadian Context, vols, monographs, doc & artifacts
Subject Interests: Army, Behav sci, Defense, Intl relations, Leadership,
Mil art, Mil hist, Operations
Open Mon-Fri 8-4:30

S   MARINE MUSEUM OF THE GREAT LAKES AT KINGSTON*, Audrey
Rushbrook Memorial Library, 55 Ontario St, K7L 2Y2. SAN 370-6427.
Tel: 613-542-2261. FAX: 613-542-0043. E-mail: curator@marmuseum.ca.
Web Site: www.marmuseum.ca. *Curator,* Ben Holthof; Staff 1 (MLS 1)
Library Holdings: Bk Titles 12,000; Per Subs 250
Publications: Jib Gems
Restriction: Open by appt only

S   NOVELIS GLOBAL TECHNOLOGY CENTRE*, Novelis Technical
Information Centre, 945 Princess St, K7L 5L9. (Mail add: PO Box 8400,
K7L 5L9), SAN 319-1893. Tel: 613-541-2071. Administration Tel:
613-541-2065. FAX: 613-541-2134. Web Site: www.novelis.com. *Mgr, Sr
Info Spec,* Brian Chenoweth; E-mail: brian.chenoweth@novelis.com
Founded 1942
Library Holdings: Bk Vols 1,000; Per Subs 20
Subject Interests: Chem, Computer modeling, Mat sci, Mechanical
testing, Metallurgy, Physics
Database Vendor: CISTI Source, Dialog, EBSCOhost, Factiva.com,
LexisNexis, Material ConneXion, MicroPatent, ProQuest, ScienceDirect,
STN International
Restriction: Open by appt only

M   PROVIDENCE CARE, Gibson Library, St Marys of the Lake Hospital,
340 Union St, K7L 5A2. (Mail add: PO Box 3600, K7L 5A2), SAN
324-4881. Tel: 613-548-7222, Ext 2218. FAX: 613-544-1184. Web Site:
www.providencecare.ca. *Dir, Libr Serv,* Karen Gagnon; E-mail:
gagnonk@providencecare.ca; Staff 2 (MLS 1, Non-MLS 1)
Subject Interests: Brain injury, Geriatrics, Gerontology, Nursing homes,
Occupational therapy, Phys therapy, Psychogeriatrics, Psychol, Recreational
therapy, Rehabilitation, Speech therapy, Spiritual care, Vocational serv
Automation Activity & Vendor Info: (Acquisitions) Inmagic, Inc.;
(Cataloging) Inmagic, Inc.; (OPAC) Inmagic, Inc.; (Serials) EBSCO Online
Database Vendor: EBSCO Information Services, EBSCOhost
Function: Doc delivery serv
Publications: Accession List
Partic in Docline
Open Mon-Fri 8:30-4:30
Restriction: In-house use for visitors, Open to others by appt, Open to
students, fac & staff

M   PROVIDENCE CARE MENTAL HEALTH SERVICES, Staff Library, 752
King St W, K7L 4X3. (Mail add: PO Box 603, K7L 4X3), SAN 324-0487.
Tel: 613-546-1101, Ext 5745. *Librn,* Karen Gagnon; E-mail:
gagnonk@providencecare.ca; Staff 1.4 (MLS 1, Non-MLS 0.4)
Founded 1965
Library Holdings: Bk Titles 4,600; Per Subs 50
Subject Interests: Mental health, Nursing, Occupational therapy, Psychiat,
Psychol
Open Mon-Fri 8:30-4:30

C   QUEEN'S UNIVERSITY*, Stauffer Library, 101 Union St, K7L 5C4.
SAN 367-536X. Circulation Tel: 613-533-2524. Interlibrary Loan Service
Tel: 613-533-2526. Reference Tel: 613-533-2527. Administration Tel:
613-533-2519. FAX: 613-533-6362. Web Site: www.stauffer.queensu.ca.
Univ Librn, Martha Whitehead; *Assoc Univ Librn,* Laurie Scott; Tel:
613-533-6000, Ext 77694; *Assoc Univ Librn,* Michael Vandenburg; Tel:
613-533-6000, Ext 74536; *Head, Coll Mgt Serv,* Sharon Musgrave; Tel:
613-533-6000, Ext 7544; *Bus Officer,* N Petri; Tel: 613-533-2518; *Coord,
Coll Develop,* Jane Philipps; Tel: 613-533-3040; *Human Res Officer,*
Shannon Tureski; Tel: 613-533-6000, Ext 75270; Staff 40 (MLS 38,
Non-MLS 2)
Founded 1841. Enrl 20,131; Highest Degree: Doctorate
Library Holdings: Bk Vols 2,410,869
Special Collections: Aborigines Coll; Artica Coll; Bibles Coll; Canadian
Studies; Eighteenth-Century English Pamphlets; Gothic Fantasy; History of
Science in North America (McNicol & Riche-Covington Colls); History,
esp Exploration, War of 1812, Travellers' Narratives, Loyalists, Local

History; Political Pamphlets; Pre-1700 Books; Private Press Books;
Scottish Studies (Scots in Canada, Burns, Presbyterians & the John
Buchan, Jas, Roy, Grace Campbell, Bishop MacDonnell & MacGillivray
Colls). Can & Prov; Oral History; UN Document Depository
Automation Activity & Vendor Info: (Cataloging) Ex Libris Group;
(Circulation) Ex Libris Group
Partic in Association of Research Libraries (ARL)
Open Mon-Fri 8:30am-11pm
Friends of the Library Group
Departmental Libraries:
BRACKEN HEALTH SCIENCES LIBRARY, Botterell Hall, Ground Flr,
18 Stuart St, K7L 3N6. Tel: 613-533-2510. Interlibrary Loan Service Tel:
613-533-3039. Reference Tel: 615-533-3176. Administration Tel:
613-533-2511. FAX: 613-533-6892. Interlibrary Loan Service FAX:
613-533-3152. Web Site: library.queensu.ca/health. *Head of Libr,*
Suzanne Maranda; Tel: 613-533-6000, Ext 74522. Subject Specialists:
Health sci, Suzanne Maranda
   Subject Interests: Health, Life sci
   Open Mon-Thurs 8:00am-11pm, Fri 8-8, Sat 10-5, Sun 10-8; Mon-Fri
   (Summer) 8-4:30
EDUCATION LIBRARY, Duncan McArthur Hall, 511 Union St at Sir
John A Macdonald Blvd, K7M 5R7, SAN 367-5572. Tel: 613-533-2191.
Reference Tel: 613-533-3193. Toll Free Tel: 866-267-7406. FAX:
613-533-2010. E-mail: education.library@queensu.ca. Web Site:
library.queensu.ca/webedu. *Head, Educ Libr,* Corrine Laverty; Staff 6.5
(MLS 2, Non-MLS 4.5)
   Founded 1968
   Open Mon-Thurs 8:30am-9pm, Fri 8:30-5, Sat & Sun 12:30-5
ENGINEERING & SCIENCE LIBRARY, Douglas Library, K7L 5C4. Tel:
613-533-2610. Reference Tel: 613-533-6981. FAX: 613-533-2584. Web
Site: library.queensu.ca/webeng. *Head Librn,* Position Currently Open
   Open Mon-Fri 8:30am-11pm
W D JORDAN SPECIAL COLLECTIONS - MUSIC, Douglas Library, 6th
Level, K7L 5C4. Tel: 613-533-2839. Reference Tel: 613-533-2510. FAX:
613-533-2584. Web Site: library.queensu.ca/webmus/sc. *Head, Spec Coll,*
Barbara Teatero; Tel: 613-533-6320; *Pub Serv Librn,* Lucinda Walls.
Subject Specialists: *Art, Music,* Lucinda Walls
   Open Mon-Fri 8:30am-10pm

CL   LAW LIBRARY, Macdonald Hall, 128 Union St, K7L 3N6, SAN
367-5696. Tel: 613-533-2842. Circulation Tel: 613-533-6346. Reference
Tel: 613-533-2465. Administration Tel: 613-533-3179. FAX:
613-533-2594. *Head of Libr,* Amy Kaufman; E-mail:
kaufman@queensu.ca
Founded 1957. Enrl 470; Fac 28; Highest Degree: Master
Library Holdings: Bk Vols 150,000; Per Subs 3,850
Special Collections: Can & Prov
Subject Interests: Can legal mat
Function: CD-ROM, Computers for patron use, Copy machines,
Electronic databases & coll, ILL available, Photocopying/Printing, Ref &
res, Scanner, Telephone ref, VHS videos, Wheelchair accessible
Restriction: Circ limited, Non-circulating coll, Open to pub for ref &
circ; with some limitations, Restricted loan policy
Friends of the Library Group

J   ST LAWRENCE COLLEGE LIBRARY*, Kingston Campus, 100
Portsmouth Ave, K7L 5A6. SAN 319-1966. Tel: 613-544-5400, Ext 1705.
Reference Tel: 613-544-5400, Ext 1248. FAX: 613-545-3914. Web Site:
www.sl.on.ca/library. *Dir, Student Serv,* Wanda Williams; *Librn,* Jill Baker;
E-mail: jillbaker@sl.on.ca; Staff 1 (MLS 1)
Founded 1967. Enrl 5,000; Fac 195
Library Holdings: Bk Vols 45,000; Per Subs 250
Automation Activity & Vendor Info: (Cataloging) SirsiDynix;
(Circulation) SirsiDynix; (Course Reserve) SirsiDynix; (OPAC) SirsiDynix
Database Vendor: EBSCOhost, ProQuest
Wireless access
Open Mon-Thurs 8am-9pm, Fri 8-4, Sat 12-4

KIRKLAND LAKE

J   NORTHERN COLLEGE OF APPLIED ARTS & TECHNOLOGY
LIBRARY, 140 Government Rd E, P2N 3L8. (Mail add: Postal Bag 2400,
P2N 3P4), SAN 319-1982. Tel: 705-567-9291, Ext 3700. FAX:
705-567-3350. E-mail: libraryk@northern.on.ca. Web Site:
www.northernc.on.ca. *Libr Tech,* Wenliang Wang
Founded 1962
Library Holdings: Bk Vols 7,900; Per Subs 46
Wireless access
Partic in Ontario Colleges Library Service (OCLS)
Open Mon-Thurs (Sept-April) 8am-9pm, Fri 8-4, Sat 10:30-3:30;
Mon-Thurs (May-Aug) 8am-9pm, Fri 8-4

P   TECK CENTENNIAL LIBRARY*, Ten Kirkland St E, P2N 1P1. SAN
319-1990. Tel: 705-567-7966. FAX: 705-568-6303. E-mail: library@tkl.ca.
Web Site: www.olsn.ca/kirklandlakepl/. *Chief Exec Officer, Head Librn,*
Cheryl Lafreniere; *Ch,* Candice Turbide; E-mail: candice.turbide@tkl.ca;

Early Childhood Educator, Jamie Cowie. Subject Specialists: *Children's prog,* Jamie Cowie; Staff 6 (MLS 1, Non-MLS 5)
Founded 1928. Pop 10,000; Circ 75,000
Library Holdings: Audiobooks 1,000; DVDs 250; Large Print Bks 2,000; Bk Titles 50,000; Per Subs 110; Talking Bks 350; Videos 1,500
Special Collections: Northern Daily News, 1923-present, microfilm
Special Services for the Deaf - Bks on deafness & sign lang
Special Services for the Blind - Audio mat

KITCHENER

C   CONESTOGA COLLEGE INSTITUTE OF TECHNOLOGY & ADVANCED LEARNING, Library Resource Centre, 299 Doon Valley Dr, N2G 4M4. SAN 319-2008. Tel: 519-748-5220, Ext 3361. FAX: 519-748-3538. E-mail: lrcinfo@conestogac.on.ca. Web Site: www.conestogac.on.ca/lrc. *Dir,* Linda Schneider; E-mail: lschneider@conestogac.on.ca; Staff 17 (MLS 3, Non-MLS 14)
Founded 1968
Library Holdings: Bk Vols 40,000; Per Subs 300
Automation Activity & Vendor Info: (OPAC) SirsiDynix
Wireless access
Open Mon-Thurs 7am-9pm, Fri 7-5, Sat 9-4, Sun 12-4

S   DOON HERITAGE CROSSROADS LIBRARY*, Ten Huron Rd, N2P 2R7. SAN 373-7810. Tel: 519-748-1914. FAX: 519-748-0009. Web Site: www.region.waterloo.on.ca. *Librn,* Stacy McLennan; E-mail: smclennan@regionofwaterloo.ca; Staff 1 (MLS 1)
Founded 1983
Library Holdings: Bk Titles 2,000; Per Subs 10
Special Collections: Oral History
Subject Interests: Local hist, Mat culture
Open Mon-Fri 8:30-4:30

R   EMMANUEL BIBLE COLLEGE*, Edna Pridham Memorial Library, 100 Fergus Ave, N2A 2H2. SAN 324-6094. Tel: 519-894-8900, Ext 232, 519-894-8900, Ext 273. FAX: 519-894-5331. E-mail: info@emmanuelbiblecollege.ca. Web Site: www.emmanuelbiblecollege.ca. *Libr Dir,* Jennifer Wohlgemut; E-mail: jwohlgemut@ebcollege.on.ca
Library Holdings: Bk Titles 24,000; Bk Vols 30,000; Per Subs 100
Special Collections: Canada East; Christian Womens' Temperance League; Evangelical Missionary Church
Subject Interests: Biblical theol, Counsel, Hist, Psychol, Theol
Automation Activity & Vendor Info: (Cataloging) Inmagic, Inc.
Open Mon, Tues & Thurs 9-9, Wed 9-7, Fri 9-5, Sat 1-5

M   GRAND RIVER HOSPITAL*, Library Services, 835 King St W, N2G 1G3. (Mail add: PO Box 9056, N2G 1G3), SAN 319-2016. Tel: 519-749-4300, Ext 2235. FAX: 519-749-4208. E-mail: libraryservices@grhosp.on.ca. *In Charge,* Tim Burns
Founded 1954
Library Holdings: Bk Titles 4,000; Per Subs 200
Subject Interests: Allied health, Med, Nursing
Wireless access
Partic in Wellington-Waterloo-Dufferin Health Library Network

P   KITCHENER PUBLIC LIBRARY, 85 Queen St N, N2H 2H1. SAN 367-5939. Tel: 519-743-0271. FAX: 519-743-1261. Web Site: www.kpl.org. *Chief Exec Officer,* Sonia Lewis; E-mail: sonia.lewis@kpl.org; *Cat,* Position Currently Open; *Pub Serv,* Ann Wood; E-mail: ann.wood@kpl.org; *Ref,* Laura Master; E-mail: laura.master@kpl.org; Staff 118.61 (MLS 22.74, Non-MLS 95.87)
Founded 1884. Pop 231,092; Circ 2,732,004
Jan 2011-Dec 2011 Income (Main Library and Branch(s)) (CAN) $9,794,293, Provincial (CAN) $286,755, City (CAN) $8,927,661, Federal (CAN) $30,710, Locally Generated Income (CAN) $511,271, Other (CAN) $37,896. Mats Exp (CAN) $1,181,378. Sal (CAN) $7,290,129
Special Collections: Waterloo County Historical Society Coll
Subject Interests: Local hist
Automation Activity & Vendor Info: (Acquisitions) Innovative Interfaces, Inc; (Cataloging) Innovative Interfaces, Inc; (Circulation) Innovative Interfaces, Inc; (OPAC) Innovative Interfaces, Inc; (Serials) Innovative Interfaces, Inc
Database Vendor: Innovative Interfaces, Inc INN - View
Wireless access
Partic in Southern Ontario Libr Serv
Open Mon-Thurs 9:30-9, Fri 9:30-5:30, Sat 9-5:30, Sun 1-5
Branches: 5
COUNTRY HILLS COMMUNITY, 1500 Block Line Rd, N2C 2S2. Tel: 519-743-3558. FAX: 519-743-3558. *Br Mgr,* Position Currently Open
FOREST HEIGHTS, 251 Fischer-Hallman Rd, N2H 2H1, SAN 367-5963. Tel: 519-743-0644. FAX: 519-743-0644. *Librn,* Susan Bloos
Open Mon-Thurs 9:30-9, Fri 9:30-5:30, Sat 9-5:30

GRAND RIVER STANLEY PARK, 175 Indian Rd, N2B 2S7, SAN 367-5998. Tel: 519-896-1736. FAX: 519-896-1736. *Librn,* Chris Schnarr
Open Mon-Thurs 9:30-9, Fri 9:30-5:30, Sat 9-5:30
Friends of the Library Group
PIONEER PARK, 150 Pioneer Dr, N2H 2H1, SAN 367-598X. Tel: 519-748-2740. FAX: 519-748-2740. *Librn,* Maureen Plomske
Open Mon-Thurs 9:30-9, Fri 9:30-5:30, Sat 9-5:30
GRACE SCHMIDT ROOM, 85 Queen St N, N2H 2H1, SAN 329-2215. Tel: 519-743-0271, Ext 252. FAX: 519-743-1261. Web Site: www.kpl.org/ref/gsr.html, www.whs.ca. *Librn,* Karen Ball-Pyatt; E-mail: karen.ball-pyatt@kpl.org; Staff 2 (MLS 1, Non-MLS 1)
Library Holdings: Bk Vols 500
Special Collections: Oral History
Subject Interests: Genealogy, Local hist
Publications: Waterloo Historical Society Annual Reports
Houses the archival collection of the Waterloo Historical Society
Restriction: Open to pub for ref only

M   ST MARY'S GENERAL HOSPITAL*, Medical Library, 911 Queen's Blvd, N2M 1B2. SAN 319-2032. Tel: 519-749-6549. FAX: 519-749-6526. *Librn,* Elaine Baldwin; E-mail: ebaldwin@smgh.ca
Founded 1962
Library Holdings: Bk Titles 1,500; Per Subs 100
Subject Interests: Cardiology, Med, Nursing, Ophthalmology, Rheumatology

L   WATERLOO LAW ASSOCIATION*, Court House, 20 Weber St E, N2H 1C3. SAN 370-6001. Tel: 519-742-0872. FAX: 519-742-4102. *Librn,* Catherine Whiteman
Founded 1894
Library Holdings: Bk Vols 15,500; Per Subs 16
Publications: WLA Members Directory (Annually); WLA Newsletter (Quarterly)

KLEINBURG

S   MCMICHAEL CANADIAN ART COLLECTION, Library & Archives, 10365 Islington Ave, L0J 1C0. SAN 323-7192. Tel: 905-893-1121, Ext 2255. FAX: 905-893-2588. E-mail: library@mcmichael.com. *Librn & Archivist,* Linda Morita; E-mail: lmorita@mcmichael.com; Staff 1 (MLS 1)
Library Holdings: Bk Vols 8,000; Per Subs 20
Special Collections: Arctic Images (Norman Hallendy Coll); Artist Archives & Canadian Art (The Group of Seven Coll); Inuit & First Nations Art & Culture
Automation Activity & Vendor Info: (Cataloging) SydneyPlus
Restriction: Non-circulating, Open by appt only

LANSDOWNE

P   LEEDS & THE THOUSAND ISLANDS PUBLIC LIBRARY*, 1B Jessie St, K0E 1L0. (Mail add: PO Box 219, K0E 1L0), SAN 319-2059. Tel: 613-659-3885. FAX: 613-659-4192. E-mail: leedsti@ltipl.net. Web Site: www.ltipl.net. *Interim Chief Exec Officer,* Erika Heesen; *Head of Libr,* Lisa Marston; E-mail: lisa@ltipl.net; Staff 1 (MLS 1)
Founded 1974. Pop 4,387
Library Holdings: Bk Vols 26,000; Per Subs 38
Mem of Ontario Library Service North
Open Mon, Tues & Thurs 1-8, Wed 9-12 & 1-8, Fri & Sat 10-2
Branches: 3
ESCOTT BRANCH, 1365 County Rd 2, Mallorytown, K0E 1R0, SAN 319-2342. Tel: 613-659-3800. FAX: 613-659-3800. E-mail: escott@ltipl.net. *Librn,* Dawne Fiegen
Founded 1975
Open Tues & Thurs 5-8, Sat 12-5
Friends of the Library Group
LYNDHURST BRANCH, 426 Lyndhurst Rd, Lyndhurst, K0E 1N0, SAN 367-1372. Tel: 613-928-2277. FAX: 613-928-2816. E-mail: lyndhurst@ltipl.net. *Librn,* Lisa Harston
Open Mon 1-5, Wed 1-8, Sat 9-1
SEELEY'S BAY BRANCH, 150 Main St, Seeley's Bay, K0H 2N0, SAN 367-1461. Tel: 613-387-3909. FAX: 613-387-2037. E-mail: seeleysbay@ltipl.net. Web Site: www.ltipl.net/seeley.html. *Br Head, Librn,* Amanda Start
Open Tues & Sat 1-5, Thurs 1-8

LARDER LAKE

P   LARDER LAKE PUBLIC LIBRARY, 69 Fourth Ave, P0K 1L0. (Mail add: PO Box 189, P0K 1L0), SAN 319-2067. Tel: 705-643-2222. FAX: 705-643-2222. E-mail: llpublib@onlink.net. Web Site: www.larderlakepubliclibrary.ca. *Chief Exec Officer, Librn,* Patricia Bodick
Founded 1940. Pop 800; Circ 15,969
Library Holdings: DVDs 525; Bk Titles 13,000; Per Subs 45
Automation Activity & Vendor Info: (Acquisitions) SirsiDynix
Wireless access

Mem of Ontario Library Service North
Open Tues & Thurs 1-8, Wed & Sat 1-4

LEAMINGTON

S   POINT PELEE NATIONAL PARK LIBRARY*, 407 Robson St, RR1,
N8H 3V4. Tel: 519-322-5700, Ext 21. FAX: 519-322-1277. E-mail:
pelee.info@pc.gc.ca. Web Site: www.parkscanada.gc.ca. *Mgr,* Monique
Oltrop; E-mail: monique.oltrop@pc.gc.ca
Library Holdings: Bk Titles 5,000; Per Subs 24
Special Collections: Botany (Herbarium Coll), specimens; Entomology
(Insects Coll), specimens
Restriction: Open to pub by appt only, Open to researchers by request,
Staff use only

LINDSAY

P   CITY OF KAWARTHA LAKES PUBLIC LIBRARY*, 190 Kent St W,
K9V 2Y6. (Mail add: PO Box 9000, K9V 2Y6), SAN 367-6080. Tel:
705-324-9411, Ext 1291. Reference Tel: 705-324-5632, Ext 268. FAX:
705-878-1859. E-mail: libraryadministration@city.kawarthalakes.on.ca.
Chief Librn, Linda Kent; E-mail: lkent@city.kawarthalakes.on.ca; *Supvr,*
Diane Lansdell; *Supvr,* Debbie Spivey; Staff 6 (MLS 1, Non-MLS 5)
Founded 2001. Pop 75,000; Circ 308,632
Library Holdings: Bk Vols 170,267
Partic in Southern Ontario Libr Serv
Open Mon-Thurs 10-8, Fri & Sat 10-5
Friends of the Library Group
Branches: 18
   BETHANY BRANCH, 1474 Hwy 7A, Bethany, L0A 1K0. Tel:
   705-277-2321. FAX: 705-277-1580. *In Charge,* Pat Wykes
   Open Mon, Wed & Fri 8:30-4:30, Tues & Thurs 8:30-7:30, Sat 10-2
   BOBCAYGEON BRANCH, 21 Canal St, Bobcaygeon, K0M 1A0. (Mail
   add: PO Box 420, Bobcaygeon, K0M 1A0), SAN 367-6110. Tel:
   705-738-2088. FAX: 705-738-0918. *Librn,* Carolyn Warren
   Open Mon & Thurs 1:30-8, Tues, Wed & Fri 10-5, Sat 10-3:30
   BURNT RIVER BRANCH, 186 Burnt River Rd, Burnt River, K0M 1C0,
   SAN 367-6145. Tel: 705-454-9646. FAX: 705-454-8465. *Librn,* Fern
   Allen
   Open Mon 3-7, Thurs 10-2, Sat 9-1
   CAMBRAY-FENELON TOWNSHIP, 2255 Elm Tree Rd, Cambray, K0M
   1E0. (Mail add: PO Box 9, Cambray, K0M 1E0), SAN 367-617X. Tel:
   705-374-4900. FAX: 705-374-4900.
   Open Tues 3-7, Wed & Sat 10-2
   CARDEN, 258 Lake Dalrymple Rd, Sebright, L0K 1W0, SAN 367-6234.
   Tel: 705-833-2845. FAX: 705-832-2273. *Librn,* Janet Hill
   Open Mon 3:30-7:30, Wed 10-2, Sat 1-5
   COBOCONK BRANCH, Nine Grandy Rd, Coboconk, K0M 1K0. (Mail
   add: PO Box 90, Coboconk, K0M 1K0), SAN 367-620X. Tel:
   705-454-3322. FAX: 705-454-2392. *In Charge,* Hodgson Beatrice
   Open Mon, Wed & Fri 8:30-4:30, Tues & Thurs 8:30-7, Sat 9-2
   DALTON, 13 Rumohr, RR 1, Sebright, L0K 1W0, SAN 367-6269. Tel:
   705-833-2858. FAX: 705-833-2752. *In Charge,* June Hill
   Open Mon & Sat 10-2, Wed 3:30-7:30
   DOWNEYVILLE BRANCH, Saint Luke's School, 335 Saint Luke's Rd
   (Downeyville) RR 5, K9V 4R5, SAN 367-6293. Tel: 705-799-5265. *In
   Charge,* Jill Potter
   Open Wed 4:30-7:30
   DUNSFORD BRANCH, 26 Community Center Rd, Dunsford, K0M 1L0.
   (Mail add: PO Box 82, Dunsford, K0M 1L0), SAN 367-6323. Tel:
   705-793-3037. FAX: 705-793-2380. *In Charge,* Jill Potter
   Open Tues 2-7, Wed 10-1, Sat 9-1
   FENELON FALLS BRANCH, 19 Market St, Fenelon Falls, K0M 1N0.
   (Mail add: PO Box 727, Fenelon Falls, K0M 1N0), SAN 367-6382. Tel:
   705-887-6300. FAX: 705-887-1532. *Supvr,* Debbie Spivey
   Open Tues & Thurs 10-8, Wed & Fri 10-5, Sat 9-2
   KINMOUNT BRANCH, 3980 County Rd 121, Kinmount, K0M 2A0, SAN
   367-6412. Tel: 705-488-3199. FAX: 705-488-1108. *In Charge,* Karen
   Kent
   Open Tues & Thurs 11-7, Sat 9-1
   KIRKFIELD SERVICE CENTRE LIBRARY, PO Box 246, 7 Monroe St,
   Kirkfield, K0M 2B0, SAN 367-6358. Tel: 705-438-3331. FAX:
   705-438-3138. E-mail: kirkfieldlibrary@kawarthalakes.on.ca. *Librn,*
   Carole May
   Open Mon & Thurs 8:30-7, Tues, Wed & Fri 8:30-4:30, Sat 9-2
   LINDSAY BRANCH, 190 Kent St W, K9V 2Y6. Tel: 705-324-5632. FAX:
   705-324-7140. *Supvr,* Diane Lansdell; *Ref,* Georgia Robinson
   Open Mon-Thurs 10-8, Fri & Sat 10-5
   LITTLE BRITAIN BRANCH, Nine Arena Rd, Little Britain, K0M 2C0.
   (Mail add: PO Box 29, Little Britain, K0M 2C0), SAN 367-6447. Tel:
   705-786-2088. FAX: 705-786-0375. *In Charge,* Karen Sproxton
   Open Mon & Sat 10-2, Thurs 4-8

   NORLAND BRANCH, 3448 County Rd 45, Norland, K0M 2L0, SAN
   367-6501. Tel: 705-454-8552. FAX: 705-454-9749. *In Charge,* Bea
   Hodgson
   Open Tues & Sat 10-2, Thurs 3:30-7:30
   OAKWOOD BRANCH, 932 Hwy 7, Oakwood, K0M 2M0. (Mail add: PO
   Box 179, Oakwood, K0M 2M0), SAN 367-6536. Tel: 705-953-9060.
   FAX: 705-953-9355. *In Charge,* Cathy Hamill-Hill
   Open Tues 11-7, Sat 10-2
   OMEMEE BRANCH, One Kings St W, Omemee, K0L 2W0. (Mail add:
   PO Box 520, Omemee, K0L 2W0), SAN 367-6560. Tel: 705-799-5711.
   FAX: 705-799-6498. *In Charge,* Dale Kennedy
   Open Mon & Sat 10-2, Wed & Thurs 3:30-8
   WOODVILLE BRANCH, 78 King St, Woodville, K0M 2T0. (Mail add:
   PO Box 130, Woodville, K0M 2T0), SAN 367-6595. Tel: 705-439-2160.
   FAX: 705-439-1726. *In Charge,* Jane Davidson
   Open Mon & Thurs 2-8, Fri & Sat 10-2

C   SIR SANDFORD FLEMING COLLEGE*, Frost Campus Library, School
of Environmental & Natural Resources, 200 Albert St S, K9V 5E6. (Mail
add: PO Box 8000, K9V 5E6), SAN 319-2113. Tel: 705-324-9144, Ext
3319. FAX: 705-878-9313. Web Site: www.flemingc.on.ca. *Exec Dir,* Grant
Meadwell
Founded 1968. Enrl 1,740; Fac 85
Library Holdings: Bk Titles 19,000; Bk Vols 20,000; Per Subs 100
Subject Interests: Arboriculture, Ecosystem mgt, Environ tech, Fish,
Forestry, Geol, Heavy equip, Natural res law, Outdoor recreation, Park
operations, Res drilling & blasting, Wildlife
Automation Activity & Vendor Info: (Circulation) SirsiDynix; (Course
Reserve) SirsiDynix; (ILL) SirsiDynix; (Media Booking) SirsiDynix;
(OPAC) SirsiDynix; (Serials) SirsiDynix
Wireless access
Open Mon-Thurs 7:45am-9pm, Fri 7:45-4:30, Sat & Sun 1-5

LISTOWEL

P   NORTHPERTH PUBLIC LIBRARY*, 260 Main St W, N4W 1A1. SAN
319-2121. Tel: 519-291-4621. FAX: 519-291-2235. E-mail:
npl@northperth.library.on.ca. Web Site: www.northperth.library.on.ca. *Chief
Librn/CEO,* Rebecca Dechert-Sage
Pop 12,000; Circ 103,177
Library Holdings: Bk Titles 52,699; Bk Vols 59,414; Per Subs 89
Subject Interests: Biog, Can hist
Wireless access
Partic in Southern Ontario Libr Serv
Open Mon-Thurs 10-8, Fri 10-5, Sat 10-3
Friends of the Library Group

LITTLE CURRENT

P   NEMI PUBLIC LIBRARY*, 50 Meredith St, P0P 1K0. (Mail add: PO Box
790, P0P 1K0), SAN 319-213X. Tel: 705-368-2444. FAX: 705-368-0708.
E-mail: nemilib@vianet.on.ca. Web Site: www.vianet.ca/comm/nemilib.
Librn, Judith Kift
Pop 2,300; Circ 24,000
Library Holdings: Bk Titles 14,000; Per Subs 20
Wireless access

P   SUCKER CREEK FIRST NATIONS PUBLIC LIBRARY*, RR 1, Box 21,
P0P 1K0. SAN 319-2148. Tel: 705-368-2228, 705-368-3696. FAX:
705-368-3563. *Librn,* Paula Kakekagumick
Founded 1975. Pop 440; Circ 2,000
Library Holdings: Bk Vols 2,100
Special Collections: Native Coll, bks, videos
Open Mon-Wed 1-3 & 6-8, Thurs 9-12, 12:30-3 & 6-8, Fri 9-12 & 12:30-3

LONDON

CR BRESCIA UNIVERSITY COLLEGE LIBRARY*, Beryl Ivey Library,
1285 Western Rd, N6G 1H2. SAN 319-2164. Tel: 519-432-8353, Ext
28250. FAX: 519-858-5137. E-mail: beryliveylibrary@uwo.ca. Web Site:
www.brescia.uwo.ca. *Dir,* James Mei; Tel: 519-432-8353, Ext 28250,
E-mail: jmei2@uwo.ca; *Librn,* Adrienne Roode; Tel: 519-432-8353, Ext
28140, E-mail: aroode@uwo.ca; Staff 4 (MLS 2, Non-MLS 2)
Founded 1919. Enrl 1,100; Highest Degree: Bachelor
Library Holdings: Bk Titles 65,000; Bk Vols 68,000; Per Subs 450
Automation Activity & Vendor Info: (Acquisitions) Innovative Interfaces,
Inc; (Cataloging) Innovative Interfaces, Inc; (Circulation) Innovative
Interfaces, Inc; (OPAC) Innovative Interfaces, Inc
Database Vendor: EBSCOhost, Innovative Interfaces, Inc INN - View,
OCLC FirstSearch, OVID Technologies, ProQuest, TLC (The Library
Corporation)
Open Mon-Thurs (Oct-Apr) 8am-10:30pm, Fri 8am-10pm, Sat 9-5, Sun
2-10; Mon-Fri (May-Sept) 8-4

GM   CHILD & PARENT RESOURCE INSTITUTE*, Dr Joseph Pozsonyi
Memorial Library, 600 Sanatorium Rd, N6H 3W7. SAN 371-9391. Tel:
519-858-2774, Ext 2076. FAX: 519-858-3913. *Supvr,* Gillian Kriter; Staff 1
(MLS 1)
Founded 1960
Library Holdings: Bk Titles 4,900; Per Subs 36
Subject Interests: Adolescent psychol, Child psychiat, Child psychology,
Consumer health info
Function: Prof lending libr
Open Mon-Fri 8-5

M   CHILDREN'S HOSPITAL OF WESTERN ONTARIO*, Dr J C Rathbun
Memorial Library, 800 Commissioners Rd E, N6A 4G5. SAN 373-6970.
Tel: 519-685-8500. FAX: 519-685-8103. E-mail: rathbunlibrary@lhsc.on.ca.
Clinical Librn, Shauna-Lee Konrad; Staff 1 (Non-MLS 1)
Founded 1972
Library Holdings: Bk Titles 500; Per Subs 42
Subject Interests: Pediatrics
Function: Res libr
Open Mon-Fri 8-4

J   FANSHAWE COLLEGE*, Library & Media Services, 1001 Fanshawe
College Blvd, N5Y 5R6. (Mail add: PO Box 7005, N5Y 5R6), SAN
319-2199. Tel: 519-452-4240. Interlibrary Loan Service Tel: 519-452-4430,
Ext 4169. FAX: 519-452-4473. Web Site: www.fanshawec.ca. *Mgr,* Martie
Grof-Iannelli; *Copyright Officer,* Meaghan Shannon; *Syst Coordr,* Linda
Crosby; *Pub Serv,* Martha Joyce; *Media Spec,* Megan Anderson; Staff 16
(MLS 4, Non-MLS 12)
Founded 1967. Enrl 10,000; Highest Degree: Bachelor
Library Holdings: e-books 20,000; Bk Titles 60,000; Per Subs 450;
Videos 5,000
Special Collections: Can & Prov
Subject Interests: Applied arts, Health sci
Automation Activity & Vendor Info: (Cataloging) SirsiDynix;
(Circulation) SirsiDynix; (OPAC) SirsiDynix
Database Vendor: EBSCOhost, ProQuest, Wilson - Wilson Web
Wireless access
Open Mon-Thurs 8:30am-10pm, Fri 8:30-4:30, Sun 1-5

C   HURON UNIVERSITY COLLEGE LIBRARY*, 1349 Western Rd, N6G
1H3. SAN 319-2202. Tel: 519-438-7224, Ext 209. FAX: 519-438-3938.
E-mail: huclibrary@uwo.ca. Web Site: www.huronuc.ca/library. *Dir, Info
Res,* Pamela MacKay; *Assoc Librn, Ref,* Dawn Easton Merritt; *Coordr,
Access Serv,* Adrianne Sarich; *Acq,* Beatrice Schmitz du Moulin; Staff 5
(MLS 2, Non-MLS 3)
Founded 1863. Enrl 1,200; Fac 75; Highest Degree: Master
Library Holdings: Bk Vols 165,000; Per Subs 110
Subject Interests: Chinese, Econ, English, Hist, Philosophy, Psychol,
Theol
Wireless access

CR   KING'S UNIVERSITY COLLEGE AT THE UNIVERSITY OF
WESTERN ONTARIO*, G Emmett Cardinal Carter Library, 266 Epworth
Ave, N6A 2M3. SAN 319-2210. Tel: 519-433-3491, Ext 4390. Circulation
Tel: 519-433-3491, Ext 4505. Reference Tel: 519-433-3491, Ext 4327. Toll
Free Tel: 800-265-4406, Ext 4390. FAX: 519-963-0307. Web Site:
www.kings.uwo.ca/library. *Chief Librn,* Claire Callaghan; E-mail:
callagha@uwo.ca; *Head, Res & Info Serv,* Susan Evans; Tel:
519-433-3491, Ext 4327, E-mail: sevans1@uwo.ca; *Assoc Librn, Head,
Tech & Info Res,* Linda M Whidden; Tel: 519-433-3491, Ext 4506, E-mail:
lwhidden@uwo.ca. Subject Specialists: *Psychol, Relig, Thanatology,* Claire
Callaghan; *English, Soc work, Sociol,* Susan Evans; *Econ, Hist, Polit sci,*
Linda M Whidden; Staff 3 (MLS 3)
Founded 1954. Enrl 3,800; Fac 185; Highest Degree: Master
Library Holdings: CDs 105; DVDs 2,301; Bk Titles 121,534; Bk Vols
135,465; Per Subs 432; Videos 446
Special Collections: Cardinal Carter Archives; Georges Bernanos (William
Bush Coll); Henry Edward Dormer Archives; Malcolm Muggeridge (Ian A
Hunter Coll); S & M Clouston 15th-18th Century Coll
Subject Interests: Peace studies, Relig, Soc justice, Soc work,
Thanatology
Automation Activity & Vendor Info: (Acquisitions) Innovative Interfaces,
Inc; (Cataloging) Innovative Interfaces, Inc; (Circulation) Innovative
Interfaces, Inc; (Course Reserve) Innovative Interfaces, Inc; (ILL)
Innovative Interfaces, Inc; (OPAC) Innovative Interfaces, Inc; (Serials)
Innovative Interfaces, Inc
Database Vendor: EBSCO Information Services, EBSCOhost, Gale
Cengage Learning, Innovative Interfaces, Inc INN - View, LexisNexis,
ProQuest
Wireless access
Function: Photocopying/Printing, Ref serv available
Special Services for the Deaf - Assistive tech
Special Services for the Blind - Assistive/Adapted tech devices, equip &
products
Restriction: Open to students, fac & staff

L   LERNERS LLP LIBRARY*, 85 Dufferin Ave, N6A 4G4. (Mail add: PO
Box 2335, Sta A, N6A 4G4), SAN 326-1972. Tel: 519-640-6355. FAX:
519-932-3355. E-mail: lerner.london@lerners.ca. Web Site: www.lerners.ca.
Mgr, Libr Serv, Michelle LaPorte; E-mail: mlaporte@lerners.ca. Subject
Specialists: *Law,* Michelle LaPorte; Staff 4 (MLS 1, Non-MLS 3)
Library Holdings: Bk Vols 10,000
Automation Activity & Vendor Info: (Acquisitions) EOS International;
(Cataloging) EOS International; (Circulation) EOS International; (OPAC)
EOS International; (Serials) EOS International
Database Vendor: EOS International
Wireless access

S   LIBRARY SERVICE OF THE COLLEGE OF FAMILY PHYSICIANS OF
CANADA, Canadian Library of Family Medicine, Rm 106K, Natural
Sciences Centre, University of Western Ontario, N6A 5B7. SAN 323-7109.
Tel: 519-661-3170. FAX: 519-661-3880. E-mail: clfm@uwo.ca. Web Site:
www.cfpc.ca/clfm. *Dir, Libr Serv,* Lynn Dunikowski; Staff 1 (MLS 1)
Subject Interests: Family med, Gen practice, Primary health care
Open Mon-Fri 9-5
Restriction: Mem only

S   LONDON FREE PRESS*, Editorial Library, 369 York St, N6A 4G1. (Mail
add: PO Box 2280, N6A 4G1), SAN 319-2237. Tel: 519-667-4559. FAX:
519-667-4528. Web Site: www.lfpress.com. *Librn,* Cheryl Chute; E-mail:
cheryl.chute@sunmedia.ca; Staff 1 (MLS 1)
Founded 1950
Library Holdings: Bk Vols 550
Special Collections: Newspaper Coll 1849-present, microfilm
Subject Interests: Current news
Restriction: Open by appt only

M   LONDON HEALTH SCIENCES CENTRE LIBRARY SERVICES*, 800
Commissioners Rd E, N6A 4G5. SAN 373-6415. Tel: 519-685-8500, Ext
75934. FAX: 519-667-6641. Web Site: www.lhsc.on.ca. *Libr Mgr,* Karla
VanKessel; E-mail: karla.vankessel@lhsc.on.ca; Staff 7 (MLS 1, Non-MLS
6)
Founded 1995
Library Holdings: AV Mats 250; e-books 150; Bk Titles 6,000; Per Subs
1,750
Subject Interests: Med, Nursing
Automation Activity & Vendor Info: (Acquisitions) Inmagic, Inc.;
(Cataloging) Inmagic, Inc.; (Circulation) Inmagic, Inc.; (Serials) Inmagic,
Inc.
Function: Doc delivery serv, For res purposes, ILL available, Outside serv
via phone, mail, e-mail & web, Photocopying/Printing, Prof lending libr,
Ref serv available, Referrals accepted, Telephone ref
Partic in Canadian Health Libraries Association; Michigan Health Sciences
Libraries Association; Ontario Health Libraries Association
Open Mon-Fri 8-4
Restriction: Open to students, fac & staff

P   LONDON PUBLIC LIBRARY, Central, 251 Dundas St, N6A 6H9. SAN
367-6625. Tel: 519-661-4600. FAX: 519-663-9013. Web Site:
www.londonpubliclibrary.ca. *Chief Exec Officer, Chief Librn,* Susanna
Hubbard Krimmer; Tel: 519-661-5143; *Dep Chief Exec Officer, Dir,*
Margaret Mitchell; Tel: 519-661-5134; Staff 222 (MLS 54, Non-MLS 168)
Founded 1894. Pop 40,000; Circ 3,412,777
Library Holdings: AV Mats 6,396; CDs 1,014; DVDs 48,954; e-books
5,773; Large Print Bks 23,427; Bk Vols 554,170; Per Subs 1,632; Talking
Bks 1,664
Special Collections: Can & Prov; Local History (London Room Coll)
a-tapes, bks, microfilm, pictures. Oral History
Subject Interests: Archit, Art, Hist, Humanities, Music
Wireless access
Publications: Access (Monthly bulletin); Annual Report; Subject-Specific
Booklists
Partic in Ont Pub Libr Info Network
Special Services for the Deaf - Bks on deafness & sign lang; High
interest/low vocabulary bks; Staff with knowledge of sign lang; TTY equip
Open Mon-Thurs 9-9, Fri 9-6, Sat 9-5
Friends of the Library Group
Branches: 16
E S BEACOCK BRANCH, 1280 Huron St, N5Y 1A8, SAN 367-6862.
    Tel: 519-451-8140. *Br Librn,* Maria Forte
    Library Holdings: Bk Vols 58,483
    Open Tues-Thurs 9-9, Fri 9-6, Sat 9-5
    Friends of the Library Group
BYRON MEMORIAL, 1295 Commissioners Rd W, N6K 1C9, SAN
    367-6714. Tel: 519-471-4000. Interlibrary Loan Service Tel:
    519-661-4600. *Br Librn,* Sarah Andrews
    Library Holdings: Bk Vols 58,542

Open Tues-Thurs 9-9, Fri 9-6, Sat 9-5
Friends of the Library Group

W O CARSON BRANCH, 465 Quebec St, N5W 3Y4, SAN 376-9720.
Tel: 519-438-4287. *Librn,* Delilah Deane Cummings
Library Holdings: Bk Vols 22,670
Open Tues & Thurs 1-5 & 6-9, Wed, Fri & Sat 9-12 & 1-5
Friends of the Library Group

CHERRYHILL, 301 Oxford St W, N6H 1S6, SAN 367-6927. Tel:
519-439-6456. *Br Librn,* Ellie Contursi
Library Holdings: Bk Vols 53,334
Open Tues-Thurs 9-9, Fri 9-6, Sat 9-5
Friends of the Library Group

CHILDREN'S, 251 Dundas St, N6A 6H9, SAN 367-6773. Tel:
519-661-4600. *Ch,* Anne McCambridge
Library Holdings: Bk Vols 50,701
Open Mon-Thurs 9-9, Fri 9-6, Sat 9-5
Friends of the Library Group

R E CROUCH BRANCH, 550 Hamilton Rd, N5Z 1S4, SAN 367-6803.
Tel: 519-673-0111. *Br Librn,* Brian Rhoden
Library Holdings: Bk Vols 43,699
Open Tues-Thurs 9-9, Fri 9-6, Sat 9-5
Friends of the Library Group

EAST LONDON, 2016 Dundas St, N5V 1R1, SAN 367-665X. Tel:
519-451-7600. *Br Librn,* Heather Heathcote
Library Holdings: Bk Vols 41,681
Open Tues-Thurs 9-9, Fri 9-6, Sat 9-5
Friends of the Library Group

GLANWORTH, 2950 Glanworth Dr, N6N 1N6, SAN 376-9739. Tel:
519-681-6797. *Br Librn,* Sarah Andrews
Library Holdings: Bk Vols 2,686
Open Tues 7pm-9pm, Sat 10am-Noon
Friends of the Library Group

JALNA, 1119 Jalna Blvd, N6E 3B3, SAN 323-9365. Tel: 519-685-6465.
Br Librn, Jodi Lewis
Library Holdings: Bk Vols 63,698
Open Tues-Thurs 9-9, Fri 9-6, Sat 9-5
Friends of the Library Group

LAMBETH BRANCH, 7112 Beattie St, Lambeth, N6P 1A2, SAN
376-9747. Tel: 519-652-2951. *Br Librn,* Sarah Andrews
Library Holdings: Bk Vols 20,180
Open Tues & Thurs 1-5 & 6-9, Wed, Fri & Sat 9-12 & 1-5
Friends of the Library Group

FRED LANDON BRANCH, 167 Wortley Rd, N6C 3P6, SAN 367-6838.
Tel: 519-439-6240. *Br Librn,* Carolyn Doyle
Library Holdings: Bk Vols 40,496
Open Tues-Thurs 9-9, Fri 9-6, Sat 9-5
Friends of the Library Group

MASONVILLE, 30 North Centre Rd, N5X 3W1, SAN 376-2165. Tel:
519-660-4646. *Br Librn,* Susan Price
Library Holdings: Bk Vols 54,309
Open Tues-Thurs 9-9, Fri 9-6, Sat 9-5
Friends of the Library Group

POND MILLS, 1166 Commissioners Rd E, N5Z 4W8, SAN 323-8407.
Tel: 519-685-1333. *Br Librn,* Kevin Moore
Library Holdings: Bk Vols 48,607
Open Tues-Thurs 9-9, Fri 9-6, Sat 9-5
Friends of the Library Group

SHERWOOD FOREST, Sherwood Forest Mall, 1225 Wonderland Rd N,
N6G 2V9, SAN 328-9699. Tel: 519-473-9965. *Br Librn,* Diane Knoppert
Library Holdings: Bk Vols 53,406
Open Tues-Thurs 9-9, Fri 9-6, Sat 9-5
Friends of the Library Group

STONEY CREEK, 920 Sunningdale Rd E, N5X 0H5, Tel: 519-930-2065.
Br Librn, Elizabeth Egleston
Open Tues-Thurs 9-9, Fri 9-6, Sat 9-5

WESTMOUNT, 3200 Wonderland Rd S, N6L 1A6, SAN 367-6935. Tel:
519-473-4708. *Br Librn,* Alastair Neely
Library Holdings: Bk Vols 51,887
Open Tues-Thurs 9-9, Fri 9-6, Sat 9-5
Friends of the Library Group

L   MIDDLESEX LAW ASSOCIATION, Law Library, Ground Flr, Unit N, 80
Dundas St, N6A 6A1. SAN 319-2253. Tel: 519-679-7046. FAX:
519-672-5917. E-mail: library@middlaw.on.ca. Web Site:
www.middlaw.on.ca. *Librn,* Gail Brown; *Librn,* Cynthia Simpson; Staff 3
(MLS 2, Non-MLS 1)
Founded 1879
Library Holdings: Bk Vols 21,000
Special Collections: Historical Coll of City (London) Directories
Database Vendor: LexisNexis
Wireless access
Restriction: Not open to pub, Private libr

S   PARMALAT CANADA, LTD*, Research & Development Library, 65
Bathurst St, N6B IN8. SAN 329-9430. Tel: 519-667-7709. FAX:
519-667-7725. Web Site: www.parmalat.ca. *In Charge,* Jackie Haldane;
Tel: 519-667-7705, E-mail: jackie_haldane@parmalat.ca
Library Holdings: Bk Vols 450
Subject Interests: Dairy, Eng, Food sci, Nutrition
Open Mon-Fri 8:30-5

M   REGIONAL MENTAL HEALTH CARE LONDON*, George E Jenkins
Library, 850 Highbury Ave N, N6A 4H1. SAN 324-4962. Tel:
519-455-5110. FAX: 519-455-3620. E-mail:
rmhcl_library@sjhc.london.on.ca. *Med Librn,* Elizabeth Russell; Tel:
519-455-5110, Ext 49685, E-mail: elizabeth.russell@sjhc.london.on.ca; *Libr
Tech,* Elizabeth Pattison; Tel: 519-455-5110, Ext 47543; Staff 2 (MLS 1,
Non-MLS 1)
Founded 1964
Library Holdings: Bk Titles 2,694; Per Subs 116
Subject Interests: Mental health, Psychiat, Psychol
Automation Activity & Vendor Info: (Cataloging) Inmagic, Inc.;
(Circulation) Inmagic, Inc.; (OPAC) Inmagic, Inc.; (Serials) Inmagic, Inc.
Database Vendor: EBSCOhost, OVID Technologies
Partic in Docline; Southwestern Ontario Health Libraries & Information
Network
Open Mon-Fri 8:30-4:15

M   SAINT JOSEPH'S HOSPITAL, Robert M McFarlane Medical Library, 268
Grosvenor St, N6A 4V2. (Mail add: PO Box 5777, N6A 4V2), SAN
325-2477. Tel: 519-646-6000, Ext 65727. Circulation Tel: 519-646-6000,
Ext 64439. FAX: 519-646-6228. *Mgr, Libr Serv,* Brad Dishan; E-mail:
brad.dishan@sjhc.london.on.ca; Staff 2 (MLS 1, Non-MLS 1)
Founded 1966
Library Holdings: Bk Titles 4,433; Per Subs 5,000
Automation Activity & Vendor Info: (Cataloging) Inmagic, Inc.;
(Circulation) Inmagic, Inc.; (OPAC) Inmagic, Inc.
Database Vendor: EBSCO Information Services, EBSCOhost, Gale
Cengage Learning, Lexi-Comp, Micromedex, OVID Technologies,
ProQuest, PubMed, ScienceDirect, Springshare, LLC, STAT!Ref (Teton
Data Systems), UpToDate, Wiley InterScience
Function: Computers for patron use, Doc delivery serv, Electronic
databases & coll, Health sci info serv, Ref serv available
Partic in Docline; Western Ontario Health Knowledge Network (WOHKN)
Open Mon-Fri 8:30-5
Restriction: Badge access after hrs, Hospital employees & physicians only,
In-house use for visitors

R   SAINT PETER'S SEMINARY*, A P Mahoney Library, 1040 Waterloo St
N, N6A 3Y1. SAN 319-227X. Tel: 519-432-1824. FAX: 519-439-5172.
Web Site: www.stpetersseminary.ca. *Chief Librn,* Claire Callaghan; Tel:
519-433-3491, Ext 4390, E-mail: calagha@uwo.ca;
Asst Librn, Circ, Ref, Frances Theilade; E-mail: ftheilad@uwo.ca; *Libr
Asst,* Rita Ulrich; E-mail: rulrich@uwo.ca; Staff 3 (MLS 2, Non-MLS 1)
Founded 1926
Library Holdings: AV Mats 2,019; Bk Titles 56,036; Bk Vols 68,421; Per
Subs 181
Subject Interests: Philosophy, Theol
Automation Activity & Vendor Info: (Acquisitions) Innovative Interfaces,
Inc - Millenium; (Cataloging) Innovative Interfaces, Inc - Millenium;
(Circulation) Innovative Interfaces, Inc - Millenium; (Course Reserve)
Innovative Interfaces, Inc - Millenium; (OPAC) Innovative Interfaces, Inc -
Millenium
Database Vendor: EBSCO Information Services, EBSCOhost, Project
MUSE, ProQuest, RefWorks, YBP Library Services
Wireless access
Open Mon & Fri 8:30-4:30, Tues-Thurs 8:30-4:30 & 7pm-10:30pm, Sat
1-4:30, Sun 1-4:30 & 7pm-10:30pm

L   SISKIND, CROMARTY, IVEY & DOWLER*, Law Library, 680 Waterloo
St, N6A 3V8. SAN 328-0446. Tel: 519-672-2121. FAX: 519-672-6065.
Web Site: www.siskinds.com. *Librn,* Michael Mcaopine; E-mail:
micheal.mcaopine@siskinds.com; Staff 1 (MLS 1)
Library Holdings: Bk Titles 200
Database Vendor: LexisNexis, WestlaweCARSWELL
Function: CD-ROM, Doc delivery serv, For res purposes, Govt ref serv,
Online searches, Ref serv available, VHS videos
Restriction: Co libr, Open to staff only

S   3M CANADA CO, Corporate Library & Information Services, 1840
Oxford St E, N5V 3R6. (Mail add: PO Box 5757, N6A 4T1), SAN
319-2288. Tel: 519-451-2500, Ext 2486. FAX: 519-452-4714. Web Site:
www.mmm.com. *In Charge,* Cheryl E Stephenson; E-mail:
cstephenson@mmm.com; Staff 2 (MLS 2)
Founded 1973
Library Holdings: Bk Titles 2,000; Per Subs 125
Restriction: Co libr

C   UNIVERSITY OF WESTERN ONTARIO, Faculty of Information &
Media Studies Graduate Resource Centre, North Campus Bldg, Rm 280,
N6A 5B7. SAN 324-4938. Tel: 519-661-2111, Ext 88489. Circulation Tel:
519-661-2111, Ext 88488. FAX: 519-661-3848. Web Site:
www.fims.uwo.ca. *Librn,* Marni Harrington; E-mail: mharring@uwo.ca;
Libr Asst, Crystel Cowen; E-mail: ccowen@uwo.ca; *Libr Asst,* Steve
Patterson; E-mail: spatter2@uwo.ca; Staff 4 (MLS 1, Non-MLS 3)
Founded 1966. Enrl 300; Highest Degree: Doctorate
Library Holdings: Bk Titles 1,500; Per Subs 150
Subject Interests: Health sci, Journalism, Libr sci, Media studies, Popular
culture, Popular music
Wireless access
Function: Ref serv available
Restriction: Authorized patrons, Badge access after hrs, Borrowing
privileges limited to fac & registered students, Borrowing requests are
handled by ILL, ID required to use computers (Ltd hrs), Non-circulating
coll

C   WESTERN UNIVERSITY - LIBRARIES, (Formerly University of Western
Ontario Libraries), 1151 Richmond St, Ste 200, N6A 3K7. SAN 367-6951.
Tel: 519-661-3166, 519-661-4807. Interlibrary Loan Service Tel:
519-661-3163. Administration Tel: 519-661-2111, Ext 84796. Information
Services Tel: 519-661-2111, Ext 84770. FAX: 519-661-3493. Web Site:
www.lib.uwo.ca. *Univ Librn,* Joyce Garnett; Tel: 519-661-3165, E-mail:
jgarnett@uwo.ca; *Assoc Univ Librn,* Eeva Munoz; Tel: 519-661-2111, Ext
86897, E-mail: ekmunoz@uwo.ca; *Asst Univ Librn, Info Res & Access,*
Karen Marshall; Tel: 519-661-2111, Ext 84850; *Univ Archivist,* Robin
Keirstead; Tel: 519-661-2111, Ext 87289, E-mail: keirste@uwo.ca; Staff 62
(MLS 45, Non-MLS 17)
Founded 1908. Enrl 35,000; Fac 1,400; Highest Degree: Doctorate
Library Holdings: e-books 502,116; e-journals 79,327; Bk Vols
3,162,463; Per Subs 6,852
Special Collections: Can & Prov
Subject Interests: Applied health sci, Dentistry, Educ, Eng, Humanities,
Journalism, Kinesiology, Law, Med, Music, Nursing, Sci, Soc sci
Automation Activity & Vendor Info: (Acquisitions) Innovative Interfaces,
Inc; (Cataloging) Innovative Interfaces, Inc; (Circulation) Innovative
Interfaces, Inc; (OPAC) Innovative Interfaces, Inc; (Serials) Innovative
Interfaces, Inc
Wireless access
Publications: A Guide to Selected Microform Collections & Sets in The D
B Weldon Library; Bibliography of Hitchins Coll; Catalogue of the R M
Bucke Coll; Guide to Canadian Newspapers on Microfilm in The D B
Weldon Library
Open Mon-Thurs 8am-11:30pm, Fri 8am-9:30pm, Sat & Sun 11-5:30
Friends of the Library Group
Departmental Libraries:

CL JOHN & DOTSA BITOVE FAMILY LAW LIBRARY, Josephine Spencer
Niblett Law Bldg, N6A 3K7, SAN 367-7109. Tel: 519-661-3171.
Administration Tel: 519-661-2111, Ext 88271. FAX: 519-661-2012. Web
Site: www.lib.uwo.ca/law. *Dir,* John Sadler; E-mail: jsadler@uwo.ca;
Staff 7 (MLS 2, Non-MLS 5)
Founded 1959. Enrl 850; Fac 40; Highest Degree: Doctorate
Library Holdings: Bk Vols 194,377; Per Subs 1,207
Subject Interests: Can law, Taxation
Function: Computers for patron use, Copy machines, Electronic
databases & coll, Handicapped accessible, ILL available,
Photocopying/Printing, Pub access computers, Ref & res, Ref serv
available, Ref serv in person, Res libr, Wheelchair accessible
Open Mon-Thurs 8:15am-10pm, Fri 8:15-5, Sat 10-5, Sun 1-8
Friends of the Library Group
EDUCATION, John George Althouse Faculty of Educ, 1137 Western Rd,
N6G 1G7, SAN 367-701X. Tel: 519-661-3172. Circulation Tel:
519-661-2111, Ext 3172. Reference Tel: 519-661-2111, Ext 88275. FAX:
519-661-3822. Web Site: www.lib.uwo.ca/education. *Dir,* Christena
McKillop; Tel: 519-661-2111, Ext 88276; Staff 2 (MLS 2)
Founded 1965. Enrl 873; Fac 42; Highest Degree: Doctorate
Library Holdings: Microforms 634,704; Bk Vols 675,064; Per Subs 548
Special Collections: Complete ERIC Coll, microfiche
Subject Interests: Elem educ
Function: Accessibility serv available based on individual needs
Open Mon-Thurs 8-7, Fri 8-5, Sat 12-5
Friends of the Library Group
C B "BUD" JOHNSTON LIBRARY, Richard Ivey School of Business,
N6A 3K7, SAN 367-6986. Tel: 519-661-3941. FAX: 519-661-2158.
E-mail: buslib@ivey.uwo.ca. Web Site: www.lib.uwo.ca/business. *Dir,*
Nicole Marshall; Tel: 519-661-2111, Ext 84842; Staff 7 (MLS 2,
Non-MLS 5)
Founded 1961. Enrl 1,169; Fac 93; Highest Degree: Doctorate
Library Holdings: Bk Vols 80,581; Per Subs 293
Special Collections: Canadian & US Company Data, microfiche. Can &
Prov
Subject Interests: Acctg, Finance, Labor relations, Mkt, Operation res
Special Services for the Deaf - ADA equip; Videos & decoder
Special Services for the Blind - Accessible computers

Open Mon-Thurs 8:30am-9pm, Fri 8:30-4:30, Sat & Sun 10-5
Friends of the Library Group
MUSIC, Talbot College, Rm 234, N6A 3K7, SAN 367-7133. Tel:
519-661-3913. Reference Tel: 519-661-2111, Ext 84846. FAX:
519-661-3927. Web Site: www.lib.uwo.ca/music. *Dir,* Monica Fazekas;
Tel: 519-661-2111, Ext 85334; Staff 8 (MLS 2, Non-MLS 6)
Founded 1963. Enrl 661; Fac 42; Highest Degree: Doctorate
Library Holdings: AV Mats 53,912; Microforms 11,782; Music Scores
69,587; Bk Vols 35,806; Per Subs 557; Videos 453
Special Collections: Gustav Mahler, Alfred Rose & Bruno Walter
(Mahler-Rose Coll), scores; Opera Coll, 1600-Early 20th Century
Subject Interests: Applied music, Hist, Music educ, Popular music,
Theory of music
Function: Accessibility serv available based on individual needs
Open Mon-Thurs 8:30-7, Fri 8:30-5, Sat & Sun 1-5
Friends of the Library Group
ALLYN & BETTY TAYLOR LIBRARY, 1151 Richmond St, Ste 2, N6A
5B7, SAN 367-7079. Tel: 519-661-3168. FAX: 519-661-3435. Web Site:
www.lib.uwo.ca/taylor. *Asst Univ Librn,* Kim Cornell; Tel: 519-661-2111,
Ext 86362, E-mail: kcornel@uwo.ca; Staff 26 (MLS 9, Non-MLS 17)
Founded 1882. Enrl 11,573; Fac 738; Highest Degree: Doctorate
Library Holdings: Bk Vols 342,226; Per Subs 1,636
Subject Interests: Chem, Chem eng, Communications, Communicative
disorders, Conserv, Dentistry, Earth sci, Electrical eng, Life sci, Mat eng,
Math sci, Mechanical eng, Med, Natural hist, Nursing, Occupational
therapy, Phys therapy
Function: Accessibility serv available based on individual needs
Open Mon-Thurs 8:30am-11:30pm, Fri 8:30am-9:30pm, Sat 11-5:30, Sun
11-9:30
Friends of the Library Group
THE D B WELDON LIBRARY, 1151 Richmond St, Ste 2, N6A 3K7. Tel:
519-661-3166. Interlibrary Loan Service Tel: 519-661-3697. Reference
Tel: 519-661-3162. Administration Tel: 519-661-2111, Ext 84806.
E-mail: dbwlib@uwo.ca. Web Site: www.lib.uwo.ca/weldon. *Asst Univ
Librn,* Dr Catherine Wilkins; Tel: 519-661-2111, Ext 84772; Staff 100
(MLS 28, Non-MLS 72)
Founded 1934. Enrl 15,000; Fac 430; Highest Degree: Doctorate
Library Holdings: Microforms 2,929,162; Bk Titles 1,500,687; Per Subs
3,346
Subject Interests: Arts, Humanities, Journalism, Libr, Media studies,
Soc sci
Database Vendor: Innovative Interfaces, Inc INN - View
Function: Accessibility serv available based on individual needs
Open Mon-Fri 8am-11:30pm, Sat 11-9, Sun 11am-11:30pm
Friends of the Library Group
WESTERN ARCHIVES, Archives & Research Collection Centre (ARCC),
1151 Richmond St, Ste 2, N6A 3K7. Tel: 519-661-4046. FAX:
519-850-2979. E-mail: archive.services@uwo.ca. Web Site:
www.lib.uwo.ca/archives. *Univ Archivist,* Robin Keirstead; Tel:
519-661-2111, Ext 87289; Staff 12 (MLS 5, Non-MLS 7)
Founded 1900
Library Holdings: Electronic Media & Resources 1,652,000;
Microforms 13,839; Bk Vols 74,665; Spec Interest Per Sub 15,381
Special Collections: Aviation History (Beatrice Hitchins Memorial Coll);
Canadian Newspapers, microfilm; Canadian Quaker Archives, 1789-1950,
microfilm; Canadian, American & British Government Publs; Edwardian
Writers (John Galt Coll); French Enlightenment & the Revolution;
History of Science & Medicine (Hannah Coll); John Milton & Miltonia
(G William Stuart Jr Coll); Richard Maurice Buckle Coll; Southwestern
Ontario Regional Coll; University Archives
Subject Interests: Local hist
Restriction: Non-circulating

L'ORIGNAL

L   PRESCOTT & RUSSELL LAW ASSOCIATION LIBRARY*, 59 Court St,
K0B 1K0. (Mail add: PO Box 540, K0B 1K0), SAN 377-3310. Tel:
613-675-2424. FAX: 613-675-1003. E-mail: prescott.law@bellnet.ca. *Libr
Asst,* Anita Regan
Library Holdings: Bk Titles 1,000; Bk Vols 1,100
Wireless access
Open Wed 9-3:30

MADOC

P   MADOC PUBLIC LIBRARY*, 20 Davidson St, K0K 2K0. (Mail add: PO
Box 6, K0K 2K0), SAN 319-2326. Tel: 613-473-4456. FAX:
613-473-4456. E-mail: madoc_public_library@bellnet.ca. Web Site:
www.madocpubliclibrary.ca. *Librn,* Susan Smith
Pop 1,266; Circ 20,000
Library Holdings: Bk Titles 23,867; Per Subs 18
Wireless access
Open Tues & Thurs 3:30-7:30, Wed & Fri 10-5, Sat 10-1
Friends of the Library Group

MANITOUWADGE

P   MANITOUWADGE PUBLIC LIBRARY, Community Ctr, Two Manitou Rd, P0T 2C0. SAN 319-2350. Tel: 807-826-3913. FAX: 807-826-4640. E-mail: manitouwadgelibrary@hotmail.com. Web Site: www.olsn.ca/manitouwadge. *Chief Exec Officer, Librn,* Janis Lamothe Founded 1961. Pop 2,300; Circ 33,032
Library Holdings: Bk Titles 29,000
Special Collections: Geco Mining Coll. Can & Prov
Subject Interests: Geol sci
Automation Activity & Vendor Info: (Cataloging) SirsiDynix; (Circulation) SirsiDynix; (OPAC) SirsiDynix; (Serials) SirsiDynix
Wireless access
Function: Bks on cassette, Computer training, Copy machines, Free DVD rentals, Holiday prog, Homebound delivery serv, ILL available, Magnifiers for reading, Music CDs, Photocopying/Printing, Prog for children & young adult, Scanner, Summer reading prog, Video lending libr
Open Mon 1-4:30 & 6:30-8:30, Tues-Thurs 10-4:30 & 6:30-8:30, Fri 10-4:30; Sat (Oct-May) 1-4:30
Friends of the Library Group

MARATHON

P   MARATHON PUBLIC LIBRARY*, 22 Peninsula Rd, P0T 2E0. (Mail add: PO Box 400, P0T 2E0), SAN 319-2377. Tel: 807-229-0740. FAX: 807-229-3336. Web Site: www.marathon.ca/article/public-library-178.asp. *Chief Exec Officer, Head Librn,* Tamara Needham; E-mail: tneedham@tbaytel.net; Staff 5 (Non-MLS 5)
Founded 1948. Pop 4,400; Circ 35,000
Library Holdings: Bk Vols 21,000; Per Subs 12
Automation Activity & Vendor Info: (Acquisitions) Follett Software; (Cataloging) Follett Software; (Circulation) Follett Software; (OPAC) Follett Software
Wireless access
Open Mon-Fri 12-5

MARKHAM

S   IBM CANADA LTD-TORONTO LAB*, Skill Centre, 8200 Warden Ave, Dept Z3, L6G 1C7. SAN 319-0994. Tel: 905-413-3555. E-mail: skills@ca.ibm.com. Web Site: www.can.ibm.com/torontolab/learning.html. *Librn,* Lada Sergeeva; Staff 2 (MLS 1, Non-MLS 1)
Library Holdings: Bk Vols 8,000; Per Subs 100
Wireless access
Open Mon-Fri 8:30-5

S   INTERNATIONAL NORTH AMERICAN LIBRARY*, 90 Nolan Ct, No 21, L3R 4L9. SAN 373-840X. Tel: 905-946-9588. FAX: 905-946-9590. E-mail: sales@ippbook.com. Web Site: www.ippbooks.com. *Acq,* Bali Sethi; *Pub Serv,* M Rupa
Founded 1993
Special Collections: Canadian Directories, Serials (American & International Reference Books & Annuals); International. Can & Prov

P   MARKHAM PUBLIC LIBRARY, Central Admin, 6031 Hwy 7, L3P 3A7. SAN 319-4442. Tel: 905-513-7977. Automation Services Tel: 905-474-5966. FAX: 905-471-6015. E-mail: comments@markham.library.on.ca. Web Site: www.markhampubliclibrary.ca. *Chief Exec Officer,* Catherine Biss; E-mail: cbiss@markham.library.on.ca
Pop 299,800
Special Collections: Black Heritage Coll; John Lunau Heritage Research Centre
Automation Activity & Vendor Info: (Circulation) SirsiDynix
Database Vendor: 3M Library Systems, Brodart
Wireless access
Partic in Southern Ontario Libr Serv
Special Services for the Blind - Bks available with recordings; Bks on cassette; Bks on CD; Home delivery serv; Large print bks
Open Mon-Fri 9-5
Branches: 7
ANGUS GLEN BRANCH, 3990 Major Mackenzie Dr E, L6C 1P8. Tel: 905-513-7977, Ext 4277. Circulation Tel: 905-513-7977, Ext 7100. Interlibrary Loan Service Tel: 905-513-7977, Ext 3711. Reference Tel: 905-513-7977, Ext 7133. Information Services Tel: 905-513-7977, Ext 7144. FAX: 905-944-3801. *Br Mgr,* Angela Tse; Tel: 905-513-7977, Ext 7150, E-mail: atse@markham.library.on.ca
Special Services for the Deaf - Coll on deaf educ
Open Mon-Thurs 9:30-9, Fri 9:30-5, Sat 9-5, Sun 1-5
CORNELL BRANCH, 6031 Hwy 7 E, L6B 0T2. Tel: 905-513-7977. *Br Mgr,* Hilary Murphy; E-mail: hmurphy@markham.library.on.ca
Subject Interests: Med
Database Vendor: 3M Library Systems, BiblioCommons
Special Services for the Blind - Bks on cassette
Open Mon-Thurs 9:30-9, Fri 9:30-5, Sat 9-5, Sun 1-5

MARKHAM VILLAGE BRANCH, 6031 Hwy 7 E, L3P 3A7, SAN 321-947X. Tel: 905-513-7977. Circulation Tel: 905-513-7977, Ext 4271. Interlibrary Loan Service Tel: 905-513-7977, Ext 3711. Automation Services Tel: 905-474-5966. Information Services Tel: 905-513-7977, Ext 4273. FAX: 905-294-7586. Web Site: www.markhampubliclibrary.ca. *Br Mgr,* Yolanda Chan; Tel: 905-513-7977, Ext 4277, E-mail: ychan@markham.library.on.ca
Database Vendor: BiblioCommons
Open Mon-Thurs 9:30-9, Fri 9:30-5, Sat 9-5, Sun 1-5
MILLIKEN MILLS BRANCH, 7600 Kennedy Rd, Unit 1, Unionville, L3R 9S5, SAN 374-6356. Tel: 905-513-7977. Circulation Tel: 905-513-7977, Ext 5337. Interlibrary Loan Service Tel: 905-513-7977, Ext 3711. Administration Tel: 905-513-7977, Ext 2111. Automation Services Tel: 905-474-5966. Information Services Tel: 905-513-7977, Ext 5336. FAX: 905-940-8326. *Br Mgr,* John Shewfelt; E-mail: jshewfelt@markham.library.on.ca
Open Mon-Thurs 9:30-9, Fri 9:30-5, Sat 9-5, Sun 1-5
THORNHILL COMMUNITY BRANCH, 7755 Bayview Ave, Thornhill, L3T 4P1, SAN 321-9488. Tel: 905-513-7977. Circulation Tel: 905-513-7977, Ext 3521. Interlibrary Loan Service Tel: 905-513-7977, Ext 3711. Information Services Tel: 905-513-7977, Ext 3523. FAX: 905-881-2935. *Br Mgr,* Mindy Freed; Tel: 905-513-7977, Ext 3524, E-mail: mfreed@markham.library.on.ca
Open Mon-Thurs 9:30-9, Fri 9:30-5, Sat 9-5, Sun 1-5
THORNHILL VILLAGE BRANCH, 10 Colborne St, Thornhill, L3T 1Z6, SAN 321-9496. Tel: 905-513-7977, Ext 3481. FAX: 905-881-0149. *Br Mgr,* Mindy Freed; Tel: 905-513-7977, Ext 3524, E-mail: mfreed@markham.library.on.ca
Open Tues & Thurs 12-8, Wed, Fri & Sat 9-5, Sun 1-5
UNIONVILLE BRANCH, 15 Library Lane, Unionville, L3R 5C4, SAN 321-950X. Tel: 905-513-7977, Ext 5517. Interlibrary Loan Service Tel: 905-513-7977, Ext 3711. Information Services Tel: 905-513-7977, Ext 5518. FAX: 905-477-8608. *Br Mgr,* Patrick Pan; Tel: 905-513-7977, Ext 5551, E-mail: ppan@markham.library.on.ca
Open Mon-Thurs 9:30-9, Fri 9:30-5, Sat 9-5, Sun 1-5

M   MARKHAM STOUFFVILLE HOSPITAL LIBRARY*, 381 Church St, L3P 7P3. (Mail add: PO Box 1800, L3P 7P3), SAN 373-6334. Tel: 905-472-7061. FAX: 905-472-7590. *Librn,* Gail Knaggs; E-mail: gknaggs@msh.on.ca; Staff 1 (Non-MLS 1)
Founded 1990
Library Holdings: CDs 34; DVDs 35; e-books 3; e-journals 7; Large Print Bks 29; Bk Titles 2,937; Per Subs 38; Videos 381
Open Mon-Thurs 9-12 & 1-4, Fri 9-1

MARMORA

P   MARMORA & LAKE PUBLIC LIBRARY*, 37 Forsyth St, K0K 2M0. (Mail add: PO Box 340, K0K 2M0), SAN 319-2393. Tel: 613-472-3122. E-mail: info@marmoralibrary.ca. *Chief Exec Officer, Librn,* Sheryl Price; *Asst Librn,* Tammie Adams
Founded 1920. Pop 3,078
Library Holdings: Bk Vols 10,000; Per Subs 13
Mem of Ontario Library Service North
Open Tues & Fri 10-5, Wed & Thurs 3-7, Sat 10-2
Friends of the Library Group

MASSEY

P   MASSEY & TOWNSHIP PUBLIC LIBRARY*, 185 Grove, P0P 1P0. (Mail add: PO Box 40, P0P 1P0), SAN 319-2407. Tel: 705-865-2641. FAX: 705-865-1781. E-mail: infomasseylibrary@gmail.com. *Librn,* Elizabeth Gamble; *Asst Librn,* Ruth DeClerck; *Asst Librn,* Jeanine Hnatuik
Founded 1960. Pop 3,500; Circ 15,000
Library Holdings: Audiobooks 313; CDs 26; DVDs 223; High Interest/Low Vocabulary Bk Vols 2,636; Large Print Bks 520; Bk Vols 19,358; Per Subs 35; Talking Bks 184; Videos 8
Special Collections: French Coll; German Coll
Special Services for the Deaf - Bks on deafness & sign lang
Special Services for the Blind - Accessible computers; Assistive/Adapted tech devices, equip & products; Audio mat; Bks on cassette; Bks on CD; Daisy reader; Extensive large print coll; Large print bks; Large screen computer & software; Low vision equip; Magnifiers
Open Mon, Wed & Fri 10-5 & 7pm-9pm, Tues 11-5, Sat (Winter) 11-1
Branches: 1
WEBBWOOD PUBLIC, 16 Main St, Webbwood, P0P 1P0. (Mail add: PO Box 40, Webbwood, P0P 1P0). Tel: 705-869-4147. FAX: 705-869-4147. E-mail: webbwoodlibrary@personainternet.com. Web Site: www.masseylibrary.com/webbwood-library.htm. *Br Librn,* Linda Lendrum
Library Holdings: Audiobooks 14; DVDs 228; High Interest/Low Vocabulary Bk Vols 11; Large Print Bks 64; Bk Titles 6,311; Bk Vols 91; Per Subs 3; Spec Interest Per Sub 1; Talking Bks 14
Open Mon, Wed & Thurs (Summer) 6am-8pm, Tues 11-1; Mon & Wed-Fri (Winter) 6pm-8pm, Tues 11-1

MATTAWA

P　　MATTAWA PUBLIC LIBRARY*, John Dixon Public Library, 370 Pine St, P0H 1V0. (Mail add: PO Box 920, P0H 1V0), SAN 319-2423. Tel: 705-744-5550. FAX: 705-744-1714. E-mail: mplibrary@efni.com. Web Site: users.efni.com/mplibrary. *Chief Exec Officer,* Lise Moore-Asselin; *ILL,* Nicole Leblant
Pop 2,644; Circ 5,000
Library Holdings: Bk Vols 50,000; Per Subs 22
Wireless access
Mem of Ontario Library Service North
Open Mon-Fri 12-8, Sat 12-4
Friends of the Library Group

MATTICE

P　　MATTICE-VAL COTE PUBLIC LIBRARY*, Hwy 11, P0L 1T0. (Mail add: PO Box 129, P0L 1T0), SAN 320-071X. Tel: 705-364-5301. FAX: 705-364-6431. E-mail: biblimat@ntl.sympatico.ca. *Librn,* Michelle Salonen
Library Holdings: Bk Vols 11,000; Per Subs 45
Wireless access
Open Mon & Thurs 1-5, Tues & Wed 1-5 & 6-8

MAYNOOTH

P　　THE MUNICIPALITY OF HASTINGS HIGHLANDS LIBRARY*, 33011 Hwy 62 N, K0L 2S0. (Mail add: Box 70, K0L 2S0), SAN 319-2431. Tel: 613-338-2262. FAX: 613-338-3292. E-mail: maynoothlibrary362@hotmail.com. *Chief Exec Officer,* Julie Andrews-Jotham
Pop 4,000; Circ 9,000
Library Holdings: Bk Titles 6,000; Bk Vols 8,000; Per Subs 15
Automation Activity & Vendor Info: (Cataloging) Winnebago Software Co; (Circulation) Winnebago Software Co
Partic in Southern Ontario Libr Serv
Open Tues 10-7, Wed-Fri 10-5, Sat 10-3

MCKELLAR

P　　MCKELLAR TOWNSHIP PUBLIC LIBRARY*, 701 Hwy 124, P0G 1C0. (Mail add: PO Box 10, Mckellar, P0G 1C0), SAN 321-8015. Tel: 705-389-2611. FAX: 705-389-2611. E-mail: mckellarlib@vianet.ca. Web Site: www.mckellarpubliclibrary.ca. *Librn,* Joan Ward; Staff 1 (MLS 1)
Founded 1982. Pop 1,400; Circ 4,672
Library Holdings: Bk Titles 7,732; Per Subs 18; Talking Bks 106
Automation Activity & Vendor Info: (Acquisitions) SIRSI WorkFlows; (Cataloging) SIRSI WorkFlows; (Circulation) SIRSI WorkFlows; (Course Reserve) SIRSI WorkFlows; (ILL) SIRSI WorkFlows; (Media Booking) SIRSI WorkFlows; (OPAC) SIRSI WorkFlows; (Serials) SIRSI WorkFlows
Database Vendor: EBSCO Auto Repair Reference, EBSCOhost
Wireless access
Mem of Ontario Library Service North
Open Wed & Thurs 12-5, Tues 12-5 & 7pm-9pm, Sat 10-1

MEAFORD

P　　MEAFORD PUBLIC LIBRARY*, 15 Trowbridge St W, N4L 1V4. SAN 319-244X. Tel: 519-538-1060, Ext 1123. FAX: 519-538-1808. E-mail: info@meafordlibrary.on.ca. Web Site: www.meafordlibrary.on.ca. *Chief Exec Officer, Chief Librn,* Cathlean Lee; E-mail: cathie@meafordlibrary.on.ca; *Tech Serv Coordr,* Marion Mower; E-mail: marion@meafordlibrary.on.ca; *ILL, Web Coordr,* Lynne Fascinato; E-mail: lynne@meafordlibrary.on.ca; *Children's Serv Coordr, Youth Serv Coordr,* Jody Seeley; E-mail: jody@meafordlibrary.on.ca; *Outreach Serv, Pub Relations,* Lori Ledingham; E-mail: lori@meafordlibrary.on.ca
Pop 11,000; Circ 70,000
Library Holdings: Bk Vols 40,000; Per Subs 35
Wireless access
Open Tues & Thurs 10-8, Wed & Fri 10-5, Sat 10-3
Friends of the Library Group

MERRICKVILLE

P　　MERRICKVILLE PUBLIC LIBRARY, 446 Main St W, K0G 1N0. (Mail add: PO Box 460, K0G 1N0), SAN 319-2458. Tel: 613-269-3326. FAX: 613-269-3326. E-mail: merrickville_library@bellnet.ca. Web Site: www.merrickvillelibrary.ca. *Librn,* Mary Kate Laphen; Staff 1 (MLS 1)
Founded 1856. Pop 3,500; Circ 34,000
Library Holdings: Bk Titles 20,000; Per Subs 30
Special Collections: Merrickville Historical Society Digital Archives; Merrickville-Wolford Genealogy Records
Automation Activity & Vendor Info: (Cataloging) Mandarin Library Automation; (Circulation) Mandarin Library Automation; (OPAC) Mandarin Library Automation
Wireless access

Function: Adult bk club, Bks on cassette, Bks on CD, Children's prog, Computers for patron use, Copy machines, Fax serv, Handicapped accessible, ILL available, Online cat, Photocopying/Printing, Pub access computers, Ref serv available, Scanner, Story hour, Summer reading prog, Web-catalog, Wheelchair accessible
Partic in Southern Ontario Libr Serv
Open Mon & Wed 6pm-8:30pm, Tues & Thurs 10-12 & 1-5, Sat 10-12 & 1-4
Friends of the Library Group

MIDHURST

P　　TOWNSHIP OF SPRINGWATER PUBLIC LIBRARY*, Midhurst Branch, 12 Finlay Mill Rd, L0L 1X0. (Mail add: PO Box 129, L0L 1X0), SAN 319-2547. Tel: 705-737-5650. FAX: 705-737-3594. E-mail: midhurst.library@springwater.ca. Web Site: www.springwater.ca. *Chief Librn,* Lynn Patkau; E-mail: lynn.patkau@springwater.ca
Pop 16,000; Circ 107,000
Library Holdings: Bk Titles 32,000; Per Subs 60
Partic in Southern Ontario Libr Serv
Open Tues 12-7, Wed 12-5, Thurs 10-7, Fri 10-5, Sat 10-3
Friends of the Library Group
Branches: 2
ELMVALE BRANCH, 50 Queen St W, Elmvale, L0L 1P0, SAN 319-1206. Tel: 705-322-1482. FAX: 705-322-0173. E-mail: elmvale.library@springwater.ca. *Chief Librn,* Lynn Patkau
Library Holdings: Bk Vols 24,000; Per Subs 27
Open Tues Noon-7, Wed Noon-5, Thurs 10-7, Fri 10-5, Sat 10-3
Friends of the Library Group
MINESING BRANCH, Minesing Community Ctr, 2347 Ronald Rd, Minesing, L0L 1Y0. (Mail add: PO Box 131, Minesing, L0L 1Y0), SAN 375-3034. Tel: 705-722-6440. FAX: 705-722-6511. E-mail: minesing.library@springwater.ca. *Chief Librn,* Lynn Patkau; Tel: 705-737-5650, Fax: 705-737-3594
Library Holdings: Bk Vols 1,000
Open Tues 1-7, Thurs 1-5, Fri 10-5
Friends of the Library Group

MIDLAND

S　　HURONIA MUSEUM*, Library & Archives, 549 Little Lake Park Rd, L4R 4P4. (Mail add: PO Box 638, L4R 4P4), SAN 373-6849. Tel: 705-526-2844. FAX: 705-527-6622. E-mail: info@huroniamuseum.com. Web Site: www.huroniamuseum.com. *Curator,* James Hunter; *Cat,* Genevieve Carter
Library Holdings: Bk Titles 2,000
Special Collections: 16th Century Huronia. Oral History
Function: Archival coll, For res purposes, Photocopying/Printing
Open Mon-Fri 9-5, Sat & Sun (Summer) 9-5
Restriction: Non-circulating

P　　MIDLAND PUBLIC LIBRARY*, 320 King St, L4R 3M6. SAN 319-2482. Tel: 705-526-4216. FAX: 705-526-1474. Web Site: midlandlibrary.com. *Chief Librn,* Bill Molesworth; *Head, Adult & Info Serv,* Gail Griffith; *Ch,* Bonnie Reynolds
Founded 1880. Pop 16,400; Circ 160,000
Library Holdings: AV Mats 3,000; CDs 2,500; DVDs 200; e-books 6,800; Electronic Media & Resources 75; Large Print Bks 1,000; Bk Vols 50,000; Per Subs 125; Talking Bks 2,000; Videos 500
Special Collections: Sainte Marie Historical Coll (Local History). Can & Prov
Automation Activity & Vendor Info: (Circulation) Auto-Graphics, Inc; (OPAC) Auto-Graphics, Inc
Wireless access
Partic in Southern Ontario Libr Serv
Open Mon-Thurs 10-9, Fri 10-6, Sat 10-4
Friends of the Library Group

MILFORD

P　　COUNTY OF PRINCE EDWARD LIBRARIES*, Ann Farwell Branch Library, 3053 County Rd 10, K0K 2P0. (Mail add: PO Box 77, K0K 2P0), SAN 373-7918. Tel: 613-476-4130. FAX: 613-476-6527. E-mail: milford@peclibrary.org.
Founded 1951. Pop 2,210; Circ 13,966
Library Holdings: Bk Vols 9,000
Subject Interests: Genealogy, Local hist
Open Tues 12-4, Thurs 11-7, Sat 10-4
Friends of the Library Group

MILLBROOK

P　　THE CAVAN MONAGHAN LIBRARIES, Millbrook Branch, One Dufferin St, L0A 1G0. SAN 319-2504. Tel: 705-932-2919. FAX: 705-932-4019. E-mail: madcapinfo@nexicom.net. *Librn,* Karla Buckborough
Founded 1894. Pop 8,600; Circ 62,000

Library Holdings: Bk Titles 12,000; Bk Vols 12,500; Per Subs 70
Wireless access
Partic in Southern Ontario Libr Serv
Open Tues & Wed 10-8, Thurs & Fri 10-5, Sat 9-2

MILTON

L   HALTON COUNTY LAW ASSOCIATION*, Court House Library, 491
Steeles Ave E, L9T 1Y7. SAN 328-0322. Tel: 905-878-1272. FAX:
905-878-8298. E-mail: hcla@bellnet.ca. *Librn,* Karen Kennett; Staff 1
(Non-MLS 1)
Library Holdings: Bk Vols 8,000; Per Subs 40
Wireless access
Open Mon-Fri 9-4:30

P   MILTON PUBLIC LIBRARY*, 1010 Main St E, L9T 6H7. Tel:
905-875-2665. FAX: 905-875-4324. Web Site: www.mpl.on.ca. *Chief Exec
Officer,* Leslie Fitch; Tel: 905-875-2665, Ext 3252, E-mail:
leslie.fitch@mpl.on.ca; *Dep Chief Librn,* Susan Mickalow; Tel:
905-875-2665 Ext 3260, E-mail: susan.mickalow@mpl.on.ca; *Circ Mgr,*
Sherri Norris; Tel: 905-875-2665, Ext 3259, E-mail:
sherri.norris@mpl.on.ca; *Info Serv,* Melanie Southern; Tel: 905-875-2665,
Ext 3265, E-mail: melanie.southern@mpl.on.ca
Wireless access
Open Mon, Fri & Sat 10-5, Tues-Thurs 10-9, Sun (Oct-Apr) 1-5

MILVERTON

P   PERTH EAST PUBLIC LIBRARY*, 19 Mill St E, N0K 1M0. SAN
319-2512. Tel: 519-595-8395. E-mail: pel@pcin.on.ca. Web Site:
www.pertheast.library.on.ca. *Actg Chief Exec Officer,* Cindy Dunbar; Staff
2.3 (Non-MLS 2.3)
Pop 12,300; Circ 74,588
Library Holdings: Bk Vols 20,816; Per Subs 17
Subject Interests: Christian
Automation Activity & Vendor Info: (Acquisitions) Horizon;
(Cataloging) Horizon; (Circulation) Horizon; (Course Reserve) Horizon;
(ILL) Horizon; (OPAC) Horizon; (Serials) Horizon
Wireless access
Function: Adult bk club, Children's prog, Computer training, Computers
for patron use, Copy machines, Digital talking bks, e-mail & chat,
Electronic databases & coll, Family literacy, Holiday prog, Home delivery
& serv to Sr ctr & nursing homes, Homebound delivery serv, Homework
prog, ILL available, Instruction & testing, OverDrive digital audio bks,
Photocopying/Printing, Preschool outreach, Prog for children & young
adult, Ref serv available
Partic in Perth County Information Network
Open Mon & Sat 10-2, Tues-Thurs 10-9
Restriction: Access at librarian's discretion
Friends of the Library Group

MINDEMOYA

P   CENTRAL MANITOULIN PUBLIC LIBRARIES, 6020 Hwy 542, P0P
1S0. (Mail add: PO Box 210, P0P 1S0), SAN 319-2520. Tel:
705-377-5334. FAX: 705-377-5334. E-mail: bookworm@amtelecom.net.
Web Site: www.centralmanitoulin.ca. *Head Librn,* Claire Cline
Founded 1957. Pop 1,910; Circ 14,000
Library Holdings: Bk Vols 15,000
Mem of Ontario Library Service North
Open Tues & Wed 10-5, Thurs 1-8, Sat (Winter) 11-1
Friends of the Library Group
Branches: 1
PROVIDENCE BAY BRANCH, 11 Mutchmor St, Providence Bay, P0P
1T0, SAN 376-8856. Tel: 705-377-4503. *Br Mgr,* Claire Cline
    Library Holdings: Bk Vols 8,000
    Open Wed 1-3:30, Fri 1-4:30
    Friends of the Library Group

MINESING

G   SIMCOE COUNTY ARCHIVES, 1149 Hwy 26, RR 2, L0L 1Y2. SAN
319-2539. Tel: 705-726-9300, Ext 1287, 705-726-9331. Administration Tel:
705-726-9300, Ext 1295. Toll Free Tel: 866-893-9300, Ext 1287. FAX:
705-725-5341. E-mail: archives@simcoe.ca. Web Site: www.simcoe.ca.
Archives Mgr, Archivist, Bruce James Beacock; E-mail:
bruce.beacock@simcoe.ca; *Asst Archivist,* Ellen Millar; Tel: 705-726-9300,
Ext 1288, E-mail: ellen.millar@simcoe.ca; *Ref Serv Coordr,* Christina
MacBain; Tel: 705-726-9300, Ext 1292, E-mail: chris.macbain@simcoe.ca;
Tech Serv, Matthew Fells; Tel: 705-726-9300, Ext 1285, E-mail:
matthew.fells@simcoe.ca; Staff 2 (Non-MLS 2)
Founded 1966
Jan 2011-Dec 2011 Income (CAN) $708,719, City (CAN) $41,000, County
(CAN) $659,958, Locally Generated Income (CAN) $7,761. Mats Exp
(CAN) $755,481, Books (CAN) $500, Manu Arch (CAN) $234, Other
Print Mats (CAN) $1,500, Micro (CAN) $2,423, Electronic Ref Mat (Incl.

Access Fees) (CAN) $500, Presv (CAN) $3,519. Sal (CAN) $330,000
(Prof (CAN) $165,000)
Library Holdings: Bk Vols 2,650
Special Collections: Ardagh & Gowan Papers; Barrie Gas Company
Fonds; Barrie Sports Hall of Fame Coll; Beck Lumber Company Records;
Cavana Survey Records Coll; County & Municipal Records; Fred Grant
Coll; History of Simcoe County; Norman D Clarke Coll; Sir Frederick
Banting Papers
Automation Activity & Vendor Info: (Cataloging) Inmagic, Inc.
Wireless access
Function: Homebound delivery serv, Photocopying/Printing, Ref serv
available, Spoken cassettes & CDs, Spoken cassettes & DVDs, Telephone
ref, VHS videos
Special Services for the Deaf - TTY equip
Open Mon-Fri 8:30-4
Restriction: Closed stack, In-house use for visitors

MISSISSAUGA

M   CREDIT VALLEY HOSPITAL*, Dr Keith G MacDonald Health Sciences
Library, 2200 Eglinton Ave W, L5M 2N1. SAN 377-4767. Tel:
905-813-2411. FAX: 905-813-3969. E-mail: cvhlibrary@cvh.on.ca. Web
Site: www.cvh.on.ca/library. *Head of Librn,* Penka I Stoyanova; E-mail:
pstoyanova@cvh.on.ca; *Librn Tech,* Melissa Paladines; Tel: 905-813-1100,
Ext 6871, E-mail: mpaladines@cvh.on.ca. Subject Specialists: *Health sci,*
Penka I Stoyanova; Staff 1.6 (MLS 1.6)
Founded 1985
Apr 2009-Mar 2010. Mats Exp (CAN) $100,000, Books (CAN) $5,000,
Per/Ser (Incl. Access Fees) (CAN) $70,000, Electronic Ref Mat (Incl.
Access Fees) (CAN) $8,000
Library Holdings: e-journals 10,000; Bk Titles 2,000; Bk Vols 2,200; Per
Subs 230
Automation Activity & Vendor Info: (Cataloging) SIRSI WorkFlows;
(Circulation) SIRSI WorkFlows; (OPAC) SIRSI WorkFlows
Database Vendor: EBSCOhost, OVID Technologies
Function: Copy machines, Doc delivery serv, Electronic databases & coll,
Fax serv, Health sci info serv, ILL available, Photocopying/Printing, Ref &
res, VHS videos
Partic in Docline; Health Science Information Consortium of Toronto;
National Network of Libraries of Medicine
Open Mon-Fri 9-5
Restriction: Circulates for staff only, Hospital staff & commun

S   E I DU PONT CANADA CO*, Central Library, 7070 Mississauga Rd,
L5N 5M8. (Mail add: Box 2200, Streetsville, L5M 2H3), SAN 369-2469.
Tel: 905-821-5782. FAX: 905-821-5519. *In Charge,* Caren Larner; E-mail:
caren.a.larner@can.dupont.com
Founded 1954
Library Holdings: Bk Titles 8,000; Bk Vols 14,000; Per Subs 257
Subject Interests: Econ, Law, Statistics
Restriction: Not open to pub

M   GLAXOSMITHKLINE*, Information Centre, 7333 Mississauga Rd N,
L5N 6L4. SAN 326-8926. Tel: 905-819-3000, Ext 6023. FAX:
905-819-3096. Web Site: www.gsk.ca. *Mgr,* Jennifer Papandreou; *Info
Spec,* Lisa Eschli
Library Holdings: Bk Titles 3,000; Per Subs 100
Subject Interests: Bus, Med, Pharmacology
Restriction: Open to staff only

S   GOLDER ASSOCIATES LTD LIBRARY*, 2390 Argentina Rd, L5N 5Z7.
SAN 325-6642. Tel: 905-567-4444, Ext 205. FAX: 905-567-6561. E-mail:
misinfocentre@golder.com. Web Site: www.golder.com. *Librn,* Stephanie
Dudgeon
Library Holdings: Bk Vols 3,500; Per Subs 400

S   HATCH RESEARCH & INFOCENTRES*, 2800 Speakman Dr, L5K 2R7.
SAN 319-504X. Tel: 905-855-7600. FAX: 905-855-8270. E-mail:
infocentre@hatch.ca. *Info Spec,* Ljiljana Radman; Tel: 905-403-4196,
E-mail: lradman@hatch.ca; Staff 2 (MLS 1, Non-MLS 1)
Founded 1960
Library Holdings: Bk Vols 9,500; Per Subs 150
Special Collections: Iron, Steel & Non-ferrous Metals Coll
Subject Interests: Metallurgy, Mining
Function: ILL available
Restriction: Co libr

S   HONEYWELL CANADA-ENGINE & SYSTEMS KNOWLEDGE
CENTRE*, 3333 Unity Dr, L5L 3S6. SAN 329-7756. Tel: 905-608-6000,
Ext 6139. FAX: 905-608-6001. Web Site: www.honeywell.com. *Tech
Supvr,* Debra Southern; E-mail: debra.southern@honeywell.com; Staff 1
(MLS 1)
Library Holdings: Bk Titles 5,000; Bk Vols 7,000; Per Subs 110

Subject Interests: Aeronaut, Aerospace, Aviation, Electric power, Electronics
Partic in Dialog Corp
Open Mon-Fri 8:30-5

P   MISSISSAUGA LIBRARY SYSTEM, Central Library, 301 Burnhamthorpe Rd W, L5B 3Y3. SAN 367-7435. Tel: 905-615-3500. FAX: 905-615-3625. E-mail: library.info@mississauga.ca. Web Site: mississauga.ca/library. *Mgr,* Anne Murphy
Automation Activity & Vendor Info: (Acquisitions) SirsiDynix; (Cataloging) SirsiDynix; (Circulation) SirsiDynix; (OPAC) SirsiDynix
Wireless access
Friends of the Library Group
Branches: 17
BURNHAMTHORPE, 3650 Dixie Rd, L4Y 3V9, SAN 367-7400. Tel: 905-615-4635. *Br Mgr,* David Penteliuk
    Friends of the Library Group
CHURCHILL MEADOWS, 3801 Thomas St, L5M 7G2. Tel: 905-615-4735. *Mgr,* Kathy Oakleaf
    Friends of the Library Group
CLARKSON, 2475 Truscott Dr, L5J 2B3, SAN 367-7559. Tel: 905-615-4840. FAX: 905-615-4841. *Mgr,* Mai Lu
    Friends of the Library Group
COOKSVILLE, 3024 Hurontario St, Ste 212, L5B 4M4. Tel: 905-615-4855. Administration FAX: 905-615-3625. *Br Mgr,* Mai Lu
    Friends of the Library Group
COURTNEYPARK, 730 Courtneypark Dr W, L5W 1L9, SAN 367-7370. Tel: 905-615-4745. *Br Mgr,* Lina Van Velzen
    Friends of the Library Group
ERIN MEADOWS, 2800 Erin Centre Blvd, L5M 6R5. Tel: 905-615-4750. *Br Mgr,* Erica Conly
LAKEVIEW, 1110 Atwater Ave, L5E 1M9. (Mail add: 301 Burnhamthorpe Rd W, L5B 3Y3), SAN 367-7494. Tel: 905-615-4805. FAX: 905-615-3625. *Mgr,* Alan Barry
LORNE PARK, 1474 Truscott Dr, L5J 1Z2, SAN 367-746X. Tel: 905-615-4845. FAX: 905-615-4846. *Br Mgr,* Diane Kendall
    Friends of the Library Group
MALTON BRANCH, 3540 Morningstar Dr, Malton, L4T 1Y2, SAN 367-7524. Tel: 905-615-4640. *Br Mgr,* Maria Politano
    Friends of the Library Group
FRANK MCKECHNIE BRANCH, 310 Bristol Rd E, L4Z 3V5. Tel: 905-615-4660. FAX: 905-615-3625. *Br Mgr,* Laura Higginson
MEADOWVALE, 6677 Meadowvale Town Centre Circle, L5N 2R5, SAN 367-7540. Tel: 905-615-4715. *Br Mgr,* Amy Colson
    Friends of the Library Group
MISSISSAUGA VALLEY, 1275 Mississauga Valley Blvd, L5A 3R8, SAN 367-7532. Tel: 905-615-4670. FAX: 905-615-4671. *Br Mgr,* Ann Jacob
    Friends of the Library Group
PORT CREDIT, 20 Lakeshore Rd E, L5G 1C8, SAN 367-7583. Tel: 905-615-4835. FAX: 905-615-4751. *Br Mgr,* Alan Barry
    Friends of the Library Group
SHERIDAN, 2225 Erin Mills Pkwy, L5K 1T9, SAN 367-7613. Tel: 905-615-4815. FAX: 905-615-4816. *Br Mgr,* Katharine Pryma
    Friends of the Library Group
SOUTH COMMON, 2233 S Millway Dr, L5L 3H7, SAN 367-7478. Tel: 905-615-4770. FAX: 905-615-4771. *Br Mgr,* Tamara Stojakovic
    Friends of the Library Group
STREETSVILLE, 112 Queen St S, L5M 1K8, SAN 367-7648. Tel: 905-615-4785. *Br Mgr,* Sandra Laird
    Friends of the Library Group
WOODLANDS, 1030 McBride Ave, L5C 1L6, SAN 367-7672. Tel: 905-615-4825. FAX: 905-615-4826. *Br Mgr,* JoAnne Storen
    Friends of the Library Group

S   PEEL DISTRICT SCHOOL BOARD, J A Turner Professional Library, 5650 Hurontario St, L5R 1C6. SAN 319-2644. Tel: 905-890-1099, Ext 2601. FAX: 905-890-4780. E-mail: proflib@peelsb.com. Web Site: www.peelschools.org. *Librn,* Jeanne Conte; Staff 3 (Non-MLS 3)
Founded 1970
Library Holdings: Bk Titles 10,000; Bk Vols 11,000; Per Subs 200
Special Collections: Curriculum Coll; Education Coll; Leadership Coll
Subject Interests: Leadership
Automation Activity & Vendor Info: (Acquisitions) SirsiDynix; (Cataloging) SirsiDynix; (Circulation) SirsiDynix; (Course Reserve) SirsiDynix; (ILL) SirsiDynix; (Media Booking) SirsiDynix; (OPAC) SirsiDynix; (Serials) SirsiDynix
Database Vendor: EBSCOhost
Wireless access
Open Mon-Thurs 8-5, Fri 8-4

S   STANDARDBRED CANADA LIBRARY*, 2150 Meadowvale Blvd, L5N 6R6. SAN 326-1751. Tel: 905-858-3060. FAX: 905-858-3111. Web Site: www.standardbredcanada.ca. *Librn,* Elynne Meaney; E-mail: emeaney@standardbredcanada.ca
Library Holdings: Bk Titles 800; Bk Vols 1,500; Per Subs 50

S   TECK METALS LTD PRODUCT TECHNOLOGY GROUP, PTC*, Gerald P Lewis Library, Sheridan Science & Technology Park, 2380 Speakman Dr, L5K 1B4. SAN 319-2571. Tel: 905-287-2276. FAX: 905-822-2882. *Info Spec,* Vera Rodic; E-mail: vera.rodic@teck.com
Founded 1964
Library Holdings: Bk Titles 3,000; Per Subs 100
Subject Interests: Lead, Product tech R&D, Uses of zinc
Function: Res libr
Restriction: Not open to pub, Open by appt only

S   VALE CANADA LIMITED, Information Service Group, 2060 Flavelle Blvd, L5K 1Z9. SAN 319-261X. Tel: 905-403-2448. FAX: 905-403-2401. Web Site: nickel.vale.com. *Supvr,* Diane Baksa; Tel: diane.baksa@vale.com; Staff 1 (Non-MLS 1)
Founded 1966
Library Holdings: Bk Titles 3,400; Bk Vols 4,000; Per Subs 90
Subject Interests: Electrochem, Extractive metallurgy, Geol, Inorganic, Mat sci, Mining, Pollution control
Automation Activity & Vendor Info: (Cataloging) Cuadra Associates; (OPAC) Cuadra Associates; (Serials) Cuadra Associates
Database Vendor: Dialog, Knovel, ScienceDirect, STN International

S   XEROX RESEARCH CENTRE OF CANADA LIBRARY*, 2660 Speakman Dr, L5K 2L1. SAN 319-2660. Tel: 905-823-7091. FAX: 905-822-7022. *Mgr,* Gordana Pavlovic; E-mail: gordana.pavlovic@xrcc.xeroxlabs.com; Staff 2 (MLS 1, Non-MLS 1)
Founded 1974
Library Holdings: AV Mats 200; Bk Titles 7,000; Bk Vols 8,000; Per Subs 250
Special Collections: Annual Reports; Audio Visual Materials; External Reports; Internal Reports
Subject Interests: Chem eng, Organic chem, Polymer chem, Xerography
Automation Activity & Vendor Info: (Acquisitions) Ex Libris Group; (Cataloging) Ex Libris Group; (Circulation) Ex Libris Group; (OPAC) Ex Libris Group; (Serials) Ex Libris Group
Database Vendor: Dialog, Factiva.com, OCLC FirstSearch, ProQuest
Publications: XRCC Library Update (Monthly bulletin)
Partic in Sheridan Park Association, Library and Information Science Committee
Restriction: Open by appt only

MITCHELL

P   WEST PERTH PUBLIC LIBRARY*, 105 Saint Andrew St, N0K 1N0. (Mail add: PO Box 100, N0K 1N0), SAN 319-2679. Tel: 519-348-9234. FAX: 519-348-4540. E-mail: wpl@pcin.on.ca. Web Site: www.westperth.library.on.ca/. *Mgr, Libr Serv,* Caroline Shewberg; *ILL Librn,* Sherri Siemon; *Circ Librn,* Janice Davey
Founded 1895. Pop 3,100
Library Holdings: Bk Vols 12,800; Per Subs 35
Partic in Perth County Information Network
Open Mon-Fri 10-12 & 2-8, Sat 10-2

MOONBEAM

P   BIBLIOTHEQUE PUBLIQUE DE MOONBEAM*, 53 St-Aubin Ave, CP 370, P0L 1V0. SAN 320-0728. Tel: 705-367-2462. FAX: 705-367-2120. E-mail: biblio@moonbeam.ca. Web Site: www.biblio.moonbeam.ca. *Chief Librn,* Gisele Belisle; E-mail: gbelisle@moonbeam.ca; *Librn,* Angèle Lauzon-Albert; Staff 2 (Non-MLS 2)
Founded 1977. Pop 1,170
Library Holdings: Bk Vols 20,000; Per Subs 40
Automation Activity & Vendor Info: (Acquisitions) Mandarin Library Automation; (Cataloging) Mandarin Library Automation
Wireless access
Function: ILL available, Ref serv available
Mem of Ontario Library Service North
Open Mon & Thurs 12-4:30 & 6:30pm-8:30pm, Tues, Wed & Fri 10-11:30 & 12:30-4:30
Friends of the Library Group

MORRISBURG

G   SAINT LAWRENCE PARKS COMMISSION*, Upper Canada Village Reference Library, 13740 County Rd 2, K0C 1X0. SAN 328-1396. Tel: 613-543-3704. FAX: 613-543-4098. TDD: 613-543-4181.
Library Holdings: Bk Titles 5,000; Per Subs 45
Special Collections: Lost Villages; Social & Political History of 19th Century Ontario
Function: Res libr
Publications: Upper Canada Village Reference Library & Archives Brochure
Restriction: Open by appt only

NAPANEE

P   **LENNOX & ADDINGTON COUNTY PUBLIC LIBRARY***, Information Services Administration Office, 97 Thomas St E, K7R 3S9. SAN 367-7702. Tel: 613-354-4883. FAX: 613-354-3112. E-mail: infoservices@lennox-addington.on.ca. Web Site: www.lennox-addington.on.ca/library/about-the-library.html. *Dir, Info Serv,* Mary Anne Evans; E-mail: mevans@lennox-addington.on.ca; Staff 2 (Non-MLS 2)
Founded 1972. Pop 42,000; Circ 152,000
Library Holdings: DVDs 500; Large Print Bks 10,000; Bk Vols 100,000; Per Subs 65
Special Collections: Fed & Prov
Partic in Southern Ontario Libr Serv
Open Mon-Fri 8:30-4:30
Branches: 8
AMHERSTVIEW BRANCH, 322 Amherst Dr, Amherstview, K7N 1S9, SAN 367-7737. Tel: 613-389-6006. FAX: 613-389-0077. E-mail: amhbrch@lennox-addington.on.ca. *Br Mgr,* Jane Vanderzande
    Library Holdings: Bk Vols 23,070
    Open Mon-Thurs 10-8, Fri & Sat 10-5
BATH BRANCH, 197 Davey St, Bath, K0H 1G0. (Mail add: PO Box 400, Bath, K0H 1G0), SAN 367-7761. Tel: 613-352-5600. E-mail: bathbrch@lennox-addington.on.ca. *Br Coordr,* Karen Scott
    Library Holdings: Bk Vols 3,500
    Open Mon 5-8, Wed 1-4 & 5-8, Fri 11-2, Sat 10-1
CAMDEN EAST BRANCH, 2832 County Rd 1, Camden East, K0K 1J0. (Mail add: PO Box 10, Camden East, K0K 1J0), SAN 367-7796. Tel: 613-378-2101. E-mail: camdbrch@lennox-addington.on.ca. *Br Coordr,* Jackie Hassefrass
    Library Holdings: Bk Vols 3,300
    Open Mon 10-3, Wed 3-8, Sat 9-12
NAPANEE BRANCH, 25 River Rd, K7R 3S6, SAN 367-7826. Tel: 613-354-2525. FAX: 613-354-7527. E-mail: napbrch@lennox-addington.on.ca. *Br Coordr,* Kim Switzer
    Library Holdings: Bk Vols 26,265
    Open Mon-Thurs 10-8, Fri & Sat 10-5
ODESSA BRANCH, 102 Main St, Odessa, K0H 2H0. (Mail add: PO Box 250, Odessa, K0H 2H0), SAN 367-7885. Tel: 613-386-3981. E-mail: odesbrch@lennox-addington.on.ca. *Br Coordr,* Jacqueline Hassefras
    Library Holdings: Bk Vols 3,500
    Open Tue 3-6. Thurs 4-7, Sat 1-4
SOUTH FREDERICKSBURGH, 2478 County Rd 8, Bath, K0H 1G0. (Mail add: PO Box 400, Bath, K0H 1G0), SAN 367-7915. Tel: 613-354-4114. E-mail: fredbrch@lennox-addington.on.ca. *Br Coordr,* Karen Scott
    Library Holdings: Bk Vols 3,500
    Open Tues 1-4, Thurs 5-8, Sat 2-5
STELLA BRANCH, 5555 Front Rd, Stella, K0H 2S0, SAN 367-794X. Tel: 613-389-9371. E-mail: stelbrch@lennox-addington.on.ca. *Br Coordr,* Karen Scott
    Library Holdings: Bk Vols 3,500
TAMWORTH BRANCH, One Ottawa St, Tamworth, K0K 3G0. (Mail add: PO Box 10, Tamworth, K0K 3G0), SAN 367-7974. Tel: 613-379-3082. E-mail: tambrch@lennox-addington.on.ca. Web Site: www.lennox-addington.on.ca. *Br Coordr,* Joan Larkin
    Library Holdings: Bk Vols 3,500
    Open Wed 2-8, Thurs 11-4, Sat 10-1

NAUGHTON

P   **WHITEFISH LAKE FIRST NATION PUBLIC LIBRARY***, PO Box 39, P0M 2M0. SAN 319-2717. Tel: 705-692-0807, FAX: 705-692-5010. E-mail: library@wlfn.com. *Librn,* Mary Jane Fraser
Pop 668; Circ 1,000
Library Holdings: Bk Titles 3,000; Bk Vols 3,100
Open Mon-Wed 2:30-6:30, Thurs 8-1:30

NEWMARKET

P   **NEWMARKET PUBLIC LIBRARY**, 438 Park Ave, L3Y 1W1. SAN 319-2741. Tel: 905-953-5110. FAX: 905-953-5104. E-mail: npl@newmarketpl.ca. Web Site: www.newmarketpl.ca. *Chief Exec Officer,* Todd Kyle; E-mail: tkyle@newmarketpl.ca; *Dep Dir,* Linda Peppiatt; E-mail: lpeppiatt@newmarketpl.ca; *Head, Adult Serv,* Heather Halliday; E-mail: hhalliday@newmarketpl.ca; *Head, Ch,* Susan Hoffman; E-mail: shoffman@newmarketpl.ca; *Syst Mgr,* Simon Chong; E-mail: schong@newmarketpl.ca; *Commun Serv,* Jennifer Leveridge; E-mail: jleveridge@newmarketpl.ca; *Digital Serv,* Michael Russell; E-mail: mrussell@newmarket.pl.ca; Staff 7 (MLS 5, Non-MLS 2)
Founded 1956. Pop 84,000; Circ 480,000
Library Holdings: Bk Titles 146,000; Bk Vols 175,000; Per Subs 258
Automation Activity & Vendor Info: (Acquisitions) Polaris Library Systems; (Cataloging) Polaris Library Systems; (Circulation) Polaris Library Systems; (OPAC) Polaris Library Systems; (Serials) Polaris Library Systems

Database Vendor: EBSCOhost
Wireless access
Partic in Southern Ontario Libr Serv
Open Tues-Thurs 9:30-9, Fri & Sat 9:30-5, Sun (Sept-May) 1-5

M   **SOUTHLAKE REGIONAL HEALTH CENTER***, Health Sciences Library, 596 Davis Dr, L3Y 2P9. SAN 375-4715. Tel: 905-895-4521, Ext 2327. FAX: 905-830-5989. Web Site: www.southlakeregional.org. *Librn,* Katherine Dedrick
Library Holdings: Bk Titles 3,000; Per Subs 100
Subject Interests: Health sci

NIAGARA FALLS

P   **NIAGARA FALLS PUBLIC LIBRARY***, 4848 Victoria Ave, L2E 4C5. SAN 367-8032. Tel: 905-356-8080. FAX: 905-356-7004. Web Site: www.nflibrary.ca. *Chief Librn,* Monika Seymour; E-mail: mseymour@nflibrary.ca; *Mgr,* Susan DiBattista; E-mail: sdibattista@nflibrary.ca; *Ch,* Inge Saczkowski; E-mail: isaczkow@nflibrary.ca; *Online Serv, Ref,* Andrew Porteus; E-mail: aporteus@nflibrary.ca; *Ref Serv,* Cathy Roy; Staff 42 (MLS 6, Non-MLS 36)
Founded 1878. Pop 83,000
Library Holdings: Bk Titles 150,000; Bk Vols 250,000; Talking Bks 2,000
Special Collections: Can
Subject Interests: Local hist
Automation Activity & Vendor Info: (OPAC) Infor Library & Information Solutions
Wireless access
Open Mon-Thurs 9-9, Fri & Sat 9-5:30, Sun (Winter) 1-5
Branches: 3
CHIPPAWA, 3763 Main St, L2G 6B3, SAN 367-8067. Tel: 905-295-4391. *Br Mgr,* Carrie Chiaramonte
    Open Mon & Tues 1-8, Wed 9-5:30, Sat 10-4
COMMUNITY CENTER, 7150 Montrose Rd, O2H 3N3. Tel: 905-371-1200. *Br Mgr,* Carrie Chiaramonte
    Open Mon-Thurs 9-8, Fri & Sat 9-5:30
STAMFORD CENTRE, Town & Country Plaza, 3643 Portage Rd N, L2J 2K8, SAN 367-8121. Tel: 905-357-0410. *Br Mgr,* Carrie Chiaramonte
    Open Mon & Thurs 9-8, Tues, Wed, Fri & Sat 9-5:30

S   **NIAGARA PARKS BOTANICAL GARDENS & SCHOOL OF HORTICULTURE**, C H Henning Library, 2565 Niagara Pkwy N, L2E 6S4. (Mail add: PO Box 150, L2E 6T2), SAN 322-7413. Tel: 905-356-8554, Ext 226. FAX: 905-356-5488. *Librn,* Ruth Stoner; E-mail: rstoner@niagaraparks.com; Staff 1 (Non-MLS 1)
Library Holdings: CDs 45; DVDs 30; Bk Titles 4,500; Per Subs 120; Videos 130
Subject Interests: Arboriculture, Hort, Landscape archit

NIAGARA-ON-THE-LAKE

S   **GENAIRE LTD LIBRARY**, 468 Niagara Stone Rd, Rural Route 4, L0S 1J0. SAN 377-4694. Tel: 905-684-1165. FAX: 905-684-2412. Web Site: www.genaireltd.com. *Tech Librn,* Gloria Furtney; Staff 1 (Non-MLS 1)
Library Holdings: Bk Vols 10,000
Restriction: Circulates for staff only

P   **NIAGARA-ON-THE-LAKE PUBLIC LIBRARY***, Ten Anderson Lane, L0S 1J0. (Mail add: PO Box 430, L0S 1J0), SAN 367-8156. Tel: 905-468-2023. FAX: 905-468-3334. Web Site: www.notlpubliclibrary.com. *Asst Mgr, Libr Serv,* Deborah Smith; E-mail: debbiesmith@notl.org; Staff 8 (MLS 1, Non-MLS 7)
Founded 1800. Pop 15,000; Circ 103,000
Library Holdings: Bk Titles 45,000; Per Subs 135
Special Collections: History of Niagara & the War of 1812 (Janet Carnochan Coll)
Automation Activity & Vendor Info: (Acquisitions) Evergreen; (Cataloging) Evergreen; (Circulation) Evergreen; (OPAC) Evergreen
Database Vendor: EBSCOhost, Gale Cengage Learning, netLibrary
Wireless access
Function: Art exhibits, CD-ROM, Home delivery & serv to Sr ctr & nursing homes, ILL available, Photocopying/Printing, Prog for children & young adult, Ref serv available, Summer reading prog
Publications: Landmarks & People of Niagara; Records of Niagara - Inventory
Partic in Southern Ontario Libr Serv
Special Services for the Blind - Talking bks
Open Tues-Fri (Fall & Spring) 9-9, Sat 9-5, Sun 1-5
Friends of the Library Group

NIPIGON

P   **CORPORATION OF THE TOWNSHIP OF NIPIGON PUBLIC LIBRARY BOARD**, Nipigon Public Library, 52 Front St, P0T 2J0. (Mail add: PO Box 728, P0T 2J0), SAN 319-2784. Tel: 807-887-3142. FAX:

807-887-3142. E-mail: nipigonpl@tbaytel.net. Web Site: www.nipigon.net.
Librn, Sumiye Sugawara; Staff 1 (Non-MLS 1)
Founded 1958. Pop 1,631; Circ 14,380
Library Holdings: AV Mats 1,140; CDs 190; DVDs 200; Large Print Bks
550; Bk Titles 13,650; Bk Vols 16,000; Per Subs 26; Talking Bks 144;
Videos 709
Subject Interests: Local hist, Local newsp
Automation Activity & Vendor Info: (Acquisitions) SIRSI WorkFlows;
(Cataloging) SIRSI WorkFlows; (Circulation) SIRSI WorkFlows; (Course
Reserve) SIRSI WorkFlows; (ILL) Fretwell-Downing; (Media Booking)
SIRSI WorkFlows; (OPAC) SIRSI WorkFlows; (Serials) SIRSI WorkFlows
Database Vendor: SirsiDynix
Wireless access
Function: Adult bk club, Fax serv, Homebound delivery serv, ILL
available, Photocopying/Printing, Prog for adults, Prog for children &
young adult, Summer reading prog, VHS videos, Workshops
Publications: NPL Annual Report; NPL Newsletter
Open Tues & Wed 1:30-5:30 & 7-9, Thurs 9-1 & 1:30-5:30, Fri 1:30-5:30,
Sat 10-1

NORTH BAY

L   NIPISSING DISTRICT LAW ASSOCIATION LIBRARY*, 360 Plouffe St,
       P1B 9L5. SAN 375-3654. Tel: 705-495-3271. Toll Free Tel: 866-899-6439.
       FAX: 705-495-3487. E-mail: nipilaws@onlink.net. *Law Librn,* Amanda
       Adams
       Library Holdings: Bk Vols 8,500; Per Subs 106
       Wireless access
       Open Mon-Thurs 8:30-3, Fri 8:30am-12:30pm

P   NORTH BAY PUBLIC LIBRARY*, 271 Worthington St E, P1B 1H1.
       SAN 319-2814. Tel: 705-474-4830. FAX: 705-495-4010. E-mail:
       library@cityofnorthbay.ca. Web Site: www.cityofnorthbay.ca/library. *Chief
       Exec Officer,* Paul Walker; E-mail: paul.walker@cityofnorthbay.ca; *Head,
       Adult Serv,* Judith Bouman; E-mail: judith.bouman@cityofnorthbay.ca;
       Head, Ch, Nora Elliott-Coutts; E-mail:
       nora.elliott-coutts@cityofnorthbay.ca; *Head, Info Serv,* Rebecca Larocque;
       E-mail: rebecca.larocque@cityofnorthbay.ca; Staff 27 (MLS 4, Non-MLS
       23)
       Founded 1895. Pop 54,982; Circ 450,000
       Library Holdings: Bk Vols 146,090; Per Subs 191
       Special Collections: Canadiana; French Coll, bks, pamphlets, rec; Picture
       File. Can & Prov
       Automation Activity & Vendor Info: (Acquisitions) Evergreen
       Wireless access
       Function: Adult bk club, Archival coll, Audiobks via web, Bks on CD,
       CD-ROM, Children's prog, Computer training, Computers for patron use,
       Copy machines, Digital talking bks, e-mail serv, Electronic databases &
       coll, Family literacy, Fax serv, Free DVD rentals, Genealogy discussion
       group, Govt ref serv, Handicapped accessible, Holiday prog, Homebound
       delivery serv, Homework prog, ILL available, Magnifiers for reading,
       Music CDs, Newsp ref libr, Online cat, Online searches, OverDrive digital
       audio bks, Photocopying/Printing, Preschool outreach, Prog for children &
       young adult, Pub access computers, Ref serv in person, Res performed for
       a fee, Scanner, Senior computer classes, Senior outreach, Spoken cassettes
       & CDs, Story hour, Summer & winter reading prog, Summer reading prog,
       Video lending libr, Web-catalog, Wheelchair accessible
       Open Mon-Thurs 9:30-9, Fri 9:30-6, Sat 9:30-4

NORTH YORK

S   CANADIAN COPPER & BRASS DEVELOPMENT ASSOCIATION
       LIBRARY*, 49 The Donway West, Ste 415, M3C 3M9. SAN 373-7012.
       Tel: 416-391-5599. FAX: 416-391-3823. Web Site: www.coppercanada.ca.
       Librn, Sandra J Knapp
       Founded 1965
       Library Holdings: Bk Titles 400; Per Subs 65

S   ONTARIO GENEALOGICAL SOCIETY LIBRARY*, 5120 Yonge St,
       M2N 5N9. (Mail add: 102 - 40 Orchard View Blvd, Toronto, M4R 1B9),
       SAN 326-6362. Tel: 416-395-5623. Administration Tel: 416-489-0734.
       FAX: 416-489-9803. E-mail: provoffice@ogs.on.ca. Web Site:
       www.ogs.on.ca. *Chair,* Len Chester; Staff 1 (MLS 1)
       Jan 2011-Dec 2011 Income (CAN) $10,000
       Library Holdings: Bk Titles 10,000; Per Subs 200
       Special Collections: Ontario Genealogical Society Coll, bks, fiche, maps,
       microfilm
       Subject Interests: Genealogy
       Wireless access
       Open Mon-Fri 9-8:30, Sat 9-5, Sun (Sept-June) 1:30-5

G   TORONTO DISTRICT SCHOOL BOARD*, Professional Library Services,
       Three Tippett Rd, M3H 2V1. SAN 320-3484. Tel: 416-395-8289. FAX:
       416-395-8292.
       Founded 1956

Library Holdings: Bk Titles 20,000; Per Subs 450
Subject Interests: Educ
Partic in Dialog Corp; Info-globe; Infomart; Utlas
Open Mon-Fri 8-5

NORWICH

S   NORWICH & DISTRICT HISTORICAL SOCIETY ARCHIVES*, 91
       Stover St N, N0J 1P0. (Mail add: RR 3, N0J 1P0), SAN 373-6253. Tel:
       519-863-3638. Administration Tel: 519-863-3101. FAX: 519-863-2343.
       E-mail: archives@norwichdhs.ca. Web Site: www.norwichdhs.ca.
       Founded 1979
       Special Collections: Genealogy, bks, fiche, files, flm, pictures & maps;
       Municipal. Oral History
       Function: Archival coll, Ref serv available
       Open Tues & Thurs 10-12 & 1-4

NORWOOD

P   ASPHODEL-NORWOOD PUBLIC LIBRARY, Norwood Branch, 2363
       County Rd 45, K0L 2V0. (Mail add: PO Box 100, K0L 2V0), SAN
       319-2822. Tel: 705-639-2228. FAX: 705-639-1880. E-mail:
       norwst@asphodelnorwood.com. *Librn,* Kris Bulloch
       Founded 1872. Pop 4,500
       Library Holdings: Bk Vols 22,000; Per Subs 50
       Automation Activity & Vendor Info: (Cataloging) Mandarin Library
       Automation; (Circulation) Mandarin Library Automation
       Wireless access
       Function: ILL available, Photocopying/Printing
       Partic in Southern Ontario Libr Serv
       Open Tues & Thurs 4-7, Wed & Fri 9-1, Sat 9-12
       Branches: 1
       WESTWOOD BRANCH, 312 Centre Line, Westwood, K0L 3B0. Tel:
          705-696-2744. FAX: 705-639-1880. E-mail:
          norwest@asphodelnorwood.com. *Librn,* Kris Bulloch
          Library Holdings: Bk Vols 22,000
          Open Mon & Wed 4-7, Thurs 4-8, Sat 10-2

OAKVILLE

P   OAKVILLE PUBLIC LIBRARY*, 120 Navy St, L6J 2Z4. SAN 367-8210.
       Tel: 905-815-2042. FAX: 905-815-2024. Web Site: www.opl.on.ca. *Chief
       Exec Officer,* Charlotte Meissner; Tel: 905-815-2031, E-mail:
       cmeissner@oakville.ca; *Dir, Serv Develop,* Janice Kullas; Tel:
       905-815-2035, E-mail: jkullas@oakville.ca; Staff 179 (MLS 3, Non-MLS
       176)
       Founded 1895. Pop 182,500; Circ 2,172,109
       Library Holdings: CDs 28,757; DVDs 25,370; Large Print Bks 6,276; Bk
       Titles 161,215; Bk Vols 318,781; Per Subs 633; Talking Bks 2,555
       Special Collections: Can & Prov
       Subject Interests: Local hist
       Automation Activity & Vendor Info: (Acquisitions) SirsiDynix;
       (Cataloging) SirsiDynix; (Circulation) SirsiDynix; (OPAC) SirsiDynix;
       (Serials) SirsiDynix
       Wireless access
       Partic in Halinet; Southern Ontario Libr Serv
       Open Mon-Thurs 9:30-9, Fri & Sat 9:30-5, Sun 1-5
       Friends of the Library Group
       Branches: 6
       CENTRAL, 120 Navy St, L6J 2Z4. Tel: 905-815-2042. FAX:
          905-815-2024. *Br Mgr,* Florence De Dominicis; Tel: 905-815-2042, Ext
          5041, E-mail: fdedominicis@oakville.ca
          Open Mon-Thurs 9:30-9, Fri & Sat 9:30-5, Sun 1-5; Mon-Thurs
          (Summer) 10-8, Fri & Sat 10-5
          Friends of the Library Group
       CLEARVIEW NEIGHBOURHOOD, 2860 Kingsway Dr, L6J 6R3. Tel:
          905-815-2033. FAX: 905-815-2034. *Br Mgr,* Nancy LeGrow; E-mail:
          nlegrow@oakville.ca
          Founded 2007
          Open Mon-Thurs 3:30-8:30, Sat 1-5
          Friends of the Library Group
       GLEN ABBEY, 1415 Third Line, L6M 3G2, SAN 371-3512. Tel:
          905-815-2039. FAX: 905-815-5978. *Br Mgr,* Lila Saab; Tel:
          905-815-2039, Ext 3596, E-mail: lsaab@oakville.ca
          Open Mon-Thurs 9:30-9, Fri & Sat 9:30-5, Sun 1-5
          Friends of the Library Group
       IROQUOIS RIDGE, 1051 Glenashton Dr, L6H 6Z4. Tel: 905-338-4247.
          FAX: 905-338-4248. *Br Mgr,* Leslie Sutherland; E-mail:
          lesliesutherland@oakville.ca
          Open Mon-Thurs 9:30-9, Fri & Sat 9:30-5, Sun 1-5
          Friends of the Library Group
       WHITE OAKS, 1070 McCraney St E, L6H 2R6, SAN 367-8245. Tel:
          905-815-2038. FAX: 905-815-5972. *Br Mgr,* Position Currently Open
          Open Mon-Thurs 9:30-8:30, Fri & Sat 9:30-5, Sun 1-5
          Friends of the Library Group

WOODSIDE, 1274 Rebecca St, L6L 1Z2, SAN 367-827X. Tel: 905-815-5954. FAX: 905-815-2036. E-mail: info@opl.on.ca. *Br Mgr,* Susan A Kun; E-mail: skun@oakville.ca
Subject Interests: Literacy, Parenting, Pre-sch children
Open Mon-Thurs 9:30-8:30, Fri & Sat 9:30-5, Sun 1-5
Friends of the Library Group

S   ROYAL CANADIAN GOLF ASSOCIATION LIBRARY & ARCHIVES*, 1333 Dorval Dr, L6J 4Z3. SAN 370-6117. Tel: 905-849-9700. FAX: 905-845-7040. E-mail: cghf@golfcanada.ca. Web Site: www.cghf.org. *Curator, Dir, Librn,* Meggan Gardner
Founded 1975
Library Holdings: Bk Vols 3,200; Per Subs 20
Wireless access
Open Mon-Sun 10-5

C   SHERIDAN COLLEGE LIBRARY*, 1430 Trafalgar Rd, L6H 2L1. SAN 367-830X. Tel: 905-845-9430. Circulation Tel: 905-845-9430, Ext 2482. Reference Tel: 905-845-9430, Ext 2197. FAX: 905-815-4123. Web Site: www.sheridanc.ca/Services/Student%20Learning%20Services/Library%20Services.aspx. *Dir,* Joan Sweeney Marsh; Tel: 905-845-9430, Ext 2480, E-mail: joan.sweeneymarsh@sheridaninstitute.ca; *Circ & Ref,* Sonam Dhargay; *Coll Liaison,* Ahtasham Rizvi; Tel: 905-845-9430, Ext 2495, E-mail: ahtasham.rizvi@sheridanc.on.ca; *Computer Support Spec,* Irene Sillius; *ILL,* Johnathan Pring; Tel: 905-459-7533, Ext 5280, E-mail: johnathan.pring@sheridanc.on.ca; *Ref & Instruction,* Kathleen Oakey; Tel: 905-459-7533, Ext 5454, E-mail: kathleen.oakey@sheridaninstitute.ca; Staff 6.5 (MLS 3.5, Non-MLS 3)
Founded 1967. Enrl 11,500; Fac 409; Highest Degree: Bachelor
Library Holdings: Bk Vols 40,000; Per Subs 130
Subject Interests: Art
Automation Activity & Vendor Info: (Acquisitions) SirsiDynix; (Cataloging) SirsiDynix; (Circulation) SirsiDynix; (Course Reserve) SirsiDynix; (OPAC) SirsiDynix; (Serials) SirsiDynix
Database Vendor: EBSCOhost, SirsiDynix
Wireless access
Function: Audio & video playback equip for onsite use, ILL available, Photocopying/Printing, Ref serv available, VHS videos, Wheelchair accessible
Partic in Bibliocentre
Open Mon-Thurs (Sept-June) 8:30am-10pm, Fri 8:30-4, Sat & Sun 11-4; Mon-Fri (July & Aug) 8:30-4:30, Sat & Sun 11-4
Departmental Libraries:
DAVIS CAMPUS, 7899 McLaughlin Rd, Brampton, L6V 1G6, SAN 367-8369. Tel: 905-459-7533. Circulation Tel: 905-459-7533, Ext 4338. Reference Tel: 905-459-7533, Ext 5280, 905-459-7533, Ext 5281. FAX: 905-874-4345. *Operations Mgr,* Marian Traynor; Tel: 905-459-7533, Ext 5283, E-mail: marian.traynor@sheridanc.on.ca; *Circ,* Steve Chan; E-mail: steve.chan1@sheridanc.on.ca; *Ref,* Johnathan Pring; E-mail: johnathan.pring@sheridanc.on.ca; *Ref,* Irene Sillius; E-mail: irene.sillius@sheridanc.on.ca; Staff 5 (MLS 1, Non-MLS 4)
Founded 1967. Enrl 4,000
Library Holdings: Bk Titles 18,000; Per Subs 80
Open Mon-Thurs 8:30am-9pm, Fri 8:30-4:30

ORANGEVILLE

P   ORANGEVILLE PUBLIC LIBRARY, One Mill St, L9W 2M2. SAN 319-2849. Tel: 519-941-0610. FAX: 519-941-4698. E-mail: infolibrary@orangeville.ca. Web Site: www.orangeville.library.on.ca. *Chief Exec Officer,* Rich Schwarzer; Tel: 519-941-0440, Ext 2243, E-mail: rschwarzer@orangeville.ca; *Chief Librn,* Darla Fraser; Tel: 519-941-0610, Ext 5222, E-mail: dfraser@orangeville.ca; *Prog & Res Coordr,* Lesley McGill; Tel: 519-941-0610, Ext 5230, E-mail: lmcgill@orangeville.ca; *Pub Serv Coordr,* Kathryn Creelman; Tel: 519-941-0610, Ext 5232, E-mail: kcreelman@orangeville.ca; *Coll & Syst Coordr,* Kim Carson; Tel: 519-941-0610, Ext 5226, E-mail: kcarson@orangeville.ca; Staff 7 (MLS 2, Non-MLS 5)
Pop 32,000; Circ 231,000
Library Holdings: Bk Titles 78,000
Subject Interests: Genealogy, Local hist
Wireless access
Partic in Southern Ontario Libr Serv
Open Mon-Thurs 10-9, Fri 10-6, Sat 10-5, Sun 1-4
Friends of the Library Group

ORILLA

P   RAMARA TOWNSHIP PUBLIC LIBRARY, Atherley Branch, 5482 Hwy 12 S, L3V 6H7. (Mail add: PO Box 158, Brechin, L0K 1B0). Tel: 705-325-5776. FAX: 705-325-8176. E-mail: info@ramarapubliclibrary.org. Web Site: www.ramarapubliclibrary.org. *Chief Exec Officer,* Janet Banfield; Staff 6 (Non-MLS 6)
Founded 1982. Pop 9,000
Library Holdings: Bk Vols 22,000

Automation Activity & Vendor Info: (Acquisitions) SirsiDynix; (Cataloging) SirsiDynix; (Circulation) SirsiDynix; (ILL) SirsiDynix; (OPAC) SirsiDynix; (Serials) SirsiDynix
Database Vendor: Canadian Reference Centre, EBSCOhost, Overdrive, Inc
Wireless access
Function: Bks on CD, CD-ROM, Photocopying/Printing, Pub access computers
Special Services for the Deaf - Assistive tech
Special Services for the Blind - Audio mat
Open Tues-Thurs 10-8, Fri 10-6, Sat 9-3
Friends of the Library Group
Branches: 1
BRECHIN BRANCH, 3242 Ramara Rd 47, Brechin, L0K 1B0. Tel: 705-484-0476. FAX: 705-484-0476.
   Library Holdings: Bk Vols 10,000
   Open Tues, Wed & Fri 10-6, Thurs 12-8, Sat 10-2

ORILLIA

C   GEORGIAN COLLEGE-ORILLIA CAMPUS*, Library Commons, 825 Memorial Ave, L3V 6S2. (Mail add: PO Box 2316, L3V 6S2). Tel: 705-325-2740. Circulation Tel: 705-325-2740, Ext 3050. Interlibrary Loan Service Tel: 705-329-2740, Ext 3052 or 3053. Reference Tel: 705-325-2740, Ext 3054. FAX: 705-329-3107. Web Site: library.georgianc.on.ca. *Librn,* Joy Martin; Tel: 705-325-2740, Ext 3051; Staff 6 (MLS 3, Non-MLS 3)
Founded 1968. Enrl 1,300; Fac 43
Library Holdings: AV Mats 1,258; Bk Vols 10,790; Per Subs 119
Automation Activity & Vendor Info: (Acquisitions) SirsiDynix; (Cataloging) SirsiDynix; (Circulation) SirsiDynix; (OPAC) SirsiDynix; (Serials) SirsiDynix
Open Mon-Thurs 7:45am-9pm, Fri 7:45-4:30, Sat 10-4
Restriction: Open to students, fac & staff

P   STEPHEN LEACOCK MEMORIAL LIBRARY MUSEUM*, Old Brewery Bay, L3V 6K5. (Mail add: PO Box 625, L3V 6K5), SAN 371-117X. Tel: 705-329-1908. FAX: 705-326-5578. E-mail: leacock@transdata.ca. Web Site: leacockmuseum.com. *Dir,* Craig Metcalf
Library Holdings: Bk Vols 6,000
Friends of the Library Group

G   ONTARIO PROVINCIAL POLICE, Eric Silk Library, 777 Memorial Ave, L3V 7V3. SAN 326-5579. Tel: 705-329-6886. FAX: 705-329-6887. E-mail: opp.ghq.library@ontario.ca. Web Site: www.opp.ca. *Librn, Mgr,* Catherine Dowd; E-mail: catherine.dowd@ontario.ca. Subject Specialists: *Can & Ont legislation & case law, Police sci,* Catherine Dowd; Staff 2 (MLS 1, Non-MLS 1)
Library Holdings: DVDs 230; Bk Vols 6,000; Per Subs 100; Videos 680
Subject Interests: Law, Law enforcement
Publications: Acquisitions List (Bi-monthly)
Open Mon-Fri 8:30-4:30

P   ORILLIA PUBLIC LIBRARY*, 36 Mississaga St W, L3V 3A6. SAN 319-2865. Tel: 705-325-2338. FAX: 705-327-1744. E-mail: info@orilliapubliclibrary.ca. Web Site: www.orilliapubliclibrary.ca. *Chief Exec Officer,* Suzanne Campbell; *Dir, Info Resources & Res,* Kelli Absalom; *AV, Ch,* Amanda Hodgkinson; *Tech Serv,* Susan Dance; Staff 8 (MLS 5, Non-MLS 3)
Founded 1911. Pop 60,000; Circ 260,879
Library Holdings: Bk Titles 104,235; Per Subs 316
Special Collections: Stephen Leacock Coll. Oral History
Subject Interests: Local hist, Orilliana
Automation Activity & Vendor Info: (Acquisitions) TLC (The Library Corporation); (Cataloging) Infor Library & Information Solutions; (Circulation) Infor Library & Information Solutions; (Course Reserve) Infor Library & Information Solutions; (ILL) Infor Library & Information Solutions; (Media Booking) Infor Library & Information Solutions; (OPAC) Infor Library & Information Solutions; (Serials) Infor Library & Information Solutions
Wireless access
Function: Teen prog
Partic in Southern Ontario Libr Serv
Open Mon-Thurs 10-8, Fri 10-6, Sat 9-5, Sun 1-4
Friends of the Library Group

OSHAWA

L   DURHAM REGION LAW ASSOCIATION*, Courthouse Library, 150 Bond St E, L1G 0A2. SAN 372-7319. Tel: 905-579-9554. FAX: 905-579-1801. E-mail: drllaw@bellnet.ca. Web Site: www.durhamlawlibrary.com. *Librn,* Monica Schjott; E-mail: mschjott@speedline.ca
Library Holdings: Bk Titles 7,000

Wireless access
Open Mon-Fri 9-4

M　LAKERIDGE HEALTH*, Library Services, One Hospital Ct, L1G 2B9.
　　SAN 321-6810. Tel: 905-576-8711. FAX: 905-721-4759. Web Site:
　　www.lakeridgehealth.on.ca. *Librn,* Ken McFarlan; Tel: 905-576-8711, Ext
　　3334, E-mail: kmcfarlan@lakeridgehealth.on.ca; *Libr Tech,* Debbie
　　Arsenault; Tel: 905-576-8711, Ext 3754; Staff 2 (MLS 1, Non-MLS 1)
　　Founded 1973
　　Library Holdings: Bk Titles 1,000; Per Subs 75
　　Subject Interests: Med, Nursing
　　Database Vendor: EBSCOhost, OVID Technologies
　　Partic in Health Science Information Consortium of Toronto
　　Open Mon-Fri 8-5

S　ROBERT MCLAUGHLIN GALLERY LIBRARY*, 72 Queen St, Civic
　　Centre, L1H 3Z3. SAN 328-3216. Tel: 905-576-3000. Web Site:
　　www.rmg.on.ca. *Coordr, Libr Serv,* Barb Duff; Tel: 905-576-3000, Ext 102,
　　E-mail: bduff@rmg.on.ca; Staff 1 (Non-MLS 1)
　　Founded 1967
　　Library Holdings: Bk Titles 9,000; Per Subs 11
　　Special Collections: "Painters Eleven" Archives; Thomas Bouckley
　　Photography Archives
　　Subject Interests: Can art
　　Automation Activity & Vendor Info: (OPAC) MINISIS Inc
　　Function: Archival coll, e-mail serv, Res libr
　　Publications: Art Exhibition Catalogues (Annual report)
　　Open Tues-Thurs 9-5
　　Restriction: Circ to mem only, In-house use for visitors

P　OSHAWA PUBLIC LIBRARY*, McLaughlin Library, 65 Bagot St, L1H
　　1N2. SAN 367-8482. Tel: 905-579-6111. FAX: 905-433-8107. E-mail:
　　oplref@oshawalibrary.on.ca. Web Site: www.oshawalibrary.on.ca. *Chief
　　Exec Officer,* J Ian Heckford; E-mail: iheckford@oshawalibrary.on.ca;
　　Head, Tech Serv, Anne Donnellan; *Mgr, Ad Serv,* Joseph Sansalone; *Mgr,
　　Ch & Youth Serv,* Kim O'Reilly; *ILL,* Diana Tckazuk; *Ref,* Jackie
　　McFarlane; Staff 16 (MLS 16)
　　Founded 1864. Pop 154,000
　　Library Holdings: Bk Vols 336,018; Per Subs 791
　　Special Collections: Automotive & Transportation, bks; Can & Prov;
　　Canadiana & Oshawa History, bks, maps, vf. State Document Depository
　　Automation Activity & Vendor Info: (Acquisitions) Infor Library &
　　Information Solutions; (Cataloging) Infor Library & Information Solutions;
　　(Circulation) Infor Library & Information Solutions; (Course Reserve)
　　Infor Library & Information Solutions; (OPAC) Infor Library &
　　Information Solutions; (Serials) Infor Library & Information Solutions
　　Database Vendor: Checkpoint Systems, Inc, EBSCOhost, Gale Cengage
　　Learning, OCLC WorldCat
　　Wireless access
　　Publications: Annual Report
　　Partic in Southern Ontario Libr Serv
　　Special Services for the Deaf - Bks on deafness & sign lang; Staff with
　　knowledge of sign lang
　　Open Mon-Thurs 9-9, Fri-Sun 9-5
　　Friends of the Library Group
　　Branches: 3
　　JESS HANN BRANCH, Lake Vista Sq, 199 Wentworth St W, L1J 6P4,
　　　SAN 367-8512. Tel: 905-579-6111, Ext 5860. Web Site:
　　　www.oshawalibrary.on.ca. *Br Supvr,* Nicole Adams; Tel: 905-579-6111,
　　　Ext 5862
　　　Library Holdings: Bk Vols 44,000
　　　Open Tues, Wed, Fri & Sat 9-5, Thurs 9-8
　　　Friends of the Library Group
　　LEGENDS, 1661 Harmony Rd N, L1H 7K5. Tel: 905-436-5461. *Head
　　　Librn,* Gail Canonaco; Staff 14 (MLS 2, Non-MLS 12)
　　　Function: Adult bk club
　　　Open Mon-Fri 9-9, Sat & Sun 9-6
　　NORTHVIEW, 250 Beatrice St E, L1G 7T6, SAN 367-8547. Tel:
　　　905-576-6040. *Br Head,* Tammy Robinson; *Librn,* Tiffany Tahman
　　　Library Holdings: Bk Vols 54,300
　　　Open Tues-Thurs 9-9, Fri & Sat 9-5
　　　Friends of the Library Group

C　UNIVERSITY OF ONTARIO INSTITUTE OF TECHNOLOGY
　　LIBRARY*, Durham College Library, 2000 Simcoe St N, L1H 7K4. (Mail
　　add: PO Box 385, L1H 7L7), SAN 760-3614. Tel: 905-721-8668, Ext
　　2214. Circulation Tel: 905-721-8668, Ext 3082. Interlibrary Loan Service
　　Tel: 905-721-2412. FAX: 905-721-3029. Web Site: www.uoit.ca/library.
　　Chief Librn, Dr Pamela Drayson; Fax: 905-721-8668, Ext 3029; *Assoc
　　Librn, Coll,* Carol Mittlestead; E-mail: carol.mittlestead@durhamc.on.ca;
　　Staff 5 (MLS 5)
　　Founded 2000. Enrl 10,000; Fac 250; Highest Degree: Doctorate
　　Apr 2007-Mar 2008. Mats Exp $1,814,000, Books (CAN) $500,000,
　　Per/Ser (Incl. Access Fees) (CAN) $1,250,000, AV Mat (CAN) $50,000,

Electronic Ref Mat (Incl. Access Fees) (CAN) $10,000, Presv (CAN)
$4,000
Library Holdings: DVDs 500; e-books 40,000; e-journals 45,000;
Electronic Media & Resources 22,000; Bk Titles 80,000; Bk Vols 100,000;
Per Subs 500; Videos 2,500
Special Collections: Can & Prov
Subject Interests: Computer sci, Energy, Health sci, Nuclear, Sci, Tech
Automation Activity & Vendor Info: (Acquisitions) SirsiDynix;
(Cataloging) SirsiDynix; (Circulation) SirsiDynix; (Course Reserve)
SirsiDynix; (ILL) OCLC; (Media Booking) SirsiDynix; (OPAC)
SirsiDynix; (Serials) SirsiDynix
Database Vendor: SirsiDynix
Wireless access
Partic in Canadian Research Knowledge Network; Ontario Council of
University Libraries
Open Mon-Thurs 8am-Midnight, Fri 8-7, Sat & Sun 10-6

OTTAWA

G　AGRICULTURE & AGRI-FOOD CANADA*, Canadian Agriculture
　　Library, Tower 6, 1341 Baseline Rd, K1A 0C5. SAN 367-8571. Tel:
　　613-773-1400. FAX: 613-773-1499. E-mail: cal-bca@agr.gc.ca. Web Site:
　　www.agr.gc.ca/cal. *Dir,* Danielle Jacques; Staff 63 (MLS 34, Non-MLS 29)
　　Founded 1910
　　Library Holdings: e-journals 11,000; Bk Vols 1,000,000; Per Subs 4,000
　　Special Collections: FAO; Historical Agriculture (Chapais Coll); USDA
　　Subject Interests: Agr
　　Partic in Council of Federal Libraries Consortium
　　Open Mon-Fri 8:30-4:30
　　Branches:
　　EASTERN CEREAL & OILSEED RESEARCH CENTRE LIBRARY, K
　　　W Neatby Bldg, 930 Carling Ave, K1A 0C6, SAN 367-8660. Tel:
　　　613-759-1806. FAX: 613-759-1924. E-mail: ooage@agr.gc.ca. *Librn,*
　　　Patricia Madaire; E-mail: patricia.madaire@agr.gc.ca; Staff 3 (MLS 1,
　　　Non-MLS 2)
　　　Founded 1919
　　　Library Holdings: Bk Titles 11,000; Bk Vols 14,000; Per Subs 200
　　　Subject Interests: Entomology, Evolution
　　PLANT RESEARCH LIBRARY, Wm Saunders Bldg No 49, CEF, 960
　　　Carling Ave, K1A 0C6, SAN 367-875X. Tel: 613-759-1368. FAX:
　　　613-759-1599. E-mail: ooagb@agr.gc.ca. *In Charge,* Lise Robillard
　　　Library Holdings: Bk Titles 12,000; Per Subs 115
　　　Special Collections: Linnean Coll
　　　Subject Interests: Botany, Mycology, Taxonomy
　　　Restriction: Not open to pub

G　AGRICULTURE & AGRI-FOOD CANADA, CANADIAN
　　AGRICULTURE LIBRARY*, Ottawa Laboratory Fallowfield, PO Box
　　11300, Sta H, K2H 8P9. Tel: 613-228-6698. FAX: 613-228-6668. E-mail:
　　ooaga@inspection.gc.ca. *Librn,* Lynne Thacker; E-mail:
　　lynne.thacker@agr.gc.ca; Staff 1 (Non-MLS 1)
　　Founded 1902
　　Library Holdings: Bk Titles 4,050; Per Subs 83
　　Subject Interests: Bacteriology, Immunology, Pathology, Veterinary med,
　　Virology
　　Restriction: Open by appt only

R　AGUDATH ISRAEL CONGREGATION*, Malca Pass Library, 1400
　　Coldrey Ave, K1Z 7P9. SAN 319-289X. Tel: 613-728-3501, Ext 232. FAX:
　　613-728-4468. E-mail: library@agudathisrael.net. Web Site:
　　agudathisrael.net. *Librn,* Jack Schecter; Staff 1 (MLS 1)
　　Founded 1960
　　Library Holdings: CDs 300; DVDs 50; Bk Titles 3,500; Videos 150
　　Subject Interests: Judaica
　　Open Thurs 9:30-4:30, Sun 9:30-12:30

J　ALGONQUIN COLLEGE LEARNING RESOURCE CENTRE*,
　　Woodroffe Campus, 1385 Woodroffe Ave, K2G 1V8. SAN 367-8784. Tel:
　　613-727-4723, Ext 5062. FAX: 613-727-7642. Web Site:
　　www.algonquincollege.com/lrc. *Actg Mgr,* Tammy Thorton; *Coordr, Librn,*
　　Brenda Mahoney; Tel: 613-727-4723, Ext 5284, E-mail:
　　mahoneb@algonquincollege.com; *Coordr, Librn,* Maureen Sheppard; Tel:
　　613-727-4723, Ext 5944, E-mail: sheppam@algonquincollege.com
　　Founded 1967
　　Library Holdings: AV Mats 6,269; e-books 16,695; Bk Vols 67,823; Per
　　Subs 309
　　Subject Interests: Applied arts, Bus, Computer sci, Health sci, Tech,
　　Trades
　　Automation Activity & Vendor Info: (Circulation) SirsiDynix; (Course
　　Reserve) SirsiDynix; (Media Booking) SirsiDynix; (OPAC) SirsiDynix;
　　(Serials) SirsiDynix
　　Database Vendor: EBSCOhost, Gale Cengage Learning, netLibrary,
　　ProQuest, Safari Books Online, WestlaweCARSWELL, Wilson - Wilson
　　Web
　　Wireless access

Departmental Libraries:
HERITAGE INSTITUTE, Seven Craig St, Perth, K7H 1X7, SAN 367-8938. Tel: 613-267-2859, Ext 5607. FAX: 613-267-3950. *Libr Tech, Operational Head,* Ann MacPhail; E-mail: macphaa@algonquincollege.com
Library Holdings: e-books 16,695; Bk Vols 10,000; Per Subs 30
OTTAWA VALLEY, 315 Pembroke St E, Pembroke, K8A 3K2, SAN 367-9055. Tel: 613-735-4700, Ext 2707. FAX: 613-735-8801. *Librn,* Patricia Kim; Tel: 613-735-4700, Ext 2779, E-mail: kimp@algonquincollege.com; *Coordr, Librn,* Mythili Kaneshalingam; E-mail: kaneshm@alongonquincollege.com

SR   ASSOCIATION FOR BAHA'I STUDIES*, Reference Library, 34 Copernicus St, K1N 7K4. SAN 374-4019. Tel: 613-233-1903, Ext 106. FAX: 613-233-3644. E-mail: abs-na@bahai-studies.ca. Web Site: www.bahai-studies.ca. *Librn,* Mrs Nilufar Gordon
Founded 1971
Library Holdings: Bk Titles 1,700; Bk Vols 3,000; Per Subs 32
Special Collections: Early Baha'i Periodicals
Open Mon-Fri 9-5
Restriction: Open to pub for ref only

G   BANK OF CANADA, Knowledge & Information Services, 234 Wellington St, K1A 0G9. SAN 319-2911. Tel: 613-782-8881. FAX: 613-782-7387. E-mail: knowinfoserv@bankofcanada.ca. Web Site: www.bank-banque-canada.ca/library. *Asst Dir, Client Relations,* Beverly Graham; Tel: 613-782-8987, E-mail: bgraham@bankofcanada.ca; Staff 18.5 (MLS 9, Non-MLS 9.5)
Founded 1935
Library Holdings: Bk Titles 35,000; Per Subs 6,000
Subject Interests: Cent banking, Econ, Finance, Macro econ policy
Automation Activity & Vendor Info: (Cataloging) SirsiDynix; (ILL) A-G Canada Ltd
Function: Res libr
Restriction: Open to pub by appt only

M   BIBLIOTHEQUE DE L'HOPITAL MONTFORT, Annie Powers Library, 713 Chemin Montreal, K1K 4A9. SAN 324-4016. Tel: 613-746-4621, Ext 6045. FAX: 613-748-4922. E-mail: lib-biblio@montfort.on.ca. *Librn,* Marie-Cecile Domecq
Library Holdings: Bk Titles 1,054; Per Subs 5
Special Collections: Health professionals (French English Lang Coll)
Subject Interests: Med, Nursing
Wireless access

R   BIBLIOTHEQUE DU COLLEGE DOMINICAIN DE PHILOSOPHIE ET DE THEOLOGIE*, Dominican College Library, 96 Empress Ave, K1R 7G3. SAN 319-325X. Tel: 613-233-5696, Ext 216. FAX: 613-233-6064. E-mail: librarian@dominican.college.ca. Web Site: www.collegedominicain.ca/new/default.html. *Librn,* Philip Fraser; *Cat,* Robert Dale; *Cat,* Imad Zakaria; Staff 1 (Non-MLS 1)
Founded 1884. Highest Degree: Doctorate
Library Holdings: Bk Vols 120,000; Per Subs 300
Subject Interests: Behav studies, Hist, Philosophy, Relig studies, Soc
Open Mon-Fri 8:30am-10pm, Sat 8:30-5

L   BORDEN LADNER GERVAIS LLP*, Law Library, World Exchange Plaza, 100 Queen St, Ste 1100, K1P 1J9. SAN 374-5880. Tel: 613-237-5160. FAX: 613-230-8842. *Dir, Libr Serv,* Neal Ferguson; Tel: 613-787-3553; Staff 2 (MLS 1, Non-MLS 1)
Library Holdings: Bk Vols 6,000; Per Subs 400
Automation Activity & Vendor Info: (Acquisitions) Horizon; (Cataloging) Horizon; (Circulation) Horizon; (Serials) Horizon
Database Vendor: Dialog, LexisNexis, Westlaw

S   BREWERS ASSOCIATION OF CANADA LIBRARY*, 45 O'Connor St, Ste 650, K1P 1A4. SAN 325-5875. Tel: 613-232-9601. FAX: 613-232-2283. E-mail: office@brewers.ca. Web Site: www.brewers.ca. *Librn,* Ed Gregory
Library Holdings: Bk Titles 580; Per Subs 20
Subject Interests: Brewing, Taxation
Restriction: Open by appt only

M   BRUYERE CONTINUING CARE LIBRARY*, 43 Bruyere St, K1N 5C8. SAN 319-3500. Tel: 613-562-6262, Ext 4054. FAX: 613-562-4237. E-mail: library@bruyere.org. Web Site: www.bruyere.org. *Mgr, Libr Serv,* Mireille Ethier-Danis; E-mail: methier@bruyere.org; *Libr Tech,* Nathalie Lalonde; Staff 3 (Non-MLS 3)
Founded 1958
Library Holdings: e-journals 300; Bk Titles 3,500
Subject Interests: Complex continuing care, Long term care, Mgt, Palliative care, Rehabilitation

Automation Activity & Vendor Info: (Acquisitions) Inmagic, Inc.; (Cataloging) Inmagic, Inc.; (Circulation) Inmagic, Inc.; (OPAC) Inmagic, Inc.; (Serials) Inmagic, Inc.
Database Vendor: EBSCOhost
Function: For res purposes, Handicapped accessible, ILL available, Photocopying/Printing
Partic in Can Libr Asn; Ont Hospital Librs Asn
Restriction: Staff & prof res

S   CANADA AVIATION MUSEUM*, Library Services, 11 Aviation Pkwy, K1K 4R3. (Mail add: 2380 Lancaster Rd, PO Box 9724, Sta T, K1G 5A3), SAN 371-7445. Tel: 613-993-2303. FAX: 613-990-3655. E-mail: aviation.info@technomuscs.ca. Web Site: www.aviation.technomuses.ca. *Head, Info Serv,* F Smith Hale; *Asst Librn,* Sylvie Bertrand; E-mail: ileslie@nmstc.ca; Staff 2 (MLS 1, Non-MLS 1)
Library Holdings: Bk Titles 12,000; Per Subs 120
Subject Interests: Aeronaut
Automation Activity & Vendor Info: (Acquisitions) SirsiDynix; (Cataloging) SirsiDynix; (Circulation) SirsiDynix; (Serials) SirsiDynix
Open Mon-Fri 9-4

S   CANADA COUNCIL FOR THE ARTS*, Reference & Documentation Centre, 350 Albert St, K1P 5V8. (Mail add: PO Box 1047, K1P 5V8), SAN 371-7739. Tel: 613-566-4414, Ext 4051. Toll Free Tel: 800-263-5588, Ext 4051. FAX: 613-566-4390. Web Site: www.canadacouncil.ca. *Asst Admin,* Melissa-Renee Boulrice; Tel: 613-566-4414, E-mail: melissa-renee.boulrice@canadacouncil.ca; Staff 4 (Non-MLS 4)
Founded 1980
Library Holdings: Bk Titles 5,000; Spec Interest Per Sub 300
Special Collections: Canada Council History Coll
Subject Interests: Arts, Culture
Function: Ref serv available
Partic in Canadian Fed Librs
Restriction: Non-circulating to the pub, Open by appt only

GL   CANADA DEPARTMENT OF JUSTICE LIBRARY*, Headquarters, EMB, Rm A-370, 284 Wellington St, K1A 0H8. SAN 319-3004. Tel: 613-957-4606. Interlibrary Loan Service Tel: 613-957-4598. Administration Tel: 613-957-4609. Reference FAX: 613-952-5792. Administration FAX: 613-952-3491. E-mail: library@justice.gc.ca. *Dir,* Fiona A McPherson; Tel: 613-957-4611, E-mail: fiona.mcpherson@justice.gc.ca; *Mgr, Coll Develop,* Marcelle Saint-Arnaud; E-mail: marcelle.saint-arnaud@justice.gc.ca; *Mgr, Ref & Res Support Serv,* Nicolas Savard; *Mgr, Syst & Tech Serv,* Jennifer Svarckopf; E-mail: jennifer.svarckopf@justice.gc.ca; Staff 16 (MLS 9, Non-MLS 7)
Founded 1868
Library Holdings: AV Mats 35,350; CDs 100; e-books 1,788; e-journals 20; Electronic Media & Resources 20; Bk Titles 28,855; Bk Vols 160,000; Per Subs 1,570; Talking Bks 130; Videos 235
Subject Interests: Law
Automation Activity & Vendor Info: (Acquisitions) Innovative Interfaces, Inc; (Cataloging) Innovative Interfaces, Inc; (Circulation) Innovative Interfaces, Inc; (ILL) Amicus; (OPAC) Innovative Interfaces, Inc; (Serials) Innovative Interfaces, Inc
Database Vendor: AZIMUT, Dialog, Factiva.com, Gale Cengage Learning, Infomart, Ingenta, Innovative Interfaces, Inc INN - View, LexisNexis, netLibrary, OVID Technologies, Quicklaw, Thomson Carswell, Westlaw, WestlaweCARSWELL, Wilson - Wilson Web
Function: Audio & video playback equip for onsite use, CD-ROM, Copy machines, Doc delivery serv, e-mail serv, Electronic databases & coll, ILL available, Online cat, Online searches, Orientations, Ref serv available, Res libr, Scanner, VHS videos, Wheelchair accessible, Workshops
Publications: AWACOU; Guide to Services (Library handbook); New Acquisitions - Nouvelles Acquisitions (Current awareness service); Service Pamphlets (Research guide)
Partic in Council of Federal Libraries Consortium
Open Mon-Fri 8:30-5
Restriction: Badge access after hrs, Borrowing requests are handled by ILL, Employees only, Not open to pub

S   CANADA INDUSTRIAL RELATIONS BOARD LIBRARY*, C D Howe Bldg, 4th Flr W, 240 Sparks St, K1A 0X8. SAN 319-3055. Toll Free Tel: 800-575-9696. E-mail: library-bibliotheque@cirb-ccri.gc.ca. *Libr Tech,* Sophie Tauvette; Staff 2 (Non-MLS 2)
Founded 1973
Library Holdings: Bk Titles 4,100; Per Subs 250
Subject Interests: Admin law, Indust relations
Automation Activity & Vendor Info: (Acquisitions) Inmagic, Inc.; (Cataloging) Inmagic, Inc.; (Circulation) Inmagic, Inc.; (OPAC) Inmagic, Inc.; (Serials) Inmagic, Inc.
Partic in Federal Librs Consortium (Canada)
Restriction: Not open to pub

S CANADA SCIENCE & TECHNOLOGY MUSEUM, Library & Information Services, 2380 Lancaster Rd, K1B 3W9. (Mail add: PO Box 9724, Stn T, K1G 5A3), SAN 368-0282. Tel: 613-991-2982. FAX: 613-990-3636. E-mail: library@technomuses.ca. Web Site: www.sciencetech.technomuses.ca. *Dir, Libr & Archive Serv,* Fiona Smith Hale; Tel: 613-993-2303, E-mail: fsmithhale@technomuses.ca; *Reader Serv,* Sylvie Bertrand; E-mail: library@technomuses.ca; Staff 4 (MLS 1, Non-MLS 3)
Founded 1967
Library Holdings: Bk Titles 26,000; Per Subs 300
Special Collections: Canadian National Railway Photographs Coll; Cycling (Shields Coll); Railway Engineering Drawings; Trade Literature
Subject Interests: Agr, Astronomy, Communications, Energy, Forestry, Graphic arts, Hist of sci & tech, Indust tech, Land transportation, Marine transportation, Mining, Phys sci, Radar, Space
Automation Activity & Vendor Info: (Acquisitions) SirsiDynix; (Cataloging) SirsiDynix; (Circulation) SirsiDynix; (OPAC) SirsiDynix; (Serials) SirsiDynix
Database Vendor: SirsiDynix
Function: Archival coll, Ref serv available
Restriction: In-house use for visitors

S CANADIAN ARTISTS' REPRESENTATION*, Publication Archives, Two Daly Ave, Ste 250, K1N 6E2. SAN 375-2577. Tel: 613-233-6161. FAX: 613-233-6162. E-mail: communications@carfac.ca. Web Site: www.carfac.ca. *Exec Dir,* April Britski
Library Holdings: Bk Vols 3,000; Per Subs 34
Open Mon-Fri 10-5

M CANADIAN ASSOCIATION OF OCCUPATIONAL THERAPISTS*, Resource Center, CTTC Bldg, Ste 3400, 1125 Colonel By Dr, K1S 5R1. SAN 375-8052. Tel: 613-523-2268. FAX: 613-523-2552. E-mail: practice@caot.ca. Web Site: www.caot.ca. *Exec Dir,* Claudia Von Zweck; E-mail: cvonzweck@caot.ca
Library Holdings: Bk Titles 100

S CANADIAN CHILD CARE FEDERATION, Resource Centre, 700 Industrial Ave, Ste 600, K1G 0Y9. SAN 373-6687. Tel: 613-729-5289. Toll Free Tel: 800-858-1412. FAX: 613-729-3159. E-mail: info@cccf-fcsge.ca. Web Site: www.cccf-fcsge.ca. *Pres & Chief Exec Officer,* Don Giesbrecht; Tel: 613-729-5289, Ext 220; Staff 2 (MLS 1, Non-MLS 1)
Founded 1988
Library Holdings: Bk Titles 5,000
Special Collections: Provincial Child Care Legislation (Special Coll), bk, files
Subject Interests: Child care, Families
Automation Activity & Vendor Info: (Acquisitions) Inmagic, Inc.; (Cataloging) Inmagic, Inc.; (Serials) Inmagic, Inc.
Restriction: Mem only, Open by appt only

S CANADIAN DENTAL ASSOCIATION RESOURCE CENTRE, 1815 Alta Vista Dr, K1G 3Y6. SAN 320-796X. Tel: 613-523-1770. Toll Free Tel: 800-267-6354. FAX: 613-523-7736. E-mail: library@cda-adc.ca. Web Site: www.cda-adc.ca. *Coordr,* Naomi Blais; Tel: 613-520-5025, E-mail: nablais@cda-adc.ca; Staff 1 (Non-MLS 1)
Founded 1951
Library Holdings: Per Subs 200
Subject Interests: Dental health, Dental hygiene, Dentistry
Wireless access
Function: ILL available
Partic in Docline
Restriction: Staff & mem only

G CANADIAN FORCES HEALTH SERVICES GROUP HEADQUARTERS LIBRARY*, 1745 Alta Vista Dr, K1A 0K6. SAN 370-7849. Tel: 613-945-6517. FAX: 613-945-6938. *Librn,* Pearl Yost; E-mail: pearl.yost@forces.gc.ca
Library Holdings: Bk Vols 4,095
Partic in Hosp Librs Group; Ont Hospital Librs Asn
Open Mon-Fri 8-4

G CANADIAN INTERNATIONAL TRADE TRIBUNAL LIBRARY*, 333 Laurier Ave W, K1A 0G7. SAN 374-4035. Tel: 613-990-8715. FAX: 613-990-2431. *Circ, Tech Serv,* Vedranka Zec; E-mail: vedranka.zec@citt-tcce.gc.ca
Founded 1989
Library Holdings: Bk Titles 7,832; Per Subs 666
Special Collections: Canadian International Trade Tribunal Reports; Tariff Board Reports; USITC Decisions Since 1954; World Trade Organization Documents
Subject Interests: Intl trade
Automation Activity & Vendor Info: (Cataloging) SydneyPlus; (Circulation) SydneyPlus; (OPAC) SydneyPlus; (Serials) SydneyPlus
Restriction: Open by appt only

M CANADIAN MEDICAL ASSOCIATION*, T Clarence Routley Library, 1867 Alta Vista Dr, K1G 0G8. SAN 319-3209. Tel: 613-731-9331, Ext 2144. Toll Free Tel: 800-663-7336, Ext 2144. FAX: 613-731-2076. Web Site: www.cma.ca. *Ref Librn,* Elizabeth Czanyo; Tel: 800-663-7336, Ext 2245, E-mail: elizabeth.czanyo@cma.ca; Staff 5 (MLS 3, Non-MLS 2)
Founded 1911
Library Holdings: Bk Titles 4,000; Per Subs 250
Subject Interests: Health econ, Health policy, Health promotion, Med ethics
Automation Activity & Vendor Info: (Acquisitions) Inmagic, Inc.; (Cataloging) Inmagic, Inc.; (Circulation) Inmagic, Inc.; (ILL) Inmagic, Inc.; (OPAC) Inmagic, Inc.; (Serials) Inmagic, Inc.
Database Vendor: Dialog, EBSCOhost, Elsevier MDL, Factiva.com, Infomart, OVID Technologies
Open Mon-Fri 8:30-4:30

G CANADIAN MUSEUM OF NATURE LIBRARY & ARCHIVES*, PO Box 3443, Sta D, K1P 6P4. SAN 368-0193. Tel: 613-364-4042. FAX: 613-364-4026. E-mail: cmnlib@mus-nature.ca. Web Site: www.nature.ca. *Head, Archives & Rec Libr,* Chantal Dussault; Tel: 613-364-4047, E-mail: cdussault@mus-nature.ca; *Acq, Ser,* Ted Sypniewski; Tel: 613-566-4734, E-mail: tsypniewski@mus-nature.ca; *Circ, ILL,* Mike Wayne; E-mail: mwayne@mus-nature.ca; Staff 3 (MLS 1, Non-MLS 2)
Founded 1842
Apr 2011-Mar 2012. Mats Exp (CAN) $90,000, Books (CAN) $15,000, Per/Ser (Incl. Access Fees) (CAN) $75,000
Library Holdings: Bk Titles 35,000; Per Subs 110
Special Collections: Mammology Anderson Coll, bks, per; Nature Art Coll; Paleontology (C M Sternberg Coll), reprints; Photographs Coll; Rare Books Coll
Subject Interests: Botany, Geol, Natural sci, Ornithology, Paleobiology, Taxonomy, Zoology
Database Vendor: Dialog, EBSCOhost, netLibrary
Function: Res libr
Open Mon-Fri 8:30-4:30

G CANADIAN NUCLEAR SAFETY COMMISSION LIBRARY, 280 Slater St, K1P 1C2. (Mail add: PO Box 1046, Sta B, K1P 5S9), SAN 322-8061. Tel: 613-995-2060. Interlibrary Loan Service Tel: 613-995-1359. FAX: 613-995-5086. E-mail: library-bibliotheque@cnsc-ccsn.gc.ca. Web Site: www.nuclearsafety.gc.ca. *Librn, Mgr,* Frank Rautenkranz; E-mail: frank.rautenkranz@cnsc-ccsn.gc.ca; *ILL/Doc Delivery Serv, Ref Serv,* Carole Blais; E-mail: carole.blais@cnsc-ccsn.gc.ca; Staff 2 (MLS 1, Non-MLS 1)
Library Holdings: CDs 240; DVDs 25; e-books 2,300; e-journals 70; Electronic Media & Resources 45; Bk Titles 52,000; Per Subs 220; Videos 160
Subject Interests: Eng, Nuclear nonproliferation, Nuclear sci, Phys sci, Radiation protection, Radioactive waste
Automation Activity & Vendor Info: (Acquisitions) Horizon; (Cataloging) Horizon; (Circulation) Horizon; (OPAC) Horizon; (Serials) Horizon
Database Vendor: Bowker, Cambridge Scientific Abstracts, CISTI Source, Dialog, EBSCOhost, IHS, LexisNexis, netLibrary, Newsbank, OCLC FirstSearch, OVID Technologies, Oxford Online, ProQuest, PubMed, Quicklaw, ScienceDirect
Function: ILL available, Wheelchair accessible
Publications: Monthly Acquisitions List (Online only); Periodical list (Online only)
Partic in Council of Federal Libraries Consortium; Horizon Users Group
Open Mon-Fri 8-5

M CANADIAN PARAPLEGIC ASSOCIATION LIBRARY*, 230-1101 Prince of Wales Dr, K2C 3W7. SAN 321-6764. Tel: 613-723-1033. FAX: 613-723-1060. E-mail: info@canparaplegic.org. Web Site: www.canparaplegic.org. *Exec Dir,* Robert White
Founded 1945
Subject Interests: Advocacy, Disability, Paraplegia, Quadriplegia, Rehabilitation, Resettlement into commun of spinal cord injured, Spinal cord injury

S CANADIAN POLICE COLLEGE LIBRARY*, Canadian Police College, One Sandridge Rd, Bldg C, K1G 3J2. (Mail add: PO Box 8900, K1G 3J2), SAN 375-8249. Tel: 613-993-3225. FAX: 613-993-2220. E-mail: library_biblio@rcmp-grc.gc.ca. Web Site: www.cpc-ccp.gc.ca/biblio, www.cpc-ccp.gc.ca/library. *Mgr,* Marc Lepage; *Syst/Electronic Res Librn,* Pierre Mullie; *Tech Serv,* Frédéric Gaudreau; Staff 12 (MLS 6, Non-MLS 6)
Founded 1936
Library Holdings: Bk Vols 30,000; Per Subs 650; Videos 2,500
Subject Interests: Criminal justice, Criminology, Police sci, Soc pathology
Publications: Accessions list; Bibliographies; List of periodicals

G   CANADIAN RADIO-TELEVISION & TELECOMMUNICATIONS
     COMMISSION INFORMATION RESOURCE CENTRE*, One Promenade
     du Portage, K1A 0N2. SAN 319-3217. Tel: 819-997-4484. FAX:
     819-994-6337. Web Site: www.crtc.gc.ca. *Mgr, Info Mgt,* Karla Weys;
     E-mail: karla.weys@crtc.gc.ca; Staff 6 (MLS 2, Non-MLS 4)
     Founded 1971
     Library Holdings: Bk Titles 6,700; Per Subs 151
     Special Collections: Canadian Radio
     Subject Interests: Broadcasting, Internet, Media, Mkt
     Automation Activity & Vendor Info: (OPAC) Inmagic, Inc.
     Database Vendor: EBSCOhost
     Function: ILL available, Ref serv available
     Partic in Council of Federal Libraries Consortium
     Open Mon-Fri 8-4:30
     Restriction: Open to pub for ref only

G   CANADIAN WAR MUSEUM*, Hartland Molson Library, One Vimy Pl,
     K1A 0M8. SAN 368-0258. Tel: 819-776-8652. FAX: 819-776-8623. Web
     Site: www.warmuseum.ca. *Dir,* Jane Naisbitt; E-mail:
     jane.naisbitt@warmuseum.ca; *Librn,* Lara Andrews; E-mail:
     lara.andrews@warmuseum.ca
     Founded 1969
     Library Holdings: Bk Vols 45,000; Per Subs 90
     Special Collections: Military Technical Manuals; Newspaper Clippings;
     Rare Book Coll; Regimental Histories
     Subject Interests: Art, Can mil hist, Heraldry
     Automation Activity & Vendor Info: (Acquisitions) Infor Library &
     Information Solutions; (Cataloging) Infor Library & Information Solutions;
     (Circulation) Infor Library & Information Solutions
     Function: ILL available
     Partic in Council of Federal Libraries Consortium; OCLC Online Computer
     Library Center, Inc

C   CARLETON UNIVERSITY LIBRARY, MacOdrum Library, 1125 Colonel
     By Dr, K1S 5B6. SAN 319-3241. Tel: 613-520-2735. Circulation Tel:
     613-520-2734. Interlibrary Loan Service Tel: 613-520-2732. Administration
     Tel: 613-520-2600, Ext 1652. FAX: 613-520-2750. Interlibrary Loan
     Service FAX: 613-521-1118. Reference FAX: 613-520-2780. E-mail:
     university_librarian@carleton.ca. Web Site: www.library.carleton.ca. *Univ
     Librn,* Margaret Haines; Tel: 613-520-2600, Ext 8260, E-mail:
     margaret_haines@carleton.ca; *Assoc Univ Librn,* Valerie Critchley; Tel:
     613-520-2600, Ext 1808, E-mail: valerie_critchley@carleton.ca; *Assoc Univ
     Librn,* Wayne Jones; Tel: 613-520-2600, Ext 8008, E-mail:
     wayne_jones@carleton.ca; *Assoc Univ Librn,* Pat Moore; Tel:
     613-520-2600, Ext 2745, E-mail: pat_moore@carleton.ca; *Head of
     Acq/Cataloging,* Colleen Neely; Tel: 613-520-2600, Ext 8140, E-mail:
     colleen_neely@carleton.ca; *Head, Coll, E-Res & Ser,* David Sharp; Tel:
     613-520-2600, Ext 8372, E-mail: david_sharp@carleton.ca; *Head, Access
     Serv,* Ingrid Draayer; Tel: 613-520-2600, Ext 2729, E-mail:
     ingrid_draayer@carleton.ca; *Head, Archives & Res Coll,* Patti Harper; Tel:
     613-520-2600, Ext 8066, E-mail: patti_harper@carleton.ca; *Head, Ref Serv,*
     Janice Scammell; Tel: 613-520-2600, Ext 2017, E-mail:
     janice_scammell@carleton.ca; *Actg Head, Maps, Data & Govt Info Ctr,*
     Frances Montgomery; Tel: 613-520-2600, Ext 8196, E-mail:
     frances_montgomery@carleton.ca; Staff 135.31 (MLS 27.28, Non-MLS
     108.03)
     Founded 1942. Highest Degree: Doctorate
     May 2010-Apr 2011. Mats Exp (CAN) $5,328,990, Books (CAN)
     $757,482, Per/Ser (Incl. Access Fees) (CAN) $495,573, Electronic Ref Mat
     (Incl. Access Fees) (CAN) $3,799,188. Sal (CAN) $8,233,090 (Prof (CAN)
     $2,911,963)
     Library Holdings: CDs 8,548; e-books 41,472,662; e-journals 76,026;
     Music Scores 34,712; Bk Titles 1,560,731; Bk Vols 1,862,021; Per Subs
     2,645; Videos 3,190
     Special Collections: Canadian Gallup Polls; Canadian, British & American
     Small-Press Poetry; Cardinal Coll; CBC Newsworld Coll; French
     Revolution; ICA Barbara Petchenik Children's Map Competition Archive;
     International Social Survey Project Coll; Maps, Atlases & Cartographic
     References; Novosti Press Agency Photograph Files; POLLARA Polls;
     Siskind Coll; Ukrainian Politics, 19th-20th Century (Batchinsky Coll);
     William Blake Coll, Trianon Press. Can & Prov
     Subject Interests: Africana, Biol, Can Inst hist microreproductions,
     Computing sci, E European studies, Econ, Eng lit, Fr lit, Hist, Journalism,
     Mass communications, Math, Philosophy, Polit sci, Psychol, Pub admin,
     Sociol, Soviet studies, Spanish lit
     Automation Activity & Vendor Info: (Acquisitions) Innovative Interfaces,
     Inc; (Cataloging) Innovative Interfaces, Inc; (Circulation) Innovative
     Interfaces, Inc; (Course Reserve) Innovative Interfaces, Inc; (ILL)
     Fretwell-Downing; (OPAC) Innovative Interfaces, Inc; (Serials) Innovative
     Interfaces, Inc
     Database Vendor: Innovative Interfaces, Inc
     Wireless access
     Publications: Data Centre News Bytes (Newsletter)
     Partic in Ontario Council of University Libraries
     Special Services for the Deaf - TTY equip

Special Services for the Blind - Computer with voice synthesizer for
visually impaired persons; Dragon Naturally Speaking software; Inspiration
software; Large screen computer & software; Reader equip; Screen reader
software; ZoomText magnification & reading software
Friends of the Library Group

M   CHILDREN'S HOSPITAL OF EASTERN ONTARIO*, Conway Library,
     401 Smyth Rd, K1H 8L1. SAN 324-4105. Tel: 613-737-7600, Ext 2206.
     FAX: 613-738-4806. E-mail: library@cheo.on.ca. *Mgr, Libr Serv,* Margaret
     Sampson; E-mail: msampson@cheo.on.ca; Staff 2 (MLS 1, Non-MLS 1)
     Founded 1974
     Library Holdings: Bk Titles 3,500; Per Subs 120
     Subject Interests: Pediatrics
     Open Mon-Fri 8-4
     Restriction: Circulates for staff only

G   CITIZEN & IMMIGRATION CANADA LIBRARY SERVICES*, 300
     Slater St, Journal Towers N, 3rd Flr, K1A 1L1. SAN 374-7433. Tel:
     613-954-1474. Circulation Tel: 613-952-7415. FAX: 613-954-7892. *Mgr,*
     Charlene Elgee; E-mail: charlene.elgee@cic.gc.ca; Staff 6 (MLS 3,
     Non-MLS 3)
     Founded 1994
     Mar 2011-Apr 2012. Mats Exp (CAN) $171,000. Sal (CAN) $400,000
     (Prof (CAN) $208,000)
     Special Collections: Canadian Citizenship & Immigration CD-ROM,
     printed mat & videos
     Automation Activity & Vendor Info: (Acquisitions) Innovative Interfaces,
     Inc; (Cataloging) Innovative Interfaces, Inc; (Circulation) Innovative
     Interfaces, Inc; (OPAC) Innovative Interfaces, Inc; (Serials) Innovative
     Interfaces, Inc

L   COMPETITION TRIBUNAL LIBRARY*, 90 Sparks St, Ste 600, K1P
     5B4. SAN 370-6222. Tel: 613-957-7850. FAX: 613-957-3170. *Librn,*
     Melanie Emart
     Library Holdings: Bk Vols 1,000; Per Subs 50
     Subject Interests: Antitrust law
     Open Mon-Fri 8-5

GL   COUNTY OF CARLETON LAW LIBRARY*, Ottawa Court House,
     2004-161 Elgin St, K2P 2K1. SAN 319-3292. Tel: 613-233-7386. FAX:
     613-238-3788. E-mail: info@ccla.ottawa.on.ca. Web Site:
     www.ccla.ottawa.on.ca. *Head Librn,* Jennifer Walker; Tel: 613-233-7386,
     Ext 225, E-mail: jwalker@ccla-abcc.ca; *Ref Librn,* Brenda Lauritzen; *Libr
     Tech,* Amanda Elliot; Staff 4 (MLS 3, Non-MLS 1)
     Founded 1888
     Library Holdings: Bk Vols 35,000; Per Subs 80
     Special Collections: Abridgements; Digests; Law Reports; Periodicals &
     Texts
     Subject Interests: Legal
     Publications: CCLA Bulletin
     Restriction: Not open to pub

S   GEORGE G CROSKERY MEMORIAL LIBRARY*, 2490 Don Reid Dr,
     K1H 1E1. SAN 319-3225. Tel: 613-232-1505. FAX: 613-232-1886. E-mail:
     info@ctf-fce.ca. Web Site: www.ctf-fce.ca. *Librn,* Alain Monette; Tel:
     613-232-1505, Ext 146, E-mail: amone@ctf-fce.ca; Staff 1 (Non-MLS 1)
     Founded 1953
     Library Holdings: Bk Titles 8,000; Per Subs 68
     Special Collections: Collective Agreements; Department of Education
     Annual Reports; Educational Law & Legislation; Teacher Organization
     Handbooks
     Subject Interests: Admin, Benefits, Cases, Certification, Collective
     bargaining, Curric, Educ, Philosophy, Psychol, Salaries, Sch law, Sociol,
     Statistics, Welfare
     Function: ILL available

G   DEPARTMENT OF CANADIAN HERITAGE*, Canadian Conservation
     Institute Library, 1030 Innes Rd, K1A 0M5. SAN 374-5341. Tel:
     613-998-3721. FAX: 613-998-4721. E-mail: cci.library@pch.gc.ca. Web
     Site: www.cci-icc.gc.ca. Staff 2 (MLS 1, Non-MLS 1)
     Founded 1972
     Library Holdings: Bk Titles 13,000; Per Subs 370; Videos 191
     Subject Interests: Conserv, Museology, Restoration
     Automation Activity & Vendor Info: (Acquisitions) Inmagic, Inc.;
     (Cataloging) Inmagic, Inc.; (OPAC) Inmagic, Inc.; (Serials) Inmagic, Inc.
     Open Tues-Fri 9-4

G   DEPARTMENT OF FINANCE & TREASURY BOARD OF CANADA
     LIBRARY, East Tower, Esplanade Laurier, 140 O'Connor St, 11th Flr,
     K1A 0G5. SAN 319-2970. Tel: 613-996-5491. FAX: 613-992-6411.
     E-mail: library.bibliotheque@fin.gc.ca.
     Founded 1947
     Library Holdings: Bk Vols 15,000; Per Subs 300

Subject Interests: Acctg, Auditing, Econ, Finance, Govt prog, Indust relations, Personnel admin, Pub admin, Pub policy
Automation Activity & Vendor Info: (Acquisitions) SirsiDynix; (Cataloging) SirsiDynix; (Circulation) SirsiDynix; (OPAC) SirsiDynix; (Serials) SirsiDynix
Restriction: Open by appt only

G   FOREIGN AFFAIRS CANADA & INTERNATIONAL TRADE CANADA, Jules Leger Library, Lester B Pearson Bldg, 125 Sussex Drive, K1A 0G2. SAN 319-2962. Reference Tel: 613-992-6150. FAX: 613-944-0222. E-mail: library-biblio.aiml@international.gc.ca. Web Site: www.international.gc.ca. *Chief Librn, Dep Dir,* Jo-Anne Valentine; Tel: 613-996-4042
Library Holdings: Bk Titles 50,000; Bk Vols 150,000; Per Subs 200
Special Collections: UN Document Depository
Subject Interests: Can foreign relations, Commerce, Econ, Intl law, Intl relations, Polit sci

GOVERNMENT OF CANADA
L   COURTS ADMINISTRATION SERVICE, TAX LIBRARY*, 200 Kent St, K1A 0M1, SAN 322-7251. Tel: 613-992-1704. FAX: 613-943-8449. Web Site: www.cas-satj.gc.ca. *Librn,* Denis Roussel; E-mail: denis.roussel@cas-satj.gc.ca; Staff 2 (MLS 1, Non-MLS 1)
Founded 1982
Library Holdings: Bk Titles 2,250; Bk Vols 12,485; Per Subs 180
Subject Interests: Acctg, Goods, Income tax, Law, Serv tax, Taxation
Automation Activity & Vendor Info: (OPAC) SydneyPlus
Database Vendor: LexisNexis, netLibrary, OCLC WorldCat

GL   FEDERAL COURTS & TAX COURT OF CANADA, COURTS ADMINISTRATION SERVICE-LIBRARY SERVICES, 90 Sparks St, K1A 0H9, SAN 326-1344. Tel: 613-995-1382. Reference Tel: 613-995-1267. FAX: 613-943-5303. E-mail: reference@cas-satj.gc.ca. *Dir, Libr & Info Serv,* Jean Weerasinghe; E-mail: jean.weerasinghe@cas-satj.gc.ca; *Head, Coll Develop,* Christina-Anne Boyle; Tel: 613-947-3906, E-mail: christina-anne.boyle@cas-satj.gc.ca; *Head, Libr Syst & Cat,* Lawrence Wardroper; Tel: 613-996-8735, E-mail: lawrence.wardroper@cas-satj.gc.ca; *Client Serv Librn,* Karon J Crummey; Tel: 613-943-0839, E-mail: karon.crummey@cas-satj.gc.ca; *Br Mgr,* Denis Roussel; Tel: 613-992-1704, Fax: 613-943-8449, E-mail: denis.roussel@cas-satj.gc.ca. Subject Specialists: *Tax,* Denis Roussel; Staff 11 (MLS 4, Non-MLS 7)
Library Holdings: AV Mats 200; e-books 2,100; Bk Vols 40,000
Subject Interests: Admin law, Citizenship, Competition law, Employment insurance, Immigration, Intellectual property, Maritime, Native law, Tax
Automation Activity & Vendor Info: (Acquisitions) SydneyPlus; (Cataloging) SydneyPlus; (Circulation) SydneyPlus; (ILL) SydneyPlus; (OPAC) SydneyPlus; (Serials) SydneyPlus
Database Vendor: AZIMUT, EBSCOhost, Gale Cengage Learning, HeinOnline, LexisNexis, Oxford Online, ProQuest, Quicklaw, Thomson Carswell, WestlaweCARSWELL
Partic in Consortium of Fed Librs
Publications: Acquisitions List; Table of Contents Service
Restriction: Not open to pub

L   GOWLING LAFLEUR HENDERSON LLP*, Law Library, 160 Elgin St, K1P 1C3. SAN 323-9063. Tel: 613-232-1781. FAX: 613-563-9869. Web Site: www.gowlings.com. *Mgr, Libr Serv,* Glenda O'Brien; Staff 3 (Non-MLS 3)
Library Holdings: Bk Titles 10,000; Per Subs 200
Subject Interests: Law
Open Mon-Fri 9-5

R   GREENBERG FAMILIES LIBRARY, 21 Nadolny Sachs PR, K2A 1R9. SAN 321-3382. Tel: 613-798-9818. FAX: 613-798-9839. E-mail: library@jccottawa.com. *Librn,* Estelle Backman; *Librn,* Jack Schecter
Founded 1955
Library Holdings: Bk Titles 10,000; Per Subs 8
Subject Interests: Judaica
Open Mon-Thurs 10-8, Fri 10-2, Sun 10-4

G   HEALTH CANADA LIBRARY*, Postal Locator 2202B, 251 Frederick Banting Driveway, K1A 0K9. SAN 329-2924. Tel: 613-957-1545. FAX: 613-941-6957. E-mail: library.bibliotheque@hc-sc.gc.ca. *Chief Librn,* Marty Lovelock; E-mail: marty.lovelock@hc-sc.gc.ca; Staff 9 (MLS 8, Non-MLS 1)
Founded 1991
Library Holdings: CDs 35; e-books 12,000; e-journals 5,500; Bk Titles 30,000; Per Subs 38
Subject Interests: Health econ, Health policy, Health promotion, Healthcare reform, Pop health
Open Mon-Fri 8:30-4:30

G   INDUSTRY CANADA, Library & Knowledge Centre, 235 Queen St, K1A 0H5. SAN 319-3136. Tel: 613-954-2728. Interlibrary Loan Service Tel: 613-954-5454. Administration Tel: 613-941-7256. FAX: 613-954-0548. E-mail: library@ic.gc.ca. *Dir,* Diane Rudzevicius; E-mail: diane.rudzevicius@ic.gc.ca; Staff 15 (MLS 8, Non-MLS 7)
Founded 1918
Library Holdings: Bk Titles 63,000; Per Subs 1,000
Subject Interests: Bus info, Corp, Develop, Economy, Indust policy, Sci, Sci policy, Small bus, Tech innovation
Restriction: Employees only

S   INSTITUT CANADIEN FRANCAIS D'OTTAWA BIBLIOTHECAIRE*, 316 Dalhousie St, K1N 7E7. (Mail add: PO Box 52073, K1N 1B4), SAN 326-9442. Tel: 613-241-3522. FAX: 613-241-3611. E-mail: icfottawa@gmail.com. *Librn,* Position Currently Open
Founded 1852
Library Holdings: Bk Vols 3,500
Restriction: Mem only

S   INTERNATIONAL DEVELOPMENT RESEARCH CENTRE LIBRARY, IDRC Library, 150 Kent St, K1G 3H9. (Mail add: PO Box 8500, K1G 3H9), SAN 321-2343. Tel: 613-236-6163. Interlibrary Loan Service Tel: 613-696-2579. Reference Tel: 613-696-2578. FAX: 613-563-3858. E-mail: library@idrc.ca, reference@idrc.ca. Web Site: www.idrc.ca/library. *Librn,* Mélanie Brunet; *Supvr, Libr & Training,* Guy Gascon; *Doc Delivery, Res Serv,* Elizabeth Debeljak; *Ref Asst,* Heidi Boraks; Staff 4 (MLS 1, Non-MLS 3)
Founded 1971
Special Collections: Brundtland Commission Archives; Rio Summit Archives
Subject Interests: Develop res, Info & communication technologies, Poverty alleviation, Sustainable develop
Open Mon-Fri 8-5

S   LEARNING DISABILITIES ASSOCIATION OF CANADA LIBRARY*, 1188 Wellington St W, Ste 201, K1Y 2Z5. SAN 377-2810. Tel: 613-238-5721. Toll Free Tel: 877-238-5332. FAX: 613-235-5391. E-mail: information@ldac-taac.ca. Web Site: www.ldac-taac.ca. *Info Spec,* Claudette Laroque; E-mail: claudette@ldac-acta.ca
Function: Ref serv available
Restriction: Circ limited, Circulates for staff only, In-house use for visitors

G   LIBRARY OF PARLIAMENT*, Parliament Bldgs, Ste 677F, K1A 0A9. SAN 368-0649. Tel: 613-992-3122. Reference Tel: 613-995-1166. Information Services Tel: 613-992-4793. Toll Free Tel: 866-599-4999. Reference FAX: 613-992-1269. Information Services FAX: 613-992-1273. Web Site: www.parl.gc.ca. *Dir,* Sonia L'Heureux
Founded 1867
Library Holdings: AV Mats 9,368; e-books 1,312; Bk Titles 700,000; Per Subs 7,148
Special Collections: Audubon Double Elephant Folio Birds of America; Canadian Political Pamphlets; Parliamentary Papers of France, Australia, United Kingdom, United Nations; Sessional Papers (1810-present); United Kingdom CTTEES (1715-present); United States (Congressional Papers). Can & Prov
Subject Interests: Can studies, Canadiana, Govt, Intl relations, Law, Law Can, Legislation, Parliamentary affairs, Parliamentary procedure, Parlimentary hist, Polit sci, Soc sci with emphasis on Canada
Automation Activity & Vendor Info: (Acquisitions) SirsiDynix; (Cataloging) SirsiDynix; (Circulation) SirsiDynix; (OPAC) SirsiDynix; (Serials) SirsiDynix
Publications: Articles List; Canada's Parliament - Democracy in Action; Current Issue Reviews; Electronic Services Offered to Parliamentarians by the Library of Parliament; History of the Federal Electoral Ridings since 1867; How Canadians Govern Themselves; Inside Canada's Parliament; Legislative Summaries; Library of Parliament - A Guide to Services; Library of Parliament - Annual Report; Library of Parliament - Strategic Outlook; Publications List; Quorum; Speakers of the Canadian House of Commons; Speakers of the Senate; The Parliament Buildings; TIPS
Open Mon-Fri 8-5
Branches
BRANCHES & INFORMATION SERVICE, Centre Block, Parliament Bldgs, K1A 0A9. Tel: 613-992-4793. Toll Free Tel: 866-599-4999. FAX: 613-992-1273. E-mail: info@parl.gc.ca. Web Site: www.parl.gc.ca. *Chief,* Barbara Pilek; Tel: 613-943-7051, E-mail: barbara.pilek@parl.gc.ca
CONFEDERATION BUILDING BRANCH, Confederation Bldg, Rm G-48, K1A 0A9. Tel: 613-992-1602. FAX: 613-996-0862. *Chief, Br & Reading,* Barbara Pilek; Tel: 613-943-7051
Open Mon-Fri 8-5
MAIN LIBRARY, Centre Block, 111 Wellington, K1A 0A9. Tel: 613-992-6953. FAX: 613-941-4087. *Chief, Br & Reading,* Barbara Pilek; Tel: 613-943-7051
Open Mon-Fri 8-5

S   MITEL CORPORATE LIBRARY, 350 Legget Dr, K2K 2W7. SAN
     326-1441. Tel: 613-592-2122, Ext 74407. FAX: 613-592-7803. *Librn,*
     Melissa Foran
     Founded 1982
     Library Holdings: Bk Titles 5,000; Per Subs 90
     Special Collections: Industry Standards
     Subject Interests: Mkt
     Wireless access
     Partic in Dialog Corp; OLAM
     Restriction: Staff use only

S   NATIONAL GALLERY OF CANADA LIBRARY, 380 Sussex Dr, K1N
     9N4. (Mail add: PO Box 427, Sta A, K1N 9N4), SAN 319-339X. Tel:
     613-998-8949. Automation Services Tel: 613-990-0584. FAX:
     613-990-9818. E-mail: erefel@gallery.ca. Web Site:
     www.gallery.ca/en/library/index.php. *Chief, Libr, Archives & Res Fel Prog,*
     Jonathan Franklin; Tel: 613-990-0590, E-mail: jfrankli@gallery.ca; *Head,*
     Archives, Documentation & Visual Res, Cyndie Campbell; Tel:
     613-990-0597, E-mail: ccampbel@gallery.ca; *Head, Coll & Database Mgt,*
     Lisa DiNoble; Tel: 613-990-0594, E-mail: ldinoble@gallery.ca; *Acq,* Julie
     Levac; Tel: 613-990-0591, E-mail: jlevac@gallery.ca; *Bibliographer,* Jo
     Beglo; Tel: 613-990-3285, E-mail: jbeglo@gallery.ca; *Cat,* Kathleen
     O'Reilly; Tel: 613-990-0592, E-mail: koreilly@gallery.ca; *Reader Serv,*
     Peter Trepanier; Tel: 613-990-0587, E-mail: ptrepani@gallery.ca; *Ser,* Mike
     Saunders; Tel: 613-991-5058, E-mail: msaunders@gallery.ca; Staff 13
     (MLS 7, Non-MLS 6)
     Founded 1918
     Library Holdings: Bk Vols 270,000; Per Subs 1,100
     Special Collections: Art Metropole; Canadian Art Documentation, files &
     microfiche, photog, slides; Canadiana; National Gallery Archives
     Subject Interests: Archit, Can art, Graphic arts, Post-mediaeval western
     painting, Sculpture
     Automation Activity & Vendor Info: (Acquisitions) Innovative Interfaces,
     Inc; (Cataloging) Innovative Interfaces, Inc; (Circulation) Innovative
     Interfaces, Inc; (OPAC) Innovative Interfaces, Inc; (Serials) Innovative
     Interfaces, Inc
     Publications: Art at Auction: A Bibliographical Listing of
     Nineteenth-Century Canadian Catalogues; Artists in Canada: A Union List
     of Artists' Files; Index to Nineteenth-Century Canadian Catalogues of Art;
     Index to the National Gallery of Canada Bulletin & Annual Bulletin;
     Library & Archives Collection Development Policy
     Partic in AG Canada; Canadian Heritage Information Network; RLIN
     (Research Libraries Information Network)

     NATURAL RESOURCES CANADA
G   BIBLIOTHEQUE DE RESSOURCES NATURELLES CANADA*, 580
     Booth St, K1A OE4, SAN 367-9144. Tel: 613-996-3919. Interlibrary
     Loan Service Tel: 613-996-0839. FAX: 613-943-8742. E-mail:
     bibliothequerncan.nrcanlibrary@nrcan.gc.ca, nrcanlibrary@nrcan.gc.ca.
     Web Site: www.nrcan.gc.ca/library/home. *Head of Libr,* Margaret
     Ahearn; Tel: 613-995-4157, E-mail: mahearn@nrcan.gc.ca
     Founded 1854
     Special Collections: Contract Reports, Research Reports. Can & prov;
     Early Exploration Coll; Ehnography, Fauna, Flora & Geography;
     Forestry, Energy, Earth Sciences, Mineral & Metals Specialized Colls;
     Map Archival Coll; Minproc; Mintec; Photo Coll (1842-present); Rare
     Books on Geology & Mineral Exploration; Science of Geology Coll; Sir
     William Logan Coll
     Subject Interests: Botany, Chem, Climate change, Earth sci,
     Entomology, Forestry, Geol, Geomatics, Hydrology (environment),
     Physics, Renewable energy
     Database Vendor: Agricola, EBSCOhost, Innovative Interfaces, Inc,
     netLibrary, OCLC FirstSearch, OCLC WorldCat, ProQuest,
     ScienceDirect, Scopus
     Partic in Council of Federal Libraries Consortium
     Open Mon-Fri 8:30-4:30
G   NATIONAL AIR PHOTO LIBRARY*, 615 Booth St, Rm 180, K1A 0E9,
     SAN 324-0657. Tel: 613-995-4560. FAX: 613-995-4568. E-mail:
     napl@nrcan.gc.ca. Web Site: nrcan.gc.ca/earth-sciences/home. *Mgr,*
     Florin Savopol; Tel: 613-943-0234
     Founded 1925

S   THE NAVY LEAGUE OF CANADA LIBRARY*, 305 Rideau St, 1st Flr,
     K1N 9E5. SAN 323-4290. Tel: 613-993-5415. FAX: 613-990-8701. E-mail:
     national@navyleague.ca. Web Site: www.navyleague.ca. *Exec Dir,* Douglas
     J Thomas
     Library Holdings: Bk Titles 500; Per Subs 10
     Subject Interests: Maritime affairs, Youth activities

S   OTTAWA CITIZEN LIBRARY*, 1101 Baxter Rd, K2C 3M4. SAN
     319-3438. Tel: 613-596-3744. Toll Free Tel: 800-267-6100, Ext 3744.
     FAX: 613-726-1198. E-mail: library@ottawacitizen.com. Web Site:
     www.ottawacitizen.com. *Chief Librn,* Lisa Tuominen
     Founded 1940

Library Holdings: Bk Vols 300
Wireless access
Partic in Infomart

M   OTTAWA HOSPITAL*, Medical Library (General Campus), 501 Smyth
     Rd, Rm 1404, K1H 8L6. SAN 319-3446. Tel: 613-737-8899, Ext 78530.
     FAX: 613-737-8521. E-mail: libraryservices@ottawahospital.on.ca. Web
     Site: www.ottawahospital.on.ca/library. *Dir,* Margaret Quirie; *Librn,* Risa
     Shorr; Staff 9 (MLS 4, Non-MLS 5)
     Founded 1935
     Library Holdings: CDs 120; DVDs 50; e-journals 3,725; Bk Vols 7,735;
     Per Subs 3,000
     Subject Interests: Allied health, Med, Nursing, Sexual abuse
     Automation Activity & Vendor Info: (Cataloging) Inmagic, Inc.; (OPAC)
     Inmagic, Inc.; (Serials) Inmagic, Inc.
     Database Vendor: EBSCOhost
     Function: ILL available
     Partic in National Network of Libraries of Medicine
     Restriction: Circulates for staff only, Med staff only
     Branches:
     CIVIC CAMPUS LIBRARY, 1053 Carling Ave, D-1, K1Y 4E9, SAN
       321-6837. Tel: 613-798-5555, Ext 14450. FAX: 613-761-5292. E-mail:
       libraryservices@toh.on.ca. *Dir,* Margaret Quirie; *Librn,* Alexandra Davis;
       Librn, Andrew Steinmetz; Staff 7 (MLS 4, Non-MLS 3)
       Founded 1960
       Library Holdings: Bk Titles 3,000; Bk Vols 4,500; Per Subs 20
       Automation Activity & Vendor Info: (Acquisitions) EBSCO Online;
       (OPAC) Inmagic, Inc.
       Database Vendor: EBSCOhost, OVID Technologies, ScienceDirect,
       STAT!Ref (Teton Data Systems), UpToDate, Wiley InterScience
       Restriction: Med staff only

G   OTTAWA OFFICE OF THE AUDITOR GENERAL*, Knowledge Centre
     Library, West Tower, 240 Sparks St, 11th Flr, K1A 0G6. SAN 370-6923.
     Tel: 613-995-3708. Reference Tel: 613-952-0213, Ext 6204. FAX:
     613-952-5131. E-mail: library@oag-bvg.gc.ca. *Dir,* Joanne Hauck
     DeMorest; *Head, Client Serv,* Susan Ross; *Head, Libr Syst, Head, Tech*
     Serv, Deborah Maclean; *Acq, Ser,* Jennifer Prins; Staff 8 (MLS 5,
     Non-MLS 3)
     Founded 1979
     Special Collections: Can Govt
     Subject Interests: Acctg, Auditing
     Automation Activity & Vendor Info: (Acquisitions) SirsiDynix;
     (Cataloging) SirsiDynix; (Circulation) SirsiDynix; (OPAC) SirsiDynix;
     (Serials) SirsiDynix

S   PLANETARY ASSOCIATION FOR CLEAN ENERGY INC*, 100
     Bronson Ave, Ste 1001, K1R 6G8. SAN 328-4158. Tel: 613-236-6265.
     FAX: 613-235-5876. E-mail: paceincnet@gmail.com. Web Site:
     pacenet.homestead.com. *Pres,* Dr Andrew Michrowski; *In Charge,*
     Monique Michaud
     Founded 1979
     Library Holdings: CDs 500; Bk Titles 7,000; Per Subs 100; Videos 500
     Function: Res libr
     Open Mon-Fri 9-5
     Restriction: Non-circulating of rare bks

G   PRIVY COUNCIL OFFICE*, Library Information Centre, 85 Sparks St,
     Rm 1000, K1A 0A3. SAN 322-7197. Tel: 613-957-5125. FAX:
     613-957-5043. E-mail: info@pco-bcp.gc.ca. Web Site: www.pco-bcp.gc.ca.
     Mgr, Michele Sura; Staff 13 (MLS 4, Non-MLS 9)
     Founded 1920
     Library Holdings: Bk Titles 35,000; Per Subs 350
     Subject Interests: Current events, Hist, Polit sci, Pub admin, Pub policy
     Automation Activity & Vendor Info: (Acquisitions) Sydney; (Cataloging)
     Sydney; (Circulation) Sydney; (OPAC) Sydney; (Serials) Sydney
     Publications: Acquisitions List; Bibliography
     Partic in Consortium of Fed Librs
     Open Mon-Fri 9-5

G   PUBLIC SAFETY CANADA*, Library & Information Centre, 340 Laurier
     Ave W, 10A, K1A 0P8. SAN 319-3357. Tel: 613-991-2787. FAX:
     613-941-6171. E-mail: library-biblio@ps-sp.gc.ca. Web Site:
     elibrary.ps-sp.gc.ca/ehome.htm. *Chief Librn,* Position Currently Open;
     Head, Info Serv, F Clemente; Tel: 613-991-2780, E-mail:
     filomena.clemente@ps-sp.gc.ca; *Head, Tech Serv,* P Jackson; Tel:
     613-991-2784, E-mail: patricia.jackson@ps-sp.gc.ca; *Acq/Cat Tech,* Diana
     Kirouac; Tel: 613-991-5677, E-mail: libacqu@ps-sp.gc.ca; Staff 5 (MLS 3,
     Non-MLS 2)
     Founded 1969
     Library Holdings: Bk Titles 25,000; Per Subs 784
     Special Collections: Inmate Publications; National Criminal Justice
     Reference Service (US), microfiche coll; Unpublished Documents Section

(originating in the Correctional Service of Canada, National Parole Board & Ministry Secretariat)
Subject Interests: Corrections, Criminal justice, Critical infrastructure, Emergency preparedness, Nat security, Parole, Police - law enforcement, Terrorism
Publications: Acquisitions List
Partic in Consortium of Fed Librs
Restriction: Open to others by appt

G　PUBLIC SERVICE ALLIANCE OF CANADA LIBRARY*, 233 Gilmour St, 2nd Flr, K2P 0P1. SAN 377-2454. Tel: 613-560-4211. FAX: 613-236-3239. E-mail: laplanl@psac-afpc.com. Web Site: www.psac-afpc.com.
Founded 1967
Library Holdings: Bk Vols 4,000; Per Subs 60
Automation Activity & Vendor Info: (Cataloging) Inmagic, Inc.; (Circulation) Inmagic, Inc.; (Serials) Inmagic, Inc.

GL　PUBLIC SERVICE LABOUR RELATIONS BOARD LIBRARY, Jacob Finkelman Library, West Tower, 6th Flr, 240 Sparks St, K1P 5V2. (Mail add: PO Box 1525, Sta B, K1P 5V2), SAN 319-308X. Tel: 613-990-1800. Toll Free Tel: 866-931-3454. FAX: 613-990-1849. E-mail: library@pslrb-crtfp.gc.ca. Web Site: www.pslrb-crtfp.gc.ca. *Mgr, Info Mgt,* Katherine Laundy; *Libr Asst,* Pierre Robichaud; Staff 2 (MLS 1, Non-MLS 1)
Founded 1967
Library Holdings: Bk Titles 5,000; Bk Vols 20,000; Per Subs 350
Subject Interests: Compensation analysis & res, Labor relations in the public sector
Automation Activity & Vendor Info: (Cataloging) EOS International; (OPAC) EOS International; (Serials) EOS International
Database Vendor: Quicklaw
Publications: Acquisitions List; Periodicals List
Partic in Council of Federal Libraries Consortium

M　ROYAL OTTAWA HEALTH CARE GROUP, Royal Ottawa Mental Health Centre Library, 1145 Carling Ave, K1Z 7K4. SAN 324-0495. Tel: 613-722-6521, Ext 6268. E-mail: library@theroyal.ca. *Mgr, Libr Serv,* Cathy MacLean
Founded 1968
Library Holdings: Bk Titles 3,700; Per Subs 180
Subject Interests: Psychiat, Psychol
Automation Activity & Vendor Info: (Acquisitions) Inmagic, Inc.; (Cataloging) Inmagic, Inc.; (OPAC) Inmagic, Inc.; (Serials) Inmagic, Inc.
Restriction: Staff use only

S　THE ROYAL SOCIETY OF CANADA LIBRARY*, 283 Sparks St, K1R 7X9. SAN 371-8875. Tel: 613-991-6990. FAX: 613-991-6996. E-mail: adminrsc@rsc.ca. Web Site: www.rsc.ca. *Access Serv,* Nancy Lessard
Library Holdings: Bk Titles 600
Publications: Calendar (1954 to date); Index (1882-1982); Presentations (1943 to 2001); Proceedings (1882 to 1999); Transactions (1882 to 2000)
Restriction: Mem only

CR　SAINT PAUL UNIVERSITY LIBRARY*, Jean-Leon Allie Library, 223 Main St, K1S 1C4. SAN 319-3497. Tel: 613-236-1393, Ext 2357. FAX: 613-751-4031. E-mail: biblio@ustpaul.ca. Web Site: www.ustpaul.ca. *Chief Librn,* André Paris; Tel: 613-236-1393, Ext 2220, E-mail: aparis@ustpaul.ca; *Cat Librn,* Alice Constantinou; Tel: 613-236-1393, Ext 2334, E-mail: aconstantinou@ustpaul.ca; *Coll Develop Librn,* Marta Samokishyn; Tel: 613-236-1393, Ext 2313, E-mail: msamokishyn@ustpaul.ca; Staff 12 (MLS 3, Non-MLS 9)
Founded 1937. Enrl 835; Fac 66; Highest Degree: Doctorate
Library Holdings: Bk Titles 426,716; Bk Vols 452,813; Per Subs 793
Special Collections: Rare Books; Roman Catholic liturgy
Subject Interests: Canon law, Medieval studies, Theol
Automation Activity & Vendor Info: (Acquisitions) SIRSI WorkFlows; (Cataloging) SIRSI WorkFlows; (Circulation) SIRSI WorkFlows; (OPAC) SirsiDynix; (Serials) SIRSI WorkFlows
Database Vendor: SirsiDynix
Wireless access
Function: Res libr
Restriction: Borrowing privileges limited to fac & registered students

S　SCOUTS CANADA*, National Office Library, 1345 Baseline Rd, K2C 0A7. SAN 319-2946. Tel: 613-224-5131. FAX: 613-224-3571. E-mail: mailbox@scouts.ca. Web Site: www.scouts.ca. *Chief Exec Officer,* Michael McKay
Founded 1961
Subject Interests: Arts, Scouting
Restriction: Staff use only

G　SERVICE CANADA LIBRARY*, 140 Promenade Du Portage, Phase 4-1, K1A 0J9. SAN 319-3012. Circulation Tel: 819-994-2603. Reference Tel: 819-994-2604. FAX: 819-953-5482. E-mail: ref.library-bibliotheque.response@sdc-dsc.gc.ca. *Chief Librn,* David Shields
Subject Interests: Educ, Employment, Fire safety, Human resource mgt, Income maint, Income security, Indust relations, Info tech, Labor market develop, Labor market info, Labor relations, Literacy, Mgt, Occupational health, Occupational safety, Occupations, Training, Unemployment, Welfare, Women, Women's issues, Workers compensation, Youth
Automation Activity & Vendor Info: (Acquisitions) Innovative Interfaces, Inc; (Cataloging) Innovative Interfaces, Inc; (Circulation) Innovative Interfaces, Inc; (ILL) Innovative Interfaces, Inc; (Serials) Innovative Interfaces, Inc

S　SPORT INFORMATION RESOURCE CENTRE (SIRC)*, 116 Rue Albert St, Ste 400, K1P 5G3. SAN 320-3468. Tel: 613-231-7472. Toll Free Tel: 800-665-6413. FAX: 613-231-3739. E-mail: info@sirc.ca. Web Site: www.sirc.com. *Pres,* Debra Gassewitz; Staff 11 (MLS 11)
Founded 1973
Library Holdings: Bk Vols 36,500; Per Subs 1,200
Subject Interests: Fitness, Leisure, Phys educ, Phys recreation, Recreation, Sports
Database Vendor: Dialog, EBSCOhost, OVID Technologies
Publications: Selected Research Themes; SIRC Thesaurus; Women, Sport & Physical Activity

G　STANDARDS COUNCIL OF CANADA*, Technical Document Centre, 270 Albert St, Ste 200, K1P 6N7. SAN 329-384X. Tel: 613-238-3222. FAX: 613-569-7808. E-mail: info@scc.ca. Web Site: www.scc.ca. *Info Res,* Anne Sharkey; Tel: 613-238-3222, Ext 460, E-mail: asharkey@scc.ca
Special Collections: Canadian, US, Foreign National & International Standards Coll
Subject Interests: Environ mgt, Quality mgt, Standardization, Standards, Tech regulations
Function: Ref serv available

S　STATISTICS CANADA LIBRARY*, 100 Tunney's Pasture Driveway, K1A 0T6. (Mail add: R H Coats Bldg, 2nd Flr, Tunney's Pasture, K1A 0T6), SAN 319-3535. Tel: 613-951-8219. FAX: 613-951-0939. E-mail: biblionet@statcan.gc.ca. Web Site: www.statcan.gc.ca/biblionet/index-eng.htm, www.statcan.gc.ca/biblionet/index-fra.htm. *Asst Dir,* Bernie Gloyn; Tel: 613-951-8218, E-mail: gloyber@statcan.ca; Staff 29 (MLS 12, Non-MLS 17)
Founded 1918
Library Holdings: Bk Vols 180,000; Per Subs 700
Special Collections: Demography (Foreign Census); Statistics (Statistics Canada Coll, Foreign Statistics Coll)
Subject Interests: Demography, Economics, Labor, Math, Methodology, Sociol, Statistical theory
Automation Activity & Vendor Info: (Acquisitions) SirsiDynix; (Cataloging) SirsiDynix; (Circulation) SirsiDynix; (ILL) Relais International; (OPAC) SirsiDynix; (Serials) SirsiDynix
Publications: Finding & Using Statistics: A Key Resource of Information on Canada & Canadians
Partic in Council of Federal Libraries Consortium
Special Services for the Blind - Computer with voice synthesizer for visually impaired persons; ZoomText magnification & reading software
Restriction: Non-circulating to the pub

GL　SUPREME COURT OF CANADA LIBRARY, 301 Wellington St, K1A 0J1. SAN 319-3543. Tel: 613-996-8120. FAX: 613-952-2832. E-mail: library-bibliotheque@scc-csc.ca. Web Site: www.scc-csc.ca/lib-bib/index-eng.asp. *Dir, Libr & Info Mgt,* Rosalie Fox; Tel: 613-996-9971, E-mail: rosalie.fox@scc-csc.ca; *Head, E-Access & Assessment,* Susan Goard; Tel: 613-996-8129, E-mail: susan.goard@scc-csc.ca; *Head, Libr Syst & Cat,* Carole Brisson; Tel: 613-947-0628, E-mail: carole.brisson@scc-csc.ca; *Mgr, Coll Develop,* Adela Romero; Tel: 613-996-0166, E-mail: adela.romero@scc-csc.ca; *Mgr, Legal Res & Client Serv,* Alicia Loo; Tel: 613-996-7996, E-mail: alicia.loo@scc-csc.ca; *Mgr, Libr, Info Mgt Syst & Standards,* Gail Rawlings; Tel: 613-996-8183, E-mail: gail.rawlings@scc-csc.ca; Staff 17 (MLS 10, Non-MLS 7)
Founded 1875
Library Holdings: Bk Titles 73,801; Bk Vols 317,337; Per Subs 2,418
Subject Interests: Civil law, Common law
Automation Activity & Vendor Info: (Acquisitions) SirsiDynix; (Cataloging) SirsiDynix; (Circulation) SirsiDynix; (Course Reserve) SirsiDynix; (ILL) Relais International; (OPAC) SirsiDynix; (Serials) SerialsSolutions
Database Vendor: AZIMUT, ebrary, EBSCOhost, Gale Cengage Learning, HeinOnline, JSTOR, LexisNexis, netLibrary, OCLC FirstSearch, Quicklaw, RefWorks, SerialsSolutions, SirsiDynix, Thomson Carswell, Westlaw, WestlaweCARSWELL, Wilson - Wilson Web
Publications: Law Journal Contents; New Library Titles (Acquisition list)

Partic in Canadian Fed Librs
Restriction: By permission only

S   TRAFFIC INJURY RESEARCH FOUNDATION OF CANADA*, Research
     Library, 171 Nepean St, Ste 200, K2P 0B4. SAN 324-4482. Tel:
     613-238-5235. Toll Free Tel: 877-238-5235. FAX: 613-238-5292. E-mail:
     tirf@tirf.ca. Web Site: www.tirf.ca. *Librn,* Steve Brown; Staff 10 (MLS 10)
     Founded 1968
     Library Holdings: Bk Titles 5,000; Per Subs 100
     Special Collections: Oral History
     Subject Interests: Med, Pharmacological, Statistical aspects, Traffic
     accidents
     Publications: Impact: Drinking & Driving (Newsletter)

S   TRANSPORTATION ASSOCIATION OF CANADA*, Transportation
     Information Service, 2323 St Laurent Blvd, K1G 4J8. SAN 319-3470. Tel:
     613-736-1350. FAX: 613-736-1395. E-mail: tis@tac-atc.ca. Web Site:
     www.tac-atc.ca. *Adminr,* Glenn Cole; Staff 1 (Non-MLS 1)
     Founded 1956
     Library Holdings: Bk Titles 19,500; Per Subs 200
     Special Collections: Great Britain Transportation & Road Research
     Laboratory Reports; National Association of Australia State Road
     Authority Publications; Transportation Association of Canada Annual
     Proceeds; Transportation Research Board Reports
     Subject Interests: Bridges, Roads, Traffic eng, Transportation, Urban
     transportation
     Automation Activity & Vendor Info: (Acquisitions) Inmagic, Inc.;
     (Cataloging) Inmagic, Inc.; (Circulation) Inmagic, Inc.; (ILL) Inmagic, Inc.;
     (OPAC) Inmagic, Inc.; (Serials) Inmagic, Inc.
     Database Vendor: Dialog, OVID Technologies

C   UNIVERSITY OF OTTAWA LIBRARIES*, Library Network, 65
     University, K1N 6N5. SAN 368-136X. Tel: 613-562-5800, 613-562-5883,
     613-562-5934. FAX: 613-562-5195. Web Site: www.biblio.uottawa.ca.
     Chief Librn, Leslie Weir; E-mail: leslie.weir@uottawa.ca; *Chief Financial
     Officer,* Gilbert Caron; Tel: 613-562-5800, Ext 3646, E-mail:
     gilbert.caron@uottawa.ca; *Access Serv & Syst,* Grace Welch; Tel:
     613-562-5228, E-mail: grace.welch@uottawa.ca; *Coll Mgt,* Gisele De
     Villers; Tel: 613-562-5800, Ext 3591, E-mail: gisele.devillers@uottawa.ca;
     Staff 37 (MLS 35, Non-MLS 2)
     Founded 1848. Enrl 32,000; Fac 1,630; Highest Degree: Doctorate
     Library Holdings: Bk Vols 2,573,156; Per Subs 16,494
     Special Collections: Canadian Women's Movement Archives. UN
     Document Depository
     Subject Interests: English, Law, Med, Slavic studies
     Automation Activity & Vendor Info: (Acquisitions) Innovative Interfaces,
     Inc; (Cataloging) Innovative Interfaces, Inc; (Circulation) Innovative
     Interfaces, Inc; (Course Reserve) Innovative Interfaces, Inc; (Media
     Booking) Innovative Interfaces, Inc; (OPAC) Innovative Interfaces, Inc;
     (Serials) Innovative Interfaces, Inc
     Publications: Annual Report
     Partic in Dialog Corp; Utlas; Westlaw
     Special Services for the Blind - Reader equip
     Friends of the Library Group
     Departmental Libraries:
CL   BRIAN DICKSON LAW LIBRARY, Fauteux Hall, 57 Louis Pasteur, K1N
     6N5, SAN 368-1424. Tel: 613-562-5845. Circulation Tel: 613-562-5812.
     FAX: 613-562-5279. Web Site: www.biblio.uottawa.ca/ftx/en/,
     www.biblio.uottawa.ca/ftx/fr/. *Dir,* Margo Jeske; Staff 3 (MLS 3)
     Library Holdings: Bk Vols 181,778; Per Subs 3,009
     Subject Interests: Civil law, Common law
CM   HEALTH SCIENCES, 451 Smyth Rd, K1H 8M5, SAN 368-1459. Tel:
     613-562-5407. Reference Tel: 613-562-5800, Ext 8294. E-mail:
     refrgn@uottawa.ca. Web Site: www.biblio.uottawa.ca/rgn/. *Dir,* Dianne
     Kharouba; E-mail: kharouba@uottawa.ca; Staff 9 (MLS 3, Non-MLS 6)
     Founded 1982
     Subject Interests: Audiology, Med, Nursing, Nutrition, Occupational
     therapy, Physiotherapy, Speech pathology
     Automation Activity & Vendor Info: (ILL) Fretwell-Downing
     Partic in Canadian Research Knowledge Network; Docline; Ontario
     Council of University Libraries
     Open Mon-Thurs 8am-10:30pm, Fri 8-8, Sat & Sun 9-7
     MAP, GOVERNMENT INFORMATION & DATA, Morisset Hall, 65
     University, No 308, K1N 9A5, SAN 373-5591. Tel: 613-562-5211. FAX:
     613-562-5195. Web Site: www.uottawa.ca/library/map. *Dir,* Susan
     Mowers; E-mail: susan.mowers@uottawa.ca; Staff 3 (MLS 3)
     Library Holdings: Bk Vols 866,059; Per Subs 16
     Special Collections: Maps Coll-Canada, Western Europe, US, Amazonia
     & French-Speaking Africa
     Publications: Acquisitions List
     MORISSET LIBRARY (ARTS & SCIENCES), 65 University, K1N 9A5,
     SAN 368-1394. Tel: 613-562-5882. FAX: 613-562-5133. Web Site:
     www.uottawa.ca/library/mrt. *Dir,* Helene Carrier; E-mail:
     helene.carrier@uottawa.ca; Staff 15 (MLS 14, Non-MLS 1)

Library Holdings: AV Mats 8,915; Bk Vols 1,124,267; Per Subs 6,000
Subject Interests: Celtic studies, Hist of med, Slovakian studies, Women
studies
Automation Activity & Vendor Info: (Circulation) Innovative
Interfaces, Inc; (Course Reserve) Innovative Interfaces, Inc; (Media
Booking) Innovative Interfaces, Inc; (OPAC) Innovative Interfaces, Inc;
(Serials) Innovative Interfaces, Inc
MUSIC, Perez Hall, 50 University, K1N 6N5, SAN 373-5613. Tel:
613-562-5209. Web Site: www.uottawa.ca/library/firestone. *Dir,* Debra
Begg; E-mail: dbegg@uottawa.ca; Staff 1 (MLS 1)
Library Holdings: Music Scores 37,062; Bk Vols 5,335; Per Subs 52
Special Collections: Scandinavian Music
Automation Activity & Vendor Info: (Circulation) Innovative
Interfaces, Inc; (Course Reserve) Innovative Interfaces, Inc; (OPAC)
Innovative Interfaces, Inc; (Serials) Innovative Interfaces, Inc

S   VIETNAMESE CANADIAN FEDERATION LIBRARY*, 249 Rochester
     St, K1R 7M9. SAN 375-197X. Tel: 613-230-8282. FAX: 613-230-8281.
     E-mail: vietfederation@yahoo.ca. *Pres,* Dr Vinh Tang; *Exec Dir,* Diep
     Trinh
     Library Holdings: Bk Titles 200

OWEN SOUND

C   GEORGIAN COLLEGE-OWEN SOUND CAMPUS*, Library Commons,
     Main Bldg, 1st Flr, Rm 206, 1450 Eighth St, N4K 5R4. Tel: 519-376-0840,
     Ext 2034. FAX: 519-376-5395. Web Site: library.georgianc.on.ca. *Libr
     Tech,* Sherri Pringle
     Library Holdings: Bk Vols 6,254; Per Subs 40
     Restriction: Open to students, fac & staff

M   GREY BRUCE HEALTH SERVICES, Health Sciences Library, 1800
     Eighth St E, N4K 6M9. (Mail add: PO Box 1800, N4K 6M9), SAN
     323-9047. Tel: 519-376-2121, Ext 2043. FAX: 519-372-3947. E-mail:
     library@gbhs.on.ca. *Librn,* Elyse Pike; Staff 1 (MLS 1)
     Library Holdings: e-books 85; e-journals 2,700; Bk Titles 500; Per Subs
     15
     Database Vendor: Eloquent Systems Inc
     Wireless access

P   OWEN SOUND & NORTH GREY UNION PUBLIC LIBRARY*, 824
     First Ave W, N4K 4K4. SAN 319-3586. Tel: 519-376-6623. FAX:
     519-376-7170. E-mail: info@owensound.library.on.ca. Web Site:
     www.owensound.library.on.ca. *Chief Librn/CEO,* Cindy Weir; Tel:
     519-376-6623, Ext 201, E-mail: cweir@owensound.library.on.ca; *Children
     & Youth Serv Librn,* Nadia Danyluk; E-mail:
     ndanyluk@owensound.library.on.ca; *Info Serv Librn,* Position Currently
     Open; *Admin & Pub Serv Mgr,* Beth Hall; E-mail:
     bhall@owensound.library.on.ca; *Adult & Commun Learning Serv Mgr,* Tim
     Nicholls Harrison; E-mail: tnicholls-harrison@owensound.library.on.ca;
     Tech Serv & Syst Mgr, Chris Carmichael; E-mail:
     carmichc@owensound.library.on.ca; Staff 14.5 (MLS 3, Non-MLS 11.5)
     Founded 1855. Pop 41,069; Circ 301,110
     Jan 2011-Dec 2011 Income (CAN) $1,324,419, Provincial (CAN) $75,980,
     City (CAN) $1,159,104, Federal (CAN) $4,200, Locally Generated Income
     (CAN) $85,135. Mats Exp (CAN) $124,250, Books (CAN) $90,481,
     Per/Ser (Incl. Access Fees) (CAN) $10,638, Micro (CAN) $1,854, AV Mat
     (CAN) $13,892, Electronic Ref Mat (Incl. Access Fees) (CAN) $7,385. Sal
     (CAN) $986,909
     Library Holdings: Audiobooks 2,016; CDs 1,099; DVDs 2,643; e-books
     32,535; Large Print Bks 1,848; Bk Titles 75,564; Bk Vols 81,734; Per Subs
     214
     Special Collections: Local History & Genealogy of Grey & Bruce
     Counties Coll. Oral History
     Subject Interests: Genealogy, Local hist
     Automation Activity & Vendor Info: (Acquisitions) SirsiDynix;
     (Cataloging) SirsiDynix; (Circulation) SirsiDynix; (OPAC) SirsiDynix
     Database Vendor: EBSCOhost, Gale Cengage Learning
     Wireless access
     Function: Adult literacy prog, Bks on CD, Children's prog, Computer
     training, Computers for patron use, Copy machines, e-mail serv, Family
     literacy, Free DVD rentals, Handicapped accessible, Homebound delivery
     serv, ILL available, Large print keyboards, Magnifiers for reading, Music
     CDs, Newsp ref libr, Online cat, Photocopying/Printing, Prog for children
     & young adult, Pub access computers, Ref serv in person, Senior computer
     classes, Story hour, Teen prog, Telephone ref, Video lending libr,
     Wheelchair accessible
     Partic in Ontario Library Consortium; Southern Ontario Libr Serv
     Open Mon-Thurs 9:30-9, Fri & Sat 9:30-5, Sun 2-5

PAKENHAM

P   MISSISSIPPI MILLS LIBRARIES*, Pakenham Library, 128 MacFarlane
     St, K0A 2X0. (Mail add: PO Box 250, K0A 2X0), SAN 319-3594. Tel:
     613-624-5306. Web Site: www.mississippimills.ca,
     www.mississippimills.ca/en/live/library.esp. *Librn,* Mariah Caswell
     Founded 1971. Pop 1,800; Circ 14,000
     Library Holdings: Large Print Bks 30; Bk Titles 11,560; Bk Vols 11,578;
     Per Subs 15; Talking Bks 389; Videos 1,281
     Automation Activity & Vendor Info: (Cataloging) L4U Library Software;
     (Circulation) L4U Library Software; (OPAC) L4U Library Software
     Open Tues & Fri 2-4 & 7pm-9pm, Thurs 1-4 & 7pm-9pm, Sat 1-5

PARIS

P   COUNTY OF BRANT PUBLIC LIBRARY*, Paris Branch, 12 William St,
     N3L 1K7. SAN 324-1637. Tel: 519-442-2433. FAX: 519-442-7582. Web
     Site: www.brant.library.on.ca. *Chief Librn,* Gay Kozak-Selby; *Ch Serv
     Librn,* Zeta Phillipo; *Br Coordr,* Christine Schriver; Staff 6 (MLS 1,
     Non-MLS 5)
     Pop 30,000; Circ 71,000
     Library Holdings: Bk Titles 34,000; Per Subs 70
     Partic in Southern Ontario Libr Serv
     Open Mon-Thurs 10-8, Fri & Sat 10-5
     Friends of the Library Group
     Branches: 4
     BURFORD BRANCH, 24 Park Ave, Burford, N0E 1A0. (Mail add: Box
       267, Burford, N0E 1A0). Tel: 519-449-5371. FAX: 519-449-5371. *Chief
       Librn,* Gay Kozak Selby; *Br Coordr,* Chris Scrivener; *Ch,* Zeta Phillipo
       Library Holdings: Bk Vols 5,000
       Open Tues & Thurs 10-8, Wed 3-8, Fri-Sat 10-2
     GLEN MORRIS BRANCH, 474 E River Rd, Glen Morris, N0B 1W0.
       (Mail add: PO Box 40, Glen Morris, N0B 1W0). Tel: 519-740-2122.
       FAX: 519-740-2122.
       Library Holdings: Bk Vols 8,000
       Open Tues & Sat 10-2, Wed & Thurs 5-8
     ST GEORGE BRANCH, 78 Main St N, St. George, N0E 1N0. (Mail add:
       PO Box 310, St. George, N0E 1N0). Tel: 519-448-1300. FAX:
       519-448-4608.
       Library Holdings: Bk Vols 4,000
       Open Tues-Thurs 10-8, Fri 10-5, Sat 10-4, Sun Noon-4
     SCOTLAND-OAKLAND BRANCH, 281 Oakland Rd, Scotland, N0E 1R0.
       (Mail add: PO Box 40, Scotland, N0E 1R0). Tel: 519-446-0181. FAX:
       519-446-0077.
       Library Holdings: Bk Vols 5,000
       Open Tues & Thurs 3-8, Wed 10-5, Fri 12-5, Sat 10-2

PARRY SOUND

P   PARRY SOUND PUBLIC LIBRARY*, 29 Mary St, P2A 1E3. SAN
     319-3616. Tel: 705-746-9601. FAX: 705-746-9601. E-mail: pspl@vianet.ca.
     Web Site: www.parrysoundlibrary.ca. *Chief Exec Officer,* Richard Sulkers;
     Asst Librn, Selena Martens; Staff 6 (MLS 1, Non-MLS 5)
     Founded 1898. Pop 7,500; Circ 54,708
     Library Holdings: Bk Titles 37,739; Bk Vols 41,029; Per Subs 41
     Automation Activity & Vendor Info: (Acquisitions) SirsiDynix;
     (Cataloging) SirsiDynix; (Circulation) SirsiDynix; (OPAC) SirsiDynix
     Wireless access
     Publications: District of Parry Sound Bibliography; Notes & Sketches on
     the History of Parry Sound
     Open Tues-Fri 10-9, Sat 10-5
     Friends of the Library Group

PEMBROKE

P   PEMBROKE PUBLIC LIBRARY*, 237 Victoria St, K8A 4K5. SAN
     319-3624. Tel: 613-732-8844. FAX: 613-732-1116. E-mail:
     fineprint@pembrokelibrary.ca. Web Site: www.pembrokelibrary.ca. *Chief
     Exec Officer,* Margaret Mau; Tel: 613-732-9178, Ext 3, E-mail:
     mmau@pembrokelibrary.ca; *Children & Teen Librn,* Karthi Rajamani; *Mgr,
     ILL,* Patti Stillman; E-mail: pstillman@pembrokelibrary.ca; *AV, Info Tech,*
     Jennifer Cross; E-mail: jcross@pembrokelibrary.ca; Staff 11 (MLS 1,
     Non-MLS 10)
     Founded 1901. Pop 23,500; Circ 172,036
     Library Holdings: AV Mats 5,954; e-books 8,237; Large Print Bks 2,205;
     Bk Vols 72,000; Per Subs 103; Talking Bks 1,004
     Subject Interests: Genealogy, Local hist
     Automation Activity & Vendor Info: (Cataloging) Follett Software;
     (Circulation) Follett Software; (OPAC) Follett Software
     Wireless access
     Function: AV serv, Homebound delivery serv, ILL available, Newsp ref
     libr, Outside serv via phone, mail, e-mail & web, Photocopying/Printing,
     Prog for children & young adult, Ref serv available, Serves mentally
     handicapped consumers, Summer reading prog, Wheelchair accessible
     Partic in Southern Ontario Libr Serv

Special Services for the Blind - Audio mat; Home delivery serv; Large
print bks; Micro-computer access & training; PC for handicapped
Open Mon-Thurs 10-9, Fri & Sat 10-5:30, Sun 1-4:30
Friends of the Library Group

L   RENFREW COUNTY LAW ASSOCIATION*, RCLA Law Library, 297
     Pembroke St E, K8A 3K2. SAN 328-0780. Tel: 613-732-4880. FAX:
     613-732-2262. E-mail: rcla@bellnet.ca. Web Site: www.rcla.on.ca. *Librn,*
     Laurie Stoddard
     Library Holdings: Bk Titles 5,600
     Open Mon-Fri 9-4

PENETANGUISHENE

P   PENETANGUISHENE PUBLIC LIBRARY, 24 Simcoe St, L9M 1R6.
     SAN 319-3640. Tel: 705-549-7164. FAX: 705-549-3932. Web Site:
     www.penetanguishene.library.on.ca. *Chief Exec Officer,* Cynthia Cote;
     E-mail: ccote@penetanguishene.library.on.ca; Staff 6 (Non-MLS 6)
     Pop 9,111; Circ 113,014
     Library Holdings: e-books 4,400; Bk Vols 49,000; Per Subs 42
     Automation Activity & Vendor Info: (Acquisitions) SirsiDynix;
     (Cataloging) SirsiDynix; (Circulation) SirsiDynix; (Course Reserve)
     SirsiDynix; (ILL) SirsiDynix; (Media Booking) SirsiDynix; (OPAC)
     SirsiDynix; (Serials) SirsiDynix
     Database Vendor: Canadian Reference Centre, CEDROM-SNi, EBSCO
     Auto Repair Reference, EBSCOhost, Gale Cengage Learning, netLibrary,
     Overdrive, Inc, World Book Online
     Wireless access
     Partic in County of Simcoe Libr Coop; Southern Ontario Libr Serv
     Open Mon-Fri 10-8, Sat 10-5
     Friends of the Library Group

PERTH

P   PERTH & DISTRICT UNION PUBLIC LIBRARY*, Perth Union Library,
     30 Herriott St, K7H 1T2. SAN 319-3659. Tel: 613-267-1224. FAX:
     613-267-7899. E-mail: info@perthunionlibrary.ca. Web Site:
     www.perthunionlibrary.ca/. *Chief Exec Officer,* Elizabeth Goldman; E-mail:
     egoldman@perthunionlibrary.ca; Staff 2 (Non-MLS 2)
     Founded 1832. Pop 18,600; Circ 142,016
     Library Holdings: Bk Vols 50,000; Per Subs 70
     Automation Activity & Vendor Info: (Cataloging) Brodart; (Circulation)
     Follett Software
     Wireless access
     Partic in Southern Ontario Libr Serv
     Open Mon 12-5, Tues 10-8, Wed & Thurs 12-8, Fri 10-5, Sat 10-3, Sun
     12-3
     Friends of the Library Group

PETAWAWA

P   PETAWAWA PUBLIC LIBRARY*, 16 Civic Centre Rd, K8H 3H5. SAN
     319-3667. Tel: 613-687-2227. FAX: 613-687-2527. E-mail:
     info@petawawapubliclibrary.ca. Web Site: www.petawawapubliclibrary.ca.
     Chief Exec Officer, Janet Coulas; E-mail: jcoulas@bellnet.ca; *Dep Chief
     Exec Officer, Mgr, Young Adult & Children's Serv,* Kelly Thompson;
     E-mail: kthompson@bellnet.ca; Staff 4 (MLS 1, Non-MLS 3)
     Founded 1975. Pop 15,998; Circ 108,365
     Library Holdings: Bk Titles 45,657; Bk Vols 45,826
     Special Collections: French Coll; Heritage Coll, large print; Military &
     Family Resource Coll
     Wireless access
     Partic in Southern Ontario Libr Serv
     Open Mon-Thurs 10-8, Fri 10-6, Sat 10-3
     Friends of the Library Group

PETERBOROUGH

G   ONTARIO MINISTRY OF NATURAL RESOURCES*, Library Services,
     300 Water St, K9J 8M5. (Mail add: PO Box 7000, K9J 8M5), SAN
     323-4886. Tel: 705-755-1888. Administration Tel: 705-755-1879. FAX:
     705-755-1882. E-mail: mnr.library@ontario.ca. *Librn,* Heath Finley;
     E-mail: heath.finley@ontario.ca; Staff 3 (MLS 2, Non-MLS 1)
     Founded 1942
     Apr 2009-Mar 2010 Income (CAN) $90,000. Mats Exp $90,000, Books
     (CAN) $10,000, Per/Ser (Incl. Access Fees) (CAN) $55,000, Electronic
     Ref Mat (Incl. Access Fees) (CAN) $25,000
     Library Holdings: AV Mats 500; CDs 247; e-books 50; e-journals 50; Bk
     Vols 100,000; Per Subs 90; Talking Bks 25; Videos 500
     Special Collections: Can & Prov
     Automation Activity & Vendor Info: (Cataloging) Inmagic, Inc.;
     (Circulation) Inmagic, Inc.; (OPAC) Inmagic, Inc.; (Serials) Inmagic, Inc.
     Database Vendor: EBSCOhost, OCLC FirstSearch, OCLC WorldCat,
     OVID Technologies
     Partic in Ont Govt Libr Coun
     Open Mon-Fri 9-4

P PETERBOROUGH PUBLIC LIBRARY*, 345 Aylmer St N, K9H 3V7.
   SAN 368-1548. Tel: 705-745-5382. FAX: 705-745-8958. E-mail:
   comments@peterborough.ca. Web Site: www.peterborough.library.on.ca.
   Head Librn, Betty-Kay Murray; Tel: 705-745-5382, Ext 2370, E-mail:
   bmurray@peterborough.ca; *Libr Mgr,* Becky Rogers; *Access Serv,* M
   Giuliani; *Adult Serv,* K Bisschop; *Coll Develop,* Laura Gardner
   Founded 1910. Pop 71,446; Circ 655,471
   Library Holdings: e-journals 32,076; Bk Vols 139,295; Per Subs 295
   Special Collections: Local History (Peterborough Coll)
   Database Vendor: SirsiDynix
   Wireless access
   Partic in Southern Ontario Libr Serv
   Open Mon-Thurs (Summer) 10:30-7; Mon-Thurs (Winter) 10-8, Fri & Sat
   10-5, Sun 2-5
   Friends of the Library Group
   Branches: 1
   DELAFOSSE, 729 Park St S, K9J 3T3, SAN 368-1572. Tel:
      705-745-8653.
      Open Tues & Thurs 2:30-7:30, Sat 10-3
      Friends of the Library Group

J SIR SANDFORD FLEMING COLLEGE OF APPLIED ARTS &
   TECHNOLOGY LIBRARY*, 599 Brealey Dr, K9J 7B1. SAN 368-1602.
   Tel: 705-749-5530. FAX: 705-749-5542. Web Site: www.flemingc.on.ca.
   Mgr, Libr & Tech Support Serv, Mark Gray; *Per,* D Sloan; Staff 1 (MLS 1)
   Founded 1968. Enrl 5,000; Fac 300
   Library Holdings: Electronic Media & Resources 1,254; Bk Titles 66,796;
   Per Subs 270
   Subject Interests: Art, Bus, Commun health, Commun serv, Computer sci,
   Computer tech, Heritage, Hospitality, Justice, Law, Nursing, Recreation,
   Tourism
   Wireless access
   Open Mon-Thurs 8-8, Fri 8-4:30, Sat & Sun 12-4

C TRENT UNIVERSITY*, Thomas J Bata Library, 1600 West Bank Dr, K9J
   7B8. SAN 368-1661. Tel: 705-748-1011, Ext 1324. FAX: 705-748-1126.
   Web Site: www.trentu.ca/admin/library/. *Univ Librn,* Robert Clarke; E-mail:
   robertclarke@trentu.ca; *Circ Librn,* Ken Field; *Info Serv Librn,* Ellen
   Olsen-Lynch; *Info Serv Librn,* Jean Luyben; *Govt Doc, Maps Librn,*
   Barbara Znamirowski; Tel: 705-748-1011, Ext 1278; *Syst Librn,* Gord
   Ripley; *Tech Serv Librn,* Marisia Scigliano; Tel: 705-748-1011, Ext 1390;
   ILL, Sharon Bosnell; Tel: 705-748-1011, Ext 5196
   Founded 1963. Enrl 6,410; Fac 246; Highest Degree: Doctorate
   Library Holdings: Electronic Media & Resources 6,000; Bk Vols 525,000;
   Per Subs 2,000
   Special Collections: Canadian Literature (Shell Coll); Canadiana; Native
   Studies; Trent Coll (Trent Valley Region)
   Partic in Ontario Univs Libr Coop Syst
   Departmental Libraries:
   ACCESS SERVICES DEPARTMENT, Thomas J Bata Library, 1600 W
      Bank Dr, K9J 7B8. Tel: 705-748-1011, Ext 1565. *Librn,* Ken Field;
      E-mail: kfield@trentu.ca; Staff 5 (MLS 1, Non-MLS 4)
      Founded 1967. Enrl 8,000; Fac 300; Highest Degree: Doctorate
      Library Holdings: Bk Titles 600,000; Per Subs 3,500
      Automation Activity & Vendor Info: (Acquisitions) SirsiDynix;
      (Cataloging) SirsiDynix; (Circulation) SirsiDynix; (Course Reserve)
      SirsiDynix; (OPAC) SirsiDynix; (Serials) SirsiDynix
      Open Mon-Fri 8am-11pm, Sat 11-8, Sun 1-11
      Friends of the Library Group
   ARCHIVES, Thomas J Bata Library, 1st Flr, 1600 W Bank Dr, K9J 7B8.
      Tel: 705-748-1011, Ext 7413. E-mail: archives@trentu.ca. Web Site:
      www.trentu.ca/library/archives. *Archivist,* Jodi Aoki
      Open Mon-Fri 9-4
   MEDIA SERVICES/INFORMATION TECHNOLOGY, Thomas J Bata
      Library, No 105, 1600 W Bank Dr, K9J 7B8. Tel: 705-748-1011, Ext
      7458. *Dir,* William Hodgson
      Open Mon-Fri 8:30-4:30
   OSHAWA CAMPUS LIBRARY, 55 Thornton Rd S, Oshawa, L1J 5Y1.
      Tel: 905-435-5102, Ext 5061. E-mail: oshawalibrary@trentu.ca. *Campus
      Librn,* Ken Field; Tel: 905-435-5102, Ext 5065, E-mail: kfield@trentu.ca;
      Libr Serv Coordr, John Wales; Tel: 905-435-5102 Ext 5062, E-mail:
      jwales@trentu.ca; Staff 4 (MLS 1, Non-MLS 3)
      Founded 2010. Enrl 1,000; Fac 30; Highest Degree: Master

PICKERING

P PICKERING PUBLIC LIBRARY*, Administrative Office, One The
   Esplanade, L1V 6K7. (Mail add: PO Box 368, L1V 2R6), SAN 368-1726.
   Tel: 905-831-6265. FAX: 905-831-6927. E-mail: help@picnet.org. Web
   Site: www.picnet.org. *Chief Exec Officer,* Cathy Grant; Tel: 905-831-6265,
   Ext 6236, E-mail: cathyg@picnet.org; Staff 53 (MLS 12, Non-MLS 41)
   Founded 1967. Pop 94,000; Circ 1,193,956
   Library Holdings: Bk Vols 150,000
   Subject Interests: Local hist

   Automation Activity & Vendor Info: (Acquisitions) SirsiDynix;
   (Cataloging) SirsiDynix; (Circulation) SirsiDynix; (Course Reserve)
   SirsiDynix; (ILL) SirsiDynix; (Media Booking) SirsiDynix; (OPAC)
   SirsiDynix; (Serials) SirsiDynix
   Wireless access
   Partic in Southern Ontario Libr Serv
   Open Mon-Fri 9:30-9, Sat 9-5, Sun 1-5
   Branches: 4
   CLAREMONT BRANCH, 4941 Old Brock Rd, Claremont, L1Y 1B1,
      SAN 368-1815. Tel: 905-649-3341. FAX: 905-649-2065. *Br Mgr,*
      Maureen McVarish
      Library Holdings: Bk Vols 9,400
      Open Tues 3-8, Thurs 9:30-5:30, Sat 1-5
      Friends of the Library Group
   GREENWOOD, 3540 Westney Rd, Greenwood, L0H 1H0, SAN 368-1785.
      Tel: 905-683-8844. *Br Mgr,* Maureen McVarish
      Library Holdings: Bk Vols 7,300
      Open Tues & Wed 9:30-1, Thurs 4-8, Sat 1-5
   PETTICOAT CREEK, 470 Kingston Rd, L1V 1A4, SAN 368-184X. Tel:
      905-420-2254. FAX: 905-420-2860. *Br Mgr,* Maureen McVarish
      Library Holdings: Bk Vols 53,000
      Open Mon-Fri 9:30-9, Sat 9-5
   WHITEVALE, 475 Whitevale Rd, L1X 2R5, SAN 368-1874. Tel:
      905-294-0967. *Br Mgr,* Maureen McVarish
      Library Holdings: Bk Vols 2,300
      Open Mon & Wed 3-7, Sat 9-12

M PURDUE PHARMA LIBRARY*, 575 Granite Ct, L1W 3W8. SAN
   371-6961. Tel: 905-420-4991. FAX: 905-420-5036. Web Site:
   www.purdue.ca. *Mgr, Info & Libr Serv,* Karen Taylor; Staff 2 (MLS 1,
   Non-MLS 1)
   Founded 1990
   Library Holdings: Per Subs 100
   Special Collections: Pharmaceutical Coll
   Subject Interests: Med

PICTON

P COUNTY OF PRINCE EDWARD LIBRARIES*, Picton Branch, 208 Main
   St, K0K 2T0. (Mail add: PO Box 260, K0K 2T0), SAN 319-3683. Tel:
   613-476-5962. FAX: 613-476-3325. E-mail: crenaud@peclibrary.org. Web
   Site: www.peclibrary.org. *Dir,* Barbara Sweet; E-mail:
   bsweet@peclibrary.org; *Ch,* Marie Dawson; *ILL,* Dianne Cranshaw
   Pop 23,000
   Library Holdings: Bk Vols 90,000; Per Subs 80
   Subject Interests: Local hist
   Partic in Southern Ontario Libr Serv
   Open Mon 12-4, Tues 10-7, Wed-Fri 10-5, Sat 10-4
   Friends of the Library Group

PLANTAGENET

P PLANTAGENET VILLAGE LIBRARY SYSTEM*, Plantagenet Public
   Library, 550 Albert St, K0B 1L0. (Mail add: PO Box 280, K0B 1L0),
   SAN 319-3691. Tel: 613-673-2051. FAX: 613-673-2051. E-mail:
   biblioplant@yahoo.com. Web Site: www.bibap.org. *Dir,* Dominique
   Lacelle; Tel: 613-679-4928, E-mail: biblio_dg@yahoo.ca; *Librn,* Lyne
   Brazeau
   Pop 2,650; Circ 7,483
   Library Holdings: Bk Vols 10,430
   Wireless access
   Open Wed & Fri 1:30-5:30 & 6:30-8:30
   Branches: 4
   ALFRED BRANCH, 330 Saint-Philippe St, Alfred, K0B 1A0. (Mail add:
      PO Box 329, Alfred, K0B 1A0), SAN 321-1681. Tel: 613-679-2663.
      FAX: 613-679-2663. *Librn,* Ginette Peladeau
      Circ 16,713
      Library Holdings: Bk Vols 11,172
      Open Mon 4-7, Tues & Thurs 1-8, Wed 10-12 & 2-5, Sat 10-2
      Friends of the Library Group
   CURRAN, 791 Mill St, Curran, K0B 1C0, SAN 324-7074. Tel:
      613-673-2072. FAX: 613-673-2072. *Librn,* Carol Mainville
      Circ 10,907
      Library Holdings: Bk Vols 11,324
      Open Tues & Thurs 1:30-4:30 & 6:30-8:30, Sat 10-1
   LEFAIVRE BRANCH, 1963 Hotel de Ville St, Lefaivre, K0B 1J0, SAN
      377-6867. Tel: 613-679-4928. FAX: 613-679-4928. E-mail:
      bibliolefaivre@yahoo.ca. *Librn,* Lyne Brazeau
      Circ 6,905
      Library Holdings: Bk Vols 10,672
      Open Tues 1-4:30 & 6pm-8pm, Thurs 11-12, 1-4:30 & 6pm-8pm
      Friends of the Library Group

WENDOVER, 3104 du Quai Ave, Wendover, K0A 3K0, SAN 324-7082.
Tel: 613-673-2923. FAX: 613-673-2923. E-mail: bibliowend@yahoo.ca.
Librn, Anne St-Pierre
Circ 4,412
Library Holdings: Bk Vols 7,988
Open Tues 6pm-8pm, Thurs 11:30-4:30 & 6-8, Sat 10-1

PORT CARLING

P   MUSKOKA LAKES LIBRARY BOARD*, The Norma Miller Alloway
Muskoka Lakes Library, 69 Joseph St, P0B 1J0. (Mail add: PO Box 189,
P0B 1J0), SAN 377-8118. Tel: 705-765-5650. FAX: 705-765-0422. E-mail:
pclib@muskoka.com. Web Site: www.muskoka.com/library. *Chief
Librn/CEO,* Sheila Durand
Library Holdings: CDs 229; DVDs 307; e-books 1,321; Large Print Bks
362; Music Scores 54; Bk Vols 50,000; Per Subs 33; Talking Bks 443;
Videos 573
Automation Activity & Vendor Info: (Cataloging) SirsiDynix;
(Circulation) SirsiDynix; (OPAC) SirsiDynix; (Serials) SirsiDynix
Database Vendor: SirsiDynix
Wireless access
Open Mon-Wed & Fri 10-5, Thurs 10-7, Sat 10-3
Friends of the Library Group
Branches: 1
BALA PUBLIC, Community Centre, 1008 Maple St, Bala, P0C 1A0.
(Mail add: PO Box 762, Bala, P0C 1A0), SAN 326-7318. Tel:
705-762-1086. E-mail: balib@muskoka.com. *Librn,* Mari Carson
Founded 1979. Pop 2,000; Circ 5,000
Special Collections: Bala & Muskoka Coll
Open Mon 4-7, Wed 1-4, Thurs 10-1, Sat 10-2

PORT COLBORNE

P   PORT COLBORNE PUBLIC LIBRARY*, 310 King St, L3K 4H1. SAN
368-1904. Tel: 905-834-6512. FAX: 905-835-5775. E-mail:
library@portcolborne.ca. Web Site: www.portcolbornelibrary.org. *Dir, Libr
Serv,* Jennifer Parry; E-mail: jenniferparry@portcolborne.ca
Founded 1886. Pop 18,000; Circ 130,000
Library Holdings: Bk Vols 65,000; Per Subs 100
Automation Activity & Vendor Info: (Acquisitions) SirsiDynix;
(Cataloging) SirsiDynix; (Circulation) SirsiDynix; (Course Reserve)
SirsiDynix; (OPAC) SirsiDynix; (Serials) SirsiDynix
Database Vendor: SirsiDynix
Wireless access
Open Mon, Tues & Thurs (Winter) 10-8, Wed, Fri & Sat 9-5; Mon, Tues
& Thurs (Summer) 10-8, Wed & Fri 9-5, Sat 9-1
Friends of the Library Group

PORT ELGIN

P   BRUCE COUNTY PUBLIC LIBRARY*, 1243 MacKenzie Rd, N0H 2C6.
SAN 368-1963. Tel: 519-832-6935. FAX: 519-832-9000. E-mail:
bruce2@brucecounty.on.ca. Web Site: library.brucecounty.on.ca. *Dir,* Ken
MacLeod; Staff 2 (MLS 2)
Founded 1967. Pop 63,000; Circ 460,410
Library Holdings: Bk Titles 110,000; Bk Vols 150,000; Per Subs 140
Special Collections: Local History
Branches: 18
CARGILL BRANCH, Major St, Cargill, N0G 1J0. (Mail add: PO Box 98,
Cargill, N0G 1J0), SAN 368-2021. Tel: 519-366-9990. FAX:
519-366-9990. E-mail: calib@brucecounty.on.ca. *Supvr,* Tracey Knapp
Open Tues 11-5, Thurs 1-7, Sat 9-12
CHESLEY BRANCH, 72 Second Ave SE, Chesley, N0G 1L0. (Mail add:
PO Box 220, Chesley, N0G 1L0), SAN 368-2056. Tel: 519-363-2239.
FAX: 519-363-0726. E-mail: chlib@brucecounty.on.ca. *Br Supvr,* Ellen
Kerr
Open Open Mon & Wed 10-5, Tues 10-6, Thurs 10-7, Fri 10-3, Sat 10-2
Friends of the Library Group
HEPWORTH BRANCH, 465 Bruce St, Hepworth, N0H 1P0. (Mail add:
PO Box 83, Hepworth, N0H 1P0), SAN 368-2145. Tel: 519-935-2030.
E-mail: helib@brucecounty.on.ca. *Librn,* Barbara Wong
Open Mon-Fri 12-3
KINCARDINE BRANCH, 727 Queen St, Kincardine, N2Z 1Z9, SAN
368-217X. Tel: 519-396-3289. FAX: 519-396-3289. E-mail:
kilib@brucecounty.on.ca. *Librn,* Charmaine Jenkins
Open Tues & Wed 10-8, Thurs & Fri 10-5, Sat 10-3, Sun 1-4
LION'S HEAD BRANCH, Main St, Lion's Head, N0H 1W0. (Mail add:
PO Box 965, Lion's Head, N0H 1W0), SAN 368-220X. Tel:
519-793-3844. FAX: 519-793-3844. E-mail: lhlib@brucecounty.on.ca. *Br
Supvr,* Clare Drury
Open Mon 12-5, Wed & Fri 10-5, Sat 10-1
Friends of the Library Group
LUCKNOW BRANCH, 526 Campbell St, Lucknow, N0G 2H0. (Mail add:
PO Box 130, Lucknow, N0G 2H0), SAN 368-2234. Tel: 519-528-3011.
E-mail: lulib@brucecounty.on.ca. *Br Supvr,* Grant Robertson
Open Tues & Thurs 3-8, Wed 1-8, Fri 9-5, Sat 10-1

MILDMAY-CARRICK BRANCH, 51 Elora St, Mildmay, N0G 2J0. (Mail
add: PO Box 87, Mildmay, N0G 2J0), SAN 368-2269. Tel:
519-367-2814. FAX: 519-367-2814. E-mail: mclib@brucecounty.on.ca.
Web Site: www.brucecap.org. *Br Supvr,* Pat Markle
Founded 1929. Pop 1,200
Function: Handicapped accessible, Homebound delivery serv, ILL
available, Photocopying/Printing, Summer reading prog, Video lending
libr, Wheelchair accessible
Open Tues 12-7, Thurs 1-8, Fri 9:30-1:30, Sat 10-12
PAISLEY BRANCH, 274 Queen St N, Paisley, N0G 2N0. (Mail add: PO
Box 219, Paisley, N0G 2N0), SAN 368-2293. Tel: 519-353-7225. FAX:
519-353-7225. E-mail: palib@brucecounty.on.ca. *Br Supvr,* Ellen Kerr
Open Mon & Wed 12-6, Fri 10-4, Sat 9-12
Friends of the Library Group
PORT ELGIN BRANCH, 708 Goderich St, N0H 2C0. (Mail add: PO Box
609, N0H 2C0), SAN 368-2323. Tel: 519-832-2201. E-mail:
pelib@brucecounty.on.ca. *Librn,* Elizabeth Carter
Open Mon & Wed 10-7, Tues 10-6, Thurs & Fri 10-5, Sat 10-3, Sun
11-2
Friends of the Library Group
RIPLEY BRANCH, 23 Jessie St, Ripley, N0G 2R0. (Mail add: PO Box
207, Ripley, N0G 2R0), SAN 368-2358. Tel: 519-395-5919. E-mail:
rilib@brucecounty.on.ca. *Br Supvr,* Grant Robertson
Open Tues 3-8, Wed 2-5, Fri 1-5, Sat 10-1
SAUBLE BEACH, 27 Community Centre Dr, RR 1, Box 11, Sauble
Beach, N0H 2G0, SAN 368-2382. Tel: 519-422-1283. FAX:
519-422-1283. E-mail: salib@brucecounty.on.ca. *Br Mgr,* Bonnie
McGann
Open Mon, Wed & Thurs 12-6, Fri 12-5, Sat 11-2
Friends of the Library Group
SOUTHAMPTON BRANCH, 215 High St, Southampton, N0H 2L0. (Mail
add: PO Box 130, Southampton, N0H 2L0), SAN 368-2412. Tel:
519-797-3586. FAX: 519-797-3586. E-mail: solib@brucecounty.on.ca. *Br
Supvr,* Elizabeth Carter
Open Mon 10-6, Tues & Thurs 10-7, Fri 10-5, Sat 10-2
Friends of the Library Group
TARA BRANCH, 67 Yonge St N, Tara, N0H 2N0. (Mail add: PO Box 59,
Tara, N0H 2N0), SAN 368-2447. Tel: 519-934-2626. E-mail:
talib@brucecounty.on.ca. *Supvr,* Ellen Kerr
Open Tues & Fri 12-6, Wed 12-5, Thurs 10-2, Sat 10-1
Friends of the Library Group
TEESWATER BRANCH, Two Clinton St S, Teeswater, N0G 2S0. (Mail
add: PO Box 430, Teeswater, N0G 2S0), SAN 368-2471. Tel:
519-392-6801. FAX: 519-392-6801. E-mail: telib@brucecounty.on.ca. *Br
Coordr,* Lynda Benninger
Open Tues, Thurs & Fri 1-5, Wed 1-7, Sat 10-1
TIVERTON BRANCH, 56 King St, Tiverton, N0G 2T0. (Mail add: PO
Box 174, Tiverton, N0G 2T0), SAN 368-2501. Tel: 519-368-5655.
E-mail: tilib@brucecounty.on.ca. *Br Supvr,* Charmaine Jenkins
Open Tues & Thurs 1-7, Fri & Sat 10-2
TOBERMORY BRANCH, 22 Bay St S, Tobermory, N0H 2R0. (Mail add:
PO Box 159, Tobermory, N0H 2R0), SAN 368-2536. Tel: 519-596-2446.
E-mail: tolib@brucecounty.on.ca. *Br Supvr,* Claire Drury
Open Tues, Wed & Fri 11-4, Sat 10-1
Friends of the Library Group
WALKERTON BRANCH, 253 Durham St, Walkerton, N0G 2V0. (Mail
add: PO Box 250, Walkerton, N0G 2V0), SAN 368-2560. Tel:
519-881-3240. FAX: 519-881-3240. E-mail: walib@brucecounty.on.ca.
Br Mgr, Tracey Knapp
Open Tues 1-8, Wed & Fri 10-5, Thurs 12-8, Sat 10-2
WIARTON BRANCH, 578 Brown St, Wiarton, N0H 2T0. (Mail add: PO
Box 250, Wiarton, N0H 2T0), SAN 368-2595. Tel: 519-534-2602. FAX:
519-534-2602. E-mail: wilib@brucecounty.on.ca. *Br Supvr,* Clare Drury
Open Tues & Thurs 10-7, Wed & Fri 10-6, Sat 10-2, Sun 1-4
Friends of the Library Group
Bookmobiles: 1

PORT HOPE

P   PORT HOPE PUBLIC LIBRARY*, 31 Queen St, L1A 2Y8. SAN
319-3713. Tel: 905-885-4712. FAX: 905-885-4181. E-mail:
library@porthope.ca. Web Site: www.phpl.ca. *Chief Librn,* Barbara
Stephenson
Founded 1912. Pop 16,500; Circ 120,000
Library Holdings: Bk Titles 30,000; Per Subs 35
Special Collections: Historical Newspaper Name Index, 1980; Port Hope
Evening Guide 1832-2013
Subject Interests: Local hist
Automation Activity & Vendor Info: (Acquisitions) SirsiDynix;
(Cataloging) SirsiDynix; (Circulation) SirsiDynix; (Course Reserve)
SirsiDynix; (ILL) Fretwell-Downing; (OPAC) SirsiDynix; (Serials)
SirsiDynix
Wireless access
Open Mon-Thurs 10-8, Fri 10-6, Sat 10-5

PORT MCNICOLL

P TAY TOWNSHIP PUBLIC LIBRARY*, Port McNicoll Branch, 715 Fourth Ave, L0K 1R0. (Mail add: PO Box 490, L0K 1R0). Tel: 705-534-3511. FAX: 705-534-3511. E-mail: pmlibrary@tay.ca. Web Site: www.tay.library.on.ca. *Head, Libr Serv,* Heather Walker; E-mail: hwalker@tay.ca; *Br Librn,* Heather Delong
Library Holdings: Bk Vols 48,311
Automation Activity & Vendor Info: (Acquisitions) Horizon; (Cataloging) Horizon; (Circulation) Horizon; (ILL) Horizon; (OPAC) Horizon; (Serials) Horizon
Wireless access
Function: Bks on CD, CD-ROM, Fax serv, Homebound delivery serv, ILL available, Online cat, Photocopying/Printing, Pub access computers, Video lending libr
Open Mon 6pm-9pm, Tues, Thurs & Fri 10-12 & 1-5, Wed 10-12, 1-5 & 6-9, Sat 9am-1pm
Branches: 2
VICTORIA HARBOUR BRANCH, 145 Albert St, Victoria Harbour, L0K 2A0. (Mail add: PO Box 158, Victoria Harbour, L0K 2A0). Tel: 705-534-3581. FAX: 705-534-3581. E-mail: vhlibrary@tay.ca. *Br Librn,* Janet McFadden
Function: Pub access computers
Open Tues, Thurs & Fri 10-12 & 1-5, Wed 10-12, 1-5 & 6pm-9pm, Sat 9am-1pm
WAUBAUSHENE BRANCH, 17 Thiffault St, Waubaushene, L0K 2C0. (Mail add: PO Box 280, Waubaushene, L0K 2C0). Tel: 705-538-1122. FAX: 705-538-1122. E-mail: wblibrary@tay.ca. *Br Librn,* Janice Waddell
Function: Pub access computers
Open Tues 1-5 & 6pm-9pm, Wed 6pm-9pm, Thurs & Fri 1-5, Sat 9-1

PORT PERRY

P SCUGOG MEMORIAL PUBLIC LIBRARY*, 231 Water St, L9L 1A8. (Mail add: PO Box 1049, L9L 1A8), SAN 319-3721. Tel: 905-985-7686. E-mail: scugogref@powergate.ca. Web Site: www.scugoglibrary.ca. *Chief Librn,* Amy Caughlin; Staff 6 (MLS 2, Non-MLS 4)
Founded 1856. Pop 22,500; Circ 231,175
Library Holdings: Bk Titles 48,000; Bk Vols 48,541; Per Subs 80
Subject Interests: Local hist
Automation Activity & Vendor Info: (Acquisitions) VTLS, Inc; (Cataloging) VTLS, Inc; (Circulation) VTLS, Inc; (OPAC) VTLS, Inc; (Serials) VTLS, Inc
Database Vendor: EBSCOhost, Gale Cengage Learning
Wireless access
Function: Art exhibits, Handicapped accessible, ILL available, Music CDs, Photocopying/Printing, Prog for adults, Prog for children & young adult, Ref serv available, Spoken cassettes & CDs, Spoken cassettes & DVDs, Summer reading prog, Telephone ref, VHS videos, Wheelchair accessible
Partic in Southern Ontario Libr Serv
Open Mon, Wed & Fri 10-6, Tues & Thurs 10-9, Sat 10-5, Sun 1-5

POWASSAN

P POWASSAN & DISTRICT UNION PUBLIC LIBRARY*, 324 Clark St, P0H 1Z0. (Mail add: Box 160, P0H 1Z0), SAN 319-373X. Tel: 705-724-3618. FAX: 705-724-5525. E-mail: powlib@onlink.net. Web Site: powlib.www2.onlink.net. *Chief Exec Officer,* Marie Rosset; E-mail: mrosset@ontera.net; Staff 1.5 (MLS 0.5, Non-MLS 1)
Pop 7,500; Circ 46,000
Library Holdings: Large Print Bks 549; Bk Titles 20,000; Bk Vols 30,505; Per Subs 40; Talking Bks 347
Automation Activity & Vendor Info: (Cataloging) SirsiDynix; (Circulation) SirsiDynix
Wireless access
Mem of Ontario Library Service North
Special Services for the Blind - Bks on cassette; Large print bks
Open Mon, Tues & Thurs (Sept-June) 10:30-8, Fri 10:30-6, Sat 10:30-3:30; Mon, Tues & Thurs (July-Aug) 11-7, Fri 11-6, Sat 11-3:30
Friends of the Library Group

PRESCOTT

P PRESCOTT PUBLIC LIBRARY*, 360 Dibble St W, K0E 1T0. (Mail add: PO Box 430, K0E 1T0), SAN 319-3748. Tel: 613-925-4340. FAX: 613-925-0100, 613-925-4381. E-mail: library@prescott.ca. Web Site: www.prescott.ca/library/index.asp. *Chief Exec Officer, Chief Librn,* Jane McGuire; E-mail: jmcguire@prescott.ca; *Asst Librn,* Susen Kaylo; Staff 4 (Non-MLS 4)
Founded 1895. Pop 4,189; Circ 23,744
Library Holdings: DVDs 701; Large Print Bks 631; Bk Titles 31,271; Per Subs 15; Talking Bks 191; Videos 47
Automation Activity & Vendor Info: (Cataloging) Duncan Systems Specialists Inc; (Circulation) Duncan Systems Specialists Inc; (ILL) Fretwell-Downing; (OPAC) Duncan Systems Specialists Inc

Database Vendor: Duncan Systems Specialists Inc, EBSCOhost, Gale Cengage Learning, ImagiNET Resources Corp
Wireless access
Function: Adult literacy prog, AV serv, Distance learning, Games & aids for the handicapped, Govt ref serv, Home delivery & serv to Sr ctr & nursing homes, Homebound delivery serv, ILL available, Large print keyboards, Magnifiers for reading, OverDrive digital audio bks, Photocopying/Printing, Prog for children & young adult, Pub access computers, Ref serv available, Scanner, Summer reading prog
Partic in Southern Ontario Libr Serv
Special Services for the Deaf - Adult & family literacy prog; Bks on deafness & sign lang; High interest/low vocabulary bks
Special Services for the Blind - Assistive/Adapted tech devices, equip & products; Computer with voice synthesizer for visually impaired persons; Dragon Naturally Speaking software; HP Scan Jet with photo-finish software; Inspiration software; Large print & cassettes; Large screen computer & software; Reader equip; Screen reader software; ZoomText magnification & reading software
Open Mon-Thurs 1-8, Fri 1-5, Sat (Sept-June) 10-2
Friends of the Library Group

RAINY RIVER

P RAINY RIVER PUBLIC LIBRARY*, 334 Fourth St, P0W 1L0. (Mail add: PO Box 308, P0W 1L0), SAN 319-3756. Tel: 807-852-3375. FAX: 807-852-3375. E-mail: libraryrr@gmail.com. Web Site: rainyriverlibrary.com. *Chief Exec Officer,* Michael Dawber
Founded 1971. Pop 2,100; Circ 12,900
Library Holdings: Bk Vols 12,000; Per Subs 15
Special Collections: Local History Coll, photos, scrapbks, tapes & written mat
Wireless access
Publications: Annual Report; Librarian's Annual Report, Local Library History
Open Tues & Thurs 2-7, Wed, Fri & Sat 11-4

RED ROCK

P RED ROCK PUBLIC LIBRARY BOARD*, 42 Salls St, P0T 2P0. (Mail add: PO Box 285, P0T 2P0), SAN 319-3772. Tel: 807-886-2558. FAX: 807-886-2558. E-mail: rrocklib@gmail.com. *Head Librn,* Nancy Carrier; *Asst Librn,* Shelley Boudreau; *Asst Librn,* Eileen Ferren
Founded 1965. Pop 900; Circ 10,000
Library Holdings: Bk Vols 18,000; Per Subs 15
Subject Interests: Local hist
Wireless access
Mem of Ontario Library Service North
Open Mon 10-12, 2-5 & 6:30-8:30, Tues & Thurs 2-5 & 6:30-8:30, Wed 10-12 & 2-5, Fri 6:30pm-8:30pm, Sun 2-4
Friends of the Library Group

RENFREW

P RENFREW PUBLIC LIBRARY, 13 Railway Ave E, K7V 3A9. SAN 319-3780. Tel: 613-432-8151. FAX: 613-432-7680. E-mail: renlib@renfrew.library.on.ca. Web Site: www.town.renfrew.on.ca/library. *Chief Exec Officer, Chief Librn,* Bettijane O'Neill; E-mail: bjoneill@renfrew.library.on.ca; Staff 5.5 (MLS 1, Non-MLS 4.5)
Founded 1898. Pop 15,000; Circ 95,000
Jan 2008-Dec 2008 Income (CAN) $394,361, Provincial (CAN) $16,720, City (CAN) $376,108, Federal (CAN) $1,533. Mats Exp (CAN) $57,300, Books (CAN) $47,000, Per/Ser (Incl. Access Fees) (CAN) $2,800, AV Mat (CAN) $5,000, Electronic Ref Mat (Incl. Access Fees) (CAN) $2,500. Sal (CAN) $222,000 (Prof (CAN) $66,000)
Library Holdings: AV Mats 2,057; e-books 1,508; e-journals 1,650; Large Print Bks 4,300; Bk Titles 37,350; Per Subs 36; Talking Bks 670
Special Collections: DVDs; Large Print & Talking Book Coll; Video Games. Municipal Document Depository; State Document Depository
Subject Interests: Early Can, Ottawa valley hist
Automation Activity & Vendor Info: (Acquisitions) Insignia Software; (Cataloging) Insignia Software; (Circulation) Insignia Software; (OPAC) Insignia Software
Wireless access
Partic in Southern Ontario Libr Serv
Open Mon-Thurs 10:30-8, Fri 10:30-5, Sat 10-4
Friends of the Library Group

RICHARDS LANDING

P ST JOSEPH TOWNSHIP PUBLIC LIBRARY, 1240 Richard St, P0R 1J0. (Mail add: PO Box 9, P0R 1J0), SAN 319-3802. Tel: 705-246-2353. FAX: 705-246-2353. E-mail: sjtlibrary@ontera.net. *Librn,* Sharon Thomas
Founded 1942. Pop 2,000; Circ 11,551
Library Holdings: Large Print Bks 87; Bk Vols 8,400; Per Subs 20
Wireless access
Mem of Ontario Library Service North

RICHMOND HILL

P   RICHMOND HILL PUBLIC LIBRARY, One Atkinson St, L4C 0H5. SAN 368-2714. Tel: 905-884-9288. Administration Tel: 905-770-0310. FAX: 905-770-0312, 905-884-6544. Web Site: www.rhpl.richmondhill.on.ca. *Chief Exec Officer,* Louise Procter Maio; *Dir, Pub Serv,* Mary Jane Celsie; *Dir, Serv Develop, Planning & Support,* Barbara Ransom
Founded 1851. Pop 174,000; Circ 2,130,539
Special Collections: Canadiana & Genealogy. Can & Prov
Automation Activity & Vendor Info: (Acquisitions) SirsiDynix; (Cataloging) SirsiDynix; (Circulation) SirsiDynix; (Course Reserve) SirsiDynix; (OPAC) SirsiDynix; (Serials) SirsiDynix
Wireless access
Open Mon-Thurs 9:30-9, Fri 9:30-6, Sat 10-5, Sun 12-5
Branches: 3
OAK RIDGES MORAINE LIBRARY, 13085 Yonge St, Unit 12, L4E 3L2, SAN 368-2749. Tel: 905-773-5533. FAX: 905-773-8107. *Br Mgr,* Cathy Peters
Open Mon 1-8, Tues & Wed 10-8, Thurs & Fri 10-6, Sat 10-5
RICHMOND GREEN LIBRARY, One William F Bell Pkwy, L4S 2T9. Tel: 905-780-0711. FAX: 905-780-1155. *Br Mgr,* Len Wong
RICHVALE LIBRARY, 40 Pearson Ave, L4C 6T7, SAN 368-2773. Tel: 905-889-2847. FAX: 905-889-2435. *Br Mgr,* Brian Bell
Open Tues & Wed 10-8, Thurs & Fri 10-6, Sat 10-5

S   YORK CENTRAL HOSPITAL*, Douglas Storms Memorial Library, Ten Trench St, L4C 4Z3. SAN 375-1759. Tel: 905-883-2018. FAX: 905-883-2135. Web Site: www.yorkcentral.com. *Librn,* Sharon Thomson; E-mail: sthomson@yorkcentral.on.ca
Library Holdings: Bk Titles 800; Per Subs 100

RIDGETOWN

C   UNIVERSITY OF GUELPH*, Ridgetown Campus Library, 120 Main St E, N0P 2C0. SAN 319-3829. Tel: 519-674-1540. FAX: 519-674-1539. E-mail: library@ridgetownc.uoguelph.ca. Web Site: www.ridgetownc.on.ca. *Libr Assoc,* Becky Clark
Founded 1954
Library Holdings: Bk Vols 16,000; Per Subs 500
Subject Interests: Agr, Biores mgt, Environment, Hort, Veterinary tech
Automation Activity & Vendor Info: (Acquisitions) Ex Libris Group; (Cataloging) Ex Libris Group; (Circulation) Ex Libris Group; (Course Reserve) Ex Libris Group; (ILL) Ex Libris Group; (Media Booking) Ex Libris Group; (OPAC) Ex Libris Group; (Serials) Ex Libris Group
Wireless access
Publications: Current Awareness Bulletin
Open Mon-Thurs (Winter) 8:30am-9pm, Fri 8:30-4:30, Sat 1-4; Mon-Fri (Summer) 8:30-4:30

ROCKLAND

P   CLARENCE-ROCKLAND PUBLIC LIBRARY*, 1525 du Parc Ave, Unit 2, K4K 1C3. SAN 319-3845. Tel: 613-446-5680. FAX: 613-446-1518. E-mail: biblioinfo@biblibclarence-rockland.ca. Web Site: www.clarence-rockland.com. *Chief Exec Officer,* Daniel Noel
Founded 1972. Pop 20,000
Library Holdings: Bk Vols 26,000; Per Subs 30
Wireless access
Partic in Southern Ontario Libr Serv
Open Mon-Thurs 9-8, Fri 9-5, Sat 10-2
Branches: 1
BOURGET BRANCH, 2240 Dollard St, Bourget, K0A 1E0. (Mail add: Box 208, Bourget, K0A 1E0), SAN 321-7167. Tel: 613-487-9488. E-mail: biblioinfo@clarence-rockland.com. *Br Head,* Monique Stenson
Founded 1950
Library Holdings: Bk Vols 47,000; Per Subs 10
Open Mon 2-5, Tues & Thurs 6-9
Friends of the Library Group

RUSSELL

P   TOWNSHIP OF RUSSELL PUBLIC LIBRARY, 1053 Concession St, Box 280, K4R 1E1. Tel: 613-445-5331. FAX: 613-445-8014. E-mail: mylibrary@russellbiblio.com. Web Site: www.russellbiblio.com. *Head of Libr,* Claire Dionne; *Br Head, Ch,* Helene Quesnel; E-mail: helene.quesnel@russellbiblio.com; *ILL, Tech Serv,* Joanne Yelle; E-mail: joanne.yelle@russellbiblio.ca
Pop 15,000
Library Holdings: DVDs 1,000; e-books 8,000; Electronic Media & Resources 200; Large Print Bks 150; Bk Titles 39,000; Bk Vols 42,000; Per Subs 60; Talking Bks 600; Videos 250
Special Collections: French Talking Books; St-Jacques Parish Records, genealogical database, microfilm. Municipal Document Depository
Wireless access

Open Mon 3-7, Tues & Thurs 1-8, Wed 9-12 & 1-8, Fri 9-12 & 1-6, Sat 10-3
Friends of the Library Group
Branches: 1
EMBRUN BRANCH, 1215 St Augustin St, Embrun, K0A 1W1, SAN 319-1222. Tel: 613-443-3636. FAX: 613-445-8014. E-mail: mabiblio@russellbiblio.com. *Chief Exec Officer,* Claire Dionne; Staff 1 (MLS 1)
Founded 1972. Pop 15,000
Library Holdings: DVDs 1,000; e-books 8,000; Bk Titles 19,000; Bk Vols 21,000; Per Subs 30; Talking Bks 150; Videos 150
Special Collections: French Talking Books; St-Jacques Parish Records, genealogical database, microfilm. Municipal Document Depository
Open Mon 3-7, Tues & Thurs 1-8, Wed 9-12 & 1-8, Fri 9-12 & 1-6, Sat 10-3
Friends of the Library Group

SAINT CATHARINES

M   HOTEL DIEU SHAVER HEALTH & REHABILITATION CENTRE*, Health Sciences Library, 541 Glenridge Ave, L2T 4C2. SAN 377-2624. Tel: 905-685-1381, Ext 85266. FAX: 905-687-3228. Web Site: dc-hdffts01.hds.local. *Libr Tech,* Dennis Sawyer
Library Holdings: Per Subs 100
Wireless access
Open Mon-Fri 8:30-4:30

G   ONTARIO MINISTRY OF TRANSPORTATION LIBRARY, 301 Saint Paul St, Ground Flr, L2R 7R4. SAN 319-1079. Tel: 905-704-2171. E-mail: mto.library@ontario.ca. *Librn,* Patricia Bartel; Staff 1 (MLS 1)
Founded 1960
Library Holdings: Bk Titles 15,000
Special Collections: MTO Reports; Transportation Research Board Publications
Subject Interests: Econ, Transportation
Automation Activity & Vendor Info: (Cataloging) Sydney
Function: ILL available
Restriction: Open by appt only

SAINT CHARLES

P   ST CHARLES PUBLIC LIBRARY*, 22 St Anne, Rm 216-217, P0M 2W0. (Mail add: PO Box 40, P0M 2W0), SAN 319-3934. Tel: 705-867-5332. FAX: 705-867-2511. E-mail: stcharles_library@yahoo.ca. *Librn,* Lorraine Dube; *Asst Librn,* Carol Vaillant
Founded 1970. Pop 1,208; Circ 10,625
Library Holdings: Bk Titles 8,500; Bk Vols 8,750; Per Subs 15
Subject Interests: Fiction (Fr & English), Genealogy, Geog, Hist
Function: Art exhibits, AV serv, Bk club(s), CD-ROM, Games & aids for the handicapped, Govt ref serv, Handicapped accessible, Home delivery & serv to Sr ctr & nursing homes, Homebound delivery serv, Homework prog, ILL available, Online searches, Photocopying/Printing, Prog for children & young adult, Ref serv available, Spoken cassettes & DVDs, Summer reading prog, Telephone ref, VHS videos
Mem of Ontario Library Service North
Open Mon & Sat 11-2, Tues, Wed & Fri 11-5, Thurs 11-7
Restriction: Non-resident fee
Friends of the Library Group

SARNIA

J   LAMBTON COLLEGE*, Library Resource Centre, 1457 London Rd, N7S 6K4. SAN 319-4000. Tel: 519-541-2441. Circulation Tel: 519-542-7751, Ext 2441. Interlibrary Loan Service Tel: 519-542-7751, Ext 3288. FAX: 519-541-2426. Web Site: library.lambtoncollege.ca, www.lambtoncollege.ca. *Dir, Campus Serv & Libr Res Ctr,* Tim Pearce; *Acq, Ref Serv,* Linda Gibbs; Staff 6 (Non-MLS 6)
Founded 1967. Enrl 2,495; Fac 110
Library Holdings: Bk Vols 43,000; Per Subs 236
Database Vendor: EBSCOhost, OVID Technologies, ProQuest
Open Mon-Thurs 7:30-8, Fri 7:30-4:30, Sun 9-4:30

S   LANXESS, INC*, Sarnia Library, 1265 S Vidal St, N7T 7M2. (Mail add: PO Box 3001, N7T 7M2), SAN 319-4019. Tel: 519-337-8251, Ext 5106. *In Charge,* Tina DeMars; Staff 1 (MLS 1)
Founded 1943
Library Holdings: Bk Vols 2,000; Per Subs 15
Subject Interests: Petrochemicals, Polymers, Rubber
Automation Activity & Vendor Info: (ILL) Amicus
Database Vendor: Dialog, Factiva.com
Partic in Sci & Tech Info Network

SAULT STE. MARIE

C   ALGOMA UNIVERSITY COLLEGE*, Arthur A Wishart Library, 1520 Queen St E, P6A 2G4. SAN 319-4035. Tel: 705-949-2101. FAX: 705-949-6583. E-mail: library@algomau.ca, reference@algomau.ca. Circulation E-mail: circulation@algomau.ca. Interlibrary Loan Service E-mail: inter-library@algomau.ca. Web Site: www.algomau.ca/wishart-library. *Univ Librn,* Ken Hernden; E-mail: ken.hernden@algomau.ca; *Pub Serv & Coll Supvr,* Penny Tyrrel; E-mail: penny.tyrrel@algomau.ca; *Access Serv,* Carol Wright; *Res Sharing Tech,* Anne Beaupre; Staff 6 (MLS 1, Non-MLS 5)
Founded 1967. Fac 35; Highest Degree: Master
May 2007-Apr 2008. Mats Exp (CAN) $8,350,000, Other Print Mats $2,650,000, Electronic Ref Mat (Incl. Access Fees) $5,700,000
Library Holdings: e-journals 20,000; Bk Vols 110,000; Per Subs 300
Subject Interests: Gen sci, Humanities, Liberal arts, Soc sci
Automation Activity & Vendor Info: (Acquisitions) SirsiDynix; (Cataloging) SirsiDynix; (Circulation) SirsiDynix; (Course Reserve) SirsiDynix; (ILL) SirsiDynix; (Media Booking) SirsiDynix; (OPAC) SirsiDynix; (Serials) SirsiDynix
Database Vendor: Cambridge Scientific Abstracts, EBSCOhost, Gale Cengage Learning, ProQuest, Wilson - Wilson Web
Open Mon-Thurs (Winter) 8:30am-10:30pm, Fri 8:30-4:30, Sat & Sun 12-5; Mon-Thurs (Summer) 8:30-8, Fri 8:30-4:30, Sun 12-5

G   NATURAL RESOURCES CANADA-CANADIAN FOREST SERVICE, Great Lakes Forestry Centre Library, 1219 Queen St E, P6A 2E5. SAN 319-4051. Tel: 705-541-5501. FAX: 705-541-5712. E-mail: glfclib@nrcan.gc.ca. *In Charge,* Shelley Hanninen
Founded 1947
Library Holdings: Bk Titles 8,000; Per Subs 180
Subject Interests: Bacteriology, Botany, Chem, Econ, Entomology, Forestry
Wireless access
Open Mon-Fri 8:30-4:30

M   SAULT AREA HOSPITAL*, Health Sciences Library, 750 Great Northern Rd, P6B 0A8. SAN 324-489X. Tel: 705-759-3434, Ext 4368. FAX: 705-759-3847. *Librn,* Kimberley Aslett; E-mail: aslettk@sah.on.ca; Staff 1 (MLS 1)
Founded 1979
Library Holdings: Bk Titles 2,700; Per Subs 100
Subject Interests: Allied health, Med, Nursing, Psychiat
Automation Activity & Vendor Info: (Acquisitions) Evergreen; (Cataloging) Evergreen; (Circulation) Evergreen; (OPAC) Evergreen
Wireless access
Function: ILL available
Partic in Canadian Health Libraries Association; Medical Library Association (MLA); Ontario Health Libraries Association
Restriction: Access at librarian's discretion, In-house use for visitors, Restricted borrowing privileges, Restricted pub use, Staff & mem only

J   SAULT COLLEGE LIBRARY*, 443 Northern Ave, P6A 5L3. SAN 319-406X. Tel: 705-759-2554, Ext 2711. Reference Tel: 705-7559-2554, Ext 2455. Administration Tel: 705-759-2554, Ext 2402. FAX: 705-759-1319. E-mail: library@saultcollege.ca. Web Site: www.saultcollege.ca/library. *Mgr, Libr Serv,* Jason Bird; Staff 1 (MLS 1)
Founded 1965. Enrl 2,219
Library Holdings: Bk Vols 25,000; Per Subs 140
Automation Activity & Vendor Info: (Circulation) SirsiDynix; (Course Reserve) SirsiDynix; (Media Booking) SirsiDynix; (OPAC) SirsiDynix; (Serials) SirsiDynix
Wireless access
Function: AV serv, ILL available, Online searches
Open Mon-Thurs 8-8, Fri 8-4:30, Sat & Sun 12-5

P   SAULT STE MARIE PUBLIC LIBRARY*, 50 East St, P6A 3C3. SAN 368-3281. Tel: 705-759-5242. Circulation Tel: 705-759-5231. Interlibrary Loan Service Tel: 705-759-5236. Automation Services Tel: 705-759-5230. FAX: 705-759-8752. E-mail: admin.library@cityssm.on.ca. Web Site: www.ssmpl.ca. *Chief Exec Officer,* Elizabeth Rossnagel; Tel: 705-759-5246, E-mail: e.ross@cityssm.on.ca; Staff 63 (MLS 5, Non-MLS 58)
Founded 1896. Pop 80,000; Circ 564,128
Jan 2007-Dec 2007 Income (Main Library and Branch(s)) (CAN) $3,182,149, Provincial (CAN) $496,921, City (CAN) $2,399,975, Locally Generated Income (CAN) $194,001, Other (CAN) $91,252
Special Collections: Archives. Can & Prov
Database Vendor: EBSCOhost
Wireless access
Special Services for the Blind - Braille bks; Descriptive video serv (DVS); Reader equip; Talking bks
Open Mon-Thurs 9-9, Fri 9-6, Sat 9-5, Sun 2-5
Friends of the Library Group

Branches: 2
CHURCHILL, 301 Lake St, P6A 4B5, SAN 368-3311. Tel: 705-759-5248. *Chief Exec Officer,* Elizabeth Rossnagel; Tel: 705-759-5246
   Library Holdings: Bk Vols 35,890
   Open Mon-Wed 1-8, Thurs 10-6, Fri 1-5, Sat 10-5
   Friends of the Library Group
KORAH, 496 Second Line W, P6C 2K4, SAN 368-3346. Tel: 705-759-5249. *Chief Exec Officer,* Elizabeth Rossnagel; Tel: 705-759-5246
   Library Holdings: Bk Vols 33,207
   Open Mon-Wed 1-8, Thurs 10-6, Fri 1-5, Sat 10-5
   Friends of the Library Group

SCARBOROUGH

S   CANADIAN ARAB FEDERATION LIBRARY*, 1057 McNicoll Ave, M1W 3W6. SAN 375-2585. Tel: 416-493-8635. FAX: 416-493-9239. E-mail: info@caf.ca. Web Site: www.caf.ca. *Pres,* Dr Farid Ayad
Library Holdings: Bk Vols 600

C   CENTENNIAL COLLEGE OF APPLIED ARTS & TECHNOLOGY*, Centennial College Libraries, 941 Progress Ave, M1G 3T8. (Mail add: PO Box 631, Sta A, M1K 5E9), SAN 368-3400. Tel: 416-289-5000. FAX: 416-289-5228. E-mail: library@centennialcollege.ca. Web Site: www.library.centennialcollege.ca. *Dir,* Gladys Watson; Tel: 416-289-5000, Ext 2601; Staff 24.6 (MLS 5.6, Non-MLS 19)
Founded 1966. Enrl 14,000; Fac 500; Highest Degree: Bachelor
Library Holdings: Bk Titles 70,000; Per Subs 350
Special Collections: Centennial Writes Coll; Daher Folk Tales Coll; John & Molly Pollock Holocaust Coll
Automation Activity & Vendor Info: (Acquisitions) SirsiDynix; (Cataloging) SirsiDynix; (Circulation) SirsiDynix; (OPAC) SirsiDynix; (Serials) SirsiDynix
Database Vendor: ACM (Association for Computing Machinery), CredoReference, EBSCOhost, Gale Cengage Learning, LexisNexis, OVID Technologies, ProQuest, Safari Books Online, SirsiDynix, Wiley
Partic in BiblioNet
Special Services for the Deaf - Closed caption videos
Special Services for the Blind - Accessible computers; Aids for in-house use; Assistive/Adapted tech devices, equip & products; Audio mat; Cassette playback machines; Closed caption display syst; Computer with voice synthesizer for visually impaired persons; Dragon Naturally Speaking software; Inspiration software; Integrated libr/media serv; Internet workstation with adaptive software; Large screen computer & software; Lending of low vision aids; Magnifiers; PC for handicapped; Ref serv; Scanner for conversion & translation of mats; Screen enlargement software for people with visual disabilities; Screen reader software; Text reader; VisualTek equip; ZoomText magnification & reading software
Open Mon-Thurs 8am-10pm, Fri 8-4, Sat & Sun 9-4:30
Departmental Libraries:
ASHTONBEE CAMPUS LIBRARY, 75 Ashtonbee Rd, M1L 4N4. (Mail add: PO Box 631, Sta A, M1K 5E9), SAN 368-3435. Tel: 416-289-5000, Ext 7000. FAX: 416-289-5017. *Dir,* Gladys Watson; *Librn,* Elizabeth Dobson; Staff 5 (MLS 1, Non-MLS 4)
   Subject Interests: Aircraft, Automotive, Avionics, Heavy-duty equip, Transportation
   Partic in BiblioNet
   Open Mon-Thurs 8am-10pm, Fri 8-4, Sat & Sun 9-4:30
   Restriction: Open to students, fac, staff & alumni
CENTRE FOR CREATIVE COMMUNICATIONS LIBRARY, 951 Carlaw Ave, Toronto, M4K 3M2. (Mail add: PO Box 631, Sta A, M1K 5E9), SAN 376-9674. Tel: 416-289-5000, Ext 8600. FAX: 416-289-5118. *Dir,* Gladys Watson; *Librn,* Gail Alexander; Staff 3 (MLS 1, Non-MLS 2)
   Subject Interests: Communication arts, Newsmedia
   Open Mon-Thurs 8am-10pm, Fri 8-4, Sat & Sun 9-4:30
MORNINGSIDE CAMPUS LIBRARY, 755 Morningside Ave, Rm 160, M1C 5J9. (Mail add: PO Box 631, Sta A, M1K 5E9). Tel: 416-289-5000, Ext 8000. FAX: 416-289-5156. *Dir,* Gladys Watson; *Librn,* Gail Alexander; *Librn,* Rosemary Stackhouse; Staff 8 (MLS 2, Non-MLS 6)
   Open Mon-Thurs 8am-10pm, Fri 8-4, Sat & Sun 9-4:30
PROGRESS CAMPUS LIBRARY, 941 Progress Ave, M1G 3T8. (Mail add: PO Box 631, Sta A, M1K 5E9), SAN 368-346X. Tel: 416-289-5000, Ext 2600. FAX: 416-289-5242. *Dir,* Gladys Watson; *Librn,* Carmen Biron; *Librn,* Eva McDonald; *Librn,* Richard Sims; Staff 14 (MLS 3, Non-MLS 11)
   Subject Interests: Bus, Eng tech
   Open Mon-Thurs 8am-10pm, Fri 8-8, Sat & Sun 9-4:30

S   MASARYK MEMORIAL INSTITUTE INC*, Czech & Slovak Library, 450 Scarborough Golf Club Rd, M1G 1H1. SAN 376-1827. Tel: 416-439-0792. Administration Tel: 416-439-4354. FAX: 416-439-6473. E-mail: office@masaryktown.ca. Web Site: masaryktown.ca. *Librn,* Dana Anoud
Library Holdings: Bk Vols 6,500

Special Collections: T G Masaryk Coll; Video-Club Coll, Czek documentary & feature films
Open Wed 4pm-9pm
Restriction: Private libr

R   SAINT AUGUSTINE'S SEMINARY LIBRARY*, 2661 Kingston Rd, M1M 1M3. SAN 320-7986. Tel: 416-261-7207, Ext 271. Circulation Tel: 416-261-7207, Ext 279. FAX: 416-261-2529. E-mail: library_sas@rogers.com. Web Site: www.staugustines.on.ca/academic/library.html. *Dir of Libr Serv,* Position Currently Open; *Librn,* Mariam Rezai-Atrie; Staff 1.6 (MLS 1.6)
Founded 1913. Enrl 98; Fac 16; Highest Degree: Master
Library Holdings: AV Mats 1,195; CDs 2; DVDs 74; Electronic Media & Resources 30; Bk Vols 40,045; Per Subs 168; Videos 242
Subject Interests: Theol
Automation Activity & Vendor Info: (Cataloging) SirsiDynix; (OPAC) SirsiDynix
Open Mon-Fri 9-12, 1-4:30 & 7-9, Sat 1-5, Sun 1-5 & 7-9
Restriction: Authorized patrons

SR   THE SALVATION ARMY ARCHIVES*, Canada & Bermuda Territory, 26 Howden Rd, M1R 3E4. Tel: 416-285-4344. FAX: 416-285-7763. E-mail: heritage_centre@can.salvationarmy.org. Web Site: www.salvationist.ca/museum-archives. *Dir,* Colonel John E Carew; Tel: 416-285-4344, Ext 25, E-mail: john_carew@can.salvationarmy.org; Staff 3 (Non-MLS 3)
Founded 1982
Library Holdings: Bk Titles 1,000
Special Collections: Salvation Army Immigration Coll, Ship Logs 1911-1929; The Salvation Army Canada & Bermuda Territory, artifacts, bks, flm, music, photos, prints. Oral History
Automation Activity & Vendor Info: (Acquisitions) Inmagic, Inc.; (Cataloging) Inmagic, Inc.; (Circulation) Inmagic, Inc.; (Serials) Inmagic, Inc.
Function: Archival coll, For res purposes, Handicapped accessible, Photocopying/Printing, Ref serv available, Res libr, Wheelchair accessible
Restriction: Open by appt only

     SCARBOROUGH HOSPITAL
M   HEALTH INFORMATION RESOURCE CENTRE, BIRCHMOUNT CAMPUS*, 3030 Birchmount Rd, M1W 3W3. Tel: 416-495-2437. FAX: 416-495-2562. E-mail: library@tsh.to. Web Site: tsh.to. *Mgr,* Tonya Mahar
     Open Mon-Fri 8:30-4:30
     HEALTH SCIENCES LIBRARY*, 3050 Lawrence Ave E, M1P 2V5, SAN 319-4108. Tel: 416-431-8114. Interlibrary Loan Service Tel: 416-431-8200, Ext 6593. FAX: 416-431-8232. E-mail: librarygen@tsh.to. *Mgr,* Tonya Mahar
     Library Holdings: e-books 21; e-journals 1,700; Bk Titles 5,000; Per Subs 300; Videos 200
     Partic in Health Science Information Consortium of Toronto
     Restriction: Staff use only

SCHREIBER

P   SCHREIBER TOWNSHIP PUBLIC LIBRARY*, 314 Scotia St, P0T 2S0. (Mail add: Box 39, P0T 2S0), SAN 319-4124. Tel: 807-824-2477. FAX: 807-824-2996. E-mail: libinfo@schreiber.ca. Web Site: www.schreiberlibrary.ca. *Librn,* Donna Mikeluk
Founded 1891. Pop 1,000; Circ 14,800
Library Holdings: AV Mats 237; CDs 106; DVDs 87; Large Print Bks 241; Bk Titles 17,544; Bk Vols 17,758; Per Subs 25; Videos 575
Special Collections: Local History Coll, photogs. Oral History
Mem of Ontario Library Service North
Open Tues & Thurs 10-5 & 7pm-9pm, Wed & Fri 10-5, Sat 1-5
Friends of the Library Group

SHANNONVILLE

P   TYENDINAGA TOWNSHIP PUBLIC LIBRARY*, 852 Melrose Rd, RR1, K0K 3A0. SAN 319-4159. Tel: 613-967-0606. FAX: 613-396-2080. E-mail: tyendinagatownshiplibrary@yahoo.ca. Web Site: www.ttpl.ca. *Librn,* Frances Smith
Pop 3,769; Circ 12,000
Library Holdings: Bk Titles 9,500; Bk Vols 12,000
Automation Activity & Vendor Info: (Acquisitions) Follett Software; (Cataloging) Follett Software; (Circulation) Follett Software; (OPAC) Follett Software; (Serials) Follett Software
Open Tues & Thurs 10-8, Sat 10-2

SHELBURNE

P   SHELBURNE PUBLIC LIBRARY*, 201 Owen Sound St, L0N 1S0. (Mail add: PO Box 127, L0N 1S0), SAN 319-4175. Tel: 519-925-2168. FAX: 519-925-6555. Web Site: www.shelburnelibrary.ca. *Chief Exec Officer,* Rose Dotten

Founded 1912. Pop 8,000; Circ 100,000
Library Holdings: Bk Vols 35,000; Per Subs 45
Wireless access
Partic in Southern Ontario Libr Serv
Open Mon-Wed 10-5, Thurs 12-8, Fri 10-7, Sat 12-5

SIMCOE

P   NORFOLK COUNTY PUBLIC LIBRARY*, Simcoe Branch, 46 Colborne St S, N3Y 4H3. Tel: 519-426-3506. Administration Tel: 519-426-8918. FAX: 519-426-0657. E-mail: norfolk.library@norfolkcounty.ca. Web Site: www.ncpl.ca. *Chief Exec Officer,* Bill Hett; Tel: 519-426-3506, Ext 1253, E-mail: bill.hett@norfolkcounty.ca; *Mgr, Coll Develop,* Heidi Goodale; E-mail: heidi.goodale@norfolkcounty.ca; *Admin Coordr,* Janet Cowan; Tel: 519-426-3506, Ext 1258, E-mail: janet.cowan@norfolkcounty.ca; Staff 46 (MLS 3, Non-MLS 43)
Pop 61,000
Library Holdings: Bk Vols 169,827; Per Subs 232; Talking Bks 2,866; Videos 6,797
Special Collections: Canadiana-Local History, bks, per, tapes
Automation Activity & Vendor Info: (Cataloging) MINISIS Inc; (Circulation) MINISIS Inc; (OPAC) MINISIS Inc
Wireless access
Publications: Bibliography of History in Norfolk Libraries; Bibliography of Holdings of Norfolk County; History of Simcoe Public Library; Selected Bibliography of Haldimand-Norfolk History, bks, newsp, per
Partic in Southern Ontario Libr Serv
Open Mon-Thurs 10-8, Fri & Sat 10-5
Friends of the Library Group
Branches: 4
DELHI BRANCH, 192 Main St of Delhi, Delhi, N4B 2M2, SAN 319-096X. Tel: 519-426-3506, Ext 2. FAX: 519-582-8376.
     Founded 1894
     Special Collections: Tobacco History of Norfolk Area, photos. Oral History
     Publications: Preserving Our Tobacco History; The Tobacco Leaf Yesterday & Today
     Open Tues & Fri 10-5, Wed & Thurs 12-7, Sat 10-2
     Friends of the Library Group
PORT DOVER BRANCH, 413 Main St, Port Dover, N0A 1N0, SAN 319-3705. Tel: 519-426-3506, Ext 3. FAX: 519-583-3496.
     Founded 1888
     Subject Interests: Local hist
     Open Tues & Fri 10-5, Wed & Thurs 12-7, Sat 10-2
     Friends of the Library Group
PORT ROWAN BRANCH, 1034 Bay St, Port Rowan, N0E 1M0. Tel: 519-426-3506, Ext 4. FAX: 519-586-3297.
     Open Tues & Fri 10-5, Wed & Thurs 12-7, Sat 10-2
     Friends of the Library Group
WATERFORD BRANCH, 15 Main St S, Waterford, N0E 1Y0, SAN 319-5929. Tel: 519-426-3506, Ext 6. Administration Tel: 519-426-3506. FAX: 519-443-6540. Administration FAX: 519-426-8918.
     Founded 1898
     Open Tues & Fri 10-5, Wed & Thurs 12-7, Sat 10-2
     Friends of the Library Group

S   NORFOLK HISTORICAL SOCIETY, Eva Brook Donly Museum & Archives, 109 Norfolk St S, N3Y 2W3. SAN 320-3328. Tel: 519-426-1583. FAX: 519-426-1584. E-mail: office@norfolklore.com. Web Site: www.norfolklore.com. *Curator,* Helen Bartens; E-mail: curator@norfolklore.com
Founded 1900
Library Holdings: CDs 25; Bk Titles 3,500; Per Subs 10
Special Collections: Canadian/American Genealogy
Subject Interests: Antiques, Genealogy, Hist, Local hist
Wireless access
Publications: Local History Pamphlets
Open Tues-Sat 10-4:30
Restriction: Open to pub for ref only
Friends of the Library Group

SIOUX LOOKOUT

P   SIOUX LOOKOUT PUBLIC LIBRARY*, 21 Fifth Ave, P8T 1B3. (Mail add: PO Box 1028, P8T 1B3), SAN 319-4191. Tel: 807-737-3660. FAX: 807-737-4046. E-mail: publiclibrary@siouxlookout.ca. Web Site: www.slpl.on.ca. *Chief Librn/CEO,* Wendy MacDonald
Founded 1958. Pop 5,200; Circ 40,000
Library Holdings: Bk Titles 32,000; Per Subs 85
Special Collections: Oral History
Wireless access
Open Mon-Wed 10-8, Thurs & Fri 10-5, Sat & Sun (Sept-June) 12-4

SIOUX NARROWS

P   SIOUX NARROWS PUBLIC LIBRARY*, PO Box 417, P0X 1N0. SAN
     319-4205. Tel: 807-226-5204. FAX: 807-226-5712. E-mail:
     library@voyageur.ca, *Librn,* Alice Motlong
     Founded 1975. Pop 300; Circ 5,683
     Library Holdings: Bk Titles 13,830; Per Subs 26
     Special Collections: National Geographic Coll
     Open Tues & Thurs (Sept-May) 5-8, Sat 11-2, Sun 1-4; Tues & Thurs
     (June-Aug) 5-8, Sat 10-2, Sun 12-4

SMITHS FALLS

P   SMITHS FALLS PUBLIC LIBRARY, 81 Beckwith St N, K7A 2B9. SAN
     319-4213. Tel: 613-283-2911. FAX: 613-283-9834. E-mail:
     smithsfallslibrary@vianet.ca. Web Site: www.smithsfallslibrary.ca. *Chief
     Librn,* Karen Schecter; *Ch,* Debra Kuehl; *Circ,* Deborah Andre; *Ref Serv,
     Ad,* Beth Lavender; Staff 6 (MLS 1, Non-MLS 5)
     Founded 1903. Pop 12,000
     Library Holdings: Large Print Bks 616; Bk Titles 41,655; Bk Vols
     43,500; Per Subs 50
     Subject Interests: Art, Bio, Bldg, Cookery, Handicrafts, Hist, Local hist,
     Sports
     Automation Activity & Vendor Info: (Cataloging) Mandarin Library
     Automation; (Circulation) Mandarin Library Automation; (OPAC)
     Mandarin Library Automation
     Database Vendor: ProQuest, World Book Online
     Wireless access
     Publications: Periodical Indexing
     Partic in Southern Ontario Libr Serv
     Open Mon-Thurs 1-5:30 & 7-9, Fri 10-5, Sat 10-4:30
     Friends of the Library Group

S   SMITHS FALLS RAILWAY MUSEUM LIBRARY & ARCHIVES*, 90
     William St W, K7A 5A5. (Mail add: PO Box 962, Smith Falls, K7A 5A5),
     SAN 373-6466. Tel: 613-283-5696. FAX: 613-283-7211. Web Site:
     www.magma.ca/~sfrm/. *Librn,* Chris Anstead
     Founded 1990
     Library Holdings: Bk Titles 500; Bk Vols 550
     Special Collections: Can Railroad Hist Asn
     Publications: Rideau Valley Dispatch (membership newsletter)
     Open Mon-Sun (May-Oct) 10-4:30

SMITHVILLE

P   WEST LINCOLN PUBLIC LIBRARY*, Smithville Public Library, 318
     Canborough St, L0R 2A0. (Mail add: Box 28, L0R 2A0). Tel:
     905-957-3756. FAX: 905-957-3219. E-mail: westlincolnlibrary@yahoo.ca.
     Web Site: westlincolnlibrary.tripod.com. *Chief Librn,* Catharine Vaughan
     Library Holdings: Bk Vols 25,000; Per Subs 37
     Automation Activity & Vendor Info: (Acquisitions) Mandarin Library
     Automation
     Open Mon & Fri 7pm-9pm, Tues-Thurs & Sat 10-5
     Branches: 2
     CAISTORVILLE BRANCH, 9549 Reg Rd 9, York St, Caistorville, N0A
     1C0. (Mail add: RR No 2, Canfield, N0A 1C0). Tel: 905-692-4290.
     FAX: 905-692-4290. *Br Mgr,* Barb Stolys
     Library Holdings: Bk Vols 11,000
     Open Mon, Wed & Thurs 6-9pm, Tues & Fri 3-5, Sat 10-2
     WELLANDPORT BRANCH, 5042 Canborough Rd, Wellandport, L0R 2J0.
     (Mail add: Box 68, Wellandport, L0R 2J0). Tel: 905-386-6792. *Br Mgr,*
     Colleen Keizer
     Library Holdings: Bk Vols 10,000
     Open Mon, Tues & Thurs 7pm-9pm, Wed & Sat 9-2

SMOOTH ROCK FALLS

P   SMOOTH ROCK FALLS PUBLIC LIBRARY*, 120 Ross Rd, P0L 2B0.
     (Mail add: PO Box 670, P0L 2B0), SAN 319-4221. Tel: 705-338-2318.
     FAX: 705-338-2330. *Librn,* Lise Gagnon
     Pop 1,800; Circ 25,448
     Library Holdings: Bk Titles 24,918; Per Subs 67
     Wireless access
     Open Mon, Thurs & Fri 2-6, Tues & Wed 2-8

SOUTH PORCUPINE

J   NORTHERN COLLEGE OF APPLIED ARTS & TECHNOLOGY
     LIBRARY, Porcupine Learning Resource Centre, 4715 Hwy 101 E, P0N
     1H0. (Mail add: PO Box 3211, Timmins, P4R 8R6), SAN 319-423X. Tel:
     705-235-7150. FAX: 705-235-7279. E-mail: libraryp@northern.on.ca. Web
     Site: www.northernc.on.ca. *Sr Libr Tech,* Shannon Arsenault; Staff 5
     (Non-MLS 5)
     Founded 1967. Enrl 1,500; Fac 300; Highest Degree: Bachelor

Library Holdings: AV Mats 1,400; CDs 200; DVDs 400; Electronic
Media & Resources 1,000; Bk Titles 30,000; Bk Vols 35,000; Per Subs
300; Videos 1,000
Special Collections: ECE Coll; Map Coll. Can & Prov
Subject Interests: Behav sci, Econ, Mining, Soc sci, Welding
Automation Activity & Vendor Info: (Acquisitions) SirsiDynix;
(Cataloging) SirsiDynix; (Circulation) SirsiDynix; (OPAC) SirsiDynix
Wireless access
Publications: Library Handbook; Student Success Handbook (Newsletter)
Partic in Ontario Colleges Library Service (OCLS)
Open Mon-Thurs 8-8, Fri 8-6, Sat & Sun 10-3
Restriction: Access at librarian's discretion, Authorized patrons, Open to
pub for ref only

SOUTH RIVER

P   SOUTH RIVER-MACHAR UNION PUBLIC LIBRARY, 63 Marie St,
     P0A 1X0. (Mail add: PO Box 190, P0A 1X0), SAN 319-4248. Tel:
     705-386-0222. FAX: 705-386-0222. E-mail: osrmlibrary@hotmail.com.
     Web Site: www.olsn.ca/srmupl. *Chief Exec Officer,* Jan Heinonen; *Asst
     Librn,* Jo-Ann Long; Staff 1 (Non-MLS 1)
     Founded 1973. Pop 1,935; Circ 16,404
     Jan 2010-Dec 2010 Income (CAN) $74,742, Provincial (CAN) $6,580,
     City (CAN) $45,266, Locally Generated Income (CAN) $14,725, Other
     (CAN) $8,171. Mats Exp (CAN) $12,498, Books (CAN) $7,098, AV Equip
     (CAN) $3,663, AV Mat (CAN) $1,337, Electronic Ref Mat (Incl. Access
     Fees) (CAN) $400. Sal (CAN) $50,754 (Prof (CAN) $31,486)
     Library Holdings: Bks on Deafness & Sign Lang 2; CDs 27; DVDs 258;
     e-books 2,000; Electronic Media & Resources 1,000; High Interest/Low
     Vocabulary Bk Vols 1,137; Large Print Bks 106; Bk Titles 7,500; Bk Vols
     7,522; Per Subs 13; Talking Bks 99
     Subject Interests: Local hist
     Automation Activity & Vendor Info: (Cataloging) SIRSI WorkFlows;
     (Circulation) SIRSI WorkFlows; (ILL) OCLC; (Media Booking) SIRSI
     WorkFlows; (OPAC) SIRSI-iBistro; (Serials) SIRSI WorkFlows
     Database Vendor: EBSCOhost, Gale Cengage Learning, netLibrary,
     Overdrive, Inc, ProQuest, TumbleBookLibrary, World Book Online
     Wireless access
     Function: Adult bk club, Art exhibits, Audiobks via web, Bks on cassette,
     Bks on CD, CD-ROM, Children's prog, Computer training, Computers for
     patron use, Copy machines, Digital talking bks, e-mail & chat, e-mail serv,
     E-Reserves, Electronic databases & coll, Fax serv, Free DVD rentals,
     Handicapped accessible, Home delivery & serv to Sr ctr & nursing homes,
     Homebound delivery serv, ILL available, Mail & tel request accepted,
     Music CDs, Online cat, Online ref, Online searches, OverDrive digital
     audio bks, Photocopying/Printing, Preschool outreach, Prog for children &
     young adult, Pub access computers, Ref serv in person, Scanner, Senior
     computer classes, Spoken cassettes & CDs, Spoken cassettes & DVDs,
     Summer reading prog, Telephone ref, VHS videos, Wheelchair accessible
     Partic in Ont Libr Serv-North
     Special Services for the Deaf - Bks on deafness & sign lang; Closed
     caption videos
     Special Services for the Blind - Audio mat; Bks on CD; Daisy reader;
     Digital talking bk; Extensive large print coll; Large print bks; Large screen
     computer & software; Playaways (bks on MP3); Talking bks
     Open Mon, Wed & Fri 3-5 & 6:30-8:30, Tues & Thurs 10:30-12:30 & 1-5,
     Sat 10-12

SPANISH

P   SPANISH PUBLIC LIBRARY*, Eight Trunk Rd, P0P 2A0. (Mail add: PO
     Box 329, P0P 2A0), SAN 319-4256. Tel: 705-844-2555. FAX:
     705-844-2555. E-mail: library@town.spanish.on.ca. *Librn,* Hanne Sauve
     Pop 864; Circ 3,653
     Library Holdings: Bk Vols 8,045
     Mem of Ontario Library Service North
     Open Tues 1-8, Wed 10-5 & 6pm-8pm, Fri 1-5

ST. CATHARINES

C   BROCK UNIVERSITY*, James A Gibson Library, 500 Glenridge Ave,
     L2S 3A1. SAN 319-3896. Tel: 905-688-5550. FAX: 905-988-5490. Web
     Site: www.brocku.ca/library. *Univ Librn,* Margaret Grove; Tel:
     905-688-5550, Ext 3226, E-mail: mgrove@brocku.ca; *Assoc Univ Librn,
     Coll & Liaison Serv,* Barbara McDonald; Tel: 905-688-5550, Ext 3949,
     E-mail: bmcdonald@brocku.ca; *Assoc Univ Librn, Serv & Facilities,*
     Debbie Kalvee; Tel: 905-688-5550, Ext 3198, E-mail: dkalvee@brocku.ca;
     Head, Circ Serv, Ian Gordon; Tel: 905-688-5550, Ext 3727, E-mail:
     igordon@brocku.ca; *Head, Spec Coll, Univ Archivist,* David Sharron; Tel:
     905-688-5550, Ext 3264, E-mail: dsharron@brocku.ca; *Bus Librn,* Linda
     Lowry; Tel: 905-688-5550, Ext 4650, E-mail: llowery@brocku.ca; Staff 62
     (MLS 19, Non-MLS 43)
     Founded 1964. Enrl 20,000; Fac 592; Highest Degree: Doctorate
     May 2006-Apr 2007. Mats Exp $2,905,650, Books $475,000, Per/Ser (Incl.
     Access Fees) $1,920,000, Electronic Ref Mat (Incl. Access Fees) $20,000.
     Sal $4,199,883 (Prof $1,292,101)

Library Holdings: AV Mats 21,988; e-books 386,429; e-journals 25,500; Music Scores 2,999; Bk Titles 400,000; Bk Vols 1,254,826; Per Subs 13,650; Videos 1,814
Special Collections: Niagara Regional Coll
Subject Interests: Applied health sci, Bus, Educ, Humanities
Automation Activity & Vendor Info: (Acquisitions) Innovative Interfaces, Inc; (Cataloging) Innovative Interfaces, Inc; (Circulation) Innovative Interfaces, Inc; (ILL) Fretwell-Downing; (OPAC) Innovative Interfaces, Inc; (Serials) Innovative Interfaces, Inc
Wireless access
Partic in Canadian Research Knowledge Network; Ontario Council of University Libraries
Open Mon-Thurs 7:30am-11pm, Fri 7:30am-8pm, Sat 10-9, Sun 11-9

S　THE CANADIAN FOUNDATION FOR THE STUDY OF INFANT DEATHS LIBRARY*, 60 James St, Ste 403, L2R 7E7. SAN 375-2542. Tel: 905-688-8884. Toll Free Tel: 800-363-7437 (Canada only). FAX: 905-688-3300. E-mail: sidsinfo@sidscanada.org. Web Site: www.sidscanada.org. Staff 2 (MLS 2)
Founded 1973
Library Holdings: Bk Vols 200
Restriction: Open to pub for ref only

L　LINCOLN COUNTY LAW ASSOCIATION LIBRARY*, 59 Church St, L2R 3C3. SAN 377-3655. Tel: 905-685-9094. FAX: 905-685-0981. E-mail: library@thelcla.ca. *Librn,* Kelly Elliott
Library Holdings: Bk Vols 9,000
Open Mon-Fri 9-5

M　NIAGARA HEALTH SYSTEM*, Library Services, 142 Queenston St, L2R 7C6. SAN 329-4196. Tel: 905-378-4647, Ext 44354. FAX: 905-704-4767. E-mail: library@niagarahealth.on.ca. Web Site: www.niagarahealth.on.ca. *Asst Librn,* Nina Kelly; *Asst Librn,* Janice Russell; Staff 3 (MLS 1, Non-MLS 2)
Founded 1978
Library Holdings: Bk Titles 1,000; Per Subs 125
Special Collections: Hospital Archives
Subject Interests: Allied health, Med, Nursing
Partic in Hamilton & District Health Library Network

S　RODMAN HALL ARTS CENTRE LIBRARY*, 109 Saint Paul Crescent, L2S 1M3. SAN 326-9523. Tel: 905-684-2925. FAX: 905-682-4733. *In Charge,* Danny Custodio
Library Holdings: Bk Titles 500; Bk Vols 800
Open Tues-Fri 12-5, Sat & Sun 1-5

S　ST CATHARINES MUSEUM*, Research Centre, 1932 Welland Canals Pkwy, RR 6, L2R 7K6. (Mail add: PO Box 3012, L2R 7C2), SAN 319-3926. Tel: 905-984-8880. Toll Free Tel: 800-305-5134. FAX: 905-984-6910. E-mail: museuminfo@stcatharines.ca. Web Site: www.stcatharineslock3museum.ca. *Curator,* Arden Phair; Tel: 905-984-8880, Ext 231, E-mail: aphair@stcatharineslock3museum.ca
Founded 1965
Library Holdings: Bk Vols 1,600; Per Subs 20
Special Collections: Alan Howard Marine Coll, photogs; Algoma Marine Coll; Benson Family Papers; Calder Family Papers; Craig Swayze Coll; DeCew Falls Waterworks Coll (1875-1970); Figure Skating (Winter Club of St Catharines Coll); Frank Scott & Sons Account; Fred Pattison Aviation Coll incl Records of No 9 EFTS (1920-1950); Girl Guides Coll; Grantham High School Coll; Grape & Wine Industry, Bright's Wines (George Hostetter Coll); Graves Shipping Papers, 19th Century; Heritage St Catharines Coll; Ingersoll Papers (Family & Business Accounts 1835-1909); Lalor Estate Coll; Maps & Plans (St Catharines Planning Dept & St Catharines Engineering Dept); Marine & Business Papers (Sylvester Neelon Coll); Marine (James Kidd Coll), photogs; Marine, English Electric & W S Tyler (Jim Gilmore Coll); Mayor Joe Reid Coll; Mayor Roy Adams Coll; McCordick Family (Anne McPherson Coll); McCordick Family Papers; Merritt Family Papers (Wendy Young Coll); Merritton High School Coll; Mid-19th Century Shipping Business Papers (Norris & Neelon Coll); Niagara Grape & Wine Festival Archives (1955-present); Niagara North Land Registry Property Records; Old Courthouse Coll (1800-1920); Ontario Winter Games Coll, 1983; Papermaking (Lincoln Sulphite Mill Coll); Press Theatre Coll; Property Records (Robert Nunnenmacher Coll); Rob Sharik Marine Coll, ship photogs; Robertson Farm (Janice Partlow Coll); Royal Canadian Legion Br 24 Coll; Skip Gillham Marine Coll; Sports Columns "Through the Sports Gate" (Jack Gatecliff Coll); St Catharines & Lincoln Historical Society Coll; St Catharines' Centennial (1976) Coll; St Catharines Equestrian Club Coll; St Catharines Standard Coll; St Catharines Wine Co Coll; Standard Fine Printing Coll; Third Welland Canal Construction (St Lawrence Seaway Coll); Welch's, Cadbury-Schweppes-Powell (Jack Collard Coll); Welland Canals Preservation Association Coll; Welland Vale Mfg Co Ltd (Ray Sheehan & Norman Shopland Colls) (.); William Hamilton Merritt Papers, micro; World Rowing Championships (1999) Coll

Subject Interests: Artifact res, Great Lakes marine hist, Local hist, Welland Canals
Open Mon, Wed & Fri 12:30-4:30
Restriction: Open to pub for ref only

P　ST CATHARINES PUBLIC LIBRARY*, Central Library, 54 Church St, L2R 7K2. SAN 368-2803. Tel: 905-688-6103. FAX: 905-688-6292. TDD: 905-688-6103. E-mail: admin@stcatharines.library.on.ca. Web Site: www.stcatharines.library.on.ca. *Chief Exec Officer,* Lilita Stripnieks; Tel: 905-688-6103, Ext 235, E-mail: lstripnieks@stcatharines.library.on.ca; *Mgr, Ad Serv,* Diane Andrusko; Tel: 905-688-6103, Ext 228, E-mail: dandrusko@stcatharines.library.on.ca; *Mgr, Br Serv,* Anna Chiota; *Bus Mgr,* Jack Foster; Tel: 905-688-6103, Ext 213, E-mail: jfoster@stcatharines.library.on.ca; *Commun Serv Mgr, Mgr, Ch Serv,* Ann McKenzie; Tel: 905-688-6103, Ext 226, E-mail: amckenzie@stcatharines.library.on.ca; *Circ Mgr,* Anne Penfold; Tel: 905-688-6103, Ext 244, E-mail: apenfold@stcatharines.library.on.ca; *Mgr, Info Tech, Network Serv,* David Bott; Tel: 905-688-6103, Ext 212, E-mail: dbott@stcatharines.library.on.ca; *Mgr, Tech Serv,* John Dunn; Tel: 905-688-6103, Ext 202, E-mail: jdunn@stcatharines.library.on.ca; Staff 70 (MLS 15, Non-MLS 55)
Founded 1888. Pop 130,926
Jan 2005-Dec 2005 Income (Main Library and Branch(s)) (CAN) $5,054,550, Provincial (CAN) $228,600, City (CAN) $4,427,500, Locally Generated Income (CAN) $398,450. Mats Exp (CAN) $902,600, Books (CAN) $619,000, Per/Ser (Incl. Access Fees) (CAN) $44,192, Micro (CAN) $88,000, AV Mat (CAN) $87,000, Electronic Ref Mat (Incl. Access Fees) (CAN) $44,808, Presv (CAN) $19,600. Sal (CAN) $3,414,250
Library Holdings: AV Mats 38,291; CDs 16,000; DVDs 16,000; e-journals 46,500; Large Print Bks 7,000; Bk Titles 211,685; Bk Vols 327,139; Per Subs 681
Subject Interests: Genealogy, Local hist
Automation Activity & Vendor Info: (Acquisitions) SirsiDynix; (Cataloging) SirsiDynix; (Circulation) SirsiDynix; (ILL) SirsiDynix; (OPAC) SirsiDynix; (Serials) SirsiDynix
Database Vendor: EBSCOhost, Gale Cengage Learning, ProQuest
Wireless access
Partic in Southern Ontario Libr Serv
Special Services for the Deaf - TDD equip
Open Tues-Thurs 10-9, Fri 10-6, Sat 9-5
Branches: 3
GRANTHAM BRANCH, 425 Carlton St, L2M 4W8, SAN 368-2838. Tel: 905-934-7511. FAX: 905-688-6292. *Br Mgr,* Anna Chiota; Tel: 905-688-6103, Ext 345, E-mail: achiota@stcatharines.library.on.ca
Founded 1888. Pop 50,000
Library Holdings: Bk Vols 58,917; Per Subs 50
Open Tues-Fri 10-8, Sat 9-5
WILLIAM HAMILTON MERRITT BRANCH, 149 Hartzel Rd, L2P 1N6, SAN 370-2251. Tel: 905-682-3568. FAX: 905-688-6292. *Br Mgr,* Anna Chiota; Tel: 905-688-6103, Ext 245, E-mail: achiota@stcatharines.library.on.ca
Library Holdings: Bk Vols 34,331; Per Subs 50
Open Tues-Fri 10-8, Sat 9-5
PORT DALHOUSIE BRANCH, 23 Brock St, L2N 5E1. (Mail add: 54 Church St, L2R 7K2), SAN 368-2897. Tel: 905-646-0220. FAX: 905-688-6292. *Br Mgr,* Anna Chiota; Tel: 905-688-6103, Ext 245
Library Holdings: Bk Vols 9,455; Per Subs 25
Subject Interests: Local hist
Open Tues 1-8, Thurs 10-8, Sat 11-4

ST. ISIDORE

P　NATION MUNICIPALITY PUBLIC LIBRARY, St Isidore Public Library, 25 Arena St, K0C 2B0. SAN 319-3950. Tel: 613-524-2252. FAX: 613-524-2545. E-mail: biblioinfo@nationmun.ca. Web Site: www.nationmunbiblio.ca. *Chief Exec Officer,* Jeanne Leroux; E-mail: jeanneleroux@nationmun.ca
Founded 1974. Pop 10,499; Circ 36,000
Jan 2005-Dec 2005 Income $224,832, Provincial $16,332, County $200,500, Locally Generated Income $8,000. Mats Exp $33,336. Sal $139,000
Library Holdings: DVDs 400; Bk Vols 41,000; Per Subs 407
Automation Activity & Vendor Info: (Cataloging) Mandarin Library Automation; (Circulation) Mandarin Library Automation; (OPAC) Mandarin Library Automation
Partic in Southern Ontario Libr Serv
Open Mon, Wed & Thurs 1:30-5:30, Tues 2-8, Fri 2-8, Sat 9-12
Branches: 2
LIMOGES BRANCH, 205 Limoges Rd, Limoges, K0A 2M0. Tel: 613-443-1630. FAX: 613-443-9643. E-mail: biblioinfo@nationmun.ca. Web Site: www.nationmunbiblio.ca. *Chief Exec Officer,* Jeanne Leroux; E-mail: jeanneleroux@nationmun.ca
Open Mon 2:30-6:30, Tues & Wed 5-8, Thurs 4-8, Fri 3-8, Sat 10-1

ST ALBERT BRANCH, 116 Principale St, Saint Albert, K0A 3C0. (Mail add: St Albert Branch, c/o 25 rue de l'arena, St Isidore, K0C 2B0). Tel: 613-987-2143. FAX: 613-987-2909. E-mail: biblioinfo@nationmun.ca. Web Site: www.nationmunbiblio.ca. *Chief Exec Officer,* Jeanne Leroux; E-mail: jeanneleroux@nationmun.ca

Open Mon & Thurs 5-8, Tues & Wed 2:30-6:30, Fri 3-8, Sat 10-1

ST. MARYS

P   ST MARY'S PUBLIC LIBRARY, 15 Church St N, N4X 1B4. (Mail add: PO Box 700, N4X 1B4), SAN 319-3969. Tel: 519-284-3346. FAX: 519-284-2630. E-mail: libraryinfo@stmaryspubliclibrary.ca. Web Site: www.stmarys.library.on.ca. *Chief Exec Officer,* Yunmi Hwang; Staff 8 (Non-MLS 8)
Founded 1904. Pop 6,293; Circ 111,000
Library Holdings: Bk Vols 30,000; Per Subs 60
Subject Interests: Local hist
Automation Activity & Vendor Info: (Acquisitions) SirsiDynix; (Cataloging) SirsiDynix; (Circulation) SirsiDynix
Database Vendor: EBSCO Auto Repair Reference, EBSCOhost, TumbleBookLibrary
Wireless access
Partic in Southern Ontario Libr Serv
Open Mon-Thurs 10:30-8, Fri 10:30-5, Sat 9-1:30
Friends of the Library Group

ST. THOMAS

P   ELGIN COUNTY PUBLIC LIBRARY*, 450 Sunset Dr, N5R 5V1. SAN 368-2927. Tel: 519-631-1460. FAX: 519-631-9209. Reference E-mail: reference@elgin-county.on.ca. Web Site: www.library.elgin-county.on.ca. *Dir, Cultural Serv,* Brain Masschaele; E-mail: bmasschaele@elgin-county.on.ca; Staff 12 (MLS 2, Non-MLS 10)
Founded 1936. Pop 50,000; Circ 271,347
Library Holdings: Audiobooks 3,869; AV Mats 529; CDs 3,185; DVDs 4,113; e-books 37,458; e-journals 32,469; Large Print Bks 4,539; Bk Titles 107,202; Bk Vols 162,717; Per Subs 126; Videos 2,607
Subject Interests: Local hist
Automation Activity & Vendor Info: (Cataloging) SirsiDynix; (Circulation) SirsiDynix
Function: CD-ROM
Partic in Ontario Library Consortium
Open Mon-Fri 8:30-4:30
Friends of the Library Group
Branches: 10
AYLMER OLD TOWN HALL BRANCH, 38 John St S, Aylmer, N5H 2C2, SAN 368-2951. Tel: 519-773-2439. FAX: 519-773-2420. E-mail: aylmerlib@elgin-county.on.ca. Web Site: www.library.elgin-county.on.ca/aylmer. *Supvr,* Christina Mayhew; E-mail: cmayhew@elgin-county.on.ca; Staff 8 (MLS 1, Non-MLS 7)
Founded 1936
Open Mon, Tues & Thurs 9:30-8:30, Fri & Sat 9:30-5
BAYHAM TOWNSHIP, 9366 Plank Rd, Straffordville, N0J 1Y0. (Mail add: PO Box 209, Straffordville, N0J 1Y0), SAN 368-3192. Tel: 519-866-3584. FAX: 519-866-3219. E-mail: bayhamlib@elgin-county.on.ca. Web Site: www.library.elgin-county.on.ca/bayham/. *Supvr,* Eileen de Jager; Staff 4 (Non-MLS 4)
Founded 1936
Open Mon, Tues & Thurs 10-8, Fri 10-5, Sat 1-4
BELMONT BRANCH, 14134 Belmont Rd, Belmont, N0L 1B0. (Mail add: PO Box 149, Belmont, N0L 1B0), SAN 368-2986. Tel: 519-644-1560. FAX: 519-644-0533. E-mail: belmontlib@elgin-county.on.ca. Web Site: www.library.elgin-county.on.ca/belmont. *Supvr,* Maria Smit; E-mail: msmit@elgin-county.on.ca; Staff 4 (Non-MLS 4)
Founded 1936
Open Mon & Thurs 2-8:30, Tues 10-8:30, Fri 2-5, Sat 10-2
FRED BODSWORTH PUBLIC LIBRARY OF PORT BURWELL, 21 Pitt St, Port Burwell, N0J 1T0. (Mail add: PO Box 189, Port Burwell, N0J 1T0), SAN 368-3044. Tel: 519-874-4754. FAX: 519-874-4436. E-mail: ptburwelllib@elgin-county.on.ca. Web Site: www.library.elgin-county.on.ca/burwell. *Supvr,* Eileen de Jagar; Staff 4 (Non-MLS 4)
Founded 1936
Open Mon 2-5, Tues & Thurs 2-7, Sat 10-12
JOHN KENNETH GALBRAITH REFERENCE LIBRARY-DUTTON BRANCH, 236 Shackleton St, Dutton, N0L 1J0. (Mail add: PO Box 69, Dutton, N0L 1J0). SAN 368-301X. Tel: 519-762-2780. FAX: 519-762-0707. E-mail: duttonlib@elgin-county.on.ca. Web Site: www.library.elgin-county.on.ca/dutton. *Supvr,* Mary Lou McMillan; E-mail: mmcmillan@elgin-county.on.ca; Staff 6 (MLS 1, Non-MLS 5)
Founded 1936
Open Mon & Tues 10-8:30, Thurs 1-8:30, Fri & Sat 10-5
Friends of the Library Group

PORT STANLEY BRANCH, 302 Bridge St, Port Stanley, N5L 1C3, SAN 368-3079. Tel: 519-782-4241. FAX: 519-782-4861. E-mail: ptstanleylib@elgin-county.on.ca. Web Site: www.library.elgin-county.on.ca/stanley. *Supvr,* Emily Finch; E-mail: efinch@elgin-county.on.ca; Staff 5 (Non-MLS 5)
Founded 1936
Open Mon, Tues & Thurs 10-8:30, Fri 1-5, Sat 9-1
RODNEY BRANCH, 207 Furnival Rd, Rodney, N0L 2C0. (Mail add: PO Box 398, Rodney, N0L 2C0), SAN 368-3109. Tel: 519-785-2100. FAX: 519-785-1734. E-mail: rodneylib@elgin-county.on.ca. Web Site: www.library.elgin-county.on.ca/rodney. *Supvr,* Shelley Fleming; E-mail: sfleming@elgin-county.on.ca; Staff 5 (Non-MLS 5)
Founded 1936
Open Mon 3-5, Tues & Thurs 3-8, Fri 10-5, Sat 10-12
SHEDDEN BRANCH, 9557 Union Rd, Shedden, N0L 2E0. (Mail add: PO Box 10, Shedden, N0L 2E0), SAN 368-3133. Tel: 519-764-2081. FAX: 519-764-2789. E-mail: sheddenlib@elgin-county.on.ca. Web Site: www.library.elgin-county.on.ca/shedden/. *Supvr,* Emily Finch; E-mail: efinch@elgin-county.on.ca; Staff 3 (Non-MLS 3)
Founded 1936
Open Tues 2:30-8:30, Thurs & Sat 2-5, Fri 10-5
SPRINGFIELD BRANCH, Malahida Community Place, 12105 Whittaker Rd, Springfield, N0L 2J0. (Mail add: PO Box 9, Springfield, N0L 2J0), SAN 368-3168. Tel: 519-765-4515. FAX: 519-765-4453. E-mail: springfieldlib@elgin-county.on.ca. Web Site: www.library.elgin-county.on.ca/spring/. *Supvr,* Maria Smit; E-mail: msmit@elgin-county.on.ca; Staff 2 (Non-MLS 2)
Founded 1936
Open Mon & Sat 2-5, Tues 2-8:30, Thurs 10-8:30
WEST LORNE BRANCH, 160A Main St, West Lorne, N0L 2P0, SAN 368-3257. Tel: 519-768-1150. FAX: 519-768-0773. E-mail: westlornelib@elgin-county.on.ca. Web Site: www.library.elgin-county.on.ca/wlorne. *Supvr,* Shelley Fleming; E-mail: sfleming@elgin-county.on.ca; Staff 4 (Non-MLS 4)
Founded 1936
Open Mon & Fri 2-5, Tues & Thurs 2-8, Sat 10-1

M   REGIONAL MENTAL HEALTH CARE ST THOMAS*, Staff Library Services, 467 Sunset Dr, N5P 3V9. SAN 324-4075. Tel: 519-631-8510, Ext 49605. FAX: 519-631-9691. Web Site: www.sjhc.london.on.ca. *Librn,* Elizabeth Russell; Tel: 519-631-8510, Ext 49685, E-mail: elizabeth.russell@sjhc.london.on.ca; Staff 2 (MLS 1, Non-MLS 1)
Founded 1974
Library Holdings: Bk Vols 1,000; Per Subs 120
Subject Interests: Allied health, Hospital admin, Nursing, Patient educ, Psychiat, Psychol
Open Mon-Fri 8:30-4:15
Branches:
PATIENT LIBRARY, 467 Sunset Dr, N5P 3V9. Tel: 519-631-8510, Ext 49605. FAX: 519-631-9691. *Med Librn,* Elizabeth Russell; Tel: 519-631-8510, Ext 49685, E-mail: elizabeth.russell@sjhc.london.on.ca
Library Holdings: Bk Vols 2,000; Per Subs 40
Subject Interests: Humor, Life skills, Patient educ
Open Mon-Fri 8:30-4:15

P   ST THOMAS PUBLIC LIBRARY*, 153 Curtis St, N5P 3Z7. SAN 319-3977. Tel: 519-631-6050. FAX: 519-631-1987. Web Site: www.st-thomas.library.on.ca. *Chief Librn,* Rudi Denham; E-mail: rdenham@st-thomas.library.on.ca; *Head, Adult Serv,* Paul Blower; E-mail: pblower@st-thomas.library.on.ca; *Head, Ch,* Heather Robinson; E-mail: hrobinson@st-thomas.library.on.ca; *Head, Circ,* Effie Lattanzio; E-mail: elattanzio@st-thomas.library.on.ca; Staff 9 (MLS 3, Non-MLS 6)
Founded 1884. Pop 35,599; Circ 365,493
Library Holdings: Bk Titles 131,961; Bk Vols 151,069; Per Subs 204
Subject Interests: Local hist
Open Mon-Fri 9-8:30, Sat 9-5
Friends of the Library Group

STAYNER

P   CLEARVIEW PUBLIC LIBRARY, Stayner Branch, 201 Huron St, L0M 1S0. (Mail add: PO Box 160, L0M 1S0), SAN 319-4272. Tel: 705-428-3595. FAX: 705-428-3595. Web Site: www.clearview.library.on.ca. *Chief Exec Officer,* Jennifer La Chapelle; E-mail: jlachapelle@clearview.ca; Staff 11 (MLS 1, Non-MLS 10)
Founded 1994. Pop 15,000; Circ 154,000
Library Holdings: Bk Titles 68,000; Per Subs 118
Subject Interests: Fed-prov govt doc, Local hist
Automation Activity & Vendor Info: (Acquisitions) SirsiDynix; (Cataloging) SirsiDynix; (Circulation) SirsiDynix; (ILL) SirsiDynix; (OPAC) SirsiDynix
Partic in Southern Ontario Libr Serv
Open Tues-Fri 10-8, Sat 10-4

Branches: 2

CREEMORE BRANCH, 165 Library St, Creemore, L0M 1G0, SAN 319-0927. Tel: 705-466-3011. FAX: 705-466-3011. *Chief Exec Officer,* Jennifer LaChapelle

Open Tues-Fri 10-5 & 7-9, Sat 10-4

Friends of the Library Group

SUNNIDALE BRANCH, 5237 Simcoe County Rd 9, New Lowell, L0M 1N0, SAN 319-2733. Tel: 705-424-6288. FAX: 705-424-6288. *Chief Exec Officer,* Jennifer La Chapelle

Open Tues & Fri 1-6, Wed & Thurs 10-8, Sat 10-2

STIRLING

P   STIRLING-RANDON PUBLIC LIBRARY*, 43 Front St W, K0K 3E0. (Mail add: PO Box 730, K0K 3E0), SAN 319-4280. Tel: 613-395-2837. *Chief Exec Officer, Head Librn,* Sue Winfield; E-mail: sue@stirlinglibrary.com; *Asst Librn,* Theresa Brennan; Staff 4 (Non-MLS 4)

Founded 1903. Pop 5,000; Circ 47,000

Library Holdings: Bk Titles 28,000; Per Subs 85

Wireless access

Partic in Southern Ontario Libr Serv

Friends of the Library Group

STONECLIFFE

P   HEAD, CLARA, & MARIA TOWNSHIP PUBLIC LIBRARY*, 15 Township Hall Rd, K0J 2K0. SAN 319-4302. Tel: 613-586-2526. FAX: 613-586-2596. E-mail: hcmlibra@xplornet.com. Web Site: hcmpubliclibrary.ca. *Librn,* Gayle Watters

Pop 300; Circ 1,800

Library Holdings: Bk Vols 2,400

Wireless access

Partic in Southern Ontario Libr Serv

Open Mon-Fri 8:30-4, Tues 6:30pm-8pm, Sat 12:30-3

STOUFFVILLE

P   WHITCHURCH-STOUFFVILLE PUBLIC LIBRARY, 30 Burkholder St, L4A 4K1. SAN 319-4329. Tel: 905-642-7323. Toll Free Tel: 888-603-4292. FAX: 905-640-1384. Web Site: www.whitchurch-library.on.ca. *Chief Exec Officer,* Carolyn Nordheimer James; *Coordr, Pub Serv,* Catherine Sword; E-mail: csword@whitchurch-library.on.ca; *Ch, Youth Serv,* Anne Houle; E-mail: ahoule@whitchurch-library.on.ca; Staff 5 (MLS 4, Non-MLS 1)

Founded 1899. Pop 40,000; Circ 237,895

Library Holdings: Bk Titles 85,969; Bk Vols 86,985; Per Subs 126

Wireless access

Open Mon-Thurs (Winter) 10-8:30, Fri 10-6, Sat 10-5, Sun 12-5; Mon-Thurs (Summer) 10-8:30, Fri & Sat 10-4

STRATFORD

P   STRATFORD PUBLIC LIBRARY*, 19 Saint Andrew St, N5A 1A2. SAN 319-4337. Tel: 519-271-0220. FAX: 519-271-3843. Web Site: www.stratford.library.on.ca. *Dir,* Sam Coghlan; Tel: 519-271-0220, Ext 15, E-mail: scoghlan@city.stratford.on.ca; Staff 7 (MLS 7)

Founded 1846. Pop 33,000; Circ 368,755

Library Holdings: AV Mats 7,013; Bk Vols 102,132; Per Subs 173; Talking Bks 1,138

Special Collections: Chalmers Public Theatre Resource Coll; Fed & Prov

Subject Interests: Performing arts, Theatre

Automation Activity & Vendor Info: (Cataloging) SirsiDynix; (Circulation) SirsiDynix; (OPAC) SirsiDynix

Database Vendor: SirsiDynix

Partic in Perth County Information Network; Southern Ontario Libr Serv

Open Mon 1-9, Tues-Thurs 10-9, Fri 10-6, Sat 10-5, Sun 2-5

Friends of the Library Group

STRATHROY

P   MIDDLESEX COUNTY LIBRARY*, 34B Frank St, N7G 2R4. (Mail add: PO Box 5007, N7G 2R4), SAN 366-9335. Tel: 519-245-8237. FAX: 519-245-8238. Web Site: www.middlesex.library.on.ca. *Dir, Info Serv,* Lindsey Brock; Tel: 519-245-8237, Ext 4022, E-mail: lbrock@middlesex.ca; *County Librn,* Julie DeVries; E-mail: jdevries@middlesex.ca; *Ch,* Patricia Wallace; *Syst Coordr,* Beverly Sweezie; Staff 14 (MLS 7, Non-MLS 7)

Founded 1963. Pop 71,000; Circ 389,048

Library Holdings: AV Mats 3,906; Large Print Bks 3,201; Bk Titles 185,000; Per Subs 434; Talking Bks 1,072

Subject Interests: Local hist

Automation Activity & Vendor Info: (Cataloging) SirsiDynix; (Circulation) SirsiDynix; (OPAC) SirsiDynix

Wireless access

Partic in Ontario Library Consortium; Southern Ontario Libr Serv

Special Services for the Blind - Talking bks

Friends of the Library Group

Branches: 14

AILSA CRAIG BRANCH, 147 Main St, Ailsa Craig, N0M 1A0, SAN 366-936X. Tel: 519-293-3441. FAX: 519-293-9319. *Supvr,* Anne Vandenbogaard; E-mail: avandenbogaard@middlesex.ca; Staff 3 (Non-MLS 3)

Open Mon & Tues 2-5 & 6:30pm-8:30pm, Wed 6:30pm-8:30pm, Thurs 10-12:30 & 2-8:30, Fri 2-5, Sat 10-1

Friends of the Library Group

DELAWARE BRANCH, 29 Young St, Delaware, N0L 1E0, SAN 366-9815. Tel: 519-652-9978. FAX: 519-652-0166. *Supvr,* Linda Verberne; Staff 1 (Non-MLS 1)

Open Tues 3-5 & 6:30pm-8:30pm, Thurs 6:30pm-8:30pm, Sat 10-Noon

DORCHESTER BRANCH, 2123 Dorchester Rd, Dorchester, N0L 1G0, SAN 366-9513. Tel: 519-268-3451. FAX: 519-268-1047. E-mail: dorchester_staff@middlesex.ca. Web Site: www.middlesex.library.on.ca/branch/dorchester.asp. *Supvr,* Kathryn Suffoletta; E-mail: ksuffoletta@middlesex.ca; *Br Asst,* Kathy Campeau; Staff 4 (Non-MLS 4)

Open Mon & Wed 2:30-8:30, Tues & Thurs 10-8:30, Fri 10-8, Sat 10-4

GLENCOE BRANCH, 178 McKellar St, Glencoe, N0L 1M0, SAN 366-9572. Tel: 519-287-2735. *Supvr,* Janice Moniz; E-mail: jmoniz@middlesex.ca; Staff 3 (Non-MLS 3)

Open Tues-Thurs 2-8:30, Fri 10-4:30, Sat 10-2

ILDERTON BRANCH, 40 Heritage Dr, Ilderton, N0M 2A0, SAN 366-9661. Tel: 519-666-1599. FAX: 519-666-2107. *Supvr,* Jean Moir; Staff 3 (Non-MLS 3)

Open Mon 1:30-8:30, Tues 2-5 & 6:30-8:30, Wed 6:30pm-8:30pm, Thurs 10-12, 2-5 & 6:30-8:30, Fri 2-5, Sat 10-1

KOMOKA BRANCH, One Tunks Lane, Komoka, N0L 1R0, SAN 366-984X. Tel: 519-657-1461. *Supvr,* Tammy Johnson; E-mail: tjohnson@middlesex.ca; Staff 5 (MLS 1, Non-MLS 4)

Open Mon & Sat 10-4, Tues 10-8, Wed-Fri 2-8

LUCAN BRANCH, 261 Main St, Lucan, N0M 2J0, SAN 366-9726. Tel: 519-227-4682. *Supvr,* Leanne Robinson; Staff 2 (Non-MLS 2)

Open Mon 2:30-8:30, Tues 2-5 & 6:30-8:30, Wed 2-5, Thurs 10-12 & 2:30-8:30, Fri 10-12 & 2-5, Sat 10-1

Friends of the Library Group

MELBOURNE BRANCH, 6570 Longwoods Rd, Melbourne, N0L 1T0, SAN 366-9750. Tel: 519-289-2405. FAX: 519-289-0191. *Supvr,* Sue King; Staff 1 (Non-MLS 1)

Open Tues 3-5, Thurs 4:30-8:30, Fri 10-Noon

MOUNT BRYDGES BRANCH, 22501 Adelaide Rd, Mount Brydges, N0L 1W0, SAN 366-9785. Tel: 519-264-1061. *Supvr,* Mary McIntyre; Staff 2 (Non-MLS 2)

Open Mon 1:30-8:30, Tues-Thurs 2-5 & 6:30-8:30, Fri 10-Noon, Sat 10-1

NEWBURY BRANCH, 22894 Hagerty St, Newbury, N0L 1Z0. (Mail add: PO Box 240, Newbury, N0L 1Z0), SAN 366-9874. Tel: 519-693-4275. FAX: 519-693-4493. *Supvr,* Diana Watson

Open Mon & Thurs 2-5, Wed 6:30pm-8:30pm

PARKHILL BRANCH, 233 Main St, Parkhill, N0M 2K0, SAN 366-9939. Tel: 519-294-6583. *Supvr,* Liz Adema; Staff 2 (Non-MLS 2)

Open Mon & Thurs 2-5 & 6:30-8:30, Tues 1:30-8:30, Wed 6:30pm-8:30pm, Fri 10-12 & 2-5, Sat 10-1

STRATHROY BRANCH, 34 Frank St, N7G 2R4, SAN 378-2409. Tel: 519-245-1290. FAX: 519-245-0647. *Supvr,* Aimee Starzynski; Staff 6 (MLS 2, Non-MLS 4)

Special Collections: Middlesex County Local History

Open Mon-Fri 10-8:30, Sat 10-4

Friends of the Library Group

THORNDALE BRANCH, 21790 Fairview Rd, Thorndale, N0M 2P0. (Mail add: PO Box 88, Thorndale, N0M 2P0), SAN 367-0023. Tel: 519-461-1150. FAX: 519-461-0561. *Supvr,* Debbie Guy; Staff 2 (Non-MLS 2)

Open Mon & Wed 2:30-8:30, Tues & Thurs 2-5 & 6:30-8:30, Fri 10-12 & 2-5, Sat 10-1

Friends of the Library Group

WARDSVILLE BRANCH, 21935 Hagerty Rd, Wardsville, N0L 2N0, SAN 366-9998. Tel: 519-693-4208. *Supvr,* Jennifer DeBruyne; Staff 1 (Non-MLS 1)

Open Tues & Fri 2-5, Thurs 6:30pm-8:30pm

STURGEON FALLS

P   WEST NIPISSING PUBLIC LIBRARY*, 225 rue Holditch, Ste 107, P2B 1T1. SAN 319-4353. Tel: 705-753-2620. FAX: 705-753-2131. E-mail: mail@wnpl.ca. *Chief Exec Officer,* Carole Marion; E-mail: cmarion@wnpl.ca; *Archives,* Frances Cockburn; *Libr Tech,* Susie Michaud; E-mail: smichaud@wnpl.ca

Founded 1963. Pop 13,650

Library Holdings: Audiobooks 87; Bks on Deafness & Sign Lang 11; CDs 745; DVDs 1,680; e-books 4,854; Large Print Bks 664; Bk Titles 47,060; Bk Vols 53,455; Per Subs 66; Talking Bks 87; Videos 2,179

Automation Activity & Vendor Info: (Cataloging) Mandarin Library Automation; (Circulation) Mandarin Library Automation; (OPAC) Mandarin Library Automation
Wireless access
Open Tues-Thurs 10-5 & 7pm-9pm, Fri 10-5, Sat 10-4
Branches: 3
CACHE BAY BRANCH, 55 Cache St, Cache Bay, P0H 1G0. (Mail add: PO Box 10, Cache Bay, P0H 1G0), SAN 319-065X. Tel: 705-753-9393. FAX: 705-753-9393. E-mail: cachebay@wnpl.ca. *Librn,* Lucienne Desjardins; *Librn,* Susie Michaud
Pop 679; Circ 3,405
Library Holdings: Bk Vols 9,500
Open Mon & Wed 10-12, Tues & Thurs 6pm-8pm
FIELD BRANCH, 59 rue Ecole, Field, P0H 1M0. (Mail add: PO Box 10, Field, P0H 1M0), SAN 319-129X. Tel: 705-758-6610. FAX: 705-758-6610. E-mail: field@wnpl.ca. *Head of Libr,* Lucienne Desjardins
Founded 1972. Pop 707; Circ 7,177
Library Holdings: Bk Titles 9,562; Bk Vols 15,500; Per Subs 11
Open Mon & Wed 6:30pm-9pm, Tues & Thurs 1-4:30
VERNER BRANCH, 11790 Hwy 64, Verner, P0H 2M0. Tel: 705-594-2800. FAX: 705-594-2800. E-mail: wncap5@onlink.net. *Head of Libr,* Diane Tellier
Open Mon & Wed 6pm-9pm, Tues 3-5, Thurs 2-5, Fri 6pm-8pm

SUDBURY

J   CAMBRIAN COLLEGE OF APPLIED ARTS & TECHNOLOGY LIBRARY*, 1400 Barrydowne Rd, P3A 3V8. SAN 368-394X. Tel: 705-524-7333. FAX: 705-566-6163. E-mail: library@cambrianc.on.ca. Web Site: www.cambriancollege.ca/departments/library/Pages/default.aspx. *Librn,* Susan Bartlett; Staff 7 (MLS 1, Non-MLS 6)
Founded 1967. Enrl 4,000; Fac 200
Library Holdings: Music Scores 840; Bk Titles 35,000; Per Subs 225; Videos 1,500
Special Collections: College Art Coll
Automation Activity & Vendor Info: (Circulation) Mandarin Library Automation; (OPAC) Mandarin Library Automation
Open Mon-Thurs 8am-10pm, Fri 8-8, Sat & Sun 11-5

P   GREATER SUDBURY PUBLIC LIBRARY*, Bibliotheque Publique de Grand Sudbury, 74 MacKenzie St, P3C 4X8. SAN 368-4121. Tel: 705-673-1155. FAX: 705-673-6145. Web Site: www.sudbury.library.on.ca. *Chief Exec Officer, Dir,* Ron Henderson; *Mgr, Libr Heritage Res,* Claire Zuleani; Staff 49 (MLS 8, Non-MLS 41)
Founded 1912. Pop 155,000
Library Holdings: Bk Vols 600,000
Special Collections: Oral History
Subject Interests: Local hist
Automation Activity & Vendor Info: (Acquisitions) Innovative Interfaces, Inc; (Cataloging) Innovative Interfaces, Inc; (Circulation) Innovative Interfaces, Inc; (Course Reserve) Innovative Interfaces, Inc; (ILL) Innovative Interfaces, Inc; (Media Booking) Innovative Interfaces, Inc; (OPAC) Innovative Interfaces, Inc; (Serials) Innovative Interfaces, Inc
Open Mon-Thurs 9-9, Fri 9-5, Sat 10-4, Sun (Oct-May) 12-4
Friends of the Library Group
Branches: 12
AZILDA BRANCH, 120 Ste-Agnus St, Azilda, P0M 1B0. (Mail add: PO Box 818, Azilda, P0M 1B0), SAN 329-7659. Tel: 705-983-3955. FAX: 705-983-4119. *Librn,* Denise Lalonde
Open Mon, Tues & Thurs 3-8, Wed & Sat 10-2
CAPREOL BRANCH, Nine Morin St, Capreol, P0M 1H0, SAN 319-0684. Tel: 705-688-3958. FAX: 705-858-1085. *Librn,* Lynn Imbeau
Library Holdings: Bk Vols 13,000; Per Subs 14
CHELMSFORD CITIZEN SERVICE CENTER PUBLIC LIBRARY, 3502 Errington St, Chelmsford, P0M 1L0, SAN 319-0781. Tel: 705-688-3963, 705-855-2593. FAX: 705-855-4629. *Librn,* Lise Paquette-Lalonde
Founded 1971. Pop 14,745; Circ 77,516
Library Holdings: Bk Vols 37,000; Per Subs 143
Open Mon-Thurs 8:30-8, Fri 9-5, Sat 10-4, Sun 1-4
CONISTON BRANCH, 32nd Ave, Coniston, P0M 1M0. Tel: 705-688-3953. FAX: 705-694-0992.
COPPER CLIFF CENTENNIAL BRANCH, 11 Balsam St, Copper Cliff, P0M 1N0. (Mail add: PO Box 790, Copper Cliff, P0M 1N0), SAN 368-4156. Tel: 705-688-3954. FAX: 705-682-0484. *Librn,* Marilyn Knoll
Library Holdings: Bk Vols 20,000
GARSON BRANCH, 214 Orell St, Garson, P3L 1V2, SAN 319-1389. Tel: 705-688-3957. FAX: 705-693-5540.
Founded 1972
Library Holdings: Bk Vols 66,141; Per Subs 36
Open Mon-Thurs 1-8, Fri & Sat 1-4
LEVACK/ ONAPING PUBLIC, One Hillside Ave, Onaping, P0M 2R0, SAN 373-0158. Tel: 705-688-3951. FAX: 705-966-1769.
Pop 5,954; Circ 54,632
Library Holdings: Bk Vols 15,400; Per Subs 17

Open Mon 10-2, Tues, Wed & Thurs 3-8, Sat 10-2
Friends of the Library Group
LIVELY BRANCH, 15 Kin Dr, Lively, P3Y 1M3. Tel: 705-688-3959. FAX: 705-692-4261.
NEW SUDBURY, 1346 Lasalle Blvd, P3A 1Z6, SAN 368-4245. Tel: 705-688-3952. *Librn,* Rebecca McArthur; Staff 9 (MLS 1, Non-MLS 8)
Founded 1960
Library Holdings: Bk Vols 47,000; Per Subs 100
Special Collections: Children's Story Hour Coll
Mem of Ontario Library Service North
Friends of the Library Group
LIONEL RHEAUME PUBLIC, 79 Main St, Dowling, P0M 1R0, SAN 321-7302. Tel: 705-688-3956. FAX: 705-855-2591. *Librn,* Diane McGirr
Library Holdings: Bk Vols 35,000
Open Mon-Thurs 9-9, Fri 9-5, Sat 10-4
Friends of the Library Group
SOUTH, 1991 Regent St S, P3E 3Z9, SAN 368-4210. Tel: 705-688-3950. FAX: 705-522-7788. *Librn,* Rebecca McArthur
Library Holdings: Bk Vols 42,114
Open Mon-Thurs 8:30am-8pm, Fri 8:30-5, Sat 10-4, Sun 1-4
VALLEY EAST, 4100 Elmview Dr, Hanmer, P3P 1J7, SAN 319-5821. Tel: 705-688-3961. FAX: 705-969-7787. *Librn,* Richard Clouthier; Staff 8 (MLS 1, Non-MLS 7)
Founded 1971
Library Holdings: Bk Vols 70,000; Per Subs 110
Subject Interests: Local hist

M   HEALTH SCIENCES NORTH, Health Sciences Library, 41 Ramsey Lake Rd, P3E 5J1. SAN 320-7994. Tel: 705-523-7100, Ext 3375. FAX: 705-523-7317. E-mail: library@hsnsudbury.ca. Web Site: www.hsnsudbury.ca/PortalEn/library. *Librn,* Irma Sauvola; E-mail: isauvola@hsnsudbury.ca; *Librn,* Jami van Haaften; E-mail: jvanhaaften@hsnsudbury.ca; Staff 4 (MLS 2, Non-MLS 2)
Automation Activity & Vendor Info: (Cataloging) Evergreen; (Circulation) Evergreen; (OPAC) Evergreen
Database Vendor: EBSCOhost, OVID Technologies
Wireless access

C   HUNTINGTON UNIVERSITY*, J W Tate Library, Laurentian Campus, 935 Ramsey Lake Rd, P3E 2C6. SAN 326-5560. Tel: 705-673-4126, Ext 220. FAX: 705-673-6917. Web Site: www.huntingtonu.ca/library. *Head Librn,* Natasha Gerolami; Tel: 705-673-4126, Ext 248, E-mail: ngerolami@laurentian.ca; Staff 1 (MLS 1)
Founded 1961. Fac 20; Highest Degree: Master
May 2011-Apr 2012. Mats Exp (CAN) $34,750, Books (CAN) $21,500, Per/Ser (Incl. Access Fees) (CAN) $3,800, Electronic Ref Mat (Incl. Access Fees) (CAN) $7,000, Presv (CAN) $2,450
Library Holdings: DVDs 1,000; e-journals 43; Bk Vols 12,115; Per Subs 30; Videos 1,150
Subject Interests: Communication studies, Ethics, Gerontology, Relig studies, Theol
Automation Activity & Vendor Info: (Acquisitions) Evergreen; (Cataloging) Evergreen; (Circulation) Evergreen; (Course Reserve) Evergreen; (OPAC) Evergreen
Wireless access
Function: Prof lending libr
Open Mon-Thurs (Winter) 9-9, Fri 9-4; Mon-Fri (Summer) 9-4:30

C   LAURENTIAN UNIVERSITY*, J N Desmarais Library, 935 Ramsey Lake Rd, P3E 2C6. SAN 368-4032. Tel: 705-675-1151, Ext 3302. Circulation Tel: 705-675-4800. Interlibrary Loan Service Tel: 705-675-1151, Ext 3317. Reference Tel: 705-675-4803. Information Services Tel: 705-675-1151, Ext 3330. Toll Free Tel: 800-461-4030. FAX: 705-675-4877. Interlibrary Loan Service FAX: 705-673-6524. Information Services FAX: 705-673-3803. Web Site: www.laurentian.ca/library. *Chair, Dept of Libr & Archives,* Sylvie Lafortune; E-mail: slafortune@laurentian.ca; *Univ Librn,* Leila Wallenius; Tel: 705-675-4841, E-mail: lwallenius@laurentian.ca; *Electronic Res Librn,* Alain Lamothe; Tel: 705-675-1151, Ext 3304, E-mail: alamothe@laurentian.ca; *Librn,* Desmond Maley; Tel: 705-675-1151, Ext 3323, E-mail: dmaley@laurentian.ca; *Librn,* Ashley Thomson; Tel: 705-675-1151, Ext 3322, E-mail: athomson@laurentian.ca; *Librn - Fr Serv,* Leila Saadaoui; Tel: 705-675-151, Ext 3319, E-mail: lsaadaoui@laurentian.ca; *Syst Librn,* Dan Scott; Tel: 705-675-1151, Ext 3315, E-mail: dscott@laurentian.ca; *Circ Supvr,* Lise Seguin; Tel: 705-675-1151, Ext 3336, E-mail: lseguin@laurentian.ca; *Archivist,* Marthe Brown; Tel: 705-675-1151, Ext 3329, E-mail: mbrown@laurentian.ca. *Subject Specialists: Archives,* Marthe Brown; Staff 31 (MLS 7, Non-MLS 24)
Founded 1960. Enrl 8,478; Fac 386; Highest Degree: Doctorate
May 2011-Apr 2012. Mats Exp (CAN) $1,985,686, Books (CAN) $273,422, Per/Ser (Incl. Access Fees) (CAN) $420,996, Electronic Ref Mat (Incl. Access Fees) (CAN) $56,753. Sal (CAN) $2,141,656 (Prof (CAN) $1,140,805)

Library Holdings: CDs 344; e-books 5,287; e-journals 190,000; Electronic Media & Resources 109; Bk Titles 433,283; Bk Vols 698,547; Per Subs 43,000; Videos 344
Special Collections: Franco-Ontarienne Coll; Mining Environment
Subject Interests: Admin, Commerce, Educ, Eng, Humanities, Justice, Law, Midwifery, Nursing, Soc work
Automation Activity & Vendor Info: (Acquisitions) Evergreen; (Cataloging) Evergreen; (Circulation) Evergreen; (Course Reserve) Evergreen; (ILL) Evergreen; (Media Booking) Evergreen; (OPAC) Evergreen; (Serials) Evergreen
Database Vendor: 3M Library Systems, Cambridge Scientific Abstracts, Dialog, EBSCOhost, Gale Cengage Learning, JSTOR, LexisNexis, netLibrary, OCLC WorldCat, OVID Technologies, ProQuest, Wilson - Wilson Web
Wireless access
Function: Archival coll
Publications: Regional & local bibliographies
Partic in Canadian Research Knowledge Network
Special Services for the Deaf - Staff with knowledge of sign lang; TTY equip
Special Services for the Blind - Assistive/Adapted tech devices, equip & products; Closed circuit TV; Closed circuit TV magnifier; Computer with voice synthesizer for visually impaired persons; Dragon Naturally Speaking software; Inspiration software; Large screen computer & software; Micro-computer access & training; Reader equip; Scanner for conversion & translation of mats; Talking calculator; ZoomText magnification & reading software
The services for Specials Needs students are through the Special Needs Office which is located in the Learning Commons, which is located in our library
Open Mon-Thurs 8:30am-2am, Fri 8:30am-10pm, Sat Noon-10pm, Sun Noon-2am

G   ONTARIO MINISTRY OF NORTHERN DEVELOPMENT, MINES & FORESTRY LIBRARY*, John B Gammon Geoscience Library, 933 Ramsey Lake Rd, Level A-3, P3E 6B5. SAN 319-5376. Tel: 705-670-5614. Toll Free Tel: 888-415-9845, Ext 5614. FAX: 705-670-5770. E-mail: mines.library.ndm@ontario.ca. Web Site: www.mndm.gov.on.ca/mines/ogs/ims/library/default_e.asp. *Libr Tech,* Johanne Roux; Staff 1 (Non-MLS 1)
Library Holdings: Bk Vols 100,000; Per Subs 40
Subject Interests: Eng geol, Geol of Ont, Maps, Mining, Theses
Automation Activity & Vendor Info: (Cataloging) Inmagic, Inc.
Database Vendor: EBSCOhost
Open Mon-Fri 8:30-5

S   SUDBURY ROCK & LAPIDARY SOCIETY LIBRARY*, 456 Kaireen St, P3E 5R9. SAN 373-8590. Tel: 705-522-5140. FAX: 705-522-5140. Web Site: www.ccfms.ca/clubs/sudbury. *Librn,* Ruth Debicki; E-mail: ed.debicki@sympatico.ca
Founded 1987
Jan 2006-Dec 2006. Mats Exp $500, Books $150, Per/Ser (Incl. Access Fees) $150, Other Print Mats $50, AV Mat $150
Library Holdings: Bk Titles 60
Special Collections: Back Issues of Lapidary Journal, Mineralogical Record, The Russian Stone & The Canadian Gemmologist, Rock & Minerals, Rock & Gen
Subject Interests: Fossils, Gems
Restriction: Not open to pub

C   UNIVERSITY OF SUDBURY LIBRARY*, 935 Ramsey Lake Rd, P3E 2C6. SAN 319-4388. Tel: 705-673-5661. FAX: 705-673-4912. Web Site: www.usudbury.ca. *Coll Develop, Dir,* Paul Laverdure; Tel: 705-673-5661, Ext 208, E-mail: plaverdure@usudbury.ca; *Head, Circ,* Jacques Trottier; Tel: 705-673-5661, Ext 216; *Tech Serv,* Angele St Amour; Tel: 705-673-5661, Ext 207, E-mail: astamour@usudbury.ca; Staff 3 (MLS 1, Non-MLS 2)
Founded 1958. Enrl 1,300; Fac 18; Highest Degree: Master
Library Holdings: Bk Vols 56,300; Per Subs 160
Special Collections: French Canadian Folklore (Coll Luc Lacourciere); Jesuit Archives
Subject Interests: Communication, Folklore, Native studies, Philosophy, Pub relations, Relig studies
Automation Activity & Vendor Info: (Cataloging) SirsiDynix; (Circulation) SirsiDynix; (OPAC) SirsiDynix
Database Vendor: EBSCOhost, SirsiDynix
Open Mon-Fri (Winter) 9-4:30; Mon-Fri (Summer) 8:30-4

SUNDRIDGE

P   SUNDRIDGE-STRONG UNION PUBLIC LIBRARY*, 110 Main St, P0A 1Z0. (Mail add: PO Box 429, P0A 1Z0). Tel: 705-384-7311. FAX: 705-384-7311. E-mail: sslibrary@hotmail.com. Web Site: www.olsn.ca/sundridgestronglibrary. *Librn,* Denise Rogers; *Asst Librn,* Brenda Lee

Founded 1978. Pop 2,500; Circ 17,424
Library Holdings: CDs 10; DVDs 16; Large Print Bks 250; Bk Titles 10,000; Bk Vols 12,000; Per Subs 13; Talking Bks 101; Videos 425
Special Collections: Local History (files, books, photos, 1881 & 1891 census)
Automation Activity & Vendor Info: (Cataloging) Follett Software; (Circulation) Follett Software
Partic in Ont Libr Serv-North
Open Mon, Tues & Fri 10-3, Wed 10-3 & 6pm-9pm, Thurs 10-5, Sat 9-Noon
Friends of the Library Group

TERRACE BAY

P   TERRACE BAY PUBLIC LIBRARY*, 1010B Hwy 17 & Selkirk Ave, P0T 2W0. (Mail add: PO Box 369, P0T 2W0), SAN 319-4418. Tel: 807-825-3315, Ext 222. FAX: 807-825-1249. E-mail: terpl@nwconx.net. Web Site: www.nwconx.net/~terpl. *Chief Exec Officer,* Mary Deschatelets; Tel: 807-825-3315, Ext 234, E-mail: m.deschatelets@terracebay.ca
Founded 1947. Pop 1,650; Circ 20,700
Library Holdings: Bk Titles 18,000; Bk Vols 20,000; Per Subs 50
Subject Interests: Foreign lang, Local hist
Automation Activity & Vendor Info: (Acquisitions) SIRSI WorkFlows; (Cataloging) SIRSI WorkFlows; (Circulation) SIRSI WorkFlows; (ILL) SIRSI WorkFlows; (OPAC) SIRSI-iBistro; (Serials) SIRSI WorkFlows
Database Vendor: EBSCOhost
Function: Archival coll, Audio & video playback equip for onsite use, CD-ROM, Computer training, Copy machines, e-mail serv, Electronic databases & coll, Fax serv, Handicapped accessible, Homebound delivery serv, ILL available, Magnifiers for reading, Mail & tel request accepted, Online searches, Orientations, Photocopying/Printing, Preschool outreach, Prog for children & young adult, Senior computer classes, Spoken cassettes & CDs, Spoken cassettes & DVDs, Summer reading prog, Telephone ref, VHS videos, Video lending libr, Wheelchair accessible
Publications: Birchwood Terrace (Local historical information); History of Jackfish (Local historical information); Terrace Bay - First 50 Years (Local historical information)
Special Services for the Deaf - Bks on deafness & sign lang
Special Services for the Blind - Audio mat; Bks & mags in Braille, on rec, tape & cassette; Bks on cassette; Bks on CD; Braille bks; Cassette playback machines; Daisy reader; Large print bks; Large screen computer & software; Talking bks

THESSALON

P   THESSALON PUBLIC LIBRARY, 187 Main St, P0R 1L0. (Mail add: PO Box 549, P0R 1L0). Tel: 705-842-2306. FAX: 705-842-5690. E-mail: library@thesslibcap.com. Web Site: www.thesslibcap.com. *Chief Exec Officer,* Sandra McKee
Library Holdings: Bk Vols 10,000
Wireless access
Open Mon, Tues, Thurs & Fri 1-5 & 7pm-9pm, Wed 10-Noon, Sat 2-5

THORNBURY

P   THE BLUE MOUNTAINS PUBLIC LIBRARY*, Leonard E Shore Memorial Library, 173 Bruce St S, N0H 2P0. (Mail add: PO Box 580, N0H 2P0), SAN 319-4426. Tel: 519-599-3681. FAX: 519-599-7951. E-mail: libraryinfo@thebluemountains.ca. Web Site: www.thebluemountainslibrary.ca. *Chief Exec Officer,* Carol Cooley; *Ch,* Jenn Perks; *Circ,* Donna St Jacques; *Tech Serv,* Laurel Moss
Pop 6,500; Circ 60,000
Library Holdings: Bk Vols 40,000; Per Subs 48
Partic in Southern Ontario Libr Serv
Open Tues & Thurs 1-8, Wed, Fri & Sat 10-5, Sun 1-4

THORNHILL

S   ANTHROPOSOPHICAL SOCIETY IN CANADA LIBRARY*, 9100 Bathurst St, Lower Level Hesperus Fellowship Community, L4J 8C7. SAN 321-6896. Tel: 905-886-5163. FAX: 905-886-4989. E-mail: library@anthroposophy.ca. Web Site: www.anthroposophy.ca. *Adminr,* Mark McAlister
Founded 1953
Library Holdings: Bk Titles 3,100; Bk Vols 4,000; Per Subs 12
Subject Interests: Anthroposophy, esp the works of Rudolf Steiner

P   VAUGHAN PUBLIC LIBRARIES*, 900 Clark Ave W, L4J 8C1. Tel: 905-653-7323. FAX: 905-709-1530. Web Site: www.vaughanpl.info. *Chief Exec Officer,* Margie Singleton
Pop 250,000; Circ 2,000,000
Library Holdings: Bk Titles 195,085; Bk Vols 399,775; Per Subs 434
Automation Activity & Vendor Info: (Acquisitions) VTLS, Inc; (Cataloging) VTLS, Inc; (Circulation) VTLS, Inc

Wireless access
Function: Homebound delivery serv, ILL available, Photocopying/Printing, Ref serv available, Telephone ref
Branches: 7
ANSLEY GROVE LIBRARY, 350 Ansley Grove Rd, Woodbridge, L4L 5C9. Tel: 905-653-7323. FAX: 905-856-6151. *Libr Coordr,* Farida Shaikh
 Open Tues-Thurs 10-9, Fri & Sat 10-5, Sun 1-5
BATHURST CLARK RESOURCE LIBRARY, 900 Clark Ave W, L4J 8C1. Tel: 905-653-7323. FAX: 905-709-1099. *Mgr,* Chin Tso
 Open Mon 1-9, Tues-Thurs 10-9, Fri & Sat 10-5, Sun 1-5
PIERRE BERTON RESOURCE LIBRARY, 4921 Rutherford Rd, Woodbridge, L4L 1A6. Tel: 905-653-7323. FAX: 905-856-5706. *Mgr,* Lisa McDonough
 Open Mon 1-9, Tues-Thurs 10-9, Fri & Sat 10-5, Sun 1-5
DUFFERIN CLARK LIBRARY, 1441 Clark Ave W, L4J 7R4. Tel: 905-653-7323. FAX: 905-660-7202. *Libr Coordr,* Miranda Yu
 Open Mon & Wed 1-9, Tues & Thurs 10-9, Sat 10-5, Sun (Sept-June) 1-5
KLEINBURG LIBRARY, 10341 Islington Ave N, Kleinburg, L0J 1C0. Tel: 905-653-7323. FAX: 905-893-2736. *Mgr,* Lisa McDonough
 Open Mon, Wed & Thurs 1-8, Tues 10-8, Sat (Sept-June) 1-5
MAPLE LIBRARY, 10190 Keele St, Maple, L6A 1G3. Tel: 905-653-7323. FAX: 905-832-4971. *Mgr, Commun Libr,* June Orrell
 Open Mon & Wed 1-9, Tues & Thurs 10-9, Sat 10-5, Sun (Sept-June) 1-5
WOODBRIDGE LIBRARY, 150 Woodbridge Ave, Woodbridge, L4L 2S7. Tel: 905-653-7323. FAX: 905-851-2322. *Libr Coordr,* Elizabeth Malak-McMullan
 Open Mon & Wed 1-9, Tues & Thurs 10-9, Sat 10-5, Sun (Sept-June) 1-5

THOROLD

P THOROLD PUBLIC LIBRARY*, 14 Ormond St N, L2V 1Y8. SAN 368-427X. Tel: 905-227-2581. FAX: 905-227-2311. E-mail: thoroldpubliclibrary@cogeco.net. Web Site: www.thoroldpubliclibrary.ca. *Chief Librn,* Patricia Bronson; E-mail: pbronson@cogeco.net; *Head, Tech Serv,* Cheryl Bowman; E-mail: cbowman@cogeco.net; Staff 3 (MLS 2, Non-MLS 1)
Founded 1858. Pop 18,500; Circ 175,000
Library Holdings: Bk Vols 86,000; Per Subs 55
Special Collections: Niagara Branch of the Ontario Genealogical Society Coll; Thorold History
Subject Interests: Genealogy, Local hist
Automation Activity & Vendor Info: (Cataloging) SirsiDynix; (Circulation) SirsiDynix
Database Vendor: SirsiDynix
Wireless access
Friends of the Library Group
Branches: 1
PORT ROBINSON BRANCH, 46 Cross St, Port Robinson, L0S 1K0, SAN 368-4334. Tel: 905-384-9513. *Chief Librn,* Patricia Bronson; Tel: 905-227-2581, Fax: 905-227-2311, E-mail: pbronson@cogeco.net
 Open Wed 2pm-8pm
 Friends of the Library Group

THUNDER BAY

L BUSET & PARTNERS, Law Library, 1121 Barton St, P7B 5N3. SAN 372-3534. Tel: 807-623-2500. FAX: 807-622-7808. Web Site: www.buset-partners.com. *Librn,* Carolyn Enns; E-mail: cenns@buset-partners.com; Staff 1 (Non-MLS 1)
Library Holdings: Bk Vols 2,800
Subject Interests: Aboriginal law, Civil litigation, Commercial law, Corp law, Environ law, Estates, Family law, Ins, Labor law, Municipal law, Personal injury, Real estate, Taxation, Wills

J CONFEDERATION COLLEGE LIBRARY*, Paterson Library Commons, 1450 Nakina Dr, P7C 4W1. (Mail add: PO Box 398, P7C 4W1), SAN 319-4469. Tel: 807-475-6241. Circulation Tel: 807-475-6219. Interlibrary Loan Service Tel: 807-475-6614. Administration Tel: 807-475-6204. Information Services Tel: 807-475-6208. FAX: 807-622-3258. E-mail: library@confederationc.on.ca. Web Site: www.confederationc.on.ca/library. *Dir,* Laraine Tapak; E-mail: tapak@confederationc.on.ca; Staff 8 (MLS 1, Non-MLS 7)
Founded 1967. Enrl 3,186; Fac 144; Highest Degree: Bachelor
Apr 2008-Mar 2009 Income (CAN) $920,063. Mats Exp (CAN) $188,247, Books (CAN) $62,887, Per/Ser (Incl. Access Fees) (CAN) $35,150, Micro (CAN) $3,000, AV Equip (CAN) $5,000, AV Mat (CAN) $19,410, Electronic Ref Mat (Incl. Access Fees) (CAN) $44,900. Sal (CAN) $647,465 (Prof (CAN) $100,000)
Library Holdings: AV Mats 4,559; e-books 5,000; High Interest/Low Vocabulary Bk Vols 100; Bk Vols 27,000; Per Subs 318

Subject Interests: Aboriginal studies, Applied arts, Learning disabilities, Literacy, Women's studies
Automation Activity & Vendor Info: (Acquisitions) SirsiDynix; (Cataloging) SirsiDynix; (Circulation) SirsiDynix; (Course Reserve) SirsiDynix; (OPAC) SirsiDynix; (Serials) SirsiDynix
Database Vendor: 3M Library Systems, ALLDATA Online, Canadian Reference Centre, Cinahl Information Systems, EBSCOhost, Electric Library, Gale Cengage Learning, netLibrary, OVID Technologies, ProQuest, ScienceDirect, SerialsSolutions, SirsiDynix
Wireless access
Function: Archival coll, Audio & video playback equip for onsite use, AV serv, Copy machines, e-mail & chat, Electronic databases & coll, Equip loans & repairs, ILL available, Music CDs, Online cat, Online ref, Online searches, Photocopying/Printing, Pub access computers, Ref serv available, Ref serv in person, Scanner, Telephone ref, VHS videos, Video lending libr, Web-catalog, Wheelchair accessible
Publications: Faculty Focus (Newsletter); Faculty Information Guide (Library handbook); General Guide to the Paterson Library Commons (Reference guide); LibGuides (Online only); Program Resource Guide (Reference guide); What's New (Newsletter)
Special Services for the Deaf - Assistive tech; Bks on deafness & sign lang; Closed caption videos; High interest/low vocabulary bks; TDD equip
Special Services for the Blind - Assistive/Adapted tech devices, equip & products; Bks on cassette; GEAC Advance
Open Mon-Thurs 8am-9pm, Fri 8-4:30, Sat 1-4, Sun 2pm-8pm

C LAKEHEAD UNIVERSITY LIBRARY*, 955 Oliver Rd, P7B 5E1. SAN 368-4369. Tel: 807-343-8205. Circulation Tel: 807-343-8225. Interlibrary Loan Service Tel: 807-343-8211. Reference Tel: 807-343-8302. Information Services Tel: 807-343-8165. FAX: 807-343-8007. E-mail: riref@lakeheadu.ca. Web Site: www.lakeheadu.ca/. *Univ Librn,* Anne Deighton; E-mail: anne.deighton@lakeheadu.ca; *Head, Coll Develop,* Louise Wuorinen; Tel: 807-343-8856, E-mail: louise.wuorinen@lakeheadu.ca; *Head, Ref & Info Serv,* Valerie Gibbons; Tel: 807-343-8165, E-mail: valerie.gibbons@lakeheadu.ca; *Head, Tech Serv,* Moira Davidson; Tel: 807-343-8315, E-mail: moira.davidson@lakeheadu.ca; *Librn,* Qing (Jason) Zou; Tel: 807-343-8251, E-mail: qing.zou@lakeheadu.ca; *Coll Develop/Ref Librn,* Trudy Russo; Tel: 807-343-8728, E-mail: trusso@lakeheadu.ca; *Electronic Serv Librn,* Debra Gold; Tel: 807-343-8129, E-mail: debra.gold@lakeheadu.ca; *Info Literacy Librn,* Janice Mutz; Tel: 807-343-8147, E-mail: janice.mutz@lakeheadu.ca; *Govt Doc,* Linda Mitchell; Tel: 807-343-8072, E-mail: linda.mitchell@lakeheadu.ca; *ILL,* Tracey Zurich; E-mail: tracey.zurich@lakeheadu.ca; Staff 11 (MLS 11)
Founded 1948. Enrl 7,671; Fac 317; Highest Degree: Doctorate
May 2008-Apr 2009. Mats Exp $1,680,824, Books (CAN) $319,873, Per/Ser (Incl. Access Fees) (CAN) $1,360,951
Library Holdings: Microforms 491,222; Bk Titles 333,777; Bk Vols 352,126
Special Collections: Local Finnish History; Northern Studies
Automation Activity & Vendor Info: (Acquisitions) Ex Libris Group; (Cataloging) Ex Libris Group; (Circulation) Ex Libris Group; (Course Reserve) Ex Libris Group; (OPAC) Ex Libris Group; (Serials) Ex Libris Group
Partic in Ontario Council of University Libraries
Open Mon-Thurs 8am-11:30pm, Fri 8am-9pm, Sat 10-7, Sun (Sept-Mar) 11-9
Departmental Libraries:
EDUCATION LIBRARY, Lakehead University, Bora Laskin Bldg, P7B 5E1, SAN 368-4393. Tel: 807-343-8718, FAX: 807-346-7996. E-mail: edlib@Lakeheadu.ca. *Univ Librn,* Anne Deighton; Tel: 807-343-8205, E-mail: anne.deighton@lakeheadu.ca; *Librn,* Gisela Scalese; Tel: 807-343-8719
 Library Holdings: Microforms 453,243; Bk Titles 40,000
 Subject Interests: Educ
 Open Mon-Thurs 8:30am-9pm, Fri 8:30-6, Sat (Sept-Mar) 12-5
ORILLIA, 500 University Ave, Orillia, L3Z 0B9. Tel: 705-330-4008. E-mail: orlibrary@lakeheadu.ca. Web Site: library.lakeheadu.ca/orillia. *Librn,* Chris Tomasini; E-mail: orlibrary@lakeheadu.ca
 May 2008-Apr 2009. Mats Exp Per/Ser (Incl. Access Fees) (CAN) $1,308
 Library Holdings: Bk Titles 8,000
 Open Mon-Thurs 8am-7:30pm, Fri 8-5, Sat 11-4

S NORTHWESTERN ONTARIO SPORTS HALL OF FAME LIBRARY*, 219 May St S, P7E 1B5. SAN 373-8248. Tel: 807-622-2852. FAX: 807-622-2736. Toll Free FAX: www.nwosportshalloffame.com. E-mail: nwosport@tbaytel.net. *Exec Dir,* Diane Imrie; *Curator,* Kathryn Elizabeth Dwyer; Staff 2 (Non-MLS 2)
Founded 1978
Library Holdings: Bk Vols 1,000
Subject Interests: Sports hist
Function: Archival coll

G ONTARIO MINISTRY OF TOURISM*, Fort William Historical Park, Jean Morrison Canadian Fur Trade Library, 1350 King Rd, P7K 1L7. SAN 324-203X. Tel: 807-473-2344. FAX: 807-473-2327. E-mail: info@fwhp.ca. Web Site: www.fwhp.ca.
Library Holdings: Bk Titles 6,500
Special Collections: Research collection on North American fur trade history & its social & material culture compiled by National Heritage Limited & Fort William Archaeological Project, including 10,000 photocopied ms
Subject Interests: Fur trade, N Am Indians, Trades
Wireless access
Special Services for the Deaf - TTY equip
Restriction: Open by appt only

S THUNDER BAY HISTORICAL MUSEUM SOCIETY LIBRARY*, 425 Donald St E, P7E 5V1. SAN 329-1642. Tel: 807-623-0801. FAX: 807-622-6880. E-mail: info@thunderbaymuseum.com. Web Site: www.thunderbaymuseum.com. *Curator,* Tory J Tronrud; Staff 1 (MLS 1)
Founded 1908
Library Holdings: Bk Titles 2,610; Per Subs 3
Special Collections: Archival Coll. Oral History
Wireless access
Publications: The Thunder Bay Historical Museum Society Papers & Records (Annually)
Restriction: Non-circulating to the pub

L THUNDER BAY LAW ASSOCIATION LIBRARY, District Courthouse Library, 277 Camelot St, P7A 4B3. SAN 328-235X. Tel: 807-344-3481. FAX: 807-345-9091. E-mail: tbla@tbaytel.net. Web Site: www.tbla.on.ca. *Librn,* Helen Heerema; Staff 1 (Non-MLS 1)
Founded 1905
Library Holdings: Bk Vols 10,000

P THUNDER BAY PUBLIC LIBRARY*, Waverley Resource Library, 285 Red River Rd, P7B 1A9. SAN 368-4423. Tel: 807-345-8275. Reference Tel: 807-624-4200. Administration Tel: 807-684-6803. FAX: 807-345-8727. Administration FAX: 807-344-5119. E-mail: commserv@tbpl.ca, reference@tbpl.ca. Web Site: www.tbpl.ca. *Chief Librn/CEO,* Gina La Force; Tel: 807-684-6802, E-mail: glaforce@tbpl.ca; *Dir, Commun Develop,* Tina Tucker; Tel: 807-684-6813, E-mail: ttucker@tbpl.ca; *Dir, Human Res,* Yvonne Wodell; Tel: 807-684-6806, E-mail: ywodell@tbpl.ca
Founded 1970. Pop 109,000; Circ 921,369
Automation Activity & Vendor Info: (Acquisitions) Innovative Interfaces, Inc - Millenium; (Cataloging) Innovative Interfaces, Inc - Millenium; (Circulation) Innovative Interfaces, Inc - Millenium
Wireless access
Publications: Annual Report; Newsletter (Quarterly)
Special Services for the Blind - Audio mat; Bks on cassette; Bks on CD; Children's Braille; Daisy reader; Home delivery serv; Internet workstation with adaptive software; Large print & cassettes; Large print bks; Magnifiers
Open Mon-Thurs 10-9, Fri & Sat 10-5, Sun 1-5
Friends of the Library Group
Branches: 3
MARY J L BLACK BRANCH, 901 S Edward St, P7E 6R2, SAN 368-4482. Tel: 807-345-8275. FAX: 807-475-7855.
  Library Holdings: Bk Vols 42,692
  Open Mon, Wed & Sat 10-5, Tues & Thurs 1-9, Fri 1-5
  Friends of the Library Group
BRODIE RESOURCE, 216 S Brodie St, P7E 1C2, SAN 368-4512. Tel: 807-345-8275. Reference Tel: 807-624-4200. FAX: 807-623-0875.
  Founded 1911
  Library Holdings: Bk Vols 108,788
  Open Mon-Wed 10-9, Thurs-Sat 10-5, Sun 1-5
COUNTY PARK, 1020 Dawson Rd, P7B 1K6, SAN 368-4520. Tel: 807-345-8275. FAX: 807-768-0233.
  Library Holdings: Bk Vols 30,949
  Open Tues & Wed 1pm-9pm, Thurs-Sat 10-5, Sun 1-5

TILLSONBURG

P TILLSONBURG PUBLIC LIBRARY*, Two Library Lane, N4G 4S7. SAN 319-4493. Tel: 519-842-5571. FAX: 519-842-2941. E-mail: publiclibrary@tillsonburg.ca. Web Site: www.ocl.net/tpl. *Dir,* Position Currently Open; Staff 1 (MLS 1)
Founded 1915. Pop 14,000; Circ 124,727
Library Holdings: Bk Vols 33,000; Per Subs 50
Subject Interests: Small libr admin
Automation Activity & Vendor Info: (Cataloging) MultiLIS; (Circulation) MultiLIS
Mem of Ontario Library Service North
Open Mon-Fri 10-5:30 & 7pm-9pm

TIMMINS

S OJIBWAY & CREE CULTURAL CENTRE, 273 Third Ave, Ste 204, P4N 1E2. SAN 329-1723. Tel: 705-267-7911. FAX: 705-267-4988. E-mail: info@occc.ca. Web Site: www.occc.ca. *Librn,* Kathy Perreault; Staff 1 (MLS 1)
Library Holdings: Bk Titles 6,500
Special Collections: Native Oriented Resource Centre. Oral History
Mem of Ontario Library Service North
Open Mon-Fri 8:30-4:30

P TIMMINS PUBLIC LIBRARY*, 320 Second Ave, P4N 4A8. SAN 368-4547. Tel: 705-360-2623. FAX: 705-360-2688. Web Site: tpl.city.timmins.on.ca. *Actg Chief Exec Officer,* Judith Heinzen; E-mail: tpl_4@city.timmins.on.ca; *Tech Serv,* Teresa Woodrow; Staff 3 (MLS 3)
Founded 1921. Pop 43,000; Circ 150,392
Library Holdings: Bk Titles 90,310; Bk Vols 94,691
Special Collections: Northern Ontario Heritage Coll
Subject Interests: Mining
Automation Activity & Vendor Info: (Acquisitions) Horizon; (Cataloging) Horizon; (Circulation) Horizon; (Course Reserve) Horizon; (ILL) Horizon; (Media Booking) Horizon; (OPAC) Horizon; (Serials) Horizon
Database Vendor: SirsiDynix
Wireless access
Mem of Ontario Library Service North
Partic in Info Network for Ontario
Open Mon-Thurs 10-8, Fri & Sat 10-5
Branches: 1
CHARLES M SHIELDS CENTENNIAL LIBRARY, 99 Bloor Ave, South Porcupine, P0N 1H0. (Mail add: PO Box 400, South Porcupine, P0N 1H0), SAN 368-4601. Tel: 705-360-2623, Ext 8590. FAX: 705-360-2688. *Head of Libr,* Kathi Martin; E-mail: kathi.martin@timmins.ca
  Circ 42,233
  Library Holdings: Bk Vols 18,747; Per Subs 30

TORONTO

L AIRD & BERLIS LLP LAW LIBRARY*, 181 Bay St, Ste 1800, Brooksfield Pl, M5J 2T9. (Mail add: PO Box 754, M5J 2T9), SAN 326-8551. Tel: 416-865-7756. Interlibrary Loan Service Tel: 416-865-3077. FAX: 416-863-1515. Web Site: www.airdberlis.com. *Librn,* Dawn Urquhart; E-mail: durquhart@airdberlis.com; Staff 3 (MLS 1, Non-MLS 2)
Library Holdings: Bk Vols 3,000; Per Subs 200
Automation Activity & Vendor Info: (OPAC) Inmagic, Inc.
Open Mon-Fri 8:30-5:30

S ALZHEIMER SOCIETY OF TORONTO, Resource Center, 20 Eglinton Ave W, Ste 1600, M4R 1K8. SAN 371-8301. Tel: 416-322-6560. FAX: 416-322-6656. E-mail: write@alzheimertoronto.org. Web Site: www.alzheimertoronto.org. *Info Res Coordr,* Margaret C Cameron; E-mail: mcameron@alzheimertoronto.org; Staff 1 (MLS 1)
Founded 1986
Library Holdings: CDs 20; DVDs 220; Electronic Media & Resources 2,000; Bk Titles 2,000; Per Subs 26; Talking Bks 10; Videos 137
Special Collections: Alzheimer's Disease & Other Dementias Coll; Children's Books, videos & DVDs; Non-English Books, videos & DVDs
Subject Interests: Alzheimers disease, Caregiving, Dementia
Database Vendor: Eloquent Systems Inc
Wireless access
Function: AV serv, Res libr
Open Mon-Fri 9-5
Restriction: Restricted borrowing privileges

S R V ANDERSON ASSOCIATES LTD LIBRARY*, 2001 Sheppard Ave E, Ste 400, M2J 4Z8. SAN 370-5471. Tel: 416-497-8600, Ext 212. FAX: 416-497-0342. Web Site: www.rvanderson.com. *Supvr, Info Mgt,* Terri Zimmer; E-mail: tzimmer@rvanderson.com; *Mkt Researcher,* Leah Swift; E-mail: lswift@rvanderson.com; Staff 2 (MLS 1, Non-MLS 1)
Library Holdings: Bk Titles 5,764; Per Subs 234
Automation Activity & Vendor Info: (Acquisitions) Inmagic, Inc.; (Cataloging) Inmagic, Inc.; (Circulation) Inmagic, Inc.; (ILL) Inmagic, Inc.; (OPAC) Inmagic, Inc.
Database Vendor: Dialog
Function: Ref & res
Open Mon-Fri 9-5
Restriction: Circulates for staff only

S ANIMAL ALLIANCE OF CANADA LIBRARY*, 221 Broadview Ave, No 101, M4M 2G3. SAN 374-9118. Tel: 416-462-9541. FAX: 416-462-9647. E-mail: contact@animalalliance.ca, info@animalalliance.ca. Web Site: www.animalalliance.ca. *Librn,* Liz White; Staff 2 (Non-MLS 2)
Founded 1990

Library Holdings: AV Mats 200; DVDs 20; Bk Titles 500; Per Subs 50; Videos 500
Restriction: Access at librarian's discretion

G   ARCHIVES OF ONTARIO LIBRARY*, 134 Ian Macdonald Blvd, M7A 2C5. SAN 319-4574. Tel: 416-327-1553. Toll Free Tel: 800-668-9933. FAX: 416-327-1999. E-mail: reference@ontario.ca. Web Site: ontario.ca/archives. *Librn,* Frank van Kalmthout; E-mail: frank.vankalmthout@ontario.ca; Staff 1 (MLS 1)
Founded 1903
Library Holdings: Bk Vols 81,000; Per Subs 100
Special Collections: Historical Almanacs 1776-1919; Historical Pamphlets
Subject Interests: Archival sci, Conserv, Govt publ, Info mgt, Local hist, Ont hist
Automation Activity & Vendor Info: (Acquisitions) MINISIS Inc; (Cataloging) MINISIS Inc; (OPAC) MINISIS Inc
Wireless access
Function: Web-catalog
Partic in Ont Govt Libr Coun
Open Mon-Fri 8:30-5

SR   ARCHIVES OF THE ROMAN CATHOLIC ARCHDIOCESE OF TORONTO*, 1155 Yonge St, Ste 505, M4T 1W2. SAN 375-0477. Tel: 416-934-3400, Ext 501. FAX: 416-934-3434. E-mail: archives@archtoronto.org. Web Site: www.archtoronto.org/archives. *Dir,* Marc Lerman
Jan 2012-Dec 2012 Income (CAN) $300,000

S   ART GALLERY OF ONTARIO*, Edward P Taylor Research Library & Archives, 317 Dundas St W, M5T 1G4. SAN 319-4582. Tel: 416-979-6642. FAX: 416-979-6602. E-mail: library_archives@ago.net. Web Site: www.ago.net/research-library-archives. *Chief Librn,* Karen McKenzie; Tel: 416-979-6660, E-mail: karen.mckenzie@ago.net; *Ref Librn,* Donald Rance; E-mail: donald_rance@ago.net; *Head, Reader Serv,* Larry Pfaff; E-mail: larry_pfaff@ago.net; *Cataloger,* Deborah Mills; E-mail: deborah_mills@ago.net; *Spec Coll Archivist,* Amy Furness; E-mail: amy_marshall@ago.net. Subject Specialists: *Artists bks,* Donald Rance; *Hist of Western art,* Larry Pfaff; *Can art,* Amy Furness; Staff 5 (MLS 4, Non-MLS 1)
Founded 1933
Library Holdings: Bk Vols 160,000; Per Subs 450
Special Collections: Art Sales Catalogues, 1800-current; Artist Documentation Files; Canadian Art & Artists' Archives; Exhibition Catalogues; Fine Illustrated Books; Museum Archives & Records
Subject Interests: Can art, European decorative arts (15th-19th century), European miniature painting, Hist of Western art, Photog, Tribal art (Oceania, North Am)
Automation Activity & Vendor Info: (Acquisitions) SirsiDynix; (Cataloging) SirsiDynix; (Circulation) SirsiDynix; (OPAC) SirsiDynix; (Serials) SirsiDynix
Database Vendor: SirsiDynix
Function: Archival coll, Computers for patron use, Copy machines, E-Reserves, Exhibits, ILL available, Online cat, Outside serv via phone, mail, e-mail & web, Ref serv in person, Wheelchair accessible
Open Wed-Fri 1-5
Restriction: Non-circulating, Open to pub for ref only, Open to students

S   ARTS & LETTERS CLUB LIBRARY*, 14 Elm St, M5G 1G7. SAN 325-2035. Tel: 416-597-0223. FAX: 416-597-9544. E-mail: archives@artsandlettersclub.ca, info@artsandlettersclub.ca. Web Site: www.artsandlettersclub.ca. *Librn,* William Denton; *Archivist,* Scott James
Founded 1908
Library Holdings: Bk Titles 4,700; Bk Vols 5,950; Per Subs 24
Special Collections: Canadian Art Coll, ms
Subject Interests: Archit, Art, Can, Lit, Painting, Theatre
Publications: Lampsletters (Newsletter)

S   ASSOCIATION OF MUNICIPALITIES OF ONTARIO, AMO Resource Centre, 200 University Ave, Ste 801, M5H 3C6. SAN 373-6822. Tel: 416-971-9856. FAX: 416-971-6191. E-mail: amo@amo.on.ca. Web Site: www.amo.on.ca. *Mgr, Info Serv,* Snezana Vukelic; Tel: 416-971-9856, Ext 322, E-mail: svukelic@amo.on.ca; *Info Analyst/Researcher,* Julia Shiu; Tel: 416-971-9856, Ext 321, E-mail: jshiu@amo.on.ca; Staff 2 (MLS 2)
Founded 1991
Library Holdings: Bk Titles 700; Per Subs 50
Special Collections: Municipal Government-Ontario, Canada & US
Subject Interests: Environ, Health serv, Municipal admin, Municipal finance, Municipal mgt, Municipal serv, Waste mgt
Automation Activity & Vendor Info: (Cataloging) Inmagic, Inc.; (Serials) Inmagic, Inc.
Function: Res libr
Restriction: Open by appt only

S   BEREAVED FAMILIES OF ONTARIO TORONTO LIBRARY*, Alison Parrott Library, 80 Woodlawn Ave, M4T 1C1. SAN 373-7640. Tel: 416-440-0290. FAX: 416-440-0304. E-mail: info@bfotoronto.ca. Web Site: www.bfotoronto.ca. *Exec Dir,* Aruna Ogale; *Prog & Vols Coordr,* Jacqueline Menagh
Library Holdings: Bk Titles 600

R   BETH TZEDEC CONGREGATION*, Max & Beatrice Wolfe Library, 1700 Bathurst St, M5P 3K3. SAN 319-4639. Tel: 416-781-3514, Ext 225. Administration Tel: 416-781-3511. FAX: 416-781-0150. E-mail: info@beth-tzedec.org. Web Site: www.beth-tzedec.org. *Librn,* Zina Glassman; Staff 2 (MLS 2)
Founded 1956
Library Holdings: Bk Vols 13,000; Per Subs 15
Subject Interests: Hebraica, Judaica
Automation Activity & Vendor Info: (Acquisitions) Follett Software; (Cataloging) Follett Software; (Circulation) Follett Software
Publications: Beth Tzedec Congregation Bulletin
Partic in Asn of Jewish Librs
Open Mon 10-6, Tues 9-6, Wed 12:30-6, Sun 10-2

L   BLAKE, CASSELS & GRAYDON LLP, Law Library, Commerce Ct W, 199 Bay St, Ste 4000, M5L 1A9. SAN 319-4647. Tel: 416-863-2650. Interlibrary Loan Service Tel: 416-863-2971. Reference Tel: 416-863-3885. FAX: 416-863-2653. E-mail: dds@blakes.com (doc delivery), research@blakes.com. Web Site: blakes.com. *Dir,* Sandra Morris; *Res,* Leanne Grilli; *Res,* Leanne Notenboom; Staff 10 (MLS 3, Non-MLS 7)
Founded 1858
Library Holdings: Electronic Media & Resources 400; Bk Titles 5,000; Per Subs 350
Special Collections: Blakes Historical Coll; Lex Mundi Files; Statutes - Provincial, Canada, International
Subject Interests: Commercial law, Computer, Constitutional, Corp law, Entertainment, Environ law, Estates, Insolvency, Intellectual property, Litigation, Real estate, Securities law, Tax
Wireless access
Function: ILL available
Publications: Blakes Current Law (Newsletter)
Restriction: Staff use only

L   BLANEY MCMURTRY LLP*, Law Library, Maritime Life Tower, Two Queen St E, Ste 1500, M5C 3G5. SAN 324-0517. Tel: 416-593-1221, Ext 3550. FAX: 416-593-5437. Web Site: www.blaney.com. *Librn,* Agnes Alcantara; E-mail: aalcantara@blaney.com
Library Holdings: Bk Titles 4,000; Bk Vols 7,000; Per Subs 15
Publications: The Bulletin

L   BORDEN LADNER GERVAIS LLP LIBRARY*, Scotia Plaza, 40 King St W, M5H 3Y4. SAN 323-7982. Tel: 416-367-6000. FAX: 416-361-2752. *Mgr,* Frances Wong; Staff 7 (MLS 4, Non-MLS 3)
Library Holdings: CDs 100; Bk Titles 6,000; Bk Vols 20,000; Per Subs 600
Subject Interests: Law
Automation Activity & Vendor Info: (Cataloging) SirsiDynix; (OPAC) SirsiDynix; (Serials) SirsiDynix
Database Vendor: Dialog, Infomart, LexisNexis, Westlaw
Publications: Newsletter
Restriction: Not open to pub

M   BRIDGEPOINT HEALTH CLINICAL LIBRARY, 14 St Matthews Rd, M4M 2B5. SAN 372-5871. Tel: 416-461-8252, Ext 2436. FAX: 416-470-6721. E-mail: clinicallibrary@bridgepointhealth.ca. *Clinical Libr Tech,* Patricia Petruga
Library Holdings: Bk Titles 200; Per Subs 11
Database Vendor: EBSCOhost
Partic in Health Science Information Consortium of Toronto
Restriction: Staff use only

SR   CANADIAN BIBLE SOCIETY LIBRARY*, Ten Carnforth Rd, M4A 2S4. SAN 326-5366. Tel: 416-757-4171. FAX: 416-757-3376. Web Site: www.biblesociety.ca. *In Charge,* Meggy Kwok
Library Holdings: Bk Vols 400; Per Subs 15
Special Collections: Old Bibles, 1477-1900s (CBS Library Museum), bks; Scripture in languages other than English (World Scriptures Coll), bks, pamphlets

CANADIAN BROADCASTING CORP
G   RADIO ARCHIVES*, 205 Wellington St W, M5G 3G7. (Mail add: Box 500 Sta A, M5W 1E6), SAN 372-5863. Tel: 416-205-5880. FAX: 416-205-8602. *Mgr,* Allison Lennox; *Sr Librn,* Elizabeth Headlam; *Sr Librn,* Linda Partington; *Sr Librn,* Ken Puley; *Libr Coordr,* Heather Palmer
Founded 1959
Library Holdings: Bk Vols 1,900

Subject Interests: Current events, Drama, Music
Restriction: Open by appt only

G   REFERENCE & IMAGE RESEARCH LIBRARIES*, 250 Front St W, M5V 3G5. (Mail add: PO Box 500, Sta A, M5W 1E6), SAN 368-4849. Tel: 416-205-3244. FAX: 416-205-3733. E-mail: reference_library@cbc.ca. *Mgr,* Michele Melady; Tel: 416-205-8501, E-mail: michele.melady@cbc.ca; Staff 10 (MLS 3, Non-MLS 7) Founded 1946
   Library Holdings: Bk Titles 20,000; Per Subs 150
   Special Collections: CBC Still Photo Coll
   Subject Interests: Broadcasting media, Canadiana, Gen news
   Automation Activity & Vendor Info: (Acquisitions) Inmagic, Inc.; (Cataloging) Inmagic, Inc.; (Circulation) Inmagic, Inc.; (Serials) Inmagic, Inc.
   Database Vendor: Dialog, EBSCOhost, Factiva.com, Gale Cengage Learning, Infomart, LexisNexis, ProQuest
   Restriction: Internal use only, Limited access for the pub

L   CANADIAN ENVIRONMENTAL LAW ASSOCIATION*, Resource Library for the Environment & the Law, 130 Spadina Ave, Ste 301, M5V 2L4. SAN 325-0261. Tel: 416-960-2284. FAX: 416-960-9392. Web Site: www.ecolawinfo.org. *Librn,* Anna Leah Harms; Tel: 416-960-2284, Ext 210, E-mail: leah@cela.ca; *Librn,* Sarah Miller; E-mail: millers@lao.on.ca; Staff 2 (MLS 2)
   Library Holdings: Bk Titles 2,100; Per Subs 90
   Special Collections: Technical & Scientific Reports
   Subject Interests: Environ, Environ law, Law reform
   Function: Electronic databases & coll
   Restriction: Open by appt only

S   CANADIAN FEDERATION OF INDEPENDENT BUSINESS*, Information Research Centre, 401-4141 Yonge St, M2P 2A6. SAN 328-4956. Tel: 416-222-8022, Ext 227. FAX: 416-222-4337. E-mail: msont@cfib.ca. *Chief Librn,* Kathy Coorsh; E-mail: kathy.coorsh@cfib.ca; Staff 2 (MLS 2)
   Founded 1980
   Library Holdings: Bk Titles 2,000
   Special Collections: Conference Papers of Small Business Conferences
   Automation Activity & Vendor Info: (Acquisitions) Inmagic, Inc.; (Cataloging) Inmagic, Inc.; (OPAC) Inmagic, Inc.; (Serials) Inmagic, Inc.
   Database Vendor: Dialog, Infomart
   Function: ILL available

C   CANADIAN FORCES COLLEGE*, Keith Hodson Memorial Library, 215 Yonge Blvd, M5M 3H9. SAN 368-4903. Tel: 416-482-6800, Ext 6846. FAX: 416-480-9935. Web Site: wps.cfc.dnd.ca. *Chief Librn,* Cathy Murphy
   Founded 1943
   Library Holdings: Bk Vols 140,000; Per Subs 850
   Subject Interests: Aeronaut, Hist, Mil art, Sci, World politics

L   CANADIAN FOUNDATION FOR CHILDREN, YOUTH & THE LAW*, Justice for Children & Youth Library, 415 Yonge St, Ste 1203, M5B 2E7. SAN 329-8647. Tel: 416-920-1633. Toll Free Tel: 866-999-5329. FAX: 416-920-5855. E-mail: info@jfcy.org. Web Site: www.jfcy.org. *Actg Exec Dir,* Mary Birdsell
   Subject Interests: Child abuse, Educ law, Mental health, Young offenders
   Open Mon-Fri 9-5

S   CANADIAN FRIENDS OF SOVIET PEOPLE LIBRARY*, 280 Queen St W, M5V 2A1. SAN 375-8060. Tel: 416-977-5819. FAX: 416-593-0781. Web Site: www.nostarcompass.org. *Librn,* Michael Lucas; E-mail: mlucas3545@aol.com
   Library Holdings: Bk Titles 1,700; Per Subs 600

S   CANADIAN INSTITUTE OF CHARTERED ACCOUNTANTS*, Information Services, Guidance & Support, 277 Wellington St W, M5V 3H2. SAN 326-9000. Tel: 416-204-3307. FAX: 416-977-8585. *Librn,* Gerald B Gerard; E-mail: jerry.gerard@cica.ca
   Founded 1980
   Library Holdings: Bk Titles 10,000; Per Subs 200
   Restriction: Not open to pub

S   CANADIAN LESBIAN & GAY ARCHIVES*, James Fraser Library, 34 Isabella St, M4Y 1N1. (Mail add: PO Box 699, Sta F, 50 Charles St E, M4Y 2NG), SAN 321-6691. Tel: 416-777-2755. E-mail: queeries@clga.ca. Web Site: www.clga.ca. *Lead Librn,* Gerry King. Subject Specialists: *Bisexual, Gay, Lesbian,* Gerry King; Staff 3 (MLS 1, Non-MLS 2)
   Founded 1973
   Library Holdings: Bk Vols 10,000; Per Subs 6,100; Spec Interest Per Sub 2,300
   Special Collections: Audio-visual Coll; Poster Coll; Realia Coll; Vertical Files Coll. Can & Prov; Oral History
   Subject Interests: Bisexual, Gay, Homosexuality, Lesbian

Function: Art exhibits
Publications: Archival Inventories; Bibliographies; Gay Archivist (Newsletter); Lesbian & Gay Archivist (Newsletter); On-line catalogue of holdings; Periodical Holdings; Photographs catalogue and finding aid
Open Tues-Thurs 7:30pm-10pm
Restriction: Closed stack, Non-circulating, Not a lending libr, Off-site coll in storage - retrieval as requested

S   CANADIAN LIFE & HEALTH INSURANCE ASSOCIATION, INC*, Resource & Information Library, One Queen St E, Ste 1700, M5C 2X9. SAN 372-6770. Tel: 416-777-2221, Ext 3070. FAX: 416-777-1895. Web Site: www.clhia.ca. *Mgr, Libr Serv,* Kolette Taber; E-mail: ktaber@clhia.ca; Staff 1.5 (MLS 1, Non-MLS 0.5)
   Founded 1938
   Library Holdings: Bk Titles 850; Per Subs 96
   Subject Interests: Employee benefits, Law, Life ins, Pensions, Tax
   Automation Activity & Vendor Info: (Acquisitions) Inmagic, Inc.; (Cataloging) Inmagic, Inc.; (Circulation) Inmagic, Inc.; (ILL) Inmagic, Inc.; (OPAC) Inmagic, Inc.; (Serials) Inmagic, Inc.
   Restriction: Access at librarian's discretion

CM   CANADIAN MEMORIAL CHIROPRACTIC COLLEGE*, CMCC Health Sciences Library, 6100 Leslie St, M2H 3J1. SAN 319-4809. Tel: 416-482-2340, Ext 158. Interlibrary Loan Service Tel: 416-482-2340, Ext 160. Reference Tel: 416-482-2340, Ext 205. FAX: 416-482-4816. Web Site: www.cmcc.ca. *Dir,* Margaret Butkovic; Tel: 416-482-2340, Ext 159, E-mail: mbutkovic@cmcc.ca; *Archivist, Coll Develop,* Steve Zoltai; Tel: 416-482-2340, Ext 206, E-mail: szoltai@cmcc.ca; *Ref Serv,* Anne Taylor-Veisey; E-mail: atveisey@cmcc.ca; Staff 3 (MLS 3)
   Founded 1945. Enrl 739; Fac 138; Highest Degree: Doctorate
   Library Holdings: AV Mats 850; e-journals 113; Bk Titles 13,735; Bk Vols 16,822; Per Subs 204
   Special Collections: History of Chiropractic, Canada
   Subject Interests: Anatomy, Athletic injuries, Chiropractic, Neurology, Nutrition, Orthopedics, Radiology
   Automation Activity & Vendor Info: (Acquisitions) EOS International; (Cataloging) EOS International; (Circulation) EOS International; (Course Reserve) EOS International; (OPAC) EOS International; (Serials) EBSCO Online
   Database Vendor: EBSCOhost
   Publications: Chiropractic Research Abstracts Coll (1984, 85, 87, 90); Index to Chiropractic Literature
   Partic in Canadian Health Libraries Association; Chiropractic Libr Consortium; Medical Library Association (MLA); Ont Libr Asn; Toronto Health Libraries Association
   Open Mon-Thurs 7:30am-10pm, Fri 7:30am-8pm, Sat 9-5, Sun 12-5
   Restriction: Non-circulating to the pub

S   CANADIAN MUSIC CENTRE*, Centre de Musique Canadienne, 20 St Joseph St, M4Y 1J9. SAN 321-7043. Tel: 416-961-6601, Ext 204. FAX: 416-961-7198. E-mail: library@musiccentre.ca. Web Site: www.musiccentre.ca. *Exec Dir,* Elisabeth Bihl; Staff 2 (MLS 1, Non-MLS 1)
   Founded 1959
   Library Holdings: AV Mats 7,000; CDs 1,000; Music Scores 17,000
   Subject Interests: Can composers, Music
   Publications: Printed Catalogues of library holdings
   Open Mon-Fri 9-5
   Branches:
   NATIONAL LIBRARY/ONTARIO REGION, 20 St Joseph St, M4Y 1J9, SAN 324-4865. Tel: 416-961-6601, Ext 204. Circulation Tel: 416-961-6601, Ext 201. FAX: 416-961-7198. E-mail: library@musiccentre.ca. Web Site: www.musiccentre.ca. *Info Coordr,* Andrea Ayotte
     Founded 1983
     Library Holdings: CDs 11,561; Music Scores 19,000; Bk Titles 200; Per Subs 35
     Special Collections: Ann Southam Audio Archive; Canadian Composer Vertical Files, bios, concert notes, photos, press
     Subject Interests: Can composers, Concert mus
     Function: Archival coll, Audio & video playback equip for onsite use, Doc delivery serv, Homebound delivery serv, Music CDs, Online cat, Online ref, Online searches, Orientations, Photocopying/Printing, Pub access computers, Ref serv available, Satellite serv, Workshops
     Publications: Notations (Newsletter)
     Open Mon-Fri 9-5
     Restriction: Circ limited
   QUEBEC REGION, 416 McGill St, Montreal, H2Y 2G1, SAN 321-706X. Tel: 514-866-3477. FAX: 514-866-0456. E-mail: quebec@musiccentre.ca. *Dir,* Sonia Paquet
     Library Holdings: AV Mats 6,000; Bk Titles 15,271; Per Subs 2,100
     Subject Interests: Can composers, Music
     Publications: Alternance (Newsletter)
     Open Mon-Fri 1-5

G CANADIAN NATIONAL EXHIBITION ARCHIVES, Exibition Place Records & Archives Unit, Exibition Pl, Two Manitoba Dr, M6K 3C3. Tel: 416-263-3658. FAX: 416-263-3591. Web Site: www.explace.on.ca. *Archivist,* Linda Cobon; E-mail: lcobon@explace.on.ca
Library Holdings: Bk Vols 1,000
Special Collections: Aviation (Canadian International Air Show Coll), archives, ms, photog; Trade Shows & Expositions (Exhibition Place Archives Coll), archives, ms, photog, prog. Oral History
Subject Interests: Agr, Aviation, Can art, Carnivals, Expositions, Fairs, Sports, Transportation
Restriction: Open by appt only

P CANADIAN NATIONAL INSTITUTE FOR THE BLIND*, Library for the Blind, 1929 Bayview Ave, M4G 3E8. SAN 319-4817. Toll Free Tel: 800-268-8818. FAX: 416-480-7700. E-mail: info@cnib.ca. Web Site: www.cnib.ca. *Pres,* John Rafferty
Founded 1906. Pop 100,000; Circ 1,500,000
Library Holdings: Bk Titles 60,000; Bk Vols 500,000; Per Subs 60
Special Collections: Music Braille Coll; Rehabilitative Aspects of Blindness, ref
Publications: Acquisitions Lists; Children's Audio Magazine, Music Magazine (Audio); CNIB Library Newsletter
Special Services for the Blind - Braille bks; Braille music coll; Spec cats; Talking bks

S CANADIAN OPERA CO*, The Margo Sandor Music Library, 227 Front St E, M5A 1E8. SAN 329-868X. Tel: 416-363-6671. FAX: 416-363-5584. Web Site: www.coc.ca. *Librn,* Catella Sherwood; *Librn,* Wayne Vogan; E-mail: waynev@coc.ca
Library Holdings: Bk Vols 6,000
Special Collections: Vocal & Orchestral Music Materials
Subject Interests: Hist of opera in Toronto, Opera performance mat

S CANADIAN ROYAL HERITAGE TRUST*, King George III Canadian Royal Heritage Library (Claudia Willetts Branch), The Fealty Heritage Ctr, 3050 Yonge St, Ste 206A, M4N 2K4. SAN 326-6621. Tel: 416-482-4909. FAX: 416-482-4909, 416-544-8082. E-mail: info@crht.ca, kg3library@crht.ca. Web Site: www.crht.ca. *Exec Dir,* Garry Toffoli
Founded 1981
Library Holdings: Bk Titles 7,000; Per Subs 15
Open Tues-Thurs 10:30-5:30
Restriction: Open to pub for ref only
Friends of the Library Group

S CANADIAN TAX FOUNDATION*, Douglas J Sherbaniuk Research Centre, 595 Bay St, Ste 1200, M5G 2N5. SAN 319-4868. Tel: 416-599-0283. Toll Free Tel: 877-733-0283. FAX: 416-599-9283. Web Site: www.ctf.ca. *Librn,* Judy Singh; E-mail: jsingh@ctf.ca
Founded 1946
Library Holdings: Bk Titles 28,000; Per Subs 150
Special Collections: Canadian Federal & Provincial Budgets, Estimates & Public Accounts; Taxation Services
Subject Interests: Econ, Fed govt finance, Intl taxation, Local govt admin, Pub finance, Taxation
Open Mon-Fri 9-5

S CANADIAN URBAN TRANSIT ASSOCIATION LIBRARY, 55 York St, Ste 1401, M5J 1R7. SAN 326-1743. Tel: 416-365-9800. FAX: 416-365-1295. E-mail: transit@cutaactu.ca. Web Site: www.cutaactu.ca. *In Charge,* Michelle Sawka; Tel: 416-365-9800, Ext 113, E-mail: techservices@cutaactu.ca
Library Holdings: Bk Titles 6,000; Bk Vols 6,250; Per Subs 35
Subject Interests: Transportation planning, Urban transportation
Publications: Library News (Acquisition list)
Restriction: Mem only

L CASSELS, BROCK & BLACKWELL LIBRARY*, Scotia Plaza, Ste 2100, 40 King St W, M5H 3C2. SAN 372-7238. Tel: 416-869-5436. Interlibrary Loan Service Tel: 416-869-5763. Reference Tel: 416-869-5981. FAX: 416-360-8877. E-mail: libraryhelp@casselsbrock.com. Web Site: www.casselsbrock.com. *Mgr,* Clare Lyons; E-mail: clyons@casselsbrock.com; *Ref Serv,* Cathy Mark; E-mail: cmark@casselsbrock.com; Staff 4 (MLS 2, Non-MLS 2)
Library Holdings: CDs 5; Bk Titles 4,500; Bk Vols 16,000; Per Subs 150
Automation Activity & Vendor Info: (OPAC) Inmagic, Inc.
Publications: Current Week (Newsletter)
Open Mon-Fri 8:30-5:30
Restriction: Access at librarian's discretion

S CENTRE FOR ADDICTION & MENTAL HEALTH LIBRARY*, 33 Russell St, M5S 2S1. SAN 319-4523. Tel: 416-595-6144. FAX: 416-595-6601. E-mail: library@camh.net. Web Site: www.camh.net. *Dir,* Sydney Jones; Tel: 416-535-8501, Ext 6999, E-mail: sydney_jones@camh.net; Staff 7.5 (MLS 4, Non-MLS 3.5)

Founded 1958
Apr 2011-Mar 2012 Income (CAN) $1,100,000. Mats Exp $335,000, Books (CAN) $35,000, Per/Ser (Incl. Access Fees) (CAN) $300,000
Library Holdings: AV Mats 1,500; e-books 125; e-journals 4,000; Bk Titles 40,000; Bk Vols 60,000; Per Subs 223
Special Collections: CAMH Staff Publications; Drug Education Materials; Temperance
Automation Activity & Vendor Info: (Acquisitions) SydneyPlus; (Cataloging) SydneyPlus; (Circulation) SydneyPlus; (OPAC) SydneyPlus; (Serials) SydneyPlus
Database Vendor: EBSCOhost, OVID Technologies
Publications: Audio-Visuals List (Acquisition list)
Partic in Docline
Open Mon, Tues, Thurs & Fri 8:30-5:30, Wed 8:30-7

S CITY OF TORONTO ARCHIVES*, 255 Spadina Rd, M5R 2V3. SAN 325-6545. Tel: 416-397-0778. FAX: 416-392-9685. E-mail: archives@toronto.ca. Web Site: www.toronto.ca/archives. *Archives Mgr,* Michele Dale
Library Holdings: Bk Vols 3,500
Open Mon-Fri 9-4:30, Sat 10-4:30

S CSA INTERNATIONAL*, Information Centre, 178 Rexdale Blvd, M9W 1R3. SAN 319-3799. Tel: 416-747-4059. Toll Free Tel: 800-463-6727. FAX: 416-747-4199. E-mail: info@csagroup.org. *Mgr,* Susan Morley; E-mail: susan.morley@csagroup.org; Staff 1 (Non-MLS 1)
Founded 1970
Library Holdings: e-journals 10; Bk Vols 4,000; Per Subs 120
Special Collections: Engineering Standards, doc
Subject Interests: Eng standards, Hist of Can Standards Asn, Production liability, Quality assurance, Standardization
Automation Activity & Vendor Info: (Acquisitions) Inmagic, Inc.; (Cataloging) Inmagic, Inc.; (Circulation) Inmagic, Inc.; (Course Reserve) Inmagic, Inc.; (ILL) Inmagic, Inc.; (Media Booking) Inmagic, Inc.; (OPAC) Inmagic, Inc.; (Serials) Inmagic, Inc.
Database Vendor: EBSCOhost, Gale Cengage Learning, IEEE (Institute of Electrical & Electronics Engineers), IHS
Wireless access
Function: Archival coll, Computers for patron use, Online searches
Open Mon-Fri 9-4
Restriction: Circulates for staff only, External users must contact libr

L DALE & LESSMANN LIBRARY*, 181 University Ave, Ste 2100, M5H 3M7. SAN 377-3175. Tel: 416-863-1010. FAX: 416-863-1009. *Librn,* Micky Wylie; Staff 1 (MLS 1)
Library Holdings: Bk Vols 2,000
Database Vendor: WestlaweCARSWELL
Restriction: Staff use only

S DANCER TRANSITION RESOURCE CENTRE*, The Lynda Hamilton Centre, 250 The Esplanade, Ste 500, M5A 1J2. SAN 376-1649. Tel: 416-595-5655. FAX: 416-595-0009. E-mail: nationaloffice@dtrc.ca. Web Site: www.dtrc.ca. *Exec Dir,* Amanda Hancox; Staff 3 (Non-MLS 3)
Founded 1985
Library Holdings: Bk Titles 600; Bk Vols 800; Per Subs 15
Subject Interests: Career develop, Dance
Function: Prof lending libr
Open Mon-Fri 10-5

L DAVIES, WARD, PHILLIPS & VINEBERG, Law Library, 155 Wellington St W, M5V 3J7. SAN 373-3254. Tel: 416-863-0900. FAX: 416-863-0871. Web Site: www.dwpv.com. *Dir, Libr Serv,* Gaye Lefebvre; Staff 5 (MLS 3, Non-MLS 2)
Restriction: Private libr

G DEFENCE RESEARCH & DEVELOPMENT CANADA-TORONTO LIBRARY, 1133 Sheppard Ave W, M3K 2C9. SAN 319-1052. Tel: 416-635-2100. FAX: 416-635-2104. E-mail: sic@drdc-rddc.gc.ca. *Head of Libr,* Stewart Harrison; Staff 1 (Non-MLS 1)
Founded 1951
Apr 2012-Mar 2013 Income (CAN) $125,000. Mats Exp (CAN) $62,000, Books (CAN) $5,000, Per/Ser (Incl. Access Fees) (CAN) $52,000, Other Print Mats (CAN) $5,000. Sal (CAN) $56,000
Library Holdings: Bk Vols 16,000; Per Subs 36
Subject Interests: Aviation med, Environ physiology, Human factors, Hyperbaric med, Life support systs
Automation Activity & Vendor Info: (Cataloging) SydneyPlus; (OPAC) SydneyPlus
Partic in Council of Federal Libraries Consortium
Restriction: Not open to pub

L   DICKINSON WRIGHT LLP LIBRARY, Ernst & Young Tower, Toronto-Dominion Centre, 222 Bay St, 18th Flr, M5K 1H1. SAN 375-3441. Tel: 416-777-0101. FAX: 416-865-1398. *Librn,* Micky Wylie; E-mail: mwylie@dickinson-wright.com; Staff 1 (MLS 1)
Library Holdings: Electronic Media & Resources 5; Bk Titles 2,000; Bk Vols 5,000; Per Subs 20
Database Vendor: CEDROM-SNi, WestlaweCARSWELL
Wireless access
Restriction: Staff use only

S   DYING WITH DIGNITY CANADA LIBRARY*, 802-55 Eglinton Ave E, M4P 1G8. SAN 374-6712. Tel: 416-486-3998. Toll Free Tel: 800-495-6156. FAX: 416-486-5562. E-mail: info@dyingwithdignity.ca. Web Site: www.dyingwithdignity.ca. *Exec Dir,* Wanda Morris; *Librn,* Trudie Ross; Staff 1 (Non-MLS 1)
Founded 1980
Library Holdings: Bk Vols 500
Subject Interests: Law, Philosophy
Function: Prof lending libr
Publications: Newsletter
Open Mon-Fri 8:30-5

G   ENVIRONMENT CANADA LIBRARY, DOWNSVIEW*, 4905 Dufferin St, M3H 5T4. SAN 319-1044. Tel: 416-739-4828. Interlibrary Loan Service Tel: 416-739-4225. Reference Tel: 416-739-5702. FAX: 416-739-4212. E-mail: librarybiblio.downsview@ec.gc.ca. Web Site: www.ec.gc.ca/bd-dl, www.ec.gc.ca/bd-dl/Default.asp?lang=En&n=8986FE6F-0. *Head, EC Libr Downsview,* Maria Latyszewskyj; E-mail: maria.latyszewskyj@ec.gc.ca; Staff 5 (MLS 3, Non-MLS 2)
Founded 1871
Library Holdings: CDs 200; DVDs 58; e-books 2,809; e-journals 225; Microforms 10,000; Bk Titles 133,592; Per Subs 300; Videos 1,079
Special Collections: Depository Coll for Published Documents of the World Meteorological Organization; Meteorological Records for Canadian Stations, 1873-; Meteorological Records for Toronto, 1839; World Climatic Data. Can & Prov
Subject Interests: Air quality, Atmospheric sci, Climatology, Environ protection, Meteorology
Automation Activity & Vendor Info: (Acquisitions) EBSCO Online; (Cataloging) Horizon; (Circulation) Horizon; (OPAC) Horizon; (Serials) Horizon
Database Vendor: American Chemical Society, American Geophysical Union, BioOne, Cambridge Scientific Abstracts, Dialog, EBSCOhost, Elsevier, Knovel, LexisNexis, netLibrary, OCLC, ProQuest, Repere, ScienceDirect, Scopus, SerialsSolutions, Springer-Verlag, STN International, Wiley
Function: Archival coll, Electronic databases & coll, ILL available, Learning ctr, Online cat, Photocopying/Printing, Pub access computers, Ref & res, VHS videos, Web-catalog
Partic in Canadian Fed Librs
Open Mon-Fri 8:30-4:30
Restriction: Open to pub for ref only
Friends of the Library Group

S   ERNST & YOUNG*, Center for Business Knowledge, Ernst & Young Tower, 222 Bay St, M5K 1J7. (Mail add: Toronto-Dominion Centre, PO Box 251, Ernst & Young Tower, M5K 1J7), SAN 319-5023. Tel: 416-943-3471. Reference Tel: 416-943-3389. Toll Free Tel: 800-475-3045. FAX: 416-943-2954. Web Site: www.ey.com. *Mgr,* Anne Bateman; Staff 14 (MLS 11, Non-MLS 3)
Founded 1961
Library Holdings: e-books 5,000; Bk Titles 50
Subject Interests: Acctg, Econ, Mkt, Tax
Publications: Library Bulletin
Restriction: Staff use only

L   FASKEN MARTINEAU DUMOULIN LLP*, Toronto Library, Bay Adelaide Centre, Box 20, 333 Bay St, Ste 2400, M5H 2T6. SAN 320-880X. Tel: 416-865-5143. Interlibrary Loan Service Tel: 416-865-4500. FAX: 416-364-7813. Web Site: www.fasken.com. *Librn,* Michele Miles; E-mail: mmiles@fasken.com; *Ref,* Aiju Yu; E-mail: ayu@fasken.com; Staff 7 (MLS 4, Non-MLS 3)
Library Holdings: Bk Vols 10,000; Per Subs 300
Subject Interests: Law
Automation Activity & Vendor Info: (Acquisitions) Inmagic, Inc.; (Cataloging) Inmagic, Inc.; (Circulation) Inmagic, Inc.; (ILL) Inmagic, Inc.; (OPAC) Inmagic, Inc.; (Serials) Inmagic, Inc.
Database Vendor: Dialog, Gale Cengage Learning, HeinOnline, Infomart, LexisNexis, WestlaweCARSWELL
Wireless access
Publications: Legislative Snapshots (Newsletter)
Open Mon-Fri 8:30-5
Restriction: Open to others by appt

L   FILION WAKELY THORUP ANGELETTI LLP*, Law Library, 150 King St W, Ste 2601, M5H 4B6. (Mail add: Box 32, M5H 4B6), SAN 372-3666. Tel: 416-408-3221. FAX: 416-408-4814. *Librn,* Naunihal Masen; Tel: 416-408-5506, E-mail: nmasen@filion.on.ca. Subject Specialists: *Employment law, Human rights, Labor law,* Naunihal Masen; Staff 2 (MLS 1, Non-MLS 1)
Library Holdings: Bk Vols 11,000; Per Subs 29
Subject Interests: Employment, Human rights, Occupational health, Occupational safety, Workers compensation
Open Mon-Fri 9-5

L   FRASER MILNER CASGRAIN LLP, BARRISTERS & SOLICITORS*, Law Library, 400 Toronto Dominion Ctr, 77 King St W, M5K 0A1. SAN 326-8942. Tel: 416-863-4581. FAX: 416-863-4592. Web Site: www.fmc-law.com. *Dir,* Yzonne MacDonald; *Librn,* Ian Colvin; Staff 4 (MLS 2, Non-MLS 2)
Library Holdings: Bk Titles 10,500; Bk Vols 11,000; Per Subs 65
Automation Activity & Vendor Info: (Cataloging) EOS International; (OPAC) EOS International; (Serials) EOS International
Partic in Can Asn of Law Librs; Toronto Asn of Law Librs

L   GARDINER ROBERTS LLP LIBRARY*, Scotia Plaza, Ste 3100, 40 King St W, M5H 3Y2. SAN 377-4678. Tel: 416-865-6600. Information Services Tel: 416-865-6728. FAX: 416-865-6636. E-mail: gr@gardiner-roberts.com. Web Site: www.gardiner-roberts.com. *Librn,* Jan Barrett; E-mail: jbarrett@gardiner-roberts.com; Staff 2 (MLS 1, Non-MLS 1)
Library Holdings: Bk Vols 2,000
Automation Activity & Vendor Info: (Cataloging) Inmagic, Inc.

C   GEORGE BROWN COLLEGE OF APPLIED ARTS & TECHNOLOGY*, Casa Loma Campus Library, 160 Kendal Ave, M5R 1M3. (Mail add: PO Box 1015, Sta B, M5T 2T9), SAN 368-511X. Tel: 416-415-5000, Ext 4634. Interlibrary Loan Service Tel: 416-415-5000, Ext 3742. Toll Free Tel: 800-265-2002. FAX: 416-415-4765. Web Site: library.georgebrown.ca. *Librn,* Ita Ferdinand-Grant; Tel: 416-415-5000, Ext 4635; *Librn,* Bill McAskill; Staff 2 (MLS 2)
Founded 1968. Enrl 9,016; Fac 735
Library Holdings: Bk Titles 27,000; Per Subs 160
Subject Interests: Archit tech, Arts, Bus, Child care, Commerce, Dental hygiene, Dental tech, Eng, Fashion, Food tech, Info tech, Jewelry, Manufacturing, Microelectronics, Nursing
Special Services for the Deaf - Bks on deafness & sign lang; High interest/low vocabulary bks; Spec interest per; Staff with knowledge of sign lang
Open Mon-Thurs 7:30am-11pm, Fri 7:30am-10pm, Sat 10-6, Sun 10-5

C   GEORGE BROWN COLLEGE OF APPLIED ARTS & TECHNOLOGY*, Saint James Campus Library, 200 King St E, M5A 3W8. (Mail add: PO Box 1015, Sta B, M5T 2T9), SAN 760-3606. Tel: 416-415-5000, Ext 2173. FAX: 416-415-2698. Web Site: library.georgebrown.ca. *Librn,* Marcia Pulleyblank; E-mail: mpulleyb@georgebrown.ca; Staff 6 (MLS 1, Non-MLS 5)
Library Holdings: Bk Titles 30,000; Per Subs 400
Subject Interests: Commerce, Commun serv, Graphic design, Hospitality, Nursing
Open Mon-Thurs 7:30am-11pm, Fri 7:30am-10pm, Sat 10-6, Sun 10-5

C   GEORGE BROWN COLLEGE OF APPLIED ARTS & TECHNOLOGY ARCHIVES*, 500 Macpherson Ave, Rm F-103, M5R 1M3. (Mail add: PO Box 1015, Sta B, M5T 2T9), SAN 368-5128. Tel: 416-415-5000, Ext 4771. Toll Free Tel: 800-265-2002, Ext 4771. FAX: 416-415-4772. *Archivist,* Clay Thibodeau; E-mail: cthibodeau@georgebrown.ca; Staff 2 (Non-MLS 2)
Founded 1975. Enrl 14,000; Fac 700; Highest Degree: Bachelor

S   THE GLOBE & MAIL LIBRARY*, Editorial Research, 444 Front St W, M5V 2S9. SAN 319-5015. Tel: 416-585-5076. Web Site: www.globeandmail.com. *Mgr, News Res & Chief Librn,* Celia Donnelly; Tel: 416-585-5229; *News Res Librn,* Stephanie Chambers; Tel: 416-585-5060; Staff 4 (MLS 3, Non-MLS 1)
Founded 1938
Library Holdings: Bk Titles 9,000; Per Subs 34
Subject Interests: Current affairs, Politics
Database Vendor: Factiva.com
Function: Newsp ref libr
Restriction: Co libr, Not open to pub

S   GOETHE-INSTITUT TORONTO LIBRARY*, North Tower, 100 University Ave, Ste 201, M5J 1V6. SAN 373-6377. Tel: 416-593-5257. FAX: 416-593-5145. E-mail: library@toronto.goethe.org. Web Site: www.goethe.de/toronto. *Head Librn,* Michelle Kay; Staff 1 (MLS 1)
Library Holdings: Bk Titles 5,500; Per Subs 15

Special Collections: Contemporary German Literature & Plays, AV & bks; German Language Textbooks
Function: Adult bk club, Audio & video playback equip for onsite use, Bks on CD, e-mail serv, ILL available, Music CDs
Publications: Acquisitions List

L   GOODMANS LLP LIBRARY*, Bay Adelaide Ctr, 333 Bay St, Ste 3400, M5H 2S7. SAN 321-5547. Tel: 416-979-2211, Ext 6070. FAX: 416-979-1234. E-mail: library@goodmans.ca. Web Site: www.goodmans.ca. *Dir, Libr Serv,* Mary Saulig; E-mail: msaulig@goodmans.ca; *Librn,* Diane Rook; Staff 5 (MLS 2, Non-MLS 3) Founded 1972
Library Holdings: Bk Vols 10,000; Per Subs 315
Subject Interests: Law
Automation Activity & Vendor Info: (Cataloging) EOS International
Restriction: Staff use only

L   GOWLING LAFLEUR HENDERSON LLP, Law Library, One First Canadian Pl, 100 King St W, Ste 1600, M5X 1G5. SAN 370-7148. Tel: 416-862-5735. Interlibrary Loan Service Tel: 416-862-3505. Reference Tel: 416-862-6261. FAX: 416-862-7661. Web Site: www.gowlings.com. *Dir,* Roslyn Theodore-McIntosh; E-mail: roslyn.theodoremcintosh@gowlings.com; *Librn,* Lily Mac; Tel: 416-862-3637, E-mail: lily.mac@gowlings.com; *Sr Ref Librn,* Suzanna LaRose; Tel: 416-862-4282, E-mail: suzanna.larose@gowlings.com; *Ref Librn,* Zdena Nagyova; Tel: 416-862-3633, E-mail: zdena.nagyova@gowlings.com; *Ref Librn/Trainer,* Joanne Berent; Tel: 416-862-4354, E-mail: joanne.berent@gowlings.com; *Ref Librn/Trainer,* Elizabeth Dingman; Tel: 416-862-7287, E-mail: elizabeth.dingman@gowlings.com; *Ref Tech,* Helen Jarvis; E-mail: helen.jarvis@gowlings.com; Staff 7 (MLS 2, Non-MLS 5)
Automation Activity & Vendor Info: (Acquisitions) Inmagic, Inc.; (Cataloging) Inmagic, Inc.; (Circulation) Inmagic, Inc.; (Course Reserve) Inmagic, Inc.; (ILL) Inmagic, Inc.; (OPAC) Inmagic, Inc.; (Serials) Inmagic, Inc.
Database Vendor: Dialog, Factiva.com, Infomart, LexisNexis, Westlaw
Publications: Acquisitions List; Information Packages; Library Brochure

L   HICKS MORLEY HAMILTON STEWART & STORIE LLP*, HMHSS Law Library, TD Ctr, 39th Flr, 77 King St W, M5H 1K8. (Mail add: TD Ctr, 37th Flr, 77 King St W, M5H 1K8), SAN 375-4960. Tel: 416-362-1011. FAX: 416-362-9680. Web Site: www.toronto.hicks.com. *Mgr,* Mrs Lorenza Tejada Thompson; Tel: 416 362-1011, Ext 7119, E-mail: lorenza@hicks.com; *Libr Tech,* Sushma Sultan; Tel: 416 362-1011, Ext 7118, E-mail: sushma-sultan@hicksmorley.com; Staff 2 (MLS 2) Founded 1972. Pop 95
Library Holdings: Bk Vols 7,500; Per Subs 90
Special Collections: Labour & Employment Law Coll. Can & Prov
Subject Interests: Educ, Environ law, Pensions, Workers compensation
Wireless access
Function: Res libr
Publications: Client Update (Newsletter); For the Record (Monthly bulletin)
Partic in Can Asn of Law Librs; Toronto Asn of Law Librs
Restriction: Not open to pub
Friends of the Library Group

S   HOCKEY HALL OF FAME*, D. K. (Doc) Seaman Hockey Resource Centre, 400 Kipling Ave, M8V 3L1. SAN 319-5066. Tel: 416-360-7735. FAX: 416-251-5770. E-mail: acquisitions@hhof.com. Web Site: www.hhof.com. *Curator, VPres,* Phil Pritchard; E-mail: ppritchard@hhof.com; *Asst Curator, Mgr,* Izak Westgate; *Archives, Res Ctr Mgr,* Craig Campbell; Tel: 416-933-8224, E-mail: campbellc@hhof.com; *Coordr,* Steve Poirier; *Archivist,* Miragh Bitove; Tel: 419-933-8224
Library Holdings: Bk Vols 1,500
Special Collections: Artifacts & Memorabilia, scrapbooks, info files, photographic/moving pictures archives
Wireless access
Publications: "Legends" Annually
Restriction: Open to pub by appt only

M   HOLLAND BLOORVIEW KIDS REHABILITAION HOSPITAL*, Health Sciences Library, 150 Kilgour Rd, M4G 1R8. SAN 370-8942. Tel: 416-425-6220, Ext 3517. Toll Free Tel: 800-363-2440, Ext 3517. FAX: 416-425-6376. Web Site: www.hollandbloorview.ca. *Mgr, Health Sci Libr & Archives,* Pui-Ying Wong; E-mail: pwong@hollandbloorview.ca. Subject Specialists: *Pediatrics, Rehabilitation,* Pui-Ying Wong; Staff 2 (MLS 1, Non-MLS 1)
Library Holdings: Bk Titles 4,000; Per Subs 50
Automation Activity & Vendor Info: (Acquisitions) SIRSI WorkFlows; (Cataloging) SIRSI WorkFlows; (Circulation) SIRSI WorkFlows; (OPAC) SIRSI WorkFlows; (Serials) SIRSI WorkFlows
Database Vendor: EBSCOhost, OVID Technologies

Partic in Health Science Information Consortium of Toronto
Open Mon-Fri 8:30-4:30

M   HOSPITAL FOR SICK CHILDREN*, Hospital Library, 555 University Ave, M5G 1X8. SAN 319-5074. Tel: 416-813-6693. Interlibrary Loan Service Tel: 416-813-6591. FAX: 416-813-7523. E-mail: hsclink@sickkids.on.ca. Web Site: www.sickkids.ca/learning/hospitallibrary. *Dir,* Elizabeth Uleryk; Tel: 416-813-6695; Staff 9 (MLS 3, Non-MLS 6) Founded 1919
Library Holdings: e-books 1,500; e-journals 1,200; Bk Titles 8,000; Bk Vols 65,000; Per Subs 300; Videos 120
Special Collections: Clinical Slide Coll; Pediatrics Coll
Subject Interests: Pediatrics
Automation Activity & Vendor Info: (Acquisitions) Horizon; (Cataloging) Horizon; (Circulation) Horizon; (OPAC) Horizon; (Serials) Horizon
Database Vendor: Checkpoint Systems, Inc, Dialog, JSTOR, Lexi-Comp, McGraw-Hill, Medline, OVID Technologies, PubMed, Springer-Verlag, STAT!Ref (Teton Data Systems), Wiley InterScience
Wireless access
Partic in Docline; Health Science Information Consortium of Toronto
Open Mon-Thurs 8-8, Fri 8-6, Sun 11-6

L   HOUSER, HENRY & SYRON LAW LIBRARY*, 145 King St W, Ste 2000, M5H 2B6. SAN 374-7867. Tel: 416-362-3411. FAX: 416-362-3757. Web Site: www.houserhenry.com. *Librn,* Sandra Findlay; E-mail: sfindlay@houserhenry.com
Library Holdings: Bk Vols 500; Per Subs 100
Restriction: Not open to pub

S   C D HOWE INSTITUTE LIBRARY, 67 Yonge St, Ste 300, M5E 1J8. SAN 325-1632. Tel: 416-865-1904, Ext 2606. FAX: 416-865-1866. E-mail: library@cdhowe.org. Web Site: www.cdhowe.org. *VPres, Res & Sr Coordr, Res,* Kristine Gray; E-mail: kgray@cdhowe.org; Staff 1 (Non-MLS 1) Founded 1973
Library Holdings: Bk Titles 3,000; Per Subs 100
Subject Interests: Econ, Pub policy
Automation Activity & Vendor Info: (Acquisitions) Inmagic, Inc.; (Cataloging) Inmagic, Inc.; (Circulation) Inmagic, Inc.; (Course Reserve) Inmagic, Inc.; (ILL) Inmagic, Inc.
Database Vendor: EBSCOhost, Factiva.com, Infomart
Function: Res libr
Restriction: Staff & mem only

J   HUMBER COLLEGE*, North Campus Libraries, 205 Humber College Blvd, M9W 5L7. (Mail add: PO Box 1900, M9W 5L7), SAN 374-4280. Tel: 416-675-5079. Reference Tel: 416-675-6622, Ext 4421. FAX: 416-675-7439. Web Site: www.library.humber.ca. *Dir,* Lynne Bentley; Tel: 416-675-4574; *Coll Develop, Per,* Maureen Hyland; Tel: 416-675-6622, Ext 4501; *Electronic Res,* Lisa Dibarbora; Tel: 416-675-6622, Ext 5593; *Ref Serv,* Nancy Pierobon
Library Holdings: Bk Titles 80,937; Bk Vols 90,421; Per Subs 969
Wireless access
Open Mon-Thurs 7:30am-10pm, Fri 7:30-6, Sat 8:30-5, Sun 12-5
Departmental Libraries:
LAKESHORE CAMPUS LIBRARY, 3199 Lakeshore Blvd W, M8V 1K8, SAN 368-5292. Tel: 416-675-6622, Ext 3250. Reference Tel: 416-675-6622, Ext 3351. FAX: 416-252-0918. *Bus Librn,* Alexandra Ross; *Coordr,* Janet Hollingsworth
Founded 1968
Library Holdings: Bk Vols 20,000; Per Subs 216
Open Mon-Thurs 7:30am-10pm, Fri 7:30-6, Sat 8.30-5, Sun 12-5

S   IBI GROUP LIBRARY, 230 Richmond St W, 5th Flr, M5V 1V6. SAN 323-7362. Tel: 416-596-1930, Ext 1250. FAX: 416-596-0644. E-mail: library@ibigroup.com. Web Site: www.ibigroup.com. *Librn,* Jennifer Osther; E-mail: josther@ibigroup.com; *Libr Tech,* Cindy Wong; Staff 3 (MLS 1, Non-MLS 2) Founded 1974
Library Holdings: Bk Titles 800; Bk Vols 6,000; Per Subs 185
Special Collections: Reports by IBI Group
Subject Interests: Archit, Transportation, Urban design, Urban planning
Automation Activity & Vendor Info: (Cataloging) Inmagic, Inc.; (Circulation) Inmagic, Inc.
Database Vendor: Dialog, Factiva.com, Infomart
Restriction: Not open to pub

C   INSTITUTE FOR CHRISTIAN STUDIES*, ICS Library, 229 College St, M5T 1R4. SAN 375-3891. Tel: 416-979-2331, Ext 250. Toll Free Tel: 888-326-5347. FAX: 416-979-2332. E-mail: librarian@icscanada.edu. Web Site: www.icscanada.edu/library. *Librn,* Isabella Guthrie-McNaughton; E-mail: iguthriemcnaughton@icscanada.edu; Staff 1 (MLS 1) Founded 1967. Enrl 156; Fac 9; Highest Degree: Doctorate
Library Holdings: Bk Titles 24,000; Bk Vols 45,000; Per Subs 35

Special Collections: Philosophy of History (MC Smit Coll), bks, pamphlets; Philosophy, Legal Theory (Herman Dooyeweerd Coll)
Subject Interests: Philosophy
Wireless access
Restriction: Non-circulating

S   INSURANCE BUREAU OF CANADA LIBRARY*, Kennedy/Martin Library, 777 Bay St, Ste 2400, M5G 2C8. SAN 325-6111. Tel: 416-362-2031, Ext 4350. FAX: 416-361-5952. Web Site: www.ibc.ca. *Mgr, Libr Serv,* Amra Porobic; E-mail: aporobic@ibc.ca; Staff 1 (MLS 1)
Founded 1968
Library Holdings: Bk Titles 8,500; Per Subs 300
Subject Interests: Automotive eng, Climate change, Ins, Law, Road safety, Statistics
Automation Activity & Vendor Info: (Acquisitions) Eloquent Systems Inc; (Cataloging) Eloquent Systems Inc; (Circulation) Eloquent Systems Inc; (OPAC) Eloquent Systems Inc; (Serials) Eloquent Systems Inc
Database Vendor: Dialog, EBSCOhost, Eloquent Systems Inc, Infomart, LexisNexis
Publications: Fact Book (Annually); How Cars Measure Up (Consumer guide)
Restriction: Open by appt only

S   INSURANCE INSTITUTE OF ONTARIO LIBRARY*, 18 King St E, 6th Flr, M5C 1C4. SAN 373-6830. Tel: 416-362-8586. FAX: 416-362-4239. Web Site: www.insuranceinstitute.ca.
Library Holdings: Bk Titles 325; Per Subs 20
Restriction: Mem only

G   INTERGOVERNMENTAL COMMITTEE ON URBAN & REGIONAL RESEARCH*, Comite Intergouvernemental de Recherches Urbaines et Regionales, 40 Wynford Dr, Ste 210, M3C 1J5. SAN 323-6153. Tel: 647-345-7004. E-mail: icurrlib@icurr.org. Web Site: www.icurr.org. *Info Serv Mgr,* Mark Phillip Rose; Tel: 416-952-1437; Staff 5 (MLS 2, Non-MLS 3)
Founded 1967
Library Holdings: Bk Titles 14,000; Per Subs 15
Subject Interests: Local govt, Urban planning
Automation Activity & Vendor Info: (Cataloging) Inmagic, Inc.; (Circulation) Inmagic, Inc.; (OPAC) Inmagic, Inc.; (Serials) Inmagic, Inc.
Function: Mail loans to mem
Restriction: Circ limited

S   ITALIAN CULTURAL INSTITUTE LIBRARY*, 496 Huron St, M5R 2R3. SAN 374-7859. Tel: 416-921-3802. FAX: 416-962-2503. E-mail: iic@esteri.it. Web Site: www.iictoronto.esteri.it. *Librn,* Paolo Marino
Library Holdings: Bk Vols 4,000
Restriction: Open to pub for ref only

S   JAPAN FOUNDATION*, Toronto Library, 131 Bloor St W, Ste 213, M5S 1R1. SAN 377-0915. Tel: 416-966-1600, Ext 238, 416-966-2935. FAX: 416-966-0957. Web Site: www.jftor.org. *Chief Librn,* Mariko Liliefeldt
Library Holdings: Per Subs 65
Partic in Can Libr Asn; Coun on East Asian Librs; Nat Coord Comt on Japanese Libr Resources; OCLC Online Computer Library Center, Inc
Open Mon & Thurs 11:30-7, Tues, Wed & Fri 11:30-4:30, Sat 12-5

C   LAIDLAW LIBRARY AT UNIVERSITY COLLEGE, UNIVERSITY OF TORONTO*, Laidlaw Wing, 2nd Flr, 15 King's College Circle, M5S 3H7. SAN 328-705X. Tel: 416-978-8107. Web Site: www.uc.utoronto.ca/library. *Librn,* Margaret Fulford; Tel: 416-978-4634, E-mail: margaret.fulford@utoronto.ca
Library Holdings: Bk Vols 35,861
Special Collections: Canadian Literature (Al Purdy Coll)
Subject Interests: Can studies, Drama, Health studies, Sexual diversity studies
Wireless access

L   LAW SOCIETY OF UPPER CANADA*, Great Library, Osgoode Hall, 130 Queen St W, M5H 2N6. SAN 319-5155. Tel: 416-947-3315. FAX: 416-869-0331. E-mail: refstaff@lsuc.on.ca. Web Site: rc.lsuc.on.ca/library/home.htm. *Mgr,* David Whelan; Tel: 416-947-3438, E-mail: dwhelan@lsuc.on.ca; *Libr Syst Adminr,* Chris Stephenson; Staff 19 (MLS 8, Non-MLS 11)
Founded 1829
Library Holdings: Bk Titles 40,000; Bk Vols 120,000; Per Subs 1,700
Subject Interests: Canadiana, Govt doc, Law
Automation Activity & Vendor Info: (Acquisitions) Ex Libris Group; (Cataloging) Ex Libris Group; (OPAC) Ex Libris Group; (Serials) Ex Libris Group
Database Vendor: HeinOnline, Quicklaw, Westlaw
Wireless access
Function: Ref serv available, Res libr
Restriction: Mem only, Open to pub by appt only

L   MCCARTHY TETRAULT LLP*, John J Robinette Library, T-D Centre, Ste 5300, Toronto Dominion Bank Tower, M5K 1E6. SAN 319-5171. Tel: 416-601-8200, Ext 542737. FAX: 416-868-0673. E-mail: natlibrary@mccarthy.ca. Web Site: www.mccarthy.ca. *Sr Dir,* Lenie Ott; *Sr Researcher,* Barbara Fingerote; Staff 4 (MLS 4)
Founded 1968
Wireless access
Restriction: Staff use only

S   MERCER HUMAN RESOURCE CONSULTING*, Information-Research Centre, 161 Bay St, M5J 2S5. (Mail add: PO Box 501, M5J 2S5), SAN 319-521X. Tel: 416-868-7697. FAX: 416-868-7171. Web Site: www.mercerhr.com. *Mgr,* Joanne Wheeler
Founded 1974
Library Holdings: Bk Titles 350; Bk Vols 1,700
Subject Interests: Actuarial sci, Compensation, Employee benefits, Financial planning, Human resource mgt, Ins (group), Personnel mgt, Taxation
Automation Activity & Vendor Info: (Cataloging) Inmagic, Inc.; (Circulation) Inmagic, Inc.; (Serials) Inmagic, Inc.
Publications: Canadian Library Bulletin
Open Mon-Fri 8:30-5

S   METRAC (METROPOLITAN ACTION COMMITTEE ON VIOLENCE AGAINST WOMEN & CHILDREN)*, 158 Spadina Rd, M5R 2T8. SAN 377-1911. Tel: 416-392-3135. Toll Free Tel: 877-558-5570. FAX: 416-392-3136. TDD: 416-392-3031. E-mail: info@metrac.org. Web Site: www.metrac.org.
Founded 1984
Library Holdings: Bk Titles 2,000
Subject Interests: Justice, Sexual assault/abuse, Violence against women, Women's issues
Wireless access
Function: For res purposes
Special Services for the Deaf - TTY equip
Restriction: Open by appt only

CM   MICHENER INSTITUTE FOR APPLIED HEALTH SCIENCES LIBRARY*, Learning Resource Centre, 222 Saint Patrick St, 2nd Flr, M5T 1V4. SAN 320-3417. Tel: 416-596-3123. FAX: 416-596-3137. E-mail: lrc@michener.ca. Web Site: www.michener.ca/lrc. *Sr Dir,* Ann Russell; Staff 3 (Non-MLS 3)
Founded 1972. Enrl 900; Fac 80
Library Holdings: Bk Vols 12,000; Per Subs 50
Special Collections: Board Examination Questions
Subject Interests: Allied health, Anesthesia tech, Cardiovascular perfusion, Chiropody, Cytology, Echocardiography, Educ, Genetics, Med tech, Nuclear med, Organizational develop, Radiography, Respiratory tech
Wireless access
Open Mon-Thurs (Winter) 8am-9pm, Fri 8-7, Sat & Sun 12-5; Mon-Fri (Summer) 8-6

M   MOUNT SINAI HOSPITAL*, Sidney Liswood Library, 600 University Ave, Rm 18-234, M5G 1X5. SAN 319-5260. Tel: 416-586-4800, Ext 4614. FAX: 416-586-4998. E-mail: library@mtsinai.on.ca. *Dir,* Sandra Kendall; Staff 5 (MLS 2, Non-MLS 3)
Founded 1967
Library Holdings: e-books 60; e-journals 1,200; Bk Titles 2,000; Per Subs 300
Automation Activity & Vendor Info: (Acquisitions) SirsiDynix; (Cataloging) SirsiDynix; (Circulation) SirsiDynix; (Course Reserve) SirsiDynix; (ILL) SirsiDynix; (Media Booking) SirsiDynix; (OPAC) SirsiDynix; (Serials) SirsiDynix
Wireless access
Function: Res libr
Partic in Health Science Information Consortium of Toronto
Open Mon-Fri 8:30-6
Restriction: Circ limited

S   NATIONAL POST LIBRARY*, 300-1450 Don Mills Rd, M3B 3R5. SAN 319-5198. Tel: 416-383-2300. FAX: 416-442-2109. *Libr Mgr,* Scott Maniquet; Staff 4 (MLS 2, Non-MLS 2)
Library Holdings: Bk Vols 3,000; Per Subs 285
Subject Interests: Finance, Pub affairs
Open Mon-Fri 9-7

C   NELLIE LANGFORD ROWELL WOMEN'S STUDY LIBRARY*, 204 Founders College, 4700 Keele St, M3J 1P3. SAN 322-7391. Tel: 416-736-2100, Ext 33219. FAX: 416-736-5732. E-mail: nlrowell@yorku.ca. Web Site: www.yorku.ca/nlrowell. *Coordr,* Vicky Drummond; E-mail: vickyd@yorku.ca
Founded 1969

Library Holdings: Bk Vols 23,000
Special Collections: Caribbean Women; Women's Movement Ephemera
Subject Interests: Feminism, Women, Women's studies
Wireless access
Publications: Margins of the Blackboard; Nellie Langford Rowell; Pamphlets on Pay Equity, Equality in Sports

S   NICKEL INSTITUTE LIBRARY*, 2700-161 Bay St, M5J 2S1. SAN 376-1967. Tel: 416-591-7999. E-mail: ni_toronto@nickelinstitute.org. Web Site: www.nickelinstitute.org. *Communications Mgr,* Stephanie Dunn; E-mail: sdunn@nickelinstitute.org

M   NORTH YORK GENERAL HOSPITAL, W Keith Welsh Library, 4001 Leslie St, M2K 1E1. SAN 368-8445. Tel: 416-756-6142. FAX: 416-756-6605. E-mail: library@nygh.on.ca. Web Site: www.nygh.on.ca/library. *Dir, Libr Serv,* Elaine Bernstein; E-mail: elaine.bernstein@nygh.on.ca
Founded 1968
Library Holdings: Bk Vols 3,500; Per Subs 25
Open Mon-Thurs 9-5

J   ONTARIO ARCHAEOLOGICAL SOCIETY LIBRARY*, 1444 Queen St E, Ste 102, M4A 2W1. (Mail add: PO Box 62066, M4A 2W1), SAN 329-2398. Tel: 416-406-5959. FAX: 416-406-5959. E-mail: oasociety@ontarioarchaeology.on.ca. Web Site; www.ontarioarchaeology.on.ca. *Exec Dir,* Lorie Harris; E-mail: executive-director@ontarioarchaeology.on.ca
Founded 1950
Library Holdings: Bk Titles 550
Subject Interests: Local hist
Wireless access
Open Tues, Wed & Thurs 9-5

S   ONTARIO CAMPS ASSOCIATION LIBRARY*, 250 Merton St, Ste 301, M4S 1B1. SAN 377-4201. Tel: 416-485-0425. FAX: 416-485-0422. E-mail: info@ontariocamps.ca. Web Site: www.ontariocamps.ca. *Exec Dir,* Heather Heagle
Library Holdings: Bk Vols 500; Per Subs 10
Open Mon-Fri 9-5
Restriction: Open to pub for ref only

J   ONTARIO COLLEGE OF ART & DESIGN*, Dorothy H Hoover Library, 100 McCaul St, M5T 1W1. SAN 319-5309. Tel: 416-977-6000, Ext 255. Reference Tel: 416-977-6000, Ext 334. FAX: 416-977-6006. Web Site: www.ocadu.ca. *Dir, Libr Serv,* Jill Patrick; E-mail: jpatrick@ocadu.ca; *Head, Instrul Serv,* Daniel Payne; Tel: 416-977-6000, Ext 217, E-mail: dpayne@ocadu.ca; *Head, Libr Syst,* James Forrester; E-mail: jforrester@ocadu.ca; *Ref & Access Serv Librn,* Robert Fabbro; Tel: 416-977-6000, Ext 343, E-mail: rfabbro@ocadu.ca; Staff 5 (MLS 5)
Founded 1876. Enrl 3,500; Fac 255; Highest Degree: Master
Library Holdings: AV Mats 4,100; Bk Vols 70,000; Per Subs 215
Subject Interests: Art, Design
Automation Activity & Vendor Info: (Acquisitions) SirsiDynix; (Cataloging) SirsiDynix; (Circulation) SirsiDynix; (Course Reserve) SirsiDynix; (OPAC) SirsiDynix; (Serials) SirsiDynix
Wireless access
Friends of the Library Group

S   ONTARIO ENERGY BOARD*, The Robert W Macaulay Library, 2300 Yonge St, Ste 2700, M4P 1E4. (Mail add: PO Box 2319, M4P 1E4), SAN 323-4223. Tel: 416-440-7655. FAX: 416-440-7656. Web Site: www.ontarioenergyboard.ca. *Librn,* Lina Buccilli; E-mail: lina.buccilli@ontarioenergyboard.ca
Library Holdings: Bk Titles 7,000; Per Subs 150
Subject Interests: Admin regulations, Electricity, Natural gas
Wireless access
Open Mon-Fri 8:30-4:45

GL   ONTARIO LEGISLATIVE LIBRARY*, Legislative Bldg, Queen's Park, M7A 1A9. SAN 319-5325. Tel: 416-325-3900. Interlibrary Loan Service Tel: 416-325-3901. FAX: 416-325-3925. Web Site: www.ontla.on.ca. *Exec Dir, Legis Librn,* Vicki Whitmell; Tel: 416-325-3939, Fax: 416-325-3909; *Dir,* Donna Burton; Tel: 416-325-3945, Fax: 416-314-8541; *Client Serv Mgr,* Wendy Reynolds; Tel: 416-325-2145; *Mgr, Coll Mgt,* Brian Tobin; Tel: 416-325-3910; Staff 34 (MLS 21, Non-MLS 13)
Founded 1867
Library Holdings: AV Mats 22; CDs 137; Bk Titles 160,729; Per Subs 427
Special Collections: British Statutes & Law Reports; Government Publications from Ontario & Other Provinces, British Parliament & United States Congress; Ontario Daily Newspapers; Ontario, Canadian & Provincial Statutes & Law Reports; Selected United States Government Documents

Subject Interests: Can hist, Law, Ont, Pub admin, Pub policy
Automation Activity & Vendor Info: (Acquisitions) Ex Libris Group; (Cataloging) Ex Libris Group; (Circulation) Ex Libris Group; (OPAC) Ex Libris Group; (Serials) Ex Libris Group
Publications: Current Issue Papers; Great Reads (Acquisition list); Ontario Government Publications Annual Catalogue; Ontario Government Publications Monthly Checklist; Press Highlights; Provincial Press; Status of Bills Report; Toronto Press Today

G   ONTARIO MINISTRY OF EDUCATION*, Brian Fleming Research Library, Mowat Block, 900 Bay St, 13th Flr, M7A 1L2. SAN 319-4906. Tel: 416-325-2652. FAX: 416-325-4235. *Mgr,* Simon Loban; Tel: 416-325-2654; Staff 2 (MLS 2)
Founded 1973
Library Holdings: Bk Vols 32,000; Per Subs 20
Special Collections: Ministry Documents Coll
Subject Interests: Educ, Mgt training
Function: ILL available, Ref serv available
Restriction: Not open to pub

G   ONTARIO MINISTRY OF FINANCE, Finance Library, 95 Grosvenor St, 1st Flr, M7A 1Y8. SAN 319-5392. Tel: 416-325-1200. FAX: 416-325-1212. E-mail: financelibrary.fin@ontario.ca. *Mgr,* Helen Katz; Tel: 416-325-1253, E-mail: helen.katz@ontario.ca; *Res Librn,* Gitta Rice; Tel: 416-325-1254, E-mail: gitta.rice@ontario.ca; *Res Librn,* Geeta Thachil; Tel: 416-325-1204, E-mail: geeta.thachil@ontario.ca; Staff 3 (MLS 3)
Founded 1944
Library Holdings: Bk Vols 33,000; Per Subs 125
Special Collections: Ontario Statutes, 1792-present
Subject Interests: Economics, Pub finance, Pub mgt
Automation Activity & Vendor Info: (Acquisitions) SydneyPlus; (Cataloging) SydneyPlus; (Circulation) SydneyPlus; (OPAC) SydneyPlus; (Serials) SydneyPlus
Database Vendor: EBSCOhost, Infomart, JSTOR, LexisNexis, Quicklaw
Function: ILL available
Publications: Library Update
Restriction: Open by appt only

GL   ONTARIO MINISTRY OF THE ATTORNEY GENERAL*, Law Library, 720 Bay St, Main Flr, M7A 2S9. SAN 319-5252. Tel: 416-326-4566. FAX: 416-326-4562. E-mail: library.mag@ontario.ca. *Mgr,* Gina Cullen; Tel: 416-326-4563
Founded 1967
Library Holdings: Bk Vols 30,000
Special Collections: English Reports
Subject Interests: Civil, Constitutional law, Criminal
Restriction: Not open to pub

GL   ONTARIO MINISTRY OF THE ATTORNEY GENERAL - COURT OF APPEAL JUSTICE JUDGES LIBRARY, Judicial Library Services, Osgoode Hall, 130 Queen St W, M5H 2N5. SAN 372-8986. Tel: 416-327-5750. FAX: 416-327-6797. Web Site: www.ontariocourts.ca. *Mgr,* Louise Hamel; Staff 4 (MLS 1, Non-MLS 3)
Library Holdings: Electronic Media & Resources 15; Bk Vols 22,000; Per Subs 10
Subject Interests: Law
Automation Activity & Vendor Info: (Cataloging) SydneyPlus; (OPAC) SydneyPlus
Database Vendor: ebrary, Gale Cengage Learning, HeinOnline, LexisNexis, Thomson Carswell, Westlaw, WestlaweCARSWELL
Restriction: Not open to pub

G   ONTARIO MINISTRY OF THE ENVIRONMENT*, Information Resource Centre, 40 Saint Clair Ave W, 11th Flr, M4V 1M2. SAN 374-5023. Tel: 416-327-1247. FAX: 416-327-2936. E-mail: irc.irc.moe@ontario.ca. *Sci Res Spec,* Denise Angeloni; Tel: 416-327-1241, E-mail: denise.angeloni@ontario.ca; Staff 1 (MLS 1)
Founded 1984
Library Holdings: Bk Vols 14,000; Per Subs 35
Subject Interests: Pesticides, Risk assessment, Toxicology
Automation Activity & Vendor Info: (Acquisitions) Inmagic, Inc.; (Cataloging) Inmagic, Inc.; (Circulation) Inmagic, Inc.; (ILL) Inmagic, Inc.; (OPAC) Inmagic, Inc.
Database Vendor: CISTI Source
Function: Prof lending libr
Restriction: Circ limited, Employees & their associates, In-house use for visitors, Limited access for the pub, Open to pub by appt only

G   ONTARIO OFFICE OF THE FIRE MARSHAL, Fire Sciences Library & Audio-Visual Resource Centre, 5775 Yonge St, 7th Flr, M2M 4J1. SAN 320-3395. Tel: 416-325-3121. FAX: 416-325-3213. E-mail: firesciences.information@ofm.ca. Web Site: www.ofm.gov.on.ca. *AV Tech,* Sophie Greco; E-mail: sophie.greco@ontario.ca; Staff 22 (MLS 1, Non-MLS 21)

Founded 1961
Apr 2012-Mar 2013. Mats Exp $41,700, Books (CAN) $18,000, Per/Ser (Incl. Access Fees) (CAN) $9,000, Other Print Mats (CAN) $4,700, AV Equip (CAN) $9,000, Electronic Ref Mat (Incl. Access Fees) (CAN) $1,000
Library Holdings: AV Mats 1,600; Bk Titles 9,500; Per Subs 150
Special Collections: Annual Reports of Dominion Fire Commissioner & Ontario Fire Marshall; Fire Journal from 1903; Ontario Fires, newsp clippings, audio-visual mat
Automation Activity & Vendor Info: (Cataloging) Inmagic, Inc.; (Circulation) Inmagic, Inc.; (OPAC) Inmagic, Inc.
Function: ILL available, Photocopying/Printing
Publications: Bibliographies; List of Monthly Acquisitions
Partic in Ont Govt Libr Coun
Open Mon-Fri 8:30-4:15

S   ONTARIO POWER GENERATION LIBRARY, 700 University Ave, H17G10, M5G 1X6. SAN 319-5317. Tel: 416-592-2715. FAX: 416-592-7532. E-mail: library@opg.com. *Librn,* Joanne Collingwood; E-mail: joanne.collingwood@opg.com; *Mgr,* Nancy Fish; Staff 6 (MLS 6)
Founded 1916
Library Holdings: Bk Vols 25,000; Per Subs 125
Subject Interests: Electrical, Environ sci, Nuclear energy, Rate, Rate structures
Partic in AG Canada

G   ONTARIO SECURITIES COMMISSION LIBRARY, 20 W Queen St, 20th Flr, M5H 3S8. SAN 326-2944. Tel: 416-593-2303. Interlibrary Loan Service Tel: 416-593-8336. FAX: 416-593-3661. Web Site: www.osc.gov.on.ca. *Mgr, Knowledge Mgt Serv,* Laura Knapp. Subject Specialists: *Bus, Legal res,* Laura Knapp; Staff 3 (MLS 2, Non-MLS 1)
Founded 1984
Library Holdings: Bk Titles 3,000; Per Subs 200
Special Collections: Ontario Securities Commission Bulletins (1949 to present)
Subject Interests: Admin law, Securities law
Automation Activity & Vendor Info: (Acquisitions) Sydney; (Cataloging) Sydney; (Circulation) Sydney; (OPAC) Sydney; (Serials) Sydney
Function: Doc delivery serv, For res purposes, Govt ref serv, ILL available, Online searches, Ref serv available, Workshops
Restriction: By permission only, Circulates for staff only, Not open to pub

G   ONTARIO WORKPLACE TRIBUNALS LIBRARY*, 505 University Ave, 7th Flr, M5G 2P2. SAN 368-5470. Tel: 416-314-3700. Administration Tel: 888-618-8846. FAX: 416-326-5164. E-mail: owtl@wst.gov.on.ca. Web Site: www.owtlibrary.on.ca. *Head Librn,* Martha Murphy; Tel: 416-314-8957; *Librn,* Kevin Jenkins; Tel: 416-314-8959; Staff 3 (MLS 2, Non-MLS 1)
Founded 1998
Library Holdings: Bk Titles 4,000; Bk Vols 13,400; Per Subs 150
Special Collections: Ontario Employment Standards Decisions; Ontario Labour Relations Board Reports; Workplace Safety & Insurance Appeals
Subject Interests: Human rights, Labor law, Pay equity, Workplace safety law
Partic in Can Asn of Law Librs; Ont Govt Libr Coun; Toronto Asn of Law Librs

L   OSLER, HOSKIN & HARCOURT LIBRARY*, One First Canadian Pl, 64th Flr, M5X 1B8. (Mail add: PO Box 50, M5X 1B8), SAN 329-9406. Tel: 416-862-4239. FAX: 416-862-6666. Web Site: www.osler.com. *Mgr,* Martin Tomlinson; E-mail: mtomlinson@osler.com; Staff 9 (MLS 5, Non-MLS 4)
Library Holdings: Bk Titles 3,000; Bk Vols 20,000; Per Subs 500
Special Collections: Can Gov
Subject Interests: Law
Restriction: Not open to pub

S   PARENT ACTION ON DRUGS LIBRARY, Seven Hawksdale Rd, Rm 121, M3K 1W3. SAN 375-6777. Tel: 416-395-4970. Toll Free FAX: 866-591-7685. E-mail: pad@parentactionondrugs.org. Web Site: www.parentactionondrugs.org. *Exec Dir,* Diane Buhler; E-mail: pad@sympatico.ca; Staff 3 (Non-MLS 3)
Founded 1983
Library Holdings: Bk Titles 50
Special Collections: Drug Prevention Coll, pamphlets, parent resources
Open Mon-Fri 9-4:30

SR   PRESBYTERIAN CHURCH IN CANADA ARCHIVES*, 50 Wynford Dr, M3C 1J7. SAN 375-0191. Tel: 416-441-1111, Ext 310. Toll Free Tel: 800-619-7301, Ext 310. FAX: 416-441-2825. Web Site: www.presbyterianarchives.ca. *Archivist,* Kim Arnold; E-mail: karnold@presbyterian.ca
Library Holdings: Bk Vols 600
Subject Interests: Church hist, Genealogy, Soc hist

Wireless access
Open Mon-Fri 9-4:45; Mon-Fri (Jul & Aug) 9-4

PRICEWATERHOUSECOOPERS
S   NATIONAL TAX RESEARCH SERVICES*, Royal Trust Tower, 77 King St W, Ste 3000, M5K 1G8. (Mail add: PO Box 82, M5K 1G8), SAN 325-1128. Tel: 416-815-5103. FAX: 416-814-3200. *Mgr,* Yasmin Chandra; E-mail: yasmin.chandra@ca.pwc.com; *Res Spec,* Agnese Caruso; E-mail: agnese.caruso@ca.pwc.com; *Res Spec,* Stacey Piesner; E-mail: stacey.piesner@ca.pwc.com; *Info Tech,* Denise Roeleveld; E-mail: denise.roeleveld@ca.pwc.com; *Info Tech,* Tischa Singh; E-mail: tischa.singh@ca.pwc.com; Staff 5 (MLS 3, Non-MLS 2)
Library Holdings: Bk Titles 4,000; Per Subs 100
Subject Interests: Law, Taxation
Database Vendor: CISTI Source, Dun & Bradstreet, EBSCOhost, Factiva.com, Infomart, LexisNexis, Mergent Online, Quicklaw, Standard & Poor's, Thomson Carswell, Westlaw
Function: For res purposes
Open Mon-Fri 8-5
Restriction: Co libr, Staff use only

G   PUBLIC HEALTH ONTARIO, Public Health Laboratories Library, 81 Resources Rd, M9P 3T1. SAN 319-6054. Tel: 416-235-5935. FAX: 416-235-6196. E-mail: phl_torontolibrary.moh@ontario.ca. Web Site: www.oahpp.ca. *Tech Serv,* Gabrielle Gaedecke; E-mail: gabrielle.gaedecke@oahpp.ca; Staff 1 (Non-MLS 1)
Founded 1963
Library Holdings: Bk Titles 3,800; Bk Vols 4,000; Per Subs 150; Spec Interest Per Sub 150
Special Collections: CLS; Guidelines
Subject Interests: Infectious diseases, Microbiology, Pub health
Partic in Health Science Information Consortium of Toronto; Ont Govt Libr Coun; Ontario Public Health Libraries Association (OPHLA)
Restriction: Staff use only

S   R B C DOMINIONS SECURITIES*, Research Library, Royal Bank Plaza, South Tower, 4th Flr, 200 Bay St, M5J 2W7. SAN 318-9104. Tel: 416-842-7588. FAX: 416-842-7555. *Librn,* Ann Ma; Tel: 416-842-7574, E-mail: ann.ma@rbccm.com
Special Collections: Canadian & US Public Company Files
Subject Interests: Finance, Securities indust
Restriction: Not open to pub, Staff use only

S   RADIATION SAFETY INSTITUTE OF CANADA*, Resource Centre, 165 Avenue Rd, Ste 300, M5R 3S4. SAN 375-5355. Tel: 416-650-9090. Toll Free Tel: 800-263-5803. FAX: 416-650-9920. E-mail: info@radiationsafety.ca. Web Site: www.radiationsafety.ca. *In Charge,* Maria Costa; Tel: 416-650-9090, Ext 21, E-mail: mcosta@radiationsafety.ca
Founded 1981

CR   REGIS COLLEGE LIBRARY*, 100 Wellesley St W, M5S 2Z5. SAN 319-5511. Tel: 416-922-5474, Ext 234. Reference Tel: 416-922-5474, Ext 236. Administration Tel: 416-922-5474, Ext 233. FAX: 416-922-2898. E-mail: regis.library@utoronto.ca. Web Site: www.regiscollege.ca/library. *Chief Librn,* Teresa Helik; Tel: 416-922-5474, Ext 235, E-mail: teresa.helik@utoronto.ca; *Head Librn,* Position Currently Open; *Cat, Ref Librn,* Mary Reynolds; Tel: 416-922-5474, Ext 233, E-mail: mary.reynolds@utoronto.ca; Staff 3.4 (MLS 3.4)
Founded 1930. Enrl 300; Highest Degree: Doctorate
May 2005-Apr 2006 Income (CAN) $290,418, Locally Generated Income (CAN) $10,461, Parent Institution (CAN) $279,957. Mats Exp (CAN) $57,500, Books (CAN) $29,000, Per/Ser (Incl. Access Fees) (CAN) $24,000, Electronic Ref Mat (Incl. Access Fees) (CAN) $1,500, Presv (CAN) $3,000. Sal (CAN) $175,604 (Prof (CAN) $102,964)
Library Holdings: AV Mats 140; Bk Vols 98,000; Per Subs 250; Videos 22
Special Collections: Archives of Jesuits of Upper Canada; John Macmurray Coll; Lonergan Research Center
Subject Interests: Jesuits, Theol
Automation Activity & Vendor Info: (Acquisitions) SirsiDynix; (Cataloging) SirsiDynix; (Circulation) SirsiDynix; (OPAC) SirsiDynix
Database Vendor: EBSCOhost, Factiva.com, Gale Cengage Learning, JSTOR, netLibrary, OCLC FirstSearch, OVID Technologies, ProQuest, Wilson - Wilson Web
Wireless access
Function: ILL available, Res libr, Wheelchair accessible
Partic in Lyrasis; Univ of Toronto Libr Automation Syst
Open Mon-Thurs 8:30-8:30, Fri 8:30-4:30, Sat 11-6; Mon-Fri (Summer) 9-4:30
Restriction: In-house use for visitors, Open to fac, students & qualified researchers, Use of others with permission of librn

M ROUGE VALLEY HEALTH SYSTEM-CENTENARY HEALTH
CENTRE*, C D Farquharson Health Sciences Library, 2867 Ellesmere Rd,
M1E 4B9. SAN 323-410X. Tel: 416-281-7101. FAX: 416-281-7360. *Librn,*
Natalia Tukhareli; E-mail: ntukhareli@rougevalley.ca; Staff 1 (Non-MLS 1)
Founded 1967
Library Holdings: Bk Vols 800; Per Subs 135
Subject Interests: Internal med, Nursing, Pediatrics, Psychiat, Surgery
Database Vendor: EBSCOhost, OVID Technologies
Wireless access
Partic in Health Science Information Consortium of Toronto
Open Mon-Fri 8:30-4:30

S ROYAL CANADIAN MILITARY INSTITUTE LIBRARY, 426 University
Ave, M5G 1S9. SAN 319-5570. Tel: 416-597-0286, Ext 128. Toll Free Tel:
800-585-1072. FAX: 416-597-6919. *Librn,* Penny Lipman; E-mail:
penny.lipman@rcmi.org; *Honorary Librn,* Arthur Manvell; Staff 2 (MLS 1,
Non-MLS 1)
Founded 1890
Library Holdings: Bk Vols 15,000
Special Collections: British Army Lists Coll; Champlain Society
Publications; The War of the Rebellion, Canadian Militia Lists
Subject Interests: Mil hist
Automation Activity & Vendor Info: (Cataloging) SoutronGLOBAL
Wireless access
Restriction: Mem only, Open to pub by appt only, Open to pub for ref
only

S ROYAL ONTARIO MUSEUM*, Library & Archives, 100 Queen's Park,
M5S 2C6. SAN 368-5500. Tel: 416-586-5595. Reference Tel:
416-586-5596. Administration Tel: 416-586-5597. FAX: 416-586-5519.
E-mail: info@rom.on.ca. Web Site: www.rom.on.ca. *Dept Head,* Arthur
Smith; Tel: 416-586-5740, E-mail: arthurs@rom.on.ca; *Librn,* Jack
Howard; Tel: 416-586-5718, E-mail: jackh@rom.on.ca; *Archivist,* Judith
Pudden; E-mail: judithp@rom.on.ca; Staff 6 (MLS 3, Non-MLS 3)
Founded 1962
Apr 2010-Mar 2011 Income (CAN) \$671,172, Locally Generated Income
(CAN) \$8,214, Parent Institution (CAN) \$662,958. Mats Exp (CAN)
\$117,655, Books (CAN) \$69,400, Per/Ser (Incl. Access Fees) (CAN)
\$46,755, Presv (CAN) \$1,500. Sal (CAN) \$469,862 (Prof (CAN)
\$250,848)
Library Holdings: CDs 12; DVDs 99; e-journals 1; Electronic Media &
Resources 1; Microforms 483; Music Scores 126; Bk Vols 179,963; Per
Subs 500; Videos 66
Special Collections: Asian Decorative Arts & Archaeology (H H Mu Far
Eastern Library); Early North American Discovery & Exploration
(Sigmund Samuel Canadiana Coll); Ornithology & Natural History
(Fleming Coll)
Subject Interests: Anthropology, Archaeology, Astronomy, Botany,
Canadiana, Decorative art, Entomology, Ethnology, Geol, Herpetology,
Ichthyology, Mammalogy, Mineralogy, Museology, Ornithology,
Paleontology, Textiles
Automation Activity & Vendor Info: (Cataloging) SIRSI WorkFlows;
(Circulation) SIRSI WorkFlows; (Course Reserve) SIRSI WorkFlows; (ILL)
OCLC FirstSearch; (OPAC) SIRSI WorkFlows; (Serials) SIRSI WorkFlows
Wireless access
Function: Archival coll, Art exhibits, e-mail & chat, e-mail serv,
Electronic databases & coll, ILL available, Online ref,
Photocopying/Printing, Pub access computers, Ref serv available, Ref serv
in person, Scanner, Web-catalog
Open Mon-Fri 10-5
Restriction: Open to pub for ref only

M SAINT JOSEPH'S HEALTH CENTRE*, George Pennal Library, 30 The
Queensway, M6R 1B5. SAN 319-5589. Tel: 416-530-6726. FAX:
416-530-6244. *Libr Serv Mgr,* Ana Jeremic; E-mail: jerema@stjoe.on.ca;
Staff 1 (Non-MLS 1)
Founded 1963
Library Holdings: e-books 85; e-journals 1,500; Bk Vols 1,000; Per Subs
38
Automation Activity & Vendor Info: (Cataloging) SIRSI WorkFlows
Database Vendor: EBSCOhost, Elsevier, MD Consult, Medline, Open Text
Corporation, OVID Technologies, ProQuest, PubMed, STAT!Ref (Teton
Data Systems), UpToDate, Wiley
Partic in Docline; Health Science Information Consortium of Toronto
Open Mon-Fri 7-3

M ST MICHAEL'S HOSPITAL*, Health Sciences Library, 209 Victoria St,
M5B 1W8. (Mail add: 30 Bond St, M5B 1W8), SAN 320-3409. Tel:
416-864-5059. Interlibrary Loan Service Tel: 416-864-5419. FAX:
416-864-5296. E-mail: hslibrary@smh.ca. *Mgr,* Sandra Iverson; Tel:
416-864-6060, Ext 77694; Staff 7 (MLS 5, Non-MLS 2)
Founded 1961
Library Holdings: Bk Titles 3,000; Per Subs 500

Subject Interests: Med
Database Vendor: OVID Technologies

S SAINT VLADIMIR INSTITUTE LIBRARY, 620 Spadina Ave, M5S 2H4.
SAN 321-091X. Tel: 416-923-3318. FAX: 416-923-8266. E-mail:
hostapchuk@stvladimir.ca, library@stvladimir.ca. Web Site:
www.stvladimir.ca. *Librn,* Halyna Ostapchuk; Staff 1 (Non-MLS 1)
Founded 1970
Library Holdings: Bk Vols 17,000; Per Subs 15
Special Collections: Canadian Ukrainians in Canadian Press, 1921 to
present; Rare Book Coll; Ukrainians in Toronto, posters
Subject Interests: Archaeology, Hist, Lit, Music, Relig
Open Tues 2-8, Wed & Fri 10-3, Thurs 3-8, Sat 2-5
Restriction: Access at librarian's discretion

S SHIBLEY RIGHTON LLP, Law Library, 250 University Ave, Ste 700,
M5H 3E5. SAN 326-3932. Tel: 416-214-5294. Interlibrary Loan Service
Tel: 416-214-5427. FAX: 416-214-5400. Interlibrary Loan Service FAX:
416-214-5426. Web Site: www.shibleyrighton.com. *Librn,* Joan Hudson;
Staff 2 (MLS 1, Non-MLS 1)
Library Holdings: Bk Titles 2,500; Per Subs 400
Automation Activity & Vendor Info: (Serials) Inmagic, Inc.
Publications: Weekly Bulletin
Restriction: Staff use only

S SNC-LAVALIN INC LIBRARY*, 195 West Mall, M9C 5K1. SAN
320-3476. Tel: 416-252-5311. FAX: 416-231-5356. Web Site:
www.snclavalin.com. *Librn,* Dr Aarash Kalra; Staff 1 (MLS 1)
Founded 1950
Library Holdings: CDs 60; e-journals 40; Bk Titles 9,000; Bk Vols
12,000; Per Subs 100
Subject Interests: Chem & petrochemical, Eng, Environment,
Infrastructure, Mining & metallurgy, Nuclear, Power, Transportation, Waste
mgt
Automation Activity & Vendor Info: (Acquisitions) Inmagic, Inc.;
(Cataloging) SIRSI Unicorn; (Circulation) SIRSI Unicorn; (OPAC) SIRSI
Unicorn; (Serials) Inmagic, Inc.
Restriction: Co libr

S SPINA BIFIDA & HYDROCEPHALUS ASSOCIATION OF ONTARIO,
Resource Centre, 555 Richmond St W, Ste 1006, M5V 3B1. (Mail add: PO
Box 103, M5V 3B1), SAN 373-7357. Tel: 416-214-1056. Toll Free Tel:
800-387-1575. FAX: 416-214-1446. E-mail: provincial@sbhao.on.ca. Web
Site: www.sbhao.on.ca. *Head of Libr,* Shauna Beaudoin
Founded 1973
Library Holdings: CDs 20; DVDs 20; Bk Titles 3,000; Per Subs 60;
Videos 50
Subject Interests: Disabilities, Educ, Employment, Hydrocephalus,
Lifestyle, Sexuality, Spina bifida
Publications: Library Listing; Video Listing

S SUN LIFE ASSURANCE COMPANY OF CANADA*, Business
Information Centre & Law Library, 150 King St W, 4th Flr, M5H 1J9.
SAN 319-5619. Tel: 416-204-3835. Interlibrary Loan Service Tel:
416-204-3840. Reference Tel: 416-204-3851. Information Services Tel:
416-204-3830. FAX: 416-595-0346. *Mgr,* Martha Foote; E-mail:
martha_foote@sunlife.com; *Res,* Faye Mitchell; E-mail:
faye_mitchell@sunlife.com; Staff 5 (MLS 2, Non-MLS 3)
Founded 1898
Library Holdings: Bk Vols 7,500; Per Subs 300
Special Collections: Actuarial Proceedings; Annual Reports
Subject Interests: Finance, Law, Life ins, Pensions

S SUN MEDIA*, News Research Centre, 333 King St E, M5A 3X5. SAN
320-3425. Tel: 416-947-2257. Toll Free Tel: 877-624-1463. FAX:
416-947-2043. E-mail: research@tor.sunpub.com. Web Site:
www.canoe.ca/Sunlib. *Mgr,* Julie Kirsh; E-mail:
julie.kirsh@tor.sunpub.com; Staff 12 (MLS 2, Non-MLS 10)
Founded 1971
Library Holdings: Bk Titles 150; Per Subs 75
Special Collections: SAVE Automated Library System, 1989-current; The
Toronto Sun Coll, newsp clips & reels; The Toronto Telegram Coll, newsp
clip & reels
Subject Interests: Current events
Partic in Info-globe; Infomart

SUNNYBROOK HEALTH SCIENCES CENTRE
M LIBRARY SERVICES, HOLLAND ORTHOPAEDIC & ARTHRITIC
CENTRE*, 43 Wellesley St E, M4Y 1H1, SAN 373-1464. Tel:
416-967-8545. FAX: 416-967-8605. E-mail:
library.requests@sunnybrook.ca. *Librn,* Carmen Genuardi; E-mail:
carmen.genuardi@sunnybrook.ca; Staff 1.25 (MLS 1.25)
Library Holdings: Bk Titles 1,105; Per Subs 16
Subject Interests: Arthritis, Arthroscopy, Orthopaedic surgery,
Orthopedics, Rehabilitation, Rheumatology

Partic in Health Sci Libr Info Consortium
Open Mon-Fri 9-5
Restriction: Hospital employees & physicians only, In-house use for visitors

M   DR R IAN MACDONALD LIBRARY*, 2075 Bayview Ave, M4N 3M5, SAN 319-5627. Tel: 416-480-6100, Ext 4562. Administration Tel: 416-480-6100, Ext 2560. FAX: 416-480-6848. *Mgr, Libr Serv,* Dr Farid Miah; E-mail: farid.miah.sw.ca; Staff 6 (MLS 2, Non-MLS 4)
Founded 1968
Library Holdings: AV Mats 1,227; e-books 10; e-journals 185; Bk Titles 3,294; Per Subs 120; Videos 250
Subject Interests: Hospital admin, Med, Mentally challenged adults, Nursing, Women's health
Automation Activity & Vendor Info: (Acquisitions) EOS International; (Cataloging) EOS International; (Circulation) EOS International; (OPAC) EOS International; (Serials) EOS International
Database Vendor: OVID Technologies
Open Mon-Fri 9-5, Sat & Sun 1-6

M   SUNNYBROOK HEALTH SCIENCES CENTRE - LIBRARY SERVICES, Sunnybrook Library Services, 2075 Bayview Ave, Rm EG-29, M4N 3M5. SAN 319-5767. Tel: 416-480-4762. FAX: 416-480-6848. E-mail: library.requests@sunnybrook.ca. *Mgr, Libr Serv,* Md Farid Miah; Tel: 416-480-6100, Ext 2560, E-mail: farid.miah@sunnybrook.ca; *Info Spec,* Henry Lam; Tel: 416-480-6100, Ext 2562, E-mail: henry.lam@sunnybrook.ca
Founded 1965
Library Holdings: e-books 100; e-journals 2,000; Electronic Media & Resources 100; Bk Vols 6,000; Per Subs 131
Subject Interests: Aging, Cancer, Cardiology, Critical care, Dermatology, Gynecology, Internal med, Neuroscience, Orthopedics, Perinatology, Pop health, Trauma, Women's health
Automation Activity & Vendor Info: (Acquisitions) SIRSI WorkFlows; (Cataloging) SIRSI WorkFlows; (Circulation) SIRSI WorkFlows; (OPAC) SIRSI WorkFlows; (Serials) SIRSI WorkFlows
Database Vendor: SirsiDynix
Wireless access
Partic in Health Science Information Consortium of Toronto
Open Mon-Fri 9-5

M   THE GORDON & RUBY SWAYZE HEALTH RESOURCE CENTRE*, 825 Coxwell Ave, M4C 3E7. SAN 368-5624. Tel: 416-469-6580, Ext 6010. FAX: 416-469-6106. E-mail: library@tegh.on.ca. *Librn,* Gurvinder Batra; Staff 1 (MLS 1)
Founded 1960
Library Holdings: Bk Titles 1,500; Per Subs 180
Subject Interests: Med, Nursing
Automation Activity & Vendor Info: (Acquisitions) SirsiDynix; (Cataloging) SirsiDynix; (Circulation) SirsiDynix; (OPAC) SirsiDynix; (Serials) SirsiDynix
Database Vendor: SirsiDynix

C   TARTU INSTITUTE LIBRARY*, 310 Bloor St W, M5S 1W4. (Mail add: 37 Groveland Crescent, Don Mills, M3A 3C4), SAN 370-7024. Tel: 416-447-8958. *Librn,* Endel Aruja; E-mail: arujae@sympatico.ca
Founded 1971
Library Holdings: Bk Titles 15,000; Bk Vols 25,000; Per Subs 30
Special Collections: Archival Materials Related to Estonians in Canada; Estonian Literature. Oral History
Automation Activity & Vendor Info: (Cataloging) Inmagic, Inc.
Publications: Annual Reports
Restriction: Open by appt only
Friends of the Library Group

S   TORONTO BOTANICAL GARDEN*, Weston Family Library, 777 Lawrence Ave E, M3C 1P2. SAN 319-0986. Tel: 416-397-1343. FAX: 416-397-1354. E-mail: library@torontobotanicalgarden.ca. Web Site: www.torontobotanicalgarden.ca/library.htm.
Founded 1959
Library Holdings: Bk Vols 8,500; Per Subs 55
Special Collections: Horticulture (Canadiana & Historical Coll)
Subject Interests: Botany, Floral arts, Garden design, Gardening
Automation Activity & Vendor Info: (Cataloging) Inmagic, Inc.; (Circulation) Inmagic, Inc.
Wireless access
Function: Archival coll, Bks on CD, CD-ROM, Children's prog, Computers for patron use, Copy machines, Handicapped accessible, Online cat, Photocopying/Printing, Ref & res, Ref serv available, VHS videos, Web-catalog, Wheelchair accessible
Open Mon-Fri 10-4, Sat & Sun 12-4
Restriction: Circ to mem only, Pub use on premises

S   TORONTO CATHOLIC DISTRICT SCHOOL BOARD*, Catholic Education Centre Professional Library, 80 Sheppard Ave E, M2N 6E8. SAN 321-7361. Tel: 416-222-8282, Ext 5324. Information Services Tel: 416-222-8282, Ext 2406. FAX: 416-229-5392. Web Site: www.tcdsb.org/library/. *Actg Librn,* Bozena Grymek-Nowinowski; *Coordr, Libr Serv,* Myra Junyk; E-mail: myra.junyk@tcdsb.org. Subject Specialists: *Lang arts,* Myra Junyk; Staff 3 (MLS 2, Non-MLS 1)
Founded 1966
Library Holdings: Bk Titles 30,000; Per Subs 400
Special Collections: Curriculum Documents Coll; ERIC Coll, micro; Historical Coll
Subject Interests: Child psychology, Children's lit, Educ, Relig
Publications: Bibliographies
Partic in Dialog Corp

S   TORONTO DOMINION BANK, Knowledge Centre, TD Economics, 55 King St W, M5K 1A2. SAN 319-566X. Tel: 416-982-8068. *Librn,* Cynthia Chan; Staff 1 (Non-MLS 1)
Founded 1960
Library Holdings: Bk Vols 734; Per Subs 174
Subject Interests: Banking, Econ, Finance, Indust
Open Mon-Fri 8-4

S   TORONTO INTERNATIONAL FILM FESTIVAL GROUP*, Film Reference Library, Two Carlton St, E Mezzanine, M5B 1J3. SAN 321-5091. Tel: 416-967-1517. FAX: 416-967-0628. E-mail: libraryservices@tiffg.ca. Web Site: www.filmreferencelibrary.ca. *Dir,* Sylvia Frank; E-mail: sylfrank@torfilmfest.ca; Staff 5 (MLS 1, Non-MLS 4)
Founded 1968
Library Holdings: CDs 200; Bk Titles 18,000; Per Subs 110; Videos 10,000
Special Collections: Cronenberg Archive Coll; Egoyan Archive Coll
Subject Interests: Film
Open Mon, Wed-Fri (Oct-Apr) 12-5, Tues 12-8; Tues, Thurs & Fri (May-Aug) 12-5

SR TORONTO JEWISH LIBRARY*, 4600 Bathurst St, 4th Flr, M2R 3V3. SAN 319-5686. Tel: 416-635-2996. FAX: 416-849-1005. E-mail: torontojewishlibrary@ujafed.org. Web Site: www.jewishtoronto.com. *Coordr,* Barbara Barak; Tel: 416-631-5843, E-mail: bbarak@ujafed.org; *Cat, Circ Asst,* Anna Skorupsky; E-mail: askorupsky@ujafed.org
Founded 1942
Library Holdings: Bk Titles 32,000; Bk Vols 40,000
Special Collections: Anita Ekstein Holocaust Resource Coll; Jewish Canadiana Coll, bks & newsp
Subject Interests: Holocaust, Israel, Judaica, Rare bks
Automation Activity & Vendor Info: (Cataloging) Mandarin Library Automation; (Circulation) Mandarin Library Automation; (OPAC) Mandarin Library Automation
Wireless access
Open Mon-Thurs 1-4

GL TORONTO LAWYERS ASSOCIATION LIBRARY*, Courthouse, 361 University Ave, M5G 1T3. SAN 319-4922. Tel: 416-327-5700. FAX: 416-947-9148. Web Site: www.tlaonline.ca. *Mgr,* Anne C Matthewman; E-mail: amatthewman@tlaonline.ca; Staff 2 (MLS 2)
Founded 1885
Library Holdings: Bk Vols 30,000
Automation Activity & Vendor Info: (Cataloging) Ex Libris Group
Open Mon-Fri 9-5

S   TORONTO MENDELSSOHN CHOIR LIBRARY*, 60 Simcoe St, M5J 2H5. SAN 373-6474. Tel: 416-598-0422, Ext 26. FAX: 416-598-2992. E-mail: library@tmchoir.org. Web Site: www.tmchoir.org. *Librn,* Lorraine Spragg. Subject Specialists: *Chorale music,* Lorraine Spragg
Library Holdings: Music Scores 90,000

SR TORONTO MONTHLY MEETING OF THE RELIGIOUS SOCIETY OF FRIENDS (QUAKERS), Friends House Library, 60 Lowther Ave, M5R 1C7. SAN 326-890X. Tel: 416-921-0368. FAX: 416-920-5214. E-mail: tmm@web.net. *Coordr,* Jane Sweet
Library Holdings: Bk Vols 9,000
Wireless access

G   TORONTO PUBLIC HEALTH LIBRARY, 277 Victoria St, 6th Flr, M5B 1W2. SAN 326-1522. Tel: 416-338-7865. FAX: 416-338-0489. E-mail: hlibrary@toronto.ca. *Sr Librn,* Bruce Gardham; E-mail: bgardha@toronto.ca; *Info Officer,* Graciela Latan; Tel: 416-338-7862, E-mail: glatan@toronto.ca; *Info Officer,* Julie Yang; Tel: 416-338-0049, E-mail: jyang@toronto.ca; Staff 3 (MLS 2, Non-MLS 1)
Jan 2011-Dec 2011. Mats Exp (CAN) $110,000, Books (CAN) $20,000, Per/Ser (Incl. Access Fees) (CAN) $70,000, Electronic Ref Mat (Incl. Access Fees) (CAN) $20,000. Sal (CAN) $261,000
Library Holdings: e-journals 15,000; Electronic Media & Resources 65; Bk Vols 11,000; Per Subs 127

Subject Interests: Health, Health admin, Health policy, Health promotion, Pub health

Automation Activity & Vendor Info: (Acquisitions) Inmagic, Inc.; (Cataloging) Inmagic, Inc.; (Circulation) Inmagic, Inc.; (OPAC) Inmagic, Inc.; (Serials) Inmagic, Inc.

Database Vendor: EBSCOhost, OVID Technologies, ProQuest, PubMed Partic in Health Science Information Consortium of Toronto; Knowledge Ontario; Ontario Public Health Libraries Association (OPHLA)

Open Mon-Fri 8:30-4:30

Restriction: External users must contact libr

P   TORONTO PUBLIC LIBRARY*, 789 Yonge St, M4W 2G8. (Mail add: Planning & Development Dept, 5120 Yonge St, 3rd Flr, M2N 5N9), SAN 368-5683. Tel: 416-393-7131. FAX: 416-393-7229. Web Site: www.torontopubliclibrary.ca. *City Librn,* Jane Pyper; *Dir of Develop, Pres, Toronto Pub Libr Found,* Heather Rumball; *Dir, Br Libr,* Anne Bailey; *Dir, Coll Mgt & City-Wide Serv,* Vickery Bowles; *Dir of Finance,* Larry Hughsam; *Dir, Human Res,* Dan Keon; *Dir, Info Tech & Fac Div,* Ron Dyck; *Dir, Mkt & Communications,* Linda Hazzan; *Dir, Planning, Policy & E-Serv Delivery,* Katherine Palmer; *Dir, Res & Ref Libr,* Linda Mackenzie Founded 1883. Pop 2,503,281; Circ 31,271,072

Library Holdings: Bk Vols 7,122,223

Special Collections: Art Room; Arthur Conan Doyle Coll; Black & Caribbean Heritage Coll; Business Information Centre; Canadian Theatre Record; Canadiana; Children's Literature Resource Coll; Consumer Health Information Service; Digital Coll; Electronic Books; Historicity:Toronto Then & Now; History of Canada (Baldwin Room); Jewish Mosaic; John Ross Robertson Coll; Languages Centre; Languages, Literature & Fine Arts; Local History Resources; Map Coll; Marguerite G Bagshaw Coll, puppetry, creative drama & theatre for children; Merril Coll of Science Fiction, Speculation & Fantasy; Native Peoples Coll; Osborne Coll of Early Children's Books; Performing Arts Centre; TD Audubon Coll; Theatre Coll Room; Toronto Star Newspaper Centre; Urban Affairs Library

Wireless access

Special Services for the Deaf - Sign lang interpreter upon request for prog

Special Services for the Blind - Braille bks; Talking bks

Friends of the Library Group

Branches: 101

AGINCOURT DISTRICT, 155 Bonis Ave, M1T 3W6, SAN 368-3524. Tel: 416-396-8943. FAX: 416-396-8956. *Br Head,* Rosa Pinto

Circ 1,140,779

Library Holdings: Bk Vols 126,640

Special Services for the Blind - Screen enlargement software for people with visual disabilities

Open Mon-Fri 9-8:30, Sat 9-5, Sun (Sept-June) 1:30-5

ALBION, 1515 Albion Rd, M9V 1B2, SAN 367-1976. Tel: 416-394-5170. FAX: 416-394-5185. *Br Head,* Haney Mussa

Circ 626,823

Library Holdings: Bk Vols 105,665

Special Services for the Blind - Screen enlargement software for people with visual disabilities

Open Mon-Thurs 9-8:30, Fri 9-6, Sat 9-5, Sun (Sept-June) 1:30-5

ALDERWOOD, 2 Orianna Dr, M8W 4Y1, SAN 367-200X. Tel: 416-394-5310. FAX: 416-394-5313. *Br Head,* Kerry Morton

Circ 170,971

Library Holdings: Bk Vols 45,201

Special Services for the Blind - Screen enlargement software for people with visual disabilities

Open Mon 10-8:30, Tues, Wed & Fri 10-6, Thurs 12:30-8:30, Sat 9-5

AMESBURY PARK, 1565 Lawrence Ave W, M6L 1A8, SAN 368-8593. Tel: 416-395-5420. FAX: 416-395-5432. *Br Head,* Carmen LaTouche

Circ 173,938

Library Holdings: Bk Vols 33,780

Special Services for the Blind - Screen enlargement software for people with visual disabilities

Open Tues & Thurs 12:30-8:30, Wed & Fri 10-6, Sat 9-5

ANNETTE STREET, 145 Annette St, M6P 1P3, SAN 368-5713. Tel: 416-393-7692. FAX: 416-393-7412. *Br Head,* Pam Mountain

Circ 169,286

Library Holdings: Bk Vols 25,293

Special Services for the Blind - Screen enlargement software for people with visual disabilities

Open Mon 10-8:30, Tues & Thurs 12:30-8:30, Wed & Fri 10-6, Sat 9-5

ARMOUR HEIGHTS, 2140 Avenue Rd, M5M 4M7, SAN 368-8607. Tel: 416-395-5430. FAX: 416-395-5433. *Br Head,* Marilyn Kruger

Circ 157,944

Library Holdings: Bk Vols 25,206

Special Services for the Blind - Screen enlargement software for people with visual disabilities

Open Tues, Thurs & Fri 10-6, Wed 12:30-8:30, Sat 9-5

BAYVIEW, Bayview Village Shopping Ctr, 2901 Bayview Ave, M2K 1E6, SAN 368-8658. Tel: 416-395-5460. FAX: 416-395-5434. *Br Head,* Jerry Lomoro

Circ 332,092

Library Holdings: Bk Vols 35,828

Special Services for the Blind - Screen enlargement software for people with visual disabilities

Open Mon 10:30-8:30, Tues & Thurs 12:30-8:30, Wed & Fri 10-6, Sat 9-5

BEACHES, 2161 Queen St E, M4L 1J1, SAN 368-5748. Tel: 416-393-7703. FAX: 416-393-7422. *Br Head,* Jennifer Ziorli

Circ 330,078

Library Holdings: Bk Vols 51,466

Special Services for the Blind - Screen enlargement software for people with visual disabilities

Open Mon-Thurs 9-8:30, Fri & Sat 9-5

BENDALE, 1515 Danforth Rd, M1J 1H5, SAN 368-3559. Tel: 416-396-8910. FAX: 416-396-3608. *Br Head,* Sandra Cox

Circ 303,557

Library Holdings: Bk Vols 32,647

Special Services for the Blind - Screen enlargement software for people with visual disabilities

Open Mon-Fri 9-8:30, Sat 9-5, Sun (Sept-Jun) 1:30-5

BLACK CREEK, North York Sheridan Mall, 1700 Wilson Ave, M3L 1B2, SAN 368-8682. Tel: 416-395-5470. FAX: 416-395-5435. *Br Head,* Nancy Velez

Circ 135,731

Library Holdings: Bk Vols 26,967

Special Services for the Blind - Screen enlargement software for people with visual disabilities

Open Tues & Thurs 12:30-8:30, Wed & Fri 10-6, Sat 9-5

BLOOR/GLADSTONE, 1101 Bloor St W, M6H 1M7, SAN 368-5772. Tel: 416-393-7674. FAX: 416-393-7502. *Br Head,* Gloria Jacobs

Circ 253,516

Library Holdings: Bk Vols 67,534

Special Services for the Blind - Screen enlargement software for people with visual disabilities

Open Mon-Fri 9-8:30, Sat 9-5, Sun (Sept-June) 1:30-5

BRENTWOOD, 36 Brentwood Rd N, M8X 2B5, SAN 367-2034. Tel: 416-394-5240. FAX: 416-394-5257. *Br Head,* Sue Wolfe

Circ 454,332

Library Holdings: Bk Vols 73,440

Special Services for the Blind - Screen enlargement software for people with visual disabilities

Open Mon-Thurs 9-8:30, Fri 9-6, Sat 9-5, Sun (Sept-June) 1:30-5

BRIDLEWOOD, Bridlewood Mall, 2900 Warden Ave, M1W 2S8, SAN 368-3583. Tel: 416-396-8960. FAX: 416-396-3604. *Br Head,* Leo Wong

Circ 438,694

Library Holdings: Bk Vols 47,114

Special Services for the Blind - Screen enlargement software for people with visual disabilities

Open Mon-Fri 9:30-8:30, Sat 9-5

BROOKBANKS, 210 Brookbanks Dr, M3A 2T8, SAN 368-8712. Tel: 416-395-5480. FAX: 416-395-5436. *Br Head,* Denise Drabkin

Circ 201,009

Library Holdings: Bk Vols 39,638

Special Services for the Blind - Screen enlargement software for people with visual disabilities

Open Tues & Thurs 12:30-8:30, Wed & Fri 10-6, Sat 9-5

BURROWS HALL, 1081 Progress Ave, M1B 5Z6, SAN 378-2263. Tel: 416-396-8740. FAX: 416-396-3559. *Br Head,* Vincent DeCaen

Circ 274,327

Library Holdings: Bk Vols 37,974

Special Services for the Blind - Screen enlargement software for people with visual disabilities

Open Tues & Thurs 12:30-8:30, Wed & Fri 10-6, Sat 9-5

ALBERT CAMPBELL, 496 Birchmount Rd, M1K 1N8, SAN 368-3613. Tel: 416-396-8890. FAX: 416-396-8901. *Br Head,* Susan Zadek

Circ 525,696

Library Holdings: Bk Vols 83,850

Special Services for the Blind - Screen enlargement software for people with visual disabilities

Open Mon 12:30-8:30, Tues-Fri 9:30-8:30, Sat 9-5, Sun (Sept-June) 1:30-5

CEDARBRAE, 545 Markham Rd, M1H 2A1, SAN 368-3648. Tel: 416-396-8850. FAX: 416-396-8864. *Br Head,* Russell Hanley

Circ 89,396

Library Holdings: Bk Vols 82,200

Special Services for the Blind - Screen enlargement software for people with visual disabilities

Open Mon-Fri 9-8:30, Sat 9-5, Sun (Sept-June) 1:30-5

CENTENNIAL, 578 Finch Ave W, M2R 1N7, SAN 368-8747. Tel: 416-395-5490. FAX: 416-395-5437. *Br Head,* Lynette Hartwell

Circ 290,430

Library Holdings: Bk Vols 38,664

Special Services for the Blind - Screen enlargement software for people with visual disabilities

Open Mon 10-8:30, Tues & Thurs 12:30-8:30, Wed & Fri 10-6, Sat 9-5

CITY HALL, Nathan Phillips Sq, 100 Queen St W, M5H 2N3, SAN 368-5861. Tel: 416-393-7650. FAX: 416-393-7421. *Br Head,* Sue Hoffman
Circ 291,101
Library Holdings: Bk Vols 28,229
Special Services for the Blind - Screen enlargement software for people with visual disabilities
Open Mon-Fri 10-6

CLIFFCREST, Cliffcrest Plaza, 3017 Kingston Rd, M1M 1P1, SAN 368-3672. Tel: 416-396-8916. FAX: 416-396-3605. *Br Head,* Judy Mak
Circ 224,201
Library Holdings: Bk Titles 24,836
Special Services for the Blind - Screen enlargement software for people with visual disabilities
Open Tues & Thurs 12:30-8:30, Wed & Fri 10-6, Sat 9-5

COLLEGE-SHAW, 766 College St, M6G 1C4, SAN 322-6255. Tel: 416-393-7668. FAX: 416-393-7418. *Br Head,* Nancy Jessop
Circ 241,560
Library Holdings: Bk Vols 28,214
Special Services for the Blind - Screen enlargement software for people with visual disabilities
Open Mon 10-8:30, Tues & Thurs 12:30-8:30, Wed & Fri 10-6, Sat 9-5

DANFORTH/COXWELL, 1675 Danforth Ave, M4C 5P2, SAN 329-6555. Tel: 416-393-7783. FAX: 416-393-7578. *Br Head,* Helen Flint
Circ 305,478
Library Holdings: Bk Vols 38,203
Special Services for the Blind - Screen enlargement software for people with visual disabilities
Open Tues & Thurs 9-8:30, Fri & Sat 9-5

DAVENPORT, 1246 Shaw St, M6G 3P1, SAN 329-6571. Tel: 416-393-7732. FAX: 416-393-7588. *Br Head,* Barb Ferguson
Circ 117,981
Library Holdings: Bk Vols 10,606
Special Services for the Blind - Screen enlargement software for people with visual disabilities
Open Tues & Thurs 12:30-8:30, Wed & Fri 10-6, Sat 9-5

DAWES ROAD, 416 Dawes Rd, M4B 2E8, SAN 368-508X. Tel: 416-396-3820. FAX: 416-396-3825. *Br Head,* Eileen Scidmore
Circ 221,311
Library Holdings: Bk Vols 43,220
Special Services for the Blind - Screen enlargement software for people with visual disabilities
Open Mon 10-8:30, Tues & Thurs 12:30-8:30, Wed & Fri 10-6, Sat 9-5

DEER PARK, 40 St Clair Ave E, M4T 1M9, SAN 368-5926. Tel: 416-393-7657. FAX: 416-393-7417. *Br Head,* Position Currently Open
Circ 404,529
Library Holdings: Bk Vols 63,636
Special Services for the Blind - Screen enlargement software for people with visual disabilities
Open Mon-Thurs 9-8:30, Fri & Sat 9-5

DON MILLS, 888 Lawrence Ave E, M3C 1P6, SAN 368-8801. Tel: 416-395-5710. FAX: 416-395-5715. *Br Head,* Denise Gordon
Circ 725,759
Library Holdings: Bk Vols 110,440
Special Services for the Blind - Screen enlargement software for people with visual disabilities
Open Mon 12:30-8:30, Tues-Thurs 9-8:30, Fri 9-6, Sat 9-5, Sun (Sept-June) 1:30-5

DOWNSVIEW, 2793 Keele St, M3M 2G3, SAN 368-8836. Tel: 416-395-5720. FAX: 416-395-5727. *Br Head,* Brenda Livingston
Circ 291,454
Library Holdings: Bk Vols 67,612
Special Services for the Blind - Screen enlargement software for people with visual disabilities
Open Mon 12:30-8:30, Tues-Thurs 9-8:30, Fri 9-5:30, Sat 9-5, Sun (Sept-June) 1:30-5

DUFFERIN/ST CLAIR, 1625 Dufferin St, M6H 3L9, SAN 368-5950. Tel: 416-393-7712. FAX: 416-393-7410. *Br Head,* Caroline Ingvaldsen
Circ 182,133
Library Holdings: Bk Vols 35,669
Special Services for the Blind - Screen enlargement software for people with visual disabilities
Open Mon 10-8:30, Tues & Thurs 12:30-8:30, Wed & Fri 10-6, Sat 9-5

EATONVILLE, 430 Burnhamthorpe Rd, M9B 2B1, SAN 367-2069. Tel: 416-394-5270. FAX: 416-394-5276. *Br Head,* Sue Patrick
Circ 513,760
Library Holdings: Bk Vols 63,452
Special Services for the Blind - Screen enlargement software for people with visual disabilities
Open Mon-Thurs 9-8:30, Fri 9-6, Sat 9-5, Sun (Sept-Jun) 1:30-5

EGLINTON SQUARE, Eglinton Square Mall, One Eglinton Sq, Unit 126, M1L 2K1, SAN 368-3702. Tel: 416-396-8920. FAX: 416-396-3557. *Br Head,* Cathy Pyper
Circ 285,956
Library Holdings: Bk Vols 31,595

Special Services for the Blind - Screen enlargement software for people with visual disabilities
Open Mon-Wed 9-8:30, Thurs 12:30-8:30, Fri & Sat 9-5

ELMBROOK PARK, Two Elmbrook Crescent, M9C 5B4, SAN 370-2030. Tel: 416-394-5290. FAX: 416-394-5295. *Br Head,* Susan Wise
Circ 174,237
Library Holdings: Bk Vols 26,762
Special Services for the Blind - Screen enlargement software for people with visual disabilities
Open Tues & Fri 10-6, Wed & Thurs 12:30-8:30, Sat 9-5

FAIRVIEW, 35 Fairview Mall Dr, M2J 4S4, SAN 368-8860. Tel: 416-395-5750. FAX: 416-395-5756. *Br Head,* Ellen Prostang; *Br Head,* Paul Robinson
Circ 1,230,935
Library Holdings: Bk Vols 181,454
Special Services for the Blind - Screen enlargement software for people with visual disabilities; Screen reader software
Open Mon-Fri 9-8:30, Sat 9-5, Sun (Sept-Jun) 1:30-5

FLEMINGDON PARK, 29 St Dennis Dr, M3C 3J3, SAN 368-8895. Tel: 416-395-5820. FAX: 416-395-5438. *Br Head,* Mounia Hanzazi
Circ 196,840
Library Holdings: Bk Vols 36,761
Special Services for the Blind - Screen enlargement software for people with visual disabilities
Open Tues & Thurs 12:30-8:30, Wed & Fri 10-6, Sat 9-5, Sun (Sept-Jun) 1:30-5

FOREST HILL, 700 Eglinton Ave W, M5N 1B9, SAN 368-5985. Tel: 416-393-7706. FAX: 416-393-7611. *Br Head,* Pam Hancock
Circ 241,450
Library Holdings: Bk Vols 45,450
Special Services for the Blind - Screen enlargement software for people with visual disabilities
Open Mon-Thurs 9-8:30, Fri & Sat 9-5

BARBARA FRUM, 20 Covington Rd, M6A 3C1, SAN 368-8623. Tel: 416-395-5440. FAX: 416-395-5447. *Br Head,* Panagiota Biros
Circ 712,019
Library Holdings: Bk Vols 111,944
Special Services for the Blind - Screen enlargement software for people with visual disabilities
Open Mon 12:30-8:30, Tues-Thurs 9-8:30, Fri 9-6, Sat 9-5, Sun (Sept-June) 1:30-5

GERRARD/ASHDALE, 1432 Gerrard St E, M4L 1Z6, SAN 368-6043. Tel: 416-393-7717. FAX: 416-393-7779. *Br Head,* Severino Ziorli
Circ 200,906
Library Holdings: Bk Vols 39,756
Special Services for the Blind - Screen enlargement software for people with visual disabilities
Open Mon 10-8:30, Tues & Thurs 12:30-8:30, Wed & Fri 10-6, Sat 9-5

GOLDHAWK PARK, 295 Alton Towers Circle, M1V 4P1, SAN 373-854X. Tel: 416-396-8964. FAX: 416-396-3561. *Br Head,* Sylvia Cheung; Staff 1 (MLS 1)
Circ 369,708
Library Holdings: Bk Vols 38,207
Special Services for the Blind - Screen enlargement software for people with visual disabilities
Open Mon-Thurs 9-8:30, Fri & Sat 9-5, Sun (Sept-Jun) 1:30-5

EVELYN GREGORY, 120 Trowell Ave, M6M 1L7. Tel: 416-394-1006. FAX: 416-394-1035. *Br Head,* Nora Lay
Circ 97,846
Library Holdings: Bk Vols 31,595
Special Services for the Blind - Screen enlargement software for people with visual disabilities
Open Mon 10-8:30, Tues & Thurs 12:30-8:30, Wed & Fri 10-6, Sat 9-5

GUILDWOOD, Guildwood Plaza, 123 Guildwood Pkwy, M1E 4V2, SAN 368-3737. Tel: 416-396-8872. FAX: 416-396-3610. *Br Head,* Frances Johnson
Circ 139,437
Library Holdings: Bk Vols 22,881
Special Services for the Blind - Screen enlargement software for people with visual disabilities
Open Tues & Thurs 12:30-8:30, Wed & Fri 10-6, Sat 9-5

HIGH PARK, 228 Roncesvalles Ave, M6R 2L7, SAN 368-6078. Tel: 416-393-7671. FAX: 416-393-7411. *Br Head,* Brian Bertrand
Circ 315,724
Library Holdings: Bk Vols 43,894
Special Services for the Blind - Screen enlargement software for people with visual disabilities
Open Mon-Thurs 9-8:30, Fri & Sat 9-5

HIGHLAND CREEK, 3550 Ellesmere Rd, M1C 3Z2, SAN 368-3761. Tel: 416-396-8876. FAX: 416-396-3562. *Br Head,* Linda Flavell
Circ 219,513
Library Holdings: Bk Vols 35,912
Special Services for the Blind - Screen enlargement software for people with visual disabilities
Open Tues & Thurs 12:30-8:30, Wed & Fri 10-6, Sat 9-5

HILLCREST, 5801 Leslie St, M2H 1J8, SAN 368-8925. Tel: 416-395-5830. FAX: 416-395-5439. *Br Head,* Mary Stone
Circ 311,868
Library Holdings: Bk Vols 44,548
Open Tues & Thurs 12:30-8:30, Wed & Fri 10-6, Sat 9-5

HUMBER BAY, 200 Park Lawn Rd, M8Y 3J1, SAN 367-2093. Tel: 416-394-5300. FAX: 416-394-5072. *Br Head,* Mark Gaudet
Circ 1,661,643
Library Holdings: Bk Vols 23,301
Open Tues & Fri 10-6, Wed & Thurs 12:30-8:30, Sat 9-5

HUMBER SUMMIT, 2990 Islington Ave, M9L 2K6, SAN 368-895X. Tel: 416-395-5840. FAX: 416-395-5426. *Br Head,* Neil McDonald
Circ 87,909
Library Holdings: Bk Vols 18,216
Open Tues & Thurs 12:30-8:30, Wed & Fri 10-6, Sat 9-5

HUMBERWOOD, 850 Humberwood Blvd, M9W 7A6, SAN 376-9682. Tel: 416-394-5210. FAX: 416-394-5215. *Br Head,* Vivien Canning
Circ 126,130
Library Holdings: Bk Vols 38,148
Open Tues & Thurs 12:30-8:30, Wed & Fri 10-6, Sat 9-5

JANE/DUNDAS, 620 Jane St, M6S 4A6, SAN 368-475X. Tel: 416-394-1014. FAX: 416-394-1025. *Br Head,* James Karanja
Circ 266,603
Library Holdings: Bk Vols 44,297
Open Mon 12:30-8:30, Tues-Thurs 9-8:30, Fri & Sat 9-5

JANE/SHEPPARD, 1906 Sheppard Ave W, M3L 1Y7, SAN 370-0933. Tel: 416-395-5966. FAX: 416-395-5427. *Br Head,* Eva Prout
Circ 133,977
Library Holdings: Bk Vols 24,665
Open Mon 10-8:30, Tues & Thurs 12:30-8:30, Wed & Fri 10-6, Sat 9-5

JONES, 118 Jones Ave, M4M 2Z9, SAN 368-6108. Tel: 416-393-7715. FAX: 416-393-7416. *Br Head,* Buch Lynda
Circ 176,701
Library Holdings: Bk Vols 26,860
Open Mon & Fri 10-6, Tues 10-8:30, Wed & Thurs 12:30-8:30, Sat 9-5

KENNEDY-EGLINTON, Liberty Square Shopping Plaza, 2380 Eglinton Ave E, M1K 2P3, SAN 329-6547. Tel: 416-396-8924. FAX: 416-396-8928. *Br Head,* Marie Belanger
Circ 146,003
Library Holdings: Bk Vols 24,616
Open Tues & Thurs 12:30-8:30, Wed & Fri 10-6, Sat 9-5

LEASIDE, 165 McRae Dr, M4G 1S8, SAN 368-5020. Tel: 416-396-3835. FAX: 416-396-3840. *Br Head,* Linda Martin
Circ 352,803
Library Holdings: Bk Vols 50,222
Open Mon-Thurs 9-8:30, Fri & Sat 9-5

LOCKE, 3083 Yonge St, M4N 2K7, SAN 368-6019. Tel: 416-393-7730. FAX: 416-393-7581. *Br Head,* Beverley Howatson
Circ 351,871
Library Holdings: Bk Vols 62,414
Open Mon-Thurs 9-8:30, Fri & Sat 9-5

LONG BRANCH, 3500 Lakeshore Blvd W, M8W 1N6, SAN 367-2123. Tel: 416-394-5320. FAX: 416-394-5326. *Br Head,* Dorota Rajewska
Circ 145,025
Library Holdings: Bk Vols 30,634
Open Tues & Thurs 12:30-8:30, Wed & Fri 10-6, Sat 9-5

MAIN STREET, 137 Main St, M4E 2V9, SAN 368-6132. Tel: 416-393-7700. FAX: 416-393-7505. *Br Head,* Susan Truong
Circ 254,059
Library Holdings: Bk Vols 37,804
Open Mon-Thurs 9-8:30, Fri & Sat 9-5

MALVERN, 30 Sewells Rd, M1B 3G5, SAN 368-377X. Tel: 416-396-8969. FAX: 416-396-3560. *Br Head,* Joanne Bainbridge
Circ 725,072
Library Holdings: Bk Vols 120,686
Mon-Fri 9-8:30, Sat 9-5, Sun (Sept-Jun) 1:30-5

MARYVALE, Parkway Mall, 85 Ellesmere Rd, M1R 4B9, SAN 368-3788. Tel: 416-396-8931. FAX: 416-396-3603. *Br Head,* Sheryl Hyland
Circ 268,684
Library Holdings: Bk Vols 39,936
Open Mon 10-8:30, Tues & Thurs 12:30-8:30, Wed & Fri 10-6, Sat 9-5

MCGREGOR PARK, 2219 Lawrence Ave E, M1P 2P5, SAN 368-3796. Tel: 416-396-8935. FAX: 416-396-3609. *Br Head,* Yonghai Ke
Circ 299,977
Library Holdings: Bk Vols 29,209
Open Tues & Thurs 12:30-8:30, Wed & Fri 10-6, Sat 9-5, Sun (Sept-June) 1:30-5

MERRIL COLLECTION OF SCIENCE FICTION, SPECULATION & FANTASY, 239 College St, 3rd Flr, M5T 1R5, SAN 374-3551. Tel: 416-393-7748. FAX: 416-393-7741. *Br Head,* Lorna Toolis
Library Holdings: Bk Vols 44,303
Open Mon-Fri 10-6, Sat 9-5
Friends of the Library Group

MIMICO CENTENNIAL, 47 Station Rd, M8V 2R1, SAN 367-2158. Tel: 416-394-5330. FAX: 416-394-5338. *Br Head,* Neil Marlow
Circ 173,886
Library Holdings: Bk Vols 40,219
Open Tues & Wed 12:30-8:30, Thurs & Fri 10-6, Sat 9-5

MORNINGSIDE, Morningside Mall, 255 Morningside Ave, M1E 3E6, SAN 368-3826. Tel: 416-396-8881. FAX: 416-396-3606. *Br Head,* Sheila Yates
Circ 272,742
Library Holdings: Bk Vols 34,570
Open Mon-Wed 9-8:30, Thurs 12:30-8:30, Fri & Sat 9-5

MOUNT DENNIS, 1123 Weston Rd, M6N 3S3, SAN 368-4784. Tel: 416-394-1008. FAX: 416-394-1036. *Br Head,* Anne Keys
Circ 125,783
Library Holdings: Bk Vols 39,597
Open Mon 10-8:30, Tues & Thurs 12:30-8:30, Wed & Fri 10-6, Sat 9-5

MOUNT PLEASANT, 599 Mount Pleasant Rd, M4S 2M5, SAN 372-0047. Tel: 416-393-7737. FAX: 416-393-7414. *Br Head,* Dulce Gomes
Circ 145,348
Library Holdings: Bk Vols 15,234
Open Tues & Thurs 12:30-8:30, Wed & Fri 10-6, Sat 9-5

NEW TORONTO, 110 Eleventh St, M8V 3G5, SAN 367-2182. Tel: 416-394-5350. FAX: 416-394-5358. *Br Head,* Anne Campbell
Circ 140,877
Library Holdings: Bk Vols 37,597
Open Tues & Fri 10-6, Wed & Thurs 12:30-8:30, Sat 9-5, Sun (Sept-June) 1:30-5

NORTH YORK CENTRAL, 5120 Yonge St, M2N 5N9, SAN 368-8771. Tel: 416-395-5535. FAX: 416-395-5668. *Dir, Res & Ref Libr,* Linda Mackenzie
Circ 1,622,092
Library Holdings: Bk Vols 438,911
Special Services for the Deaf - TTY equip
Special Services for the Blind - Screen enlargement software for people with visual disabilities; Screen reader software
Open Mon-Fri 9-8:30, Sat 9-5, Sun (Sept-June) 1:30-5
Friends of the Library Group

NORTHERN DISTRICT, 40 Orchard View Blvd, M4R 1B9, SAN 368-6167. Tel: 416-393-7610. FAX: 416-393-7742. *Br Head,* Kathy Staal
Circ 505,619
Library Holdings: Bk Vols 143,451
Open Mon-Fri 8:30-6

NORTHERN ELMS, 123B Rexdale Blvd, Unit 5, M9W 1P1, SAN 372-5227. Tel: 416-394-5230. FAX: 416-394-5235. *Br Head,* Bert Providence
Circ 95,852
Library Holdings: Bk Vols 22,521
Open Tues & Wed 12:30-8:30, Thurs & Fri 10-6, Sat 9-5

OAKWOOD VILLAGE LIBRARY & ARTS CENTRE, 341 Oakwood Ave, M6E 2W1, SAN 377-7855. Tel: 416-394-1040. FAX: 416-394-1039. *Br Head,* Colleen Mowatt
Circ 123,597
Library Holdings: Bk Vols 30,100
Open Mon 10-8:30, Tues & Thurs 12:30-8:30, Wed & Fri 10-6, Sat 9-5

OSBORNE COLLECTION OF EARLY CHILDREN'S BOOKS, 239 College St, 4th Flr, M5T 1R5, SAN 374-7220. Tel: 416-393-7753. FAX: 416-393-7635. *Br Head,* Leslie McGrath
Library Holdings: Bk Vols 75,000
Special Collections: Historical Children's Literature
Open Mon-Fri 10-6, Sat 9-5
Friends of the Library Group

PALMERSTON, 560 Palmerston Ave, M6G 2P7, SAN 368-6191. Tel: 416-393-7680. FAX: 416-393-7420. *Br Head,* RoseMarie Spearpoint
Circ 218,404
Library Holdings: Bk Vols 30,673
Open Mon 10-8:30, Tues & Thurs 12:30-8:30, Wed & Fri 10-6, Sat 9-5

PAPE/DANFORTH, 701 Pape Ave, M4K 3S6, SAN 368-5896. Tel: 416-393-7727. FAX: 416-393-7503. *Br Head,* Suk Yin Ng
Circ 445,268
Library Holdings: Bk Vols 50,806
Open Mon-Fri 9-8:30, Sat 9-5, Sun (Sept-Jun) 1:30-5

PARKDALE, 1303 Queen St W, M6K 1L6, SAN 368-6221. Tel: 416-393-7686. FAX: 416-393-7705. *Br Head,* Miranda Huska
Circ 356,848
Library Holdings: Bk Vols 63,789
Open Mon-Fri 9-8:30, Sat 9-5, Sun (Sept-Jun) 1:30-5

PARLIAMENT STREET, 269 Gerrard St E, M5A 2G6, SAN 368-6256. Tel: 416-393-7663. FAX: 416-393-7413. *Br Head,* Barrie Gray
Circ 277,682
Library Holdings: Bk Vols 49,649
Open Mon-Fri 9-8:30, Sat 9-5, Sun (Sept-Jun) 1:30-5

PERTH/DUPONT, 1589 Dupont St, M6P 3S5, SAN 368-6280. Tel: 416-393-7677. FAX: 416-393-7724. *Br Head,* Carmen Martino
Circ 83,603

Library Holdings: Bk Vols 16,861
Open Tues & Thurs 12:30-8:30, Wed & Fri 10-6, Sat 9-5
PLEASANT VIEW, 575 Van Horne Ave, M2J 4S8, SAN 368-8984. Tel: 416-395-5940. FAX: 416-395-5419. *Br Head,* Karen Knott
Circ 210,856
Library Holdings: Bk Vols 28,344
Open Tues & Thurs 12:30-8:30, Wed & Fri 10-6, Sat 9-5
PORT UNION, 5450 Lawrence Ave E, M1C 3B2, SAN 368-3850. Tel: 416-396-8885. FAX: 416-396-3558. *Br Head,* Patricia Anaka
Circ 196,212
Library Holdings: Bk Vols 32,516
Open Mon 10-8:30, Tues & Thurs 12:30-8:30, Wed & Fri 10-6, Sat 9-5
QUEEN/SAULTER, 765 Queen St E, M4M 1H3, SAN 368-6299. Tel: 416-393-7723. FAX: 416-393-7423. *Br Head,* Miguelita Costes
Circ 88,833
Library Holdings: Bk Vols 17,146
Open Tues & Thurs 12:30-8:30, Wed & Fri 10-6, Sat 9-5
REXDALE, 2243 Kipling Ave, M9W 4L5, SAN 367-2212. Tel: 416-394-5200. FAX: 416-394-5205. *Br Head,* Eliseo Zompanti
Circ 123,525
Library Holdings: Bk Vols 25,766
Open Tues & Fri 10–6, Wed & Thurs 12:30–8:30, Sat 9–5
RICHVIEW, 1806 Islington Ave, M9P 3N3, SAN 367-2247. Tel: 416-394-5120. FAX: 416-394-5158. *Br Head,* Margot Clarke
Circ 808,368
Library Holdings: Bk Vols 151,948
Open Mon-Thurs 9-8:30, Fri 9-6, Sat 9-5, Sun (Sept-June) 1:30-5
RIVERDALE, 370 Broadview Ave, M4K 2M8, SAN 368-6310. Tel: 416-393-7720. FAX: 416-393-7424. *Br Head,* Niki Lawrence
Circ 364,781
Library Holdings: Bk Vols 53,771
Open Mon-Thurs 9-8:30, Fri & Sat 9-5
RUNNYMEDE, 2178 Bloor St W, M6S 1M8, SAN 368-6345. Tel: 416-393-7697. FAX: 416-393-7574. *Br Head,* Brenda Beaton
Circ 433,689
Library Holdings: Bk Vols 62,719
Open Mon-Thurs 9-8:30, Fri 9-6, Sat 9-5, Sun (Sept-June) 1:30-5
ST CLAIR-SILVERTHORN, 1748 St Clair Ave W, M6N 1J3, SAN 368-6353. Tel: 416-393-7709. FAX: 416-393-7409. *Br Head,* Lillian Necakov-Avalos
Circ 70,471
Library Holdings: Bk Vols 12,995
Open Tues & Thurs 12:30-8:30, Wed & Fri 10-6, Sat 9-5
ST JAMES TOWN, 495 Sherbourne St, M4X 1K7. Tel: 416-393-7744. FAX: 416-393-7562. *Br Head,* Jean Lee
Circ 271,997
Library Holdings: Bk Vols 54,871
Open Tues & Thurs 12:30-8:30, Wed & Fri 10-6, Sat 9-5
ST LAWRENCE, 171 Front St E, M5A 4H3, SAN 368-6361. Tel: 416-393-7655. FAX: 416-393-7419. *Br Head,* Linda Goldman
Circ 175,741
Library Holdings: Bk Vols 28,428
Open Mon 10-8:30, Tues & Thurs 12:30-8:30, Wed & Fri 10-6, Sat 9-5
SANDERSON, 327 Bathurst St, M5T 1J1, SAN 368-5837. Tel: 416-393-7653. FAX: 416-393-7702. *Br Head,* Kathryn Quan
Circ 299,171
Library Holdings: Bk Vols 47,096
Open Mon-Thurs 9-8:30, Fri & Sat 9-5
MARIA A SHCHUKA BRANCH, 1745 Eglinton Ave W, M6E 2H4, SAN 368-4768. Tel: 416-394-1000. FAX: 416-394-1034. *Br Head,* Graziela Pimentel
Circ 289,271
Library Holdings: Bk Titles 98,426
Open Mon-Thurs 9-8:30, Fri 9-6, Sat 9-5, Sun (Sept-June) 1:30–5
LILLIAN H SMITH BRANCH, 239 College St, M5T 1R5, SAN 368-5802. Tel: 416-393-7746. FAX: 416-393-7609. *Br Head,* Sarah Bradley
Circ 569,097
Library Holdings: Bk Vols 97,167
Open Mon-Thurs 9-8:30, Fri 9-6, Sat 9-5, Sun (Sept-June) 1:30-5
SPADINA ROAD, Ten Spadina Rd, M5R 2S7, SAN 368-637X. Tel: 416-393-7666. FAX: 416-393-7415. *Br Head,* Mariella Bertelli
Circ 196,421
Library Holdings: Bk Vols 32,285
Special Collections: Native Peoples' Coll
Open Tues & Thurs 12:30-8:30, Wed & Fri 10-6, Sat 9-5
STEELES, Bamburgh Gardens Shopping Plaza, 375 Bamburgh Circle, M1W 3Y1, SAN 328-915X. Tel: 416-396-8975. FAX: 416-396-3602. *Br Head,* Rita Au
Circ 322,190
Library Holdings: Bk Vols 34,412
Open Mon-Fri 9-8:30, Sat 9-5

S WALTER STEWART BRANCH, 170 Memorial Park Ave, M4J 2K5, SAN 368-4997. Tel: 416-396-3975. FAX: 416-396-3842. *Br Head,* Jean Kowalewski
Circ 425,320
Library Holdings: Bk Vols 88,261
Open Mon-Fri 9-8:30, Sat 9-5, Sun (Sept-June) 1:30-5
SWANSEA MEMORIAL, 95 Lavinia Ave, M6S 3H9, SAN 368-640X. Tel: 416-393-7695. FAX: 416-393-7552. *Br Head,* Brenda Beaton
Circ 39,266
Library Holdings: Bk Vols 9,173
Open Tues & Thurs 10-12 & 1-6, Wed 1-8, Sat 10-5
TAYLOR MEMORIAL, 1440 Kingston Rd, M1N 1R3, SAN 368-3885. Tel: 416-396-8939. FAX: 416-396-3601. *Br Head,* Renuka Jeyanayagam
Circ 126,374
Library Holdings: Bk Vols 22,287
Open Tues & Thurs 12:30-8:30, Wed & Fri 10-6, Sat 9-5
THORNCLIFFE, 48 Thorncliffe Park Dr, M4H 1J7, SAN 368-5055. Tel: 416-396-3865. FAX: 416-396-3866. *Br Head,* Susan Guglielmin
Circ 12,013
Library Holdings: Bk Vols 43,127
Open Mon-Fri 9-8:30, Sat 9-5
TODMORDEN ROOM, 1081 1/2 Pape Ave (at Torrens), M4K 3W6, SAN 378-228X. Tel: 416-396-3875. FAX: 416-396-3864. *Br Head,* Susan Farmer
Circ 50,583
Library Holdings: Bk Vols 7,128
Open Tues & Thurs 12:30-5 & 6-8:30, Wed & Sat 9-12 & 1-5
TORONTO REFERENCE LIBRARY, 789 Yonge St, M4W 2G8. Tel: 416-395-5577. FAX: 416-393-7147. *Dir, Res & Ref Libr,* Linda Mackenzie
Circ 282,685
Library Holdings: Bk Vols 1,455,545
Special Services for the Deaf - TTY equip
Special Services for the Blind - Daisy reader; Magnifiers; Screen enlargement software for people with visual disabilities; Screen reader software; Talking bks
Open Mon-Thurs 9:30-8:30, Fri 9:30-5:30, Sat 9-5, Sun (Sept-June) 1:30-5
Friends of the Library Group
URBAN AFFAIRS, Metro Hall, 55 John St, M5V 3C6, SAN 378-2204. Tel: 416-397-7241. FAX: 416-397-7245. *Br Head,* Judy Curry
Circ 45,517
Library Holdings: Bk Vols 103,547
Special Collections: Don River Reports; The Campaign to Save Toronto's Old City Hall, docs & papers on microfiche
Subject Interests: Archit, Arts, Culture, Econ develop, Environ planning, Environ pollution, Housing, Law, Municipal finance, Municipal govt, Municipal serv, Urban design, Urban geog, Urban hist, Urban planning, Urban sociol, Urban transportation
Special Services for the Blind - Screen enlargement software for people with visual disabilities
Open Mon & Tues 9:30-6, Wed-Fri 9:30-8
VICTORIA VILLAGE, 184 Sloane Ave, M4A 2C4, SAN 368-9077. Tel: 416-395-5950. FAX: 416-395-5418. *Br Head,* Rosa De Barros
Circ 105,032
Library Holdings: Bk Vols 22,291
Open Tues & Thurs 12:30-8:30, Wed & Fri 10-6, Sat 9-5
WESTON, Two King St, M9N 1K9, SAN 368-4814. Tel: 416-394-1016. FAX: 416-394-1037. *Br Head,* Luidmila Cibic
Circ 143,560
Library Holdings: Bk Vols 36,260
Open Mon 10-8:30, Tues & Thurs 12:30-8:30, Wed & Fri 10-6, Sat 9-5
WOODSIDE SQUARE, Woodside Square Mall, 1571 Sandhurst Circle, M1V 1V2, SAN 368-3915. Tel: 416-396-8979. FAX: 416-395-3563. *Br Head,* Mary Massoud
Circ 646,220
Library Holdings: Bk Vols 52,445
Open Mon-Thurs 9-8:30, Fri & Sat 9-5
WOODVIEW PARK, 16 Bradstock Rd, M9M 1M8, SAN 368-9107. Tel: 416-395-5960. FAX: 416-395-5417. *Br Head,* Kathryn Watson
Circ 96,461
Library Holdings: Bk Vols 18,649
Open Tues, Wed & Fri 10-6, Thurs 12:30-8:30, Sat 9-5
WYCHWOOD, 1431 Bathurst St, M5R 3J2, SAN 368-6434. Tel: 416-393-7683. FAX: 416-393-7665. *Br Head,* Isobel Lang
Circ 235,915
Library Holdings: Bk Vols 40,156
Open Mon-Thurs 9-8:30, Fri & Sat 9-5
YORK WOODS, 1785 Finch Ave W, M3N 1M6, SAN 368-9131. Tel: 416-395-5980. FAX: 416-395-5991. *Br Head,* Denise Piper
Circ 416,586
Library Holdings: Bk Vols 91,891
Open Mon 12:30-8:30, Tues-Thurs 9-8:30, Fri 9-6, Sat 9-5, Sun (Sep-June) 1:30-5

YORKVILLE, 22 Yorkville Ave, M4W 1L4, SAN 368-6469. Tel: 416-393-7660. FAX: 416-393-7725. *Br Head,* Tiziano Vanola Circ 323,783
Library Holdings: Bk Vols 45,553
Open Mon-Thurs 9-8:30, Fri & Sat 9-5
Bookmobiles: 2

M   TORONTO REHAB*, Library Services, 550 University Ave, M5G 2A2. SAN 323-9004. Tel: 416-597-3422, Ext 3050. FAX: 416-591-6515. Web Site: www.torontorehab.on.ca. *Mgr,* Doreen Millman-Wilson; Tel: 416-597-3422, Ext 3750, E-mail: millman-wilson.doreen@torontorehab.on.ca; *Acq,* Elizabeth Johnson; *Electronic Res,* Marcia Winterbottom; *Info Res,* Joy Shanfield; *ILL,* Doris Extavour; *ILL,* Holly Phillips; E-mail: phillips.holly@torontorehab.on.ca; Staff 6 (MLS 3, Non-MLS 3)
Founded 1998
Library Holdings: Bk Titles 5,000; Bk Vols 6,000; Per Subs 125
Database Vendor: EBSCOhost, OVID Technologies, ProQuest
Function: ILL available
Partic in Health Science Information Consortium of Toronto
Open Mon-Fri 8:30-5

S   TORONTO STAR NEWSPAPERS LTD LIBRARY*, One Yonge St, 5th Flr, M5E 1E6. SAN 319-5708. Tel: 416-869-4491. FAX: 416-865-3994. Web Site: www.thestar.ca. *Mgr,* Carol Elder; Staff 9 (MLS 5, Non-MLS 4)
Library Holdings: Bk Vols 4,000; Per Subs 38
Special Collections: Electronic Clip Files; Events, Places, Subjects & People, photog; Personalities, micro
Subject Interests: Biog, Current events, Regional happenings
Restriction: Staff use only

G   TORONTO URBAN DEVELOPMENT SERVICES*, City Planning Library, Metro Hall, 22nd Flr, M5V 3C6. SAN 319-5694. Tel: 416-392-1526. FAX: 416-392-3821. *Librn,* Deborah Fowler; Staff 1 (MLS 1)
Founded 1958
Library Holdings: Bk Vols 8,000; Per Subs 250
Subject Interests: Design especially Toronto, Urban planning
Automation Activity & Vendor Info: (Acquisitions) Sydney; (Cataloging) Sydney; (Circulation) Sydney; (OPAC) Sydney; (Serials) Sydney
Open Mon-Fri 9-5

L   TORYS LLP LIBRARY*, 79 Wellington St W, Ste 3000, M5K 1N2. (Mail add: PO Box 270, Toronto-Dominion Centre, M5K 1N2), SAN 325-6529. Tel: 416-865-8158. FAX: 416-865-7380. E-mail: libserv@torys.com. *Mgr, Libr Serv,* Nicholas Watt; Tel: 416-865-7626, E-mail: nwatt@torys.com; *Ref Librn,* Jennifer Lee; Tel: 416-865-8159, E-mail: jlee@torys.com; *Ref Librn,* Clare Mauro; Tel: 416-945-7704, E-mail: cmauro@torys.com. Subject Specialists: *Corporate law, Law, Securities law,* Nicholas Watt; *Intellectual property, Law,* Jennifer Lee; *Civil procedure, Law, Litigation,* Clare Mauro; Staff 10.5 (MLS 4, Non-MLS 6.5)
Library Holdings: e-journals 100; Bk Vols 20,000; Per Subs 250
Special Collections: Legal Memoranda
Subject Interests: Corp law, Finance, Financial institutions, Securities
Automation Activity & Vendor Info: (Acquisitions) EOS International; (Cataloging) EOS International; (Circulation) EOS International; (OPAC) EOS International; (Serials) EOS International
Database Vendor: CISTI Source, Dialog, Dun & Bradstreet, EOS International, Factiva.com, Gale Cengage Learning, HeinOnline, Hoovers, Infomart, LexisNexis, OCLC FirstSearch, PubMed, Quicklaw, Westlaw, Westlaw Business, WestlaweCARSWELL
Function: ILL available
Publications: Legal Research Handbook; Library Handbook; Library Report
Restriction: Employee & client use only

S   TOWERS PERRIN INFORMATION CENTRE*, South Tower, Ste 1501, 175 Bloor St E, M4W 3T6. SAN 326-7407. Tel: 416-960-2600. FAX: 416-960-2819. *Librn,* Karen Tarbox; Tel: 416-960-2609, E-mail: karen.tarbox@towersperrin.com; *Coordr, Libr Serv,* Heidi Wyma; Tel: 416-960-2790, E-mail: heidi.wyma@towersperrin.com; *Cat,* Charmaine Wunsch; Tel: 416-960-2842, E-mail: charmaine.wunsch@towersperrin.com; *Info Spec,* Rosemary Hatnay; Tel: 416-960-7449, E-mail: rosemary.hatnay@towersperrin.com; *Info Spec,* Adrianne Petitti; Tel: 416-960-2836, E-mail: adrianne.petitti@towersperrin.com; Staff 5 (MLS 5)
Founded 1978
Subject Interests: Compensation, Employee benefits, Pensions, Taxation
Restriction: Staff use only

CR TYNDALE UNIVERSITY COLLEGE & SEMINARY*, J William Horsey Library, 25 Ballyconnor Ct, M2M 4B3. SAN 319-6119. Tel: 416-226-6380. Circulation Tel: 416-226-6620, Ext 2125. Reference Tel: 416-226-6620, Ext 2126. FAX: 416-218-6765. E-mail: library@tyndale.ca. Web Site: www.tyndale.ca/library. *Dir,* Hugh Rendle; Tel: 416-226-6620, Ext 6716,

E-mail: hrendle@tyndale.ca; *Educ Librn,* Mark Mueller; Tel: 416-226-6620, Ext 2227, E-mail: mmueller@tyndale.ca; *Acq,* Becky Wismer; Tel: 416-226-6620, Ext 2128, E-mail: bwismer@tyndale.ca; *Pub Serv,* Armen Svadjian; *Tech Serv,* Maria Ho. Subject Specialists: *Educ,* Mark Mueller; Staff 9 (MLS 3, Non-MLS 6)
Founded 1894. Enrl 1,300; Fac 40; Highest Degree: Master
Library Holdings: Bk Vols 132,000; Per Subs 500
Special Collections: Percival J Baldwin Puritan Coll
Subject Interests: Biblical studies, Christian ministry, Theol
Automation Activity & Vendor Info: (Acquisitions) Ex Libris Group; (Cataloging) Ex Libris Group; (Circulation) Ex Libris Group; (OPAC) Ex Libris Group
Database Vendor: Canadian Reference Centre, ebrary, EBSCOhost, Elsevier, Ex Libris Group, Gale Cengage Learning, Haworth Pres Inc, Ingram Library Services, JSTOR, OCLC ArticleFirst, OCLC CAMIO, OCLC FirstSearch, OVID Technologies, Project MUSE, ProQuest
Open Mon-Thurs 8am-10:30pm, Fri 8-7, Sat 10-5

SR UNITED CHURCH OF CANADA*, Victoria University Archives, 95 Charles St W, M5S 1K7. (Mail add: 73 Queen's Park Crescent E, M5S 1K7), SAN 329-9937. Tel: 416-585-4563. Reference Tel: 416-585-4564. Automation Services Tel: 416-585-4565. FAX: 416-585-4584. E-mail: info@unitedchurcharchives.ca. Web Site: www.unitedchurcharchives.ca. *Archives Dir,* Sharon Larade; E-mail: sharon.larade@utoronto.ca; Staff 5 (MLS 2, Non-MLS 3)
Founded 1972
Library Holdings: Bk Titles 12,000; Bk Vols 20,000; Per Subs 50
Subject Interests: Can church, Methodist hist, Missions & missionaries, Presbyterianism, Relig educ, Relig studies, Soc action, Soc hist, Soc welfare, Temperance soc
Automation Activity & Vendor Info: (Acquisitions) SirsiDynix; (Cataloging) SirsiDynix; (OPAC) SirsiDynix; (Serials) SirsiDynix
Database Vendor: SirsiDynix
Function: ILL available
Partic in Univ of Toronto Libr Automation Syst
Restriction: Non-circulating

S   UNITED EMPIRE LOYALISTS' ASSOCIATION OF CANADA LIBRARY*, George Brown House, 202 - 50 Baldwin St, M5T 1L4. SAN 321-7248. Tel: 416-591-1783. E-mail: uelac@uelac.org. Web Site: www.uelac.org. *Pres,* Robert C McBride
Founded 1968
Special Collections: American Revolutionary War Coll; Genealogy Coll (Family Histories of Descendants of Loyalists)
Publications: American Revolutionary War; Early History & Genealogical Publication; Index to the Loyalist Gazette; Loyalist Gazette
Restriction: Not open to pub

S   UNITED STEELWORKERS OF AMERICA LIBRARY*, 234 Eglinton Ave E, 8th Flr, M4P 1K7. SAN 323-7311. Tel: 416-487-1571. FAX: 416-482-5548. Web Site: www.uswa.ca. *Librn,* Jackie Edwards; E-mail: jedwards@uswa.ca
Library Holdings: Bk Titles 800
Special Collections: Stelabor Coll dating back to the 1940s, per
Partic in Toronto Indust Relations Librns
Restriction: Open by appt only

UNIVERSITY HEALTH NETWORK
M   HEALTH SCIENCES LIBRARY*, 610 University Ave, 5th Flr, M5G 2M9, SAN 319-5295. Tel: 416-946-4482. Interlibrary Loan Service Tel: 416-340-4121. FAX: 416-946-2084. Web Site: www.uhn.ca/Education/library_services.asp. *Dir,* Bogusia Trojan; E-mail: boguslawa.trojan@uhn.on.ca
Founded 1957
Library Holdings: Bk Vols 15,000
Subject Interests: Hematology, Med biophysics, Molecular biol, Oncology, Radiotherapy
Automation Activity & Vendor Info: (Acquisitions) SydneyPlus; (Cataloging) SydneyPlus; (Circulation) SydneyPlus; (OPAC) SydneyPlus; (Serials) SydneyPlus
Partic in Health Science Information Consortium of Toronto
Open Mon-Fri 8:30-7
M   TORONTO GENERAL HOSPITAL HEALTH SCIENCES LIBRARY*, University Health Network, 200 Elizabeth St, ENI 418, M5G 2C4, SAN 319-5678. Tel: 416-340-3429. FAX: 416-340-4384. E-mail: uhnlibraries@uhn.on.ca. Web Site: www.uhn.on.ca/education/library_services.asp. *Dir,* Bogusia Trojan; E-mail: boguslawa.trojan@uhn.on.ca
Founded 1964
Library Holdings: Bk Vols 22,000
Special Collections: History of Medicine
Subject Interests: Cardiology, Neuroscience, Oncology, Transplantation

Automation Activity & Vendor Info: (Cataloging) EOS International; (Circulation) EOS International; (OPAC) EOS International; (Serials) EOS International

Database Vendor: EBSCOhost, Elsevier, EOS International, Ex Libris Group, Natural Standard, OVID Technologies, Oxford Online, ProQuest Partic in Docline; Health Science Information Consortium of Toronto
Open Mon-Fri 8:30-8, Sat 10-5

C   UNIVERSITY OF TORONTO LIBRARIES*, 130 St George St, M5S 1A5. SAN 368-6493. Tel: 416-978-8450. Reference Tel: 416-978-6215. FAX: 416-978-1608. E-mail: libraryinfo@library.utoronto.ca. Web Site: library.utoronto.ca/. *Chief Librn,* Carole Moore; Tel: 416-978-2292, E-mail: carole.moore@utoronto.ca; *Dir, Tech & Info Serv,* Marshall Clinton; Tel: 416-978-7649, E-mail: m.clinton@utoronto.ca; *Head, Coll Develop,* Graham Bradshaw; Tel: 416-978-2289, E-mail: graham.bradshaw@utoronto.ca
Founded 1827. Enrl 62,731; Fac 2,101; Highest Degree: Doctorate
Library Holdings: Bk Vols 9,346,479; Per Subs 53,547
Special Collections: UN Document Depository
Automation Activity & Vendor Info: (Acquisitions) SirsiDynix; (Cataloging) SirsiDynix; (Circulation) SirsiDynix
Publications: University of Toronto Libraries Newsletter; UTL News
Partic in OCLC Online Computer Library Center, Inc
Open Mon-Fri 8:30-11
Friends of the Library Group
Departmental Libraries:
A D ALLEN CHEMISTRY LIBRARY, Lash Miller Laboratories, Rm 480, 80 St George St, M5S 3H6, SAN 368-6825. Tel: 416-978-3587. FAX: 416-946-8059. Web Site: www.chem.utoronto.ca/facilities/chemlib/. *Librn,* Patricia Meindl; E-mail: pmeindl@chem.utoronto.ca. Subject Specialists: *Chem,* Patricia Meindl; Staff 1 (MLS 1)
Highest Degree: Doctorate
Library Holdings: Bk Vols 21,151
ASTRONOMY & ASTROPHYSICS, 60 Saint George St, Rm 1306, M5S 1A7, SAN 368-6671. Tel: 416-978-4268. FAX: 416-946-7287. E-mail: astlibr@astro.utoronto.ca; library@astro.utoronto.ca. Web Site: www.astro.utoronto.ca/library.html. *Librn,* Lee Robbins
Founded 1935
Library Holdings: Bk Vols 36,038
Special Collections: David Dunlap Observatory Coll
Function: Archival coll
Open Mon-Fri 9-5
BUSINESS INFORMATION CENTRE LIBRARY, Joseph L Rotman School of Management, 105 Saint George St, M5S 1A5, SAN 368-7333. Tel: 416-978-3421. FAX: 416-978-1920. E-mail: bicstaff@rotman.utoronto.ca. Web Site: www.mgmt.utoronto.ca/bic/. *Mgr,* Sean Forbes; Tel: 416-978-1924
Library Holdings: Bk Vols 19,500
Open Mon-Thurs 8:45am-9:30pm, Fri 8:45-5, Sat 12-5, Sun 1-5
CR   CAVEN LIBRARY, Knox College, 59 Saint George St, M5S 2E6, SAN 368-7783. Tel: 416-978-4504. FAX: 416-971-2133. E-mail: knox.college@utoronto.ca. Web Site: www.utoronto.ca:80/knox/knoxlib.htm. *Chief Librn,* Joan Pries; Tel: 416-978-6090, E-mail: joan.pries@utoronto.ca; *Acq, Cataloger,* Anna Golodnitsky; Tel: 416-978-6719, E-mail: knox.readerservices@utoronto.ca. Subject Specialists: *Interdisciplinary studies, Theol,* Joan Pries
Library Holdings: Bk Vols 80,000; Per Subs 224
Special Collections: Soren Aabye Kierkegaard first editions
Subject Interests: Presbyterianism, Reform church hist, Theol
Automation Activity & Vendor Info: (Acquisitions) SIRSI WorkFlows; (Cataloging) SIRSI WorkFlows; (Circulation) SIRSI WorkFlows; (Course Reserve) Blackboard Inc; (OPAC) SIRSI WorkFlows; (Serials) SIRSI WorkFlows
CENTRE FOR REFORMATION & RENAISSANCE STUDIES, Victoria University, E J Pratt Library, 71 Queen's Park Crescent E, M5S 1K7, SAN 368-6795. Tel: 416-585-4468. FAX: 416-585-4430. Web Site: www.crrs.ca.
Library Holdings: Bk Vols 41,000
Special Collections: Erasmus Coll; Rare Book Coll
Subject Interests: Confraternities, Erasmus, Humanism, Northern renaissance, Reformation
Publications: A Reformation Debate: Karlstadt, Emser & Eck on Sacred Images; An Annotated Catalogue of Early Editions of Erasmus at the Centre for Reformation & Renaissance Studies, Toronto; Bibles, Theological Treatise & other Religious Literature, 1491-1700, at the CRRS; Galateo: A Renaissance Treatise on Manners; Humanist Editions of Statues & Histories at the CRRS; Humanist Editions of the Classics at the CRRS; International Directory of Renaissance & Reformation Associations & Institutes (1993); Language & literature: Early Printed Books at the CRRS; Published Books (1499-1700) on science, medicine & natural history at the CRRS; Register of Sermons Preached at Paul's Cross 1534-1642; Seven Dialogues; The Layman on Wisdom & the

Mind; The Profession of the Religious & the Falsely-Believed & Forged Donation of Constantine
Open Mon-Fri 9-5
CENTRE OF CRIMINOLOGY, 14 Queens Park Crescent W, M5S 3K9, SAN 368-6949. Tel: 416-978-7068. FAX: 416-978-4195. Web Site: library.utoronto.ca/www/libraries_crim/crimhome.htm. *Librn,* Tom Finlay; Tel: 416-978-7068, Ext 236, E-mail: tom.finlay@utoronto.ca; *Ref Librn,* Andrea Shier; Tel: 416-978-7068, Ext.245, E-mail: andrea.shier@utoronto.ca
Library Holdings: Bk Vols 26,332
Open Mon-Fri (Winter) 9-5; Mon-Fri (Summer) 9-4:30
CHENG YU TUNG EAST ASIAN LIBRARY, John P Robarts Research Library, 130 St George St, Rm 8049, M5S 1A5, SAN 368-7007. Tel: 416-978-3300. Reference Tel: 416-978-1024. FAX: 416-978-0863. Web Site: library.utoronto.ca/www/east. *Librn,* Anna U; Tel: 416-978-7690, E-mail: anna.u@utoronto.ca; *Coll & Res Librn,* Hana Kim
Library Holdings: Bk Vols 301,998
Open Mon-Thurs 9-7:30, Fri 9-6
JOHN H DANIELS FACULTY OF ARCHITECTURE, LANDSCAPE & DESIGN, Shore + Moffat Library, 230 College St, 2nd Flr, M5T 1R2, SAN 368-6647. Tel: 416-978-2649. FAX: 416-971-2094. *Librn,* Irene Puchalski; Tel: 416-978-6787, E-mail: irene.puchalski@daniels.utoronto.ca; *Libr Tech,* Lisa Doherty; E-mail: lisa.doherty@daniels.utoronto.ca
Library Holdings: Bk Vols 32,000
Open Mon-Thurs 9-9, Fri 9-7, Sat 12-5
DATA, MAP & GOVERNMENT INFORMATION SERVICES, John P Robarts Library, 130 Saint George St, 5th Flr, M5S 1A5, SAN 368-7368. Tel: 416-978-3931 (govt & map info), 416-978-5589 (Data Library & GIS Service). FAX: 416-946-0522. E-mail: gis.maps@utoronto.ca. Web Site: www.chass.utoronto.ca:8080/datalib. *Head of Librr,* Marcel Fortin; Tel: 416-978-7628
Library Holdings: Bk Vols 410,000
Open Mon-Fri 10-5
ROBERTSON DAVIES LIBRARY, Massey College, Four Devonshire Pl, M5S 2E1, SAN 368-7392. Tel: 416-978-2893. FAX: 416-978-1759. *Librn,* PJ MacDougall; Staff 2 (MLS 1, Non-MLS 1)
Founded 1963
Library Holdings: Bk Vols 45,000; Per Subs 16
Special Collections: 19th Century Colour Printing, Bookbinding & Illustration Processes (Ruari McLean Coll); Carl Dair Archives; Working 19th Century Printing Presses
Open Mon-Fri 10-12:30 & 2-5
Restriction: Closed stack, External users must contact libr, Non-circulating, Open to pub by appt only
CM   DENTISTRY LIBRARY, 124 Edward St, Rm 267, M5G 1G6, SAN 368-6973. Tel: 416-979-4916. FAX: 416-979-4936. E-mail: library.dentistry@utoronto.ca. Web Site: dentistry.library.utoronto.ca. *Head of Librr,* Helen He; Tel: 416-979-4916, Ext 4371, E-mail: helen.he@utoronto.ca; Staff 3 (MLS 2, Non-MLS 1)
Library Holdings: Bk Vols 26,647
DEPARTMENT OF FINE ART, Sidney Smith Hall, Rm 6032B, 100 Saint George St, M5S 3G3, SAN 368-7155. Tel: 416-978-5006. FAX: 416-978-1491. *Chief Librn,* Margaret English; E-mail: margaret.english@utoronto.ca
Founded 1930. Highest Degree: Doctorate
Library Holdings: Bk Vols 33,000
Subject Interests: Exhibition catalogs
Function: Ref serv available
Open Mon-Tues 10-6, Wed-Thurs 10-8, Fri 10-5
Restriction: Non-circulating
DEPARTMENT OF PHYSICS, McLennan Physical Laboratories, 60 St George St, Rm 211C, M5S 1A1, SAN 368-7546. Tel: 416-978-5188. FAX: 416-978-5919. Web Site: www.physics.utoronto.ca/library/. *Librn,* Barbara Chu; E-mail: bchu@physics.utoronto.ca; *Libr Tech,* Elizabeth Glover; E-mail: eglover@physics.utoronto.ca
Library Holdings: Bk Vols 34,270
Open Mon-Fri 9-5
ENGINEERING & COMPUTER SCIENCE LIBRARY, Sandford Fleming Bldg, Rm 2402, Ten King's College Rd, M5S 1A5. (Mail add: Engineering and Computer Science Library, University of Toronto, M5S 1A5), SAN 368-7066. Tel: 416-978-6494. Reference Tel: 416-978-6578. FAX: 416-971-2091. E-mail: engincs.lib@utoronto.ca. *Librn,* Wang Jiabin; E-mail: jiabin.wang@utoronto.ca; *Librn,* Cristina Sewerin; E-mail: cris.sewerin@utoronto.ca
Library Holdings: Bk Vols 157,259
Open Mon-Thurs 8:30am-10:30pm, Fri 8:30-6, Sat 9-5, Sun 1-6
FACULTY OF INFORMATION INFORUM, 140 Saint George St, 4th Flr, M5S 3G6, SAN 368-7309. Tel: 416-978-7060. FAX: 416-978-5769. Web Site: www.ischool.utoronto.ca/services/inforum-is. *Dir,* Joe Cox; Tel: 416-978-5766, E-mail: joe.cox@utoronto.ca; *Coll & Pub Serv Coordr,* Elisa Sze; Tel: 416-978-7071, E-mail: elisa.sze@utoronto.ca; *Outreach & Instrul Coordr,* Kathleen Scheaffer; Tel: 416-978-5770, E-mail: kathleen.scheaffer@utoronto.ca; *Ref & Web Content Coordr,* Nalini Singh; Tel: 416-978-7069, E-mail: nalini.singh@utoronto.ca; *Circ & Pub*

Serv Tech, Anna Oh; Tel: 416-978-5767, E-mail: anna.oh@utoronto.ca; *Coll Tech,* Nadia Moro; Tel: 416-978-5765, E-mail: nadia.moro@utoronto.ca; *Ser & Acq Tech,* Meera Thirunavukarasu; Tel: 416-978-5542, E-mail: meera.thirunavukarasu@utoronto.ca; *Syst Tech,* Tony Lemmens; Tel: 416-978-7168, E-mail: tony.lemmens@utoronto.ca; *Sr IT Adminr,* Ivan Sestak; Tel: 416-978-6121, E-mail: ivan.sestak@utoronto.ca; *Syst Adminr,* Gabriel Moga; Tel: 416-978-6122, E-mail: gabriel.moga@utoronto.ca; *Sr Web Developer,* Dvornyak Alex; Tel: 416-978-6120, E-mail: alex.dvornyak@utoronto.ca; Staff 11 (MLS 4, Non-MLS 7)
Founded 1928. Enrl 600; Fac 35; Highest Degree: Doctorate
Library Holdings: AV Mats 1,000; Bk Vols 120,000; Per Subs 500
Special Collections: Subject Analysis Systems Coll; Theses Coll
Automation Activity & Vendor Info: (Course Reserve) SirsiDynix; (ILL) Fretwell-Downing; (OPAC) Endeca Technologies, Inc; (Serials) SirsiDynix
FACULTY OF MUSIC, Edward Johnson Bldg, 80 Queens Park Crescent, M5S 1A1, SAN 368-7422. Tel: 416-978-3734. FAX: 416-978-5571. Web Site: www.utoronto.ca/music/html/frames/library/libhome.htm. *Librn,* Kathleen McMorrow; Tel: 416-978-6920, E-mail: k.mcmorrow@utoronto.ca
Library Holdings: Bk Vols 203,817
Open Mon-Thurs 8:30am-8:45pm, Fri 8:30-5:45

CM FAMILY & COMMUNITY MEDICINE LIBRARY, 500 University Ave, M5G 1V7. Tel: 416-978-5606. FAX: 416-978-3912. E-mail: dfcm.library@utoronto.ca. Web Site: www.dfcm.utoronto.ca/library.htm. *Librn,* Robyn Butcher; E-mail: dfcm.librarian@utoronto.ca; *Librn,* Rita Shaughnessy; E-mail: r.shaughnessy@utoronto.ca; *Libr Tech,* Iveta Lewis; Tel: 416-946-3071, E-mail: iveta.lewis@utoronto.ca; Staff 3 (MLS 2, Non-MLS 1)
Fac 1,500
Library Holdings: Bk Titles 1,500; Per Subs 10
Special Collections: Medical Education
Subject Interests: Family med
Function: Photocopying/Printing, Ref serv available
Open Mon-Fri 9-5
FIRST NATIONS HOUSE LIBRARY, 563 Spadine Ave, 3rd Flr, M5S 1A5. Tel: 416-978-0413. FAX: 416-978-1893. E-mail: fnh.info@utoronto.ca; gsunion@epas.utoronto.ca. Web Site: www.fnh.utoronto.ca. *Br Mgr,* Position Currently Open
Founded 1992
Library Holdings: Bk Vols 1,000; Per Subs 25
Function: Photocopying/Printing
Open Mon-Fri 9-5
THOMAS FISHER RARE BOOKS LIBRARY, 120 St George St, M5S 1A5. Tel: 416-978-6107. FAX: 416-978-1667. Web Site: www.library.utoronto.ca/fisher. *Dir,* Richard London; E-mail: richard.landon@utoronto.ca; *Head of Libr,* Anne Dondertman; Tel: 416-978-5332, E-mail: anne.dondertman@utoronto.ca
Founded 1973
Library Holdings: Bk Vols 600,000
Open Mon-Fri 9-5
Restriction: Non-circulating
GERSTEIN SCIENCE INFORMATION CENTRE, Seven & Nine Kings College Circle, M5S 1A5. Tel: 416-978-2280. Interlibrary Loan Service Tel: 416-978-3327. FAX: 416-971-2848. E-mail: ask.gerstein@utoronto.ca. Web Site: www.library.utoronto.ca/gerstein/. *Dir,* Joan Leishman; Tel: 416-978-7662, E-mail: j.leishman@utoronto.ca; *Instrul Serv Librn,* Carla Hagstrom; Tel: 416-978-7668, E-mail: carla.hagstrom@utoronto.ca
Library Holdings: Bk Vols 757,152
Subject Interests: Med
Function: Doc delivery serv, ILL available, Photocopying/Printing, Ref serv available
Open Mon-Thurs 8:30am-11pm, Fri 8:30-6, Sat 9am-10pm, Sun 1-10 (Sept-Apr)
JOHN W GRAHAM LIBRARY, UNIVERSITY OF TRINITY COLLEGE, Trinity College, Six Hoskin Ave, M5S 1H8, SAN 368-7848. Tel: 416-978-2653. Administration Tel: 416-978-4398. Information Services Tel: 416-978-5851. FAX: 416-978-2797. Web Site: www.trinity.utoronto.ca/library/wel_lib.htm. *Nicholls Librn & Dir Graham Libr,* Linda Wilson Corman; E-mail: linda.corman@utoronto.ca; Staff 7.5 (MLS 3.5, Non-MLS 4)
Founded 1852. Highest Degree: Doctorate
Library Holdings: Bk Vols 200,000
Special Collections: Churchill Coll; SPCK Coll; Strachan Coll; Works of Richard Hooker (W Speed Hill Coll)
Subject Interests: Anglican Church hist, Eng lit, English (Lang), Intl relations, Theol
Automation Activity & Vendor Info: (Acquisitions) SIRSI WorkFlows; (Cataloging) Robyn WorkFlows; (Circulation) SIRSI WorkFlows; (OPAC) SirsiDynix; (Serials) SIRSI WorkFlows
Function: Archival coll, Audio & video playback equip for onsite use, Computers for patron use, Copy machines, Electronic databases & coll, ILL available, Online cat, Online info literacy tutorials on the web & in

blackboard, Orientations, Photocopying/Printing, Ref serv available, Wheelchair accessible
Publications: Ex Libris (Periodical)
Open Mon-Thurs 8:30am-11:45pm, Fri 8:30am-8:45pm, Sat 9-8:45, Sun 1-11:45
Restriction: Open to fac, students & qualified researchers
Friends of the Library Group
INDUSTRIAL RELATIONS CENTRE, Jean & Dorothy Newman Library, 121 Saint George St, M5S 1A1, SAN 368-7244. Tel: 416-978-2928. Automation Services Tel: 416-978-0191. FAX: 416-978-5694. Web Site: www.chass.utoronto.ca/cir/. *Librn,* Victoria Skelton; E-mail: cirhr.library@utoronto.ca; *Tech Librn,* Monica Hypher; E-mail: monica.hypher@utoronto.ca
Library Holdings: Bk Vols 10,000
Open Mon-Thurs 10-6, Fri 10-5
INNIS COLLEGE LIBRARY, Two Sussex Ave, M5S 1J5, SAN 328-7017. Tel: 416-978-4497. FAX: 416-946-0168. Web Site: www.utoronto.ca/innis/library. *Librn,* Leonard Ferstman; E-mail: l.ferstman@utoronto.ca
Library Holdings: Bk Vols 5,000
Special Collections: Cinema Studies
Subject Interests: Cinema
Open Mon-Fri 9:30-5
PETRO JACYK CENTRAL & EAST EUROPEAN RESOURCE CENTRE, 130 St George St, Rm 3008, M5S 1A5. Tel: 416-978-0588. Administration Tel: 416-978-1288. FAX: 416-971-2636. E-mail: jacyk.centre@utoronto.ca. Web Site: pjrc.library.utoronto.ca. *Head of Libr,* Dr Ksenya Kiebuzinski, PhD; *Res Spec,* Wasyl Sydorenko; Staff 4 (MLS 2, Non-MLS 2)
Library Holdings: Bk Vols 3,500
Function: Ref & res
Open Mon-Fri 10-6
Restriction: Ref only
CR JOHN M KELLY LIBRARY, University of Saint Michael's College, 113 Saint Joseph St, M5S 1J4, SAN 368-7813. Tel: 416-926-7114. Reference Tel: 416-926-1300, Ext 3444. FAX: 416-926-7262. Web Site: www.utoronto.ca/stmikes/library/. *Dir, Libr & Archives,* Jonathan Bengtson; E-mail: jbengtson@utoronto.ca; *Assoc Dir, Libr & Archives,* Dave - Hagelaar; Tel: 416-926-7250, E-mail: d.hagelaar@utoronto.ca; *Ref Librn,* Richard Carter; E-mail: richard.carter@utoronto.ca; *Head, Pub Serv,* Noel S Mcferran; E-mail: noel.mcferran@utoronto.ca; Staff 11.8 (MLS 6, Non-MLS 5.8)
Founded 1852. Highest Degree: Doctorate
Library Holdings: Bk Vols 372,000
Special Collections: Centre d'Eludes sur le Naturalisme (Zola); Centre d'Etudes Romantiques; Chesterton Coll; New Man Coll; Recusant & Counter-Reformation Materials; Soulerin Coll
Automation Activity & Vendor Info: (Cataloging) SIRSI WorkFlows
Function: Archival coll, Art exhibits, Audio & video playback equip for onsite use, Bks on CD, CD-ROM, Computers for patron use, Copy machines, Doc delivery serv, e-mail serv, E-Reserves, Electronic databases & coll, Fax serv, Free DVD rentals, Handicapped accessible, ILL available, Mail & tel request accepted, Music CDs, Online cat, Online info literacy tutorials on the web & in blackboard, Online ref, Online searches, Orientations, Photocopying/Printing, Res libr, Scanner, Spoken cassettes & CDs, Spoken cassettes & DVDs, Telephone ref, VHS videos, Web-catalog, Workshops, Writing prog
Open Mon-Fri 8:30am-11:45pm, Sat 10am-11:45pm, Sun 1-11-45
Restriction: Authorized patrons
Friends of the Library Group
CL BORA LASKIN LAW LIBRARY, 78 Queen's Park, M5S 2C5, SAN 368-7279. Tel: 416-978-1073. Interlibrary Loan Service Tel: 416-946-7833. Reference Tel: 416-978-1072. FAX: 416-978-8396. Web Site: www.law-lib.utoronto.ca. *Chief Librn,* John Papadopoulos; E-mail: john.papadopoulos@utoronto.ca
Library Holdings: AV Mats 56,002; Bk Vols 265,000; Per Subs 2,413
Open Mon-Thurs 8:45am-11pm, Fri 8:45-8, Sat & Sun 10-8
MATHEMATICAL SCIENCES, Sidney Smith Hall, 100 Saint George St, Rm 622, M5S 1A1, SAN 368-7406. Tel: 416-978-8624. FAX: 416-978-4107. *Librn,* Bruce Garrod; E-mail: bruce.garrod@utoronto.ca
Library Holdings: Bk Vols 33,411
Open Mon-Fri 9-5
MEDIA COMMONS, 130 St George St, M5S 1A5, SAN 368-6701. Tel: 416-978-6520. FAX: 416-978-8707. *Dir,* Brock Silversides; Tel: 416-978-7119, E-mail: brock.silversides@utoronto.ca; *Media Librn,* Shauna Dorskind; Tel: 416-978-6785, E-mail: shauna.dorskind@utoronto.ca; *Archivist,* Michelle Wilder; Tel: 416-978-4601, E-mail: michelle.wilder@utoronto.ca
Library Holdings: Bk Vols 472
Open Mon-Fri 9-Noon, 2-5
MISSISSAUGA LIBRARY, 3359 Mississauga Rd, Mississauga, L5L 1C6, SAN 368-7120. Tel: 905-828-5235. FAX: 905-569-4320. Reference E-mail: askutml.utm@utoronto.ca. Web Site: www.erin.utoronto.ca/library. *Librn,* Position Currently Open
Library Holdings: Bk Vols 306,912

NEW COLLEGE - IVEY LIBRARY, 20 Willcocks St, M5S 1A1, SAN 328-7033. Tel: 416-978-2493. FAX: 416-978-0554. *Libm,* Position Currently Open
Library Holdings: Bk Vols 25,000
Subject Interests: Women's studies
Open Mon-Thurs 9am-11pm, Fri 9-5, Sat 1-5, Sun 2pm-9pm
NORANDA EARTH SCIENCES LIBRARY, Five Bancroft Ave, 2nd Flr, M5S 1A5, SAN 368-6760. Tel: 416-978-3024. FAX: 416-971-2101. E-mail: earth.sciences@utoronto.ca. Web Site: www.library.utoronto.ca/earth/. *Libm,* Christina Tooulias-Santolin
Library Holdings: Bk Vols 91,508
Open Mon-Thurs 9-9, Fri 9-6, Sat 9-5
PONTIFICAL INSTITUTE FOR MEDIAEVAL STUDIES, 113 Saint Joseph St, M5S 1J4, SAN 368-7600. Tel: 416-926-7146. FAX: 416-926-7262. Web Site: www.pims.ca/library. *Dir, Libr & Archives,* Jonathan Bengtson; E-mail: j.bengtson@utoronto.ca; *Ref Libm,* William Edwards; Tel: 416-926-1300, Ext 3423, E-mail: pims.library@utoronto.ca; *Curator, Rare Bks,* James Farge; E-mail: james.farge@utoronto.ca
Library Holdings: Bk Vols 150,000
Special Collections: Mediaeval Manuscripts; Microfilms of Manuscripts; Monastic Foundations Image Coll
ROBARTS LIBRARY, 130 St George St, M5S 1A5, SAN 118-9948. Tel: 416-978-2294. FAX: 416-978-1608. Web Site: www.library.utoronto.ca/robarts. *Head, Access Serv, Head, Info Serv,* Lari Langford; Tel: 416-978-2898, E-mail: lari.langford@utoronto.ca; *Head, Ref,* Jenny Mendelsohn; Tel: 416 946-5519, E-mail: jenny.mendelsohn@utoronto.ca
Library Holdings: Bk Titles 100,424; Bk Vols 9,346,479; Per Subs 26,382
Subject Interests: Humanities
Open Mon-Fri 8:30am-11pm, Sat 9am-10pm, Sun 1pm-10pm
SCARBOROUGH LIBRARY, Scarborough College, 1265 Military Trail, Scarborough, M1C 1A4, SAN 368-766X. Tel: 416-287-7481. FAX: 416-287-7507. Web Site: www.library.scar.utoronto.ca. *Head Libm,* Victoria Owen; E-mail: owen@utsc.utoronto.ca; *Acq Libm,* Marla Miller; Tel: 416-287-7497, E-mail: miller@utsc.utoronto.ca; *Media Libm,* Heather Glerum; E-mail: glerum@utsc.utoronto.ca
Library Holdings: Bk Vols 246,794; Per Subs 2,037
Partic in Utlas
VICTORIA UNIVERSITY LIBRARY, 71 Queens Park Crescent E, M5S 1K7, SAN 368-7872. Tel: 416-585-4471. Interlibrary Loan Service Tel: 416-585-4470. FAX: 416-585-4591. E-mail: victoria.library@utoronto.ca. Web Site: library.vicu.utoronto.ca. *Chief Libm,* Dr Robert Brandeis; Tel: 416-585-4472, E-mail: robert.brandeis@utoronto.ca; *Ref Libm,* K Wishart; Tel: 416-585-4551, Ext 316; *Syst Libm,* Doug Fox; E-mail: douglas.fox@utoronto.ca; *Head, Bibliog Serv,* Carmen Socknat; E-mail: carmen.socknat@utoronto.ca; *Head, Reader Serv,* Lisa J Sherlock; E-mail: lis.sherlock@utoronto.ca; *Acq,* Pat Corbett; E-mail: pat.corbett@utoronto.ca; *Reader Serv,* Beverly A Branton; E-mail: bev.branton@utoronto.ca. Subject Specialists: *Theol,* K Wishart; *Theol,* Doug Fox
Library Holdings: Bk Vols 261,171
Special Collections: Baxter Coll, prints; Canadian Literary Manuscripts; Claire Pratt Coll; Coburn Coll; E J Pratt Coll, bks, mss; Erasmus Coll; Norman Jewison Archive; Northrop Frye, books, mss; Reformation & Renaissance Coll; S T Coleridge Coll, bks, mss; Tennyson Coll; V Woolf-Bloomsbury-Hogarth Press Coll; Wesleyana Coll; William Blake Coll
Subject Interests: Church hist, Humanities, Soc sci, Theol
Publications: A P Coleman, Geologist, 1852-1939; Bloomsbury: Books, Art & Design; Guide to Canadian Manuscript Collections; Guide to the Northrop Frye Papers; William Blake & His Contemporaries: An exhibition selected from the Bentley Collection at Victoria University Special Services for the Blind - Computer access aids; Computer with voice synthesizer for visually impaired persons; Internet workstation with adaptive software; Scanner for conversion & translation of mats; Screen enlargement software for people with visual disabilities; Screen reader software; ZoomText magnification & reading software
Friends of the Library Group

C   UNIVERSITY OF TORONTO LIBRARIES*, Ontario Institute for Studies in Education, 252 Bloor St W, M5S 1V6. SAN 321-3706. Tel: 416-978-1850. Reference Tel: 416-978-1860. FAX: 416-926-4737. E-mail: askeloise@oise.utoronto.ca. Web Site: www.oise.utoronto.ca/ec/library/. *Chief Libm,* Carole Moore; Tel: 416-978-2292, E-mail: cmoore@oise.utoronto.ca; *Cat, Head, Tech Serv,* Stephanie Swift; E-mail: sswift@oise.utoronto.ca; *Coll Develop,* Julie Hannaford; Tel: 416-978-1702, E-mail: jhannaford@oise.utoronto.ca; *Distance Educ Coordr,* Patricia Serafini; Tel: 416-978-1903, E-mail: pserafini@oise.utoronto.ca; Staff 25 (MLS 6, Non-MLS 19)
Founded 1965. Enrl 4,000; Fac 160; Highest Degree: Doctorate
Library Holdings: Bk Vols 381,891; Per Subs 1,212
Special Collections: Franco-Ontarienne Coll; Modern Language Coll; Ontario Department of Education Historical Publications; Ontario School

Textbooks 1840 to date; Paulo Freire Resource Coll; Women's Educational Resources Coll
Subject Interests: Curric, Educ software, Higher educ, Hist of educ, Linguistics, Psychol, Sociol, Statistical methodology
Automation Activity & Vendor Info: (Acquisitions) SirsiDynix; (Cataloging) SirsiDynix; (Circulation) SirsiDynix; (Course Reserve) SirsiDynix; (OPAC) SirsiDynix; (Serials) SirsiDynix
Wireless access
Function: Res libr
Publications: Index to Paulo Freire Resource Coll; J R Kidd: A Bibliography of His Writings; OISE Theses Catalogue; Ontario Textbook Coll Catalogue
Special Services for the Blind - Bks on cassette
Open Mon-Thurs 8:30am-10pm, Fri 8:30-5, Sat 9-5, Sun (Sept-May) 1-6
Restriction: Open to students, fac & staff

S   VALE INCO LTD*, Business Library, South Tower, Ste 1600, Royal Bank Plaza, 200 Bay St, M5J 2K2. SAN 321-0073. Tel: 416-361-7518. FAX: 416-361-7781. Web Site: www.inco.com. *Libm,* Christina Wu; E-mail: christina.wu@valeinco.com. Subject Specialists: *Legal, Mkt,* Christina Wu; Staff 2 (MLS 1, Non-MLS 1)
Founded 1995
Library Holdings: Bk Titles 1,116; Bk Vols 10,000; Per Subs 360
Special Collections: Annual Reports, papers
Subject Interests: Econ, Environ health, Exploration, Finance, Geol, Investment, Mineral proc, Mining, Occupational, Pub relations
Database Vendor: Bloomberg, Dialog, EBSCOhost, Factiva.com, HeinOnline, LexisNexis, Quicklaw, Thomson Carswell
Function: Doc delivery serv
Restriction: Not open to pub

S   WALKER NOTT DRAGICEVIC ASSOCIATES LTD LIBRARY*, 90 Eglinton Ave E, Ste 701, M4P 2Y3. SAN 375-3778. Tel: 416-968-3511. FAX: 416-960-0172. Web Site: www.wndplan.com. *Libm,* Jutta Szep; Staff 1 (MLS 1)
Founded 1988
Library Holdings: Bk Titles 12,500; Bk Vols 12,600; Per Subs 37; Spec Interest Per Sub 19
Subject Interests: Environ impact assessment, Urban design, Urban planning, Zoning
Automation Activity & Vendor Info: (Cataloging) Inmagic, Inc.
Open Mon-Wed & Fri 8-5
Restriction: Not a lending libr

S   WATTS, GRIFFIS & MCOUAT LTD LIBRARY*, Eight King St E, Ste 400, M5C 1B5. SAN 323-7303. Tel: 416-364-6244. FAX: 416-864-1675. Web Site: www.wgm.on.ca. *In Charge,* Sandra Panbay
Founded 1962
Library Holdings: Bk Titles 9,000; Per Subs 100
Special Collections: In-House Reports
Subject Interests: Earth sci, Geol
Automation Activity & Vendor Info: (Acquisitions) Inmagic, Inc.; (Cataloging) Inmagic, Inc.
Publications: Quarterly Acquisitions List
Open Mon-Fri 9-5

S   WEIRFOULDS LIBRARY*, The Exchange Tower, Ste1600, 130 King St W, M5X 1J5. (Mail add: PO Box 480, M5X 1J5), SAN 326-1468. Tel: 416-365-1110. FAX: 416-365-1876. E-mail: library@weirfoulds.com. *Managing Libm,* Kay Samuels; Tel: 416-947-5057, E-mail: ksamuels@weirfoulds.com; *Ref,* Position Currently Open; *ILL, Tech Serv,* Maggie Day-Myron; Tel: 416-365-1110, Ext 2327, E-mail: mday@weirfoulds.com; Staff 4 (MLS 2, Non-MLS 2)
Founded 1960
Library Holdings: Bk Titles 5,300; Bk Vols 16,000; Per Subs 850
Special Collections: Environmental, corporate and commercial laws
Subject Interests: Admin law, Civil litigation, Commercial law, Corp law, Environ law, Health law, Intellectual property law, Municipal law, Securities law, Tax law
Automation Activity & Vendor Info: (Acquisitions) Inmagic, Inc.; (Cataloging) Inmagic, Inc.; (ILL) Inmagic, Inc.; (OPAC) Inmagic, Inc.; (Serials) Inmagic, Inc.
Database Vendor: Dialog, LexisNexis
Publications: Newsletters

S   WEST MISSISSAUGA JAZZ MUDDIES LIBRARY*, 90 Prince George Dr, M9B 2X8. SAN 375-2178. Tel: 416-231-4055. FAX: 416-239-6284. E-mail: jazzcol@rogers.com. *Pres,* Eugene Miller
Library Holdings: Bk Titles 4,500; Per Subs 2,000

M   WEST PARK HEALTHCARE CENTRE*, Health Disciplines Library, 82 Buttonwood Ave, M6M 2J5. SAN 323-6110. Tel: 416-243-3600, Ext 2048. FAX: 416-243-8947. Web Site: 204.50.92.64. *Libm,* John Tagg; E-mail: jtagg@westpark.org; Staff 0.6 (MLS 0.6)

Founded 1979
Library Holdings: Bk Titles 1,000; Per Subs 60
Special Collections: TB History (DR Gale Coll), bks, journals, med instruments, med recs, pathological specimens, photog, plaques. Oral History
Subject Interests: Respiratory med, Tuberculosis
Restriction: Staff use only

G WORKPLACE SAFETY & INSURANCE BOARD*, Reference Library, 200 Front St W, 17th Flr, M5V 3J1. SAN 319-5406. Tel: 416-344-4962. FAX: 416-344-4050. E-mail: reference_library@wsib.on.ca. *Info Res Mgr,* Carolyn Archer; Tel: 416-344-5660; *Policy Publ & Info Res Coordr,* Christina Ciraco; Tel: 416-344-4335; *Policy Publ & Info Res Coordr,* Angie Servello-Cammack; Tel: 416-344-6384; *Info Res Spec,* Yee Ching Chang; Tel: 416-344-4052, E-mail: yee_ching_chang@wsib.on.ca; *Info Res Spec,* David A Roy; E-mail: david_a_roy@wsib.on.ca; Staff 5 (MLS 3, Non-MLS 2)
Founded 1986
Library Holdings: Bk Vols 8,500; Per Subs 150
Special Collections: Canadian Workers' Compensation Systems
Subject Interests: Legal, Med, Occupational health, Safety, Vocational rehabilitation, Workers compensation
Automation Activity & Vendor Info: (Acquisitions) SydneyPlus; (Cataloging) SydneyPlus; (Circulation) SydneyPlus; (OPAC) SydneyPlus; (Serials) SydneyPlus
Database Vendor: Dialog, EBSCOhost, Factiva.com, LexisNexis, Quicklaw
Open Mon-Fri 9-4

C YORK UNIVERSITY LIBRARIES*, Scott Library, 4700 Keele St, M3J 1P3. SAN 367-1135. Tel: 416-736-5601. Interlibrary Loan Service Tel: 416-736-5808. FAX: 416-736-5451. Web Site: www.library.yorku.ca. *Univ Librn,* Cynthia Archer; Tel: 416-736-5935, E-mail: carcher@yorku.ca; *Assoc Univ Librn, Info Serv,* Brent Roe; E-mail: broe@yorku.ca; *Archivist, Spec Coll Librn,* Michael Moir; Tel: 416-736-2100, Ext 22457, E-mail: mmoir@yorku.ca; *Computer Serv,* Robert Thompson; E-mail: rthompson@yorku.ca; Staff 54 (MLS 39, Non-MLS 15)
Founded 1959. Enrl 37,546; Fac 1,170; Highest Degree: Doctorate
Library Holdings: Bk Vols 2,487,083; Per Subs 17,356
Special Collections: American & English Literature of the 19th & 20th Centuries, bks & mss; Canadiana, bks & mss; Music, Theatre & Visual Arts Coll. Can & Prov
Automation Activity & Vendor Info: (Acquisitions) SirsiDynix; (Cataloging) SirsiDynix; (Circulation) SirsiDynix
Partic in Association of Research Libraries (ARL); OCLC Online Computer Library Center, Inc
Departmental Libraries:
PETER F BRONFMAN BUSINESS LIBRARY, Schulich School of Business, Seymour Schulich Bldg, Rm S237, 4700 Keele St, M3J 1P3, SAN 367-116X. Tel: 416-736-5139. FAX: 416-736-5687. *Head Librn,* Elizabeth Watson; E-mail: watson@yorku.ca; Staff 3 (MLS 3)
Founded 2003
Library Holdings: e-journals 10,000; Electronic Media & Resources 30; Bk Vols 25,000; Per Subs 360
Automation Activity & Vendor Info: (OPAC) SirsiDynix
Restriction: Open to researchers by request, Open to students, fac & staff
LESLIE FROST LIBRARY, GLENDON CAMPUS, 2275 Bayview Ave, M4N 3M6, SAN 319-5783. Tel: 416-487-6726. Reference Tel: 416-487-6729. FAX: 416-487-6705. Web Site: www.library.yorku.ca/depts/frost/frost.htm. *Br Head,* Julie Drexler; Tel: 416-736-2100, Ext 88262, E-mail: drexler@yorku.ca; Staff 9 (MLS 4, Non-MLS 5)
Founded 1960. Enrl 2,000; Fac 100; Highest Degree: Master
Library Holdings: Bk Vols 275,000; Per Subs 900
Special Collections: Bilingual (French/English) Translation Materials
Subject Interests: Humanities, Intl studies, Liberal arts, Linguistics, Soc sci

CL OSGOODE HALL LAW SCHOOL LIBRARY, One Scholar's Walk, York University, M3J 1P3. (Mail add: 4700 Keele St, M3J 1P3), SAN 367-1224. Tel: 416-736-5205. Circulation Tel: 416-736-5206. Interlibrary Loan Service Tel: 416-736-5588. Reference Tel: 416-736-5207. FAX: 416-736-5298. E-mail: lawill@yorku.ca. Web Site: library.osgoode.yorku.ca. *Chief Librn,* Louis Mirando; Tel: 416-736-5646, E-mail: lmirando@osgoode.yorku.ca; *Head, Pub Serv,* Yemisi Dina; Tel: 416-650-8404, E-mail: ydina@osgoode.yorku.ca; *Head, Tech Serv,* Tim Knight; Tel: 416-650-8403, E-mail: tknight@osgoode.yorku.ca; *Ref Librn,* Daniel Perlin; Tel: 416-736-5380, E-mail: dperlin@osgoode.yorku.ca; *Ref Librn,* Sharon Wang; Tel: 416-736-5893, E-mail: swang@osgoode.yorku.ca; Staff 19 (MLS 5, Non-MLS 14)
Founded 1892. Enrl 1,042; Fac 82; Highest Degree: Doctorate
Special Collections: Early Anglo-American Legal Materials; Early Legal Canadiana
Subject Interests: Can legal lit & hist, Legal hist

Function: Writing prog
Restriction: Vols & interns use only
STEACIE SCIENCE & ENGINEERING LIBRARY, 4700 Keele St, M3J 1P3, SAN 367-1259. Tel: 416-736-5639. FAX: 416-736-5452. *Head Librn,* Leila Fernandez; E-mail: leilaf@yorku.ca; Staff 5 (MLS 3, Non-MLS 2)
Founded 1970
Library Holdings: Bk Titles 74,000; Bk Vols 178,000
VISUAL ARTS SLIDE LIBRARY, York Campus, Phase II, 4700 Keele St, Ste 257, M3J 1P3, SAN 325-1365. Tel: 416-736-5534. FAX: 416-736-5447. *Digital Media Coordr,* Lillian Heinson
Founded 1971. Enrl 55,000; Highest Degree: Doctorate
Library Holdings: Per Subs 20
Special Collections: Anderson-Alinari Photo Coll; T A Heinrich Coll
Function: Archival coll
Restriction: Open to students, fac & staff
VISUAL RESOURCE CENTRE, Room 257 Goldfarb Centre of Fine Arts, 4700 Keele St, M3J 1P3. Tel: 416-736-2100, Ext 33494. *In Charge,* Lillian Heinson; E-mail: lheinson@yorku.ca

TRENTON

P QUINTE WEST PUBLIC LIBRARY*, Seven Creswell Dr, K8V 6X5. SAN 368-7996. Tel: 613-394-3381. FAX: 613-394-2079. Web Site: www.library.quintewest.com. *Chief Exec Officer,* Rita Turtle; E-mail: ritat@quintewest.ca; *ILL Coordr,* Linda C Lafonde; Tel: 613-394-3381, Ext 3316; *Ch,* Rosemary Kirby; E-mail: rosemaryk@quintewest.ca; *Ref,* Robert Amesse; E-mail: roberta@quintewest.ca; Staff 3 (MLS 3)
Founded 1920. Pop 43,000; Circ 225,760
Library Holdings: Bk Titles 122,189; Per Subs 205
Subject Interests: Local hist
Automation Activity & Vendor Info: (Acquisitions) SirsiDynix; (Cataloging) SirsiDynix; (Circulation) SirsiDynix; (ILL) Fretwell-Downing; (OPAC) SirsiDynix; (Serials) SirsiDynix
Wireless access
Partic in Southern Ontario Libr Serv
Open Mon-Wed 9:30-8, Thurs & Fri 9:30-6, Sat 9:30-4
Friends of the Library Group

UXBRIDGE

P UXBRIDGE TOWNSHIP PUBLIC LIBRARY*, Nine Toronto St S, L9P 1P7. (Mail add: PO Box 279, L9P 1P7), SAN 319-5813. Tel: 905-852-9747. FAX: 905-852-9749. E-mail: upl@interhop.net. Web Site: www.uxlib.com. *Librn,* Jane Dubis; Staff 6 (MLS 1, Non-MLS 5)
Founded 1870. Pop 14,500; Circ 133,029
Library Holdings: Bk Vols 49,561; Per Subs 78
Subject Interests: Gen databases
Publications: The Old Town Clock (newsletter)
Open Mon, Wed, Fri & Sat 10-5, Tues & Thurs 10-9, Sun 1-5
Friends of the Library Group
Branches: 1
ZEPHYR BRANCH, 13000 Concession 39, Zephyr, L0E 1T0. (Mail add: PO Box 51, Zephyr, L0E 1T0), SAN 377-6751. Tel: 905-473-2375. FAX: 905-473-2375. Web Site: www.uxlib.com. *Librn,* Nancy Bongard
Library Holdings: Bk Vols 8,000
Open Tues & Thurs 1:30pm-8:30pm, Sat 2-5
Friends of the Library Group

VANKLEEK HILL

P VANKLEEK HILL PUBLIC LIBRARY*, 94 Main St E, K0B 1R0. (Mail add: PO Box 520, K0B 1R0), SAN 319-5856. Tel: 613-678-2216. FAX: 613-678-2216. E-mail: library@champlaintwplibrary.ca. *Librn,* Linda Poyser
Pop 1,711; Circ 48,173
Library Holdings: Bk Vols 24,000; Per Subs 22
Open Mon-Fri 1-5 & 7pm-8:30pm, Sat 10-Noon

VINELAND STATION

G AGRICULTURE & AGRI-FOOD CANADA*, Southern Crop Protection & Food Research Centre Vineland Library, 4902 Victorian Ave N, L0R 2E0. (Mail add: PO Box 6000, L0R 2E0), SAN 319-5864. Tel: 905-562-4113, Ext 212. FAX: 905-562-4335. Web Site: www.agr.gc.ca. *Librn,* Sheridan Lynne Alder; E-mail: sheridan.alders@agr.gc.ca; Staff 1 (MLS 1)
Founded 1967
Library Holdings: Bk Vols 500
Subject Interests: Diseases, Pests of fruits, Pests of trees
Database Vendor: OVID Technologies
Function: Res libr
Restriction: Staff use only

VIRGINIATOWN

P   MCGARRY PUBLIC LIBRARY*, One 27th St, P0K 1X0. (Mail add: PO
     Box 250, P0K 1X0), SAN 319-5880. Tel: 705-634-2312. FAX:
     705-634-2312. E-mail: mcgarry@onlnet.net. Web Site:
     mcgarrypubliclibrary.8m.com. *Librn,* Anne-Marie Boucher; Staff 1 (MLS
     1)
     Founded 1950. Pop 800; Circ 12,098
     Library Holdings: Bk Titles 11,802; Bk Vols 12,884; Per Subs 31
     Special Collections: French & English Videos (Entertainment &
     Educational, Adult & Juvenile)
     Database Vendor: EBSCOhost
     Function: ILL available
     Mem of Ontario Library Service North
     Open Mon, Wed & Fri 1-4, Tues & Thurs 6pm-9pm
     Friends of the Library Group

WAINFLEET

P   WAINFLEET TOWNSHIP PUBLIC LIBRARY*, 19M9 Park St, L0S 1V0.
     (Mail add: PO Box 118, L0S 1V0), SAN 319-5899. Tel: 905-899-1277.
     FAX: 905-899-2495. E-mail: dariusz@wainfleetlibrary.ca. Web Site:
     www.wainfleetlibrary.ca. *Chief Librn,* Lorrie Atkinson; E-mail:
     latkinson@wainfleetlibrary.ca; Staff 9 (MLS 1, Non-MLS 8)
     Founded 1966. Pop 6,258; Circ 34,282
     Library Holdings: Bk Vols 29,500
     Subject Interests: Genealogy, Wainfleet hist
     Wireless access
     Function: Archival coll, AV serv, Handicapped accessible, ILL available,
     Photocopying/Printing, Prog for children & young adult, Ref serv available,
     Summer reading prog, Wheelchair accessible
     Restriction: In-house use for visitors

WASAGA BEACH

P   WASAGA BEACH PUBLIC LIBRARY*, 120 Glenwood Dr, L0L 2P0.
     (Mail add: PO Box 530, L0L 2P0), SAN 319-5910. Tel: 705-429-5481.
     FAX: 705-429-5481. E-mail: wblibrary@georgian.net. *Librn,* Jackie
     Marshall; *Asst Librn,* Patricia Heath
     Founded 1972. Pop 5,125; Circ 39,404
     Library Holdings: Bk Titles 15,000; Bk Vols 16,000; Per Subs 50

WATERLOO

C   CONRAD GREBEL UNIVERSITY COLLEGE LIBRARY*, 140
     Westmount Rd N, N2L 3G6. SAN 321-3439. Tel: 519-885-0220, Ext
     24238. FAX: 519-885-0014. E-mail: greblweb@uwaterloo.ca. Web Site:
     grebel.uwaterloo.ca. *Librn & Archivist,* Laureen Harder-Gissing; E-mail:
     lharderg@uwaterloo.ca; *Asst Librn,* Ruth Steinman; E-mail:
     resteinm@uwaterloo.ca; Staff 1 (MLS 1)
     Founded 1964. Fac 17; Highest Degree: Master
     Library Holdings: CDs 2,200; DVDs 120; Bk Vols 39,000; Per Subs
     10,000; Videos 150
     Special Collections: Mennonite Archives of Ontario Coll, doc & unbound
     paper. Oral History
     Subject Interests: Biblical studies, Hist, Mennonite-Anabaptist theol,
     Music, Peace studies
     Automation Activity & Vendor Info: (Acquisitions) Ex Libris Group;
     (Cataloging) Ex Libris Group; (Circulation) Ex Libris Group
     Wireless access
     Partic in OCLC Online Computer Library Center, Inc
     Open Mon-Thurs (Winter) 8:30-9, Fri 8:30-4:30, Sat 1-5; Mon-Fri (Spring)
     8:30-4:30

JR   GREAT LAKES BIBLE COLLEGE LIBRARY*, Waterloo Campus, 470
     Glenelm Crescent, N2L 5C8. Tel: 519-342-3040. Toll Free FAX:
     888-316-7678. Web Site: www.glbc.ca. *Dean,* Dave Knutson; E-mail:
     daknutson@gmail.com
     Library Holdings: Bk Titles 4,000

C   WILFRID LAURIER UNIVERSITY LIBRARY*, Laurier Library, 75
     University Ave W, N2L 3C5. SAN 319-5945. Tel: 519-884-0710.
     Circulation Tel: 519-884-0710, Ext 3414. Interlibrary Loan Service Tel:
     519-884-0710, Ext 3814. Reference Tel: 519-884-0710, Ext 3222.
     Administration Tel: 519-884-0710, Ext 3381. Automation Services Tel:
     519-884-0710, Ext 3999. FAX: 519-884-3209. E-mail: libweb@wlu.ca.
     Web Site: library.wlu.ca. *Chief Librn,* Sharon Brown; Tel: 519-884-0710,
     Ext 3380, E-mail: sbrown@wlu.ca; *Head, Cat,* Matt Tales; Tel:
     519-884-0710, Ext 3839, E-mail: mtales@wlu.ca; *Head, Circ,* Vera Fesnak;
     Tel: 519-884-0710, Ext 3413, E-mail: vfesnak@wlu.ca; *Head, Ref,*
     Deborah Wills; Tel: 519-884-0710, Ext 3384, E-mail: dwills@wlu.ca; *Acq
     Mgr,* Helen Sagi; Tel: 519-884-0710, Ext 2475, E-mail: hsagi@wlu.ca;
     Admin Mgr, Nancy Peltier; Tel: 519-884-0710, Ext 3642, E-mail:
     npeltier@wlu.ca; *Coll Develop,* Position Currently Open; *Spec Coll &
     Archives Librn,* Julia Hendry; Tel: 519-884-0710, Ext 3825, E-mail:
     jhendry@wlu.ca; Staff 60 (MLS 16, Non-MLS 44)

Founded 1911. Enrl 12,708; Fac 482; Highest Degree: Doctorate
Library Holdings: CDs 17,000; e-books 35,000; e-journals 12,300; Music
Scores 115,000; Bk Titles 689,000; Per Subs 2,000
Special Collections: Lutheran Church; University Archives
Subject Interests: Environ law, Environ studies, Environment, Liberal arts,
Music, Relig
Automation Activity & Vendor Info: (Cataloging) Ex Libris Group;
(Circulation) Ex Libris Group; (Course Reserve) Ex Libris Group; (ILL)
Ex Libris Group; (OPAC) Ex Libris Group; (Serials) Ex Libris Group
Wireless access
Publications: Annual Report of Librarian; Bibliographical & Reference
Aids

C   RENISON UNIVERSITY COLLEGE LIBRARY, Lusi Wong Library, 240
     Westmount Rd N, N2L 3G4. Tel: 519-884-4400, 519-884-4404, Ext 28646.
     FAX: 519-884-5135. Web Site: uwaterloo.ca/renison/lusi-wong-library.
     Librn, Lois E Clifford; *Libr Asst,* Tammy Kavanaugh; Staff 2 (MLS 1,
     Non-MLS 1)
     Highest Degree: Master
     Library Holdings: Bk Titles 6,000; Per Subs 85
     Subject Interests: Applied lang studies, E Asian studies, English as a
     second lang, Relig studies, Soc develop, Soc work, Studies in Islam
     Automation Activity & Vendor Info: (Acquisitions) Ex Libris Group;
     (Cataloging) Ex Libris Group; (Circulation) Ex Libris Group; (Course
     Reserve) Atlas Systems - Ares; (OPAC) Ex Libris Group
     Wireless access
     Open Mon-Thurs (Fall & Winter) 8:30am-9:30pm, Fri 8:30-4, Sat 1-5;
     Mon-Thurs (Spring & Summer) 8:30am-9pm, Fri 8:30-4

CR   SAINT JEROME'S UNIVERSITY LIBRARY*, 290 Westmount Rd N,
     N2L 3G3. SAN 319-597X. Tel: 519-884-8111, Ext 28271. Circulation Tel:
     519-884-8110, Ext 28285. FAX: 519-884-5759. Web Site: www.sju.ca.
     Univ Librn, Lorna Rourke; E-mail: lerourke@library.uwaterloo.ca; Staff 3
     (MLS 1, Non-MLS 2)
     Founded 1962. Enrl 1,050; Fac 38; Highest Degree: Master
     Library Holdings: Bk Vols 40,000; Per Subs 320
     Special Collections: Archives of Saint Jerome's College & the
     Congregation of the Resurrection
     Subject Interests: English, Family, Hist, Liberal arts, Marriage, Psychol,
     Relig studies, Sociol
     Automation Activity & Vendor Info: (Acquisitions) Ex Libris Group;
     (Cataloging) Ex Libris Group; (Circulation) Ex Libris Group; (Course
     Reserve) Ex Libris Group; (OPAC) Ex Libris Group; (Serials) Ex Libris
     Group
     Wireless access
     Partic in TriUniversity Group of Libraries (TUG)
     Open Mon-Thurs 9am-9:30pm, Fri 9-4:30, Sat & Sun 1-5

C   UNIVERSITY OF WATERLOO LIBRARY, Dana Porter Library, 200
     University Ave W, N2L 3G1. SAN 368-8054. Tel: 519-888-4567, Ext
     32282. Circulation Tel: 519-888-4567, Ext 84600. Interlibrary Loan Service
     Tel: 519-888-4567, Ext 32598. Reference Tel: 519-888-4567, Ext 35763.
     FAX: 519-888-4320. Interlibrary Loan Service FAX: 519-888-4323. Web
     Site: www.lib.uwaterloo.ca. *Univ Librn,* Mark Haslett; Tel: 519-888-4567,
     Ext 33568, E-mail: mhaslett@uwaterloo.ca; *Assoc Univ Librn, Digital &
     Discovery Serv,* Pascal Calarco; Tel: 519-888-4567, Ext 38215, E-mail:
     pvcalarco@uwaterloo.ca; *Assoc Univ Librn, Info Res & Serv,* Susan
     Routliffe; Tel: 519-888-4567, Ext 33312, E-mail: sroutlif@uwaterloo.ca;
     Dir, Organizational Serv, Sharon Lamont; Tel: 519-888-4567, Ext 33519,
     E-mail: sljlamon@uwaterloo.ca; *Head, Acq,* Aloysius Leonard; Tel:
     519-888-4567, Ext 35430, E-mail: aleonard@uwaterloo.ca; *Head, Circ
     Serv,* Alex McCulloch; Tel: 519-888-4567, Ext 35326, E-mail:
     iamccull@uwaterloo.ca; *Head, Info Serv & Res,* Annie Belanger; E-mail:
     am2belan@uwaterloo.ca; *Head, Spec Coll,* Susan Mavor; Tel:
     519-888-4567, Ext 33122, E-mail: ssmavor@uwaterloo.ca; *Mgr, Cat Dept,*
     Betty Graf; Tel: 519-888-4567, Ext 36584, E-mail: bgraf@uwaterloo.ca;
     Mgr, Libr Communications & Develop, Nancy Collins; Tel: 519-888-4567,
     Ext 32446, E-mail: ncollins@uwaterloo.ca; Staff 36 (MLS 30, Non-MLS 6)
     Founded 1957. Enrl 33,800; Fac 1,100; Highest Degree: Doctorate
     Library Holdings: AV Mats 453; Microforms 1,715,194; Bk Vols
     2,046,934; Per Subs 35,583
     Special Collections: Breithaupt Hewetson Clark Coll; British Women's
     periodicals, 1893-1977; Canadiana (Sol Eisen Coll); Eric Gill Coll, bks,
     engravings; Eucild's Elements & History of Mathematics; Golden Cockerel
     & Nonesuch (Private Press Coll), bks, ephemera; Henry H Crapo Dance
     Coll; Kitchener-Waterloo YWCA Papers (1905-1985); KW Oktoberfest Inc
     Archives; K-W Record Photographic Negative Coll; Library of George
     Santayana; Robert Southey (B R Davis Coll); Rosa Breithaupt Clark
     Architecture Coll; Seagram Museum Library & Archives; William Blake
     Coll; Women's Studies (Lady Aberdeen Coll), bks, ephemera
     Automation Activity & Vendor Info: (Acquisitions) Ex Libris Group;
     (Cataloging) Ex Libris Group; (Circulation) Ex Libris Group; (OPAC) Ex
     Libris Group
     Wireless access

Publications: Bibliography; news@your library
Partic in Canadian Research Knowledge Network; Ontario Council of
University Libraries; TriUniversity Group of Libraries (TUG);
Wellington-Waterloo-Dufferin Health Library Network
Friends of the Library Group
Departmental Libraries:
DAVIS CENTRE LIBRARY, 200 University Ave W, N2L 3G1. Tel:
519-888-4567, Ext 37469. FAX: 519-888-4311. *Univ Librn,* Mark
Haslett; Tel: 519-888-4567, Ext 33568, Fax: 519-888-4320, E-mail:
mhaslett@uwaterloo.ca; *Head, Info Serv & Res,* Jennifer Haas; Tel:
519-888-4567, Ext. 37469, E-mail: j2haas@uwaterloo.ca. Subject
Specialists: *Eng, Math, Sci,* Jennifer Haas
Friends of the Library Group
MUSAGETES ARCHITECTURE LIBRARY, Seven Melville St S,
Cambridge, N1S 2H4. Circulation Tel: 519-888-4567, Ext 27607.
Information Services Tel: 519-888-4567, Ext 27620. Web Site:
www.lib.uwaterloo.ca/musagetes/index.html. *Br Head,* Michele Laing;
E-mail: mlaing@library.uwaterloo.ca
UNIVERSITY MAP LIBRARY, 200 University Ave W, N2L 3G1. Tel:
519-888-4567, Ext 32795. Web Site:
www.lib.uwaterloo.ca/locations/umd/index.html. *Mgr, Univ Map Libr &
Br Libr Serv,* Richard Pinnell; Tel: 519-888-4567, Ext 33412, E-mail:
rhpinnel@uwaterloo.ca
WITER LEARNING RESOURCE CENTRE, Optometry Bldg, Rm 2101,
N2L 3G1. Tel: 519-888-4005. FAX: 519-725-0784. E-mail:
optlib@uwaterloo.ca. Web Site:
optometry.uwaterloo.ca/witer-learning-resource-centre. *Liaison/Spec
Librn,* Kathy MacDonald; Tel: 519-888-4567, Ext 38538, E-mail:
kamacdon@uwaterloo.ca
Special Collections: Optometry & Physiological Optics Materials Coll

P   WATERLOO PUBLIC LIBRARY*, 35 Albert St, N2L 5E2. SAN
319-5988. Tel: 519-886-1310. FAX: 519-886-7936. Web Site: www.wpl.ca.
Chief Librn, Cathy Matyas; E-mail: cmatyas@wpl.ca; Staff 70 (MLS 9,
Non-MLS 61)
Founded 1897. Pop 103,813; Circ 900,000
Library Holdings: Bk Vols 240,113; Per Subs 259
Special Collections: Prov
Function: AV serv, For res purposes, Govt ref serv, Handicapped
accessible, Homebound delivery serv, ILL available, Magnifiers for reading,
Outside serv via phone, mail, e-mail & web, Prog for children & young
adult, Summer reading prog, Telephone ref
Open Mon-Thurs 10-9, Fri & Sat 10-5:30, Sun 1-4
Branches: 1
MCCORMICK BRANCH, 500 Parkside Dr, N2L 5J4, SAN 377-8452. Tel:
519-885-1920. FAX: 519-885-0076. *Mgr,* Doreen Disney

WAWA

P   WAWA PUBLIC LIBRARY*, 40 Broadway Ave, P0S 1K0. (Mail add: PO
Box 1730, P0S 1K0), SAN 319-5996. Tel: 705-856-2062. Circulation Tel:
705-856-2062, Ext 290. Administration Tel: 705-856-2062, Ext 291. FAX:
705-856-1488. Web Site: www.mtpl.on.ca. *Exec Dir, Head Librn,* Jayne
Griffith; E-mail: jgriffith@wawa.cc; Staff 1 (Non-MLS 1)
Pop 3,000; Circ 25,000
Automation Activity & Vendor Info: (Cataloging) SIRSI WorkFlows;
(Circulation) SIRSI WorkFlows
Function: Homebound delivery serv, ILL available, Photocopying/Printing,
Prog for children & young adult, Summer reading prog, VHS videos,
Wheelchair accessible
Special Services for the Deaf - Bks on deafness & sign lang; Closed
caption videos
Special Services for the Blind - Audio mat; Bks on CD; Large print bks;
Ref serv; Talking bks

WELLAND

J   NIAGARA COLLEGE OF APPLIED ARTS & TECHNOLOGY*,
Tecumseh Learning Resource Centre, 300 Woodlawn Rd, L3C 7L3. SAN
319-602X. Tel: 905-735-2211, Ext 7767. Automation Services Tel:
905-735-2211, Ext 7731. FAX: 905-736-6021. Web Site:
www.niagarac.on.ca/lrc. *Librn,* Patricia Labonte; E-mail:
tlabonte@niagarac.on.ca; Staff 7 (MLS 1, Non-MLS 6)
Founded 1967. Enrl 6,200; Fac 240; Highest Degree: Bachelor
Library Holdings: Bk Vols 55,000; Per Subs 450
Subject Interests: Broadcasting, Commun studies, Communications,
Health
Automation Activity & Vendor Info: (Acquisitions) Horizon
Database Vendor: EBSCOhost, ProQuest
Partic in College Bibliocentre
Open Mon-Thurs 8-8, Fri 8-5

Departmental Libraries:
GLENDALE, 135 Taylor Rd, RR 4, Niagara on the Lake, L0S 1J0, SAN
378-1569. Tel: 905-641-2252, Ext 4413. FAX: 905-988-4313. *Librn,*
Ralph Laird; Tel: 905-641-2252, Ext 4402, E-mail:
rlaird@niagarac.on.ca; Staff 4 (MLS 1, Non-MLS 3)
Founded 1967. Enrl 6,200; Fac 240; Highest Degree: Bachelor
Library Holdings: Bk Vols 55,000; Per Subs 450
Partic in College Bibliocentre
Open Mon-Thurs 8-8, Fri 8-5, Sun 12-4

P   WELLAND PUBLIC LIBRARY*, 50 The Boardwalk, L3B 6J1. SAN
368-8321. Tel: 905-734-6210. FAX: 905-734-8955. E-mail:
info@welland.library.on.ca. Web Site: www.welland.library.on.ca. *Chief
Exec Officer,* Janet C Booth; E-mail: jcbooth@welland.library.on.ca; *Pub
Serv,* Stephen Hanns; E-mail: shanns@welland.library.on.ca; Staff 8 (MLS
5, Non-MLS 3)
Founded 1922. Pop 48,411; Circ 267,837
Jan 2005-Dec 2005 Income (CAN) $1,697,165, Provincial (CAN)
$145,878, City (CAN) $1,378,100, Federal (CAN) $895, Locally Generated
Income (CAN) $96,353, Other (CAN) $75,939. Mats Exp (CAN)
$137,457, Books (CAN) $106,267, Per/Ser (Incl. Access Fees) (CAN)
$8,682, AV Mat (CAN) $8,809, Electronic Ref Mat (Incl. Access Fees)
(CAN) $12,314, Presv (CAN) $1,385. Sal (CAN) $997,646
Library Holdings: CDs 2,285; Large Print Bks 2,916; Bk Titles 83,364;
Per Subs 196; Talking Bks 932; Videos 4,287
Special Collections: French Language Coll; Welland County Local History
Coll. Can & Prov
Subject Interests: Multilingual
Automation Activity & Vendor Info: (Cataloging) SirsiDynix;
(Circulation) SirsiDynix; (OPAC) SirsiDynix
Database Vendor: EBSCOhost, SirsiDynix
Wireless access
Partic in Ontario Library Consortium

WELLINGTON

P   COUNTY OF PRINCE EDWARD LIBRARIES*, Wellington Branch, 261
Main St, K0K 3L0. (Mail add: PO Box 370, K0K 3L0), SAN 319-6038.
Tel: 613-399-2023. E-mail: wellington@peclibrary.org. *Librn,* Dianne
Cranshaw
Founded 1926. Circ 24,873
Library Holdings: Bk Titles 12,000; Bk Vols 13,000; Per Subs 32
Partic in Southern Ontario Libr Serv
Open Tues & Thurs 2-8, Wed, Fri & Sat 10-4
Friends of the Library Group

WEST HILL

J   WEST HILL COLLEGIATE INSTITUTE*, H A C Farrow Library, 350
Morningside Ave, M1E 3G3. SAN 319-6046. Tel: 416-396-6864. FAX:
416-396-8300. *Librn,* Penny Young
Enrl 1,400
Library Holdings: Bk Vols 25,000
Open Mon-Fri 8:15-3:30

WESTON

M   HUMBER RIVER REGIONAL HOSPITAL*, Health Sciences Library, 200
Church St, M9N 1N8. SAN 329-1901. Tel: 416-243-4597. FAX:
416-243-4236. E-mail: healthscienceslibrary@hrrh.on.ca. Web Site:
www.hrrh.on.ca. *Health Sci Librn,* Carmen Alcade; Staff 1 (MLS 1)
Library Holdings: Bk Titles 1,200; Per Subs 200
Subject Interests: Allied health sci, Med, Nursing
Partic in Health Science Information Consortium of Toronto

WESTPORT

P   WESTPORT PUBLIC LIBRARY, Three Spring St, K0G 1X0. (Mail add:
PO Box 28, K0G 1X0), SAN 319-6062. Tel: 613-273-3223. FAX:
613-273-3460. E-mail: library@rideau.net. *Librn,* Pamela Stuffles
Pop 1,476; Circ 13,366
Library Holdings: Bk Titles 13,500; Bk Vols 13,700
Open Mon & Fri 1-5, Tues & Sat 10-2, Thurs 2-7
Friends of the Library Group

WHITBY

P   WHITBY PUBLIC LIBRARY*, 405 Dundas St W, L1N 6A1. SAN
368-8380. Tel: 905-668-6531. FAX: 905-668-7445. Web Site:
www.whitbylibrary.on.ca. *Dir,* Ian Ross; E-mail:
ianross@whitbylibrary.on.ca; Staff 49 (MLS 6, Non-MLS 43)
Founded 1852. Pop 110,000; Circ 1,081,120
Jan 2006-Dec 2006 Income (Main Library and Branch(s)) (CAN)
$3,969,889, Provincial (CAN) $99,982, City (CAN) $3,690,015, Federal
(CAN) $6,519, Locally Generated Income (CAN) $173,373. Mats Exp
(CAN) $402,409, Books (CAN) $289,447, Per/Ser (Incl. Access Fees)

(CAN) $19,997, Manu Arch (CAN) $11,986, Micro (CAN) $4,681, AV Mat (CAN) $35,526, Electronic Ref Mat (Incl. Access Fees) (CAN) $40,772. Sal (CAN) $2,252,921
Library Holdings: Bk Titles 140,433; Bk Vols 214,596; Per Subs 274
Special Collections: Can & Prov
Automation Activity & Vendor Info: (Acquisitions) SirsiDynix; (Cataloging) SirsiDynix; (Circulation) SirsiDynix; (OPAC) SirsiDynix
Database Vendor: EBSCOhost, Electric Library, Gale Cengage Learning, Grolier Online, netLibrary, ProQuest
Wireless access
Function: Art exhibits, CD-ROM, Computer training, Copy machines, Electronic databases & coll, Handicapped accessible, Homebound delivery serv, ILL available, Mail & tel request accepted, Music CDs, Online ref, Prog for adults, Prog for children & young adult, Spoken cassettes & CDs, Summer reading prog, Telephone ref, VHS videos, Wheelchair accessible
Publications: Booklists; Monthly Bulletin of Events
Partic in Southern Ontario Libr Serv
Open Mon-Fri 9:30-9, Sat 9-5
Branches: 3
BROOKLIN BRANCH, Eight Vipond Rd, Brooklin, L1M 1B3, SAN 368-8410. Tel: 905-655-3191. *Br Supvr,* Sandra Mammone; Staff 4 (Non-MLS 4)
Open Tues-Thurs 10-9, Fri & Sat 9-5
ROSSLAND BRANCH, 701 Rossland Rd E, L1N 8Y9, SAN 370-1352. Tel: 905-668-1886. *Br Supvr,* Lianne Browne; Staff 3 (Non-MLS 3)
Open Tues & Wed 10-6, Thurs 12-8, Sat 10-2
WHITBY ARCHIVES, 405 Dundas St W, L1N 6A1, SAN 373-7470. Tel: 905-668-6531, Ext 2023. E-mail: archives@whitbylibrary.on.ca. Web Site: www.ourontario.ca/whitby, www.whitbylibrary.on.ca. *Archivist,* Sarah Ferencz; Staff 2 (MLS 1, Non-MLS 1)
Founded 1968. Pop 100,000
Jan 2012-Dec 2012 Income $15,000. Mats Exp $12,000
Special Collections: Genealogy; Land Records; Newspapers; Photographs; Private Coll
Function: Archival coll, Electronic databases & coll, Outreach serv
Open Mon-Fri 9:30-5
Restriction: Non-circulating, Open evenings by appt, Open to pub for ref only

WHITE RIVER

P　WHITE RIVER PUBLIC LIBRARY, 123 Superior St, P0M 3G0. (Mail add: PO Box 458, P0M 3G0), SAN 319-6070. Tel: 807-822-1113. FAX: 807-822-1113. E-mail: wrlib@nwconx.net. Web Site: www.whiteriverlibrary.com. *Chief Exec Officer,* Janet Ramage; *Asst Librn, Syst,* Terry Delaney
Library Holdings: Bk Vols 5,000
Open Mon, Tues & Thurs (Summer) 10-5, Wed 1-8:30, Fri 1-3; Mon (Winter) 2:30-5, Wed & Fri 6-8:30, Sat 10-12:30

WHITNEY

S　ALGONQUIN PARK VISITOR CENTRE*, Library & Archives, PO Box 219, K0J 2M0. SAN 329-4447. Tel: 613-637-2828. FAX: 613-637-2138. E-mail: info@algonquinpark.on.ca. Web Site: www.algonquinpark.on.ca. *In Charge,* Rick Stronks; E-mail: rick.stronks@mnr.gov.on.ca
Library Holdings: CDs 20; DVDs 10; Bk Titles 1,150; Per Subs 10; Videos 160
Special Collections: Reprint Coll. Oral History
Subject Interests: Archives, Newsp clipping files
Restriction: Open by appt only

WILLOWDALE

S　NATIONAL AUTOMOBILE, AEROSPACE & GENERAL WORKERS UNION OF CANADA, CAW-Canada Library, 205 Placer Ct, M2H 3H9. SAN 373-8361. Tel: 416-497-4110. FAX: 416-495-6552. E-mail: library@caw.ca. Web Site: www.caw.ca. *Librn,* Kathy Bennett; E-mail: bennettk@caw.ca; Staff 1.5 (MLS 1, Non-MLS 0.5)
Founded 1986
Library Holdings: Bk Titles 1,500; Per Subs 200
Automation Activity & Vendor Info: (Cataloging) Inmagic, Inc.; (Circulation) Inmagic, Inc.; (Serials) Inmagic, Inc.
Restriction: Authorized scholars by appt

WINDSOR

M　CANADIAN MENTAL HEALTH ASSOCIATION*, Windsor-Essex County Branch, 1400 Windsor Ave, N8X 3L9. SAN 373-3289. Tel: 519-255-7440. FAX: 519-255-7817. Web Site: www.cmha-wecb.on.ca. *Dir of Advan,* Patti Lauzon
Library Holdings: Bk Vols 1,400; Per Subs 20

L　ESSEX LAW ASSOCIATION LAW LIBRARY*, Superior Courthouse, 245 Windsor Ave, N9A 1J2. SAN 320-3492. Tel: 519-252-8418. FAX: 519-252-9686. E-mail: essexlaw@mnsi.net. *Librn,* Douglas Hewitt
Founded 1884
Library Holdings: Bk Vols 15,000
Subject Interests: Can law

M　HOTEL-DIEU GRACE HOSPITAL*, Medical Library, 1030 Ouellette Ave, N9A 1E1. SAN 327-2680. Tel: 519-973-4411, Ext 3178, 519-973-4411, Ext 3528. FAX: 519-973-0642. E-mail: library@hdgh.org. Web Site: www.hdgh.org. *Dir,* Toni Janik; Staff 3 (MLS 1, Non-MLS 2)
Library Holdings: e-books 110; e-journals 8,000; Bk Vols 1,500; Per Subs 350
Automation Activity & Vendor Info: (Acquisitions) EOS International; (Cataloging) EOS International; (Circulation) EOS International; (OPAC) EOS International; (Serials) EOS International
Partic in Canadian Health Libraries Association; CLA; Ont Hospital Librs Asn

S　INTERNATIONAL JOINT COMMISSION*, Great Lakes Regional Office Reference Resource Center, 100 Ouellette Ave, 8th Flr, N9A 6T3. SAN 319-6143. Tel: 519-257-6700. FAX: 519-257-6740. Web Site: www.ijc.org. *In Charge,* Mae Carter; Tel: 519-257-6703, E-mail: carterm@windsor.ijc.org
Founded 1975
Library Holdings: Per Subs 20
Special Collections: I J C Archive
Subject Interests: Great Lakes water quality, Planning, Related res
Publications: Bibliography of Great Lake Diversions; Bibliography of Reports Issued Under the Great Lakes Water Quality Agreement; Pollution from Land Use Activities Reference Group Bibliography
Restriction: Staff use only

S　MULTICULTURAL COUNCIL OF WINDSOR & ESSEX COUNTY LIBRARY*, 245 Janette Ave, N9A 4Z2. SAN 377-3396. Tel: 519-255-1127. FAX: 519-255-1435. E-mail: contact@themcc.com. Web Site: www.themcc.com. *Exec Dir,* Kathie Thomas; Staff 39 (MLS 39)
Library Holdings: Bk Vols 500

J　ST CLAIR COLLEGE OF APPLIED ARTS & TECHNOLOGY LIBRARY*, 2000 Talbot Rd W, N9A 6S4. SAN 319-6151. Tel: 519-972-2739. FAX: 519-972-2757. Web Site: www.stclaircollege.ca. *Mgr, Libr Serv,* Cynthia Crump
Founded 1967
Library Holdings: Bk Vols 40,000; Per Subs 200
Special Collections: Government Documents
Subject Interests: Applied arts, Trades
Wireless access
Open Mon-Thurs 7:45am-10pm, Fri 7:45-6, Sat 9-5

C　UNIVERSITY OF WINDSOR, Leddy Library, 401 Sunset Ave, N9B 3P4. SAN 368-9220. Tel: 519-253-3000, Ext 3161. Circulation Tel: 519-253-3000, Ext 3402. Interlibrary Loan Service Tel: 519-253-3000, Ext 3195. Reference Tel: 519-253-3000, Ext 3190. Web Site: www.uwindsor.ca/library. *Dean of Libr,* Gwendolyn Ebbett; E-mail: gebbett@uwindsor.ca; *Assoc Dean of Libr,* Joan Dalton; Tel: 519-253-3000, Ext 3165; *Assoc Dean of Libr,* Cathy Maskell; Tel: 519-253-3000, Ext 3165; *Head, Acq,* Shuzhen Zhao; Tel: 519-253-3000, Ext 3162; *Syst Mgr,* Guoying (Grace) Liu; Tel: 519-253-3000, Ext 3160; *Archivist,* Brian Owens; Tel: 519-253-3000, Ext 3851; *Info Serv,* Peter Zimmerman; Tel: 519-253-3000, Ext 3180; Staff 22 (MLS 22)
Founded 1857. Enrl 13,190; Fac 523; Highest Degree: Doctorate
Library Holdings: Bk Vols 1,567,813
Special Collections: Classics & Misc (Leddy Coll); Katherine Mansfield Coll, bks & letters
Database Vendor: OCLC FirstSearch, OVID Technologies, ProQuest, TLC (The Library Corporation), Wilson - Wilson Web
Partic in Canadian Association of Research Libraries
Departmental Libraries:
CL　PAUL MARTIN LAW LIBRARY, Ron W Ianni Law Bldg, 401 Sunset Ave, N9B 3P4. Tel: 519-253-3000, Ext 2977. FAX: 519-973-7064. Web Site: www.uwindsor.ca/lawlibrary. *Actg Law Librn & Lectr in Law,* Annette Demers; Staff 10 (MLS 2, Non-MLS 8)
Founded 1967. Enrl 600; Highest Degree: Bachelor
Library Holdings: Bk Vols 232,501; Per Subs 1,436
Subject Interests: Commonwealth, Law Can, US
Open Mon-Thurs 8:30am-11:50pm, Fri 8:30-4:50, Sat 11-4:50, Sun 1-11:50

S　WINDSOR COMMUNITY MUSEUM*, Windsor Public Library, 254 Pitt St W, N9A 5L5. SAN 371-1838. Tel: 519-253-1812. FAX: 519-253-0919. E-mail: wmuseum@windsorpubliclibrary.com. Web Site: www.windsorpubliclibrary.com/museum. *Asst Curator,* Madelyn Della Valle; Staff 3 (Non-MLS 3)

Founded 1958
Library Holdings: Bk Vols 410; Spec Interest Per Sub 10
Special Collections: History of Windsor/Detroit Area; Museology
Function: Archival coll
Publications: Newsletter (Quarterly)
Open Tues-Sat 10-5, Sun (May-Sept) 2-5
Restriction: Non-circulating
Friends of the Library Group

P   WINDSOR PUBLIC LIBRARY*, 850 Ouellette Ave, N9A 4M9. SAN
     368-931X. Tel: 519-255-6770, Ext 4425. FAX: 519-255-7207. Web Site:
     www.windsorpubliclibrary.com. *Chief Exec Officer,* Barry Holmes
     Founded 1894. Pop 212,000; Circ 1,500,000
     Library Holdings: Bk Vols 603,066; Per Subs 250
     Special Collections: Can & Prov
     Automation Activity & Vendor Info: (Acquisitions) SirsiDynix;
     (Cataloging) SirsiDynix; (Circulation) SirsiDynix; (OPAC) SirsiDynix
     Partic in Dialog Corp; Info-globe; Infomart; Southern Ontario Libr Serv
     Friends of the Library Group
     Branches: 10
     BRIDGEVIEW, 1295 Campbell Ave, N9B 3M7, SAN 368-9379. Tel:
        519-253-7340. FAX: 519-253-3472.
        Library Holdings: Bk Vols 42,000
        Open Mon & Wed 12-8, Tues & Thurs 10-6, Fri & Sat 9-5 (Sept-May)
        Friends of the Library Group
     NIKOLA BUDIMIR MEMORIAL, 1310 Grand Marais Rd W, N9E 1E4,
        SAN 368-9409. Tel: 519-969-5880. FAX: 519-969-7947.
        Library Holdings: Bk Vols 64,326
        Open Mon-Wed 10-9, Thurs 10-6, Fri & Sat 9-5, Sun 1-5 (Sept-May)
        Friends of the Library Group
     CENTRAL LIBRARY, 850 Ouellette Ave, N9A 4M9. Tel: 519-255-6770.
        TDD: 519-252-4775. *Mgr,* Karen Bonasso
        Library Holdings: Bk Vols 491,186
        Special Collections: Automotive History Coll; Municipal Archives
        Subject Interests: Local hist
        Special Services for the Deaf - TDD equip
        Open Mon-Thurs 9-9, Fri & Sat 9-5, Sun 1-5 (Sept-May)
        Friends of the Library Group
     FONTAINEBLEAU, 3030 Rivard, N8T 2J2.
        Founded 2005
        Library Holdings: Bk Vols 52,000
     FOREST GLADE-OPTIMIST, 3211 Forest Glade Dr, N8R 1W7, SAN
        368-9522. Tel: 519-735-6803. FAX: 519-735-2339.
        Library Holdings: Bk Vols 53,627
        Open Mon-Wed 1-9, Thurs 10-6, Fri & Sat 9-5 (Sept-May)
        Friends of the Library Group
     REMINGTON PARK, 2710 Lillian St, N8X 4B5, SAN 368-9417. Tel:
        519-966-3441. FAX: 519-966-3854.
        Library Holdings: Bk Vols 20,000
        Open Tues & Thurs 12-8, Sat 9-5 (Sept-May)
        Friends of the Library Group
     RIVERSIDE, 6275 Wyandotte St E, N8S 1N5, SAN 368-9433. Tel:
        519-945-7568. FAX: 519-945-2871.
        Library Holdings: Bk Vols 56,000
        Open Mon-Wed 10-9, Thurs 10-6, Fri & Sat 9-5, Sun 1-5 (Sept-May)
        Friends of the Library Group
     SANDWICH, 3312 Sandwich St W, N9C 1B1. Tel: 519-253-8492.
        Library Holdings: Bk Vols 35,000
        Open Mon-Wed 12-8, Thurs 10-6, Sat 9-5 (Sept-May)
     SEMINOLE, 4285 Seminole St, N8Y 1Z5, SAN 368-9468. Tel:
        519-945-6467. FAX: 519-945-3404.
        Library Holdings: Bk Vols 42,584
        Open Mon & Wed 12-8, Tues & Thurs 10-6, Sat 9-5 (Sept-May)
        Friends of the Library Group
     SOUTH WALKERVILLE, 1425 Tecumseh Rd E, N8W 1C2, SAN
        368-9492. Tel: 519-253-3600. FAX: 519-253-6554.
        Library Holdings: Bk Vols 38,068
        Open Mon & Wed 12-8, Tues & Thurs 10-6, Sat 9-5 (Sept-May)
        Friends of the Library Group

M   WINDSOR REGIONAL HOSPITAL, Health Sciences Library,
     Metropolitan Campus, 1995 Lens Ave, N8W 1L9. SAN 374-4914. Tel:
     519-254-5577, Ext 52329. E-mail: library@wrh.on.ca. Web Site:
     www.wrh.on.ca. *Coordr, Librn,* Mary Ellen Bechard; Tel: 519-254-5577,
     Ext 52706; Staff 2 (MLS 1, Non-MLS 1)
     Founded 1911
     Library Holdings: Bk Titles 7,000; Per Subs 350
     Automation Activity & Vendor Info: (Acquisitions) EOS International;
     (Cataloging) EOS International; (Circulation) EOS International; (Course
     Reserve) EOS International; (Media Booking) EOS International; (OPAC)
     EOS International
     Database Vendor: EBSCOhost
     Partic in Medical Library Association (MLA); Ont Hospital Librs Asn
     Open Mon-Fri 8-4

S   WINDSOR STAR LIBRARY*, 167 Ferry St, N9A 4M5. SAN 319-6178.
     Tel: 519-255-5711. FAX: 519-255-5515. *Librn,* Denise Chuk
     Founded 1940
     Library Holdings: Bk Vols 2,500
     Subject Interests: Automotive indust, Great Lakes region,
     Multiculturalism, Race relations

WOODSTOCK

L   OXFORD LAW ASSOCIATION LIBRARY, Courthouse, 415 Hunter St,
     N4S 4G6. (Mail add: PO Box 1678, N4S 0A9), SAN 372-6231. Tel:
     519-539-7711. FAX: 519-539-7962. *Libr Tech,* Shabira Tamachi; Staff 1
     (MLS 1)
     Library Holdings: Bk Titles 750; Bk Vols 2,000
     Automation Activity & Vendor Info: (OPAC) Ex Libris Group
     Database Vendor: LexisNexis
     Function: For res purposes
     Restriction: Not open to pub

P   WOODSTOCK PUBLIC LIBRARY*, 445 Hunter St, N4S 4G7. SAN
     319-6186. Tel: 519-539-4801. FAX: 519-539-5246. Web Site:
     www.woodstock.library.on.ca. *Chief Librn,* Gary Baumbach; E-mail:
     gbaumbach@woodstock.library.on.ca; *Adult Serv, Info Serv,* Susan Start;
     E-mail: sstart@woodstock.library.on.ca; *Ch,* Darlene Pretty; E-mail:
     dpretty@woodstock.library.on.ca; *Circ,* K Scott; E-mail:
     kscott@woodstock.library.on.ca; Staff 9 (MLS 7, Non-MLS 2)
     Founded 1835. Pop 33,061; Circ 333,394
     Library Holdings: e-journals 4,001; Bk Titles 118,400; Per Subs 140
     Special Collections: Local History Pertaining to Woodstock & to Oxford
     County
     Automation Activity & Vendor Info: (Cataloging) SirsiDynix;
     (Circulation) SirsiDynix; (OPAC) SirsiDynix
     Database Vendor: EBSCOhost, Gale Cengage Learning, netLibrary,
     ProQuest
     Partic in Southern Ontario Libr Serv
     Open Mon-Fri (Sept-June) 10-8:30, Sat 10-5, Sun 1-5
     Friends of the Library Group

WYOMING

P   LAMBTON COUNTY LIBRARY, Headquarters, 787 Broadway St, N0N
     1T0. (Mail add: PO Box 3100, N0N 1T0), SAN 369-027X. Tel:
     519-845-3324. FAX: 519-845-0700. E-mail:
     library.headquarters@county-lambton.on.ca. Web Site: www.lclmg.org. *Gen
     Mgr,* Robert Tremain; Tel: 519-845-3324, Ext 5236, E-mail:
     robert.tremain@county-lambton.on.ca; *Br Serv Mgr,* Carol Gardiner; Tel:
     519-845-3324, Ext 5238, E-mail: carol.gardiner@county-lambton.on.ca;
     Adult Serv, Kevin Coates; Tel: 519-845-3324, Ext 5233, E-mail:
     kevin.coates@county-lambton.on.ca; *Pub Serv,* Susie Beynon; Tel:
     519-337-3291, E-mail: susie.beynon@county-lambton.on.ca; *Tech Serv,*
     Krystyna Stalmach; Tel: 519-845-3324, Ext 5221, E-mail:
     krystyna.stalmach@county-lambton.on.ca; Staff 205 (MLS 10, Non-MLS
     195)
     Founded 1967. Pop 126,000; Circ 996,322
     Library Holdings: Audiobooks 5,335; CDs 9,100; DVDs 16,100; Bk
     Titles 275,821; Bk Vols 500,591; Per Subs 497; Videos 4,000
     Special Collections: Local History (Lambton Coll). Can & Prov
     Automation Activity & Vendor Info: (Acquisitions) Infor Library &
     Information Solutions; (Cataloging) Infor Library & Information Solutions;
     (Circulation) Infor Library & Information Solutions; (OPAC) Infor Library
     & Information Solutions
     Database Vendor: Gale Cengage Learning
     Wireless access
     Function: Archival coll, AV serv, Homebound delivery serv, ILL available,
     Prog for children & young adult, Ref serv available, Summer reading prog
     Publications: Leaflet (Newsletter)
     Open Mon-Fri 9-5
     Branches: 26
     ALVINSTON BRANCH, 3251 River St, Alvinston, N0N 1A0. (Mail add:
        PO Box 44, Alvinston, N0N 1A0), SAN 369-030X. Tel: 519-898-2921.
        E-mail: alvinston.library@county-lambton.on.ca.
        Open Tues, Thurs & Fri 10-5 & 6-8:30, Sat 10-1:30
     ARKONA BRANCH, 16 Smith St, Arkona, N0M 1B0. (Mail add: PO Box
        12, Arkona, N0M 1B0), SAN 369-0334. Tel: 519-828-3406. E-mail:
        arkona.library@county-lambton.on.ca.
        Open Tues & Thurs 3-8, Sat 10-Noon
     BRIGDEN BRANCH, 1540 Duncan St, Brigden, N0N 1B0. (Mail add: PO
        Box 339, Brigden, N0N 1B0), SAN 369-0369. Tel: 519-864-1142.
        E-mail: brigden.library@county-lambton.on.ca.
        Open Mon, Tues & Thurs 4-9, Sat 9-2
     BRIGHTS GROVE BRANCH, 2618 Hamilton Rd, Brights Grove, N0N
        1C0. (Mail add: PO Box 339, Brights Grove, N0N 1C0), SAN 369-0393.
        Tel: 519-869-2351. E-mail: brightsgrove.library@county-lambton.on.ca.
        Open Mon-Thurs 9:30-8, Sat & Sun 11-3

CAMLACHIE BRANCH, 6745 Camlachie Rd, Camlachie, N0N 1E0, SAN 369-0423. Tel: 519-899-2202. E-mail: camlachie.library@county-lambton.on.ca.
Open Mon & Wed 4-8, Sat 9-1

CORUNNA BRANCH, 417 Lyndock St, Corunna, N0N 1G0. (Mail add: PO Box 460, Corunna, N0N 1G0), SAN 369-0458. Tel: 519-862-1132. E-mail: corunna.library@county-lambton.on.ca.
Open Mon-Thurs 10-8, Fri & Sat 10-2, Sun 11-2

COURTRIGHT BRANCH, 1533 Fourth St, Courtright, N0N 1H0. (Mail add: PO Box 182, Courtright, N0N 1H0), SAN 369-0482. Tel: 519-867-2712. E-mail: courtright.library@county-lambton.on.ca.
Open Tues & Thurs 3-8, Sat 9:30-11:30

FLORENCE BRANCH, 6213 Mill St, Florence, N0P 1R0. (Mail add: PO Box 102, Florence, N0P 1R0), SAN 369-0504. Tel: 519-692-3213. E-mail: florence.library@county-lambton.on.ca.
Open Tues & Thurs 4pm-8pm, Sat 10-2

FOREST BRANCH, 61 King St W, Forest, N0N 1J0, SAN 369-0512. Tel: 519-786-5152. E-mail: forest.library@county-lambton.on.ca.
Open Mon-Fri 9:30-8, Sat 9:30-5, Sun 12-5

GRAND BEND BRANCH, 15 Gill Rd, Grand Bend, N0M 1T0. (Mail add: PO Box 117, Grand Bend, N0M 1T0), SAN 369-0547. Tel: 519-238-2067. E-mail: grandbend.library@county-lambton.on.ca.
Open Mon, Tues, Thurs & Fri 9-2 & 7pm-9pm, Wed & Sat 9-2

INWOOD BRANCH, 6504 James St, Inwood, N0N 1K0. (Mail add: PO Box 41, Inwood, N0N 1K0), SAN 369-0571. Tel: 519-844-2491. E-mail: inwood.library@county-lambton.on.ca.
Open Tues & Thurs 4-8, Sat 9-1

MALLROAD, 1362 Lambton Mall Rd, Sarnia, N7S 5A1, SAN 369-0601. Tel: 519-542-2580. E-mail: mallroad.library@county-lambton.on.ca.
Open Mon-Fri 9:30-8, Sat 9:30-5, Sun 12-5

MANDAUMIN, RR 1, 3021 Confederation Line, N0N 1T0, SAN 369-0636. Tel: 519-383-8085. E-mail: mandaumin.library@county-lambton.on.ca.
Open Mon & Wed 4-7, Tues 9-12, Sat 2-5

MOORETOWN BRANCH, Mooretown Sports Complex, 1166 Emily St, Mooretown, N0N 1M0, SAN 369-0644. Tel: 519-867-2823. E-mail: mooretown.library@county-lambton.on.ca.
Open Mon, Wed & Fri 9-1 (Summer); Mon & Wed 4-8, Sat 9-1 (Winter)

OIL SPRINGS BRANCH, 4596 Oil Springs Line, Oil Springs, N0N 1P0. (Mail add: PO Box 126, Oil Springs, N0N 1P0), SAN 369-0660. Tel: 519-834-2670. E-mail: oilsprings.library@county-lambton.on.ca.
Open Tues & Thurs 4-8, Sat 9-1

PETROLIA BRANCH, 4200 Petrolia Line, Petrolia, N0N 1R0. (Mail add: PO Box 70, Petrolia, N0N 1R0), SAN 369-0695. Tel: 519-882-0771. E-mail: petrolia.library@county-lambton.on.ca.
Open Mon-Thurs 10-8, Fri 12-5, Sat 9-2, Sun 12-3

POINT EDWARD BRANCH, 220 Michigan Ave, Point Edward, N7V 1E8, SAN 372-5200. Tel: 519-336-3291. E-mail: pointedward.library@county-lambton.on.ca.
Open Mon-Wed 2-7, Thurs & Sat 10-3

PORT FRANKS BRANCH, 9997 Port Franks Rd, Port Franks, N0M 2L0. (Mail add: Unit 2, Port Franks, N0M 2L0), SAN 369-0725. Tel: 519-243-2820. E-mail: portfranks.library@county-lambton.on.ca.
Open Tues & Thurs 3-8, Sat 10-12

PORT LAMBTON BRANCH, 507 Stoddard St, Port Lambton, N0P 2B0. (Mail add: PO Box 250, Port Lambton, N0P 2B0), SAN 369-075X. Tel: 519-677-5217. E-mail: portlambton.library@county-lambton.on.ca.
Open Mon, Wed, & Thurs 6pm-9om, Sat 9-12

SARNIA BRANCH, 124 S Christina St, Sarnia, N7T 2M6, SAN 319-4027. Tel: 519-337-3291. FAX: 519-344-3041. E-mail: sarnia.library@county-lambton.on.ca. Web Site: www.lclmg.org.
Founded 1900. Pop 128,975
Special Collections: Can & Prov
Open Mon-Thurs 9:30-9, Fri & Sat 9:30-5:30, Sun 2-5 (Oct-May)

SHETLAND, RR 2, 1279 Shetland Rd, Florence, N0P 1R0, SAN 369-0784. Tel: 519-695-3330. E-mail: shetland.library@county-lambton.on.ca.
Open Mon 7pm-9pm, Wed & Thurs 3-5 & 7pm-9pm, Sat 1-5

SOMBRA BRANCH, 3536 St Clair Pkwy, Sombra, N0P 2H0. (Mail add: PO Box 211, Sombra, N0P 2H0), SAN 369-0814. Tel: 519-892-3711. E-mail: sombra.library@county-lambton.on.ca.
Open Tues & Thurs 3-8, Sat 10-12

THEDFORD BRANCH, Legacy Ctr, 16 Allen St, Thedford, N0M 2N0. (Mail add: PO Box 70, Thedford, N0M 2N0), SAN 369-0849. Tel: 519-296-4459. E-mail: thedford.library@county-lambton.on.ca.
Open Tues 2-5 & 7pm-9pm, Thurs 7pm-9pm, Fri 10-12, Sat 1-4

WATFORD BRANCH, 5317 Nauvoo Rd, Watford, N0M 2S0. (Mail add: PO Box 9, Watford, N0M 2S0), SAN 369-0938. Tel: 519-876-2204. E-mail: watford.library@county-lambton.on.ca.
Open Mon, Tues & Thurs 10-8, Fri 10-4, Sat 9-1

WILKESPORT BRANCH, General Delivery, 1349 Wilkesport Line, Wilkesport, N0P 2R0, SAN 369-0946. Tel: 519-864-4000. E-mail: wilkesport.library@county-lambton.on.ca.
Open Mon, Wed & Thurs 5-8, Sat 9-12

WYOMING BRANCH, 536 Niagara St, N0N 1T0. (Mail add: PO Box 357, N0N 1T0), SAN 369-0962. Tel: 519-845-0181. E-mail: wyoming.library@county-lambton.on.ca.
Open Mon-Thurs 2-7, Fri 10-4, Sat 10-10

Bookmobiles: 1

YARKER

LENNOX & ADDINGTON COUNTY PUBLIC LIBRARY*, Yarker Branch, 4315 County Rd 1, K0K 3N0. SAN 367-8008. Tel: 613-377-1673. E-mail: yarbrch@lennox-addington.on.ca. *Librn,* Janice McBoy
Library Holdings: Bk Titles 3,000
Open Mon & Tues 5-8, Wed 1-4, Thurs 9-12, Sat 10-1

PRINCE EDWARD ISLAND

Date of Statistics: FY 2008-2009
Total Volumes in Public Libraries: 371,228
Volumes Per Capita: 2.73
Total Public Library Circulation: 766,922
   Circulation Per Capita: 5.75
Total Public Library Income: $2,489,800
   Source of Income: Appropriations
   Expenditures Per Capita: $18.32
Number of County or Multi-County Libraries: 1

CHARLOTTETOWN

G   AGRICULTURE & AGRI-FOOD CANADA*, Canadian Agriculture
Library-Charlottetown, 440 University Ave, C1A 4N6. SAN 319-6194. Tel:
902-566-6861. FAX: 902-566-6821. E-mail: pcag@agr.gc.ca. *Head, Info
Ctr,* Barrie Stanfield; E-mail: stanfieldb@agr.gc.ca; Staff 1 (MLS 1)
Founded 1910
Library Holdings: Bk Vols 3,500; Per Subs 13
Special Collections: Prince Edward Island Agricultural History Coll, bks,
pamphlets
Subject Interests: Agr, Animal nutrition, Botany, Crop sci, Entomology,
Plant nematology, Plant pathology, Soil sci
Automation Activity & Vendor Info: (Cataloging) Infor Library &
Information Solutions; (Circulation) Infor Library & Information Solutions;
(OPAC) Infor Library & Information Solutions; (Serials) Infor Library &
Information Solutions
Partic in Can Agr Libr Network
Open Mon-Fri 8:30-12 & 1-5

S   BIO FOOD TECH (FTC ENTERPRISES LIMITED), BioFoodTech
Library, (Formerly Prince Edward Island Food Technology Centre), 101
Belvedere Ave, C1A 7N8. (Mail add: PO Box 2000, C1A 7N8), SAN
377-2535. Tel: 902-368-5548. FAX: 902-368-5549. Web Site:
www.gov.pe.ca/ftc. *Exec Dir,* Jim Smith
Library Holdings: Bk Titles 1,020; Per Subs 50
Database Vendor: Dialog
Open Mon-Fri 8:30-4:30

P   CONFEDERATION CENTRE PUBLIC LIBRARY*, Charlottetown Public
Library, Queen & Richmond St, C1A 8G8. (Mail add: PO Box 7000, C1A
8G8), SAN 319-6208. Tel: 902-368-4642. FAX: 902-368-4652. E-mail:
ccpl@gov.pe.ca. Web Site: www.library.pe.ca. *Prov Librn,* Allan J Groen;
Tel: 902-368-4649; *Chief Librn,* Kathleen Eaton; Tel: 902-368-4654,
E-mail: keeaton@gov.pe.ca; *Ch,* Barbara Kissick; *Ref,* Gary Ramsay; Staff
21 (MLS 3, Non-MLS 18)
Founded 1965. Pop 32,245; Circ 330,056
Library Holdings: Bk Titles 100,920
Special Collections: Prince Edward Island Coll
Automation Activity & Vendor Info: (Acquisitions) SirsiDynix;
(Cataloging) SirsiDynix; (Circulation) SirsiDynix; (Media Booking)
SirsiDynix
Database Vendor: Gale Cengage Learning, OCLC FirstSearch
Special Services for the Blind - Talking bks
Open Mon, Fri & Sat 10-5, Tues-Thurs 10-9, Sun 1-5
Friends of the Library Group

C   HOLLAND COLLEGE LIBRARY SERVICES*, 140 Weymouth St, C1A
4Z1. SAN 372-6541. Tel: 902-566-9558. FAX: 902-566-9522. E-mail:
library@hollandcollege.com. Web Site: www.hollandcollege.com/library.
Mgr, Libr Serv, Patricia Doucette; E-mail:
pmdoucette@hollandcollege.com; *Librn,* Liane Belway; Tel: 902-888-6752,

E-mail: nlbelway@hollandcollege.com; *Librn,* Louise Mould; E-mail:
lmould@hollandcollege.com; *Librn,* Larry Tweed; E-mail:
ldtweed@hollandcollege.com; *Res Ctr Mgr,* Leslie Holt-Dalziel; Tel:
902-566-9635, E-mail: ljholt@hollandcollege.com; *Res Ctr Mgr,* Jean
Lykow; Tel: 902-888-6738, E-mail: jlykow@hollandcollege.com; *Res Ctr
Mgr,* Rose MacDonald; Tel: 902-894-6837, E-mail:
romacdonald@hollandcollege.com; *Web Developer,* Donnie Bowers;
E-mail: dbowers@hollandcollege.com; Staff 7 (MLS 4, Non-MLS 3)
Founded 1969. Enrl 3,250; Fac 175
Library Holdings: Bk Titles 32,000; Bk Vols 48,000; Per Subs 400
Special Collections: Canada - Selective Depository
Automation Activity & Vendor Info: (Acquisitions) Horizon;
(Cataloging) Horizon; (Circulation) Horizon; (OPAC) Horizon; (Serials)
Horizon
Database Vendor: EBSCOhost, Elsevier, Greenwood Publishing Group,
McGraw-Hill, ProQuest
Function: ILL available
Open Mon-Thurs 8:30am-9pm, Fri 8:30-5, Sun 12-5

L   LAW SOCIETY OF PRINCE EDWARD ISLAND LIBRARY*, 42 Water
St, C1A 1A4. SAN 377-2837. Tel: 902-368-6099. FAX: 902-368-7557.
Librn, Pam Borden; E-mail: pborden@lawlib.pe.ca
Jun 2005-May 2006. Mats Exp (CAN) $109,900, Per/Ser (Incl. Access
Fees) (CAN) $67,900, Electronic Ref Mat (Incl. Access Fees) (CAN)
$42,000. Sal (CAN) $34,000
Library Holdings: Bk Titles 1,055; Bk Vols 14,000; Per Subs 20
Database Vendor: Gale Cengage Learning, Quicklaw
Open Mon-Wed & Fri 1-6, Thurs 8-12 & 1-6
Restriction: Non-circulating

M   PRINCE EDWARD ISLAND ASSOCIATION FOR COMMUNITY
LIVING*, Resource Library, 158 Belvedere Ave, Ste 1, C1A 2Z1. SAN
375-6815. Tel: 902-566-4844. FAX: 902-368-8057. E-mail: info@peiacl.ca.
Web Site: www.peiacl.ca. *Exec Dir,* Bridget Cairns; E-mail:
bridget@peiacl.ca; Staff 2 (MLS 1, Non-MLS 1)
Founded 1956
Library Holdings: AV Mats 100; Bks on Deafness & Sign Lang 20; Bk
Titles 1,500; Per Subs 20; Talking Bks 1,500
Subject Interests: Attention deficit disorder, Autism, Communication,
Employment, Housing, Parenting, Self help, Sexuality
Open Mon-Fri 9-4

M   QUEEN ELIZABETH HOSPITAL*, Frank J MacDonald Library, 60
Riverside Dr, C1A 8T5. (Mail add: PO Box 6600, C1A 8T5), SAN
324-461X. Tel: 902-894-2371. FAX: 902-894-0259, 902-894-2424. E-mail:
qehlibrary@ihis.org. Web Site: www.qehlibrarypei.ca. *Librn,* Julie A Cole;
E-mail: jacole@ihis.org
Founded 1982
Library Holdings: Bk Titles 500; Per Subs 85
Subject Interests: Health sci
Automation Activity & Vendor Info: (Cataloging) Inmagic, Inc.

Partic in National Network of Libraries of Medicine
Open Mon-Fri 8-4

C UNIVERSITY OF PRINCE EDWARD ISLAND*, Robertson Library, 550 University Ave, C1A 4P3. SAN 319-6224. Tel: 902-566-0343. Circulation Tel: 902-566-0583. Interlibrary Loan Service Tel: 902-566-0445. Reference Tel: 902-566-0696. FAX: 902-628-4305. E-mail: reference@upei.ca. Web Site: www.upei.ca/library/. *Actg Univ Librn*, Suzanne Jones; Tel: 902-566-0460, E-mail: sjones@upei.ca; *Actg Syst Librn*, Gord Ripley; *Instrul Serv Librn*, Betty Jeffrey; *Coll Develop*, Norine Hanus; *Spec Coll Librn*, Simon Lloyd; *Access Serv, Bibliographer*, Sharon Neill; *Info Serv*, Cathy Callaghan. Subject Specialists: *Health serv*, Dawn Hooper; Staff 26 (MLS 8, Non-MLS 18)
Founded 1969. Enrl 3,000; Fac 180; Highest Degree: Doctorate
Library Holdings: Bk Titles 307,552
Special Collections: Prince Edward Island Coll
Automation Activity & Vendor Info: (Acquisitions) SirsiDynix; (Cataloging) SirsiDynix; (Circulation) SirsiDynix; (Course Reserve) SirsiDynix; (ILL) Relais International; (OPAC) SirsiDynix; (Serials) SirsiDynix
Database Vendor: Cambridge Scientific Abstracts, ProQuest, ScienceDirect, SirsiDynix, SirsiDynix
Partic in Dialog Corp
Open Mon-Thurs 8am-10pm, Fri 8-6, Sat 11-5, Sun 12-9
Friends of the Library Group

G VETERAN AFFAIRS CANADA LIBRARY, 125 Maple Hills Dr, C1C 0B6. (Mail add: PO Box 7700, C1A 8M9), SAN 329-210X. Tel: 902-368-0531. FAX: 902-370-4895. E-mail: library-bibliotheque@vac-acc.gc.ca. Web Site: www.vac-acc.gc.ca/general/. *Librn*, Heidi Lund; E-mail: heidi.lund@vac-acc.gc.ca; Staff 3 (MLS 1, Non-MLS 2)
Library Holdings: Bk Titles 5,000; Per Subs 50
Subject Interests: Govt doc, Healthcare, Mil hist
Publications: Accession Lists; List of Periodicals
Restriction: Open to dept staff only

MORELL

P PRINCE EDWARD ISLAND PUBLIC LIBRARY SERVICE, 89 Red Head Rd, C0A 1S0. (Mail add: PO Box 7500, C0A 1S0), SAN 369-0997. Tel: 902-961-7320. Interlibrary Loan Service Tel: 902-961-7314. FAX: 902-961-7322. E-mail: plshq@gov.pe.ca. Web Site: www.library.pe.ca. *Prov Librn*, Kathleen Eaton; Tel: 902-961-7316; *Syst Librn*, Liam O'Hare; Tel: 902-961-7323
Founded 1933. Pop 140,000; Circ 823,600
Library Holdings: Bk Titles 203,000; Bk Vols 323,000; Per Subs 600
Special Collections: Can; Prince Edward Island History, bks, micro
Automation Activity & Vendor Info: (Acquisitions) SirsiDynix; (Cataloging) SirsiDynix; (Circulation) SirsiDynix; (OPAC) SirsiDynix
Database Vendor: Bowker, Gale Cengage Learning, Overdrive, Inc, TumbleBookLibrary
Wireless access
Open Mon-Fri 8-4
Friends of the Library Group
Branches: 26
ABRAM VILLAGE PUBLIC, a/s ecole Evangeline RR3, Wellington, Abram Village, C0B 2E0, SAN 369-108X. Tel: 902-854-2491. FAX: 902-854-2981. E-mail: abram@gov.pe.ca. *Libr Tech,* Doris Arsenault
Open Tues 6pm-9pm, Wed & Sat 1-4, Thurs 1-4 & 6pm-9pm
ALBERTON PUBLIC, 460 Main St, Alberton, C0B 1B0. (Mail add: PO Box 449, Alberton, C0B 1B0), SAN 369-111X. Tel: 902-853-3049. E-mail: alberton@gov.pe.ca. *Br Tech,* Kelly Gillis
Open Mon 12:30-5, Wed 10:30-12 & 12:30-5, Fri 12:30-5 & 6:30pm-8:30pm
BIBLIOTHEQUE DR J EDMOND ARSENAULT, Hillsborough Parc, 5 rue Acadienne, Charlottetown, C1C 1M2, SAN 374-4302. Tel: 902-368-6092. E-mail: carrefour@gov.pe.ca. *Br Librn,* Lyne Cadieux
Open Mon, Tues, Thurs & Fri 9-11 & 11:30-4:30, Wed 9-11, 11:30-3 & 5-7
BIBLIOTHEQUE J-HENRI-BLANCHARD, Five Maris Stella, Summerside, C1N 3Y5. Tel: 902-432-2748. FAX: 902-888-1686. E-mail: blanchard@gov.pe.ca. *Librn,* Julie Thiffeault
Founded 2003
Open Mon 10:30-11:30 & 12-3, Tues 9-12 & 2-5, Wed 12-3 & 5-8, Sat 9-1
Friends of the Library Group
BORDEN-CARLETON PUBLIC, 244 Borden Ave, Borden, C0B 1X0, SAN 369-1144. Tel: 902-437-6492. E-mail: borden-carleton@gov.pe.ca. *Libr Tech,* Sharon Leard
Open Tues & Fri 3-7, Thurs 10-Noon
BREADALBANE PUBLIC, 4023 Dixon Rd, Breadalbane, C0A 1E0, SAN 369-1179. Tel: 902-964-2520. E-mail: breadalbane@gov.pe.ca. *Libr Tech,* Joan Sutton
Open Tues & Sat 2-5, Thurs 4-8

CONFEDERATION CENTRE PUBLIC
See Separate Entry in Charlottetown
CORNWALL PUBLIC, 39 Lowther Dr, Cornwall, C0A 1H0, SAN 322-6069. Tel: 902-629-8415. E-mail: cornwall@gov.pe.ca. *Librn,* Pam Wheatley
Open Tues & Wed 1-5:30 & 6-8:30, Fri & Sat 8:30-1
CRAPAUD PUBLIC, 20424 Trans Canada Hwy, Crapaud, C0A 1J0, SAN 369-1209. Tel: 902-658-2297. E-mail: crapaud@gov.pe.ca. *Libr Tech,* Luann Molyneaux
Open Wed & Thurs 2pm-7pm, Sat 9-12
GEORGETOWN PUBLIC, 36 Kent St, Georgetown, C0A 1L0, SAN 369-1233. Tel: 902-652-2832. E-mail: georgetown@gov.pe.ca. *Libr Tech,* Mary Cameron
Open Tues & Thurs 4pm-8pm, Wed 9:30am-11:30am
GOVERNMENT SERVICES LIBRARY, Basement, Jones Bldg, 11 Kent St, Charlottetown, C1A 7N8. (Mail add: PO Box 2000, Charlottetown, C1A 7N8), SAN 369-1055. Tel: 902-368-4653. E-mail: gsl@gov.pe.ca. *Librn,* Nichola Cleaveland; E-mail: nacleave@gov.pe.ca; Staff 1 (MLS 1)
Library Holdings: Bk Vols 7,000; Per Subs 35
Special Collections: Canada & PEI Government Documents; Public Administration & Management Coll
Automation Activity & Vendor Info: (Circulation) SIRSI WorkFlows
Open Mon-Fri 1:30-5
HUNTER RIVER PUBLIC, 19816 Rte 2, Hunter River, C0A 1N0, SAN 369-1268. Tel: 902-964-2800. E-mail: hunter_river@gov.pe.ca. *Librn,* Pam Wheatley
Open Tues 6pm-8:30pm, Wed 5:30-8:30, Thurs 11-1:30 & 2-5, Fri & Sat 2-5
KENSINGTON PUBLIC, 55 Victoria St, Kensington, C0B 1M0, SAN 369-1292. Tel: 902-836-3721. E-mail: kensington@gov.pe.ca. *Br Librn,* Stephanie Campbell
Open Tues 9:30am-1:30pm, Thurs 2:30pm-7pm, Sat 9:30am-1pm
KINKORA PUBLIC, 45 Anderson St, Kinkora, C0B 1N0, SAN 369-1306. Tel: 902-887-2172. E-mail: kinkora@gov.pe.ca. *Libr Tech,* Catherine Arsenault
Open Tues 2-6, Wed 3pm-7pm, Fri 10-Noon
MONTAGUE PUBLIC, 273 Queen's Rd, Montague, C0A 1R0, SAN 369-1322. Tel: 902-838-2928. E-mail: montague@gov.pe.ca. *Libr Tech,* Position Currently Open
Open Tues & Sat 12:30-5:30, Wed & Thurs 12:30-5:30 & 6pm-8:30pm, Fri 9:30-11:30 & 12:30-5:30
MORELL PUBLIC, 89 Red Head Rd, C0A 1S0, SAN 369-1357. Tel: 902-961-3389. E-mail: morell@edu.pe.ca. *Br Librn,* Maria Van De Cappelle
Open Tues-Thurs 3pm-7pm, Sat 9-Noon
MOUNT STEWART PUBLIC, 104 Main St, Mount Stewart, C0A 1T0, SAN 369-1381. Tel: 902-676-2050. E-mail: mtstewart@gov.pe.ca. *Br Librn,* Maria Van De Cappelle
Open Mon & Fri 3pm-7pm, Wed 10-2
MURRAY HARBOUR PUBLIC, 1381 Main St, Murray Harbour, C0A 1V0, SAN 369-1411. Tel: 902-962-3875. E-mail: murray_harbour@gov.pe.ca. *Libr Tech,* Kay MacLean
Open Mon & Tues 5:30pm-8:30pm, Wed & Thurs 1:30-4:30, Fri 11-12 & 1:30-4:30
MURRAY RIVER LEONA GIDDINGS MEMORIAL LIBRARY, 1066 McInnis Rd, Murray River, C0A 1V0, SAN 369-1446. Tel: 902-962-2667. E-mail: murray_river@gov.pe.ca. *Libr Tech,* Kay MacLean
Open Tues & Sat 1:30-4:30, Wed & Thurs 5:30pm-8:30pm
O'LEARY PUBLIC, 18 Community St, O'Leary, C0B 1V0, SAN 369-1470. Tel: 902-859-8788. E-mail: o'leary@gov.pe.ca. *Br Librn,* Nancy McNally
Open Tues 1-5:30, Thurs 10-12:30 & 1-5:30, Fri 1-5:30 & 6pm-8pm
ST PETERS PUBLIC, 1968 Cardigan Rd, St. Peters, C0A 2A0, SAN 369-1500. Tel: 902-961-3415. E-mail: st_peter's@gov.pe.ca. *Libr Tech,* Ann MacInnis
Open Tues 1-5 & 6pm-8pm, Thurs 1-5, Sat 10-Noon
SOURIS PUBLIC, 75 Main St, Souris, C0A 2B0. (Mail add: PO Box 603, Souris, C0A 2B0), SAN 369-1535. Tel: 902-687-2157. E-mail: souris@gov.pe.ca. *Libr Tech,* Kathy MacEwen
Open Tues 1-5, Fri 1-5 & 6pm-8pm, Sat 9:30-12:30
STRATFORD PUBLIC, 57 Bunbury Rd, Stratford, C1B 1T8. Tel: 902-569-7441. E-mail: stratford@edu.pe.ca. *Br Librn,* Jane McKinney
Founded 2001
Open Tues, Fri & Sat 2-5, Wed 5pm-8pm, Thurs 10:30-1:30 & 2-5
SUMMERSIDE ROTARY LIBRARY, 192 Water St, Summerside, C1N 1B1, SAN 369-156X. Tel: 902-436-7323, 902-888-8370. FAX: 902-888-8055. E-mail: summerside@gov.pe.ca. *Librn,* Jean-Francois Savaria
Subject Interests: Local hist
Open Tues 10-9, Wed & Thurs 10-5:30, Fri & Sat 10-5, Sun 1-5
TIGNISH PUBLIC, 103 School St, Tignish, C0B 2B0, SAN 369-1594. Tel: 902-882-7363. E-mail: tignish@gov.pe.ca. *Libr Tech,* Diane McCue
Open Tues, Thurs & Sat 1-4:30, Fri 1:30-4:30 & 6pm-8:30pm

TYNE VALLEY PUBLIC, 19 Allen Rd, Tyne Valley, C0B 2C0, SAN 369-1624. Tel: 902-831-2928. E-mail: tyne_valley@gov.pe.ca. *Libr Tech,* Carolyn Millar
Open Tues & Thurs 3pm-7pm, Sat 10:30-12:30

SUMMERSIDE

S   PRINCE COUNTY HOSPITAL*, Medical Library, 65 Roy Boates Ave, C1N 6M8. SAN 325-7932. Tel: 902-438-4200. FAX: 902-438-4221. Web Site: www.gov.pe.ca/hir. *Health Res Ctr Coordr,* Kathy Evans; Tel: 902-438-4225
Library Holdings: Bk Vols 3,000; Per Subs 30
Database Vendor: Gale Cengage Learning
Open Mon-Fri 8-4
Friends of the Library Group

Date of Statistics: FY 2007
Population: 7,686,038
Population Served by Public Libraries: 7,322,905
Total Volumes in Public Libraries: 21,782,010
    Volumes Per Capita: 2.97
Total Public Library Circulation: 46,111,974
    Circulation Per Capita: 6.29
Total Public Library Income: $299,271,941
    Income Per Capita: $40.86
Provincial Aid to Public Libraries: $70,326,403
Number of Regional Systems: 11

ALMA

P   BIBLIOTHEQUE MUNICIPALE D'ALMA*, 500 Collard, G8B 1N2. SAN 325-0229. Tel: 418-669-5139. FAX: 418-669-5089. Web Site: www.ville.alma.qc.ca/mini_site.php?idMini=175. *Dir,* Martin Bouchard; *Tech Serv,* Rachelle Hudon; Staff 5 (MLS 1, Non-MLS 4)
Founded 1968. Pop 31,000; Circ 191,000
Jan 2008-Dec 2008 Income (CAN) $852,000, Provincial (CAN) $101,000, City (CAN) $701,000, Other (CAN) $50,000. Mats Exp (CAN) $115,000, Books (CAN) $90,000, Per/Ser (Incl. Access Fees) (CAN) $10,000, AV Mat (CAN) $6,000, Presv (CAN) $9,000. Sal (CAN) $557,000 (Prof (CAN) $68,000)
Library Holdings: AV Mats 2,800; Bk Vols 78,000; Per Subs 128; Talking Bks 180
Special Collections: Municipal Document Depository
Subject Interests: Regional lit
Automation Activity & Vendor Info: (Acquisitions) SirsiDynix; (Cataloging) SirsiDynix; (Circulation) SirsiDynix; (ILL) OCLC; (OPAC) SirsiDynix
Database Vendor: SirsiDynix
Wireless access
Open Mon-Wed & Fri 12-8, Thurs 9-8, Sat 10-4:30, Sun 12-4:30

AMOS

P   BIBLIOTHEQUE MUNICIPALE DE AMOS*, 222 Front St E, J9T 1H3. SAN 319-6259. Tel: 819-732-6070. FAX: 819-732-3242. E-mail: bibliotheque@ville.amos.qc.ca. Web Site: www.ville.amos.qc.ca. *Dir,* Linda Langlois
Circ 9,200
Library Holdings: Bk Vols 39,600
Open Mon-Fri 1:30-9, Sat & Sun 1-5

ASBESTOS

P   BIBLIOTHEQUE MUNICIPALE D'ASBESTOS*, 351 Saint Luc Blvd, J1T 2W4. SAN 319-6283. Tel: 819-879-4363. FAX: 819-879-0608. E-mail: bibliasbestos@cgocable.ca. *Dir,* Julie Fontaine; Staff 2 (MLS 1, Non-MLS 1)
Founded 1958. Pop 7,000; Circ 50,067
Library Holdings: Bk Vols 18,980

BAIE COMEAU

P   BIBLIOTHEQUE MUNICIPALE ALICE-LANE*, Six Ave Radisson, G4Z 1W4. SAN 319-6291. Tel: 418-296-8305. FAX: 418-296-8328. *Dir,* Yvon Grondin
Founded 1961. Pop 27,000
Library Holdings: Bk Vols 90,000; Per Subs 159
Open Mon-Thurs 12-9, Fri-Sun 12-5
Friends of the Library Group

C   CEGEP DE BAIE-COMEAU*, Centre de Documentation, 537 boul Blanche, G5C 2B2. SAN 322-8029. Tel: 418-589-5707, Ext 325. Reference Tel: 418-589-5707, Ext 321. FAX: 418-589-9842. E-mail: biblio@cegep-baie-comeau.qc.ca. Web Site: cegep-baie-comeau.qc.ca. *Head of Librn,* Michel Paquette; E-mail: mipaquet@cegep-baie-comeau.qc.ca; *Librn Tech,* Danielle Boudreault; E-mail: daniboud@cegep-baie-comeau.qc.ca; *Librn Tech,* Melanie Cote-Foster; E-mail: mfoster@cegep-baie-comeau.qc.ca; Staff 4 (MLS 1, Non-MLS 3)
Founded 1959. Enrl 1,000; Fac 17
Library Holdings: Bk Vols 53,000; Per Subs 155
Special Collections: US Document Depository
Subject Interests: Humanities, Nat sci
Database Vendor: SirsiDynix

BAIE D'URFE

P   BIBLIOTHEQUE MUNICIPALE DE LA BAIE D'URFE*, Baie-d'Urfe Municipal Library, 20551 chemin du Bord du Lac, H9X 1R3. SAN 319-6305. Tel: 514-457-3274. E-mail: baiedurfelibrary@bellnet.ca. *Pres,* Cloudagh Bassermann; E-mail: bbasserm@yahoo.com
Founded 1966. Pop 3,900; Circ 19,618
Jan 2006-Dec 2006 Income (CAN) $44,500, Provincial (CAN) $11,500, City (CAN) $32,000, Locally Generated Income (CAN) $1,000. Mats Exp (CAN) $20,000, Books (CAN) $15,000, Per/Ser (Incl. Access Fees) (CAN) $2,000, AV Mat (CAN) $2,000, Electronic Ref Mat (Incl. Access Fees) (CAN) $1,000. Sal (CAN) $17,900
Library Holdings: AV Mats 2,516; Bk Titles 30,360; Bk Vols 32,923; Per Subs 47
Special Collections: Early Childhood Education Coll. Municipal Document Depository
Partic in Mandarin
Open Mon, Tues, Thurs & Fri 2:30-5 & 7:30-9, Wed 10-12 & 2:30-9, Sat 10-12, Sun (Winter) 2-4

BAIE SAINT-PAUL

M   CENTRE HOSPITALIER DE CHARLEVOIX*, Bibliotheque Medicale, 74 Blvd Ambroise-Fafard, G3Z 2J6. SAN 324-4350. Tel: 418-435-5150. Reference Tel: 418-435-5150, Ext 2217. FAX: 418-435-0212, 418-435-6451. *Librn,* Louise Leblanc
Mar 2009-Feb 2010. Mats Exp (CAN) $11,700, Books (CAN) $5,000, Per/Ser (Incl. Access Fees) (CAN) $5,000, Other Print Mats (CAN) $200, AV Mat (CAN) $1,500. Sal (CAN) $48,700
Library Holdings: AV Mats 40; DVDs 10; Bk Titles 2,800; Per Subs 40; Videos 290
Special Collections: Can & Prov
Subject Interests: Geriatric, Mental health, Mental retardation, Nursing, Psychiat, Psychol, Rehabilitation
Publications: Bibliographies; Info-biblio (monthly new books & articles of periodicals)
Partic in National Network of Libraries of Medicine
Open Mon-Fri 8-4

BEACONSFIELD

P BIBLIOTHEQUE DE BEACONSFIELD*, 303 Boulevard, H9W 4A7.
SAN 319-6313. Tel: 514-428-4460. Circulation Tel: 514-428-4470.
Reference Tel: 514-428-4473. FAX: 514-428-4477. E-mail:
bibliotheque@beaconsfield.ca. Web Site: www.beaconsfieldbiblio.ca. *Dir,*
Beverley Gilbertson; Tel: 514-428-4466, E-mail:
beverley.gilbertson@beaconsfield.ca; *Head, Pub Serv,* Cathy Maxwell; *Coll
Develop,* Nicole Tremblay; Staff 19 (MLS 3, Non-MLS 16)
Founded 1951. Pop 19,300; Circ 220,000
Library Holdings: Bk Titles 80,000; Per Subs 300
Special Collections: Foreign Language Books (German, Dutch & Spanish)
Subject Interests: Children's lit, Local hist
Automation Activity & Vendor Info: (Acquisitions) SirsiDynix;
(Cataloging) SirsiDynix; (Circulation) SirsiDynix; (OPAC) SirsiDynix;
(Serials) SirsiDynix
Database Vendor: SirsiDynix
Wireless access
Open Mon 1-9, Tues-Fri 10-9, Sat 10-5, Sun 1-5
Friends of the Library Group

BEAUPORT

P RESEAU DES BIBLIOTHEQUES DE LA VILLE DE QUEBEC,
Bibliotheque Etienne-Parent, 3515 Clemenceau, G1C 7R5. SAN 321-2955.
Tel: 418-641-6501, Ext 3545. FAX: 418-666-6173. Web Site:
www.bibliothequesdequebec.qc.ca. *Dir,* Denis Couture
Founded 1982. Pop 76,000; Circ 533,000
Library Holdings: Bk Titles 63,500; Bk Vols 80,400; Per Subs 126
Subject Interests: Local hist
Automation Activity & Vendor Info: (Acquisitions) SirsiDynix;
(Cataloging) SirsiDynix; (Circulation) SirsiDynix; (Course Reserve)
SirsiDynix; (ILL) SirsiDynix; (Media Booking) SirsiDynix; (OPAC)
SirsiDynix; (Serials) SirsiDynix
Open Mon-Fri 10-9, Sat & Sun 10-5
Friends of the Library Group

BELOEIL

P BIBLIOTHEQUE DE BELOEIL*, 620 rue Richelieu, J3G 5E8. SAN
319-6321. Tel: 450-467-7872. FAX: 450-467-3257. E-mail:
biblio@ville.beloeil.qc.ca. Web Site: www.ville.beloeil.qc.ca/bibli. *Librn,*
Johanne Guevremont
Founded 1960. Pop 19,306; Circ 100,000
Library Holdings: Bk Vols 60,000; Per Subs 125

BOIS-DES-FILION

P BOIS-DES-FILION LIBRARY*, 60, 36 ie'me Ave S, J6Z 2J6. SAN
377-0656. Tel: 450-621-2041. FAX: 450-621-8483. E-mail:
biblio@ville.bois-des-filion.qc.ca. Web Site: www.ville.bois-des-filion.qc.ca.
Librn, Marc Bineault
Library Holdings: Bk Titles 17,000; Bk Vols 20,000; Per Subs 40
Partic in Libr Asn of Can; Libr Asn of Quebec & Montreal

BOUCHERVILLE

P BIBLIOTHEQUE MONTARVILLE-BOUCHER DE LA BRUERE*, 501
Chemin Du Lac, J4B 6V6. SAN 319-633X. Tel: 450-463-7120. FAX:
450-449-6865. *Dir,* Sylvie Provost
Founded 1962. Circ 322,640
Library Holdings: Bk Vols 77,000
Subject Interests: Canadiana, Genealogy

BROSSARD

P BIBLIOTHEQUE DE BROSSARD*, 7855 San Francisco Ave, J4X 2A4.
SAN 328-3151. Tel: 450-923-6350. FAX: 450-923-7042. E-mail:
bibliotheque.brossard@ville.brossard.qc.ca. Web Site:
www.ville.brossard.qc.ca/biblio. *Dir,* Suzanne Payette; Tel: 450-923-6350,
Ext 6291; *Coll Develop, Tech Serv,* Linda Page; Tel: 450-923-6350, Ext
6278, E-mail: linda.page@ville.brossard.qc.ca; *ILL,* Diane Murphy; Tel:
450-923-6350, Ext 6286, E-mail: diane.murphy@ville.brossard.qc.ca;
Outreach Serv Librn, Ref, Martha Frey; Tel: 450-923-6350, Ext 6285,
E-mail: martha.frey@ville.brossard.qc.ca; *Pub Serv,* Brigitte Gagnon; Tel:
450-923-6350, Ext 6288, E-mail: brigitte.gagnon@ville.brossard.qc.ca;
Staff 26 (MLS 7, Non-MLS 19)
Founded 1976. Pop 66,110; Circ 422,041
Library Holdings: Bk Vols 220,000; Per Subs 478
Subject Interests: Bus, Local hist
Automation Activity & Vendor Info: (Acquisitions) Isacsoft Inc (ISF);
(Cataloging) Isacsoft Inc (ISF); (Circulation) Isacsoft Inc (ISF); (OPAC)
Isacsoft Inc (ISF); (Serials) Isacsoft Inc (ISF)
Publications: History of Brossard (Local historical information)
Open Mon & Fri 1:30-9:30, Tues & Thurs 9:30-9:30, Sat 10-5, Sun 11-5
Friends of the Library Group

CAP-CHAT

P CENTRE REGIONAL DE SERVICE AUX BIBLIOTHEQUE PUBLIQUE
DE PRET GASPESIE ISLE DE LA MADELENE*, 31 Rue des Ecoliers,
CP 430, G0J 1E0. SAN 321-2637. Tel: 418-786-5597. FAX: 418-786-2024.
Web Site: www.crsbpgim.qc.ca. *Dir,* Aurelien Bisson
Pop 84,500
Library Holdings: Bk Vols 140,000

CHARLESBOURG

P BIBLIOTHEQUE DE CHARLESBOURG*, 7950 First Ave, G1H 2Y4.
SAN 321-2769. Tel: 418-641-6287. FAX: 418-624-7886. E-mail:
bibliotheque.charlesbourg@ville.quebec.qc.ca. *In Charge,* Lina Rousseau
Pop 73,000
Library Holdings: Bk Titles 106,000

S CENTRE DE VEILLE SUR L'EFFICACITE ENERGETIQUE*, 5700, 4e
Ave Ouest, 4e Etage, Bureau B405, G1H 6R1. SAN 373-7306. Tel:
418-627-6379. Toll Free Tel: 877-727-6655. FAX: 418-643-5828. E-mail:
aee@aee.gouv.qc.ca. Web Site: www.aee.gouv.qc.ca. *Librn,* Lucette Fraser;
Tel: 418-627-6379, Ext 8030; Staff 1 (MLS 1)
Library Holdings: Bk Vols 6,000; Per Subs 100
Open Mon-Fri 8:30-12 & 1-4:30

C COLLEGE DE LIMOILOU-CAMPUS DE CHARLESBOURG*, Centre
des Medias, 7600 Third Ave E, G1H 7L4. SAN 375-3840. Tel:
418-647-6600, Ext 3611. Reference Tel: 418-647-6600, Ext 3653. Web
Site: www.climoilou.qc.ca. *Ref Serv,* Marcelle Lauzon; E-mail:
mlauzon@climoilou.qc.ca; Staff 5 (MLS 1, Non-MLS 4)
Founded 1991. Enrl 1,650; Fac 100
Library Holdings: Bk Titles 28,000; Bk Vols 30,000; Per Subs 120
Automation Activity & Vendor Info: (Acquisitions) SirsiDynix;
(Cataloging) SirsiDynix; (Circulation) SirsiDynix
Database Vendor: EBSCOhost
Function: Res libr
Partic in RESDOC
Open Mon-Thurs 7:45-6, Fri 7:45-5

CHARNY

P CENTRE REGIONAL DE SERVICES AUX BIBLIOTHEQUES
PUBLIQUES DE LA CAPITALE-NATIONALE ET DE LA
CHAUDIERE-APPALACHES INC*, Réseau BIBLIO CNCA, 3189 rue
Albert-Demers, G6X 3A1. SAN 321-1738. Tel: 418-832-6166. Toll Free
Tel: 866 446-6166. FAX: 418-832-6168. E-mail:
info@reseaubibliocnca.qc.ca. Web Site: www.reseaubibliocnca.qc.ca. *Dir,*
Lucie Gobeil; Staff 16 (MLS 3, Non-MLS 13)
Founded 1977. Pop 218,713
Library Holdings: Bk Titles 171,437; Bk Vols 617,678
Automation Activity & Vendor Info: (Acquisitions) SirsiDynix;
(Cataloging) SirsiDynix; (Circulation) SirsiDynix; (OPAC) SirsiDynix;
(Serials) SirsiDynix
Database Vendor: SirsiDynix
Publications: Annual Report; Guides; Le Passeur (Bulletin)

CHATEAUGUAY

P CHATEAUGUAY MUNICIPAL LIBRARY*, 25 Maple Blvd, J6J 3P7.
SAN 319-6372. Tel: 450-698-3085. FAX: 450-698-3109. *Dir,* Celine
Lussier; *Librn,* Marcotta Veronique; *Acq,* Michel St-Onge; *Cat,* Jocelyne
Brunet; *Pub Serv,* Joelle Desmarchait; *Pub Serv,* Christian Tautchier; *Tech
Serv,* Monique Larouche; *Tech Serv,* Marie-France Martel; Staff 1 (MLS 1)
Founded 1968. Pop 38,200; Circ 190,000
Library Holdings: Bks on Deafness & Sign Lang 86,000; Bk Vols
106,000; Per Subs 215
Open Mon Noon-9, Tues-Fri 9-9, Sat 10-5, Sun 12-5

CHICOUTIMI

P BIBLIOTHEQUE PUBLIQUE DE CHICOUTIMI*, 155, rue Racine Est,
G7H 1R5. SAN 319-6399. Tel: 418-698-3000, Ext 4181, 418-698-5350.
Reference Tel: 418-698-5350, Ext 4184. Administration Tel: 418-698-3000,
Ext 4179. FAX: 418-698-5359. Web Site: www.ville.saguenay.qc.ca/biblio.
Admin Dir, Chief Librn, Claude Dumais; Tel: 418-698-3000, Ext 4179,
E-mail: claude.dumais@ville.saguenay.qc.ca; *Acq & Develop, Asst Dir,
Commun Outreach,* France Léger; Tel: 418-698-3000, Ext 4180, E-mail:
france.leger@ville.saguenay.qc.ca; *Asst Dir, Human Res & Phys Plant,*
Carole Brassard; Tel: 418-698-3000, Ext 4177, E-mail:
carole.brassard@ville.saguenay.qc.ca; Staff 29 (MLS 2, Non-MLS 27)
Founded 1950. Pop 65,000
Library Holdings: AV Mats 11,128; CDs 4,512; DVDs 947; Bk Vols
153,627; Per Subs 275; Talking Bks 450; Videos 5,669
Special Collections: Youth Coll. Can & Prov
Automation Activity & Vendor Info: (Cataloging) SIRSI Unicorn;
(Circulation) SIRSI WorkFlows; (Serials) EBSCO Online

Database Vendor: CEDROM-SNi, Repere
Function: Art exhibits, Children's prog, Computer training, Computers for patron use, Copy machines, Electronic databases & coll, Fax serv, Free DVD rentals, Handicapped accessible, Mail & tel request accepted, Music CDs, Newsp ref libr, Online cat, Online searches, Spoken cassettes & CDs, Story hour, Summer reading prog, Telephone ref, Web-catalog, Wheelchair accessible
Open Mon-Fri (Winter) 12:30-8, Sat 10-5, Sun 12-5; Mon-Thurs (Summer) 12:30-8, Fri 12:30-5, Sat 1-5

J CEGEP DE CHICOUTIMI*, Centre des Medias, 534 Jacques-Cartier, Est, G7H 1Z6. SAN 319-6402. Tel: 418-549-9520, Ext 337. Circulation Tel: 418-549-9520, Ext 333. Reference Tel: 418-549-9520, Ext 345. Automation Services Tel: 418-549-9520, Ext 364. FAX: 418-549-1315. Web Site: www.cegep-chicoutimi.qc.ca/cdm/index.htm. *Coordr,* Gilles Cusson; *Acq,* Clothilde Brillant; *Per,* Johanne Gauthier; *Ref,* Louis Gaudreau; Staff 2 (MLS 2)
Founded 1967. Enrl 2,600; Fac 275
Library Holdings: Bk Titles 62,000; Bk Vols 70,000; Per Subs 225
Subject Interests: Archit, Art, Computers, Flight training, Hist, Med
Partic in Regard

P CENTRE D'ARCHIVES DU SAGUENAY-LAC-SAINT-JEAN*, 930 rue Jacques Cartier E Bureau C-103, G7H 7K9. SAN 319-6240. Tel: 418-698-3516. FAX: 418-698-3758. E-mail: archives.saguenay@banq.qc.ca. Web Site: www.banq.qc.ca. *Librn,* Audrey Bouchard
Pop 26,322; Circ 311,354
Library Holdings: Bk Vols 2,000,000
Open Mon-Fri 8:30-12 & 1-4:30

M COMPLEXE HOSPITALIER DE LA SAGAMIE*, 305 Ave Saint Vallier, CP 5006, G7H 5H6. SAN 325-7916. Tel: 418-541-1000, 418-541-1234, Ext 2496. FAX: 418-541-1145. *In Charge,* Marcelle Frigon; E-mail: marcelle.frigon@chs02.qc.ca
Library Holdings: Bk Vols 3,000

SR SEMINAIRE DE CHICOUTIMI BIBLIOTHEQUE*, 679 rue Chabanel, G7H 1Z7. SAN 325-7894. Tel: 418-693-8448. FAX: 418-693-8449. *Dir,* Marcel Bergeron

C UNIVERSITE DU QUEBEC A CHICOUTIMI BIBLIOTHEQUE*, 555 Blvd de l'Universite E, G7H 2B1. SAN 319-6437. Tel: 418-545-5011, Ext 5631. FAX: 418-693-5896. *Dir,* Johanne Belley; Staff 43 (MLS 13, Non-MLS 30)
Founded 1969. Enrl 4,132; Fac 199; Highest Degree: Doctorate
Library Holdings: Bk Vols 238,000; Per Subs 4,200
Special Collections: Canadiana
Partic in Dialog Corp; SDC Info Servs

COATICOOK

P BIBLIOTHEQUE DE COATICOOK, INC*, 34 rue Main Est, J1A 1N2. SAN 319-6445. Tel: 819-849-4013. FAX: 819-849-0479. E-mail: biblcoat@bibliotheque.coaticook.qc.ca. Web Site: www.bibliotheque.coaticook.qc.ca. *Dir,* Patrick Falardeau
Founded 1958. Pop 9,800; Circ 44,384
Library Holdings: Bk Vols 28,892; Per Subs 84
Open Tues-Thurs 1:30-5:30, Fri 1:30-9, Sat 9-12, Sun 12-3

COTE SAINT-LUC

P ELEANOR LONDON COTE SAINT LUC PUBLIC LIBRARY*, Cote Saint-Luc Public Library, 5851 Blvd Cavendish, H4W 2X8. SAN 319-6453. Tel: 514-485-6900. FAX: 514-485-6966. Web Site: www.elcslpl.org/. *Dir, Libr Serv,* Jannie West
Founded 1966. Pop 31,739; Circ 575,442
Library Holdings: Bk Vols 187,028
Wireless access
Open Mon-Sun 10-10

DE SOREL TRACY

P BIBLIOTHEQUE DE SOREL TRACY*, 3015, up Leisure, Recreation, J3P 7K1. (Mail add: PO Box 368, Sorel-Tracy, J3R 1C2), SAN 370-6788. Tel: 450-742-8321. FAX: 450-764-8894. E-mail: bibliotheque@ville.sorel-tracy.qc.ca. *Librn,* Alain Larouche; E-mail: alain.larouche@ville.sorel-tracy.qc.ca; Staff 1 (MLS 1)
Founded 1987. Pop 12,900
Library Holdings: Bk Titles 106,000; Per Subs 86
Special Collections: State Document Depository
Open Mon & Tues 10-12 & 1:30-5, Wed-Fri 10-12 & 1:30-8, Sat 9-12 & 1-5, Sun 1-5

DOLLARD-DES-ORMEAUX

P BIBLIOTHEQUE DE DOLLARD-DES-ORMEAUX, 12001 Blvd de Salaberry, H9B 2A7. Tel: 514-684-1496. FAX: 514-684-9569. E-mail: bibliotheque@ddo.qc.ca. Web Site: www.ville.ddo.qc.ca. *Div Mgr, Libr & Culture,* Lise Brosseau; Tel: 514-684-1012, Ext 402, E-mail: lbrosseau@ddo.qc.ca; Staff 6 (MLS 5, Non-MLS 1)
Founded 1992. Pop 50,154; Circ 311,837
Jan 2011-Dec 2011 Income (CAN) \$2,506,552, Provincial (CAN) \$117,500, City (CAN) \$2,331,106, Locally Generated Income (CAN) \$57,946. Mats Exp (CAN) \$243,728, Books (CAN) \$171,892, Per/Ser (Incl. Access Fees) (CAN) \$27,186, AV Mat (CAN) \$16,870, Electronic Ref Mat (Incl. Access Fees) (CAN) \$27,780. Sal (CAN) \$1,654,858
Library Holdings: Audiobooks 2,107; CDs 3,256; DVDs 2,942; e-books 629; e-journals 20; Electronic Media & Resources 381; Bk Vols 149,618; Per Subs 273
Automation Activity & Vendor Info: (Acquisitions) Infor Library & Information Solutions; (Cataloging) Infor Library & Information Solutions; (Circulation) Infor Library & Information Solutions; (ILL) OCLC; (OPAC) Infor Library & Information Solutions; (Serials) Infor Library & Information Solutions
Database Vendor: Infor Library & Information Solutions
Wireless access
Function: Adult bk club, Adult literacy prog, Audiobks via web, Bk club(s), Bk reviews (Group), Bks on CD, CD-ROM, Chess club, Children's prog, Citizenship assistance, Computer training, Computers for patron use, Copy machines, Digital talking bks, Doc delivery serv, e-mail serv, E-Reserves, Electronic databases & coll, Free DVD rentals, Handicapped accessible, Homebound delivery serv, Homework prog, ILL available, Large print keyboards, Literacy & newcomer serv, Magnifiers for reading, Mail & tel request accepted, Music CDs, Online cat, Orientations, Outreach serv, Outside serv via phone, mail, e-mail & web, OverDrive digital audio bks, Photocopying/Printing, Prog for adults, Prog for children & young adult, Pub access computers, Ref & res, Ref serv available, Ref serv in person, Res libr, Story hour, Summer reading prog, Teen prog, Telephone ref, Wheelchair accessible, Workshops, Writing prog
Special Services for the Blind - Bks on CD; Large print bks; Magnifiers
Open Mon-Fri 10-9, Sat & Sun 9-5

DORVAL

P BIBLIOTHEQUE DE DORVAL*, Dorval Library, 1401 Chemin du Bord du Lac, H9S 2E5. SAN 369-1683. Tel: 514-633-4170. FAX: 514-633-4177. E-mail: biblio@ville.dorval.qc.ca. *Supvr,* Linda Burdayron; E-mail: lburdayron@ville.dorval.qc.ca
Founded 1967. Pop 17,715; Circ 243,389
Library Holdings: Bk Vols 68,320
Subject Interests: Aviation, Local hist
Open Mon-Thurs 10-9, Fri-Sun (Winter) 10-5

G CENTRE DE REFERENCE TECHNIQUE*, Technical Reference Centre, 700 Leigh Capreol St, NAI-CRT, Rm 0135, H4Y 1G7. SAN 374-499X. Tel: 514-633-3589. FAX: 514-420-5801. E-mail: trc-qbc@tc.gc.ca. *Head, Info Serv,* Jacques Bisson; E-mail: bissonj@tc.gc.ca. Subject Specialists: *Aircraft,* Jacques Bisson; Staff 2 (Non-MLS 2)
Founded 1956
Library Holdings: Bk Titles 4,000; Per Subs 12
Subject Interests: Aircraft maintenance, Aviation
Function: Govt ref serv
Restriction: Staff use only

S NOVARTIS PHARMACEUTICALS CANADA, INC*, Documentation Services, 385 Bouchard Blvd, H9F 1A9. SAN 326-1387. Tel: 514-631-6775, Ext 3302. Interlibrary Loan Service Tel: 514-633-7880, Ext 7551. FAX: 514-631-8851. Web Site: www.novartis.ca. *Info Spec,* Wendy Blue; Staff 1 (MLS 1)
Library Holdings: Bk Titles 3,000; Per Subs 80
Subject Interests: Endocrinology, Immunology, Neurology
Automation Activity & Vendor Info: (Acquisitions) Ex Libris Group; (Cataloging) Ex Libris Group; (Circulation) Ex Libris Group; (OPAC) Ex Libris Group; (Serials) Ex Libris Group
Database Vendor: Dialog, OVID Technologies
Open Mon-Fri 8-4:30
Restriction: Staff use only

DRUMMONDVILLE

P BIBLIOTHEQUE MUNICIPALE COME-SAINT-GERMAIN*, 545 rue des Ecoles, J2B 1J6. SAN 319-647X. Tel: 819-474-8841, 819-478-6573. Circulation Tel: 819-478-6590. FAX: 819-478-0399. E-mail: biblio@ville.drummondville.qc.ca. Web Site: www.ville.drummondville.qc.ca. *Dir,* Joceline-Andree Turcotte; Tel: 819-478-6588; *Librn,* Michel LeBlanc; E-mail: mleblanc@ville.drummondville.qc.ca
Founded 1949. Circ 238,818

Library Holdings: Bk Vols 105,000; Per Subs 430
Special Collections: Can & Prov Doc Dep
Subject Interests: Agr, Area, Drummondville, Genealogy, Quebec lit
Publications: Archives on Video; Feuillet d'information; listes
bibliographiques; Recquil de gestion (non public); seasonal leaflets
Open Tues 11-5, Wed 12:30-8, Thurs & Fri 1:30-8, Sat & Sun 10-4

EAST BROUGHTON

P BIBLIOTHEQUE MUNICIPALE*, 372A Ave Du College, G0N 1G0. SAN
   321-3226. Tel: 418-427-3408, 418-427-4900. FAX: 418-427-3478,
   418-427-3514. *Dir,* Roger Lessard
   Library Holdings: Bk Vols 34,000; Per Subs 20
   Open Mon-Fri 8-6

FARNHAM

P BIBLIOTHEQUE DE FARNHAM, INC*, 479 rue Hotel de Ville, J2N
   2H3. SAN 319-6488. Tel: 450-293-3375. FAX: 450-293-2989. E-mail:
   bibliofarnham@bellnet.ca. Web Site: bibliofarnham.ca. *Dir,* Patrick
   Falardeau
   Founded 1957. Pop 7,000; Circ 36,000
   Library Holdings: Bk Vols 32,000
   Subject Interests: Applied sci, Computers, Countries, Political problems,
   Pure
   Publications: Special Thematic
   Open Tues 1-6, Wed & Fri 6-8, Thurs 1-8, Sat 9-12

FERMONT

P BIBLIOTHEQUE PUBLIQUE DE FERMONT*, 130 Le Carrefour CP 10,
   G0G 1J0. SAN 372-7300. Tel: 418-287-3227. FAX: 418-287-3274. Web
   Site: www.crrstv.net/~bibliof. *Head Librn,* Aline Martel; *Asst Librn,*
   Mireille Lavoie; Staff 1 (MLS 1)
   Founded 1979. Pop 3,400
   Library Holdings: Bk Titles 20,000; Bk Vols 22,000; Per Subs 27

GASPE

M CENTRE HOSPITALIER DE GASPE*, Bibliotheque Medicale, 215 York
   Blvd W, G4X 2W2. SAN 327-8492. Tel: 418-368-3301. FAX:
   418-368-6850. Web Site: www.chgaspe.qc.ca. *Librn,* Michel Desjardins
   Library Holdings: Bk Vols 750; Per Subs 85
   Open Mon-Fri 8-4

G GOVERNMENT OF QUEBEC - AGRICULTURE FISHERIES &
   FOODS*, Centre de Documentation des Peches et de l'Agriculture, 96
   Montee de Sandy-Beach, No 205, G4X 2V6. SAN 373-7977. Tel:
   418-368-7615. FAX: 418-360-8211. *Acq, Doc, Ref,* Paul Carrier; *Circ, Per,*
   Gislain Chapedos; Staff 3 (MLS 1, Non-MLS 2)
   Founded 1946
   Library Holdings: Bk Titles 12,000; Per Subs 100
   Special Collections: Agriculture, bks, serials; Fisheries, bks, serials

GATINEAU

P BIBLIOTHEQUE MUNICIPALE DE GATINEAU*, 144, boul de l'Hôpital,
   local 317, J8T 7S7. (Mail add: CP 1970, succ Hull, J8X 3Y9), SAN
   319-650X. Tel: 819-243-2345, Ext 2548. Toll Free Tel: 866-299-2002.
   FAX: 819-243-2399. TDD: 819-243-2345, Ext 2513. E-mail:
   biblio@gatineau.ca. Web Site: www.ville.gatineau.qc.ca/bibliotheque. *Chief
   Librn,* Carole Laguë; E-mail: lague.carole@gatineau.ca; *Ch,* Andrée Côté;
   Tel: 819-243-2345, Ext 7462. E-mail: cote.andree@gatineau.ca; *Outreach
   Librn,* Position Currently Open; *Pub Relations Librn,* André-Yves
   Duchesne; Tel: 819-595-7464, Fax: 819-595-7479, E-mail:
   duchesne.andre-yves@gatineau.ca; *Pub Serv Librn,* Position Currently
   Open; *Ref Serv Librn,* Martine Plouffe; Tel: 819-243-2345, Ext 2513, Fax:
   819-243-2569, E-mail: plouffe.martine@gatineau.ca; *Res Librn,* Ingrid
   Moisil; Tel: 819-243-2345, Ext 2567, Fax: 819-243-2306, E-mail:
   moisil.ingrid@gatineau.ca; *Tech Serv Librn,* Francois Gagnon; Tel:
   819-243-2345, Ext 2510, E-mail:
   gagon.francois@gatineau.ca; *Adult Serv,* Guy Dubois; Tel: 819-243-2345,
   Ext 7461, Fax: 819-595-7487, E-mail: dubois.guy@gatineau.ca; Staff 36
   (MLS 10, Non-MLS 26)
   Founded 1937. Pop 245,629; Circ 1,453,681
   Jan 2006-Dec 2006 Income (CAN) $7,194,504, Provincial (CAN)
   $656,800, City (CAN) $6,113,873, Locally Generated Income (CAN)
   $380,601, Other (CAN) $43,230. Mats Exp (CAN) $1,377,838, Books
   (CAN) $964,364, Per/Ser (Incl. Access Fees) (CAN) $58,714, AV Mat
   (CAN) $102,438, Electronic Ref Mat (Incl. Access Fees) (CAN) $18,954,
   Presv (CAN) $233,368. Sal (CAN) $3,487,560
   Library Holdings: CDs 12,795; DVDs 1,898; Electronic Media &
   Resources 496; Large Print Bks 4,809; Bk Titles 22,900; Bk Vols 577,621;
   Per Subs 935; Talking Bks 1,580; Videos 15,778
   Special Collections: Municipal Document Depository; State Document
   Depository

Automation Activity & Vendor Info: (Acquisitions) Horizon;
(Cataloging) Horizon; (Circulation) Horizon; (OPAC) SirsiDynix; (Serials)
Horizon
Database Vendor: CEDROM-SNi, EBSCO Information Services, ProQuest
Publications: Guide de l'usager / Users' Guide (Library handbook)
Partic in Consortium d'acquisition de ressources electroniques du Quebec
(CAREQ)
Open Mon-Thurs 10-9, Fri 10-6, Sat & Sun 11-5

P BIBLIOTHEQUE MUNICIPALE DE GATINEAU*, Édifice Pierre Papin,
   CP 1970 Succ. Hull, J8X 3Y9. SAN 325-2434. Circulation Tel: 819
   986-5293. Reference Tel: 819 243-2345, Ext 2513. Administration Tel:
   819-243-2345, Ext 2548. Circulation FAX: 819 986-4206. Reference FAX:
   819 243-2569. Web Site: www.ville.gatineau.qc.ca/bibliotheque. *Head
   Librn,* Carole Lague; E-mail: lague.carole@gatineau.ca; *Ad,* Guy Dubois;
   Outreach Librn, Kayleigh Felice; *Pub Serv Mgr,* Louise Beaulieu-Couture;
   Mgr, Ch Serv, Nancy Bilodeau; *Ref Serv Mgr,* Martine Plouffe; E-mail:
   plouffe.martine@gatineau.gc.ca; *Pub Serv Mgr,* Claudine Patry; *Res Mgr,*
   Noëlle Gratton-Tétreault; *Mgr, Tech Serv,* François Gagnon; *Mgr, User
   Serv,* André-Yves Duchesne
   Founded 1938. Pop 254,549; Circ 1,624,003
   Jan 2009-Dec 2009 Income (CAN) $7,695,426, Provincial (CAN)
   $682,800, City (CAN) $6,490,264, Locally Generated Income (CAN)
   $519,562, Other (CAN) $2,800. Mats Exp (CAN) $1,117,218, Books
   (CAN) $910,271, Per/Ser (Incl. Access Fees) (CAN) $68,506, Micro
   (CAN) $2,747, AV Mat (CAN) $85,654, Electronic Ref Mat (Incl. Access
   Fees) (CAN) $50,040. Sal (CAN) $3,583,992 (Prof (CAN) $632,941)
   Library Holdings: Audiobooks 1,220; AV Mats 32,566; CDs 15,606;
   DVDs 10,838; Electronic Media & Resources 7; Large Print Bks 3,728;
   Microforms 2,828; Bk Titles 234,190; Bk Vols 569,405; Per Subs 367;
   Videos 6,122
   Special Collections: Canadiana (on Gatineau) genealogy
   Subject Interests: Local hist
   Automation Activity & Vendor Info: (Acquisitions) SirsiDynix;
   (Cataloging) SirsiDynix; (Circulation) SirsiDynix; (OPAC) SirsiDynix;
   (Serials) SirsiDynix
   Publications: Annual Report
   Open Mon & Thurs 10-9, Fri 10-6, Sat & Sun 11-5
   Friends of the Library Group
   Branches: 2
   SUCCURSALE AURELIEN-DOUCET, 207 Mont-Bleu, Hull, J8Z 3G3,
     SAN 370-1107. Tel: 819-595-7490. FAX: 819-595-7376.
     Library Holdings: Bk Titles 15,000; Bk Vols 27,000
     Open Mon & Thurs 12-9, Fri 12-6, Sat 11-5
     Friends of the Library Group
   SUCCURSALE LUCIEN-LALONDE, 225 Berri, Hull, J8Y 4K1, SAN
     369-1772. Tel: 819-595-7480. FAX: 819-595-7479.
     Library Holdings: Bk Titles 28,500; Bk Vols 47,000
     Open Mon & Thurs 12-9, Fri 12-6, Sat 11-5, Sun 12-5

G CANADA DEPARTMENT OF ABORIGINAL AFFAIRS & NORTHERN
   DEVELOPMENT, Departmental Library, Ten Wellington St, Rm 1400,
   14th Flr, K1A 0H4. SAN 319-2989. Tel: 819-997-0811. Interlibrary Loan
   Service Tel: 819-994-1347. FAX: 819-953-5491. E-mail:
   reference@aadnc-aandc.gc.ca. Web Site: www.aadnc-aandc.gc.ca/library.
   Staff 12 (MLS 8, Non-MLS 4)
   Founded 1966
   Library Holdings: e-books 5,000; e-journals 10,000; Bk Vols 60,000; Per
   Subs 900
   Subject Interests: Aboriginal people, Artic Can
   Automation Activity & Vendor Info: (Cataloging) VTLS, Inc;
   (Circulation) VTLS, Inc; (OPAC) VTLS, Inc; (Serials) VTLS, Inc
   Function: ILL available
   Publications: Acquisitions List; Various Subject Bibliographies

G CANADA SCHOOL OF PUBLIC SERVICE LIBRARY*, 241 Cité des
   jeunes Blvd, K1N 6Z2. SAN 328-1671. Tel: 819-953-5295. Interlibrary
   Loan Service Tel: 819-953-5613. FAX: 819-953-1702. E-mail:
   bibliast@csps-efpc.gc.ca. *Officer,* Darlene Nadeau; E-mail:
   darlene.nadeau@csps-efpc.gc.ca; *ILL,* France Viau; E-mail:
   france.viaux@csps-efpc.gc.ca; Staff 6 (MLS 4, Non-MLS 2)
   Founded 1991
   Library Holdings: DVDs 1,300; Bk Titles 10,000; Per Subs 120; Videos
   50
   Special Collections: Collection on Diversity
   Subject Interests: Leadership, Mgt, Pub admin, Training lang
   Partic in Council of Federal Libraries Consortium
   Open Mon-Fri 8-4

G CANADIAN INTERNATIONAL DEVELOPMENT AGENCY*,
   International Development Information Centre, 200 Promenade du Portage,
   8th Flr, K1A 0G4. SAN 319-6534. Tel: 819-953-1035. FAX:
   819-953-8132. E-mail: cidi.idic@acdi-cida.gc.ca. *Dir,* Marc Lepage;
   E-mail: marc.lepage@acdi-cida.gc.ca

Founded 1965
Library Holdings: Bk Vols 22,000; Per Subs 1,400
Special Collections: International Development
Subject Interests: Intl aid & developing countries

S   CANADIAN MUSEUM OF CIVILIZATION LIBRARY*, 100 Laurier St,
K1A 0M8. SAN 328-784X. Tel: 819-776-7173. Interlibrary Loan Service
Tel: 819-776-7174. FAX: 819-776-7152. E-mail: library@civilization.ca.
Web Site: geoweb.civilization.ca:8001. *Head of Libr,* Brigitte LaFond; Tel:
819-776-7151, E-mail: brigitte.lafond@civilization.ca; *Ref Serv,* Sylvia
Mauro; Tel: 819-776-8479, E-mail: sylvia.mauro@civilization.ca; Staff 3
(MLS 3)
Founded 1854
Library Holdings: AV Mats 1,000; CDs 100; e-books 1,000; Bk Titles
61,000; Bk Vols 76,000; Per Subs 2,400
Special Collections: Indians of North America Coll. Can & Prov
Subject Interests: Archaeology, Ethnology, Folklore, Hist, Mus studies
Automation Activity & Vendor Info: (Acquisitions) Infor Library &
Information Solutions; (Cataloging) Infor Library & Information Solutions;
(Circulation) Infor Library & Information Solutions; (OPAC) Infor Library
& Information Solutions; (Serials) Infor Library & Information Solutions
Function: Audio & video playback equip for onsite use, Doc delivery serv,
For res purposes, Homebound delivery serv, ILL available, Online searches,
Outside serv via phone, mail, e-mail & web, Photocopying/Printing, Ref
serv available, Res libr, Telephone ref
Publications: Bibliography Series
Partic in Canadian Fed Librs
Special Services for the Deaf - TDD equip
Open Mon-Fri (May-Sept) 9-5; Tues-Fri (Oct-April) 9-5
Restriction: Open to pub for ref only, Pub use on premises, Restricted
borrowing privileges

S   CANADIAN TRANSPORTATION AGENCY LIBRARY*, 15 Eddy St,
K1A 0N9. SAN 319-3233. Tel: 819-997-7160. FAX: 819-953-9815.
E-mail: cta.library@cta-otc.gc.ca. *Mgr,* Alison Hale; Tel: 819-953-0482;
Staff 1 (MLS 1)
Founded 1968
Library Holdings: Bk Titles 23,000; Per Subs 250
Subject Interests: Econ, Transportation law
Function: Govt ref serv
Publications: Accessions List

M   CENTRE HOSPITALIER DES VALLEES DE L'OUTAOUAIS
BIBLIOTHEQUE*, Hospital de Hull, 116, Blvd Lionel-Emond, J8Y 1W7.
SAN 319-6542. Tel: 819-595-6050. FAX: 819-595-6098. E-mail:
dianne_couture@ssss.gouv.qc.ca.
Founded 1961
Library Holdings: Bk Vols 800; Per Subs 130
Automation Activity & Vendor Info: (Acquisitions) Inmagic, Inc.;
(Circulation) Inmagic, Inc.; (ILL) Inmagic, Inc.; (Serials) Inmagic, Inc.
Database Vendor: OVID Technologies
Function: Prof lending libr
Restriction: Mem only
Friends of the Library Group

M   CSSS DE GATINEAU - HOPITAL PIERRE-JANET, Centre de
Documentation, 20, rue Pharand, J9A 1K7. SAN 325-2094. Tel:
819-771-7761, Ext 8380. FAX: 819-771-1506. Web Site:
www.chpj.ca/biblio. *Librn,* Mahalya Havard; E-mail:
mahalya_havard@ssss.gouv.qc.ca; Staff 2 (MLS 1, Non-MLS 1)
Subject Interests: Psychiat, Psychol
Wireless access
Restriction: Staff use only

G   DEPARTMENT OF CANADIAN HERITAGE*, Knowledge Centre, 15
Eddy St, 2nd Flr, K1A 0M5. SAN 319-6550. Tel: 819-953-0527.
Interlibrary Loan Service Tel: 819-997-5467. Reference Tel: 819-953-7738.
FAX: 819-953-7988. E-mail: pch_library@pch.gc.ca. *Mgr, Libr Serv,* Eric
Wees; Tel: 819-994-5724, E-mail: eric_wees@pch.gc.ca; *Head, Cat, Syst
Adminr,* Jacques Brodeur; Tel: 819-994-5915, E-mail:
jacques_brodeur@pch.gc.ca; *Head, Ref,* Michelle Ryan; E-mail:
michelle_ryan@pch.gc.ca; Staff 11 (MLS 2, Non-MLS 9)
Founded 1993
Apr 2006-Mar 2007. Mats Exp (CAN) $214,000, Books (CAN) $25,000,
Per/Ser (Incl. Access Fees) (CAN) $40,000, Micro (CAN) $7,000,
Electronic Ref Mat (Incl. Access Fees) (CAN) $142,000
Library Holdings: CDs 125; DVDs 215; e-books 750; e-journals 40;
Electronic Media & Resources 40; Bk Vols 59,000; Per Subs 300; Videos
460
Special Collections: Can & Prov
Subject Interests: Amateur sport, Art & archit, Can cultural content, Can
hist, Cultural industries, Historic sites, Human rights, Multiculturalism, Nat
parks, Official langs, Shared citizenship, Soc cohesion

Automation Activity & Vendor Info: (Cataloging) Infor Library &
Information Solutions; (Circulation) Infor Library & Information Solutions;
(ILL) Relais International; (OPAC) Infor Library & Information Solutions;
(Serials) Infor Library & Information Solutions
Database Vendor: Cambridge Scientific Abstracts, Dialog, EBSCOhost,
Factiva.com, Infomart, LexisNexis, netLibrary, OCLC FirstSearch, OCLC
WorldCat, OVID Technologies, ProQuest
Function: Doc delivery serv, For res purposes, Govt ref serv, Handicapped
accessible, ILL available, Photocopying/Printing, Ref serv available, Res
libr, Wheelchair accessible
Partic in Council of Federal Libraries Consortium
Special Services for the Deaf - Assistive tech; Bks on deafness & sign
lang; Staff with knowledge of sign lang; TDD equip
Special Services for the Blind - Assistive/Adapted tech devices, equip &
products; Braille equip; Dragon Naturally Speaking software
Restriction: Co libr, In-house use for visitors, Open to pub for ref only,
Open to students, Pub use on premises

G   ENVIRONMENT CANADA*, Departmental Library, Place Vincent
Massey, 2nd Flr, 351 Saint Joseph Blvd, K1A 0H3. SAN 324-3397.
Circulation Tel: 819-997-2580. Interlibrary Loan Service Tel:
819-953-1374. Reference Tel: 819-997-1767. FAX: 819-997-5349. Web
Site: www.ec.gc.ca/library. *Actg Chief Librn,* J McIntosh; Tel:
819-953-1373; Staff 9 (MLS 4, Non-MLS 5)
Founded 1971
Library Holdings: e-journals 95; Bk Titles 65,000
Subject Interests: Biodiversity, Climatology, Environ chem, Environ
impact analysis, Environment, Global warming, Meteorology, Pollution,
Pollution prevention, Sustainable develop, Water res
Automation Activity & Vendor Info: (Acquisitions) SirsiDynix;
(Cataloging) SirsiDynix; (Circulation) SirsiDynix; (OPAC) SirsiDynix;
(Serials) SirsiDynix
Database Vendor: SirsiDynix
Partic in Council of Federal Libraries Consortium
Open Mon-Fri 8:30-4:30
Restriction: Open to pub for ref only

G   INDUSTRY CANADA*, Canadian Intellectual Property Office Resource
Centre, 50 Victoria St, C229, Place du Portage Phase I, K1A 0C9. SAN
325-5891. Tel: 819-953-1886. FAX: 819-997-5585. E-mail:
cro-crc@ic.gc.ca. *Mgr,* Rita Bolar; E-mail: rita.bolar@ic.gc.ca; Staff 7
(MLS 2, Non-MLS 5)
Special Collections: Annual Reports from Patent Offices Worldwide
Subject Interests: Intellectual property, Sci, Tech
Automation Activity & Vendor Info: (Acquisitions) Infor Library &
Information Solutions; (Cataloging) Infor Library & Information Solutions;
(Circulation) Infor Library & Information Solutions; (ILL)
Fretwell-Downing; (OPAC) Infor Library & Information Solutions;
(Serials) Infor Library & Information Solutions
Function: ILL available, Ref serv available
Partic in Council of Federal Libraries Consortium

G   LIBRARY & ARCHIVES CANADA*, Bibliothèque et Archives Canada,
550 De la Cité Blvd, K1A 0N4. SAN 319-3403. Tel: 613-992-6969 (TTY),
613-996-5115. Interlibrary Loan Service Tel: 613-996-7527. FAX:
613-995-6274. Interlibrary Loan Service FAX: 613-996-4424. E-mail:
reference@bac-lac.gc.ca. Web Site: www.collectionscanada.gc.ca. *Dep
Head & Librn & Archivist of Can,* Daniel J Caron, PhD; Tel:
819-934-5800, Fax: 819-934-5888, E-mail: danielj.caron@bac-lac.gc.ca;
Secy Gen & Dir Gen, Communications Bur, Fabien Lengellé; Tel:
819-934-5717, Fax: 819-934-5839, E-mail: fabien.lengelle@bac-lac.gc.ca;
Sr Dir Gen, Corporate Resourcing Br & CFO, Mark C Melanson; Tel:
819-934-4627, Fax: 819-934-5262, E-mail: mark.melanson@bac-lac.gc.ca;
Actg Dir General, Strategic Res, Richard RG Brown; Tel: 819-934-5808,
Fax: 819-934-7539, E-mail: richard.brown@bac-lac.gc.ca; *Asst Dep
Minister, Acq Sector,* Jean-Stéphen Piché; Tel: 819-934-5790, Fax:
819-934-4422, E-mail: jean-stephen.piche@bac-lac.gc.ca; *Asst Dep
Minister, Coll Mgt Sector,* Doug Rimmer; Tel: 819-934-4618, Fax:
819-934-5262, E-mail: doug.rimmer@bac-lac.gc.ca; *Asst Dep Minister, Res
Discovery Sector,* Cecilia Muir; Tel: 613-992-7059, Fax: 613-992-5315,
E-mail: cecilia.muir@bac-lac.gc.ca; *Actg Chief, Audit & Evaluation Exec,*
Sandra Lopes; Tel: 613-897-8719, Fax: 819-934-7539, E-mail:
sandra.lopes@bac-lac.gc.ca
Founded 2004
Special Collections: Canadian Materials, documentary art, educ kits, govt
publs & doc, monographs, ms, newsp, per, philately, sound rec; Children's
Literature Coll; Multimedia & Special Colls; Rare Book Coll; Rare
Hebraic & Judaic Coll; Reference & Geneology Service. Can & Prov
Subject Interests: Can documentary heritage, Canadiana, Libr & archival
sci
Wireless access
Function: ILL available
Restriction: Open to pub for ref & circ; with some limitations
Friends of the Library Group

S   SOCIETE DE GENEALOGIE DE L'OUTAOUAIS BIBLIOTHEQUE*, 855, boul de la Gappe, J8T 8H9. SAN 373-8051. Tel: 819-568-8798, 819-643-0888. FAX: 819-568-5933. E-mail: sgo@genealogieoutaouais.com. Web Site: www.genealogieoutaouais.com/. *Adminr,* Suzane Career; Tel: 819-686-0291, E-mail: suzane@videotron.ca; *Res,* Serge Coutu
Founded 1978
Library Holdings: Bk Titles 1,600; Bk Vols 1,800
Special Collections: Parish Registers on microfilm
Subject Interests: Genealogy
Publications: L'Outaouais Genealogique (4 times/yr) (Newsletter)

S   TRANSLATION BUREAU DOCUMENTATION CENTRE*, 70 Crémazie St, 8th Flr, K1A 0S5. Tel: 819-997-0858. FAX: 819-994-3735. E-mail: ncrtra.documentation@tpsgc-pwgsc.gc.ca. *Chief, Documentation Serv,* Claire Bourassa; E-mail: claire.bourassa@tpsgc-pwgsc.gc.ca

G   TRANSPORTATION SAFETY BOARD OF CANADA LIBRARY, Place du Centre, 200 Promenade du Portage, 4th Flr, K1A 1K8. SAN 371-6090. FAX: 819-997-2239. E-mail: bibliotheque/library@bst-tsb.gc.ca, library@tsb.gc.ca. *Librn,* Rosemary Richards; Tel: 819-994-8020, E-mail: rosemary.richards@bst-tsb.gc.ca; *Tech Serv,* Rita Pascolo; Tel: 819-953-1574, E-mail: rita.pascolo@bst-tsb.gc.ca; Staff 2 (MLS 1, Non-MLS 1)
Library Holdings: Bk Titles 20,000; Per Subs 50
Special Collections: Transportation Accident Reports from Canada, USA, UK, France, Australia & New Zealand
Subject Interests: Transportation safety
Automation Activity & Vendor Info: (Cataloging) Horizon; (Circulation) Horizon; (OPAC) Horizon; (Serials) Horizon
Database Vendor: OCLC FirstSearch
Function: Doc delivery serv, ILL available, Ref serv available
Open Mon-Fri 8-4
Restriction: Borrowing requests are handled by ILL, External users must contact libr, Open to pub with supv only

C   UNIVERSITE DU QUEBEC EN OUTAOUAIS*, Service de la Bibliotheque, 283, Blvd Alexandre-Tache, Case postale 1250, succ Hull, J8X 3X7. SAN 319-6569. Tel: 819-595-3900, Ext 1790. Interlibrary Loan Service Tel: 819-595-3900, Ext 1798. Reference Tel: 819-595-3900, Ext 1628, 819-595-3900, Ext 2375. Information Services Tel: 819-595-3900, Ext 1624, 819-595-3900, Ext 2370. Toll Free: 800-567-1283. FAX: 819-773-1669. E-mail: bibliotheque@uqo.ca. Web Site: biblio.uqo.ca. *Dir,* Helene Larouche; E-mail: helene.larouche@uqo.ca; *Assoc Dir,* Daniel Godon; Tel: 819-595-3900, Ext 1945, E-mail: daniel.dogon@uqo.ca; *Coll Develop Librn, Ref Librn,* Danielle Boisvert; Tel: 819-595-3900, Ext 2374, E-mail: danielle.boisvert@uqo.ca; *Coll Develop Librn, Ref Librn,* Simon Bouisset; Tel: 819-595-3900, Ext 2373, E-mail: simon.bouisset@uqo.ca; *Coll Develop Librn, Ref Librn,* Marie-Helene Labory; Tel: 819-595-3900, Ext 1856, E-mail: marie-helene.labory@uqo.ca; *Coll Develop Librn, Ref Librn,* Carmen Rousseau; Tel: 819-595-3900, Ext 1860, E-mail: carmen.rousseau@uqo.ca; *Syst Librn,* Sylvie Gervais; Tel: 819-595-3900, Ext 1789, E-mail: sylvie.gervais@uqo.ca; *ILL,* Jacinthe Sirois; E-mail: jacinthe.sirois@uqo.ca. Subject Specialists: *Acctg, Bus,* Daniel Godon; *Nursing, Psychol,* Danielle Boisvert; *Educ, Terminology, Translation,* Simon Bouisset; *Acctg, Bus,* Marie-Helene Labory; *Art, Computer sci,* Carmen Rousseau; Staff 7 (MLS 7)
Founded 1972. Enrl 3,499; Fac 183; Highest Degree: Doctorate
Library Holdings: AV Mats 13,684; CDs 656; DVDs 1,310; e-books 8,000; e-journals 13,000; Bk Titles 189,680; Per Subs 1,370; Videos 2,332
Subject Interests: Acctg, Admin, Arts, Computer sci, Educ, Health, Indust relations, Soc sci, Soc work
Automation Activity & Vendor Info: (ILL) Fretwell-Downing
Database Vendor: EBSCOhost, OCLC FirstSearch, ProQuest
Publications: Annual Report; Bibliographies; Guides
Partic in Canadian Research Knowledge Network; CREPUQ

GRANBY

P   BIBLIOTHEQUE PAUL-O-TREPANIER*, 11 rue Dufferin, J2G 4W5. SAN 319-6518. Tel: 450-776-8310. FAX: 450-776-8313. E-mail: bibliotheque@ville.granby.qc.ca. Web Site: www.biblio.ville.granby.qc.ca/bibliotheque. *Dir,* Rejeanne Rheault
Pop 45,223; Circ 167,228
Library Holdings: Bk Vols 80,353; Per Subs 219

C   CEGEP DE GRANBY HAUTE-YAMASKA*, Service de la Bibliotheque et des technologies educatives et du soutien aux TI, 235 Saint Jacques St, J2G 3N1. (Mail add: PO Box 7000, J2G 3N1), SAN 322-7006. Tel: 450-372-6614, Ext 1205. FAX: 450-372-6565. Web Site: www.cegepgranby.qc.ca/biblio. *Acq, Librn, Pub Serv,* Daniel Marquis; E-mail: dmarquis@cegepgranby.qc.ca; *Circ,* Jacinthe Parent; *Per,* Isabelle Racine; *Tech Serv,* Joanne Deschamps; Staff 2 (MLS 1, Non-MLS 1)
Founded 1970. Enrl 3,700; Fac 190

Library Holdings: CDs 4,267; DVDs 1,453; Bk Titles 55,674; Per Subs 465; Videos 3,785
Special Collections: Federal Govt; Tourisme -Voyages. Oral History
Publications: User Guide

P   HAUTE-YAMASKA*, 135-1 Principale, J2G 2V1. SAN 370-6354. Tel: 450-372-4500. FAX: 450-372-9904. E-mail: info@shhy.org. Web Site: www.shhy.org. *Dir,* Richard Racine; Staff 3 (MLS 2, Non-MLS 1)
Founded 1976. Pop 70,000
Library Holdings: Bk Titles 10,000
Special Collections: Agriculture (French Canadian Breeders Association); Industry (Miner Rubber Coll), doc; Quebec-Eastern Townships

JOLIETTE

C   CEGEP REGIONAL DE LANAUDIERE A JOLIETTE*, 20 rue Saint Charles Sud, J6E 4T1. SAN 319-6585. Tel: 450-759-1661. FAX: 450-759-4468, 450-759-7120. Web Site: biblio-joliette.collanaud.qc.ca/biblio. *Asst Dir,* Marie-Carole McKenzie
Library Holdings: Bk Vols 100,000; Per Subs 450
Database Vendor: LibLime
Wireless access
Partic in RESDOC

S   MUSEE D'ART DE JOLIETTE*, Documentary Center, 145 Wilfrid-Corbeil St, J6E 4T4. SAN 320-3506. Tel: 450-756-0311. FAX: 450-756-6511. Web Site: www.musee.joliette.org. *Dir,* Gaetane Verna
Founded 1976
Library Holdings: Bk Vols 1,000
Subject Interests: Archit, Art, Biog
Restriction: Staff use only

JONQUIERE

P   BIBLIOTHEQUE MUNICIPALE DE JONQUIERE*, 2850 Davis Pl, G7X 7W7. SAN 319-6607. Tel: 418-699-6068, 418-699-6069. FAX: 418-699-6046. E-mail: webbiblio@ville.saguenay.qc.ca. Web Site: www.ville.saguenay.qc.ca. *Dir,* France Leger; E-mail: france.ledger@ville.saguenay.qc.ca
Founded 1944. Pop 56,503; Circ 267,614
Library Holdings: Bk Titles 78,659; Bk Vols 155,443; Per Subs 98
Special Collections: Can & Prov
Subject Interests: Genealogy, Local hist
Automation Activity & Vendor Info: (Cataloging) SirsiDynix; (Circulation) SirsiDynix; (OPAC) SirsiDynix; (Serials) SirsiDynix
Database Vendor: SirsiDynix
Open Mon-Wed 10-8, Thurs & Fri 10-5, Sat 10-4

J   CEGEP DE JONQUIERE*, Centre de Resources Educatives, 2505 rue St Hubert, G7X 7W2. SAN 319-6615. Tel: 418-547-2191. FAX: 418-547-0917. E-mail: biblio@cjonquiere.qc.ca. Web Site: www.cjonquiere.qc.ca. *Dir,* J P Dufour; *Acq, Asst Librn,* Helene Jeannotte; *AV,* Celine LaPointe; *Cat,* Line Kenny; *Ref,* Armande Dery-Allard; *Ref,* Fabienne Simard; *Tech Serv,* Huguette Martel; Staff 6 (MLS 2, Non-MLS 4)
Founded 1958. Enrl 3,050; Fac 278
Library Holdings: AV Mats 4,000; Bk Titles 104,000; Bk Vols 140,000; Per Subs 331
Special Collections: State Document Depository
Subject Interests: Art, Communications, Media, Nautical sci, Rare bks
Automation Activity & Vendor Info: (Serials) EBSCO Online
Database Vendor: EBSCOhost
Function: Photocopying/Printing, Ref serv available
Publications: L'Indicateur
Partic in RESDOC
Open Mon-Thurs 8am-9pm, Fri 8-5, Sat 1-5
Friends of the Library Group

KIRKLAND

P   BIBLIOTHEQUE DE KIRKLAND*, 17100 Hymus Blvd, H9J 2W2. SAN 326-646X. Tel: 514-630-2726. FAX: 514-630-2716. Web Site: www.ville.kirkland.qc.ca/english/index.htm. *Head Librn,* Sonia Djevalikian; *Tech Serv-Section Head,* Annie Tetreault; E-mail: atetreault@ville.kirkland.qc.ca; *Head, Youth Serv,* Elizabeth Lemyre
Founded 1974. Pop 20,446; Circ 141,732
Library Holdings: Bk Vols 57,965
Database Vendor: 3M Library Systems, EBSCOhost, Electric Library, Grolier Online, ProQuest
Wireless access
Open Mon-Fri 10-9, Sat & Sun (Winter) 12-4

KNOWLTON

P   BIBLIOTHEQUE COMMEMORATIVE PETTES*, Pettes Memorial
Library, 276 rue Knowlton, J0E 1V0. SAN 319-6712. Tel: 450-243-6128.
FAX: 450-243-5272. Web Site: www.endirect.qc.ca/~pettes. *Librn,* Jana
Marie Valasek; Staff 4 (MLS 1, Non-MLS 3)
Founded 1894. Pop 5,500; Circ 41,404
Library Holdings: Bk Vols 20,967; Per Subs 50; Talking Bks 627
Subject Interests: Local hist
Automation Activity & Vendor Info: (Cataloging) Mandarin Library
Automation; (Circulation) Mandarin Library Automation; (OPAC)
Mandarin Library Automation
Open Mon, Tues, Thurs & Fri 12-4:30, Wed 10-4:30, Sat 10-4

LA BAIE

P   BIBLIOTHEQUE MUNICIPALE DE LA BAIE*, 1911 Sixth Ave, G7B
1S1. SAN 319-8405. Tel: 418-697-5085. FAX: 418-697-5087. Web Site:
www.ville.seguenay.qc.ca/biblio. *Dir,* Anne Lebel
Founded 1961. Pop 21,647
Library Holdings: Bk Vols 70,000; Per Subs 70
Special Collections: Can
Open Mon 1:30-9, Tues-Fri 10-9, Sat & Sun 1-5; Mon-Thurs (Summer)
9-9

LA MALBAIE

P   BIBLIOTHEQUE PUBLIQUE DE LA MALBAIE*, Bibliotheque
Laure-Conan, 363 rue Saint-Etienne (Chapel Community Center), G5A
1S8. (Mail add: 395 rue Saint-Etienne, G5A 1S8), SAN 319-6658. Tel:
418-665-6027. FAX: 418-665-6481. E-mail: bibl.malbaie@qc.aira.com.
Web Site: www.ville.lamalbaie.qc.ca/fr/bibliotheques. *Dir,* Marie-Claire
Fortin; E-mail: respo.biblio@qc.aira.com
Founded 1960. Pop 9,150
Library Holdings: CDs 500; Bk Vols 16,000; Per Subs 50
Open Mon, Wed & Fri 1:30-4:30 & 6:30-9, Tues & Thurs 6:30-9, Sat
9:30-3:30

LA POCATIERE

J   CEGEP DE LA POCATIERE*, Bibliotheque Francois-Hertel, 140 Fourth
Ave, G0R 1Z0. SAN 322-6891. Tel: 418-856-1525. FAX: 418-856-4589.
Web Site: www.cegeplapocatiere.qc.ca. *Acq, Librn, Pub Serv,* Marc-André
Chevrette; *Cat,* Jocelyne Dubé; Staff 6 (MLS 1, Non-MLS 5)
Library Holdings: Bk Vols 42,000; Per Subs 250
Special Collections: Canada & Quebec Gov; Oeuvres de Francois Hertel;
Robotic Coll
Wireless access
Publications: Guide de l'usager, Catalogue des Productions Audiovisuelles
et des Publications du cegep de La Pocatiere; La Recherche Documentaire

J   INSTITUT DE TECHNOLOGIE AGRO-ALIMENTAIRE, CAMPUS
LAPOCATIERE*, Centre de Documentation, 401 rue Poire, G0R 1Z0.
SAN 319-6623. Tel: 418-856-1110, Ext 258. FAX: 418-856-1719. Web
Site: www.ita.qc.ca. *Librn,* Pierre Duncan
Founded 1859. Enrl 500
Library Holdings: Bk Titles 12,250; Per Subs 325
Subject Interests: Agr, Environ, Fisheries

S   SOCIETE HISTORIQUE DE LA COTE-DU-SUD BIBLIOTHEQUE*, 100
Fourth Ave, G0R 1Z0. SAN 375-0752. Tel: 418-856-2104. FAX:
418-856-2104. E-mail: archsud@bellnet.ca. Web Site: www.shcds.org. *Pres,*
Gaetan Godbout
Library Holdings: Bk Vols 2,500; Per Subs 25
Subject Interests: Genealogy, Hist
Friends of the Library Group

LA PRAIRIE

P   CENTRE REGIONAL DE SERVICES AUX BIBLIOTHEQUES
PUBLIQUES DE LA MONTEREGIE*, 275 rue Conrad-Pelletier, J5R
4V1. SAN 321-0987. Tel: 450-444-5433. FAX: 450-659-3364. Web Site:
www.reseaubibliomonteregie.qc.ca. *Exec Dir,* Jacqueline Labelle; E-mail:
jacqueline.labelle@reseaubibliomonteregie.qc.ca; Staff 13 (MLS 3,
Non-MLS 10)
Founded 1978. Pop 168,495; Circ 660,476
Library Holdings: Bk Titles 314,487; Bk Vols 625,553
Special Collections: Can & Prov
Automation Activity & Vendor Info: (Acquisitions) SirsiDynix;
(Cataloging) SirsiDynix; (Circulation) SirsiDynix; (ILL) OCLC; (OPAC)
SirsiDynix
Database Vendor: SirsiDynix
Wireless access
Function: ILL available
Publications: Annual Report; Contact Express (Quarterly); Le Bon Choix
Restriction: Not open to pub

LA SALLE

C   CENTRE DE DOCUMENTATION COLLEGIALE*, 1111 rue Lapierre,
H8N 2J4. SAN 374-6259. Tel: 514-364-3320, Ext 241. FAX:
514-364-2627. E-mail: infocdc@cdc.qc.ca. Web Site: www.cdc.qc.ca.
Librn, Isabelle LaPlante; E-mail: ilaplante@cdc.qc.ca; *Acq, Circ,* Carole
Hebert; *Cat,* Yves Juillet; Staff 3 (MLS 1, Non-MLS 2)
Founded 1991
Library Holdings: Bk Titles 22,000; Per Subs 250
Subject Interests: Educ
Automation Activity & Vendor Info: (Acquisitions) MultiLIS;
(Cataloging) MultiLIS
Open Mon-Fri 9-12 & 1-5

LA TUQUE

P   BIBLIOTHEQUE MUNICIPALE DE LA TUQUE*, 575 rue St-Eugene,
G9X 2T5. (Mail add: 375 St-Joseph, G9X 1L5), SAN 319-6704. Tel:
819-523-3100. FAX: 819-523-4487. E-mail:
bibliotheque@ville.latuque.qc.ca. *Head Librn,* Alain Michaud; Staff 2
(MLS 1, Non-MLS 1)
Founded 1961. Pop 13,000; Circ 60,000
Jan 2006-Dec 2006. Mats Exp (CAN) $74,500, Books (CAN) $62,000,
Per/Ser (Incl. Access Fees) (CAN) $7,500, AV Equip (CAN) $5,000
Library Holdings: CDs 3,000; DVDs 200; Large Print Bks 150; Bk Vols
35,000; Per Subs 98
Automation Activity & Vendor Info: (Cataloging) MultiLIS; (Circulation)
MultiLIS; (OPAC) MultiLIS
Function: Adult bk club, Art exhibits, CD-ROM, Handicapped accessible,
Homebound delivery serv, ILL available, Photocopying/Printing, Prog for
children & young adult, Ref serv available, Spoken cassettes & CDs,
Spoken cassettes & DVDs, Summer reading prog, Wheelchair accessible,
Workshops
Open Tues & Wed 9:30-12 & 1:30-5, Thurs 9:30-12 & 1:30-8, Sat 9-12 &
1-4:30

LAC SAINT-CHARLES

P   BIBLIOTHEQUE MUNICIPALE*, 530 Delage St, Office 102, G3G 1J2.
SAN 321-3196. Tel: 418-641-6121. FAX: 419-849-2849. *Librn,* Denise
Ferland
Founded 1981. Pop 9,064
Library Holdings: Bk Titles 8,000
Open Mon & Tues 1-4:30 & 7-9, Wed 4-9, Thurs 1-4:30, Fri 7-9, Sat
9:30-12:30

LACHINE

S   ROLLS-ROYCE (CANADA) LIBRARY*, 9500 Cote de Liesse, H8T 1A2.
SAN 319-6763. Tel: 514-631-3541, Ext 2499. FAX: 514-636-9969. *Librn,*
Juliette Martin
Library Holdings: Bk Vols 1,000

LACHUTE

P   BIBLIOTHEQUE JEAN-MARC-BELZILE*, 378, rue Principale, J8H 1Y2.
SAN 319-6771. Tel: 450-562-3781, Ext 215. Interlibrary Loan Service Tel:
450-562-3781, Ext 214. FAX: 450-562-1431. E-mail:
biblio@ville.lachute.qc.ca. Web Site: www.ville.lachute.qc.ca/biblio. *Head
Librn,* Emilie Paquin; Tel: 450-562-3781, Ext 255, E-mail:
epaquin@ville.lachute.qc.ca; Staff 7 (MLS 1, Non-MLS 6)
Founded 1959. Pop 15,035; Circ 83,000
Library Holdings: Bk Titles 50,000; Per Subs 96
Subject Interests: Genealogy, Hort
Automation Activity & Vendor Info: (Cataloging) SirsiDynix;
(Circulation) SirsiDynix; (OPAC) SirsiDynix
Database Vendor: CEDROM-SNi
Wireless access
Open Tues 10-6, Wed & Thurs 1-8, Fri 1-6, Sat & Sun 10-4

L'ASSOMPTION

C   COLLEGE DE L'ASSOMPTION*, Bibliotheque Secondaire, 270 boul
l'Ange-Gardien, J5W 1R7. SAN 319-664X. Tel: 450-589-5621, Ext 258.
FAX: 450-589-2910. E-mail: dirgen@classomption.qc.ca. Web Site:
www.classomption.qc.ca. *Dir of Educ,* Denyse Verret; *Tech Serv,* Pascal
Belanger
Founded 1833. Highest Degree: Doctorate
Library Holdings: Bk Titles 18,000; Per Subs 200
Special Collections: Prov; Theatre (Fonds Charbonneau)
Open Mon-Fri 8am-8:30pm

LAVAL

P   BIBLIOTHEQUES DE LAVAL*, 1535 boul Chomedey, H7V 3Z4. SAN
328-168X. Tel: 450-978-6888, Ext 5649. Interlibrary Loan Service Tel:
450-978-6888, Ext 5877. Administration Tel: 450-978-6888, Ext 5981.
FAX: 450-978-5833. Administration FAX: 450-978-5835. E-mail:
adm-biblio@ville.laval.qc.ca. Web Site: www.info.ville.laval.qc.ca. *Dir of
Communications, Dir, Commun Develop, Dir, Cultural Serv,* Paul Lemay;
Asst Dir of Br, Marc Deblois; *Asst Dir, Strategy & Planning,* Jean-Pierre
Tessier; *Coll Develop Coordr, Coordr, Cat & Acq, Prog Coordr,*
Jean-François Roulier; Staff 44 (MLS 18, Non-MLS 26)
Founded 1971. Pop 376,425; Circ 2,733,816
Library Holdings: AV Mats 28,314; CDs 6,406; DVDs 14,970; Electronic
Media & Resources 2; Large Print Bks 980; Bk Titles 267,376; Bk Vols
644,232; Per Subs 1,816; Talking Bks 493
Special Collections: History & Genealogy Coll
Wireless access
Function: CD-ROM, Children's prog, Handicapped accessible, Music CDs,
Photocopying/Printing, Prog for adults, Ref serv available, Story hour
Partic in Consortium d'acquisition de ressources electroniques du Quebec
(CAREQ)

M   CENTRE DE SANTE ET SERVICES SOCIAUX DE LAVAL - CITE DE
LA SANTE*, Bibliotheque du CSSS de Laval, 1755 boul Rene-Laennec,
H7M 3L9. SAN 324-3869. Tel: 450-975-5493. FAX: 450-975-5572.
E-mail: biblio.cssssl@ssss.gouv.qc.ca. Web Site: catalogue.cssslaval.qc.ca,
www.bibliocssssl.wordpress.com. *Librn,* France Pontbriand; Tel:
450-668-1010, Ext 23215, E-mail: fpontbriand.csssl@ssss.gouv.qc.ca; Staff
2.6 (MLS 1.6, Non-MLS 1)
Founded 1978
Library Holdings: Bk Titles 5,000; Per Subs 100
Subject Interests: Family practice
Publications: Cyberlettre (Monthly newsletter)

C   COLLEGE MONTMORENCY BIBLIOTHEQUE*, 475 Boul de L Avenir,
H7N 5H9. SAN 322-9033. Tel: 450-975-6274. FAX: 450-381-2263. Web
Site: www.cmontmorency.qc.ca/biblio/. *Librn,* Georges Langlois; *Librn,*
Philippe Lavigueur; E-mail: plavigueur@cmontmorency.qc.ca; Staff 11
(MLS 1, Non-MLS 10)
Library Holdings: Bk Titles 60,000; Bk Vols 70,000
Automation Activity & Vendor Info: (Acquisitions) BiblioMondo;
(Cataloging) BiblioMondo; (Circulation) BiblioMondo; (OPAC)
BiblioMondo; (Serials) BiblioMondo
Publications: Nouveaute's

S   CORRECTIONAL SERVICE OF CANADA*, Establissement Leclerc
Bibliotheque, 400 Montee Saint Francois, H7C 1S7. SAN 375-3816. Tel:
450-664-1320, Ext 5505. FAX: 450-664-6719. *Librn,* Phillipe Bodson;
Staff 7 (MLS 1, Non-MLS 6)
Library Holdings: Bk Titles 7,000; Per Subs 25
Open Mon-Wed 6-8

SR   FOREIGN MISSIONS SOCIETY OF QUEBEC LIBRARY, 180 Place
Juge Desnoyers, H7G 1A4. SAN 328-5103. Tel: 450-667-4190. FAX:
450-667-4194. *Dir,* Bertrand Roy
Library Holdings: Bk Vols 25,000; Per Subs 121

C   INRS - INSTITUT ARMAND-FRAPPIER - BIBLIOTHEQUE*, 531 blvd
des Prairies, H7V 1B7. SAN 328-3801. Tel: 450-687-5010, Ext 4340.
Circulation Tel: 450-687-5010, Ext 4267. Interlibrary Loan Service Tel:
450-687-5010, Ext 4266. Administration Tel: 450-687-5010, Ext 4205.
FAX: 450-686-5501. Web Site: sdis.inrs.ca. *Librn,* Michel Courcelles;
E-mail: michel.courcelles@iaf.inrs.ca; *Librn,* Diane Sauve; E-mail:
diane.sauve@iaf.inrs.ca; *ILL & Distance Libr Serv Spec,* Danielle
Chartrand; E-mail: prets-entre-biblio@iaf.inrs.ca; *Pub Serv,* Josette
Bourdages; Tel: 450-687-5010, Ext 4267, E-mail:
josette.bourdages@iaf.inrs.ca; Staff 4 (MLS 2, Non-MLS 2)
Founded 1938. Highest Degree: Doctorate
Library Holdings: e-journals 4,260; Bk Vols 7,000; Per Subs 4,600
Subject Interests: Animal health, Bacteriology, Epidemiology, Human
health, Immunology, Microbiology, Toxicology, Virology
Wireless access
Function: Computers for patron use, Copy machines, Electronic databases
& coll, For res purposes, Health sci info serv, ILL available, Online
searches, Ref & res, Web-catalog
Partic in Canadian Research Knowledge Network; CREPUQ
Open Mon-Fri 9-5
Restriction: External users must contact libr

M   JEWISH REHABILITATION HOSPITAL MEDICAL LIBRARY*, 3205 Pl
Alton Goldbloom, H7V 1R2. SAN 324-4342. Tel: 450-688-9550, Ext 226.
FAX: 450-688-3673. *Librn,* Irene D Shanefield; E-mail:
irene_shanefield_hjr@ssss.gouv.qc.ca
Founded 1979

Library Holdings: Bk Titles 800; Per Subs 70
Special Collections: Oral History
Open Mon-Fri 8-5

LAVAL-DES-RAPIDES

S   MATERIAL HANDLING ASSOCIATION OF QUEBEC*, Information
Center, 62A Labelle, H7N 2S3. SAN 373-6180. Tel: 450-662-3717. FAX:
450-662-6096. *Librn,* Stephanie Vonka
Founded 1986
Library Holdings: Bk Titles 500; Bk Vols 550; Per Subs 56
Open Mon-Fri 8:30-4:30

LEVIS

P   BIBLIOTHEQUE MUNICIPALE DE LEVIS*, Seven Mgr Gosselin, G6V
5J9. SAN 373-7780. Tel: 418-838-4126. FAX: 418-838-4124. Web Site:
www.bibliotheques.qc.ca. *In Charge,* Julie Labrecque; E-mail:
jlabrecque@ville.levis.qc.ca
Founded 1974. Pop 39,000
Library Holdings: Bk Vols 63,324

J   COLLEGE DE LEVIS*, Bibliotheque Alphonse-Desjardins, Nine rue Mgr
Gosselin, G6V 5K1. SAN 319-681X. Tel: 418-833-1249, Ext 140. FAX:
418-833-1974. Web Site: www.collegedelevis.qc.ca/~biblio. *Coll Develop,
Managing Librn, Purchasing,* Christian LaCroix; E-mail:
clacroix@collegedelevis.qc.ca; Staff 2 (MLS 1, Non-MLS 1)
Founded 1964. Enrl 950
Library Holdings: Bk Vols 20,000; Per Subs 75
Subject Interests: Canadiana, Regional hist
Function: ILL available, Photocopying/Printing
Open Mon-Fri 8:30-4:30
Restriction: Access at librarian's discretion, Open to students, fac & staff,
Use of others with permission of librn

S   CONFEDERATION DES CAISSES POPULAIRES ET D'ECONOMIE
DES JARDINS DU QUEBEC*, Service de Documentation de Reference,
100 Ave des Commandeurs, G6V 7N5. SAN 319-6828. Tel: 418-835-8444.
FAX: 418-833-5873. Staff 8 (MLS 3, Non-MLS 5)
Founded 1963
Library Holdings: Bk Titles 31,000
Subject Interests: Banking, Finance, Sociol
Open Mon 8:30-4:30
Restriction: Staff use only

LONGUEUIL

S   BIBLIOTHEQUE DE L'INSTITUT NAZARETH ET LOUIS-BRAILLE*,
1111 St Charles St W, J4K 5G4. SAN 319-762X. Tel: 450-463-1710. Toll
Free Tel: 800-361-7063. FAX: 450-463-0243. Web Site: www.inlb.qc.ca.
Librn, Linda Laberge; Staff 8 (MLS 1, Non-MLS 7)
Founded 1911
Library Holdings: Bk Titles 11,000
Special Collections: Braille Books; Music Braille Books; Talking Books
Open Tues-Fri 10-12 & 2-7

P   BIBLIOTHEQUE MUNICIPALE DE GREENFIELD PARK*, 225 rue
Empire, Greenfield Park, J4V 1T9. SAN 325-2396. Tel: 450-463-7140.
FAX: 450-466-8112. E-mail:
bibliotheque.greenfieldpark@ville.longueuil.qc.ca. *Librn,* Lise Lasleur; Staff
2 (MLS 2)
Circ 90,000
Library Holdings: Bk Vols 43,547; Per Subs 63
Special Collections: Large Print Coll- Pocket Books Coll
Open Mon, Tues, Thurs & Fri 1-9, Sat 1-4, Sun 1-5

P   BIBLIOTHEQUES PUBLIQUES DE LONGUEUIL*, 100 rue
Saint-Laurent Ouest, J4H 1M1. SAN 369-1802. Tel: 450-463-7180. FAX:
450-646-8080. Web Site: www.longueuil.ca/vieux-longueuil/bibliotheque.
Actg Br Mgr, Jean-Francois Hetu; E-mail:
jean-francois.hetu@ville.longueuil.qc.ca; Staff 5 (MLS 5)
Founded 1967. Pop 135,634; Circ 1,006,446
Library Holdings: Bk Vols 257,543; Per Subs 364
Special Collections: History (J-Z-Leon Patenaude Coll)
Subject Interests: Genealogy, Handicraft, Lore, Quebec hist
Automation Activity & Vendor Info: (Acquisitions) MultiLIS;
(Cataloging) MultiLIS
Publications: Bulletin (Quarterly)
Branches: 4
CLAUDE-HENRI GRIGNON BRANCH, 1660 rue Bourassa, J4J 3A4,
SAN 369-1837. Tel: 450-463-7180. *Libr Tech,* Carole Denault; Fax:
450-646-6710
    Library Holdings: Bk Vols 42,000
    Subject Interests: Genealogy, Quebec hist

'ST-JEAN-BAPTISTE BRANCH, 700, rue Duvernay, J4K 4L1. *Pub Serv,*
Sylvie Beaudoin
SUCCURSALE FATIMA, 2130 rue Jean-Louis, J4H 1M1. (Mail add: c/o
Succursale Jaques Ferron, 5 rue St. Laurent Quest, J4H 1M1), SAN
369-1845. Tel: 450-463-7180. *Tech Librn,* Sylvie Beaudoin
Library Holdings: Bk Vols 5,487
SUCCURSALE GEORGES-DOR, 2760 Chemin de Chambly, J4L 1M7,
SAN 369-1861. Tel: 450-463-7180. *Librn,* Diane Lavigne
Library Holdings: Bk Vols 43,799

C   COLLEGE EDOUARD-MONTPETIT BIBLIOTHEQUE*, 945 Chemin de
Chambly, J4H 3M6. SAN 369-1896. Tel: 450-679-2631, Ext 2461.
Circulation Tel: 450-679-2631, Ext 6047. Interlibrary Loan Service Tel:
450-679-2631, Ext 2462. FAX: 450-677-2945. Web Site;
www2.college-em.qc.ca/biblio. *Dir of Libr,* Louis-Marie Dussault; Tel:
450-678-3561, Ext 4236, E-mail: louis-marie.dussault@college-em.qc.ca;
Pub Serv, Nancie Lamontagne; E-mail:
nancie.lamontagne@college-em.qc.ca; *Tech Serv,* Michelle Chartier; Tel:
450-679-2631, Ext 2609, E-mail: michelle.chartier@college-em.qc.ca; Staff
2 (MLS 2)
Founded 1967. Enrl 6,700; Highest Degree: Associate
Library Holdings: CDs 400; DVDs 1,000; Bk Titles 75,000; Bk Vols
100,000; Per Subs 314; Videos 6,000
Special Collections: State Document Depository
Subject Interests: Archit, Art, Behav sci, Econ, Natural sci, Soc sci
Automation Activity & Vendor Info: (Acquisitions) SirsiDynix;
(Cataloging) SirsiDynix; (Circulation) SirsiDynix; (OPAC) SirsiDynix;
(Serials) SirsiDynix
Database Vendor: CEDROM-SNi, EBSCOhost, SirsiDynix
Open Mon-Thurs 8-8, Fri 8-6, Sat 9-1
Departmental Libraries:
ECOLE NATIONALE D'AEROTECHNIQUE BIBLIOTHEQUE, 5555
Place de la Savane, Saint Hubert, J3Y 8Y9, SAN 374-728X. Tel:
450-678-3560, Ext 4254. FAX: 450-678-3240. E-mail:
ena.biblio@college-em.qc.ca. Web Site: www.college-em.qc.ca. *Librn,*
Lise Chaillez; Staff 1 (MLS 1)
Founded 1964. Enrl 700
Library Holdings: Bk Titles 17,000; Bk Vols 25,000; Per Subs 105
Subject Interests: Aeronaut

G   HEALTH CANADA*, Health Protection Branch Regional Library, 1001
Boul St Laurent Ouest, J4K 1C7. SAN 324-4067. Tel: 450-928-4189. FAX:
450-928-4102. E-mail: bibliotheques_quebec@hc-sc.gc.ca. Web Site:
www.hc-sc.gc.ca. *Libr Tech,* Chantal Labonte
Founded 1971
Library Holdings: Bk Titles 2,600; Per Subs 98
Subject Interests: Analytical chem, Bacteriology, Biochem,
Chromatography, Cosmetics, Drugs of abuse, Environ health, Food, Food
chem, Forensic chem, Microbiology, Nutrition, Organic chem,
Pharmaceuticals, Pharmacology, Toxicology
Open Mon-Fri 8:30-4:30

S   PRATT & WHITNEY CANADA, INC LIBRARY*, 1000 Blvd
Marie-Victorin, MS 01RA4, J4G 1A1. SAN 319-6852. Tel: 450-677-9411,
Ext 2607. FAX: 450-647-9469. *Online Serv, Ref,* Lyzane St Amour
Founded 1957
Subject Interests: Aeronautical, Aircraft gas turbine engines, Mechanical
eng
Database Vendor: Cambridge Scientific Abstracts, Dialog
Restriction: Not open to pub

LORETTEVILLE

P   BIBLIOTHEQUE MUNICIPALE DE
LORETTEVILLE-CHRYSTINE-BROUILLET*, 264 Rue Racine, G2B
1E7. SAN 319-6860. Tel: 418-641-6120. FAX: 418-842-3866. E-mail:
cbrouillet@icqbdq.qc.ca. Web Site: www.bibliothequesdequebec.qc.ca. *In
Charge,* Nancy Duchesneau
Founded 1962. Pop 15,000
Library Holdings: Bk Vols 40,000; Per Subs 100
Automation Activity & Vendor Info: (Cataloging) SIRSI Unicorn;
(Circulation) SIRSI Unicorn; (OPAC) SIRSI Unicorn
Database Vendor: Repere
Open Tues-Fri 1-8, Sat 10-5, Sun 12-5

MANIWAKI

G   BIBLIOTHEQUE MUNICIPALE JR L'HEUREUX*, 14 Comeau St, J9E
2R8. SAN 328-8145. Tel: 819-449-2738. *Librn,* Jocelyne LeClair
Founded 1967
Library Holdings: Bk Vols 8,000; Per Subs 15
Open Mon-Wed (Winter) 2-5, Thurs & Fri 2-5 & 6-8, Sat 1-4; Mon-Wed
(Summer) 1:30-4:30, Thurs & Fri 1:30-4:30 & 6-8

MARIEVILLE

P   BIBLIOTHEQUE COMMEMORATIVE DESAUTELS*, 1801 DuPont St,
J3M 1J7. SAN 319-6887. Tel: 450-460-4444, Ext 271. FAX:
450-460-3526. Web Site: www.ville.marieville.qc.ca. *Dir,* Daniel Lalonde;
E-mail: d.lalonde@ville.marieville.qc.ca; Staff 3 (MLS 1, Non-MLS 2)
Founded 1967. Pop 7,650; Circ 51,000
Jan 2006-Dec 2006 Income $231,000. Mats Exp $48,150, Books $36,000,
Per/Ser (Incl. Access Fees) $4,000, AV Equip $1,000, Presv $7,150. Sal
$149,635
Library Holdings: Bk Vols 40,000
Special Collections: Can
Automation Activity & Vendor Info: (Cataloging) SirsiDynix;
(Circulation) SirsiDynix
Open Tues & Wed 8:30-12 & 1-8, Thurs & Fri 8:30-12 & 1-4:30, Sat 9-12

MONT-JOLI

G   DEPARTMENT OF FISHERIES & OCEANS CANADA*, Institut
Maurice-Lamontagne Library, 850 route de la Mer, G5H 3Z4. (Mail add:
PO Box 1000, G5H 3Z4), SAN 329-8620. Tel: 418-775-0552. Interlibrary
Loan Service Tel: 418-775-0537. Reference Tel: 418-775-0551. FAX:
418-775-0538. E-mail: biblioiml@dfo-mpo.gc.ca. Web Site:
www.dfo-mpo.gc.ca/libraries-bibliotheques/quebec-fra.htm. *Head Librn,*
Christine Lemay; E-mail: christine.lemay@dfo-mpo.gc.ca; *Tech Serv,*
Marie-Hélène Beauchesne; E-mail:
marie-helene.beauchesne@dfo-mpo.gc.ca
Founded 1987
Library Holdings: AV Mats 230; e-books 1,900; Bk Titles 61,000; Per
Subs 294
Subject Interests: Ecotoxicology, Fisheries, Hydrography, Marine sci,
Navigation, Oceanography
Database Vendor: BioOne, Cambridge Scientific Abstracts, ISI Web of
Knowledge, netLibrary, OCLC FirstSearch, OCLC WorldCat,
Springer-Verlag
Function: ILL available, Res libr, Telephone ref
Restriction: Non-circulating to the pub, Open to pub for ref only
Friends of the Library Group

MONT-LAURIER

P   BIBLIOTHEQUE MUNICIPALE DE MONT-LAURIER, 385 rue du Pont,
J9L 2R5. SAN 319-6895. Tel: 819-623-1833. FAX: 819-623-7079. *Librn,*
Sophie Monette; E-mail: smonette@villemontlaurier.qc.ca; Staff 2 (MLS 1,
Non-MLS 1)
Pop 13,500
Library Holdings: DVDs 138; Large Print Bks 190; Bk Titles 39,371; Bk
Vols 47,520; Per Subs 47
Automation Activity & Vendor Info: (Acquisitions) BiblioMondo;
(Cataloging) BiblioMondo; (Circulation) BiblioMondo; (OPAC)
BiblioMondo; (Serials) BiblioMondo
Wireless access
Open Mon-Fri 10-8, Sat 10-4:30

MONTREAL

M   ALLAN MEMORIAL INSTITUTE OF PSYCHIATRY*, Eric D Wittkower
Library, Royal Victoria Hospital, 1025 Pine Ave W, H3A 1A1. SAN
319-695X. Tel: 514-934-1934, Ext 34528. FAX: 514-843-1731. E-mail:
ami.library@muhc.mcgill.ca. Web Site: muhclibraries.mcgill.ca/ami.php.
Libr Asst, Alex Amar
Subject Interests: Psychiat, Psychoanalysis, Psychopharmacology
Friends of the Library Group

SR   ANGLICAN CHURCH OF CANADA ARCHIVES*, Diocese of Montreal
Archives, 1444 Union Ave, H3A 2B8. SAN 371-4683. Tel: 514-843-6577,
Ext 254. FAX: 514-843-6344. E-mail: archives@montreal.anglican.ca. Web
Site: www.montreal.anglican.ca. *Archivist,* Dr Richard Virr
Special Collections: Diocese of Montreal Administrative Records
Restriction: Non-circulating

R   ARCHIVES PROVINCIALES DES CAPUCINS*, 3650 Blvd de la
Rousseliere, H1A 2X9. SAN 370-6605. Tel: 514-642-5391, Ext 347. FAX:
514-642-5033. *Librn,* Jean-Charles Côté; Tel: 514-642-5391, Ext 308,
E-mail: jeanccote@yahoo.ca; *Libr Tech,* France Guilbert; E-mail:
franceguilbert@hotmail.com
Founded 1977
Jan 2010-Dec 2010. Mats Exp (CAN) $800, Books (CAN) $50, Per/Ser
(Incl. Access Fees) (CAN) $50, Electronic Ref Mat (Incl. Access Fees)
(CAN) $350, Presv (CAN) $250. Sal (CAN) $16,780
Library Holdings: AV Mats 32; DVDs 3; Bk Vols 1,000; Per Subs 17
Special Collections: Capucins of Canada History-East Province (1890-)
Wireless access
Function: Archival coll
Publications: Les Capucins de l'Est du Canada 1632 a nos jours, 1982

Open Mon-Fri 9-3:30
Restriction: Open to pub by appt only

S ARTEXTE INFORMATION CENTRE*, 460 Saint-Catherine W, Ste 508, H3B 1A7. SAN 323-6676. Tel: 514-874-0049. E-mail: info@artexte.ca. Web Site: www.artexte.ca. *Dir,* Sylvie Gilbert; *Info Spec,* John Latour; Staff 3 (MLS 2, Non-MLS 1)
Founded 1981
Library Holdings: CDs 200; DVDs 200; Bk Titles 17,000; Per Subs 50
Special Collections: Artists Files; Exhibition Catalogs
Subject Interests: Contemporary art
Automation Activity & Vendor Info: (Acquisitions) Inmagic, Inc.; (Cataloging) Inmagic, Inc.; (OPAC) Inmagic, Inc.
Function: Photocopying/Printing, Ref serv available
Publications: The Directory of Publications on Canadian Contemporary Art
Open Wed-Sat 10:30-5:30
Restriction: Non-circulating

S ASSOCIATION PARITAIRE POUR LA SANTE ET LA SECURITE DU TRAVAIL - SECTEUR AFFAIRES MUNICIPALES*, 715 Square Victoria, Ste 710, H2Y 2H7. SAN 328-5359. Tel: 514-849-8373, Ext 230. Toll Free Tel: 800-465-1754. FAX: 514-849-8873. Toll Free FAX: 800-465-6578. E-mail: apsamdoc@apsam.com. Web Site: centredoc.csst.qc.ca. *Librn,* Claire Vezina; Staff 1 (Non-MLS 1)
Founded 1985
Library Holdings: CDs 21; DVDs 29; Bk Vols 3,865; Per Subs 35; Videos 121
Special Collections: NFPA Codes (Updated)
Subject Interests: Fire fighters, Law enforcement, Occupational health, Occupational safety, Pub transportation, Sewage treatment
Automation Activity & Vendor Info: (Cataloging) Isacsoft Inc (ISF); (Circulation) Isacsoft Inc (ISF); (Serials) Isacsoft Inc (ISF)
Open Mon-Fri 9-4:30

S BANQUE NATIONALE DU CANADA*, Centre de Documentation, 600 rue de la Gauchetiere ouest, H3B 4L2. SAN 325-3287. Tel: 514-394-5000, Ext 5470. FAX: 514-394-4167. *Info Spec,* Ghyslaine Rheault; E-mail: ghyslaine.rheault@bnc.ca; Staff 2 (MLS 1, Non-MLS 1)
Founded 1986
Library Holdings: Bk Titles 4,000; Per Subs 700
Subject Interests: Banking, Banks, Econ, Finance
Publications: Info Doc
Open Mon-Fri 8:30-5

S BCA RESEARCH GROUP LIBRARY*, 1002 Sherbrooke St W, Ste 1600, H3A 3L6. SAN 375-5592. Tel: 514-499-9550. FAX: 514-843-1763. Web Site: www.bcaresearch.com. *Mgr,* Jane Patterson
Founded 1992
Library Holdings: Bk Titles 2,000; Per Subs 400
Subject Interests: Finance
Automation Activity & Vendor Info: (Cataloging) Inmagic, Inc.
Restriction: Not open to pub

SR BIBLIOTHEQUE ALBERT-LE-GRAND*, 2715 Côte Ste-Catherine, H3T 1B6. SAN 325-8335. Tel: 514-731-3603, Ext 307. FAX: 514-731-0676. E-mail: albertlegrand@1221yahoo.ca. *Librn,* Aubin Luc
Library Holdings: Bk Vols 80,000
Open Tues-Fri 10-6

R BIBLIOTHEQUE DE LA COMPAGNIE DE JESUS, Bibliothèque des Jésuites, Collège Jean-de-Brebeuf, L B4-25, 3200, Ch Côte-Sainte-Catherine, H3T 1C1. SAN 372-6908. Tel: 514-342-9342, Ext 5466. E-mail: bibliojesus@brebeuf.qc.ca. *Dir, Librn,* Marc Mambuku Umba. Subject Specialists: *Classical studies, Law, Philosophy,* Marc Mambuku Umba; Staff 1 (MLS 1)
Founded 1882
Library Holdings: Bk Titles 200,000; Per Subs 250
Special Collections: 16th to 19th Century Books (Manuscript & Rare Bks); Ancient & Rare Books (16th Century & On); Former Jesuit College, Founded in 1635, Rare Books (New France Books); Philosophy & Theology (Jesuit Education)
Subject Interests: Canadiana, Philosophy, Theol

L BIBLIOTHEQUE DU CAIJ MONTREAL*, One Notre-Dame East, 17th Flr, Rm 17.50, H2Y 1B6. SAN 319-7018. Tel: 514-866-2057. Toll Free Tel: 877-666-2057. FAX: 514-879-8592. Toll Free FAX: 866-879-9470. Web Site: www.caij.qc.ca. *Dir, Libr Network,* Isabelle Pilon; Staff 9 (MLS 4, Non-MLS 5)
Founded 1828
Library Holdings: Bk Titles 100,000
Subject Interests: Law
Wireless access

G BIBLIOTHEQUE ET ARCHIVES NATIONALES DU QUEBEC, 475 de Maisonneuve E, H2L 5C4. SAN 319-7069. Tel: 514-873-1100. Toll Free Tel: 800-363-9028. FAX: 514-873-9312. E-mail: info@banq.qc.ca. Web Site: www.banq.qc.ca. *Pres & Chief Exec Officer,* Guy Berthiaume; Tel: 514-873-1101, Ext 3250, Fax: 514-864-3818, E-mail: pdg@banq.qc.ca; *Secy Gen,* Carole Payen; Tel: 514-873-1101, Ext 3255, E-mail: carole.payen@banq.qc.ca; *Dir,* Danny Boulanger; Tel: 514-873-1101, Ext 3241, E-mail: danny.boulanger@banq.qc.ca; *Dir,* Louise Boutin; Tel: 514-873-1101, Ext 3129, E-mail: louise.boutin@banq.qc.ca; *Dir,* Normand Charbonneau; Tel: 514-873-1101, Ext 6408, E-mail: normand.charbonneau@banq.qc.ca; *Dir,* Benoit Ferland; Tel: 514-873-1101, Ext 3752, E-mail: benoit.ferland@banq.qc.ca; *Dir,* Dominique Hétu; Tel: 514-873-1101, Ext 3237, E-mail: dominique.hetu@banq.qc.ca; *Dir,* Isabelle Lafrance; Tel: 514-873-1101, Ext 3203, E-mail: isabelle.lafrance@banq.qc.ca; *Dir,* François Montreuil; Tel: 514-873-1101, Ext 3287, E-mail: francois.montreuil@banq.qc.ca; *Dir,* Helene Roussel; Tel: 514-873-1101, Ext 3245, E-mail: helene.roussel@banq.qc.ca; *Dir,* Nicole Vallières; Tel: 514-873-1101, Ext 6714, E-mail: nicole.vallieres@banq.qc.ca. Subject Specialists: *Legal,* Carole Payen; *Human resources,* Danny Boulanger; *Admin,* Louise Boutin; *Archives,* Normand Charbonneau; *Conserv,* Benoit Ferland; *Communications, Pub relations,* Dominique Hétu; *Legal affairs,* Isabelle Lafrance; *Info tech, Telecommunication,* François Montreuil; *Cultural prog,* Nicole Vallières
Founded 1967
Wireless access
Publications: A Rayons Ouverts; Revue de BAnQ
Open Tues-Fri 10-10, Sat & Sun 10-6
Friends of the Library Group

R BIBLIOTHEQUE FRANCISCAINE PROVINCIALE DES CAPUCINS*, 3650 boul de la Rousseliere, H1A 2X9. SAN 370-7385. Tel: 514-642-5391, Ext 347. FAX: 514-642-5033. *Librn,* Jean-Charles Côté; Tel: 514-642-5391, Ext 308, E-mail: jeanccote@yahoo.ca; *Libr Tech,* France Guilbert; E-mail: franceguilbert@hotmail.com
Jan 2010-Dec 2010. Mats Exp (CAN) $4,000, Books (CAN) $1,000, Per/Ser (Incl. Access Fees) (CAN) $1,000, Electronic Ref Mat (Incl. Access Fees) (CAN) $1,500, Presv (CAN) $500. Sal (CAN) $16,780
Library Holdings: Bk Vols 21,000; Per Subs 200
Special Collections: Franciscan Coll
Subject Interests: Missions, Theol
Wireless access
Function: Archival coll, Copy machines, Electronic databases & coll, Photocopying/Printing
Publications: Repertoire des livres Franciscains des Capucins de l'Est du Canada, 1993
Open Mon-Fri 9-3:30
Restriction: Internal circ only, Open to pub by appt only, Pub by appt only

C BIBLIOTHEQUE LAURENT-MICHEL-VACHER*, College Ahuntsic Bibliotheque, 9155 rue St-Hubert, H2M 1Y8. SAN 319-728X. Tel: 514-389-5921, Ext 2240. FAX: 514-389-1422. Web Site: www.collegeahuntsic.qc.ca. *Academy Librn,* Jean Lemaire; E-mail: jean.lemaire@collegeahuntsic.qc.ca
Founded 1967
Library Holdings: Bk Vols 88,000; Per Subs 550
Open Mon-Thurs 8-8, Fri 8-5, Sat 12-4

P BIBLIOTHEQUE PUBLIQUE JUIVE*, Jewish Public Library, One carré Cummings, 5151 ch de la Cote Ste Catherine, H3W 1M6. SAN 319-7085. Tel: 514-345-2627. Reference Tel: 514-345-2627, Ext 3001. FAX: 514-342-6477. E-mail: info@jplmontreal.org. Web Site: www.jewishpubliclibrary.org. *Exec Dir,* Michael Crelinsten; Tel: 514-345-2627, Ext 3222; *Head Biblio & Info Serv,* Eddie Paul; Tel: 514-345-2627, Ext 3004; *Head, Norman Berman Children's Libr,* Penny Fransblow; Tel: 514-345-2627, Ext 3028, E-mail: penny.fransblow@jplmontreal.org; Staff 16 (MLS 5, Non-MLS 11)
Founded 1914. Pop 90,000; Circ 174,346
Special Collections: 15th-19th Century Judaica (Rare Book Coll); Archives, ms, photog, etc; German Judaica, 19th-20th Centuries; Irving Layton Library; Jewish Canadiana Coll, ephemera; Yiddish Periodicals; Yizkor Coll
Subject Interests: Gen fiction, Judaica
Automation Activity & Vendor Info: (Acquisitions) VTLS, Inc; (Cataloging) VTLS, Inc; (Circulation) VTLS, Inc; (OPAC) VTLS, Inc; (Serials) VTLS, Inc
Database Vendor: ABC-CLIO, EBSCOhost, ProQuest, YBP Library Services
Wireless access
Function: Bks on CD, CD-ROM, Computer training, Computers for patron use, Copy machines, e-mail serv, Electronic databases & coll, ILL available, Music CDs, Online cat, Online ref, Online searches, Orientations,

Photocopying/Printing, Prog for children & young adult, Pub access computers, Scanner, Spoken cassettes & CDs, Telephone ref
Special Services for the Deaf - Assistive tech
Special Services for the Blind - Audio mat; Bks available with recordings; Bks on cassette; Bks on CD; Large print bks
Open Mon-Wed 10-9, Thurs 10-6, Fri 10-1, Sun (Sept-June) 10-5
Restriction: Circ to mem only, Closed stack, Non-circulating coll, Non-circulating of rare bks
Friends of the Library Group

P   BIBLIOTHEQUES DE MONTREAL, 801, rue Brennan, 5e Etage, Bureau 5206, H3C 0G4. SAN 369-3279. Tel: 514-872-1608. FAX: 514-872-0530. *Dir of Libr,* Louise Guillemette-Labory; E-mail: lglabory@ville.montreal.qc.ca; *Chief, Libr Serv/Commun Serv, Outreach Serv Librn,* Ivan Filion; Tel: 514-872-9075, E-mail: ifilion@ville.montreal.qc.ca; *Chief, Info Tech Serv, Planning & Develop Librn,* Luc Jodoin; Tel: 514-872-2918, E-mail: ljodoin@ville.montreal.qc.ca; *Database Mgt, Planning & Develop Librn,* Miguelle Dube; Tel: 514-872-8771, E-mail: miguelledube@ville.montreal.qc.ca; *Planning & Develop Librn, Syst Analyst,* Christian Pecquet; Tel: 514-872-2741, E-mail: christianpecquet@ville.montreal.qc.ca; *Tech Serv Mgr,* Brigitte Raymond; Tel: 514-872-1542, E-mail: braymond@ville.montreal.qc.ca; *Communications Coordr,* Claire Rocher; Tel: 514-872-9080, Fax: 514-872-1155, E-mail: crocher@ville.montreal.qc.ca; *Coll Develop, Prog Coordr,* Marie Désilets; Tel: 514-872-2449, E-mail: marie_desilets@ville.montreal.qc.ca; *Coordr, Tech Serv,* Michel Claveau; Tel: 514-872-6563, E-mail: mclaveau@ville.montreal.qc.ca; *Acq,* Henriette Auger; Tel: 514-872-1539, E-mail: henriette_auger@ville.montreal.qc.ca; *Libr Spec, Tech Serv,* Renaud Arcand; Tel: 514-872-1892, E-mail: renaud_arcand@ville.montreal.qc.ca; *Coll Develop, Youth Serv,* Marie-France Genest; Tel: 514-872-2910; Staff 611 (MLS 119, Non-MLS 492)
Founded 1902. Pop 1,651,235; Circ 10,277,388
Jan 2011-Dec 2011 Income (Main Library and Branch(s)) (CAN) $83,541,400, Provincial (CAN) $4,543,327, City (CAN) $77,706,447, Locally Generated Income (CAN) $86,338, Other (CAN) $1,205,288. Mats Exp (CAN) $6,626,268, Books (CAN) $4,978,270, Per/Ser (Incl. Access Fees) (CAN) $525,684, Other Print Mats (CAN) $63,332, AV Mat (CAN) $716,172, Electronic Ref Mat (Incl. Access Fees) (CAN) $342,810. Sal (CAN) $51,739,283
Library Holdings: Audiobooks 15,032; AV Mats 271,861; Braille Volumes 118; CDs 125,411; DVDs 136,070; Electronic Media & Resources 10,843; Large Print Bks 29,335; Music Scores 6,326; Bk Titles 911,064; Bk Vols 3,780,175; Per Subs 16,503
Special Collections: Dr Armand Frappier's Personal Coll; Genealogy Coll; History Coll; Music Scores; Nautical Maps; Stamps; Yves Ryan's Archives
Automation Activity & Vendor Info: (Acquisitions) Innovative Interfaces, Inc; (Cataloging) Innovative Interfaces, Inc; (Circulation) Innovative Interfaces, Inc; (Media Booking) Innovative Interfaces, Inc; (OPAC) Innovative Interfaces, Inc; (Serials) Innovative Interfaces, Inc
Wireless access
Partic in Consortium d'acquisition de ressources electroniques du Quebec (CAREQ)
Friends of the Library Group
Branches: 43
AHUNTSIC, 10300, rue Lajeunesse, H3L 2E5, SAN 369-3368. Tel: 514-872-0568. FAX: 514-872-0518. *Chef de Section,* Lucie Bernier; Tel: 514-872-6993, E-mail: luciebernier@ville.montreal.qc.ca; *Chef de Div,* Francine Elhadad; Tel: 514-872-8421, Fax: 514-872-4601, E-mail: felhadad@ville.montreal.qc.ca; Staff 28 (MLS 4, Non-MLS 24)
Founded 1953. Circ 557,097
Library Holdings: Audiobooks 468; AV Mats 7,162; Braille Volumes 3; CDs 2,690; DVDs 4,446; Electronic Media & Resources 449; Large Print Bks 1,244; Music Scores 830; Bk Vols 128,336; Per Subs 581
Open Mon 12-6, Tues & Wed 1-9, Thurs 10-9, Fri 10-6, Sat 10-5, Sun 12-5
BELLEVILLE, 10400, avenue de Belleville, H1H 4Z7, SAN 369-4925. Tel: 514-328-4000, Ext 4140. FAX: 514-328-4298. *Chef de Div,* Cécile Lointier; Tel: 514-328-4000, Ext 4131 or 4128, E-mail: cecile.lointier@ville.montreal.qc.ca; *Chef de Section,* Jean-François Cusson; Tel: 514-328-4000, Ext 5620, E-mail: jean-francois.cusson@ville.montreal.qc.ca; *Chef de Section,* France Genest; Tel: 514-328-4000, Ext 4130, Fax: 514-328-4298, E-mail: france.genest@ville.montreal.qc.ca; Staff 4 (Non-MLS 4)
Founded 1973. Circ 78,244
Library Holdings: Audiobooks 88; AV Mats 3,545; CDs 2,230; DVDs 1,288; Electronic Media & Resources 214; Music Scores 4; Bk Vols 31,397; Per Subs 123
Open Mon-Thurs 10-9, Fri 9-1, Sat & Sun 12-5
BENNY, 3465, avenue Benny, H4B 2R9, SAN 369-3422. Tel: 514-872-4147 (Adults), 514-872-4636 (Youth). FAX: 514-872-0515. *Chef de Div,* Linda Boileau; Tel: 514-868-4021, Fax: 514-872-4585, E-mail: lboileau@ville.montreal.qc.ca; *Chef de Section,* Valérie Comte; Tel:

514-872-7367, E-mail: valerie.comte@ville.montreal.qc.ca; Staff 9 (MLS 2, Non-MLS 7)
Founded 1956. Circ 219,354
Library Holdings: Audiobooks 367; AV Mats 3,241; Braille Volumes 1; CDs 374; DVDs 2,859; Electronic Media & Resources 251; Large Print Bks 363; Music Scores 6; Bk Vols 52,381; Per Subs 206
Open Mon, Sat & Sun 10-5, Tues & Wed 12-8, Thurs & Fri 10-6
CARTIERVILLE, 5900, rue De Salaberry, H4J 1J1, SAN 369-3333. Tel: 514-872-6989. FAX: 514-872-0510. *Chef de Div,* Francine Elhadad; Tel: 514-872-8421, Fax: 514-872-4601, E-mail: felhadad@ville.montreal.qc.ca; *Chef de Section,* Sylvie Cantin; Tel: 514-868-5916, E-mail: scantin@ville.montreal.qc.ca; Staff 13 (MLS 4, Non-MLS 9)
Founded 1966. Circ 201,224
Library Holdings: Audiobooks 357; AV Mats 3,983; CDs 1,643; DVDs 2,318; Electronic Media & Resources 148; Large Print Bks 340; Music Scores 44; Bk Vols 76,879; Per Subs 327
Open Mon 1-8, Tues & Wed 10-8, Thurs 10-6, Fri 12-6, Sat 10-5, Sun 12-5
CHARLEROI, 4740, rue de Charleroi, H1H 1V2, SAN 369-4917. Tel: 514-328-4000, Ext 4135 (adult), 514-328-4000, Ext 4238 (young adult). FAX: 514-328-4298. *Chef de Div,* Cécile Lointier; Tel: 514-328-4000, Ext 4131 or 4128, E-mail: cecile.lointier@ville.montreal.qc.ca; *Chef de Section,* Jean-François Cusson; Tel: 514-328-4000, Ext 5620, E-mail: jean-francois.cusson@ville.montreal.qc.ca; *Chef de Section,* France Genest; Tel: 514-328-4000, Ext 4130, Fax: 514-328-4298, E-mail: france.genest@ville.montreal.qc.ca; Staff 8 (Non-MLS 8)
Founded 1970. Circ 105,200
Library Holdings: Audiobooks 223; AV Mats 5,723; CDs 3,153; DVDs 1,624; Electronic Media & Resources 209; Large Print Bks 218; Music Scores 142; Bk Vols 41,146; Per Subs 201
Open Mon-Thurs 10-9, Fri 9-1, Sat & Sun 12-5
COTE-DES-NEIGES, 5290, chemin de la Côte-des-Neiges, H3T 1Y2, SAN 322-6077. Tel: 514-872-5118 (Children's Servs), 514-872-6603 (Adults). FAX: 514-872-0516. *Chef de Div,* Linda Boileau; Tel: 514-868-4021, E-mail: lboileau@ville.montreal.qc.ca; *Chef de Section,* Robert Chamberot; Tel: 514-872-2935, E-mail: rchamberot@ville.montreal.qc.ca; Staff 24 (MLS 2, Non-MLS 22)
Founded 1983. Circ 408,388
Library Holdings: Audiobooks 195; AV Mats 6,024; CDs 225; DVDs 5,797; Electronic Media & Resources 117; Large Print Bks 1,217; Music Scores 78; Bk Vols 118,964; Per Subs 459
Open Mon, Sat & Sun 10-5, Tues & Wed 12-8, Thurs & Fri 10-6
FRONTENAC, 2550, rue Ontario Est, H2K 1W7, SAN 370-4572. Tel: 514-872-7888. FAX: 514-872-7893. *Chef de Div,* Michel Demers; Tel: 514-872-5594, E-mail: mdemers_1@ville.montreal.qc.ca; *Bibliothecaire Responsable,* Johanne Prud'homme; Tel: 514-872-7889, E-mail: johanneprudhomme@ville.montreal.qc.ca; Staff 13 (MLS 1, Non-MLS 12)
Founded 1989. Circ 227,880
Library Holdings: Audiobooks 270; AV Mats 6,084; Braille Volumes 2; CDs 2,020; DVDs 4,058; Electronic Media & Resources 217; Large Print Bks 598; Music Scores 27; Bk Vols 83,195; Per Subs 219
Open Mon & Fri 12-6, Tues-Thurs 10-8, Sat 10-5, Sun 12-5
GEORGES-VANIER, 2450, rue Workman, H3J 1L8, SAN 369-3937. Tel: 514-872-2001 (Adult Servs), 514-872-2002 (Children's Servs). FAX: 514-872-0511. *Chef de Div,* Chantal Beaulieu; Tel: 514-872-3067, E-mail: chantalbeaulieu@ville.montreal.qc.ca; *Chef de Section,* Louise Robichaud; Tel: 514-872-3763, E-mail: louiserobichaud@ville.montreal.qc.ca; Staff 8 (MLS 2, Non-MLS 6)
Founded 1985. Circ 97,348
Library Holdings: Audiobooks 2; AV Mats 3,140; Braille Volumes 1; CDs 930; DVDs 2,200; Electronic Media & Resources 116; Large Print Bks 21; Music Scores 22; Bk Vols 38,491; Per Subs 159
Open Mon 12-6, Tues 10-8, Wed 1-8, Thurs & Fri 10-6, Sat & Sun 10-5
HAUT-ANJOU, 7070, rue Jarry Est, H1J 1G4. Tel: 514-493-8271. FAX: 514-493-8273. *Chef de Div,* Magdalena Michalowska; Tel: 514-493-8262, E-mail: mmichalowska@ville.montreal.qc.ca; *Chef de Section,* Olivier Barrette; Tel: 514-493-8270, E-mail: olivier.barrette@ville.montreal.qc.ca; Staff 4 (Non-MLS 4)
Founded 1990. Circ 42,271
Library Holdings: AV Mats 88; DVDs 88; Large Print Bks 5; Music Scores 3; Bk Vols 16,792; Per Subs 54
Open Mon-Fri 12-8, Sat 9:30-5, Sun 11-5
HENRI-BOURASSA, 5400, boulevard Henri-Bourassa Est, H1G 2S9, SAN 369-4895. Tel: 514-328-4000, Ext 4125 (Adult serv), 514-328-4000, Ext 4134 (Children's serv). FAX: 514-328-4298. *Chef de Div,* Cécile Lointier; Tel: 514-328-4000, Ext 4131 or 4128, E-mail: cecile.lointier@ville.montreal.qc.ca; *Chef de Section,* Jean-François Cusson; Tel: 514-328-4000, Ext 5620, E-mail: jean-francois.cusson@ville.montreal.qc.ca; *Chef de Section,* France Genest; Tel: 514-328-4000, Ext 4130, E-mail: france.genest@ville.montreal.qc.ca; Staff 30 (MLS 3, Non-MLS 27)
Founded 1970. Circ 292,954

Library Holdings: Audiobooks 358; AV Mats 8,938; CDs 4,517; DVDs 4,043; Electronic Media & Resources 307; Large Print Bks 1,245; Music Scores 329; Bk Vols 83,716; Per Subs 558

Open Mon-Thurs 10-9, Fri 9-5, Sat & Sun 10-5

HOCHELAGA, 1870, rue Davidson, H1W 2Y6, SAN 369-3570. Tel: 514-872-3666. FAX: 514-872-0521. *Chef de Div,* Richard Paulhus; Tel: 514-872-6629, Fax: 514-872-4617, E-mail: rpaulhus@ville.montreal.qc.ca; *Chef de Section,* Sylvie Burelle; Tel: 514-872-6733, Fax: 514-872-0522, E-mail: sburelle@ville.montreal.qc.ca; Staff 4 (MLS 1, Non-MLS 3)

Founded 1964. Circ 59,578

Library Holdings: Audiobooks 19; AV Mats 1,242; Braille Volumes 4; CDs 455; DVDs 784; Electronic Media & Resources 148; Large Print Bks 1; Music Scores 17; Bk Vols 28,419; Per Subs 49

Open Mon, Sat & Sun 10-5, Tues & Wed 12-8, Thurs & Fri 10-6

ILE-DES-SOEURS, 260, rue Elgar, H3E 1C9, SAN 373-6202. Tel: 514-765-7266. FAX: 514-765-7264. *Chef de Div,* Daniel Felton; Tel: 514-732-7337, E-mail: danielfelton@ville.montreal.qc.ca; Staff 8 (MLS 1, Non-MLS 7)

Founded 1990. Circ 111,515

Library Holdings: Audiobooks 152; AV Mats 5,218; CDs 3,004; DVDs 2,040; Electronic Media & Resources 14; Large Print Bks 190; Music Scores 92; Bk Vols 54,712; Per Subs 167

Open Mon, Wed & Thurs 1-9, Tues 10-9, Fri 10-6, Sat & Sun 12-5

INTERCULTURELLE, 6767, chemin de la Côte-des-Neiges, Montréal, H3S 2T6. Tel: 514-868-4715 (Adults), 514-868-4716 (Young adult). *Chef de Div,* Linda Boileau; Tel: 514-868-4021, E-mail: lboileau@ville.montreal.qc.ca; *Chef de Section,* Valérie Comte; Tel: 514-872-7367, E-mail: valerie.comte@ville.montreal.qc.ca; Staff 22 (MLS 3, Non-MLS 19)

Founded 2005. Circ 334,588

Library Holdings: Audiobooks 1,021; AV Mats 13,133; CDs 6,133; DVDs 6,479; Electronic Media & Resources 604; Large Print Bks 1,526; Music Scores 318; Bk Vols 130,946; Per Subs 369

Open Mon, Sat & Sun 10-5, Tues & Wed 12-8, Thurs & Fri 10-6

JEAN-CORBEIL, 7500, avenue Goncourt, H1K 3X9. Tel: 514-493-8260. FAX: 514-493-8273. E-mail: bibliotheque.jean.corbeil@ville.montreal.qc.ca. *Chef de Div,* Magdalena Michalowska; Tel: 514-493-8262, E-mail: mmichalowska@ville.montreal.qc.ca; *Chef de Section,* Olivier Barrette; Tel: 514-493-8270, E-mail: olivier.barrette@ville.montreal.qc.ca; Staff 17 (MLS 5, Non-MLS 12)

Founded 1984. Circ 234,228

Library Holdings: Audiobooks 286; AV Mats 6,773; CDs 4,849; DVDs 1,560; Electronic Media & Resources 7; Large Print Bks 454; Music Scores 365; Bk Vols 109,749; Per Subs 160

Open Mon-Fri 12-8, Sat 9:30-5, Sun 11-5

L'ILE-BIZARD, 500, montée de l'Église, H9C 1G9. Tel: 514-620-6257. FAX: 514-620-4153. *Chef de Div,* Robert Potvin; Tel: 514-620-6199, Fax: 514-620-0707, E-mail: rpotvin@ville.montreal.qc.ca; *Bibliothecaire Responsable,* Sophie David; Tel: 514-620-7400, E-mail: sophiedavid@ville.montreal.qc.ca; Staff 8 (MLS 1, Non-MLS 7)

Founded 1971. Pop 18,300; Circ 91,305

Library Holdings: Audiobooks 88; AV Mats 5,849; CDs 3,614; DVDs 1,970; Large Print Bks 243; Bk Vols 51,013; Per Subs 248

Open Mon-Thurs 10-9, Fri 10-6, Sat & Sun 11-5

L'OCTOGONE, 1080, avenue Dollard, H8N 2T9, SAN 319-6674. Tel: 514-367-6376. FAX: 514-367-6604. *Chef de Div,* Marie-Andree Marcoux; Tel: 514-367-6488, E-mail: mamarcoux@ville.montreal.qc.ca; *Chef de Section,* Saida Meridja; Tel: 514-367-4384, E-mail: saida.meridja@ville.montreal.qc.ca; Staff 32 (MLS 7, Non-MLS 25)

Founded 1984. Pop 76,958; Circ 635,320

Library Holdings: Audiobooks 22; AV Mats 14,961; CDs 6,686; DVDs 8,098; Electronic Media & Resources 697; Large Print Bks 1,299; Bk Vols 209,999; Per Subs 2,124

Open Mon-Thurs 10-9, Fri-Sun 10-5

Friends of the Library Group

LA PETITE-PATRIE, 6707, avenue De Lorimier, H2G 2P8, SAN 328-8811. Tel: 514-872-1732 (Children's serv), 514-872-1733 (Adult serv). FAX: 514-872-0526. *Chef de Div,* Line Ferland; Tel: 514-872-6557, E-mail: lineferland@ville.montreal.qc.ca; *Chef de Section,* Françoise Ménard; Tel: 514-872-4735, E-mail: francoise.menard@ville.montreal.qc.ca; *Bibliothecaire Responsable,* Véronique L'Helgouach; Tel: 514-872-1734, E-mail: veroniquelhelgouach@ville.montreal.qc.ca; Staff 5 (MLS 1, Non-MLS 4)

Founded 1987. Circ 200,231

Library Holdings: Audiobooks 179; AV Mats 4,290; Braille Volumes 2; CDs 2,323; DVDs 1,965; Electronic Media & Resources 234; Large Print Bks 631; Music Scores 57; Bk Vols 76,496; Per Subs 404

Open Mon 1-6, Tues 1-8, Wed 10-8, Thurs 10-7, Fri 10-6, Sat & Sun 10-5

LANGELIER, 6473, rue Sherbrooke Est, H1N 1C5, SAN 369-3597. Tel: 514-872-2640 (Adult serv), 514-872-4227 (Children's serv). FAX: 514-872-0523. *Chef de Div,* Richard Paulhus; Tel: 514-872-6629, Fax: 514-872-4617, E-mail: rpaulhus@ville.montreal.qc.ca; *Chef de Section,*

Josée Valiquette; Tel: 514-872-1529, E-mail: jovaliquette@ville.montreal.qc.ca; Staff 9 (MLS 1, Non-MLS 8)

Founded 1980. Circ 329,191

Library Holdings: Audiobooks 216; AV Mats 6,469; Braille Volumes 3; CDs 2,756; DVDs 3,700; Electronic Media & Resources 315; Large Print Bks 166; Music Scores 48; Bk Vols 70,514; Per Subs 373

Open Mon, Sat & Sun 10-5, Tues & Wed 12-8, Thurs & Fri 10-6

LE PREVOST, 7355 Ave Christophe-Colomb, H2R 2S5, SAN 322-6387. Tel: 514-872-1523 (Adult serv), 514-872-1526 (Children's serv). FAX: 514-872-0529. *Librn,* Danielle Keable; Tel: 514-872-1525, E-mail: daniellekeable@ville.montreal.qc.ca

Founded 1983. Pop 54,775; Circ 346,560

Library Holdings: Bk Vols 86,265

Open Mon 1-6, Tues 1-8:30, Wed 10-8:30, Thurs & Fri 10-6, Sat & Sun 10-5

MAISON CULTURELLE ET COMMUNAUTAIRE, 12002, boulevard Rolland, H1G 3W1. Tel: 514-328-4000, Ext 5626. *Chef de Div,* Cécile Lointier; Tel: 514-328-4000, Ext 4131 or 4128, E-mail: cecile.lointier@ville.montreal.qc.ca; *Chef de Section,* Jean-François Cusson; Tel: 514-328-4000, Ext 5620, E-mail: jean-francois.cusson@ville.montreal.qc.ca; *Chef de Section,* France Genest; Tel: 514-328-4000, Ext 4130, E-mail: france.genest@ville.montreal.qc.ca; Staff 13 (MLS 2, Non-MLS 11)

Founded 2006. Circ 180,175

Library Holdings: Audiobooks 197; AV Mats 5,952; Braille Volumes 70; CDs 2,372; DVDs 3,307; Electronic Media & Resources 95; Large Print Bks 419; Music Scores 305; Bk Vols 51,048; Per Subs 310

Open Mon-Thurs 10-9, Fri 9-5, Sat & Sun 10-5

MAISONNEUVE, 4120 rue Ontario Est, H1V 1J9, SAN 369-3643. Tel: 514-872-4213 (Adult serv), 514-872-4214 (Children's serv). FAX: 514-872-0522. *Librn,* Francois Seguin; Tel: 514-872-6976, E-mail: francoseguin@ville.montreal.qc.ca

Founded 1981. Pop 42,480; Circ 198,554

Library Holdings: Bk Vols 59,437

Open Mon, Thurs & Fri 12-7, Tues & Wed 10-8, Sat 10-5, Sun 12-5

MARIE-UGUAY, 6052, rue Monk, H4E 3H6, SAN 369-3929. Tel: 514-872-4097 (Adult serv), 514-872-4414 (Children's serv). FAX: 514-872-0513. *Chef de Div,* Chantal Beaulieu; Tel: 514-872-3067, E-mail: chantalbeaulieu@ville.montreal.qc.ca; *Chef de Section,* Daniel Legault; Tel: 514-872-2313, E-mail: daniel.legault@ville.montreal.qc.ca; Staff 10 (MLS 2, Non-MLS 8)

Founded 1982. Circ 133,425

Library Holdings: Audiobooks 166; AV Mats 6,448; CDs 3,347; DVDs 3,091; Electronic Media & Resources 259; Large Print Bks 133; Music Scores 79; Bk Vols 59,169; Per Subs 190

Open Mon, Thurs & Fri 10-6, Tues 1-8, Wed 10-8, Sat 10-5, Sun 12-5

MERCIER, 8105, rue Hochelaga, H1L 2K9, SAN 370-4580. Tel: 514-872-8738 (Adult serv), 514-872-8739 (Children's serv). FAX: 514-872-0524. *Chef de Div,* Richard Paulhus; Tel: 514-872-6629, Fax: 514-872-4617, E-mail: rpaulhus@ville.montreal.qc.ca; *Chef de Section,* Amélie Harbec; Tel: 514-872-8737, E-mail: amelie.harbec@ville.montreal.qc.ca; Staff 9 (MLS 1, Non-MLS 8)

Founded 1989. Circ 224,161

Library Holdings: Audiobooks 292; AV Mats 6,421; CDs 3,195; DVDs 3,188; Electronic Media & Resources 333; Large Print Bks 270; Music Scores 104; Bk Vols 82,232; Per Subs 279

Open Mon & Sun 11-5, Tues & Wed 11-8, Thurs & Fri 10-6, Sat 10-5

MILE END, 5434, avenue du Parc, H2V 4G7, SAN 369-3678. Tel: 514-872-2141 (Adult serv), 514-872-2142 (Children's serv). FAX: 514-872-0531. *Chef de Div,* Anne-Marie Collins; Tel: 514-872-9966, E-mail: acollins@ville.montreal.qc.ca; *Bibliothecaire Responsable,* Lyne Olivier; Tel: 514-872-6982, E-mail: lyneolivier@ville.montreal.qc.ca

Founded 1982. Circ 243,136

Library Holdings: Audiobooks 415; AV Mats 6,026; Braille Volumes 1; CDs 2,688; DVDs 3,333; Electronic Media & Resources 114; Large Print Bks 279; Music Scores 18; Bk Vols 63,857; Per Subs 379

Open Mon & Thurs 10-6, Tues & Wed 10-8, Fri 12-6, Sat 10-5, Sun 12-5

NOTRE-DAME-DE-GRACE, 3755, rue Botrel, H4A 3G8, SAN 328-879X. Tel: 514-872-2377 (Children's serv), 514-872-2398 (Adult serv). FAX: 514-872-0517. *Chef de Div,* Linda Boileau; Tel: 514-868-4021, E-mail: lboileau@ville.montreal.qc.ca; *Chef de Section,* Robert Chamberot; Tel: 514-872-2935, E-mail: rchamberot@ville.montreal.qc.ca; Staff 10 (MLS 2, Non-MLS 8)

Founded 1984. Circ 203,603

Library Holdings: Audiobooks 413; AV Mats 3,136; CDs 416; DVDs 2,716; Electronic Media & Resources 115; Large Print Bks 210; Music Scores 1; Bk Vols 53,993; Per Subs 195

Open Mon, Sat & Sun 10-5, Tues & Wed 12-8, Thurs & Fri 10-6

PARC-EXTENSION, 421, rue Saint-Roch, H3N 1K2, SAN 378-1828. Tel: 514-872-6071. FAX: 514-872-6152. *Chef de Div,* Mireille Cliche; Tel: 514-868-3444, E-mail: mcliche@ville.montreal.qc.ca; *Chef de Section,* Chantal Trottier; Tel: 514-872-7416, E-mail: chantaltrottier@ville.montreal.qc.ca; Staff 16 (MLS 3, Non-MLS 13)

Founded 2004. Circ 252,900

Library Holdings: Audiobooks 456; AV Mats 4,524; CDs 1,572; DVDs 2,721; Electronic Media & Resources 398; Large Print Bks 371; Music Scores 220; Bk Vols 100,082; Per Subs 324

Open Mon & Fri 12-6, Tues & Wed 10-8:30, Thurs 10-6, Sat 10-5, Sun 12-5

PERE-AMBROISE, 2093, rue de la Visitation, H2L 3C9, SAN 373-5877. Tel: 514-872-1633. FAX: 514-872-1626. *Div Head,* Michel Demers; Tel: 514-872-5594, E-mail: mdemers_1@ville.montreal.qc.ca; *Head Librn,* Isabelle Pellerin; Tel: 514-872-9541, E-mail: isabelle.pellerin@ville.montreal.qc.ca; Staff 6 (MLS 1, Non-MLS 5) Founded 1941. Circ 129,941

Library Holdings: Audiobooks 220; AV Mats 6,031; Braille Volumes 5; CDs 2,591; DVDs 3,428; Electronic Media & Resources 141; Large Print Bks 189; Music Scores 10; Bk Vols 56,379; Per Subs 201

Open Mon & Thurs 9:30-5, Tues 9:30-8, Wed 9:30-6, Fri & Sat 10-5, Sun 12-5

PIERREFONDS, 13555, boulevard Pierrefonds, H9A 1A6. Tel: 514-620-4181. FAX: 514-620-5503. *Chef de Div,* Louise Zampini; Tel: 514-620-4181, Ext 2210, E-mail: lzampini@ville.montreal.qc.ca; *Chef de Section,* Ève Durocher; Tel: 514-620-4181, Ext 2219, E-mail: edurovher@ville.montreal.qc.ca; Staff 30 (MLS 6, Non-MLS 24) Founded 1960. Circ 412,461

Library Holdings: Audiobooks 1,409; AV Mats 8,440; Braille Volumes 1; CDs 5,455; DVDs 2,833; Electronic Media & Resources 225; Large Print Bks 2,304; Music Scores 6; Bk Vols 186,735; Per Subs 593

Open Mon-Thurs 10-9, Fri 10-6, Sat & Sun 10-5

PLATEAU-MONT-ROYAL, 465, avenue du Mont-Royal Est, H2J 1W3, SAN 328-8838. Tel: 514-872-2270 (Adult serv), 514-872-2271 (Children's serv). FAX: 514-872-0532. *Chef de Div,* Anne-Marie Collins; Tel: 514-872-9966, E-mail: acollins@ville.montreal.qc.ca; *Bibliothecaire Responsable,* Vesna Dell'Olio; Tel: 514-872-0725, E-mail: vdellolio@ville.montreal.qc.ca Founded 1984. Circ 304,354

Library Holdings: Audiobooks 212; AV Mats 3,903; Braille Volumes 3; CDs 258; DVDs 3,628; Electronic Media & Resources 215; Large Print Bks 260; Music Scores 707; Bk Vols 80,858; Per Subs 532

Open Mon 12-5, Tues & Wed 10-8, Thurs 12-8, Fri 12-6, Sat & Sun 10-5

POINTE-AUX-TREMBLES, 14001, rue Notre-Dame Est, H1A 1T9, SAN 371-344X. Tel: 514-872-6987 (Adult serv), 514-872-9170 (Children's serv). FAX: 514-872-0525. *Chef de Div,* Claude Toupin; Tel: 514-872-2102, E-mail: ctoupin@ville.montreal.qc.ca; *Bibliothecaire Responsable,* Nicole St-Vincent; Tel: 514-872-0644, E-mail: nstvincent@ville.montreal.qc.ca; Staff 15 (MLS 3, Non-MLS 12) Founded 1983. Circ 233,581

Library Holdings: Audiobooks 311; AV Mats 1,077; Braille Volumes 1; CDs 321; DVDs 755; Electronic Media & Resources 187; Large Print Bks 541; Music Scores 39; Bk Vols 68,488; Per Subs 279

Open Mon & Sun 12-5, Tues & Wed 10-8, Thurs & Fri 10-6, Sat 10-5

RIVIERE-DES-PRAIRIES, 9001, boulevard Perras, H1E 3J7, SAN 376-026X. Tel: 514-872-9425 (Adult serv), 514-872-9494 (Children's serv). FAX: 514-872-9650. *Chef de Div,* Claude Toupin; Tel: 514-872-2102, E-mail: ctoupin@ville.montreal.qc.ca; *Bibliothecaire Responsable,* Joanne Dion; Tel: 514-872-9386, E-mail: jdion@ville.montreal.qc.ca; Staff 14 (MLS 3, Non-MLS 11) Founded 1995. Circ 192,021

Library Holdings: Audiobooks 306; AV Mats 1,673; CDs 323; DVDs 1,325; Electronic Media & Resources 179; Large Print Bks 492; Music Scores 200; Bk Vols 114,702; Per Subs 362

Open Mon & Sun 12-5, Tues & Wed 10-8, Thurs & Fri 10-6, Sat 10-5

ROBERT-BOURASSA, 41, avenue Saint-Just, H2V 4T7, SAN 319-8324. Tel: 514-495-6208. FAX: 514-495-6287. *Chef de Div,* Maryse Bouchard; Tel: 514-495-6270, E-mail: maryse_bouchard@ville.montreal.qc.ca; *Chef de Section,* Christiane St-Onge; Tel: 514-495-6209, E-mail: christianestonge@ville.montreal.qc.ca; Staff 15 (MLS 3, Non-MLS 12) Founded 1965. Pop 24,535; Circ 166,895

Library Holdings: Audiobooks 607; AV Mats 4,373; CDs 2,784; DVDs 1,173; Electronic Media & Resources 17; Large Print Bks 598; Music Scores 49; Bk Vols 76,816; Per Subs 295

Open Mon-Fri 1-9, Sat & Sun 10-6

ROSEMONT, 3131, boulevard Rosemont, H1Y 1M4, SAN 369-3724. Tel: 514-872-4701 (Adult serv), 514-872-6139 (Children's serv). FAX: 514-872-0527. *Chef de Div,* Line Ferland; Tel: 514-872-6557, E-mail: lineferland@ville.montreal.qc.ca; *Chef de Section,* Françoise Ménard; Tel: 514-872-4735, E-mail: francoise.menard@ville.montreal.qc.ca; Staff 4 (Non-MLS 4) Founded 1951. Circ 354,024

Library Holdings: Audiobooks 103; AV Mats 7,434; Braille Volumes 2; CDs 3,632; DVDs 3,760; Electronic Media & Resources 568; Large Print Bks 582; Music Scores 87; Bk Vols 87,038; Per Subs 329

Open Mon & Tues 1-8, Wed & Fri 10-6, Thurs 10-7, Sat & Sun 10-5

ROXBORO, 110, rue Cartier, H8Y 1G8, SAN 319-8766. Tel: 514-684-8247. FAX: 514-684-8563. *Chef de Div,* Louise Zampini; Tel: 514-620-4181, Ext 2210, E-mail: lzampini@ville.montreal.qc.ca; *Chef de Section,* Maurice Houle; Tel: 514-620-4181, Ext 2212, E-mail: mauricehoule@ville.montreal.qc.ca; Staff 5 (MLS 1, Non-MLS 4) Founded 1961. Circ 55,097

Library Holdings: Audiobooks 188; AV Mats 2,347; CDs 1,141; DVDs 1,155; Electronic Media & Resources 13; Large Print Bks 132; Bk Vols 53,438; Per Subs 165

Open Mon-Wed 1-9, Thurs 10-9, Fri 10-6, Sat 10-5, Sun 1-5

SAINT-CHARLES, 2333, rue Mullins (adultes), 1050, rue Hibernia (jeunes), H3K 3E3, SAN 369-3759. Tel: 514-872-3035 (jeunes), 514-872-3092 (adultes). *Chef de Div,* Chantal Beaulieu; Tel: 514-872-3067, E-mail: chantalbeaulieu@ville.montreal.qc.ca; *Chef de Section,* Louise Robichaud; Tel: 514-872-3763, E-mail: louiserobichaud@ville.montreal.qc.ca; Staff 8 (MLS 2, Non-MLS 6) Founded 1976. Circ 115,602

Library Holdings: Audiobooks 7; AV Mats 5,218; Braille Volumes 1; CDs 2,135; DVDs 3,074; Electronic Media & Resources 183; Large Print Bks 80; Music Scores 6; Bk Vols 43,744; Per Subs 282

Open Mon & Thurs-Fri 9-6, Tues-Wed 1-8, Sat 10-5, Sun 12-6

SAINT-HENRI, 4707, rue Notre-Dame Ouest, H4C 1S9, SAN 369-3694. Tel: 514-872-2879. FAX: 514-872-0512. *Chef de Div,* Chantal Beaulieu; Tel: 514-872-3067, E-mail: chantalbeaulieu@ville.montreal.qc.ca; *Chef de Section,* Daniel Legault; Tel: 514-872-2313, E-mail: daniel.legault@ville.montreal.qc.ca; Staff 8 (MLS 2, Non-MLS 6) Founded 1965. Circ 114,141

Library Holdings: Audiobooks 35; AV Mats 3,357; CDs 1,038; DVDs 2,319; Electronic Media & Resources 62; Large Print Bks 67; Music Scores 35; Bk Vols 39,492; Per Subs 262

Open Mon & Thurs-Fri 10-6, Tues 1-8, Wed 10-8, Sat 10-5, Sun 12-5

SAINT-LAURENT, 1380, rue de l'Église, H4L 2H2, SAN 319-8928. Tel: 514-855-6130, Ext 4747. FAX: 514-855-6129. *Chef de Div,* Andrée Tremblay; Tel: 514-855-6130, Ext 4722, E-mail: andree.tremblay@ville.montreal.qc.ca; *Chef de Section, Serv de Techniques,* Hélène Diamond; Tel: 514-855-6000, Ext 4728, E-mail: helene.diamond@ville.montreal.qc.ca; *Chef de Section, Serv Publics,* Dominique Gazo; Tel: 514-855-6000, Ext 4726, E-mail: dominique.gazo@ville.montreal.qc.ca; *Bibliothecaire Responsable,* Agnès Lassonde; Tel: 514-855-6000, E-mail: agnes.lassonde@ville.montreal.qc.ca; Staff 34 (MLS 8, Non-MLS 26) Founded 1950. Pop 91,946; Circ 524,379

Library Holdings: Audiobooks 1,076; AV Mats 19,239; CDs 10,334; DVDs 7,853; Electronic Media & Resources 253; Large Print Bks 1,873; Bk Vols 150,585; Per Subs 497

Open Mon-Wed 10-9, Thurs 10-8, Fri 10-6, Sat & Sun 10-5

SAINT-LEONARD, 8420, boulevard Lacordaire, H1R 3G5, SAN 319-8936. Tel: 514-328-8500, Ext 8592. FAX: 514-328-7002. *Chef de Div,* Sylvie Vézina; Tel: 514-328-8500, Ext 8517, E-mail: sylvie.vezina@ville.montreal.qc.ca; *Bibliothecaire Responsable,* Julie Leclair; Tel: 514-328-8500, Ext 8521, E-mail: julie.leclair@ville.montreal.qc.ca; Staff 29 (MLS 5, Non-MLS 24) Founded 1966. Pop 74,769; Circ 333,344

Library Holdings: Audiobooks 226; AV Mats 12,766; CDs 7,478; DVDs 2,160; Electronic Media & Resources 2,079; Large Print Bks 1,455; Bk Vols 203,346; Per Subs 1,558

Open Mon 1-9, Tues-Thurs 10-9, Fri 10-6, Sat 10-5, Sun 1-5

SAINT-MICHEL, 7601, rue François-Perrault, H2A 3L6, SAN 369-3813. Tel: 514-872-3899 (Adult serv), 514-872-4250 (Children's serv). FAX: 514-872-0528. *Chef de Div,* Mireille Cliche; Tel: 514-868-3444, E-mail: mcliche@ville.montreal.qc.ca; *Chef de Section,* Suzanne Thibault; Tel: 514-872-3910, E-mail: suzannethibault@ville.montreal.qc.ca; Staff 11 (MLS 3, Non-MLS 8) Founded 1970. Circ 251,158

Library Holdings: Audiobooks 142; AV Mats 3,695; Braille Volumes 5; CDs 1,385; DVDs 2,274; Electronic Media & Resources 163; Large Print Bks 336; Music Scores 42; Bk Vols 85,102; Per Subs 274

Open Mon 12-6, Tues 12-8:30, Wed 10-8:30, Thurs & Fri 10-6, Sat 10-5, Sun 12-5

SAINT-PIERRE, 183, rue des Érables, H8R 1B1. Tel: 514-634-3471, Ext 826. FAX: 514-634-8194. *Chef de Div,* Francine Hoffman; Tel: 514-634-3471, Ext 304, E-mail: fhoffman@ville.montreal.qc.ca; *Chef de Section,* Francine Dupuis; Tel: 514-634-3471, Ext 336, E-mail: francinedupuis@ville.montreal.qc.ca; Staff 4 (Non-MLS 4) Founded 1966. Circ 28,111

Library Holdings: Audiobooks 93; AV Mats 1,675; CDs 519; DVDs 638; Bk Vols 18,039; Per Subs 71

Open Mon-Wed 1-9, Thurs-Sat 9-5, Sun 12-5

SALABERRY, 4170, rue De Salaberry, H4J 1H1, SAN 369-3872. Tel: 514-872-1521. FAX: 514-872-0519. *Chef de Div,* Francine Elhadad; Tel: 514-872-8421, Fax: 514-872-4601, E-mail: felhadad@ville.montreal.qc.ca; *Chef de Section,* Sylvie Cantin; Tel: 514-868-5916, E-mail: scantin@ville.montreal.qc.ca; Staff 5 (MLS 1, Non-MLS 4) Founded 1964. Circ 97,565

Library Holdings: Audiobooks 4; AV Mats 1,488; Braille Volumes 1; CDs 7; DVDs 1,480; Electronic Media & Resources 81; Large Print Bks 3; Music Scores 4; Bk Vols 28,967; Per Subs 82
Open Mon, Thurs & Fri 9-5, Tues & Wed 9-6, Sat 11-5, Sun 12-5
SAUL-BELLOW, 3100, rue Saint-Antoine, H8S 4B8, SAN 319-6755. Tel: 514-634-3471, Ext 338 (Young adult), 514-634-3471, Ext 339 (Adults). FAX: 514-634-8194. *Chef de Div,* Francine Hoffman; Tel: 514-634-3471, Ext 304, E-mail: fhoffman@ville.montreal.qc.ca; *Chef de Section,* Francine Dupuis; Tel: 514-634-3471, Ext 336, E-mail: francinedupuis@ville.montreal.qc.ca; Staff 16 (MLS 4, Non-MLS 12)
Founded 1973. Circ 245,769
Library Holdings: Audiobooks 737; AV Mats 6,098; CDs 3,820; DVDs 1,970; Large Print Bks 1,292; Music Scores 840; Bk Vols 93,906; Per Subs 380
Open Mon-Thurs 9-9, Fri & Sat 9-5, Sun 10-5
VERDUN, 5955, rue Bannantyne, H4H 1H6, SAN 369-5646. Tel: 514-765-7170, 514-765-7172 (Adult serv), 514-765-7173 (Children's Servs). FAX: 514-765-7167. *Chef de Div,* Daniel Felton; Tel: 514-765-7281, E-mail: danielfelton@ville.montreal.qc.ca; Staff 17 (MLS 3, Non-MLS 14)
Founded 1975. Circ 206,763
Library Holdings: Audiobooks 452; AV Mats 12,707; CDs 7,460; DVDs 5,018; Electronic Media & Resources 186; Large Print Bks 381; Music Scores 232; Bk Vols 144,475; Per Subs 713
Open Mon, Wed & Thurs 1-9, Tues 10-9, Fri 10-6, Sat & Sun 12-5
Bookmobiles: 1

L   BORDEN LADNER GERVAIS LLP LIBRARY*, 1000 de la Gauchetiere W, Ste 900, H3B 5H4. SAN 325-8408. Tel: 514-954-3159. FAX: 514-954-1905. Web Site: www.blgcanada.com. *Head Librn,* Ronald Charest; E-mail: rcharest@blgcanada.com; *Acq,* Julie Brousseau; *Res Serv Spec,* Isabelle Lizotte; *Tech Serv,* Danielle Babin; E-mail: dbabin@mcmastergervais.qc.ca; Staff 4 (MLS 2, Non-MLS 2)
Founded 1980
Library Holdings: Bk Titles 8,000; Bk Vols 20,000; Per Subs 350
Automation Activity & Vendor Info: (Acquisitions) SirsiDynix; (Cataloging) SirsiDynix; (Circulation) SirsiDynix; (OPAC) SirsiDynix; (Serials) SirsiDynix
Database Vendor: Dialog, Factiva.com, Infomart, LexisNexis, Westlaw
Function: Res libr

S   BUSINESS DEVELOPMENT BANK OF CANADA RESEARCH & INFORMATION CENTER*, Five Place Ville Marie, 3rd Flr, H3B 5E7. SAN 329-8817. Tel: 514-283-7632. FAX: 514-283-0439. *Sr Info Spec,* Odette Lavoie; E-mail: odette.lavoie@bdc.ca; Staff 5 (MLS 3, Non-MLS 2)
Library Holdings: Bk Titles 6,000; Per Subs 100
Subject Interests: Small bus develop banking
Partic in Dialog Corp

G   CANADA DEPARTMENT OF JUSTICE MONTREAL HEADQUARTERS LIBRARY*, East Tower, 9th flr, No 200 Quest boul Rene-Levesque W, H2Z 1X4. SAN 326-0046. Tel: 514-283-6674, 514-283-8739. FAX: 514-283-6425. *Librn,* Andre Archambault; *Asst Librn,* Linda Cryans; Staff 2 (MLS 2)
Founded 1982
Library Holdings: Bk Titles 24,000; Per Subs 250
Subject Interests: Law, Law enforcement
Publications: Acquisitions List

SR   CANADIAN CENTRE FOR ECUMENISM LIBRARY*, 1819, René-Lévesque ouest, Bureau No 003, H3H 2P5. SAN 319-7131. Tel: 514-937-9176. FAX: 514-937-4986. Web Site: www.oikoumene.ca/collections/library. *Libr Coordr,* Bernice Baranowski; *Archivist,* Francoise Martel; Staff 3 (MLS 3)
Founded 1963
Library Holdings: CDs 50; DVDs 50; Bk Titles 7,000; Bk Vols 7,250; Per Subs 150
Special Collections: Histoire de l'Eglise (2000 Ans de Christianisme); World Council of Churches, Geneva, Switzerland, Publications
Subject Interests: Bible, Can churches, Christian churches, Ecology, Ecumenism, Ethics, Hist of relig, Interchurch, Interfaith dialogue, Ministry, Native people, Relig freedom, Spirituality, Theol, World relig
Publications: Ecumenism (Quarterly); Oecumenisme (Quarterly)

R   CANADIAN JEWISH CONGRESS CHARITIES COMMITTEE, National Archives, 1590 Docteur Penfield Ave, H3G 1C5. SAN 319-714X. Tel: 514-931-7531. FAX: 514-931-0548. E-mail: archives@cjccc.ca. Web Site: www.cjccc.ca. *Archivist,* Janice Rosen; Staff 2 (MLS 1, Non-MLS 1)
Founded 1934
Library Holdings: Bk Titles 1,500
Subject Interests: Can Jewish hist
Publications: Canadian Jewish Archives Series
Restriction: Open to pub for ref only

S   THE CANADIAN ZIONIST FEDERATION*, Israel Information Center, One Carre Cummings Sq, Ste 206, 5151 Cote St Catherine, H3W 1M6. SAN 373-6547. Tel: 514-739-7300, Ext 3100. FAX: 514-739-9412. *Dir,* Florence Simon
Founded 1985
Special Collections: Israel-Zionism, bks, flms, pamphlets, videos

S   CEGEP DU VIEUX MONTREAL LIBRARY*, 255 Ontario St E, H2X 1X6. SAN 328-3119. Tel: 514-982-3437. FAX: 514-982-3448. Web Site: www.cvm.qc.ca. *Coordr,* Lise Vincent; Tel: 514-982-3437, Ext 2580, E-mail: lvincent@cvm.qc.ca; *Librn,* Michel Chops; E-mail: mhache@cvm.qc.ca
Library Holdings: Bk Vols 100,000; Per Subs 500
Subject Interests: Art
Database Vendor: EBSCOhost, SirsiDynix
Open Mon-Thurs 8am-9pm, Fri 8-5

J   CEGEP MARIE-VICTORIN BIBLIOTHEQUE*, 7000 rue Marie-Victorin, H1G 2J6. SAN 319-7360. Tel: 514-325-0150, Ext 2363. FAX: 514-328-3840. Web Site: www.resdoc.ccsr.qc.ca/biblio/marie. *Coordr,* Alain Vezina; E-mail: alain.vezina@collegemv.qc.ca
Founded 1965
Library Holdings: Bk Vols 67,000
Subject Interests: Behav sci, Humanities, Natural sci, Relig studies, Soc sci

S   CENTRE CANADIEN D'ARCHITECTURE/CANADIAN CENTRE FOR ARCHITECTURE, 1920 rue Baile, H3H 2S6. SAN 322-8878. Tel: 514-939-7000. Circulation Tel: 514-939-7011. FAX: 514-939-7020. E-mail: ref@cca.qc.ca. Web Site: www.cca.qc.ca. *Head, Acq,* Kathryn Kollar; E-mail: kkollar@cca.qc.ca; *Head, Coll Cat,* Judy Silverman; E-mail: jsilverm@cca.qc.ca; *Head, User Serv,* Renata Guttman; E-mail: rguttman@cca.qc.ca; Staff 10 (MLS 7, Non-MLS 3)
Founded 1979
Library Holdings: Bk Titles 192,000; Bk Vols 240,000; Per Subs 700
Special Collections: Architectural Toys & Games; Architectural Trade Catalogues; Early Architectual Treatises; English Country House Guides; Fortifications; Frank Lloyd Wright; Italian Regional Histories & City Guides; Portraits of Architects; Russian Architecture; World Fairs
Subject Interests: Archit, Archit hist, Landscape design, Urban planning
Automation Activity & Vendor Info: (Acquisitions) SirsiDynix; (Cataloging) SirsiDynix; (OPAC) SirsiDynix; (Serials) SirsiDynix
Database Vendor: SirsiDynix
Wireless access
Partic in OCLC Online Computer Library Center, Inc
Restriction: Open by appt only

S   CENTRE CANADIEN D'ETUDES ET DE COOPERATION INTERNATIONALE*, Centre de Documentation, 3000 Omer-Lavallee, H1Y 3R8. SAN 319-7255. Tel: 514-875-9911, Ext 288. FAX: 514-875-6469. E-mail: info@ceci.ca. Web Site: www.ceci.ca. *Doc,* Carmen Houle; E-mail: carmenh@ceci.ca
Founded 1958
Library Holdings: Bk Titles 20,000; Per Subs 120
Subject Interests: Asia, Develop of Third World countries, Latin Am, Mainly Africa

S   CENTRE D'ANIMATION, DE DEVELOPPEMENT ET DE RECHERCHE EN EDUCATION-BIBLIOTHEQUE*, 1940 Est Blvd Henri Bourassa, H2B 1S2. SAN 319-7247. Tel: 514-381-8891, Ext 246. FAX: 514-381-4086. E-mail: info@cadre.qc.ca. Web Site: www.cadre.qc.ca. *Librn,* Roland Desrosiers; E-mail: desrosiersr@cadre.qc.ca. Subject Specialists: *Pvt educ,* Roland Desrosiers; Staff 1 (MLS 1)
Founded 1968
Library Holdings: Bk Titles 7,100; Per Subs 40
Subject Interests: Primary educ, Pvt educ, Secondary educ
Automation Activity & Vendor Info: (Cataloging) CDS-ISIS (Unesco)

S   CENTRE DE DOCUMENTATION SUR L'EDUCATION DES ADULTES ET LA CONDITION FEMININE, 110 rue Ste-Therese, Ste 101, H2Y 1E6. SAN 323-7052. Tel: 514-876-1180. Toll Free Tel: 866-972-1180 (Canada only). FAX: 514-876-1325. E-mail: info@cdeacf.ca. Web Site: www.cdeacf.ca. *Dir Gen,* Genevieve Dorais-Beauregard; *Commun Serv Coordr,* Astou Niang; *Coordr, Doc,* Sharon Hackett; Staff 12 (MLS 3, Non-MLS 9)
Founded 1983
Apr 2011-Mar 2012 Income (CAN) $1,261,110. Sal (CAN) $818,747
Library Holdings: e-books 1,825; e-journals 58; Electronic Media & Resources 3,875; High Interest/Low Vocabulary Bk Vols 518; Bk Titles 31,119; Bk Vols 39,050; Spec Interest Per Sub 100; Videos 622
Special Collections: Directory of Researchers & Research in Adult Education & Literacy in Canada; Feminist Archives; Literacy & Adult Basic Education Coll; Organizations Working in Adult Education & Women's Issues

Subject Interests: Adult learning, Adult literacy, Women's studies
Wireless access
Publications: Bibliographie sélective (Bibliographies); NetFemmes, EFA, Horizon Alpha (Monthly bulletin); Pour voir plus loin (Acquisition list); Rapport annuel (Annual report)
Partic in ASTED
Friends of the Library Group

M   **CENTRE HOSPITALIER DE L'UNIVERSITE DE MONTREAL***, Hôpital St Luc Library, 1058 rue Saint Denis, H2X 3J4. SAN 325-5166. Tel: 514-890-8000, Ext 35867. FAX: 514-412-7317. E-mail: 06_chum_biblio_st-luc@ssss.gouv.qc.ca. *Librn,* Andre Allard; E-mail: andre.allard.chum@ssss.gouv.qc.ca; Staff 4 (MLS 1, Non-MLS 3)
Library Holdings: Bk Titles 12,200; Per Subs 400
Subject Interests: Alcohol abuse, Drug abuse, Hospital admin
Automation Activity & Vendor Info: (Acquisitions) Infor Library & Information Solutions; (Cataloging) Infor Library & Information Solutions; (Circulation) Infor Library & Information Solutions; (OPAC) Infor Library & Information Solutions; (Serials) Infor Library & Information Solutions
Database Vendor: OVID Technologies
Partic in Association des Bibliotheques de la Sante Affiliees a L'Universite de Montreal

M   **CENTRE HOSPITALIER JACQUES VIGER***, Centre de Documentation, 1051 rue St Hubert, H2L 3Y5. SAN 324-3915. Tel: 514-842-7180, Ext 2104. FAX: 514-842-1212. *In Charge,* Danielle Cayer
Library Holdings: Bk Titles 500; Per Subs 45
Subject Interests: Geriatrics, Gerontology, Med, Nursing
Open Wed & Fri 8-4:30

S   **CENTRE INTERNATIONAL DE CRIMINOLOGIE COMPAREE***, Centre de Documentation, 3150 Jean-Brillant, Local C-4110, H3T 1N8. (Mail add: Universite de Montreal Centre de documentation - criminologie, CP 6128 Succursale Centre-ville, H3C 3J7), SAN 325-8297. Tel: 514-343-6534. FAX: 514-343-2269. *Doc,* Aniela Belina; E-mail: belina@cicc.umontreal.ca
Subject Interests: Crime, Criminal justice, Criminology, Juv delinquency, Penology, Police, Private security, Victimology
Open Mon, Tues, Thurs & Fri 9-12 & 1:30-5, Wed 1:30-5
Restriction: Borrowing privileges limited to fac & registered students, Open to pub for ref only, Open to researchers by request, Open to students, fac & staff

G   **CENTRE JEUNESSE DE MONTREAL - INSTITUT UNIVERSITAIRE***, Bibliotheque, 1001 boul de Maisonneuve est, 5ieme etage, H2L 4R5. SAN 325-8270. Tel: 514-896-3396. FAX: 514-896-3483. E-mail: bibliotheque@cjm-iu.qc.ca. Web Site: www.centrejeunessedemontreal.qc.ca/bibliotheque. *Librn,* Paule Asselin; *Librn,* Jeanne Bazinet; *Tech Serv,* Suzanne Payeur; Staff 3 (MLS 2, Non-MLS 1)
Library Holdings: AV Mats 714; Bk Titles 30,000; Per Subs 80
Subject Interests: Child welfare, Juv delinquency, Youth
Database Vendor: OVID Technologies
Function: For res purposes

GL   **CHAMBRE DES NOTAIRES DU QUEBEC***, Centre de Documentation, Tour Bourse 800 Victoria Pl, H4Z 1L8. SAN 328-4832. Tel: 514-879-1793, Ext 240. FAX: 514-879-1697. *Asst Dir,* Lise Lachance; E-mail: lise.lachance@cdnq.org
Library Holdings: Bk Titles 5,965; Per Subs 500
Subject Interests: Law

M   **CHU SAINTE-JUSTINE***, Centre d'information, 3175 Chemin Cote-Sainte-Catherine, H3T 1C5. SAN 319-7565. Tel: 514-345-4681. Interlibrary Loan Service Tel: 514-345-4682. FAX: 514-345-4806. Web Site: www.chu-sainte-justine.org/cise. *Head of Libr,* Louis-Luc Lecompte; E-mail: louis-luc_lecompte@ssss.gouv.qc.ca; *Ref,* Louise Jolin; E-mail: louise_jolin@ssss.gouv.qc.ca. Subject Specialists: *Child psychiat, Neonatology, Pediatrics,* Louis-Luc Lecompte; Staff 2 (MLS 2)
Founded 1936
Library Holdings: AV Mats 2,700; e-journals 230; Bk Vols 9,500; Per Subs 420
Special Collections: Mediatheque, AV mat; Parent Information Resources
Subject Interests: Adolescence, Child psychiat, Neonatology, Pediatric nursing, Pediatrics
Automation Activity & Vendor Info: (Acquisitions) BiblioMondo; (Cataloging) BiblioMondo; (Circulation) BiblioMondo; (OPAC) BiblioMondo; (Serials) BiblioMondo
Database Vendor: OVID Technologies
Publications: Guide Info-Famille (2008) (Reference guide)
Open Mon-Wed 8-8, Thurs & Fri 8-6

M   **CHUM, HOPITAL NOTRE-DAME,** Bibliothèque médicale, 1560 rue Sherbrooke Est, H2L 4M1. SAN 319-7964. Tel: 514-890-8000, Ext 27217. Interlibrary Loan Service Tel: 514-890-8000, Ext 25842. Information

Services Tel: 514-890-8000, Ext 26862. FAX: 514-412-7569. E-mail: biblio.hnd.chum@ssss.gouv.qc.ca. *Chief Librn,* Diane St-Aubin; Tel: 514-890-8000, Ext 14269, E-mail: diane.st-aubin.chum@ssss.gouv.qc.ca; Staff 4 (MLS 1, Non-MLS 3)
Founded 1930
Library Holdings: Bk Vols 30,000; Per Subs 286
Subject Interests: Allied sci, Med
Automation Activity & Vendor Info: (Acquisitions) Infor Library & Information Solutions; (Cataloging) Infor Library & Information Solutions; (Circulation) Infor Library & Information Solutions; (Course Reserve) Infor Library & Information Solutions; (OPAC) Infor Library & Information Solutions; (Serials) Infor Library & Information Solutions
Database Vendor: OVID Technologies
Partic in Association des Bibliotheques de la Sante Affiliees a L'Universite de Montreal

S   **CINEMATHEQUE QUEBECOISE***, Mediatheque Guy-L-Cote, 335 boul de Maisonneuve est, H2X 1K1. SAN 324-5209. Tel: 514-842-9768, Ext 262. FAX: 514-842-1816. Web Site: www.cinematheque.qc.ca. *Librn,* Rene Beauclair; E-mail: rbeauclair@cinematheque.qc.ca; *Ref,* Julienne Boudreau; E-mail: jboudreau@cinematheque.qc.ca; *Ref,* Julie Dubuc; E-mail: jdubuc@cinematheque.qc.ca; *Ref,* Lorraine Le Blanc; E-mail: lleblanc@cinematheque.qc.ca; *Ref,* Manon Viens; E-mail: mviens@cinematheque.qc.ca; Staff 6 (MLS 1, Non-MLS 5)
Founded 1970
Library Holdings: Bk Titles 45,000; Per Subs 450
Subject Interests: Cinema, Television, Video
Publications: Reperes Bibliographiques (irregular)
Open Tues-Fri 1-8

S   **CMC ELECTRONICS INC LIBRARY***, 600 Dr Frederick Philips Blvd, H4M 2S9. SAN 319-7158. Tel: 514-748-3000, Ext 4577, 514-748-3148. FAX: 514-748-3100. Web Site: www.cmcelectronics.ca. *Librn,* Mary Thomson
Founded 1952
Library Holdings: Bk Titles 4,500; Per Subs 150
Subject Interests: Avionics, Electronics
Restriction: Staff use only

C   **COLLEGE DE BOIS-DE-BOULOGNE BIBLIOTHEQUE,** 10555, ave de Bois-de-Boulogne, H4N 1L4. SAN 372-8404. Tel: 514-332-3000, Ext 6467. FAX: 514-332-0083. Web Site: www.bdeb.qc.ca/services-aux-etudiants/bibliotheque. *Chief Librn,* Marthe Francoeur; Staff 1 (MLS 1)
Founded 1968. Enrl 2,800
Library Holdings: DVDs 522; Electronic Media & Resources 16; Bk Titles 47,811; Bk Vols 56,328; Per Subs 125
Automation Activity & Vendor Info: (Acquisitions) BiblioMondo; (Cataloging) BiblioMondo; (Circulation) BiblioMondo; (Course Reserve) BiblioMondo; (OPAC) BiblioMondo; (Serials) BiblioMondo
Wireless access
Open Mon-Thurs 7:40-6:15, Fri 7:40-5

C   **COLLEGE DE MAISONNEUVE CENTRE DES MEDIAS***, 3800 Est rue Sherbrooke E, H1X 2A2. SAN 319-731X. Tel: 514-254-7131. Circulation Tel: 514-254-7131, Ext 4221. Interlibrary Loan Service Tel: 514-254-7131, Ext 4730. Reference Tel: 514-254-7131, Ext 4733. FAX: 514-254-2517. E-mail: biblio@cmaisonneuve.qc.ca. Web Site: www.cmaisonneuve.qc.ca. *Coordr,* Marjolaine Millette; Tel: 514-254-7131, Ext 4239, E-mail: mmillette@cmaisonneuve.qc.ca; *Acq, ILL,* Lise Ulrich; E-mail: lulrich@cmaisonneuve.qc.ca; *Bibliog Instr, Ref,* Nathalie Ouellet; Tel: 514-254-7131, Ext 4279, E-mail: nouellet@cmaisonneuve.qc.ca; *Bibliog Instr, Ref,* Mario Paille; Tel: 514-254-7131, Ext 4770, E-mail: mpaille@cmaisonneuve.qc.ca; Staff 21 (MLS 3, Non-MLS 18)
Founded 1952. Enrl 7,082
Special Collections: Can & Prov
Automation Activity & Vendor Info: (Acquisitions) SirsiDynix; (Cataloging) SirsiDynix; (Circulation) SirsiDynix; (OPAC) SirsiDynix; (Serials) SirsiDynix
Function: AV serv, Res libr
Publications: Fiche Technique d Utilisation De Canadian Reference Center; Guide cle Recherche du Catalogue; Guide de Recherche E-STAT; Guide de Recherche Internet; Guide de Recherche sur Biblio Branchee; Guide de Recherche sur Repere; Guide des Cederoms; Guide pour citer un Document electronique; Guide pour citer un document paper ou audiovisuel; List of Periodicals; Methodologie de Recherche; Rapport Annuel

C   **COLLEGE DE MONTREAL BIBLIOTHEQUE***, 1931 Ouest rue Sherbrooke, H3H 1E3. SAN 319-7328. Tel: 514-933-7397. FAX: 514-933-3225. E-mail: cdm@college-montreal.qc.ca. Web Site: www.college-montreal.qc.ca. *Dir,* Margarite Trenblay
Founded 1961
Library Holdings: Bk Vols 10,000

Special Collections: Canadian & French History (secondary school)
Subject Interests: Secondary sch educ

J   COLLEGE DE ROSEMONT (CEGEP) BIBLIOTHEQUE*, 6400 16th
Ave, H1X 2S9. SAN 319-7336. Tel: 514-376-1620, Ext 265. FAX:
514-376-1440. Web Site: www.resdoc.ccsr.qc.ca/biblio/rosem. *Dir,* Josee
Corriveau; E-mail: jcorriveau@crosemont.qc.ca; *Acq,* Nicole Desnoyers;
Cat, Diane Gloutnay; *Res,* Maryse Desaulniers
Founded 1969
Library Holdings: AV Mats 4,413; Bk Titles 56,444; Per Subs 154
Partic in RESDOC
Open Mon-Wed 8am-9pm, Thurs 8-6, Fri 8-4:30

M   COLLEGE DES MEDECINS DU QUEBEC, Centre de Documentation,
2170 Rene-Levesque Blvd W, H3H 2T8. SAN 319-8049. Tel:
514-933-4441, Ext 5253, 514-933-4441, Ext 5254. FAX: 514-933-9112.
E-mail: cdoc@cmq.org. *Libr Tech,* Helene Landry; *Libr Tech,* Guylaine
Lavigne
Founded 1961
Subject Interests: Health serv, Med educ, Med ethics
Restriction: Not open to pub

C   COLLEGE JEAN-DE-BREBEUF*, Bibliotheque de Pavillon Lalemant,
5625 rue Decelles, H3T 1W4. SAN 319-7344. Tel: 514-342-9342, Ext
5261. FAX: 514-342-1558. E-mail: bibliocol@brebeuf.qc.ca. Web Site:
www.brebeuf.qc.ca. *Ref Serv Coordr,* Genevieve Everaere; E-mail:
genevieve.everaere@brebeuf.qc.ca; Staff 7 (MLS 3, Non-MLS 4)
Founded 1958. Enrl 1,550; Fac 116
Library Holdings: Bk Titles 63,796; Bk Vols 70,338; Per Subs 325
Subject Interests: Can hist, Cinema, Fine arts, Philosophy, Polit sci
Database Vendor: EBSCOhost

C   COLLEGE LASALLE*, Centre de Documentation et Support Didactique,
Bureau 4100, 2000 Saint Catherine St W, H3H 2T2. SAN 323-9101. Tel:
514-939-2006, Ext 4470. Toll Free Tel: 800-363-3541. FAX:
514-939-7292. Web Site: www.clasalle.com. *Librn,* Elisabeth Lebel;
E-mail: elebel@clasalle.com; *AV,* Gilles Dion; Tel: 514-939-2006, Ext
4439; *Ref,* Renee-Claude Larouche; Tel: 514-939-2006, Ext 4503; *Tech
Serv,* Sylvie Auger; Tel: 514-939-2006, Ext 4407; Staff 4 (MLS 1,
Non-MLS 3)
Enrl 2,000; Highest Degree: Master
Library Holdings: Bk Titles 7,000; Bk Vols 12,000; Per Subs 200
Subject Interests: Computer sci, Fashion, Hotel, Mgt, Tourism
Publications: New Acquisitions List
Open Mon-Thurs 7:30am-8pm, Fri 7:30-6

J   COLLEGE MARIE DE FRANCE LIBRARY*, 4635 chemin Queen Mary,
H3W 1W3. SAN 319-7352. Tel: 514-737-1177. FAX: 514-737-0789. Web
Site: www.mariedefrance.qc.ca. *Dir,* Jean Pierre Giraud; *Librn,* Esther
Legendre; *Librn,* Agnes Sedjro
Library Holdings: Bk Vols 2,500
Open Mon-Thurs 7:30-7, Fri 7:30-6

C   COLLEGE NOTRE DAME LIBRARY*, 3791 Queen Marie Rd, H3V
1A8. SAN 319-7379. Tel: 514-739-3371. FAX: 514-739-4833. E-mail:
info@collegenotre-dame.qc.ca. Web Site: www.collegenotre-dame.qc.ca.
Librn, Colette Leduc
Library Holdings: Bk Titles 50,000; Per Subs 110
Open Mon-Fri 8-7

C   COLLEGE O'SULLIVAN LIBRARY*, 1191 de la Montagne, H3G 1Z2.
SAN 323-6501. Tel: 514-866-4622. Toll Free Tel: 800-621-8055. FAX:
514-866-0668. Web Site: www.osullivan.edu. *Librn,* Jose Descheneaux;
E-mail: jdescheneaux@osullivan.edu
Founded 1976. Enrl 500; Fac 10
Library Holdings: Bk Titles 3,200; Bk Vols 5,000; Per Subs 23
Open Mon-Fri 8:30-6

G   COMMISSION DE LA SANTE ET DE LA SECURITE DU TRAVAIL,
Centre de Documentation, 1199 rue de Bleury, 4th Flr, H3B 3J1. SAN
324-7430. Tel: 514-906-3760. Toll Free Tel: 1-888-873-3160. FAX:
514-906-3820. E-mail: documentation@csst.qc.ca. Web Site:
www.centredoc.csst.qc.ca. Staff 12 (MLS 8, Non-MLS 4)
Founded 1979
Library Holdings: AV Mats 1,500; Bk Titles 60,000; Bk Vols 120,000;
Per Subs 200
Subject Interests: Occupational health, Occupational safety
Automation Activity & Vendor Info: (Acquisitions) BiblioMondo;
(Cataloging) BiblioMondo; (Circulation) BiblioMondo; (OPAC)
BiblioMondo; (Serials) BiblioMondo
Publications: Bibliographies sélectives; Liste des Nouvelles Acquisitions;
Repertoire des Documents Audio Visuel: Sante et Securite en Images;
Thesaurus CSST

G   COMMISSION DES VALEURS MOBILIERES DU QUEBEC
BIBLIOTHEQUE*, 800 Square Victoria, 22nd Flr, CP 246, H4Z 1G3.
SAN 370-744X. Tel: 514-940-2199, Ext 4494. FAX: 514-873-3090. Web
Site: www.cvmq.com. *Cat, Pub Serv, Tech Serv,* Lucie LaFrance; E-mail:
lucie.lafrance@cvmq.com; *Pub Serv, Ref,* Gilles Lachance; *Pub Serv, Ref
Serv, Tech Serv,* Annik Zimmer; Staff 4 (MLS 2, Non-MLS 2)
Founded 1971
Library Holdings: Bk Titles 10,000; Bk Vols 17,000; Per Subs 210
Subject Interests: Securities
Publications: Acquisition List (bi-monthly)

C   CONCORDIA UNIVERSITY LIBRARIES, 1400 de Maisonneuve Blvd W,
LB 209, H3G 1M8. (Mail add: 1455 de Maisonneuve Blvd W, LB 209,
H3G 1M8), SAN 369-2221. Tel: 514-848-2424, Ext 7777. Interlibrary
Loan Service Tel: 514-848-2424, Ext 7716. Reference Tel: 514-848-2424,
Ext 7700, 514-848-2424, Ext 7722. Administration Tel: 514-848-2424, Ext
7743. Information Services Tel: 514-848-2424, Ext 7706. FAX:
514-848-2882. Interlibrary Loan Service FAX: 514-848-2801. E-mail:
lib.admin@concordia.ca. Web Site: library.concordia.ca. *Univ Librn,* Gerald
Beasley; Tel: 514-848-2424, Ext 7695, E-mail:
gerald.beasley@concordia.ca; *Dir, Vanier Libr,* Dubravka Kapa; Tel:
514-848-2424, Ext 7721, Fax: 514-848-2804, E-mail:
dubravka.kap@concordia.ca; *Dir, Webster Libr,* Dr Guylaine Beaudry; Tel:
514-848-2424, Ext 7699, E-mail: guylaine.beaudry@concordia.ca; *Assoc
Univ Librn, Coll Serv,* Cynthia Holt; Tel: 514-848-2424, Ext 5255, E-mail:
cynthia.holt@concordia.ca; *Assoc Univ Librn, Info Tech & Syst,* Jean-Marc
Edwards; Tel: 514-848-2424, Ext 7732, E-mail:
jean-marc.edwards@concordia.ca; *Assoc Univ Librn, Personnel &
Communications,* David Thirlwall; Tel: 514-848-2424, Ext 7693, E-mail:
david.thirlwall@conconcordia.ca; *Mgr, Budget & Fac,* Alexander Konyari;
Tel: 514-848-2424, Ext 7761, E-mail: alex.konyari@concordia.ca; Staff 40
(MLS 35, Non-MLS 5)
Founded 1974. Highest Degree: Doctorate
May 2011-Apr 2012. Mats Exp (CAN) $4,260,955
Library Holdings: CDs 41,992; DVDs 5,599; e-books 331,762;
Microforms 1,305,078; Music Scores 3,609; Bk Titles 1,549,127; Bk Vols
1,840,355; Per Subs 63,686
Special Collections: Adrien Arcand Coll; Christopher Fry's Works;
Concordia Theses & MBA Papers; Gay & Lesbian Coll; Irving Layton
Coll; James Card Coll; Peter Desbarats Coll; Quinn Coll; René Balcer
Archives. Can & Prov
Subject Interests: Admin, Arts, Commerce, Computer sci, Eng, Fine arts,
Sci
Automation Activity & Vendor Info: (Cataloging) Innovative Interfaces,
Inc; (Circulation) Innovative Interfaces, Inc; (ILL) Innovative Interfaces,
Inc; (OPAC) Innovative Interfaces, Inc
Database Vendor: EBSCOhost, Elsevier, Gale Cengage Learning,
LexisNexis, Mergent Online, OCLC FirstSearch, Thomson - Web of
Science, Wilson - Wilson Web
Wireless access
Partic in Canadian Research Knowledge Network; CREPUQ
Friends of the Library Group
Departmental Libraries:
COUNSELLING & DEVELOPMENT, CAREER RESOURCE CENTRE,
1455 de Maisonneuve Blvd W, H-440, H3G 1M8. Tel: 514-848-2424,
Local 3556. FAX: 514-848-4534. Web Site: cdev.concordia.ca/cnd/crc.
Librn, Marlis Hubbard; Tel: 514-848-2424, Local 7385, E-mail:
marhub@alcor.concordia.ca; *Assoc Librn,* Susan Hawke; E-mail:
hawke@alcor.concordia.ca; Staff 2 (MLS 2)
Founded 1950. Enrl 32,530; Fac 2,000; Highest Degree: Doctorate
Library Holdings: CDs 50; DVDs 80; Bk Titles 10,000; Per Subs 30;
Spec Interest Per Sub 22; Videos 30
Special Collections: Disabled, Women & Labour
Subject Interests: Career planning, Educ planning, Financial aid, Job
hunting techniques, Travel
Automation Activity & Vendor Info: (Acquisitions) FileMaker;
(Cataloging) FileMaker; (Circulation) FileMaker; (OPAC) FileMaker
Function: CD-ROM, Computers for patron use, e-mail serv, Online
searches, Ref serv available, Referrals accepted, Telephone ref
Publications: Acquisitions List
Restriction: Access at librarian's discretion, Open to pub for ref & circ;
with some limitations, Open to students, fac & staff
FACULTY OF FINE ARTS SLIDE LIBRARY, 1395 Rene Levesque Blvd
W, H3G 2M5. (Mail add: VA Bldg, Rm VA433, 1455 de Maisonneuve
Blvd W, H3G 1M8), SAN 370-9183. Tel: 514-848-2424, Ext 4274. FAX:
514-848-8627. *Curator,* Janice Anderson; E-mail:
janicea@vax2.concordia.ca. Subject Specialists: *Can art,* Janice
Anderson; Staff 1 (Non-MLS 1)
Founded 1969. Highest Degree: Doctorate
Library Holdings: AV Mats 300,000
Special Collections: Canadian Sculpture, Mid-19th & 20th Century;
Quebec Stained Glass
Subject Interests: 20th Century Can art, Archit, Art hist, Ceramics,
Contemporary art hist, Fibres

Open Mon-Thurs 8:15-6, Fri 8:15-4
Restriction: Open to fac, students & qualified researchers

S   CONSERVATOIRE DE MUSIQUE DE MONTREAL BIBLIOTHEQUE*,
4750 Ave Henri-Julien, H2T 2C8. SAN 369-2167. Tel: 514-873-4031.
FAX: 514-873-3346. E-mail: cmm.bib@conservatoire.gouv.qc.ca. Web Site:
www.conservatoire.gouv.qc.ca/montreal/bibliotheque.html. *Librn,* Denise
Prince; Tel: 514 873-3485, E-mail: denise.prince@conservatoire.gouv.qc.ca;
Staff 6 (MLS 1, Non-MLS 5)
Founded 1942. Highest Degree: Master
Library Holdings: Per Subs 81
Special Collections: Music (Cooper Coll, Arthur Garami Coll, Jean
Deslauriers Coll); Scores & Manuscripts of the 16th, 17th & 18th
Centuries; Wilfrid Pelletier Coll
Subject Interests: Analysis, Chamber music, Composition, Hist, Opera,
Orchestra, Theory
Automation Activity & Vendor Info: (Acquisitions) BiblioMondo;
(Cataloging) BiblioMondo; (Circulation) BiblioMondo; (OPAC)
BiblioMondo; (Serials) BiblioMondo
Publications: Foldings on Research Strategy; Foldings on Service; List of
New Acquisitions
Open Mon-Fri 9-7, Sat 11-4
Restriction: Not open to pub, Open to students, fac & staff

M   CSSS DU COEUR-DE L'ILE-HOPITAL JEAN-TALON*, Bibliotheque
Medicale, 1385, Jean-Talon Est, H2E 1S6. SAN 328-2791. Tel:
514-495-6767, Ext 6420. FAX: 514-495-6738. Web Site:
www.santemontreal.qc.ca/csss/coeordelile/fr/default.aspx?.
Founded 1961
Library Holdings: CDs 56; Bk Vols 1,795; Per Subs 61; Videos 58
Partic in Docline
Open Mon-Fri 8-11 & 12-3:30
Restriction: Staff use only
Friends of the Library Group

L   DE GRANDPRE CHAIT LIBRARY*, 1000 de la Gauchetiere Ouest, Ste
2900, H3B 4W5. SAN 375-3670. Tel: 514-878-4311. FAX: 514-878-4333.
Librn, Ruth Veilleux; Staff 2 (MLS 1, Non-MLS 1)
Founded 1928
Library Holdings: Bk Titles 8,000
Partic in Muse; Soquiz; Westlaw
Open Mon-Fri 8:15-6

M   DOUGLAS MENTAL HEALTH UNIVERSITY INSTITUTE*, Charles
Cahn Library, 6875 LaSalle Blvd, Perry Pavilion, Rm E4501, H4H 1R3.
SAN 319-9401. Tel: 514-762-3029. FAX: 514-762-3039. E-mail:
biblio@douglas.mcgill.ca. *Chief Librn,* Benoit Cameron; *Libr Tech,*
Marie-Line Rioux
Library Holdings: Bk Vols 5,000; Per Subs 200

C   ECOLE DE TECHNOLOGIE SUPERIEURE (SERVICE DE LA
BIBLIOTHEQUE)*, 1100 rue Notre-Dame Ouest, H3C 1K3. SAN
375-488X. Tel: 514-396-8946. Circulation Tel: 514-396-8960. Interlibrary
Loan Service Tel: 514-396-8585. Reference Tel: 514-396-8591. FAX:
514-396-8633. E-mail: biblio@etsmtl.ca. Web Site: www.etsmtl.ca/biblio.
Coll Develop, Dir, Louise Thibaudeau; E-mail:
louise.thibaudeau@etsmtl.ca; *Librn,* Bernard Bizimana; E-mail:
bernard.bizimana@etsmtl.ca; *Librn, Webmaster,* Denis Levasseur; E-mail:
denis.levasseur@etsmtl.ca; *Librn,* Paul Marchand; E-mail:
paul.marchand@etsmtl.ca; *Circ,* Lucette Lapointe; E-mail:
lucette.lapointe@etsmtl.ca; *Bibliog Instr, Ref,* Edith Healy; E-mail:
edith.healy@etsmtl.ca; *ILL,* Danielle Fournier; E-mail:
danielle.fournier@etsmtl.ca; *Per,* Anne Goyette; E-mail:
anne.goyette@etsmtl.ca; *Cat,* Gaston Fournier; E-mail:
gaston.fournier@etsmtl.ca; Staff 18 (MLS 6, Non-MLS 12)
Founded 1974. Enrl 3,857; Fac 90; Highest Degree: Doctorate
Library Holdings: AV Mats 410; e-books 5,000; Electronic Media &
Resources 1,905; Bk Vols 60,053; Per Subs 4,000
Special Collections: Rapports techniques de l'ETS
Subject Interests: Eng
Database Vendor: Dialog, netLibrary, OCLC FirstSearch
Publications: Biblio-listes (Reference guide)

C   ECOLE POLYTECHNIQUE DE MONTREAL BIBLIOTHEQUE*, 2500,
chemin de Polytechnique, H3T 1J4. (Mail add: CP 6079, succursale
Centre-ville, H3C 3A7), SAN 319-7468. Tel: 514-340-4666. Circulation
Tel: 514-340-4849. Interlibrary Loan Service Tel: 514-340-4846. Reference
Tel: 514-340-4665. FAX: 514-340-4026. E-mail: biblio@polytml.ca. Web
Site: www.polymtl.ca/biblio. *Dir,* Richard Dumont; E-mail:
rdumont@polymtl.ca; *Head, Coll Develop,* Marc Hiller; E-mail:
mhiller@polymtl.ca; *Head, Ref,* Marie-Helene Dupuis; E-mail:
mhdupuis@polymtl.ca; *Head, Syst Serv,* Greg Whitney; E-mail:
gwhitney@polymtl.ca; *Head, Tech Serv,* Minh-Thu Nguyen; E-mail:
mtnguyen@polymtl.ca; *Info Serv,* Manon Du Ruisseau; E-mail:

manon.du.ruisseau@polymtl.ca; *Info Serv,* Genevieve
Gamache-Vaillancourt; *Info Serv,* Huguette Mallet; E-mail:
hmallet@polymtl.ca; *Info Serv,* Madeleine Proulx; E-mail:
mproulx@polymtl.ca; *Tech Serv,* Luc Foucault; E-mail:
lfoucault@polymtl.ca; *Tech Serv,* Andre Maltais; E-mail:
amaltais@polymtl.ca; Staff 11 (MLS 11)
Founded 1873. Enrl 6,000; Fac 225; Highest Degree: Doctorate
Special Collections: Can; Industrial Catalogs Coll; Technical Standards
Subject Interests: Applied sci, Eng
Wireless access
Publications: Infotech
Open Mon-Thurs (Sept-Apr) 8:30am-9:55pm, Fri 8:30am-8:55pm, Sat 10-5

G   EMPLOI QUEBEC*, Centre de Documentation, 276 rue St-Jacques, 6e
etage, H2Y 1N3. SAN 374-5503. Tel: 514-864-3086. Interlibrary Loan
Service Tel: 514-864-4969. FAX: 514-864-3239. E-mail:
documentationeq@mess.gouv.qc.ca. *Librn,* Nicole Dumoulin; E-mail:
nicole.dumoulin@mess.gouv.qc.ca; *Libr Tech,* Stephanie Vachon; E-mail:
stephanie.vachon@mess.gouv.qc.ca; Staff 1 (MLS 1)
Founded 1993
Library Holdings: AV Mats 80; CDs 150; Bk Titles 10,000; Per Subs 400
Subject Interests: Econ, Educ
Publications: News List
Open Mon-Fri 8:30-4:30

L   FASKEN MARTINEAU DUMOULIN LLP*, Law Library, 800 Victoria
Sq, H4Z 1E9. (Mail add: PO Box 242, H4Z 1E9), SAN 372-7424. Tel:
514-397-7400, 514-397-7439. Reference Tel: 514-397-5154, 514-397-7632.
FAX: 514-397-7600. *Dir,* Stephanie Grenier; Tel: 514-397-4320, E-mail:
sgrenier@mtl.fasken.com; *Librn,* Sylvie Hetu; Tel: 514-397-5154, E-mail:
shetu@mtl.fasken.com; *Librn,* Nathalie St-Jacques; Tel: 514-397-7632,
E-mail: nstjacques@mtl.fasken.com; *Asst Librn,* Danielle Gilbert; E-mail:
dgilbert@mtl.fasken.com; Staff 6 (MLS 3, Non-MLS 3)
Founded 1920
Library Holdings: e-journals 28; Electronic Media & Resources 139; Bk
Titles 8,493; Per Subs 428; Videos 10
Special Collections: Can & Prov
Function: Res libr
Open Mon-Fri 8-6
Restriction: Mem only

M   FEDERATION DES MEDECINS SPECIALISTES DU QUEBEC
BIBLIOTHEQUE*, Two Complexe Desjardins, Ste 3000, H5B 1G8. (Mail
add: CP 216 Succ Desjardins, H5B 1G8), SAN 372-9028. Tel:
514-350-5000. FAX: 514-350-5100. Web Site: www.fmsq.org. *Librn,*
Angele L'Heureux
Library Holdings: Bk Vols 5,000; Per Subs 150
Subject Interests: Med

S   FEDERATION DES TRAVAILLEURS ET TRAVAILLEUSES DU
QUEBEC*, Centre de Documentation, 565 Cremazie Blvd E, Ste 12100,
H2M 2W3. SAN 373-7322. Tel: 514-383-8025. FAX: 514-383-0502. Web
Site: www.ftq.qc.ca. *Head of Libr,* Isabelle Reny; E-mail: ireny@ftq.qc.ca;
Staff 1 (MLS 1)
Founded 1957
Library Holdings: AV Mats 480; CDs 81; DVDs 24; Bk Titles 11,000;
Per Subs 74; Videos 375
Subject Interests: Economy, Labor, Soc sci, Unions
Restriction: Non-circulating, Open by appt only

L   FRASER MILNER CASGRAIN LIBRARY*, One Place Ville Marie, 39th
Flr, H3B 4M7. SAN 328-2783. Tel: 514-878-8800. FAX: 514-866-2241.
Librn, Sonya Eder; Tel: 514-878-8890, E-mail: sonya.eder@fmc-law.com;
Staff 3 (MLS 1, Non-MLS 2)
Library Holdings: Bk Titles 10,000; Per Subs 400
Subject Interests: Civil law, Commercial, Corporate, Environment,
Finance, Intellectual property, Labor, Taxation
Automation Activity & Vendor Info: (Acquisitions) EOS International;
(Cataloging) EOS International; (Circulation) EOS International; (ILL)
EOS International; (Serials) EOS International
Database Vendor: LexisNexis
Function: ILL available
Restriction: Not open to pub, Private libr

G   GOVERNMENT DU QUEBEC MINISTERE DE L'IMMIGRATION ET
DES COMMUNAUTES CULTURELLES*, MICC Centre de
Documentation, 360 McGill St, ss-14, H2Y 2E9. SAN 319-7506. Tel:
514-873-3255, Ext 20207. FAX: 514-864-2468. Web Site:
www.micc.gouv.qc.ca.
Founded 1968
Library Holdings: Bk Titles 20,920; Bk Vols 31,820; Per Subs 315
Subject Interests: Immigration, Minorities, Refugees
Publications: Revue de Presse

C HEC MONTREAL*, Myriam & J Robert Ouimet Library, 3000, chemin de la Cote-Sainte-Catherine, H3T 2A7. SAN 319-745X. Tel: 514-340-6220. Interlibrary Loan Service Tel: 514-340-6230. Reference Tel: 514-340-3851. FAX: 514-340-5639. E-mail: biblio.info@hec.ca. Web Site: www.hec.ca/biblio. *Dir,* Maureen Clapperton; Tel: 514-340-6689; *Head, Tech Serv,* Bernard Bizimana; Tel: 514-340-6217; *Head, User Serv,* Sylvain Champagne; Tel: 514-340-6211; *Librn,* Caroline Archambault; Tel: 514-340-6221; *Librn,* Diane Begin; Tel: 514-340-6223; *Librn,* Michelle Champagne; Tel: 514-340-6224; *Librn,* Jean-Yves Cote; Tel: 514-340-3657; *Librn,* Francine Gendron; Tel: 514-340-6215; Staff 8 (MLS 8)
Founded 1910. Enrl 11,000; Fac 240; Highest Degree: Doctorate
Library Holdings: AV Mats 2,923; e-books 17,912; Electronic Media & Resources 52,230; Microforms 17,101; Bk Titles 241,634; Bk Vols 366,280; Per Subs 4,153
Subject Interests: Acctg for bus mgt, Bus admin, Distribution mgt, Economics, Electronic commerce, Financial mgt, Info syst, Mgt, Mkt, Operations mgt, Production mgt, Retail mgt
Automation Activity & Vendor Info: (Acquisitions) SirsiDynix; (Cataloging) SirsiDynix; (Circulation) SirsiDynix; (ILL) Fretwell-Downing; (OPAC) SirsiDynix; (Serials) SirsiDynix
Database Vendor: SirsiDynix
Function: Doc delivery serv, ILL available, Online searches, Ref serv available

M HOPITAL HOTEL-DIEU DU CHUM, Centre de Documentation, 3840 rue St-Urbain, H2W 1T8. SAN 319-7530. Tel: 514-890-8000, Ext 14355. Reference Tel: 514-890-8000, Ext 14781. Administration Tel: 514-890-8000, Ext 14269. E-mail: biblio.hdm.chum@ssss.gouv.qc.ca. Web Site: bibliothequeduchum.ca. *Actg Dir,* Diane St-Aubin; E-mail: diane.st-aubin@ssss.gouv.qc.ca; *Syst Librn,* Jonathan Laporte; Tel: 514-890-8000, Ext 27217. E-mail: jonathan.laporte.chum@ssss.gouv.qc.ca; *Acq,* Johanne Chaperon; E-mail: johanne.chaperon@ssss.gouv.qc.ca; *Doc Delivery,* Pierre Mercier; E-mail: pierre.mercier.chum@ssss.gouv.qc.ca; Staff 3 (MLS 1, Non-MLS 2)
Founded 1947
Library Holdings: e-journals 200; Bk Titles 1,000; Per Subs 200
Subject Interests: Med
Automation Activity & Vendor Info: (ILL) Relais International; (OPAC) Infor Library & Information Solutions
Database Vendor: OVID Technologies, UpToDate
Partic in Association des Bibliotheques de la Sante Affiliees a L'Universite de Montreal

M HOPITAL LOUIS-H LAFONTAINE*, Documentation Centre, 7401 Hochelaga, H1N 3M5. SAN 319-7697. Tel: 514-251-4000, Ext 2964. FAX: 514-251-0270. E-mail: centrededocumentation.hlhl@ssss.gouv.qc.ca. Web Site: www.hlhl.qc.ca/centre-de-documentation/qui-sommes-nous.html. *Librn Spec,* Marie Désilets; Tel: 514-251-4000, Ext 2332, E-mail: mdesilets.hlhl@ssss.gouv.qc.ca; *Tech Spec,* Guyane Choquette-Poulin; Tel: 514-251-4000, Ext 3291, E-mail: gchoquette-poulin.hlhl@ssss.gouv.qc.ca; *Tech Spec,* Marc-Yvan Custeau; Tel: 514-251-4000, Ext 2963, E-mail: mcusteau@ssss.gouv.qc.ca; *Tech Spec,* Jacqueline Rochefort; Tel: 514-251-4000, Ext 2965, E-mail: jrochefo@ssss.gouv.qc.ca. Subject Specialists: *Psychiat,* Marie Désilets; Staff 4 (MLS 1, Non-MLS 3)
Founded 1948
Library Holdings: Bk Vols 6,000; Per Subs 100
Subject Interests: Psychiat
Open Mon-Fri 8:30-4

M HOPITAL MAISONNEUVE-ROSEMONT*, Bibliotheque Medicale, 5415 boul de l'Assomption, H1T 2M4. SAN 319-7549. Tel: 514-252-3462. Interlibrary Loan Service Tel: 514-252-3463. FAX: 514-252-3574. Web Site: biblio.hmr.qc.ca. *Chief Librn,* Helene Lauzon; E-mail: hlauzon.hmr@ssss.gouv.qc.ca; *Acq,* Lucie Grise; E-mail: lgrise.hmr@ssss.gouv.qc.ca; *ILL,* Donatien Michaud; E-mail: dmichaud.hmr@ssss.gouv.qc.ca; *Ref,* Odette Hinse; Staff 4 (MLS 1, Non-MLS 3)
Founded 1955
Apr 2009-Mar 2010. Mats Exp (CAN) $185,264, Books (CAN) $4,350, Per/Ser (Incl. Access Fees) (CAN) $158,914, Electronic Ref Mat (Incl. Access Fees) (CAN) $20,000. Sal (CAN) $108,335 (Prof (CAN) $80,000)
Library Holdings: CDs 40; DVDs 20; e-journals 355; Electronic Media & Resources 15; Bk Titles 3,165; Bk Vols 5,114; Per Subs 451; Videos 15
Subject Interests: Bone marrow transplant, Family med, Hematology, Immunology, Kidney transplant, Med, Nursing, Oncology, Ophthalmology, Para-nursing, Pediatrics, Psychiat
Automation Activity & Vendor Info: (Acquisitions) BiblioMondo; (Cataloging) BiblioMondo; (Circulation) BiblioMondo; (OPAC) BiblioMondo; (Serials) BiblioMondo
Function: Computers for patron use, Copy machines, Doc delivery serv, Electronic databases & coll, Fax serv, Health sci info serv, ILL available
Publications: Patients & Family Booklets (Documents)
Partic in Association des Bibliotheques de la Sante Affiliees a L'Universite de Montreal; Consortium des Bibliotheques du RUIS Universite Laval

Open Mon-Fri 8-5
Restriction: Access at librarian's discretion, Authorized patrons, Clients only, Hospital employees & physicians only, Hospital staff & commun, Lending to staff only, Med & nursing staff, patients & families, Not open to pub

M HOPITAL RIVIERE-DES-PRAIRIES*, Bibliotheque du Personnel, 7070 boul Perras, H1E 1A4. SAN 324-4024. Tel: 514-323-7260, Ext 2316. FAX: 514-323-3512. Web Site: www.hrdp.qc.ca. *In Charge,* Martine Ouellet; *Libr Tech,* Isabelle Barette; Staff 2 (MLS 1, Non-MLS 1)
Library Holdings: Bk Vols 8,000; Per Subs 70
Special Collections: Can & Prov
Subject Interests: Child & adolescent psychiat & psychol, Mental deficiency
Partic in Association des Bibliotheques de la Sante Affiliees a L'Universite de Montreal

M HOSPITAL SANTA CABRINI*, Centre de Documentation, 5655 est Saint Zotique, H1T 1P7. SAN 324-4032. Tel: 514-252-6488. FAX: 514-252-6432. *Tech Serv,* Diane Seguin; E-mail: dseguin@ssss.gouv.qc.ca; *Tech Serv,* Helene Prezeau
Library Holdings: AV Mats 200; Bk Titles 4,200; Per Subs 128
Subject Interests: Emergency med, Family practice, Gynecology, Internal med, Nursing, Obstetrics, Surgery
Open Mon-Fri 8:30-4:30
Restriction: Staff use only

S HYDRO QUEBEC BIBLIOTHEQUE*, 800, De Maisonneuve E, blvd, 2nd Flr, H2L 4M8. SAN 319-7573. Tel: 514-840-3000, Ext 5939. FAX: 514-840-5044. E-mail: bibliotheque@hydro.qc.ca. *Actg Librn,* France Bélanger; *Actg Librn,* André Fradette; *Actg Librn,* Pierre Gaudreau; *Actg Librn,* Marcel Ouellet; Staff 5 (MLS 3, Non-MLS 2)
Founded 1962
Library Holdings: Bk Titles 16,000; Bk Vols 22,000; Per Subs 25
Subject Interests: Electrical utilities, Energy, Eng, Mkt, Tech standards
Partic in Dialog Corp

S INFO ENTREPRENEURS, Strategic Information Centre, 380 Saint Antoine Ouest, Bureau W 204, H2Y 3X7. SAN 319-7808. Tel: 514-496-4636. Interlibrary Loan Service Tel: 514-496-5928. Administration Tel: 514-496-5927. Toll Free Tel: 800-322-4636. FAX: 514-496-5934. Web Site: www.infoentrepreneurs.org. *Supvr,* Cindy Desmarais; Staff 6 (MLS 4, Non-MLS 2)
Founded 1994
Library Holdings: Electronic Media & Resources 20
Special Collections: Entrepreneurship Coll
Subject Interests: Bus, Govt aid & subsidies, Intl trade, Ratings
Wireless access
Open Mon-Fri 9-3

CR INSTITUT DE FORMATION THEOLOGIQUE DE MONTREAL BIBLIOTHEQUE, 2065, rue Sherbrooke Ouest, H3H 1G6. SAN 326-3991. Tel: 514-935-1169. FAX: 514-935-5497. E-mail: biblio@iftm.ca. Web Site: www.iftm.ca. *Borrower Serv Librn,* Odette Dallaire; *Acq of Monographs,* Marie-Hélène De Montigny; E-mail: achats@iftm.ca; Staff 2 (Non-MLS 2)
Founded 1841. Enrl 108; Highest Degree: Master
Library Holdings: CDs 73; Bk Vols 153,510; Per Subs 142; Videos 245
Special Collections: Patrology Coll
Subject Interests: Philosophy, Theol
Open Mon-Thurs 8:30-12 & 1-5, Fri 8:30-12 & 12:30-3

M INSTITUT DE READAPTION GINGRAS-LINDSAY-DE-MONTREAL*, Centre de Documentation, 6300 Darlington Ave, H3S 2J4. SAN 325-8386. Tel: 514-340-2085, Ext 2270. FAX: 514-340-2716. *Actg Adminr,* Lucie Pelletier; Staff 1 (Non-MLS 1)
Apr 2008-Mar 2009 Income (CAN) $71,000. Mats Exp (CAN) $28,950, Books (CAN) $4,400, Per/Ser (Incl. Access Fees) (CAN) $24,200, Presv (CAN) $350. Sal Prof (CAN) $52,918
Library Holdings: CDs 5; DVDs 10; e-books 10; e-journals 270; Bk Vols 4,000; Per Subs 100; Videos 10
Subject Interests: Neuropsychology, Nursing, Occupational therapy, Phys therapy, Physiatry, Rehabilitation
Partic in Association des Bibliotheques de la Sante Affiliees a L'Universite de Montreal
Open Mon-Fri 8:30-12 & 1-4:30

M INSTITUT DE RECHERCHES CLINIQUES DE MONTREAL LIBRARY*, 110 Pine Ave W, Rm 2340, H2W 1R7. Tel: 514-987-5596. FAX: 514-987-5675. E-mail: biblio@ircm.qc.ca. Web Site: www.ircm.qc.ca. *Librn,* Nicole Campeau; Tel: 514-987-5599, E-mail: campean@ircm.qc.ca; *Tech Serv,* Claudia Jones; Tel: 514-987-5598, E-mail: jonesc@ircm.qc.ca; *Tech Serv,* Martine Lauzier; E-mail: lauziem@ircm.qc.ca

Library Holdings: Bk Titles 3,000; Per Subs 100
Partic in Association des Bibliotheques de la Sante Affiliees a L'Universite de Montreal
Open Mon-Fri 8-5

S   INSTITUT RAYMOND-DEWAR REHABILITATION CENTRE FOR THE DEAF, DEAFBLIND & HARD OF HEARING*, Centre de Documentation, 3600, rue Berri, H2L 4G9. SAN 326-2545. Tel: 514-284-2214, Ext 3610. FAX: 514-284-5086. E-mail: biblio@raymond-dewar.gouv.qc.ca. *Dir,* Rachel Graveline; Staff 1 (MLS 1) Founded 1984
Library Holdings: AV Mats 500; Bks on Deafness & Sign Lang 3,000; Bk Titles 4,500; Bk Vols 8,000; Per Subs 90
Special Collections: History of the Deaf (Quebec, Canada & other countries); Sign Language Dictionaries
Subject Interests: Audiology, Deaf culture, Deaf hist, Deafness, Sign lang, Speech disorders
Function: Res libr
Publications: Summaries of Periodicals (quarterly) (Index to periodicals) Special Services for the Deaf - Bks on deafness & sign lang; Captioned film dep; Spec interest per; Staff with knowledge of sign lang; TTY equip; Videos & decoder

C   INSTITUT TECCART INC LIBRARY*, 3030 Hochelaga, H1W 1G2. SAN 373-6679. Tel: 514-526-2501. Toll Free Tel: 866-832-2278. FAX: 514-526-9192. E-mail: info@teccart.qc.ca. Web Site: www.teccart.qc.ca. *Librn,* Pierre Dewolf
Founded 1945. Enrl 120
Library Holdings: Bk Vols 2,000; Per Subs 75
Special Collections: Invention & Technology (Comment C A Marche Coll)

M   INSTITUT UNIVERSITAIRE DE GERIATRIE DE MONTREAL*, Medical Library, 4565 Chemin Queen Mary, H3W 1W5. SAN 319-809X. Tel: 514-340-2800, Ext 3266. FAX: 514-340-2815. Web Site: www.iugm.qc.ca. *Chief Librn,* Audrey Attia; E-mail: audrey.attia.iugm@ssss.gouv.qc.ca
Founded 1947
Library Holdings: Bk Titles 10,000; Per Subs 175
Subject Interests: Chronic care, Geriatrics, Gerontology, Neuropsychology, Related specialities

S   INSTITUTE PHILIPPE PINEL DE MONTREAL BIBLIOTHEQUE*, 10905 Henri Bourassa Blvd E, H1C 1H1. SAN 319-7662. Tel: 514-648-8461, Ext 557. FAX: 514-881-3706. Web Site: www.pinel.qc.ca. *Librn,* Normand Beaudet; E-mail: normand_beaudet@ssss.gouv.qc.ca
Founded 1970
Library Holdings: Bk Titles 8,000; Per Subs 60
Subject Interests: Criminology, Legal psychiat, Psychiat
Restriction: Open by appt only

S   INTERNATIONAL CIVIL AVIATION ORGANIZATION*, Web & Library, 999 University St, H3C 5H7. SAN 319-7689. Tel: 514-954-8207. FAX: 514-954-6077. Web Site: www.icao.int. *Libr Asst,* Ghislaine Giroux; E-mail: ggiroux@icao.int; Staff 2 (Non-MLS 2)
Founded 1946
Library Holdings: Bk Vols 20,000; Per Subs 143
Special Collections: Academie de Droit International, 1923 to date, Recueil de cours; International Law
Subject Interests: Aeronaut, Air, Air transport, Aviation med, Intl law, Law, Meteorology
Restriction: Open by appt only

SR   INTERNATIONAL INSTITUTE OF INTEGRAL HUMAN SCIENCES LIBRARY*, 1974 de Maisonneuve W, H3H 1K5. (Mail add: PO Box 1387, Sta H, H3G 2N3), SAN 329-224X. Tel: 514-937-8359. FAX: 514-937-5380. E-mail: mrossner@iiihs.org. Web Site: www.iiihs.com. *Librn,* Bibiane Lyman
Founded 1976. Enrl 200; Fac 10
Library Holdings: Bk Vols 10,000
Subject Interests: Comparative relig, Consciousness studies, Healing
Function: Ref serv available, Res libr
Open Mon-Fri 1-7

S   ITALIAN CULTURAL INSTITUTE*, 1200 Dr Penfield Ave, H3A 1A9. SAN 328-3941. Tel: 514-849-3473. FAX: 514-849-2569. Web Site: www.italcultur.org. *Actg Dir,* Giovanna Jatropelli
Library Holdings: Bk Titles 10,000; Per Subs 119
Open Mon-Thurs 9-1 & 2-5, Fri 9-1

S   JARDIN BOTANIQUE DE MONTREAL BIBLIOTHEQUE*, 4101 Sherbrooke St E, H1X 2B2. SAN 329-7748. Tel: 514-872-1440, 514-872-1824. FAX: 514-872-5167. E-mail:

jardin_botanique@ville.montreal.qc.ca. Web Site: www.ville.montreal.qc.ca/jardin/biblio/biblio.htm, www.ville.montreal.qc.ca/jardin/jardin.htm. *Librn,* Celine Arseneault; E-mail: celine_arseneault@ville.montreal.qc.ca; *Asst Librn, Libr Tech,* Guy Frenette; E-mail: guy_frenette@ville.montreal.qc.ca; *Curator,* Lise Servant; *Info Spec,* Steluta Ovesia; Staff 1 (MLS 1)
Library Holdings: Bk Vols 30,000; Per Subs 250
Special Collections: Curtis Botanical Illustration Mag, bd per, watercolors; Documentation Center on Japanese Horticulture & Japan
Subject Interests: Botany, Hort, Landscape archit, Urban forestry
Publications: Publications au Jardin Botanique de Montreal
Open Mon-Sat 9-4:30

S   KPMG RESEARCH*, 2000 McGill College Ave Ste 1900, H3A 3H8. SAN 322-7898. Tel: 514-840-2254. FAX: 514-840-2162. Web Site: www.kpmg.ca. *Res,* Claude Gagnon; E-mail: claudegagnon@kpmg.ca; *Res,* Jimmy Gallant; Tel: 514-840-2362, E-mail: jgallant@kpmg.ca; *Res,* Samantha Sohmer; Tel: 514-840-2252, E-mail: ssohmer@kpmg.ca; Staff 2 (MLS 2)
Library Holdings: Bk Vols 2,000; Per Subs 100
Subject Interests: Acctg, Auditing, Taxation, Transportation
Automation Activity & Vendor Info: (Cataloging) Inmagic, Inc.; (Serials) Inmagic, Inc.
Publications: Acquisitions List
Open Mon-Fri 8:30-5

S   KSH SOLUTIONS*, One Pl Alexis Nihon, 3400 Maisonneuve West Bureau 1600, H3Z 3B8. SAN 328-4484. Tel: 514-932-4611. FAX: 514-932-9700. *Librn,* Dorothy Monstad; E-mail: dmonstad@ksh.ca
Founded 1976
Library Holdings: Bk Titles 2,500; Per Subs 20
Subject Interests: Eng
Open Mon-Thurs 8:30am-10:30am

G   LABORATOIRE DE SCIENCES JUDICIAIRES ET DE MEDICINE LEGALE, Centre de Documentation, Ministere de la Securite Publique Edifice Wilfrid Derome, 1701 rue Parthenais, 12th Flr, H2K 3S7. SAN 326-3762. Tel: 514-873-3301, Ext 61446. FAX: 514-873-4847. E-mail: lsjml-bib@msp.gouv.qc.ca. *Librn,* Guylaine Marion; *Asst Librn,* Zineb Bahi; Tel: 514-873-3301, Ext 61565; Staff 2 (MLS 1, Non-MLS 1)
Founded 1968
Library Holdings: e-journals 30; Bk Titles 5,000; Per Subs 70
Special Collections: Dr Wilfrid Derome Collection
Subject Interests: Forensic medicine, Forensic sci
Automation Activity & Vendor Info: (Acquisitions) Inmagic, Inc.; (Cataloging) Inmagic, Inc.; (Media Booking) Inmagic, Inc.; (OPAC) Inmagic, Inc.; (Serials) Inmagic, Inc.
Function: Govt ref serv
Publications: Liste des nouvelles acquisitions (Acquisition list)
Open Mon-Fri 8-12 & 1-4
Restriction: Access at librarian's discretion
Friends of the Library Group

S   LAFLEUR & BROWN LIBRARY*, One Place Ville Marie, 37th Flr, H3B 3P4. SAN 326-3649. Tel: 514-878-9641. FAX: 514-878-1450. Web Site: www.gowlings.com. *Librn,* Linda Ramsay; Tel: 514-392-9538; Staff 2 (MLS 1, Non-MLS 1)
Library Holdings: Bk Titles 3,000; Per Subs 425
Subject Interests: Corporate law
Restriction: Not open to pub

S   LE DEVOIR*, Centre de Documentation, 2050 rue de Bleury, 9th Flr, H3A 3M9. SAN 319-7700. Tel: 514-985-3333. FAX: 514-985-3360. Web Site: www.ledevoir.com. *Librn,* Gilles Pare; E-mail: gpare@ledevoir.com
Founded 1972
Subject Interests: Econ, Politics, Relig studies
Open Mon-Fri 8-7

G   RACINE LOUISE DOCUMENTATION CENTER*, 500 Sherbrooke W, H3A 3G6. SAN 326-2979. Tel: 514-499-5188. FAX: 514-873-4900. *Dir,* Daniel Collette; *Acq, Tech Serv,* Lynda Pilote; E-mail: lynda.pilote@loto-quebe.com; *Circ, Per,* Carole Dumont; *Tech Serv,* Anne Marie Sinard; E-mail: anne-marie.simards@loto-quebec.com; Staff 2 (MLS 2)
Founded 1978
Library Holdings: Bk Titles 4,000; Per Subs 400
Subject Interests: Gambling
Open Mon-Fri 8:30-4

S   LOWER CANADA COLLEGE LIBRARY*, 4090 Royal Ave, H4A 2M5. SAN 372-7742. Tel: 514-482-9916. FAX: 514-482-0195. Web Site: www.lcc.ca. *Head Librn,* Maria Varvarikos; E-mail: mvarvarikos@lcc.ca; Staff 6 (MLS 1, Non-MLS 5)
Library Holdings: Bk Titles 27,000

M MAIMONIDES HOSPITAL GERIATRIC CENTRE*, Health Information Centre, 5795 Caldwell Ave, H4W 1W3. SAN 321-673X. Tel: 514-483-2121, Ext 2217. FAX: 514-483-1086. Web Site: www.maimonides.net. *Head, Archives & Patient Info,* Nidaa Karnib; Tel: 514-483-2121, Ext 2299
Founded 1966
Library Holdings: Bk Titles 2,000; Per Subs 100
Automation Activity & Vendor Info: (Cataloging) Inmagic, Inc.; (Circulation) Inmagic, Inc.; (OPAC) Inmagic, Inc.
Database Vendor: OVID Technologies
Publications: Resource Subject Guide
Open Mon-Fri 9-5

C MCGILL UNIVERSITY LIBRARIES*, 3459 McTavish St, H3A 1Y1. SAN 369-2612. Tel: 514-398-4677. FAX: 514-398-3561. E-mail: doadmin.library@mcgill.ca. Web Site: www.mcgill.ca/library. *Dir,* Janine Schmidt; Tel: 514-398-1840, E-mail: janine.schmidt@mcgill.ca; *Assoc Dir, Client Serv, Humanities, Law, Mgt & Soc Sci,* Carole Urbain; Tel: 514-398-5725, Fax: 514-398-7184, E-mail: carole.urbain@Mcgill.ca; *Assoc Dir, Client Serv, Sci, Health & Eng,* Louis Houle; Tel: 514-398-4763, Fax: 514-398-3903, E-mail: louis.houle@mcgill.ca; *Assoc Dir, Coll Serv,* Joseph Hafner; Tel: 514-398-4788, Fax: 514-398-8919, E-mail: joseph.hafner@mcgill.ca; *Assoc Dir, Libr Tech Serv,* Louise O'Neill; Tel: 514-398-5898, Fax: 514-398-8919, E-mail: louise.oneill@mcgill.ca; *Assoc Dir, Planning & Res,* Diane Koen; Tel: 514-398-2149, E-mail: diane.koen@mcgill.ca; Staff 65 (MLS 64, Non-MLS 1)
Founded 1821. Enrl 33,258; Fac 2,575; Highest Degree: Doctorate
Special Collections: 16th & 17th Century Tracts (Redpath Coll); Architecture (Blackader Coll); Blake Coll; Canadiana (Arkin Coll & Lande Coll); Early Geology (Adams Coll); Entomology (Lyman Coll); History of Science & Medicine (Osler Coll); Hume Coll; Kierkegaard Coll; Leacock Coll; Marionettes (Stearn Coll); Napoleon Coll; Natural History & Ornithology (Blacker-Wood Coll); Printing (Colgate Coll); Shakespeare Coll; UN, Can, Prov & Food/Agr Orgn
Automation Activity & Vendor Info: (Acquisitions) Ex Libris Group; (Cataloging) Ex Libris Group; (Circulation) Ex Libris Group; (Course Reserve) Ex Libris Group; (ILL) Fretwell-Downing; (Media Booking) Ex Libris Group; (OPAC) Ex Libris Group; (Serials) Ex Libris Group
Database Vendor: 3M Library Systems, ABC-CLIO, Academy of Political Science, ACM (Association for Computing Machinery), Agricola, Alexander Street Press, American Chemical Society, American Mathematical Society, American Psychological Association (APA), Annual Reviews, ARTstor, ASCE Research Library, AZIMUT, Baker & Taylor, BioOne, Blackwell's, Bloomberg, Bowker, BWI, Cambridge Scientific Abstracts, Canadian Reference Centre, Cinahl Information Systems, CISTI Source, Commonwealth Business Media, Community of Science (COS), Coutts Information Service, Dialog, Dun & Bradstreet, ebrary, EBSCO Information Services, EBSCOhost, Elsevier, Elsevier MDL, Emerald, EOS International, Ex Libris Group, Factiva.com, Facts on File, Gale Cengage Learning, Greenwood Publishing Group, Grolier Online, H W Wilson, Haworth Pres Inc, HeinOnline, Hoovers, IEEE (Institute of Electrical & Electronics Engineers), IHS, IOP, ISI Web of Knowledge, Jane's, JSTOR, Knovel, Kompass, Lexi-Comp, LexisNexis, Majors, Marquis Who's Who, McGraw-Hill, Medlib, Medline, Mergent Online, Micromedex, MicroPatent, Modern Language Association, Nature Publishing Group, netLibrary, Newsbank, OCLC ArticleFirst, OCLC FirstSearch, OCLC Openly Informatics, OCLC WorldCat, OCLC-RLG, OneSource, OVID Technologies, Oxford Communications, Oxford Online, Project MUSE, ProQuest, PubMed, Quicklaw, ReferenceUSA, RefWorks, Safari Books Online, ScienceDirect, Springer-Verlag, Standard & Poor's, STN International, Swets Information Services, Sybase, Tech Logic, TechBooks, Thomson - Web of Science, Thomson Carswell, UpToDate, ValueLine, WebMD, Westlaw, WestlaweCARSWELL, Wiley, Wilson - Wilson Web, World Book Online, YBP Library Services
Wireless access
Publications: Fontanus
Partic in Association of Research Libraries (ARL); Canadian Association of Research Libraries; Canadian Research Knowledge Network; CREPUQ
Special Services for the Deaf - ADA equip
Special Services for the Blind - Accessible computers
Friends of the Library Group
Departmental Libraries:
BLACKADER-LAUTERMAN LIBRARY OF ARCHITECTURE & ART, Redpath Library Bldg, 3459 McTavish St, H3A 1Y1, SAN 369-2884. Tel: 514-398-4742. FAX: 514-398-6695. Web Site: www.mcgill.ca/blackader. *Librn,* Marilyn Berger; E-mail: marilyn.berger@mcgill.ca; Staff 1 (MLS 1)
Founded 1922
Library Holdings: Bk Titles 80,093; Bk Vols 85,702; Per Subs 353
Automation Activity & Vendor Info: (Acquisitions) Ex Libris Group; (Cataloging) Ex Libris Group; (Circulation) Ex Libris Group; (OPAC) Ex Libris Group; (Serials) Ex Libris Group
Oprn Mon-Fri (Winter) 9-5; Mon-Thurs (Summer) 9-5

MARVIN DUCHOW MUSIC LIBRARY, New Music Bldg, 3rd Flr, 527 Sherbrooke St W, H3A 1E3, SAN 369-3120. Tel: 514-398-4695. Interlibrary Loan Service Tel: 514-398-3426. FAX: 514-398-8276. Web Site: www.mcgill.ca/library/library-using/branches/music-library. *Head Librn,* Cynthia Leive
Library Holdings: AV Mats 89,993; CDs 27,632; DVDs 1,934; Microforms 194; Music Scores 52,359; Bk Titles 24,243; Bk Vols 28,034; Per Subs 237; Videos 307
Special Collections: Bassoon (Bruce Bower Coll), music, parts, scores; David Edelberg/Handel Coll, bks, scores, sound rec; Fonds Discographique Noël-Vallerand; Marvin Duchow Coll, correspondence, ms compositions, teaching mat; Sheet Music Coll (incl Roger Doucet Coll), 19th & Early 20th Centuries
Open Mon-Thurs 8am-11pm, Fri 8-7, Sat 11-7, Sun Noon-11
EDUCATION & CURRICULUM LAB, 3700 McTavish St, 1st Flr, H3A 1Y2, SAN 369-2973. Tel: 514-398-8109. FAX: 514-398-2165. Web Site: www.mcgill.ca/education-library. *Librn,* Marilyn Cohen; E-mail: marilyn.cohen@mcgill.ca
Library Holdings: e-books 504; Bk Titles 105,570; Bk Vols 120,533; Per Subs 503
Open Mon-Thurs 8:30am-9pm, Fri 8:30-6, Sat 10-6, Sun 11-6
Friends of the Library Group

CL NAHUM GELBER LAW LIBRARY, 3660 Peel St, H3A 1W9, SAN 369-2701. Tel: 514-398-4715. FAX: 514-398-3585. E-mail: law.library@mcgill.ca. Web Site: www.mcgill.ca/law-library. *Libr Supvr-Popular Libr,* Mary Lourenço; *Civil Law Librn,* Daniel Boyer; *Law Librn,* John Hobbins; E-mail: john.hobbins@mcgill.ca; Staff 12 (MLS 4, Non-MLS 8)
Founded 1950. Enrl 818; Fac 39; Highest Degree: Doctorate
Library Holdings: Bk Titles 79,413; Bk Vols 96,485; Per Subs 2,574
Special Collections: J P Humphrey Human Rights Coll; Wainwright Pre-Napoleanic French Law
Subject Interests: Civil law, Common law, Comparative law, Human rights, Intl law
Database Vendor: Ex Libris Group
WALTER HITSCHFELD GEOGRAPHIC INFORMATION CENTRE, Burnside Hall, Rm 524, 805 Sherbrooke St W, H3A 2K6, SAN 369-2876. Tel: 514-398-7453, 514-398-8095. FAX: 514-398-7437. E-mail: gic.library@mcgill.ca. Web Site: www.mcgill.ca/gic. *Coordr, Electronic Res,* Anastasia Khouri; *Info Spec,* Joanna Hobbins; Staff 1 (MLS 1)
Library Holdings: AV Mats 231,969; Electronic Media & Resources 200; Bk Titles 3,808; Bk Vols 3,934; Per Subs 25
Special Collections: Airphotos; Geospatial Data; Maps, Atlases & Globes
Open Mon-Thurs 10-9, Fri 10-5, Sat & Sun 12-5
HUMANITIES & SOCIAL SCIENCES, McLennan Library Bldg, 3459 McTavish St, H3A 1Y1, SAN 369-2760. Tel: 514-398-4734. Interlibrary Loan Service Tel: 514-398-4732. FAX: 514-398-7184. TDD: 514-398-3422. E-mail: mclennan.library@mcgill.ca. Web Site: www.mcgill.ca/hssl. *Assoc Dir,* Carole Urbain Urbain
Library Holdings: e-books 148; Bk Titles 1,001,781; Bk Vols 1,219,939; Per Subs 3,561
Automation Activity & Vendor Info: (Acquisitions) Ex Libris Group; (Cataloging) Ex Libris Group; (Circulation) Ex Libris Group
Friends of the Library Group
ISLAMIC STUDIES, Morrice Hall, 3485 McTavish St, H3A 1Y1, SAN 369-3031. Tel: 514-398-4685. FAX: 514-398-8189. Web Site: www.mcgill.ca/islamic_library. *Head Librn,* Anaïs Salamon; Tel: 514-398-4688; Staff 2 (MLS 1, Non-MLS 1)
Founded 1952. Enrl 71; Fac 17; Highest Degree: Doctorate
Library Holdings: Bk Vols 130,927; Per Subs 363
Subject Interests: Islamic world

CM LIFE SCIENCES LIBRARY, McIntyre Medical Science Bldg, 3655 Promenade Sir William Osler, H3G 1Y6, SAN 369-2795. Tel: 514-398-4475, Ext 09115. Circulation Tel: 514-398-4475, Ext 09220. Administration Tel: 514-398-4475, Ext 09042. Information Services Tel: 514-398-4475, Ext 09185. FAX: 514-398-3890. Circulation FAX: 514-398-5782. Web Site: www.health.library.mcgill.ca. *Instrul Serv Librn,* Lori Kloda; Tel: 514-398-4475, Ext 09528, E-mail: lori.kloda@mcgill.ca; *Instrul Serv Librn,* Deborah Meert; Tel: 514-398-4475, Ext 09844, E-mail: deborah.meert@mcgill.ca; *Coll Develop,* Valerie Fortin; Tel: 514-398-4475, Ext 09671, E-mail: valerie.fortin@mcgill.ca; *Computer Serv,* Angella Lambrou; Tel: 514-398-4475, Ext 09184, E-mail: angella.lambrou@mcgill.ca; *Info Serv,* Deanna Cowan; Tel: 514-398-4475, Ext 09669, E-mail: deanna.cowan@mcgill.ca; Staff 22 (MLS 6, Non-MLS 16)
Founded 1823
Library Holdings: AV Mats 167; Bks on Deafness & Sign Lang 220; e-journals 1,695; Bk Titles 91,916; Bk Vols 109,099; Per Subs 877
Subject Interests: Allied health, Biomed sci, Dentistry, Med, Nursing
Function: Res libr
Open Mon-Fri 8:30am-9pm, Sat & Sun 12-5
Restriction: Open to students, fac & staff

MACDONALD CAMPUS, 21111 Lakeshore Rd, Sainte Anne de Bellevue, H9X 3V9, SAN 369-2736, Tel: 514-398-7881, FAX: 514-398-7960. E-mail: macdonald.library@mcgill.ca. Web Site: www.mcgill.ca/macdonald-library. *Head Librn,* Natalie Waters; Tel: 514-398-7876, E-mail: natalie.waters@mcgill.ca. Subject Specialists: *Biores eng, Environment, Parasitology,* Natalie Waters; Staff 8 (MLS 3, Non-MLS 5)
Founded 1907. Highest Degree: Doctorate
Library Holdings: Bk Titles 48,416; Bk Vols 53,384; Per Subs 694
Special Collections: Canadian, Quebec & FAO Documents. UN Document Depository
Subject Interests: Agr, Environ sci, Food, Nutrition, Parasitology
Automation Activity & Vendor Info: (Acquisitions) Ex Libris Group; (Cataloging) Ex Libris Group; (Circulation) Ex Libris Group; (OPAC) Ex Libris Group; (Serials) Ex Libris Group
Partic in CREPUQ
Open Mon-Thurs 8:30am-10pm, Fri 8:30-6, Sat & Sun 12-8
OSLER LIBRARY, McIntyre Medical Sciences Bldg, 3655 Promenade Sir William Osler, H3G 1Y6, SAN 369-2825, Tel: 514-398-4475, Ext 09873. FAX: 514-398-5747. E-mail: osler.library@mcgill.ca. Web Site: www.mcgill.ca/osler_library. *Librn,* Pamela Miller. Subject Specialists: *Hist of med,* Pamela Miller
Library Holdings: Bk Titles 77,244; Per Subs 120
Friends of the Library Group
EDWARD ROSENTHALL MATHEMATICS & STATISTICS LIBRARY, Burnside Hall, Rm 1105, 805 Sherbrooke St W, H3A 2K6, SAN 369-3090, Tel: 514-398-4676. FAX: 514-398-3899. E-mail: roselib@math.mcgill.ca. Web Site: www.mcgill.ca/rosenthall. *Librn,* Marika Asimakopulos; Tel: 514-398-7430
Library Holdings: Bk Titles 4,321; Bk Vols 4,668; Per Subs 267
Open Mon-Fri 10-4
HOWARD ROSS LIBRARY OF MANAGEMENT, Samuel Bronfman Bldg, 1001 Sherbrooke St W, 2nd Flr, H3A 1G5, SAN 369-321X. Tel: 514-398-4690. Circulation Tel: 514-398-4690, Ext 00863. Interlibrary Loan Service Tel: 514-398-4690, Ext 00862. Reference Tel: 514-398-4690, Ext 00865. FAX: 514-398-5046. E-mail: management.library@mcgill.ca. Web Site: www.mcgill.ca. *Head Librn,* Amber Lannon; *Libr Supvr-Popular Libr,* Peter Martinek; Tel: 514-398-4690, Ext 00864; *Librn,* Beth Dunning; *Librn,* Rajiv Johal; *Librn,* Judy Symansky; *Circ Asst,* Traudi Leisser; Tel: 514-398-4690, Ext 09272; *ILL/Doc Delivery Serv,* Dorothy Lawson; *Reserves,* Gail Veli; Tel: 514-398-4690, Ext 04553; *Ser,* Sylvia Little; Tel: 514-398-8268; Staff 7.5 (MLS 3.5, Non-MLS 4)
Founded 1943
Library Holdings: Bk Titles 47,407; Bk Vols 48,769; Per Subs 656
Open Mon-Thurs 9-9, Fri 9-6, Sat 10-6
SCHULICH LIBRARY OF SCIENCE & ENGINEERING, Macdonald Stewart Library Bldg, 809 Sherbrooke St W, H3A 2K6, SAN 369-318X. Tel: 514-398-4769. FAX: 514-398-3903. E-mail: schulich.library@mcgill.ca. Web Site: www.mcgill.ca/schulich. *Librn,* Louis Houle; E-mail: louis.houle@mcgill.ca
Library Holdings: Bk Titles 121,973; Bk Vols 151,830; Per Subs 1,465

L   MCMILLAN BIRCH MENDELSOHN LIBRARY*, 1000 Sherbrooke St W, 27th Flr, H3A 3G4. SAN 374-5619. Tel: 514-987-5000, 514-987-5043. FAX: 514-987-1213. Web Site: www.mcmbm.com. *Librn,* Mary Kelly; E-mail: mary.kelly@mcmbm.com
Library Holdings: Bk Titles 2,700; Bk Vols 8,000

G   MEDIATHEQUE, INSTITUT DE TOURISME ET D'HOTELLERIE DU QUEBEC*, 3535, rue Saint-Denis, Local 1.97, H2X 3P1. SAN 329-2967. Tel: 514-282-5114. Toll Free Tel: 800-361-5111. FAX: 514-282-5105. E-mail: mediatheque@ithq.qc.ca. Web Site: www.ithq.qc.ca. *Libr Serv Mgr,* Guylaine Simard; Tel: 514-282-5141, E-mail: simard-guylaine@ithq.qc.ca; Staff 6 (MLS 1, Non-MLS 5)
Founded 1975
Jul 2007-Jun 2008. Mats Exp (CAN) $57,000, Books (CAN) $35,000, AV Mat (CAN) $22,000
Library Holdings: AV Mats 3,043; Bk Titles 24,689; Bk Vols 28,433; Per Subs 196
Special Collections: Professional Recipes; Restaurant menus
Subject Interests: Cookery, Food, Food serv mgt, Hotel mgt, Recipes, Restaurant mgt, Tourism, Wine
Automation Activity & Vendor Info: (Cataloging) Mandarin Library Automation; (Circulation) Mandarin Library Automation; (OPAC) Mandarin Library Automation
Database Vendor: EBSCOhost
Wireless access
Function: ILL available
Publications: Babillard (Newsletter); Guide de la Mediatheque (Library handbook); Les banques accessibles sur le site WEB (Reference guide); Liste des cederoms, DVD-roms et des liens internet (Acquisition list); Liste des menus (Periodical); Liste des nouvelles acquisitions (Acquisition list); Liste des Periodiques (Index to periodicals)

S   MERCER HUMAN RESOURCE CONSULTING*, Information Centre, 1981 McGill College Ave, Ste 800, H3A 3T5. SAN 319-7778. Tel: 514-285-1802. FAX: 514-285-8831. Web Site: www.mercerhr.com. *Librn,* Elise Rettinger
Founded 1975
Library Holdings: Bk Vols 2,380; Per Subs 180
Subject Interests: Compensation, Employee benefits, Group ins, Human resources, Pensions
Automation Activity & Vendor Info: (Acquisitions) Inmagic, Inc.; (Cataloging) Inmagic, Inc.; (Circulation) Inmagic, Inc.; (OPAC) Inmagic, Inc.; (Serials) Inmagic, Inc.
Database Vendor: Factiva.com
Open Mon-Fri 8-5:30

M   MONTREAL ASSOCIATION FOR THE BLIND*, Constance-Lethbridge Rehabilitation Centre Library, 7005 de Maisonneuve Blvd W, H4B 1T3. SAN 324-3656. Tel: 514-487-1891, Ext 220. FAX: 514-487-5494. *Librn,* David Chevrier
Founded 1950
Library Holdings: Bk Titles 2,500; Bk Vols 3,500; Per Subs 90
Subject Interests: Blindness, Handicaps, Phys med, Rehabilitation
Automation Activity & Vendor Info: (Cataloging) Inmagic, Inc.; (Circulation) Inmagic, Inc.; (OPAC) Inmagic, Inc.
Open Mon-Fri 8:30-4:30

S   MONTREAL ASSOCIATION FOR THE INTELLECTUALLY HANDICAPPED LIBRARY*, 633 Cremazie Blvd E, Ste 100, H2M 1L9. SAN 320-8052. Tel: 514-381-2307. FAX: 514-381-0454. E-mail: amdi@delegation.ca. Web Site: www.delegation.ca/amdi
Library Holdings: Bk Vols 1,500; Per Subs 70
Subject Interests: Law, Med, Mental deficiency educ, Soc sci
Publications: Bon A' Quoi On Jove; Early Infant Stimulation Makes a Difference (pamphlet); Entre Nous...Parents (newsletter); La Boite A' Outils

M   MONTREAL CHEST INSTITUTE, Medical Library, 3650 Saint Urbain St, J5 26, H2X 2P4. SAN 319-7824. Tel: 514-934-1934, Ext 32593. FAX: 514-849-3824. Web Site: muhclibraries.mcgill.ca/mci.php. *Med Librn,* Ibtisam M Mahmoud; E-mail: ibtisam.mahmoud@muhc.mcgill.ca
Founded 1965
Library Holdings: Bk Vols 393; Per Subs 9
Subject Interests: Med on chest diseases, Respiratory diseases
Function: ILL available
Open Mon-Thurs 10-3
Restriction: Open to students, fac & staff

M   MONTREAL CHILDREN'S HOSPITAL*, Medical Library, 2300 Tupper St, H3H 1P3. SAN 319-7832. Tel: 514-412-4400, Ext 22054. FAX: 514-412-4345. Web Site: www.mchlib.mcgill.ca/index.htm. *Librn,* Joanne Baird; Staff 2 (MLS 2)
Founded 1946
Library Holdings: Bk Titles 6,000; Per Subs 100
Subject Interests: Child psychiat, Pediatrics
Automation Activity & Vendor Info: (Cataloging) Inmagic, Inc.
Database Vendor: OVID Technologies
Partic in National Network of Libraries of Medicine
Open Mon-Thurs 8:30-6:30, Fri 8:30-4:45

G   MONTREAL CITY HALL*, Management of Documents & Archives, 275 Notre Dame St E, R-113, H2Y 1C6. SAN 319-7840. Tel: 514-872-9092. FAX: 514-872-3475. Web Site: ville.montreal.qc.ca. *Dept Head,* Marc Lebele; E-mail: mlebele@ville.montreal.qc.ca; *Actg Librn,* Mario Robert; E-mail: mrobert@ville.montreal.qc.ca; *Archivist,* Denys Chouinard; Tel: 514-872-3496, E-mail: dchouinard@ville.montreal.qc.ca
Founded 1913
Library Holdings: Bk Vols 6,000; Per Subs 50
Subject Interests: Hist of Montreal, Municipal admin
Open Mon-Fri 8:30-12 & 1-4:30

G   MONTREAL CITY PLANNING DEPARTMENT*, Centre de Documentation, 303 Notre-Dame est Bureau 5A-37, H2Y 3Y8. SAN 329-7667. Tel: 514-872-4119. FAX: 514-872-7726. *Info Res, Librn,* Ginette Dugas; E-mail: ginettedugas@ville.montreal.qc.ca
Library Holdings: Electronic Media & Resources 2,000; Bk Titles 18,000; Per Subs 70
Special Collections: Municipal Document Depository
Subject Interests: Archaeology, Archit, Sustainable develop, Urban planning
Database Vendor: Dialog
Function: Res libr
Open Mon-Fri 9-5
Restriction: Access for corporate affiliates, External users must contact librn, Internal circ only, Limited access for the pub, Open to dept staff only, Open to others by appt

M MONTREAL GENERAL HOSPITAL*, Medical Library, 1650 Cedar Ave, Rm E6-157, H3G 1A4. SAN 319-7867. Tel: 514-934-1934, Ext 35293, 514-934-1934, Ext 43057. FAX: 514-934-8250. E-mail: library.mgh@muhc.mcgill.ca. Web Site: muhclibraries.mcgill.ca. *Chief Librn,* Elizabeth Lamont; Staff 3 (MLS 1, Non-MLS 2)
Founded 1955
Library Holdings: Bk Titles 2,200; Per Subs 100
Subject Interests: Consumer health info, Dentistry, Med, Surgery
Open Mon-Fri 8-5

S MONTREAL MUSEUM OF FINE ARTS, Art Reference Library, 3430 Ave du Musee, H3G 2C7. (Mail add: CP 3000, Succursole H, H3G 2T9), SAN 319-7883. Tel: 514-285-1600, Ext 159. FAX: 514-285-5655. E-mail: biblio@mbamtl.org. *Head Librn,* Joanne Dery; E-mail: jdery@mbamtl.org; Staff 4 (MLS 2, Non-MLS 2)
Founded 1882
Library Holdings: Bk Vols 82,200; Per Subs 631
Special Collections: Canadian Artists, clippings, auction catalogues
Subject Interests: Applied arts, Canadiana, Decorative art, Fine arts
Automation Activity & Vendor Info: (Acquisitions) SIRSI Unicorn; (Cataloging) SIRSI Unicorn; (Circulation) SIRSI Unicorn; (OPAC) SIRSI Unicorn; (Serials) SIRSI Unicorn
Database Vendor: SirsiDynix

M MONTREAL NEUROLOGICAL INSTITUTE HOSPITAL LIBRARY*, 3801 University St, Rm 285, H3A 2B4. SAN 319-7891. Tel: 514-398-1980. FAX: 514-398-5077. *Chief Librn,* Carol Wiens; E-mail: carol.wiens@mail.mcgill.ca; Staff 2 (MLS 1, Non-MLS 1)
Founded 1934
Library Holdings: Bk Titles 14,000; Per Subs 109
Automation Activity & Vendor Info: (Acquisitions) Inmagic, Inc.; (Cataloging) Inmagic, Inc.; (Circulation) Inmagic, Inc.; (OPAC) Inmagic, Inc.; (Serials) Inmagic, Inc.
Open Mon-Thurs 8am-9pm, Fri 8:30-6:30, Sat 9-4, Sun 10-4

S MORNEAU SOBECO LIBRARY*, 500 Rene-Levesque Blvd W, Ste 1200, H2Z 1W7. SAN 370-6036. Tel: 514-878-9090, Ext 8299. FAX: 514-875-2673. Web Site: www.morneausobeco.com. *Librn, Ref,* Martine Vadnais; E-mail: mvadnais@morneausobeco.com; *Circ, Per, Tech Serv,* Natalie Lauzon
Library Holdings: Bk Titles 5,000; Per Subs 150
Open Mon-Fri 8-5

S NATIONAL FILM BOARD OF CANADA*, NFB Montreal, 3155 Cote de Liesse, H4N 2N4. SAN 376-2181. Tel: 514-283-9045. FAX: 514-283-9811. E-mail: research@nfb.ca. Web Site: www.nfb.ca. *Librn,* Katherine Kasirer; *Librn,* Christiane Talbot; Tel: 514 283-9046, E-mail: c.talbot@onf.ca. *Subject Specialists: Animation, Can film, Documentary film,* Katherine Kasirer; *Animation, Can film, Documentary film,* Christiane Talbot; Staff 3 (MLS 2, Non-MLS 1)
Founded 1939
Library Holdings: AV Mats 10,000; Bk Titles 15,000; Per Subs 40
Special Collections: Films-Notebooks
Automation Activity & Vendor Info: (Acquisitions) Mandarin Library Automation; (Cataloging) Mandarin Library Automation; (OPAC) Marcive, Inc
Function: AV serv, Computers for patron use, Electronic databases & coll, Online ref
Open Tues-Sun Noon-9
Restriction: Employee & client use only

S NATIONAL THEATRE SCHOOL OF CANADA LIBRARY*, 5030 Rue Saint Denis, H2J 2L8. SAN 319-793X. Tel: 514-842-7954, Ext 125. FAX: 514-842-5661. Web Site: thalia.ent-nts.ca, www.ent-nts.ca. *Dir,* Wolfgang Noethlichs; E-mail: wolfgangnoethlichs@ent-nts.ca; *Tech Serv Librn,* Simon Barry; Tel: 514 842-7954, Ext 112, E-mail: simonbarry@ent-nts.ca; *Asst Librn,* Monique Forest; *Tech Serv,* Marianne Boudreau; Staff 5 (MLS 1, Non-MLS 4)
Founded 1941
Library Holdings: AV Mats 1,903; DVDs 272; Bk Titles 70,000; Per Subs 60; Videos 1,394
Special Collections: Architecture Coll; Costume History Coll; Fine Arts Coll; Performing Arts Coll; Theatre Coll
Subject Interests: Archives
Automation Activity & Vendor Info: (Acquisitions) BiblioMondo; (Cataloging) BiblioMondo; (Circulation) BiblioMondo; (OPAC) BiblioMondo; (Serials) BiblioMondo
Open Mon 9am-11pm, Tues 11-6, Wed 9-6, Thurs 9-7, Fri 11-5:30

S NORTON ROSE CANADA LLP LIBRARY, One Place Ville Marie, Ste 2500, H3B 1R1. SAN 319-7980. Tel: 514-847-4701. FAX: 514-286-5474. Web Site: www.nortonrose.com. *Regional Librn Serv Dir,* Carole Mehu; E-mail: carole.mehu@nortonrose.com; *Ref Serv,* Renee Lauzier; *Ref Serv,*

Julie Lavallee; *Ref Serv,* Carol Slutsky; *Tech Serv,* Louise Beauregard; *Tech Serv,* Caroline Brisson; *Tech Serv,* Maria Panza
Founded 1879
Library Holdings: Bk Vols 20,000
Special Collections: Canadian Law
Automation Activity & Vendor Info: (Acquisitions) SIRSI WorkFlows
Wireless access

G OFFICE FRANCO-QUEBECOIS POUR LA JEUNESSE LIBRARY*, 11 Rene Levesque E, H2X 3Z6. SAN 377-5534. Tel: 514-873-4255. FAX: 514-873-0067. E-mail: info@ofqj.gouv.qc.ca. Web Site: www.ofqj.gouv.qc.ca. *Librn,* Michel Lagace; Staff 1 (MLS 1)
Library Holdings: Bk Vols 2,000; Per Subs 60
Open Mon-Fri 9-5

M ORDRE DES INFIRMIERES ET INFIRMIERS DU QUEBEC*, Centre de Documentation, 4200 Boul Dorchester Ouest, H3Z 1V4. SAN 319-8006. Tel: 514-935-2501, Ext 277. FAX: 514-935-5273. E-mail: cdoc@oiiq.org. Web Site: www.oiig.org. *Chief Librn,* Maryse Dumas; E-mail: maryse.dumas@oiig.org; Staff 4 (MLS 1, Non-MLS 3)
Founded 1964
Library Holdings: Bk Vols 14,000; Per Subs 380
Subject Interests: Admin, Educ, Health, Nursing, Psychol, Sociol
Automation Activity & Vendor Info: (Acquisitions) SirsiDynix; (Cataloging) SirsiDynix; (Circulation) SirsiDynix; (Course Reserve) SirsiDynix; (OPAC) SirsiDynix; (Serials) SirsiDynix
Database Vendor: SirsiDynix
Open Mon-Fri (Winter) 9-5; Mon-Fri (Summer) 8:30-4:30

S THE POLISH LIBRARY*, McGill University, 3479 Peel St, H3A 1W7. SAN 325-8424. Tel: 514-398-6978. E-mail: info@biblioteka.info. Web Site: www.biblioteka.info. *Dir,* Hanna M Pappius; *Librn,* Stefan Wladysiuk; E-mail: stefan.wladysiuk@mail.mcgill.ca; Staff 2 (MLS 2)
Founded 1943
Library Holdings: Bk Vols 41,000
Publications: Biuletyn Informacyjny (Annually)

CR PRESBYTERIAN COLLEGE LIBRARY*, The Joseph C McLelland Library, 3495 University St, H3A 2A8. SAN 319-8022. Tel: 514-288-5256. FAX: 514-288-8072. *Librn,* Dr Daniel J Shute; E-mail: dshute@presbyteriancollege.ca; Staff 1 (MLS 1)
Founded 1867. Enrl 30; Fac 6; Highest Degree: Master
Library Holdings: Bk Titles 22,000; Per Subs 65
Special Collections: Antiquarian Books (Sebright Memorial Coll); Migne's Patrology
Subject Interests: Hist, Reformed theol, Theol
Wireless access
Open Mon-Fri 9-12 & 1-5

G QUEBEC COMMISSION DES SERVICES JURIDIQUES LIBRARY*, Two Complexe Desjardins, Ste 1404, H5B 1B3. (Mail add: CP 123, Succ Desjardins, H5B 1B3), SAN 371-764X. Tel: 514-873-3562. FAX: 514-873-9263. *Documentalist,* Francine Godin
Founded 1973
Library Holdings: Bk Titles 3,800; Per Subs 100
Subject Interests: Law
Function: Res libr
Restriction: Not open to pub

S QUEBEC OFFICE QUEBECOIS DE LA LANGUE FRANCAISE BIBLIOTHEQUE, 125 W Sherbrooke, H2X 1X4. SAN 321-3420. Tel: 514-873-2996, 514-873-2997. FAX: 514-873-2868. E-mail: qmolf@oqlf.gouv.qc.ca. Web Site: www.oqlf.gouv.qc.ca. *Librn,* Chantal Robinson; E-mail: chantal.robinson@oqlf.gouv.qc.ca; Staff 1 (MLS 1)
Founded 1969
Library Holdings: Bk Titles 19,000; Per Subs 50
Special Collections: Techniques de L'ingenieur
Subject Interests: Linguistics
Publications: Acquisitions list; Bibliographies; List of Periodicals; Repertoire des Publications de l'office de la Langue Francaise
Open Mon-Fri 1-4:30

S RAYMOND CHABOT GRANT THORNTON LIBRARY*, 600 de la Gauchetiere W, Ste 1900, H3B 4L8. SAN 371-1633. Tel: 514-878-2691. Reference Tel: 514-393-4844. FAX: 514-878-2127. *Librn,* Michele Bernard; E-mail: bernard.michele@rcgt.com; Staff 3 (MLS 1, Non-MLS 2)
Founded 1979
Library Holdings: Bk Vols 9,000; Per Subs 120
Subject Interests: Acctg
Automation Activity & Vendor Info: (Cataloging) Inmagic, Inc.; (OPAC) Inmagic, Inc.
Database Vendor: EBSCOhost, Factiva.com, ProQuest
Open Mon-Fri 8:30-5

S READER'S DIGEST MAGAZINES LTD*, Editorial Library, 1100 Ouest Boul Rene-Levesque, H3B 5H5. SAN 369-4178. Tel: 514-940-7229. FAX: 514-940-7337. Web Site: www.readersdigest.ca. *Librn,* Pierre Charlebois
Founded 1973
Library Holdings: Bk Titles 3,250; Per Subs 185
Subject Interests: Canadiana, Human interest
Restriction: Staff use only

L ROBINSON, SHEPPARD & SHAPIRO*, Law Library, 800 Place Victoria, Ste 4700, H4Z 1H6. SAN 328-4506. Tel: 514-393-4009. FAX: 514-878-1865. *Librn,* Angela Tietolman; E-mail: atietolman@rsslex.com
Library Holdings: Bk Vols 12,500
Database Vendor: Infomart, LexisNexis, Westlaw
Partic in EUREKA; Quicklaw Inc; SOQUIJ; Westlaw
Open Mon-Fri 9-5
Restriction: Staff use only

ROYAL VICTORIA HOSPITAL
M MEDICAL LIBRARY*, 687 Pine Ave W, Rm H4-01, H3A 1A1, SAN 369-4232. Tel: 514-934-1934, Ext 35290. FAX: 514-843-1483. E-mail: rvh.library@muhc.mcgill.ca. Web Site: muhclibraries.mcgill.ca/rvh.php. *Chief Librn,* Elizabeth Lamont; E-mail: elizabeth.lamont@muhc.mcgill.ca; *Librn,* Robyn Maler; E-mail: rvh.library@muhc.mcgill.ca; *Librn,* Martin Morris; E-mail: martin.morris@muhc.mcgill.ca; *Libr Tech,* Vincent Caetano; E-mail: vincent.caetano@muhc.mcgill.ca; *Libr Tech,* George Mallari-Lee; E-mail: george.mallari-lee@muhc.mcgill.ca
Founded 1945
Library Holdings: Bk Titles 3,000; Per Subs 175
Partic in BRS; National Network of Libraries of Medicine
Open Mon-Fri 9-6

M WOMEN'S PAVILION LIBRARY, 687 Pine Ave W, Rm F 4-24, H3A 1A1, SAN 369-4267. Tel: 514-934-1934, Ext 34738. FAX: 514-843-1678. Web Site: muhclibraries.mcgill.ca/wp.php. *Librn,* Irina Iavorskaia; Staff 0.62 (MLS 0.62)
Founded 1957
Library Holdings: Bk Vols 480; Per Subs 30
Subject Interests: Gynecology, Obstetrics
Function: CD-ROM, Doc delivery serv, Electronic databases & coll, Fax serv, Online cat, Online ref, Online searches, Orientations, Photocopying/Printing, Ref serv available, Scanner, Workshops
Restriction: Authorized personnel only, Badge access after hrs, Borrowing privileges limited to fac & registered students, Med staff & students

M SAINT MARY'S HOSPITAL*, Health Sciences Library, 3830 Lacombe Ave, H3T 1M5. SAN 319-812X. Tel: 514-345-3511, Ext 3317. FAX: 514-734-2695. Web Site: www.smhc.qc.ca. *Librn,* Gilles Teasdale; E-mail: gilles.teasdale@ssss.gouv.qc.ca; Staff 1 (MLS 1)
Founded 1952
Library Holdings: Bk Vols 2,000; Per Subs 125
Subject Interests: Family med, Gynecology, Med, Nursing, Obstetrics, Psychiat, Surgery

G SERVICES DOCUMENTAIRES MULTIMEDIA, INC*, 5650 Iberville, Ste 620, H2G 2B3. SAN 321-6918. Tel: 514-382-0895. FAX: 514-384-9139. *In Charge,* Denis Brunet; Staff 2 (MLS 1, Non-MLS 1)
Founded 1971
Library Holdings: Bk Titles 4,500; Per Subs 213
Restriction: Staff use only

S SIMONE DE BEAUVOIR LIBRARY*, Reading Room, Concordia Univ, Simone de Beauvoir Inst, MU-401, 2170 Bishop St, H3G 1M8. (Mail add: Concordia Univ, Simone de Beauvoir Inst, MU-401, 1455 de Maisonneuve Blvd W, H3G 1M8). Tel: 514-848-2424, Ext 2377. Administration Tel: 514-848-2424, Ext 2370. Web Site: www.concordia.ca. *Head Librn,* Isabelle Lamoureux; Staff 1 (MLS 1)
Founded 1978
Library Holdings: AV Mats 55; Bk Titles 4,000; Spec Interest Per Sub 4
Subject Interests: Aboriginal studies, Environ issues, Feminism, Gay & lesbian, Peace studies, Women's health, Women's studies
Open Mon-Thurs 10-4
Friends of the Library Group

M SIR MORTIMER B DAVIS JEWISH GENERAL HOSPITAL*, Health Sciences Library, 3755 Cote Ste Catherine Rd, A-200, H3T 1E2. SAN 369-237X. Tel: 514-340-8222, Ext 5927. Circulation Tel: 514-340-8222, Ext 2391. Interlibrary Loan Service Tel: 514-340-8222, Ext 5928. FAX: 514-340-7552. Web Site: www.library.jgh.ca. *Chief Librn,* Arlene Greenberg; Tel: 514-340-8222, Ext 5930; *Acq of New Ser, Ser, Web Coordr,* Kathleen Blagrave; *Acq of Monographs, Cat, Web Coordr,* Donna M Gibbons; Tel: 514-340-8222, Ext 2391; *Coll & Res Librn,* Manxue Chen; Tel: 514-340-8222, Ext 2453; *ILL,* Blanka Glowacki; Tel:

514-340-8222, Ext 5928; *Ser,* Elisabeth Breier; Staff 5 (MLS 2, Non-MLS 3)
Founded 1950
Library Holdings: Bk Titles 47,000; Per Subs 300
Special Collections: Drazin Memorial Library on Judaica & Medical Ethics; Patient & Family Resource Centre Consumer Health Coll
Subject Interests: Clinical med, Hospital admin, Med, Nursing, Nutrition, Phys therapy, Related sci, Speech pathology
Publications: Medical Library Newsletter (Bi-annually)
Partic in BRS; Can-Ole; Canadian Health Libraries Association; Montreal Health Libr Asn; National Network of Libraries of Medicine
Open Mon-Thurs 8:30-7:30, Fri 8:30-4:30
Friends of the Library Group
Branches:
DR HENRY KRAVITZ LIBRARY-INSTITUTE OF COMMUNITY & FAMILY PSYCHIATRY, 4333 Cote Ste Catherine Rd, H3T 1E4, SAN 322-6360. Tel: 514-340-8210, Ext 5243. FAX: 514-340-8104. E-mail: icfplib.jgh@mail.mcgill.ca. Web Site: www.jgh.ca. *Librn,* Teodora Constantinescu; Staff 1 (MLS 1)
Library Holdings: Bk Vols 2,300
Subject Interests: Psychiat
HOPE & COPE LIBRARY, 3755 Cote Ste Catherine Rd, H3T 1E2. Tel: 514-340-8255. FAX: 514-340-8605. *Dir,* Suzanne O'Brien
Library Holdings: Bk Vols 1,000
Special Collections: Palliative; Radiotherapy
Subject Interests: Cancer patients, Families
Open Mon-Fri 8:30-4:30
LADY DAVIS INSTITUTE FOR MEDICAL RESEARCH, 3755 Cote Ste Catherine Rd, H3T1E2. Tel: 514-340-8260, Ext 3795. FAX: 514-340-7502. Web Site: www.ldilibrary.jgh.ca. *Librn,* Marek Pukteris; E-mail: mpukteri@ldi.jgh.mcgill.ca; Staff 1 (MLS 1)
Library Holdings: Bk Titles 100; Per Subs 95

S SNC-LAVALIN, INC LIBRARY*, 455 boul Rene-Levesque ouest, H2Z 1Z3. SAN 319-8235. Tel: 514-393-1000, Ext 2888. FAX: 514-866-6709. *Chief Librn,* Lynda Thivierge
Founded 1911
Library Holdings: Bk Vols 10,000; Per Subs 300
Subject Interests: Eng
Publications: Biblio-Bulletin (library bulletin); New Acquisitions

G SOCIETE DE TRANSPORT DE MONTREAL*, Centre de Documentation, 800 Gauchetiere St O, Bureau 9740, H5A 1J6. SAN 319-7913. Tel: 514-280-6109. FAX: 514-280-6126. Web Site: www.stm.info. *Archivist, Chief Librn,* Andre Vigneau; E-mail: andre.vigneau@stm.info; Staff 2 (MLS 1, Non-MLS 1)
Founded 1968
Jan 2008-Dec 2008. Mats Exp (CAN) $110,000
Library Holdings: Bk Titles 2,500; Bk Vols 4,500; Per Subs 350
Subject Interests: Eng, Finance, Law, Policy, Pub transit
Database Vendor: OVID Technologies
Function: Archival coll, Doc delivery serv, Res libr, Telephone ref
Restriction: Open by appt only

S SOCIETE GENEALOGIQUE CANADIENNE-FRANCAISE*, Maison de la Genealogie, 3440 Davidson St., H1W 2Z5. SAN 373-7985. Tel: 514-527-1010. FAX: 514-527-0265. E-mail: info@sgcf.com. Web Site: www.sgcf.com. *Dir,* Micheline Perreault
Founded 1943
Library Holdings: Bk Titles 15,000; Bk Vols 18,000; Per Subs 307
Subject Interests: Genealogy, Hist
Publications: Memoires
Open Mon & Tues 4:30-10, Thurs-Sat 9:30-4:30

S SOCIETE GENERALE DE FINANCEMENT DU QUEBEC*, Centre de Documentation, 600 de La Gauchetiere ouest, Bureau 1500, H3B 4L8. SAN 370-7296. Tel: 418-876-9290. FAX: 418-395-8055. *Info Spec, Res Serv Spec,* Marlene Tanguay; E-mail: mtanguay@sgfqc.com
Founded 1998
Library Holdings: Bk Vols 2,000; Per Subs 50
Restriction: Staff use only

S SOCIETE RADIO-CANADA BIBLIOTHEQUE*, 1400 est boul Rene-Levesque, H2L 2M2. SAN 321-2386. Tel: 514-597-4804. FAX: 514-597-6236. Web Site: www.radio-canada.ca. *Mgr,* Johanne Lacroix; Staff 9 (MLS 7, Non-MLS 2)
Library Holdings: Bk Titles 40,000; Per Subs 478
Subject Interests: Canadiana, Costume, Radio, Television
Database Vendor: Dialog, Infomart, LexisNexis

S STEWART MUSEUM*, David M Stewart Library, The Old Fort St Helen's Island, H3C 4G6. (Mail add: PO Box 1200, Sta A, H3C 2Y9), SAN 319-8197. Tel: 514-861-6701. FAX: 514-284-0123. Web Site: www.stewart-museum.org. *Coll Mgr,* Normand Trudel; E-mail: ntrudel@stewart-museum.org

Founded 1974
Library Holdings: Bk Titles 8,392; Per Subs 31
Special Collections: Books Printed Before 1763 (Chevalier de Johnstone Coll); French & Canadian Military History (David M Stewart Coll), rare manuals, treatises; History New France (David M Stewart Coll), rare bks, maps & doc
Subject Interests: Can mil hist, Hist of New France
Function: Res libr
Publications: 4 M's Bulletin (Irregular)
Restriction: Open by appt only

S   TECSULT, INC*, Library Department, 85 W Saint Catherine, H2X 3P4. SAN 325-7851. Tel: 514-287-8500, Ext 8546. FAX: 514-287-8531. E-mail: biblitec@tecsult.com. *Librn,* Veronique Pepin
Library Holdings: Bk Titles 8,000

S   TOWERS PERRIN*, Information Centre, 1800 McGill College Ave, Ste 2200, H3A 3J6. SAN 329-8035. Tel: 514-982-2172. FAX: 514-982-9269. *Info Assoc,* Dawn Chipps; Staff 1 (MLS 1)
Library Holdings: Bk Vols 1,500; Per Subs 26
Database Vendor: Factiva.com, LexisNexis
Function: Ref & res
Restriction: Employees only

S   TREBAS INSTITUTE, Montreal Campus Library-Resource Center, East Tower, 6th Flr, 550 Sherbrooke St W, H3A 1B9. SAN 371-4691. Tel: 514-845-4141. FAX: 514-845-2581. Web Site: www.trebas.com. *Pres,* David Leonard
Founded 1979. Enrl 250; Fac 25
Library Holdings: Bk Vols 3,000; Per Subs 50
Subject Interests: Copyright law, Entertainment, Film production, Video production

S   UNIVERSITE DU QUEBEC*, Bibliotheque des Arts, CP 8889, Succ Centre-Ville, 1255 Rue St Denis, Locale-A-1200, H3C 3P3. SAN 319-8243. Tel: 514-987-6134. FAX: 514-987-0262. Web Site: www.uqam.ca. *Dir,* Patricia Black; E-mail: black.patricia@uqam.ca; *Librn,* Gisèle Guay; *Librn,* Lucie Séguin
Founded 1925
Library Holdings: Bk Vols 80,000
Special Collections: Fine Arts Coll

C   UNIVERSITE DU QUEBEC A MONTREAL BIBLIOTHEQUE*, CP 8889 Succ Centre-Ville, H3C 3P3. SAN 319-8251. Tel: 514-987-3824. FAX: 514-987-3542. Web Site: www.bibliotheques.uqam.ca. *Dir,* Lucy Gardner; *Dir, Coll Develop,* Marie-Jeanne Préfontaine; Staff 44 (MLS 42, Non-MLS 2)
Founded 1969. Highest Degree: Doctorate
Library Holdings: AV Mats 19,183; Bk Titles 1,598,814; Per Subs 8,972
Special Collections: Art Slides Coll; Artist's Books; Maps & Aerial Photographs
Subject Interests: Archit, Art, Econ, Educ, Humanities, Literary studies, Music, Sexology, Soc, Soc law
Publications: InfoSphere
Open Mon-Fri 9am-10pm, Sat & Sun Noon-5

S   VUES & VOIX, 1055 boul Rene-Levesque E bur 501, H2L 4S5. SAN 319-7727. Tel: 514-282-1999. Toll Free Tel: 800-361-0635. Interlibrary Loan Service Toll Free Tel: 866-269-2113. FAX: 514-282-1676. E-mail: info@vuesetvoix.com. Web Site: www.vuesetvoix.com. *Librn,* Yvonne Senechal
Founded 1976
Library Holdings: Talking Bks 13,000
Special Collections: Raised Line Drawings accompanying Talking Books in Specific Topics
Special Services for the Blind - Talking bks

MONTREAL-EST

P   BIBLIOTHEQUE DE MONTREAL-EST*, 11370 rue Notre-Dame Est, 3e etage, H1B 2W6. SAN 319-8294. Tel: 514-868-4222, 514-868-4223. FAX: 514-868-4225, 514-868-5277. *Libr Tech,* Anne-Marie Dufort; E-mail: anne-marie.dufort@montreal-est.ca; Staff 1 (MLS 1)
Founded 1967. Pop 3,796; Circ 42,000
Library Holdings: Bk Vols 28,371
Open Mon-Fri (Winter) 10-8:30, Sat 1-5; Mon (Summer) 12-8, Tues & Wed 10-5:30, Thurs 12-8, Fri 10-5:30

NICOLET

S   ECOLE NATIONALE DE POLICE DU QUEBEC*, Centre de Documentation, 350 rue Marguerite d'Youville, J3T 1X4. SAN 329-4145. Tel: 819-293-8631, Ext 6256. FAX: 819-293-8625. Web Site: www.enpq.qc.ca. *Librn,* Daniel Arcand; E-mail: darcand@enpq.qc.ca

Founded 1970
Library Holdings: AV Mats 591; Bk Vols 7,200; Per Subs 102
Open Mon-Fri 8:30-12:30 & 1:30-4:30

R   SEMINAIRE DE NICOLET LIBRARY*, 900 Blvd Louis Frechette, Bureau 110, J3T 1V5. SAN 319-8316. Tel: 819-293-4838. FAX: 819-293-4543. E-mail: seminairedenicolet@sogetel.net. Web Site: www.archives-seminaire-nicolet.qc.ca. *Librn,* Marie Pelletier
Founded 1825
Library Holdings: Bk Vols 100,000
Subject Interests: Art, Hist, Relig studies

NOTRE-DAME DU LAC

P   BIBLIOTHEQUE MUNICIPALE*, 681 Commercial, G0L 1X0. SAN 321-2483. Tel: 418-899-6004. *Dir,* Judith Pelerin
Library Holdings: Bk Vols 1,000
Automation Activity & Vendor Info: (Circulation) MultiLIS
Open Tues-Thurs 2-4 & 7-8

OUTREMONT

S   CENTRE DE RECHERCHE LIONEL-GROULX*, 261 Bloomfield Ave, H2V 3R6. SAN 319-7611. Tel: 514-271-4759, Ext 226. FAX: 514-271-6369. Web Site: site.rdaq.qc.ca/crlg. *Librn,* Yves Devin; E-mail: yves.devin@cam.org
Founded 1956
Library Holdings: Bk Titles 35,000; Per Subs 1,000
Special Collections: (Fonds Rene-Desmarais), clippings; 19th Century Quebec History (Fonds J-J-Girouard), mss; 20th Century Quebec History; 20th Century Quebec History (Fonds; Fonds Anatole-Vanier; Fonds Gerard-Filion, Fonds de L'Action Nationale; Fonds J Z Leon Patenaude; Georges-Pelletier, Fonds Maxime-Raymond, Fonds du Bloc populaire canadien, Fonds Commission; Latin-American History (Fonds d'Etudes latino-americaines); Laurendeau-Dunton, Fonds de la Ligue de la defense du Canada), mss; Lionel-Groulx, Fonds Michel-Brochu, Fonds Leo-Paul-Desrosiers, Fonds Andre-Laurendeau, Fonds
Subject Interests: Can hist, Fr Can hist, Fr civilization in Am
Publications: Le livre d'orgue de Montreal - facsimile

C   COLLEGE STANISLAS LIBRARY*, 780 Blvd Dollard, H2V 3G5. SAN 319-7387. Tel: 514-273-9521, Ext 244. FAX: 514-273-3409. E-mail: cdi@stanislas.qc.ca. Web Site: www.stanislas.qc.ca. *Librn,* Marie Olivier
Library Holdings: Bk Vols 23,000; Per Subs 60

C   PAUL-GERIN-LAJOIE-D'OUTREMONT LIBRARY*, 475 Bloomfield, H2V 3R9. SAN 319-8014. Tel: 514-276-3746. FAX: 514-276-9283. *Librn,* Michele Mailloux
Founded 1953
Library Holdings: Bk Vols 20,000
Wireless access

PINCOURT

P   BIBLIOTHEQUE MUNICIPALE DE PINCOURT*, 225 boul Pincourt, J7V 9T2. SAN 319-8340. Tel: 514-425-1104. FAX: 514-425-6668. E-mail: bibliotheque@villepincourt.qc.ca. Web Site: www.villepincourt.qc.ca. *In Charge,* Sylvie de Repentigny
Founded 1965. Pop 13,600; Circ 76,416
Library Holdings: CDs 436; DVDs 2,063; Bk Vols 37,537; Per Subs 45
Wireless access

POINTE-CLAIRE

P   BIBLIOTHEQUE PUBLIQUE DE POINTE-CLAIRE, Centrale/Central, 100 av Douglas-Shand, H9R 4V1. SAN 369-495X. Tel: 514-630-1218. Circulation Tel: 514-630-1218, Ext 1623 (Children's), 514-630-1218, Ext 1624 (Adults). Interlibrary Loan Service Tel: 514-630-1218, Ext 1692. Reference Tel: 514-630-1218, Ext 1630. FAX: 514-630-1261. E-mail: bibliotheque@ville.pointe-claire.qc.ca, ill@ville.pointe-claire.qc.ca. Web Site: www.ville.pointe-claire.qc.ca/library. *Head Librn,* Celine Laperriere; Tel: 514-630-1217, E-mail: laperrierec@ville.pointe-claire.qc.ca; Staff 7 (MLS 7)
Founded 1965. Pop 30,732; Circ 497,942
Jan 2010-Dec 2010 Income (Main Library and Branch(s)) $172,332, Provincial (CAN) $74,700, Locally Generated Income (CAN) $97,632. Mats Exp $486,200, Books (CAN) $345,000, Per/Ser (Incl. Access Fees) (CAN) $30,000, Micro (CAN) $4,000, AV Mat (CAN) $53,700, Electronic Ref Mat (Incl. Access Fees) (CAN) $53,500
Library Holdings: Audiobooks 4,805; AV Mats 3,105; Braille Volumes 11; CDs 13,303; DVDs 5,177; e-books 207; Electronic Media & Resources 25; Large Print Bks 3,700; Microforms 92; Bk Vols 201,136; Per Subs 459; Videos 3,072
Automation Activity & Vendor Info: (Acquisitions) BiblioMondo; (Cataloging) BiblioMondo; (Circulation) BiblioMondo; (OPAC) BiblioMondo; (Serials) BiblioMondo

Wireless access
Function: Adult bk club, After school storytime; Bk club(s), Bks on cassette, Bks on CD, CD-ROM, Chess club, Children's prog, Computer training, Computers for patron use, Copy machines, Digital talking bks, Doc delivery serv, e-mail serv, E-Reserves, Electronic databases & coll, Free DVD rentals, Genealogy discussion group, Handicapped accessible, Holiday prog, Home delivery & serv to Sr ctr & nursing homes, Homebound delivery serv, ILL available, Magnifiers for reading, Mail & tel request accepted, Music CDs, Online cat, Online ref, Online searches, Orientations, Outreach serv, Outside serv via phone, mail, e-mail & web, OverDrive digital audio bks, Photocopying/Printing, Preschool outreach, Prog for adults, Prog for children & young adult, Pub access computers, Ref serv in person, Senior computer classes, Spoken cassettes & CDs, Spoken cassettes & DVDs, Story hour, Summer & winter reading prog, Summer reading prog, Teen prog, Telephone ref, VHS videos, Web-catalog, Wheelchair accessible, Workshops, Writing prog
Open Mon-Fri 10-9, Sat 9-5, Sun 1-5
Friends of the Library Group
Branches: 1
VALOIS BRANCH, 68 av Prince-Edward, H9R 4C7, SAN 369-5018. Tel: 514-630-1219. FAX: 514-695-9924. *Br Coordr,* Kathy Wilson; E-mail: wilsonk@ville.pointe-claire.qc.ca
Founded 1991
Open Mon, Wed & Fri 1-9, Sat 1-5
Friends of the Library Group

S   LAFARGE CANADA, INC*, Technical Library, 334 Avro Ave, H9R 5W5. SAN 323-7095. Tel: 514-428-7277. FAX: 514-428-0049. *Info Officer,* Nathalie Cayouette; E-mail: nathalie.cayouette@lafarge-na.com
Founded 1988
Library Holdings: Bk Vols 2,200; Per Subs 100
Database Vendor: Dialog
Publications: Biblio News, Techno News (monthly newsletters)
Restriction: Not open to pub

M   LAKESHORE GENERAL HOSPITAL*, Medical Library, 160 Stillview Rd, H9R 2Y2. SAN 319-8375. Tel: 514-630-2225, Ext 6499. FAX: 514-630-5111. *Librn,* Hakima Amoura; Staff 1 (MLS 1)
Founded 1965
Library Holdings: Bk Titles 800; Per Subs 62
Subject Interests: Health admin, Med, Nursing
Automation Activity & Vendor Info: (OPAC) Inmagic, Inc.
Publications: Liste d'acquisition; Liste des Videos
Restriction: Staff use only
Friends of the Library Group

M   PFIZER CANADA, INC*, Library & Information Services, 17300 Trans-Canada Hwy, H9J 2M5. (Mail add: PO Box 800, H9J 2M5), SAN 324-4091. Tel: 514-426-7060. FAX: 514-426-7558. *Mgr,* Sharon Pipon; *Info Spec,* Maureen Goodwin; *Info Spec,* Jocelyne LeClevc
Library Holdings: Bk Titles 3,000; Per Subs 200
Subject Interests: Cardiovascular, Med, Pharmacology, Psychiat, Rheumatology
Partic in Data Star; Dialog Corp; National Network of Libraries of Medicine

S   PULP & PAPER RESEARCH INSTITUTE OF CANADA*, Paprican Library, 570 Saint Jean Blvd, H9R 3J9. SAN 319-8391. Tel: 514-630-4100. FAX: 514-630-4134. Web Site: www.paprican.ca. *In Charge,* Roberta Roberts; E-mail: roberta.roberts@fpinnovations.ca; Staff 4 (MLS 2, Non-MLS 2)
Founded 1925
Subject Interests: Pulp
Publications: Book Catalog

QUEBEC

G   ASSEMBLEE NATIONALE DU QUEBEC BIBLIOTHEQUE*, 1035 Rue des Parlementaires, Edifice Pamphile-Lemay, G1A 1A3. SAN 319-8421. Tel: 418-643-4408. FAX: 418-646-3207. E-mail: bibliotheque@assnat.qc.ca. Web Site: www.assnat.qc.ca. *Dir,* Philippe Sauvageau; Tel: 418-643-2708, E-mail: psauvageau@assnat.qc.ca; *Dir, Info Resources & Res,* Daniel Allaire; Tel: 418-644-5536, E-mail: dallaire@assnat.qc.ca; *Dir of Tech Serv,* Clement Lebel; Tel: 418-528-1262, Fax: 418-646-4873, E-mail: clebel@assnat.qc.ca; *Archivist,* Jocelyn St-Pierre; Tel: 418-643-1272, Fax: 418-646-4873, E-mail: jstpierre@assnat.qc.ca; *Reader Serv,* Jean-Luc Fortin; Tel: 418-643-2708, E-mail: jean-luc.fortin/padm/bi@asnat.qc.ca; Staff 43 (MLS 12, Non-MLS 31)
Founded 1802
Library Holdings: Bk Titles 451,000; Bk Vols 955,000; Per Subs 942
Special Collections: Canadiana (Fonds Pierre-Joseph-Olivier Chauveau); Droit (Fonds Pollette); Government Documents (British Parliamentary Papers)

Subject Interests: Behav sci, Econ, Hist, Law, Parliamentary procedure, Polit sci, Soc
Automation Activity & Vendor Info: (Acquisitions) BiblioMondo; (Cataloging) BiblioMondo; (Circulation) BiblioMondo; (ILL) BiblioMondo; (OPAC) BiblioMondo; (Serials) BiblioMondo
Database Vendor: Dialog, EBSCOhost, LexisNexis, OVID Technologies, TLC (The Library Corporation)
Publications: Annual report; Bibliographie et Documentation; Bibliographies, Dictionaire des Parlementaires Quebecois, 1792-1992; Bulletin; Catalogue des Publications; Debats de l'Assemblee Legislative, 1867-1962; Journal des D-ebats: Index
Partic in Riseau Informatisi des Bibliothhques Gouvernementales du Quibec
Open Mon-Fri 8:30-4:30

J   BIBLIOTHEQUE DU CEGEP LIMOILOU*, 1300 Eighth Ave, G1G 5L5. SAN 369-5220. Tel: 418-647-6600. FAX: 418-647-6793. E-mail: biblio@climoilou.qc.ca. Web Site: www.climoilou.qc.ca. *Coordr, Librn,* Maud Godin; Staff 12 (MLS 1, Non-MLS 11)
Founded 1967. Enrl 7,000; Fac 500
Library Holdings: AV Mats 2,299; Bk Vols 80,950; Per Subs 370
Special Collections: Gabriel-Garcia-Marquez Coll
Automation Activity & Vendor Info: (Acquisitions) MultiLIS; (Cataloging) MultiLIS; (Circulation) MultiLIS; (OPAC) MultiLIS; (Serials) MultiLIS
Database Vendor: EBSCOhost
Function: Photocopying/Printing
Partic in RESDOC

P   BIBLIOTHEQUE GABRIELLE-ROY*, 350 est Saint-Joseph, G1K 3B2. SAN 369-5042. Tel: 418-641-6789. FAX: 418-641-6787. E-mail: courrier@icqbdq.qc.ca. Web Site: www.bibliothequesdequebec.qc.ca. *Dir,* Marie Goyette; Staff 8 (MLS 8)
Founded 1848. Pop 166,000
Library Holdings: Bk Vols 447,000
Subject Interests: Art
Wireless access
Publications: Annual report
Branches: 14
BIBLIOTHEQUE CHRYSTINE-BROUILLET, 264 rue Racine, G2B 1E6. Tel: 418-641-6120. *In Charge,* Marion Bernier
BIBLIOTHEQUE ALIETTE-MARCHAND, 233 Pierre-Bertrand Blvd, G1M 2C7. Tel: 418-641-6223. *In Charge,* Martine Caouette
BIBLIOTHEQUE LE TOURNESOL, 530, rue Delage, G3G 1J2. Tel: 418-641-6121. *In Charge,* Denise Ferland
CANARDIERE, 1601, Chemin De La Canardiere, G1J 2E1, SAN 369-5077. Tel: 418-641-6793. *In Charge,* Nadia Pizzamiglio
COLLEGE-DES-JESUITES, 1120 Blvd Rene-Levesques Ouest, G1S 4W4, SAN 369-5190. Tel: 418-641-6792. *In Charge,* Lise Beaudoin
JEAN-BAPTISTE-DUBERGER, 2475 Central Blvd, G1P 4S1, SAN 378-1690. Tel: 418-641-6799. *In Charge,* Isabelle Picard
LEBOURGNEUF, 1650 Blvd la Morille, G2K 2L2, SAN 376-9666. Tel: 418-641-6794. *Librn,* Marik Trépanier
LES SAULES, 2035 Blvd Masson, G1P 1J3, SAN 369-5131. Tel: 418-641-6796. *In Charge,* Isabelle Picard
NEUFCHATEL, 4060 rue Blain, G2B 4P3, SAN 369-5182. Tel: 418-641-6794. *In Charge,* Nancy Duchesneau
SAINT-ALBERT, Five rue des Ormes, G1L 1M5, SAN 325-4054. Tel: 418-641-6793. *In Charge,* Nadia Pizzamiglio
SAINT-ANDRE, 2155 Blvd Bastien, G2B 1B8, SAN 325-4070. Tel: 418-641-6790. *Chief Librn,* Marik Trépanier
SAINT-CHARLES, 400 Fourth Ave, G1J 2Z9, SAN 325-4038. Tel: 418-641-6795. *In Charge,* Nadia Pizzamiglio
SAINT-JEAN-BAPTISTE, 755 rue Saint-Jean, G1R 1R1, SAN 369-5212. Tel: 418-641-6798. *In Charge,* Lise Beaudoin
VIEUX-QUEBEC, 37 rue Sainte-Angele, G1R 4G5, SAN 369-5239. Tel: 418-641-6797. *Chief Librn,* Josée Tardif

G   BIBLIOTHEQUE MINISTERIELLE/MINISTERE DE LA CULTURE ET DES COMMUNICATIONS DU QUEBEC*, Bldg Guy Frégault, 225 Grande Allee Est, Block C, G1R 5G5. SAN 323-5904. Tel: 418 380-2325, Ext 7006. FAX: 418-380-2326. Web Site: www.mcccf.gouv.qc.ca/. *Librn,* Jonathan Gailloux; Staff 3 (MLS 1, Non-MLS 2)
Founded 1994
Library Holdings: Bk Titles 20,000; Per Subs 200
Subject Interests: Arts, Communications, Culture
Automation Activity & Vendor Info: (Acquisitions) BiblioMondo; (Cataloging) BiblioMondo; (Circulation) BiblioMondo; (Serials) BiblioMondo

S   CENTRALE DES SYNDICATS DU QUEBEC*, Centre de Documentation, 320, rue St-Joseph Est, bur 100, G1K 9E7. SAN 319-8464. Tel: 418-649-8888. FAX: 418-649-8800. E-mail: documentation@csq.qc.net. Web Site: www.csq.qc.net. *In Charge,* Sylvie A Painchaud; Staff 1 (MLS 1)

Founded 1965
Library Holdings: Bk Titles 19,005; Per Subs 120
Special Collections: Archives de la CSQ
Subject Interests: Economics, Educ, Labor unions, Trade unions
Publications: Publications de la Centrale
Restriction: Open by appt only

L   CENTRE D'ACCES A L'INFORMATION JURIDIQUE-BIBLIOTHEQUE
    DE QUEBEC*, 300 Boul Jean-Lesage, Palais de Justice Ste 503, G1K
    8K6. SAN 319-8448. Tel: 418-525-0057. FAX: 418-525-4208. Web Site:
    www.caij.qc.ca. *Librn,* Francine Pelletier; E-mail: fpelletier@caij.qc.ca;
    Tech Serv, Johanne Paquin
    Founded 1849
    Library Holdings: Bk Vols 40,000
    Special Collections: Jurisprudence, (Law Reviews)

M   CENTRE DE PEDOPSYCHIATRIE DU CHUQ*, Bibliotheque Medicale,
    One Ave Du-Sacre Coeur, G1N 2W1, SAN 328-5405. Tel: 418-529-6851,
    Ext 278. FAX: 418-691-0751. *Head of Librn,* Marie-Josee Blais; E-mail:
    marie-josee.blais@chuq.qc.ca. Subject Specialists: *Child psychiat,*
    Marie-Josee Blais; Staff 1 (MLS 1)
    Library Holdings: Bk Titles 4,000; Per Subs 35
    Subject Interests: Psychiat

G   CENTRE DE SERVICES PARTAGES DU QUEBEC, Bibliotheque
    Cecile-Rouleau, 700 rue St-Amable, RC, G1R 5E5. SAN 319-8626. Tel:
    418-643-1515. FAX: 418-646-8132. E-mail: bcr@cspq.gouv.qc.ca. Web
    Site: www.bibliotheque.gouv.qc.ca. *Libr Mgr,* Martine Frenette; E-mail:
    bcr@cspq.gouv.qc.ca; Staff 6 (MLS 5, Non-MLS 1)
    Founded 1972
    Library Holdings: DVDs 150; Bk Vols 240,000; Per Subs 750; Videos
    1,200
    Special Collections: Can & Prov
    Subject Interests: Computer sci, Economy, Educ, Environment,
    Intergovernmental affairs, Mgt, Native people, Pub admin, Quebec law,
    Road safety, Tourism
    Automation Activity & Vendor Info: (Acquisitions) Best-Seller, Inc;
    (Cataloging) Best-Seller, Inc; (Circulation) Best-Seller, Inc; (OPAC)
    Best-Seller, Inc; (Serials) Best-Seller, Inc
    Database Vendor: CEDROM-SNi, EBSCO Information Services
    Wireless access
    Open Mon-Fri 8:30-4:30

M   CENTRE HOSPITALIER ROBERT-GIFFARD - INSTITUT
    UNIVERSITAIRE EN SANTE MENTALE*, Centre de Documentation,
    2601 rue de la Canardiere, G1J 2G3. SAN 319-8472. Tel: 418-663-5300.
    FAX: 418-666-9416. E-mail: biblio@crulrg.ulaval.ca. *Adminr,* Murielle
    Lavoie; Tel: 418-663-5000, Ext 6607, E-mail:
    murielle_lavoie@ssss.gouv.qc.ca; Staff 2 (Non-MLS 2)
    Founded 1927
    Library Holdings: Bk Vols 3,000; Per Subs 50
    Subject Interests: Psychiat
    Partic in Consortium des Bibliotheques du RUIS Universite Laval
    Restriction: Mem organizations only

C   COLLEGE BART BIBLIOTHEQUE*, 751 cote d'Abraham, G1R 1A2.
    SAN 375-3905. Tel: 418-522-3906. FAX: 418-522-5456. E-mail:
    info@bart.qc.ca. Web Site: www.bart.qc.ca. *Librn,* Sandra Jacques;
    E-mail: sandra.jacques@bart.qc.ca
    Founded 1974. Enrl 300
    Library Holdings: Bk Vols 5,064; Per Subs 30
    Subject Interests: Law

C   COLLEGE FRANCOIS-XAVIER-GARNEAU-CENTRE DES MEDIAS*,
    1660 Blvd de l'Entente, G1S 4S3. SAN 319-8502. Tel: 418-688-8310, Ext
    2220. FAX: 418-688-0087. Web Site: www.cegep-fxg.qc.ca/biblio. Staff 11
    (MLS 1, Non-MLS 10)
    Founded 1970. Enrl 6,000
    Library Holdings: Bk Titles 90,000; Per Subs 290
    Function: Ref serv available
    Open Mon-Thurs 7:45am-10pm, Fri 7:45-6

C   COLLEGE MERICI - BIBLIOTHEQUE*, 755 Grande Allée Ouest, G1S
    1C1. SAN 325-2507. Tel: 418-683-1591. Toll Free Tel: 800-208-1463.
    FAX: 418-682-8938. Web Site:
    www.merici.ca/outils/carrefour_de_linformation.html. *Dir,* Maryse Messely;
    Tel: 418-683-2104, Ext 2213, E-mail: mmessely@college-merici.qc.ca; *Cat,
    Tech Serv,* Tina Latulippe; Tel: 418-683-2104, Ext 2249, E-mail:
    tlatulippe@college-merici.qc.ca; Staff 4 (MLS 1, Non-MLS 3)
    Enrl 1,100
    Library Holdings: AV Mats 13,000; CDs 150; DVDs 1,000; e-books 9;
    Electronic Media & Resources 10; Bk Titles 40,000; Per Subs 175; Videos
    1,000

Subject Interests: Arts, Food serv mgt, Hotel bus, Liberal arts, Orthotic,
Prosthetics, Restaurant, Sci, Tourism
Wireless access
Partic in Regard; RESDOC
Open Mon-Thurs 8-8, Fri 8-5

CR COLLEGE SAINT-CHARLES-GARNIER BIBLIOTHEQUE*, 1150 Blvd
    Rene Levesque W, G1S 1V7. SAN 320-8079. Tel: 418-681-0107. FAX:
    418-681-0118. Web Site: www.collegegarnier.qc.ca. *Dir,* Carol Beaudim
    Library Holdings: Bk Titles 6,000; Per Subs 40

G   COMMISSION D'ACCES A L'INFORMATION*, Centre de
    Documentation, 575, Rue St-Amable No. 1.10, G1R 2G4. SAN 373-8310.
    Tel: 418-528-1355. Toll Free Tel: 888-528-7741. FAX: 418-529-3102.
    E-mail: cai.communications@cai.gouv.qc.ca. Web Site: www.cai.gouv.qc.ca.
    In Charge, Suzanne Plante
    Founded 1983
    Library Holdings: Bk Vols 2,000; Per Subs 50

G   COMMISSION DE TOPONYMIE DU QUEBEC BIBLIOTHEQUE*, 750,
    boul Charest Est, RC, G1K 9M1. SAN 373-9023. Tel: 418-646-9609. FAX:
    418-528-1373. E-mail: qqolf@oqlf.gouv.qc.ca, topo@toponymie.gouv.qc.ca.
    Web Site: www.toponymie.gouv.qc.ca. *Librn,* Mihaela Ardeleanu-Ionita;
    Staff 1 (MLS 1)
    Founded 1977
    Library Holdings: Bk Titles 6,000; Bk Vols 6,500; Per Subs 25
    Special Collections: Geographicals Names; Municipality History;
    Toponymy
    Partic in Reseau Informatise des Bibliotheques du Gouvernement du
    Quebec
    Open Mon-Fri 8:30-4:30

G   COMMISSION DES NORMES DU TRAVAIL*, Centre de Documentation,
    400 blvd Jean-Lesage, 6th Flr, G1K 8W1. SAN 329-2347. Tel:
    418-525-1661. FAX: 418-528-2219. E-mail: bibli.srm@cnt.gouv.qc.ca. *Tech
    Serv,* Lucie Fecteau; Staff 2 (MLS 1, Non-MLS 1)
    Founded 1978
    Library Holdings: Bk Vols 2,000; Per Subs 136
    Publications: Acquisition Summary
    Restriction: Staff use only

S   COMMISSION SCOLAIRE DE LA CAPITALE*, Bibliotheque du
    Personnel, Louis-Jolliet, 1201 De Le Pointe-Aux-Lievres, G1N 4M1. SAN
    319-8499. Tel: 418-525-8230. FAX: 418-525-8772. E-mail:
    adm2@cscapitale.qc.ca. Web Site: www.cscapitale.qc.ca. *Dir,* Jacques
    Jerard; *Librn,* Louise Radmam
    Founded 1965
    Subject Interests: Educ
    Open Mon-Fri 8-12 & 1-4

G   CONSEIL DE LA LANGUE FRANCAISE*, Centre de Documentation,
    800 Place Youville, 13e Etage, G1R 3P4. SAN 323-6447. Tel:
    418-643-2740. FAX: 418-644-7654. Web Site: www.cslf.gouv.qc.ca. *Librn,*
    Mireille Gagne; Tel: 418-646-1127, E-mail: mireille.gagne@cslf.gouv.qc.ca
    Library Holdings: Bk Titles 4,500; Per Subs 110
    Open Mon-Fri 8:30-5

S   CONSERVATOIRE DE MUSIQUE DE QUEBEC BIBLIOTHEQUE*, 270
    rue Saint-Amable, G1R 5G1. SAN 372-6746. Tel: 418-643-2190, Ext 234.
    FAX: 418-644-9658. Web Site: www.conservatoire.gouv.qc.ca/quebec.
    Interim Head Librn, Dominique Dube; Tel: 418-643-2190, Ext 224, E-mail:
    dominique.dube@conservatoire.gouv.qc.ca; *Cat,* Claire Tremblay; Tel:
    418-643-2190, Ext 232, E-mail: claire.tremblay@mcc.gouv.qc.ca; *Circ,*
    Robert Deblois; Staff 2 (Non-MLS 2)
    Founded 1944
    Library Holdings: Bk Titles 33,000; Bk Vols 60,000; Per Subs 32
    Special Collections: Music History & Local (Fonds Vezina Coll), Archives
    Subject Interests: Music
    Automation Activity & Vendor Info: (Cataloging) BiblioMondo; (OPAC)
    BiblioMondo
    Function: ILL available
    Partic in Reseau Informatise des Bibliotheques du Gouvernement du
    Quebec
    Open Mon-Wed & Fri 9:30-6, Thurs 1-6

C   ECOLE NATIONALE D'ADMINISTRATION PUBLIQUE LIBRARIES*,
    555 Blvd Charest E, G1K 9E5. SAN 322-7308. Tel: 418-641-3000. FAX:
    418-641-3060. *Dir,* Alain Gagnon; E-mail: alain_gagnon@enap.uquebec.ca
    Founded 1969
    Library Holdings: Bk Titles 60,157; Per Subs 407
    Subject Interests: Econ, Psychol, Pub admin, Pub mgt, Sociol

Publications: Bulletin signaletique des acquisitions; Guide bibliographique en administiration publique; Liste des publications et rapports de recherche du personnel de l'Enap; Vient de paraitre
Open Mon-Fri 8-10:30, Sat 8:30-5
Departmental Libraries:
BIBLIOTHEQUE (MONTREAL CAMPUS), 4750 Ave Henri-Julien, 5e etage, Montreal, H2T 3E5, SAN 325-4445. Tel: 514-849-3989. Interlibrary Loan Service Tel: 514-849-3989, Ext 2962. Reference Tel: 514-849-3989, Ext 3578. Administration Tel: 514-849-3989, Ext 2901. Information Services Tel: 514-849-3989, Ext 2960. FAX: 514-849-3369. Web Site: www.enap.ca/enap-fra/bibliotheque/index.html. *Head of Libr,* Francine Lanouette; E-mail: francine.lanouette@enap.ca; Staff 4 (MLS 1, Non-MLS 3)
Library Holdings: Bk Vols 54,077; Per Subs 1,662
Subject Interests: Intl admin, Local admin, Pub admin
Open Mon-Thurs 8:30-4:30, Fri 8:30-12:30

S   FPINNOVATIONS-FORINTEK*, Eastern Division Library, 319 rue Franquet, G1P 4R4. SAN 329-2647. Tel: 418-659-2647. FAX: 418-659-2922. Web Site: www.fpinnovations.ca. *Librn,* Johanne Lachance; E-mail: johanne.lachance@ftinnovations.ca; *Librn,* Odile Fleury
Library Holdings: Bk Vols 25,000; Per Subs 250
Special Collections: Standards, Patents & Translations
Subject Interests: Bicontrol, Forest products, Wood composites, Wood eng, Wood sci
Partic in Dialog Corp
Open Mon-Fri 8:30-4:30

M   HOPITAL DE L'ENFANT JESUS*, Bibliotheque Charles-Auguste-Gauthier, 1401 18th St, G1J 1Z4. SAN 321-6853. Tel: 418-649-5686. FAX: 418-649-5627. *Libr Tech, Team Leader,* Zorica Djordjevic; *Libr Tech,* Lucie Côté
Founded 1964
Library Holdings: Bk Titles 3,500; Per Subs 175
Subject Interests: Neurology
Open Mon-Fri 8:30-4:30

M   HOPITAL L'HOTEL-DIEU DE QUEBEC*, Medical Library, 11 Cote du Palais, G1R 2J6. SAN 319-8529. Tel: 418-525-4444. FAX: 418-691-5468. E-mail: biblio.phdq@dechuq.ulaval.ca. Web Site: www.dechuq.ulaval.ca. *In Charge,* Justine Bilobeau
Library Holdings: Bk Vols 3,698; Per Subs 274
Subject Interests: Documentation on cancer, Nephrology

M   HOSPITAL DU SAINT-SACREMENT*, Bibliotheque Delage-Couture, 1050, Chemin Sainte-Foy, G1S 4L8. Tel: 418-682-7511, Ext 2128. FAX: 418-682-7730. *Libr Tech, Team Leader,* Zorica Djordjevic; *Libr Tech,* Sylvie Marcoux
Library Holdings: Bk Titles 2,422; Bk Vols 99

G   INSTITUT DE LA STATISTIQUE DU QUEBEC, Centre d'Information et de Documentation, 200 Chemin Ste Foy, 3e etage, G1R 5T4. SAN 374-6062. Tel: 418-691-2401. Toll Free Tel: 800-463-4090. FAX: 418-643-4129. E-mail: cid@stat.gouv.qc.ca. Web Site: www.stat.gouv.qc.ca. *Coordr,* Manon Leclerc; E-mail: manon.leclerc@stat.gouv.qc.ca; Staff 9 (MLS 1, Non-MLS 8)
Founded 1978
Library Holdings: Bk Titles 7,000; Bk Vols 18,000; Per Subs 240
Special Collections: Statistics Canada Coll, bks, CD-ROM & microfiche
Open Mon-Fri 8:30-4:30

C   INSTITUT NATIONAL DE LA RECHERCHE SCIENTIFIQUE, UNIVERSITE DU QUEBEC, Service de documentation et d'information specialisees INRS/CGC-Q, 490 de la Couronne, local 1401, G1K 9A9. SAN 373-7713. Tel: 418-654-2577. Interlibrary Loan Service Tel: 418-654-3727. Reference Tel: 418-654-2663. FAX: 418-654-2660. E-mail: sdis@adm.inrs.ca. Web Site: sdis.inrs.ca. *Libr Mgr,* Jean-Daniel Bourgault; E-mail: jean-daniel.bourgault@ete.inrs.ca; *Circ,* Pascale Dion; E-mail: pascale.dion@ete.inrs.ca; *ILL & Distance Libr Serv Spec,* Chantal Paquin; Tel: 418-654-3707, E-mail: chantal_paquin@ete.inrs.ca; *Tech Serv,* Anne Robitaille; Tel: 418-654-2588, E-mail: anne_robitaille@ete.inrs.ca; Staff 4 (MLS 1, Non-MLS 3)
Founded 1970. Enrl 100; Fac 40; Highest Degree: Doctorate
Library Holdings: Bk Titles 25,000; Per Subs 4,500
Special Collections: INRS-Eau, Terre et Environnement / Rapports de recherche
Subject Interests: Earth sci, Environ sci, Water sci
Automation Activity & Vendor Info: (Cataloging) Ex Libris Group; (Circulation) Ex Libris Group; (Course Reserve) Ex Libris Group; (ILL) Fretwell-Downing; (OPAC) Ex Libris Group
Database Vendor: American Chemical Society, American Mathematical Society, Blackwell's, Cambridge Scientific Abstracts, CEDROM-SNi, CISTI Source, EBSCOhost, Elsevier, IOP, ISI Web of Knowledge, Nature Publishing Group, OCLC WorldCat, Oxford Online, ProQuest, Repere,

Sage, ScienceDirect, Springer-Verlag, Thomson - Web of Science, Wiley InterScience
Wireless access
Partic in Canadian Research Knowledge Network; CREPUQ

GM   INSTITUT UNIVERSITAIRE DE CARDIOLOGIE ET DE PNEUMOLOGIE DE QUEBEC BIBLIOTHEQUE, 2725 Chemin Ste-Foy, G1V 4G5. SAN 322-8835. Tel: 418-656-4563. FAX: 418-656-4720. E-mail: biblio@criucpq.ulaval.ca. *Chief Librn,* Jocelyne Bellemare; *Libr Tech,* Julie Emond; Staff 2 (MLS 1, Non-MLS 1)
Founded 1960
Library Holdings: Per Subs 200
Subject Interests: Cardiology, Internal med, Respiratory med
Function: Health sci info serv

S   INTER-AMERICAN ORGANIZATION FOR HIGHER EDUCATION LIBRARY*, 333, Grande Allee Est, Bureau 230, G1R 2H8. SAN 374-7891. Tel: 418-650-1515. FAX: 418-650-1519. E-mail: secretariat@oui-iohe.qc.ca. Web Site: www.oui-iohe.qc.ca. *Exec Dir,* Marcil Hamelin
Library Holdings: Bk Vols 2,000
Open Mon-Fri 9-5

S   LES ARCHIVES DE LA VILLE DE QUEBEC, 350 rue Saint Joseph E, 4th Flr, G1B 3B2. SAN 370-713X. Tel: 418-641-6214. FAX: 418-641-6702. Web Site: www.ville.quebec.qc.ca/archives. *Dir, Div Archives,* Dorais Jacques
Library Holdings: Bk Titles 5,000
Open Tues-Fri 8:30-12 & 1-4

S   LITERARY & HISTORICAL SOCIETY OF QUEBEC LIBRARY*, 44 Chaussee des Ecossais, G1R 4H3. SAN 319-857X. Tel: 418-694-9147. FAX: 418-694-0754. E-mail: lhsqlibrary@morrin.org. Web Site: www.morrin.org. *Mgr,* Virginie Haustrate; E-mail: virginiehaustrate@morrin.org; Staff 1 (Non-MLS 1)
Founded 1824
Library Holdings: Large Print Bks 200; Bk Vols 30,000; Per Subs 20; Talking Bks 25
Special Collections: Canadiana
Subject Interests: Local hist
Function: Homebound delivery serv, Workshops
Open Tues 12-9, Wed-Fri 12-4, Sat 10-4, Sun 1-4

G   MINISTERE DE LA JUSTICE*, Bibliotheque du Ministere de la Justice, 1200 route de l'Eglise, 4th Flr, G1V 4M1. SAN 322-7553. Tel: 418-643-8409. FAX: 418-643-9749. E-mail: biblio.justice@justice.gouv.qc.ca. *Librn,* Solange Fortier; E-mail: sfortier@justice.gouv.qc.ca; *Cat,* Martine Boivin; Staff 3 (MLS 1, Non-MLS 2)
Founded 1965
Library Holdings: Bk Vols 22,500; Per Subs 180
Subject Interests: Admin of justice, Criminology, Law
Restriction: Staff use only

G   MINISTERE DE LA SANTE ET DES SERVICES SOCIAUX*, Service des Ressources Documentaires, 1075, Chemin Ste-Foy, 5e etage, G1S 2M1. SAN 319-8618. Tel: 418-266-7007. FAX: 418-266-7024. E-mail: pebservdoc@msss.gouv.qc.ca. Web Site: www.ribg.gouv.qc.ca. *Cat,* Denis Perreault; Tel: 418-266-7015, E-mail: denis.perreault@msss.gouv.qc.ca; *ILL, Ref,* Annie Lachance; Tel: 418-266-7018, E-mail: annie.lachance@msss.gouv.qc.ca; *Ref,* Louise Guy; Tel: 418-266-7017; *Ref,* Annie Racicot; Staff 2 (MLS 2)
Founded 1970
Library Holdings: AV Mats 200; Bk Titles 28,766; Bk Vols 56,000; Per Subs 400
Special Collections: WHO Publication Coll
Subject Interests: Day care, Evaluation, Health, Health manpower, Health planning, Health promotion, Med, Med econ, Nursing, Nutrition, Occupational health, Phys educ, Psychol, Pub health, Soc work
Automation Activity & Vendor Info: (Acquisitions) BiblioMondo; (Cataloging) BiblioMondo; (Circulation) BiblioMondo; (OPAC) BiblioMondo
Publications: Informations Documentaires
Partic in Reseau Informatise des Bibliotheques du Gouvernement du Quebec
Special Services for the Deaf - Bks on deafness & sign lang; Spec interest per

G   MINISTERE DES AFFAIRES MUNICIPALES ET DE REGIONS*, Centre de Documentation, 10 rue Pierre-Olivier-Chauveau, Sous-sol, Aile Chauveau, G1R 4J3. SAN 319-8510. Tel: 418-691-2018. FAX: 418-528-8970. E-mail: centre.doc@mamr.gouv.qc.ca. *Librn,* Julie Limoges
Founded 1976

Library Holdings: Bk Vols 12,000
Subject Interests: Assessment, Housing, Local politics, Municipal admin, Real estate, Surburban, Urban planning
Publications: Acquisitions list; serials list

G MINISTERE DES FINANCES BIBLIOTHEQUE*, 12 rue St Louis, Bureau 2-12, G1R 5L3. SAN 373-773X. Tel: 418-691-2256. FAX: 418-643-9911. E-mail: bibliotheque@finances.gouv.qc.ca. Web Site: www.ribg.gouv.qc.ca. *Librn,* Michele Lavoie; E-mail: michele.lavoie@finances.gouv.qc.ca; *Cat,* France Blouin; Tel: 418-644-7297, E-mail: france.blouin@finances.gouv.qc.ca; *Circ,* Isabelle Leduc; Tel: 418-644-7303, E-mail: isabelle.leduc@finances.gouv.qc.ca; Staff 3 (Non-MLS 3)
Founded 1990
Library Holdings: Bk Titles 31,615; Per Subs 117
Subject Interests: Economy, Finance, Law, Pub finance
Automation Activity & Vendor Info: (Acquisitions) BiblioMondo; (Cataloging) BiblioMondo; (Circulation) BiblioMondo; (OPAC) BiblioMondo; (Serials) BiblioMondo
Publications: Nouveautes (Accession list)
Partic in Reseau Informatise des Bibliotheques du Gouvernement du Quebec

G MINISTERE DES RESSOURCES NATURELLES ET DE LA FAUNE*, 5700 4e Ave Ouest, B-201, G1H 6R1. SAN 319-8456. Tel: 418-627-8686. FAX: 418-644-1124. E-mail: bibliotheque@mrnf.gouv.qc.ca. *Head Librn, Ref Librn,* Annie Turner; Tel: 418-627-8686, Ext 3552, E-mail: annie.turner@mrnf.gouv.qc.ca; *Acq of Monographs, Ser,* Marie-Claude Pellerin; Tel: 418-627-8686, Ext 3545, E-mail: marie-claude.pellerin@mrnf.gouv.qc.ca; *Cat,* Lynda Racine; Tel: 418-627-8686, Ext 3597, E-mail: lynda.racine@mrnf.gouv.qc.ca; *ILL,* Sylvie Laliberte; Tel: 418-627-8686, Ext 3554, E-mail: sylvie.laliberte@mrnf.gouv.qc.ca; Staff 7 (MLS 1, Non-MLS 6)
Founded 1969
Library Holdings: Bk Titles 55,000; Bk Vols 57,000; Per Subs 500
Special Collections: Forestry & Geology (Ministere des Ressources Naturelles, USDA Forest Service, Forest Canada); Geological Survey of Canada; Mines (US Bureau of Mines)
Subject Interests: Chem, Conserv, Energy, Entomology, Forest econ, Forestry, Geol, Hydraulics, Hydrol, Land surveying geodesy, Law, Metallurgy, Meteorology, Mines, Mining, Pollution, Wildlife
Automation Activity & Vendor Info: (Acquisitions) BiblioMondo; (Cataloging) BiblioMondo; (Circulation) BiblioMondo; (OPAC) BiblioMondo; (Serials) BiblioMondo
Database Vendor: Dialog, EBSCOhost, Elsevier MDL, OCLC FirstSearch, OCLC WorldCat, OVID Technologies
Function: Computers for patron use, Electronic databases & coll, Handicapped accessible, Online cat, Outside serv via phone, mail, e-mail & web, Photocopying/Printing, Prof lending libr, Ref serv available
Partic in Reseau Informatise des Bibliotheques du Gouvernement du Quebec
Restriction: Circulates for staff only

S MUSEE DE LA CIVILISATION - BIBLIOTHEQUE DU SEMINAIRE DE QUEBEC*, Service des Archives et de la Documentation, Nine rue de l'Universite, G1R 5K1. (Mail add: Box 155, Succ B, G1K 7A6), SAN 377-4945. Tel: 418-643-2158. Toll Free Tel: 866-710-8031. FAX: 418-692-5206. E-mail: archives@mcq.org. Web Site: www.mcq.org. *Dir,* Danielle Aubin; *Librn,* Lan Tran; *Tech Serv,* Pierrette LaFond; *Tech Serv,* Martine Malenfant
Library Holdings: Bk Vols 180,000
Subject Interests: Econ, Hist, Rare bks, Sci
Function: Ref serv available
Open Tues-Thurs 8:30-12 & 1:30-4:30
Restriction: Non-circulating coll

S MUSEE NATIONAL DES BEAUX-ARTS DU QUEBEC BIBLIOTHEQUE, Parc des Champs-de-Bataille, G1R 5H3. SAN 320-3549. Tel: 418-644-6460. Reference Tel: 418-644-6460, Ext 3341. FAX: 418-643-2478. E-mail: bibliom@mnba.qc.ca. Web Site: www.mnba.qc.ca. *Head, Coll Serv, Res,* Pierre B Landry; Staff 5 (MLS 2, Non-MLS 3)
Founded 1933
Library Holdings: AV Mats 57; CDs 34; DVDs 69; Electronic Media & Resources 64; Microforms 191; Bk Titles 40,000; Spec Interest Per Sub 125; Videos 138
Special Collections: Artists Archives; Artists Files; Research Archives
Subject Interests: Fine arts, Mus studies
Automation Activity & Vendor Info: (Acquisitions) BiblioMondo; (Cataloging) BiblioMondo; (Circulation) BiblioMondo; (OPAC) BiblioMondo
Partic in Reseau Informatise des Bibliotheques Gouvernementales du Quebec (RIBG)

G QUEBEC CONSEIL DE LA FAMILLE ET DE L'ENFANCE*, Centre De Documentation, 900 Rene-Levesque Blvd E, 8e etage, G1R 6B5. SAN 374-5627. Tel: 418-646-5865. Toll Free Tel: 877-221-7024 (Quebec Province only). FAX: 418-643-9832. E-mail: conseil.famille.enfance@cfe.gouv.qc.ca. Web Site: www.cfe.gouv.qc.ca. *Doc,* Suzanne Lamy; Staff 1 (MLS 1)
Founded 1989
Library Holdings: Bk Titles 4,000; Per Subs 50
Special Collections: Can & Prov

G QUEBEC MINISTERE DE L'AGRICULTURE DES PECHERIES ET DE L'ALIMENTATION BIBLIOTHEQUE*, 200 Chemin Sainte-Foy, 1er etage, G1R 4X6. SAN 319-860X. Tel: 418-380-2100, Ext 3504. FAX: 418-380-2175. E-mail: bibli200@mapaq.gouv.qc.ca. *Librn,* Ann Lafont; E-mail: ann.lafont@mapaq.gouv.qc.ca
Library Holdings: Bk Vols 31,000; Per Subs 500
Special Collections: Publications of the Ministere de l'Agriculture, des Pecheries et de l'Alimentation
Subject Interests: Agr, Nutrition, Veterinary sci

G QUEBEC MINISTERE DES TRANSPORTS, Centre de Documentation, 700 est boul Rene-Levesque, G1R 5H1. SAN 329-3327. Tel: 418-643-3578. FAX: 418-646-2343. E-mail: doc-qtr@mtq.gouv.qc.ca. Web Site: www.mtq.gouv.qc.ca/portal/page/portal/accueil/publications/centre_documentation. *Librn,* Jose Vinals; E-mail: jose.vinals@mtq.gouv.qc.ca; Staff 17 (MLS 3, Non-MLS 14)
Founded 1978
Library Holdings: Bk Titles 65,000; Per Subs 800
Subject Interests: Transportation

G REVENU QUEBEC BIBLIOTHEQUE*, 3800 rue de Marly, Secteur 6-2-9, G1X 4A5. SAN 320-3522. Tel: 418-652-5765. FAX: 418-577-5039. E-mail: bibliotheque@mrq.gouv.qc.ca. *Librn,* Veronique Cayouette; E-mail: veronique.cayouette@mrq.gouv.qc.ca
Founded 1961
Library Holdings: Bk Titles 10,000; Bk Vols 13,000; Per Subs 125
Subject Interests: Income, Law, Taxation
Automation Activity & Vendor Info: (Cataloging) BiblioMondo; (Circulation) BiblioMondo; (OPAC) BiblioMondo
Database Vendor: LexisNexis, SirsiDynix, WestlaweCARSWELL

SR SOEURS URSULINES DE QUEBEC ARCHIVES*, 18 Rue Donnacona, G1R 3Y7. SAN 327-1366. Tel: 418-692-2523. FAX: 418-692-1356. *Archivist,* Marie-Andrée Fortier. Subject Specialists: *Hist, Relig, Sch texts,* Marie-Andrée Fortier
Library Holdings: Bk Vols 25,000
Special Collections: Canadian religious & school books (1588-1994)
Open Tues-Thurs 9-12 & 1-4

C TELE-UNIVERSITE*, Bibliotech at distance, 455 rue du Parvis, G1K 9H6. SAN 375-0868. Tel: 418-657-2747. Interlibrary Loan Service Tel: 418-657-274, Ext 5331. Toll Free Tel: 800-463-4728. FAX: 418-657-2094. E-mail: peb_qquqt@uquebec.ca. Web Site: www.biblio.teluq.uqam.ca. *Actg Univ Librn,* Claude Tousignant; E-mail: ctousign@teluq.uquebec.ca; *Asst Univ Librn, Pub Serv,* Dominique Avoine; E-mail: davoine@teluq.uquebec.ca; *Acq of New Ser,* Nicole Boutet; E-mail: nboutet@teluq.uquebec.ca; *Ref,* Parisse Potvin; E-mail: ppotvin@teluq.uquebec.ca
Jun 2006-May 2007. Mats Exp (CAN) $26,547, Books (CAN) $12,545, Per/Ser (Incl. Access Fees) (CAN) $14,002. Sal (CAN) $348,486 (Prof (CAN) $138,565)
Library Holdings: Bk Vols 13,596; Per Subs 2,687
Subject Interests: Distance educ
Database Vendor: Blackwell's, EBSCOhost, Elsevier, Emerald, IOP, JSTOR, OCLC ArticleFirst, OCLC FirstSearch, OCLC WorldCat, Oxford Online, ProQuest, PubMed, Repere, ScienceDirect, Scopus, Springer-Verlag, Thomson - Web of Science, Wiley InterScience, Wilson - Wilson Web

UNIVERSITE LAVAL BIBLIOTHEQUE

C BIBLIOTHEQUE DES SCIENCES HUMAINES ET SOCIALES*, Pavillon Jean-Charles-Bonenfant, 2345, allée des Bibliothèques, G1V 0A6. Circulation Tel: 418-656-2131, Ext 5351. Interlibrary Loan Service Tel: 418-656-2573. Reference Tel: 418-656-3344. FAX: 418-656-3048. E-mail: bibl@bibl.ulaval.ca. Web Site: www.bibl.ulaval.ca. *Dir,* Loubna Ghaouti; *Head, Prof Serv,* Chantal St-Louis; *Head, Ref,* Susanne Brillant; *Circ, ILL & Distance Libr Serv Spec, Reserves,* Sarah Samson; Staff 93 (MLS 24, Non-MLS 69)
Highest Degree: Doctorate
Library Holdings: Bk Vols 3,801,000
Subject Interests: 19th Century Fr musical press, Arts, Can lit, Fr, Fr Canadian, Fr Canadian folklore, Fr modern, Humanities, Law, Philos of sci, Philos-Aristotelian, Quebec geog, Quebec studies, Soc sci, Thomist

Automation Activity & Vendor Info: (Acquisitions) SirsiDynix;
(Cataloging) SirsiDynix; (Circulation) SirsiDynix; (ILL)
Fretwell-Downing; (OPAC) SirsiDynix; (Serials) SirsiDynix
Function: Homebound delivery serv, ILL available,
Photocopying/Printing, Ref serv available, Res libr
Restriction: Open to students, fac & staff

C   BIBLIOTHEQUE SCIENTIFIQUE*, Pavillon Alexandre-Vachon, 1045 rue
de la Médecine, G1V 0A6, SAN 369-531X. Circulation Tel:
418-656-2131, Ext 2638. Interlibrary Loan Service Tel: 418-656-2131,
Ext 7193. Reference Tel: 418-656-3967. FAX: 418-656-7699. E-mail:
bibl@bibl.ulaval.ca. Web Site: www.bibl.ulaval.ca. *Head Librn,* Guy
Bilodeau; Tel: 418-656-2131, Ext 2948, E-mail:
guy.bilodeau@bibl.ulaval.ca; Staff 30 (MLS 9, Non-MLS 21)
Founded 1852. Highest Degree: Doctorate
Library Holdings: Per Subs 2,082
Subject Interests: Agr, Eng, Forest, Health sci, Sci
Automation Activity & Vendor Info: (Acquisitions) SirsiDynix;
(Cataloging) SirsiDynix; (Circulation) SirsiDynix; (Course Reserve)
SirsiDynix; (ILL) Fretwell-Downing; (OPAC) SirsiDynix; (Serials)
SirsiDynix
Partic in Canadian Research Knowledge Network; CREPUQ
Open Mon-Fri 8am-11pm, Sat & Sun 10-4:30
Restriction: Badge access after hrs

QUEBEC CITY

G   NATURAL RESOURCES CANADA-FORESTRY*, Laurentian Forestry
Centre Library, 1055 rue du PEPS, G1V 4C7. (Mail add: PO Box 10380,
Stn Sainte-Foy, G1V 4C7), SAN 319-9037. Tel: 418-648-4850. Interlibrary
Loan Service Tel: 418-648-4428. FAX: 418-648-3433. E-mail:
lfc.ill@nrcan.gc.ca. Web Site: www.cfl.scf.rncan.gc.ca/bib-lib_internet/.
Mgr, Libr Serv, Deirdre Moore; E-mail: dmoore@nrcan.gc.ca; Staff 2
(MLS 1, Non-MLS 1)
Founded 1952
Library Holdings: AV Mats 100; e-books 450; Bk Titles 12,000; Per Subs
150
Subject Interests: Botany, Entomology, Forest res, Forestry econs,
Mycology, Silviculture, Vegetal genetics

REPENTIGNY

P   BIBLIOTHEQUE DE REPENTIGNY*, One Place d'Evry, J6A 8H7. SAN
319-8677. Tel: 450-470-3001, Ext 3427. Reference Tel: 450-470-3001, Ext
3428. FAX: 450-470-3079. E-mail: bibliotheque@ville.repentigny.qc.ca.
Web Site: www.ville.repentigny.qc.ca/bibliotheque. *Librn,* Celyne Ross;
Coll Develop, Chantal Brocleur; Staff 7 (MLS 3, Non-MLS 4)
Founded 1964. Pop 74,485; Circ 407,763
Library Holdings: AV Mats 7,831; Large Print Bks 916; Bk Titles
137,741; Bk Vols 183,466; Per Subs 183
Subject Interests: Child, Fiction, Govt publ, Non-fiction bks for adults

RIGAUD

P   COLLEGE BOURGET BIBLIOTHEQUE*, 65 rue Saint Pierre, J0P 1P0.
SAN 373-6431. Tel: 450-451-0815. FAX: 450-451-4171. E-mail:
bibliotheque@collegebourget.qc.ca. Web Site: www.collegebourget.qc.ca.
Dir, Sylvain Christin; *Dir,* Ghislaine Desjardins; *Access Serv & Syst, Acq,*
Anne Bradley; *Access Serv & Syst,* Linda Lambert; Staff 6 (MLS 1,
Non-MLS 5)
Founded 1850. Pop 10,000
Library Holdings: Bk Titles 85,000; Per Subs 10
Open Mon-Fri 8-4

RIMOUSKI

P   BIBLIOTHEQUE LISETTE-MORIN (MUNICIPALE DE RIMOUSKI)*,
110 de l'Eveche est, CP 710, G5L 7C7. SAN 321-2602. Tel:
418-724-3164. FAX: 418-724-3139. E-mail:
bibliotheque.lisette-morin@ville.rimouski.qc.ca. Web Site:
www.ville.rimouski.qc.ca. *Librn,* Nicole Gagnon
Pop 45,000
Library Holdings: Bk Vols 100,000

S   SOCIETE GENEALOGIQUE DE L'EST DU QUEBEC
BIBLIOTHEQUE*, Societe de Genealogie et d'Archives de Rimouski, 110
Rue de L'Eveche EST, G5L 1X9. SAN 373-7845. Tel: 418-724-3242.
FAX: 418-724-3242. E-mail: info@sgar.org. Web Site: www.sgar.org. *Pres,*
Guy Bernier; Tel: 418-723-5323, E-mail: guy-bernier@globetrotter.net
Founded 1979
Library Holdings: Bk Titles 13,000; Bk Vols 14,700; Per Subs 70
Special Collections: Cardex; Drouin (male, female); Drouin Microfilms
(1635-1940)
Subject Interests: Genealogy
Publications: L'Estuaire Genealogique (Bulletin)
Open Mon-Thurs 9-11 & 1-4
Friends of the Library Group

C   UNIVERSITE DU QUEBEC A RIMOUSKI - BIBLIOTHEQUE*, 300
Allee des Ursulines, G5L 3A1. (Mail add: CP 3300, G5L 3A1), SAN
321-3692. Tel: 418-723-1986, Ext 1470. Circulation Tel: 418-723-1986,
Ext 1476. Interlibrary Loan Service Tel: 418-723-1986, Ext 1437. FAX:
418-724-1621. E-mail: bibliotheque@uqar.qc.ca. Web Site:
www.uqar.uquebec.ca. *Dir,* Denis Boisvert; E-mail:
denis_boisvert@uqar.qc.ca; *Coordr, Access Serv, Coordr, Coll Develop,
Coordr, Ref (Info Serv),* Josee Pelletier; Tel: 418-723-1986, Ext 1479,
E-mail: josee_pelletier@uqar.qc.ca; *Coordr, Acq, Coordr, Circ, Coordr, Ser,*
Dr Lino Tremblay; Tel: 418-723-1986, Ext 1474, E-mail:
lino_tremblay@uqar.qc.ca; Staff 13 (MLS 7, Non-MLS 6)
Founded 1969. Enrl 2,630; Fac 135; Highest Degree: Doctorate
Library Holdings: AV Mats 3,168; e-journals 8,000; Bk Vols 225,439; Per
Subs 1,515
Special Collections: Documentation Regionale de l'Est du Quebec. Oral
History
Database Vendor: Cambridge Scientific Abstracts, Dialog, EBSCOhost,
LexisNexis, ProQuest, ScienceDirect
Partic in CREPUQ

RIVIERE-DU-LOUP

P   BIBLIOTHEQUE MUNICIPALE FRANCOISE-BEDARD, 67 rue du
Rocher, G5R 1J8. SAN 319-8715. Tel: 418-862-4252. FAX: 418-862-3478.
Web Site: www.ville.riviere-du-loup.qc.ca/biblio. *Chief Librn,* Sylvie
Michaud; Tel: 418-867-6669; Staff 2.5 (MLS 1, Non-MLS 1.5)
Founded 1980. Pop 19,150; Circ 94,184
Jan 2011-Dec 2011 Income (CAN) $567,345, Provincial (CAN) $68,100,
City (CAN) $476,918, Locally Generated Income (CAN) $22,327. Mats
Exp (CAN) $105,262, Books (CAN) $81,879, Per/Ser (Incl. Access Fees)
(CAN) $7,415, AV Mat (CAN) $10,847, Electronic Ref Mat (Incl. Access
Fees) (CAN) $5,121. Sal (CAN) $340,309
Library Holdings: Audiobooks 340; CDs 4,239; DVDs 230; Large Print
Bks 1,891; Bk Titles 59,153; Bk Vols 65,177; Per Subs 106
Subject Interests: Genealogy, Local hist
Automation Activity & Vendor Info: (Cataloging) SIRSI WorkFlows;
(Circulation) SIRSI WorkFlows; (OPAC) SIRSI-iBistro
Database Vendor: CEDROM-SNi
Function: Accessibility serv available based on individual needs, Adult bk
club, After school storytime, Bk club(s), Bks on CD, CD-ROM, Children's
prog, Computer training, Computers for patron use, Copy machines, e-mail
serv, E-Reserves, Electronic databases & coll, Exhibits, Free DVD rentals,
ILL available, Instruction & testing, Magnifiers for reading, Mail & tel
request accepted, Mus passes, Music CDs, Online cat, Orientations,
Photocopying/Printing, Preschool outreach, Preschool reading prog, Prog
for adults, Prog for children & young adult, Ref serv available, Ref serv in
person, Scanner, Senior computer classes, Spoken cassettes & CDs, Story
hour, Summer reading prog, Telephone ref
Special Services for the Blind - Accessible computers; Bks on CD; Large
print bks; Magnifiers; ZoomText magnification & reading software
Open Mon-Fri 12-8, Sat 10-5, Sun 1-5

C   CEGEP RIVIERE DU-LOUP-BIBLIOTHEQUE*, 80 rue Frontenac, G5R
1R1. SAN 323-5807. Tel: 418-862-6903, Ext 2238. FAX: 418-862-4959.
Web Site: www.bibliotheque.cegep-rdl.qc.ca/outils.html. *Librn,* Joanne
Laforest; E-mail: joalaf@cegep-rdl.qc.ca; *Ref,* Diane Ouellet; Tel:
418-862-6903, Ext 2326, E-mail: diaoue@cegep-rdl.qc.ca; *Tech Serv,* Marie
Bourbeau; Tel: 418-862-6903, Ext 2325, E-mail:
mbourbeau@cegep-rdl.qc.ca; Staff 5 (MLS 1, Non-MLS 4)
Enrl 1,221; Fac 15
Library Holdings: Per Subs 130
Wireless access

P   CENTRE REGIONAL DE SERVICES AUX BIBLIOTHEQUES
PUBLIQUES DU BAS-SAINT-LAURENT*, 465 St Pierre, G5R 4T6. SAN
321-0979. Tel: 418-867-1682. FAX: 418-867-3434. E-mail:
crsbp.bsl@crsbp.net. Web Site: www.crsbp.net. *Librn,* Jean Chabot
Founded 1979. Pop 108,824; Circ 389,568
Library Holdings: Bk Titles 79,358; Bk Vols 197,556
Special Collections: Bas-St-Laurent Area
Automation Activity & Vendor Info: (Acquisitions) SirsiDynix;
(Cataloging) SirsiDynix; (Circulation) SirsiDynix; (OPAC) SirsiDynix
Database Vendor: SirsiDynix

ROSEMERE

P   BIBLIOTHEQUE H J HEMENS*, Bibliothèque de Rosemère, 339 Chemin
Grande-Cote, J7A 1K2. SAN 319-8731. Tel: 450-621-6132. FAX:
450-621-6131. E-mail: biblio@ville.rosemere.qc.ca. Web Site:
www.ville.rosemere.qc.ca/biblio. *Dir,* Marc Bineault; E-mail:
mbineault@ville.rosemere.qc.ca; *Tech Serv Team Leader,* Ginette
Corbeil-Rivet; *Tech Serv,* Chantal Maille; *Tech Serv,* Annette Roy
Founded 1946. Pop 14,193; Circ 138,728

Library Holdings: Audiobooks 626; CDs 1,650; DVDs 300; Bk Titles 72,400; Bk Vols 77,000; Per Subs 174
Automation Activity & Vendor Info: (Cataloging) BiblioMondo; (Circulation) BiblioMondo; (Course Reserve) BiblioMondo; (OPAC) BiblioMondo
Wireless access

ROUYN-NORANDA

C   BIBLIOTHEQUE CEGEP ET UNIVERSITE DU QUEBEC EN ABITIBI-TEMISCAMINGUE*, Bibliotheque CAT-UQAT, 425 Blvd du College, BP 8000, J9X 5M5. SAN 371-5299. Tel: 819-762-0931. Toll Free Tel: 866-234-3728. FAX: 819-762-2071. Web Site: www.uqat.uquebec.ca. *Dir,* Francois Delachevrotiere; Tel: 819-762-0931, Ext 1112, E-mail: francois.delachevrotiere@uqat.ca; Staff 2 (MLS 2)
Founded 1971. Enrl 4,300; Highest Degree: Master
Library Holdings: Bk Vols 225,036; Per Subs 620
Special Collections: James Bay Coll; Northwestern Quebec, bks, micro
Subject Interests: Educ
Automation Activity & Vendor Info: (Acquisitions) Ex Libris Group; (Cataloging) OCLC WorldCat; (Circulation) Ex Libris Group; (OPAC) Ex Libris Group
Wireless access
Open Mon-Thurs 8am-9:45pm, Fri 8am-8:45pm, Sat & Sun 12-4:15

P   BIBLIOTHEQUE MUNICIPALE DE ROUYN-NORANDA*, 201 Ave Dallaire, J9X 4T5. SAN 319-874X. Tel: 819-762-0944. FAX: 819-797-7136. Web Site: www.biblrn.qc.ca. *Dir, Libr Serv,* Charlotte Baril; Staff 5 (MLS 1, Non-MLS 4)
Founded 1947. Pop 29,600; Circ 350,000
Library Holdings: Bk Vols 100,000; Per Subs 100
Subject Interests: English, Multilingual
Publications: Annual report
Open Mon-Fri 1-9, Sat & Sun 1-5

C   CEGEP DE L'ABITIBI - TEMISCAMINGUE BIBLIOTHEQUE*, 425 Boul du College, J9X 5M5. (Mail add: CP 8000, J9X 5M5), SAN 369-5344. Tel: 819-762-0931, Ext 1216. FAX: 819-762-2071. Web Site: www.uqat.ca/bibliotheque. *Dir,* François de la Chevrotière; *ILL,* Gisele Neas; *Ref,* David Fournier-Viger; Staff 2 (MLS 2)
Founded 1953. Enrl 2,300
Library Holdings: Bk Vols 225,036; Per Subs 620
Special Collections: Northwestern Quebec, bk, microform. Can & Prov
Open Mon-Thurs 8am-9:45pm, Fri 8am-8:45pm, Sat & Sun Noon-4:15

P   CENTRE REGIONALE DE SERVICES AUX BIBLIOTHEQUES PUBLIQUES DE L'ABITIBI-TEMISCAMINGUE-NORD-DU-QUEBEC*, Centre Regional Biblio, 20 Quebec Ave, J9X 2E6. SAN 321-2629. Tel: 819-762-4305. FAX: 819-762-5309. E-mail: info@crsbpat.qc.ca. Web Site: www.crsbpat.qc.ca. *Dir,* Norman Fink; Staff 9 (MLS 4, Non-MLS 5)
Founded 1976. Pop 58,299; Circ 269,439
Library Holdings: Bk Titles 75,507; Bk Vols 142,645; Per Subs 660
Special Collections: Provincial
Database Vendor: SirsiDynix
Publications: L'Echange (Bi-monthly)

SAINT BENOIT-DU-LAC

SR   BIBLIOTHEQUE DE L'ABBAYE SAINT-BENOIT*, J0B 2M0. SAN 319-8774. Tel: 819-843-4080. FAX: 819-868-1861. Web Site: www.st-benoit-du-lac.com. *Librn,* Martin Chamberlain
Founded 1912
Library Holdings: Bk Vols 80,000

SAINT BRUNO-DE-MONTARVILLE

P   BIBLIOTHEQUE MUNICIPALE DE SAINT-BRUNO-DE-MONTARVILLE*, 82 Seigneurial W, J3V 5N7. SAN 319-8782. Tel: 450-645-2950. Administration Tel: 450-653-2443, Ext 2850. FAX: 450-441-8485. E-mail: bibliotheque@stbruno.ca. Web Site: www.ville.stbruno.qc.ca/bibliotheque. *Coll Develop, Dir,* Jean-Marc Lynch; Staff 9 (MLS 1, Non-MLS 8)
Founded 1961. Pop 25,000; Circ 175,000
Library Holdings: Bk Titles 75,000; Bk Vols 85,000; Per Subs 137
Special Collections: Can & Prov
Automation Activity & Vendor Info: (Acquisitions) BiblioMondo; (Cataloging) BiblioMondo; (Circulation) BiblioMondo; (OPAC) BiblioMondo; (Serials) BiblioMondo

SAINT CHARLES BORROMEE

M   CENTRE DE SANTE ET DE SERVICES SOCIAUX DU NORD DE LANAUDIERE BIBLIOTHEQUE*, Medical Staff Library, 1000 Blvd Ste-Anne, J6E 6J2. SAN 319-6577. Tel: 450-759-8222. FAX:

450-759-7343. E-mail: csssnl.bibliotheque@ssss.gouv.qc.ca. *Librn,* Nancy Gadoury; *Libr Tech,* Christiane Rondeau
Founded 1964
Library Holdings: Bk Titles 2,000; Per Subs 150
Subject Interests: Med, Nursing, Psychiat, Psychol
Restriction: Staff use only

SAINT CONSTANT

S   EXPORAIL ARCHIVES LIBRARY*, The Canadian Railway Museum, 110 St Pierre, J5A 1G7. SAN 325-9846. Tel: 450-638-1522, Ext 237. FAX: 450-638-1563. E-mail: info@exporail.org. Web Site: www.exporail.org. *Archivist,* Josee Vallerand
Library Holdings: Bk Titles 6,000; Per Subs 800
Subject Interests: Railway hist
Open Mon-Fri 10-5

SAINT EUSTACHE

P   BIBLIOTHEQUE MUNICIPALE GUY-BELISLE SAINT EUSTACHE*, 80 blvd Arthur Sauve, J7R 2H7. SAN 322-676X. Tel: 450-974-5035. FAX: 450-974-5054. Web Site: www.ville.saint-eustache.qc.ca. *Coll Develop, Dir,* Nicole Grimard; E-mail: ngrimard@ville.saint-eustache.qc.ca; Staff 1 (MLS 1)
Pop 40,000
Library Holdings: Bk Vols 132,840; Per Subs 240
Special Collections: Canada & Quebec Govt
Subject Interests: Genealogy, Hist, Patrimony
Automation Activity & Vendor Info: (Acquisitions) Innovative Interfaces, Inc; (Cataloging) Innovative Interfaces, Inc; (Circulation) Innovative Interfaces, Inc; (Course Reserve) Innovative Interfaces, Inc; (ILL) Innovative Interfaces, Inc; (Media Booking) Innovative Interfaces, Inc; (OPAC) Innovative Interfaces, Inc; (Serials) Innovative Interfaces, Inc
Open Mon-Fri 9-9, Sat & Sun 9-5

SAINT FELICIEN

P   BIBLIOTHEQUE MUNICIPALE DE SAINT FELICIEN*, 1209 Blvd Sacre-Coeur, G8K 2R5. SAN 319-8790. Tel: 418-679-5334. FAX: 418-679-2178. E-mail: loisirs@ville.stfelicien.qc.ca. *Librn,* Joanne LaPrise; *ILL,* Danielle LaPierre; *ILL,* Nathalie Tremblay; *Libr Tech,* Francine Menard
Pop 9,058; Circ 19,281
Library Holdings: Bk Vols 30,000; Per Subs 43

C   CEGEP DE SAINT FELICIEN*, Centre de Documentation, 1105 boul Hamel, G8K 2R8. (Mail add: CP 7300, G8K 2R8), SAN 322-8371. Tel: 418-679-5412, Ext 284. FAX: 418-679-1040. E-mail: biblio@cstfelicien.qc.ca. Web Site: www.cstfelicien.qc.ca. *Librn,* Serge Berube; Staff 3 (MLS 1, Non-MLS 2)
Founded 1971. Enrl 998
Library Holdings: Bk Titles 65,000; Per Subs 125
Subject Interests: Nat sci
Open Mon-Thurs 8-8, Fri 8-5

SAINT JACQUES

P   BIBLIOTHEQUE MUNICIPALE*, 16 rue Marechal, CP 370, J0K 2R0. SAN 319-8855. Tel: 450-831-2296. FAX: 450-839-2387. Web Site: www.biblio@st-jacques.org. *In Charge,* Lisette Noury
Pop 3,800; Circ 13,847
Library Holdings: Bk Vols 11,000

SAINT JEROME

P   BIBLIOTHEQUE MARIE-ANTOINETTE-FOUCHER*, 185 rue Du Palais, J7Z 1X6. SAN 319-8898. Tel: 450-432-0589. FAX: 450-436-1211. *Dir,* Claudine Richer; Tel: 450-432-1226; Staff 19 (MLS 1, Non-MLS 18)
Founded 1949. Pop 60,000
Library Holdings: Bk Vols 50,000; Per Subs 100
Automation Activity & Vendor Info: (Acquisitions) MultiLIS; (Cataloging) MultiLIS; (Circulation) MultiLIS; (OPAC) MultiLIS
Open Mon & Wed 12-8, Sat 9-5, Sun 12-4

SAINT LAMBERT

J   CHAMPLAIN REGIONAL COLLEGE*, George Wallace Library, 900 Riverside Dr, J4P 3P2. SAN 319-8901. Tel: 450-672-7360. Circulation Tel: 450-672-7360, Ext 221. Reference Tel: 450-672-7360, Ext 345. FAX: 450-672-2152. *Libr Coordr,* Nicole Hache; E-mail: nhache@champlaincollege.qc.ca; *Ref,* Dale Huston; E-mail: huston@champlaincollege.qc.ca; Staff 2 (MLS 2)
Founded 1972. Enrl 2,400; Fac 165
Library Holdings: Bk Vols 80,000; Per Subs 250
Automation Activity & Vendor Info: (OPAC) SirsiDynix
Database Vendor: EBSCOhost, ProQuest

P   SAINT LAMBERT MUNICIPAL LIBRARY, 490 Mercille Ave, J4P 2L5. SAN 369-5433. Tel: 450-466-3910. FAX: 450-923-6512. E-mail: bibliotheque@ville.saint-lambert.qc.ca. Web Site: www.ville.saint-lambert.qc.ca/biblio. *Dir,* Guylaine Pellerin; Staff 1 (MLS 1)
Founded 1954. Pop 21,700; Circ 203,500
Library Holdings: Bk Titles 101,786; Per Subs 151
Automation Activity & Vendor Info: (Acquisitions) BiblioMondo; (Cataloging) BiblioMondo; (Circulation) BiblioMondo; (Course Reserve) BiblioMondo; (ILL) BiblioMondo; (Media Booking) BiblioMondo; (OPAC) BiblioMondo; (Serials) BiblioMondo
Friends of the Library Group
Branches: 1
PREVILLE, 120 de Poitou, J4S 1E1, SAN 369-5468. Tel: 450-923-6510.
   Dir, Guylaine Pellerin
   Library Holdings: Bk Titles 14,200
   Open Tues-Fri 1:30-4, Sat 10-12

SAINT LAURENT

S   ABBOTT LABORATORIES LTD LIBRARY*, 8401 Trans Canada Hwy, Ville St'Laurent, H4S 1Z1. SAN 319-6917. Tel: 514-832-7000. FAX: 514-832-7800. *Librn,* Georgette Vincze
Founded 1944
Library Holdings: Bk Vols 1,000; Per Subs 135
Subject Interests: Med, Mkt

S   CAE, INC*, Engineering Reference Library, 8585 Cote de Liesse Rd, H4L 4X4. (Mail add: PO Box 1800, H4L 4X4), SAN 319-7093. Tel: 514-341-6780, Ext 2113. FAX: 514-734-5616. Web Site: www.cae.ca. *Librn,* Margaret Ford; E-mail: margaret.ford@cae.com
Library Holdings: Bk Titles 5,200; Bk Vols 7,000; Per Subs 400
Subject Interests: Air traffic control, Communications, Electrical power, Electronics, Eng, Nuclear power, Simulators, Space tech

J   CEGEP DE SAINT-LAURENT BIBLIOTHEQUE*, 625 Boul Ste-Croix, H4L 3X7. SAN 319-7212. Tel: 514-747-6521. FAX: 514-748-1249, 514-855-1942. Web Site: www.cegep-st-laurent.qc.ca/bibliotheque/bibliotheque.htm. *Coordr,* Pierre Sasseville; E-mail: psasseville@cegep_st_laurent.qc.ca; *Acq,* Johanne Desjardins; *Circ,* Josee Barrette; *Per,* Mireille Cherrier; *Tech Serv,* Yolande Felx
Founded 1847. Enrl 3,545; Fac 229
Library Holdings: AV Mats 2,025; CDs 3,790; Music Scores 7,557; Bk Titles 81,000; Per Subs 586
Subject Interests: Arts, Humanities, Sciences
Publications: Guide & bibliographies
Open Mon-Thurs 8-6, Fri 8-4:30

S   NATIONAL FILM BOARD OF CANADA*, Information Management, 3155 Cote-de-Liesse Rd, H4N 2N4. (Mail add: PO Box 6100, Montreal, H3C 3H5), SAN 369-3961. Tel: 514-496-1044. FAX: 514-283-9811. Web Site: www.nfb.ca. *Chief Info Officer,* James Roberts; E-mail: j.a.roberts@nfb.ca; Staff 3 (MLS 3)
Founded 1940
Library Holdings: Bk Vols 15,000; Per Subs 1,100
Special Collections: Challenge For Change, Norman McLaren
Subject Interests: Canadiana, Moving pictures, Television, Video

C   VANIER COLLEGE LIBRARY*, Information Technology Centre, 821 Ave Sainte-Croix, H4X 3L9. SAN 321-7086. Tel: 514-744-7500, Ext 7540. Interlibrary Loan Service Tel: 514-744-7500, Ext 7544. FAX: 514-744-7545. Web Site: www.vaniercollege.qc.ca. *Acq & Coll,* Carol-Anne Inglis; *Instruction & Ref Librn,* Rose De Souza; *Ser Tech & PT Librn,* Nina Arabian; Staff 3 (MLS 3)
Founded 1969. Enrl 5,600; Fac 450
Library Holdings: Bk Vols 97,000; Per Subs 700
Special Collections: Can
Automation Activity & Vendor Info: (Acquisitions) BiblioMondo; (Cataloging) BiblioMondo; (Circulation) BiblioMondo; (Course Reserve) BiblioMondo; (ILL) BiblioMondo; (Media Booking) BiblioMondo; (OPAC) BiblioMondo; (Serials) BiblioMondo
Database Vendor: ProQuest

S   WYETH CANADA, SCIENTIFIC INFORMATION*, 1025 Boul Marcel-Laurin, H4R 1J6. SAN 319-6968. Tel: 514-748-3734. FAX: 514-744-0550. *Mgr,* Meredith Giffin; Staff 3 (MLS 3)
Founded 1937
Subject Interests: Chem, Med
Automation Activity & Vendor Info: (OPAC) Fretwell-Downing
Open Mon-Fri 8:30-4:30

SAINT NICOLAS

P   BIBLIOTHEQUE MUNICIPALE*, 220 rue du Pont, G7A 1T7. SAN 321-2742. Tel: 418-835-8588. FAX: 418-835-5297. Web Site: www.bibliotheques.qc.ca. *In Charge,* Martine Boulay
Library Holdings: Bk Vols 45,000
Special Collections: French Coll, bks, novels, mag
Open Tues, Wed & Thurs 1-9, Fri 6pm-9pm, Sat & Sun 1-5

SAINT-CASIMIR

P   BIBLIOTHEQUE JEAN-CHARLES MAGNAN*, 510 boul de la Montagne, G0A 3L0. SAN 321-3099. Tel: 418-339-2543. FAX: 418-339-3105. *Librn,* Ange-Aimee Asselin
Founded 1980. Pop 1,575
Library Holdings: Bk Vols 2,000; Per Subs 10
Open Tues 1:30-3:30, Thurs 6:30pm-8:30pm

SAINT-CLEMENT

P   BIBLIOTHEQUE MUNICIPALE*, 25 A Rue St Pierre, G0L 2N0. SAN 321-2505. Tel: 418-963-2258. FAX: 418-963-2619. E-mail: st_clement@videotron.ca. *Librn,* Therese St Pierre
Library Holdings: Bk Vols 1,500
Automation Activity & Vendor Info: (OPAC) MultiLIS
Open Wed 7am-8:30pm

SAINTE THERESE

P   BIBLIOTHEQUE MUNICIPALE DE SAINTE-THERESE*, 150 Boul du Seminaire, J7E 1Z2. SAN 322-8258. Tel: 450-434-1442. FAX: 450-434-6070. Web Site: www.ville.sainte-therese.qc.ca/biblio. *Dir,* Lise Theriault; E-mail: ltheriault@ville.sainte-therese.qc.ca; *Pub Serv,* Nicole Bouchard; *Tech Serv,* Dominique Bourget; Staff 4 (MLS 1, Non-MLS 3)
Founded 1975. Pop 27,000
Library Holdings: AV Mats 1,646; Bk Vols 89,000; Per Subs 250; Talking Bks 500
Special Collections: Can & Que
Subject Interests: Travel
Automation Activity & Vendor Info: (Acquisitions) BiblioMondo; (Cataloging) BiblioMondo; (Circulation) BiblioMondo
Open Mon-Fri (Winter) 10-9, Sat 9-4, Sun 12-5; Mon-Fri (Summer) 10-9

SAINTE-ANNE-DE-BELLEVUE

P   BIBLIOTHEQUE MUNICIPALE DE SAINTE-ANNE-DE-BELLEVUE*, 40, rue Saint-Pierre, H9X 1Y6. Tel: 514-457-1940. FAX: 514-457-7146. Web Site: www.reseaubiblioduquebec.qc.ca. *Librn,* Josée Caron; Tel: 514-457-5248, E-mail: jcaron@ville.sainte-anne-de-bellevue.qc.ca
Founded 1980. Pop 5,035; Circ 28,815
Library Holdings: AV Mats 819; CDs 450; DVDs 175; Bk Vols 18,000
Automation Activity & Vendor Info: (Cataloging) MultiLIS; (Circulation) MultiLIS; (Course Reserve) MultiLIS; (OPAC) MultiLIS
Wireless access
Open Mon-Wed 12-8, Thurs 4-8, Sat & Sun (Winter) 11-3

S   EMS TECHNOLOGIES CANADA, LTD LIBRARY*, 21025 Trans-Canada Hwy, H9X 3R2. SAN 319-8987. Tel: 514-457-2150, Ext 3259. FAX: 514-425-3048. Web Site: www.elmg.com. *In Charge,* Lola Olczak; Staff 1 (MLS 1)
Founded 1977
Library Holdings: AV Mats 500; e-books 50; Bk Titles 10,500; Per Subs 150
Subject Interests: Aeronaut, Communications, Electronic, Electronics, Market res, Mat sci, Satellites, Space flight, Specifications, Standards
Automation Activity & Vendor Info: (Cataloging) Inmagic, Inc.; (Circulation) Inmagic, Inc.; (OPAC) Inmagic, Inc.; (Serials) Inmagic, Inc.
Database Vendor: OCLC FirstSearch
Publications: Accession Lists; Current Awareness; Current Contents
Partic in OCLC Online Computer Library Center, Inc
Restriction: Access at librarian's discretion, Access for corporate affiliates, By permission only, Circulates for staff only, Co libr, Lending to staff only, Non-circulating to the pub, Not open to pub, Open by appt only, Open to others by appt, Open to researchers by request, Staff use only

M   HOPITAL SAINTE-ANNE*, Centre de Documentation, 305 boul des Anciens-Combattants, H9X 1Y9. SAN 377-5305. Tel: 514-457-3440. FAX: 514-457-2761. *In Charge,* S Lavoie
Library Holdings: Bk Vols 1,500; Per Subs 40

C   JOHN ABBOTT COLLEGE, Library Media Services, 21,275 Lakeshore Rd, H9X 3L9. (Mail add: PO Box 2000, H9X 3L9), SAN 326-4335. Tel: 514-457-6610, Ext 5335. Circulation Tel: 514-457-6610, Ext 5330. Reference Tel: 514-457-6610, Ext 5331. E-mail: library.ref@johnabbott.qc.ca. Web Site: www.johnabbott.qc.ca. *Chairperson, Libr Media Serv Head Librn,* Lesley Lawrence; E-mail:

lesley.lawrence@johnabbott.qc.ca; *Head, Pub Serv,* Marek Pukteris; E-mail: marek.pukteris@johnabbott.qc.ca; *Head, Tech Serv,* Carolyn Littlejohns; E-mail: carolyn.littlejohns.qc.ca; *Ref Serv,* Ian Young; E-mail: ian.young@johnabbott.qc.ca; Staff 11 (MLS 4, Non-MLS 7)
Founded 1972. Enrl 6,000; Fac 400
Library Holdings: AV Mats 4,000; Bk Titles 61,000; Bk Vols 85,000; Per Subs 200
Special Collections: Can & Prov
Database Vendor: OPALS (Open-source Automated Library System)
Wireless access
Open Mon-Thurs 8-6, Fri 8-4:30

MCGILL UNIVERSITY
See Montreal

SAINTE-ANNE-DES-MONTS

S   SOCIETE D'HISTOIRE ET D'ARCHEOLOGIE DES MONTS, INC*, 675 Blvd Saint Anne Ouest, G4V 1T9. SAN 370-6338. Tel: 418-763-7871. E-mail: genealogie@globetrotter.net. *Dir,* Roland Provost; *Asst Librn,* Michel Levesque; Staff 1 (MLS 1)
Founded 1970
Library Holdings: Bk Vols 40,000
Special Collections: Oral History
Subject Interests: Genealogy, Local hist

SAINTE-ETIENNE

P   BIBLIOTHEQUE D'ALBERT ROUSSEAU*, 711 ave Albert Rousseau, G6J 1Z7. SAN 321-2785. Tel: 418-831-6492. FAX: 418-831-6107. E-mail: bibliolevis@ville.levis.qc.ca. *Dir,* Marie Lavoie
Library Holdings: Bk Vols 30,000; Per Subs 25
Open Tues-Thurs 1-9, Fri 6pm-9pm, Sat & Sun 1-5

SAINTE-FOY

G   AGRICULTURE & AGRI-FOOD CANADA*, Library Research Centre, 2560 Hochelaga Blvd, G1V 2J3. SAN 321-8430. Tel: 418-657-7985, Ext 239. FAX: 418-648-2402. *Dir,* Francine Bernard; E-mail: francine.bernard@agr.gc.ca; Staff 1 (Non-MLS 1)
Founded 1967
Library Holdings: Bk Titles 9,000; Per Subs 85
Subject Interests: Breeding, Cereal, Clay soils, Cold resistance, Forage, Molecular biol, Nitrogen fixation, Pathology, Soil conservation
Automation Activity & Vendor Info: (Cataloging) Infor Library & Information Solutions
Restriction: Staff use only

G   ARCHIVES NATIONALES DU QUEBEC BIBLIOTHEQUE*, Cite Universitaire, Pavillon Louis Jacques Casault, CP 10450, G1V 4N1. SAN 372-7246. Tel: 418-644-4797. FAX: 418-646-4254. E-mail: anq-biblio@mcc.gov.qc.ca. Web Site: www.banq.qc.ca. *Dir,* Anastassia Khouri; Staff 2 (MLS 1, Non-MLS 1)
Founded 1920
Library Holdings: Bk Vols 30,000; Per Subs 36
Special Collections: Archives Management; Genealogy; Government Institutions; History of French America
Open Mon-Fri 10:30-4:30

P   BIBLIOTHEQUE MUNICIPALE DE SAINTE-FOY*, 999 Place de Ville, CP 218, G1V 4E1. SAN 319-8995. Tel: 418-641-6301. Reference Tel: 418-641-6277. FAX: 418-654-4172. *Ref,* Andree Cote
Founded 1967. Pop 74,328; Circ 399,633
Library Holdings: Bk Titles 119,203
Subject Interests: Archit, Art, Genealogy, Musical scores
Open Mon & Sun 1-5, Tues-Thurs Noon-9, Fri 1-9, Sat 10-5

C   CEGEP DE SAINTE-FOY BIBLIOTHEQUE, 2410 Chemin Sainte-Foy, G1V 1T3. SAN 319-9029. Tel: 418-659-6600, Ext 3714. FAX: 418-659-4563. Web Site: www.cegep-ste-foy-qc.ca. *AV, Media Spec,* Denis Thibault; Staff 6 (MLS 6)
Founded 1918. Enrl 6,100
Library Holdings: Bk Vols 90,000; Per Subs 400
Open Mon-Fri 8:30am-9pm, Sat & Sun 12-4:30

G   CONSEIL SUPERIEUR DE L'EDUCATION*, Centre de Documentation, 1175 ave Lavigerie, Bureau 180, G1V 5B2. SAN 323-908X. Tel: 418-643-2845, 418-644-0753. FAX: 418-644-2530. E-mail: panorama@cse.gouv.qc.ca. Web Site: www.cse.gouv.qc.ca. *Dir, Res Serv,* Francesco Arena; E-mail: francesco.arena@cse.gouv.qc.ca; Staff 2 (Non-MLS 2)
Founded 1965
Library Holdings: e-books 153; Bk Titles 7,500; Per Subs 45
Subject Interests: Educ
Restriction: Staff use only

S   SOCIETE DE GENEALOGIE DE QUEBEC*, 1210 av du Seminaire, CP 9066, G1V 4A8. SAN 373-8337. Tel: 418-651-9127. FAX: 418-651-2643. E-mail: sgq@total.net. Web Site: www.sgq.qc.ca. *Pres,* Mariette Parent
Founded 1961
Library Holdings: Bk Titles 3,000; Bk Vols 4,000; Per Subs 35
Subject Interests: Genealogy
Publications: L'Ancetre

SAINT-FABIAN DE PANET

P   BIBLIOTHEQUE MUNICIPALE DE SAINT-FABIEN DE PANET*, 199, Saint Bilodeau, G0R 2J0. SAN 321-3048. Tel: 418-249-4471. FAX: 418-249-2507. *Librn,* Michelle Thibodeau
Founded 1980. Pop 1,053
Open Tues & Wed 6:30pm-9pm

SAINT-GEORGES DE BEAUCE

C   CEGEP BEAUCE-APPALACHES BIBLIOTHEQUE*, 1055 116e rue, G5Y 3G1. SAN 372-7475. Tel: 418-228-8896, Ext 220. FAX: 418-228-0562. *Dir, Libr Serv,* Yvon Bernard
Library Holdings: Bk Vols 42,000; Per Subs 110
Open Mon-Fri 8-5:30 & 6:30-9:30

SAINT-HYACINTHE

CR   BIBLIOTHEQUE DU SEMINAIRE DE SAINT-HYACINTHE, 650 rue Girouard Est, J2S 2Y2. SAN 374-518X. Tel: 450-774-8977. FAX: 450-774-7101. E-mail: bssh@cgocable.ca. Web Site: www.bibssh.qc.ca. *Dir, Libr Serv,* Bernard Auger. Subject Specialists: *Indexing,* Bernard Auger; Staff 1 (MLS 1)
Founded 1811
Jul 2012-Jun 2013 Income (CAN) $89,000. Mats Exp (CAN) $7,000, Books (CAN) $4,500, Per/Ser (Incl. Access Fees) (CAN) $2,500. Sal (CAN) $43,000
Library Holdings: Bk Vols 200,000; Per Subs 12
Special Collections: Rare Religious Books, 1511-1900
Subject Interests: Can hist, Fr lit, Roman Catholic relig
Automation Activity & Vendor Info: (Acquisitions) Concepts Logiques 4DI Inc; (Cataloging) Concepts Logiques 4DI Inc; (Circulation) Concepts Logiques 4DI Inc; (ILL) Concepts Logiques 4DI Inc; (OPAC) Concepts Logiques 4DI Inc; (Serials) Concepts Logiques 4DI Inc
Database Vendor: Concepts Logiques 4DI Inc
Function: Ref serv available

G   CANADA AGRICULTURE & AGRI-FOOD CANADA*, CAL Information Center-St-Hyacinthe, 3600 Blvd Casavant W, J2S 8E3. SAN 372-6401. Tel: 450-768-3247, 450-773-1105. FAX: 450-773-8461. E-mail: qshag@agr.gc.ca. Web Site: www.agr.gc.ca. *Head, Libr & Info Serv,* Pierre Di Campo; E-mail: pierre.dicampo@agr.gc.ca; *Coordr, Doc,* Lucie Allaire; *Libr Tech,* Helen Simard-Vermette; Staff 2 (MLS 1, Non-MLS 1)
Library Holdings: Bk Titles 10,000; Per Subs 45
Open Mon-Fri 8:30-5

R   CEGEP DE SAINT-HYACINTHE BIBLIOTHEQUE*, 3000 rue Boulle, J2S 1H9. SAN 319-8839. Tel: 450-773-6800. FAX: 450-773-9971. *Librn,* Louis Blaise-Cote
Founded 1929
Library Holdings: Bk Vols 80,000; Per Subs 250
Special Collections: Canadiana
Subject Interests: Educ, Humanities, Sci, Textiles
Open Mon-Thurs 8am-8:30pm, Fri 8-5

M   CENTRE DE SANTE ET DE SERVICES SOCIAUX RICHELIEU-YAMASKA*, Bibliotheque Romeo-Germain, 2750 boul Laframboise, J2S 4Y8. SAN 375-3646. Tel: 450-771-3333, Ext 3242. FAX: 450-771-3552. *Mgr,* Alain Dery; E-mail: alain.dery@rrsss16.gouv.qc.ca
Library Holdings: Bk Vols 5,000; Per Subs 80
Subject Interests: Med

P   MEDIATHEQUE MASKOUTAINE*, 2720 rue Dessaulles, J2S 2V7. SAN 325-2116. Tel: 450-773-1830. FAX: 450-773-3398. E-mail: info@mediatheque.qc.ca. Web Site: www.mediatheque.qc.ca. *Admin Dir,* Yves Tanguay; E-mail: tanguayy@mediatheque.qc.ca; *Asst Admin,* Denis Bourassa; Staff 77 (MLS 3, Non-MLS 74)
Founded 1954. Pop 59,204; Circ 402,304
Jan 2007-Dec 2007 Income (CAN) $2,111,721, Provincial (CAN) $273,200, City (CAN) $1,588,477, Locally Generated Income (CAN) $178,860, Other (CAN) $71,184. Mats Exp (CAN) $416,410, Books (CAN) $330,828, Per/Ser (Incl. Access Fees) (CAN) $22,333, AV Mat (CAN) $55,561, Electronic Ref Mat (Incl. Access Fees) (CAN) $7,688. Sal (CAN) $753,113

Library Holdings: CDs 8,865; DVDs 4,275; Electronic Media & Resources 1,107; Large Print Bks 2,275; Bk Titles 131,254; Bk Vols 170,856; Per Subs 319; Talking Bks 1,320; Videos 5,497
Special Collections: Maskoutana
Automation Activity & Vendor Info: (Acquisitions) SIRSI Unicorn; (Cataloging) SIRSI Unicorn; (Circulation) SIRSI Unicorn; (Course Reserve) SIRSI Unicorn; (OPAC) SIRSI-iBistro; (Serials) SIRSI Unicorn
Database Vendor: CEDROM-SNi
Wireless access
Publications: Liste Collective des Periodiques des Bibliotheques de la Monteregie
Open Mon-Thurs 12-9, Fri 10-9, Sat & Sun 10-5
Friends of the Library Group

SAINT-JACQUES DE LEEDS

P　　BIBLIOTHEQUE MUNICIPALE DE SAINT-JACQUES DE LEEDS*, 425 Principale St, G0N 1J0. SAN 321-2874. Tel: 418-424-3181. FAX: 418-424-0126. *Librn,* Esther Mercier
Founded 1979. Pop 769
Open Tues & Wed 12:45-3, Thurs 7pm-8:30pm

SAINT-JEAN-CHRYSOSTOME

P　　BIBLIOTHEQUE MUNICIPALE*, 959, rue de l'Hotel de ville, G6Z 2N8. SAN 319-8944. Tel: 418-839-5242. FAX: 418-834-4719. *Dir,* Suzanne Rochesort
Founded 1964. Pop 10,604; Circ 52,905
Library Holdings: Bk Vols 34,472; Per Subs 79
Subject Interests: Govt
Open Tues-Wed 1-9, Thurs-Fri 1-8, Sat 1-4

SAINT-JEAN-SUR-RICHELIEU

G　　AGRICULTURE CANADA*, Research Station Library, 430 Gouin Blvd, J3B 3E6. SAN 321-8449. Tel: 450-346-4494. FAX: 450-346-7740. *Librn,* Pierre DiCampo; *Libr Tech,* Lise LaValle
Founded 1950
Library Holdings: Bk Titles 12,000; Per Subs 205
Special Collections: Organic agriculture
Subject Interests: Hort
Publications: Bibliographies; Library Bulletin; Recent Acquisitions; Upcoming Conferences
Partic in Agricat
Open Mon-Fri 8-12 & 1-4
Restriction: Open to pub for ref only

SAINT-JEAN-SUR-RICHELIEU

P　　BIBLIOTHEQUES MUNICIPALES DE SAINT-JEAN-SUR-RICHELIEU, 180, rue Laurier, CP 1025, J3B 7B2. SAN 319-8863. Tel: 450-357-2111. Circulation Tel: 450-357-2118, 450-359-2452. Interlibrary Loan Service Tel: 450-359-2692. Reference Tel: 450-357-2120. Administration Tel: 450-357-2113. FAX: 450-359-2457. E-mail: biblio@ville.saint-jean-sur-richelieu.qc.ca. Web Site: www.ville.saint-jean-sur-richelieu.qc.ca/bibliotheques. *Head Librn,* Camille Bricault; Tel: 450-357-2112, E-mail: c.bricault@ville.saint-jean-sur-richelieu.qc.ca; Staff 51 (MLS 4, Non-MLS 47)
Founded 1959. Pop 92,448; Circ 559,660
Jan 2011-Dec 2011 Income (CAN) $3,024,485, Provincial (CAN) $253,700, City (CAN) $2,620,054, Locally Generated Income (CAN) $139,553, Other (CAN) $11,178. Mats Exp (CAN) $3,024,485, Books (CAN) $379,852, Per/Ser (Incl. Access Fees) (CAN) $22,913, AV Mat (CAN) $37,325, Electronic Ref Mat (Incl. Access Fees) (CAN) $13,727, Presv (CAN) $24,500. Sal (CAN) $1,914,940 (Prof (CAN) $343,000)
Library Holdings: CDs 9,182; DVDs 9,469; Electronic Media & Resources 181; Bk Titles 146,194; Bk Vols 226,351; Per Subs 268; Talking Bks 3,415
Special Collections: Local History, bk, flm & micro
Automation Activity & Vendor Info: (Acquisitions) BiblioMondo; (Cataloging) BiblioMondo; (Circulation) BiblioMondo; (OPAC) BiblioMondo; (Serials) BiblioMondo
Database Vendor: 3M Library Systems, Brodart, CEDROM-SNi, EBSCO Information Services, Isacsoft Inc (ISF), OCLC, Repere
Wireless access
Function: Adult bk club, AV serv, Bks on CD, Children's prog, Computer training, Computers for patron use, Copy machines, Electronic databases & coll, Free DVD rentals, Games & aids for the handicapped, Holiday prog, Magnifiers for reading, Mail & tel request accepted, Microfiche/film & reading machines, Music CDs, Online cat, Outreach serv, Photocopying/Printing, Preschool reading prog, Prog for adults, Prog for children & young adult, Pub access computers, Ref & res, Ref serv in person, Scanner, Spoken cassettes & CDs, Spoken cassettes & DVDs, Story hour, Summer reading prog, Web-catalog, Workshops
Special Services for the Deaf - Assisted listening device

Special Services for the Blind - Accessible computers; Bks on CD; Large print bks; Low vision equip; ZoomText magnification & reading software
Open Mon, Thurs & Fri 1-8:30, Wed 10-8:30, Sat & Sun 10-5
Restriction: Non-resident fee

SAINT-JEAN-SUR-RICHELIEU

C　　CEGEP ST JEAN SUR RICHELIEU BIBLIOTHEQUE*, 30 boul du Seminaire, CP 1018, J3B 7B1. SAN 322-7499. Tel: 450-347-5301, Ext 2333. FAX: 450-347-3329, 450-358-9350. E-mail: biblio@cstjean.qc.ca. Web Site: www.cstjean.qc.ca. *Assoc Dir, Pub Serv,* Jean-Pierre Guillet; E-mail: jean-pierre.guillet@cstjean.qc.ca; *Admin Librn,* Robert Dufort; E-mail: robert.dufort@cstjean.qc.ca; *Acq,* Denise Boucher; E-mail: denise.boucher@cstjean.qc.ca; *Acq,* Helene Piedalue; E-mail: helene.piedalue@cstjean.qc.ca; *Circ,* Manon Benoit; E-mail: manon.benoit@cstjean.qc.ca; *Circ,* Johanne Labbe; E-mail: johanne.labbe@cstjean.qc.ca; *Per,* Lucie Bouret; E-mail: lucie.bouret@cstjean.qc.ca; *Pub Serv,* Johanne Lorion; E-mail: johanne.lorion@cstjean.qc.ca; Staff 7 (MLS 1, Non-MLS 6)
Founded 1961. Enrl 2,300; Fac 300
Jul 2005-Jun 2006. Mats Exp (CAN) $64,603, Books (CAN) $50,000, Per/Ser (Incl. Access Fees) (CAN) $10,306, Presv (CAN) $4,297. Sal (CAN) $257,000 (Prof (CAN) $62,715)
Library Holdings: AV Mats 25,000; CDs 500; DVDs 15; Bk Titles 63,000; Bk Vols 75,000; Per Subs 175; Videos 1,500
Subject Interests: Hist
Database Vendor: GRICS
Partic in RESDOC
Open Mon-Thurs 8am-9:30pm, Fri 8-4, Sat & Sun 12-4

C　　COLLEGE MILITAIRE ROYAL DE SAINT-JEAN LIBRARY*, 15 rue Jaques-Cartier Nord, J3B 8R8. SAN 319-8871. Tel: 450-358-6608. FAX: 450-358-6929. *Dir,* Paul Tremblay; *Librn,* Life LaFleche; Staff 4 (MLS 4)
Founded 1952. Enrl 700; Highest Degree: Master
Library Holdings: Bk Vols 180,000; Per Subs 750
Special Collections: X
Subject Interests: Computer sci, Mil, Strategic studies
Partic in Dobis; Utlas
Open Mon-Fri 8-5

SAINT-LEONARD DE PORTNEUF

P　　BIBLIOTHEQUE MUNICIPALE*, 260 Pettigrew, G0A 4A0. SAN 321-320X. Tel: 418-337-6741. FAX: 418-337-6742. E-mail: saintleonard@derytele.com. Web Site: www.municipalite.st-leonard.qc.ca. *Librn,* Ginette Poquet
Pop 1,059
Library Holdings: Bk Vols 1,200; Per Subs 12
Open Mon-Fri 8-12 & 1-5

SAINT-REGIS

L　　THE MOHAWK COUNCIL OF AKWESASNE*, Research Library & Archival Services, Angus Mitchell Memorial Bldg, N0M 1A0. (Mail add: PO Box 579, Cornwall, K6H 5T3), SAN 321-8406. Tel: 613-575-1500, 613-575-2222. FAX: 613-575-1726. Web Site: www.akwesasne.ca. *Archivist,* Sharon Peters
Founded 1977
Library Holdings: Bk Titles 400
Special Collections: St Regis Band Council Archives
Subject Interests: Environ contaminants, Indian rights, Law
Open Mon-Fri 8-4

SAINT-SIMEON

P　　BIBLIOTHEQUE MUNICIPALE DE SAINT-SIMEON*, 502 St-Laurent, G0T 1X0. (Mail add: PO Box 98, G0T 1X0), SAN 321-3021. Tel: 418-638-2691. *Dir,* Sylvie Asselin; *Asst Dir,* Lyse Leblond; E-mail: leblondlyse@msn.com
Library Holdings: Bk Vols 1,500

SAINT-TITE-DES CAPS

J　　COLLEGE SAINT-ALPHONSE LIBRARY*, 97 Ave de la Montagne, G0A 4J0. SAN 319-8952. Tel: 418-823-2759. FAX: 418-823-2838. E-mail: csa_secretariat@vl.videotron.ca. Web Site: www.collegestalphonse.qc.ca. *Dir,* Diane Paradis
Founded 1896
Library Holdings: Bk Vols 40,000

SEPT ILES

P　　BIBLIOTHEQUE LOUIS-ANGE-SANTERRE, 500, ave Jolliet, G4R 2B4. SAN 319-907X. Tel: 418-964-3355. FAX: 418-964-3353. Web Site: www.ville.sept-iles.qc.ca. *Dir,* Sylvie Pelletier; *Librn,* Claude Charest; E-mail: claude.charest@ville.sept-iles.qc.ca; Staff 1 (MLS 1)

Founded 1953. Pop 26,500; Circ 135,000
Library Holdings: Audiobooks 150; CDs 1,500; DVDs 3,000; Large Print
Bks 300; Bk Vols 75,000; Per Subs 120
Subject Interests: Local hist
Automation Activity & Vendor Info: (Cataloging) SirsiDynix;
(Circulation) SirsiDynix; (OPAC) SirsiDynix; (Serials) SirsiDynix
Wireless access

P CENTRE REGIONAL SERVICES AUX BIBLIOTHEQUES PUBLIQUES
DE LA COTE-NORD, INC*, 59 Napoleon, G4R 5C5. SAN 321-0960. Tel:
418-962-1020. FAX: 418-962-5124. Web Site: www.crsbpcn.qc.ca. *Dir,*
Jean-Roch Gagnon; E-mail: jrgagnon@globetrotter.qc.ca; Staff 2 (MLS 1,
Non-MLS 1)
Founded 1979. Pop 30,606
Library Holdings: Bk Titles 50,336; Bk Vols 85,129; Per Subs 154
Special Collections: Cote Nord; Hunting & Fishing (French & English);
Plants & Shrubs (French)
Partic in ASTED
Open Mon-Fri 8-4:30

SHAWINIGAN

P BIBLIOTHEQUE MUNICIPALE DE SHAWINIGAN*, 550 Av de Hotel
de Ville, CP 400, G9N 6V3. SAN 319-9088. Tel: 819-536-7218. FAX:
819-536-0808. E-mail: bibliotheque@shawinigan.ca. Web Site:
www.bibliomcq.ca/shawinigan. *Dir,* Charlotte Picary-Lecours; Staff 1
(MLS 1)
Founded 1923. Pop 21,000; Circ 92,812
Library Holdings: Bk Titles 65,000; Per Subs 155; Videos 1,450
Open Tues & Fri 1-8, Sat 10:30-5

SHERBROOKE

C JOHN BASSETT MEMORIAL LIBRARY*, 2600 College St, J1M 0C8.
SAN 319-6801. Tel: 819-822-9600. Circulation Tel: 819-822-9600, Ext
2605. Interlibrary Loan Service Tel: 819-822-9600, Ext 2710. Reference
Tel: 819-822-9600, Ext 2608. FAX: 819-822-9644. E-mail:
llemay@ubishops.ca. Web Site: www.ubishops.ca/library_info. *Univ Librn,*
Bruno Gnassi; Tel: 819-822-9600, Ext 2483. E-mail: bgnassi@ubishops.ca;
Acq, Lorraine Smith; Tel: 819-822-9600, Ext 2283. E-mail:
lsmith@ubishops.ca; *ILL,* Lee-Ann St-Onge; E-mail: ill@ubishops.ca; Staff
7 (MLS 7)
Founded 1843. Enrl 2,100; Fac 120; Highest Degree: Master
Jul 2006-Jun 2007. Mats Exp (CAN) $686,969, Books (CAN) $169,742,
Per/Ser (Incl. Access Fees) (CAN) $501,317, Presv (CAN) $10,002. Sal
(CAN) $1,167,946 (Prof (CAN) $493,417)
Library Holdings: AV Mats 24,732; CDs 5,511; DVDs 1,831; e-journals
22,701; Bk Titles 263,471; Bk Vols 453,443; Per Subs 1,127
Special Collections: Canadiana (McKinnon Coll), bks & micro; Local
History (Eastern Townships Historical Coll). Can & Prov
Subject Interests: Bus, Educ, Humanities
Automation Activity & Vendor Info: (Acquisitions) Infor Library &
Information Solutions; (Cataloging) Infor Library & Information Solutions;
(Circulation) Infor Library & Information Solutions; (Course Reserve)
Infor Library & Information Solutions; (ILL) A-G Canada Ltd; (OPAC)
Infor Library & Information Solutions; (Serials) Infor Library &
Information Solutions
Database Vendor: American Chemical Society, ARTstor, BioOne,
EBSCOhost, Emerald, Gale Cengage Learning, Hoovers, IOP, ISI Web of
Knowledge, Mergent Online, ProQuest, ScienceDirect, SerialsSolutions,
Springer-Verlag, Wilson - Wilson Web
Wireless access
Function: Archival coll, CD-ROM, Govt ref serv, ILL available,
Magnifiers for reading, Music CDs, Newsp ref libr, Online searches,
Orientations, Photocopying/Printing, Ref serv available, VHS videos,
Wheelchair accessible
Publications: Student Guides to Reference Sources; Subject Lists
Partic in Canadian Research Knowledge Network; CREPUQ

P BIBLIOTHEQUE MUNICIPALE EVA-SENECAL*, Sherbrooke Municipal
Library, 450 Marquette St, J1H 1M4. SAN 319-910X. Tel: 819-821-5861.
FAX: 819-822-6110. E-mail: bibliotheque@ville.sherbrooke.qc.ca. Web
Site: ville.sherbrooke.qc.ca. *Dir,* Linda Travis; *Head, Adult Serv,* Andre
Bruneau; *Head, Ch,* Jeanne Desautels; *Head, Tech Serv,* Luce Marquis;
Staff 38 (MLS 4, Non-MLS 34)
Founded 1954. Pop 146,000; Circ 639,000
Library Holdings: AV Mats 29,000; Bk Titles 166,000; Bk Vols 185,000;
Per Subs 372; Talking Bks 1,800
Automation Activity & Vendor Info: (Acquisitions) Isacsoft Inc (ISF);
(Cataloging) Isacsoft Inc (ISF); (Circulation) Isacsoft Inc (ISF); (OPAC)
Isacsoft Inc (ISF); (Serials) Isacsoft Inc (ISF)

C CEGEP DE SHERBROOKE*, Centre des Medias, 475 rue du Cegep, J1E
4K1. SAN 373-7551. Tel: 819-564-6350, Ext 5231, 819-564-6350, Ext
5233. Reference Tel: 819-564-6350, Ext 5238. Administration Tel:

819-564-6350, Ext 5195. FAX: 819-564-4025. E-mail:
cmedias@cegepsherbrooke.qc.ca. Web Site: www.cegepsherbrooke.qc.ca.
Dir, Therese Letourneau; E-mail:
therese.letourneau@cegepsherbrooke.qc.ca; *Librn,* Francine Pelletier;
E-mail: francine.pelletier@cegepsherbrooke.qc.ca; *Reader Serv,* Louise
Marceau; E-mail: louise.marceau@cegepsherbrooke.qc.ca; Staff 3 (MLS 1,
Non-MLS 2).
Founded 1968. Enrl 6,500; Fac 500
Library Holdings: Bk Titles 94,000; Bk Vols 100,000; Per Subs 290
Subject Interests: Computer, Ecology, Mechanics, Music, Nursing
Wireless access
Function: ILL available
Partic in RESDOC
Open Mon-Thurs 8am-9:45pm, Fri 8-4:45

M CENTRE HOSPITALIER UNIVERSITAIRE DU SHERBROOKE
BIBLIOTHEQUE*, Hotel-Dieu, 580 rue Bowen S, J1G 2E8. SAN
319-9118. Tel: 819-346-1110, Ext 2-1126. FAX: 819-822-6745. *Librn,*
Gilberte Poirier; E-mail: g.poirier@abacom.com; Staff 1 (MLS 1)
Founded 1954
Library Holdings: Bk Vols 5,600; Per Subs 161
Subject Interests: Cardiology, Hospital admin, Internal med, Nursing,
Surgery
Restriction: Staff use only

R GRAND SEMINAIRE DES SAINTS APOTRES LIBRARY*, Archeveche
de Sherbrooke Cathedral, 130 rue de la Cathedrale, J1H 4M1. SAN
319-9126. Tel: 819-563-9934, Ext 217. FAX: 819-562-0125. *Librn,*
Solange Bonneau, Sr
Founded 1940
Library Holdings: Bk Vols 28,000; Per Subs 130
Special Collections: Migne Coll
Subject Interests: Theol
Open Mon-Thurs 1:30-4

S LA SOCIETE D'HISTOIRE DE SHERBROOKE, Sherbrooke Historical
Society, 275, rue Dufferin, J1H 4M5. SAN 319-9134. Tel: 819-821-5406.
FAX: 819-821-5417. *Exec Dir,* Michel Harnois; *Archivist,* Karine Savary
Founded 1927
Library Holdings: Bk Titles 8,000; Per Subs 30
Special Collections: Local History Archives, newsp
Subject Interests: Eastern Townships in the Province of Quebec,
Especially Sherbrooke region
Wireless access
Restriction: Authorized personnel only

C UNIVERSITE DE SHERBROOKE SERVICE DES BIBLIOTHEQUES ET
ARCHIVES, Cite Universitaire, J1K 2R1. SAN 369-5492. Tel:
819-821-7550. Circulation Tel: 819-821-7858. Interlibrary Loan Service
Tel: 819-821-8000, Ext 62563. Information Services Tel: 819-821-8000,
Ext 62557. Toll Free Tel: 866-506-2433. FAX: 819-821-7096. Web Site:
www.usherbrooke.ca/biblio. *Dir,* Sylvie Belzile; Staff 26 (MLS 23,
Non-MLS 3)
Founded 1954. Enrl 18,000; Fac 850; Highest Degree: Doctorate
May 2010-Apr 2011. Mats Exp (CAN) $4,990,000, Books (CAN)
$645,000, Per/Ser (Incl. Access Fees) (CAN) $3,845,000, Presv (CAN)
$40,000. Sal (CAN) $4,462,000
Library Holdings: CDs 12,440; e-books 109,000; e-journals 60,970; Bk
Titles 552,167; Bk Vols 840,000; Per Subs 14,386; Videos 4,440
Special Collections: Can & Prov
Automation Activity & Vendor Info: (Acquisitions) SirsiDynix;
(Cataloging) SirsiDynix; (Circulation) SirsiDynix; (ILL) Fretwell-Downing;
(OPAC) SerialsSolutions; (Serials) SirsiDynix

SILLERY

P BIBLIOTHEQUE CHARLES H BLAIS*, 1445 ave Maguire, G1T 2W9.
SAN 373-7314. Tel: 418-641-6276. FAX: 418-684-2169. E-mail:
bibliotheque.charles_h._blais@ville.quebec.qc.ca. Web Site:
www.bibliotheques.qc.ca/bchb/index.htm. *In Charge,* Madaline Dumeis;
E-mail: madeleine.dumais@ville.quebec.qc.ca; Staff 2 (MLS 1, Non-MLS
1)
Founded 1982. Pop 12,519; Circ 97,092
Library Holdings: Bk Titles 39,000; Bk Vols 43,015; Per Subs 102
Special Services for the Deaf - Bks on deafness & sign lang

S COLLEGE JESUS-MARIE DE SILLERY BIBLIOTHEQUE*, 2047
Chemin Saint-Louis, G1T 1P3. SAN 372-7750. Tel: 418-687-9250, Ext 19.
FAX: 418-687-9847. Web Site: www.cjmds.qc.ca. *Librn, Ref,* Lorrayne
Beaucage; Staff 3 (MLS 1, Non-MLS 2)
Library Holdings: Bk Titles 10,000; Bk Vols 11,000; Per Subs 60
Open Mon-Fri 7:30-5:30

G　　REGIE DE L'ASSURANCE-MALADIE DU QUEBEC*, Center de
　　　Documentation, 1125 Chemin Saint-Louis, 7E, G1S 1E7. SAN 321-7132.
　　　Tel: 418-682-5118. FAX: 418-528-6864. *In Charge,* Louise Guy
　　　Founded 1969
　　　Library Holdings: Bk Titles 3,000; Per Subs 20
　　　Special Collections: National Library of Canada
　　　Subject Interests: Human resources, Med

R　　SEMINAIRE DES PERES MARISTES BIBLIOTHEQUE, 2315 Chemin
　　　St-Louis, G1T 1R5. SAN 319-9185. Tel: 418-651-4944. FAX:
　　　418-651-6841. *Librn,* Andree Lepine
　　　Enrl 630
　　　Library Holdings: Bk Vols 17,000
　　　Subject Interests: Can hist, General reading, Lit

SOREL-TRACY

P　　BIBLIOTHEQUE MUNICIPALE DE SOREL-TRACY*, 145 rue George,
　　　J3P 1C7. SAN 319-9193. Tel: 450-780-5750. FAX: 450-780-5758. Web
　　　Site: www.ville.sorel-tracy.qc.ca/. *Librn,* Guy Desjardins; E-mail:
　　　guy.desjardins@ville.sorel-tracy.qc.ca
　　　Founded 1947. Pop 25,000
　　　Library Holdings: Bk Titles 49,000; Per Subs 100
　　　Special Collections: Can & Prov
　　　Subject Interests: Genealogy, Rare bks

S　　RIO TINTO IRON & TITANIUM INC*, 1625 Rte Marie-Victorin, J3R
　　　1M6. SAN 319-9207. Tel: 450-746-3000, 450-746-3077. FAX:
　　　450-746-3391. *In Charge,* Suzette Coumoyer; Tel: 450-746-3000, Ext
　　　2065; Staff 1 (MLS 1)
　　　Founded 1950
　　　Library Holdings: Bk Titles 8,000; Per Subs 200
　　　Special Collections: Patents
　　　Subject Interests: Chem, Physics
　　　Open Mon-Fri 9-4

STANBRIDGE EAST

S　　MISSISQUOI HISTORICAL SOCIETY, Missisquoi Museum Research
　　　Library, Two River St, J0J 2H0. SAN 319-9215. Tel: 450-248-3153. FAX:
　　　450-248-0420. Web Site: www.missisquoimuseum.ca,
　　　www.museemissisquoi.ca. *Curator,* Heather Darch; *Archivist,* Judy A
　　　Antle; E-mail: jantle@missisquoimuseum.ca. Subject Specialists:
　　　Genealogy, Judy A Antle
　　　Founded 1967
　　　Library Holdings: Bk Titles 4,500
　　　Special Collections: Genealogical Reference (Archives Annex Coll)
　　　Subject Interests: Antiques, Can hist, Canadiana, Genealogy, Old books,
　　　Rare
　　　Publications: Biennial History Reports

STANSTEAD

J　　STANSTEAD COLLEGE*, John C Colby Memorial Library, 450 Dufferin
　　　St, J0B 3E0. Tel: 819-876-7891, Ext 226. FAX: 819-876-5891. E-mail:
　　　lgetty@stansteadcollege.com. Web Site: www.stansteadcollege.com. *Librn,*
　　　Liz Getty; *Asst Librn,* Keri Reynolds; Tel: 819-876-7891, Ext 278
　　　Founded 1872. Enrl 228; Fac 29
　　　Library Holdings: Bk Titles 20,000; Per Subs 100

SUTTON

P　　BIBLIOTHEQUE MUNICIPALE ET SCOLAIRE DE SUTTON, 19
　　　Highland St, J0E 2K0. SAN 319-9231. Tel: 450-538-5843. FAX:
　　　450-538-4286. Web Site: www.reseaubibliodequebec.qc.ca/sutton. *Coordr,*
　　　Lisa Charbonneau
　　　Pop 3,960; Circ 23,500
　　　Library Holdings: Bk Titles 20,000
　　　Automation Activity & Vendor Info: (Acquisitions) SirsiDynix;
　　　(Cataloging) SirsiDynix; (Circulation) SirsiDynix; (Course Reserve)
　　　SirsiDynix; (ILL) SirsiDynix; (Media Booking) SirsiDynix; (OPAC)
　　　SirsiDynix; (Serials) SirsiDynix
　　　Database Vendor: Repere
　　　Wireless access
　　　Open Mon, Wed, Fri & Sat 10-12, Tues & Thurs 10-12 & 6:30-8:30

TEMISCAMING

P　　BIBLIOTHEQUE MUNICIPALE*, PO Box 730, J0Z 3R0. SAN
　　　319-924X. Tel: 819-627-9778. FAX: 819-627-3019. *Librn,* Suzelle Plante
　　　Pop 2,097
　　　Library Holdings: Bk Vols 12,000
　　　Open Mon-Wed 7am-9pm, Thurs 8-4

TERREBONNE

P　　BIBLIOTHEQUE MUNICIPALE*, 855 lle-des-moulins, J6W 4N7. SAN
　　　319-9258. Tel: 450-961-2001, Ext 1116. *Dir,* Francoise Martin
　　　Pop 85,000; Circ 661,729
　　　Library Holdings: Bk Vols 234,253
　　　Subject Interests: Genealogy, Local hist

THETFORD MINES

P　　BIBLIOTHEQUE DE LA POLYVALENTE DE THETFORD MINES*,
　　　561 rue St Patrick, G6G 5W1. SAN 328-1361. Tel: 418-338-7832. FAX:
　　　418-338-7851. E-mail: polytm@hotmail.com. *In Charge,* Luce Ebert
　　　Pop 1,700
　　　Library Holdings: Bk Vols 25,000; Per Subs 34
　　　Open Mon-Fri 8-4

GM　CENTRE DE SANTE ET DE SERVICES SOCIAUX DE LA REGION DE
　　　THETFORD*, Bibliotheque, 1717 rue Notre-Dame Est, G6G 2V4. SAN
　　　374-5996. Tel: 418-338-7777, Ext 4019. FAX: 418-338-7786. *Tech Serv,*
　　　Jacinthe Ouellet; E-mail: jouellet@ssss.gouv.qc.ca
　　　Library Holdings: Bk Titles 2,500; Per Subs 300
　　　Open Mon-Fri 8:30-4:30

S　　LAB CHRYSOTILE, INC*, Quality Control-Research & Development
　　　Library, Rte 112, G6H 2M9. SAN 370-6567. Tel: 418-338-7500, Ext 644.
　　　FAX: 418-338-7664. *Mgr,* Pierre Laroche
　　　Founded 1986
　　　Library Holdings: Bk Vols 340; Per Subs 6
　　　Open Mon-Fri 8-5
　　　Restriction: Staff use only

TORONTO

S　　THE BANK OF NOVA SCOTIA LIBRARY, Scotia Library Services,
　　　(Formerly The Bank of Nova Scotia Business Information Services), 44
　　　King St W, M5H 1H1. SAN 319-4612. Tel: 416-866-4403. FAX:
　　　416-866-4036. *Chief Librn,* Marion Miwa; E-mail:
　　　marion.miwa@scotiabank.com; Staff 18 (MLS 10, Non-MLS 8)
　　　Founded 1951
　　　Library Holdings: Bk Vols 10,000; Per Subs 2,000
　　　Subject Interests: Finance
　　　Function: Res libr
　　　Publications: Library Bulletin (Irregular)
　　　Restriction: Employees only

TROIS-PISTOLES

P　　BIBLIOTHEQUE MUNICIPALE ANNE-MARIE-D'AMOURS, 145, rue
　　　de l'Arena, G0L 4K0. SAN 319-9274. Tel: 418-851-2374. FAX:
　　　418-851-3567. *Librn,* Karen Dionne
　　　Founded 1967. Pop 4,551; Circ 19,783
　　　Library Holdings: Bk Vols 12,000

TROIS-RIVIERES

G　　BIBLIOTHEQUE SPORT ET LOISIR, MINISTERE DE L'EDUCATION,
　　　DU LOISIR ET DU SPORT*, 100 Laviolette, Bur 306, G9A 5S9. SAN
　　　323-9349. Tel: 819-371-6033, Ext 4429. FAX: 819-371-6992. *Librn,*
　　　Micheline Denis; Staff 1 (MLS 1)
　　　Founded 1985
　　　Library Holdings: Bk Vols 5,880; Per Subs 80
　　　Subject Interests: Health promotion, Injury prevention, Leisure, Sport

P　　BIBLIOTHEQUES DE TROIS-RIVIERES*, Bibliotheque Gatien-Lapointe,
　　　1425 Place de l'Hotel de Ville, CP 1713, G9A 5L9. SAN 319-9290. Tel:
　　　819-372-4645. Circulation Tel: 819-372-4615. FAX: 819-693-1892. Web
　　　Site: www.biblio.v3r.net. *Dir,* Michel Lacoursiere; E-mail:
　　　mlacoursiere@v3r.net; *Head, Adult Serv, Head, Ch,* Lisette Beauchemin;
　　　E-mail: lbeauchemin@v3r.net; *Ref Serv,* Marie-Claude Taillon; E-mail:
　　　mtaillon@v3r.net; *Tech Serv,* Odette Pelletier; E-mail: opelletier@v3r.net;
　　　Staff 6 (MLS 5, Non-MLS 1)
　　　Founded 1946. Pop 128,000; Circ 980,000
　　　Library Holdings: Per Subs 200
　　　Special Collections: Trifluviana
　　　Automation Activity & Vendor Info: (Acquisitions) BiblioMondo;
　　　(Cataloging) BiblioMondo; (Circulation) BiblioMondo; (Course Reserve)
　　　BiblioMondo; (ILL) BiblioMondo; (Media Booking) BiblioMondo; (OPAC)
　　　BiblioMondo; (Serials) BiblioMondo
　　　Publications: Annual Report; Library Handbook
　　　Partic in ASTED
　　　Branches: 3
　　　BIBLIOTHEQUE ALINE-PICHE, 5575 boul Jean-XXIII, G8Z 4A8. Tel:
　　　　819-374-6525. FAX: 819-374-5126. *Media Spec,* Denise Lemay

BIBLIOTHEQUE DE POINTE-DU-LAC (SIMONE-L-ROY), 500 rue de la Grande-Allee, G0X 1Z0. Tel: 819-377-4289. FAX: 819-377-7116. *Media Spec,* Louise Houle

BIBLIOTHEQUE MAURICE-LORANGER, 70 rue Parè, G8T 6V8, SAN 319-6348. Tel: 819-378-8826. FAX: 819-378-5539. *Media Spec,* Richard-Alain Valois
Circ 26,093
Library Holdings: Bk Vols 30,000; Per Subs 75

C   CEGEP DE TROIS-RIVIERES BIBLIOTHEQUE*, 3175 Laviolette, G9A 5E6. (Mail add: 3500 de Courval CP97, G9A-5E6), SAN 319-9339. Tel: 819-376-1721, Ext 2609. FAX: 819-693-3844. E-mail: bibliotheque@cegeptr.qc.ca, solange.thibeault@cegeptr.qc.ca. Web Site: biblio.cegeptr.qc.ca. *Coll Develop, Dir, Ref,* Daniele Baillargeon; *Acq,* Solange Coulombe; *AV, Coll Develop,* Monique Paradis; Staff 12 (MLS 3, Non-MLS 9)
Founded 1968. Enrl 4,300
Jul 2005-Jun 2006. Mats Exp (CAN) $129,200, Books (CAN) $47,880, Per/Ser (Incl. Access Fees) (CAN) $49,400, AV Mat (CAN) $31,920. Sal (CAN) $482,089
Library Holdings: AV Mats 69,823; CDs 392; DVDs 176; Bk Vols 96,000; Per Subs 300; Videos 4,194
Special Collections: Materiautheque Coll; Mediatheque Coll; Pulp & Paper Coll
Publications: Guide de la Bibliothique; Liste des Periodiques Courants; Liste Regionale des Periodiques
Partic in RESDOC
Open Mon-Thurs 8-7:50, Fri 8-4:50

M   CENTRE HOSPITALIER REGIONAL TROIS-RIVIERES PAVILLON STE-MARIE*, 1991 boul du Carmel, G8Z 3R9. SAN 319-9312. Tel: 819-697-3333, Ext 69878. FAX: 819-378-9850. *Chief Librn,* Liane Dube
Founded 1961
Library Holdings: Bk Titles 3,200; Per Subs 65
Partic in OCLC Online Computer Library Center, Inc

P   CENTRE REGIONAL DE SERVICES AUX BIBLIOTHEQUES PUBLIQUES*, Centre-du-Quebec-Lanaudiere-Mauricie, 3125 rue Girard, G8Z 2M4. SAN 319-9282. Tel: 819-375-9623. FAX: 819-375-0132. Web Site: www.reseaubibliocqlm.qc.ca. *Dir,* Helene Arseneau
Founded 1961. Pop 222,837; Circ 850,030
Library Holdings: Bk Vols 498,185
Open Mon-Fri 8:30-4:30

S   LE SEMINAIRE SAINT-JOSEPH DE TROIS-RIVIERES, Archives du Seminaire de Trois-Rivieres, 858 rue Laviolette, local 221, G9A 5S3. SAN 328-1485. Tel: 819-376-4459, Ext 135. FAX: 819-378-0607. Web Site: site.rdaq.qc.ca/seminairedetrois-rivieres. *Archivist, Dir,* Suzanne Girard; *Archivist,* Christian Lalancette
Founded 1918
Library Holdings: Bk Vols 10,000
Special Collections: Manuscripts, Maps, Photographs
Subject Interests: Educ, Families, Hist, Politics, Relig
Function: Archival coll, Photocopying/Printing, Ref serv available, Telephone ref
Open Tues-Fri 9-12 & 1:30-4:15
Restriction: In-house use for visitors, Not a lending libr

G   MINISTERE DE LA CULTURE*, Conservatory of Music, 587 rue Radisson, G9A 2C8. SAN 325-2027. Tel: 819-371-6748. FAX: 819-371-6955. Web Site: www.conservatoire.gouv.qc.ca. *Librn,* Guy Lefebvre
Founded 1979
Library Holdings: Bk Titles 400
Special Collections: Private Musical (Anais Allard Rousseau Coll), musical scores, parts, bks

C   UNIVERSITE DU QUEBEC A TROIS-RIVIERES - SERVICE DE LA BIBLIOTHEQUE*, Pavillon Albert-Tessier, 3351 Blvd des Forges, G9A 5H7. (Mail add: Pavillon Albert-Tessier, CP 500, G9A 5H7), SAN 319-9347. Tel: 819-376-5005. FAX: 819-376-5144. E-mail: webmestre-biblio@uqtr.ca. Web Site: www.uqtr.ca/biblio. *Dir,* Benoit Seguin; Tel: 819-376-5011, Ext 2265, E-mail: benoit.seguin@uqtr.ca; Staff 11 (MLS 11)
Founded 1969. Enrl 6,896; Fac 340; Highest Degree: Doctorate
Special Collections: Etudes Quebecoises. Can & Prov
Subject Interests: Acctg, Arts, Biochem, Biol, Biophysics, Bus, Chem, Chiropractic, Communication, Computer sci, Educ, Eng, Fr Can studies, Geog, Hist, Math, Nursing, Philosophy, Physics, Psychol, Sports leisure

VAL-BELAIR

S   DEFENCE R&D CANADA-VALCARTIER LIBRARY*, 2459 Pie-XI Blvd N, G3J 1X5. SAN 319-9371. Tel: 418-844-4000, Ext 4262. FAX: 418-844-4624. E-mail: val-biblio@drdc-rddc.gc.ca. *Librn,* Carol Lefrancois;

Tel: 418-844-4000, Ext 4244; *Tech Serv,* Christiane Potvin; Staff 4 (MLS 1, Non-MLS 3)
Founded 1945
Library Holdings: Bk Vols 20,000; Per Subs 300
Subject Interests: Chem, Electrical eng, Electro optics, Math, Mil sci, Physics
Automation Activity & Vendor Info: (Acquisitions) BiblioMondo; (Circulation) BiblioMondo; (OPAC) BiblioMondo
Publications: Accession list

VAL-D'OR

P   BIBLIOTHEQUE MUNICIPALE DE VAL-D'OR*, 600, 7e Rue, J9P 3P3. SAN 319-9355. Tel: 819-824-2666. FAX: 819-825-3062. E-mail: biblvd@ville.valdor.qc.ca. *In Charge,* Guilbert Nicole; Tel: 819-874-7469, Ext 222, E-mail: guilbertn@ville.valdor.qc.ca
Founded 1952. Pop 30,000; Circ 225,000
Library Holdings: Bk Vols 70,000; Per Subs 110

M   HOSPITAL CENTER OF VAL D'OR*, Bibliotheque Medicale, 725 Sixth St, J9P 3Y1. SAN 319-9363. Tel: 819-825-5858. FAX: 819-825-7919. *In Charge,* Cynthia Richard; E-mail: cynthia_richard@ssss.gouv.qc.ca
Library Holdings: Bk Vols 510
Partic in National Network of Libraries of Medicine

S   SOQUEM, INC*, Centre de Documentation, 600, ave Centrale, J9P 1P8. SAN 370-5609. Tel: 819-874-3773. FAX: 819-874-3770. Web Site: www.soquem.qc.ca. *Admin Officer,* Lucie Beaudoin
Founded 1965
Library Holdings: Bk Vols 8,500
Subject Interests: Geol
Publications: Acquisitions list (Monthly)

VALLEYFIELD

J   CEGEP DE VALLEYFIELD BIBLIOTHEQUE*, 80 St Thomas St, J6T 4J7. SAN 319-938X. Tel: 450-370-4860. FAX: 450-377-6011. E-mail: biblio.a.frappier@colval.qc.ca. *Admin Dir,* Andre Deschamps; E-mail: andre.deschamps@colval.qc.ca; *Admin Dir,* Andre Grenier; E-mail: andre.grenier@ville.valleyfield.qc.ca; Staff 2 (MLS 2)
Founded 1997
Library Holdings: Bk Vols 100,000; Per Subs 139
Special Collections: UN Document Depository

VARENNES

S   INSTITUT DE RECHERCHE D'HYDRO-QUEBEC BIBLIOTHEQUE*, 1800 Lionel-Boulet Blvd, CP 1000, J3X 1S1. SAN 324-0010. Tel: 450-652-8999. FAX: 450-652-8040. E-mail: biblio.ireq@ireq.ca. *Libr Serv Supvr,* Regis Cote; Tel: 450-652-1343, E-mail: cote.regis@ireq.ca; *Libr Tech,* Yvon Lavoie; *Libr Tech,* Christiane Ostiguy; *Ref Serv,* Helene Lemaire; Tel: 450-652-8022, E-mail: lemaire.helene@ireq.ca; Staff 2 (MLS 1, Non-MLS 1)
Founded 1970
Library Holdings: Bk Titles 40,000; Per Subs 400
Special Collections: IEEE Publications, Chemical Abstracts, Canadian Electrical Association Reports
Subject Interests: Electricity, Electronics, Energy
Restriction: Open to pub upon request

VAUDREUIL-DORION

P   BIBLIOTHEQUE MUNICIPALE*, 51 rue Jeannotte, J7V 6E6. SAN 377-0672. Tel: 450-455-5588. FAX: 450-455-5653. E-mail: biblio@vaudreuil-dorion.qc.ca. Web Site: www.ville.vaudreuil-dorion.qc.ca/Bibliotheque/. *Dir,* Michelle Dupuy; E-mail: mdupuy@ville.vaudreuil-dorion.qc.ca; *Chief of Br Serv,* Helene Diamond; *Tech Coordr,* Jean Gagnon
Library Holdings: Bk Titles 50,000; Bk Vols 60,000; Per Subs 200
Open Tues-Fri 1:30-9

S   PERKINELMER OPTOELECTRONICS LIBRARY*, 22001 Dumberry, J7V 8P7. SAN 371-845X. Tel: 450-424-2510, Ext 3370. FAX: 450-424-3413. Web Site: www.perkinelmer.com. *In Charge,* Sam Zhang; Staff 1 (Non-MLS 1)
Library Holdings: Bk Titles 3,500; Bk Vols 4,100; Per Subs 15
Special Collections: RCA Review
Subject Interests: Physics
Restriction: Staff use only

VICTORIAVILLE

P   BIBLIOTHEQUE CHARLES-EDOUARD-MAILHOT*, 2, rue de L'Ermitage, G6P 6T2. (Mail add: CP 370, G6P 6T2), SAN 319-941X. Tel: 819-758-8441. FAX: 819-758-9432. *Libr Coordr,* Sylvie Filiatrault; Staff 12 (MLS 1, Non-MLS 11)

Founded 1948. Pop 40,853
Library Holdings: CDs 6,225; DVDs 263; Large Print Bks 515; Bk Vols 119,552; Per Subs 215; Talking Bks 623
Special Collections: Local History (Fonds Alcide-Fleury Coll)
Automation Activity & Vendor Info: (Acquisitions) BiblioMondo; (Cataloging) BiblioMondo; (Circulation) BiblioMondo; (OPAC) BiblioMondo; (Serials) BiblioMondo
Function: Home delivery & serv to Sr ctr & nursing homes, Magnifiers for reading, Photocopying/Printing, Prog for children & young adult, Ref serv available, Summer reading prog, Telephone ref, Wheelchair accessible
Publications: Livraison Spéciale (Serials catalog)
Partic in Consortium d'acquisition de ressources electroniques du Quebec (CAREQ)
Special Services for the Deaf - Assistive tech
Special Services for the Blind - Assistive/Adapted tech devices, equip & products
Open Mon 5-8, Tues 1-8, Wed & Thurs 10-8, Fri 10-5, Sat & Sun 10-4
Restriction: Badge access after hrs
Branches: 1
BIBLIOTHEQUE ALCIDE-FLEURY, 841, blvd des Bois-Francs Sud, G6P 5W3. (Mail add: 2, rue de l'Ermitage, Case postale 370, G6P 6T2), SAN 374-4450. Tel: 819-357-8240. Administration Tel: 819-758-8441. FAX: 819-357-2099. Administration FAX: 819-758-9432. *Pub Serv, Ref Serv,* Helene St-Martin; Staff 5 (Non-MLS 5)
Founded 1958
   Library Holdings: AV Mats 909; Bk Titles 36,883; Bk Vols 38,940; Per Subs 45

J   CEGEP DE VICTORIAVILLE*, Centre de Documentation, 475 rue Notre Dame E, G6P 4B3. SAN 369-5700. Tel: 819-758-6401, Ext 2486. FAX: 819-758-2729. Web Site: www.cgpvicto.qc.ca. *Librn,* Marjolaine Bechard
Founded 1963
Library Holdings: Bk Vols 52,000; Per Subs 300
Special Collections: Woodworking Coll
Subject Interests: Regional hist
Open Mon-Wed 8am-9pm, Thurs 8-5, Fri 8-4
Departmental Libraries:
E'COLE QUEBECOISE DU MEUBLE ET DU BOIS OUVRE, 765 Est Notre Dame, G6P 4B3, SAN 369-5735. Tel: 819-758-6401, Ext 2621. FAX: 819-758-2729. *Librn,* Marjo Bechard

M   CSSS D'ARTHABASKA-ERABLE, Medical Library, 5 rue des Hospitalieres, G6P 6N2. SAN 319-6267. Tel: 819-357-2030, Ext 2185. FAX: 819-357-6060. *Documentation Tech,* Annie Lemay
Founded 1960
Library Holdings: Bk Titles 1,500; Per Subs 60
Friends of the Library Group

VILLE DE DEUX-MONTAGNES

P   BIBLIOTHEQUE MUNICIPALE DE DEUX-MONTAGNES, 200 rue Henri-Dunant, J7R 4W6. SAN 326-503X. Tel: 450-473-2702. FAX: 450-473-2816. Web Site: www.ville.deux-montagnes.qc.ca/bibliotheque. *Dir,* Johanne Chaput; E-mail: jchaput@ville.deux-montagnes.qc.ca; Staff 7 (MLS 3, Non-MLS 4)
Pop 17,626
Library Holdings: Audiobooks 176; AV Mats 1,726; DVDs 109; Electronic Media & Resources 4; Bk Titles 77,920; Bk Vols 78,631; Per Subs 128
Automation Activity & Vendor Info: (Cataloging) SIRSI WorkFlows; (Circulation) SIRSI WorkFlows; (OPAC) SIRSI-iBistro
Wireless access
Open Mon-Fri (Winter) 1-8, Sat & Sun 1-4:30; Mon-Thurs (Summer) 1-8, Fri 1-6

WARWICK

P   BIBLIOTHEQUE MUNICIPALE DE WARWICK*, Bibliotheque P Rodolphe Baril, 181 rue Saint-Louis, J0A 1M0. SAN 319-9428. Tel: 819-358-4325. FAX: 819-358-4326. E-mail: bibliowarwick@cablovision.com. *Dir,* France P Gendron

Founded 1969. Pop 4,907
Library Holdings: Bk Titles 26,013; Bk Vols 29,135; Per Subs 60
Function: Doc delivery serv

WATERLOO

P   WATERLOO PUBLIC LIBRARY*, CP 700, 650 Rue de la Cour, J0E 2N0. SAN 319-9436. Tel: 450-539-2268. FAX: 450-539-2528. E-mail: biblio@cacwaterloo.qc.ca. Web Site: www.cacwaterloo.qc.ca/biblio. *Librn,* Gisele Dupuis; E-mail: ntsgisele816@netscape.net
Founded 1900. Circ 25,000
Library Holdings: Audiobooks 20; Large Print Bks 200; Bk Vols 25,000; Per Subs 75
Special Collections: Journal de Waterloo 1921-53; Waterloo Advertiser 1856-1924
Open Mon-Fri 9:30-11:30 & 1-5, Sat 10-12 & 1-4 & Sun 1-4

WESTMOUNT

S   ATWATER LIBRARY & COMPUTER CENTRE*, 1200 Atwater Ave, H3Z 1X4. SAN 319-6984. Tel: 514-935-7344. FAX: 514-935-1960. E-mail: info@atwaterlibrary.ca. Web Site: www.atwaterlibrary.ca. *Exec Dir,* Lynn Verge; *Tech Serv,* Rani Yoganathan; Staff 2 (Non-MLS 2)
Founded 1828
Library Holdings: Bk Vols 38,000; Per Subs 70
Special Collections: Archives of the Mechanics' Institute of Montreal, 1828-present; Quebec Writers' Federation Coll; The Scottish Coll
Subject Interests: Art, Biog, Can hist, Computer sci, Fiction, Geog, Local hist
Automation Activity & Vendor Info: (Acquisitions) Mandarin Library Automation; (Cataloging) Mandarin Library Automation; (Circulation) Mandarin Library Automation; (OPAC) Mandarin Library Automation
Wireless access
Function: Adult bk club, Adult literacy prog, Bks on cassette, Citizenship assistance, Computer training, Computers for patron use, e-mail & chat, Electronic databases & coll, Fax serv, Govt ref serv, Literacy & newcomer serv, Photocopying/Printing, Prog for adults, Pub access computers, Ref serv available, Scanner, Senior computer classes, Senior outreach, Workshops
Publications: Annual report; Newsletter
Open Mon & Wed 10-8, Tues, Thurs & Fri 10-6, Sat 10-5

J   DAWSON COLLEGE LIBRARY*, 3040 Sherbrooke St W, H3Z 1A4. SAN 319-7425. Tel: 514-931-8731. Circulation Tel: 514-931-8731, Ext 1620. Reference Tel: 514-931-8731, Ext 1731. FAX: 514-931-3567. E-mail: refdesk@dawsoncollege.qc.ca. Web Site: dolls.dawsoncollege.qc.ca. *Dir,* Raymond Boucher; Tel: 514-931-8731, Ext 1204, E-mail: rboucher@dawsoncollege.qc.ca; *Coordr, Pub Serv,* Carolyn Gilmore; Tel: 514-931-8731, Ext 1736, E-mail: cgilmore@dawsoncollege.qc.ca; *Ref Serv,* Janice Belanger; Tel: 514-931-8731, Ext 1733, E-mail: jkelly@dawsoncollege.qc.ca; *Ref Serv,* David Jones; Tel: 514-931-8731, Ext 1734, E-mail: djones@dawsoncollege.qc.ca; *Tech Serv,* Anne Scott; Tel: 514-931-8731, Ext 1796, E-mail: ascott@dawsoncollege.qc.ca; Staff 12 (MLS 12)
Founded 1969. Enrl 7,000; Fac 450
Library Holdings: Bk Titles 92,000; Bk Vols 107,200; Per Subs 320
Automation Activity & Vendor Info: (Acquisitions) MultiLIS; (Cataloging) MultiLIS; (Circulation) MultiLIS; (Course Reserve) MultiLIS; (OPAC) MultiLIS; (Serials) MultiLIS
Database Vendor: SirsiDynix

M   FEDERATION DES MEDECINS OMNIPRATICIENS DU QUEBEC, Centre de Documentation, Two Place Alexis Nihon, 20e étage, 2000-3500 boul de Maisonneuve Ouest, H3Z 3C1. SAN 324-3400. Tel: 514-878-1911, Ext 258. Toll Free Tel: 800-361-8499. FAX: 514-878-4455. E-mail: info@fmoq.org. Web Site: www.fmoq.org. *Head of Libr,* Marie Paule Saint-Gelais; E-mail: mpsaintgelais@fmoq.org
Library Holdings: Bk Vols 8,000; Per Subs 250
Subject Interests: Med econ, Med law, Med legis, Soc med

Date of Statistics: FY 2009
Population, 2006: 968,147
Population Served by Public Libraries: 968,147
Total Volumes in Public Libraries: 3,503,450
　　Volumes Per Capita: 3.62
Total Public Library Circulation: 9,879,610
　　Circulation Per Capita: 10.2
Number of Regional Libraries: 10 Library Systems plus a
　Provincial Library & Literacy Office

AIR RONGE

P　PAHKISIMON NUYE?AH LIBRARY SYSTEM, 118 Avro Pl. (Mail add: Bag Service 6600, La Ronge, S0J 1L0), SAN 374-6003. Tel: 306-425-4525. Toll Free Tel: 866-396-8818. FAX: 306-425-4572. E-mail: PNLSOffice@pnls.lib.sk.ca. Web Site: www.pnls.lib.sk.ca. *Dir,* Audrey Mark; *Asst Dir,* Harriet Roy; *Archives Mgr,* Graham Guest; Staff 7 (MLS 1, Non-MLS 6)
　Founded 1990. Pop 36,557
　Library Holdings: Bk Vols 64,781; Per Subs 30
　Special Collections: Aboriginal, multimedia; Fur trade; Northern Saskatchewan, multimedia
　Automation Activity & Vendor Info: (Cataloging) Innovative Interfaces, Inc - Millenium; (Circulation) Innovative Interfaces, Inc - Millenium; (ILL) Innovative Interfaces, Inc - Millenium; (OPAC) Innovative Interfaces, Inc - Millenium
　Publications: Word's Worth
　Member Libraries: Ayamicikiwikamik Public Library; Beauval Public Library; Dave O'Hara Community Library; Ile a la Crosse Public Library; Keethanow Public Library; La Ronge Public Library; Peayamechikee Public Library; Tawowikamik Public Library; Wisewood Library
　Partic in Saskatchewan Information & Library Services (SILS)
　Special Services for the Deaf - Bks on deafness & sign lang; High interest/low vocabulary bks
　Special Services for the Blind - Braille bks; Talking bks
　Open Mon-Fri 8-5

BEAUVAL

P　BEAUVAL PUBLIC LIBRARY*, Bag Service, No 9000, S0M 0G0. Tel: 306-288-2022, Ext 3304. FAX: 306-288-2222. E-mail: sb@pnls.lib.sk.ca. Web Site: beauvallibrary.piczo.com. *Librn,* Edquist Carol
　Library Holdings: Bk Vols 15,000; Per Subs 15
　Mem of Pahkisimon Nuye?ah Library System
　Open Mon & Tues 9-7, Thurs & Fri 9-9, Sun1-5

BUFFALO NARROWS

P　WISEWOOD LIBRARY*, PO Box 309, S0M 0J0. Tel: 306-235-4240. FAX: 306-235-4511. E-mail: wisewoodlibrary@nlsd113.net. *Librn,* Darlene Petit
　Library Holdings: Bk Vols 25,000; Per Subs 30
　Mem of Pahkisimon Nuye?ah Library System
　Open Mon & Wed 1-5 & 7pm-9pm, Tues, Thurs & Fri 1-5

CARONPORT

CR　BRIERCREST COLLEGE & SEMINARY*, Archibald Library, 510 College Dr, S0H 0S0. SAN 319-9487. Tel: 306-756-3252. Administration Tel: 306-756-3262. FAX: 306-756-5521. E-mail: library@briercrest.ca. Web Site: www.briercrest.ca/library. *Dir,* Brad Doerksen; Staff 6 (MLS 1, Non-MLS 5)
　Founded 1935. Enrl 800; Fac 40; Highest Degree: Master

　Library Holdings: e-books 6,000; e-journals 14,000; Music Scores 2,153; Bk Vols 80,000; Per Subs 180
　Special Collections: Eric Coll, microfiche
　Subject Interests: Bible, Christian ministry, Theol
　Automation Activity & Vendor Info: (Acquisitions) Horizon; (Cataloging) Horizon; (Circulation) Horizon; (ILL) Amicus; (OPAC) Horizon; (Serials) Horizon
　Database Vendor: Alexander Street Press, Canadian Reference Centre, CEDROM-SNi, EBSCO Auto Repair Reference, EBSCOhost, Gale Cengage Learning, JSTOR, netLibrary
　Wireless access
　Open Mon-Thurs 8am-10pm, Fri 8am-9pm, Sat 11-9

ESTON

C　ESTON COLLEGE, A D Marshall Library, 730 First St SE, S0L 1A0. (Mail add: PO Box 579, S0L 1A0), SAN 327-1234. Tel: 306-962-3621. Toll Free Tel: 888-440-3424. FAX: 306-962-3810. *Libr Asst,* Darla Lowenberg; Staff 1 (Non-MLS 1)
　Founded 1979. Enrl 70; Fac 10; Highest Degree: Bachelor
　Library Holdings: e-books 725; e-journals 100; Bk Titles 16,430; Per Subs 15
　Subject Interests: Relig
　Database Vendor: ProQuest
　Function: Audio & video playback equip for onsite use, CD-ROM, Copy machines, Electronic databases & coll, Handicapped accessible, ILL available, Mail & tel request accepted, Mail loans to mem, Online searches, Orientations, Photocopying/Printing, Ref & res, Ref serv available, Telephone ref, VHS videos, Wheelchair accessible

HUMBOLDT

S　PRAIRIE AGRICULTURAL MACHINERY INSTITUTE LIBRARY*, 2215 Eighth Ave, S0K 2A0. (Mail add: PO Box 1150, S0K 2A0), SAN 321-5253. Tel: 306-682-5033. Toll Free Tel: 800-567-7264. FAX: 306-682-5080. E-mail: humboldt@pami.ca. Web Site: www.pami.ca. *Librn,* Sharon Doepker
　Founded 1974
　Library Holdings: Bk Titles 2,500; Per Subs 45
　Subject Interests: Agr, Econ, Electronics, Energy, Machinery testing
　Open Mon-Fri 8:30-5

ILE A LA CROSSE

P　ILE A LA CROSSE PUBLIC LIBRARY*, PO Box 540, S0M 1C0. Tel: 306-833-3027. FAX: 306-833-2189. Web Site: www.icsd112.ca. *Libr Adminr,* Linda Ryckman; E-mail: lpryckman@hotmail.com
　Library Holdings: Bk Vols 19,000
　Mem of Pahkisimon Nuye?ah Library System
　Open Mon-Thurs 4pm-8pm

INDIAN HEAD

G   AGRICULTURE & AGRI-FOOD CANADA*, Indian Head Research Farm, RR No 1 Government Rd, S0G 2K0. (Mail add: PO Box 760, S0G 2KO), SAN 319-9495. Tel: 306-695-2274, 306-695-5220. FAX: 306-695-3445. Web Site: www4.agr.gc.ca. *Librn,* Aidan Beaubier; E-mail: aidan.beaubier@agr.gc.ca
   Library Holdings: Bk Vols 2,400
   Open Mon-Fri 8-4:30

LA LOCHE

P   DAVE O'HARA COMMUNITY LIBRARY*, Bag Service, No 4, S0M 1G0. Tel: 306-822-2151. FAX: 306-822-2280. E-mail: daveohara.sll@pnls.lib.sk.ca. *Librn,* Priscilla Wolverine
   Library Holdings: Bk Vols 18,000
   Mem of Pahkisimon Nuye?ah Library System
   Open Mon-Thurs 10-12, 1-5 & 6:30pm-8:30pm, Sun 1-5

LA RONGE

P   LA RONGE PUBLIC LIBRARY*, 1212 Hildebrand Dr, S0J 1L0. (Mail add: PO Box 5680, S0J 1L0). Tel: 306-425-2160. FAX: 306-425-3883. Web Site: pnls.lib.sk.ca/laronge. *Librn,* Rosemary Loeffler; E-mail: r.loeffler.slg@pnls.lib.sk.ca; *Libr Tech,* Judy Anglestad; E-mail: janglestad@pnls.lib.sk.ca
   Library Holdings: AV Mats 2,500; Bk Vols 21,000; Per Subs 48
   Automation Activity & Vendor Info: (Acquisitions) Innovative Interfaces, Inc - Millenium; (Cataloging) Innovative Interfaces, Inc - Millenium; (Circulation) Innovative Interfaces, Inc - Millenium; (Course Reserve) Innovative Interfaces, Inc - Millenium; (ILL) Innovative Interfaces, Inc - Millenium; (OPAC) Innovative Interfaces, Inc - Millenium
   Mem of Pahkisimon Nuye?ah Library System
   Open Mon & Fri 12-5, Tues-Thurs 12-9, Sat 11-5

LLOYDMINSTER

J   LAKELAND COLLEGE*, Lloydminster Campus Library, 2602 59th Ave, Bag 6600, S9V 1Z3. Circulation Tel: 780-871-5731. FAX: 780-871-5410.
   Library Holdings: Bk Vols 26,000
   Open Mon-Thurs 8:15am-11pm, Fri 8:15-4:30, Sat 1-6, Sun 2-9

MOOSE JAW

P   HARRISON MEMORIAL LIBRARY*, Seventh Ave SW, S6H 4R2. (Mail add: PO Box 1300, S6H 4R2), SAN 319-9525. Tel: 306-694-3096. FAX: 306-694-3003. *Librn,* Mary Tkach; Tel: 306-694-3000, E-mail: mary.tkach@gov.sk.ca
   Library Holdings: Bk Vols 5,500
   Restriction: Staff use only

CR   INTERNATIONAL BIBLE COLLEGE LIBRARY*, 401 Trinity Lane, S6H 0E3. SAN 325-0105. Tel: 306-692-4041. FAX: 306-692-7968. E-mail: ibc.administrator@sasktel.net. Web Site: www.ibiblecollege.com. *Librn,* Lyle Esau
   Library Holdings: Bk Titles 6,000; Bk Vols 7,000; Per Subs 40
   Subject Interests: Bible, Pentecostal theol, Practical theol, Theol
   Open Mon-Fri 9-12 & 1-4:30

P   PALLISER REGIONAL LIBRARY, 366 Coteau St W, S6H 5C9. SAN 319-955X. Tel: 306-693-3669. FAX: 306-692-5657. Web Site: www.palliserlibrary.ca. *Dir,* Janet Smith; E-mail: jsmith@palliser.lib.sk.ca; *Rural Br Supvr,* Arwen Rudolph; Staff 6 (MLS 5, Non-MLS 1)
   Founded 1973. Pop 54,200; Circ 553,300
   Jan 2011-Dec 2011 Income (Main Library and Branch(s)) (CAN) $5,060,153, Provincial (CAN) $680,708, City (CAN) $944,363, Federal (CAN) $34,420, County (CAN) $3,366,482, Locally Generated Income (CAN) $12,000, Other (CAN) $22,180. Mats Exp (CAN) $327,465, Books (CAN) $239,869, Per/Ser (Incl. Access Fees) (CAN) $16,310, AV Mat (CAN) $48,005, Electronic Ref Mat (Incl. Access Fees) (CAN) $23,281. Sal (CAN) $1,369,950
   Library Holdings: Audiobooks 3,589; CDs 4,369; DVDs 15,828; e-books 22,838; Large Print Bks 9,020; Bk Vols 280,358; Per Subs 685
   Subject Interests: Local hist
   Automation Activity & Vendor Info: (Acquisitions) Innovative Interfaces, Inc - Millenium; (Cataloging) Innovative Interfaces, Inc - Millenium; (Circulation) Innovative Interfaces, Inc - Millenium; (ILL) Relais International; (Media Booking) IME; (OPAC) Innovative Interfaces, Inc - Millenium; (Serials) Innovative Interfaces, Inc - Millenium
   Database Vendor: Bowker, CEDROM-SNi, EBSCOhost, Gale Cengage Learning, Innovative Interfaces, Inc, Marcive, Inc, Overdrive, Inc, Thomson Carswell, TLC (The Library Corporation), TumbleBookLibrary
   Function: Accelerated reader prog, Adult bk club, Adult literacy prog, After school storytime, Archival coll, Art exhibits, Audiobks via web, Bk club(s), Bks on cassette, Bks on CD, CD-ROM, Children's prog, Computer training, Computers for patron use, Copy machines, Digital talking bks, Distance learning, e-mail & chat, Electronic databases & coll, Family literacy, Free DVD rentals, Holiday prog, Home delivery & serv to Sr ctr & nursing homes, Homebound delivery serv, Homework prog, ILL available, Literacy & newcomer serv, Mail loans to mem, Music CDs, Online cat, Prog for adults, Prog for children & young adult, Pub access computers, Ref serv in person, Scanner, Senior computer classes, Senior outreach, Spoken cassettes & CDs, Spoken cassettes & DVDs, Story hour, Summer & winter reading prog, Summer reading prog, VHS videos, Video lending libr, Workshops, Writing prog
   Publications: @palliser (Newsletter); For The Record (Newsletter); Update
   Partic in Saskatchewan Information & Library Services (SILS)
   Friends of the Library Group
   Branches: 20
   ASSINIBOIA & DISTRICT PUBLIC LIBRARY, 201 Third Ave W, Assiniboia, S0H 0B0. (Mail add: Box 940, Assiniboia, S0H 0B0), SAN 321-1428. Tel: 306-642-3631. E-mail: assiniboia@palliser.lib.sk.ca. *Librn,* Carol Munro; *Asst Librn,* Lois Seeley; Staff 1 (Non-MLS 1)
   Pop 4,067; Circ 30,502
   Library Holdings: Bk Vols 25,608
   Open Mon, Tues, Thurs & Fri 10-5, Wed 10-9, Sat 12-5
   AVONLEA BRANCH, 201 Main St W, Avonlea, S0H 0C0. (Mail add: Box 351, Avonlea, S0H 0C0), SAN 321-1436. Tel: 306-868-2076. FAX: 306-868-2221. E-mail: avonlea@palliser.lib.sk.ca. *Librn,* Randi Edmonds
   Pop 732; Circ 7,236
   Library Holdings: Bk Vols 7,594
   Open Tues 5-8, Wed & Fri 1-5, Thurs 12-5
   BETHUNE BRANCH, Community Hall, 524 East St, Bethune, S0G 0H0. (Mail add: Box 116, Bethune, S0G 0H0), SAN 321-1444. Tel: 306-638-3046. E-mail: bethune@palliser.lib.sk.ca. *Librn,* Roberta Curtis
   Pop 450; Circ 10,000
   Library Holdings: Bk Vols 7,209
   Open Tues 2-8, Wed 10:30-4:30, Fri 10-3
   BRIERCREST BRANCH, Community Ctr, Main St, Briercrest, S0H 0K0. (Mail add: Box 97, Briercrest, S0H 0K0), SAN 321-1452. Tel: 306-799-2137. E-mail: briercrest@palliser.lib.sk.ca. *Librn,* Lisa Nestman
   Pop 505; Circ 3,616
   Library Holdings: Bk Vols 7,071
   Open Tues & Thurs 6pm-9:30pm, Wed 9-Noon
   CORONACH BRANCH, 111A Centre St, Coronach, S0H 0Z0. (Mail add: Box 30, Coronach, S0H 0Z0), SAN 321-1487. Tel: 306-267-3260. E-mail: coronach@palliser.lib.sk.ca. Web Site: www.palliser.lib.sk.ca/coronach/coronach.htm. *Librn,* Marlene McBurney; *Asst Librn,* Deena McCarter
   Pop 1,133; Circ 13,341
   Library Holdings: Bk Vols 14,361
   Open Mon 9:30-12 & 1-5:30, Tues-Thurs 9:30-12:30 & 1-6, Sat 9:30-12:30 & 1-4:30
   CRAIK BRANCH, 611 First Ave, Craik, S0G 0V0. (Mail add: Box 339, Craik, S0G 0V0), SAN 321-1495. Tel: 306-734-2388. FAX: 306-734-2388. E-mail: craik@palliser.lib.sk.ca. *Librn,* Jo McAlpine; Staff 1 (Non-MLS 1)
   Pop 795; Circ 9,205
   Library Holdings: Bk Vols 10,831
   Open Tues 10-12, 1:30-5 & 7-9, Wed-Fri 1:30-5
   DAVIDSON BRANCH, 314 Washington Ave, Davidson, S0G 1A0. (Mail add: Box 754, Davidson, S0G 1A0), SAN 321-1509. Tel: 306-567-2022. FAX: 306-567-2081. E-mail: davidson@palliser.lib.sk.ca. *Librn,* September Brooke; *Asst Librn,* Debbie Shearwood; Staff 1 (Non-MLS 1)
   Pop 1,612; Circ 12,070
   Library Holdings: Bk Vols 11,816
   Open Tues & Thurs 9:30-11:30 & 1-5, Wed 12-8, Fri & Sat 1-5
   ELBOW BRANCH, 402 Minto St, Elbow, S0H 1J0. (Mail add: Box 10, Elbow, S0H 1J0), SAN 321-1517. Tel: 306-854-2220. E-mail: elbow@palliser.lib.sk.ca. *Librn,* Leeanne Hurlburt
   Pop 800; Circ 8,072
   Library Holdings: Bk Vols 9,796
   Open Wed-Fri 12:30-5:30
   HOLDFAST BRANCH, 125 Roberts St, Holdfast, S0G 2H0. (Mail add: Box 205, Holdfast, S0G 2H0), SAN 321-1525. Tel: 306-488-2140. E-mail: holdfast@palliser.lib.sk.ca. *Librn,* Tammy Bilsky
   Pop 674; Circ 4,794
   Library Holdings: Bk Vols 6,198
   Open Wed & Thurs (Summer) 11-5; Wed & Thurs (Winter) 12-6
   IMPERIAL BRANCH, 310 Royal St Town Office, Imperial, S0G 2J0. (Mail add: Box 238, Imperial, S0G 2J0), SAN 321-1533. Tel: 306-963-2272. FAX: 306-963-2445. E-mail: imperial@palliser.lib.sk.ca. *Br Librn,* Donalda McLellan
   Pop 683; Circ 8,995
   Library Holdings: Bk Vols 9,351
   Function: Bks on cassette, Bks on CD, Wheelchair accessible
   Open Tues 11-4, Wed 9:30-4:30, Thurs 11-5 & 6:30-8
   LOREBURN BRANCH, 528 Main St, Loreburn, S0H 2S0. (Mail add: Box 172, Loreburn, S0H 2S0), SAN 321-1541. Tel: 306-644-2026. FAX: 306-644-2150. E-mail: loreburn@palliser.lib.sk.ca. *Librn,* Sue Ann Abbott

Pop 313; Circ 2,613
Library Holdings: Bk Vols 6,000
Open Tues & Wed 3:30-7, Thurs 3:30-8:30
MOOSE JAW PUBLIC LIBRARY, 461 Langdon Crescent, S6H 0X6, SAN 321-155X. Tel: 306-692-2787. FAX: 306-692-3368. E-mail: librarian.smj@sasktel.net. Web Site: www.moosejawlibrary.ca. *Librn,* Karon Selzer; Staff 16.9 (MLS 3, Non-MLS 13.9)
Founded 1913. Pop 33,000; Circ 307,012
Jan 2011-Dec 2011 Income (CAN) $937,733, Provincial (CAN) $9,386, City (CAN) $913,943, Federal (CAN) $9,404, Locally Generated Income (CAN) $5,000. Mats Exp (CAN) $247,421, Books (CAN) $160,137, Per/Ser (Incl. Access Fees) (CAN) $15,000, Manu Arch (CAN) $1,300, Micro (CAN) $800, AV Mat (CAN) $38,000, Electronic Ref Mat (Incl. Access Fees) (CAN) $32,184. Sal (CAN) $693,441
Library Holdings: Audiobooks 6,836; CDs 4,692; DVDs 5,767; e-books 18,477; Microforms 1,055; Bk Vols 130,263; Per Subs 500; Talking Bks 2,072; Videos 954
Special Collections: Archives Coll
Subject Interests: Local hist
Automation Activity & Vendor Info: (ILL) Innovative Interfaces, Inc - Millenium
Database Vendor: Canadian Reference Centre, Checkpoint Systems, Inc, EBSCO Auto Repair Reference, EBSCO Information Services, ProQuest
Function: Adult bk club, After school storytime, Archival coll, Audio & video playback equip for onsite use, Audiobks via web, BA reader (adult literacy), Bk club(s), Bks on cassette, Bks on CD, CD-ROM, Children's prog, Computer training, Computers for patron use, Copy machines, Digital talking bks, Doc delivery serv, Electronic databases & coll, Family literacy, Free DVD rentals, Holiday prog, Home delivery & serv to Sr ctr & nursing homes, Homebound delivery serv, ILL available, Magnifiers for reading, Mail & tel request accepted, Music CDs, Online cat, Orientations, Outreach serv, Outside serv via phone, mail, e-mail & web, OverDrive digital audio bks, Photocopying/Printing, Printer for laptops & handheld devices, Prog for adults, Prog for children & young adult, Pub access computers, Ref & res, Ref serv available, Ref serv in person, Scanner, Senior computer classes, Spoken cassettes & CDs, Spoken cassettes & DVDs, Story hour, Summer reading prog, Teen prog, Telephone ref, VHS videos, Web-catalog, Wheelchair accessible
Publications: Lines & Links (Newsletter)
Special Services for the Blind - Closed circuit TV; Reader equip
Open Mon-Thurs 9:30-9, Fri & Sat 9:30-6, Sun 1-5
Friends of the Library Group
MORTLACH BRANCH, 112 Rose St, Mortlach, S0H 3E0. (Mail add: Box 36, Mortlach, S0H 3E0), SAN 321-1568. Tel: 306-355-2202. E-mail: mortlach@palliser.lib.sk.ca. Web Site: www.palliser.lib.sk.ca/mortlach/mortlach.htm. *Librn,* Vi Domeij
Pop 419; Circ 3,472
Library Holdings: Bk Vols 3,943
Open Tues 9-1, Wed 3-7, Fri 1-4:30
MOSSBANK BRANCH, 310 Main St, Mossbank, S0H 3G0. (Mail add: Box 422, Mossbank, S0H 3G0), SAN 321-1576. Tel: 306-354-2474. FAX: 306-354-2646. E-mail: mossbank@palliser.lib.sk.ca. *Librn,* Jenna Hysiuk
Pop 895; Circ 5,239
Library Holdings: Bk Vols 11,481
Open Tues 9-12:30 & 2-5, Wed 9-12:30 & 2-5:30, Fri 1-5
RIVERHURST BRANCH, 324 Teck St, Riverhurst, S0H 3P0. (Mail add: Box 37, Riverhurst, S0H 3P0), SAN 321-1584. Tel: 306-353-2130. E-mail: riverhurst@palliser.lib.sk.ca. *Librn,* Donna Miner
Pop 351; Circ 2,466
Library Holdings: Bk Vols 6,196
Open Tues 1-7, Thurs 9:30-3
ROCKGLEN BRANCH, 1018 Centre St, Rockglen, S0H 3R0. (Mail add: Box 148, Rockglen, S0H 3R0), SAN 321-1592. Tel: 306-476-2350. FAX: 306-476-2339. E-mail: rockglen@palliser.lib.sk.ca. *Librn,* Angela Stewart
Pop 1,002; Circ 9,713
Library Holdings: Bk Vols 7,684
Open Mon & Fri 12-5, Wed 10:30-5
ROULEAU BRANCH, 204 Main St, Rouleau, S0G 4H0. (Mail add: Box 238, Rouleau, S0G 4H0), SAN 321-1606. Tel: 306-776-2322. E-mail: rouleau@palliser.lib.sk.ca. *Librn,* Dee Colibaba
Pop 574; Circ 4,663
Library Holdings: Bk Vols 7,352
Open Mon & Wed 6-9, Tues 1:30-5:15, Fri 1:30-5
TUGASKE BRANCH, 106 Ogema St, Tugaske, S0H 4B0. (Mail add: Box 10, Tugaske, S0H 4B0), SAN 321-1614. Tel: 306-759-2215. E-mail: tugaske@palliser.lib.sk.ca. Web Site: www.palliser.lib.sk.ca/tugaske/tugaske.htm. *Librn,* Morgan Freeman
Pop 806; Circ 4,621
Library Holdings: Bk Vols 6,934
Open Tues 1-8, Wed 5-8, Thurs 9-12
WILLOW BUNCH BRANCH, Two Ave F S, Willow Bunch, S0H 4K0. (Mail add: Box 280, Willow Bunch, S0H 4K0), SAN 321-1622. Tel: 306-473-2393. E-mail: willowbunch@palliser.lib.sk.ca. *Librn,* Barb Gibbons

Pop 590; Circ 6,081
Library Holdings: Bk Vols 8,524
Open Tues & Thurs 1-5, Wed 2-8:30
WOOD MOUNTAIN BRANCH, Second Ave W, Wood Mountain, S0H 4L0. (Mail add: Box 62, Wood Mountain, S0H 4L0), SAN 321-1630. Tel: 306-266-2110. E-mail: woodmountain@palliser.lib.sk.ca. *Librn,* Gus Gere
Pop 198; Circ 2,047
Library Holdings: Bk Vols 4,440
Open Tues 10:30-4:30

C   SIAST-SASKATCHEWAN INSTITUTE OF APPLIED SCIENCE & TECHNOLOGY*, Palliser Campus Library, 600 Saskatchewan St W, S6H 4R4. (Mail add: PO Box 1420, S6H 4R4), SAN 319-9576. Tel: 306-691-8233. Interlibrary Loan Service Tel: 306-694-3256. FAX: 306-694-3427. E-mail: libpal@siast.sk.ca. Web Site: www.siast.sk.ca/libraries. *Dir, Libr Serv,* Heather West; E-mail: west@siast.sk.ca; *Librn,* Beverley Brooks; E-mail: brooks@siast.sk.ca; Staff 2 (MLS 2)
Founded 1961. Enrl 1,700
Jul 2006-Jun 2007 Income (CAN) $275,000. Mats Exp $133,000, Books (CAN) $100,000, Per/Ser (Incl. Access Fees) (CAN) $33,000
Library Holdings: Bk Vols 19,000; Per Subs 200
Subject Interests: Indust
Automation Activity & Vendor Info: (Acquisitions) SirsiDynix; (Cataloging) SirsiDynix; (Circulation) SirsiDynix; (Course Reserve) SirsiDynix; (ILL) Fretwell-Downing; (Media Booking) SirsiDynix; (OPAC) SirsiDynix; (Serials) SirsiDynix
Database Vendor: ebrary, EBSCOhost, Gale Cengage Learning, netLibrary, OCLC FirstSearch, OVID Technologies, ProQuest, ScienceDirect
Wireless access
Open Mon-Thurs (Winter) 8am-9pm, Fri 8-5, Sat 9-5, Sun 1-5; Mon-Fri (Summer) 8-4:30

MUENSTER

C   SAINT PETER'S ABBEY & COLLEGE LIBRARY, 100 College Dr, S0K 2Y0. (Mail add: PO Box 40, S0K 2Y0), SAN 319-9592. Tel: 306-682-7860. FAX: 306-682-4402. E-mail: library@stpeters.sk.ca. Web Site: www.stpeterscollege.ca. *Libr Serv Mgr,* Brenda McNabb; E-mail: mcnabbb@stpeters.sk.ca; Staff 2 (Non-MLS 2)
Founded 1903
Library Holdings: Bk Vols 40,000; Per Subs 100
Subject Interests: German Americana, German Canadiana, Monastic hist, Theol

NIPAWIN

SR   NIPAWIN BIBLE COLLEGE LIBRARY*, Hwy 35 S, S0E 1E0. (Mail add: PO Box 1986, S0E 1E0), SAN 370-565X. Tel: 306-862-5095. Toll Free Tel: 888-862-5095. FAX: 306-862-3651. *Dir,* Wes Dobson; *Librn,* Charlotte Thiessen
Founded 1934
Library Holdings: Bk Titles 10,500; Per Subs 160
Special Collections: Religious Volumes
Wireless access
Open Mon-Sat 8-11

NORTH BATTLEFORD

M   BATTLEFORDS UNION HOSPITAL*, Medical Library, 1092 107th St, S9A 1Z1. SAN 319-9606. Tel: 306-446-6641. FAX: 306-446-4114.
Library Holdings: Bk Titles 2,400; Per Subs 30
Restriction: Staff use only

P   LAKELAND LIBRARY REGION*, 1302 100 St, S9A 0V8. SAN 319-9614. Tel: 306-445-6108. FAX: 306-445-5717. Web Site: www.lakeland.lib.sk.ca. *Dir,* Donna Challis; E-mail: dchallis@lakeland.lib.sk.ca; *Mgr,* Jacky Bauer; E-mail: jbauer@lakeland.lib.sk.ca; *Rural Br Supvr,* Lane Jackson; E-mail: ljackson@lakeland.lib.sk.ca; Staff 9 (Non-MLS 9)
Founded 1972. Pop 72,294
Library Holdings: Bk Vols 267,209
Special Collections: North American Indians Coll
Subject Interests: NW Sask hist
Automation Activity & Vendor Info: (Acquisitions) Innovative Interfaces, Inc - Millenium; (Cataloging) Innovative Interfaces, Inc - Millenium; (Circulation) Innovative Interfaces, Inc - Millenium; (OPAC) Innovative Interfaces, Inc - Millenium
Function: Ref serv available
Member Libraries: Lloydminster Public Library
Special Services for the Blind - Talking bks
Open Mon-Fri 8:30-5

Branches: 31

BATTLEFORD BRANCH, 201 22nd St W, Battleford, S0M 0E0. (Mail add: PO Box 220, Battleford, S0M 0E0). Tel: 306-937-2646. FAX: 306-937-6631. *Librn,* Rita Kuntz
Open Mon 1-9, Tues 12-6, Wed 10-1 & 1:30-5:30, Thurs 12:30-5:30

BORDEN BRANCH, 303 First Ave, Borden, S0K 0N0. (Mail add: PO Box 58, Borden, S0K 0N0). Tel: 306-997-2220. *Librn,* Diane Sylvester
Open Tues 3-6, Wed 10:30-4:30, Fri 1:30-4:30

CUT KNIFE BRANCH, Box 595, Cut Knife, S0M 0N0. Tel: 306-398-2342. *Librn,* Ceinnie Kortright
Library Holdings: Bk Vols 4,243
Open Tues & Thurs 1-4, Wed 1-5

DENZIL BRANCH, Box 188, Denzil, S0L 0S0. Tel: 306-358-2118. FAX: 306-358-4828. *Librn,* Carrie McKee
Library Holdings: Bk Vols 2,763
Open Tues & Thurs 12:30-3:30

EDAM BRANCH, 1000 Main St, Edam, S0M 0V0. (Mail add: PO Box 203, Edam, S0M 0V0). Tel: 306-397-2223. FAX: 306-397-2626. *Librn,* Karlie King
Open Mon 12:30-4:30, Wed 3-7, Thurs 10-1

GLASLYN BRANCH, Box 501, Glaslyn, S0M 0Y0. Tel: 306-342-4748. *Librn,* Jenine Willumeit
Open Tues 10-2, Thurs 1-4

GOODSOIL BRANCH, 301 Main St N, Goodsoil, S0M 1A0. (Mail add: Box 129, Goodsoil, S0M 1A0). Tel: 306-238-2155. FAX: 306-238-2155. *Librn,* Sarah Degenhardt
Open Wed 10-4, Thurs 1-7

HAFFORD BRANCH, Box 520, Hafford, S0J 1A0. Tel: 306-549-2373. FAX: 306-549-2333. *Librn,* Carol Hermann
Open Tues-Thurs 12-4

LASHBURN BRANCH, 95 Main St E, Lashburn, S0M 1H0. (Mail add: Box 160, Lashburn, S0M 1H0). Tel: 306-285-4144. *Librn,* Kathy Berg
Library Holdings: Bk Vols 7,329
Open Tues 4-7, Wed 6:30-9:30, Fri 10-4

LOON LAKE BRANCH, Box 216, Loon Lake, S0M 1L0. Tel: 306-837-2186. *Librn,* Lucy Berube
Open Tues & Thurs 1-7

MACKLIN BRANCH, Box 652, Macklin, S0L 2C0. Tel: 306-753-2933. FAX: 306-753-3234. *Librn,* Leanne Shapka
Open Tues & Thurs 3-7, Wed & Fri 1:30-5

MAIDSTONE BRANCH, Box 429, Maidstone, S0M 1M0, Tel: 306-893-4153. FAX: 306-893-4158. *Librn,* Lorna Foster
Open Tues 9:30-1 & 1:30-5, Wed 1-5 & 5:30-8, Fri 9:30-1

MAKWA BRANCH, 111 Main St, Makwa, S0M 1N0. Tel: 306-236-3995. *Librn,* Lucy Berude
Open Wed 10-4

MARSDEN BRANCH, 104 Centre St, Marsden, S0M 1P0. (Mail add: PO Box 328, Marsden, S0M 1P0). Tel: 306-826-5666. *Librn,* Denise Polkinghorne
Open Tues, Thurs & Fri 1-5

MARSHALL BRANCH, 13 Main St, Marshall, S0M 1R0. Tel: 306-387-6155. *Librn,* Barb Holt
Library Holdings: Bk Vols 4,000
Open Tues 9-3, Thurs 4-7

MAYFAIR BRANCH, PO Box 70, Mayfair, S0M 1S0. Tel: 306-246-4465. E-mail: mayfair.lib@lakeland.lib.sk.ca. *Librn,* Teresa Toews
Library Holdings: Bk Titles 20,000; Per Subs 12
Open Tues 10-2, Wed 5-8, Thurs 10-1

MAYMONT BRANCH, PO Box 102, Maymont, S0M 1T0. Tel: 306-389-2006. *Librn,* Joeleen Milman
Founded 1972
Open Tues 1-6, Fri 9-Noon

MEADOW LAKE BRANCH, SPMC Box 9000, 320 Centre St, Meadow Lake, S9X 1V8. Tel: 306-236-5396. FAX: 306-236-6282. *Librn,* Tara Million
Open Mon-Thurs 10-5:30, Fri & Sat 10-5

MEDSTEAD BRANCH, Box 13, Medstead, S0M 1W0. Tel: 306-342-4988. *In Charge,* Shannon Englot
Open Tues 10-5, Thurs 1-5

MEOTA BRANCH, Box 214, Meota, S0M 1X0. Tel: 306-892-2004. FAX: 306-892-2004. E-mail: meota.lib@lakeland.lib.sk.ca. *Librn,* Deborah Pearce
Open Tues & Wed 5-8:30, Thurs & Sat 1-5

NEILBURG BRANCH, Box 174, Neilburg, S0M 2C0. Tel: 306-823-4234. *Librn,* Sharon Schempp
Open Tues 11-6, Thurs 1-8, Fri 10-3

NORTH BATTLEFORD PUBLIC LIBRARY, 1392 101st St, S9A 1A2, SAN 376-2173. Tel: 306-445-3206. FAX: 306-445-6454. Web Site: www.northbattlefordlibrary.com. *Librn,* Karen Sabraw; E-mail: librarian.northbattleford@lakeland.lib.sk.ca
Founded 1916. Pop 14,500; Circ 191,173
Library Holdings: Bk Vols 83,000; Per Subs 121
Open Mon 12:30-9, Tues, Fri & Sat 10-5:30, Wed & Thurs 10-9, Sun 1:30-5:30

PARADISE HILL BRANCH, Second Ave, No 104, Paradise Hill, S0M 2Go. (Mail add: PO Box 187, Paradise Hill, S0M 2Go). Tel: 306-344-4741. Web Site: www.lakeland.lib.sk.ca/llr/pabranch.htm. *Librn,* Dianne Palsich
Open Mon 9:30-11:30 & 1-5, Tues 5-10, Fri 12-5

PAYNTON BRANCH, 201 First St E, Paynton, S0M 2J0. Tel: 306-895-2175. *Librn,* Sonja Margerison
Open Tues 12:30-5:30, Thurs 3-8

PIERCELAND BRANCH, PO Box 250, Pierceland, S0M 2K0. Tel: 306-839-2166. *Librn,* Anita Kajner
Library Holdings: Bk Vols 2,000
Open Tues & Wed 1-5:30

RABBIT LAKE BRANCH, Box 146, Rabbit Lake, S0M 2L0. Tel: 306-824-2089. *Librn,* Melita Hildebrand
Open Tues 10-4, Wed 3-6

RADISSON BRANCH, Box 161, Radisson, S0K 3L0. Tel: 306-827-4521. *Librn,* Shirley Hosegood
Open Tues 1-5, Wed 4-7, Fri 2-5

ST WALBURG BRANCH, 154 Main St, St. Walburg, S0M 2T0. (Mail add: Box 154, St. Walburg, S0M 2T0). Tel: 306-248-3250.
Open Tues 3-8, Wed 1-5, Thurs 11-5, Fri 10-1

SASKATCHEWAN HOSPITAL, PO Box 39, S9A 2X8, SAN 327-1250. Tel: 306-446-6863. FAX: 306-446-6810. *Librn,* Position Currently Open
Library Holdings: Bk Vols 1,600; Per Subs 44
Open Tues 10-11:30 & 12-2, Thurs 9am-11:30am

SPEERS BRANCH, Main St, Speers, S0M 2V0. Tel: 306-246-4866. *Librn,* Colleen Wicks
Open Mon & Thurs 2-5, Wed 9:30-12:30

TURTLEFORD BRANCH, Box 146, Turtleford, S0M 2Y0. Tel: 306-845-2074. *Librn,* Norma Corrigal
Open Mon & Wed 10-6, Tues & Thurs 10-4:30, Fri 10-4

PELICAN NARROWS

P   TAWOWIKAMIK PUBLIC LIBRARY*, PO Box 100, S0P 0E0. Tel: 306-632-2161. FAX: 306-632-2022. E-mail: spn@pnls.lib.sk.ca. *Head Librn,* Merle Bighetty; E-mail: M.Bighetty.spn@pnls.lib.sk.ca
Library Holdings: Bk Vols 15,000; Per Subs 50
Automation Activity & Vendor Info: (Cataloging) Chancery SMS; (Circulation) Chancery SMS; (OPAC) Chancery SMS
Mem of Pahkisimon Nuye?ah Library System
Open Mon-Fri 9-6

PINEHOUSE LAKE

P   PEAYAMECHIKEE PUBLIC LIBRARY*, Box 160, S0J 2B0. Tel: 306-884-4888. FAX: 306-884-2164. *Librn,* Sophie McCallum
Library Holdings: AV Mats 300; Bk Vols 5,000; Per Subs 17
Mem of Pahkisimon Nuye?ah Library System
Open Mon-Thurs 11-7

PRINCE ALBERT

P   JOHN M CUELENAERE PUBLIC LIBRARY*, 125 12th St E, S6V 1B7. SAN 322-7057. Tel: 306-763-8496. Administration Tel: 306-763-8322. FAX: 306-763-3816. E-mail: library@jmcpl.ca. Web Site: www.jmcpl.ca. *Dir,* Alex Juorio; Tel: 306-763-4150, E-mail: ajuorio@jmcpl.ca; Staff 9 (MLS 3, Non-MLS 6)
Founded 1973. Pop 40,000; Circ 358,395
Jan 2007-Dec 2007 Income (CAN) $1,288,980, City (CAN) $1,245,480, County (CAN) $3,000, Locally Generated Income (CAN) $40,500. Mats Exp (CAN) $173,728, Books (CAN) $121,203, Per/Ser (Incl. Access Fees) (CAN) $27,948, AV Mat (CAN) $23,577, Electronic Ref Mat (Incl. Access Fees) (CAN) $1,000. Sal (CAN) $802,884
Library Holdings: AV Mats 4,623; CDs 3,617; DVDs 701; High Interest/Low Vocabulary Bk Vols 656; Large Print Bks 4,513; Bk Titles 109,509; Bk Vols 127,477; Per Subs 498; Talking Bks 150
Special Collections: Maps; Microfilm; Pamphlets; Sewing Patterns
Database Vendor: EBSCOhost, Gale Cengage Learning, ProQuest, SirsiDynix
Wireless access
Function: Govt ref serv, Handicapped accessible, Health sci info serv, Home delivery & serv to Sr ctr & nursing homes, ILL available
Publications: Cuelenaere Contact (Newsletter)
Partic in Saskatchewan Information & Library Services (SILS)
Open Mon-Thurs 9-9, Fri & Sat 9-5:30

C   GABRIEL DUMONT INSTITUTE OF METIS STUDIES & APPLIED RESEARCH LIBRARY*, 48 12th St E, S6V 1B2. SAN 371-8441. Tel: 306-922-6466. FAX: 306-763-4834. Web Site: www.gdi.local. *Librn,* Sharon Wood; E-mail: sharon.wood@gdi.gdins.org; Staff 2 (MLS 1, Non-MLS 1)
Founded 1989. Enrl 200; Fac 17; Highest Degree: Master
Library Holdings: CDs 500; DVDs 200; Music Scores 200; Bk Vols 20,000; Per Subs 30

Subject Interests: Multicultural studies, Teacher educ
Database Vendor: EBSCOhost
Partic in RegLIN Consortium
Open Mon-Fri 8-4:30

M   PRINCE ALBERT PARKLAND HEALTH REGION LIBRARY*, PAPHR
Library, 1200 24th St W, S6V 5T4. SAN 319-9657. Tel: 306-765-6026.
FAX: 306-765-6062. *Librn,* Suzy Bear; E-mail: sbear@paphr.sk.ca
Subject Interests: Med, Pub health, Surgical
Wireless access
Function: Health sci info serv
Open Mon-Fri 8-4:30
Restriction: Non-circulating to the pub

C   SIAST LIBRARIES*, Woodland Campus, 1100 15th St E, S6V 6G1. (Mail
add: PO Box 3003, S6V 6G1), SAN 370-6818. Tel: 306-765-1550. FAX:
306-953-7064. E-mail: woodlandlibrary@siast.sk.ca. Web Site:
www.siast.sk.ca/libraries. *Head Librn,* Regan Gunningham; Staff 6 (MLS 2,
Non-MLS 4)
Founded 1988. Enrl 2,500; Highest Degree: Doctorate
Library Holdings: Per Subs 400
Automation Activity & Vendor Info: (Acquisitions) SirsiDynix;
(Cataloging) SirsiDynix; (Circulation) SirsiDynix; (OPAC) SirsiDynix;
(Serials) SirsiDynix
Database Vendor: EBSCOhost, Gale Cengage Learning, netLibrary,
OCLC FirstSearch, OCLC WorldCat, OVID Technologies, SerialsSolutions,
SirsiDynix
Function: ILL available
Special Services for the Deaf - Bks on deafness & sign lang; Staff with
knowledge of sign lang
Open Mon-Thurs 7:30am-9pm, Fri 7:30-5, Sat & Sun 10-5
Restriction: Restricted borrowing privileges

P   WAPITI REGIONAL LIBRARY*, 145 12th St E, S6V 1B7. SAN
319-9665. Tel: 306-764-0712. FAX: 306-922-1516. E-mail:
wapiti@panet.pa.sk.ca. Web Site: www.panet.pa.sk.ca. *Regional Dir,* John
Murray; E-mail: jmurray@panet.pa.sk.ca; *Asst Regional Dir,* Joan Weldon;
Staff 114 (MLS 6, Non-MLS 108)
Founded 1950. Pop 119,392; Circ 744,381
Library Holdings: Bk Vols 509,665
Automation Activity & Vendor Info: (Acquisitions) SirsiDynix;
(Cataloging) SirsiDynix; (Circulation) SirsiDynix; (Course Reserve)
SirsiDynix; (ILL) SirsiDynix; (Media Booking) SirsiDynix; (OPAC)
SirsiDynix; (Serials) SirsiDynix
Database Vendor: EBSCOhost
Publications: Wapiti
Open Mon-Fri 8-5:30
Branches: 46
ALVENA PUBLIC LIBRARY, Business/Commerce Complex, 101 Main
St, Alvena, S0K 0E0. (Mail add: Box 94, Alvena, S0K 0E0). Tel:
306-943-2003. E-mail: alvcirc@panet.pa.sk.ca. *Br Librn,* Charlotte Kuhn
Open Tues 9-6
ARBORFIELD PUBLIC LIBRARY, 201 Main St, Arborfield, S0E 0A0.
(Mail add: PO Box 223, Arborfield, S0E 0A0). Tel: 306-769-8533.
E-mail: arbcirc@panet.pa.sk.ca. *Br Librn,* Ruth LaForge
Open Tues 4:30-8:30, Thurs 10-4, Fri 1-4
ARCHERWILL PUBLIC LIBRARY, First Ave, Archerwill, S0E 0B0. Tel:
306-323-2128. E-mail: arccirc@panet.pa.sk.ca. *Librn,* Sandra Bender
Library Holdings: Bk Vols 3,000
Open Tues 4-7, Thurs 1-6
BIG RIVER PUBLIC LIBRARY, 606 First St N, Big River, S0J 0E0.
(Mail add: Box 154, Big River, S0J 0E0). Tel: 306-469-2152. E-mail:
bigcirc@panet.pa.sk.ca. *Br Librn,* Meada Wilson
Open Mon 11-6, Wed 10-6, Fri 12-6
BIRCH HILLS PUBLIC LIBRARY, 126 McCallum Ave, Birch Hills, S0J
0G0. (Mail add: Box 396, Birch Hills, S0J 0G0). Tel: 306-749-3281.
E-mail: bircirc@panet.pa.sk.ca. *Librn,* Joanne Bzdel
Open Tues 12-4 & 5-8, Thurs & Fri 12-4:30
BJORKDALE PUBLIC LIBRARY, 105 Hara Ave, Bjorkdale, S0E 0E0.
(Mail add: Box 210, Bjorkdale, S0E 0E0). Tel: 308-886-2119. E-mail:
bjocirc@panet.pa.sk.ca. *Br Librn,* Lorraine Bishop
Open Tues & Thurs 12-6, Fri 10-3
BLAINE LAKE PUBLIC LIBRARY, CNR Station, Blaine Lake, S0J 0J0.
Tel: 306-497-3130. E-mail: blacirc@panet.pa.sk.ca. *Librn,* Renee Antonie
Open Tues 12-5, Wed & Fri 1-5, Thurs 5-8
CANWOOD PUBLIC LIBRARY, 660 Main St, Canwood, S0J 0K0. (Mail
add: Box 23, Canwood, S0J 0K0). *Librn,* Hildergarde Butz
Open Tues & Fri 1-5
CARROT RIVER PUBLIC LIBRARY, Town Office/Library Complex,
Main St, Carrot River, S0E 0L0. (Mail add: Box 1001, Carrot River, S0E
0L0). Tel: 306-768-2501. E-mail: carcirc@panet.pa.sk.ca. *Librn,* Maria
Doerkson
Open Tues 11-5, Wed 5pm-8pm, Thurs 10-5

CHOICELAND PUBLIC LIBRARY, 116 First St E, Choiceland, S0J 0M0.
(Mail add: Box 250, Choiceland, S0J 0M0). Tel: 306-428-2216. E-mail:
chocirc@panet.pa.sk.ca. *Librn,* Rita Holman
Open Tues & Thurs 11-5, Wed 3:30-7:30
CHRISTOPHER LAKE PUBLIC LIBRARY, RM Office on Hwy 263,
Christopher Lake, S0J 0N0. (Mail add: Box 27, Christopher Lake, S0J
0N0). Tel: 306-982-4763. E-mail: chrcirc@panet.pa.sk.ca. *Librn,* Barb
Hazeltine
Open Wed 1-7:30, Thurs 12-7:30
CUDWORTH PUBLIC LIBRARY, 426 Second Ave, Cudworth, S0K 1B0.
(Mail add: Box 321, Cudworth, S0K 1B0). Tel: 306-256-3530. E-mail:
cudcirc@panet.pa.sk.ca. *Librn,* Shirley Osmond
Open Tues 12-4, Thurs 1-5, Fri 5-8
DEBDEN PUBLIC LIBRARY, 3 204 Second Ave E, Debden, S0J 0S0.
(Mail add: PO Box 143, Debden, S0J 0S0). Tel: 306-724-2240. E-mail:
debcirc@panet.pa.sk.ca. *Librn,* Aline Hannon
Open Mon 3-7, Wed 10-4
DUCK LAKE PUBLIC LIBRARY, 410 Victoria Ave, Duck Lake, S0K
1J0. (Mail add: Box 490, Duck Lake, S0K 1J0), SAN 327-8417. Tel:
306-467-2016. E-mail: duccirc@panet.pa.sk.ca. *Librn,* Dianne Perrin
Database Vendor: EBSCOhost
Open Tues & Wed 12-5
GRONLID PUBLIC LIBRARY, One Railway Ave, Gronlid, S0E 0W0.
(Mail add: Box 192, Gronlid, S0E 0W0). Tel: 306-277-4633. FAX:
306-277-4633. E-mail: grocirc@panet.pa.sk.ca. *Librn,* Barb Dick
Open Wed & Thurs 12-6
HUDSON BAY PUBLIC LIBRARY, 130 Main St, Hudson Bay, S0E 0Y0.
(Mail add: Box 1109, Hudson Bay, S0E 0Y0). Tel: 306-865-3110.
E-mail: hudcirc@panet.pa.sk.ca. *Librn,* Glennys Binkley
Open Mon-Wed, Fri & Sat 1-6, Thurs 1-5 & 6-8
HUMBOLDT REID-THOMPSON PUBLIC LIBRARY, 705 Main St,
Humboldt, S0K 2A0. (Mail add: Box 1330, Humboldt, S0K 2A0). Tel:
306-682-2034. FAX: 306-682-3035. E-mail: humcirc@wapitilibrary.ca.
Web Site: www.wapitilibrary.ca. *Librn,* Rose Ward
Open Mon-Wed 11-9, Thurs & Fri 11-6, Sat 1-4
KINISTINO PUBLIC LIBRARY, 210 Kinistino Ave, Kinistino, S0J 1H0.
(Mail add: Box 774, Kinistino, S0J 1H0). Tel: 306-864-2537. E-mail:
kincirc@panet.pa.sk.ca. *Librn,* Jill Johnson
Open Tues-Thurs 12:30-5:00
LEASK PUBLIC LIBRARY, First Ave RM Office Complex, Leask, S0J
1M0. (Mail add: Box 117, Leask, S0J 1M0). Tel: 306-466-4577. *Librn,*
Beryle Peake; *Librn,* Connie Peake
Open Tues, Fri & Sat 1-5:30
LEOVILLE PUBLIC LIBRARY, Box 129, Leoville, S0J 1N0. Tel:
306-984-2057. E-mail: leocirc@panet.pa.sk.ca. *Librn,* Gladys Henri
Open Tues & Thurs 10-3
MARCELIN PUBLIC LIBRARY, 100 First Ave, Marcelin, S0J 1R0. Tel:
306-226-2110. E-mail: marcirc@panet.pa.sk.ca. *Librn,* Peggy
Barber-Grenier
Open Tues 10-4, Thurs 3-8
MELFORT PUBLIC LIBRARY, 106 Crawford Ave W, Melfort, S0E 1A0.
(Mail add: Box 429, Melfort, S0E 1A0). Tel: 306-752-2022. E-mail:
melcirc@panet.pa.sk.ca. *Librn,* Penny Markland
Open Mon & Fri 10-6, Tues-Thurs 9:30-9, Sat 10-5
MISTATIM PUBLIC LIBRARY, Railway Ave, Mistatim, S0E 1B0. (Mail
add: Box 10, Mistatim, S0E 1B0). Tel: 306-889-2008. E-mail:
miscirc@panet.pa.sk.ca. *Librn,* Yolanda Tremblay
Open Tues 10-6, Thurs 11-5
NAICAM PUBLIC LIBRARY, 109 Centre St, Naicam, S0K 2Z0. (Mail
add: Box 587, Naicam, S0K 2Z0). Tel: 306-874-2156. E-mail:
naicirc@panet.pa.sk.ca. *Librn,* Darla Christianson
Open Tues & Fri 12-5, Wed & Thurs 1-5
NIPAWIN PUBLIC LIBRARY, 501 Second St E, Nipawin, S0E 1E0.
(Mail add: Box 1720, Nipawin, S0E 1E0). Tel: 306-862-4867. E-mail:
nipcirc@panet.pa.sk.ca. *Librn,* Nancy Budd
Open Mon & Fri 9-6, Tues & Thurs 9-8, Sat 1-6
PADDOCKWOOD PUBLIC LIBRARY, First St N, Paddockwood, S0J
1Z0. (Mail add: Box 178, Paddockwood, S0J 1Z0). Tel: 306-989-4522.
E-mail: padcirc@panet.pa.sk.ca. *Librn,* Joan Carriere
Open Wed 10-2 & 6-8
PILGER PUBLIC LIBRARY, 622 Main St, Pilger, S0K 3G0. (Mail add:
Box 116, Pilger, S0K 3G0). Tel: 306-367-4809. E-mail:
padcirc@panet.pa.sk.ca. *Librn,* Bernice Keller
Open Tues & Thurs 3-8
PORCUPINE PLAIN PUBLIC LIBRARY, 310 Elm St, Porcupine Plain,
S0E 1H0. (Mail add: Box 162, Porcupine Plain, S0E 1H0). Tel:
306-278-2488. E-mail: porcirc@panet.pa.sk.ca. *Librn,* Joanne Yacyshyn
Open Tues & Wed 10-5, Thurs 10-4
PRAIRIE RIVER PUBLIC LIBRARY, General Delivery, Two Arras St,
Prairie River, S0E 1J0. Tel: 306-889-4521. E-mail:
pracirc@panet.pa.sk.ca. *Librn,* Pat Danku
Open Tues 9-12 & 6:30-9:30, Thurs 9:30-12, 1-3 & 6:30-9:30

PRUD'HOMME PUBLIC LIBRARY, 45 Government Rd, Prud'homme, S0K 3K0. (Mail add: Box 249, Prud'homme, S0K 3K0). Tel: 306-654-2221. FAX: 306-654-4411. E-mail: prucirc@panet.pa.sk.ca. *Librn,* Jennifer Wesdyk
Open Tues & Thurs 4-7

ST BENEDICT PUBLIC LIBRARY, Center Street, Village Office, Saint Benedict, S0K 3T0. (Mail add: PO Box 10, Saint Benedict, S0K 3T0). Tel: 306-289-2072. E-mail: sbencirc@panet.pa.sk.ca. *Librn,* LeeAnn Hannotte
Open Tues 12:30-5:30, Fri 5pm-8pm

ST BRIEUX PUBLIC LIBRARY, 50 Third Ave, St. Brieux, S0K 3V0. (Mail add: Box 70, St. Brieux, S0K 3V0). Tel: 306-275-2133. E-mail: sbricirc@panet.pa.sk.ca. *Librn,* Alaine Derla
Open Tues & Thurs 3:30-6:30, Wed 3:30-7:30

ST LOUIS PUBLIC LIBRARY, 205 Second St, St. Louis, S0J 2C0. (Mail add: Box 70, St. Louis, S0J 2C0). Tel: 306-422-8511. E-mail: sloucirc@panet.pa.sk.ca. *Librn,* Janine Planeuf
Open Wed 4-9, Thurs 4-8

SASKATCHEWAN PENITENTIARY, Box 160, S6V 5R6. Tel: 306-765-8000, Ext 5643. *Librn,* Erin McCrum; *Librn,* Maureen Reid
Open Mon-Fri 1-5 & 6-9

SHELL LAKE PUBLIC LIBRARY, Main St, Village Office, Shell Lake, S0J 2G0. Tel: 306-427-2272. E-mail: shllcirc@panet.pa.sk.ca. *Librn,* Pat Pelchat
Open Tues 12:30-4:30, Wed 1-4

SHELLBROOK PUBLIC LIBRARY, 105 Railway Ave W, Shellbrook, S0J 2E0. (Mail add: Box 490, Shellbrook, S0J 2E0). Tel: 306-747-3419. E-mail: shbrcirc@panet.pa.sk.ca. *Librn,* Alanna Carswell
Open Mon & Thurs 2pm-6:30pm, Tues & Wed 2-8, Fri 10-4

SMEATON PUBLIC LIBRARY, Main Street, Village Office, Smeaton, S0J 2J0. (Mail add: PO Box 149, Smeaton, S0J 2J0). Tel: 306-426-2049. E-mail: smecirc@panet.pa.sk.ca. *Librn,* Gayle Olson
Open Tues & Wed 1-5

JAMES SMITH PUBLIC LIBRARY, Box 3848, Melfort, S0E 1A0. Tel: 306-864-2955. E-mail: jsfncirc@panet.pa.sk.ca. *Librn,* Marcelynn Constant
Open Mon, Tues, Thurs & Fri 8:15-3:45, Wed 8:15-4

SPIRITWOOD PUBLIC LIBRARY, 200 Main St, Spiritwood, S0J 2M0. (Mail add: Box 177, Spiritwood, S0J 2M0). Tel: 306-883-2337. E-mail: spicirc@panet.pa.sk.ca. *Librn,* Joyce Carriere
Open Tues & Fri 9:30-4:30, Wed 10:30-4:30

STAR CITY PUBLIC LIBRARY, 400 Fourth St, Star City, S0E 1P0. (Mail add: Box 371, Star City, S0E 1P0). Tel: 306-863-4364. E-mail: stacirc@panet.pa.sk.ca. *Librn,* Dena MacKenzie
Open Mon & Wed 5:30-8:30, Tues & Thurs 1-5:30

STURGEON LAKE PUBLIC LIBRARY, RR 1, Site 12, Shellbrook, S0J 0E0. (Mail add: Box 24, Shellbrook, S0J 0E0). Tel: 306-764-5506. *Librn,* Sharon Daniels
Open Wed 9-3

TISDALE COMMUNITY LIBRARY, 800 - 101st St, Tisdale, S0E 1T0. (Mail add: Box 2499, Tisdale, S0E 1T0). Tel: 306-873-4767. E-mail: tiscirc@panet.pa.sk.ca. *Librn,* Isabel Hankins-Wilk
Open Mon-Thurs 8-8, Fri 8-5, Sat 1-5

VONDA PUBLIC LIBRARY, 204 Main St, Vonda, S0K 4N0. (Mail add: Box 160, Vonda, S0K 4N0). Tel: 306-258-2035. E-mail: voncirc@panet.pa.sk.ca. *Librn,* Jennifer Wesdyk
Open Mon 1-6:30, Wed 2:30-8

WAKAW PUBLIC LIBRARY, 121 Main St, Wakaw, S0K 4P0. (Mail add: Box 464, Wakaw, S0K 4P0). Tel: 306-233-5552. E-mail: wakcirc@panet.pa.sk.ca. *Librn,* Lisa Hubert
Open Tues & Fri 10-4:30, Wed 10:30-4:30

WELDON PUBLIC LIBRARY, Box 55, Weldon, S0J 3A0. Tel: 306-887-4466. E-mail: welcirc@panet.pa.sk.ca. *Librn,* Joanne Kayser
Open Tues & Thurs 12-5:30

WHITE FOX PUBLIC LIBRARY, 301 Elinor St, White Fox, S0J 3B0. Tel: 306-276-5800. E-mail: whicirc@panet.pa.sk.ca. *Librn,* Grace Adrian
Open Wed 1:30-6:30, Thurs 9-1

REGINA

C CAMPION COLLEGE LIBRARY, University of Regina, 3737 Wascana Pkwy, S4S 0A2. SAN 319-9681. Tel: 306-359-1202. FAX: 306-359-1200. Web Site: www.campioncollege.ca. *Libr Coordr,* Nancy McNeil; Staff 2 (Non-MLS 2)
Founded 1918. Enrl 1,200; Fac 29; Highest Degree: Bachelor
May 2010-Apr 2011. Mats Exp (CAN) $59,000, Books (CAN) $30,000, Per/Ser (Incl. Access Fees) (CAN) $27,000, AV Equip (CAN) $2,000. Sal (CAN) $94,500
Library Holdings: Bk Vols 50,000; Per Subs 100; Videos 740
Special Collections: Jesuitica Coll; Women & Religion Coll
Subject Interests: Can hist, English lit, Film studies, Medieval studies, Philosophy, Relig studies, Theol
Automation Activity & Vendor Info: (Acquisitions) Ex Libris Group; (Cataloging) Ex Libris Group; (Circulation) Ex Libris Group; (Course

Reserve) Ex Libris Group; (OPAC) Ex Libris Group; (Serials) EBSCO Online
Database Vendor: Cambridge Scientific Abstracts, Dialog, EBSCOhost, Gale Cengage Learning, JSTOR, netLibrary, OCLC WorldCat, OVID Technologies, ProQuest, ScienceDirect
Wireless access
Open Mon-Thurs 8:30am-9pm, Fri 8:30-4:30, Sat & Sun 1-5

C FIRST NATIONS UNIVERSITY OF CANADA*, Regina Campus Library, One First Nations Way, S4S 7K2. SAN 327-1137. Tel: 306-790-5950, Ext 3425. FAX: 306-790-5990. Web Site: www.fnuniv.ca. *Univ Librn,* Phyllis G Lerat; Tel: 306-790-5950, Ext 3425; E-mail: plerat@firstnationsuniversity.ca; *Libr Tech,* Belle Young; Tel: 306-790-5950, Ext 3427; Staff 3 (MLS 1, Non-MLS 2)
Founded 1977. Highest Degree: Master
Library Holdings: Bk Titles 60,000; Per Subs 35
Special Collections: Can & Prov
Automation Activity & Vendor Info: (Acquisitions) Ex Libris Group; (Cataloging) Ex Libris Group; (Circulation) Ex Libris Group; (Course Reserve) Ex Libris Group; (ILL) Ex Libris Group; (Media Booking) Ex Libris Group; (OPAC) Ex Libris Group; (Serials) Ex Libris Group
Database Vendor: EBSCOhost, OCLC FirstSearch
Publications: Annotated video list; periodical list
Open Mon-Thurs (Winter) 8am-8:10pm, Fri 8-4:10, Sat & Sun 11:30-4:10; Mon-Fri (Summer) 8:30-4:10
Departmental Libraries:
NORTHERN CAMPUS LIBRARY, 1301 Central Ave, Prince Albert, S6V 4W1, SAN 377-7472. Tel: 306-765-3333. Toll Free Tel: 800-267-6303. FAX: 306-765-3330. Web Site: www.fnuniv.ca/index.php/library-2. *Libr Tech,* Arlette Alcock; Tel: 306-765-3333, Ext 7430, E-mail: aalcock@fnuniv.ca; *Libr Tech,* Glenda Goertzen; Tel: 306-765-3333, Ext 7425, E-mail: ggoertzen@fnuniv.ca; Staff 2 (MLS 1, Non-MLS 1)
Founded 1991
Library Holdings: Bk Vols 15,000; Per Subs 60
Special Collections: Can & Prov
Open Mon & Fri 8:30-4:30, Tues-Thurs 8:30-8
SASKATOON CAMPUS LIBRARY, 226 20th St E, Saskatoon, S7K 0A6, SAN 377-7456. Tel: 306-931-1800, Ext 5425. FAX: 306-931-1847. *Head Librn,* Phyllis Lerat; Tel: 306-790-5950, Ext 3425; *Libr Tech,* Hongru Liu; Staff 2 (MLS 1, Non-MLS 1)
Founded 1985. Highest Degree: Master
Library Holdings: Bk Vols 14,000; Per Subs 85
Special Collections: Can & Prov
Open Mon-Thurs (Sept-April) 8:30-6, Fri 8:30-4:30; Mon-Fri (May-Aug) 8:30-4:30

C GABRIEL DUMONT INSTITUTE LIBRARY*, College West, Rm 218, 3737 Wascana Pkwy, S4S 0A2. SAN 329-7705. Tel: 306-347-4124. FAX: 306-565-0809. Web Site: www.gdins.org. *Librn,* Marilyn Belhumeur; E-mail: marilyn.belhumeur@uregina.ca; Staff 3 (MLS 2, Non-MLS 1)
Founded 1980. Enrl 400; Fac 45; Highest Degree: Bachelor
Library Holdings: Bk Titles 25,000; Bk Vols 30,000; Per Subs 50
Special Collections: Metis Historical Archive (60,000 docs). Oral History
Automation Activity & Vendor Info: (ILL) Ex Libris Group; (OPAC) Ex Libris Group
Open Mon-Fri 8-5

L LAW SOCIETY OF SASKATCHEWAN LIBRARIES*, Court House, 2425 Victoria Ave, S4P 3M3. (Mail add: PO Box 5032, S4P 3M3), SAN 369-5883. Tel: 306-569-8020. FAX: 306-569-0155. E-mail: reference@lawsociety.sk.ca. Web Site: www.lawsociety.sk.ca/library. *Librn,* Ken Fox; *Librn,* Maxine Seeley
Founded 1905
Library Holdings: Bk Vols 50,000
Special Collections: Law Reports; Law Text Books; Unreported Saskatchewan judgements
Automation Activity & Vendor Info: (Acquisitions) Inmagic, Inc.; (Cataloging) Inmagic, Inc.; (Circulation) Inmagic, Inc.; (Course Reserve) Inmagic, Inc.; (ILL) Inmagic, Inc.; (Media Booking) Inmagic, Inc.; (OPAC) Inmagic, Inc.; (Serials) Inmagic, Inc.
Publications: Builders' Lien Act-A Practitioners' Manual; Queen's Bench Rules of Saskatchewan Annotated
Open Mon-Fri 9-12 & 1-4
Branches:
SASKATOON COURT HOUSE, 520 Spadina Crescent E, Saskatoon, S7K 3G7, SAN 369-5913. Tel: 306-933-5141. FAX: 306-933-5166. E-mail: reference@lawsociety.sk.ca. Web Site: www.lawsociety.sk.ca. *Librn,* Peta Bates
Library Holdings: Bk Vols 15,000
Open Mon-Fri 9-12 & 1-4

G MINISTRY OF HIGHWAYS & INFRASTRUCTURE*, Materials-Research Library, 1855 Victoria Ave, S4P 3T5. SAN 369-6219. Tel: 306-787-4800. FAX: 306-787-8700. *Librn,* Joanne Paisig
Founded 1958

Library Holdings: Bk Titles 1,000; Per Subs 50
Special Collections: Annual Reports of Department of Highways &
Transportation
Subject Interests: Asphalt, Construction, Design, Geotechnical, Grain
transportation, Hwy planning, Maintenance, Road mat, Safety
Publications: Acquistions List (Quarterly)
Open Mon-Fri 8-12 & 1-5

S   MUSEUMS ASSOCIATION OF SASKATCHEWAN*, Resource Library,
424 McDonald St, S4N 6E1. SAN 375-9261. Tel: 306-780-9279. FAX:
306-780-9463. E-mail: mas@saskmuseums.org. Web Site:
www.saskmuseums.org. *Exec Dir,* Wendy Fitch; Tel: 306-780-9280
Library Holdings: Bk Titles 1,400; Per Subs 19
Subject Interests: Mus practice
Function: Mail loans to mem
Open Mon-Fri 8-4

G   PRAIRIE FARM REHABILITATION ADMINISTRATION*, Information
Centre, 408-1800 Hamilton St, S4P 4L2. SAN 319-9703. Tel:
306-780-3855. FAX: 306-780-5018. E-mail: srre@agr.gc.ca. *Mgr,* Position
Currently Open; *Coordr,* Barb Senkow; Tel: 360-780-8408; Staff 2 (MLS
1, Non-MLS 1)
Founded 1966
Library Holdings: Bk Titles 20,000; Per Subs 500
Subject Interests: Drought, Res conserv mgt, Rural develop, Soil sci,
Water res
Open Mon-Fri 8-4

S   REGINA LEADER-POST LTD LIBRARY*, 1964 Park St, S4P 3G4. (Mail
add: PO Box 2020, S4P 3G4), SAN 319-9827. Tel: 306-781-5234. FAX:
306-565-2588. *Head Librn,* Sue Marshall; E-mail:
smarshall@leaderpost.com; Staff 1 (MLS 1)
Special Collections: Clippings; Government Documents; Microfiche;
Microfilm; Photography; Scrapbooks
Function: Newsp ref libr
Restriction: Co libr

P   REGINA PUBLIC LIBRARY*, Library Directors Office, 2311 12th Ave,
S4P 0N3. (Mail add: PO Box 2311, S4P 3Z5), SAN 369-5948. Tel:
306-777-6099. Circulation Tel: 306-777-6022. Interlibrary Loan Service
Tel: 306-777-6024. Reference Tel: 306-777-6120. FAX: 306-949-7263.
Web Site: www.reginalibrary.ca. *Chief Exec Officer, Libr Dir,* Jeff Barber;
E-mail: jbarber@reginalibrary.ca; *Dep Dir,* Julie McKenna; E-mail:
jmckenna@reginalibrary.ca; Staff 94 (MLS 41, Non-MLS 53)
Founded 1909. Pop 189,400; Circ 2,734,411
Library Holdings: Bk Vols 388,754
Special Collections: Dunlop Art Gallery; Prairie History Coll
Subject Interests: Archit, Art, Econ, Literacy, Local hist
Database Vendor: EBSCOhost
Publications: Community Information Directory 1988-89; On the Street
Where You Live; RPL Film Catalogue
Special Services for the Blind - Reader equip
Open Mon-Thurs 9:30-9, Fri 9:30-6, Sat 9:30-5, Sun 1:30-5
Branches: 8
ALBERT, 1401 Robinson St, S4T 2N7, SAN 369-5972. Tel:
   306-777-6076. FAX: 306-949-7265. *Br Head,* Wendy Sinclair; E-mail:
   wsinclair@reginalibrary.ca
   Library Holdings: Bk Vols 24,084
   Special Collections: Native Indian Collection
   Open Mon & Thurs 9:30-6, Tues & Wed 1-9, Fri 9:30-5, Sat 12-5
GEORGE BOTHWELL BRANCH, 2787 Gordon Rd, S4S 6H7, SAN
   326-7849. Tel: 306-777-6091. FAX: 306-949-7267. *Br Head,* Myrna
   Crawford; E-mail: mcrawfor@reginalibrary.ca
   Open Mon, Tues & Fri 9:30-6, Wed & Thurs 9:30-9, Sat 9:30-5, Sun
   1:30-5
CONNAUGHT, 3435 13th Ave, S4T 1P8, SAN 369-6006. Tel:
   306-777-6078. *Librn,* Tanya Rogoschewsky
   Library Holdings: Bk Vols 30,370
   Open Tues 9:30-9, Wed 1-9, Thurs & Fri 9:30-6, Sat 12-5
GLEN ELM, 1601 Dewdney Ave E, S4N 4N6, SAN 369-6030. Tel:
   306-777-6080. FAX: 306-949-7268. *Librn,* Charles Ottosen; E-mail:
   cottosen@reginalibrary.ca
   Library Holdings: Bk Vols 58,745
   Open Tues & Fri 9:30-6, Wed 1-9, Thurs 9:30-9, Sat 9:30-5, Sun
   (Sept-June) 1:30-5
PRINCE OF WALES, 445-14th Ave, S4N 6T5, SAN 369-6057. Tel:
   306-777-6085. FAX: 306-949-7272. *Br Mgr,* Leo Deveau; E-mail:
   ldeveau@reginalibrary.ca
   Library Holdings: Bk Vols 18,590
   Database Vendor: EBSCOhost
   Open Mon, Tues & Fri 9:30-6, Wed & Thurs 1-9, Sat 9:30-5, Sun 1:30-5
REGENT PLACE, 331 Albert St, S4R 2N6, SAN 369-6065. Tel:
   306-777-6086. FAX: 306-949-7269. *Librn,* Erin Fradette; E-mail:
   efradatte@regionalibrary.ca
   Library Holdings: Bk Vols 41,087

Database Vendor: EBSCOhost
   Open Mon, Tues, & Fri 9:30-6, Wed 1-9, Thurs 9:30-9, Sat 9:30-5, Sun
   1:30-5
SHERWOOD VILLAGE, 6121 Rochdale Blvd, S4X 2R1, SAN 369-6073.
   Tel: 306-777-6088. FAX: 306-949-7270. *Librn,* Marguerite Porter;
   E-mail: mporter@reginalibrary.ca
   Library Holdings: Bk Vols 60,733
   Open Mon & Thurs 9:30-6, Tues & Wed 9:30-9, Sat 9:30-5
SUNRISE, 3130 E Woodhams Dr, S4V 2P9, SAN 373-0913. Tel:
   306-777-6095. FAX: 306-949-7271. *Librn,* Janet Hilderman; E-mail:
   jhilderman@reginalibrary.ca
   Open Mon, Thurs & Fri 9:30-6, Tues & Wed 9:30-9, Sat 9:30-5, Sun
   1:30-5

M   REGINA QU'APPELLE HEALTH REGION*, Health Sciences Library,
1440 14th Ave, S4P 0W5. SAN 319-9819. Tel: 306-766-4142. FAX:
306-766-3839. E-mail: library@rqhealth.ca. *Dir,* Susan Baer; Tel:
306-766-3830, E-mail: susan.baer@rqhealth.ca; Staff 8 (MLS 3, Non-MLS
5)
Subject Interests: Health sci
Open 8-4:30

REGINA-QU'APPELLE HEALTH REGION

M   HEALTH SCIENCES LIBRARY-WASCANA*, 2180 23rd Ave, S4S 0A5,
SAN 321-561X. Tel: 306-766-5441. FAX: 306-766-5460. *Librn,* Joan
Harmsworth Dow; Staff 1 (Non-MLS 1)
Founded 1958
Library Holdings: Bk Titles 2,500; Per Subs 100
Subject Interests: Geriatrics, Phys med, Physically handicapped,.
Rehabilitation
Automation Activity & Vendor Info: (Acquisitions) Ex Libris Group;
(Cataloging) Ex Libris Group; (Circulation) Ex Libris Group
Database Vendor: Gale Cengage Learning, OVID Technologies
Function: Doc delivery serv
Partic in Docline; Murlin
Open Mon-Thurs 8:30-4:30

M   PASQUA HOSPITAL LIBRARY, 4101 Dewdney Ave, S4T 1A5, SAN
320-8087. Tel: 306-766-2370. FAX: 306-766-2565. *Libr Tech,* Lily
Walter-Smith; E-mail: lily.waltersmith@rqhealth.ca; Staff 1 (Non-MLS 1)
Founded 1953
Library Holdings: Bk Vols 800; Per Subs 75
Automation Activity & Vendor Info: (Acquisitions) Ex Libris Group;
(Cataloging) Ex Libris Group; (Circulation) Ex Libris Group; (Serials)
EBSCO Online
Database Vendor: OVID Technologies
Restriction: Not open to pub

S   ALEX ROBB RESOURCE CENTER*, 1600 Fourth Ave, S4R 8C8. SAN
377-4732. Tel: 306-523-3055. FAX: 306-523-3031. E-mail:
alex.robb@rbe.sk.ca. Web Site: www.rbe.sk.ca. *Libr Tech,* Jodi Terhorst
Library Holdings: Bk Titles 7,400; Bk Vols 8,000
Open Mon-Fri 8-11:55 & 1-4:25

S   ROYAL CANADIAN MOUNTED POLICE TRAINING ACADEMY*,
RCMP Resource Centre, 5600 11th Ave W, S4P 3J7, (Mail add: PO Box
6500, S4P 3J7), SAN 327-103X. Circulation Tel: 306-780-6973. Reference
Tel: 306-780-8096. Administration Tel: 306-780-7052. Administration
FAX: 306-780-7599. E-mail: librarydepot@rcmp-grc.gc.ca. *Librn,* George
Charlebois; Staff 4 (MLS 2, Non-MLS 2)
Library Holdings: Bk Vols 10,000; Per Subs 273; Videos 1,500
Subject Interests: Can law, Law enforcement
Automation Activity & Vendor Info: (Acquisitions) Ex Libris Group;
(Cataloging) Ex Libris Group; (Circulation) Ex Libris Group; (Course
Reserve) Ex Libris Group; (ILL) Ex Libris Group; (Media Booking) Ex
Libris Group; (OPAC) Ex Libris Group; (Serials) Ex Libris Group
Database Vendor: Gale Cengage Learning, LexisNexis, ProQuest
Partic in Multitype Libr Coun; RegLIN Consortium
Open Mon-Fri 8-5
Restriction: Open to pub by appt only, Restricted access

M   SASKATCHEWAN CANCER AGENCY*, Allan Blair Cancer Centre
Library, 4101 Dewdney Ave, S4T 7T1. SAN 321-1703. Tel: 306-766-2203.
FAX: 306-766-6222. *Librn,* Michelle Zahayko; E-mail:
michelle.zahayko@saskcancer.ca
Founded 1948
Library Holdings: Bk Titles 300; Per Subs 82
Subject Interests: Nursing, Oncology, Physics, Radiation therapy
Open Mon-Fri 8-4:30

S   SASKATCHEWAN CHORAL FEDERATION LIBRARY*, 201-1870
Lorne St, S4P 2L7. SAN 376-186X. Tel: 306-780-9230. Toll Free Tel:
877-524-6725. FAX: 306-781-6021. E-mail: information@saskchoral.ca.
Web Site: www.saskchoral.ca. *Exec Dir,* Denise Gress
Open Mon-Fri 8:30-5

S SASKATCHEWAN GENEALOGICAL SOCIETY LIBRARY*, 110 - 1514 11th Ave, S4P 0H2. (Mail add: PO Box 1894, S4P 3E1), SAN 327-1110. Tel: 306-780-9207. FAX: 306-780-3615. E-mail: sgslibrary@sasktel.net. Web Site: www.saskgenealogy.com. *Exec Dir,* Linda Dunsmore-Porter; *Librn,* Megan Ashcroft; Staff 2 (MLS 1, Non-MLS 1)
Founded 1969
Library Holdings: Bk Titles 20,178; Per Subs 153
Special Collections: Family Histories; Germans to America Series, Volumes 1-67; Index to 1881 Census for England & Wales; Index to Births, Marriages, & Deaths - England & Wales; Index to Ontario Vital Statistics, 1867 to most recent release; Metis Scrip Records; National Burial Index for England & Wales, 2nd Edition; Ontario Cemetery Records, microfilm & paper; Ontario Land Records; Saskatchewan Cemetery Records; Saskatchewan Henderson's Directories; Saskatchewan Local History Books; Saskatchewan Obituary File; Saskatchewan Residents Index (SRI); Zichydorf Village Association Coll
Subject Interests: Genealogy, Hist, Maps
Publications: The Bulletin (Quarterly)
Open Mon-Fri 10-4:30

L SASKATCHEWAN GOVERNMENT INSURANCE*, Legal Library, Government Insurance, 2260 11th Ave, 14th Flr, S4P 0J9. SAN 319-9916. Tel: 306-751-1219. FAX: 306-352-0933. *Librn,* Reina Wylie
Library Holdings: Bk Vols 3,800; Per Subs 10
Special Collections: English Report; Lloyd's Law Reports
Subject Interests: Ins law
Open Mon-Fri 8-5

SASKATCHEWAN JUSTICE
GL CIVIL LAW LIBRARY*, 900 - 1874 Scarth St, S4P 4B3, SAN 369-6456. Tel: 306-787-8955. FAX: 306-787-0581. *In Charge,* Vicki Strickland; Tel: 306-787-8382, E-mail: vicki.strickland@gov.sk.ca
Restriction: Not open to pub
GL COURT OF APPEAL LIBRARY*, Court House, 2425 Victoria Ave, S4P 4W6, SAN 369-6391. Tel: 306-787-7399. FAX: 306-787-0505. *Librn,* Ann Marie Melvie; E-mail: amelvie@sasklawcourts.ca; Staff 1 (MLS 1)
Library Holdings: Bk Vols 5,000; Per Subs 30
GL COURT OF THE QUEEN'S BENCH*, Court House, 2425 Victoria Ave, S4P 3V7, SAN 369-6421. Tel: 306-787-7809. FAX: 306-787-7160. *Mgr,* Sharon West
Subject Interests: Law
Restriction: Not open to pub

G SASKATCHEWAN LABOUR RELATIONS & WORKPLACE SAFETY LIBRARY*, 300 - 1870 Albert St, S4P 4W1. SAN 327-1072. Tel: 306-787-2429. FAX: 306-798-5190. E-mail: library@lab.gov.sk.ca. Web Site: www.lrws.gov.sk.ca. *Librn,* Mary-Ellen Illingworth; Staff 1 (MLS 1)
Library Holdings: Bk Titles 3,000; Per Subs 200

G SASKATCHEWAN LEGISLATIVE LIBRARY, 234-2405 Legislative Dr, S4S 0B3. SAN 319-9762. Tel: 306-787-2276. Circulation Tel: 306-787-1823. Administration Tel: 306-787-2277. FAX: 306-787-5856. Administration FAX: 306-787-1772. E-mail: reference@legassembly.sk.ca. Web Site: www.legassembly.sk.ca/library. *Legis Librn,* Melissa Bennett; E-mail: mbennett@legassembly.sk.ca; *Asst Legis Librn,* Patricia M Kolesar; Tel: 306-787-9379, E-mail: pkolesar@legassembly.sk.ca; *Dir, Ref,* Leslie Polsom; Tel: 306-787-1825, E-mail: lpolsom@legassembly.sk.ca; *Dir, Support Serv,* Bette Desjarlais; Tel: 306-787-2278, Fax: 306-787-7400, E-mail: bdesjarlais@legassembly.sk.ca; *Mem Serv Librn,* Maria Swarbrick; Tel: 306-787-7663, E-mail: mswarbrick@legassembly.sk.ca; Staff 15 (MLS 7, Non-MLS 8)
Founded 1887
Apr 2011-Mar 2012 Income (CAN) $1,806,000. Mats Exp (CAN) $398,000, Books (CAN) $62,000, Per/Ser (Incl. Access Fees) (CAN) $153,000, Micro (CAN) $48,500, Electronic Ref Mat (Incl. Access Fees) (CAN) $127,500, Presv (CAN) $7,000. Sal (CAN) $1,153,000
Library Holdings: Electronic Media & Resources 16,437; Bk Vols 155,000; Per Subs 1,605
Special Collections: Saskatchewan Government Publications (official repository); Saskatchewan Local Histories. Can & Prov
Subject Interests: Govt doc, Hist, Law, Political, Soc sci with emphasis on Canada
Automation Activity & Vendor Info: (Acquisitions) Ex Libris Group; (Cataloging) Ex Libris Group; (Circulation) Ex Libris Group; (OPAC) Ex Libris Group; (Serials) Ex Libris Group
Database Vendor: CEDROM-SNi, Dialog, EBSCO Information Services, Gale Cengage Learning, Infomart, JSTOR, LexisNexis, OCLC FirstSearch, ProQuest, Quicklaw, Thomson Carswell
Wireless access
Publications: Annual Report; Checklist of Saskatchewan Government Publications (Accession list); Publications of the Governments of the Northwest Territories, 1876-1905 & the Province of Saskatchewan, 1905-1952 (Bibliographies); Saskatchewan Local Histories at the Legislative Library (Bibliographies)

Partic in RegLIN Consortium
Open Mon-Fri 9-5

S SASKATCHEWAN PARKS & RECREATION ASSOCIATION, Resource Centre for Sport, Culture & Recreation, 100-1445 Park St, S4N 4C5. SAN 370-5498. Tel: 306-780-9439. Circulation Tel: 306-780-9206. Toll Free Tel: 800-563-2555. FAX: 306-780-9257. E-mail: resourcecentre@spra.sk.ca. Web Site: www.spra.sk.ca/information. Staff 3 (MLS 2, Non-MLS 1)
Founded 1984
Library Holdings: CDs 660; DVDs 1,600; Electronic Media & Resources 100; Bk Titles 4,900; Videos 430
Special Collections: Parks & Open Spaces; Physical Activity & Fitness; Recreation & Facility Management; Sports & Coaching; Volunteer & Nonprofit Management
Automation Activity & Vendor Info: (Cataloging) SydneyPlus; (Circulation) SydneyPlus; (ILL) SydneyPlus; (Serials) SydneyPlus
Database Vendor: EBSCOhost
Open Mon-Fri 8:30-5

P SASKATCHEWAN PROVINCIAL LIBRARY & LITERACY OFFICE, 409A Park St, S4N 5B2. SAN 319-9959. Tel: 306-787-2973. Circulation Tel: 306-787-2987. Interlibrary Loan Service Tel: 306-787-2983. Administration FAX: 306-787-2029. E-mail: srp.adm@prov.lib.sk.ca. Web Site: www.lib.sk.ca. *Prov Librn,* Brett Waytuck
Founded 1953
Apr 2012-Mar 2013. Mats Exp (CAN) $66,500, Books (CAN) $35,500, Per/Ser (Incl. Access Fees) (CAN) $16,500, Electronic Ref Mat (Incl. Access Fees) (CAN) $14,500. Sal (CAN) $1,176,000
Library Holdings: Bk Titles 97,000
Special Collections: Last Copy Fiction; Library Science Coll; Multilingual Colls. Can & Prov
Automation Activity & Vendor Info: (Acquisitions) Innovative Interfaces, Inc - Millenium; (Cataloging) Innovative Interfaces, Inc - Millenium; (Circulation) Innovative Interfaces, Inc - Millenium; (Course Reserve) Innovative Interfaces, Inc - Millenium; (ILL) Innovative Interfaces, Inc - Millenium; (Media Booking) Innovative Interfaces, Inc - Millenium; (OPAC) Innovative Interfaces, Inc - Millenium; (Serials) Innovative Interfaces, Inc - Millenium
Publications: Directory of Saskatchewan Libraries; Library Systems Statistical Summary; Saskatchewan Bibliography; Think Globally - Search Locally
Partic in Province-wide Libr Electronic Info Syst
Open Mon-Fri 8-5

S SASKTEL CORPORATE LIBRARY*, 2121 Saskatchewan Dr, 12th Flr, S4P 3Y2. SAN 319-9967. Tel: 306-777-2899. FAX: 306-359-9022. *Librn,* Charlene Kramer; E-mail: charlene.kramer@sasktel.com; Staff 3 (MLS 3)
Founded 1980
Library Holdings: Bk Vols 5,500; Per Subs 350
Subject Interests: Computing, Personnel mgt
Automation Activity & Vendor Info: (Cataloging) Sydney
Database Vendor: Dialog, EBSCOhost
Function: ILL available
Publications: Libr Bulletin
Restriction: Not open to pub, Restricted loan policy

J SIAST-SASKATCHEWAN INSTITUTE OF APPLIED SCIENCE & TECHNOLOGY*, Wascana Campus Library, 4500 Wascana Pkwy, S4P 3S7. (Mail add: PO Box 7150, S4P 3S7), SAN 369-6480. Tel: 306-775-7408. Reference Tel: 306-798-0453. Toll Free Tel: 1-866-460-4430. FAX: 306-798-0560. E-mail: wascanalibrary@siast.sk.ca. *Prog Head, Emergent Technologies Librn,* Val Younge; Tel: 306-775-7411, E-mail: youngev@siast.sk.ca; *Distance Educ Librn,* Juliet Nelson; E-mail: nielsenju@siast.sk.ca; *Mkt Librn,* Rian Misfeldt; Tel: 306-775-7413, E-mail: misfeldt@siast.sk.ca; *Serv Assessment Librn,* Robin Canham; Tel: 306-665-7409, E-mail: canhamr@siast.sk.ca; *Syst Adminr,* Duane Meyers; Tel: 306-775-7403, E-mail: meyers@siast.sk.ca; Staff 10 (MLS 3, Non-MLS 7)
Founded 1972. Enrl 3,500; Fac 350
Library Holdings: Bk Titles 40,000; Per Subs 680
Subject Interests: Agr, Allied health, Basic educ, Dental assisting, Dental hygiene, Early childhood educ, Literacy, Nursing, Off educ
Automation Activity & Vendor Info: (Acquisitions) SirsiDynix; (Cataloging) SirsiDynix; (Circulation) SirsiDynix; (Course Reserve) SirsiDynix; (Media Booking) SirsiDynix; (OPAC) SirsiDynix; (Serials) SirsiDynix
Database Vendor: EBSCOhost, Gale Cengage Learning, netLibrary, OCLC FirstSearch, OVID Technologies
Publications: LibraryTutor CD-ROM
Partic in Province-wide Libr Electronic Info Syst
Special Services for the Deaf - Assistive tech
Special Services for the Blind - Assistive/Adapted tech devices, equip & products
Open Mon-Thurs 7:30am-10pm, Fri 7:30-4:30, Sat 9-5, Sun 11-7

UNIVERSITY OF REGINA

C   **DR JOHN ARCHER LIBRARY***, 3737 Wascana Pkwy, S4S 0A2, SAN 319-9983. Tel: 306-585-4295. Circulation Tel: 306-585-4133. Reference Tel: 306-585-4134. FAX: 306-585-4878. Web Site: www.uregina.ca/library. *Libr Adminr,* Daria Snow; Tel: 306-585-5110, Fax: 306-585-4878, E-mail: daria.snow@uregina.ca; Staff 22 (MLS 19, Non-MLS 3)
Founded 1967. Enrl 10,014; Fac 406; Highest Degree: Doctorate
May 2010-Apr 2011 Income (CAN) $8,665,889. Mats Exp (CAN) $3,158,625, Books (CAN) $943,666, Per/Ser (Incl. Access Fees) (CAN) $2,243,233, Other Print Mats (CAN) $28,163, Micro (CAN) $144,563, Electronic Ref Mat (Incl. Access Fees) (CAN) $846,625. Sal (CAN) $3,551,587 (Prof (CAN) $1,827,625)
Library Holdings: AV Mats 13,612; CDs 14,118; e-books 192,262; e-journals 95,396; Microforms 1,216,291; Music Scores 10,531; Bk Titles 677,951; Bk Vols 1,083,037; Per Subs 805; Videos 2,690
Automation Activity & Vendor Info: (Acquisitions) Ex Libris Group; (Cataloging) Ex Libris Group; (Circulation) Ex Libris Group; (Course Reserve) Ex Libris Group; (OPAC) Ex Libris Group; (Serials) Ex Libris Group
Database Vendor: Alexander Street Press, Annual Reviews, Cambridge Scientific Abstracts, CEDROM-SNi, ebrary, EBSCOhost, Elsevier, Emerald, Gale Cengage Learning, IEEE (Institute of Electrical & Electronics Engineers), IHS, JSTOR, LexisNexis, McGraw-Hill, Nature Publishing Group, netLibrary, OCLC FirstSearch, OCLC WorldCat, OVID Technologies, Oxford Online, ProQuest, RefWorks, Sage, SerialsSolutions, Swets Information Services, Wilson - Wilson Web
Function: Audio & video playback equip for onsite use, ILL available, Ref serv available, Res libr
Partic in OCLC Online Computer Library Center, Inc
Special Services for the Blind - Computer with voice synthesizer for visually impaired persons
Open Mon-Thurs & Sun 8am-11pm, Fri & Sat 8-7:30

C   **LUTHER COLLEGE LIBRARY***, University of Regina, 3737 Wascana Pkwy, S4S 0A2, SAN 326-453X. Tel: 306-585-5030. FAX: 306-585-5267. E-mail: luther.library@regina.ca. Web Site: www.luthercollege.edu. *Libr Coordr,* Carla L Flengeris; E-mail: carla.flengeris@luthercollege.edu; Staff 1 (Non-MLS 1)
Founded 1971. Enrl 800; Fac 20; Highest Degree: Bachelor
Library Holdings: AV Mats 170; Bk Vols 20,000; Per Subs 46
Subject Interests: Art hist, Geog, Lit, Lutheran church, Musicology, Psychol, Relig, Renaissance hist, Sociol, Tourism
Automation Activity & Vendor Info: (Acquisitions) Ex Libris Group; (Cataloging) Ex Libris Group; (Circulation) Ex Libris Group; (Course Reserve) Ex Libris Group; (ILL) Ex Libris Group; (OPAC) Ex Libris Group
Partic in Canadian Research Knowledge Network; Council of Prairie & Pacific University Libraries
Open Mon-Thurs 8:15-5:30, Fri 8:15-4:45
Restriction: Borrowing privileges limited to fac & registered students

SANDY BAY

P   **AYAMICIKIWIKAMIK PUBLIC LIBRARY***, PO Box 240, S0P 0G0. Tel: 306-754-2139. FAX: 306-754-2130. E-mail: ssbpp@pnls.lib.sk.ca. *In Charge,* Gerri Merasty; E-mail: g.merasty.ssbp@pnls.lib.sk.ca
Library Holdings: Bk Vols 16,000; Per Subs 35; Videos 100
Mem of Pahkisimon Nuye?ah Library System
Open Mon-Fri 5pm-9pm

SASKATOON

S   **AUTISM TREATMENT SERVICES OF SASKATCHEWAN, INC LIBRARY***, Autism Services Resource Centre, 609 25th St E, S7K 0L7. SAN 375-6726. Tel: 306-665-7013. FAX: 306-665-7011. E-mail: admin@autismservices.ca. Web Site: www.autismservices.ca. *Admin Serv,* Pat Kuechle
Library Holdings: CDs 10; DVDs 10; Bk Titles 400; Bk Vols 500; Per Subs 10; Videos 10
Subject Interests: Asperger's syndrome, Autism
Restriction: Mem only, Not open to pub

G   **CANADA AGRICULTURE & AGRI-FOOD CANADA***, Canadian Agriculture Library, Saskatoon, 107 Science Pl, S7N 0X2. SAN 319-9991. Tel: 306-956-7222. FAX: 306-956-7247. E-mail: library-saskatoon@agr.gc.ca. Web Site: www.agr.gc.ca/cal/saskatoon_e.html. *Librn,* Joan Martin; Staff 2 (MLS 1, Non-MLS 1)
Founded 1957
Library Holdings: Bk Vols 7,000; Per Subs 150
Special Collections: Safety Coll
Subject Interests: Agr, Agronomy, Crop breeding, Entomology, Molecular genetics, Phys sci, Plant breeding, Protection

Function: Doc delivery serv, For res purposes, Govt ref serv, ILL available, Res libr
Open Mon-Fri 8-4:30

R   **COLLEGE OF EMMANUEL & ST CHAD LIBRARY***, 114 Seminary Crescent, S7N 0X3. SAN 320-0027. Tel: 306-975-1554. FAX: 306-934-2683. E-mail: library.esc@usask.ca. Web Site: reindex.net/STU. *Head Librn, Saskatoon Theol Union Libr,* Sarah Benson; *Libr Tech,* Anna Gerscher; Staff 0.65 (MLS 0.25, Non-MLS 0.4)
Founded 1879. Enrl 35; Fac 4; Highest Degree: Doctorate
Library Holdings: Bk Vols 37,000; Per Subs 90
Subject Interests: Relig, Theol
Open Mon & Tues 8:30-3:30

G   **ENVIRONMENT CANADA LIBRARY***, National Hydrology Research Ctr, 11 Innovation Blvd, S7N 3H5. SAN 372-7181. Tel: 306-975-4096. Circulation Tel: 306-975-5559. Interlibrary Loan Service Tel: 306-975-5003. FAX: 306-975-5513. E-mail: library.biblio.saskatoonec@ec.gc.ca. *Librn,* Warren Wulff; Staff 1 (MLS 1)
Founded 1986
Library Holdings: Bk Vols 75,000; Per Subs 6,000
Special Collections: Canadian Glacier Information Centre; Hammer-Rawson Limnological Coll; Snow & Ice Reprints. Can & Prov
Automation Activity & Vendor Info: (ILL) OCLC
Partic in Dialog Corp
Open Mon-Fri 8:30-4
Restriction: Restricted borrowing privileges

SR   **JEWISH COMMUNITY CENTER SASKATOON***, Reverend David Avol Memorial Library, Congregation Agudas Israel, 715 McKinnon Ave, S7H 2G2. SAN 375-829X. Tel: 306-343-7023. FAX: 306-343-1244. Web Site: agudasisrael.org. *Librn,* Patricia Pavey
Library Holdings: Bk Titles 2,600
Special Collections: Yiddish Book Coll
Open Mon 4-6

R   **LUTHERAN THEOLOGICAL SEMINARY LIBRARY***, Otto Olson Memorial Library, 114 Seminary Crescent, S7N 0X3. Tel: 306-966-7869. FAX: 306-966-7852. E-mail: library.lts@usask.ca. Web Site: reindex.net/STU. *Libr Tech,* Leif Steistol; Staff 1 (Non-MLS 1)
Founded 1966. Enrl 50; Fac 7; Highest Degree: Master
Library Holdings: Bk Titles 45,000; Per Subs 60
Open Mon-Fri 8:30-4:30

L   **MCKERCHER LLP**, Law Library, 374 Third Ave S, S7K 1M5. SAN 329-1138. Tel: 306-653-2000. FAX: 306-653-2699. Web Site: www.mckercher.ca. *In Charge,* Sandy Welsh; E-mail: s.welsh@mckercher.ca; Staff 1 (Non-MLS 1)
Founded 1986
Library Holdings: Bk Titles 1,500; Bk Vols 5,000; Per Subs 35
Automation Activity & Vendor Info: (Cataloging) Insignia Software; (Circulation) Insignia Software; (ILL) Insignia Software; (OPAC) Insignia Software
Function: Res libr
Restriction: Staff use only

S   **MENDEL ART GALLERY & CIVIC CONSERVATORY LIBRARY***, 950 Spadina Crescent E, S7K 3L6. (Mail add: PO Box 569, S7K 3L6), SAN 375-4871. Tel: 306-975-7616. Reference Tel: 306-385-7383. FAX: 306-975-7698. E-mail: library@mendel.ca. Web Site: www.mendel.ca. Staff 1 (Non-MLS 1)
Founded 1966
Library Holdings: AV Mats 10; Bk Titles 7,800; Per Subs 30
Special Collections: Western Canadian Art, exhibition cat, vf
Subject Interests: Art hist
Function: Archival coll, For res purposes
Restriction: Open by appt only

S   **MOHYLA INSTITUTE LIBRARY**, 1240 Temperance St, S7N 0P1. SAN 320-0078. Tel: 306-653-1944. FAX: 306-653-1902. Web Site: www.mohyla.ca.
Founded 1918
Library Holdings: Bk Vols 10,000
Special Collections: Archives of Ukrainian Newspapers; Rare books
Subject Interests: Ukrainian lit
Publications: Mohyla Institute Newsletter
Open Mon-Fri 8:30-4:30

S   **NUTANA COLLEGIATE INSTITUTE***, Memorial Library & Art Gallery, 411 11th St E, S7N 0E9. SAN 320-0094. Tel: 306-683-7583. FAX: 306-683-7587. *Librn,* Silvia Regnier
Founded 1909
Library Holdings: Bk Vols 10,000; Per Subs 20
Special Collections: Canadian Artists (Memorial Art Gallery), paintings & wood cuts

Automation Activity & Vendor Info: (Acquisitions) Follett Software; (Cataloging) Follett Software; (Circulation) Follett Software; (Course Reserve) Follett Software; (ILL) Follett Software; (Media Booking) Follett Software; (OPAC) Follett Software; (Serials) Follett Software
Database Vendor: EBSCOhost
Open Mon-Fri 8:30-4

S   POS PILOT PLANT CORP LIBRARY*, 118 Veterinary Rd, S7N 2R4. SAN 321-5334. Tel: 306-978-2800, Ext 811, 306-978-2811. FAX: 306-975-3766. *Res Librn,* Aleksandra Hankey; Staff 1 (Non-MLS 1)
Founded 1974
Library Holdings: Bk Titles 3,500; Per Subs 60
Special Collections: Government Publications; POS Archives
Subject Interests: Food sci
Automation Activity & Vendor Info: (Acquisitions) Inmagic, Inc.; (Cataloging) Inmagic, Inc.; (Circulation) Inmagic, Inc.; (Course Reserve) Inmagic, Inc.; (ILL) Inmagic, Inc.; (Media Booking) Inmagic, Inc.; (OPAC) Inmagic, Inc.; (Serials) Inmagic, Inc.
Database Vendor: Dialog
Publications: Exposure; POSabilities; Processing Profile
Restriction: Open to pub upon request

S   POTASH CORPORATION OF SASKATCHEWAN INC*, Library Services, 122 First Ave S, Ste 500, S7K 7G3. SAN 321-5113. Tel: 306-933-8501. Web Site: www.potashcorp.com. *Coordr,* Dee Neufeld
Founded 1979
Library Holdings: Bk Titles 5,000; Bk Vols 5,500; Per Subs 350
Special Collections: PCS Clipping File (Historical)
Subject Interests: Agr, Chem, Fertilizers, Geol, Law, Mining, Mkt, Transportation
Restriction: Staff use only

S   S E D SYSTEMS, INC LIBRARY*, 18 Innovation Blvd, S7K 3P7. (Mail add: PO Box 1464, S7K 3P7), SAN 320-0108. Tel: 306-931-3425. FAX: 306-933-1486. *Librn,* Shelley Davis; E-mail: davis@sedsystems.ca
Founded 1968
Library Holdings: Bk Titles 1,500; Per Subs 50
Subject Interests: Satellite communications, Space systs
Restriction: Open to pub for ref only

R   SAINT ANDREW'S COLLEGE LIBRARY, 1121 College Dr, S7N 0W3. SAN 320-0116. Tel: 306-966-8983. Toll Free Tel: 877-644-8970. FAX: 306-966-8981. E-mail: standrews.library@usask.ca. Web Site: reindex.net/STU. *Head Librn, Saskatoon Theol Union Libr,* Sarah Benson; *Libr Tech,* Mallory Wiebe; Staff 1.26 (MLS 0.26, Non-MLS 1)
Founded 1913. Enrl 60; Highest Degree: Master
Library Holdings: Bk Titles 36,000; Per Subs 134
Subject Interests: Church hist, Soc issues, Theol, Women's studies
Open Mon-Fri 8:30-4:30

M   ST PAUL'S HOSPITAL OF SASKATOON, Medical Library, 1702 20th St W, S7M 0Z9. SAN 321-6780. Tel: 306-655-5224. FAX: 306-655-5209. *Libr Tech,* Colleen Haichert; E-mail: colleen.haichert@saskatoonhealthregion.ca
Founded 1960
Library Holdings: Bk Titles 300; Per Subs 100
Database Vendor: OVID Technologies
Restriction: Staff use only

C   SAINT THOMAS MORE COLLEGE-UNIVERSITY OF SASKATCHEWAN*, Shannon Library, 1437 College Dr, S7N 0W6. SAN 320-0124. Tel: 306-966-8916. FAX: 306-966-8909. Web Site: www.stmcollege.ca. *Dir,* Dr Donna Brockmeyer; Tel: 306-966-8962, E-mail: donna.brockmeyer@usask.ca; Staff 2 (MLS 1, Non-MLS 1)
Founded 1936. Fac 35; Highest Degree: Bachelor
Library Holdings: Bk Titles 45,000; Bk Vols 55,000; Per Subs 150
Special Collections: Canadian Catholic Church Coll; Catholic Authors; Elizabethan & Jacobean Studies; St Thomas More
Automation Activity & Vendor Info: (Acquisitions) Innovative Interfaces, Inc; (Cataloging) Innovative Interfaces, Inc; (Circulation) Innovative Interfaces, Inc; (Course Reserve) Innovative Interfaces, Inc; (ILL) Innovative Interfaces, Inc; (Media Booking) Innovative Interfaces, Inc; (OPAC) Innovative Interfaces, Inc; (Serials) Innovative Interfaces, Inc
Publications: Women & The Church
Open Mon-Thurs (Winter) 8:30am-10pm, Fri 8:30-5, Sat 10-5, Sun 12-9; Mon-Fri (Summer) 10-2

S   SASKATCHEWAN INDIAN CULTURAL CENTRE, Library & Information Services, 305 - 2555 Grasswood Rd E, S7T 0K1. SAN 320-0035. Tel: 306-244-1146. FAX: 306-665-6520. E-mail: info@sicc.sk.ca. Web Site: www.sicc.sk.ca. *Libr Tech,* Evelyn Daniels; E-mail: evelyn.daniels@sicc.sk.ca
Founded 1973. Highest Degree: Master

Library Holdings: Bk Titles 8,200; Bk Vols 11,237; Per Subs 28
Subject Interests: Mat on Indian people of N Am
Open Mon-Thurs 8:30-5, Fri 8:30-4

S   SASKATCHEWAN TEACHERS' FEDERATION*, Stewart Resource Centre, 2317 Arlington Ave, S7J 2H8. SAN 320-0140. Tel: 306-373-1660. FAX: 306-374-1122. E-mail: src@stf.sk.ca. Web Site: www.stf.sk.ca. *Librn,* Joan Elliott; Staff 5 (MLS 2, Non-MLS 3)
Founded 1970
Library Holdings: Bk Titles 22,000; Per Subs 250
Subject Interests: Econ, Educ, Psychol
Database Vendor: EBSCOhost
Open Mon-Fri 8:30-5

P   SASKATOON PUBLIC LIBRARY*, Frances Morrison Library, 311-23rd St E, S7K 0J6. SAN 369-660X. Tel: 306-975-7558. Interlibrary Loan Service Tel: 306-975-7561. Administration Tel: 306-975-7630. Information Services Tel: 306-975-7555. FAX: 306-975-7542. Information Services FAX: 306-975-7521. Web Site: www.saskatoonlibrary.ca. *Dir,* Zenon Zuzak; Tel: 306-975-7575, E-mail: z.zuzak@saskatoonlibrary.ca; *Dep Dir, Planning & Support Serv,* Ann-Marie Mathieu; Tel: 306-975-7586, E-mail: a.matheiu@saskatoonlibrary.ca; *Commun Relations Librn,* Carol Johner; Tel: 306-975-7530, E-mail: c.johner@saskatoonlibrary.ca; *Mgr, Adult & Info Serv,* Gwen Thomson; Tel: 306-975-7564, E-mail: g.thomson@saskatoonlibrary.ca; *Br Pub Serv Mgr,* Jannay Thiessen; Tel: 306-975-8131, E-mail: j.thiessen@saskatoonlibrary.ca; *Cent Libr Serv Mgr,* Trudy Harder; Tel: 306-975-7567, E-mail: t.harder@saskatoonlibrary.ca; *Info Tech Serv Mgr,* Bryan McCabe; Tel: 306-975-8136, E-mail: b.mccabe@saskatoonlibrary.ca; *Coordr, Outreach Serv,* Gwen Schmidt; Tel: 306-975-7606, E-mail: g.schmidt@saskatoonlibrary.ca; Staff 132 (MLS 37, Non-MLS 95)
Founded 1913. Pop 206,800; Circ 4,028,803
Library Holdings: Bk Vols 845,927; Per Subs 1,200
Special Collections: Canada Coll; Historical Children's Coll; Local History, bks, micro, pamphlets
Subject Interests: Performing arts
Automation Activity & Vendor Info: (Acquisitions) Innovative Interfaces, Inc - Millenium; (Cataloging) Innovative Interfaces, Inc - Millenium; (Circulation) Innovative Interfaces, Inc - Millenium; (OPAC) Innovative Interfaces, Inc - Millenium; (Serials) Innovative Interfaces, Inc - Millenium
Database Vendor: ALLDATA Online, Bowker, CEDROM-SNi, EBSCOhost, Gale Cengage Learning, Overdrive, Inc, ProQuest, TumbleBookLibrary, World Book Online
Wireless access
Function: Wheelchair accessible
Publications: Annual Report; Programme brochures
Partic in Saskatchewan Information & Library Services (SILS)
Special Services for the Blind - Assistive/Adapted tech devices, equip & products; Daisy reader; Newsp reading serv; Talking bks
Open Mon-Thurs 10-9, Fri & Sat 10-6, Sun (Sept-May) 1-5:30
Friends of the Library Group
Branches: 6
CARLYLE KING BRANCH, Cosmo Civic Centre, 3130 Laurier Dr, S7L 5J7, SAN 369-6634. Tel: 306-975-7592. FAX: 306-975-7588. *Br Head,* Barbara Palmer; Tel: 306-975-7595, E-mail: b.palmer@saskatoonlibrary.ca
Open Mon 1-9, Tues-Fri 10-9, Sat 10-6, Sun (Sept-May) 1-5:30
Friends of the Library Group
RUSTY MACDONALD BRANCH, 225 Primrose Dr, S7K 5E4, SAN 378-1933. Tel: 306-975-7600. FAX: 306-975-7603. *Br Head,* Rochelle Raeber; Tel: 306-975-7605
Open Mon-Fri 10-9, Sat 10-6, Sun (Sept-May) 1-5:30
Friends of the Library Group
MAYFAIR BRANCH, 602 33rd St W, S7L 0W1, SAN 369-6642. Tel: 306-975-7591. *Supvr,* Lisa Fortier; Tel: 306-975-7749, E-mail: l.fortier@saskatoonlibrary.ca
Open Tues & Thurs 1-9, Wed & Sat 1-5, Fri 1-6, Sun (Sept-May) 1-5:30
Friends of the Library Group
ALICE TURNER BRANCH, 110 Nelson Rd, S7S 1K7, SAN 378-195X. Tel: 306-975-8127. FAX: 306-975-8130. *Librn,* Ann Foster; E-mail: a.foster@saskatoonlibrary.ca
Open Mon-Wed 10-9, Thurs-Sat 10-6, Sun (Sept-May) 1-5:30
Friends of the Library Group
J S WOOD BRANCH, 1801 Lansdowne Ave, S7H 2C4, SAN 369-6669. Tel: 306-975-7590. FAX: 306-975-7636. *Br Head,* Patricia Caldwell; Tel: 306-975-7595
Open Mon-Fri 1-9, Sat 10-6, Sun (Sept-May) 1-5:30
Friends of the Library Group
CLIFF WRIGHT BRANCH, Lakewood Civic Center, 1635 McKercher Dr, S7H 5J9, SAN 328-7157. Tel: 306-975-7550. FAX: 306-975-7632. *Br Head,* Patricia Caldwell; Tel: 306-975-7545
Open Mon-Fri 10-9, Sat 10-6, Sun (Sept-May) 1-5:30
Friends of the Library Group

C   SIAST-SASKATCHEWAN INSTITUTE OF APPLIED SCIENCE & TECHNOLOGY*, SIAST Kelsey Campus Library, ldylwyld Dr & 33rd St W, S7K 3R5. (Mail add: PO Box 1520, S7K 3R5). Tel: 306-659-4040. Interlibrary Loan Service Tel: 306-659-4167. FAX: 306-964-1222. Web Site: www.siast.sk.ca/libraries. *Head Librn,* Fabian Harrison; Tel: 306-659-4240, E-mail: harrisonf@siast.sk.ca; *ILL,* Fern Cruickshank; E-mail: fern.cruickshank@siast.sk.ca; Staff 12 (MLS 2, Non-MLS 10) Founded 1963. Enrl 10,444; Fac 320; Highest Degree: Associate
Library Holdings: High Interest/Low Vocabulary Bk Vols 25; Bk Titles 19,000; Bk Vols 30,000; Per Subs 550; Videos 5,000
Subject Interests: Adult basic educ, Natural sci, Nursing, Technologies, Trades
Automation Activity & Vendor Info: (Acquisitions) SirsiDynix; (Cataloging) SirsiDynix; (Circulation) SirsiDynix; (Media Booking) SirsiDynix; (OPAC) SirsiDynix; (Serials) SirsiDynix
Database Vendor: EBSCOhost, Gale Cengage Learning, OCLC FirstSearch, OCLC WorldCat, OVID Technologies, ProQuest, SerialsSolutions
Open Mon-Thurs (Sept-June) 7:30am-9pm, Fri 7:30-5, Sat & Sun 10-5; Mon-Fri (July-Aug) 8-4:30

P   UKRAINIAN CANADIAN CONGRESS - SASKATCHEWAN PROVINCIAL COUNCIL INC*, Library Resource Centre, 4-2345 Avenue C N, S7L 5Z5. SAN 374-7611. Tel: 306-652-5850. Toll Free Tel: 888-652-5850. FAX: 306-665-2127. E-mail: uccspc@ucc.sk.ca. Web Site: www.ucc.sk.ca. *Exec Dir,* Danylo Puderak
Founded 1971
Library Holdings: Bk Vols 1,800
Function: Photocopying/Printing, Scanner
Open Mon-Fri 10-5
Restriction: Not a lending libr

S   UKRAINIAN MUSEUM OF CANADA LIBRARY*, 910 Spadina Crescent E, S7K 3H5. SAN 326-7423. Tel: 306-244-3800. FAX: 306-652-7620. Web Site: www.umc.sk.ca. *Dir,* Janet Danyliuk
Founded 1936
Library Holdings: Bk Titles 11,000; Bk Vols 12,000
Special Collections: History & Ethnography (Save The Ukrainian Canadian Heritage Coll), three dimensional, print, photogs, oral hist, archival mats
Subject Interests: Lit
Publications: Embroidery Designs & Stitches; Heritage Patterns; Museum News; Pysanka Kit; Pysanka: Icon of the Universe; Saskatchewan's Ukrainian historic sites along the Yellowhead route; Ukrainian Historic Sites of Central Saskatchewan: Travel Guide
Restriction: Open by appt only
Friends of the Library Group

C   UNIVERSITY OF SASKATCHEWAN LIBRARIES, Murray Library, Three Campus Dr, S7N 5A4. SAN 369-6693. Tel: 306-966-6005. Interlibrary Loan Service Tel: 306-966-6002. FAX: 306-966-6040. E-mail: uaskref@library.usask.ca. Web Site: library.usask.ca. *Dean of Libr,* Vicki Williamson; Tel: 306-966-5942; *Assoc Dean of Libr,* Ken Ladd; Tel: 306-966-5946; *Asst Dean,* Jill Crawley-Low; Tel: 306-966-7425; Staff 143 (MLS 37, Non-MLS 106)
Founded 1912. Highest Degree: Doctorate
May 2007-Apr 2008. Mats Exp (CAN) $8,643,653, Books (CAN) $2,152,080, Per/Ser (Incl. Access Fees) (CAN) $6,418,080, Presv (CAN) $73,493. Sal (CAN) $8,586,790 (Prof (CAN) $3,090,675)
Library Holdings: Audiobooks 103,847; e-journals 34,886; Bk Titles 1,548,869; Bk Vols 2,418,869; Per Subs 50,135
Special Collections: Canadiana (Shortt Coll); Conrad Aiken; Sorokin
Subject Interests: Agr, Humanities, Law, Med, Soc sci, Veterinary
Automation Activity & Vendor Info: (Acquisitions) Innovative Interfaces, Inc; (Cataloging) Innovative Interfaces, Inc; (Circulation) Innovative Interfaces, Inc; (Course Reserve) Innovative Interfaces, Inc
Database Vendor: EBSCOhost, OCLC FirstSearch
Wireless access
Partic in Association of Research Libraries (ARL); Canadian Association of Research Libraries
Open Tues-Fri 8-6, Sat & Sun 12-5
Departmental Libraries:
EDUCATION, Education Bldg, Rm 2003, 28 Campus Dr, S7N 0X1. Tel: 306-966-5973. FAX: 306-966-2444. Web Site: library.usask.ca/education. *Head Librn,* L Currie
   Library Holdings: Bk Vols 22,000
   Special Collections: Professional & Curriculum Materials, multi-media
ENGINEERING, 1B08 Engineering Bldg, 57 Campus Dr, S7N 5A9, SAN 369-6758. Tel: 306-966-5976. FAX: 306-966-1352. E-mail: uaskengi@library.usask.ca. Web Site: library.usask.ca/engineering. *Librn,* Lyn Currie; Tel: 306-966-5978; Staff 4.5 (MLS 1, Non-MLS 3.5)
   Library Holdings: Audiobooks 3,066; Bk Vols 61,873
   Open Tues-Fri 8-6, Sat & Sun 12-5

HEALTH SCIENCES, Health Sciences Bldg, Rm B-205, 107 Wiggins Rd, S7N 5E5, SAN 369-6847. Tel: 306-966-5991. FAX: 306-966-5918. E-mail: uaskhsl@library.usask.ca. Web Site: library.usask.ca/hsl. *Head Librn,* Susan Murphy
   Library Holdings: AV Mats 11,206; e-journals 5,050; Bk Titles 48,943; Bk Vols 166,060; Per Subs 5,739
   Subject Interests: Dentistry, Med, Nursing
   Open Tues & Thurs 8am-10pm, Fri 8-6, Sat 10-6, Sun 12-8

CL   LAW, Law Bldg, Rm 8, 15 Campus Dr, S7N 5A6, SAN 369-6812. Tel: 306-966-5999, 306-966-6053. FAX: 306-966-6162. E-mail: uasklaw@library.usask.ca. Web Site: library.usask.ca/law. *Librn,* Greg Wurzer
   Library Holdings: AV Mats 793; e-journals 1,549; Bk Titles 42,766; Bk Vols 167,488; Per Subs 2,134
   Automation Activity & Vendor Info: (OPAC) Innovative Interfaces, Inc
   Database Vendor: LexisNexis, Westlaw
   Open Tues-Thurs 8-4:30, Fri 8-4
NATURAL SCIENCES LIBRARY, 180 Geology Bldg, 114 Science Pl, S7N 5E2, SAN 369-6782. Tel: 306-966-6047. FAX: 306-966-1911. E-mail: uasksci@library.usask.ca. *Head Librn,* Lyn Currie; Tel: 306-966-6049, Fax: 306-966-6040
   Library Holdings: AV Mats 240; Bk Vols 168,878
   Subject Interests: Chem, Chem eng, Geol, Nutrition, Physics
   Open Tues-Fri 8:30-4:30

CM   WESTERN COLLEGE OF VETERINARY MEDICINE, WCVM Bldg, Rm 3110, 52 Campus Dr, S7N 5B4, SAN 369-6936. Tel: 306-966-7205. FAX: 306-966-7207. E-mail: uaskvet@library.usask.ca. Web Site: library.usask.ca/vetmed. *Librn,* Christine Neilson; Staff 1 (MLS 1)
   Founded 1969. Highest Degree: Doctorate
   Library Holdings: AV Mats 84; Bk Vols 42,221
   Subject Interests: Med, Veterinary med
   Open Tues-Fri 8-4

S   WESTERN DEVELOPMENT MUSEUM*, George Shepherd Library, 2935 Melville St, S7J 5A6. SAN 324-6175. Tel: 306-934-1400. FAX: 306-934-4467. E-mail: info@wdm.ca. Web Site: www.wdm.ca. *Curator,* Warren Clubb; Tel: 306-934-1400, Ext 228, E-mail: wclubb@wdm.ca; Staff 1 (Non-MLS 1)
Founded 1972
Library Holdings: AV Mats 10,000; Bk Titles 3,500; Bk Vols 10,000; Per Subs 25
Special Collections: Agricultural Machinery Catalogue Coll
Subject Interests: Agr, Transportation, Western Can hist
Automation Activity & Vendor Info: (Cataloging) LibraryWorld, Inc; (OPAC) LibraryWorld, Inc
Function: Res libr
Restriction: Non-circulating, Open by appt only

STANLEY MISSION

P   KEETHANOW PUBLIC LIBRARY*, PO Box 70, S0J 2P0. Tel: 306-635-2104. FAX: 306-635-2050. *Librn,* Lucy Ratt; E-mail: l.ratt.ssk@pnls.lib.sk.ca
Library Holdings: DVDs 55; Bk Vols 8,000; Per Subs 9; Videos 100
Mem of Pahkisimon Nuye?ah Library System
Open Mon, Tues & Thurs 8:30-12, 1-5 & 7pm-9pm, Fri 8:30-12 & 1-5

SWIFT CURRENT

G   AGRICULTURE & AGRI-FOOD CANADA*, Semiarid Prairie Agricultural Research Centre Library, One Airport Rd, S9H 3X2. (Mail add: PO Box 1030, S9H 3X2), SAN 320-0191. Tel: 306-778-7260. FAX: 306-778-3188. *Librn,* Aidan Beaubier; E-mail: aidan.beaubier@agr.gc.ca
Library Holdings: Bk Vols 15,500
Subject Interests: Agr, Agr eng, Agrometeorology, Animal husbandry, Botany, Chem, Dryland farming systems, Soil sci
Partic in Consortium of Fed Librs
Restriction: Not open to pub

P   CHINOOK REGIONAL LIBRARY*, 1240 Chaplin St W, S9H 0G8. SAN 320-0205. Tel: 306-773-3186. FAX: 306-773-0434. E-mail: chinook@chinook.lib.sk.ca. Web Site: www.chinooklibrary.ca. *Dir,* Heather Walker; E-mail: hwalker@chinook.lib.sk.ca; *Automation Supvr,* Lynette Butts; E-mail: butts@chinook.lib.sk.ca; *Circ Supvr,* Doreen Roberts; E-mail: droberts@chinook.lib.sk.ca; *Coll Coordr,* Nora Honsey; E-mail: nhonsey@chinook.lib.sk.ca; *Acq,* Judy Mauer; E-mail: jmauer@chinook.lib.sk.ca; *ILL,* Wendy Muri
Founded 1971. Pop 53,000; Circ 313,589
Library Holdings: Audiobooks 675; Bk Vols 158,707; Videos 662
Automation Activity & Vendor Info: (Acquisitions) Innovative Interfaces, Inc - Millenium; (Cataloging) Innovative Interfaces, Inc - Millenium; (Circulation) Innovative Interfaces, Inc - Millenium; (OPAC) Innovative Interfaces, Inc - Millenium
Database Vendor: Gale Cengage Learning, ProQuest, SirsiDynix
Open Mon-Fri 8-12 & 1-5

Branches: 33

ABBEY BRANCH, 133 Main St, Abbey, S0N 0A0. (Mail add: PO Box 185, Abbey, S0N 0A0). Tel: 306-689-2202. E-mail: abbey@chinook.lib.sk.ca. *Librn,* Marilyn Turgeon; *Asst Librn,* Linda Haggart; *Asst Librn,* Mary Main
Founded 1971
Open Mon (Winter) 4pm-9pm, Wed 6pm-9pm, Fri 12-5; Mon (Summer) 12-5, Wed 6pm-9pm

BURSTALL BRANCH, Martin St & Hamilton Ave, Burstall, S0N 0H0. (Mail add: PO Box 309, Burstall, S0N 0H0). Tel: 306-679-2177. E-mail: burstall@chinook.lib.sk.ca. *Librn,* Karen Dieterle; *Asst Librn,* Cindy Ressler
Founded 1979
Open Mon & Wed 1-5 & 7pm-9pm, Thurs 2-5

CABRI BRANCH, PO Box 18, Cabri, S0N 0J0. Tel: 306-587-2911. E-mail: cabri@chinook.lib.sk.ca. *Librn,* Joy Handwork; *Asst Librn,* Heather Arnelien
Founded 1971
Open Mon, Wed & Fri 1-5

CENTRAL BUTTE BRANCH, Box 276, Central Butte, S0H 0T0. Tel: 306-796-4660. E-mail: centralbutte@chinook.lib.sk.ca. *Librn,* Sandra Yonge; *Asst Librn,* Ann Lloyd
Founded 1972
Open Tues 9:30-2, Wed 5pm-9pm, Fri 2-6

CHAPLIN BRANCH, Second Ave Hall Complex, Chaplin, S0H 0V0. (Mail add: PO Box 225, Chaplin, S0H 0V0). Tel: 306-395-2524. E-mail: chaplin@chinook.lib.sk.ca. *Librn,* Gayla Gane; *Asst Librn,* Geri Ball; *Asst Librn,* Nadin Blaczczok
Founded 1973
Open Mon & Wed 2-7, Fri 9-Noon

CLIMAX BRANCH, PO Box 323, Climax, S0N 0N0. Tel: 306-293-2229. E-mail: climax@chinook.lib.sk.ca. *Librn,* Nancy Glenn; *Asst Librn,* Lorna Smith
Founded 1974
Open Tues & Fri 1-6

CONSUL BRANCH, PO Box 121, Consul, S0N 0P0. Tel: 306-299-2118. E-mail: consul@chinook.lib.sk.ca. *Librn,* Linda Brown; *Asst Librn,* Dennetta Warberg
Founded 1972
Open Mon & Wed 1-4, Fri 9-12

EASTEND BRANCH, Eastend Memorial Hall, Eastend, S0N 0T0. (Mail add: PO Box 91, Eastend, S0N 0T0). Tel: 306-295-3788. E-mail: eastend@chinook.lib.sk.ca. *Librn,* Lorraine Armstrong; *Asst Librn,* Gail Bock; *Asst Librn,* Denise Gebhardt
Founded 1971
Open Tues (Summer) 12:30-4:30, Wed & Sat 1:30-4:30, Thurs 6pm-9pm; Tues (Winter) 12:30-4:30, Wed, Thurs & Sat 1:30-4:30

FOX VALLEY BRANCH, 85 Centre St E, Fox Valley, S0N 0V0. (Mail add: PO Box 145, Fox Valley, S0N 0V0). Tel: 306-666-2045. E-mail: foxvalley@chinook.lib.sk.ca. *Librn,* Valerie Reinboldt; *Asst Librn,* Rebecca Hudec
Founded 1974
Open Tues & Fri (Winter) 12-4:30, Wed 6:30pm-9:30pm; Tues (Summer) 12-4:30, Wed 6:30pm-9:30pm

FRONTIER BRANCH, First St W, Frontier, S0N 0W0. (Mail add: Box 269, Frontier, S0N 0W0). Tel: 306-296-4667. E-mail: frontier@chinook.lib.sk.ca. *Librn,* Holly Johnson; *Asst Librn,* Marilyn Nelson; *Asst Librn,* Janet Wilkinson
Founded 1971
Open Wed 12:30-4:30, Thurs 12-3 & 6pm-9pm

GLENTWORTH BRANCH, Glentworth School, Glentworth, S0H 1V0. (Mail add: PO Box 209, Glentworth, S0H 1V0). Tel: 306-266-4804. E-mail: glentworth@chinook.lib.sk.ca. *Librn,* Marla Gavelin; *Asst Librn,* Tanya Fehr
Founded 1974
Open Mon-Wed 2-5, Tues 10-3:30, Thurs 10-3:30 & 4-8

GRAVELBOURG BRANCH, Box 568, Gravelbourg, S0H 1X0. Tel: 306-648-3177. E-mail: gravelbourg@chinook.lib.sk.ca. *Librn,* Valarie Alix
Founded 1974
Open Tues & Thurs 12-5, Wed 9:30-11:30 & 12-5

GULL LAKE BRANCH, 1377 Conrad Ave, Gull Lake, S0N 1A0. (Mail add: PO Box 653, Gull Lake, S0N 1A0). Tel: 306-672-3277. E-mail: gulllake@chinook.lib.sk.ca. *Librn,* Sandy Kettner; *Asst Librn,* Lianne LeFaive; *Asst Librn,* Kathy Springer
Founded 1971
Open Mon 10-5, Tues & Thurs 1-8, Wed 1-6, Fri 1-5

HAZLET BRANCH, Railway Ave, Hazlet, S0N 1E0. (Mail add: PO Box 73, Hazlet, S0N 1E0). Tel: 306-678-2155. E-mail: hazlet@chinook.lib.sk.ca. *Librn,* Elaine Little; *Asst Librn,* Noel Anderson
Founded 1974
Open Tues 1:30-6, Thurs 11-4

HERBERT BRANCH, 517 Herbert Ave, Herbert, S0H 2A0. (Mail add: PO Box 176, Herbert, S0H 2A0). Tel: 306-784-2484. E-mail: herbert@chinook.lib.sk.ca. *Librn,* Evelyn Nickel; *Asst Librn,* Heather Meyers
Founded 1972
Open Mon & Wed 6pm-9pm, Tues 1-4:30 & 5-8, Fri 1-4:30, Sat 9-Noon

HODGEVILLE BRANCH, Main St, Hodgeville, S0H 2B0. (Mail add: PO Box 68, Hodgeville, S0H 2B0). Tel: 306-677-2223. E-mail: hodgeville@chinook.lib.sk.ca. *Librn,* Elizabeth Haubrich; *Asst Librn,* Ann Haubrich; *Asst Librn,* Bev Seibel
Founded 1971
Open Tues & Fri 1:15-5:15, Wed 3-7

KINCAID BRANCH, Village Office, Kincaid, S0H 2J0. (Mail add: PO Box 146, Kincaid, S0H 2J0). Tel: 306-264-3910. E-mail: kincaid@chinook.lib.sk.ca. *Librn,* Trudy Turgeon; *Asst Librn,* Debbie Robertson
Founded 1971
Open Mon 9-12, Wed 11-5, Fri 2-5

LAFLECHE BRANCH, 157 Main St, Lafleche, S0H 2K0. (Mail add: PO Box 132, Lafleche, S0H 2K0). Tel: 306-472-5466. E-mail: lafleche@chinook.lib.sk.ca. *Librn,* Gloria McIvor; *Asst Librn,* Anne Sproule
Founded 1975
Open Tues 9:30-2, Wed 4pm-7pm, Thurs 10-1, Fri 2-5

LEADER BRANCH, 151 First St W, Leader, S0N 1H0. (Mail add: Box 40, Leader, S0N 1H0). Tel: 306-628-3830. E-mail: leader@chinook.lib.sk.ca. *Librn,* Lois Smith; *Asst Librn,* Cindy Buscholl; *Asst Librn,* Stephanie Hilger
Founded 1971
Open Mon 1-4 & 5-8, Tues-Thurs 9-12 & 1-5, Fri 9-12 & 1-3

MANKOTA BRANCH, Village Office Complex, First Ave, Mankota, S0H 2W0. (Mail add: PO Box 373, Mankota, S0H 2W0). Tel: 306-478-2401. E-mail: mankota@chinook.lib.sk.ca. *Librn,* Maggie Brown; *Asst Librn,* Cheryl Martin
Founded 1972
Open Tues-Thurs (Winter) 1-5; Mon-Fri (Summer) 1-5

MAPLE CREEK BRANCH, 205 Jasper St, Maple Creek, S0N 1N0. (Mail add: PO Box 760, Maple Creek, S0N 1N0). Tel: 306-662-3522. E-mail: maplecreek@chinook.lib.sk.ca. *Librn,* Ev Southwood; *Asst Librn,* Georgina Kimber
Founded 1971. Pop 3,000; Circ 20,000
Open Mon, Thurs & Sat 1-5, Tues 12-5, Wed 1-5 & 6:30pm-8:30pm, Fri 1-6

MORSE BRANCH, Village Recreational Complex, Main St, Morse, S0H 3C0. (Mail add: PO Box 64, Morse, S0H 3C0). Tel: 306-629-3335. E-mail: morse@chinook.lib.sk.ca. *Librn,* Donna Fafard
Founded 1971
Open Mon 1-4, Tues & Wed 1-5

PENNANT BRANCH, PO Box 10, Pennant, S0N 1X0. Tel: 306-626-3316. E-mail: pennant@chinook.lib.sk.ca. *Librn,* Caralee Laturnus
Founded 1975
Open Tues & Thurs 12:30-5

PONTEIX BRANCH, 130 First Ave E, Ponteix, S0N 1Z0. (Mail add: Box 700, Ponteix, S0N 1Z0). Tel: 306-625-3353. E-mail: ponteix@chinook.lib.sk.ca. *Librn,* Roxanne Bedard
Founded 1971
Open Tues & Thurs 1-5:30, Wed 9:30-11:30, 1-5:30 & 7-8:30

PRELATE BRANCH, Village Office, Main St, Prelate, S0N 2B0. (Mail add: Drawer 40, Prelate, S0N 2B0). Tel: 306-673-2340. E-mail: prelate@chinook.lib.sk.ca. *Librn,* Darlene Wagner
Founded 1972
Open Tues & Thurs 1-4:30, Wed 1:30-4:30

SCEPTRE BRANCH, 128 Kingsway, Sceptre, S0N 2H0. (Mail add: PO Box 128, Sceptre, S0N 2H0). Tel: 306-623-4244. E-mail: sceptre@chinook.lib.sk.ca. *Librn,* Sherry Egeland; *Asst Librn,* Krista Marlin
Founded 1975
Open Tues 1:30-4:30

SHAUNAVON BRANCH, Grand Coteau Heritage & Cultural Ctr, 440 Centre St, Shaunavon, S0N 2M0. (Mail add: PO Box 1116, Shaunavon, S0N 2M0). Tel: 306-297-3844. E-mail: shaunavon@chinook.lib.sk.ca. *Librn,* Ellen Rae Overand; *Asst Librn,* Janice Fischer
Founded 1971
Open Mon, Wed, Fri & Sat 12-5, Tues & Thurs 12-7:30

STEWART VALLEY BRANCH, Box 1, Stewart Valley, S0N 2P0. E-mail: stewartvalley@chinook.lib.sk.ca. *Librn,* Kathy King
Founded 1971
Open Mon 2-5 & 7-9, Fri 2-5

SWIFT CURRENT BRANCH, R C Dahl Ctr, 411 Herbert St E, S9H 1M5. Tel: 306-778-2752. Toll Free Tel: 800-773-5564. FAX: 306-773-8769. *Librn,* Christopher Harrow; E-mail: charrow@chinook.lib.sk.ca
Founded 1971
Function: Photocopying/Printing, Ref serv available
Open Mon-Thurs 9-9, Fri 9-6, Sat 10-5, Sun 1-5

TOMPKINS BRANCH, Main St, Tompkins, S0N 2S0. (Mail add: PO Box 203, Tompkins, S0N 2S0). Tel: 306-622-2255. E-mail: tompkins@chinook.lib.sk.ca. *Librn,* Lynne Baumann; *Asst Librn,* Arlene Willows
Founded 1973
Open Tues & Thurs 9:30-4:30
VAL MARIE BRANCH, Val Marie Village Complex, Val Marie, S0N 2T0. (Mail add: PO Box 93, Val Marie, S0N 2T0). Tel: 306-298-2133. E-mail: valmarie@chinook.lib.sk.ca. *Librn,* Judy Gunter; *Asst Librn,* Marilyn Magee
Founded 1972
Open Tues & Wed 9:30-4
VANGUARD BRANCH, Library/Musem Bldg, Dominion St, Vanguard, S0N 2V0. (Mail add: PO Box 85, Vanguard, S0N 2V0). Tel: 306-582-2244. E-mail: vanguard@chinook.lib.sk.ca. *Librn,* Melanie Clark; *Asst Librn,* Hailey Clark; *Asst Librn,* Kim Rousseaux
Founded 1971
Open Mon (Winter) 12-3, Wed 6pm-9pm, Fri 10-1; Mon (Summer) 12-3, Wed 6pm-9pm, Fri 9-Noon

TURTLEFORD

P   THUNDERCHILD LIBRARY*, Thunderchild First Nation, 1032 100th St, S0M 2Y0. (Mail add: PO Box 600, S0M 2Y0). Tel: 306-845-3779. FAX: 306-845-3866. *Librn,* Bonnie Stone
Library Holdings: Bks on Deafness & Sign Lang 5; CDs 80; DVDs 20; High Interest/Low Vocabulary Bk Vols 100; Bk Titles 5,000; Videos 40
Open Mon-Fri 9-3:30

WEYBURN

P   SOUTHEAST REGIONAL LIBRARY*, 49 Bison Ave, S4H 0H9. SAN 320-0221. Tel: 306-848-3100. Interlibrary Loan Service Tel: 306-848-3106. FAX: 306-842-2665. E-mail: admin@southeast.lib.sk.ca. Interlibrary Loan Service E-mail: ill@southeast.lib.sk.ca. Web Site: www.southeast.lib.sk.ca. *Dir,* Allan R Johnson; Tel: 306-848-3101, E-mail: allan@southeast.lib.sk.ca; *Br Mgr,* James Richards; Tel: 306-848-3102, E-mail: jrichards@southeast.lib.sk.ca; *Syst Mgr,* Susan Atkinson; Tel: 306-848-3104, E-mail: susan@southeast.lib.sk.ca; *Acq,* Patty Clampitt; Tel: 306-848-3107, E-mail: pattyc@southeast.lib.sk.ca; *Cat,* Cindy Bourassa; Tel: 306-848-3108, E-mail: cindy@southeast.lib.sk.ca; Staff 91 (MLS 4, Non-MLS 87)
Founded 1966. Pop 99,500; Circ 400,000
Library Holdings: Audiobooks 1,700; e-books 9,200; Bk Vols 450,000
Automation Activity & Vendor Info: (Acquisitions) SirsiDynix; (Cataloging) SirsiDynix; (Circulation) SirsiDynix; (Course Reserve) SirsiDynix; (ILL) SirsiDynix; (Media Booking) SirsiDynix; (OPAC) SirsiDynix; (Serials) SirsiDynix
Database Vendor: EBSCOhost
Function: Computers for patron use, Distance learning, Homebound delivery serv, ILL available, Ref serv available
Special Services for the Blind - Talking bks
Open Mon-Fri 8-4:30
Branches: 47
ALAMEDA BRANCH, 200-Fifth St, Alameda, S0C 0A0. (Mail add: Box 144, Alameda, S0C 0A0). Tel: 306-489-2066. E-mail: alameda@southeast.lib.sk.ca. *Librn,* Diane Miller
Library Holdings: Bk Vols 7,128
Open Mon, Fri & Sat 1-4:30, Wed 9:30-3
ARCOLA BRANCH, 127 Main St, Arcola, S0C 0G0. (Mail add: Box 389, Arcola, S0C 0G0). Tel: 306-455-2321. E-mail: arcola@southeast.lib.sk.ca. *Librn,* Shauna Daku; *Asst Librn,* Marcie Erick
Library Holdings: Bk Vols 6,000
Function: AV serv, Homebound delivery serv
Special Services for the Blind - Home delivery serv; Large print & cassettes; Talking bks
Open Tues & Thurs 9-1 & 2-5, Wed 3-6
BALGONIE BRANCH, 129 Railway St E, Balgonie, S0G 0E0. (Mail add: PO Box 389, Balgonie, S0G 0E0). Tel: 306-771-2332. E-mail: balgonie@southeast.lib.sk.ca. *Librn,* Donna Jank
Library Holdings: Bk Vols 15,000
Function: AV serv, Homebound delivery serv
Special Services for the Blind - Home delivery serv; Large print & cassettes; Talking bks
Open Mon 1-5, Tues & Thurs 3:30-8:30, Wed 9-12, Fri 1-5
BENGOUGH BRANCH, 301 Main St, Bengough, S0C 0K0. (Mail add: PO Box 71, Bengough, S0C 0K0). Tel: 306-268-2022. E-mail: bengough@southeast.lib.sk.ca. *Librn,* Fay Adam; *Asst Librn,* Kelly Raymond
Library Holdings: Bk Vols 10,000
Function: AV serv, Homebound delivery serv
Special Services for the Blind - Home delivery serv; Large print & cassettes; Talking bks
Open Mon 11-3, Tues 9-Noon, Wed 4-8, Thurs 1-5

BIENFAIT BRANCH, 414 Main St, Bienfait, S0C 0M0. (Mail add: PO Box 520, Bienfait, S0C 0M0). Tel: 306-388-2995. FAX: 306-388-2883. E-mail: bienfait@southeast.lib.sk.ca. *Librn,* Sheila Farstad; *Asst Librn,* Annette Eby
Library Holdings: Bk Vols 8,500
Function: AV serv, Homebound delivery serv
Special Services for the Blind - Home delivery serv; Large print & cassettes; Talking bks
Open Mon 1-6, Tues 3-6, Wed 9-1, Thurs 5-8
BROADVIEW BRANCH, 515 Main St, Broadview, S0G 0K0. (Mail add: Box 590, Broadview, S0G 0K0). Tel: 306-696-2414. E-mail: broadview@southeast.lib.sk.ca. *Librn,* Christine Judy
Library Holdings: Bk Vols 7,000
Function: AV serv, Homebound delivery serv
Special Services for the Blind - Home delivery serv; Large print & cassettes; Talking bks
Open Wed 1:30-7, Fri 11:30-5, Sat 11-3
CARLYLE BRANCH, 119 Souris W, Carlyle, S0C 0R0. (Mail add: PO Box 417, Carlyle, S0C 0R0). Tel: 306-453-6120. FAX: 306-453-6120. E-mail: carlyle@southeast.lib.sk.ca. Web Site: southeast.lib.sk.ca/Southeast/Docs/carlyle.html. *Librn,* Rita Kyle; *Asst Librn,* Carolyn McMillan
Library Holdings: Bk Vols 6,200
Function: AV serv, Homebound delivery serv
Special Services for the Blind - Home delivery serv; Large print & cassettes; Talking bks
Open Tues & Thurs 10-12 & 1-5, Wed 10-1 & 2-6, Sat 12:30-4:30
CARNDUFF BRANCH, 506 Anderson Ave, Carnduff, S0C 0S0. (Mail add: PO Box 6, Carnduff, S0C 0S0). Tel: 306-482-3255. E-mail: carnduff@southeast.lib.sk.ca. *Librn,* Marjorie Johnson
Library Holdings: Bk Vols 9,000
Function: AV serv, Homebound delivery serv
Special Services for the Blind - Home delivery serv; Large print & cassettes; Talking bks
Open Mon, Tues & Thurs 9-12 & 1-6, Wed 9-12 & 1-8, Fri 9-12 & 1-3
ESTEVAN BRANCH, Leisure Ctr, 701 Souris Ave N, Estevan, S4A 2T1. Tel: 306-636-1620, 306-636-1626. FAX: 306-634-5830. E-mail: estevan@southeast.lib.sk.ca. *Librn,* Kate-Lee Donohoe; *Asst Librn,* Barb Dodd; Staff 8 (MLS 1, Non-MLS 7)
Founded 1908. Pop 10,000; Circ 46,000
Library Holdings: Audiobooks 450; Bk Vols 33,000
Special Collections: Can & Prov
Function: AV serv, Homebound delivery serv
Special Services for the Blind - Home delivery serv; Large print & cassettes; Talking bks
Open Mon-Thurs 9-8, Fri & Sat 9:30-6, Sun 1-4
FILLMORE BRANCH, 51 Main St, Fillmore, S0G 1N0. (Mail add: PO Box 68, Fillmore, S0G 1N0). Tel: 306-722-3369. E-mail: fillmore@southeast.lib.sk.ca. *Librn,* Tracy Jones; *Asst Librn,* Courtney Milos
Library Holdings: Bk Vols 9,400
Function: AV serv, Homebound delivery serv
Special Services for the Blind - Home delivery serv; Large print & cassettes; Talking bks
Open Tues 10-12 and 1-5, Wed 2-6
FORT QU'APPELLE BRANCH, 140 Company Ave S, Fort Qu'Appelle, S0G 1S0. (Mail add: PO Box 218, Fort Qu'Appelle, S0G 1S0). Tel: 306-332-6411. E-mail: fort.qu'appelle@southeast.lib.sk.ca. *Librn,* Barb Badiuk; *Asst Librn,* Lois Haug
Library Holdings: Bk Vols 4,700
Function: AV serv, Homebound delivery serv
Special Services for the Blind - Home delivery serv; Large print & cassettes; Talking bks
Open Tues 12:30-6, Wed & Thurs 1:30-7, Fri 9-2, Sat 10:30-4
GAINSBOROUGH BRANCH, 401 Railway Ave, Gainsborough, S0C 0Z0. (Mail add: PO Box 57, Gainsborough, S0C 0Z0). Tel: 306-685-2229. E-mail: gainsborough@southeast.lib.sk.ca. *Librn,* Marjorie Johnson; *Asst Librn,* Marilyn Harder
Library Holdings: Bk Vols 9,000
Function: AV serv, Homebound delivery serv
Special Services for the Blind - Home delivery serv; Large print & cassettes; Talking bks
Open Tues & Wed 9-12, Thurs 2-6
GLENAVON BRANCH, 311 Railway Ave, Glenavon, S0G 1Y0. (Mail add: PO Box 162, Glenavon, S0G 1Y0). Tel: 306-429-2180. E-mail: glenavon@southeast.lib.sk.ca. *Librn,* Sabrina Silversides
Library Holdings: Bk Vols 11,000
Function: AV serv, Homebound delivery serv
Special Services for the Blind - Home delivery serv; Large print & cassettes; Talking bks
Open Tues 1-6, Thurs 11-4
GRENFELL BRANCH, 710 Desmond Ave, Grenfell, S0G 2B0. (Mail add: PO Box 876, Grenfell, S0G 2B0). Tel: 306-697-2455. E-mail: grenfell@southeast.lib.sk.ca. *Librn,* Anne Neuls
Library Holdings: Bk Vols 9,700

Function: AV serv, Homebound delivery serv

Special Services for the Blind - Home delivery serv; Large print & cassettes; Talking bks

Open Tues 9:30-12:30 & 1-6, Thurs 9:30-12:30 & 1-5, Fri 12-5

INDIAN HEAD BRANCH, 419 Grand Ave, Indian Head, S0G 2K0. (Mail add: Box 986, Indian Head, S0G 2K0). Tel: 306-695-3922. E-mail: indian.head@southeast.lib.sk.ca. *Librn,* Colleen Reynard

Library Holdings: Bk Vols 9,405

Open Tues 1-5, Wed 10-12, 1-5 & 6-8, Fri 9:30-12 & 1-5:30, Sat 10-12 & 1-5

KENNEDY BRANCH, 235 Scott St, Kennedy, S0G 2R0. (Mail add: PO Box 217, Kennedy, S0G 2R0). Tel: 306-538-2020. E-mail: kennedy@southeast.lib.sk.ca. *Librn,* Carolyn McMillan

Library Holdings: Bk Vols 6,700

Function: AV serv, Homebound delivery serv

Special Services for the Blind - Home delivery serv; Large print & cassettes; Talking bks

Open Tues 2-7, Fri 9:30-2

KIPLING BRANCH, 207 Sixth Ave, Kipling, S0G 2S0. (Mail add: PO Box 608, Kipling, S0G 2S0). Tel: 306-736-2911. E-mail: kipling@southeast.lib.sk.ca. *Librn,* Sheila Roberton

Library Holdings: Bk Vols 14,000

Function: AV serv, Homebound delivery serv

Special Services for the Blind - Home delivery serv; Large print & cassettes; Talking bks

Open Tues 1-5, Wed 6pm-9pm, Thurs 10:30-3:30 & 6-9, Fri 12:30-5:30

LAKE ALMA BRANCH, Hwy 18, Lake Alma, S0C 1M0. (Mail add: PO Box 216, Lake Alma, S0C 1M0). Tel: 306-447-2061. E-mail: lake.alma@southeast.lib.sk.ca. *Librn,* Bernice Bloor; *Asst Librn,* Jennifer Throssell

Library Holdings: Bk Vols 4,000

Function: AV serv, Homebound delivery serv

Special Services for the Blind - Home delivery serv; Large print & cassettes; Talking bks

Open Tues 3-6, Wed 2-5, Thurs 10-2

LAMPMAN BRANCH, 302 Main St, Lampman, S0C 1N0. (Mail add: PO Box 9, Lampman, S0C 1N0). Tel: 306-487-2202. E-mail: lampman@southeast.lib.sk.ca. *Librn,* Martha Engel

Library Holdings: Bk Vols 6,500

Function: AV serv, Homebound delivery serv

Special Services for the Blind - Home delivery serv; Large print & cassettes; Talking bks

Open Tues 11-2:30 & 3-6:30, Wed & Thurs 9:30-1 & 1:30-5:30

LUMSDEN BRANCH, 20 Third Ave, Lumsden, S0G 3C0. (Mail add: PO Box 496, Lumsden, S0G 3C0). Tel: 306-731-1431. E-mail: lumsden@southeast.lib.sk.ca. *Librn,* Carol Fisher

Library Holdings: Bk Vols 7,000

Function: AV serv, Homebound delivery serv

Special Services for the Blind - Home delivery serv; Large print & cassettes; Talking bks

Open Mon & Wed 3-8, Fri & Sat 10-3

MANOR BRANCH, 23 Main St, Manor, S0C 1R0. (Mail add: PO Box 188, Manor, S0C 1R0). Tel: 306-448-2266. FAX: 306-448-2266. E-mail: manor@southeast.lib.sk.ca. Web Site: www.southeasy.lib.sk.ca. *Librn,* Rita Kyle

Library Holdings: Bk Vols 5,000

Function: AV serv, Homebound delivery serv

Special Services for the Blind - Home delivery serv; Large print & cassettes; Talking bks

Open Mon 10-12 & 2-4, Wed & Fri 12:30-6

MARYFIELD BRANCH, 201 Barrows St, Maryfield, S0G 3K0. (Mail add: Box 160, Maryfield, S0G 3K0). Tel: 306-646-2148. E-mail: maryfield@southeast.lib.sk.ca. *Librn,* Doreen Jurkovic

Library Holdings: Bk Vols 6,000

Function: AV serv, Homebound delivery serv

Special Services for the Blind - Home delivery serv; Large print & cassettes; Talking bks

Open Tues 10-3, Wed 2-7

MIDALE BRANCH, Civic Ctr, 128 Haslem St, Midale, S0C 1S0. (Mail add: PO Box 478, Midale, S0C 1S0). Tel: 306-458-2263. E-mail: midale@southeast.lib.sk.ca. *Head Librn,* Tara-Lee McIndoe

Library Holdings: Bk Vols 7,500

Function: AV serv, Homebound delivery serv

Special Services for the Blind - Home delivery serv; Large print & cassettes; Talking bks

Open Tues 3:30-6, Wed 2-6, Thurs 4-8, Fri 10-2

MILESTONE BRANCH, 112 Main St, Milestone, S0G 3L0. (Mail add: PO Box 549, Milestone, S0G 3L0). Tel: 306-436-2112. E-mail: milestone@southeast.lib.sk.ca. *Librn,* Diana Cook

Library Holdings: Bk Vols 1,000

Function: AV serv, Homebound delivery serv

Special Services for the Blind - Home delivery serv; Large print & cassettes; Talking bks

Open Mon 9-Noon, Wed 2-5 & 6-8, Fri 6-8

MONTMARTRE BRANCH, 136 Central Ave, Montmartre, S0G 3M0. (Mail add: PO Box 360, Montmartre, S0G 3M0). Tel: 306-424-2029. E-mail: montmartre@southeast.lib.sk.ca. *Librn,* Lillian Ripplinger

Library Holdings: Bk Vols 7,500

Function: AV serv, Homebound delivery serv

Special Services for the Blind - Home delivery serv; Large print & cassettes; Talking bks

Open Mon 1-5, Wed 11-12:30 & 1-5:30, Thurs 3-8, Fri 12-5

MOOSOMIN BRANCH, 701 Main St, Moosomin, S0G 3N0. (Mail add: PO Box 845, Moosomin, S0G 3N0). Tel: 306-435-2107. E-mail: moosomin@southeast.lib.sk.ca. *Librn,* Deanne Boast

Library Holdings: Bk Vols 11,000

Function: AV serv, Homebound delivery serv

Special Services for the Blind - Home delivery serv; Large print & cassettes; Talking bks

Open Mon 1-5, Tues, Wed & Fri 9-12 & 1-5, Thurs 12-4 & 5-8

OGEMA BRANCH, 117 Main St, Ogema, S0C 1Y0. (Mail add: PO Box 460, Ogema, S0C 1Y0). Tel: 306-459-2985. E-mail: ogema@southeast.lib.sk.ca. *Librn,* Valerie Dunn

Library Holdings: Bk Vols 9,000

Function: AV serv, Homebound delivery serv

Special Services for the Blind - Home delivery serv; Large print & cassettes; Talking bks

Open Mon 9-1, Tues & Thurs 1:30-7

OUNGRE BRANCH, Lyndale School, Oungre, S0C 1Z0. (Mail add: PO Box 88, Oungre, S0C 1Z0). Tel: 306-456-2662. E-mail: oungre@southeast.lib.sk.ca. *Librn,* Allison Newton

Library Holdings: Bk Vols 8,100

Function: AV serv, Homebound delivery serv

Special Services for the Blind - Home delivery serv; Large print & cassettes; Talking bks

Open Tues & Wed 10-3

OXBOW BRANCH, 516 Prospect Ave, Oxbow, S0C 2B0. (Mail add: PO Box 387, Oxbow, S0C 2B0). Tel: 306-483-5175. E-mail: oxbow@southeast.lib.sk.ca. *Librn,* Shirley Berntson

Library Holdings: Audiobooks 250; AV Mats 25; Bk Vols 8,100; Per Subs 14

Function: AV serv, Homebound delivery serv

Special Services for the Blind - Home delivery serv; Large print & cassettes; Talking bks

Open Tues 2-5, Wed 2-7, Thurs 9:30-2:30, Fri & Sat 1:30-5

PANGMAN BRANCH, 120 Mergens St, Pangman, S0C 2C0. (Mail add: PO Box 113, Pangman, S0C 2C0). Tel: 306-442-2119. E-mail: pangman@southeast.lib.sk.ca. *Librn,* Carol Colbow

Library Holdings: Bk Vols 6,200

Function: AV serv, Homebound delivery serv

Special Services for the Blind - Home delivery serv; Large print & cassettes; Talking bks

Open Tues 9-12 & 2-5, Fri 2-6

PILOT BUTTE BRANCH, Third St & Second Ave, Pilot Butte, S0G 3Z0. (Mail add: PO Box 668, Pilot Butte, S0G 3Z0). Tel: 306-781-3403. E-mail: pilot.butte@southeast.lib.sk.ca. *Librn,* Connie LaRonge-Mohr

Library Holdings: Bk Vols 3,500

Function: AV serv, Homebound delivery serv

Special Services for the Blind - Home delivery serv; Large print & cassettes; Talking bks

Open Tues 1:30-4:30 & 5-8, Wed 9-12 & 1-5, Thurs 12:30-4:30 & 5-8, Fri 12:30-5:30

QU'APPELLE BRANCH, Town Hall, 25-9th Ave, Qu'Appelle, S0G 4A0. (Mail add: PO Box 450, Qu'Appelle, S0G 4A0). Tel: 306-699-2902. FAX: 306-699-2306. E-mail: quappelle@southeast.lib.sk.ca. *Br Librn,* Elizabeth Fries

Library Holdings: Audiobooks 200; Bk Vols 4,000

Function: AV serv, Homebound delivery serv

Special Services for the Blind - Home delivery serv; Large print & cassettes; Talking bks

Open Wed 2-5 & 6-8, Thurs 1-5, Fri 10-12 & 1-5

RADVILLE BRANCH, 420 Floren St, Radville, S0C 2G0. (Mail add: PO Box 791, Radville, S0C 2G0). Tel: 306-869-2742. E-mail: radville@southeast.lib.sk.ca. *Librn,* Erin Nordin

Library Holdings: Bk Vols 10,500

Function: AV serv, Homebound delivery serv

Special Services for the Blind - Home delivery serv; Large print & cassettes; Talking bks

Open Tues & Fri 10-1, Wed 3-8, Thurs 2-6

REDVERS BRANCH, 23B Railway Ave, Redvers, S0C 2H0. (Mail add: PO Box 392, Redvers, S0C 2H0). Tel: 306-452-3255. E-mail: redvers@southeast.lib.sk.ca. *Librn,* Windell Seargeant

Library Holdings: Bk Vols 2,000

Function: AV serv, Homebound delivery serv

Open Tues & Thurs 9:30-12 & 12:30-5:30, Wed 3-8, Fri 10-3

REGINA BEACH BRANCH, 133 Donovel Crescent, Regina Beach, S0G 4C0. (Mail add: Box 10, Regina Beach, S0G 4C0). Tel: 306-729-2062. E-mail: regina.beach@southeast.lib.sk.ca. *Librn,* Lorie Gejdos

Library Holdings: Bk Vols 8,500

Function: AV serv, Homebound delivery serv

Special Services for the Blind - Home delivery serv; Large print & cassettes; Talking bks

Open Tues & Thurs 3-8, Fri & Sat 10-2

ROCANVILLE BRANCH, 218 Ellice St, Rocanville, S0A 3L0. (Mail add: PO Box 263, Rocanville, S0A 3L0). Tel: 306-645-2088. E-mail: rocanville@southeast.lib.sk.ca. *Librn,* Carol Greening

Library Holdings: Bk Vols 9,000

Function: AV serv, Homebound delivery serv

Special Services for the Blind - Home delivery serv; Large print & cassettes; Talking bks

Open Tues & Thurs 1:30-5, Wed 9-12 & 1:30-6:30

SEDLEY BRANCH, 224 Broadway Ave, Sedley, S0G 4K0. (Mail add: PO Box 231, Sedley, S0G 4K0). Tel: 306-885-4505. FAX: 306-885-4506. E-mail: sedley@southeast.lib.sk.ca. *Librn,* Julie Lapointe

Library Holdings: Bk Vols 7,300

Function: AV serv, Homebound delivery serv

Special Services for the Blind - Home delivery serv; Large print & cassettes; Talking bks

Open Mon 10-1, Tues & Thurs 4:30-8

STOUGHTON BRANCH, 232 Main St, Stoughton, S0G 4T0. (Mail add: PO Box 595, Stoughton, S0G 4T0). Tel: 306-457-2484. E-mail: stoughton@southeast.lib.sk.ca. *Librn,* Laura Sabados

Library Holdings: Bk Vols 7,000

Function: AV serv, Computers for patron use, Homebound delivery serv

Special Services for the Blind - Home delivery serv; Large print & cassettes; Talking bks

Open Tues 3:30-8, Wed 1:30-5:30, Thurs 10-1 & 1:30-5:30, Sat 10-2

VIBANK BRANCH, 101 Second Ave, Vibank, S0G 4Y0. (Mail add: PO Box 241, Vibank, S0G 4Y0). Tel: 306-762-2270. E-mail: vibank@southeast.lib.sk.ca. *Br Librn,* Betty Kuntz

Library Holdings: Bk Vols 11,000

Function: AV serv, Homebound delivery serv

Special Services for the Blind - Home delivery serv; Large print & cassettes; Talking bks

Open Mon 1-4:30, Wed 5-8, Fri 9-12:30

WAPELLA BRANCH, 519 S Railway St, Wapella, S0G 4Z0. (Mail add: PO Box 130, Wapella, S0G 4Z0). Tel: 306-532-4419. E-mail: wapella@southeast.lib.sk.ca. *Librn,* Sharon Matheson

Library Holdings: Bk Vols 3,500

Function: AV serv, Homebound delivery serv

Special Services for the Blind - Home delivery serv; Large print & cassettes; Talking bks

Open Tues & Thurs 3-6:30, Wed 9-Noon

WAWOTA BRANCH, 308 Railway Ave, Wawota, S0G 5A0. (Mail add: PO Box 65, Wawota, S0G 5A0). Tel: 306-739-2375. E-mail: wawota@southeast.lib.sk.ca. *Librn,* Sylvia Jewkes

Library Holdings: Bk Vols 10,000

Function: AV serv, Homebound delivery serv

Special Services for the Blind - Home delivery serv; Large print & cassettes; Talking bks

Open Tues 10-12 & 1-5, Wed 1:30-5:30, Thurs 3-8

WEYBURN BRANCH, 45 Bison Ave NE, S4H 0H9. Tel: 306-842-4352, 306-848-3950. FAX: 306-842-1255. E-mail: weyburn@southeast.lib.sk.ca. *Librn,* Kam Teo; Staff 5 (MLS 1, Non-MLS 4)

Pop 10,000

Library Holdings: CDs 200; DVDs 100; Bk Vols 40,000

Function: AV serv, Homebound delivery serv

Special Services for the Blind - Home delivery serv; Large print & cassettes; Talking bks

Open Mon-Thurs 9:30-8:30, Fri & Sat 9:30-6, Sun 1-5

WHITE CITY BRANCH, Community Ctr, 12 Ramm Ave, White City, S4L 5B1. (Mail add: PO Box 308, White City, S0G 5B0). Tel: 306-781-2118. E-mail: white.city@southeast.lib.sk.ca. *Librn,* Lori-Lee Harris

Library Holdings: Bk Vols 9,300

Function: AV serv, Homebound delivery serv

Special Services for the Blind - Home delivery serv; Large print & cassettes; Talking bks

Open Mon & Wed 5pm-9pm, Tues 1-5:30 & 6-9, Fri 9-1:30

WHITEWOOD BRANCH, 731 Lalonde St, Whitewood, S0G 5C0. (Mail add: PO Box 488, Whitewood, S0G 5C0). Tel: 306-735-4233. FAX: 306-735-4233. E-mail: whitewood@southeast.lib.sk.ca. *Librn,* Irene Blyth; *Asst Librn,* Valerie Kitzul

Library Holdings: Bk Vols 5,000

Function: AV serv, Homebound delivery serv

Special Services for the Blind - Home delivery serv; Large print & cassettes; Talking bks

Open Tues 10-1 & 2-5, Thurs 10:30-1:30 & 2:30-6, Fri 12:30-4

WINDTHORST BRANCH, 202 Angus St, Windthorst, S0G 5G0. (Mail add: Box 220, Windthorst, S0G 5G0). Tel: 306-224-2159. E-mail: windthorst@southeast.lib.sk.ca. *Librn,* Jill Taylor

Library Holdings: Bk Vols 6,000

Function: AV serv, Homebound delivery serv

Special Services for the Blind - Home delivery serv; Large print & cassettes; Talking bks

Open Tues & Wed 5-8, Thurs 10:30-12:30 & 1-5

WOLSELEY BRANCH, 500 Front St, Wolseley, S0G 5H0. (Mail add: Box 398, Wolseley, S0G 5H0). Tel: 306-698-2221. E-mail: wolseley@southeast.lib.sk.ca. *Librn,* Sharon Jeeves

Library Holdings: Bk Vols 3,000

Function: AV serv, Homebound delivery serv

Special Services for the Blind - Home delivery serv; Large print & cassettes; Talking bks

Open Tues 10:30-2:30 & 3:30-6:30, Wed 2-5, Fri 11-4

YELLOW GRASS BRANCH, 213 Souris St, Yellow Grass, S0G 5J0. (Mail add: PO Box 381, Yellow Grass, S0G 5J0). Tel: 306-465-2574. E-mail: yellow.grass@southeast.lib.sk.ca. *Librn,* Betty Guest

Library Holdings: Bk Vols 9,000

Function: AV serv, Homebound delivery serv

Special Services for the Blind - Home delivery serv; Large print & cassettes; Talking bks

Open Mon 3:30-6:30, Wed 3-7, Fri 9-Noon

M   TATAGWA VIEW*, Medical Library, 808 Souris Valley Rd, S4H 2Z9. SAN 320-0213. Tel: 306-842-8398. FAX: 306-842-8341. Web Site: www.suncountry.sk.ca. *Librn,* Stella Swertz; Tel: 306-842-8360, E-mail: stella.swertz@schr.sk.ca

Library Holdings: Bk Vols 1,700

Special Collections: Sask Hosp Research Papers

Subject Interests: Gerontology, Med, Nursing, Psychiat, Psychol

Restriction: Open by appt only

YORKTON

P   PARKLAND REGIONAL LIBRARY*, Hwy 52 W, S3N 3Z4. (Mail add: PO Box 5049, S3N 3Z4), SAN 320-0256. Tel: 306-783-7022. FAX: 306-782-2844. E-mail: office@parkland.lib.sk.ca. Web Site: www.parkland.lib.sk.ca. *Dir,* Deirdre Crichton; E-mail: dcrichton@parkland.lib.sk.ca; *Asst Librn,* Sher Temoin; E-mail: stemoin@parkland.lib.sk.ca; *Database Mgr, Syst Coordr,* M Patrick; E-mail: mpatrick@parkland.lib.sk.ca; *Acq,* Patti Anderson; E-mail: panderso@parkland.lib.sk.ca; *Info Serv,* P Stroud; E-mail: pstroud@parkland.lib.sk.ca; *ILL,* Anna Marie Gage; E-mail: amgage@parkland.lib; Staff 3 (MLS 3)

Founded 1968. Pop 92,200

Library Holdings: DVDs 3,723; e-journals 7,000; Large Print Bks 4,833; Bk Titles 45,866; Bk Vols 56,194; Talking Bks 7,363

Automation Activity & Vendor Info: (Acquisitions) SirsiDynix; (Cataloging) SirsiDynix; (Circulation) SirsiDynix

Database Vendor: EBSCOhost

Publications: Parkland Newsletter

Partic in Utlas

Open Mon-Wed 10-9, Thurs & Fri 10-6, Sat & Sun 1-5

Branches: 51

ANNAHEIM BRANCH, PO Box 15, Annaheim, S0K 0G0. Tel: 306-598-2155. *Librn,* Corinne Zawrucha

Open Tues 1-5, Wed 3-7

BALCARRES BRANCH, 209 Main St, Balcarres, S0G 0C0. (Mail add: PO Box 640, Balcarres, S0G 0C0). Tel: 306-334-2966. E-mail: balcarres@parkland.lib.sk.ca. *Librn,* Stephanie Paus

Open Tues 1-7, Wed 1-6, Fri 10-3

BREDENBURY BRANCH, TD Bank Bldg, Bredenbury, S0A 0H0. (Mail add: PO Box 222, Bredenbury, S0A 0H0). Tel: 306-898-4683. E-mail: bredenbury@parkland.lib.sk.ca. *Librn,* Andrea Rosin

Open Tues 9:30-4:30, Wed 4-7, Sat 10-2

BUCHANAN BRANCH, 315 Central, Buchanan, S0A 0J0. (Mail add: PO Box 323, Buchanan, S0A 0J0). Tel: 306-592-2137. E-mail: buchananlib@sasktel.net. *Librn,* Marie Kupchinski

Open Tues 1-5, Thurs & Fri 2-6

CANORA BRANCH, 223 Eighth Ave, Canora, S0A 0L0. (Mail add: PO Box 694, Canora, S0A 0L0). Tel: 306-563-6877. E-mail: canora@parkland.lib.sk.ca. *Librn,* Gina Dergousoff

Open Mon 3:30-8, Tues 1-5, Wed 2:30-8, Thurs 11-5, Fri 3:30-7:30, Sat 12-5

CHURCHBRIDGE BRANCH, 114 Rankin Rd, Churchbridge, S0A 0M0. (Mail add: PO Box 530, Churchbridge, S0A 0M0). Tel: 306-896-2322. E-mail: churchbridge@parkland.lib.sk.ca. *Librn,* Jocelyn Mehrer

Open Tues 1-7, Wed-Fri 1-5

CUPAR BRANCH, 217 Stanley St, Cupar, S0A 0Y0. (Mail add: PO Box 520, Cupar, S0A 0Y0). Tel: 306-723-4749. E-mail: cupar@parkland.lib.sk.ca. *Librn,* Ann Lucas

Open Wed & Fri 10:30-5

EARL GREY BRANCH, Main St, Earl Grey, S0A 1J0. (Mail add: PO Box 237, Earl Grey, S0A 1J0). Tel: 306-939-2212. E-mail: earlgrey@parkland.lib.sk.ca. *Librn,* Larry Bailey

Open Tues 2-7, Thurs 6-9

ELFROS BRANCH, Nackra St, Elfros, S0A 0V0. (Mail add: PO Box 70, Elfros, S0A 0V0). Tel: 306-328-2175. *Librn,* Karen Buck
Open Tues 5-8, Thurs 1-4

ENGLEFELD BRANCH, PO Box 22, Englefeld, S0K 1N0. Tel: 306-287-3497. E-mail: englefeld@parkland.lib.sk.ca. *Librn,* Deb Andrews
Open Tues & Thurs 10-2, Wed 4-8

ESTERHAZY BRANCH, 624 Main St, Esterhazy, S0A 0X0. (Mail add: PO Box 1329, Esterhazy, S0A 0X0). Tel: 306-745-6406. E-mail: esterhazy@parkland.lib.sk.ca. *Librn,* Susan Slotsve
Open Tues-Thurs 12-5 & 6-9, Fri 12-4, Sat 10-3

FOAM LAKE BRANCH, 402 Cameron St, Foam Lake, S0A 1A0. (Mail add: PO Box 181, Foam Lake, S0A 1A0). Tel: 306-272-3660. E-mail: foamlake@parkland.lib.sk.ca. *Librn,* Fiona Emuke
Open Tues-Thurs 10:30-4:30

GOVAN BRANCH, PO Box 40, Govan, S0G 1Z0, SAN 325-1012. Tel: 306-484-2122. E-mail: govan@parkland.lib.sk.ca. *Librn,* Vicky Wilson
Library Holdings: Bk Vols 3,000
Special Collections: Saskatchewan History Room Coll, bks, pictures
Open Tues & Thurs 9:30-12:30 & 1-5

INVERMAY BRANCH, 301 Fourth Ave N, Invermay, S0A 1M0. (Mail add: PO Box 59, Invermay, S0A 1M0). Tel: 306-593-4990. E-mail: invermay@parkland.lib.sk.ca. *Librn,* Judith Bansley
Open Tues & Wed 12-4

ITUNA BRANCH, 317 Fourth Ave N, Ituna, S0A 1N0. (Mail add: PO Box 550, Ituna, S0A 1N0). Tel: 306-795-2672. E-mail: ituna@parkland.lib.sk.ca. *Librn,* Gale Brick
Open Tues & Wed 12-5, Thurs 11-5

JANSEN BRANCH, Main St, Jansen, S0K 2B0. (Mail add: PO Box 217, Jansen, S0K 2B0). Tel: 306-364-2122. E-mail: jansen@parkland.lib.sk.ca. *Librn,* Kathy Jones
Open Mon & Wed 4-8

KAMSACK BRANCH, 235 Second St, Kamsack, S0A 1S0. (Mail add: PO Box 1870, Kamsack, S0A 1S0). Tel: 306-542-3787. E-mail: kamsack@parkland.lib.sk.ca. *Librn,* Nicole Larson
Open Mon & Fri 4-7:30, Tues & Thurs 11-5, Wed 2-7:30, Sat 1-4:30

KELLIHER BRANCH, 413 Second Ave, Kelliher, S0A 1V0. (Mail add: PO Box 161, Kelliher, S0A 1V0). Tel: 306-675-2110. E-mail: kelliher@parkland.lib.sk.ca. *Librn,* Merrilee Grunert
Open Tues 9-12 & 2-5, Wed & Thurs 2-6

KELVINGTON BRANCH, 201 Main St, Kelvington, S0A 1W0. (Mail add: PO Box 429, Kelvington, S0A 1W0). Tel: 306-327-4322. E-mail: kelvington@parkland.lib.sk.ca. *Librn,* Kim Kizlyk
Open Tues & Fri 10-2, Wed & Thurs 11-4

LAKE LENORE BRANCH, PO Box 34, Lake Lenore, S0K 2J0. Tel: 306-368-2500. E-mail: lakelenore@parkland.lib.sk.ca. *Librn,* Lucille Eberle
Open Tues 4-8, Wed & Thurs 4-7

LANGENBURG BRANCH, PO Box 549, Langenburg, S0A 2A0. Tel: 306-743-5394. E-mail: langenburg@parkland.lib.sk.ca. *Librn,* Marlies Nerbas
Special Services for the Blind - Large print bks
Open Mon & Thurs 1-6, Tues 9-1, Wed 3:30-7:30

LEMBERG BRANCH, PO Box 339, Lemberg, S0A 2B0. Tel: 306-335-2267. E-mail: lemberg@parkland.lib.sk.ca. *Librn,* Barbara Kanciruk
Open Mon 1-4:30. Tues 6-9, Wed 10-2:30, Fri 1-4

LEROY BRANCH, PO Box 310, LeRoy, S0K 2P0. Tel: 306-286-3356. E-mail: leroy@parkland.lib.sk.ca. *Librn,* Sarah Thompson
Open Mon 10-2, Wed 2-6, Fri 9-4

LINTLAW BRANCH, PO Box 157, Lintlaw, S0A 2H0. Tel: 306-325-2166. *Librn,* Barb Semko
Open Tues 9-1, Fri 12:30-4:30

LIPTON BRANCH, 1103 Shamrock Ave, Lipton, S0G 3B0. (Mail add: PO Box 111, Lipton, S0G 3B0). Tel: 306-336-2288. E-mail: lipton@parkland.lib.sk.ca. *Librn,* Marlene Fink
Open Wed & Thurs 11-6

MACNUTT BRANCH, PO Box 150, MacNutt, S0A 2K0. *Librn,* Tammy Antony
Open Tues 1-5, Fri 3-7

MELVILLE BRANCH, 444 Main St, Melville, S0A 2P0. (Mail add: PO Box 489, Melville, S0A 2P0). Tel: 306-728-2171. E-mail: melville@parkland.lib.sk.ca. *Asst Librn,* Merissa Kiesowapy
Open Mon & Sat 1-5, Tues & Wed 11-5 & 6-9, Thurs & Fri 11-5

MUENSTER BRANCH, 307 Railway St, Muenster, S0K 2Y0. Tel: 306-682-5252. E-mail: muenster@parkland.lib.sk.ca. *Librn,* Monica Keefer
Open Tues 10:30-4:30, Wed 2:30-7:30, Thurs 1-5

NEUDORF BRANCH, 103 Main St, Neudorf, S0A 2T0. (Mail add: PO Box 156, Neudorf, S0A 2T0). Tel: 306-748-2553. E-mail: neudorf@parkland.lib.sk.ca. *Librn,* Crystal Campbell
Open Tues 6-9, Wed 5-8, Fri 11-3

NORQUAY BRANCH, 25 Main St, Norquay, S0A 2V0. (Mail add: PO Box 459, Norquay, S0A 2V0). Tel: 306-594-2766. E-mail: norquay@parkland.lib.sk.ca. *Librn,* Jody Abbott
Open Tues & Thurs 12:30-5, Wed 10-3

PELLY BRANCH, 300 W 2nd St, Pelly, S0A 2Z0. (Mail add: PO Box 40, Pelly, S0A 2Z0). Tel: 306-595-2243. E-mail: pelly@parkland.lib.sk.ca. *Librn,* Judy Mazurin
Open Tues 10-3, Thurs 3-8

PREECEVILLE BRANCH, PO Box 663, Preeceville, S0A 3B0. Tel: 306-547-3444. E-mail: preeceville@parkland.lib.sk.ca. *Librn,* Fay Alberts
Open Tues 2-6, Wed 11-6, Thurs & Fri 2-5:30

PUNNICHY BRANCH, PO Box 550, Punnichy, S0A 3C0. Tel: 306-835-2265. E-mail: punnichy@parkland.lib.sk.ca. *Librn,* Kathleen Graessli
Open Tues 3-7, Fri 10-2

QUILL LAKE BRANCH, PO Box 638, Quill Lake, S0A 3E0. Tel: 306-383-2242. E-mail: quilllake@parkland.lib.sk.ca. *Librn,* Wendy Chatman
Open Tues & Thurs 9:30-4:30

RAYMORE BRANCH, PO Box 244, Raymore, S0A 3J0. Tel: 306-746-2166. E-mail: raymore@parkland.lib.sk.ca. *Librn,* Sheila Lamont
Open Tues 1-7, Wed 1-5, Thurs 10-4

ROSE VALLEY BRANCH, 300 Centre St, Rose Valley, S0E 1M0. (Mail add: PO Box 384, Rose Valley, S0E 1M0). Tel: 306-322-2001. E-mail: rosevalley@parkland.lib.sk.ca. *Librn,* Cheryl Holt
Open Tues 2-6, Wed 12-6, Fri 10-2

SALTCOATS BRANCH, 117 Allen Ave, Saltcoats, S0A 3R0. (Mail add: PO Box 220, Saltcoats, S0A 3R0). Tel: 306-744-2911. E-mail: saltcoats@parkland.lib.sk.ca. *Librn,* Laura Hutchings
Open Tues & Thurs 3:30-7:30, Wed 9-12 & 12:30-3:30

SEMANS BRANCH, 103 King St, Semans, S0A 3S0. (Mail add: PO Box 220, Semans, S0A 3S0). Tel: 306-524-2224. E-mail: semans@parkland.lib.sk.ca. *Librn,* Phyllis James
Open Tues 9-12 & 1-4, Wed 11-3, Thurs 1-5

SOUTHEY BRANCH, 260 Keats St, Southey, S0G 4P0. Tel: 306-726-2907. E-mail: southey@parkland.lib.sk.ca. *Librn,* Connie Lillejord
Open Tues & Wed 1-5, Thurs & Fri 10-2

SPALDING BRANCH, PO Box 37, Spalding, S0K 4C0. Tel: 306-872-2184. E-mail: spalding@parkland.lib.sk.ca. *Librn,* Olwen Hoffman
Open Tues 12-5, Thurs 10-4, Sat 12-3

SPRINGSIDE BRANCH, 19 Main St, Springside, S0A 3V0. (Mail add: PO Box 388, Springside, S0A 3V0). Tel: 306-792-4743. E-mail: springside@parkland.lib.sk.ca. *Librn,* Mary Anne Ockochinski
Open Tues 1-7, Thurs 1-6, Fri 9:30-12:30

SPY HILL BRANCH, 316 Main St, Spy Hill, S0A 3W0. (Mail add: PO Box 160, Spy Hill, S0A 3W0). Tel: 306-534-2122. E-mail: spyhill@parkland.lib.sk.ca. *Librn,* Jean Istace
Open Tues 2-8, Thurs 11:30-5:30

STOCKHOLM BRANCH, PO Box 173, Stockholm, S0A 3Y0. Tel: 306-793-2102. E-mail: stockholm@parkland.lib.sk.ca. *Librn,* Carol Closson
Open Tues 9:30-5:30, Thurs 9:30-4:30

STRASBOURG BRANCH, 113 Pearson St, Strasbourg, S0G 4V0. (Mail add: PO Box 331, Strasbourg, S0G 4V0). Tel: 306-725-3239. E-mail: strasbourg@parkland.lib.sk.ca. *Librn,* Angela Kuderewko
Open Tues 10:30-2:30 & 3-6, Thurs & Fri 10:30-4:30

STURGIS BRANCH, 222 Main St, Sturgis, S0A 4A0. (Mail add: PO Box 194, Sturgis, S0A 4A0). Tel: 306-548-2824. E-mail: sturgis@parkland.lib.sk.ca. *Librn,* Helen Scheller
Open Tues 2-6, Wed 12-6, Thurs 11-5

THEODORE BRANCH, PO Box 448, Theodore, S0A 4C0. Tel: 306-647-2315. *Librn,* Valerie Blades
Open Tues & Thurs 1-5

WADENA BRANCH, 86 First St NE, Wadena, S0A 4J0. (Mail add: PO Box 297, Wadena, S0A 4J0). Tel: 306-338-2293. E-mail: wadena@parkland.lib.sk.ca. *Librn,* Cara Elthinstone
Open Tues-Thurs 12-5, Fri 9-Noon

WATSON BRANCH, Main St, Watson, S0K 4V0. (Mail add: PO Box 489, Watson, S0K 4V0). Tel: 306-287-3642. E-mail: watson@parkland.lib.sk.ca. *Librn,* Kathleen McNulty
Open Tues-Thurs 11-5

WISHART BRANCH, PO Box 48, Wishart, S0A 4R0. Tel: 306-576-2150. E-mail: wishart@parkland.lib.sk.ca. *Librn,* Donna McDougall
Open Tues 1-4, Fri 12-4

WYNYARD BRANCH, 431 Bosworth St, Wynyard, S0A 4T0. (Mail add: PO Box 477, Wynyard, S0A 4T0). Tel: 306-554-3321. E-mail: wynyard@parkland.lib.sk.ca. *Librn,* Brenda Laxdal
Open Tues 11-6, Wed & Thurs 1-7, Fri & Sat 10-2

YORKTON BRANCH, 93 W Broadway St, S3N 0L9, SAN 376-2076. Tel: 306-783-3523. FAX: 306-782-5524. E-mail: yorkton@parkland.lib.sk.ca. *Mgr, Pub Serv,* Melody Maye Wood; E-mail: mwood@parkland.lib.sk.ca;
Staff 12 (MLS 1, Non-MLS 11)
Founded 1912. Pop 20,000; Circ 100,000
Open Mon-Wed 10-9, Thurs & Fri 10-6, Sat 12-4, Sun (Oct-May) 1-5

Date of Statistics: FY 2010-2011
Population, 2009: 34,667
Population Served by Public Libraries: 34,667
Total Public Library Circulation: 171,893
Expenditures Per Capita (O & M): $50.10
**Public libraries income includes centralized acquisition &
  processing of library materials for all Yukon public libraries**

DAWSON CITY

S   DAWSON CITY MUSEUM & HISTORICAL SOCIETY*, Klondike
    History Library, PO Box 303, Y0B 1G0. Tel: 867-993-5291 ext 24. FAX:
    867-993-5839. E-mail: dcmuseum@yknet.yk.ca. Web Site:
    www.dawsonmuseum.ca. *Exec Dir,* Laura Mann; E-mail:
    lmann@dawsonmuseum.ca
    Library Holdings: Bk Titles 1,000
    Special Collections: Dawson Photog Coll. Oral History
    Subject Interests: Local hist
    Restriction: Non-circulating

WHITEHORSE

G   DEPARTMENT OF COMMUNITY SERVICES, GOVERNMENT OF
    YUKON, Yukon Public Libraries, 1171 First Ave, Y1A 0G9. (Mail add:
    PO Box 2703, Y1A 2C6), SAN 369-6960. Tel: 867-667-5239. Reference
    Tel: 867-667-3668. Administration Tel: 867-667-8062. FAX: 867-393-6333.
    E-mail: whitehorse.library@gov.yk.ca. Reference E-mail:
    reference.pls@gov.yk.ca. Web Site: www.pac.gov.yk.ca, www.ypl.gov.yk.ca.
    Dir, Julie Ourom; Tel: 867-667-5447, E-mail: julie.ourom@gov.yk.ca; *Br
    Serv Librn,* Don Allen; Tel: 867-667-5448, E-mail: don.allen@gov.yk.ca;
    Pub Prog Librn, Mairi Macrae; Tel: 867-667-5228, E-mail:
    mairi.macrae@gov.yk.ca; *Tech Serv Librn,* Debbie Hawco; E-mail:
    debbie.hawco@gov.yk.ca; *Circ Supvr,* Jacqueline Cameron; Tel:
    867-667-5413, E-mail: jacqueline.cameron@gov.yk.ca; Staff 13 (MLS 3,
    Non-MLS 10)
    Founded 1962. Pop 30,469; Circ 172,000
    Library Holdings: Bk Titles 145,423; Per Subs 340
    Special Collections: Northern Books Coll; Yukon History Coll
    Automation Activity & Vendor Info: (Cataloging) TLC (The Library
    Corporation); (Circulation) TLC (The Library Corporation)
    Database Vendor: TLC (The Library Corporation)
    Function: Alaskana res, Audio & video playback equip for onsite use, AV
    serv, Games & aids for the handicapped, Govt ref serv, Handicapped
    accessible, ILL available, Large print keyboards, Magnifiers for reading,
    Photocopying/Printing, Prog for adults, Prog for children & young adult,
    Ref serv available, Summer reading prog, Telephone ref, Wheelchair
    accessible
    Open Mon-Fri 10-9, Sat 10-6, Sun 1-9
    Friends of the Library Group
    Branches:
    BEAVER CREEK COMMUNITY, Beaver Creek Fire Hall, Beaver Creek,
        Y0B 1A0. (Mail add: General Delivery, Beaver Creek, Y0B 1A0), SAN
        378-1356. Tel: 867-862-7622. FAX: 867-862-7904. E-mail:
        bclib@klondiker.com. *Chair,* Position Currently Open
    BURWASH LANDING COMMUNITY, Kluane First Nation Bldg, 1093
        Alaska Hwy, Burwash Landing, Y0B 1V0. (Mail add: PO Box 18,
        Burwash Landing, Y0B 1V0), SAN 378-1372. Tel: 867-841-4707. FAX:
        867-841-5904. E-mail: bllib@klondiker.com. *Chair,* Rose Blair

CARMACKS COMMUNITY, Tantalus School, One Tantalus Crescent,
    Carmacks, Y0B 1C0. (Mail add: PO Box 131, Carmacks, Y0B 1C0),
    SAN 325-4232. Tel: 867-863-5901. FAX: 867-863-5814. E-mail:
    cmlib@klondiker.com. *Chair,* Christian Woods-Hindson
DAWSON CITY COMMUNITY, Robert Service School, Dawson City,
    Y0B 1G0. (Mail add: PO Box 1410, Dawson City, Y0B 1C0), SAN
    369-6995. Tel: 867-993-5571. FAX: 867-993-6770. E-mail:
    dclib@klondiker.com. *Chair,* Bonnie Barber
    Special Collections: Klondike Goldrush Coll
FARO COMMUNITY, Del Van Gorder School, Faro, Y0B 1K0. (Mail
    add: PO Box 279, Faro, Y0B 1K0), SAN 369-7053. Tel: 867-994-2684.
    FAX: 867-994-2236, 867-994-3342. E-mail: flib@klondiker.com. *Chair,*
    Doris Unruh
HAINES JUNCTION COMMUNITY, Haines Junction Admininstration
    Bldg, Haines Junction, Y0B 1L0. (Mail add: PO Box 5350, Haines
    Junction, Y0B 1L0), SAN 369-7088. Tel: 867-634-2215. FAX:
    867-634-2400. *Chair,* Wenda Lythgoe
    Special Collections: Mountaineering (Kluane National Park Coll)
ISABELLE PRINGLE COMMUNITY, PO Box 93, Carcross, Y0B 1B0,
    SAN 325-4216. Tel: 867-821-3801. FAX: 867-821-3801. E-mail:
    iplib@klondiker.com. *Chair,* Bill Pringle
MAYO COMMUNITY, Mayo Administration Bldg, Mayo, Y0B 1M0.
    (Mail add: PO Box 158, Mayo, Y0B 1M0), SAN 369-7118. Tel:
    867-996-2541. FAX: 867-996-2203. E-mail: mlib@klondiker.com. *Dir of
    Libr,* Julie Ourom
OLD CROW COMMUNITY, Chief Zzeh Gittlit School, Old Crow, Y0B
    1N0. (Mail add: PO Box 101, Old Crow, Y0B 1N0), Tel: 867-966-3031.
    E-mail: oclib@klondiker.com. *Chair,* Megan Williams
PELLY CROSSING COMMUNITY, Eliza Van Bibber School, Pelly
    Crossing, Y0B 1P0. (Mail add: PO Box 108, Pelly Crossing, Y0B 1P0).
    Tel: 867-537-3041. FAX: 867-537-3103. E-mail: pclib@klondiker.com.
    Chair, Donna Conley
ROSS RIVER COMMUNITY, Ross River School, Ross River, Y0B 1S0.
    (Mail add: General Delivery, Ross River, Y0B 1S0), SAN 329-6199. Tel:
    867-969-2909. E-mail: rrlib@klondiker.com. *Chair,* Lynne Harris
TAGISH COMMUNITY, Tagish Community Association Bldg, Tagish,
    Y0B 1T0. (Mail add: PO Box 69, Tagish, Y0B 1T0). Tel: 867-399-3418.
    E-mail: tglib@klondiker.com. *Chair,* Gloria DeVillers
    Special Services for the Blind - Talking bks
TESLIN COMMUNITY, Teslin Community Bldg, Teslin, Y0A 1B0. (Mail
    add: PO Box 58, Teslin, Y0A 1B0), SAN 369-7134. Tel: 867-390-2802.
    E-mail: tslib@klondiker.com. *Chair,* Wes Wirth
WATSON LAKE COMMUNITY, Watson Lake Administration Bldg, 701
    Adela Trail, Watson Lake, Y0A 1C0. (Mail add: PO Box 843, Watson
    Lake, Y0A 1C0), SAN 369-7142. Tel: 867-536-7517. FAX:
    867-536-7515. E-mail: wllib@klondiker.com. *Chair,* Barb Millen
    Subject Interests: Alaska hwy
    Friends of the Library Group
WHITEHORSE PUBLIC, 2071 Second Ave, Y1A 2C6. (Mail add: Box
    2703 C-23, Y1A 2C6). Tel: 867-667-5239. FAX: 867-393-6333. *Br Serv
    Librn,* Don Allen; Tel: 867-667-5448, E-mail: don.allen@gov.yk.ca
    Founded 1961. Pop 31,587

Library Holdings: Bk Vols 75,000
Special Collections: Klondike Goldrush Coll. Can & Prov
Automation Activity & Vendor Info: (OPAC) TLC (The Library Corporation)
Open Mon-Fri 10-9, Sat 10-6, Sun 1-9
Friends of the Library Group

G   DEPARTMENT OF INDIAN AFFAIRS & NORTHERN DEVELOPMENT*, Yukon Region Library, 335-300 Main St, Y1A 2B5. (Mail add: 345-300 Main St, Y1A 2B5), SAN 373-8884. Tel: 867-667-3111. FAX: 867-667-3888. E-mail: yukonlibrary@inac.gc.ca. Web Site: www.inac.gc.ca. *Head of Librr,* Aimee Ellis; Staff 3 (MLS 2, Non-MLS 1)
Founded 1991
Library Holdings: Bk Titles 25,000; Per Subs 102
Special Collections: Earth Sciences Coll
Automation Activity & Vendor Info: (Acquisitions) VTLS, Inc; (Cataloging) VTLS, Inc; (Circulation) VTLS, Inc; (Serials) VTLS, Inc
Open Mon-Fri 8-4:30

G   ENVIRONMENT CANADA*, Conservation & Protection Yukon Branch Library, 91782 Alaska Hwy, Y1A 5B7. SAN 321-3676. Tel: 867-667-3407. FAX: 867-667-7962. *Librn,* Murray Munn; E-mail: murray.munn@ec.gc.ca
Library Holdings: Bk Titles 4,200; Per Subs 12
Subject Interests: Beaufort sea develop, Environ concerns in the north, Hazardous substances, Hydrocarbon, Mine effluent, Northern pipelines, Water quality
Open Mon-Fri 8-4:30

S   LEARNING DISABILITES ASSOCIATION OF YUKON*, Information Services-Resource Centre, 107 Main St, Y1A 2A7. Tel: 867-668-5167. FAX: 867-668-6504. E-mail: ldayoffice@northwestel.net. Web Site: www.nald.ca/lday.htm. *Pres,* Anne King
Founded 1973
Library Holdings: Bk Titles 1,400; Bk Vols 2,200; Per Subs 10
Open Mon-Fri 8:30-5

J   YUKON COLLEGE LIBRARY*, 500 College Dr, Y1A 5K4. (Mail add: PO Box 2799, Y1A 5K4), SAN 324-3842. Tel: 867-668-8870. Reference Tel: 867-668-8727. FAX: 867-668-8808. E-mail: library@yukoncollege.yk.ca. Web Site: library.yukoncollege.yk.ca. *Managing Librn,* Robert Sutherland; Tel: 867-668-8888, E-mail: rsutherland@yukoncollege.yk.ca; *Cat/Syst Librn,* Derek Yap; E-mail: dyap@yukoncollege.yk.ca; *Info Literacy, Ref Librn,* Aline Goncalves; E-mail: agoncalves@yukoncollege.yk.ca; *Acq, Ser,* Jane Haydock; E-mail:

jhaydoc@yukoncollege.yukoncollege.yk.ca; *AV,* Jerry Kearn; E-mail: jkearn@yukoncollege.yk.ca; *Circ/Reserves,* Genevieve O'Neil; E-mail: goneil@yukoncollege.yk.ca; Staff 6 (MLS 3, Non-MLS 3)
Founded 1983
Library Holdings: Bk Titles 40,000; Per Subs 500
Special Collections: Northern Economic Development, Northern Studies, Northern Building Construction
Database Vendor: Dialog, EBSCOhost
Wireless access
Publications: Acquisitions List; Newsletter (Irregular)
Partic in BC Electronic Library Network

G   YUKON DEPARTMENT OF ENVIRONMENT LIBRARY, 10 Burns Rd, Y1A 4Y9. (Mail add: PO Box 2703, Y1A 2C6), SAN 329-2037. Tel: 867-667-3029. Toll Free Tel: 800-661-0408, Ext 3029 (Yukon Territory). FAX: 867-393-7197. Web Site: www.environmentyukon.gov.yk.ca. *Librn,* Vicki McCollum; E-mail: vicki.mccollum@gov.yk.ca; *Asst Librn,* Melanie Lucas; E-mail: melanie.lucas@gov.yk.ca; Staff 2 (Non-MLS 2)
Library Holdings: Bk Titles 7,100; Per Subs 120
Function: For res purposes, ILL available
Open Mon-Fri 8-4:30
Restriction: Circulates for staff only, Pub use on premises

S   YUKON HISTORICAL & MUSEUMS ASSOCIATION LIBRARY*, 3126 Third Ave, Y1A 1E7. Tel: 867-667-4704. FAX: 867-667-4506. Web Site: www.heritageyhukon.vs.
Founded 1977
Library Holdings: Bk Titles 70
Special Collections: First Nations Culture; Yukon History
Open Mon-Fri 10-5

GL   YUKON PUBLIC LAW LIBRARY, Yukon Law Courts, 2134 Second Ave, Y1A 2C6. (Mail add: Box 2703, Stn Main, Y1A 2C6). Tel: 867-667-3086. FAX: 867-393-6212. E-mail: yukon.law.library@gov.yk.ca. Web Site: www.justice.gov.yk.ca/prog/cs/library.html. *Librn,* Tanya Astika
Library Holdings: Bk Titles 15,000; Per Subs 50
Open Mon-Fri 9-2

G   YUKON WOMEN'S DIRECTORATE LIBRARY*, 404 Hanson St, Ste 1, Y1A 1Y8. (Mail add: PO Box 2703, Y1A 2C6). Tel: 867-667-3030. FAX: 867-393-6270. E-mail: womens.directorate@gov.yk.ca. Web Site: www.womensdirectorate.gov.yk.ca. *In Charge,* Lorie Larose
Library Holdings: Bk Titles 3,000; Per Subs 12
Open Mon-Fri 8-5

LIBRARY INFORMATION

Networks and Consortia

Library Schools and Training Courses

Library Systems

Libraries for the Blind
and Physically Handicapped

Libraries Serving the
Deaf and Hearing Impaired

State and Provincial
Public Library Agencies

State School Library Agencies

National Interlibrary Loan Codes
for the United States

United States Armed
Forces Libraries Overseas

NETWORKS, CONSORTIA & OTHER COOPERATIVE LIBRARY ORGANIZATIONS

These organizations are listed alphabetically by state or province.

ALABAMA

ALABAMA HEALTH LIBRARIES ASSOCIATION, INC*, (ALHeLa), University of Alabama, Lister Hill Library, 1530 Third Ave S, Birmingham, 35294-0013. SAN 372-8218. Tel: 205-975-8313. FAX: 205-934-2230. Web Site: southmed.usouthal.edu/library/alhela/. *Pres,* Lee Vacovich; E-mail: lvucovi@uab.edu
Founded 1980
Member Libraries: 43
Primary Functions: Increase & maintain the total health science information resources & services available; strengthen & promote existing health libraries & the professional skills of health information personnel by providing opportunities for continuing education; encourage the formation of new libraries & provide consulting services to developing Alabama health science libraries; through joint effort, utilize more effectively the resources of individual libraries

LIBRARY MANAGEMENT NETWORK, INC, (LMN), 2132 Sixth Ave SE, Ste 106, Decatur, 35601. SAN 322-3906. Tel: 256-308-2529. FAX: 256-308-2533. Web Site: www.lmn.lib.al.us. *Syst Coordr,* Charlotte Moncrief; E-mail: charlotte@lmn.lib.al.us
Founded 1983
Member Libraries: 4 comm coll, 2 high sch & 2 pub
Primary Functions: To operate an automated integrated library system; to offer access to the collective resources of the region to members & to the public via maintaining a web site; to establish a common database among members using MARC standards; to provide on a cooperative basis, automated management services for member libraries, i.e. circulation, offline backup circulation, MARC bibliographic processing, authority control, online public access catalog, federated searching & web-mail

MARINE ENVIRONMENTAL SCIENCES CONSORTIUM*, Dauphin Island Sea Lab, 101 Bienville Blvd, Dauphin Island, 36528. SAN 322-0001. Tel: 251-861-2141. FAX: 251-861-4646. E-mail: disl@disl.org. Web Site: www.disl.org. *Coordr,* John Dindo
Member Libraries: 22
Primary Functions: Provides marine-related education & research for Alabama; serves as a repository for marine-related holdings for all schools & marine agencies

NETWORK OF ALABAMA ACADEMIC LIBRARIES, c/o Alabama Commission on Higher Education, 100 N Union St, Montgomery, 36104. (Mail add: PO Box 302000, Montgomery, 36130-2000), SAN 322-4570. Tel: 334-242-2211. FAX: 334-242-0270. Web Site: www.ache.state.al.us/naal. *Dir,* Ronald P Leonard; E-mail: ron.leonard@ache.alabama.gov
Founded 1984
Member Libraries: 21 acad, 8 affiliates, 1 pub & 6 spec
Primary Functions: Collection development; digital collection development; interlibrary loan; continuing education; preservation; electronic access to information

ALASKA

ALASKA LIBRARY NETWORK*, (ALN), PO Box 100585, Anchorage, 99501-0585. SAN 371-0688. Tel: 907-269-6567. FAX: 907-269-6580. E-mail: aln@alaska.gov. Web Site: alaskalibrarynetwork.org. *Dir,* Nina Malyshev
Founded 2007
Member Libraries: 61 acad, med, pub, sch & spec
Primary Functions: Coordinate statewide access to commercial electronic resources, including EBSCO & Live Homework Help; coordinate ListenAlaska digital audio book collection consortia; discount purchase programs

ARIZONA

MARICOPA COUNTY COMMUNITY COLLEGE DISTRICT*, Library Technology Services, 2411 W 14th St, Tempe, 85281-6942. SAN 322-0060. Tel: 480-731-8774. FAX: 480-731-8787. Web Site: www.maricopa.edu/lts. *Dir of Tech Serv,* Thomas Saudargas; E-mail: thomas.saudargas@domail.maricopa.edu; *Project Leader,* Lori Threlkeld; Tel: 480-731-8776, E-mail: lori.threlkeld@domail.maricopa.edu; *Syst Programmer,* Cheryl Laieski; Tel: 480-731-8918, E-mail: cheryl.laieski@domail.maricopa.edu
Partic in Maryland Association of Health Science Librarians
Member Libraries: 10 community cols, associated satellite sites & centralized tech serv located at District Serv Support Ctr
Primary Functions: Maintains union district bibliographic database on the Dynix Horizon integrated library system; provides interlibrary loan services via OCLC; centralized ordering, receiving, cataloging & processing; maintains Horizon Information Portal interface

ARKANSAS

ARKANSAS AREA HEALTH EDUCATION CENTER CONSORTIUM*, (AHEC), Sparks Regional Medical Ctr, 1001 Tawson Ave, Fort Smith, 72901-4992. (Mail add: PO Box 17006, Fort Smith, 72917-7006), SAN 329-3734. Tel: 479-441-5337. FAX: 479-441-5339. *Dir,* Grace Anderson; E-mail: grace@sparks.org
Member Libraries: 7
Primary Functions: Interlibrary loan services; cooperation-cooperative acquisitions; resource sharing

ARKANSAS INDEPENDENT COLLEGES & UNIVERSITIES*, Firstar Bldg, One Riverfront Pl, Ste 610, North Little Rock, 72114. SAN 322-0079. Tel: 501-378-0843. FAX: 501-374-1523. Web Site: www.arkindcolleges.org. *Pres,* Kearney E Dietz; E-mail: kdietz@alltel.net
Founded 1954
Member Libraries: 11
Primary Functions: Acquisitions; interlibrary loan; fund-raising

NORTHEAST ARKANSAS HOSPITAL LIBRARY CONSORTIUM*, 223 E Jackson, Jonesboro, 72401. SAN 329-529X. Tel: 870-972-1290. FAX: 870-931-0839. *Dir,* Karen Crosser; E-mail: kcrosser@ahecne.uams.edu
Founded 1979

Member Libraries: 28 med
Primary Functions: Sharing union list of journals, books and audio-visual materials

SOUTH ARKANSAS FILM COOP*, c/o Malvern-Hot Spring County Library, 202 E Third St, Malvern, 72104. SAN 321-5938. Tel: 501-332-5441. FAX: 501-332-6679. E-mail: hotspringcountylibrary@yahoo.com. *Dir,* Tammy Carter; E-mail: tammyc1965@yahoo.com
Founded 1983
Member Libraries: 20 pub
Primary Functions: A film cooperative serving the twenty-seven counties in the southern half of Arkansas

CALIFORNIA

BAY AREA LIBRARY & INFORMATION NETWORK*, (BayNet), 1462 Cedar St, Berkeley, 94702. SAN 371-0610. Tel: 415-355-2826. E-mail: infobay@baynetlibs.org. Web Site: www.baynetlibs.org. *Pres,* Debbie Abilock; E-mail: dabilock@gmail.com; *VPres,* Nicole Greenland; Tel: 510-436-1462, E-mail: greenland@hnu.edu; *Adminr,* Rose Falanga; Tel: 510-525-4726, E-mail: infobay@exo.net; *Treas,* Sharon Miller; Tel: 415-393-0113, E-mail: smiller@milibrary.org
Founded 1983
Member Libraries: 146, incl 37 acad, 38 other, 14 pub, 16 sch & 41 spec
Primary Functions: To strengthen connections among all types of libraries & information centers; to promote communication, professional development, cooperation & innovative resource sharing

BERKELEY INFORMATION NETWORK*, (BIN), Berkeley Public Library, 2090 Kittredge St, Berkeley, 94704. Tel: 510-981-6150, 510-981-6166. FAX: 510-981-6246. Web Site: www.berkeleypubliclibrary.org. *Mgr,* Jane Scantlebury; E-mail: jscantlebury@ci.berkeley.ca.us
Founded 1980
Primary Functions: Functions as information & referral service at the Berkeley Public Library connecting people with local information sources

CALIFA*, 32 W 25th Ave, Ste 201, San Mateo, 94403. Tel: 650-572-2746. Toll Free Tel: 866-209-5439 (CA only). FAX: 650-349-5089. E-mail: califa@califa.org. Web Site: www.califa.org. *Exec Dir,* Linda Crowe; *Serv Consult,* Roberto Esteves; *Serv Mgr,* Anthony Costa
Founded 2002
Member Libraries: 250
Primary Functions: Delivery of cost effective services for members

CLAREMONT UNIVERSITY CONSORTIUM*, (CUC), 150 E Eighth St, Claremont, 91711. Tel: 909-621-8026, 909-621-8150. FAX: 909-621-8681. Web Site: www.cuc.claremont.edu. *Chief Exec Officer,* Robert Walton
Founded 1925
Member Libraries: 8 acad
Primary Functions: Central coordinating & agency service for the 7 Claremont colleges

CONSORTIUM FOR OPEN LEARNING*, 333 Sunrise Ave, No 229, Roseville, 95661-3480. SAN 329-4412. Tel: 916-788-0660. FAX: 916-788-0696. *Operations Mgr,* Sandra Scott-Smith; E-mail: sss@calweb.com
Founded 1972
Member Libraries: 18 commun col
Primary Functions: Members offer educational programming to students over open broadcast, cable, ITFS, classroom & Internet

CONSUMER HEALTH INFORMATION PROGRAM & SERVICES*, (CHIPS), 12350 Imperial Hwy, Norwalk, 90650. SAN 372-8110. Tel: 562-868-4003. FAX: 562-868-4065. E-mail: referenceservices@gw.colapl.org. Web Site: www.colapublib.org/services/chips.html. *Librn,* Amy Beteilho
Founded 1976
Member Libraries: 88 county
Primary Functions: Provide information & extended reference service on health, diseases, disorders, types of therapy, prescription drugs & physician credentials

49-99 COOPERATIVE LIBRARY SYSTEM, c/o Southern California Library Cooperative, 248 E Foothill Blvd, Ste 101, Monrovia, 91016. SAN 301-6218. Tel: 626-359-6111. FAX: 626-359-0001. *Dir,* Rosario Garza
Founded 1968
Member Libraries: 6

GOLD COAST LIBRARY NETWORK*, 3437 Empresa Dr, Ste C, San Luis Obispo, 93401-7355. Tel: 805-543-6082. FAX: 805-543-9487. Web Site: www.goldcoastlibraries.org. *Admin Dir,* Maureen Theobald; E-mail: mtheobald@blackgold.org
Member Libraries: 11 acad, 8 pub & 19 spec
Primary Functions: Serves academic, public & special libraries in San Luis Obispo, Santa Barbara & Ventura counties & provides services that facilitate resource sharing & connectivity among its members

NATIONAL NETWORK OF LIBRARIES OF MEDICINE PACIFIC SOUTHWEST REGION, (NN/LM PSR), Louise M Darling Biomedical Library, 12-077 Ctr for Health Science, Box 951798, Los Angeles, 90095-1798. SAN

372-8234. Tel: 310-825-1200. Toll Free Tel: 800-338-7657. FAX: 310-825-5389. E-mail: psr-nnlm@library.ucla.edu. Web Site: nnlm.gov/psr. *Dir,* Judy Consales; Tel: 310-825-5781, E-mail: consales@library.ucla.edu; *Assoc Dir,* Alan Carr; Tel: 310-825-7263, E-mail: acarr@library.ucla.edu
Founded 1969
Member Libraries: 696
Primary Functions: Serves the health information needs of librarians, healthcare practitioners, administrators, investigators, educators & consumers in the Pacific Southwest & Pacific Basin; coordinates interlibrary lending & other cooperative services among health sciences libraries in the region; through training, demonstrations & exhibits; reaches out to health care professionals & consumers to promote their use of the biomedical information resources of the National Library of Medicine, including Medline, PubMed, MedlinePlus & ClinicalTrials.gov; provides support & training to health sciences library staff, health professionals & those who provide information to the public, in using biomedical resources available through the Internet

NEVADA MEDICAL LIBRARY GROUP*, (NMLG), Barton Memorial Hospital Library, 2170 South Ave, South Lake Tahoe, 96150. (Mail add: PO Box 9578, South Lake Tahoe, 96158-2578), SAN 370-0445. Tel: 530-543-5844. FAX: 530-541-4697. *Sr Exec Coordr,* Laurie Anton; E-mail: lanton@bartonhealth.org
Founded 1978
Member Libraries: 40 med
Primary Functions: Networking & cooperating in acquisitions; ILL

NORTHERN CALIFORNIA ASSOCIATION OF LAW LIBRARIES*, (NOCALL), 268 Bush St, No 4006, San Francisco, 94104. SAN 323-5777. E-mail: admin@nocall.org. Web Site: www.nocall.org. *Pres,* Coral Henning; Tel: 916-874-6013, E-mail: chenning@saclaw.org; *VPres,* Kelly Browne; Tel: 916-874-7427, E-mail: kbrowne@saclaw.org
Founded 1979
Member Libraries: 400
Primary Functions: Union list for participating libraries; consultant committees for law firms; educational seminars relating to law librarianship; government relations committee; Internet committee

NORTHERN CALIFORNIA CONSORTIUM OF PSYCHOLOGY LIBRARIES*, (NCCPL), Argosy University, San Franscisco Bay Area Campus, 1005 Atlantic Ave, Alameda, 94133. SAN 371-9006. Tel: 510-837-3715. Web Site: www.nccpl.org. *Pres,* Julie Griffith; E-mail: jgriffith@argosy.edu
Founded 1985
Member Libraries: 18 acad & med
Primary Functions: Facilitate exchange of information & resources among Northern California libraries specializing in psychology studies; develop policies for resource sharing

PENINSULA LIBRARIES AUTOMATED NETWORK*, (PLAN), 2471 Flores St, San Mateo, 94403-4000. SAN 371-5035. Tel: 650-349-5538. FAX: 650-349-5089. Web Site: plsinfo.org. *Dir, Info Tech,* Monica Schultz; E-mail: schultz@plsinfo.org; *Database Mgr,* John Boggs; E-mail: boggs@plsino.org; *Syst,* Josh Shreffler; E-mail: shreffler@plsinfo.org
Founded 1982
Member Libraries: 9 (includes commun, col & pub)
Primary Functions: Shared automated circulation, cataloging & online catalog system

SAN BERNARDINO, INYO, RIVERSIDE COUNTIES UNITED LIBRARY SERVICES*, (SIRCULS), 555 W Sixth St, San Bernardino, 92410. SAN 322-0222. Tel: 909-381-8257. FAX: 909-888-3171. E-mail: ils@inlandlib.org. Web Site: inlandlib.org. *Exec Dir,* Vera Skop; E-mail: vskop@inlandlib.org
Founded 1975
Member Libraries: Acad, pub, sch & spec
Primary Functions: Interlibrary loan; reference; delivery

SAN FRANCISCO BIOMEDICAL LIBRARY NETWORK*, (SFBLN), San Franscisco General Hospital UCSF/ Barnett-Briggs Medical Library, 1001 Potrero Ave, Bldg 30, First Fl, San Francisco, 94110. SAN 371-2125. Tel: 415-206-6639. E-mail: fishbon@ucsfmedctr.org. Web Site: mountzion.ucsfmedicalcenter.org/library/sfbln.html. *Coordr,* Graham Joy; E-mail: jgraham@sfghdean.ucsf.edu
Founded 1978
Member Libraries: 18 health sci
Primary Functions: To provide for the cooperative development & resource sharing of member institutions

SANTA CLARITA INTERLIBRARY NETWORK, (SCILNET), Powell Library, 21726 Placerita Canyon Rd, Santa Clarita, 91321. SAN 371-8964. Tel: 661-362-2271. FAX: 661-362-2719. *Librn,* John Stone
Founded 1985
Member Libraries: 16 acad, pub, sch & spec
Primary Functions: Improve quality of service to citizens of Santa Clarita through interlibrary cooperation, including mutual borrowing privileges, union listings, shared technology & continuing education workshops

SERRA COOPERATIVE LIBRARY SYSTEM, c/o San Diego Public Library, 820 E St, San Diego, 92101. SAN 301-3510. Tel: 619-232-1225. Web Site: www.serralib.org. *Syst Coordr,* Vera Skop; E-mail: vskop@serralib.org

SOUTHERN CALIFORNIA LIBRARY COOPERATIVE, (SCLC), 248 E Foothill Blvd, Ste 101, Monrovia, 91016-5522. SAN 371-3865. Tel: 626-359-6111. FAX: 626-359-0001. E-mail: sclchq@socallibraries.org. Web Site: www.socallibraries.org. *Dir,* Rosario Garza
Founded 1965
Member Libraries: 48 pub
Primary Functions: Provide communication, delivery & training services to associate & member libraries; administer grant projects; offer professional development training & workshops

SUBSTANCE ABUSE LIBRARIANS & INFORMATION SPECIALISTS*, (SALIS), PO Box 9513, Berkeley, 94709-0513. SAN 372-4042. FAX: 510-985-6459. E-mail: salis@salis.org. Web Site: salis.org. *Exec Dir,* Andrea L Mitchell; E-mail: amitchell@salis.org
Founded 1978
Member Libraries: 150 acad, hospital, med & pub
Primary Functions: Promote the dissemination of knowledge & objective, accurate information about the use & abuse of alcohol, tobacco & other drugs; serve as a communications network for those working in the field; encourage cooperation & linkages among members & information centers; serve as a member advocate on matters of common interest; support professional development of members

COLORADO

AUTOMATION SYSTEM COLORADO CONSORTIUM*, (ASCC), c/o Delta Public Library, 211 W Sixth St, Delta, 81416. Tel: 970-872-4317. Web Site: ascc.lib.co.us. *Tech Consult,* Connie Wolfrom
Founded 2004
Member Libraries: 63
Primary Functions: Deliver SirsiDynix library automation system, including circulation, cataloging, serials & acquisition functions, as well as a web-accessible catalog

COLORADO ALLIANCE OF RESEARCH LIBRARIES*, 3801 E Florida Ave, Ste 515, Denver, 80210. SAN 322-3760. Tel: 303-759-3399. FAX: 303-759-3363. Web Site: www.coalliance.org. *Exec Dir,* Alan Charnes; Tel: 303-759-3399, Ext 104, E-mail: alan@coalliance.org
Founded 1973
Member Libraries: 1 pub & 9 univ
Primary Functions: Vehicle for members to cooperate for the benefit of their users & the public; Cooperative agreements in ILL; Joint acquisition of unusual or expensive items; Online acquisitions

COLORADO ASSOCIATION OF LAW LIBRARIES*, PO Box 13363, Denver, 80201. SAN 322-4325. Tel: 303-492-7535. FAX: 303-492-2707. Web Site: www.aallnet.org/chapter/coall. *Pres,* Tracy Leming; E-mail: tleming@bhf-law.com
Founded 1977
Member Libraries: 100
Primary Functions: General networking & resource sharing; continuing education; information programs

COLORADO COUNCIL OF MEDICAL LIBRARIANS*, (CCML), PO Box 101058, Denver, 80210-1058. SAN 370-0755. Tel: 303-724-2124. FAX: 303-724-2154. Web Site: www.ccmlnet.org. *Pres,* Gene Gardner; E-mail: gene.gardner@uchsc.edu; *Librn,* Lilian Hoffecker; E-mail: lilian.hoffecker@uchsc.edu
Founded 1957
Member Libraries: 108 med
Primary Functions: Provides opportunities for professional growth through networking, educational & organizational participation; collaborates with other organizations to increase public understanding & support of our profession; monitors developments in health care & information science & assesses their impact on the profession & its future.

COLORADO LIBRARY CONSORTIUM*, (CLiC), 770 W Hampden Ave, Ste 75, Centennial, 80112. SAN 371-3970. Tel: 303-422-1150. Toll Free Tel: 888-206-2695. FAX: 303-431-9752. Web Site: www.clicweb.org. *Exec Dir,* Jim Duncan; E-mail: jduncan@clicweb.org
Founded 2004
Member Libraries: 453
Primary Functions: Consulting; Continuing Education; Cooperative Purchases; Support Services; Management of courier sysyem including links to other states and a discarded book recycle program; manage a Koha-based Ils for member libraries

CONNECTICUT

BIBLIOMATION*, 32 Crest Rd, Middlebury, 06762. Tel: 203-577-4070. Toll Free Tel: 800-327-4765 (Conn only). FAX: 203-577-4077. Web Site: www.biblio.org. *Chief Exec Officer,* Mike Simonds; Tel: 203-577-4070, Ext 106, E-mail: msimonds@biblio.org; *Asst Dir,* Amy Terlaga; Tel: 203-577-4070, Ext 101, E-mail:

terlaga@biblio.org; *Bus Mgr,* Nancy Mazer; Tel: 203-577-4070, Ext 104, E-mail: nmazer@biblio.org
Founded 1980
Member Libraries: 60 pub & 16 sch
Primary Functions: Telecommunications, technological & ILS automation services

CAPITAL AREA HEALTH CONSORTIUM*, 270 Farmington Ave, Ste 352, Farmington, 06032-1994. SAN 322-0370. Tel: 860-676-1110. Toll Free Tel: 888-372-2242. FAX: 860-676-1303. Web Site: www.cahc.org. *Pres,* Karen Goodman
Primary Functions: Provides support services for Graduate Medical Education programs sponsored primarily by the University of Connecticut School of Medicine; provides an inter-institutional forum to improve collaboration among its members

CONNECTICUT LIBRARY CONSORTIUM, 234 Court St, Middletown, 06457-3304. SAN 322-0389. Tel: 860-344-8777. FAX: 860-344-9199. E-mail: clc@ctlibrarians.org. Web Site: www.ctlibrarians.org. *Exec Dir,* Jennifer Keohane; E-mail: jkeohane@ctlibrarians.org
Founded 2003
Member Libraries: Over 800 Connecticut public, academic, school, & special libraries
Primary Functions: Statewide membership collaborative serving all types of Connecticut libraries by helping them strengthen their ability to serve their users.

COUNCIL OF STATE LIBRARY AGENCIES IN THE NORTHEAST*, (COSLINE), Connecticut State Library, 231 Capitol Ave, Hartford, 06106. SAN 322-0451. Tel: 860-757-6510. FAX: 860-757-6503.
Founded 1972
Member Libraries: State libr agencies of CT, DE, MA, MD, ME, NH, NJ, NY, PA, RI, VT & WV
Primary Functions: Provides coordination of planning for regional multitype library cooperation

CTW LIBRARY CONSORTIUM*, Olin Memorial Library, Wesleyan University, Middletown, 06459-6065. SAN 329-4587. Tel: 860-685-3887. FAX: 860-685-2661. *Managing Dir,* Patricia Tully; *Librn, Collaborative Pojects,* Lorraine Huddy; Tel: 860-685-3844
Founded 1987
Member Libraries: 3
Primary Functions: Shared computer system; running Endeavor Voyager; resource sharing through a delivery service; FAX network

HARTFORD CONSORTIUM FOR HIGHER EDUCATION*, 950 Main St, Ste 314, Hartford, 06103. SAN 322-0443. Tel: 860-906-5016. FAX: 860-906-5118. Web Site: www.hartfordconsortium.org. *Exec Dir,* Rosanne Druckman; E-mail: rdruckman@ccc.commnet.edu
Founded 1972
Member Libraries: 11 col & univ
Primary Functions: Standard borrowing & visiting privileges for students & faculty of member institutions; coordination

LIBRARIES ONLINE, INC*, (LION), 100 Riverview Ctr, Ste 252, Middletown, 06457. SAN 322-3922. Tel: 860-347-1704. FAX: 860-346-3707. Web Site: www.lioninc.org. *Exec Dir,* Alan Hagyard; E-mail: ahagyard@lioninc.org; *Assoc Dir,* Andrew Gardner; E-mail: agardner@lioninc.org
Founded 1982
Member Libraries: 22
Primary Functions: Provides members with an integrated library system, shared bibliographic database & cataloging utility, telecommunications, wide & local area network services, internet, email, web services & electronic databases

LIBRARY CONNECTION, INC*, 599 Matianuck Ave, Windsor, 06095-3567. Tel: 860-298-5322. FAX: 860-298-5328. Web Site: www.libraryconnection.info. *Exec Dir,* George Christian; *Automation Librn,* Katherine Bade; *Automation Librn,* Patricia Kiser; *Network Adminr,* Ken Sutton
Founded 2003
Member Libraries: 27 acad & pub
Primary Functions: Shared online public access catalog & information system (SIRSI)

NORTH ATLANTIC HEALTH SCIENCES LIBRARIES, INC*, (NAHSL), University of Vermont Medical School, Dana Medical Library, Medical Education Center, Burlington, 05405. SAN 371-0599. Tel: 508-656-3483. FAX: 508-656-0762. Web Site: www.nahsl.org. *Chair,* Marianne Burke; E-mail: marianne.burke@uvm.edu
Founded 1957
Member Libraries: 229 Librarians
Primary Functions: Encourage communication & networking among health science libraries in New England; provide continuing education opportunities for the membership

DELAWARE

CENTRAL DELAWARE LIBRARY CONSORTIUM*, Dover Public Library, 45 S State St, Dover, 19901. SAN 329-3696. Tel: 302-736-7030. FAX: 302-736-5087. Web Site: www.doverpubliclibrary.org. *Dir,* Margery Kirby Cyr; Tel: 302-736-7032,

E-mail: margery.cyr@lib.de.us; *Asst Dir,* Joan Stover; Tel: 302-736-4220, E-mail: joan.stover@lib.de.us
Founded 1982
Member Libraries: 3
Primary Functions: OCLC cataloging association

DELAWARE LIBRARY CONSORTIUM*, (DLC), Delaware Academy of Medicine, 4765 Ogletown Stanton Rd, Ste L10, Newark, 19713. SAN 329-3718. Tel: 302-733-1122. FAX: 302-733-3885. E-mail: library@delamed.org. Web Site: www.delamed.org. *Dir,* P J Grier; Tel: 302-376-0314
Founded 1979
Member Libraries: 7 acad, med & spec
Primary Functions: Sharing access to OCLC

DISTRICT OF COLUMBIA

COMPUTER SCIENCES CORPORATION, ERIC Project, 655 15th St NW, Ste 500, Washington, 20005. SAN 322-161X. Tel: 202-741-4200. FAX: 202-628-3205. Web Site: www.eric.ed.gov. *Dir,* Lawrence Henry; Tel: 202-741-4224, E-mail: lhenry9@csc.com
Primary Functions: Acquisitions; electronic cataloging, indexing, abstracting; receiving & dispatch; document control & analysis; authority-list maintenance, including lexicographic analysis; editing; data preparation; computer processing; computerized typesetting; system file maintenance; database management & distribution, computer programming reference responses

COUNCIL FOR CHRISTIAN COLLEGES & UNIVERSITIES*, 321 Eighth St NE, Washington, 20002. SAN 322-0524. Tel: 202-546-8713. FAX: 202-546-8913. E-mail: council@cccu.org. Web Site: www.cccu.org. *Pres,* Paul R Corts
Founded 1976
Member Libraries: 105 col
Primary Functions: Sharing resources that deal with the integration of Christian faith, learning & living; publication of Choose a Christian College

DISTRICT OF COLUMBIA AREA HEALTH SCIENCE LIBRARIES, (DCAHSL), Washington. (Mail add: PO Box 96920, Washington, 20090-6920), SAN 323-9918. Tel: 202-863-2518. E-mail: resources@acog.org. Web Site: www8.georgetown.edu/dml/dcahsl/index.html. *Treas,* Debra G Scarborough
Founded 1969
Member Libraries: 30
Primary Functions: Exchange of ideas; discussion of problems & issues of concern; encourage & establish cooperative resource sharing projects; sponsor continuing education & instructive programming

FEDLINK*, Federal Library & Information Network, c/o Federal Library & Information Center Committee, 101 Independence Ave SE, Adams Bldg, Rm 217, Washington, 20540-4935. SAN 322-0761. Tel: 202-707-4800. FAX: 202-707-4818. E-mail: flicc@loc.gov. Web Site: www.loc.gov/flicc/fedlink.html. *Exec Dir,* Roberta I Shaffer; E-mail: rsha@loc.gov
Founded 1977
Member Libraries: 1200 fed librs & info ctrs
Primary Functions: Contracting for on-line services, information retrieval, cataloging & retrospective conversion, interlibrary loan services, document delivery, books procurement & serials subscriptions; instruction & training on OCLC products & services, the Internet & other library-related technologies

INTERLIBRARY USERS ASSOCIATION*, (IUA), c/o Urban Institute Library, 2100 M St NW, Washington, 20037. SAN 322-1628. Tel: 202-261-5534. FAX: 202-223-3043. Web Site: www.lib.umd.edu/guests/iua/iuahome.html. *Pres,* Nancy L Minter; E-mail: nminter@urban.org
Founded 1964
Member Libraries: 45
Primary Functions: Reciprocal interlibrary lending & borrowing

TRANSPORTATION RESEARCH BOARD*, 500 Fifth St NW, Washington, 20001. SAN 370-582X. Tel: 202-334-2990. FAX: 202-334-2527. Web Site: www.trb.org. *Mgr, Info Serv,* Barbara Post; E-mail: bpost@nas.edu
Founded 1968
Member Libraries: 1 spec
Primary Functions: Prepare & maintain bibliographic database of transportation research & research in progress

WASHINGTON THEOLOGICAL CONSORTIUM*, 487 Michigan Ave NE, Washington, 20017-1585. SAN 322-0842. Tel: 202-832-2675. FAX: 202-526-0818. E-mail: wtc@washtheocon.org. Web Site: www.washtheocon.org. *Exec Dir,* Larry Golemon; E-mail: lgolemon@washtheocon.org
Founded 1967
Member Libraries: 16
Primary Functions: Interlibrary loan; acquisitions; Union List of Serials

FLORIDA

CENTRAL FLORIDA LIBRARY COOPERATIVE*, (CFLC), 431 E Horatio Ave, Ste 230, Maitland, 32751. SAN 371-9014. Tel: 407-644-9050. FAX: 407-644-7023. E-mail: contactus@cflc.net. Web Site: www.cflc.net. *Exec Dir,* Marta Westall
Founded 1989

Member Libraries: 84 acad, pub & spec
Primary Functions: Promote resource sharing; members participate in OCLC group access program & union list of serials project; internet access, continuing education

COLLEGE CENTER FOR LIBRARY AUTOMATION*, (CCLA), 1753 W Paul Dirac Dr, Tallahassee, 32310. Tel: 850-922-6044. FAX: 850-922-4869. E-mail: servicedesk@cclaflorida.org. Web Site: www.cclaflorida.org. *Exec Dir,* Richard Madaus, PhD; *Dep Exec Dir,* Ann Armbrister; *Communications Coordr,* Mark Adams
Founded 1989
Member Libraries: 60
Primary Functions: Provide OPAC, catalogue, databases to community colleges, as well as an integrated library system

FLORIDA CENTER FOR LIBRARY AUTOMATION*, (FCLA), 5830 NW 39th Ave, Gainesville, 32606. Tel: 352-392-9020. FAX: 352-392-9185. E-mail: fclmin@ufl.edu. Web Site: www.fcla.edu. *Dir,* James Corey; Tel: 352-392-9020, Ext 322, E-mail: jcorey@ufl.edu; *Asst Dir, Digital Serv,* Phyllis Caplan; Tel: 352-392-9020, Ext 324, E-mail: pcaplan@ufl.edu; *Asst Dir, Libr Serv,* Michele Newberry; Tel: 352-392-9020, Ext 349, E-mail: fclmin@ufl.edu
Founded 1984
Member Libraries: 11 acad
Primary Functions: Provide computer services to libraries of state universities

FLORIDA LIBRARY INFORMATION NETWORK, R A Gray Bldg, State Library & Archives of Florida, Tallahassee, 32399-0250. SAN 322-0869. Tel: 850-245-6600. FAX: 850-245-6744. E-mail: library@dos.myflorida.com. Web Site: dlis.dos.state.fl.us. *Bur Chief,* Cathy Moloney; Tel: 850-245-6687, E-mail: cathy.moloney@dos.myflorida.com; *Lending Serv Librn,* Linda Pulliam; Tel: 850-245-6672, E-mail: linda.pulliam@dos.myflorida.com
Founded 1968
Member Libraries: 28 commun col, 78 dist media ctr, 43 pvt acad, 87 pub, 226 spec, 1 state & 13 state univ
Primary Functions: Statewide cooperative for interlibrary loan & resource sharing. The State Library serves as network headquarters; receives title, photocopy & subject requests by e-mail, OCLC & FAX from over 525 libraries in Florida & fills & refers them to member libraries; using FLIN protocols based on geographic proximity

NORTHEAST FLORIDA LIBRARY INFORMATION NETWORK*, (NEFLIN), 2233 Park Ave, Ste 402, Orange Park, 32073. Tel: 904-278-5620. FAX: 904-278-5625. E-mail: office@neflin.org. Web Site: www.neflin.org. *Exec Dir,* Brad Ward; E-mail: brad@neflin.org; *Asst Dir,* Stephanie Fazenbaker Race; E-mail: stephanie@neflin.org; *Continuing Educ Coordr,* Patricia Hay; E-mail: patty@neflin.org
Founded 1992
Member Libraries: 39 (incl 19 acad, 18 pub & 2 spec)
Primary Functions: Resource sharing, continuing education & online technology (Internet, consulting, databases & survey workstation)

PANHANDLE LIBRARY ACCESS NETWORK*, (PLAN), Five Miracle Strip Loop, Ste 8, Panama City Beach, 32407-3850. SAN 370-047X. Tel: 850-233-9051. FAX: 850-235-2286. Web Site: www.plan.lib.fl.us. *Exec Dir,* William P Conniff; E-mail: wconniff@plan.lib.fl.us
Founded 1991
Member Libraries: 46 acad, pub, sch & spec
Primary Functions: To provide services & programs which promote & enhance resource sharing amoung libraries in a 17-county region of the Florida Panhandle; Current projects include the Panhandle Union List of Serials (PULSE) through the OCLC Union Listing subsystem; continuing education workshops; loading non-OCLC MARC records into the OCLC database, the retrospective conversion of those PLAN libraries with no MARC records; consulting for libraries on technical and organizational issues

SEFLIN - SOUTHEAST FLORIDA LIBRARY INFORMATION NETWORK, INC, Wimberly Library, Office 452, Florida Atlantic University, 777 Glades Rd, Boca Raton, 33431. SAN 370-0666. Tel: 561-208-0984. Toll Free Tel: 877-733-5460. FAX: 561-208-0995. Web Site: www.seflin.org. *Exec Dir,* Jeannette Smithee; E-mail: smithee@seflin.org; *Dir, Info Serv,* Charles Mayberry; E-mail: mayberry@seflin.org; *Mrg, Admin Serv,* Irina Galilova; E-mail: galilova@seflin.org; *Mgr, Staff Develop,* Lois Albertson; E-mail: training@seflin.org
Founded 1986
Member Libraries: Acad, pub & sch
Primary Functions: To cultivate cooperation & coordination among libraries of all types, nurture efficient & effective information resource sharing; advance technological innovation; provide staff development opportunities; advocate for our libraries & their patrons

SOUTHWEST FLORIDA LIBRARY NETWORK*, (SWFLN), Bldg III, Unit 7, 12751 Westlinks Dr, Fort Myers, 33913. Tel: 239-225-4225. Toll Free Tel: 877-793-5699. FAX: 239-225-4229. E-mail: swfln@fgcu.edu. Web Site: www.swfln.org. *Exec Dir,* Sondra Taylor-Furbee; E-mail: staylorf@fgcu.edu
Founded 1993

Member Libraries: 45
Primary Functions: Provide member libraries with cost-effective sharing of library materials, staff training & evaluation; help libraries make the best technology decisions

TAMPA BAY LIBRARY CONSORTIUM, INC*, 1202 Tech Blvd, Ste 202, Tampa, 33619. SAN 322-371X. Tel: 813-622-8252, 813-740-3963. FAX: 813-628-4425. Web Site: www.tblc.org. *Exec Dir,* Charlie Parker; E-mail: cparker@tblc.org
Founded 1979
Member Libraries: 99 acad, pub, sch & spec
Primary Functions: Promotion of Interlibrary Cooperation with emphasis on continuing education, resource sharing & a shared integrated automated library system (CLSI)

TAMPA BAY MEDICAL LIBRARY NETWORK*, (TABAMLN), Florida Hospital College of Health Sciences, 671 Winyah Dr, Orlando, 32803-1226. SAN 322-0885. Tel: 407-303-9798. Toll Free Tel: 800-500-7747. FAX: 407-303-9408. Web Site: www.tblc.org/tabamln/index.shtml. *Pres,* Deanna Stevens; E-mail: deanna.stevens@fhchs.edu
Founded 1975
Member Libraries: 30
Primary Functions: Continuing education; interlibrary loans & document delivery

GEORGIA

ASSOCIATION OF SOUTHEASTERN RESEARCH LIBRARIES*, (ASERL), c/o SOLINET, 1438 W Peachtree St NW, Ste 200, Atlanta, 30309-2955. SAN 322-1555. Tel: 404-892-0943. Toll Free Tel: 800-999-8558. FAX: 404-892-7879. Web Site: www.aserl.org. *Exec Dir,* John Burger; E-mail: jburger@solinet.net
Founded 1956
Member Libraries: 37 acad & 7 state
Primary Functions: To promote cooperative enterprises among member research libraries

ATLANTA HEALTH SCIENCE LIBRARIES CONSORTIUM*, Fran Golding Medical Library at Scottish Rite, 1001 Johnson Ferry Rd NE, Atlanta, 30342-1600. Tel: 404-785-2157. FAX: 404-785-2155. Web Site: www.ghsla.org/AHSLC. *Pres,* Kate Daniels; E-mail: kate.daniels@choa.org
Founded 1974
Member Libraries: 24
Primary Functions: Interlibrary loan exchange; coordination of acquisitions; continuing education for members; improvement of library services

ATLANTA REGIONAL COUNCIL FOR HIGHER EDUCATION*, (ARCHE), 50 Hurt Plaza, Ste 735, Atlanta, 30303-2923. SAN 322-0990. Tel: 404-651-2668. FAX: 404-880-9816. E-mail: arche@atlantahighered.org. Web Site: www.atlantahighered.org. *Pres,* Michael Gerber
Founded 1938
Member Libraries: 19 pub & pvt col & univ, plus six affiliated libr
Primary Functions: Interlibrary loan & interlibrary use; other cooperative activities in areas of civil rights holdings & professional development

GEORGIA INTERACTIVE NETWORK FOR MEDICAL INFORMATION, (GAIN), c/o Mercer University School of Medicine, 1550 College St, Macon, 31207. SAN 370-0577. Tel: 478-301-2515. Toll Free Tel: 800-425-4246. FAX: 478-301-2051. E-mail: gain.info@gain.mercer.edu. Web Site: gain.mercer.edu. *Prog Coordr,* David Greenebaum; Tel: 478-301-2827, E-mail: greenebaum_dc@mercer.edu
Founded 1983
Member Libraries: 46
Primary Functions: Provides reference & database searching; online union catalog; interlibrary loan; fax; electronic document delivery; current alert & full-text services

GEORGIA ONLINE DATABASE, (GOLD), c/o Public Library Services, 1800 Century Pl NE, Ste 150, Atlanta, 30345-4304. SAN 322-094X. Tel: 404-235-7200. FAX: 404-235-7201. Web Site: www.georgialibraries.org/lib/gold. *Asst State Librn, Libr Develop,* Alan Harkness; Tel: 404-235-7134, E-mail: aharkness@georgialibraries.org
Member Libraries: 211 acad, county, hosp, pub, regional, sch & spec
Primary Functions: Statewide interlibrary lending network; union list of serials for Georgia; group access capability through OCLC

LYRASIS*, 1438 W Peachtree St NW, Ste 200, Atlanta, 30309-2955. SAN 322-0974. Tel: 404-892-0943. Toll Free Tel: 800-999-8558. FAX: 404-892-7879. Web Site: www.lyrasis.org. *Exec Dir,* Kate Nevins
Founded 1973
Member Libraries: 2500 col, jr col, pub, sch, spec & state
Primary Functions: Regional library system cooperative providing access, training & support for OCLC services & products; supports a regional preservation program; database licensing services; education, training & brokerage/discount rates for information retrieval database services

METRO ATLANTA LIBRARY ASSOCIATION*, (MALA), PO Box 14948, Atlanta, 30324. SAN 378-2549. Tel: 678-915-7207. FAX: 678-915-7471. E-mail: mala-a@comcast.net. Web Site: www.matllib.org. *Pres,* Steven Vincent; Tel: 404-371-8072

Founded 1982
Member Libraries: 130 individual & institutional
Primary Functions: Continuing education & networking of librarians, media specialists & information scientists in the Atlanta area

HAWAII

HAWAII LIBRARY CONSORTIUM*, (HLC), c/o Hawaii Business Research Library, 590 Lipoa Pkwy, No 136, Kihei, 96753. Tel: 808-875-2408. Web Site: www.hlc.hawaii.edu. *Pres,* Sonia I King; E-mail: soniai@hawaii.edu; *President-Elect,* Diane Sakai; Tel: 808-455-0378, E-mail: dsakai@hawaii.edu
Founded 2002
Member Libraries: 5 col, 33 pvt sch & 51 pub
Primary Functions: To increase, enhance & facilitate cooperation among libraries in the State of Hawaii through consortial purchasing of resources, expanding access to resources, & encouraging partnerships between & among member libraries; to support training & professional development relative to purchased resources, expanding access to resources, & effective partnerships among member libraries

HAWAII-PACIFIC CHAPTER OF THE MEDICAL LIBRARY ASSOCIATION*, (HPC-MLA), Health Sciences Library, 651 Ilalo St MEB, Honolulu, 96813. SAN 371-3946. Tel: 808-692-0810. FAX: 808-692-1244. Web Site: hpcmla.mlanet.org. *Chair,* A Lee Adams; E-mail: annisa@hawaii.edu; *Continuing Educ Chair,* Mabel Trafford; E-mail: mabel.trafford@medd.army.mil
Primary Functions: Promote the educational, scientific & professional growth of its members & member organizations in health sciences library service & in the Medical Library Association; encourage cooperation & communication among its members in the Hawaii-Pacific area

IDAHO

CANYON OWYHEE LIBRARY GROUP, LTD*, (COLG), PO Box 340, Marsing, 83639. Tel: 208-896-4112. Web Site: colg.lili.org. *Pres,* Peggy Rabe
Founded 1989
Member Libraries: Over 30 pub sch & private libr
Primary Functions: A cooperative venture among public school & private libraries; uses WLN's LaserCat as a shared union catalog; cooperative collection development; materials delivery system; reciprocal borrowing agreement; Union Periodical List & COLG Video Catalog

COOPERATIVE INFORMATION NETWORK*, (CIN), 8385 N Government Way, Hayden, 83835-9280. SAN 323-7656. Tel: 208-772-5612. FAX: 208-772-2498. E-mail: hay@cin.kcl.org. Web Site: cin.wash-id.net, cinlibraries.org. *Fiscal Agent,* John W Hartung; Tel: 208-772-5612, Ext 16, E-mail: jhartung@cin.kcl.org; *Coordr,* larry Almeida; E-mail: lalmeida@cin.kcl.org
Founded 1984
Member Libraries: 15 pub, 2 sch & 2 spec
Primary Functions: Shared automated database for cataloging, circulation, OPAC

IDAHO HEALTH INFORMATION ASSOCIATION*, (IHIA), c/o Eastern Idaho Regional Medical Center, PO Box 2077, Idaho Falls, 83403. SAN 371-5078. Tel: 208-529-6077. FAX: 208-529-7014. Web Site: ihia.lili.org. *Dir,* Kathy Fatkin; E-mail: library@dataway.net; *Treas,* Amy Claybaugh; E-mail: claybaua@slrmc.org
Founded 1971
Member Libraries: 18 med/hosp
Primary Functions: Resource sharing; continuing education

LIBRARY CONSORTIUM OF EASTERN IDAHO*, (LCEI), 113 S Garfield, Pocatello, 83204-3235. SAN 323-7699. Tel: 208-237-2192. Web Site: lcei.lili.org. *Chair,* Linda Rasmussen; Tel: 208-425-3695, E-mail: gracedistlibra@dcdi.net; *Treas,* Heidi Riddoch; Tel: 208-357-7801, E-mail: hriddoch@cableone.net
Founded 1999
Member Libraries: 20 pub
Primary Functions: Shared automated circulation system

LYNX! CONSORTIUM*, c/o Boise Public Library, 715 S Capitol Blvd, Boise, 83702-7195. SAN 375-0086. Tel: 208-384-4238, 208-384-4485. FAX: 208-384-4025. Web Site: www.boisepubliclibrary.org.
Founded 1979
Member Libraries: 11
Primary Functions: Shared automated circulation & online public access catalog

WESTERN COUNCIL OF STATE LIBRARIES, INC*, Idaho Commission for Libraries, 325 W State St, Boise, 83702-6055. Tel: 208-334-2150. FAX: 208-334-4016. Web Site: www.westernco.org. *Pres,* Ann Joslin; E-mail: ann.joslin@libraries.idaho.gov
Founded 1977
Member Libraries: 21
Primary Functions: Improve library services in the West; provide means for enunciating a position of western state librarians on national & regional matters of common concern; develop resource sharing; foster staff development

ILLINOIS

AREAWIDE HOSPITAL LIBRARY CONSORTIUM OF SOUTHWESTERN ILLINOIS*, (AHLC), c/o St Elizabeth Hosp Health Sci Libr, 211 S Third St, Belleville, 62222. SAN 322-1016. Tel: 618-234-2120, Ext 2011. FAX: 618-222-4614. *Coordr,* Kim Whittborn
Founded 1974
Member Libraries: 9
Primary Functions: Facilitating ILL activities among members, between consortia & within the Medical Library Network; improving communication between members; providing reference service, educational programs, a forum for information exchange & coordinated acquisitions

ASSOCIATION OF CHICAGO THEOLOGICAL SCHOOLS*, (ACTS), Univ of St Mary of the Lake, 1000 E Maple Ave, Mundelein, 60060. SAN 370-0658. Tel: 847-970-4860. *Chair,* Thomas Baima; E-mail: tbaima@usml.edu
Founded 1968
Member Libraries: 11
Primary Functions: Provides student cross registration; library cooperation; faculty interest groups; joint programs

CENTER FOR RESEARCH LIBRARIES*, 6050 S Kenwood, Chicago, 60637-2804. SAN 322-1032. Tel: 773-955-4545. FAX: 773-955-4339. Web Site: www.crl.edu. *Pres,* Bernard F Reilly; Tel: 773-955-4545, Ext 334, E-mail: breilly@crl.edu; *VPres,* Position Currently Open
Founded 1949
Member Libraries: 239 col, independent res librs & univ
Primary Functions: Houses, preserves & circulates research materials for use by member libraries; purchases materials for cooperative use

CHICAGO & SOUTH CONSORTIUM*, Jackson Park Hospital & Medical Center, 7531 S Stony Island Ave, Chicago, 60649-3993. SAN 322-1067. Tel: 773-947-7653. *Coordr,* Andrew Paradise; E-mail: andyanne@hotmail.com
Founded 1974
Member Libraries: 19 acad & med
Primary Functions: Interlibrary loan; staff development; resource sharing

CHICAGO AREA MUSEUM LIBRARIES, (CAML), c/o Library, The Field Museum, 1400 S Lake Shore Dr, Chicago, 60605-2496. SAN 371-392X. Tel: 312-665-7970. FAX: 312-665-7893. *Mus Librn,* Christine Giannoni; E-mail: cgiannoni@fieldmuseum.org
Founded 1989
Member Libraries: 30 libr & 15 mus
Primary Functions: Function as a forum for communication & cooperation among Chicago area museum libraries; provide a network for intermuseum library services

COMMITTEE ON INSTITUTIONAL COOPERATION*, 1819 S Neil St, Ste D, Champaign, 61820-7271. Tel: 217-333-8475. FAX: 217-244-7127. E-mail: cic@staff.cic.net. Web Site: cic.net. *Dir,* Barbara Mcfadden Allen; Tel: 217-244-9240, E-mail: bmallen@staff.cic.net
Founded 1958
Member Libraries: 12 Acad
Primary Functions: Foster collaboration to benefit research & instruction

CONSORTIUM OF ACADEMIC & RESEARCH LIBRARIES IN ILLINOIS*, (CARLI), 100 Trade Ctr Dr, Ste 303, Champaign, 61820. SAN 322-3736. Tel: 217-244-7593. Toll Free Tel: 866-904-5873. FAX: 217-244-7596. E-mail: support@carli.illinois.edu. Web Site: www.carli.illinois.edu. *Exec Dir,* Susan Singleton; Tel: 217-244-5167, E-mail: ssingle@uillinois.edu; *Dir, Admin & Planning,* Tom Dorst; Tel: 217-206-7856; *Dir, Coll Serv,* Elizabeth Clarage; Tel: 217-753-9168; *Dir, Electronic Res,* Cindy Clennon; Tel: 217-333-4895; *Dir, User Serv,* Kristine Hammerstrand; *Assoc Dir, Syst Serv,* Brandon Gant; Tel: 217-333-4802; *Asst Dir, Communications,* Margaret Chambers; Tel: 217-333-2618; *Chief Financial Officer, Bus & Finance Serv,* Connie Walsh; Tel: 217-333-4802
Founded 2005
Member Libraries: 153
Primary Functions: Electronic resource purchases; collection assessment; union catalog/resource sharing services

COUNCIL OF DIRECTORS OF STATE UNIVERSITY LIBRARIES IN ILLINOIS, (CODSULI), Southern Illinois Univ Sch of Med Library, 801 N Rutledge, Springfield, 62702-4910. (Mail add: PO Box 19625, Springfield, 62794-9625), SAN 322-1083. Tel: 217-545-0994. FAX: 217-545-0988. Web Site: codsuli.org.
Founded 1977
Member Libraries: 13 Illinois Pub Univ Libr
Primary Functions: Promote the advancement of public academic libraries in Illinois through cooperation, exchange of information, research, standards, & advocacy.

EAST CENTRAL ILLINOIS CONSORTIUM*, Eastern Illinois University, Booth Library, 600 LincolnAve, Charleston, 61920. SAN 322-1040. Tel: 217-581-7549. FAX: 217-581-7534. *Mgr,* Stacey Knight-Davis; E-mail: cfslk@eiu.edu
Founded 1975
Member Libraries: 10 acad, med & spec
Primary Functions: Interlibrary loan; reference

FOX VALLEY HEALTH SCIENCE LIBRARY CONSORTIUM*, c/o Delnor-Community Hospital, 300 Randall Rd, Geneva, 60134. SAN 329-3831. Tel: 630-208-4299. *Coordr,* Paula Olson
Founded 1975
Member Libraries: 15
Primary Functions: Facilitate interlibrary cooperation in resource sharing & continuing education

HEART OF ILLINOIS LIBRARY CONSORTIUM*, 511 NE Greenleaf, Peoria, 61603. SAN 322-1113, *Chairperson,* Leslie Menz
Member Libraries: 29 acad, med & spec
Primary Functions: Continuing education; advice on journal acquisitions; resource & expertise sharing; Medline access & backup reference

ILLINOIS LIBRARY & INFORMATION NETWORK, (ILLINET), c/o Illinois State Library, Gwendolyn Brooks Bldg, 300 S Second St, Springfield, 62701-1796. SAN 322-1148. Tel: 217-782-2994. FAX: 217-785-4326. Web Site: www.cyberdriveillinois.com/library/isl/isl.html. *Dir,* Anne Craig; E-mail: acraig@ilsos.net
Member Libraries: 5166 acad, pub, sch & spec librs, 3 regional multitype libr systs
Primary Functions: Interlibrary loan; cooperative reference; access to research & reference centers; delivery; cooperative collection development; continuing education; services to the blind & physically handicapped; access to OCLC & staff support for training & administration of its use; access to electronic resources

ILLINOIS OFFICE OF EDUCATIONAL SERVICES*, 2450 Foundation Dr, Ste 100, Springfield, 62703-5464. SAN 371-5108. Tel: 217-786-3010. Toll Free Tel: 800-252-4822. FAX: 217-786-3020. E-mail: info@ioes.org. *Dir,* Rebecca Woodhull; Tel: 217-786-3010, Ext 231, E-mail: rwoodhull@ioes.org
Founded 1971
Primary Functions: Provide free loan education materials to teachers & trainers

LIBRAS, INC*, North Park University, 3225 W Foster Ave, Chicago, 60625-4895. SAN 322-1172. Tel: 773-244-5584. FAX: 773-244-4891. Web Site: libras.org. *Pres,* Mark Vargas; Tel: 773-298-3350, E-mail: vargas@sxu.edu
Founded 1965
Member Libraries: 17
Primary Functions: Interlibrary loan & resource sharing; staff development & continuing education

METROPOLITAN CONSORTIUM OF CHICAGO*, Chicago School of Professional Psychology, 325 N Wells St, Chicago, 60610. SAN 322-1180. Tel: 312-329-6633. FAX: 312-644-6075. *Coordr,* Margaret White
Member Libraries: 25 acad, med & spec
Primary Functions: Interlibrary loan; serial holdings list; continuing education; informal consultation; cooperative projects

NATIONAL NETWORK OF LIBRARIES OF MEDICINE GREATER MIDWEST REGION*, (NN-LM GMR), c/o Library of Health Sci, Univ Illinois at Chicago, 1750 W Polk St, M/C 763, Chicago, 60612-4330. SAN 322-1202. Tel: 312-996-2464. Toll Free Tel: 800-338-7657. FAX: 312-996-2226. Web Site: nnlm.gov/gmr/. *Dir,* Kathryn Carpenter; *Assoc Dir,* Ruth Holst
Founded 1965
Member Libraries: 31 regional librs & over 100 info ctrs
Primary Functions: Resources for members of the National Network of Library of Medicine (NN/LM) Greater Midwest Region; coordination of regional interlibrary loan; coordination of education, training & outreach programs for health science librarians & health care professionals; subcontracts management & development; internet education & training; regional blog & other publications

NETWORK OF ILLINOIS LEARNING RESOURCES IN COMMUNITY COLLEGES*, (NILRC), c/o Kishwaukee College, 21193 Malta Rd, Malta, 60150. (Mail add: PO Box 120, Blanchardville, 53516-0120). Tel: 608-523-4094. FAX: 608-523-4072. Web Site: www.nilrc.org. *Exec Off Bus Mgr,* Lisa Sikora; E-mail: lsikora@nilrc.org
Founded 1975
Member Libraries: 50 acad
Primary Functions: Enhance the service provided by post-secondary resource center libraries & alternative delivery programs to their institutions & respective communities

SYSTEM WIDE AUTOMATED NETWORK*, (SWAN), c/o Metropolitan Library System, 125 Tower Dr, Burr Ridge, 60527-5783. Tel: 630-734-5000. Toll Free Tel: 866-734-2004. FAX: 630-734-5050. Web Site: www.mls.lib.il.us; swan.sls.lib.il.us. *Dir,* Aaron Skog; E-mail: skoga@mls.lib.il.us
Founded 1974
Member Libraries: 3 commun col, 74 pub, 2 spec
Primary Functions: Library automation services

INDIANA

CENTRAL INDIANA HEALTH SCIENCE LIBRARIES CONSORTIUM, Indiana University School of Med Library, 975 W Walnut IB109, Indianapolis, 46202. SAN 322-1245. Tel: 317-274-8358. FAX: 317-274-4056. Web Site:

cihslc.pbworks.com/w/page/4229306/frontpage. *Officer,* Elaine Skopelja; E-mail: eskopelj@iupui.edu
Founded 1973
Member Libraries: 15
Primary Functions: Networking in cooperative activities; facilitating resource sharing among members; providing professional development & educational opportunities

CONSORTIUM OF COLLEGE & UNIVERSITY MEDIA CENTERS*, (CCUMC), Indiana University, Franklin Hall 0009, 601 E Kirkwood Ave, Bloomington, 47405-1223. SAN 322-1091. Tel: 812-855-6049. FAX: 812-855-2103. E-mail: ccumc@ccumc.org. Web Site: www.ccumc.org. *Exec Dir,* Aileen Scales; *Admin Serv,* Kirsten Phillips
Founded 1971
Member Libraries: 750 univ
Primary Functions: Advocate the accessibility & effective use of educational media; provide leadership in the development of standards for the effective implementation & management of instructional technology in higher education; foster cooperative efforts among colleges & universities & other institutions, agencies, foundations & organizations in the solution of mutual problems; gather & disseminate information about educational, professional & operational issues, including statistics important to the profession; develop & provide programs & services that will enable members to most effectively support the missions of their institutions; provide profesional development opportunities for members; inspire, generate & coordinate research & scholarship that advances the mission of the Consortium

EVANSVILLE AREA LIBRARY CONSORTIUM*, 3700 Washington Ave, Evansville, 47750. SAN 322-1261. Tel: 812-485-4151. FAX: 812-485-7564. *Coordr,* Jane Saltzman
Member Libraries: 23
Primary Functions: Support of quality patient care through efficient dissemination of information; promotion of high standards of library service; cooperative sharing of resources through interlibrary loan; provision of continuing education seminars & workshops

EVERGREEN INDIANA CONSORTIUM, Indiana State Library, 315 W Ohio St, Indianapolis, 46202. Tel: 317-605-4518. FAX: 317-232-0002. Web Site: www.in.gov/library/evergreen.htm. *Coordr,* Shauna Borger; E-mail: sborger@library.IN.gov
Founded 2008
Member Libraries: 100
Primary Functions: Cooperative, open-source, integrated library automation services; facilitating resource sharing among multi-type member libraries; cataloging; statistics

INDIANA STATE DATA CENTER*, Indiana State Library, 315 W Ohio St, Indianapolis, 46202. SAN 322-1318. Tel: 317-232-3733. FAX: 317-232-3728. Web Site: www.in.gov/library/isdc.htm. *Coordr,* Katie Springer; E-mail: kspringer@library.in.gov
Founded 1978
Member Libraries: 26
Primary Functions: Provides access to current & historical census data on Indiana & its communities; information available in print, fiche, internet, CD-ROM or through Stats-Indiana & the Indiana Business Research Center, Federal-State cooperative with the US Census Bureau

NORTHEAST INDIANA HEALTH SCIENCE LIBRARIES CONSORTIUM*, (NEIHSL), Univ Saint Francis Vann Library, 2701 Spring St, Fort Wayne, 46808. SAN 373-1383. Tel: 260-399-7700, Ext 6065. FAX: 260-399-8166. *Coordr,* Lauralee Aven; E-mail: laven@sf.edu
Founded 1978
Member Libraries: 10 acad, med, pub & spec
Primary Functions: Resource sharing; Union List of Serials; professional support & development; statistics; collection development; special projects

IOWA

CONSORTIUM OF USER LIBRARIES*, (CUL), Libr for the Blind & Physically Handicapped, Iowa Dept for the Blind, 524 Fourth St, Des Moines, 50309-2364. Tel: 515-281-1333. FAX: 515-281-1263, 515-281-1378. Web Site: www.consortiumofuserlibraries.org. *Pres,* Position Currently Open
Founded 1990
Member Libraries: 6
Primary Functions: Provides a flexible & unique automated system for libraries for the Blind & Physically Handicapped to tailor the library services needs of each individual patron

DUBUQUE (IOWA) AREA LIBRARY INFORMATION CONSORTIUM*, c/o NE Iowa Community College, Burton Payne Library, 10250 Sundown Rd, Peosta, 52068. Tel: 563-556-5110, Ext 269. FAX: 563-557-0340. *Coordr,* Deb Seiffert
Founded 1979
Member Libraries: 12 acad, pub, sch & spec

Primary Functions: Interlibrary loan exchange among members; cooperative exchange of audiovisual materials; avoiding duplication of expensive materials; free exchange of materials; Serials Locator List; provide continuing education for member library staff

IOWA PRIVATE ACADEMIC LIBRARY CONSORTIUM*, (IPAL), c/o Buena Vista University Library, 610 W Fourth St, Storm Lake, 50588. SAN 329-5311. Tel: 712-749-2127, 749-2203. Toll Free Tel: 800-383-2821. FAX: 712-749-2059. E-mail: library@bvu.edu. Web Site: www.bvu.edu/library. *Pres,* Rodney N Henshaw; Fax: 712-749-2033
Founded 1891
Primary Functions: Meet annually to share ideas; photocopy exchange; group grant projects; annual statistics publications; group purchasing

LINN COUNTY LIBRARY CONSORTIUM*, Russell D Cole Library, 620 3rd St SW, Mount Vernon, 52314-1012. SAN 322-4597. Tel: 319-895-4259. Web Site: www.lclc.org. *Pres,* Jason Bengtson; E-mail: jbengtson@kaplan.edu; *VPres,* Boyd Broughton; E-mail: bbroughton@mtmercy.edu
Founded 1968
Member Libraries: 23
Primary Functions: Information sharing among librarians; serials list; resource sharing; opportunities for professional development

POLK COUNTY BIOMEDICAL CONSORTIUM*, c/o Broadlawns Medical Center Library, 1801 Hickman Rd, Des Moines, 50314. SAN 322-1431. Tel: 515-282 2394. FAX: 515-282 5634. *Treas,* Elaine Hughes; E-mail: ehughes@broadlawns.org
Member Libraries: 11
Primary Functions: Interlibrary loan; in-service education activities; resource sharing

QUAD CITY AREA BIOMEDICAL CONSORTIUM*, Great River Medical Ctr Library, 1221 S Gear Ave, West Burlington, 52655. SAN 322-435X. Tel: 319-768-4075. FAX: 319-768-4080. *Coordr,* Sarah Goff
Member Libraries: 14
Primary Functions: To promote & improve the quality of health sciences library services within member libraries to more effectively meet their informational needs; to encourage, promote & extend cooperative library services among members; to provide opportunities for professional interaction, counseling & education among member librarians

SIOUX CITY LIBRARY COOPERATIVE, (SCLC), c/o Sioux City Public Library, 529 Pierce St, Sioux City, 51101-1203. SAN 329-4722. Tel: 712-255-2933, Ext 255. FAX: 712-279-6432. *Chairperson,* Betsy Thompson
Member Libraries: 8
Primary Functions: Reciprocal Use Agreement to operate libraries so that each agency's service population will benefit. Promote the purpose & objectives of each agency.

STATE OF IOWA LIBRARIES ONLINE*, (SILO), State Library of Iowa, 1112 E Grand, Des Moines, 50319. SAN 322-1415. Tel: 515-281-4105. Toll Free Tel: 800-248-4483. FAX: 515-281-6191. Web Site: www.statelibraryofiowa.org/ld/silo/index. *State Librn,* Mary Wegner
Founded 1995
Member Libraries: 500
Primary Functions: Provide libraries with interlibrary loans; email service; web hosting

KANSAS

ASSOCIATED COLLEGES OF CENTRAL KANSAS, (ACCK), 210 S Main St, McPherson, 67460. SAN 322-1474. Tel: 620-241-5150. FAX: 620-241-5153. Web Site: www.acck.edu/ics.
Founded 1966
Member Libraries: 6 church-related cols
Primary Functions: Union Lists of Serials; reference works & bibliographies; cooperative programs of education & service

DODGE CITY LIBRARY CONSORTIUM*, c/o Comanche Intermediate Center, 1601 First Ave, Dodge City, 67801. SAN 322-4368. Tel: 620-227-1609. FAX: 620-227-4862.
Member Libraries: 14 col, pub, sch & spec
Primary Functions: Cooperation on common problems; communications improvement; resource sharing

KANSAS REGENTS LIBRARY DATABASE CONSORTIUM*, (RLDC), c/o Emporia State University, William Allen White Library, 1200 Commercial St, Emporia, 66801. Tel: 620-341-5480. E-mail: rldc@ku.edu. Web Site: www.lib.ku.edu/rldc. *Chair,* Cynthia Akers; E-mail: akerscyn@emporia.edu
Founded 1996
Member Libraries: 16 Acad, 3 Pub
Primary Functions: Purchase electronic resources (primarily databases) on a consortial basis

STATE LIBRARY OF KANSAS*, Statewide Resource Sharing Division, 300 SW Tenth Ave, Rm 343 N, Topeka, 66612-1593. SAN 329-5621. Tel: 785-296-3875. Toll Free Tel: 800-432-3919. FAX: 785-368-7291. Web Site: www.kslib.info. *Dir*, Patti Butcher; E-mail: pattib@kslib.info
Founded 2005
Primary Functions: Administers grant programs to foster interlibrary cooperation; sponsors cooperative long-range planning efforts & Administers statewide Resource sharing programs

KENTUCKY

ASSOCIATION OF INDEPENDENT KENTUCKY COLLEGES & UNIVERSITIES*, (AIKCU), 484 Chenault Rd, Frankfort, 40601. SAN 322-1490. Tel: 502-695-5007. FAX: 502-695-5057. Web Site: www.aikcu.org. *Pres*, Gary S Cox; E-mail: gary@mail.aikcu.org
Founded 1970
Member Libraries: 20 acad
Primary Functions: Interlibrary cooperation

EASTERN KENTUCKY HEALTH SCIENCE INFORMATION NETWORK*, (EKHSIN), c/o Camden-Carroll Library, Morehead State University, Morehead, 40351. SAN 370-0631. Tel: 606-783-6860. FAX: 606-784-2178. Web Site: ekhsin.morehead-st.edu. *Libr Dir*, Tammy Jenkins; E-mail: tjenkins@st-claire.org; *Libr Tech*, Crystal J Wright; Tel: 606-783-6861, E-mail: cjwright@st-claire.org
Founded 1977
Member Libraries: 8 acad & med
Primary Functions: Provides professional library services; online searching; reference information; interlibrary loans; cataloging; consulting

KENTUCKIANA METROVERSITY, INC*, 109 E Broadway, Louisville, 40202. SAN 322-1504. Tel: 502-897-3374. FAX: 502-895-1647. Web Site: www.metroversity.org. *Exec Dir*, Dr Daniel Ash
Founded 1969
Member Libraries: 7 col, univ & sem
Primary Functions: Interlibrary loan; Union List of Serials; Union Film Catalog

KENTUCKY MEDICAL LIBRARY ASSOCIATION*, VA Med Ctr, Libr Servs 142D, 800 Zorn Ave, Louisville, 40206-1499. SAN 370-0623. Tel: 502-287-6240. FAX: 502-287-6134. *Head Librn*, Gene M Haynes; Tel: 502-287-6240, Ext 5584, E-mail: gene.haynes@va.gov
Founded 1972
Member Libraries: 34
Primary Functions: Cooperative services; continuing education

SOUTHEASTERN CHAPTER OF THE AMERICAN ASSOCIATION OF LAW LIBRARIES*, (SEAALL), c/o University of Kentucky, Law Library, 620 S Limestone St, Lexington, 40506-0048. Tel: 859-257-8347. FAX: 859-323-4906. Web Site: www.aallnet.org/chapter/seaall. *Pres*, Osborne Amy; E-mail: amyo@uky.edu; *Treas*, Paula Tajeda; E-mail: ptejedo@charlestonlaw.org
Member Libraries: 500
Primary Functions: Promote law librarianship; develop & increase the usefulness of law libraries, particularly those in the southeastern US

THEOLOGICAL EDUCATION ASSOCIATION OF MID AMERICA*, (TEAM-A), Southern Baptist Theological Seminary, 2825 Lexington Rd, Louisville, 40280. SAN 377-5038. Tel: 502-897-4807. FAX: 502-897-4600. Web Site: www.eteama.org. *Dir, Info Res*, Ken Boyd; E-mail: ken_boyd@asburyseminary.edu; *Librn*, Tim Browning; E-mail: tbrowning@lextheo.edu; *Librn*, Monica Corcoran; E-mail: mcorcoran@saintmeinrad.edu; *Librn*, Douglas Gragg; E-mail: dgragg@lpts.edu; *Librn*, Bruce Keisling; E-mail: bkeisling@sbts.edu
Founded 1959
Member Libraries: 5 theol sem
Primary Functions: Coordinate & cooperate with member theological seminaries in the Greater Louisville/Lexington, KY area

LOUISIANA

CENTRAL LOUISIANA MEDICAL CENTER LIBRARY CONSORTIUM*, (CLMLC), 2495 Shreveport Hwy, 142D, Alexandria, 71306. (Mail add: PO Box 8784, Alexandria, 71306-1784). Tel: 318-619-9102. FAX: 318-619-9144. E-mail: clmlc8784@yahoo.com. Web Site: www.clmlc.org. *Coordr*, Miriam J Brown
Founded 1997
Member Libraries: 7
Primary Functions: Facilitates sharing of information resources among Louisiana medical libraries; upkeeps combined holdings for all medical & health science libraries for members; offers automation seminars; offers Internet training & consortia licensing for members

HEALTH SCIENCES LIBRARY ASSOCIATION OF LOUISIANA*, (HSLAL), LSUHSC-New Orleans Library, 433 Bolivar St, Box B3-1, New Orleans, 70112. SAN 375-0035. Web Site: www.hslal.org. *Pres*, Marlene Bishop; Tel: 504-568-6109, Fax: 504-568-7718, E-mail: mbisho@lsuhsc.edu
Founded 1976

Member Libraries: 48
Primary Functions: To encourage & promote cooperation & communication among the librarians & library managers of health sciences institutions in the state of Louisiana

LOAN SHARK*, State Library of Louisiana, 701 N Fourth St, Baton Rouge, 70802. (Mail add: State Library of Louisiana, PO Box 131, Baton Rouge, 70821-0131), SAN 371-6880. Tel: 225-342-4920, 342-4918. FAX: 225-219-4725. *Head, Access Serv*, Kytara A Gaudin; E-mail: kgaudin@state.lib.la.us
Founded 1987
Member Libraries: 68 pub
Primary Functions: Provides an automated interlibrary loan referral system & use of statewide online catalog

THE LOUISIANA LIBRARY NETWORK*, LOUIS, Information Technology Services, 200 Frey Computing Services Ctr, Baton Rouge, 70803. Web Site: louis.lsu.edu. *Exec Dir*, Sara Zimmerman; E-mail: sara@lsu.edu
Founded 1992
Member Libraries: 45 acad & 5 spec
Primary Functions: Provide library automation, digital library, and interlibrary loan support and services for member libraries. License access to electronic resources for all Louisiana public and private academic libraries.

NEW ORLEANS EDUCATIONAL TELECOMMUNICATIONS CONSORTIUM*, 6400 Press Dr, New Orleans, 70126. (Mail add: 5000 W Esplanade Ave, No 290, Metairie, 70006), SAN 329-5214. Tel: 504-524-0350. E-mail: noetc@noetc.org. Web Site: www.noetc.org.
Member Libraries: 6
Primary Functions: To identify & foster methods by which its member institutions acquire & utilize the emerging technologies pursuant to each member's academic mission; to facilitate the research, development, funding & effective implementation of these technologies to support technology-enhanced instruction & related activities

MAINE

HEALTH SCIENCE LIBRARY INFORMATION CONSORTIUM*, (HSLIC), 211 Marginal Way, No 245, Portland, 04101. SAN 322-1601. Tel: 207-795-2561. FAX: 207-795-2569. *Chairperson*, Kathy Brunjes; E-mail: brunjesk@cmhc.org
Founded 1973
Member Libraries: 50 incl acad, hosp, inst & spec med
Primary Functions: Biomedical communications network for Maine; identifies & shares resources; provides interlibrary loan & continuing education; serves as clearing house for interstate arrangements to initiate & maintain cooperation among libraries involved in delivering health or medical information & consumer health information

MARYLAND

MARYLAND ASSOCIATION OF HEALTH SCIENCE LIBRARIANS*, (MAHSL), VA Medical HealthCare System, Medical Library, Ten N Greene St, Baltimore, 21201. SAN 377-5070. Tel: 401-605-7093. Web Site: www.mahsl.umaryland.edu. *Co-Pres*, Brittany Rice; Tel: 301-896-3199, E-mail: brice@suburbanhospital.org; *Coordr*, Deborah Thomas; Tel: 443-849-2531, E-mail: dathomas@gbmc.org; *Treas*, Joanna Lin; E-mail: joanna.lin@med.va.gov
Founded 1970
Member Libraries: 80
Primary Functions: Promote a more thorough knowledge of health science librarians through instructional programs; foster communication within the health science library profession

MARYLAND INTERLIBRARY LOAN ORGANIZATION*, (MILO), c/o Enoch Pratt Free Library, 400 Cathedral St, Baltimore, 21201-4484. SAN 343-8600. Tel: 410-396-5498. FAX: 410-396-5837. E-mail: milo@prattlibrary.org. Web Site: www.prattlibrary.org. *Mgr*, Emma E Beaven
Member Libraries: 536
Primary Functions: Interlibrary loan; document delivery; information-reference service; consultation; service to Maryland government agencies

NATIONAL NETWORK OF LIBRARIES OF MEDICINE*, (NN-LM), Nat Libr of Med, 8600 Rockville Pike, Rm B1E03, Bethesda, 20894. SAN 373-0905. Tel: 301-496-4777. FAX: 301-480-1467. Web Site: www.nnlm.gov. *Dir*, Angela Ruffin
Founded 1967
Member Libraries: 4700 health sci
Primary Functions: Administers program to ensure equal access to information to all US health professionals and the general public; programs funded by the National Library of Medicine & carried out in eight geographic regions through contracts with eight major medical libraries

NATIONAL NETWORK OF LIBRARIES OF MEDICINE SOUTHEASTERN ATLANTIC REGION*, (NNLM-SEA), Univ Md Health Scis & Human Servs Libr, 601 W Lombard St, Baltimore, 21201-1512. SAN 322-1644. Tel: 410-706-2855. Toll Free Tel: 800-338-7657. FAX: 410-706-0099. E-mail: hshsl-NIMsea@hshsl.umaryland.edu. Web Site: www.nnlm.nlm.nih.gov/sea/. *Dir*, Mary J Tooey
Founded 1983

Member Libraries: Over 940 health sci librs
Primary Functions: Program emphasizes provision of basic level of information services to health care providers through network by: promoting training & library development at the community level; encouraging state & local cooperative library efforts; coordinating regional interlibrary loan network; training of health professionals in the use of the US National Library of Medicine's products & services; provides referral information for health professionals needing information; exhibits at health professional meetings; funds projects related to provision of information to health care provider especially in rural areas or those who serve minority populations

US NATIONAL LIBRARY OF MEDICINE*, (NLM), 8600 Rockville Pike, Bethesda, 20894. SAN 322-1652. Tel: 301-594-5983. Toll Free Tel: 888-346-3656. FAX: 301-402-1384. Web Site: www.nlm.nih.gov. *Coordr,* Martha Fishel; Tel: 301-496-5501, Fax: 301-402-9334
Founded 1836
Member Libraries: Domestic & international health sci librs, health professionals, researches & gen public
Primary Functions: Delivers authoritative health information to Americans & to people around the world through services including: MEDLINE/PubMed, MedlinePlus, the NLM Gateway, ClinicalTrials.gov, LocatorPlus, TOXNET, Images from the History of Medicine & Profiles in Science. NLM's mission, in conjunction with its National Network of Libraries of Medicine (NN/LM), is to assist the advancement of medical & related sciences & to aid the dissemination & exchange of scientific & other information important to the progress of medicine & to the public health

WASHINGTON RESEARCH LIBRARY CONSORTIUM, (WRLC), 901 Commerce Dr, Upper Marlboro, 20774. SAN 373-0883. Tel: 301-390-2000. FAX: 301-390-2020. Web Site: www.wrlc.org. *Exec Dir,* Mark Jacobs; *Dir, Info Serv,* Bruce Hulse; *Dir, Info Tech,* Jim Austin
Founded 1987
Member Libraries: 9 acad
Primary Functions: Shared online catalog & database system; cooperative collection development; shared offsite storage facility; reciprocal borrowing & document delivery

MASSACHUSETTS

BOSTON BIOMEDICAL LIBRARY CONSORTIUM*, (BBLC), c/o Dana Farber Cancer Trust, 44 Binney St, Boston, 02115. SAN 322-1725, *Pres,* Christine Fleuried; Tel: 617-632-2489, Fax: 617-632-2488
Founded 1980
Member Libraries: 16 acad, hosp & res inst
Primary Functions: Interlibrary loan; Union List of Periodicals; continuing education; Cooperative group purchasing

BOSTON LIBRARY CONSORTIUM, INC*, McKim Bldg, 700 Boylston St, Boston, 02117. SAN 322-1733. Tel: 617-262-0380. FAX: 617-262-0163. E-mail: admin@blc.org. Web Site: www.blc.org. *Exec Dir,* Melissa Trevvett; E-mail: mtrevvett@blc.org
Founded 1970
Member Libraries: 19 acad, pub, res & state
Primary Functions: Support resource sharing & enhancement of services to users through programs in cooperative collecting, access to electronic resources & physical collections & enhanced resource sharing; facilitate access to research materials at member institutions by member online catalogs & other information resources, interlibrary loan enhanced by the virtual catalog, on-site use of most member libraries & borrowing privileges for qualified researchers

CAPE LIBRARIES AUTOMATED MATERIALS SHARING NETWORK*, (CLAMS), 270 Communication Way, Unit 4E, Hyannis, 02601. SAN 370-579X. Tel: 508-790-4399. FAX: 508-771-4533. Web Site: www.clamsnet.org. *Exec Dir,* Gayle Simundza; E-mail: gsimundza@clamsnet.org
Member Libraries: 32
Primary Functions: Resource sharing network via automated integrated library system

CENTRAL & WESTERN MASSACHUSETTS AUTOMATED RESOURCE SHARING*, (C/W MARS), 67 Millbrook St, Ste 201, Worcester, 01606. SAN 322-3973. Tel: 508-755-3323, Ext 30. FAX: 508-755-3721. Web Site: www.cwmars.org. *Exec Dir,* Joan Kuklinski; E-mail: jkuklins@cwmars.org; *Network Serv,* Susan Hopkins; Tel: 508-755-3323, Ext 18, E-mail: shopkins@cwmars.org
Founded 1982
Member Libraries: 148
Primary Functions: Provides library automation system, cataloging, shared databases, training, support & Internet access

COOPERATING LIBRARIES OF GREATER SPRINGFIELD, (CLGS), Springfield Technical Community College, One Armory Sq, Springfield, 01102. SAN 322-1768. Tel: 413-755-4565. FAX: 413-755-6315. E-mail: lcoakley@stcc.edu. *Coordr,* Lynn Coakley; E-mail: lcoakley@stcc.edu
Founded 1962
Member Libraries: 10
Primary Functions: Cooperative circulation; intra-cooperative borrowing

FENWAY LIBRARIES ONLINE, INC*, (FLO), c/o Wentworth Institute Technology, 550 Huntington Ave, Boston, 02115. SAN 373-9112. Tel: 617-442-2384. FAX: 617-442-1519. Web Site: www.flo.org. *Exec Dir,* Walter Stine
Founded 1987
Member Libraries: 10 acad & mus
Primary Functions: Provides online library & information services, including a shared bibliographic database, cataloging, acquisitions & serials control

MASSACHUSETTS HEALTH SCIENCES LIBRARIES NETWORK*, (MAHSLIN), Lamar soutter Library, UMass Medical School, 55 Lake Ave, n, worcester, 01655. SAN 372-8293. Tel: 508-856-1966. Web Site: www.mahslin.org. *Pres,* Sally A Gore; E-mail: sally.gore@umassmed.edu
Founded 1970
Member Libraries: 129 med
Primary Functions: Enhancement of health services & health information access for the people of Massachusetts

MERRIMACK VALLEY LIBRARY CONSORTIUM*, 1600 Osgood St, North Andover, 01845. SAN 322-4384. Tel: 978-557-1050. FAX: 978-557-8101. E-mail: netmail@mvlc.org. Web Site: www.mvlc.org. *Exec Dir,* Lawrence Rungren; Tel: 978-557-5409, E-mail: lrungren@mvlc.org
Founded 1982
Member Libraries: 35 pub
Primary Functions: Cataloging; circulation control; interlibrary loan; resource sharing; public access catalog; online periodical database & access to the Internet

MINUTEMAN LIBRARY NETWORK*, Ten Strathmore Rd, Natick, 01760-2419. SAN 322-4252. Tel: 508-655-8008. FAX: 508-655-1507. Web Site: www.mln.lib.ma.us. *Exec Dir,* Susan McAlister; E-mail: smcalister@minlib.net
Founded 1983
Member Libraries: 6 acad & 35 pub
Primary Functions: Resource sharing network; integrated library system; cataloging; OCLC through Nelinet Automated System; Innovative Interfaces; Millennium

NATIONAL NETWORK OF LIBRARIES OF MEDICINE NEW ENGLAND REGION*, (NN-LM NER), University of Massachusetts Medical School, 222 Maple Ave, Shrewsbury, 01545-2732. SAN 372-5448. Tel: 508-856-5979. Toll Free Tel: 800-338-7657. FAX: 508-856-5977. Web Site: nnlm.gov/ner. *Dir,* Elaine Martin; *Assoc Dir,* Javier Crespo
Founded 1991
Member Libraries: 454 med
Primary Functions: Provide free access to information to all health care providers in New England

NORTH OF BOSTON LIBRARY EXCHANGE, INC, (NOBLE), 26 Cherry Hill Dr, Danvers, 01923. SAN 322-4023. Tel: 978-777-8844. FAX: 978-750-8472. Web Site: www.noblenet.org. *Exec Dir,* Ronald A Gagnon; *Mgr, Libr Serv,* Elizabeth B Thomsen; *Syst Coordr,* Martha J Driscoll
Founded 1980
Member Libraries: 9 acad, 17 pub, 1 sch & 1 spec
Primary Functions: Resource sharing; automated circulation control; online union catalog; cooperative cataloging; acquisitions; serials; gateway services; collection management; PC support; Internet services; electronic resources; digital library & repository

NORTHEAST CONSORTIUM OF COLLEGES & UNIVERSITIES IN MASSACHUSETTS*, (NECCUM), Merrimack College, 315 Turnpike St, North Andover, 01845. SAN 371-0602. Tel: 978-556-3400. FAX: 978-556-3738. *Pres,* Richard Santagati; *Adminr,* Linda Murphy
Founded 1981
Member Libraries: 10 acad
Primary Functions: Enhance education opportunities of students & faculty of member institutions in Northeastern Massachusetts

NORTHEASTERN CONSORTIUM FOR HEALTH INFORMATION*, (NECHI), Lowell General Hospital Health Science Library, 295 Varnum Ave, Lowell, 01854. SAN 322-1857. Tel: 978-937-6247. FAX: 978-937-6855. Web Site: www.lowellgeneral.org/go/health-information/health-sciences-library/. *Librn,* Donna Beales
Member Libraries: 2 col & 14 hospital
Primary Functions: Interlibrary loan; resource sharing; continuing education

SAILS, INC*, 547 W Groves St, Ste 4, Middleboro, 02346. SAN 378-0058. Tel: 508-946-8600. FAX: 508-946-8605. Web Site: www.sailsinc.org. *Pres,* Robin Glasser; *Exec Dir,* Deborah K Conrad; E-mail: dconrad@sailsinc.org
Founded 1995
Member Libraries: 73 sites
Primary Functions: Administration of a multi-type resource sharing network

SOUTHEASTERN MASSACHUSETTS CONSORTIUM OF HEALTH SCIENCE LIBRARIES*, (SEMCO), Charlton Medical Library, 363 Highland Ave, Fall River, 02720. SAN 322-1873. Tel: 508-679-7196. FAX: 508-679-7458. *Chair,* Nicola Pallotti; E-mail: PallottiN@southcoast.org

Member Libraries: 13 acad, hospital & med
Primary Functions: To cooperate in the exchange of information; to share existing resources in the form of free interlibrary loans; professional development

WESTERN MASSACHUSETTS HEALTH INFORMATION CONSORTIUM*, Baystate Medical Ctr Health Sciences Library, 759 Chestnut St, Springfield, 01199. SAN 329-4579. Tel: 413-794-1865. FAX: 413-794-1974. *Pres,* Susan La Forter; Tel: 413-787-2053
Member Libraries: 3 acad, 13 hosp & 8 individual
Primary Functions: Serving the information needs of residents & health professionals in Western Massachusetts

MICHIGAN

DETROIT AREA CONSORTIUM OF CATHOLIC COLLEGES*, c/o Sacred Heart Seminary, 2701 Chicago Blvd, Detroit, 48206. SAN 329-482X. Tel: 313-883-8500. FAX: 313-883-8594. *Dir of Libr,* Christopher Spilker
Founded 1971
Member Libraries: 5
Primary Functions: To provide an opportunity for members to meet for information exchange

DETROIT AREA LIBRARY NETWORK, (DALNET), 5048 Gullen Mall, 6th Flr SEL, Detroit, 48202. Tel: 313-577-6789. FAX: 313-577-1231. E-mail: info@dalnet.org. Web Site: www.dalnet.org. *Exec Dir,* Steven K Bowers; E-mail: sbowers@wayne.edu
Founded 1985
Member Libraries: 20 mem/23 inst (incl 9 acad, 1 pub, 1 pub/spec, 8 spec, & 1 k-12/spec)
Primary Functions: To advance research & learning; run library systems for ILS members; provide training & technical support; supports participation in group digital projects; encourage reciprocal borrowing & interlibrary loan; provides funding for state-wide delivery

LAKELAND LIBRARY COOPERATIVE*, 4138 Three Mile Rd NW, Grand Rapids, 49534-1134. SAN 308-132X. Tel: 616-559-5253. FAX: 616-559-4329. Web Site: www.llcoop.org. *Dir,* Sandra Wilson; Tel: 616-559-5253, Ext 201, E-mail: sandra@llcoop.org; *Asst Dir,* Martha Pitchford; Tel: 616-559-5253, Ext 202, E-mail: martha@llcoop.org; *Info Tech Dir,* Thom Riley; E-mail: thom@llcoop.org; *Syst Coordr,* Sheryl VanderWagen; E-mail: sheryl@llcoop.org
Founded 1978
Member Libraries: 41
Primary Functions: Shared integrated online system for OPAC, circulation, acquisitions; delivery service; world-wide ILL service; consulting services; group discounts from vendors

THE LIBRARY NETWORK, (TLN), 41365 Vincenti Ct, Novi, 48375. SAN 370-596X. Tel: 248-536-3100. FAX: 248-536-3099. Web Site: tln.lib.mi.us. *Dir,* James Pletz; E-mail: jpletz@tln.lib.mi.us; *Mgr, Network Serv,* Angelina Michelini; E-mail: amichelini@tln.lib.mi.us; *Mgr, Tech Serv,* James Flury; E-mail: jflury@tln.lib.mi.us; *Shared Automation Syst Coordr,* Anne Neville; E-mail: aneville@tln.lib.mi.us; *Controller,* Rick Rosekrans; E-mail: rosekrans@tln.lib.mi.us
Founded 1978
Member Libraries: 64 pub
Primary Functions: Shared ILS; Acquisitions; Cataloging; Delivery; Consulting; Continuing Education; Networking & Technology

MICHIGAN HEALTH SCIENCES LIBRARIES ASSOCIATION*, (MHSLA), 1407 Rensen St, Ste 4, Lansing, 48910. SAN 323-987X. Tel: 517-394-2774. FAX: 517-394-2675. Web Site: www.mhsla.org. *Pres,* Sheila Bryant; E-mail: bryants@mail.lib.msu.edu
Founded 1963
Member Libraries: 160 acad & med
Primary Functions: To further health sciences librarianship by assisting members to demonstrate a positive impact on health care within their communities; networking for sharing of resources; educational opportunities for members; application of research in library science to health care; provision of a professional support system; financial viability

MID-MICHIGAN LIBRARY LEAGUE*, 210 1/2 N Mitchell, Cadillac, 49601-1835. SAN 307-9325. Tel: 231-775-3037. Toll Free Tel: 800-968-0046. FAX: 231-775-1749. Toll Free FAX: 800-968-3297. Web Site: www.mmll.org. *Dir,* James Lawrence; E-mail: lawrencej@mmll.org; *ILL Coordr,* Jack Sheehan; E-mail: jack@mmll.org
Special Services for the Blind - Large print bks

MIDEASTERN MICHIGAN LIBRARY COOPERATIVE*, 503 S Saginaw St, Ste 839, Flint, 48502. SAN 346-5187. Tel: 810-232-7119. FAX: 810-232-6639. *Dir,* Denise Hooks; E-mail: dhooks@flint.org

PALNET*, 1040 W Bristol Rd, Flint, 48507. Tel: 810-766-4070. Web Site: www.palnet.info. *Dir,* Vince Molosky
Founded 1991
Member Libraries: 13 acad
Primary Functions: Library automation project that serves the libraries of Baker College (10 statewide sites), Mott Community College (Flint & Southern Lakes sites) & Kettering University

SOUTHEASTERN MICHIGAN LEAGUE OF LIBRARIES*, (SEMLOL), Lawrence Technological University, 21000 W Ten Mile Rd, Southfield, 48075. SAN 322-4481. Tel: 248-204-3000. FAX: 248-204-3005. Web Site: www.semlol.org. *Treas,* Gary Cocozzoli; E-mail: gcocozzol@ltu.edu
Founded 1980
Member Libraries: 41
Primary Functions: Promote understanding of members' needs & services; develop vehicles for sharing resources & improving & coordinating services; promote development of professional skills & abilities; exchange ideas & provide channels of communication

SOUTHWEST MICHIGAN LIBRARY COOPERATIVE*, 305 Oak St, Paw Paw, 49079-1364. SAN 308-2156. Tel: 269-657-4698. FAX: 269-657-4494. Web Site: www.swmlc.info. *Dir,* Rick Hulsey; Tel: 269-968-8166, E-mail: rhulsey@willard.lib.mi.us
Founded 1977

SUBURBAN LIBRARY COOPERATIVE*, (SLC), 44750 Delco Blvd, Sterling Heights, 48313. SAN 373-9082. Tel: 586-685-5750. FAX: 586-685-3010. Web Site: www.libcoop.net. *Interim Dir,* Arthur M Woodford; E-mail: woodfora@libcoop.net; *Cataloger,* Lauren Boggs; E-mail: boggsl@libcoop.net; *ILL,* Kim Shearer; E-mail: shearerk@libcoop.net; *Syst Librn,* Amy Shaughnessy; E-mail: shaughna@libcoop.net
Founded 1978
Member Libraries: 21 pub
Primary Functions: Services to libraries: shared automated system (SIRSI-Unicorn); negotiating contracts & quantity discounts; continuing education; publicity & public relations

UPPER PENINSULA OF MICHIGAN HEALTH SCIENCE LIBRARY CONSORTIUM*, c/o Marquette General Health System, 580 W College Ave, Marquette, 49855. SAN 329-4803. Tel: 906-225-3429. FAX: 906-225-3524. Web Site: www.mgh.org/library. *Libr Mgr,* Janis Lubenow
Founded 1974
Member Libraries: 2 med
Primary Functions: A cooperative exchange of resources sharing, interlibrary loans & duplicate journal exchange; holds an annual educational workshop with Michigan Health Science Association

UPPER PENINSULA REGION OF LIBRARY COOPERATION, INC*, 1615 Presque Isle Ave, Marquette, 49855. SAN 329-5540. Tel: 906-228-7697. FAX: 906-228-5627. Web Site: als2.web.uproc.lib.mi.us/uproc. *Treas,* Suzanne Dees
Founded 1984
Member Libraries: 102
Primary Functions: Facilitate the sharing of information resources among the libraries of Michigan's Upper Peninsula; encourage libraries of Michigan's Upper Peninsula to institute such cost-effective practices & procedures which may be made possible through Upper Peninsula wide interlibrary cooperation; enable libraries of Michigan's Upper Peninsula to link up & interact with other regional & national electronic bibliographic communication systems; operate Sirsi ILS for 84 libraries

VALLEY LIBRARY CONSORTIUM*, 3210 Davenport Ave, Saginaw, 48602-3495. Tel: 989-497-0925. FAX: 989-497-0918. Web Site: www.vlc.lib.mi.us. *Exec Dir,* Randall Martin; Tel: 898-497-0925, Ext 5, E-mail: l.martin@valleylibrary.org
Founded 1980
Member Libraries: 25
Primary Functions: To provide the greater Saginaw Valley community with access to shared library & information resources through quality, cost-effective automated services for member libraries

MINNESOTA

CAPITAL AREA LIBRARY CONSORTIUM*, (CALCO), c/o Minnesota Dept of Transportation, Library MS155, 395 John Ireland Blvd, Saint Paul, 55155. SAN 374-6127. Tel: 651-296-5272. FAX: 651-297-2354. Web Site: www.libraries.state .mn.us. *Librn,* Shirley Sherkow
Founded 1973
Member Libraries: 18 state govt
Primary Functions: Cooperation among member libraries to enhance information services in state government

CENTRAL MINNESOTA LIBRARIES EXCHANGE*, (CMLE), Miller Ctr, Rm 130-D, Saint Cloud State University, Saint Cloud, 56301-4498. SAN 322-3779. Tel: 320-308-2950. Toll Free Tel: 800-657-3796. FAX: 320-654-5131. E-mail: cmle@stcloudstate.edu. *Dir,* Patricia A Post
Founded 1979
Member Libraries: 285 acad, regional pub systs, sch & spec
Primary Functions: Interlibrary loan; phone-in reference service to participating libraries; expense-paid delivery of interloan materials; workshops; newsletter; development of bibliographic data bases

COOPERATING LIBRARIES IN CONSORTIUM*, (CLIC), 1619 Dayton Ave, Ste 204, Saint Paul, 55104. SAN 322-1970. Tel: 651-644-3878. FAX: 651-644-6258. Web Site: www.clic.edu. *Exec Dir,* Ruth Dukelow; *Syst Adminr,* Steven Waage
Founded 1969

Member Libraries: 15 librs
Primary Functions: Reciprocal borrowing; Union Catalog in online format; Access to the Union Catalog (CLICnet) is via Internet (www.clicnet.clic.edu); delivery service for documents & interlibrary loan; OCLC online cataloging; reciprocal photocopy service for non-circulating materials; joint staff-development programs; joint research & investigations; joint purchase of equipment, services & materials; daily courier exchange system with MINITEX; MnLINK Gateway participant

METRONET*, 1619 Dayton Ave, Ste 314, Saint Paul, 55104. SAN 322-1989. Tel: 651-646-0475. FAX: 651-649-3169. E-mail: information@metrolibraries.net. Web Site: www.metrolibraries.net. *Exec Dir,* Ann Walker Smalley; E-mail: ann@metronet.lib.mn.us
Founded 1979
Member Libraries: 725
Primary Functions: Resource sharing; long-range planning; communications systems; continuing education

METROPOLITAN LIBRARY SERVICE AGENCY*, (MELSA), 1619 Dayton Ave, No 314, Saint Paul, 55104-6206. SAN 371-5124. Tel: 651-645-5731. FAX: 651-649-3169. E-mail: melsa@melsa.org. Web Site: www.melsa.org. *Exec Dir,* Chris D Olson; Tel: 651-645-5731, Ext 105, E-mail: chris@melsa.org; *Bus Mgr,* Mona Scott; E-mail: mona@melsa.org
Founded 1969
Member Libraries: 8 libr syst
Primary Functions: Manage state & federal grant aid for reciprocal services; Internet services; collection development; database purchasing; homework help; Museum Adventure Pass; automation reimbursement & assistance

MINITEX LIBRARY INFORMATION NETWORK, Univ Minn Twin Cities, 15 Andersen Library, 222 21st Ave S, Minneapolis, 55455-0439. SAN 322-1997. Tel: 612-624-4002. FAX: 612-624-4508. Web Site: www.minitex.umn.edu/. *Dir,* Valerie Horton; Tel: 612-624-2839, E-mail: vhorton@umn.edu
Founded 1969
Member Libraries: 228 acad, govt, pub & spec
Primary Functions: Shared licensing of reference databases online, Web homepage & courier delivery systems; support resource-sharing among & between libraries; reference & information service; online bibliographic searching; workshops & skills development programs; Union List of Serials; OCLC services; reciprocal arrangement with Wisconsin Interlibrary Loan Service contractual arrangements with North & South Dakota periodical exchange service; discounts through group purchase of certain items, cooperative cataloging

MINNESOTA LIBRARY INFORMATION NETWORK*, (MnLINK), University of Minnesota-Twin Cities, 15 Andersen Library, 222 21st Ave S, Minneapolis, 55455-0439. Tel: 612-624-8096. Toll Free Tel: 800-462-5348. FAX: 612-624-4508. Web Site: www.mnlink.org. *Info Spec,* Nick Banitt; E-mail: banit006@umn.edu
Founded 1997
Member Libraries: 600
Primary Functions: Coordinate with libraries to facilitate resource sharing & make Minnesota resources available to Minnesotans

MINNESOTA THEOLOGICAL LIBRARY ASSOCIATION*, (MTLA), Luther Seminary Library, 2375 Como Ave, Saint Paul, 55108. SAN 322-1962. Tel: 651-641-3447. Web Site: www.stthomas.edu/mtla. *Chair,* David Stewart; *Chair,* Bruce Eldevik
Member Libraries: 5
Primary Functions: Coordinates interlibrary loans, certain acquisitions, resource sharing, professional development & collection development

NORTH COUNTRY LIBRARY COOPERATIVE*, 5528 Emerald Ave, Mountain Iron, 55768-2069. SAN 322-3795. Tel: 218-741-1907. Toll Free Tel: 800-950-4401. FAX: 218-741-1908. Web Site: www.nclcmn.org. *Dir,* Linda J Wadman; E-mail: lwadman@arrowhead.lib.mn.us
Founded 1979
Member Libraries: 12 acad, 29 pub, 110 sch & 22 spec
Primary Functions: To encourage & develop sharing of resources among all types of libraries in the seven counties of northeastern Minnesota as well as encourage professional development & expertise; to support a common database consisting of regional holdings in member libraries; provide members with workshop opportunities & administer a delivery system for ILL

NORTHERN LIGHTS LIBRARY NETWORK*, 103 Graystone Plaza, Detroit Lakes, 56501-3041. SAN 322-2004. Tel: 218-847-2825. FAX: 218-847-1461. E-mail: nloffice@nlln.org. Web Site: www.nlln.org. *Exec Dir,* Kathy B Enger; E-mail: kbenger@nlln.org
Founded 1979
Primary Functions: Multi-county, multi-type system facilitating cooperative activities among all types of libraries in the northwest 23 counties of Minnesota; resource sharing, communications, long-range planning, database development, continuing education

SOUTHCENTRAL MINNESOTA INTER-LIBRARY EXCHANGE*, (SMILE), 1400 Madison Ave, No 622, Mankato, 56001. SAN 321-3358. Tel: 507-625-7555. FAX: 507-625-4049. E-mail: smile@tds.lib.mn.us. Web Site: smilelibrary.info. *Dir,* Nancy Katharine Steele; E-mail: nsteel@tds.lib.mn.us

Founded 1979
Member Libraries: 146 acad, pub, sch & spec
Primary Functions: Continuing education; delivery service; interlibrary loan; monthly newsletter; web site; electronic resources; honorariums for professional development; regional planning; grant assistance; library advocacy

SOUTHEASTERN LIBRARIES COOPERATING, (SELCO), 2600 19th St NW, Rochester, 55901-0767. SAN 308-7417. Tel: 507-288-5513. Toll Free Tel: 800-992-5061. FAX: 507-288-8697. Web Site: www.selco.info. *Exec Dir,* Ann Hutton; E-mail: ann@selco.info; *Asst Dir,* Michael Scott; *Automation Librn,* Donovan Lambright
Founded 1971
Member Libraries: 87
Primary Functions: Staff development; delivery; consultation on all library matters; interlibrary loan coordination; large print rotating collection, cooperative programming; public relations & publicity; continuing education & training; management of 11-county wide area network; cataloging; scholarships; homepage hosting; web catalog; electronic resources; library advocacy; PC support; public internet management

SOUTHWEST AREA MULTICOUNTY MULTITYPE INTERLIBRARY EXCHANGE*, (SAMMIE), 109 S Fifth St, Ste 30, Marshall, 56258-1240. SAN 322-2039. Tel: 507-532-9013. FAX: 507-532-2039. E-mail: info@sammie.org. Web Site: www.sammie.org. *Dir,* Robin Chaney; E-mail: robin@sammie.org
Founded 1979
Member Libraries: 210
Primary Functions: Interlibrary cooperation programs; one of seven multicounty multitype library systems in state

TWIN CITIES BIOMEDICAL CONSORTIUM*, (TCBC), c/o Fairview University Medical Ctr, 2450 Riverside Ave, Minneapolis, 55455. SAN 322-2055. Tel: 612-273-6595. FAX: 612-273-2675. *Mgr,* Colleen Olsen; Tel: 612-273-6595
Primary Functions: Develop a strong network of biomedical libraries in Twin Cities area & improve efficiency of access to biomedical information; provide educational opportunities to members

MISSISSIPPI

CENTRAL MISSISSIPPI LIBRARY COUNCIL*, (CMLC), c/o Millsaps College Library, 1701 N State St, Jackson, 39210. SAN 372-8250. Tel: 601-974-1070. FAX: 601-974-1082. *Adminr, Treas,* Tom Henderson; E-mail: hendetw@millsaps.edu
Founded 1976
Member Libraries: 20 acad, pub & spec
Primary Functions: Promote access to books & other informational materials among libraries in central Mississippi; provide reference services to patrons of member libraries; develop interlibrary loan cooperation & staff development opportunities

MISSISSIPPI ELECTRONIC LIBRARIES ONLINE*, (MELO), Mississippi State Board for Community & Junior Colleges, 3825 Ridgewood Rd, Jackson, 39211. Tel: 601-432-6518. FAX: 601-432-6363. E-mail: melo@colin.edu. Web Site: www.colin.edu/vcclib. *Dir,* Audra Kimball; *Mgr,* Kathleen Hutchison
Founded 2000
Member Libraries: 15
Primary Functions: To support students in Mississippi virtual community colleges

MISSOURI

GREATER WESTERN LIBRARY ALLIANCE*, (GWLA), 5109 Cherry St, Kansas City, 64110. Tel: 816-926-8765. FAX: 816-926-8790. Web Site: www.gwla.org. *Exec Dir,* Joni Blake; E-mail: joni@gwla.org; *Prog Officer for Digital Coll,* Jim Dilline; E-mail: jim@gwla.org; *Prog Officer for Res Sharing,* Anne McKee; E-mail: anne@gwla.org
Founded 1998
Member Libraries: 30 acad & 1 spec
Primary Functions: Resource sharing: helping members maximize resources in a collaborative way

HEALTH SCIENCES LIBRARY NETWORK OF KANSAS CITY, INC*, (HSLNKC), University of Missouri-Kansas City Health Sciences Library, 2411 Holmes St, Kansas City, 64108-2792. SAN 322-2098. Tel: 816-235-1880. FAX: 816-235-6570. *Dir,* Dr Peggy Mullaly-Quijas
Founded 1974
Member Libraries: 31 hospital, med ctr, coll & med soc
Primary Functions: Courier service; interlibrary loan; Union Lists of Serials; professional opportunities

KANSAS CITY LIBRARY SERVICE PROGRAM*, (KC-LSP), Kansas City Public Library, 14 W Tenth St, Kansas City, 64105-1702. Tel: 816-701-3400, Ext 3520. Toll Free Tel: 866-755-5252. FAX: 816-701-3401. E-mail: kclcsupport@kclibrary.org. Web Site: www.kclconline.org. *Coordr,* Steven Knapp; Tel: 816-701-3551, E-mail: stevenknapp@kclibrary.org
Founded 1991
Member Libraries: 23

Primary Functions: A service program of the Kansas City Public Library, providing a full-featured library automation system (SirsiDynix), complete with web-based public access & reporting; direct patron borrowing & access to 2.1 million circulating items

MID-AMERICA LIBRARY ALLIANCE/KANSAS CITY METROPOLITAN LIBRARY & INFORMATION NETWORK*, (MALA/KCMLIN), 15624 E 24 Hwy, Independence, 64050. SAN 322-2101. Tel: 816-521-7257. FAX: 816-461-0966. Web Site: www.kcmlin.org. *Exec Dir,* Susan Burton; E-mail: susanburton@kcmlin.org
Founded 1978
Open Mon-Fri 8-4
Member Libraries: 187
Primary Functions: Centralized interlibrary loan communication & delivery service; staff development & continuing education; KC Metrolink Project

SAINT LOUIS REGIONAL LIBRARY NETWORK*, 341 Sappington Rd, Saint Louis, 63122. SAN 322-2209. Tel: 314-395-1305. Web Site: www.slrln.org. *Coordr,* Bernyce Christiansen
Founded 1978
Member Libraries: 102 acad, health related, pub, sch & spec
Primary Functions: Reciprocal library services, including directory of area libraries, an INFO-PASS system, staff-development programs, cooperative purchasing, collection development & preservation, newsletter & information publications

NEBRASKA

ICON LIBRARY CONSORTIUM*, Univ of Nebr, McGoogan Libr of Med, Nebr Med Ctr, Box 986705, Omaha, 68198-6705. Tel: 402-559-7099. FAX: 402-559-5498. Web Site: www.iconlibrary.org. *Exec Secy,* Mary Helms
Founded 1990
Member Libraries: 60, incl 20 inst
Primary Functions: Provide resources to health science libraries, libraries with either a health science program or public libraries with a consumer health science information focus & to individuals in health care occupations, either professional or in-training

SOUTHEAST NEBRASKA LIBRARY SYSTEM*, 5730 R St, Ste C-1, Lincoln, 68505. SAN 322-4732. Tel: 402-467-6188. Toll Free Tel: 800-288-6063. FAX: 402-467-6196. Web Site: www.selsne.org. *Pres,* Glenda Willnerd; E-mail: gwilln@lps.org; *Adminr,* Brenda Ealey; E-mail: bsealey@alltel.net
Member Libraries: 206 acad, pub, sch & spec
Primary Functions: Coordinating & encouraging cooperation among multitype libraries, including interlibrary loan & reference services, providing continuing education & consultation

NEVADA

DESERT STATES LAW LIBRARY CONSORTIUM*, Wiener-Rogers Law Libr, William S Boyd Sch Law, 4505 Maryland Pkwy, Las Vegas, 89154-1080. (Mail add: PO Box 451080, Las Vegas, 89154-1080). Tel: 702-895-2400. FAX: 702-895-2416. Web Site: www.law.unlv.edu/library/desertstates. *Coll Develop Librn,* Matthew Wright; Tel: 702-895-2409
Founded 2003
Member Libraries: 8 law
Primary Functions: Facilitates cooperative collection development & resource sharing programs as well as other collaborative projects among its law school libraries in Arizona, Colorado, New Mexico, Nevada & Vermont

INFORMATION NEVADA, Interlibrary Loan Dept, Nevada State Library & Archives, 100 N Stewart St, Carson City, 89701-4285. SAN 322-2276. Tel: 775-684-3381. Toll Free Tel: 800-922-2880. FAX: 775-684-3330. *Asst Adminr, Libr & Develop Serv,* Karen Starr; Fax: 775-684-3311; E-mail: kstarr@admin.nv.gov; *ILL Librn,* Hope Williams; Fax: 775-684-3355, E-mail: hwilliams@admin.nv.gov
Founded 1977
Primary Functions: Coordinates statewide interlibrary loan network

NEW HAMPSHIRE

GMILCS, INC*, 1701B Hooksett Rd, Hooksett, 03106. Tel: 603-485-4286. FAX: 603-485-4246. E-mail: helpdesk@gmilcs.org. Web Site: www.gmilcs.org. *Chair,* Dianne Hathaway; E-mail: dianneh@goffstown.lib.nh.us
Founded 1992
Member Libraries: 9 pub, 3 acad
Primary Functions: Shared automation system

HEALTH SCIENCES LIBRARIES OF NEW HAMPSHIRE & VERMONT*, Breene Memorial Library, New Hampshire Hospital, 36 Clinton St, Concord, 03246. SAN 371-6864. Tel: 603-527-2837. FAX: 603-527-7197. Web Site: ibrary.umassmed.edu/hslnhvt. *Admin Coordr,* Marion Allen; Tel: 603-271-5420, E-mail: mallen@dhhs.state.nh.us
Founded 1972
Member Libraries: 35 acad, med, resource & tech
Primary Functions: Promote all interests of health sciences librarianship

LIBRARIANS OF THE UPPER VALLEY COOP*, (LUV Coop), c/o Hanover Town Library, 130 Etna Rd, Etna, 03750. (Mail add: PO Box 207, Etna, 03750), SAN 371-6856. Tel: 603-643-3116. *Coordr,* Barbara Prince; E-mail: etna.library@hanovernh.org
Founded 1977
Member Libraries: 26 pub & 2 acad
Primary Functions: Improve library service through cooperative purchase of materials; interlibrary loan of materials; exchange of information; presentation of workshops & demonstrations of interest to school & public librarians

MERRI-HILL-ROCK LIBRARY COOPERATIVE*, c/o Kimball Library, Three Academy Ave, Atkinson, 03811-2299. SAN 329-5338. Tel: 603-362-5234. FAX: 603-362-4791. *Interim Dir,* Caroline Birr
Member Libraries: 20 pub & 2 acad
Primary Functions: Meet monthly to share ideas, speakers come to discuss topics of interest to librarians

NEW ENGLAND LAW LIBRARY CONSORTIUM, INC*, (NELLCO), Nine Drummer Rd, Keene, 03431. SAN 322-4244. Tel: 603-357-3385. FAX: 603-357-2075. Web Site: www.nellco.org. *Exec Dir,* Tracy L Thompson-Przylucki; E-mail: tracy.thompson@nellco.org
Founded 1983
Member Libraries: 100 law libraries
Primary Functions: Interlibrary loan; virtual reference; legal scholarship repository; collaborative web page development; internships & exchanges; newsletter; union catalog for members; cooperative acquisitions

NEW HAMPSHIRE COLLEGE & UNIVERSITY COUNCIL*, Three Barrell Ct, Ste 100, Concord, 03301-8543. SAN 322-2322. Tel: 603-225-4199. FAX: 603-225-8108. Web Site: www.nhcuc.org. *Pres,* Thomas R Horgan; E-mail: horgan@nhcuc.org
Founded 1966
Member Libraries: 18
Primary Functions: Interlibrary loan; joint acquisition; reciprocal borrowing privileges; Union List of Serials; NELINET participation; resource sharing

NUBANUSIT LIBRARY COOPERATIVE*, c/o Peterborough Town Library, Two Concord St, Peterborough, 03458. SAN 322-4600. Tel: 603-924-8040. FAX: 603-924-8041.
Founded 1971
Member Libraries: 30
Primary Functions: Staff development; discussion of regional & statewide library issues

NEW JERSEY

BASIC HEALTH SCIENCES LIBRARY NETWORK*, (BHSL), Overlook Hospital Health Science Library, 99 Beauvoir Ave, Summit, 07902. SAN 371-4888. Tel: 908-522-2886. FAX: 908-522-2274. *Coordr,* Pat Regenberg; E-mail: pat.regenberg@atlantichealth.org
Founded 1986
Member Libraries: 450 acad & med
Primary Functions: Resource sharing; interlibrary loan

BERGEN COUNTY COOPERATIVE LIBRARY SYSTEM, (BCCLS), 810 Main St, Hackensack, 07601. Tel: 201-489-1904. FAX: 201-489-4215. E-mail: bccls@bccls.org. Web Site: www.bccls.org. *Exec Dir,* Robert William White; E-mail: robert@bccls.org; *Dir, Libr Serv,* Arlene Sahraie; E-mail: arlene@bccls.org; *Cat & Training Librn,* Luca Manna; E-mail: luca@bccls.org; *Integrated Syst Librn,* Trevor Diamond; E-mail: trevor@bccls.org; *Admin Serv,* Patricia Loughnane; E-mail: pat@bccls.org; *Coll Develop,* Ruth Greenberg; E-mail: ruth@bccls.org; *Info Tech,* Eric Lozauskas; E-mail: eric@bccls.org; *Internet Serv,* Laurie Meeske; E-mail: laurie@bccls.org
Founded 1979
Member Libraries: All 61 public libraries in Bergen County plus Bloomfield, Glen Ridge, Livingston, Millburn, Montclair, Nutley, Roseland, West Caldwell in Essex County, Hoboken, North Bergen, Secaucus, Weehawken in Hudson County & Hawthorne in Passaic County
Primary Functions: Resource sharing & other shared automated services

BERGEN PASSAIC HEALTH SCIENCES LIBRARY CONSORTIUM*, c/o Englewood Hospital & Medical Ctr, Health Sciences Library, 350 Engle St, Englewood, 07631. SAN 371-0904. Tel: 201-894-3069. FAX: 201-894-9049. *Coordr,* Lia Sabbagh; E-mail: lia.sabbagh@ehmc.com
Founded 1975
Member Libraries: 20 acad & med
Primary Functions: Increase local cooperation among area hospitals & facilitate ILL

BURLINGTON LIBRARIES INFORMATION CONSORTIUM*, (BLINC), Five Pioneer Blvd, Westampton, 08060. Tel: 609-267-9660. FAX: 609-267-4091. E-mail: hq@bcls.lib.nj.us. Web Site: www.bcls.lib.nj.us. *Coordr,* Gale Sweet; E-mail: gsweet@bcls.lib.nj.us
Founded 1985

Member Libraries: 2 commun col, 16 pub & 2 sch
Primary Functions: Resource & technology sharing among libraries (SirsiDynix Horizon Software)

INTEGRATED INFORMATION SOLUTIONS*, 600 Mountain Ave, Rm 1B 202, Murray Hill, 07974. SAN 329-5400. Tel: 908-582-4840. FAX: 908-582-3146. *Mgr,* M E Brennan
Member Libraries: 1
Primary Functions: To provide reference, circulation, document delivery & database access & to manage the corporation's intellectual property

LIBRARIES OF MIDDLESEX AUTOMATION CONSORTIUM, (LMxAC), 1030 Saint Georges Ave, Ste 203, Avenel, 07001. SAN 329-448X. Tel: 732-750-2525. FAX: 732-750-9392. Web Site: www.lmxac.org. *Exec Dir,* Eileen Palmer; E-mail: empalmer@lmxac.org
Founded 1986
Member Libraries: 27
Primary Functions: To maintain & operate cooperative automated library system

LIBRARYLINKNJ, THE NEW JERSEY LIBRARY COOPERATIVE, 44 Stelton Rd, Ste 330, Piscataway, 08854. SAN 371-5116. Tel: 732-752-7720. Toll Free Tel: 866-505-5465. FAX: 732-752-7785. Toll Free FAX: 800-793-8007. Web Site: librarylinknj.org. *Exec Dir,* Cheryl O'Connor; E-mail: coconnor@librarylinknj.org; *Asst Dir,* Joanne Roukens; E-mail: jroukens@librarylinknj.org
Founded 1985
Member Libraries: 2000 acad, corp, inst, med, pub & sch
Primary Functions: LibraryLinkNJ empowers libraries to serve their clientele more effectively & enhances the value of member libraries to their communities

MONMOUTH-OCEAN BIOMEDICAL INFORMATION CONSORTIUM*, (MOBIC), Community Medical Ctr, 99 Hwy 37 W, Toms River, 08755. SAN 329-5389. Tel: 732-557-8117. FAX: 732-557-8354. *Librn,* Reina Reisler; E-mail: rreisler@sbhcs.com
Member Libraries: 15
Primary Functions: To provide medical information to the staff

MORRIS AUTOMATED INFORMATION NETWORK*, (MAIN), c/o Morris County Library, 30 East Hanover Ave, Whippany, 07981. (Mail add: PO Box 900, Morristown, 07963-0900), SAN 322-4058. Tel: 973-631-5353. FAX: 973-631-5366. Web Site: www.mainlib.org. *Dir,* Jeremy Jenynak
Member Libraries: 33 pub
Primary Functions: Operate a shared collection management, resource sharing & circulation system maintain bibliographic database; provide public access to the Internet from all member libraries; provide an Internet-accessible web catalog & patron reservation system

MORRIS-UNION FEDERATION, 214 Main St, Chatham, 07928. SAN 310-2629. Tel: 973-635-0603. FAX: 973-635-7827.
Founded 1974
Member Libraries: 7
Primary Functions: Provides interlibrary services; member libraries contribute to budget to purchase specialty books & increase access to information for residents in membership area

NEW JERSEY HEALTH SCIENCES LIBRARY NETWORK*, (NJHSN), Overlook Hospital Library, 99 Beauvoir Ave, Summit, 07902. SAN 371-4829. Tel: 908-522-2886. FAX: 908-522-2274. *Libr Mgr,* Patricia Regenberg; E-mail: pat.regenberg@atlantichealth.org
Founded 1980
Member Libraries: 96 med
Primary Functions: Interlibrary loan; resource sharing; education

NEW JERSEY LIBRARY NETWORK*, Library Development Bureau, 185 W State St, Trenton, 08608. (Mail add: PO Box 520, Trenton, 08625-0520), SAN 372-8161. Tel: 609-278-2640, Ext 152. FAX: 609-278-2650. Web Site: www.njstatelib.org. *Assoc State Librn, Libr Develop,* Kathleen Moeller-Peiffer; E-mail: kpeiffer@njstatelib.org
Founded 1984
Member Libraries: 2600 acad, inst, pub, sch & spec
Primary Functions: Provides residents with full & equal access to library programs & materials not available within their communities; promotes cooperation among libraries; provides a number of statewide services & additional services through the New Jersey State Library & Regional Library Cooperatives; reference services to supplement those provided by the member libraries; interlibrary loan services; delivery services for library materials; access to online databases; consultant services; in-service training; preservation; conservation & disaster-preparedness programs; public relations; provides supplemental reference in specific subjects to all Network member libraries through contracts with Newark Public Library, New Jersey State Library, Rutgers University & the University of Medicine & Dentistry of New Jersey

VIRTUAL ACADEMIC LIBRARY ENVIRONMENT*, (VALE), William Paterson University Library, 300 Pompton Rd, Wayne, 07470-2103. Tel: 973-720-3179. FAX: 973-720-3171. Web Site: www.valenj.org. *Coordr,* Judy Avrin
Founded 1998

Member Libraries: 53 acad
Primary Functions: To facilitate access to scholarly resources by leveraging the group's purchasing power for cost-effective access to electronic databases; to promote resource sharing among member libraries

NEW MEXICO

ALLIANCE FOR INNOVATION IN SCIENCE & TECHNOLOGY INFORMATION*, (AISTI), 369 Montezuma Ave, No 237, Santa Fe, 87501. Toll Free Tel: 888-901-4144. Toll Free FAX: 800-315-6956. Web Site: www.aisti.org. *Exec Dir,* Corinne Lebrunn; E-mail: cl@aisti.org
Founded 1992
Member Libraries: 16 acad, govt & pvt
Primary Functions: Acquire scientific & technology information to create collaborative tool sets exploiting these to the best advantage for researchers; forum for sharing of ideas & collaboration

ESTACADO LIBRARY INFORMATION NETWORK*, (ELIN), 509 N Shipp, Hobby, 88240. Tel: 575-397-9328. FAX: 575-397-1508.
Founded 1996
Member Libraries: 2 acad & 5 pub
Primary Functions: To share common items & patron databases & provide more online databases to all patrons, free of charge

NEW MEXICO CONSORTIUM OF ACADEMIC LIBRARIES*, Dean's Office, University Libraries MSC 053020, Albuquerque, 87131-0001. SAN 371-6872. Web Site: lib.nmsu.edu/nmcal. *Pres,* Ruben Aragon
Founded 1988
Member Libraries: 28 acad
Primary Functions: Provides the means to present the unified position of New Mexico's public & private academic libraries on key issues affecting them to governmental committees, the public & other appropriate bodies provides the means to devise & carry out projects of common usefulness such as: enhanced library cooperation for resource sharing, collection development & improved funding for library acquisitions in all academic libraries

NEW MEXICO CONSORTIUM OF BIOMEDICAL & HOSPITAL LIBRARIES*, c/o St Vincent Hospital, 455 St Michaels Dr, Santa Fe, 87505. SAN 322-449X. Tel: 505-820-5218. FAX: 505-989-6478. *Chair,* Albert Robinson; E-mail: albert.robinson@stvin.org
Founded 1981
Member Libraries: 13
Primary Functions: Interlibrary loan; consultation; resource sharing

NEW YORK

ACADEMIC LIBRARIES OF BROOKLYN*, Long Island University Library-LLC 517, One University Plaza, Brooklyn, 11201. SAN 322-2411. Tel: 718-488-1081. FAX: 718-780-4057. Web Site: www.liu.edu.
Founded 1963
Member Libraries: 8 col
Primary Functions: Interlibrary loan; open access; Union periodicals list; Brooklyn bibliography

ASSOCIATED COLLEGES OF THE SAINT LAWRENCE VALLEY*, SUNY Potsdam, 288 Van Housen Extension, Potsdam, 13676-2299. SAN 322-242X. Tel: 315-267-3331. FAX: 315-267-2389. Web Site: associatedcolleges.org. *Exec Dir,* Anneke J Larrance; E-mail: larranaj@potsdam.edu
Founded 1970
Member Libraries: 4
Primary Functions: Interlibrary loan; professional development for staff

BROOKLYN-QUEENS-STATEN ISLAND-MANHATTAN-BRONX HEALTH SCIENCES LIBRARIANS*, (BQSIMB), 150 55th St, Brooklyn, 11220. Tel: 718-630-7200. FAX: 718-630-8918. Web Site: www.bqsimb.org. *Pres,* Irina Meyman; E-mail: imeyman@lmcmc.com
Founded 1968
Primary Functions: To bring together persons of this constituted geographic area engaged in providing professional health sciences library services for the following objectives: furthering their specialized knowledge; exchange of information; improvements & developments of resources; identifying special needs & coordinating all library services & activities with existing area groups, libraries & programs

CAPITAL DISTRICT LIBRARY COUNCIL*, (CDLC), 28 Essex St, Albany, 12206. SAN 322-2446. Tel: 518-438-2500. FAX: 518-438-2872. Web Site: www.cdlc.org. *Exec Dir,* Jean K Sheviak; E-mail: jsheviak@cdlc.org; *Asst Dir,* Christine M Walker; E-mail: cwalker@cdlc.org; *Archivist,* Susan D'Entremont; E-mail: sd'entremont@cdlc.org; *Cat,* Suzanne Rahn; E-mail: srahn@cdlc.org; *Hospital Libr Serv Coordr,* Christopher Tosh; E-mail: ctosh@cdlc.org; *Res Sharing Spec,* Marie Noonan; E-mail: mnoonan@cdlc.org
Founded 1967
Member Libraries: 22 acad, 11 hospitals, 3 pub libr systs, 4 sch libr systs & 28 spec
Primary Functions: Enhance access to information, encourage resource sharing, & promote library interests for all CDLC members through a wide variety of

programs & services: ILL; Union Catalog of monographs & list of serials; bibliographic & reference services; regional automation projects; Hospital Library Service Program; NY State Coordinated Collection Development Program; cooperative cataloging projects; consortial purchases; delivery service to member libraries; DAP program for direct borrowing privileges to individual patrons; Documentary Heritage Program serving historical societies, museum & archives

CENTRAL NEW YORK LIBRARY RESOURCES COUNCIL*, (CLRC), 6493 Ridings Rd, Syracuse, 13206-1195. SAN 322-2454. Tel: 315-446-5446. FAX: 315-446-5590. Web Site: www.clrc.org. *Exec Dir,* Penelope J Klein; E-mail: pjklein@clrc.org
Founded 1967
Member Libraries: 55 acad, med, pub, sch & spec
Primary Functions: Interlibrary loan processing; materials delivery; bibliographic access through union lists & catalogs & collection development; continuing education; conservation & preservation; local administration of specialized state & federal library programs for regional automation & hospital library services; promotion of interlibrary communication & cooperation for enhanced service to library users in the region; Internet training & connectivity; documentary heritage & archives program; regional electronic list serv CNYLIB-L & web site http://clrc.org

CONNECT NY*, Rochester Institute of Technology, 90 Lomb Memorial Dr, Rochester, 14623. Tel: 585-475-2050. Web Site: www.connectny.info. *Exec Dir,* Bart Harloe
Founded 2002
Member Libraries: 13 acad
Primary Functions: Shared catalog/collection via Inn-Reach

COUNCIL OF ARCHIVES & RESEARCH LIBRARIES IN JEWISH STUDIES*, (CARLJS), 330 Seventh Ave, 21st Flr, New York, 10001. SAN 371-053X. Tel: 212-629-0500. FAX: 212-629-0508. E-mail: fjc@jewishculture.org. Web Site: www.jewishculture.org. *Operations Dir,* Michelle Moskowitz Brown; E-mail: mmoskowitzbrown@jewishculture.org
Founded 1973
Member Libraries: 40 acad, pub & spec
Primary Functions: Coordinate & plan information sharing of projects all related to Jewish studies & topic; coordinate CARLJS-RLG Consortia for block purchase of RLIN searches

LIBRARY ASSOCIATION OF ROCKLAND COUNTY*, (LARC), PO Box 917, New City, 10956-0917. Tel: 845-359-3877. Web Site: www.rocklandlibraries.org. *Pres,* Sara Nugent; E-mail: snugent@rcls.org; *VPres,* Janet Lukas; Tel: 845-786-3060, E-mail: jlukas@rcls.org
Member Libraries: 17 pub
Primary Functions: To support & promote public libraries, public library development & public library services in Rockland County

LIBRARY CONSORTIUM OF HEALTH INSTITUTIONS IN BUFFALO*, (LCHIB), Abbott Hall, SUNY at Buffalo, 3435 Main St, Buffalo, 14214. SAN 329-367X. Tel: 716-829-3900, Ext 143. FAX: 716-829-2211. E-mail: hubnet@buffalo.edu, Ulb-lchib@buffalo.edu. Web Site: hubnet.buffalo.edu. *Exec Dir,* Martin E Mutka
Founded 1988
Member Libraries: 10
Primary Functions: Cooperative collection development, library services & interlibrary loan; manage & provide access to share electronics resources over wide area network HUB NET

LONG ISLAND LIBRARY RESOURCES COUNCIL*, (LILRC), 627 N Sunrise Service Rd, Bellport, 11713. SAN 322-2489. Tel: 631-675-1570. Web Site: www.lilrc.org. *Dir,* Herbert Biblo; E-mail: director@lilrc.org; *Asst Dir,* Min Liu; E-mail: minliu@lilrc.org
Founded 1966
Member Libraries: 173 acad, med, pub, sch & spec
Primary Functions: Interlibrary loan location (last resort); direct access (Research Loan Program); online Union List of Serials; cooperative acquisitions, Hospital Library Services Program; OCLC union listing; Coordinated Collection Development Program; continuing education programs & workshops; Internet Gateway & OCLC FirstSearch access; regional digitization program (Long Island Memories); Documentary Heritage Program

MEDICAL & SCIENTIFIC LIBRARIES OF LONG ISLAND*, (MEDLI), c/o Palmer Sch of Libr & Info Sci, C W Post Campus, Long Island Univ, Brookville, 11548. SAN 322-4309. Tel: 516-299-2866. FAX: 516-299-4168. Web Site: www.medli.net. *Chair,* Mary Westermann-Cicio; E-mail: westerma@liu.edu; *Pres,* Christina Rivera
Founded 1962
Member Libraries: 50
Primary Functions: Initiate, sponsor & contribute to any educational programs pertaining to medicine & related subjects

METROPOLITAN NEW YORK LIBRARY COUNCIL*, (METRO), 57 E 11th St, 4th Flr, New York, 10003-4605. SAN 322-2500. Tel: 212-228-2320. FAX: 212-228-2598. Web Site: www.metro.org. *Exec Dir,* Dottie Hiebing; E-mail: dhiebing@metro.org; *VPres,* Norman J Jacknis; *Treas,* Hal F Higginbotham

Founded 1964
Member Libraries: 270
Primary Functions: Training professional development in resource sharing; coordinate digitization projects

NEW YORK STATE HIGHER EDUCATION INITIATIVE*, (NYSHEI), 22 Corporate Woods Blvd, Albany, 12211-2350. (Mail add: c/o Nylink, State University Plaza, Albany, 12246). Toll Free Tel: 800-342-3353. FAX: 518-432-4346. E-mail: nyshei@nyshei.org. Web Site: www.nyshei.org. *Exec Dir,* Jason Kramer; Tel: 518-443-5444
Founded 2000
Member Libraries: 140
Primary Functions: Advocacy for academic, public, private & research libraries needing funding for databases & facilities.

NORTHEAST FOREIGN LAW LIBRARIES COOPERATIVE GROUP*, Columbia University Library, 435 W 116th St, New York, 10027. SAN 375-0000. Tel: 212-854-1411. FAX: 212-854-3295. *Coordr,* Silke Sahl
Member Libraries: 7
Primary Functions: To share & promote collection development among member libraries

NORTHERN NEW YORK LIBRARY NETWORK*, 6721 US Hwy 11, Potsdam, 13676. SAN 322-2527. Tel: 315-265-1119. Toll Free Tel: 877-833-1674. FAX: 315-265-1881. E-mail: info@nnyln.org. Web Site: www.nnyln.org. *Exec Dir,* John J Hammond; E-mail: john@nnyln.org; *Head, Bibliog Serv, Syst Mgr,* Thomas Blauvelt; E-mail: blauvelt@northnet.org; *Bus Mgr,* Phil Jones; E-mail: philj@nnyln.org; *Communications Coordr, Regional Coordr,* Pamela Ouimet; E-mail: pouimet@nnyln.org; *Regional Coordr,* Bridget Doyle; E-mail: doyle@nnyln.net
Founded 1965
Member Libraries: 67 acad, hospital, pub, res, sch & spec
Primary Functions: Reciprocal borrowing; interlibrary loan; paper & electronic union lists & directories; electronic mail; cooperative acquisition of library materials; continuing education for librarians & archivists; publication program; catalog support; bibliographic center; joint grants & research projects; computerized literature searches; conservation & preservation of historical materials; hospital library program; library regional automation program; public relations; automated services; shared access to commercial online database; technical assistance to special collections, archives & historical documents repositories; regional web catalog (ICEPAC) - www.icepac.net & regional interlibrary loan system (ICICILL); newspaper digitization

ROCHESTER REGIONAL LIBRARY COUNCIL*, 390 Packetts Landing, Fairport, 14450. SAN 322-2535. Tel: 585-223-7570. FAX: 585-223-7712. E-mail: rrlc@rrlc.org. Web Site: www.rrlc.org. *Exec Dir,* Kathleen M Miller; E-mail: kmiller@rric.org; *Librn,* April Younglove; *Mem Serv Librn,* Laura Osterhout; *Outreach Librn,* Barbara Clambor; *Bus Mgr,* Susan Vanderwall
Founded 1966
Member Libraries: 54 acad, hospital, pub, res, sch, seminary & spec
Primary Functions: Interlibrary loan; photocopies; consortial purchases of electronic resources; OCLC processing center courier service; hospital library services; regional borrower's card; coordinated collection development program; regional automation program; continuing education programs for staff development; gifts & exchange program; directory of area libraries & resources; Union List of Serials; Union List of Historical Maps; Union catalog on the web (http://rrlc.library.net); preservation of library materials, grant applications; share databases, automation & technology

SOUTH CENTRAL REGIONAL LIBRARY COUNCIL*, Clinton Hall, 108 N Cayuga St, Ithaca, 14850. SAN 322-2543. Tel: 607-273-9106. FAX: 607-272-0740. E-mail: scrlc@scrlc.org. Web Site: www.scrlc.org. *Exec Dir,* Mary-Carol Lindbloom; E-mail: mclindbloom@scrlc.org
Founded 1967
Member Libraries: 75
Primary Functions: Resource sharing; continuing education; grantsmanship; consulting & focus groups; legislative advocacy; hospital library services program: consortial purchase of e-resources, regional digitizing program

SOUTHEASTERN NEW YORK LIBRARY RESOURCES COUNCIL*, (SENYLRC), 21 S Elting Corners Rd, Highland, 12528-2805. SAN 322-2551. Tel: 845-883-9065. FAX: 845-883-9483. Web Site: www.senylrc.org. *Exec Dir,* John L Shaloiko; E-mail: shaloiko@senylrc.org
Founded 1965
Member Libraries: Over 80 acad, med, pub, sch libr systs & spec; 24 Assoc
Primary Functions: Coordinates cooperative automation, interlibrary loan, delivery, electronic resource group discounts & admin reference services & retrospective conversion; publishes Union Catalog; maintains Union List of Serials; offers staff-development workshops, continuing education & consultations; publishes directories brochures; database searching; hospital library program; database maintenance; archival assistance; Conservation & Preservation assistance

SUNYCONNECT*, Office of Library & Information Services, SUNY Plaza, Albany, 12246. Tel: 518-443-5577. FAX: 518-443-5358. Web Site: www.sunyconnect.suny.edu. *Asst Provost for Libr & Info Serv,* Carey Hatch; E-mail: carey.hatch@suny.edu; *Coordr, Electronic Res,* John Schumacher; E-mail: john.shumacher@suny.edu

Founded 2000
Member Libraries: 61
Primary Functions: Share collection & services across State University of New York

UNITED NATIONS SYSTEM ELECTRONIC INFORMATION ACQUISITIONS CONSORTIUM*, (UNSEIAC), c/o United Nations Library, 220 E 42nd St Rm, DN-2426, New York, 10017. SAN 377-855X. Tel: 212-963-2026. FAX: 212-963-2608. E-mail: unseiac@un.org. Web Site: www.un.org/depts/dhl. *Coordr,* Kikuko Maeyama; E-mail: maeyamak@un.org
Founded 1998
Member Libraries: 55
Primary Functions: Share cost of & access to electronic information resources within the United Nations System

WESTERN NEW YORK LIBRARY RESOURCES COUNCIL*, 4455 Genesee St, Buffalo, 14225. (Mail add: PO Box 400, Buffalo, 14225-0400), SAN 322-2578. Tel: 716-633-0705. FAX: 716-633-1736. Web Site: www.wnylrc.org. *Exec Dir,* Sheryl Knab; E-mail: sknab@wnylrc.org; *Digital Serv & Circuit Librn,* Karlen Chase
Founded 1966
Member Libraries: 83 acad, corporate, hospital, pub, res, sch & spec
Primary Functions: To foster & develop multi-type interlibrary cooperation, sharing & interlibrary loan among junior college, college, university, public, research, industrial, school, technical, hospital & medical libraries; to extend & improve library services to the professions, business, industry & the general public

NORTH CAROLINA

CAPE FEAR HEALTH SCIENCES INFORMATION CONSORTIUM*, 1601 Owen Dr, Fayetteville, 28301. SAN 322-3930. Tel: 910-671-5046. FAX: 910-671-5337. *Dir,* Katherine Mcginniss; E-mail: mcginn01@srmc.org
Member Libraries: 17 acad, hospital, med & spec
Primary Functions: Reciprocal borrowing; interlibrary loan; union lists; gift & exchange of library material; consultations; access to numerous in-house databases

DIALOG CORP*, 2250 Perimeter Park Dr, Ste 300, Morrisville, 27560-8893. SAN 322-0176. Tel: 919-804-6400. Toll Free Tel: 800-334-2564. FAX: 919-804-6410. Web Site: www.dialog.com.
Founded 1972
Primary Functions: Provider of Online, Internet, Intranet as well as CD-ROM-based information; hosts over 900 databases covering news, business, science & technology, medicine, intellectual property & other subject areas; includes flagship Web-based services of Dialog Web & DataStarSM Web for information professionals; guided search services of Dialog SelectSM for end users; Dialog@SiteSM for Intranet, Dialog Direct, customized e-mail current awareness service & UnCover periodical & document delivery service

NORTH CAROLINA AREA HEALTH EDUCATION CENTERS*, Univ NC Health Sci Libr, CB 7585, Chapel Hill, 27599-7585. SAN 323-9950. Tel: 919-962-0700. Web Site: www.ncahec.net. *Dir,* Diana McDuffee; Tel: 919-966-0963
Founded 1972
Member Libraries: 4 acad & 11 med
Primary Functions: Coordinate activities statewide of all AHEC Consortia

NORTH CAROLINA COMMUNITY COLLEGE SYSTEM*, 200 W Jones St, Raleigh, 27603-1379. SAN 322-2594. Tel: 919-807-7100. FAX: 919-807-7164, 919-807-7175. Web Site: www.ncccs.cc.nc.us. *Assoc VPres, Learning Tech Syst,* Dr Bill Randall
Founded 1963
Member Libraries: 58 commun cols
Primary Functions: To manage a statewide system of community colleges; to assist the colleges in providing essential services including support to provide technical services support; to provide collection development/management services; to provide leadership in library information technology initiatives

NORTHWEST AHEC LIBRARY AT HICKORY*, Catawba Medical Ctr, 810 Fairgrove Church Rd, Hickory, 28602. SAN 322-4708. Tel: 828-326-3662. FAX: 828-326-3484. *Dir,* Karen Lee Martinez; E-mail: martinez@wfubmc.edu
Founded 1976
Member Libraries: 1 col, 2 commun col, 3 hospital & 2 state inst
Primary Functions: Coordinated collection development; resource sharing; circuit librarian to healthcare institutions; staff development; mediated literature searches; end-user training; general medical reference

NORTHWEST AHEC LIBRARY AT SALISBURY*, c/o Rowan Regional Medical Ctr, 612 Mocksville Ave, Salisbury, 28144. SAN 322-4589. Tel: 704-210-5069. FAX: 704-636-5050. Web Site: northwestahec.wfubmc.edu/link/index.htm. *Coordr,* Nancy Stine
Member Libraries: 9 col, hospital & med
Primary Functions: Provide professional library services at each hospital library; provide workshops for staff development & coordination

NORTHWEST AHEC LIBRARY INFORMATION NETWORK*, Wake Forest University School of Medicine, Medical Center Blvd, Winston-Salem, 27157-1060. SAN 322-4716. Tel: 336-713-7700. FAX: 336-713-7701. *Dir,* Mike Lischke
Member Libraries: 4
Primary Functions: Outreach; resource sharing; centralized technical services; computer searching; audiovisual collection; circuit librarian & consultation; staff development

TRIANGLE RESEARCH LIBRARIES NETWORK, Wilson Library, CB No 3940, Chapel Hill, 27514-8890. SAN 329-5362. Tel: 919-962-8022. FAX: 919-962-4452. Web Site: www.trln.org. *Exec Dir,* Mona C Couts; *Project Librn,* Derek Rodriguez; Staff 4 (MLS 3, Non-MLS 1)
Founded 1977
Member Libraries: 10
Primary Functions: Collaborative organization of Duke University, North Carolina Central University, North Carolina State University & The University of North Carolina at Chapel Hill, the purpose of which is to marshal the financial, human & information resources of their research libraries through cooperative efforts in order to create a rich & unparalleled knowledge environment that furthers the universities' teaching, research & service missions

WESTERN NORTH CAROLINA LIBRARY NETWORK*, (WNCLN), c/o Appalachian State University, 218 College St, Boone, 28608. SAN 376-7205. Tel: 828-262-2774. FAX: 828-262-3001. Web Site: wncln.wncln.org. *Librn,* Catherine Wilkinson; E-mail: wilkinsncl@appstate.edu
Founded 1985
Member Libraries: 3
Primary Functions: Maintenance & enhancement of an integrated library system (Innopac: wncln.wncln.org); sharing of library materials through a network delivery service; development of cooperative collection management policies

NORTH DAKOTA

CENTRAL DAKOTA LIBRARY NETWORK*, Morton Mandan Public Library, 609 W Main St, Mandan, 58554-3149. SAN 373-1391. Tel: 701-667-5365. Toll Free Tel: 800-260-4291. E-mail: mortonmandanlibrary@cdln.info. Web Site: www.mortonmandanlibrary.org. *Dir,* Kelly Steckler
Founded 1990
Member Libraries: 18
Primary Functions: Facilitate & enhance the sharing of resources & services; improve access to & dissemination of knowledge & information; provide online public access catalog

MID-AMERICA LAW LIBRARY CONSORTIUM*, (MALLCO), Univ of North Dakota School of Law, Thormodsgard Library, Grand Forks, 58202. (Mail add: 2968 Second Ave N, Grand Forks, 58202-9004), SAN 371-6813. Tel: 701-777-2204. FAX: 701-777-4956. *Interim Dir,* Rhonda Schwartz
Founded 1980
Member Libraries: 20 acad
Primary Functions: Promotion of resource sharing; cooperation among member schools

TRI-COLLEGE UNIVERSITY LIBRARIES CONSORTIUM*, NDSU Downtown Campus, 650 NP Ave, No 110, Fargo, 58102. SAN 322-2047. Tel: 701-231-8170. FAX: 701-231-7205. Web Site: www.tri-college.org. *In Charge,* Sonia Hohnadel; E-mail: sonia.hohnadel@ndsu.edu
Member Libraries: 3 acad
Primary Functions: Interlibrary loan; reciprocal borrowing; film library; computer-based Union list of serials; computer-based Union catalog of monographs; coordinated acquisitions; member of OCLC/MINITEX Network, MnSCU/PALS

OHIO

ASSOCIATION OF CHRISTIAN LIBRARIANS, (ACL), PO Box 4, Cedarville, 45314. Tel: 937-766-2255. FAX: 937-766-5499. E-mail: info@acl.org. Web Site: www.acl.org. *Pres,* Frank Quinn; *VPres,* Rodney Birch; *Treas,* Sheila Carlblom
Founded 1956
Member Libraries: 556
Primary Functions: Strengthen libraries through professional development of evangelical librarians; scholarship; and spiritual encouragement for service in higher education

CENTRAL OHIO HOSPITAL LIBRARY CONSORTIUM*, 127 S Davis Ave, Columbus, 43222. SAN 371-084X. Tel: 614-234-5214. FAX: 614-234-1257. E-mail: library@mchs.com. Web Site: www.mccn.edu/library. *Dir,* Stevo Roksandic; Tel: 614-234-1644, E-mail: sroksandic@mchs.com
Founded 1978
Primary Functions: Cooperative group of hospital & academic medical libraries to collect & assist to keep updated in medical field

CHRISTIAN LIBRARY CONSORTIUM, (CLC), c/o ACL, PO Box 4, Cedarville, 45314. Tel: 937-766-2255. FAX: 937-766-5499. E-mail: info@acl.org. Web Site: www.acl.org. *Coordr,* Beth Purtee
Founded 1991

Member Libraries: 187
Primary Functions: Resource sharing; vendor discounts; purchasing agreement for religious e-books

COLUMBUS AREA LIBRARY & INFORMATION COUNCIL OF OHIO*, (CALICO), c/o Westerville Public Library, 126 S State St, Westerville, 43081. SAN 371-683X. Tel: 614-882-7277. FAX: 614-882-5369.
Member Libraries: 45 acad, corp, med, pub & spec
Primary Functions: Allows members to share knowledge, experience & ideas for continued development & improvement of services to the central Ohio area

CONSORTIUM OF POPULAR CULTURE COLLECTIONS IN THE MIDWEST*, (CPCCM), c/o Popular Culture Library, Bowling Green State University, Bowling Green, 43403-0600. SAN 370-5811. Tel: 419-372-2450. FAX: 419-372-7996. Web Site: www.bgsu.edu/colleges/library/pcl/pcl.html, poplcult.lms.kent.edu. *Head Librn,* Nancy Down; Tel: 419-372-6054
Founded 1990
Member Libraries: 12 acad
Primary Functions: Seeks to promote popular culture materials through cooperative collection development, access, preservation & promotion of research

THE FIVE COLLEGES OF OHIO*, 102 Allen House, Kenyon College, Gambier, 43022. Tel: 740-427-5377. FAX: 740-427-5390. E-mail: ohiofive@gmail.com. Web Site: www.ohio5.org. *Exec Dir,* Susan Palmer; *Chmn,* Georgia Nugent
Founded 1995
Member Libraries: 5
Primary Functions: Fosters closer cooperation & understanding by coordinating operating functions, administrative services, developing collaborative academic programs & resource sharing

NORTHEAST OHIO REGIONAL LIBRARY SYSTEM*, (NEO-RLS), 4445 Mahoning Ave NW, Warren, 44483. SAN 322-2713. Tel: 330-847-7744. FAX: 330-847-7704. Web Site: www.neo-rls.org. *Exec Dir,* William Martino; E-mail: bill.martino@neo-rls.org
Founded 1972
Member Libraries: 91 acad, pub, sch & spec
Primary Functions: Continuing Education; cooperative purchasing; consultant services; technology services; ListenOhio

NORTHWEST REGIONAL LIBRARY SYSTEM*, (NORWELD), 181 1/2 S Main St, Bowling Green, 43402. SAN 322-273X. Tel: 419-352-2903. FAX: 419-353-8310. Web Site: www.norweld.lib.oh.us. *Dir,* Allan Gray
Member Libraries: 50 pub
Primary Functions: Interlibrary loan; reference service; large print book circuit; public relations; regional & local library planning; consultant services; delivery service

OCLC ONLINE COMPUTER LIBRARY CENTER, INC*, 6565 Kilgour Pl, Dublin, 43017-3395. SAN 322-2748. Tel: 614-764-6000. Toll Free Tel: 800-848-5878. FAX: 614-718-1017. E-mail: oclc@oclc.org. Web Site: www.oclc.org. *Pres & Chief Exec Officer,* Jay Jordon; *Chief Financial Officer, Treas,* Rick J Schwieterman
Founded 1967
Member Libraries: 52,000
Primary Functions: Engages in computer library services & research; OCLC systems help libraries locate, acquire, catalog & lend books & other library materials; OCLC reference services provide electronic journals & online information used by researchers, students, faculty & scholars, as well as professional librarians; NetLibrary, a division of OCLC, offers an easy-to-use information retrieval system for accessing the full text of reference, scholarly & professional books & other e-content; more than 52,000 libraries contribute to &/or use info in WorldCat (Online Union Catalog), the world's largest database of library bibliographic information; through affiliated US regional networks, service centers & distributors, provides cataloging, database services, resource sharing, conversion & contract cataloging in 95 countries & territories; publishes the Dewey Decimal Classification, the world's most widely used classification system; OCLC Digital Collection & Preservation Services provides high quality microfilming, access & dissemination options for libraries, archives & museums

OHIO HEALTH SCIENCES LIBRARY ASSOCIATION*, (OHSLA), South Pointe Hospital, Medical Library, 20000 Harvard Rd, Warrensville Heights, 44122. Tel: 216-491-7454. FAX: 216-491-7650. Web Site: www.ohslanet.org. *Pres,* Michelle Kraft; E-mail: mkraft@cchseast.org
Founded 1994
Member Libraries: 100
Primary Functions: Statewide networking with other health information professionals & opportunities for cooperative ventures with other Ohio health science libraries

OHIO LIBRARY & INFORMATION NETWORK, (OhioLINK), 35 E Chestnut St, 8th Flr, Columbus, 43215-2541. SAN 374-8014. Tel: 614-485-6722. FAX: 614-228-1807. E-mail: info@ohiolink.edu. Web Site: www.ohiolink.edu. *Exec Dir,* Gwen Evans; Tel: 614-485-6726, E-mail: gwen@ohiolink.edu
Founded 1989
Member Libraries: 88 acad & State Library of Ohio

Primary Functions: Provide Ohio students, faculty & researchers with the information they need for teaching & research; provide access to & delivery of millions of books & other library materials, millions of electronic articles, electronic research databases, e-books, images, videos, sounds, theses & dissertations from Ohio students

OHIO NETWORK OF AMERICAN HISTORY RESEARCH CENTERS*, Ohio Historical Society Archives-Library, 1982 Velma Ave, Columbus, 43211-2497. SAN 323-9624. Tel: 614-297-2510. FAX: 614-297-2546. E-mail: reference@ohiohistory.org. Web Site: www.ohiohistory.org.
Founded 1970
Primary Functions: The Ohio Network of American History Research Centers was established in 1970 to aid in the collection, preservation & use of research materials documenting the history of the state; member respositories include the University of Akron, Bowling Green State University, the University of Cincinnati, the Ohio Historical Society, Ohio University, the Western Reserve Historical Society, Wright State University & the Youngstown Historical Center of Industry & Labor

OHIO PUBLIC LIBRARY INFORMATION NETWORK*, (OPLIN), 2323 W Fifth Ave, Ste 130, Columbus, 43204. Tel: 614-728-5252. FAX: 614-728-5256. E-mail: support@oplin.org. Web Site: www.oplin.org. *Exec Dir,* Stephen Hedges
Founded 1996
Member Libraries: 251 pub
Primary Functions: Internet service provider for public libraries

OHIONET*, 1500 W Lane Ave, Columbus, 43221-3975. SAN 322-2764. Tel: 614-486-2966. Toll Free Tel: 800-686-8975. FAX: 614-486-1527. Web Site: www.ohionet.org. *Exec Officer,* Michael P Butler; E-mail: mpbutler@ohionet.org
Founded 1977
Member Libraries: 3000 acad, med, pub, sch, spec & theol
Primary Functions: Membership organization consisting of all types of libraries, information centers & related organizations located in Ohio, Pennsylvania & West Virginia; Provide high quality, cost-effective services & products in response to member needs. Facilitate cooperative & reciprocal programs & support the application of information technologies which benefit members; OHIONET develops programs & services that provide members with opportunities to utilize the latest technologies & resources. Services include training, support & discounted prices on the full range of OCLC services; online services, e.g., Dialog & BRS; & other library supplies. Member services include training & workshops, brokerage & discount rates for database services, diversity speaking engagements, consulting, Web design & hosting, internet services

RURAL OHIO VALLEY HEALTH SCIENCES LIBRARY NETWORK*, (ROVHSLN), Southern State Community College- South, 12681 US Rte 62, Sardinia, 45171. Tel: 937-695-0307, Ext 3681. FAX: 937-695-1440. Web Site: www.rovhsln.org. *Mgr,* Mary Ayres; E-mail: mayres@sscc.edu
Founded 1993
Member Libraries: 15
Primary Functions: Networking & continuing education through teleconferences

SOUTHEAST REGIONAL LIBRARY SYSTEM*, (SERLS), 252 W 13th St, Wellston, 45692. SAN 322-2756. Tel: 740-384-2103. Toll Free Tel: 800-759-1537. FAX: 740-384-2106. E-mail: dirserls@oplin.org. Web Site: www.serls.org. *Exec Dir,* Mary Leffler; Tel: 740-384-2103, Ext 5; *Treas,* Mandy Sabine
Founded 1973
Member Libraries: 24
Primary Functions: Consulting services; interlibrary loan; references services; continuing education

SOUTHWEST OHIO & NEIGHBORING LIBRARIES*, (SWON), 10901 Reed Hartman Hwy, Ste 120, Blue Ash, 45242. SAN 322-2675. Tel: 513-751-4422. Toll Free Tel: 800-680-6314. FAX: 513-751-0463. E-mail: info@swonlibraries.org. Web Site: www.swonlibraries.org. *Exec Dir,* Melanie A Blau-McDonald; E-mail: melanie@swonlibraries.org
Founded 1976
Member Libraries: 80 acad, pub, sch & spec
Primary Functions: Direct lending; interlibrary loan; delivery service; cooperative acquisition of education videos; continuing education; newsletter & special directories; coordinated disaster-preparedness effort; information exchange; group discounts; web site & discussion lists, digitization project, technology training & consultation service

SOUTHWESTERN OHIO COUNCIL FOR HIGHER EDUCATION*, (SOCHE), Miami Valley Research Park, 3155 Research Blvd, Ste 204, Dayton, 45420-4015. SAN 322-2659. Tel: 937-258-8890. FAX: 937-258-8899. E-mail: soche@soche.org. Web Site: www.soche.org. *Exec Dir,* Sean Creighton; Tel: 937-258-8890, Ext 11, E-mail: sean.creighton@soche.org
Founded 1967
Member Libraries: 21 acad, corp, law, med, mil, tech & theol
Primary Functions: Resource sharing; delivery system; 16mm film catalog; joint & cooperative acquisitions; staff development

STATE ASSISTED ACADEMIC LIBRARY COUNCIL OF KENTUCKY*, (SAALCK), c/o SWON Libraries, 10815 Indeco Dr, Ste 200, Cincinnati, 45241. (Mail add: 1748 Greatwood Dr, Florence, 41042), SAN 371-2222. Tel: 513-751-4422. Toll Free Tel: 800-254-2803. FAX: 513-751-0463. E-mail:

saalck@saalck.org. Web Site: www.saalck.org. *Exec Dir,* Dr Anne Abate; E-mail:
anne@saalck.org
Founded 1973
Member Libraries: 8 acad, 20 commun col
Primary Functions: Provide leadership for academic libraries of the state & for all
libraries in developing a unified vision for effective resource sharing by initiating a
vision for the virtual library in support of the virtual university

THEOLOGICAL CONSORTIUM OF GREATER COLUMBUS*, (TCGC), Trinity
Lutheran Seminary, 2199 E Main St, Columbus, 43209-2334. Tel: 614-384-4646.
FAX: 614-238-0263. Web Site: www.tcgcohio.org. *Libr Syst Mgr,* Ray Olson;
E-mail: rolson@trinitylutheranseminary.edu
Founded 1967
Member Libraries: 3 acad
Primary Functions: Sharing of theological resources

OKLAHOMA

GREATER OKLAHOMA AREA HEALTH SCIENCES LIBRARY
CONSORTIUM*, (GOAL), Mercy Memorial Health Ctr-Resource Ctr, 1011 14th
Ave NW, Ardmore, 73401. SAN 329-3858. Tel: 580-220-6625. FAX:
580-220-6599. *Pres,* Catherine Ice
Member Libraries: 16 med
Primary Functions: Networking of medical library; interlibrary loan; sharing of
resources; continuing education

OKLAHOMA HEALTH SCIENCES LIBRARY ASSOCIATION*, (OHSLA),
University of Oklahoma - HSC Bird Health Science Library, 1000 S L Young Blvd,
Oklahoma City, 73190. (Mail add: PO Box 26901, Oklahoma City, 73126-0901),
SAN 375-0051. Tel: 405-271-2285, Ext 48755. FAX: 405-271-3297. *Dir,* Clinton
M Thompson, Jr; E-mail: marty-thompson@ouhsc.edu
Member Libraries: 3 col/univ, 3 health ctr libs & 20 hosp
Primary Functions: Continuing education; sharing of resources

OREGON

CHEMEKETA COOPERATIVE REGIONAL LIBRARY SERVICE*, c/o
Chemeketa Community College, 4000 Lancaster Dr NE, Salem, 97305-1453. (Mail
add: PO Box 14007, Salem, 97309-7070), SAN 322-2837. Tel: 503-399-5105.
FAX: 503-399-7316. E-mail: cocl@chemeketa.edu. Web Site: www.ccrls.org.
Coordr, Linda Cochrane; E-mail: cocl@chemeketa.edu
Founded 1973
Member Libraries: 18 acad & pub
Primary Functions: Daily courier service; automation; cataloging service

COASTAL RESOURCE SHARING NETWORK*, (CRSN), c/o Tillamook County
Library, 1716 Third St, Tillamook, 97141. Tel: 503-842-4792. FAX: 503-815-8194.
Web Site: www.beachbooks.org. *Pres,* Jill Tierce; E-mail: jtierce@beachbooks.org
Founded 1991
Member Libraries: 5 city, 2 col, 1 county & 1 libr district
Primary Functions: Provide library network services in northeast Oregon

COOS COUNTY LIBRARY SERVICE DISTRICT*, Tioga Hall, 1988 Newmark
Ave, Coos Bay, 97420. SAN 322-4279. Tel: 541-888-1529. FAX: 541-888-1529.
Web Site: www.cooslibraries.org. *Dir,* Mary Jane Fisher; Tel: 541-888-7393,
E-mail: mjfisher@socc.edu; *Outreach Serv Librn,* Irene Luoto; Tel: 541-888-7273,
E-mail: iluoto@socc.edu; *Network Adminr,* Sean Park; Tel: 541-888-7459, E-mail:
spark@cclsd.org
Founded 1980
Member Libraries: 1 commun col, 8 pub
Primary Functions: Provides the following services for Coos County Libraries:
Courier van service; centralized interlibrary loan switching; reference & referral;
direct outreach library services to inmates, nursing home & homebound patrons;
online searches; satellite libraries

GORGE LINK LIBRARY CONSORTIUM*, c/o Hood River County Library, 601
State St, Hood River, 97031. Tel: 541-387-7064. E-mail:
gorgelinklibrary@gorge.net. Web Site: www.gorgelinklibrary.org. *Syst Adminr,*
Jayne Guidinger
Founded 1993
Member Libraries: 1 high sch, 2 high sch/pub, 5 pub & 1 spec
Primary Functions: Share Sirsi Dynix Symphony integrated library system
(circulation/cataloging/OPAC)

LIBRARY INFORMATION NETWORK OF CLACKAMAS COUNTY*, (LINCC),
16239 SE McLoughlin Blvd, Ste 208, Oak Grove, 97267-4654. SAN 322-2845.
Tel: 503-723-4888. FAX: 503-794-8238. Web Site: www.lincc.org. *Libr Syst
Analyst,* George Yobst; E-mail: george@lincc.org
Founded 1977
Member Libraries: 11
Primary Functions: Interlibrary loan; courier service; administration of automated
library system; centralized MARC cataloging via OCLC; centralized ILL via
OCLC; reference service; continuing education; administrative functions; circulation
- SirsiDynix Symphony (turnkey system)

ORBIS CASCADE ALLIANCE, 2288 Oakmont Way, Eugene, 97401-5519. SAN
377-8096. Tel: 541-246-2470. FAX: 541-246-2477. Web Site:
www.orbiscascade.org. *Chair,* Jay Starratt; *Exec Dir,* John Helmer; Tel:
541-246-2470, Ext 205
Founded 1993
Member Libraries: 37 pvt & pub col & univ (Ore & Wash)
Primary Functions: Online patron-initiated borrowing direct from the union
catalog between all member libraries; reciprocal borrowing agreements for on-site
borrowing; union catalog continuously updated real-time over internet; electronic
resource licensing projects; contract administrator for library courier service;
Northwest Digital Archives program

OREGON HEALTH SCIENCES LIBRARIES ASSOCIATION*, (OHSLA), Oregon
Health & Science University Library, 3181 SW Sam Jackson Park Rd, Portland,
97239-3098. SAN 371-2176. Tel: 503-494-3462. FAX: 503-494-3322. E-mail:
library@ohsu.edu. *Dir,* Position Currently Open
Member Libraries: 50 health sci
Primary Functions: Organization for professionals in health science librarianship
providing continuing education development; resource sharing & information
exchange for its members

PORTLAND AREA LIBRARY SYSTEM*, (PORTALS), Port Community College,
SYLIB202, Portland, 97219. (Mail add: PO Box 19000, Portland, 97219). Tel:
503-977-4571. FAX: 503-977-4977. Web Site: www.portals.org. *Coordr,* Roberta
Richards; E-mail: rrichard@pcc.edu
Founded 1992
Member Libraries: 12 acad & 2 pub
Primary Functions: To meet the research & educational needs of people in the
greater Portland, Oregon area through cooperative & creative access to information
resources & services

SOUTHERN OREGON LIBRARY FEDERATION*, c/o Klamath County Library,
126 S Third St, Klamath Falls, 97601. SAN 322-2861. Tel: 541-882-8894. FAX:
541-882-6166. *Dir,* Andy Swanson; E-mail: aswanson@co.klamath.or.us
Member Libraries: 25 col, high sch, jr col, pub & spec
Primary Functions: Improving library service by establishing & maintaining
cooperative projects including interlibrary loan, Union Lists & newsletters

SOUTHERN OREGON LIBRARY INFORMATION SYSTEM*, (SOLIS), 724 S
Central Ave, Ste 112, Medford, 97501. Tel: 541-772-2141. FAX: 541-772-2144.
E-mail: solis_97501@yahoo.com. Web Site: solis.lib.or.us. *Syst Adminr,* Marian
Stoner; E-mail: stonerm@solis.lib.or.us; *Network Adminr,* Robert Jensen; E-mail:
admin@solis.lib.or.us
Founded 1999
Primary Functions: Provides an integrated library system; network services

WASHINGTON COUNTY COOPERATIVE LIBRARY SERVICES, 111 NE
Lincoln St, MS No 58, Hillsboro, 97124-3036. SAN 322-287X. Tel: 503-846-3222.
FAX: 503-846-3220. Web Site: www.wccls.org. *Mgr,* Eva Calcagno
Founded 1976
Member Libraries: 12 pub, plus col, high sch, spec & univ
Primary Functions: Interlibrary communication; courier service; online searching
& interlibrary loan service; library development for community libraries; universal
access to all public libraries; outreach to homebound; youth services coordination;
branch coordination; automation centralized cataloging, on-line public access
catalog & circulation including Internet access; public relations, staff training &
development; provide 60% of operating funding to member libraries; jail library
service; Spanish language support; outreach to Daycare; management of the West
Slope Library

PENNSYLVANIA

BERKS COUNTY LIBRARY ASSOCIATION*, (BCLA), Reading Public Library,
100 S Fifth St, Reading, 19602. SAN 371-0866. Tel: 610-478-9035, 610-655-6350.
Web Site: www.reading.lib.pa.us/berks_libraries/bcla. *Pres,* Jennifer Balas; *VPres,*
Celia Colby; Tel: 610-373-9888
Founded 1967
Member Libraries: 85 acad, med, pub & sch
Primary Functions: Social & professional sharing of problems, ideas & sharing of
resources

CENTRAL PENNSYLVANIA CONSORTIUM*, (CPC), Dickinson College, 249 W
Louther St, Carlisle, 17013. (Mail add: PO Box 1773, Carlisle, 17013-2896), SAN
322-2896. Tel: 717-245-1984. FAX: 717-245-1807. E-mail: cpc@dickinson.edu.
Web Site: www.dickinson.edu/prorg/cpc. *Pres,* Katherine Haley Will; *Chair,* Janet
M Riggs
Founded 1968
Member Libraries: 3 acad
Primary Functions: Interlibrary loan; interconsortium cooperation; journals
analysis & redistribution; audio tapes sharing; online network administration

CENTRAL PENNSYLVANIA HEALTH SCIENCES LIBRARY ASSOCIATION*,
(CPHSLA), Office for Research Protections, the Pennsylvania State University, 212
Kern Graduate Bldg, University Park, 16802. SAN 375-5290. FAX: 814-865-1775.
Web Site: www.cphsla.org. *Pres,* Tracie Kahler; Tel: 814-863-8699, Fax:
814-863-8699, E-mail: tkahler@psu.edu
Founded 1972

Member Libraries: 45
Primary Functions: Stimulate interests in & strengthen health services libraries in Central Pennsylvania by providing a means of communication & exchange of information resources; provide opportunities for resource sharing & institutional cooperation; continuing education of members

COOPERATING HOSPITAL LIBRARIES OF THE LEHIGH VALLEY AREA*, Saint Luke's Hospital, Estes Library, 801 Ostrum St, Bethlehem, 18015. SAN 371-0858. Tel: 610-954-3407. FAX: 610-954-4651. *Chairperson,* Sharon Hrabina; Tel: 570-476-3515; *Treas,* Diana Frantz; E-mail: frantz@slhn.org
Founded 1976
Member Libraries: 11 med, nursing
Primary Functions: Organization of health science libraries dedicated to resource sharing & education

DELAWARE VALLEY INFORMATION CONSORTIUM*, (DEVIC), St Mary Medical Ctr Medical Library, 1201 Langhorne-Newtown Rd, Langhorne, 19047. Tel: 215-710-2012. FAX: 215-710-4638. Web Site: devic-libraries.net. *Dir,* Jacqueline Luizzi; E-mail: jluizzi@stmaryealthcare.org
Founded 1979
Open Mon - Fri 8:30 - 4:30
Member Libraries: 35
Primary Functions: Provides free interlibrary loan

EASTERN MENNONITE ASSOCIATED LIBRARIES & ARCHIVES*, (EMALA), 2215 Millstream Rd, Lancaster, 17602. SAN 372-8226. Tel: 717-393-9745. FAX: 717-393-8751. *Chair,* Edsel Burdge, Jr
Founded 1961
Member Libraries: 8 spec (Mennonite & Anabaptist coll)
Primary Functions: Promote cooperation & foster discussion concerning operations, collection management & resources of Mennonite libraries, archives & museums; provide financial support for publication of Mennonite & Anabaptist research

ERIE AREA HEALTH INFORMATION LIBRARY COOPERATIVE*, (EAHILC), Gannon University, Nash Library, 109 University Sq, Erie, 16541. SAN 371-0564. Tel: 814-871-7667. FAX: 814-871-5566. *Chair,* Deborah West; Tel: 814-871-7667, E-mail: west001@gannon.edu
Member Libraries: 25
Primary Functions: Healthcare

GREATER PHILADELPHIA LAW LIBRARY ASSOCIATION*, (GPLLA), Wolf, Block, Schorr & Solis-Cohen LLP Library, 25th fl, 1650 Arch St, Philadelphia, 19103. SAN 373-1375. Toll Free Tel: 215-977-2779. Web Site: www.gplla.org. *Pres,* Monica Almendarez; E-mail: malmendarez@wolfblock.com; *Treas,* Deborah Botke; Tel: 215-979-1715
Founded 1970
Member Libraries: 230
Primary Functions: Promote librarianship; develop & increase the usefulness of law libraries; cultivate the science of law librarianship; foster a spirit of cooperation among the members of the profession

HSLC/ACCESS PA*, (Health Science Libraries Consortium), 3600 Market St, Ste 550, Philadelphia, 19104-2646. SAN 323-9780. Tel: 215-222-1532. FAX: 215-222-0416. E-mail: support@hslc.org. Web Site: www.accesspa.state.pa.us, www.hslc.org. *Exec Dir,* Joseph C Scorza; *Assoc Dir,* Alan C Simon; *Asst Dir,* Cindy A Pitchon
Founded 1988
Member Libraries: 100 HSLC; 3018 Access PA
Primary Functions: Cooperative programs in automated systems; statewide electronic interlibrary loan system; statewide online union catalog; subscription database services; POWER Library program; federated search service; Ask Here PA virtual reference service; Access PA Digital Repository

INTERLIBRARY DELIVERY SERVICE OF PENNSYLVANIA*, (IDS), c/o Bucks County IU, No 22, 705 N Shady Retreat Rd, Doylestown, 18901. SAN 322-2942. Tel: 215-348-2940, Ext 1620. Toll Free Tel: 800-770-4822, Ext 1620. FAX: 215-348-8315. E-mail: ids@bucksiu.org. Web Site: www.bucksiu.org. *Admin Dir,* Pamela Newman Dinan
Member Libraries: 224 acad, pub, sch & spec
Primary Functions: Interlibrary loan; delivery service

KEYSTONE LIBRARY NETWORK*, Dixon University Ctr, 2986 N Second St, Harrisburg, 17110-1201. Tel: 717-720-4088. FAX: 717-720-4453. Web Site: www.passhe.edu/kln. *Coordr,* Mary Lou Sowden; E-mail: msowden@passhe.edu
Founded 1998
Member Libraries: 18 col, state & univ
Primary Functions: Collections sharing; common library system; electronic content licensing; training including information literacy videos; electronic content presentation; ILL; document delivery; bookbinding contract

LAUREL HIGHLANDS HEALTH SCIENCE LIBRARY CONSORTIUM*, 361 Sunrise Rd, Dayton, 16222. SAN 322-2950. Tel: 814-341-0242. FAX: 814-266-8230. *Dir,* Rhonda Yeager
Member Libraries: 10 acad, med & spec
Primary Functions: Local resource sharing; efficient use of available financial resources; quick distribution of health-science information required by users; shared

online searching; clearinghouse of consumer health information; telephone information system - Health-line; shared telefax network; shared catalog - Medcat - Library Master; instruction of users in Grateful-Med; Silver Platter CD-ROM; Internet

LEHIGH VALLEY ASSOCIATION OF INDEPENDENT COLLEGES*, 130 W Greenwich St, Bethlehem, 18018. SAN 322-2969. Tel: 610-625-7888. FAX: 610-625-7891. Web Site: www.lvaic.org. *Exec Dir,* Dr Bonnie Lynch; Tel: 610-625-7892, E-mail: lynche@lvaic.org; *Dir, Admin Serv,* Mary Ann Williams; Tel: 610-625-7889, E-mail: williamsma@lvaic.org
Founded 1969
Member Libraries: 6 acad
Primary Functions: Mutual notification of purchase or intent to purchase; delivery services; photocopying services; production or maintenance of Union catalogs, lists & directories; reciprocal borrowing privileges; interlibrary loan system involving association member colleges & area public libraries

MONTGOMERY COUNTY LIBRARY & INFORMATION NETWORK CONSORTIUM, (MCLINC), 301 Fayette St, 2nd Flr, Conshohocken, 19428. Tel: 610-238-0580. FAX: 610-238-0581. Web Site: www.mclinc.org. *Pres,* Anne Frank
Founded 1995
Member Libraries: 16 pub
Primary Functions: Connect all free libraries & provide for their computer needs throughout Montgomery county

NATIONAL NETWORK OF LIBRARIES OF MEDICINE MIDDLE ATLANTIC REGION*, (NN-LM MAR), University of Pittsburgh, 3550 Terrace St, 200 Scaife Hall, Pittsburgh, 15261. Toll Free Tel: 800-338-7657 (Press 1). E-mail: rml@library.med.nyu.edu. Web Site: nnlm.gov/mar. *Exec Dir,* Renae Barger
Member Libraries: 815
Primary Functions: Serving Region 1: New York, New Jersey, Pennsylvania & Delaware; coordinates document delivery; outreach programs; provides health professionals with equal access to biomedical information; improve the public's access to information to enable them to make informed decisions about their health; provides workshop instructors, NLM trainers; publishes bi-monthly electronic newsletter; serves as national training center for librarians & health professionals from all 50 states

NORTHEASTERN PENNSYLVANIA LIBRARY NETWORK*, c/o Marywood University Library, 2300 Adams Ave, Scranton, 18509-1598. SAN 322-2993. Tel: 570-348-6260. FAX: 570-961-4769. Web Site: www.npln.org. *Exec Dir,* Catherine H Schappert; E-mail: cschappert@marywood.edu
Founded 1956
Member Libraries: 11 acad & 2 pub
Primary Functions: Interlibrary loan; Union List of Serials; continuing education

NORTHWEST INTERLIBRARY COOPERATIVE OF PENNSYLVANIA, (NICOP), Mercyhurst University Library, 501 E 38th St, Erie, 16546. SAN 370-5862. Tel: 814-824-2190. FAX: 814-824-2219. *Archivist,* Earleen Glaser
Founded 1972
Member Libraries: 29 incl acad, law, med, pub & spec
Primary Functions: Strengthen library resources & services in Northwestern Pennsylvania through interlibrary loan; Union List of Serials; reciprocal borrowing privileges; continuing education; mutually supporting acquisitions & preservation activities

PENNSYLVANIA LIBRARY ASSOCIATION, 220 Cumberland Pkwy, Ste 10, Mechanicsburg, 17055. Tel: 717-766-7663. FAX: 717-766-5440. Web Site: www.palibraries.org. *Exec Dir,* Glenn R Miller; *Pres,* Paula Gilbert
Founded 1901
Member Libraries: 1500 individuals, 300 institutions
Primary Functions: Provide leadership development, continuing education & advocacy on behalf of libraries

PHILADELPHIA AREA CONSORTIUM OF SPECIAL COLLECTIONS LIBRARIES*, (PACSCL), c/o The Historical Society of Pennsylvania, 1300 Locust St, Philadelphia, 19107. (Mail add: PO Box 22642, Philadelphia, 19110-2642), SAN 370-7504. Tel: 215-985-1445. FAX: 215-985-1446. Web Site: www.pacscl.org. *Exec Dir,* Laura Blanchard; E-mail: lblanchard@pacscl.org
Founded 1985
Member Libraries: 28 acad, pvt res, pub & res
Primary Functions: Encourages diverse audiences to explore & engage with member libraries' uniquely rich holdings & through collaboration, strengthens these collections & the institutions that preserve them

SOUTHEASTERN PENNSYLVANIA THEOLOGICAL LIBRARY ASSOCIATION*, (SEPTLA), c/o Biblical Seminary, 200 N Main St, Hatfield, 19440. SAN 371-0793. Tel: 215-368-5000, Ext 234. Web Site: www.atla.com/septla. *Chair,* Daniel LaValla; E-mail: dlavalla@biblical.edu
Founded 1965
Member Libraries: 19 acad
Primary Functions: Promote cooperation among member libraries for ILL, Union List of Serials, resource sharing & exchange of ideas particularly among the different denominations of member libraries

STATE SYSTEM OF HIGHER EDUCATION LIBRARY COOPERATIVE*, (SSHELCO), c/o Bailey Library, Slippery Rock Univ of Pennsylvania, Slippery Rock, 16057. Tel: 724-738-2630. FAX: 724-738-2661. *Dir,* Philip Tramdack
Founded 1962
Member Libraries: 14
Primary Functions: Cooperative resource sharing among the libraries in the state system of higher education & shared automated systems

SUSQUEHANNA LIBRARY COOPERATIVE, (SLC), Lock Haven University, Stevenson Library, 401 N Fairview St, Lock Haven, 17745. SAN 322-3051. Tel: 570-484-2310. FAX: 570-484-2506. Web Site: www.slclibrary.org. *Interim Dir, Libr & Info Serv,* Joby Topper; Tel: 570-484-2465, E-mail: jtopper@lhup.edu
Founded 1973
Member Libraries: 14 acad, med, pub & spec
Primary Functions: Interlibrary loan; Shared information; reference cooperation; reciprocal borrowing privileges; Ariel network; continuing education

TRI-STATE COLLEGE LIBRARY COOPERATIVE, (TCLC), c/o Rosemont College Library, 1400 Montgomery Ave, Rosemont, 19010-1699. SAN 322-3078. Tel: 610-525-0796. FAX: 610-525-1939. E-mail: office@tclclibs.org. Web Site: www.tclclibs.org. *Coordr,* Ellen Gasiewski
Founded 1967
Member Libraries: 46
Primary Functions: Educational programs; interlibrary loan; direct borrowing; continuing education awards

RHODE ISLAND

LIBRARY OF RHODE ISLAND NETWORK*, (LORI), c/o Office of Library & Info Services, One Capitol Hill, 2nd Flr, Providence, 02908-5870. SAN 371-6821. Tel: 401-574-9300. FAX: 401-574-9320. Web Site: www.olis.ri.gov. *Libr Serv Dir,* Howard Boksenbaum; E-mail: howardbm@olis.ri.gov
Founded 1964
Member Libraries: 350 acad, law, med, pub, sch & other spec
Primary Functions: ILL resource sharing; interlibrary delivery; statewide programming in libraries; state agency consulting services; electronic communications; library directories; talking books plus; library construction

OCEAN STATE LIBRARIES, (OSL), 300 Centerville Rd, Ste 103 S, Warwick, 02886-0226. SAN 329-4560. Tel: 401-738-2200. FAX: 401-736-8949. E-mail: support@oslri.net. Web Site: www.oslri.org. *Exec Dir,* Joan Gillespie; E-mail: jgillespie@oslri.net
Member Libraries: 50
Primary Functions: Provide materials, services & electronic resources to Rhode Island libraries & community

SOUTH CAROLINA

CHARLESTON ACADEMIC LIBRARIES CONSORTIUM*, (CALC), PO Box 118067, Charleston, 29423-8067. SAN 371-0769. Tel: 843-574-6088. FAX: 843-574-6484. *Chair,* Drucie Gullion
Founded 1993
Member Libraries: 6
Primary Functions: Interlibrary loan among academics; reciprocal borrowing

COLUMBIA AREA MEDICAL LIBRARIANS' ASSOCIATION*, (CAMLA), University of South Carolina, School of Medicine Library, 6311 Garner's Ferry Rd, Columbia, 29209. SAN 372-9400. Tel: 803-733-3361. FAX: 803-733-1509. Web Site: uscm.med.sc.edu/camla.htm. *Pres,* Roz Anderson; E-mail: roz@med.sc.edu; *Dir,* Ruth Riley; E-mail: ruth@med.sc.edu; *Asst Dir, Info Serv,* Laura Kane; E-mail: laura@med.sc.edu; *Syst Librn, Treas,* Bridget Livingston
Member Libraries: 10
Primary Functions: To exchange ideas, work closely & support each others services

PARTNERSHIP AMONG SOUTH CAROLINA ACADEMIC LIBRARIES*, (PASCAL), 1333 Main St, Ste 305, Columbia, 29201. Tel: 803-734-0900. FAX: 803-734-0901. Web Site: pascalsc.org. *Exec Dir,* Rick Moul; *Tech Prog Dir,* Victor Jenkinson; Tel: 803-734-0911, E-mail: vjenkinson@pascalsc.org; *Acad Res Coordr,* Alisa Whitt; Tel: 803-734-0912, E-mail: awhitt@pascalsc.org
Founded 2001
Member Libraries: 58 acad
Primary Functions: Respond to the information-access crisis facing South Carolina

SOUTH CAROLINA AHEC*, c/o Medical University of SC, 19 Hagood Ave, Ste 802, Charleston, 29425. (Mail add: PO Box 250814, Charleston, 29425-0814), SAN 329-3998. Tel: 843-792-4431. FAX: 843-792-4430. Web Site: www.scahec.net. *Exec Dir,* David Garr; E-mail: garrdr@musc.edu
Founded 1972
Member Libraries: 12
Primary Functions: Retains physicians & other health care providers in the state; provides educational programs to health care professionals

SOUTH CAROLINA LIBRARY NETWORK*, 1430 & 1500 Senate St, Columbia, 29201. (Mail add: PO Box 11469, Columbia, 29211-1469), SAN 322-4198. Tel: 803-734-8666. FAX: 803-734-8676. Web Site: www.scln.statelibrary.sc.gov. *Dir, Libr Develop,* Denise Lyons
Founded 1943
Member Libraries: 172 acad, pub & spec
Primary Functions: Interlibrary loan; locator service; bibliographic assistance; reference & research assistance; staff development; automation & network planning; online database administration

SOUTH DAKOTA

SOUTH DAKOTA LIBRARY NETWORK*, (SDLN), 1200 University, Unit 9672, Spearfish, 57799-9672. SAN 371-2117. Tel: 605-642-6835. Toll Free Tel: 800-245-5690. FAX: 605-642-6472. Web Site: www.sdln.net. *Dir,* Warren Wilson; Tel: 605-642-6930, E-mail: wwilson@sdln.net
Founded 1988
Member Libraries: 70
Primary Functions: Automated library network; resource sharing

TENNESSEE

CONSORTIUM OF SOUTHERN BIOMEDICAL LIBRARIES*, (CONBLS), Meharry Medical College, 1005 Dr D B Todd Blvd, Nashville, 37208. SAN 370-7717. Tel: 615-327-6728. FAX: 615-327-6448. Web Site: www.nab.edu/conbls. *Chair,* Barbara Shearer; E-mail: barbara.shearer@med.fsu.edu; *Ref Librn,* Marvelyn E Thompson; E-mail: thompsonm@mmc.edu
Founded 1982
Member Libraries: 17 med
Primary Functions: To exchange information & share resources; to participate in cooperative programs

KNOXVILLE AREA HEALTH SCIENCES LIBRARY CONSORTIUM*, (KAHSLC), UT Preston Med Libr, 1924 Alcoa Hwy, Knoxville, 37920. SAN 371-0556. Tel: 865-305-9525. FAX: 865-305-9527. Web Site: gsm.utmck.edu/library/kahslc/kahslc.htm. *Pres,* Cynthia Vaughn; Tel: 865-305-9526, E-mail: cvaughn@mc.utmck.edu
Founded 1976
Member Libraries: 15 acad, commun col, hosp, med, pub & spec
Primary Functions: For better communication between health science libraries; cooperate in exchange of information & share existing resources; continuing education

TENNESSEE HEALTH SCIENCE LIBRARY ASSOCIATION*, (THeSLA), Holston Valley Med Ctr Health Sciences Library, 130 W Ravine Rd, Kingsport, 37660. SAN 371-0726. Tel: 423-224-6870. FAX: 423-224-6014. *Coordr, Libr Serv,* Sharon M Brown; E-mail: sharon_m_brown@wellmont.org
Founded 1977
Member Libraries: 55 acad, hosp & med
Primary Functions: To promote the profession & to provide education by exchange of information & materials

TRI-CITIES AREA HEALTH SCIENCES LIBRARIES CONSORTIUM*, (TCAHSLC), East Tenn State Univ, James H Quillen Col of Med, Medical Library, Johnson City, 37614. (Mail add: PO Box 70693, Johnson City, 37614-1710), SAN 329-4099. Tel: 423-439-6252. FAX: 423-439-7025. Web Site: qcom.etsu.edu/medlib/tcahslc. *Dir,* Biddanda Ponnappa; E-mail: ponnappa@mail.etsu.edu
Member Libraries: 10
Primary Functions: Provides education & resource sharing, outreach & training to health care professionals in 17 counties of upper East Tennessee

WOLF RIVER LIBRARY CONSORTIUM*, c/o Germantown Community Library, 1925 Exeter Rd, Germantown, 38138-2815. Tel: 901-757-7323. FAX: 901-756-9940. Web Site: www.germantown-library.org. *Dir,* Melody Pittman
Founded 2005
Member Libraries: 4 commun
Primary Functions: Provide mutual support for collection development, subscription to online databases & integrated online catalog

TEXAS

ABILENE LIBRARY CONSORTIUM, 3305 N Third St, Ste 301, Abilene, 79603. SAN 322-4694. Tel: 325-672-7081. FAX: 325-672-7082. Web Site: www.alc.org. *Exec Dir,* Edward J Smith
Founded 1989
Member Libraries: 5
Primary Functions: To deliver higher quality library services to our communities through resource sharing and collaboration

AMIGOS LIBRARY SERVICES, INC, 14400 Midway Rd, Ste 200, Dallas, 75244-3509. SAN 322-3191. Tel: 972-851-8000. Toll Free Tel: 800-843-8482. FAX: 972-991-6061. E-mail: amigos@amigos.org. Web Site: www.amigos.org. *Pres & Chief Exec Officer,* Bonnie Juergens; Tel: 972-340-2820, E-mail: juergens@amigos.org; *Chief Communications & Membership Develop Officer,* Tracy Byerly; Tel: 972-340-2893, E-mail: byerly@amigos.org; *Chief Financial*

Officer, Charles Cason; Tel: 972-340-2846, E-mail: cason@amigos.org; *Chief Mem Serv Officer,* Laura Kimberly; Tel: 972-340-2864, E-mail: kimberly@amigos.org; *Imaging & Presv Serv Mgr,* Gina Minks; Tel: 972-340-2825, E-mail: minks@amigos.org; *Mem Discount Serv Mgr,* Gerrye McEntire; Tel: 972-340-2818, E-mail: mcentire@amigos.org
Founded 1974
Member Libraries: Over 850 acad, cultural heritage, pub, sch, spec & state institutions
Primary Functions: Member discounts on databases & supplies; resource sharing; consulting & training on cataloging, digital imaging, preservation & library technologies

COUNCIL OF RESEARCH & ACADEMIC LIBRARIES*, (CORAL), PO Box 290236, San Antonio, 78280-1636. SAN 322-3213. Tel: 210-458-4885. *Coordr,* Rosemary Vasquez; E-mail: rosemary.vasquez@utsa.edu
Member Libraries: 32 acad, mil inst, pvt & pub
Primary Functions: Strengthening area resources & services through circulation & interlibrary loan agreements; grant proposals; publish Union List of member holdings of serials; workshops; cooperative acquisitions programs; area data bank of holdings in machine format

DEL NORTE BIOSCIENCES LIBRARY CONSORTIUM, El Paso Community Coll, El Paso, 79998. (Mail add: PO Box 20500, El Paso, 79998), SAN 322-3302. Tel: 915-831-4458. FAX: 915-831-4639. *Coordr,* Kristin Sanchez; E-mail: gsanc127@epcc.edu
Member Libraries: 17
Primary Functions: Stimulate use of bioscience libraries through interlibrary loan & reciprocal copying services; produce & maintain a list of library services for health professionals in the El Paso regional area

HARRINGTON LIBRARY CONSORTIUM*, 413 E Fourth Ave, Amarillo, 79101. (Mail add: PO Box 2171, Amarillo, 79189), SAN 329-546X. Tel: 806-378-6037. FAX: 806-378-6038. Web Site: www.harringtonlc.org, www.hlc-lib.org/. *Dir,* Donna Littlejohn; E-mail: donna.littlejohn@amarillolibrary.org
Founded 1982
Member Libraries: 102 incl commun cols, elem schs, high schs, learning res ctrs, middle schs, pub & tech cols, pvt elem schools.
Primary Functions: To promote resource sharing; to provide access to information through a common automated integrated system

HEALTH LIBRARIES INFORMATION NETWORK*, (Health LINE), UT Southwestern Medical Ctr Libr, 5323 Harry Hines Blvd, Dallas, 75390-9049. SAN 322-3299. Tel: 214-648-2626. FAX: 214-648-2826.
Member Libraries: 20 hospital & health sci institutions
Primary Functions: Provide support network for health sciences librarians who provide service to physicians, nurses, hospital administrators, faculty, professional med students & technical personnel interlibrary loan

HOUSTON AREA LIBRARY AUTOMATED NETWORK*, (HALAN), Houston Public Library, 500 McKinney Ave, Houston, 77002. Tel: 832-393-1411. FAX: 832-393-1427. E-mail: website@hpl.lib.tx.us. Web Site: www.halan.lib.tx.us. *Chief,* Judith Hiott
Founded 1988
Member Libraries: 1 commun col & 7 pub
Primary Functions: Primary provider of information technology services in support of an integrated library system

HOUSTON AREA RESEARCH LIBRARY CONSORTIUM*, (HARLiC), c/o University of Houston Libraries, 114 University Libraries, Houston, 77204-2000. SAN 322-3329. Tel: 713-743-9807. FAX: 713-743-9811. Web Site: www.harlic.org. *Pres,* Dana Rooks
Founded 1978
Member Libraries: 4 academic, 2 medical & 1 public
Primary Functions: Reciprocal borrowing privileges & consult about collection development; resource sharing & preservation; technical services, systems & automation development; staff development

NATIONAL NETWORK OF LIBRARIES OF MEDICINE SOUTH CENTRAL REGION*, (NN/LM SCR), c/o HAM-TMC Library, 1133 John Freeman Blvd, Houston, 77030-2809. SAN 322-3353. Tel: 713-799-7880. Toll Free Tel: 800-338-7657. FAX: 713-790-7030. E-mail: nnlm-scr@exch.library.tmc.edu. Web Site: nnlm.gov/scr. *Dir,* L Maximillian Buja; Tel: 713-799-7177, E-mail: l.maximillian.buja@exch.library.tmc.edu; *Assoc Dir,* Renée Bougard; E-mail: michelle.malizia@exch.library.tmc.edu; *Tech Coordr,* Emily Hurst; Tel: 713-799-7189, E-mail: emily.hurst@exch.library.tmc.edu
Member Libraries: 891 health sci, pub & other libr insts located in AR, LA, NM, OK & TX
Primary Functions: Document delivery; consultation & outreach; training for academic, medical, hospital & public libraries, consumers, healthcare providers, & public health departments; resource sharing; consortia development; Internet training; bibliographic instruction; course development

SOUTH CENTRAL ACADEMIC MEDICAL LIBRARIES CONSORTIUM*, (SCAMeL), c/o Lewis Library-UNTHSC, 3500 Camp Bowie Blvd, Fort Worth, 76107. SAN 372-8269. Tel: 817-735-2380. FAX: 817-735-5158. *Dir,* Daniel Burgard; E-mail: daniel.burgard@unthsc.edu

Founded 1982
Member Libraries: 14 acad med ctrs
Primary Functions: Provide interlibrary loan, cooperative acquisitions, continuing education & management training, research, statistical data comparison, networking

TEXAS COUNCIL OF ACADEMIC LIBRARIES*, (TCAL), VC/UHV Library, 2602 N Ben Jordan, Victoria, 77901. (Mail add: c/o Texas Library Association, 3355 Bee Cave Rd, Ste 401, Austin, 78746), SAN 322-337X. Tel: 361-570-4150. FAX: 361-570-4155. Web Site: www.txla.org/groups/tcal. *Chairperson,* Dr Joe Dahlstrom; E-mail: dahlstromj@uhv.edu
Member Libraries: Pub & pvt col & univ
Primary Functions: State contract for binding & book acquisition; statistics compilation; legislative action; liaison with Coordinating Board for Institutions of Higher Learning in library matters; liaison with Texas Legislative Budget Board; development of networks to meet specific information needs

TEXAS NAVIGATOR GROUP, (Formerly Texnet), PO Box 12927, Austin, 78711. SAN 322-3396. Tel: 512-463-5406. FAX: 512-936-2306. Web Site: www.tsl.state.tx.us. *Coordr,* Sue Bennett
Primary Functions: Sharing resources through interlibrary loan with Texas public libraries

TEXSHARE - TEXAS STATE LIBRARY & ARCHIVES COMMISSION, 1201 Brazos, Austin, 78701. (Mail add: PO Box 12927, Austin, 78711). Tel: 512-463-5465. Toll Free Tel: 800-252-9386. FAX: 512-936-2306. E-mail: texshare@tsl.state.tx.us. Web Site: www.tsl.state.tx.us/texshare/index.html. *Consortia Serv,* Beverley Shirley; Tel: 512-463-5433, E-mail: bshirley@tsl.state.tx.us
Founded 1988
Primary Functions: TexShare is a cooperative program designed to improve library service to Texans. TexShare focuses on the efficient sharing of library holdings, with an emphasis on electronic information resources & traditional collections of books & journals

UTAH

NATIONAL NETWORK OF LIBRARIES OF MEDICINE MIDCONTINENTAL REGION*, (NN-LM MCR), Univ Utah, Spencer S Eccles Health Sci Libr, Bldg 589, Ten N 1900 E, Salt Lake City, 84112-5890. SAN 322-225X. Tel: 801-587-3412. Toll Free Tel: 800-338-7657. FAX: 801-581-3632. Web Site: nnlm.gov/mcr/. *Dir,* Wayne J Peay; *Assoc Dir,* Claire Hamasu
Founded 2001
Member Libraries: 400
Primary Functions: Consultation; education; online training & services; regional planning services for the development of information access programs within Clorado, Kansas, Missouri, Nebraska, Utah & Wyoming, for the improvement of medical library service for health professionals

UTAH ACADEMIC LIBRARY CONSORTIUM, (UALC), University of Utah, 295 S 1500 E, Salt Lake City, 84112-0860. SAN 322-3418. Tel: 801-581-3852, 801-581-7701. FAX: 801-585-7185. E-mail: UALCmail@library.utah.edu. Web Site: www.ualc.net. *Fiscal Agent,* Carol Jost; E-mail: carol.jost@utah.edu; *Exec Secy,* Kimberly Rollins; E-mail: kim.rollins@utah.edu
Founded 1971
Member Libraries: 26
Primary Functions: Cooperate in continually improving the availaiility and delivery of library and information services to the higher education community in the state of Utah and to partner libraries in Nevada.

UTAH HEALTH SCIENCES LIBRARY CONSORTIUM*, c/o Univ Utah, Spencer S Eccles Health Sci Library, Ten N 1900 East, Salt Lake City, 84112-5890. SAN 376-2246. Tel: 801-585-5743. FAX: 801-581-3632. Web Site: library.med.utah.edu/twiki/bin/view/UHSLC/AboutUhslc. *Chair,* Emily Eresuma; Tel: 801-662-1391, E-mail: emily.eresuma@imail.org
Member Libraries: 13 acad, hosp, spec & VA
Primary Functions: To improve healthcare through development & fostering of a cooperative network of health sciences libraries in Utah; resource sharing; development of standards to assure quality in the provision of library services; to advocate the value of libraries & librarians to their institutions, hospital administrators & health care professionals

VERMONT

VERMONT RESOURCE SHARING NETWORK, Vermont Dept of Libraries, 109 State St, Montpelier, 05609-0601. SAN 322-3426. Tel: 802-828-3261. FAX: 802-828-1481. *Ref Librn,* Gerrie Denison
Member Libraries: 500 acad, pub, sch & spec
Primary Functions: Coordination of statewide interlibrary loan network & the Vermont Automated Library System; maintenance of Vermont Union Catalog; maintenance of Reference Services Unit; supervision of DOL-UVM Access Office at University of Vermont; coordination of continuing education offerings in the area of reference; maintenance of library science collection; coordination of online search services

VIRGINIA

AMERICAN INDIAN HIGHER EDUCATION CONSORTIUM*, (AIHEC), 121 Oronoco St, Alexandria, 22314. SAN 329-4056. Tel: 703-838-0400. FAX: 703-838-0388. E-mail: info@aihec.org. Web Site: www.aihec.org. *Exec Dir,* Gerald Gipp
Founded 1972
Member Libraries: 33 inst
Primary Functions: Promotes tribal college & university curriculum

LYNCHBURG AREA LIBRARY COOPERATIVE, c/o Sweet Briar College Library, PO Box 1200, Sweet Briar, 24595. SAN 322-3450. Tel: 434-381-6315. FAX: 434-381-6173. Web Site: old.library.sbc.edu/lalc/lalcdirectory.html.
Founded 1974
Member Libraries: 25 acad, pub & spec
Primary Functions: Interlibrary loan; reference collection access; Union List of Serials (Blue Ridge Union List - OCLC); staff development programs; automation projects

LYNCHBURG INFORMATION ONLINE NETWORK*, (LION), 2315 Memorial Ave, Lynchburg, 24503. SAN 374-6097. Tel: 434-381-6311. FAX: 434-381-6173. *Dir,* John G Jaffee; Tel: 434-381-6139, E-mail: jgjaffee@sbc.edu
Founded 1988
Member Libraries: 5 (incl 2 acad, 2 pub & 1 spec)
Primary Functions: Shared library automation system; interlibrary loan; courier service

NASA LIBRARIES INFORMATION SYSTEM-NASA GALAXIE*, NASA Langley Research Ctr, MS 185 - Technical Library, Two W Durand St, Hampton, 23681-2199. SAN 322-0788. Tel: 757-864-2356. FAX: 757-864-2375. E-mail: tech-library@larc.nasa.gov. Web Site: library.larc.nasa.gov.
Member Libraries: 13 NASA libraries in US
Primary Functions: NASA Galaxie contains bibliographic information on the holdings for the NASA libraries, including books, technical reports, journals & electronic media such as audio & video tapes & internet resources; the system utilizes Sirsi's library management system

RICHMOND ACADEMIC LIBRARY CONSORTIUM*, (RALC), Virginia Commonwealth University, James Branch Cabell Library, 901 Park Ave, Richmond, 23284. (Mail add: PO Box 2033, Richmond, 23284-2033), SAN 322-3469. Tel: 804-828-1107, 804-828-1110. FAX: 804-828-0151, 804-828-1105. Web Site: www.library.vcu.edu/services/ralc.html. *Officer, Univ Librn,* John E Ulmschneider; E-mail: jeulmschneider@vcu.edu
Founded 1972
Member Libraries: 10 acad
Primary Functions: Further the development of academic libraries; sponsor projects for the mutual benefit of its members; sponsor activities in professional development & continuing education; promote resource sharing through interlibrary lending, document delivery, direct borrowing by patrons, shared collection development & automated networking; shared media resources through the Richmond Academic Film-Video Co-operative

SOUTHSIDE VIRGINIA LIBRARY NETWORK*, (SVLN), Longwood University, 201 High St, Farmville, 23909-1897. SAN 372-8242. Tel: 434-395-2431, 434-395-2433. FAX: 434-395-2453. Web Site: www.longwood.edu/library. *Dean of Libr,* Suzy Szasz Palmer; Tel: 434-395-2083
Founded 1984
Member Libraries: 47 incl acad, commun col, institutional, pub, sch & spec
Primary Functions: Provide a forum for professional concerns of the Southside Virginia library community; share resources through interlibrary loan & serials union listing; survey membership on needs & share results through newsletters & directory; plan continuing education workshops; pursue funding for library networking in South-Central Virginia

SOUTHWESTERN VIRGINIA HEALTH INFORMATION LIBRARIANS, (SWVAHILI), Carilion Health Sciences Library, Belleview at Jefferson St, Roanoke, 24033. SAN 323-9527. Tel: 540-689-1771. FAX: 540-689-1770. *Chair,* George Curran; E-mail: gcurran@rhcc.com
Founded 1982
Member Libraries: 12 acad & med
Primary Functions: Exchange information & ideas; provide short programs on various health science library functions & activities

UNITED STATES ARMY TRAINING & DOCTRINE COMMAND*, Library Program Office, US Army Hq TRADOC, Seven Bernard Rd, Fort Monroe, 23651. SAN 322-418X. Tel: 757-788-2155. FAX: 757-788-5544. *Dir,* Amy Loughran; E-mail: amy.loughran@us.army.mil
Member Libraries: 22 army, sch & tech
Primary Functions: Provision of network service

VIRGINIA INDEPENDENT COLLEGE & UNIVERSITY LIBRARY ASSOCIATION*, c/o Mary Helen Cochran Library, Sweet Briar College, Sweet Briar, 24595. SAN 374-6089. Tel: 434-381-6139. FAX: 434-381-6173. *Dir,* John Jaffee
Member Libraries: 32 pvt acad
Primary Functions: ILL resource sharing; union listing; staff cooperation & communication; cooperative projects; library directories

VIRGINIA TIDEWATER CONSORTIUM FOR HIGHER EDUCATION*, (VTC), 4900 Powhatan Ave, Norfolk, 23529. SAN 329-5486. Tel: 757-683-3183. FAX: 757-683-4515. E-mail: lgdotolo@aol.com. Web Site: www.vtc.odu.edu. *Pres,* Dr Lawrence G Dotolo; *Prog Mgr,* Nicola V Beltz
Founded 1973
Member Libraries: 15
Primary Functions: Cross registration; interlibrary borrowing for students & faculty; sponsor of grants; operation of television channel for higher educational programming; off-campus centers on military bases; educational opportunity center; summer institute on college teaching; certificate on college teaching; security & emergency preparedness programs; substance abuse prevention programs; cooperative international programs; college access programs

VIRTUAL LIBRARY OF VIRGINIA*, (VIVA), George Mason University, Fenwick B222, Fairfax, 22030. (Mail add: George Mason University, MSC 2FL, Fairfax, 22030-4444). Tel: 703-993-4652. FAX: 703-993-4662. Web Site: www.vivalib.org. *Dir,* Katherine Perry; E-mail: kperry@gmu.edu; *Assoc Dir,* Tansy Matthews; Tel: 703-993-2694, E-mail: tmatthe6@gmu.edu
Founded 1994
Member Libraries: 73 acad
Primary Functions: Group acquisition of electronic resources & promotion of use of these products; promote & assist resource sharing & interlibrary loan among members

WASHINGTON

COOPERATING LIBRARIES IN OLYMPIA*, (CLIO), The Evergreen State College Library, L2300, Olympia, 98505. SAN 329-4528. Tel: 360-867-6260. FAX: 360-867-6790. *Dean, Libr Serv,* Lee Lyttle; *Syst Adminr,* Steven Metcalf
Founded 1997
Member Libraries: 3
Primary Functions: To acquire & operate an integrated library system

INLAND NORTHWEST HEALTH SCIENCES LIBRARIES, (INWHSL), PO Box 10283, Spokane, 99209-0283. SAN 370-5099. Tel: 509-368-6973. FAX: 509-358-7928. *Treas,* Robert Pringle; E-mail: rpringle@wsu.edu
Founded 1989
Member Libraries: 12 incl acad & med
Primary Functions: Facilitate cooperative efforts among members; promote continuing education for information professionals; provide a forum for discussion of mutual problems & concerns that members encounter in providing health care information

NATIONAL NETWORK OF LIBRARIES OF MEDICINE PACIFIC NORTHWEST REGION, (NNLM-PNR), T-344 Health Sciences Bldg, University of Washington, Seattle, 98195. (Mail add: Box 357155, University of Washington, Seattle, 98195-7155), SAN 322-3485. Tel: 206-543-8262. Toll Free Tel: 800-338-7657. FAX: 206-543-2469. E-mail: nnlm@uw.edu. Web Site: nnlm.gov/pnr. *Assoc Dir,* Catherine Burroughs; Tel: 206-543-9261, E-mail: cburroug@u.washington.edu
Founded 1968
Member Libraries: 81 acad, 105 hospitals, 29 pub, & 159 other
Primary Functions: With responsibility for the region comprising Alaska, Idaho, Montana, Oregon & Washington, serve as the regional coordinating & service agency under contract to the National Library of Medicine (NLM); supplement local services to guarantee access to information needed by those engaged in health care, research & education; coordinate regional use of DOCLINE; promote the use of online information services; promote use of Internet & provide Internet training for librarians & health professionals; provide Web page for the NN-LM PNR; collect & analyze data, plan & consult for development of more effective services; coordinate efforts to provide training & continuing education for health sciences librarians; promote development of health sciences library consortia & statewide health information networks

PALOUSE AREA LIBRARY INFORMATION SERVICES*, (PALIS), c/o Neill Public Library, 210 N Grand Ave, Pullman, 99163. SAN 375-0132. Tel: 509-334-3595. FAX: 509-334-6051. Web Site: www.neill-lib.org/palis.htm. *Dir,* Andriette Pieron; Tel: 509-338-3269, E-mail: andriette@neill-lib.org
Founded 1992
Member Libraries: 21 acad, pub & sch
Primary Functions: A cooperative venture among public, school & academic libraries; cooperative collection development & materials delivery system; explores resource sharing opportunities

WASHINGTON IDAHO NETWORK*, (WIN), Gonzaga University, Foley Center Library, 502 E Boone Ave, AD 95, Spokane, 99258. Tel: 509-313-6545. Toll Free Tel: 800-388-2008. FAX: 509-313-5904. E-mail: winsupport@gonzaga.edu. Web Site: www.wash-id.net. *Pres,* Eileen Bell-Garrison; Tel: 509-313-6535, E-mail: bellgarrison@gonzaga.edu
Founded 2000
Member Libraries: 95 acad, elem, high sch, legal, med & pub
Primary Functions: Shared library automation system & central site support for Ex Libris automation services

WEST VIRGINIA

MID-ATLANTIC LAW LIBRARY COOPERATIVE*, (MALLCO), College of Law Library, West Virginia University, Morgantown, 26506-6135. SAN 371-0645. Tel: 304-293-7641. FAX: 304-293-6020. Web Site: law.wvu.edu/library. *Libr Dir,* Camille M Riley; E-mail: camille.riley@mail.wvu.edu
Founded 1980
Member Libraries: 15 acad, bar, law, pub & state law
Primary Functions: Sharing of concerns & information among members; interlibrary loan; sharing in joint projects such as Union Lists, micro, etc

WISCONSIN

ARROWHEAD HEALTH SCIENCES LIBRARY NETWORK*, Wisconsin Indianhead Technical College, 505 Pine Ridge Dr, Shell Lake, 54817. SAN 322-1954. Tel: 715-468-2815, Ext 2298. Toll Free Tel: 800-243-9482. FAX: 715-468-2819. Web Site: www.witc.edu. *Coordr,* Judy Lyons; E-mail: jlyons@witc.edu
Member Libraries: 15 acad, med & spec
Primary Functions: Interlibrary loan; reference assistance; continuing education; collection development; cooperative acquisitions; on-line search services

FOX RIVER VALLEY AREA LIBRARY CONSORTIUM*, (FRVALC), c/o University of Wisconsin Oshkosh, Polk Library, 800 Algona Blvd, Oshkosh, 54901. SAN 322-3531. Tel: 920-424-3348, 920-424-4333. Toll Free Tel: 800-574-5041. FAX: 920-424-2175. Web Site: www.focol.org/frvalc. *Coordr,* Position Currently Open
Founded 1975
Member Libraries: 32
Primary Functions: Shared resources; workshops; journal exchange; Union List of books, periodicals & catalogs

FOX VALLEY LIBRARY COUNCIL*, c/o OWLS, 225 N Oneida St, Appleton, 54911. SAN 323-9640. Tel: 920-832-6190. FAX: 920-832-6422. Web Site: www.focol.org/edu-lib/fvlc. *Pres,* Joy Schwarz
Founded 1977
Member Libraries: 95 acad, pub, sch & spec
Primary Functions: To promote cooperation among all types of libraries & information centers in the Fox Valley area

NORTH EAST WISCONSIN INTERTYPE LIBRARIES, INC, (NEWIL), 515 Pine St, Green Bay, 54301. SAN 322-3574. Tel: 920-448-4413. FAX: 920-448-4420. Web Site: www.newil.org. *Coordr,* Jamie Matczak; E-mail: jmatczak@mail.nfls.lib.wi.us
Founded 1967
Member Libraries: 95 acad, med, pub, sch & spec
Primary Functions: Interlibrary loan; resource & material sharing

NORTHWESTERN WISCONSIN HEALTH SCIENCE LIBRARY CONSORTIUM*, c/o Gundersen Lutheran Medical Center, 1900 South Ave, Mail Stop H01-011, Lacrosse, 54601. Tel: 608-775-5410. FAX: 608-775-6343. Web Site: www.whsla.mcw.edu. *Treas,* Eileen Severson
Primary Functions: Promote & share medical information & new technologies

SOUTH CENTRAL WISCONSIN HEALTH SCIENCE LIBRARY CONSORTIUM*, c/o Fort Healthcare Medical Library, 611 Sherman Ave E, Fort Atkinson, 53538. SAN 322-4686. Tel: 920-568-5194. FAX: 920-568-5195. *Coordr,* Carrie Garity; E-mail: carrie.garity@forthc.com
Member Libraries: 35
Primary Functions: Interlibrary loan; inservice education; member of Mid-West Federated Network of Public Libraries

SOUTHEASTERN WISCONSIN HEALTH SCIENCE LIBRARY CONSORTIUM*, Veteran's Admin Ctr Medical Library, 5000 W National Ave, Milwaukee, 53295. SAN 322-3582. Tel: 414-384-2000, Ext 42342. FAX: 414-382-5334. *Coordr,* Janice Curnes; E-mail: janice.curnes@med.va.gov
Founded 1974
Member Libraries: 19 health
Primary Functions: Shared resources; continuing education

SOUTHEASTERN WISCONSIN INFORMATION TECHNOLOGY EXCHANGE, INC*, (SWITCH), 6801 N Yates Rd, Milwaukee, 53217-3985. SAN 371-3962. Tel: 414-351-2423. FAX: 414-228-4146. Web Site: topcat.switchinc.org. *Coordr,* William A Topritzhofer; E-mail: btopritz@switchinc.org; *Instrul Serv Librn,* Jennifer Schmidt; E-mail: jschmidt@switchinc.org
Founded 1988
Member Libraries: 8 acad
Primary Functions: Dedicated to the advancement of open information technologies & shared electronic resources among information-providing institutions; operates a union database & shared integrated library system utilizing Innovative Interfaces software

UNIVERSITY OF WISCONSIN SYSTEM SCHOOL LIBRARY EDUCATION CONSORTIUM*, (UWSSLEC), Grad & Continuing Educ, Univ Wisconsin-Whitewater, 800 W Main St, Whitewater, 53190. Tel: 262-472-1463. Toll Free Tel: 800-621-5376. FAX: 262-472-5210. E-mail: lenchoc@uww.edu. Web

Site: www.uwsslec.org. *Co-Dir,* Dr E Anne Zarinnia; E-mail: zarinnie@uww.edu; *Co-Dir,* Dr Eileen E Schroeder
Founded 1998
Member Libraries: Univ Wisconsin-Whitewaater, University of Wisconsin Madison, UW-Eau Claire, UW Oshkosh, UW-Superior
Primary Functions: Library education; provide access to licensure in school library media & technology

WISCONSIN LIBRARY SERVICES*, (WILS), 728 State St, Rm 464, Madison, 53706-1494. SAN 322-3612. Tel: 608-265-4167. Interlibrary Loan Service Tel: 608-263-4981. Automation Services Tel: 608-265-0580. FAX: 608-262-6067. Interlibrary Loan Service FAX: 608-263-3684. Web Site: www.wils.wisc.edu. *Dir,* Kathryn Schneider Michaelis; Tel: 608-263-2773, E-mail: schneid@wils.wisc.edu; *ILL Librn,* Joy Pohlman; *ILL Librn,* Bob Shaw; *Automation Syst Coordr,* Allen Wenzel; *Coordr, ILL,* Eric Robinson; E-mail: erobinson@wils.wisc.edu; *Coordr of Res Serv,* Tom Zillner
Founded 1972
Member Libraries: 66 acad, 69 pub, 273 sch districts, 43 spec, 13 state agency & 16 vo-tech
Primary Functions: Interlibrary loan; document delivery; resource sharing; OCLC access; shared cataloging; cooperative purchasing & licensing for Wisconsin libraries

WISCONSIN PUBLIC LIBRARY CONSORTIUM*, (WPLC), c/o South Central Library System, 5250 E Terrace Dr, Madison, 53718. Web Site: www.wplc.info. *Dir,* Phyllis Davis; Tel: 608-246-7975, Fax: 608-246-7958, E-mail: pbdavis@scls.lib.wi.us; *Project Mgr,* Jane Richard
Founded 2000
Member Libraries: 17 pub
Primary Functions: To undertake research & development &/or new technology projects for public library systems

WISCONSIN VALLEY LIBRARY SERVICE, (WVLS), 300 N First St, Wausau, 54403. SAN 371-3911. Tel: 715-261-7250. FAX: 715-261-7259. Web Site: wvls.lib.wi.us. *Dir,* Marla Rae Sepnafski; Tel: 715-261-7251, E-mail: msepnafs@wvls.org; *Asst Dir, ILS Adminr,* Inese Christman; Tel: 715-261-7257, E-mail: ichristman@wvls.org; *IT Dir,* Joshua Klingbeil; Tel: 715-261-7252, E-mail: jklingbeil@wvls.org
Founded 1961
Member Libraries: 25 pub, 187 sch & 25 spec
Primary Functions: Provide backup reference, referral & courier services to member libraries; provide professional consultant services to member library personnel & trustees; provide structure for interlibrary loan among libraries

WISPALS LIBRARY CONSORTIUM*, c/o Gateway Technical College, 3520 30th Ave, Kenosha, 53144-1690. Tel: 262-564-2602. FAX: 262-564-2787. Web Site: www.wispals.org. *Coordr,* Jennifer Brosek; E-mail: brosekj@gtc.edu
Founded 1989
Member Libraries: 11 tech col districts
Primary Functions: Provide access to shared library automation system; member library resources & library staff training opportunities; negotiate on behalf of member colleges; access to electronic databases at reduced cost; represent the Wisconsin technical college library community to state & national organizations

WYOMING

WYLD NETWORK*, c/o Wyoming State Library, 516 S Greeley Hwy, Cheyenne, 82002-0060. SAN 371-0661. Tel: 307-777-6339. Toll Free Tel: 800-264-1281. FAX: 307-777-6289. E-mail: wyldstaff@will.state.wy.us. Web Site: www-wsl.state.wy.us/wyld. *State Librn,* Lesley Boughton; Tel: 307-777-5911, E-mail: lbough@state.wy.us; *Prog Mgr,* Brian A Greene; E-mail: bgreen@state.wy.us
Founded 1984
Member Libraries: Statewide multitype with 49 members in almost 90 acad, K-12, pub, spec & state locations
Primary Functions: Coordinate ILL activity (F-D, OCLC, Sirsi); maintain statewide database (Sirsi); statewide PAC (Sirsi); automated circulation service (Sirsi); assist & help consortium members in these & other areas

VIRGIN ISLANDS

VILINET*, Virgin Islands Library & Information Network, c/o Division of Libraries, Archives & Museums, 23 Dronningens Gade, Saint Thomas, 00802. SAN 322-3639. Tel: 340-773-5715. FAX: 340-773-3257. E-mail: info@vilinet.net. Web Site: www.library.gov.vi, virginislandspace.org/vinineta.htm. *Territorial Dir of Libr, Archives & Mus,* Ingrid Bough; E-mail: ingrid.bough@dpnr.gov.vi
Founded 1988
Member Libraries: 26, incl 7 pub, 17 sch & 2 univ
Primary Functions: Interlibrary loan; library automation; legislation

ALBERTA

NEOS LIBRARY CONSORTIUM, Cameron Library, 5th Flr, University of Alberta, Edmonton, T6G 2J8. Tel: 780-492-0075. FAX: 780-492-8302. Web Site: www.neoslibraries.ca. *Mgr,* Anne Carr-Wiggin; E-mail: anne.carr-wiggin@ualberta.ca

Founded 1996
Member Libraries: 17
Primary Functions: Shared Integrated Library System & related services.
Professional development & training

THE ALBERTA LIBRARY, (TAL), 6-14, Seven Sir Winston Churchill Sq,
Edmonton, T5J 2V5. Tel: 780-414-0805. FAX: 780-414-0806. E-mail:
admin@thealbertalibrary.ab.ca. Web Site: www.thealbertalibrary.ab.ca. *Chief Exec
Officer,* Maureen Woods; Tel: 780-414-0805, Ext 224, E-mail:
mwoods@thealbertalibrary.ab.ca
Founded 1997
Member Libraries: 49
Primary Functions: Optimize resources & services among member libraries in a
dynamic model of collaboration

BRITISH COLUMBIA

BC ACADEMIC HEALTH COUNCIL*, (BCAHC), 402-1770 W Seventh Ave,
Vancouver, V6J 4Y6. Tel: 604-739-3910, Ext 228. FAX: 604-739-3931. E-mail:
info@bcahc.ca. *Chief Exec Officer,* Laureen Styles
Founded 2003
Member Libraries: 21 acad, 3 govt & 2 spec
Primary Functions: Effective collaboration, partnership & leadership by senior
leaders in health care & education

BC ELECTRONIC LIBRARY NETWORK*, (BC ELN), WAC Bennett Library, 7th
Flr, Simon Fraser University, 8888 University Dr, Burnaby, V5A 1S6. Tel:
778-782-7003. FAX: 778-782-3023. E-mail: office@eln.bc.ca. Web Site:
www.eln.bc.ca. *Exec Dir,* Anita Cocchia; Tel: 778-782-7004, E-mail:
anitac@eln.bc.ca
Founded 1989
Member Libraries: 29 acad
Primary Functions: Develop, promote & maintain system-wide mechanisms that
allow post-secondary libraries to meet the expanding information needs of the
province's learners, researchers & educators, at the lowest possible cost

BRITISH COLUMBIA COLLEGE & INSTITUTE LIBRARY SERVICES*,
Langara College Library, 100 W 49th Ave, Vancouver, V5Y 2Z6. SAN 329-6970.
Tel: 604-323-5639. FAX: 604-323-5544. E-mail: cils@langara.bc.ca. Web Site:
www.langara.bc.ca/cils. *Dir,* Mary Anne Epp; Tel: 604-323-5627, Fax:
604-323-5577, E-mail: maepp@langara.bc.ca
Founded 1984
Member Libraries: 22 colleges served
Primary Functions: Locates, produces & provides library materials in forms
acessible to students with print disabilities; interlibrary loan; electronic text, large
print, digital audio & DAISY production & reference information service

COUNCIL OF PRAIRIE & PACIFIC UNIVERSITY LIBRARIES*, (COPPUL),
2005 Sooke Rd, Victoria, V9B 5Y2. Tel: 250-391-2554. FAX: 250-391-2556.
E-mail: coppul@royalroads.ca. Web Site: www.coppul.ca. *Exec Dir,* Alexander
Slade
Founded 2000
Member Libraries: 20
Primary Functions: Resource sharing; collective purchasing; document delivery

ELECTRONIC HEALTH LIBRARY OF BRITISH COLUMBIA*, (e-HLbc), c/o
Bennett Library, 8888 University Dr, Burnaby, V5A 1S6. Tel: 778-782-5440. FAX:
778-782-3023. E-mail: info@ehlbc.ca. Web Site: ehlbc.ca. *Coordr,* JoAnne
Newyear-Ramirez; E-mail: joannen@ehlbc.ca
Founded 2006
Member Libraries: 24 acad & 9 govt
Primary Functions: To facilitate cross-sectoral collaboration, support, training &
sharing health information resources among BC's academic & healthcare
community

PUBLIC LIBRARY INTERLINK*, c/o Burnaby Public Library-Kingsway Branch,
7252 Kingsway, Burnaby, V5E 1G3. SAN 318-8272. Tel: 604-517-8441. FAX:
604-517-8410. E-mail: info@interlinklibraries.ca. Web Site:
www.interlinklibraries.ca. *Operations Mgr,* Rita Avigdor
Founded 1994
Member Libraries: 18 pub
Primary Functions: Fosters & promotes the provision of quality library services to
residents through open access to member libraries with free access & reciprocal
borrowing

MANITOBA

MANITOBA LIBRARY CONSORTIUM, INC*, (MLCI), c/o Library
Administration, University of Winnipeg, 515 Portage Ave, Winnipeg, R3B 2E9.
SAN 372-820X. Tel: 204-786-9801. FAX: 204-783-8910. Web Site:
www.mlcinc.mb.ca. *Chair,* Patricia Burt; Tel: 204-632-2382, Fax: 204-697-4791,
E-mail: pburt@rrc.mb.ca
Founded 1991

Member Libraries: 54 acad, govt, health, pub, sch & spec
Primary Functions: Initiate & coordinate projects & activities related to resource
sharing & library networking; maintain cooperative relationships with groups or
agencies with similar goals

NOVA SCOTIA

MARITIMES HEALTH LIBRARIES ASSOCIATION*, (MHLA-ABSM), WK
Kellogg Health Sciences Library, 5850 College St, Halifax, B3H 1X5. SAN
370-0836. Tel: 902-494-2483. FAX: 902-494-3750. Web Site:
www.chla-absc.ca/mhla. *Librn,* Shelley McKibbon; E-mail: mckibbon@dal.ca
Member Libraries: 35 med
Primary Functions: Promote continuity among health science libraries; promote
continuing education & development activities

NOVANET*, The Consortium of Nova Scotia Academic Libraries, 84 Chain Lake
Dr, No 402, Halifax, B3S 1A2. SAN 372-4050. Tel: 902-453-2470. FAX:
902-453-2369. E-mail: office@novanet.ns.ca. Web Site: www.novanet.ns.ca. *Mgr,*
Bill Slauenwhite; E-mail: bill.slauenwhite@novanet.ns.ca
Founded 1988
Member Libraries: 10 acad
Primary Functions: Enhance access to information & knowledge through
cooperation among the member institutions for the benefit of their user
communities

ONTARIO

CANADIAN ASSOCIATION OF RESEARCH LIBRARIES*, 350 Albert St, Ste
600, Ottawa, K1R 1B1. SAN 323-9721. Tel: 613-562-5385. FAX: 613-562-5297.
E-mail: carladm@uottawa.ca. Web Site: www.carl-abrc.ca/. *Exec Dir,* Brent Roe;
Tel: 613-562-5800, Ext 3652, E-mail: carl@uottawa.ca; *Prog Officer,* Katherine
McColgan; Tel: 613-562-5800, Ext 2768, E-mail: katherine.mccolgan@uottawa.ca;
Res Officer, Diego Argáez; Tel: 613-562-5800, Ext 2427, E-mail:
carlrpo@uottawa.ca
Founded 1976
Member Libraries: 27 acad & 3 nat
Primary Functions: To provide organized leadership for the Canadian Research
Library community in the development of policies & programs which maintain &
improve scholarly communication; to work toward the realization of a national
research library resource-sharing network in the areas of collection development,
conservation & access; to increase the capacity of individual member libraries to
provide effective support & encouragement to postgraduate study & research at
national, regional & local levels

CANADIAN HEALTH LIBRARIES ASSOCIATION*, (CHLA-ABSC), 39 River
St, Toronto, M5A 3P1. SAN 370-0720. Tel: 416-646-1600. FAX: 416-646-9460.
E-mail: info@chla-absc.ca. Web Site: www.chla-absc.ca. *Pres,* Miriam Ticoll;
E-mail: president@chla-absc.ca; *VPres,* Jeff Mason; E-mail:
vicepresident@chla-absc.ca
Founded 1976
Member Libraries: 450 allied health sci & med
Primary Functions: To encourage the professional development of its members
whose foremost concern is for the dissemination of health sciences information to
those in research, education & patient care

CANADIAN RESEARCH KNOWLEDGE NETWORK*, (CRKN), Preston Sq,
Tower 2, 200 343 Preston St, Ottawa, K1S IN4. Tel: 613-907-7040. FAX:
866-903-9094. Web Site: www.researchknowledge.ca. *Exec Dir,* Deb deBruijn; Tel:
613-907-7029, E-mail: debruijn@researchknowledge.ca; *Dir, Content Prog,* Jobin
Yves; Tel: 613-907-7033, E-mail: jobin@researchknowledge.ca
Founded 2004
Member Libraries: 73 acad
Primary Functions: Expand digital content for the academic research enterprise in
Canada. Through the coordinated leadership of librarians, researchers and
administrators, undertakes largescale content acquisition and licensing initiatives in
order to build knowledge infrastructure and research capacity in Canada's
universities.

CONSORTIUM OF ONTARIO LIBRARIES*, (COOL), 111 Peter St, Ste 902,
Toronto, M5V 2H1. Tel: 416-961-1669. Toll Free Tel: 800-387-5765. FAX:
416-961-5122. *Dir,* Barbara Franchetto; Tel: 416-961-1669, Ext 5104, E-mail:
bfranchetto@sols.org
Founded 1998
Member Libraries: 40 acad & 325 pub
Primary Functions: To negotiate consortia agreements for electronic resources

HAMILTON & DISTRICT HEALTH LIBRARY NETWORK*, c/o St Josephs
Healthcare Hamilton, Sherman Libray, Rm T2305, 50 Charlton Ave E, Hamilton,
L8N 4A6. SAN 370-5846. Tel: 905-522-1155, Ext 3410. FAX: 905-540-6504.
Coordr, Jean Maragno; E-mail: jmaragno@stjosham.on.ca
Founded 1967
Member Libraries: 8 health care
Primary Functions: Promote quality information services by sharing resources
between member libraries

HEALTH SCIENCE INFORMATION CONSORTIUM OF TORONTO*, c/o Gerstein Sci Info Ctr, Univ Toronto, Nine King's College Circle, Toronto, M5S 1A5. SAN 370-5080. Tel: 416-978-6359. FAX: 416-971-2637. Web Site: www.library.utoronto.ca/hsict. *Exec Dir,* Miriam Ticoll; E-mail: miriam.ticoll@utoronto.ca
Founded 1990
Member Libraries: 35 inst
Primary Functions: Collaborate to promote advances in health care through optimal use of information resources, technologies & collective expertise; ensure optimal access to electronic & print resources on a consortium-wide basis; coordinate new technology to streamline resources sharing; rationalize information services to allow for the most effective use of local institution library budgets; support the patient care, teaching, research & community outreach mandates of the Consortium members

ONTARIO COUNCIL OF UNIVERSITY LIBRARIES*, (OCUL), 130 Saint George St, Toronto, M5S 1A5. Tel: 416-946-0578. FAX: 416-978-6755. Web Site: www.ocul.on.ca. *Exec Dir,* Kathy Scardellato; E-mail: kathy.scardellato@ocul.on.ca; *Projects Officer,* Faye Abrams; E-mail: faye.abrams@ocul.on.ca
Founded 1967
Member Libraries: 20 acad
Primary Functions: Seeks to enhance information services through resource sharing, collective purchasing, document delivery & many similar activities

ONTARIO LIBRARY CONSORTIUM*, (OLC), Owen Sound & North Grey Union Public Library, 824 First Ave W, Owen Sound, N4K 4K4. (Mail add: c/o Margaret Rule, OLC Treasurer, Middlesex County Bldg, 399 Ridout St N, London, N6A 2P1). Web Site: www.onlibcon.on.ca. *Pres,* Judy Armstrong; Tel: 519-376-6623, E-mail: jbarms@owensound.library.on.ca; *Sr VPres & Chief Financial Officer,* Margaret Rule; *Coordr,* Katherine Slimman; Tel: 905-627-8662, E-mail: k.slimman@sympatico.ca
Founded 1986
Member Libraries: 19 libr systs, 13 county & regional municipality, 6 medium-sized pub libr located in southern Ontario
Primary Functions: OLC continues to develop library processes together, through joint custom programming, negotiations of bulk rates with vendors, and co-operative training and support. Priorities, activities and membership costs of the OLC are determined by the members

PARRY SOUND & AREA ACCESS NETWORK*, c/o Parry Sound Public Library, 29 Mary St, Parry Sound, P2A 1E3. Tel: 705-746-9601. FAX: 705-746-9601. E-mail: pspl@vianet.ca. Web Site: www.pspl.on.ca/paan. *Chair,* Laurine Tremaine; *Vice Chair,* Lori Guillemette
Founded 2001
Member Libraries: 1 health ctr & 8 pub
Primary Functions: Public education & access to internet information resources

PERTH COUNTY INFORMATION NETWORK*, (PCIN), c/o Stratford Public Library, 19 Saint Andrew St, Stratford, N5A 1A2. Tel: 519-271-0220. FAX: 519-271-3843. Web Site: www.pcin.on.ca. *Chief Exec Officer,* Sam Coglin; Tel: 519-271-0220, Ext 15
Founded 2000
Member Libraries: 1 archives & 3 pub
Primary Functions: Public information access

SHARED LIBRARY SERVICES*, (SLS), South Huron Hospital, Shared Library Services, 24 Huron St W, Exeter, N0M 1S2. SAN 323-9500. Tel: 519-235-5168. FAX: 519-235-2742. E-mail: shha.sls@shha.on.ca. Web Site: www.wohkn.ca. *Librn,* Linda Wilcox
Founded 1981

Member Libraries: 11 hosp
Primary Functions: Provision of both reference & technical library services to contracted hospitals

SOUTHWESTERN ONTARIO HEALTH LIBRARIES & INFORMATION NETWORK*, (SOHLIN), St Joseph's Health Care London - Regional Mental Health Staff Libraries, 467 Sunset Dr, St. Thomas, N5P 3V9. Tel: 519-631-8510, Ext 49685. Web Site: www.chla-absc.ca/sohlin. *Pres,* Elizabeth Russell; E-mail: elizabeth.russell@sjhc.london.on.ca
Founded 1971
Member Libraries: 35
Primary Functions: Promoting & providing access to health information & resources to health professionals & communities in southwestern Ontario

TORONTO HEALTH LIBRARIES ASSOCIATION*, (THLA), 3409 Yonge St, Toronto, M4N 2L0. (Mail add: PO Box 94056, Toronto, M4N 2L0), SAN 323-9853. Tel: 416-485-0377. FAX: 416-485-6877. E-mail: medinfoserv@rogers.com. Web Site: www.thla.ca. *Pres,* Graziela Alexandria; Tel: 905-828-3231; *Treas,* Stoyanova Penka; E-mail: treasurer@thia.ca
Founded 1965
Member Libraries: 80 acad, govt & med
Primary Functions: To promote the provision of quality library service to the health community; to encourage communication & cooperation among members & to foster their professional development

QUEBEC

ASSOCIATION DES BIBLIOTHEQUES DE LA SANTE AFFILIEES A L'UNIVERSITE DE MONTREAL*, (ABSAUM), c/o Health Library Univ Montreal, Pavillon Roger-Gaudry, 2900 Boul Edouard-Montpetit, 6e Etage, Salle L-623, Montreal, H3C 3J7. (Mail add: PO Box 76128 Sta Downtown, Montreal, H3C 3J7), SAN 370-5838. Tel: 514-343-6826. FAX: 514-343-2350. Web Site: www.bib.umontreal.ca/sa. *Dir,* Monique St-Jean
Founded 1979
Member Libraries: 15 acad
Primary Functions: Interlibrary loan services; sharing periodical development collection; mutual assistance

CANADIAN HERITAGE INFORMATION NETWORK*, (CHIN), 15 Eddy St, 4th Flr, Gatineau, K1A 0M5. SAN 329-3076. Tel: 819-994-1200. Toll Free Tel: 800-520-2446. FAX: 819-994-9555. E-mail: service@chin.gc.ca. Web Site: www.chin.gc.ca. *Actg Exec Dir,* Claudette Lévesque
Founded 1972
Primary Functions: Allows museum professionals to take advantage of information technologies. In addition to reference & training resources, offers three national inventories of museum collections through Artefacts Canada: Humanities, Natural Sciences & Archaeological Sites, each offering information on millions of objects. Through the Virtual Museum of Canada's Internet gateway (virtualmuseum.ca), CHIN & the museum community provide the general public with new access to the stories & treasures held in trust by Canada's heritage institutions

RESEAU BIBLIO DE L'OUTAOUAIS*, 2295 Saint-Louis St, Gatineau, J8T 5L8. SAN 319-6526. Tel: 819-561-6008. FAX: 819-561-6767. Web Site: www.crsbpo.qc.ca. *Dir Gen,* Sylvie Thibault; E-mail: sylvie.thibault@crsbpo.qc.ca
Founded 1964
Primary Functions: Maintain & develop document collections, document processing services & other technical or professional library science services; develop & maintain training & information sessions, activities & cultural development programs in the field of library science

LIBRARY SCHOOLS AND TRAINING COURSES

Library Schools are listed alphabetically by state or province.

This section provides the name of the school, its address, name of the director or dean, names of the staff members, number of yearly visiting faculty, date the program was established, type of school (private, public or denominational), entrance exams required, degrees offered, scholarships granted, and enrollment. The entries also list data on tuition for graduate and undergraduate students, the course offered, and the availability of evening and summer school classes.

The schools marked with an asterisk (*) are those which did not reply to the questionnaire sent to them.

The schools marked with a dagger (†) are those which have first professional degree programs that are accredited by the American Library Association Committee on Accreditation as of 1995 based on the Standards of Accreditations adopted by the ALA Council in 1972.

Once a program is accredited under these standards, periodic revisits for purposes of continuing accreditation are scheduled by the Committee.

A list of the programs accredited by the ALA is issued twice yearly and is available on request to: "Accredited List," American Library Association, 50 East Huron St., Chicago, Illinois 60611, or visit ALA website at www.ala.org.

ALABAMA

ALABAMA STATE UNIVERSITY, COLLEGE OF EDUCATION*, Library Education Media Program, 915 S Jackson St, Montgomery, 36104. (Mail add: PO Box 271, Montgomery, 36101-0271). Tel: 334-229-6829, 334-229-8801. FAX: 334-229-6831. Web Site: www.alasu.edu. *Coordr,* Dr Agnes H Bellel; E-mail: abellel@alasu.edu
Prog estab 1949. Sch type: Pub. Scholarships offered; Enrl: Grad: 50
Ent Req: Undergrad degree in educ & classroom teaching experience
Tuition: Non-resident Undergraduate $2,320 Per semester; Non-resident Graduate $170 Per credit hour; Resident Undergraduate $1,160 Per semester; Resident Graduate $85 Per credit hour
Degrees & Hours Offered: AA, Teacher Certification, 18 to 24 sem hrs; M.Ed., Libr Educ major, 33 sem hrs; M.Ed., Specialist in Library Media, 36 sem hrs
Special Courses: Communication, Instructional Design, Literature for Children & Young Adults & Management for School Programs
Evening Session, Summer Session

AUBURN UNIVERSITY*, Department of Educational Foundations, Leadership & Technology, 4036 Haley Ctr, Auburn, 36849-5221. Tel: 334-844-4460. FAX: 334-844-3072. Web Site: www.auburn.edu. *Prof,* Judith Lechner; E-mail: lechnjv@auburn.edu; *Assoc Prof,* Susan H Bannon; E-mail: bannosh@auburn.edu; *Assoc Prof,* Sherida Downer; E-mail: downesh@auburn.edu
Prog estab 1969. Sch type: Pub; Enrl: Grad: 220
Tuition: Non-resident Graduate $6,345 Per semester; Resident Graduate $2,115 Per semester
Type of Training Offered: School
Degrees & Hours Offered: MS
Evening Session, Summer Session

JACKSONVILLE STATE UNIVERSITY*, College of Education, Department of Educational Resources, Library Media Program, 700 Pelham Rd N, Jacksonville, 36265. Tel: 256-782-5011, 256-782-5096. FAX: 256-782-5321, 256-782-8136. Web Site: jsu.edu. *Prog Chair,* Dr Betty Morris; E-mail: bmorris@jsu.edu
Prog estab 1965. Sch type: Pub; Enrl: Grad: 30
Degrees & Hours Offered: MS, Educ, 37 sem hrs
Special Courses: Automation, Management, Young Adult Literature
Evening Session, Summer Session

† UNIVERSITY OF ALABAMA, School of Library & Information Studies, 514 Main Library, Tuscaloosa, 35487. (Mail add: PO Box 870252, Tuscaloosa, 35487-0252). Tel: 205-348-4610. FAX: 205-348-3746. Web Site: www.slis.ua.edu. *Dir, Prof,* Heidi Julien; *Prof,* Elizabeth Aversa; *Prof,* Steve Miller; *Prof,* Charles Osburn; *Prof,* Danny Wallace; *Assoc Prof,* Anna Embree; *Assoc Prof,* Steven MacCall; *Asst Prof,* Dan Albertson; *Asst Prof,* Laurie Bonnici; *Asst Prof,* Jennifer Campbell-Meier; *Asst Prof,* Melissa Johnston; *Asst Prof,* Jamie Campbell Naidoo; *Asst Prof,* Robert Riter; *Asst Prof,* Jeff Weddle
Prog estab 1970. Sch type: Pub; Enrl: Grad: 280; Fac 14

Ent Req: GRE or MAT & GPA of 3.0 on a 4.0 syst
Tuition: Non-resident Graduate $11,475 Per semester; Resident Graduate $4,600 Per semester
Type of Training Offered: Public
Degrees & Hours Offered: MLIS, 36 sem hrs; Ph.D., 24 to 48 sem hrs; MFA, Bk Arts, 60 sem hrs
Special Courses: Archives, Book Arts, Children's Literature, Economics of Information, Information Policy, Information Science, Instructional Design, Media (AV), Printing & Book Design, Systems Analysis & Young Adult Literature
Evening Session, Internet Courses, Summer Session, Weekend Session

UNIVERSITY OF SOUTH ALABAMA*, Department of Professional Studies, Educational Media Program, 3800 UCOM-University Commons, Mobile, 36688. Tel: 251-380-2861. FAX: 251-380-2713. Web Site: www.southalabama.edu/coe. *Chair,* Dr Charles Guest; *Assoc Prof,* Dr Mary Ann Robinson; E-mail: mrobinson@usouthal.edu
Sch type: Pub
Tuition: Non-resident Graduate $460 Per credit hour; Resident Graduate $218 Per credit hour
Degrees & Hours Offered: M.Ed., Educ Media, 33 sem hrs
Internet Courses

ARIZONA

ARIZONA STATE UNIVERSITY*, College of Education, Division of Curriculum & Instruction Graduate Programs, Farmer Bldg 434, Tempe, 85287. (Mail add: PO Box 871911, Tempe, 85287-1911). Tel: 480-965-4602. FAX: 480-965-1863. E-mail: cnigrad@asu.edu. Web Site: www.asu.edu. *Exec Dir,* Dr Robert Rutherford; *Prof,* Dr James Christie; Tel: 480-965-2314, E-mail: jchristie@asu.edu; *Prof,* Dr Barbara Guzzetti; E-mail: guzzetti@asu.edu
Tuition: Non-resident Graduate $4,320 Per semester; Resident Graduate $994 Per semester
Degrees & Hours Offered: Certificate, 18 hrs
Evening Session, Summer Session

MESA COMMUNITY COLLEGE*, Library Information Technology Program, Paul A Elsner Library, 1833 W Southern Ave, Mesa, 85202. Tel: 480-461-7686. FAX: 480-461-7681. Web Site: www.mc.maricopa.edu/library/lbt. *Libr Dir,* Chas Moore; E-mail: chas.moore@mcmail.maricopa.edu
Prog estab 1967. Sch type: Pub; Enrl: Undergrad: 35; Fac 9
Ent Req: Open enrollment
Tuition: Non-resident Undergraduate $90 Per credit hour; Resident Undergraduate $65 Per credit hour
Type of Training Offered: Library & Information Science
Degrees & Hours Offered: AAS, Electronic Res, Libr Info Systs, Libr Tech Servs, Multimedia, Pub Servs, 24 sem hrs in LBT, 64 credit hr total; Certificate, Basic Certificate - Introduction to Libr Info Servs & Practical Skills, 20; Certificate, Advanced Certificate - Basic & Specialized courses leading to thorough background as Libr Info Tech, 30; Certificate,

Practitioners Certificate - Will qualify students working as Libr Mgr or Dir to apply for certification through the Regional Western Coun of State Librs Practitioner Certification Prog, 23; Certificate, Sch Libr Media Ctr Certificate - Prepares & upgrades the skills of staff working in sch libr media centers, 28
Continuing Education, Evening Session, Internet Courses, Summer Session, Weekend Session

NORTHLAND PIONEER COLLEGE*, Department of Library Media Technology, PO Box 610, Holbrook, 86025-0610. Tel: 928-532-6123. Toll Free Tel: 800-266-7845. FAX: 928-532-6121. Web Site: www.npc.edu/lmt. *Prog Chair,* Sherry French; E-mail: sherry.french@npc.edu
Prog estab 1976. Sch type: Pub; Enrl: Undergrad: 15
Tuition: Non-resident Undergraduate $80 Per credit hour; Resident Undergraduate $48 Per credit hour
Degrees & Hours Offered: AAS, 64 sem hrs; Certificate, Libr Media Tech, 30 sem hrs
Internet Courses

† UNIVERSITY OF ARIZONA*, School of Information Resources & Library Science, 1515 E First St, Tucson, 85719. Tel: 520-621-3565. FAX: 520-621-3279. E-mail: sirls@u.arizona.edu. Web Site: www.sir.arizona.edu. *Dir, Prof,* Dr Jana Bradley; E-mail: janabrad@u.arizona.edu; *Asst Dir,* Leslie Ann Kent Kunkel, E-mail: lkunkel@u.arizona.edu; *Asst Prof,* Peter Botticelli; *Assoc Dir, Info Serv, Assoc Prof,* Dr Martin Fricke; Tel: 520-621-3491, E-mail: mfricke@u.arizona.edu
Prog estab 1971. Sch type: Pub. Scholarships offered; Enrl: Grad: 285; Fac 9
Ent Req: Admission requirements: GRE, B average, two letters of recommendation, application form, official transcripts, resume, letter of introduction. Admission is competitive. Graduation requirements: Completion of 36 credits & an electronic portfolio
Tuition: Non-resident Graduate $3,300 Per course; Resident Graduate $1,500 Per course
Degrees & Hours Offered: MA, 36 sem hrs; Ph.D., 48 sem hrs
Continuing Education, Evening Session, Internet Courses, Online & Blended Courses, Professional Development, Summer Session, Weekend Session

ARKANSAS

UNIVERSITY OF CENTRAL ARKANSAS*, Library & Information Technologies, College of Education, PO Box 4918, Conway, 72032-5001. Tel: 501-450-3177, 501-450-5497. FAX: 501-450-5680. Web Site: www.uca.edu. *Coordr,* Dr Stephanie Huffman; Tel: 501-450-5430, E-mail: steph@uca.edu
Prog estab 1980. Sch type: Pub; Fac 3
Tuition: Non-resident Graduate $300 Per credit hour; Resident Graduate $150 Per credit hour
Type of Training Offered: School
Degrees & Hours Offered: MS, Libr Media & Info Tech, 36
Evening Session, Summer Session

CALIFORNIA

CALIFORNIA STATE UNIVERSITY, LONG BEACH, Librarianship Program, Dept of Advanced Studies in Education & Counseling, 1250 Bellflower Blvd, Long Beach, 90840-2201. Tel: 562-985-4517. FAX: 562-985-4534. E-mail: edpac-lmt@csulb.edu. Web Site: www.csulb.edu/lmt. *Coordr,* Dr Lesley S J Farmer; Tel: 562-985-4509, E-mail: lfarmer@csulb.edu
Prog estab 1968. Sch type: Pub; Enrl: Grad: 75; Fac 4
Ent Req: Undergraduate degree, 3.0 GPA, letters of recommendation, writing proficiency, teaching credential & CBEST for credential program
Tuition: Non-resident Graduate $671 Per unit; Resident Graduate $2,337 Part-time; Regional Graduate $299 Per unit
Type of Training Offered: School Library Media Certificate
Degrees & Hours Offered: Certificate, Teacher Librn, 27 credit hrs; MA, Educational Technology and Media Leadership, 36-39 credit hrs
Special Courses: Information Literacy/Reference, Library Media Materials for Elementary & Secondary Schools, Library Technologies, Management & Administration
Distance Learning, Internet Courses, Online & Blended Courses, Summer Session, Weekend Session

CITRUS COLLEGE*, Library Technology Program, 1000 W Foothill Blvd, Glendora, 91741-1899. Tel: 626-914-8643. FAX: 626-963-2531. Web Site: www.citruscollege.edu/library. *Dean,* John R Thompson; E-mail: jthompson@citruscollege.edu
Sch type: Pub; Enrl: Undergrad: 35
Tuition: Non-resident Undergraduate $150 Per course; Resident Undergraduate $18 Per course
Degrees & Hours Offered: Certificate, Libr Tech, 18 sem hrs; AS, Libr Tech, 18 sem hrs

Special Courses: Audio-Visual Library Services, Children's Library Services & Certificate in Libr Tech
Internet Courses

CITY COLLEGE OF SAN FRANCISCO, Library Information Technology Program, 50 Phelan Ave, Rm 517, San Francisco, 94112. Tel: 415-452-5519. FAX: 415-452-5478. Web Site: www.ccsf.edu/library. *Chair,* Christopher Kox; E-mail: ckox@ccsf.edu
Sch type: Pub; Enrl: Undergrad: 75
Degrees & Hours Offered: AA, Library Assisting, 18 units in the major & 42 units general education & electives; Certificate, Library Assisting, 17 units minimum
Special Courses: Continuing Education Workshops
No Summer Sessions

FOOTHILL COLLEGE, 12345 El Monte Rd, Los Altos Hills, 94022-4599. Tel: 650-949-7086. FAX: 650-949-7123. Web Site: www.foothill.edu/library. *Librn,* Micaela Agyare; *Librn,* Kay Jones; *Librn,* Mary Thomas; *Librn,* Pam Wilkes
Sch type: Pub
Tuition: Resident Undergraduate $31 Per unit

HARTNELL COLLEGE*, Library-Media Technology, 411 Central Ave, Salinas, 93901. Tel: 831-755-6700. FAX: 831-759-6084. *Dir,* Gary Hughes; E-mail: ghughes@hartnell.cc.ca.us; *Librn,* William Rawson; E-mail: wrawson@hartnell.edu
Tuition: Non-resident Undergraduate $149 Per unit; Resident Undergraduate $26 Per unit
Degrees & Hours Offered: AA, Libr Med Tech; Certificate, Libr Med Tech
Special Courses: Children's Literature & Media (AV), Computers, Libraries & other Continuing Education
No Summer Sessions

PALOMAR COLLEGE*, Library Technology Program, 1140 W Mission Rd, San Marcos, 92069-1487. Tel: 760-744-1150, Ext 2618. FAX: 760-761-3500. E-mail: cbundy@palomar.edu. Web Site: www.palomar.edu/library/librtech/default.htm. *Dean,* Dr Mark W Vernoy; Tel: 760-744-1150, Ext 2759, E-mail: mvernoy@palomar.edu; *Chair,* Judy J Cater; Tel: 760-744-1150, E-mail: jcater@palomar.edu
Prog estab 1965. Sch type: Pub; Enrl: Undergrad: 35; Fac 5
Tuition: Non-resident Undergraduate $149 Per unit; Resident Undergraduate $26 Per unit
Type of Training Offered: Library Technician
Degrees & Hours Offered: AA, Libr Tech, 60 sem hrs; Certificate, 28 units
Special Courses: Children's Literature; Media (AV) & Computer Technology
No Summer Sessions

† SAN JOSE STATE UNIVERSITY*, School of Library & Information Science, One Washington Sq, San Jose, 95192-0029. Tel: 408-924-2490. FAX: 408-924-2476. E-mail: sanjoseslis@gmail.com. Web Site: slisweb.sjsu.edu. *Dir, Prof,* Dr Sandy Hirsh; E-mail: sandy.hirsh@sjsu.edu; *Assoc Dir, Prof,* Dr Linda Main; E-mail: linda.main@sjsu.edu; *Mrg, Admin Serv,* Kristina Luna; Tel: 408-924-2492, E-mail: kristina.luna@sjsu.edu
Prog estab 1954. Sch type: Pub. Scholarships offered; Enrl: Grad: 2,000; Fac 125
Ent Req: B average
Tuition: Non-resident Graduate $474 Per unit
Type of Training Offered: Special
Degrees & Hours Offered: MLIS, 43
Distance Learning, Internet Courses

UNIVERSITY OF CALIFORNIA AT BERKELEY*, School of Information, 102 South Hall, Berkeley, 94720-4600. Tel: 510-642-1464. FAX: 510-642-5814. Web Site: www.ischool.berkeley.edu/. *Dean,* Annalee Saxenian; E-mail: anno@ischool.berkeley.edu; *Asst Dean,* Position Currently Open
Tuition: Non-resident Graduate $7,598 Per semester; Resident Graduate $2,269 Per semester
Type of Training Offered: Public
Degrees & Hours Offered: Ph.D.
Special Courses: Archives Management, Catalog Design, Children's Literature, Data Processing, Economics of Information, History of Printing & Publishing, Information Retrieval Theory, Information Systems Design, Information Systems Management, Law, Media (AV), Systems Analysis & Use of Database Management Systems

† UNIVERSITY OF CALIFORNIA, LOS ANGELES*, Department of Information Studies, Graduate School of Education & Information Studies, 2320 Moore Hall, Mail Box 951521, Los Angeles, 90095-1521. Tel: 310-825-8799. FAX: 310-206-3076. Web Site: is.gseis.ucla.edu. *Chair,* Gregory Leazer
Sch type: Pub; Enrl: Grad: 200

Tuition: Non-resident Graduate $25,810 Per year; Resident Graduate
$10,768 Per year
Type of Training Offered: Special
Degrees & Hours Offered: Certificate, Archival Studies, Libr Studies,
Informatics, 36 qtr hrs; MA, Moving Image Archive Studies, 72 qtr hrs;
MLIS, Archival Studies, Libr Studies, Informatics, 72 qtr hrs; Ph.D., Info
Studies: Evidence, Retrieval, Policy, Seeking, Structures, Inst &
Professions, 72 qtr hrs; MLIS/MA, Latin Am Studies Articulated Prog, 84
qtr hrs; MLIS/MBA, 96 qtr hrs Concurrent Program
Special Courses: Advanced Issues in Archival Sciences, American
Archives & Manuscripts, Analytical Bibliography, Automation of Library
Processes, Development of Multimedia Resources, Health & Life Sciences
Libraries, Human/Computer Communication, Information Seeking
Behavior, Internship, Legal Bibliography, Preservation, Principles of
Information Systems Analysis & Design, Public Libraries, Special
Libraries, Thesaurus Construction, University & Research Libraries &
User-Centered Design of Information Retrieval Systems

COLORADO

† UNIVERSITY OF DENVER, Library & Information Science Program,
Morgridge College of Education, Katherine A Ruffatto Hall, 1999 E Evans
Ave, Denver, 80208. Tel: 303-871-2747. Toll Free Tel: 800-835-1607.
FAX: 303-871-2709. E-mail: edinfo@du.edu. Web Site: www.du.edu/LIS.
Chair, Clara Sitter, PhD; Tel: 303-871-3587, E-mail: csitter@du.edu; *Acad
Serv Assoc,* Nick Heckart; E-mail: nheckart@du.edu
Prog estab 1995. Sch type: Pvt; Enrl: Grad: 175
Ent Req: Undergrad degree. Does not require GRE
Type of Training Offered: School
Degrees & Hours Offered: MLIS, 58 credit hrs
Special Courses: Practicum
Evening Session

UNIVERSITY OF NORTHERN COLORADO*, Educational Technology
Program, McKee Hall 518, 501 20th St, Greeley, 80639. Tel:
970-351-2816. FAX: 970-351-1622. Web Site: www.unco.edu/cebs/edtech/.
Dir, Susan Hutchinson
Prog estab 1991. Sch type: Pub. Scholarships offered; Enrl: Grad: 150; Fac
6
Ent Req: GPA of 3.0 for last 60 hrs; GRE for PhD
Tuition: Non-resident Graduate $5,230 Per semester; Resident Graduate
$1,275 Per semester
Type of Training Offered: School
Degrees & Hours Offered: Certificate, Sch Libr Media, 26; MA, Sch Libr
Media, Educ Tech, 30-32; Ph.D., Educ Tech, 67
Special Courses: Online MA Programs
Evening Session, Summer Session

CONNECTICUT

† SOUTHERN CONNECTICUT STATE UNIVERSITY*, Department of
Information & Library Science, 501 Crescent St, New Haven, 06515. Tel:
203-392-5781. Toll Free Tel: 888-500-7278. FAX: 203-392-5780. E-mail:
ils@southernct.edu. Web Site: www.southernct.edu/ils. *Dean,* Dr Edward
Harris; Tel: 203-392-5701, Fax: 203-392-5748, E-mail:
harrise1@southernct.edu; *Prof,* Dr Mary Brown; Tel: 203-392-5772,
E-mail: brownm6@southernct.edu; *Prof,* Dr James Kusack; Tel:
203-392-5706, E-mail: kusackj1@southernct.edu; *Prof,* Dr Gwendolyn
Nowlan; Tel: 203-392-5711, E-mail: nowlang1@southernct.edu;
Chairperson, Prof, Dr Josephine Sche; Tel: 203-392-5710, E-mail:
schej1@southernct.edu; *Assoc Prof,* Dr Arlene Bielefield; Tel:
203-392-5708, E-mail: bielefielda1@southernct.edu; *Assoc Prof,* Nancy
Disbrow; Tel: 203-392-5702, E-mail: disbrown1@southernct.edu; *Assoc
Prof,* Dr Chang Suk Kim; Tel: 203-392-5191, E-mail:
kimc1@southernct.edu; *Assoc Prof,* Dr Hak Joon Kim; Tel: 203-392-5764,
E-mail: kimh1@southernct.edu; *Assoc Prof,* Dr Yan Quan Liu; Tel:
203-392-5763, E-mail: liuy1@southernct.edu; *Assoc Prof,* Dr Jane McGinn;
Tel: 203-392-5086, E-mail: mcginnj1@southernct.edu; *Assoc Prof,* Dr Elsie
Okobi; Tel: 203-392-5709, E-mail: okobie1@southernct.edu; *Assoc Prof,*
Dr Eino Sierpe; Tel: 203-392-6883, E-mail: sierpee1@southernct.edu; *Asst
Prof,* Gayle Bogel; Tel: 203-392-5704, E-mail: bogelg1@southernct.edu
Prog estab 1954. Sch type: Pub. Scholarships offered; Enrl: Grad: 275,
Undergrad: 46; Fac 13
Ent Req: 90 credits Liberal Arts, GPA 2.5
Tuition: Non-resident Undergraduate $8,158 Per semester; Non-resident
Graduate $8,814 Full-time; Non-resident Graduate $506 Part-time; Resident
Undergraduate $3,590 Per semester; Resident Graduate $4,286 Full-time;
Resident Graduate $506 Part-time
Type of Training Offered: Special
Degrees & Hours Offered: BS, Libr Info Serv, 120 including 30 credits in
LS; BS, Libr Info Serv minor, 18 sem hrs; Diploma, Sixth Year:
Information Studies/Art of the Oral Tradition, 30 sem hrs; MLS, 36 sem
hrs
Special Courses: Digital Librarian, Information Seeking Behavior,
Information Systems/Technology, Legal Bibliography, Media (AV), Medical

Bibliography, Online Information Retrieval & Preservation of Library
Materials, Special Topics - Current Relevant Issues Presented
Evening Session, Internet Courses, Summer Session

DISTRICT OF COLUMBIA

† CATHOLIC UNIVERSITY OF AMERICA*, School of Library &
Information Science, Marist Hall, 228, 620 Michigan Ave NE, Washington,
20064. Tel: 202-319-5085. FAX: 202-319-5574. E-mail: cua-slis@cua.edu.
Web Site: slis.cua.edu. *Dean,* Dr Ingrid Hshieh-Yee; E-mail:
hsiehyee@cua.edu; *Assoc Dean,* Dr Sydney Pierce; Tel: 202-319-5877,
E-mail: pierce@cua.edu
Prog estab 1938. Sch type: Den. Scholarships offered; Enrl: Grad: 250
Ent Req: Undergrad GPA of 3.0 OR GRE scores of 1000, plus 3 letters of
reference, personal statement & transcripts
Tuition: Non-resident Graduate $1,195 Per credit hour; Non-resident
Graduate $15,000 Per semester; Resident Graduate $1,195 Per credit hour;
Resident Graduate $15,000 Per semester
Type of Training Offered: School Library Media Certificate
Degrees & Hours Offered: Certificate, Sch Libr Media Studies, 24; MLS,
Libr Sci, Sch Libr Media Studies, 36; MLS, Libr Sci, Sch Libr Media
Studies, 30 with previous grad degree
Evening Session, Internet Courses, Summer Session

FLORIDA

† FLORIDA STATE UNIVERSITY, COLLEGE OF COMMUNICATION &
INFORMATION*, School of Library & Information Studies, 142
Collegiate Loop, Tallahassee, 32306-2100. (Mail add: Louis Shores Bldg,
MC 2100, Tallahassee, 32306-2100). Tel: 850-644-5775. FAX:
850-644-9763. Web Site: slis.cci.fsu.edu. *Dean, Col of Communication &
Info,* Dr Lawrence W Dennis; Tel: 850-644-8741, E-mail:
larry.dennis@cci.fsu.edu; *Asst Dean,* Ebrahim Randeree; Tel:
850-645-5674, E-mail: ebrahim.randeree@cci.fsu.edu; *Dir, Prof,* Dr
Corinne Jorgensen; Tel: 850-644-8116, E-mail:
corinne.jorgensen@cci.fsu.edu; *Dir, Acad & Res Tech,* Dr Peter E
Jorgensen; Tel: 850-644-4139, E-mail: peter.jorgensen@cci.fsu.edu; *Dir,
Info Inst, Prof,* Dr Charles McClure; Tel: 850-644-8109, E-mail:
charles.mcclure@cci.fsu.edu; *Assoc Prof, Dir, PALM Ctr,* Dr Nancy
Everhart; Tel: 850-644-8122, E-mail: nancy.everhart@cci.fsu.edu; *Asst Prof,
Assoc Dir, PALM Ctr,* Dr Marcia Mardis; Tel: 850-644-3392, E-mail:
marcia.mardis@cci.fsu.edu
Prog estab 1947. Sch type: Pub. Scholarships offered; Enrl: Grad: 12,
Grad: 51, Undergrad: 310, Grad: 569; Fac 30
Ent Req: GRE or other graduate admissions test, GPA of 3.0 on a 4.0
scale; letters of reference
Tuition: Non-resident Undergraduate $675 Per credit hour; Non-resident
Graduate $1,059 Per credit hour; Resident Graduate $428 Per credit hour
Type of Training Offered: Special
Degrees & Hours Offered: BS, Information Technology, 120 semester
hrs; Certificate, Information Architecture; Leadership & Management;
Museum Studies; Reference Services; School Library Media Leadership;
Youth Services, 12-15 credit hours; MA, Information Studies, 36 semester
hrs; MS, Information Studies, 36 semester hrs; Ph.D., Information Studies,
Varies, normally around 60. 24 credit hours in residence required by
university; EdS, Specialist Degree; focused area of interest, 30 credit hours
Special Courses: Advanced Web Applications, Health Informatics,
Information Architecture, Information Security, Information Storage &
Retrieval, International & Comparative Information Services, International
Literature for Youth, Introduction to Legal Resources, Leadership in
Reading, Metadata, Multicultural Literature for Youth, Museum Studies,
Storytelling, Usability Analysis
Distance Learning, Evening Session, Internet Courses, Online & Blended
Courses, Summer Session, Weekend Session

UNIVERSITY OF CENTRAL FLORIDA*, Educational Research
Technology & Leadership, College of Education, PO Box 161250, Orlando,
32816. Tel: 407-823-5175. FAX: 407-823-4880. Web Site: www.ucf.edu/.
Assoc Prof, Dr Atsusi Hirumi; Tel: 407-823-1760, E-mail:
hirumi@mail.ucf.edu; *Assoc Prof,* Glenda Gunter; Tel: 407-823-3502,
E-mail: ggunter@mail.ucf.edu; *Assoc Prof,* Dr Judy Lee; E-mail:
jlee@mail.ucf.edu; *Asst Prof,* Dr Atkinson Tom; Tel: 407-823-3763,
E-mail: atkinson@mail.ucf.edu; *Coordr,* Dr Amy Scheick; Tel:
407-823-0228, E-mail: ascheick@mail.ucf.edu
Sch type: Pub; Enrl: Grad: 150
Ent Req: GRE 850; GPA 3.0 for last 60 units of Bachelor degree
Tuition: Non-resident Graduate $913 Per credit hour; Resident Graduate
$241 Per credit hour
Type of Training Offered: School
Degrees & Hours Offered: Certificate, Educ Media, 12 sem hrs;
Certificate, Educ Tech, 16 sem hrs; Certificate, E-Learning, 16 sem hrs;
MA, Educ Tech, 39 sem hrs; M.Ed., Educ Media, 39 sem hrs; Ph.D., Instr
Tech, 99 sem hrs (dependent on MA)
Evening Session, Internet Courses, Summer Session

† UNIVERSITY OF SOUTH FLORIDA, School of Information, 4202 Fowler Ave, CIS 1040, Tampa, 33620-7800. Tel: 813-974-3520. FAX: 813-974-6840. E-mail: lisinfo@cas.usf.edu. Web Site: www.cas.usf.edu/lis. *Dir,* James E Andrews, PhD; Tel: 813-974-2108, E-mail: jimandrews@usf.edu; *Asst Dir, Instr,* Diane Austin; E-mail: dianeaustin.usf.edu; *Distinguished Univ Prof,* Kathleen de la Pena McCook; E-mail: kmccook@tampabay.rr.com; *Prof Emeritus,* Anna Perrault; E-mail: perraulta@cas.usf.edu; *Prof,* Dr John Gathegi; Tel: 813-974-5322, E-mail: jgathegi@usf.edu; *Prof,* Vicki L Gregory; E-mail: gregory@usf.edu; *Assoc Prof,* Dr James Andrews; E-mail: jimandrews@usf.edu; *Assoc Prof,* Dr Cora Dunkley; E-mail: cdunkley@usf.edu; *Assoc Prof,* Dr Jung Won Yoon; E-mail: jyoon@usf.edu; *Asst Prof,* Dr Hong Huang; Tel: 813-974-6361, E-mail: honghuang@usf.edu; *Asst Prof,* Dr Edward Schneider; Tel: 813-974-7540, E-mail: efschneider@usf.edu; *Asst Prof,* Dr Jinfang Niu; Tel: 813-974-6837, E-mail: jinfang@usf.edu; *Instr,* Linda Alexander; E-mail: lalexander@usf.edu; *Instr,* Richard Austin; E-mail: raustin@usf.edu; *Instr,* Kiersten Cox; E-mail: kcox@usf.edu; *Instr,* Dr Heiko Haubitz; Tel: 813-974-7650, E-mail: heiko@usf.edu; *Instr,* Dr John Sullivan; Tel: 813-974-2370, E-mail: jjsullivan@usf.edu; *Instr,* Maria Treadwell; E-mail: mtreadwell@cas.usf.edu
Prog estab 1965. Sch type: Pub. Scholarships offered; Enrl: Grad: 600; Fac 28
Ent Req: GRE minimum 800, GPA of 3.0 on a 4.0 syst, or GRE minimum 1000
Tuition: Non-resident Graduate $855 Per credit hour; Resident Graduate $431 Per credit hour
Type of Training Offered: Special
Degrees & Hours Offered: MA, Libr & Info Sci, 39 sem hrs
Special Courses: Adult Services, Children's Literature, Genealogy, Health Sciences Librarianship, Information Science, Law Librarianship, Library Personnel Management, Media (AV), Organization of Knowledge, Web Page Design & Management, Young Adult Literature
Evening Session, Internet Courses, Summer Session

GEORGIA

GEORGIA COLLEGE & STATE UNIVERSITY*, Education Library Media, Campus Box 079, Milledgeville, 31061. Tel: 478-445-5004, Ext 2515. FAX: 478-445-2513. Web Site: www.gcsu.edu/educaton. *Prof,* Dr Diane Gregg
Prog estab 1933. Sch type: Pub; Enrl: Grad: 80
Ent Req: Bachelor's & graduation in upper half of class; writing test adminstered on campus
Tuition: Non-resident Graduate $450 Per credit hour; Resident Graduate $215 Per credit hour
Degrees & Hours Offered: M.Ed., Edu Tech- Major Libr, Media Servs, 36 sem hrs
Special Courses: Instructional technology, Web based Resources, Production of multi-media products
Evening Session, Summer Session

UNIVERSITY OF GEORGIA, Department of Educational Psychology & Instructional Technology, College of Education, 224 River's Crossing, Athens, 30602-7144. Tel: 706-542-4110. FAX: 706-542-4032. E-mail: slmedia@uga.edu. Web Site: slm.uga.edu. *Dept Head/Prof,* Dr Robert Branch; *Prog Head/Prof,* Lloyd Rieber, PhD; *Assoc Prof, Learning, Design & Tech Prog Coordr,* Dr Michael Orey; *Sch Libr Emphasis Area Coordr,* Christa Harrelson Deissler, PhD; E-mail: cdeiss@uga.edu; *Assoc Prof,* Ikeson Choi, PhD; *Asst Prof,* ChanMin Kim, PhD; *Asst Prof,* Theodore J Kopcha, PhD; *Lecturer,* Greg Clinton
Sch type: Pub; Enrl: Grad: 70; Fac 16
Ent Req: GRE with GPA of 2.6
Tuition: Non-resident Graduate $5,187 Per semester; Resident Graduate $1,587 Per semester
Type of Training Offered: School Library Media Certificate
Degrees & Hours Offered: M.Ed., Sch Libr Media, 36 sem hrs; Ph.D., Learning, Design, & Technology, 67 sem hrs; EdS, Sch Libr Media, 30 sem hrs
Special Courses: Administration of Media Services, Information Literacy, Information Services, Information Technology
Internet Courses, Online & Blended Courses, Summer Session, Weekend Session

UNIVERSITY OF WEST GEORGIA*, Department of Media & Instructional Technology, 1601 Maple St, Carrollton, 30118. Tel: 678-839-6558. FAX: 678-839-6153. Web Site: www.westga.edu/mit. *Chair,* Dr Barbara McKenzie; Tel: 678-839-6149, E-mail: bmckenzi@westga.edu
Sch type: Pub; Enrl: Grad: 500; Fac 12
Tuition: Non-resident Graduate $543 Per credit hour; Resident Graduate $136 Per credit hour
Type of Training Offered: School
Degrees & Hours Offered: M.Ed., Media, 36 sem hrs (may be taken concurrently with Education Degree)

Special Courses: Children's Materials, Diffusion of Innovations, Distance Education Courses, Instructional Design, Issues in Instructional Technology, Media Production, Media Program & Microcomputer Technology, Planning Research in Education
Evening Session, Internet Courses, Summer Session

† VALDOSTA STATE UNIVERSITY*, Master of Library & Information Program, Odum Library - MLIS, 1500 N Patterson St, Valdosta, 31698-0144. Tel: 229-333-5966. FAX: 229-259-5055. E-mail: mlis@valdosta.edu. Web Site: www.valdosta.edu/mlis. *Univ Librn,* Dr George R Gaumond; Tel: 229-333-5860, E-mail: ggaumond@valdosta.edu; *Dir, Prof,* Dr Wallace C Koehler; Tel: 229-245-3732, E-mail: wkoehler@valdosta.edu; *Assoc Prof,* Dr Anita Ondrusek; Tel: 229-245-3742, E-mail: alondrus@valdosta.edu; *Asst Prof,* Dr William Meehan; Tel: 229-249-2726, E-mail: wfmeehan@valdosta.edu; *Asst Prof,* Linda Most; Tel: 229-245-6534, E-mail: lrmost@valdosta.edu; *Asst Prof,* Dr Fatih Oguz; Tel: 229-245-3715, E-mail: foguz@valdosta.edu
Prog estab 2001. Sch type: Pub; Enrl: Grad: 178; Fac 6
Degrees & Hours Offered: MLIS, 39

HAWAII

† UNIVERSITY OF HAWAII*, Library & Information Science Program, 2550 The Mall, Honolulu, 96822. Tel: 808-956-7321. FAX: 808-956-5835. E-mail: slis@hawaii.edu. Web Site: www.hawaii.edu/lis. *Assoc Prof, Chair,* Dr Andrew B Wertheimer; E-mail: wertheim@hawaii.edu; *Prof,* Violet Harada; *Prof,* Peter Jacso; *Prof,* Rebecca Knuth; *Prof,* Diane Nahl; *Assoc Prof,* Luz Quiroga; *Asst Prof,* Noriko Asato; *Asst Prof,* Rich Gazan
Prog estab 1965. Sch type: Pub. Scholarships and fellowships offered; Enrl: Grad: 110
Tuition: Non-resident Graduate $1,116 Per credit hour; Resident Graduate $458 Per credit hour
Type of Training Offered: Special
Degrees & Hours Offered: Certificate, Advan Libr Info, 15 sem hrs & thesis; MLIS, 42 sem hrs
Special Courses: Asian Research Materials, Conservation, Database Design & Creation, Hawaiian & Pacific Information Systems, Human Dimension of Information Systems, Information Policy & Planning, International Librarianship, School & Media Librarianship
Distance Learning, Evening Session, Summer Session

IDAHO

COLLEGE OF SOUTHERN IDAHO, Library & Information Science Program, Gerald R Meyerhoeffer Bldg, Main Flr, Twin Falls, 83303. (Mail add: PO Box 1238, Twin Falls, 83303-1238). Tel: 208-732-6501. FAX: 208-736-3087. Web Site: www.csi.edu/library. *Dir,* Teri Fattig; E-mail: tfattig@csi.edu
Sch type: Pub; Enrl: Undergrad: 15
Ent Req: HS Diploma or GED
Tuition: Non-resident Undergraduate $280 Per credit hour; Resident Undergraduate $110 Per credit hour
Degrees & Hours Offered: AA, Libr Sci, 66 sem hrs
Internet Courses
Friends of the Library Group

ILLINOIS

CHICAGO STATE UNIVERSITY*, Library Science & Communications Media Program, 9501 S King Dr, Chicago, 60628-1598. Tel: 773-995-2503. *Asst Prof,* Dr Gayles E Evans
Sch type: Pub; Fac 3
Tuition: Non-resident Undergraduate $3,628 Per semester; Resident Undergraduate $1,479 Per semester
Degrees & Hours Offered: MS, Libr Sci, 38 sem hrs
Special Courses: Children's Literature, Government Documents, Information Science, Instructional Design, International Comparative Librarianship, Media (AV), TV & AV Production & Young Adult Literature & Storytelling
Evening Session, Summer Session

COLLEGE OF DUPAGE*, Library & Information Technology Program, 425 Fawell Blvd, Glen Ellyn, 60137. Tel: 630-942-2597. FAX: 630-858-8757. Web Site: www.cod.edu/lta. *Coordr,* Carol Sturz; E-mail: sturzc@cod.edu
Enrl: Undergrad: 140
Tuition: Non-resident Undergraduate $305 Per semester hour; Resident Undergraduate $116 Per semester hour
Degrees & Hours Offered: AAS, Libr Tech, 64 sem hrs; Certificate, Libr Tech, 31 sem hrs
Evening Session, Internet Courses, Summer Session, Video Courses, Weekend Session

COLLEGE OF LAKE COUNTY*, Library-Media Technology, 19351 W
Washington St, Grayslake, 60030. Tel: 847-543-2469. FAX: 847-223-7690.
Web Site: yyz.clcillinois.edu/lta. *Dept Chair,* Ann Chernaik; E-mail:
achernaik@clcillinois.edu
Enrl: Undergrad: 40
Degrees & Hours Offered: AAS, Libr Tech Assist, 60 Credit hrs;
Certificate, Libr Tech Assist, 32 Credit hrs
Evening Session

† **DOMINICAN UNIVERSITY***, Graduate School of Library & Information
Science, 7900 W Division St, River Forest, 60305. Tel: 708-524-6845.
FAX: 708-524-6657. E-mail: gslis@dom.edu. Web Site:
www.gslis.dom.edu. *Dean, Prof,* Susan Roman; *Assoc Prof, Dir, PhD Prog,*
Tonyia J Tidline; *Asst Prof, Dir, Sch Libr Media Prog,* Don W Hamerly
Prog estab 1930. Sch type: Pvt; Enrl: Grad: 524; Fac 18
Tuition: Resident Graduate $2,235 Per course
Type of Training Offered: Special
Degrees & Hours Offered: Certificate, Spec Studies: Law Librarianship,
Libr Admin, Sch Media (if not taken as part of MLIS prog), Tech Servs &
Knowledge Mgt, 15 credit hrs beyond MLIS; 12 hrs for Knowledge Mgt
Certificate; MLIS, MBA, Master of Divinity, Pub Hist, Mus Hist, 36 credit
hrs (12 courses) for MLIS, additional for dual degrees; MLIS, 36 credit hrs
(12 courses); MS, Masters of Sci in Knowledge Mgt (MSKM), 39 credit
hrs (13 courses); Ph.D., Libr & Info Sci, 36 credit hrs (beyond Master's
degree) plus dissertation
Special Courses: Archives, Health Sciences, Information Resources
Management, Law Libraries, Librarianship, Music, Public Services,
Special, Academic, Public, School Media, Rare Books & Special
Collections, Technical Services, Theological
Continuing Education, Evening Session, Internet Courses, Online &
Blended Courses, Professional Development, Summer Session, Weekend
Session

ILLINOIS CENTRAL COLLEGE, Library Technical Assistant Program,
One College Dr, L445, East Peoria, 61635-0001. Tel: 309-694-5508. FAX:
309-694-5473. Web Site:
www.icc.edu/library/librarytechnicalassistantprogram.asp. *LSTA Coordr,*
Pam Thomas; E-mail: pthomas@icc.edu
Prog estab 1971. Sch type: Pub; Enrl: Undergrad: 30; Fac 7
Tuition: Resident Undergraduate $106 Per credit hour
Degrees & Hours Offered: AA, Libr Tech, 64 sem hrs
Evening Session, No Summer Sessions

† **UNIVERSITY OF ILLINOIS AT URBANA-CHAMPAIGN**, Graduate
School of Library & Information Science, Library & Information Science
Bldg, 501 E Daniel St, Champaign, 61820-6211. Tel: 217-333-3280. Toll
Free Tel: 800-982-0914. FAX: 217-244-3302. E-mail: gslis@illinois.edu.
Web Site: www.lis.illinois.edu. *Interim Dean, Prof,* Allen Renear; *Assoc
Dean, Prof,* J Stephen Downie; *Assoc Dean, Prof,* Linda Smith; *Asst Dean,*
Cindy Ashwill; *Asst Dean,* Rae-Anne Montague; *Asst Dean,* Diana Stroud;
Prof, Abdul Alkalimat; *Prof,* Alistair Black; *Prof,* Susan G Davis; *Prof,* Les
Gasser; *Prof,* Carole Palmer; *Prof,* Dan Schiller; *Prof,* Michael Twidale;
Assoc Prof, Catherine Blake; *Assoc Prof,* David Dubin; *Assoc Prof,* Jon
Gant; *Assoc Prof,* Christine Jenkins; *Assoc Prof,* Lori Kendall; *Assoc Prof,*
Kathryn La Barre; *Assoc Prof,* Jerome McDonough; *Assoc Prof,* Terry
Weech; *Asst Prof,* Nicole Cooke; *Asst Prof,* Jana Diesner; *Asst Prof,* Miles
Efron; *Asst Prof,* Emily Knox; *Asst Prof,* Bonnie Mak; *Asst Prof,* Kate
McDowell; *Asst Prof,* Carol Tilley; *Asst Prof,* Vetle Torvik; *Asst Prof,* Kate
Williams
Prog estab 1893. Sch type: Pub. Scholarships offered; Enrl: Grad: 702; Fac
27
Ent Req: For MS, CAS, PhD need GPA of 3.0 on a scale of 4.0; for MS
need a Baccalaureate; for CAS need a MS in LIS; for PhD need a BA/BS
or MS in LIS or closely related field
Tuition: Non-resident Graduate $11,858 Per semester; Resident Graduate
$6,508 Per semester
Type of Training Offered: Special
Degrees & Hours Offered: Certificate, Advan Studies, 40 sem hrs; MS,
40 sem hrs; Ph.D., 80 sem hrs
Special Courses: Archives, Business Information, Children's Literature,
Community Information Systems, Designing Universally Accessible WWW
Resources, Electronic Publishing & Information Processing Standards,
Information Consulting, Information Retrieval, Inquiry Teaching &
Learning, Interfaces to Information Systems, Legal Bibliography, Medical
Reference, Music Bibliography, Preservation, Slavic Bibliography, Young
Adult Literature
Internet Courses, Summer Session

WILBUR WRIGHT COLLEGE*, Library Technology Program, 4300 N
Narragansett, Chicago, 60634. Tel: 773-481-8400, 773-777-7900. FAX:
773-481-8407. Web Site: wright.ccc.edu/library. *Coordr,* Richard Bazile;
E-mail: rbazile@ccc.edu
Enrl: Undergrad 35
Tuition: Resident Undergraduate $62 Per credit hour

Degrees & Hours Offered: AAS, Libr Tech, 60 sem hrs; Certificate, Libr
Tech, 12 sem hrs
Special Courses: CD-ROM Technologies, Children's Service Media (AV)

INDIANA

INDIANA STATE UNIVERSITY*, College of Education, Library Media
Specialist Program, Curric, Instruction & Media Tech Dept, Terre Haute,
47809. Tel: 812-237-2960. Toll Free Tel: 800-444-4723, 800-468-6478.
FAX: 812-237-4556. Web Site:
soe.indstate.edu/cimt/library_media_cert.htm. *Prof,* Dr Scott Davis; Tel:
812-237-2954, E-mail: scott.davis@indstate.edu
Prog estab 1969. Sch type: Pub. Scholarships offered; Enrl: Grad: 115
Tuition: Non-resident Graduate $262 Per credit hour
Type of Training Offered: School
Degrees & Hours Offered: Certificate, Libr certification grad & undergrad
levels, 27 sem hrs
Special Courses: Administration, Cataloging & Classification,
Foundations, Literature, Production of Media Practicum, Reference
Internet Courses
Open Mon-Fri 7:30-4:30

† **INDIANA UNIVERSITY***, School of Library & Information Science,
Wells Library 001, 1320 E Tenth St, Bloomington, 47405-3907. SAN
340-9805. Tel: 812-855-2018. Toll Free Tel: 888-335-7547. FAX:
812-855-6166. E-mail: slis@indiana.edu. Web Site: www.slis.indiana.edu.
Dean, Dr Debora Shaw; E-mail: shawd@indiana.edu
Tuition: Non-resident Graduate $1,124 Per credit hour; Resident Graduate
$386 Per credit hour
Type of Training Offered: Library & Information Science
Degrees & Hours Offered: MLS; Ph.D.; MIS; MIS/MLS; SpLIS
Special Courses: Archives & Manuscripts, Children's Sources & Services,
Descriptive Bibliography, Electronic Commerce, Human Computer
Interaction, Government Documents, Information Retrieval, Legal
Bibliography, Online Information Retrieval, Preservation, Rare Books
Librarianship, Web Management

IOWA

† **UNIVERSITY OF IOWA**, School of Library & Information Science, 3087
Main Library, Iowa City, 52242-1420. Tel: 319-335-5707. FAX:
319-335-5374. E-mail: slis@uiowa.edu. Web Site: slis.uiowa.edu. *Dir, Ctr
for the Bk,* Timothy Barrett; *Interim Dir,* Dr Daniel Berkowitz; *Assoc Prof,*
Dr David Eichmann; E-mail: david-eichmann@uiowa.edu; *Assoc Prof,* Dr
James K Elmborg; *Assoc Prof,* Julia Leonard; *Asst Prof,* Dr Andre Brock;
Asst Prof, Dr Haowei Hsieh; *Asst Prof,* Dr Patricia Katopol; *Asst Prof,* Dr
Jennifer Pierce; *Asst Prof,* Dr Joan Bessman Taylor; *Asst Admin,* Kit
Austin
Prog estab 1967. Sch type: Pub. Scholarships offered; Enrl: Grad: 90
Ent Req: BA, GRE, GPA of 3.0, statement of purpose, three letters of
recommendation.
Tuition: Resident Graduate $3,950 Per semester
Type of Training Offered: Special
Degrees & Hours Offered: MA, Libr & Info Sci, 36 sem hrs

UNIVERSITY OF NORTHERN IOWA*, School Library Media Studies,
Library 121, Rod Library, Cedar Falls, 50613. Tel: 319-273-2050. FAX:
319-273-2913. Web Site: www.uni.edu/coe/ci/slms. *Interim Coordr,* Karla
Krueger; Tel: 319-273-7241, E-mail: karla.krueger@uni.edu
Prog estab 1969. Sch type: Pub. Scholarships offered; Enrl: Undergrad: 20,
Grad: 60; Fac 2
Ent Req: 3.0 GPA Teaching License
Tuition: Non-resident Undergraduate $7,014 Per semester; Non-resident
Graduate $7,550 Per semester; Resident Undergraduate $3,056 Per
semester; Resident Graduate $3,481 Per semester
Type of Training Offered: School
Degrees & Hours Offered: BA, Minor in Library Media Specialist, 24
sem hrs; MA, School Media Libr Studies, 35-37 sem hrs
Special Courses: Library Resources for Children, Library Automation
Systems & Networking, School Library Media Curriculum Development,
Seminar in Inquiry Learning & Information Literacy (Web-based), Library
Resources for Young Adults
Distance Learning, Evening Session, Summer Session

KANSAS

† **EMPORIA STATE UNIVERSITY***, School of Library & Information
Management, 1200 Commercial St, Campus Box 4025, Emporia,
66801-4025. Tel: 620-341-5203. Toll Free Tel: 800-552-4770. FAX:
620-341-5233. E-mail: sliminfo@emporia.edu. Web Site: slim.emporia.edu.
Dean, Gwen Alexander; Tel: 800-552-4770, Ext 5203, E-mail:
galexan1@emporia.edu; *Tech Mgr,* Yvonne Ballester; Tel: 800-552-4770,
Ext 5271, E-mail: yballest@emporia.edu
Prog estab 1902. Sch type: Pub; Enrl: Grad: 328, Undergrad: 35; Fac 10
Ent Req: GRE scores

Tuition: Non-resident Graduate $4,942 Per semester; Non-resident Graduate $424 Per credit hour; Resident Graduate $1,758 Per semester; Resident Graduate $158 Per credit hour
Type of Training Offered: Librarianship
Degrees & Hours Offered: BA, Info Res Studies, 124 hrs; MLS, Sch Libr Media Certification, Legal Info Mgt Certificate, Info Mgt Certificate, Archives Studies Certificate, 36 hrs; Ph.D., Libr & Info Mgt, 52 hrs
Weekend Session

FORT HAYS STATE UNIVERSITY*, Department of Teacher Education, Rarick Hall, Rm 243, 600 Park St, Hays, 67601-4099. Tel: 785-628-4204. FAX: 785-628-4140. Web Site: www.fhsu.edu/te. *Asst Prof,* Dr Beth Walizer; E-mail: bwalizer@fhsu.edu
Sch type: Pub; Enrl: Grad: 25
Tuition: Non-resident Graduate $174 Per credit hour; Resident Graduate $174 Per credit hour
Type of Training Offered: School
Degrees & Hours Offered: M.Ed., Educ with SLM endorsement, 42 sem hrs
Special Courses: Action Research in Library, Computer Use in the Library

KENTUCKY

MURRAY STATE UNIVERSITY*, Library Media Program, 3201 Alexander Hall, Murray, 42071-3309. Tel: 270-809-2500. Toll Free Tel: 800-272-4678. FAX: 270-809-3799. *Chair,* Dr Jo Robertson; *Prof,* Sharon Gill; *Asst Dean,* Dr Rene Campoy
Prog estab 1930. Sch type: Pub. Scholarships offered; Enrl: Undergrad: 35, Grad: 10
Ent Req: 2.5 GPA
Special Courses: Media, Preparation & Utilization of School Library Media & Print-Nonprint Curriculum
Evening Session, Internet Courses

† UNIVERSITY OF KENTUCKY, School of Library & Information Science, 320 Little Library Bldg, Lexington, 40506-0224. Tel: 859-257-8876. FAX: 859-257-4205. E-mail: ukslis@uky.edu. Web Site: cis.uky.edu/lis. *Dir,* Dr Jeffrey T Huber; E-mail: jeff.huber@uky.edu; *Prof,* Dr Donald Case; Tel: 859-257-8415, E-mail: dcase@uky.edu; *Assoc Prof,* Dr Sujin Kim; Tel: 859-281-0110, E-mail: sujinkim@uky.edu; *Assoc Prof,* Joseph Miller; Tel: 859-257-8854, E-mail: jbmill00@uky.edu; *Assoc Prof,* Dr Lisa O'Connor; Tel: 859-257-5679, E-mail: loconnor@uky.edu; *Asst Prof,* Dr Bradley Wade Bishop; Tel: 859-257-3970, E-mail: wade.bishop@uky.edu; *Asst Prof,* Dr Namjoo Choi; Tel: 859-257-4113, E-mail: namjoo.choi@uky.edu; *Asst Prof,* Mrs Jamey Herdelin; Tel: 859-257-4161, E-mail: jamey.herdelin@uky.edu; *Asst Prof,* Dr Shannon M Oltmann; Tel: 859-257-0788, E-mail: shannon.oltmann@uky.edu; *Asst Prof,* Dr Stephanie D Reynolds; Tel: 859-257-5894, E-mail: stepahnie.reynolds.@uky.edu; *Asst Prof,* Dr Ning Yu; Tel: 859-257-4109, E-mail: ning.yu@uky.edu; *Asst Prof,* Dr Hong Zhang; Tel: 859-257-4136, E-mail: hong.zhang@uky.edu
Prog estab 1933. Sch type: Pub. Scholarships offered; Enrl: Grad: 254; Fac 12
Ent Req: GRE & UGPA of 2.75
Tuition: Non-resident Graduate $10,773 Per semester; Resident Graduate $5,229 Per semester
Type of Training Offered: Special
Degrees & Hours Offered: MA, Libr Sci, 36 sem hrs; MLS, Libr & Info Sci, 36 sem hrs
Special Courses: Information Retrieval, Information Policy, Medical Informatics
Distance Learning, Evening Session, Summer Session

WESTERN KENTUCKY UNIVERSITY, SCHOOL OF TEACHER EDUCATION*, Library Media Education, 1092 Gary A Ransdell Hall, Normal St, WKU No 61030, Bowling Green, 42101-1030. (Mail add: 1906 College Heights Blvd, No 61030, Bowling Green, 42101-1030). Tel: 270-745-2435, 270-745-5414. FAX: 270-745-6322. E-mail: lmeinfo@wku.edu, marge.maxwell@wku.edu. Web Site: www.wku.edu/lme. *Prof,* Dr Robert C Smith; Tel: 270-779-4950, E-mail: robert.smith@wku.edu; *Assoc Prof, Prog Coordr,* Dr Marge Maxwell; E-mail: marge.maxwell@wku.edu; *Asst Prof,* Dr Barbara Fiehn; Tel: 270-745-6123, E-mail: barbara.fiehn@wku.edu; *Asst Prof,* Dr Cynthia Houston; Tel: 270-745-4662, E-mail: cynthia.houston@wku.edu; *Asst Prof, Coordr of Educ Res Ctr,* Roxanne Spencer; Tel: 270-745-3147, E-mail: roxanne.spencer@wku.edu
Prog estab 1929. Sch type: Pub. Scholarships offered; Enrl: Grad: 325
Ent Req: GAP Score (GRE Verbal & GRE Quantitative X Undergrad GPA) = 2500 & GRE Analytical Writing Score = 3.5. GAP score may be waived for applicants with first Master's degree
Tuition: Regional Graduate $475 Per credit hour
Type of Training Offered: School Library Media Certificate
Degrees & Hours Offered: Certificate, Educ Tech for teacher certification, non-teacher prep, 12 credit hrs; MS, Libr Media Educ, P-12 Libr Media Spec, Educ Tech Spec, non-teacher certified Ky Pub Libr credential, non-teacher Educ Tech spec, 30-33

Special Courses: Children's Literature, Collection Management, Instructional Design, Integration of Technology, Issues in Educational Technology, Management of Educational Networks, Storytelling, Technology Production
Evening Session, Internet Courses, Summer Session

LOUISIANA

† LOUISIANA STATE UNIVERSITY, School of Library & Information Science, 267 Coates Hall, Baton Rouge, 70803. Tel: 225-578-3158. FAX: 225-578-4581. E-mail: slis@lsu.edu. Web Site: slis.lsu.edu. *Dir,* Dr Beth Paskoff; E-mail: bpaskoff@lsu.edu; *Prof,* Dr Alma Dawson; E-mail: notaed@lsu.edu; *Prof,* Dr Elizabeth Dow; E-mail: edow1@lsu.edu; *Assoc Prof,* Dr Carol Barry; E-mail: lsbary@lsu.edu; *Assoc Prof,* Dr Boryung Ju; E-mail: bju1@lsu.edu; *Assoc Prof,* Dr Michelynn McKnight; E-mail: mmck@lsu.edu; *Assoc Prof,* Dr Suzanne Stauffer; E-mail: stauffer@lsu.edu; *Asst Prof,* Tao Jin; E-mail: taojin@lsu.edu; *Asst Prof,* Dr Robin Kurz; E-mail: rkurx@lsu.edu; *Asst Prof,* Dr Yejun Wu; E-mail: wuyj@lsu.edu
Prog estab 1931. Sch type: Pub. Scholarships offered; Enrl: Grad: 180; Fac 11
Ent Req: BA, 3.0 GPA, GRE, TOEFL & letters of recommendation
Tuition: Non-resident Graduate $11,481 Per semester; Non-resident Graduate $1,715 Per 3 credit hour; Resident Graduate $3,785 Per semester; Resident Graduate $909 Per 3 credit hour
Type of Training Offered: Special
Degrees & Hours Offered: MLIS, 40 sem hrs
Special Courses: Archives, Health Sciences, Information Science, Joint Degree with Computer Science, Joint Degree with History
Distance Learning, Evening Session, Internet Courses, Online & Blended Courses, Summer Session

LOUISIANA TECH UNIVERSITY*, Curriculum Instruction Leadership Library Science, College of Education, PO Box 3163, Ruston, 71272. Tel: 318-257-3712, 318-257-4606. FAX: 318-257-2960. Web Site: www.latech.edu. *Dean,* Dr David Gullatt; E-mail: gullattd@latech.edu
Prog estab 1940. Sch type: Pub. Scholarships offered; Enrl: Undergrad: 20, Grad: 20
Ent Req: BA, BS
Tuition: Non-resident Undergraduate $1,449 Per quarter; Resident Undergraduate $784 Per quarter
Type of Training Offered: School
Degrees & Hours Offered: BA, Elem Ed Libr Sci, 125 sem hrs; BA, Libr Sci minor, 125 sem hrs
Special Courses: Children's Literature, Library Automation, Storytelling & Young Adult Literature
Evening Session, Summer Session

MCNEESE STATE UNIVERSITY*, Burton College of Education, 4205 Ryan St, Lake Charles, 70605. Tel: 337-475-5432. Toll Free Tel: 800-622-3352. FAX: 337-475-5467. Web Site: www.mcneese.edu. *Dean,* Wayne Fetter; E-mail: wfetter@mcneese.edu
Sch type: Pub; Fac 54
Tuition: Resident Undergraduate $1,219 Per semester; Resident Graduate $1,521 Per semester
Type of Training Offered: School
Degrees & Hours Offered: BA, Educ with Add - On Endorsement & Libr Sci, 21 sem hrs; BS, Educ with Add - On Endorsement & Libr Sci, 21 sem hrs
Special Courses: Cataloging & Classification, Children's Literature, Educational Technology, Library Administration, Reference & Young Adult Literature
Evening Session, Internet Courses, Summer Session

SOUTHEASTERN LOUISIANA UNIVERSITY*, Department of Educational Leadership & Technology, PO Box 10549, Hammond, 70402. Tel: 985-549-5713. FAX: 985-549-5712. *Chair,* Dr Mike Richardson
Sch type: Pub
Type of Training Offered: School
Degrees & Hours Offered: Certificate, Libr Sci, 21 hrs
Special Courses: Bibliotherapy, Information Literacy, Technology for the Library
Evening Session, Summer Session

UNIVERSITY OF LOUISIANA AT MONROE*, Department of Educational Leadership & Counseling, 306 Strauss Hall, 700 University Ave, Monroe, 71209. Tel: 318-342-1246. FAX: 318-342-1213. Web Site: www.ulm.edu/elc. *Dept Head, Prof,* Dr Charles Pryor; E-mail: cpryor@ulm.edu; *Assoc Dean,* Dr Glenda Holland; *Assoc Prof,* Dr Lamar Woodham; Tel: 318-362-3008, E-mail: woodham@ulm.edu
Enrl: Undergrad: 20, Grad: 15
Tuition: Non-resident Undergraduate $2,412 Per semester; Resident Undergraduate $1,026 Per semester
Degrees & Hours Offered: BS, Libr Sci minor, 21 sem hrs, 9 hrs grad credit with Med Educ Media

Special Courses: Children's Literature, Informational Sources, Media (AV), Organization of Library Materials, School Library Administrations & Young Adult Literature
Evening Session, Summer Session

UNIVERSITY OF LOUISIANA AT LAFAYETTE*, Department of School Librarianship, USL Sta, Box 42051, Lafayette, 70504. Tel: 337-482-6405. FAX: 337-482-5904. Web Site: www.coe.louisiana.edu. *Dir,* Dr Mary Jane Ford; E-mail: mjf5352@louisiana.edu
Prog estab 1939. Sch type: Pub; Enrl: Undergrad: 15
Type of Training Offered: School
Degrees & Hours Offered: BA, Libr Sci minor or Add-On Certification, 21 sem hrs; BS, Libr Sci minor or Add-On Certification, 21 sem hrs
Special Courses: Children's Literature, Young Adult Literature
Evening Session, Summer Session

UNIVERSITY OF NEW ORLEANS*, Department of Curriculum & Instruction, Program in Library Science, College of Education, Rm 342, New Orleans, 70148. Tel: 504-280-6251, 504-280-6528. FAX: 504-280-1120. *Dean,* Dr James Meza; E-mail: jmeza@uno.edu; *Assoc Dean,* James Miller; *Assoc Dean,* Janet D Williams; *Dir,* George North; *Prof,* Jill B Fatzer; E-mail: jfatzer@uno.edu; *Assoc Prof,* Pat Austin
Prog estab 1962. Sch type: Pub; Fac 2
Tuition: Non-resident Undergraduate $4,878 Per semester; Resident Undergraduate $1,356 Per semester
Type of Training Offered: School
Degrees & Hours Offered: Certificate, 21 sem hrs; M.Ed., Libr Sci, 33 sem hrs
Special Courses: Children's Literature, Teaching Information Literacy
Evening Session, Summer Session

MARYLAND

MCDANIEL COLLEGE*, School Library Program, Graduate Studies, Two College Hill, Westminster, 21157-4390. Tel: 410-857-2501. FAX: 410-857-2515. Web Site: www2.mcdaniel.edu/slm. *Coordr,* Dr Ramona N Kerby; Tel: 410-857-2507; E-mail: rkerby@mcdaniel.edu
Sch type: Pvt; Enrl: Grad: 100; Fac 4
Ent Req: Baccalaureate Degree
Type of Training Offered: School
Degrees & Hours Offered: MS, Libr Sci, 33 sem hrs
Evening Session, Online & Blended Courses, Summer Session

† UNIVERSITY OF MARYLAND*, College of Information Studies, 4105 Hornbake Bldg, College Park, 20742-4345. Tel: 301-405-2033. FAX: 301-314-9145. TDD: 301-405-2040. Web Site: www.clis.umd.edu. *Dean,* Dr Jennifer Preece; E-mail: preece@umd.edu; *Assoc Dean, Res,* Dr Douglas Oard; E-mail: oard@glue.umd.edu
Prog estab 1965. Sch type: Pub. Scholarships offered; Enrl: Grad: 500; Fac 20
Ent Req: Bachelor's, GRE & letters of recommendation
Tuition: Non-resident Graduate $886 Per credit hour; Resident Graduate $411 Per credit hour
Type of Training Offered: Special
Degrees & Hours Offered: MLS, 36 sem hrs; MLS, Archives, Records & Info Mgt; Sch Libr Media; Pub Libr; Health Sci Info; Info Policy; Lifelong Access; Info Tech, 36 sem hrs; Ph.D., 60 sem hrs & 12 hrs dissertation research; MIM, Strategic Mgt of Info; SocioTech Applications, 36 sem hrs; MA/MLS, 54 sem hrs
Evening Session, Internet Courses, Summer Session

MASSACHUSETTS

BOSTON UNIVERSITY*, Educational Media & Technology Program, School of Education, No 2 Sherborn St, Boston, 02215. Tel: 617-353-3181, 617-353-3182. FAX: 617-353-3924. Web Site: emt.bu.edu/program. *Coordr,* David Whittier; E-mail: whittier@bu.edu
Prog estab 1960. Sch type: Pvt; Enrl: Grad: 45; Fac 1
Ent Req: GRE or MAT & letters of recommendation; Statement of qualifications and objectives
Type of Training Offered: College
Degrees & Hours Offered: M.Ed., Educ Media & Tech, 36 sem hrs
Special Courses: Database & Web Integration for Educators, Designing Educational Multimedia, Distance Education, Instructional Video, Interactive Software Development, Internet & WWW for Educators
Evening Session, Summer Session

SALEM STATE UNIVERSITY, Library Media Studies Program, Graduate School, 352 Lafayette St, Salem, 01970. Tel: 978-542-6000, 978-542-7044. FAX: 978-542-7215. Web Site: www.salemstate.edu. *Dean,* Dr Carol Glod; *Coordr,* Peter Smith; E-mail: psmith@salemstate.edu
Prog estab 1973. Enrl: Grad: 30
Tuition: Non-resident Graduate $780 Per credit hour; Resident Graduate $510 Per credit hour
Type of Training Offered: School

Degrees & Hours Offered: M.Ed., Libr Media Servs, 36 credits
Evening Session, Summer Session

† SIMMONS COLLEGE, Graduate School of Library & Information Science, 300 The Fenway, Boston, 02115. Tel: 617-521-2800. FAX: 617-521-3192. Web Site: www.simmons.edu/gslis. *Dean, Prof,* Michele V Cloonan; *Dir, Sch Libr Teacher Prog & Prof of Practice,* Mary F Zilonis; *Prof,* Peter Hernon; *Prof,* James M Matarazzo; *Prof,* Carolyn S Schwartz; *Prof of Practice,* Martha Mahard; *Assoc Prof of Practice,* Donna Webber; *Assoc Prof,* Jeannette Bastian; *Assoc Prof,* Gerald Benoit; *Assoc Prof,* Robin Peek; *Asst Prof,* Naresh Agarwal; *Asst Prof,* Joel Blanco-Rivera; *Asst Prof,* Monica Colon-Aguirre; *Asst Prof,* Lisa Hussey; *Asst Prof,* Daniel Joudrey; *Asst Prof,* Melanie Kimball; *Asst Prof,* Rebecca Morris; *Asst Prof,* Amy Pattee; *Asst Prof,* Laura Saunders; *Asst Prof,* Rong Tang; *Asst Prof,* Mary Wilkins-Jordan; *Asst Prof,* Kathy Wisser; *Vis Prof,* Ross Harvey
Prog estab 1902. Sch type: Pvt. Scholarships offered; Enrl: Grad: 750; Fac 23
Ent Req: BA or equivalent & 3.0 GPA
Tuition: Resident Graduate $1,129 Per credit hour
Type of Training Offered: School
Degrees & Hours Offered: MA, Part of MA/MS dual-degree. MA in Children's Lit, 57-60 sem hrs; MA, Part of an MA/MS dual-degree. The MA is in Hist, the MS is with an Archives concentration, 57-60 sem hrs; MS, 39 sem hrs; Ph.D., Library and Information Science, (LIS) or Managerial Leadership in the information professions (MLIP), 39 Sem Hours
Special Courses: Administration of Archives & Manuscript Collections, Applied Information Systems Design, Competitive Intelligence, Information/Organization Ethics, Intellectual Freedom & Censorship, Medical Librarianship, Modern Publishing & Librarianship, Music Librarianship, Photographic Archives, Visual Information, Preservation Management, Digital Asset Management, XML, Database Management, Information Retrieval, User Instruction, Indexing & Thesaurus Constitution
Continuing Education, Distance Learning, Online & Blended Courses, Professional Development, Summer Session

MICHIGAN

† UNIVERSITY OF MICHIGAN*, School of Information, 304 West Hall, 1085 S University, Ann Arbor, 48109-1107. Tel: 734-763-2285. FAX: 734-764-2475. Web Site: www.si.umich.edu. *Dean, Prof,* Martha E Pollack; E-mail: pollckm@umich.edu; *Assoc Dean, Prof,* Thomas Finholt; E-mail: finholt@umich.edu; *Assoc Dean, Prof,* Jeffrey MacKie-Mason; E-mail: jmm@umich.edu; *Prof,* Daniel Atkins; E-mail: atkins@umich.edu; *Prof,* Francis Blouin; E-mail: fblouin@umich.edu; *Prof,* Yan Chen; E-mail: yanchen@umich.edu; *Prof,* Michael Cohen; E-mail: mdc@umich.edu; *Prof,* Edmund Durfee; E-mail: durfee@umich.edu; *Prof,* Joan C Durrance; E-mail: durrance@umich.edu; *Prof,* C Olivia Frost; E-mail: cfrost@umich.edu; *Prof,* George Furnas; E-mail: furnas@umich.edu; *Prof,* Karen Markey; E-mail: ylime@umich.edu; *Prof,* Paul Resnick; E-mail: presnik@umich.edu; *Prof,* Douglas E Van Houweling; E-mail: dvh@umich.edu; *Assoc Prof,* Steven P Abney; E-mail: abney@umich.edu; *Assoc Prof,* Mark Ackerman; E-mail: ackerm@umich.edu; *Assoc Prof,* Paul Conway; E-mail: pconway@umich.edu; *Assoc Prof,* Paul Edwards; E-mail: pne@umich.edu; *Assoc Prof,* Robert Frost; *Assoc Prof,* Margaret Hedstrom; E-mail: hedstrom@umich.edu; *Assoc Prof,* Dragomir Radev; E-mail: radev@umich.edu; *Assoc Prof,* Soo Young Rieh; E-mail: rieh@umich.edu; *Assoc Prof,* Victor Rosenberg; E-mail: victorr@umich.edu; *Assoc Prof,* Elizabeth Yakel; E-mail: yakel@umich.edu; *Asst Prof,* Lada A Adamic; E-mail: ladamic@umich.edu; *Asst Prof,* Ixchel Faniel; E-mail: ifaniel@umich.edu; *Asst Prof,* Steven J Jackson; E-mail: sjackso@umich.edu; *Asst Prof,* Mick McQuaid; E-mail: mcq@umich.edu; *Asst Prof,* Mark W Newman; E-mail: mwnewman@umich.edu; *Asst Prof,* Rahul Sami; E-mail: rsami@umich.edu; *Asst Prof,* Tiffany Veinot; E-mail: tveinot@umich.edu
Prog estab 1926. Sch type: Pub. Scholarships offered; Enrl: Grad: 350, Grad: 48
Ent Req: Doctoral
Tuition: Non-resident Graduate $16,628 Per semester; Resident Graduate $8,271 Per semester
Degrees & Hours Offered: MS, 48 credit hrs; Ph.D., 36 credit hrs

† WAYNE STATE UNIVERSITY*, School of Library & Information Science, 106 Kresge Library, Detroit, 48202. Tel: 313-577-1825. Toll Free Tel: 877-263-2665. FAX: 313-577-7563. E-mail: asklis@wayne.edu. Web Site: slis.wayne.edu. *Dean,* Dr Sandra G Yee; Tel: 313-577-4020, E-mail: aj0533@wayne.edu; *Assoc Dean,* Dr Stephen T Bajjaly; Tel: 313-577-0350, E-mail: dx1042@wayne.edu; *Acad Serv Officer III,* Jennifer L Bondy; Tel: 313-577-2523, E-mail: aa1676@wayne.edu; *Acad Serv Officer II,* Megen R Drulia; Tel: 313-577-8543, E-mail: ay6086@wayne.edu; *Acad Serv Officer I,* Matthew D Fredericks; Tel: 313-577-2446, E-mail: aj8416@wayne.edu; *Prof,* Dr Robert P Holley; E-mail: aa3805@wayne.edu; *Prof,* Dr Dian E Walster; E-mail: ah1984@wayne.edu; *Assoc Prof,* Dr Hermina G B Anghelescu; E-mail: ag7662@wayne.edu; *Assoc Prof,* Dr John H Heinrichs; E-mail: ai2824@wayne.edu; *Assoc Prof,* Dr Gordon Barrick

Neavill; E-mail: aa3401@wayne.edu; *Asst Prof,* Dr Joan Beaudoin; E-mail: ee4525@wayne.edu; *Asst Prof,* Dr Deborah Charbonneau; E-mail: ao8245@wayne.edu; *Asst Prof,* Dr Kafi Kumasi; E-mail: ak4901@wayne.edu; *Asst Prof,* Dr Stephanie Maatta Smith; E-mail: es7746@wayne.edu; *Asst Prof,* Dr Jennifer Pecoskie; E-mail: ep1859@wayne.edu; *Asst Prof,* Dr Joseph M Turrini; E-mail: au5177@wayne.edu; *Asst Prof,* Dr Xiangmin E Zhang; E-mail: ae9101@wayne.edu; *Sr Lecturer,* Dr Bin Li; E-mail: ax9064@wayne.edu; *E-Learning Instrul Support Lectr,* David M Foote; Tel: 313-577-5328, E-mail: bb0875@wayne.edu; *Practicum Coordr,* Jennifer Gustafson; E-mail: ad9667@wayne.edu; *Prof in Residence,* Judith J Field; E-mail: aa4101@wayne.edu

Prog estab 1940. Sch type: Pub; Enrl: Grad: 585; Fac 15
Tuition: Non-resident Graduate $1,196 Per credit hour; Resident Graduate $576 Per credit hour
Type of Training Offered: Special
Degrees & Hours Offered: Certificate, Archival Admin, 15 credit hrs; Certificate, Post Master-Specialist, 30 credit hrs; Certificate, Info Mgt for Librarians, 15 plus 3 credit prerequisite; Certificate, Rec & Info Mgt, 15 plus 3 credit prerequisite; Certificate, Pub Libr Servs to Ch & YA, 15; Certificate, Grad Certificate in Arts & Mus Librarianship, 15; Certificate, Urban Librarianship, 15; MLIS, 36 credit hrs; MLIS/MA, Hist, 57 credit hrs
Special Courses: Archives, Arts & Museum Librarianship, Children's Literature, Database Concepts & Applications, Educational Technology, Government Information Resources, Indexing & Abstracting, Information Architecture, Information Behavior, Information Policy, Integrated Library Systems, Legal Information Resources, Medical Libraries, Microcomputer Applications, Multicultural Information Services & Resources, Productivity Tools, Records Management, Urban Libraries, Web Development, Young Adult Literature
Distance Learning, Evening Session, Internet Courses, Online & Blended Courses, Professional Development, Summer Session, Weekend Session

MINNESOTA

COLLEGE OF SAINT SCHOLASTICA*, Educational Media & Technology Program, 1200 Kenwood Ave, Duluth, 55811-4199. Tel: 218-723-6155. FAX: 218-723-6709. Web Site: www.css.edu/gradedm.xml. *Dir,* Marie Kelsey; E-mail: mkelsey@css.edu
Sch type: Pvt; Enrl: Grad: 25
Ent Req: GPA 2.8
Type of Training Offered: School
Degrees & Hours Offered: BA, Educ Media, 128 sem hrs; M.Ed., Educ Media, 34 sem hrs
Distance Learning, Evening Session, Internet Courses

MINNESOTA STATE UNIVERSITY, MANKATO*, Library Media Education, College of Education, Armstrong Hall AH 313, Mankato, 56001-8400. Tel: 507-389-5708. FAX: 507-389-5751. Web Site: www.musu.edu/ksp/lme. *Asst Prof, Prog Coordr,* Dr Deborah Jesseman; Tel: 507-389-5662, E-mail: deborah.jesseman@mnsu.edu
Prog estab 1971. Sch type: Pub. Scholarships offered
Tuition: Non-resident Graduate $386 Per credit hour; Resident Graduate $256 Per credit hour
Type of Training Offered: College
Degrees & Hours Offered: Certificate, Sch Libr Media Specialist License, 28 sem hrs; MS, Libr Sci, 34 sem hrs
Special Courses: Children's Literature, Information Science, Media & Technology, Records Management
Internet Courses, Summer Session

SAINT CATHERINE UNIVERSITY, Information Management Department, (Formerly College of Saint Catherine), 2004 Randolph Ave, Mailstop No 4125, Saint Paul, 55105. Tel: 651-690-6802. FAX: 651-690-8724. E-mail: imdept@stkate.edu. Web Site: www.stkate.edu/~mlisweb. *Assoc Dean, Prog Dir,* Deborah Grealy, PhD; E-mail: dsgrealy@stkate.edu; *Asst Prog Dir,* Deborah Torres; *Assoc Prof,* David Lesniaski, PhD; E-mail: dalesniaski@stkate.edu; *Assoc Prof,* Sook Lim, PhD; E-mail: slim@stkate.edu; *Asst Prof,* Heidi Hammond, PhD; E-mail: hkhammond@stkate.edu; *Asst Prof,* Sarah Park, PhD; E-mail: spark@stkate.edu; *Asst Prof,* Sheri Ross, PhD; E-mail: svtross@stkate.edu; *Asst Prof,* Kyunghye Yoon, PhD; E-mail: kyoon@stkate.edu; *Asst Prof,* Joyce Yukawa, PhD; *Coordr, Instrul Tech,* Nicolas Steffel; E-mail: nsteffel@stkate.edu
Prog estab 1917. Sch type: Pvt; Enrl: Grad: 188; Fac 8
Ent Req: 3.0 GPA
Tuition: Resident Graduate $796 Per credit hour
Degrees & Hours Offered: MLS; MLIS, 136 sem hrs
Evening Session

SAINT CLOUD STATE UNIVERSITY*, Center for Information Media, Learning Resources & Technology Services, 720 Fourth Ave S, Saint Cloud, 56301-4498. Tel: 320-308-2084. FAX: 320-308-4778. E-mail: lrtsinfo@stcloudstate.edu. Web Site: lrts.stcloudstate.edu. *Interim Dean,*

Ruth Zietlow; E-mail: razietlow@stcloudstate.edu; *Dean,* Position Currently Open; *Assoc Dean for Instruction & Educ Tech,* Mark Baas; E-mail: mjbaas@stcloudstate.edu
Sch type: Pub. Scholarships offered
Type of Training Offered: College
Degrees & Hours Offered: BA, Info Media minor, 18 or 24 sem hrs; BS, Info Media major, 36 sem hrs; BS, Info Media minor, 18 or 24 sem hrs; MS, Info Media, 39 or 42 sem hrs

MISSISSIPPI

† THE UNIVERSITY OF SOUTHERN MISSISSIPPI*, School of Library & Information Science, 118 College Dr, No 5146, Hattiesburg, 39406-0001. Tel: 601-266-4228. FAX: 601-266-5774. E-mail: slis@usm.edu. Web Site: www.usm.edu/slis. *Dir,* Dr M Jay Norton; E-mail: slis@usm.edu
Prog estab 1926. Sch type: Pub; Fac 10
Tuition: Non-resident Undergraduate $5,311 Full-time; Non-resident Graduate $5,311 Full-time; Non-resident Graduate $1,005 Per 3 credit hour; Resident Undergraduate $2,297 Full-time; Resident Graduate $2,297 Per credit hour; Resident Graduate $765 Per 3 credit hour
Type of Training Offered: School Library Media Certificate
Degrees & Hours Offered: BA, with or without Sch Libr Media specialization (impacts sem hrs required), 39 sem hrs for major; Certificate, Miss supplemental Sch Libr Media Specialist endorsement, 21 undergrad hrs, A level; MLIS, with or without Sch Libr Media specialization (impacts sem hrs required), 39 sem hrs; SLIS, with or without Sch Libr Media specialization (impacts sem hrs required), 36-48 sem hrs beyond the MLIS
Special Courses: Archives, British Studies, Children's Literature, Information Management & Media (AV)
Evening Session, Internet Courses, Summer Session, Weekend Session

MISSOURI

MISSOURI STATE UNIVERSITY*, Department of Library Science, Duane G Meyer Library, 901 S National Ave, Springfield, 65897. Tel: 417-836-4525. FAX: 417-836-4764. E-mail: library@missouristate.edu. *Dean,* Neosha Mackey; *Assoc Prof, Dir, Curric Res Ctr,* Cheryl Jones; *Coordr, Libr Sci,* Bill Edgar; Tel: 417-836-4529; *Prof,* Lynn S Cline; *Prof,* Marilyn McCroskey; *Assoc Prof,* Drew Beisswenger; *Assoc Prof,* James A Coombs; *Assoc Prof,* David Richards; *Asst Prof,* David Adams; *Asst Prof,* Dea Borneman; *Asst Prof,* Edward DeLong; *Asst Prof,* Betty Evans; *Asst Prof,* Crystal Gale; *Asst Prof,* Joshua Lambert; *Asst Prof,* Andrea Miller; *Asst Prof,* Vern Reeder; *Asst Prof,* Byron Stewart; *Asst Prof,* Tammy Stewart; *Asst Prof,* Tracy Stout; *Asst Prof,* Rebecca Thompson; *Asst Prof,* Raegan Wiechert
Prog estab 1960. Sch type: Pub; Enrl: 80
Type of Training Offered: School
Degrees & Hours Offered: BA, Libr Sci minor, 18-22 sem hrs; BS, Educ; BS, Libr Sci minor, 18-22 sem hrs; Certificate, Post Bacc LMS Certification
Evening Session, Summer Session

UNIVERSITY OF CENTRAL MISSOURI, Library Science & Information Services Program, Dept of Educational Leadership & Human Development, Lovinger 4101, Warrensburg, 64093. Tel: 660-543-8633. Toll Free Tel: 877-729-8266. FAX: 660-543-4164. E-mail: antrim@ucmo.edu. Web Site: www.ucmo.edu/lis. *Chair, Coordr, Prof,* Dr Patricia Antrim; E-mail: antrim@ucmo.edu; *Assoc Prof,* Dr Jennifer Robins; Tel: 660-543-8879, E-mail: jrobins@ucmo.edu; *Instr,* Sandra Jenkins; Tel: 660-543-4150, E-mail: sjenkins@ucmo.edu; *Instr,* Floyd Pentlin; Tel: 660-543-4910, E-mail: fpentlin@ucmo.edu
Prog estab 1964. Sch type: Pub. Scholarships offered; Enrl: Grad: 200
Ent Req: 2.75 GPA, 3 letters of recommendation & interview
Tuition: Non-resident Undergraduate $448 Per credit hour; Non-resident Graduate $316 Per credit hour; Resident Undergraduate $238 Per credit hour; Resident Graduate $316 Per credit hour
Type of Training Offered: School Library Media Certificate
Degrees & Hours Offered: MS, Sch Libr Media, 36 sem hrs; EdS, Human Servs (Learning Res), 30 sem hrs
Special Courses: Libraries & Librarianship, Library Materials for Children & Youth, School Library Administration, Using Online Resources
Online & Blended Courses

† UNIVERSITY OF MISSOURI-COLUMBIA, School of Information Science & Learning Technology, 303 Townsend Hall, Columbia, 65211. Tel: 573-882-4546. Toll Free Tel: 877-747-5868. FAX: 573-884-2917. E-mail: sislt@missouri.edu. Web Site: lis.missouri.edu. *Dir,* John Wedman; E-mail: wedmanj@missouri.edu; *Prof,* John M Budd; E-mail: buddj@missouri.edu; *Prof,* Sanda Erdelez; E-mail: erdelezs@missouri.edu; *Prof,* Gail Fitzgerald; E-mail: fitzgeraldg@missouri.edu; *Prof,* David H Jonassen; E-mail: jonassen@missouri.edu; *Prof,* Jim Laffey; E-mail: laffeyj@missouri.edu; *Prof,* Rose Marra; E-mail: marrar@missouri.edu; *Assoc Prof,* Denice Adkins; E-mail: adkinsde@missouri.edu; *Assoc Prof,* Julie Caplow; E-mail: caplowj@missouri.edu; *Assoc Prof,* Tom Kochtanek; E-mail: kochtanekt@missouri.edu; *Assoc Prof,* Joi Moore; E-mail:

moorejoi@missouri.edu; *Asst Prof,* Jenny Bossaller; E-mail:
bossallerj@missouri.edu; *Asst Prof,* Twyla Gibson; E-mail:
gibsontg@missouri.edu; *Asst Prof,* Heather Lea Moulaison; E-mail:
moulaisonhe@missouri.edu; *Teaching Prof,* Linda Esser; E-mail:
esserl@missouri.edu; *Assoc Teaching Prof,* Jane Howland; E-mail:
howlandj@missouri.edu; *Asst Teaching Prof,* Aimee Klimczak; E-mail:
klimczaka@missouri.edu; *Asst Teaching Prof, Kans City,* Chris LeBeau;
E-mail: lebeauc@umkc.edu; *Asst Teaching Prof, St Louis,* Karen Robinson;
E-mail: robinsonkar@umsl.edu
Prog estab 1966. Sch type: Pub. Scholarships offered; Enrl: Grad: 250
Ent Req: Undergrad degree & 3.0 GPA (last 60 hrs) & GRE
Tuition: Non-resident Graduate $532 Per credit hour; Resident Graduate
$337 Per credit hour
Type of Training Offered: Special
Degrees & Hours Offered: MA, Libr Sci, 42 hrs; M.Ed., Educ Tech, 32
hrs; Ph.D., Info Sci & Learning Tech, 80-100
Special Courses: Digital Humanities & Information, Digital Libraries,
Emerging Technologies in Libraries, Ethics & Information, History of
Books & Printing, Intellectual Freedom, International & Comparative
Libraries, Materials for Children & Teens, Reader Advisory Services,
Social Constructs of Information, Special Libraries & Information Centers,
Web Usability
Co-operative Education Prog, Distance Learning, Evening Session, Internet
Courses, Online & Blended Courses, Summer Session

MONTANA

MONTANA STATE UNIVERSITY*, College of Education, Health &
Human Development, Library Media, 213 Reid Hall, Bozeman, 59717.
(Mail add: PO Box 172880, Bozeman, 59717-2880). Tel: 406-994-3120.
FAX: 406-994-3261. E-mail: libmedia@montana.edu. Web Site:
www.montana.edu/libmedia. *Dir,* Dr Janis Bruwelheide; E-mail:
janisb@montana.edu
Prog estab 1967. Sch type: Pub; Enrl: Grad: 45
Ent Req: Graduate school library media K-12 certification only for post
BS teachers
Tuition: Resident Graduate $275 Per credit hour
Type of Training Offered: School Library Media Certificate
Degrees & Hours Offered: Certificate, School Libr Media K-12, 21 sem
hrs
Special Courses: Library Media K-12
Internet Courses

UNIVERSITY OF MONTANA, Phyllis J Washington College of Education
& Human Sciences, 32 Campus Dr, Missoula, 59812-6346. Tel:
406-243-4841. FAX: 406-243-4908. Web Site:
www.coehs.umt.edu/departments/currinst/libmedia/default.php. *Chair, Prof,*
Position Currently Open; *Assoc Prof,* Sandra Williams; Tel: 406-243-4073,
E-mail: sandra.williams@umontana.edu
Enrl: Grad: 30
Type of Training Offered: School Library Media Certificate
Degrees & Hours Offered: BA, Libr Sci Minor, 25 sem hrs; M.Ed.,
Libr-Media Endorsement, 44 sem hrs
Special Courses: Administration, Children's & Young Adult Literature,
Collection Development, Curriculum, Practicum, Reference, Technical
Processing
Internet Courses

NEBRASKA

CHADRON STATE COLLEGE, Library Media Specialist Program, Reta
King Library, 300 E 12th St, Chadron, 69337-2675. Tel: 308-432-6271.
FAX: 308-432-6409. Web Site: www.csc.edu/library. *Asst Prog Dir,* Shawn
Hartman
Prog estab 1965. Enrl: Undergrad: 23
Degrees & Hours Offered: BA, Libr Media Specialist major, 21 sem hrs;
BS, Libr Media Specials major & endorsement, 33 sem hrs
Internet Courses, No Summer Sessions

UNIVERSITY OF NEBRASKA AT OMAHA*, Library Science Program,
College of Education, Roskens 308, Omaha, 68182-0163. Tel:
402-554-2119. Toll Free Tel: 800-858-8648, Ext 2119. FAX:
402-554-2125. Web Site: www.unomaha.edu/libraryed. *Coordr,* Dr Rebecca
Pasco; E-mail: rpasco@unomaha.edu
Enrl: Undergrad: 100, Grad: 200
Type of Training Offered: School Library Media Certificate
Degrees & Hours Offered: BS, Libr Sci major or minor, 30 sem hrs; MS,
Elem Educ, Secondary Educ or Reading, 36 sem hrs
Co-operative Education Prog, Distance Learning, Online & Blended
Courses, Weekend Session

NEW JERSEY

† RUTGERS, THE STATE UNIVERSITY OF NEW JERSEY*, School of
Communication, Information & Library Studies, Four Huntington St, New
Brunswick, 08901-1071. Tel: 732-932-7500, Ext 8955. FAX:
732-932-2644. Web Site: scils.rutgers.edu. *Chairperson, Prof,* Nicholas
Belkin; E-mail: nick@belkin.rutgers.edu; *Dean, Prof,* Gustav W Friedrich;
E-mail: gusf@scils.rutgers.edu; *Assoc Dean, Prof,* Betty J Turock; E-mail:
bturock@scils.rutgers.edu; *Prof,* James D Anderson; E-mail:
jda@scils.rutgers.edu; *Prof,* Paul Kantor; E-mail: kantor@scils.rutgers.edu;
Prof, Carol C Kuhlthau; E-mail: kuhlthau@scils.rutgers.edu; *Prof,* Tefko
Saracevic; E-mail: tefko@scils.rutgers.edu; *Prof,* Kay Vandergrift; E-mail:
kvander@scils.rutgers.edu; *Assoc Prof,* Kay Ann Cassell; *Assoc Prof,* Carol
Gordon; *Assoc Prof,* Ross Todd; E-mail: rtodd@scils.rutgers.edu; *Assoc
Prof,* Daniel O O'Connor; E-mail: oconnor@scils.rutgers.edu; *Assoc Prof,*
Jana Varlejs; E-mail: varlejs@scils.rutgers.edu; *Asst Prof,* Lisa Covi;
E-mail: covi@scils.rutgers.edu; *Asst Prof,* Marija Dalbello; E-mail:
dalbello@scils.rutgers.edu; *Asst Prof,* Claire McInerney; E-mail:
clairemc@scils.rutgers.edu; *Asst Prof,* Gheorghe Muresan; E-mail:
muresan@scils.rutgers.edu; *Asst Prof,* Anselm Spoerri; E-mail:
aspoerri@scils.rutgers.edu; *Asst Prof,* Nina Wacholder; E-mail:
nina@scils.rutgers.edu; *Asst Prof,* Mark Winston; E-mail:
mwinston@scils.rutgers.edu; *Asst Prof,* Xiangmin Zhang; E-mail:
xzhang@scils.rutgers.edu
Prog estab 1953. Sch type: Pub. Scholarships offered; Enrl: Grad: 304; Fac
18
Ent Req: GRE, 3.0 GPA, letters of recommendation & personal statement
Tuition: Non-resident Graduate $6,511 Per semester; Non-resident
Graduate $500 Per credit hour; Resident Graduate $4,597 Per semester;
Resident Graduate $338 Per credit hour
Type of Training Offered: Special
Degrees & Hours Offered: MLIS, Libr & Info Studies, 36 credit hrs;
Ph.D., Communication, Info & Libr Studies
Special Courses: Academic Librarianship, Information Retrieval, Human
Information Behavior, Information Science, Information Technology,
Management Services, Scientific & Technical Information, Reference &
Information Service, Services for Children & Young Adults, School Media
Services, Special Librarianship, Technical Services
Evening Session, Summer Session

WILLIAM PATERSON UNIVERSITY*, School Library Media
Concentration Program, College of Education, 1600 Valley Rd, Wayne,
07470. Tel: 973-720-2331, 973-720-2980. FAX: 973-720-2585. Web Site:
www.unomaha.edu/libraryed. *Prog Chair,* Jane B Hutchison; E-mail:
hutchisonj@wpunj.edu; *Prof,* Michelle Kowalsky; E-mail:
knowalsky@wpvnj.edu; *Prof,* Yvonne Roux; E-mail: rouxy@wpunj.edu
Prog estab 1952. Sch type: Pub; Enrl: Grad: 51; Fac 2
Ent Req: GPA 2.75, NJ Teaching Certificate, GRE 450, MAT 388
Tuition: Non-resident Graduate $841 Per credit hour; Resident Graduate
$542 Per credit hour
Type of Training Offered: School Library Media Certificate
Degrees & Hours Offered: M.Ed., Sch Libr Media Program, 36 credit hrs
Special Courses: Children's & Adolescent Literature, Field Experiences in
School Library Media Centers, Foundations of School Librarianship,
Information Sources & Services, Instructional Design, Management of the
School Library Media Program, Technical Processes
Evening Session, Internet Courses, Summer Session

NEW MEXICO

NATIONAL AMERICAN UNIVERSITY*, 1601 Rio Rancho Blvd, Ste
200, Rio Rancho, 87124. Tel: 505-348-3750. FAX: 505-348-3705. *Syst Dir
of Libr,* Benjamin Wakashige; Tel: 505-348-3746
Enrl: Undergrad: 300
Degrees & Hours Offered: AAS; BS; MBA; MM

THE UNIVERSITY OF NEW MEXICO*, Educational Media Library
Science Program, Travelstead Hall, MSC 05 3040, Tireman Library, 119
COE UNM, Albuquerque, 87131-0001. Tel: 505-277-6384, 505-277-7260.
FAX: 505-277-8427. E-mail: saticoy@unm.edu. *Dir,* Leslie Chamberlin
Prog estab 1970. Sch type: Pub; Enrl: Undergrad: 22, Grad: 18; Fac 1
Ent Req: 24 credits, 8 three-unit classes.
Type of Training Offered: School Library Media Certificate
Distance Learning, Evening Session, Internet Courses, Summer Session,
Weekend Session

NEW YORK

† LONG ISLAND UNIVERSITY*, Palmer School of Library & Information
Science, C W Post Campus, 720 Northern Blvd, Brookville, 11548-1300.
Tel: 516-299-2866. FAX: 516-299-4168. E-mail: palmer@liu.edu. Web
Site: www.palmer.cwpost.liu.edu. *Dir,* Linda Ryan; Tel: 516-299-4109,
E-mail: linda.ryan@liu.edu; *Dir, PhD Prog, Prof,* Dr Gregory Hunter; Tel:
516-299-7171, E-mail: ghunter@liu.edu; *Dir, Sch Media Prog,* Dr Bea
Baaden; Tel: 516-299-3818, E-mail: bea.baaden@liu.edu; *Prof,* Dr Michael
Koenig; Tel: 516-299-2176, E-mail: mkoenig@liu.edu; *Prof,* Dr Lucienne

Maillet; Tel: 516-299-2175, E-mail: mailletl@liu.edu; *Prof,* Dr John Regazzi; Tel: 516-299-3322, E-mail: john.regazzi@liu.edu; *Prof,* Dr William Saffady; Tel: 516-299-2179, E-mail: wsaffady@liu.edu; *Prof,* Dr Amy Spaulding; Tel: 516-299-2172, E-mail: spauldg@liu.edu; *Assoc Prof,* Dr Heting Chu; Tel: 516-299-2177, E-mail: hchu@liu.edu; *Assoc Prof,* Dr Seth Magot; Tel: 516-299-2176, E-mail: magot@liu.edu; *Assoc Prof,* Dr Deirdre Stam; Tel: 212-998-2680, E-mail: deirdre.stam@liu.edu; *Assoc Prof,* Dr Mary Westermann; Tel: 516-299-2178, E-mail: westerma@liu.edu; *Asst Prof,* Dr Thomas Krichel; Tel: 516-299-2843, E-mail: thomas.krichel@liu.edu; *Asst Prof,* Dr Qiping Zhang; Tel: 516-299-2180, E-mail: qiping.zhang@liu.edu
Prog estab 1959. Sch type: Pvt. Scholarships offered; Enrl: Grad: 450; Fac 15
Ent Req: 3.0 GPA, letters of recommendation, transcripts, essay & resume
Type of Training Offered: Special
Degrees & Hours Offered: Certificate, Archives & Rec Mgt, 15 credits; Certificate, Pub Libr Mgt, 15 credits; MS, Libr & Info Sci, 36 credits; Ph.D., Info Studies, 60 credits; MLIS/MA, Dual-degree prog with New York Univ
Special Courses: Abstracting & Indexing, Archives, Artist's Books, Building Digital Libraries, Business & Economic Resources, Children's Literature, Descriptive Cataloging, Digital Preservation, Electronic Resources, Encoded Archival Description, Government Information, Health Sciences Sources & Services, History of the Book, Information Networks, Instructional Design & Leadership, Knowledge Management, Library Services for the Special Populations, Preservation, Rare Books, Records Management, School Media Centers, Special Collections of NYC, Storytelling, Subject Analysis
Evening Session, Online & Blended Courses, Summer Session, Weekend Session

† PRATT INSTITUTE*, School of Information & Library Science, 144 W 14th St, 6th Flr, New York, 10011-7301. Tel: 212-647-7682. Toll Free Tel: 800-331-0834. FAX: 212-367-2492. E-mail: infosils@pratt.edu. Web Site: www.pratt.edu/sils. *Dean,* Tula Giannini; E-mail: giannini@pratt.edu
Prog estab 1890. Sch type: Pvt; Enrl: Grad: 250; Fac 37
Ent Req: GPA 3.0, TOEFL 600
Tuition: Resident Graduate $675 Per credit hour
Type of Training Offered: Public
Degrees & Hours Offered: MLIS, Advanced Certificate in Libr & Info Sci, Library Media Specialist, 36 sem hrs incl individual research courses; MLIS/MA, Art Hist
Special Courses: Abstracting & Indexing, Business, Economics & Statistical Sources, Conservation & Preservation of Archival & Library Materials, Database Design, Digital Archiving, Digital Libraries, Government Info Sources, Interpersonal Communication for Information Professionals, Legal Research Methods & Law, Management Archives & Special Collections, Museums & Library Research, On-line Data Bases in Business, On-line Data Bases in Social Sciences & Humanities, On-line Data Base Searching & Services, Professional Writing, Records Management, Thesaurus Design & Construction
Summer Session

† QUEENS COLLEGE OF THE CITY UNIVERSITY OF NEW YORK, Graduate School of Library & Information Studies, Benjamin Rosenthal Library, Rm 254, 65-30 Kissena Blvd, Flushing, 11367. Tel: 718-997-3790. FAX: 718-997-3797. E-mail: qc_gslis@qc.cuny.edu. Web Site: www.qc.edu/. *Chair, Dir,* James Marcum; *Chief Librn,* Robert Shaddy; *Prof,* Mary K Chelton; *Prof,* Harry M Kibiridge; *Prof,* Thomas T Surprenant; *Asst Prof,* Ben Alexander; *Asst Prof,* Ping Li; *Assoc Prof,* Roberta Brody; *Assoc Prof,* Colleen Cool; *Assoc Prof,* Linda Cooper; *Assoc Prof,* Claudia Perry; *Assoc Prof,* Kwong Bor Ng; *Instr,* Valero Walter
Prog estab 1955. Sch type: Pub. Scholarships offered; Fac 13
Tuition: Non-resident Graduate $675 Per credit hour; Resident Graduate $4,345 Per semester; Resident Graduate $365 Per credit hour
Degrees & Hours Offered: MLS, 36 credits
Special Courses: Art Librarianship, Bibliographic Control of Non-print Materials, Business Reference, Children's Literature, Digital Libraries, Fundamentals of Library Conservation & Preservation, Geographic Information Science, Health Sciences, Issues & Applications, Law Librarianship, Library Conservation & Preservation, Media (AV), Mythology & Folklore for Children & Adolescents, Planning & Delivering Services to Youth in the Public Library, Public Library Services for Children & Young Adults, Reading Motivation Techniques for Children & Adolescents, Resources for the School Curriculum, Young Adult Literature
Evening Session, Summer Session

† SAINT JOHN'S UNIVERSITY, Division of Library & Information Science, Saint Augustine Hall, Rm 408, 8000 Utopia Pkwy, Jamaica, 11439. Tel: 718-990-6200. FAX: 718-990-2071. Web Site: www.stjohns.edu/academics/graduate/liberalarts/department/library. *Dir,* Jeffrey Olson, PhD; Tel: 718-990-5705, E-mail: olsonj@stjohns.edu; *Asst Dir,* Rosann Kelly; Tel: 718-990-1457, E-mail: kellyr1@stjohns.edu; *Assoc Prof,* Kevin Rioux, PhD; Tel: 718-990-1458, E-mail: riouxk@stjohns.edu; *Assoc Prof,* Katherine Shelfer, PhD; E-mail: shelferk@stjohns.edu; *Assoc*

Prof, Kristin Szylivan, PhD; Tel: 718-990-5239, E-mail: szylviank@stjohns.edu; *Assoc Prof,* James Vorbach, PhD; Tel: 718-990-1834, E-mail: vorbachj@stjohns.edu; *Asst Prof,* Christine Angel, PhD; Tel: 718-990-1452, E-mail: angelc@stjohns.edu; *Asst Prof,* Shari Lee, PhD; Tel: 718-990-1451, E-mail: lees2@stjohns.edu
Prog estab 1937. Sch type: Pvt; Enrl: Grad: 100; Fac 7
Ent Req: Bachelor's Degree, B average & letters of recommendation, statement of professional goals
Tuition: Resident Graduate $1,105 Per credit hour
Type of Training Offered: Special
Degrees & Hours Offered: Certificate, Law Librarianship, Archives, Public Librarianship, Academic Librarianship, Special Librarianship, Youth Librarianship, School Librarianship, 24 sem hrs; MLS, Library Science, 36 sem hrs
Special Courses: Archives & Records, Children's Literature, Children & Young Adult Literature, Competitive Intelligence, Database Management, Goverment Information, Indexing & Abstracting, Knowledge Management, Law Library Administration, Library Automation, Media Design & Production, Metadata, Networks, Online Databases, Popular Materials, Preservation & Conservation, Services to Diverse Populations, Social Justice, Web Design,
Distance Learning, Evening Session, Online & Blended Courses, Summer Session

† SYRACUSE UNIVERSITY*, School of Information Studies, Center for Science & Technology, Rm 4-206, Syracuse, 13244-4100. Tel: 315-443-2911. FAX: 315-443-5673. E-mail: ischool@syr.edu. Web Site: ischool.syr.edu. *Dean,* Elizabeth D Liddy
Prog estab 1896. Sch type: Pvt. Scholarships offered; Enrl: Undergrad: 550, Grad: 740; Fac 41
Ent Req: GRE & letters of recommendation
Tuition: Resident Undergraduate $12,860 Per semester; Resident Graduate $806 Per credit hour
Type of Training Offered: Public
Degrees & Hours Offered: BS, Info Mgt & Tech, 120 sem hrs; Certificate, Info Systs & Telecommunications Mgt; Certificate, Info Security Mgt; Certificate, Sch Media; Certificate, Digital Libr; MLIS, 36 sem hrs; MS, Info Mgt, 42 sem hrs; MS, Telecommunications & Network Mgt, 36 sem hrs; Ph.D., Info Transfer, 78 sem hrs
Special Courses: Behavior of Information Users, Biomedical Information, Computer Programming, Database Management Systems, Electronic Commerce, Governments & Information, Information Processing Industry, Information Resources Management, Information Policy, Information Retrieval, Information Science, Project Management, Records Management, School Media Management, Strategic Management of Information Resources, Systems Analysis, Telecommunications, Youth Services
Evening Session, Summer Session

† UNIVERSITY AT ALBANY, STATE UNIVERSITY OF NEW YORK, Department of Information Studies, College of Computing and Information, Draper 116, 135 Western Ave, Albany, 12222. Tel: 518-442-5110. FAX: 518-442-5367. E-mail: infostudies@albany.edu. Web Site: www.albany.edu/informationstudies/. *Chair,* Dr Philip B Eppard; Tel: 518-442-5119, Fax: peppard@albany.edu; *Asst to the Chair,* Daphne Jorgensen; E-mail: djorgensen@albany.edu; *Assoc Prof,* Dr Deborah Lines Andersen; Tel: 518-442-5122, E-mail: dla@albany.edu; *Assoc Prof,* Dr Hemalata Iyer; Tel: 518-442-5116, E-mail: hiyer@albany.edu; *Assoc Prof,* Dr Abebe Rorissa; Tel: 518-442-5123, E-mail: arorissa@albany.edu; *Assoc Prof,* Dr Joette Stefl-Mabry; Tel: 518-442-5120, E-mail: jstefl@albany.edu; *Asst Prof,* Dr Donghee Sinn; Tel: 518-442-5117, E-mail: dsinn@albany.edu; *Asst Prof,* Dr Ozlem Uzuner; Tel: 518-442-4687, E-mail: ouzuner@albany.edu; *Asst Prof,* Dr Xiaojun Yuan; Tel: 518-591-8746, E-mail: xyuan@albany.edu; *Serv Prof,* Frank D'Andraia; Tel: 518-442-5118, E-mail: fdandraia@albany.edu
Prog estab 1926. Sch type: Pub. Scholarships offered; Enrl: Grad: 300
Ent Req: Bachelor's Degree, GRE or other grad degree & letters of recommendation
Tuition: Non-resident Graduate $8,340 Per semester; Non-resident Graduate $695 Per credit hour; Resident Graduate $4,685 Per semester; Resident Graduate $390 Per credit hour
Type of Training Offered: Public
Degrees & Hours Offered: Certificate, Advan Study, 30 credits; MA, English or Hist with Info Sci, 58 credits; MS, English or Hist with Info Sci, 58 credits; MS, Info Sci, 42 credits; Ph.D., Info Sci, 60 credits
Special Courses: Archives, Children's Literature, Literature for Young Adults, Teaching Fundamentals for School Libraries, Fundamentals of XML, Preservation Management, Rare Books, Records Management,Public Libraries, Database Design & Development, Archival Representation, Information Literacy Instruction, Developing User Interface, Web Database Programming, Information Systems, Academic Libraries & Higher Education,
Evening Session, Summer Session, Weekend Session

† UNIVERSITY AT BUFFALO, STATE UNIVERSITY OF NEW YORK*, Department of Library & Information Studies, 534 Baldy Hall, Buffalo, 14260. Tel: 716-645-2412. FAX: 716-645-3775. E-mail:

ub-lis@buffalo.edu. Web Site: www.gsc.buffalo.edu/lis. *Chair,* Dagobert Soergel; *Prof,* Judith Robinson; *Assoc Prof,* Kay Bishop; *Assoc Prof,* Lorna Peterson; *Asst Prof,* Brenda Battleson; *Asst Prof,* Dr Melanie Kimball; *Asst Prof,* Joseph Meloche; *Asst Prof,* Valerie Nesset; *Asst Prof,* Anne Perrault; *Asst Prof,* Dr Ying Sun; *Asst Prof,* Dr Jiangiang Wang

Prog estab 1966. Sch type: Pub. Scholarships offered; Enrl: Grad: 280; Fac 12

Ent Req: 3.0 GPA & letters of reference, BA or BS

Tuition: Non-resident Graduate $438 Per credit hour; Non-resident Graduate $6,000 Per semester; Resident Graduate $288 Per credit hour; Resident Graduate $4,000 Per semester

Type of Training Offered: School Library Media Certificate

Degrees & Hours Offered: MLS, 36 sem hrs

Special Courses: Bibliographic Instruction, Business Info Sources, Data Base Management Systems, Digital Information Retrieval, Digital Libraries, Government Info, Indexing & Surrogation, Information Systems Analysis & Design, Intellectual Freedom, International Publishing, Marketing of Information Services, Music Librarianship, Networking Technologies, Records Management

Evening Session, Summer Session

NORTH CAROLINA

APPALACHIAN STATE UNIVERSITY*, Library Science Program, RCOE, Dept of LES, 311 Edwin Duncan Hall, Boone, 28608. Tel: 828-262-7236. Toll Free Tel: 800-355-4084. FAX: 828-262-6035. Web Site: www.ced.appstate.edu/departments/les/programs/lbsci. *Prof,* Dr Nita Matzen; E-mail: matzennj@appstate.edu; *Prof,* Dr Robert Sanders; E-mail: sandersrl@appstate.edu; *Prof,* Dr Carol Truett; E-mail: truettca@appstate.edu; *Prof,* Dr Linda Veltze; E-mail: veltzela@appstate.edu; *Instr,* Dr Rao Aluri; *Instr,* Karen Lowe

Prog estab 1937. Sch type: Pub. Scholarships offered; Enrl: Grad: 120

Ent Req: GRE & 3.0 undergrad

Tuition: Non-resident Graduate $2,994 Per 3 credit hour; Non-resident Graduate $6,277 Per semester; Resident Graduate $609 Per 3 credit hour; Resident Graduate $1,506 Per semester

Type of Training Offered: School

Degrees & Hours Offered: MLS, Libr Sci; School (K-12) Public Librarianship, 37-45 sem hrs

Evening Session, Summer Session, Weekend Session

EAST CAROLINA UNIVERSITY*, Department of Library Science, 101 Umstead Residence Hall, Greenville, 27858-4353. (Mail add: 1000 E Fifth St, Mail Stop 172, Greenville, 27858). Tel: 252-328-6621. FAX: 252-328-4368. Web Site: www.ecu.edu/cs-educ/lsit1/index.cfm. *Chair,* Dr Elaine Yontz; Tel: 252-737-1150, E-mail: yontzm@ecu.edu; *Prof,* Dr Plummer Alson Jones, Jr; Tel: 252-328-6803, E-mail: jonesp@ecu.edu; *Assoc Prof,* Dr Ruth C Clark; E-mail: clarkc@ecu.edu; *Asst Prof,* Dr Lane Kaye Dotson; Tel: 252-328-2787, E-mail: dotsonl@ecu.edu; *Asst Prof,* Dr John Harer; Tel: 252-328-4389, E-mail: harerj@ecu.edu; *Asst Prof,* Dr Jami Jones; E-mail: jonesj@ecu.edu; *Asst Prof,* Dr Barbara M Marson; E-mail: marsonb@ecu.edu; *Asst Prof,* Dr Gail Munde; Tel: 252-737-1151, E-mail: mundeg@ecu.edu; *Asst Prof,* Dr Patrick Valentine; Tel: 252-737-1570, E-mail: valentinep@ecu.edu

Prog estab 1939. Sch type: Pub. Scholarships offered; Enrl: Grad: 205

Ent Req: MAT or GRE, satisfactory GPA & undergrad degree & letters of recommendation

Tuition: Non-resident Graduate $2,154 Per course; Resident Graduate $567 Per course

Type of Training Offered: Librarianship

Degrees & Hours Offered: MLS, 39 sem hrs

Special Courses: Financial Management Public Library Organizations (online), Genealogy for Librarians (online), Online Cataloging, Small Computer Applications, Storytelling

Summer Session

† NORTH CAROLINA CENTRAL UNIVERSITY*, School of Library & Information Sciences, 1801 Fayetteville St, Durham, 27707. (Mail add: PO Box 19586, Durham, 27707-0021). Tel: 919-530-6485. FAX: 919-530-6402. E-mail: iowens@nccu.edu; *Assoc Dean, Prof,* Robert E Burgin; E-mail: rburgin@mindspring.com; *Prof,* Robert M Ballard; E-mail: rballard@nccu.edu; *Prof,* Beverly Jones; *Assoc Prof,* Ismail Abdullahi; E-mail: iabdullahi@nc.rr.com; *Assoc Prof,* Kalyani Ankem; E-mail: kankem@nccu.edu; *Assoc Prof,* Pauletta B Bracy; E-mail: pbracy@nccu.edu; *Asst Prof,* Deborah Swain; E-mail: dswaine@nccu.edu; *Assoc Prof,* Diane Neal; E-mail: dneal@nccu.edu; *Assoc Prof,* Gabe Peterson; E-mail: gpeterson@nccu.edu; *Asst Prof,* Eun-Young Yoo; E-mail: eunyoung@nccu.edu; *Librn,* Virginia Purefoy Jones; E-mail: vpjones@nccu.edu

Prog estab 1939. Sch type: Pub. Scholarships offered; Enrl: Grad: 237

Ent Req: GRE, SAT, GPA, Bachelor's, Letters of reference

Tuition: Non-resident Graduate $6,436 Per semester; Resident Graduate $1,683 Per semester

Type of Training Offered: Special

Degrees & Hours Offered: MLS, Archives, 36 sem hrs

Special Courses: African American Coll, Computer - Based Info Storage Retrieval Systems, Early Childhood Libr Specialist Program, Expert Systems, Ethnic Materials, Info Science Program & Meta-Data Analysis

Evening Session, Summer Session, Weekend Session

† UNIVERSITY OF NORTH CAROLINA AT CHAPEL HILL*, School of Information & Library Science, CB No 3360, 100 Manning Hall, Chapel Hill, 27599-3360. Tel: 919-962-8366. FAX: 919-962-8071. E-mail: info@ils.unc.edu. Web Site: www.sils.unc.edu. *Dean,* Dr Gary Marchionini; E-mail: march@ils.unc.edu; *Assoc Dean, Acad Affairs,* Barbara M Wildemuth; *Univ Librn,* Rebecca Vargha

Prog estab 1931. Sch type: Pub. Scholarships offered; Enrl: Undergrad: 50, Grad: 300

Ent Req: GRE, 3.0 GPA & letters of reference

Tuition: Non-resident Graduate $19,012 Per year; Resident Graduate $5,014 Per year

Type of Training Offered: Public

Degrees & Hours Offered: BS, Info Sci, 120 sem hrs; MS, Info Sci, 48 sem hrs; MS, Libr Sci, 48 sem hrs; Ph.D., Info & Libr Sci

Special Courses: Archives & Cultural Heritage Information Management, Artificial Intelligence, Children's Literature, Health Science Literature, Information Retrieval, Internet Resources & Services, Law, Library History, Management & Human Resources, Network Applications, Online Databases, Rare Books & Manuscripts, Records Management, Telecommunications & Young Adult Literature

Evening Session, Summer Session

† UNIVERSITY OF NORTH CAROLINA AT GREENSBORO*, Department of Library & Information Studies, School of Education, 349 Curry Bldg, Greensboro, 27402. (Mail add: PO Box 26170, Greensboro, 27402-6170). Tel: 336-334-3477. FAX: 336-334-5060. Web Site: www.uncg.edu/ils/department/index.html. *Chair,* Dr Orvin Lee Shiflett, PhD; Tel: 336-334-3481, E-mail: olshifle@uncg.edu; *Prof,* Dr James V Carmichael, Jr; Tel: 336-334-3478, E-mail: Jim_Carmichael@uncg.edu; *Assoc Prof,* Dr Pamela P Barron, PhD; Tel: 336-334-3476, E-mail: ppbarron@uncg.edu; *Assoc Prof,* Dr Julie Hersberger, PhD; Tel: 336-334-3482, E-mail: jahersbe@uncg.edu; *Asst Prof,* Dr Sandra D Andrews, PhD; Tel: 336-334-5738, E-mail: sdandre2@uncg.edu; *Instr,* Anthony S Chow, PhD; Tel: 336-334-3411, E-mail: aschow@uncg.edu; *Instr,* Nora Bird; Tel: 336-256-0162, E-mail: njbird@uncg.edu; *Instr,* Linda Gann; Tel: 336-334-3479, E-mail: lagann@uncg.edu; *Sch Libr Media,* Sue Spencer; Tel: 336-334-3373, E-mail: srspencer@uncg.edu

Sch type: Pub; Enrl: Grad: 375

Ent Req: Bachelor's & GRE scores

Tuition: Non-resident Graduate $7,368 Per semester; Resident Graduate $1,734 Per semester

Type of Training Offered: Special

Degrees & Hours Offered: MLIS, 36 sem hrs

Evening Session, Summer Session

NORTH DAKOTA

MAYVILLE STATE UNIVERSITY*, Library Science Program, 330 Third St NE, Mayville, 58257-1299. Tel: 701-788-2301. Toll Free Tel: 800-437-4104, Ext 34814. FAX: 701-788-4846. Web Site: www.mayvillestate.edu. *Dir,* Kelly Kornkven; E-mail: Kelly.Kornkven@mayvillestate.edu

Sch type: Pub; Enrl: Undergrad: 10

Tuition: Resident Undergraduate $166 Per credit hour; Regional Undergraduate $249 Per credit hour

Type of Training Offered: School

Degrees & Hours Offered: BA, Educ with Libr Sci Minor, 25 sem hrs; BS, Educ with Libr Sci Minor, 25 sem hrs

Distance Learning, Internet Courses, Summer Session

VALLEY CITY STATE UNIVERSITY*, Library Media & Information Science Program, 101 College St SW, Valley City, 58072-4098. Tel: 701-845-7276. FAX: 701-845-7437. Web Site: library.vcsu.edu. *Dir,* Donna V James; E-mail: donna.james@vcsu.edu

Sch type: Pub; Enrl: Grad: 20, Undergrad: 20; Fac 3

Ent Req: GPA 3.0

Tuition: Resident Undergraduate $199 Per credit hour; Resident Graduate $236 Per credit hour

Type of Training Offered: School

Degrees & Hours Offered: BA, Libr Media & Info Sci minor, 20 sem hrs; BS, Libr Media & Info Sci minor, 20 sem hrs; BS, Educ, Libr Media & Info Sci minor, 20 sem hrs

Internet Courses

OHIO

† KENT STATE UNIVERSITY*, School of Library & Information Science, 314 Library, Kent, 44242-0001. (Mail add: PO Box 5190, Kent, 44242-0001). Tel: 330-672-2782. FAX: 330-672-7965. E-mail: slisinform@kent.edu. Web Site: www.slis.kent.edu. *Dir,* Dr Richard Rubin; *Prof,* Dr Carolyn Brodie; *Prof,* Dr Thomas Froehlich; *Prof,* Dr Marcia Lei

Zeng; *Assoc Prof,* Dr Greg Byerly; *Assoc Prof,* Dr Donald Wicks; *Assoc Prof,* Dr Yin Zhang; *Asst Prof,* Dr Belinda Boon; *Asst Prof,* Dr Yungrang Laura Cheng; *Asst Prof,* Karl Fast; *Asst Prof,* Karen Gracy; *Asst Prof,* Dr Megan Harper; *Asst Prof,* Dr Jason Holmes; *Asst Prof,* Frank Lambert; *Asst Prof,* Miriam Matteson; *Asst Prof,* Dr David Robins; *Asst Prof,* Daniel Roland; *Asst Prof,* Dr Athena Salaba; *Instr,* Jodi Kearns; *Instr,* Mary Anne Nichols

Prog estab 1946. Sch type: Pub. Scholarships offered; Enrl: Grad: 633; Fac 16

Ent Req: GRE, 3.0 GPA & BA or BS

Tuition: Non-resident Graduate $7,990 Per semester; Non-resident Graduate $728 Per credit hour; Resident Graduate $4,484 Per semester; Resident Graduate $408 Per credit hour

Type of Training Offered: Public

Degrees & Hours Offered: MLIS, 36 sem hrs

Special Courses: Archives, Automation, Business/Finance, Children's Literature, Electronic Publishing, Ethics, Field Experience, Government Documents, Humanities, Human Resource Management, Indexing Abstracting, Information Retrieval, Information Science, Network Resources, On-Line Searching, Preservation, Science/Technology, Social Sciences, Young Adult Literature

Evening Session, Summer Session

WRIGHT STATE UNIVERSITY*, College of Education & Human Services, 421 Allyn Hall, 3640 Colonel Glenn Hwy, Dayton, 45435-0001. Tel: 937-775-2509. FAX: 937-775-4855. Web Site: www.cehs.wright.edu. *Dir, Libr Media Prog,* Susan Berg; Tel: 937-775-4148, E-mail: susan.berg@wright.edu

Prog estab 1972. Sch type: Pub; Enrl: Grad: 120; Fac 4

Tuition: Non-resident Undergraduate $3,186 Per quarter; Non-resident Undergraduate $296 Per credit hour; Non-resident Graduate $3,742 Per quarter; Non-resident Graduate $351 Per credit hour; Resident Undergraduate $148 Per credit hour; Resident Undergraduate $1,593 Per quarter; Resident Graduate $203 Per credit hour; Resident Graduate $1,914 Per quarter

Type of Training Offered: School

Degrees & Hours Offered: MA, Libr Media, 48 qtr hrs; M.Ed., Libr Media, 48 qtr hrs

Special Courses: Cataloging & Classification, Computer Education Courses, Field Experience, Information Retrieval, Library & Research Skills, Media (AV), Multimedia Development, Production of Materials, TV Production & Young Adult Literature

Evening Session, Summer Session

OKLAHOMA

UNIVERSITY OF CENTRAL OKLAHOMA*, Instructional Media Education, 100 N University Dr, Edmond, 73034. (Mail add: Box 193 - LIB 129, Edmond, 73034-0193). Tel: 405-974-5437. FAX: 405-974-3857. Web Site: www.uco.edu. *Prof,* Dr Pat Couts; Tel: 405-974-5888, E-mail: pcouts@uco.edu; *Prof,* Dr Jill Rooker; E-mail: jrooker@uco.edu

Enrl: Grad: 60

Ent Req: Prior teaching certification; 2.75 undergrad GPA

Tuition: Non-resident Graduate $427 Per credit hour; Resident Graduate $180 Per credit hour

Type of Training Offered: School Library Media Certificate

Degrees & Hours Offered: M.Ed., Instrul Media - Libr Info, 36 sem hrs

Special Courses: Cataloging, Effective Writing, Elements of Web Design, Graphic & Video Production, Library Materials for Elementary Schools, Library Materials for Secondary Schools, Materials Selection, PR & Information Skills, Reference & Bibliography, School Library Administration

Distance Learning, Evening Session, Online & Blended Courses, Summer Session, Weekend Session

† UNIVERSITY OF OKLAHOMA, School of Library & Information Studies, Bizzell Memorial Library, 401 W Brooks, Rm 120, Norman, 73019-6032. Tel: 405-325-3921. FAX: 405-325-7648. E-mail: slisinfo@lists.ou.edu. Web Site: slis.ou.edu. *Dir, Prof,* Dr Cecelia M Brown, PhD; E-mail: cbrown@ou.edu; *Prof,* Dr Connie J Van Fleet, PhD; E-mail: cvanfleet@ou.edu; *Assoc Prof,* Dr June M Abbas, PhD; E-mail: jmabbas@ou.edu; *Assoc Prof,* Dr Susan Burke, PhD; E-mail: sburke@ou.edu; *Assoc Prof,* Dr Rhonda Harris Taylor, PhD; E-mail: rtaylor@ou.edu; *Asst Prof,* Dr Yong-Mi Kim, PhD; Tel: 918-660-3364, E-mail: yongmi@ou.edu; *Asst Prof,* Dr Kyungwon Koh, PhD; E-mail: kkoh@ou.edu; *Asst Prof,* Dr Betsy Van der Veer Martens, PhD; Tel: 918-660-3376, E-mail: bvmartens@ou.edu; *Asst Prof,* Dr Ellen Rubenstein, PhD; E-mail: erubenstein@ou.edu; *Asst Prof,* Dr John Snead, PhD; E-mail: jsnead@ou.edu; *Asst Prof,* Dr Kelvin White, PhD; E-mail: kwhite@ou.edu; *Instr,* Stacy Zemke; E-mail: szemke@ou.edu

Prog estab 1929. Sch type: Pub. Scholarships offered; Enrl: Grad: 204; Fac 12

Ent Req: 3.2 GPA, 3 letters of reference & statement of purpose & goals, GRE scores

Tuition: Non-resident Undergraduate $669 Per credit hour; Non-resident Graduate $802 Per credit hour; Resident Undergraduate $282 Per credit hour; Resident Graduate $325 Per credit hour

Type of Training Offered: Special

Degrees & Hours Offered: BA, Information Studies (BAIS), 124 sem hrs; MLIS, Library and Information Studies (MLIS), 36 sem hrs; MS, Knowledge Management (MSKM), 36 sem hrs

Special Courses: Biomedical Information Program

Distance Learning, Evening Session, Internet Courses, Online & Blended Courses, Summer Session, Video Courses, Weekend Session

OREGON

WESTERN OREGON UNIVERSITY*, Information Technology, 345 N Monmouth Ave, Monmouth, 97361-1396. Tel: 503-838-8039, 503-838-8492. FAX: 503-838-8228. *Coordr,* Dana Ulveland

Tuition: Non-resident Undergraduate $3,246 Per quarter; Non-resident Graduate $3,070 Per quarter; Resident Undergraduate $1,066 Per quarter; Resident Graduate $1,723 Per quarter

Type of Training Offered: Public

Special Courses: Children's & Young Adult Literature, Media (AV) Computer Application in Libraries, Emerging Technologies

PENNSYLVANIA

† CLARION UNIVERSITY OF PENNSYLVANIA, Department of Library Science, 840 Wood St, Clarion, 16214. Tel: 814-393-2271. Toll Free Tel: 866-272-5612. FAX: 814-393-2150. E-mail: libsci@clarion.edu. Web Site: www.clarion.edu/libsci. *In Charge,* Lois Dulavitch; E-mail: ldulavitch@clarion.edu

Prog estab 1937. Sch type: Pub; Enrl: Undergrad: 50, Grad: 350; Fac 12

Ent Req: GPA of 3.0

Tuition: Non-resident Undergraduate $9,642 Per year; Non-resident Graduate $4,380 Per semester; Resident Undergraduate $6,428 Per year; Resident Graduate $4,290 Per semester; International Undergraduate $4,821 Per semester; International Graduate $4,380 Per semester

Type of Training Offered: Special

Degrees & Hours Offered: BS, ED-Libr Sci, 120 credits; BS, Liberal Studies with Libr Sci concentration, 120 credits; Certificate, post-MS Certificate of Advan Study, 15 credits; MLIS/MA, MA in Applied Hist is offered in conjunction with Shippensburg Univ; MSLS, Libr Sci, 36 credits; MSLS, Libr Sci with PA med serv certification, 36 credits; MSLS/JD, offered in conjunction with Widener Univ Sch of Law

Special Courses: Archival Management of Small Repositories, Business Reference Sources, Children's Literature, Digital Libraries, Instructional Strategies, Integrated Technologies, Multicultural Library Services, Online Information Retrieval, Preservation of Library Materials, Rural Library Services, Special Collection Representation & Records Management, Young Adult Literature

† DREXEL UNIVERSITY*, The iSchool at Drexel, College of Information Science & Technology, Rush Bldg, Rm 306, 30 N 33rd St, Philadelphia, 19104-2875. (Mail add: 3141 Chestnut St, Philadelphia, 19104-2875). Tel: 215-895-2474. FAX: 215-895-2494. E-mail: istinfo@drexel.edu. Web Site: www.ischool.drexel.edu. *Dean,* David E Fenske, PhD; E-mail: fenske@drexel.edu; *Assoc Dean, Res & Undergrad Educ, Prof,* Michael E Atwood, PhD; E-mail: atwood@drexel.edu; *Dir, Inst for Healthcare Informatics, Res & Teaching Prof,* Prudence W Dalrymple, PhD; E-mail: pdalrymple@drexel.edu; *Assoc Prof, Dir, Sch Libr Media Prog,* Delia Neuman, PhD; E-mail: dneuman@drexel.edu; *Assoc Dean, Acad Affairs, Prof,* Eileen G Abels, PhD; E-mail: eabels@drexel.edu; *PhD Prog Dir, Prof,* Susan Wiedenbeck, PhD; E-mail: sw53@drexel.edu; *Prof,* Katherine W McCain, PhD; E-mail: mccainkw@drexel.edu; *Prof,* Il-Yeol Song, PhD; E-mail: song@drexel.edu; *Assoc Prof,* Denise E Agosto, PhD; E-mail: dea@drexel.edu; *Assoc Prof,* Robert B Allen, PhD; E-mail: rba@drexel.edu; *Assoc Prof,* Chaomei Chen, PhD; E-mail: chaomei.chen@drexel.edu; *Assoc Prof,* M Carl Drott, PhD; E-mail: drott@drexel.edu; *Assoc Prof,* Susan Gasson, PhD; E-mail: sgasson@drexel.edu; *Assoc Prof,* Gregory W Hislop, PhD; E-mail: hislopg@drexel.edu; *Assoc Prof,* Xiaohua Tony Hu, PhD; E-mail: Xh29@drexel.edu; *Assoc Prof,* Xia Lin, PhD; E-mail: xlin@drexel.edu; *Assoc Prof,* Gerry Stahl, PhD; E-mail: Gerry.Stahl@drexel.edu; *Assoc Prof,* Rosina Weber, PhD; E-mail: rosina@drexel.edu; *Assoc Prof,* Christopher C Yang, PhD; E-mail: Chris.Yang@drexel.edu; *Asst Prof,* Yuan An, PhD; E-mail: yuan.an@drexel.edu; *Asst Prof,* Sean P Goggins, PhD; E-mail: sgoggins@drexel.edu; *Asst Prof,* Michael Khoo, PhD; E-mail: khoo@drexel.edu; *Asst Prof,* Jiexun Jason Li, PhD; E-mail: Jiexun.Li@drexel.edu; *Asst Prof,* Jung-ran Park, PhD; E-mail: jung-ran.Park@ischool.drexel.edu; *Asst Prof,* Michelle L Rogers, PhD; E-mail: mrogers@drexel.edu; *Asst Prof,* Lisl Zach, PhD; E-mail: lisl@drexel.edu; *Assoc Teaching Prof,* Susan E Davis, PhD; E-mail: sedavis@drexel.edu; *Assoc Teaching Prof,* Lee Leitner, PhD; E-mail: Lee.Leitner@ischool.drexel.edu; *Assoc Teaching Prof,* Linda S Marion, PhD; E-mail: linda.marion@drexel.edu; *Assoc Teaching Prof,* Valerie Ann Yonker, PhD; E-mail: vay22@drexel.edu; *Assoc Teaching Prof,* Martin

Donaldson; E-mail: Martin.Donaldson@drexel.edu; *Asst Teaching Prof,* Glenn Booker; E-mail: gbooker@drexel.edu; *Asst Teaching Prof,* Catherine D Collins; E-mail: collins@drexel.edu; *Asst Teaching Prof,* Belinha De Abreu, PhD; E-mail: bdeabreu@drexel.edu; *Asst Teaching Prof,* Peter Grillo, PhD; E-mail: Pg54@drexel.edu; *Asst Teaching Prof,* Alison M Lewis, PhD; E-mail: alewis@drexel.edu; *Asst Teaching Prof,* Vanessa J Morris; E-mail: vmorris@drexel.edu; *Asst Teaching Prof,* Thomas J Smith; E-mail: tj@drexel.edu; *iSchool Prog Leader, DU Univ Ctr for Grad Studies, Sacramento, Teaching Prof,* Toni Carbo, PhD; E-mail: Toni.Carbo@ischool.drexel.edu

Prog estab 1892. Sch type: Pvt. Scholarships offered; Enrl: Undergrad: 288, Grad: 858; Fac 39

Ent Req: GRE (may be waived), B average or better, letters of recommendation, transcripts, resume, personal statement

Type of Training Offered: Library & Information Science

Degrees & Hours Offered: BS, Info Syst, 188; BS, Info Tech, 188; BS, Software Eng, 188; Certificate, Healthcare Informatics, 9; Certificate, Advan Cert Info Studies & Tech (ACIST), 24; MS, Libr & Info Sci, 45; MS, Info Syst, 45; MS, Software Eng, 45; Ph.D., Info Studies, 45

Special Courses: Healthcare Informatics; Optional Concentrations in Archival Studies, Competitive Intelligence & Knowledge Management, Digital Libraries, Library & Information Services, School Library Media, & Youth Services

Evening Session, Internet Courses, Professional Development, Summer Session

KUTZTOWN UNIVERSITY*, Department of Library Science, Kutztown, 19530. Tel: 610-683-4300. FAX: 610-683-1326. E-mail: long@kutztown.edu. *Dept Chair,* Dr Eloise Long; E-mail: long@kutztown.edu; *Instr,* Nancy Latanision; E-mail: latanasi@kutztown.edu; *Instr,* Roseanne Perkins; E-mail: rperkins@kutztown.edu

Prog estab 1921. Sch type: Pub. Scholarships offered; Enrl: Undergrad: 60, Grad: 100; Fac 3

Ent Req: BA with 3.0 GPA or better & GRE

Tuition: Resident Undergraduate $3,120 Per semester; Resident Graduate $416 Per credit hour

Degrees & Hours Offered: BS, Educ with major in Libr Sci K-12, 120 sem hrs; MLS, Libr Sci, 36 sem hrs

Internet Courses

NORTHAMPTON COMMUNITY COLLEGE, Library Technical Assistant Program, 3835 Green Pond Rd, Bethlehem, 18020. Tel: 610-861-5358. FAX: 610-861-5373. *Dir, Libr Serv,* Sandra L Sander; *Instr,* Dr Elizabeth Fordon; E-mail: efordon@northampton.edu; *Instr,* Mary Garm; E-mail: mgarm@northampton.edu; *Instr,* Marjorie Stern; E-mail: mstern@northampton.edu; *Instr,* Martha Stevenson; E-mail: mstevenson@northampton.edu; *Instr,* Scott Thomas; E-mail: sthomas@northampton.edu

Prog estab 1968. Sch type: Pub; Enrl: Undergrad: 30

Tuition: Non-resident Undergraduate $438 Per course

Degrees & Hours Offered: Diploma, 15 credit hrs

Internet Courses

† UNIVERSITY OF PITTSBURGH*, School of Information Sciences, 135 N Bellefield Ave, Pittsburgh, 15260. Tel: 412-624-5230. Toll Free Tel: 800-672-9435. FAX: 412-624-5231. E-mail: inquiry@mail.sis.pitt.edu. Web Site: www2.sis.pitt.edu. *Dean,* Ronald L Larsen; *Assoc Dean, Prof,* Mary Kay Biagini; *Prof,* Toni Carbo; *Prof,* Richard Cox; *Prof,* Margaret Kimmel; *Prof,* Richard A Thompson; *Prof,* Martin Weiss; *Prof,* Taieb Znati; *Assoc Prof,* Ellen Detlefsen; *Assoc Prof,* Roger Flynn; *Assoc Prof,* Stephen Hirtle; *Assoc Prof,* C Michael Lewis; *Assoc Prof,* Douglas Metzler; *Assoc Prof,* Paul Munro; *Assoc Prof,* Michael Spring; *Assoc Prof,* David Tipper; *Assoc Prof,* Christinger Tomer; *Assoc Prof,* Martin B H Weiss; *Asst Prof,* Susan Alman; *Asst Prof,* Peter Brusilovsky; *Asst Prof,* Marek Druzdel; *Asst Prof,* Karen Gracy; *Asst Prof,* Daqing He; *Asst Prof,* Judith Jablonski; *Asst Prof,* James Joshi; *Asst Prof,* Joseph Kabara; *Asst Prof,* Hassan Karimi; *Asst Prof,* Sherry Koshman; *Asst Prof,* Prashant Krishnamurthy; *Asst Prof,* Glenn Ray; *Asst Prof,* Stuart Shulman; *Asst Prof,* Kenneth Sochats; *Asst Prof,* Vladimir Zadorozhny; *Lecturer,* Robert Perkoski

Prog estab 1962. Sch type: Pvt. Scholarships offered; Enrl: Grad: 606, Undergrad: 118; Fac 31

Ent Req: 2.0 GPA & 3rd yr standing

Tuition: Non-resident Undergraduate $11,175 Per semester; Non-resident Undergraduate $931 Per credit hour; Non-resident Graduate $13,545 Per semester; Non-resident Graduate $1,118 Per credit hour; Resident Undergraduate $6,121 Per semester; Resident Undergraduate $510 Per credit hour; Resident Graduate $7,346 Per semester; Resident Graduate $601 Per credit hour

Type of Training Offered: Public

Degrees & Hours Offered: BS, Info Sci, 30 credit hrs; MLIS, Libr & Info Sci, 36 credit hrs; MS, Info Sci, 36 credit hrs; MS, Telecom, 36 credit hrs; Ph.D., Info Sci & Tele, 60 credit hrs; Ph.D., Libr & Info Sci, 54 credit hrs

Special Courses: Archives & Records Management, Cognitive Science, Field Experience, Image Databases, Indexing & Abstracting, Information

Storage & Retrieval, Information Systems Design, Law Librarianship, Management of Library Automation, Medical Informatics, Personnel Issues, Rare Books & Preservation, Research Methods & Statistics, Resources for Youth, School Librarianship, Systems Integration, Telecommunications & Networking

Evening Session, Summer Session

RHODE ISLAND

† UNIVERSITY OF RHODE ISLAND*, Graduate School of Library & Information Studies, Rodman Hall, 94 W Alumni Ave, Ste 2, Kingston, 02881-0815. Tel: 401-874-2878, 401-874-2947. FAX: 401-874-4964. E-mail: gslis@etal.uri.edu. Web Site: www.uri.edu/artsci/lsc. *Dir, Prof,* Dr E Gale Eaton; Tel: 401-874-4651, E-mail: geaton@uri.edu; *Asst Dir, Prof,* Dr C Herbert Carson; Tel: 401-874-4646, E-mail: chcarson@uri.edu; *Prof,* Dr Donna L Gilton; Tel: 401-874-4630, E-mail: dgilton@uri.edu; *Prof,* Dr W Michael Havener; Tel: 401-874-4651, E-mail: mhavener@uri.edu; *Prof,* Dr Yan Ma; Tel: 401-874-2819, E-mail: yanma@uri.edu; *Prof,* Dr Cheryl A McCarthy; Tel: 401-874-4654, E-mail: chermc@uri.edu; *Assoc Prof,* Dr Naomi Caldwell; Tel: 401-874-2278, E-mail: inpeacencw@aol.com; *Asst Prof,* Dr Suellen Adams; Tel: 401-874-4740, E-mail: suellen@mac.com

Prog estab 1963. Sch type: Pub. Scholarships offered; Enrl: Grad: 210; Fac 40

Ent Req: GRE, MAT or advanced degree; 3.0 GPA, Bachelor's; 2 letters of recommendation; resume

Tuition: Non-resident Graduate $19,044 Per year; Resident Graduate $6,936 Per year; Regional Graduate $10,404 Per year

Type of Training Offered: Special

Degrees & Hours Offered: Certificate, Library Media (TCP); Certificate, 15, Information Literacy Instruction; MLIS, 42

Special Courses: Digital Resources for Children & Youth, Health Sciences Librarianship, Information Ethics, Information Policy, Law Librarianship, Library Preservation, Multiculturalism in Libraries, Rare Book Librarianship, Special Collections & Archives, Visual Information Science

Evening Session, Internet Courses, Online & Blended Courses, Summer Session

SOUTH CAROLINA

† UNIVERSITY OF SOUTH CAROLINA*, School of Library & Information Science, 1501 Greene St, Columbia, 29208. Tel: 803-777-3858. FAX: 803-777-7938. Web Site: www.libsci.sc.edu. *Dean,* Charles Bierbauer; Tel: 803-777-4105, Fax: 803-777-4103, E-mail: bierbau@gwm.sc.edu; *Assoc Dean,* Gayle Douglas; E-mail: gayle.douglas@sc.edu; *Dir, Prof,* Samantha K Hastings; E-mail: hhastings@gwm.sc.edu; *Assoc Prof,* Patricia E Feehan; E-mail: pfeehan@gwm.sc.edu; *Assoc Prof,* Donna M Shannon; E-mail: dshannon@sc.edu; *Assoc Prof,* Nancy P Zimmerman; E-mail: nzimmerman@gwm.sc.edu; *Asst Prof,* Jennifer Arns; E-mail: jarns@gwm.sc.edu; *Asst Prof,* Kim Jinmook; E-mail: jinmook@gwm.sc.edu; *Asst Prof,* Judith Marley; E-mail: marleyj@gwm.sc.edu; *Asst Prof,* Jennifer Marshall; E-mail: jmarshall@sc.edu; *Asst Prof,* Anne Perrault; E-mail: perrault@gwm.sc.edu; *Asst Prof,* Feili Tu; E-mail: feilitu@sc.edu; *Sr Instr,* Christyn G Billinsky; E-mail: cbllinsky@sc.edu; *Instr,* Heidi L Hoerman; E-mail: hoerman@sc.edu

Enrl: Grad: 504

Ent Req: GPA 3.0, 950 on combined v & q of GRE, 410 on MAT

Tuition: Non-resident Graduate $816 Per credit hour; Resident Graduate $384 Per credit hour

Type of Training Offered: Special

Degrees & Hours Offered: Certificate, Graduate Study in Libr & Info Sci, 18 sem hrs; MLIS, Libr & Info Sci, 36 sem hrs; SLIS, Libr & Info Sci, 30 sem hrs

Special Courses: Automation, Business Information Services, Children's Literature, Information Retrieval, Information Science, Library Service to the Handicapped, Media (AV) & Young Adult Literature

Evening Session, Summer Session

SOUTH DAKOTA

BLACK HILLS STATE UNIVERSITY, Library Media Program, E Y Berry Library Learning Ctr, 1200 University St, Unit 9676, Spearfish, 57799-9676. Tel: 605-642-6250, 605-642-6834. FAX: 605-642-6298. Web Site: iis.bhsu.edu/lis/librarymedia/index.cfm. *Assoc Dir,* Scott Ahola; Tel: 605-642-6359, E-mail: scott.ahola@bhsu.edu; *Archives, Spec Coll,* Roberta Sago; Tel: 605-642-6361, E-mail: roberta.sago@bhsu.edu; *Bibliog Serv,* Michael Tolan; Tel: 605-642-6356, E-mail: michael.tolan@bhsu.edu

Sch type: Pub; Fac 5

Tuition: Non-resident Undergraduate $289 Per credit hour; Resident Undergraduate $289 Per credit hour; Resident Graduate $383 Per credit hour

Type of Training Offered: School Library Media Certificate

Degrees & Hours Offered: BS, Library Media minor, 20; Certificate, Library Media online, 20

Special Courses: Library Technology
Internet Courses, Summer Session

TENNESSEE

EAST TENNESSEE STATE UNIVERSITY*, Educational Media &
Educational Technology, Dept Curriculum & Instruction, Warf-Pickel Hall,
PO Box 70684, Johnson City, 37614-1709. Tel: 423-439-7595. FAX:
423-439-8362. Web Site: www.etsu.edu/coe/cuai/emet-ma.asp,
www.etsu.edu/coe/cuai/library_media_certification.asp. *Grad Coordr, Sch
Libr Media,* Linda Steele; Tel: 423-439-7851, E-mail: steelel@etsu.edu
Prog estab 1948. Sch type: Pub; Enrl: Grad: 45; Fac 5
Ent Req: 3.0 GPA
Tuition: Non-resident Graduate $446 Per credit hour; Resident Graduate
$288 Per credit hour
Degrees & Hours Offered: M.Ed., Sch Libr Media, 36 sem hrs; M.Ed.,
Educ Tech, 36
Special Courses: Adult Literature, Children's Literature, Issues in Media,
Media (AV), Storytelling
Evening Session, Internet Courses, Summer Session, Weekend Session

MIDDLE TENNESSEE STATE UNIVERSITY*, Womack Family
Department of Educational Leadership, Library Science, PO Box 91,
Murfreesboro, 37132. Tel: 615-898-2804. FAX: 615-898-2859. Web Site:
mtweb.mtsu.edu/kpatten. *Prof,* Kathy Boudreau-Henry; E-mail:
kpatten@mtsu.edu; *Prof,* Sandra G Sanders
Sch type: Pub; Enrl: 55; Grad: 50
Tuition: Non-resident Undergraduate $3,206 Per semester; Non-resident
Undergraduate $515 Per credit hour; Non-resident Graduate $3,517 Per
semester; Non-resident Graduate $606 Per credit hour; Resident
Undergraduate $908 Per semester; Resident Undergraduate $147 Per credit
hour; Resident Graduate $1,219 Per semester; Resident Graduate $238 Per
credit hour
Type of Training Offered: School
Degrees & Hours Offered: M.Ed., Admin & Supv Libr Sci, 33 sem hrs
Special Courses: Cataloging, Children's Literature, Integration of
Curriculum, Learning Theory & Technology, Reference, Young Adult
Literature
Distance Learning, Internet Courses, Summer Session

TENNESSEE TECHNOLOGICAL UNIVERSITY*, Library Science
Program, College of Education - Dept of Curriculum & Instruction, PO
Box 5042, Cookeville, 38505. Tel: 931-372-3181. FAX: 931-372-6270.
Web Site: www.tntech.edu/. *Dean,* Dr Larry Peach; E-mail:
lpeach@tntech.edu
Sch type: Pub
Tuition: Non-resident Graduate $6,803 Per semester; Resident Graduate
$2,549 Per semester
Type of Training Offered: School
Degrees & Hours Offered: MA, Educ - Curriculum & Instruction, 33 sem
hrs; MA, Libr Sci, 33 sem hrs; MA, Reading Specialist, 33 sem hrs
Special Courses: Administration, Cataloging, Children's Literature,
Reference Sources, Young Adult Literature,
Evening Session, Summer Session

TREVECCA NAZARENE UNIVERSITY*, Library & Information Science
Program, School of Education, 333 Murfreesboro Rd, Nashville,
37210-2877. Tel: 615-248-1201, 615-248-1205. Toll Free Tel:
888-210-4868. FAX: 615-248-1597. Web Site: www.trevecca.edu/. *Dean,*
Dr Esther Swink; E-mail: eswink@trevecca.edu; *Assoc Prof,* Ruth
Kinnersley; *Asst Prof,* Priscilla Speer; *Prog Coordr,* Judy Bivens; Tel:
615-248-1206, E-mail: jbivens@trevecca.edu
Sch type: Pvt; Enrl: Grad: 45
Ent Req: MAT or GRE, 2.7 GPA
Type of Training Offered: School
Degrees & Hours Offered: MLIS, 33 credit hours

UNIVERSITY OF MEMPHIS*, Instruction & Curriculum Leadership,
College of Education, 406 Ball Hall Educ Bldg, Memphis, 38152. Tel:
901-678-2365. FAX: 901-678-3881. E-mail: coe@memphis.edu. Web Site:
www.coe.memphis.edu/icl. *Chair, Prof,* Ramona Mahood
Sch type: Pub. Scholarships offered; Enrl: Grad: 400; Fac 2
Ent Req: GRE 2.7 GPA
Tuition: Non-resident Undergraduate $203 Per credit hour; Non-resident
Graduate $228 Per credit hour; Resident Undergraduate $63 Per credit
hour; Resident Graduate $88 Per credit hour
Type of Training Offered: School
Degrees & Hours Offered: MS, 39 sem hrs; MAT
Evening Session, Summer Session

† UNIVERSITY OF TENNESSEE, KNOXVILLE*, School of Information
Sciences, 451 Communications Bldg, 1345 Circle Park Dr, Knoxville,
37996-0341. Tel: 865-974-2148. FAX: 865-974-4967. E-mail: sis@utk.edu.
Web Site: www.sis.utk.edu. *Dir,* Edwin M Cortez; *Prof,* Dania Bilal; *Prof,*
J Michael Pemberton; *Prof,* Carol Tenopir; E-mail: ctenopir@utk.edu;
Assoc Prof, Kimberly Black; *Assoc Prof,* Peiling Wang; *Assoc Prof,* Jinx

Stapleton Watson; *Assoc Prof,* Gretchen Whitney; *Asst Prof,* Lorraine
Normore; *Asst Prof,* Bharat Mehra; Tel: 865-974-5917, E-mail:
bmehra@utk.edu; *Asst Prof,* Vandana Singh; Tel: 865-974-2785, E-mail:
vandana@utk.edu; *Asst Prof,* Dr Cindy Welch; Tel: 865-974-7918, E-mail:
cwelch11@utk.edu
Prog estab 1971. Sch type: Pub. Scholarships offered; Enrl: Grad: 225; Fac
12
Ent Req: GRE & 3.0 GPA
Tuition: Non-resident Graduate $4,896 Per semester; Resident Graduate
$1,854 Per semester
Type of Training Offered: School Library Media Certificate
Degrees & Hours Offered: MS, 42 sem hrs
Special Courses: Youth Services in Public & School Libraries
Evening Session, Summer Session

TEXAS

SAM HOUSTON STATE UNIVERSITY*, Department of Library Science,
1921 Ave J, Huntsville, 77340. (Mail add: PO Box 2236, Huntsville,
77341-2236). Tel: 936-294-1151. Toll Free Tel: 866-232-5287. FAX:
936-294-1153. E-mail: rjl006@shsu.edu. Web Site:
www.shsu.edu/libraryscience. *Chair, Prof,* Dr Mary A Berry; Tel:
936-294-1150, E-mail: lis_mab@shsu.edu; *Prof,* Dr Frank Hoffmann; Tel:
936-294-1289, E-mail: lis_fwh@shsu.edu; *Prof,* Dr Teri Lesesne; Tel:
936-294-3673, E-mail: lis_tsl@shsu.edu; *Assoc Prof,* Dr Rosemary Chance;
E-mail: rxc001@shsu.edu; *Assoc Prof,* Dr Joanna Fountain; Tel:
936-294-4133, E-mail: jff001@shsu.edu; *Assoc Prof,* Dr Tricia Kuon; Tel:
936-294-3365, E-mail: tav005@shsu.edu; *Asst Prof,* Holly A Weimar; Tel:
936-294-3158, E-mail: haw001@shsu.edu; *Instr,* Sara Catherine Howard;
Tel: 936-294-4641, E-mail: lis_sch@shsu.edu; *Instr,* Robin O Krig; E-mail:
lis_rok@shsu.edu
Prog estab 1937. Sch type: Pub. Scholarships offered; Enrl: Grad: 200; Fac
9
Ent Req: GRE & 3.0 GPA
Tuition: Non-resident Undergraduate $677 Per credit hour; Non-resident
Graduate $650 Per credit hour; Resident Undergraduate $402 Per credit
hour; Resident Graduate $400 Per credit hour
Type of Training Offered: School
Degrees & Hours Offered: MLS, 36 sem hrs
Special Courses: Literature for Children, Technolo
Summer Session

TEXAS A & M UNIVERSITY - COMMERCE, Department of
Educational Leadership, 2600 S Neal St, Commerce, 75428. (Mail add: PO
BOX 3011, Commerce, 75429). Tel: 903-886-5500, 903-886-5607. FAX:
903-886-5507. Web Site: www.tamu-commerce.edu. *Dir,* Dr Lee Waller
Enrl: Grad: 75
Ent Req: MS or school librarian certification only
Tuition: Non-resident Graduate $1,291 Per 3 credit hour; Resident
Graduate $517 Per 3 credit hour
Type of Training Offered: Library & Information Science
Degrees & Hours Offered: M.Ed., 36 Sem hrs; MS, 36 sem hrs
Evening Session, Internet Courses, Online & Blended Courses, Summer
Session

† TEXAS WOMAN'S UNIVERSITY*, School of Library & Information
Studies, PO Box 425438, Denton, 76204-5438. Tel: 940-898-2602. FAX:
940-898-2611. E-mail: slis@twu.edu. Web Site: www.libraryschool.net.
Dir, Prof, Dr Ling Hwey Jeng
Sch type: Pub. Scholarships offered; Enrl: Grad: 501; Fac 1
Ent Req: BA, 3.0 GPA for last 2 yrs
Tuition: Non-resident Graduate $4,200 Per semester; Resident Graduate
$1,500 Per semester
Type of Training Offered: Public
Degrees & Hours Offered: MA, Libr Sci, 39 credits; MLS, Libr Sci, 36
credits; Ph.D., Libr Sci, 90 credits beyond the bachelor's
Special Courses: Academic Libraries, Children's Literature & Services,
Materials & Services for Very Young Child, Nonfiction for Children &
Young Adults, Public Libraries
Internet Courses, Summer Session, Weekend Session

UNIVERSITY OF HOUSTON-CLEAR LAKE*, School Library &
Information Science Program, 2700 Bay Area Blvd, Houston, 77058-1098.
Tel: 281-283-3577. FAX: 281-283-3630. Web Site: www.uhcl.edu/soe.
Assoc Prof, Maureen White; E-mail: white@uhcl.edu; *Asst Prof,* Jane
Claes; E-mail: claesj@uhcl.edu
Prog estab 1975. Sch type: Pub; Enrl: Grad: 70; Fac 5
Ent Req: BA, Texas Teaching Certification & GRE
Tuition: Non-resident Graduate $1,399 Per course; Resident Graduate $697
Per course
Type of Training Offered: School
Degrees & Hours Offered: MS, 39
Special Courses: Children's Literature, Information Storage & Retrieval,
Media (AV) & Young Adult Literature, Media Technology, School Library
Administration
Evening Session, Summer Session, Weekend Session

† UNIVERSITY OF NORTH TEXAS*, College of Information, Department of Library & Information Sciences, 1155 Union Circle, Denton, 76203-5017. (Mail add: PO Box 311068, Denton, 76203-1068). Tel: 940-565-2445. Toll Free Tel: 877-275-7547. FAX: 940-565-3101. E-mail: lis-school@unt.edu. Web Site: www.lis.unt.edu. *Dean,* Dr Herman L Totten, PhD; E-mail: totten@unt.edu; *Assoc Dean, Academics, Assoc Dir, PhD Prog,* Dr Linda Schamber; E-mail: linda.schamber@unt.edu; *Assoc Dean, Res, Assoc Prof, Dir, Tex Ctr for Digital Knowledge,* Dr William E Moen; E-mail: william.moen@unt.edu; *Chair, Prof,* Dr Suliman Hawamdeh; E-mail: suliman.hawamdeh@unt.edu; *Prof,* Dr Brian C O'Connor; *Prof,* Dr Phillip Turner; Tel: 940-565-4462, E-mail: pturner@unt.edu; *Prof & Dir, Houston Prog,* Dr Ana D Cleveland; *Prof Emeritus,* Dr Donald Cleveland; *Prof Emeritus,* Dr Barbara L Stein-Martin; *Assoc Prof, Dir, Ga, Nev, SWIM, LEAP Cohorts,* Dr Yvonne J Chandler; E-mail: yvonne.chandler@unt.edu; *Assoc Prof,* Dr Jiangping Chen; E-mail: jiangping.chen@unt.edu; *Assoc Prof,* Dr Yunfei Du; Tel: 940-565-3565, E-mail: ydu@unt.edu; *Assoc Prof,* Dr Elizabeth Figa; E-mail: elizabeth.figa@unt.edu; *Assoc Prof,* Dr Martin Halbert; E-mail: martin.halbert@unt.edu; *Assoc Prof,* Dr Shawne Miksa; E-mail: shawne.miksa@unt.edu; *Assoc Prof,* Dr Guillermo Oyarce; E-mail: guillermo.oyarce@unt.edu; *Assoc Prof,* Dr Maurice Wheeler; E-mail: maurice.wheeler@unt.edu; *Assoc Prof, Modified Serv,* Carol Simpson; *Asst Prof,* Dr Janet Hilbun; E-mail: janet.hilbun@unt.edu; *Asst Prof,* Dr Jeonghyun Annie Kim; *Asst Prof,* Barbara Schultz-Jones; E-mail: bjones@unt.edu; *Asst Prof,* Dr Daniella Smith; E-mail: daniella.Smith@unt.edu; *Asst Prof,* Dale Thompson; E-mail: dthompson@unt.edu; *Asst Prof,* Dr Oksana Zavalina; E-mail: zavalina.oksana@unt.edu; *Instr,* Dr Larry Enoch; E-mail: larry.enoch@unt.edu
Prog estab 1939. Sch type: Pub. Scholarships offered; Enrl: Grad: 1,010, Undergrad: 47
Ent Req: ACT or SAT
Tuition: Non-resident Undergraduate $500 Per credit hour; Non-resident Graduate $550 Per credit hour; Resident Undergraduate $450 Per credit hour; Resident Graduate $500 Per credit hour
Type of Training Offered: Special
Degrees & Hours Offered: BS, Info Sci major, 128 sem hrs; MS, Libr Sci or Info Sci, 36 hrs; Ph.D., Info Sci, 60 sem hrs
Special Courses: Communications & the Use of Information, Economics of Information, Horizon Technologies for Library & Information Centers, Human Information & Communication Behavior, Information Networks, Information Resources & Services in Culturally Diverse Communities, Information Retrieval Design, Information Retrieval Theory, Internet Applications for Information Professionals, Legal Information & Access Services, Management of Information Resources in Organizations, Medical Informatics, Music Libraries, Preservation, Product Management for Information Systems, Rare Books, Records Management, Scholarly & Scientific Communication, Telecommunications for Information Professionals, Website Development, Youth Programs & Storytelling
Continuing Education, Evening Session, Internet Courses, Professional Development, Summer Session, Weekend Session

† UNIVERSITY OF TEXAS AT AUSTIN*, School of Information, One University Sta, D7000, Austin, 78712-0390. Tel: 512-471-3821. FAX: 512-471-3971. E-mail: info@ischool.utexas.edu. Web Site: www.ischool.utexas.edu. *Dir,* Ellen Cunningham-Kruppa; *Dean, Prof,* Andrew Dillon; *Assoc Dean,* Mary Lynn Rice-Lively; *Prof,* Donald G Davis, Jr; *Prof,* Philip Doty; *Prof,* Patricia Galloway; *Prof,* David B Gracy; *Prof,* Julie Hallmark; *Prof,* E Glynn Harmon; *Prof,* Barbara F Immroth; *Prof,* W Bernard Lukenbill; *Prof,* Francis L Miksa; *Prof,* Loriene Roy; *Prof,* Brooke E Sheldon; *Assoc Prof,* Randolph Bias; *Asst Prof,* Hsin-Liang Chen; *Asst Prof,* Luis Francisco-Revilla; *Asst Prof,* Gary Geisler; *Asst Prof,* Donald Turnbull; *Asst Prof,* Lynn Westbrook
Prog estab 1948. Sch type: Pub. Scholarships offered; Enrl: Grad: 300
Ent Req: GRE & letters of reference
Tuition: Non-resident Graduate $5,229 Per semester; Resident Graduate $2,112 Per semester
Type of Training Offered: Special
Degrees & Hours Offered: MS, Info Studies, 40 sem hrs; Ph.D., Info Studies
Special Courses: Archives & Manuscripts, Architecture & Usability Studies, Audio Preservation & Reformatting, Children's Literature, Classification Theory, Cognitive Science, Competitive Intelligence, Database-Mgt Principles & Applications, Developing Media Collections, Electronic & Digital Records, Electronic Online Info Resources, Health Informatics, Image Processing, Indexing & Categorization of Informational Materials, Info Materials, Info Mgt, Info Policy, Info Resources in Business, Info Resources in Law, Info Services for Hispanic Americans, Issues in Contemporary Publishing, Library History, Mgt of Library Automation, Modern Info Retrieval, Network Security, Photograph & Cinema Archives, Preservation in Digital Environment, Preservation of Archival Material & Conservation of Library, Printing History, Rare Books & Special Collections, Records Mgt, Research in Library & Info Science, Subject Cataloging, Systems Analysis
Evening Session, Internet Courses, Summer Session

UTAH

SOUTHERN UTAH UNIVERSITY SHERRATT LIBRARY*, School Library Media Program, 351 W University Blvd, Cedar City, 84720. Tel: 435-865-8031, 435-865-8172. FAX: 435-865-8152. E-mail: chalmers@suu.edu. Web Site: www.li.suu.edu/page/school-library-media-program-about. *Dir, Libr Media Prog,* Verlene Schafer; E-mail: verleneschafer@suu.edu
Prog estab 1980. Sch type: Pub; Enrl: Grad: 3, Undergrad: 150; Fac 9
Tuition: Non-resident Undergraduate $2,603 Per course; Non-resident Graduate $1,128 Per course; Resident Undergraduate $789 Per course; Resident Graduate $878 Per course
Type of Training Offered: College
Degrees & Hours Offered: BA, Libr Media Endorsement, 18 sem hrs; BA, Libr Media minor, 18 sem hrs; BS, Libr Media Endorsement, 18 sem hrs; BS, Libr Media minor, 18 sem hrs; M.Ed., Sch Libr Media Endorsements, 42 sem hrs
Special Courses: Library Computer & Reference Skills, Library Media Practicum, Library Technical Services, Managing a Media Center, Technology for Library Media Teachers, Utilization of Literature in the Classroom
Internet Courses

UTAH STATE UNIVERSITY*, Department of Instructional Technology-School Library Media, 2830 Old Main Hill, Education, Bldg 215, Logan, 84322. Tel: 435-797-2694. FAX: 435-797-2693. Web Site: www.inst.usu.edu. *Dept Head, Prof,* Mimi Recker; Tel: 435-797-2692, E-mail: mimi.recker@usu.edu
Sch type: Pub; Enrl: Grad: 150
Ent Req: GPA 3.0
Type of Training Offered: College
Degrees & Hours Offered: M.Ed., Libr Media, 36 sem hrs; MS, Instrul Design, 39 sem hrs; Ph.D., Instrul Tech, 62 hrs beyond Masters
Special Courses: Authoring Languages, Computer Application, Instructional Development, Instructional Simulation, Multimedia Design & Development, Performance Technology
Evening Session, Summer Session

VIRGINIA

OLD DOMINION UNIVERSITY LEARNING RESOURCES CENTER*, College of Education, Department of Curriculum & Instruction, College of Education, Rm 244, 5215 Hampton Blvd, Norfolk, 23529-0161. (Mail add: Department of Curriculum & Instruction, Darden College of Education, Rm 145, Norfolk, 23529-0161). Tel: 757-683-3284. FAX: 757-683-5862. Web Site: www.education.odu.edu/eci/libsci. *Coordr,* Dr Carrol Doll; Tel: 757-683-3222, E-mail: cdoll@odu.edu
Prog estab 1975. Sch type: Pub; Enrl: Grad: 100
Tuition: Non-resident Graduate $715 Per credit hour; Resident Graduate $285 Per credit hour
Type of Training Offered: Librarianship
Degrees & Hours Offered: M.Ed., Sch Librarianship, 35 credit hrs

WASHINGTON

HIGHLINE COMMUNITY COLLEGE*, Library & Information Services Program, 2400 S 240th St, Des Moines, 98198. (Mail add: PO Box 98000, Des Moines, 98198). Tel: 206-878-3710, Ext 3234. FAX: 206-870-3776. E-mail: lisinquiry@highline.edu. Web Site: lis.highline.edu. *Dir,* Monica Luce; Tel: 206-878-3710, Ext 3230
Prog estab 1967. Sch type: Pub; Enrl: Undergrad: 100; Fac 6
Tuition: Non-resident Undergraduate $109 Per credit hour; Resident Undergraduate $96 Per credit hour; International Undergraduate $268 Per credit hour
Type of Training Offered: School Library Media Certificate
Degrees & Hours Offered: AAS, Libr Paraprof, 64-66 req plus electives for total 90 qtr hrs; Certificate, Libr Paraprof, 64-66 req
Special Courses: Book Repair, Business Reference, Collection Development, Legal Reference, Library Administration & Management, Medical Reference, School Libraries
Co-operative Education Prog, Internet Courses, Professional Development

SPOKANE FALLS COMMUNITY COLLEGE, Library & Information Services Program, Bldg 2 MS 3020, W3410 Fort George Wright Dr, Spokane, 99224-5288. SAN 372-5340. Tel: 509-533-3809. Toll Free Tel: 888-509-7944. FAX: 509-533-3144. E-mail: librarytechnician@spokanefalls.edu. Web Site: spokanefalls.edu/TechProf/LibraryTech/Home.aspx, www.spokanefalls.edu. *Prog Lead/Mgr,* Paula D Swan; E-mail: paula.swan@spokanefalls.edu
Prog estab 1977. Sch type: Pub. Scholarships offered; Enrl: Undergrad: 40; Fac 2
Ent Req: High sch diploma or GED (unless an international student). Also those with prior college can transfer in courses.

Tuition: Non-resident Undergraduate $145 Per credit hour; Resident Undergraduate $106 Per credit hour; International Undergraduate $278 Per credit hour

Type of Training Offered: School Library Media Certificate

Degrees & Hours Offered: AAS, Online library science 2 year degree program, 90 quarter credits; AAS, Online education paraprofessional, school library media emphasis, 90 quarter credits; Certificate, School Library Media Online one year certificate, 41 quarter credits

Special Courses: ALA Library Support Staff Certification Program; College Credit for Prior or Current Library Work Experience Program; No textbooks required for library science classes.

Co-operative Education Prog, Continuing Education, Distance Learning, Internet Courses

† UNIVERSITY OF WASHINGTON*, The Information School, Mary Gates Hall, Ste 370, Campus Box 352840, Seattle, 98195-2840. Tel: 206-685-9937. FAX: 206-616-3152. E-mail: info@ischool.washington.edu. Web Site: www.ischool.washington.edu. *Prof & Dean,* Harry Bruce; E-mail: harryb@u.washington.edu; *Assoc Dean, Res, Prof,* Robert Mason; E-mail: rmmason@uw.edu; *Assoc Dean, Academics,* Matthew Saxton; E-mail: msaxton@u.washington.edu; *Dir, Info Tech, Sr Lecturer,* Scott Barker; E-mail: barker@uw.edu; *Prof,* Michael Eisenberg; E-mail: mbe@uw.edu; *Prof,* Raya Fidel; E-mail: fidelr@u.washington.edu; *Prof,* Karen Fisher; E-mail: fisher@u.washington.edu; *Prof,* Batya Friedman; E-mail: batya@u.washington.edu; *Prof,* Sherrilynne Fuller; E-mail: sfuller@uw.edu; *Prof,* David Levy; E-mail: dmlevy@u.washington.edu; *Assoc Prof,* Terrence Brooks; E-mail: tabrooks@u.washington.edu; *Assoc Prof,* Allyson Carlyle; E-mail: acarlyle@u.washington.edu; *Assoc Prof,* Efthimis Efthimiadis; E-mail: efthimis@u.washington.edu; *Assoc Prof,* David Hendry; E-mail: dhendry@u.washington.edu; *Assoc Prof,* Joseph Janes; E-mail: jwj@u.washington.edu; *Assoc Prof,* David McDonald; E-mail: dwmc@u.washington.edu; *Assoc Prof,* Cheryl Metoyer; E-mail: metoyer@uw.edu; *Assoc Prof,* Adam Moore; E-mail: moore2@uw.edu; *Assoc Prof,* Wanda Pratt; E-mail: wpratt@u.washington.edu; *Assoc Prof,* Jochen Scholl; E-mail: scholl@uw.edu; *Assoc Prof,* Stuart Sutton; E-mail: sasutton@u.washington.edu; *Asst Prof,* Karine Barzilai-Nahon; E-mail: karineb@u.washington.edu; *Asst Prof,* Kevin Desouza; E-mail: kdesouza@uw.edu; *Asst Prof,* Ricardo Gomez; E-mail: rgomez@uw.edu; *Asst Prof,* Julie Kientz; E-mail: jkientz@uw.edu; *Asst Prof,* Andrew Ko; E-mail: ajko@uw.edu; *Asst Prof,* Jin Ha Lee; E-mail: jinhalee@uw.edu; *Asst Prof,* Hazel Taylor; E-mail: hztaylor@uw.edu; *Asst Prof,* Joseph Tennis; E-mail: jtennis@uw.edu; *Asst Prof,* Jacob Wobbrock; E-mail: wobbrock@uw.edu; *Cleary Prof of Ch & Youth Serv,* Eliza Dresang; E-mail: edresang@uw.edu; *Sr Lecturer,* Robert Boiko; E-mail: bboiko@uw.edu; *Sr Lecturer,* Lorraine Bruce; E-mail: lbruce@uw.edu; *Sr Lecturer,* Michael Crandall; E-mail: mikecran@uw.edu; *Sr Lecturer,* Nancy Gershenfeld; E-mail: ngersh@uw.edu; *Sr Lecturer,* Barbara Endicott-Popovsky; E-mail: endicott@uw.edu; *Sr Lecturer,* Trent Hill; E-mail: tghill62@uw.edu; *Sr Lecturer,* Jeffrey Kim; E-mail: jykim@u.washington.edu; *Sr Lecturer,* Elizabeth Marcoux; E-mail: elm2@u.washington.edu; *Lecturer,* Lisa Fusco; E-mail: lfusco@uw.edu; *Lecturer,* Bob Larson; E-mail: blabob@uw.edu; *Lecturer,* D A Clements; E-mail: daclem@uw.edu

Prog estab 1911. Sch type: Pub. Scholarships offered; Enrl: Grad: 378, Undergrad: 70; Fac 40

Ent Req: BS-Admission to the University of Washington & prerequisite courses

Tuition: Non-resident Undergraduate $5,116 Per quarter; Non-resident Graduate $5,365 Per quarter; Resident Undergraduate $1,545 Per quarter; Resident Graduate $2,336 Per quarter

Type of Training Offered: Public

Degrees & Hours Offered: BS, Informatics; MLIS; MS, Info Mgt; Ph.D., Info Sci

Special Courses: Data Resource Management, Electronic Information & Records Management, Law Librarianship Program, School Library Media Endorsement for K-12 Teachers, Web Administration, Web Consultant for Small Businesses, Web Technology Essentials, XML Standards & Technologies

Evening Session

WEST VIRGINIA

FAIRMONT STATE COLLEGE, SCHOOL OF EDUCATION*, Online Library Science Program, 1201 Locust Ave, Fairmont, 26554. Tel: 304-367-4733. FAX: 304-367-4677. E-mail: library@fairmontstate.edu. *Dir of Libr Serv,* Thelma Hutchins; Tel: 304-367-4122, E-mail: Thelma.Hutchins@fairmontstate.edu; *Asst Prof,* Robert Hammonds; Tel: 304-367-4697, E-mail: rhammonds@fairmontstate.edu; *Asst Prof,* Sharon Mazure; Tel: 304-367-4622, E-mail: smazure@fairmontstate.edu

Prog estab 1968. Sch type: Pub; Enrl: Undergrad: 52; Fac 3

Tuition: Non-resident Undergraduate $350 Per credit hour; Resident Undergraduate $159 Per credit hour

Type of Training Offered: School Library Media Certificate

Degrees & Hours Offered: Certificate, Sch Libr Media, 24 sem hrs

Internet Courses, Summer Session

WISCONSIN

UNIVERSITY OF WISCONSIN-EAU CLAIRE*, Foundations of Education Dept, 105 Garfield Ave, Eau Claire, 54702. (Mail add: PO Box 4004, Eau Claire, 54702-4004). Tel: 715-836-2635. FAX: 715-836-5099. *Chair,* Dr Dwight C Watson; *Prof,* Dr Mark Clark; *Assoc Prof,* Dr Jill Pinkney Pastrana; *Assoc Prof,* Dr Jill Prushiek; *Asst Prof,* Dr Barbara Erdman; *Asst Prof,* Dr Carol Koroghlanian; *Sr Lecturer,* Robert A Reid

Prog estab 1954. Sch type: Pub. Scholarships offered; Enrl: Grad: 20

Tuition: Non-resident Undergraduate $367 Per credit hour; Non-resident Graduate $595 Per credit hour; Resident Undergraduate $120 Per credit hour; Resident Graduate $194 Per credit hour

Degrees & Hours Offered: BA, with Libr Sci minor, 24 sem hrs; BS, with Libr Sci minor, 24 sem hrs

Special Courses: Adolescent Literature, Children's Literature, Computers in Education

Evening Session, Summer Session

† UNIVERSITY OF WISCONSIN-MADISON*, School of Library & Information Studies, 4217 H C White Hall, 600 N Park St, Madison, 53706. Tel: 608-263-2900. FAX: 608-263-4849. E-mail: uw-slis@slis.wisc.edu. Web Site: www.slis.wisc.edu. *Dir, Prof,* Louise S Robbins; Tel: 608-263-2908, E-mail: lrobbins@slis.wisc.edu; *Prof,* Patricia Flately Brennan; Tel: 608-263-5251, E-mail: pbrennan@engr.wisc.edu; *Assoc Prof,* Anne Lundin; Tel: 608-265-4733, E-mail: alundin@wisc.edu; *Asst Prof,* Anuj Desai; Tel: 608-263-7605, E-mail: acdesai@witz.edu; *Asst Prof,* Greg Downey; Tel: 608-263-2916, E-mail: gdowney@wisc.edu; *Asst Prof,* Kristin Eschenfelder; Tel: 608-263-2105, E-mail: eschenfelder@wisc.edu; *Asst Prof,* Kyung-Sun Kim; Tel: 608-263-2941, E-mail: kskim@slis.wisc.edu; *Asst Prof,* Madge Hildebrandt Klais; Tel: 608-263-2943, E-mail: mhklais@wisc.edu; *Asst Prof,* Ciaran Trace; Tel: 608-262-2955, E-mail: trace@wisc.edu

Prog estab 1906. Sch type: Pub. Scholarships offered; Enrl: Grad: 257; Pop 235; Fac 1

Ent Req: Bachelor's, 3.0 GPA, 90 sem hrs of Liberal Arts & Scis, letters of ref (2 acad & 1 more either prof or acad)

Tuition: Non-resident Undergraduate $10,143 Per semester; Non-resident Graduate $12,005 Per semester; Resident Undergraduate $3,143 Per semester; Resident Graduate $4,370 Per semester

Type of Training Offered: School Library Media Certificate

Degrees & Hours Offered: Certificate, Specialist, 24 credits beyond MA with major paper & oral defense; MA, Libr & Info Studies, 42 sem hrs with a minimum 40 hr practicum; Ph.D., 32 credit hrs

Special Courses: Archives, Children's & Young Adult Literature & Services, Corporate & Specialized Information Services, Database Design, Digital Divides & Differences, Geographies of Information, Government Information Sources, Health Information Systems, Information Architecture, Information Sources, Intellectual Freedom, Library History, Mass Media & Global Communication, Online Reference, Reading Interests of Adults, Reference Services & Materials, Research Methods, School Library Media Specialist, Storytelling & Oral Literature

Continuing Education, Professional Development

† UNIVERSITY OF WISCONSIN-MILWAUKEE*, School of Information Studies, 510 Bolton Hall, 3120 N Maryland Ave, Milwaukee, 53211. (Mail add: PO Box 413, Milwaukee, 53201-0413). Tel: 414-229-4707. Toll Free Tel: 888-349-3432. FAX: 414-229-6699. E-mail: soisinfo@uwm.edu. Web Site: www.uwm.edu/dept/SOIS. *Dean, Prof,* Dr Johannes J Britz; E-mail: britz@uwm.edu; *Assoc Dean, Prof,* Dr Hope Olson; *Asst Dean,* Chad Zahrt

Prog estab 1966. Sch type: Pub. Scholarships offered; Enrl: Grad: 500, Undergrad: 180; Fac 1

Ent Req: GRE or MAT, Bachelor's, B average & letters of recommendation

Tuition: Non-resident Undergraduate $9,488 Per semester; Non-resident Graduate $11,443 Per semester; Resident Undergraduate $3,112 Per semester; Resident Graduate $4,260 Per semester

Type of Training Offered: Special

Degrees & Hours Offered: BS, Info Resources, 120 sem hrs; Certificate, Libr & Info Sci, 18 sem hrs; Certificate, Advan Study, 24 sem hrs beyond MLIS; Certificate, Archives and Records Administration, 15 sem hrs beyond MLIS or master's in closely related field; MLIS, 36 sem hrs; Ph.D., Info Sci, Educ & Media Tech

Special Courses: Archives, Archives Automation, Bibliometrics, Book Binding & Repair, Children's Literature, Computerized Information Systems, Electronic Networking & Information Services, Goverment Documents, Health Sciences & Information Services, Information Marketing, Information Systems Analysis & Designs, Information & Communications Technology, Microcomputers in Libraries, Law Librarianship, Law Library Administration, Legal Bibliography, Library Automation, Library Resources on the Internet, Map Librarianship, Media (AV), Multimedia, Music Librarianship, On-Line Information Retrieval, Records Management, Storytelling & Young Adult Literature

Evening Session, Internet Courses, Summer Session

UNIVERSITY OF WISCONSIN OSHKOSH*, Department of Human Services & Professional Leadership, 800 Algoma Blvd, Oshkosh, 54901. Tel: 920-424-0881. FAX: 920-424-0858. E-mail: hspl@uwosh.edu. Web Site: www.coehs.uwosh.edu. *Prof,* Dr Janet Hagen; Tel: 920-424-0336, E-mail: hagen@uwosh.edu; *Assoc Prof,* Dr Susan Cramer; Tel: 920-424-0338, E-mail: cramer@uwosh.edu; *Assoc Prof,* Dr Penny Garcia; E-mail: garcia@uwosh.edu; *Assoc Prof,* Dr Henry Winterfeldt; E-mail: winterfe@uwosh.edu; *Asst Prof,* Dr Annette Smith; Tel: 920-424-7252, E-mail: smith@uwosh.edu
Prog estab 1951. Sch type: Pub
Tuition: Non-resident Undergraduate $4,274 Per semester; Non-resident Graduate $5,326 Per semester; Resident Undergraduate $1,303 Per semester; Resident Graduate $1,712 Per semester
Type of Training Offered: School
Degrees & Hours Offered: BA, Libr Sci minor, 24 sem hrs; BS, Libr Sci minor, 24 sem hrs; MS, Educational Leadership, 36 sem hrs
Special Courses: School Library Media Specialist
Evening Session, Internet Courses, Summer Session, Weekend Session

UNIVERSITY OF WISCONSIN-SUPERIOR*, Library Science Department, Belknap & Catlin, PO Box 2000, Superior, 54880. Tel: 715-394-8343. FAX: 715-394-8462. Web Site: www.uwsuper.edu/acaddept/libs/index.cfm. *Assoc Prof, Chair,* Debra Nordgren; Tel: 715-394-8233, E-mail: dnordgre@uwsuper.ed; *Asst Prof,* Peter Nordgren; Tel: 715-394-8528, E-mail: pnordgre@uwsuper.edu; *Assoc Prof,* Laura Jacobs; Tel: 715-394-8359, E-mail: ljacobs@uwsuper.edu; *Asst Prof,* Ella Cross; Tel: 715-394-8512, E-mail: ecross@uwsuper.edu
Sch type: Pub; Enrl: Grad: 350, Undergrad: 2,500; Fac 4
Tuition: Non-resident Undergraduate $9,980 Per year; Non-resident Graduate $20,132 Per year; Resident Undergraduate $2,438 Per year; Resident Graduate $5,972 Per year
Type of Training Offered: School
Degrees & Hours Offered: BA, Libr Sci minor, 24 sem hrs; BS, Libr Sci minor, 24 sem hrs
Special Courses: Administration of a School Media Program, Children's Literature, Collection Development, Curriculum Leadership & the Library Media Program, Directed Studies in Librarianship, Educational Communications & Technology, Foundations of Information Literacy, Information Resources & Services, Library Practice, Library Research Methods, Organizing Library & Media Materials & Young Adult Literature, Trends in K-12 Literature
Co-operative Education Prog, Evening Session, Summer Session

UNIVERSITY OF WISCONSIN-WHITEWATER*, Library & Information Technology, 800 W Main St, Whitewater, 53190. Tel: 262-472-1380. FAX: 262-472-2841. E-mail: edfound@uww.edu. *Assoc Prof,* Dr Eileen Schroeder; E-mail: schroede@uww.edu; *Assoc Prof,* E Anne Zarinnia; E-mail: zarinnia@uww.edu
Enrl: Undergrad: 30
Tuition: Non-resident Undergraduate $1,485 Per 3 credit hour; Non-resident Graduate $2,390 Per 3 credit hour; Resident Undergraduate $421 Per 3 credit hour; Resident Graduate $753 Per 3 credit hour
Degrees & Hours Offered: BA, Libr Media minor, 24 sem hrs; BS, Libr Media minor, 24 sem hrs; MS, Curriculum & Instruction with Library & Information Technology Emphasis
Evening Session, Summer Session

PUERTO RICO

† UNIVERSITY OF PUERTO RICO, RIO PIEDRAS CAMPUS*, Graduate School of Information Sciences & Technologies, PO Box 21906, San Juan, 00931-1906. Tel: 787-764-0000, Ext 1286, 787-764-0000, Ext 5028. FAX: 787-764-2311. Web Site: egcti.upr.edu. *Dir, Prof,* Consuelo Figueras; E-mail: consuelof@compuserve.com; *Prof,* Jorge Encarnacion-Torres; E-mail: jencarn@rrpac.upr.clu.edu; *Prof,* Eliut Flores-Caraballo; E-mail: eflores@rrpac.upr.clu.edu; *Prof,* Susan Freiband; E-mail: sfreiba@rrpac.upr.clu.edu; *Prof,* Mariano Maura-Sardo; E-mail: mmaura@rrpac.upr.clu.edu; *Prof,* Luisa Vigo-Cepeda; E-mail: lvigo@rrpac.upr.clu.edu; *Assoc Prof,* Betsaida Velez-Natal; E-mail: bvelez@rrpac.upr.clu.edu; *Asst Prof,* Jose A Sanchez-Lugo; E-mail: jsanche1@rrpac.upr.clu.edu; *Instr,* Sarai Lastra; E-mail: slastra@rrpac.upr.clu.edu
Prog estab 1969. Sch type: Pub; Enrl: Grad: 165; Fac 2
Ent Req: Bachelor's, 3.00 PAEG
Tuition: Non-resident Graduate $1,500 Per semester; Resident Graduate $75 Per credit hour
Type of Training Offered: Public
Degrees & Hours Offered: Certificate, Post Bachelor - School Librarian, 22 sem hrs; Certificate, Post Bachelor - Analyst in Electronic Resources, 21 sem hrs; Certificate, Post Bachelor - Archives & Records Mgt, 18 sem hrs; Certificate, Post Master - Legal Specialist, 18 sem hrs; Certificate, Post Master - Library Administrator, 16 sem hrs; Certificate, Post Master - Info Consultant, 20 sem hrs; MIS, 38 sem hrs
Special Courses: Abstracting & Indexing, Automation of Information Services, Bibliographic Instruction, Information Needs Analysis, Latin American Bibliography, Legal Bibliography, Music Bibliography, Systems Analysis
Evening Session

ALBERTA

GRANT MACEWAN COLLEGE*, Information Management & Library Technology Program, 10700-104 Ave, 5-107B, Edmonton, T5J 4S2. Tel: 780-497-5274. FAX: 780-497-5385. Web Site: www.macewan.ca. *Coordr,* Tony Fell; E-mail: fellt@macewan.ca
Prog estab 1971. Sch type: Pub. Scholarships offered; Enrl: Undergrad: 70
Tuition: Resident Undergraduate $7,250 Per year
Special Courses: Children & Young Adult Services, Database Applications, Information System Design, Web Development

SAIT POLYTECHNIC, Library Information Technology, 1301 - 16 Ave NW, Calgary, T2M 0L4. Tel: 403-284-7231, 403-284-8897. Toll Free Tel: 877-284-7248. FAX: 403-284-7238. E-mail: lit.info@sait.ca. Web Site: www.sait.ca. *Libr Mgr,* Susan Brayford
Prog estab 1968. Sch type: Pub
Type of Training Offered: Library Technician
Degrees & Hours Offered: Certificate, Libr Operations Asst (Distance Educ), 288 approx hrs Basic Level, 384 approx hrs Advan Level; Diploma, Libr Tech (2-year day prog), 1,460 hrs
Special Courses: Acquisitions & Serials, Cataloguing & Classification, Circulation, Collection Development (Children, Young Adult & Adult), Communication Skills, Designing Web Tools for Libraries, Information Services, Library Automation, Library Management, Library Marketing, Library Network Technology, Managing Digital Content, Records Management
Continuing Education, Internet Courses

† UNIVERSITY OF ALBERTA*, School of Library & Information Studies, 3-20 Rutherford S, Edmonton, T6G 2J4. Tel: 780-492-4578. FAX: 780-492-2430. E-mail: slis@ualberta.ca. Web Site: www.slis.ualberta.ca. *Dir,* Ernie Ingles; *Prof & Grad Coordr,* Dr Margaret Mackey; *Prof,* Dr Toni Samek; *Assoc Prof,* Dr Ali Shiri; *Assoc Prof,* Dr Dangzhi Zhao; *Asst Prof,* Dr Dinesh Rathi
Prog estab 1968. Sch type: Pub. Scholarships offered; Enrl: Grad: 120
Ent Req: Bachelor's & 3.0 GPA on scale of 4.0
Tuition: Non-resident Graduate $11,000 Per year; Resident Graduate $5,800 Per year (CAN)
Type of Training Offered: Library & Information Science
Degrees & Hours Offered: MLIS, 48 credits; MLIS/MA
Special Courses: Advanced Research Methods, Archives, Children's Literature, Conservation & Preservation, Contemporary Theories & Practices of Reading, Globalization, Diversity & Information, Government Publications, History of the Book, Information Retrieval, Instructional Practices in Library & Information Services, Internet, Intellectual Freedom, Knowledge Management, Multi-media Texts for Young People, Practicum, Records Management, Young Adult Literature
Evening Session, Internet Courses, Summer Session, Weekend Session

BRITISH COLUMBIA

LANGARA COLLEGE*, Library & Information Technology Program, 100 W 49th Ave, Vancouver, V5Y 2Z6. Tel: 604-323-5364, 604-323-5862. FAX: 604-323-5010. Web Site: www.langara.bc.ca/libtech. *Chair,* Carol Elder
Prog estab 1967. Sch type: Pub. Scholarships offered; Enrl: Undergrad: 100
Tuition: Resident Undergraduate $79 Per credit hour (CAN)
Degrees & Hours Offered: Diploma, 64 credit hrs
Special Courses: Children's Library Service, Information Handling & Internet, Information Retrieval, Multi-Media Libraries
Evening Session, Internet Courses

† UNIVERSITY OF BRITISH COLUMBIA, School of Library, Archival & Information Studies, The Irving K Barber Centre, 1961 E Mall, Ste 470, Vancouver, V6T 1Z1. Tel: 604-822-2404. FAX: 604-822-6006. E-mail: slais.info@ubc.ca. Web Site: www.slais.ubc.ca. *Dir, Prof,* Caroline Haythornthwaite; *Prof,* Luciana Duranti; *Prof,* Edie Rasmussen; *Prof,* Judith Saltman; *Asst Prof,* Luanne Freund; *Asst Prof,* Richard Kopak; *Asst Prof,* Victoria Lemieux; *Asst Prof,* Aaron Loehrlein; *Asst Prof,* Eric Meyers; *Asst Prof,* Giovanni Michetti; *Asst Prof,* Lisa Nathan; *Asst Prof,* Heather O'Brien; *Sr Instr,* Mary Sue Stephenson
Prog estab 1961. Sch type: Pub; Enrl: Grad: 280; Fac 13
Ent Req: Bachelor's & achieved a minimum overall average in the B+ grade range (76% at UBC) in third & fourth year level courses
Tuition: Resident Graduate $4,350 Per year (CAN); Resident Graduate $4,448 Per year (CAN); International Graduate $7,641 Per year (CAN)
Degrees & Hours Offered: Certificate, Archival, Libr & Info Studies, 24 credits; MA, Children's Lit, 30 credits; MAS, 48 credits; MLIS, 48 credits; Ph.D., Archival, Libr & Info Studies; MAS/MLIS, 81 credits; MAS/MLIS
Special Courses: Archival Administration, Archival Appraisal, Bibliographic Control, Electronic Records, Information Retrieval,

Management, Records Management, Serving Groups with Special Needs, Youth Literature & Services

Evening Session, Summer Session

MANITOBA

RED RIVER COLLEGE*, Library & Information Technology Program, W210B-160 Princess St, Winnipeg, R3B 1K9. Tel: 204-949-8477. FAX: 204-949-0032. Web Site: www.rrc.mb.ca. *Instr,* Brian Rountree; Tel: 204-949-8476; *Instr,* Sherri Vokey; E-mail: svokey@rrc.mb.ca
Prog estab 1963. Sch type: Pub; Enrl: Undergrad: 30; Fac 2
Degrees & Hours Offered: Diploma

NOVA SCOTIA

† DALHOUSIE UNIVERSITY*, School of Information Management, 6100 University Ave, Halifax, B3H 3J5. Tel: 902-494-3656. FAX: 902-494-2451. E-mail: sim@dal.ca. Web Site: www.sim.management.dal.ca. *Dean,* David Wheeler; *Dir,* Dr Fiona Black; E-mail: fiona.black@dal.ca; *Prof,* Dr Bertrum MacDonald; *Assoc Prof,* Dr Haidar Moukdad; *Assoc Prof,* Dr Louise Spiteri; *Asst Prof,* Dr Keith Lawson; *Lecturer,* Vivian Howard; *Lecturer,* Sandra Toze; *Prog Coordr,* JoAnn Watson; Tel: 902-494-2471, E-mail: joann.watson@dal.ca
Prog estab 1969. Sch type: Pub. Scholarships offered; Enrl: Grad: 110
Ent Req: GPA 3.0 (B average), TOEFL 600 (250 computer testing)
Tuition: Resident Graduate $804 Per course
Type of Training Offered: Library & Information Science
Degrees & Hours Offered: MLIS, 48 sem hrs; MLS/JD; MLIS/MBA; MLIS/MPA; MLIS/MREM
Special Courses: Applications for Information Management, Archives, Cataloging & Classification, Collections Management, Database Management Systems, Digital Libraries, Electronic Access to Information, Electronic Text Design, Government Information Resources, Health Sciences Literature & Information Sources, History of the Book, Human Computer Interaction, Indexing & Abstracting, Information in Society, Information Literacy; Information Policy, Information Retrieval, Info Sources & Retrieval, Info Sources in the Humanities/Social Sciences, Information Sources in Science in Technology, International Perspectives, Legal Literature & Librarianship, Organizational Management & Strategy, Organization of Information, Quantitative Methods, Records Management, Research Methods, Resources for Business Intelligence, Services & Resources for Children, Services & Resources for Young Adults, Special Topics in Information Management, Systems Analysis, Users & Services
Summer Session

ONTARIO

ALGONQUIN COLLEGE OF APPLIED ARTS & TECHNOLOGY*, Library & Information Technician Program, 1385 Woodroffe Ave, Ottawa, K2G 1V8. Tel: 613-727-4723, Ext 5066. FAX: 613-727-7759. Web Site: www.algonquincollege.com. *Coordr,* C M Nason; E-mail: nasonm@algonquincollege.com
Prog estab 1967. Sch type: Pub; Enrl: 40
Tuition: Resident Graduate $1,914 Per semester; International Graduate $3,742 Per semester
Distance Learning

SENECA COLLEGE OF APPLIED ARTS & TECHNOLOGY*, Library & Information Technician Diploma Program, 1750 Finch Ave E, Toronto, M2J 2X5. Tel: 416-491-5050. FAX: 416-491-4606. Web Site: www.senecac.on.ca. *Coordr, Prof,* Deborah Kay; Tel: 416-491-5050, Ext 2744; *Prof,* Delia Antonacci; Tel: 416-491-5050, Ext 6733; *Prof,* Katherine More; Tel: 416-491-5050, Ext 6706
Prog estab 1967. Sch type: Pub; Enrl: Undergrad: 120
Ent Req: High school diploma
Tuition: Resident Undergraduate $2,000 Per year (CAN)
Degrees & Hours Offered: Diploma
Evening Session, Summer Session

† UNIVERSITY OF TORONTO*, Faculty of Information, iSchool@Toronto, 140 St George St, Toronto, M5S 3G6. Tel: 416-978-3234. FAX: 416-978-5762. E-mail: help.ischool@utoronto.ca, inquire.ischool@utoronto.ca. Web Site: www.ischool.utoronto.ca. *Dean,* Seamus Ross; E-mail: seamus.ross@utoronto.ca; *Assoc Dean, Res,* Lynne Howarth; E-mail: lynne.howarth@utoronto.ca; *Assoc Dean, Acad,* Heather MacNeil; E-mail: h.macneil@utoronto.ca; *Asst Dean, Admin,* Susan Brown; Tel: 416-978-8588, E-mail: susan.brown@utoronto.ca; *Dir, Info Serv,* Joe Cox; E-mail: joe.cox@utoronto.ca; *Registrar & Dir, Student Serv,* Adriana Rossini; Tel: 416-978-8589, E-mail: adriana.rossini@utoronto.ca
Prog estab 1928. Sch type: Pub. Scholarships offered; Enrl: Grad: 570; Fac 25
Tuition: Domestic Graduate $10,000 Per year (CAN); International Graduate $22,000 Per year (CAN)
Degrees & Hours Offered: Ph.D.; MISt, Master of Info in Archives & Rec Mgt, Critical Info Studies, Info Syst & Design, Knowledge Mgt &

Info Mgt, Libr & Info Sci; MISt/JD, Joint MI & JD degree; MM, Master of Mus Studies
Special Courses: Advocacy & Library Issues, Analyzing Information Systems, Archives Concepts & Issues, Archives Programs & Services, Archives Science Functions, Database Design, Designing Information Systems, Information & its Social Contexts, Information Literacy, Information Policy, Information Resources & Services, Introduction to Bibliographic Control, Introduction to Information Systems, Introduction to Information Technology, Library Administration, Management of Information Organizations, Organizing & Storing Information, Research Methods, Resources & Library Collections
Continuing Education, Evening Session, Professional Development, Summer Session

UNIVERSITY OF TORONTO*, Faculty of Education, School Librarianship Dept, 371 Bloor St W, Rm 213, Toronto, M5S 2R7. Tel: 416-978-6246, 416-978-8833. FAX: 416-978-6775. Web Site: www.oise.utoronto.ca.
Prog estab 1961. Sch type: Pub; Enrl: Undergrad: 200; Fac 15
Tuition: Resident Undergraduate $825 Per semester
Special Courses: Children's Literature, Information Technology, School Libraries, Young Adult Literature
Evening Session, Summer Session

† UNIVERSITY OF WESTERN ONTARIO*, Graduate Programs in Library & Information Science, Faculty of Information & Media Studies, North Campus Bldg, Rm 240, London, N6A 5B7. Tel: 519-661-4017. FAX: 519-661-3506. E-mail: mlisinfo@uwo.ca. Web Site: www.fims.uwo.ca. *Dean,* Dr Thomas Carmichael; E-mail: fimsdean@uwo.ca; *Prog Coordr,* Dr Gloria Leckie; E-mail: leckie@uwo.ca
Prog estab 1966. Sch type: Pub; Enrl: Grad: 283, Grad: 26
Ent Req: For PhD: 4 yr undergrad degree & Master's degree in Libr & Info Sci from ALA-accredited sch
Tuition: Domestic Graduate $3,427 Per term (Masters) (CAN); Domestic Graduate $2,757 Per term (Doctorate) (CAN); International Graduate $5,546 Per term (Doctorate) (CAN); International Graduate $7,420 Per term (Masters) (CAN)
Type of Training Offered: Special
Degrees & Hours Offered: MLIS, 15 courses; Ph.D., Info & Soc; Info Organization & Technologies, 6 courses
Special Courses: Archival Reference Services; Digital Libraries; Human Resource Management; Information Policy; Information Visualization; Instructional Strategies for Information Professionals; Issues in Distance Learning for Public & Academic Libraries; Knowledge Management; Legal Issues for Information Professionals; Prospect Research & Fundraising
Co-operative Education Prog, Evening Session, Summer Session

QUEBEC

CEGEP TROIS-RIVIERES*, Dept Techniques Documentation, 3500 rue De Courval, Trois-Rivieres, G9A 5E6. Tel: 819-376-1721, Ext 3722. E-mail: tech.documentation@cegeptr.qc.ca. Web Site: tech-doc.cegeptr.qc.ca/.
Prog estab 1968. Sch type: Pub
Type of Training Offered: Library Technician
Degrees & Hours Offered: Diploma, DEC Techniques de la Documentation - Libr Tech
Special Courses: Archives, Information & Library Technologies, Information Science, MARC21, RCAA2, RDDA, Records Management

COLLEGE DE MAISONNEUVE*, Techniques de la Documentation, 3800, rue Sherbrooke Est, Montreal, H1X 2A2. Tel: 514-254-7131. FAX: 514-251-9741. E-mail: tdo@cmaisonneuve.qc.ca. *Prof,* Ginette Allard; *Prof,* Lise Brotherton; *Prof,* Guy Champagne; *Prof,* Luce Anne Courchesne; *Prof,* Pierre Manseau; *Prof,* Nicole Rene; *Prof,* Katy Simard; *Prof,* France Vinet
Prog estab 1975. Sch type: Pub; Enrl: Undergrad: 120
Special Courses: Archives, Data Processing in Documentation, Information Retrieval, Media (AV) & Records Management

COLLEGE FRANCOIS-XAVIER-GARNEAU*, Techniques de la Documentation, 1660 blvd de l'Entente, Quebec, G1S 4S3. Tel: 418-688-8310, Ext 3504. FAX: 418-681-9384. E-mail: communications@cegep-fxg.qc.ca. Web Site: www.cegep-fxg.qc.ca. *Coordr,* Mario Goupil; E-mail: mgoupil@cegep-fxg.qc.ca; *Prof,* Melanie DeBuhan; E-mail: mdebuhan@cegep-fxg.qc.ca; *Prof,* Amelie Frenette; E-mail: afrenette@cegep-fxg.qc.ca; *Prof,* Aline Neron; E-mail: aneron@cegep-fxg.qc.ca; *Prof,* Carole Robitaille; E-mail: crobitaille@cegep-fxg.qc.ca; *Prof,* Dominique Trottier; E-mail: dtrottier@cegep-fxg.qc.ca; *Tech Serv,* Josée Gaudreau; E-mail: jgaudreau@cegep-fxg.qc.ca
Prog estab 1971. Sch type: Pub. Scholarships offered; Enrl: Undergrad: 125; Fac 23
Special Courses: Archives & Documentation, Records Management

COLLEGE LIONEL-GROULX*, Department des Techniques de la Documentation, 100, rue Duquet, Sainte-Therese, J7E 3G6. Tel: 450-430-3120, Ext 407. FAX: 450-971-7883. Web Site: www.clg.qc.ca/coord/adr/adr.html. *Dir,* Johanne Pessier; *Prof,* Michelle Bujdd-Plouffe; *Prof,* Jean-Pierre Chabot; *Prof,* Daniele Daoust; *Prof,* Genevieve Fortin
Prog estab 1972. Sch type: Pub; Enrl: Undergrad: 55
Special Courses: Media (AV) & Records Management

† MCGILL UNIVERSITY*, School of Information Studies, 3661 Peel St, Montreal, H3A 1X1. Tel: 514-398-4204. FAX: 514-398-7193. E-mail: sis@mcgill.ca. Web Site: www.mcgill.ca/sis. *Assoc Prof, Dir,* France Bouthillier; Tel: 514-398-3362, E-mail: france.bouthillier@mcgill.ca; *Prof,* J Andrew Large; Tel: 514-398-3360, E-mail: andrew.large@mcgill.ca; *Prof,* Peter F McNally; Tel: 514-398-3367, E-mail: peter.mcnally@mcgill.ca; *Assoc Prof,* Jamshid Beheshti; Tel: 514-398-3366, E-mail: jamshid.beheshti@mcgill.ca; *Assoc Prof,* Kimiz Dalkir; Tel: 514-398-3364, E-mail: kimiz.dalkir@mcgill.ca; *Assoc Prof,* Catherine Guastavino; Tel: 514-398-1709, E-mail: catherine.guastavino@mcgill.ca; *Asst Prof,* Elaine Menard; Tel: 514-398-3368, E-mail: elaine.menard@mcgill.ca; *Assoc Prof,* Eun Park; Tel: 514-398-3364, E-mail: eun.park@mcgill.ca; *Asst Prof,* Joan Bartlett; Tel: 514-398-6976, E-mail: joan.bartlett@mcgill.ca
Prog estab 1904. Sch type: Pub. Scholarships offered; Enrl: Grad: 205; Fac 9
Tuition: Non-resident Graduate $6,100 Per year (CAN); Resident Graduate $3,200 Per year (CAN); International Graduate $13,495 Per year (non-Canadian) (CAN)
Type of Training Offered: Library & Information Science
Degrees & Hours Offered: Certificate, Grad Level, 15 credit hrs; Diploma, Grad Level, 30 credit hrs; MLIS, Archival Studies, Knowledge Mgt, Librarianship, 48 credits; Ph.D., Information Studies
Special Courses: Abstracting & Indexing, Archival Principles & Practice, Bibliographic & Factual Sources, Bioinformatics Resources, Business Information, Classification & Cataloging, Corporate Information Centres, Descriptive Bibliography, Financial Management, Government Information, Health Sciences Information, History of Books & Printing, Humanities & Social Sciences Information, Human Resources in Libraries, Independent Study, Information Agency Management, Information Policy, Information Resource Management, Information Storage & Retrieval Systems, Information System Design, Information Users & Services, Knowledge Management, Law Information, Library Systems, Marketing Information

Services, Multimedia Systems, Organization of Information, Public Libraries, Practicum in Information Services, Quantitative Methods & Bibliometrics, Research Principles & Analysis, Research Project, Scientific & Technical Information, Selected Topics in Library & Information Studies, Systems Thinking

† UNIVERSITE DE MONTREAL*, Ecole de Bibliotheconomie et des Sciences de l'Information, 3150, rue Jean-Brillant, bur C-2004, Montreal, H3T 1N8. (Mail add: CP 6128, succ Centre-ville, Montreal, H3C 3J7). Tel: 514-343-6044. FAX: 514-343-5753. E-mail: ebsiinfo@ebsi.umontreal.ca. Web Site: www.ebsi.umontreal.ca. *Dir,* Jean-Michel Salaun; *Prof,* Rejean Savard; *Prof,* James Turner; *Assoc Prof,* Clement Arsenault; *Assoc Prof,* Pierrette Bergeron; *Assoc Prof,* Lyne Da Sylva; *Assoc Prof,* Michele Hudon; *Assoc Prof,* Eric Leroux; *Assoc Prof,* Yves Marcoux; *Asst Prof,* Christine Dufour; *Asst Prof,* Dominic Forest; *Asst Prof,* Audrey Laplante; *Asst Prof,* Yvon Lemay; *Asst Prof,* Sabine Mas; *Asst Prof,* Dominique Maurel
Prog estab 1961. Sch type: Pub; Enrl: Grad: 218, Undergrad: 100; Fac 16
Ent Req: BA with B average for Master
Tuition: Resident Undergraduate $1,200 Per semester; Resident Graduate $1,200 Per semester
Type of Training Offered: Library & Information Science
Degrees & Hours Offered: Certificate, Archival Studies, 30 credits; Certificate, Digital Info Mgt, 30 credits; Ph.D., Info Studies, 90 credits; MIS, Info Studies, 51 credits
Special Courses: Archives & Records Management, Digital Information Management, Information Science, Librarianship

SASKATCHEWAN

SIAST KELSEY CAMPUS, Library & Information Technology, 107 Fourth Ave S, Saskatoon, S7K 5X2. (Mail add: PO Box 1520, Saskatoon, S7K 3R5). Tel: 306-659-3850. Toll Free Tel: 866-467-4278. FAX: 306-933-6490. Web Site: www.siast.sk.ca. *Prog Head,* Cynthia Bretell; E-mail: cynthia.bretell@siast.sk.ca
Prog estab 1969. Sch type: Pub. Scholarships offered; Enrl: Undergrad: 30; Fac 2
Ent Req: Grade 12, English A & B
Tuition: Resident Undergraduate $3,000 Per year
Degrees & Hours Offered: Diploma

LIBRARY SYSTEMS

Serving as an index to library systems in the United States and Canada, this section lists the functions of each state's or province's systems and includes an alphabetical listing of the individual systems within each state/province.

Complete data for each system can be found in the Library Section of this directory, unless the state/provincial heading is followed by an (N), in which case the information can be found in the Network Section. A system followed by a library name in parentheses has its entry alphabetized under the library name, not under the system name.

ALABAMA

The state of Alabama has the following Library Systems, which provide easily accessible services through branches and cooperating libraries.

Single County Systems (public libraries only):

Anniston-Calhoun County Library, Anniston
Baldwin County Library System, Robertsdale
DeKalb County Public Library, Fort Payne
Escambia County Cooperative Library System, Atmore
Harrison Regional Library, Columbiana
Jefferson County Library Cooperative, Birmingham
Lauderdale County Regional Library, Florence
Marengo Library System, Demopolis
Marshall County Cooperative Library, Guntersville
Pickens County Cooperative Library, Carrollton
Sumter County Library System, Livingston

Multi-County Systems (public libraries only):

Cheaha Regional Library, Heflin
Carl Elliott Regional Library, Jasper
Horseshoe Bend Regional Library, Dadeville
Northwest Regional Library, Winfield

ALASKA

Alaska has seven public libraries or systems, which operate multiple libraries within a Borough government:

Anchorage Public Library, Anchorage
Bristol Bay Borough Libraries, Naknek
Chukchi Consortium Library, Kotzebue
Fairbanks North Star Borough Public Library, Fairbanks
Juneau Public Library, Juneau
Mantanuska-Susitna Borough Libraries, Palmer
Tuzzy Consortium Library, Barrow

ARIZONA

The state of Arizona has fifteen county libraries of which eleven are Library Districts with secondary taxing authority.

Single-Type Library Districts:

Apache County Library District, Saint Johns
Cochise County Library District, Bisbee
Flagstaff City-Coconino County Public Library, Flagstaff
Gila County Library District, Globe
Maricopa County Library District, Phoenix
Mohave County Library District, Kingman
Navajo County Library District, Holbrook
Pinal County Library District, Florence
Pima County Public Library, Tucson
Yavapai County Free Library District, Prescott
Yuma County Library District, Yuma

Single-Type Library Coops:

Greenlee County Library System, Clifton
Nogales City-Santa Cruz County Library, Nogales
Parker Public Library, Parker
Safford City-Graham County Library, Safford

ARKANSAS

Public library service in Arkansas is provided through fifty-one library systems within five library development districts.

Library Development District I

Arkansas River Valley Regional Library, Dardanelle
Baxter County Library, Mountain Home
Bella Vista Public Library, Bella Vista
Bentonville Public Library, Bentonville
Boone County Library, Harrison
Carroll & Madison Library System, Berryville
Crawford County Library, Van Buren
Fayetteville Public Library, Fayetteville
Fort Smith Public Library, Fort Smith
Marion County Library, Jasper
Newton County Library, Jasper
Pope County Library System, Russellville
Rogers Public Library, Rogers
Scott-Sebastian Regional Library, Greenwood
Searcy County Library, Marshall
Siloam Springs Public Library, Siloam Springs
Washington County Library, Fayetteville

Library Development District II

Crowley Ridge Regional Library, Jonesboro
East Central Arkansas Regional Library, Wynne
Forrest City Public Library, Forrest City
Jackson County Library, Newport
Lawrence County Library, Walnut Ridge
Mississippi-Crittendon County Library System, Blytheville
Northeast Arkansas Regional Library, Paragould
Trumann Public Library, Trumann
West Memphis Public Library, West Memphis
White River Regional Library, Batesville

Library Development District III

Central Arkansas Library System, Little Rock
Conway County Library, Morrilton
Faulkner-Van Buren Regional Library, Conway
William F Laman Public Library, North Little Rock
Lonoke-Prairie County Library, Lonoke
Mid-Arkansas Regional Library, Malvern
Saline County Public Library, Benton
White County Library System, Searcy

Library Development District IV

Barton Library, El Dorado
Calhoun County Library, Hampton
Clark County Library, Arkadelphia
Columbia County Library, Magnolia
Garland County Library, Hot Springs
LaFayette County Library, Lewisville
Montgomery County Library, Mount Ida
Polk County Library, Mena
Public Library of Camden & Ouachita County, Camden
Texarkana Public Library, Texarkana

Library Development District V

Arkansas County Library, Stuttgart
Ashley County Library, Hamburg
Phillips-Lee-Monroe Regional Library, Helena
Public Library of Pine Bluff & Jefferson County, Pine Bluff
Southeast Arkansas Regional Library, Monticello

CALIFORNIA

The state of California has nine public library systems which provide resource sharing & interlibrary cooperation.

California Library Services Act (CLSA) Systems:

Black Gold Cooperative Library System (BLACK GOLD), San Luis Obispo
49-99 Cooperative Library System, Monrovia
Inland Library System (INLAND), Riverside
NorthNet Library System (NLS), Santa Rosa
Pacific Library Partnership (PLP), San Mateo
San Joaquin Valley Library System (SJVLS), Fresno
Serra Cooperative Library System (SERRA), San Diego
Southern California Library Cooperative (SCLC), Monrovia

COLORADO

Colorado is a division of the state department of education, and is charged with providing multi-type services for libraries throughout the state. Services to improve libraries and resident's access to materials are offered through technology-based programs, professional development, and direct consulting by staff. The Talking Book and state publications libraries meet walk-in needs.

CONNECTICUT (N)

Connecticut has the Connecticut Library Consortium, a statewide membership collaborative serving all types of Connecticut libraries.

DELAWARE

The state of Delaware has a multitude of library governance, including: county, city, and independent libraries.

FLORIDA

Residents of the state of Florida have access to public library service through 39 countywide library systems, 8 multi-county regional library systems and 35 municipal libraries. There are also 5 multi-type library consortia that coordinate resource sharing and cooperative programming in 5 regions of the state.

Regional Public Libraries:

Heartland Library Cooperative, Sebring
New River Public Library Cooperative, Lake Butler
Northwest Regional Library System, Panama City
PAL Public Library Cooperative, Palatka
Panhandle Public Library Cooperative System, Marianna
Suwannee River Regional Library, Live Oak
Three Rivers Regional Library System, Mayo
Wilderness Coast Public Libraries (WILD), Monticello

Countywide Public Libraries:

Brevard County Library System, Cocoa
Broward County Division of Libraries, Fort Lauderdale
Charlotte County Library System, Port Charlotte
Citrus County Library System, Beverly Hills
Clay County Public Library, Orange Park
Collier County Public Library, Naples
Columbia County Public Library, Lake City
Flagler County Public Library, Palm Coast
Gadsden County Public Library, Quincy
Hendry County Library System, Clewiston
Hernando County Library System, Brooksville
Hillsborough County Public Library Cooperative, Tampa

Indian River County Library, Vero Beach
Jacksonville Public Library System, Jacksonville
Lake County Public Library System, Tavares
Lee County Library System, Fort Myers
Leon County Public Library System, Tallahassee
Manatee County Public Library System, Bradenton
Marion County Public Library System, Ocala
Martin County Public Library, Stuart
Miami-Dade Public Library System, Miami
Monroe County Public Library, Key West
Nassau County Public Library, Fernandina Beach
Okaloosa County Public Library Cooperative, Niceville
Orange County Library District, Orlando
Osceola County Public Library System, Kissimmee
Palm Beach County Library System, West Palm Beach
Pasco County Library Cooperative, Hudson
Pinellas Public Library Cooperative Inc, Clearwater
Polk County Library Cooperative, Bartow
Saint Johns County Public Library, Saint Augustine
Saint Lucie County Library System, Fort Pierce
Santa Rosa County Library System, Milton
Sarasota County Library System, Sarasota
Seminole County Public Library System, Casselberry
Sumter County Library System, Wildwood
Volusia County Public Library System, Daytona Beach
Walton County Public Library System, DeFuniak Springs
West Florida Public Library System, Pensacola

Multitype Library Cooperatives (MLCs):

Northeast Florida Library Information Network, Orange Park
Panhandle Library Access Network, Panama City Beach
Southeast Florida Library Information Network, Boca Raton
Southwest Florida Library Network, Fort Myers
Tampa Bay Library Consortium, Tampa

Municipal Libraries:

Altamonte Springs City Library, Altamonte Springs
Apalachicola Municipal Library, Apalachicola
Boca Raton Public Library, Boca Raton
Boynton Beach City Library, Boynton Beach
Brockway Memorial Library, Miami Shores
Citrus Springs Memorial Library, Citrus Springs
Delray Beach Public Library, Delray Beach
Eustis Memorial Library, Eustis
Flagler Beach Library, Flager Beach
Fort Myers Beach Public Library, Fort Myers Beach
Doreen Gauthier Lighthouse Point Library, Lighthouse Point
Hialeah Public Libraries, Hialeah
Highland Beach Library, Highland Beach
Helen B Hoffman Plantation Library, Plantation
Indian Rocks Beach Library, Indian Rocks Beach
Lake Park Public Library, Lake Park
Lake Worth Public Library, Lake Worth
Lantana Public Library, Lantana
Lynn Haven Public Library, Lynn Haven
Maitland Public Library, Maitland
J Turner Moore Memorial Library, Manalapan
New Port Richey Public Library, New Port Richey
North Miami Beach Public Library, North Miami Beach
North Miami Public Library, North Miami
North Palm Beach Library, North Palm Beach
Oakland Park Library, Oakland Park
Herman B Oberman Public Library, Dunnellon
Palm Springs Public Library, Palm Springs
Parkland Library, Parkland
Riviera Beach Public Library, Rivera Beach
Sanibel Public Library District, Sanibel
Shalimar Public Library, Shalimar
Richard C Sullivan Public Library of Wilton Manors, Wilton Manors
West Palm Beach Public Library, West Palm Beach
Winter Park Public Library, Winter Park

GEORGIA

The state of Georgia has 33 Multi-county Regional Library Systems and 28 County Library Systems. These systems provide comprehensive public library service to their service areas. All areas of the state are served by public libraries.

Regional Systems:

Athens Regional Library, Athens
Bartram Trail Regional Library, Washington
Chattahoochee Valley Regional Library, Columbus
Cherokee Regional Library, LaFayette

Chestatee Regional Library, Dawsonville
Coastal Plain Regional Library, Tifton
De Soto Trail Regional Library, Camilla
East Central Georgia Regional Library, Augusta
Flint River Regional Library, Griffin
Sara Hightower Regional Library, Rome
Kinchafoonee Regional Library, Dawson
Lake Blackshear Regional Library, Americus
Live Oak Public Libraries, Savannah
Middle Georgia Regional Library, Macon
Mountain Regional Library, Young Harris.
Northeast Georgia Regional Library, Clarkesville
Northwest Georgia Regional Library, Dalton
Ocmulgee Regional Library System, Eastman
Oconee Regional Library, Dublin
Ohoopee Regional Library, Vidalia
Okefenokee Regional Library System, Waycross
Piedmont Regional Library, Winder
Pine Mountain Regional Library System, Manchester
Satilla Regional Library, Douglas
Screven-Jenkins Regional Library, Sylvania
Sequoyah Regional Library, Canton
South Georgia Regional Library, Valdosta
Southwest Georgia Regional Library, Bainbridge
Statesboro Regional Library, Statesboro
Three Rivers Regional Library System, Brunswick
Troup-Harris Regional Library System, La Grange
Uncle Remus Regional Library System, Madison
West Georgia Regional Library, Carrollton

County Systems:

Atlanta-Fulton Public Library, Atlanta
Bartow County Library System, Cartersville
Brooks County Library, Quitman
Catoosa County Library System, Ringgold
Chattooga County Library, Summerville
Clayton County Library System, Jonesboro
Cobb County Public Library System, Marietta
Conyers-Rockdale Library System, Conyers
Coweta County Public Library, Newnan
DeKalb County Public Library, Decatur
Dougherty County Public Library, Albany
Elbert County Public Library, Elberton
Fitzgerald-Ben Hill County Library, Fitzgerald
Forsyth County Public Library, Cumming
Gwinnett County Public Library, Lawrenceville
Hall County Public Library, Gainesville
Hart County Library, Hartwell
Henry County Library System, McDonough
Houston County Public Libraries, Perry
Jefferson County Library, Louisville
Lee County Public Library, Leesburg
Moultrie-Colquiott County Library, Moultrie
Newton County Library System, Covington
Peach Public Libraries, Fort Valley
Roddenbery Memorial Library, Cairo
Thomas County Public Library System, Thomasville
Twin Lakes Library System, Milledgeville
Worth County Public Library, Sylvester

HAWAII

The state of Hawaii has one Public Library System, which administers free comprehensive statewide library resources and information services to the residents, government agencies, libraries and the library profession.

Library System:

Hawaii State Public Library System, Honolulu

IDAHO (N)

Definition: The Idaho Commission for Libraries defines a network as an electronic means of sharing resources among member libraries of a consortium. At a minimum, a network consists of a shared integrated library system that is web-accessible and allows multi-site searching both from within the network and remotely, and interlibrary loan service among all network members.

Library Networks:

Cooperative Information Network, CIN
Inland Northwest Council of Libraries, INCOL
Inland Northwest Library Association Network, INLAN
LYNX! Consortium
Valley Library Network, VALNet

Washington Idaho Network, WIN
Westend Library Consortium, WELCOM

Definition: The Idaho Commission for Libraries defines a consortium as a group of libraries that join together for one or more cooperative purposes. A consortium provides the infrastructure through which these services are delivered. A consortium has a mission, goals and objectives that are outlined in a long range or strategic planning document. It also has an organizational structure that includes governance, administration, staffing, and sustainable finding.

Library Consortia:

Canyon Owyhee Library Group, COLG
Libraries By A River, LIBRI
Library Consortium of Eastern Idaho, LCEI
Valley Mountain Library Consortium, VMLC

ILLINOIS

The state of Illinois has three regional library systems. The multitype library systems cover the state geographically with system membership held by public, academic, school and special libraries. The one public library system serves the city of Chicago. Each library system participates in SILC, the Statewide Illinois Library Catalog.

LIBRARY SYSTEMS

Chicago Public Library, Chicago
Illinois Heartland Library System, Decatur
Reaching Across Illinois Library System, Burr Ridge

INDIANA

The residents of the State of Indiana have access to 237 public library systems, through 35 city & town library systems, 31 partial county (half or more of the total townships) library systems, 24 countywide library systems, 143 township library systems and 4 endowed library systems.

Public Library Systems:

Adams Public Library System
Akron Carnegie Public Library
Alexandria-Monroe Public Library
Alexandrian Public Library
Allen County Public Library
Anderson Public Library
Andrews-Dallas Township Public Library
Argos Public Library
Attica Public Library
Aurora Public Library District
Avon-Washington Township Public Library
Bartholomew County Public Library
Barton Rees Pogue Memorial Public Library
Batesville Memorial Public Library
Bedford Public Library
Beech Grove Public Library
Bell Memorial Public Library
Benton County Public Library
Berne Public Library
Bicknell-Vigo Township Public Library
Bloomfield-Eastern Greene County Public Library
Boonville-Warrick County Public Library
Boswell Grant Township Public Library
Bourbon Public Library
Brazil Public Library
Bremen Public Library
Bristol-Washington Township Public Library
Brook-Iroquois-Washington Township Public Library
Brookston-Prairie Township Public Library
Brown County Public Library
Brownsburg Public Library
Brownstown Public Library
Butler Carnegie Public Library
Cambridge City Public Library
Camden-Jackson Township Public Library
Carmel Clay Public Library
Carnegie Public Library of Steuben County
Centerville-Center Township Public Library
Charlestown Clark County Public Library
Churubusco Public Library
Clayton-Liberty Township Public Library
Clinton Public Library
Coatesville-Clay Township Public Library
Colfax-Perry Township Public Library
Converse-Jackson Township Public Library
Covington-Veedersburg Public Library

Crawford County Public Library
Crawfordsville District Public Library
Crown Point Community Public Library
Culver-Union Township Public Library
Danville-Center Township Public Library
Darlington Public Library
Delphi Public Library
Dublin Public Library
Dunkirk Public Library
Earl Park Public Library
East Chicago Public Library
Eckhart Public Library
Edinburgh Wright-Hageman Public Library
Elkhart Public Library
Evansville-Vanderburgh Public Library
Fairmount Public Library
Farmland Public Library
Fayette County Public Library
Flora-Monroe Public Library
Fort Branch-Johnson Township Public Library
Fortville-Vernon Township Public Library
Francesville-Salem Township Public Library
Frankfort-Clinton County Contractual Public Library
Franklin County Public Library District
Fremont Public Library
Fulton County Public Library
Garrett Public Library
Gary Public Library
Gas City-Mill Township Public Library
Goodland & Grant Township Public Library
Goshen Public Library
Greensburg Decatur County Contractual Public Library
Greentown & Eastern Howard School Public Library
Greenwood Public Library
Hagerstown-Jefferson Township Public Library
Hamilton East Public Library
Hamilton North Public Library
Hammond Public Library
Hancock County Public Library
Harrison County Public Library
Hartford City Public Library
Henry Henley Public Library
Huntingburg Public Library
Huntington City-Township Public Library
Hussy-Mayfield Memorial Public Library
Indianapolis-Marion County Public Library
Jackson County Public Library
Jasonville Public Library
Jasper County Public Library
Jasper-Dubois County Contractual Public Library
Jay County Public Library
Jefferson County Public Library
Jeffersonville Township Public Library
Jennings County Public Library
Johnson County Public Library
Jonesboro Public Library
Joyce Public Library
Kendallville Public Library
Kentland-Jefferson Township Public Library
Kewanna-Union Township Public Library
Kingman-Millcreek Public Library
Kirklin Public Library
Knightstown Public Library
Knox County Public Library
Kokomo-Howard County Public Library
La Crosse Public Library
La Grange Public Library
La Porte County Public Library
Ladoga-Clark Township Public Library
Lake County Public Library
Lawrenceburg Public Library
Lebanon Public Library
Ligonier Public Library
Lincoln Heritage Public Library
Linden Carnegie Public Library
Linton Public Library
Logansport-Cass County Public Library
Loogootee Public Library
Lowell Public Library
Marion Public Library
Matthews Public Library
Melton Public Library
Michigan City Public Library
Middlebury Community Public Library
Middletown Fall Creek Township Public Library

Milford Public Library
Mishawaka-Penn-Harris Public Library
Mitchell Community Public Library
Monon Town and Township Public Library
Monroe County Public Library
Monterey-Tippecanoe Township Public Library
Montezuma Public Library
Monticello-Union Township Public Library
Montpelier-Harrison Township Public Library
Mooresville Public Library
Morgan County Public Library
Morrisson Reeves Library
Muncie-Center Township Public Library
Nappanee Public Library
New Albany-Floyd County Public Library
New Carlisle & Olive Township Public Library
New Castle-Henry County Public Library
New Harmony Workingmen's Institute
Newton County Public Library
Noble County Public Library
North Judson-Wayne Township Public Library
North Madison County Public Library System
North Manchester Public Library
North Webster Community Public Library
Oakland City-Columbia Township Public Library
Odon Winkelpleck Public Library
Ohio County Public Library
Ohio Township Public Library System
Orleans Town & Township Public Library
Osgood Public Library
Otterbein Public Library
Owen County Public Library
Owensville Carnegie Public Library
Oxford Public Library
Paoli Public Library
Peabody Public Library
Pendleton Community Public Library
Penn Township Public Library
Perry County Public Library
Peru Public Library
Pierceton & Washington Township Public Library
Pike County Public Library
Plainfield-Guilford Township Public Library
Plymouth Public Library
Porter County Public Library System
Poseyville Carnegie Public Library
Princeton Public Library
Pulaski County Public Library
Putnam County Public Library
Remington-Carpenter Township Public Library
Ridgeville Public Library
Roachdale-Franklin Township Public Library
Roann Paw-Paw Township Public Library
Roanoke Public Library
Rockville Public Library
Royal Center-Boone Township Public Library
Rushville Public Library
Salem-Washington Township Public Library
Scott County Public Library
Shelby County Public Library
Sheridan Public Library
Shoals Public Library
South Whitley-Cleveland Township Public Library
Speedway Public Library
Spencer County Public Library
Spiceland Town Township Public Library
St Joseph County Public Library
Starke County Public Library System
Sullivan County Public Library
Swayzee Public Library
Switzerland County Public Library
Syracuse-Turkey Creek Township Public Library
Thorntown Public Library
Tippecanoe County Public Library
Tipton County Public Library
Tyson Library Association, Inc
Union City Public Library
Union County Public Library
Van Buren Public Library
Vermillion County Public Library
Vigo County Public Library
Wabash Carnegie Public Library
Wakarusa-Olive & Harrison Township Public Library
Walkerton-Lincoln Township Public Library
Walton & Tipton Township Public Library

Wanatah Public Library
Warren Public Library
Warsaw Community Public Library
Washington Carnegie Public Library
Washington Township Public Library
Waterloo Grant Township Public Library
Waveland-Brown Township Public Library
Wells County Public Library
West Lafayette Public Library
West Lebanon-Pike Township Public Library
Westchester Public Library
Westfield Washington Public Library
Westville-New Durham Township Public Library
Whiting Public Library
Willard Library of Evansville
Williamsport -Washington Township Public Library
Winchester Community Public Library
Wolcott Community Public Library
Worthington Jefferson Township Public Library
York Township Public Library
Yorktown-Mount Pleasant Township Public Library

IOWA

Iowa no longer have Regional Library Service Areas.

KANSAS

The state of Kansas has seven Library Systems, which act as a library service to libraries and to those not served, by a local library.

Library Systems:

Central Kansas Library System, Great Bend
North Central Kansas Library System, Manhattan
Northeast Kansas Library System, Lawrence
Northwest Kansas Library System, Norton
South Central Kansas Library System, Hutchinson
Southeast Kansas Library System, Iola
Southwest Kansas Library System, Dodge City

KENTUCKY

Kentucky has Field Consultants headquartered in eight Regions who develop, extend and improve library service and provide information to the citizens of the Commonwealth.

Regions:

Region 1 - Murray
Region 2 - Bowling Green
Region 3 - Columbia
Region 4 - Frankfort
Region 5 - Frankfort
Region 6 - Frankfort
Region 7 - Hazard
Region 8 - Ashland

LOUISIANA

In the 64 parishes, there are 68 public libraries. Sixty of these are parish-wide; one is a two-parish consolidated unit; one is a bi-city library in a parish without parish-wide service; the others are independent city libraries in parishes with parish-wide service; and one is a district library serving three towns and their outlying areas.

MAINE

The state of Maine has one Regional Library System serving three Library Districts. The Maine Regional Library System was created to improve library service for the citizens of Maine. Membership consists of public, school, academic, & special libraries.

Library System:

The Maine Regional Library System is administered by the Maine State Library in Augusta.

Library Districts:

Public Law 626, enacted in 1973, established three library service districts based on population:
Central Maine Library District, Augusta
Northeastern Maine Library District, Bangor
Southern Maine Library District, Portland

MARYLAND

The state of Maryland has three Regional Libraries and one State Library Resource Center. Regional Libraries are the intermediate link between local libraries and the State Library Resource Center and other resources in the state. They are a vital part of the Maryland library network, a network recognized nationally for its excellence and innovation. Automation and extraordinary growth in information technology is transforming library services. Maryland's Regional Libraries, by providing leadership in cooperative resource sharing, training, and technical assistance in non-metropolitan areas, plays a pivotal role in the delivery of information to Maryland residents, while the State Library Resource Center provides access to specialized materials and services in its reference and research collections.

Library Systems:

Eastern Shore Regional Library, Salisbury
Southern Maryland Regional Library Association, Charlotte Hall
State Library Resource Center, Baltimore
Western Maryland Public Libraries, Hagerstown

MASSACHUSETTS

The state of Massachusetts has one regional library system that provides services to 1,700 Massachusetts libraries throughout the Commonwealth.

Massachusetts Library System, Danvers

MICHIGAN (N)

With state funds authorized by Public Act 89 of 1977, Michigan has 11 Library Cooperatives. A Library Cooperative is the library or service center designated by the cooperative board to provide services as specified by the cooperative plan and provided to public libraries participating in the cooperative. Michigan in addition has 2 multi-type regions of cooperation based on the cooperatives.

Cooperative Libraries:

Detroit Library Cooperative, Detroit
Lakeland Library Cooperative, Grand Rapids
Mideastern Michigan Library Cooperative, Flint
Mid-Michigan Library League, Cadillac
Northland Library Cooperative, Lapeer
Southwest Michigan Library Cooperative, Baule Creek
Superiorland Library Cooperative, Marquette
Suburban Library League, Sterling Heights
The Library Network, Novi
White Pine Library Cooperative, Saginaw
Woodlands Library Cooperative, Albion

Multi-Type Regions of Cooperation: (N)

Northland Interlibrary System, Alpena
Upper Peninsula Region of Library Cooperation, Marquette

MINNESOTA

The state of Minnesota has six Federated Regional Public Library Systems and six Consolidated Regional Public Library Systems. In a manner appropriate to their organizational structures, they support or provide minimum levels of library service to residents of the areas they serve. In addition, seven multi-county multi-type library systems coordinate cooperative programs among academic, public, school and special libraries.

Federated Public Library Systems:

Arrowhead Library System, Mountain Iron
Metropolitan Library Service Agency, Saint Paul
Plum Creek Library System, Worthington
Southeastern Libraries Cooperating, Rochester
Traverse des Sioux Library System, Mankato
Viking Library System, Fergus Falls

Consolidated Public Library Systems:

East Central Regional Library, Cambridge
Great River Regional Library, Saint Cloud
Kitchigami Regional Library, Pine River
Lake Agassiz Regional Library, Moorhead
Northwest Regional Library, Thief River Falls
Pioneerland Library System, Willmar

Multi-County Multi-Type Library Systems:

Central Minnesota Library Exchange, Saint Cloud
Metronet, Saint Paul
North Country Library Cooperative, Mountain Iron
Northern Lights Library Network, Detroit Lakes
Southcentral Minnesota Inter-Library Exchange, Mankato
Southeast Library System, Rochester

Southwest Area Multi-county Interlibrary Exchange, Marshall

MISSISSIPPI

The state of Mississippi has sixteen Regional Systems. In addition, there are thirty-two County Libraries in Mississippi. There are also two independent public libraries in the state.

Regional Libraries:

Central Mississippi Regional Library, Brandon
Copiah-Jefferson Regional Library, Hazlehurst
Dixie Regional Library, Pontotoc
East Mississippi Regional Library, Quitman
First Regional Library, Hernando
Jackson-George Regional Library, Pascagoula
Kemper-Newton Regional Library, Union
Lee-Itawamba Library System, Tupelo
Lincoln-Lawrence-Franklin Regional Library, Brookhaven
Mid-Mississippi Regional Library System, Kosciusko
Natchez Adams Wilkinson Library (Formerly Homochitto Valley), Natchez
Northeast Regional Library, Corinth
Pike-Amite-Walthall Library System, McComb
Pine Forest Regional Library, Richton
South Delta Library Services, Yazoo City
South Mississippi Regional Library, Columbia
Tombigbee Regional Library, West Point

MISSOURI

ILL lending for public libraries in the state is done through an OCLC statewide license paid for by the Missouri State Library.

A statewide courier service supports materials delivery for public libraries.
A statewide system for Internet access is partially supported for public libraries through an appropriation to the Missouri State Library.

MONTANA

The state of Montana has six Library Federations, which incorporate all city, county and district public libraries. Member libraries gain strength from a larger unit without losing individual control.

Library Federations:

Broad Valleys Federation, Lewis & Clark Public Library, Helena
Golden Plains Federation, Phillips County Library
Pathfinder Federation, Fairfield/Teton Public Library
Sagebrush Federation, Miles City Public Library
South Central Federation, Carnegie Public Library
Tamarack Federation, Missoula Public Library

NEBRASKA

The state of Nebraska has six regional multi-type Library Systems that provide services to libraries within multi-county areas. The library systems provide continuing education and training, and other services for the benefit of library staff and library users.

Systems:

Eastern Library System
Meridian Library System
Northeast Library System
Panhandle Library System
Republican Valley Library System
Southeast Library System

NEVADA

The state of Nevada has seven automated library networks, each of which provides interlibrary loan and resource sharing. Two are based in public libraries, one is a consortium of central and northern Nevada public libraries, one is a community college, and two are housed at universities. The seven networks communicate via a digital system for statewide resource sharing.

Automated Library Networks:

Cooperative Libraries Automated Network (CLAN) Headquarters, Nevada State Library and Archives
Henderson District Public Libraries
Southern Network, Headquarters, Las Vegas/Clark County Library District
Truckee Meadows Community College
University of Nevada, Las Vegas
University of Nevada, Reno Library
Washoe County Library

NEW HAMPSHIRE

The NH State Library maintains an online statewide union catalog. 479 multi-type member libraries share access to the web-based system to contribute their holdings and to borrow Interlibrary Loan materials.

Multi-Type Library System:

New Hampshire Automated Information System

NEW JERSEY

The state of New Jersey has one Library Cooperative and three Statewide Services Contract Libraries which facilitate interlibrary reference and loan. The Library Cooperative, through contracts and partnerships with local libraries, provide direct access to expanded resources and services, such as material delivery, shares specialized service and staff skills and develops a coordinated plan of library services to serve patron needs in a specific geographic area. Membership is voluntary and multi-type (academic, institutional, public, school and special libraries). The cooperative is funded by state aid formula.

NEW MEXICO

The state of New Mexico has no library system.

NEW YORK

The state of New York has twenty-three Public Library Systems, nine Reference and Research Library Resources Systems, and forty-one School Library Systems, which reinforce local public, academic and school libraries in meeting the needs of their primary users through the sharing of resources and personnel services.

Public Library Systems:

Brooklyn Public Library, Brooklyn
Buffalo & Erie County Public Library, Buffalo
Chautauqua-Cattaraugus Library System, Jamestown
Clinton-Essex-Franklin Library System, Plattsburgh
Finger Lakes Library System, Ithaca
Four County Library System, Vestal
Mid-Hudson Library System, Poughkeepsie
Mid-York Library System, Utica
Mohawk Valley Library System, Schenectady
Monroe County Library System, Rochester
Nassau Library System, Uniondale
Nioga Library System, Lockport
North County Library System, Watertown
Onondaga County Public Library, Syracuse
Pioneer Library System, Canandaigua
Queens Borough Public Library, Jamaica
Ramapo Catskill Library System, Middletown
Southern Adirondack Library System, Saratoga Springs
Southern Tier Library System, Painted Post
Suffolk Cooperative Library System, Bellport
The New York Public Library, New York
Upper Hudson Library System, Albany
Westchester Library System, Ardsley

Reference and Research Library Resources Systems:

Capital District Library Council for Reference and Research Resources, Albany
Central New York Library Resources Council, Syracuse
Long Island Library Resources Council Inc, Bellport
Metropolitan New York Library Council (METRO), New York
Northern New York Library Network, Potsdam
Rochester Regional Library Council, Fairport
South Central Regional Library Council, Ithaca
Southeastern New York Library Resources Council, Highland
Western New York Library Resources Council, Buffalo

School Library Systems:

Albany-Schoharie-Schenectady-Saratoga BOCES School Library System
Broome-Tioga BOCES School Library System
Buffalo City School Library System
Cattaraugus-Allegany-Erie-Wyoming BOCES School Library System
Cayuga-Onondaga BOCES School Library System
Clinton-Essex-Warren-Washington BOCES School Library System
Delaware-Chenango-Madison-Otsego BOCES School Library System
Dutchess BOCES School Library System
Eastern Suffolk, (Suffolk 1) BOCES School Library System
Erie 1 BOCES School Library System
Erie 2-Chautauqua-Cattaraugus BOCES School Library System
Franklin-Essex-Hamilton BOCES School Library System
Genesee-Livingston-Steuben-Wyoming (Genesee Valley) BOCES School Library System
Hamilton-Fulton-Montgomery BOCES School Library System

Jefferson-Lewis-Hamilton-Herkimer-Oneida BOCES School Library System
Madison-Oneida BOCES School Library System
Monroe 1-BOCES School Library System
Monroe 2-Orleans BOCES School Library System
Nassau School Library System
New York City School Library System
Oneida-Herkimer-Madison BOCES School Library System
Onondaga-Cortland-Madison BOCES School Library System
Ontario-Seneca-Yates-Cayuga-Wayne (Wayne-Finger Lakes) BOCES School
    Library System
Orange-Ulster BOCES School Library System
Orleans-Niagara BOCES School Library System
Oswego BOCES School Library System
Otsego-Delaware-Schoharie-Greene (Otsego Northern Catskills) BOCES School
    Library System
Putnam Westchester BOCES School Library System
Rensselaer-Columbia-Greene (Questar III) BOCES School Library System
Rochester City School Library System
Rockland BOCES School Library System
St Lawrence-Lewis BOCES School Library System
Schuyler-Steuben-Chemung-Tioga-Allegany BOCES School Library System
Sullivan BOCES School Library System
Syracuse City School Library System
Tompkins-Seneca-Tioga BOCES School Library System
Ulster BOCES School Library System
Washington-Saratoga-Warren-Hamilton-Essex BOCES School Library System
Westchester (Southern Westchester or Westchester 2) BOCES School Library
    System
Western Suffolk, (Suffolk 2) BOCES School Library System
Yonkers City School Library System

NORTH CAROLINA

North Carolina public libraries are organized into fourteen regional (multi-county)
systems and fifty-three single-county systems. These systems have a total of 324
branch libraries. The state also has ten independent municipal public libraries.

NORTH DAKOTA

North Dakota has a statewide online library catalog.

OHIO

The state of Ohio has four chartered regional library systems which develop services
and resources within a region to meet the needs of the users.

Chartered Regional Library Systems:

Northeast Ohio Regional Library System (NEO-RLS), Warren
Northwest Regional Library System, (NORWELD), Bowling Green
Southeast Regional Library System (SERLS), Wellston
Southwest Ohio and Neighboring Libraries (SWON), Blue Ash

OKLAHOMA

The state of Oklahoma has eight Library Systems, six Multi-County and two
City-County Systems. The Multi-County Systems provide public library service in
two or more counties under a consolidated administration and governance, with a
stable financial base.

Library Systems:

Chickasaw Regional Library System, Ardmore
Eastern Oklahoma District Library System, Muskogee
Metropolitan Library System, Oklahoma City
Pioneer Library System, Norman
Southeastern Public Library System of Oklahoma, McAlester
Southern Prairie Library System, Altus
Tulsa City-County Library, Tulsa
Western Plains Library System, Clinton

OREGON (N)

The state of Oregon has seven cooperative library systems, which derive their
operating income exclusively from local tax sources. These systems provide a variety
of services including cooperative automation, outreach services, interlibrary loan,
courier service, books-by-mail, bookmobile, reference back-up and general
cooperation. The seven systems serve 41.77% of Oregon's total population.

Cooperative Library Systems:

Chemeketa Cooperative Regional Library Service, Salem
Coos County Library Service District, Coos Bay
Library Information Network of Clackamas County, Oak Grove
Lincoln County Library District, Newport
Umatilla County Special Library District, Pendleton

Wasco County Library Service District, The Dalles
Washington County Cooperative Library Service, Hillsboro

PENNSYLVANIA

The state of Pennsylvania has thirty-three Public Library Systems. The systems are
federations of independent libraries which have joined together to serve a county or
township. They provide interlibrary loan and, in some cases, centralized ordering and
processing. The chief benefit is that residents of the county or township have free use
of any library in the system.

Library Systems:

Adams County Library System, Gettysburg
Allegheny County Library Association, Pittsburgh
Beaver County Library System, Aliquippa
Bedford County Federated Library System, Bedford
Berks County Library System, Reading
Blair County Library System, Altoona
Bradford County Library System, Troy
Bucks County Free Library, Doylestown
Butler County Library System, Butler
Cambria County Library System, Johnstown
Centre County Federation of Public Libraries, State College
Chester County Library System, Exton
Clarion County Library System, Clarion
Crawford County Federated Library System, Meadville
Cumberland County Library System, Carlisle
Delaware County Library System, Media
Franklin County Library System, Chambersburg
Greene County Library System, Jefferson
Jefferson County Library System, Brockway
Lackawanna County Library System, Scranton
Lawrence County Federated Library System, New Castle
Lebanon County Library System, Lebanon
Library System of Lancaster County, Lancaster
Luzerne County Library System, Wilkes-Barre
Lycoming County Library System, Williamsport
Potter-Tioga County Library System, Coudersport
Schuylkill County Library System, Pottsville
Somerset County Federated Library System, Somerset
Union County Library System, Lewisburg
Washington County Library System, Washington
Wayne Library Authority, Honesdale
Westmoreland County Federated Library System, Greensburg
York County Library System, York

RHODE ISLAND (N)

The state of Rhode Island established The Library of Rhode Island (LORI) network in
1989, as a multitype network to promote resource sharing and interlibrary
cooperation. Approximately 206 libraries belong to LORI, including public,
academic, health sciences and school libraries as well as state agency libraries and a
historical society. Libraries annually certify that they comply with network standards,
which are regulations on file with the Office of the Secretary of State, in order to
receive: interlibrary loan, First Search and Clearinghouse services, interlibrary
delivery, e-rate application support, and technology plan consulting.

SOUTH CAROLINA

The state of South Carolina has 42 Public Library Systems. Each system provides
services to an entire county or to a region composed of several counties, thus serving
the entire state.

SOUTH DAKOTA (N)

The state of South Dakota has the member supported S.D. Library Network
(SDLN). Participation is voluntary for individual libraries. The system provides
resource sharing, communications & provision for out-of-state services.

TENNESSEE

The state of Tennessee has 12 multi-county regional library systems, which provide
support services to public libraries in 91 counties.

Multi-County Library Systems:

Buffalo River Regional Library, Columbia
Clinch River Regional Library, Clinton
Falling Water River Regional Library, Cookeville
Hatchie River Regional Library, Jackson
Holston River Regional Library, Johnson City
Obion River Regional Library, Martin
Ocoee River Regional Library, Athens
Red River Regional Library, Clarksville

Stones River Regional Library, Murfreesboro

The state also has 4 single-county library systems that provide direct library services to residents of those counties.

Single-County Library Systems:
Chattanooga-Hamilton County Bicentennial Library, Chattanooga
Knox County Public Library System, Knoxville
Memphis-Shelby County Public Library & Information Center, Memphis
Nashville Public Library, Nashville

Other Library Systems with Multiple Branches:
Collegedale Public Library, Collegedale
East Ridge City Library, East Ridge
Germantown Community Library, Germantown
La Vergne Public Library, La Vergne
Lucius E & Elsie C Burch, Jr Library, Collierville
Mary E Tippit, Townsend
Millington Public Library, Millington

Mount Carmel Public Library, Mount Carmel
Oak Ridge Public Library, Oak Ridge
Sam T Wilson Public Library, Arlington
Signal Mountain Library, Signal Mountain

TEXAS

Texas has 5 Regional Library Systems in the state. The system project allows member libraries from each region to participate in cooperative services such as continuing education and consulting, technical assistance, special services and programs.The 5 library systems are listed below:

Regional Library Systems:
Big Country Library System, Abilene Public Library
Central Texas Library System, Inc., Austin
Nicholson Memorial Library, Garland
North Texas Library Partners, Fort Worth
West Texas Library System, Lubbock

Library Networks:
Harrington Library Consortium

UTAH

In the State of Utah, public libraries are established by State statute under the jurisdiction of a city or a county government. There are 44 certified city public library systems and 12 from counties, as well as 7 Native American tribal libraries. In addition, the State Library manages mobile library services to 14 counties with nine bookmobiles equipped with computers and wireless Internet access serving rural and remote areas of the State. The Utah State Library manages the State's digital library of government publications.

As a division of the Department of Heritage and Arts, the Utah State Library is also established under State statute to oversee the development of libraries across the State, and has adopted a vision to lead Utah's library community by preparing them to face the challenges of the 21st Century. This State Library provides funding, training, professional advice and technical assistance to library directors, staff, and trustees throughout Utah.

Through PUBLIC PIONEER: *Utah's Online Library,* the State Library offers all residents of the State access to a broad range of full-text databases featuring unique business resources, tools for research and homework, career information, genealogy research, and downloadable media. Additionally, the State Library assists residents of all ages who are blind, visually impaired, physically or print-disabled by providing audio books, books in large print and one of the largest collections of books in Braille in the world.

VERMONT

The state of Vermont has no library systems.

VIRGINIA

The state of Virginia has no Library Systems.

WASHINGTON

Washington State has twenty-six public library districts serving an aggregate population of 5,062,760 across thirty-six of the state's thirty-nine counties. Another 1,584,270 people are served by thirty-six municipal libraries. At least one public library (either municipal, county or multi-county library) exists in every county in Washington State, serving at least a portion of the total population of that county.

WEST VIRGINIA

The state of West Virginia has thirteen service center libraries.

Service Center Libraries:
Cabell County Public Library, Huntington
Clarksburg-Harrison County Public Library, Clarksburg
Craft Memorial Library, Bluefield
Greenbrier County Public Library, Lewisburg
Kanawha County Public Library, Charleston
Keyser-Mineral County Public Library, Keyser
Martinsburg-Berkeley County Public Library, Martinsburg
Mary H Weir Public Library, Weirton
Morgantown Public Library, Morgantown
Moundsville-Marshall County Public Library, Moundsville
Parkersburg & Wood County Public Library, Parkersburg
South Charleston Public Library, South Charleston
Upshur County Public Library, Buckhannon

WISCONSIN

The state of Wisconsin has seventeen Public Library Systems which provide an organizational and service structure to make the most efficient use of library resources through cooperative arrangements among system members. The following are county and multi-county organizations.

Public Library Systems:
Arrowhead Library System, Janesville
Eastern Shores Library System, Sheboygan
Indianhead Federated Library System, Eau Claire
Kenosha County Library System, Kenosha
Lakeshores Library System, Waterford
Manitowoc-Calumet Library System, Manitowoc
Mid-Wisconsin Federated Library System, Horicon
Milwaukee County Federated Library System, Milwaukee
Nicolet Federated Library System, Green Bay
Northern Waters Library Service, Ashland
Outagamie Waupaca Library System, Appleton
South Central Library System, Madison
Southwest Wisconsin Library System, Fennimore
Waukesha County Federated Library System, Waukesha
Winding Rivers Library System, La Crosse
Winnefox Library System, Oshkosh
Wisconsin Valley Library Service, Wausau

WYOMING

Each of the twenty-three counties in the state of Wyoming forms a Library System.

CANADA

ALBERTA

Alberta has seven Cooperative Library Systems which work to improve the quality of public library service in the province. The first three systems serve public libraries. The other four provide services to both public libraries and school libraries.

Library Systems:
Chinook Arch Regional Library System, Lethbridge
Marigold Library System, Strathmore
Northern Lights Library System, Elk Point
Parkland Regional Library, Lacombe
Peace Library System, Grande Prairie
Shortgrass Library System, Medicine Hat
Yellowhead Regional Library, Spruce Grove

BRITISH COLUMBIA

British Columbia has 6 Library Federations, 2 Integrated Public Library Systems, 3 Regional Library Districts, 28 Municipal Public Libraries & 38 Public Library Associations serving the province.

Library Federations:
Island Link Library Federation, Victoria
Kootenay Library Federation, Castlegor
North Central Library Federation, Burns Lake
North Coast Library Federation, Terrace
North East Library Federation, Hudson's Hope
Public Library InterLINK, Burnaby

Regional Library Districts:

Fraser Valley Regional Library, Abbotsford
Okanagan Regional Library District, Kelowna
Vancouver Island Regional Library, Nanaimo

Integrated Public Library Systems:

Cariboo Regional District Library System, Williams Lake
Thompson-Nicola Regional District Library System, Kamloops

NEW BRUNSWICK

In New Brunswick, public library services are offered through a partnership between the provincial government and participating municipalities. New Brunswick Public Library Service (NBPLS) is the agency responsible for the management and development of public library services in the province. NBPLS has been part of the New Brunswick Department of Post Secondary Education Training & Labour since February 14, 2006. NBPLS is made up of one provincial office, 5 regional offices, 63 public libraries, 11 public-school libraries and 3 bookmobiles.

Regional Offices:

Albert-Westmorland-Kent Library Region, Moncton
Chaleur Library Region, Campbellton
Fundy Library Region, Saint John
Haut-Saint-Jean Library Region, Edmundston
York Library Region, Fredericton

NEWFOUNDLAND & LABRADOR

The Provincial Information and Library Resources Board of Newfoundland and Labrador is responsible for public library services throughout the province. The Board operates 96 public libraries offering a range of services including: printed materials, DVDs, CDs, e-content, public access computers with free Internet access, Wi-Fi and a variety of library programs. Communities without public libraries are served through books-by-mail. The libraries are organized into four geographic divisions, Provincial Resource, Eastern, Central and West Newfoundland/Labrador. There are also three divisions located at the provincial headquarters, which have provincial responsibilities: Administration, Technical Services and Information Technology. The Board's website is: www.nlpl.ca.

NORTHWEST TERRITORIES

There are 14 public libraries in the Northwest Territories, all community run and supported by Public Library Services, a government unit located in Hay River, NT, Canada.

NOVA SCOTIA

Public library service in Nova Scotia is provided by nine Regional Libraries serving 54 municipalities through 83 service points.

Regional Libraries:

Annapolis Valley Regional Library, Bridgetown
Cape Breton Regional Library, Sydney
Colchester - East Hants Public Library, Truro
Cumberland Public Libraries, Amherst
Eastern Counties Regional Library, Mulgrave
Halifax Public Libraries, Dartmouth
Pictou - Antigonish Regional Library, New Glasgow
South Shore Public Libraries, Hebbville

Western Counties Regional Library, Yarmouth

PRINCE EDWARD ISLAND

The Prince Edward Island Public Library Service is the Regional Library System, which provides public library services to the entire province. Service is provided directly by the province, which provides staff and materials. The local community provides the facility to house the library.

QUEBEC

In 2007 Quebec had eleven Centres regionaux de services aux bibliotheques publiques (CRSBP), also called Reseaux BIBLIO, which promote library services in municipalities with population under 5000. 692 public libraries are served by CRSBP.

125 public libraries promote library service in municipalities with population over 5001.

Bibliotheque ET Archives nationales du Quebec (BAnQ), a national institution, has as part of its mission to assemble, preserve permanently and disseminate Quebec's published documentary heritage together with any related document of cultural interest, and documents relating to Quebec that are published outside Quebec.

SASKATCHEWAN

Saskatchewan has seven regional library systems, two municipal library systems, and a northern federation of educational and public libraries, which deliver public library services. All library systems in Saskatchewan cooperate with each other in extensive resource sharing to foster a one-province library system, which provides service to all residents. The Saskatchewan Provincial Library, in cooperation with all types of libraries, develops and coordinates library services throughout the province.

Regional Library Systems:

Chinook Regional Library, Swift Current
Lakeland Library Region, North Battleford
Palliser Regional Library, Moose Jaw
Parkland Regional Library, Yorkton
Southeast Regional Library, Weyburn
Wapiti Regional Library, Prince Albert
Wheatland Regional Library, Saskatoon

Municipal Library Systems:

Regina Public Library, Regina
Saskatoon Public Library, Saskatoon

Federated System:

Pahkisimon Nuye Ah Library System, La Ronge
Saskatchewan Provincial Library

YUKON

Public Libraries Branch of the Community Development Division of the Department of Community Services provides public library service in Yukon through a distributed network with a central library in Whitehorse and fourteen community libraries. Public libraries provides centralized administrative and consultative services, a Web PAC comprising the holdings of public libraries plus the Yukon Archives Library, the cataloguing, processing and distribution of materials, programming and promotion, reference services and a Yukon-wide ILL network.

LIBRARIES FOR THE BLIND AND PHYSICALLY HANDICAPPED

Through designated regional and subregional libraries, the National Library Service for the Blind and Physically Handicapped, Library of Congress (NLS) provides free library service to print-handicapped individuals. This index serves as a guide for locating libraries, which provide recordings and Braille materials for their patrons.

Each regional library has an individual entry in the Library Section of this directory. Each subregional library has a sub-entry under the library it is a part of. For statistics on NLS (Karen Keninger, Director), see the Library of Congress entry.

For Canada, this index lists the headquarters of the Canadian National Institute for the Blind (Jim Sanders, President). It also lists Canadian institutions, which have facilities for assisting blind and physically handicapped patrons.

ALABAMA

Regional

Alabama Public Library Service, Division for the Blind & Physically Handicapped, Montgomery

Subregional

Alabama Institute for the Deaf & Blind, Library & Resource Center for the Blind & Physically Handicapped, Talladega

Houston Love Memorial Library, Division for the Blind & Physically Handicapped, Dothan

Huntsville-Madison County Public Library, Subregional Library for the Blind & Physically Handicapped, Huntsville

Tuscaloosa Public Library, Subregional Library for the Blind & Physically Handicapped, Tuscaloosa

ALASKA

Regional

Alaska State Library, Talking Book Center, Anchorage

ARIZONA

Regional

Arizona State Braille & Talking Book Library, Phoenix

ARKANSAS

Regional

Arkansas State Library Services for the Blind & Physically Handicapped, Little Rock

Subregional

Columbia County Library/Library for the Blind & Physically Handicapped, Magnolia

CALIFORNIA

Regional

California State Library /Braille & Talking Book Library, Sacramento
Braille Institute Library Services, Los Angeles

Subregional

Fresno County Public Library, Talking Book Library for the Blind, Fresno

COLORADO

Regional

Colorado Talking Book Library, Denver

CONNECTICUT

Regional

Connecticut State Library, Library for the Blind & Physically Handicapped, Rocky Hill

DISTRICT OF COLUMBIA

Regional

DC Regional Library for the Blind & Physically Handicapped, Washington

FLORIDA

Regional

Bureau of Braille & Talking Book Library Services, Daytona Beach

Subregional

Broward County Division of Libraries, Talking Book Library, Fort Lauderdale
Jacksonville Public Library, Talking Books/Special Needs Library, Jacksonville
Lee County Library System, Talking Books, North Fort Myers
Miami-Dade Public Library System, Talking Books, Miami
Orange County Library District, Talking Books Section, Orlando
Pinellas Talking Book Library, Clearwater
Tampa-Hillsborough County Public Library System, Hillsborough Talking Book Library, Tampa

GEORGIA

Regional

Georgia Library for Accessible Services, Atlanta

Subregional

Cherokee Regional Library System, North Georgia Talking Books Center, Lafayette

Sara Hightower Regional Library, Rome Subregional Library for People with Disabilities, Rome
Live Oak Public Libraries, Library for the Blind & Physically Handicapped, Savannah
Middle Georgia Regional Library System Library for the Blind & Physically Handicapped, Macon
Oconee Regional Library, Talking Book Center, Dublin
South Georgia Regional Library System, Talking Books Center, Valdosta
Southwest Georgia Regional Library, Bainbridge Subregional Library for the Blind & Physically Handicapped-Talking Book Center, Bainbridge

HAWAII

Regional

Hawaii State Public Library System, Library for the Blind & Physically Handicapped, Honolulu

IDAHO

Regional

Idaho School for the Deaf & Blind Library, Gooding
Idaho Commission for Libraries, Talking Book Service, Boise

ILLINOIS

Regional

Illinois State Library, Talking Book & Braille Service, Springfield

Subregional

Mid-Illinois Talking Book Center, East Peoria

INDIANA

Regional

Indiana State Library, Indiana Talking Book & Braille Library, Indianapolis

Subregional

Bartholomew County Public Library, Subregional Library for the Blind & Physically Handicapped, Columbus
Evansville-Vanderburgh Public Library, Talking Books Service, Evansville
Lake County Public Library, Talking Book Service, Merrillville

IOWA

Regional

Iowa Regional Library for the Blind & Physically Handicapped, Des Moines

KANSAS

Regional

Kansas State Library, Kansas Talking Books Service, Emporia

Subregional

Central Kansas Library System, Subregional Library for the Blind & Physically Handicapped, Great Bend
North Central Kansas Libraries System, Subregional Talking Books, Manhattan
Southwest Kansas Library System, Talking Books, Dodge City
Topeka & Shawnee County Public Library, Subregional Library for the Blind & Physically Handicapped, Topeka

KENTUCKY

Regional

Kentucky Regional Library for the Blind & Physically Handicapped, Kentucky Talking Book Library, Frankfort

Subregional

LOUISIANA
Regional

State Library of Louisiana, Services for the Blind & Physically Handicapped, Baton Rouge

MAINE

Regional

Maine Regional Library for the Blind & Physically Impaired, Augusta

MARYLAND

Regional

Maryland State Library for the Blind & Physically Handicapped, Baltimore

MASSACHUSETTS

Regional

Perkins School for the Blind, Braille & Talking Book Library, Watertown

Subregional

Worcester Public Library, Talking Book Library, Worcester

MICHIGAN

Regional

Michigan Commission for the Blind -Braille & Talking Book Library, Lansing
Wayne County Regional Library for the Blind & Physically Handicapped, Westland

Subregional

Ann Arbor District Library, Washtenaw Library for the Blind & Physically Disabled, Ann Arbor
Detroit Public Library, Detroit Subregional Library for the Blind & Physically Handicapped, Detroit
Genesee District Library, Library for the Blind and Physically Handicapped, Flint
Kent District Library, Library for the Blind & Physically Handicapped, Wyoming
Macomb County Library, Macomb Library for the Blind & Physically Handicapped, Clinton Township
Muskegon Area District Library, Blind & Physically Handicapped Library, Muskegon
Traverse Area District Library, Subregional Library for the Blind & Physically Handicapped, Traverse City
Upper Peninsula Library for the Blind & Physically Handicapped, Marquette

MINNESOTA

Regional

Minnesota Braille & Talking Book Library, Faribault

MISSISSIPPI

Regional

Mississippi Library Commission, Blind & Physically Handicapped Library Services, Jackson

MISSOURI

Regional

Missouri State Library, Wolfner Library for the Blind & Physically Handicapped, Jefferson City

NEBRASKA

Regional

Nebraska Library Commission Talking Book & Braille Service, Lincoln

NEVADA

Regional

Nevada State Library & Archives, Regional Library for the Blind & Physically Handicapped, Carson City

NEW HAMPSHIRE

Regional

New Hampshire State Library, Talking Book Services, Concord

NEW JERSEY

Regional

New Jersey State Library/Talking Book & Braille Center, Trenton

NEW MEXICO

Regional

New Mexico State Library, Library for the Blind & Physically Handicapped, Santa Fe

NEW YORK

Regional

The New York Public Library - Astor, Lenox & Tilden Foundations, Andrew Heiskell Braille & Talking Book Library, New York
New York State Library, Talking Book & Braille Library, Albany

Subregional

Suffolk Cooperative Library System, Long Island Talking Book Library, Bellport

NORTH CAROLINA

Regional

North Carolina Regional Library for the Blind & Physically Handicapped, Raleigh

OHIO

Regional

Cleveland Public Library, Ohio Library for the Blind & Physically Handicapped, Cleveland

OKLAHOMA

Regional

Oklahoma Library for the Blind & Physically Handicapped, Oklahoma City

OREGON

Regional

Oregon State Library Talking Book & Braille Services, Salem

PENNSYLVANIA

Regional

Carnegie Library of Pittsburgh, Library for the Blind & Physically Handicapped, Pittsburgh
Free Library of Philadelphia, Library for the Blind & Physically Handicapped, Philadelphia

RHODE ISLAND

Regional

State of Rhode Island Office of Library & Information Services, Talking Books Plus, Providence

SOUTH CAROLINA

Regional

South Carolina State Library, Talking Book Services, Columbia

SOUTH DAKOTA

Regional

South Dakota State Library, Braille & Talking Book Library, Pierre

TENNESSEE

Regional

Tennessee Regional Library for the Blind & Physically Handicapped, Nashville

TEXAS

Regional

Texas State Library & Archives Commission, Talking Book Program, Austin

Subregional

Coldspring Area Public Library, Coldspring

UTAH

Regional

Utah State Library Division, Program for the Blind & Disabled, Salt Lake City

VERMONT

Regional

Vermont Regional Library for the Blind & Physically Handicapped, Berlin

VIRGINIA

Regional

Virginia Department for the Blind & Vision Impaired Library & Resource Center, Richmond

Subregional

Alexandria Library, Talking Books, Alexandria
Central Rappahannock Regional Library, Fredericksburg Subregional for the Blind-Physically Handicapped, Fredericksburg
Staunton Public Library, Talking Book Center, Staunton
Virginia Beach Public Library Department/ Subregional Library for the Blind & Handicapped, Bayside Special Library Services, Virginia Beach

WASHINGTON

Regional

Washington Talking Book & Braille Library, Seattle

WEST VIRGINIA

Subregional

Cabell County Public Library, Services for the Blind & Physically Handicapped, Huntington
Parkersburg & Wood County Public Library, Services for the Blind & Physically Handicapped, Parkersburg
West Virginia School for the Blind Library, Romney

WISCONSIN

Regional

Wisconsin Regional Library for the Blind & Physically Handicapped, Milwaukee

PUERTO RICO

Regional

Puerto Rico Regional Library for the Blind & Physically Handicapped, Biblioteca Regional para Ciegos y Fisicamente Impedidos de Puerto Rico, San Juan

VIRGIN ISLANDS

Regional

Virgin Islands Division of Libraries, Archives & Museums, Regional Library for the Blind & Physically Handicapped, Saint Croix

CANADA
NOVA SCOTIA

Saint Mary's University, Ferguson Library for Print Handicapped Students, Halifax

ONTARIO

Canadian National Institute for the Blind, Library for the Blind, Toronto

LIBRARIES SERVING THE DEAF AND HEARING IMPAIRED

Although no federal agency provides material for deaf and impaired patrons, as the National Library Service for the Blind and Physically Handicapped does for the blind, libraries are doing so on their own. Many offer TDD reference service, whereby a deaf patron can call the library and key in a request; have available staff that know sign language; and provide books and periodicals of special interest to the deaf as well as captioned films and projectors.

What follows is an index to those libraries, which have available TDD reference service or other services available for the deaf and hearing impaired. This index is a clear indication that libraries are concerned with serving deaf patrons and that they are letting American Library Directory know of their services.

For the TDD number of a specific library, as well as information on the other services available for the deaf and hearing impaired, see the "Special Services for the Deaf" paragraph in each individual entry in the library section.

ALABAMA

Alabama Public Library Service, Montgomery
Alabama Public Library Service, Division for the Blind & Physically Handicapped, Montgomery
Birmingham Public Library, Birmingham
Wallace Community College-Dothan, Phillip G Hamm Library-LRC System, Dothan

ALASKA

Alaska Department of Natural Resources, Division of Mining, Land & Water Library, Anchorage
Alaska Department of Natural Resources, Public Information Center, Anchorage
Anchorage Public Library, Z J Loussac Public Library, Anchorage
Special Education Service Agency, Anchorage
United States National Park Service, Klondike Gold Rush International Historical Park Library, Skagway

ARIZONA

Apache Junction Public Library, Apache Junction
Arizona State Schools for the Deaf & Blind Library, Tucson
Casa Grande Public Library, Casa Grande
Chandler Public Library, Chandler
Mesa Public Library, Mesa
Glendale Public Library, Glendale
Mesa Community College, Paul A Elsner Library & High Technology Complex, Mesa
Nogales-Santa Cruz County Public Library, Nogales
Page Public Library, Page
Phoenix Public Library, Phoenix
    Acacia, Phoenix
    Burton Barr Central Library, Phoenix
    Century, Phoenix
    Cesar Chavez, Phoenix
    Cholla, Phoenix
    Desert Broom, Phoenix
    Desert Sage, Phoenix
    Harmon, Phoenix
    Ironwood, Phoenix
    Mesquite, Phoenix
    Ocotillo, Phoenix
    Palo Verde, Phoenix
    Saguaro, Phoenix
    Yucca, Phoenix
Pinal County Library District, Florence
Scottsdale Public Library System, Scottsdale

Mustang Library, Scottsdale
University of Arizona, East Asian Collection, Tucson
Yuma County Library District Yuma

ARKANSAS

Arkansas School for the Deaf Library, Little Rock
Arkansas State Library, Little Rock
Arkansas State Library Services for the Blind & Physically Handicapped, Little Rock
Arkansas State University-Beebe, Abington Memorial Library, Beebe
Central Arkansas Library System, Little Rock
Fort Smith Public Library, Fort Smith
University of Arkansas at Little Rock, Ottenheimer Library, Little Rock

CALIFORNIA

Alameda County Library, Fremont
    Albany Branch, Albany
    Castro Valley Branch, Castro Valley
    Dublin Branch, Dublin
    Fremont Main Library, Fremont
    Newark Branch, Newark
    San Lorenzo Branch, San Lorenzo
    Union City Branch, Union City
Alameda Free Library, Alameda
Arcadia Public Library, Arcadia
Berkeley Public Library, Berkeley
Burbank Public Library, Burbank
California Department of Alcohol & Drug Programs, Resource Center Library, Sacramento
California State Library, Sacramento
California State University, Northridge, Delmar T Oviatt Library, Northridge
    National Center on Deafness-PEPNet Resource Center, Northridge
California State University, Sacramento Library, Sacramento
California State University, San Marcos Library, San Marcos
County of Los Angeles Public Library, Downey
Cuyamaca College Library, El Cajon
De Anza College, A Robert DeHart Learning Center, Cupertino
Evergreen Valley College Library, San Jose
Fresno County Public Library, Fresno
Glendale Public Library, Glendale
    Montrose-Crescenta, Montrose
Golden West College, R Dudley Boyce Library & Learning Center, Huntington Beach
Hayward Public Library, Hayward
Hemet Public Library, Hemet
Humboldt County Library, Eureka

Long Beach Public Library & Information Center, Long Beach
Los Angeles County Metropolitan Transportation Authority, Dorothy Peyton Gray
    Transportation Library-Research Center, Los Angeles
Monrovia Public Library, Monrovia
Monterey Park Bruggemeyer Library, Monterey Park Public Library, Monterey Park
Virginia Reid Moore Marine Research Library, Cabrillo Marine Aquarium Library,
    San Pedro
Napa City-County Library, Napa
Oakland Public Library, Oakland
    Main Library, Oakland
Oceanside Public Library, Oceanside
Oxnard Public Library, Oxnard
Pacific Grove Public Library, Pacific Grove
Palm Springs Public Library, Palm Springs
Palo Alto City Library, Palo Alto
    Mitchell Park, Palo Alto
Palomar College Library-Media Center, San Marcos
Pasadena Public Library, Pasadena
Pomona Public Library, Pomona
Richmond Public Library, Richmond
Sacramento Public Library, Sacramento
    Rio Linda Neighborhood Library, Rio Linda
San Diego Public Library, Central Library, San Diego
    City Heights Weingart, San Diego
    Mira Mesa, San Diego
    North Park, San Diego
    Otay Mesa-Nestor, San Diego
San Jose City College Library, San Jose
    Cesar E Chavez Library, San Jose
San Jose Public Library, Dr Martin Luther King Jr Library, San Jose
San Jose State University, King Library, San Jose
Santa Barbara City College, Eli Luria Library, Santa Barbara
Santa Clara City Library, Santa Clara
Santa Monica Public Library, Santa Monica
Sea World Library, San Diego
Sonoma County Library, Santa Rosa
Southwestern College Library, Chula Vista
Stanislaus County Law Library, Modesto
    Visalia Headquarters Branch, Visalia
University of California Berkeley, Berkeley
US National Park Services, Cabrillo National Monument Library, San Diego
Ventura County Library, Ventura
Virginia Reid Moore Marine Research Library, Cabrillo Marine Aquarium Library,
    San Pedro
Washington Hospital Healthcare System, Community Health Resource Library,
    Fremont
Watsonville Public Library, Watsonville
West Hills College Lemoore Library, Lemoore
Yorba Linda Public Library, Yorba Linda

COLORADO

Adams State College, Nielsen Library, Alamosa
Aurora Public Library, Administration - Department of Library & Cultural Services,
    Aurora
Edwin A Bemis Public Library, Littleton Public Library, Littleton
Denver Public Library, Denver
    Eugene Field, Denver
    Hampden, Denver
    Ross-Cherry Creek, Denver
    Schlessman, Denver
    Virginia Village, Denver
Englewood Public Library, Englewood
Jefferson County Public Library, Belmar Branch, Lakewood
Loveland Public Library, Loveland
Mesa County Public Library District, Grand Junction
Colorado Mesa University, Tomlinson Library, Grand Junction
Morgan Community College Library, Fort Morgan
National Stroke Association Library, Englewood
Pikes Peak Library District, Colorado Springs
Poudre River Public Library District, Fort Collins
Pueblo City-County Library District, Robert Hoag Rawlings Public Library, Pueblo
United States Department of Justice, National Institute of Corrections Information
    Center, Aurora
United States Geological Survey Library, Denver

CONNECTICUT

Avon Free Public Library, Avon
Bridgeport Public Library, Bridgeport
Derby Public Library, Harcourt Wood Memorial, Derby
Hartford Public Library, Hartford
Manchester Public Library, Mary Cheney Library, Manchester

Naugatuck Valley Community College, Max R Traurig Learning Resource Center
    Library, Waterbury
New Haven Free Public Library, New Haven
New Milford Public Library, New Milford
Northwestern Connecticut Community College Library, Winsted
Russell Library, Middletown
Silas Bronson Library, Waterbury
South Windsor Public Library, South Windsor
University of Connecticut, School of Law Library, Hartford
West Hartford Public Library, Noah Webster Memorial Library, West Hartford
    Julia Faxon Branch, West Hartford
West Haven Public Library, West Haven
Windham Community Memorial Hospital, Grant Health Sciences Library,
    Willimantic

DELAWARE

Rehoboth Beach Public Library, Rehoboth Beach
Margaret S Sterck School for the Deaf Library, Newark

DISTRICT OF COLUMBIA

District of Columbia Library for the Blind & Physically Handicapped, Washington
District of Columbia Public Library, Washington
    Dorothy I Height/Benning Neighborhood Library, Washington
    Martin Luther King Jr Memorial Library, Washington
Gallaudet University Library, Washington
Library of Congress, National Library Service for the Blind & Physically
    Handicapped, Washington
National Library of Education, Washington
United States Commission on Civil Rights, National Clearinghouse Library,
    Washington
United States Department of Justice-Justice Libraries, Washington
United States Equal Employment Opportunity Commission Library, Washington
United States Senate Library, Washington
US Architectural & Transportation Barriers Compliance Board, Technical
    Resources Library, Washington
US National Park Service, Frederick Douglass NHS Library, Washington

FLORIDA

Alachua County Library District, Headquarters Library, Gainesville
Boca Raton Public Library, Boca Raton
Boynton Beach City Library, Boynton Beach
Broward County Division of Libraries, Main Library, Fort Lauderdale
    Talking Book Library, Fort Lauderdale
    West Regional, Plantation
Citrus County Library System, Beverly Hills
    Central Ridge, Beverly Hills
    Coastal Region, Crystal River
    Floral City Public, Floral City
    Homosassa Library, Homosassa
    Lakes Region, Inverness
College of Central Florida Citrus Campus Learning Resources Center, Citrus
    Campus Library, Lecanto
Columbia County Public Library, Lake City
Elsie Quirk Public Library of Englewood, Englewood
Eustis Memorial Library, Eustis
Florida Department of Elder Affairs, Information Clearinghouse, Tallahassee
Florida Department of State, Division of Library & Information Service, State
    Library & Archives of Florida, Tallahassee
Florida Gulf Coast University Library, Fort Myers
Florida International University, Glen Hubert Library, North Miami
Florida International University, Steven & Dorothea Green Library, Miami
Florida State University Libraries, Tallahassee
    Paul A M Dirac Science Library, Tallahassee
    Robert Manning Strozier Library, Tallahassee
Fort Myers Beach Public Library, Fort Myers Beach
Fruitville Public Library, Sarasota
Hernando County Public Library System, Lykes Memorial Library, Brooksville
Jacksonville Public Library, Jacksonville
    Regency Square, Jacksonville
Largo Public Library, Largo
Lee County Library System, Fort Myers
    Bonita Springs Public, Bonita Springs
    Cape Coral-Lee County Public, Cape Coral
    Captiva Memorial, Captiva
    Dunbar Jupiter Hammon Library, Fort Myers
    East County Regional, Lehigh Acres
    Lakes Regional, Fort Myers
    North Fort Myers Public, North Fort Myers
    Outreach Services, Estero

Pine Island, Bokeelia
Riverdale, Fort Myers
South County Regional, Estero
LeRoy Collins Leon County Public Library System, Tallahassee
Dr B L Perry Jr, Branch, Tallahassee
Lake Jackson, Tallahassee
Marion County Public Library System, Ocala
Martin County Library System, Blake Library, Stuart
Miami-Dade Public Library System, Miami
North Indian River County Library, Sebastian
North Miami Public Library, E May Avil Library, North Miami
North Port Public Library, North Port
Orange County Library District, Orlando Public Library, Orlando
Osceola Library System, Hart Memorial Central Library & Ray Shanks Law
Library, Kissimmee
Palm Beach County Library System, West Palm Beach
Pasco County Library System, Hudson
Centennial Park, Holiday
Hudson Regional, Hudson
Hugh Embry Branch, Dade City
Land O' Lakes Branch, Land O' Lakes
New River, Zephyrhills
Regency Park, New Port Richey
South Holiday Branch, Holiday
Pinellas Talking Book Library, Clearwater
Polk State College, James W Dowdy Memorial Library, Winter Haven
Safety Harbor Public Library, Safety Harbor
Saint Johns County Public Library System, Southeast Branch Library &
Administrative Headquarters, Saint Augustine
Saint Lucie County Library System, Fort Pierce
Lakewood Park, Fort Pierce
Saint Petersburg Public Library, Saint Petersburg
Satellite Beach Public Library, Satellite Beach
Selby Public Library, Sarasota
South Mainland Library, Micco
Suwannee River Regional Library, Live Oak
Tampa-Hillsborough County Public Library System, Hillsborough Talking Books
Library, Tampa
Tampa-Hillsborough County Public Library System, John F Germany Public
Library, Tampa
Taylor County Public Library, Perry
Umatilla Public Library, Umatilla
University of North Florida, Thomas G Carpenter Library, Jacksonville
University of South Florida Library System, Tampa Campus, Tampa
University of West Florida, John C Pace Library, Pensacola
Volusia County Public Library, Daytona Beach
DeLand Area Public, DeLand
Wakulla County Public Library, Crawfordville

GEORGIA

Atlanta-Fulton Public Library System, Atlanta
Clayton State University, Morrow
Coastal Plain Regional Library, Headquarters, Tifton
Coweta Public Library System, A Mitchell Powell Jr Public Library, Newnan
DeKalb County Public Library, Clarkson Branch, Clarkson
East Georgia College Library, Swainsboro
Emory University Libraries, Robert W Woodruff Library, Atlanta
Gainesville State College, John Harrison Hosch Library, Gainesville
Gwinnett County Public Library, Lawrenceville
Hall County Library System, Main Library, Gainesville Branch
East Hall & Special Needs Library, Gainesville
Sara Hightower Regional Library, Rome
Live Oak Public Libraries, Savannah
Library for the Blind & Physically Handicapped, Macon
Newton County Library System, Covington
Thomas County Public Library System, Thomasville
US Bureau of the Census, Atlanta Regional Office Library, Atlanta

HAWAII

Hawaii State Public Library System, Honolulu
Aiea Public, Aiea
Hilo Public, Hilo
Kapaa Public, Kapaa
Lanai Public & School, Lanai City
Molokai Public, Kaunakakai
University of Hawaii, Thomas Hale Hamilton Library, Honolulu
University of Hawaii , William S Richardson School of Law Library, Honolulu
University of Hawaii at Hilo Library, Edwin H Mookini Library, Hilo

IDAHO

Boise Public Library / Main Library, Boise
Boise Public Library / Library! at Hillcrest , Boise

ILLINOIS

Algonquin Area Public Library District, Algonquin
Alpha Park Public Library District, Bartonville
Antioch District Library, Antioch
Arlington Heights Memorial Library, Arlington Heights
Auburn Public Library, Auburn
Bartlett Public Library District, Bartlett
Batavia Public Library District, Batavia
Belleville Public Library, Belleville
Bellwood Public Library, Bellwood
Berwyn Public Library, Berwyn
Champaign Public Library, Champaign
Chicago Community Trust Library, Chicago
Chicago Public Library, Chicago
Blackstone, Chicago
Hegewisch, Chicago
Conrad Sulzer Regional, Chicago
Carter G Woodson Regional, Chicago
Chicago Ridge Public Library, Chicago Ridge
Chillicothe Public Library District, Chillicothe
Decatur Public Library, Decatur
Deerfield Public Library, Deerfield
DeKalb Public Library, Haish Memorial Library, De Kalb
Des Plaines Public Library, Des Plaines
Dixon Public Library, Dixon
Downers Grove Public Library, Downers Grove
Eastern Illinois University, Booth Library, Charleston
Eisenhower Public Library District, Harwood Heights
Ela Area Public Library District, Lake Zurich
Elk Grove Village Public Library, Elk Grove Village
Elmhurst Public Library, Elmhurst
Flagg-Rochelle Public Library District, Rochelle
Forest Park Public Library, Forest Park
Fountaindale Public Library District, Bolingbrook
Romeoville Branch, Romeoville
Fox Lake District Library, Fox Lake
Fremont Public Library District, Mundelein
Galesburg Public Library, Galesburg
Geneva Public Library, Geneva
Glen Carbon Centennial Library, Glen Carbon
Glencoe Public Library, Glencoe
Glenside Public Library District, Glendale Heights
Glenview Public Library, Glenview
Grayslake Area Public Library District, Grayslake
Harvey Public Library District, Harvey
Havana Public Library District, Havana
Highland Park Public Library, Highland Park
Hinsdale Public Library, Hinsdale
Hoopeston Public Library, Hoopeston
Illinois Early Childhood Intervention Clearinghouse Library, Springfield
Illinois School for the Deaf, Library for the Deaf, Jacksonville
Illinois State Library, Springfield
Illinois State University, Milner Library, Normal
Indian Prairie Public Library District, Darien
Indian Trails Public Library District, Wheeling
Jacksonville Public Library, Jacksonville
John D & Catherine T MacArthur Foundation Library, Chicago
Kewanee Public Library District, Kewanee
La Grange Park Public Library District, La Grange Park
Lake Forest Library, Lake Forest
Lincoln Library, The Public Library of Springfield Illinois, Springfield
Maywood Public Library District, Maywood
Moline Public Library, Moline
Morton Grove Public Library, Morton Grove
Mount Prospect Public Library, Mount Prospect
Naperville Public Library, Naper Boulevard Library, Naperville
New Lenox Public Library District, New Lenox
Niles Public Library District, Niles
Northern Illinois University, University Libraries, De Kalb
Park Ridge Public Library, Park Ridge
Passavant Area Hospital, Sibert Library, Jacksonville
Peoria Public Library Downtown, Peoria
Prevention First, Inc, Lura Lynn Ryan Prevention Research Library, Chicago
Rantoul Public Library, Rantoul
Reddick Library, Ottawa
Robinson Public Library District, Robinson
Rockford Public Library, Rockford
Roselle Public Library District, Roselle

Round Lake Area Public Library District, Round Lake
Schaumburg Township District Library, Schaumburg
Shorewood-Troy Public Library District, Shorewood
Skokie Public Library, Skokie
Spertus Institute of Jewish Studies, Norman & Helen Asher Library, Chicago
St Charles Public Library District, Saint Charles
Sugar Grove Public Library District, Sugar Grove
Sycamore Public library, Sycamore
University of Illinois Library at Urbana-Champaign, Undergraduate, Urbana
Villa Park Public Library, Villa Park
Warren-Newport Public Library District, Gurnee
Wauconda Area Public Library District, Wauconda
Westchester Public Library, Westchester
Wheaton Public Library, Wheaton
William Rainey Harper College, Resources for Learning, Palatine
Wilmette Public Library District, Wilmette
Woodbridge Public Library, Woodbridge
Zion-Benton Public Library District, Zion

INDIANA

Allen County Public Library, Fort Wayne
Anderson City, Anderson, Stony Creek & Union Townships Public Library, Anderson
Brown County Public Library, Nashville
Brownsburg Public Library, Brownsburg
Carmel Clay Public Library, Carmel
East Chicago Public Library, East Chicago
Frankfort Community Public Library, Frankfort
Garrett Public Library, Garrett
Greenwood Public Library, Greenwood
Indiana Historical Society Library, William Henry Smith Memorial Library, Indianapolis
Indiana State Library, Indianapolis
Indiana State Library, Indiana Talking Book & Braille Library, Indianapolis
Indiana University, Indiana Institute on Disability & Community, Bloomington
Indianapolis-Marion County Public Library, Indianapolis
Jackson County Public Library, Seymour Library, Seymour
Logansport State Hospital Staff Library, Logansport
Marion Public Library, Marion
Porter County Public Library System, Valparaiso
    Valparaiso Public (Central), Valparaiso
Pulaski County Public Library, Winamac
Saint Joseph County Public Library, South Bend
Vigo County Public Library, Terre Haute
West Lafayette Public Library, West Lafayette

IOWA

Council Bluffs Public Library, Council Bluffs
Daveport Public Library, Davenport
Iowa Regional Library for the Blind & Physically Handicapped, Des Moines
Mount Pleasant Public Library, Mount Pleasant
University of Northern Iowa Library, Rod Library, Cedar Falls
Waterloo Public Library, Waterloo

KANSAS

Johnson County Library, Overland Park
    Antioch, Merriam
    Blue Valley, Overland Park
    Corinth, Prairie Village
    Gardner Branch, Gardner
    Lackman, Lenexa
    Leawood Pioneer Branch, Leawood
    Oak Park, Overland Park
Kansas State Historical Society, Library & Archives Division, Topeka
Olathe Public Library, Olathe
Topeka & Shawnee County Public Library, Topeka
University of Kansas Life Span Institute, Research & Training Center on Independent Living Library, Lawrence
Wichita Public Library, Wichita

KENTUCKY

Boyle County Public Library, Danville Library, Inc, Danville
Kentucky Horse Park, International Museum of the Horse, Lexington
University of Kentucky Libraries, William T Young Library, Lexington

LOUISIANA

Louisiana House of Representatives, David R Poynter Legislative Research Library, Baton Rouge
Louisiana State University Libraries, Paul M Herbert Law Center, Baton Rouge
McNeese State University, Lether E Frazar Memorial Library, Lake Charles
Rapides Parish Library, Alexandria
State Library of Louisiana, Baton Rouge

MAINE

Bowdoin College Library, Brunswick
Kennebec Valley Community College, Lunder Library, Fairfield
Lewiston Public Library, Lewiston
Maine Education Center for the Deaf & Hard of Hearing, Governor Baxter School for the Deaf Library, Falmouth
Maine State Law & Legislative Reference Library, Augusta
University of Southern Maine, University Libraries, Portland

MARYLAND

Baltimore County Public Library, Towson
Calvert Marine Museum Library, Solomons
Cecil County Public Library, Elkon Central Library, Elkton
Charles County Public Library, La Plata Branch, La Plata
Dorchester County Public Library, Cambridge
Enoch Pratt Free Library, Baltimore
Frederick County Public Libraries, Frederick
Howard County Library, Columbia
    Central, Columbia
    East Columbia, Columbia
    Elkridge Branch, Elkridge
    Miller Branch & Historical Center, Ellicott City
    Savage, Columbia
Maryland Department of Natural Resources, Carter Library & Information Resource Center, Annapolis
Maryland State Library for the Blind & Physically Handicapped, Baltimore
Montgomery College, Rockville
    Germantown Campus Library, Germantown
    Takoma Park Campus Library, Takoma Park
    Aspen Hill Library, Rockville
    Bethesda Library, Bethesda
    Chevy Chase Library, Chevy Chase
    Damascus Library, Damascus
    Davis Library, Bethesda
    Gaithersburg Interim Library, Gaithersburg
    Germantown Library, Germantown
    Kensington Park Library, Kensington
    Little Falls Library, Bethesda
    Long Branch, Silver Spring
    Olney Library, Olney
    Poolesville Library, Poolesville
    Potomac Library, Potomac
    Marilyn J Praisner, Burtonsville
    Quince Orchard Library, Gaithersburg
    Rockville Library, Rockville
    Silver Spring Library, Silver Spring
    Twinbrook Library, Rockville
    Wheaton Library, Wheaton
    White Oak Library, Silver Spring
NASA, Goddard Space Flight Center Library-Homer E Newell Memorial, Greenbelt
National Institute of Arthritis & Musculoskeletal & Skin Diseases, Bethesda
National Rehabilitation Information Center, Lanham
Prince George's County Memorial Library System, Hyattsville
    Surratts-Clinton Branch, Clinton
Public Library Association of Annapolis & Anne Arundel County, Inc, Headquarters, Annapolis
Ruth Enlow Library of Garrett County, Oakland
Riverdale Presbyterian Church Library, Hyattsville
Talbot County Free Library, Easton
The Library at Springfield Hospital Center, Sykesville
United States Department of Agriculture, National Agricultural Library, Beltsville
University of Baltimore, Langsdale Library, Baltimore
University of Maryland Libraries, Theodore R McKeldin Library, College Park
Washington County Free Library, Hagerstown

MASSACHUSETTS

Acton Memorial Library, Acton
Adams Free Library, Adams
Bedford Free Public Library, Bedford

Berkshire Athenaeum, Pittsfield Public Library, Pittsfield
Bridgewater Public Library, Bridgewater
Cambridge Public Library, Cambridge
Concord Free Public Library, Concord
Thomas Crane Public Library, Quincy
Everett Public Libraries, Frederick E Parlin Memorial, Everett
Fall River Public Library, Fall River
Framingham Public Library, Framingham
Greenfield Community College Library, Greenfield
Jones Library, Inc, Amherst
Needham Free Public Library, Needham
New Bedford Free Public Library, New Bedford
New England Sinai Hospital, Medical Library, Stoughton
Northeastern University Libraries, Snell Library, Boston
Frederick E Parlin Memorial Library, Everett
Peabody Essex Museum, Phillips Library, Salem
Plymouth Public Library, Plymouth
Pollard Memorial Library, Lowell
Springfield City Library, Central Branch, Springfield
Springfield Technical Community College Library, Springfield
State Transportation Library, Boston
Taunton Public Library, Taunton
The State Library of Massachusetts, George Fingold Library, Boston
Watertown Free Public Library, Watertown
Wellesley Free Library, Wellesley
West Springfield Public Library, West Springfield
Wilmington Memorial Library, Wilmington
Worcester Polytechnic Institute, George C Gordon Library, Worcester
Worcester Public Library, Talking Book Library, Worcester

MICHIGAN

Bay County Library System, Bay City
Bullard Sanford Memorial Library, Vassar
Capital Area District Library, Lansing
Clinton-Macomb Public Library, Clinton Township
    South, Clinton Township
Dearborn Public Library, Dearborn
Detroit Public Library, Detroit
    Detroit Public Library, Detroit Subregional Library for the Blind & Physically
        Handicapped, Detroit
Ferris State University, Library for Information, Technology & Education, Big
    Rapids
Grace A Dow Memorial Library, Midland
Harrison Community Library, Harrison
Herrick District Library, Holland
Kellogg Community College, Emory W Morris Learning Resource Center, Battle
    Creek
Lansing Community College Library, Lansing
Library of Michigan, Lansing
Library of Michigan Service for the Blind & Physically Handicapped, Lansing
Lincoln Township Public Library, Stevensville
Macomb County Library, Macomb Library for the Blind & Physically
    Handicapped, Clinton Township
Michigan Department of Community Health, Center for Forensic Psychiatry
    Library, Saline
Michigan State University Library, East Lansing
Monroe County Library System, Monroe
    Bedford, Temperance
    Blue Bush, Monroe
    Carleton Branch, Carleton
    Dorsch Memorial, Monroe
    Dundee Branch, Dundee
    Ellis Reference & Information Center, Monroe
    Erie Branch, Erie
    Frenchtown-Dixie, Monroe
    Ida Branch, Ida
    Maybee Branch, Maybee
    L S Navarre Branch, Monroe
    Rasey Memorial, Luna Pier
    South Rockwood Branch, South Rockwood
    Summerfield - Petersburg Branch, Petersburg
    Robert A Vivian Branch, Monroe
Muskegon Area District Library, Muskegon
    Blind & Physically Handicapped Library, Muskegon
    Egelston Branch, Muskegon
    Fruitport Branch, Fruitport
    Holton Branch, Holton
    Montague Branch, Montague
    Muskegon Heights Branch, Muskegon
    Norton Shores Jacob O Funkhouser Branch, Muskegon
    Ravenna Branch, Ravenna
    North Muskegon Walker Branch, North Muskegon
Northern Michigan University, Lydia M Olson Library, Marquette

Novi Public Library, Novi
Oak Park Public Library, Oak Park
Oakland County Library for the Visually & Physically Impaired, Pontiac
Orion Township Public Library, Lake Orion
Plymouth District Library, Plymouth
Public Libraries of Saginaw, Hoyt Main Library, Saginaw
Rochester Hills Public Library, Rochester
Saint Clair County Library System, STAR (Special Technologies Alternate
    Resources), Port Huron
Saint Clair Shores Public Library, Saint Clair Shores
Spies Public Library, Menominee
Traverse Area District Library, Traverse City
Troy Public Library, Troy
United States Army Corps of Engineers - Detroit District, IM-R Library, Detroit
Warren Public Library, Arthur J Miller Branch, Warren
Wayne County Regional Library for the Blind & Physically Handicapped, Westland
West Bloomfield Township Public Library, West Bloomfield

MINNESOTA

Austin Public Library, Austin
Blue Earth Community Library, Blue Earth
Dakota County Library System, Eagan
Debra S Fish Early Childhood Resource Library, Saint Paul
Duluth Public Library, Duluth
Fire-EMS-Safety Center Library, St Paul
Debra S Fish Early Childhood Resource Library, Saint Paul
Grand Rapids Area Library, Grand Rapids
Hibbing Public Library, Hibbing
Minneapolis Community & Technical College Library, Minneapolis
Minnesota Attorney General Library, Saint Paul
Mn/DOT Library, Saint Paul
Normandale Community College Library, Bloomington
Northfield Public Library, Northfield
Red Wing Public Library, Red Wing
Rochester Public Library, Rochester
Saint Paul Public Library, Saint Paul
South Saint Paul Public Library, South Saint Paul

MISSISSIPPI

Mississippi Library Commission, Jackson
University of Mississippi, John Davis Williams Library, University

MISSOURI

Daniel Boone Regional Library, Columbia Public Library-Headquarters, Columbia
    Callaway County Public Library, Fulton
Boonslick Regional Library, Sedalia
Cass County Public Library, Harrisonville
Ferguson Municipal Public Library, Ferguson
Mercer County Library, Princeton
Missouri State Library, Wolfner Library for the Blind & Physically Handicapped,
    Jefferson City
Missouri State University, Duane G Meyer Library, Springfield
Missouri Western State College, Hearnes Center, Saint Joseph
Northeast Missouri Library Service, Kahoka
Rockhurst University, Greenlease Library, Kansas City
Saint Charles City County Library District, Corporate Parkway Branch, Wentzville
    Deer Run, O'Fallon
    Middendorf-Kredell, O'Fallon
    Spencer Road, Saint Peters
Saint Louis Community College, Florissant Valley Campus Library, Ferguson
    Florissant Valley Campus Library, Ferguson
    Forest Park Campus Library, Saint Louis
Saint Louis County Library, Saint Louis
Saint Louis Public Library, Saint Louis
Sedalia Public Library, Sedalia
St Joseph Public Library, Saint Joseph
The Kansas City Public Library, Kansas City
University of Central Missouri, James C Kirkpatrick Library, Warrensburg

MONTANA

Bozeman Public Library, Bozeman
Lewis & Clark Library, Helena
Montana School for the Deaf & Blind Library, Great Falls
Montana State Library, Helena
Parmly Billings Library, South Central Federation of Libraries, Billings
University of Montana, Maureen & Mike Mansfield Library

NEBRASKA

Beatrice Public Library, Beatrice
Hastings Public Library, Hastings
Lied Scottsbluff Public Library, Scottsbluff
Lincoln City Libraries, Bennett Martin Library, Lincoln
Metropolitan Community College Library, Omaha
Omaha Public Library, W Dale Clark Library, Omaha

NEVADA

Nevada State Library & Archives, Regional Library for the Blind & Physically
  Handicapped, Carson City
Nevada Supreme Court Library, Carson City
University of Nevada, Las Vegas Libraries, Lied Library, Las Vegas

NEW HAMPSHIRE

Derry Public Library, Derry
Nashua Public Library, Nashua

NEW JERSEY

Burlington County Library, Westampton
East Brunswick Public Library, East Brunswick
Edison Township Free Public Library, Edison
Middlesex County Cultural & Heritage Commission, Resource & Reference
  Library, New Brunswick
Monmouth County Library, Manalapan
Morris County Library, Whippany
New Jersey Historical Society Library, Newark
New Jersey State Library, Trenton
    New Jersey State Library, New Jersey Library for the Blind & Physically
      Handicapped, Trenton
Prevention First, Prevention & Education Resource Center, Ocean
Ruth L Rockwood Memorial Library, Public Library of Livingston, Livingston

NEW MEXICO

Thomas Branigan Memorial Library, Las Cruces
Los Alamos County Library System, Los Alamos
National Park Service, Aztec Ruins National Monument Library, Aztec
New Mexico Highlands University, Thomas C Donnelly Library, Las Vegas
Santa Fe Public Library, Santa Fe
University of New Mexico, Zimmerman Library, Albuquerque

NEW YORK

Babylon Public Library, Babylon
Bethlehem Public Library, Delmar
Brentwood Public Library, Brentwood
Brighton Memorial Library, Rochester
College of Staten Island Library, Staten Island
East Meadow Public Library, East Meadow
Finger Lakes Library System, Ithaca
Levittown Public Library, Levittown
Lindenhurst Memorial Library, Lindenhurst
The New York Public Library - Astor, Lenox & Tilden Foundations, New York
    Bronx Library Center, Bronx
    Donnell Library Center, New York
    Andrew Heiskell Braille & Talking Book, New York
    Mid-Manhattan Library, New York
North Babylon Public Library, North Babylon
Onondaga County Public Library , Robert P Kinchen Central Library, Syracuse
Penfield Public Library, Penfield
Plainview-Old Bethpage Public Library, Plainview
Queens Borough Public Library, Queens Library, Jamaica
Rochester Institute of Technology, National Technical Institute for the Deaf,
  Rochester
Shelter Rock Public Library, Albertson
Suffolk Cooperative Library System, Bellport
    Long Island Talking Book Library, Bellport
SUNY Upstate Medical University, Health Sciences Library, Syracuse

NORTH CAROLINA

Buncombe County Public Libraries, Asheville
Cape Fear Community College, Learning Resource Center, Wilmington

Cumberland County Public Library & Information Center, Headquarters,
  Fayetteville
Duke University, William R Perkins Library System, Durham
Durham County Library, Durham
East Carolina University, William E Laupus Health Sciences Library, Greenville
High Point Public Library, High Point
New Hanover County Public Library, Wilmington
North Carolina Regional Library for the Blind & Physically Handicapped, Raleigh
Pitt Community College, Learning Resources Center, Greenville
Rowan Public Library, Salisbury
Union County Public Library, Monroe
University of North Carolina at Asheville, D Hiden Ramsey Library, Asheville
University of North Carolina at Chapel Hill, Walter Royal Davis Library, Chapel
  Hill
Western Piedmont Community College, Phifer Learning Resources Center,
  Morganton

NORTH DAKOTA

Minot Public Library, Minot
North Dakota State Library, Bismarck
North Dakota State University Libraries, Fargo
University of North Dakota, Chester Fritz Library, Grand Forks

OHIO

Akron-Summit County Public Library, Akron
Ashtabula County District Library, Ashtabula
    Geneva Public, Geneva
Chillicothe & Ross County Public Library, Chillicothe
Cleveland Heights-University Heights Public Library, Cleveland Heights
    Coventry Village, Cleveland Heights
Cleveland Public Library, Cleveland
Columbus Metropolitan Library, Columbus
    Driving Park, Columbus
    Dublin Branch, Dublin
    Franklinton, Columbus
    Gahanna Branch, Gahanna
    Hilliard Branch, Hilliard
    Hilltop, Columbus
    Karl Road, Columbus
    Martin Luther King Branch, Columbus
    Linden Branch, Columbus
    Livingston Branch, Columbus
    Main Library, Columbus
    New Albany Branch, New Albany
    Northside, Columbus
    Northwest, Columbus
    Outreach Division, Columbus
    Parsons, Columbus
    Reynoldsburg Branch, Reynoldsburg
    Shepard Branch, Columbus
    South High, Columbus
    Southeast, Columbus
    Whetstone Branch, Columbus
    Whitehall Branch, Columbus
Conneaut Public Library, Conneaut
Cuyahoga County Public Library, Parma
    Fairview Park Branch, Fairview Park
Elyria Public Library System, Elyria
Ella M Everhard Public Library, Wadsworth Public Library, Wadsworth
Fairfield County District Library, Lancaster
Lorain Public Library System, Lorain
Mansfield-Richland County Public Library, Mansfield
Medina County District Library, Medina
Northeast Behavioral Healthcare Library, Toledo Campus Library, Toledo
Ohio School for the Deaf Library, Columbus
Orville Public Library, Orville
Portage County District Library, Garrettsville
Portsmouth Public Library Portsmouth
Preble County District Library, Eaton
Public Library of Youngstown & Mahoning County, Youngstown
Public Utilities Commission of Ohio Library, Columbus
Sinclair Community College, Learning Resources Center, Dayton
Warren-Trumbull County Public Library, Warren
Willard Memorial Library, Willard
    Greenwich Public Library, Greenwich

OKLAHOMA

Bartlesville Public Library, Bartlesville
Oklahoma Library for the Blind & Physically Handicapped, Oklahoma City

Rose State College, Learning Resources Center, Midwest City
Southeastern Public Library System of Oklahoma, McAlester
Stillwater Public Library, Stillwater
Tulsa City-County Library System, Tulsa
University of Tulsa Libraries, McFarlin Library, Tulsa

OREGON

Beaverton City Library, Beaverton
Corvallis-Benton County Public Library, Corvallis
Dallas Public Library, Dallas
Douglas County Library System, Roseburg
Eugene Public Library, Eugene
Hillsboro Public Library, Hillsboro
Klamath County Library Services District, Klamath Falls
Multnomah County Library, Portland
Newport Public Library, Newport
Oregon State Library Talking Book & Braille Services, Salem
Oregon State University Libraries, The Valley Library, Corvallis
Portland Community College Library, Administration, Portland
Salem Public Library, Salem
Tigard Public Library, Tigard
Umpqua Community College Library, Roseburg
Washington County Cooperative Library Services, Hillsboro
Western Oregon University, Wayne & Lynn Hamersly Library, Monmouth

PENNSYLVANIA

Abington Township Public Library, Abington Free Library, Abington
AIDS Library, Philadelphia
Butler Area Public Library, Butler
Carnegie Library of Pittsburgh, Pittsburgh
Citizens Library, Washington
East Stroudsburg University, Kemp Library, East Stroudsburg
Erie County Public Library/Raymond M Blasco MD Memorial Library, Erie
Free Library of Philadelphia, Philadelphia
Green Tree Public Library, Pittsburgh
Mt Lebanon Public Library, Pittsburgh
Seton Hill University, Reeves Memorial Library, Greensburg
State Library of Pennsylvania, Harrisburg
US Department of Interior, National Park Service, Hopewell Furnace National
    Historic Site Resource Center, Elverson

RHODE ISLAND

Cumberland Public Library, Edward J Hayden Library, Cumberland
Marian J Mohr Memorial Library, Johnston
Pawtucket Public Library, Pawtucket
Providence Public Library, Providence
Robert L Carothers Library & Learning Commons, Kingston

SOUTH CAROLINA

Clemson University Libraries/ RM Cooper Library, Clemson
Horry County Memorial Library/ Administration, Conway
    Conway Branch, Conway
    North Myrtle Beach, North Myrtle Beach
    Socastee, Myrtle Beach
    Surfside Beach Branch, Surfside Beach
Richland County Public Library, Columbia
South Carolina School for the Deaf & the Blind, Jesse Franklin Cleveland Learning
    Resource Center, Spartanburg
South Carolina State Library, Columbia
    Talking Book Services, Columbia
Spartanburg County Public Libraries, Spartanburg

SOUTH DAKOTA

Vermillion Public Library, Vermillion

TENNESSEE

Chattanooga-Hamilton County Bicentennial Library, Chattanooga
East Tennessee State University, Sherrod Library, Johnson City
Jefferson City Public Library, Jefferson City
Knox County Public Library System, Lawson McGee Library-East Tennessee
    History Center, Knoxville
Memphis Public Library & Information Center, Benjamin L Hooks Central Library,
    Memphis
Motlow State Community College Libraries, Clayton-Glass Library, Tullahoma

TEXAS

Amarillo Public Library, Amarillo
Arlington Public Library System, George W Hawkes Central Library, Arlington
Beaumont Public Library System, Beaumont
Brownsville Public Library, Brownsville
Coldspring Area Public Library, Coldspring
Dallas Public Library, Dallas
Del Mar College, William F White Jr Library, Corpus Christi
Fort Bend County Libraries, George Memorial Library, Richmond
    Cinco Ranch, Katy
    First Colony, Sugar Land
    Albert George Branch, Needville
    Bob Lutts Fulshear Simonton Branch, Fulshear
    Missouri City Branch, Missouri City
    Sugar Land Branch, Sugar Land
Fort Worth Public Library, Fort Worth
Georgetown Public Library, Georgetown
Harlingen Public Library, Harlingen
Harris County Public Library, Houston
    Baldwin Boettcher Branch, Humble
Houston Public Library, Houston
    Southwest Collegiate Institute for the Deaf-Resource Center, Big Spring
San Antonio Public Library, San Antonio
Sterling Municipal Library, Baytown
Temple Public Library, Temple
Texas Christian University, Mary Couts Burnett Library, Fort Worth
Tom Green County Library System, San Angelo
University of Texas-Pan American Library, Edinburg
Weatherford College Library, Weatherford

UTAH

Orem Public Library, Orem
Salt Lake City Public Library, Salt Lake City
The Church of Jesus Christ of Latter-day Saints. Family History Library, Salt Lake
    City
United States Army Dugway Proving Ground, Dugway Post Library, Dugway
Utah State Library Division, Salt Lake City
    Program for the Blind & Disabled, Salt Lake City
Weber County Library, Ogden

VIRGINIA

Alexander Library, Alexandria
    Charles E Beatley, Jr Central, Alexandria
    Talking Books, Alexandria
American Counseling Association, Professional Library, Alexandria
Arlington County Department of Libraries, Arlington Public Library, Arlington
    Central Library, Arlington
Blue Ridge Community College, Houff Library, Weyers Cave
Central Rappahannock Regional Library, Fredericksburg Subregional for the
    Blind-Physically Handicapped, Fredericksburg
Christopher Newport University, Paul & Rosemary Trible Library, Newport News
George Mason University Libraries, Fenwick Library, Fairfax
    Arlington Campus, Arlington
    Johnson Center, Fairfax
    Mercer Library, Prince William Campus, Manassas
Hampton Public Library, Hampton
Jefferson-Madison Regional Library, Central Library, Charlottesville
Loudoun County Public Library, Leesburg
    Cascades Branch, Potomac Falls
    Lovettsville Branch, Lovettsville
    Middleburg Branch, Middleburg
    Outreach Services, Leesburg
    Purcellville Branch, Purcellville
    Rust Branch, Leesburg
    Sterling Branch, Sterling
Newport News Public Library System, Newport News
    Pearl Bailey Branch, Newport News
    Virgil I Grissom Branch, Newport News
    Main Street, Newport News
    West Avenue, Newport News
    Manassas Campus, Manassas
Pamunkey Regional Library, Hanover
    Atlee Branch, Mechanicsville
    Richard S Gillis Jr - Ashland Branch, Ashland
    Goochland Branch, Goochland
    Hanover Branch, Hanover
    King & Queen, Saint Stephen's Church
    Lois Wickham Jones-Montpelier Branch, Hanover

Mechanicsville Branch, Mechanicsville
Cochrane Rockville Branch, Rockville
Upper King William, King William
West Point Branch, West Point
Prince William Public Library System, Prince William
   Bull Run Regional, Manassas
   Central, Manassas
   Chinn Park Regional, Prince William
Roanoke Public Libraries, Roanoke
Roanoke County Public Library, Roanoke
The Library of Virginia, Richmond
Virginia Commonwealth University, James Cabell Branch Library, Richmond
Virginia Department of Historic Resources, Archives-Research Library, Richmond

WASHINGTON

Bellingham Public Library, Bellingham
Highline Community College Library, Des Moines
King County Rural Library District , King County Library System, Issaquah
Kitsap Regional Library, Bremerton
Northwest Library on Deaf Culture & History, Community Service Center for the
   Deaf & Hard of Hearing, Seattle
Mason General Hospital Library , Shelton
Pierce County Library System, Tacoma
Puyallup Public Library, Puyallup
Renton Public Library, Renton
Sno-Isle Libraries, Lynnwood Branch, Lynnwood
Spokane Public Library, Spokane
   East Side, Spokane
   Hillyard, Spokane
   Indian Trail, Spokane
   South Hill
Tacoma Community College Library, Pearl A Wanamaker Library, Tacoma
Tacoma Public Library, Tacoma
The Seattle Public Library, Seattle
University of Puget Sound, Collins Memorial Library, Tacoma
Washington Talking Book & Braille Library, Seattle
Whatcom County Law Library, Bellingham

WEST VIRGINIA

Cabell County Public Library, Huntington
Hampshire County Public Library, Romney
Southern West Virginia Community & Technical College, Harless Library, Mount
   Gay
West Virginia School for the Deaf & Blind Library, Romney

WISCONSIN

Appleton Public Library, Appleton
Aram Public Library, Delavan
Brookfield Public Library, Brookfield
Brown County Library, Green Bay
Hedberg Public Library, Janesville
L E Phillips Memorial Public Library, Eau Claire
La Crosse Public Library, La Crosse
Madison Public Library, Madison
McMillan Memorial Library, Wisconsin Rapids
Milwaukee Public Library, Milwaukee
   Martin Luther King Jr Branch, Milwaukee
Oshkosh Public Library, Oshkosh

St Francis Public Library, Saint Francis
Superior Public Library, Superior
United States Forest Service, Forest Products Laboratory Library, Madison
University of Wisconsin-Milwaukee, Golda Meir Library, Milwaukee
University of Wisconsin-Stout Library, Menomonie
Waukesha County Federated Library System, Waukesha
Waukesha Public Library, Waukesha
West Allis Public Library, West Allis
Wisconsin Regional Library for the Blind & Physically Handicapped, Milwaukee

WYOMING

Albany County Public Library, Laramie
Laramie County Community College Library, Cheyenne
Laramie County Library System, Cheyenne
Sheridan County Public Library System, Sheridan Fulmer Public Library, Sheridan

CANADA
ALBERTA

Calgary Public Library, Calgary
University of Alberta, Humanities & Social Sciences Library, Edmonton

BRITISH COLUMBIA

College of New Caledonia Library, Prince George
Greater Victoria Public Library Board, Victoria
Justice Institute of British Columbia Library, New Westminster
New Westminster Public Library, New Westminster
Vancouver Community College, King Edward & City Centre Campus Libraries,
   Vancouver

MANITOBA

Canada-Manitoba Business Service Centre Library, Winnipeg

NOVA SCOTIA

Halifax Public Library, Alderney Gate, Dartmouth
Pictou-Antigonish Regional Library, New Glasgow

ONTARIO

Brampton Library, Brampton
Canada Mortgage & Housing Corp, Canadian Housing Information Centre, Ottawa
Metrac (Metropolitan Action Committee on Violence Against Women & Children),
   Toronto
Saint Lawrence Parks Commission, Upper Canada Village Reference Library,
   Morrisburg
St Catharines Public Library, St. Catharines
Windsor Public Library, Windsor

QUEBEC

Bibliotheque Municipale de Gatineau, Gatineau
McGill University Libraries, Humanities & Social Sciences, Montreal

STATE AND PROVINCIAL PUBLIC LIBRARY AGENCIES

Listed below are the agencies concerned with Public Library extension work. Entries include the names of the persons in charge of this work. For detailed information see entries in the Library Section.

NATIONAL LIBRARY OF EDUCATION, 400 Maryland Ave SW, BE 101, Washington, DC 20202-5523. Tel: 202-205-5015. FAX: 202-401-0547; 202-260-7364. E-mail: library@ed.gov. *Dir,* Position Currently Open. (NLE conducts surveys of libraries, learning resources and educational technology.)

ALABAMA PUBLIC LIBRARY SERVICE, 6030 Monticello Dr, Montgomery 36130. Tel: 334-213-3900. FAX: 334-213-3993. *Dir,* Rebecca Mitchell

ALASKA STATE LIBRARY, 333 Willoughby Ave, Juneau 99801. (Mail add: PO Box 110571, 99811-0571). Tel: 907-465-2910. FAX: 907-465-2151. E-mail: asl@alaska. gov. *Dir, Libr, Archives & Mus,* Linda Thibodeau

ARIZONA STATE LIBRARY, ARCHIVES & PUBLIC RECORDS, 1700 W Washington, Rm 200, Phoenix 85007. Tel: 602-926-4035. FAX: 602-256-7983. E-mail: services@lib.az.us. *State Librn,* Joan Clark

ARKANSAS STATE LIBRARY, 900 W Capitol, Ste 100, Little Rock 72201-3108. Tel: 501-682-1527, 501-682-1526. FAX: 501-682-1899. *State Librn,* Carolyn Ashcraft

CALIFORNIA STATE LIBRARY, 900 N St, Sacramento 95814. (Mail add: PO Box 942837, 94237-0001). Tel: 916-654-0188. FAX: 916-376-5310. E-mail: cslsinfo@library.ca.gov. *State Librn,* Stacey Aldrich

COLORADO STATE LIBRARY, 201 E Colfax Ave, Rm 309, Denver 80203-1799. Tel: 303-866-6900. FAX: 303-866-6940. *Exec Dir,* Eugene Hainer

CONNECTICUT STATE LIBRARY, 231 Capitol Ave, Hartford 06106-1537. Tel: 860-757-6510. FAX: 860-757-6503. *State Librn,* Kendall Wiggin

STATE OF DELAWARE, DELAWARE DIVISION OF LIBRARIES, 121 Duke of York St, Dover 19901. Tel: 302-739-4748. FAX: 302-739-6787. *Dir,* Dr Anne E Norman

DISTRICT OF COLUMBIA PUBLIC LIBRARY, 901 G St NW, Washington, DC 20001-4599. Tel: 202-727-1101. FAX: 202-727-1129. *Chief Librn,* Ginnie Cooper

FLORIDA DEPARTMENT OF STATE, DIVISION OF LIBRARY & INFORMATION SERVICES, State Library & Archives of Florida, R A Gray Bldg, 500 S Bronough St, Tallahassee 32399-0250. Tel: 850-245-6600. FAX: 850-245-6735. E-mail:info@dos. myflorida.com. *State Librn,* Judith Ring

GEORGIA PUBLIC LIBRARY SERVICE, 1800 Century Place, Ste 150, Atlanta 30345-4304. Tel: 404-235-7200. FAX: 404-235-7201. *State Librn,* Dr Lamar Veatch

HAWAII STATE PUBLIC LIBRARY SYSTEM, Office of the State Librarian, 44 Merchant St, Honolulu 96813. Tel: 808-586-3704. FAX: 808-586-3715. *State Librn,* Richard Burns

IDAHO COMMISSION FOR LIBRARIES, Idaho State Library, 325 W State St, Boise 83702-6072. Tel: 208-334-2150. FAX: 208-334-4016. *State Librn,* Ann Joslin. *Assoc State Librn,* Marjorie Hooper

ILLINOIS STATE LIBRARY, Gwendolyn Brooks Bldg, 300 S Second St, Springfield 62701-1713. Tel: 217-782-2994. FAX: 217-785-4326. E-mail: islinformationonline@il-sos.net. *Dir,* Anne Craig

INDIANA STATE LIBRARY, 315 West Ohio St, Indianapolis 46202. Tel: 317-232-3675. FAX: 317-232-3728. *State Librn,* Roberta Brooker

STATE LIBRARY OF IOWA, 1112 E Grand Ave, Des Moines 50319. Tel: 515-281-4105. FAX: 515-281-6191. *State Librn,* Mary Wegner

KANSAS STATE LIBRARY, State Capitol Bldg, 300 SW Tenth Ave, Rm 312N, Topeka 66612-1593. Tel: 785-296-3296. FAX: 785-296-6650. E-mail: infodesk@library.ks.gov. *State Librn,* Jo Budler

KENTUCKY DEPARTMENT FOR LIBRARIES & ARCHIVES, 300 Coffee Tree Rd, Frankfort 40601. (Mail Add: PO 537, 40602). Tel: 502-564-8300. FAX: 502-564-5773. *State Librn,* Wayne Onkst

STATE LIBRARY OF LOUISIANA, 701 N Fourth St, Baton Rogue 70821-5232. (Mail add: PO Box 131, 70821-0131). Tel: 225-342-4923. FAX: 225-219-4804. E-mail: admin@state.lib.la.us. *State Librn,* Rebecca Hamilton. *Dep State Librn,* Diane Brown

MAINE STATE LIBRARY, LMA Bldg, 230 State St, Augusta 04333. (Mail Add: LMA Bldg, 64 State House Sta, 04333-0064). Tel: 207-287-5600. FAX: 207-287-5615. E-mail: reference.desk@maine.gov. *State Librn,* Linda Lord

MARYLAND STATE DEPARTMENT OF EDUCATION, Division of Library Development & Services, 200 W Baltimore St, Baltimore 21201-2595. Tel: 410-767-0435. FAX: 410-333-2507. *State Librn,* Irene Padilla

MASSACHUSETTS BOARD OF LIBRARY COMMISSIONERS, 98 N Washington St, Ste 401, Boston 02114. Tel: 617-725-1860. FAX: 617-725-0140. *Dir,* Robert C Maier

LIBRARY OF MICHIGAN, 702 W Kalamazoo St, Lansing 48915. (Mail add: PO Box 30007, 48909-0007). Tel: 517-373-1580. FAX: 517-373-5700. E-mail: librarian@michigan.gov. *State Librn,* Nancy Robertson

MISSISSIPPI LIBRARY COMMISSION, 3881 Eastwood Dr, Jackson 39211. Tel: 601-432-4039. FAX: 601-432-4480. E-mail: mlcref@mlc.lib.ms.us; mslib@mlc.lib. ms.us. *Exec Dir,* Sharman Smith

MISSOURI STATE LIBRARY, James C Kirkpatrick State Information Ctr, 600 W Main St, Jefferson City 65101-1532, (Mail add: PO Box 387, 65102-0387). Tel: 573-751-2751. FAX: 573-751-3612. E-mail: moslill@sos.mo.gov. *State Librn,* Margaret Conroy

MONTANA STATE LIBRARY, 1515 E Sixth Ave, Helena 59620-1800. (Mail Add: PO Box 201800). Tel: 406-444-3115. FAX: 406-444-0266. E-mail: MSLReference@mt.gov. *State Librn,* Jennie Stapp

NEBRASKA LIBRARY COMMISSION, The Atrium, 1200 N St, Ste 120, Lincoln, 68508-2023. Tel: 402-471-4016. FAX: 402-471-2083. *Dir,* Rod Wagner

NEVADA STATE LIBRARY & ARCHIVES, 100 N Stewart St, Carson City 89701-4285. Tel: 775-684-3360. FAX: 775-684-3330. *Admin,* Daphne DeLeon

NEW HAMPSHIRE STATE LIBRARY, 20 Park St, Concord 03301-6314, Tel: 603-271-2392. FAX: 603-271-2205, 603-271-6826. E-Mail: nhslill@dcr.nh.gov. *State Librn,* Michael York

NEW JERSEY STATE LIBRARY, 185 W State St, Trenton 08618. (Mail add: PO Box 520, 08625-0520). Tel: 609-278-2640. FAX: 609-278-2652. E-mail: refdesk@njs-statelib.org. *State Librn,* Mary Chute

NEW MEXICO STATE LIBRARY, 1209 Camino Carlos Rey, Santa Fe 87507. Tel: 505-476-9700. FAX: 505-476-9701. *Interim State Librn,* Benjamin Wakeshige

NEW YORK STATE LIBRARY, State Education Department, Cultural Education Center, Empire State Plaza, Albany 12230. Tel: 518-474-5961. FAX: 518-474-5786. E-mail: circ@mail.nysed.gov, nyslweb@mail.nysed.gov. *State Librn,* Bernard Margolis

STATE LIBRARY OF NORTH CAROLINA, 109 E Jones St, (Mail add: 4640 Mail Service Ctr, Raleigh 27699-4640). Tel: 919-807-7400. FAX: 919-733-8748. *State Librn,* Cal Shepard. *Asst State Librn,* Laura O'Donoghue

NORTH DAKOTA STATE LIBRARY, 604 East Blvd Ave, Dept 250, Bismarck 58505-0800. Tel: 701-328-2492. FAX: 701-328-2040. E-mail: statelib@nd.gov. *State Librn,* Hulen Bivins

STATE LIBRARY OF OHIO, 274 E First Ave, Ste 100, Columbus 43201. Tel: 614-644-7061. FAX: 614-466-3584. E-mail: refhelp@sloma.state.oh.us. *State Librn,* Beverly Cain

OKLAHOMA DEPARTMENT OF LIBRARIES, 200 NE 18th St, Oklahoma City 73105. Tel: 405-521-2502. FAX: 405-525-7804. *Dir,* Susan McVey

OREGON STATE LIBRARY, 250 Winter St NE, Salem 97301-3950. Tel: 503-378-4243. FAX: 503-585-8059. E-mail: reference@library.state.or.us. *State Librn,* MaryKay Dahlgreen

STATE LIBRARY OF PENNSYLVANIA, 607 South Dr, Forum Bldg, Harrisburg 17120-0600. Tel: 717-783-5950; 717-787-4307. FAX: 717-787-9127. *Dir,* Alice Lubrecht

STATE OF RHODE ISLAND OFFICE OF LIBRARY & INFORMATION SERVICES, One Capitol Hill, 4th Flr, Providence 02908. Tel: 401-574-9300. FAX: 401-574-9320. *Chief Librn,* Howard Boksenbaum

SOUTH CAROLINA STATE LIBRARY, 1430-1500 Senate St, Columbia 29201. (Mail add: PO Box 11469, 29211). Tel: 803-734-8666. FAX: 803-734-8676. E-mail: reference@statelibrary.sc.gov. *Dir,* Position Currently Open

SOUTH DAKOTA STATE LIBRARY, 800 Governors Dr, Pierre 57501-2294. Tel: 605-773-3131. FAX: 605-773-6962. E-mail: library@state.sd.us. *State Librn,* Dan Siebersma

TENNESSEE STATE LIBRARY & ARCHIVES, 403 Seventh Ave N, Nashville 37243-0312. Tel: 615-741-2764. FAX: 615-741-6471, 615-532-2472. E-mail: reference.tsla@tn.gov. *State Librn,* Chuck Sherrill

TEXAS STATE LIBRARY & ARCHIVES COMMISSION, 1201 Brazos, Austin 78701. (Mail add: PO Box 12927, 78711-2927). Tel: 512-463-5460. FAX: 512-463-5436. E-mail: info@tsl.state.tx.us. *Dir,* Peggy D Rudd

UTAH STATE LIBRARY DIVISION, 250 N 1950 W, Ste A, Salt Lake City 84116-7901. Tel: 801-715-6777. FAX: 801-715-6767. *Dir,* Donna Jones Morris

STATE OF VERMONT DEPARTMENT OF LIBRARIES, 109 State St, Montpelier 05609-0601. Tel: 802-828-3261. FAX: 802-828-2199. E-mail: lib.rls@state.vt.us. *Librn,* Martha Reid

THE LIBRARY OF VIRGINIA, 800 E Broad St, Richmond 23219-8000. Tel: 804-692-3592. FAX: 804-692-3594. *State Librn,* Sandra G Treadway

WASHINGTON STATE LIBRARY, 6880 Capital Blvd S, Tumwater 98501-5513, (Mail add: PO Box 42460, Olympia 98504-2460). Tel: 360-704-5200. FAX: 360-586-7575. *Actg State Librn,* Rand Simmons. *Dep State Librn,* Marlys Rudeen

WEST VIRGINIA LIBRARY COMMISSION, State Capital Complex, 1900 Kanawha Blvd, Charleston 25305-0620. Tel: 304-558-2041. FAX: 304-558-2044. E-mail: web_one@wvlc.lib.wv.us. *State Librn,* Karen Goff

WISCONSIN DEPARTMENT OF PUBLIC INSTRUCTION, Division for Libraries, Technology & Community Learning, 125 S Webster St, Madison 53707. (Mail add: PO Box 7841, 53707-7841). Tel: 608-266-2205. FAX: 608-266-8770. *Asst State Superintendent,* Kurt Kiefer

WYOMING STATE LIBRARY, 2800 Central Ave, Cheyenne 82002. Tel: 307-777-6333. FAX: 307-777-6289. E-mail: refdesk@state.wy.us. *State Librn,* Lesley Boughton

AMERICAN SAMOA OFFICE OF LIBRARY SERVICES, American Library Bldg, Pago Pago 96799. (Mail add: PO Box 1329, 96799-1329). Tel: 684-699-2170. FAX: 684-699-2193. *Asst Dir,* Bessie Manase

COMMONWEALTH OF PUERTO RICO, Library & Information Services Program, Cesar Gonzalez Ave, San Juan 00919. (Mail add: PO Box 190759, 00919-0759). Tel: 787-759-2000, Ext 2822. FAX: 787-753-6945. *Dir,* Sandra Castro

VIRGIN ISLANDS DIVISION OF LIBRARIES, ARCHIVES & MUSEUMS, 23 Dronningens Gade, Saint Thomas 00802. Tel: 340-774-3407. FAX: 340-775-1887. *Territorial Dir,* Ingrid Bough

ALBERTA DEPARTMENT OF CULTURE & COMMUNITY SPIRIT, Provincial Archives of Alberta, Reference Library, 8555 Roper Rd, Edmonton T6E 5W1. Tel: 780-427-1750. FAX: 780-427-4646. E-mail: paa@gov.ab.ca. *Exec Dir,* Leslie Latta-Guthrie

BRITISH COLUMBIA MINISTRY OF EDUCATION, Public Library Services Branch, 620 Superior St, Fifth Fl, Victoria V8V 1V2, (Mail add: PO Box 9831, Stn Prov Govt, V8W 9T1). Tel: 250-356-1791. FAX: 250-953-3225. E-mail: plsb@gov.bc.ca. *Dir,* Jacqueline van Dyke

NOVA SCOTIA PROVINCIAL LIBRARY, 2021 Brunswick St, 2nd Flr, Halifax B3K 2Y5. (Mail add: Box 578, B3J 2S9). Tel: 902-424-2457. FAX: 902-424-0633. E-mail: nspl@gov.ns.ca. *Dir,* Jennifer Evans

ARCHIVES OF ONTARIO LIBRARY, 134 Ian Macdonald Blvd, Toronto M7A 2C5. Tel: 416-327-1600. FAX: 416-327-1999. E-mail: reference@ontario.ca. *Librn,* Frank van Kalmthout

PRINCE EDWARD ISLAND PUBLIC LIBRARY SERVICE, 89 Red Head Rd, Morell C0A 1S0. (Mail add: PO Box 7500). Tel: 902-961-7320. FAX: 902-961-7322. E-mail: plshq@gov.pe.ca. *Prov Librn,* Kathleen Eaton

SASKATCHEWAN PROVINCIAL LIBRARY, 409A Park St, Regina S4N 5B2. Tel: 306-787-2973. FAX: 306-787-2029. E-mail: srp.adm@prov.lib.sk.ca. *Prov Librn,* Brett Waytuck

DEPARTMENT OF COMMUNITY SERVICES, Yukon Public Libraries, 2071 Second Ave, Whitehorse Y1A 2C6. (Mail add: PO Box 2703). Tel: 867-667-5239. FAX: 867-393-6333. E-mail: whitehorse.library@gov.yk.ca; reference.pls@gov.yk.ca. *Dir,* Julie Ourom

ALABAMA DEPARTMENT OF EDUCATION, 5114 Gordon Persons Bldg, PO Box 302101, Montgomery 36104-2101. Tel: 334-242-9702. Fax: 334-242-9708. Web Site: www.alsde.edu. *Superintendent of Educ,* Thomas R Bice. Tel: 334-242-9700. E-mail: tbice@alsde.edu

ALASKA STATE LIBRARY, Alaska Department of Education & Early Development, 801 W Tenth St, Ste 200, Juneau 99801. Tel: 907-465-2802. Fax: 907-465-4156. *Commissioner of Educ,* Mike Hanley. E-mail: mike.hanley@alaska.gov

ARIZONA DEPARTMENT OF EDUCATION, Bin 2, 1535 W Jefferson, Phoenix 85007-3280. Tel: 602-542-5460. Fax: 602-542-5440. Web Site: www.azed.gov. *Superintendent of Pub Instruction,* John Huppenthal. E-mail: adeinbox@azed.gov

ARKANSAS DEPARTMENT OF EDUCATION, Education Buildings, 304A, Four Capitol Mall, Little Rock 72201-1071. Tel: 501-682-4475. Fax: 501-682-1079. *Commissioner of Educ,* Tom W Kimbrell. E-mail: tom.kimbrell@arkansas.gov

CALIFORNIA STATE LIBRARY, Library & Courts Bldg1, Rm 220, 914 Capitol Mall, Sacramento 95814 (Mail add: PO Box 942837, 94237-0001). Tel: 916-654-0266. Fax: 916-654-0064. *State Libr Dir,* Stacy Aldrich. E-mail: csl_adm@library.ca.gov

COLORADO STATE LIBRARY, Colorado Department of Education, 201 E Colfax, Rm 309, Denver 80203. Tel: 303-866-6772. Fax: 303-866-6940. Web Site: www.cde.state.co.us. *Commissioner of Educ,* Robert Hammond. E-mail commissioner@cde.state.co.us

CONNECTICUT STATE DEPARTMENT OF EDUCATION, 165 Capitol Ave, Hartford 06106-1630. Tel: 860-713-6553. Fax: 860-713-7018. *Commissioner of Educ,* Stefan Pryor. E-mail stefan.pryor@ct.gov

DELAWARE STATE DEPARTMENT OF EDUCATION, John G Townsend Bldg, Ste 2, 401 Federal St, Dover 19901-1402, Tel: 302-739-4601. Fax: 302-739-4654. Web Site: www.doe.k12.de.us. *Secy of Educ,* Lillian Lowrey. E-mail: lillian.lowrey@doe.k12.de.us

FLORIDA DEPARTMENT OF EDUCATION, 325 W Gaines St, Turlington Bldg, Ste 1514, Tallahassee 32399. Tel: 850-245-0874. Fax: 850-245-0826. *Commissioner of Educ,* Gerard Robinson. Tel: 850-245-9663. E-mail: commissioner@fldoe.org

GEORGIA DEPARTMENT OF EDUCATION, 1754 Twin Towers E, 205 Jesse Hill Jr Dr, Atlanta 30334. Tel: 404-656-2608. Fax: 404-656-5744. Web Site: www.doe.k12.ga.us. *Prog Mgr,* Judy Serritella. E-mail: jserrite@doe.k12.ga.us

HAWAII STATE DEPARTMENT OF EDUCATION, School Library Services, 475 22nd Ave, Bldg 302, Rm 205, Honolulu 96816. Tel: 808-733-9150. Fax: 808-733-9154. Web Site: sls.k12.hi.us. *Adminr,* Donna Shiroma. E-mail: donna_shiroma@notes.k12.hi.us

IDAHO STATE DEPARTMENT OF EDUCATION, 650 W State St, PO Box 83720, Boise 83720-0027. Tel: 208-332-6800. Fax: 208-334-2228. *Div of Innovation & Choice,* Val Fenske. Tel: 208-332-6967. E-mail: vafenske@sde.idaho.gov

ILLINOIS STATE BOARD OF EDUCATION, 100 N First St, Springfield 62777-0001. Tel: 217-557-7323. Fax: 217-782-7937. Web Site: www.isbe.net. *Principal Consult,* Jamey Baiter. E-mail: jbaiter@isbe.net.

INDIANA DEPARTMENT OF EDUCATION, Center for School Improvement & Performance, 101 W Ohio St, Indianapolis 46204. Tel: 317-232-9129. Fax: 800-527-4930.

Superintendent of Pub Instruction, Dr Tony Bennett. Tel: 317-232-6665. E-mail: tbennett@doe.in.us

KANSAS STATE DEPARTMENT OF EDUCATION, 120 SE Tenth Ave, Topeka 66612-1182. Tel 785-296-2144. Fax 785-296-3523. Web Site: www.ksde.org. *Commissioner of Educ,* Dr Diane DeBacker. Tel: 785-296-3202. E-mail: ddebacker@ksde.org

KENTUCKY STATE DEPARTMENT OF EDUCATION, 500 Mero St, Frankfort 40601. Tel: 502-564-2106, Ext 4507. Fax: 502-564-6470. Web Site: www.education.ky.gov. *Libr Media Prog Consult,* Donna M Travillian. E-mail: donna.travillian@education.ky.gov

LOUISIANA STATE DEPARTMENT OF EDUCATION, Division Curriculum Standard, Claiborne Bldg 1201, N Third St, PO Box 94064, Baton Rouge 70804-9064. Tel: 225-342-9969. Fax: 225-342-0178. Web Site: www.doe.state.la.us. *Ancillary Res,* Dr Jackie Bobbett. E-mail: jackie.bobbett@la.gov

MAINE STATE LIBRARY, 64 State House Station, Augusta 04333. Tel: 207-287-5620. Fax: 207-287-5624. *Sch Libr & Tech Plan Coordr,* Pam Goucher. E-mail: pam.goucher@maine.gov

MARYLAND STATE DEPARTMENT OF EDUCATION, Division of Instruction, 200 W Baltimore St, Baltimore 21201. Web Site: www.marylandpublicschools.org. *Asst State Superintendent for Instruction,* Colleen Seremet. Tel: 410-767-0316. Fax: 410-333-2369. *Dir, Instrul Tech & Sch Libr Media,* Jayne Moore. Tel: 410-767-0382. E-mail: jmoore@msde.state.md.us

MASSACHUSETTS DEPARTMENT OF EDUCATION, 350 Main St, Malden 02148. Tel: 781-338-3000. Fax: 781-338-3770, Web Site: www.doe.mass.edu. *Commissioner of Educ,* Mitchell D Chester.

MISSISSIPPI STATE DEPARTMENT OF EDUCATION, 359 North West St, PO Box 771, Jackson 39205. Tel: 601-359-2586. Fax: 601-359-2040. Web Site: www.mde.k12.ms.us. *Visual & Performing Arts & Libr Media Spec,* Limeul Eubanks. E-mail: leubanks@mde.k12.ms.us

MISSOURI STATE DEPARTMENT OF EDUCATION, 205 Jefferson St, PO Box 480, Jefferson City 65102. Tel: 573-526-4219. Fax: 573-526-0651. *Libr Media & Tech Consult,* Curt Fuchs

MONTANA OFFICE OF PUBLIC INSTRUCTION, 1227 11th Ave, PO Box 202501, Helena 59620-2501. Tel: 406-444-3680. Fax: 406-444-2893. E-mail: OPISupt@opi.mt.gov. Web Site: www.opi.mt.gov. *Superintendent,* Denise Juneau. Tel: 406-444-5658, 406-444-9299.

NEBRASKA DEPARTMENT Of EDUCATION, 301 S Centennial Mall South, PO Box 94987 Lincoln, NE 68509. Tel: 402-471-2295. Fax: 402-471-0117. Web Site: www.education.ne.gov. *Dir of Instrul Tech,* Mike Kozak. Tel: 402-471-0533. E-mail: mike.kozak@nebraska.gov

NEVADA DEPARTMENT OF EDUCATION, Technology Team, 700 E Fifth St, Capitol Complex, Carson City 89701. Tel: 775-687-9202. Web Site: www.doe.nv.gov. *Superintendent,* Dr Keith W Rheault. Tel: 775-687-9217. E-mail: krheault@doe.nv.gov. *Libr Learning Res Consult,* Bill Strader. Tel: 775-687-6627. E-mail: bstrader@doe.nv.gov

NEW HAMPSHIRE STATE DEPARTMENT OF EDUCATION, 101 Pleasant St, Concord 03301-3860. Web Site: www.education.nh.gov. *Commissioner,* Dr Virginia Barry. Tel: 603-271-3144. Fax: 603-271-1953. E-mail: virginia.barry@doe.nh.gov

NEW JERSEY STATE DEPARTMENT OF EDUCATION, Division of Education Standards & Programs, Office of Language Arts Literacy Education, 100 Riverview Plaza, (Mail add: PO Box 500, Trenton 08625-0500). Tel: 609-292-6245. Fax: 609-292-7276. *Lang Arts Literacy Coordr,* Marcia Ashhurst-Whiting. Tel: 609-292-3206

NEW MEXICO STATE DEPARTMENT OF EDUCATION, Public Education Bldg, 300 Don Gaspar Ave, Santa Fe 87501-2786. Tel: 505-827-6559. Fax: 505-827-6694. *Coordr of Arts, Media & Libr,* Vicki Breen. E-mail: vicki.breen@state.nm.us

NEW YORK STATE EDUCATION DEPARTMENT, 89 Washington Ave, Education Bldg, Albany 12234. Web Site: www.nysed.gov. *Sch Libr Media Serv Assoc,* John Brock. Tel: 518-474-5922. Fax: 518-473-4884. E-mail: jbrock@mail.nysed.gov

PUBLIC SCHOOLS OF NORTH CAROLINA, North Carolina Department of Public Instruction, K-12 Curriculum, Instruction & Technology Division, Instructional Technology Section, 6364 Mail Service Center, Raleigh 27699-6364. Tel: 919-807-3292. Fax: 919-807-3290. Web Site: www.ncwiseowl.org. *Instrul Tech Section Chief,* Neill Kimrey. Tel: 919-807-3270. E-mail: nkimrey@dpi.nc.gov

NORTH DAKOTA STATE DEPARTMENT OF PUBLIC INSTRUCTION, State Capitol Bldg, Ninth Fl, 600 E Boulevard Ave, Bismarck 58505-0440. Tel: 701-328-2260. Web Site: www.dpi.state.nd.us. *Dir of Sch Approval & Accreditation,* Linda M Paluck. Tel: 701-328-1718. Fax: 701-328-4770. E-mail: lpaluck@nd.gov

OHIO DEPARTMENT OF EDUCATION, 25 S Front St, Columbus 43215-4183. Tel: 614-466-1317. Fax: 614-387-0421. Web Site: www.ode.state.oh.us. *Curric & Instruction, Sch Libr,* Sasheen Phillips. Tel: 614-387-2206. E-mail: sasheen.phillips@ode.state.oh.us

OKLAHOMA STATE DEPARTMENT OF EDUCATION, 2500 N Lincoln Blvd, Oklahoma City 73105-4599. Tel: 405-521-3301. Fax: 405-521-6205. Web Site: www.sde.state.ok.us. Superintendent of Pub Instruction, Janet Barresi

    Documents/Media Production Section. Tel: 405-521-3103. *Media Production Dir,* Marty Fulk. *Publ Coordr,* Frances Lee

PENNSYLVANIA DEPARTMENT OF EDUCATION, Resources for School Libraries, Commonwealth Libraries, 333 Market St, Harrisburg 17126-0333. Tel: 717-783-2646. Fax: 717-783-5420. *Res Librn,* Eileen Kocher

RHODE ISLAND DEPARTMENT OF EDUCATION, Shepard Bldg, 255 Westminster St, Providence 02903-3414. Tel: 401-222-4600. Fax: 401-222-6178. Web Site: www.ride.ri.gov

SOUTH CAROLINA DEPARTMENT OF EDUCATION, District Technology Services, 1429 Senate St, Columbia 29201. Tel: 803-734-7000. Fax: 803-734-4064. *Tech Spec,* Barbara Solomon. E-mail: bsolomon@ed.sc.gov

SOUTH DAKOTA STATE LIBRARY, 800 Governors Dr, Pierre 57501-2294. Tel: 605-773-3131. Fax: 605-773-6962. Web Site: library.sd.gov. *State Librn,* Dan Siebersma. E-mail: Dan.Siebersma@state.sd.us

TENNESSEE DEPARTMENT OF EDUCATION, 5th Fl, Andrew Johnson Tower, 710 James Robertson Pkwy, Nashville 37243-0379. Tel: 615-253-2113. Fax: 615-532-8536. Web: www.state.tn.us. *Dir of Text Bk Serv,* Morgan Branch. Tel: 615-253-3160. E-mail: Morgan.Branch@state.tn.us

TEXAS EDUCATION AGENCY, 1701 N Congress Ave, Austin 78701-1494. Tel: 512-463-9581. Fax: 512-463-9090. *Curric, Libr Serv:* Karen Kahan

UTAH STATE OFFICE OF EDUCATION, Library Media, 250 E 500 S, PO Box 144200, Salt Lake City 84114-4200. Tel: 801-538-7789. Fax: 801-538-7769. Web Site: www.usoe.k12.ut.us/curr/library/. *Spec,* Georgia M Loutensock. E-mail:georgia.loutensock@schools.utah.gov

VERMONT DEPARTMENT OF EDUCATION, 120 State St, Montpelier 05620-2501. Tel: 802-828-3135. Web Site: www.education.vermont.gov. *Commissioner,* Armando Vilaseca

VIRGINIA STATE DEPARTMENT OF EDUCATION, James Monroe Bldg, 101 N 14th St, PO Box 2120, Richmond 23218-2120. Tel: 804-225-2825. Fax: 804-371-2455. Web Site: www.doe.virginia.gov. *Off of Educ Tech & Libr Serv Dir,* Dr Tammy McGraw. Tel: 804-225-4429. E-mail: Tammy.McGraw@doe.virginia.gov

WASHINGTON OFFICE OF THE STATE SUPERINTENDENT OF PUBLIC INSTRUCTION, Old Capitol Bldg, PO Box 47200, Olympia 98504-7200. TDD: 360-664-3631. Web Site: www.k12.wa.us. *Superintendent Pub Instruction,* Randy Dorn. Tel: 360-725-6004. E-mail: Randy.Dorn@k12.wa.us. *Dir, Title I, LAP, Title V,* Gayle Pauley. Tel: 360-725-6100. Fax: 360-586-3305. E-mail: Gayle.Pauley@k12.wa.us

WEST VIRGINIA STATE DEPARTMENT OF EDUCATION, 1900 Kanawha Blvd, Capitol Complex Bldg 6, Rm B-346, Charleston 25305. Tel: 304-558-7880. Fax: 304-558-2584. Web Site: www.wvde.state.wv.us. *Exec Dir, Off of Instrul Tech,* Brenda Williams. E-mail brendaw@access.k12.wv.us

WISCONSIN STATE DEPARTMENT OF PUBLIC INSTRUCTION, 125 S Webster St, PO Box 7841, Madison 53707. Tel: 608-266-2205. Fax: 608-266-8770. Web: www.dpi.wi.gov. *Asst State Superintendent, Div for Libr Tech & Commun Learning,* Kurt Kiefer. E-mail: kurt.kiefer@dpi.wi.gov

    Instructional Media & Technology Team. *Dir,* Stephen Sanders. E-mail:stephen.sanders@dpi.wi.gov. *Tech Consult,* Stuart J Ciske. *Sch Libr Media Consult,* Nancy Anderson

    Public Library Development Team. *Dir,* John Debacher. *Libr Serv & Tech Act Coordr,* Terrie Howe. *Libr Tech Consult,* Robert Bocher.

    Interlibrary Loan & Resource Sharing Team. 2109 S Stoughton Rd, Madison 53716. Tel: 608-224-6161. *Dir,* Sally J Drew. *Chief, Ref & ILL,* Martha Berninger. *Chief, Res Sharing Tech,* David Sleasman

    Library & Statistical Information Center Team. *Librn,* Kay Ihlenfeldt

WYOMING DEPARTMENT OF EDUCATION, Hathaway Bldg, 2nd Flr, 2300 Capitol Ave, Cheyenne 82002-0050. Tel: 307-777-7675. Fax: 307-777-6234. *State Superintendent of Pub Instruction,* Cindy Hill. E-mail Cindy.Hill@wyo.gov

GUAM PUBLIC SCHOOL SYSTEM, Curriculum & Instruction Improvement, PO Box DE, Hagatna 96932. Tel: 671-475-0457. Fax: 671-472-5003. Web Site: www.gdoe.net. *Dep Superintendent,* Geri James. Tel: 671-300-1247. E-mail: gjames@doe.edu.gu

NORTHERN MARIANA ISLANDS, Public School System Library Program. PO Box 501370, Saipan, 96950. Fax: 01-670-664-3796. *Contact,* Rita A Sablan. E-mail: sablanr@pss.cnmi.mp

COMMONWEALTH OF PUERTO RICO, DEPARTMENT OF EDUCATION, Public Library Services Division, PO Box 190759, San Juan 00919-0759. Tel: 787-754-1120. Fax: 787-754-0843. *Dir,* Aura Roderigues

VIRGIN ISLANDS DEPARTMENT OF EDUCATION, Media Library Services, 1834 Kongens Gade, Charlotte Amalie, Saint Thomas 00802-6742. Tel: 340-775-2250, Ext 8534. Fax: 340-777-3673. Web Site: www.sttj.k12.vi. *Coordr Media Libr Serv,* Nancy Christie. E-mail: nchristie@sttj.k12.vi

Interlibrary Loan Code for the United States

The "Interlibrary Loan Code for the United States" is reprinted with permission of the Reference and User Services Association (RUSA), a division of the American Library Association (ALA), www.ala.org/rusa.

Prepared by the Interlibrary Loan Committee, Reference and User Services Association (RUSA), 1994, revised 2001. Revised 2008, by the Sharing and Transforming Access to Resources Section (STARS).

For more detailed information about the provisions of this code, please see the accompanying explanatory supplement.

Introduction

The Reference and User Services Association, acting for the American Library Association in its adoption of this code, recognizes that the sharing of material between libraries is an integral element in the provision of library service and believes it to be in the public interest to encourage such an exchange.

In the interest of providing quality service, libraries have an obligation to obtain material to meet the informational needs of users when local resources do not meet those needs. Interlibrary Loan (ILL), a mechanism for obtaining material, is essential to the vitality of all libraries.

The effectiveness of the national interlibrary loan system depends upon participation of libraries of all types and sizes.

This code establishes principles that facilitate the requesting of material by a library and the provision of loans or copies in response to those requests. In this code, "material" includes books, audiovisual materials, and other returnable items as well as copies of journal articles, book chapters, excerpts, and other non-returnable items.

1.0 Definition

1.1 Interlibrary loan is the process by which a library requests material from, or supplies material to, another library.

2.0 Purpose

2.1 The purpose of interlibrary loan as defined by this code is to obtain, upon request of a library user, material not available in the user's local library.

3.0 Scope

3.1 This code regulates the exchange of material between libraries in the United States.

3.2 Interlibrary loan transactions with libraries outside of the United States are governed by the International Federation of Library Associations and Institutions' International Lending: Principles and Guidelines for Procedure.

4.0 Responsibilities of the Requesting Library

4.1 Establish, promptly update, and make available an interlibrary borrowing policy.

4.2 Ensure the confidentiality of the user.

4.3 Describe completely and accurately the requested material following accepted bibliographic practice.

4.4 Identify libraries that own the requested material and check and adhere to the policies of potential supplying libraries.

4.5 When no libraries can be identified as owning the needed material, requests may be sent to libraries believed likely to own the material, accompanied by an indication that ownership is not confirmed.

4.6 Transmit interlibrary loan requests electronically whenever possible.

4.7 For copy requests, comply with the U.S. copyright law (Title 17, U.S. Code) and its accompanying guidelines.

4.8 Assume responsibility for borrowed material from the time it leaves the supplying library until it has been returned to and received by the supplying library. This includes all material shipped directly to and/or returned by the user. If damage or loss occurs, provide compensation or replacement, in accordance with the preference of the supplying library.

4.9 Assume full responsibility for user-initiated transactions.

4.10 Honor the due date and enforce any use restrictions specified by the supplying library. The due date is defined as the date the material is due to be checked-in at the supplying library.

4.11 Request a renewal before the item is due. If the supplying library does not respond, the requesting library may assume that a renewal has been granted extending the due date by the same length of time as the original loan.

4.12 All borrowed material is subject to recall. Respond immediately if the supplying library recalls an item.

4.13 Package material to prevent damage in shipping and comply with any special instructions stated by the supplying library.

4.14 Failure to comply with the provisions of this code may be reason for suspension of service by a supplying library.

5.0 Responsibilities of the Supplying Library

5.1 Establish, promptly update, and make available an interlibrary lending policy.

5.2 Consider filling all requests for material regardless of format.

5.3 Ensure the confidentiality of the user.

5.4 Process requests in a timely manner that recognizes the needs of the requesting library and/or the requirements of the electronic network or transmission system being used. If unable to fill a request, respond promptly and state the reason the request cannot be filled.

5.5 When filling requests, send sufficient information with each item to identify the request.

5.6 Indicate the due date and any restrictions on the use of the material and any special return packaging or shipping requirements. The due date is defined as the date the material is due to be checked-in at the supplying library.

5.7 Ship material in a timely and efficient manner to the location specified by the requesting library. Package loaned material to prevent loss or damage in shipping. Deliver copies electronically whenever possible.

5.8 Respond promptly to requests for renewals. If no response is sent, the requesting library may assume that a renewal has been granted extending the due date by the same length of time as the original loan.

5.9 Loaned material is subject to recall at any time.

5.10 Failure to comply with the provisions of this code may lead to suspension of service to the requesting library.

Supplemental Documentation

For more detailed information, please see the accompanying explanatory supplement.

Interlibrary Loan Code for the United States

For Use with the Interlibrary Loan Code for the United States (May 2008)

This Explanatory Supplement is intended to amplify specific sections of the Interlibrary Loan Code for the United States, providing fuller explanation and specific examples for text that is intentionally general and prescriptive. Topical headings refer to the equivalent sections in the Code. Libraries are expected to comply with the Code, using this Supplement as a source for general direction.[1]

Introduction

The U.S. Interlibrary Loan Code, first published in 1917 and adopted by The American Library Association in 1919, is designed to provide a code of behavior for requesting and supplying material within the United States. This code does not override individual or consortial agreements or regional or state codes which may be more liberal or more prescriptive. This national code is intended to provide guidelines for exchanges between libraries where no other agreement applies. The code is intended to be adopted voluntarily by U.S. libraries and is not enforced by an oversight body. However, as indicated below, supplying libraries may suspend service to borrowing libraries that fail to comply with the provisions of this code.

This interlibrary loan code describes the responsibilities of libraries to each other when requesting material for users. Increasingly, libraries are allowing users to request material directly from suppliers. This code makes provision for direct patron requesting and at the same time affirms the responsibility of the patron's library for the safety and return of the borrowed material, or for paying the cost of a non-returnable item sent directly to the patron.

Technology has expanded access options beyond traditional library-to-library transactions. Unmediated requests, direct-to-user delivery, purchase-on-demand options, and increasing full-text availability are exciting developments in resource sharing. At present, the Interlibrary Loan Code reflects established practices. However, libraries and other information centers are encouraged to explore and use nontraditional means where available to ensure maximum accessibility and convenience for users. More information for libraries interested in new ideas for resource sharing can be found at: http://www.ala.org/ala/rusa/rusaourassoc/rusa-sections/stars/starssection

1. Definition

The Interlibrary Code for the United States covers transactions between two libraries. Transactions between libraries and commercial document suppliers or library fee-based services are contractual arrangements beyond the scope of these guidelines.

The terms "requesting library" and "supplying library" are used in preference to "borrowing" and "lending" to cover the exchange of copies as well as loans.

2. Purpose

Interlibrary loan (ILL) is intended to complement local collections and is not a substitute for good library collections intended to meet the routine needs of users. ILL is based on a tradition of sharing resources between various types and sizes of libraries and rests on the belief that no library, no matter how large or well supported, is self-sufficient in today's world. It is also evident that some libraries are net borrowers (borrow more than they lend) and others are net lenders (lend more than they borrow), but the system of interlibrary loan still rests on the belief that all libraries should be willing to lend if they are willing to borrow.

3. Scope

The conduct of international interlibrary loan is regulated by the rules set forth in the *IFLA document International Lending: Principles and Guidelines for Procedure*.[2]

Although the U.S. shares a common border with Canada and Mexico, it is important to remember that these countries have their own library infrastructures and ILL codes. The *IFLA Principles and Guidelines* regulate the exchange of material between institutions across these borders. Further, U.S. librarians would be wise to inform themselves of customs requirements that take precedence over library agreements when material is shipped across these national borders, e.g., as described in the Association of Research Libraries' *Transborder Interlibrary Loan: Shipping Interlibrary Loan Materials from the U.S. to Canada*.[3]

4. Responsibilities of the Requesting Library

4.1 Written Policies

A library's interlibrary loan borrowing policy should be available in a written format that is readily accessible to all library users. Whenever possible the borrowing policy should be posted on the library's Web site as well as be available in paper copy at public service desks or wherever other library user handouts are provided.

4.2 Confidentiality

Interlibrary loan transactions, like circulation transactions, are confidential library records. Interlibrary loan personnel are encouraged to be aware of local/state confidentiality rules and laws as they relate to interlibrary loan transactions. Appropriate steps, such as using identification numbers or codes rather than users' names, should be taken to maintain confidentiality. However, it is not a violation of this code to include a user's name on a request submitted to a supplier. Policies and procedures should be developed regarding the retention of ILL records and access to this information. ILL personnel should also be aware of privacy issues when posting requests for assistance or using the text of ILL requests as procedural examples. ALA's Office for Intellectual Freedom has developed a number of policies regarding confidentiality of library records.[4]

ILL staff should adhere to the American Library Association's (ALA) Code of Ethics[5], specifically principle III, that states: "We protect each library user's right to privacy and confidentiality with respect to information sought or received and resources consulted, borrowed, acquired or transmitted."

4.3 Complete Bibliographic Citation

A good bibliographic description is the best assurance that the user will receive the item requested. Rather than detail these descriptive elements, the code requires the requesting library to include whatever data provides the best indication of the desired material, whether an alphanumeric string or an extensive bibliographic citation. The important point is that this description be exact enough to avoid unnecessary work on the part of the supplier and frustration on the part of the user. For example, journal title verification rather than article level verification would be sufficient.

4.4 Identifying Appropriate Suppliers

Requesting libraries should use all resources at their disposal to determine ownership of a particular title before sending a request to a potential supplier. Many libraries contribute their holdings to major bibliographic utilities such as DOCLINE and/or OCLC and make their individual catalogs freely available via the Internet. The interlibrary loan listserv (ill-l@webjunction.org) or other ILL-related lists are also excellent sources for the requesting library to verify and/or locate particularly difficult items.

The requesting library is encouraged to use resources such as the OCLC *Policies Directory* to determine lending policies including any applicable charges, before requesting material.

The requesting library should clearly state on the request an amount that meets or exceeds the charges of suppliers to which the request is sent. The requesting library is responsible for payment of any fees charged by the supplying library that are less than or equal to the amount stated on its request. Libraries are encouraged to use electronic invoicing capabilities such as OCLC's Interlibrary Loan Fee Management (IFM) system or the Electronic Fund Transfer System used by medical libraries.

4.5 Sending Unverified Requests

Despite the requirements in Sec. 4.4 and 4.5 that an item should be completely and accurately described and located, the code recognizes that it is not always possible to verify and/or locate a particular item. For example, a request may be sent to a potential supplier with strong holdings in a subject or to the institution at which the dissertation was written.

4.6 Transmitting the Request

The code recommends electronic communication. For many libraries, sending requests electronically means using the ILL messaging systems associated with DOCLINE, OCLC, other products that use the ISO ILL Protocol, or structured email requests.

Lacking the ability to transmit in this fashion, the requesting library should send a completed ALA interlibrary loan request form via fax, Internet transmission, or mail; use a potential supplier's web request form; or otherwise provide the necessary information via email message or conventional letter. Whatever communication method is used, the requesting library should identify and use the appropriate address or number for ILL requests.

The requesting library should include a street address, a postal box number, an IP address, a fax number, and an email address to give the supplying library delivery options. Any special needs, such as for a particular edition, language, or rush delivery, should be included on the request.

In addition, because the primary purpose of interlibrary loan is to provide material for relatively short term use by an individual, the requesting library should communicate with the supplying library in advance if the material is needed for other uses (such as course reserves, classroom or other group viewing of audio-visual material or for an extended loan period, especially of a textbook).

4.7 Copy Requests

The requesting library is responsible for complying with the provisions of Section 108(g)(2) Copyright Law[6] and the *Guidelines for the Proviso of Subsection* 108(g)(2) prepared by the National Commission on New Technological Uses of Copyrighted Works (the CONTU Guidelines).[7]

4.8 Responsibility of the Requester

The requesting library assumes an inherent risk when material is supplied through interlibrary loan. Although the number is small, some material is lost or damaged at some point along the route from the supplier and back again. The requesting library's responsibility for this loss is based on the concept that if the request had not been made, the material would not have left the supplier's shelf, and thus would not have been put at risk. This section clearly states that the requesting library is responsible for the material from the time it leaves the supplying library until its safe return to the supplying library.

If the requesting library asks for delivery at a location away from the library (such as to the user's home), the requesting library is likewise responsible for the material during this delivery and return process. In any case, a final decision regarding replacement, repair, or compensation rests with the supplying library.

Borrowed items should be returned in the condition in which they were received at the requesting library. In particular, adhesive labels or tape should not be affixed directly to any borrowed item.

It is the responsibility of the requesting library to pay invoices received or to notify the supplying library of any billing questions not later than six months from the billing date for the charges in question. The requesting library should also make every attempt to resolve billing questions within six months of notifying the supplying library of an apparent billing error.

Although the code stipulates that the requesting library is required to pay if billed for a lost or damaged item, the supplying library is not necessarily required to charge for a lost item. In the case of lost material, the requesting and supplying libraries may need to work together to resolve the matter. For instance, the library shipping the material may need to initiate a trace with the delivery firm.

4.9 Responsibility for Unmediated ILL Requests

Some requesting libraries permit users to initiate online ILL requests that are sent directly to potential supplying libraries. A requesting library that chooses to allow its users to order materials through interlibrary loan without mediation accepts responsibility for these requests as if they have been placed by library staff. The supplying library may assume that the user has been authenticated and authorized to place requests and that the requesting library assumes full responsibility for transaction charges, the safety and return of material, and the expense of replacement or repair.

4.10 Due Date and Use Restrictions

This code makes a departure from earlier codes that described due dates in terms of a "loan period" which was interpreted as the length of time a requesting library could retain the material before returning it. The primary object of this section is to provide a clear definition of due date as the date the material must be checked in at the supplying library. This definition brings ILL practice into alignment with automated circulation procedures and is intended to facilitate interoperability of ILL and circulation applications.

The requesting library should develop a method for monitoring due dates so that material can be returned to and checked in at the supplying library by the due date assigned by the supplying library.

The requesting library is responsible for ensuring compliance with any use restrictions specified by the supplying library such as "library use only" or "no photocopying."

4.11 Renewals

When the supplying library denies a renewal request the material should be returned by the original due date or as quickly as possible if the renewal is denied after the due date has passed.

4.12 Recalls

The response to a recall may be the immediate return of the material, or timely communication with the supplying library to negotiate a new due date.

When the material has been recalled, the requesting library is encouraged to return the material via an expedited delivery carrier such as UPS, FedEx, or USPS Priority Mail.

4.13 Shipping

It is the ultimate responsibility of the requesting library to return materials in the same condition in which they were received as noted in section 4.8 of the *Interlibrary Loan Code for the United States.*

It is the responsibility of the requesting library to follow the shipping and packaging requirements, including insurance and preferred shipping method, as stipulated by the supplying library. Packaging is defined as the outer material, which may be a box, padded envelope, etc. Wrapping is defined as an inner covering for the item such as paper or bubble wrap.

If no shipping or packaging methods are specified, the requesting library's regular form of shipment should be used.

If packaging material has been used previously, remove or mark out old addresses, postal marks, etc. to avoid misdirection. Do not reuse old, frayed, ripped, or decaying packaging and wrapping materials - discard it instead. Clearly address all packages with both the destination and return addresses properly attached to the packaging material.

In accordance with United States Postal Service guidelines, tape is the preferred sealing methods on all types of packages. Remember that wrapping and packaging materials will most likely be reused. So, please use tape judiciously. If staples must be used, do not use industrial (e.g. copper) staples if at all possible. Copper staples make it very difficult to reuse wrapping and packaging materials and are not ergonomically sound.

Use wrapping and packaging material that is appropriate to the size and format of the material being shipped. Too small or too large packaging will not adequately protect materials during transportation. Remember to use appropriate wrapping to avoid shifting and damage to the contents.

For special formats, consult the appropriate ALA Guidelines:

- American Library Association. Association for Library Collections and Technical Services. *Guidelines for Packaging and Shipping Magnetic Tape Recording and Optical Discs (CD-ROM and CD-R) Carrying Audio, Video, and/or Data*, n.d.

- American Library Association. Association for Library Collection and Technical Services. *Guidelines for Packaging and Shipping Microforms*, 1989.

- American Library Association. Association for Library Collections and Technical Services. *Guidelines for Preservation Photocopying of Replacement Pages*, 1990.

- American Library Association. Video Round Table. *Guidelines for the Interlibrary Loan of Audiovisual Formats*, 1998.

- American Library Association. Association of College and Research Libraries. Ad Hoc Committee on the Interlibrary Loan of Rate and Unique Materials. *Guidelines for the Interlibrary Loan of Rare and Unique Materials*, 2004.

4.14 Suspension of Service

Repeated or egregious breaches of this code may result in the requesting library's inability to obtain material. Examples of actions that may result in suspension include lost or damaged books, allowing "library use only" books to leave the library, or failing to pay the supplier's charges. A supplying library should not suspend service to a requesting library without first attempting to resolve the problem(s).

5. Responsibilities of the Supplying Library

5.1 Lending Policy

The lending policy should be clear, detailed, and readily available to requesting libraries. The policy should include among other things, schedule of fees and charges, overdue fines, non-circulating items/categories, current shipping instructions, calendar for service suspensions, penalties for late payments, etc. While a supplying library may charge additional fees for the rapid delivery of requested material, it is recommended that no additional fees be charged for the routine supply of documents via electronic means.

The supplying library is encouraged to make its lending policy available in print, on the library's Web site, and in resources such as the *OCLC Policies Directory*. The supplying library should be willing to fill requests for all types and classes of users, and all types of libraries, regardless of their size or geographic location.

5.2 Material Format

Supplying libraries are encouraged to lend as liberally as possible regardless of the format of the material requested, while retaining the right to determine what material will be supplied. It is the obligation of the supplying library to consider the loan of material on a case by case basis. Supplying libraries are encouraged to lend audiovisual material, newspapers, and other categories of material that have traditionally been non-circulating.

Supplying libraries are encouraged to follow *ACRL's Guidelines for the Interlibrary Loan of Rare and Unique Materials*[8] and the *Guidelines for Interlibrary Loan of Audiovisual Formats.*[9]

If permitted by copyright law, the supplying library should consider providing a copy in lieu of a loan rather than giving a negative response.

Supplying libraries should be aware of the provisions of license agreements for electronic resources that may either permit or prohibit use of an electronic resource to fill interlibrary copying requests.

5.3 Confidentiality

The supplying library has a responsibility to safeguard the confidentiality of the individual requesting the material. The sharing of the user's name between requesting and supplying library is not, of itself, a violation of confidentiality. However, the supplying library should not require the user's name if the requesting library chooses not to provide it. If the name is provided, the supplying library needs to take care not to divulge the identity of the person requesting the material.

5.4 Timely Processing

The supplying library has a responsibility to act promptly on all requests. If a supplying library cannot fill a request within a reasonable time then it should respond promptly. The response should be sent via the same method the requesting library used to send the request, or by otherwise contacting the requesting library directly. Some ILL messaging systems such as OCLC and DOCLINE have built-in time periods after which requests will either expire or be sent to another institution. The supplying library should respond before this time expires rather than allow requests to time-out.

Providing a reason for an unfilled request helps the requesting library determine what additional steps, if any, may be taken to access the requested item. For example, "noncirculating" indicates the item is likely available for on-site use while "in use" indicates that another request at a later date might be filled. Providing no reason or simply stating "policy problem" or "other" without providing additional information deprives the requesting library of important information and can lead to time-consuming follow-up for both libraries.

Timely processing of a loan or copy may involve other library departments, such as circulation, copy services, and the mailroom. The interlibrary loan department is responsible for ensuring that material is delivered expeditiously, irrespective of internal library organizational responsibilities.

The supplying library should, when charging for materials, make every effort to allow for a variety of payment options. Payment through electronic crediting and debiting services such as OCLC's ILL Fee Management (IFM) system or other non-invoicing payment forms such as IFLA vouchers should be encouraged. The supplying library that charges should make every effort to accept the use of vouchers, coupons, or credit cards.

It is the responsibility of the supplying library to send final bills for service not later than six months after the supply date, final overdue notices not later than six months after the final due date, and final bills for replacement of lost material not later than one year after the final due date. The supplying library should resolve billing questions within six months of receiving notice of an apparent billing error.

5.5 Identifying the Request

The supplying library should send sufficient identifying information with the material to allow the requesting library to identify the material and process the request quickly. Such information may include a copy of the request, the requestor's transaction number, or the user's ID or name. Failure to include identifying information with the material can unduly delay its processing and may risk the safety of the material.

Supplying libraries are encouraged to enclose an accurate and complete return mailing label.

5.6 Use Restrictions and Due Date

Although it is the responsibility of the requesting library to ensure the safe treatment and return of borrowed material, the supplying library should provide specific instructions when it is lending material that needs special handling. These instructions might include the requirement that material be used only in a monitored special collections area, no photocopying, library use only, specific return packaging/shipping instructions, etc. The supplying library should not send "library use only" material directly to a user.

The supplying library should clearly indicate the date on which it expects the loan to be discharged in its circulation system. As explained in section 4.10 above, this code has moved away from the concept of a loan period, to a definite date that accommodates the sending and return of material as well as sufficient time for the use of the material. For example, a supplying library might establish a due date of six (6) weeks for the purpose of providing one (1) week for shipping, four (4) weeks for use, and one (1) week for the return trip and check-in.

5.7 Delivery and Packaging

The location specified by the requesting library may include the requesting library, a branch or departmental library, or the individual user.

It is the responsibility of the supplying library:

- to judge whether an item is suitable for shipment and circulation. If a damaged item is sent, the supplying library should note all prior damage (such as loose pages or loose spine) and not hold the requesting library responsible for subsequent damage.

- to take care that the material it sends out is properly packaged to protect the item from damage even though the requesting library will be held responsible for material damaged in shipment to specify the shipping method, as well as insurance, for returning materials and if any special wrapping or packaging is required. See section 4.13 above for definitions and other important information regarding wrapping and packaging.

- to provide a complete street address if asking for return via UPS, FedEx, etc. (Many supplying libraries find it safer and more cost effective to ship all material via expedited carriers).

- to work with the requesting library when tracing a lost or damaged item if the commercial delivery firm is responsible for reimbursement for losses in transit.

5.8 Renewals

The supplying library should respond affirmatively or negatively to all renewal requests. The supplying library is encouraged to grant the renewal request if the material is not needed by a local user.

5.9 Recalls

The supplying library may recall material at its discretion at any time. Increasingly, some libraries are finding it more effective to request the material on ILL for a local user rather than to recall material in use by another library.

5.10 Service Suspension

A supplying library should not suspend service without first attempting to address the problem(s) with the requesting library.

References

[1] Boucher, Virginia. *Interlibrary Loan Practices Handbook*. Chicago, IL: American Library Association, 1997. Though written in light of an earlier code, the Practices Handbook contains many useful and practical details on interlibrary loan procedures.

[2] International Federation of Library Associations and Institutions. *International Lending: Principles and Guidelines for Procedure*. 2001.

[3] Transborder Interlibrary Loan: *Shipping Interlibrary Loan Materials from the U.S. to Canada*. 1999. (note: Pricing information is out of date)

[4] American Library Association. Office for Intellectual Freedom. *Policy on Confidentiality of Library Records*. 1986.

American Library Association. Office for Intellectual Freedom. *Policy Concerning Confidentiality of Personally Identifiable Information about Library Users.* 2004.

[5] American Library Association. Committee on Professional Ethics. *Code of Ethics.* Chicago, American Library Association, 1995.

[6] Copyright Law of the United States of America Chapter 1, Section 108: Limitations on the exclusive rights: *Reproduction by libraries and archives.*

[7] National Commission on New Technological Uses of Copyrighted Works. *Guidelines on Photocopying Under Interlibrary Loan Arrangements.*

[8] American Library Association. Association of College and Research Libraries. Ad Hoc Committee on the Interlibrary

Loan of Rate and Unique Materials. *Guidelines for the Loan of Rare and Unique Materials.* 2004.

[9] American Library Association. Video Round Table. *Guidelines for Interlibrary Loan of Audiovisual Formats.* 1998.

[10] Hilyer, Lee. *Interlibrary loan and document delivery: best practices for operating and managing interlibrary loan services in all libraries.* New York: Haworth Information Press, 2006. (Co-published simultaneously as *Journal of interlibrary loan, document delivery & electronic reserve,* volume 16, numbers 1/2, 2006)

[11] Hilyer, Lee. *Interlibrary loan and document delivery in the larger academic library: a guide for university, research, and larger public libraries.* Binghamton, NY: Haworth Information Press, 2002. (Co-published simultaneously as *Journal of interlibrary loan, document delivery & information supply,* v. 13, nos. 1/2, 2002)

UNITED STATES ARMED FORCES LIBRARIES OVERSEAS

This section lists all libraries serving the Armed Forces overseas. Libraries in Alaska, Hawaii, Guam and Puerto Rico are included since the Department of the Air Force, Army and Navy treats these areas administratively as being overseas.

For the librarians in charge of library programs for the Armed Forces in the United States as well as overseas, see the entries in the Library Section for the Department of the Air Force, Randolph AFB, Texas; Department of the Army, Alexandria, Virginia; and Department of the Navy, Pensacola, Florida.

UNITED STATES AIR FORCE

ACC (Air Combat Command)

FL4486/Base Library, 65 SVS/SVMG, Bldg T208, APO AE 09720-5000. SAN 323-0066

FL4528/Base Library, 5 SVS/SVMG, 210 Missile Ave, Unit 1, Bldg 156, Minot AFB ND 58705-9850

FL4600/Base Library, 55 SVS/SVMG, 510 Custer Dr, Suite 101, Bldg 73, Offutt AFB NE 68113-2150. SAN 350-199X

FL4608/Base Library, 2 SVS/SVMG, 744 Douhet Dr, Bldg 4244, Barksdale AFB LA 71110-2428. SAN 342-7447

FL4625/Base Library, 509 SVS/SVMG, 750 Arnold, Bldg 527, Whiteman AFB MO 65305-5019. SAN 349-9413

FL4661/Base Library, 349 3rd Ave, Bldg 6142, Dyess AFB TX 79607-1242. SAN 378-0236. *Dir,* Cheryl Smith

FL4686/Base Library, 9 SVS/SVMG, 17849 16th St, Bldg 25219, Beale AFB CA 95903-1611. SAN 331-4944

FL4690/Base Library, 28 SVS/SVMG, 2650 Doolittle Dr, Bldg 3910, Ellsworth AFB SD 57706-4820. SAN 360-4144

FL4800/Bateman Library, 42 Ash Ave, Bldg 161, Langley AFB VA 23665. SAN 363-0064

FL4801/Base Library, 49 SVS/SVMG, 596 Fourth St, Bldg 224, Holloman AFB NM 88330-8038. SAN 351-6482

FL4803/Base Library, 20 SVS/SVMG, 451 Johnson St, Bldg 405, Shaw AFB SC 29152-5127. SAN 360-3601

FL4809/Base Library, 4 SVS/SVMG, 1520 Goodson St, Bldg 3660, Seymour Johnson AFB NC 27531-2461. SAN 355-158X

FL4830/Base Library, 347 SVS/SVMG, 5107 Austin Ellipse, Suite A, Bldg 103, Moody AFB GA 31699-1594. SAN 339-0845

FL4852/Base Library, 99 SVS/SVMG, 4311 N Washington Blvd, Bldg 312, Suite 101, Las Vegas NV 89191-7064. SAN 350-3798

FL4855/Base Library, 27 SVS/SVMG, 107 W Trident Ave, Bldg 75, Cannon AFB NM 88103-5211. SAN 351-6393

FL4867/CA-STINFO/AFTAC, 1030 S Highway A1A, Bldg 989, Room A1-S3, Patrick AFB, FL 32925

FL4877/Base Library, 355 SVS/SVMG, 5427 E Madera St, Bldg 4339, Davis Monthan AFB AZ 85707-4930. SAN 330-5619

FL4897/Base Library, 366 SVS/SVMG, 520 Phantom Ave, Bldg 2427, Mountain Home AFB ID 83648-5224. SAN 339-6789

FL4899/Command Librarian, HQ ACC/A7SM, 200 Sweeney Blvd, Suite 313, Bldg 220, Langley AFB VA 23665-2795. SAN 378-0252

AETC (Air Education & Training Command)

FL3000/Command Librarian, HQ AETC/SVPC, 100 H St E, Suite 5, Bldg 905, Randolph AFB TX 78150-4398. SAN 370-2413

FL3003/Medical Library, 59 MDW/MSIL, 2200 Bergquist Dr, Suite 1, Bldg 4550, Lackland AFB TX 78236-5300. SAN 378-0627

FL3010/McBride Library, 81 MSG/SVMG, 512 Larcher Blvd, Bldg 2222, Keesler AFB MS 39534-2345. SAN 348-6036

FL3020/Base Library, 82 SPTG/SVMG, 425 3rd Ave, Bldg 312, Sheppard AFB TX 76311-3043. SAN 362-3343

FL3021/Academic Library, 882 TRG/TSOL, 939 Missile Rd, Bldg 1900, Sheppard AFB TX 76311-2245. SAN 362-3408

FL3022/Base Library, 14 SVS/SVMG, 37 D St, Bldg 715, Columbus AFB MS 39710-5102. SAN 348-2553

FL3029/Base Library, 71 FTW/CSSL, 446 McAffrey Ave, Suite 24, Bldg 314, Vance AFB OK 73705-5710

FL3030/Base Library, 17 SPTG/SVMG, 271 Ft Phantom Hill Ave, Bldg 712, Goodfellow AFB TX 76908-4711. SAN 361-7645

FL3046/Academic Library, DLIELC/LEAAB, 2230 Andrews Ave, Bldg 7447, Lackland AFB TX 78236-5203. SAN 316-5574.

FL3047/Base Library, 37 SPTG/SVMG, 1930 George Ave, Bldg 6114, Lackland AFB TX 78236-5518. SAN 378-0279

FL3061/Academic Library, 336 TRSS/OSFL, 1040 W Survival Loop, Bldg 1256, Ste 122D, Fairchild AFB WA 99011-8628. SAN 363-6518

FL3089/Base Library, 12 SPTG/SVMG, 5th St E, Bldg 598, Randolph AFB TX 78150-4405. SAN 362-1901

FL3099/Base Library, 47 MSG/SVMG, 427 4th St, Bldg 257, Laughlin AFB TX 78843-5125. SAN 362-1030

FL3300/Base Library, 42 SPTG/SVMG, 481 Williamson St, Bldg 1110, Gunter Annex, Maxwell AFB AL 36114-3117

FL3319/Academic Library, AFIT/LD, 2950 Hobson Way, Bldg 642, Wright-Patterson AFB OH 45433-7765. SAN 357-3664

FL3368/Library, Air University Library, AUL/LD, 600 Chennault Circle, Bldg 1405, Maxwell AFB AL 36112-6424. SAN 300-1431

FL4419/Base Library, 97 SVS/SVMG, 109 E Ave, Bldg 65, Altus AFB OK 73523-5134. SAN 357-4806

FL4460/Base Library, 314 SVS/SVMG, 976 Cannon Dr, Bldg 976, Little Rock AFB AR 72099-5289. SAN 331-2518

FL4819/Base Library, 325 SVS/SVMG/45, 640 Suwannee Rd, Bldg 916, Tyndall AFB FL 32403-5531. SAN 338-1994

FL4887/Base Library, 56 SVS/SVMG, 7424 N Homer Dr, Bldg 219, Luke AFB AZ 85309-1220. SAN 330-6216

AFMC (Air Force Material Command)

FL2000/Command Librarian, HQ AFMC/A7VP, 4375 Chidlaw Rd, Bldg 262, Rm N-237, Wright-Patterson AFB OH 45433-5006. SAN 329-4501

FL2020/Base Library, 75 MSG/SVMG, 7415 8th St, Bldg 440, Hill AFB UT 84056-5006. SAN 362-4455

FL2030/Base Library, 72 MSG/SVMG, 6120 Arnold St, Bldg 5702, Tinker AFB OK 73145-8101. SAN 357-7058

FL2060/Base Library, 78 MSG/SVMG, 620 Ninth St, Suite 100, Bldg 905, Robins AFB GA 31098-1469. SAN 370-2375

FL2300/Base Library, 88 MSG/SVMG, 5435 Hemlock St, Wright-Patterson AFB OH 45433-5424. SAN 357-3575

FL2802/AFRL Technical Library, Det 1 AFRL/WSC, 2950 Hobson Way, Bldg 642, Wright-Patterson AFB OH 45433-7765. SAN 357-3605

FL2804/AEDC Technical Library, 100 Kindel Dr, Suite C212, Arnold AFB TN 37389-3212. SAN 360-5078

FL2805/Base Library, 95 MSG/SVMG, 5 W Yeager Blvd, Bldg 2665, Edwards AFB CA 93524-1295. SAN 331-9083

FL2806/AFFTC Technical Library, 412 TW/ENTL, 307 E Popson Ave, Bldg 1400, Rm 110, Edwards AFB CA 93524-6630. SAN 331-9113

FL2807/Research Library, AFRL/VSIL Library, Five Wright St, Bldg 1103, Hanscom AFB MA 01731-3004. SAN 345-2646

FL2809/Phillips Site Technical Library, AFRL/PSTL, 3550 Aberdeen Ave SE, Bldg 419, Kirtland AFB NM 87117-5776. SAN 351-6571

FL2810/AFRL Rome Research Site, Information Dir Tech Library, AFRL/FOIL, 525 Brooks Rd. Bldg 3, West Wing, Rome NY 13441-4505. SAN 352-5031

FL2823/Base Library, 96 SVS/SVMG, 305 West F St, Bldg 278, Eglin AFB FL 32542-6842. SAN 337-386X

FL2825/AFRL Munitions Directorate Technical Library, 203 W Eglin Blvd, Suite 300, Eglin AFB FL 32542-6843. SAN 337-3924

FL2830/Technical Library, NAIC/DEKA, 4180 Watson Way, Bldg 856, Wright Patterson AFB, OH 45433-5648

FL2835/Base Library, 66 SVS/SVMG, 98 Barksdale St, Bldg 1530, Hanscom AFB MA 01731-1807. SAN 345-2670

FL2855/Aeromedical Library, AFRL/HEDM, 2511 Kennedy Dr, Brooks City-Base, AFB TX 78235-5116. SAN 361-3178

FL2857/Base Library, 311 MSG/SVMG, 8080 Outercircle Rd, Suite 1, Brooks AFB TX 78235-5228. SAN 361-3119

FL4469/Base Library, 377 SVS/SVMG, 2050-B 2nd St SE, Bldg 20204, Kirtland AFB 87117-5525. SAN 351-6547

FL7050/AFRL Tyndall Site, Technical Information Center, AFRL/MLQP, 139 Barnes Drive, Suite 2, Bldg 1120, Tyndall AFB FL 32403-5323. SAN 324-5845

AFSPC (Air Force Space Command)

FL2500/Base Library, 21 SVS/SVMG, 201 W Stewart Ave, Bldg 1171, Peterson AFB CO 80914-1600. SAN 335-976X

FL2507/Base Library, 821 SPTS/SVRL, Bldg 362, Unit 82501, APO AE 09704-5000. SAN 327-3318

FL2508/Command Librarian, HQ AFSPC/MSVXL, 150 Vandenberg Ave, Suite 1105, Bldg 1, Rm 3400, Peterson AFB CO 80914-4210. SAN 378-0511

FL2513/45th SW Technical Library, 1030 South Hwy A1A, Bldg 989, Rm A1-S3, Patrick AFB FL 32925-0127. SAN 337-968X

FL2520/Base Library, 45 SVS/SVMG, 842 Falcon Ave, Bldg 722, Patrick AFB FL 32925-3439. SAN 337-971X

FL2827/Vandenberg AFB Technical Library, 30 SW ACTA-SC,144 Tenth St, Bldg 7525, Rm 155, Vandenberg AFB CA 93437-5200. SAN 335-217X

FL4610/Base Library, 30 MSG/SVMG, 100 Community Loop, Bldg 10343-A, Vandenberg AFB CA 93437-6111. SAN 326-0720

FL4613/Base Library, 90 SVS/SVMG, 7205 Randall Ave, Bldg 214, F E Warren AFB WY 82005-2988. SAN 365-2386

FL4626/Base Library, 341 SVS/SVMG, 7356 Fourth Ave N, Malmstrom AFB, MT 59402-7506. SAN 350-0497

AFSVA (Air Force Services Agency)

FL4400/Base Library, AFIAA HQ 11 MSG/SVMG, 410 Tinker St, Bldg 4439, Bolling AFB DC 20032-0703. SAN 337-0895

FL4414/AF Weather Technical Library, AFCCC/DOR, 151 Patton Ave, Rm 358, Asheville, NC 28801-5002. SAN 378-0643

FL4417/Base Library, 16 SVS/SVMG, 443 Cody Ave, Bldg 90337, Hurlburt Field, FL 32544-5435. SAN 378-0686

FL7000/USAF Academy Library, HQ USAFA/DFLIB, 2354 Fairchild Dr, Suite 3A15, USAF Academy, CO 80840-6214. SAN 336-0067

FL7005/Base Library, 10 SVS/SVMG, 5136 Redtail Dr, Suite H103, USAF Academy, CO 80840-2600. SAN 336-0091

FL7011/AFLMA Technical Library, AFLMA/TL, 501 Ward St, Bldg 205, Maxwell AFB, Gunter Annex-MAFB, AL 36114. SAN 378-0708

FL7058/AF Historical Stuides Office Library, AF/HOH HSO/HOR, Three Brookley Ave, Box 94, Bolling AFB DC 20332-5000. SAN 378-066X

FL7072 453 EWS/EWD Research, 102 Hall Blvd, Suite 315, Bldg 2000, San Antonio, TX 78243-7016

AMC (Air Mobility Command)

FL4401/Command Librarian, HQ AMC/A7SFG, 507 Symington Dr, Suite W121. Scott AFB IL 62225-5022. SAN 378-0767

FL4407 Scott AFB Library, 375 SVS/SVMG, 510 Ward Dr, Scott AFB IL 62225-5360. SAN 340-7551

FL4418/Base Library, 437 SVS/SVMG, 106 W McCaw St, Bldg 215, Charleston AFB, SC 29404-4700. SAN 360-0548

FL4425/Base Library, 89 SVS/SVMG, Brookley & D St, Bldg 1642, Andrews AFB MD 20762-5984. SAN 378-0724

FL4427/Base Library, 60 SVS/SVMG, 510 Travis Ave, Bldg 436, Travis AFB CA 94535-2168. SAN 335-1904

FL4479/Base Library, 62 SVS/SVMG, 851 Lincoln Blvd, McChord AFB WA 98438-1317. SAN 363-678X

FL4484/Base Library, 305 SVS/SVMG, 2603 Tuskegee Airmen Ave, McGuire AFB NJ 08641-5016. SAN 350-8560

FL4488/Base Library, 43 SVS/SVMG, 396 Sonic St, Bldg 373, Pope AFB NC 28308-2902. SAN 355-0354

FL4497/Base Library, 436 SVS/SVMG, 262 Chad St, Rm 208, Dover AFB DE 19902-7235. SAN 336-5913

FL4499/Ronald R Fogleman Library, Air Mobility Warfare Center, 5656 Texas Ave, Ft Dix, NJ 08640-7406. SAN 378-0740

FL4620/Base Library, 92 SVS/SVMG, Two W Castle St, Fairchild AFB WA 99011-8532. SAN 363-6518

FL4621/Base Library, 22 SVS/SVMG, 53476 Wichita St, Bldg 412, McConnell AFB KS 67221. SAN 342-1171

FL4659/Base Library, 319 SVS/SVMG, 511 Holzapple St, Bldg 201, Grand Forks AFB ND 58205-6320. SAN 355-3744

FL4814/Base Library, 6 SVS/SVMG, 8102 Condor St, Bldg 252, MacDill AFB FL 33621-5013. SAN 337-7105

PACAF (Pacific Air Forces Command)

FL5000/Base Library, 3 SVS/SVMG, 10480 22nd St, Elmendorf AFB AK 99506-2550. SAN 330-4655

FL5004/Base Library, 354 SVS/SVMG, 2539 Central Ave, Suite 100, Eielson AFB, AK 99702-1299. SAN 330-4620

FL5205/Base Library, 35 SVS/SVMG, Unit 5019, Misawa AB Japan, APO AP 96319-5019. SAN 323-0082

FL5209/Base Library, 374 MSG/SVMG, Unit 5119, Bldg 617, Yokota AB Japan, APO AP 96328-5119. SAN 323-0104

FL5239/PACAF Command Librarian, HQ PACAF/SVPRL, Bldg 1102, 25 East St, Suite K112, Hickam AFB, HI 96853-5431. SAN 378-0783

FL5240/Base Library, 36 SVS/SVMG, Unit 14004, Box 28, Andersen AFB Guam, APO AP 96543-4004. SAN 365-4575

FL5260/Base Library, 15 SVS/SVMG, 990 Mills Ave, Bldg 595, Hickam AFB HI 96853-5316. SAN 339-3844

FL5270/Base Library, 18 SVS/SVMG, Unit 5135, Box 20, Kadena AB Okinawa Japan, APO AP 96368-5135. SAN 323-0147

FL5284/Base Library, 8 SVS/SVMG, Unit 2105, Kunsan AB Korea, APO AP 96264-2105. SAN 323-0103

FL5294/Base Library, 51 SVS/SVMG, Unit 2065, Bldg 921, Osan AB Korea, APO AP 96278-2065. SAN 323-018X

USAFE (US Air Forces Europe)

FL5500/Command Librarian, HQ USAFE/A7SXL, Unit 3050, Box 30, APO AE 09094-5030

FL5510/Library Service Center, HQ USAFE/A7SXLC, Unit 3050, Box 30, APO AE 09094-5030. SAN 323-0201

FL5518/Base Library, 100 SVS/SVMG, Unit 4905, Box 245, APO AE 09459-5000

FL5530/Base Library, 435 SVS/SVMGK, Unit 3240, Box 510, APO AE 09094-5000. SAN 323-0287

FL5531/Base Library, 425 ABS/SVMG, Unit 6870, Box 33, APO AE 09821-5000. SAN 323-0309

FL5537/Base Library, 422 ABS/SVMG, Unit 5845, Box 20, APO AE 09494-0022. SAN 378-0805

FL5587/Base Library, 48 SVS/SVMI, Unit 5185, Box 240, APO AE 09464-5000. SAN 323-0384

FL5604/Base Library, 435 SVS/SVMG-S, Unit 4125, Box 155, APO AE 09136-5000

FL5606/Branch Library, 52 SV/SVMG-B, Unit 3820, Box 85, APO AE 09126. SAN 323-0449

FL5612/Base Library, 435 SVS/SVMG, Unit 3240, Box 535, APO AE 09094-0535. SAN 323-0465

FL5621/Base Library, 52 SVS/SVMG, Unit 3670, Box 90, APO AE 09126-7090. SAN 323-2328.

FL5643/Base Library, 423 ABS/SVMG, Unit 5570, Box 85, Bldg 678, APO AE 09470-7085. SAN 323-2360

FL5670/Base Library, PSC 45, Unit 8405, APO AE 09468-5000

FL5682/Base Library, 31 SVS/SVMG, Unit 6122, Box 50, APO AE 09604-2250. SAN 323-2425

FL5685/Base Library, 39 SVS/SVMG, Unit 8915, Box 165, APO AE 09824-5000. SAN 323-2441

UNITED STATES ARMY

PACIFIC

-Installation Management Agency, Library Program, H Place, Bldg 104, Fort Shafter, Hawaii 96858-5520

ALASKA

-Post Library, Bldg 7, Chilkoot Ave, IMPA FRAHRE PL, Fort Richardson, AK 99505-0055. SAN 376-6314

-Post Library, 1060 Gaffney Rd, No 6600, Ft Wainwright, AK 99703-6600. SAN 330-4957

HAWAII

-Aliamanu Library, Attn: APVG-GAF-RL (AMR), 1782 Bougainvillea Loop, Honolulu, HI 96818. SAN 371-3067

-Ft Shafter Library, Attn: APVG-GAF-RL (FS), Bldg. 650, Ft Shafter, HI 96858-5000. SAN 339-5677

-Medical Library, Tripler Army Medical Center, One Jarrett White Rd., HI 96859-5000. SAN 339-5766

-Sergeant Rodney J Yano Post Library, Attn: APVG-GAF-RL, Bldg. 560 Schofield Barracks, HI 96857-5000. SAN 339-5707

JAPAN

-USAG Japan, Unit 45006, Attn: IMPA-JA-MWR-L, Camp Zama Community Library, APO AP 96343-5006. SAN 323-1364

Okinawa

-USAG Japan, Attn: IM PA-JA-MWO-RL, Torii Library, APO AP 96376-5115. SAN 323-1380

EUROPE

The United States Army Libraries, Europe, is a professionally administered systems network of 38 libraries (main, branch, hospital, and confinement libraries) in Germany, Belgium, Holland and Italy. These general libraries support the education programs for military personnel from high school through graduate-level, military training, technical mission-related requirements of the United States Army and the informational and general-reading needs of the military community. The Command Reference Center provides specialized command-wide reference, research, and interlibrary loan services to the command and staff sections of the various military headquarters, libraries and students, and serves as the network outlet to reference sources in the United States.

-ANSBACH Comm. Library, USAG Ansbach, Unit 28614, Box 55, Bldg 5083 Bleidorn Village, APO AE 09177. SAN 323-0961

-Brussels Library, USAG Brussels, Unit 8100, Box 07, APO AE 09714. SAN 323-0740

-Europe Region Librarian, IMA SFM-EU-MWR. Unit 29351, APO AE 09014. SAN 323-0503

-Europe Regional Library & Support Center, Attn IMEU-MWO-L, Unit 29351, APO AE 09014-9351. SAN 323-052X

-Joint Forces Command HQ Brunssum Library, USAG Schinner, Unit 21601, APO AE 09703. SAN 323-0740

-Landstuhl Library, Kleber Kaserne, USAG Kaiserslautern LRMC, APO AE 09180. SAN 323-0600

-Pioneer Library, USAG Hessen Hanau, Unit 20193, Box 0029, APO AE 09165-0029. SAN 323-0902

-SHAPE International Library, USAG Benelux, Unit 21420, APO AE 09705. SAN 375-8826

-Sullivan Library, USAG Mannheim, Unit 29901, Box 6, APO AE 09086. SAN 323-066X

-US Army Library, Camp Eberle USAG Vicenz Unit 31410, Box 80, APO AE 09630. SAN 323-1321

-US Army Library, Camp Darby Library, USAG Livorno, Unit 31301, Box 70, APO AE 09613. SAN 323-1305

-US Army Library, Patch Barracks, USAG Stuttgart, Unit 30401, APO AE 09107. SAN 323-1224

-US Army Library, USAG Heidelberg, Unit 29237 PHV, APO AE 09102-0010. SAN 323-1313

-US Army Library, USAG Baumholder, Unit 23746, APO AE 09034. SAN 323-0805

-US Army Library, Leighton Barracks, USAG Franconia, Unit 26230, APO AE 09244. SAN 323-1240

-US Army Library, Ledward Barracks, USAG Schweinfurt, CMR 457, PO Box 1507, APO AE 09033. SAN 232-1208

-US Army Library, USAG Bamberg, Unit 27535, APO AE 09139. SAN 323-0162

-US Army Library, Grafenwoehr, Unit 28130, Bldg. 445, APO AE 09114-5413. SAN 323-1267

-US Army Library, Rose Barracks, USAG Grafenwoehr, Bldg 2222, Unit 28038, APO AE 09112. SAN 372-5553

-US Army Library, USAG Hohenfels, Bldg 49, Unit 28216 Hohenfels, APO AE 09173. SAN 323-1275

-US Army Library, USAG Darmstadt, Unit 29500, Box 0035, APO AE 09175-0035. SAN 323-0821

-Wiesbaden Airbase Library, USAG Weisbaden, Unit 29623, APO 09096. SAN 323-0929

KOREA

-Camp Casey Library, USAG Camp Casey, Unit 15614, Bldg. S-2648. APO AP 96224-5614. SAN 323-1461

-Camp Hovey, Library, 2D BDE, 2ID, Unit 15058, APO AP 96224-5058. SAN 323-150X

-Camp Red Cloud, Library, CRD DPCA Solet SG, Unit 15303, APO AP 96258-5303. SAN 323-1569

-Camp Stanley, Library, HQ, 2nd Inf Div, Artillery, Unit 15564, APO AP 96257-5564. SAN 323-1623

-Camp Long, Library, Unit 15579, APO AP 96297-5579. SAN 323-1887

  -Camp Humphreys Library, Unit 15593, Bldg S-301, APO AP 96271-5593

  -Camp Walker Library, CRD, Bldg S-335, 20th Support Group, Unit 15494, APO 96218-5494

-Camp Carroll, Library, CRD, ADCFA, DCA, 20th Support GP, Unit 15476, APO AP 96260-5748. SAN 323-214X

  -Hannam Village, Library, Unit 15333, Bldg T6150, CRD APO AP 96205-5333. SAN 322-6425

-Korea Regional Librarian, IMA SFIM-Ko-MWR, APO AP 96205-5333. SAN 372-557X

-Korea Regional Reference Center & Yongsan, Library, Unit 15333, APO AP 96205-5333. SAN 323-1828

PUERTO RICO

-Fort Buchanan Post Library, Bldg 518, 218 Brook St, Fort Buchanan, PR 00934-5013. SAN 365-5024

UNITED STATES NAVY AND MARINE CORPS LIBRARIES

Allied Naval Forces Southern Europe, Headquarters Command, General Library, PSC 813 Box 5, FPO AE 09620-0000. SAN 323-2700

Command Naval Activity, ROTA, General Library, PSC 819 Box 14, FPO AE 09645-2000. SAN 326-8187

Library Processing Center, COMMARCORBASEJAPAN, Camp Butler, IMOT 35023, FPO AP 96373-5023. SAN 323-2824

US Naval Air Facility Atsugi Japan, MWR Library, PSC 477 Box 20 MWR, FPO AP 96306-1220. SAN 323-3340

US Naval Forces Marianas, MWR Library, PSC 455 Box 169, AP APO 96540-1099. SAN 323-2603

US Naval Station Guantanamo, Station Library, PSC 1005 Box 14, APO AE 09593-0114. SAN 323-2689

US Naval Air Station Sigonella IT, General Library, PSC 812 Box 470, FPO AE 09627-0824. SAN 323-3367

US Fleet Activities, MWR Library, Code 6054, PSC 473 Box 60, FPO AP 96319-1105. SAN 373-8418

US Naval Support Activity Gaeta IT, MWR Monte Orlando Library, PSC 811 Box 03 FPO AE 09609-1001. SAN 323-3308

US Naval Air Station Keflavik IC, General Library, PSC 1003 Box 43, FPO AE 09728-0343. SAN 323-2581

US Naval Support Activity La Maddalena IT, MWR Library, PSC 816 Box 1795, FPO AE 09612-0051. SAN 323-3324

US Naval Support Activity Naples IT, General Library, PSC 817 Box 9, FPO AE 09622-0009. SAN 375-8842

US Fleet Activities Sasebo, MWR Dept Main Base Library, PSC 476 Box 5, FPO AP 96322-1190. SAN 323-3405

US Command Fleet Activities Chinhae Korea, General Library, PSC 479, FPO AP 96269-1100. SAN 329-5672

US Naval Radio Receiving Facility Kamiseya JA, General Library, PSC 478A, FPO AP 96313-1800. SAN 323-3162

US Naval Support Activity Souda Bay GR, General Library, PSC 814 Box 13, FPO AE 09865-0063. SAN 372-5111

US Command Fleet Activities Yokosuka JA, Code 6112, MWR Library, Yokohama Detachment Br, PSC 473 Box 60, FPO AP 96349-1105. SAN 323-262X

US Naval Support Activity Bahrain, General Library, PSC 451 Box 116, FPO AE 09834-2800. SAN 323-3588

US Marine Corps Air Station Iwakuni JA, MCCS Station Library, PSC 561 Box 1867, FPO AP 96810-1867. SAN 323-2808

US Marine Corps Base Hawaii, MWR Base Library Box 63073, Kaneohe Bay, HI 96863-3073. SAN 339-6037

US Marine Corps Base Hawaii, MWR Library, Box 64123, Camp H M Smith, HI 96861-4123. SAN 339-6061

INDEXES

Organization Index

Personnel Index

ORGANIZATION INDEX

Air Force, Army and Navy are listed under United States.

The letter (N) after an organization name indicates that the organization will be found in the Networks and Consortia section.

Letter-by-letter alphabetization is used. Universities, colleges or junior colleges named after a person are alphabetized by the person's first name, e.g., Sarah Lawrence College will be found under S. Any other library or institution named after a person will be alphabetized by the person's last name, e.g., Martin Luther King Libarary will be found under K.

A T Still University, Mesa AZ p. 68
A T Still University of Health Sciences, Kirksville MO p. 1342
AAHS Reference Library, *see* American Aviation Historical Society, Huntington Beach CA p. 158
Aalfs Wilbur Library, *see* Sioux City Public Library, Sioux City IA p. 844
Aaron A H Health Sciences Library, *see* Buffalo General Health System, Buffalo NY p. 1597
AARP, Washington DC p. 391
Abbell Joseph & Dora Library, *see* Congregation Rodfei Zedek, Chicago IL p. 611
Abbell Maxwell Library, *see* North Suburban Synagogue Beth El, Highland Park IL p. 656
Abbeville County Library System, Abbeville SC p. 2179
Abbeville Memorial Library, Abbeville AL p. 3
Abbey of Gethsemani Library, Trappist KY p. 936
Abbey of Regina Laudis Library, Bethlehem CT p. 330
Abbot Public Library, Marblehead MA p. 1102
Abbotsford Public Library, Abbotsford WI p. 2577
Abbott, Abbott Park IL p. 587
Abbott Edith Memorial Library, *see* Grand Island Public Library, Grand Island NE p. 1400
Abbott Laboratories Ltd Library, Saint Laurent QC p. 2909
Abbott Library, Sunapee NH p. 1466
Abbott Memorial Library, Dexter ME p. 983
Abbott Memorial Library, South Pomfret VT p. 2436
Abbott Northwestern Hospital, *see* Allina Health Library Services, Minneapolis MN p. 1258
Abbottsfield-Penny McKee, *see* Edmonton Public Library, Edmonton AB p. 2700
Abel W H Memorial Library, *see* Timberland Regional Library, Montesano WA p. 2543
Abell George T & Gladys H Library Center, *see* Austin College, Sherman TX p. 2387
Abelson Echikson Ehrenkrantz Memorial Library, *see* Temple Sharey Tefilo-Israel, South Orange NJ p. 1531
Abercrombie Lelia Historical Resource Center, *see* Pensacola Historical Society, Pensacola FL p. 481
Aberdeen District Library, Aberdeen ID p. 569
Aberdeen Hospital, New Glasgow NS p. 2784
Aberdeen Public Library, *see* Mitchell Alexander Public Library, Aberdeen SD p. 2209
Abernathy Public Library, Abernathy TX p. 2271
Abilene Christian University, Abilene TX p. 2271
Abilene Educational Center Library, *see* Cisco College, Abilene TX p. 2297
Abilene Library Consortium (N), Abilene TX p. 2955

Abilene Public Library, Abilene KS p. 855
Abilene Public Library, Abilene TX p. 2271
Abington College Library, *see* Pennsylvania State University, Abington PA p. 2025
Abington Community Library, Clarks Summit PA p. 2045
Abington Free Library, *see* Abington Township Public Library, Abington PA p. 2025
Abington Memorial Hospital, Abington PA p. 2025
Abington Memorial Hospital, Willow Grove PA p. 2157
Abington Memorial Library, *see* Arkansas State University, Beebe AR p. 94
Abington Presbyterian Church Library, Abington PA p. 2025
Abington Public Library, Abington MA p. 1047
Abington Social Library, Abington CT p. 329
Abington Township Public Library, Abington PA p. 2025
Abiquiu Public Library, Abiquiu NM p. 1547
Abplanalp Josephine S Library, *see* University of New England Libraries, Portland ME p. 978
Abraham Baldwin Agricultural College, Tifton GA p. 554
Abrahams Milton R & Pauline S Library, *see* Joslyn Art Museum, Omaha NE p. 1413
Abrahams Milton R, *see* Omaha Public Library, Omaha NE p. 1414
Abram Village Public, *see* Prince Edward Island Public Library Service, Abram Village PE p. 2876
Abramson Madlyn & Leonard Center for Jewish Life, North Wales PA p. 2099
ABSAUM (N), *see* Association des Bibliotheques de la Sante Affiliees, Montreal QC p. 2960
Absecon Public Library, Absecon NJ p. 1469
ACA Library of Savannah College of Art & Design, Atlanta GA p. 510
Acacia Library, *see* Phoenix Public Library, Phoenix AZ p. 76
Academic Libraries of Brooklyn (N), Brooklyn NY p. 2949
Academy Art Museum, Easton MD p. 1027
Academy for Educational Development, Washington DC p. 391
Academy of Art University Library, San Francisco CA p. 240
Academy of Motion Picture Arts & Sciences, Beverly Hills CA p. 128
Academy of Natural Sciences of Philadelphia, Philadelphia PA p. 2102
Acadia Municipal Library, Acadia Valley AB p. 2683
Acadia Parish Library, Crowley LA p. 948
Acadia University, Wolfville NS p. 2786

Access-AIC Services Library, Ann Arbor MI p. 1150
ACCK (N), *see* Associated Colleges of Central Kansas, McPherson KS p. 2943
Accokeek Foundation Library, Accokeek MD p. 1009
ACES Educational Center for the Arts, New Haven CT p. 355
Achilles Frances Mulhall Library, *see* Whitney Museum of American Art, New York NY p. 1702
Acker David D Library, Fort Belvoir VA p. 2464
Ackerman Irving P MD Health Sciences Library, *see* Kaiser-Permanente Medical Center, Los Angeles CA p. 171
Ackley Public Library, Ackley IA p. 791
ACL (N), *see* Association of Christian Librarians, Cedarville OH p. 2951
Acme Municipal Library, Acme AB p. 2683
Acopian Center for Conservation Learning, Orwigsburg PA p. 2101
Acorn Public Library District, Oak Forest IL p. 683
Acosta Moreno Esperanza Regional, *see* El Paso Public Library, El Paso TX p. 2316
ACT Information Resource Center, Iowa City IA p. 822
Acterra Environmental Library, Palo Alto CA p. 204
Acton Memorial Library, Acton MA p. 1047
Acton Public Library, Old Saybrook CT p. 363
Acton Public Library, Acton ME p. 973
ACTS (N), *see* Association of Chicago Theological Schools, Mundelein IL p. 2942
Acuren Group, Inc, Edmonton AB p. 2697
Acworth Silsby Library, Acworth NH p. 1437
Ada Community Library, Boise ID p. 570
Ada Public Library, Ada OH p. 1851
Ada Public Library, Ada OK p. 1955
Ada Public Library, *see* Lake Agassiz Regional Library, Ada MN p. 1265
Adair County Public Library, Columbia KY p. 910
Adair County Public Library, Kirksville MO p. 1342
Adair Public Library, Adair IA p. 791
Adamany David Undergraduate Library, *see* Wayne State University Libraries, Detroit MI p. 1173
Adams & Reese Law Library, New Orleans LA p. 959
Adams Center Free Library, Adams Center NY p. 1567
Adams County Historical Society Archives, Hastings NE p. 1401
Adams County Historical Society Library, Gettysburg PA p. 2059
Adams County Law Library, Gettysburg PA p. 2059
Adams County Library, Hettinger ND p. 1844
Adams County Library, Adams WI p. 2577

Adams County Library System, Gettysburg PA p. 2059

Adams County Public Library, Manchester OH p. 1912

Adams Dr & Mrs J F Memorial Library, *see* Cannon County Library System, Woodbury TN p. 2269

Adams Free Library, Adams MA p. 1047

Adams Free Library, Adams NY p. 1567

Adams Henry C Memorial Library, Prophetstown IL p. 692

Adams James P Library, *see* Rhode Island College, Providence RI p. 2174

Adams Memorial Library, Latrobe PA p. 2078

Adams Memorial Library, Central Falls RI p. 2164

Adams Park Library, *see* Atlanta-Fulton Public Library System, Atlanta GA p. 511

Adams Paul M Memorial Library, *see* Rocky Mountain College, Billings MT p. 1374

Adams-Pratt Oakland County Law Library, Pontiac MI p. 1218

Adams Public Library, Adams OR p. 1989

Adams Public Library System, Decatur IN p. 735

Adams State University, Alamosa CO p. 287

Adams-Vines Library, *see* Arkansas Northeastern College, Blytheville AR p. 95

Adamstown Area Library, Adamstown PA p. 2025

Adamsville Public Library, Adamsville AL p. 3

Adat Shalom Synagogue, Farmington Hills MI p. 1177

Adath Israel Synagogue, Cincinnati OH p. 1868

Adcock Ernest J Library, *see* Holmes Community College, Ridgeland MS p. 1314

Addiction Research Center Library, *see* National Institute on Drug Abuse, Baltimore MD p. 1016

Addictions Foundation of Manitoba, Winnipeg MB p. 2753

Addictions Services Library, *see* Eastern Health, St. John's NL p. 2772

Addiego Peter Health Sciences Library, *see* Nassau University Medical Center, East Meadow NY p. 1617

Addison Public Library, Addison IL p. 587

Addison Public Library, Addison NY p. 1567

Addison Township Public Library, Leonard MI p. 1203

Addlestone Marlene & Nathan Library, *see* College of Charleston, Charleston SC p. 2184

Adel Public Library, Adel IA p. 791

Adelphi University, Hauppauge NY p. 1634

Adelphi University, New York NY p. 1667

Adelphi University Libraries, Garden City NY p. 1625

Adelson Library, *see* Cornell University Library, Ithaca NY p. 1641

ADI Ltd Library, Fredericton NB p. 2762

Adirondack Community College Library, Queensbury NY p. 1725

Adirondack Correctional Facility Library, Ray Brook NY p. 1726

Adirondack Museum Library, Blue Mountain Lake NY p. 1583

Adkins Rocky J Public Library, Sandy Hook KY p. 934

Adler Planetarium & Astronomy Museum, Chicago IL p. 604

Adler Pollock & Sheehan PC Library, Providence RI p. 2171

Adler School of Professional Psychology, Chicago IL p. 605

ADM Research Library, *see* Archer Daniels Midland Co, Decatur IL p. 633

Administrative Office of the United States Courts Library, Washington DC p. 391

Admiral Nimitz National Museum of the Pacific War, Fredericksburg TX p. 2325

Adrian College, Adrian MI p. 1147

Adrian Public Library, Adrian MI p. 1147

Adriance Memorial Library, *see* Poughkeepsie Public Library District, Poughkeepsie NY p. 1723

Adventist Health System, DeLand FL p. 437

Adventist Hinsdale Hospital, Hinsdale IL p. 656

Advocate Illinois Masonic Medical Center, Chicago IL p. 605

Advocate Library, *see* Capital City Press, Baton Rouge LA p. 942

Advocate Library, *see* Cumberland Public Libraries, Advocate Harbour NS p. 2777

Advocate Lutheran General Hospital, Park Ridge IL p. 688

Advocate Trinity Hospital, Chicago IL p. 605

Advocates for Youth, Washington DC p. 391

AECom Canada Ltd, Winnipeg MB p. 2754

AECOM Library, Los Angeles CA p. 168

AECOM Library, Vernon Hills IL p. 714

Aero Systems Engineering Inc Library, Saint Paul MN p. 1277

Aerodyne Research, Inc, Billerica MA p. 1054

Aeromedical Library, *see* United States Air Force, Brooks AFB TX p. 2292

Aerospace Corp, El Segundo CA p. 146

Aerospace Museum Association of Calgary Library, Calgary AB p. 2687

Aesthetic Realism Foundation, New York NY p. 1667

Aetna, Hartford CT p. 344

AEW Capital Management LP, Boston MA p. 1054

Affinity Medical Center, Massillon OH p. 1915

AFIWC Library, *see* United States Air Force, San Antonio TX p. 2383

African American Library at the Gregory School, *see* Houston Public Library, Houston TX p. 2339

African American Museum & Library, Cedar Rapids IA p. 800

African-American Research Library & Cultural Center, *see* Broward County Division of Libraries, Fort Lauderdale FL p. 441

Afro-American Historical Society Museum Library, Jersey City NJ p. 1492

Afton Free Library, Afton NY p. 1567

Agassiz Library, *see* Fraser Valley Regional Library, Agassiz BC p. 2723

Agave Library, *see* Phoenix Public Library, Phoenix AZ p. 76

Agawam Public Library, Agawam MA p. 1048

Agency Public Library, Agency IA p. 791

Agere Systems, Allentown PA p. 2026

Agnes Scott College, Decatur GA p. 529

Agness Community Library, Agness OR p. 1989

Agoos Medical Library, *see* Beth Israel Deaconess Medical Center, Boston MA p. 1055

Agricultural Research Service, Midwest Area, Peoria IL p. 689

Agriculture & Agri-Food Canada, Beaverlodge AB p. 2685

Agriculture & Agri-Food Canada, Lethbridge AB p. 2709

Agriculture & Agri-Food Canada, Ottawa ON p. 2827

Agriculture & Agri-Food Canada, Charlottetown PE p. 2875

Agriculture & Agri-Food Canada, Sainte-Foy QC p. 2910

Agriculture & Agri-Food Canada, Indian Head SK p. 2918

Agriculture & Agri-Food Canada, Swift Current SK p. 2927

Agriculture & Agri-Food Canada, Canadian Agriculture Library, Kentville NS p. 2783

Agriculture & Agri-Food Canada, Ottawa ON p. 2827

Agriculture & Agri-Food Canada, Vineland Station ON p. 2868

Agriculture Canada, Saint-Jean-Sur-Richelieu QC p. 2911

Agrium, Inc, Redwater AB p. 2715

Agudas Achim Congregation, Bexley OH p. 1860

Agudath Israel Congregation, Ottawa ON p. 2827

Aguilar Public Library, Aguilar CO p. 287

AHEC (N), *see* Arkansas Area Health Education Center Consortium, Fort Smith AR p. 2937

AHLC (N), *see* Areawide Hospital Library Consortium of Southwestern Illinois, Belleville IL p. 2942

Ahmadiyya Movement In Islam Inc, Washington DC p. 391

Ahmadiyya Muslim Association Library, Winnipeg MB p. 2754

Ahoskie Public Library, *see* Albemarle Regional Library, Ahoskie NC p. 1835

Ahrens Memorial Library, *see* United States Air Force, Holloman AFB NM p. 1557

Ai Miami International University, Miami FL p. 464

AIB College of Business Library, Des Moines IA p. 808

AIDS Coalition of Nova Scotia Library, Halifax NS p. 2780

AIDS Library, Philadelphia PA p. 2102

Aiea Public Library, *see* Hawaii State Public Library System, Aiea HI p. 561

AIHEC (N), *see* American Indian Higher Education Consortium, Alexandria VA p. 2957

AIKCU (N), *see* Association of Independent Kentucky Colleges & Universities, Frankfort KY p. 2944

Aiken-Bamberg-Barnwell-Edgefield Regional Library System, Aiken SC p. 2179

Aiken Technical College Library, Graniteville SC p. 2195

Aims Community College, Greeley CO p. 311

Aina Haina Public Library, *see* Hawaii State Public Library System, Honolulu HI p. 561

Ainsworth Annie Porter Memorial Library, Sandy Creek NY p. 1738

Ainsworth Public Library, Ainsworth NE p. 1391

Ainsworth Public Library, Williamstown VT p. 2439

Air & Waste Management Association Library, Pittsburgh PA p. 2121

Air Force Association, Arlington VA p. 2448

Air Force Flight Test Center, *see* United States Air Force, Edwards AFB CA p. 144

Air Force Institute of Technology Academic Library, *see* United States Air Force, Wright-Patterson AFB OH p. 1951

Air Force Research Laboratory, Eglin AFB FL p. 439

Air Force Research Laboratory Library, *see* United States Air Force, Hanscom AFB MA p. 1093

Wright Research Technical Library, *see* United States Air Force, Wright-Patterson AFB OH p. 1951

McConnell Air Force Base Library, *see* United States Air Force, Wichita KS p. 900

Fairchild Muir S Research Information Center, *see* United States Air Force, Maxwell AFB AL p. 24

Aird & Berlis LLP Law Library, Toronto ON p. 2849

Airdrie Public Library, Airdrie AB p. 2683

Airline Pilots Association International, Herndon VA p. 2471

Aiso Library, Monterey CA p. 189

AISTI (N), *see* Alliance for Innovation in Science & Technology Information, Santa Fe NM p. 2949

Aitkin Memorial District Library, Croswell MI p. 1167

Aitkin Public Library, *see* East Central Regional Library, Aitkin MN p. 1243

Ajax Public Library, Ajax ON p. 2791

Akerman, Senterfitt & Eidson PA, Orlando FL p. 475

Akerman Senterfitt LLP Law Library, Washington DC p. 391

Akin Free Library, Pawling NY p. 1716

Akin, Gump, Strauss, Hauer & Feld Library, Dallas TX p. 2304

Akin, Gump, Strauss, Hauer & Feld LLP, Washington DC p. 391

Akin, Gump, Strauss, Hauer & Feld LLP, San Antonio TX p. 2379

Akiva Library, *see* Jewish Federation Libraries, Nashville TN p. 2256

Akron Art Museum, Akron OH p. 1851

Akron Carnegie Public Library, Akron IN p. 723

Akron Department of Planning & Urban Development Library, Akron OH p. 1851

Akron General Medical Center, Akron OH p. 1851

Akron Law Library, Akron OH p. 1851

Akron Library, *see* Newstead Public Library, Akron NY p. 1567

Akron Public Library, Akron AL p. 3

Akron Public Library, Akron CO p. 287

Akron Public Library, Akron IA p. 791

Akron-Summit County Public Library, Akron OH p. 1851

Akwesasne Cultural Center Library, Hogansburg NY p. 1637

AkzoNobel, Strongsville OH p. 1937

Purdy Al, *see* County of Prince Edward Libraries, Ameliasburgh ON p. 2792

Alabama A&M University, Huntsville AL p. 21

Alabama Department of Archives & History Research Room, Montgomery AL p. 27

Alabama Department of Corrections, Elmore AL p. 15

Alabama Department of Corrections, Springville AL p. 36

Alabama Health Libraries Association, Inc (N), Birmingham AL p. 2937

Alabama Institute for the Deaf & Blind, Talladega AL p. 36

Alabama League of Municipalities Library, Montgomery AL p. 27

Alabama Power Co, Birmingham AL p. 6

Alabama Public Library Service, Montgomery AL p. 27

Alabama Southern Community College, Monroeville AL p. 26

Alabama State University, Montgomery AL p. 28, 2961

Alabama Supreme Court & State Law Library, Montgomery AL p. 28

Alachua County Historic Trust, Gainesville FL p. 448

Alachua County Library District, Gainesville FL p. 448

Alamance Community College, Graham NC p. 1795

Alamance County Historic Properties Commission, Graham NC p. 1795

Alamance County Public Libraries, Burlington NC p. 1778

Alamance Regional Medical Center, Burlington NC p. 1779

Alameda County Law Library, *see* Witkin Bernard E Alameda County Law Library, Oakland CA p. 199

Alameda County Library, Fremont CA p. 149

Alameda County Medical Center, Oakland CA p. 196

Alameda Free Library, Alameda CA p. 119

McCollough Alameda Research Library, *see* Tippecanoe County Historical Association, Lafayette IN p. 759

Alamogordo Public Library, Alamogordo NM p. 1547

Alamosa Public Library, Alamosa CO p. 287

Murphy Robert L Memorial Library, *see* Albuquerque-Bernalillo County Library System, Albuquerque NM p. 1548

Alanson Area Public Library, Alanson MI p. 1148

Alaska Bible College Library, Glennallen AK p. 48

Alaska Christian College, Soldotna AK p. 53

Alaska Department of Law, Juneau AK p. 49

Alaska Department of Natural Resources, Anchorage AK p. 43

Alaska Heritage Museum & Library, Anchorage AK p. 43

Alaska Housing Finance Corp, Anchorage AK p. 43

Alaska Library Network (N), Anchorage AK p. 2937

Alaska Masonic Library & Museum, Anchorage AK p. 43

Alaska Native Medical Center, Anchorage AK p. 43

Alaska Oil & Gas Conservation Commission Library, Anchorage AK p. 43

Alaska Resources Library & Information Services, Anchorage AK p. 43

Alaska State Archives, Juneau AK p. 49

Alaska State Court Law Library, Anchorage AK p. 44

Alaska State Department of Corrections, Eagle River AK p. 47

Alaska State Legislature, Juneau AK p. 49

Alaska State Library, Anchorage AK p. 44

Alaska State Library, Juneau AK p. 49

Alaska Vocational Technical Center, Seward AK p. 53

Albany College of Pharmacy & Health Sciences, Albany NY p. 1567

Albany County Public Library, Laramie WY p. 2657

Albany Institute of History & Art, Albany NY p. 1567

Albany Law School, Albany NY p. 1568

Albany Medical College, Albany NY p. 1568

Albany Public Library, Albany NY p. 1568

Albany Public Library, Albany OR p. 1989

Albany Public Library, Albany WI p. 2577

Albany Public Library, *see* Great River Regional Library, Albany MN p. 1274

Albany Public Library District, Albany IL p. 587

Albany State University, Albany GA p. 507

Albany Town Library, Albany VT p. 2417

Albemarle Corp Library, Baton Rouge LA p. 942

Albemarle Regional Library, Winton NC p. 1835

Albert City Public Library, Albert City IA p. 791

Albert Einstein College of Medicine, Bronx NY p. 1585

Albert Lea Public Library, Albert Lea MN p. 1239

Albert-Westmorland-Kent Regional Library, Moncton NB p. 2765

Alberta Association for Community Living, Edmonton AB p. 2697

Alberta Beach Municipal Library, Alberta Beach AB p. 2683

Alberta Bible College Learning Resource Centre, Calgary AB p. 2687

Alberta Children's Hospital Knowledge Centre, Calgary AB p. 2687

Alberta College Campus Library, *see* MacEwan Grant University Library, Edmonton AB p. 2701

Alberta College of Art & Design, Calgary AB p. 2687

Alberta Committee of Citizens with Disabilities Library, Edmonton AB p. 2697

Alberta Culture, Edmonton AB p. 2697

Alberta Department of Environment Library, Edmonton AB p. 2698

Alberta Distance Learning Centre, Barrhead AB p. 2684

Alberta Genealogical Society Library & Research Centre, Edmonton AB p. 2698

Alberta Government Library, Edmonton AB p. 2698

Alberta Health Services, Ponoka AB p. 2713

Alberta Historical Resources Foundation Library, Edmonton AB p. 2698

Alberta Hospital-Edmonton Library, *see* Alberta Health Services, Edmonton AB p. 2714

Alberta Human Services, Calgary AB p. 2687

Alberta Innovates-Technology Futures, Edmonton AB p. 2698

Alberta Law Libraries, Calgary AB p. 2687

Alberta Law Libraries, Edmonton AB p. 2698

Alberta Law Libraries, Lethbridge AB p. 2709

Alberta Law Libraries, Peace River AB p. 2713

Alberta Law Libraries - Camrose, Camrose AB p. 2694

Alberta Law Libraries - Canmore, Canmore AB p. 2694

Alberta Law Libraries - Edson, Edson AB p. 2703

Alberta Law Libraries - Fort Saskatchewan, Fort Saskatchewan AB p. 2704

Alberta Law Libraries - High Prairie, High Prairie AB p. 2706

Alberta Law Libraries - Hinton, Hinton AB p. 2707

Alberta Law Libraries - Leduc, Leduc AB p. 2709

Alberta Law Libraries - Saint Albert, St. Albert AB p. 2717

Alberta Law Libraries - Sherwood Park, Sherwood Park AB p. 2716

Alberta Law Libraries - Stony Plain, Stony Plain AB p. 2718

Alberta Law Libraries - Vermilion, Vermilion AB p. 2720

Alberta Law Libraries - Red Deer, Red Deer AB p. 2714

Alberta Legislature Library, Edmonton AB p. 2699

Alberta School for the Deaf Library, Edmonton AB p. 2699

Alberta Teachers' Association Library, Edmonton AB p. 2699

Alberta Wilderness Association, Calgary AB p. 2687

Alberta Work Centre, *see* Alberta Human Services, Calgary AB p. 2687

Alberto Culver Co, Melrose Park IL p. 673

Alberton Public, *see* Prince Edward Island Public Library Service, Alberton PE p. 2876

Albertsons Library, *see* Boise State University, Boise ID p. 570

Albertus Magnus College Library, New Haven CT p. 355

Albertville Public Library, Albertville AL p. 3

Albion Area Public Library, Albion PA p. 2026

Albion College, Albion MI p. 1148

Albion Correctional Facility, *see* New York State Department of Correctional Services, Albion NY p. 1571

Albion District Library, Albion MI p. 1148

Albion Municipal Library, Albion IA p. 792

Albion Public Library, Albion IL p. 587

Albion Public Library, Albion ME p. 973

Albion Public Library, Albion NE p. 1391

Albizu Miranda Carlos Library, San Juan PR p. 2675

Albright College, Reading PA p. 2132

Albright Memorial Library, *see* Scranton Public Library, Scranton PA p. 2137

Albright-Knox Art Gallery, Buffalo NY p. 1596

Albuquerque-Bernalillo County Library System, Albuquerque NM p. 1547

Albuquerque Museum of Art & History, Albuquerque NM p. 1548

Alburg Public Library, Alburg VT p. 2417

Alcoa Technical Center Library, Alcoa Center PA p. 2026

Alcohol Research Group Library, Emeryville CA p. 146

Alcona County Library System, Harrisville MI p. 1188

Alcorn State University, Alcorn State MS p. 1293

Alcott Louisa May Memorial Association Library, Concord MA p. 1082

Alcuin Library, *see* Saint John's University, Collegeville MN p. 1246

Alden-Ewell Free Library, Alden NY p. 1571

Alden George I, *see* Quinsigamond Community College, Worcester MA p. 1144

Alden Manor, *see* Elmont Public Library, Elmont NY p. 1620

Alden Vernon R Library, *see* Ohio University Libraries, Athens OH p. 1856

Alder Flats Public Library, Alder Flats AB p. 2683

Alderman Library, *see* University of Virginia, Charlottesville VA p. 2454

Aldersgate United Methodist Church Library, Rochester NY p. 1728

Alderson-Broaddus College, Philippi WV p. 2569

Alderson Library, Alderson WV p. 2553

Aldrich Chemical Co, Inc Library, Milwaukee WI p. 2616

Aldrich Free Public Library, Moosup CT p. 353

Aldrich Museum of Contemporary Arts Library, Ridgefield CT p. 365

Aldrich Public Library, Barre VT p. 2418

Alegent Health Bergan Mercy Medical Center, Omaha NE p. 1411

Alert Bay Public Library & Museum, Alert Bay BC p. 2724

Alexander Archibald Stevens Library, *see* Rutgers University Libraries, New Brunswick NJ p. 1508

Alexander County Library, Taylorsville NC p. 1827

Alexander Donald L Library, *see* Allegany College of Maryland Library, Cumberland MD p. 1026

Alexander Hezekiah Homesite, *see* Charlotte Museum of History, Charlotte NC p. 1782

Alexander Library, *see* North Las Vegas Library District, North Las Vegas NV p. 1432

Alexander Margaret Walker Library, *see* Jackson/Hinds Library System, Jackson MS p. 1303

Alexander Memorial, *see* Cape May County Historical & Genealogical Society Library, Cape May Court House NJ p. 1477

Alexander Memorial Library, Cotulla TX p. 2303

Alexander Public Library, Alexander IA p. 792

Alexander-Smith Library, *see* New Providence Presbyterian Church, Maryville TN p. 2247

Alexander Will W Library, *see* Dillard University, New Orleans LA p. 960

William H & Marion C Alexander Family Library, *see* Dauphin County Library System, Hummelstown PA p. 2064

Alexandria Daily Town Talk Library, Alexandria LA p. 939

Alexandria Holland Free Public Library, Milford NJ p. 1502

Alexandria Library, Alexandria VA p. 2444

Alexandria-Monroe Public Library, Alexandria IN p. 723

Alexandria Public Library, Alexandria OH p. 1853

Alexandria Public Library, Alexandria SD p. 2210

Alexandria Technical College Library, Alexandria MN p. 1239

Alexandrian Public Library, Mount Vernon IN p. 766

Alexian Brothers Medical Library, Elk Grove Village IL p. 641

Alfaro Angel Quintero Library, *see* University of Puerto Rico Library System, San Juan PR p. 2677

Alford Lionel Regional, *see* Wichita Public Library, Wichita KS p. 901

Alfred University, Alfred NY p. 1572

Alger Maximum Correctional Facility Library, *see* Michigan Department of Corrections, Munising MI p. 1212

Alger Public Library, Alger OH p. 1854

Algiers Regional, *see* New Orleans Public Library, New Orleans LA p. 962

Algoma Public Library, Algoma WI p. 2577

Algoma University College, Sault Ste. Marie ON p. 2840

Algona-Pacific Library, *see* King County Library System, Pacific WA p. 2516

Algona Public Library, Algona IA p. 792

Algonquin Area Public Library District, Algonquin IL p. 588

Algonquin College Learning Resource Centre, Ottawa ON p. 2827

Algonquin College of Applied Arts & Technology, Ottawa ON p. 2978

Algonquin Park Visitor Centre, Whitney ON p. 2871

Alhambra Public Library, Alhambra CA p. 120

ALHeLa (N), *see* Alabama Health Libraries Association, Inc, Birmingham AL p. 2937

Aliamanu Library, *see* United States Army, Honolulu HI p. 565

Aliante Library, *see* North Las Vegas Library District, North Las Vegas NV p. 1432

Alice Lloyd College, Pippa Passes KY p. 933

Aliceville Public Library, Aliceville AL p. 4

Alief Center, *see* Houston Community College - Southwest College, Houston TX p. 2338

Alief Continuing Education Center, *see* Houston Community College - Southwest College, Houston TX p. 2338

Alix Public Library, Alix AB p. 2683

Alkek Albert B Library, *see* Texas State University-San Marcos, San Marcos TX p. 2385

All Childrens' Hospital, Saint Petersburg FL p. 487

All Cossack Museum & Library, *see* New Kuban Education & Welfare Association, Buena NJ p. 1476

All Saints Catholic Church, Dallas TX p. 2304

All Saints Healthcare, Racine WI p. 2632

All Souls Unitarian Church, Indianapolis IN p. 749

Allaire Village Inc, Farmingdale NJ p. 1485

Allan Memorial Institute of Psychiatry, Montreal QC p. 2887

Allara Frank M Library, *see* Pikeville College, Pikeville KY p. 933

Allegan District Library, Allegan MI p. 1148

Allegany College of Maryland Library, Cumberland MD p. 1026

Allegany County Circuit Court Law Library, Cumberland MD p. 1026

Allegany County Historical Museum Library, Belmont NY p. 1580

Allegany County Library System, Cumberland MD p. 1026

Allegany Public Library, Allegany NY p. 1572

Alleghany County Public Library, Sparta NC p. 1824

Allegheny College Library, Meadville PA p. 2086

Allegheny County Health Department Library, Pittsburgh PA p. 2121

Allegheny County Law Library, Pittsburgh PA p. 2121

Allegheny General Hospital, Pittsburgh PA p. 2121

Allegheny Valley Hospital, Natrona Heights PA p. 2094

Allegheny Wesleyan College Library, Salem OH p. 1933

Allen A D Chemistry Library, *see* University of Toronto Libraries, Toronto ON p. 2865

Allen Charlotte Whitney Library, *see* University of Rochester, Rochester NY p. 1733

Allen College, Waterloo IA p. 849

Allen Community College Library, Iola KS p. 873

Allen Correctional Institution Library, Lima OH p. 1909

Allen County Historical Society, Lima OH p. 1909

Allen County Law Library, Lima OH p. 1909

Allen County Law Library Association, Inc, Fort Wayne IN p. 740

Allen County Public Library, Fort Wayne IN p. 740

Allen County Public Library, Scottsville KY p. 934

Allen George E Library, *see* Northeast Regional Library, Booneville MS p. 1297

Allen Gordon P Learning Resources Center, *see* Piedmont Community College, Roxboro NC p. 1821

Allen Hampton B Library, Wadesboro NC p. 1827

Allen James B Library, *see* Jefferson State Community College, Birmingham AL p. 8

Allen Library, *see* Montgomery County Public Library, Biscoe NC p. 1827

Allen Memorial Library, *see* Cleveland Health Sciences Library, Cleveland OH p. 1876

Allen Memorial Library, *see* United States Army, Fort Polk LA p. 949

Allen Memorial Library, *see* Valley City State University Library, Valley City ND p. 1848

Allen Memorial Public Library, Hawkins TX p. 2331

Allen Mildred P Memorial, *see* University of Hartford Libraries, West Hartford CT p. 376

Allen Park Public Library, Allen Park MI p. 1149

Allen Public Library, Allen OK p. 1955

Allen Public Library, Allen TX p. 2273

Allen University Library, Columbia SC p. 2186

Allen Warren D Music Library, *see* Florida State University Libraries, Tallahassee FL p. 494

Allendale County Library, *see* Allendale-Hampton-Jasper Regional Library, Allendale SC p. 2180

Allendale-Hampton-Jasper Regional Library, Allendale SC p. 2180

Allendale Public Library, *see* Lee Memorial Library, Allendale NJ p. 1469

Allendale Township Library, Allendale MI p. 1149

Allens Hill Free Library, Bloomfield NY p. 1583

Allenstown Public Library, Allenstown NH p. 1437

Allentown Public Library, Allentown PA p. 2026

Allerton Public Library, Allerton IA p. 792

Allerton Public Library District, Monticello IL p. 675

Allerton Robert C Library, *see* Honolulu Academy of Arts, Honolulu HI p. 564

Alliance for Children & Families, Milwaukee WI p. 2616

Alliance for Innovation in Science & Technology Information (N), Santa Fe NM p. 2949

Alliance Public Library, Alliance NE p. 1391

Alliance Public Library, Alliance AB p. 2683

Alliant International University, Alhambra CA p. 120

Alliant International University, Fresno CA p. 150

Alliant International University, San Diego CA p. 230

Alliant International University, San Francisco CA p. 240

Allin Township Library, Stanford IL p. 707

Allina Health Library Services, Minneapolis MN p. 1258

Alling Dorothy Memorial Library, Williston VT p. 2440

Allison John Richard Library, *see* Regent College, Vancouver BC p. 2742

Allison Ora Byram Memorial Library, *see* Mid-America Baptist Theological Seminary, Cordova TN p. 2232

Allison Public Library, Allison IA p. 792

Allison Transmission Inc, Indianapolis IN p. 749

Allnutt Health Sciences Library, *see* Saint Elizabeth Medical Center, Edgewood KY p. 911

Alloway Norma Marion Library, *see* Trinity Western University, Langley BC p. 2731

Alloway Norma Miller, *see* Muskoka Lakes Library Board, Port Carling ON p. 2837

Allstate Insurance Co, Northbrook IL p. 682

Allyn Lyman Art Museum Library, New London CT p. 359

Alma-Bacon County Public, *see* Okefenokee Regional Library, Alma GA p. 557

Alma College Library, Alma MI p. 1149

Alma Public Library, Alma AR p. 93

Alma Public Library, Alma MI p. 1149

Alma Public Library, Alma WI p. 2577

Almena City Library, Almena KS p. 855

Almond Tea Gallery Library, Cuyahoga Falls OH p. 1892

Almont District Library, Almont MI p. 1149

Almonte Library, *see* Mississippi Mills Libraries, Almonte ON p. 2792

ALN (N), *see* Alaska Library Network, Anchorage AK p. 2937

Alondra Library, *see* County of Los Angeles Public Library, Norwalk CA p. 140

Alpena Community College, Alpena MI p. 1150

Alpena County Library, Alpena MI p. 1150

Alpha Park Public Library District, Bartonville IL p. 592

Alpharetta Library, *see* Atlanta-Fulton Public Library System, Alpharetta GA p. 511

Alphin Albert Music Library, *see* Boston Conservatory, Boston MA p. 1056

Alpine County Library, Markleeville CA p. 184

Alpine Public, *see* Apache County Library District, Alpine AZ p. 80

Alpine Public Library, Alpine TX p. 2273

ALS Society of British Columbia, Vancouver BC p. 2740

Alsea Community Library, *see* Corvallis-Benton County Public Library, Alsea OR p. 1994

Alsip-Merrionette Park Public Library District, Alsip IL p. 588

Alston & Bird Law Library, Atlanta GA p. 510

Alston & Bird, LLP Library, New York NY p. 1667

Alta Bates Medical Center, Berkeley CA p. 126

Alta Community Library, Alta IA p. 792

Alta Vista Public Library, Alta Vista IA p. 792

Altadena Library District, Altadena CA p. 120

Altamaha Technical College Library, Jesup GA p. 536

Altamont Free Library, Altamont NY p. 1572

Altamont Public Library, Altamont IL p. 588

Altamont Public Library, Altamont KS p. 855

Altamont Public Library, Altamont TN p. 2223

Altamonte Springs City Library, Altamonte Springs FL p. 425

Altamonte Springs Library, *see* City College, Altamonte Springs FL p. 425

Alternative Energy Resources Organization Library, Helena MT p. 1381

Alternative Press Center Library, Chicago IL p. 605

Altheimer Public Library, *see* Pine Bluff & Jefferson County Library System, Altheimer AR p. 112

Alton Public Library, Alton IA p. 792

Alton Public Library, *see* Oregon County Library District, Alton MO p. 1319

Altona Correctional Facility Library, *see* New York State Department of Corrections & Community Supervision, Altona NY p. 1573

Altoona Area Public Library, Altoona PA p. 2028

Altoona Hospital, Altoona PA p. 2028

Altoona Public Library, Altoona IA p. 792

Altoona Public Library, Altoona KS p. 855

Altoona Public Library, Altoona WI p. 2577

Altru Health System, Grand Forks ND p. 1842

Altschul Medical Library, *see* Monmouth Medical Center, Long Branch NJ p. 1497

Altus Public Library, Altus OK p. 1955

American Physical Therapy Association, Alexandria VA p. 2445

American Planning Association, Chicago IL p. 606

American Printing House for the Blind, Inc, Louisville KY p. 923

American Psychiatric Association, Arlington VA p. 2448

American Psychological Association, Washington DC p. 392

American Public Power Association Library, Washington DC p. 392

American Public Transportation Association, Washington DC p. 392

American Red Cross, West Henrietta NY p. 1766

American Red Cross Holland Laboratory, Rockville MD p. 1037

American Rhinologic Society Library, Warwick NY p. 1762

American River College Library, Sacramento CA p. 220

American Rose Society Library, Shreveport LA p. 967

American Samoa Community College Library, Mapusaga AS p. 2665

American Samoa Office of Library Services, Pago Pago AS p. 2665

American Scientific Corp Library, Chula Vista CA p. 134

American Society for Nondestructive Testing Library, Columbus OH p. 1883

American Society for Psychical Research Inc Library, New York NY p. 1668

American Society for Quality, Milwaukee WI p. 2617

American Society of Abdominal Surgeons, Melrose MA p. 1104

American Society of Anesthesiologists, Park Ridge IL p. 688

American Society of Health-System Pharmacists, Bethesda MD p. 1021

American Society of International Law Library, Washington DC p. 393

American Society of Landscape Architects, Washington DC p. 393

American Society of Military History Library, South El Monte CA p. 270

American Sokol Educational & Physical Culture Organization, Brookfield IL p. 598

American Sports Medicine Institute, Birmingham AL p. 6

American Standards Testing Bureau, Inc, New York NY p. 1669

American Swedish Historical Museum Library, Philadelphia PA p. 2103

American Swedish Institute, Minneapolis MN p. 1258

American Theatre Organ Society, Inc, Joliet IL p. 659

American Truck Historical Society, Kansas City MO p. 1336

American University, Washington DC p. 393

American University Library, Washington DC p. 393

American Veterinary Medical Association Library, Schaumburg IL p. 700

American Watchmakers-Clockmakers Institute Library, Harrison OH p. 1904

American Water Works Association, Denver CO p. 298

Americus Township Library, Americus KS p. 855

Amerind Foundation, Inc, Dragoon AZ p. 61

Amery Public Library, Amery WI p. 2577

Ames Free Library, North Easton MA p. 1112

Ames Library, see Illinois Wesleyan University, Bloomington IL p. 595

Ames Library of South Asia, see University of Minnesota Libraries-Twin Cities, Minneapolis MN p. 1262

Ames Public Library, Ames IA p. 792

Amesbury Public Library, Amesbury MA p. 1048

AMG International Library, Chattanooga TN p. 2226

Amgen Inc Library, Thousand Oaks CA p. 274

Amherst College, Amherst MA p. 1048

Amherst County Public Library, Amherst VA p. 2447

Amherst Public Library, Amherst NY p. 1573

Amherst Public Library, Amherst OH p. 1854

Amherst Town Library, Amherst NH p. 1437

Amigos Library Services, Inc (N), Dallas TX p. 2955

Amisk Public Library, Amisk AB p. 2683

Amistad Research Center, New Orleans LA p. 959

Amity Public Library, Amity OR p. 1990

Amity Township Public Library, Cornell IL p. 631

Amityville Public Library, Amityville NY p. 1573

Amory Municipal Library, see Tombigbee Regional Library System, Amory MS p. 1318

Amos Health Science Library, see Mercy Health Partners, Muskegon MI p. 1212

Amos John B Library, see Western Hemisphere Institute for Security Cooperation, Fort Benning GA p. 533

Amos Music Library, see Miami University Libraries, Oxford OH p. 1926

Amos Press, Inc Library, Sidney OH p. 1934

Amridge University Library, Montgomery AL p. 28

Amsterdam Free Library, Amsterdam NY p. 1573

AMT Management Services Library, Winnipeg MB p. 2754

Ana G Mendez University System, Orlando FL p. 475

Anacortes Public Library, Anacortes WA p. 2507

Anacostia Community Museum Library, see Smithsonian Libraries, Washington DC p. 414

Anadarko Community Library, Anadarko OK p. 1956

Anaheim Public Library, Anaheim CA p. 120

Anaheim Regional Medical Center, Anaheim CA p. 121

Anamosa Public Library, Anamosa IA p. 793

Anamosa State Penitentiary, Anamosa IA p. 793

Anasazi Heritage Center Library, Dolores CO p. 304

Anchor Point Public Library, Anchor Point AK p. 43

Anchorage Daily News Library, Anchorage AK p. 44

Anchorage Museum, Anchorage AK p. 44

Anchorage Public Library, Anchorage AK p. 44

Ancilla College, Donaldson IN p. 736

Andale District Library, Andale KS p. 855

Andalusia Public Library, Andalusia AL p. 4

Andalusia Township Library, Andalusia IL p. 588

Anders Norma Public Library, Dysart IA p. 812

Andersen Air Force Base Library, see United States Air Force, APO AP GU p. 2667

Andersen Horticultural Library, see University of Minnesota Libraries-Twin Cities, Chaska MN p. 1262

Anderson City, Anderson, Stony Creek & Union Townships Public Library, Anderson IN p. 723

Anderson County Library, Anderson SC p. 2180

Anderson County Public Library, Lawrenceburg KY p. 919

Anderson Creek Public, see Harnett County Public Library, Bunn Level NC p. 1807

Anderson Dwight Music Library, see University of Louisville Libraries, Louisville KY p. 926

Anderson E Ross Library, see Dean College, Franklin MA p. 1090

Anderson J C Library, see University of South Carolina Sumter, Sumter SC p. 2206

Anderson-Jensen Lillian, see Mondak Heritage Center, Sidney MT p. 1388

Anderson Joseph Cook Library, see University of Southern Mississippi Library, Hattiesburg MS p. 1300

Anderson, Kill & Olick, New York NY p. 1669

Anderson L C Memorial Library, Metter GA p. 544

Anderson Larz Auto Museum Library & Archives, Brookline MA p. 1071

Anderson-Lee Library, Silver Creek NY p. 1744

Anderson Library/Jepson Center for the Arts, see Telfair Museum of Art, Savannah GA p. 551

Anderson M D Cancer Center Research Medical Library, see University of Texas, Houston TX p. 2344

Anderson M D Library, see University of Houston, Houston TX p. 2343

Anderson, McPharlin & Conners LLP Library, Los Angeles CA p. 168

Anderson Memorial Library & Archives, see Emporia State University, Emporia KS p. 866

Anderson R V Associates Ltd Library, Toronto ON p. 2849

Anderson University, Anderson IN p. 724

Anderson University Library, Anderson SC p. 2181

Anderson Victor E, see Lincoln City Libraries, Lincoln NE p. 1405

Anderson William E Library Penn Hills, Pittsburgh PA p. 2121

Anderson William M Library, see West Shore Community College, Scottville MI p. 1226

Andes Public Library, Andes NY p. 1574

Andover Free Library, Andover NY p. 1574

Andover-Harvard Theological Library, see Harvard Library, Cambridge MA p. 1074

Andover Historical Society Library, Andover MA p. 1049

Andover Newton Theological School, Newton Centre MA p. 1110

Andover Public Library, Andover CT p. 329

Andover Public Library, Andover KS p. 856

Andover Public Library, Andover ME p. 973

Andover Public Library, Andover NH p. 1437

Andover Public Library, Andover OH p. 1854

Andrew College, Cuthbert GA p. 527

Andrew Public Library, Andrew AB p. 2683

Andrews & Kurth LLP Library, Washington DC p. 393

Andrews Arthur Memorial Library, see Grand Rapids Community College, Grand Rapids MI p. 1184

Andrews C Blythe, Jr Public Library, see Tampa-Hillsborough County Public Library System, Tampa FL p. 497

Andrews County Library, Andrews TX p. 2275

Andrews Dallas Township Public Library, Andrews IN p. 724

Andrews Public Library, Andrews NC p. 1773

Andrews University, Berrien Springs MI p. 1157

Androscoggin Historical Society, Auburn ME p. 973

Androscoggin Valley Hospital, Berlin NH p. 1439

Andruss Harvey A Library, see Bloomsburg University of Pennsylvania, Bloomsburg PA p. 2035

Aneta Public, see Carnegie Regional Library, Aneta ND p. 1842

Angel Mounds State Historic Site Library, Evansville IN p. 738

Angelica Free Library, Angelica NY p. 1574

Angelina College Library, Lufkin TX p. 2358

Angelo State University, San Angelo TX p. 2378

Angelou Maya, see Stockton-San Joaquin County Public Library, Stockton CA p. 273

Angelou Maya, see Wichita Public Library, Wichita KS p. 901

Angier Public, see Harnett County Public Library, Angier NC p. 1807

Anglican Church of Canada Archives, Montreal QC p. 2887

Anglican Church of Canada, Saint John NB p. 2767

Anglican Diocesan Archives & Medley Library, see Diocesan Synod of Fredericton, Fredericton NB p. 2763

Angola Public Library, Angola NY p. 1574

Anheuser-Busch Co, Inc, Saint Louis MO p. 1353

Animal Alliance of Canada Library, Toronto ON p. 2849

Anita Public Library, Anita IA p. 793

AnMed Health Medical Library, Anderson SC p. 2181

Ann Arbor District Library, Ann Arbor MI p. 1150

Anna Community, see Shelby County Libraries, Anna OH p. 1935

Fernald Anna Field Library, Detroit ME p. 983

Anna Maria College, Paxton MA p. 1116

Annandale Public Library, see Great River Regional Library, Annandale MN p. 1274

Annapolis Valley Regional Library, Bridgetown NS p. 2778

Annawan-Alba Township Library, Annawan IL p. 589

Anne Arundel Community College, Arnold MD p. 1011

Annenberg Library & Communications Center, see Pine Manor College, Chestnut Hill MA p. 1081

Annville Free Library, Annville PA p. 2029

Arizona Department of Corrections - Adult Institutions, Buckeye AZ p. 58

Arizona Department of Corrections - Adult Institutions, Douglas AZ p. 61

Arizona Department of Corrections - Adult Institutions, Florence AZ p. 63

Arizona Department of Corrections - Adult Institutions, Globe AZ p. 64

Arizona Department of Corrections - Adult Institutions, Goodyear AZ p. 65

Arizona Department of Corrections - Adult Institutions, Marana AZ p. 68

Arizona Department of Corrections - Adult Institutions, Phoenix AZ p. 71

Arizona Department of Corrections - Adult Institutions, Safford AZ p. 79

Arizona Department of Corrections - Adult Institutions, San Luis AZ p. 80

Arizona Department of Corrections - Adult Institutions, Tucson AZ p. 85

Arizona Department of Corrections - Adult Institutions, Winslow AZ p. 90

Arizona Department of Corrections, Arizona State Prison, Fort Grant AZ p. 63

Arizona Department of Economic Security, Coolidge AZ p. 60

Arizona Department of Education Library, Phoenix AZ p. 71

Arizona Department of Environmental Quality Library, Phoenix AZ p. 71

Arizona Department of Transportation Library, Phoenix AZ p. 71

Arizona Geological Survey, Tucson AZ p. 85

Arizona Health Sciences Library, *see* University of Arizona, Tucson AZ p. 88

Arizona Historical Foundation, Tempe AZ p. 83

Arizona Historical Society, Tucson AZ p. 85

Arizona Historical Society Library, Flagstaff AZ p. 62

Arizona Historical Society Library, Yuma AZ p. 90

Arizona Historical Society Museum Library & Archives, Tempe AZ p. 83

Arizona Museum for Youth Library, Mesa AZ p. 68

Arizona Republic Library, Phoenix AZ p. 71

Arizona-Sonora Desert Museum Library, Tucson AZ p. 85

Arizona State Braille & Talking Book Library, Phoenix AZ p. 72

Arizona State Hospital Library, Phoenix AZ p. 72

Arizona State Library, Archives & Public Records, Phoenix AZ p. 72

Arizona State Museum Library, Tucson AZ p. 85

Arizona State Parks, Winslow AZ p. 90

Douglas Library, *see* Arizona Department of Corrections - Adult Institutions, Douglas AZ p. 61

Eyman Library, *see* Arizona Department of Corrections - Adult Institutions, Florence AZ p. 63

Arizona State Prison Complex Florence Libraries, Florence AZ p. 63

Globe Library, *see* Arizona Department of Corrections - Adult Institutions, Globe AZ p. 64

Lewis Library, *see* Arizona Department of Corrections - Adult Institutions, Buckeye AZ p. 58

Perryville Library, *see* Arizona Department of Corrections - Adult Institutions, Goodyear AZ p. 65

Phoenix Library, *see* Arizona Department of Corrections - Adult Institutions, Phoenix AZ p. 71

Safford Resource Library, *see* Arizona Department of Corrections - Adult Institutions, Safford AZ p. 79

Tucson Library, *see* Arizona Department of Corrections - Adult Institutions, Tucson AZ p. 85

Winslow Library, *see* Arizona Department of Corrections - Adult Institutions, Winslow AZ p. 90

Yuma Library, *see* Arizona Department of Corrections - Adult Institutions, San Luis AZ p. 80

Arizona State Schools for the Deaf & the Blind Library, Tucson AZ p. 85

Arizona State University, Tempe AZ p. 2961

Arizona State University, College of Law, Tempe AZ p. 83

Arizona State University Libraries, Tempe AZ p. 83

Arizona Training Program-Division of Developmental Disabilities, *see* Arizona Department of Economic Security, Coolidge AZ p. 60

Arizona Western College & NAU Yuma, Yuma AZ p. 90

Arkansas Area Health Education Center Consortium (N), Fort Smith AR p. 2937

Arkansas Arts Center, Little Rock AR p. 105

Arkansas Baptist College Library, Little Rock AR p. 105

Arkansas City Public Library, Arkansas City KS p. 856

Arkansas Democrat Gazette News Library, Little Rock AR p. 105

Arkansas Department of Correction, Pine Bluff AR p. 112

Arkansas Department of Correction Library System, Pine Bluff AR p. 112

Arkansas Geological Survey Library, Little Rock AR p. 105

Arkansas History Commission Library, Little Rock AR p. 105

Arkansas Independent Colleges & Universities (N), North Little Rock AR p. 2937

Arkansas Methodist Hospital, Paragould AR p. 111

Arkansas Northeastern College, Blytheville AR p. 95

Arkansas River Valley Regional Library System, Dardanelle AR p. 97

Arkansas School for the Deaf Library, Little Rock AR p. 105

Arkansas State Library, Little Rock AR p. 105

Arkansas State University, Beebe AR p. 94

Arkansas State University, Newport AR p. 111

Arkansas State University, State University AR p. 115

Arkansas State University-Searcy, Searcy AR p. 114

Arkansas State University-Mountain Home, Mountain Home AR p. 110

Arkansas Supreme Court Library, Little Rock AR p. 105

Arkansas Tech University, Russellville AR p. 113

Arkansas Valley Correctional Facility Library, *see* Colorado Department of Corrections, Crowley CO p. 297

Arkansas Workers' Compensation Commission Library, Little Rock AR p. 106

Arkoma Public Library, Arkoma OK p. 1957

Arkport Village Book Center, Arkport NY p. 1575

Arley Public Library, Arley AL p. 4

Arlington Baptist College, Arlington TX p. 2276

Arlington City Library, Arlington KS p. 856

Arlington Community Library, Arlington SD p. 2210

Arlington Community Library, *see* Sno-Isle Libraries, Arlington WA p. 2542

Arlington County Department of Libraries, Arlington VA p. 2448

Arlington Heights Memorial Library, Arlington Heights IL p. 589

Arlington Public Library, Arlington IA p. 794

Arlington Public Library, Arlington MN p. 1240

Arlington Public Library, Arlington NE p. 1392

Arlington Public Library, Arlington OR p. 1990

Arlington Public Library, *see* Arlington County Department of Libraries, Arlington VA p. 2448

Arlington Public Library System, Arlington TX p. 2276

Arma City Library, Arma KS p. 856

Armacost George & Verda Library, *see* University of Redlands, Redlands CA p. 215

Armacost Peter H Library, *see* Eckerd College, Saint Petersburg FL p. 488

Armada Free Public Library, Armada MI p. 1154

Armenian Apostolic Church of America, New York NY p. 1669

Armenian Cultural Foundation Library, Arlington MA p. 1050

Armenian Library & Museum of America, Inc, Watertown MA p. 1133

Armenian Missionary Association of America Library, Paramus NJ p. 1517

Armenian Numismatic Society Research Library, Pico Rivera CA p. 208

Armona Community Library, Armona CA p. 122

Armor School Research Library, *see* United States Army, Fort Knox KY p. 913

Armoral Tuttle Public Library, New Plymouth ID p. 581

Armour Public Library, Armour SD p. 2210

Arms Library Association, Shelburne Falls MA p. 1123

Armstrong Atlantic State University, Savannah GA p. 549

Armstrong Chapel Church Library, *see* United Methodist Church, Cincinnati OH p. 1873

Armstrong Lena Public Library, Belton TX p. 2288

Armstrong Library, *see* Middlebury College Library, Middlebury VT p. 2428

Armstrong Public Library, Armstrong IA p. 794

Armstrong Township Public Library, Earlton ON p. 2803

Army & Navy Club Library, Washington DC p. 393

Army Corps of Engineers Philadelphia Library, *see* United States Army, Philadelphia PA p. 2118

Army Logistics Library, *see* United States Army, Fort Lee VA p. 2465

Army Times Publishing Co Library, Springfield VA p. 2496

Arnason Muriel Library (Willowbrook), *see* Fraser Valley Regional Library, Langley BC p. 2723

Arneson Methodist Library, *see* Park Nicollet Institute, Saint Louis Park MN p. 1277

Arnold & Porter Library, Washington DC p. 393

Arnold & Porter LLP Law Library, San Francisco CA p. 240

Arnold Arboretum Horticultural Library, *see* Harvard Library, Jamaica Plain MA p. 1074

Arnold Engineering Development Center Technical Library, *see* United States Air Force, Arnold AFB TN p. 2223

Arnold Library, *see* Hutchinson Fred Cancer Research Center, Seattle WA p. 2528

Arnold Library, *see* Straub Clinic & Hospital, Honolulu HI p. 565

Arnold R T Public, *see* Southside Regional Library, South Hill VA p. 2452

Arnold's Cove Public Library, Arnold's Cove NL p. 2769

Arnolds Park Public Library, Arnolds Park IA p. 794

Arnprior Public Library, Arnprior ON p. 2792

Arnstein & Lehr LLP Library, Chicago IL p. 606

Arrendale State Prison, *see* Georgia Department of Corrections, Alto GA p. 508

Arrigoni Helen T Library, *see* Iona College, New Rochelle NY p. 1666

Arrowhead Correctional Center Library, *see* Colorado Department of Corrections, Canon City CO p. 293

Arrowhead Health Sciences Library Network (N), Shell Lake WI p. 2958

Arrowhead Library System, Mountain Iron MN p. 1267

Arrowhead Library System, Janesville WI p. 2599

Arrowhead Regional Medical Center, Colton CA p. 135

Arroyo Seco Regional, *see* Los Angeles Public Library System, Los Angeles CA p. 173

Art & Architecture Library, *see* Southern University, Baton Rouge LA p. 944

Art Center College of Design, Pasadena CA p. 205

Art Center Manatee, Bradenton FL p. 429

Art Center of Battle Creek Library, Battle Creek MI p. 1155

Art Center of Waco Library, Waco TX p. 2395

Art Circle Public Library, Crossville TN p. 2232

Art Complex Museum, Duxbury MA p. 1085

Art Gallery of Hamilton, *see* Bostwick Muriel Isabel Library, Hamilton ON p. 2808

Art Gallery of Nova Scotia Library, Halifax NS p. 2780

Art Gallery of Ontario, Toronto ON p. 2850

Art Institute of Atlanta Library, Atlanta GA p. 511

Art Institute of Boston Library, *see* Lesley University, Boston MA p. 1062

Atlanta-Fulton Public Library System, Atlanta GA p. 511

Atlanta Health Science Libraries Consortium (N), Atlanta GA p. 2941

Atlanta History Center, Atlanta GA p. 513

Atlanta Medical Center, Atlanta GA p. 513

Atlanta Metropolitan State College Library, Atlanta GA p. 513

Atlanta Public Library, Atlanta TX p. 2277

Atlanta Public Library District, Atlanta IL p. 590

Atlanta Regional Commission, Atlanta GA p. 513

Atlanta Regional Council for Higher Education (N), Atlanta GA p. 2941

Atlanta Technical College, Atlanta GA p. 513

Atlanta University Center, Atlanta GA p. 513

Atlanta VA Medical Center Library, Decatur GA p. 529

Atlantic Baptist University, Moncton NB p. 2765

Atlantic Cape Community College, Mays Landing NJ p. 1500

Atlantic Care Regional Medical Center, Atlantic City NJ p. 1469

Atlantic City Free Public Library, Atlantic City NJ p. 1469

Atlantic County Historical Society Library, Somers Point NJ p. 1529

Atlantic County Library System, Mays Landing NJ p. 1500

Atlantic Highlands Public Library Association, Atlantic Highlands NJ p. 1470

Atlantic Provinces Economic Council Library, Halifax NS p. 2780

Atlantic Provinces Special Education Authority Library, Halifax NS p. 2780

Atlantic Public Library, Atlantic IA p. 795

Atlantic School of Theology Library, Halifax NS p. 2780

Atlantic Union College, South Lancaster MA p. 1125

Atlin Learning Centre Library, see Northern Lights College, Atlin BC p. 2724

Atmore Public Library, Atmore AL p. 5

Atoka County Library, see Chickasaw Regional Library System, Atoka OK p. 1957

Attalla-Etowah County Public Library, Attalla AL p. 5

Attica City Library, Attica KS p. 857

Attica Correctional Facility, Attica NY p. 1575

Attica Public Library, Attica IN p. 725

Attleboro Public Library, Attleboro MA p. 1050

Attorney General's Law Library, see California Department of Justice, Sacramento CA p. 222

Attorney General's Office, Baltimore MD p. 1011

Attorney General's Office, Olympia WA p. 2522

Atwater Library & Computer Centre, Westmount QC p. 2915

Atwater Memorial, see North Branford Library Department, North Branford CT p. 361

Atwater Public Library, Atwater MN p. 1240

Atwood Alaska Resource Center, see Anchorage Museum, Anchorage AK p. 44

Atwood-Hammond Public Library, Atwood IL p. 591

Atwood Pierce LLP, Portland ME p. 996

Atwood Public Library, Atwood KS p. 857

Au Gres Community, see Iosco-Arenac District Library, Au Gres MI p. 1176

Au Sable Forks Free Library, Au Sable Forks NY p. 1575

Aubrey Area Library, Aubrey TX p. 2277

Auburn Avenue Research Library on African-American Culture & History, see Atlanta-Fulton Public Library System, Atlanta GA p. 511

Auburn Cord Duesenberg Museum, Auburn IN p. 725

Auburn Correctional Facility Library, Auburn NY p. 1575

Auburn Hills Public Library, Auburn Hills MI p. 1154

Auburn Memorial Library, Auburn NE p. 1392

Auburn Public, see Piedmont Regional Library, Auburn GA p. 557

Auburn Public Library, Auburn AL p. 5

Auburn Public Library, Auburn IL p. 591

Auburn Public Library, Auburn IA p. 795

Auburn Public Library, Auburn ME p. 973

Auburn Public Library, Auburn MA p. 1051

Auburn University, Auburn AL p. 5

Auburn University, Montgomery AL p. 28

Auburn University, Auburn AL p. 2961

Auburndale Community Library, see Queens Borough Public Library, Flushing NY p. 1644

Auburndale Public Library, Auburndale FL p. 425

Aucremann Medical Library, see Bayfront Medical Center, Saint Petersburg FL p. 487

Auditor General's Library, Tallahassee FL p. 492

Audrain County Historical Society, Mexico MO p. 1345

Audubon Naturalist Society Library, Chevy Chase MD p. 1024

Audubon Park Public Library, Audubon Park NJ p. 1470

Audubon Public Library, Audubon IA p. 795

Audubon Regional Library, Clinton LA p. 947

Audubon Society of New Hampshire, Concord NH p. 1442

Audubon Society of Rhode Island, Smithfield RI p. 2176

Auer Library, see Fort Wayne Museum of Art, Fort Wayne IN p. 741

Auerbach Art Library, see Wadsworth Atheneum, Hartford CT p. 348

Auglaize County Law Library, Wapakoneta OH p. 1944

Auglaize County Public District Library, Wapakoneta OH p. 1944

Augsburg College, Minneapolis MN p. 1258

Augusta County Library, Fishersville VA p. 2464

Augusta Memorial Public Library, Augusta WI p. 2579

Augusta Public Library, Augusta KS p. 857

Augusta Richmond County Historical Society, Augusta GA p. 518

Augusta-Richmond County Public Library, see East Central Georgia Regional Library, Augusta GA p. 519

Augusta State Medical Prison, see Georgia Department of Corrections, Grovetown GA p. 536

Augusta State University, Augusta GA p. 518

Augusta Technical College, Augusta GA p. 519

Augusta Township Public Library, Brockville ON p. 2797

Augustana College, Sioux Falls SD p. 2218

Augustana College Library, Rock Island IL p. 696

Augustana Faculty Library, see University of Alberta, Camrose AB p. 2694

Augustana Lutheran Church Library, Denver CO p. 298

Augustine Library, see Saint Norbert Abbey, De Pere WI p. 2587

Auld Public Library, Red Cloud NE p. 1417

Auld-Doudna Public Library, Guide Rock NE p. 1400

Aulds Henry L Memorial, see Bossier Parish Central Library, Bossier City LA p. 946

Aullwood Audubon Center & Farm, Dayton OH p. 1892

Aultman Hospital, Canton OH p. 1863

Auraria Library, Denver CO p. 298

Aurelia Public Library, Aurelia IA p. 795

Aurelius Library, see Capital Area District Libraries, Mason MI p. 1200

Aurora College, Fort Smith NT p. 2775

Aurora College, Inuvik NT p. 2775

Aurora Free Library, Aurora NY p. 1576

Aurora Health Care Libraries, Milwaukee WI p. 2617

Aurora Historical Society, East Aurora NY p. 1616

Aurora History Museum Library, Aurora CO p. 288

Aurora Memorial, see Portage County District Library, Aurora OH p. 1901

Aurora Public Library, Aurora CO p. 288

Aurora Public Library, Aurora IL p. 591

Aurora Public Library, Aurora IA p. 795

Aurora Public Library, Aurora MN p. 1240

Aurora Public Library, Aurora ON p. 2793

Aurora Public Library District, Aurora IN p. 725

Aurora Research Institute Library, see Aurora College, Inuvik NT p. 2775

Aurora Town Public Library, East Aurora NY p. 1616

Aurora University, Aurora IL p. 591

Aurora West Allis Medical Center, West Allis WI p. 2647

Austin College, Sherman TX p. 2387

Austin Community College, Austin TX p. 2278

Austin County Library System, Wallis TX p. 2398

Austin Ella Bess Library, see Jackson/Hinds Library System, Terry MS p. 1303

Austin Ethel L Library, see South Congregational Church, Granby CT p. 341

Austin Graduate School of Theology, Austin TX p. 2278

Austin History Center, see Austin Public Library, Austin TX p. 2278

Austin Memorial Library, Cleveland TX p. 2298

Austin Peay State University, Clarksville TN p. 2228

Austin Presbyterian Theological Seminary, Austin TX p. 2278

Austin Public Library, Austin MN p. 1240

Austin Public Library, Austin TX p. 2278

Austrian Cultural Forum Library, New York NY p. 1669

Autauga-Prattville Public Library, Prattville AL p. 34

Autaugaville Public, see Autauga-Prattville Public Library, Autaugaville AL p. 34

Autism Society of British Columbia Library, Burnaby BC p. 2725

Autism Society of Michigan Library, Okemos MI p. 1215

Autism Treatment Services of Saskatchewan, Inc Library, Saskatoon SK p. 2925

Automation System Colorado Consortium (N), Delta CO p. 2939

Automotive Research Library, see Blackhawk Museum, Danville CA p. 139

Autry Library, see Autry National Center, Los Angeles CA p. 168

Autry National Center, Los Angeles CA p. 168

Autry State Prison, see Georgia Department of Corrections, Pelham GA p. 547

Avalon Free Public Library, Avalon NJ p. 1470

Avalon Public Library, Avalon PA p. 2030

Ave Maria School of Law Library, Naples FL p. 471

Avella Area Public Library, Avella PA p. 2030

Avenal State Prison, see California Department of Corrections Library System, Avenal CA p. 221

Aventis Pharmaceuticals Library, Bridgewater NJ p. 1474

Avera Sacred Heart Hospital, Yankton SD p. 2222

Avera Saint Luke's Hospital, Aberdeen SD p. 2209

Averett University Library, Danville VA p. 2459

Avery Architectural & Fine Arts Library, see Columbia University, New York NY p. 1674

Avery County Morrison Public Library, Newland NC p. 1813

Avery-Mitchell-Yancey Regional Library System, Burnsville NC p. 1779

Avery Research Center, Pasadena CA p. 205

Aviation Applied Technology Directorate, Technical Library, see United States Army, Fort Eustis VA p. 2464

Aviation Hall of Fame & Museum Library of New Jersey, Teterboro NJ p. 1533

Aviation Technical Library, see United States Army, Fort Rucker AL p. 18

Avil E May Library, see North Miami Public Library, North Miami FL p. 473

Avila University, Kansas City MO p. 1336

Avoca Free Library, Avoca NY p. 1576

Avoca Public Library, Avoca IA p. 795

Avon Free Library, Avon NY p. 1577

Avon Free Public Library, Avon CT p. 329

Avon Grove Library, West Grove PA p. 2154

Avon Lake Public Library, Avon Lake OH p. 1856

Avon Park Correctional Facility, Avon Park FL p. 426

Avon Park Public Library, Avon Park FL p. 426

Avon Public, see Eagle Valley Library District, Avon CO p. 305

Avon Public Library, Avon MA p. 1051

Ballard Jr/Sr High School IMC, see Huxley Public Library, Huxley IA p. 821

Ballard Nora Library, see Stanislaus County Free Library, Waterford CA p. 188

Ballard, Spahr LLP Library, Philadelphia PA p. 2103

Balloch Grace Memorial Library, Spearfish SD p. 2220

Ballston Spa Public Library, Ballston Spa NY p. 1577

Balmertown Public Library, Balmertown ON p. 2793

Balmorhea Public Library, Balmorhea TX p. 2286

Balsam Lake Public Library, Balsam Lake WI p. 2580

Baltimore Bar Library, see Library Company of the Baltimore Bar, Baltimore MD p. 1015

Baltimore City Community College, Baltimore MD p. 1011

Baltimore City Department of Legislative Reference Library, Baltimore MD p. 1011

Baltimore County Circuit Court Library, Towson MD p. 1044

Baltimore County Historical Society Library, Hunt Valley MD p. 1032

Baltimore County Public Library, Towson MD p. 1044

Baltimore Hebrew Congregation, Baltimore MD p. 1011

Baltimore International College, Baltimore MD p. 1011

Baltimore Metropolitan Council, Baltimore MD p. 1012

Baltimore Museum of Art, Baltimore MD p. 1012

Baltimore Museum of Industry, Baltimore MD p. 1012

Baltimore Sun Library, see Tribune Co, Baltimore MD p. 1018

Balzekas Museum of Lithuanian Culture, Chicago IL p. 606

Bamfield Marine Sciences Centre Library, see Western Canadian Universities, Bamfield BC p. 2724

Bancroft Library, see University of California, Berkeley, Berkeley CA p. 127

Bancroft Memorial Library, Hopedale MA p. 1096

Bancroft Public Library, Bancroft IA p. 795

Bancroft Public Library, Bancroft NE p. 1392

Bancroft Public Library, Salem NY p. 1737

Bancroft Public Library, Bancroft ON p. 2793

Bandon Public Library, Bandon OR p. 1991

Banff Centre, Banff AB p. 2684

Banff Public Library, Banff AB p. 2684

Bangor Campus Library, see Bangor Theological Seminary, Bangor ME p. 975

Bangor Daily News Library, Bangor ME p. 975

Bangor Historical Society Library, Bangor ME p. 975

Bangor Public Library, Bangor ME p. 975

Bangor Public Library, Bangor PA p. 2031

Bangor Theological Seminary, Bangor ME p. 975

Bangor Theological Seminary, Portland ME p. 996

Bank of America Merrill Lynch & Co, New York NY p. 1669

Bank of Canada, Ottawa ON p. 2828

Bank of Nova Scotia Library, Toronto QC p. 2913

Bank Street College of Education Library, New York NY p. 1669

Bankhead Courts Library, see Atlanta-Fulton Public Library System, Atlanta GA p. 511

Bankier Library, see Brookdale Community College, Lincroft NJ p. 1495

Banks County Public, see Piedmont Regional Library, Homer GA p. 557

Banks Public Library, Banks OR p. 1991

Banks R L & Associates Inc Library, Arlington VA p. 2449

Banks William & Evelyn Library, see La Grange College, La Grange GA p. 537

Banner & Witcoff, Ltd Library, Chicago IL p. 606

Banner Boswell Medical Center, Sun City AZ p. 82

Banner Desert Medical Center, Mesa AZ p. 68

Banner Good Samaritan Medical Center, Phoenix AZ p. 72

Banning Library District, Banning CA p. 125

Bannon Health Sciences Library, see Saint Elizabeth Regional Health, Lafayette IN p. 759

Banque Nationale du Canada, Montreal QC p. 2888

Bapst Art Library, see Boston College Libraries, Chestnut Hill MA p. 1080

Baptist Bible College, Springfield MO p. 1365

Baptist Bible College & Seminary, Clarks Summit PA p. 2045

Baptist College of Florida, Graceville FL p. 450

Baptist College of Health Sciences, Memphis TN p. 2247

Baptist General Conference History Center, Saint Paul MN p. 1277

Baptist General Convention of Texas, Brenham TX p. 2291

Baptist Health Medical Center Library, see Gilbreath Margaret Clark Library, Little Rock AR p. 107

Baptist Health System, San Antonio TX p. 2379

Baptist Health Systems, Jackson MS p. 1302

Baptist Hospital, Pensacola FL p. 481

Baptist Hospital, Nashville TN p. 2255

Baptist Hospital East, Louisville KY p. 923

Baptist Hospital of Miami, Miami FL p. 464

Baptist Joint Committee Library, Washington DC p. 394

Baptist Medical Center Library, Montgomery AL p. 28

Baptist Medical Center Princeton, Birmingham AL p. 6

Baptist Missionary Association, Jacksonville TX p. 2347

Baptist University of the Americas, San Antonio TX p. 2379

Baraboo Public Library, Baraboo WI p. 2580

Barack, Ferrazzano, Kirshbaum & Nagelberg Library, Chicago IL p. 607

Baraga Maximum Facility Library, see Michigan Department of Corrections, Baraga MI p. 1155

Barbee G V Sr, see Brunswick County Library, Oak Island NC p. 1824

Barber Doris K Memorial Library, see Spaulding Rehabilitation Hospital, Boston MA p. 1067

Barber Irving K Learning Centre, see University of British Columbia Library, Vancouver BC p. 2743

Barber Scotia College, Concord NC p. 1785

Barbershop Harmony Society, Nashville TN p. 2255

Barberton Public Library, Barberton OH p. 1857

Barbour Clifford E Library, see Pittsburgh Theological Seminary, Pittsburgh PA p. 2127

Barclay College, Haviland KS p. 870

Barclay H Douglas Law Library, see Syracuse University College of Law, Syracuse NY p. 1753

Barclay Public Library District, Warrensburg IL p. 715

Barco Law Library, see University of Pittsburgh, Pittsburgh PA p. 2129

Bard College, Annandale-on-Hudson NY p. 1574

Bard College at Simon's Rock, Great Barrington MA p. 1092

Bard Graduate Center Library, New York NY p. 1669

Bard Library, see Baltimore City Community College, Baltimore MD p. 1011

Bare Hill Correctional Facility Library, Malone NY p. 1656

Barger-Richardson LRC, see Oakland City University, Oakland City IN p. 771

Baright Hollis & Helen Public Library, Ralston NE p. 1417

Barium & Chemicals, Inc, Steubenville OH p. 1936

Barker Darwin R Library, Fredonia NY p. 1624

Barker Free Library, Barker NY p. 1577

Barkerville Historic Town Library & Archives, Barkerville BC p. 2725

Barkman Frank & Marie, see Pueblo City-County Library District, Pueblo CO p. 321

Barksdale Medical Library, Lynchburg VA p. 2475

Barlow Respiratory Hospital, Los Angeles CA p. 168

Barlow Robert W Memorial Library, Iowa Falls IA p. 824

Barnard College, New York NY p. 1669

Barnard E T Library, see Otter Tail County Historical Society, Fergus Falls MN p. 1251

Barnard Library, La Crosse KS p. 876

Barnes-Jewish Hospital, Saint Louis MO p. 1353

Barnes Reading Room, Everest KS p. 866

Barnes Ward E Library, see University of Missouri-Saint Louis Libraries, Saint Louis MO p. 1362

Barnesville Hutton Memorial Library, Barnesville OH p. 1857

Barnesville-Lamar County Library, see Flint River Regional Library, Barnesville GA p. 535

Barnesville Public Library, see Lake Agassiz Regional Library, Barnesville MN p. 1266

Barnet Public Library, Barnet VT p. 2417

Barnett-Briggs Medical Library, see San Francisco General Hospital, San Francisco CA p. 245

Barnett-Hall Library, see Palo Alto Medical Foundation, Palo Alto CA p. 204

Barnett Mary Memorial Library, Guthrie Center IA p. 820

Barneveld Free Library Association, Barneveld NY p. 1578

Barneveld Public Library, Barneveld WI p. 2580

Barnhart Joe Bee County Public Library, Beeville TX p. 2288

Barnsdall Public Library, Barnsdall OK p. 1957

Barnstable Law Library, Barnstable MA p. 1051

Barnwell Public Library, Barnwell AB p. 2684

Baron-Forness Library, see Edinboro University of Pennsylvania, Edinboro PA p. 2053

Barr Library, see Minnesota Department of Health, Saint Paul MN p. 1279

Barr Memorial Library, see Saint Thomas Aquinas Church, Ames IA p. 793

Barr Memorial Library, see United States Army, Fort Knox KY p. 913

Barr W W Law Library, Clarion PA p. 2045

Barratt's Chapel & Museum Library, see United Methodist Church, Frederica DE p. 383

Barret Paul Jr Library, see Rhodes College, Memphis TN p. 2251

Barrett Kate Waller, see Alexandria Library, Alexandria VA p. 2444

Barrett Kim Memorial Library, see Hospital for Special Surgery, New York NY p. 1681

Barrett Library, see Allen College, Waterloo IA p. 849

Barrett Memorial Library, Williams Bay WI p. 2649

Barrett Paradise Friendly Library, Cresco PA p. 2048

Barrhead Public Library, Barrhead AB p. 2684

Barrie Public Library, Barrie ON p. 2793

Barrigar Gail Katherine Library, see Kaplan University, Davenport IA p. 806

Barrington Public Library, Barrington NH p. 1438

Barrington Public Library, Barrington RI p. 2163

Barrington Public Library District, Barrington IL p. 592

Barrins Edward F Memorial Library, Tucson AZ p. 85

Barron County Library, see University of Wisconsin, Rice Lake WI p. 2634

Barron Library, see Hendry County Library System, Labelle FL p. 433

Barron Public Library, Barron WI p. 2580

Barry Edith Cleaves Library, see Brick Store Museum, Kennebunk ME p. 988

Barry Gerald A Memorial Library, see Tompkins Cortland Community College, Dryden NY p. 1615

Barry-Lawrence Regional Library, Monett MO p. 1346

Barry Marion C Memorial Library, see Monroe County Seneca Park Zoo, Rochester NY p. 1730

Barry Public Library, Barry IL p. 592

Barry University, Miami FL p. 464

Barry's Bay & Area Public Library, Barry's Bay ON p. 2794

Barryton Public Library, Barryton MI p. 1155

Barsky Paul Memorial Library, see Kennedy Memorial Hospitals, Turnersville NJ p. 1536

Barstow College, Barstow CA p. 125

Barstow Frederic D Memorial Library, see Chittenden Public Library, Chittenden VT p. 2421

Barth Learning Resource Center, see Del Mar College, Corpus Christi TX p. 2302

Bear Lake County Free Library, Montpelier ID
p. 579

Bear Library, Bear DE p. 381

Bear Mountain Trailside Museums Library, Bear
Mountain NY p. 1579

Bear Point Community Library, Bear Canyon AB
p. 2685

Bearden Public Library, *see* Columbia County
Library, Bearden AR p. 108

Beardslee Library, *see* Western Theological
Seminary, Holland MI p. 1191

Beardsley & Memorial Library, Winsted CT p. 379

Beardsley Robert B Arts Reference Library, *see*
Ruthmere Museum, Elkhart IN p. 737

Beardstown Houston Memorial Library, Beardstown
IL p. 593

Beasley Firm, LLC, Philadelphia PA p. 2103

Beatley Charles E Jr, *see* Alexandria Library,
Alexandria VA p. 2444

Beatley Library, *see* Simmons College, Boston MA
p. 1066

Beaton Institute, *see* Cape Breton University Library,
Sydney NS p. 2785

Beatrice Public Library, Beatrice NE p. 1393

Beatrice State Developmental Center, Beatrice NE
p. 1393

Beatty Library District, Beatty NV p. 1425

Beauchamp Botanical Library, National City CA
p. 193

Beaufort County Community College Library,
Washington NC p. 1828

Beaufort County Library, Beaufort SC p. 2181

Beaufort, Hyde & Martin County Regional Library,
Washington NC p. 1828

Beaumont Enterprise Library, Beaumont TX p. 2287

Beaumont Hospital, Grosse Pointe MI p. 1187

Beaumont Juvenile Correctional Center, Beaumont
VA p. 2450

Beaumont Library District, Beaumont CA p. 125

Beaumont Public, *see* Beaumont Public Library
System, Beaumont TX p. 2287

Beaumont Public Library System, Beaumont TX
p. 2287

Beaumont William Army Medical Library, *see*
United States Army, El Paso TX p. 2317

Beaumont William Hospital, Royal Oak MI p. 1223

Beauregard Parish Library, DeRidder LA p. 948

Beauval Public Library, Beauval SK p. 2917

Beaver Area Memorial Library, Beaver PA p. 2031

Beaver City Public Library, Beaver City NE p. 1393

Beaver County Law Library, Beaver PA p. 2031

Beaver County Library System, Monaca PA p. 2090

Beaver County Pioneer Library, Beaver OK p. 1958

Beaver Creek Township Library, *see* Crawford
County Library System, Grayling MI p. 1186

Beaver Dam Community Hospitals, Beaver Dam WI
p. 2581

Beaver Dam Community Library, Beaver Dam WI
p. 2581

Beaver Falls Library, Beaver Falls NY p. 1579

Beaver Island District Library, Beaver Island MI
p. 1156

Beaver Patrick Memorial Library, *see* Hickory
Public Library, Hickory NC p. 1801

Beaver Public Library, Beaver UT p. 2403

Beaver Thomas Free Library, Danville PA p. 2049

Beaver Valley Public Library, Fruitvale BC p. 2728

Beaverbrook Art Gallery Library, Fredericton NB
p. 2762

Beavercreek Community Library, *see* Greene County
Public Library, Beavercreek OH p. 1951

Beaverhead County Museum Association Library,
Dillon MT p. 1377

Beaverlodge Public Library, Beaverlodge AB
p. 2685

Beaverton City Library, Beaverton OR p. 1991

Beavertown Community Library, *see* Snyder County
Libraries, Beavertown PA p. 2138

Bechtold Paul Library, *see* Catholic Theological
Union, Chicago IL p. 607

Beck Bookman Library, Holton KS p. 872

Beck John A Jr Library, *see* Butler County
Community College, Butler PA p. 2040

Beck Library, *see* Western Nevada Community
College, Fallon NV p. 1426

Beck Marianne Memorial Library, Howey in the
Hills FL p. 451

Beck William C Health Science Library & Resource
Center, Sayre PA p. 2136

Becker Bernard Medical Library, *see* Washington
University Libraries, Saint Louis MO p. 1362

Becker Charles E Library, *see* Benedictine
University Library, Springfield IL p. 666

Becker College, Leicester MA p. 1098

Becker College, Worcester MA p. 1143

Becker County Historical Society, Detroit Lakes MN
p. 1247

Becker Library, *see* Great River Regional Library,
Becker MN p. 1274

Becket Athenaeum, Inc Library, Becket MA p. 1051

Beckman Coulter, Inc, Miami FL p. 464

Beckwith Music Library, *see* Bowdoin College
Library, Brunswick ME p. 979

Becton, Dickinson & Co, Franklin Lakes NJ p. 1486

Becton Dickinson & Company, Research Triangle
Park NC p. 1819

Bedford County Historical Society & Pioneer
Library, *see* Pioneer Historical Society of
Bedford County Inc, Bedford PA p. 2032

Bedford County Library, Bedford PA p. 2031

Bedford Free Library, Bedford NY p. 1579

Bedford Free Public Library, Bedford MA p. 1052

Bedford Hills Correctional Facility Library, *see* New
York Department of Correctional Services,
Bedford Hills NY p. 1579

Bedford Hills Free Library, Bedford Hills NY
p. 1579

Bedford Historical Society Library, Bedford OH
p. 1858

Bedford Institute of Oceanography Library, *see*
Canada Department of Fisheries & Oceans,
Dartmouth NS p. 2778

Bedford Park Public Library District, Bedford Park
IL p. 593

Bedford Public Library, Bedford IN p. 726

Bedford Public Library, Bedford IA p. 796

Bedford Public Library, Bedford NH p. 1438

Bedford Public Library, Bedford TX p. 2287

Bedford Public Library System, Bedford VA p. 2450

Bedford-Somerset Mental Health, Somerset PA
p. 2141

Bedsole J L Library, *see* University of Mobile,
Mobile AL p. 26

Bee Cave Public Library, Bee Cave TX p. 2288

Beebe George H Communications Library, *see*
Boston University Libraries, Boston MA p. 1058

Beebe Lucius Memorial Library, Wakefield MA
p. 1132

Beebe Marcus P Memorial Library, Ipswich SD
p. 2213

Beebe Medical Center, Lewes DE p. 384

Beebe Public, *see* White County Regional Library
System, Beebe AR p. 114

Beech Grove Public Library, Beech Grove IN p. 726

Beech-Nut Nutrition Corp Library, Canajoharie NY
p. 1600

Beecher Community Library, Beecher IL p. 593

Beeghly L A Library, *see* Juniata College,
Huntingdon PA p. 2070

Beeghly L A Library, *see* Ohio Wesleyan University,
Delaware OH p. 1896

Beeghly Library, *see* Heidelberg University, Tiffin
OH p. 1938

Beekley Licia & Mason Community Library, New
Hartford CT p. 355

Beekman Library, Hopewell Junction NY p. 1637

Beene-Pearson Public Library, South Pittsburg TN
p. 2266

Beering Steven C Medical Library, *see* Indiana
University School of Medicine-Northwest Center
for Medical Education, Gary IN p. 745

Beersheba Springs Public Library, Beersheba
Springs TN p. 2224

Beeson Lucille Stewart Law Library, *see* Samford
University Library, Birmingham AL p. 9

Begley Library & Instructional Technology Center,
see Schenectady County Community College,
Schenectady NY p. 1740

Behan Health Science Library, *see* Jefferson
Regional Medical Center, Pittsburgh PA p. 2125

Behringer-Crawford Museum, Covington KY p. 910

Beinecke Richard S Medical Library, *see* Good
Samaritan Medical Center, West Palm Beach FL
p. 502

Beiseker Municipal Library, Beiseker AB p. 2685

Beit Midrash Library-Dr Arnold L Segel Library
Center, *see* Temple Israel Library, Boston MA
p. 1067

Beit Yisrael Library, *see* Morristown Jewish Center,
Morristown NJ p. 1505

Bekkum Memorial Library, Westby WI p. 2648

Belcher Memorial Library, Gaysville VT p. 2424

Belden Cora J Library, Rocky Hill CT p. 365

Belding Alvah N Memorial Library, Belding MI
p. 1156

Belding Memorial Library, Ashfield MA p. 1050

Beldon Noble Memorial Library, Essex NY p. 1621

Belen Public Library, Belen NM p. 1552

Belfast Free Library, Belfast ME p. 977

Belfast Public Library, Belfast NY p. 1579

Belfer Center for Science & International Affairs
Library, *see* Harvard Library, Cambridge MA
p. 1074

Belfry Public, *see* Pike County Public Library
District, Belfry KY p. 932

Belgrade Community Library, Belgrade MT p. 1373

Belgrade Public Library, Belgrade ME p. 977

Belhaven Public, *see* Beaufort, Hyde & Martin
County Regional Library, Belhaven NC p. 1828

Belhaven University, Jackson MS p. 1303

Belington Public Library, Belington WV p. 2554

Belk Carol Grotnes Library, *see* Appalachian State
University, Boone NC p. 1776

Belk Carol Grotnes Library, *see* Elon University,
Elon NC p. 1791

Bell Alexander Graham Association for the Deaf &
Hard of Hearing, Washington DC p. 394

Bell Alexander Graham National Historic Site,
Baddeck NS p. 2777

Bell County Forestry Library, Pineville KY p. 933

Bell Helicopter Textron, Inc, Fort Worth TX p. 2321

Bell Island Public Library, Bell Island NL p. 2769

Bell J W & Dorothy Library, *see* Crichton College,
Memphis TN p. 2248

Bell James Ford Library, *see* University of
Minnesota Libraries-Twin Cities, Minneapolis
MN p. 1262

Bell James Ford Library, *see* General Mills, Inc,
Minneapolis MN p. 1260

Bell L Nelson Library, *see* Montreat College,
Montreat NC p. 1810

Bell-Marsh Memorial Library, *see* East Texas
Medical Center, Tyler TX p. 2393

Bell Mary & Jeff Library, *see* Texas A&M
University-Corpus Christi, Corpus Christi TX
p. 2302

Bell Memorial Library, Nunda NY p. 1708

Bell Memorial Public Library, Mentone IN p. 763

Bell Mertys W Library, *see* Guilford Technical
Community College, Jamestown NC p. 1803

Bell-Pittman Library Resource Center, *see* Wilson
Medical Center Library, Wilson NC p. 1831

Bell Ralph Pickard Library, *see* Mount Allison
University Libraries & Archives, Sackville NB
p. 2766

Bell-Whittington Public Library, Portland TX
p. 2372

Bella Vista Historical Society Museum Library,
Bella Vista AR p. 94

Bella Vista Public Library, Bella Vista AR p. 94

Bellaire City Library, Bellaire TX p. 2288

Bellaire Public Library, Bellaire MI p. 1156

Bellaire Public Library, Bellaire OH p. 1858

Bellarmine University, Louisville KY p. 923

Belle Center Free Public Library, Belle Center OH
p. 1858

Belle Fourche Public Library, Belle Fourche SD
p. 2210

Belle Isle Library, *see* Metropolitan Library System
in Oklahoma County, Oklahoma City OK
p. 1972

Belle Plaine City Library, Belle Plaine KS p. 857

Belle Plaine Community Library, Belle Plaine IA
p. 796

Berrien Springs Community Library, Berrien Springs MI p. 1157

Berry College, Mount Berry GA p. 546

Berry Creek Community Library, Brooks AB p. 2686

Berry E Y Library-Learning Center, *see* Black Hills State University, Spearfish SD p. 2220

Berry Johnnie Mae Library, *see* Cincinnati State Technical & Community College, Cincinnati OH p. 1869

Berry Memorial Library, Bar Mills ME p. 976

Berryville Public Library, Berryville AR p. 95

Berstler Lois High Community Health Library, Hershey PA p. 2068

Benld Frank Bertetti Public Library, Benld IL p. 594

Berthoud Public Library, Berthoud CO p. 289

Bertolet Memorial Library District, Leaf River IL p. 664

Berton Pierre Resource Library, *see* Vaughan Public Libraries, Woodbridge ON p. 2848

Bertrand Ellen Clarke Library, *see* Bucknell University, Lewisburg PA p. 2080

Berwick Public Library, Berwick ME p. 977

Berwyn Municipal Library, Berwyn AB p. 2685

Berwyn Public Library, Berwyn IL p. 594

Besore Lilian S Memorial Library, Greencastle PA p. 2062

Besse Ralph M Library, *see* Ursuline College, Pepper Pike OH p. 1929

Bessemer Public Library, Bessemer AL p. 6

Bessemer Public Library, Bessemer MI p. 1157

Bessemer Trust Co, New York NY p. 1670

Best Robin Library, *see* Vancouver Aquarium Marine Science Centre, Vancouver BC p. 2743

Beth Ahabah Museum & Archives, *see* Congregation Beth Ahabah Museum & Archives Trust, Richmond VA p. 2488

Beth David Congregation, Miami FL p. 464

Beth David Reform Congregation, Gladwyne PA p. 2060

Beth El Hebrew Congregation Library & Information Center, Alexandria VA p. 2445

Beth El Ner Tamid Library, Broomall PA p. 2038

Beth El Ner Tamid Synagogue, *see* Rosen Horace J & Idabell Library, Mequon WI p. 2615

Beth-El Synagogue, Saint Louis Park MN p. 1277

Beth-El Temple Center, Belmont MA p. 1053

Beth Elohim Library, *see* Main Line Reform Temple, Wynnewood PA p. 2158

Beth Emet Synagogue, Evanston IL p. 643

Beth Hillel Congregation Library, Wilmette IL p. 719

Beth Israel Community Library, *see* Beth Israel Synagogue, Vineland NJ p. 1538

Beth Israel Deaconess Medical Center, Boston MA p. 1055

Beth Israel Deaconess Medical Center, Needham MA p. 1108

Beth Israel Medical Center, New York NY p. 1670

Beth Israel Synagogue, Vineland NJ p. 1538

Beth Shalom Congregation, Overland Park KS p. 887

Beth Sholom Congregation, Elkins Park PA p. 2053

Beth Tzedec Congregation, Toronto ON p. 2850

Bethalto Public Library District, Bethalto IL p. 594

Bethany-Calvary United Methodist Church Library, Wauwatosa WI p. 2647

Bethany College, Lindsborg KS p. 880

Bethany College, Mary Cutlip Center, Bethany WV p. 2554

Bethany Library, *see* Metropolitan Library System in Oklahoma County, Bethany OK p. 1972

Bethany Lutheran College Memorial Library, Mankato MN p. 1257

Bethany Presbyterian Church Library, Sacramento CA p. 220

Bethany Presbyterian Church Library, Rochester NY p. 1728

Bethany Public Library, Bethany PA p. 2033

Bethea Katherine Shaw Hospital, Dixon IL p. 636

Bethel College, Mishawaka IN p. 765

Bethel College Library, North Newton KS p. 885

Bethel Library Association, Bethel ME p. 977

Bethel Park Public Library, Bethel Park PA p. 2033

Bethel Public Library, Bethel CT p. 330

Bethel Public Library, Bethel VT p. 2419

Bethel Seminary Library, Saint Paul MN p. 1277

Bethel University, McKenzie TN p. 2247

Bethel University Library, Saint Paul MN p. 1277

Bethel-Tulpehocken Public Library, Bethel PA p. 2033

Bethesda Library, *see* Montgomery County Public Libraries, Bethesda MD p. 1038

Bethesda Memorial Hospital, Boynton Beach FL p. 429

Bethesda Mennonite Church Library, Henderson NE p. 1402

Bethesda North Hospital, Cincinnati OH p. 1868

Bethesda United Methodist Church Library, Bethesda MD p. 1021

Bethlehem Area Public Library, Bethlehem PA p. 2033

Bethlehem Lutheran Church Library, Saint Charles IL p. 699

Bethlehem Public Library, Bethlehem CT p. 330

Bethlehem Public Library, Bethlehem NH p. 1439

Bethlehem Public Library, Delmar NY p. 1614

Bethpage Public Library, Bethpage NY p. 1581

Bethune-Cookman College, Daytona Beach FL p. 435

Bethune Public, *see* Kershaw County Library, Bethune SC p. 2182

Betsie Valley District Library, Thompsonville MI p. 1230

Bettencourt Medical Library, *see* Shattuck Lemuel Hospital, Jamaica Plain MA p. 1097

Bettendorf Public Library Information Center, Bettendorf IA p. 796

Bettsville Public Library, Bettsville OH p. 1859

Betze Stephen J Library, *see* Delaware Technical & Community College, Georgetown DE p. 383

Beulah Heights University, Atlanta GA p. 513

Beveridge & Diamond PC Library, Washington DC p. 394

Beverly Free Library, Beverly NJ p. 1472

Beverly Hills Public Library, Beverly Hills CA p. 129

Beverly Historical Society, Beverly MA p. 1053

Beverly Hospital, Montebello CA p. 189

Beverly Hospital Library, Beverly MA p. 1053

Beverly Public Library, Beverly MA p. 1053

Bevevino Mary Kintz Library, *see* College of Misericordia, Dallas PA p. 2048

Bevier Engineering Library, *see* University of Pittsburgh, Pittsburgh PA p. 2128

Bevill State Community College, Fayette AL p. 17

Bevill State Community College Library, Hamilton AL p. 19

Bevill State Community College, Jasper AL p. 23

Bevill State Community College, Sumiton AL p. 36

Bevill Tom Public, *see* Cullman County Public Library System, Hanceville AL p. 13

Bexar County Law Library, San Antonio TX p. 2379

Bexar County Medical Library Association, San Antonio TX p. 2379

Bexley Public Library, Bexley OH p. 1860

BHSL (N), *see* Basic Health Sciences Library Network, Summit NJ p. 2948

Bianchi Angelo & Harriet Library, *see* Eastchester Historical Society, Eastchester NY p. 1618

Bibb Basil G Library, *see* University of Rochester Medical Center, Rochester NY p. 1734

Bibi Jannat Library, *see* Muslim Education & Welfare Foundation of Canada, Surrey BC p. 2738

Bible Holiness Movement Library, Penticton BC p. 2735

Biblical Theological Seminary Library, Hatfield PA p. 2067

Bibliomation (N), Middlebury CT p. 2939

Biblioteca Dennis Soto, *see* Universidad Adventista de las Antillas, Mayaguez PR p. 2674

Biblioteca Regional para Ciegos y Fisicamente Impedidos de Puerto Rico, *see* Puerto Rico Regional Library for the Blind & Physically Handicapped, San Juan PR p. 2676

Biblioteca Rene Marques, *see* Inter-American University of Puerto Rico, Arecibo PR p. 2671

Biblioteca Victor M Pons Gil, *see* University of Puerto Rico Library, Cayey Campus, Cayey PR p. 2672

Bibliotheque Albert-le-Grand, Montreal QC p. 2888

Bibliotheque Alcide-Fleury, *see* Bibliotheque Charles-Edouard-Mailhot, Victoriaville QC p. 2915

Bibliotheque Alfred-Monnin, *see* College Universitaire de Saint-Boniface, Winnipeg MB p. 2755

Bibliotheque Aliette-Marchand, *see* Bibliotheque Gabrielle-Roy, Quebec QC p. 2903

Bibliothèque Allard Regional Library, Saint Georges MB p. 2751

Bibliotheque Alphonse-Desjardins, *see* College de Levis, Levis QC p. 2886

Bibliotheque Cecile-Rouleau, *see* Centre de Services Partages du Quebec, Quebec QC p. 2904

Bibliotheque Cegep et Universite du Quebec en Abitibi-Temiscamingue, Rouyn-Noranda QC p. 2908

Bibliotheque Charles-Auguste-Gauthier, *see* Hopital De L'Enfant Jesus, Quebec QC p. 2905

Bibliotheque Charles-Edouard-Mailhot, Victoriaville QC p. 2914

Bibliotheque Charles H Blais, Sillery QC p. 2912

Bibliotheque Commemorative Desautels, Marieville QC p. 2887

Bibliotheque Commemorative Pettes, Knowlton QC p. 2885

Bibliotheque d'Albert Rousseau, Sainte-Etienne QC p. 2910

Bibliotheque de Beaconsfield, Beaconsfield QC p. 2880

Bibliotheque de Beaumont Library, Beaumont AB p. 2685

Bibliotheque de Beloeil, Beloeil QC p. 2880

Bibliotheque de Brossard, Brossard QC p. 2880

Bibliotheque de Charlesbourg, Charlesbourg QC p. 2880

Bibliotheque de Coaticook, Inc, Coaticook QC p. 2881

Bibliotheque de Dollard-des-Ormeaux, Dollard-des-Ormeaux QC p. 2881

Bibliotheque de Dorval, Dorval QC p. 2881

Bibliotheque de Farnham, Inc, Farnham QC p. 2882

Bibliotheque de Kirkland, Kirkland QC p. 2884

Bibliotheque de l'Abbaye Saint-Benoit, Saint Benoit-du-Lac QC p. 2908

Bibliotheque de l'Hopital Montfort, Ottawa ON p. 2828

Bibliotheque de l'Institut Nazareth et Louis-Braille, Longueuil QC p. 2886

Bibliotheque de la Compagnie de Jesus, Montreal QC p. 2888

Bibliotheque de la Polyvalente de Thetford Mines, Thetford Mines QC p. 2913

Bibliotheque de Montreal Est, Montreal-Est QC p. 2902

Bibliotheque de Pavillon Lalemant, *see* College Jean-de-Brebeuf, Montreal QC p. 2894

Bibliotheque de Repentigny, Repentigny QC p. 2907

Bibliotheque de Sorel Tracy, De Sorel Tracy QC p. 2881

Bibliotheque de St Isidore, St. Isidore AB p. 2717

Bibliotheque Delage Couture, *see* Hospital du Saint-Sacrement, Quebec QC p. 2905

Bibliotheque Dentinger, Falher AB p. 2704

Arsenault Dr J Edmond, *see* Prince Edward Island Public Library Service, Charlottetown PE p. 2876

Bibliotheque Dre-Marguerite-Michaud, *see* York Library Region, Fredericton NB p. 2764

Bibliotheque du CAIJ Montreal, Montreal QC p. 2888

Bibliotheque du Cegep Limoilou, Quebec QC p. 2903

Bibliotheque du College Dominicain de Philosophie et de Theologie, Ottawa ON p. 2828

Bibliotheque du Personnel, *see* Commission Scolaire de la Capitale, Quebec QC p. 2904

Bibliotheque du Seminaire de Saint-Hyacinthe, Saint-Hyacinthe QC p. 2910

Bibliotheque et Archives nationales du Quebec, Montreal QC p. 2888

Billington Library, *see* Johnson County Community College, Overland Park KS p. 888

Billups R A Memorial Library, *see* Cottonlandia Museum, Greenwood MS p. 1299

Biloxi Central Library, *see* Harrison County Library System, Biloxi MS p. 1299

BIN (N), *see* Berkeley Information Network, Berkeley CA p. 2938

Binger Public Library, Binger OK p. 1958

Bingham McCutchen, San Francisco CA p. 240

Bingham McCutchen LLP, Boston MA p. 1055

Bingham Memorial Hospital, Blackfoot ID p. 569

BIO FOOD TECH (FTC Enterprises Limited), Charlottetown PE p. 2875

BioFoodTech Library, *see* BIO FOOD TECH (FTC Enterprises Limited), Charlottetown PE p. 2875

Biogen Idec Inc Library, Cambridge MA p. 1072

Biola University Library, La Mirada CA p. 162

Birch Hills Public Library, *see* Wapiti Regional Library, Birch Hills SK p. 2921

Birchard Public Library of Sandusky County, Fremont OH p. 1900

Bird City Public Library, Bird City KS p. 858

Bird E S Library, *see* Syracuse University Library, Syracuse NY p. 1754

Bird Island Public Library, Bird Island MN p. 1241

Bird Robert M Health Sciences Library, *see* University of Oklahoma Health Sciences Center, Oklahoma City OK p. 1975

Bird Walter D Memorial Library & Archives, *see* Becker County Historical Society, Detroit Lakes MN p. 1247

Birkhoff George David Mathematical Library, *see* Harvard Library, Cambridge MA p. 1074

Birmingham Museum of Art, Birmingham AL p. 7

Birmingham News, Birmingham AL p. 7

Birmingham Public Library, Birmingham AL p. 7

Birmingham Public Library, Birmingham IA p. 796

Birmingham-Southern College, Birmingham AL p. 8

Birmingham Temple Library, Farmington Hills MI p. 1177

Birnamwood Public, *see* Shawano City-County Library, Birnamwood WI p. 2637

Birnbaum Henry Library, *see* Pace University Library, New York NY p. 1696

Biro Louis L Law Library, *see* Marshall John Law School, Chicago IL p. 618

Bisbee City Library, *see* Copper Queen Library, Bisbee AZ p. 58

Bisbee Mining & Historical Museum, Bisbee AZ p. 58

Bishop & McKenzie LLP, Barristers & Solicitors Library, Edmonton AB p. 2699

Bishop Baraga Association Archives, Marquette MI p. 1206

Bishop Bernice P Museum Library & Archives, Honolulu HI p. 560

Bishop Hodges Library, *see* Wheeling Jesuit University, Wheeling WV p. 2575

Bishop Jones Library, *see* Saint Mark's Episcopal Church, San Antonio TX p. 2381

Bishop Memorial Library, *see* Luzerne County Historical Society, Wilkes-Barre PA p. 2155

Bishop Minnie Slade Library, *see* Bishop State Community College, Mobile AL p. 25

Bishop State Community College, Mobile AL p. 25

Bishop Veron & Doris Library, *see* Lebanon Valley College, Annville PA p. 2029

Bishops Library-Rock Point, *see* Episcopal Church Center, Burlington VT p. 2420

Bismarck State College Library, Bismarck ND p. 1837

Bismarck Veterans Memorial Public Library, Bismarck ND p. 1837

Bison Community Library, Bison KS p. 858

Bitove John & Dotsa Family Law Library, *see* Western University - Libraries, London ON p. 2819

Bitterroot Public Library, Hamilton MT p. 1380

Bixby George Holmes Memorial Library, Francestown NH p. 1447

Bixby Memorial Free Library, Vergennes VT p. 2437

Bixler Art & Music Library, *see* Colby College Libraries, Waterville ME p. 1005

Bjorkdale Public Library, *see* Wapiti Regional Library, Bjorkdale SK p. 2921

Black & Veatch, Overland Park KS p. 887

Black Barron F, *see* Norfolk Public Library, Norfolk VA p. 2481

Black Bridge Library, Dime Box TX p. 2314

Black Canyon City Community Library, Black Canyon City AZ p. 58

Black Creek Village Library, Black Creek WI p. 2582

Black Cultural Centre for Nova Scotia Library, Dartmouth NS p. 2778

Black Earth Public Library, Black Earth WI p. 2582

Black Gold Cooperative Library System, San Luis Obispo CA p. 253

Black Hawk College, Moline IL p. 674

Black Hawk College-East Campus, Galva IL p. 648

Black Heritage Library & Multicultural Center, Findlay OH p. 1899

Black Hills State University, Spearfish SD p. 2220, 2973

Black Marianna Library, Bryson City NC p. 1778

Black Mary J L, *see* Thunder Bay Public Library, Thunder Bay ON p. 2849

Black River Falls Public Library, Black River Falls WI p. 2582

Black River Technical College Library, Pocahontas AR p. 113

Black Watch Memorial Library, Ticonderoga NY p. 1755

Blackader-Lauterman Library, *see* McGill University Libraries, Montreal QC p. 2898

Blackburn College, Carlinville IL p. 600

Blackburn Correctional Complex Library, Lexington KY p. 920

Blackduck Community Library, Blackduck MN p. 1241

Blackfalds Public Library, Blackfalds AB p. 2685

Blackfeet Community College, Browning MT p. 1376

Blackfoot Public Library, Blackfoot ID p. 569

Blackhawk Museum, Danville CA p. 139

Blackhawk Technical College Library, Janesville WI p. 2599

Blackmer Library, *see* Erie Business Center South, New Castle PA p. 2095

Blackmore Lenora Public Library, Windsor MO p. 1372

Blackmore Library, *see* Capital University, Columbus OH p. 1883

Blackmur Memorial Library, Water Valley MS p. 1317

Blackshear Memorial Library, *see* Okefenokee Regional Library, Blackshear GA p. 557

Blackstone James Memorial Library, Branford CT p. 331

Blackstone Public Library, Blackstone MA p. 1054

Blackwater Regional Library, Courtland VA p. 2458

Blackwell Library, *see* Salisbury University, Salisbury MD p. 1040

Blackwell Lucien E West Philadelphia Regional, *see* Free Library of Philadelphia, Philadelphia PA p. 2107

Blackwell Public Library, Blackwell OK p. 1958

Blackwell R E Memorial, *see* Pine Forest Regional Library, Collins MS p. 1314

Blackwood Rotary Library, *see* Camden County Library System, Blackwood NJ p. 1538

Bladen Community College Library, Dublin NC p. 1787

Bladen County Public Library, Elizabethtown NC p. 1791

Blagg-Huey Mary Evelyn Library, *see* Texas Woman's University Libraries, Denton TX p. 2312

Blaine County Library, Chinook MT p. 1376

Blaine Lake Public Library, *see* Wapiti Regional Library, Blaine Lake SK p. 2921

Blaine Public Library, Blaine TN p. 2224

Blair Allan Cancer Centre Library, *see* Saskatchewan Cancer Agency, Regina SK p. 2923

Blair-Caldwell African American Research Library, *see* Denver Public Library, Denver CO p. 301

Blair County Law Library, Hollidaysburg PA p. 2069

Blair County Library System, Altoona PA p. 2028

Blair Library, *see* Fayetteville Public Library, Fayetteville AR p. 99

Blair Memorial Library, Clawson MI p. 1163

Blair Memorial Library, *see* Kent State University, East Liverpool OH p. 1897

Blair-Preston Public Library, Blair WI p. 2582

Blair Public Library, Blair NE p. 1394

Blairstown Public Library, Blairstown IA p. 797

Blairsville Public Library, Blairsville PA p. 2035

Blaisdell F William Medical Library, *see* University of California, Davis, Sacramento CA p. 225

Blaisdell Memorial Library, Nottingham NH p. 1461

Blake, Cassels & Graydon LLP, Toronto ON p. 2850

Blake Library, *see* Martin County Library System, Stuart FL p. 491

Blake Library, *see* University of Maine at Fort Kent, Fort Kent ME p. 986

Blake Memorial Library, East Corinth VT p. 2423

Blakesburg Public Library, Blakesburg IA p. 797

Blakley William A Library, *see* University of Dallas, Irving TX p. 2347

Blanchard Community Library, *see* Blanchard-Santa Paula Public Library District, Santa Paula CA p. 266

Blanchard Judith Rozier Library, *see* Tampa Museum of Art, Tampa FL p. 498

Blanchard Learning Resources Center, *see* Ohlone College, Fremont CA p. 149

Blanchard Public, *see* Pioneer Library System, Blanchard OK p. 1970

Blanchard-Santa Paula Public Library District, Santa Paula CA p. 266

Blanchardville Public Library, Blanchardville WI p. 2582

Blanchester Public Library, Blanchester OH p. 1860

Blanco County South Library District, Blanco TX p. 2290

Bland Correctional Center, Bland VA p. 2451

Bland Schuyler Otis Memorial Library, *see* United States Merchant Marine Academy, Kings Point NY p. 1649

Bland W T Public Library, Mount Dora FL p. 470

Blanden Memorial Art Museum, Fort Dodge IA p. 816

Blanding Public Library, Rehoboth MA p. 1120

Blandinsville-Hire District Library, Blandinsville IL p. 595

Blaney McMurtry LLP, Toronto ON p. 2850

Blank Rome LLP, Philadelphia PA p. 2103

Blank Rome LLP Library, Washington DC p. 394

Blank Rome LLP Library, New York NY p. 1670

Blankenbuehler John H Memorial Library, *see* Hobart Institute of Welding Technology, Troy OH p. 1941

Blasco Raymond M MD Memorial Library, *see* Erie County Public Library, Erie PA p. 2055

Blaustein Library, *see* American Jewish Committee, New York NY p. 1668

Blauvelt Free Library, Blauvelt NY p. 1583

Blazer Paul G Library, *see* Kentucky State University, Frankfort KY p. 914

Blecher & Collins, Los Angeles CA p. 168

Bledsoe County Public Library, Pikeville TN p. 2263

Bleskacek G E Memorial Library, Bloomer WI p. 2582

Blessed Edmund Rice School of Pastoral Ministry, Arcadia FL p. 425

Blessed Pope John XXIII National Seminary Library, Weston MA p. 1139

Blessing Health Professions Library, Quincy IL p. 693

Bleyhl Community Library, Grandview WA p. 2516

BLINC (N), *see* Burlington Libraries Information Consortium, Westampton NJ p. 2948

Blind Children's Fund Library, Mount Pleasant MI p. 1211

Blind River Public Library, Blind River ON p. 2795

Blinn College Library, Brenham TX p. 2291

Bliss Memorial Library, *see* First United Methodist Church, Shreveport LA p. 968

Bliss Memorial Public Library, Bloomville OH p. 1860

Bonner General Hospital, Sandpoint ID p. 583

Bonner Springs City Library, Bonner Springs KS p. 858

Bonnette Nancy, *see* Aiken-Bamberg-Barnwell-Edgefield Regional Library System, Wagener SC p. 2179

Bonneville Power Administration Library, Portland OR p. 2010

Bonney Memorial Library, Cornish ME p. 982

Bonnyville Municipal Library, Bonnyville AB p. 2686

Bonte Fred Library, *see* Parkland Health & Hospital System, Dallas TX p. 2309

Booher Library, *see* Episcopal Theological Seminary of the Southwest, Austin TX p. 2280

Book Club of California, San Francisco CA p. 240

Booker Health Sciences Library, *see* Jersey Shore University Medical Center, Neptune NJ p. 1507

Boone Area Library, Birdsboro PA p. 2035

Boone County Library, Harrison AR p. 102

Boone County Public Library, Burlington KY p. 908

Boone Daniel, *see* Saint Louis County Library, Ellisville MO p. 1358

Boone Daniel Regional Library, Columbia MO p. 1324

Boone-Madison Public Library, Madison WV p. 2564

Boonsboro Free Library, *see* Washington County Free Library, Boonsboro MD p. 1031

Boonslick Regional Library, Sedalia MO p. 1364

Boonton Holmes Public Library, Boonton NJ p. 1473

Boonville Community Public Library, Boonville NC p. 1777

Boonville Correctional Center, *see* Missouri Department of Corrections, Boonville MO p. 1334

Boonville-Warrick County Public Library, Boonville IN p. 729

Boot Hill Museum, Dodge City KS p. 863

Booth & Dimock Memorial Library, Coventry CT p. 334

Booth Cyrenius H Library, Newtown CT p. 361

Booth Fannie Brown Memorial Library, Center TX p. 2296

Booth Library, *see* Davis & Elkins College, Elkins WV p. 2558

Booth Library, *see* Eastern Illinois University, Charleston IL p. 603

Booth Mrs Arthur W Library, *see* Chemung County Historical Society, Inc, Elmira NY p. 1619

Booth University College, Winnipeg MB p. 2754

Boothbay Harbor Memorial Library, Boothbay Harbor ME p. 978

Boothby Nan Memorial Library, *see* Cochrane Public Library, Cochrane AB p. 2695

Bor Medical Library, *see* Cambridge Hospital-Cambridge Health Alliance, Cambridge MA p. 1072

Borbas Hope Okemos Library, *see* Capital Area District Libraries, Okemos MI p. 1200

Borchardt Learning Center, *see* MacCormac College Library, Chicago IL p. 618

Borchert John R Map Library, *see* University of Minnesota Libraries-Twin Cities, Minneapolis MN p. 1262

Borden-Carleton Public, *see* Prince Edward Island Public Library Service, Borden PE p. 2876

Borden Gail Public Library District, Elgin IL p. 640

Borden Ladner Gervais LLP, Ottawa ON p. 2828

Borden Ladner Gervais LLP Library, Calgary AB p. 2688

Borden Ladner Gervais LLP Library, Vancouver BC p. 2740

Borden Ladner Gervais LLP Library, Toronto ON p. 2850

Borden Ladner Gervais LLP Library, Montreal QC p. 2892

Border Regional Library, Virden MB p. 2753

Boreham Library, *see* University of Arkansas Fort Smith, Fort Smith AR p. 101

Boren David L Library, *see* Seminole State College, Seminole OK p. 1977

Borgess Medical Center Library, Kalamazoo MI p. 1196

Boricua College, Brooklyn NY p. 1589

Boricua College, New York NY p. 1671

Borja Olympio T Memorial Library, *see* Northern Marianas College, Saipan MP p. 2669

Borland Health Sciences Library, *see* University of Florida Health Science Center-Jacksonville, Jacksonville FL p. 455

Borough of Folcroft Public Library, Folcroft PA p. 2057

Borough of Manhattan Community College Library, New York NY p. 1671

Bortz Library, *see* Hampden Sydney College, Hampden Sydney VA p. 2468

Boscawen Public Library, Boscawen NH p. 1439

Boscobel Public, *see* Hildebrand Memorial Library, Boscobel WI p. 2582

Thun Library, *see* Pennsylvania State University, Reading PA p. 2133

Bose McKinney & Evans LLP, Indianapolis IN p. 749

Boshes Natalie A & Louis D Library for the Neurosciences, Chicago IL p. 607

Bosler Free Library, Carlisle PA p. 2041

Bosque Farms Public Library, Bosque Farms NM p. 1552

Bossard Dr Samuel L Memorial Library, *see* Gallia County District Library, Gallipolis OH p. 1901

Bosshard John Memorial, *see* La Crosse County Library, Bangor WI p. 2598

Bossier Parish Central Library, Bossier City LA p. 945

Bossier Parish Community College Library, Bossier City LA p. 946

Boston Architectural College, Boston MA p. 1055

Boston Athenaeum, Boston MA p. 1056

Boston Baptist College Library, Boston MA p. 1056

Boston Bar Library, *see* Fraser Valley Regional Library, Boston Bar BC p. 2723

Boston Biomedical Library Consortium (N), Boston MA p. 2945

Boston Carnegie Public Library, *see* Thomas County Public Library System, Boston GA p. 553

Boston College, Newton Centre MA p. 1110

Boston College Libraries, Chestnut Hill MA p. 1080

Boston Conservatory, Boston MA p. 1056

Boston Free Library, Boston NY p. 1584

Boston Globe, Boston MA p. 1056

Boston Herald, Boston MA p. 1056

Boston Library Consortium Inc (N), Boston MA p. 2945

Boston Psychoanalytic Society & Institute, Inc, Newton MA p. 1109

Boston Public Library, Boston MA p. 1056

Boston University, Boston MA p. 2967

Boston University Libraries, Boston MA p. 1058

Bostwick Muriel Isabel Library, Hamilton ON p. 2808

Bostwick Public, *see* Putnam County Library System, Palatka FL p. 478

Bosveld Library on Applied Poetry, *see* Pudding House Innovative Writers Programs, Columbus OH p. 1890

Boswell & Grant Township Public Library, Boswell IN p. 729

Boswell Mabel Memorial, *see* Saline County Public Library, Bryant AR p. 95

Boswell Thomas E Memorial Library, *see* First Presbyterian Church, Evanston IL p. 643

Bosworth Memorial Library, *see* Lexington Theological Seminary, Lexington KY p. 921

Botanical Research Institute of Texas Library, Fort Worth TX p. 2321

Botetourt County Library, Roanoke VA p. 2493

Bothell Regional Library, *see* King County Library System, Bothell WA p. 2517

Bothin Library, *see* San Francisco Conservatory of Music, San Francisco CA p. 245

Bothwell George, *see* Regina Public Library, Regina SK p. 2923

Botsford Hospital, Farmington Hills MI p. 1177

Bottineau County Public Library, Bottineau ND p. 1838

Bottineau Pierre, *see* Hennepin County Library, Minneapolis MN p. 1263

Botts Memorial Library & Archives, *see* Resurrection Metropolitan Community Church, Houston TX p. 2341

Boulder City Library, Boulder City NV p. 1425

Boulder Community Hospital, Boulder CO p. 290

Boulder County Corrections Library, Boulder CO p. 290

Boulder Junction Public Library, Boulder Junction WI p. 2583

Boulder Laboratories Main Library, *see* United States Department of Commerce, Boulder CO p. 291

Boulder Public Library, Boulder CO p. 290

Boulevard Park Library, *see* King County Library System, Seattle WA p. 2517

Boundary County District Library, Bonners Ferry ID p. 572

Bourbon Public Library, Bourbon IN p. 729

Bourbonnais Public Library District, Bourbonnais IL p. 596

Bourke Memorial Library, *see* Cayuga County Community College, Auburn NY p. 1576

Bourne Frances T Jacaranda Public Library, Venice FL p. 501

Bourne Jonathan Public Library, Bourne MA p. 1068

Bouwhuis Andrew L Library, *see* Canisius College, Buffalo NY p. 1597

Bovard Sarah Stewart Memorial Library, Tionesta PA p. 2145

Bovey Public Library, Bovey MN p. 1242

Bovina Library Association, Bovina Center NY p. 1584

Bow Island Municipal Library, Bow Island AB p. 2686

Bowden Public Library, Bowden AB p. 2686

Bowditch & Dewey, Worcester MA p. 1143

Bowditch Ingersoll Library, *see* Brigham & Women's Faulkner Hospital, Boston MA p. 1059

Bowdoin College Library, Brunswick ME p. 979

Bowdoinham Public Library, Bowdoinham ME p. 978

Bowen Island Public Library, Bowen Island BC p. 2725

Bowen Otis & Elizabeth Library, *see* Bethel College, Mishawaka IN p. 765

Bowerston Public Library, Bowerston OH p. 1860

Bowie Public Library, Bowie TX p. 2290

Bowie State University, Bowie MD p. 1022

Bowlby Eva K Public Library, Waynesburg PA p. 2152

Bowld Kathryn Sullivan Music Library, *see* Southwestern Baptist Theological Seminary Libraries, Fort Worth TX p. 2323

Bowles Life Center, *see* Grand Prairie Public Library System, Grand Prairie TX p. 2329

Bowling Green State University, Huron OH p. 1905

Bowling Green State University Libraries, Bowling Green OH p. 1861

Bowling Library, *see* Judson College, Marion AL p. 24

Bowman & Brooke, Minneapolis MN p. 1259

Bowman Library, *see* Menlo College, Atherton CA p. 122

Bowman Mary Jane & James L, *see* Handley Regional Library, Stephens City VA p. 2503

Bowman Regional Public Library, Bowman ND p. 1839

Box Butte County Law Library, Alliance NE p. 1391

Boxer University Library, *see* Franklin Rosalind University of Medicine & Science, North Chicago IL p. 682

Boxford Town Library, Boxford MA p. 1069

Boy's Town National Research Hospital, Omaha NE p. 1411

Boyce James P Centennial Library, *see* Southern Baptist Theological Seminary, Louisville KY p. 925

Boyce R Dudley Library, *see* Golden West College, Huntington Beach CA p. 158

Boyce William T Library, *see* Fullerton College, Fullerton CA p. 153

Boyceville Public Library, Boyceville WI p. 2583

Boyd County Public Library, Ashland KY p. 905

Boyd J D Library, *see* Alcorn State University, Alcorn State MS p. 1293

Boyd Katharine L Library, *see* Sandhills Community College, Pinehurst NC p. 1814

Boyden Library, Foxborough MA p. 1089

Boyden Public Library, Boyden IA p. 797

Boydstun Q B Library, Fort Gibson OK p. 1963

Boyer Raymond F Resource Center, *see* Michigan Molecular Institute, Midland MI p. 1208

Boyer-Reinstein Julia Library, *see* Cheektowaga Public Library, Cheektowaga NY p. 1606

Boyertown Community Library, Boyertown PA p. 2036

Boyle County Public Library, Danville KY p. 911

Boyle Public Library, Boyle AB p. 2686

Boylston Public Library, Boylston MA p. 1069

Boyne District Library, Boyne City MI p. 1159

Boyne Regional Library, Carman MB p. 2748

Boynton Beach City Library, Boynton Beach FL p. 429

Boynton Public Library, Templeton MA p. 1131

Bozeman Public Library, Bozeman MT p. 1375

BQSIMB (N), *see* Brooklyn-Queens-Staten Island-Manhattan-Bronx Health Sciences Libraries, Brooklyn NY p. 2949

Bracebridge Public Library, Bracebridge ON p. 2796

Bracewell & Giuliani LLP, Washington DC p. 394

Bracewell J S Neighborhood Library, *see* Houston Public Library, Houston TX p. 2339

Bracken Alexander M Library, *see* Ball State University Libraries, Muncie IN p. 766

Bracken County Public Library, Brooksville KY p. 908

Bracken Health Sciences Library, *see* Queen's University, Kingston ON p. 2814

Bracken Memorial Library, Woodstock CT p. 380

Brackett Library, *see* Harding University, Searcy AR p. 114

Brackin Harl V Library, *see* Museum of Flight, Seattle WA p. 2529

Braddock Carnegie Library, Braddock PA p. 2037

Bradenton Beach Public Library, *see* Tingley Memorial Library, Bradenton Beach FL p. 430

Bradford Anderson Oglesby Public Library, *see* Markham Public Library, Markham IL p. 670

Bradford Area Public Library, Bradford PA p. 2037

Bradford County Library System, Troy PA p. 2146

Bradford County Public Library, Starke FL p. 491

Bradford Memorial Library, El Dorado KS p. 864

Bradford Memorial Library, *see* First Congregational Church, Mansfield OH p. 1912

Bradford Public Library, Bradford OH p. 1861

Bradford Public Library, Bradford VT p. 2419

Bradford Public Library District, Bradford IL p. 597

Bradford Regional Medical Center, Bradford PA p. 2037

Bradford-West Gwillimbury Public Library, Bradford ON p. 2796

Bradley, Arant, Rose & White, Birmingham AL p. 8

Bradley Beach Public Library, Bradley Beach NJ p. 1474

Bradley Blanche Memorial Library, *see* Cathlamet Public Library, Cathlamet WA p. 2511

Bradley Public Library District, Bradley IL p. 597

Bradley University, Peoria IL p. 690

Bradner Eric J Library, *see* Schoolcraft College, Livonia MI p. 1204

Bradshaw H Grady Chambers County Library, Valley AL p. 39

Brady Library of the Health Sciences, *see* Mercy Hospital of Pittsburgh, Pittsburgh PA p. 2126

Braille Circulating Library, Inc, Richmond VA p. 2488

Braille Institute Library Services, Los Angeles CA p. 168

Braille Philosophers Library & Press, Santa Maria CA p. 265

Brainerd Memorial Library, Haddam CT p. 343

Brainerd Memorial Library, Danville VT p. 2422

Brainerd Public Library, Brainerd MN p. 1242

Braintree Historical Society, Inc Library, Braintree MA p. 1069

Braken Vera Library, *see* Medicine Hat College Library, Medicine Hat AB p. 2711

Brakensiek Clifton M Library, *see* County of Los Angeles Public Library, Bellflower CA p. 141

Bramlage Dorothy Public Library, Junction City KS p. 874

Bramley Jordan Library, Jordan NY p. 1648

Brammer R Iris Public Library, Narrows VA p. 2479

Brampton Library, Brampton ON p. 2796

Bramson Ort College, Forest Hills NY p. 1623

Branch District Library, Coldwater MI p. 1164

Modeste Bedient Memorial Library, *see* Branchport Library, Branchport NY p. 1584

Branchville Correctional Facility Library, Branchville IN p. 729

Brandeis School of Law Library, *see* University of Louisville Libraries, Louisville KY p. 926

Brandeis University Libraries, Waltham MA p. 1132

Brandel Library, *see* North Park University, Chicago IL p. 620

Brandley Theodore Library, *see* Stirling Municipal Library, Stirling AB p. 2718

Brandon Free Public Library, Brandon VT p. 2419

Brandon Public Library, Brandon MS p. 1294

Brandon Public Library, Brandon WI p. 2583

Brandon Regional Health Authority, Brandon MB p. 2747

Brandon Regional Library, *see* Tampa-Hillsborough County Public Library System, Brandon FL p. 497

Brandon Township Public Library, Ortonville MI p. 1215

Brandon University, Brandon MB p. 2747

Brandywine Community Library, Topton PA p. 2146

Brandywine Conservancy, Inc, Chadds Ford PA p. 2043

Brandywine Hospital & Trauma Center, Coatesville PA p. 2046

Brandywine Hundred Library, Wilmington DE p. 387

Brandywine River Museum Library, *see* Brandywine Conservancy, Inc, Chadds Ford PA p. 2043

Branford Public Library, *see* Suwannee River Regional Library, Branford FL p. 461

Branigan Thomas Memorial Library, Las Cruces NM p. 1557

Brannon Jackie Correctional Center Library, McAlester OK p. 1968

Brant Historical Society Library, Brantford ON p. 2796

Brantford Public Library, Brantford ON p. 2796

Brantigan Otto C Medical Library, *see* Saint Joseph Medical Center, Towson MD p. 1045

Brantley County Library, *see* Three Rivers Regional Library System, Nahunta GA p. 522

Brantley Nola Memorial Library, *see* Houston County Public Library System, Warner Robins GA p. 547

Brantley Public Library, Brantley AL p. 10

Braswell Memorial Public Library, Rocky Mount NC p. 1820

Brattleboro Memorial Hospital, Brattleboro VT p. 2419

Brattleboro Retreat, Brattleboro VT p. 2419

Braude William G Library, *see* Temple Beth El Congregation Sons of Israel & David, Providence RI p. 2175

Braun Research Library, *see* Autry National Center, Los Angeles CA p. 168

Brause Jack Library, *see* New York University, New York NY p. 1695

Brawley Public Library, Brawley CA p. 129

Bray Thomas Library, *see* Saint Paul's Episcopal Church, Washington DC p. 413

Brazil Public Library, Brazil IN p. 729

Brazoria County Law Library, Angleton TX p. 2275

Brazoria County Library System, Angleton TX p. 2275

Brazosport College Library, Lake Jackson TX p. 2352

Bread for the World Library, Washington DC p. 394

Breadalbane Public, *see* Prince Edward Island Public Library Service, Breadalbane PE p. 2876

Breathitt County Public Library, Jackson KY p. 919

Brechner Joseph L Research Center, *see* Orange County Regional History Center, Orlando FL p. 477

Breckenridge Library, Breckenridge TX p. 2291

Breckenridge Public Library, *see* Lake Agassiz Regional Library, Breckenridge MN p. 1266

Breckinridge County Public Library, Hardinsburg KY p. 915

Breckinridge Health Care Inc Library, Hyden KY p. 918

Breeden Memorial Library & Literacy Center, Leavenworth IN p. 761

Breene Dorothy M Memorial Library, *see* New Hampshire Hospital, Concord NH p. 1442

Brees Anton Carillon Library, *see* Bok Tower Gardens, Lake Wales FL p. 458

Breese Public Library, Breese IL p. 597

Brehm C E Memorial Public Library, Mount Vernon IL p. 677

Breitman Memorial Library, *see* Beverly Hospital, Montebello CA p. 189

Bremen Public Library, Bremen IN p. 729

Bremen Public Library, Bremen ME p. 978

Rushcreek Memorial, *see* Fairfield County District Library, Bremen OH p. 1908

Bremer Anne Memorial Library, *see* San Francisco Art Institute, San Francisco CA p. 244

Bremer Pond Memorial Library, Pittsburg NH p. 1462

Bremond Public Library & Visitors Center, Bremond TX p. 2291

Bren Del Win Centennial Library, Deloraine MB p. 2748

Brenau University, Gainesville GA p. 534

Brendle Thomas R Memorial Library & Museum, *see* Historic Schaefferstown, Inc, Schaefferstown PA p. 2136

Brendlinger Library, *see* Montgomery County Community College, Blue Bell PA p. 2036

Brengle Library, *see* Salvation Army School for Officer Training, Suffern NY p. 1750

Brenizer Public Library, Merna NE p. 1408

Brennan Law Library, *see* Thomas M Cooley Law School Libraries, Lansing MI p. 1202

Brennan Library, *see* Lasell College, Newton MA p. 1109

Brenner Library, *see* Congregation Emanuel Library, Denver CO p. 300

Brenner Library, *see* Quincy University, Quincy IL p. 693

Brent Centreville Public Library, Centreville AL p. 11

Brentwood Library, Pittsburgh PA p. 2121

Brentwood Library, Brentwood TN p. 2225

Brentwood Library, *see* Contra Costa County Library, Brentwood CA p. 209

Brentwood Public Library, Brentwood MO p. 1320

Brentwood Public Library, Brentwood NY p. 1584

Brescia University, Owensboro KY p. 931

Brescia University College Library, London ON p. 2816

Brethren in Christ Historical Library & Archives, *see* Messiah College, Grantham PA p. 2087

Breton Municipal Library, Breton AB p. 2686

Brevard College, Brevard NC p. 1777

Brevard Community College, Melbourne FL p. 463

Brevard Community College, Palm Bay FL p. 479

Brevard Community College, Titusville FL p. 500

Brevard Correctional Institution Library, *see* Florida Department of Corrections, Cocoa FL p. 433

Brevard County Law Library, *see* Brewer A Max Memorial Law Library, Viera FL p. 502

Brevard County Library System, Cocoa FL p. 433

Brevort Township Community, *see* Bayliss Public Library, Moran MI p. 1226

Brewer A Max Memorial Law Library, Viera FL p. 502

Brewer Albert P Library, *see* Calhoun Community College, Decatur AL p. 14

Brewer Jane Blain Memorial, *see* Pine Forest Regional Library, Mount Olive MS p. 1314

Brewer Public Library, Brewer ME p. 978

Brewer Public Library, Richland Center WI p. 2634

Brewers Association of Canada Library, Ottawa ON p. 2828

Brewster Ladies' Library Association, Brewster MA p. 1069

Brewster Library, *see* Essex County Historical Society, Elizabethtown NY p. 1618

Brewster Public Library, Brewster NY p. 1584

Brewster Public Library, *see* North Central Regional Library, Brewster WA p. 2548

Brewton-Parker College, Mount Vernon GA p. 546

Brewton Public Library, Brewton AL p. 10

Briar Cliff University, Sioux City IA p. 843

Briarcliff Manor Public Library, Briarcliff Manor NY p. 1585

Briarcliffe College Library, Bethpage NY p. 1581

Briargate Library, *see* Pikes Peak Library District, Colorado Springs CO p. 296

Briarwood Community Library, *see* Queens Borough Public Library, Briarwood NY p. 1644

Briceville Public Library, Briceville TN p. 2225

Brick Store Museum, Kennebunk ME p. 988

Brickell Edward E Medical Sciences Library, *see* Eastern Virginia Medical School, Norfolk VA p. 2481

Brickfield, Burchette, Ritts & Stone Law Library, Washington DC p. 394

Bridge Academy Public Library, Dresden ME p. 984

Bridge City Correctional Center for Youth Library, Bridge City LA p. 946

Bridge City Public Library, Bridge City TX p. 2291

Bridgenorth Library, *see* Smith-Ennismore-Lakefield Public Library, Bridgenorth ON p. 2797

Bridgepoint Health Clinical Library, Toronto ON p. 2850

Bridgeport Community, *see* North Central Regional Library, Bridgeport WA p. 2548

Bridgeport Hospital, Bridgeport CT p. 331

Bridgeport Law Library, *see* Connecticut Judicial Branch Law Libraries, Bridgeport CT p. 344

Bridgeport Public Library, Bridgeport CT p. 331

Bridgeport Public Library, Bridgeport MI p. 1159

Bridgeport Public Library, Bridgeport NE p. 1394

Bridgeport Public Library, Bridgeport TX p. 2291

Bridgeport Public Library, Bridgeport WV p. 2555

Bridger Memorial, *see* Bladen County Public Library, Bladenboro NC p. 1791

Bridger Public Library, Bridger MT p. 1375

Bridgestone Americas Center for Research & Technology, *see* Bridgestone/Firestone Research LLC, Akron OH p. 1852

Bridgestone/Firestone Research LLC, Akron OH p. 1852

Bridgeton Free Public Library, Bridgeton NJ p. 1474

Bridgeview Public Library, Bridgeview IL p. 597

Bridgeville Public Library, Bridgeville DE p. 381

Bridgeville Public Library, Bridgeville PA p. 2037

Bridgewater College, Bridgewater VA p. 2452

Bridgewater Free Library, Bridgewater NY p. 1585

Bridgewater Library Association, Bridgewater CT p. 332

Bridgewater Public Library, Bridgewater MA p. 1070

Bridgewater State College, Bridgewater MA p. 1070

Bridgewater Town Library, Plymouth NH p. 1462

Bridgman Public Library, Bridgman MI p. 1159

Bridgton Academy Library, North Bridgton ME p. 993

Bridgton Hospital, Bridgton ME p. 978

Bridgton Public Library, Bridgton ME p. 979

Bridwell Library, *see* Southern Methodist University, Dallas TX p. 2310

Bridwell Margaret Art Library, *see* University of Louisville Libraries, Louisville KY p. 926

Brielle Public Library, Brielle NJ p. 1475

Brier Community Library, *see* Sno-Isle Libraries, Brier WA p. 2542

Briercrest College & Seminary, Caronport SK p. 2917

Briger & Associates Library, New York NY p. 1671

Briggs & Morgan, Minneapolis MN p. 1259

Briggs Evelyn Goldberg Memorial Library, Iron River WI p. 2599

Briggs Hilton M Library, *see* South Dakota State University, Brookings SD p. 2210

Briggs Lawrence County Public Library, Ironton OH p. 1906

Briggs Public Library, Saint Johns MI p. 1225

Briggs Rodney A Library, *see* University of Minnesota-Morris, Morris MN p. 1267

Brigham & Women's Faulkner Hospital, Boston MA p. 1059

Brigham & Women's Hospital, Boston MA p. 1059

Brigham Carl Campbell Library, *see* Educational Testing Service, Princeton NJ p. 1522

Brigham City Library, Brigham City UT p. 2403

Brigham H F Free Public Library, Bakersfield VT p. 2417

Brigham Memorial Library, Sharon WI p. 2636

Brigham Young University, Provo UT p. 2411

Brigham Young University-Idaho, Rexburg ID p. 582

Brigham Young University-Hawaii, Laie HI p. 567

Brighton District Library, Brighton MI p. 1159

Brighton Memorial Library, Brighton IL p. 597

Brighton Memorial Library, Rochester NY p. 1728

Brighton Public Library, Brighton ON p. 2797

Brigus Public Library, Brigus NL p. 2769

Brill Abraham A Library, *see* New York Psychoanalytic Institute, New York NY p. 1690

Brill Jack Medical Library, *see* Saint John West Shore Hospital, Westlake OH p. 1947

Brillion Public Library, Brillion WI p. 2583

Brimfield Public Library, Brimfield IL p. 597

Brimfield Public Library, Brimfield MA p. 1070

Brimhall Grant R Library, *see* Thousand Oaks Library, Thousand Oaks CA p. 275

Brimley H H Memorial Library, *see* North Carolina State Museum of Natural Sciences, Raleigh NC p. 1816

Briner Library, *see* Central Christian College of Kansas, McPherson KS p. 883

Brinkerhoff Earth Resources Information Center, *see* University of Wyoming Libraries, Laramie WY p. 2658

Brinks, Hofer, Gilson & Lione, Chicago IL p. 607

Brinson Sr Lewis I Library, *see* Wiregrass Georgia Technical College, Fitzgerald GA p. 532

Brisbane Library, *see* San Mateo County Library, Brisbane CA p. 255

Briscoe Dolph Library, *see* University of Texas Health Science Center, San Antonio TX p. 2383

Bristol Area Library, Pemaquid ME p. 995

Bristol Bay Borough Libraries, Naknek AK p. 51

Bristol Community College, Fall River MA p. 1087

Bristol Historical Preservation Society Library, Bristol RI p. 2163

Bristol Hospital & Health Care Group, Bristol CT p. 332

Bristol Law Library, Taunton MA p. 1130

Bristol Library, Canandaigua NY p. 1601

Bristol Public Library, Bristol CT p. 332

Bristol Public Library, Bristolville OH p. 1861

Bristol Public Library, Bristol VA p. 2452

Bristol Regional Medical Center Library, Bristol TN p. 2225

Bristol-Washington Township Public Library, Bristol IN p. 729

Bristow Public Library, Bristow OK p. 1959

Britain Memorial, *see* Killgore Memorial Library, Sunray TX p. 2314

British Columbia College & Institute Library Services (N), Vancouver BC p. 2959

British Columbia Courthouse Library Society, Prince George BC p. 2736

British Columbia Genealogical Society, Surrey BC p. 2738

British Columbia Institute of Technology Library, Burnaby BC p. 2725

British Columbia Land Surveyors Foundation, Sidney BC p. 2737

British Columbia Legislative Library, Victoria BC p. 2744

British Columbia Library, *see* ALS Society of British Columbia, Vancouver BC p. 2740

British Columbia Ministry of Education, Victoria BC p. 2745

British Columbia Ministry of Energy & Mines, Victoria BC p. 2745

British Columbia Ministry of Forests Library, Victoria BC p. 2745

British Columbia Securities Commission, Vancouver BC p. 2740

Britt Area Library, Britt ON p. 2797

Britt Public Library, Britt IA p. 797

Brittain Library, *see* First Presbyterian Church of the Covenant, Erie PA p. 2055

Brittingham Harold H Memorial Library, *see* Metrohealth Medical Center, Cleveland OH p. 1880

Britton Public Library, Britton SD p. 2210

Broad Brook Public Library, Broad Brook CT p. 332

Broad Channel Community Library, *see* Queens Borough Public Library, Broad Channel NY p. 1644

Broad Robert Medical Library, *see* Cayuga Medical Center at Ithaca, Ithaca NY p. 1641

Broad Shepard Law Center Library, *see* Nova Southeastern University Libraries, Fort Lauderdale FL p. 444

Broadcast Pioneers Library, *see* University of Maryland Libraries, College Park MD p. 1025

Broadhurst Library, *see* Nazarene Theological Seminary, Kansas City MO p. 1340

Broadlawns Medical Center, Des Moines IA p. 808

Broadview Public Library District, Broadview IL p. 597

Broadwater School & Community Library, Townsend MT p. 1389

Broadway Community Library, *see* Queens Borough Public Library, Long Island City NY p. 1644

Brock Benjamin L Medical Library, *see* Holley A G State Hospital, Lantana FL p. 460

Brock Township Public Library, Beaverton ON p. 2794

Brock University, St. Catharines ON p. 2842

Brock William E Memorial Library, *see* Oklahoma State University Libraries, Stillwater OK p. 1978

Brockbridge Correctional Facility Library, Jessup MD p. 1033

Brockenbrough Eleanor S Library, *see* Museum of the Confederacy, Richmond VA p. 2489

Brockton Hospital Library, Brockton MA p. 1070

Brockton Law Library, *see* Commonwealth of Massachusetts - Trial Court, Brockton MA p. 1071

Brockton Public Library System, Brockton MA p. 1070

Brockville Public Library, Brockville ON p. 2797

Brockway Memorial Library, Miami Shores FL p. 470

Brodhead Memorial Public Library, Brodhead WI p. 2583

Brodsky Saul Jewish Community Library, Saint Louis MO p. 1353

Broken Bow Public Library, Broken Bow NE p. 1394

Broken Bow Public Library, Broken Bow OK p. 1959

Brokenhead River Regional Library, Beausejour MB p. 2747

Bromenn Healthcare, Normal IL p. 681

Bromfield Louis Library, *see* Ohio State University LIBRARIES, Mansfield OH p. 1887

Bronfman Peter F Business Library, *see* York University Libraries, Toronto ON p. 2868

Bronson Methodist Hospital, Kalamazoo MI p. 1196

Bronson Public, *see* Levy County Public Library System, Bronson FL p. 430

Bronson Public Library, Bronson KS p. 858

Bronson Silas Library, Waterbury CT p. 374

Bronx Community College Library & Learning Center, Bronx NY p. 1586

Bronx County Historical Society, Bronx NY p. 1586

Bronxville Public Library, Bronxville NY p. 1588

Brook-Iroquois-Washington Public Library, Brook IN p. 729

Brookdale Center Klau Library, *see* Hebrew Union College-Jewish Institute of Religion, New York NY p. 1681

Brookdale Community College, Lincroft NJ p. 1495

Brookdale University Medical Center, Brooklyn NY p. 1589

Brooke Army Medical Center Library, *see* United States Army, Fort Sam Houston TX p. 2320

Brooke County Public Library, Wellsburg WV p. 2574

Brooke-Gould Memorial, *see* Preble County District Library, Eaton OH p. 1897

Brunswick Public Library, Brunswick MO p. 1321

Brunswick Public Library, Brunswick NE p. 1395

Brunswick Public Library Association, Brunswick ME p. 979

Bruton Memorial Library, Plant City FL p. 484

Bruun Memorial Public Library, Humboldt NE p. 1402

Bruyere Continuing Care Library, Ottawa ON p. 2828

Bruyns Otto Public Library of Northfield, Northfield NJ p. 1515

Bryan-Bennett Library, Salem IL p. 700

Bryan Cave Law Library, Washington DC p. 395

Bryan Cave LLP, Santa Monica CA p. 265

Bryan Cave LLP, Saint Louis MO p. 1353

Bryan Cave LLP, New York NY p. 1671

Bryan College Library, Dayton TN p. 2232

Bryan College Station Public Library System, Bryan TX p. 2292

Bryan G Werber Psychiatric Hospital Library, Columbia SC p. 2187

Bryan-Lang Historical Library, Woodbine GA p. 557

Bryan Memorial, see Sampson-Clinton Public Library, Newton Grove NC p. 1784

Bryan Public Library, see Tombigbee Regional Library System, West Point MS p. 1317

BryanLGH College of the Health Sciences, Lincoln NE p. 1404

BryanLGH Medical Center Library, see BryanLGH College of the Health Sciences, Lincoln NE p. 1404

Bryant & Stratton Business College, Buffalo NY p. 1596

Bryant & Stratton College Library, Albany NY p. 1568

Bryant & Stratton College Library, Virginia Beach VA p. 2498

Bryant & Stratton College Library, Milwaukee WI p. 2617

Bryant Free Library, Cummington MA p. 1083

Bryant Jean Gould Library of Women's Study, see Florida State University Libraries, Tallahassee FL p. 494

Bryant Library, Roslyn NY p. 1735

Bryant Library, see Great River Regional Library, Sauk Centre MN p. 1274

Bryant Thelma Dingus Library, Wallace NC p. 1827

Bryant Tyrone, see Broward County Division of Libraries, Fort Lauderdale FL p. 441

Bryant University, Smithfield RI p. 2176

Bryn Athyn College, Bryn Athyn PA p. 2038

Bryn Mawr College, Bryn Mawr PA p. 2039

Bryn Mawr Hospital Library, Bryn Mawr PA p. 2039

Bryn Mawr Presbyterian Church, Bryn Mawr PA p. 2039

Bucci Joseph F Health Sciences Library, see Frick Hospital, Mount Pleasant PA p. 2093

Buchalter, Nemer, Los Angeles CA p. 169

Buchanan County Genealogical Society Library, Independence IA p. 822

Buchanan County Public Library, Grundy VA p. 2467

Buchanan District Library, Buchanan MI p. 1160

Buchanan-Haralson Public Library, see West Georgia Regional Library, Buchanan GA p. 524

Buchanan Ingersoll & Rooney PC, Philadelphia PA p. 2103

Buchanan Ingersoll PC, Washington DC p. 395

Buchanan James Foundation for the Preservation of Wheatland Library, Lancaster PA p. 2076

Buchanan Library, see Lethbridge College, Lethbridge AB p. 2709

Buck Consultants Knowledge Center, see Buck Consultants LLC, Secaucus NJ p. 1529

Buck Consultants LLC, Secaucus NJ p. 1529

Buck Memorial Library, Bucksport ME p. 980

Buck Pearl S Birthplace Foundation, Hillsboro WV p. 2560

Buckels Marvin Library, see Red Rocks Community College, Lakewood CO p. 315

Buckeye Public Library, Buckeye AZ p. 58

Buckham Memorial Library, Faribault MN p. 1250

Buckhead Library, see Atlanta-Fulton Public Library System, Atlanta GA p. 511

Buckingham Correctional Center, Dillwyn VA p. 2460

Buckingham County Public, see Central Virginia Regional Library, Dillwyn VA p. 2463

Buckland Public Library, Shelburne Falls MA p. 1123

Buckley Public Library, Poteau OK p. 1976

Bucklin Public Library, Bucklin KS p. 858

Buckman Laboratories International, Inc, Memphis TN p. 2248

Bucknell University, Lewisburg PA p. 2080

Bucks County Community College Library, Newtown PA p. 2097

Bucks County Courier Times Library, Levittown PA p. 2080

Bucks County Free Library, Doylestown PA p. 2050

Bucks County Historical Society, Doylestown PA p. 2050

Bucks County Law Library, Doylestown PA p. 2050

Bucyrus Public Library, Bucyrus OH p. 1862

Buda Public Library, Buda TX p. 2293

Budden W A Library, see University of Western States, Portland OR p. 2015

Bude Public Library, see Lincoln-Lawrence-Franklin Regional Library, Bude MS p. 1294

Budge O Cope Library, see Vanguard University of Southern California, Costa Mesa CA p. 137

Budimir Nikola Memorial, see Windsor Public Library, Windsor ON p. 2872

Budner William P Youth Library, see Temple Emanu-El, Dallas TX p. 2311

Buehler A C Library, see Elmhurst College, Elmhurst IL p. 642

Bueker John & Michele Research Library, see Saginaw Art Museum, Saginaw MI p. 1224

Buena Park Library District, Buena Park CA p. 129

Buena Vista Correctional Complex Library, Buena Vista CO p. 293

Buena Vista Minimum Center Library, see Colorado Department of Corrections, Buena Vista CO p. 293

Buena Vista Public, see Rockbridge Regional Library, Buena Vista VA p. 2474

Buena Vista Public Library, Buena Vista CO p. 293

Buena Vista University Library, Storm Lake IA p. 846

Buffalo & Erie County Public Library System, Buffalo NY p. 1596

Buffalo Bill Historical Center, Cody WY p. 2653

Buffalo Center Public Library, Buffalo Center IA p. 797

Buffalo Creek Memorial Library, Man WV p. 2564

Buffalo General Health System, Buffalo NY p. 1597

Buffalo History Museum Research Library, Buffalo NY p. 1597

Buffalo Library, see Great River Regional Library, Buffalo MN p. 1274

Buffalo Museum of Science, Buffalo NY p. 1597

Buffalo News Library, Buffalo NY p. 1597

Buffalo Public Library, Buffalo OK p. 1959

Buffalo Public Library, Buffalo TX p. 2293

Buffalo River Regional Library, Columbia TN p. 2231

Buhl Henry Library, see Grove City College, Grove City PA p. 2063

Buhl Library of Social Work, see University of Pittsburgh, Pittsburgh PA p. 2128

Buhl Public Library, Buhl ID p. 572

Buhl Public Library, Buhl MN p. 1243

Buhler Public Library, Buhler KS p. 859

Buisson Paul School of Architecture Reference Library, see University of Miami Libraries, Coral Gables FL p. 434

Buley Hilton C Library, see Southern Connecticut State University, New Haven CT p. 356

Buley Joe Memorial Library, Third Lake IL p. 709

Bull, Housser & Tupper Library, Vancouver BC p. 2740

Bull Run Regional, see Prince William Public Library System, Manassas VA p. 2486

Bull Shoals Library, Bull Shoals AR p. 96

Bullard Community Library, Bullard TX p. 2293

Bullard Sanford Memorial Library, Vassar MI p. 1233

Bullis George C Memorial Library, Maybrook NY p. 1659

Bullitt County Public Library, Shepherdsville KY p. 935

Bullitt Dorothy Stimson Library, see Seattle Art Museum, Seattle WA p. 2530

Bullivant, Houser & Bailey, Portland OR p. 2010

Bultema Memorial Library, see Grace Bible College, Grand Rapids MI p. 1184

Bulverde Area Rural Library District, Bulverde TX p. 2293

Buna Public Library, Buna TX p. 2293

Bunch Lila D Library, see Belmont University, Nashville TN p. 2255

Bunche Ralph J Center for African-American Studies Library, see University of California, Los Angeles, Los Angeles CA p. 179

Bunche Ralph J Library, see United States Department of State, Washington DC p. 419

Buncombe County Public Libraries, Asheville NC p. 1774

Bunker Hill Community College, Boston MA p. 1059

Bunker Hill Public Library District, Bunker Hill IL p. 598

Bunker Paul G Memorial Medical Library, see Avera Saint Luke's Hospital, Aberdeen SD p. 2209

Bunker Ruth Memorial Library, see Dacotah Prairie Museum, Aberdeen SD p. 2209

Bunkerville Library, see Las Vegas-Clark County Library District, Bunkerville NV p. 1429

Bunnvale Public Library, Califon NJ p. 1476

Bunting Library, see Newark United Methodist Church, Newark DE p. 385

Burbank Public Library, Burbank CA p. 130

Burch & Cracchiolo, Phoenix AZ p. 72

Burch Lucius E & Elsie C Library, Collierville TN p. 2230

Burchfield Charles E Archives & Library, see Burchfield Penney Art Center, Buffalo NY p. 1597

Burchfield Penney Art Center, Buffalo NY p. 1597

Burdett Community Library, Burdett KS p. 859

Bureau County Historical Society Museum & Library, Princeton IL p. 692

Bureau of Braille & Talking Book Library Services, Daytona Beach FL p. 435

Bureau of Economic Geology, see University of Texas Libraries, Austin TX p. 2283

Bureau of Labor Statistics, see United States Department of Labor, New York NY p. 1702

Bureau of Land Management, Ukiah CA p. 277

Bureau of Land Management, Craig CO p. 297

Bureau of Land Management, Salmon ID p. 583

Bureau of Land Management, North Bend OR p. 2008

Bureau of Land Management, Saint George UT p. 2411

Bureau of Land Management Library, Fairbanks AK p. 47

Bureau of Land Management Library, Denver CO p. 298

Bureau of Land Management Library, Winnemucca NV p. 1435

Bureau of Land Management Library, Vernal UT p. 2416

Bureau of National Affairs, Inc Library, Arlington VA p. 2449

Bureau of Prisons, El Reno OK p. 1962

Bureau of Prisons Federal Medical Center Library, see United States Department of Justice, Fort Worth TX p. 2324

Bureau of Reclamation Library, see United States Department of the Interior, Denver CO p. 303

Bureau of Topographic & Geologic Survey Library, see Pennsylvania Department of Conservation & Natural Resources, Middletown PA p. 2089

Burger Warren E Library, see William Mitchell College of Law, Saint Paul MN p. 1283

Burges Richard Regional, see El Paso Public Library, El Paso TX p. 2316

Burgess Marie Blair Library, see Spartanburg Methodist College, Spartanburg SC p. 2205

Burgettstown Community Library, Burgettstown PA p. 2039

Byron Public Library, Byron NE p. 1395
Byron Public Library District, Byron IL p. 598
Byzantine Catholic Seminary of Saints Cyril & Methodius Library, Pittsburgh PA p. 2122
C Berger Group, Inc Library, Carol Stream IL p. 601
C/W MARS (N), *see* Central & Western Massachusetts Automated Resource Sharing, Worcester MA p. 2945
Cabarrus County Public Library, Concord NC p. 1785
Cabarrus Health Sciences Library, *see* Northeast Medical Center, Concord NC p. 1785
Cabell County Public Library, Huntington WV p. 2561
Cabell James, *see* Virginia Commonwealth University Libraries, Richmond VA p. 2492
Cabot Godfrey Lowell Science Library, *see* Harvard Library, Cambridge MA p. 1074
Cabot Performance Materials Library, Boyertown PA p. 2037
Cabot Public Library, Cabot VT p. 2421
Cabrillo College, Aptos CA p. 121
Cabrillo Marine Aquarium Library, *see* Moore Virginia Reid Marine Research Library, San Pedro CA p. 256
Cabrillo National Monument Library, *see* United States National Park Service, San Diego CA p. 238
Cabrini College Library, Radnor PA p. 2132
Cachelin Mary Jane Library, *see* Virginia University of Lynchburg, Lynchburg VA p. 2476
Cachiaras G H Memorial Library, *see* Crossroads College, Rochester MN p. 1272
Cadbury Henry J Library, *see* Philadelphia Yearly Meeting of the Religious Society of Friends, Philadelphia PA p. 2115
Cade John B Library, *see* Southern University, Baton Rouge LA p. 944
Cadence Health - Central Dupage Hospital, Winfield IL p. 720
Cades Schutte, Honolulu HI p. 560
Cadillac-Wexford Public Library, Cadillac MI p. 1160
Cadott Community Library, Cadott WI p. 2584
Cadwalader, Wickersham & Taft, Washington DC p. 395
Cadwalader, Wickersham & Taft Library, New York NY p. 1671
Cady George P & Susan Platt Library, Nichols NY p. 1705
CAE, Inc, Saint Laurent QC p. 2909
CAE USA, Inc Library, Tampa FL p. 496
Caestecker Public Library, Green Lake WI p. 2596
Cagan Crossings Community Library, *see* Lake County Library System, Clermont FL p. 500
Cagle Lena Public Library, Bridgeport AL p. 11
Cahill, Gordon & Reindel Library, Washington DC p. 395
Cahill, Gordon & Reindel Library, New York NY p. 1671
Cahn Charles Library, *see* Douglas Mental Health University Institute, Montreal QC p. 2895
Cahokia Mounds State Historic Site Library, *see* Illinois Historic Preservation Agency, Collinsville IL p. 630
Cahokia Public Library District, Cahokia IL p. 599
Cahoon Museum of American Art, Cotuit MA p. 1083
Cain Pierce C Learning Resource Center, *see* Gadsden State Community College, Anniston AL p. 18
Cairn University, Langhorne PA p. 2078
Cairo Public Library, Cairo IL p. 599
Cairo Public Library, Cairo NY p. 1600
CAL Information Center, *see* Canada Agriculure & Agri Food Canada, Saint-Hyacinthe QC p. 2910
Calabasas Public Library, *see* City of Calabasas Library, Calabasas CA p. 131
Calais Free Library, Calais ME p. 980
Calaveras County Law Library, San Andreas CA p. 226
Calaveras County Library, San Andreas CA p. 226
CALC (N), *see* Charleston Academic Libraries Consortium, Charleston SC p. 2955

Calcasieu Parish Public Library, Lake Charles LA p. 953
CALCO (N), *see* Capital Area Library Consortium, Saint Paul MN p. 2946
Calder Louis Memorial Library, *see* University of Miami, Miami FL p. 469
Calderone Mary S Library, *see* SIECUS, New York NY p. 1700
Caldwell College, Caldwell NJ p. 1476
Caldwell Community College & Technical Institute, Hudson NC p. 1803
Caldwell County Public Library, Lenoir NC p. 1806
Caldwell-Lake George Library, Lake George NY p. 1650
Caldwell Memorial, *see* Adams Memorial Library, Derry PA p. 2079
Caldwell Parish Library, Columbia LA p. 947
Caldwell Public Library, Caldwell ID p. 572
Caldwell Public Library, Caldwell KS p. 859
Caldwell Public Library, Caldwell NJ p. 1476
Caldwell Public Library, Caldwell OH p. 1863
Caledon Public Library, Bolton ON p. 2795
Caledonia Library, Caledonia NY p. 1600
Caledonia Public, *see* Columbus-Lowndes Public Library, Caledonia MS p. 1297
Caledonia Public Library, Caledonia MN p. 1243
Calef Memorial Library, Washington VT p. 2438
Calera Public Library, Calera AL p. 11
Calgary Academy Library, Calgary AB p. 2688
Calgary Board of Education, Calgary AB p. 2688
Calgary Health Region, Calgary AB p. 2688
Calgary Herald Library, Calgary AB p. 2688
Calgary Public Library, Calgary AB p. 2688
Calhoun Alexander, *see* Calgary Public Library, Calgary AB p. 2689
Calhoun Community College, Decatur AL p. 14
Calhoun Correction Institution Library, Blountstown FL p. 427
Calhoun County Library, Hampton AR p. 102
Calhoun County Library, Saint Matthews SC p. 2204
Calhoun County Library, Port Lavaca TX p. 2371
Calhoun County Library, *see* Kinchafoonee Regional Library System, Edison GA p. 528
Calhoun County Museum & Cultural Center, Saint Matthews SC p. 2204
Calhoun County Public Library, Blountstown FL p. 427
Calhoun County Public Library, Grantsville WV p. 2560
Calhoun-Gordon County Library, *see* Northwest Georgia Regional Library System, Calhoun GA p. 528
Calhoun Memorial Library, Chetek WI p. 2585
Calhoun Public Library, Calhoun TN p. 2226
Calhoun State Prison, *see* Georgia Department of Corrections, Morgan GA p. 545
CALICO (N), *see* Columbus Area Library & Information Council of Ohio, Westerville OH p. 2952
Califa (N), San Mateo CA p. 2938
California Academy of Sciences Library, San Francisco CA p. 240
California Area Public Library, California PA p. 2040
California Baptist University, Riverside CA p. 216
California Christian College, Fresno CA p. 150
California College of the Arts Libraries, Oakland CA p. 196
California Court of Appeal, San Diego CA p. 230
California Court of Appeal Fifth Appellate District Library, Fresno CA p. 150
California Court of Appeal Third Appellate District Library, Sacramento CA p. 220
California Department of Alcohol & Drug Programs, Sacramento CA p. 220
California Department of Corrections, Norco CA p. 194
California Department of Corrections Library System, Sacramento CA p. 220
California Department of Justice, Sacramento CA p. 222
California Department of Justice Library, San Diego CA p. 230
California Energy Commission Library, Sacramento CA p. 222

California Environmental Protection Agency Public Library, Sacramento CA p. 222
California Highway Patrol, Sacramento CA p. 222
California Historical Society, San Francisco CA p. 240
California Hospital Medical Center Los Angeles, Los Angeles CA p. 169
California Institute of Integral Studies, San Francisco CA p. 240
California Institute of Technology, Pasadena CA p. 205, 206
California Institute of the Arts, Valencia CA p. 278
California Institution for Men, *see* California Department of Corrections Library System, Chino CA p. 221
California Institution for Women, *see* California Department of Corrections Library System, Corona CA p. 221
California Lutheran University, Thousand Oaks CA p. 274
California Maritime Academy Library, Vallejo CA p. 278
California Men's Colony-West, *see* California Department of Corrections Library System, San Luis Obispo CA p. 221
California Men's Colony-East, *see* California Department of Corrections Library System, San Luis Obispo CA p. 221
California Pacific Medical Center, San Francisco CA p. 241
California Polytechnic State University, San Luis Obispo CA p. 253
California Province of the Society of Jesus, Los Gatos CA p. 180
California Regional Water Quality Control Board, Oakland CA p. 196
California Rehabilitation Center Library, *see* California Department of Corrections, Norco CA p. 194
California School for the Blind, Fremont CA p. 149
California School for the Deaf Library, Riverside CA p. 216
California Second District Court of Appeals, Los Angeles CA p. 169
California State Archives, Sacramento CA p. 222
California State Board of Equalization, Sacramento CA p. 222
California State Court of Appeal, Riverside CA p. 216
California State Department of Corporations Library, Sacramento CA p. 222
California State Department of Food & Agriculture, Sacramento CA p. 222
California State Department of Health Services, Oakland CA p. 196
California State Department of Transportation, Sacramento CA p. 222
California State Department of Water Resources, Sacramento CA p. 223
California State Legislative Counsel, Sacramento CA p. 223
California State Library, Sacramento CA p. 223
California State Library, San Francisco CA p. 241
California State Polytechnic University Library, Pomona CA p. 211
California State Prison, Los Angeles County, *see* California Department of Corrections Library System, Lancaster CA p. 221
California State Prison, Sacramento Inmate Library, *see* California Department of Corrections Library System, Represa CA p. 221
California State Prison-Solano, *see* California Department of Corrections Library System, Vacaville CA p. 221
California State Railroad Museum Library, Sacramento CA p. 223
California State University, Baker CA p. 123
California State University, Bakersfield CA p. 123
California State University, Moss Landing CA p. 192
California State University, San Marcos CA p. 254
California State University, Chico, Chico CA p. 133
California State University Dominguez Hills, Carson CA p. 132

Canada Department of Justice, Edmonton AB p. 2699

Canada Department of Justice, Vancouver BC p. 2740

Canada Department of Justice Library, Ottawa ON p. 2828

Canada Department of Justice Montreal Headquarters Library, Montreal QC p. 2892

Canada Department of National Defence, Dartmouth NS p. 2779

Canada Department of National Defence, Halifax NS p. 2780

Canada Department of National Defence, Borden ON p. 2796

Canada Industrial Relations Board Library, Ottawa ON p. 2828

Canada Institute for Scientific & Technical Information, Penticton BC p. 2735

Canada/Manitoba Business Service Centre, Winnipeg MB p. 2754

Canada-Newfoundland Offshore Petroleum Board Library, St. John's NL p. 2771

Canada School of Public Service Library, Gatineau QC p. 2882

Canada Science & Technology Museum, Ottawa ON p. 2829

Canaday Mariam Coffin Library, see Bryn Mawr College, Bryn Mawr PA p. 2039

Canadian Agriculture Library, Lacombe AB p. 2708

Canadian Agriculture Library, see Agriculture & Agri-Food Canada, Ottawa ON p. 2827

Canadian Agriculture Library, see Agriculture & Agri-Food Canada, Charlottetown PE p. 2875

Canadian Agriculture Library-Fredericton, Fredericton NB p. 2762

Canadian Agriculture Library-Harrow, Harrow ON p. 2811

Canadian Agriculture Library-Lethbridge, see Agriculture & Agri-Food Canada, Lethbridge AB p. 2709

Canadian Agriculture Library, see Canada Agriculture & Agri-Food Canada, Saskatoon SK p. 2925

Canadian Agriculture Library - Summerland, Summerland BC p. 2738

Canadian Agriculture Library-Winnipeg, Winnipeg MB p. 2754

Canadian Arab Federation Library, Scarborough ON p. 2840

Canadian Artists' Representation, Ottawa ON p. 2829

Canadian Association of Occupational Therapists, Ottawa ON p. 2829

Canadian Association of Research Libraries (N), Ottawa ON p. 2959

Canadian Baptist Archives, Hamilton ON p. 2808

Canadian Bible Society Library, Toronto ON p. 2850

Canadian Broadcasting Corp, Toronto ON p. 2850

Canadian Centre for Ecumenism Library, Montreal QC p. 2892

Canadian Centre for Occupational Health & Safety (CCOHS), Hamilton ON p. 2808

Canadian Child Care Federation, Ottawa ON p. 2829

Canadian Coast Guard College Library, see Canada Department of Fisheries & Oceans, Sydney NS p. 2784

Canadian Conservation Institute Library, see Department of Canadian Heritage, Ottawa ON p. 2830

Canadian Consulate General Library, New York NY p. 1671

Canadian Copper & Brass Development Association Library, North York ON p. 2825

Canadian County Historical Museum Library, El Reno OK p. 1962

Canadian Dental Association Resource Centre, Ottawa ON p. 2829

Canadian Environmental Law Association, Toronto ON p. 2851

Canadian Federation of Independent Business, Toronto ON p. 2851

Canadian Forces College, Toronto ON p. 2851

Canadian Forces Health Services Group Headquarters Library, Ottawa ON p. 2829

Canadian Forces Health Services Training Centre, see Canada Department of National Defence, Borden ON p. 2796

Canadian Foundation for Children, Youth & the Law, Toronto ON p. 2851

Canadian Foundation for the Study of Infant Deaths Library, St. Catharines ON p. 2843

Canadian Friends of Soviet People Library, Toronto ON p. 2851

Canadian Grain Commission Library, Winnipeg MB p. 2754

Canadian Health Libraries Association (N), Toronto ON p. 2959

Canadian Heritage Information Network (N), Gatineau QC p. 2960

Canadian Institute of Chartered Accountants, Toronto ON p. 2851

Canadian Institute of Resources Law, Calgary AB p. 2691

Canadian Intellectual Property Office, see Industry Canada, Gatineau QC p. 2883

Canadian International Development Agency, Gatineau QC p. 2882

Canadian International Trade Tribunal Library, Ottawa ON p. 2829

Canadian Jewish Congress Charities Committee, Montreal QC p. 2892

Canadian Lesbian & Gay Archives, Toronto ON p. 2851

Canadian Library of Family Medicine, see Library Service of the College of Family Physicians of Canada, London ON p. 2817

Canadian Life & Health Insurance Association, Inc, Toronto ON p. 2851

Canadian Lutheran Bible Institute, Camrose AB p. 2694

Canadian Medical Association, Ottawa ON p. 2829

Canadian Memorial Chiropractic College, Toronto ON p. 2851

Canadian Mennonite University Library, Winnipeg MB p. 2754

Canadian Mental Health Association, Windsor ON p. 2871

Canadian Museum of Civilization Library, Gatineau QC p. 2883

Canadian Museum of Nature Library & Archives, Ottawa ON p. 2829

Canadian Music Centre, Toronto ON p. 2851

Canadian National Exhibition Archives, Toronto ON p. 2852

Canadian National Institute for the Blind, Toronto ON p. 2852

Canadian Nuclear Safety Commission Library, Ottawa ON p. 2829

Canadian Opera Co, Toronto ON p. 2852

Canadian Pacific Railway, Calgary AB p. 2691

Canadian Paraplegic Association, Winnipeg MB p. 2754

Canadian Paraplegic Association Library, Ottawa ON p. 2829

Canadian Police College Library, Ottawa ON p. 2829

Canadian Radio-Television & Telecommunications Commission Library, Ottawa ON p. 2830

Canadian Reformed Theological Seminary Library, see Theological College of the Canadian Reformed Churches Library, Hamilton ON p. 2811

Canadian Research Knowledge Network (N), Ottawa ON p. 2959

Canadian Royal Heritage Trust, Toronto ON p. 2852

Canadian Tax Foundation, Toronto ON p. 2852

Canadian Transportation Agency Library, Gatineau QC p. 2883

Canadian University College Library, Lacombe AB p. 2708

Canadian Urban Transit Association Library, Toronto ON p. 2852

Canadian War Museum, Ottawa ON p. 2830

Canadian Wildlife Federation, Kanata ON p. 2812

Canadian Zionist Federation, Montreal QC p. 2892

Canajoharie Library & Art Gallery, Canajoharie NY p. 1601

Canal Fulton Public Library, Canal Fulton OH p. 1863

Canal Society of New Jersey, Stanhope NJ p. 1532

Canastota Public Library, Canastota NY p. 1601

Canby Public Library, Canby MN p. 1244

Canby Public Library, Canby OR p. 1993

CancerCare Manitoba Library, Winnipeg MB p. 2755

Candler Medical Library, see Saint Joseph's-Candler, Savannah GA p. 550

Candler Scott, see DeKalb County Public Library, Decatur GA p. 529

Cando Community Library, Cando ND p. 1839

Candor Free Library, Candor NY p. 1602

Caney City Library, Caney KS p. 859

Canfield Martha Memorial Free Library, Arlington VT p. 2417

Canisius College, Buffalo NY p. 1597

Canizaro Library at Ave Maria University, Ave Maria FL p. 426

Canmore Public Library, Canmore AB p. 2694

Cannavino James A Library, see Marist College, Poughkeepsie NY p. 1722

Cannell Lewis D Library, see Clark College, Vancouver WA p. 2545

Cannelton Public Library, Cannelton IN p. 731

Cannon Beach Library, Cannon Beach OR p. 1993

Cannon County Library System, Woodbury TN p. 2269

Cannon Falls Library, Cannon Falls MN p. 1244

Cannon Free Library, Delhi NY p. 1613

Cannon Memorial Library, see Saint Leo University, Saint Leo FL p. 487

Canon City Public Library, Canon City CO p. 293

Canonie Marialyce Great Lakes Research Library, see Michigan Maritime Museum, South Haven MI p. 1227

Canterbury Public Library, Canterbury CT p. 333

Canton Free Library, Canton NY p. 1602

Canton Historical Society Library, Collinsville CT p. 334

Canton Historical Society Library, Canton MA p. 1079

Canton Museum of Art Library, Canton OH p. 1863

Canton Public Library, Canton CT p. 333

Canton Public Library, Canton MA p. 1079

Canton Public Library, Canton MI p. 1160

Canton Public Library, Canton MO p. 1321

Canton Public Library, Canton SD p. 2211

Canton Public Library, see Madison County Library System, Canton MS p. 1295

Canton Township Library, Canton KS p. 859

Cantor Rubin Kaplan Memorial Library, see Congregation Beth Yeshurun, Houston TX p. 2334

Cantor Ted Cotler Memorial Library, see Temple Isaiah, Lafayette CA p. 163

Cantril Public Library, Cantril IA p. 798

Cantwell Community-School Library, Cantwell AK p. 46

Canwood Public Library, see Wapiti Regional Library, Canwood SK p. 2921

Canyon Area Library, Canyon TX p. 2294

Canyon Country Jo Anne Darcy Library, see Santa Clarita Public Library, Santa Clarita CA p. 263

Canyon de Chelly National Monument Library, see National Park Service, Chinle AZ p. 60

Canyon Lake Community Church Library, Canyon Lake CA p. 131

Canyon Lake Library, see Riverside County Library System, Canyon Lake CA p. 217

Canyon Owyhee Library Group, Ltd (N), Marsing ID p. 2941

Capac Public, see Saint Clair County Library System, Capac MI p. 1219

Cape Ann Museum Library/Archives, Gloucester MA p. 1091

Cape Breton District Health Authority, Sydney NS p. 2784

Cape Breton Regional Library, Sydney NS p. 2785

Cape Breton University Library, Sydney NS p. 2785

Cape Canaveral Public Library, Cape Canaveral FL p. 431

Cape Cod Community College, West Barnstable MA p. 1136

Cape Cod Hospital, Hyannis MA p. 1096

Carney Claire T Library, *see* University of Massachusetts Dartmouth Library, North Dartmouth MA p. 1112

Caro Area District Library, Caro MI p. 1161

Carol Stream Public Library, Carol Stream IL p. 601

Carolina Library Services, Inc, Chapel Hill NC p. 1780

Carolina Population Center Library, Chapel Hill NC p. 1780

Caroline County Public Library, Denton MD p. 1027

Caroline Library Inc, Milford VA p. 2479

Caroline Municipal Library, Caroline AB p. 2694

Carondelet Saint Mary's Hospital, Tucson AZ p. 86

Carp Lake Township Library, White Pine MI p. 1237

Carpenter Alma M Public Library, Sourlake TX p. 2388

Carpenter-Carse Library, Hinesburg VT p. 2425

Carpenter Coy C School of Medicine, *see* Wake Forest University, Winston-Salem NC p. 1834

Carpenter Dr Robert Memorial Library, *see* North Adams Regional Hospital, North Adams MA p. 1111

Carpenter Elizabeth Public Library of New Hope, *see* Huntsville-Madison Public Library, New Hope AL p. 21

Carpenter Josiah Library, Pittsfield NH p. 1462

Carpenter Juanita Library, *see* Oak Grove Lutheran Church, Richfield MN p. 1272

Carpenter Library, *see* South Piedmont Community College, Monroe NC p. 1815

Carpenter Memorial Library, Cle Elum WA p. 2512

Carpenter Rhys Library for Art, Archaeology & Cities, *see* Bryn Mawr College, Bryn Mawr PA p. 2039

Carpenter Technology Corp, Reading PA p. 2133

Carpenter Thomas G Library, *see* University of North Florida, Jacksonville FL p. 455

Carr Emily, *see* Greater Victoria Public Library Board, Victoria BC p. 2745

Carr Emily Institute of Art & Design Library, Vancouver BC p. 2740

Carr Health Sciences Library, *see* Somerville Hospital, Somerville MA p. 1124

Carr Research Laboratory, Inc Library, Natick MA p. 1107

Carrabassett Valley Library, Carrabassett ME p. 981

Carraway Gertrude Research Library, *see* Tryon Palace, New Bern NC p. 1812

Carrell Brandon Medical Library, *see* Texas Scottish Rite Hospital, Dallas TX p. 2311

Carriage Museum of America Library, Lexington KY p. 920

Carrico Philip N, *see* Campbell County Public Library District, Fort Thomas KY p. 909

Carrier Mills-Stonefort Public Library District, Carrier Mills IL p. 601

Carrington City Library, Carrington ND p. 1839

Carroll & Madison Library System, Berryville AR p. 95

Carroll, Burdick & McDonough, San Francisco CA p. 241

Schoerner Roger Technical Library, *see* West Georgia Technical College, Carrollton GA p. 556

Carroll College, Helena MT p. 1381

Carroll College, Waukesha WI p. 2644

Carroll Community College, Westminster MD p. 1045

Carroll County District Library, Carrollton OH p. 1865

Carroll County Farm Museum, Westminster MD p. 1045

Carroll County Library, Huntingdon TN p. 2237

Carroll County Public, *see* Galax-Carroll Regional Library, Hillsville VA p. 2466

Carroll County Public Library, Carrollton KY p. 909

Carroll County Public Library, Westminster MD p. 1045

Carroll Medical Library, *see* University of Arkansas for Medical Sciences, El Dorado AR p. 98

Carroll Public Library, Carroll IA p. 798

Carroll Public Library, Carroll NE p. 1395

Carrollton-North Carrollton Public Library, Carrollton MS p. 1295

Carrollton Public, *see* Blackwater Regional Library, Carrollton VA p. 2458

Carrollton Public Library, Carrollton AL p. 11

Carrollton Public Library, Carrollton IL p. 601

Carrollton Public Library, Carrollton MO p. 1322

Carrollton Public Library, Carrollton TX p. 2295

Carrolltown Public Library, Carrolltown PA p. 2042

Carrot River Public Library, *see* Wapiti Regional Library, Carrot River SK p. 2921

Carruthers Center for Inner City Studies, *see* Northeastern Illinois University, Chicago IL p. 621

Carson City Correctional Facility Library, *see* Michigan Department of Corrections, Carson City MI p. 1161

Carson City Hospital, Carson City MI p. 1161

Carson City Library, Carson City NV p. 1425

Carson City Public Library, Carson City MI p. 1161

Carson County Public Library, Panhandle TX p. 2368

Carson James H Library, *see* Lees-McRae College, Banner Elk NC p. 1775

Carson Lucy Memorial Library, *see* University of Montana Western, Dillon MT p. 1378

Carson Nancy, *see* Aiken-Bamberg-Barnwell-Edgefield Regional Library System, North Augusta SC p. 2179

Carson-Newman College, Jefferson City TN p. 2239

Carson Rachel Council, Inc Library, Silver Spring MD p. 1041

Carson-Tahoe Regional Medical Center, Carson City NV p. 1425

Carson W O, *see* London Public Library, London ON p. 2818

Carstairs Public Library, Carstairs AB p. 2694

Carter Amon Museum of American Art, Fort Worth TX p. 2321

Carter County Library District, Van Buren MO p. 1370

Carter G Emmett Cardinal Library, *see* King's University College, London ON p. 2817

Carter James Earl Library, *see* Georgia Southwestern State University, Americus GA p. 508

Carter Jimmy Presidential Library & Museum, *see* National Archives & Records Administration, Atlanta GA p. 517

Carter Larue D Memorial Hospital, Indianapolis IN p. 749

Carter, Ledyard & Milburn Library, New York NY p. 1671

Carter Library, *see* Ivy Tech Community College, Evansville IN p. 738

Carter Library, *see* Maryland Department of Natural Resources, Annapolis MD p. 1010

Carter Memorial Library, *see* Omro Public Library, Omro WI p. 2627

Carter Music Resources Center, *see* Louisiana State University Libraries, Baton Rouge LA p. 943

Carter Walter P Library, *see* Sojourner-Douglass College, Baltimore MD p. 1017

Carteret Community College Library, Morehead City NC p. 1810

Carteret County Public Library, Beaufort NC p. 1776

Carteret Public Library, Carteret NJ p. 1478

Carthage College, Kenosha WI p. 2601

Carthage Free Library, Carthage NY p. 1603

Carthage Library, *see* Henley Henry Public Library, Carthage IN p. 731

Carthage Public Library, Carthage MO p. 1322

Carthage Public Library District, Carthage IL p. 601

Cartographic Information Center, *see* Louisiana State University Libraries, Baton Rouge LA p. 943

Cartwright Arthur LRC Library, *see* Wayne County Community College District, Detroit MI p. 1172

Carus Chemical Co, La Salle IL p. 662

Caruth Mabel Peters Learning Resource Center, *see* Baylor University Libraries, Dallas TX p. 2396

Caruthersville Public Library, Caruthersville MO p. 1322

Carver Bible College Library, Atlanta GA p. 514

Carver County Historical Society Library, Waconia MN p. 1287

Carver County Library, Chaska MN p. 1245

Carver George Washington Library, *see* Sheppard Memorial Library, Greenville NC p. 1799

Carver George Washington National Monument Library, *see* United States National Park Service, Diamond MO p. 1327

Carver Homes Library, *see* Atlanta-Fulton Public Library System, Atlanta GA p. 511

Carver Joyce Memorial Library, *see* Soldotna Public Library, Soldotna AK p. 54

Carver Public Library, Carver MA p. 1079

Cary Area Public Library District, Cary IL p. 601

Cary Institute of Ecosystem Studies Library, Millbrook NY p. 1661

Cary Library, Houlton ME p. 988

Cary Medical Center, Caribou ME p. 981

Cary Memorial Library, Wayne ME p. 1006

Cary Memorial Library, Lexington MA p. 1099

Caryville Public Library, Caryville TN p. 2226

Casa Blanca Library & Family Learning Center, *see* Riverside Public Library, Riverside CA p. 218

Casa Grande Public Library, Casa Grande AZ p. 59

Casa Grande Valley Historical Society, Casa Grande AZ p. 59

Cascade County Historical Society Archives, Great Falls MT p. 1379

Cascade Foothills Library, Dexter OR p. 1995

Cascade Park Community Library, *see* Fort Vancouver Regional Library District, Vancouver WA p. 2546

Cascade Public Library, Cascade ID p. 572

Cascade Public Library, Cascade IA p. 799

Casco Public Library, Casco ME p. 981

Case Everett Needham Library, *see* Colgate University, Hamilton NY p. 1633

Case Memorial Library, Orange CT p. 364

Case Memorial Library, Kenduskeag ME p. 988

Case Western Reserve University, Cleveland OH p. 1875

Casemate Museum Library, Fort Monroe VA p. 2465

Casey County Public Library, Liberty KY p. 922

Casey Memorial Library, *see* United States Army, Fort Hood TX p. 2320

Casey Public Library, Casey IA p. 799

Casey Township Library, Casey IL p. 602

Caseyville Public Library District, Caseyville IL p. 602

Cash Joseph Harper Memorial Library, *see* American Indian Research Project, Vermillion SD p. 2220

Cashmere Community, *see* North Central Regional Library, Cashmere WA p. 2548

Cashton Memorial Library, Cashton WI p. 2584

Casper College, Casper WY p. 2651

Cass County Public Library, Harrisonville MO p. 1330

Cass District Library, Cassopolis MI p. 1161

Cass Lake Community Library, Cass Lake MN p. 1244

Cass Libbie A Memorial Library, Springfield NH p. 1465

Cassels, Brock & Blackwell Library, Toronto ON p. 2852

Casselton Public Library, Casselton ND p. 1839

Cassville Public Library, *see* Eckstein Memorial Library, Cassville WI p. 2584

Castell W R Central Library, *see* Calgary Public Library, Calgary AB p. 2689

Castillo De San Marcos & Fort Matanzas National Monuments, Saint Augustine FL p. 486

Castle Rock Public Library, Castle Rock WA p. 2511

Castlegar & District Public Library, Castlegar BC p. 2726

Castleton Free Library, Castleton VT p. 2421

Castleton Public Library, Castleton-on-Hudson NY p. 1603

Castleton State College, Castleton VT p. 2421

Castlewood Xpress Library, *see* Arapahoe Library District, Centennial CO p. 305

Castor Municipal Library, Castor AB p. 2694

Castroville Public Library, Castroville TX p. 2295

Caswell Learning Resources Center, *see* Piedmont Community College, Yanceyville NC p. 1821

Catahoula Parish Library, Harrisonburg LA p. 950

Catalina Public Library, Catalina NL p. 2769

The Center - Resources for Teaching & Learning Library, Arlington Heights IL p. 589

Centerburg Public Library, Centerburg OH p. 1866

Centers for Disease Control, Cincinnati OH p. 1868

Centers for Disease Control & Prevention, Atlanta GA p. 514

Centers for Disease Control & Prevention Public Health Library & Information Center, Morgantown WV p. 2566

Centerville-Center Township Public Library, Centerville IN p. 731

Centerville Community Library, Centerville SD p. 2211

Centerville Public Library Association, Inc, Centerville MA p. 1079

Centinela Hospital Medical Center, Inglewood CA p. 159

Centinela State Prison, see California Department of Corrections Library System, Imperial CA p. 221

Central & Western Massachusetts Automated Resource Sharing (N), Worcester MA p. 2945

Central Alabama Community College, Alexander City AL p. 3

Central Arizona College, Apache Junction AZ p. 57

Central Arizona College, Coolidge AZ p. 60

Central Arizona College, Winkelman AZ p. 90

Central Arkansas Library System, Little Rock AR p. 106

Central Arkansas Veterans Healthcare System, Little Rock AR p. 106

Central Baptist College, Conway AR p. 96

Central Baptist Hospital Library, Lexington KY p. 920

Central Baptist Theological Seminary, Shawnee KS p. 894

Central Bible College, Springfield MO p. 1366

Central Brevard Library & Reference Center, Cocoa FL p. 433

Central California Women's Facility, see California Department of Corrections Library System, Chowchilla CA p. 221

Central Carolina Community College, Sanford NC p. 1823

Central Carolina Technical College Library, Sumter SC p. 2206

Central Christian Church Library, Lexington KY p. 920

Central Christian College of Kansas, McPherson KS p. 883

Central Christian College of the Bible Library, Moberly MO p. 1345

Central Citizens' Library District, Clifton IL p. 630

Central City Public Library, Central City NE p. 1395

Central College, Pella IA p. 838

Central Community College, Columbus NE p. 1396

Central Community College, Grand Island NE p. 1400

Central Community College, Hastings Campus, Hastings NE p. 1401

Central Connecticut State University, New Britain CT p. 353

Central Dakota Library Network (N), Mandan ND p. 2951

Central Delaware Library Consortium (N), Dover DE p. 2939

Central Florida Community College, Ocala FL p. 473

Central Florida Library Cooperative (N), Maitland FL p. 2940

Central Florida Reception Center, Orlando FL p. 475

Central Georgia Technical College Library, Macon GA p. 540

Central Great Plains Research Station Library, see USDA Agricultural Research Service, Akron CO p. 287

Central Indiana Health Science Libraries Consortium (N), Indianapolis IN p. 2942

Central Islip Public Library, Central Islip NY p. 1604

Central Kansas Library System, Great Bend KS p. 869

Central Lake District Library, Central Lake MI p. 1162

Central Lakes College Library, Brainerd MN p. 1242

Central Louisiana Medical Center Library Consortium (N), Alexandria LA p. 2944

Central Louisiana State Hospital, Pineville LA p. 965

Central Lutheran Church Library, Minneapolis MN p. 1259

Central Maine Technical College Library, Auburn ME p. 974

Central Maine Medical Center, Lewiston ME p. 989

Central Manitoulin Public Libraries, Mindemoya ON p. 2822

Central Methodist College, Fayette MO p. 1327

Central Michigan University, Mount Pleasant MI p. 1211

Central Minnesota Libraries Exchange (N), Saint Cloud MN p. 2946

Central Mississippi Correctional Facility Library, see Mississippi Department of Corrections, Pearl MS p. 1311

Central Mississippi Library Council (N), Jackson MS p. 2947

Central Mississippi Medical Center, Jackson MS p. 1303

Central Mississippi Regional Library System, Brandon MS p. 1294

Central Nevada Museum & Historical Society, Tonopah NV p. 1434

Central New Mexico Community College Libraries, Albuquerque NM p. 1548

Central New York Library Resources Council (N), Syracuse NY p. 2950

Central New York Regional Planning & Development Board, Syracuse NY p. 1751

Central Ohio Hospital Library Consortium (N), Columbus OH p. 2951

Central Oklahoma Juvenile Center Library, Tecumseh OK p. 1980

Central 1 Credit Union Corporate Information Centre, Vancouver BC p. 2740

Central Oregon Community College Barber Library, Bend OR p. 1991

Central Pennsylvania College Library, Summerdale PA p. 2144

Central Pennsylvania Consortium (N), Carlisle PA p. 2953

Central Pennsylvania District Library Center, see Centre County Library & Historical Museum, Bellefonte PA p. 2032

Central Pennsylvania Health Sciences Library Association (N), University Park PA p. 2953

Central Piedmont Community College Library, Charlotte NC p. 1781

Central Presbyterian Church Library, Terre Haute IN p. 781

Central Presbyterian Church Library, Kansas City MO p. 1337

Central Rappahannock Regional Library, Fredericksburg VA p. 2465

Central Regional Integrated Health Authority, Gander NL p. 2770

Central Square Library, Central Square NY p. 1605

Central State University, Wilberforce OH p. 1948

Central Texas College, Killeen TX p. 2350

Central Texas Library System, Inc, Austin TX p. 2280

Central Texas Veterans Health Care System Library Service, see Department of Veterans Affairs, Temple TX p. 2390

Central United Methodist Church Library, Decatur AL p. 14

Central United Methodist Church Library, Albuquerque NM p. 1549

Central Utah Correctional Facility Library, see Utah Department of Corrections, Gunnison UT p. 2406

Central Vermont Medical Center, Berlin VT p. 2419

Central Village Public Library, Central Village CT p. 333

Central Virginia Community College Library, Lynchburg VA p. 2475

Central Virginia Regional Library, Farmville VA p. 2463

Central Virginia Training Center, Lynchburg VA p. 2475

Central Washington Hospital, Wenatchee WA p. 2548

Central Washington University, Ellensburg WA p. 2514

Central Wyoming College Library, Riverton WY p. 2659

Centrale des Syndicats du Quebec, Quebec QC p. 2903

Centralia College, Centralia WA p. 2511

Centralia Community Library, Centralia KS p. 860

Centralia Correctional Center Library, Centralia IL p. 602

Centralia Public Library, Centralia MO p. 1323

Centralia Regional Library District, Centralia IL p. 602

Centralia Timberland Library, see Timberland Regional Library, Centralia WA p. 2543

Centrastate Healthcare System Library, Freehold NJ p. 1487

Centre Canadien d'Architecture, Montreal QC p. 2892

Centre Canadien d'Etudes et de Cooperation, Montreal QC p. 2892

Centre College of Kentucky, Danville KY p. 911

Centre County Law Library, Bellefonte PA p. 2032

Centre County Library & Historical Museum, Bellefonte PA p. 2032

Centre d'Animation, de Developpement et de Recherche en Education-Bibliotheque, Montreal QC p. 2892

Centre d'acces a l'Information Juridique, Quebec QC p. 2904

Centre d'Archives du Saguenay-Lac-Saint-Jean, Chicoutimi QC p. 2881

Centre de Documentation Collegiale, La Salle QC p. 2885

Centre de documentation sur l'education des adultes, Montreal QC p. 2892

Centre de Pedopsychiatrie du CHUQ, Quebec QC p. 2904

Centre de Recherche Lionel-Groulx, Outremont QC p. 2902

Centre de Reference Technique, Dorval QC p. 2881

Centre de Santé et de Services Sociaux du Nord de Lanaudière Bibliothèque, Saint Charles Borromee QC p. 2908

Centre de Sante et de Services Sociaux Richeliue-Yamaska, Saint-Hyacinthe QC p. 2910

Centre de Santé et de Services Sociaux de la Région de Thetford, Thetford Mines QC p. 2913

Centre de Santé et Services Sociaux de Laval, Laval QC p. 2886

Centre de Services Partages du Quebec, Quebec QC p. 2904

Centre de Veille Sur l'efficacite Energetique, Charlesbourg QC p. 2880

Centre for Addiction & Mental Health Library, Toronto ON p. 2852

Centre for Christian Studies Library, Winnipeg MB p. 2755

Centre for Indigenous Environmental Resources, Winnipeg MB p. 2755

Centre for Mennonite Brethren Studies Archive, Winnipeg MB p. 2755

Centre for Nursing Studies Learning Resource Centre, see Eastern Health, St. John's NL p. 2772

Centre for Suicide Prevention, 2005, Calgary AB p. 2691

Centre Hospitalier de Charlevoix, Baie Saint-Paul QC p. 2879

Centre Hospitalier de Gaspe, Gaspe QC p. 2882

Centre Hospitalier de l'Universite de Montreal, Montreal QC p. 2893

Centre Hospitalier des Vallees de l'Outaouais Bibliotheque, Gatineau QC p. 2883

Centre Hospitalier Jacques Viger, Montreal QC p. 2893

Centre Hospitalier Regional trois-Rivieres Pavillon St-Joseph, Trois-Rivieres QC p. 2914

Centre Hospitalier Robert-Giffard, Quebec QC p. 2904

Centre Hospitalier Universitaire du Sherbrooke Bibliotheque, Sherbrooke QC p. 2912

Chartiers-Houston Community Library, Houston PA p. 2070

Chevy Chase Library, *see* Montgomery County Public Libraries, Chevy Chase MD p. 1038

Chase Emory A Memorial Law Library, *see* New York State Supreme Court Library, Catskill NY p. 1603

Chase Library, West Harwich MA p. 1137

Chase Library, *see* Chase Township Public Library, Chase MI p. 1162

Chase Manhattan Bank, New York NY p. 1672

Chase Salmon P College of Law Library, *see* Northern Kentucky University, Highland Heights KY p. 917

Chase Township Public Library, Chase MI p. 1162

Chase Virginius H Special Collections Center, *see* Bradley University, Peoria IL p. 690

Chastek Library, *see* Gonzaga University School of Law, Spokane WA p. 2536

Chateaugay Memorial Library, Chateaugay NY p. 1605

Chateauguay Municipal Library, Chateauguay QC p. 2880

Chatelain Jane O'Brien West Bank Regional, *see* Jefferson Parish Library, Harvey LA p. 956

Chatfield Brass Band, Inc, Chatfield MN p. 1245

Chatfield College Library, Saint Martin OH p. 1933

Chatfield Public Library, Chatfield MN p. 1245

Chatham Area Public Library District, Chatham IL p. 604

Chatham College, Pittsburgh PA p. 2124

Chatham County Public Libraries, Siler City NC p. 1823

Chatham-Kent Public Library, Chatham ON p. 2799

Chatham Public Library, Chatham NY p. 1605

Chatham Public Library, *see* York Library Region, Miramichi NB p. 2764

Chatlos Library, *see* Florida College, Temple Terrace FL p. 500

Chatsworth Historical Society, Chatsworth CA p. 133

Chatsworth-Murray County Library, *see* Northwest Georgia Regional Library System, Chatsworth GA p. 528

Chatsworth Township Library, Chatsworth IL p. 604

Chattahoochee Public Library, *see* Gadsden County Public Library, Chattahoochee FL p. 485

Chattahoochee Technical College Library, Marietta GA p. 542

Chattahoochee Valley Community College, Phenix City AL p. 33

Chattahoochee Valley Libraries, Columbus GA p. 525

Chattanooga-Hamilton County Bicentennial Library, Chattanooga TN p. 2226

Chattanooga State Community College, Chattanooga TN p. 2227

Chattanooga Times Free Press Library, Chattanooga TN p. 2227

Chatton Milton J Medical Library, *see* Santa Clara Valley Medical Center, San Jose CA p. 252

Chattooga County Library, Summerville GA p. 552

Chauncey Public, *see* Nelsonville Public Library, Chauncey OH p. 1920

Chautauqua-Cattaraugus Library System, Jamestown NY p. 1646

Chautauqua County Historical Society Library, Westfield NY p. 1768

Chautauqua Institution Library, *see* Smith Memorial Library, Chautauqua NY p. 1606

Chauvin Municipal Library, Chauvin AB p. 2695

Chavez Cesar E, *see* Oakland Public Library, Oakland CA p. 198

Chavez Cesar E Library, *see* San Jose City College Library, San Jose CA p. 250

Chavez Cesar Library, *see* Phoenix Public Library, Laveen AZ p. 76

Chavez Cesar Library, *see* Salinas Public Library, Salinas CA p. 226

Chavis Vance H Lifelong Learning, *see* Greensboro Public Library, Greensboro NC p. 1796

Chazy Public Library, Chazy NY p. 1606

Cheaha Regional Library, Heflin AL p. 20

Cheatham County Public Library, Ashland City TN p. 2223

Chebeague Island Library, Chebeague Island ME p. 982

Cheboygan Area Public Library, Cheboygan MI p. 1162

Cheek James E Learning Resources Center, *see* Shaw University, Raleigh NC p. 1817

Cheektowaga Public Library, Cheektowaga NY p. 1606

Cheland Community, *see* North Central Regional Library, Chelan WA p. 2548

Chelmsford Citizen Service Center Public Library, *see* Greater Sudbury Public Library, Chelmsford ON p. 2846

Chelmsford Public Library, Chelmsford MA p. 1079

Chelsea District Library, Chelsea MI p. 1163

Chelsea Public Library, Chelsea IA p. 801

Chelsea Public Library, Chelsea MA p. 1080

Chelsea Public Library, Chelsea OK p. 1959

Chelsea Public Library, Chelsea VT p. 2421

Cheltenham Township Library System, Glenside PA p. 2061

Chemeketa Community College Library, Salem OR p. 2017

Chemeketa Cooperative Regional Library Service (N), Salem OR p. 2953

Chemtura Corp, Middlebury CT p. 351

Chemung County Historical Society, Inc, Elmira NY p. 1619

Chemung County Library District, Elmira NY p. 1619

Chenango Memorial Hospital, Norwich NY p. 1708

Cheney Library, Hoosick Falls NY p. 1637

Cheney Mary Library, *see* Manchester Public Library, Manchester CT p. 350

Cheney Public Library, Cheney KS p. 860

Cheney's Grove Township Library, Saybrook IL p. 700

Cheng David & Lorraine Library, *see* William Paterson University of New Jersey, Wayne NJ p. 1540

Cheng Yu Tung East Asian Library, *see* University of Toronto Libraries, Toronto ON p. 2865

Chenoa Public Library District, Chenoa IL p. 604

Cherokee-City-County Public Library, Cherokee OK p. 1959

Cherokee County Law Library, *see* Sequoyah Regional Library System, Canton GA p. 523

Cherokee County Public Library, Centre AL p. 11

Cherokee County Public Library, Gaffney SC p. 2194

Cherokee Heritage Center Archives, *see* Cherokee National Historical Society, Park Hill OK p. 1975

Cherokee Mental Health Institute, Cherokee IA p. 801

Cherokee National Historical Society, Park Hill OK p. 1975

Cherokee Public Library, Cherokee AL p. 12

Cherokee Public Library, Cherokee IA p. 801

Cherokee Regional Library System, LaFayette GA p. 538

Arlene Cherry Memorial, *see* Lonoke Prairie County Regional Library Headquarters, Cabot AR p. 108

Cherry County Historical Society Library, Valentine NE p. 1422

Cherry Hill Public Library, Cherry Hill NJ p. 1478

Cherry Hospital, Goldsboro NC p. 1795

Cherry Jim Learning Resource Center, *see* Georgia Perimeter College, Clarkston GA p. 525

Cherry Valley Memorial Library, Cherry Valley NY p. 1606

Cherry Valley Public Library District, Cherry Valley IL p. 604

Cherryfield Free Public Library, Cherryfield ME p. 982

Cherryvale Public Library, Cherryvale KS p. 860

Chesapeake & Ohio Canal National Historical Park Library, *see* National Park Service, Hagerstown MD p. 1031

Chesapeake & Ohio Historical Society Archives, Clifton Forge VA p. 2457

Chesapeake Bay Maritime Museum Library, Saint Michaels MD p. 1040

Chesapeake Biological Laboratory, *see* University of Maryland Center for Environmental Science, Solomons MD p. 1042

Chesapeake College, Wye Mills MD p. 1046

Chesapeake Public Library, Chesapeake VA p. 2456

Cheshire Library, *see* Connecticut Correctional Institution, Cheshire CT p. 334

Cheshire Medical Center, Keene NH p. 1452

Cheshire Public Library, Cheshire CT p. 333

Cheshire Public Library, Cheshire MA p. 1080

Chesley Memorial Library, Northwood NH p. 1461

Chesnutt Charles W Library, *see* Fayetteville State University, Fayetteville NC p. 1793

Chestatee Regional Library System, Dawsonville GA p. 529

Chester College of New England, Chester NH p. 1441

Chester County Archives & Records Services Library, West Chester PA p. 2153

Chester County Historical Society, West Chester PA p. 2153

Chester County Hospital Library, West Chester PA p. 2153

Chester County Law Library, West Chester PA p. 2153

Chester County Library, Chester SC p. 2185

Chester County Library System, Exton PA p. 2056

Chester County Public Library, Henderson TN p. 2237

Chester Library, Chester NJ p. 1478

Chester Mental Health Center, Chester IL p. 604

Chester Public Library, Chester CT p. 334

Chester Public Library, Chester IL p. 604

Chester Public Library, Chester NE p. 1395

Chester Public Library, Chester NH p. 1441

Chester Public Library, Chester NY p. 1606

Chester Springs Library, Chester Springs PA p. 2044

Chesterfield County Library, Chesterfield SC p. 2186

Chesterfield County Public Library, Chesterfield VA p. 2456

Chesterfield Public Library, Chesterfield MA p. 1080

Chesterfield Public Library, Chesterfield NH p. 1441

Chesterfield Township Library, Chesterfield MI p. 1163

Chestermere Public Library, Chestermere AB p. 2695

Chestnut Dr Walter Public Library, *see* Haut-Saint-Jean Regional Library, Hartland NB p. 2762

Chestnut Hill College, Philadelphia PA p. 2104

Chestnut Hill Hospital, Philadelphia PA p. 2104

Chetco Community Public Library, Brookings OR p. 1992

Chetopa City Library, Chetopa KS p. 860

Chetwynd Public Library, Chetwynd BC p. 2726

Chevron Global Library, *see* Chevron Information Technology Company, Division of Chevron USA, Inc, Richmond CA p. 216

Chevron Global Library Houston, Houston TX p. 2334

Chevron Information Technology Company, Division of Chevron USA, Inc, Richmond CA p. 216

Chevron Law Library, Houston TX p. 2334

Chewelah Public Library, Chewelah WA p. 2512

Cheyenne Mountain Library, *see* Pikes Peak Library District, Colorado Springs CO p. 296

Cheyenne Mountain Zoological Park Library, Colorado Springs CO p. 294

Cheyenne Wells Public Library, Cheyenne Wells CO p. 294

Cheyney University, Cheyney PA p. 2044

Chi John W Memorial Medical Library, *see* Ingham Regional Medical Center, Lansing MI p. 1201

Chicago & South Consortium (N), Chicago IL p. 2942

Chicago Academy of Sciences, Chicago IL p. 607

Chicago Area Museum Libraries (N), Chicago IL p. 2942

Chicago Bridge & Iron Co, Bloomfield NJ p. 1473

Chicago Community Trust Library, Chicago IL p. 607

Chicago Heights Public Library, Chicago Heights IL p. 628

Chicago History Museum, Chicago IL p. 607

Clarke Athalie Irvine Library, *see* House Ear Institute, Los Angeles CA p. 171

Clarke Bruce C Library, *see* United States Army, Fort Leonard Wood MO p. 1328

Clarke County Library, *see* Handley Regional Library, Berryville VA p. 2503

Clark David A School of Law Library, *see* University of the District of Columbia, Washington DC p. 421

Clarke Historical Library, *see* Central Michigan University, Mount Pleasant MI p. 1211

Clarke J R Public Library, Covington OH p. 1892

Clarke John Henrik Africana Library, *see* Cornell University Library, Ithaca NY p. 1641

Clarke Library, *see* Aspen Institute, Aspen CO p. 288

Clarke University, Dubuque IA p. 811

Clarkesville-Habersham County Library, Clarkesville GA p. 524

Clarkia District Library, Clarkia ID p. 573

Clarks Public Library, Clarks NE p. 1396

Clarksburg-Harrison Public Library, Clarksburg WV p. 2557

Clarksburg Town Library, Clarksburg MA p. 1082

Clarkson College Library, Omaha NE p. 1411

Clarkson Public Library, Clarkson NE p. 1396

Clarkson University Library, Potsdam NY p. 1721

Clarksville Area Public Library, *see* Southside Regional Library, Clarksville VA p. 2452

Clarksville-Montgomery County Public Library, Clarksville TN p. 2229

Clarksville Public Library, Clarksville IA p. 802

Clarkton Public, *see* Bladen County Public Library, Clarkton NC p. 1791

Clatskanie Library District, Clatskanie OR p. 1993

Clatsop Community College, Astoria OR p. 1990

Claude Public Library, Claude TX p. 2297

Clausen Miller Research Services Dept, Chicago IL p. 611

Claverack Free Library, Claverack NY p. 1607

Claxton-Hepburn Medical Center Library, Ogdensburg NY p. 1709

Clay-Battelle Public Library, *see* Morgantown Public Library, Blacksville WV p. 2566

Clay Center Carnegie Library, Clay Center KS p. 861

Clay Center for the Arts & Sciences of West Virginia, Charleston WV p. 2556

Clay Center Public Library, Clay Center NE p. 1396

Clay County Archives & Historical Library, Liberty MO p. 1343

Clay County Library, *see* Kinchafoonee Regional Library System, Fort Gaines GA p. 528

Clay County Public Library, Manchester KY p. 928

Clay County Public Library, Celina TN p. 2226

Clay County Public Library, Clay WV p. 2558

Clay County Public Library System, Orange Park FL p. 475

Clay Springs Public Library, Clay Springs AZ p. 60

Claymont Public Library, Claymont DE p. 381

Claymont Public Library, Uhrichsville OH p. 1942

Claypool Nancy Sue Health Information Center, *see* Saint Mary's Health Center, Saint Louis MO p. 1361

Claysburg Area Public Library, Claysburg PA p. 2045

Clayton City Library, Clayton KS p. 861

Clayton County Library System, Jonesboro GA p. 536

Clayton Group Services, Inc, Novi MI p. 1214

Clayton-Liberty Township Public Library, Clayton IN p. 732

Clayton Library, *see* Contra Costa County Library, Clayton CA p. 209

Clayton Library Center for Genealogical Research, *see* Houston Public Library, Houston TX p. 2339

Clayton Mayme A Library & Museum, Culver City CA p. 138

Clayton Public Library, Clayton NM p. 1553

Clayton Public Library District, Clayton IL p. 629

Clayton State University, Morrow GA p. 545

Clayton Town & County Library, Clayton AL p. 12

Clayton-Glass Library, *see* Motlow State Community College Libraries, Tullahoma TN p. 2267

Claytor Archer A Library, *see* Public Libraries of Saginaw, Saginaw MI p. 1224

Clayville Library Association, Clayville NY p. 1607

CLC (N), *see* Christian Library Consortium, Cedarville OH p. 2951

Clear Creek Baptist Bible College, Pineville KY p. 933

Clear Lake City Library, Clear Lake SD p. 2211

Clear Lake Public Library, Clear Lake IA p. 802

Clear Lake Public Library, Clear Lake WI p. 2585

Clearbrook Library, *see* Fraser Valley Regional Library, Abbotsford BC p. 2723

Clearfield County Law Library, Clearfield PA p. 2045

Clearfield County Public Library, Curwensville PA p. 2048

Clearfield Public Library, Clearfield IA p. 802

Clearview Neighbourhood, *see* Oakville Public Library, Oakville ON p. 2825

Clearview Public Library, Stayner ON p. 2844

Clearwater Christian College, Clearwater FL p. 431

Clearwater County Free Library District, Weippe ID p. 585

Clearwater Marine Aquarium Library, Clearwater FL p. 432

Clearwater Memorial Public Library, Orofino ID p. 581

Clearwater Public Library, Clearwater KS p. 861

Clearwater Public Library, Clearwater NE p. 1396

Clearwater Public Library System, Clearwater FL p. 432

Clearwater United Church Library, *see* First United Methodist Church, Clearwater FL p. 432

Cleary, Gottlieb, Steen & Hamilton LLP Library, New York NY p. 1673

Cleary University Library, Howell MI p. 1192

Cleaves Nathan & Henry B Law Library, Portland ME p. 996

Cleburne County Library, Heber Springs AR p. 103

Cleburne Public Library, Cleburne TX p. 2297

Clegg John C Public Library, Central City IA p. 801

Clemens Library, *see* College of Saint Benedict, Saint Joseph MN p. 1277

Clement Whittington W Learning Resources Center, *see* Danville Community College, Danville VA p. 2459

Clementon Memorial Library, Clementon NJ p. 1479

Clements William L Library, *see* University of Michigan, Ann Arbor MI p. 1152

Clemons Library, *see* University of Virginia, Charlottesville VA p. 2455

Clemson University Libraries, Clemson SC p. 2186

Clendaniel Estella C Library, *see* Eastern Shore Hospital Center, Cambridge MD p. 1022

Clendening History of Medicine Library, *see* Kansas University Medical Center, Kansas City KS p. 875

Clermont College Library, *see* University of Cincinnati, Batavia OH p. 1858

Clermont County Law Library Association, Batavia OH p. 1857

Clermont County Public Library, Batavia OH p. 1857

Clermont Public Library, Clermont IA p. 802

Cleveland Botanical Garden, Cleveland OH p. 1876

Cleveland Bradley County Public Library, Cleveland TN p. 2229

Cleveland Chiropractic College, Overland Park KS p. 887

Cleveland Clinic Alumni Library, Cleveland OH p. 1876

Cleveland Community College, Shelby NC p. 1823

Cleveland County Library System, Shelby NC p. 1823

Cleveland County Mid-Arkansas Regional Library, *see* Sturgis Roy & Christine Library, Rison AR p. 113

Cleveland Health Sciences Library, Cleveland OH p. 1876

Cleveland Heights-University Heights Public Library, Cleveland Heights OH p. 1882

Cleveland Institute of Art, Cleveland OH p. 1877

Cleveland Institute of Music, Cleveland OH p. 1877

Cleveland Jesse Franklin Learning Resource Center, *see* South Carolina School for the Deaf & the Blind, Spartanburg SC p. 2204

Cleveland Law Library Association, Cleveland OH p. 1877

Cleveland-Marshall Law Library, *see* Cleveland State University, Cleveland OH p. 1878

Cleveland Metroparks Zoo Library, Cleveland OH p. 1877

Cleveland Museum of Art, Cleveland OH p. 1877

Cleveland Museum of Natural History, Cleveland OH p. 1877

Cleveland Psychoanalytic Center Library, Cleveland Heights OH p. 1882

Cleveland Public Library, Cleveland OH p. 1877, 1878

Cleveland Ruth R Memorial Library, *see* Cleveland Chiropractic College, Overland Park KS p. 887

Cleveland State Community College Library, Cleveland TN p. 2229

Cleveland State University, Cleveland OH p. 1878

Cleveland Susan Colgate Library, *see* Colby-Sawyer College, New London NH p. 1459

Clever Public Library, Clever MO p. 1323

Clewiston Public Library, *see* Hendry County Library System, Clewiston FL p. 433

CLGC (N), *see* Cooperating Libraries of Greater Springfield, Springfield MA p. 2945

CLiC (N), *see* Colorado Library Consortium, Centennial CO p. 2939

CLIC (N), *see* Cooperating Libraries in Consortium, Saint Paul MN p. 2946

Clifford A H Mathematics Research Library, *see* Tulane University, New Orleans LA p. 963

Clifford Chance LLP Library, New York NY p. 1673

Cliffside Park Free Public Library, Cliffside Park NJ p. 1479

Clifton Community Library, Cranberry Lake NY p. 1612

Clifton Forge Public Library, Clifton Forge VA p. 2457

Clifton Park-Halfmoon Public Library, Clifton Park NY p. 1607

Clifton Public Library, Clifton AZ p. 60

Clifton Public Library, Clifton IL p. 630

Clifton Public Library, Clifton KS p. 861

Clifton Public Library, Clifton NJ p. 1479

Clifton Springs Library, Clifton Springs NY p. 1607

Climax Public Library, *see* Lake Agassiz Regional Library, Climax MN p. 1266

Clinch County Public, *see* Okefenokee Regional Library, Homerville GA p. 557

Clinch River Regional Library, Clinton TN p. 2230

Cline-Keller Library, *see* Bartholomew County Historical Society, Columbus IN p. 733

Cline Library, *see* Northern Arizona University, Flagstaff AZ p. 62

Cline-Tunnell Library, *see* Western Seminary, Portland OR p. 2015

Clint ISD Public Library, Clint TX p. 2298

Clinton Community College, Plattsburgh NY p. 1718

Clinton Community College Library, Clinton IA p. 803

Clinton Community Library, Rhinebeck NY p. 1727

Clinton Community Library, *see* Sno-Isle Libraries, Clinton WA p. 2542

Clinton Correctional Facility Library, Dannemora NY p. 1613

Clinton County Law Library, Wilmington OH p. 1949

Clinton County Public Library, Albany KY p. 905

Clinton District Library, *see* Morgantown Public Library, Morgantown WV p. 2566

Clinton-Essex-Franklin Library System, Plattsburgh NY p. 1718

Clinton Junior College Library, Rock Hill SC p. 2202

Clinton-Macomb Public Library, Clinton Township MI p. 1164

Clinton Public, *see* Laurens County Library, Clinton SC p. 2199

Clinton Public Library, Clinton IN p. 732

Clinton Public Library, Clinton IA p. 803

Clinton Public Library, Clinton TN p. 2230

Clinton Public Library, Clinton WI p. 2585

Clinton Public Library, *see* Western Plains Library System, Clinton OK p. 1960

Clinton Township Public Library, Waterman IL p. 715

Clinton Township Public Library, Clinton MI p. 1163

Clinton William J Presidential Library & Museum, *see* National Archives & Records Administration, Little Rock AR p. 107

Clintonville Public Library, Clintonville WI p. 2586

CLIO (N), *see* Cooperating Libraries in Olympia, Olympia WA p. 2957

Clive Public Library, Clive IA p. 803

Clive Public Library, Clive AB p. 2695

CLMLC (N), *see* Central Louisiana Medical Center Library Consortium, Alexandria LA p. 2944

Cloisters Library, *see* Metropolitan Museum of Art, New York NY p. 1686

Cloquet Public Library, Cloquet MN p. 1246

Close Anne Springs Library, *see* York Technical College Library, Rock Hill SC p. 2203

Close O H Youth Correctional Facility Library, *see* California Youth Authority, Stockton CA p. 272

Closter Public Library, Closter NJ p. 1479

Cloud County Community College Library, Concordia KS p. 862

Cloud County Historical Society Museum Library, Concordia KS p. 862

Cloughly O J Alumni Library, *see* Saint Louis College of Pharmacy, Saint Louis MO p. 1357

Clouter Joseph E Memorial Public Library, *see* Catalina Public Library, Catalina NL p. 2769

Clover Park Technical College Library, Lakewood WA p. 2519

Clover Public, *see* York County Library, Clover SC p. 2203

Clover Public Library District, Woodhull IL p. 721

Cloverdale Regional, *see* Sonoma County Library, Cloverdale CA p. 267

Clovis-Carver Public Library, Clovis NM p. 1553

Clovis Community College Library, Clovis NM p. 1553

Clovis Regional, *see* Fresno County Public Library, Clovis CA p. 152

CLRC (N), *see* Central New York Library Resources Council, Syracuse NY p. 2950

Clutier Public Library, Clutier IA p. 803

Clyde Public Library, Clyde KS p. 861

Clyde Public Library, Clyde OH p. 1882

Clyde Public Library, Clyde TX p. 2298

Clyde-Savannah Public Library, Clyde NY p. 1608

Clymer Public Library, Pocono Pines PA p. 2131

Clymer Rolla A Research Library, El Dorado KS p. 865

Clymer-French Creek Free Library, Clymer NY p. 1608

CMC Electronics Inc Library, Montreal QC p. 2893

CMLC (N), *see* Central Mississippi Library Council, Jackson MS p. 2947

CMLE (N), *see* Central Minnesota Libraries Exchange, Saint Cloud MN p. 2946

Coachella Library, *see* Riverside County Library System, Coachella CA p. 217

Coady & Tompkins Memorial, *see* Eastern Counties Regional Library, Margaree Forks NS p. 2783

Coahoma Community College, Clarksdale MS p. 1295

Coal City Public Library District, Coal City IL p. 630

Coaldale Public Library, Coaldale AB p. 2695

Coalfield Public Library, Coalfield TN p. 2230

Coalgate Public Library, Coalgate OK p. 1961

Coalinga District Library, *see* Coalinga-Huron Library District, Coalinga CA p. 135

Coalinga-Huron Library District, Coalinga CA p. 135

Coalmont Public Library, Coalmont TN p. 2230

Coastal Bend College, Beeville TX p. 2288

Coastal Bend College, Kingville TX p. 2351

Coastal Carolina Community College, Jacksonville NC p. 1803

Coastal Carolina University, Conway SC p. 2191

Coastal Plain Regional Library, Tifton GA p. 554

Coastal Resource Sharing Network (N), Tillamook OR p. 2953

Coastal State Prison, *see* Georgia Department of Corrections, Garden City GA p. 535

Coates Library, *see* Trinity University, San Antonio TX p. 2383

Coatesville Area Public Library, Coatesville PA p. 2046

Coatesville-Clay Township Public Library, Coatesville IN p. 732

Cobalt Public Library, Cobalt ON p. 2800

Cobb County Public Library System, Marietta GA p. 542

Cobb Institute of Archaelogy Library, Mississippi State MS p. 1308

Cobb J E Library, *see* Central Baptist College, Conway AR p. 96

Cobb Mary Wallace Memorial Library, *see* Northwest Regional Library, Vernon AL p. 40

Cobb Public Library, Cobb WI p. 2586

Cobey Minnie Memorial Library, Columbus OH p. 1884

Cobleigh Public Library, Lyndonville VT p. 2427

Cobourg Public Library, Cobourg ON p. 2800

Cobre Valley Community Hospital, Globe AZ p. 64

Coburn Free Library, Owego NY p. 1713

Cochise College Library, Douglas AZ p. 61

Cochise County Law Library, Bisbee AZ p. 58

Cochise County Library District, Bisbee AZ p. 58

Cochiti Lake Public Library, Cochiti Lake NM p. 1553

Cochiti Pueblo Community Library, Cochiti NM p. 1553

Cochran County Love Memorial Library, Morton TX p. 2363

Cochran Mary Helen Library, *see* Sweet Briar College, Sweet Briar VA p. 2497

Cochran Public Library, *see* Henry County Public Library System, Stockbridge GA p. 544

Cochrane Public Library, Cochrane AB p. 2695

Cochrane Public Library, Cochrane ON p. 2800

Cochrane-Woods Library, *see* Nebraska Wesleyan University, Lincoln NE p. 1406

Cochranton Area Public Library, Cochranton PA p. 2046

Cockrell Hill Public Library, Dallas TX p. 2305

Cocoa Beach Public Library, Cocoa Beach FL p. 433

Coconino Community College, Flagstaff AZ p. 62

Coconino County Law Library & Self-Help Center, Flagstaff AZ p. 62

Cocopah Tribal Library, Somerton AZ p. 82

CODSULI (N), *see* Council of Directors of State University Libraries in Illinois, Springfield IL p. 2942

Coe Charles Willard Memorial Library, *see* Mount Saint Mary's College, Los Angeles CA p. 175

Coe College, Cedar Rapids IA p. 800

Coe Levi E Library, Middlefield CT p. 351

Coe William Robertson Ornithology Library, *see* Yale University Library, New Haven CT p. 357

Coeburn Community, *see* Lonesome Pine Regional Library, Coeburn VA p. 2504

Coeur d'Alene Public Library, Coeur d'Alene ID p. 573

Cofer Library, *see* Truett-McConnell College, Cleveland GA p. 525

Coffee Correctional Facility, *see* Georgia Department of Corrections, Nicholls GA p. 546

Coffee County Lannom Memorial Public Library, Tullahoma TN p. 2267

Coffee County-Manchester Library, Manchester TN p. 2246

Coffee Creek Correctional Facility, *see* Oregon State Penitentiary, Wilsonville OR p. 2018

Coffeeville Public Library, Coffeeville MS p. 1296

Coffey County Library, Burlington KS p. 859

Coffeyville Community College, Coffeyville KS p. 861

Coffeyville Public Library, Coffeyville KS p. 861

Cofrin David A Library, *see* University of Wisconsin-Green Bay, Green Bay WI p. 2596

Coggon Public Library, Coggon IA p. 803

Cogswell Polytechnical College Library, Sunnyvale CA p. 273

Cohasset Historical Society Library, Cohasset MA p. 1082

Cohen & Grigsby PC, Pittsburgh PA p. 2124

Cohen Albert D Management Library, *see* University of Manitoba Libraries, Winnipeg MB p. 2758

Cohen David, *see* Free Library of Philadelphia, Philadelphia PA p. 2107

Cohen L Lewis Memorial Library, *see* Weiss Louis A Memorial Hospital, Chicago IL p. 627

Cohen Morris Raphael Library, *see* City College of the City University of New York, New York NY p. 1672

Cohn Charles Memorial Library, *see* North Shore Synagogue, Syosset NY p. 1751

Cohocton Public Library, Cohocton NY p. 1608

Cohoes Public Library, Cohoes NY p. 1608

Coil Henry Wilson Masonic Library & Museum, *see* Grand Lodge Free & Accepted Masons of California, San Francisco CA p. 242

Coin Public Library, Coin IA p. 803

Cokato Library, *see* Great River Regional Library, Cokato MN p. 1275

Coke County Library, Robert Lee TX p. 2376

Coker Charles W & Joan S Library, *see* Coker College, Hartsville SC p. 2198

Coker College, Hartsville SC p. 2198

Colburn Phyllis Ann Memorial Family Library, *see* Children's Hospital of Michigan, Detroit MI p. 1169

Colby College Libraries, Waterville ME p. 1005

Colby Community College, Colby KS p. 861

Colby John C Memorial Library, *see* Stanstead College, Stanstead QC p. 2913

Colby Memorial Library, Danville NH p. 1444

Colby Public Library, Colby WI p. 2586

Colby-Sawyer College, New London NH p. 1459

Colby William E Memorial Library, *see* Sierra Club, San Francisco CA p. 247

Colchester - East Hants Regional Library, Truro NS p. 2785

Colchester District Library, Colchester IL p. 630

Colchester Historical Society Archives Library, Truro NS p. 2786

Cold Lake Public Library, Cold Lake AB p. 2695

Cold Spring Harbor Laboratory, Cold Spring Harbor NY p. 1609

Cold Spring Harbor Library, Cold Spring Harbor NY p. 1609

Cold Spring Harbor Whaling Museum Library, Cold Spring Harbor NY p. 1609

Cold Spring Library, *see* Great River Regional Library, Cold Spring MN p. 1275

Coldspring Area Public Library, Coldspring TX p. 2298

Coldwater Memorial Public Library, Coldwater ON p. 2800

Coldwater Public Library, Coldwater OH p. 1882

Coldwater-Wilmore Regional Library, Coldwater KS p. 861

Cole Bruce Memorial Library, *see* Saint Joseph's Hospital, Tucson AZ p. 87

Cole Donald M & Jameson Annex Library, *see* South Dakota State Penitentiary, Sioux Falls SD p. 2219

Georgina Cole Library, *see* Carlsbad City Library, Carlsbad CA p. 132

Cole Houston Library, *see* Jacksonville State University Library, Jacksonville AL p. 22

Cole Memorial Library, Enfield ME p. 984

Cole-Mitte Joanne Memorial Library, Bertram TX p. 2289

Cole Norwood Library, *see* Skagit Valley College, Mount Vernon WA p. 2521

Cole Robert L & Sara Marcy Library, *see* Rensselaer at Hartford, Hartford CT p. 347

Cole Russell D Library, *see* Cornell College, Mount Vernon IA p. 834

Cole Thomas Winston Sr Library, *see* Wiley College, Marshall TX p. 2360

Colebrook Public Library, Colebrook NH p. 1442

Coleman Area Library, Coleman MI p. 1165

Coleman Bessie, *see* Chicago Public Library, Chicago IL p. 608

Coleman College Library, San Diego CA p. 231

Coleman John B Library, *see* Prairie View A&M University, Prairie View TX p. 2372

Colonial Williamsburg Foundation, Williamsburg VA p. 2502

Colony City Library, Colony KS p. 862

Colony Public Library, The Colony TX p. 2392

Colorado Agency for Jewish Education, Denver CO p. 299

Colorado Alliance of Research Libraries (N), Denver CO p. 2939

Colorado Association of Law Libraries (N), Denver CO p. 2939

Colorado Christian University Library, Lakewood CO p. 314

Colorado College, Colorado Springs CO p. 294

Colorado Correctional Center Library, *see* Colorado Department of Corrections, Golden CO p. 309

Colorado Council of Medical Librarians (N), Denver CO p. 2939

Colorado Department of Corrections, Buena Vista CO p. 293

Colorado Department of Corrections, Canon City CO p. 293

Colorado Department of Corrections, Crowley CO p. 297

Colorado Department of Corrections, Delta CO p. 298

Colorado Department of Corrections, Denver CO p. 299

Colorado Department of Corrections, Fort Lyon CO p. 308

Colorado Department of Corrections, Golden CO p. 309

Colorado Department of Corrections, Limon CO p. 316

Colorado Department of Corrections, Model CO p. 318

Colorado Department of Corrections, Pueblo CO p. 320

Colorado Department of Corrections, Rifle CO p. 321

Colorado Department of Corrections, Sterling CO p. 323

Colorado Department of Education, Adult Education & Family Literacy, *see* Colorado State Literacy Resource Center, Denver CO p. 299

Colorado Department of Transportation Library, Denver CO p. 299

Colorado Division of State Archives & Public Records Library, Denver CO p. 299

Colorado Division of Wildlife, Fort Collins CO p. 307

Colorado Joint Legislative Council, Denver CO p. 299

Colorado Library Consortium (N), Centennial CO p. 2939

Colorado Mental Health Institute at Fort Logan, Denver CO p. 299

Colorado Mental Health Institute of Pueblo, Pueblo CO p. 320

Colorado Mesa University, Grand Junction CO p. 310

Colorado Mountain College, Glenwood Springs CO p. 309

Colorado Mountain College, Steamboat Springs CO p. 322

Colorado Mountain College, Leadville CO p. 316

Colorado Northwestern Community College Library, Rangely CO p. 321

Colorado Railroad Historical Foundation, Inc, Golden CO p. 309

Colorado River Indian Tribes Public Library-Archives, Parker AZ p. 70

Colorado School of Mines, Golden CO p. 309

Colorado Ski Museum-Ski Hall of Fame, Vail CO p. 324

Colorado Springs Fine Arts Center Library, Colorado Springs CO p. 295

Colorado Springs Pioneers Museum, Colorado Springs CO p. 295

Colorado State Department of Natural Resources, Denver CO p. 299

Colorado State Library, Denver CO p. 299

Colorado State Literacy Resource Center, Denver CO p. 299

Colorado State Penitentiary Library, *see* Colorado Department of Corrections, Canon City CO p. 293

Colorado State University Libraries, Fort Collins CO p. 307

Colorado State University Pueblo Library, Pueblo CO p. 320

Colorado Supreme Court Library, Denver CO p. 300

Colorado Talking Book Library, Denver CO p. 300

Colorado Technical University Library, Colorado Springs CO p. 295

Colorado Territorial Correctional Facility, Canon City CO p. 294

Colorado Water Conservation Board Library, *see* Colorado State Department of Natural Resources, Denver CO p. 299

Colorado Women's Correctional Facility, *see* Colorado Department of Corrections, Canon City CO p. 293

Colpoys Library, *see* Caritas Carney Hospital, Dorchester MA p. 1084

Colquitt Regional Medical Center, Moultrie GA p. 545

Colton Hall Museum Library, Monterey CA p. 189

Colton Hepburn Library, Colton NY p. 1609

Colton Public Library, Colton CA p. 135

Columbia Area Medical Librarians' Association (N), Columbia SC p. 2955

Columbia Basin College Library, Pasco WA p. 2523

Columbia Bible College, Abbotsford BC p. 2723

Columbia College, Columbia MO p. 1324

Columbia College, Columbia SC p. 2187

Columbia College Chicago Library, Chicago IL p. 611

Columbia College Hollywood, Tarzana CA p. 274

Columbia College Library, Sonora CA p. 269

Columbia College Library, Vancouver BC p. 2740

Columbia College of Nursing Library, Glendale WI p. 2594

Columbia Correctional Institution Library, Lake City FL p. 457

Columbia Correctional Institution Library, Portage WI p. 2631

Columbia County Historical & Genealogical Society Library, Bloomsburg PA p. 2036

Columbia County Historical Society Library, Kinderhook NY p. 1649

Columbia County Library, Magnolia AR p. 108

Columbia County Public Library, Lake City FL p. 457

Columbia County Public Library, *see* East Central Georgia Regional Library, Evans GA p. 519

Columbia County Rural Library District, Dayton WA p. 2514

Columbia County Traveling Library Authority, Bloomsburg PA p. 2036

Columbia Daily Tribune Library, *see* Tribune Publishing Co, Columbia MO p. 1325

Columbia Environmental Research Center Library, Columbia MO p. 1324

Columbia Gorge Community College Library, The Dalles OR p. 2020

Columbia-Greene Community College Library, Hudson NY p. 1638

Columbia Heights Public Library, Columbia Heights MN p. 1246

Columbia International University, Columbia SC p. 2187

Columbia Marion County Library, *see* South Mississippi Regional Library, Columbia MS p. 1296

Columbia Memorial Hospital, Hudson NY p. 1638

Columbia Missourian Newspaper Library, *see* University of Missouri-Columbia, Columbia MO p. 1325

Columbia Museum of Art, Columbia SC p. 2187

Columbia Public Library, Columbia IL p. 631

Columbia Public Library, Columbia PA p. 2046

Columbia Public Library, *see* Boone Daniel Regional Library, Columbia MO p. 1324

Columbia Resource Centre, *see* Columbia Bible College, Abbotsford BC p. 2723

Columbia River Maritime Museum Library, Astoria OR p. 1990

Columbia Saint Mary's Ozaukee Campus, Mequon WI p. 2615

Columbia State Community College, Columbia TN p. 2231

Columbia Theological Seminary, Decatur GA p. 529

Columbia Township Library, Unionville MI p. 1232

Columbia University, New York NY p. 1674

Columbian Newspaper Information Resource Center, Vancouver WA p. 2545

Columbiana County Law Library, Lisbon OH p. 1910

Columbiana Public Library, Columbiana AL p. 13

Columbiana Public Library, Columbiana OH p. 1883

Columbus Area Library & Information Council of Ohio (N), Westerville OH p. 2952

Columbus College of Art & Design, Columbus OH p. 1884

Columbus County Public Library, Whiteville NC p. 1829

Columbus Dispatch Editorial Library, Columbus OH p. 1884

Columbus Hospital, Newark NJ p. 1510

Columbus Junction Public Library, Columbus Junction IA p. 804

Columbus Law Library Association, Columbus OH p. 1884

Columbus-Lowndes Public Library, Columbus MS p. 1297

Columbus Memorial Library, *see* Organization of American States, Washington DC p. 412

Columbus Metropolitan Library, Columbus OH p. 1884

Columbus Public Library, Columbus KS p. 862

Columbus Public Library, Columbus NE p. 1396

Columbus Public Library, Columbus WI p. 2586

Columbus Public Library, Headquarters, *see* Chattahoochee Valley Libraries, Columbus GA p. 525

Columbus Regional Healthcare System, Columbus GA p. 526

Columbus State Community College Library, Columbus OH p. 1885

Columbus State University Libraries, Columbus GA p. 526

Columbus Technical College Library, Columbus GA p. 526

Columbus Village Public Library, Columbus NM p. 1554

Colusa County Free Library, Colusa CA p. 135

Colville Confederated Tribe Library, Nespelem WA p. 2521

Colville Public Library, Colville WA p. 2513

Colwich Community Library, Colwich KS p. 862

Comanche Public Library, Comanche TX p. 2299

Combined Community Library, Ordway CO p. 319

Comer B B Memorial Library, Sylacauga AL p. 36

Comfort Public Library, Comfort TX p. 2299

Comfort Public Library, *see* Neuse Regional Library, Trenton NC p. 1805

Comfrey Public Library, Comfrey MN p. 1246

Comite Intergouvernemental de Recherches Urbaines et Regionales, *see* Intergovernmental Committee on Urban & Regional Research, Toronto ON p. 2855

Commack Public Library, Commack NY p. 1609

Commerce Public, *see* Piedmont Regional Library, Commerce GA p. 557

Commerce Public Library, Commerce TX p. 2300

Commercial Appeal News Library, Memphis TN p. 2248

Commissariat of the Holy Land USA, *see* Franciscan Monastery Library, Washington DC p. 401

Commission d'Acces A L'Information, Quebec QC p. 2904

Commission de la Sante et de la Securite, Montreal QC p. 2894

Commission de Toponymie du Quebec Bibliotheque, Quebec QC p. 2904

Commission des Normes du Travail, Quebec QC p. 2904

Commission des Valeurs Mobilieres du Quebec Bibliotheque, Montreal QC p. 2894

Commission of Public Records, Santa Fe NM p. 1562

Connelly Library, *see* La Salle University, Philadelphia PA p. 2111

Connelly Library, *see* Moore College of Art & Design, Philadelphia PA p. 2112

Conner Dick Correctional Center Leisure Library, Hominy OK p. 1965

Conner-Graham Memorial, *see* Pine Forest Regional Library, Seminary MS p. 1314

Conner Prairie, Fishers IN p. 740

Connetquot Public Library, Bohemia NY p. 1583

Connors State College, Warner OK p. 1985

ConocoPhillips Library Network, Houston TX p. 2334

Conrad Grebel University College Library, Waterloo ON p. 2869

Conrad Public Library, Conrad IA p. 804

Conrad Public Library, Conrad MT p. 1377

Conran Memorial Library, Hayti MO p. 1330

Consad Research Corp Library, Pittsburgh PA p. 2124

Conseil de la Langue Francaise, Quebec QC p. 2904

Conseil Superieur de l'Education, Sainte-Foy QC p. 2910

Conservatoire de Musique de Montreal, Montreal QC p. 2895

Conservatoire de Musique de Quebec Bibliotheque, Quebec QC p. 2904

Conshohocken Free Library, *see* Montgomery County-Norristown Public Library, Conshohocken PA p. 2098

Consort Municipal Library, Consort AB p. 2695

Consortium for Open Learning (N), Roseville CA p. 2938

Consortium Library, *see* University of Alaska Anchorage, Anchorage AK p. 45

Consortium of Academic & Research Libraries (N), Champaign IL p. 2942

Consortium of College & University Media Centers (N), Bloomington IN p. 2943

Consortium of Nova Scotia Academic Libraries (N), *see* Novanet, Halifax NS p. 2959

Consortium of Ontario Libraries (N), Toronto ON p. 2959

Consortium of Popular Culture Collections in the Midwest (N), Bowling Green OH p. 2952

Consortium of Southern Biomedical Libraries (N), Nashville TN p. 2955

Consortium of User Libraries (N), Des Moines IA p. 2943

Constableville Village Library, Constableville NY p. 1609

Constance-Lethbridge Rehabilitation Centre Library, *see* Montreal Association for the Blind, Montreal QC p. 2899

Constantine Township Library, Constantine MI p. 1166

Consulate General of Sweden, New York NY p. 1676

Consumer Electronics Association, Arlington VA p. 2449

Consumer Health Information Program & Services (N), Norwalk CA p. 2938

Consumer Health Library, *see* United States Army, Fort Gordon GA p. 533

Consumer Reports, Yonkers NY p. 1771

Consumers Energy, Jackson MI p. 1195

Contra Costa College Library, San Pablo CA p. 256

Contra Costa County Library, Pleasant Hill CA p. 208

Contra Costa County Office of Education, Pleasant Hill CA p. 210

Contra Costa County Public Law Library, Martinez CA p. 184

Contra Costa Times News Research Department, Walnut Creek CA p. 282

Converse College, Spartanburg SC p. 2204

Converse Consultants East Library, Whippany NJ p. 1544

Converse County Library, Douglas WY p. 2654

Converse Free Library, Lyme NH p. 1454

Converse J D Memorial Medical Library, *see* Winter Haven Hospital, Winter Haven FL p. 505

Converse Jackson Township Public Library, Converse IN p. 734

Converse Library, *see* Bryn Mawr Presbyterian Church, Bryn Mawr PA p. 2039

Converse Public Library, Converse TX p. 2301

Conway County Library Headquarters, Morrilton AR p. 110

Conway Data, Inc Library, Norcross GA p. 547

Conway E A Medical Center Library, *see* LSU Health Sciences Center, Monroe LA p. 957

Conway Hall Public, *see* Pine Forest Regional Library, Petal MS p. 1314

Conway Library, *see* Children's Hospital of Eastern Ontario, Ottawa ON p. 2830

Conway Public Library, Conway NH p. 1444

Conway Springs City Library, Conway Springs KS p. 862

Conyers-Rockdale Library System, Conyers GA p. 527

Cook Albert S Library, *see* Towson University, Towson MD p. 1045

Cook County Hospital Libraries, Chicago IL p. 611

Cook County Law Library, Chicago IL p. 611

Cook Dr & Mrs Peter C Library, *see* Northwood University, West Palm Beach FL p. 502

Cook F Maxine & Thomas W Memorial Library, *see* La Grande Public Library, La Grande OR p. 2003

Cook Inlet Pre-Trial Facility Library, Anchorage AK p. 45

Cook Jane Bancroft Library, *see* New College of Florida, Sarasota FL p. 490

Cook Mary L Public Library, Waynesville OH p. 1945

Cook Memorial Library, Tamworth NH p. 1466

Cook Memorial Public Library District, Libertyville IL p. 665

Cook Perry Memorial Public Library, Shauck OH p. 1934

Cook Public Library, Cook MN p. 1246

Cook William & Gayle Music Library, *see* Indiana University Bloomington, Bloomington IN p. 727

Cooke County Library, Gainesville TX p. 2326

Cooke Ethel Miner Historical Library, *see* Rocky Hill Historical Society, Rocky Hill CT p. 366

Cooksey Phyllis Resource Center, *see* Planned Parenthood of Minnesota & South Dakota, Minneapolis MN p. 1261

COOL (N), *see* Consortium of Ontario Libraries, Toronto ON p. 2959

Cooledge Belle Community Library, *see* Sacramento Public Library, Sacramento CA p. 224

Cooley Dickinson Hospital, Northampton MA p. 1113

Cooley George R Science Library, *see* Colgate University, Hamilton NY p. 1633

Cooley Godward Kronish LLP Library, San Francisco CA p. 241

Cooley Harold D Library, *see* Nashville Public Library, Nashville NC p. 1812

Cooley LLP, New York NY p. 1676

Coolidge Calvin Library, *see* Castleton State College, Castleton VT p. 2421

Coolidge Library, Solon ME p. 1001

Coolidge Public Library, Coolidge AZ p. 61

Coolidge Public Library, *see* Thomas County Public Library System, Coolidge GA p. 553

Coolville Public, *see* Nelsonville Public Library, Coolville OH p. 1920

Coon George Public Library, Princeton KY p. 933

Coon Rapids Public Library, Coon Rapids IA p. 804

Cooper Argie Public Library, Shelbyville TN p. 2265

Cooper E M Memorial Public Library, Wilmington NY p. 1770

Cooper John Hughes, *see* Richland County Public Library, Columbia SC p. 2188

Cooper Landing Community Library, Cooper Landing AK p. 46

Cooper Memorial Library, *see* Lake County Library System, Clermont FL p. 500

Cooper R M Library, *see* Clemson University Libraries, Clemson SC p. 2186

Cooper River Memorial, *see* Charleston County Public Library, Charleston Heights SC p. 2183

Cooper Thomas Library, *see* University of South Carolina, Columbia SC p. 2189

Cooper Union for Advancement of Science & Art Library, New York NY p. 1676

Cooper, White & Cooper, San Francisco CA p. 241

Cooper-Hewitt, National Design Museum Library, *see* Smithsonian Libraries, New York City DC p. 414

Cooperating Hospital Libraries of the Lehigh Valley Area (N), Bethlehem PA p. 2954

Cooperating Libraries in Consortium (N), Saint Paul MN p. 2946

Cooperating Libraries in Olympia (N), Olympia WA p. 2957

Cooperating Libraries of Greater Springfield (N), Springfield MA p. 2945

Cooperative Information Network (N), Hayden ID p. 2941

Cooperative Oxford Laboratory Library, Oxford MD p. 1036

Cooperstown Public Library, Cooperstown PA p. 2047

Coopersville Area District Library, Coopersville MI p. 1166

Coos Bay Public Library, Coos Bay OR p. 1993

Coos County Library Service District (N), Coos Bay OR p. 2953

Copeland Public Library, Copeland KS p. 862

Copiague Memorial Public Library, Copiague NY p. 1610

Copiah-Jefferson Regional Library System, Hazlehurst MS p. 1301

Copiah-Lincoln Community College, Mendenhall MS p. 1308

Copiah-Lincoln Community College, Natchez MS p. 1309

Copiah-Lincoln Community College, Wesson MS p. 1317

Copland Aaron School of Music Library, *see* Queens College, Flushing NY p. 1623

Coplay Public Library, Coplay PA p. 2047

Copley Helen K & James S Library, *see* University of San Diego, San Diego CA p. 239

Copley Hospital Medical Library, Morrisville VT p. 2430

Coppell Public Library, Coppell TX p. 2301

Copper Development Association, New York NY p. 1676

Copper Mountain College, Joshua Tree CA p. 161

Copper Queen Library, Bisbee AZ p. 58

Copper Valley Community Library, Glennallen AK p. 49

Copperas Cove Public Library, Copperas Cove TX p. 2301

Coppin State College, Baltimore MD p. 1012

COPPUL (N), *see* Council of Prairie & Pacific University Libraries, Victoria BC p. 2959

Coquille Public Library, Coquille OR p. 1993

Coquitlam Public Library, Coquitlam BC p. 2726

CORAL (N), *see* Council of Research & Academic Libraries, San Antonio TX p. 2956

Coralville Public Library, Coralville IA p. 804

Coraopolis Memorial Library, Coraopolis PA p. 2047

Corban University Library, Salem OR p. 2017

Corbett Lynn Library, *see* Southern Methodist College, Orangeburg SC p. 2202

Corbin Chester C Public Library, Webster MA p. 1134

Corbin Memorial Library, *see* Somerset County Library System, Crisfield MD p. 1036

Corbin Public Library, Corbin KY p. 910

Corbit-Calloway Memorial Library, Odessa DE p. 386

Corcoran Gallery of Art College/College of Art & Design, Washington DC p. 396

Corcoran Library, *see* Corcoran Gallery of Art College/College of Art & Design, Washington DC p. 396

Cordell Public Library, *see* Western Plains Library System, Cordell OK p. 1960

Cordes Lakes Public Library, Cordes Lakes AZ p. 61

Cordova District Library, Cordova IL p. 631

Cordova Public Library, Cordova AK p. 46

Core Library, *see* Kansas Geological Survey Library, Lawrence KS p. 877

Corette Jack & Sallie Library, *see* Carroll College, Helena MT p. 1381

Corfu Free Library, Corfu NY p. 1610

Corgan D Leonard Library, *see* King's College, Wilkes-Barre PA p. 2155

Corinth Free Library, Corinth NY p. 1610

Corinth Public Library, *see* Northeast Regional Library, Corinth MS p. 1297

Cornelia-Habersham County Library, Cornelia GA p. 527

Cornelius Public Library, Cornelius OR p. 1994

Cornell College, Mount Vernon IA p. 834

Cornell Ida, *see* Woodbury Public Library, Central Valley NY p. 1605

Cornell Julien & Virginia Library, *see* Vermont Law School, South Royalton VT p. 2436

Cornell Public Library, Cornell WI p. 2586

Cornell University Library, Ithaca NY p. 1641

Cornerstone University, Grand Rapids MI p. 1184

Cornette Library, *see* West Texas A&M University, Canyon TX p. 2294

Corning City Library, Corning KS p. 862

Corning Community College, Corning NY p. 1610

Corning Museum of Glass, Corning NY p. 1611

Corning Public Library, Corning AR p. 97

Corning Public Library, Corning IA p. 804

Corning Warren H Library, *see* Holden Arboretum, Kirtland OH p. 1908

Cornish College of the Arts Library, Seattle WA p. 2527

Cornwall Free Library, Cornwall CT p. 334

Cornwall Free Public Library, Cornwall VT p. 2422

Cornwall Public, *see* Prince Edward Island Public Library Service, Cornwall PE p. 2876

Cornwall Public Library, Cornwall NY p. 1611

Cornwall Public Library, Cornwall ON p. 2801

Corona Public Library, Corona CA p. 136

Coronado Public Library, Coronado CA p. 136

Coronation Memorial Library, Coronation AB p. 2695

Corporation of the City of Burlington, Burlington ON p. 2798

Corporation of the Township of Nipigon Public Library Board, Nipigon ON p. 2824

Corps of Engineers Alaska, *see* United States Army, Elmendorf AFB AK p. 47

Corps of Engineers Buffalo Technical Library, *see* United States Army, Buffalo NY p. 1599

Corps of Engineers Fort Worth Technical Library, *see* United States Army, Fort Worth TX p. 2324

Corps of Engineers Memphis Library, *see* United States Army, Memphis TN p. 2252

Corps of Engineers New England Library, *see* United States Army, Concord MA p. 1083

Corps of Engineers New Orleans Technical Library, *see* United States Army, New Orleans LA p. 963

Corps of Engineers Omaha Library, *see* United States Army, Omaha NE p. 1414

Corps of Engineers Rock Island Technical Library, *see* United States Army, Rock Island IL p. 696

Corps of Engineers Sacramento Technical Information Center, *see* United States Army, Sacramento CA p. 225

Corps of Engineers Saint Paul Technical Library, *see* United States Army, Saint Paul MN p. 1282

Corps of Engineers Technical Library, *see* United States Army, Jacksonville FL p. 455

Corpus Christi Museum of Science & History, Corpus Christi TX p. 2301

Corpus Christi Public Libraries, Corpus Christi TX p. 2301

Corrales Community Library, Corrales NM p. 1554

Correctional Institution for Women, Clinton NJ p. 1479

Correctional Service of Canada, Bath ON p. 2794

Correctional Service of Canada, Laval QC p. 2886

Correctional Service of Canada-Pacific Region, Agassiz BC p. 2724

Correctional Services of Canada, Dorchester NB p. 2762

Correctionville Public Library, Correctionville IA p. 804

Corrigan Memorial Library, *see* Saint Joseph's Seminary, Yonkers NY p. 1771

Corriher-Linn-Black Library, *see* Catawba College, Salisbury NC p. 1821

Corry Public Library, Corry PA p. 2047

Corsicana Public Library, Corsicana TX p. 2302

Cortese Library, *see* California Christian College, Fresno CA p. 150

Cortez Public Library, Cortez CO p. 297

Cortland Community Library, Cortland IL p. 631

Cortland County Historical Society, Cortland NY p. 1611

Cortland Free Library, Cortland NY p. 1611

Corvallis-Benton County Public Library, Corvallis OR p. 1994

Corwith Public Library, Corwith IA p. 804

Cosbey Winifred Library, *see* Elkhart County Historical Society, Inc, Bristol IN p. 729

Cosby Community Library, Cosby TN p. 2232

Cosgrove Library, *see* Truman College, Chicago IL p. 625

Coshocton Public Library, Coshocton OH p. 1891

COSLINE (N), *see* Council of State Library Agencies In The Northeast, Hartford CT p. 2939

Cosmos Club Library, Washington DC p. 396

Cosner Library, *see* Germanna Community College, Fredericksburg VA p. 2466

Cossatot Community College of the University of Arkansas, DeQueen AR p. 97

Cossitt Frederick H Library, *see* Granby Public Library, North Granby CT p. 341

Costa Anthony Pio Memorial Library, *see* Fairfield Public Library, Fairfield NJ p. 1485

Dungan Donald, *see* OC Public Libraries, Costa Mesa CA p. 258

Costilla County Library, San Luis CO p. 322

Cosumnes River College Library, Sacramento CA p. 223

Cote Saint-Luc Public Library, *see* London Eleanor Cote Saint Luc Public Library, Cote Saint-Luc QC p. 2881

Cottage Grove Library & Community Center, Cottage Grove OR p. 1995

Cottage Health System, Santa Barbara CA p. 260

Cottet Gerard Library, *see* Pennsylvania College of Optometry, Elkins Park PA p. 2054

Cottey College, Nevada MO p. 1347

Cotton G Robert Regional Correctional Facility Library, Jackson MI p. 1195

Cotton Mary Public Library, Sabetha KS p. 892

Cottonlandia Museum, Greenwood MS p. 1299

Cottonwood County Historical Society Library, Windom MN p. 1289

Cottonwood Public Library, Cottonwood AZ p. 61

Cottrell E J Memorial Library, Atlanta NY p. 1575

Cotuit Library, Cotuit MA p. 1083

Coudersport Public Library, Coudersport PA p. 2047

Coulee City Community, *see* North Central Regional Library, Coulee City WA p. 2548

Coulter Public Library, Coulter IA p. 804

Coulter Sidney B Library, *see* Onondaga Community College, Syracuse NY p. 1752

Coulterville Public Library, Coulterville IL p. 631

Council Bluffs Public Library, Council Bluffs IA p. 805

Council District Library, Council ID p. 573

Council for Advancement & Support of Education, Washington DC p. 397

Council for Christian Colleges & Universities (N), Washington DC p. 2940

Council for Relationships Library, Philadelphia PA p. 2105

Council Grove Public Library, Council Grove KS p. 862

Council of Archives & Research Libraries in Jewish Studies (N), New York NY p. 2950

Council of Directors of State University Libraries in Illinois (N), Springfield IL p. 2942

Council of Governments of the Central Naugatuck Valley Library, Waterbury CT p. 374

Council of Michigan Foundations, Grand Haven MI p. 1183

Council of Prairie & Pacific University Libraries (N), Victoria BC p. 2959

Council of Research & Academic Libraries (N), San Antonio TX p. 2956

Council of State Library Agencies In The Northeast (N), Hartford CT p. 2939

Council on Foreign Relations Library, New York NY p. 1676

Council on Foundations, Arlington VA p. 2449

Council Tree Library, *see* Poudre River Public Library District, Fort Collins CO p. 308

Council Valley Free Library, *see* Council District Library, Council ID p. 573

Country Hills Community, *see* Kitchener Public Library, Kitchener ON p. 2815

Country Music Hall of Fame & Museum, Nashville TN p. 2255

Countway Francis A Library of Medicine, *see* Harvard Library, Boston MA p. 1074

County College of Morris, Randolph NJ p. 1525

County of Brant Public Library, Paris ON p. 2835

County of Carleton Law Library, Ottawa ON p. 2830

County of Los Angeles Public Library, Downey CA p. 140

County of Prince Edward Libraries, Ameliasburgh ON p. 2792

County of Prince Edward Libraries, Bloomfield ON p. 2795

County of Prince Edward Libraries, Consecon ON p. 2800

County of Prince Edward Libraries, Milford ON p. 2821

County of Prince Edward Libraries, Picton ON p. 2836

County of Prince Edward Libraries, Wellington ON p. 2870

Coupeville Community Library, *see* Sno-Isle Libraries, Coupeville WA p. 2542

Courant Institute of Mathematical Sciences, *see* New York University, New York NY p. 1695

Courier Library, Findlay OH p. 1899

Court of Appeals Eleventh Circuit Library, Atlanta GA p. 514

Court Square Community Library, *see* Queens Borough Public Library, Long Island City NY p. 1644

Courtland Community Library, Courtland KS p. 862

Courtland Community Operated Neighborhood Library, *see* Sacramento Public Library, Courtland CA p. 224

Courtland Public Library, Courtland AL p. 13

Courtright Memorial Library, *see* Otterbein University, Westerville OH p. 1946

Courts Administration Service, Tax Library, *see* Government of Canada, Ottawa ON p. 2831

Courville-Abbott Memorial Library, *see* White Memorial Medical Center, Los Angeles CA p. 180

Coutts Herbert T Education & Physical Education Library, *see* University of Alberta, Edmonton AB p. 2702

Coutts Municipal Library, Coutts AB p. 2695

Cove City Public Library, Cove City NC p. 1785

Cove Library, Cove OR p. 1995

Covenant College, Lookout Mountain GA p. 539

Covenant Health, Knoxville TN p. 2241

Covenant Health System, Lubbock TX p. 2357

Covenant Medical Center, Waterloo IA p. 850

Covenant Medical Library, *see* Covenant Health System, Lubbock TX p. 2357

Covenant Theological Seminary, Saint Louis MO p. 1354

Covenant United Methodist Church, Springfield PA p. 2142

Coventry Public Library, Coventry RI p. 2164

Covidien, Saint Louis MO p. 1354

Covina Public Library, Covina CA p. 137

Covington & Burling LLP, Washington DC p. 397

Covington George W Memorial Library, *see* Copiah-Jefferson Regional Library System, Hazlehurst MS p. 1301

Covington-Veedersburg Public Library, Covington IN p. 734

Cowan Memorial Library, *see* Anglican Church of Canada, Saint John NB p. 2767

Cowen Library, Cowen WV p. 2558

Coweta Public Library, Coweta OK p. 1961

Coweta Public Library System, Newnan GA p. 546

Cowles Harriet Cheney Memorial Library, *see* Whitworth University, Spokane WA p. 2538

Cowles Library, *see* Drake University, Des Moines IA p. 809

Cowley County Community College, Arkansas City KS p. 856

Cowley County Historical Society Museum Library, Winfield KS p. 902

Cox Angie Williams Public Library, Pardeeville WI p. 2629

Cox Anne Spencer Library, *see* Northeast Regional Library, Baldwyn MS p. 1297

Cox, Castle & Nicholson LLP Library, Los Angeles CA p. 169

Cox Sidney Library of Music & Dance, *see* Cornell University Library, Ithaca NY p. 1641

Cox Smith Matthews Inc, San Antonio TX p. 2379

Cox T Elmer Library, Greeneville TN p. 2236

CoxHealth Libraries, Springfield MO p. 1366

Coxsackie Correctional Facility Library, Coxsackie NY p. 1612

Coyle Free Library, Chambersburg PA p. 2043

Cozby William T Library, *see* Coppell Public Library, Coppell TX p. 2301

Cozean C H Library, *see* Mineral Area College, Park Hills MO p. 1349

Cozen O'Connor, Philadelphia PA p. 2105

CPC (N), *see* Central Pennsylvania Consortium, Carlisle PA p. 2953

CPCCM (N), *see* Consortium of Popular Culture Collections in the Midwest, Bowling Green OH p. 2952

CPHSLA (N), *see* Central Pennsylvania Health Sciences Library Association, University Park PA p. 2953

CPI Canada, Inc, Georgetown ON p. 2806

CRA International Library, Boston MA p. 1060

Crab Orchard Public Library District, Marion IL p. 670

Crabtree Correctional Center, Helena OK p. 1965

Cracchiolo Andrea Library, *see* Cochise College Library, Sierra Vista AZ p. 61

Craft Memorial Library, Bluefield WV p. 2555

Crafton Hills College Library, Yucaipa CA p. 286

Crafton Public Library, Pittsburgh PA p. 2124

Crafton United Presbyterian Church Library, Pittsburgh PA p. 2124

Craftsbury Public Library, Craftsbury Common VT p. 2422

Cragin Memorial Library, Colchester CT p. 334

Cragsmoor Free Library, Cragsmoor NY p. 1612

Craig Memorial Library, *see* Miami Valley Hospital, Dayton OH p. 1893

Craig Public Library, Craig AK p. 46

Craighead County Jonesboro Public Library, Jonesboro AR p. 104

Craigsville Library, Craigsville WV p. 2558

Craik Donald W Engineering Library, *see* University of Manitoba Libraries, Winnipeg MB p. 2758

Crain Communications Inc, Chicago IL p. 612

Cranberry Lake Library, *see* Clifton Community Library, Cranberry Lake NY p. 1612

Cranberry Public Library, Cranberry Township PA p. 2047

Cranbrook Academy of Art Library, Bloomfield Hills MI p. 1158

Cranbrook Public Library, Cranbrook BC p. 2727

Cranbury Public Library, Cranbury NJ p. 1480

Crandall-Combine Community Library, Crandall TX p. 2303

Crandall Prudence Museum Library, *see* Connecticut Commission on Culture & Tourism, Canterbury CT p. 333

Crandall Public Library, Glens Falls NY p. 1629

Crandon Public Library, Crandon WI p. 2587

Crane County Library, Crane TX p. 2303

Crane J W Memorial Library, *see* University of Manitoba Libraries, Winnipeg MB p. 2758

Crane Julia E Memorial Library, *see* State University of New York College at Potsdam, Potsdam NY p. 1722

Crane Thomas Public Library, Quincy MA p. 1119

Cranford Free Public Library, Cranford NJ p. 1480

Cranford United Methodist Church Library, Cranford NJ p. 1480

Cranston Public Library, Cranston RI p. 2164

Crapaud Public, *see* Prince Edward Island Public Library Service, Crapaud PE p. 2876

Cravath Memorial Library, Hay Springs NE p. 1401

Cravath, Swaine & Moore LLP, New York NY p. 1676

Craven Community College, New Bern NC p. 1812

Craven-Pamlico-Carteret Regional Library System, New Bern NC p. 1812

Crawford C C Memorial Library, *see* Dallas Christian College, Dallas TX p. 2305

Crawford County Federated Library System, Meadville PA p. 2086

Crawford County Historical Society, Meadville PA p. 2086

Crawford County Library System, Grayling MI p. 1186

Crawford County Public Library, English IN p. 737

Crawford County Public, *see* Middle Georgia Regional Library System, Roberta GA p. 541

Crawford Ethelbert B Public Library, Monticello NY p. 1662

Crawford Library, *see* Valve Manufacturers Association of America, Washington DC p. 421

Crawford Long Hospital - Emory Healthcare, Atlanta GA p. 514

Crawford Pearle L Memorial Library, Dudley MA p. 1085

Crawford Public, *see* Columbus-Lowndes Public Library, Crawford MS p. 1297

Crawford Public, *see* Delta County Libraries, Crawford CO p. 313

Crawford Public Library, Crawford NE p. 1396

Crawfordsville District Public Library, Crawfordsville IN p. 734

Crazy Horse Memorial Library, Crazy Horse SD p. 2211

CRC Press Inc Library, Boca Raton FL p. 428

Credit Valley Hospital, Mississauga ON p. 2822

Creech James Bryan Public Library, *see* Public Library of Johnston County & Smithfield, Four Oaks NC p. 1824

Creighton Public Library, Creighton NE p. 1396

Creighton University, Omaha NE p. 1412

Cremona Municipal Library, Cremona AB p. 2696

Crenshaw Cornelia Memorial Library, *see* Memphis Public Library, Memphis TN p. 2250

Crerar John Library, *see* University of Chicago Library, Chicago IL p. 626

Crescent City Public Library, *see* Putnam County Library System, Crescent City FL p. 478

Crescent Community Library, Crescent OK p. 1961

Crescent Heights Baptist Church Library, Abilene TX p. 2272

Crescent Hill Baptist Church Library, Louisville KY p. 923

Cresco Public Library, Cresco IA p. 805

Cresskill Public Library, Cresskill NJ p. 1480

Cressman Library, *see* Cedar Crest College, Allentown PA p. 2026

Cresson Public Library, Cresson PA p. 2048

Crested Butte Library, *see* Gunnison Public Library of the Gunnison County Library District, Crested Butte CO p. 312

Crestline Public Library, Crestline OH p. 1892

Creston-Dement Library District, Creston IL p. 631

Creston Public Library Association, Creston BC p. 2727

Crestview Public Library, *see* Sikes Robert L F Public Library, Crestview FL p. 434

Crestwood Public Library District, Crestwood IL p. 631

Creswell Library, *see* Lane Library District, Creswell OR p. 1995

Crete Public Library, Crete NE p. 1396

Crete Public Library District, Crete IL p. 632

Creve Coeur Public Library District, Creve Coeur IL p. 632

Crew Public Library, Salem IA p. 842

Crew's Library, *see* United States Navy, Camp Pendleton CA p. 131

Crichton College, Memphis TN p. 2248

Cridersville Public Library, *see* Auglaize County Public District Library, Cridersville OH p. 1944

Criss Dr C C & Mabel L Library, *see* University of Nebraska at Omaha, Omaha NE p. 1414

Cristal USA, Inc, Glen Burnie MD p. 1030

Criswell College, Dallas TX p. 2305

Crittenden County Library, Marion AR p. 109

Crittenden County Public Library, Marion KY p. 928

Crittenton Hospital Medical Center, Rochester MI p. 1221

Crivitz Public Library, *see* Marinette County Library System, Crivitz WI p. 2612

CRKN (N), *see* Canadian Research Knowledge Network, Ottawa ON p. 2959

Crocker House Museum Library, *see* Macomb County Historical Society, Mount Clemens MI p. 1210

Crockett County Public Library, Ozona TX p. 2367

Crockett Library, *see* Contra Costa County Library, Crockett CA p. 209

Crockett Memorial Library, Alamo TN p. 2223

Crockett Public Library, Crockett TX p. 2303

Croghan Free Library, Croghan NY p. 1612

Cromaine District Library, Hartland MI p. 1189

Cromwell Belden Public Library, Cromwell CT p. 334

Cronk Betty Memorial Library, *see* Everest Institute, Rochester NY p. 1729

Crook Community Library, Crook CO p. 297

Crook County Library, Prineville OR p. 2016

Crook County Library, Sundance WY p. 2660

Crooked Tree District Library, Walloon Lake MI p. 1234

Crookston Public Library, *see* Lake Agassiz Regional Library, Crookston MN p. 1266

Crop Diversification Centre South Library, Brooks AB p. 2686

Crosby County Library, Crosbyton TX p. 2303

Crosby County Pioneer Memorial Museum Library, Crosbyton TX p. 2303

Crosby Margaret Reed Memorial Library, *see* Pearl River County Library System, Picayune MS p. 1311

Crosby Public Library, Antwerp NY p. 1574

Croskery George G Memorial Library, Ottawa ON p. 2830

Cross Cancer Institute Library, Edmonton AB p. 2700

Cross City Correctional Institution Library, Cross City FL p. 434

Cross' Mills Public Library, Charlestown RI p. 2164

Cross Plains Public Library, Cross Plains TX p. 2303

Crossett Library, *see* Bennington College, Bennington VT p. 2418

Crossett Public Library, Crossett AR p. 97

Crossfield Municipal Library, Crossfield AB p. 2696

Crossroads Bible College, Indianapolis IN p. 750

Crossroads College, Rochester MN p. 1272

Crossroads Public Library, *see* West Georgia Regional Library, Acworth GA p. 524

Crossville Public Library, Crossville AL p. 13

Crosswicks Library Co, Crosswicks NJ p. 1481

Crosswicks Public Library, *see* Crosswicks Library Co, Crosswicks NJ p. 1481

Croton Free Library, Croton-on-Hudson NY p. 1612

Crouch Fine Arts Library, *see* Baylor University Libraries, Waco TX p. 2396

Crouch R E, *see* London Public Library, London ON p. 2818

Crouse Hospital Library, Syracuse NY p. 1751

Crow Canyon Archaeological Center, Cortez CO p. 297

Crow Wing County Historical Society Archives Library, Brainerd MN p. 1242

Crowder College, Neosho MO p. 1347

Crowell Library, *see* Moody Bible Institute, Chicago IL p. 619

Crowell Public Library, San Marino CA p. 254

Crowheart Public Library, Crowheart WY p. 2654

Crowley, Haughey, Hanson, Toole & Dietrich Library, Billings MT p. 1374

Crowley Public Library, Crowley TX p. 2304

Crowley Ridge Regional Library, Jonesboro AR p. 104

Dade County Public Library, *see* Cherokee Regional Library System, Trenton GA p. 538

Dadeville Public Library, Dadeville AL p. 14

Daemen College Library, Amherst NY p. 1573

Dafoe Elizabeth Library, *see* University of Manitoba Libraries, Winnipeg MB p. 2758

Daggett Eleanor Public Library, Chama NM p. 1553

D'Agostino Frank J MD Medical Library, *see* Easton Hospital, Easton PA p. 2052

Dahlgren Memorial Library, *see* Georgetown University, Washington DC p. 402

Dahlgren Public Library, Dahlgren IL p. 632

Dailey Memorial Library, Derby VT p. 2423

Daingerfield Public Library, Daingerfield TX p. 2304

Dakota City Public Library, Dakota City NE p. 1397

Dakota College at Bottineau Library, Bottineau ND p. 1839

Dakota County Historical Society, South Saint Paul MN p. 1285

Dakota County Library System, Eagan MN p. 1249

Dakota County Technical College Library, Rosemount MN p. 1273

Dakota State University, Madison SD p. 2214

Dakota Wesleyan University, Mitchell SD p. 2215

Daland Memorial Library, Mont Vernon NH p. 1458

Dale & Lessmann Library, Toronto ON p. 2852

Dale Gertrude Angel Library, *see* Southeast Kentucky Community & Technical College, Cumberland KY p. 911

Daleville Public Library, Daleville AL p. 14

Daley Richard J Library, *see* Chicago Public Library, Chicago IL p. 608

Daley Richard J Library, *see* University of Illinois at Chicago, Chicago IL p. 627

Daley Richard M, *see* Chicago Public Library, Chicago IL p. 608

Dalhousie Centennial Library, *see* Chaleur Library Region, Dalhousie NB p. 2761

Dalhousie University, Halifax NS p. 2780, 2978

Dali Museum Library, *see* Dali Salvador Foundation Inc, Saint Petersburg FL p. 487

Dali Salvador Foundation Inc, Saint Petersburg FL p. 487

Dallam-Hartley County Library, Dalhart TX p. 2304

Dallas Baptist University, Dallas TX p. 2305

Dallas Christian College, Dallas TX p. 2305

Dallas County Community College District, Dallas TX p. 2305

Dallas County Community College District, Mesquite TX p. 2362

Dallas County Historical Society, Buffalo MO p. 1321

Dallas County Law Library, Dallas TX p. 2305

Dallas County Library, Fordyce AR p. 100

Dallas County Library, Buffalo MO p. 1321

Dallas Historical Society, Dallas TX p. 2305

Dallas Municipal Archives, Dallas TX p. 2306

Dallas Museum of Art, Dallas TX p. 2306

Dallas Public Library, Dallas OR p. 1995

Dallas Public Library, Dallas TX p. 2306

Dallas Public Library, Dallas WI p. 2587

Dallas Theological Seminary, Dallas TX p. 2307

Dalles-Wasco County Library, The Dalles OR p. 2020

Dally Memorial Library, Sardis OH p. 1934

DALNET (N), *see* Detroit Area Library Network, Detroit MI p. 2946

Dalton Community Library, Dalton PA p. 2048

Dalton Free Public Library, Dalton MA p. 1083

Dalton Public Library, Dalton NE p. 1397

Dalton Public Library, Dalton NH p. 1444

Dalton State College, Dalton GA p. 528

Daly City Public Library, Daly City CA p. 138

Daly Elizabeth Kerns Library, *see* Northern Wyoming Community College District - Gillette, Gillette WY p. 2655

Daly John D, *see* Daly City Public Library, Daly City CA p. 138

Daly Leo A Co Library, Honolulu HI p. 560

Damascus Library, *see* Montgomery County Public Libraries, Damascus MD p. 1038

D'Amour Library, *see* Western New England University, Springfield MA p. 1128

Dana-Farber Cancer Institute, Boston MA p. 1060

Dana John Cotton Library, *see* Rutgers University Libraries, Newark NJ p. 1512

Dana John Cotton Library, *see* Woodstock Historical Society, Inc, Woodstock VT p. 2441

Dana Marshall N Memorial Library, *see* Clackamas Community College, Oregon City OR p. 2009

Dana Medical Library, *see* University of Vermont Libraries, Burlington VT p. 2421

Cord Memorial Library, *see* Woodbury County Library, Danbury IA p. 834

Danbury Hospital, Danbury CT p. 335

Danbury Law Library, *see* Connecticut Judicial Branch Law Libraries, Danbury CT p. 344

Danbury Public Library, Danbury CT p. 335

Danbury Public Library, Danbury NC p. 1786

Danbury Scott-Fanton Museum & Historical Society, Danbury CT p. 335

Dance Notation Bureau Library, New York NY p. 1676

Dancer Transition Resource Centre, Toronto ON p. 2852

Dandridge Memorial Library, Dandridge TN p. 2232

Dane County Legal Resource Center, *see* Wisconsin State Law Library, Madison WI p. 2611

Dane County Library Service, Madison WI p. 2606

Dane County Regional Planning Commission Library, Madison WI p. 2606

Danforth Charles B Public Library, Barnard VT p. 2417

Danforth H Raymond Library, *see* New England College, Henniker NH p. 1451

Danforth Memorial Library, *see* Paterson Free Public Library, Paterson NJ p. 1518

Danforth Museum of Art, Framingham MA p. 1089

Danforth Public Library, Danforth ME p. 983

D'Angelo Law Library, *see* University of Chicago Library, Chicago IL p. 626

DeMaio Paul Library, *see* Broward County Division of Libraries, Dania Beach FL p. 441

Daniel John H, *see* Southside Virginia Community College, Keysville VA p. 2472

Daniel Library, *see* Citadel, Charleston SC p. 2184

Daniel Vista J Memorial, *see* Noxubee County Library System, Shuqualak MS p. 1307

Daniel Webster College, Nashua NH p. 1458

Daniels County Free Library, Scobey MT p. 1388

Daniels John H Faculty of Architecture, Landscape & Design, *see* University of Toronto Libraries, Toronto ON p. 2865

Dannemora Free Library, Dannemora NY p. 1613

Dansville Library, *see* Capital Area District Libraries, Dansville MI p. 1200

Dansville Public Library, Dansville NY p. 1613

Danvers Township Library, Danvers IL p. 632

Danville Area Community College Library, Danville IL p. 632

Danville-Center Township Public Library, Danville IN p. 735

Danville Community College, Danville VA p. 2459

Danville Library, *see* Contra Costa County Library, Danville CA p. 209

Danville Library Inc, *see* Boyle County Public Library, Danville KY p. 911

Danville Public, *see* Public Library of Mount Vernon & Knox County, Danville OH p. 1919

Danville Public Library, Danville IL p. 633

Danville Public Library, Danville VA p. 2459

Danville Regional Medical Center, Danville VA p. 2460

Daphne Public Library, Daphne AL p. 14

DAR Library, *see* National Society of the Daughters of the American Revolution, Washington DC p. 411

Darby Community Public Library, Darby MT p. 1377

Darby Foundation, Fort Smith AR p. 100

Darby Free Library, Darby PA p. 2049

Darcy Library of Beulah, Beulah MI p. 1157

Darden Graduate School of Business-Camp Library, *see* University of Virginia, Charlottesville VA p. 2455

Dare County Library, Manteo NC p. 1808

Dare Ruby E Library, *see* Greenville College, Greenville IL p. 652

Dargan E C Library, Nashville TN p. 2255

Darien Historical Society, Inc Library, Darien CT p. 336

Darien Library, Darien CT p. 336

Darien Public Library, Darien WI p. 2587

Darke County Law Library, *see* Greenville Law Library Association, Greenville OH p. 1903

Darling Hugh & Hazel Law Library, *see* University of California Los Angeles Library, Los Angeles CA p. 178

Darling Hugh & Hazel Library, *see* Hope International University, Fullerton CA p. 154

Darling Louise M Biomedical Library, *see* University of California Los Angeles Library, Los Angeles CA p. 178

Darling Marine Center Library, *see* University of Maine, Walpole ME p. 1004

Darling Roger E Memorial Library, *see* Ashland Theological Seminary, Ashland OH p. 1855

Darlington County Historical Commission, Darlington SC p. 2192

Darlington County Library, Darlington SC p. 2192

Darlington Public Library, Darlington IN p. 735

Darrington Community Library, *see* Sno-Isle Libraries, Darrington WA p. 2542

Dart John L, *see* Charleston County Public Library, Charleston SC p. 2183

Dartmouth College Library, Hanover NH p. 1450

Dartmouth Heritage Museum Library, Dartmouth NS p. 2779

Dartmouth Public Libraries, Dartmouth MA p. 1084

Darton College, Albany GA p. 507

Darwell Public Library, Darwell AB p. 2696

Dassel Public Library, Dassel MN p. 1247

Daugherty Public Library District, Dupo IL p. 638

Daughters of Charity Health Care System, Los Angeles CA p. 169

Daughters of the Republic of Texas Library at the Alamo, San Antonio TX p. 2379

Daume Mary K Library, *see* Monroe County Library System, Monroe MI p. 1209

Dauphin County Law Library, Harrisburg PA p. 2064

Dauphin County Library System, Harrisburg PA p. 2064

Davee Chalmer Library, *see* University of Wisconsin-River Falls, River Falls WI p. 2635

Davenport Public Library, Davenport IA p. 806

Davenport Public Library, Davenport NE p. 1397

Davenport Public Library, Davenport WA p. 2513

Davenport University, Grand Rapids MI p. 1184

David Edward M Research Library, Philadelphia PA p. 2105

David Library of the American Revolution, Washington Crossing PA p. 2151

Davidson College, Davidson NC p. 1786

Davidson County Community College, Lexington NC p. 1806

Davidson County Public Library System, Lexington NC p. 1806

Davidson Library, *see* University of California, Santa Barbara, Santa Barbara CA p. 261

Davie County Public Library, Mocksville NC p. 1809

Davies Memorial Library, Lower Waterford VT p. 2427

Davies Public Library, *see* Arapahoe Library District, Deer Trail CO p. 305

Davies Robertson Library, *see* University of Toronto Libraries, Toronto ON p. 2865

Davies, Ward, Phillips & Vineberg, Toronto ON p. 2852

Daviess County Library, Gallatin MO p. 1329

Daviess County Public Library, Owensboro KY p. 931

Davis & Co, Vancouver BC p. 2740

Davis & Elkins College, Elkins WV p. 2558

Davis Addie Memorial Library, Mountain View OK p. 1969

Davis Arthur Vining Library, *see* Mote Marine Laboratory Library, Sarasota FL p. 489

Davis Austin Public Library, *see* Tampa-Hillsborough County Public Library System, Odessa FL p. 497

Davis Brown Law Firm, Des Moines IA p. 808

Davis Carl Jr, MD Medical Library, *see* NorthShore University HealthSystem, Skokie IL p. 703

Davis Center for Russian & Eurasian Studies Fung Library, *see* Harvard Library, Cambridge MA p. 1074

Davis Centre Library, *see* University of Waterloo Library, Waterloo ON p. 2870

Davis College, Toledo OH p. 1939

Davis Community Church Library, Davis CA p. 139

Davis County Library, Farmington UT p. 2405

Holmes Davis Dalton Memorial Library, *see* Bridgton Public Library, Bridgton ME p. 979

Davis Edwin M Memorial Library, *see* Avoca Public Library, Avoca IA p. 795

Davis Friends Meeting Library, Davis CA p. 139

Davis, Graham & Stubbs LLP, Denver CO p. 300

Davis H F Memorial Library, *see* Colby Community College, Colby KS p. 861

Davis Harmer E Transportation Library, *see* Institute of Transportation Studies Library, Berkeley CA p. 127

Davis Ivan O Library, *see* Liberty Library, Liberty ME p. 990

Davis J M Arms & Historical Museum, Claremore OK p. 1960

Davis James & Leah Memorial Library, *see* Chicago Sinai Congregation, Chicago IL p. 610

Davis Jeanette Albiez Library, *see* University of Rio Grande, Rio Grande OH p. 1931

Davis Jeff County Library, Fort Davis TX p. 2320

Davis Jeff Public Library, *see* Satilla Regional Library, Hazlehurst GA p. 530

Davis Jefferson Campus Learning Resource Center, *see* Mississippi Gulf Coast Community College, Gulfport MS p. 1300

Davis Jefferson Parish Library, Jennings LA p. 952

Davis John Memorial Library, *see* First Baptist Church, Winston-Salem NC p. 1832

Davis Julia, *see* Saint Louis Public Library, Saint Louis MO p. 1360

Davis Kathryn & Shelby Cullom Library, *see* Saint John's University Library, New York NY p. 1725

Davis Lee Library, *see* San Jacinto College, Pasadena TX p. 2369

Davis Library, *see* Montgomery County Public Libraries, Bethesda MD p. 1038

Davis M R Public Library, *see* First Regional Library, Southaven MS p. 1301

Davis Maribelle M Library, *see* Plano Public Library System, Plano TX p. 2370

Davis Marion Memorial, *see* McDowell County Public Library, Old Fort NC p. 1809

Davis Mark J Jr Memorial, *see* Natrona County Public Library, Edgerton WY p. 2652

Davis Memorial Library, Limington ME p. 990

Davis Memorial Library, *see* Methodist College, Fayetteville NC p. 1793

Davis Polk & Wardwell Library, New York NY p. 1677

Davis Public Library, Stoddard NH p. 1465

Davis Public Library, *see* Chickasaw Regional Library System, Davis OK p. 1957

Davis Stanley K Library, *see* Samaritan Albany General Hospital, Albany OR p. 1989

Davis William Memorial Library, *see* Emanuel Synagogue, Oklahoma City OK p. 1971

Davis Wright Tremaine LLP, Seattle WA p. 2527

Davisville Free Library, North Kingstown RI p. 2170

Dawes Arboretum Library, Newark OH p. 1921

Dawson City Museum & Historical Society, Dawson City YT p. 2933

Dawson College Library, Westmount QC p. 2915

Dawson Community College Library, Glendive MT p. 1379

Dawson County Library, Lamesa TX p. 2353

Dawson County Library, *see* Chestatee Regional Library System, Dawsonville GA p. 529

Dawson Creek Municipal Public Library, Dawson Creek BC p. 2727

Dawson Dana Library, *see* Saint Paul School of Theology, Kansas City MO p. 1341

Dawson Hubert M Library, *see* Temple College, Temple TX p. 2391

Dawson J M Church, *see* Baylor University Libraries, Waco TX p. 2396

Dawson Public Library, Dawson MN p. 1247

Dawson Technical Institute, Chicago IL p. 612

Day Pitney LLP, Boston MA p. 1060

Day Pitney LLP, Florham Park NJ p. 1486

Daysland Public Library, Daysland AB p. 2696

Dayton Art Institute, Dayton OH p. 1892

Dayton Law Library, Dayton OH p. 1892

Dayton Memorial Library, *see* Regis University, Denver CO p. 303

Dayton Metro Library, Dayton OH p. 1892

Dayton Public Library, Dayton IA p. 807

Daytona Beach Community College Library, Daytona Beach FL p. 435

Daytona Beach Regional, *see* Volusia County Public Library, Daytona Beach FL p. 436

DC Court of Appeals Library, Washington DC p. 397

DC Regional Library for the Blind & Physically Handicapped, Washington DC p. 397

DCAHSL (N), *see* District of Columbia Area Health Science Libraries, Washington DC p. 2940

DDB Chicago, Chicago IL p. 612

DDB Worldwide, New York NY p. 1677

De Anza College, Cupertino CA p. 138

De Grandpre Chait Library, Montreal QC p. 2895

de la Parte Louis, *see* University of South Florida, Tampa FL p. 498

de Lancie John Library, *see* Rock Milton L Resource Center, Philadelphia PA p. 2115

De Leon City County Library, De Leon TX p. 2311

De Paul Library, *see* University of Saint Mary, Leavenworth KS p. 879

De Rodriguez Ramonita G, *see* Free Library of Philadelphia, Philadelphia PA p. 2107

de Rothschild Edmond Library, *see* Park Avenue Synagogue, New York NY p. 1697

De Soto Public Library, De Soto IA p. 807

De Soto Public Library, De Soto MO p. 1327

De Soto Public Library, De Soto WI p. 2588

De Soto Trail Regional Library, Camilla GA p. 522

Deaconess Hospital, Evansville IN p. 738

Deaconess Hospital, Oklahoma City OK p. 1971

Deadwood Public Library, Deadwood SD p. 2211

Deaf Services Commission of Iowa, Des Moines IA p. 808

Deaf Smith County Library, Hereford TX p. 2332

Dealey G B Library, *see* Dallas Historical Society, Dallas TX p. 2305

Dean Bashford Memorial Library, *see* American Museum of Natural History Library, New York NY p. 1668

Dean College, Franklin MA p. 1090

Dean Edwin W Sr Memorial Library, *see* Centinela Hospital Medical Center, Inglewood CA p. 159

Deane Barbara & Maurice A Law Library, *see* Hofstra University Law Library, Hempstead NY p. 1635

de Angeli Marguerite, *see* Lapeer District Library, Lapeer MI p. 1202

Dearborn County Hospital, Lawrenceburg IN p. 760

Dearborn Frederick M Library, *see* Metropolitan Hospital Center, New York NY p. 1686

Dearborn Heights City Libraries, Dearborn Heights MI p. 1168

Dearborn Historical Museum Library, Dearborn MI p. 1167

Dearborn Public Library, Dearborn MI p. 1167

Death Valley National Park Research Libraries, *see* National Park Service, Death Valley CA p. 140

Deats Hiram E Memorial Library, *see* Hunterdon County Historical Society, Flemington NJ p. 1486

DeBary Public, *see* Volusia County Public Library, DeBary FL p. 436

Debden Public Library, *see* Wapiti Regional Library, Debden SK p. 2921

DeBenedictis Henrietta Library, *see* Massachusetts College of Pharmacy & Health Sciences, Boston MA p. 1063

Debevoise & Plimpton Library, Washington DC p. 397

Debevoise & Plimpton, New York NY p. 1677

DeBlois Austen K Library, *see* Palmer Theological Seminary, Wynnewood PA p. 2158

DeBolt Public Library, DeBolt AB p. 2696

Deborah Heart & Lung Center, Browns Mills NJ p. 1475

Deborah Library, *see* Congregation Beth Israel, West Hartford CT p. 375

Gragg Gilbert H Library, *see* Southwest Georgia Regional Library, Bainbridge GA p. 521

Decatur County Library, Decaturville TN p. 2232

Decatur Genealogical Society Library, Decatur IL p. 633

Decatur Herald & Review Library, Decatur IL p. 633

Decatur Learning Resources Center, *see* Georgia Perimeter College, Decatur GA p. 525

Decatur Memorial Hospital, Decatur IL p. 633

Decatur Public, *see* Kemper-Newton Regional Library System, Decatur MS p. 1316

Decatur Public Library, Decatur AL p. 14

Decatur Public Library, Decatur IL p. 633

Decatur Public Library, Decatur TX p. 2311

Dechert Law Library, Boston MA p. 1060

Dechert Law Library, New York NY p. 1677

Dechert Library, Philadelphia PA p. 2105

Dechert LLP, Washington DC p. 397

Decker Library, *see* Maryland Institute College of Art, Baltimore MD p. 1015

Deckerville Public Library, Deckerville MI p. 1168

Decorah Public Library, Decorah IA p. 807

Dedham Historical Society Library, Dedham MA p. 1084

Dedham Public Library, Dedham MA p. 1084

Deel Jonnie B Memorial, *see* Lonesome Pine Regional Library, Clintwood VA p. 2504

Deep River Public Library, Deep River CT p. 336

Deer Creek District Library, Deer Creek IL p. 634

Deer Isle-Stonington Historical Society, Deer Isle ME p. 983

Deer Lodge Public Library, Deer Lodge TN p. 2233

Deer Park Public Library, Deer Park NY p. 1613

Deer Park Public Library, Deer Park TX p. 2311

Deer Park Public Library, Deer Park WI p. 2588

Deere & Co Library, Moline IL p. 674

White Percy, *see* Broward County Division of Libraries, Deerfield Beach FL p. 441

Deerfield Correctional Center, Capron VA p. 2453

Deerfield Public Library, Deerfield IL p. 634

Deerfield Public Library, Deerfield WI p. 2588

Deering Public Library, Deering NH p. 1444

Dees Eula Memorial Library, *see* Northeast Mississippi Community College, Booneville MS p. 1294

Defence R&D Canada-Valcartier Library, Val-Belair QC p. 2914

Defence Research & Development Canada-Altantic Library, *see* Canada Department of National Defence, Dartmouth NS p. 2779

Defence Research & Development Canada, Toronto ON p. 2852

Defense Institute of Security Assistance Management Library, *see* United States Department of Defense, Wright-Patterson AFB OH p. 1951

Defense Language Institute, *see* United States Department of the Air Force, Lackland AFB TX p. 2352

Defense Technical Information Center, Fort Belvoir VA p. 2464

Defiance College, Defiance OH p. 1895

Defiance Public Library, Defiance OH p. 1895

DeForest Area Public Library, DeForest WI p. 2588

Degen John A Resource Room, *see* Florida State University Libraries, Tallahassee FL p. 494

Degenkolb Engineers Library, San Francisco CA p. 241

Degenshein George A MD Memorial Library, *see* Maimonides Medical Center, Brooklyn NY p. 1593

Degenstein Community Library, Sunbury PA p. 2144

Degolyer & MacNaughton Library, Dallas TX p. 2307

DeGolyer Library of Special Collections, *see* Southern Methodist University, Dallas TX p. 2310

Degroodt Franklin T Library, Palm Bay FL p. 479

DeHart A Robert Learning Center, *see* De Anza College, Cupertino CA p. 138

DeHoff Memorial Branch, *see* Stark County District Library, Canton OH p. 1864

Dehon Leo Library, *see* Sacred Heart School of Theology, Franklin WI p. 2593

DeKalb County Public Library, Fort Payne AL p. 17

DeKalb County Public Library, Decatur GA p. 529

Dekalb Medical Center, Decatur GA p. 530

DeKalb Public Library, DeKalb IL p. 635

DeKoven Center Library, *see* DeKoven Foundation, Racine WI p. 2632

DeKoven Foundation, Racine WI p. 2632

Del City Library, *see* Metropolitan Library System in Oklahoma County, Del City OK p. 1972

Del Mar College, Corpus Christi TX p. 2302

Del Norte Biosciences Library Consortium (N), El Paso TX p. 2956

Del Norte County Historical Society Museum Library, Crescent City CA p. 137

Del Norte County Library District, Crescent City CA p. 137

Del Norte Public Library, Del Norte CO p. 297

Del Paso Heights Library, *see* Sacramento Public Library, Sacramento CA p. 224

Del Toro Fulladosa Josefina, Rare Books & Manuscripts, *see* University of Puerto Rico Library System, San Juan PR p. 2677

Delafield Public Library, Delafield WI p. 2588

DeLaMare Library, *see* University of Nevada-Reno, Reno NV p. 1433

Delanco Public Library, Delanco NJ p. 1481

DeLand Area Public, *see* Volusia County Public Library, DeLand FL p. 436

Delano Library, *see* Great River Regional Library, Delano MN p. 1275

DeLap Loyd Law Library, *see* Klamath County Library Services District, Klamath Falls OR p. 2002

Delaware Agricultural Museum & Village Library-Archives, Dover DE p. 381

Delaware Art Museum, Wilmington DE p. 387

Delaware City Public Library, Delaware City DE p. 381

Delaware Correctional Center Law Library, Smyrna DE p. 386

Delaware County Community College Library, Media PA p. 2087

Delaware County District Library, Delaware OH p. 1895

Delaware County Historical Society, Chester PA p. 2044

Delaware County Law Library Association, Delaware OH p. 1895

Delaware County Library, Jay OK p. 1966

Delaware County Library System, Media PA p. 2087

Delaware County Supreme Court Law Library, Delhi NY p. 1613

Delaware Division of Substance Abuse & Mental Health, New Castle DE p. 384

Delaware Historical Society Research Library, Wilmington DE p. 387

Delaware Indian Resource Center, *see* Westchester County Department of Parks, Recreation & Conservation, Cross River NY p. 1612

Delaware Library Consortium (N), Newark DE p. 2940

Delaware Museum of Natural History Library, Wilmington DE p. 387

Delaware Public Archives, Dover DE p. 382

Delaware River Basin Commission Library, Ewing NJ p. 1484

Delaware State Law Library in Kent County, Dover DE p. 382

Delaware State University, Dover DE p. 382

Delaware Technical & Community College, Dover DE p. 382

Delaware Technical & Community College, Georgetown DE p. 383

Delaware Technical & Community College, Newark DE p. 385

Delaware Technical & Community College, Wilmington DE p. 387

Delaware Township Library, Valley Falls KS p. 898

Delaware Township Library Association, Dingmans Ferry PA p. 2049

Delaware Valley College of Science & Agriculture, Doylestown PA p. 2050

Delaware Valley Hospital, Walton NY p. 1762

Delaware Valley Information Consortium (N), Langhorne PA p. 2954

Delburne Municipal Library, Delburne AB p. 2696

Delevan-Yorkshire Public Library, Delevan NY p. 1613

Delgado Community College, New Orleans LA p. 959

Delhi Public Library, Delhi IA p. 807

Delia Municipal Library, Delia AB p. 2696

Delmar Public Library, Delmar DE p. 381

Delmont Public Library, Delmont PA p. 2049

Delnor Community Hospital, Geneva IL p. 648

Deloitte & Touche, Vancouver BC p. 2741

Deloitte & Touche Library, Washington DC p. 397

Deloitte & Touche LLP, Minneapolis MN p. 1259

DeLoria Vine, Jr Library, *see* Smithsonian Libraries, Suitland DC p. 414

Delphi Public Library, Delphi IN p. 735

Delphos Public Library, Delphos KS p. 863

Delphos Public Library, Delphos OH p. 1896

Delray Beach Public Library, Delray Beach FL p. 437

Delta City Library, Delta UT p. 2404

Delta College Library, University Center MI p. 1232

Delta Community Library, Delta Junction AK p. 47

Delta Correctional Center Library, *see* Colorado Department of Corrections, Delta CO p. 298

Delta County Libraries, Hotchkiss CO p. 313

Delta County Public Library, Cooper TX p. 2301

Delta Public Library, Delta OH p. 1896

Delta Public Library, *see* Delta County Libraries, Delta CO p. 313

Delta State University, Cleveland MS p. 1296

Delta Township District Library, Lansing MI p. 1200

Delton District Library, Delton MI p. 1169

Deltona Regional, *see* Volusia County Public Library, Deltona FL p. 436

Demarest Public Library, Demarest NJ p. 1481

DeMary Memorial Library, Rupert ID p. 583

Demmer Edward U Memorial Library, Three Lakes WI p. 2642

Demopolis Public Library, *see* Marengo Library System, Demopolis AL p. 15

DeNeve Felipe, *see* Los Angeles Public Library System, Los Angeles CA p. 173

Denison Ella Strong Library, *see* Claremont Colleges Library, Claremont CA p. 134

Denison Public Library, Denison TX p. 2312

Denison University Libraries, Granville OH p. 1902

Denmark Public Library, Denmark ME p. 983

Denmark Technical College, Denmark SC p. 2192

Dennis Memorial, *see* Sussex County Library System, Newton NJ p. 1514

Dennis Memorial Library Association, Dennis MA p. 1084

Dennysville-Lincoln Memorial Library, Dennysville ME p. 983

Denton Public, *see* Davidson County Public Library System, Denton NC p. 1806

Denton Public Library, Denton MT p. 1377

Denton Public Library, Denton TX p. 2312

Denver Academy Library, Denver CO p. 300

Denver Art Museum Library, Denver CO p. 300

Denver Botanic Gardens, Denver CO p. 300

Denver Medical Library, *see* Health One Presbyterian-Saint Luke's Medical Center, Denver CO p. 302

Denver Museum of Nature & Science, Denver CO p. 300

Denver Public Library, Denver CO p. 300

Denver Public Library, Denver IA p. 808

Denver Seminary, Littleton CO p. 317

Denver Women's Correctional Facility Library, *see* Colorado Department of Corrections, Denver CO p. 299

Denville Free Public Library, Denville NJ p. 1481

Department of Canadian Heritage, Ottawa ON p. 2830

Department of Canadian Heritage, Gatineau QC p. 2883

Department of Community Services, Government of Yukon, Whitehorse YT p. 2933

Department of Conservation & Natural Resources, Dauphin Island AL p. 14

Department of Correctional Education, State Farm VA p. 2496

Department of Corrections, Machiasport ME p. 991

Department of Corrections, Custer SD p. 2211

Department of Finance & Treasury Board Canada Library, Ottawa ON p. 2830

Department of Fisheries & Oceans Canada, Mont-Joli QC p. 2887

Department of Fisheries & Oceans Canada, Central & Arctic Region, Winnipeg MB p. 2755

Department of Government Services, Government of Newfoundland & Labrador, Mount Pearl NL p. 2770

Department of Human Services-Youth Corrections, Colorado Springs CO p. 295

Department of Human Services, Englewood CO p. 306

Department of Human Services-Youth Corrections, Golden CO p. 309

Department of Human Services, Greeley CO p. 311

Department of Human Services-Youth Corrections, Pueblo CO p. 320

Department of Human Services-Youth Corrections, Denver CO p. 301

Department of Indian Affairs, Whitehorse YT p. 2934

Department of Instructional Technology-School Library Media, *see* Utah State University, Logan UT p. 2975

Department of Justice, St. John's NL p. 2772

Department of Mental Health, Saint Elizabeths Hospital, Washington DC p. 397

Department of Natural Resources, Government of Newfoundland & Labrador, St. John's NL p. 2772

Department of Veteran Affairs, Tomah WI p. 2642

Department of Veterans Affairs, Tuscaloosa AL p. 38

Department of Veterans Affairs, Prescott AZ p. 78

Department of Veterans Affairs, Tucson AZ p. 86

Department of Veterans Affairs, Loma Linda CA p. 165

Department of Veterans Affairs, San Francisco CA p. 241

Department of Veterans Affairs, Denver CO p. 301

Department of Veterans Affairs, Grand Junction CO p. 310

Department of Veterans Affairs, Wilmington DE p. 387

Department of Veterans Affairs, Washington DC p. 397

Department of Veterans Affairs, Miami FL p. 465

Department of Veterans Affairs, Boise ID p. 570

Department of Veterans Affairs, Hines IL p. 656

Department of Veterans Affairs, Indianapolis IN p. 750

Department of Veterans Affairs, Topeka KS p. 896

Department of Veterans Affairs, Alexandria LA p. 939

Department of Veterans Affairs, Shreveport LA p. 968

Department of Veterans Affairs, Augusta ME p. 974

Department of Veterans Affairs, Bedford MA p. 1052

Department of Veterans Affairs, Leeds MA p. 1098

Department of Veterans Affairs, Ann Arbor MI p. 1151

Department of Veterans Affairs, Battle Creek MI p. 1155

Department of Veterans Affairs, Saginaw MI p. 1223

Department of Veterans Affairs, Minneapolis MN p. 1259

Department of Veterans Affairs, Columbia MO p. 1324

Department of Veterans Affairs, Saint Louis MO p. 1354

Department of Veterans Affairs, Lyons NJ p. 1497

Department of Veterans Affairs, Bath NY p. 1578

Department of Veterans Affairs, Bronx NY p. 1586

Department of Veterans Affairs, Brooklyn NY p. 1592

Dexter Library, *see* Northland College, Ashland WI p. 2579

Dexter Public Library, Dexter IA p. 810

Dexter Public Library, Dexter NM p. 1554

Di Peso Charles Library, *see* Cochise College Library, Douglas AZ p. 61

Diablo Valley College Library, Pleasant Hill CA p. 210

Diack Samuel L Library, *see* Oregon Health & Science University, OGI School of Science & Engineering, Beaverton OR p. 1991

Diagnostic & Evaluation Center Library, Lincoln NE p. 1404

Dialog Corp (N), Morrisville NC p. 2951

Diamond Arthur W Law Library, *see* Columbia University, New York NY p. 1674

D'Iberville Public, *see* Harrison County Library System, D'Iberville MS p. 1299

Dibner Bern Library of Science & Technology, *see* Polytechnic Institute of NYU, Brooklyn NY p. 1594

Dibner Library of the History of Science & Technology, *see* Smithsonian Libraries, Washington DC p. 414

Dickens County-Spur Public Library, Spur TX p. 2388

Dickens Public Library, Dickens IA p. 811

Dickerman Library, Wadsworth Center, *see* New York State Department of Health, Albany NY p. 1569

Dickerson John H Heritage, *see* Volusia County Public Library, Daytona Beach FL p. 436

Dickerson-Johnson Library & Learning Resource Center, *see* Coahoma Community College, Clarksdale MS p. 1295

Dickey Alfred Public Library, Jamestown ND p. 1844

Dickhaut Library, *see* Methodist Theological School in Ohio Library, Delaware OH p. 1895

Dickinson Area Public Library, Dickinson ND p. 1840

Dickinson College, Carlisle PA p. 2041

Dickinson County Library, Iron Mountain MI p. 1193

Dickinson Donald C & Elizabeth M Research Center, *see* National Cowboy & Western Heritage Museum, Oklahoma City OK p. 1973

Dickinson George Sherman Music Library, *see* Vassar College Library, Poughkeepsie NY p. 1724

Dickinson Memorial Library, Northfield MA p. 1114

Dickinson Public Library, Dickinson TX p. 2313

Dickinson S White Memorial Library, Whately MA p. 1140

Dickinson State University, Dickinson ND p. 1840

Dickinson Wright LLP Library, Toronto ON p. 2853

Dickinson Wright PLLC Library, Bloomfield Hills MI p. 1159

Dickinson Wright PLLC Library, Detroit MI p. 1170

Dickson Brian Law Library, *see* University of Ottawa Libraries, Ottawa ON p. 2834

Dickson County Public Library, Dickson TN p. 2233

Dickson Mounds Museum Library, Lewistown IL p. 665

Dickstein Shapiro LLP, Washington DC p. 398

Didsbury Municipal Library, Didsbury AB p. 2696

Dieppe Public, *see* Albert-Westmorland-Kent Regional Library, Dieppe NB p. 2765

Dietzman Allen Library, Livingston WI p. 2605

Dighton Historical Society Museum Library, Dighton MA p. 1084

Dighton Public Library, Dighton MA p. 1084

Dike Public Library, Dike IA p. 811

Dillard James W Library, *see* Frank Phillips College, Borger TX p. 2290

Dillard University, New Orleans LA p. 960

Dilley Public Library, Dilley TX p. 2314

Dillingham Public Library, Dillingham AK p. 47

Dillon City Library, Dillon MT p. 1378

Dillon Clarence Public Library, Bedminster NJ p. 1471

Dillon County Library, Dillon SC p. 2192

Dillsboro Public, *see* Aurora Public Library District, Dillsboro IN p. 725

Dillsburg Area Public Library, Dillsburg PA p. 2049

Dillwyn Correctional Center, Dillwyn VA p. 2460

DiMenna-Nyselius Library, *see* Fairfield University, Fairfield CT p. 339

Dimeo Mary & James Library, *see* Sacred Heart Academy, Hamden CT p. 343

Dimmick Memorial Library, Jim Thorpe PA p. 2073

Dimmit County Public Library, Carrizo Springs TX p. 2295

Dinand Library, *see* College of the Holy Cross, Worcester MA p. 1143

Dine College, Tsaile AZ p. 85

Dine College, Crownpoint NM p. 1554

Dine College, Shiprock NM p. 1565

Dingell John D VA Medical Center, *see* Department of Veterans Affairs Library Service, Detroit MI p. 1169

Dingell John LRC Library, *see* Wayne County Community College District, Taylor MI p. 1230

Dinsmore & Shohl Library, Cincinnati OH p. 1870

Diocesan Resource Center, Providence RI p. 2172

Diocesan Synod of Fredericton, Fredericton NB p. 2763

Diocese of Amarillo, Amarillo TX p. 2274

Diocese of Boise, Boise ID p. 571

Diocese of Colorado Springs, Colorado Springs CO p. 295

Diocese of La Crosse Archives, La Crosse WI p. 2602

Diocese of Montreal Archives, *see* Anglican Church of Canada Archives, Montreal QC p. 2887

Diocese of Olympia, Seattle WA p. 2527

Diocese of Pittsburgh, Pittsburgh PA p. 2125

Dirac Paul A M Science Library, *see* Florida State University Libraries, Tallahassee FL p. 495

Direction des Ressources Educatives Francaises, Saint Boniface MB p. 2751

Disciples of Christ Historical Society Library & Archives, Nashville TN p. 2256

Distance Education & Training Council, Washington DC p. 398

Distefano Memorial Library, *see* Central Louisiana State Hospital, Pineville LA p. 965

District Council 37 Library, *see* College of New Rochelle, New York NY p. 1674

District of Columbia Area Health Science Libraries (N), Washington DC p. 2940

District of Columbia Department of Corrections, Washington DC p. 398

District of Columbia Public Library, Washington DC p. 398

District of Columbia Superior Court Judges Library, Washington DC p. 399

Dittrick Medical History Center, *see* Cleveland Health Sciences Library, Cleveland OH p. 1877

Diver Arvilla E Memorial Library, Schaghticoke NY p. 1740

Divernon Township Library, Divernon IL p. 636

Divide County Public Library, Crosby ND p. 1839

Divine Word College, Epworth IA p. 814

Divinity School Library, *see* Duke University Libraries, Durham NC p. 1787

Divinity School Library, *see* Yale University Library, New Haven CT p. 357

Division of Juvenile Justice of Department of Corrections, Camarillo CA p. 131

Division of Legislative Services Reference Center, Richmond VA p. 2488

Division of Mining, Land & Water Library, *see* Alaska Department of Natural Resources, Anchorage AK p. 43

Dix Dorothea Psychiatric Center, Bangor ME p. 975

Dix Hills Jewish Center Library, Dix Hills NY p. 1614

Dixie County Public Library, Cross City FL p. 435

Dixie Regional Library System, Pontotoc MS p. 1311

Dixie State College of Utah, Saint George UT p. 2411

Dixon Amanda E Neighborhood Library, *see* Houston Public Library, Houston TX p. 2339

Dixon Correctional Center Library, Dixon IL p. 637

Dixon Correctional Institute, Jackson LA p. 951

Dixon Gallery & Gardens Library, Memphis TN p. 2248

Dixon Homestead Library, Dumont NJ p. 1481

Dixon John Public Library, *see* Mattawa Public Library, Mattawa ON p. 2821

Dixon Public Library, Dixon CA p. 140

Dixon Public Library, Dixon IL p. 637

Dixon School of Nursing Library, *see* Abington Memorial Hospital, Willow Grove PA p. 2157

Dixon Township Library, Argonia KS p. 856

DLA Piper United States LLP, East Palo Alto CA p. 144

DLA Piper US LLP, San Diego CA p. 231

DLA Piper US LLP, Washington DC p. 399

DLA Piper US LLP, Chicago IL p. 612

DLA Piper US LLP, Baltimore MD p. 1012

DLA Piper US LLP, New York NY p. 1677

DLC (N), *see* Delaware Library Consortium, Newark DE p. 2940

Doane College, Crete NE p. 1396

Doane Dr Grace O Alden Public Library, Alden IA p. 792

Doane William Howard Library, *see* Denison University Libraries, Granville OH p. 1902

Dobbs Ferry Public Library, Dobbs Ferry NY p. 1615

Doblitz Ray Memorial Library, *see* Ohev Shalom Synagogue, Wallingford PA p. 2150

Dobson Community Library, Dobson NC p. 1786

Dockery Dr Carl D Library, *see* Tri-County Community College, Murphy NC p. 1812

Doctor Edwin E Lehr Library, *see* San Jacinto College North, Houston TX p. 2342

Doctors Community Hospital, Lanham MD p. 1034

Doctor's Hospital, Baptist Health, Coral Gables FL p. 434

Doctors Library, *see* Saint Vincent's Medical Center, Jacksonville FL p. 454

Doctors Medical Center, Modesto CA p. 187

Doctors' Memorial Library, *see* Arkansas Methodist Hospital, Paragould AR p. 111

Doddridge County Public Library, West Union WV p. 2574

Dodge Center Public Library, Dodge Center MN p. 1247

Dodge City Community College, Dodge City KS p. 863

Dodge City Library Consortium (N), Dodge City KS p. 2943

Dodge City Public Library, Dodge City KS p. 863

Dodge Correctional Institution Library, Waupun WI p. 2646

Dodge County Historical Society, Fremont NE p. 1399

Dodge County Historical Society Library, Mantorville MN p. 1258

Dodge County Library, *see* Ocmulgee Regional Library System, Eastman GA p. 531

Dodge Library, West Chazy NY p. 1765

Dodge Memorial Library, Rouses Point NY p. 1736

Dodge Memorial Public Library, Olive Branch IL p. 685

Dodge State Prison, *see* Georgia Department of Corrections, Chester GA p. 524

Dodgeville Public Library, Dodgeville WI p. 2588

Doerun Municipal Library, *see* Moultrie-Colquitt County Library, Doerun GA p. 546

Dog River Public Library, *see* West Georgia Regional Library, Douglasville GA p. 524

Dogwood Library, *see* Atlanta-Fulton Public Library System, Atlanta GA p. 512

Doheny Eye Institute, Los Angeles CA p. 170

Doherty Grace Library, *see* Centre College of Kentucky, Danville KY p. 911

Doherty Robert Pace & Ada Mary Library, *see* University of Saint Thomas, Houston TX p. 2344

Dolan Springs Community Library, *see* Mohave County Library District, Dolan Springs AZ p. 67

Dolby Laboratories, Inc, San Francisco CA p. 242

Dole Ruth Memorial Library, Burrton KS p. 859

Dolezal George, *see* Monroe County Public Library, Marathon FL p. 456

Dolgeville-Manheim Public Library, Dolgeville NY p. 1615

Dolloff Richard H Medical Library, *see* Cooley Dickinson Hospital, Northampton MA p. 1113

Drug Enforcement Administration Library, *see* United States Department of Justice, Arlington VA p. 2450

Drumheller Public Library, Drumheller AB p. 2697

Drummond Public Library, Drummond WI p. 2588

Drummond School & Community Library, Drummond MT p. 1378

Drumright Public Library, Drumright OK p. 1961

Drury University, Springfield MO p. 1366

Drusch Professional Library, Saint Louis MO p. 1354

Druskin Sidney Memorial Library, *see* New York College of Podiatric Medicine, New York NY p. 1689

Dry Point Township Library, Cowden IL p. 631

Dry R R Memorial Library, *see* Erie Community College-North, Williamsville NY p. 1769

Dryden Public Library, Dryden ON p. 2802

Dryden Township Library, Dryden MI p. 1174

Du Bois Public Library, Du Bois PA p. 2050

Du Bois W E B, *see* Gary Public Library, Gary IN p. 744

Du Bois W E B Library, *see* University of Massachusetts Amherst, Amherst MA p. 1049

Du Pont De Nemours & Co, Inc, Circleville OH p. 1875

Du Quoin Public Library, Du Quoin IL p. 637

Duane Morris LLP Library, Philadelphia PA p. 2106

Duba Lawrence Research Library, *see* Behringer-Crawford Museum, Covington KY p. 910

Dublin Public Library, Dublin IN p. 736

Dublin Public Library, Dublin NH p. 1445

Dublin Public Library, Dublin TX p. 2314

DuBois Campus Library, *see* Pennsylvania State University, Du Bois PA p. 2051

Dubreuilville Public Library, Dubreuilville ON p. 2802

Dubuque County Library, Asbury IA p. 794

Dubuque (Iowa) Area Library Information Consortium (N), Peosta IA p. 2943

Duchesne Library, Duchesne UT p. 2404

Duchess & District Public Library, Duchess AB p. 2697

Duchow Marvin Music Library, *see* McGill University Libraries, Montreal QC p. 2898

Duck Hill Public, *see* Mid-Mississippi Regional Library System, Duck Hill MS p. 1306

Duck Lake Public Library, *see* Wapiti Regional Library, Duck Lake SK p. 2921

Ducks Unlimited Canada Library, *see* Institute for Wetland & Waterfowl Research Library, Stonewall MB p. 2752

Ducktown Community Library, Ducktown TN p. 2233

Duckworth Henry & J Lon Memorial Library, *see* Young Harris College, Young Harris GA p. 558

Dudley Literacy Center, *see* Boston Public Library, Roxbury MA p. 1057

Dudley Observatory Library, Schenectady NY p. 1740

Dudley Township Public Library, Satanta KS p. 893

Dudley-Tucker Library, Raymond NH p. 1463

Duff & Phelps, Chicago IL p. 613

Dufferin Clark Library, *see* Vaughan Public Libraries, Thornhill ON p. 2848

Duffield Public Library, Duffield AB p. 2697

Dufur School-Community Library, Dufur OR p. 1995

Dugan Library, *see* Newman University, Wichita KS p. 900

Duggan Library, *see* Hanover College, Hanover IN p. 748

Dugger Public, *see* Sullivan County Public Library, Dugger IN p. 780

Dugway Proving Ground Tech Library, *see* West Desert Technical Information Center, Dugway UT p. 2405

Duke Energy Corp, Charlotte NC p. 1783

Duke James B Library, *see* Furman University Libraries, Greenville SC p. 2195

Duke James B Memorial Library, *see* Johnson C Smith University, Charlotte NC p. 1783

Duke University Libraries, Durham NC p. 1787

Dukes Law Library, Edgartown MA p. 1087

Dulaney-Browne Library, *see* Oklahoma City University, Oklahoma City OK p. 1974

Dulany Memorial, *see* Little Dixie Regional Libraries, Paris MO p. 1346

Dulany Memorial Library, Salisbury MO p. 1364

Dulany Memorial Library, *see* William Woods University, Fulton MO p. 1328

Duluth News Tribune Library, Duluth MN p. 1247

Duluth Public Library, Duluth MN p. 1247

Dumbarton Oaks Research Library, *see* Harvard Library, Washington MA p. 1074

Dummer Public Library, Milan NH p. 1457

Dumont Community Library, Dumont IA p. 812

Dumphy John J Memorial Library, *see* Saint Vincent Hospital, Worcester MA p. 1144

Dunagan J Conrad Library, *see* University of Texas of the Permian Basin, Odessa TX p. 2366

Dunbar Community Library, Dunbar PA p. 2051

Dunbar Free Library, Grantham NH p. 1448

Dunbar Jupiter Hammon Public Library, *see* Lee County Library System, Fort Myers FL p. 445

Dunbar Paul Laurence, *see* Dallas Public Library, Dallas TX p. 2306

Dunbar Paul Lawrence, *see* Vernon Parish Library, Leesville LA p. 955

Dunbar Public, *see* Kanawha County Public Library, Dunbar WV p. 2556

Dunbarton Public Library, Dunbarton NH p. 1445

Duncan James M Jr, *see* Alexandria Library, Alexandria VA p. 2444

Duncan Mary Public Library, Benson NC p. 1776

Duncan Public Library, Duncan AZ p. 61

Duncan Public Library, Duncan OK p. 1961

Duncan-Traner Community Library, *see* Washoe County Library System, Reno NV p. 1434

Duncanville Public Library, Duncanville TX p. 2314

Duncombe Public Library, Duncombe IA p. 812

Dundalk Library, *see* Community College of Baltimore County, Baltimore MD p. 1023

Dundee Library, Dundee NY p. 1616

Dundee Library, *see* Fox River Valley Public Library District, Dundee IL p. 637

Dundee Public Library, Dundee FL p. 438

Dundy County Library, Benkelman NE p. 1394

Dunedin Public Library, Dunedin FL p. 438

Dunellen Public Library, Dunellen NJ p. 1481

Dunham Hall Library, *see* Windham Textile & History Museum, Willimantic CT p. 378

Dunham Public Library, Whitesboro NY p. 1769

Dunham Tavern Museum Library, Cleveland OH p. 1879

Dunkerton Public Library, Dunkerton IA p. 812

Dunkirk Free Library, Dunkirk NY p. 1616

Dunkirk Public Library, Dunkirk IN p. 736

Dunklin County Library, Kennett MO p. 1341

Dunlap Bailey H Memorial Public Library, La Feria TX p. 2351

Dunlap Public Library, Dunlap IA p. 812

Dunlap Public Library District, Dunlap IL p. 638

Dunlap S M Memorial Library, Italy TX p. 2347

Dunn Center Public Library, Dunn Center ND p. 1840

Dunn Library, *see* Simpson College, Indianola IA p. 822

Dunn Margaret, *see* Caledon Public Library, Mayfield ON p. 2795

Dunn Public, *see* Harnett County Public Library, Dunn NC p. 1807

Dunn Sir James Law Library, *see* Dalhousie University, Halifax NS p. 2780

Dunn Willie Mae Library, *see* Copiah-Lincoln Community College, Natchez MS p. 1309

Dunnellon Public Library, *see* Marion County Public Library System, Dunnellon FL p. 474

Dunstable Free Public Library, Dunstable MA p. 1085

Dunwoody College of Technology, Minneapolis MN p. 1259

Dupage Library, *see* Robert Morris University, Aurora IL p. 592

Duplin County Historical Foundation, Rose Hill NC p. 1821

Duplin County Library, Kenansville NC p. 1804

Dupont Alfred I Hospital for Children, Wilmington DE p. 387

DuPont-Ball Library, *see* Stetson University, DeLand FL p. 437

DuPont Jessie Ball Library, *see* University of the South, Sewanee TN p. 2265

Dupont Jessie Ball Memorial Library, Stratford VA p. 2497

Dupre Edith Garland Library, *see* University of Louisiana at Lafayette, Lafayette LA p. 953

Duquesne University, Pittsburgh PA p. 2125

Duraleigh Road Community Library, *see* Wake County Public Library System, Raleigh NC p. 1817

Durand Public Library, Durand WI p. 2589

Durango Public Library, Durango CO p. 304

Durant Public, *see* Mid-Mississippi Regional Library System, Durant MS p. 1306

Durant Will & Ariel, *see* Los Angeles Public Library System, Los Angeles CA p. 173

Durfee Mike State Prison, Springfield SD p. 2220

Durham Charles L, *see* Free Library of Philadelphia, Philadelphia PA p. 2107

Durham College Library, *see* University of Ontario Institute of Technology Library, Oshawa ON p. 2827

Durham County Library, Durham NC p. 1788

Durham Public Library, Durham CT p. 336

Durham Public Library, Durham NH p. 1445

Durham Region Law Association, Oshawa ON p. 2826

Durham Technical Community College, Durham NC p. 1788

Durick Library, *see* Saint Michaels College, Colchester VT p. 2422

Durland Alternatives Library, Ithaca NY p. 1642

Durland Anne Carry Memorial Library, *see* Durland Alternatives Library, Ithaca NY p. 1642

Durr William E, *see* Kenton County Public Library, Independence KY p. 910

Durst Seymour B Library, *see* Real Estate Board of New York, New York NY p. 1698

Dutchess Community College Library, Poughkeepsie NY p. 1722

Dutchess County Genealogical Society Library, Poughkeepsie NY p. 1722

Dutton Public Library, Dutton MT p. 1378

Duval County Law Library, Jacksonville FL p. 452

Duval County-San Diego Public Library, San Diego TX p. 2384

Duxbury Free Library, Duxbury MA p. 1085

DVA-WNY Healthcare System, Buffalo NY p. 1597

Dvoracek Memorial Library, Wilber NE p. 1423

Dwight Correctional Center Library, *see* Illinois Department of Corrections, Dwight IL p. 638

Dwight Library, Dwight KS p. 864

Dyckman Free Library, Sleepy Eye MN p. 1284

Dye F W & Bessie Memorial Library, *see* Texas Woman's University, Dallas TX p. 2311

Dye M R Public Library, *see* First Regional Library, Horn Lake MS p. 1301

Dyer Edythe L Community Library, Hampden ME p. 987

Dyer Library, Saco ME p. 999

Dyersburg State Community College, Dyersburg TN p. 2233

Dyess Public Library, Dyess AR p. 98

Dying With Dignity Canada Library, Toronto ON p. 2853

Dykema Gossett PLLC, Chicago IL p. 613

Dykema Gossett PLLC, Bloomfield Hills MI p. 1159

Dykema Gossett PLLC, Detroit MI p. 1171

Dykes Archie R Library of Health Sciences, *see* University of Kansas Medical Center, Kansas City KS p. 876

Dykes Eva B Library, *see* Oakwood College, Huntsville AL p. 22

Dykes W I Library, *see* University of Houston-Downtown, Houston TX p. 2343

D'Youville College, Buffalo NY p. 1597

e-HLbc (N), *see* Electronic Health Library of British Columbia, Burnaby BC p. 2959

E I du Pont Canada Co, Mississauga ON p. 2822

E I Du Pont De Nemours & Co, Inc, Newark DE p. 385

E'cole Quebecoise du Meuble et du Bois Ouvre, *see* Cegep de Victoriaville, Victoriaville QC p. 2915

Eastern Idaho Regional Medical Center, Idaho Falls ID p. 576

Eastern Idaho Technical College, Idaho Falls ID p. 576

Eastern Illinois University, Charleston IL p. 603

Eastern Irrigation District, Brooks AB p. 2686

Eastern Kentucky Correctional Complex Library, West Liberty KY p. 937

Eastern Kentucky Health Science Information Network (N), Morehead KY p. 2944

Eastern Kentucky University Libraries, Richmond KY p. 933

Eastern Lancaster County Library, New Holland PA p. 2096

Eastern Long Island Hospital, Greenport NY p. 1631

Eastern Louisiana Mental Health Systems, Jackson LA p. 951

Eastern Maine Community College Library, Bangor ME p. 975

Eastern Maine Medical Center, Bangor ME p. 976

Eastern Mennonite Associated Libraries & Archives (N), Lancaster PA p. 2954

Eastern Mennonite University, Harrisonburg VA p. 2470

Eastern Michigan University, Ypsilanti MI p. 1237

Eastern Monroe Public Library, Stroudsburg PA p. 2143

Eastern Nazarene College, Quincy MA p. 1119

Eastern Nebraska Genealogical Society Library, Fremont NE p. 1399

Eastern New Mexico University, Portales NM p. 1560

Eastern New Mexico University - Roswell, Roswell NM p. 1561

Eastern Oklahoma District Library System, Muskogee OK p. 1969

Eastern Oklahoma State College Library, Wilburton OK p. 1986

Eastern Oregon University, La Grande OR p. 2003

Eastern Shore Community College, Melfa VA p. 2478

Eastern Shore Hospital Center, Cambridge MD p. 1022

Eastern Shore Public Library, Accomac VA p. 2443

Eastern Shores Library System, Sheboygan WI p. 2637

Eastern State Hospital, Lexington KY p. 920

Eastern State Hospital, Williamsburg VA p. 2503

Eastern State Hospital, see Washington State Library, Medical Lake WA p. 2545

Eastern Township Public Library, Crofton NE p. 1396

Eastern University, Saint Davids PA p. 2135

Eastern Virginia Medical School, Norfolk VA p. 2481

Eastern Washington University, Cheney WA p. 2512

Eastern Wyoming College Library, Torrington WY p. 2661

Eastfield College Library, Mesquite TX p. 2362

Eastford Public Library, Eastford CT p. 338

Eastham Public Library, Eastham MA p. 1086

Eastland Centennial Memorial Library, Eastland TX p. 2315

Eastman Chemical, West Elizabeth PA p. 2154

Eastman Chemical Co, Kingsport TN p. 2240

Eastman George House, Rochester NY p. 1729

Easton Area Public Library & District Center, Easton PA p. 2052

Easton Hospital, Easton PA p. 2052

Easton Library, Greenwich NY p. 1631

Easton Public Library, Easton CT p. 338

Easton's Public Library, see Ames Free Library, North Easton MA p. 1112

Eastpointe Memorial Library, Eastpointe MI p. 1176

Easttown Library & Information Center, Berwyn PA p. 2033

Eastvale Library, see Riverside County Library System, Corona CA p. 217

Eastwood A J Library, see Limestone College, Gaffney SC p. 2194

Eaton Public Library, Eaton CO p. 305

Eaton Rapids Public Library, Eaton Rapids MI p. 1176

Eatontown Library, Eatontown NJ p. 1482

Eau Claire District Library, Eau Claire MI p. 1176

Eau Claire Leader-Telegram Newsroom Library, Eau Claire WI p. 2589

Eau Gallie Public Library, Melbourne FL p. 463

Ebensburg Cambria Public Library, Ebensburg PA p. 2052

Eberly Family Special Collections Library, see Pennsylvania State University Libraries, University Park PA p. 2148

Eberly Library, see Waynesburg College, Waynesburg PA p. 2152

Ebling Library, see University of Wisconsin-Madison, Madison WI p. 2609

Eccles-Lesher Memorial Library, Rimersburg PA p. 2134

Eccles Spencer S, see University of Utah, Salt Lake City UT p. 2414

Echo Public Library, Echo OR p. 1995

Eckels Memorial Library, Oakland IA p. 836

Eckerd College, Saint Petersburg FL p. 488

Eckert M Beven Memorial Library, see Mason County Library, Mason TX p. 2360

Eckfeldt Thomas Memorial Medical Library, see Monadnock Community Hospital, Peterborough NH p. 1461

Eckhardt-Gramatte Music Library, see University of Manitoba Libraries, Winnipeg MB p. 2758

Eckhart Library, see University of Chicago Library, Chicago IL p. 627

Eckhart Public Library, Auburn IN p. 725

Eckles Library, see George Washington University, Washington DC p. 402

Eckstein Memorial Library, Cassville WI p. 2584

Eckville Municipal Library, Eckville AB p. 2697

Ecole de Technologie Superieure (Service de la bibliotheque), Montreal QC p. 2895

Ecole Nationale d'Aerotechnique Bibliotheque, see College Edouard-Montpetit Bibliotheque, Saint Hubert QC p. 2887

Ecole Nationale d'Administration Publique Libraries, Quebec QC p. 2904

Ecole Nationale de Police du Quebec, Nicolet QC p. 2902

Ecole Polytechnique de Montreal Bibliotheque, Montreal QC p. 2895

Ecology & Environment Inc, Library, Lancaster NY p. 1651

Economic Policy Institute, Washington DC p. 399

Economics Research Associates Library, Washington DC p. 399

Economists Inc Library, Washington DC p. 399

Ecorse Public Library, Ecorse MI p. 1176

Ecosystems International Inc Library, Millersville MD p. 1035

ECPI University, Charlotte NC p. 1783

ECPI University, Greensboro NC p. 1796

ECPI University, Raleigh NC p. 1815

ECPI University, Columbia SC p. 2187

ECPI University, Greenville SC p. 2195

ECPI University, Manassas VA p. 2477

ECPI University, Virginia Beach VA p. 2498

ECRI Institute Library, Plymouth Meeting PA p. 2130

Ector County Library, Odessa TX p. 2366

Ecumenical Theological Seminary, Detroit MI p. 1171

Edberg Municipal Library, Edberg AB p. 2697

Eddy Mary Baker Library, Boston MA p. 1060

Eddyville Public Library, Eddyville IA p. 813

Eden Library, Eden NY p. 1618

Eden Public Library, Eden TX p. 2315

Edens J Drake Library, see Columbia College, Columbia SC p. 2187

Edgartown Free Public Library, Edgartown MA p. 1087

Edgecombe Community College, Tarboro NC p. 1826

Edgecombe County Memorial Library, Tarboro NC p. 1826

Edgeley Public, see South Central Area Library, Edgeley ND p. 1840

Edgemont Public Library, Edgemont SD p. 2212

Edgerton Public Library, Edgerton MN p. 1249

Edgerton Public Library, Edgerton WI p. 2590

Edgerton Public Library, Edgerton AB p. 2697

Edgewater Free Public Library, Edgewater NJ p. 1483

Edgewater Public, see Volusia County Public Library, Edgewater FL p. 436

Edgewood College Library, Madison WI p. 2606

Edgewood Community Library, Edgewood NM p. 1554

Edgewood Library, see Mellor C C Memorial Library, Edgewood PA p. 2053

Edgewood Public Library, Edgewood IA p. 813

Edinboro University of Pennsylvania, Edinboro PA p. 2053

Edinburgh Wright-Hageman Public Library, Edinburgh IN p. 736

Edison College, Punta Gorda FL p. 485

Edison Community College Library, Piqua OH p. 1930

Edison Electric Institute, Washington DC p. 399

Edison State College, Fort Myers FL p. 444

Edison State College, Naples FL p. 471

Edison Township Free Public Library, Edison NJ p. 1483

Editorial Projects in Education Library, Bethesda MD p. 1021

Edmeston Free Library & Museum, Edmeston NY p. 1618

Edmond Library, see Metropolitan Library System in Oklahoma County, Edmond OK p. 1972

Edmonds Community College Library, Lynnwood WA p. 2520

Edmondson Memorial, see Dixie Regional Library System, Vardaman MS p. 1312

Edmondson Public Library, Edmondson AR p. 98

Edmonson County Public Library, Brownsville KY p. 908

Edmonton Autism Society Library, Edmonton AB p. 2700

Edmonton Humane Society, Edmonton AB p. 2700

Edmonton Police, Edmonton AB p. 2700

Edmonton Public Library, Edmonton AB p. 2700

Edmund Cardinal Szoka Library, see Sacred Heart Major Seminary, Detroit MI p. 1171

Edna Public Library, Edna KS p. 864

Edson Public Library, Edson AB p. 2703

Education Management Corporation, Denver CO p. 301

Education Northwest, Portland OR p. 2010

Educational Broadcasting Corp, New York NY p. 1677

Educational Communications, Inc, Los Angeles CA p. 170

Educational Information & Resource Center, Mullica Hill NJ p. 1506

Educational Leadership Institute Library, Thiensville WI p. 2642

Educational Research Service, Alexandria VA p. 2445

Educational Testing Service, Princeton NJ p. 1522

Edward Hospital Library, Naperville IL p. 678

Edward Waters College Library, Jacksonville FL p. 452

Edwards Angell Palmer & Dodge LLP, Boston MA p. 1060

Edwards J Joel Public Library, see Flint River Regional Library, Zebulon GA p. 535

Edwards Jacob Library, Southbridge MA p. 1126

Edwards Jessie J Public Library, see First Regional Library, Coldwater MS p. 1301

Edwards Joan C School of Medicine, see Marshall University Libraries, Huntington WV p. 2562

Edwards Jonathan Library, see Berkshire Community College, Pittsfield MA p. 1117

Edwards Kathleen Clay Family, see Greensboro Public Library, Greensboro NC p. 1796

Edwards Lois Morgan Memorial, see Union County Public Library, Marshville NC p. 1810

Edwards Mary D Public Library, Willington CT p. 378

Edwards Public Library, Southampton MA p. 1126

Edwards Public Library, Henrietta TX p. 2332

Edwardsburgh/Cardinal Public Library, Cardinal ON p. 2798

Edwardsville Public Library, Edwardsville IL p. 639

Effigy Mounds National Monument Library, *see* United States National Park Service, Harpers Ferry IA p. 820

Effingham Community Library, Effingham KS p. 864

Effingham Public Library, Effingham NH p. 1446

Egan Joseph F Memorial Supreme Court Library, Schenectady NY p. 1740

Egan William A Library, *see* University of Alaska Southeast, Juneau AK p. 50

Egegik Village Library, Egegik AK p. 47

Egremont Free Library, South Egremont MA p. 1125

Egypt Lake Partnership Library, *see* Tampa-Hillsborough County Public Library System, Tampa FL p. 497

Ehrman Frederick L Medical Library, *see* New York University School of Medicine, New York NY p. 1695

Eiche Robert E Library, *see* Pennsylvania State University Altoona College, Altoona PA p. 2028

Eighth Judicial District Library, *see* New York Supreme Court, Buffalo NY p. 1598

882nd Training Group Academic Library, *see* United States Air Force, Sheppard AFB TX p. 2386

89th Malcolm Grow Medical Group, *see* United States Air Force, Andrews AFB MD p. 1009

Einstein Albert Healthcare Network, Philadelphia PA p. 2106

Einstein Emanuel Memorial Library, *see* Pompton Lakes Public Library, Pompton Lakes NJ p. 1521

Eiseley Loren Corey, *see* Lincoln City Libraries, Lincoln NE p. 1405

Eisenhower Army Medical Center, *see* United States Army, Fort Gordon GA p. 533

Eisenhower Dwight D Library, *see* National Archives & Records Administration, Abilene KS p. 855

Eisenhower Dwight D Public Library, Totowa NJ p. 1535

Eisenhower Mamie Doud Public Library, Broomfield CO p. 292

Eisenhower Medical Center, Rancho Mirage CA p. 213

Eisenhower Public Library District, Harwood Heights IL p. 654

Eisman Malcolm Memorial Library, *see* Temple Am Echad, Lynbrook NY p. 1655

Eisner Memorial Library, *see* Red Bank Public Library, Red Bank NJ p. 1525

Eiteljorg Museum of American Indians & Western Art, Indianapolis IN p. 750

Ekalaka Public Library, Ekalaka MT p. 1378

EKHSIN (N), *see* Eastern Kentucky Health Science Information Network, Morehead KY p. 2944

Ekstrom William F Library, *see* University of Louisville Libraries, Louisville KY p. 927

El Cajon First Presbyterian Church Library, El Cajon CA p. 145

El Camino College, Torrance CA p. 275

El Camino Hospital Library & Information Center, Mountain View CA p. 192

El Camino Los Gatos Health Library, Los Gatos CA p. 180

El Camino Real Library, *see* County of Los Angeles Public Library, Los Angeles CA p. 141

El Centro College, Dallas TX p. 2307

El Centro Public Library, El Centro CA p. 145

El Cerrito Library, *see* Contra Costa County Library, El Cerrito CA p. 209

El Cerrito Library, *see* Riverside County Library System, Corona CA p. 217

El Dorado Correctional Facility Library, *see* Kansas Department of Corrections, El Dorado KS p. 865

El Dorado County Law Library, Placerville CA p. 208

El Dorado County Library, Placerville CA p. 208

El Monte Museum of History Library, El Monte CA p. 146

El Paso Community College Library, El Paso TX p. 2315

El Paso County Bar Assocoation Law Library, Colorado Springs CO p. 295

El Paso County Law Library, El Paso TX p. 2316

El Paso Museum of Art, El Paso TX p. 2316

El Paso Public Library, El Paso IL p. 640

El Paso Public Library, El Paso TX p. 2316

El Progreso Memorial Library, Uvalde TX p. 2394

El Reno Carnegie Library, El Reno OK p. 1962

El Rito Public Library, El Rito NM p. 1554

El Segundo Public Library, El Segundo CA p. 146

Ela Area Public Library District, Lake Zurich IL p. 663

Elaine Library, *see* Phillips-Lee-Monroe Regional Library, Elaine AR p. 103

Elba Public Library, Elba AL p. 15

Elberon Public Library, Elberon IL p. 813

Elbert County Library District, Elizabeth CO p. 305

Elbert County Public Library, Elberton GA p. 532

Elbin Paul N Library, *see* West Liberty University, West Liberty WV p. 2574

Elbow Lake Public Library, Elbow Lake MN p. 1249

Elbridge Free Library, Elbridge NY p. 1618

Eldon Public Library, Eldon IA p. 813

Eldon Public Library, Eldon MO p. 1327

Eldora Public Library, Eldora IA p. 813

Eldorado Memorial Public Library District, Eldorado IL p. 640

Eldredge Public Library, Chatham MA p. 1079

Eleanor Slator Hospital, Pascoag RI p. 2170

Elections Manitoba Library, *see* Legislative Assembly, Winnipeg MB p. 2756

Electra Public Library, Electra TX p. 2317

Electronic Computer Programming College Inc Library, Chattanooga TN p. 2227

Electronic Health Library of British Columbia (N), Burnaby BC p. 2959

Elfrida Library, *see* Cochise County Library District, Elfrida AZ p. 58

Elftman Memorial Library, *see* Salvation Army College for Officer Training at Crestmont, Rancho Palos Verdes CA p. 213

Elgin Community College, Elgin IL p. 640

Elgin Community Library, Elgin OK p. 1963

Elgin County Public Library, St. Thomas ON p. 2844

Elgin Mental Health Center Library, Elgin IL p. 641

Elgin Public Library, Elgin IA p. 814

Elgin Public Library, Elgin NE p. 1398

Elgin Public Library, Elgin ND p. 1840

Elgin Public Library, Elgin OR p. 1995

Elgin Public Library, Elgin TX p. 2318

Lilly Eli & Co, Indianapolis IN p. 751

Elias, Matz, Tiernan & Herrick LLP, Washington DC p. 399

Elida Public Library, Elida NM p. 1554

Elim Community Library, Elim AK p. 47

ELIN (N), *see* Estacado Library Information Network, Hobby NM p. 2949

Elizabeth City State University, Elizabeth City NC p. 1790

Elizabeth Public Library, Elizabeth NJ p. 1483

Elizabeth Township Library, Elizabeth IL p. 641

Elizabethton-Carter County Public Library, Elizabethton TN p. 2233

Elizabethtown College, Elizabethtown PA p. 2053

Elizabethtown Community & Technical College Library, Elizabethtown KY p. 912

Elizabethtown Library Association, Elizabethtown NY p. 1618

Elizabethtown Public Library, Elizabethtown PA p. 2053

Elizabethtown-Kitley Township Public Library, Addison ON p. 2791

Elizabethville Area Library, *see* Dauphin County Library System, Elizabethville PA p. 2064

Elk City Carnegie Library, Elk City OK p. 1963

Elk City Community Library, Elk City ID p. 574

Elk Grove Community Library, *see* Sacramento Public Library, Elk Grove CA p. 225

Elk Grove Village Public Library, Elk Grove Village IL p. 641

Elk Horn Public Library, Elk Horn IA p. 814

Elk Lake Public Library, Elk Lake ON p. 2803

Elk Point Public Library, Elk Point AB p. 2703

Elk Rapids District Library, Elk Rapids MI p. 1176

Elk River Free Library District, Elk River ID p. 574

Elk River Library, *see* Great River Regional Library, Elk River MN p. 1275

Elk Township Library, Peck MI p. 1217

Elkader Public Library, Elkader IA p. 814

Elkford Public Library, Elkford BC p. 2727

Elkhart County Historical Society, Inc, Bristol IN p. 729

Elkhart Lake Public Library, Elkhart Lake WI p. 2590

Elkhart Public Library, Elkhart IN p. 737

Elkhart Public Library District, Elkhart IL p. 642

Elkhorn City Public, *see* Pike County Public Library District, Elkhorn City KY p. 932

Elkins Park Free Library, *see* Cheltenham Township Library System, Elkins Park PA p. 2061

Elkins Public Library, Elkins AR p. 98

Elkins Public Library, Canterbury NH p. 1440

Elkins-Randolph County Public Library, Elkins WV p. 2558

Elkland Area Community Library, Elkland PA p. 2054

Elko County Library, *see* Elko-Lander-Eureka County Library System, Elko NV p. 1426

Elko-Lander-Eureka County Library System, Elko NV p. 1426

Elks Tuberculosis Library, *see* Barlow Respiratory Hospital, Los Angeles CA p. 168

Elkton Public Library, *see* Giles County Public Library, Elkton TN p. 2264

Ellenburg Center Library, Ellenburg Center NY p. 1618

Ellenburg Sarah A Munsil Free Library, Ellenburg Depot NY p. 1619

Ellendale Public Library, Ellendale ND p. 1840

Ellender Allen J Memorial Library, *see* Nicholls State University, Thibodaux LA p. 971

Ellensburg Public Library, Ellensburg WA p. 2514

Ellenville Public Library & Museum, Ellenville NY p. 1619

Ellicottville Memorial Library, Ellicottville NY p. 1619

Ellington Joyce, *see* San Jose Public Library, San Jose CA p. 251

Ellinwood School & Community Library, Ellinwood KS p. 865

Elliot Hospital, Manchester NH p. 1455

Elliot Lake Public Library, Elliot Lake ON p. 2803

Elliott Carl Regional Library System, Jasper AL p. 23

Elliott G M Library, *see* Cincinnati Christian University, Cincinnati OH p. 1869

Elliott Public Library, Elliott IA p. 814

Ellis County Historical Society Archives, Hays KS p. 870

Ellis Dean B Library, *see* Arkansas State University, State University AR p. 115

Ellis Eleanor Public Library, *see* Phelps Public Library, Phelps WI p. 2629

Ellis Elmer Library, *see* University of Missouri-Columbia, Columbia MO p. 1325

Ellis Hospital, Schenectady NY p. 1740

Ellis Memorial Library, Port Aransas TX p. 2371

Ellis Public Library, Ellis KS p. 865

Ellis Reference & Information Center, *see* Monroe County Library System, Monroe MI p. 1210

Ellisburg Free Library, Ellisburg NY p. 1619

Ellison Marie Memorial Library, Del Rio TN p. 2233

Ellison Ralph Library, *see* Metropolitan Library System in Oklahoma County, Oklahoma City OK p. 1972

Ellisville Public, *see* Laurel-Jones County Library System, Inc, Ellisville MS p. 1307

Ellsworth Community College, Iowa Falls IA p. 824

Ellsworth Correctional Facility Inmate Library, *see* Kansas Department of Corrections, Ellsworth KS p. 865

Ellsworth Public Library, Ellsworth IA p. 814

Ellsworth Public Library, Ellsworth ME p. 984

Ellsworth Public Library, Ellsworth WI p. 2591

Ellwood City Area Public Library, Ellwood City PA p. 2054

Elm Creek Public Library, Elm Creek NE p. 1398

Elm Creek Township Library, Wilsey KS p. 902

Elm Grove Public Library, Elm Grove WI p. 2591

Elma Public Library, Elma IA p. 814
Elma Public Library, Elma NY p. 1619
Elmendaro Township Library, Hartford KS p. 870
Elmer Library, Elmer NJ p. 1484
Elmhurst College, Elmhurst IL p. 642
Elmhurst Community Library, *see* Queens Borough Public Library, Elmhurst NY p. 1644
Elmhurst Historical Museum Library, Elmhurst IL p. 642
Elmhurst Hospital Center, Elmhurst NY p. 1619
Elmhurst Memorial Healthcare, Elmhurst IL p. 642
Elmhurst Public Library, Elmhurst IL p. 642
Elmira College, Elmira NY p. 1619
Elmira Correctional Facility Library, *see* New York State Department of Correctional Services, Elmira NY p. 1620
Elmont Public Library, Elmont NY p. 1620
Elmore Public Library, Elmore MN p. 1250
Elmwood Park Public Library, Elmwood Park IL p. 642
Elmwood Park Public Library, Elmwood Park NJ p. 1484
Elmwood Public Library, Elmwood NE p. 1398
Elmwood Public Library, Elmwood WI p. 2591
Elmworth Community Library, Elmworth AB p. 2703
Elon University, Elon NC p. 1791
Eloy Public Library, Eloy AZ p. 62
Elroy Community Library, Del Valle TX p. 2312
Elroy Public Library, Elroy WI p. 2591
Elsa Public Library, Elsa TX p. 2318
Elsie Public Library, Elsie MI p. 1176
Elsmere Public Library, Wilmington DE p. 387
Elsner Paul A Library & High Technology Complex, *see* Mesa Community College Library, Mesa AZ p. 68
Elting Memorial Library, New Paltz NY p. 1665
Elwood Public Library, Elwood NE p. 1398
Elwood Public Library, East Northport NY p. 1617
Elwood Public Library, *see* North Madison County Public Library, Elwood IN p. 737
Elwood Township Carnegie Library, Ridge Farm IL p. 694
Elwood Walter Museum Library, Amsterdam NY p. 1574
Ely Library, *see* Westfield State University, Westfield MA p. 1138
Ely Public Library, Ely IA p. 814
Ely Public Library, Ely MN p. 1250
Ely State Prison - Law Library, *see* Nevada Department of Corrections, Ely NV p. 1427
Ely State Prison Library, *see* Nevada Department of Corrections, Ely NV p. 1427
Elyria Public Library System, Elyria OH p. 1898
EMALA (N), *see* Eastern Mennonite Associated Libraries & Archives, Lancaster PA p. 2954
Emanuel Congregation, Chicago IL p. 613
Emanuel Medical Center Library, Turlock CA p. 277
Emanuel Synagogue, Oklahoma City OK p. 1971
Emanuel Synagogue Library, West Hartford CT p. 376
Embroiderers Guild of America Inc Library, Louisville KY p. 923
Embry Hugh, *see* Pasco County Library System, Dade City FL p. 451
Embry-Riddle Aeronautical University, Prescott AZ p. 78
Embry-Riddle Aeronautical University, Daytona Beach FL p. 435
Embudo Valley Public Library, Dixon NM p. 1554
Emerson Chase Memorial Library, Deer Isle ME p. 983
Emerson College Library, Boston MA p. 1060
Emerson Hospital Medical Library, Concord MA p. 1083
Emerson Library, *see* Webster University, Saint Louis MO p. 1363
Emerson Process Management, Marshalltown IA p. 830
Emerson Process Management eLibrary, Round Rock TX p. 2377
Emerson Public Library, Emerson IA p. 814
Emerson Public Library, Emerson NE p. 1398
Emerson Public Library, Emerson NJ p. 1484

Emerson Ruth M Library, *see* American Institute of Baking, Manhattan KS p. 881
Emery County Library, Castle Dale UT p. 2403
EMH Regional Healthcare System, Elyria OH p. 1898
Emily Center Library, *see* Phoenix Children's Hospital, Phoenix AZ p. 76
Emiot Israel Memorial Yiddish Library, *see* Jewish Community Center of Greater Rochester, Rochester NY p. 1730
Emmanuel Bible College, Kitchener ON p. 2815
Emmanuel College, Boston MA p. 1060
Emmanuel College Library, Franklin Springs GA p. 534
Emmanuel School of Religion Library, Johnson City TN p. 2239
Emmaus Bible College Library, Dubuque IA p. 811
Emmaus Public Library, Emmaus PA p. 2054
Emmetsburg Public Library, Emmetsburg IA p. 814
Emmett Public Library, Emmett ID p. 574
Emo Public Library, Emo ON p. 2804
Emory & Henry College, Emory VA p. 2460
Emory University Libraries, Atlanta GA p. 514
Emory University School of Law, Atlanta GA p. 514
Empire Health Services, Spokane WA p. 2535
Empire State College, Saratoga Springs NY p. 1738
Empire State Development Library, Albany NY p. 1569
Emploi Quebec, Montreal QC p. 2895
Emporia Public Library, Emporia KS p. 865
Emporia State University, Emporia KS p. 865, 2965
Empress Municipal Library, Empress AB p. 2703
Emprise Bank Research Library, *see* Wichita Art Museum, Wichita KS p. 901
Emrick Robert J MD Medical Library, *see* Wilcox Memorial Hospital, Lihue HI p. 567
EMS Technologies Canada, Ltd Library, Sainte-Anne-de-Bellevue QC p. 2909
EnCana Corp, Calgary AB p. 2691
Encarnacion Valdes Library, *see* Pontifical Catholic University Of Puerto Rico, Ponce PR p. 2674
Enchant Community Library, Enchant AB p. 2703
Encyclopaedia Britannica Inc, Chicago IL p. 613
Endeavor Public Library, Endeavor WI p. 2591
Enderlin Municipal Library, Enderlin ND p. 1840
Endicott College Library, Beverly MA p. 1054
Endometriosis Association Library & Reading Room, Milwaukee WI p. 2618
Enfield Free Public Library, Enfield NH p. 1446
Enfield-Medium Library, *see* Connecticut Correctional Institution, Enfield CT p. 338
Enfield Public Library, Enfield CT p. 338
Engel Library, *see* Temple Emanu-El, Birmingham AL p. 9
Engelhard Corp, Iselin NJ p. 1491
Engineering Systems Inc Library, Aurora IL p. 591
Engl Michael S Family Foundation Research Center Library, *see* O'Keeffe Georgia Museum, Santa Fe NM p. 1563
England Joseph W Library, *see* University of the Sciences in Philadelphia, Philadelphia PA p. 2120
Englehart Public Library, Englehart ON p. 2804
Englewood Charlotte Public, *see* Charlotte County Library System, Englewood FL p. 484
Englewood Christian Church Library, Indianapolis IN p. 751
Englewood Hospital & Medical Center, Englewood NJ p. 1484
Englewood Public Library, Englewood CO p. 306
Englewood Public Library, Englewood NJ p. 1484
Englewood Public Library, Englewood TN p. 2234
English Lutheran Church Library, La Crosse WI p. 2603
English-Speaking Union, New York NY p. 1677
Enid Library, *see* Northwestern Oklahoma State University Libraries, Enid OK p. 1963
Enlow Ruth Library of Garrett County, Oakland MD p. 1035
Ennis Public Library, Ennis TX p. 2318
Enoch Pratt Free Library, Baltimore MD p. 1012
Enosburgh Public Library, Enosburg Falls VT p. 2423
Ensanian Physicochemical Institute, Eldred PA p. 2053

ENSCO, Inc, Springfield VA p. 2496
Enterprise Library, Brockton MA p. 1071
Enterprise Library, *see* Las Vegas-Clark County Library District, Las Vegas NV p. 1429
Enterprise Public, *see* East Mississippi Regional Library System, Enterprise MS p. 1313
Enterprise Public Library, Enterprise AL p. 15
Enterprise Public Library, Enterprise KS p. 866
Enterprise Public Library, Enterprise OR p. 1996
Enterprise State Community College, Enterprise AL p. 16
Enterprise State Community College, Ozark AL p. 33
Entiat Community, *see* North Central Regional Library, Entiat WA p. 2548
Entwistle Public Library, Entwistle AB p. 2703
Enumclaw Public Library, Enumclaw WA p. 2515
Environment Canada, Vancouver BC p. 2741
Environment Canada, Dartmouth NS p. 2779
Environment Canada, Gatineau QC p. 2883
Environment Canada, Whitehorse YT p. 2934
Environment Canada Library, Saskatoon SK p. 2925
Environment Canada Library, Burlington, Burlington ON p. 2798
Environment Canada Library, Downsview, Toronto ON p. 2853
Environmental Protection Agency, Washington DC p. 399
Environmental Protection Agency, Athens GA p. 509
Environmental Protection Agency, Ann Arbor MI p. 1151
Environmental Protection Agency, New York NY p. 1677
Environmental Protection Agency, Dallas TX p. 2308
Environmental Protection Agency Library - RTP, Research Triangle Park NC p. 1819
Environmental Protection Agency - R S Kerr Environmental Research, Ada OK p. 1955
Environmental Research Associates Inc Library, Villanova PA p. 2149
Enzon Pharmaceuticals, Inc, Piscataway NJ p. 1520
Ephesus Public, *see* West Georgia Regional Library, Roopville GA p. 524
Ephraim Public Library, Ephraim UT p. 2405
Ephrata Public Library, Ephrata PA p. 2054
Ephrata Public Library, *see* North Central Regional Library, Ephrata WA p. 2548
Epilepsy Foundation, Landover MD p. 1034
Episcopal Church Center, Burlington VT p. 2420
Episcopal Church Library, *see* Immanuel Church, Highlands, Wilmington DE p. 388
Episcopal Diocese of Connecticut, Hartford CT p. 345
Episcopal Diocese of Massachusetts, Boston MA p. 1060
Episcopal Diocese of Missouri Archives, Saint Louis MO p. 1354
Episcopal Diocese of Western North Carolina, Asheville NC p. 1775
Episcopal Divinity School - Sherrill Library, Cambridge MA p. 1073
Episcopal Theological Seminary of the Southwest, Austin TX p. 2280
Epp Jake Library, Steinbach MB p. 2752
Epps Memorial, *see* Calcasieu Parish Public Library, Lake Charles LA p. 953
Epsom Public Library, Epsom NH p. 1446
Epstein, Becker & Green, New York NY p. 1677
Epworth Library, *see* First United Methodist Church, Gainesville FL p. 449
Epworth United Methodist Church Library, Toledo OH p. 1939
Equity Diversity & Education Library, *see* University of Colorado Boulder, Boulder CO p. 291
ERIC Project (N), *see* Computer Sciences Corporation, Washington DC p. 2940
Erick Community Library, Erick OK p. 1963
Erickson Gordon Music Library, *see* University of North Dakota, Grand Forks ND p. 1843
Erickson Walton Public Library, Morley MI p. 1210
Erico, Inc, Solon OH p. 1935
Ericson Public Library, Boone IA p. 797
Erie Area Health Information Library Cooperative (N), Erie PA p. 2954

Exponent, Menlo Park CA p. 185

EXPORAIL Archives Library, Saint Constant QC p. 2908

Export-Import Bank of the United States, Washington DC p. 399

Bethune Dr Mary McLeod, *see* Los Angeles Public Library System, Los Angeles CA p. 173

Express News Corp, San Antonio TX p. 2379

Extrusion Engineers Library, Branchburg NJ p. 1474

Ezra-Habonim, The Niles Township Jewish Congregation, Skokie IL p. 702

Fabian & Clendenin, Salt Lake City UT p. 2412

Fabricators & Manufacturers Association International, Rockford IL p. 696

Factoryville Public Library, Factoryville PA p. 2057

iSchool@Toronto, *see* University of Toronto, Toronto ON p. 2978

Faegre & Benson, LLP, Boulder CO p. 290

Faegre & Benson, LLP, Denver CO p. 302

Faegre & Benson, LLP, Minneapolis MN p. 1259

Faegre Baker Daniels Library, Indianapolis IN p. 751

Fahey Robert J Health Sciences Library, *see* Lawrence Memorial Hospital of Medford, Medford MA p. 1104

Fair Bluff Community, *see* Columbus County Public Library, Fair Bluff NC p. 1829

Fair Haven Free Library, Fair Haven VT p. 2424

Fair Haven Library, Fair Haven NJ p. 1485

Fair Haven Public Library, Fair Haven NY p. 1621

Fair Oaks-Orangevale Community Library, *see* Sacramento Public Library, Fair Oaks CA p. 225

Fairbank Center for Chinese Studies Collection, *see* Harvard Library, Cambridge MA p. 1075

Fairbank John Memorial Library, *see* Booth University College, Winnipeg MB p. 2754

Fairbank Public Library, Fairbank IA p. 815

Fairbanks Correctional Center Library, Fairbanks AK p. 47

Fairbanks Memorial Hospital Library, Fairbanks AK p. 47

Fairbanks Museum & Planetarium, Saint Johnsbury VT p. 2434

Fairbanks North Star Borough Public Library & Regional Center, Fairbanks AK p. 47

Fairborn Community Library, *see* Greene County Public Library, Fairborn OH p. 1951

Fairburn Hobgood-Palmer Library, *see* Atlanta-Fulton Public Library System, Fairburn GA p. 512

Fairbury Public Library, Fairbury NE p. 1398

Fairchild Aerial Photography Collection, *see* Whittier College, Whittier CA p. 283

Fairchild Public Library, Fairchild WI p. 2591

Fairchild Sherman Library, *see* California Institute of Technology, Pasadena CA p. 206

Fairchild Tropical Botanic Garden, Miami FL p. 465

Fairfax Bar Association Library, *see* Fairfax Public Law Library, Fairfax VA p. 2461

Fairfax Community Library, Fairfax VT p. 2424

Fairfax County Public Library, Fairfax VA p. 2461

Fairfax Public Law Library, Fairfax VA p. 2461

Fairfax Public Library, Fairfax IA p. 815

Fairfax Public Library, Fairfax MN p. 1250

Fairfax Public Library, Fairfax OK p. 1963

Fairfield Area Library, Fairfield PA p. 2057

Fairfield Area Library, *see* Henrico County Public Library, Henrico VA p. 2471

Fairfield Bay Library, Inc, Fairfield Bay AR p. 99

Fairfield Civic Center, *see* Solano County Library, Fairfield CA p. 148

Fairfield County District Library, Lancaster OH p. 1908

Fairfield County Library, Winnsboro SC p. 2207

Fairfield Lane Library, *see* Lane Public Libraries, Fairfield OH p. 1904

Fairfield Library Association, Inc, Fairfield TX p. 2318

Fairfield Museum & History Center, Fairfield CT p. 339

Fairfield Public Library, Fairfield CT p. 339

Fairfield Public Library, Fairfield IL p. 645

Fairfield Public Library, Fairfield IA p. 815

Fairfield Public Library, Fairfield NE p. 1398

Fairfield Public Library, Fairfield NJ p. 1485

Fairfield Simon Public Library, East Douglas MA p. 1086

Fairfield University, Fairfield CT p. 339

Fairfield/Teton Public Library, Fairfield MT p. 1378

Fairgrove District Library, Fairgrove MI p. 1177

Fairhope Public Library, Fairhope AL p. 16

Fairlee Public Library, Fairlee VT p. 2424

Fairleigh Dickinson University, Hackensack NJ p. 1489

Fairleigh Dickinson University, Madison NJ p. 1497

Fairleigh Dickinson University, Teaneck NJ p. 1532

Fairmont First Baptist Church, Fairmont NC p. 1792

Fairmont Public Library, Fairmont NE p. 1398

Fairmont State College, School of Education, Fairmont WV p. 2976

Fairmont State University, Fairmont WV p. 2558

Fairmount Community Library, Syracuse NY p. 1751

Fairmount Public Library, Fairmount IN p. 739

Fairport Harbor Public Library, Fairport Harbor OH p. 1899

Fairport Public Library, Fairport NY p. 1621

Fairview City Library, Fairview OK p. 1963

Fairview Free Public Library, Fairview NJ p. 1485

Fairview Heights Public Library, Fairview Heights IL p. 645

Fairview Hospital, Cleveland OH p. 1879

Fairview Public, *see* Cullman County Public Library System, Cullman AL p. 13

Fairview Public, *see* Marion County Public Library, Fairview WV p. 2559

Fairview Public Library, Margaretville NY p. 1658

Fairview Public Library, Fairview AB p. 2704

Fairview Public Library, *see* Henry County Public Library System, Stockbridge GA p. 544

Fairview-Ridges Hospital, Burnsville MN p. 1243

Fairview-Southdale Hospital, Edina MN p. 1249

Fairway, *see* Maricopa County Library District, Sun City AZ p. 74

Fairwood Library, *see* King County Library System, Renton WA p. 2517

Faith Baptist Bible College, Ankeny IA p. 793

Faith Evangelical Seminary Library, Tacoma WA p. 2538

Faith Memorial Library, Wallace NE p. 1422

Faith Presbyterian Church Library, Baltimore MD p. 1013

Faith Public Library, Faith SD p. 2212

Faith Theological Seminary Library, Baltimore MD p. 1013

Falcone Noreen Reale Library, *see* Le Moyne College, Syracuse NY p. 1751

Falconer Biology Library, *see* Stanford University Libraries, Stanford CA p. 271

Falconer Public Library, Falconer NY p. 1621

Fales Library, *see* New York University, New York NY p. 1695

Fales Robert M Health Sciences Library, *see* SEAHEC Medical Library, Wilmington NC p. 1831

Falher Municipal Library, *see* Bibliotheque Dentinger, Falher AB p. 2704

Falk Library of the Health Sciences, *see* University of Pittsburgh, Pittsburgh PA p. 2129

Falkville Public Library, Falkville AL p. 16

Fall Creek Public Library, Fall Creek WI p. 2591

Fall River Historical Society Museum-Library, Fall River MA p. 1088

Fall River Law Library, *see* Massachusetts Trial Court Law Libraries, Fall River MA p. 1088

Fall River Public Library, Fall River KS p. 866

Fall River Public Library, Fall River MA p. 1088

Falling Water River Regional Library, Cookeville TN p. 2231

Fallon County Library, Baker MT p. 1373

Falls City Library & Arts Center, Falls City NE p. 1398

Falls City Public Library, Falls City TX p. 2318

Fallsburg Library Inc, South Fallsburg NY p. 1745

Fallsington Library, Fallsington PA p. 2057

Falmouth Area Library, Falmouth MI p. 1177

Falmouth Historical Society, Falmouth MA p. 1088

Falmouth Hospital, Falmouth MA p. 1088

Falmouth Memorial Library, Falmouth ME p. 985

Falmouth Public Library, Falmouth MA p. 1088

Falvey Memorial Library, *see* Villanova University, Villanova PA p. 2149

Family & Community Medicine Library, *see* University of Toronto Libraries, Toronto ON p. 2866

Fannin County Public Library, *see* Mountain Regional Library System, Blue Ridge GA p. 558

Fannin Library, *see* Phoenix College, Phoenix AZ p. 76

Fanning Thelma Memorial Library, Nanton AB p. 2712

Fanshawe College, London ON p. 2817

Fanwood Memorial Library, Fanwood NJ p. 1485

Far Eastern Research Library, Plato MN p. 1271

Far Rockaway Community Library, *see* Queens Borough Public Library, Far Rockaway NY p. 1644

Faraday Library, *see* Northern Illinois University Libraries, DeKalb IL p. 635

Farallones Marine Sanctuary Association, San Francisco CA p. 242

Farella, Braun & Martel, San Francisco CA p. 242

Fargo L D Public Library, Lake Mills WI p. 2604

Fargo Public Library, Fargo ND p. 1841

Farha George J Medical Library, *see* University of Kansas School of Medicine-Wichita, Wichita KS p. 900

Faribault County Library Service, Blue Earth MN p. 1242

Faribault Public Library, *see* Buckham Memorial Library, Faribault MN p. 1250

Farley Eileen T Learning Resources Center, *see* Bristol Community College, Fall River MA p. 1087

Farley Library, *see* Wilkes University, Wilkes-Barre PA p. 2156

Farm & Food Care Ontario Library, Guelph ON p. 2806

Farman Free Library, Ellington NY p. 1619

Farmer City Public Library, Farmer City IL p. 645

Farmer George R Jr College of Law Library, *see* West Virginia University Libraries, Morgantown WV p. 2566

Farmers Branch Manske Library, Farmers Branch TX p. 2319

Farmers Insurance Group Library, Los Angeles CA p. 170

Farmersburg Public, *see* Sullivan County Public Library, Farmersburg IN p. 780

Farmersburg Public Library, Farmersburg IA p. 815

Farmingdale Public Library, Farmingdale NY p. 1621

Farmingdale State College of New York, Farmingdale NY p. 1622

Farmington Area Public Library District, Farmington IL p. 645

Farmington Community Library, Farmington Hills MI p. 1177

Farmington Library, Farmington CT p. 340

Farmington Public Library, Farmington IA p. 816

Farmington Public Library, Farmington ME p. 985

Farmington Public Library, Farmington MO p. 1327

Farmington Public Library, Farmington NM p. 1555

Farmland Public Library, Farmland IN p. 739

Farmville-Prince Edward Library, *see* Central Virginia Regional Library, Farmville VA p. 2463

Farmville Public Library, Farmville NC p. 1792

Farnam Public Library, Farnam NE p. 1398

Farnham Frank C Company Inc Library, Media PA p. 2087

Farnhamville Public Library, Farnhamville IA p. 816

Farnsworth Public Library, Oconto WI p. 2626

Farquhar Grover C Library, *see* Missouri School for the Deaf, Fulton MO p. 1328

Farquharson C D Health Sciences Library, *see* Rouge Valley Health System, Toronto ON p. 2858

Farr Alice M Library, Aurora NE p. 1392

Farr Regional Library, *see* High Plains Library District, Greeley CO p. 312

Farris Management Ltd, Vancouver BC p. 2741

Farrow H A C Library, *see* West Hill Collegiate Institute, West Hill ON p. 2870

Farwell Ann, *see* County of Prince Edward Libraries, Milford ON p. 2821

Ferris Joel E Research Library & Archives, *see* Northwest Museum of Art & Culture-Eastern Washington State Historical Society, Spokane WA p. 2536

Ferris Library for Information, Technology & Education, *see* Ferris State University Library, Big Rapids MI p. 1158

Ferris Public Library, Ferris TX p. 2319

Ferris State University, Grand Rapids MI p. 1184

Ferris State University Library, Big Rapids MI p. 1158

Ferrum College, Ferrum VA p. 2463

Fertile Public Library, Fertile IA p. 816

Fertile Public Library, *see* Lake Agassiz Regional Library, Fertile MN p. 1266

Festus Public Library, Festus MO p. 1327

FHI360 Library Services, Durham NC p. 1789

Field-Carnegie Library, Odebolt IA p. 836

Field Clark Library & Archives, *see* Maxwell Museum Association of Anthropology, Albuquerque NM p. 1549

Field Evelyn S Library, *see* Raritan Valley Community College, Somerville NJ p. 1530

Field Library, Northfield MA p. 1114

Field Library of Peekskill, Peekskill NY p. 1716

Field Memorial Library, Conway MA p. 1083

Field Memorial Library, *see* Bolivar County Library System, Shaw MS p. 1296

Field Museum of Natural History Library, Chicago IL p. 613

Fielding Graduate University, Santa Barbara CA p. 260

Fields Barbara Memorial Library, *see* Midstate College, Peoria IL p. 690

Fields Mildred G Memorial Library, Milan TN p. 2253

Fields Octavia Memorial, *see* Harris County Public Library, Humble TX p. 2336

Fife Lake Public Library, Fife Lake MI p. 1178

Fifth Ward Neighborhood Library, *see* Houston Public Library, Houston TX p. 2339

Fig Garden Regional, *see* Fresno County Public Library, Fresno CA p. 152

Figge Art Museum, Davenport IA p. 806

Filer Public Library, Filer ID p. 574

Files Loyd Research Library, *see* Museum of Western Colorado, Grand Junction CO p. 311

Filger Public Library, Minonk IL p. 674

Filion Wakely Thorup Angeletti LLP, Toronto ON p. 2853

Fillmore County Historical Society, Fountain MN p. 1252

Fillmore Riley, Winnipeg MB p. 2755

Filson Historical Society Library, Louisville KY p. 923

Financial Accounting Foundation Library, Norwalk CT p. 362

Finch Lucy Cooper Library, *see* Peace College, Raleigh NC p. 1816

Finch Memorial Public Library, Arnold NE p. 1392

Finch William E Jr Archives, *see* Historical Society of the Town of Greenwich, Cos Cob CT p. 334

Findlay-Hancock County District Public Library, Findlay OH p. 1899

Findley Alexander Community Library, Findley Lake NY p. 1622

Findley Timothy Memorial Library, *see* Brock Township Public Library, Cannington ON p. 2794

Finger Lakes Community College, Canandaigua NY p. 1601

Finger Lakes Library System, Ithaca NY p. 1642

Fingerlakes Developmental Disabilities Service Office Monroe Developmental Center, Rochester NY p. 1729

Fingold George Library, *see* State Library of Massachusetts, Boston MA p. 1067

Fink Harold Memorial Library, *see* Coney Island Hospital, Brooklyn NY p. 1592

Finkelman Jacob Library, *see* Public Service Labour Relations Board Library, Ottawa ON p. 2833

Finkelstein Memorial Library, Spring Valley NY p. 1746

Findlandia University, Hancock MI p. 1187

Finley Hospital, Dubuque IA p. 811

Finley-Sharon Library, Finley ND p. 1841

Finnegan, Henderson, Farabow, Garrett & Dunner, Washington DC p. 400

Finney County Public Library, Garden City KS p. 868

Finney Memorial Library, *see* Columbia State Community College, Columbia TN p. 2231

Finney Memorial Library, *see* Saint Mary Corwin Medical Center, Pueblo CO p. 321

Finney Theodore M Music Library, *see* University of Pittsburgh, Pittsburgh PA p. 2129

Finnish American Heritage Center & Historical Archive, *see* Findlandia University, Hancock MI p. 1188

Fintel Library, *see* Roanoke College, Salem VA p. 2495

Fiorello H LaGuardia Community College Library, Long Island City NY p. 1654

Fire Sciences Library & Audio-Visual Resource Centre, *see* Ontario Office of the Fire Marshal, Toronto ON p. 2856

Firefighters' Museum of Nova Scotia Library, Yarmouth NS p. 2786

Firelands College Library, *see* Bowling Green State University, Huron OH p. 1905

Firestone Idabelle Audio Library, *see* New England Conservatory of Music, Boston MA p. 1064

Firestone Library, *see* Princeton University, Princeton NJ p. 1523

First Assembly of God Library, North Little Rock AR p. 111

First Baptist Church, Rosedale MS p. 1314

First Baptist Church, Brevard NC p. 1777

First Baptist Church, Marion NC p. 1808

First Baptist Church, Winston-Salem NC p. 1832

First Baptist Church, Miami OK p. 1968

First Baptist Church, Salem OR p. 2017

First Baptist Church, Arlington TX p. 2277

First Baptist Church, Longview TX p. 2356

First Baptist Church, Luling TX p. 2358

First Baptist Church Library, Gainesville FL p. 449

First Baptist Church Library, Ashland KY p. 906

First Baptist Church Library, Melrose MA p. 1104

First Baptist Church Library, Minneapolis MN p. 1259

First Baptist Church Library, Kennett MO p. 1342

First Baptist Church Library, Union MO p. 1369

First Baptist Church Library, Greensboro NC p. 1796

First Baptist Church Library, Lancaster PA p. 2076

First Baptist Church Library, Sioux Falls SD p. 2218

First Baptist Church Library, Murfreesboro TN p. 2254

First Baptist Church Library, McAllen TX p. 2360

First Baptist Church Library, Richmond VA p. 2488

First Baptist Church Library-Waukesha, Waukesha WI p. 2645

First Baptist Church of Blanchard, Blanchard LA p. 945

First Baptist Church of Dallas, Dallas TX p. 2308

First Baptist Church of Highland Park Library, Landover MD p. 1034

First Baptist Church of Lakewood Library, Long Beach CA p. 166

First Baptist Church of West Terre Haute, West Terre Haute IN p. 787

First Centenary United Methodist Church, Chattanooga TN p. 2227

First Cerebral Palsy of New Jersey, Belleville NJ p. 1471

First Christian Church, Knoxville TN p. 2241

First Christian Church (Disciples of Christ) Library, Omaha NE p. 1412

First Christian Church Library, Saint Joseph MO p. 1352

First Christian Church Library, New Castle PA p. 2096

First Christian Church Library, Lubbock TX p. 2357

First Christian Reformed Church Library, Zeeland MI p. 1238

First Church of Christ Congregational, West Hartford CT p. 376

First Church of the Brethren Library, York PA p. 2159

First Congregational Church, Mansfield OH p. 1912

First Congregational Church Library, Palo Alto CA p. 204

First Congregational Church Library, Greeley CO p. 311

First Congregational Church Library, Stamford CT p. 369

First Congregational Church Library, Auburn MA p. 1051

First Congregational Church, Colorado Springs CO p. 295

First Congregational United Church of Christ, Saint Joseph MI p. 1225

First District Court of Appeal Library, Tallahassee FL p. 492

First Division Museum at Cantigny, *see* McCormick Colonel Robert R Research Center, Wheaton IL p. 718

First Judicial District of Pennsylvania, Philadelphia PA p. 2106

First Lutheran Church, Red Wing MN p. 1271

First Lutheran Church, Johnstown PA p. 2073

First Lutheran Church Library, Sioux Falls SD p. 2218

First Mennonite Church Library, Reedley CA p. 216

First Meridian Heights Library, *see* United Presbyterian Church, Indianapolis IN p. 755

First Nation Library, *see* Wahta Mohawks, Bala ON p. 2793

First Nations House Library, *see* University of Toronto Libraries, Toronto ON p. 2866

First Nations University of Canada, Regina SK p. 2922

First Parish Church of Norwell, Norwell MA p. 1115

First Plymouth Congregational Church, Englewood CO p. 306

First Presbyterian Church, Colorado Springs CO p. 295

First Presbyterian Church, Evanston IL p. 643

First Presbyterian Church, Cranford NJ p. 1480

First Presbyterian Church, Ardmore PA p. 2029

First Presbyterian Church, Lansdowne PA p. 2078

First Presbyterian Church, Houston TX p. 2335

First Presbyterian Church Library, Monrovia CA p. 189

First Presbyterian Church Library, Upland CA p. 278

First Presbyterian Church Library, Shreveport LA p. 968

First Presbyterian Church Library, Hastings NE p. 1401

First Presbyterian Church Library, Albuquerque NM p. 1549

First Presbyterian Church Library, Charlotte NC p. 1783

First Presbyterian Church Library, Mansfield OH p. 1912

First Presbyterian Church Library, Norwalk OH p. 1924

First Presbyterian Church Library, Phoenixville PA p. 2120

First Presbyterian Church Library, El Paso TX p. 2317

First Presbyterian Church Library, Yakima WA p. 2550

First Presbyterian Church of Arlington Library, Arlington VA p. 2449

First Presbyterian Church of Charleston, Charleston WV p. 2556

First Presbyterian Church of Flint, Flint MI p. 1179

First Presbyterian Church of Gadsden Library, Gadsden AL p. 18

First Presbyterian Church of San Diego Library, San Diego CA p. 231

First Presbyterian Church of the Covenant, Erie PA p. 2055

First Reformed Church of Schenectady, Schenectady NY p. 1740

First Regional Library, Hernando MS p. 1301

First Southern Baptist Church Library, Tucson AZ p. 86

First Unitarian Universalist Society of Albany, Albany NY p. 1569

First United Methodist Church, Alhambra CA p. 120

First United Methodist Church, Clearwater FL p. 432

First United Methodist Church, Gainesville FL p. 449

First United Methodist Church, Shreveport LA p. 968

First United Methodist Church, Oak Ridge TN p. 2262

First United Methodist Church Library, Palo Alto CA p. 204

First United Methodist Church Library, Pasadena CA p. 206

First United Methodist Church Library, Boulder CO p. 290

First United Methodist Church Library, Glen Ellyn IL p. 650

First United Methodist Church Library, Normal IL p. 681

First United Methodist Church Library, Hyattsville MD p. 1032

First United Methodist Church Library, Mount Pleasant MI p. 1211

First United Methodist Church Library, Los Alamos NM p. 1559

First United Methodist Church Library, Sylvania OH p. 1938

First United Methodist Church Library, Tulsa OK p. 1980

First United Methodist Church Library, Austin TX p. 2280

First United Methodist Church Library, Lufkin TX p. 2358

First United Methodist Church Library, Richardson TX p. 2374

First United Methodist Church Library, Green Bay WI p. 2595

FirstEnergy Corp, Akron OH p. 1853

Fischer Fred C Library, Belleville MI p. 1156

Fish & Neave IP Group of Ropes Gray LLP Library, New York NY p. 1678

Fish & Wildlife Research Institute, Saint Petersburg FL p. 488

Fish Creek, see Calgary Public Library, Calgary AB p. 2689

Fish Debra S Early Childhood Resource Library, Saint Paul MN p. 1278

Fish Dorothy Coastal Resource Library at Wells Reserve, Wells ME p. 1006

Fish Lake Library, Dyer NV p. 1426

Fishbeck, Thompson, Carr & Huber, Grand Rapids MI p. 1184

Fishbon Harris M Memorial Library, see UCSF Medical Center at Mount Zion, San Francisco CA p. 247

Fishburn Junius P Music Library, see Sweet Briar College, Sweet Briar VA p. 2497

Fisher B L Library, see Asbury Theological Seminary, Wilmore KY p. 938

Fisher College Library, Boston MA p. 1061

Fisher Control International Information Center, see Emerson Process Management, Marshalltown IA p. 830

Fisher Edward Gauche Public Library, Athens TN p. 2224

Fisher Family Archives & Library, see Clark County Historical Society, Springfield OH p. 1935

Fisher Fine Arts Library, see University of Pennsylvania Libraries, Philadelphia PA p. 2119

Fisher L P Public Library, see Haut-Saint-Jean Regional Library, Woodstock NB p. 2762

Fisher Laura Kramer Library, see Institute for Clinical Social Work Library, Chicago IL p. 615

Fisher Robert M Library, see John F Kennedy University Libraries, Pleasant Hill CA p. 210

Fisher Thomas Rare Books Library, see University of Toronto Libraries, Toronto ON p. 2866

Fisher-Whiting Memorial Library, Mapleton IA p. 829

Fisheries & Marine Institute - Dr C R Barrett Library, see Memorial University of Newfoundland, St. John's NL p. 2772

Fisheries & Oceans Canada, Sidney BC p. 2737

Fisheries & Oceans Canada, Vancouver BC p. 2741

Fisheries & Oceans Canada, Saint Andrews NB p. 2766

Fisheries & Oceans Canada, St. John's NL p. 2772

Fishers Island Library, Fishers Island NY p. 1622

Fishkill Correctional Facility Library, Beacon NY p. 1579

Fishkill Historical Society, Fishkill NY p. 1622

Fishman R Jack Library, see Walters State Community College Library, Morristown TN p. 2253

Fisk University, Nashville TN p. 2256

Fiske Free Library, Claremont NH p. 1441

Fiske Public Library, Wrentham MA p. 1146

Fitch Library, see West Hills Community College, Coalinga CA p. 135

Fitchburg Law Library, see Massachusetts Trial Court, Fitchburg MA p. 1089

Fitchburg Public Library, Fitchburg MA p. 1089

Fitchburg State College, Fitchburg MA p. 1089

Fitzgerald-Ben Hill County Library, Fitzgerald GA p. 532

Fitzgerald Library, see Saint Mary's University of Minnesota, Winona MN p. 1289

FitzPatrick James A Library, see Miner William H Agricultural Research Institute, Chazy NY p. 1606

Fitzwilliam Town Library, Fitzwilliam NH p. 1447

Five Colleges of Ohio (N), Gambier OH p. 2952

Five Rivers Public Library, Parsons WV p. 2569

Five Towns College Library, Dix Hills NY p. 1614

Flag Research Center Library, Winchester MA p. 1141

Flagg Lois A, see Jackson/Hinds Library System, Edwards MS p. 1303

Flagg-Rochelle Public Library District, Rochelle IL p. 695

Flagler Beach Library, Flagler Beach FL p. 440

Flagler College, Saint Augustine FL p. 486

Flagler Community Library, Flagler CO p. 306

Flagler County Public Library, Palm Coast FL p. 479

Flagstaff City-Coconino County Public Library System, Flagstaff AZ p. 62

Flagstaff Medical Center, Flagstaff AZ p. 62

Flaschner Disabilities Library, see Mental Health Legal Advisors Committee, Boston MA p. 1064

Flasher Public Library, Flasher ND p. 1841

Flat River Community Library, Greenville MI p. 1186

Flat Rock Public Library, Flat Rock MI p. 1178

Flatbush Community Library, Flatbush AB p. 2704

Flathead County Library, Kalispell MT p. 1384

Flathead Valley Community College Library, Kalispell MT p. 1384

Flatonia Public Library, Flatonia TX p. 2319

Flatwoods Public, see Greenup County Public Libraries, Flatwoods KY p. 915

Flaxman John M Library, see School of the Art Institute of Chicago, Chicago IL p. 624

Fleche Marie Memorial Library, Berlin NJ p. 1472

Fleck Paul D Library & Archives, see Banff Centre, Banff AB p. 2684

Fleece G Allen Library, see Columbia International University, Columbia SC p. 2187

Fleet Library at RISD, see Rhode Island School of Design Library, Providence RI p. 2174

Fleetwood Area Public Library, Fleetwood PA p. 2057

Fleischmann Max C Medical Library, see Saint Mary's Regional Medical Center, Reno NV p. 1432

Fleisher Edwin A Collection of Orchestral Music, see Free Library of Philadelphia, Philadelphia PA p. 2107

Fleming Brian Research Library, see Ontario Ministry of Education, Toronto ON p. 2856

Fleming Community Library, Fleming CO p. 306

Fleming County Public Library, Flemingsburg KY p. 912

Fleming Library, see Grand Canyon University, Phoenix AZ p. 73

Flemington Free Public Library, Flemington NJ p. 1486

Flenniken Public Library, Carmichaels PA p. 2042

Fleschner Thomas E Memorial Library, Birch Run MI p. 1158

Flesh Public Library, Piqua OH p. 1930

Flesherton Public Library, see Grey Highlands Public Library, Flesherton ON p. 2805

Fletcher Free Library, Burlington VT p. 2420

Fletcher George N Public Library, see Alpena County Library, Alpena MI p. 1150

Fletcher J V Library, Westford MA p. 1138

Fletcher John Gould, see Central Arkansas Library System, Little Rock AR p. 106

Fletcher Library, see Arizona State University Libraries, Glendale AZ p. 83

Fletcher Memorial Library, Hampton CT p. 344

Fletcher Memorial Library, Ludlow VT p. 2427

Fletcher Stephen H Library, see Alpena Community College, Alpena MI p. 1150

Felwellin Memorial Library, Shabbona IL p. 701

Flexon R G Memorial Library, see God's Bible School & College Library, Cincinnati OH p. 1870

Flin Flon Public Library, Flin Flon MB p. 2748

Flinn Lewis B Medical Library, see Christiana Hospital Library, Newark DE p. 385

Flint-Groves Baptist Church Library, Gastonia NC p. 1794

Flint Hills Technical College Library, Emporia KS p. 866

Flint Institute of Arts, Flint MI p. 1179

Flint Memorial Library, North Reading MA p. 1113

Flint Memorial Library, see New Hope Christian College, Eugene OR p. 1997

Flint Public Library, Middleton MA p. 1105

Flint Public Library, Flint MI p. 1179

Flint River Regional Library, Griffin GA p. 535

McCarty Public Library, see Genesee District Library, Flint MI p. 1180

FLO (N), see Fenway Libraries Online, Inc, Boston MA p. 2945

Flomaton Public Library, Flomaton AL p. 17

Flora-Monroe Township Public Library, Flora IN p. 740

Flora Public Library, Flora IL p. 646

Flora Public Library, see Madison County Library System, Flora MS p. 1295

Floral City Public, see Citrus County Library System, Floral City FL p. 427

Floral Park Public Library, Floral Park NY p. 1622

Florala Public Library, Florala AL p. 17

Florence Community Library, Florence AZ p. 63

Florence County Library, Florence WI p. 2592

Florence County Library System, Florence SC p. 2193

Florence-Darlington Technical College Libraries, Florence SC p. 2193

Florence-Lauderdale Public Library, Florence AL p. 17

Florence Library, see County of Los Angeles Public Library, Los Angeles CA p. 141

Florence Nan Library, see United Nations Association In Canada, Winnipeg Branch, Winnipeg MB p. 2757

Florence Public, see Cape Breton Regional Library, Florence NS p. 2785

Florence Public Library, Florence KS p. 866

Florence Public Library, Florence MS p. 1298

Florence Public Library, Florence TX p. 2319

Florence Township Public Library, Roebling NJ p. 1527

Flores Nieves M Memorial Library, see Guam Public Library, Hagatna GU p. 2667

Flores Patricio Neighborhood Library, see Houston Public Library, Houston TX p. 2339

Florham Park Public Library, Florham Park NJ p. 1486

Florida Agricultural & Mechanical University, Orlando FL p. 475

Florida Agricultural & Mechanical University Libraries, Tallahassee FL p. 492

Florida Atlantic University, Boca Raton FL p. 428

Florida Atlantic University, Fort Pierce FL p. 446

Florida Atlantic University, Jupiter FL p. 455

Florida Atlantic University, Port Saint Lucie FL p. 485

Florida Attorney General's Law Library, Tallahassee FL p. 493

Florida Center for Library Automation (N), Gainesville FL p. 2940

Florida Christian College Library, Kissimmee FL p. 456

Florida Coastal School of Law Library, Jacksonville FL p. 452

Florida College, Temple Terrace FL p. 500

Florida Department of Agriculture & Consumer Services, Gainesville FL p. 449

Florida Department of Agriculture & Consumer Services, Tallahassee FL p. 493

Florida Department of Children & Families, Pembroke Pines FL p. 481

Florida Department of Corrections, Arcadia FL p. 425

Florida Department of Corrections, Belle Glade FL p. 427

Florida Department of Corrections, Bonifay FL p. 428

Florida Department of Corrections, Bowling Green FL p. 429

Florida Department of Corrections, Bristol FL p. 430

Florida Department of Corrections, Brooksville FL p. 430

Florida Department of Corrections, Bushnell FL p. 431

Florida Department of Corrections, Chipley FL p. 431

Florida Department of Corrections, Clermont FL p. 432

Florida Department of Corrections, Cocoa FL p. 433

Florida Department of Corrections, Crestview FL p. 434

Florida Department of Corrections, Daytona Beach FL p. 436

Florida Department of Corrections, De Funiak Springs FL p. 437

Florida Department of Corrections, East Palatka FL p. 438

Florida Department of Corrections, Florida City FL p. 440

Florida Department of Corrections, Fort Lauderdale FL p. 443

Florida Department of Corrections, Jasper FL p. 455

Florida Department of Corrections, Lake Butler FL p. 457

Florida Department of Corrections, Madison FL p. 462

Florida Department of Corrections, Malone FL p. 462

Florida Department of Corrections, Mayo FL p. 463

Florida Department of Corrections, Miami FL p. 465

Florida Department of Corrections, Milton FL p. 470

Florida Department of Corrections, Ocala FL p. 473

Florida Department of Corrections, Okeechobee FL p. 474

Florida Department of Corrections, Perry FL p. 483

Florida Department of Corrections, Polk City FL p. 484

Florida Department of Corrections, Punta Gorda FL p. 485

Florida Department of Corrections, Raiford FL p. 485

Florida Department of Corrections, Sanderson FL p. 489

Florida Department of Corrections, Sneads FL p. 491

Florida Department of Corrections, Trenton FL p. 500

Florida Department of Corrections, Zephyrhills FL p. 505

Florida Department of Education, Tallahassee FL p. 493

Florida Department of Elder Affairs, Tallahassee FL p. 493

Florida Department of Environmental Protection, Tallahassee FL p. 493

Florida Department of Highway Safety & Motor Vehicles, Tallahassee FL p. 493

Florida Department of State, Tallahassee FL p. 493

Florida Department of Transportation, Tallahassee FL p. 494

Florida Diagnostic & Learning Resource System, Fort Lauderdale FL p. 443

Florida Free Library, Florida MA p. 1089

Florida Geological Survey Research Library, *see* Florida Department of Environmental Protection, Tallahassee FL p. 493

Florida Gulf Coast University Library, Fort Myers FL p. 444

Florida Historical Society, Cocoa FL p. 433

Florida Hospital, Orlando FL p. 475

Florida Hospital College of Health Sciences, Orlando FL p. 475

Florida Hospital-Tampa, Tampa FL p. 496

Florida Institute of Phosphate Research, Bartow FL p. 426

Florida Institute of Technology, Melbourne FL p. 463

Florida International University, Miami FL p. 465

Florida International University, North Miami FL p. 472

Florida Keys Community College Library, Key West FL p. 456

Florida Library Information Network (N), Tallahassee FL p. 2940

Florida Medical Entomology Laboratory Library, *see* University of Florida, Vero Beach FL p. 502

Florida Memorial University, Miami Gardens FL p. 469

Florida Office of Financial Regulation, Tallahassee FL p. 494

Florida Public, *see* Napoleon Public Library, Napoleon OH p. 1920

Florida Public Library, Florida NY p. 1623

Florida Solar Energy Center, Cocoa FL p. 433

Florida Southern College, Lakeland FL p. 459

Florida State College at Jacksonville, Jacksonville FL p. 452

Florida State Hospital, Chattahoochee FL p. 431

Florida State Prison Library, *see* Florida Department of Corrections, Raiford FL p. 485

Florida State University, Tallahassee FL p. 494, 2963

Florida State University Libraries, Tallahassee FL p. 494

Florida Supreme Court Library, Tallahassee FL p. 495

Florida Technical College Library, Orlando FL p. 476

Florida Times Union, Jacksonville FL p. 453

Florida Today Newspaper Library, Melbourne FL p. 463

Florissant Public Library, *see* Rampart Public Library District, Florissant CO p. 326

Flossmoor Public Library, Flossmoor IL p. 646

Flower Mound Public Library, Flower Mound TX p. 2319

Flower Roswell P Memorial Library, Watertown NY p. 1763

Flower-Sprecher Veterinary Library, *see* Cornell University Library, Ithaca NY p. 1641

Floyd Carolyn Library, *see* Kodiak College, Kodiak AK p. 51

Floyd County Historical Society Museum Library, Charles City IA p. 801

Floyd County Library, Floydada TX p. 2319

Floyd County Public Library, Prestonsburg KY p. 933

Floyd Medical Center Library, Rome GA p. 548

Floyd Memorial Library, Greenport NY p. 1631

Fluor, Greenville SC p. 2195

Fluor Corp, Sugar Land TX p. 2389

Flushing Hospital Medical Center, Flushing NY p. 1623

Flushing Library, *see* Queens Borough Public Library, Flushing NY p. 1644

Fluvanna County Library, Fork Union VA p. 2464

Fluvanna Free Library, Jamestown NY p. 1646

Fly Fishing Discovery Center, *see* Federation of Flyfishers, Livingston MT p. 1385

Fly Murry H Learning Resources Center, *see* Odessa College, Odessa TX p. 2366

Flynt Roy A Memorial, *see* Georgia Department of Transportation, Forest Park GA p. 532

FM Global, Norwood MA p. 1115

FM Global Library, Johnston RI p. 2167

Foard County Library, Crowell TX p. 2303

Fobes Memorial Library, Oakham MA p. 1116

Fogelman Raymond Library, *see* New School, New York NY p. 1688

Fogelson Library, *see* Santa Fe University of Art & Design, Santa Fe NM p. 1564

Fogg James Lemont Memorial Library, *see* Art Center College of Design, Pasadena CA p. 205

Fogg Library, *see* Tufts Library, South Weymouth MA p. 1140

Fogg William Library, Eliot ME p. 984

Fogler Raymond H Library, *see* University of Maine, Orono ME p. 994

Fohrman Library, *see* Condell Medical Center, Libertyville IL p. 665

FOI Services Inc Library, Gaithersburg MD p. 1030

Foley & Hoag LLP Library, Boston MA p. 1061

Foley & Lardner Library, Chicago IL p. 613

Foley & Lardner, Milwaukee WI p. 2618

Foley & Lardner LLP, Los Angeles CA p. 170

Foley & Lardner LLP, Washington DC p. 400

Foley Center Library, *see* Gonzaga University, Spokane WA p. 2536

Foley Doris Library for Historical Research, *see* Nevada County Library, Nevada City CA p. 193

Foley Library, *see* Great River Regional Library, Foley MN p. 1275

Foley Public Library, Foley AL p. 17

Folger Shakespeare Library, Washington DC p. 400

Folks Frances L Memorial Library, *see* Loogootee Public Library, Loogootee IN p. 762

Follett David L Memorial Library, *see* New York State Supreme Court Sixth District, Norwich NY p. 1708

Folsom Lake College Library, Folsom CA p. 148

Folsom Library, *see* Rensselaer Libraries, Troy NY p. 1756

Folsom Public Library, Folsom CA p. 148

Folsom State Prison, *see* California Department of Corrections Library System, Represa CA p. 221

Fond Du Lac Circuit Court, Fond du Lac WI p. 2592

Fond du Lac County Historical Society, Fond du Lac WI p. 2592

Fond Du Lac Public Library, Fond du Lac WI p. 2592

Fonda Public Library, Fonda IA p. 816

Fondren Library, *see* Rice University, Houston TX p. 2341

Fondren Library, *see* Southern Methodist University, Dallas TX p. 2310

Fondulac Public Library District, East Peoria IL p. 638

Fong Optometry & Health Sciences Library, *see* University of California, Berkeley, Berkeley CA p. 128

Fontana Public Library, Fontana WI p. 2592

Fontana Regional Library, Bryson City NC p. 1778

Fontanelle Public Library, Fontanelle IA p. 816

Fontbonne University, Saint Louis MO p. 1354

Fontenot Memorial, *see* Calcasieu Parish Public Library, Vinton LA p. 954

Food & Drug Administration, Atlanta GA p. 515

Food & Drug Administration Biosciences Library, *see* United States Department of Health & Human Services, Silver Spring MD p. 1039

Food Development Centre Library, *see* Manitoba Agriculture, Food & Rural Initiatives, Portage la Prairie MB p. 2750

Food Marketing Institute, Arlington VA p. 2449

Foote Marvin W Youth Services Center, *see* Department of Human Services, Englewood CO p. 306

Foothill College, Los Altos Hills CA p. 167, 2962

Foothills Art Center, Golden CO p. 309

Foothills Correctional Institution Library, *see* North Carolina Department of Correction, Morganton NC p. 1811

FOR Sto-Rox Library, McKees Rocks PA p. 2085

Forbes Library, Northampton MA p. 1113

Forbes Regional Hospital, Monroeville PA p. 2091

Forbush Memorial Library, Westminster MA p. 1139

Ford Benson Research Center, *see* Ford Henry, Dearborn MI p. 1167

Ford City Library, Ford KS p. 867

Ford City Public Library, Ford City PA p. 2058

Ford Edith B Memorial Library, Ovid NY p. 1713

Fort Ward Museum, Alexandria VA p. 2445

Fort Wayne Museum of Art, Fort Wayne IN p. 741

Fort Wayne News-Sentinel Library, Fort Wayne IN p. 741

Morrison Jean Canadian Fur Trade Library, see Ontario Ministry of Tourism, Thunder Bay ON p. 2849

Fort Worth Library, Fort Worth TX p. 2321

Fort Worth Museum of Science & History Library, Fort Worth TX p. 2322

Forte John Dennis Library, see Alabama Southern Community College, Monroeville AL p. 26

Fortier Library, see White Mountains Community College, Berlin NH p. 1439

Fortier Memorial Library, see Manistee County Historical Museum, Manistee MI p. 1205

Fortress of Louisbourg Library, Louisbourg NS p. 2783

Fortson Public Library, see Henry County Public Library System, Hampton GA p. 544

Fortune Public Library, Fortune NL p. 2770

Fortville-Vernon Township Public Library, Fortville IN p. 743

49-99 Cooperative Library System (N), Monrovia CA p. 2938

45th Space Wing Technical Library, see United States Air Force, Patrick AFB FL p. 481

Forum Health-Western Reserve Healthcare, Youngstown OH p. 1952

Foss Oscar Memorial Library, Center Barnstead NH p. 1440

Fossil Public Library, Fossil OR p. 1998

Fossil Ridge Public Library, Braidwood IL p. 597

Fosston Public Library, see Lake Agassiz Regional Library, Fosston MN p. 1266

Foster Associates, Inc Library, Bethesda MD p. 1021

Foster Betty Public Library, Ponder TX p. 2371

Foster City Library, see San Mateo County Library, Foster City CA p. 255

Foster Community Library, see Capital Area District Libraries, Lansing MI p. 1200

Foster Dwight Public Library, Fort Atkinson WI p. 2592

Foster E P Library, see Ventura County Library, Ventura CA p. 280

Foster Emily Health Sciences Library, see Women and Children's Hospital of Buffalo, Buffalo NY p. 1600

Foster Frank B Research Room, see Evanston History Center Library & Archives, Evanston IL p. 643

Foster Library, see King County Library System, Tukwila WA p. 2517

Foster Memorial Library, see Strong Public Library, Strong ME p. 1003

Foster Public Library, Foster RI p. 2166

Foster Sumner & Laura Library, see University of Michigan, Ann Arbor MI p. 1152

Foster William F Public, see Lonoke Prairie County Regional Library Headquarters, England AR p. 108

Foundation Center-Cleveland Library, Cleveland OH p. 1880

Foundation Center Library, New York NY p. 1679

Foundation Center-San Francisco Library, San Francisco CA p. 242

Foundation Center Washington DC Library, Washington DC p. 401

Foundation for Blind Children Library & Media Center, Phoenix AZ p. 73

Foundation for Blood Research Library, Scarborough ME p. 1000

Foundation for Economic Education Library, Irvington NY p. 1640

Foundation for Student Communication, Princeton NJ p. 1522

Founders Library, see Los Angeles Southwest College, Los Angeles CA p. 174

Founders Memorial Library, see Northern Illinois University Libraries, DeKalb IL p. 635

Founding Church of Scientology, Washington DC p. 401

Fountain Library, see Pikes Peak Library District, Fountain CO p. 296

Fountain-New Library, see Brewton-Parker College, Mount Vernon GA p. 546

Fountaindale Public Library District, Bolingbrook IL p. 596

Four County Library System, Vestal NY p. 1761

Four Fathers Memorial, see Cumberland Public Libraries, Amherst NS p. 2777

Four Mile Correctional Center Library, see Colorado Department of Corrections, Canon City CO p. 293

Four Star Public Library District, Mendon IL p. 673

Fournarakis Dimitrios Medical Library, see Richmond University Medical Center, Staten Island NY p. 1748

Fourth Presbyterian Church, Bethesda MD p. 1021

Fowler Clifton Library, see Colorado Christian University Library, Lakewood CO p. 314

Fowler Emily Central Library, see Denton Public Library, Denton TX p. 2312

Fowler Helen Library, see Denver Botanic Gardens, Denver CO p. 300

Fowler Memorial, see Concord Free Public Library, Concord MA p. 1082

Fowler Public Library, Fowler CO p. 308

Fowler Public Library, Fowler KS p. 867

Fowler Richard S Memorial Library, see Hall of Flame, Phoenix AZ p. 73

Fowlerville District Library, Fowlerville MI p. 1181

Fox Clardy, see El Paso Public Library, El Paso TX p. 2316

Fox Creek Municipal Library, Fox Creek AB p. 2705

Fox Edith M Library, see Public Library of Arlington, Arlington MA p. 1050

Fox Harbour Public Library, Fox Harbour NL p. 2770

Fox Herbert Memorial Library, see Pennsylvania State Department of Health, Lionville PA p. 2082

Fox Lake Correctional Institution Library, Fox Lake WI p. 2593

Fox Lake Public District Library, Fox Lake IL p. 646

Fox Lake Public Library, Fox Lake WI p. 2593

Fox Point Library, see Providence Community Library, Providence RI p. 2173

Fox River Grove Public Library District, Fox River Grove IL p. 646

Fox River Valley Area Library Consortium (N), Oshkosh WI p. 2958

Fox River Valley Public Library District, Dundee IL p. 637

Fox Rothschild LLP, Philadelphia PA p. 2106

Fox Terry Library, see Fraser Valley Regional Library, Port Coquitlam BC p. 2723

Fox Valley Health Science Library Consortium (N), Geneva IL p. 2942

Fox Valley Library Council (N), Appleton WI p. 2958

Fox Valley Technical College, Appleton WI p. 2578

Fox Valley Technical College, Oshkosh WI p. 2627

Foxburg Free Library, Foxburg PA p. 2058

FPInnovations-Forintek, Quebec QC p. 2905

Frackville Free Public Library, Frackville PA p. 2058

Framingham Public Library, Framingham MA p. 1090

Framingham State College, Framingham MA p. 1090

Frances-Henry Library, see Hebrew Union College-Jewish Institute of Religion, Los Angeles CA p. 170

Francesville-Salem Township Public Library, Francesville IN p. 743

Francis Marion University, Florence SC p. 2194

Francis Roger B, see Saint Joseph County Public Library, South Bend IN p. 779

Franciscan Friars of the Atonement Library, Garrison NY p. 1627

Franciscan Monastery Library, Washington DC p. 401

Franciscan University of Steubenville, Steubenville OH p. 1936

Franco-American Centre Bibliotheque, Manchester NH p. 1455

Franco Dr Frank A Library Learning Center, see Alvernia University, Reading PA p. 2132

Franco Jorge Medical Library, see O'Connor Hospital Medical Library, San Jose CA p. 250

Frank Lloyd Wright School of Architecture, Scottsdale AZ p. 80

Frank Morris Neighborhood Library, see Houston Public Library, Houston TX p. 2339

Frank Phillips College, Borger TX p. 2290

Frank Willie Library, see Seminole Tribe of Florida, Clewiston FL p. 474

Frankenmuth Historical Association, Frankenmuth MI p. 1181

Frankenmuth Historical Museum Library, see Frankenmuth Historical Association, Frankenmuth MI p. 1181

Frankford Public Library, Frankford DE p. 383

Frankfort Career Development Center Library, Frankfort KY p. 913

Frankfort City Library, Frankfort KS p. 867

Frankfort Community Public Library, Frankfort IN p. 743

Frankfort Free Library, Frankfort NY p. 1624

Frankfort Public Library District, Frankfort IL p. 646

Franklin & Marshall College, Lancaster PA p. 2076

Franklin Ben Center Library, see Franklin Memorial Hospital, Farmington ME p. 985

Franklin Benjamin, see Los Angeles Public Library System, Los Angeles CA p. 173

Franklin College, Franklin IN p. 743

Franklin Community Library, see Sacramento Public Library, Elk Grove CA p. 225

Franklin Correctional Facility, Malone NY p. 1656

Franklin County Law Library, see Franklin County Law Library Association, Chambersburg PA p. 2043

Franklin County Law Library Association, Chambersburg PA p. 2043

Franklin County Library, Louisburg NC p. 1807

Franklin County Library, Winchester TN p. 2269

Franklin County Library, Mount Vernon TX p. 2364

Franklin County Library District, Preston ID p. 582

Franklin County Library System, Chambersburg PA p. 2043

Franklin County Public Library, Eastpoint FL p. 438

Franklin County Public Library, Rocky Mount VA p. 2495

Franklin County Public Library, see Lincoln-Lawrence-Franklin Regional Library, Meadville MS p. 1295

Franklin County Public Library District, Brookville IN p. 730

Franklin Free Library, Franklin NY p. 1624

Franklin Grove Public Library, Franklin Grove IL p. 647

Franklin Institute Library, Philadelphia PA p. 2106

Franklin Lakes Free Public Library, Franklin Lakes NJ p. 1486

Franklin Law Library, see Massachusetts Trial Court, Greenfield MA p. 1092

Franklin Medical Center, Greenfield MA p. 1092

Franklin Memorial Hospital, Farmington ME p. 985

Franklin Memorial Library, Swainsboro GA p. 552

Franklin Parish Library, Winnsboro LA p. 972

Franklin Park Public Library District, Franklin Park IL p. 647

Franklin Pierce University Library, Rindge NH p. 1463

Franklin Public Library, Franklin MA p. 1090

Franklin Public Library, Franklin MI p. 1181

Franklin Public Library, Franklin NE p. 1399

Franklin Public Library, Franklin NH p. 1447

Franklin Public Library, Franklin PA p. 2058

Franklin Public Library, Franklin WI p. 2593

Franklin Rosalind University of Medicine & Science, North Chicago IL p. 682

Franklin-Springboro Public Library, Franklin OH p. 1900

Franklin Square Public Library, Franklin Square NY p. 1624

Franklin Township Free Public Library, Somerset NJ p. 1529

Franklin Township Public Library, Franklinville NJ p. 1487

Franklin University Library, Columbus OH p. 1886

Frum Barbara, *see* Toronto Public Library, Toronto ON p. 2861

FRVALC (N), *see* Fox River Valley Area Library Consortium, Oshkosh WI p. 2958

Fry Mabel C Public Library, Yukon OK p. 1987

Frye Art Museum Library, Seattle WA p. 2527

Fryeburg Public Library, Fryeburg ME p. 986

FTP Library, *see* Elgin Mental Health Center Library, Elgin IL p. 641

Fuchsberg Jacob D Law Center Library, *see* Touro College, Central Islip NY p. 1605

Fugro, Inc, Houston TX p. 2335

Fugro West, Ventura CA p. 279

Fujitsu, Sunnyvale CA p. 273

Fulbright & Jaworski Library, San Antonio TX p. 2380

Fulbright & Jaworski LLP, Los Angeles CA p. 170

Fuld Helene College of Nursing, New York NY p. 1679

Fulda Memorial Library, Fulda MN p. 1252

Fulford Harlie Memorial, *see* Oconee Regional Library, Wrightsville GA p. 531

Fuller Public Library, Hillsboro NH p. 1451

Fuller Ralph Henry Medical Library, *see* Carondelet Saint Mary's Hospital, Tucson AZ p. 86

Fuller Theological Seminary, Pasadena CA p. 206

Fullerton College, Fullerton CA p. 153

Fullerton Public Library, Fullerton CA p. 154

Fullerton Public Library, Fullerton NE p. 1399

Fulton County Association, Wauseon OH p. 1945

Fulton County Historical Society, Inc, Rochester IN p. 776

Fulton County Law Library, Atlanta GA p. 515

Fulton County Library, Salem AR p. 114

Fulton County Library, McConnellsburg PA p. 2085

Fulton County Public Library, Rochester IN p. 776

Fulton Dr Robert E Regional, *see* Atlanta-Fulton Public Library System, Alpharetta GA p. 512

Fulton-Hayden Memorial Library, *see* Amerind Foundation, Inc, Dragoon AZ p. 61

Fulton L R Library & Audiovisual Center, *see* New Brunswick Community College, Saint John NB p. 2767

Fulton-Montgomery Community College, Johnstown NY p. 1648

Fulton Public Library, Fulton KY p. 914

Fulton Public Library, Fulton NY p. 1625

Fulton Public Library, *see* Schmaling Memorial Public Library District, Fulton IL p. 647

Fulton Ralph J & Virginia A Library, *see* Clarion County Historical Society, Clarion PA p. 2045

Fulton State Hospital, Fulton MO p. 1328

Fultondale Public Library, Fultondale AL p. 18

Fund for Modern Courts Library, New York NY p. 1679

Funderburg Library, *see* Manchester College, North Manchester IN p. 769

Funk Agricultural, Consumer & Environmental Sciences, *see* University of Illinois Library at Urbana-Champaign, Urbana IL p. 712

Funkhouser Virginia Health Sciences Library, *see* RMH Healthcare, Harrisonburg VA p. 2470

Furman University Libraries, Greenville SC p. 2195

Furnas County Law Library, Beaver City NE p. 1393

Furnas Leto M Information Resource Center, *see* Illinois Mathematics & Science Academy, Aurora IL p. 591

Furness Helen Kate Free Library, Wallingford PA p. 2150

Furth Harold P Library, *see* Princeton University, Princeton NJ p. 1523

Fuss & O'Neill Inc, Manchester CT p. 349

Fyles James T Library, *see* British Columbia Ministry of Energy & Mines, Victoria BC p. 2745

G A R Memorial Library, West Newbury MA p. 1137

Gabbs Community Library, Gabbs NV p. 1428

Gable & Gotwals, Inc, Tulsa OK p. 1980

Gabriel Annie Library, *see* California Baptist University, Riverside CA p. 216

Gabriel Dumont Institute Library, Regina SK p. 2922

Gabriel Dumont Institute of Metis Studies & Applied Research Library, Prince Albert SK p. 2920

Gabriele Library, *see* Immaculata University, Immaculata PA p. 2071

Gackle Public Library, Gackle ND p. 1842

Gadsden County Public Library, Quincy FL p. 485

Gadsden Public Library, Gadsden AL p. 18

Gadsden State Community College, Gadsden AL p. 18

Gadsen Correctional Institution Library, Quincy FL p. 485

Gafney Library, Inc, Sanbornville NH p. 1464

GAIN (N), *see* Georgia Interactive Network for Medical Information, Macon GA p. 2941

Gaines County Library, Seminole TX p. 2386

Gainesville Correctional Institution Library, Gainesville FL p. 449

Gainesville State College, Oakwood GA p. 547

Gainesville State College, Watkinsville GA p. 556

Gainesville VA Medical Center, *see* United States Department of Veterans Affairs, Gainesville FL p. 449

Gaithersburg Interim Library, *see* Montgomery County Public Libraries, Gaithersburg MD p. 1038

Galahad Public Library, Galahad AB p. 2705

Galax-Carroll Regional Library, Galax VA p. 2466

Galax Public Library, *see* Galax-Carroll Regional Library, Galax VA p. 2466

Galbraith John Kenneth Reference Library, *see* Elgin County Public Library, Dutton ON p. 2844

Gale Free Library, Holden MA p. 1095

Gale Library, Newton NH p. 1460

Gale Medical Library, *see* Littleton Regional Hospital, Littleton NH p. 1454

Galena Public Library, Galena KS p. 868

Galena Public Library District, Galena IL p. 647

Gales Ferry Library, *see* Ledyard Public Libraries, Gales Ferry CT p. 349

Galesburg Memorial Library, Galesburg MI p. 1182

Galesburg Public Library, Galesburg IL p. 648

Galesville Public Library, Galesville WI p. 2593

Galeton Public Library, Galeton PA p. 2059

Galeucia Kenneth W Memorial Library, *see* Hesser College, Manchester NH p. 1455

Galien Township Public Library, Galien MI p. 1182

Galion Public Library Association, Galion OH p. 1901

Gallagher & Kennedy, Phoenix AZ p. 73

Gallagher Library, *see* University of Calgary Library, Calgary AB p. 2693

Gallagher Marian Gould Law Library, *see* University of Washington Libraries, Seattle WA p. 2534

Gallatin County Public Library, Warsaw KY p. 936

Gallaudet University Library, Washington DC p. 401

Galleria Library, *see* Henderson District Public Libraries, Henderson NV p. 1428

Gallia County District Library, Gallipolis OH p. 1901

Gallier Florence, *see* Duplin County Library, Magnolia NC p. 1804

Gallier House Library, New Orleans LA p. 960

Gallison Memorial Library, Harrington ME p. 987

Gallitzin Public Library, Gallitzin PA p. 2059

Gallop, Johnson & Neuman LC, Saint Louis MO p. 1355

Galloupe Charles W Memorial Library, *see* Beverly Historical Society, Beverly MA p. 1053

Galt Neighborhood Library, *see* Sacramento Public Library, Galt CA p. 225

Galt Ocean Mile Reading Center, *see* Broward County Division of Libraries, Fort Lauderdale FL p. 441

Galter Health Sciences Library, *see* Northwestern University, Chicago, Chicago IL p. 621

Galucci-Cirio Amelia V Library, *see* Fitchburg State College, Fitchburg MA p. 1089

Galva Public Library, Galva IA p. 817

Galva Public Library District, Galva IL p. 648

Galvan Robert J Law Library, *see* El Paso County Law Library, El Paso TX p. 2316

Galveston College, Galveston TX p. 2326

Galveston District Corps of Engineers Library, *see* United States Army, Galveston TX p. 2326

Galvin Paul V Library, *see* Illinois Institute of Technology, Chicago IL p. 615

Galway Public Library, Galway NY p. 1625

Gambaiani Benny Public Library, Shell Rock IA p. 842

Gambier Public, *see* Public Library of Mount Vernon & Knox County, Gambier OH p. 1919

Gamble George Library, Danbury NH p. 1444

Gammon John B Geoscience Library, *see* Ontario Ministry of Northern Development, Mines & Forestry Library, Sudbury ON p. 2847

Gananoque Public Library, Gananoque ON p. 2806

Gann Rae & Joseph Library, *see* Hebrew College, Newton Centre MA p. 1110

Gannett Co Inc, Lansing MI p. 1201

Gannett-Estes Library, *see* Southeastern Bible College Library, Birmingham AL p. 9

Gannett Frank E Memorial Library, *see* Utica College, Utica NY p. 1759

Gannett Newspapers, Vestal NY p. 1761

Gannett-Tripp Library, *see* Elmira College, Elmira NY p. 1619

Gannon University, Erie PA p. 2055

Ganser Helen A Library, *see* Millersville University, Millersville PA p. 2090

Gant John R Library, *see* Wisconsin School for the Deaf, Delavan WI p. 2588

Garber Aaron Library, *see* Siegal College of Judaic Studies, Cleveland OH p. 1881

Garbrecht Donald L Law Library, *see* University of Maine School of Law, Portland ME p. 997

Garceau Library, *see* St Vincent Hospital & Health Services, Indianapolis IN p. 755

Garcia Dr Hector P Memorial Library, Mercedes TX p. 2362

Garcia Sam Western Avenue Library, *see* Avondale Public Library, Avondale AZ p. 57

Garcia Venito Public Library & Archives, Sells AZ p. 81

Garden City Community College, Garden City KS p. 868

Garden City Library, Garden City ID p. 574

Garden City Public, *see* Cullman County Public Library System, Garden City AL p. 13

Garden City Public Library, Garden City MI p. 1182

Garden City Public Library, Garden City NY p. 1626

Garden Grove Public Library, Garden Grove IA p. 817

Garden Grove Regional Library, *see* OC Public Libraries, Garden Grove CA p. 258

Garden Home Community Library, Portland OR p. 2010

Garden Plain Community Library, Garden Plain KS p. 868

Garden Ridge Library, Garden Ridge TX p. 2327

Garden State Youth Correctional Facility Library, Yardville NJ p. 1546

Garden Valley District Library, Garden Valley ID p. 574

Dear Mayme Library, *see* County of Los Angeles Public Library, Gardena CA p. 141

Gardendale Martha Moore Public Library, Gardendale AL p. 18

Gardenview Horticultural Park Library, Strongsville OH p. 1937

Gardere & Wynne, Dallas TX p. 2308

Gardere, Wynne & Sewell Library, Houston TX p. 2335

Gardiner Library, Gardiner NY p. 1626

Gardiner Public Library, Gardiner ME p. 986

Gardiner Roberts LLP Library, Toronto ON p. 2853

Gardner-Harvey Library, *see* Miami University-Middletown, Middletown OH p. 1917

Gardner Isabella Stewart Museum Library, Boston MA p. 1061

Gardner John C Memorial Library, *see* First Presbyterian Church, Colorado Springs CO p. 295

Gardner Leon P Health Science Library, *see* Provena Saint Joseph Medical Center, Joliet IL p. 660

Gardner Public Library, Wakefield NE p. 1422

Gardner-Webb University, Boiling Springs NC p. 1776

Garfield County Library, Jordan MT p. 1384

Georgetown Public Library, Georgetown IL p. 649
Georgetown Public Library, Georgetown TX p. 2327
Georgetown University, Washington DC p. 402
Georgia Archives, Morrow GA p. 545
Georgia College & State University, Milledgeville GA p. 544, 2964
Georgia Department of Corrections, Alto GA p. 508
Georgia Department of Corrections, Chester GA p. 524
Georgia Department of Corrections, Columbus GA p. 526
Georgia Department of Corrections, Davisboro GA p. 528
Georgia Department of Corrections, Forsyth GA p. 532
Georgia Department of Corrections, Garden City GA p. 535
Georgia Department of Corrections, Glennville GA p. 535
Georgia Department of Corrections, Grovetown GA p. 536
Georgia Department of Corrections, Hardwick GA p. 536
Georgia Department of Corrections, Hawkinsville GA p. 536
Georgia Department of Corrections, Helena GA p. 536
Georgia Department of Corrections, Jackson GA p. 536
Georgia Department of Corrections, Leesburg GA p. 539
Georgia Department of Corrections, Morgan GA p. 545
Georgia Department of Corrections, Mount Vernon GA p. 546
Georgia Department of Corrections, Nicholls GA p. 546
Georgia Department of Corrections, Oglethorpe GA p. 547
Georgia Department of Corrections, Pelham GA p. 547
Georgia Department of Corrections, Reidsville GA p. 547
Georgia Department of Corrections, Sparta GA p. 552
Georgia Department of Corrections, Office of Library Services, Valdosta GA p. 554
Georgia Department of Corrections, Trion GA p. 554
Georgia Department of Corrections, Unadilla GA p. 554
Georgia Department of Corrections, Waycross GA p. 557
Georgia Department of Corrections, Office of Library Services, Zebulon GA p. 558
Georgia Department of Corrections, Wrightsville GA p. 558
Georgia Department of Transportation, Forest Park GA p. 532
Georgia Diagnostic & Classification State Prison, see Georgia Department of Corrections, Jackson GA p. 536
Georgia Gulf Corp Library, Plaquemine LA p. 965
Georgia Health Sciences University, Augusta GA p. 520
Georgia Highlands College Libraries, Rome GA p. 548
Georgia-Hill Library, see Atlanta-Fulton Public Library System, Atlanta GA p. 512
Georgia Historical Society Library, Savannah GA p. 550
Georgia Institute of Technology, Atlanta GA p. 515
Georgia Interactive Network for Medical Information (N), Macon GA p. 2941
Georgia Library for Accessible State-wide Services, Atlanta GA p. 515
Georgia Military College, Milledgeville GA p. 544
Georgia Northwestern Technical College, Rome GA p. 548
Georgia Online Database (N), Atlanta GA p. 2941
Georgia Perimeter College, Clarkston GA p. 525
Georgia Piedmont Technical College, Covington GA p. 527
Georgia Power Co-Southern Co, Atlanta GA p. 515
Georgia Public Library, Fairfax VT p. 2424
Georgia Public Library Service, Atlanta GA p. 515

Georgia Southern University, Statesboro GA p. 552
Georgia Southwestern State University, Americus GA p. 508
Georgia State Prison, see Georgia Department of Corrections, Reidsville GA p. 547
Georgia State University Library, Atlanta GA p. 516
Georgian Bay Township Library, Honey Harbour ON p. 2811
Georgian College, Barrie ON p. 2794
Georgian College-Orillia Campus, Orillia ON p. 2826
Georgian College-Owen Sound Campus, Owen Sound ON p. 2834
Georgian Court University, Lakewood NJ p. 1493
GEP Dodge Library, Bennington NH p. 1439
Gerald Area Library, Gerald MO p. 1329
Gerald Lynn Law Library, see Lee County Law Library, Fort Myers FL p. 445
Geraldine Public Library, Geraldine AL p. 18
Gerboth Walter W Music Library, see Brooklyn College Library, Brooklyn NY p. 1590
Gere Charles H, see Lincoln City Libraries, Lincoln NE p. 1405
Gering Public Library, Gering NE p. 1399
German Cultural Center Library, see Goethe-Institut New York, New York NY p. 1680
German Historical Institute Library, Washington DC p. 403
German Society of Pennsylvania, Philadelphia PA p. 2110
German-Masontown Public Library, Masontown PA p. 2085
Germanna Community College, Fredericksburg VA p. 2466
Germanna Community College, Locust Grove VA p. 2475
Germantown Community Library, Germantown TN p. 2235
Germantown Community Library, Germantown WI p. 2594
Germantown Historical Society, Philadelphia PA p. 2110
Germantown Library, Germantown NY p. 1628
Germantown Library, see Montgomery County Public Libraries, Germantown MD p. 1038
Germantown Public Library, Germantown OH p. 1901
Germantown Public Library District, Germantown IL p. 649
Germany John F Public Library, see Tampa-Hillsborough County Public Library System, Tampa FL p. 497
Gerontological Society of America, Washington DC p. 403
Gerontology Research Center Library, see National Institute on Aging, Baltimore MD p. 1016
Gerrish Scott & Wesley Library, see Anchorage Public Library, Girdwood AK p. 44
Gerrish-True Health Sciences Library, see Central Maine Medical Center, Lewiston ME p. 989
Gerrity Memorial Library, see United States Air Force, Hill AFB UT p. 2406
Gerstein Science Information Centre, see University of Toronto Libraries, Toronto ON p. 2866
Gerstenburg Carriage Reference Library, see Long Island Museum of American Art, History & Carriages, Stony Brook NY p. 1749
Getty Research Institute, Los Angeles CA p. 170
Gettysburg College, Gettysburg PA p. 2059
Gettysburg National Military Park Library, Gettysburg PA p. 2060
Getz Oscar Museum of Whiskey History, Bardstown KY p. 906
Getz Stan Media Center & Library, see Berklee College of Music Library, Boston MA p. 1055
GHEC Library, see Mississippi Delta Community College, Greenville MS p. 1309
Ghost Ranch Conference Center Library, Abiquiu NM p. 1547
GIA Library, see Liddicoat Richard T Gemological Library, Carlsbad CA p. 132
Giannini Foundation Library, see University of California, Berkeley, Berkeley CA p. 128
Gibb Hamilton A R Islamic Seminar Library, see Harvard Library, Cambridge MA p. 1075

Gibbon Public Library, Gibbon MN p. 1252
Gibbon Public Library, Gibbon NE p. 1399
Gibbons Municipal Library, Gibbons AB p. 2705
Gibbons PC, Newark NJ p. 1510
Gibbs College of Boston, Boston MA p. 1061
Gibbs Library, Washington ME p. 1005
Gibbs Memorial Library, Mexia TX p. 2362
Gibbsboro Public Library, Gibbsboro NJ p. 1487
Gibson Charles W Public Library, Buckhannon WV p. 2555
Gibson County Memorial Library, Trenton TN p. 2267
Gibson, Dunn & Crutcher, Los Angeles CA p. 170
Gibson, Dunn & Crutcher, New York NY p. 1680
Gibson James A Library, see Brock University, St. Catharines ON p. 2842
Gibson James I Library, see Henderson District Public Libraries, Henderson NV p. 1428
Gibson Library, see Kentucky Mountain Bible College, Jackson KY p. 919
Gibson Library, see Providence Care, Kingston ON p. 2814
Gibson Memorial Library, Creston IA p. 805
Gibson R E Library, see Johns Hopkins University, Applied Physics Laboratory, Laurel MD p. 1034
Gibsons & District Public Library, Gibsons BC p. 2728
Giddings Public Library, Giddings TX p. 2328
Gila County Historical Museum Library, Globe AZ p. 64
Gila County Law Library, Globe AZ p. 64
Gila County Library District, Globe AZ p. 64
Gilbert Addison Hospital, Gloucester MA p. 1091
Gilbert Library, Inc, Northfield CT p. 362
Gilbert Public Library, Gilbert MN p. 1252
Gilbert Public Library, Friend NE p. 1399
Gilbertsville Free Library, Gilbertsville NY p. 1628
Gilbreath Memorial Library, Winnsboro TX p. 2401
Gilchrist County Public Library, Trenton FL p. 500
Gilcrease Thomas Institute of American History & Art, Tulsa OK p. 1981
Giles County Public Library, Pulaski TN p. 2263
Gilford Public Library, Gilford NH p. 1448
Gilkey Mary City Library, Dayton OR p. 1995
Gill Gail P Consumer Health Library, see Christiana Hospital Library, Newark DE p. 385
Gill Library, see College of New Rochelle, New Rochelle NY p. 1666
Gill Library, see Southwest Tennessee Community College, Memphis TN p. 2251
Gill Memorial Library, Paulsboro NJ p. 1519
Gillespie Public Library, Gillespie IL p. 649
Gillett Public Library, Gillett WI p. 2594
Gilliam County Library, Condon OR p. 1993
Gilliam Elvis Maxine Memorial Public Library, Wilmer TX p. 2401
Gilliam Youth Services Center Library, see Department of Human Services-Youth Corrections, Denver CO p. 301
Gillis Richard S Jr, see Pamunkey Regional Library, Ashland VA p. 2469
Gilliss James Melville Library, see United States Naval Observatory, Washington DC p. 421
Gilman-Danforth District Library, Gilman IL p. 649
Gilman Museum Library, Hellertown PA p. 2068
Gilman Public Library, Gilman IA p. 818
Gilman Public Library, Alton NH p. 1437
Gilmanton Corner Public Library, Gilmanton NH p. 1448
Gilmanton Iron Works Public Library, Gilmanton Iron Works NH p. 1448
Gilmer Claud H Memorial Library, Rocksprings TX p. 2376
Gilmer County Public, see Sequoyah Regional Library System, Ellijay GA p. 523
Gilmer Public Library, Glenville WV p. 2559
Gilmore City Public Library, Gilmore City IA p. 818
Gilmore Irving S Music Library, see Yale University Library, New Haven CT p. 357
Gilpin County Public Library District, Black Hawk CO p. 289
Gilroy Library, see Santa Clara County Library District, Gilroy CA p. 181
Gilsum Public Library, Gilsum NH p. 1448
Giltner Public Library, Giltner NE p. 1400

Gimbel Adam & Sophie Design Library, *see* New School, New York NY p. 1688

Giner Electrochemical Systems LLC Library, Newton MA p. 1109

Gingrich F Wilbur Library, *see* Albright College, Reading PA p. 2132

Ginn Edwin Library, *see* Tufts University, Medford MA p. 1104

Ginsberg Allen Library, *see* Naropa University Library, Boulder CO p. 290

Giorgetti Library, *see* College of Saint Joseph, Rutland VT p. 2434

Giovale Library, *see* Westminster College, Salt Lake City UT p. 2415

Girard Free Library, Girard OH p. 1902

Girard Public Library, Girard KS p. 868

Girard Township Library, Girard IL p. 649

Girl Scouts of the USA, Savannah GA p. 550

Givin Amelia S Free Library, Mount Holly Springs PA p. 2093

Glace Bay Public, *see* Cape Breton Regional Library, Glace Bay NS p. 2785

Glacier Bay National Park & Preserve Library, *see* National Park Service, Gustavus AK p. 49

Glacier County Library, Cut Bank MT p. 1377

Gladbrook Public Library, Gladbrook IA p. 818

Glades Correctional Institution Library, *see* Florida Department of Corrections, Belle Glade FL p. 427

Glades County Public Library, Moore Haven FL p. 470

Gladewater Public Library, *see* Lee Public Library, Gladewater TX p. 2328

Gladstone Area School & Public Library, Gladstone MI p. 1183

Gladstone Public Library, Gladstone OR p. 1999

Gladwin County District Library, Gladwin MI p. 1183

Gladwyne Free Library, Gladwyne PA p. 2060

Glankler Brown, Memphis TN p. 2248

Glann John D Library, *see* Peninsula College Library, Port Angeles WA p. 2524

Glasco City Library, Glasco KS p. 868

Glascock County Library, *see* Oconee Regional Library, Gibson GA p. 531

Glasgow City-County Library, Glasgow MT p. 1379

Glasgow James A Library, *see* Northwest-Shoals Community College, Phil Campbell AL p. 34

Glasgow Public, *see* Rockbridge Regional Library, Glasgow VA p. 2474

Glass D R Library, *see* Texas College, Tyler TX p. 2393

Glass E Gordon MD Memorial Library, *see* Muhlenberg Regional Medical Center, Plainfield NJ p. 1521

Glass Memorial Library, *see* Johnson Bible College, Knoxville TN p. 2241

Glassboro Public, *see* Gloucester County Library System, Glassboro NJ p. 1507

Glatfelter Lee R Library, *see* Penn State University York, York PA p. 2159

Glatfelter Memorial Library, Spring Grove PA p. 2142

GlaxoSmithKline, Mississauga ON p. 2822

GlaxoSmithKline Pharmaceuticals, Philadelphia PA p. 2110

Gleason Ellen Library, *see* Santa Ynez Valley Historical Society, Santa Ynez CA p. 268

Gleason Memorial Library, Gleason TN p. 2235

Gleason Public Library, Carlisle MA p. 1079

Glebe House Museum Library, *see* Seabury Society for the Preservation of the Glebe House, Inc, Woodbury CT p. 380

Gledhill Library, *see* Santa Barbara Historical Museum, Santa Barbara CA p. 260

Glee Merritt Kelley Community Library, Wolcott VT p. 2440

Gleeson Richard A Library-Charles & Nancy Geschke Resource Center, *see* University of San Francisco, San Francisco CA p. 248

Gleichen & District Library, Gleichen AB p. 2705

Glen Avon Library, *see* Riverside County Library System, Riverside CA p. 217

Glen Carbon Centennial Library, Glen Carbon IL p. 649

Glen Cove Public Library, Glen Cove NY p. 1628

Glen Elder Library, Glen Elder KS p. 868

Glen Ellyn Public Library, Glen Ellyn IL p. 650

Glen Lake Community Library, Empire MI p. 1177

Glen Oaks Community College Library, Centreville MI p. 1162

Glen Oaks Community Library, *see* Queens Borough Public Library, Glen Oaks NY p. 1644

Glen Ridge Free Public Library, Glen Ridge NJ p. 1488

Glen Rock Public Library, Glen Rock NJ p. 1488

Glen Ullin Public Library, Glen Ullin ND p. 1842

Glenbow Museum Library, Calgary AB p. 2691

Glencoe Public Library, Glencoe IL p. 650

Glencoe Public Library, Glencoe MN p. 1252

Glendale Adventist Medical Center Library, Glendale CA p. 155

Glendale Area Public Library Inc, Coalport PA p. 2046

Glendale Community College, Glendale AZ p. 64

Glendale Community College Library, Glendale CA p. 155

Glendale Community Library, *see* Queens Borough Public Library, Glendale NY p. 1644

Glendale Public Library, Glendale AZ p. 64

Glendale Public Library, Glendale CA p. 155

Glendale University, Glendale CA p. 155

Glendive Public Library, Glendive MT p. 1379

Glendora Public Library & Cultural Center, Glendora CA p. 156

Glenmary Novitiate Library, *see* Home Missioners of America, Cincinnati OH p. 1870

Glenn John H Research Center, *see* NASA, Cleveland OH p. 1880

Glenn Memorial United Methodist Church Library, Atlanta GA p. 516

Glenns Ferry Public Library, Glenns Ferry ID p. 574

Glennville Public, *see* Ohoopee Regional Library System, Glennville GA p. 556

Glenolden Library, Glenolden PA p. 2061

Glenrose Rehabilitation Hospital, Edmonton AB p. 2701

Glens Falls-Queensbury Historical Association, Glens Falls NY p. 1629

Glenshaw Public Library, Glenshaw PA p. 2061

Glenside Free Library, *see* Cheltenham Township Library System, Glenside PA p. 2061

Glenside Public Library District, Glendale Heights IL p. 650

Glenstone Baptist Church, Springfield MO p. 1366

Glenview Public Library, Glenview IL p. 650

Glenville State College, Glenville WV p. 2559

Glenwood & Souris Regional Library, Souris MB p. 2752

Glenwood City Public Library, Glenwood City WI p. 2594

Glenwood Community Library, *see* Greensboro Public Library, Greensboro NC p. 1796

Glenwood-Lynwood Public Library District, Glenwood IL p. 651

Glenwood Municipal Library, Glenwood AB p. 2705

Glenwood Public Library, Glenwood IA p. 818

Glenwood Public Library, Glenwood MN p. 1252

Glenwood Resource Center, Glenwood IA p. 818

Glew William B MD Health Sciences Library, *see* Washington Hospital Center, Washington DC p. 422

Glidden Public Library, Glidden IA p. 818

Global Drug Information Center McWhorter School of Pharmacy, *see* Samford University Library, Birmingham AL p. 9

Global Intelligence Group, New York NY p. 1680

Global Issues Resource Center Library, Highland Hills OH p. 1904

Globe & Mail Library, Toronto ON p. 2853

Globe Institute of Technology, New York NY p. 1680

Globe Public Library, Globe AZ p. 65

Glocester Manton Free Public Library, Chepachet RI p. 2164

Gloucester City Library, Gloucester City NJ p. 1488

Gloucester County College Library, Sewell NJ p. 1529

Gloucester County Historical Society Library, Woodbury NJ p. 1545

Gloucester County Law Library, Woodbury NJ p. 1545

Gloucester County Library, Gloucester VA p. 2467

Gloucester County Library System, Mullica Hill NJ p. 1507

Gloucester, Lyceum & Sawyer Free Library, Gloucester MA p. 1091

Glouster Public, *see* Nelsonville Public Library, Glouster OH p. 1920

Glover Memorial Library, *see* Altoona Hospital, Altoona PA p. 2028

Glover Public Library, Glover VT p. 2424

Gloversville Public Library, Gloversville NY p. 1629

GMILCS, Inc (N), Hooksett NH p. 2948

Gnadenhutten Public Library, Gnadenhutten OH p. 1902

GOAL (N), *see* Greater Oklahoma Area Health Sciences Library Consortium, Ardmore OK p. 2953

Gobbel Luther L Library, *see* Lambuth University, Jackson TN p. 2238

Goddard Burton L Library, *see* Gordon-Conwell Theological Seminary, South Hamilton MA p. 1125

Goddard College, Plainfield VT p. 2432

Goddard Library, *see* University Center Rochester, Rochester MN p. 1273

Goddard Memorial Library, *see* Oroville Hospital, Oroville CA p. 202

Goddard Public Library, Goddard KS p. 869

Goddard Robert Hutchings Library, *see* Clark University, Worcester MA p. 1143

Goddard Space Flight Center Library-Homer E Newell Memorial, *see* NASA, Greenbelt MD p. 1030

Goddard Space Flight Center, Wallops Flight Facility Library, *see* NASA, Wallops Island VA p. 2500

Godel Memorial Library, *see* Northwest Regional Library, Warren MN p. 1286

Godfrey Memorial Library, Middletown CT p. 351

Godine Morton R Library, *see* Massachusetts College of Art & Design, Boston MA p. 1063

God's Bible School & College Library, Cincinnati OH p. 1870

Godwin R C Memorial Library, *see* Craven Community College, New Bern NC p. 1812

Goessel Public Library, Goessel KS p. 869

Goethe-Institut New York, New York NY p. 1680

Goethe-Institut Toronto Library, Toronto ON p. 2853

Goethe-Institut Atlanta Library, *see* Friends of Goethe, Inc, Atlanta GA p. 515

Goff Bob, *see* Natrona County Public Library, Mills WY p. 2652

Goff-Nelson Memorial Library, Tupper Lake NY p. 1757

Goffstown Public Library, Goffstown NH p. 1448

Gogebic Community College, Ironwood MI p. 1194

Golberg Library & Resource Center, *see* Hamner Institutes for Health Sciences, Research Triangle Park NC p. 1819

Golconda Public Library, Golconda IL p. 651

GOLD (N), *see* Georgia Online Database, Atlanta GA p. 2941

Gold Coast Library Network (N), San Luis Obispo CA p. 2938

Gold Coast Public Library, Glen Head NY p. 1628

Gold, Weems, Bruser, Sues & Rundell, Alexandria LA p. 939

Golden Gate Baptist Theological, Scottsdale AZ p. 80

Golden Gate Baptist Theological, Brea CA p. 129

Golden Gate Baptist Theological Seminary Library, Mill Valley CA p. 186

Golden Gate Baptist Theological, Centennial CO p. 294

Golden Gate Baptist Theological, Vancouver WA p. 2546

Golden Gate University, San Francisco CA p. 242

Golden Library, *see* Eastern New Mexico University, Portales NM p. 1560

Golden Plains Library Federation, Malta MT p. 1385

Golden Shores Community Library, *see* Mohave County Library District, Topock AZ p. 67

Golden Valley County Library, Beach ND p. 1837

Golden West College, Huntington Beach CA p. 158

Goldendale Community Library, *see* Fort Vancouver Regional Library District, Goldendale WA p. 2546

Golder Associates, Inc, Redmond WA p. 2525

Golder Associates Ltd Library, Mississauga ON p. 2822

Golder Associates, Ltd, Burnaby BC p. 2725

Goldey Beacom College, Wilmington DE p. 388

Goldfarb School of Nursing at Barnes-Jewish College, Saint Louis MO p. 1355

Goldfield Public Library, *see* Silverpeak Library, Goldfield NV p. 1434

Goldman Lillian, *see* Yale University Library, New Haven CT p. 358

Goldsby Sandra C Library, *see* Mid-South Community College, West Memphis AR p. 117

Goldsmith Civic Garden Center - Sybile Malloy Memorial, *see* Memphis Botanic Garden Foundation, Inc, Memphis TN p. 2249

Goldstein Library, *see* Florida State University Libraries, Tallahassee FL p. 495

Goldston Public Library, *see* Chatham County Public Libraries, Goldston NC p. 1823

Goldthwait Polar Library, *see* Byrd Polar Research Center, Columbus OH p. 1883

Goldwater Memorial Hospital, New York NY p. 1680

Goldwater Robert Library, *see* Metropolitan Museum of Art, New York NY p. 1686

Goldwyn Frances Howard, *see* Los Angeles Public Library System, Los Angeles CA p. 173

Goleman Library, *see* San Joaquin Delta College, Stockton CA p. 272

Golemon Library & Learning Resources Center, *see* Ranger College, Ranger TX p. 2373

Goliad County Library, Goliad TX p. 2328

Golisano B Thomas Library, *see* Roberts Wesleyan College & Northeastern Seminary, Rochester NY p. 1731

Gondring Florence L Library, *see* Stanislaus County Free Library, Ceres CA p. 188

Gonser Louisa Community Library, Kutztown PA p. 2075

Gonzaga University, Spokane WA p. 2536

Gonzaga University School of Law, Spokane WA p. 2536

Gonzales Public Library, Gonzales TX p. 2328

Good Harold & Wilma Library, *see* Goshen College, Goshen IN p. 745

Good Leonard A Community Library, Ogden IA p. 836

Good LeRoy V Library, *see* Monroe Community College, Rochester NY p. 1730

Good Samaritan Church Library, Pinellas Park FL p. 483

Good Samaritan Hospital, Los Angeles CA p. 170

Good Samaritan Hospital, Baltimore MD p. 1013

Good Samaritan Hospital, West Islip NY p. 1766

Good Samaritan Hospital Library, Vincennes IN p. 784

Good Samaritan Hospital Library, Dayton OH p. 1893

Good Samaritan Hospital Library, *see* TriHealth, Inc, Cincinnati OH p. 1873

Good Samaritan Hospital Medical Library, *see* Krohn Memorial Library, Lebanon PA p. 2079

Good Samaritan Medical Center, West Palm Beach FL p. 502

Good Samaritan Regional Health Center, Mount Vernon IL p. 678

Good Samaritan Regional Medical Center, Corvallis OR p. 1994

Good Shepherd Medical Center, Longview TX p. 2356

Good Shepherd Medical Library, Allentown PA p. 2026

Goodall City Library, Ogallala NE p. 1411

Goodall Louis B Memorial Library, Sanford ME p. 999

Goodhue County Historical Society Library, Red Wing MN p. 1271

Goodhue Memorial Library, *see* Pilgrim Congregational Church, Nashua NH p. 1459

Gooding Public Library, Gooding ID p. 574

Goodland & Grant Township Public Library, Goodland IN p. 745

Goodland Public Library, Goodland KS p. 869

Goodlett Caroline Meriwether Library, *see* United Daughters of the Confederacy, Richmond VA p. 2491

Goodman Ida Long Memorial Library, Saint John KS p. 892

Goodman Keshen, *see* Halifax Public Libraries, Halifax NS p. 2779

Goodman Public, *see* Mid-Mississippi Regional Library System, Goodman MS p. 1306

Goodmans LLP Library, Toronto ON p. 2854

Goodnight Memorial Library, Franklin KY p. 914

Goodnow Library, Sudbury MA p. 1129

Goodrich Memorial Library, Newport VT p. 2430

Goodson Felix Library, *see* Williams Baptist College, Walnut Ridge AR p. 116

Goodspeed Musicals, East Haddam CT p. 337

Goodsprings Library, *see* Las Vegas-Clark County Library District, Goodsprings NV p. 1429

Goodstein Foundation Library, *see* Casper College, Casper WY p. 2651

Goodwater Public Library, Goodwater AL p. 18

Goodwin Library, Farmington NH p. 1447

Goodwin Memorial Library, Hadley MA p. 1093

Goodwin Procter, Boston MA p. 1061

Goose Creek Township Carnegie Library, De Land IL p. 633

Gordo Public Library, Gordo AL p. 19

Gordon & Rees LLP, San Francisco CA p. 242

Gordon Asa H Library, *see* Savannah State University, Savannah GA p. 551

Gordon Bruce Memorial Library, *see* Beth Emet Synagogue, Evanston IL p. 643

Gordon City Library, Gordon NE p. 1400

Gordon College, Wenham MA p. 1136

Gordon College Library, Barnesville GA p. 521

Gordon-Conwell Theological Seminary, South Hamilton MA p. 1125

Gordon, Feinblatt, Rothman, Hoffberger & Hollander, Baltimore MD p. 1013

Gordon George C Library, *see* Worcester Polytechnic Institute, Worcester MA p. 1145

Gordon Health Sciences Library, *see* Children's Hospital & Research Center Oakland, Oakland CA p. 196

Gordon Library, *see* University of Arkansas Community College at Morrilton, Morrilton AR p. 110

Gordon-Nash Library, New Hampton NH p. 1459

Gordon Public, *see* Middle Georgia Regional Library System, Gordon GA p. 541

Gordon Virgil & Josephine Memorial Library, Sealy TX p. 2385

Gordon, Arata, McCollam, Duplantis & Egan Law Library, New Orleans LA p. 960

Gore Bay Union Public Library, Gore Bay ON p. 2806

Gore Place Society, Inc Library, Waltham MA p. 1133

Gorge LINK Library Consortium (N), Hood River OR p. 2953

Gorham Free Library, Gorham NY p. 1629

Gorham-Macbane Public Library, Springfield TN p. 2266

Gorham Public Library, Gorham NH p. 1448

Gorton Music & Dance Library, *see* University of Kansas Libraries, Lawrence KS p. 878

Goshen College, Goshen IN p. 745

Goshen County Library, Torrington WY p. 2661

Goshen Free Public Library, Goshen MA p. 1091

Goshen Historical Society Library, Goshen CT p. 341

Goshen Public, *see* Rockbridge Regional Library, Goshen VA p. 2474

Goshen Public Library, Goshen CT p. 341

Goshen Public Library, Goshen IN p. 746

Goshen Public Library & Historical Society, Goshen NY p. 1629

Gothenburg Public Library, Gothenburg NE p. 1400

Gottesman D Samuel Library, *see* Albert Einstein College of Medicine, Bronx NY p. 1585

Gottesman Libraries, *see* Teachers College, Columbia University, New York NY p. 1701

Gottesman Mendel Library of Hebraica-Judaica, *see* Yeshiva University Libraries, New York NY p. 1704

Gottfredson Don M Library of Criminal Justice, *see* Rutgers University Libraries, Newark NJ p. 1513

Gottlieb Memorial Hospital, Melrose Park IL p. 673

Goucher College Library, Baltimore MD p. 1014

Gould Laurence McKinley Library, *see* Carleton College, Northfield MN p. 1269

Gould Memorial Library, *see* College of Coastal Georgia, Brunswick GA p. 521

Goulston & Storrs, PC, Boston MA p. 1061

Gouverneur Correctional Facility, Gouverneur NY p. 1629

Gove City Library, Gove KS p. 869

Government du Quebec Ministere de l'Immigration et des Communaute's Culturelles, Montreal QC p. 2895

Government of Canada, Ottawa ON p. 2831

Government of Newfoundland & Labrador, St. John's NL p. 2772

Government of Quebec, Gaspe QC p. 2882

Government of the Northwest Territories, Yellowknife NT p. 2775

Government Printing Office, Washington DC p. 403

Government Services Library, *see* Prince Edward Island Public Library Service, Charlottetown PE p. 2876

Governor Baxter School for the Deaf Library, *see* Maine Education Center for the Deaf & Hard of Hearing, Falmouth ME p. 985

Governors State University Library, University Park IL p. 711

Gowanda Correctional Facility Library, *see* New York State Department of Correctional Services, Gowanda NY p. 1630

Gowanda Free Library, Gowanda NY p. 1630

Gowling Lafleur Henderson LLP, Ottawa ON p. 2831

Gowling Lafleur Henderson LLP, Toronto ON p. 2854

Gowrie Public Library, Gowrie IA p. 818

GPLLA (N), *see* Greater Philadelphia Law Library Association, Philadelphia PA p. 2954

GRA Inc Library, Jenkintown PA p. 2072

Grace Bible College, Grand Rapids MI p. 1184

Grace College & Grace Theological Seminary, Winona Lake IN p. 789

Grace Cottage Hospital Library, *see* Otis Health Care Center, Townshend VT p. 2437

Grace District Library, Grace ID p. 575

Grace Library, *see* Carlow University, Pittsburgh PA p. 2122

Grace Lutheran Church Library, Show Low AZ p. 82

Grace Lutheran Church Library, La Grange IL p. 662

Grace Lutheran Church Library, Wayzata MN p. 1288

Hunt Grace M Memorial English Reading Room, *see* University of California Los Angeles Library, Los Angeles CA p. 178

Grace Medical Center, Lubbock TX p. 2357

Grace Presbyterian Church, Jenkintown PA p. 2072

Grace University Library, Omaha NE p. 1413

Grace W R & Co, Columbia MD p. 1025

Grace W R & Co Library, Cambridge MA p. 1073

Graceland Museum-American Saddlebred Horse Museum Library, *see* Audrain County Historical Society, Mexico MO p. 1345

Graceland University, Lamoni IA p. 826

Graceville Public Library, Graceville MN p. 1252

Gradient, Cambridge MA p. 1073

Graduate Institute of Applied Linguistics, Dallas TX p. 2308

Graduate School of Public & International Affairs Economics Library, *see* University of Pittsburgh, Pittsburgh PA p. 2129

Graduate Theological Union Library, Berkeley CA p. 126

Grady Oscar Public Library, Saukville WI p. 2636

Graese Clifford E Community Health Library, *see* Orlando Health, Orlando FL p. 477

Graettinger Public Library, Graettinger IA p. 818

Graysville Public Library, Graysville TN p. 2235
Graziano John A Memorial Library, *see* Samuel Merritt College, Oakland CA p. 199
Great Basin College Library, Elko NV p. 1427
Great Bay Community College, Stratham NH p. 1465
Great Bend Public Library, Great Bend KS p. 869
Great Cranberry Library, Cranberry Isles ME p. 982
Great Falls Genealogy Society Library, Great Falls MT p. 1380
Great Falls Public Library, Great Falls MT p. 1380
Great Lakes Bible College Library, Waterloo ON p. 2869
Great Lakes Christian College, Lansing MI p. 1201
Great Lakes Colleges Association, Philadelphia PA p. 2110
Great Lakes Forestry Centre Library, *see* Natural Resources Canada-Canadian Forest Service, Sault Ste. Marie ON p. 2840
Great Lakes Historical Society, Vermilion OH p. 1943
Great Library, *see* Law Society of Upper Canada, Toronto ON p. 2855
Great Library, *see* Manitoba Law Library, Inc, Winnipeg MB p. 2757
Great Meadow Correctional Facility Library, Comstock NY p. 1609
Great Neck Library, Great Neck NY p. 1630
Great River Medical Center Library, West Burlington IA p. 852
Great River Regional Library, Saint Cloud MN p. 1274
Great Smoky Mountains National Park Library, *see* United States National Park Service, Gatlinburg TN p. 2235
Great Valley Library, *see* Pennsylvania State University, Malvern PA p. 2083
Greater Baltimore Medical Center, Baltimore MD p. 1014
Greater Canonsburg Public Library, Canonsburg PA p. 2041
Greater Egypt Regional Planning & Development Commission, Carbondale IL p. 600
Greater Louisville, Inc, Louisville KY p. 923
Greater Madawaska Public Library, Calabogie ON p. 2798
Greater Oklahoma Area Health Sciences Library Consortium (N), Ardmore OK p. 2953
Greater Philadelphia Law Library Association (N), Philadelphia PA p. 2954
Greater Portland Landmarks, Inc, Portland ME p. 996
Greater Sudbury Public Library, Sudbury ON p. 2846
Greater Vancouver Regional District Library, Burnaby BC p. 2725
Greater Victoria Public Library Board, Victoria BC p. 2745
Greater West Bloomfield Historical Society, Orchard Lake MI p. 1215
Greater West Central Public Library District, Augusta IL p. 591
Greater Western Library Alliance (N), Kansas City MO p. 2947
Grebing Grace Public Library, Dell City TX p. 2312
Greece Public Library, Greece NY p. 1630
Greeley & Hansen Engineering Library, Chicago IL p. 614
Greeley County Library, Tribune KS p. 898
Greeley Mary Medical Center Library, Ames IA p. 793
Greeley Village Public Library, Greeley NE p. 1400
Green Art Research Library, *see* Old Jail Art Center, Albany TX p. 2272
Green Bay Correctional Institution Library, Green Bay WI p. 2595
Green Cecil H Library, *see* Stanford University Libraries, Stanford CA p. 270
Green County Public Library, Greensburg KY p. 915
Green-Field Benjamin B National Alzheimer's Library, *see* Alzheimer's Association, Chicago IL p. 605
Green Forest Public Library, Green Forest AR p. 101

Green Francis Harvey Library, *see* West Chester University, West Chester PA p. 2153
Green Free Library, Canton PA p. 2041
Green Free Library, Wellsboro PA p. 2152
Green Grove Public Library, Niton Junction AB p. 2712
Green Haven Correctional Facility Library, *see* New York State Department of Correctional Services, Stormville NY p. 1750
Green Hills Public Library District, Palos Hills IL p. 687
Green House Cancer Resource Center, El Paso TX p. 2317
Green Learning Center, *see* Texas Health Presbyterian Hospital Library, Dallas TX p. 2311
Green Mountain College Library, Poultney VT p. 2432
Green River Community College, Auburn WA p. 2507
Green Springs Memorial, *see* Birchard Public Library of Sandusky County, Green Springs OH p. 1900
Green Steven & Dorothea Library, *see* Florida International University, Miami FL p. 465
Green Tom County Library System, San Angelo TX p. 2378
Green Tree Public Library, Pittsburgh PA p. 2125
Greenawalt Library, *see* Northwestern Health Sciences University, Bloomington MN p. 1242
Greenback Public Library, Greenback TN p. 2236
Greenbaum, Rowe, Smith & Davis LLP, Woodbridge NJ p. 1545
Greenberg Families Library, Ottawa ON p. 2831
Greenberg Glusker Fields Claman & Machtinger & LLP Library, Los Angeles CA p. 170
Greenberg Traurig LLP, Miami FL p. 465
Greenberg Traurig LLP, New York NY p. 1680
Greenblatt Robert B MD Library, *see* Georgia Health Sciences University, Augusta GA p. 520
Greenbridge Library, *see* King County Library System, Seattle WA p. 2517
Greenbrier County Public Library, Lewisburg WV p. 2563
Greenbrier Historical Society Archives, Lewisburg WV p. 2564
Greenburgh Public Library, Elmsford NY p. 1620
Greenbush Public Library, *see* Northwest Regional Library, Greenbush MN p. 1286
Greendale Public Library, Greendale WI p. 2596
Greene & Greene Archives, San Marino CA p. 255
Greene Cordelia A Library, Castile NY p. 1603
Greene Correctional Facility, Coxsackie NY p. 1612
Greene County Historical Society, Coxsackie NY p. 1612
Greene County Law Library, Xenia OH p. 1951
Greene County Law Library, Waynesburg PA p. 2152
Greene County Library, *see* Uncle Remus Regional Library System, Greensboro GA p. 542
Greene County Library System, Jefferson PA p. 2072
Greene County Public Library, Paragould AR p. 111
Greene County Public Library, Xenia OH p. 1951
Greene County Public Library, *see* Neuse Regional Library, Snow Hill NC p. 1805
Greene Public Library, Greene IA p. 819
Greene Public Library, Greene RI p. 2166
Greenebaum, Doll & McDonald, Lexington KY p. 920
Greenebaum, Doll & McDonald, Louisville KY p. 923
Greeneville Green County Public Library, Greeneville TN p. 2236
Greenfield Albert M Library, *see* University of the Arts University Libraries, Philadelphia PA p. 2119
Greenfield Community College Library, Greenfield MA p. 1092
Greenfield Library, *see* Saint John's College Library, Annapolis MD p. 1011
Greenfield Library, *see* Stephenson Memorial Library, Greenfield NH p. 1449
Greenfield Public Library, Greenfield IL p. 652
Greenfield Public Library, Greenfield IA p. 819

Greenfield Public Library, Greenfield MA p. 1092
Greenfield Public Library, Greenfield WI p. 2596
Greenforest Community Baptist Church-Christian Academic Center Library, Decatur GA p. 530
Greenhoe Library-Rainbow Children's Library, *see* Memorial Presbyterian Church, Midland MI p. 1208
Greenland Rita & Leo Library & Archive, *see* Anti-Defamation League, New York NY p. 1669
Greenleaf Abbie Library, Franconia NH p. 1447
Greenleaf Library, *see* Copper Mountain College, Joshua Tree CA p. 161
Greenlease Library, *see* Rockhurst University, Kansas City MO p. 1340
Greenley Thomas D Library, *see* Farmingdale State College of New York, Farmingdale NY p. 1622
Greensboro College, Greensboro NC p. 1796
Greensboro Free Library, Greensboro VT p. 2425
Greensboro Historical Museum Archives Library, Greensboro NC p. 1796
Greensboro Public Library, Greensboro NC p. 1796
Greensburg-Decatur County Public Library, Greensburg IN p. 746
Greensburg Hempfield Area Library, Greensburg PA p. 2062
Greensfelder, Hemker & Gale, PC Library, Saint Louis MO p. 1355
Greentown Public Library, Greentown IN p. 747
Greenup County Public Libraries, Greenup KY p. 915
Greenup Township Public Library, Greenup IL p. 652
Greenville Area Public, *see* Pine Mountain Regional Library, Greenville GA p. 542
Greenville Area Public Library, Greenville PA p. 2063
Greenville College, Greenville IL p. 652
Greenville County Library System, Greenville SC p. 2196
Greenville County Planning Department, Greenville SC p. 2196
Greenville Hospital System, Greenville SC p. 2196
Greenville Law Library Association, Greenville OH p. 1903
Greenville News-Piedmont Library, Greenville SC p. 2197
Greenville Public Library, Greenville IL p. 652
Greenville Public Library, Greenville NY p. 1631
Greenville Public Library, Greenville OH p. 1903
Greenville Public Library, Greenville RI p. 2166
Greenville Public Library, *see* Suwannee River Regional Library, Greenville FL p. 461
Greenville Technical College Library, Greenville SC p. 2197
Greenville-Butler County Public Library, Greenville AL p. 19
Greenwell Springs Road Regional, *see* East Baton Rouge Parish Library, Baton Rouge LA p. 943
Greenwich Department of Health Library, Greenwich CT p. 341
Greenwich Free Library, Greenwich NY p. 1632
Greenwich Hospital, Greenwich CT p. 341
Greenwich Library, Greenwich CT p. 341
Greenwich Public Library, *see* Willard Memorial Library, Greenwich OH p. 1948
Greenwood County Historical Society Library, Eureka KS p. 866
Greenwood County Library, Greenwood SC p. 2197
Greenwood Genetic Center Library, Greenwood SC p. 2197
Greenwood Janet D Library, *see* Longwood University, Farmville VA p. 2463
Greenwood Lake Public Library, Greenwood Lake NY p. 1632
Greenwood-Leflore Public Library System, Greenwood MS p. 1299
Greenwood Library, *see* Mississippi Delta Community College, Greenwood MS p. 1309
Greenwood Public, *see* Sussex County Department of Libraries, Greenwood DE p. 383
Greenwood Public Library, Greenwood IN p. 747
Greenwood Public Library, Greenwood NE p. 1400
Greenwood Public Library, Greenwood WI p. 2597
Greenwood Public Library, Greenwood BC p. 2729
Greenwood Reading Center, Greenwood NY p. 1632

Greer Memorial, *see* Apache County Library District, Greer AZ p. 80

Greer Music Library, *see* Connecticut College, New London CT p. 360

Gregg-Graniteville Library, *see* University of South Carolina Aiken, Aiken SC p. 2180

Gregg Memorial Library, *see* First Congregational Church, Colorado Springs CO p. 295

Gregory Evelyn, *see* Toronto Public Library, Toronto ON p. 2861

Gregory Francis A, *see* District of Columbia Public Library, Washington DC p. 398

Gregory Public Library, Gregory SD p. 2212

Greig Memorial Library, Oneida IL p. 685

Grems-Doolittle Library, *see* Schenectady County Historical Society, Schenectady NY p. 1740

Grenola Public Library, Grenola KS p. 870

Gresham Newton Library, *see* Sam Houston State University, Huntsville TX p. 2345

Gressette Learning Resources Center, *see* Orangeburg-Calhoun Technical College, Orangeburg SC p. 2201

Gretna Public Library, Gretna NE p. 1400

Grey Bruce Health Services, Owen Sound ON p. 2834

Grey Eagle Community Library, *see* Great River Regional Library, Grey Eagle MN p. 1275

Grey Highlands Public Library, Flesherton ON p. 2805

Grey Nuns Community Hospital-Caritas Health Group, Edmonton AB p. 2701

Greystone Park Psychiatric Hospital, Morris Plains NJ p. 1504

Gridley Public Library District, Gridley IL p. 653

Gries Library, *see* Suburban Temple, Beachwood OH p. 1858

Griffin Free Public Library, Auburn NH p. 1438

Griffin Hospital, Derby CT p. 336

Griffin Memorial Hospital, Norman OK p. 1970

Griffin-Spalding County Library, *see* Flint River Regional Library, Griffin GA p. 535

Griffin Technical College Library, Griffin GA p. 535

Griffith Observatory Library, Los Angeles CA p. 170

Griffith Silas L Memorial Library, Danby VT p. 2422

Grifton Public Library, Grifton NC p. 1799

Grigg Medical Library, *see* Lincoln John C Health Network, Phoenix AZ p. 74

Griggs County Public Library, Cooperstown ND p. 1839

Grignon Claude-Henri, *see* Bibliotheques Publiques de Longueuil, Longueuil QC p. 2886

Grimes Public Library, Grimes IA p. 819

Grimsby Public Library, Grimsby ON p. 2806

Grimshaw Municipal Library, Grimshaw AB p. 2706

Grimshaw Public Library, *see* Grimshaw Municipal Library, Grimshaw AB p. 2706

Grinnell College Libraries, Grinnell IA p. 819

Grinnell Library Association, Wappingers Falls NY p. 1762

Grissom Virgil I, *see* Newport News Public Library System, Newport News VA p. 2480

Griswold Library, *see* Green Mountain College Library, Poultney VT p. 2432

Griswold Memorial Library, Colrain MA p. 1082

Griswold Public Library, Griswold IA p. 819

Groesbeck Maffett Public Library, Groesbeck TX p. 2330

Groffe Memorial Library, Grayville IL p. 652

Grolier Club of New York Library, New York NY p. 1680

Groninger Library, *see* United States Army, Fort Eustis VA p. 2465

Gronlid Public Library, *see* Wapiti Regional Library, Gronlid SK p. 2921

Grosse Ile Presbyterian Church Library, Grosse Ile MI p. 1187

Grosse Pointe Public Library, Grosse Pointe Farms MI p. 1187

Groton Free Public Library, Groton VT p. 2425

Groton Public Library, Groton CT p. 342

Groton Public Library, Groton MA p. 1093

Groton Public Library, Groton NY p. 1632

Group Health Cooperative, Seattle WA p. 2527

Group Technology Library & Information Services, Naperville IL p. 678

Grout Museum of History & Science, Waterloo IA p. 850

Grove City College, Grove City PA p. 2063

Grove City Community Library, Grove City PA p. 2063

Grove City Public Library, Grove City MN p. 1253

Grove Family Library, Chambersburg PA p. 2043

Grove Hill Public Library, Grove Hill AL p. 19

Grove Public Library, Grove OK p. 1964

Grove United Methodist Church Library, West Chester PA p. 2153

Groveland Correctional Facility Library, Sonyea NY p. 1745

Groves Public Library, Groves TX p. 2330

Groveton Public Library, Groveton TX p. 2330

Grow Brimson Library, *see* Northern Baptist Theological Seminary, Lombard IL p. 667

Grundy County-Jewett Norris Library, Trenton MO p. 1368

Grundy Margaret R Memorial Library, Bristol PA p. 2037

Grunigen Medical Library, *see* University of California Library, Orange CA p. 160

Gruver City Library, Gruver TX p. 2330

Guam Community College, Mangilao GU p. 2667

Guam Law Library, Hagatna GU p. 2667

Guam Public Library, Hagatna GU p. 2667

Guebert Arnold Library, *see* Concordia University College of Alberta, Edmonton AB p. 2700

Guelph General Hospital, Guelph ON p. 2806

Guelph Public Library, Guelph ON p. 2807

Guerneville Regional, *see* Sonoma County Library, Guerneville CA p. 267

Guernsey County District Public Library, Cambridge OH p. 1863

Guernsey County Law Library, Cambridge OH p. 1863

Guernsey Memorial Library, Norwich NY p. 1708

Guggenheim Memorial Library, *see* Monmouth University, West Long Branch NJ p. 1541

Guha Atin, MD Medical Library, Washington DC p. 403

Guilderland Public Library, Guilderland NY p. 1632

Guildhall Public Library, Guildhall VT p. 2425

Guilford College, Greensboro NC p. 1796

Guilford Free Library, Guilford CT p. 342

Guilford Free Library, Guilford VT p. 2425

Guilford Hazel W Memorial, *see* Beaufort, Hyde & Martin County Regional Library, Aurora NC p. 1828

Guilford Memorial Library, Guilford ME p. 987

Guilford Technical Community College, Jamestown NC p. 1803

Guillermin A Pierre Library, *see* Liberty University Library, Lynchburg VA p. 2475

Guin Marilyn Potts Library, *see* Oregon State University, Newport OR p. 2008

Guiteau Foundation Library, *see* Irvington Public Library, Irvington NY p. 1640

Gulf Beaches Public Library, Madeira Beach FL p. 462

Gulf Coast Library, *see* University of Southern Mississippi, Long Beach MS p. 1307

Richard G Cox - Gulf Coast Library, *see* University of Southern Mississippi Library MS p. 1300

Gulf Coast Research Laboratory, Ocean Springs MS p. 1310

Gulf Coast State College Library, Panama City FL p. 480

Gulf Correctional Institution Library, Wewahitchka FL p. 504

Gulf County Public, *see* Northwest Regional Library System, Port Saint Joe FL p. 481

Gulf Gate Public Library, Sarasota FL p. 489

Gulf Publishing Co Library, Houston TX p. 2335

Gulfport Library, *see* Harrison County Library System, Gulfport MS p. 1299

Gulfport Public Library, Gulfport FL p. 450

Gumberg Library, *see* Duquesne University, Pittsburgh PA p. 2125

Gund Jessica Memorial Library, *see* Cleveland Institute of Art, Cleveland OH p. 1877

Gundersen Adolf, MD Health Sciences Library, *see* Gundersen Lutheran Health System, La Crosse WI p. 2603

Gundersen Lutheran Health System, La Crosse WI p. 2603

Gundry Lewis P Health Sciences Library, *see* Saint Agnes Healthcare, Baltimore MD p. 1017

Gunlocke Memorial Library, *see* Wayland Free Library, Wayland NY p. 1765

Gunn Memorial Library, Inc, Washington CT p. 374

Gunn Memorial Public Library, Yanceyville NC p. 1835

Gunnin Architecture Library, *see* Clemson University Libraries, Clemson SC p. 2186

Gunnison Civic Library, Gunnison UT p. 2406

Gunnison Public Library, *see* Bolivar County Library System, Gunnison MS p. 1296

Gunnison Public Library of the Gunnison County Library District, Gunnison CO p. 312

Gunston Hall Plantation Library & Archives, Mason Neck VA p. 2478

Gunter Carl N Sr, *see* Rapides Parish Library, Pineville LA p. 940

Gunter Library, *see* Gulf Coast Research Laboratory, Ocean Springs MS p. 1310

Guntersville Public Library, Guntersville AL p. 19

Gurdon Public, *see* Clark County Library, Gurdon AR p. 93

Gurley Public Library, *see* Huntsville-Madison Public Library, Gurley AL p. 21

Gustafson Raymond Archives Library & Debra Bernhardt Archives, *see* Iron County Historical Museum, Caspian MI p. 1161

Gustavus Adolphus College, Saint Peter MN p. 1283

Gustavus Public Library, Gustavus AK p. 49

Gutekunst Public Library, State Center IA p. 846

Gutenberg College, Eugene OR p. 1996

Guthrie Ben-Lac Du Flambeau Public Library, Lac Du Flambeau WI p. 2604

Guthrie CSD & King County Consolidated Library, Guthrie TX p. 2330

Guthrie Memorial Library - Hanover's Public Library, Hanover PA p. 2064

Guthrie Public Library, Guthrie OK p. 1964

Guthrie Theater Foundation, Minneapolis MN p. 1260

Gutman Library-Research Center, *see* Harvard Library, Cambridge MA p. 1075

Gutman Paul J Library, *see* Philadelphia University, Philadelphia PA p. 2115

Guttenberg Public Library, Guttenberg IA p. 820

Guymon Public Library, Guymon OK p. 1964

Guysborough Historical Society, Guysborough NS p. 2780

Guyton Library, *see* Blue Mountain College, Blue Mountain MS p. 1294

Gwinnett County Law Library, Lawrenceville GA p. 538

Gwinnett County Public Library, Lawrenceville GA p. 538

Gwinnett Technical College Library, Lawrenceville GA p. 539

GWLA (N), *see* Greater Western Library Alliance, Kansas City MO p. 2947

Gwynedd-Mercy College, Gwynedd Valley PA p. 2063

Gypsum Community Library, Gypsum KS p. 870

Gypsum Public, *see* Eagle Valley Library District, Gypsum CO p. 305

H Councill Trenholm State Technical College Library, Montgomery AL p. 28

Thode H G Library of Science & Engineering, *see* McMaster University Library, Hamilton ON p. 2810

H O K. Inc, Houston TX p. 2335

Haakenson Philip N Health Sciences Library, *see* North Dakota State University Libraries, Fargo ND p. 1841

Haakon County Public Library, Philip SD p. 2216

Haas Robert B Family Arts Library, *see* Yale University Library, New Haven CT p. 358

Haas Ruth A Library, *see* Western Connecticut State University, Danbury CT p. 335

Haass Pauline Public Library, Sussex WI p. 2642

HACC Central Pennsylvania's Community College, Gettysburg PA p. 2060

Hackensack University Medical Center, Hackensack NJ p. 1489

HackensackUMC Mountainside, Montclair NJ p. 1503

Hackettstown Free Public Library, Hackettstown NJ p. 1489

Hackettstown Regional Medical Center, Hackettstown NJ p. 1489

Hackley Public Library, Muskegon MI p. 1212

Hackney Library, *see* Barton College, Wilson NC p. 1831

Haddon Heights Public Library, Haddon Heights NJ p. 1489

Haddonfield Public Library, Haddonfield NJ p. 1489

Hadley-Luzerne Public Library, Lake Luzerne NY p. 1650

Hagaman Memorial Library, East Haven CT p. 337

Hagan Norma Perkins Memorial Library, *see* University of the Cumberlands/Cumberland College, Williamsburg KY p. 937

Hagan-Pedigo Library, *see* Baptist Hospital East, Louisville KY p. 923

Hagerstown Community College Library, Hagerstown MD p. 1030

Hagerstown Jefferson Township Public Library, Hagerstown IN p. 747

Hagerty Library, *see* Drexel University Libraries, Philadelphia PA p. 2105

Haggard Memorial Library, *see* East Dallas Christian Church, Dallas TX p. 2307

Haggard W O Jr Library, *see* Plano Public Library System, Plano TX p. 2370

Haggerty Patrick & Beatrice Library, *see* Mount Mary College, Milwaukee WI p. 2621

Haggin Museum, Stockton CA p. 272

Hagley Museum & Library, Wilmington DE p. 388

Hahn Grace O Health Science Library, *see* Deaconess Hospital, Evansville IN p. 738

Hahn, Loeser & Parks, Cleveland OH p. 1880

Hahnemann Library, *see* Drexel University Health Sciences Libraries, Philadelphia PA p. 2105

Hail George Free Library, Warren RI p. 2177

Hailey Public Library, Hailey ID p. 575

Haines Alyce L Biomedical Library, *see* Maui Memorial Medical Center, Wailuku HI p. 567

Haines Borough Public Library, Haines AK p. 49

Haines City Public Library, Haines City FL p. 450

Haines Falls Free Library, Haines Falls NY p. 1632

Haines Richard D Medical Library, *see* Scott & White Healthcare, Temple TX p. 2390

Haish Memorial Library, *see* DeKalb Public Library, DeKalb IL p. 635

HALAN (N), *see* Houston Area Library Automated Network, Houston TX p. 2956

Haldimand County Public Library, Dunnville ON p. 2802

Hale & Dorr Library, Boston MA p. 1061

Hale Center Public Library, Hale Center TX p. 2330

Hale County Public Library, Greensboro AL p. 19

Hale Library, *see* Observatories of the Carnegie Institution of Washington, Pasadena CA p. 206

Hale Nathan Library, *see* Tulsa City-County Library, Tulsa OK p. 1983

Hale Robert Beverley Library, *see* South Kingstown Public Library, Wakefield RI p. 2171

Haledon Free Public Library, Haledon NJ p. 1490

Hales Corners Library, Hales Corners WI p. 2597

Haley & Aldrich Inc, Library, Boston MA p. 1061

Haleyville Public Library, Haleyville AL p. 19

Half Hollow Hills Community Library, Dix Hills NY p. 1615

Half Moon Bay Library, *see* San Mateo County Library, Half Moon Bay CA p. 256

Haliburton County Public Library, Haliburton ON p. 2807

Halifax Community College Library, Weldon NC p. 1829

Halifax County Library, Halifax NC p. 1799

Halifax County-South Boston Regional Library, Halifax VA p. 2467

Halifax North Memorial, *see* Halifax Public Libraries, Halifax NS p. 2779

Halifax Public Libraries, Dartmouth NS p. 2779

Hall Ahira Memorial Library, Brocton NY p. 1585

Hall County Library System, Gainesville GA p. 534

Hall Grace Memorial Library, Montgomery MA p. 1107

Hall Helen Library, League City TX p. 2354

Hall James O Research Center Library, *see* Maryland National Capital Park & Planning Commission, Clinton MD p. 1024

Hall Kenneth E Learning Resource Center, *see* East Saint Louis Community College Center, East Saint Louis IL p. 639

Hall Linda Library, Kansas City MO p. 1337

Hall Mattie D Memorial Library, *see* First Baptist Church, Rosedale MS p. 1314

Hall Memorial Library, Ellington CT p. 338

Hall Memorial Library, Northfield NH p. 1461

Hall of Flame, Phoenix AZ p. 73

Hall Paul Library & Maritime Museum, *see* Seafarer's Harry Lundeberg School of Seamanship, Piney Point MD p. 1036

Hall Samuel Read Library, *see* Lyndon State College, Lyndonville VT p. 2427

Hall Sharlot Archives & Library, *see* Prescott Historical Society, Prescott AZ p. 78

Hall Thomas A, Sr Library, *see* Klein Ann Forensic Center, West Trenton NJ p. 1542

Hall-Voyer Foundation, Honey Grove TX p. 2333

Hall Wilbur C Law Library, *see* Washington & Lee University, Lexington VA p. 2474

Hall William H Free Library, *see* Cranston Public Library, Cranston RI p. 2165

Halle Bruce T Library, *see* Eastern Michigan University, Ypsilanti MI p. 1237

Halle Diane M Library, *see* Endicott College Library, Beverly MA p. 1054

Hallett Jesse F Memorial Library, Crosby MN p. 1247

Halliburton Energy Services, Duncan OK p. 1961

Halliburton Energy Services, Houston TX p. 2335

Hallmark Cards, Inc, Kansas City MO p. 1337

Hallock Medical Library, *see* Connecticut Valley Hospital, Middletown CT p. 351

Hallock Public Library, *see* Northwest Regional Library, Hallock MN p. 1286

Hallock Sarah Hull Free Library, Milton NY p. 1661

Halls Public Library, Halls TN p. 2236

Halstead Public Library, Halstead KS p. 870

Haltom City Public Library, Haltom City TX p. 2330

Halton County Law Association, Milton ON p. 2822

Halton District School Board, Burlington ON p. 2798

Halton Hills Public Library, Georgetown ON p. 2806

Ham Ennis & Nancy Library, *see* Rochester College, Rochester Hills MI p. 1222

Hamady Michael H & Robert M Health Sciences Library, *see* Hurley Medical Center, Flint MI p. 1180

Hamann Memorial Library, Anthon IA p. 794

Hamber Eric Library, *see* University of British Columbia Library, Vancouver BC p. 2743

Hamburg Center, Hamburg PA p. 2063

Hamburg Public Library, Hamburg IA p. 820

Hamburg Public Library, Hamburg NY p. 1632

Hamburg Public Library, Hamburg PA p. 2063

Hamburg Township Library, Hamburg MI p. 1187

Hamden Public Library, Hamden CT p. 343

Hamer Donald W Maps Library, *see* Pennsylvania State University Libraries, University Park PA p. 2148

Hamer Fannie Lou Library, *see* Jackson/Hinds Library System, Jackson MS p. 1303

Hamersly Wayne & Lynn Library, *see* Western Oregon University, Monmouth OR p. 2006

Hamilton & District Health Library Network (N), Hamilton ON p. 2959

Hamilton Alexander Memorial Free Library, Blue Ridge Summit PA p. 2036

Hamilton B F Library, *see* Franklin College, Franklin IN p. 743

Hamilton Beth Safety Library, *see* Triodyne Inc, Glenview IL p. 651

Hamilton City Library, Hamilton KS p. 870

Hamilton College, Clinton NY p. 1607

Hamilton College Library, Lincoln NE p. 1404

Hamilton Correctional Institution Library, *see* Florida Department of Corrections, Jasper FL p. 455

Hamilton County Governmental Law Library, Chattanooga TN p. 2227

Hamilton County Library, Syracuse KS p. 895

Hamilton East Public Library, Noblesville IN p. 769

Hamilton Health Sciences, Hamilton ON p. 2808

Hamilton Jim E Correctional Center, Hodgen OK p. 1965

Hamilton Law Association Library, Hamilton ON p. 2808

Hamilton Library, *see* Cumberland County Historical Society, Carlisle PA p. 2041

Hamilton Longie Dale Memorial Library, *see* Copiah-Jefferson Regional Library System, Wesson MS p. 1301

Hamilton Marshall W Library, *see* North Florida Community College Library, Madison FL p. 462

Hamilton Medical Center, Dalton GA p. 528

Hamilton Memorial Library, Chester MA p. 1080

Hamilton North Public Library, Cicero IN p. 732

Hamilton Parks Public Library, Trimble TN p. 2267

Hamilton Public Library, Hamilton IL p. 653

Hamilton Public Library, Hamilton MO p. 1329

Hamilton Public Library, Hamilton NY p. 1633

Hamilton Public Library, Hamilton TX p. 2330

Hamilton Public Library, Hamilton ON p. 2808

Hamilton Public Library, *see* Tombigbee Regional Library System, Hamilton MS p. 1318

Hamilton Spectator Library, Hamilton ON p. 2810

Hamilton Sundstrand, Rockford IL p. 697

Hamilton Thomas Hale Library, *see* University of Hawaii at Manoa Library, Honolulu HI p. 565

Hamilton Township Public Library, Hamilton NJ p. 1490

Hamilton-Wenham Public Library, South Hamilton MA p. 1125

Hamilton Wentworth Catholic District School Board, Hamilton ON p. 2810

Hamlet Public, *see* Leath Thomas Memorial Library, Hamlet NC p. 1820

Hamlin-Lincoln County Public Library, Hamlin WV p. 2560

Hamlin Memorial Library, Smethport PA p. 2141

Hamlin Memorial Library-Paris Hill, South Paris ME p. 1001

Hamlin Public Library, Hamlin NY p. 1633

Hamline University, Saint Paul MN p. 1278

Hamm Phillip G Library, *see* Wallace Community College-Dothan, Dothan AL p. 15

Hamma Library, *see* Trinity Lutheran Seminary, Columbus OH p. 1891

Hammermill Library, *see* Mercyhurst College, Erie PA p. 2056

Hammond Community Library, Hammond WI p. 2597

Hammond Free Library, Hammond NY p. 1633

Hammond Library, *see* Chicago Theological Seminary, Chicago IL p. 611

Hammond Library of Crown Point NY, Crown Point NY p. 1612

Hammond Public Library, Hammond IN p. 747

Hamner Institutes for Health Sciences, Research Triangle Park NC p. 1819

Hamner James L Public Library, Amelia VA p. 2447

Hamon Arts Library, *see* Southern Methodist University, Dallas TX p. 2310

Hampden Law Library, *see* Massachusetts Trial Court, Springfield MA p. 1127

Hampden Sydney College, Hampden Sydney VA p. 2468

Hampden-Booth Theatre Library at the Players, New York NY p. 1680

Hampshire College Library, Amherst MA p. 1048

Hampshire County Public Library, Romney WV p. 2570

Hampshire Law Library, *see* Massachusetts Trial Court, Northampton MA p. 1113

Hampstead Public Library, Hampstead NH p. 1449

Hampton Bays Public Library, Hampton Bays NY p. 1633

Hampton Community Library, Allison Park PA p. 2028

Harrisburg Area Community College, Harrisburg PA p. 2065

Harrisburg Area Community College, Lancaster PA p. 2076

Harrisburg Area Community College, Lebanon PA p. 2079

Harrisburg Area Community College, York PA p. 2159

Harrisburg District Library, *see* Harrisburg Public Library District, Harrisburg IL p. 653

Harrisburg Hospital Library, Harrisburg PA p. 2065

Harrisburg Public Library, Harrisburg OR p. 2000

Harrisburg Public Library District, Harrisburg IL p. 653

Harrisburg University of Science & Technology, Harrisburg PA p. 2065

Harrison A R Learning Resources Center, *see* Redlands Community College, El Reno OK p. 1963

Harrison B J Library, *see* Marshalltown Community College, Marshalltown IA p. 830

Harrison Community Library, Harrison MI p. 1188

Harrison County Historical Museum, Marshall TX p. 2360

Harrison County Law Library, Gulfport MS p. 1299

Harrison County Library System, Gulfport MS p. 1299

Harrison County Public Library, Corydon IN p. 734

Harrison Donald C Health Sciences Library, *see* University of Cincinnati Libraries, Cincinnati OH p. 1874

Harrison G Lamar Library, *see* Langston University, Langston OK p. 1967

Harrison Mel Memorial Library, *see* Temple Judea, Coral Gables FL p. 434

Harrison Memorial Hospital, Bremerton WA p. 2510

Harrison Memorial Library, Carmel CA p. 132

Harrison Memorial Library, Moose Jaw SK p. 2918

Harrison Public, *see* Kootenai-Shoshone Area Libraries, Harrison ID p. 575

Harrison Public Library, Harrison NJ p. 1490

Harrison Public Library, Harrison NY p. 1634

Harrison Regional Library System, Columbiana AL p. 13

Harrison Richard B Community Library, *see* Wake County Public Library System, Raleigh NC p. 1818

Harrison Village Library, Harrison ME p. 987

Harrison W Walworth Public Library, Greenville TX p. 2329

Harrisonburg-Rockingham Historical Society Library, Dayton VA p. 2460

Harrisville Free Library, Harrisville NY p. 1634

Harrisville Public Library, Harrisville MS p. 1300

Harrisville Public Library, Harrisville NH p. 1451

Harrodsburg Historical Society, Harrodsburg KY p. 916

Harrodsburg Mercer County Research Library, *see* Harrodsburg Historical Society, Harrodsburg KY p. 916

Harry E K Library of Fishes, *see* IGFA Fishing Hall of Fame & Museum, Dania Beach FL p. 435

Hart Area Public Library, Hart MI p. 1188

Hart County Library, Hartwell GA p. 536

Hart County Public Library, Munfordville KY p. 930

Hart Gilbert Library, Wallingford VT p. 2438

Hart-Holifield Emily B Library, *see* Compton Community College Library, Compton CA p. 136

Hart John C Memorial Library, Shrub Oak NY p. 1743

Hart Memorial Central Library, *see* Osceola Library System, Kissimmee FL p. 456

Hart Stella Memorial Public Library, Smiley TX p. 2387

Hart Stephen H Library, *see* History Colorado, Denver CO p. 302

Harte Bret, *see* Long Beach Public Library, Long Beach CA p. 167

Harte Janet F Public, *see* Corpus Christi Public Libraries, Corpus Christi TX p. 2301

Harter, Secrest & Emery LLP, Rochester NY p. 1729

Hartfield Library, *see* Henderson Community College, Henderson KY p. 917

Hartford City Public Library, Hartford City IN p. 748

Hartford Conservatory, Hartford CT p. 345

Hartford Consortium For Higher Education (N), Hartford CT p. 2939

Hartford Hospital, Hartford CT p. 345

Hartford Law Library, *see* Connecticut Judicial Branch Law Libraries, Hartford CT p. 344

Hartford Library, Hartford VT p. 2425

Hartford Library, *see* Scott-Sebastian Regional Library, Hartford AR p. 101

Hartford Medical Society, Farmington CT p. 340

Hartford Public Library, Hartford CT p. 345

Hartford Public Library, Hartford MI p. 1188

Hartford Public Library, Hartford WI p. 2597

Hartford Public Library, *see* McGregor-McKinney Public Library, Hartford AL p. 20

Hartford Public Library District, Hartford IL p. 653

Hartford Seminary Library, Hartford CT p. 346

Hartford Steam Boiler Inspection & Insurance Co, Hartford CT p. 347

Hartigan John D Medical Library, *see* Alegent Health Bergan Mercy Medical Center, Omaha NE p. 1411

Hartington Public Library, Hartington NE p. 1401

Hartland Public Libraries, Hartland VT p. 2425

Hartland Public Library, West Hartland CT p. 376

Hartland Public Library, Hartland ME p. 987

Hartland Public Library, Hartland WI p. 2597

Hartley Public Library, Hartley IA p. 820

Hartman Library, *see* Johnson & Johnson Pharmaceutical Research & Development, Raritan NJ p. 1525

Hartnell College, Salinas CA p. 2962

Hartnell College Library, Salinas CA p. 226

Hartness Library, *see* Vermont Technical College, Randolph Center VT p. 2433

Hartselle Public Library, Hartselle AL p. 20

Hartshorn Family Association Library, Conover NC p. 1785

Hartshorne Public Library, Hartshorne OK p. 1964

Hartstein Ray, *see* Oakton Community College Library, Skokie IL p. 703

Hartsville Memorial, *see* Darlington County Library, Hartsville SC p. 2192

Hartwick College, Oneonta NY p. 1710

Hartzler Sadie A Library, *see* Eastern Mennonite University, Harrisonburg VA p. 2470

Hartzmark Lee & Dolores Library, Beachwood OH p. 1858

Harvard College Library, *see* Harvard Library, Cambridge MA p. 1075

Harvard Diggins Public Library, Harvard IL p. 654

Harvard Forest Library, *see* Harvard Library, Petersham MA p. 1075

Harvard Library, Cambridge MA p. 1073

Harvard Library in New York, New York NY p. 1680

Harvard Musical Association Library, Boston MA p. 1062

Harvard Public Library, Harvard MA p. 1094

Harvard Public Library, Harvard NE p. 1401

Harvard-Smithsonian Center for Astrophysics Library, Cambridge MA p. 1077

Harvard-Yenching Library, *see* Harvard Library, Cambridge MA p. 1075

Cushing Harvey, *see* Yale University Library, New Haven CT p. 358

Harvey Memorial Library, Parkman ME p. 995

Harvey Public Library, Harvey ND p. 1844

Harvey Public Library District, Harvey IL p. 654

Harvey William R & Norma B Library, *see* Hampton University, Hampton VA p. 2468

Harvin Clarendon County Library, Manning SC p. 2199

Harwich Port Library Association, Harwich Port MA p. 1094

Harwinton Public Library, Harwinton CT p. 348

Harwood E C Library, *see* American Institute for Economic Research, Great Barrington MA p. 1092

Haseltine Library, *see* Missouri State University, Springfield MO p. 1367

Haselwood Library, *see* Olympic College, Bremerton WA p. 2510

Haskell County Library, Haskell TX p. 2331

Haskell Free Library, Inc, Derby Line VT p. 2423

Haskell Indian Nations University, Lawrence KS p. 877

Haskell Library, *see* French Institute-Alliance Francaise Library, New York NY p. 1679

Haskell Memorial Library, *see* University of Pittsburgh at Titusville, Titusville PA p. 2146

Haskell Township Library, Sublette KS p. 895

Haskett Elva L, *see* Anaheim Public Library, Anaheim CA p. 120

Haslett Library, *see* Capital Area District Libraries, Haslett MI p. 1200

Hassard Bonnington, San Francisco CA p. 242

Hastie William H Library, *see* United States Court of Appeals, Philadelphia PA p. 2118

Hastings Center, Garrison NY p. 1627

Hastings College, Hastings NE p. 1401

Hastings College of the Law Library, *see* University of California, San Francisco CA p. 248

Hastings Memorial Library, Grant NE p. 1400

Hastings Museum of Natural & Cultural History Library, Hastings NE p. 1401

Hastings-on-Hudson Public Library, Hastings-on-Hudson NY p. 1634

Hastings Public Library, Hastings MI p. 1189

Hastings Public Library, Hastings NE p. 1401

Hastings Public Library, Hastings PA p. 2067

Hastings Regional Center, Hastings NE p. 1401

Haston Free Public Library, North Brookfield MA p. 1112

Haston Library, Franklin VT p. 2424

Hatboro Baptist Church Library, Hatboro PA p. 2067

Hatch-Billops Collection, Inc Library, New York NY p. 1681

Hatch Energy Library, Calgary AB p. 2691

Hatch Library, *see* Bay Path College, Longmeadow MA p. 1100

Hatch Public Library, Hatch NM p. 1556

Hatch Public Library, Mauston WI p. 2613

Hatch Research & InfoCentres, Mississauga ON p. 2822

Hatch Science Library, *see* Bowdoin College Library, Brunswick ME p. 979

Hatcher Harlan Graduate Library, *see* University of Michigan, Ann Arbor MI p. 1153

Hatchie River Regional Library, Jackson TN p. 2238

Hatfield Mark O Library, *see* Willamette University, Salem OR p. 2018

Hatfield Public Library, Hatfield MA p. 1094

Hathaway G H Library, *see* White James Memorial Library, Assonet MA p. 1086

Hathaway Library of Conservation & Natural History, *see* Audubon Society of Rhode Island, Smithfield RI p. 2176

Hatley Hughes Inez Research Library, *see* Harrison County Historical Museum, Marshall TX p. 2360

Hatton School & Public Library, Hatton ND p. 1844

Hauenstein Grace Library, *see* Aquinas College, Grand Rapids MI p. 1183

Hauge Memorial Library, Osseo WI p. 2628

Haughton Peter D Memorial Library, *see* Harness Racing Museum & Hall of Fame, Goshen NY p. 1629

Hauppauge Center Library, *see* Adelphi University, Hauppauge NY p. 1634

Hauppauge Public Library, Hauppauge NY p. 1634

Hauptman-Woodward Medical Research Institute, Buffalo NY p. 1598

Hauser Eric V Memorial Library, *see* Reed College, Portland OR p. 2014

Hauser Willet Architectural Glass Library, Philadelphia PA p. 2110

Haut-Saint-Jean Regional Library, Edmundston NB p. 2762

Haute-Yamaska, Granby QC p. 2884

Havana Public, *see* Gadsden County Public Library, Havana FL p. 485

Havana Public Library District, Havana IL p. 654

Havelock-Craven County Public Library, Havelock NC p. 1800

Haven Public Library, Haven KS p. 870

Haverford College, Haverford PA p. 2067

Hebrew Union College-Jewish Institute of Religion, Cincinnati OH p. 1870

Hebron Library, Hebron NH p. 1451

Hebron Public, *see* Porter County Public Library System, Hebron IN p. 783

Hebron Public Library, Hebron ND p. 1844

Hebron Secrest Library, Hebron NE p. 1402

HEC Montreal, Montreal QC p. 2896

Hector Public Library, Hector MN p. 1254

Hedberg Library, *see* Carthage College, Kenosha WI p. 2601

Hedberg Public Library, Janesville WI p. 2599

Hedrick Public Library, Hedrick IA p. 820

Heermance Memorial Library, Coxsackie NY p. 1612

Heffernan Margaret Avery Reference Library, *see* Sioux City Art Center, Sioux City IA p. 844

Hefner W G VA Medical Center Library, *see* Department of Veterans Affairs, Salisbury NC p. 1822

Hege Library, *see* Guilford College, Greensboro NC p. 1796

Heggan Margaret E Free Public Library, Sewell NJ p. 1529

Heginbotham Library, Holyoke CO p. 313

Heidelberg University, Tiffin OH p. 1938

Height Dorothy I/Benning Neighborhood Library, *see* District of Columbia Public Library, Washington DC p. 398

Heights Neighborhood Library, *see* Houston Public Library, Houston TX p. 2339

Heilig Resource Center, *see* North Carolina Synod of the ELCA, Salisbury NC p. 1822

Heintzelman Donald S Wildlife Library, *see* Wildlife Information Center, Slatington PA p. 2140

Heinz H J Co, Warrendale PA p. 2151

Heisey Collectors of America, Inc, Newark OH p. 1922

Heiskell Andrew Braille & Talking Book Library, *see* New York Public Library - Astor, Lenox & Tilden Foundations, New York NY p. 1691

Heisler Municipal Library, Heisler AB p. 2706

Hekman Library, *see* Calvin College & Calvin Theological Seminary, Grand Rapids MI p. 1184

Held-Poage Historical Research Library, *see* Mendocino County Historical Society, Ukiah CA p. 277

Heldman Learning Resource Center, *see* West Los Angeles College Library, Culver City CA p. 138

Lewis Library, *see* Phillips Community College of the University of Arkansas, Helena AR p. 103

Helena Township Public Library, Alden MI p. 1148

Helix Public Library, Helix OR p. 2000

Hellenic College-Holy Cross Greek Orthodox School of Theology, Brookline MA p. 1071

Hellertown Area Library, Hellertown PA p. 2068

Helling Madelyn Library, *see* Nevada County Library, Nevada City CA p. 193

Hellman Neil Library, *see* College of Saint Rose, Albany NY p. 1568

Hellmuth, Obata & Kassabaum, Inc Library, Dallas TX p. 2308

Hellmuth, Obata & Kassabaum, Inc, Saint Louis MO p. 1355

Helmerich Peggy V Library, *see* Tulsa City-County Library, Tulsa OK p. 1983

Helmke Walter E Library, *see* Indiana University-Purdue University, Fort Wayne IN p. 741

Helper City Library, Helper UT p. 2406

Helvetia Library, Helvetia WV p. 2560

Hemens H J Bibliotheque, Rosemere QC p. 2907

Hemenway & Barnes, Boston MA p. 1062

Hemet Public Library, Hemet CA p. 158

Heminger Health Library, *see* Central Washington Hospital, Wenatchee WA p. 2548

Hemingford Public Library, Hemingford NE p. 1402

Hemisphere Engineering Inc Library, Edmonton AB p. 2701

Hemphill County Library, Canadian TX p. 2294

Hempstead County Library, *see* Southwest Arkansas Regional Library, Hope AR p. 103

Hempstead Public Library, Hempstead NY p. 1634

Henderson Community College, Henderson KY p. 917

Henderson County, Athens TX p. 2277

Henderson County Public Library, Henderson KY p. 917

Henderson County Public Library, Hendersonville NC p. 1801

Henderson County Public Library District, Biggsville IL p. 595

Henderson District Public Libraries, Henderson NV p. 1428

Henderson Free Library, Henderson NY p. 1635

Henderson Isabel, *see* Torrance Public Library, Torrance CA p. 276

Henderson John F Public Library, Westville OK p. 1986

Henderson Memorial Public Library Association, Jefferson OH p. 1906

Henderson Porter Library, *see* Angelo State University, San Angelo TX p. 2378

Henderson Public, Henderson MN p. 1254

Henderson Simon & Louise Library, *see* Morris Lon College, Jacksonville TX p. 2347

Henderson State University, Arkadelphia AR p. 93

Henderson-Wilder Library, *see* Upper Iowa University, Fayette IA p. 816

Henderson Zach S Library, *see* Georgia Southern University, Statesboro GA p. 552

Hendersonville Martin Curtis Public Library, Hendersonville TN p. 2237

Hendren Scott Medical Library, *see* Integris Southwest Medical Center, Oklahoma City OK p. 1972

Hendrick Medical Center, Abilene TX p. 2272

Hendricks Dr R A Memorial Library, *see* Saint Luke's Hospital, Maumee OH p. 1915

Hendrix College, Conway AR p. 97

Hendry County Library System, Clewiston FL p. 433

Hendry Dixon, *see* Indian River State College, Okeechobee FL p. 474

Henika District Library, Wayland MI p. 1235

Henington David M Alief Regional Library, *see* Houston Public Library, Houston TX p. 2339

Henkle-Holliday Memorial, *see* Marion Public Library, La Rue OH p. 1914

Henley Henry Public Library, Carthage IN p. 731

Hennepin County Law Library, Minneapolis MN p. 1260

Hennepin County Library, Minnetonka MN p. 1263

Hennepin County Medical Center, Minneapolis MN p. 1260

Hennepin History Museum Library, *see* Historical Society of Hennepin County, Minneapolis MN p. 1260

Hennessey Public Library, Hennessey OK p. 1965

Henning C H Library, *see* Niagara Parks Botanical Gardens & School of Horticulture, Niagara Falls ON p. 2824

Henri-Bourassa, *see* Bibliothèques de Montrèal, Montreal QC p. 2889

Henrico County Public Library, Henrico VA p. 2471

Henry County Historical Society, New Castle IN p. 768

Henry County Law Library, Napoleon OH p. 1919

Henry County Library, Eminence KY p. 912

Henry County Library, Clinton MO p. 1323

Henry County Public Library System, McDonough GA p. 544

Henry Dorothy E Memorial, *see* Sussex County Library System, Vernon NJ p. 1514

Henry Ford Community College, Dearborn MI p. 1167

Henry O Museum Library, Austin TX p. 2280

Henry Patrick, *see* Fairfax County Public Library, Vienna VA p. 2461

Henry Patrick Memorial, *see* Campbell County Public Library, Brookneal VA p. 2495

Henry Patrick School District Public Library, Deshler OH p. 1896

Henry Public Library, Henry IL p. 655

Henryetta Public Library, Henryetta OK p. 1965

Henryville Correctional Facility Library, Henryville IN p. 748

Hepburn Library of Edwards, Edwards NY p. 1618

Hepburn Library of Hermon, Hermon NY p. 1635

Hepburn Library of Lisbon, Lisbon NY p. 1652

Hepburn Library of Madrid, Madrid NY p. 1656

Hepburn Library of Norfolk, Norfolk NY p. 1706

Hepburn Library of Waddington, Waddington NY p. 1761

Hepler City Library, Hepler KS p. 871

Herb Society of America Library, Kirtland OH p. 1907

Hercules Library, *see* Contra Costa County Library, Hercules CA p. 209

Herington Public Library, Herington KS p. 871

Heritage Christian Reformed Church Library, Kalamazoo MI p. 1197

Heritage College & Seminary Library, Cambridge ON p. 2798

Heritage Institute, *see* Algonquin College Learning Resource Centre, Perth ON p. 2828

Heritage Museum & Cultural Center, Saint Joseph MI p. 1225

Heritage Park Regional Library, *see* OC Public Libraries, Irvine CA p. 258

Heritage Public Library, McDonald PA p. 2085

Heritage Public Library, Providence Forge VA p. 2486

Heritage Society Library, Houston TX p. 2336

Heritage University, Toppenish WA p. 2541

Heritage Valley Health System, Beaver PA p. 2031

Heritage Village Archives & Library, *see* Pinellas County Government, Largo FL p. 460

Heritage Winnipeg Corp Library, Winnipeg MB p. 2755

Herkimer County Community College Library, Herkimer NY p. 1635

Herkimer County Historical Society Library, Herkimer NY p. 1635

Herkimer County Law Library, Herkimer NY p. 1635

Hermann-Grima House Library, New Orleans LA p. 960

Hermann Memorial Library, *see* Sullivan County Community College, Loch Sheldrake NY p. 1653

Hermiston Public Library, Hermiston OR p. 2000

Hernando Correctional Institution Library, *see* Florida Department of Corrections, Brooksville FL p. 430

Hernando County Public Library System, Brooksville FL p. 430

Hernando Public Library, *see* First Regional Library, Hernando MS p. 1301

Herr Jane I Annetta M Memorial Library, Mifflinburg PA p. 2089

Herrera Felipe Library, *see* Inter-American Development Bank Library, Washington DC p. 405

Herrick District Library, Holland MI p. 1190

Herrick Health Sciences Library, *see* Alta Bates Medical Center, Berkeley CA p. 126

Herrick Margaret Library, *see* Academy of Motion Picture Arts & Sciences, Beverly Hills CA p. 128

Herrick Memorial Library, Wellington OH p. 1945

Herrick Memorial Library, *see* Alfred University, Alfred NY p. 1572

Herrick Township Public Library, Herrick IL p. 655

Herrin City Library, Herrin IL p. 655

Herron Art Library, *see* Indiana University-Purdue University, Indianapolis IN p. 753

Hershey Foods Corp, Hershey PA p. 2069

Hershey Public Library, Hershey PA p. 2069

Hertford County Library, *see* Albemarle Regional Library, Winton NC p. 1835

Hervey Memorial, *see* Licking County Library, Utica OH p. 1922

Herzberg Institute of Astrophysics, *see* Canada Institute for Scientific & Technical Information, Penticton BC p. 2735

Herzfeld Bob Memorial Library, *see* Saline County Public Library, Benton AR p. 94

Herzing College Library, Winter Park FL p. 505

Herzing College Library, Atlanta GA p. 516

Herzing College Library, Madison WI p. 2606

Herzstein Albert & Ethel Library, *see* San Jacinto Museum of History, La Porte TX p. 2352

Hesburgh Libraries, Notre Dame IN p. 770

Hesperia Community Library, Hesperia MI p. 1189

Hess Corp, Houston TX p. 2337

Hessel William Library, *see* Lake Michigan College, Benton Harbor MI p. 1156

Hesseltine Public Library, Wilbur WA p. 2550

Hesser College, Manchester NH p. 1455

Hesston College, Hesston KS p. 871

Hesston Public Library, Hesston KS p. 871

Hester Memorial Library, *see* North Greenville University, Tigerville SC p. 2206

Heterick Memorial Library, *see* Ohio Northern University, Ada OH p. 1851

Heutte Fred Horticultural Library, Norfolk VA p. 2481

Heuvelton Free Library, Heuvelton NY p. 1636

Hewes Library, *see* Monmouth College, Monmouth IL p. 675

Hewitt Public Library, Hewitt TX p. 2332

Hewlett Flora Lamson Library, *see* Graduate Theological Union Library, Berkeley CA p. 126

Hewlett-Woodmere Public Library, Hewlett NY p. 1636

Heyworth Public Library District, Heyworth IL p. 655

Hialeah-John F Kennedy Library, Hialeah FL p. 450

Hiawatha Public Library, Hiawatha IA p. 821

Hibbing Public Library, Hibbing MN p. 1254

Hibbs Russell A Memorial Library, *see* New York Orthopaedic Hospital-Columbia University, New York NY p. 1690

Hickman County Memorial Library, Clinton KY p. 909

Hickman County Public Library, Centerville TN p. 2226

Hickman-Johnson-Furrow Library Center, *see* Morningside College, Sioux City IA p. 844

Hickman Public, *see* Fulton Public Library, Hickman KY p. 914

Hickmans Crossroads Library, *see* Brunswick County Library, Calabash NC p. 1824

Hickory Flat Public, *see* Sequoyah Regional Library System, Canton GA p. 523

Hickory Flat Public Library, *see* Benton County Library System, Hickory Flat MS p. 1293

Hickory Public Library, Hickory NC p. 1801

Hickox Edward J & Gena G Library, *see* Naismith Memorial Basketball Hall of Fame, Springfield MA p. 1127

Hicks Gerald Memorial Library, *see* Lorain County Historical Society, Elyria OH p. 1898

Hicks J F Memorial Library, *see* Virginia Intermont College, Bristol VA p. 2453

Hicks John W Undergraduate Library, *see* Purdue University Libraries, West Lafayette IN p. 786

Hicks Leanna Public Library, Inkster MI p. 1193

Hicks Morley Hamilton Stewart & Storie LLP, Toronto ON p. 2854

Hicksville Public Library, Hicksville NY p. 1636

Hidalgo County Law Library, Edinburg TX p. 2315

Hidalgo County Library System, Pharr TX p. 2369

Hidalgo Public Library, Hidalgo TX p. 2332

Hiebert Library, *see* Fresno Pacific University, Fresno CA p. 153

Higginbotham/Bryson, *see* Shreve Memorial Library, Greenwood LA p. 969

Higgins Armory Museum, Worcester MA p. 1144

Higgins Public Library, Higgins TX p. 2332

Higgs, Fletcher & Mack LLP, San Diego CA p. 231

High Bridge Public Library, High Bridge NJ p. 1490

High Carolyn T Memorial Library, *see* Columbus County Public Library, Whiteville NC p. 1829

High Desert State Prison, *see* California Department of Corrections Library System, Susanville CA p. 221

High Desert State Prison Library, *see* Nevada Department of Corrections, Indian Springs NV p. 1428

High Level Municipal Library, High Level AB p. 2706

High Library, *see* Elizabethtown College, Elizabethtown PA p. 2053

High Museum of Art Library, Atlanta GA p. 516

High Plains Library District, Greeley CO p. 311

High Plains Museum Library, McCook NE p. 1408

High Point Public Library, High Point NC p. 1802

High Point University, High Point NC p. 1802

High Prairie Library, *see* Pikes Peak Library District, Falcon CO p. 296

High Prairie Municipal Library, High Prairie AB p. 2707

High River Centennial Library, High River AB p. 2707

High Street Christian Church, Akron OH p. 1853

Highgate Public Library, Highgate Center VT p. 2425

Highgrove Library, *see* Riverside County Library System, Highgrove CA p. 217

Highland Beach Library, Highland Beach FL p. 451

Highland City Library, Highland UT p. 2406

Highland Community College Library, Freeport IL p. 647

Highland Community College Library, Highland KS p. 871

Highland Community Library, Johnstown PA p. 2073

Highland County District Library, Hillsboro OH p. 1904

Highland County Law Library, Hillsboro OH p. 1904

Highland County Public Library, Monterey VA p. 2479

Highland Falls Library, Highland Falls NY p. 1636

Highland Hospital Library, Rochester NY p. 1729

Highland Park Library, Highland Park TX p. 2333

Highland Park Presbyterian Church, Dallas TX p. 2308

Highland Park Public Library, Highland Park IL p. 655

Highland Park Public Library, Highland Park NJ p. 1490

Highland Park United Methodist Church Library, Dallas TX p. 2308

Highland Presbyterian Church, New Castle PA p. 2096

Highland Public Library, Highland NY p. 1636

Highland Township Public Library, Highland MI p. 1189

Highlands County Library System, Sebring FL p. 491

Highlands Ranch Library, *see* Douglas County Libraries, Highlands Ranch CO p. 294

Highline Community College, Des Moines WA p. 2975

Highline Community College Library, Des Moines WA p. 2514

Hightower Memorial, *see* Pine Mountain Regional Library, Thomaston GA p. 542

Hightower Memorial Library, York AL p. 41

Hightower Sara Regional Library, Rome GA p. 549

Hightstown Memorial, *see* Mercer County Library System, Hightstown NJ p. 1494

Highwood Public Library, Highwood IL p. 656

Hignett Travis P Memorial Library, *see* IFDC Library, Muscle Shoals AL p. 32

Hiland Mountain Correctional Center Library, *see* Alaska State Department of Corrections, Eagle River AK p. 47

Hilandar Research Library & Research Center for Medieval Slavic Studies, *see* Ohio State University LIBRARIES, Columbus OH p. 1888

Hilbert College, Hamburg NY p. 1632

Hildebrand C B Public, *see* Burke County Public Library, Hildebran NC p. 1811

Hildebrand Memorial Library, Boscobel WI p. 2582

Hilding Medical & Health Sciences Library, *see* Saint Luke's Hospital, Duluth MN p. 1248

Hildreth Public Library, Hildreth NE p. 1402

Hill A P, *see* Petersburg Public Library, Petersburg VA p. 2484

Hill B J Library, Holland TX p. 2333

Hill City Public Library, Hill City SD p. 2213

Hill College Library, Hillsboro TX p. 2333

Hill Correctional Center Library, Galesburg IL p. 648

Hill Emily S, *see* Duplin County Library, Faison NC p. 1804

Hill James J Reference Library, Saint Paul MN p. 1278

Hill Jerome Reference Library, *see* Anthology Film Archives, New York NY p. 1669

Hill Jim Dan Library, *see* University of Wisconsin-Superior, Superior WI p. 2641

Hill Kathleen Library, *see* Group Health Cooperative, Seattle WA p. 2528

Hill Laurie Library, Heron MT p. 1383

Hill Leslie Pinckney Library, *see* Cheyney University, Cheyney PA p. 2044

Hill Lewis Dana Memorial Library, Center Lovell ME p. 982

Hill Library, Center Strafford NH p. 1440

Hill Public Library, Hill NH p. 1451

Hill Stella Memorial Library, Alto TX p. 2273

Hill Tillman Public Library of Hazel Green, *see* Huntsville-Madison Public Library, Hazel Green AL p. 21

Hillcrest Community Library, *see* Queens Borough Public Library, Flushing NY p. 1644

Hillcrest Hospital, Mayfield Heights OH p. 1915

Hillcrest Medical Center Library, Tulsa OK p. 1981

Hillcrest Public Library, Cuba KS p. 862

Hillendahl Arnold L Neighborhood Library, *see* Houston Public Library, Houston TX p. 2339

Hillerman Tony, *see* Albuquerque-Bernalillo County Library System, Albuquerque NM p. 1548

Hillman James Frazer Health Science Library, *see* University of Pittsburgh Medical Center Shadyside, Pittsburgh PA p. 2129

Hillman Library, *see* Ezra-Habonim, The Niles Township Jewish Congregation, Skokie IL p. 702

Hillman Library, *see* University of Pittsburgh, Pittsburgh, *see* University of Pittsburgh PA p. 2128, 2129

Hillsboro City Library, Hillsboro TX p. 2333

Hillsboro Community Library, Hillsboro NM p. 1556

Hillsboro Public, *see* Pocahontas County Free Libraries, Hillsboro WV p. 2565

Hillsboro Public Library, Hillsboro IL p. 656

Hillsboro Public Library, Hillsboro IA p. 821

Hillsboro Public Library, Hillsboro KS p. 872

Hillsboro Public Library, Hillsboro OR p. 2000

Hillsboro Public Library, Hillsboro WI p. 2598

Hillsborough Community College, Tampa FL p. 496

Hillsborough County Historic Commission Library, *see* Tampa Bay History Center, Tampa FL p. 497

Hillsborough County Law Library, Manchester NH p. 1455

Hillsborough Public, *see* Albert-Westmorland-Kent Regional Library, Hillsborough NB p. 2765

Hillsborough Public, *see* Somerset County Library System, Hillsborough NJ p. 1475

Hillsborough Talking Book Library, *see* Tampa-Hillsborough County Public Library System, Tampa FL p. 497

Hillsdale College, Hillsdale MI p. 1190

Hillsdale Community Library, Hillsdale MI p. 1190

Hillsdale Free Public Library, Hillsdale NJ p. 1491

Hillsdale Free Will Baptist College Library, Moore OK p. 1969

Hillside Public Library, Hillside IL p. 656

Hillside Public Library, Hillside NJ p. 1491

Hillside Public Library, New Hyde Park NY p. 1665

Hillview Free Library, Diamond Point NY p. 1614

Hillwood Estate, Museum & Gardens, Washington DC p. 403

Hillyer Art Library, *see* Smith College Libraries, Northampton MA p. 1114

Hilo Public Library, *see* Hawaii State Public Library System, Hilo HI p. 562

Hilton Conrad N Library, *see* Culinary Institute of America, Hyde Park NY p. 1639

Hilton Ida Library, *see* Three Rivers Regional Library System, Darien GA p. 522

Hilton Union Public Library, Hilton Beach ON p. 2811

Hilty Mae Memorial Library, *see* Texas Chiropractic College, Pasadena TX p. 2369

Himmelfarb Paul Health Sciences Library, *see* George Washington University, Washington DC p. 402

Hinckley, Allen & Snyder LLP, Providence RI p. 2172

Hinckley Library, *see* Northwest College, Powell WY p. 2659

Hinckley Public Library, *see* East Central Regional Library, Hinckley MN p. 1244

Hinckley Public Library District, Hinckley IL p. 656

Hinds Community College, Raymond MS p. 1313

Hineline Richard H Research Center, *see* Camden County Historical Society, Camden NJ p. 1476

Hines Creek Municipal Library, Hines Creek AB p. 2707

Hingham Public Library, Hingham MA p. 1095

Hink Louise & Lucille-Tama Public Library, Tama IA p. 847

Hinkle Walter C Memorial Library, *see* State University of New York, College of Technology, Alfred NY p. 1572

Hinrichs Merle A International Business Information Centre, *see* Thunderbird School of Global Management, Glendale AZ p. 64

Hinsdale County Library District, Lake City CO p. 314

Hinsdale Public Library, Hinsdale IL p. 656

Hinsdale Public Library, Hinsdale MA p. 1095

Hinsdale Public Library, Hinsdale NH p. 1451

Hinshaw & Culbertson Library, Chicago IL p. 614

Hinton Elmer Memorial Library, *see* Portland Public Library, Portland TN p. 2263

Hinton Municipal Library, Hinton AB p. 2707

Hinton Public Library, Hinton OK p. 1965

Hiram College Library, Hiram OH p. 1905

Hiram Halle Memorial Library, *see* Pound Ridge Library, Pound Ridge NY p. 1724

Hirons J Wilbur Library, *see* Goldey Beacom College, Wilmington DE p. 388

Hirsch Library Museum of Fine Arts, Houston, Houston TX p. 2337

Hirshhorn Museum & Sculpture Garden Library, *see* Smithsonian Libraries, Washington DC p. 415

Hiscock & Barclay LLP, Buffalo NY p. 1598

Hispanic Culture Foundation Resource Library, Albuquerque NM p. 1549

Hispanic Society of America Library, New York NY p. 1681

Historic Arkansas Museum Library, Little Rock AR p. 106

Historic Bethlehem Partnership Library, Bethlehem PA p. 2034

Historic Charlton Park Village & Museum Library, Hastings MI p. 1189

Historic Courthouse Museum Library, Lakeport CA p. 163

Historic Deerfield Inc & Pocumtuck Valley Memorial Association Libraries, Deerfield MA p. 1084

Historic House Museum Library, *see* Buck Pearl S Birthplace Foundation, Hillsboro WV p. 2560

Historic Hudson Valley Library, Tarrytown NY p. 1754

Historic Huguenot Street Library, New Paltz NY p. 1665

Historic Jefferson College Library, Washington MS p. 1317

Historic Landmarks Foundation of Indiana, Indianapolis IN p. 751

Historic Mobile Preservation Society, Mobile AL p. 25

Historic New England, Boston MA p. 1062

Historic New Orleans Collection, New Orleans LA p. 960

Historic Northampton, Northampton MA p. 1113

Historic Restoration Resources Library, *see* Alamance County Historic Properties Commission, Graham NC p. 1795

Historic Rugby, Rugby TN p. 2264

Historic Saint Mary's City, Saint Mary's City MD p. 1040

Historic Schaefferstown, Inc, Schaefferstown PA p. 2136

Historic Westville, Inc Library, Lumpkin GA p. 540

Historic White Pine Village Research Library, *see* Mason County Historical Society, Ludington MI p. 1204

Historical & Cultural Society of Clay County, Moorhead MN p. 1265

Historical & Genealogical Society of Indiana County, Indiana PA p. 2071

Historical Association of Southern Florida, Miami FL p. 465

Historical Evaluation & Research Organization, Stevensville MD p. 1043

Historical Society of Alpine County, Markleeville CA p. 184

Historical Society of Berks County, Reading PA p. 2133

Historical Society of Carroll County Library, Westminster MD p. 1046

Historical Society of Cheshire County, Keene NH p. 1452

Historical Society of Dauphin County Library, Harrisburg PA p. 2065

Historical Society of Haddonfield Library, Haddonfield NJ p. 1489

Historical Society of Hennepin County, Minneapolis MN p. 1260

Historical Society of Long Beach, Long Beach CA p. 166

Historical Society of Michigan, East Lansing MI p. 1175

Historical Society of Moorestown Library, Moorestown NJ p. 1504

Historical Society of Ocean Grove, Ocean Grove NJ p. 1516

Historical Society of Old Newbury Library, Newburyport MA p. 1109

Historical Society of Old Yarmouth Library, Yarmouth Port MA p. 1146

Historical Society of Palm Beach County, West Palm Beach FL p. 502

Historical Society of Pennsylvania, Philadelphia PA p. 2110

Historical Society of Porter County, Valparaiso IN p. 783

Historical Society of Princeton, Princeton NJ p. 1522

Historical Society of Quincy & Adams County Library, Quincy IL p. 693

Historical Society of Rockland County Library, New City NY p. 1664

Historical Society of Seattle & King County, Seattle WA p. 2528

Historical Society of the Cocalico Valley Library, Ephrata PA p. 2054

Historical Society of the Town of Greenwich, Cos Cob CT p. 334

Historical Society of Western Pennsylvania, Pittsburgh PA p. 2125

Historical Society of York County Library & Archives, *see* York County Heritage Trust, York PA p. 2160

Historical Society Serving Sleepy Hollow & Tarrytown, Tarrytown NY p. 1754

History Center in Tompkins County, Ithaca NY p. 1642

History Colorado, Denver CO p. 302

History Museum & Historical Society of Western Virginia Library, Roanoke VA p. 2493

History of Science Library - Cabot Science Library, *see* Harvard Library, Cambridge MA p. 1075

History San Jose, San Jose CA p. 249

Hitchcock Genevieve Miller Public Library, Hitchcock TX p. 2333

Hitchcock Memorial Museum & Library, Westfield VT p. 2439

Hitschfeld Walter Geographic Information Centre, *see* McGill University Libraries, Montreal QC p. 2898

HIV North Society, Grande Prairie AB p. 2705

Hiwassee College, Madisonville TN p. 2246

Hjorth Norman E Memorial Library, *see* Trinity Presbyterian Church Library, Cherry Hill NJ p. 1478

HLC (N), *see* Hawaii Library Consortium, Kihei HI p. 2941

Ho-Ho-Kus Public Library, *see* Worth Pinkham Memorial Library, Ho-Ho-Kus NJ p. 1491

Hoag Memorial Hospital Presbyterian, Newport Beach CA p. 194

Hoar Reuben Library, Littleton MA p. 1099

Hoard Historical Museum Library, Fort Atkinson WI p. 2593

Hobart & William Smith Colleges, Geneva NY p. 1627

Hobart Historical Society, Inc, Hobart IN p. 748

Hobart Institute of Welding Technology, Troy OH p. 1941

Hobart Public Library, Hobart OK p. 1965

Hobbs Charlotte E Memorial Library, Lovell ME p. 991

Hobbs Public Library, Hobbs NM p. 1556

Hobby Memorial Library, *see* Texas A&M University Central Texas, Killeen TX p. 2350

Hobby Oveta Culp Memorial Library, *see* Central Texas College, Killeen TX p. 2350

Hobe Sound Bible College Library, Hobe Sound FL p. 451

Hoboken Public Library, Hoboken NJ p. 1491

Hobson Rae Memorial Library, Republic KS p. 891

Hoch Heritage Center, *see* Fort Lauderdale Historical Society, Fort Lauderdale FL p. 443

Hockessin Public Library, Hockessin DE p. 384

Hockey Hall of Fame, Toronto ON p. 2854

Hocking College Library, Nelsonville OH p. 1920

Hocking Correctional Facility Library, Nelsonville OH p. 1920

Hockley County Memorial Library, Levelland TX p. 2355

Hocutt-Ellington Memorial, *see* Public Library of Johnston County & Smithfield, Clayton NC p. 1824

Hodges J M Library, *see* Wharton County Junior College, Wharton TX p. 2399

Hodges John C University Libraries, *see* University of Tennessee, Knoxville, Knoxville TN p. 2243

Hodgett Ferriss Library, *see* Memorial University of Newfoundland, Corner Brook NL p. 2772

Hodgkins Public Library District, Hodgkins IL p. 657

Hodgson Russ LLP, Buffalo NY p. 1598

Hodson Keith Memorial Library, *see* Canadian Forces College, Toronto ON p. 2851

Hoeganaes Corp Library, Cinnaminson NJ p. 1479

Hoesch Memorial Public Library, Alma NE p. 1391

Hoffman Helen B Plantation Library, Plantation FL p. 484

Hoffman Memorial Library, *see* Rabbinical College of America, Morristown NJ p. 1505

Hoffmann-La Roche, Inc, Nutley NJ p. 1515

Hofheimer Elise N Art Library, *see* Old Dominion University Libraries, Norfolk VA p. 2483

Hofheimer Henry Clay II Library, *see* Virginia Wesleyan College, Norfolk VA p. 2483

Hofman Catherine Dickson, *see* Warren County Library, Blairstown NJ p. 1472

Hofstra University, Hempstead NY p. 1635

Hofstra University Law Library, Hempstead NY p. 1635

Hog Hammock Community Library, *see* Three Rivers Regional Library System, Sapelo Island GA p. 522

Hogan & Hartson LLP, Washington DC p. 403

Hogan & Hartson LLP Law Library, New York NY p. 1681

Hogan Elsie S Community Library, Willcox AZ p. 89

Hogansville Public Library, *see* Troup-Harris Regional Library System, Hogansville GA p. 538

Hoghaug Paul Library, *see* Lake Region State College, Devils Lake ND p. 1839

Hogue Grady C Learning Resource Center Library, *see* Coastal Bend College, Beeville TX p. 2288

Hogue Library, *see* Christian Life College Library, Stockton CA p. 272

Hoisington Public Library, Hoisington KS p. 872

Hokah Public Library, Hokah MN p. 1254

Hoke County Public Library, Raeford NC p. 1815

Hoke Library, *see* Martin County Library System, Jensen Beach FL p. 492

Holbrook Library, *see* United States Air Force, Ellsworth AFB SD p. 2212

Holbrook Public Library, Holbrook AZ p. 65

Holbrook Public Library, Holbrook MA p. 1095

Holcomb T L Library, *see* American Baptist College, Nashville TN p. 2255

Holden Arboretum, Kirtland OH p. 1908

Hopital Sainte-Anne, Sainte-Anne-de-Bellevue QC p. 2909

Hôpital St Luc Library, *see* Centre Hospitalier de l'Universite de Montreal, Montreal QC p. 2893

Hopkins & Carley Library, San Jose CA p. 249

Hopkins County-Madisonville Public Library, Madisonville KY p. 927

Hopkins Public Library, Hopkins MI p. 1191

Hopkinsville-Christian County Public Library, Hopkinsville KY p. 918

Hopkinsville Community College Library, Hopkinsville KY p. 918

Hopkinton Public Library, Hopkinton IA p. 821

Hopkinton Public Library, Hopkinton MA p. 1096

Hopkinton Town Library, Contoocook NH p. 1444

Hopkinton Town Library, Hopkinton NY p. 1638

Hopland Research & Extension Center Library, Hopland CA p. 158

Hopper George W Law Library, *see* University of Wyoming, Laramie WY p. 2657

Hopper Research Library, *see* Butler Institute of American Art, Youngstown OH p. 1952

Hopping, Green & Sams, Tallahassee FL p. 495

Mann Horace Library, *see* Northwest Missouri State University, Maryville MO p. 1345

Horgan Paul Library, *see* New Mexico Military Institute, Roswell NM p. 1561

Horicon Free Public Library, Brant Lake NY p. 1584

Horicon Public Library, Horicon WI p. 2598

Horizon Health Network, Miramichi NB p. 2765

Horizon Health Network, Moncton NB p. 2765

Horlock House History Center, *see* Navasota Public Library, Navasota TX p. 2365

Horn Everett Public Library, Lexington TN p. 2245

Horn Library, *see* Babson College, Babson Park MA p. 1051

Hornbake R Lee Library, *see* University of Maryland Libraries, College Park MD p. 1025

Horne Library, *see* South Piedmont Community College, Polkton NC p. 1814

Hornell Public Library, Hornell NY p. 1638

Hornepayne Public Library, Hornepayne ON p. 2811

Horner Joseph Memorial Library, *see* German Society of Pennsylvania, Philadelphia PA p. 2110

Horrmann Library, *see* Wagner College, Staten Island NY p. 1748

Horry County Memorial Library, Conway SC p. 2191

Horry-Georgetown Technical College, Conway SC p. 2191

Horse Cave Free Public Library, Horse Cave KY p. 918

Horseheads Free Library, *see* Chemung County Library District, Horseheads NY p. 1619

Horseshoe Bend District Library, Horseshoe Bend ID p. 576

Horseshoe Bend Public Library, *see* Izard County Library, Horseshoe Bend AR p. 104

Horseshoe Bend Regional Library, Dadeville AL p. 14

Horsey J William Library, *see* Tyndale University College & Seminary, Toronto ON p. 2864

Horsham Township Library, Horsham PA p. 2069

Horst Janice, *see* San Bernardino County Library, Lucerne Valley CA p. 228

Horticultural Society of New York, Inc Library, New York NY p. 1681

Horton Free Public Library, Horton KS p. 872

Hortonville Public Library, Hortonville WI p. 2598

Hosch John Harrison Library, *see* Gainesville State College, Oakwood GA p. 547

Hospers Public Library, Hospers IA p. 821

Hospital Center of Val D'or, Val-d'Or QC p. 2914

Hospital du Saint-Sacrement, Quebec QC p. 2905

Hospital for Sick Children, Toronto ON p. 2854

Hospital for Special Surgery, New York NY p. 1681

Hospital of Central Connecticut, New Britain CT p. 354

Hospital Santa Cabrini, Montreal QC p. 2896

Hospitality, Labor & Management Library, *see* Cornell University Library, Ithaca NY p. 1641

Host Bruce J Center, *see* Collins LeRoy Leon County Public Library System, Tallahassee FL p. 492

Hostos Community College Library, Bronx NY p. 1587

Hot Springs County Library, Thermopolis WY p. 2661

Hot Springs Public Library, Hot Springs SD p. 2213

Hotchkin Memorial Library, *see* Rogers Environmental Education Center, Sherburne NY p. 1743

Hotchkiss Library of Sharon, Inc, Sharon CT p. 367

Hotchkiss Public, *see* Delta County Libraries, Hotchkiss CO p. 313

Hotel-Dieu Grace Hospital, Windsor ON p. 2871

Hotel Dieu Shaver Health & Rehabilitation Centre, Saint Catharines ON p. 2839

Hotel Queen Mary Historical Archives, *see* RMS Foundation, Inc, Long Beach CA p. 167

Houff Library, *see* Blue Ridge Community College, Weyers Cave VA p. 2502

Houghton Arthur A Jr Library, *see* Corning Community College, Corning NY p. 1610

Houghton College, Houghton NY p. 1638

Houghton International, Valley Forge PA p. 2149

Houghton Lake Public Library, Houghton Lake MI p. 1192

Houghton Library, *see* Harvard Library, Cambridge MA p. 1075

Houghton Memorial Library, *see* Huntingdon College, Montgomery AL p. 29

Houghton Willard J Library, *see* Houghton College, Houghton NY p. 1638

Houlka Public, *see* Dixie Regional Library System, Houlka MS p. 1312

Hourigan, Kluger & Quinn, Kingston PA p. 2074

Housatonic Community College Library, Bridgeport CT p. 331

House Memorial Public Library, Pender NE p. 1416

House Ear Institute, Los Angeles CA p. 171

House Robert B Undergraduate, *see* University of North Carolina at Chapel Hill, Chapel Hill NC p. 1781

Houser, Henry & Syron Law Library, Toronto ON p. 2854

Housing Advocates, Inc, Cleveland OH p. 1880

Houston Academy of Medicine, Houston TX p. 2337

Houston Area Library Automated Network (N), Houston TX p. 2956

Houston Area Research Library Consortium (N), Houston TX p. 2956

Houston Baptist University, Houston TX p. 2337

Houston Chronicle Library, Houston TX p. 2337

Houston Community College, Houston TX p. 2337

Houston Community College Central College, Houston TX p. 2337

Houston Community College Northeast College, Houston TX p. 2337

Houston Community College - Northwest College, Houston TX p. 2338

Houston Community College - Southwest College, Houston TX p. 2338

Houston County Historical Commission Archives, Crockett TX p. 2303

Houston County Public Library, Erin TN p. 2234

Houston County Public Library System, Perry GA p. 547

Houston Love Memorial Library, Dothan AL p. 15

Houston Memorial Library, *see* Murray-Colloway County Hospital, Murray KY p. 930

Houston Metropolitan Research Center, *see* Houston Public Library, Houston TX p. 2339

Houston Museum of Decorative Arts, Chattanooga TN p. 2227

Houston Museum of Natural Science Library, Houston TX p. 2338

Houston Public Library, Houston TX p. 2338

Houston Public Library, Houston BC p. 2729

Houston Sam Regional Library & Research Center, *see* Texas State Library & Archives Commission, Liberty TX p. 2283

Houston-Tillotson University, Austin TX p. 2280

Howard Beach Community Library, *see* Queens Borough Public Library, Howard Beach NY p. 1644

Howard City Library, Howard KS p. 872

Howard College - San Angelo Library, San Angelo TX p. 2379

Howard Community College Library, Columbia MD p. 1025

Howard County Detention Center, *see* Howard County Library System, Columbia MD p. 1026

Howard County Junior College, Big Spring TX p. 2289

Howard County Library, Big Spring TX p. 2289

Howard County Library, *see* Southwest Arkansas Regional Library, Nashville AR p. 103

Howard County Library System, Columbia MD p. 1026

Howard Lake Library, *see* Great River Regional Library, Howard Lake MN p. 1275

Howard Payne University, Brownwood TX p. 2292

Howard Public Library, Hornell NY p. 1638

Howard Ray W Library Technology Center, *see* Shoreline Community College, Shoreline WA p. 2535

Howard-Tilton Memorial Library, *see* Tulane University, New Orleans LA p. 963

Howard University Libraries, Washington DC p. 403

Howe C D Institute Library, Toronto ON p. 2854

Howe Community Library, Howe TX p. 2345

Howe David A Public Library, Wellsville NY p. 1765

Howe John Library, *see* Albany Public Library, Albany NY p. 1568

Howe Library, Hanover NH p. 1450

Howe Memorial Library, Breckenridge MI p. 1159

Howe Percy R Memorial Library, *see* Forsyth Institute, Boston MA p. 1061

Howell Bruce I Library, *see* Wake Technical Community College, Raleigh NC p. 1818

Howell Carnegie District Library, Howell MI p. 1192

Howell Julian M Library, *see* Southside Virginia Community College Libraries, Alberta VA p. 2444

Howells Public Library, Howells NE p. 1402

Hower Mary Medical Library, Akron OH p. 1853

Howey in the Hills Library, *see* Beck Marianne Memorial Library, Howey in the Hills FL p. 451

Howitt Dr William Memorial Learning Centre, *see* Guelph General Hospital, Guelph ON p. 2806

Howland Public Library, Beacon NY p. 1579

Howorth Library, *see* Mississippi Museum of Art, Jackson MS p. 1305

Hoyle, Fickler, Herschel & Mathes LLP, Philadelphia PA p. 2111

Hoyt Lakes Public Library, Hoyt Lakes MN p. 1254

Hoyt Library, Kingston PA p. 2074

Hoyt Thomas H Memorial, *see* Merrimac Public Library, Merrimac MA p. 1105

HPC-MLA (N), *see* Hawaii-Pacific Chapter of the Medical Library Association, Honolulu HI p. 2941

HPL Express Discovery Green, *see* Houston Public Library, Houston TX p. 2339

HPL Express Southwest, *see* Houston Public Library, Houston TX p. 2339

Hruska Roman L & Victoria E Memorial Public Library, David City NE p. 1397

HSC Learning Resource Center, *see* West Virginia University, Charleston WV p. 2557

HSLAL (N), *see* Health Sciences Library Association of Louisiana, New Orleans LA p. 2944

HSLC/Access PA (N), Philadelphia PA p. 2954

HSLIC (N), *see* Health Science Library Information Consortium, Portland ME p. 2944

HSLNKC (N), *see* Health Sciences Library Network of Kansas City, Inc, Kansas City MO p. 2947

Huachuca City Public Library, Huachuca City AZ p. 65

Hubbard David Allan Library, *see* Fuller Theological Seminary, Pasadena CA p. 206

Hubbard Free Library, Hallowell ME p. 987

Hubbard Memorial Library, Ludlow MA p. 1101

Hubbard Public Library, Hubbard IA p. 821

Hubbard Public Library, Hubbard OH p. 1905

Hubbard-Roycroft Elbert Museum, *see* Aurora Historical Society, East Aurora NY p. 1616

Huntsville-Madison Public Library, Huntsville AL p. 21

Huntsville Memorial Hospital, Huntsville TX p. 2345

Huntsville Museum of Art Library, Huntsville AL p. 21

Huntsville Public Library, Huntsville TN p. 2237

Huntsville Public Library, Huntsville TX p. 2345

Huntsville Public Library, Huntsville ON p. 2811

Hupp Medical Library, see Ohio Valley Medical Center, Wheeling WV p. 2574

Hurd D A Library, North Berwick ME p. 993

Hurley Library District, Hurley NY p. 1639

Hurley Medical Center, Flint MI p. 1180

Hurley Public Library, Hurley WI p. 2599

Huron City Museums Library, Port Austin MI p. 1219

Huron County Courthouse Library, see Huron Law Association, Goderich ON p. 2806

Huron County Law Library, Bad Axe MI p. 1155

Huron County Law Library Association, Norwalk OH p. 1924

Huron County Library, Clinton ON p. 2799

Huron Law Association, Goderich ON p. 2806

Huron Public Library, Huron OH p. 1906

Huron Public Library, Huron SD p. 2213

Huron Shores Public Library, Iron Bridge ON p. 2812

Huron University College Library, London ON p. 2817

Huronia Museum, Midland ON p. 2821

Hurst Library, see Northwest University, Kirkland WA p. 2519

Hurst Public Library, Hurst TX p. 2345

Hurston Zora Neale, see Saint Lucie County Library System, Fort Pierce FL p. 447

Hurt-Battelle Memorial Library of West Jefferson, West Jefferson OH p. 1946

Husch Blackwell Sanders LLP, Saint Louis MO p. 1355

Huskins Mildred & J P Library, see Mitchell Community College, Statesville NC p. 1826

Husky Energy Corporate Library, Calgary AB p. 2692

Hussar Municipal Library, Hussar AB p. 2707

Hussey-Mayfield Memorial Public Library, Zionsville IN p. 789

Husson University, Bangor ME p. 976

Hustisford Community Library, Hustisford WI p. 2599

Hutchens Harriett K Library, see Southwest Baptist University Libraries, Bolivar MO p. 1320

Hutchins-Atwell Public Library, Hutchins TX p. 2346

Hutchins Library, see Berea College, Berea KY p. 907

Hutchinson Community College, Hutchinson KS p. 873

Hutchinson Correctional Facility Central Library, see Kansas Department of Corrections, Hutchinson KS p. 873

Hutchinson County Library, Borger TX p. 2290

Hutchinson Fred Cancer Research Center, Seattle WA p. 2528

Hutchinson Memorial Library, Randolph WI p. 2632

Hutchinson Public Library, Hutchinson KS p. 873

Hutchinson Public Library, Hutchinson MN p. 1254

Hutchison Bruce, see Greater Victoria Public Library Board, Victoria BC p. 2745

Huttonsville Correctional Center Library, Huttonsville WV p. 2562

Huxford Genealogical Society Inc, Homerville GA p. 536

Huxley College of the Environment, Bellingham WA p. 2508

Huxley Public Library, Huxley IA p. 821

Hyannis Public Library Association, Hyannis MA p. 1096

Hyattville Library, see Big Horn County Library, Hyattville WY p. 2651

Hyconeechee Regional Library, Hillsborough NC p. 1802

Hyde Collection Library, Glens Falls NY p. 1629

Hyde County Library, Highmore SD p. 2212

Hyde Joshua Public Library, Sturbridge MA p. 1129

Hyde Park Free Library, Hyde Park NY p. 1640

Hyde Park Historical Society Archives, Hyde Park MA p. 1097

Hyde Park Public Library, Hyde Park PA p. 2070

Hyder Public Library, Hyder AK p. 49

Hydro Quebec Bibliotheque, Montreal QC p. 2896

Hydrosource Associates Library, Ashland NH p. 1438

Hyndman Londonderry Public Library, Hyndman PA p. 2070

Hynek J Allen Center for UFO Studies, Chicago IL p. 614

Hyrum Library, Hyrum UT p. 2406

Hythe Public Library, Hythe AB p. 2707

Iacoboni Angelo M Library, see County of Los Angeles Public Library, Lakewood CA p. 142

IAHS (Institute for Applied Health Sciences) Library, see Mohawk College Library, Hamilton ON p. 2810

Iberia Parish Library, New Iberia LA p. 959

Iberville Parish Library, Plaquemine LA p. 965

IBI Group Library, Toronto ON p. 2854

IBM Canada Ltd-Toronto Lab, Markham ON p. 2820

IBM Corp, Hopewell Junction NY p. 1638

IBM Corp, Yorktown Heights NY p. 1772

IBM Corp, Austin TX p. 2280

IBM Mid-Hudson Valley Library, see IBM Corp, Hopewell Junction NY p. 1638

Ice Miller LLP, Indianapolis IN p. 751

ICF Consulting Inc, Sacramento CA p. 224

ICF International, see ICF Consulting Inc, Sacramento CA p. 224

ICON Library Consortium (N), Omaha NE p. 2948

Ida Grove Public Library, Ida Grove IA p. 822

Ida Public Library, Belvidere IL p. 594

Idabel Public Library, Idabel OK p. 1966

Idaho Commission for Libraries, Boise ID p. 571

Idaho Correctional Institution-Orofino Library, see Idaho State Correctional Institution Library, Orofino ID p. 577

Idaho Falls Public Library, Idaho Falls ID p. 576

Idaho Health Information Association (N), Idaho Falls ID p. 2941

Idaho Health Sciences Library, see Idaho State University, Pocatello ID p. 582

Idaho Legislative Reference Library, Boise ID p. 571

Idaho National Laboratory, Idaho Falls ID p. 576

Idaho Power Co, Boise ID p. 571

Idaho School for the Deaf & Blind Library, Gooding ID p. 574

Idaho Springs Public Library, Idaho Springs CO p. 313

Idaho State Correctional Institution Library, Kuna ID p. 577

Idaho State Historical Society, Boise ID p. 571

Idaho State Law Library, Boise ID p. 571

Idaho State University, Pocatello ID p. 581

Idalou Community Library, Idalou TX p. 2346

Ideal Public, see Middle Georgia Regional Library System, Ideal GA p. 541

Ider Public Library, Ider AL p. 22

Idlewild Public Library, Idlewild MI p. 1193

IDRC Library, see International Development Research Centre Library, Ottawa ON p. 2831

IDS (N), see Interlibrary Delivery Service of Pennsylvania, Doylestown PA p. 2954

Idyllwild Library, see Riverside County Library System, Idyllwild CA p. 217

IFA World Resource Center, see International Franchise Association, Washington DC p. 405

IFAS Indian River Research & Education Center, see University of Florida, Fort Pierce FL p. 447

IFDC Library, Muscle Shoals AL p. 32

IGFA Fishing Hall of Fame & Museum, Dania Beach FL p. 435

Igloolik Research Centre Library, see Nunavut Research Institute, Igloolik NU p. 2789

Ignace Public Library, Ignace ON p. 2812

Ignacio Community Library District, Ignacio CO p. 313

IHIA (N), see Idaho Health Information Association, Idaho Falls ID p. 2941

IHM Library/Resource Center, Monroe MI p. 1209

Ihrig Wilson & Associates Library, Oakland CA p. 196

IISOH Library, see International Institute for Sport History Library, State College PA p. 2143

ILA Library, see National Rifle Association, Fairfax VA p. 2462

Ile a la Crosse Public Library, Ile a la Crosse SK p. 2917

Iliff School of Theology, Denver CO p. 302

Ilion Free Public Library, Ilion NY p. 1640

ILLINET (N), see Illinois Library & Information Network, Springfield IL p. 2942

Illinois Agricultural Association, Bloomington IL p. 595

Illinois Appellate Court, Mount Vernon IL p. 678

Illinois Auditor General Library, Springfield IL p. 704

Illinois Central College, East Peoria IL p. 638, 2965

Illinois College, Jacksonville IL p. 658

Illinois Colllege, Petersburg IL p. 691

Illinois College of Optometry Library, Chicago IL p. 614

Illinois CPA Society, Chicago IL p. 614

Illinois Criminal Justice Information Authority Library, Chicago IL p. 614

Illinois Department of Commerce & Economic Opportunity, see Illinois State Data Center Cooperative, Springfield IL p. 705

Illinois Department of Corrections, Canton IL p. 599

Illinois Department of Corrections, Dwight IL p. 638

Illinois Department of Corrections, East Saint Louis IL p. 639

Illinois Department of Corrections, Ina IL p. 658

Illinois Department of Corrections, Jacksonville IL p. 658

Illinois Department of Corrections, Kewanee IL p. 661

Illinois Department of Corrections, Sheridan IL p. 702

Illinois Department of Corrections, Sumner IL p. 709

Illinois Department of Corrections, Vienna IL p. 714

Illinois Department of Employment Security, Chicago IL p. 615

Illinois Department of Natural Resources, Metropolis IL p. 673

Illinois Department of Transportation, Springfield IL p. 704

Illinois Early Intervention Clearinghouse, Champaign IL p. 603

Illinois Eastern Community College, Fairfield IL p. 645

Illinois Environmental Protection Agency Library, Springfield IL p. 704

Illinois Historic Preservation Agency, Collinsville IL p. 630

Illinois Historic Preservation Agency, Galena IL p. 647

Illinois State Historical Library, Springfield IL p. 705

Illinois Institute of Art, Schaumburg IL p. 700

Illinois Institute of Art - Chicago Library, Chicago IL p. 615

Illinois Institute of Technology, Chicago IL p. 615

Illinois Institute of Technology, Summit Argo IL p. 709

Illinois Library & Information Network (N), Springfield IL p. 2942

Illinois Lodge of Research, Normal IL p. 681

Illinois Mathematics & Science Academy, Aurora IL p. 591

Illinois Office of Educational Services (N), Springfield IL p. 2942

Illinois Prairie District Public Library, Metamora IL p. 673

Illinois Railway Museum, Union IL p. 711

Illinois River Correctional Center Library, see Illinois Department of Corrections, Canton IL p. 599

Illinois School for the Deaf, Jacksonville IL p. 658

Illinois School for the Visually Impaired Library, Jacksonville IL p. 658

Illinois State Archives, Springfield IL p. 705

Illinois State Data Center Cooperative, Springfield IL p. 705

Institute Archives & Special Collections, *see* Massachusetts Institute of Technology Libraries, Cambridge MA p. 1078

Institute for Advanced Study Libraries, Princeton NJ p. 1522

Institute for Advanced Study of Human Sexuality, San Francisco CA p. 242

Institute for American Indian Studies, Washington CT p. 374

Institute for Basic Research in Developmental Disabilities Library, *see* New York State Office of Mental Retardation & Developmental Disabilities, Staten Island NY p. 1748

Institute for Childhood Resources, San Francisco CA p. 243

Institute for Christian Studies, Toronto ON p. 2854

Institute for Clinical Social Work Library, Chicago IL p. 615

Institute for Creation Research Library, Dallas TX p. 2308

Institute for Defense Analyses Library, Alexandria VA p. 2445

Institute for Defense Analysis Library, Princeton NJ p. 1522

Institute for Foreign Policy Analysis, Inc, Cambridge MA p. 1077

Institute for Human Services Education, Truro NS p. 2786

Institute for Parapsychology, *see* Rhine Research Center, Durham NC p. 1790

Institute for Psychoanalysis, Chicago, Chicago IL p. 615

Institute for Research on Labor & Employment Library, *see* University of California, Berkeley, Berkeley CA p. 128

Institute for Study of Earth & Man, *see* Southern Methodist University, Dallas TX p. 2310

Institute for Supply Management, Tempe AZ p. 84

Institute for Wetland & Waterfowl Research Library, Stonewall MB p. 2752

Institute of American Indian & Alaska Native Culture & Arts Development Library, Santa Fe NM p. 1562

Institute of American Indian Arts Library, *see* Institute of American Indian & Alaska Native Culture & Arts Development Library, Santa Fe NM p. 1562

Institute of Arctic & Alpine Research, *see* University of Colorado Boulder, Boulder CO p. 292

Institute of Business Appraisers, Inc Library, Plantation FL p. 484

Institute of Contemporary Art Library, Boston MA p. 1062

Institute of Design & Construction, Brooklyn NY p. 1592

Institute of Environmental Sciences & Technology Library, Arlington Heights IL p. 590

Institute of Fine Arts Conservation Center Library, *see* New York University, New York NY p. 1695

Institute of Food & Agricultural Sciences Library, *see* University of Florida, Tropical Research & Education Center, Homestead FL p. 451

Institute of Govermental Studies, *see* University of California-Berkeley, Berkeley CA p. 127

Institute of Governmental Affairs Library & Data Archive, *see* University of California, Davis, Davis CA p. 139

Institute of Governmental Studies, *see* University of California, Berkeley, Berkeley CA p. 128

Institute of Heraldry Library, *see* United States Army, Fort Belvoir VA p. 2464

Institute of Historical Survey Foundation Library, Las Cruces NM p. 1558

Institute of Internal Auditors Library, Altamonte Springs FL p. 425

Institute of International Finance Library, Washington DC p. 404

Institute of Jazz Studies, *see* Rutgers University Libraries, Newark NJ p. 1513

Institute of Living Medical Library, *see* Hartford Hospital, Hartford CT p. 345

Institute of Noetic Sciences Library, Petaluma CA p. 207

Institute of Ocean Sciences Library, *see* Fisheries & Oceans Canada, Sidney BC p. 2737

Institute of Surgical Research Library, *see* United States Army, Fort Sam Houston TX p. 2321

Institute of Transportation Engineers, Washington DC p. 404

Institute of Transportation Studies Library, Berkeley CA p. 127

Institute on World War II & the Human Experience Library, *see* Florida State University, Tallahassee FL p. 494

Institute Philippe Pinel de Montreal, Montreal QC p. 2897

Insurance Bureau of Canada Library, Toronto ON p. 2855

Insurance Information Institute Library, New York NY p. 1682

Insurance Institute for Highway Safety Library, Arlington VA p. 2449

Insurance Institute of Ontario Library, Toronto ON p. 2855

Insurance Library Association of Boston, Boston MA p. 1062

Integrated Information Solutions (N), Murray Hill NJ p. 2949

Integris Baptist Medical Center, Oklahoma City OK p. 1972

Integris Southwest Medical Center, Oklahoma City OK p. 1972

Inter-American Development Bank Library, Washington DC p. 405

Inter-American University-Fajardo Campus, Fajardo PR p. 2672

Inter-American University of Puerto Rico, Aguadilla PR p. 2671

Inter-American University of Puerto Rico, Arecibo PR p. 2671

Inter-American University of Puerto Rico, Barranquitas PR p. 2671

Inter-American University of Puerto Rico, Bayamon PR p. 2671

Inter-American University of Puerto Rico, Guayama PR p. 2673

Inter-American University of Puerto Rico, Mercedita PR p. 2674

Inter-American University of Puerto Rico, San German PR p. 2675

Inter-American University of Puerto Rico, Hato Rey PR p. 2673

Inter-American Organization, Quebec QC p. 2905

Interchurch Center, New York NY p. 1682

Intercultural Communication Institute & Summer Institute, Portland OR p. 2011

Intercultural Development Research Association Library, San Antonio TX p. 2380

Interfaith Resource Center, Wilmington DE p. 388

Intergovernmental Committee on Urban & Regional Research, Toronto ON p. 2855

Interlachen Public Library, *see* Putnam County Library System, Interlachen FL p. 478

Interlaken Public Library, Interlaken NY p. 1640

Interlakes Oncology Medical Library, Rochester NY p. 1729

Interlibrary Delivery Service of Pennsylvania (N), Doylestown PA p. 2954

Interlibrary Users Association (N), Washington DC p. 2940

Interlochen Center for the Arts, Interlochen MI p. 1193

Interlochen Public Library, Interlochen MI p. 1193

Intermountain Health Care, Salt Lake City UT p. 2412

Internal Revenue Service, Washington DC p. 405

International Academy of Design & Technology, Tampa FL p. 496

International Academy of Design & Technology, Chicago IL p. 615

International Association of Educators for World Peace, Huntsville AL p. 21

International Bible College Library, Moose Jaw SK p. 2918

International Brotherhood of Teamsters, Washington DC p. 405

International Business College Library, Fort Wayne IN p. 742

International Business College Library, Indianapolis IN p. 754

International Cadmium Association Library, Great Falls VA p. 2467

International Center for Research on Women Library, Washington DC p. 405

International Center of Photography Library, New York NY p. 1683

International City-County Management Association Library, Washington DC p. 405

International Civil Aviation Organization, Montreal QC p. 2897

International College Library, Naples FL p. 471

International Copper Association Ltd, New York NY p. 1683

International Council of Shopping Centers, New York NY p. 1683

International Crane Foundation, Baraboo WI p. 2580

International Data Corp Library, San Mateo CA p. 255

International Development Research Centre Library, Ottawa ON p. 2831

International Falls Public Library, International Falls MN p. 1254

Federation of Flyfishers, Livingston MT p. 1385

International Flavors & Fragrances, Inc, Union Beach NJ p. 1537

International Food Policy Research Institute, Washington DC p. 405

International Foundation of Employee, Brookfield WI p. 2583

International Franchise Association, Washington DC p. 405

International Graduate University Library, Washington DC p. 405

International Institute for Sport History Library, State College PA p. 2143

International Institute for Sustainable Development, Winnipeg MB p. 2756

International Institute of Integral Human Sciences Library, Montreal QC p. 2897

International Joint Commission, Windsor ON p. 2871

International Longshore & Warehouse Union, San Francisco CA p. 243

International Mission Board, Southern Baptist Convention, Richmond VA p. 2488

International Museum of Surgical Science Library, Chicago IL p. 616

International North American Library, Markham ON p. 2820

International Parking Institute, Fredericksburg VA p. 2466

International Personnel Management Association, Alexandria VA p. 2446

International Reading Association Library, Newark DE p. 385

International Society Daughters of Utah Pioneers, Salt Lake City UT p. 2412

International Society for Vehicle Preservation Library, Tucson AZ p. 86

International Society of Parametric Analysts, Huntsville AL p. 22

International Specialty Products, Wayne NJ p. 1539

International Stamp Collectors Society Library, Van Nuys CA p. 279

International Tennis Hall of Fame & Museum Library (IRC), Newport RI p. 2169

International Trademark Association Library, New York NY p. 1683

International Tsunami Information Center Library, *see* UNESCO-Intergovernmental Oceanographic Commission, Honolulu HI p. 565

International Union of United Automobile, Aerospace & Agricultural Implement Workers, Detroit MI p. 1171

International Wild Waterfowl Association, Spring Hope NC p. 1825

Intertek Testing Services, Coquitlam BC p. 2727

Inuvik Centennial Library, Inuvik NT p. 2775

Inver Hills Community College Library, Inver Grove Heights MN p. 1254

Invermere Public Library, Invermere BC p. 2729

Inverness Public, *see* Sunflower County Library System, Inverness MS p. 1302

Investigative Reporters & Editors Inc, Columbia MO p. 1324

Jackson County Library Services, Medford OR p. 2005

Jackson County Memorial Library, Edna TX p. 2315

Jackson County Public Library, Walden CO p. 325

Jackson County Public Library, Seymour IN p. 777

Jackson County Public Library, McKee KY p. 928

Jackson County Public Library, Sylva NC p. 1826

Jackson County Public Library, see Holland Charles Ralph Memorial Library, Gainesboro TN p. 2235

Jackson County Public Library System, Marianna FL p. 462

Jackson District Library, Jackson MI p. 1195

Jackson-George Regional Library System, Pascagoula MS p. 1310

Jackson Heights Community Library, see Queens Borough Public Library, Jackson Heights NY p. 1644

Jackson/Hinds Library System, Jackson MS p. 1303

Jackson Hospital & Clinic, Inc, Montgomery AL p. 29

Jackson John A & Katherine G Municipal Library, see Bridgeport Public Library, Bridgeport TX p. 2291

Jackson Kelly, Charleston WV p. 2556

Jackson Laboratory, Bar Harbor ME p. 976

Jackson Larry A Library, see Lander University, Greenwood SC p. 2197

Jackson Larry R, see Lakeland Public Library, Lakeland FL p. 459

Jackson Lewis A Library, see Indiana Wesleyan University, Marion IN p. 762

Jackson Lewis LLP, New York NY p. 1683

Jackson-Madison County General Hospital, Jackson TN p. 2238

Jackson-Madison County Library, Jackson TN p. 2238

Jackson Margaret Memorial Library, see Unitarian Universalist Congregation, Binghamton NY p. 1582

Jackson Memorial Library, Tenants Harbor ME p. 1003

Jackson Parish Library, Jonesboro LA p. 952

Jackson Park Hospital Library, Chicago IL p. 616

Jackson Paul K Memorial Library, see Shepherds Theological Seminary Library, Cary NC p. 1780

Jackson Public Library, Jackson MO p. 1334

Jackson Public Library, Jackson NH p. 1452

Jackson State Community College Library, Jackson TN p. 2238

Jackson State University, Jackson MS p. 1303

Jackson Stonewall House, Lexington VA p. 2474

Jackson Walker, LLP Library, Austin TX p. 2280

Jackson Walker LLP, Dallas TX p. 2308

Jackson Walter Clinton & Harold Schiffman, see University of North Carolina at Greensboro, Greensboro NC p. 1797

Jacksonville Correctional Center Library, see Illinois Department of Corrections, Jacksonville IL p. 658

Jacksonville Developmental Center Library, Jacksonville IL p. 659

Jacksonville Public Library, Jacksonville AL p. 22

Jacksonville Public Library, Jacksonville FL p. 453

Jacksonville Public Library, Jacksonville IL p. 659

Jacksonville Public Library, Jacksonville TX p. 2347

Jacksonville State University, Jacksonville AL p. 2961

Jacksonville State University Library, Jacksonville AL p. 22

Jacksonville University, Jacksonville FL p. 454

Jacobs Canada Inc, Calgary AB p. 2692

Jacobs Engineering Library, Houston TX p. 2340

Jacobs Julius Health Sciences Library, see Saint Thomas Hospital, Nashville TN p. 2258

Jacobs Mary Memorial, see Somerset County Library System, Rocky Hill NJ p. 1475

Jacobs Memorial Library, see Illinois Valley Community College, Oglesby IL p. 684

Jacobson Jack Memorial Library, see Temple on the Heights, Pepper Pike OH p. 1929

Jacoby Matthew Memorial Library, see Divine Word College, Epworth IA p. 814

Petro Jacyk Central & East European Resource Centre, see University of Toronto Libraries, Toronto ON p. 2866

Jaffe Raitt Heuer & Weiss, Southfield MI p. 1228

Jaffee Medical Library, see Baptist Hospital of Miami, Miami FL p. 464

Jaffrey Public Library, Jaffrey NH p. 1452

Jamaica Hospital Medical Center, Jamaica NY p. 1643

Jamaica Memorial Library, Jamaica VT p. 2426

Jamaica Public Library, Jamaica IA p. 824

Jamail Center for Legal Research, see University of Texas Libraries, Austin TX p. 2284

Jamerson J Robert Memorial Library, Appomattox VA p. 2448

James Gerald B Library, see Rockingham Community College, Wentworth NC p. 1829

James Library Center for the Arts, see First Parish Church of Norwell, Norwell MA p. 1115

James Madison University Libraries & Educational Technologies, Harrisonburg VA p. 2470

James Memorial Library, Saint James MO p. 1352

James Price Memorial Library, Tipton MO p. 1368

James Sprunt Community College Library, Kenansville NC p. 1804

James Terry Resource Library, see Upper Grand District School Board, Guelph ON p. 2807

James Zoe Memorial Library, see American Truck Historical Society, Kansas City MO p. 1336

Jamesburg Public Library, Jamesburg NJ p. 1492

Jameson Health System Library, New Castle PA p. 2096

Jameson Memorial Hospital, see Jameson Health System Library, New Castle PA p. 2096

Jameson William J Law Library, see University of Montana, Missoula MT p. 1386

Jamestown City Library, Jamestown KS p. 874

Jamestown College, Jamestown ND p. 1844

Jamestown Community College, Jamestown NY p. 1647

Jamestown Community Library, see Greene County Public Library, Jamestown OH p. 1951

Jamestown Philomenian Library, Jamestown RI p. 2167

Jamestown Public Library, Jamestown NC p. 1803

Jamieson Memorial Library, see Washington County Historical Society, Hagerstown MD p. 1031

Jamison John B MD Memorial Library, see Flagstaff Medical Center, Flagstaff AZ p. 62

Janesville Public, see Waseca-Le Sueur Regional Library, Janesville MN p. 1287

Janesville Public Library, Janesville IA p. 824

Jannasch Nils Library, see Maritime Museum of the Atlantic, Halifax NS p. 2781

Jannes Library, see Kansas City Art Institute Library, Kansas City MO p. 1338

Japan-American Society of Washington DC Library, Washington DC p. 405

Japan Foundation, Toronto ON p. 2855

Japan Society, New York NY p. 1683

Japanese American National Library, San Francisco CA p. 243

Jaqua John E Law Library, see University of Oregon Libraries, Eugene OR p. 1997

Jaques Anna Hospital, Newburyport MA p. 1109

Jaquett Josephine Memorial Library, see Salem County Historical Society, Salem NJ p. 1528

Jaquith Public Library, Marshfield VT p. 2428

Jardin Botanique de Montreal Bibliotheque, Montreal QC p. 2897

Jarrett Mamye Library, see East Texas Baptist University, Marshall TX p. 2359

Jarvie Public Library, Jarvie AB p. 2707

Jason William C Library, see Delaware State University, Dover DE p. 382

Jasonville Public Library, Jasonville IN p. 756

Jasper County Library, see Uncle Remus Regional Library System, Monticello GA p. 542

Jasper County Public Library, Rensselaer IN p. 774

Jasper-Dubois County Contractual Public Library, Jasper IN p. 756

Jasper Free Library, Jasper NY p. 1647

Jasper Municipal Library, Jasper AB p. 2707

Jasper Public Library, Jasper AL p. 23

Jasper Public Library, Jasper TN p. 2239

Jasper Public Library, Jasper TX p. 2348

Jasper Public Library, see Suwannee River Regional Library, Jasper FL p. 461

Jay County Public Library, Portland IN p. 773

Jay John Homestead State Historic Site Library, see New York State Office of Parks, Recreation & Historic Preservation, Katonah NY p. 1648

Jay-Niles Memorial Library, North Jay ME p. 994

Jay-Rollins Library, see McMurry University, Abilene TX p. 2272

JBI International, New York NY p. 1683

Jean-Leon Allie Library, see Saint Paul University Library, Ottawa ON p. 2833

Jeanes William Memorial Library, Lafayette Hill PA p. 2075

Jeannette Public Library Association, Jeannette PA p. 2072

Jeffers Annie Thompson Library, see Jackson/Hinds Library System, Bolton MS p. 1303

Jefferson Carnegie Library, Jefferson TX p. 2348

Jefferson City Public Library, Jefferson City TN p. 2239

Jefferson College Library, Hillsboro MO p. 1331

Jefferson College of Health Sciences, Roanoke VA p. 2494

Jefferson Community & Technical College, Louisville KY p. 924

Jefferson Community College Library, Steubenville OH p. 1936

Jefferson County District Library, Menan ID p. 578

Jefferson County Historical Society Library, Watertown NY p. 1763

Jefferson County Law Library, Birmingham AL p. 8

Jefferson County Law Library Association, Steubenville OH p. 1936

Jefferson County Library, High Ridge MO p. 1330

Jefferson County Library, see Copiah-Jefferson Regional Library System, Fayette MS p. 1301

Jefferson County Library District, Madras OR p. 2004

Jefferson County Library System, Louisville GA p. 539

Jefferson County Library System, Boulder MT p. 1375

Jefferson County Public Law Library, Louisville KY p. 924

Jefferson County Public Library, Lakewood CO p. 315

Jefferson County Public Library, Monticello FL p. 470

Jefferson County Rural Library District, Port Hadlock WA p. 2524

Jefferson Davis Community College, Brewton AL p. 11

Jefferson Health System, Paoli Memorial Hospital, Paoli PA p. 2101

Jefferson Hills Library, Jefferson Hills PA p. 2072

Jefferson Library, see Jefferson Thomas Foundation Inc, Charlottesville VA p. 2454

Jefferson-Madison Regional Library, Charlottesville VA p. 2453

Jefferson National Expansion Memorial Library, Saint Louis MO p. 1355

Jefferson Parish Library, Metairie LA p. 956

Jefferson Public, see Piedmont Regional Library, Jefferson GA p. 557

Jefferson Public Library, Jefferson IA p. 824

Jefferson Public Library, Jefferson ME p. 988

Jefferson Public Library, Jefferson NH p. 1452

Jefferson Public Library, Jefferson OR p. 2001

Jefferson Public Library, Jefferson WI p. 2600

Jefferson Regional Medical Center, Pittsburgh PA p. 2125

Jefferson State Community College, Birmingham AL p. 8

Jefferson Thomas, see Fairfax County Public Library, Falls Church VA p. 2461

Jefferson Thomas Foundation Inc, Charlottesville VA p. 2454

Jefferson Thomas Library, see National American University, Rapid City SD p. 2217

Jefferson Thomas National Accelerator Facility Library, Newport News VA p. 2480

Jefferson Township Public Library, Oak Ridge NJ p. 1515

Johnson James Weldon, *see* Saint Petersburg Public Library, Saint Petersburg FL p. 488

Johnson Jay Public Library, Quinter KS p. 891

Johnson Jerry Crail Earth Sciences & Map Library, *see* University of Colorado Boulder, Boulder CO p. 292

Johnson Lawrence V Library, *see* Southern Polytechnic State University, Marietta GA p. 543

Johnson Library, *see* Olympic College, Shelton WA p. 2510

Johnson Lionel Washington Memorial Library, *see* New Hampshire Youth Services Center, Manchester NH p. 1456

Johnson Louis A VA Library Service, *see* Department of Veterans Affairs, Clarksburg WV p. 2557

Johnson Lyndon B National Historical Park, *see* National Park Service, Johnson City TX p. 2348

Johnson Lyndon Baines Library & Museum, Austin TX p. 2281

Johnson Martin & Osa Safari Museum, Chanute KS p. 860

Johnson Mary Lou Hardin County District Library, Kenton OH p. 1907

Johnson Memorial, *see* Dauphin County Library System, Millersburg PA p. 2064

Johnson Memorial, *see* Defiance Public Library, Hicksville OH p. 1895

Johnson Memorial Hospital, Stafford Springs CT p. 369

Johnson Mildred Library, *see* North Dakota State College of Science, Wahpeton ND p. 1849

Johnson Milo P Library, *see* Mount San Jacinto College, San Jacinto CA p. 249

Johnson Norman B Memorial Library, *see* First Reformed Church of Schenectady, Schenectady NY p. 1740

Johnson Oscar G Veterans Affairs Medical Center, Iron Mountain MI p. 1194

Johnson Oscar Memorial Library, Silverhill AL p. 36

Johnson Pauline Library, Lundar MB p. 2749

Johnson Public Library, Johnson VT p. 2426

Johnson Public Library, Darlington WI p. 2587

Johnson R H Library, Sun City West AZ p. 82

Johnson Ralph Memorial Library, *see* Saint Paul's United Methodist Church, Las Cruces NM p. 1558

Johnson Robert Wood Foundation, Princeton NJ p. 1522

Johnson Robert Wood Library, *see* University of Medicine & Dentistry of New Jersey, New Brunswick NJ p. 1509

Johnson Robert Wood University Hospital, Rahway NJ p. 1524

Johnson Seymour Air Force Base Library, *see* United States Air Force, Seymour Johnson AFB NC p. 1823

Johnson Space Center, *see* NASA, Houston TX p. 2341

Johnson State College Library, Johnson VT p. 2426

Johnson State Prison, *see* Georgia Department of Corrections, Wrightsville GA p. 558

Johnson W L D Neighborhood Library, *see* Houston Public Library, Houston TX p. 2339

Johnson Walter Memorial Library, *see* Nordic Heritage Museum, Seattle WA p. 2529

Johnsonburg Public Library, Johnsonburg PA p. 2073

Johnsonville Public Library, *see* Florence County Library System, Johnsonville SC p. 2193

Johnston C B "Bud" Library, *see* Western University - Libraries, London ON p. 2819

Johnston City Public Library, Johnston City IL p. 659

Johnston Community College Library, Smithfield NC p. 1824

Johnston Edith G, *see* South Georgia Regional Library System, Lake Park GA p. 555

Johnston Faith Memorial, *see* Chippewa River District Library, Rosebush MI p. 1211

Johnston Garvin H Library, *see* Pearl River Community College, Poplarville MS p. 1312

Johnston Hardwick Memorial Library, *see* Hiwassee College, Madisonville TN p. 2246

Johnston Mary Memorial Library, *see* Iosco-Arenac District Library, Standish MI p. 1176

Johnston Memorial Library, *see* Virginia State University, Petersburg VA p. 2484

Johnston Public Library, Johnston IA p. 824

Johnston Public Library, Baxter Springs KS p. 857

Johnston Richard M Health Sciences Library, *see* Western Pennsylvania Hospital, Pittsburgh PA p. 2129

Johnstown Public Library, Johnstown NY p. 1648

Joice Public Library, Joice IA p. 825

Joint Archives of Holland, *see* Hope College, Holland MI p. 1190

Lewis-McChord Libraries, *see* United States Army, Joint Base Lewis McChord WA p. 2518

Joint Commission, Oakbrook Terrace IL p. 684

Joint Forces Staff College Library, Norfolk VA p. 2481

Joint Free Public Library of the Chathams, Chatham NJ p. 1478

Joint World Bank-International Monetary Fund Library, Washington DC p. 405

Joliet Junior College, Joliet IL p. 659

Joliet Library, *see* Illinois Youth Center, Joliet IL p. 659

Joliet Public Library, Joliet IL p. 660

Joliet Public Library, Joliet MT p. 1383

Jolys Regional Library, Saint Pierre Jolys MB p. 2751

Jonas Charles R Library, *see* Lincoln County Public Library, Lincolnton NC p. 1807

Jonas Harvey A, *see* Gaston College, Lincolnton NC p. 1786

Jones B F Memorial Library, Aliquippa PA p. 2026

Jones Cecil Harding Library, *see* Grace Presbyterian Church, Jenkintown PA p. 2072

Jones Charles P Memorial Library, Covington VA p. 2458

Jones Charles T Library, *see* Central Pennsylvania College Library, Summerdale PA p. 2144

Jones College, Jacksonville FL p. 454

Jones County Junior College, Ellisville MS p. 1298

Jones County Public, *see* Middle Georgia Regional Library System, Gray GA p. 541

Jones Creek Regional, *see* East Baton Rouge Parish Library, Baton Rouge LA p. 943

Jones D A, *see* New Tecumseth Public Library, Beeton ON p. 2792

Jones Day, Los Angeles CA p. 171

Jones Day, Washington DC p. 406

Jones Day, Atlanta GA p. 516

Jones Day, Chicago IL p. 616

Jones Day, Cleveland OH p. 1880

Jones Day, Columbus OH p. 1886

Jones Day, Pittsburgh PA p. 2126

Jones Day, Dallas TX p. 2308

Jones Day, Houston TX p. 2340

Jones Elizabeth Library, Grenada MS p. 1299

Jones Extension Library, *see* Metropolitan Library System in Oklahoma County, Jones OK p. 1972

Jones G Eric Library, *see* Atlantic Union College, South Lancaster MA p. 1125

Jones George M Library Association, Lynchburg VA p. 2475

Jones Glenn A Memorial Library, Johnstown CO p. 314

Jones James Addison Library, *see* Brevard College, Brevard NC p. 1777

Jones James Addison Library, *see* Greensboro College, Greensboro NC p. 1796

Jones Jesse H Library, *see* Baylor University Libraries, Waco TX p. 2396

Jones Library, *see* National Theatre Conservatory, Denver CO p. 302

Jones Library, Inc, Amherst MA p. 1048

Jones Lois Wickham, *see* Pamunkey Regional Library, Montpelier VA p. 2469

Jones Margaret Public, *see* De Soto Trail Regional Library, Sylvester GA p. 522

Jones Memorial Library, Orleans VT p. 2431

Jones Memorial Library, *see* First United Methodist Church, Oak Ridge TN p. 2262

Jones Memorial Library, *see* Jones George M Library Association, Lynchburg VA p. 2475

Jones Montfort & Allie B Memorial Library, *see* Bristow Public Library, Bristow OK p. 1959

Jones Music Library, *see* Baldwin Wallace University, Berea OH p. 1859

Jones Public Library, Dayton TX p. 2311

Jones R T Memorial Library, *see* Sequoyah Regional Library System, Canton GA p. 523

Jones Robert B Memorial Library, Lynnville TN p. 2246

Jones Robert R Public Library, Coal Valley IL p. 630

Jones Seby Library, *see* Toccoa Falls College, Toccoa Falls GA p. 554

Jones T J Library, *see* North Central University Library, Minneapolis MN p. 1261

Jones W C "Billy" Jr Memorial, *see* Halifax County Library, Littleton NC p. 1799

Jones W Yerby Memorial Library, *see* Erie County Medical Center, Buffalo NY p. 1598

Jonesboro Public Library, Jonesboro IL p. 660

Jonesboro Public Library, Jonesboro IN p. 756

Jonestown Community Library, Jonestown TX p. 2348

Jonesville District Library, Jonesville MI p. 1196

Jonesville Public Library, Jonesville NC p. 1804

Joos Dennis Memorial Library, West Stewartstown NH p. 1467

Joplin Public Library, Joplin MO p. 1335

Jordaan Memorial Library, Larned KS p. 877

Jordan Hospital, Plymouth MA p. 1118

Jordan Public Library, *see* Scott County Library System, Jordan MN p. 1284

Raymond Jordan Boyd Public Library, Boyd TX p. 2290

Jordan Valley District Library, East Jordan MI p. 1174

Jordan W D Special Collections - Music, *see* Queen's University, Kingston ON p. 2814

Jordanville Public Library, Jordanville NY p. 1648

Jordon Richard & Lila J Library, *see* Eastern Idaho Technical College, Idaho Falls ID p. 576

Joseph City Library, Joseph OR p. 2001

Lee Joseph Memorial Library, *see* National Recreation & Park Association, Ashburn VA p. 2450

Josephine Community Libraries, Inc, Grants Pass OR p. 1999

Josephine County Historical Society, Grants Pass OR p. 1999

Josephine County Law Library, Grants Pass OR p. 1999

Josephine-Louise Public Library, Walden NY p. 1762

Josephs Martin Library, *see* Temple Sinai, Dresher PA p. 2050

Josey Health Sciences Library, Columbia SC p. 2187

Joshua Public Library, Joshua TX p. 2348

Joshua Tree National Park Research Library, *see* United States National Park Service, Twentynine Palms CA p. 277

Joslin Diabetes Center, Inc, Boston MA p. 1062

Joslin Memorial Library, Waitsfield VT p. 2438

Joslyn Art Museum, Omaha NE p. 1413

Josten Werner Performing Arts Library, *see* Smith College Libraries, Northampton MA p. 1114

Jourdanton Community Library, Jourdanton TX p. 2348

Journal Gazette Library, Fort Wayne IN p. 742

Joy Charles R Library, *see* First Unitarian Universalist Society of Albany, Albany NY p. 1569

Joyce Public Library, Orland IN p. 771

Joyner J Y Library, *see* East Carolina University, Greenville NC p. 1798

JSI Research & Training Institute Library, *see* Snow John, Inc, Boston MA p. 1067

Judaica Library, *see* Jewish Community Center On The Palisades, Tenafly NJ p. 1533

Judge Edward S Marquez, *see* El Paso Public Library, El Paso TX p. 2316

Judge George W Armstrong Library, *see* Natchez Adams Wilkinson Library Service, Natchez MS p. 1309

Judge Kathryn J DuFour Law Library, *see* Catholic University of America, Washington DC p. 395

Judson College, Marion AL p. 24

Judson University, Elgin IL p. 641

Juilliard School, New York NY p. 1684

Julesburg Public Library, Julesburg CO p. 314

Julien & Schlesinger, PC, New York NY p. 1684

Junction City Public Library, Junction City OR p. 2001

Juneau Public Libraries, Juneau AK p. 50

Juneau Public Library, Juneau WI p. 2600

Jung C G Institute of Los Angeles, Los Angeles CA p. 171

Jung C G Institute of San Francisco, San Francisco CA p. 243

Jung-Kellogg Library, *see* Missouri Baptist College Library, Saint Louis MO p. 1356

Junginger Karl Memorial Library, Waterloo WI p. 2644

Jungman J Frank Neighborhood Library, *see* Houston Public Library, Houston TX p. 2339

Juniata College, Huntingdon PA p. 2070

Juniata County Library Inc, Mifflintown PA p. 2089

Junior Board Cancer Resource Library, *see* Christiana Hospital Library, Newark DE p. 385

Juniper Library, *see* Phoenix Public Library, Phoenix AZ p. 76

Juravinski Cancer Centre Library, *see* Hamilton Health Sciences, Hamilton ON p. 2808

Justice Institute of British Columbia Library, New Westminster BC p. 2734

Justice Public Library District, Justice IL p. 660

Justice Steven H Grimes Law Library, *see* Polk County Law Library, Bartow FL p. 427

Justin Community Library, Justin TX p. 2348

Justus May Memorial Library, Monteagle TN p. 2253

Juvenile Correction Center Library, Saint Anthony ID p. 583

JWB Children's Services Council of Pinellas County, Pinellas Park FL p. 483

K T Analytics Inc Library, Oakland CA p. 197

K&L Gates Law Library, Charlotte NC p. 1783

K&L Gates Library, Pittsburgh PA p. 2126

K&L Gates Library, Dallas TX p. 2309

K&L Gates LLP, Washington DC p. 406

K&L Gates LLP, Chicago IL p. 616

K&L Gates LLP, Boston MA p. 1062

Kacmarcik Education Resource Center, *see* Columbia Saint Mary's Ozaukee Campus, Mequon WI p. 2615

Kadey Memorial Library, *see* Saint John's Episcopal Cathedral, Albuquerque NM p. 1550

KAHSLC (N), *see* Knoxville Area Health Sciences Library Consortium, Knoxville TN p. 2955

Kahuku Public & School Library, *see* Hawaii State Public Library System, Kahuku HI p. 562

Kahului Public Library, *see* Hawaii State Public Library System, Kahului HI p. 562

Kaibab Paiute Public Library, Fredonia AZ p. 64

Kailua-Kona Public Library, *see* Hawaii State Public Library System, Kailua-Kona HI p. 562

Kailua Public Library, *see* Hawaii State Public Library System, Kailua HI p. 562

Kaimuki Public Library, *see* Hawaii State Public Library System, Honolulu HI p. 562

Kaiser Herman & Kate Library, *see* Tulsa City-County Library, Tulsa OK p. 1983

Kaiser Permanente, Portland OR p. 2011

Kaiser Permanente Health Sciences Library, South San Francisco CA p. 270

Kaiser-Permanente Medical Center, Bellflower CA p. 125

Kaiser-Permanente Medical Center, Fontana CA p. 148

Kaiser-Permanente Medical Center, Los Angeles CA p. 171

Kaiser-Permanente Medical Center, Oakland CA p. 197

Kaiser-Permanente Medical Center, Redwood City CA p. 215

Kaiser-Permanente Medical Center, Riverside CA p. 217

Kaiser-Permanente Medical Center, Sacramento CA p. 224

Kaiser-Permanente Medical Center, San Diego CA p. 231

Kaiser-Permanente Medical Center, San Francisco CA p. 243

Kaiser-Permanente Medical Center, San Rafael CA p. 257

Kaiser Permanente Northwest Regional, Clackamas OR p. 1993

Kalama Public Library, Kalama WA p. 2518

Kalamazoo College, Kalamazoo MI p. 1197

Kalamazoo Institute of Arts, Kalamazoo MI p. 1197

Kalamazoo Public Library, Kalamazoo MI p. 1197

Kalamazoo Valley Community College Libraries, Kalamazoo MI p. 1197

Kales Carl Memorial Library, *see* Beth-El Temple Center, Belmont MA p. 1053

Kalihi-Palama Public Library, *see* Hawaii State Public Library System, Honolulu HI p. 562

Kalispell Regional Medical Center, Kalispell MT p. 1384

Kalkaska County Library, Kalkaska MI p. 1198

Kalmbach A C Memorial Library, *see* National Model Railroad Association, Chattanooga TN p. 2228

Kalmbach Publishing Co Library, Waukesha WI p. 2645

Kalona Public Library, Kalona IA p. 825

Kalsec, Inc, Kalamazoo MI p. 1197

Kaltreider-Benfer Library, Red Lion PA p. 2134

Kamiel Max L Library, *see* Masonic Medical Research Laboratory Library, Utica NY p. 1758

Kanab City Library, Kanab UT p. 2406

Kanabec County Historical Society, Mora MN p. 1267

Kanabec History Center, *see* Kanabec County Historical Society, Mora MN p. 1267

Kanawha County Public Library, Charleston WV p. 2556

Kanawha Public Library, Kanawha IA p. 825

Kandiyohi County Historical Society, Willmar MN p. 1288

Kaneohe Public Library, *see* Hawaii State Public Library System, Kaneohe HI p. 562

Kaneville Public Library, Kaneville IL p. 660

Kankakee Community College, Kankakee IL p. 660

Kankakee County Historical Society Museum Library, Kankakee IL p. 661

Kankakee Public Library, Kankakee IL p. 661

Kanopolis Public Library, Kanopolis KS p. 875

Kansas City Art Institute Library, Kansas City MO p. 1338

Kansas City Kansas Community College Library, Kansas City KS p. 875

Kansas City, Kansas Public Library, Kansas City KS p. 875

Kansas City Library Service Program (N), Kansas City MO p. 2947

Kansas City Public Library, Kansas City MO p. 1338

Kansas City University of Medicine & Biosciences D'Angelo Library, Kansas City MO p. 1338

Kansas Community Memorial Library, Kansas IL p. 661

Kansas Department of Corrections, Beloit KS p. 857

Kansas Department of Corrections, El Dorado KS p. 865

Kansas Department of Corrections, Ellsworth KS p. 865

Kansas Department of Corrections, Hutchinson KS p. 873

Kansas Department of Corrections, Lansing KS p. 877

Kansas Department of Corrections, Larned KS p. 877

Kansas Department of Corrections, Topeka KS p. 896

Kansas Department of Transportation Library, Topeka KS p. 896

Kansas Geological Survey Library, Lawrence KS p. 877

Kansas Heritage Center Library, Dodge City KS p. 863

Kansas Public Library, Kansas OK p. 1966

Kansas Regents Library Database Consortium (N), Emporia KS p. 2943

Kansas State Historical Society, Topeka KS p. 896

Kansas State Library, Emporia KS p. 866

Kansas State University at Salina, Salina KS p. 893

Kansas State University Libraries, Manhattan KS p. 881

Kansas Supreme Court, Topeka KS p. 896

Kansas University Medical Center, Kansas City KS p. 875

Kansas Wesleyan University, Salina KS p. 893

Kapaa Public Library, *see* Hawaii State Public Library System, Kapaa HI p. 562

Kapiolani Community College Library, Honolulu HI p. 564

Kapiolani Medical Center Library, Honolulu HI p. 564

Kaplan Career Institute Resource Room, *see* Thompson Institute, Harrisburg PA p. 2066

Kaplan Mordecai M Library, *see* Reconstructionist Rabbinical College Library, Wyncote PA p. 2158

Kaplan University, Cedar Falls IA p. 799

Kaplan University, Cedar Rapids IA p. 800

Kaplan University, Council Bluffs IA p. 805

Kaplan University, Davenport IA p. 806

Kaplan University, Des Moines IA p. 810

Kaplan University, Mason City IA p. 830

Kaplan University, South Portland ME p. 1001

Kaplan University Hagerstown Library, Hagerstown MD p. 1031

Kaplan, McLaughlin & Diaz Architects Library, San Francisco CA p. 243

Kapolei Public Library, *see* Hawaii State Public Library System, Kapolei HI p. 562

Kapp Frederic T Memorial Library, *see* Cincinnati Psychoanalytic Institute, Cincinnati OH p. 1869

Kappe Library, *see* Southern California Institute of Architecture, Los Angeles CA p. 177

Kapuskasing Public Library, Kapuskasing ON p. 2812

Kardon-Northeast - Sol Schoenbach Library, *see* Settlement Music School, Philadelphia PA p. 2117

Kare Morley R Library, *see* Monell Chemical Senses Center, Philadelphia PA p. 2112

Karesh Coleman Law Library, *see* University of South Carolina, Columbia SC p. 2190

Karjala Research Center, *see* Itasca County Historical Society, Grand Rapids MN p. 1253

Karl Mary Memorial, *see* Daytona Beach Community College Library, Daytona Beach FL p. 435

Karlen Memorial Library, Beemer NE p. 1393

Karrmann Elton S Library, *see* University of Wisconsin-Platteville, Platteville WI p. 2630

Karn Jane Medical Library, *see* Lewistown Hospital, Lewistown PA p. 2081

Karnes City Public Library, Karnes City TX p. 2348

Karnes County Library System, Falls City TX p. 2319

Karr Tuttle Campbell, Seattle WA p. 2528

Karre Fred Memorial Library, *see* Southeastern Community College Library, Keokuk IA p. 852

Kasilof Public Library, Kasilof AK p. 50

Kaskaskia College Library, Centralia IL p. 602

Kaslo & District Public Library, Kaslo BC p. 2730

Kass Judaic Library, *see* Jewish Community Center of Greater Washington, Rockville MD p. 1037

Kasson Public Library, Kasson MN p. 1255

Katahdin Public Library, Island Falls ME p. 988

Katonah Village Library, Katonah NY p. 1648

Katten Muchin Rosenman LLP, Washington DC p. 406

Katten Muchin Rosenman LLP, New York NY p. 1684

Katten, Muchin, Rosenman LLP Library, Chicago IL p. 616

Katz Bennett D Library, *see* University of Maine at Augusta Libraries, Augusta ME p. 975

Katz Joel A Law Library, *see* University of Tennessee, Knoxville TN p. 2243

Katzen Raphael Associates International Inc Library, Cincinnati OH p. 1870

Kauai Community College, Lihue HI p. 567

Kauai Community Correctional Center Library, Lihue HI p. 567

Kaubisch Memorial Public Library, Fostoria OH p. 1900

Kaufman County Library, Kaufman TX p. 2349

Kaufman Donald Bruce, *see* Los Angeles Public Library System, Los Angeles CA p. 173

Kaukauna Public Library, Kaukauna WI p. 2600

Kaw City Public Library, Kaw City OK p. 1966

Kaweah Delta Health Care District Library, Visalia CA p. 280

Kay Mary Inc, Addison TX p. 2272

Kaye Scholer LLP, Los Angeles CA p. 171

Kaye Scholer LLP, New York NY p. 1684

KC-LSP (N), *see* Kansas City Library Service Program, Kansas City MO p. 2947

Keaau Public & School Library, *see* Hawaii State Public Library System, Keaau HI p. 562

Kealakekua Public Library, *see* Hawaii State Public Library System, Kealakekua HI p. 562

Kean University, Union NJ p. 1537

Kearl Jim & Mary Library of Cardston, Cardston AB p. 2694

Kearney & Area Public Library, Kearney ON p. 2812

Kearney Public Library, Kearney NE p. 1403

Kearny County Library, Lakin KS p. 877

Kearny Library, *see* Pomeroy Arthur E Public Library, Kearny AZ p. 66

Kearny Public Library, Kearny NJ p. 1493

Keck Memorial Library, Wapello IA p. 849

Kedgwick Public, *see* Haut-Saint-Jean Regional Library, Kedgwick NB p. 2762

Keefe Science Library, *see* Amherst College, Amherst MA p. 1048

Keel Jimmie B Regional Library, *see* Tampa-Hillsborough County Public Library System, Tampa FL p. 497

Keeler Ruth Memorial Library, North Salem NY p. 1707

Keen Mountain Correctional Center, Oakwood VA p. 2483

Keen Sally Stretch Memorial Library, Vincentown NJ p. 1537

Keene Gayle Nelson Public Library, *see* Otonabee-South Monaghan Township Public Library, Keene ON p. 2812

Keene Memorial Library, Fremont NE p. 1399

Keene Public Library, Keene NH p. 1452

Keene Public Library, Keene NY p. 1648

Keene State College, Keene NH p. 1453

Keene Valley Library Association, Keene Valley NY p. 1648

Keeneland Association, Lexington KY p. 920

Keeneland Library, *see* Keeneland Association, Lexington KY p. 920

Keephills Public Library, Duffield AB p. 2697

Keeseville Free Library, Keeseville NY p. 1648

Keeter John Ed Public Library of Saginaw, *see* Saginaw Public Library, Saginaw TX p. 2378

Keethanow Public Library, Stanley Mission SK p. 2927

Keewatin Public Library, Keewatin MN p. 1255

Keffer Charles J Library, *see* University of Saint Thomas, Minneapolis MN p. 1282

Keg River Community Library, Keg River AB p. 2708

Kegler, Brown, Hill & Ritter, Columbus OH p. 1886

Kegoayah Kozga Public Library, Nome AK p. 52

Kehillat Israel Reconstructionist Congregation, Pacific Palisades CA p. 203

Keiser George Camp Library, *see* Middle East Institute, Washington DC p. 408

Keiser Public, *see* Mississippi County Library System, Keiser AR p. 95

Keiser University Library System, Fort Lauderdale FL p. 443

Kellar Library, *see* Baptist Missionary Association, Jacksonville TX p. 2347

Kellenberger Edward P Library, *see* Northwest Christian University, Eugene OR p. 1997

Keller Christoph Jr Library, *see* General Theological Seminary, New York NY p. 1679

Keller Helen Public Library, Tuscumbia AL p. 39

Keller Helen Services for the Blind, Hempstead NY p. 1635

Keller J J & Associates, Inc, Neenah WI p. 2624

Keller Library, *see* Colville Confederated Tribe Library, Keller WA p. 2521

Keller Public Library, Dexter MO p. 1327

Keller Public Library, Keller TX p. 2349

Keller Rohrback LLP Library, Seattle WA p. 2528

Keller Rosa, *see* New Orleans Public Library, New Orleans LA p. 962

Kelley, Drye & Warren, Washington DC p. 406

Kelley Drye & Warren, New York NY p. 1684

Kelley House Museum, Inc, Mendocino CA p. 184

Kelley Library, Salem NH p. 1464

Kelley Mildred M Library, *see* Art Institute of Dallas, Dallas TX p. 2304

Kellock Library, *see* Omohundro Institute of Early American History & Culture, Williamsburg VA p. 2503

Kellogg, Brown & Root Library, Houston TX p. 2340

Kellogg Community College, Battle Creek MI p. 1155

Kellogg Free Library, Cincinnatus NY p. 1606

Kellogg-Hubbard Library, Montpelier VT p. 2429

Kellogg-Kroc Information Center, *see* Hesburgh Libraries, Notre Dame IN p. 770

Kellogg Library, *see* Union County College Libraries, Elizabeth NJ p. 1480

Kellogg Memorial Research Library, *see* Cortland County Historical Society, Cortland NY p. 1611

Kellogg Public Library, Kellogg ID p. 577

Kellogg W K Health Sciences Library, *see* Dalhousie University, Halifax NS p. 2780

Kelly, Hart & Hallman, Fort Worth TX p. 2322

Kelly J Clarence Library, *see* Pennsylvania State University, Greater Allegheny, McKeesport PA p. 2085

Kelly James J Library, *see* Saint Gregory's University, Shawnee OK p. 1977

Kelly John M Library, *see* University of Toronto Libraries, Toronto ON p. 2866

Kelly Library, *see* Emory & Henry College, Emory VA p. 2460

Kelly Memorial Library, *see* Richard J Daley College, Chicago IL p. 623

Kellyville Public Library, Kellyville OK p. 1966

Kelman Charles D Library, Wills Eye Hospital, Philadelphia PA p. 2111

Kelso Public Library, Kelso WA p. 2518

Kelver Public Library, *see* Arapahoe Library District, Byers CO p. 306

Kemmerer Library Harding Township, New Vernon NJ p. 1510

Kemp Library, *see* East Stroudsburg University, East Stroudsburg PA p. 2051

Kemp Memorial, *see* Cobb County Public Library System, Marietta GA p. 543

Kemp-Sugg Memorial, *see* Leath Thomas Memorial Library, Ellerbe NC p. 1820

Kemper-Newton Regional Library System, Union MS p. 1316

Kenai Community Library, Kenai AK p. 50

Kenai Peninsula College Library, Soldotna AK p. 53

Kenan Research Center, *see* Atlanta History Center, Atlanta GA p. 513

Kenan Veterinary Medical Library, *see* North Carolina State University Libraries, Raleigh NC p. 1816

Kendalia Public Library, Kendalia TX p. 2349

Kendall Belle Sherman Neighborhood Library, *see* Houston Public Library, Houston TX p. 2339

Kendall College Library, Chicago IL p. 616

Kendall College of Art & Design Library, *see* Ferris State University, Grand Rapids MI p. 1184

Kendall Public Library, Kendall WI p. 2601

Kendallville Public Library, Kendallville IN p. 756

Kendrick Klaude Library, *see* Evangel University, Springfield MO p. 1366

Kendrick Memorial Library, Brownfield TX p. 2292

Kenedy Public Library, Kenedy TX p. 2349

Kenilworth Historical Society, Kenilworth IL p. 661

Kenilworth Public Library, Kenilworth NJ p. 1493

Kenly Public, *see* Public Library of Johnston County & Smithfield, Kenly NC p. 1824

Kennan Institute for Advanced Russian Studies, *see* Woodrow Wilson International Center for Scholars Library, Washington DC p. 423

Kennard Frances E Public Library, Meshoppen PA p. 2088

Kennebec Public Library, Kennebec SD p. 2213

Kennebec Valley Community College, Fairfield ME p. 985

Kennebunk Free Library, Kennebunk ME p. 988

Kennedale Public Library, Kennedale TX p. 2349

Kennedy Caroline Library, *see* Dearborn Heights City Libraries, Dearborn Heights MI p. 1168

Kennedy Free Library, Kennedy NY p. 1649

Kennedy Gerald D Reference Library, *see* San Joaquin County Historical Museum, Lodi CA p. 165

Kennedy Institute of Ethics, *see* National Reference Center for Bioethics Literature, Washington DC p. 411

Kennedy James Public Library, Dyersville IA p. 812

Kennedy John F, *see* Gary Public Library, Gary IN p. 745

Kennedy John F, *see* Muncie Public Library, Muncie IN p. 767

Kennedy John F, *see* Solano County Library, Vallejo CA p. 148

Kennedy John F Jr Library, *see* Dearborn Heights City Libraries, Dearborn Heights MI p. 1168

Kennedy John F Library, *see* Hutchinson Community College, Hutchinson KS p. 873

Kennedy John F Memorial Library, Wallington NJ p. 1539

Kennedy John F Memorial Library, *see* California State University, Los Angeles, Los Angeles CA p. 169

Kennedy John F Memorial Library, *see* Eastern Washington University, Cheney WA p. 2512

Kennedy John F Memorial Library, *see* Piscataway Township Free Public Library, Piscataway NJ p. 1520

Kennedy John F Presidential Library, *see* National Archives & Records Administration, Boston MA p. 1064

Kennedy John F School of Government, *see* Harvard Library, Cambridge MA p. 1075

Kennedy John F, *see* NASA, Kennedy Space Center FL p. 455

Kennedy-King College, City Colleges of Chicago Library, Chicago IL p. 616

Kennedy Library of Konawa, Konawa OK p. 1967

Kennedy/Martin Library, *see* Insurance Bureau of Canada Library, Toronto ON p. 2855

Kennedy Memorial Hospitals, Cherry Hill NJ p. 1478

Kennedy Memorial Hospitals, Turnersville NJ p. 1536

Kennedy Public Library, *see* Northwest Regional Library, Kennedy AL p. 40

Kennedy Robert E Library, *see* California Polytechnic State University, San Luis Obispo CA p. 253

Kennedy Robert F Memorial Library, *see* University of Guam, Mangilao GU p. 2667

Kennedy Sarita East Law Library, *see* Saint Mary's University, San Antonio TX p. 2381

Kennedy-Jenks Consultants, Inc Library, San Francisco CA p. 243

Kennedy-King College Library, *see* Kennedy-King College, City Colleges of Chicago Library, Chicago IL p. 616

Kennesaw Mountain National Battlefield Park Library, *see* National Park Service, Kennesaw GA p. 537

Kennesaw State University, Kennesaw GA p. 537

Kenora Public Library, Kenora ON p. 2812

Kenosha County Historical Society, Kenosha WI p. 2601

Kenosha Medical Center Library, *see* United Hospital System, Kenosha WI p. 2601

Kenosha Public Library, Kenosha WI p. 2601

Kenosha Public Museums Library, Kenosha WI p. 2601

Kenrick-Glennon Seminary, Saint Louis MO p. 1355

Kensett Public Library, Kensett IA p. 825

Kensington Community-School Library, Kensington KS p. 876

Kensington Library, *see* Contra Costa County Library, Kensington CA p. 209

Kensington Park Library, *see* Montgomery County Public Libraries, Kensington MD p. 1038

King Martin Luther Jr Library, *see* Atlanta-Fulton Public Library System, Atlanta GA p. 512

King Martin Luther Jr Library, *see* Aurora Public Library, Aurora CO p. 288

King Martin Luther Jr Memorial, *see* District of Columbia Public Library, Washington DC p. 398

King Martin Luther Jr Memorial, *see* Rapides Parish Library, Alexandria LA p. 940

King Martin Luther Jr Regional Library, *see* Sacramento Public Library, Sacramento CA p. 225

King Mary Ann Health Sciences Library, *see* Fairview-Southdale Hospital, Edina MN p. 1249

King Memorial Library, Machias NY p. 1656

King Public Library, King NC p. 1804

King Reta E Library, *see* Chadron State College, Chadron NE p. 1395

King Ross Memorial Public Library, Mount Pearl NL p. 2770

King Township Public Library, King City ON p. 2812

Kingfisher Memorial Library, Kingfisher OK p. 1966

Kingman Carnegie Public Library, Kingman KS p. 876

Kingman Public Library, Kingman IN p. 757

King's College, Wilkes-Barre PA p. 2155

Kings County Law Library, Hanford CA p. 156

Kings County Library, Hanford CA p. 156

Kings Landing Library, Prince William NB p. 2766

Kings Mountain National Military Park Library, Blacksburg SC p. 2182

King's University College, Edmonton AB p. 2701

King's University College, London ON p. 2817

Kingsborough Community College, Brooklyn NY p. 1592

Kingsbrook Jewish Medical Center, Brooklyn NY p. 1592

Kingsgate Regional Library, *see* King County Library System, Kirkland WA p. 2517

Kingsley Public Library, Kingsley IA p. 825

Kingsport Public Library & Archives, Kingsport TN p. 2240

Kingston Community Library, Kingston AR p. 105

Kingston Community Public Library, *see* Opperman Jacquelin E Memorial Library, Kingston MI p. 1199

Kingston Frontenac Public Library, Kingston ON p. 2813

Kingston Hospital Medical Library, Kingston NY p. 1649

Kingston Library, Kingston NY p. 1650

Kingston Public Library, Kingston MA p. 1097

Kingston Public Library, Kingston TN p. 2241

Kingsville Public Library, Kingsville OH p. 1907

Kingswood University, Sussex NB p. 2767

Kingwood Center Library, Mansfield OH p. 1912

Kingwood College Library, *see* Lone Star College System, Kingwood TX p. 2340

Kingwood Public Library, Kingwood WV p. 2563

Kinistino Public Library, *see* Wapiti Regional Library, Kinistino SK p. 2921

Kinkora Public, *see* Prince Edward Island Public Library Service, Kinkora PE p. 2876

Kinlaw Library, *see* Asbury University, Wilmore KY p. 938

Kinmundy Public Library, Kinmundy IL p. 661

Kinnelon Public Library, Kinnelon NJ p. 1493

Kinney County Public Library, Brackettville TX p. 2291

Kinney Memorial Library, Hanlontown IA p. 820

Kinney Memorial Library, Hartwick NY p. 1634

Kinney Public Library, Kinney MN p. 1255

Kino Institute Diocesan Library, Phoenix AZ p. 73

Kinsel Harry L Library, *see* Metcalf & Eddy Inc, Wakefield MA p. 1132

Kinsley Public Library, Kinsley KS p. 876

Kinsman Free Public Library, Kinsman OH p. 1907

Kinston-Lenoir County Public Library, *see* Neuse Regional Library, Kinston NC p. 1805

Kinuso Municipal Library, Kinuso AB p. 2708

Kinyaa'aanii Charlie Benally Library, *see* Dine College, Tsaile AZ p. 85

Kiowa County Library, Greensburg KS p. 869

Kiowa County Public Library District, Eads CO p. 305

Kiowa Public Library, Kiowa KS p. 876

Kiracofe-Lewis Memorial Library, *see* Kaplan University Hagerstown Library, Hagerstown MD p. 1031

Kirby Free Library of Salisbury Center, Salisbury Center NY p. 1737

Kirby Library, *see* Wyoming Seminary, Kingston PA p. 2074

Kirby Library of Government & Law, *see* Lafayette College, Easton PA p. 2052

Kirby Marian Sutherland Library, Mountain Top PA p. 2093

Kirbyville Public Library, Kirbyville TX p. 2351

Kirchner-French Memorial Library, Peterson IA p. 838

Kirk Library, *see* Centralia College, Centralia WA p. 2511

Kirk Wanda, *see* Kern County Library, Rosamond CA p. 124

Kirkendall Public Library, Ankeny IA p. 794

Kirdendoll C A Learning Resources Center, *see* Miles College, Fairfield AL p. 16

Kirkland & Ellis, New York NY p. 1684

Kirkland & Ellis Library, Washington DC p. 406

Kirkland & Ellis LLP Library, Chicago IL p. 616

Kirkland Public Library, Kirkland IL p. 661

Kirkland Town Library, Clinton NY p. 1608

Kirklin Public Library, Kirklin IN p. 757

Kirkpatrick, Lockhart, Preston, Gates, Ellis, Washington DC p. 406

Kirkpatrick James C Library, *see* University of Central Missouri, Warrensburg MO p. 1371

Kirkpatrick Pam, *see* New Tecumseth Public Library, Tottenham ON p. 2792

Kirkwood Community College Library, Cedar Rapids IA p. 800

Kirkwood Library, Wilmington DE p. 388

Kirkwood Public Library, Kirkwood MO p. 1342

Kirtland Community College Library, Roscommon MI p. 1223

Kirtland Public Library, Kirtland OH p. 1908

Kirwin City Library, Kirwin KS p. 876

Kishwaukee College Library, Malta IL p. 669

Kismet Public Library, Kismet KS p. 876

Kissam Leo T Memorial Library, *see* Fordham University School of Law, New York NY p. 1678

Kissler Library & Research Center, *see* Saint Alphonsus Health System, Boise ID p. 571

Kistler Gertrude Memorial Library, *see* Rosemont College Library, Rosemont PA p. 2135

Kitchell Memorial Library, Morrisonville IL p. 676

Kitchener Public Library, Kitchener ON p. 2815

Kitchigami Regional Library, Pine River MN p. 1270

Kitimat Museum & Archives, Kitimat BC p. 2731

Kitimat Public Library Association, Kitimat BC p. 2731

Kitsap County Historical Society, Bremerton WA p. 2510

Kitsap County Law Library, Port Orchard WA p. 2524

Kitsap Regional Library, Bremerton WA p. 2510

Kitscoty Public Library, Kitscoty AB p. 2708

Kittanning Public Library, Kittanning PA p. 2074

Kittay Rosalind Keshin Public Library, West Rupert VT p. 2439

Kittochtinny Historical Society Library, Chambersburg PA p. 2043

Klamath Community College, Klamath Falls OR p. 2001

Klamath County Library Services District, Klamath Falls OR p. 2001

Klamath County Museum & Baldwin Hotel Museum, Klamath Falls OR p. 2002

Klau Library, *see* Hebrew Union College-Jewish Institute of Religion, Cincinnati OH p. 1870

Kleberg Robert J Public Library, Kingsville TX p. 2350

Kleene Stephen Cole Mathematics Library, *see* University of Wisconsin-Madison, Madison WI p. 2609

Klehr, Harrison, Harvey, Branzburg & Ellers, Philadelphia PA p. 2111

Klein-Amdur Library, *see* Temple Beth Tzedek, Amherst NY p. 1573

Klein Ann Forensic Center, West Trenton NJ p. 1542

Klemme Public Library, Klemme IA p. 825

Klinck Memorial Library, *see* Concordia University, River Forest IL p. 694

Kline Nathan S Institute for Psychiatric Research, Orangeburg NY p. 1711

Kling Memorial Library, Grundy Center IA p. 819

Klohn Crippen Berger Ltd, Calgary AB p. 2692

Klohn Crippen Berger Ltd, Vancouver BC p. 2741

Klohn Hans W Commons, *see* University of New Brunswick, Saint John Campus, Saint John NB p. 2767

Klondike Gold Rush International Historical Park Library, *see* United States National Park Service, Skagway AK p. 53

Klondike History Library, *see* Dawson City Museum & Historical Society, Dawson City YT p. 2933

Klosterman H J Chemistry Library, *see* North Dakota State University Libraries, Fargo ND p. 1841

Klutznick Law Library, *see* Creighton University, Omaha NE p. 1412

Knapp, Petersen & Clarke, Glendale CA p. 155

Knesseth Israel Synagogue Library, Gloversville NY p. 1629

Knight-Capron Library, *see* Lynchburg College, Lynchburg VA p. 2476

Knight Laura Children's Library, *see* First United Methodist Church, Gainesville FL p. 449

Knight Library, *see* University of Oregon Libraries, Eugene OR p. 1997

Knight Memorial Library, *see* Providence Community Library, Providence RI p. 2173

Knights of Columbus Supreme Council Archives, New Haven CT p. 355

Knightstown Public Library, Knightstown IN p. 757

Knipe David Memorial Library, *see* Bawlf Public Library, Bawlf AB p. 2684

Knoedler Art Library, New York NY p. 1684

Knoedler Memorial Library, Augusta KY p. 906

Knolls Atomic Power Laboratory Inc, Library, Schenectady NY p. 1740

Knott County Public Library, Hindman KY p. 918

Knott Library, *see* Saint Mary's Seminary & University, Baltimore MD p. 1017

Knotts AF Public, *see* Levy County Public Library System, Yankeetown FL p. 430

Knowledge Systems Institute, Skokie IL p. 703

Knox College, Galesburg IL p. 648

Knox Community Hospital, Mount Vernon OH p. 1919

Knox County Governmental Law Library, Knoxville TN p. 2241

Knox County Historical Society Library, Edina MO p. 1327

Knox County Public, *see* Northeast Missouri Library Service, Edina MO p. 1336

Knox County Public Library, Vincennes IN p. 784

Knox County Public Library, Barbourville KY p. 906

Knox County Public Library System, Knoxville TN p. 2241

Knox Dudley Library, *see* Naval Postgraduate School, Monterey CA p. 190

Knox Memorial Library, *see* Austin County Library System, Wallis TX p. 2398

Knox Public Library, Knox PA p. 2075

Knoxville Area Health Sciences Library Consortium (N), Knoxville TN p. 2955

Knoxville College, Knoxville TN p. 2242

Knoxville-Knox County Metropolitan Planning Commission Library, Knoxville TN p. 2242

Knoxville Public Library, Knoxville IL p. 661

Knoxville Public Library, Knoxville IA p. 825

Knoxville Public Library, Knoxville PA p. 2075

Knoxville Tennessee Campus Library, *see* National College VA p. 2495

Knutson Memorial Library, Coon Valley WI p. 2586

Koch Industries Invista, Waynesboro VA p. 2501

Kodiak College, Kodiak AK p. 51

Kodiak Public Library, *see* Johnson A Holmes Memorial Library, Kodiak AK p. 51

Ladish Co, Cudahy WI p. 2587
Ladner Pioneer Library, *see* Fraser Valley Regional Library, Delta BC p. 2724
Ladoga-Clark Township Public Library, Ladoga IN p. 759
Ladson Genealogical Library, *see* Ohoopee Regional Library System, Vidalia GA p. 556
Ladwig Jack R Memorial Library, *see* Hometown Public Library, Hometown IL p. 657
Lady Davis Institute for Medical Research, *see* Sir Mortimer B Davis Jewish General Hospital, Montreal QC p. 2901
Lady Lake Public Library, Lady Lake FL p. 457
Ladysmith Public Library, *see* Rusk County Community Library, Ladysmith WI p. 2604
LA84 Foundation, Los Angeles CA p. 171
Lafarge Canada, Inc, Pointe-Claire QC p. 2903
Lafayette College, Easton PA p. 2052
Lafayette County Library, Lewisville AR p. 105
Lafayette County Public Library, Mayo FL p. 463
Lafayette County-Oxford Public Library, *see* First Regional Library, Oxford MS p. 1301
Lafayette Library, *see* Contra Costa County Library, Lafayette CA p. 209
Lafayette Natural History Museum & Planetarium, Lafayette LA p. 952
Lafayette-Orinda Presbyterian Church Library, Lafayette CA p. 163
Lafayette Pilot Public Library, *see* Bradshaw H Grady Chambers County Library, Lafayette AL p. 39
Lafayette Public Library, Lafayette CO p. 314
Lafayette Public Library, Lafayette LA p. 952
LaFayette Public Library, LaFayette NY p. 1650
Lafayette-Yalobusha Technical Center Library, *see* Northwest Mississippi Community College, Oxford MS p. 1310
Lafitte Jean National Historical Park & Preserve, New Orleans LA p. 960
Lafleur & Brown Library, Montreal QC p. 2897
Lafourche Parish Public Library, Thibodaux LA p. 970
Lago Vista Public Library, Lago Vista TX p. 2352
LaGrange County Public Library, LaGrange IN p. 759
Laguna Public Library, Laguna NM p. 1557
Laguna Vista Public Library, Laguna Vista TX p. 2352
Lahaina Public Library, *see* Hawaii State Public Library System, Lahaina HI p. 562
Lahey Clinic Medical Center Library, Burlington MA p. 1072
Lahontan Basin Medical Library, *see* Carson-Tahoe Regional Medical Center, Carson City NV p. 1425
Laidlaw Library at University College, Toronto ON p. 2855
Laingsburg Public Library, Laingsburg MI p. 1199
Laird Flora M Memorial Library, *see* Myrtle Point Library, Myrtle Point OR p. 2007
Laird Henry Library, Belpre KS p. 858
Lake Agassiz Regional Library, Moorhead MN p. 1265
Lake Alfred Public Library, Lake Alfred FL p. 457
Lake Andes Carnegie Public Library, Lake Andes SD p. 2214
Lake Area Technical Institute Library, Watertown SD p. 2221
Lake Benton Public Library, Lake Benton MN p. 1255
Lake Blackshear Regional Library System, Americus GA p. 508
Lake Bluff Public Library, Lake Bluff IL p. 663
Lake Charles Memorial Hospital, Lake Charles LA p. 954
Lake Cities Library, Lake Dallas TX p. 2352
Lake City Community College, Lake City FL p. 457
Lake City Public Library, Lake City IA p. 826
Lake City Public Library, Lake City MN p. 1255
Lake City Public Library, Lake City TN p. 2244
Lake City Public Library, *see* Florence County Library System, Lake City SC p. 2193
Lake City Public Library, *see* Hinsdale County Library District, Lake City CO p. 314

Lake Community Branch, *see* Stark County District Library, Uniontown OH p. 1864
Lake Correctional Institution Library, *see* Florida Department of Corrections, Clermont FL p. 432
Lake County Central Law Library, Gary IN p. 745
Lake County Discovery Museum, Wauconda IL p. 716
Lake County Historical Society, Painesville OH p. 1926
Lake County Historical Society Library, Tavares FL p. 499
Lake County Law Library, Lakeport CA p. 163
Lake County Law Library, *see* Block William D Memorial Law Library, Waukegan IL p. 716
Lake County Library, Lakeport CA p. 163
Lake County Library District, Lakeview OR p. 2003
Lake County Library System, Tavares FL p. 499
Lake County Planning Resource Center, Libertyville IL p. 665
Lake County Public Library, Leadville CO p. 316
Lake County Public Library, Merrillville IN p. 763
Lake Elsinore Library, *see* Riverside County Library System, Lake Elsinore CA p. 217
Lake Erie College, Painesville OH p. 1926
Lake Erie College of Osteopathic Medicine, Erie PA p. 2055
Lake Forest College, Lake Forest IL p. 663
Lake Forest Library, Lake Forest IL p. 663
Lake Geneva Public Library, Lake Geneva WI p. 2604
Lake Health, Concord Twp OH p. 1891
Lake Helen Public, *see* Volusia County Public Library, Lake Helen FL p. 436
Lake Hills Library, *see* King County Library System, Bellevue WA p. 2517
Lake Land College Library, Mattoon IL p. 671
Lake Lillian Public Library, Lake Lillian MN p. 1255
Lake Linden-Hubbell Public & School Library, Lake Linden MI p. 1199
Lake Los Angeles Library, *see* County of Los Angeles Public Library, Palmdale CA p. 142
Lake Mead National Recreation Area Library, Boulder City NV p. 1425
Lake Michigan College, Benton Harbor MI p. 1156
Lake Mills Public Library, Lake Mills IA p. 826
Lake Odessa Community Library, Lake Odessa MI p. 1199
Lake Oswego Public Library, Lake Oswego OR p. 2003
Lake Panasoffkee Library, Lake Panasoffkee FL p. 458
Lake Park Public Library, Lake Park FL p. 458
Lake Park Public Library, Lake Park IA p. 826
Lake Placid Memorial Library, Lake Placid FL p. 458
Lake Placid Public Library, Lake Placid NY p. 1650
Lake Public Library, Lake MS p. 1306
Lake Region Community College, Laconia NH p. 1453
Lake Region Public Library, Devils Lake ND p. 1839
Lake Region State College, Devils Lake ND p. 1839
Lake Shore Railway Historical Society, North East PA p. 2099
Lake Spokane Library, Nine Mile Falls WA p. 2522
Lake-Sumter Community College Library, Leesburg FL p. 461
Lake Superior State University, Sault Sainte Marie MI p. 1226
Lake Tahoe Community College, South Lake Tahoe CA p. 270
Lake Tamarisk Library, *see* Riverside County Library System, Desert Center CA p. 217
Lake Travis Community Library, Austin TX p. 2281
Lake View Public Library, Lake View IA p. 826
Lake Villa District Library, Lake Villa IL p. 663
Lake Village Memorial Township Library, *see* Newton County Public Library, Lake Village IN p. 760
Lake Wales Public Library, Lake Wales FL p. 458
Lake Washington Technical College, Kirkland WA p. 2519
Lake Whitney Public Library, Whitney TX p. 2400
Lake Worth Public Library, Lake Worth FL p. 459

Lake Wylie Public, *see* York County Library, Lake Wylie SC p. 2203
Lakehead University Library, Thunder Bay ON p. 2848
Lakehills Area Library, Lakehills TX p. 2352
Lakeland College, Plymouth WI p. 2630
Lakeland College, Lloydminster SK p. 2918
Lakeland College Library, Vermilion AB p. 2720
Lakeland Community College Library, Kirtland OH p. 1908
Lakeland Hospital - Saint Joseph, Saint Joseph MI p. 1225
Lakeland Hospital-Niles, Niles MI p. 1214
Lakeland Library Cooperative (N), Grand Rapids MI p. 2946
Lakeland Library Region, North Battleford SK p. 2919
Lakeland Public Library, Lakeland FL p. 459
Lakeland Regional Library, Killarney MB p. 2749
Lakeland Regional Medical Center, Lakeland FL p. 459
Lakeland Specialty Hospital, Berrien Center MI p. 1157
Lakeport Library, *see* Lake County Library, Lakeport CA p. 163
Goss Ossian Wilbur Reading Room, *see* Laconia Public Library, Laconia NH p. 1453
Lakeridge Health, Oshawa ON p. 2827
Lakes Arthur Library, *see* Colorado School of Mines, Golden CO p. 309
Lakes Country Public Library, Lakewood WI p. 2604
Lakes District Library, *see* College of New Caledonia, Burns Lake BC p. 2726
Lakes Region General Hospital, Laconia NH p. 1453
Lakes Regional, *see* Lee County Library System, Fort Myers FL p. 445
Lakeshore General Hospital, Pointe-Claire QC p. 2903
Lakeshore Museum Center Archives, Muskegon MI p. 1212
Lakeshore Technical College Library, Cleveland WI p. 2585
Lakeshores Library System, Waterford WI p. 2644
Lakeside Library, *see* Riverside County Library System, Lake Elsinore CA p. 217
Lakeside Public Library, Lakeside OR p. 2003
Lakeview Area Public Library, Sandy Lake PA p. 2136
Lakeview Community Library, Random Lake WI p. 2632
Lakeview Public Library, Rockville Centre NY p. 1734
Lakeville Public Library, Lakeville MA p. 1097
Lakewood Historical Society Library, Lakewood OH p. 1908
Lakewood Memorial Library, Lakewood NY p. 1651
Lakewood Neighborhood Library, *see* Houston Public Library, Houston TX p. 2339
Lakewood Public Library, Lakewood OH p. 1908
Lakewood's Heritage Center Library, Lakewood CO p. 315
Lakota City Library, Lakota ND p. 1845
Lakota Public Library, Lakota IA p. 826
Lallouise Florey McGraw Public Library, Vincent AL p. 39
Lam David Management Research Library, *see* University of British Columbia Library, Vancouver BC p. 2743
Laman William F Public Library, North Little Rock AR p. 111
Lamar Community College Library, Lamar CO p. 315
Lamar County Library System, Purvis MS p. 1312
Lamar Memorial Library, *see* Maryville College, Maryville TN p. 2247
Lamar Public Library, Lamar CO p. 316
Lamar State College, Port Arthur TX p. 2371
Lamar State College-Orange Library, Orange TX p. 2367
Lamar University, Beaumont TX p. 2287
Lamb County Library, Littlefield TX p. 2356
Lamb Frank I, *see* Pueblo City-County Library District, Pueblo CO p. 321

Lauderhill Towne Centre Library, *see* Broward County Division of Libraries, Lauderhill FL p. 441

Laughlin Library, *see* Las Vegas-Clark County Library District, Laughlin NV p. 1429

Laughlin Memorial Library, Ambridge PA p. 2028

Lauinger Joseph Mark Library, *see* Georgetown University, Washington DC p. 402

Laumeier Sculpture Park Library & Archive, Saint Louis MO p. 1355

Launders Science Library, *see* Saint Lawrence University, Canton NY p. 1602

Laupahoehoe Public & School Library, *see* Hawaii State Public Library System, Laupahoehoe HI p. 562

Laupus William E Health Sciences Library, *see* East Carolina University, Greenville NC p. 1798

Laurel Community Learning Center, Laurel NE p. 1403

Laurel County Public Library District, London KY p. 922

Laurel Highlands Health Sciences Library Consortium (N), Dayton PA p. 2954

Laurel Highlands Library, *see* State Correctional Institution, Somerset PA p. 2141

Laurel-Jones County Library, *see* Laurel-Jones County Library System, Inc, Laurel MS p. 1306

Laurel-Jones County Library System, Inc, Laurel MS p. 1306

Laurel Public Library, Laurel DE p. 384

Laurel Public Library, Laurel MT p. 1384

Laurel Public Library, *see* Franklin County Public Library District, Laurel IN p. 730

Laurel University Library, High Point NC p. 1802

Laurelton Community Library, *see* Queens Borough Public Library, Laurelton NY p. 1645

Laurens County Library, Laurens SC p. 2199

Laurens Public Library, Laurens IA p. 827

Laurentian Forestry Centre Library, *see* Natural Resources Canada-Forestry, Quebec City QC p. 2907

Laurentian University, Sudbury ON p. 2846

Laurie Blanche & Irving Music Library, *see* Rutgers University Libraries, New Brunswick NJ p. 1509

Laurier Library, *see* Laurier Wilfrid University Library, Waterloo ON p. 2869

Laurier Wilfrid University Library, Waterloo ON p. 2869

Lauritsen Charles C Library, *see* Aerospace Corp, El Segundo CA p. 146

Lava Beds National Monument Research Library, *see* National Park Service, Tulelake CA p. 276

Lavaca Library, *see* Scott-Sebastian Regional Library, Lavaca AR p. 102

Laval-Goupil Public Library, *see* Chaleur Library Region, Shippagan NB p. 2761

LaValley Law Library, *see* University of Toledo, Toledo OH p. 1941

Lavery Library, *see* Saint John Fisher College, Rochester NY p. 1732

LaVista Correctional Facility Library, *see* Colorado Department of Corrections, Pueblo CO p. 320

Law & Consumer Affairs Library, *see* Housing Advocates, Inc, Cleveland OH p. 1880

Law Library, *see* Norton Rose Canada LLP, Calgary AB p. 2692

Law Library Association of Saint Louis, Saint Louis MO p. 1355

Law Library for San Bernardino County, San Bernardino CA p. 227

Law Library of Louisiana, New Orleans LA p. 960

Law Library of Montgomery County, Norristown PA p. 2098

Law Library of Orange County, *see* NYS Supreme Court, Goshen NY p. 1629

Law Library of Wolff & Samson, West Orange NJ p. 1541

Law Office of Daniel D Skuret Pc Library, Ansonia CT p. 329

Law Society of New Brunswick Library, Fredericton NB p. 2763

Law Society of Newfoundland Library, St. John's NL p. 2772

Law Society of Prince Edward Island Library, Charlottetown PE p. 2875

Law Society of Saskatchewan Libraries, Regina SK p. 2922

Law Society of Upper Canada, Toronto ON p. 2855

Lawler Francis J, *see* New Bedford Free Public Library, New Bedford MA p. 1108

Lawler Public Library, Lawler IA p. 827

Lawrance Marion Memorial Library, Gratis OH p. 1903

Lawrence & Memorial Hospital, New London CT p. 360

Lawrence Carl G Library, *see* Durfee Mike State Prison, Springfield SD p. 2220

Lawrence Correctional Center Library, *see* Illinois Department of Corrections, Sumner IL p. 709

Lawrence County Federated Library System, New Castle PA p. 2096

Lawrence County Law Library, New Castle PA p. 2096

Lawrence County Bar Library Association, Ironton OH p. 1906

Lawrence County Library, Walnut Ridge AR p. 116

Lawrence County Public Library, Moulton AL p. 31

Lawrence County Public Library, Louisa KY p. 923

Lawrence County Public Library, Lawrenceburg TN p. 2244

Lawrence County Public Library, *see* Lincoln-Lawrence-Franklin Regional Library, Monticello MS p. 1295

Lawrence General Hospital, Lawrence MA p. 1097

Lawrence Law Library, Lawrence MA p. 1097

Lawrence Library, Pepperell MA p. 1117

Lawrence Livermore National Laboratory, Livermore CA p. 164

Lawrence Memorial Hospital of Medford, Medford MA p. 1104

Lawrence Memorial Library, Bristol VT p. 2420

Lawrence Memorial Public Library, Climax MI p. 1163

Lawrence Memorial Public Library, *see* Albemarle Regional Library, Windsor NC p. 1835

Lawrence Public Library, Lawrence KS p. 877

Lawrence Public Library, Fairfield ME p. 985

Lawrence Public Library, Lawrence MA p. 1098

Lawrence Public Library District, Lawrenceville IL p. 664

Lawrence Samuel Crocker Library, *see* Grand Lodge of Masons in Massachusetts, Boston MA p. 1061

Lawrence Technological University Library, Southfield MI p. 1228

Lawrence University, Appleton WI p. 2578

Lawrenceburg Public Library District, Lawrenceburg IN p. 760

Lawrie Library, *see* Indiana Veteran's Home, West Lafayette IN p. 786

Laws Railroad Museum & Historical Site Library, Bishop CA p. 129

Lawson Edith S Library, *see* Jefferson Parish Library, Westwego LA p. 956

Lawson Research Library, *see* Kandiyohi County Historical Society, Willmar MN p. 1288

Lawson State Community College Library, Bessemer AL p. 6

Lawson State Community College Library, Birmingham AL p. 8

Lawtey Correctional Institution Library, *see* Florida Department of Corrections, Raiford FL p. 485

Lawton George Memorial Library, *see* National Psychological Association for Psychoanalysis, Inc, New York NY p. 1688

Lawton Memorial Library, La Farge WI p. 2604

Lawton Public Library, Lawton MI p. 1203

Lawton Public Library, Lawton OK p. 1967

Lay Park Community Resource Center, *see* Athens Regional Library System, Athens GA p. 508

Layland Museum, Cleburne TX p. 2298

LCEI (N), *see* Library Consortium of Eastern Idaho, Pocatello ID p. 2941

LCHIB (N), *see* Library Consortium of Health Institutions in Buffalo, Buffalo NY p. 2950

LDS Business College Library, Salt Lake City UT p. 2413

LDS Hospital Medical Library, *see* Intermountain Health Care, Salt Lake City UT p. 2412

Le Bonheur Children's Medical Center, Memphis TN p. 2249

Le Center Public, *see* Waseca-Le Sueur Regional Library, Le Center MN p. 1287

Le Devoir, Montreal QC p. 2897

Le Grand Pioneer Heritage Library, Le Grand IA p. 827

Le Mars Public Library, Le Mars IA p. 827

Le Moyne College, Syracuse NY p. 1751

Le Roy Public Library, Le Roy MN p. 1256

Le Seminaire Saint-Joseph de Trois-Rivieres, Trois-Rivieres QC p. 2914

Le Sueur Public, *see* Waseca-Le Sueur Regional Library, Le Sueur MN p. 1287

Leach Library, Londonderry NH p. 1454

Leach Public Library, Wahpeton ND p. 1849

Leach Public Library, Irasburg VT p. 2426

Leachville Public, *see* Mississippi County Library System, Leachville AR p. 95

Leacock Stephen Memorial Library Museum, Orillia ON p. 2826

Leadership Library, *see* Presidential Archives, Odessa TX p. 2366

Leadore Community Library, Leadore ID p. 577

Leaf-Chronicle Co Library, Clarksville TN p. 2229

Leaf Rapids Public Library, Leaf Rapids MB p. 2749

League of American Orchestras, New York NY p. 1685

League of Arab States, Washington DC p. 406

League of Minnesota Cities Library, Saint Paul MN p. 1278

Leakesville Public, *see* Pine Forest Regional Library, Leakesville MS p. 1314

Leakey Library, *see* Real County Public Library, Leakey TX p. 2354

Leal J Gilbert Learning Resource Center, *see* Texas State Technical College, Harlingen TX p. 2331

Leander Public Library, Leander TX p. 2354

Learning Center, Missoula MT p. 1386

Learning Disabilites Association of Yukon, Whitehorse YT p. 2934

Learning Disabilities Association of British Columbia-Vancouver Chapter, Vancouver BC p. 2741

Learning Disabilities Association of Canada Library, Ottawa ON p. 2831

LearningLinks Resource Centre, Calgary AB p. 2692

Leask Public Library, *see* Wapiti Regional Library, Leask SK p. 2921

Leath Thomas Memorial Library, Rockingham NC p. 1820

Leatherby Libraries, *see* Chapman University, Orange CA p. 200

Leavenworth Community, *see* North Central Regional Library, Leavenworth WA p. 2549

Leavenworth Public Library, Leavenworth KS p. 879

Lebanon College Library, Lebanon NH p. 1453

Lebanon-Community Library, Lebanon KS p. 879

Lebanon Community Library, Lebanon PA p. 2079

Lebanon Correctional Institution Library, Lebanon OH p. 1909

Lebanon County Historical Society Library, Lebanon PA p. 2079

Lebanon County Law Library, Lebanon PA p. 2080

Lebanon County Library System, Lebanon PA p. 2080

Lebanon-Laclede County Library, Lebanon MO p. 1343

Lebanon Public Library, Lebanon IL p. 664

Lebanon Public Library, Lebanon IN p. 761

Lebanon Public Library, Lebanon NH p. 1454

Lebanon Public Library, Lebanon OH p. 1909

Lebanon Public Library, Lebanon OR p. 2004

Lebanon VA Medical Center Library, Lebanon PA p. 2080

Lebanon Valley College, Annville PA p. 2029

Lebanon-Wilson County Library, Lebanon TN p. 2245

LeClaire Community Library, LeClaire IA p. 827

Lecompte Karl Miles Memorial Library, Corydon IA p. 804

Ledding Library of Milwaukie, Milwaukie OR p. 2006

Letcher Public Library, Letcher SD p. 2214
Lethbridge College, Lethbridge AB p. 2709
Lethbridge Public Library, Lethbridge AB p. 2709
LeTourneau University, Longview TX p. 2356
Letts Public Library, Letts IA p. 827
Levack Public/ Onaping Public, see Greater Sudbury
    Public Library, Onaping ON p. 2846
Levant Heritage Library, Levant ME p. 989
Leverett Library, Leverett MA p. 1099
Levi Heywood Memorial Library, Gardner MA
    p. 1090
Watkins Levi Learning Resource Center, see
    Alabama State University, Montgomery AL
    p. 28
Levin Louis R Memorial Library, see Curry College,
    Milton MA p. 1106
Levine Sklut Judaic Library & Resource Center,
    Charlotte NC p. 1783
Levinson/Axelrod Library, Edison NJ p. 1483
Levitt Library, see Mercy Medical Center, Des
    Moines IA p. 810
Levitt Library Learning Center, see York College,
    York NE p. 1424
Levittown Public Library, Levittown NY p. 1652
Levy & Droney, Farmington CT p. 340
Levy County Public Library System, Bronson FL
    p. 430
Levy Economics Institute Library, see Bard College,
    Annandale-on-Hudson NY p. 1574
Levy Gustave L & Janet W Library, see Mount
    Sinai School of Medicine, New York NY
    p. 1687
Levy Leon Dental Medicine Library, see University
    of Pennsylvania Libraries, Philadelphia PA
    p. 2119
Lewellen Public Library, Lewellen NE p. 1404
Lewes Public Library, Lewes DE p. 384
Lewis & Clark College, Portland OR p. 2011
Lewis & Clark Community College, Godfrey IL
    p. 651
Lewis & Clark Library, Helena MT p. 1382
Lewis & Clark Trail Heritage Foundation, Inc, Great
    Falls MT p. 1380
Lewis & Roca Library, Phoenix AZ p. 74
Lewis A C Memorial Library, see Grambling State
    University, Grambling LA p. 950
Lewis, Brisbois, Bisgaard & Smith, Los Angeles CA
    p. 171
Lewis-Clark State College Library, Lewiston ID
    p. 578
Lewis College of Business, Detroit MI p. 1171
Lewis Cooper Junior Memorial Library, Opelika AL
    p. 32
Lewis County General Hospital, Lowville NY
    p. 1655
Lewis County Law Library, Lowville NY p. 1655
Lewis County Law Library, Chehalis WA p. 2512
Lewis County Public Library, Vanceburg KY p. 936
Lewis County Public Library, Hohenwald TN
    p. 2237
Lewis G Pillow Memorial Library, see Memphis
    College of Art, Memphis TN p. 2249
Lewis George & Leona Library, see Albany College
    of Pharmacy & Health Sciences, Albany NY
    p. 1567
Lewis Gerald P Library, see Teck Metals Ltd
    Product Technology Group, PTC, Mississauga
    ON p. 2823
Lewis Gibson D Health Science Library, see
    University of North Texas Health Science Center
    at Fort Worth, Fort Worth TX p. 2324
Lewis Hazel M Library, Powers OR p. 2015
Lewis Library, see Loyola University Chicago
    Libraries, Chicago IL p. 617
Lewis Library of Glasgow, Glasgow MO p. 1329
Lewis Music Library, see Massachusetts Institute of
    Technology Libraries, Cambridge MA p. 1078
Lewis Public Library, Lewis IA p. 828
Lewis, Rice & Fingersh Law Library, Saint Louis
    MO p. 1355
Lewis Ron E Library, see Lamar State
    College-Orange Library, Orange TX p. 2367
Lewis Rufus A, see Montgomery City-County Public
    Library System, Montgomery AL p. 29
Lewis University Library, Romeoville IL p. 698

Lewis W B Public Library, Deep River ON p. 2802
Lewis W W Memorial, see Cape Breton Regional
    Library, Louisbourg NS p. 2785
Lewisboro Library, South Salem NY p. 1745
Lewisohn Irene Costume Reference Library, see
    Metropolitan Museum of Art, New York NY
    p. 1686
Lewison Memorial Library, see Mount Sinai
    Hospital Medical Center, Chicago IL p. 619
Lewiston-Auburn College Library, see University of
    Southern Maine, Lewiston ME p. 990
Lewiston City Library, Lewiston ID p. 578
Lewiston Public, see Montmorency County Public
    Libraries, Lewiston MI p. 1154
Lewiston Public Library, Lewiston ME p. 989
Lewiston Public Library, Lewiston MI p. 1203
Lewiston Public Library, Lewiston NY p. 1652
Lewiston Public Library, Lewiston UT p. 2407
Lewistown Hospital, Lewistown PA p. 2081
Lewistown Public Library, Lewistown MT p. 1384
Lewisville Community Library, see Chester County
    Library, Richburg SC p. 2186
Lewisville Public Library, Lewisville ID p. 578
Lewisville Public Library System, Lewisville TX
    p. 2355
Lexington College Library, Chicago IL p. 616
Lexington County Public Library System, Lexington
    SC p. 2199
Lexington Historical Society, Inc, Lexington MA
    p. 1099
Lexington Public, see Mid-Mississippi Regional
    Library System, Lexington MS p. 1306
Lexington Public Library, Lexington KY p. 920
Lexington Public Library, Lexington NE p. 1404
Lexington Public Library District, Lexington IL
    p. 665
Lexington Theological Seminary, Lexington KY
    p. 921
Lexmark Library, see University of Kentucky
    Libraries, Lexington KY p. 922
Libby Memorial Library, Old Orchard Beach ME
    p. 994
Liberal Memorial Library, Liberal KS p. 879
Liberty Center Public Library, Liberty Center OH
    p. 1909
Liberty Correctional Institution Library, see Florida
    Department of Corrections, Bristol FL p. 430
Liberty County Library, Chester MT p. 1376
Liberty Hall Historic Site Library, Frankfort KY
    p. 914
Liberty Hill Public Library, Liberty Hill TX p. 2355
Liberty Lake Municipal Library, Liberty Lake WA
    p. 2520
Liberty Library, Liberty ME p. 990
Liberty Municipal Library, Liberty TX p. 2355
Liberty Mutual Group, Boston MA p. 1062
Liberty Public Library, Liberty NY p. 1652
Liberty University Library, Lynchburg VA p. 2475
Libhart Jimmie Library, see Cochise County Library
    District, Bowie AZ p. 58
Librarians of the Upper Valley Coop (N), Etna NH
    p. 2948
Libraries of Middlesex Automation Consortium (N),
    Avenel NJ p. 2949
Libraries Online, Inc (N), Middletown CT p. 2939
Library & Archives Canada, Gatineau QC p. 2883
Library & Information Technologies, see University
    of Central Arkansas, Conway AR p. 2962
Library Association of La Jolla, La Jolla CA p. 161
Library Association of Rockland County (N), New
    City NY p. 2950
Library Association of Warehouse Point, East
    Windsor CT p. 337
Library at Birmingham Botanical Garden,
    Birmingham AL p. 8
Library at Cedar Creek Lake, Seven Points TX
    p. 2386
Library at Springfield Hospital Center, Sykesville
    MD p. 1043
Library at the Mariners' Museum, Newport News
    VA p. 2480
Library Company of Burlington, Burlington NJ
    p. 1476
Library Company of Philadelphia, Philadelphia PA
    p. 2112

Library Company of the Baltimore Bar, Baltimore
    MD p. 1015
Library Connection, Inc (N), Windsor CT p. 2939
Library Consortium of Eastern Idaho (N), Pocatello
    ID p. 2941
Library Consortium of Health Institutions in Buffalo
    (N), Buffalo NY p. 2950
Library District Number One, Doniphan County,
    Troy KS p. 898
Library for Family & Community Medicine, see
    University of Missouri-Columbia, Columbia MO
    p. 1326
Library for the Blind & Physically Handicapped,
    Little Rock AR p. 106
Library for the Blind & Physically Handicappe, see
    Hawaii State Public Library System HI p. 562
Library Information Network of Clackamas County
    (N), Oak Grove OR p. 2953
Library Management Network, Inc (N), Decatur AL
    p. 2937
Library Network (N), Novi MI p. 2946
Library of Architecture, Design & Construction, see
    Auburn University, Auburn AL p. 6
Library of Congress, Washington DC p. 406
Library of Graham, Graham TX p. 2329
Library of Hattiesburg, Petal, Forrest County,
    Hattiesburg MS p. 1300
Library of Historical Society of Newburgh Bay &
    the Highlands, Newburgh NY p. 1704
Library of Michigan, Lansing MI p. 1201
Library of Parliament, Ottawa ON p. 2831
Library of Rhode Island Network (N), Providence RI
    p. 2955
Library of Rush University Medical Center, Chicago
    IL p. 617
Library of the French Cultural Center Alliance
    Francaise of Boston, Boston MA p. 1062
Library of the Friends of Boerner Botanical Gardens,
    Hales Corners WI p. 2597
Library of the Legal Aid Society of Westchester
    County, White Plains NY p. 1768
Library of the Marine Corps, Quantico VA p. 2486
Library of the Polisher Research Institute, see
    Abramson Madlyn & Leonard Center for Jewish
    Life, North Wales PA p. 2099
Library of the US Courts, South Bend IN p. 779
Library of the US Courts, Reno NV p. 1432
Library of Virginia, Richmond VA p. 2489
Library Service of the College of Family Physicians
    of Canada, London ON p. 2817
Library System of Lancaster County, Lancaster PA
    p. 2077
LibraryLinkNJ, The New Jersey Library Cooperative
    (N), Piscataway NJ p. 2949
LIBRAS, Inc (N), Chicago IL p. 2942
Licking County Law Library Association, Newark
    OH p. 1922
Licking County Library, Newark OH p. 1922
Licking Memorial Hospital, Newark OH p. 1922
Liddicoat Richard T Gemological Library, Carlsbad
    CA p. 132
Lidgerwood City Library, Lidgerwood ND p. 1845
Liebling-Wood Library, see O'Neill Eugene Theater
    Center, Waterford CT p. 375
Lied Battle Creek Public Library, Battle Creek NE
    p. 1392
Lied Imperial Public Library, Imperial NE p. 1402
Lied Irwin Public Library, Irwin IA p. 824
Lied Library, see University of Nevada, Las Vegas
    Libraries, Las Vegas NV p. 1430
Lied Pierce Public Library, Pierce NE p. 1416
Lied Public Library, Clarinda IA p. 802
Lied Public Library, Essex IA p. 815
Lied Randolph Public Library, Randolph NE p. 1417
Lied Scottsbluff Public Library, Scottsbluff NE
    p. 1418
Lied Winside Public Library, Winside NE p. 1423
Lief Leonard Library, see Lehman College, City
    University of New York, Bronx NY p. 1587
LIFE Center, see Rehabilitation Institute of Chicago,
    Chicago IL p. 622
Life Chiropractic College-West Library, Hayward
    CA p. 158
Life Pacific College Alumni Library, San Dimas CA
    p. 239

Litchfield Carnegie Public Library, Litchfield IL p. 667
Litchfield District Library, Litchfield MI p. 1203
Litchfield Historical Society, Litchfield CT p. 349
Litchfield Law Library, *see* Connecticut Judicial Branch Law Libraries, Litchfield CT p. 344
Litchfield Public Library, Litchfield MN p. 1256
Litchfield Public Library, *see* Wolcott Oliver Library, Litchfield CT p. 349
Literary & Historical Society of Quebec Library, Quebec QC p. 2905
Lithgow Public Library, Augusta ME p. 974
Lithia Springs Public Library, *see* West Georgia Regional Library, Lithia Springs GA p. 524
Lithuanian Research & Studies Center, Inc, Chicago IL p. 617
Lititz Public Library, Lititz PA p. 2082
Little Big Horn College Library, Crow Agency MT p. 1377
Little Company of Mary Hospital, Evergreen Park IL p. 645
Little Compton Free Public Library, *see* Brownell Library, Little Compton RI p. 2168
Little Dixie Regional Libraries, Moberly MO p. 1345
Little E H Library, *see* Davidson College, Davidson NC p. 1786
Little Elm Public Library, Little Elm TX p. 2356
Little Falls Library, *see* Montgomery County Public Libraries, Bethesda MD p. 1038
Little Falls Public Library, Little Falls NJ p. 1495
Little Falls Public Library, Little Falls NY p. 1652
Little Falls Public Library, *see* Great River Regional Library, Little Falls MN p. 1275
Little Ferry Free Public Library, Little Ferry NJ p. 1496
Little G R Library, *see* Elizabeth City State University, Elizabeth City NC p. 1790
Little Lucille Fine Arts Library, *see* University of Kentucky Libraries, Lexington KY p. 922
Little Memorial Library, *see* Midway College, Midway KY p. 929
Little Priest Tribal College Library, Winnebago NE p. 1423
Little River Community Library, Little River KS p. 880
Little Rock Public Library, Little Rock IA p. 828
Little Saxton B Free Library, Inc, Columbia CT p. 334
Little Silver Public Library, Little Silver NJ p. 1496
Little Traverse History Museum Library, Petoskey MI p. 1217
Little Wood River District Library, Carey ID p. 572
Littler Mendelson Library, San Francisco CA p. 243
Littlestown Library, Littlestown PA p. 2082
Littleton Historical Museum Research Center, Littleton CO p. 317
Littleton Public Library, Littleton NH p. 1454
Littleton Public Library, *see* Bemis Edwin A Public Library, Littleton CO p. 316
Littleton Regional Hospital, Littleton NH p. 1454
Littman Barbara & Leonard, *see* New Jersey Institute of Technology, Newark NJ p. 1511
Live Oak County Library, George West TX p. 2327
Live Oak Library, *see* County of Los Angeles Public Library, Arcadia CA p. 142
Live Oak Public Libraries, Savannah GA p. 550
Livengood Charles H Jr Memorial Library, *see* North Carolina Department of Labor, Raleigh NC p. 1815
Livermore Mary Library, *see* University of North Carolina at Pembroke, Pembroke NC p. 1814
Livermore Public Library, Livermore CA p. 164
Livermore Public Library, Livermore IA p. 828
Livermore Public Library, Livermore ME p. 990
Liverpool Public Library, Liverpool NY p. 1653
Livingston A E Health Sciences Library, *see* Bromenn Healthcare, Normal IL p. 681
Livingston Correctional Facility Library, Sonyea NY p. 1745
Livingston County Library, Chillicothe MO p. 1323
Livingston Free Library, Livingston NY p. 1653
Livingston Library, *see* Shorter College, Rome GA p. 549

Livingston Library, *see* Webb Institute, Glen Cove NY p. 1628
Livingston Manor Free Library, Livingston Manor NY p. 1653
Livingston Parish Library, Livingston LA p. 955
Livingston-Park County Public Library, Livingston MT p. 1385
Livingston Public Library, *see* Dietzman Allen Library, Livingston WI p. 2605
Livingston Public Library, *see* Rockwood Ruth L Memorial Library, Livingston NJ p. 1496
Livingston Public Library, *see* Tartt Ruby Pickens Public Library, Livingston AL p. 24
Livingstone College, Salisbury NC p. 1822
Livonia Public Library, Livonia MI p. 1203
Livonia Public Library, Livonia NY p. 1653
Lizard Butte Public Library, Marsing ID p. 578
Lizzadro Museum of Lapidary Art Library, Elmhurst IL p. 642
Llano County Library System, Llano TX p. 2356
Llano County Public Library, *see* Llano County Library System, Llano TX p. 2356
Lloyd Library & Museum, Cincinnati OH p. 1870
Lloydminster Public Library, Lloydminster AB p. 2710
LMI Library, McLean VA p. 2478
LMN (N), *see* Library Management Network, Inc, Decatur AL p. 2937
LMxAC (N), *see* Libraries of Middlesex Automation Consortium, Avenel NJ p. 2949
Loan SHARK (N), Baton Rouge LA p. 2944
Lock Haven University of Pennsylvania, Lock Haven PA p. 2082
Lock Museum of America, Inc Library, Terryville CT p. 372
Locke E D Public Library, *see* McFarland Public Library, McFarland WI p. 2614
Locke Lord Bissell & Liddell LLP, Chicago IL p. 617
Locke Reynolds LLP, Indianapolis IN p. 755
Lockhart Public Library, *see* Clark Dr Eugene Public Library, Lockhart TX p. 2356
Lockheed Martin, Moorestown NJ p. 1504
Lockheed Martin, Manassas VA p. 2477
Lockheed Martin Corp, Orlando FL p. 476
Lockheed Martin Corp, Gaithersburg MD p. 1030
Lockheed Martin Corp, Syracuse NY p. 1752
Lockheed Martin Missiles & Fire Control, Grand Prairie TX p. 2329
Lockheed Martin Space Systems Company, Littleton CO p. 317
Lockheed Martin Systems Integration, Owego NY p. 1713
Lockport Public Library, Lockport NY p. 1653
Lockridge, Grindal, Nauen PLLP, Minneapolis MN p. 1260
Lockwood, Andrews & Newnam, Inc, Houston TX p. 2340
Lockwood Public Library, Lockwood MO p. 1343
Locust Grove Public Library, Locust Grove OK p. 1967
Locust Grove Public Library, *see* Henry County Public Library System, Locust Grove GA p. 544
Locust Valley Library, Locust Valley NY p. 1654
Loda Township Library, *see* Smith A Herr & E E Smith Library, Loda IL p. 667
Loden-Daniel Library, *see* Freed-Hardeman University, Henderson TN p. 2237
Lodi Memorial Library, Lodi NJ p. 1496
Lodi Public Library, Lodi CA p. 165
Lodi Whittier Library, Lodi NY p. 1654
Lodi Woman's Club Public Library, Lodi WI p. 2605
Loeb & Loeb LLP, New York NY p. 1685
Loeb Eda Kuhn Music Library, *see* Harvard Library, Cambridge MA p. 1076
Loeb Frances Library, *see* Harvard Library, Cambridge MA p. 1076
Logan Area Public Library, Logan WV p. 2564
Logan Correctional Center Library, Lincoln IL p. 666
Logan County Libraries, Bellefontaine OH p. 1859
Logan County Public Library, Russellville KY p. 934
Logan County Public Library, Stapleton NE p. 1420

Logan-Hocking County District Library, Logan OH p. 1910
Logan John A Library, *see* Rose-Hulman Institute of Technology, Terre Haute IN p. 781
Logan Library, Logan UT p. 2407
Logan Patient's Library, *see* Atascadero State Hospital, Atascadero CA p. 122
Logan Professional Library, *see* Atascadero State Hospital, Atascadero CA p. 122
Logan Public Library, Logan IA p. 828
Logan Public Library, Logan KS p. 880
Logan Regional Medical Center, Logan WV p. 2564
Logan Sallie Public Library, Murphysboro IL p. 678
Logan University/College of Chiropractic Library, Chesterfield MO p. 1323
Logan W M Library, *see* Schreiner University, Kerrville TX p. 2350
Logansport-Cass County Public Library, Logansport IN p. 761
Logansport State Hospital, Logansport IN p. 761
Logue Library, *see* Chestnut Hill College, Philadelphia PA p. 2104
LOMA, Atlanta GA p. 516
Loma Linda University, Loma Linda CA p. 165
Lomason Neva Memorial Library, *see* West Georgia Regional Library, Carrollton GA p. 523
Lombard Historical Society Library, Lombard IL p. 667
Lombard Public Library, *see* Plum Helen M Memorial Public Library District, Lombard IL p. 667
Lomira Public Library, Lomira WI p. 2605
Lomond Municipal Library, Lomond AB p. 2710
Lompoc Public Library, Lompoc CA p. 165
London Eleanor Cote Saint Luc Public Library, Cote Saint-Luc QC p. 2881
London Free Press, London ON p. 2817
London Health Sciences Centre Library Services, London ON p. 2817
London Public Library, London OH p. 1911
London Public Library, London ON p. 2817
Lone Oak Area Public Library, Lone Oak TX p. 2356
Lone Rock Public Library, Lone Rock WI p. 2605
Lone Star College System, Houston TX p. 2340
Lone Tree Library, *see* Douglas County Libraries, Lone Tree CO p. 294
Lonesome Pine Regional Library, Wise VA p. 2504
Long Augustus C Health Sciences Library, *see* Columbia University, New York NY p. 1675
Long Beach City College, Long Beach CA p. 166
Long Beach Jewish Community Center - The Alpert JCC, Long Beach CA p. 166
Long Beach Medical Center, Long Beach NY p. 1654
Long Beach Memorial/Miller Children's Hospital, Long Beach CA p. 166
Long Beach Museum of Art Library, Long Beach CA p. 166
Long Beach Public Library, Long Beach CA p. 166
Long Beach Public Library, Long Beach MS p. 1307
Long Beach Public Library, Long Beach NY p. 1654
Long Branch Free Public Library, Long Branch NJ p. 1496
Long County Library, *see* Three Rivers Regional Library System, Ludowici GA p. 522
Long Creek Youth Development Center Library, *see* Maine Department of Corrections, South Portland ME p. 1001
Long Dr Hugo Library, *see* Saint James Hospital & Health Centers, Chicago Heights IL p. 628
Long Earl K Library, *see* University of New Orleans, New Orleans LA p. 964
Long Hill Township Public Library, Gillette NJ p. 1487
Long Huey P Memorial Law Library, Baton Rouge LA p. 943
Long Island City Community Library, *see* Queens Borough Public Library, Long Island City NY p. 1645
Long Island Community Library, Long Island KS p. 880
Long Island Community Library, Long Island ME p. 990

Lowe Dorothy J Memorial Public Library, *see* Tombigbee Regional Library System, Nettleton MS p. 1318

Lowe Public Library, Shinnston WV p. 2572

Lowell Community Library, Lowell VT p. 2427

Lowell Correctional Annex, *see* Florida Department of Corrections, Ocala FL p. 473

Lowell Correctional Institution Library (Main Unit), *see* Florida Department of Corrections, Ocala FL p. 473

Lowell General Hospital, Lowell MA p. 1100

Lowell Law Library, *see* Massachusetts Trial Court, Lowell MA p. 1100

Lowell Observatory Library, Flagstaff AZ p. 62

Lowell Public Library, Lowell IN p. 762

Lowell Public Library, Lowell WI p. 2605

Lowenstein Sandler PC Library, Roseland NJ p. 1527

Lower Canada College Library, Montreal QC p. 2897

Lower Columbia College, Longview WA p. 2520

Lower Macungie Library, Macungie PA p. 2083

Lower Merion Library System, Ardmore PA p. 2029

Lower Providence Community Library, Eagleville PA p. 2051

Lowgap Public Library, Lowgap NC p. 1807

Lowndes County Historical Society & Museum, Valdosta GA p. 555

Lowry Fannie D Memorial, *see* Chesterfield County Library, Jefferson SC p. 2186

Lowry Nature Center Library, Victoria MN p. 1286

Lowville Free Library, Lowville NY p. 1655

Loxley Public Library, Loxley AL p. 24

Loyal Public Library, Loyal WI p. 2605

Loyalist College Library, *see* Parrott Centre, Belleville ON p. 2795

Loyola Law Library, *see* Loyola University New Orleans, New Orleans LA p. 961

Loyola Law School, Los Angeles CA p. 175

Loyola Marymount University, Los Angeles CA p. 175

Loyola-Notre Dame Library, Inc, Baltimore MD p. 1015

Loyola University Chicago Libraries, Chicago IL p. 617

Loyola University New Orleans, New Orleans LA p. 961

Lozano Rudy Library, *see* Chicago Public Library, Chicago IL p. 609

LSU Health Sciences Center, Monroe LA p. 957

LSU School of Veterinary Medicine Library, *see* Louisiana State University Libraries, Baton Rouge LA p. 944

Lt Robert J Rubel Memorial Library, *see* Orthopaedic Hospital, Los Angeles CA p. 176

LTG Associates Library, Takoma Park MD p. 1043

LTK Engineering Services Library, Ambler PA p. 2028

Lubbock Christian University Library, Lubbock TX p. 2357

Lubbock Public Library, Lubbock TX p. 2357

Lubrizol Library & Research Center, Wickliffe OH p. 1947

Lucas Bob Memorial Library & Literacy Center, *see* Altadena Library District, Altadena CA p. 120

Lucas County Law Library, Toledo OH p. 1939

Lucas Jim Checotah Public Library, Checotah OK p. 1959

Lucas Laird Memorial Library & Archives, *see* Winona County Historical Society, Winona MN p. 1290

Lucas Signatone Corp Library, Gilroy CA p. 154

Lucas Vane B Memorial Library, *see* American College, Bryn Mawr PA p. 2038

Lucasfilm Research Library, San Rafael CA p. 257

Luce, Forward, Hamilton & Scripps, San Diego CA p. 231

Luce Stephen B Library, *see* State University of New York Maritime College, Bronx NY p. 1588

Lucedale-George County Public Library, *see* Jackson-George Regional Library System, Lucedale MS p. 1310

Luck Public Library, Luck WI p. 2606

Luckett Luther Correctional Complex Library, La Grange KY p. 919

Ludden Memorial Library, Dixfield ME p. 983

Ludington Public Library, Bryn Mawr PA p. 2039

Luebke Arthur L Memorial Library, *see* Beloit Historical Society, Beloit WI p. 2581

Lufkin Memorial, *see* Benjamin Franklin Institute of Technology, Boston MA p. 1055

Lukens John N Library, *see* Independent Presbyterian Church, Birmingham AL p. 8

Lum, Danzis, Drasco & Positan, Roseland NJ p. 1527

Lum Y T & Louise Lee Library, *see* Appraisal Institute, Chicago IL p. 606

Lumberton Public, *see* Lamar County Library System, Lumberton MS p. 1312

Lumberton Public Library, Lumberton TX p. 2358

Lumcon Library, *see* Louisiana Universities Marine Consortium, Chauvin LA p. 947

Lummis Warren Genealogical & Historical Library, *see* Cumberland County Genealogical & Historical Society Library, Greenwich NJ p. 1488

Lummus Technology Library, *see* Chicago Bridge & Iron Co, Bloomfield NJ p. 1473

Lumpkin County Library, *see* Chestatee Regional Library System, Dahlonega GA p. 529

Lumpkin Library, *see* Blackburn College, Carlinville IL p. 600

Lunar & Planetary Institute, Houston TX p. 2340

Lund Consumer Health Information Center, *see* Emerson Hospital Medical Library, Concord MA p. 1083

Lundberg Gust E Learning Resource Center, *see* Black Hawk College-East Campus, Galva IL p. 648

Lunder Library, *see* Kennebec Valley Community College, Fairfield ME p. 985

Lunenburg Public Library, Lunenburg MA p. 1101

Lunney Robert F Library, *see* Edmonton Police, Edmonton AB p. 2700

Lunsford James J Law Library, Tampa FL p. 497

Lupton T Cartter & Margaret Rawlings Library, *see* University of Tennessee at Chattanooga Library, Chattanooga TN p. 2228

Luria Eli Library, *see* Santa Barbara City College, Santa Barbara CA p. 260

Luria Medical Library, *see* Einstein Albert Healthcare Network, Philadelphia PA p. 2106

Lurie Ann & Robert H Children's Memorial Hospital, Chicago IL p. 618

Lurleen B Wallace Community College Library, Andalusia AL p. 4

Luso-American Education Foundation, *see* Luso-American Life Insurance Society, Lexington MA p. 1099

Luso-American Life Insurance Society, Lexington MA p. 1099

Luther Area Public Library, Luther MI p. 1204

Luther College, Decorah IA p. 807

Luther College Library, *see* University of Regina, Regina SK p. 2925

Luther Extension Library, *see* Metropolitan Library System in Oklahoma County, Luther OK p. 1973

Luther Library, *see* Midland Lutheran College, Fremont NE p. 1399

Luther Rice Seminary, Lithonia GA p. 539

Luther Seminary Library, Saint Paul MN p. 1278

Lutheran Brethren Seminary, Fergus Falls MN p. 1251

Lutheran Medical Center, Brooklyn NY p. 1593

Lutheran Medical Center School of Nursing, Saint Louis MO p. 1355

Lutheran School of Theology at Chicago & McCormick Theological Seminary, Chicago IL p. 618

Lutheran Theological Seminary, Gettysburg PA p. 2060

Lutheran Theological Seminary, Philadelphia PA p. 2112

Lutheran Theological Seminary Library, Saskatoon SK p. 2925

Lutheran Theological Southern Seminary, Columbia SC p. 2188

Lutherans For Life Library, Nevada IA p. 834

Luttrell Public Library, Luttrell TN p. 2245

Lutts Bob Fulshear Simonton, *see* Fort Bend County Libraries, Fulshear TX p. 2375

Lutz Aleta E VA Medical Center & Health Science Libary, *see* Department of Veterans Affairs, Saginaw MI p. 1223

LUV Coop (N), *see* Librarians of the Upper Valley Coop, Etna NH p. 2948

Luverne Public Library, Luverne AL p. 24

Luverne Public Library, Luverne IA p. 828

Luxora Public, *see* Mississippi County Library System, Luxora AR p. 95

Luzerne County Community College Library, Nanticoke PA p. 2094

Luzerne County Historical Society, Wilkes-Barre PA p. 2155

Luzerne County Medical Society Library, Wilkes-Barre PA p. 2155

Lycoming College, Williamsport PA p. 2156

Lycoming County Law Library, *see* Brown James V Library of Williamsport & Lycoming County, Williamsport PA p. 2156

Lydon Library, *see* University of Massachusetts Lowell Libraries, Lowell MA p. 1101

Lykes Memorial Library, *see* Hernando County Public Library System, Brooksville FL p. 430

Lyman Library, Boston MA p. 1063

Lyman Public Library, Lyman NE p. 1407

Lyme Academy College of Fine Arts, Old Lyme CT p. 363

Lyme Free Library, Chaumont NY p. 1605

Lyme Historical Society Library, Old Lyme CT p. 363

Lyme Public Library, Lyme CT p. 349

Lynbrook Public Library, Lynbrook NY p. 1655

Lynch Public Library, Lynch NE p. 1407

Lynchburg Area Library Cooperative (N), Sweet Briar VA p. 2957

Lynchburg College, Lynchburg VA p. 2476

Lynchburg General Hospital, Lynchburg VA p. 2476

Lynchburg Information Online Network (N), Lynchburg VA p. 2957

Lynchburg Public Library, Lynchburg VA p. 2476

Lyndhurst Free Public Library, Lyndhurst NJ p. 1497

Lyndon Carnegie Library, Lyndon KS p. 880

Lyndon State College, Lyndonville VT p. 2427

Lynn Haven Public Library, Lynn Haven FL p. 461

Lynn Lake Library, Lynn Lake MB p. 2749

Lynn Museum & Historical Society Library, Lynn MA p. 1101

Lynn Public Library, Lynn MA p. 1101

Lynn University Library, Boca Raton FL p. 428

Lynnfield Public Library, Lynnfield MA p. 1101

Lynnville Public Library, Lynnville IA p. 828

Lynnwood Community Library, *see* Sno-Isle Libraries, Lynnwood WA p. 2542

LYNX! Consortium (N), Boise ID p. 2941

Lyon College, Batesville AR p. 93

Lyon County, Library District One, Allen KS p. 855

Lyon County Library System, Yerington NV p. 1435

Lyon County Public Library, Eddyville KY p. 911

Lyon Township Public Library, South Lyon MI p. 1227

Lyons Depot Library, Lyons CO p. 318

Lyons Falls Free Library, Lyons Falls NY p. 1656

Lyons Harrye B Design Library, *see* North Carolina State University Libraries, Raleigh NC p. 1816

Lyons Memorial Library, *see* College of the Ozarks, Point Lookout MO p. 1349

Lyons Public Library, Lyons IL p. 668

Lyons Public Library, Lyons KS p. 880

Lyons Public Library, Lyons NE p. 1407

Lyons Public Library, Lyons NY p. 1656

Lyons Public Library, Lyons OR p. 2004

Lyons Township District Library, Lyons MI p. 1204

Lyrasis (N), Atlanta GA p. 2941

Lytle Public Library, Lytle TX p. 2358

Lytton Public Library, Lytton IA p. 828

M-C Community Library, Cleghorn IA p. 802

M-C River Valley Public Library District, Meredosia IL p. 673

Maag William F Jr Library, *see* Youngstown State University, Youngstown OH p. 1953

Maaskant Simona Library, *see* King's University College, Edmonton AB p. 2701

Maass Clara Medical Center, Belleville NJ p. 1471

Mabee JE & LE Library, *see* University of the Incarnate Word, San Antonio TX p. 2384

Mabee Learning Center, *see* Oklahoma Baptist University, Shawnee OK p. 1977

Mabee Learning Resources Center, *see* Wayland Baptist University, Plainview TX p. 2370

Mabee Legal Information Center, *see* University of Tulsa Libraries, Tulsa OK p. 1984

Mabee Library, *see* Sterling College, Sterling KS p. 895

Mabee Library, *see* Washburn University, Topeka KS p. 897

Mabee Library & Learning Resource Center, *see* Mid-America Nazarene University, Olathe KS p. 886

Mabee Myrtle Library, *see* Great River Regional Library, Belgrade MN p. 1275

Mabee-Simpson Library, *see* Lyon College, Batesville AR p. 93

Mabel Public Library, Mabel MN p. 1256

Mac Freddie Corporate Information Resource Center, McLean VA p. 2478

Macalester College, Saint Paul MN p. 1278

Macaron Fred Library, Springer NM p. 1565

MacArthur John D & Catherine T Foundation Library, Chicago IL p. 618

MacArthur John D Library, *see* Florida Atlantic University, Jupiter FL p. 455

MacArthur Memorial Library & Archives, Norfolk VA p. 2481

Macaulay Robert W Library, *see* Ontario Energy Board, Toronto ON p. 2856

MacCormac College Library, Chicago IL p. 618

Macculloch Hall Historical Museum Archives, Morristown NJ p. 1505

Macdermid, Inc Library, Waterbury CT p. 374

MacDonald Angus L Library, *see* Saint Francis Xavier University, Antigonish NS p. 2777

MacDonald, Dettwiler & Associates Library, Richmond BC p. 2736

MacDonald Dr Keith G Health Sciences Library, *see* Credit Valley Hospital, Mississauga ON p. 2822

MacDonald Dr R Ian Library, *see* Sunnybrook Health Sciences Centre, Toronto ON p. 2859

MacDonald Frank J Library, *see* Queen Elizabeth Hospital, Charlottetown PE p. 2875

Macdonald-Kelce Library, *see* University of Tampa, Tampa FL p. 499

MacDonald Public Library, New Baltimore MI p. 1213

MacDonald Rusty, *see* Saskatoon Public Library, Saskatoon SK p. 2926

MacDonell Elizabeth M Memorial, *see* Allen County Historical Society, Lima OH p. 1909

Mace Borden Library, *see* North Carolina School of Science & Mathematics Library, Durham NC p. 1789

Macedon Public Library, Macedon NY p. 1656

MacEwan Grant University Library, Edmonton AB p. 2701

Macfee & Taft Law Offices, Oklahoma City OK p. 1972

MacInnis Jamie A Memorial Library, *see* Art Institute of California, San Francisco Library, San Francisco CA p. 240

Mack Alexander Memorial Library, *see* Bridgewater College, Bridgewater VA p. 2452

Mack J S Library, *see* Bob Jones University, Greenville SC p. 2195

Mack Paul & Harriett Library, *see* Northampton Community College, Bethlehem PA p. 2034

Mackall, Crounse & Moore, Minneapolis MN p. 1260

Mackay District Library, MacKay ID p. 578

MacKay Library, *see* Union County College Libraries, Cranford NJ p. 1480

Mackenzie, Hughes LLP, Syracuse NY p. 1752

MacKenzie Public Library, Mackenzie BC p. 2731

Mackie George Library, *see* Fraser Valley Regional Library, Delta BC p. 2724

Mackin Hazel Community Library, Roberts WI p. 2635

Mackinac Island Public Library, Mackinac Island MI p. 1204

Mackinaw Area Public Library, Mackinaw City MI p. 1204

Mackinaw District Public Library, Mackinaw IL p. 668

Macksville City Library, Macksville KS p. 881

MacLean Hector Public, *see* Robeson County Public Library, Fairmont NC p. 1808

Maclean Neil John Health Sciences Library, *see* University of Manitoba Libraries, Winnipeg MB p. 2758

Maclure Library, Pittsford VT p. 2432

MacMillan H R Library, *see* Vancouver School of Theology Library, Vancouver BC p. 2744

MacMillan Hugh F Law Library, *see* Emory University School of Law, Atlanta GA p. 514

MacMullen Library, *see* Maritime Museum of San Diego, San Diego CA p. 232

MacMurray College, Jacksonville IL p. 659

MacNeal Hospital, Berwyn IL p. 594

MacOdrum Library, *see* Carleton University Library, Ottawa ON p. 2830

Macomb Community College Libraries, Warren MI p. 1234

Macomb County Educational Resource Center, *see* Right to Life of Michigan, Saint Clair Shores MI p. 1224

Macomb County Historical Society, Mount Clemens MI p. 1210

Macomb County Library, Clinton Township MI p. 1164

Macomb Library for the Blind & Physically Handicapped, *see* Macomb County Library, Clinton Township MI p. 1164

Macomb Public Library District, Macomb IL p. 668

Macon County Law Library, Decatur IL p. 634

Macon County Public Library, Franklin NC p. 1794

Macon County Public Library, Lafayette TN p. 2244

Macon County-Tuskegee Public Library, Tuskegee AL p. 39

Macon Public Library, Macon MO p. 1344

Macon State College Library, Macon GA p. 540

Macon State Prison, *see* Georgia Department of Corrections, Oglethorpe GA p. 547

Macon Telegraph Library, Macon GA p. 540

MacPhaidin Library, *see* Stonehill College, Easton MA p. 1086

MacPherson Stuart Public Library, *see* Lac La Biche County Library Board, Lac La Biche AB p. 2708

MacRae Library, *see* Nova Scotia Agricultural College Library, Truro NS p. 2786

Macsherry Library, Alexandria Bay NY p. 1572

Madawaska Public Library, Madawaska ME p. 991

Madbury Public Library, Madbury NH p. 1455

Madden Henry Library, *see* California State University, Fresno, Fresno CA p. 150

Maddock Community Library, Maddock ND p. 1845

Maddox Lucy Memorial, *see* De Soto Trail Regional Library, Blakely GA p. 522

Madeline Island Public Library, La Pointe WI p. 2604

Madera County Historical Society, Madera CA p. 181

Madera County Law Library, Madera CA p. 181

Madera County Library, Madera CA p. 181

Madigan Army Medical Center Library, *see* United States Army, Tacoma WA p. 2540

Madigan Roger & Peggy Library, Williamsport PA p. 2156

Madill City County Library, Madill OK p. 1967

Madison Area Technical College, Madison WI p. 2606

Madison Community Hospital, Madison SD p. 2214

Madison Correctional Institution Library, *see* Florida Department of Corrections, Madison FL p. 462

Madison County Historical Museum, Edwardsville IL p. 639

Madison County Historical Society Library, Oneida NY p. 1710

Madison County Law Library, Edwardsville IL p. 639

Madison County Law Library, London OH p. 1911

Madison County Library, Madisonville TX p. 2359

Madison County Library, *see* Thompson-Hickman Free County Library, Virginia City MT p. 1389

Madison County Library, Inc, Madison VA p. 2477

Madison County Library System, Canton MS p. 1295

Madison County Public Library, Huntsville AR p. 104

Madison County Public Library, Richmond KY p. 934

Madison County Public Library, Marshall NC p. 1809

Madison Dolley, *see* Fairfax County Public Library, McLean VA p. 2461

Madison Heights Public Library, Madison Heights MI p. 1205

Madison-Jefferson County Public Library, Madison IN p. 762

Madison Library, Madison NH p. 1455

Madison Library District, Rexburg ID p. 582

Madison Parish Library, Tallulah LA p. 970

Madison Public Library, Madison IL p. 669

Madison Public Library, Madison KS p. 881

Madison Public Library, Madison ME p. 991

Madison Public Library, Madison MN p. 1257

Madison Public Library, Madison NE p. 1408

Madison Public Library, Madison NJ p. 1498

Madison Public Library, Madison OH p. 1912

Madison Public Library, Madison SD p. 2214

Madison Public Library, Madison WI p. 2606

Madison Public Library, *see* Huntsville-Madison Public Library, Madison AL p. 21

Madison Public Library, *see* Madison County Library System, Madison MS p. 1295

Madison Public Library, *see* Suwannee River Regional Library, Madison FL p. 461

Madison Township Historical Society, Matawan NJ p. 1500

Madison Valley Public Library, Ennis MT p. 1378

Madisonville Community College, Madisonville KY p. 927

Madisonville Public Library, Madisonville TN p. 2246

Madoc Public Library, Madoc ON p. 2819

Madonna Rehabilitation Hospital, Lincoln NE p. 1405

Madonna University Library, Livonia MI p. 1204

Madre Maria Teresa Guevara Library, *see* University of the Sacred Heart, Santurce PR p. 2678

Madrid Public Library, Madrid IA p. 828

Magale John F Memorial Library, *see* Centenary College of Louisiana, Shreveport LA p. 967

Magale Library, *see* Southern Arkansas University, Magnolia AR p. 108

Magdalena Public Library, Magdalena NM p. 1560

Magee Public Library, Magee MS p. 1307

Magee Rehabilitation Hospital, Philadelphia PA p. 2112

Magill James P Library, *see* Haverford College, Haverford PA p. 2067

Magness W H & Edgar Community House & Library, McMinnville TN p. 2247

Magnetawan First Nation Public Library, Britt ON p. 2797

Magnin George E Medical Library, *see* Marshfield Clinic, Marshfield WI p. 2613

Magnolia Library, *see* Baton Rouge Community College, Baton Rouge LA p. 942

Magnolia Library Center, Gloucester MA p. 1091

Magoffin County Library, Salyersville KY p. 934

Magrath Public Library, Magrath AB p. 2710

Maguire Charlotte Edwards Medical Library, *see* Florida State University Libraries, Tallahassee FL p. 495

Maguire Raymer Jr Learning Resources Center, West Campus, *see* Valencia Community College, Orlando FL p. 478

Mahaffey Thomas J Jr Business Information Center, *see* Hesburgh Libraries, Notre Dame IN p. 770

Mahan Edna Hall Library, *see* Correctional Institution for Women, Clinton NJ p. 1479

Mahan Oldham County Public, *see* Oldham County Public Library, Goshen KY p. 919

Mahanoy City Public Library, Mahanoy City PA p. 2083

Maharishi University of Management Library, Fairfield IA p. 815

Mahnomen Public Library, *see* Lake Agassiz Regional Library, Mahnomen MN p. 1266

Mahomet Public Library District, Mahomet IL p. 669

Mahoney A P Library, *see* Saint Peter's Seminary, London ON p. 2818

Mahoney Library, *see* College of Saint Elizabeth, Morristown NJ p. 1504

Mahoning Law Library Association, Youngstown OH p. 1952

Mahopac Public Library, Mahopac NY p. 1656

MAHSL (N), *see* Maryland Association of Health Science Librarians, Baltimore MD p. 2944

MAHSLIN (N), *see* Massachusetts Health Sciences Libraries Network, worcester MA p. 2945

Mahwah Public Library, Mahwah NJ p. 1498

Maida Adam Cardinal Alumni Library, *see* SS Cyril & Methodius Seminary, Orchard Lake MI p. 1215

Maimonides Hospital Geriatric Centre, Montreal QC p. 2898

Maimonides Medical Center, Brooklyn NY p. 1593

MAIN (N), *see* Morris Automated Information Network, Whippany NJ p. 2949

Main-a-Dieu Public, *see* Cape Breton Regional Library, Main-a-Dieu NS p. 2785

Main Line Reform Temple, Wynnewood PA p. 2158

Maine Charitable Mechanic Association Library, Portland ME p. 996

Maine College of Art, Portland ME p. 996

Maine Correctional Center Library, *see* Maine Department of Corrections, Windham ME p. 1007

Maine Department of Corrections, Charleston ME p. 982

Maine Department of Corrections, South Portland ME p. 1001

Maine Department of Corrections, Warren ME p. 1004

Maine Department of Corrections, Windham ME p. 1007

Maine Department of Marine Resources, West Boothbay Harbor ME p. 1006

Maine Department of Transportation Library, Augusta ME p. 974

Maine Education Center for the Deaf & Hard of Hearing, Falmouth ME p. 985

Maine General Medical Center, Waterville ME p. 1005

Maine General Medical Center Library, Augusta ME p. 974

Maine Historical Society, Portland ME p. 996

Maine Maritime Academy, Castine ME p. 981

Maine Maritime Museum, Bath ME p. 976

Maine Medical Center Library, Portland ME p. 997

Maine Regional Library for the Blind & Physically Impaired, Augusta ME p. 974

Maine State Law & Legislative Reference Library, Augusta ME p. 974

Maine State Library, Augusta ME p. 974

Maine State Prison Library, *see* Maine Department of Corrections, Warren ME p. 1004

Maitland Public Library, Maitland FL p. 462

Major George B Collings Memorial, *see* Virginia War Museum, Newport News VA p. 2480

Major Hillard Library, *see* Chesapeake Public Library, Chesapeake VA p. 2456

Majure Evelyn Taylor Library, *see* Jackson/Hinds Library System, Utica MS p. 1303

Makawao Public Library, *see* Hawaii State Public Library System, Makawao HI p. 563

Maki Library, *see* Findlandia University, Hancock MI p. 1187

Maki Sulo & Aileen Research Library, *see* Desert Research Institute, Las Vegas NV p. 1429

MALA (N), *see* Metro Atlanta Library Association, Atlanta GA p. 2941

MALA/KCMLIN (N), *see* Mid-America Library Alliance, Independence MO p. 2948

Malaspina University-College Library, Nanaimo BC p. 2732

Malca Pass Library, *see* Agudath Israel Congregation, Ottawa ON p. 2827

Malcho Thomas J Memorial Library, *see* Humber River Regional Hospital, Downsview ON p. 2802

Malcolm Lydia Library, *see* Henderson District Public Libraries, Henderson NV p. 1428

Malcolm X College Library, Chicago IL p. 618

Malden Historical Society, Malden MA p. 1102

Malden Public Library, Malden MA p. 1102

Malheur County Library, Ontario OR p. 2008

Mallaig Public Library, *see* Bibliotheque Mallaig Library, Mallaig AB p. 2710

Mallard Public Library, Mallard IA p. 829

MALLCO (N), *see* Mid-America Law Library Consortium, Grand Forks ND p. 2951

MALLCO (N), *see* Mid-Atlantic Law Library Cooperative, Morgantown WV p. 2958

Mallet Chemistry Library, *see* University of Texas Libraries, Austin TX p. 2284

Malley Henry A Memorial Library, Broadus MT p. 1375

Mallinckrodt Baker, Inc, Phillipsburg NJ p. 1519

Mallory Tracy Burr Memorial Library, *see* Massachusetts General Hospital, Boston MA p. 1063

Malloy/Jordon East Winston Heritage Center, *see* Forsyth County Public Library, Winston-Salem NC p. 1832

Malone University, Canton OH p. 1863

Malta Community Center, *see* Round Lake Library, Malta NY p. 1736

Malta Township Public Library, Malta IL p. 669

Maltman Memorial Public Library, Wood River NE p. 1424

Malvern-Hot Spring County Library, Malvern AR p. 108

Malvern Public Library, Malvern IA p. 829

Malvern Public Library, Malvern PA p. 2083

Malverne Public Library, Malverne NY p. 1657

Maly Eugene H Memorial Library, *see* Athenaeum of Ohio, Cincinnati OH p. 1868

Mamakating Library, Wurtsboro NY p. 1771

Mamaroneck Public Library District, Mamaroneck NY p. 1657

Mamies Place Childrens Library & Learning Center, *see* Russell Adelia McConnell Library, Alexander City AL p. 4

Mammoth Public Library, Mammoth AZ p. 68

Manasquan Public Library, Manasquan NJ p. 1499

Manassas National Battlefield Park Library, Manassas VA p. 2477

Manatee Community College Library, Bradenton FL p. 429

Manatee County Law Library, Bradenton FL p. 429

Manatee County Public Library System, Bradenton FL p. 429

Manatt, Phelps & Phillips LLP, Washington DC p. 408

Mancelona Township Library, Mancelona MI p. 1205

Manchester-by-the-Sea Public Library, Manchester-by-the-Sea MA p. 1102

Manchester City Library, Manchester NH p. 1455

Manchester College, North Manchester IN p. 769

Manchester Community College, Manchester NH p. 1455

Manchester Community College Library, Manchester CT p. 350

Manchester District Library, Manchester MI p. 1205

Manchester Historic Association Library, Manchester NH p. 1456

Manchester Historical Museum, Manchester-by-the-Sea MA p. 1102

Manchester Public Library, Manchester CT p. 350

Manchester Public Library, Manchester IA p. 829

Manchester Public Library, *see* Adams County Public Library, Manchester OH p. 1912

Mancini Nicholas Library Information Center, *see* Hamilton Wentworth Catholic District School Board, Hamilton ON p. 2810

Mancos Public Library, Mancos CO p. 318

Mancuso Frank O Neighborhood Library, *see* Houston Public Library, Houston TX p. 2339

Manderino Louis L Library, *see* California University of Pennsylvania, California PA p. 2040

Maner Memorial Library, *see* Cisco College, Cisco TX p. 2297

Manhasset Public Library, Manhasset NY p. 1657

Manhattan Center Library, *see* Adelphi University, New York NY p. 1667

Manhattan Christian College Library, Manhattan KS p. 881

Manhattan College, Riverdale NY p. 1727

Manhattan Community Library, Manhattan MT p. 1386

Manhattan-Elwood Public Library District, Manhattan IL p. 669

Manhattan Public Library, Manhattan KS p. 881

Manhattan School of Music, New York NY p. 1685

Manhattanville College Library, Purchase NY p. 1724

Manheim Community Library, Manheim PA p. 2084

Manheim Township Public Library, Lancaster PA p. 2077

Manila Public, *see* Mississippi County Library System, Manila AR p. 96

Manilla Public Library, Manilla IA p. 829

Manistee County Historical Museum, Manistee MI p. 1205

Manistee County Library, Manistee MI p. 1205

Manistique School & Public Library, Manistique MI p. 1206

Manitoba Agriculture, Food & Rural Initiatives, Portage la Prairie MB p. 2750

Manitoba Association of Playwrights Library, Winnipeg MB p. 2756

Manitoba Crafts Museum & Library, Winnipeg MB p. 2756

Manitoba Department of Culture, Heritage & Tourism, Winnipeg MB p. 2756

Manitoba Department of Education, Winnipeg MB p. 2756

Manitoba Department of Finance, Winnipeg MB p. 2756

Manitoba Department of Justice, Winnipeg MB p. 2756

Manitoba Developmental Centre Memorial Library, Portage la Prairie MB p. 2750

Manitoba Genealogical Society Inc Library, Winnipeg MB p. 2756

Manitoba Hydro Library, Winnipeg MB p. 2756

Manitoba Incorporated Library-Tony Mann, *see* Canadian Paraplegic Association, Winnipeg MB p. 2754

Manitoba Indigenous Culture-Educational Center, Winnipeg MB p. 2756

Manitoba Labour Board Library, Winnipeg MB p. 2757

Manitoba Law Library, Inc, Winnipeg MB p. 2757

Manitoba Library Consortium, Inc (N), Winnipeg MB p. 2959

Manitoba Museum, Winnipeg MB p. 2757

Manitoba School for the Deaf Multimedia Center, Winnipeg MB p. 2757

Manitou Regional Library, Manitou MB p. 2749

Manitou Springs Public Library, Manitou Springs CO p. 318

Manitouwadge Public Library, Manitouwadge ON p. 2820

Manitowoc-Calumet Library System, Two Rivers WI p. 2643

Manitowoc Public Library, Manitowoc WI p. 2612

Mankato City Library, Mankato KS p. 882

Mankoff Resource Center, Dallas TX p. 2309

Manley Dwight N Numismatic Library, *see* American Numismatic Association Library, Colorado Springs CO p. 294

Manlius Library, Manlius NY p. 1657

Manly Public Library, Manly IA p. 829

Mann Albert R Library, *see* Cornell University Library, Ithaca NY p. 1642

Mann'Arthur L Memorial Library, *see* West Paris Public Library, West Paris ME p. 1006

Mann Kristine Library, New York NY p. 1685

Mannford Public Library, Mannford OK p. 1967

Manning H V Library, *see* Claflin University, Orangeburg SC p. 2201

Manning Mabel, *see* Chicago Public Library, Chicago IL p. 609

Manning Municipal & District Library, Manning AB p. 2711

Manning Public Library, Manning IA p. 829

Mannington Public, *see* Marion County Public Library, Mannington WV p. 2559

Mannsville Free Library, Mannsville NY p. 1657

Mannville Centenial Public Library, Mannville AB p. 2711

Manoa Public Library, *see* Hawaii State Public Library System, Honolulu HI p. 563

Manomet Center for Conservation Sciences Library, Manomet MA p. 1102

Manor College, Jenkintown PA p. 2072

Manor Harold C Library, *see* Palm Beach State College, Lake Worth FL p. 459

Manor Public Library, Manor PA p. 2084

Manross Memorial, *see* Bristol Public Library, Forestville CT p. 332

Mansbach Memorial Library, *see* Ashland Community & Technical College, Ashland KY p. 905

Mansfield Art Center Library, *see* Mansfield Fine Arts Guild, Inc, Mansfield OH p. 1912

Mansfield Fine Arts Guild, Inc, Mansfield OH p. 1912

Mansfield Free Public Library, Mansfield PA p. 2084

Mansfield Historical Society, Storrs CT p. 370

Mansfield Library, *see* Scott-Sebastian Regional Library, Mansfield AR p. 102

Mansfield Maureen & Mike Library, *see* University of Montana, Missoula MT p. 1386

Mansfield Public Library, Mansfield Center CT p. 350

Mansfield Public Library, Mansfield MA p. 1102

Mansfield Public Library, Temple NH p. 1466

Mansfield Public Library, Mansfield TX p. 2359

Mansfield Public Library, *see* Blue Ridge Township Public Library, Mansfield IL p. 670

Mansfield-Richland County Public Library, Mansfield OH p. 1912

Mansfield University, Mansfield PA p. 2084

Manship Luther Medical Library, *see* Saint Dominic-Jackson Memorial Hospital, Jackson MS p. 1305

Manson Community, *see* North Central Regional Library, Manson WA p. 2549

Manson Public Library, Manson IA p. 829

Manti Public Library, Manti UT p. 2407

Mantor Library, *see* University of Maine at Farmington, Farmington ME p. 985

Manuel George M Memorial Library, *see* Piedmont Baptist College & Graduate School, Winston-Salem NC p. 1833

Manufacturers Association of Central New York Library, Syracuse NY p. 1752

Manville Public Library, Manville NJ p. 1499

MAPA Regional Library, *see* Metropolitan Area Planning Agency, Omaha NE p. 1413

Maple Park Public Library District, Maple Park IL p. 670

Maple Rapids Public Library, Maple Rapids MI p. 1206

Maple Ridge Public Library, *see* Fraser Valley Regional Library, Maple Ridge BC p. 2724

Maple Springs Baptist Bible College & Seminary Library, Capitol Heights MD p. 1023

Maple Woods Community College Library, *see* Metropolitan Community College, Kansas City MO p. 1339

Maplesville Public Library, *see* Chilton Clanton Library, Maplesville AL p. 12

Maplewood Memorial Library, Maplewood NJ p. 1499

Maplewood Public Library, Maplewood MO p. 1344

Maquoketa Public Library, Maquoketa IA p. 829

Maquon Public Library District, Maquon IL p. 670

Marana Community Correctional Facility Library, *see* Arizona Department of Corrections - Adult Institutions, Marana AZ p. 68

Maranatha Baptist Bible College, Watertown WI p. 2644

Marathon County Historical Society Library, Wausau WI p. 2646

Marathon County Public Library, Wausau WI p. 2646

Marathon Public, *see* Alpine Public Library, Marathon TX p. 2273

Marathon Public Library, Marathon IA p. 829

Marathon Public Library, Marathon ON p. 2820

Marble Alexander Library, *see* Joslin Diabetes Center, Inc, Boston MA p. 1062

Marble Falls Public, *see* Burnet County Library System, Marble Falls TX p. 2293

Marble Public Library, Marble MN p. 1258

Marble Rock Public Library, Marble Rock IA p. 829

Marble Valley Regional Correctional Facility, Rutland VT p. 2434

Marblehead Museum & Historical Society Library, Marblehead MA p. 1102

Marcelin Public Library, *see* Wapiti Regional Library, Marcelin SK p. 2921

Marceline Carnegie Library, Marceline MO p. 1344

Marcellus Free Library, Marcellus NY p. 1657

Marcellus Township-Wood Memorial Library, Marcellus MI p. 1206

March Clarence E Library, *see* Androscoggin Historical Society, Auburn ME p. 973

Marchais Jacques Museum of Tibetan Art Library, Staten Island NY p. 1747

Marcus Gladys Library, *see* Fashion Institute of Technology-SUNY, New York NY p. 1678

Marcus Public Library, Marcus IA p. 829

Mardigian Library, *see* University of Michigan-Dearborn, Dearborn MI p. 1168

Marengo County Public Library, Linden AL p. 23

Marengo Library System, Demopolis AL p. 15

Marengo Public Library, Marengo IA p. 830

Marengo-Union Library District, Marengo IL p. 670

Marfa Public Library, Marfa TX p. 2359

Gilbreath Margaret Clark Library, Little Rock AR p. 107

Margate City Public Library, Margate City NJ p. 1499

Margen Sheldon Public Health Library, *see* University of California, Berkeley, Berkeley CA p. 128

Margolies Dr Michael Library, *see* Coatesville Area Public Library, Coatesville PA p. 2046

Maria College of Albany Library, Albany NY p. 1569

Marian College, Indianapolis IN p. 755

Marian Court College, Swampscott MA p. 1130

Marian Library, *see* University of Dayton Libraries, Dayton OH p. 1894

Marian University, Fond du Lac WI p. 2592

Marianjoy Rehabilitation Hospital, Wheaton IL p. 718

Marianna Community Public Library, Marianna PA p. 2084

Maricopa Community Library, Maricopa AZ p. 68

Maricopa County Community College District (N), Tempe AZ p. 2937

Maricopa County Jail Library, Phoenix AZ p. 74

Maricopa County Library District, Phoenix AZ p. 74

Marienville Area Public Library, *see* Forest County Library, Marienville PA p. 2084

Marietta College, Marietta OH p. 1913

Marietta Memorial Hospital, Marietta OH p. 1913

Marietta Public Library, *see* Northeast Regional Library, Marietta MS p. 1297

Marigold Library System, Strathmore AB p. 2718

Marilla Free Library, Marilla NY p. 1658

Marin County Free Library, San Rafael CA p. 257

Marin County Law Library, San Rafael CA p. 257

Marin General Hospital, Greenbrae CA p. 156

Marin History Museum Library, San Rafael CA p. 257

Marine Biological Laboratory Woods Hole Oceanographic Institution Library, Woods Hole MA p. 1142

Marine City Public, *see* Saint Clair County Library System, Marine City MI p. 1219

Marine Corps Base Hawaii Libraries, Kaneohe Bay HI p. 566

Marine Corps Logistics Base Library, *see* United States Navy, Albany GA p. 507

Marine Corps Recruit Depot Library, San Diego CA p. 231

Marine Environmental Sciences Consortium (N), Dauphin Island AL p. 2937

Marine Institute Library, *see* University of Georgia, Sapelo Island GA p. 549

Marine Museum at Fall River, Inc Library, Fall River MA p. 1088

Marine Museum of the Great Lakes, Kingston ON p. 2814

Marine Products Library, Quincy MA p. 1119

Marine Resources Library, Charleston SC p. 2184

Marinette County Law Library, Marinette WI p. 2612

Marinette County Library System, Marinette WI p. 2612

Maring-Hunt Library, *see* Muncie Public Library, Muncie IN p. 767

Marion Carnegie Library, Marion IL p. 670

Marion City Library, Marion KS p. 882

Marion Correctional Institution Library, Ocala FL p. 474

Marion Correctional Institution Library, Marion OH p. 1914

Marion County Law Library, Indianapolis IN p. 755

Marion County Law Library, Marion OH p. 1914

Marion County Law Library, Salem OR p. 2017

Marion County Library, Yellville AR p. 117

Marion County Library, Marion SC p. 2200

Marion County Public Library, Lebanon KY p. 919

Marion County Public Library, Fairmont WV p. 2559

Marion County Public Library, *see* Chattahoochee Valley Libraries, Buena Vista GA p. 526

Marion County Public Library System, Ocala FL p. 474

Marion County Sub-District Library, Palmyra MO p. 1348

Marion General Hospital, Marion IN p. 763

Marion General Hospital, Marion OH p. 1914

Marion ISD Community Library, Marion TX p. 2359

Marion Military Institute, Marion AL p. 24

Marion Oaks Public Library, *see* Marion County Public Library System, Ocala FL p. 474

Marion-Perry County Library, Marion AL p. 24

Marion Public Library, Marion IN p. 763

Marion Public Library, Marion IA p. 830

Marion Public Library, Marion NY p. 1658

Marion Public Library, Marion OH p. 1914

Marion Public Library, Marion WI p. 2613

Mariposa County Law Library, Mariposa CA p. 183

Mariposa County Library, Mariposa CA p. 183

Mariposa Museum Library, Peterborough NH p. 1461

Marissa Public Library, Marissa IL p. 670

Marist College, Poughkeepsie NY p. 1722

Marist College Library, Washington DC p. 408

Maritime Museum of British Columbia Library, Victoria BC p. 2745

Maritime Museum of San Diego, San Diego CA p. 232

Maritime Museum of the Atlantic, Halifax NS p. 2781

Maritimes Health Libraries Association (N), Halifax NS p. 2959

Marjorie Mews Public Library, St. John's NL p. 2772

Markham Anne Parrish Library, *see* Mid-Continent College, Mayfield KY p. 928

Markham Public Library, Markham IL p. 670

Markham Public Library, Markham ON p. 2820

Markham Stouffville Hospital Library, Markham ON p. 2820

Markle Public Library, *see* Huntington City Township Public Library, Markle IN p. 748

Markosian Library, *see* Salt Lake Community College Libraries, Salt Lake City UT p. 2413

Markowitz Jewel K Library, *see* Beth David Reform Congregation, Gladwyne PA p. 2060

Marks Fine Arts Library, *see* Danforth Museum of Art, Framingham MA p. 1089

Marks Maud Smith, *see* Harris County Public Library, Katy TX p. 2336

Marks-Quitman County Library, Marks MS p. 1307

Markus Rita & Frits Library & Scientific Commons, *see* Rockefeller University, New York NY p. 1698

Marlboro College, Marlboro VT p. 2428

Marlboro County Library, Bennettsville SC p. 2182

Marlboro Free Library, Marlboro NY p. 1658

Marlborough Gallery Library, New York NY p. 1685

Marlborough Public Library, Marlborough MA p. 1103

Marlette District Library, Marlette MI p. 1206

Marlin Public Library, see Chilton Pauline & Jane Memorial Public Library, Marlin TX p. 2359

Marlow Town Library, Marlow NH p. 1457

Marmion Academy Library, Aurora IL p. 592

Marmion Library, see Church of the Incarnation, Dallas TX p. 2305

Marmora & Lake Public Library, Marmora ON p. 2820

Maroa Public Library District, Maroa IL p. 670

Marple Public Library, Broomall PA p. 2038

Marquand Library Art & Archaeology, see Princeton University, Princeton NJ p. 1524

Marquat Memorial Library, see United States Army, Fort Bragg NC p. 1794

Marquette Community Library, Marquette KS p. 882

Marquette County Historical Society, Marquette MI p. 1206

Marquette General Health System, Marquette MI p. 1206

Marquette Heights Public Library, Marquette Heights IL p. 671

Marquette Pere District Library, Clare MI p. 1163

Marquette University, Milwaukee WI p. 2618

Marquette University Libraries, Milwaukee WI p. 2618

Marrero Lillian, see Free Library of Philadelphia, Philadelphia PA p. 2108

Marriott Library, see University of Utah, Salt Lake City UT p. 2415

Marrowbone Public Library District, Bethany IL p. 594

Mars Area Public Library, Mars PA p. 2084

Mars Hill College, Mars Hill NC p. 1809

Marseilles Public Library, Marseilles IL p. 671

J Frank Marsh Library, see Concord University, Athens WV p. 2553

Marshall & Melhorn, Toledo OH p. 1939

Marshall A D Library, see Eston College, Eston SK p. 2917

Marshall Community Health Library, Placerville CA p. 208

Marshall Community Library, Marshall WI p. 2613

Marshall County Cooperative Library, Albertville AL p. 3

Marshall County Historical Society Library, Lacon IL p. 662

Marshall County Historical Society Library, Plymouth IN p. 773

Marshall County Library System, Holly Springs MS p. 1302

Marshall County Memorial Library, Lewisburg TN p. 2245

Marshall County Public Library System, Benton KY p. 907

Marshall District Library, Marshall MI p. 1207

Marshall Eric Aquatic Research Library, see Department of Fisheries & Oceans Canada, Central & Arctic Region, Winnipeg MB p. 2755

Marshall George C Foundation Research Library, Lexington VA p. 2474

Marshall John, see Fairfax County Public Library, Alexandria VA p. 2461

Marshall John, see Fauquier County Public Library, Marshall VA p. 2501

Marshall John Law School, Chicago IL p. 618

Marshall-Lyon County Library, Marshall MN p. 1258

Marshall Memorial Library, Deming NM p. 1554

Marshall Public Library, Pocatello ID p. 582

Marshall Public Library, Marshall IL p. 671

Marshall Public Library, Marshall MO p. 1344

Marshall Public Library, Marshall TX p. 2360

Marshall Thurgood, see Chicago Public Library, Chicago IL p. 609

Marshall Thurgood Law Library, see University of Maryland, Baltimore, Baltimore MD p. 1019

Marshall Thurgood Library, see Bowie State University, Bowie MD p. 1022

Marshall Thurgood School of Law Library, see Texas Southern University, Houston TX p. 2342

Marshall University Libraries, Huntington WV p. 2561

Marshalltown Community College, Marshalltown IA p. 830

Marshalltown Public Library, Marshalltown IA p. 830

Marshallville Public, see Middle Georgia Regional Library System, Marshallville GA p. 541

Marshfield Clinic, Marshfield WI p. 2613

Marshfield Public Library, Marshfield WI p. 2613

Marston Memorial Historical Center & Archives, see Free Methodist Church of North America, Indianapolis IN p. 751

Marstons Mills Public Library, Marstons Mills MA p. 1103

Martelle Public Library, Martelle IA p. 830

Martha's Vineyard Museum, Edgartown MA p. 1087

Martin Army Community Hospital Library, see United States Army, Fort Benning GA p. 532

Martin Bennett Public Library, see Lincoln City Libraries, Lincoln NE p. 1404

Martin Community College Library, Williamston NC p. 1830

Martin Correctional Institution Library, Indiantown FL p. 452

Martin County Historical Society, Inc, Fairmont MN p. 1250

Martin County Law Library, see Martin County Library System, Stuart FL p. 492

Martin County Library, Fairmont MN p. 1250

Martin County Library, Stanton TX p. 2389

Martin County Library System, Stuart FL p. 491

Martin County Public Library, Inez KY p. 918

Martin Elizabeth Rasmussen Memorial Library, New Hartford IA p. 835

Martin Francis, see New York Public Library - Astor, Lenox & Tilden Foundations, Bronx NY p. 1692

Martin Frank Lee Memorial Journalism Library, see University of Missouri-Columbia, Columbia MO p. 1326

Martin J W Library, see Northwestern Oklahoma State University, Alva OK p. 1956

Martin Luther College Library, New Ulm MN p. 1268

Martin Memorial, see Beaufort, Hyde & Martin County Regional Library, Williamston NC p. 1828

Martin Memorial Library, Williamston NC p. 1830

Martin Memorial Library, York PA p. 2159

Martin Methodist College, Pulaski TN p. 2264

Martin Mildred B Branch, see Rapides Parish Library, Pineville LA p. 940

Martin Music Library, see New Orleans Baptist Theological Seminary, New Orleans LA p. 961

Martin Paul Law Library, see University of Windsor, Windsor ON p. 2871

Martin Regional Library, see Tulsa City-County Library, Tulsa OK p. 1983

Martin Thomas Memorial Library, see Southern Research Institute, Birmingham AL p. 9

Martin Township Public Library, Colfax IL p. 630

Martindale Bobby Memorial Library, Grand Junction TN p. 2235

Martinez Library, see Contra Costa County Library, Martinez CA p. 209

Martins Ferry Public Library, Martins Ferry OH p. 1914

Martinsburg Community Library, Martinsburg PA p. 2084

Martinsburg Public Library, see Martinsburg-Berkeley County Public Library, Martinsburg WV p. 2565

Martinsburg-Berkeley County Public Library, Martinsburg WV p. 2565

Martinsville Public Library District, Martinsville IL p. 671

Marvell Library, see Phillips-Lee-Monroe Regional Library, Marvell AR p. 103

Marvin Dwight Learning Resources Center, see Hudson Valley Community College, Troy NY p. 1756

Marvin Memorial Library, Shelby OH p. 1934

Marwayne Public Library, Marwayne AB p. 2711

Marx Brothers Library & Archives, see Freedonia Gazette, New Hope PA p. 2097

Marx Robert S Law Library, see University of Cincinnati, Cincinnati OH p. 1874

Mary Baldwin College, Staunton VA p. 2496

Marygrove College Library, Detroit MI p. 1171

Maryland Association of Health Science Librarians (N), Baltimore MD p. 2944

Maryland Correctional Institution for Women Library, Jessup MD p. 1033

Maryland Correctional Institution-Hagerstown Library, Hagerstown MD p. 1031

Maryland Correctional Institution-Jessup Library, Jessup MD p. 1033

Maryland Correctional Training Center Library, Hagerstown MD p. 1031

Maryland Department of Legislative Services Library, Annapolis MD p. 1010

Maryland Department of Natural Resources, Annapolis MD p. 1010

Maryland Department of Planning Library, Baltimore MD p. 1015

Maryland General Hospital, Baltimore MD p. 1015

Maryland Historical Society Library, Baltimore MD p. 1015

Maryland House of Correction Library, Jessup MD p. 1033

Maryland Institute College of Art, Baltimore MD p. 1015

Maryland Interlibrary Loan Organization (N), Baltimore MD p. 2944

Maryland National Capital Park & Planning Commission, Clinton MD p. 1024

Maryland Pharmacists Association Library, Baltimore MD p. 1015

Maryland State Department of Education, Baltimore MD p. 1015

Maryland State Division of Labor & Industry, Laurel MD p. 1035

Maryland State Law Library, Annapolis MD p. 1010

Maryland State Library for the Blind & Physically Handicapped, Baltimore MD p. 1015

Marylhurst University, Marylhurst OR p. 2004

Marymount College Library, Rancho Palos Verdes CA p. 213

Marymount Manhattan College, New York NY p. 1685

Marymount University, Arlington VA p. 2449

Marystown Public Library, Marystown NL p. 2770

Marysville Community Library, see Sno-Isle Libraries, Marysville WA p. 2542

Marysville Public, see Saint Clair County Library System, Marysville MI p. 1219

Marysville Public Library, Marysville KS p. 882

Marysville Public Library, Marysville OH p. 1915

Marysville-Rye Library, Marysville PA p. 2084

Maryville College, Maryville TN p. 2247

Maryville Public Library, Maryville MO p. 1344

Maryville University Library, Saint Louis MO p. 1356

Marywood University Library, Scranton PA p. 2137

Masaryk Memorial Institute Inc, Scarborough ON p. 2840

Mascoutah Public Library, Mascoutah IL p. 671

Mashantucket Pequot Museum & Research Center, Mashantucket CT p. 350

Mashpee Public Library, Mashpee MA p. 1103

Masland Library, see Cairn University, Langhorne PA p. 2078

Mason City Public, see Mason County Library System, Mason WV p. 2570

Mason City Public Library, Mason City IA p. 830

Mason City Public Library District, Mason City IL p. 671

Mason County District Library, Ludington MI p. 1204

Mason County Historical Society, Ludington MI p. 1204

Mason County Library, Mason TX p. 2360

Mason County Library System, Point Pleasant WV p. 2570

Mason County Public Library, Maysville KY p. 928

Mason-Dixon Public Library, Stewartstown PA p. 2143

Mayo Clinic Scottsdale Libraries, Scottsdale AZ p. 80

Mayo Correctional Institution Library, *see* Florida Department of Corrections, Mayo FL p. 463

Mayo Foundation, Rochester MN p. 1272

Mayor Joe V Sanchez Public Library, Weslaco TX p. 2399

Mayor Salvatore Mancini Union Free Public Library, *see* North Providence Union Free Library, North Providence RI p. 2170

Maysville Community & Technical College Library, Maysville KY p. 928

Maysville Public, *see* Piedmont Regional Library, Maysville GA p. 557

Maysville Public Library, *see* Neuse Regional Library, Maysville NC p. 1805

Mayview State Hospital, Bridgeville PA p. 2037

Mayville District Public Library, Mayville MI p. 1207

Mayville Library, Mayville NY p. 1659

Mayville Public Library, Mayville ND p. 1846

Mayville Public Library, Mayville WI p. 2613

Mayville State University, Mayville ND p. 1846, 2971

Chavez Cesar Library, *see* County of Los Angeles Public Library, Maywood CA p. 142

Maywood Public Library, Maywood NJ p. 1500

Maywood Public Library District, Maywood IL p. 672

Mazamas Library & Archives, Portland OR p. 2011

Mazinaigan Waakaaigant - Red Cliff Public Library, Bayfield WI p. 2580

Mazomanie Free Library, Mazomanie WI p. 2614

McAlester Public Library, McAlester OK p. 1968

McAllen Memorial Library, McAllen TX p. 2360

McArthur Public Library, Biddeford ME p. 977

MCAS Station Library, *see* United States Marine Corps, Jacksonville NC p. 1803

McAteer Charles Y Library, *see* American Association of Variable Star Observers, Cambridge MA p. 1072

McAuliffe Christa Corrigan, *see* Framingham Public Library, Framingham MA p. 1090

McBain Community Library, McBain MI p. 1207

McBee Depot Library, *see* Chesterfield County Library, McBee SC p. 2186

McBride & District Public Library, McBride BC p. 2731

McBride Art Reference Library, *see* Grand Rapids Art Museum, Grand Rapids MI p. 1184

McBride Library, *see* United States Air Force, Keesler AFB MS p. 1306

McBride Memorial Library, Berwick PA p. 2033

McBride Oleta Media Center, *see* Glenstone Baptist Church, Springfield MO p. 1366

McBurney Memorial, *see* Davis Jefferson Parish Library, Welsh LA p. 952

McCabe Library, *see* Swarthmore College, Swarthmore PA p. 2144

McCain Andrew & Laura Public Library, *see* Haut-Saint-Jean Regional Library, Florenceville-Bristol NB p. 2762

McCain Library, *see* Agnes Scott College, Decatur GA p. 529

McCain Library, *see* Erskine College & Theological Seminary, Due West SC p. 2193

McCain Virgil B Jr Learning Resource Center, *see* Snead State Community College, Boaz AL p. 10

McCain William David Library & Archives, *see* University of Southern Mississippi Library, Hattiesburg MS p. 1301

McCall Public Library, McCall ID p. 578

McCardle Library, *see* Vicksburg & Warren County Historical Society, Vicksburg MS p. 1317

McCarter & English, Newark NJ p. 1510

McCarthy Tetrault Library, Vancouver BC p. 2741

McCarthy Tétrault LLP, Toronto ON p. 2855

McCarthy Tetrault LLP Library, Calgary AB p. 2692

McCarthy Walter T Law Library, Arlington VA p. 2449

McCartney Library, *see* Geneva College, Beaver Falls PA p. 2031

McCauley Hannah V Library, *see* Ohio University-Lancaster Library, Lancaster OH p. 1909

McCaw Foundation Library of Asian Art, *see* Seattle Art Museum, Seattle WA p. 2530

McClanahan Butch Memorial Library, *see* Ignacio Community Library District, Ignacio CO p. 313

McClatchy E K Neighborhood Library, *see* Sacramento Public Library, Sacramento CA p. 225

McClatchy Washington Bureau Library, Washington DC p. 408

McClellan Center, *see* Gadsden State Community College, Anniston AL p. 18

McClellan Julia Crowder Memorial Library, Mounds OK p. 1969

McClintock-Ensminger Library, *see* Southern Union State Community College, Wadley AL p. 40

McClung Nellie, *see* Greater Victoria Public Library Board, Victoria BC p. 2745

McClure Community Library, *see* Snyder County Libraries, McClure PA p. 2138

McClure Reed Law Firm Library, Seattle WA p. 2528

McCollum Public, *see* Jefferson County Library System, Wrens GA p. 539

McComb Public Library, McComb OH p. 1916

McComb Public Library, *see* Pike-Amite-Walthall Library System, McComb MS p. 1307

McConathy Nancy L Public Library, Sauk Village IL p. 700

McCone George Memorial County Library, Circle MT p. 1377

McConnell James Memorial Library, *see* Cape Breton Regional Library, Sydney NS p. 2785

McConnell John Preston Library, *see* Radford University, Radford VA p. 2487

McConnell Valdes, Hato Rey PR p. 2673

McConnico Jack Memorial Library, Selmer TN p. 2265

McCook Community College, McCook NE p. 1408

McCook Public Library, McCook NE p. 1408

McCook Public Library District, McCook IL p. 672

McCord Memorial Library, North East PA p. 2099

McCormick & Co, Inc, Hunt Valley MD p. 1032

McCormick, Barstow, Sheppard, Wayte & Carruth, Fresno CA p. 153

McCormick Colonel Robert R Research Center, Wheaton IL p. 718

McCormick County Library, McCormick SC p. 2200

McCormick Katharine Dexter Library, *see* Planned Parenthood Federation of America, Inc, New York NY p. 1697

McCormick Library, *see* Harrisburg Area Community College, Harrisburg PA p. 2065

McCormick Riverfront Library, *see* Dauphin County Library System, Harrisburg PA p. 2064

McCormick Robert R Memorial Library, *see* American Conservatory of Music, Hammond IN p. 747

McCormick Robert R Tribune Foundation Library, *see* Roosevelt University, Schaumburg IL p. 623

McCowan Memorial Library, Pitman NJ p. 1520

McCowen Ruth Public Library, *see* Elida Public Library, Elida NM p. 1554

McCoy Larry W Learning Resource Center, *see* Northwest-Shoals Community College, Muscle Shoals AL p. 32

McCoy Lavenia Public Library, *see* Pine River Public Library District, Bayfield CO p. 289

McCoy Memorial Library, McLeansboro IL p. 672

McCoy Public Library, Shullsburg WI p. 2638

McCracken County Public Library, Paducah KY p. 932

McCracken Public Library, McCracken KS p. 882

McCracken Research Library, *see* Buffalo Bill Historical Center, Cody WY p. 2653

McCrane Eva Alice Kashmere Gardens Neighborhood Library, *see* Houston Public Library, Houston TX p. 2339

McCrary Marjorie Walker Memorial, *see* Lonoke Prairie County Regional Library Headquarters, Lonoke AR p. 108

McCray Rube Memorial, *see* Columbus County Public Library, Lake Waccamaw NC p. 1829

McCreary County Public Library District, Whitley City KY p. 937

MCCS Hawaii Libraries, *see* Marine Corps Base Hawaii Libraries, Kaneohe Bay HI p. 566

MCCS Lifelong Learning Library, *see* United States Marine Corps, Twentynine Palms CA p. 277

McCullough John G Free Library Inc, North Bennington VT p. 2430

McCully-Moiliili Public Library, *see* Hawaii State Public Library System, Honolulu HI p. 563

McCune Osage Township Library, McCune KS p. 882

McDaniel College, Westminster MD p. 1046, 2967

McDermott Eugene Library, *see* University of Texas at Dallas, Richardson TX p. 2374

McDermott Library, *see* United States Air Force Academy Libraries, USAF Academy CO p. 324

McDermott, Will & Emery Law Library, Chicago IL p. 618

McDonald Army Health Center Library, Fort Eustis VA p. 2464

McDonald Ben F, *see* Corpus Christi Public Libraries, Corpus Christi TX p. 2301

McDonald County Library, Pineville MO p. 1349

McDonald Elvin Horticultural Library, *see* Monmouth County Park System, Middletown NJ p. 1502

McDonald Hopkins, LPA, Cleveland OH p. 1880

McDonald W J, *see* Rapides Parish Library, Glenmora LA p. 940

McDonald Library, *see* Oregon National Primate Research Center, Beaverton OR p. 1991

McDonald Memorial Library, *see* Xavier University, Cincinnati OH p. 1875

McDonald Public Library, McDonald KS p. 882

McDowell County Public Library, Marion NC p. 1808

McDowell Public Library, Welch WV p. 2573

McDowell Technical Community College Library, Marion NC p. 1809

McEachern Annie Hubbard Public, *see* Robeson County Public Library, Saint Pauls NC p. 1808

McEachern Leora H Library of Local History, *see* Duplin County Historical Foundation, Rose Hill NC p. 1821

MCEER Information Service, *see* Multidisciplinary Center for Earthquake Engineering Research, Buffalo NY p. 1598

McElroy, Deutsch, Mulvaney & Carpenter, LLP, Morristown NJ p. 1505

McElvain Catherine Library, *see* School for Advanced Research Library, Santa Fe NM p. 1564

McElveen Library, *see* United States Air Force, Shaw AFB SC p. 2204

McElwain Edward Memorial Library, Peach Springs AZ p. 71

McEntegart Hall Library, *see* Saint Joseph's College, Brooklyn NY p. 1594

McEwen Robert C Library, *see* United States Army, Fort Drum NY p. 1623

McFarland Andrew Mental Health Center, Springfield IL p. 706

McFarland Public Library, McFarland WI p. 2614

McFarlane Robert M Medical Library, *see* Saint Joseph's Hospital, London ON p. 2818

McFarlin Library, *see* University of Tulsa Libraries, Tulsa OK p. 1984

McGarry Public Library, Virginiatown ON p. 2869

McGaw Library & Learning Center, *see* Alice Lloyd College, Pippa Passes KY p. 933

McGhee Lawson Library, *see* Knox County Public Library System, Knoxville TN p. 2241

McGill Library, *see* Westminster College, New Wilmington PA p. 2097

McGill University, Sainte-Anne-de-Bellevue QC p. 2910

McGill University, Montreal QC p. 2979

McGill University Libraries, Montreal QC p. 2898

McGinley Memorial Public Library, McGregor TX p. 2361

McGinnis, Lochridge & Kilgore, LLP, Austin TX p. 2281

McGirt-Horton, *see* Greensboro Public Library, Greensboro NC p. 1796

McGlannan Health Sciences Library, Baltimore MD p. 1016

Meadville-Lombard Theological School Library, Chicago IL p. 618

Meadville Medical Center, Meadville PA p. 2086

Meadville Public Library, Meadville PA p. 2086

Meaford Public Library, Meaford ON p. 2821

Meagher County City Library, White Sulphur Springs MT p. 1390

Meany George Memorial Archives Library, Silver Spring MD p. 1041

Mears Library, *see* University of Sioux Falls, Sioux Falls SD p. 2219

Mebane Public Library, *see* Alamance County Public Libraries, Mebane NC p. 1779

Mecca Library, *see* Riverside County Library System, Mecca CA p. 218

Mechanic Falls Public Library, Mechanic Falls ME p. 991

Mechanics' Institute Library, San Francisco CA p. 243

Mechanicsburg Public Library, Mechanicsburg OH p. 1916

Mechanicsville Library, *see* Atlanta-Fulton Public Library System, Atlanta GA p. 512

Mechanicsville Public Library, Mechanicsville IA p. 831

Mechanicville District Public Library, Mechanicville NY p. 1659

Mechon Yochsin, *see* World Jewish Genealogy Organization Library, Brooklyn NY p. 1595

Medaille College Library, Buffalo NY p. 1598

Medal of Honor Memorial Library, *see* United States Army, Fort George G. Meade MD p. 1028

Medcenter One, Bismarck ND p. 1838

MedCentral Health System, Mansfield OH p. 1913

Meder Charles J Library, *see* Finger Lakes Community College, Canandaigua NY p. 1601

Medfield Historical Society Library, Medfield MA p. 1103

Medfield Memorial Public Library, Medfield MA p. 1103

Medford Public Library, Medford MA p. 1104

Medford Public Library, Medford OK p. 1968

Medgar Evers College, Brooklyn NY p. 1593

Media Center-Douglass Library, *see* Rutgers University Libraries, New Brunswick NJ p. 1509

Media-Upper Providence Free Library, Media PA p. 2087

Mediapolis Public Library, Mediapolis IA p. 831

Mediatheque, Institut de Tourisme et d'hotellerie du Quebec, Montreal QC p. 2899

Mediatheque Maskoutaine, Saint-Hyacinthe QC p. 2910

Mediatheque Pere Louis Lamontagne, *see* York Library Region, Miramichi NB p. 2764

Medical & Scientific Libraries of Long Island (N), Brookville NY p. 2950

Medical College of Wisconsin Libraries, Milwaukee WI p. 2619

Medical Cybernetics Foundation Library, *see* United Medical Technologies Corp, Jacksonville FL p. 455

Medical Group Management Association, Englewood CO p. 306

Medical Library, *see* Hotel-Dieu Grace Hospital, Windsor ON p. 2871

Medical Research Institute of Infectious Diseases Library, *see* United States Army, Frederick MD p. 1029

Medical Research Library of Brooklyn, *see* State University of New York Downstate Medical Center, Brooklyn NY p. 1595

Medical University of South Carolina Library, Charleston SC p. 2184

Medicine Hat College Library, Medicine Hat AB p. 2711

Medicine Hat Public Library, Medicine Hat AB p. 2711

Medicine Spring Library, *see* Blackfeet Community College, Browning MT p. 1376

Medieval Institute Library, *see* Hesburgh Libraries, Notre Dame IN p. 770

Medina Community Library, Medina TX p. 2361

Medina County District Library, Medina OH p. 1916

Medina County Law Library Association, Medina OH p. 1917

Medina Memorial Hospital, Medina NY p. 1659

Medium Price Security Library, *see* Rhode Island Department of Corrections, Cranston RI p. 2165

MEDLI (N), *see* Medical & Scientific Libraries of Long Island, Brookville NY p. 2950

MedStar Franklin Square Medical Center, Baltimore MD p. 1016

Medway Public Library, Medway MA p. 1104

Meehan Memorial Lansing Public Library, Lansing IA p. 827

Meek Paul Library, *see* University of Tennessee at Martin, Martin TN p. 2246

Meeker Regional Library District, Meeker CO p. 318

Meekins Library, Williamsburg MA p. 1140

Meem Library, *see* Saint John's College, Santa Fe NM p. 1563

Meharry Medical College Library, Nashville TN p. 2257

Meherrin Regional Library, Lawrenceville VA p. 2473

Mehoopany Area Library, Mehoopany PA p. 2088

Meigs County - Decatur Public Library, Decatur TN p. 2232

Meigs County District Public Library, Pomeroy OH p. 1930

Meigs Public Library, *see* Thomas County Public Library System, Meigs GA p. 553

Meijer Hendrik Library, *see* Muskegon Community College, Muskegon MI p. 1213

Meinders Community Library, Pipestone MN p. 1271

Meinhardt Memorial Library, *see* Art Institute of Fort Lauderdale, Fort Lauderdale FL p. 440

Meir Golda Library, *see* University of Wisconsin-Milwaukee Libraries, Milwaukee WI p. 2621

Meisel Nancy Petricoff Library, *see* Adath Israel Synagogue, Cincinnati OH p. 1868

Melbourne Beach Public Library, Melbourne Beach FL p. 464

Melbourne Public Library, Melbourne FL p. 463

Melbourne Public Library, Melbourne IA p. 831

Melbourne Public Library, *see* Izard County Library, Melbourne AR p. 109

Melcher-Dallas Public Library, Melcher-Dallas IA p. 831

Melcher Lucile Y Neighborhood Library, *see* Houston Public Library, Houston TX p. 2339

Melfort Public Library, *see* Wapiti Regional Library, Melfort SK p. 2921

Melick Library, *see* Eureka College, Eureka IL p. 643

Melissa Public Library, *see* City of Melissa Public Library, Melissa TX p. 2361

Melita Library, *see* Southwestern Manitoba Regional Library, Melita MB p. 2749

Mellinger Memorial Library, Morning Sun IA p. 833

Mellman Grace Community (Temecula County Center Library), *see* Riverside County Library System, Temecula CA p. 218

Mellon Andrew W Foundation, New York NY p. 1685

Mellon Institute Library, *see* Carnegie Mellon University, Pittsburgh PA p. 2124

Mellon Jennie King Library, *see* Chatham College, Pittsburgh PA p. 2124

Mellon M G Library of Chemistry, *see* Purdue University Libraries, West Lafayette IN p. 787

Mellor C C Memorial Library, Edgewood PA p. 2053

Melnyk Alice Public Library, Two Hills AB p. 2720

MELO (N), *see* Mississippi Electronic Libraries Online, Jackson MS p. 2947

Melrose Library, *see* Great River Regional Library, Melrose MN p. 1275

Melrose Park Public Library, Melrose Park IL p. 673

Melrose Public Library, Melrose MA p. 1104

Melrose Public Library, *see* Putnam County Library System, Melrose FL p. 478

MELSA (N), *see* Metropolitan Library Service Agency, Saint Paul MN p. 2947

Melton Arthur W Library, *see* American Psychological Association, Washington DC p. 392

Melton G T Learning Resources Center, *see* Lake City Community College, Lake City FL p. 457

Melton Public Library, French Lick IN p. 744

Melville Frank Jr Memorial Library, *see* Stony Brook University, Stony Brook NY p. 1749

Melville Library, Pine Bluff AR p. 112

Melvin Public Library, Melvin IL p. 673

Melvin Public Library, Melvin IA p. 831

Melvindale Public Library, Melvindale MI p. 1208

Memorial Hall Library, Andover MA p. 1049

Memorial Health University Medical Center, Savannah GA p. 550

Memorial Healthcare System, Hollywood FL p. 451

Memorial Hospital, Colorado Springs CO p. 295

Memorial Hospital, Easton MD p. 1027

Memorial Hospital, North Conway NH p. 1460

Memorial Hospital, Albany NY p. 1569

Memorial Hospital, Fremont OH p. 1900

Memorial Hospital at Gulfport, Gulfport MS p. 1300

Memorial Hospital Library, Belleville IL p. 593

Memorial Hospital Library, York PA p. 2159

Memorial Hospital of South Bend, South Bend IN p. 779

Memorial Hospital of Sweetwater County, Rock Springs WY p. 2659

Memorial Hospitals Association, Modesto CA p. 187

Memorial Library, *see* Chicago Academy of Sciences, Chicago IL p. 607

Memorial Library of Little Valley, Little Valley NY p. 1653

Memorial Library of Nazareth & Vicinity, Nazareth PA p. 2095

Memorial Medical Center, Springfield IL p. 706

Memorial Medical Library, *see* Saint Francis Hospital, Evanston IL p. 644

Memorial Park, *see* Calgary Public Library, Calgary AB p. 2690

Memorial Presbyterian Church, Midland MI p. 1208

Memorial Public Library of the Borough of Alexandria, Alexandria PA p. 2026

Memorial Regional Hospital Library, *see* Memorial Healthcare System, Hollywood FL p. 451

Memorial Sloan-Kettering Cancer Center Medical Library, New York NY p. 1685

Memorial University of Newfoundland, St. John's NL p. 2772

Memphis Botanic Garden Foundation, Inc, Memphis TN p. 2249

Memphis Brooks Museum of Art Library, Memphis TN p. 2249

Memphis College of Art, Memphis TN p. 2249

Memphis Pink Palace Museum Library, Memphis TN p. 2249

Memphis Public, *see* Saint Clair County Library System, Memphis MI p. 1219

Memphis Public Library, Memphis TX p. 2362

Memphis Public Library, Memphis TN p. 2249

Memphis Theological Seminary Library, Memphis TN p. 2250

Memramcook Public, *see* Albert-Westmorland-Kent Regional Library, Memramcook NB p. 2765

Menan-Annis Public Library, *see* Jefferson County District Library, Menan ID p. 578

Menands Public Library, Menands NY p. 1659

Menard Public Library, Menard TX p. 2362

Menasha Public Library, Menasha WI p. 2614

Menaul Historical Library of the Southwest, Albuquerque NM p. 1549

Mendel Art Gallery & Civic Conservatory Library, Saskatoon SK p. 2925

Mendel Music Library, *see* Princeton University, Princeton NJ p. 1524

Mendenhall Public Library, Mendenhall MS p. 1308

Mendes & Mount, LLP, New York NY p. 1686

Mendham Borough Library, Mendham NJ p. 1501

Mendham Township Library, Brookside NJ p. 1475

Mendocino Art Center Library, Mendocino CA p. 184

Mendocino College Library, Ukiah CA p. 277

Mendocino County Historical Society, Ukiah CA p. 277

Mendocino County Law Library, Ukiah CA p. 277

Mendocino County Library District, Ukiah CA p. 277

Mendon Township Library, Mendon MI p. 1208

Metroplex Commuter Facility Library, *see* Texas A&M University-Commerce, Mesquite TX p. 2300

Metropolis Public Library, Metropolis IL p. 673

Metropolitan Area Planning Agency, Omaha NE p. 1413

Metropolitan Club, Washington DC p. 408

Metropolitan College of New York Library, New York NY p. 1686

Metropolitan Community College, Kansas City MO p. 1339

Metropolitan Community College Library, Omaha NE p. 1413

Metropolitan Consortium of Chicago (N), Chicago IL p. 2942

Metropolitan Council for Educational Opportunity Library, Roxbury MA p. 1121

Metropolitan Council Library, Saint Paul MN p. 1279

Metropolitan Hospital Center, New York NY p. 1686

Metropolitan Library Service Agency (N), Saint Paul MN p. 2947

Metropolitan Library System in Oklahoma County, Oklahoma City OK p. 1972

Metropolitan Milwaukee Fair Housing Council, Milwaukee WI p. 2619

Metropolitan Museum of Art, New York NY p. 1686

Metropolitan Nashville General Hospital, Nashville TN p. 2257

Metropolitan New York Library Council (N), New York NY p. 2950

Metropolitan Opera Archives, New York NY p. 1687

Metropolitan State Hospital, Norwalk CA p. 195

Metropolitan State University, Saint Paul MN p. 1279

Metropolitan Transition Center Library, Baltimore MD p. 1016

Metropolitan Transportation Commission, Oakland CA p. 197

Metropolitan Water Reclamation District, Chicago IL p. 618

MetroSouth Medical Center, Blue Island IL p. 596

Metrowest Medical Center, Framingham MA p. 1090

Metuchen Public Library, Metuchen NJ p. 1501

Metzgar Marshall R Medical Library, *see* Pocono Medical Center, East Stroudsburg PA p. 2051

Meuser Mary Memorial Library, Easton PA p. 2052

Mexican American Opportunity Foundation, Montebello CA p. 189

Mexico-Audrain County Library District, Mexico MO p. 1345

Mexico Free Public Library, Mexico ME p. 992

Mexico Public Library, Mexico NY p. 1660

Meyer Adolf Library, *see* Johns Hopkins University Libraries, Baltimore MD p. 1014

Meyer Anna, *see* Ouachita Parish Public Library, Monroe LA p. 957

Meyer Duane G Library, *see* Missouri State University, Springfield MO p. 1366

Meyer George B Sr Neighborhood Library, *see* Houston Public Library, Houston TX p. 2339

Meyer Hazel L Memorial Library, De Smet SD p. 2211

Meyer John E Eye Library, *see* Callahan Eye Foundation Hospital, Birmingham AL p. 8

Meyer Library, *see* California College of the Arts Libraries, Oakland CA p. 196

Meyer, Suozzi, English & Klein, Garden City NY p. 1626

Meyercord Library, *see* Highland Park Presbyterian Church, Dallas TX p. 2308

Meyers Henry & Delia Library, *see* Jewish Community Center of Metropolitan Detroit, West Bloomfield MI p. 1235

Meyers Library, *see* Reform Congregation Keneseth Israel, Elkins Park PA p. 2054

Meyersdale Public Library, Meyersdale PA p. 2088

MFL Occupational Health Centre, Winnipeg MB p. 2757

Mgr Paquet Public Library, *see* Chaleur Library Region, Caraquet NB p. 2761

Mgr Robichaud Public Library, *see* Chaleur Library Region, Beresford NB p. 2761

MHLA-ABSM (N), *see* Maritimes Health Libraries Association, Halifax NS p. 2959

MHSLA (N), *see* Michigan Health Sciences Libraries Association, Lansing MI p. 2946

Miami Children's Hospital Medical Library, Miami FL p. 466

Miami Correctional Facility, Bunker Hill IN p. 730

Miami County Law Library, Troy OH p. 1941

Miami County Museum, Peru IN p. 772

Miami Dade College, Homestead FL p. 451

Miami Dade College, Miami FL p. 466

Miami-Dade County Law Library, Miami FL p. 466

Miami-Dade Public Library System, Miami FL p. 466

Miami Herald, Miami FL p. 467

Miami-Jacobs College, Dayton OH p. 1893

Miami Memorial-Gila County Library, Miami AZ p. 69

Miami Public Library, Miami OK p. 1968

Miami University-Hamilton Campus, Hamilton OH p. 1904

Miami University Libraries, Oxford OH p. 1926

Miami University-Middletown, Middletown OH p. 1917

Miami Valley Hospital, Dayton OH p. 1893

Miccosukee Community Library, Miami FL p. 467

Miceli Victor Law Library, *see* Riverside County Law Library, Riverside CA p. 217

Michael Best & Friedrich LLP, Milwaukee WI p. 2619

Michael Marie Library, *see* Saint Francis Xavier University, Antigonish NS p. 2777

Michener Institute for Applied Health Sciences Library, Toronto ON p. 2855

Michener James A, *see* Bucks County Free Library, Quakertown PA p. 2050

Michener James A Library, *see* University of Northern Colorado Libraries, Greeley CO p. 312

Michigan City Public Library, Michigan City IN p. 764

Michigan Commission for the Blind- Braille & Talking Book Library, Lansing MI p. 1201

Michigan Department of Community Health, Saline MI p. 1225

Michigan Department of Corrections, Baraga MI p. 1155

Michigan Department of Corrections, Carson City MI p. 1161

Michigan Department of Corrections, Detroit MI p. 1171

Michigan Department of Corrections, Freeland MI p. 1182

Michigan Department of Corrections, Jackson MI p. 1196

Michigan Department of Corrections, Kingsley MI p. 1198

Michigan Department of Corrections, Manistee MI p. 1206

Michigan Department of Corrections, Marenisco MI p. 1206

Michigan Department of Corrections, Munising MI p. 1212

Michigan Department of Corrections, Muskegon MI p. 1212

Michigan Department of History, Arts & Libraries, Lansing MI p. 1201

Michigan Department of Natural Resources, Institute for Fisheries Research, Ann Arbor MI p. 1151

Michigan Department of Transportation Library, Lansing MI p. 1201

Michigan Health Sciences Libraries Association (N), Lansing MI p. 2946

Michigan Jewish Institute Library, Oak Park MI p. 1215

Michigan Legislative Service Bureau, Lansing MI p. 1202

Michigan Maritime Museum, South Haven MI p. 1227

Michigan Masonic Museum & Library, Grand Rapids MI p. 1185

Michigan Molecular Institute, Midland MI p. 1208

Michigan Municipal League Library, Ann Arbor MI p. 1151

Michigan Psychoanalytic Institute & Society, Farmington Hills MI p. 1178

Michigan Public, *see* Carnegie Regional Library, Michigan ND p. 1842

Michigan Road Community Library, *see* Frankfort Community Public Library, Michigantown IN p. 743

Michigan State Department of Natural Resources & Environment Library, Lansing MI p. 1202

Michigan State University, East Lansing MI p. 1175

Michigan State University, Hickory Corners MI p. 1189

Michigan State University Library, East Lansing MI p. 1175

Michigan Technological University, Houghton MI p. 1191

Mickel Library, *see* Converse College, Spartanburg SC p. 2204

Mickelsen Community Library, *see* United States Army, Fort Bliss TX p. 2320

Mid-America Baptist Theological Seminary, Cordova TN p. 2232

Mid-America Christian University, Oklahoma City OK p. 1973

Mid-America College of Funeral Service Library, Jeffersonville IN p. 756

Mid-America Law Library Consortium (N), Grand Forks ND p. 2951

Mid-America Library Alliance (N), Independence MO p. 2948

Mid-America Nazarene University, Olathe KS p. 886

Mid-America Reformed Seminary Library, Dyer IN p. 736

Mid-Arkansas Regional Library, *see* Malvern-Hot Spring County Library, Malvern AR p. 108

Mid-Coast Hospital, Brunswick ME p. 979

Mid-Columbia Libraries, Kennewick WA p. 2518

Mid-Columbia Medical Center, The Dalles OR p. 2021

Mid-Continent College, Mayfield KY p. 928

Mid-Continent Public Library, Independence MO p. 1332

Mid-County Regional Library, *see* Charlotte County Library System, Port Charlotte FL p. 484

Mid Florida Research & Education, Apopka FL p. 425

Mid-Hudson Forensic Psychiatric Center Library, New Hampton NY p. 1665

Mid-Hudson Library System, Poughkeepsie NY p. 1723

Mid-Manhattan Library, *see* New York Public Library - Astor, Lenox & Tilden Foundations, New York NY p. 1692

Mid Michigan Community College, Harrison MI p. 1188

Mid-Michigan Correctional Facility Library, Saint Louis MI p. 1225

Mid-Michigan Library League (N), Cadillac MI p. 2946

Mid-Mississippi Regional Library System, Kosciusko MS p. 1306

Mid-South Community College, West Memphis AR p. 117

Mid State Correctional Facility Library, Wrightstown NJ p. 1546

Mid State Medical Center, Meriden CT p. 351

Mid-State Technical College, Marshfield WI p. 2613

Mid-State Technical College, Stevens Point WI p. 2639

Mid-State Technical College Library, Wisconsin Rapids WI p. 2650

Mid-Valley Regional, *see* Los Angeles Public Library System, North Hills CA p. 173

Mid-Wisconsin Federated Library System, Horicon WI p. 2598

Mid-York Library System, Utica NY p. 1758

Mid-Atlantic Law Library Cooperative (N), Morgantown WV p. 2958

Mid-Illinois Talking Book Center, East Peoria IL p. 639

Middendorf A Carter Library, *see* National Aquarium in Baltimore, Baltimore MD p. 1016

Middle Country Public Library, Centereach NY p. 1604

Middle East Institute, Washington DC p. 408

Middle Georgia College, Cochran GA p. 525

Middle Georgia Regional Library System, Macon GA p. 540

Middle Georgia Technical College, Warner Robins GA p. 556

Middle Haddam Public Library, Middle Haddam CT p. 351

Middle Tennessee State University, Murfreesboro TN p. 2254, 2974

Middle Village Community Library, *see* Queens Borough Public Library, Middle Village NY p. 1645

Middleborough Public Library, Middleborough MA p. 1105

Middlebrook Grace Family Learning Center, *see* Banner Good Samaritan Medical Center, Phoenix AZ p. 72

Middleburg Community Library, *see* Snyder County Libraries, Middleburg PA p. 2138

Middleburg Heights Community Church Library, Middleburg Heights OH p. 1917

Middleburgh Library Association, Middleburgh NY p. 1660

Middlebury College Library, Middlebury VT p. 2428

Middlebury Community Public Library, Middlebury IN p. 764

Middlebury Public Library, Middlebury CT p. 351

Middlefield Library, *see* Geauga County Public Library, Middlefield OH p. 1867

Middlefield Public Library, Middlefield MA p. 1105

Middlemas George & Sherry Arts & Humanities Library, *see* Pennsylvania State University Libraries, University Park PA p. 2148

Middleport Free Library, Middleport NY p. 1660

Middlesborough-Bell County Public, Middlesboro KY p. 929

Middlesex Community College, Middletown CT p. 351

Middlesex Community College, Bedford MA p. 1052

Middlesex Community College, Lowell MA p. 1100

Middlesex County Adult Correction Center Library, North Brunswick NJ p. 1514

Middlesex County College Library, Edison NJ p. 1483

Middlesex County Cultural & Heritage Commission, New Brunswick NJ p. 1508

Middlesex County Historical Society Library, Middletown CT p. 352

Middlesex County Law Library, New Brunswick NJ p. 1508

Middlesex County Library, Strathroy ON p. 2845

Middlesex County Public Library, Urbanna VA p. 2498

Middlesex Hospital, Middletown CT p. 352

Middlesex Law Association, London ON p. 2818

Middlesex Law Library at Cambridge, Cambridge MA p. 1078

Middlesex Public Library, Middlesex NJ p. 1501

Middlesex Reading Center, Middlesex NY p. 1660

Middleton Community Library, Middleton TN p. 2253

Middleton Public Library, Meridian ID p. 579

Middleton Public Library, Middleton WI p. 2616

Middletown Fallcreek Township Public Library, Middletown IN p. 765

Middletown Free Library, Lima PA p. 2082

Middletown Public Library, Middletown NJ p. 1501

Middletown Public Library, Middletown OH p. 1917

Middletown Public Library, Middletown PA p. 2089

Middletown Public Library, Middletown RI p. 2168

Middletown Regional Hospital, Middletown OH p. 1918

Middletown Springs Public Library, Middletown Springs VT p. 2429

Middletown Thrall Library, Middletown NY p. 1660

Middleville Free Library, Middleville NY p. 1661

Mideastern Michigan Library Cooperative (N), Flint MI p. 2946

Midfield Public Library, Midfield AL p. 25

Midkiff Public, *see* Rankin Public Library, Midkiff TX p. 2373

Midland College, Midland TX p. 2363

Midland County Historical Society Library, Midland MI p. 1208

Midland County Public Library, Midland TX p. 2363

Midland Lutheran College, Fremont NE p. 1399

Midland Park Memorial Library, Midland Park NJ p. 1502

Midland Public Library, Midland ON p. 2821

Midlands Technical College Library, West Columbia SC p. 2207

Midlothian Public Library, Midlothian IL p. 674

MidMichigan Medical Center, Midland MI p. 1208

Midstate College, Peoria IL p. 690

Midvale District Library, Midvale ID p. 579

Midway College, Midway KY p. 929

Midway Public Library, Midway BC p. 2731

Midwest Archeological Center Library, *see* National Park Service, Lincoln NE p. 1405

Midwest City Library, *see* Metropolitan Library System in Oklahoma County, Midwest City OK p. 1973

Midwest Historical & Genealogical Society, Inc Library, Wichita KS p. 900

Midwest Old Settlers & Threshers Association, Mount Pleasant IA p. 833

Midwest Research Institute, Kansas City MO p. 1339

Midwestern Baptist College, Orion MI p. 1215

Midwestern Baptist Theological Seminary Library, Kansas City MO p. 1339

Midwestern State University, Wichita Falls TX p. 2400

Midwestern University, Olympia Fields IL p. 685

Midwestern University Library, Downers Grove IL p. 637

Mifflin Community Library, Shillington PA p. 2139

Mifflin County Historical Society Library & Museum, Lewistown PA p. 2081

Mifflin County Library, Lewistown PA p. 2081

Migel M C Library & Barr Research Library, *see* American Printing House for the Blind, Inc, Louisville KY p. 923

Migrant Legal Action Program Library, Washington DC p. 408

Mikkelsen Library, *see* Augustana College, Sioux Falls SD p. 2218

Milaca Community Library, *see* East Central Regional Library, Milaca MN p. 1244

Milam Max, *see* Central Arkansas Library System, Perryville AR p. 106

Milan-Berlin Township Public Library, Milan OH p. 1918

Milan Public Library, Milan MI p. 1209

Milan Public Library, Milan NH p. 1457

Milan Public Library, *see* Fields Mildred G Memorial Library, Milan TN p. 2253

Milanof-Schock Library, Mount Joy PA p. 2093

Milbank, Tweed, Hadley & McCloy, Los Angeles CA p. 175

Milbridge Public Library, Milbridge ME p. 992

Mile Bluff Medical Center, Mauston WI p. 2613

Miles & Stockbridge PC Library, Baltimore MD p. 1016

Miles City Public Library, Miles City MT p. 1386

Miles College, Fairfield AL p. 16

Miles Community College Library, Miles City MT p. 1386

Miles Davison Library, Calgary AB p. 2692

Miles Memorial Hospital, Damariscotta ME p. 983

Miles Susie E Library, *see* Shiloh Baptist Church, Washington DC p. 414

Miley Library, *see* Indian River State College, Fort Pierce FL p. 446

Milford District Library, Milford IL p. 674

Milford Free Library, Milford NY p. 1661

Milford Memorial Library, Milford IA p. 832

Milford Public Library, Milford CT p. 352

Milford Public Library, Milford DE p. 384

Milford Public Library, Milford IN p. 765

Milford Public Library, Milford MI p. 1209

Milford Public Library, Milford NJ p. 1502

Milford Public Library, Milford UT p. 2407

Milford Town Library, Milford MA p. 1105

Milholland Elizabeth Library, *see* Highland Presbyterian Church, New Castle PA p. 2096

Mililani Public Library, *see* Hawaii State Public Library System, Mililani HI p. 563

Military Occupational Specialty Library, *see* United States Army, Fort Wainwright AK p. 48

Milk River Municipal Library, Milk River AB p. 2711

Mill City Library, Mill City OR p. 2006

Mill Creek Community Library, *see* Sno-Isle Libraries, Mill Creek WA p. 2542

Mill Memorial Library, Nanticoke PA p. 2094

Mill Pond Public Library, Kingston WI p. 2602

Mill Valley Public Library, Mill Valley CA p. 186

Millbrae Library, *see* San Mateo County Library, Millbrae CA p. 256

Millbrook Free Library, Millbrook NY p. 1661

Millbrook Public Library, Millbrook AL p. 25

Millburn Free Public Library, Millburn NJ p. 1502

Millbury Public Library, Millbury MA p. 1106

Mille Lacs Community Library, *see* East Central Regional Library, Isle MN p. 1244

Miller & Chevalier, Washington DC p. 408

Miller & Martin PLLC, Chattanooga TN p. 2227

Miller Anna Museum Library, Newcastle WY p. 2658

Miller Arthur J, *see* Warren Public Library, Warren MI p. 1234

Miller, Canfield, Paddock & Stone Library, Detroit MI p. 1171

Miller Carson K Library, *see* Washington State Community College, Marietta OH p. 1914

Miller Clifton M Library, *see* Washington College, Chestertown MD p. 1023

Miller David Memorial Library, *see* CoxHealth Libraries, Springfield MO p. 1366

Miller E Kirkbride Art Research Library, *see* Baltimore Museum of Art, Baltimore MD p. 1012

Miller Elisabeth C Library, *see* University of Washington Botanic Gardens, Seattle WA p. 2533

Miller Emerson R, *see* Licking County Library, Newark OH p. 1922

Miller Harold A Marine Biology Library, *see* Stanford University Libraries, Pacific Grove CA p. 271

Miller Howard Public Library, Zeeland MI p. 1238

Miller Ira Memorial Library, *see* Michigan Psychoanalytic Institute & Society, Farmington Hills MI p. 1178

Miller J Cloyd Library, *see* Western New Mexico University, Silver City NM p. 1565

Miller James W Learning Resources Center, *see* Saint Cloud State University, Saint Cloud MN p. 1276

Miller Jean Memorial Library, *see* Riverside Presbyterian Church, Jacksonville FL p. 454

Miller, Johnson, Snell & Cummiskey, Grand Rapids MI p. 1185

Miller/Knopf Career Resource Library, *see* Simmons College, Boston MA p. 1067

Miller Library, *see* Colby College Libraries, Waterville ME p. 1005

Miller Library, *see* Cornerstone University, Grand Rapids MI p. 1184

Miller Library, *see* Keystone College, La Plume PA p. 2075

Miller Library, *see* McPherson College, McPherson KS p. 883

Miller Lyda Library, *see* White County Regional Library System, Bald Knob AR p. 115

Miller Mary Library, *see* Hesston College, Hesston KS p. 871

Miller Memorial Central Library, *see* Hamden Public Library, Hamden CT p. 343

Miller Memorial Library, *see* University of Wisconsin-Richland, Richland Center WI p. 2634

Miller Nash LLP Library, Portland OR p. 2011

Miller Philip S Library, *see* Douglas County Libraries, Castle Rock CO p. 294

Miller R C Memorial, *see* Beaumont Public Library System, Beaumont TX p. 2287

Miller Robert, *see* Annapolis Valley Regional Library, Bridgetown NS p. 2778

Miller Stratvert PA, Albuquerque NM p. 1549

Miller U Grant Library, *see* Washington & Jefferson College Library, Washington PA p. 2151

Miller Will C Memorial Library, *see* Southwest Texas Junior College, Uvalde TX p. 2394

Miller William H Law Library, Evansville IN p. 739

Millersville University, Millersville PA p. 2090

Millet Public Library, Millet AB p. 2711

Millhaven Institution Inmate Library, *see* Correctional Service of Canada, Bath ON p. 2794

Millicent Library, Fairhaven MA p. 1087

Milligan College, Milligan College TN p. 2253

Milligan Public Library, Milligan NE p. 1408

Milliken & Company, Spartanburg SC p. 2204

Millikin University, Decatur IL p. 634

Milling, Benson, Woodward Library, New Orleans LA p. 961

Millington Arbela District Library, Millington MI p. 1209

Millington Public Library, Millington TN p. 2253

Millinocket Memorial Library, Millinocket ME p. 992

Millinocket Regional Hospital, Millinocket ME p. 992

Millis Public Library, Millis MA p. 1106

Millport Public Library, *see* Northwest Regional Library, Millport AL p. 40

Mills & Petrie Memorial Library, Ashton IL p. 590

Mills College, Oakland CA p. 197

Mills Law Library, San Francisco CA p. 244

Mills Memorial Library, *see* McMaster University Library, Hamilton ON p. 2810

Mills Music Library, *see* University of Wisconsin-Madison, Madison WI p. 2609

Mills Paul C Archives of California Art, *see* Oakland Museum of California Art Library, Oakland CA p. 197

Mills-Peninsula Health Services Library, Burlingame CA p. 131

Millsaps College, Jackson MS p. 1303

Millsaps-Wilson Library, *see* Millsaps College, Jackson MS p. 1303

Millsboro Public Library, Millsboro DE p. 384

Millstadt Library, Millstadt IL p. 674

Millstein Library, *see* University of Pittsburgh at Greensburg, Greensburg PA p. 2062

Milltown Public Library, Milltown NJ p. 1502

Milltown Public Library, Milltown WI p. 2616

Millville Free Public Library, Millville MA p. 1106

Millville Public Library, Millville NJ p. 1502

Milne David & Joyce Public Library, Williamstown MA p. 1140

Milne James M Library, *see* State University of New York, College at Oneonta, Oneonta NY p. 1711

Milne Library, *see* State University of New York College at Geneseo, Geneseo NY p. 1627

Milner Library, *see* Illinois State University, Normal IL p. 681

Milner Stanley A Library, *see* Edmonton Public Library, Edmonton AB p. 2700

MILO (N), *see* Maryland Interlibrary Loan Organization, Baltimore MD p. 2944

Milo Free Public Library, Milo ME p. 992

Milo Municipal Library, Milo AB p. 2711

Milo Public Library, Milo IA p. 832

Milpitas Public, *see* Santa Clara County Library District, Milpitas CA p. 181

Milstein Philip L Family College Library, *see* Columbia University, New York NY p. 1675

Milton Free Public Library, Milton Mills NH p. 1458

Milton-Freewater Public Library, Milton-Freewater OR p. 2006

Milton Library, *see* Hallock Sarah Hull Free Library, Milton NY p. 1661

Milton Public, *see* Sussex County Department of Libraries, Milton DE p. 383

Milton Public Library, Milton IA p. 832

Milton Public Library, Milton MA p. 1106

Milton Public Library, Milton PA p. 2090

Milton Public Library, Milton VT p. 2429

Milton Public Library, Milton WI p. 2616

Milton Public Library, Milton ON p. 2822

Milton-Union Public Library, West Milton OH p. 1946

Milwaukee Academy of Medicine Library, Milwaukee WI p. 2619

Milwaukee Area Technical College, Mequon WI p. 2615

Milwaukee Area Technical College, Milwaukee WI p. 2619

Milwaukee Area Technical College, Oak Creek WI p. 2626

Milwaukee Area Technical College, West Allis WI p. 2647

Milwaukee Art Museum Library, Milwaukee WI p. 2619

Milwaukee County Federated Library System, Milwaukee WI p. 2619

Milwaukee County Historical Society, Milwaukee WI p. 2619

Milwaukee Institute of Art & Design Library, Milwaukee WI p. 2619

Milwaukee Jewish Council for Community Relations, Milwaukee WI p. 2620

Milwaukee Journal Sentinel, Milwaukee WI p. 2620

Milwaukee Legal Resource Center, *see* Wisconsin State Law Library, Milwaukee WI p. 2611

Milwaukee Public Library, Milwaukee WI p. 2620

Milwaukee Public Museum, Milwaukee WI p. 2620

Milwaukee School of Engineering, Milwaukee WI p. 2620

Milwaukee Secure Detention Facility Library, Milwaukee WI p. 2621

Mims/Scottsmoor Public Library, Mims FL p. 470

Mina-Luning Library, *see* Mineral County Public Library, Mina NV p. 1428

Minatare Public Library, Minatare NE p. 1408

Minburn Public Library, Minburn IA p. 832

Minden Library, *see* Douglas County Public Library, Minden NV p. 1431

Mine Safety & Health Administration Library, *see* United States Department of Labor, Beaver WV p. 2553

Mineola Memorial Library, Mineola NY p. 1661

Mineola Memorial Library, Inc, Mineola TX p. 2363

Miner Edward G Library, *see* University of Rochester Medical Center, Rochester NY p. 1734

Miner Memorial Library, East Lempster NH p. 1446

Miner William H Agricultural Research Institute, Chazy NY p. 1606

Mineral Area College, Park Hills MO p. 1349

Mineral County Museum & Historical Society Library, Superior MT p. 1389

Mineral County Public Library, Superior MT p. 1389

Mineral County Public Library, Hawthorne NV p. 1428

Mineral County Regional Library, Creede CO p. 297

Mineral-Gold Public Library District, Mineral IL p. 674

Mineral Point Public Library, Mineral Point WI p. 2622

Mineral Springs Hospital, Banff AB p. 2684

Minerals Management Service, *see* United States Department of the Interior, New Orleans LA p. 964

Miners' Museum Library, Glace Bay NS p. 2780

Minersville Public Library, Minersville UT p. 2407

Minersville Public Library, *see* Minersville Public Library Association Inc, Minersville PA p. 2090

Minersville Public Library Association Inc, Minersville PA p. 2090

Minerva Free Library, Sherman NY p. 1743

Minerva Public Library, Minerva OH p. 1918

Mingei International Museum, San Diego CA p. 232

Mingo County Library, Delbarton WV p. 2558

Minisink Valley Historical Society Library, Port Jervis NY p. 1721

Ministere de la Culture, Trois-Rivieres QC p. 2914

Ministere de la Justice, Quebec QC p. 2905

Ministere de la Sante et des Services Sociaux, Quebec QC p. 2905

Ministere Des Affaires Municipales et de Regions, Quebec QC p. 2905

Ministere des Finances Bibliotheque, Quebec QC p. 2906

Ministere des Ressources naturelles et de la Faune, Quebec QC p. 2906

Ministry of Highways & Infrastructure, Regina SK p. 2922

Ministry of the Attorney General General, Vancouver BC p. 2741

MINITEX Library Information Network (N), Minneapolis MN p. 2947

Minneapolis College of Art & Design Library, Minneapolis MN p. 1260

Minneapolis Community & Technical College, Minneapolis MN p. 1261

Minneapolis Institute of Arts, Minneapolis MN p. 1261

Minneapolis Public Library, Minneapolis KS p. 883

Minnedosa Regional Library, Minnedosa MB p. 2750

Minneola City Library, Minneola KS p. 883

Minneota Public Library, Minneota MN p. 1263

Minnesota Attorney General Library, Saint Paul MN p. 1279

Minnesota Braille & Talking Book Library, Faribault MN p. 1251

Minnesota Correctional Facility, Bayport MN p. 1240

Minnesota Correctional Facility - Faribault-Rogers Library, *see* Minnesota Department of Corrections, Faribault MN p. 1251

Minnesota Correctional Facility - Lino Lakes, *see* Minnesota Department of Corrections, Lino Lakes MN p. 1256

Minnesota Correctional Facility - Oak Park Heights, *see* Minnesota Department of Corrections, Stillwater MN p. 1285

Minnesota Correctional Facility - Red Wing, *see* Minnesota Department of Corrections, Red Wing MN p. 1271

Minnesota Correctional Facility - Rush City, *see* Minnesota Department of Corrections, Rush City MN p. 1273

Minnesota Correctional Facility - St Cloud, *see* Minnesota Department of Corrections, Saint Cloud MN p. 1276

Minnesota Correctional Facility - Shakopee, *see* Minnesota Department of Corrections, Shakopee MN p. 1284

Minnesota Correctional Facility - Willow River/Moose Lake, *see* Minnesota Department of Corrections, Moose Lake MN p. 1266

Minnesota Department of Corrections, Faribault MN p. 1251

Minnesota Department of Corrections, Lino Lakes MN p. 1256

Minnesota Department of Corrections, Moose Lake MN p. 1266

Minnesota Department of Corrections, Red Wing MN p. 1271

Minnesota Department of Corrections, Rush City MN p. 1273

Minnesota Department of Corrections, Saint Cloud MN p. 1276

Minnesota Department of Corrections, Shakopee MN p. 1284

Minnesota Department of Corrections, Stillwater MN p. 1285

Minnesota Department of Corrections, Togo MN p. 1286

Minnesota Department of Employment & Economic Development Library, Saint Paul MN p. 1279

Minnesota Department of Health, Saint Paul MN p. 1279

Minnesota Department of Revenue Library, Saint Paul MN p. 1279

Minnesota Department of Transportation Library, Saint Paul MN p. 1279

Minnesota Geological Survey Library, Saint Paul MN p. 1280

Minnesota Historical Society Library, Saint Paul MN p. 1280

Minnesota Legislative Reference Library, Saint Paul MN p. 1280

Minnesota Library Information Network (N), Minneapolis MN p. 2947

Minnesota Orchestra Music Library, Minneapolis MN p. 1261

Minnesota Pollution Control Agency Library, Saint Paul MN p. 1280

Minnesota State College Southeast Technical LRC, Winona MN p. 1289

Mohawk Community Library, Sycamore OH p. 1937
Mohawk Correctional Facility Library, Rome NY p. 1735
Mohawk Council of Akwesasne, Saint-Regis QC p. 2911
Mohawk Valley Community College Library, Utica NY p. 1759
Mohawk Valley Library System, Schenectady NY p. 1740
Mohawk Valley Psychiatric Center, Utica NY p. 1759
Mohr Marian J Memorial Library, Johnston RI p. 2167
Mohyla Institute Library, Saskatoon SK p. 2925
Moise Memorial Library, Santa Rosa NM p. 1565
Mokena Community Public Library District, Mokena IL p. 674
Molalla Public Library, Molalla OR p. 2006
Moline Public Library, Moline IL p. 674
Moline Public Library, Moline KS p. 884
Molloy College, Rockville Centre NY p. 1734
Molokai Public Library, see Hawaii State Public Library System, Kaunakakai HI p. 563
Molson Hartland Library, see Canadian War Museum, Ottawa ON p. 2830
Molstead Library, see North Idaho College Library, Coeur d'Alene ID p. 573
Monaca Public Library, Monaca PA p. 2090
Monadnock Community Hospital, Peterborough NH p. 1461
Monahan Library, see Northeastern Junior College, Sterling CO p. 323
Monastic Library, see Saint Joseph's Abbey, Spencer MA p. 1126
Moncrief Army Hospital Medical Library, see United States Army, Fort Jackson SC p. 2194
Moncton Area Lawyers Association, Moncton NB p. 2766
Moncton Public, see Albert-Westmorland-Kent Regional Library, Moncton NB p. 2765
Mondak Heritage Center, Sidney MT p. 1388
Mondamin Public Library, Mondamin IA p. 832
Mondor-Eagen Library, see Anna Maria College, Paxton MA p. 1116
Mondovi Public Library, Mondovi WI p. 2623
Monell Chemical Senses Center, Philadelphia PA p. 2112
Monessen Public Library & District Center, Monessen PA p. 2091
Moneta/Smith Mountain Lake Library, see Bedford Public Library System, Moneta VA p. 2451
Mongan Mary Ann Library, see Kenton County Public Library, Covington KY p. 910
Monhegan Memorial Library, Monhegan ME p. 992
Monmouth Beach Library, Monmouth Beach NJ p. 1502
Monmouth College, Monmouth IL p. 675
Monmouth County Historical Association Library & Archives, Freehold NJ p. 1487
Monmouth County Library, Manalapan NJ p. 1498
Monmouth County Park System, Middletown NJ p. 1502
Monmouth Medical Center, Long Branch NJ p. 1497
Monmouth-Ocean Biomedical Information Consortium (N), Toms River NJ p. 2949
Monmouth Public Library, Monmouth OR p. 2006
Monmouth University, West Long Branch NJ p. 1541
Mono County Free Library, Mammoth Lakes CA p. 182
Mono County Law Library, Bridgeport CA p. 129
Monon Town & Township Public Library, Monon IN p. 765
Monona Public Library, Monona WI p. 2623
Monongahela Area Library, Monongahela PA p. 2091
Monroe City Public Library, Monroe City MO p. 1347
Monroe Clinic, Monroe WI p. 2623
Monroe College, Bronx NY p. 1588
Monroe Community College, Rochester NY p. 1730
Monroe Community Library, Monroe ME p. 992
Monroe Community Library, see Corvallis-Benton County Public Library, Monroe OR p. 1994

Monroe Community Library, see Sno-Isle Libraries, Monroe WA p. 2542
Monroe County Community College, Monroe MI p. 1209
Monroe County District Library, Woodsfield OH p. 1949
Monroe County Genealogical Society, Albia IA p. 791
Monroe County Historical Association, Stroudsburg PA p. 2144
Monroe County Historical Museum, Monroe MI p. 1209
Monroe County Law Library, Stroudsburg PA p. 2144
Monroe County Library, see Flint River Regional Library, Forsyth GA p. 535
Monroe County Library, see Phillips-Lee-Monroe Regional Library, Clarendon AR p. 103
Monroe County Library System, Monroe MI p. 1209
Monroe County Library System, Rochester NY p. 1730
Monroe County Local History Room & Library, Sparta WI p. 2639
Monroe County Public Library, Monroeville AL p. 27
Monroe County Public Library, Key West FL p. 456
Monroe County Public Library, Bloomington IN p. 728
Monroe County Public Library, Tompkinsville KY p. 936
Monroe County Public Library, Union WV p. 2573
Monroe County Seneca Park Zoo, Rochester NY p. 1730
Monroe Free Library, Monroe NY p. 1662
Monroe J Edgar & Louise S Library, see Loyola University New Orleans, New Orleans LA p. 961
Monroe Public Library, Monroe IA p. 832
Monroe Public Library, Monroe Bridge MA p. 1106
Monroe Public Library, Monroe NH p. 1458
Monroe Public Library, Monroe UT p. 2407
Monroe Public Library, Monroe WI p. 2623
Monroe Township Public Library, Monroe Township NJ p. 1502
Monroe - Walton County Library, see Uncle Remus Regional Library System, Monroe GA p. 542
Monroeton Public Library, Monroeton PA p. 2091
Monroeville Public Library, Monroeville OH p. 1918
Monroeville Public Library, Monroeville PA p. 2091
Monroney Mike Aeronautical Center Library, see Federal Aviation Administration, Oklahoma City OK p. 1972
Monrovia Public Library, Monrovia CA p. 189
Monrovia Public Library, see Huntsville-Madison Public Library, Huntsville AL p. 21
Monsanto-Calgene Campus Library, Davis CA p. 139
Monsanto Company, Saint Louis MO p. 1356
Monseigneur Plourde Public, see Haut-Saint-Jean Regional Library, Saint Francois NB p. 2762
Monseigneur W J Conway Public, see Haut-Saint-Jean Regional Library, Edmundston NB p. 2762
Monseignor Fremiot Torres Oliver, see Pontifical Catholic University Of Puerto Rico, Ponce PR p. 2675
Monsen Martin Regional Library, see Bristol Bay Borough Libraries, Naknek AK p. 51
Monsignor James C Turro Seminary Library, South Orange NJ p. 1530
Monsignor William Barry Memorial Library, see Barry University, Miami FL p. 464
Monson Free Library, Monson MA p. 1106
Monson Free Public Library, Monson ME p. 992
Montague H Laddie, see Pennsylvania State University - Dickinson School of Law, Carlisle PA p. 2042
Montague Public, see Prince Edward Island Public Library Service, Montague PE p. 2876
Montague Public Libraries, Turners Falls MA p. 1131
Montana Bible College Library, Bozeman MT p. 1375
Montana Department of Commerce, Helena MT p. 1382

Montana Department of Corrections, Boulder MT p. 1375
Montana Department of Corrections, Miles City MT p. 1386
Montana Historical Society, Helena MT p. 1382
Montana Legislative Reference Center, Helena MT p. 1382
Montana Masonic Library, Helena MT p. 1382
Montana Office of Public Instruction, Helena MT p. 1382
Montana School for the Deaf & Blind Library, Great Falls MT p. 1380
Montana State Department of Natural Resources & Conservation, Helena MT p. 1382
Montana State Hospital Library, Warm Springs MT p. 1390
Montana State Library, Helena MT p. 1383
Montana State Prison Library, Deer Lodge MT p. 1377
Montana State University, Billings MT p. 1374
Montana State University, Bozeman MT p. 2969
Montana State University - Great Falls College of Technology, Great Falls MT p. 1380
Montana State University Libraries, Bozeman MT p. 1375
Montana State University-Northern, Havre MT p. 1381
Montana Tech Library, Butte MT p. 1376
Montante Family Library, see D'Youville College, Buffalo NY p. 1597
Montauk Library, Montauk NY p. 1662
Montcalm Community College Library, Sidney MI p. 1227
Montclair Free Public Library, Montclair NJ p. 1503
Montclair State University, Montclair NJ p. 1503
Montefiore Hospital-North Division, Bronx NY p. 1588
Montefiore Medical Center, Bronx NY p. 1588
Montello Public Library, Montello WI p. 2623
Monterey Bay Aquarium Library, Monterey CA p. 189
Monterey County Free Libraries, Marina CA p. 182
Monterey County Law Library, Salinas CA p. 226
Monterey History & Art Association, Monterey CA p. 189
Monterey Institute for Research & Astronomy, Marina CA p. 183
Monterey Institute of International Studies, Monterey CA p. 190
Monterey Library, Monterey MA p. 1107
Monterey Museum of Art Library, Monterey CA p. 190
Monterey Park Bruggemeyer Library, Monterey Park CA p. 190
Monterey Park Public Library, see Monterey Park Bruggemeyer Library, Monterey Park CA p. 190
Monterey Peninsula College Library, Monterey CA p. 190
Monterey Public Library, Monterey CA p. 190
Monterey-Tippecanoe Township Public Library, Monterey IN p. 765
Montes-Gallo Delia Library, see Texas Tech University Health Sciences, El Paso TX p. 2358
Montevideo-Chippewa County Public Library, Montevideo MN p. 1265
Montezuma Public Library, Montezuma IN p. 766
Montezuma Public Library, Montezuma IA p. 833
Montezuma Public, see Middle Georgia Regional Library System, Montezuma GA p. 541
Montezuma Township Library, Montezuma KS p. 884
Montfort Public Library, Montfort WI p. 2623
Montgomery G V Sonny VA Medical Center Library, Jackson MS p. 1305
Montgomery & Andrews, Santa Fe NM p. 1562
Montgomery Area Public Library, Montgomery PA p. 2092
Montgomery City-County Public Library System, Montgomery AL p. 29
Montgomery City Public Library, Montgomery City MO p. 1347
Montgomery College, Rockville MD p. 1037
Montgomery College Library, see Lone Star College System, Conroe TX p. 2340

Montgomery Community College Library, Troy NC p. 1827

Montgomery County Circuit Court, Rockville MD p. 1038

Montgomery County Community College, Blue Bell PA p. 2036

Montgomery County Correctional Facility, *see* Montgomery County Public Libraries, Boyds MD p. 1038

Montgomery County Department of History & Archives, Fonda NY p. 1623

Montgomery County Historical Society Library, Rockville MD p. 1038

Montgomery County Law Library, Montgomery AL p. 31

Montgomery County Library, Mount Ida AR p. 110

Montgomery County Library & Information Network Consortium (N), Conshohocken PA p. 2954

Montgomery County Memorial Library System, Conroe TX p. 2300

Montgomery County Planning Commission Library, Norristown PA p. 2098

Montgomery County Public, *see* Ohoopee Regional Library System, Mount Vernon GA p. 556

Montgomery County Public Libraries, Rockville MD p. 1038

Montgomery County Public Library, Troy NC p. 1827

Montgomery County-Norristown Public Library, Norristown PA p. 2098

Montgomery-Floyd Regional Library System, Christiansburg VA p. 2457

Montgomery Frederick S Library, *see* Butte College Library, Oroville CA p. 201

Montgomery Free Library, Montgomery NY p. 1662

Montgomery Hospital, Norristown PA p. 2099

Montgomery House, McEwensville PA p. 2085

Montgomery Jack C VA Medical Center, Muskogee OK p. 1969

Montgomery Library, *see* Campbellsville University, Campbellsville KY p. 909

Montgomery Library, *see* Fairchild Tropical Botanic Garden, Miami FL p. 465

Montgomery Library, *see* Westminster Theological Seminary, Glenside PA p. 2062

Montgomery Library Resource Center, *see* Johns Hopkins University Libraries, Rockville MD p. 1037

Montgomery, Mccracken, Walker & Rhoads LLP Library, Philadelphia PA p. 2112

Montgomery Memorial Library, Jewell IA p. 824

Montgomery Presbyterian Church Library, Cincinnati OH p. 1871

Montgomery Public, *see* Waseca-Le Sueur Regional Library, Montgomery MN p. 1287

Montgomery State Prison, *see* Georgia Department of Corrections, Mount Vernon GA p. 546

Montgomery Town Library, Montgomery Center VT p. 2429

Montgomery Watson Harza Library, Chicago IL p. 619

Monticello Library, *see* Great River Regional Library, Monticello MN p. 1275

Monticello Public Library, Monticello WI p. 2623

Monticello Union Township Public Library, Monticello IN p. 766

Montieth Library, *see* Alma College Library, Alma MI p. 1149

Montmorency County Public Libraries, Atlanta MI p. 1154

Montour Falls Memorial Library, Montour Falls NY p. 1662

Montpelier Public Library, Montpelier IN p. 766

Montpelier Public Library, Montpelier OH p. 1918

Montreal Association for the Blind, Montreal QC p. 2899

Montreal Association for the Intellectually Handicapped Library, Montreal QC p. 2899

Montreal Chest Institute, Montreal QC p. 2899

Montreal Children's Hospital, Montreal QC p. 2899

Montreal City Hall, Montreal QC p. 2899

Montreal City Planning Department, Montreal QC p. 2899

Montreal General Hospital, Montreal QC p. 2900

Montreal Museum of Fine Arts, Montreal QC p. 2900

Montreal Neurological Institute Hospital Library, Montreal QC p. 2900

Montreat College, Montreat NC p. 1810

Jennings Library, *see* Genesee District Library, Montrose MI p. 1180

Montrose Public Library, Montrose IA p. 833

Montrose Regional Library District, Montrose CO p. 318

Montserrat College of Art, Beverly MA p. 1054

Montvale Free Public Library, Montvale NJ p. 1503

Montvale Library, *see* Bedford Public Library System, Montvale VA p. 2451

Montverde Library, *see* Lehmann Helen Memorial Library, Montverde FL p. 470

Montville Township Public Library, Montville NJ p. 1504

Monument Library, *see* Pikes Peak Library District, Monument CO p. 296

Moody Bible Institute, Chicago IL p. 619

Moody Community Library, Moody TX p. 2363

Moody County Resource Center, Flandreau SD p. 2212

Moody Mary Northern Municipal Library, *see* Fairfield Library Association, Inc, Fairfield TX p. 2318

Moody Medical Library, *see* University of Texas Medical Branch, Galveston TX p. 2326

Moody Memorial Library, *see* Baylor University Libraries, Waco TX p. 2396

Moody Memorial Library, *see* Houston Baptist University, Houston TX p. 2337

Moody Nettie Neighborhood Library, *see* Houston Public Library, Houston TX p. 2339

Moody W L Jr Library, *see* Blinn College Library, Brenham TX p. 2291

Mooers Free Library, Mooers NY p. 1663

Mookini Edwin H Library, *see* University of Hawaii at Hilo Library, Hilo HI p. 559

Moon D R Memorial Library, Stanley WI p. 2639

Moon F Franklin Library, *see* State University of New York, College of Environmental Science & Forestry, Syracuse NY p. 1753

Moon Henry Lee Library & Civil Rights Archives, Baltimore MD p. 1016

Moon Township Public Library, Moon Township PA p. 2092

Mooneyham Public Library, Forest City NC p. 1794

Moore & Van Allen PLLC, Charlotte NC p. 1783

Moore Ann Carroll Children's Library, *see* Utah State University, Logan UT p. 2407

Moore Arthur J Methodist Library, *see* United Methodist Church - South Georgia Conference, Saint Simons Island GA p. 549

Moore Bessie Boehm Library, *see* Stone County Library, Mountain View AR p. 110

Moore Cecil B, *see* Free Library of Philadelphia, Philadelphia PA p. 2108

Moore Claude Health Sciences Library, *see* University of Virginia, Charlottesville VA p. 2455

Moore College of Art & Design, Philadelphia PA p. 2112

Moore County Library, Carthage NC p. 1779

Moore County Library, *see* Killgore Memorial Library, Dumas TX p. 2314

Moore County Public Library, Lynchburg TN p. 2245

Moore Family Library, Grinnell KS p. 870

Moore Franklin F Library, *see* Rider University, Lawrenceville NJ p. 1494

Moore Free Library, Newfane VT p. 2430

Moore Haven Correctional Facility, *see* GEO Corporation, Moore Haven FL p. 470

Moore Henry D Library, Steuben ME p. 1003

Moore Mary C Public Library, *see* Lacombe Public Library, Lacombe AB p. 2709

Moore Memorial Library, Greene NY p. 1631

Moore Memorial Library District, Hillsdale IL p. 656

Moore Memorial Public Library, Texas City TX p. 2392

Moore Parlett Library, *see* Coppin State College, Baltimore MD p. 1012

Moore Public, *see* Pioneer Library System, Moore OK p. 1970

Moore Public Library, Lexington MI p. 1203

Moore Public Library, Moore MT p. 1387

Moore Virginia Reid Marine Research Library, San Pedro CA p. 256

Moore William J, *see* University of Kansas, Department of Religious Studies, Lawrence KS p. 878

Moores Creek Battlefield Library, *see* United States National Park Service, Currie NC p. 1786

Moores Memorial Library, Christiana PA p. 2044

Moorestown Public Library, Moorestown NJ p. 1504

Mooresville Public Library, Mooresville IN p. 766

Mooresville Public Library, Mooresville NC p. 1810

Moorhead Public Library, Moorhead IA p. 833

Moorhead Public Library, *see* Lake Agassiz Regional Library, Moorhead MN p. 1266

Moorland-Spingarn Research Center, *see* Howard University Libraries, Washington DC p. 404

Moorpark City Library, Moorpark CA p. 191

Moorpark College Library, Moorpark CA p. 191

Moose Jaw Public Library, *see* Palliser Regional Library, Moose Jaw SK p. 2919

Moose Lake Public Library, Moose Lake MN p. 1266

Moose Pass Public Library, Moose Pass AK p. 51

Moosilauke Public Library, North Woodstock NH p. 1461

Mora Public Library, Mora MN p. 1267

Moraga Historical Society Archives, Moraga CA p. 191

Moraga Library, *see* Contra Costa County Library, Moraga CA p. 209

Moraine Park Technical College, West Bend WI p. 2648

Moraine Park Technical College Library, Beaver Dam WI p. 2581

Moraine Park Technical College Library, Fond du Lac WI p. 2592

Moraine Valley Community College Library, Palos Hills IL p. 687

Moran Jan Collier City Learning Library, *see* Broward County Division of Libraries, Pompano Beach FL p. 442

Moran Pierre, *see* Elkhart Public Library, Elkhart IN p. 737

Moran Public Library, Moran KS p. 884

Moravia Public Library, Moravia IA p. 833

Moravian Archives, Bethlehem PA p. 2034

Moravian Church in America, Winston-Salem NC p. 1833

Moravian College & Moravian Theological Seminary, Bethlehem PA p. 2034

Moravian Historical Society, Nazareth PA p. 2095

Moravian Music Foundation, Winston-Salem NC p. 1833

Morbito Joseph F Architecture Library, *see* Kent State University Libraries, Kent OH p. 1907

Moreau Basil Anthony Memorial Library, *see* Buda Public Library, Buda TX p. 2293

Morehead Albert H Memorial Library, *see* American Contract Bridge League, Memphis TN p. 2247

Morehead State University, Morehead KY p. 929

Morehouse Parish Library, Bastrop LA p. 941

Morehouse School of Medicine Library, Atlanta GA p. 517

Morell Public, *see* Prince Edward Island Public Library Service, Morell PE p. 2876

Morenci Community Library, Morenci AZ p. 69

Moreno Valley Public Library, Moreno Valley CA p. 191

Moretown Memorial Library, Moretown VT p. 2429

Morgade Robert Library, *see* Martin County Library System, Stuart FL p. 492

Morgan & Gotcher Law Office Library, Greenville TX p. 2330

Morgan Charles S Technical Library, *see* National Fire Protection Association, Quincy MA p. 1119

Morgan City Public Library, Morgan City LA p. 958

Morgan Community College Library, Fort Morgan CO p. 308

Morgan County Bar Association Library, McConnelsville OH p. 1916

Morgan County Library, Versailles MO p. 1371

Morgan County Library, Morgan UT p. 2408

Morgan County Library, *see* Uncle Remus Regional Library System, Madison GA p. 542

Morgan County Public Library, Martinsville IN p. 763

Morgan County Library, West Liberty KY p. 937

Morgan County Public Library, Berkeley Springs WV p. 2554

Morgan David P Memorial Library, *see* Kalmbach Publishing Co Library, Waukesha WI p. 2645

Morgan J P Chase & Co, New York NY p. 1687

Morgan Jane Memorial Library, Cambria WI p. 2584

Morgan Juliette Hampton Memorial Library, *see* Montgomery City-County Public Library System, Montgomery AL p. 30

Morgan Lewis & Bochius LLP, Washington DC p. 408

Morgan, Lewis & Bockius LLP, Miami FL p. 468

Morgan, Lewis & Bockius LLP, Philadelphia PA p. 2112

Morgan Library, New York NY p. 1687

Morgan Library, *see* Grace College & Grace Theological Seminary, Winona Lake IN p. 789

Morgan Lucile L Public Library, Heflin AL p. 20

Morgan Memorial Library, *see* Suffolk Public Library System, Suffolk VA p. 2497

Morgan Public Library, Morgan MN p. 1267

Morgan State University, Baltimore MD p. 1016

Morgan Vincent Music Library, *see* Amherst College, Amherst MA p. 1048

Morgantown Public Library, Morgantown WV p. 2566

Moriarty Community Library, Moriarty NM p. 1560

Morikami Museum, Delray Beach FL p. 437

Morinville Public Library, Morinville AB p. 2711

Morison Robert S Memorial Library, *see* Hastings Center, Garrison NY p. 1627

Morisset Library, *see* University of Ottawa Libraries, Ottawa ON p. 2834

Moritz John Library, *see* Nebraska Methodist College, Omaha NE p. 1413

Moritz Michael E Law Library, *see* Ohio State University LIBRARIES, Columbus OH p. 1888

Morley Library, Painesville OH p. 1927

Morley Public Library, Morley IA p. 833

Morneau Sobeco Library, Montreal QC p. 2900

Morneault Abel J Memorial Library, Van Buren ME p. 1004

Morning Call, Allentown PA p. 2027

Morningside College, Sioux City IA p. 844

Morocco Community Library, *see* Newton County Public Library, Morocco IN p. 760

Morofsky Walter F Memorial Library, *see* Michigan State University, Hickory Corners MI p. 1189

Morrill Memorial & Harris Library, Strafford VT p. 2437

Morrill Memorial Library, Norwood MA p. 1115

Morrill Public Library, Hiawatha KS p. 871

Morrill Public Library, Morrill NE p. 1409

Morrin Municipal Library, Morrin AB p. 2712

Morris Arboretum Library, *see* University of Pennsylvania Libraries, Philadelphia PA p. 2119

Morris Area Public Library District, Morris IL p. 675

Morris Arthur J Law Library, *see* University of Virginia, Charlottesville VA p. 2455

Morris Automated Information Network (N), Whippany NJ p. 2949

Morris College, Sumter SC p. 2206

Morris County Historical Society, Morristown NJ p. 1505

Morris County Law Library, Morristown NJ p. 1505

Morris County Library, Whippany NJ p. 1544

Morris Delyte W Library, *see* Southern Illinois University Carbondale, Carbondale IL p. 600

Morris Emory W Learning Resource Center, *see* Kellogg Community College, Battle Creek MI p. 1155

Morris James LLP, Wilmington DE p. 388

Morris John A Library, *see* National Museum of Racing & Hall of Fame, Saratoga Springs NY p. 1738

Morris Library, *see* Gaston College, Dallas NC p. 1786

Morris Lon College, Jacksonville TX p. 2347

Morris, Manning & Martin Library LLP, Washington DC p. 408

Morris Medical Library, *see* Summa Barberton Citizens Hospital, Barberton OH p. 1857

Morris, Nichols, Arsht & Tunnell, LLP, Wilmington DE p. 388

Morris Plains Library, Morris Plains NJ p. 1504

Morris Public Library, Morris CT p. 353

Morris Public Library, Morris MN p. 1267

Morris-Union Federation (N), Chatham NJ p. 2949

Morris Watson B Medical Library, *see* Runnells Specialized Hospital, Berkeley Heights NJ p. 1472

Morris Willie, *see* Jackson/Hinds Library System, Jackson MS p. 1303

Morrison & Foerster LLP, Denver CO p. 302

Morrison & Foerster LLP Library, Los Angeles CA p. 175

Morrison Dr Samuel Medical Library, *see* Good Samaritan Hospital, Baltimore MD p. 1013

Morrison Frances Library, *see* Saskatoon Public Library, Saskatoon SK p. 2926

Morrison, Mahoney LLP, Boston MA p. 1064

Morrison Regional Library, *see* Charlotte Mecklenburg Library, Charlotte NC p. 1782

Morrison-Talbott Library, Waterloo IL p. 715

Morrison University Library, Reno NV p. 1432

Morrisson-Reeves Library, *see* Wayne Township Library, Richmond IN p. 775

Morristown & Morris Township Library, Morristown NJ p. 1505

Morristown Centennial Library, Morrisville VT p. 2430

Morristown-Hamblen Library, Morristown TN p. 2253

Morristown Jewish Center, Morristown NJ p. 1505

Morristown Memorial Hospital Medical Library, Morristown NJ p. 1505

Morristown National Historical Park Library, *see* National Park Service, Morristown NJ p. 1505

Morristown Public Library, Morristown NY p. 1663

Morrisville Free Library Association, Morrisville PA p. 2093

Morrisville Public Library, Morrisville NY p. 1663

Morrow Grant III MD Library, *see* Ohio State University LIBRARIES, Columbus OH p. 1889

Morrow Memorial United Methodist Church, Maplewood NJ p. 1499

Morse Institute Library, Natick MA p. 1107

Morse Julia Adams Memorial Library, Greene ME p. 986

Morse Leonard Campus Medical Library, *see* Metro West Medical Center, Natick MA p. 1107

Mortensen W H Library, *see* University of Hartford Libraries, West Hartford CT p. 376

Mortimer Rare Book Room, *see* Smith College Libraries, Northampton MA p. 1114

Mortimer William J Library, *see* LIMRA International InfoCenter, Windsor CT p. 379

Mortola Edward & Doris Library, *see* Pace University, Pleasantville NY p. 1719

Morton Arboretum, Lisle IL p. 667

Morton College Library, Cicero IL p. 629

Morton County Library, Elkhart KS p. 865

Morton Grove Public Library, Morton Grove IL p. 676

Morton Hospital, a Steward Family Hospital, Taunton MA p. 1130

Morton-James Public Library, Nebraska City NE p. 1409

Morton Mandan Public Library, Mandan ND p. 1845

Morton Memorial Library, Pine Hill NY p. 1718

Morton Memorial Library & Community House, Rhinecliff NY p. 1727

Morton Plant Mease Health Care, Clearwater FL p. 432

Morton Public Library, Morton MS p. 1309

Morton Public Library District, Morton IL p. 676

Morton Sterling Library, *see* Morton Arboretum, Lisle IL p. 667

Morton Township Public Library, Mecosta MI p. 1207

Morton William Smith Library, *see* Union Theological Seminary & Presbyterian School, Richmond VA p. 2490

Mortvedt Robert A L Library, *see* Pacific Lutheran University, Tacoma WA p. 2539

Mosak Sol & Elaine Library, *see* Adler School of Professional Psychology, Chicago IL p. 605

Mose Hudson Tapia Public Library, Bayou La Batre AL p. 6

Moses Cone Health System, Greensboro NC p. 1797

Moses Lake Community, *see* North Central Regional Library, Moses Lake WA p. 2549

Moses Taylor Hospital Medical Library, Scranton PA p. 2137

Mosheim Public Library, Mosheim TN p. 2253

Mosier Valley Library, Mosier OR p. 2007

Moss John F Library, *see* Texas A&M University-Texarkana, Texarkana TX p. 2392

Moss Landing Marine Laboratories Library, *see* California State University, Moss Landing CA p. 192

Moss Memorial Library, Hayesville NC p. 1800

Moss Memorial Library, *see* Delgado Community College, New Orleans LA p. 959

Moss Thomas W Jr, *see* Tidewater Community College Learning Resources Center, Norfolk VA p. 2483

Moss Walter O Medical Library, *see* Lake Charles Memorial Hospital, Lake Charles LA p. 954

Mosser John Public Library District, Abingdon IL p. 587

Mossey Michael Alex Library, *see* Hillsdale College, Hillsdale MI p. 1190

Mote Marine Laboratory Library, Sarasota FL p. 489

Mother Theresa Hackelmeier Memorial Library, *see* Marian College, Indianapolis IN p. 755

Mother Whiteside Memorial Library, Grants NM p. 1556

Motion Picture & Television Fund, Woodland Hills CA p. 285

Motion Picture Archives, *see* Cinema Arts, Inc, Newfoundland PA p. 2097

Motley County Library, Matador TX p. 2360

Motlow State Community College Libraries, Tullahoma TN p. 2267

Motorcycle Industry Council, Irvine CA p. 160

Motorola, Inc, Schaumburg IL p. 701

Motorola Technical & Business Library, Fort Lauderdale FL p. 443

Mott Community College, Flint MI p. 1180

Mott Library, *see* Mott Community College, Flint MI p. 1180

Mott Public Library, Mott ND p. 1847

Mott Stanton Memorial Library, *see* New York State Archaeological Association, Southold NY p. 1746

Moulton Marilyn L Library, *see* Northeastern Vermont Regional Hospital, Saint Johnsbury VT p. 2435

Moultonborough Public Library, Moultonborough NH p. 1458

Moultrie-Colquitt County Library, Moultrie GA p. 545

Moultrie County Historical & Genealogical Society Library, Sullivan IL p. 708

Moultrie Technical College Library, Moultrie GA p. 546

Mounce & Green, Meyers, Safi & Galatzan, El Paso TX p. 2317

Mound Bayou Public, *see* Bolivar County Library System, Mound Bayou MS p. 1296

Mound Center Library, Sinsinawa WI p. 2638

Mound City Public Library, Mound City IL p. 676

Mound City Public Library, Mound City MO p. 1347

Mound Correctional Facility Library, *see* Michigan Department of Corrections, Detroit MI p. 1171

Mound Valley Public Library, Mound Valley KS p. 884

Moundridge Public Library, Moundridge KS p. 884

Mounds Public Library, Mounds IL p. 676

Moundsville-Marshall County Public Library, Moundsville WV p. 2567

Moundview Memorial Hospital, Friendship WI p. 2593

Muldrow Public Library, Muldrow OK p. 1969

Mule Creek State Prison, *see* California Department of Corrections Library System, Ione CA p. 221

Muleshoe Area Public Library, Muleshoe TX p. 2364

Mulford Healh Science Library, *see* University of Toledo, Toledo OH p. 1940

Mullan Public Library, Mullan ID p. 580

Mullen John K of Denver Memorial Library, *see* Catholic University of America, Washington DC p. 395

Mullens Area Public, *see* Wyoming County Public Library, Mullens WV p. 2570

Mulliken District Library, Mulliken MI p. 1212

Multicultural Association of Nova Scotia Library, Halifax NS p. 2781

Multicultural Council of Windsor & Essex County Library, Windsor ON p. 2871

Multidisciplinary Center for Earthquake Engineering Research, Buffalo NY p. 1598

Multnomah County Library, Portland OR p. 2011

Multnomah Law Library, Portland OR p. 2012

Multnomah University, Portland OR p. 2012

Mulvane Public Library, Mulvane KS p. 884

Muncie Center Township Public Library, Muncie IN p. 767

Muncie Public Library, Muncie IN p. 767

Muncy Historical Society & Museum of History, Muncy PA p. 2093

Muncy Public Library, Muncy PA p. 2093

Mundare Municipal Library, Mundare AB p. 2712

Mundt Karl E Library, *see* Dakota State University, Madison SD p. 2214

Munford-Tipton Memorial Library, Munford TN p. 2254

Munger, Tolles & Olson LLP, Los Angeles CA p. 176

Municipal Association of South Carolina, Columbia SC p. 2188

Municipal Research & Services Center of Washington Library, Seattle WA p. 2528

Municipal Technical Advisory Service Library, Knoxville TN p. 2242

Municipality of Hastings Highlands Library, Maynooth ON p. 2821

Munitions Directorate Technical Library, *see* Air Force Research Laboratory, Eglin AFB FL p. 439

Munro Dr E H Library, *see* Saint Mary's Hospital, Grand Junction CO p. 311

Munson Healthcare, Traverse City MI p. 1231

Munson Memorial, *see* Jones Library, Inc, South Amherst MA p. 1049

Munson-Williams-Proctor Arts Institute Library, Utica NY p. 1759

Muntz Robert R Library, *see* University of Texas at Tyler Library, Tyler TX p. 2394

Murchison Clint W Memorial Library, *see* Henderson County, Athens TX p. 2277

Murchison Ginger Learning Resource Center, *see* Trinity Valley Community College Library, Athens TX p. 2277

Murdock Learning Resource Center, *see* George Fox University, Newberg OR p. 2007

Murphree John A H Law Library, Gainesville FL p. 449

Murphy Art & Architecture Library, *see* University of Kansas Libraries, Lawrence KS p. 878

Murphy Eleanor E Library, *see* Huntsville-Madison Public Library, Huntsville AL p. 21

Murphy Helen, *see* Huntington Beach Public Library System, Huntington Beach CA p. 159

Murphy-Jahn Library, Chicago IL p. 619

Murphy John C Memorial, *see* College of Lake County, Grayslake IL p. 652

Murphy Library Resource Center, *see* University of Wisconsin-La Crosse, La Crosse WI p. 2603

Murphy Memorial Library, Monona IA p. 832

Murphy Memorial Library, Livingston TX p. 2356

Murphy Memorial Library, *see* Baptist Bible College & Seminary, Clarks Summit PA p. 2045

Murphy Oil Corp, El Dorado AR p. 98

Murphy Public Library, Murphy NC p. 1812

Murphy, Sheneman, Julian & Rogers, San Francisco CA p. 244

Murphy Thomas B, *see* West Georgia Technical College, Waco GA p. 556

Murphy William K Health Sciences Memorial Library, *see* Veterans Home of California, Yountville CA p. 285

Murray-Colloway County Hospital, Murray KY p. 930

Murray-Green Library, *see* Roosevelt University, Chicago IL p. 623

Murray Harbour Public, *see* Prince Edward Island Public Library Service, Murray Harbour PE p. 2876

Murray Library, *see* Messiah College, Mechanicsburg PA p. 2087

Murray Lynn Memorial Library, Chester WV p. 2557

Murray Memorial Library, *see* Good Samaritan Regional Medical Center, Corvallis OR p. 1994

Murray Public Library, Murray IA p. 834

Murray Public Library, Murray UT p. 2408

Murray River Leona Giddings Memorial Library, *see* Prince Edward Island Public Library Service, Murray River PE p. 2876

Murray State College, Tishomingo OK p. 1980

Murray State University, Murray KY p. 930, 2966

Murrayville Library, *see* Fraser Valley Regional Library, Langley BC p. 2724

Murrell Katie Library, *see* Lindsey Wilson College, Columbia KY p. 910

Murrell Memorial Library, Marshall MO p. 1344

Murrieta Public Library, Murrieta CA p. 192

Gregg Murry C Learning Resources, *see* J F Ingram State Technical College Library, Deatsville AL p. 14

Murrysville Community Library, Murrysville PA p. 2094

Murtha Cullina LLP Library, Hartford CT p. 347

Musagetes Architecture Library, *see* University of Waterloo Library, Cambridge ON p. 2870

Muscatine Art Center, Muscatine IA p. 834

Muscle Shoals Public Library, Muscle Shoals AL p. 32

Muscoda Public Library, Muscoda WI p. 2623

Muse William T Law Library, *see* University of Richmond, Richmond VA p. 2491

Musee D'Art de Joliette, Joliette QC p. 2884

Musee de la Civilisation, Quebec QC p. 2906

Musee Heritage Museum, St. Albert AB p. 2717

Musee national des beaux-arts du Quebec Bibliotheque, Quebec QC p. 2906

Museum of American Glass, Millville NJ p. 1502

Museum of Art & History Library, Santa Cruz CA p. 264

Museum of Arts & Sciences, Daytona Beach FL p. 436

Museum of Contemporary Art Library, Chicago IL p. 619

Museum of Contemporary Art San Diego, La Jolla CA p. 161

Museum of Contemporary Craft Library, Portland OR p. 2012

Museum of Early Trades & Crafts Library, Madison NJ p. 1498

Museum of Fine Arts, Saint Petersburg FL p. 488

Museum of Fine Arts, Boston, Boston MA p. 1064

Museum of Flight, Seattle WA p. 2529

Museum of Independent Telephony Library, Abilene KS p. 855

Museum of Indian Arts & Culture, *see* Museum of New Mexico, Santa Fe NM p. 1562

Museum of Jewish Heritage, New York NY p. 1687

Museum of Mobile, Mobile AL p. 26

Museum of Modern Art Library, New York NY p. 1687

Museum of National Center of Afro-American Artists, Boston MA p. 1064

Museum of Nature & Science, Dallas TX p. 2309

Museum of New Mexico, Santa Fe NM p. 1562

Museum of North Idaho Inc Archives, Coeur d'Alene ID p. 573

Museum of Northern Arizona-Harold S Colton Memorial Library, Flagstaff AZ p. 62

Museum of Russian Culture, Inc Library, San Francisco CA p. 244

Museum of the American Indian Library, Novato CA p. 196

Museum of the American Railroad, Dallas TX p. 2309

Museum of the Cherokee Indian, Cherokee NC p. 1784

Museum of the City of New York, New York NY p. 1687

Museum of the Confederacy, Richmond VA p. 2489

Museum of the Fur Trade Library, Chadron NE p. 1395

Museum of the Great Plains, Lawton OK p. 1967

Museum of Transportation, Saint Louis MO p. 1357

Museum of Ventura County, Ventura CA p. 279

Museum of Western Art Library, Kerrville TX p. 2349

Museum of Western Colorado, Grand Junction CO p. 311

Museum of Women Pilots Library, *see* Ninety-Nines, Inc, Oklahoma City OK p. 1973

Museum of York County, Rock Hill SC p. 2202

Museums Association of Saskatchewan, Regina SK p. 2923

Museums of Oglebay Institute Library, Wheeling WV p. 2574

Music Center of Los Angeles Archives, Los Angeles CA p. 176

Music Library, *see* Wichita State University Libraries, Wichita KS p. 902

Musick, Peeler & Garrett Library, Los Angeles CA p. 176

Musick Ruth Ann Library, *see* Fairmont State University, Fairmont WV p. 2558

Muskego Public Library, Muskego WI p. 2623

Muskegon Area District Library, Muskegon MI p. 1212

Muskegon Community College, Muskegon MI p. 1213

Muskegon Correctional Facility Library, *see* Michigan Department of Corrections, Muskegon MI p. 1212

Muskingum County Genealogical Society Library, Zanesville OH p. 1953

Muskingum County Law Library, Zanesville OH p. 1953

Muskingum County Library System, Zanesville OH p. 1953

Muskingum University Library, New Concord OH p. 1920

Muskogee Law Library Association, Muskogee OK p. 1969

Muskogee Public Library, Muskogee OK p. 1969

Muskoka Lakes Library Board, Port Carling ON p. 2837

Muslim Education & Welfare Foundation of Canada, Surrey BC p. 2738

Musmanno William J Memorial Library, *see* Pittsburgh Institute of Mortuary Science, Pittsburgh PA p. 2127

Musselman Library, *see* Bluffton University, Bluffton OH p. 1860

Musselman Library, *see* Gettysburg College, Gettysburg PA p. 2059

Musselman-South Berkeley Community Library, *see* Martinsburg-Berkeley County Public Library, Inwood WV p. 2565

Musser Public Library, Muscatine IA p. 834

Musser R D Library, *see* Weyerhaeuser Charles A Memorial Museum, Little Falls MN p. 1256

Mustang Library, *see* Scottsdale Public Library, Scottsdale AZ p. 81

Mustang Public Library, Mustang OK p. 1969

Mutual UFO Network, Inc, Greeley CO p. 312

MWR Library, *see* United States Navy, Great Lakes IL p. 652

Myerberg Julius & Doris Library, *see* Baltimore Hebrew Congregation, Baltimore MD p. 1011

Myers Charles C Library, *see* University of Dubuque Library, Dubuque IA p. 812

Myers Isabel Briggs Memorial Library, *see* Center for Applications of Psychological Type, Gainesville FL p. 449

Myers Library, *see* Ottawa University, Ottawa KS p. 887

Myers Memorial Library, Frewsburg NY p. 1625

National Coffee Association Library, New York NY p. 1687

National College, Salem VA p. 2495

National College of Business & Technology, Knoxville TN p. 2243

National College of Naturopathic Medicine Library, Portland OR p. 2012

National Concrete Masonry Association Library, Herndon VA p. 2471

National Cotton Council of America Library, Cordova TN p. 2232

National Council of Teachers of English Library, Urbana IL p. 711

National Cowboy & Western Heritage Museum, Oklahoma City OK p. 1973

National Defense University Library, *see* United States Department of Defense, Washington DC p. 418

National Economic Research Associates, Inc, White Plains NY p. 1768

National Economic Research Associates, Inc Library, Washington DC p. 409

National Economic Research Associates, Inc Library, Los Angeles CA p. 176

National Emergency Training Center, *see* United States Fire Administration, Emmitsburg MD p. 1028

National Employment Law Project Library, New York NY p. 1688

National Endowment for Democracy Library, Washington DC p. 409

National Endowment for the Humanities Library, Washington DC p. 409

National Energy Board Library, Calgary AB p. 2692

National Energy Technology Laboratory Library, *see* United States Department of Energy, Morgantown WV p. 2566

National Environmental Satellite Data & Information Services, Seattle WA p. 2529

National Epilepsy Library®, *see* Epilepsy Foundation, Landover MD p. 1034

National Film Board of Canada, Montreal QC p. 2900

National Film Board of Canada, Saint Laurent QC p. 2909

National Fire Protection Association, Quincy MA p. 1119

National Football Foundation's College, South Bend IN p. 779

National Forest Service Library, Fort Collins CO p. 307

National Gallery of Art Library, Washington DC p. 409

National Gallery of Canada Library, Ottawa ON p. 2832

National Geodetic Survey Library, Silver Spring MD p. 1041

National Geographic Society Library, Washington DC p. 410

National Grocers Association Library, Arlington VA p. 2450

National Ground Water Association, Westerville OH p. 1946

National Guard Memorial Library, Washington DC p. 410

National Hispanic University, San Jose CA p. 250

National Humanities Center Library, Research Triangle Park NC p. 1819

National Hunters Association Inc Library, Knightdale NC p. 1805

National Hurricane Center, *see* United States National Oceanic & Atmospheric, Miami FL p. 468

National Indian Law Library, Boulder CO p. 291

National Institute for Occupational Safety & Health, Pittsburgh PA p. 2126

National Institute for Occupational Safety & Health Library, *see* Centers for Disease Control, Cincinnati OH p. 1868

National Institute of Arthritis & Musculoskeletal, Bethesda MD p. 1021

National Institute of Corrections Information Center, *see* United States Department of Justice, Aurora CO p. 288

National Institute of Environmental Health Sciences Library, Research Triangle Park NC p. 1819

National Institute of Justice, Washington DC p. 410

National Institute of Standards & Technology Research Library, Gaithersburg MD p. 1030

National Institute on Aging, Baltimore MD p. 1016

National Institute on Drug Abuse, Baltimore MD p. 1016

National Institutes of Health Library, Bethesda MD p. 1021

National Investigations Committee on Unidentified Flying Objects, Chatsworth CA p. 133

National Jewish Archive of Broadcasting, *see* Jewish Museum, New York NY p. 1683

National Jewish Health, Denver CO p. 302

National Labor Relations Board Library, Washington DC p. 410

National Library of Education, Washington DC p. 410

National Library of International Trade, *see* United States International Trade Commission, Washington DC p. 420

National Library of Medicine, Bethesda MD p. 1022

National Library Service for the Blind & Physically Handicapped, *see* Library of Congress, Washington DC p. 407

National Louis University Library & Learning Support, Chicago IL p. 619

National Marine Fisheries Service, Juneau AK p. 50

National Marine Fisheries Service, Kodiak AK p. 51

National Marine Fisheries Service, Santa Cruz CA p. 264

National Marine Fisheries Service, Miami FL p. 468

National Marine Fisheries Service, Panama City FL p. 480

National Marine Fisheries Service, Honolulu HI p. 565

National Marine Fisheries Service, Pascagoula MS p. 1311

National Marine Fisheries Service, Seattle WA p. 2529

National Model Railroad Association, Chattanooga TN p. 2228

National Monument Library, *see* Castillo De San Marcos & Fort Matanzas National Monuments, Saint Augustine FL p. 486

National Multiple Sclerosis Society, New York NY p. 1688

National Museum of American History Library, *see* Smithsonian Libraries, Washington DC p. 415

National Museum of American Jewish Military History Library, Washington DC p. 410

National Museum of Natural History Library, *see* Smithsonian Libraries, Washington DC p. 415

National Museum of Racing & Hall of Fame, Saratoga Springs NY p. 1738

National Museum of Women in the Arts, Washington DC p. 410

National Music Museum Library, *see* University of South Dakota, Vermillion SD p. 2221

National Network of Libraries of Medicine (N), Bethesda MD p. 2944

National Network of Libraries of Medicine Greater Midwest Region (N), Chicago IL p. 2942

National Network of Libraries of Medicine Midcontinental Region (N), Salt Lake City UT p. 2956

National Network of Libraries of Medicine Middle Atlantic Region (N), Pittsburgh PA p. 2954

National Network of Libraries of Medicine New England Region (N), Shrewsbury MA p. 2945

National Network of Libraries of Medicine Pacific Northwest Region (N), Seattle WA p. 2957

National Network of Libraries of Medicine Pacific Southwest Region (N), Los Angeles CA p. 2938

National Network of Libraries of Medicine South Central Region (N), Houston TX p. 2956

National Network of Libraries of Medicine Southeastern Atlantic Region (N), Baltimore MD p. 2944

National Oceanic & Atmospheric Administration, Miami FL p. 468

National Oceanic & Atmospheric Administration, Silver Spring MD p. 1042

National Oceanic & Atmospheric Administration, Princeton NJ p. 1522

National Oceanic & Atmospheric Administration, Asheville NC p. 1775

National Opinion Research Center Library, Chicago IL p. 620

National Park Community College Library, Hot Springs AR p. 104

National Park Service, Gustavus AK p. 49

National Park Service, Sitka AK p. 53

National Park Service, Chinle AZ p. 60

National Park Service, Petrified Forest National Park AZ p. 71

National Park Service, Tucson AZ p. 86

National Park Service, Death Valley CA p. 140

National Park Service, Mineral CA p. 187

National Park Service, San Francisco CA p. 244

National Park Service, Tulelake CA p. 276

National Park Service, Estes Park CO p. 306

National Park Service, Fort Oglethorpe GA p. 533

National Park Service, Kennesaw GA p. 537

National Park Service, Macon GA p. 541

National Park Service, Hagerstown MD p. 1031

National Park Service, Sharpsburg MD p. 1041

National Park Service, Republic MO p. 1350

National Park Service, Van Buren MO p. 1370

National Park Service, Deer Lodge MT p. 1377

National Park Service, Gering NE p. 1399

National Park Service, Lincoln NE p. 1405

National Park Service, Omaha NE p. 1413

National Park Service, Morristown NJ p. 1505

National Park Service, Aztec NM p. 1552

National Park Service, Mountainair NM p. 1560

National Park Service, Stillwater NY p. 1749

National Park Service, Sulphur OK p. 1979

National Park Service, Hot Springs SD p. 2213

National Park Service, Interior SD p. 2213

National Park Service, Shiloh TN p. 2265

National Park Service, El Paso TX p. 2317

National Park Service, Fort Davis TX p. 2320

National Park Service, Johnson City TX p. 2348

National Park Service, American Fork UT p. 2403

National Park Service, Appomattox VA p. 2448

National Park Service, Richmond VA p. 2489

National Park Service, Yorktown VA p. 2505

National Park Service, Bayfield WI p. 2581

National Park Service, Moose WY p. 2658

National Park Service Department of Interior, Saugus MA p. 1122

National Park Service, Department of Interior, Farmington PA p. 2057

National Park Service Independence National Historical Park, Philadelphia PA p. 2113

National Park Service Library, Lakewood CO p. 315

National Post Library, Toronto ON p. 2855

National Postal Museum Library, *see* Smithsonian Libraries, Washington DC p. 415

National Presbyterian Church & Center, Washington DC p. 410

National Press Club, Washington DC p. 411

National Psychological Association for Psychoanalysis, Inc, New York NY p. 1688

National PTA, Chicago IL p. 620

National Radio Astronomy Observatory Library, Charlottesville VA p. 2454

National Railway Historical Society, Atlanta Chapter, Duluth GA p. 531

National Railway Historical Society Library, Philadelphia PA p. 2113

National Recreation & Park Association, Ashburn VA p. 2450

National Reference Center for Bioethics Literature, Washington DC p. 411

National Rehabilitation Information Center, Landover MD p. 1034

National Renewable Energy Library, Golden CO p. 310

National Restaurant Association, Washington DC p. 411

National Rifle Association, Fairfax VA p. 2462

National Right to Life Library, Washington DC p. 411

National Safety Council Library, Itasca IL p. 658

National School Boards Association Library, Alexandria VA p. 2446

Neosho County Community College, Chanute KS p. 860

Neosho/Newton County Library, Neosho MO p. 1347

Neosho Public Library, Neosho WI p. 2625

Nephi Public Library, Nephi UT p. 2408

Neponset Public Library, Neponset IL p. 679

Neptune City Library, Neptune City NJ p. 1507

Neptune Public Library, Neptune NJ p. 1507

Ner Israel Rabbinical College Library, Baltimore MD p. 1017

Nesbitt Library, *see* Pennsylvania State University, Wilkes-Barre Commonwealth College, Lehman PA p. 2080

Nesbitt Memorial Library, Columbus TX p. 2299

Neshaminy-Warwick Presbyterian Church Library, Warminster PA p. 2150

Neshkoro Public Library, Neshkoro WI p. 2625

Neshoba County Public Library, Philadelphia MS p. 1311

Nesmith Library, Windham NH p. 1468

Ness City Public Library, Ness City KS p. 884

Nestle Purina Pet Care Co, Saint Louis MO p. 1357

Network of Alabama Academic Libraries (N), Montgomery AL p. 2937

Network of Illinois Learning Resources in Community Colleges (N), Malta IL p. 2942

Neumann College Library, Aston PA p. 2030

Neumann Library, *see* University of Houston - Clear Lake, Houston TX p. 2343

Neuschafer Community Library, Fremont WI p. 2593

Neuse Regional Library, Kinston NC p. 1805

Neustadt Public, *see* West Grey Public Library, Neustadt ON p. 2803

Nevada County Historical Society, Nevada City CA p. 193

Nevada County Library, Nevada City CA p. 193

Nevada County Library, *see* Southwest Arkansas Regional Library, Prescott AR p. 103

Nevada Department of Corrections, Carson City NV p. 1426

Nevada Department of Corrections, Ely NV p. 1427

Nevada Department of Corrections, Indian Springs NV p. 1428

Nevada Department of Corrections, Lovelock NV p. 1431

Nevada Department of Cultural Affairs, Reno NV p. 1432

Nevada Historical Society, *see* Nevada Department of Cultural Affairs, Reno NV p. 1432

Nevada Legislative Counsel Bureau, Carson City NV p. 1426

Nevada Medical Library Group (N), South Lake Tahoe CA p. 2938

Nevada Power Co Library, Las Vegas NV p. 1430

Nevada Public Library, Nevada IA p. 834

Nevada Public Library, Nevada MO p. 1348

Nevada State College, Henderson NV p. 1428

Nevada State Library & Archives, Carson City NV p. 1426

Nevada State Museum, Las Vegas NV p. 1430

Nevada State Museum, Carson City NV p. 1426

Nevada Supreme Court Library, Carson City NV p. 1426

Nevada Youth Training Center Library, Elko NV p. 1427

Neville Chemical Co, Pittsburgh PA p. 2126

Neville Public Museum of Brown County Library, Green Bay WI p. 2595

Nevins Anne Diocesan Library, *see* Blessed Edmund Rice School of Pastoral Ministry, Arcadia FL p. 425

Nevins Memorial Library, Methuen MA p. 1105

New Albany Community Library, New Albany PA p. 2095

New Albany-Floyd County Public Library, New Albany IN p. 768

New Albin Public Library, New Albin IA p. 834

New Alexandria Public Library, New Alexandria PA p. 2095

New Athens District Library, New Athens IL p. 679

New Augusta Public, *see* Pine Forest Regional Library, New Augusta MS p. 1314

New Baden Public Library, New Baden IL p. 679

New Bedford Free Public Library, New Bedford MA p. 1108

New Bedford Law Library, New Bedford MA p. 1108

New Bedford Whaling Museum Research Library, *see* Old Dartmouth Historical Society, New Bedford MA p. 1109

New Berlin Library, New Berlin NY p. 1664

New Berlin Public Library, New Berlin WI p. 2625

New Bern-Craven County Public Library, New Bern NC p. 1812

New Boston Public Library, New Boston TX p. 2365

New Braintree Public Library, New Braintree MA p. 1109

New Braunfels Public Library, New Braunfels TX p. 2365

New Bremen Public, *see* Auglaize County Public District Library, New Bremen OH p. 1944

New Brighton Public Library, New Brighton PA p. 2095

New Britain Museum of American Art Library, New Britain CT p. 354

New Britain Public Library, New Britain CT p. 354

New Brunswick College of Craft & Design Library, Fredericton NB p. 2763

New Brunswick Community College, Moncton NB p. 2766

New Brunswick Community College, Saint John NB p. 2767

New Brunswick Department of Post-Secondary Education, Training & Labour Library, Fredericton NB p. 2763

New Brunswick Emergency Measures Organization Library, Fredericton NB p. 2763

New Brunswick Free Public Library, New Brunswick NJ p. 1508

New Brunswick Legislative Library, Fredericton NB p. 2763

New Brunswick Museum Archives & Research Library, Saint John NB p. 2767

New Brunswick Public Library Service, Fredericton NB p. 2763

New Brunswick Theological Seminary, New Brunswick NJ p. 1508

New Buffalo Township Public Library, New Buffalo MI p. 1213

New Canaan Historical Society Library, New Canaan CT p. 354

New Canaan Library, New Canaan CT p. 354

New Carlisle & Olive Township Public Library, New Carlisle IN p. 768

New Carlisle Public Library, New Carlisle OH p. 1920

New Castle County Law Library, Wilmington DE p. 388

New Castle-Henry County Public Library, New Castle IN p. 768

New Castle Library, New Castle NH p. 1459

New Castle Public Library, New Castle DE p. 384

New Castle Public Library, New Castle PA p. 2096

New Center for Psychoanalysis Library, Los Angeles CA p. 176

New City Free Library, New City NY p. 1664

New College of Florida, Sarasota FL p. 490

New Cumberland Public Library, New Cumberland PA p. 2096

New Durham Public Library, New Durham NH p. 1459

New England Air Museum, Windsor Locks CT p. 379

New England Baptist Hospital, Boston MA p. 1064

New England Bible College Library, South Portland ME p. 1001

New England College, Henniker NH p. 1451

New England College of Optometry Library, Boston MA p. 1064

New England Conservatory of Music, Boston MA p. 1064

New England Electric Railway Historical Society, Kennebunkport ME p. 989

New England Historic Genealogical Society Library, Boston MA p. 1065

New England Institute of Technology Library, East Greenwich RI p. 2166

New England Law Library Consortium, Inc (N), Keene NH p. 2948

New England Public Library, New England ND p. 1847

New England School of Law Library, Boston MA p. 1065

New England Sinai Hospital & Rehabilitation Center, Stoughton MA p. 1129

New England Wild Flower Society, Inc, Framingham MA p. 1090

New England Wireless & Steam Museum, East Greenwich RI p. 2166

New Fairfield Free Public Library, New Fairfield CT p. 354

New Florence Community Library, New Florence PA p. 2096

New Georgia Public Library, *see* West Georgia Regional Library, Dallas GA p. 524

New Glarus Public Library, New Glarus WI p. 2625

New Gloucester Public Library, New Gloucester ME p. 993

New Hampshire Antiquarian Society Library, Hopkinton NH p. 1452

New Hampshire College & University Council (N), Concord NH p. 2948

New Hampshire Department of Corrections, Berlin NH p. 1439

New Hampshire Department of Corrections, Goffstown NH p. 1448

New Hampshire Department of Health & Human Services, Concord NH p. 1442

New Hampshire Department of Justice, Concord NH p. 1442

New Hampshire Division of Public Health Services, Concord NH p. 1442

New Hampshire Family Voices Library, Concord NH p. 1442

New Hampshire Historical Society Library, Concord NH p. 1442

New Hampshire Hospital, Concord NH p. 1442

New Hampshire Law Library, Concord NH p. 1443

New Hampshire State Library, Concord NH p. 1443

New Hampshire State Prison Library, Concord NH p. 1443

New Hampshire Youth Services Center, Manchester NH p. 1456

New Hampton Public Library, New Hampton IA p. 834

New Hanover County Public Library, Wilmington NC p. 1830

New Hartford Public Library, New Hartford NY p. 1665

New Haven Community Library, New Haven VT p. 2430

New Haven Free Public Library, New Haven CT p. 355

New Haven Law Library, *see* Connecticut Judicial Branch Law Libraries, New Haven CT p. 344

New Haven Museum & Historical Society, New Haven CT p. 356

New Haven Public, *see* Mason County Library System, New Haven WV p. 2570

New Hebron Public Library, *see* Lincoln-Lawrence-Franklin Regional Library, New Hebron MS p. 1295

New Holstein Public Library, New Holstein WI p. 2625

New Hope Christian College, Eugene OR p. 1997

New Ipswich Library, New Ipswich NH p. 1459

New Jersey City University, Jersey City NJ p. 1492

New Jersey Department of Corrections, Avenel NJ p. 1470

New Jersey Department of Corrections, Bridgeton NJ p. 1474

New Jersey Department of Environmental Protection, Trenton NJ p. 1535

New Jersey Department of Labor Library, Trenton NJ p. 1535

New Jersey Department of Law & Public Safety, Trenton NJ p. 1535

New Jersey Department of Transportation, Trenton NJ p. 1535

New Jersey Health Sciences Library Network (N), Summit NJ p. 2949

New York State Academy of Fire Science Library, *see* New York State Department of State-Office of Fire Prevention & Control, Montour Falls NY p. 1662

New York State Court of Appeals Library, Albany NY p. 1569

New York State Department of Correctional Services, Albany NY p. 1569

New York State Department of Correctional Services, Albion NY p. 1571

New York State Department of Correctional Services, Elmira NY p. 1620

New York State Department of Correctional Services, Gowanda NY p. 1630

New York State Department of Correctional Services, Hudson NY p. 1638

New York State Department of Correctional Services, Ogdensburg NY p. 1709

New York State Department of Correctional Services, Ossining NY p. 1712

New York State Department of Correctional Services, Stormville NY p. 1750

New York State Department of Correctional Services, Watertown NY p. 1763

New York State Department of Corrections & Community Supervision, Altona NY p. 1573

New York State Department of Health, Albany NY p. 1569

New York State Department of Law Library, Albany NY p. 1569

New York State Department of Law Library, New York NY p. 1694

New York State Department of State-Office of Fire Prevention & Control, Montour Falls NY p. 1662

New York State Division for Historic Preservation, Cazenovia NY p. 1604

New York State Division of Housing & Community Renewal, New York NY p. 1694

New York State Higher Education Initiative (N), Albany NY p. 2950

New York State Historical Association, Cooperstown NY p. 1610

New York State Judicial Department, Rochester NY p. 1731

New York State Legislative Library, Albany NY p. 1569

New York State Library, Albany NY p. 1569, 1570

New York State Nurses Association Library, Latham NY p. 1651

New York State Office of Mental Retardation & Developmental Disabilities, Staten Island NY p. 1748

New York State Office of Parks, Recreation & Historic Preservation, Katonah NY p. 1648

New York State Office of Parks Recreation & Historic Preservation, Kingston NY p. 1650

New York State Office of Parks, Recreation & Historic Preservation, Newburgh NY p. 1705

New York State Office of Parks, Recreation & Historic Preservation, Oswego NY p. 1713

New York State Office of the State Comptroller Library, Albany NY p. 1570

New York State Psychiatric Institute, New York NY p. 1694

New York State Supreme Court, Brooklyn NY p. 1594

New York State Supreme Court, Kingston NY p. 1650

New York State Supreme Court, New York NY p. 1695

New York State Supreme Court, Poughkeepsie NY p. 1723

New York State Supreme Court, Watertown NY p. 1763

New York State Supreme Court Fourth District, Plattsburgh NY p. 1719

New York State Supreme Court Library, Catskill NY p. 1603

New York State Supreme Court Library - Binghamton, Binghamton NY p. 1582

New York State Supreme Court Library, Brooklyn, Brooklyn NY p. 1594

New York State Supreme Court, Troy NY p. 1756

New York State Supreme Court Sixth District, Norwich NY p. 1708

New York State Unified Court System, Syracuse NY p. 1752

New York State Veterans Home Library, Oxford NY p. 1714

New York Supreme Court, Auburn NY p. 1576

New York Supreme Court, Bath NY p. 1578

New York Supreme Court, Buffalo NY p. 1598

New York Supreme Court, Utica NY p. 1759

New York Supreme Court Appellate Div, Albany NY p. 1570

New York Times, Washington DC p. 411

New York Times, New York NY p. 1695

New York University, New York NY p. 1695

New York University School of Law Library, New York NY p. 1695

New York University School of Medicine, New York NY p. 1695

Newark Beth Israel Medical Center, Newark NJ p. 1511

Newark Free Library, Newark DE p. 385

Newark Museum Library, Newark NJ p. 1511

Newark Public Library, Newark NJ p. 1511

Newark Public Library, Newark NY p. 1704

Newark Public Library, Newark TX p. 2365

Newark United Methodist Church, Newark DE p. 385

Newaygo Area District Library, Newaygo MI p. 1214

Newberg Public Library, Newberg OR p. 2007

Newbern City Library, Newbern TN p. 2261

Newberry College, Newberry SC p. 2201

Newberry Correctional Facility Library, Newberry MI p. 1214

Newberry County Library, Newberry SC p. 2201

Newberry Library, Chicago IL p. 620

Newboro, *see* Rideau Lakes Public Library, Newboro ON p. 2803

Newbrook Public Library, Newbrook AB p. 2712

Newburgh Free Library, Newburgh NY p. 1705

Newburgh Library, *see* Ohio Township Public Library System, Newburgh IN p. 768

Newbury College Library, Brookline MA p. 1071

Newbury Public Library, Newbury NH p. 1460

Newbury Public Library Station, *see* Geauga County Public Library, Newbury OH p. 1867

Newbury Town Library, Byfield MA p. 1072

Newburyport Public Library, Newburyport MA p. 1109

Newcastle Public, *see* Pioneer Library System, Newcastle OK p. 1970

Newcomb Lawrence Library, *see* New England Wild Flower Society, Inc, Framingham MA p. 1090

Newcomerstown Public Library, Newcomerstown OH p. 1922

Newell Public Library, Newell IA p. 835

Newell Public Library, Newell SD p. 2216

Newfane Free Library, Newfane NY p. 1705

Newfield Public, *see* Gloucester County Library System, Newfield NJ p. 1507

Newfield Public Library, Newfield NY p. 1705

Newfield Village Library & Reading Room, West Newfield ME p. 1006

Newfoundland & Labrador Oil & Gas Industries Association, St. John's NL p. 2773

Newfoundland & Labrador Teachers' Association Library, St. John's NL p. 2773

Newfoundland Area Public Library, Newfoundland PA p. 2097

Newfoundland Department of Municipal & Provincial Affairs, St. John's NL p. 2773

Newfoundland Department of Natural Resources Library, Corner Brook NL p. 2770

Newfoundland Historical Society Library, St. John's NL p. 2773

Newhall Public Library, Newhall IA p. 835

Newhope Library, *see* Santa Ana Public Library, Santa Ana CA p. 259

NEWIL (N), *see* North East Wisconsin Intertype Libraries, Inc, Green Bay WI p. 2958

Newkirk Public Library, Newkirk OK p. 1970

Newman Catholic Student Center, Tucson AZ p. 86

Newman Center Library, *see* Saint Lawrence Catholic Church, Minneapolis MN p. 1261

Newman Grove Public Library, Newman Grove NE p. 1409

Newman Library, *see* Virginia Polytechnic Institute & State University Libraries, Blacksburg VA p. 2451

Newman Regional Library District, Newman IL p. 680

Newman Riga Library, Churchville NY p. 1606

Newman Theological College Library, Edmonton AB p. 2701

Newman University, Wichita KS p. 900

Newman William & Anita Library, *see* Baruch College-CUNY, New York NY p. 1670

Newman William R Library, *see* University of Manitoba Libraries, Winnipeg MB p. 2759

Newmarket Historical Society, Newmarket NH p. 1460

Newmarket Public Library, Newmarket NH p. 1460

Newmarket Public Library, Newmarket ON p. 2824

Newnam Clara Drinkwater Library, *see* Mississippi County Library District, Charleston MO p. 1323

Newport Aeronautical Sales Corp Library, Newport Beach CA p. 194

Newport Beach Public Library, Newport Beach CA p. 194

Newport Free Library, Newport NY p. 1705

Newport Historical Society Library, Newport RI p. 2169

Newport Hospital, Newport RI p. 2169

Newport Library, *see* Arkansas State University, Newport AR p. 111

Newport News Campus Library, *see* ECPI University, Newport News VA p. 2499

Newport News Public Library System, Newport News VA p. 2480

Newport Public Library, Newport ME p. 993

Newport Public Library, Newport NC p. 1813

Newport Public Library, Newport OR p. 2007

Newport Public Library, Newport PA p. 2097

Newport Public Library, Newport RI p. 2169

Newport Public Library, *see* Pend Oreille County Library District, Newport WA p. 2522

Newport Way Library, *see* King County Library System, Bellvue WA p. 2517

News & Observer Publishing Co, Raleigh NC p. 1815

News-Gazette Library, Champaign IL p. 603

News Tribune Library, Tacoma WA p. 2539

Newsday, Inc Library, Melville NY p. 1659

Newspaper Association of America, Vienna VA p. 2498

Newspaper Guild-CWA, Washington DC p. 411

Newstead Public Library, Akron NY p. 1567

Newsweek, Inc, New York NY p. 1696

Newton Correctional Facility, Newton IA p. 835

Newton County Library System, Covington GA p. 527

Newton County Public Library, Jasper AR p. 104

Newton County Public Library, Lake Village IN p. 760

Newton County Public Library, Newton TX p. 2365

Newton Falls Public Library, Newton Falls OH p. 1922

Newton Free Library, Newton Centre MA p. 1110

Newton History Museum at The Jackson Homestead, Newton MA p. 1110

Newton Phinehas S Library, Royalston MA p. 1121

Newton Public Library, Newton AL p. 32

Newton Public Library, Newton IA p. 835

Newton Public Library, Newton KS p. 884

Newton Public Library & Museum, Newton IL p. 680

Newton Town Library, Newton UT p. 2408

Newton-Wellesley Hospital, Newton Lower Falls MA p. 1111

Newtown Historic Association, Inc, Newtown PA p. 2098

Newtown Library Co, Newtown PA p. 2098

Newtown Public Library, Newtown Square PA p. 2098

Nexant Inc, White Plains NY p. 1768

Nexen Inc Library, Calgary AB p. 2692

Ney Elisabet Museum Library, Austin TX p. 2281

NHTI, Concord's Community College, Concord NH p. 1443

Norris Visual Science Library, *see* Doheny Eye Institute, Los Angeles CA p. 170

Norristown State Hospital, Norristown PA p. 2099

North Adams Community Memorial Library, North Adams MI p. 1214

North Adams Public Library, North Adams MA p. 1111

North Adams Public Library, *see* Adams County Public Library, Seaman OH p. 1912

North Adams Regional Hospital, North Adams MA p. 1111

North American Center for Marianist Studies, Dayton OH p. 1894

North American Radio Archives, Wildomar CA p. 284

North American Youth Sport Institute, Kernersville NC p. 1804

North Andover Historical Society Library, North Andover MA p. 1111

North Arkansas College Library, Harrison AR p. 102

North Arlington Free Public Library, North Arlington NJ p. 1514

North Atlantic Health Sciences Libraries, Inc (N), Burlington CT p. 2939

North Attleboro Public Library, *see* Richards Memorial Library, North Attleboro MA p. 1112

North Babylon Public Library, North Babylon NY p. 1706

North Baker Research Library, *see* California Historical Society, San Francisco CA p. 240

North Baltimore Public Library, North Baltimore OH p. 1923

North Battleford Public Library, *see* Lakeland Library Region, North Battleford SK p. 2920

North Bay Public Library, North Bay ON p. 2825

North Bend Public Library, North Bend NE p. 1410

North Bend Public Library, North Bend OR p. 2008

North Bergen Free Public Library, North Bergen NJ p. 1514

North Berkeley Public Library, *see* Martinsburg-Berkeley County Public Library, Falling Waters WV p. 2565

North Bingham County District Library, Shelley ID p. 584

North Bonneville Community Library, *see* Fort Vancouver Regional Library District, North Bonneville WA p. 2546

North Branch Area Library, North Branch MN p. 1268

North Branch Township Library, North Branch MI p. 1214

North Branford Library Department, North Branford CT p. 361

North Bridgton Public Library, North Bridgton ME p. 993

North Brunswick Free Public Library, North Brunswick NJ p. 1514

North Canton Public Library, North Canton OH p. 1923

North Carolina Agricultural & Technical State University, Greensboro NC p. 1797

North Carolina Aquarium Library, Manteo NC p. 1808

North Carolina Area Health Education Centers (N), Chapel Hill NC p. 2951

North Carolina Biotechnology Center Library, Research Triangle Park NC p. 1820

North Carolina Central University, Durham NC p. 1789, 2971

North Carolina Community College System (N), Raleigh NC p. 2951

North Carolina Department of Correction, Elizabeth City NC p. 1791

North Carolina Department of Correction, Maury NC p. 1809

North Carolina Department of Correction, Morganton NC p. 1811

North Carolina Department of Labor, Raleigh NC p. 1815

North Carolina Justice Academy, Salemburg NC p. 1821

North Carolina Legislative Library, Raleigh NC p. 1815

McNeill Charles R Library, *see* North Carolina Office of Archives & History, Beaufort NC p. 1808

North Carolina Museum of Art, Raleigh NC p. 1815

North Carolina Museum of Life & Science Library, Durham NC p. 1789

North Carolina Office of Archives & History, Manteo NC p. 1808

North Carolina Regional Library for the Blind & Physically Handicapped, Raleigh NC p. 1815

North Carolina School of Science & Mathematics Library, Durham NC p. 1789

North Carolina State Museum of Natural Sciences, Raleigh NC p. 1816

North Carolina State University Libraries, Raleigh NC p. 1816

North Carolina Supreme Court Library, Raleigh NC p. 1816

North Carolina Synod of the ELCA, Salisbury NC p. 1822

North Carolina Wesleyan College, Rocky Mount NC p. 1821

North Castle Public Library, Armonk NY p. 1575

North Central College, Naperville IL p. 679

North Central Correctional Facility, Rockwell City IA p. 841

North Central Kansas Libraries System, Manhattan KS p. 881

North Central Michigan College Library, Petoskey MI p. 1217

North Central Missouri College Library, Trenton MO p. 1369

North Central Nevada Historical Society, Winnemucca NV p. 1435

North Central Regional Library, Wenatchee WA p. 2548

North Central Texas College Library, Gainesville TX p. 2326

North Central University Library, Minneapolis MN p. 1261

North Chatham Free Library, North Chatham NY p. 1706

North Chicago Public Library, North Chicago IL p. 682

North Colorado Medical Center, Greeley CO p. 312

North Conway Public Library, North Conway NH p. 1460

North Country Community College Library, Saranac Lake NY p. 1738

North Country Health System, Newport VT p. 2430

North Country Library Cooperative (N), Mountain Iron MN p. 2947

North Country Library System, Watertown NY p. 1763

North County Regional, *see* Charlotte Mecklenburg Library, Huntersville NC p. 1782

North Dade Regional, *see* Miami-Dade Public Library System, Miami FL p. 467

North Dakota Department of Corrections, Mandan ND p. 1845

North Dakota Legislative Council Library, Bismarck ND p. 1838

North Dakota Prevention Resource Center Library, Bismarck ND p. 1838

North Dakota School for the Deaf Library, Devils Lake ND p. 1839

North Dakota State College of Science, Wahpeton ND p. 1849

North Dakota State Hospital, Jamestown ND p. 1844

North Dakota State Library, Bismarck ND p. 1838

North Dakota State University Libraries, Fargo ND p. 1841

North Dakota Supreme Court, Bismarck ND p. 1838

North Dakota Veterans Home Library, Lisbon ND p. 1845

North Dakota Vision Services-School for the Blind, Grand Forks ND p. 1842

North Dakota Youth Correctional Center Library, *see* North Dakota Department of Corrections, Mandan ND p. 1845

North Davidson Public, *see* Davidson County Public Library System, Welcome NC p. 1806

North Donald K C Library, *see* Heritage University, Toppenish WA p. 2541

North East Multi-Regional Training, North Aurora IL p. 681

North East Wisconsin Intertype Libraries, Inc (N), Green Bay WI p. 2958

North English Public Library, North English IA p. 835

North Fairfield Public Library, *see* Willard Memorial Library, North Fairfield OH p. 1948

North Florida Community College Library, Madison FL p. 462

North Florida/South Georgia Veterans Health System, Lake City FL p. 458

North Forest Park Community Library, *see* Queens Borough Public Library, Forest Hills NY p. 1645

North Fort Myers Public, *see* Lee County Library System, North Fort Myers FL p. 445

North Freedom Public Library, North Freedom WI p. 2626

North Garland Branch, *see* Nicholson Memorial Library System, Garland TX p. 2327

North General Hospital, New York NY p. 1696

North Georgia College & State University, Dahlonega GA p. 527

North Georgia Technical College Library, Blairsville GA p. 521

North Georgia Technical College Library, Clarkesville GA p. 524

North Gorham Public Library, Gorham ME p. 986

North Greenbush Public Library, Wynantskill NY p. 1771

North Greenville University, Tigerville SC p. 2206

North Grenville Public Library, Kemptville ON p. 2812

North Haledon Free Public Library, North Haledon NJ p. 1514

North Hampton Public Library, North Hampton NH p. 1461

North Harris College Library, *see* Lone Star College System, Houston TX p. 2340

North Haven Library, North Haven ME p. 994

North Haven Memorial Library, North Haven CT p. 362

North Hennepin Community College Library, Brooklyn Park MN p. 1243

North Hero Public Library, North Hero VT p. 2430

North Highlands/Antelope Library, *see* Sacramento Public Library, Antelope CA p. 225

North Hills Community Library, *see* Queens Borough Public Library, Little Neck NY p. 1645

North Hollywood Regional, *see* Los Angeles Public Library System, North Hollywood CA p. 174

North Idaho College Library, Coeur d'Alene ID p. 573

North Idaho Correctional Institution Library, Cottonwood ID p. 573

North Indian River County Library, Sebastian FL p. 490

North Iowa Area Community College Library, Mason City IA p. 831

North Island College, Campbell River BC p. 2726

North Island College, Courtenay BC p. 2727

North Island College, Port Alberni BC p. 2735

North Jersey Media Group Library, Hackensack NJ p. 1489

North Judson-Wayne Township Public Library, North Judson IN p. 769

North Kansas City Hospital, North Kansas City MO p. 1348

North Kansas City Public Library, North Kansas City MO p. 1348

North Kawartha Public Library, Apsley ON p. 2792

North Kern State Prison, *see* California Department of Corrections Library System, Delano CA p. 221

North Kingstown Free Library, North Kingstown RI p. 2170

North Kohala Public Library, *see* Hawaii State Public Library System, Kapaau HI p. 563

North Lake College Library, Irving TX p. 2347

North Las Vegas Library District, North Las Vegas NV p. 1432

North Liberty Community Library, North Liberty IA p. 835

North Logan City Library, North Logan UT p. 2408

Northern Essex Community College, Haverhill MA p. 1094

Northern Forestry Centre, Edmonton AB p. 2702

Northern Great Plains Research Laboratory Library, Mandan ND p. 1846

Northern Illinois University Libraries, DeKalb IL p. 635

Northern Inyo Hospital, Bishop CA p. 129

Northern Kentucky University, Highland Heights KY p. 917

Northern Lakes College Library, Grouard AB p. 2706

Northern Lakes College Library, Slave Lake AB p. 2716

Northern Lights College, Atlin BC p. 2724

Northern Lights College, Fort Saint John BC p. 2728

Northern Lights College, Hudson's Hope BC p. 2729

Northern Lights College Library, Dawson Creek BC p. 2727

Northern Lights Library Network (N), Detroit Lakes MN p. 2947

Northern Lights Library System, Elk Point AB p. 2703

Northern Maine Community College Library, Presque Isle ME p. 998

Northern Marianas College, Saipan MP p. 2669

Northern Michigan Hospital, Petoskey MI p. 1217

Northern Michigan University, Marquette MI p. 1206

Northern New Hampshire Correctional Facility Library, see New Hampshire Department of Corrections, Berlin NH p. 1439

Northern New Mexico College, Espanola NM p. 1555

Northern New York Library Network (N), Potsdam NY p. 2950

Northern Oklahoma College, Tonkawa OK p. 1980

Northern Onondaga Public Library, North Syracuse NY p. 1707

Northern Plains Public Library, Ault CO p. 288

Northern Prairie Wildlife Research Center Library, see United States Geological Survey, Jamestown ND p. 1845

Northern Regional Jail Correctional Facility, Moundsville WV p. 2567

Northern State Prison Library, Newark NJ p. 1512

Northern State University, Aberdeen SD p. 2209

Northern Tier Library Association, Gibsonia PA p. 2060

Northern Virginia Community College Libraries, Annandale VA p. 2447

Northern Wake Library, see Wake Technical Community College, Raleigh NC p. 1818

Northern Waters Library Service, Ashland WI p. 2579

Northern Wayne Community Library, Lakewood PA p. 2076

Northern Westchester Hospital, Mount Kisco NY p. 1664

Northern Wyoming Community College District, Sheridan WY p. 2660

Northern Wyoming Community College District - Gillette, Gillette WY p. 2655

Northfield Public Library, Northfield MN p. 1269

Northhampton Area Public Library, Northampton PA p. 2100

Loar Barbara, see DeKalb County Public Library, Tucker GA p. 530

Northlake Public Library District, Northlake IL p. 683

Northland College, Ashland WI p. 2579

Northland Community & Technical College Library, East Grand Forks MN p. 1249

Northland Community & Technical College Library, Thief River Falls MN p. 1285

Northland International University Library, Dunbar WI p. 2588

Northland Pioneer College, Holbrook AZ p. 2962

Northland Pioneer College Libraries, Holbrook AZ p. 65

Northland Public Library, Pittsburgh PA p. 2126

Northline Library, see Houston Community College Northeast College, Houston TX p. 2338

Northminster Presbyterian Church, New Castle PA p. 2096

Northminster Presbyterian Church Library, Washington DC p. 412

Northminster Presbyterian Church Library, Cincinnati OH p. 1871

Northperth Public Library, Listowel ON p. 2816

Northpoint Training Center, Burgin KY p. 908

Northpointe Regional, see Indiana University of Pennsylvania, Freeport PA p. 2071

Northport-East Northport Public Library, Northport NY p. 1707

Northport Historical Society, Northport NY p. 1707

Northridge Hospital, Northridge CA p. 195

Northrop Bent Memorial Library, Fairfield VT p. 2424

Northrop Grumman Corp, Los Angeles CA p. 176

Northrop Grumman Corp, Rolling Meadows IL p. 698

Northrop Grumman Corp, Baltimore MD p. 1017

Northrop Grumman IT-TASC, Chantilly VA p. 2453

Northrop Grumman Mission Systems, Reston VA p. 2487

Northrop Grumman Norden Systems, Norwalk CT p. 362

Northrup Preston G Memorial Library, see Texas Biomedical Research Institute, San Antonio TX p. 2383

NorthShore University HealthSystem, Skokie IL p. 703

Northside Hospital, Atlanta GA p. 517

Northside Library, see Atlanta-Fulton Public Library System, Atlanta GA p. 512

Northside Medical Center Library, see Forum Health-Western Reserve Healthcare, Youngstown OH p. 1952

Northumberland County Law Library, Sunbury PA p. 2144

Northumberland Library, Groveton NH p. 1449

Northumberland Public Library, Inc, Heathsville VA p. 2471

Northville District Library, Northville MI p. 1214

Northville Public Library, Northville NY p. 1708

Northwest AHEC, Salisbury NC p. 1822

Northwest AHEC Library at Hickory (N), Hickory NC p. 2951

Northwest AHEC Library at Salisbury (N), Salisbury NC p. 2951

Northwest AHEC Library Information Network (N), Winston-Salem NC p. 2951

Northwest Area Health Education Center Library, see Northwest Area Health Education Center Library at Hickory, Hickory NC p. 1802

Northwest Area Health Education Center Library at Boone, Boone NC p. 1777

Northwest Area Health Education Center Library at Hickory, Hickory NC p. 1802

Northwest Arkansas Community College Library, Bentonville AR p. 95

Northwest Arkansas Genealogy Society, Bentonville AR p. 95

Northwest Atlantic Fisheries Organization Library, Dartmouth NS p. 2779

Northwest Christian University, Eugene OR p. 1997

Northwest College, Powell WY p. 2659

Northwest Community College Library, Terrace BC p. 2739

Northwest Community Hospital, Arlington Heights IL p. 590

Northwest Florida State College, Niceville FL p. 472

Northwest Florida Water Management District, Havana FL p. 450

Northwest Geophysical Associates Inc Library, Corvallis OR p. 1994

Northwest Georgia Regional Library System, Dalton GA p. 528

Northwest Georgia Talking Book Library, see Hightower Sara Regional Library, Rome GA p. 549

Northwest Hospital & Medical Center, Seattle WA p. 2529

Northwest Hospital Center, Randallstown MD p. 1037

Northwest Indian College Library, Bellingham WA p. 2508

Northwest Interlibrary Cooperative of Pennsylvania (N), Erie PA p. 2954

Northwest Iowa Community College Library, Sheldon IA p. 842

Northwest Kansas Heritage Center, Brewster KS p. 858

Northwest Kansas Library System, Norton KS p. 885

Northwest Library on Deaf Culture & History, Seattle WA p. 2529

Northwest Mississippi Community College, Oxford MS p. 1310

Northwest Mississippi Community College, Senatobia MS p. 1315

Northwest Mississippi Community College, Southaven MS p. 1315

Northwest Missouri State University, Maryville MO p. 1344

Northwest Museum of Art & Culture-Eastern Washington State Historical Society, Spokane WA p. 2536

Northwest Nazarene University, Nampa ID p. 580

Northwest Point Reservoir Library, Brandon MS p. 1294

Northwest Regional, see Maricopa County Library District, Surprise AZ p. 75

Northwest Regional Library, Winfield AL p. 40

Northwest Regional Library, Thief River Falls MN p. 1286

Northwest Regional Library, Buffalo SD p. 2211

Northwest Regional Library System, Panama City FL p. 480

Northwest Regional Library System (N), Bowling Green OH p. 2952

Northwest-Shaols Community College, Muscle Shoals AL p. 32

Northwest-Shoals Community College, Phil Campbell AL p. 34

Northwest State Community College Library, Archbold OH p. 1854

Northwest State Correctional Facility, Swanton VT p. 2437

Northwest Technical Institute, Springdale AR p. 115

Northwest University, Kirkland WA p. 2519

Northwest Vista College, San Antonio TX p. 2380

Northwestern College, Chicago IL p. 621

Northwestern College, Orange City IA p. 836

Northwestern College, Saint Paul MN p. 1280

Northwestern Connecticut Community College Library, Winsted CT p. 379

Northwestern Health Sciences University, Bloomington MN p. 1242

Northwestern Medical Center Library, Saint Albans VT p. 2434

Northwestern Memorial Hospital, Chicago IL p. 621

Northwestern Michigan College, Traverse City MI p. 1231

Northwestern Oklahoma State University, Alva OK p. 1956

Northwestern Oklahoma State University Libraries, Enid OK p. 1963

Northwestern Ontario Sports Hall of Fame Library, Thunder Bay ON p. 2848

Northwestern Regional Library, Elkin NC p. 1791

Northwestern State University Libraries, Leesville LA p. 955

Northwestern State University Libraries, Natchitoches LA p. 958

Northwestern State University Libraries, Shreveport LA p. 968

Northwestern Technical College Library, Rock Spring GA p. 548

Northwestern University Library, Evanston IL p. 644

Northwestern University, Chicago, Chicago IL p. 621

Northwestern Wisconsin Health Science Library Consortium (N), Lacrosse WI p. 2958

Northwood City Library, Northwood ND p. 1847

Northwood Public Library, Northwood IA p. 836

Northwood University, West Palm Beach FL p. 502

Northwood University, Midland MI p. 1208

Northwood University Library, Cedar Hill TX p. 2296

Norton Audubon Hospital, Louisville KY p. 925

Norton Correctional Facility, Norton KS p. 885

Oakley Library District, Oakley ID p. 581

Oakley Millard Library, Livingston TN p. 2245

Oakley Public Library, Oakley KS p. 885

Oaklyn Memorial Library, Oaklyn NJ p. 1515

Oakmont Carnegie Library, Oakmont PA p. 2100

Oakridge Public Library, Oakridge OR p. 2008

Oaks Correctional Facility Library, *see* Michigan Department of Corrections, Manistee MI p. 1206

Oakton Community College Library, Des Plaines IL p. 636

Oakton Community College Library, Skokie IL p. 703

Oakton Library, *see* Fairfax County Public Library, Oakton VA p. 2461

Oakville Public Library, Oakville ON p. 2825

Oakwood College, Huntsville AL p. 22

Oakwood Correctional Facility Library, Lima OH p. 1910

Oakwood Hospital Medical Library, Dearborn MI p. 1167

Oakwood Public Library District, Oakwood IL p. 684

Oakwood Village Library & Arts Centre, *see* Toronto Public Library, Toronto ON p. 2862

Ober, Kaler, Grimes & Shriver Law Library, Baltimore MD p. 1017

Oberlin City Library, Oberlin KS p. 885

Oberlin College Library, Oberlin OH p. 1924

Oberlin Public Library, Oberlin OH p. 1925

Oberndorf Meyera E Central Library, *see* Virginia Beach Public Library Department, Virginia Beach VA p. 2500

Obion County Public Library, Union City TN p. 2268

Obion River Regional Library, Martin TN p. 2246

Oblon, Spivak, Alexandria VA p. 2446

Oboler Eli M Library, *see* Idaho State University, Pocatello ID p. 581

O'Brien Frances Memorial Library, Blue River OR p. 1992

O'Brien Kevin F Health Sciences Library, *see* Marquette General Health System, Marquette MI p. 1206

Observatories of the Carnegie Institution of Washington, Pasadena CA p. 206

OC Public Libraries, Santa Ana CA p. 258

Ocasek Oliver Medical Library, *see* Northeastern Ohio Universities College of Medicine, Rootstown OH p. 1932

Occidental College Library, Los Angeles CA p. 176

Occidental Oil & Gas Corp Library, Houston TX p. 2341

Occupational Health & Safety Library & Information Services, *see* Department of Government Services, Government of Newfoundland & Labrador, Mount Pearl NL p. 2770

Occupational Safety & Health Administration Library, *see* United States Department of Labor, Seattle WA p. 2533

Ocean City Free Public Library, Ocean City NJ p. 1515

Ocean City Historical Museum, Ocean City NJ p. 1516

Ocean County College Library, Toms River NJ p. 1533

Ocean County Historical Society, Toms River NJ p. 1534

Ocean County Library, Toms River NJ p. 1534

Ocean Medical Center, Brick NJ p. 1474

Ocean Park Memorial Library, Ocean Park ME p. 994

Ocean Shores Public Library, Ocean Shores WA p. 2522

Ocean Springs Municipal Library, *see* Jackson-George Regional Library System, Ocean Springs MS p. 1310

Ocean State Libraries (N), Warwick RI p. 2955

Ocean Township Historical Museum Library, Ocean NJ p. 1515

Ocean Vicinage Law Library, Toms River NJ p. 1535

Oceana Public, *see* Wyoming County Public Library, Oceana WV p. 2570

Oceanic Free Library, Rumson NJ p. 1528

Oceanic Institute Library, Waimanalo HI p. 568

Oceanside Library, Oceanside NY p. 1709

Oceanside Public Library, Oceanside CA p. 199

Ocheyedan Public Library, Ocheyedan IA p. 836

Ochsner Clinic Foundation, New Orleans LA p. 962

Ochsner Medical Library & Archives, *see* Ochsner Clinic Foundation, New Orleans LA p. 962

OCLC Library, Dublin OH p. 1896

OCLC Online Computer Library Center, Inc (N), Dublin OH p. 2952

Ocmulgee National Monument Library, *see* National Park Service, Macon GA p. 541

Ocmulgee Regional Library System, Eastman GA p. 531

Ocoee River Regional Library, Athens TN p. 2224

Oconee County Public Library, Walhalla SC p. 2207

Oconee Regional Library, Dublin GA p. 531

O'Connor Catherine B Library, *see* Boston College Libraries, Weston MA p. 1081

O'Connor Dennis M Public Library, Refugio TX p. 2373

O'Connor Hospital Medical Library, San Jose CA p. 250

Oconomowoc Public Library, Oconomowoc WI p. 2626

Oconto Falls Community Library, Oconto Falls WI p. 2626

Ocotillo Library & Workforce Literacy Center, *see* Phoenix Public Library, Phoenix AZ p. 76

Fellin Octavia Public Library, Gallup NM p. 1556

OCUL (N), *see* Ontario Council of University Libraries, Toronto ON p. 2960

Odegaard Undergraduate Library, *see* University of Washington Libraries, Seattle WA p. 2534

Odell Public Library, Morrison IL p. 676

Odell Public Library District, Odell IL p. 684

Odem Public Library, Odem TX p. 2366

Odenville Public Library, Odenville AL p. 32

Odessa College, Odessa TX p. 2366

Odessa Public Library, Odessa WA p. 2522

Odin Community, *see* Centralia Regional Library District, Odin IL p. 602

Odin, Feldman & Pittleman Library, Fairfax VA p. 2462

O'Donnell Mayo Hayes Library, *see* Monterey History & Art Association, Monterey CA p. 189

O'Donoghue Medical Library, *see* Saint Anthony Hospital, Oklahoma City OK p. 1975

Odum Library, *see* Valdosta State University, Valdosta GA p. 555

Oelwein Public Library, Oelwein IA p. 836

Oesterle Library, *see* North Central College, Naperville IL p. 679

O'Fallon Public Library, O'Fallon IL p. 684

Office Franco-Quebecois pour la Jeunesse Library, Montreal QC p. 2900

Office of Navajo Nation Library, Window Rock AZ p. 90

Ogden Arnot Medical Center, Elmira NY p. 1620

Ogden Farmers' Library, Spencerport NY p. 1746

Ogden Library, Ogden KS p. 886

Ogden Rose Public Library, Ogden IL p. 684

Ogden William B Free Library, Walton NY p. 1762

Ogdensburg Correctional Facility General Library, *see* New York State Department of Correctional Services, Ogdensburg NY p. 1709

Ogdensburg Public Library, Ogdensburg NY p. 1709

Ogeechee Technical College Library, Statesboro GA p. 552

Ogema Public Library, Ogema WI p. 2627

Ogemaw District Library, Rose City MI p. 1223

Ogilvy Public Relations Worldwide Information Center, New York NY p. 1696

Oglala Lakota College, Kyle SD p. 2213

Oglala/White Clay College Center, *see* Oglala Lakota College, Oglala SD p. 2214

Oglesby Public Library, Oglesby IL p. 685

Oglethorpe Public, *see* Middle Georgia Regional Library System, Oglethorpe GA p. 541

Oglethorpe University, Atlanta GA p. 517

O'Grady Library, *see* Saint Martin's University, Lacey WA p. 2519

Ogunquit Memorial Library, Ogunquit ME p. 994

O'Hara Dave Community Library, La Loche SK p. 2918

Ohev Shalom Synagogue, Wallingford PA p. 2150

Ohio Agricultural Research & Development Center Library, Wooster OH p. 1950

Ohio Attorney General, Columbus OH p. 1886

Ohio Bureau of Worker's Compensation, Columbus OH p. 1886

Ohio Christian University, Circleville OH p. 1875

Ohio College of Podiatric Medicine Library, Independence OH p. 1906

Ohio County Law Library, Wheeling WV p. 2574

Ohio County Public Library, Rising Sun IN p. 775

Ohio County Public Library, Hartford KY p. 916

Ohio County Public Library, Wheeling WV p. 2574

Ohio Dominican University Library, Columbus OH p. 1886

Ohio Genealogical Society Library, Bellville OH p. 1859

Ohio Health-Riverside Methodist Hospital, Columbus OH p. 1887

Ohio Health Sciences Library Association (N), Warrensville Heights OH p. 2952

Ohio Historical Society, Columbus OH p. 1887

Ohio Historical Society, Marietta OH p. 1913

Ohio Legislative Service Commission Library, Columbus OH p. 1887

Ohio Library & Information Network (N), Columbus OH p. 2952

Ohio Library for the Blind & Physically Handicapped, *see* Cleveland Public Library OH p. 1878

Ohio Network of American History Research Centers (N), Columbus OH p. 2952

Ohio Northern University, Ada OH p. 1851

Ohio Public Library District, Ohio IL p. 685

Ohio Public Library Information Network (N), Columbus OH p. 2952

Ohio Reformatory for Women, Marysville OH p. 1915

Ohio School for the Deaf Library, Columbus OH p. 1887

Ohio State University LIBRARIES, Columbus OH p. 1887

Ohio Township Public Library System, Newburgh IN p. 768

Ohio University, Ironton OH p. 1906

Ohio University, Saint Clairsville OH p. 1933

Ohio University Chillicothe Campus, Chillicothe OH p. 1867

Ohio University-Lancaster Library, Lancaster OH p. 1909

Ohio University Libraries, Athens OH p. 1856

Ohio University-Zanesville/ Zane State College, Zanesville OH p. 1954

Ohio Valley General Hospital Library, McKees Rocks PA p. 2085

Ohio Valley Medical Center, Wheeling WV p. 2574

Ohio Valley University Library, Vienna WV p. 2573

Ohio Wesleyan University, Delaware OH p. 1896

Ohioana Library, Columbus OH p. 1890

OhioLINK (N), *see* Ohio Library & Information Network, Columbus OH p. 2952

OHIONET (N), Columbus OH p. 2952

Ohlone College, Fremont CA p. 149

Ohoopee Regional Library System, Vidalia GA p. 555

OHR Kodesh Congregation, Chevy Chase MD p. 1024

OHSLA (N), *see* Ohio Health Sciences Library Association, Warrensville Heights OH p. 2952

OHSLA (N), *see* Oklahoma Health Sciences Library Association, Oklahoma City OK p. 2953

OHSLA (N), *see* Oregon Health Sciences Libraries Association, Portland OR p. 2953

Oil City Library, Oil City PA p. 2100

Oil Information Library of Wichita Falls, Wichita Falls TX p. 2401

Ojibway & Cree Cultural Centre, Timmins ON p. 2849

Ojibway Correctional Facility Library, *see* Michigan Department of Corrections, Marenisco MI p. 1206

Okaloosa Correctional Institution Library, *see* Florida Department of Corrections, Crestview FL p. 434

Okanagan College Library, Kelowna BC p. 2730

Ontario Camps Association Library, Toronto ON
p. 2856
Ontario City Library, Ontario CA p. 200
Ontario College of Art & Design, Toronto ON
p. 2856
Ontario Council of University Libraries (N), Toronto
ON p. 2960
Ontario County Historical Society Library,
Canandaigua NY p. 1601
Ontario Energy Board, Toronto ON p. 2856
Ontario Genealogical Society Library, North York
ON p. 2825
Ontario Institute for Studies in Education, see
University of Toronto Libraries, Toronto ON
p. 2867
Ontario Legislative Library, Toronto ON p. 2856
Ontario Library Consortium (N), Owen Sound ON
p. 2960
Ontario Ministry of Education, Toronto ON p. 2856
Ontario Ministry of Finance, Toronto ON p. 2856
Ontario Ministry of Natural Resources, Peterborough
ON p. 2835
Ontario Ministry of Northern Development, Mines &
Forestry Library, Sudbury ON p. 2847
Ontario Ministry of the Attorney General, Toronto
ON p. 2856
Ontario Ministry of the Attorney General - Court
of Appeal Justice Judges Library, Toronto ON
p. 2856
Ontario Ministry of the Environment, Toronto ON
p. 2856
Ontario Ministry of Tourism, Thunder Bay ON
p. 2849
Ontario Ministry of Transportation Library, Saint
Catharines ON p. 2839
Ontario Office of the Fire Marshal, Toronto ON
p. 2856
Ontario Police College Library, Aylmer ON p. 2793
Ontario Power Generation Library, Toronto ON
p. 2857
Ontario Provincial Police, Orillia ON p. 2826
Ontario Public Library, Ontario NY p. 1711
Ontario Public Library, Ontario WI p. 2627
Ontario Securities Commission Library, Toronto ON
p. 2857
Ontario Workplace Tribunals Library, Toronto ON
p. 2857
Ontonagon Township Library, Ontonagon MI
p. 1215
Oostburg Public Library, Oostburg WI p. 2627
Opelousas-Eunice Public Library, Opelousas LA
p. 965
Opheim Community Library, Opheim MT p. 1387
OPIRG Guelph Library, Guelph ON p. 2807
OPLIN (N), see Ohio Public Library Information
Network, Columbus OH p. 2952
Opp Public Library, Opp AL p. 32
Oppenheimer Wolff & Donnelly Library,
Minneapolis MN p. 1261
Opperman Jacquelin E Memorial Library, Kingston
MI p. 1199
O'Quinn Law Library, see University of Houston,
Houston TX p. 2343
Oracle Public Library, Oracle AZ p. 70
Oradell Free Public Library, Oradell NJ p. 1516
Oral Roberts University Library, Tulsa OK p. 1981
Oram Wilfred, see Cape Breton Regional Library,
North Sydney NS p. 2785
Orange Beach Public Library, Orange Beach AL
p. 33
Orange Campus Library, see ITT Technical Institute,
Orange CA p. 201
Orange City Public, see Volusia County Public
Library, Orange City FL p. 436
Orange City Public Library, Orange City IA p. 837
Orange Coast College Library, Costa Mesa CA
p. 137
Orange County Community College Library,
Middletown NY p. 1660
Orange County Library, Orange VA p. 2483
Orange County Library District, Orlando FL p. 476
Orange County Museum of Art Library, Newport
Beach CA p. 194
Orange County Public Law Library, Santa Ana CA
p. 259

Orange County Public Library, Hillsborough NC
p. 1802
Orange County RDMD Technical Library, Santa Ana
CA p. 259
Orange County Regional History Center, Orlando FL
p. 477
Orange County Sheriff-Coroner, Santa Ana CA
p. 259
Orange Grove Public, see Harrison County Library
System, Gulfport MS p. 1299
Orange Grove School & Public Library, see Salinas
Alicia City of Alice Public Library, Orange
Grove TX p. 2273
Orange Park Public Library, see Clay County Public
Library System, Orange Park FL p. 475
Orange Public Library, Orange NJ p. 1516
Orange Public Library, Orange TX p. 2367
Orange Public Library & History Center, Orange CA
p. 201
Orangeburg-Calhoun Technical College, Orangeburg
SC p. 2201
Orangeburg County Library, Orangeburg SC p. 2201
Orangeburg Library, Orangeburg NY p. 1711
Orangevale Neighborhood Library, see Sacramento
Public Library, Orangevale CA p. 225
Orangeville Public Library, Orangeville PA p. 2101
Orangeville Public Library, Orangeville ON p. 2826
Orangewood Presbyterian Church Library, Phoenix
AZ p. 75
Orbach Raymond L Science Library, see University
of California, Riverside Libraries, Riverside CA
p. 219
Orbis Cascade Alliance (N), Eugene OR p. 2953
ORC Worldwide, New York NY p. 1696
Orcas Island Library District, Eastsound WA p. 2514
Orchard Park Public Library, Orchard Park NY
p. 1712
Orchard Public Library, Orchard NE p. 1415
Orcutt & Cole Memorial Research Library, see
American Morgan Horse Institute, Middlebury
VT p. 2428
Ord Township Library, Ord NE p. 1415
Order of Carmelites Library, see Whitefriars Hall,
Washington DC p. 422
Order of Servants of Mary (Servites), USA Province,
Chicago IL p. 622
Ordre des Infirmieres et Infirmiers du Quebec,
Montreal QC p. 2900
Oreana Public Library, see Argenta-Oreana Public
Library District, Oreana IL p. 685
Oregon City Public Library, Oregon City OR
p. 2009
Oregon Coast Community College Library, Newport
OR p. 2008
Oregon Coast History Center Library, Newport OR
p. 2008
Oregon College of Art & Craft Library, Portland OR
p. 2012
Oregon College of Oriental Medicine Library,
Portland OR p. 2013
Oregon County Library District, Alton MO p. 1319
Oregon Department of Geology & Mineral
Industries, Portland OR p. 2013
Oregon Department of Transportation Library, Salem
OR p. 2017
Oregon Health & Science University Library,
Portland OR p. 2013
Oregon Health & Science University, OGI School of
Science & Engineering, Beaverton OR p. 1991
Oregon Health Sciences Libraries Association (N),
Portland OR p. 2953
Oregon Historical Society Research Library, Portland
OR p. 2013
Oregon Institute of Technology Library, Klamath
Falls OR p. 2002
Oregon Legislative Library, Salem OR p. 2017
Oregon National Primate Research Center, Beaverton
OR p. 1991
Oregon Public Library, Oregon MO p. 1348
Oregon Public Library, Oregon WI p. 2627
Oregon Public Library District, Oregon IL p. 686
Oregon Research Institute Library, Eugene OR
p. 1997
Oregon School for the Deaf Library, Salem OR
p. 2018

Oregon State Correctional Institution, Salem OR
p. 2018
Oregon State Library, Salem OR p. 2018
Oregon State Library Talking Book & Braille
Services, Salem OR p. 2018
Oregon State Penitentiary Library, Salem OR
p. 2018
Oregon State University, Bend OR p. 1992
Oregon State University, Newport OR p. 2008
Oregon State University Libraries, Corvallis OR
p. 1994
Oregon Trail Library District, Boardman OR p. 1992
Oregon Zoo Animal Management Library, Portland
OR p. 2013
Orem Public Library, Orem UT p. 2409
Orendorff Harold S Library, see Indiana University
of Pennsylvania, Indiana PA p. 2071
Orford Free Library, Orfordville NH p. 1461
Orford Social Library, Orford NH p. 1461
Orfordville Public Library, Orfordville WI p. 2627
Organization Development Institute Library,
Chesterland OH p. 1867
Organization for Economic Cooperation &
Development, Washington DC p. 412
Organization for Tropical Studies Library, Durham
NC p. 1789
Organization of American States, Washington DC
p. 412
Origami USA Library, New York NY p. 1696
Orillia Public Library, Orillia ON p. 2826
Orinda, see Contra Costa County Library,
Orinda CA p. 209
Orion Township Public Library, Lake Orion MI
p. 1199
Oriskany Public Library, Oriskany NY p. 1712
Orland Free Library, Orland CA p. 201
Orland Hills Public Library District, Orland Hills IL
p. 686
Orland Park Public Library, Orland Park IL p. 686
Orlando Health, Orlando FL p. 477
Orlando Museum of Art, Orlando FL p. 477
Orlando Public Library, see Orange County Library
District, Orlando FL p. 476
Orleans Correctional Facility Library, Albion NY
p. 1571
Orleans County Historical Society, Inc, Brownington
VT p. 2420
Orleans Public Library, La Fargeville NY p. 1650
Orleans Town & Township Public Library, Orleans
IN p. 771
Ormond Beach Public, see Volusia County Public
Library, Ormond Beach FL p. 436
Oro Valley Public Library, Oro Valley AZ p. 70
Orono Public Library, Orono ME p. 994
Oroville Community, see North Central Regional
Library, Oroville WA p. 2549
Oroville Hospital, Oroville CA p. 202
Orr & Reno Law Library, Concord NH p. 1443
Orr's Island Library, Orr's Island ME p. 995
Orradre Michel Library, see Santa Clara University,
Santa Clara CA p. 263
Orrick, Herrington & Sutcliffe, New York NY
p. 1696
Orrick, Herrington & Sutcliffe LLP, San Francisco
CA p. 244
Orrington Public Library, Orrington ME p. 995
Orrville Public Library, Orrville OH p. 1925
Ort Lewis J Library, see Frostburg State University,
Frostburg MD p. 1029
Orthodox Church in America, Syosset NY p. 1751
Orthopaedic Hospital, Los Angeles CA p. 176
Ortiz Juan Cancio Library, see Inter-American
University of Puerto Rico, San German PR
p. 2675
Orton Memorial Library of Geology, see Ohio State
University LIBRARIES, Columbus OH p. 1889
Ortonville Public Library, Ortonville MN p. 1270
Orwell Free Library, Orwell VT p. 2431
Orwell Library, Orwell NY p. 1712
Orwell Library Association, see Grand Valley Public
Library, Orwell OH p. 1925
Orwig Music Library, see Brown University,
Providence RI p. 2172
Orwigsburg Area Free Public Library, Orwigsburg
PA p. 2101

Pacific & Yukon Region Library, *see* Environment Canada, Vancouver BC p. 2741

Pacific Asia Museum Library, Pasadena CA p. 206

Pacific Gas & Electric Co, San Francisco CA p. 244

Pacific Grove Public Library, Pacific Grove CA p. 203

Pacific Hospital of Long Beach, Long Beach CA p. 167

Pacific Institute for Research & Evaluation, Berkeley CA p. 127

Pacific Lutheran University, Tacoma WA p. 2539

Pacific Newspaper Group Library, Vancouver BC p. 2742

Pacific Northwest Campus, *see* Golden Gate Baptist Theological, Vancouver WA p. 2546

Pacific Northwest College of Art, Portland OR p. 2013

Pacific Northwest National Laboratory, Richland WA p. 2526

Pacific Oaks College, Pasadena CA p. 206

Pacific Resources for Education & Learning, Honolulu HI p. 565

Pacific Salmon Commission Library, Vancouver BC p. 2742

Pacific States University Library, Los Angeles CA p. 176

Pacific Studies Center, Mountain View CA p. 192

Pacific Union College, Angwin CA p. 121

Pacific University Library, Forest Grove OR p. 1998

Pacific Whale Foundation Library, Wailuku HI p. 568

Pacifica Foundation, North Hollywood CA p. 194

Pacifica Radio Archives, *see* Pacifica Foundation, North Hollywood CA p. 194

Pacifica Sanchez Library, *see* San Mateo County Library, Pacifica CA p. 256

Pacifica Sharp Park Library, *see* San Mateo County Library, Pacifica CA p. 256

Pack Audrey Memorial Library, Spring City TN p. 2266

Packanack Community Church Library, Wayne NJ p. 1540

Packard Library, *see* Columbus College of Art & Design, Columbus OH p. 1884

Packer Engineering Inc, Naperville IL p. 679

Packwaukee Public Library, Packwaukee WI p. 2629

PACSCL (N), *see* Philadelphia Area Consortium of Special Collections Libraries, Philadelphia PA p. 2954

Padberg Frank T Medical Library, *see* Saint Vincent Health Systems Library, Little Rock AR p. 107

Paddock Music Library, *see* Dartmouth College Library, Hanover NH p. 1450

Paddockwood Public Library, *see* Wapiti Regional Library, Paddockwood SK p. 2921

Paden City Public Library, Paden City WV p. 2568

Page Charles, *see* Tulsa City-County Library, Sand Springs OK p. 1983

Page Inman E Library, *see* Lincoln University of Missouri, Jefferson City MO p. 1334

Page Memorial, *see* Moore County Library, Aberdeen NC p. 1779

Page Public, *see* Massanutten Regional Library, Luray VA p. 2470

Page Public Library, Page AZ p. 70

Pageland Community Library, *see* Chesterfield County Library, Pageland SC p. 2186

Pahala Public & School Library, *see* Hawaii State Public Library System, Pahala HI p. 563

Pahkisimon Nuye ah Library System, Air Ronge SK p. 2917

Pahoa Public & School Library, *see* Hawaii State Public Library System, Pahoa HI p. 563

Pahrump Community Library, Pahrump NV p. 1432

Paier College of Art, Inc Library, Hamden CT p. 343

Paiewonsky Ralph M Library, *see* University of the Virgin Islands, Saint Thomas VI p. 2679

Paige Memorial Library, Hardwick MA p. 1094

Paine College, Augusta GA p. 520

Paine Memorial Free Library, Willsboro NY p. 1770

Paisley County Library, *see* Lake County Library System, Paisley FL p. 500

Pajaro Valley Historical Association, Watsonville CA p. 282

Pakenham Library, *see* Mississippi Mills Libraries, Pakenham ON p. 2835

Chavez Fray Angelico History Library, *see* Museum of New Mexico, Santa Fe NM p. 1562

Palacios Library, Inc, Palacios TX p. 2368

Palatine Public Library District, Palatine IL p. 686

Palatka Public Library, *see* Putnam County Library System, Palatka FL p. 478

Palco Public Library, Palco KS p. 889

Palenske Maud Preston Memorial Library, Saint Joseph MI p. 1225

Paleontological Research Institution Library, Ithaca NY p. 1643

Palermo Community Library, Palermo ME p. 995

Palestine Public Library, Palestine TX p. 2368

Palestine Public Library District, Palestine IL p. 687

Paley Samuel Library, *see* Temple University Libraries, Philadelphia PA p. 2117

PALIS (N), *see* Palouse Area Library Information Services, Pullman WA p. 2957

Palisades Free Library, Palisades NY p. 1714

Palisades Park Free Public Library, Palisades Park NJ p. 1517

Palliser Regional Library, Moose Jaw SK p. 2918

Palm Bay Public Library, Palm Bay FL p. 479

Palm Beach Atlantic University, West Palm Beach FL p. 502

Palm Beach County Law Library, West Palm Beach FL p. 503

Palm Beach County Library System, West Palm Beach FL p. 503

Palm Beach Post Library, West Palm Beach FL p. 503

Palm Beach State College, Belle Glade FL p. 427

Palm Beach State College, Boca Raton FL p. 428

Palm Beach State College, Lake Worth FL p. 459

Palm Beach State College, Palm Beach Gardens FL p. 479

Palm Desert Library, *see* Riverside County Library System, Palm Desert CA p. 218

Palm Harbor Library, Palm Harbor FL p. 480

Palm Springs Art Museum Library, Palm Springs CA p. 203

Palm Springs Public Library, Palm Springs CA p. 203

Palm Springs Public Library, Palm Springs FL p. 480

Palmdale City Library, Palmdale CA p. 203

Palmedo Roland National Ski Library, *see* United States National Ski Hall of Fame, Ishpeming MI p. 1194

Palmer College of Chiropractic, Davenport IA p. 806

Palmer College of Chiropractic, San Jose CA p. 250

Palmer Correctional Center, Palmer AK p. 52

Palmer David D Health Sciences Library, *see* Palmer College of Chiropractic, Davenport IA p. 806

Palmer Dr Eddy, *see* Hackettstown Regional Medical Center, Hackettstown NJ p. 1489

Palmer Lake Library, *see* Pikes Peak Library District, Palmer Lake CO p. 296

Palmer Library, Palmer NE p. 1416

Palmer Memorial Library, *see* Easton Area Public Library & District Center, Easton PA p. 2052

Palmer Memorial Library, *see* Texarkana College, Texarkana TX p. 2391

Palmer Public Library, Palmer AK p. 52

Palmer Public Library, Palmer IA p. 837

Palmer Public Library, Palmer MA p. 1116

Palmer Public Library, Palmer TN p. 2263

Palmer School of Library & Information Science, *see* Long Island University, Brookville NY p. 2969

Palmer Sophia F Library, *see* WKH/LWW American Journal of Nursing, New York NY p. 1703

Palmer Theological Seminary, Wynnewood PA p. 2158

Palmerton Area Library Association, Palmerton PA p. 2101

Palmyra Community Library, Palmyra NY p. 1714

Palmyra Memorial Library, Palmyra NE p. 1416

Palmyra Public Library, Palmyra PA p. 2101

PALnet (N), Flint MI p. 2946

Palo Alto City Library, Palo Alto CA p. 204

Palo Alto College, San Antonio TX p. 2380

Palo Alto Medical Foundation, Palo Alto CA p. 204

Palo Alto Research Center, Palo Alto CA p. 204

Palo Alto University, Palo Alto CA p. 204

Palo Verde College, Blythe CA p. 129

Palo Verde Library, *see* Phoenix Public Library, Phoenix AZ p. 76

Palo Verde Valley Library District, Blythe CA p. 129

Paloma Valley Library, *see* Riverside County Library System, Menifee CA p. 218

Palomar College, San Marcos CA p. 2962

Palomar College Library - Media Center, San Marcos CA p. 254

Palomino Horse Breeders of America Library, Tulsa OK p. 1982

Palomino Library, *see* Scottsdale Public Library, Scottsdale AZ p. 81

Palos Community Hospital, Palos Heights IL p. 687

Palos Heights Public Library, Palos Heights IL p. 687

Palos Park Public Library, Palos Park IL p. 688

Palos Verdes Library District, Rolling Hills Estates CA p. 219

Palouse Area Library Information Services (N), Pullman WA p. 2957

Pamlico Community College, Grantsboro NC p. 1795

Pamlico County Library, Bayboro NC p. 1776

Pamplico Public Library, *see* Florence County Library System, Pamplico SC p. 2193

Pamunkey Regional Library, Hanover VA p. 2469

Pan American Health Organization Headquarters Library, Washington DC p. 412

Pana Public Library, *see* Carnegie-Schuyler Library, Pana IL p. 688

Pangburn Public, *see* White County Regional Library System, Pangburn AR p. 115

Panhandle Library Access Network (N), Panama City Beach FL p. 2940

Panhandle-Plains Historical Museum, Canyon TX p. 2294

Pankhurst Memorial Library, Amboy IL p. 588

Pannell Library, *see* New Mexico Junior College, Hobbs NM p. 1556

Panola College, Carthage TX p. 2295

Panora Public Library, Panora IA p. 838

Paola Free Library, Paola KS p. 889

Paoli Public Library, Paoli IN p. 772

Paonia Public, *see* Delta County Libraries, Paonia CO p. 313

PAPHR Library, *see* Prince Albert Parkland Health Region Library, Prince Albert SK p. 2921

Papove Anna Memorial Library, *see* British Columbia Land Surveyors Foundation, Sidney BC p. 2737

Pappas Law Library, *see* Boston University Libraries, Boston MA p. 1058

Paprican Library, *see* Pulp & Paper Research Institute of Canada, Pointe-Claire QC p. 2903

Parade Editorial Library, *see* Parade Publications, Inc, New York NY p. 1697

Parade Publications, Inc, New York NY p. 1697

Paradise Valley Community College Library, Phoenix AZ p. 75

Paradise Valley Municipal Library, Paradise Valley AB p. 2713

Paramus Public Library, Paramus NJ p. 1517

Parapsychology Foundation Inc, Greenport NY p. 1631

Parchment Community Library, Parchment MI p. 1216

Pardee Frederick S Management Library, *see* Boston University Libraries, Boston MA p. 1058

Pardee Katherine M & George M Jr Legal Research Center, *see* University of San Diego, San Diego CA p. 239

Parent Action on Drugs Library, Toronto ON p. 2857

Parents Helping Parents Library, San Jose CA p. 250

Parents, Let's Unite for Kids, Billings MT p. 1374

Paris-Bourbon County Library, Paris KY p. 932

Paris Carnegie Public Library, Paris IL p. 688

Paris Junior College, Paris TX p. 2368

Paris Public Library, South Paris ME p. 1001

Paris Public Library, Paris TX p. 2368

Paris Regional Medical Center-North Library, *see* Essent Corp, Paris TX p. 2368

Patton Museum of Cavalry & Armor Emert L Davis Memorial Library, *see* United States Army, Fort Knox KY p. 913

Patton Public Library, Patton PA p. 2101

Patton State Hospital, Patton CA p. 207

Patuxent Institution Library, Jessup MD p. 1033

Paul D Camp Community College Library, Franklin VA p. 2465

Paul-Gerin-Lajoie D'Outremont Library, Outremont QC p. 2902

Paul, Hastings, Janofsky & Walker, Atlanta GA p. 517

Paul, Hastings, Janofsky & Walker LLP, Los Angeles CA p. 176

Paul Memorial Library, Newfields NH p. 1460

Paul Quinn College, Dallas TX p. 2309

Paul Smiths College of Arts & Sciences, Paul Smiths NY p. 1715

Paul, Weiss, Rifkind, Wharton & Garrison Library, New York NY p. 1697

Paulding County Carnegie Library, Paulding OH p. 1928

Paulding County Public Library, *see* West Georgia Regional Library, Dallas GA p. 524

Paulina June & George Pollak Library, Fullerton CA p. 154

Paullina Public Library, Paullina IA p. 838

Pavilion Public Library, Pavilion NY p. 1715

Pavillion Public Library, Pavillion WY p. 2658

Pavo Public Library, *see* Thomas County Public Library System, Pavo GA p. 554

Paw Paw District Library, Paw Paw MI p. 1217

Paw Paw Public Library, Paw Paw WV p. 2569

Paw Paw Public Library District, Paw Paw IL p. 689

Pawhuska Public Library, Pawhuska OK p. 1976

Pawlet Public Library, Pawlet VT p. 2431

Pawling Free Library, Pawling NY p. 1716

Pawnee City Public Library, Pawnee City NE p. 1416

Pawnee Public Library, Pawnee IL p. 689

Pawnee Public Library, Pawnee OK p. 1976

Pawtucket Public Library, Pawtucket RI p. 2171

Paxton Carnegie Library, Paxton IL p. 689

Paxton Public Library, Paxton NE p. 1416

Payette Associates, Boston MA p. 1066

Payette Public Library, Payette ID p. 581

Payne Bishop Library, *see* Virginia Theological Seminary, Alexandria VA p. 2446

Payne Burton Library, *see* Northeast Iowa Community College, Peosta IA p. 838

Payne Theological Seminary, Wilberforce OH p. 1948

Paynesville Library, *see* Great River Regional Library, Paynesville MN p. 1275

Payson City Library, Payson UT p. 2410

Payson Daniel Carroll Medical Library, *see* North Shore University Hospital, Manhasset NY p. 1657

Payson Library, *see* Pepperdine University Libraries, Malibu CA p. 182

Payson Public Library, Payson AZ p. 70

Payton Benjamin F Learning Resources Center, *see* Benedict College Library, Columbia SC p. 2186

PCIN (N), *see* Perth County Information Network, Stratford ON p. 2960

Pea Ridge Community Library, Pea Ridge AR p. 111

Pea Ridge Military Park Library, *see* United States National Park Service, Garfield AR p. 101

Peabody & Arnold LLP, Boston MA p. 1066

Peabody Essex Museum, Salem MA p. 1121

Peabody Frances W Research Library, *see* Greater Portland Landmarks, Inc, Portland ME p. 996

Peabody George, *see* Thetford Town Library, Post Mills VT p. 2437

Peabody George Library, *see* Johns Hopkins University Libraries, Baltimore MD p. 1014

Peabody Historical Society & Museum, Peabody MA p. 1116

Peabody Institute Library, Peabody MA p. 1116

Peabody Institute Library of Danvers, Danvers MA p. 1083

Peabody Library, *see* Vanderbilt University, Nashville TN p. 2261

Peabody Memorial Library, Jonesport ME p. 988

Peabody Public Library, Columbia City IN p. 733

Peabody Robert S Museum of Archaeology, *see* Phillips Academy, Andover MA p. 1049

Peabody Township Library, Peabody KS p. 889

Peace College, Raleigh NC p. 1816

Peace Library System, Grande Prairie AB p. 2705

Peace River Bible Institute Library, Sexsmith AB p. 2716

Peace River Municipal Library, Peace River AB p. 2713

Peace River Museum, Archives & Mackenzie Centre, Peace River AB p. 2713

Peace Roger C Hospital Library, *see* Greenville Hospital System, Greenville SC p. 2197

Peach Public Libraries, Fort Valley GA p. 533

Peacham Library, Peacham VT p. 2431

Peachtree City Library, *see* Flint River Regional Library, Peachtree City GA p. 535

Peachtree Library, *see* Atlanta-Fulton Public Library System, Atlanta GA p. 512

Peachtree Presbyterian Church, Atlanta GA p. 517

Peapack & Gladstone Public, *see* Somerset County Library System, Peapack NJ p. 1475

Pearce B C Learning Resources Center, *see* Saint John's River State College, Palatka FL p. 478

Pearisburg Public Library, Pearisburg VA p. 2484

Pearl City Public Library, *see* Hawaii State Public Library System, Pearl City HI p. 563

Pearl City Public Library District, Pearl City IL p. 689

Pearl Public Library, Pearl MS p. 1311

Pearl River Community College, Poplarville MS p. 1312

Pearl River County Library System, Picayune MS p. 1311

Pearl River Public Library, Pearl River NY p. 1716

Pearlington Public Library, *see* Hancock County Library System, Pearlington MS p. 1294

Pearlman Memorial Library, *see* Central Bible College, Springfield MO p. 1366

Pearsall Elizabeth Braswell Memorial Library, *see* North Carolina Wesleyan College, Rocky Mount NC p. 1821

Pearsall Public Library, Pearsall TX p. 2369

Pearson Library, *see* California Lutheran University, Thousand Oaks CA p. 274

Pearson Public Library, *see* Satilla Regional Library, Pearson GA p. 531

Pease Public Library, Plymouth NH p. 1462

Peavey Memorial Library, Eastport ME p. 984

Peayamechikee Public Library, Pinehouse Lake SK p. 2920

Pecatonica Public Library District, Pecatonica IL p. 689

Peck Memorial Library, Marathon NY p. 1657

Peckar & Abramson, River Edge NJ p. 1526

Peckham Barbara Research Library, *see* Champaign County Historical Museum, Champaign IL p. 602

Peconic Bay Medical Center, Riverhead NY p. 1728

Pedersen & Houpt Library, Chicago IL p. 622

Pederson Nellie Civic Library, Clifton TX p. 2298

Peebles Public Library, *see* Adams County Public Library, Peebles OH p. 1912

Peek Iva Jane Public Library, Decatur AR p. 97

Peel District School Board, Mississauga ON p. 2823

Peeples Vernon Learning Resource Center, *see* Edison College, Punta Gorda FL p. 485

Pegues Godfrey Public Library, *see* Newark Public Library, Newark TX p. 2365

Peine H A Memorial Library, Minier IL p. 674

Peirce College Library, Philadelphia PA p. 2113

Pejepscot Historical Society, Brunswick ME p. 980

Pekin Public Library, Pekin IL p. 689

Pelahatchie Public Library, Pelahatchie MS p. 1311

Pelham Library, Pelham MA p. 1117

Pelham Public Library, Pelham AL p. 33

Pelham Public Library, Pelham NH p. 1461

Pelham Public Library, Fonthill ON p. 2805

Symmes F W, *see* Greenville County Library System, Greenville SC p. 2196

Pelican Bay State Prison, *see* California Department of Corrections Library System, Crescent City CA p. 222

Pelican Public Library, Pelican AK p. 52

Pelican Rapids Public Library, Pelican Rapids MN p. 1270

Pell City Library, Pell City AL p. 33

Pell Marine Science Library, *see* University of Rhode Island, Narragansett RI p. 2168

Pella Public Library, Pella IA p. 838

Pelletier Lawrence Lee Library, *see* Allegheny College Library, Meadville PA p. 2086

Pellissippi State Technical Community College, Knoxville TN p. 2243

Pember Library & Museum of Natural History, Granville NY p. 1630

Pemberton Public Library, Pemberton BC p. 2735

Pemberton Community Library, *see* Burlington County Library, Browns Mills NJ p. 1543

Pemberville Public Library, Pemberville OH p. 1928

Pembina City Library, Pembina ND p. 1847

Pembroke Library Association, Pembroke ME p. 995

Young Walter C Resource Center, *see* Broward County Division of Libraries, Pembroke Pines FL p. 442

Pembroke Public, *see* Robeson County Public Library, Pembroke NC p. 1808

Pembroke Public Library, Pembroke GA p. 547

Pembroke Public Library, Pembroke MA p. 1117

Pembroke Public Library, Pembroke ON p. 2835

Pembroke Town Library, Pembroke NH p. 1461

Pen Bay Medical Center, Rockport ME p. 999

Pence Law Library, Washington College of Law, *see* American University, Washington DC p. 393

Pend Oreille County Library District, Newport WA p. 2521

Pender County Public Library, Burgaw NC p. 1778

Pender Island Public Library, Pender Island BC p. 2735

Pendergraft Ross Library & Technology Center, *see* Arkansas Tech University, Russellville AR p. 113

Pendergrass Public, *see* Piedmont Regional Library, Pendergrass GA p. 557

Pendergrast James Memorial Library, *see* Albany State University, Albany GA p. 507

Pendle Hill Library, Wallingford PA p. 2150

Pendleton Alice L Library, Islesboro ME p. 988

Pendleton Community Library, Pendleton IN p. 772

Pendleton Correctional Facility, Pendleton IN p. 772

Pendleton County Library, Franklin WV p. 2559

Pendleton County Public Library, Falmouth KY p. 912

Pendleton District Historical, Recreational, Pendleton SC p. 2202

Pendleton Public Library, Pendleton OR p. 2009

Penetanguishene Public Library, Penetanguishene ON p. 2835

Penfield Library, *see* Polk Museum of Art, Lakeland FL p. 459

Penfield Library, *see* State University of New York at Oswego, Oswego NY p. 1713

Penfield Public Library, Penfield NY p. 1716

Penhold & District Public Library, Penhold AB p. 2713

Peninsula Center Library, *see* Palos Verdes Library District, Rolling Hills Estates CA p. 219

Peninsula College Library, Port Angeles WA p. 2524

Peninsula Community Library, Traverse City MI p. 1231

Peninsula Hospital Center, Far Rockaway NY p. 1621

Peninsula Libraries Automated Network (N), San Mateo CA p. 2938

Peninsula Library & Historical Society, Peninsula OH p. 1928

Peninsula Public Library, Lawrence NY p. 1651

Peninsula Regional Medical Center, Salisbury MD p. 1040

Peninsula Temple Beth El Library, San Mateo CA p. 255

Penn Area Library, Harrison City PA p. 2066

Penn Commercial Business/Technical School, Washington PA p. 2151

Penn Presbyterian Medical Center, Philadelphia PA p. 2113

Penn State Erie, Erie PA p. 2056

Penn State University York, York PA p. 2159

Penn Wynne Library, Wynnewood PA p. 2158

Peters Reg Resource Centre, *see* Alberta Association for Community Living, Edmonton AB p. 2697

Peters Township Public Library, McMurray PA p. 2086

Peters William Wesley Library, *see* Frank Lloyd Wright School of Architecture, Scottsdale AZ p. 80

Petersburg-Barrett Memorial Library, *see* Pike County Public Library, Petersburg IN p. 773

Petersburg National Battlefield Library, *see* United States Department of the Interior, Petersburg VA p. 2484

Petersburg Public Library, Petersburg AK p. 52

Petersburg Public Library, Petersburg IL p. 691

Petersburg Public Library, Petersburg NE p. 1416

Petersburg Public Library, Petersburg TX p. 2369

Petersburg Public Library, Petersburg VA p. 2484

Petersburgh Public Library, Petersburgh NY p. 1717

Petersham Memorial Library, Petersham MA p. 1117

Peterson Dutton S Memorial Library, Odessa NY p. 1709

Peterson Marvin K Library, *see* University of New Haven, West Haven CT p. 377

Peterson Memorial Library, *see* Walla Walla University Libraries, College Place WA p. 2513

Peterson Walter R Library & Media Center, *see* Nashua Community College, Nashua NH p. 1458

Peterstown Public Library, Peterstown WV p. 2569

Pethick Betty Memorial Library, *see* First Presbyterian Church, Cranford NJ p. 1480

Petit-Rocher Public Library, *see* Chaleur Library Region, Petit-Rocher NB p. 2761

Petitcodiac Public, *see* Albert-Westmorland-Kent Regional Library, Petitcodiac NB p. 2765

Petoskey Public Library, Petoskey MI p. 1217

Petrie Harry L Public Library, *see* Linton Public Library, Linton ND p. 1845

Petrified Forest National Park Library, *see* National Park Service, Petrified Forest National Park AZ p. 71

Petroleum County Community Library, Winnett MT p. 1390

Petroleum Museum Library & Hall of Fame, Midland TX p. 2363

Petros Public Library, Petros TN p. 2263

Pettaquamscutt Genealogy Library, *see* Pettaquamscutt Historical Society, Kingston RI p. 2167

Pettaquamscutt Historical Society, Kingston RI p. 2167

Pettee Memorial Library, Wilmington VT p. 2440

Pettes Memorial Library, *see* Bibliotheque Commemorative Pettes, Knowlton QC p. 2885

Pettigrew Museum Library, *see* Siouxland Heritage Museums, Sioux Falls SD p. 2218

Pettigrew Regional Library, Plymouth NC p. 1814

Pettis Olive G Library, Goshen NH p. 1448

Petzinger Library, *see* Haggin Museum, Stockton CA p. 272

Pew Charitable Trusts Library, Washington DC p. 413

Pew Charitable Trusts Library, Philadelphia PA p. 2114

Pew Joseph N Jr Medical Library, *see* Bryn Mawr Hospital Library, Bryn Mawr PA p. 2039

Pew Learning Center & Ellison Library, *see* Warren Wilson College, Swannanoa NC p. 1826

Pewaukee Public Library, Pewaukee WI p. 2629

Pfau John M Library, *see* California State University, San Bernardino, San Bernardino CA p. 227

Pfeiffer Annie Merner Library, *see* West Virginia Wesleyan College, Buckhannon WV p. 2555

Pfeiffer G A Library, *see* Pfeiffer University, Misenheimer NC p. 1809

Pfeiffer Henry Library, *see* MacMurray College, Jacksonville IL p. 659

Pfeiffer Library, *see* Tiffin University, Tiffin OH p. 1938

Pfeiffer Library at Charlotte, *see* Pfeiffer University, Charlotte NC p. 1809

Pfeiffer Physics Library, *see* Washington University Libraries, Saint Louis MO p. 1363

Pfeiffer University, Misenheimer NC p. 1809

Pfizer Canada, Inc, Pointe-Claire QC p. 2903

Pflugerville Community Library, Pflugerville TX p. 2369

Pfohl Anthony C Health Sciences Library, *see* Mercy Medical Center - Dubuque, Dubuque IA p. 812

Pharr Memorial Library, Pharr TX p. 2369

Phelan Memorial Library, *see* San Bernardino County Library, Phelan CA p. 228

Phelps Community Memorial Library, Phelps NY p. 1717

Phelps Dunbar LLP, New Orleans LA p. 963

Phelps Dunbar, Jackson MS p. 1305

Phelps Hal C Archives, *see* Miami County Museum, Peru IN p. 772

Phelps Public, *see* Pike County Public Library District, Phelps KY p. 932

Phelps Public Library, Phelps WI p. 2629

Phelps Tavern Museum, *see* Simsbury Historical Society Archives, Simsbury CT p. 367

Phenix City-Russell County Library, Phenix City AL p. 33

Phenomenex Library, Torrance CA p. 276

Phifer Learning Resources Center, *see* Western Piedmont Community College, Morganton NC p. 1811

Philadelphia & Elkins Park Suburban Center Library, *see* Congregation Rodeph Shalom, Philadelphia PA p. 2104

Philadelphia Archdiocesan Historical Research Center, Wynnewood PA p. 2158

Philadelphia Area Consortium of Special Collections Libraries (N), Philadelphia PA p. 2954

Philadelphia City Archives, Philadelphia PA p. 2114

Philadelphia City Institute, *see* Free Library of Philadelphia, Philadelphia PA p. 2109

Philadelphia College of Osteopathic Medicine, Philadelphia PA p. 2114

Philadelphia Corporation for Aging Library, Philadelphia PA p. 2114

Philadelphia Historical Commission Library, Philadelphia PA p. 2114

Philadelphia Museum of Art Library, Philadelphia PA p. 2114

Philadelphia Newspapers, Inc, Philadelphia PA p. 2114

Philadelphia Orchestra Library, Philadelphia PA p. 2115

Philadelphia Public Library, Philadelphia TN p. 2263

Philadelphia University, Philadelphia PA p. 2115

Philadelphia VA Medical Center, Philadelphia PA p. 2115

Philadelphia Yearly Meeting of the Religious Society of Friends, Philadelphia PA p. 2115

Philadelphia Zoo Library, Philadelphia PA p. 2115

Philander Smith College, Little Rock AR p. 107

Philatelic Foundation, New York NY p. 1697

Philbrick-James Library, Deerfield NH p. 1444

Philbrick Popular Library, *see* Free Library of Philadelphia, Philadelphia PA p. 2109

Philbrook Museum of Art, Tulsa OK p. 1982

Philippi Public Library, Philippi WV p. 2569

Philipsburg Public Library, Philipsburg MT p. 1387

Phillips Academy, Andover MA p. 1049

Phillips Charles B Library, *see* Aurora University, Aurora IL p. 591

Phillips Collection Library, Washington DC p. 413

Phillips Community College of the University of Arkansas, DeWitt AR p. 98

Phillips Community College of the University of Arkansas, Helena AR p. 103

Phillips Community College of the University of Arkansas, Stuttgart AR p. 116

Phillips County Library, Malta MT p. 1385

Phillips County Library, *see* Phillips-Lee-Monroe Regional Library, Helena AR p. 103

Phillips Dr Walter Health Sciences Library, *see* Englewood Hospital & Medical Center, Englewood NJ p. 1484

Phillips Free Library, Homer NY p. 1637

Phillips Free Public Library, Phillipston MA p. 1117

Phillips Graduate Institute Library, Chatsworth CA p. 133

Phillips Harry Memorial Library, *see* United States Court of Appeals, Nashville TN p. 2260

Phillips Hugh J Library, *see* Mount Saint Mary's University, Emmitsburg MD p. 1027

Phillips L E Memorial Public Library, Eau Claire WI p. 2590

Phillips Library, *see* Peabody Essex Museum, Salem MA p. 1121

Phillips, McFall, McCaffrey, McVay & Murrah Pc, Oklahoma City OK p. 1975

Phillips Memorial Library, *see* Providence College, Providence RI p. 2173

Phillips Public Library, Phillips ME p. 995

Phillips Public Library, Phillips WI p. 2629

Phillips Seymour J Health Sciences Library, *see* Beth Israel Medical Center, New York NY p. 1670

Phillips Site Technical Library, *see* United States Air Force, Kirtland AFB NM p. 1557

Phillips Sixty Six Research Library, Bartlesville OK p. 1958

Phillips State Prison, Buford GA p. 522

Phillips Stephen Memorial Library, *see* Penobscot Marine Museum, Searsport ME p. 1000

Phillips T W Memorial Library, *see* Bethany College, Mary Cutlip Center, Bethany WV p. 2554

Phillips Theological Seminary Library, Tulsa OK p. 1982

Phillips, Lytle LLP Library, Buffalo NY p. 1598

Phillips-Lee-Monroe Regional Library, Helena AR p. 103

Phillipsburg City Library, Phillipsburg KS p. 890

Phillipsburg Free Public Library, Phillipsburg NJ p. 1520

Philmont Museum & Seton Memorial Library, Cimarron NM p. 1553

Philmont Public Library, Philmont NY p. 1717

Philo Public Library District, Philo IL p. 691

Philomath Community Library, *see* Corvallis-Benton County Public Library, Philomath OR p. 1994

Philomathean Free Library, *see* Belleville Public Library, Belleville NY p. 1580

Philosophical Research Society Library, Los Angeles CA p. 176

Phoenicia Library, Phoenicia NY p. 1717

Phoenix Art Museum Library, Phoenix AZ p. 75

Phoenix Children's Hospital, Phoenix AZ p. 76

Phoenix College, Phoenix AZ p. 76

Phoenix Indian Medical Center Library, *see* Indian Health Services, Phoenix AZ p. 73

Phoenix Public Library, Phoenix AZ p. 76

Phoenix Public Library, Phoenix NY p. 1717

Phoenix School of Law, Phoenix AZ p. 76

Phoenix VA Health Care System, Phoenix AZ p. 77

Phoenixville Public Library, Phoenixville PA p. 2120

Pi Beta Phi Patient/Family Library, *see* Texas Children's Hospital, Houston TX p. 2342

Piantino Louis J, *see* West Haven Public Library, West Haven CT p. 377

Piatt County Historical & Genealogical Society Library, Monticello IL p. 675

Pickaway Correctional Institution Library, Orient OH p. 1925

Pickaway County District Public Library, Circleville OH p. 1875

Pickaway County Law Library Association, Circleville OH p. 1875

Pickens County Cooperative Library, Carrollton AL p. 11

Pickens County Library System, Easley SC p. 2193

Pickens County Public, *see* Sequoyah Regional Library System, Jasper GA p. 523

Pickens Grace M Public Library, Holdenville OK p. 1965

Pickens Public, *see* Mid-Mississippi Regional Library System, Pickens MS p. 1306

Pickering Educational Resources Library, *see* Boston University Libraries, Boston MA p. 1058

Pickering Public Library, Pickering ON p. 2836

Pickerington Public Library, Pickerington OH p. 1929

Pickett County Public Library, Byrdstown TN p. 2225

Pickett Library, *see* Alderson-Broaddus College, Philippi WV p. 2569

Plain Community Branch, *see* Stark County District Library, Canton OH p. 1865

Plain Dealer Publishing Co, Cleveland OH p. 1881

Plainedge Public Library, Massapequa NY p. 1658

Plainfield-Guilford Township Public Library, Plainfield IN p. 773

Plainfield Public Library, Plainfield IA p. 838

Plainfield Public Library, Plainfield NJ p. 1521

Plainfield Public Library, Plainfield WI p. 2630

Plainfield Public Library District, Plainfield IL p. 691

Plains Community Library, Plains KS p. 890

Plains Public Library District, Plains MT p. 1387

Plainsboro Free Public Library, Plainsboro NJ p. 1521

Plainview Carnegie Public Library, Plainview NE p. 1417

Plainview-Old Bethpage Public Library, Plainview NY p. 1718

Plainview Public Library, Plainview MN p. 1271

Plainville Memorial Library, Plainville KS p. 890

Plainville Public Library, Plainville CT p. 364

Plainville Public Library, Plainville MA p. 1118

Plaistow Public Library, Plaistow NH p. 1462

Plamondon Municipal Library, *see* Lac La Biche County Library Board, Plamondon AB p. 2708

PLAN (N), *see* Panhandle Library Access Network, Panama City Beach FL p. 2940

PLAN (N), *see* Peninsula Libraries Automated Network, San Mateo CA p. 2938

Planetary Association for Clean Energy Inc, Ottawa ON p. 2832

PlaneTree Health Library, Cupertino CA p. 138

Planetree Health Resource Center, *see* Mid-Columbia Medical Center, The Dalles OR p. 2021

Plankinton Community Library, Plankinton SD p. 2217

Planned Parenthood Federation of America, Inc, New York NY p. 1697

Planned Parenthood of Greater Cleveland, Inc Library, Cleveland OH p. 1881

Planned Parenthood of Indiana, Indianapolis IN p. 755

Planned Parenthood of Minnesota & South Dakota, Minneapolis MN p. 1261

Planned Parenthood of Southern New England, New Haven CT p. 356

Planned Parenthood of Western Pennsylvania, Pittsburgh PA p. 2127

Planned Parenthood of Wisconsin, Inc, Milwaukee WI p. 2621

Planning & Forecasting Consultants Library, Houston TX p. 2341

Plano Community Library District, Plano IL p. 691

Plano Public Library System, Plano TX p. 2370

Plantagenet Public Library, *see* Plantagenet Village Library System, Plantagenet ON p. 2836

Plantagenet Village Library System, Plantagenet ON p. 2836

Plaquemines Parish Library, Belle Chasse LA p. 945

Plaster Rock Public-School Library, *see* Haut-Saint-Jean Regional Library, Plaster Rock NB p. 2762

Platt Jan Kaminis Regional Library, *see* Tampa-Hillsborough County Public Library System, Tampa FL p. 498

Platt Memorial Library, Shoreham VT p. 2435

Platte County Public Library, Wheatland WY p. 2661

Platte Valley Youth Services Center Library, *see* Department of Human Services, Greeley CO p. 311

Plattekill Public Library, Modena NY p. 1662

Platteville Public Library, Platteville CO p. 320

Platteville Public Library, Platteville WI p. 2630

Plattsburgh Public Library, Plattsburgh NY p. 1719

Plattsmouth Public Library, Plattsmouth NE p. 1417

Playboy Enterprises, Inc, Chicago IL p. 622

Pleak Mariam Library, *see* Hobart Historical Society, Inc, Hobart IN p. 748

Pleasant Grove Christian Church Library, Dallas TX p. 2309

Pleasant Grove Public Library, Pleasant Grove AL p. 34

Pleasant Grove Public Library, Pleasant Grove UT p. 2410

Pleasant Hill Library, Hastings MN p. 1253

Pleasant Hill Library, *see* Contra Costa County Library, Pleasant Hill CA p. 209

Pleasant Hill Public Library, Pleasant Hill IA p. 839

Pleasant Hills Public Library, Pleasant Hills PA p. 2130

Pleasant Mount Public Library, Pleasant Mount PA p. 2130

Pleasant Valley Free Library, Pleasant Valley NY p. 1719

Pleasant Valley State Prison, *see* California Department of Corrections Library System, Coalinga CA p. 222

Pleasanton Lincoln Library, *see* Linn County Library District No 5, Pleasanton KS p. 890

Pleasanton Public Library, Pleasanton CA p. 210

Pleasanton Public Library, Pleasanton TX p. 2371

Pleasants County Public Library, Saint Marys WV p. 2571

Pleasantville Neighborhood Library, *see* Houston Public Library, Houston TX p. 2339

Plimoth Plantation, Plymouth MA p. 1118

Plough Library, *see* Christian Brothers University, Memphis TN p. 2248

Plover Public Library, Plover IA p. 839

Plum Borough Community Library, Plum Borough PA p. 2130

Plum City Public Library, Plum City WI p. 2630

Plum Creek Library System, Worthington MN p. 1291

Plum Helen M Memorial Public Library District, Lombard IL p. 667

Plum Lake Public Library, Sayner WI p. 2636

Plumas County Law Library, Quincy CA p. 212

Plumas County Library, Quincy CA p. 212

Plumas County Museum Library, Quincy CA p. 212

Plumb Joseph H Memorial Library, Rochester MA p. 1120

Plumb Memorial Library, Shelton CT p. 367

Plummer Public Library, Plummer ID p. 581

Plunkett & Cooney, Bloomfield Hills MI p. 1159

Plymouth Congregational Church, Seattle WA p. 2529

Plymouth District Library, Plymouth MI p. 1218

Plymouth Historical Museum Archives, Plymouth MI p. 1218

Plymouth Library, Plymouth NE p. 1417

Plymouth Library Association, Plymouth CT p. 364

Plymouth Public Library, Plymouth IN p. 773

Plymouth Public Library, Plymouth MA p. 1118

Plymouth Public Library, Plymouth PA p. 2130

Plymouth Public Library, Plymouth WI p. 2631

Plymouth State University, Plymouth NH p. 1462

Plympton Public Library, Plympton MA p. 1118

PNG News Research Library, *see* Pacific Newspaper Group Library, Vancouver BC p. 2742

Poage W R Legislative Library, *see* Baylor University Libraries, Waco TX p. 2396

Pocahontas County Free Libraries, Marlinton WV p. 2564

Pocahontas Public Library, Pocahontas IA p. 839

Pocatello Women's Correctional Center Library, *see* Idaho State Correctional Institution Library, Pocatello ID p. 577

Pocono Medical Center, East Stroudsburg PA p. 2051

Pocono Mountain Public Library, Tobyhanna PA p. 2146

Poe Edgar Allen, *see* Charleston County Public Library, Sullivan's Island SC p. 2183

Poestenkill Public Library, Poestenkill NY p. 1720

Pogue Barton Rees Memorial Library, Upland IN p. 782

Pohick Regional, *see* Fairfax County Public Library, Burke VA p. 2461

Poindexter Library, *see* Richmont Graduate University, Chattanooga TN p. 2228

Poinsett County Public Library, Harrisburg AR p. 102

Point Loma Nazarene University, San Diego CA p. 232

Point Marion Public Library, Point Marion PA p. 2131

Point Park University Library, Pittsburgh PA p. 2127

Point Pelee National Park Library, Leamington ON p. 2816

Point Reyes Bird Observatory Library, Petaluma CA p. 208

Point Reyes National Seashore Library, *see* United States National Park Service, Point Reyes Station CA p. 211

Pointe Coupee Parish Library, New Roads LA p. 964

Pointer Emily Jones Library, *see* First Regional Library, Como MS p. 1302

Poland Public Library, Poland NY p. 1720

Poland's Millennium Library, Los Angeles CA p. 177

Police Officer Standards & Training Council, *see* Connecticut Police Academy, Meriden CT p. 350

Policke Alfred Medical Library, *see* Adventist Health System, DeLand FL p. 437

Polier Shad Memorial Library, *see* American Jewish Congress, New York NY p. 1668

Polish Genealogical Society of Connecticut Inc, New Britain CT p. 354

Polish Institute of Arts & Sciences in America, Inc, New York NY p. 1697

Polish Library, Washington DC p. 413

Polish Library, Montreal QC p. 2900

Polish Museum of America Library, Chicago IL p. 622

Politi Leo, *see* Fresno County Public Library, Fresno CA p. 152

Polk City Community Library, Polk City FL p. 484

Polk City Community Library, Polk City IA p. 839

Polk County Biomedical Consortium (N), Des Moines IA p. 2943

Polk County Historical & Genealogical Library, Bartow FL p. 426

Polk County Law Library, Bartow FL p. 427

Polk County Library, Bolivar MO p. 1320

Polk County Library, *see* Southwest Arkansas Regional Library, Mena AR p. 103

Polk County Public Library, Columbus NC p. 1785

Polk Library, *see* University of Wisconsin Oshkosh, Oshkosh WI p. 2628

Polk Museum of Art, Lakeland FL p. 459

Polk Public Library, Polk NE p. 1417

Polk State College, Winter Haven FL p. 504

Polk-Demilly Correctional Institution Library, *see* Florida Department of Corrections, Polk City FL p. 484

Polkville Public Library, Morton MS p. 1309

Pollack Library-Landowne Bloom Library, *see* Yeshiva University Libraries, New York NY p. 1704

Pollard Memorial Library, Lowell MA p. 1100

Pollins Calvin E Memorial Library, *see* Westmoreland County Historical Society, Greensburg PA p. 2063

Pollocksville Public Library, *see* Neuse Regional Library, Pollocksville NC p. 1805

Polo Public Library District, Polo IL p. 691

Polsinelli Shughart PC, Kansas City MO p. 1340

Polsinelli Shughart, Saint Louis MO p. 1357

Polson City Library, Polson MT p. 1387

Polytechnic Institute of NYU, Brooklyn NY p. 1594

Pomerantz Marvin A Business Library, *see* University of Iowa Libraries, Iowa City IA p. 824

Pomeroy Arthur E Public Library, Kearny AZ p. 66

Pomeroy Public Library, Pomeroy IA p. 839

Pomeroy Public, *see* Ashby Denny Memorial Library, Pomeroy WA p. 2523

Pomfret Public Library, Pomfret CT p. 364

Pomona Public Library, Pomona CA p. 211

Pomona Valley Hospital Medical Center, Pomona CA p. 211

Pomonok Community Library, *see* Queens Borough Public Library, Flushing NY p. 1645

Pompton Lakes Public Library, Pompton Lakes NJ p. 1521

Ponca City Library, Ponca City OK p. 1976

Ponca Public Library, Ponca NE p. 1417

Ponce de Leon Library, *see* Atlanta-Fulton Public Library System, Atlanta GA p. 512

Powell John Wesley Library of Anthropology, *see*
Smithsonian Libraries, Washington DC p. 415
Powell John Wesley Memorial Museum Library,
Page AZ p. 70
Powell Memorial Library, Troy MO p. 1369
Powell River Public Library, Powell River BC
p. 2735
Powell Robert L Library, Santa Clarita CA p. 263
Powell William Estes Memorial, *see* Pine Forest
Regional Library, Beaumont MS p. 1314
Power Howard Anderson Memorial Library,
Pittsburgh PA p. 2127
Power Patrick Library, *see* Saint Mary's University,
Halifax NS p. 2782
Power Thomas S Library, *see* United States Air
Force, Offutt AFB NE p. 1411
Powers Annie Library, *see* Bibliotheque de l'Hopital
Montfort, Ottawa ON p. 2828
Powers Library, Moravia NY p. 1663
Powers Memorial Library, Palmyra WI p. 2629
Powhatan County Public Library, Powhatan VA
p. 2485
Powhatan, James River & Deep Meadow
Correctional Center, *see* Department of
Correctional Education, State Farm VA p. 2496
Poy Sippi Public Library, Poy Sippi WI p. 2631
Poydras Julian, *see* Pointe Coupee Parish Library,
Rougon LA p. 965
Poynette Public Library, Poynette WI p. 2631
Poynter David R Legislative Research Library, *see*
Louisiana House of Representatives, Baton
Rouge LA p. 943
Poynter Institute for Media Studies, Saint Petersburg
FL p. 488
Poynter Nelson Memorial Library, *see* University of
South Florida Saint Petersburg, Saint Petersburg
FL p. 488
Pozsonyi Dr Joseph Memorial Library, *see* Child &
Parent Resource Institute, London ON p. 2817
PPG Industries, Inc, Pittsburgh PA p. 2128
PPH Medical Library, Escondido CA p. 147
PQ Corp, Conshohocken PA p. 2047
Prairie Agricultural Machinery Institute Library,
Humboldt SK p. 2917
Prairie Bible Institute, Three Hills AB p. 2719
Prairie City Public Library, Prairie City IA p. 839
Prairie Community Library, Cottonwood ID p. 573
Prairie County Library, Terry MT p. 1389
Prairie Creek Public Library District, Dwight IL
p. 638
Prairie Crocus Regional Library, Rivers MB p. 2751
Prairie du Chien Memorial Library, Prairie du Chien
WI p. 2631
Prairie du Sac Public Library, Prairie du Sac WI
p. 2631
Prairie Farm Rehabilitation Administration, Regina
SK p. 2923
Prairie Grove Public Library, Prairie Grove AR
p. 113
Prairie Research Institute Library, *see* University
of Illinois Library at Urbana-Champaign,
Champaign IL p. 712
Prairie-River Library District, Lapwai ID p. 577
Prairie River Public Library, *see* Wapiti Regional
Library, Prairie River SK p. 2921
Prairie Skies Public Library District, Ashland IL
p. 590
Prairie State College Library, Chicago Heights IL
p. 628
Prairie Trails Museum of Wayne County Iowa
Library, *see* Wayne County Historical Society,
Corydon IA p. 804
Prairie Trails Public Library District, Burbank IL
p. 598
Prairie View A&M University, Prairie View TX
p. 2372
Prairie View City Library, *see* Sunshine City
Library, Prairie View KS p. 891
Praisner J Marilyn, *see* Montgomery County Public
Libraries, Burtonsville MD p. 1039
Pratt & Whitney, San Jose CA p. 250
Pratt & Whitney Canada, Inc Library, Longueuil QC
p. 2887
Pratt & Whitney Rocketdyne, Inc, Canoga Park CA
p. 131

Pratt Community College, Pratt KS p. 891
Pratt Edward L Library, *see* Cincinnati Children's
Hospital, Cincinnati OH p. 1868
Pratt Eliot D Library, *see* Goddard College,
Plainfield VT p. 2432
Pratt Franklin N Library, *see* Tufts Library, East
Weymouth MA p. 1140
Pratt Institute, New York NY p. 2970
Pratt Institute Libraries, Brooklyn NY p. 1594
Pratt-Journeycake Library, *see* Central Baptist
Theological Seminary, Shawnee KS p. 894
Pratt Lydia Taft Library, West Dummerston VT
p. 2439
Pratt Memorial, *see* Allendale-Hampton-Jasper
Regional Library, Ridgeland SC p. 2180
Pratt Memorial Library, Fulton MS p. 1298
Pratt Memorial Library, New Milford PA p. 2097
Pratt Paul Memorial Library, Cohasset MA p. 1082
Pratt Public Library, Pratt KS p. 891
Prattsburgh Library, Prattsburgh NY p. 1724
Praxair, Inc Library, Tonawanda NY p. 1755
Pray Donald E Law Library, *see* University of
Oklahoma, Norman OK p. 1971
Preble County District Library, Eaton OH p. 1897
Preformed Line Products Co, Mayfield Village OH
p. 1916
Premont Public Library, *see* Salinas Alicia City of
Alice Public Library, Premont TX p. 2273
Prendergast James Library Association, Jamestown
NY p. 1647
Prentice Cathy Memorial Library, *see* Wilhoit Public
Library, Wilhoit AZ p. 89
Prentis Memorial Library, *see* Temple Beth El,
Bloomfield Hills MI p. 1159
Prentiss Public, *see* South Mississippi Regional
Library, Prentiss MS p. 1297
Presbyterian Church in Canada Archives, Toronto
ON p. 2857
Presbyterian Church of Chatham Township Library,
Chatham NJ p. 1478
Presbyterian Church of the Atonement Library,
Silver Spring MD p. 1042
Presbyterian Church (USA) Department of History,
Philadelphia PA p. 2115
Presbyterian College, Clinton SC p. 2186
Presbyterian College Library, Montreal QC p. 2900
Presbyterian Historical Society, *see* Presbyterian
Church (USA) Department of History,
Philadelphia PA p. 2115
Presbyterian Hospital, Albuquerque NM p. 1549
Presbyterian Hospital, New York NY p. 1697
Presbyterian Hospital, Charlotte NC p. 1783
Presbyterian Intercommunity Hospital, Whittier CA
p. 283
Presbytery of Long Island, Commack NY p. 1609
Presbytery of Western North Carolina, Morganton
NC p. 1811
Prescott & Russell Law Association Library,
L'Orignal ON p. 2819
Prescott City Public Library, Prescott KS p. 891
Prescott College Library, Prescott AZ p. 78
Prescott Historical Society, Prescott AZ p. 78
Prescott Memorial Library, *see* Louisiana Tech
University, Ruston LA p. 966
Prescott Public Library, Prescott AZ p. 78
Prescott Public Library, Prescott IA p. 839
Prescott Public Library, Prescott WI p. 2631
Prescott Public Library, Prescott ON p. 2838
Prescott Valley Public Library, Prescott Valley AZ
p. 79
Presence Mercy Medical Center, Aurora IL p. 592
Presentation Center Library, Fargo ND p. 1841
Presentation College Library, Aberdeen SD p. 2209
Presho Public Library, Presho SD p. 2217
President Millard Fillmore Library, Fillmore UT
p. 2406
Presidential Archives, Odessa TX p. 2366
Presque Isle Community Library, Presque Isle WI
p. 2631
Presque Isle District Library, Rogers City MI
p. 1222
Press Sun-Bulletin Library, *see* Gannett Newspapers,
Vestal NY p. 1761
Presser Music Library, *see* West Chester University,
West Chester PA p. 2154

Preston Cordelia B Memorial Library, Orleans NE
p. 1415
Preston J T L Library, *see* Virginia Military Institute,
Lexington VA p. 2474
Preston Medical Library, *see* University of
Tennessee Graduate School of Medicine,
Knoxville TN p. 2243
Preston Public Library, Preston CT p. 364
Preston Public Library, Preston IA p. 839
Preston Public Library, Preston MN p. 1271
Preston Town-County Library of Hot Springs, Hot
Springs MT p. 1383
Preston Tye Memorial Library, Canyon Lake TX
p. 2295
Preti Flaherty Beliveau & Pachios, Portland ME
p. 997
Pretlow Mary D Anchor, *see* Norfolk Public Library,
Norfolk VA p. 2482
Pretty Prairie Public Library, Pretty Prairie KS
p. 891
Preus Library, *see* Luther College, Decorah IA
p. 807
Prevention First, Ocean NJ p. 1515
Prevention First Inc, Chicago IL p. 622
Prevention Information Center Library, Lakewood
CO p. 315
Prevention Pathways, Norfolk NE p. 1410
Prevo Library, *see* DePauw University, Greencastle
IN p. 746
Prewett Library, *see* Contra Costa County Library,
Antioch CA p. 209
Price Brothers Co Library, Dayton OH p. 1894
Price City Library, Price UT p. 2410
Price Hollis F Library, *see* LeMoyne-Owen College,
Memphis TN p. 2249
Price Leontyne Library, *see* Rust College, Holly
Springs MS p. 1302
Price-Pottenger Nutrition Foundation Library, Lemon
Grove CA p. 163
Price Waterhouse Coopers LLP, Detroit MI p. 1171
Priceville Public Library, Priceville AL p. 34
PricewaterhouseCoopers, Toronto ON p. 2857
PricewaterhouseCoopers Library, Vancouver BC
p. 2742
Prichard Public Library, Prichard AL p. 34
Prickett, Jones, Elliott, Wilmington DE p. 388
Pridham Edna Memorial Library, *see* Emmanuel
Bible College, Kitchener ON p. 2815
Priest Bill J Institute, *see* Dallas County Community
College District, Dallas TX p. 2305
Priest Lake Public Library, Priest Lake ID p. 582
Priestly Diana M Law Library, *see* University of
Victoria Libraries, Victoria BC p. 2746
Prim Library, *see* Sierra Nevada College, Incline
Village NV p. 1428
Primary Children's Medical Center Library, Salt
Lake City UT p. 2413
Jacobsen Lawrence Library, *see* University of
Wisconsin-Madison, Madison WI p. 2609
Primghar Public Library, Primghar IA p. 839
Primrose Public Library, Primrose NE p. 1417
Prince Albert Parkland Health Region Library,
Prince Albert SK p. 2921
Prince County Hospital, Summerside PE p. 2877
Prince Edward Island Association for Community
Living, Charlottetown PE p. 2875
Prince Edward Island Public Library Service, Morell
PE p. 2876
Prince George Public Library, Prince George BC
p. 2736
Prince George Regional Hospital, Prince George BC
p. 2736
Prince George's County, Upper Marlboro MD
p. 1045
Prince George's Community College, Largo MD
p. 1034
Prince George's County Memorial, Hyattsville MD
p. 1032
Prince George's Hospital Center, Cheverly MD
p. 1024
Prince John F Library, *see* Glendale Community
College, Glendale AZ p. 64
Prince Memorial Library, Cumberland ME p. 982
Prince of Peace Lutheran Church Library,
Milwaukee WI p. 2621

Pupillo Anthony A Library, *see* Lincoln College of New England, Southington CT p. 368

Purcell Public, *see* Pioneer Library System, Purcell OK p. 1970

Purcell Rossie, *see* Houston Love Memorial Library, Columbia AL p. 15

Purchase College Library, *see* State University of New York, Purchase NY p. 1724

Purchase Free Library, Purchase NY p. 1724

Purdue Library, *see* Purdue Pharma LP & Associated Companies, Stamford CT p. 369

Purdue Pharma Library, Pickering ON p. 2836

Purdue Pharma LP & Associated Companies, Stamford CT p. 369

Purdue University, Hammond IN p. 747

Purdue University Libraries, West Lafayette IN p. 786

Purdue University North Central Library, Westville IN p. 787

Purdy-Kresge Library, *see* Wayne State University Libraries, Detroit MI p. 1173

Purvis Library, *see* University of Guelph, Kemptville ON p. 2812

Purvis Malcolm Library, *see* Montgomery County Memorial Library System, Magnolia TX p. 2300

Purvis Public, *see* Lamar County Library System, Purvis MS p. 1313

Pusey Nathan Marsh Library, *see* Mellon Andrew W Foundation, New York NY p. 1685

Pushnik Family Library, *see* Harrisburg Area Community College, Lebanon PA p. 2079

Puskarich Public Library, Cadiz OH p. 1862

Putnam Correctional Institution Library, *see* Florida Department of Corrections, East Palatka FL p. 438

Putnam County District Library, Ottawa OH p. 1925

Putnam County Historical Society & Foundry School Museum Library, Cold Spring NY p. 1608

Putnam County Library, Hurricane WV p. 2562

Putnam County Library, *see* Uncle Remus Regional Library System, Eatonton GA p. 542

Putnam County Library System, Palatka FL p. 478

Putnam County Library System, Cookeville TN p. 2231

Putnam County Public Library, Greencastle IN p. 746

Putnam County Public Library, Unionville MO p. 1370

Putnam County Public Library District, Hennepin IL p. 654

Putnam District Library, Nashville MI p. 1213

Putnam Law Library, *see* Connecticut Judicial Branch Law Libraries, Putnam CT p. 344

Putnam Museum of History & Natural Science, Davenport IA p. 806

Putnam Northern Westchester BOCES, Yorktown Heights NY p. 1772

Putnam Public Library, Putnam CT p. 365

Putnam Valley Free Library, Putnam Valley NY p. 1725

Putnamville Correctional Facility, Greencastle IN p. 746

Putney Public Library, Putney VT p. 2433

Puyallup Public Library, Puyallup WA p. 2525

Pyle Ernie, *see* Albuquerque-Bernalillo County Library System, Albuquerque NM p. 1548

Quad City Area Biomedical Consortium (N), West Burlington IA p. 2943

Quad Graphics Library, *see* Southern Crescent Technical College Library - Flint Campus, Thomaston GA p. 553

Quail Botanical Gardens Foundation Inc Library, Encinitas CA p. 146

Qualla Boundary Public Library, Cherokee NC p. 1784

Quarles & Brady, Milwaukee WI p. 2621

Quarryville Library, Quarryville PA p. 2132

Quartzsite Public Library, Quartzsite AZ p. 79

Quatrefoil Library, Saint Paul MN p. 1280

Quebec Commission Des Services Juridiques Library, Montreal QC p. 2900

Quebec Conseil de la Famille et de l'Enfance, Quebec QC p. 2906

Quebec Ministere De L'Agriculture Des Pecheries Et De L'Alimentation Bibliotheque, Quebec QC p. 2906

Quebec Ministere des Transports, Quebec QC p. 2906

Quebec Office quebecois de la Langue Francaise Bibliotheque, Montreal QC p. 2900

Quechee Public Library Association, Quechee VT p. 2433

Queen Anne's County Free Library, Centreville MD p. 1023

Queen Elizabeth Hospital, Charlottetown PE p. 2875

Queen Elizabeth II Hospital, Grande Prairie AB p. 2706

Queen Elizabeth II Library, *see* Memorial University of Newfoundland, St. John's NL p. 2773

Queen Lane Library, *see* Drexel University Libraries, Philadelphia PA p. 2105

Queen Memorial, *see* Free Library of Philadelphia, Philadelphia PA p. 2109

Queen of Peace Hospital Library, Mitchell SD p. 2215

Queen of the Holy Rosary College Library, Fremont CA p. 150

Queens Borough Public Library, Jamaica NY p. 1643

Queens College, Flushing NY p. 1623

Queen's College Library, St. John's NL p. 2773

Queens College of the City University of New York, Flushing NY p. 2970

Queens County Supreme Court Library, Jamaica NY p. 1646

Queens Library, *see* Queens Borough Public Library, Jamaica NY p. 1643

Queen's University, Kingston ON p. 2814

Queens University of Charlotte, Charlotte NC p. 1784

Queens Village Community Library, *see* Queens Borough Public Library, Queens Village NY p. 1645

Queensboro Hill Community Library, *see* Queens Borough Public Library, Flushing NY p. 1645

Queensborough Community College, Bayside NY p. 1579

Quemado Public Library, Quemado TX p. 2373

Quesnel Library, Quesnel BC p. 2736

Quest Diagnostics, Inc, San Juan Capistrano CA p. 252

Quetico Park, Atikokan ON p. 2793

Quigley Library, *see* Colorado Mountain College, Glenwood Springs CO p. 309

Quillen James H College of Medicine Library, *see* East Tennessee State University, Johnson City TN p. 2239

Quillen James H VA Medical Center, Mountain Home TN p. 2254

Quimby Dorothy W Library, *see* Unity College, Unity ME p. 1004

Quimby Memorial Library, *see* Southwestern College, Santa Fe NM p. 1564

Quimby Public Library, Quimby IA p. 839

Quince Orchard Library, *see* Montgomery County Public Libraries, Gaithersburg MD p. 1039

Quincy College, Quincy MA p. 1119

Quincy Community, *see* North Central Regional Library, Quincy WA p. 2549

Quincy Historical Society Library, Quincy MA p. 1120

Quincy Medical Center Library, Quincy MA p. 1120

Quincy Public Library, Quincy IL p. 693

Quincy University, Quincy IL p. 693

Quinebaug Valley Community College Library, Danielson CT p. 335

Quinn Anthony Library, *see* County of Los Angeles Public Library, Los Angeles CA p. 143

Quinn Library, *see* Fordham University Library at Lincoln Center, New York NY p. 1678

Quinn Library, *see* Ohio University Chillicothe Campus, Chillicothe OH p. 1867

Quinney S J Law Library, *see* University of Utah, Salt Lake City UT p. 2415

Quinnipiac University, Hamden CT p. 343

Quinsigamond Community College, Worcester MA p. 1144

Quinte West Public Library, Trenton ON p. 2868

Quirk C J Health Sciences Library, *see* Watertown Memorial Hospital, Watertown WI p. 2644

Quirk Elsie Public Library of Englewood, Englewood FL p. 439

Quisenberry Library, *see* Jackson/Hinds Library System, Clinton MS p. 1303

Quitman County Library, *see* Kinchafoonee Regional Library System, Georgetown GA p. 528

Quitman Public Library, Quitman TX p. 2373

Quitman Public Library, *see* East Mississippi Regional Library System, Quitman MS p. 1313

Quoddy Tides Foundation Marine Library, Eastport ME p. 984

Quogue Library, Quogue NY p. 1725

R B C Dominions Securities, Toronto ON p. 2857

Rabbi A N Schwartz Library, *see* Telshe Yeshiva College, Wickliffe OH p. 1947

Rabbi Dudley Weinberg Library, *see* Congregation Emanu-El B'Ne Jeshurun Library, Milwaukee WI p. 2617

Rabbi Edward E Klein Memorial Library, *see* Wise Stephen Free Synagogue, New York NY p. 1703

Rabbi Mordecai S Halpern Memorial Library, *see* Congregation Beth Shalom, Oak Park MI p. 1215

Rabbinical College of America, Morristown NJ p. 1505

Raborn Robert E Medical Library, *see* Bethesda Memorial Hospital, Boynton Beach FL p. 429

Rabun County Public Library, Clayton GA p. 525

Racadio Sam J Library, *see* San Bernardino County Library, Highland CA p. 229

Rachal Ed Memorial Library, Falfurrias TX p. 2318

Racine Art Museum Library, Racine WI p. 2632

Racine Correctional Institution Library, Sturtevant WI p. 2641

Racine County Law Library, Racine WI p. 2632

Racine Heritage Museum, Racine WI p. 2632

Racine Public Library, Racine WI p. 2632

Rackemann, Sawyer & Brewster Library, Boston MA p. 1066

Racquet & Tennis Club Library, New York NY p. 1698

Radcliff Library, *see* Schoolcraft College, Garden City MI p. 1204

Radcliffe Public Library, Radcliffe IA p. 839

Raddall Thomas H Library, *see* South Shore Regional Libraries, Liverpool NS p. 2783

Radford Public Library, Radford VA p. 2487

Radford University, Radford VA p. 2487

Radgowski Correctional Institution Library, Uncasville CT p. 373

Radiation Safety Institute of Canada, Toronto ON p. 2857

Radiological Society of North America, Oak Brook IL p. 683

Radium Hot Springs Public Library, Radium Hot Springs BC p. 2736

Radnor Memorial Library, Wayne PA p. 2152

Radway & District Municipal Library, Radway AB p. 2714

Rady Children's Hospital - San Diego, San Diego CA p. 232

Radzinowicz Criminology Reading Room, *see* Florida State University Libraries, Tallahassee FL p. 495

Raether Howard C Library, Brookfield WI p. 2583

Ragsdale Maude P Public Library, *see* West Georgia Regional Library, Hiram GA p. 524

Rahway Public Library, Rahway NJ p. 1525

Railroad & Heritage Museum Library, Temple TX p. 2390

Railway Mail Service Library, Inc, Boyce VA p. 2452

Rainbow City Public Library, Rainbow City AL p. 34

Rainbow Lake Municipal Library, Rainbow Lake AB p. 2714

Rainbow Library, *see* Las Vegas-Clark County Library District, Las Vegas NV p. 1429

Rainbow Resource Centre Library, Winnipeg MB p. 2757

Rainelle Municipal Public Library, Rainelle WV p. 2570

Raines David, *see* Shreve Memorial Library, Shreveport LA p. 970

Rainier City Library, Rainier OR p. 2016

Rains County Public Library, Emory TX p. 2318

Rains William M Law Library, *see* Loyola Law School, Los Angeles CA p. 175

Rainsville Public Library, Rainsville AL p. 34

Rainwater Earle A Memorial Library, Childersburg AL p. 12

Rainy River Community College Library, International Falls MN p. 1254

Rainy River Public Library, Rainy River ON p. 2838

Rake Public Library, Rake IA p. 840

Rakow Juilette K & Leonard S Research Library, *see* Corning Museum of Glass, Corning NY p. 1611

RALC (N), *see* Richmond Academic Library Consortium, Richmond VA p. 2957

Raleigh County Public Library, Beckley WV p. 2554

Raleigh Public Library, Raleigh MS p. 1313

Ralls County Library, Center MO p. 1322

Ralpho Township Public Library, Elysburg PA p. 2054

Ralston Edna Public Library, Larimore ND p. 1845

Ramaker Library & Learning Resource Center, *see* Northwestern College, Orange City IA p. 836

Ramapo Catskill Library System, Middletown NY p. 1660

Ramapo College of New Jersey, Mahwah NJ p. 1498

Ramara Township Public Library, Orillia ON p. 2826

Ramey & Flock, PC, Tyler TX p. 2393

Ramos Angel Fundacion Library, *see* Ponce School of Medicine Library, Ponce PR p. 2674

Rampart Public Library District, Woodland Park CO p. 326

Ramsay John W Research Library, *see* New England Air Museum, Windsor Locks CT p. 379

Ramsayer Research Library, *see* McKinley William Presidential Library & Museum, Canton OH p. 1864

Ramsdell Public Library, Housatonic MA p. 1096

Ramsey County Law Library, Saint Paul MN p. 1280

Ramsey County Library, Shoreview MN p. 1284

Ramsey D Hiden Library, *see* University of North Carolina at Asheville, Asheville NC p. 1775

Ramsey Free Public Library, Ramsey NJ p. 1525

Ramsey Public Library, Ramsey IL p. 693

Ramsley Alvin O Technical Library, *see* United States Army, Natick MA p. 1108

Rancho Cordova Community Library, *see* Sacramento Public Library, Sacramento CA p. 225

Rancho Cucamonga Public Library, Rancho Cucamonga CA p. 213

Rancho Los Amigos Medical Center, Downey CA p. 144

Rancho Mirage Public Library, Rancho Mirage CA p. 213

Rancho Santa Ana Botanic Garden Library, Claremont CA p. 135

Rand Anne Research Library, *see* International Longshore & Warehouse Union, San Francisco CA p. 243

RAND Corp, Arlington VA p. 2450

RAND Corporation Library, Santa Monica CA p. 266

RAND-Washington Library, *see* RAND Corp, Arlington VA p. 2450

Rand William H & Lucy F Memorial Library, North Troy VT p. 2431

Randal Helen Library, *see* College of Registered Nurses of British Columbia Library, Vancouver BC p. 2740

Randall Library, Stow MA p. 1129

Randall Public Library, Randall KS p. 891

Randall William Madison Library, Wilmington NC p. 1831

Randolph A Philip Memorial Library, *see* Borough of Manhattan Community College Library, New York NY p. 1671

Randolph Circuit Court, Winchester IN p. 788

Randolph College, Lynchburg VA p. 2476

Randolph Community College, Asheboro NC p. 1773

Randolph County Library, Pocahontas AR p. 113

Randolph County Library, *see* Kinchafoonee Regional Library System, Cuthbert GA p. 528

Randolph County Public Library, Asheboro NC p. 1774

Randolph-Decker Library, *see* Clyde Public Library, Clyde KS p. 861

Randolph Free Library, Randolph NY p. 1726

Randolph-Macon College, Ashland VA p. 2450

Randolph Public Library, Randolph IA p. 840

Randolph Public Library, Randolph NH p. 1463

Randolph Township Free Public Library, Randolph NJ p. 1525

Raney Olivia Local History Library, *see* Wake County Public Library System, Raleigh NC p. 1818

Rangeley Public Library, Rangeley ME p. 998

Rangely Regional Library, Rangely CO p. 321

Ranger City Library, Ranger TX p. 2373

Ranger College, Ranger TX p. 2373

Rankin Jeannette Library Program, *see* United States Institute of Peace, Washington DC p. 420

Rankin Public Library, Rankin TX p. 2373

Rankin W A Memorial Library, Neodesha KS p. 884

Ransom Charles A District Library, Plainwell MI p. 1218

Ransom Harry Center, *see* University of Texas Libraries, Austin TX p. 2284

Ransom Memorial Public Library, Altona IL p. 588

Ransom Public Library, Ransom KS p. 891

Ransom Reverdy C Memorial Library, *see* Payne Theological Seminary, Wilberforce OH p. 1948

Ransomville Free Library, Ransomville NY p. 1726

Rantoul Public Library, Rantoul IL p. 693

Rapaport Professional Library, *see* Osawatomie State Hospital, Osawatomie KS p. 886

Rapid City Public Library, Rapid City SD p. 2217

Rapid City Regional Hospital, Rapid City SD p. 2217

Rapid City Regional Library, Rapid City MB p. 2750

Rapides Parish Library, Alexandria LA p. 940

Rapides Regional Medical Center, Alexandria LA p. 940

Rappahannock Community College, Warsaw VA p. 2501

Rappahannock Community College Library, Glenns VA p. 2467

Rappahannock County Library, Washington VA p. 2501

Raquette Lake Free Library, Raquette Lake NY p. 1726

Raritan Bay Medical Center, Perth Amboy NJ p. 1519

Raritan Public Library, Raritan NJ p. 1525

Raritan Valley Community College, Somerville NJ p. 1530

Rasche Memorial Library, *see* Milwaukee Area Technical College, Milwaukee WI p. 2619

Rasey Memorial, *see* Monroe County Library System, Luna Pier MI p. 1210

Rasmuson Elmer E Library, *see* University of Alaska Fairbanks, Fairbanks AK p. 48

Rasmussen College, Rockford IL p. 697

Rathbun Bryce C, *see* Kern County Library, Bakersfield CA p. 124

Rathbun Dr J C Memorial Library, *see* Children's Hospital of Western Ontario, London ON p. 2817

Rathbun Free Memorial Library, East Haddam CT p. 337

Rauchholz Memorial Library, Hemlock MI p. 1189

Raugust Library, *see* Jamestown College, Jamestown ND p. 1844

Rauner Special Collections Library, *see* Dartmouth College Library, Hanover NH p. 1450

Raushenbush Esther Library, *see* Sarah Lawrence College, Bronxville NY p. 1588

Ravalli County Museum, Hamilton MT p. 1381

Ravenna Public Library, Ravenna NE p. 1417

Ravenna Public Library, *see* Reed Memorial Library, Ravenna OH p. 1931

Rawle & Henderson, Philadelphia PA p. 2115

Rawlings Robert Hoag Public Library, *see* Pueblo City-County Library District, Pueblo CO p. 320

Rawlins Municipal Library, Pierre SD p. 2216

Rawls Walter Cecil Library, *see* Blackwater Regional Library, Courtland VA p. 2458

Rawlyk George A Library, *see* Atlantic Baptist University, Moncton NB p. 2765

Rawson Deborah Memorial Library, Jericho VT p. 2426

Rawson Memorial District Library, Cass City MI p. 1161

Ray Brook Federal Correctional Institution Library, Ray Brook NY p. 1726

Ray County Historical Society & Museum Library, Richmond MO p. 1350

Ray County Library, Richmond MO p. 1350

Ray Issac Medical Library, *see* Butler Hospital, Providence RI p. 2172

Ray Lewis A, *see* Cobb County Public Library System, Smyrna GA p. 543

Ray Quinney & Nebeker PC, Salt Lake City UT p. 2413

Ray Township Library, Ray MI p. 1220

Rayburn Correctional Center Library, Angie LA p. 941

Rayburn Helen H Public, *see* Lewis County Public Library, Vanceburg KY p. 936

Rayburn Sam Library & Museum, Bonham TX p. 2290

Raymond Chabot Grant Thornton Library, Montreal QC p. 2900

Raymond Library, *see* Jackson/Hinds Library System, Raymond MS p. 1303

Raymond Library, *see* Yakima Valley Community College, Yakima WA p. 2550

Raymond Memorial Library, *see* East Hartford Public Library, East Hartford CT p. 337

Raymond Public Library, Raymond MN p. 1271

Raymond Public Library, Raymond AB p. 2714

Raymond Village Library, Raymond ME p. 999

Rayner Thelma Memorial Library, *see* Bolivar County Library System, Merigold MS p. 1296

Raynham Public Library, Raynham MA p. 1120

Raynor Memorial Libraries, *see* Marquette University Libraries, Milwaukee WI p. 2618

Rayovac, Madison WI p. 2607

Raytheon Co, Portsmouth RI p. 2171

Raytheon Co, Dallas TX p. 2309

Raytheon Co, Marlborough MA p. 1103

Raytheon Co, Sudbury MA p. 1130

Raytheon, Inc, Dallas TX p. 2309

Raytheon Technical Library, Tucson AZ p. 87

RCMP Centennial Library, Fort Macleod AB p. 2704

RCS Community Library, Ravena NY p. 1726

Read Louise Adelia Memorial Library, Hancock NY p. 1634

Read Philip Memorial Library, Plainfield NH p. 1462

Read Victoria, *see* Martins Ferry Public Library, Flushing OH p. 1915

Reade International Corp, East Providence RI p. 2166

Reader's Digest Association Inc Library, New York NY p. 1698

Reader's Digest Magazines Ltd, Montreal QC p. 2901

Readfield Community Library, Readfield ME p. 999

Reading Area Community College, Reading PA p. 2133

Reading Community Library, Reading MI p. 1220

Reading Public Library, Reading MA p. 1120

Reading Public Library, Reading PA p. 2133

Reading Public Library, Reading VT p. 2433

Reading Public Museum Library, Reading PA p. 2134

Reading Room Association of Gouverneur, Gouverneur NY p. 1629

Readington Township Library, Whitehouse Station NJ p. 1544

Readlyn Community Library, Readlyn IA p. 840

Readsboro Community Library, Readsboro VT p. 2433

Readstown Public Library, Readstown WI p. 2633

Reagan County Library, Big Lake TX p. 2289

Reagan L B Health Sciences Library, *see* Virtua Memorial Hospital Of Burlington County, Mount Holly NJ p. 1506

Reagan Ronald Presidential Library & Museum, *see* National Archives & Records Administration, Simi Valley CA p. 269

Real County Public Library, Leakey TX p. 2354

Real Estate Board of New York, New York NY p. 1698

Real Estate Commission Library, Boise ID p. 571

Ream Louise Library, *see* Heisey Collectors of America, Inc, Newark OH p. 1922

Reaney Margaret Memorial Library, Saint Johnsville NY p. 1737

Reardan Memorial Library, Reardan WA p. 2525

Reber Memorial Library, Raymondville TX p. 2373

Rebok Memorial Library, *see* General Conference of Seventh-Day Adventists, Silver Spring MD p. 1041

Reception & Medical Center Library (Main Unit), *see* Florida Department of Corrections, Lake Butler FL p. 457

Reconstructionist Rabbinical College Library, Wyncote PA p. 2158

Record Library, Stockton CA p. 272

Recording for the Blind & Dyslexic, Princeton NJ p. 1524

Rector Public Library, Rector AR p. 113

Red Bank Public Library, Red Bank NJ p. 1525

Red Bud Public Library, Red Bud IL p. 694

Red Clay State Historic Area Library, Cleveland TN p. 2230

Red Creek Free Library, Red Creek NY p. 1726

Red Deer & District Archives, Red Deer AB p. 2714

Red Deer College Library, Red Deer AB p. 2714

Red Deer Public Library, Red Deer AB p. 2714

Red Deer Regional Hospital Centre, *see* Alberta Health Services, Red Deer AB p. 2714

Red Feather Lakes Community Library, Red Feather Lakes CO p. 321

Red Hook Public Library, Red Hook NY p. 1726

Red Jacket Community Library, Shortsville NY p. 1743

Red Lake Falls Public Library, *see* Northwest Regional Library, Red Lake Falls MN p. 1286

Red Lodge Carnegie Library, Red Lodge MT p. 1387

Red Mill Museum Library, Clinton NJ p. 1479

Red Oak Public Library, Red Oak IA p. 840

Red Oak Public Library, Red Oak TX p. 2373

Red River College, Winnipeg MB p. 2978

Red River College Library, Winnipeg MB p. 2757

Red River County Public Library, Clarksville TX p. 2297

Red River North Regional Library, Selkirk MB p. 2751

Red River Parish Library, Coushatta LA p. 947

Red River Public Library, Red River NM p. 1560

Red River Regional Library, Clarksville TN p. 2229

Red Rock Public Library Board, Red Rock ON p. 2838

Red Rocks Community College, Lakewood CO p. 315

Red Waller Community Library, Malakoff TX p. 2359

Red Wing Public Library, Red Wing MN p. 1271

Redbank Valley Public Library, New Bethlehem PA p. 2095

Redcliff Public Library, Redcliff AB p. 2715

Reddick Library, Ottawa IL p. 686

Reddick Mary Lou Public Library, Lake Worth TX p. 2352

Reddick Public Library, *see* Marion County Public Library System, Reddick FL p. 474

Reddin A R Memorial Library, *see* Southeastern Baptist College, Laurel MS p. 1307

Redeemer College Library, Ancaster ON p. 2792

Redfield Carnegie Library, Redfield SD p. 2217

Redfield Library, *see* South Dakota Developmental Center, Redfield SD p. 2218

Redfield Nell J, *see* Truckee Meadows Community College, Reno NV p. 1433

Redfield Public Library, Redfield IA p. 840

Redfield Public Library, *see* Pine Bluff & Jefferson County Library System, Redfield AR p. 112

Redford Township District Library, Redford MI p. 1220

Redgranite Public Library, Redgranite WI p. 2633

Redington-Fairview General Hospital, Skowhegan ME p. 1000

Redish Jules Memorial Medical Library, *see* South Nassau Communities Hospital, Oceanside NY p. 1709

Redlands Community College, El Reno OK p. 1963

Redmond Regional Library, *see* King County Library System, Redmond WA p. 2517

Redondo Beach Public Library, Redondo Beach CA p. 215

Redstone Scientific Information Center, *see* United States Army, Redstone Arsenal AL p. 34

Redwater Public Library, Redwater AB p. 2715

Redwood City Public Library, Redwood City CA p. 215

Redwood Empire Association, San Francisco CA p. 244

Redwood Falls Public Library, Redwood Falls MN p. 1272

Redwood Library & Athenaeum, Newport RI p. 2169

Reed City Public Library, Reed City MI p. 1221

Reed College, Portland OR p. 2014

Reed Daniel A Library, *see* State University of New York at Fredonia, Fredonia NY p. 1624

Reed Free Library, Surry NH p. 1466

Reed Ira C Public Library, Lafayette IL p. 663

Reed John F Library, *see* Fort Lewis College Library, Durango CO p. 305

Reed Martha Stecher Art Reference Library, *see* Akron Art Museum, Akron OH p. 1851

Reed Memorial Library, Carmel NY p. 1603

Reed Memorial Library, Ravenna OH p. 1931

Reed Rufus M Public, *see* Martin County Public Library, Lovely KY p. 918

Reed Smith LLP, Oakland CA p. 198

Reed Smith LLP, Washington DC p. 413

Reed Smith LLP, Philadelphia PA p. 2115

Reed Smith LLP, Pittsburgh PA p. 2128

Reed William G Library, *see* Timberland Regional Library, Shelton WA p. 2544

Reedley College Library, Reedley CA p. 216

Reedsburg Public Library, Reedsburg WI p. 2633

Rees Mina Library, *see* City University of New York, New York NY p. 1673

Reese Library, *see* Augusta State University, Augusta GA p. 518

Reese Resource Center Library, *see* Central Christian College of the Bible Library, Moberly MO p. 1345

Reese Unity District Library, Reese MI p. 1221

Reeseville Public Library, Reeseville WI p. 2633

Reeve Christopher & Dana Foundation, Short Hills NJ p. 1529

Reeve Christopher & Dana Paralysis Resource Center Foundation Library, *see* Reeve Christopher & Dana Foundation, Short Hills NJ p. 1529

Reeves County Library, Pecos TX p. 2369

Reeves David L Medical Library, *see* Cottage Health System, Santa Barbara CA p. 260

Reeves Health Sciences Library, *see* Bridgeport Hospital, Bridgeport CT p. 331

Reeves Library, *see* Moravian College & Moravian Theological Seminary, Bethlehem PA p. 2034

Reeves Memorial Library, *see* Seton Hill University, Greensburg PA p. 2062

Reeves Memorial Library, *see* Westminster College, Fulton MO p. 1328

Reeves Suzanne Library, *see* Lee County Library, Sanford NC p. 1823

Wilson Library, *see* University of Minnesota Libraries-Twin Cities, Minneapolis MN p. 1262

Reform Congregation Keneseth Israel, Elkins Park PA p. 2054

Reform Public Library, Reform AL p. 35

Reformed Episcopal Seminary, Blue Bell PA p. 2036

Reformed Presbyterian Theological Seminary Library, Pittsburgh PA p. 2128

Reformed Theological Seminary Library, Oviedo FL p. 478

Reformed Theological Seminary Library, Jackson MS p. 1305

Regenstein Joseph Library, *see* University of Chicago Library, Chicago IL p. 626

Regent College, Vancouver BC p. 2742

Regent University, Virginia Beach VA p. 2499

Regent University Library, Virginia Beach VA p. 2499

Regents Center Library, *see* University of Kansas Libraries, Overland Park KS p. 878

Regie de L'Assurance-Maladie du Quebec, Sillery QC p. 2913

Regina Leader-Post Ltd Library, Regina SK p. 2923

Regina Library, *see* Rivier College, Nashua NH p. 1459

Regina Public Library, Regina SK p. 2923

Regina Qu'Appelle Health Region, Regina SK p. 2923

Regina-Qu'Appelle Health Region, Regina SK p. 2923

Region of Waterloo Library, Baden ON p. 2793

Regional Appalachian Center - Media Library, *see* Children's Museum of Oak Ridge, Oak Ridge TN p. 2262

Regional Foundation Library, Austin TX p. 2281

Regional Medical Center, Fort Smith AR p. 101

Regional Medical Center, Madisonville KY p. 928

Regional Medical Center of Orangeburg & Calhoun Counties, Orangeburg SC p. 2201

Regional Medical Center of San Jose, San Jose CA p. 250

Regional Medical Library, Jonesboro AR p. 105

Regional Mental Health Care London, London ON p. 2818

Regional Mental Health Care Saint Thomas, St. Thomas ON p. 2844

Regional Treatment Centre/Pacific Institution Library, Abbotsford BC p. 2724

Regional West Medical Center Library, Scottsbluff NE p. 1418

Regions Hospital, Saint Paul MN p. 1281

Regis College Library, Weston MA p. 1139

Regis College Library, Toronto ON p. 2857

Regis University, Denver CO p. 303

Rehabilitation & Research Library, *see* TIRR Memorial Hermann, Houston TX p. 2343

Rehabilitation Institute of Chicago, Chicago IL p. 622

Rehabilitation Institute of Michigan, Detroit MI p. 1171

Rehabilitation International, New York NY p. 1698

Rehoboth Beach Public Library, Rehoboth Beach DE p. 386

Reid Charles E, *see* Paramus Public Library, Paramus NJ p. 1517

Reid Memorial, *see* Passaic Public Library, Passaic NJ p. 1518

Reid Memorial Library, *see* Lewis & Clark Community College, Godfrey IL p. 651

Reilly William F Library, *see* Gibbs College of Boston, Boston MA p. 1061

Reily Mickey Public Library, Corrigan TX p. 2302

Reinbeck Public Library, Reinbeck IA p. 840

Reinert-Alumni Memorial Library, *see* Creighton University, Omaha NE p. 1412

Reinhardt University, Waleska GA p. 556

Reinhart Boerner Van Deuren SC, Milwaukee WI p. 2621

Reinsch Emerson G Library, *see* Marymount University, Arlington VA p. 2449

Reinstein Memorial, *see* Cheektowaga Public Library, Cheektowaga NY p. 1606

Reiss-Davis Child Study Center, Los Angeles CA p. 177

Rembrandt Public Library, Rembrandt IA p. 840

Remington-Carpenter Township Public Library, Remington IN p. 774

Remington College, Tampa FL p. 497

Remington College Library, Lafayette LA p. 953

Remsen Public Library, Remsen IA p. 840

Rend Lake College, Ina IL p. 658

Rendall T S Library, *see* Prairie Bible Institute, Three Hills AB p. 2719

Renfrew County Law Association, Pembroke ON p. 2835

RichLyn Library, *see* Huntington College, Huntington IN p. 748

Richmond Academic Library Consortium (N), Richmond VA p. 2957

Richmond Art Museum Library, Richmond IN p. 775

Richmond Beach Library, *see* King County Library System, Shoreline WA p. 2517

Richmond Community College Library, Hamlet NC p. 1800

Richmond County Public Library, Warsaw VA p. 2501

Richmond Ed & Hazel Public Library, Aransas Pass TX p. 2276

Richmond Free Library, Richmond VT p. 2434

Richmond Free Public Library, Richmond MA p. 1120

Richmond Green Library, *see* Richmond Hill Public Library, Richmond Hill ON p. 2839

Richmond Heights Memorial Library, Richmond Heights MO p. 1350

Richmond Hill Community Library, *see* Queens Borough Public Library, Richmond Hill NY p. 1645

Richmond Hill Public Library, Richmond Hill GA p. 548

Richmond Hill Public Library, Richmond Hill ON p. 2839

Richmond Library, *see* Great River Regional Library, Richmond MN p. 1275

Richmond Memorial Library, Marlborough CT p. 350

Richmond Memorial Library, Batavia NY p. 1578

Richmond Museum of History, Richmond CA p. 216

Richmond National Battlefield Park Headquarters Library, *see* National Park Service, Richmond VA p. 2489

Richmond Newspapers, Inc Library, Richmond VA p. 2489

Richmond Public Library, Richmond CA p. 216

Richmond Public Library, Richmond KS p. 891

Richmond Public Library, Richmond NH p. 1463

Richmond Public Library, Richmond UT p. 2411

Richmond Public Library, Richmond VA p. 2489

Richmond Public Library, Richmond BC p. 2736

Richmond/Senator Milton Marks, *see* San Francisco Public Library, San Francisco CA p. 246

Richmond State Hospital, Richmond IN p. 775

Richmond Township Library, Palmer MI p. 1216

Richmond University Medical Center, Staten Island NY p. 1748

Richmont Graduate University, Chattanooga TN p. 2228

Richter Otto G Library, *see* University of Miami Libraries, Coral Gables FL p. 434

Richton Park Public Library District, Richton Park IL p. 694

Richton Public, *see* Pine Forest Regional Library, Richton MS p. 1314

Richvale Library, *see* Richmond Hill Public Library, Richmond Hill ON p. 2839

Richville Free Library, Richville NY p. 1727

Richville Library, Standish ME p. 1002

Richwood North Union Public Library, Richwood OH p. 1931

Richwood Public Library, Richwood WV p. 2570

Ricker Alvan Bolster Memorial Library, Poland ME p. 996

Rickman Claude R Library, *see* Southern Wesleyan University, Central SC p. 2183

Ricke Memorial Library (Yazoo Library Association), Yazoo City MS p. 1318

Rico Public, *see* Dolores County Public Library, Rico CO p. 304

Ridderheim Health Science Library, *see* Parkview Hospital, Fort Wayne IN p. 742

Rideau Lakes Public Library, Elgin ON p. 2803

Rider University, Lawrenceville NJ p. 1494

Ridge Career Center Library, Winter Haven FL p. 505

Ridge Library, *see* Mercyhurst College, North East PA p. 2056

Ridgefield Community Library, *see* Fort Vancouver Regional Library District, Ridgefield WA p. 2546

Ridgefield Library Association Inc, Ridgefield CT p. 365

Ridgefield Park Free Public Library, Ridgefield Park NJ p. 1526

Ridgefield Public Library, Ridgefield NJ p. 1526

Ridgeland Public Library, *see* Madison County Library System, Ridgeland MS p. 1295

Ridgely Margaret Memorial Library, *see* Christ Church Cathedral, Indianapolis IN p. 750

Ridgely Public Library, Ridgely TN p. 2264

Ridgemont Public Library, Mount Victory OH p. 1919

Ridgeville Public Library, Ridgeville IN p. 775

Ridgewater College Library, Hutchinson MN p. 1254

Ridgewater College Library, Willmar MN p. 1289

Ridgewood Community Library, *see* Queens Borough Public Library, Ridgewood NY p. 1645

Ridgewood Public Library, Ridgewood NJ p. 1526

Ridgway Library District, Ridgway CO p. 321

Ridgway Memorial Library, *see* Bullitt County Public Library, Shepherdsville KY p. 935

Ridgway Public Library, Ridgway PA p. 2134

Ridley John B Research Library, *see* Quetico Park, Atikokan ON p. 2793

Ridley Park Public Library, Ridley Park PA p. 2134

Ridley Township Public Library, Folsom PA p. 2057

Riecker Memorial Library, *see* Saint Joseph Mercy Hospital, Ann Arbor MI p. 1151

Riegelsville Public Library, Riegelsville PA p. 2134

Rieger Memorial Library, Haskell OK p. 1965

Riel Louis, *see* Winnipeg Public Library, Winnipeg MB p. 2760

Riemenschneider Bach Institute, *see* Baldwin Wallace University, Berea OH p. 1859

Rienzi Public Library, *see* Northeast Regional Library, Rienzi MS p. 1297

Riffe Vernal G, *see* Portsmouth Public Library, New Boston OH p. 1931

Rifkind Robert Gore Center, *see* Los Angeles County Museum of Art, Los Angeles CA p. 172

Rifle Correctional Center, *see* Colorado Department of Corrections, Rifle CO p. 321

Rigby Public Library, Rigby ID p. 582

Riggs Austen Center, Inc, Stockbridge MA p. 1129

Riggs Austen Fox Library, *see* Riggs Austen Center, Inc, Stockbridge MA p. 1129

Right to Life League of Southern California Library, Pasadena CA p. 207

Right to Life of Michigan, Grand Rapids MI p. 1185

Right to Life of Michigan, Lansing MI p. 1202

Right to Life of Michigan, Saint Clair Shores MI p. 1224

Rike Charles J Memorial Library, Farmersville TX p. 2319

Riker, Danzig, Scherer, Hyland & Perretti, Morristown NJ p. 1505

Cream Riletta L, *see* Camden County Library System, Camden NJ p. 1538

Riley City Library, Riley KS p. 892

Riley County Historical Museum, Manhattan KS p. 882

Riley County Kansas Genealogical Society Library, Manhattan KS p. 882

Riley-Hickingbotham Library, *see* Ouachita Baptist University, Arkadelphia AR p. 93

Riley John E Library, *see* Northwest Nazarene University, Nampa ID p. 580

Riley Louise, *see* Calgary Public Library, Calgary AB p. 2690

Riley Park Community, *see* Vancouver Public Library, Vancouver BC p. 2744

Rim Community Library, Heber AZ p. 65

Rimbey Municipal Library, Rimbey AB p. 2715

Rimrock Foundation Library, Billings MT p. 1374

Rincker Memorial Library, *see* Concordia University Wisconsin, Mequon WI p. 2615

Ring Elizabeth L Neighborhood Library, *see* Houston Public Library, Houston TX p. 2340

Ringer Larry J Library, *see* Bryan College Station Public Library System, College Station TX p. 2292

Ringling College of Art & Design, Sarasota FL p. 490

Ringling John & Mable Museum of Art Library, Sarasota FL p. 490

Ringsmuth Al Library, *see* Great River Regional Library, Waite Park MN p. 1275

Ringsted Public Library, Ringsted IA p. 840

Ringtown Area Library, Ringtown PA p. 2135

Ringwood Public Library, Ringwood NJ p. 1526

Rinker Harry & Diane Law Library, *see* Chapman University School of Law, Orange CA p. 200

Rinn Vincent G Law Library, *see* DePaul University Libraries, Chicago IL p. 612

Rio Abajo Community Library, La Joya NM p. 1557

Rio Community Library, Rio WI p. 2634

Rio Grande Bible Institute & Language School, Edinburg TX p. 2315

Rio Grande City Public Library, Rio Grande City TX p. 2375

Rio Hondo Community College Library, Whittier CA p. 283

Rio Hondo Public Library, Rio Hondo TX p. 2376

Rio Linda Neighborhood Library, *see* Sacramento Public Library, Rio Linda CA p. 225

Rio Rancho Public Library, Rio Rancho NM p. 1560

Rio Salado College, Tempe AZ p. 84

Rio Tinto Iron & Titanium Inc, Sorel-Tracy QC p. 2913

Rio Vista Library, *see* Solano County Library, Rio Vista CA p. 148

Ripberger Public, *see* Southside Regional Library, Kenbridge VA p. 2452

Ripley Free Library, Ripley NY p. 1727

Ripley Public Library, *see* Northeast Regional Library, Ripley MS p. 1297

Ripon College, Ripon WI p. 2634

Ripon Public Library, Ripon WI p. 2634

Rippey Loyd & Dorothy Library, *see* University of Oregon, Charleston OR p. 1993

Rippey Public Library, Rippey IA p. 840

Ririe City Library, Ririe ID p. 583

Rising City Community Library, Rising City NE p. 1418

Rison-Beecher Vera B Library, *see* Genesee District Library, Flint MI p. 1180

Ritchie County Public Library, Harrisville WV p. 2560

Ritchie Gladys Johnson Library, Jacksboro TX p. 2347

Rittenberg Law Library, *see* Saint John's University Library, Queens NY p. 1725

Rittenhouse Moses F, *see* Lincoln Public Library, Vineland ON p. 2794

Ritter Library, *see* Baldwin Wallace University, Berea OH p. 1859

Ritter Public Library, Vermilion OH p. 1943

Rittner Augusta Floral Library, *see* Rittners School of Floral Design Library, Boston MA p. 1066

Rittners School of Floral Design Library, Boston MA p. 1066

Ritz Francis U & Mary F Library, *see* Dutchess Community College Library, Poughkeepsie NY p. 1722

Ritz Maurice Resource Center, *see* Planned Parenthood of Wisconsin, Inc, Milwaukee WI p. 2621

Ritzville Library District No 2, Ritzville WA p. 2526

River Christian Reformed Church Library, Redlands CA p. 214

River Edge Free Public Library, River Edge NJ p. 1526

River Falls Public Library, River Falls WI p. 2634

River Forest Public Library, River Forest IL p. 694

River Grove Public Library District, River Grove IL p. 694

River Hebert Library, *see* Cumberland Public Libraries, River Hebert NS p. 2777

River Oaks Public Library, River Oaks TX p. 2376

River Parishes Community College Library, Sorrento LA p. 970

River Rapids District Library, Chesaning MI p. 1163

River Region Medical Center Library, Vicksburg MS p. 1317

River Road Library, *see* Bridgewater Town Library, Plymouth NH p. 1462

River Vale Free Public Library, River Vale NJ p. 1526

River Valley Community College, Claremont NH p. 1442

Rock Hill Public Library, Rock Hill MO p. 1351
Rock Island County Illinois Genealogical Society Library, Moline IL p. 675
Rock Island County Law Library, Rock Island IL p. 696
Rock Island Public Library, Rock Island IL p. 696
Rock Milton L Resource Center, Philadelphia PA p. 2115
Rock Rapids Public Library, Rock Rapids IA p. 840
Rock River Library District, Silvis IL p. 702
Rock Springs Library, see Sweetwater County Library System, Rock Springs WY p. 2655
Rock Springs Public Library, Rock Springs WI p. 2635
Rock Valley College Library, Rockford IL p. 697
Rock Valley Public Library, Rock Valley IA p. 841
Rockaway Borough Free Public Library, Rockaway NJ p. 1527
Rockaway Township Free Public Library, Rockaway NJ p. 1527
Rockbridge Regional Library, Lexington VA p. 2474
Rockcastle County Library, Mount Vernon KY p. 930
Rockdale Temple, Cincinnati OH p. 1873
Rockefeller John D Jr Library, see Brown University, Providence RI p. 2172
Rockefeller John D Jr Library, see Colonial Williamsburg Foundation, Williamsburg, see Colonial Williamsburg Foundation, see Colonial Williamsburg Foundation VA p. 2502
Rockefeller Laurance S Library, see California Institute of Integral Studies, San Francisco CA p. 240
Rockefeller University, New York NY p. 1698
Rockford Carnegie Library, Rockford OH p. 1932
Rockford College, Rockford IL p. 697
Rockford Institute Library, Rockford IL p. 697
Rockford Memorial Hospital, Rockford IL p. 697
Rockford Public Library, Rockford AL p. 35
Rockford Public Library, Rockford IL p. 697
Rockford Public Library, Rockford IA p. 841
Rockford Public Library, see Great River Regional Library, Rockford MN p. 1275
Rockhurst University, Kansas City MO p. 1340
Rockingham Community College, Wentworth NC p. 1829
Rockingham County Public Library, Eden NC p. 1790
Rockingham Free Public Library, Bellows Falls VT p. 2418
Rockland Community College Library, Suffern NY p. 1750
Rockland Graduate Center, see Iona College, Pearl River NY p. 1666
Rockland Memorial Library, Rockland MA p. 1120
Rockland Public Library, Rockland ME p. 999
Rockland School Community Library, Rockland ID p. 583
Rockport Public Library, Rockport ME p. 999
Rockport Public Library, Rockport MA p. 1121
Rockrimmon Library, see Pikes Peak Library District, Colorado Springs CO p. 296
Rockview Library, see State Correctional Institution, Bellefonte PA p. 2032
Rockville Centre Public Library, Rockville Centre NY p. 1734
Rockville Correctional Facility Library, Rockville IN p. 776
Rockville Law Library, see Connecticut Judicial Branch Law Libraries, Rockville CT p. 344
Rockville Library, see Montgomery County Public Libraries, Rockville MD p. 1039
Rockville Public Library, Rockville IN p. 776
Rockville Public Library, Inc, Vernon CT p. 373
Rockwall County Library, Rockwall TX p. 2377
Rockwell Automation Library, Milwaukee WI p. 2621
Rockwell City Public Library, Rockwell City IA p. 841
Rockwell Public Library, Rockwell IA p. 841
Rockwell Scientific Co, Thousand Oaks CA p. 275
Rockwood Public Library, Rockwood TN p. 2264
Rockwood Ruth L Memorial Library, Livingston NJ p. 1496

Rocky Boy Public Library, see Stone Child College, Box Elder MT p. 1375
Rocky Ford Public Library, Rocky Ford CO p. 322
Rocky Hill Historical Society, Rocky Hill CT p. 366
Rocky Mount Historical Association Library, Piney Flats TN p. 2263
Rocky Mountain College, Billings MT p. 1374
Rocky Mountain College Library, Calgary AB p. 2692
Rocky Mountain College of Art & Design Library, Lakewood CO p. 315
Rocky Mountain House Public Library, Rocky Mountain House AB p. 2715
Rocky Mountain Laboratories Library, see NIH, National Institute of Allergy & Infectious Diseases, Hamilton MT p. 1380
Rocky Mountain National Park Library, see National Park Service, Estes Park CO p. 306
Rocky River Public Library, Rocky River OH p. 1932
Rockyford Municipal Library, Rockyford AB p. 2715
Rockyview General Hospital Knowledge Centre, see Calgary Health Region, Calgary AB p. 2688
Rod Library, see University of Northern Iowa Library, Cedar Falls IA p. 799
Rodale Inc, Emmaus PA p. 2054
Roddenbery Memorial Library, Cairo GA p. 522
Roddy Clyde W Library, Dayton TN p. 2232
Roden M E Memorial Library, see Ocmulgee Regional Library System, Hawkinsville GA p. 532
Rodenberg Billie Davis Memorial Library, see Temple Beth El, Hollywood FL p. 451
Rodeo Cummunity Library, see Contra Costa County Library, Rodeo CA p. 209
Rodgers George H & Ella M Memorial Library, Hudson NH p. 1452
Rodham Olivia Memorial Library, Nelson NH p. 1459
Rodino Peter W Jr Law Library, see Seton Hall University, Newark NJ p. 1513
Rodman Hall Arts Centre Library, St. Catharines ON p. 2843
Rodman Public Library, Rodman NY p. 1734
Rodman Public Library, Alliance OH p. 1854
Roehl Winona Library, see First Christian Church, Knoxville TN p. 2241
Roeliff Jansen Community Library Association, Inc, Hillsdale NY p. 1636
Roesch Library, see University of Dayton Libraries, Dayton OH p. 1894
Roger Williams University Library, Bristol RI p. 2163, 2164
Rogers Corporation, Rogers CT p. 366
Rogers Environmental Education Center, Sherburne NY p. 1743
Rogers Free Library, Bristol RI p. 2164
Rogers James A Library, see Francis Marion University, Florence SC p. 2194
Rogers James E College of Law Library, see University of Arizona, Tucson AZ p. 89
Rogers John Memorial Public Library, Dodge NE p. 1397
Rogers Lauren Museum of Art Library, Laurel MS p. 1307
Rogers Library, see Pennsauken Free Public Library, Pennsauken NJ p. 1519
Rogers Medical Library, see Jaques Anna Hospital, Newburyport MA p. 1109
Rogers Memorial Library, Southampton NY p. 1745
Rogers Public Library, Rogers AR p. 113
Rogers State Prison, see Georgia Department of Corrections, Reidsville GA p. 547
Rogers State University Library, Claremore OK p. 1960
Rogers Will Library, Claremore OK p. 1960
Rogers Will Memorial Museum Library, Claremore OK p. 1960
Rogersville Public Library, Rogersville AL p. 35
Rogue Community College, Grants Pass OR p. 1999
Rohm & Haas Co, Spring House PA p. 2142
Rohnert Part-Cotati Regional, see Sonoma County Library, Rohnert CA p. 268

Rohrbach Library, see Kutztown University, Kutztown PA p. 2075
Rohrer E, see Camden County College Library, Cherry Hill NJ p. 1473
Rohrer William G Memorial Library, see Camden County Library System, Westmont NJ p. 1538
Rokeby Museum, Ferrisburg VT p. 2424
Roland Library, see Hannibal-LaGrange University, Hannibal MO p. 1329
Roland Public Library, Roland IA p. 841
Rolette Public Library, Rolette ND p. 1848
Rolfe Public Library, Rolfe IA p. 841
Rolfing James E Memorial Library, see Trinity International University, Deerfield IL p. 635
Rolla Free Public Library, Rolla MO p. 1351
Rolla Public Library, Rolla ND p. 1848
Rolling Hills Consolidated Library, Saint Joseph MO p. 1352
Rolling Hills Public Library, Rolling Hills AB p. 2715
Rolling Meadows Library, Rolling Meadows IL p. 698
Rollins College, Winter Park FL p. 505
Rollinsford Public Library, Rollinsford NH p. 1464
Rolloff C A Law Library, Montevideo MN p. 1265
Rolls-Royce, Indianapolis IN p. 755
Rolls-Royce (Canada) Library, Lachine QC p. 2885
Rolvaag Memorial Library, Glasoe Science Library, Halvorson Music Library, see Saint Olaf College, Northfield MN p. 1269
Roman Catholic Archdiocese of Los Angeles, Mission Hills CA p. 187
Roman Catholic Diocese of Fresno Library, Fresno CA p. 153
Romanek Library, see North Shore Congregation Israel, Glencoe IL p. 650
Romanian Cultural Institute, New York NY p. 1698
Romanian Ethnic Arts Museum Library, Cleveland OH p. 1881
Romanko Patricia Public Library, Parma ID p. 581
Rome Historical Society, Rome NY p. 1735
Romeo District Library, Washington MI p. 1235
Romney Miles Memorial Library, see Ravalli County Museum, Hamilton MT p. 1381
Romoland Library, see Riverside County Library System, Romoland CA p. 218
Romulus Public Library, Romulus MI p. 1222
Ronan City Library, Ronan MT p. 1388
Ronceverte Public Library, Ronceverte WV p. 2571
Rondo Community Outreach Library, see Saint Paul Public Library, Saint Paul MN p. 1281
Roodhouse Public Library, Roodhouse IL p. 698
Rooney Mary & Andrew Library, see Saint Mary-of-the-Woods College Library, Saint Mary-of-the-Woods IN p. 777
Castle Point & Franklin Delano Roosevelt Medical Center Libraries, see VA Hudson Valley Health Care System, Montrose NY p. 1663
Roosevelt County Library, Wolf Point MT p. 1390
Roosevelt Franklin D Presidential Library, see National Archives & Records Administration, Hyde Park NY p. 1640
Roosevelt Hospital, New York NY p. 1698
Roosevelt Public Library, Roosevelt NY p. 1735
Roosevelt Theodore National Park Library, Medora ND p. 1846
Roosevelt University, Chicago IL p. 623
Roosevelt Warm Springs Institute, Warm Springs GA p. 556
Ropers, Majeski, Kohn & Bentley, Redwood City CA p. 215
Ropes & Gray LLP Library, Boston MA p. 1066
Roscoe Free Library, Roscoe NY p. 1735
Rose Benjamin Library, Cleveland OH p. 1881
Rose Bud Public, see White County Regional Library System, Rose Bud AR p. 115
Rose Creek Public, see Sequoyah Regional Library System, Woodstock GA p. 523
Rose Free Library, Rose NY p. 1735
Rose Hill Community, see Lonesome Pine Regional Library, Rose Hill VA p. 2504
Rose Hill Community Memorial Library, see Duplin County Library, Rose Hill NC p. 1804
Rose Hill Public Library, Rose Hill KS p. 892

Rural Retreat Public, *see* Wythe-Grayson Regional Library, Rural Retreat VA p. 2472

Rush Charles Andrew Learning Center & N E Miles Library, *see* Birmingham-Southern College, Birmingham AL p. 8

Rush City Public Library, Rush City MN p. 1273

Rush-Copley Medical Center, Aurora IL p. 592

Rush Oak Park Hospital Library, Oak Park IL p. 684

Rush Public Library, Rush NY p. 1736

Rush Richard H Library, *see* Edison State College, Fort Myers FL p. 444

Rushbrook Audrey Memorial Library, *see* Marine Museum of the Great Lakes, Kingston ON p. 2814

Rushford Free Library, Rushford NY p. 1736

Rushford Public Library, Rushford MN p. 1273

Rushmore Memorial, *see* Woodbury Public Library, Highland Mills NY p. 1636

Rushville Public Library, Rushville IL p. 699

Rushville Public Library, Rushville IN p. 776

Rushville Public Library, Rushville NE p. 1418

Rusk County Community Library, Ladysmith WI p. 2604

Rusk County Library, Henderson TX p. 2332

Ruska William F Library, *see* Becker College, Worcester MA p. 1143

Ruskin, Moscou & Faltischek PC, Uniondale NY p. 1758

Russell & District Regional Library, Russell MB p. 2751

Russell Adelia McConnell Library, Alexander City AL p. 4

Russell Bertrand Society, Inc Library, Wilder VT p. 2439

Russell Bessie K, *see* Huntsville-Madison Public Library, Huntsville AL p. 21

Russell C M Museum Library, Great Falls MT p. 1380

Russell Cave National Monument Library, Bridgeport AL p. 11

Russell County Public Library, Jamestown KY p. 919

Russell County Public Library, Lebanon VA p. 2473

Russell Helen Crocker Library of Horticulture, *see* San Francisco Botanical Garden Society at Strybing Arboretum, San Francisco CA p. 244

Russell Library, Middletown CT p. 352

Russell Memorial, *see* Chesapeake Public Library, Chesapeake VA p. 2456

Russell Memorial Library, Acushnet MA p. 1047

Russell Memorial Library, Monkton VT p. 2429

Russell Memorial Library, *see* Saint Paul's College, Lawrenceville VA p. 2473

Russell Public Library, Russell KS p. 892

Russell Public Library, Russell MA p. 1121

Russell Public Library, Russell NY p. 1736

Russell Resource Library, *see* Institute for Human Services Education, Truro NS p. 2786

Russell Thomas D Library, *see* Central Alabama Community College, Alexander City AL p. 3

Russellville Public Library, Russellville AL p. 35

Rust College, Holly Springs MS p. 1302

Rutan & Tucker Library, Costa Mesa CA p. 137

Rutgers University Libraries, Camden NJ p. 1476

Rutgers University Libraries, New Brunswick NJ p. 1508

Rutgers University Libraries, Newark NJ p. 1512

Rutgers University Library for the Center for Law & Justice, Newark NJ p. 1513

Rutgers, The State University of New Jersey, New Brunswick NJ p. 2969

Rutherford County Library, Spindale NC p. 1825

Rutherford (Humanities & Social Sciences) Library, *see* University of Alberta, Edmonton AB p. 2702

Rutherford Library, South Bristol ME p. 1001

Rutherford Public Library, Rutherford NJ p. 1528

Ruthmere Museum, Elkhart IN p. 737

Ruthven Public Library, Ruthven IA p. 841

Rutland Free Library, Rutland VT p. 2434

Rutland Free Public Library, Rutland MA p. 1121

Rutland Library, *see* Three Rivers Community College Library, Poplar Bluff MO p. 1349

Rutland Regional Medical Center, Rutland VT p. 2434

Rutledge Public Library, Rutledge TN p. 2264

Rutledge State Prison, *see* Georgia Department of Corrections, Columbus GA p. 526

Ryan-Biggs Associates PC Library, Clifton Park NY p. 1607

Ryan T Calvin Library, *see* University of Nebraska at Kearney, Kearney NE p. 1403

Ryan Library, *see* Iona College, New Rochelle NY p. 1666

Ryan Library, *see* Point Loma Nazarene University, San Diego CA p. 232

Ryan Lura Lynn Prevention Library, *see* Prevention First Inc, Chicago IL p. 622

Ryan Lura Lynn Prevention Research Library, Chicago IL p. 623

Ryan-Matura Library, *see* Sacred Heart University, Fairfield CT p. 339

Ryan Memorial Library, *see* Anthony Cardinal Bevilacqua Theological Research Center, Wynnewood PA p. 2158

Ryan W Gordon, *see* Portsmouth Public Library, Lucasville OH p. 1931

Rycroft Municipal Library, Rycroft AB p. 2715

Rye Free Reading Room, Rye NY p. 1736

Rye Historical Society Library, Rye NY p. 1736

Rye Public Library, Rye NH p. 1464

Ryegate Corner Public Library, East Ryegate VT p. 2423

Ryerson & Burnham Libraries, *see* Art Institute of Chicago, Chicago IL p. 606

Ryerson Nature Library, Deerfield IL p. 635

Ryerss Museum & Library, Philadelphia PA p. 2116

Rylander Memorial Library, *see* San Saba County Library, San Saba TX p. 2385

S E D Systems, Inc Library, Saskatoon SK p. 2926

SAALCK (N), *see* State Assisted Academic Library Council of Kentucky, Cincinnati OH p. 2952

Sabina Public Library, Sabina OH p. 1932

Sabinal Public Library, Sabinal TX p. 2378

Sabine Parish Library, Many LA p. 956

Sabshin Melvin Library & Archives, *see* American Psychiatric Association, Arlington VA p. 2448

Sac & Fox National Public Library, Stroud OK p. 1979

Sac City Public Library, Sac City IA p. 841

Sachem Public Library, Holbrook NY p. 1637

Sachs Hanns Medical Library, *see* Boston Psychoanalytic Society & Institute, Inc, Newton MA p. 1109

Sachs Samuel C, *see* Saint Louis County Library, Chesterfield MO p. 1359

Sachse Public Library, Sachse TX p. 2378

Sackler Medical Library, *see* Greenwich Hospital, Greenwich CT p. 341

Sackville Public, *see* Albert-Westmorland-Kent Regional Library, Sackville NB p. 2765

Sacramento Archives & Museum Collection Center, Sacramento CA p. 224

Sacramento Area Council of Governments Library, Sacramento CA p. 224

Sacramento City College, Sacramento CA p. 224

Sacramento County Public Law Library, Sacramento CA p. 224

Sacramento Public Library, Sacramento CA p. 224

Sacred Heart Academy, Hamden CT p. 343

Sacred Heart Health System, Pensacola FL p. 482

Sacred Heart Hospital, Allentown PA p. 2027

Sacred Heart Hospital, Eau Claire WI p. 2590

Sacred Heart Library, *see* Providence Regional Medical Center Everett, Everett WA p. 2515

Sacred Heart Major Seminary, Detroit MI p. 1171

Sacred Heart Medical Center at RiverBend, Springfield OR p. 2020

Sacred Heart School of Theology, Franklin WI p. 2593

Sacred Heart University, Fairfield CT p. 339

Saddle Brook Free Public Library, Saddle Brook NJ p. 1528

Saddleback College, Mission Viejo CA p. 187

Saddletowne Library, *see* Calgary Public Library, Calgary AB p. 2690

Saegertown Area Library, Saegertown PA p. 2135

Safety Harbor Public Library, Safety Harbor FL p. 486

Saffell Thomas F Library, *see* Garden City Community College, Garden City KS p. 868

Safford City-Graham County Library, Safford AZ p. 79

Sagamore Hill National Historic Site Library, Oyster Bay NY p. 1714

Sage Colleges, Albany NY p. 1570

Sage Colleges, Troy NY p. 1756

Sage Gardner A Library, *see* New Brunswick Theological Seminary, New Brunswick NJ p. 1508

Sage Memorial Library, *see* Barber Scotia College, Concord NC p. 1785

Sage Russell Foundation Library, New York NY p. 1698

Saginaw Art Museum, Saginaw MI p. 1224

Saginaw Correctional Facility Library, *see* Michigan Department of Corrections, Freeland MI p. 1182

Saginaw County Law Library, Saginaw MI p. 1224

Saginaw Public Library, Saginaw TX p. 2378

Saginaw Valley State University, University Center MI p. 1232

Saguache County Public Library, Saguache CO p. 322

Saguaro Library, *see* Phoenix Public Library, Phoenix AZ p. 76

Sahara West Library, *see* Las Vegas-Clark County Library District, Las Vegas NV p. 1429

Sahatdjian Library, *see* California State University, Fresno, Fresno CA p. 151

Sahyun Library, *see* Santa Barbara County Genealogical Society, Santa Barbara CA p. 260

SAILS, Inc (N), Middleboro MA p. 2945

Saint Agnes Healthcare, Baltimore MD p. 1017

Saint Albans Community Library, *see* Queens Borough Public Library, Saint Albans NY p. 1645

Saint Albans Free Library, Saint Albans VT p. 2434

Saint Albert Public Library, St. Albert AB p. 2717

Saint Alexius Medical Center Library, Bismarck ND p. 1838

Saint Alphonsus Health System, Boise ID p. 571

Saint Ambrose University Library, Davenport IA p. 806

Saint Andrew's Abbey, Cleveland OH p. 1881

Saint Andrew's College Library, Saskatoon SK p. 2926

Saint Andrew's College Library, *see* University of Manitoba, Winnipeg MB p. 2758

Saint Andrews Regional, *see* Charleston County Public Library, Charleston SC p. 2183

Saint Andrews Regional, *see* Richland County Public Library, Columbia SC p. 2188

Saint Andrews University, Laurinburg NC p. 1805

Saint Anselm College, Manchester NH p. 1456

Saint Ansgar Public Library, *see* Nissen Public Library, Saint Ansgar IA p. 842

Saint Anthony Hospital, Oklahoma City OK p. 1975

Saint Anthony Medical Center, Crown Point IN p. 734

Saint Anthony's Health Care Library, Saint Petersburg FL p. 488

Saint-Antoine Public, *see* Albert-Westmorland-Kent Regional Library, Saint Antoine NB p. 2765

Saint Augustine Center Library, *see* Saint John's River State College, Saint Augustine FL p. 479

Saint Augustine College Library, Chicago IL p. 623

Saint Augustine Historical Society, Saint Augustine FL p. 486

Saint Augustine Library, *see* The College of Saint Mary Magdalen, Warner NH p. 1467

Saint Augustine Preservation Department Library, Saint Augustine FL p. 486

Saint Augustine's College, Raleigh NC p. 1817

Saint Augustine's Seminary Library, Scarborough ON p. 2841

Saint Barnabas Hospital, Bronx NY p. 1588

Saint Barnabas Medical Center, Livingston NJ p. 1496

Saint Basil College Library, Stamford CT p. 369

Saint Bede's Library, *see* Saint Giles' Episcopal Church, Northbrook IL p. 682

Saint Benedict Public Library, *see* Wapiti Regional Library, Saint Benedict SK p. 2922

Saint Bernardine Library, *see* Thomas Aquinas College, Santa Paula CA p. 267

San Bernardino Valley College Library, San Bernardino CA p. 229

San Bruno Public Library, San Bruno CA p. 230

San Carlos Correctional Facility Library, *see* Colorado Department of Corrections, Pueblo CO p. 320

San Carlos Library, *see* San Mateo County Library, San Carlos CA p. 256

San Carlos Public Library, San Carlos AZ p. 80

San Diego Aero-Space Museum, Inc, San Diego CA p. 232

San Diego Christian College Library, El Cajon CA p. 145

San Diego City College, San Diego CA p. 232

San Diego County Library, San Diego CA p. 233

San Diego County Public Law Library, San Diego CA p. 234

San Diego Family History Center, San Diego CA p. 234

San Diego Historical Society, San Diego CA p. 235

San Diego Mesa College Library, San Diego CA p. 235

San Diego Miramar College, San Diego CA p. 235

San Diego Model Railroad Museum, San Diego CA p. 235

San Diego Museum of Art Library, San Diego CA p. 235

San Diego Museum of Man, San Diego CA p. 235

San Diego Natural History Museum, San Diego CA p. 235

San Diego Public Library, San Diego CA p. 235

San Diego State University, Calexico CA p. 131

San Diego State University Library & Information Access, San Diego CA p. 237

San Francisco African-American Historical & Cultural Society, San Francisco CA p. 244

San Francisco Art Institute, San Francisco CA p. 244

San Francisco Bay Region Library, *see* California Regional Water Quality Control Board, Oakland CA p. 196

San Francisco Biomedical Library Network (N), San Francisco CA p. 2938

San Francisco Botanical Garden Society at Strybing Arboretum, San Francisco CA p. 244

San Francisco Camerawork, San Francisco CA p. 245

San Francisco Center for Psychoanalysis, San Francisco CA p. 245

San Francisco Chronicle Library, San Francisco CA p. 245

San Francisco Conservatory of Music, San Francisco CA p. 245

San Francisco General Hospital, San Francisco CA p. 245

San Francisco Law Library, San Francisco CA p. 245

San Francisco Law School Library at Alliant, San Francisco CA p. 245

San Francisco Maritime Library, San Francisco CA p. 245

San Francisco Municipal Railway Library, San Francisco CA p. 245

San Francisco Museum of Modern Art, San Francisco CA p. 245

San Francisco Performing Arts Library & Museum, San Francisco CA p. 246

San Francisco Public Library, San Francisco CA p. 246

San Francisco State University, San Francisco CA p. 247

San Gorgonio Memorial Hospital, Banning CA p. 125

San Jacinto College, Pasadena TX p. 2369

San Jacinto College North, Houston TX p. 2342

San Jacinto College South, Houston TX p. 2342

San Jacinto Library, *see* Riverside County Library System, San Jacinto CA p. 218

San Jacinto Museum of History, La Porte TX p. 2352

San Joaquin College of Law Library, Clovis CA p. 135

San Joaquin County Historical Museum, Lodi CA p. 165

San Joaquin County Law Library, Stockton CA p. 272

San Joaquin Delta College, Stockton CA p. 272

San Joaquin General Hospital, French Camp CA p. 150

San Joaquin Valley Library System, Fresno CA p. 153

San Jose City College Library, San Jose CA p. 250

San Jose Mercury News Library, San Jose CA p. 250

San Jose Museum of Art Library, San Jose CA p. 250

San Jose Public Library, San Jose CA p. 250

San Jose State University, San Jose CA p. 251, 2962

San Juan Bautista City Library, San Juan Bautista CA p. 252

San Juan Capistrano Library, *see* OC Public Libraries, San Juan Capistrano CA p. 259

San Juan College Library, Farmington NM p. 1555

San Juan County Archaeological Research Center, Bloomfield NM p. 1552

San Juan County Library, Monticello UT p. 2408

San Juan Island Library District, Friday Harbor WA p. 2516

San Juan Public Library, San Juan TX p. 2384

San Leandro Public Library, San Leandro CA p. 252

San Luis Obispo County Law Library, San Luis Obispo CA p. 253

San Luis Obispo County Library, San Luis Obispo CA p. 253

San Manuel Public Library, San Manuel AZ p. 80

San Marcos Public Library, San Marcos TX p. 2384

San Mateo County, San Mateo CA p. 255

San Mateo County History Museum & Archives, Redwood City CA p. 215

San Mateo County Law Library, Redwood City CA p. 216

San Mateo County Library, San Mateo CA p. 255

San Mateo Public Library, San Mateo CA p. 256

San Miguel County Public Library District 1, Telluride CO p. 323

San Miguel Library District 2, Norwood CO p. 319

San Pablo Library, *see* Contra Costa County Library, San Pablo CA p. 209

San Patricio County Library System, Sinton TX p. 2387

San Pedro Regional, *see* Los Angeles Public Library System, San Pedro CA p. 174

San Quentin State Prison Library, *see* California Department of Corrections Library System, San Quentin CA p. 222

San Rafael Public Library, San Rafael CA p. 257

San Ramon Library, *see* Contra Costa County Library, San Ramon CA p. 209

San Saba County Library, San Saba TX p. 2385

San Xavier Library, Tucson AZ p. 88

Sanborn English Library, *see* Dartmouth College Library, Hanover NH p. 1450

Sanborn Public Library, Sanborn IA p. 842

Sanborn-Pekin Free Library, Sanborn NY p. 1738

Sanbornton Public Library, Sanbornton NH p. 1464

Sanchez Richard M Library, *see* Navarro College, Corsicana TX p. 2303

Sand Creek Library, *see* Pikes Peak Library District, Colorado Springs CO p. 296

Sand Hill Public Library, Sand Hill MS p. 1314

Sand Lake Town Library, Averill Park NY p. 1576

Sandburg Carl, *see* Livonia Public Library, Livonia MI p. 1204

Sanders Amy, *see* Central Arkansas Library System, Sherwood AR p. 106

Sanders Public, *see* Apache County Library District, Sanders AZ p. 80

Sanders Stanny Library, *see* Mississippi Delta Community College, Moorhead MS p. 1309

Sandersville Technical College, Sandersville GA p. 549

Sandhills Community College, Pinehurst NC p. 1814

Sandia Baptist Church, Albuquerque NM p. 1550

Sandia Medical Library, Albuquerque NM p. 1550

Sandia National Laboratories, Livermore CA p. 164

Sandia National Laboratories, Albuquerque NM p. 1550

Sandisfield Free Public Library, Sandisfield MA p. 1122

Sandor Margo Music Library, *see* Canadian Opera Co, Toronto ON p. 2852

Sandown Public Library, Sandown NH p. 1465

Sandstone Public Library, Sandstone MN p. 1283

Sandusky Bay Law Library Association, Inc, Sandusky OH p. 1934

Sandusky County Law Library, Fremont OH p. 1900

Sandusky District Library, Sandusky MI p. 1226

Sandusky Library, Sandusky OH p. 1934

Sandwich District Library, Sandwich IL p. 700

Sandwich Glass Museum Library, Sandwich MA p. 1122

Sandwich Public Library, Sandwich MA p. 1122

Sandy Bay Historical Society & Museums Library, Rockport MA p. 1121

Sandy Public Library, Sandy OR p. 2019

Sandy Spring Museum Library, Sandy Spring MD p. 1041

Sandy Springs Regional Library, *see* Atlanta-Fulton Public Library System, Sandy Springs GA p. 512

Sandy Valley Library, *see* Las Vegas-Clark County Library District, Sandy Valley NV p. 1430

Sanford-Brown College, Collinsville IL p. 631

Sanford Health Library, Fargo ND p. 1841

Sanford Museum & Planetarium, Cherokee IA p. 802

Sanford William K Town Library, Loudonville NY p. 1655

Sanger Public Library, Sanger TX p. 2385

Sangerville Public Library, Sangerville ME p. 1000

Sangudo Public Library, Sangudo AB p. 2716

Sanibel Public Library District, Sanibel FL p. 489

Sanilac District Library, Port Sanilac MI p. 1220

Sanofi Aventis, Malvern PA p. 2083

Santa Ana College, Santa Ana CA p. 259

Santa Ana Public Library, Santa Ana CA p. 259

Santa Ana Pueblo Community Library, Bernalillo NM p. 1552

Santa Anna Library, Santa Anna TX p. 2385

Santa Barbara Botanic Garden Library, Santa Barbara CA p. 260

Santa Barbara City College, Santa Barbara CA p. 260

Santa Barbara County Genealogical Society, Santa Barbara CA p. 260

Santa Barbara County Law Library, Santa Maria CA p. 265

Santa Barbara Historical Museum, Santa Barbara CA p. 260

Santa Barbara Mission, Santa Barbara CA p. 261

Santa Barbara Museum of Art, Santa Barbara CA p. 261

Santa Barbara Museum of Natural History Library, Santa Barbara CA p. 261

Santa Barbara News Press Library, Santa Barbara CA p. 261

Santa Barbara Public Library, Santa Barbara CA p. 261

Santa Clara City Library, Santa Clara CA p. 262

Santa Clara County Law Library, San Jose CA p. 252

Santa Clara County Library District, Los Gatos CA p. 180

Santa Clara County Office of Education, San Jose CA p. 252

Santa Clara Pueblo Community Library, Espanola NM p. 1555

Santa Clara University, Santa Clara CA p. 263

Santa Clara Valley Medical Center, San Jose CA p. 252

Santa Clara Valley Water District Library, San Jose CA p. 252

Santa Clarita Interlibrary Network (N), Santa Clarita CA p. 2938

Santa Clarita Public Library, Santa Clarita CA p. 263

Santa Cruz City-County Library System Headquarters, Santa Cruz CA p. 264

Santa Cruz County Law Library, Santa Cruz CA p. 264

Santa Fe Community College, Gainesville FL p. 449

Santa Fe Community College Library, Santa Fe NM p. 1563

Santa Fe Institute Library, Santa Fe NM p. 1563

Schizophrenia Society of Nova Scotia Library, Dartmouth NS p. 2780

Schlafer Shirley K Library, *see* American Folk Art Museum, New York NY p. 1668

Schlagle Mr & Mrs F L, *see* Kansas City, Kansas Public Library, Kansas City KS p. 875

Schleicher County Public Library, Eldorado TX p. 2317

Schlesinger Arthur & Elizabeth Library, *see* Harvard Library, Cambridge MA p. 1076

Schleswig Public Library, Schleswig IA p. 842

Schlow Centre Region Library, State College PA p. 2143

Schlumberger-Doll Research, Cambridge MA p. 1078

Schmaling Memorial Public Library District, Fulton IL p. 647

Schmeller Kurt R Library, *see* Queensborough Community College, Bayside NY p. 1579

Schmid Marvin & Virginia Law Library, *see* University of Nebraska-Lincoln, Lincoln NE p. 1407

Schmidt Grace Room, *see* Kitchener Public Library, Kitchener ON p. 2815

Schmidt Library, *see* York College of Pennsylvania, York PA p. 2160

Schmidt Martin F Research Library, *see* Kentucky Historical Society, Frankfort KY p. 913

Schnader, Harrison, Segal & Lewis Library, Philadelphia PA p. 2116

Schnare Paul & Helen Library, *see* Saint Charles Community College Library, Cottleville MO p. 1326

Schneider Minnie Resource Center, *see* Hollister Incorporated, Libertyville IL p. 665

Schneidewind Library, *see* Union Congregational Church, Montclair NJ p. 1503

Schnepp Kenneth H Professional Library, *see* Memorial Medical Center, Springfield IL p. 706

Schnepp Professional Library, Springfield IL p. 706

Schnitzler Thomas P Library, *see* Monroe College, Bronx NY p. 1588

Schoenbaum Library, *see* University of Charleston, Charleston WV p. 2556

Schoharie County Historical Society, Schoharie NY p. 1741

Schoharie Free Association Library, Schoharie NY p. 1741

Scholastic Inc Library, New York NY p. 1699

Scholes Library of Ceramics, *see* Alfred University, Alfred NY p. 1572

Schollenberger Maude Gowan Memorial Library, *see* Wichita Center for the Arts, Wichita KS p. 901

Schomburg Center for Research in Black Culture, *see* New York Public Library - Astor, Lenox & Tilden Foundations, New York NY p. 1693

School for Advanced Research Library, Santa Fe NM p. 1564

School Library Media Concentration Program, *see* William Paterson University, Wayne NJ p. 2969

School of Aerospace Medicine, *see* Franzello AeroMedical Library, Dayton OH p. 1893

School of Art & Design, *see* Montgomery College, Takoma Park MD p. 1037

School of Communication, Information & Library Studies, *see* Rutgers, The State University of New Jersey, New Brunswick NJ p. 2969

School of Information, *see* University of California at Berkeley, Berkeley CA p. 2962

School of Information Studies, *see* Syracuse University, Syracuse NY p. 2970

Harnish Jerene Appleby Law Library, *see* Pepperdine University Libraries, Malibu CA p. 182

School of Law Library, *see* Seattle University, Seattle WA p. 2532

School of Library & Information Science, *see* University of South Carolina, Columbia SC p. 2973

School of Library & Information Studies, *see* Florida State University, Tallahassee FL p. 2963

School of Management & Labor Relations, *see* Rutgers University Libraries, New Brunswick NJ p. 1509

School of Ocean & Earth Science & Technology Library, Honolulu HI p. 565

School of Professional Studies in Business & Education, *see* Johns Hopkins University Libraries, Baltimore MD p. 1014

School of Professional Studies in Business & Education Library, *see* Johns Hopkins University Libraries, Columbia MD p. 1026

School of the Art Institute of Chicago, Chicago IL p. 624

School of Visual Arts, New York NY p. 1699

Schoolcraft College, Livonia MI p. 1204

Schoolcraft Community Library, Schoolcraft MI p. 1226

Schreeder, Wheeler & Flint LLP, Atlanta GA p. 518

Schreiber Abner & Mary Jewish Music Library, *see* Gratz College, Melrose Park PA p. 2088

Schreiber Township Public Library, Schreiber ON p. 2841

Schreiner Memorial Library, Lancaster WI p. 2605

Schreiner University, Kerrville TX p. 2350

Schreyer William & Joan Business Library, *see* Pennsylvania State University Libraries, University Park PA p. 2148

Schricker Henry F, *see* Starke County Public Library System, Knox IN p. 757

Schriner Memorial Library, *see* Mercy Hospital of Tiffin, Tiffin OH p. 1938

Schroeder Public Library, Keystone IA p. 825

Schroeder Walter Library, *see* Milwaukee School of Engineering, Milwaukee WI p. 2620

Schroeter, Goldmark & Bender Library, Seattle WA p. 2530

Schroon Lake Public Library, Schroon Lake NY p. 1741

Schrup Nicholas J Library, *see* Clarke University, Dubuque IA p. 811

Schulenburg Public Library, Schulenburg TX p. 2385

Schuler Kenneth W Learning Resources Center, *see* Thaddeus Stevens College of Technology, Lancaster PA p. 2078

Schulich Library of Science & Engineering, *see* McGill University Libraries, Montreal QC p. 2899

Schulkoski Kathryn Library, Eureka SD p. 2212

Schulte Roth & Zabel LLP, New York NY p. 1699

Schulz Jean & Charles, *see* Sonoma State University Library, Rohnert Park CA p. 219

Schumacher Edward G Memorial Library, *see* Northwestern College, Chicago IL p. 621

Schuman William Music Library, *see* Sarah Lawrence College, Bronxville NY p. 1589

Schurz Franklin D Library, *see* Indiana University South Bend, South Bend IN p. 778

Schusterman-Benson Library, *see* Tulsa City-County Library, Tulsa OK p. 1983

Schuyler Public Library, Schuyler NE p. 1418

Schuyler Technical Library, Moorpark CA p. 191

Schuylerville Public Library, Schuylerville NY p. 1741

Schuylkill County Law Library, Pottsville PA p. 2131

Schuylkill Haven Free Public Library, Schuylkill Haven PA p. 2136

Schuylkill Medical Center East, Pottsville PA p. 2131

Schuylkill Valley Community Library, Leesport PA p. 2080

Schwabe, Williamson & Wyatt Library, Portland OR p. 2014

Schwan Marvin M Library, *see* Wisconsin Lutheran College Library, Milwaukee WI p. 2622

Schwartz Arnold A Memorial Library, *see* Dunellen Public Library, Dunellen NJ p. 1481

Schwartz B Davis Memorial Library, *see* Long Island University Post, Brookville NY p. 1595

Schwartz Irving, *see* El Paso Public Library, El Paso TX p. 2316

Schwartz Joseph & Elizabeth Library, *see* Beth Sholom Congregation, Elkins Park PA p. 2053

Schwartz Marie Smith Medical Library, *see* Brookdale University Medical Center, Brooklyn NY p. 1589

Schwartzbach Saul Memorial Library, *see* Prince George's Hospital Center, Cheverly MD p. 1024

Schwarzman Stephen A Building, *see* New York Public Library - Astor, Lenox & Tilden Foundations, New York NY p. 1693

Schwenkfelder Library & Heritage Center, Pennsburg PA p. 2102

Schwerin Ursula C Library, *see* New York City Technical College, Brooklyn NY p. 1594

Schwimmer Marshall B & Viola R Library, *see* Temple Jeremiah, Northfield IL p. 683

Schwob Simon Medical Library, *see* Columbus Regional Healthcare System, Columbus GA p. 526

Schwob Simon Memorial Library, *see* Columbus State University Libraries, Columbus GA p. 526

Science Museum of Minnesota, Saint Paul MN p. 1282

Scientists Center for Animal Welfare Library, Greenbelt MD p. 1030

SCILNET (N), *see* Santa Clarita Interlibrary Network, Santa Clarita CA p. 2938

Scio Free Library, Scio NY p. 1741

Scio Public Library, Scio OR p. 2019

Scioto County Law Library, Portsmouth OH p. 1931

Scioto Juvenile Correctional Facility Library, *see* State of Ohio Department of Corrections, Delaware OH p. 1896

Scituate Historical Society Library, Scituate MA p. 1123

Scituate Town Library, Scituate MA p. 1123

SCLC (N), *see* Sioux City Library Cooperative, Sioux City IA p. 2943

SCLC (N), *see* Southern California Library Cooperative, Monrovia CA p. 2939

Scolaro, Shulman, Cohen, Fetter & Burstein, PC, Syracuse NY p. 1753

Scotch Plains Public Library, Scotch Plains NJ p. 1528

Scotia Library Services, *see* Bank of Nova Scotia Library, Toronto QC p. 2913

Scotia Public Library, Scotia NE p. 1418

Scotland County Memorial Library, Memphis MO p. 1345

Scotland County Memorial Library, Laurinburg NC p. 1805

Scotland Neck Memorial, *see* Halifax County Library, Scotland Neck NC p. 1799

Scotland Public Library, Scotland CT p. 366

Scott & White Healthcare, Temple TX p. 2390

Scott Albert L Library, Alabaster AL p. 3

Scott Community College Library, Bettendorf IA p. 796

Scott County Library, Scott City KS p. 893

Scott County Library, *see* Scott-Sebastian Regional Library, Waldron AR p. 102

Scott County Library System, Eldridge IA p. 813

Scott County Library System, Savage MN p. 1283

Scott County Public, *see* Lonesome Pine Regional Library, Gate City VA p. 2504

Scott County Public Library, Scottsburg IN p. 777

Scott County Public Library, Georgetown KY p. 915

Scott County Public Library, Oneida TN p. 2262

Scott John W Health Sciences Library, *see* University of Alberta, Edmonton AB p. 2702

Scott Library, *see* York University Libraries, Toronto ON p. 2868

Scott Memorial Library, *see* Thomas Jefferson University, Philadelphia PA p. 2118

Scott Paul M Library, *see* Montserrat College of Art, Beverly MA p. 1054

Scott-Sebastian Regional Library, Greenwood AR p. 101

Scott T B Library, Merrill WI p. 2616

Scott Township Public Library, Scott Township PA p. 2136

Scottdale Public Library, Scottdale PA p. 2137

ScottHulse, PC, El Paso TX p. 2317

Scottish Rite Library, Washington DC p. 413

Scottish Rite Masonic Library, San Diego CA p. 238

Scottish Rite Masonic Museum & Library, Inc, Lexington MA p. 1099

Scotts Bluff National Monument, Oregon Trail Museum Library, *see* National Park Service, Gering NE p. 1399

Services Documentaires Multimedia, Inc, Montreal QC p. 2901

Servite Provincial Library, *see* Order of Servants of Mary (Servites), USA Province, Chicago IL p. 622

Sesser Public Library, Sesser IL p. 701

Sessions, Fishman, Nathan & Israel LLP Library, New Orleans LA p. 963

Sessions Rube Memorial Library, Wells TX p. 2399

Seton Elizabeth Library, *see* College of Mount Saint Vincent, Bronx NY p. 1586

Seton Hall University, Newark NJ p. 1513

Seton Hall University Libraries, South Orange NJ p. 1530

Seton Health Systems, Troy NY p. 1757

Seton Hill University, Greensburg PA p. 2062

Seton Medical Center, Daly City CA p. 139

Settlement Music School, Philadelphia PA p. 2116

Seufert Memorial Library, *see* Norwegian American Hospital, Chicago IL p. 621

Seven Oaks General Hospital Library, *see* University of Manitoba, Winnipeg MB p. 2758

Seven Oaks General Hospital Library, *see* University of Manitoba Libraries, Winnipeg MB p. 2759

Seventh Day Baptist Historical Society Library, Janesville WI p. 2600

Seventy-Eighth Street Community Library, *see* Tampa-Hillsborough County Public Library System, Tampa FL p. 498

Sever H E Memorial, *see* Northeast Missouri Library Service, Kahoka MO p. 1336

Severson National Information Center, *see* Alliance for Children & Families, Milwaukee WI p. 2616

Sevier County Public Library System, Sevierville TN p. 2265

Seville Community, *see* Medina County District Library, Seville OH p. 1916

Seville Township Public Library, Riverdale MI p. 1221

Seward & Kissel LLP, New York NY p. 1699

Seward Community Library Museum, Seward AK p. 53

Seward County Community College, Liberal KS p. 879

Seward House Museum, Auburn NY p. 1576

Seward Marine Center Library, *see* University of Alaska Fairbanks, School of Fisheries & Ocean Sciences, Seward AK p. 53

Seward Memorial Library, Seward NE p. 1419

Sewell Warren P Memorial Library, *see* West Georgia Regional Library, Bremen GA p. 524

Sewell Warren P Memorial Library of Bowdon, *see* West Georgia Regional Library, Bowdon GA p. 524

Sewickley Public Library, Inc, Sewickley PA p. 2139

Sewickley Township Public Library, Herminie PA p. 2068

Sexsmith Shannon Municipal Library, Sexsmith AB p. 2716

Sexton Design & Technology Library, *see* Dalhousie University, Halifax NS p. 2780

Sexuality Education Resource Centre, Winnipeg MB p. 2757

Seyfarth & Shaw New York Library, New York NY p. 1699

Seyfarth Shaw, Washington DC p. 413

Seyfarth Shaw, Chicago IL p. 624

Seyfarth Shaw Library, Los Angeles CA p. 177

Seymour Community Library, Seymour IA p. 842

Seymour Henry M Library, *see* Sunflower County Library System, Indianola MS p. 1302

Seymour Henry W Library, *see* Knox College, Galesburg IL p. 648

Seymour Library, Brockport NY p. 1585

Seymour Library, *see* Jackson County Public Library, Seymour IN p. 777

Seymour Mary E Memorial Free Library, Stockton NY p. 1749

Seymour Public Library, Seymour CT p. 366

Seymour Public Library District, Auburn NY p. 1576

SFBLN (N), *see* San Francisco Biomedical Library Network, San Francisco CA p. 2938

SGT Yano Library, *see* United States Army, Schofield Barracks HI p. 567

Shaare Emeth Temple, Saint Louis MO p. 1361

Shackelford County Library, Albany TX p. 2272

Shacknove - Saint John's Medical Staff Library, Santa Monica CA p. 266

Shadek-Fackenthal Library, *see* Franklin & Marshall College, Lancaster PA p. 2076

Shadelands Ranch Historical Museum, Walnut Creek CA p. 282

Shady Grove Adventist Hospital, Rockville MD p. 1039

Shafer Library, *see* University of Findlay, Findlay OH p. 1899

Shafer Robert Memorial Library, *see* Presbyterian Hospital, Albuquerque NM p. 1549

Shaheen E J Library, *see* Glen Oaks Community College Library, Centreville MI p. 1162

Shain Charles E Library, *see* Connecticut College, New London CT p. 359

Shake Library, *see* Vincennes University, Vincennes IN p. 784

Shaker Heights Public Library, Shaker Heights OH p. 1934

Shaker Library, New Gloucester ME p. 993

Shaker Museum & Library, Old Chatham NY p. 1710

Shaker Village of Pleasant Hill Museum Library, Harrodsburg KY p. 916

Shakespeare Data Bank, Inc Library, Evanston IL p. 644

Shakespeare Society Of America, Moss landing CA p. 192

Shakopee Public Library, *see* Scott County Library System, Shakopee MN p. 1284

Shaler North Hills Library, Glenshaw PA p. 2061

Shalimar Public Library, Shalimar FL p. 491

Shallenberger Book Arts Library & Archives, *see* Sweet Briar College, Sweet Briar VA p. 2497

Shamokin & Coal Township Public Library, Inc, Shamokin PA p. 2139

Shamrock Public Library, Shamrock TX p. 2386

Shanahan Thomas J Library, *see* Marymount Manhattan College, New York NY p. 1685

Shanklin Florence Soule Memorial, *see* Lincoln County Public Library, Denver NC p. 1807

Shannon & Wilson, Inc, Seattle WA p. 2532

Shannon Library, *see* Saint Thomas More College-University of Saskatchewan, Saskatoon SK p. 2926

Shannon Medical Center Library, San Angelo TX p. 2379

Shanower Library, *see* Geauga County Historical Society, Burton OH p. 1862

Shapiro David C Memorial Law Library, *see* Northern Illinois University Libraries, DeKalb IL p. 636

Shapiro Developmental Center, Kankakee IL p. 661

Shapiro Library, *see* Southern New Hampshire University, Manchester NH p. 1456

Shapiro Max Memorial Library, *see* Beth-El Synagogue, Saint Louis Park MN p. 1277

Shapiro Science Library, *see* University of Michigan, Ann Arbor MI p. 1153

Shapiro Undergraduate Library, *see* University of Michigan, Ann Arbor MI p. 1153

Shapleigh Community Library, Shapleigh ME p. 1000

Shared Library Services (N), Exeter ON p. 2960

Sharkey-Issaquena County Library, Rolling Fork MS p. 1314

Sharon Hill Public Library, Sharon Hill PA p. 2139

Sharon Hospital, Sharon CT p. 367

Sharon Public Library, Sharon MA p. 1123

Sharon Public Library, Sharon TN p. 2265

Sharon Regional Health System, Sharon PA p. 2139

Sharon Springs Free Library, Sharon Springs NY p. 1742

Sharon Springs Public Library, Sharon Springs KS p. 894

Sharp County Library, Hardy AR p. 102

Sharp HealthCare, San Diego CA p. 238

Sharp Memorial Hospital Medical Library, *see* Sharp HealthCare, San Diego CA p. 238

Sharp Peter Jay Library, *see* Manhattan School of Music, New York NY p. 1685

Sharpe William Jr, Hospital, Weston WV p. 2574

Sharpsburg Public, *see* Washington County Free Library, Sharpsburg MD p. 1031

Shasta College Library, Redding CA p. 214

Shasta County Public Law Library, Redding CA p. 214

Shasta Historical Society, Redding CA p. 214

Shasta Public Libraries, Redding CA p. 214

Shatford J D Memorial, *see* Halifax Public Libraries, Hubbards NS p. 2779

Shattuck Lemuel C Memorial Archival Library, *see* Bisbee Mining & Historical Museum, Bisbee AZ p. 58

Shattuck Lemuel Hospital, Jamaica Plain MA p. 1097

Shattuck Public Library, Shattuck OK p. 1977

Shaver Engineering Library, *see* University of Kentucky Libraries, Lexington KY p. 922

Shaw & Stone Library, *see* Boston Architectural College, Boston MA p. 1055

Shaw Dr Memorial Library, Mount Vernon ME p. 992

Shaw Joseph & Elizabeth Public Library, Clearfield PA p. 2046

Shaw Library, Mercer ME p. 991

Shaw Memorial Library, Plainfield MA p. 1118

Shaw Public Library, Greenville ME p. 987

Shaw University, Raleigh NC p. 1817

Shaw Watha T Daniel Interim Library, *see* District of Columbia Public Library, Washington DC p. 398

Shawangunk Correctional Facility Library, Wallkill NY p. 1762

Shawano City-County Library, Shawano WI p. 2636

Shawnee Community College Library, Ullin IL p. 711

Shawnee Correctional Center Library, *see* Illinois Department of Corrections, Vienna IL p. 714

Shawnee Mission Medical Center Library, Shawnee Mission KS p. 894

Shawnee Public, *see* Pioneer Library System, Shawnee OK p. 1970

Shawnee State University, Portsmouth OH p. 1931

Shawneetown Public Library, Shawneetown IL p. 701

Shchuka Maria A, *see* Toronto Public Library, Toronto ON p. 2863

Shea James J Sr Memorial Library, *see* American International College, Springfield MA p. 1126

Shearing Plough BioPharma, Palo Alto CA p. 204

Shearman & Sterling Library, Washington DC p. 414

Shearman & Sterling LLP, San Francisco CA p. 247

Shearman & Sterling LLP Library, New York NY p. 1699

Sheatsley Paul B Library, *see* National Opinion Research Center Library, Chicago IL p. 620

Sheboygan County Historical Research, Sheboygan Falls WI p. 2638

Sheboygan Falls Memorial Library, Sheboygan Falls WI p. 2638

Sheboygan Press Library, Sheboygan WI p. 2637

Shedd Free Library, Washington NH p. 1467

Shedd John G Aquarium Library, Chicago IL p. 624

Shedd-Porter Memorial Library, Alstead NH p. 1437

Shediac Public, *see* Albert-Westmorland-Kent Regional Library, Shediac NB p. 2765

Sheehan Phinney Bass & Green PA Library, Manchester NH p. 1456

Sheep River Library, Turner Valley AB p. 2719

Sheets Millard Library, *see* Otis College of Art & Design Library, Westchester CA p. 283

Sheets Philip Family, *see* Shelby County Libraries, Botkins OH p. 1935

Sheffield Botanical Library, *see* Atlanta Botanical Garden, Atlanta GA p. 511

Sheffield Public Library, Sheffield AL p. 36

Sheffield Public Library, Sheffield IL p. 702

Sheffield Public Library, Sheffield IA p. 842

Sheffield Township Library, Sheffield PA p. 2139

Shelbina Carnegie Public Library, Shelbina MO p. 1365

Shelburn Public, *see* Sullivan County Public Library, Shelburn IN p. 780

Shelburne County Archives & Genealogical Society Library, Shelburne NS p. 2784

Sidney Memorial Public Library, Sidney NY p. 1743
Sidney Memorial Public Library, Unadilla NY
p. 1757
Sidney Public Library, Sidney IA p. 843
Sidney Public Library, Sidney MT p. 1388
Sidney Public Library, Sidney NE p. 1419
Siebers James J Memorial Library, *see* Kimberly
Public Library, Kimberly WI p. 2602
SIEC Library, *see* Centre for Suicide Prevention,
2005, Calgary AB p. 2691
SIECUS, New York NY p. 1700
Siegal College of Judaic Studies, Cleveland OH
p. 1881
Siegel Eli Collection, *see* Aesthetic Realism
Foundation, New York NY p. 1667
Siegel Jacob E Library, *see* Adat Shalom
Synagogue, Farmington Hills MI p. 1177
Siegesmund Engineering Library, *see* Purdue
University Libraries, West Lafayette IN p. 787
Siemens Corporate Research, Inc, Princeton NJ
p. 1524
Siena College, Loudonville NY p. 1655
Siena Heights University Library, Adrian MI p. 1147
Sierra Club, San Francisco CA p. 247
Sierra College Library, Grass Valley CA p. 156
Sierra County Law Library, Downieville CA p. 144
Sierra Joint Community College District, Rocklin
CA p. 219
Sierra Madre Public Library, Sierra Madre CA
p. 269
Sierra Nevada College, Incline Village NV p. 1428
Sierra Nevada Memorial Hospital, Grass Valley CA
p. 156
Sierra Research Library, Sacramento CA p. 225
Sierra Vista Public Library, Sierra Vista AZ p. 82
Sifton Carolyn-Helene Fuld Library, *see* University
of Manitoba Libraries, Winnipeg MB p. 2759
Sigma-Aldrich Corp, Saint Louis MO p. 1361
Sigma Alpha Epsilon Fraternity & Foundation,
Evanston IL p. 644
Signal Hill Public Library, Signal Hill CA p. 269
Signal Mountain Public Library, Signal Mountain
TN p. 2265
Signal Peak Library, *see* Central Arizona College,
Coolidge AZ p. 60
Sigourney Public Library, Sigourney IA p. 843
Sikes Robert L F Public Library, Crestview FL
p. 434
Sikeston Public Library, Sikeston MO p. 1365
Silber Saul Memorial Library, *see* Hebrew
Theological College, Skokie IL p. 702
Siletz Public Library, Siletz OR p. 2019
Silk Eric Library, *see* Ontario Provincial Police,
Orillia ON p. 2826
SILO (N), *see* State of Iowa Libraries Online, Des
Moines IA p. 2943
Siloam Springs Public Library, Siloam Springs AR
p. 115
Silsbee Public Library, Silsbee TX p. 2387
Silsby Free Public Library, Charlestown NH p. 1441
Silver Bay Public Library, Silver Bay MN p. 1284
Silver City Public Library, Silver City IA p. 843
Silver Cross Hospital Medical Library, Joliet IL
p. 660
Silver Falls Library District, Silverton OR p. 2020
Silver Hill Hospital, New Canaan CT p. 354
Silver Lake College, Manitowoc WI p. 2612
Silver Lake Community, *see* Community Library,
Silver Lake WI p. 2636
Silver Lake Library, Silver Lake KS p. 894
Silver Spring Library, *see* Montgomery County
Public Libraries, Silver Spring MD p. 1039
Silverman Sidney Library & Learning Resource
Center, *see* Bergen Community College,
Paramus NJ p. 1517
Silverpeak Library, Silverpeak NV p. 1434
Silverton Public Library, Silverton CO p. 322
Silvis Public Library, *see* Rock River Library
District, Silvis IL p. 702
Simcoe County Archives, Minesing ON p. 2822
Simek Frances L Memorial Library, Medford WI
p. 2614
Simi Valley Historical Society & Museum, Simi
Valley CA p. 269

Simi Valley Hospital & Health Cares Services, Simi
Valley CA p. 269
Simmons College, Boston MA p. 1066, 2967
Simmons College of Kentucky Library, Louisville
KY p. 925
Simon Fraser University Library, Burnaby BC
p. 2725
Simon Fraser University Vancouver Library,
Vancouver BC p. 2742
Simon, Peragine, Smith & Redfearn LLP, New
Orleans LA p. 963
Simon Wiesenthal Center & Museum of Tolerance,
Los Angeles CA p. 177
Simone de Beauvoir Library, Montreal QC p. 2901
Simons Harry Library, *see* Beth David Congregation,
Miami FL p. 464
Simpson Albert B Historical Library, *see* National
Archives of The Christian & Missionary
Alliance, Colorado Springs CO p. 295
Simpson College, Indianola IA p. 822
Simpson Friench Memorial Library, Hallettsville TX
p. 2330
Simpson, Gumpertz & Heger, Inc Library, Waltham
MA p. 1133
Simpson John Woodruff Memorial Library, East
Craftsbury VT p. 2423
Simpson Joseph T Public Library, Mechanicsburg
PA p. 2087
Simpson Kate Love Morgan County Library,
McConnelsville OH p. 1916
Simpson Library, *see* California College of the Arts
Libraries, San Francisco CA p. 196
Simpson Library, *see* University of Mary
Washington, Fredericksburg VA p. 2466
Simpson Memorial Library, Carmel ME p. 981
Simpson, Thacher & Bartlett, New York NY p. 1700
Simpson University, Redding CA p. 214
Sims Linus A Memorial Library, *see* Southeastern
Louisiana University, Hammond LA p. 950
Sims Nicholas P Library, Waxahachie TX p. 2398
Simsbury Historical Society Archives, Simsbury CT
p. 367
Simsbury Public Library, Simsbury CT p. 367
Sinai Hospital of Baltimore, Baltimore MD p. 1017
Sinai Temple, Los Angeles CA p. 177
Sinclair Community College Library, Dayton OH
p. 1894
Sinclair Gregg M Library, *see* University of Hawaii
at Manoa Library, Honolulu HI p. 566
Sinclairville Free Library, Sinclairville NY p. 1744
Sing Sing Correctional Facility Library, *see* New
York State Department of Correctional Services,
Ossining NY p. 1712
Singing River Hospital System, Pascagoula MS
p. 1311
Singletary Memorial Library, Rusk TX p. 2378
Singleton J W Education Library, *see* Halton District
School Board, Burlington ON p. 2798
Sink R F Memorial Library, *see* United States Army,
Fort Campbell KY p. 912
Sinking Spring Public Library, Sinking Spring PA
p. 2140
Sinte Gleska University Library, Mission SD p. 2215
Sinton Public Library, Sinton TX p. 2387
Sioux Center Public Library, Sioux Center IA p. 843
Sioux City Art Center, Sioux City IA p. 844
Sioux City Library Cooperative (N), Sioux City IA
p. 2943
Sioux City Public Library, Sioux City IA p. 844
Sioux County Public Library, Harrison NE p. 1400
Sioux Lookout Public Library, Sioux Lookout ON
p. 2841
Sioux Narrows Public Library, Sioux Narrows ON
p. 2842
Sioux Rapids Memorial Library, Sioux Rapids IA
p. 844
Siouxland Heritage Museums, Sioux Falls SD
p. 2218
Siouxland Libraries, Sioux Falls SD p. 2218
Sipperstein Marvin Medical Center Library, *see*
Department of Veterans Affairs, San Francisco
CA p. 241
Sir Alexander Galt Museum & Archives, Lethbridge
AB p. 2710

Sir Mortimer B Davis Jewish General Hospital,
Montreal QC p. 2901
Sir Sandford Fleming College, Lindsay ON p. 2816
Sir Sandford Fleming College of Applied Arts &
Technology Library, Peterborough ON p. 2836
Sir William Stephenson, *see* Winnipeg Public
Library, Winnipeg MB p. 2760
SIRCULS (N), *see* San Bernardino, Inyo, Riverside
Counties United Library Services, San
Bernardino CA p. 2938
Sirek William M Educational Resource Center, *see*
Fox Valley Technical College, Appleton WI
p. 2578
Sirote & Permutt, PC, Birmingham AL p. 9
Siskind, Cromarty, Ivey & Dowler, London ON
p. 2818
Siskiyou County Museum Library, Yreka CA p. 285
Siskiyou County Public Law Library, Yreka CA
p. 285
Siskiyou County Public Library, Yreka CA p. 286
Sisseton Memorial Library, Sisseton SD p. 2219
Sisseton Wahpeton College Library, Sisseton SD
p. 2219
Sisson Ruby M Memorial Library, Pagosa Springs
CO p. 319
Sister Frances Flanigan Medical Library, *see*
Community Health Partners, Lorain OH p. 1911
Sister Helen Sheehan Library, *see* Trinity University,
Washington DC p. 417
Sister Joseph Patient & Visitor Library, *see* Mayo
Clinic Libraries, Rochester MN p. 1272
Sister Ludgera Library & Learning Resource Center,
see Saint Francis Medical Center College of
Nursing, Peoria IL p. 690
Sister Stella Louise Health Science Library, *see*
Saints Mary & Elizabeth Medical Center,
Chicago IL p. 624
Sisterhood B'nai Jacob Library, *see* Congregation
B'Nai Jacob, Phoenixville PA p. 2120
Saint Joseph Hospital, Cheektowaga NY p. 1606
Sisters of Charity Hospital Medical Library, Buffalo
NY p. 1598
Sisters of Saint Mary of Namur, Buffalo NY p. 1599
Sisters of The Immaculate Conception Convent
Library, Putnam CT p. 365
Sisters, Servants of the Immaculate Heart of Mary
Archives, Immaculata PA p. 2071
Sistersville Public Library, Sistersville WV p. 2572
SIT Graduate Institute/SIT Study Abroad,
Brattleboro VT p. 2420
Sitka National Historical Park Library, *see* National
Park Service, Sitka AK p. 53
Sitting Bull College Library, Fort Yates ND p. 1842
Siuslaw Public Library District, Florence OR
p. 1998
Six Mile Regional Library District, Granite City IL
p. 651
Skadden, Arps, Slate, Meagher & Flom, New York
NY p. 1700
Skadden, Arps, Slate, Meagher & Flom, Washington
DC p. 414
Skadden, Arps, Slate, Meagher & Flom, Wilmington
DE p. 388
Skadden, Arps, Slate, Meagher & Flom, Chicago IL
p. 624
Skaggs David Research Center, *see* United States
Department of Commerce, Boulder CO p. 291
Skagit County Historical Museum, La Conner WA
p. 2519
Skagit County Law Library, Mount Vernon WA
p. 2521
Skagit Valley College, Mount Vernon WA p. 2521
Skagway Public Library, Skagway AK p. 53
Skaneateles Library Association, Skaneateles NY
p. 1744
Skeen Library, *see* New Mexico Institute of Mining
& Technology, Socorro NM p. 1565
Skene Memorial Library, Fleischmanns NY p. 1622
Skidaway Institute of Oceanography Library,
Savannah GA p. 551
Skidmore College, Saratoga Springs NY p. 1738
Skidmore, Owings & Merrill, New York NY p. 1700
Skidmore, Owings & Merrill Library, Chicago IL
p. 625
Skidompha Public Library, Damariscotta ME p. 983

Smooth Rock Falls Public Library, Smooth Rock Falls ON p. 2842

Smurfit-Stone Public Library, *see* Chaleur Library Region, Bathurst NB p. 2761

Smyrna Public, *see* Linebaugh Public Library System of Rutherford County, Smyrna TN p. 2254

Smyrna Public Library, Smyrna DE p. 386

Smyrna Public Library, Smyrna GA p. 551

Smyrna Public Library, Smyrna NY p. 1744

Smyth-Bland Regional Library, Marion VA p. 2477

Smyth Herbert Weir Classical Library, *see* Harvard Library, Cambridge MA p. 1076

Smyth Public Library, Candia NH p. 1440

Snake River School Community Library, Blackfoot ID p. 569

SNC-Lavalin Inc Library, Toronto ON p. 2858

Snc-Lavalin, Inc Library, Montreal QC p. 2901

Snead State Community College, Boaz AL p. 10

Sneden Margaret Library Information Commons, *see* Davenport University, Grand Rapids MI p. 1184

Snell Library, *see* Northeastern University Libraries, Boston MA p. 1065

Sno-Isle Libraries, Tulalip WA p. 2541

Snohomish Community Library, *see* Sno-Isle Libraries, Snohomish WA p. 2542

Snohomish County Law Library, Everett WA p. 2515

Snow College, Ephraim UT p. 2405

Snow John, Inc, Boston MA p. 1067

Snow Lake Community Library, Snow Lake MB p. 2752

Snow Library, Orleans MA p. 1116

Snowden John G Memorial Library, *see* Lycoming College, Williamsport PA p. 2156

Snowflake-Taylor Public Library, Snowflake AZ p. 82

SNR Denton, New York NY p. 1700

SNR Denton LLP Library, Washington DC p. 415

Snyder Archive, *see* Pajaro Valley Historical Association, Watsonville CA p. 282

Snyder County Historical Society, Inc Library, Middleburg PA p. 2089

Snyder County Libraries, Selinsgrove PA p. 2138

Snyder Leonard P Memorial, *see* Washington County Free Library, Clear Spring MD p. 1031

Snyder O J Memorial Library, *see* Philadelphia College of Osteopathic Medicine, Philadelphia PA p. 2114

Snyder Public Library, Snyder NE p. 1419

Soap Lake Community, *see* North Central Regional Library, Soap Lake WA p. 2549

SOCHE (N), *see* Southwestern Ohio Council for Higher Education, Dayton OH p. 2952

Social Security Administration Library, Baltimore MD p. 1017

Societe de Genealogie de l'Outaouais Bibliotheque, Gatineau QC p. 2884

Societe de Genealogie de Quebec, Sainte-Foy QC p. 2910

Societe de Transport de Montreal, Montreal QC p. 2901

Societe d'Histoire de Sherbrooke, Sherbrooke QC p. 2912

Societe d'Histoire et d'Archeologie des Monts, Inc, Sainte-Anne-des-Monts QC p. 2910

Societe Genealogique Canadienne-Francaise, Montreal QC p. 2901

Societe Genealogique de l'Est du Quebec Bibliotheque, Rimouski QC p. 2907

Societe Generale de Financement du Quebec, Montreal QC p. 2901

Societe Historique de la Cote-du-Sud Bibliotheque, La Pocatiere QC p. 2885

Societe Radio-Canada Bibliotheque, Montreal QC p. 2901

Society For Academic Achievement Library, Quincy IL p. 693

Society for the Study of Male Psychology & Physiology Library, Montpelier OH p. 1918

Society of Actuaries Library, Schaumburg IL p. 701

Society of Christian Schools In British Columbia Library, Langley BC p. 2731

Society of Cost Estimating & Analysis Library, *see* International Society of Parametric Analysts, Huntsville AL p. 22

Society of Mayflower Descendants, Oakland CA p. 199

Society of Naval Architects & Marine Engineers Library, Jersey City NJ p. 1493

Society of the Cincinnati Library, Washington DC p. 416

Society of the Four Arts Library, Palm Beach FL p. 479

Society Promoting Environmental Conservation, Vancouver BC p. 2742

Socorro Public Library, Socorro NM p. 1565

Soda Springs Public Library, Soda Springs ID p. 584

Sodus Community Library, Sodus NY p. 1744

Sodus Township Library, Sodus MI p. 1227

Soeurs Ursulines de Quebec Archives, Quebec QC p. 2906

Sofia University Library, Palo Alto CA p. 205

Software Engineering Institute Library, *see* Carnegie Mellon University, Pittsburgh PA p. 2124

SOHLIN (N), *see* Southwestern Ontario Health Libraries, St. Thomas ON p. 2960

Sohn Memorial Library, *see* Fort Hamilton Hospital, Hamilton OH p. 1903

Sojourner-Douglass College, Baltimore MD p. 1017

Sola Gerardo Selles Library, *see* University of Puerto Rico Library System, San Juan PR p. 2678

Solano Community College Library, Fairfield CA p. 148

Solano County Library, Fairfield CA p. 148

Soldier Public Library, Soldier IA p. 845

Soldiers Grove Public Library, Soldiers Grove WI p. 2638

Soldiers Memorial Library, Hiram ME p. 987

Soldotna Public Library, Soldotna AK p. 54

SOLIS (N), *see* Southern Oregon Library Information System, Medford OR p. 2953

Soliz Albert H Library, *see* Ventura County Library, Oxnard CA p. 280

Sollars Library, *see* Sears W E Youth Center, Poplar Bluff MO p. 1349

Solomon Blanche R Memorial Library, Headland AL p. 20

Solomon Medical Library, *see* Saint Mary's Medical Center, San Francisco CA p. 244

Solomon Public Library, Solomon KS p. 894

Solon Public Library, Solon IA p. 845

Solvay Public Library, Solvay NY p. 1745

Somers Historical Society Library, Somers NY p. 1745

Somers Library, Somers NY p. 1745

Somers Public Library, Somers CT p. 367

Somers Public Library, Somers IA p. 845

Somerset Community College Library, Somerset KY p. 935

Somerset County Circuit Court Library, Princess Anne MD p. 1036

Somerset County Federated Library System, Somerset PA p. 2141

Somerset County Historical Society, Bridgewater NJ p. 1475

Somerset County Law Library, Somerville NJ p. 1530

Somerset County Law Library, Somerset PA p. 2141

Somerset County Library, Somerset PA p. 2141

Somerset County Library System, Princess Anne MD p. 1036

Somerset County Library System, Bridgewater NJ p. 1475

Somerset County Park Commission, Basking Ridge NJ p. 1470

Somerset Public Library, Somerset MA p. 1124

Somerset Public Library, Somerset WI p. 2638

Somersworth Public Library, Somersworth NH p. 1465

Somervell County Library, Glen Rose TX p. 2328

Somerville-Fayette County Library, Somerville TN p. 2266

Somerville Hospital, Somerville MA p. 1124

Somerville Library, Somerville NJ p. 1530

Somerville Public Library, Somerville MA p. 1124

Somesville Library Association, Mount Desert ME p. 992

Sommers, Schwartz, Silver & Schwartz, Southfield MI p. 1228

Sommerville Mary Free Library, Mound City KS p. 884

Somonauk Public Library District, Somonauk IL p. 703

Sonabend Family Library, *see* Temple Emanu-El, Long Beach NY p. 1654

Sonnenschein, Nath & Rosenthal, Chicago IL p. 625

Sonoco Products Co, Inc, Hartsville SC p. 2198

Sonoma County Law Library, Santa Rosa CA p. 267

Sonoma County Library, Santa Rosa CA p. 267

Sonoma State University Library, Rohnert Park CA p. 219

Sonoma Valley Regional, *see* Sonoma County Library, Sonoma CA p. 268

Sons of Norway, Minneapolis MN p. 1261

Sons of Utah Pioneers Library, *see* National Society of Sons of Utah Pioneers, Salt Lake City UT p. 2413

Soper Morris A Library, *see* Morgan State University, Baltimore MD p. 1016

Soquem, Inc, Val-d'Or QC p. 2914

Sordoni-Burich Library, *see* National University of Health Sciences, Lombard IL p. 667

Sorensen A V, *see* Omaha Public Library, Omaha NE p. 1414

Sorensen Library, *see* County of Los Angeles Public Library, Whittier CA p. 143

Sorini Ernest & Kellie Medical Library, *see* Oakwood Hospital Medical Library, Dearborn MI p. 1167

Soukup Herter Library & Resource Center, *see* Elmhurst Memorial Healthcare, Elmhurst IL p. 642

Sound Shore Health System of Westchester, New Rochelle NY p. 1667

Souris Public, *see* Prince Edward Island Public Library Service, Souris PE p. 2876

Soutar Memorial Library, Boise City OK p. 1958

South American Explorers Library, Ithaca NY p. 1643

South Arkansas Community College, El Dorado AR p. 98

South Arkansas Film Coop (N), Malvern AR p. 2938

South Bannock Library District, Downey ID p. 573

South Bay Correctional Facility Library, *see* Geo Group Inc, South Bay FL p. 491

South Baylo University Library, Anaheim CA p. 121

South Beloit Public Library, South Beloit IL p. 703

South Bend Museum of Art Library, South Bend IN p. 779

South Berwick Public Library, South Berwick ME p. 1001

South Boise Women's Correctional, *see* Idaho State Correctional Institution Library, Kuna ID p. 577

South Boston Public Library, *see* Halifax County-South Boston Regional Library, South Boston VA p. 2467

South Brunswick Public Library, Monmouth Junction NJ p. 1502

South Burlington Community Library, South Burlington VT p. 2435

Crawford E R, *see* Community College of Allegheny County, West Mifflin PA p. 2154

South Carolina AHEC (N), Charleston SC p. 2955

South Carolina Attorney General's Office Library, Columbia SC p. 2188

South Carolina Commission on Higher Education Library, Columbia SC p. 2189

South Carolina Confederate Relic Room & Military Museum Library, Columbia SC p. 2189

South Carolina Department of Archives & History, Columbia SC p. 2189

South Carolina Historical Society Library, Charleston SC p. 2185

South Carolina Library Network (N), Columbia SC p. 2955

South Carolina Public Service Authority, Moncks Corner SC p. 2200

South Carolina School for the Deaf & the Blind, Spartanburg SC p. 2204

Southeast Regional, *see* Maricopa County Library District, Gilbert AZ p. 75

Southeast Regional Laboratory Library, *see* Food & Drug Administration, Atlanta GA p. 515

Southeast Regional Library, Weyburn SK p. 2929

Southeast Regional Library System (N), Wellston OH p. 2952

Southeast State Correctional Facility Library, Windsor VT p. 2440

Southeast Steuben County Library, Corning NY p. 1611

Southeastern Baptist College, Laurel MS p. 1307

Southeastern Baptist Theological Seminary Library, Wake Forest NC p. 1827

Southeastern Bible College Library, Birmingham AL p. 9

Southeastern Chapter of the American Association of Law Libraries (N), Lexington KY p. 2944

Southeastern Community College Library, West Burlington IA p. 852

Southeastern Community College Library, Whiteville NC p. 1830

Southeastern Correctional Institution Library, *see* State of Ohio Department of Corrections, Lancaster OH p. 1909

Southeastern Illinois College, Harrisburg IL p. 653

Southeastern Libraries Cooperating (N), Rochester MN p. 2947

Southeastern Louisiana University, Hammond LA p. 950, 2966

Southeastern Massachusetts Consortium of Health Science Libraries (N), Fall River MA p. 2945

Southeastern Michigan League of Libraries (N), Southfield MI p. 2946

Southeastern New York Library Resources Council (N), Highland NY p. 2950

Southeastern Oklahoma State University, Durant OK p. 1961

Southeastern Pennsylvania Theological Library Association (N), Hatfield PA p. 2954

Southeastern Public Library System of Oklahoma, McAlester OK p. 1968

Southeastern Railway Museum Library, *see* National Railway Historical Society, Atlanta Chapter, Duluth GA p. 531

Southeastern Regional Medical Center, Lumberton NC p. 1808

Southeastern Technical College, Glennville GA p. 535

Southeastern Technical College, Vidalia GA p. 556

Southeastern Technical College Library, Swainsboro GA p. 553

Southeastern Tennessee State Regional Correction Facility Library, *see* Tennessee Department of Corrections, Pikeville TN p. 2263

Southeastern University, Lakeland FL p. 460

Southeastern Wisconsin Health Science Library Consortium (N), Milwaukee WI p. 2958

Southeastern Wisconsin Information Technology Exchange, Inc (N), Milwaukee WI p. 2958

Southern Adirondack Library System, Saratoga Springs NY p. 1739

Southern Adventist University, Collegedale TN p. 2230

Southern Alberta Art Gallery Library, Lethbridge AB p. 2710

Southern Alberta Institute of Technology Library, Calgary AB p. 2693

Southern Area Library, Lost Creek WV p. 2564

Southern Arizona VA Healthcare System, *see* Department of Veterans Affairs, Tucson AZ p. 86

Southern Arkansas University, Magnolia AR p. 108

Southern Arkansas University Tech-Library, Camden AR p. 96

Southern Baptist Historical Library & Archives, Nashville TN p. 2258

Southern Baptist Theological Seminary, Louisville KY p. 925

Southern Boone County Public Library, *see* Boone Daniel Regional Library, Ashland MO p. 1324

Pollard Frank & Jane Library, *see* Golden Gate Baptist Theological, Brea CA p. 129

Southern California College of Optometry, Fullerton CA p. 154

Southern California Genealogical Society, Burbank CA p. 130

Southern California Institute of Architecture, Los Angeles CA p. 177

Southern California Library Cooperative (N), Monrovia CA p. 2939

Southern California Library for Social Studies & Research, Los Angeles CA p. 177

Southern California Seminary Library, *see* San Diego Christian College Library, El Cajon CA p. 145

Southern California University of Health Sciences, Whittier CA p. 283

Southern College of Optometry Library, Memphis TN p. 2251

Southern Connecticut State University, New Haven CT p. 356, 2963

Southern Crescent Technical College Library - Flint Campus, Thomaston GA p. 553

Southern Crop Protection & Food Research Centre Vineland Library, *see* Agriculture & Agri-Food Canada, Vineland Station ON p. 2868

Southern Harbour Public Library, Southern Harbour NL p. 2770

Southern Highland Craft Guild, Asheville NC p. 1775

Southern Illinois University Carbondale, Carbondale IL p. 600

Southern Illinois University Edwardsville, Alton IL p. 588

Southern Illinois University Edwardsville, Edwardsville IL p. 639

Southern Illinois University School of Medicine Library, Springfield IL p. 706

Southern Lehigh Public Library, Center Valley PA p. 2043

Southern Maine Community College Library, South Portland ME p. 1002

Southern Maine Library District, Portland ME p. 997

Southern Maine Medical Center, Biddeford ME p. 978

Southern Maryland Hospital Center Library, Clinton MD p. 1024

Southern Maryland Regional Library Association, Inc, Charlotte Hall MD p. 1023

Southern Methodist College, Orangeburg SC p. 2202

Southern Methodist University, Dallas TX p. 2310

Southern Nazarene University, Bethany OK p. 1958

Southern New England School of Law Library, North Dartmouth MA p. 1112

Southern New Hampshire University, Manchester NH p. 1456

Southern New Mexico Correctional Facility Library, *see* New Mexico Corrections Department, Las Cruces NM p. 1558

Southern Oaks Library, *see* Metropolitan Library System in Oklahoma County, Oklahoma City OK p. 1973

Southern Ocean Medical Center, Manahawkin NJ p. 1498

Southern Oregon Library Federation (N), Klamath Falls OR p. 2953

Southern Oregon Library Information System (N), Medford OR p. 2953

Southern Oregon University, Ashland OR p. 1990

Southern Pines Public Library, Southern Pines NC p. 1824

Southern Polytechnic State University, Marietta GA p. 543

Southern Poverty Law Center, Montgomery AL p. 31

Southern Prairie Library System, Altus OK p. 1955

Southern Regional Area Health Education Center, Fayetteville NC p. 1793

Southern Regional Council, Inc, Atlanta GA p. 518

Southern Regional Education Board Library, Atlanta GA p. 518

Southern Research Institute, Birmingham AL p. 9

Southern State Community College, Hillsboro OH p. 1904

Southern States Energy Board, Norcross GA p. 547

Southern Tier Library System, Painted Post NY p. 1714

Southern Union State Community College, Wadley AL p. 40

Southern University, Baton Rouge LA p. 944

Southern University at Shreveport, Shreveport LA p. 970

Southern Utah University, Cedar City UT p. 2404

Southern Utah University Sherratt Library, Cedar City UT p. 2975

Southern Vermont College Library, Bennington VT p. 2419

Southern Virginia University, Buena Vista VA p. 2453

Southern Wasco County Library, Maupin OR p. 2004

Southern Wesleyan University, Central SC p. 2183

Southern West Virginia Community & Technical College, Danville WV p. 2558

Southern West Virginia Community & Technical College, Mount Gay WV p. 2567

Southern West Virginia Community & Technical College, Saulsville WV p. 2571

Southern West Virginia Community & Technical College, Williamson WV p. 2575

Southfield Public Library, Southfield MI p. 1228

Southgate Community Library, *see* Sacramento Public Library, Sacramento CA p. 225

Southgate Community Library, *see* Wake County Public Library System, Raleigh NC p. 1818

Southgate Public Library, Dundalk ON p. 2802

Southgate Veterans Memorial Library, Southgate MI p. 1229

Southglenn Public, *see* Arapahoe Library District, Centennial CO p. 306

Southington Public Library & Museum, Southington CT p. 368

Southlake Public Library, Southlake TX p. 2388

Southlake Regional Health Center, Newmarket ON p. 2824

Southold Free Library, Southold NY p. 1746

Southold Historical Society Museum Library, Southold NY p. 1746

Southport Memorial Library, Southport ME p. 1002

SouthShore Regional Library, *see* Tampa-Hillsborough County Public Library System, Ruskin FL p. 498

Southside Baptist Church, Lakeland FL p. 460

Southside Hospital Medical Library, *see* North Shore LIJ Health System, Bay Shore NY p. 1578

Southside Regional Library, Boydton VA p. 2452

Southside Regional Medical Center, Petersburg VA p. 2484

Southside Virginia Community College, Keysville VA p. 2472

Southside Virginia Community College Libraries, Alberta VA p. 2444

Southside Virginia Library Network (N), Farmville VA p. 2957

Southwest Applied Technology College, Cedar City UT p. 2404

Southwest Area Multicounty Multitype Interlibrary Exchange (N), Marshall MN p. 2947

Southwest Arkansas Regional Archives, Washington AR p. 117

Southwest Arkansas Regional Library, Hope AR p. 103

Southwest Baptist University Libraries, Bolivar MO p. 1320

Southwest College of Naturopathic Medicine & Health Sciences Library, Tempe AZ p. 84

Southwest Collegiate Institute for the Deaf, *see* Howard County Junior College, Big Spring TX p. 2289

Southwest County Regional, *see* Palm Beach County Library System, Boca Raton FL p. 503

Southwest Florida College, Fort Myers FL p. 446

Southwest Florida Library Network (N), Fort Myers FL p. 2940

Southwest Florida Regional Planning Council Library, Fort Myers FL p. 446

Southwest Florida Water Management District Library, Brooksville FL p. 431

Southwest Georgia Regional Library, Bainbridge GA p. 521

Southwest Georgia Technical College Library, Thomasville GA p. 553

Southwest Harbor Public Library, Southwest Harbor ME p. 1002

Southwest Health Center, Platteville WI p. 2630

Southwest Kansas Library System, Dodge City KS p. 864

Southwest Louisiana Genealogical Library, *see* Calcasieu Parish Public Library, Lake Charles LA p. 954

Southwest Michigan Library Cooperative (N), Paw Paw MI p. 2946

Southwest Minnesota State University Library, Marshall MN p. 1258

Southwest Mississippi Community College, Summit MS p. 1315

SouthWest Ohio & Neighboring Libraries (N), Blue Ash OH p. 2952

Southwest Ohio Regional Depository SWORD, *see* Miami University Libraries, Middletown OH p. 1926

Southwest Oklahoma City Public Library, *see* Pioneer Library System, Oklahoma City OK p. 1970

Southwest Public Libraries, Grove City OH p. 1903

Southwest Regional Library, *see* Atlanta-Fulton Public Library System, Atlanta GA p. 512

Southwest Research & Information Center Library, Albuquerque NM p. 1550

Southwest School of Arts Library, San Antonio TX p. 2383

Southwest Tennessee Community College, Memphis TN p. 2251

Southwest Texas Junior College, Uvalde TX p. 2394

Southwest Virginia Community College Library, Cedar Bluff VA p. 2453

Southwest Washington Medical Center Library, Vancouver WA p. 2546

Southwest Wisconsin Library System, Fennimore WI p. 2591

Southwestern Adventist University, Keene TX p. 2349

Southwestern Assemblies of God University, Waxahachie TX p. 2398

Southwestern Baptist Theological Seminary Libraries, Fort Worth TX p. 2323

Southwestern Behavioral Healthcare, Inc, Evansville IN p. 739

Southwestern Christian College, Terrell TX p. 2391

Southwestern Christian University Library, Bethany OK p. 1958

Southwestern College, Phoenix AZ p. 77

Southwestern College, Winfield KS p. 902

Southwestern College, Santa Fe NM p. 1564

Southwestern College Library, Chula Vista CA p. 134

Southwestern Community College, Creston IA p. 805

Southwestern Community College Library, Sylva NC p. 1826

Southwestern Illinois College, Granite City IL p. 651

Southwestern Illinois College Library, Belleville IL p. 593

Southwestern Illinois Correctional Center Library, *see* Illinois Department of Corrections, East Saint Louis IL p. 639

Southwestern Illinois Metropolitan & Regional Planning Commission, Collinsville IL p. 631

Southwestern Indian Polytechnic Institute Libraries, Albuquerque NM p. 1550

Southwestern Manitoba Regional Library, Melita MB p. 2749

Southwestern Michigan College, Dowagiac MI p. 1174

Southwestern Ohio Council for Higher Education (N), Dayton OH p. 2952

Southwestern Oklahoma State University, Weatherford OK p. 1985

Southwestern Ontario Health Libraries (N), St. Thomas ON p. 2960

Southwestern Oregon Community College, Coos Bay OR p. 1993

Southwestern University, Los Angeles CA p. 177

Southwestern University, Georgetown TX p. 2327

Southwestern Vermont Health Care, Bennington VT p. 2419

Southwestern Virginia Health Information Librarians (N), Roanoke VA p. 2957

Southwestern Virginia Mental Health Institute Library, Marion VA p. 2477

Southwestern Virginia Training Center, Hillsville VA p. 2472

Southwick Public Library, Southwick MA p. 1126

Southworth Library, *see* Dartmouth Public Libraries, Dartmouth MA p. 1084

Southworth Library, *see* State University of New York College of Technology, Canton NY p. 1602

Southworth Library Association, Dryden NY p. 1615

Soutter Lamar Library, *see* University of Massachusetts Medical School, Worcester MA p. 1144

Souvay Charles L Memorial Library, *see* Kenrick-Glennon Seminary, Saint Louis MO p. 1355

Sowder Bob G Library, *see* Lord Fairfax Community College, Warrenton VA p. 2479

Soyinfo Center Library, Lafayette CA p. 163

Schwerdtfeger Library, *see* University of Wisconsin-Madison, Madison WI p. 2609

Space Telescope Science Institute Library, Baltimore MD p. 1017

Spahr Engineering Library, *see* University of Kansas Libraries, Lawrence KS p. 878

Spalding Memorial Library, Athens PA p. 2030

Spalding Public Library, Spalding NE p. 1420

Spalding University Library, Louisville KY p. 925

Spangler Library, *see* Cleveland County Library System, Lawndale NC p. 1823

Spangler William Library, *see* Atlantic Cape Community College, Mays Landing NJ p. 1500

Spanish Fork Public Library, Spanish Fork UT p. 2416

Spanish Peaks Library District, Walsenburg CO p. 325

Spanish Public Library, Spanish ON p. 2842

Spanish Springs Library, *see* Washoe County Library System, Sparks NV p. 1434

Sparrow Health Sciences Library, *see* Sparrow Health System, Lansing MI p. 1202

Sparrow Health System, Lansing MI p. 1202

Sparta Free Library, Sparta WI p. 2639

Sparta Public Library, Sparta IL p. 704

Sparta Public Library, Sparta NJ p. 1531

Sparta Township Library, Sparta MI p. 1229

Spartan College of Aeronautics & Technology Library, Tulsa OK p. 1982

Spartanburg Community College Library, Spartanburg SC p. 2205

Spartanburg County Public Libraries, Spartanburg SC p. 2205

Spartanburg Methodist College, Spartanburg SC p. 2205

Spartanburg Regional Medical Center, Spartanburg SC p. 2205

Sparwood Public Library, Sparwood BC p. 2737

Spaulding Harriet M Library, *see* New England Conservatory of Music, Boston MA p. 1064

Spaulding Memorial Library, Sebago ME p. 1000

Spaulding Rehabilitation Hospital, Boston MA p. 1067

Spear MN Memorial Library, Shutesbury MA p. 1124

Speare Alden Memorial Library, *see* Chelsea Public Library, Chelsea VT p. 2421

Spears Center for Pastoral Research Library, *see* HealthCare Chaplaincy, New York NY p. 1681

Spearville Township Library, Spearville KS p. 895

Special Collections/Long Island Studies Institute, *see* Hofstra University, Hempstead NY p. 1635

Special Education Service Agency, Anchorage AK p. 45

Special Libraries Association, Alexandria VA p. 2446

Speckler Library, *see* Calumet College of Saint Joseph, Whiting IN p. 787

Spectrum Health, Grand Rapids MI p. 1186

Speed Art Museum Library, Louisville KY p. 925

Speed Leland Library, *see* Mississippi College, Clinton MS p. 1296

Speedway Public Library, Speedway IN p. 780

Speer Library, *see* Princeton Theological Seminary, Princeton NJ p. 1522

Speer Memorial Library, Mission TX p. 2363

Spellman John Library, *see* Grays Harbor College, Aberdeen WA p. 2507

Spellman Museum of Stamps & Postal History Library, Weston MA p. 1139

Spellman Nancy W Memorial Library, *see* American Institute for Chartered Property Casualty Underwriters & Insurance, Malvern PA p. 2083

Spellman Oliver B Law Libray, *see* Southern University, Baton Rouge LA p. 944

Spencer Art Reference Library, *see* Nelson-Atkins Museum of Art, Kansas City MO p. 1340

Spencer County Public Library, Rockport IN p. 776

Spencer County Public Library, Taylorsville KY p. 936

Spencer Glover Memorial Library, Rush Springs OK p. 1977

Spencer Library, Spencer NY p. 1746

Spencer Library, *see* United Theological Seminary of the Twin Cities, New Brighton MN p. 1267

Spencer Library, *see* Imperial Valley College, Imperial CA p. 159

Spencer Public Library, Spencer IA p. 845

Spencer Public Library, Spencer NC p. 1825

Spencer Research Library, *see* University of Kansas Libraries, Lawrence KS p. 878

Spencer Stuart Library, Chicago IL p. 625

Spencer Township Library, Spencer NE p. 1420

Spencerian College Lexington, *see* Sullivan University Library, Lexington KY p. 926

Sperling-Mack-Kronberg Holocaust Library, *see* JFSA Holocaust Resource Center, Las Vegas NV p. 1429

Sperry Albert F Library, *see* ISA - The International Society of Automation, Research Triangle Park NC p. 1819

Sperry Marine, Charlottesville VA p. 2454

Spertus Institute of Jewish Studies, Chicago IL p. 625

Spi Supplies Division of Structure Probe, Inc, West Chester PA p. 2153

Spiceland Town-Township Public Library, Spiceland IN p. 780

Spicer Library, Spicer MN p. 1285

Spiegel & McDiarmid LLP, Washington DC p. 416

Spies Public Library, Menominee MI p. 1208

Spillman Library, North Fond du Lac WI p. 2625

Spillville Public Library, Spillville IA p. 845

Spina Bifida & Hydrocephalus Association of Ontario, Toronto ON p. 2858

Spindale Public Library, Spindale NC p. 1825

Spindler George W Memorial Library, Woodland MI p. 1237

Spirit Lake Public Library, Spirit Lake IA p. 845

Spirit River Municipal Library, Spirit River AB p. 2717

Spiritwood Public Library, *see* Wapiti Regional Library, Spiritwood SK p. 2922

Spiro Public Library, Spiro OK p. 1978

Spishock Library, *see* Navy Personnel Research, Studies & Technology, Millington TN p. 2253

Spiva George A Library, *see* Missouri Southern State University, Joplin MO p. 1336

Spokane Community College Library, Spokane WA p. 2536

Spokane County Law Library, Spokane WA p. 2536

Spokane County Library District, Spokane WA p. 2536

Spokane Falls Community College, Spokane WA p. 2537, 2975

Spokane Public Library, Spokane WA p. 2537

Spokesman-Review, Spokane WA p. 2538

Spoon River College Library, Canton IL p. 599

Spoon River Public Library District, Cuba IL p. 632

Spooner Memorial Library, Spooner WI p. 2639

Sport Information Resource Centre (SIRC), Ottawa ON p. 2833

Sports Illustrated Library, New York NY p. 1700

Spotswood Public Library, Spotswood NJ p. 1531

Sprague Harry A Library, *see* Montclair State University, Montclair NJ p. 1503

Sprague Public Library, Baltic CT p. 330

Sprague Public Library, Sprague WA p. 2538

Sprauve Elaine Ione Library, Saint John VI p. 2679

Elaine Ione Sprauve Library, *see* Virgin Islands Division of Libraries, Archives & Museums VI p. 2680

Sprehe Ralph W & Bernice S Library, *see* Centralia Regional Library District, Hoffman IL p. 602

Spring Arbor University, Spring Arbor MI p. 1229

Spring Branch Memorial, *see* Harris County Public Library, Houston TX p. 2336

Spring City Free Public Library, Spring City PA p. 2142

Spring Creek Correctional Center Library, Seward AK p. 53

Spring Garden Road Memorial, *see* Halifax Public Libraries, Halifax NS p. 2779

Spring Green Community Library, Spring Green WI p. 2639

Spring Grove Hospital Center, Catonsville MD p. 1023

Spring Hill College, Mobile AL p. 26

Spring Lake District Library, Spring Lake MI p. 1229

Spring Lake Public Library, Spring Lake NJ p. 1532

Spring Township Library, Wyomissing PA p. 2159

Spring Valley Library, *see* Las Vegas-Clark County Library District, Las Vegas NV p. 1430

Spring Valley Public Library, Spring Valley MN p. 1285

Spring Valley Public Library, Spring Valley WI p. 2639

Springbank Township Library, Allen NE p. 1391

Springboro Public Library, Springboro PA p. 2142

Springdale Free Public Library, Springdale PA p. 2142

Springdale Public Library, Springdale AR p. 115

Springfield Art Association, Springfield IL p. 706

Springfield Art Museum, Springfield MO p. 1367

Springfield City Library, Springfield MA p. 1127

Springfield College, Springfield MA p. 1128

Springfield Free Public Library, Springfield NJ p. 1532

Springfield-Greene County Library District, Springfield MO p. 1367

Springfield Hospital Library, Springfield VT p. 2436

Springfield Hospital Medical Library, Springfield PA p. 2142

Springfield Library, Springfield Center NY p. 1747

Springfield Memorial Library, Springfield NE p. 1420

Springfield Museum of Art Library, Springfield OH p. 1936

Springfield News-Leader Library, Springfield MO p. 1368

Springfield News-Sun Library, Springfield OH p. 1936

Springfield Public Library, Springfield MN p. 1285

Springfield Public Library, Springfield OR p. 2020

Springfield Public Library, *see* Northwest Regional Library System, Springfield FL p. 481

Springfield Technical Community College Library, Springfield MA p. 1128

Springfield Town Library, Springfield VT p. 2436

Springfield Township Library, Davisburg MI p. 1167

Springfield Township Library, Springfield PA p. 2142

Springhill Miners Memorial Library, *see* Cumberland Public Libraries, Springhill NS p. 2777

Springlake-Earth Community Library, Springlake TX p. 2388

Springmier Community Library, Tiffin IA p. 847

Springport Free Library, Union Springs NY p. 1757

Springs Elliot White Business Library, *see* University of South Carolina, Columbia SC p. 2190

Springstowne Library, *see* Solano County Library, Vallejo CA p. 148

Springtown Public Library, Springtown TX p. 2388

Springvale Public Library, Springvale ME p. 1002

Springville Memorial Library, Springville IA p. 845

Springville Public Library, Springville UT p. 2416

Sprouse Nigel Memorial Library, Callaway NE p. 1395

Spruce Grove Public Library, Spruce Grove AB p. 2717

Spruce Pine Public Library, Spruce Pine NC p. 1825

Spruce View Public Library, Spruce View AB p. 2717

Squamish Public Library, Squamish BC p. 2738

Squire Eleanor Library, *see* Cleveland Botanical Garden, Cleveland OH p. 1876

Squire, Sanders & Dempsey, Columbus OH p. 1890

Squire, Sanders & Dempsey Library, Washington DC p. 416

Squire Sanders & Dempsey LLC Library, Miami FL p. 468

Squires Patrick Library, *see* Nevada System of Higher Education, Reno NV p. 1432

Sri Aurobindo Sadhana Peetham Library, Lodi CA p. 165

SRI International, Menlo Park CA p. 185

SS Cyril & Methodius Seminary, Orchard Lake MI p. 1215

SSHELCO (N), *see* State System of Higher Education Library Cooperative, Slippery Rock PA p. 2955

Saint Francis Public Library, Saint Francis WI p. 2635

Staats Joan Library, *see* Jackson Laboratory, Bar Harbor ME p. 976

Staatsburg Library, Staatsburg NY p. 1747

Stacks Rare Coin Company of NY, New York NY p. 1700

Stacyville Public Library, Stacyville IA p. 845

Stafford Creek Correctional Center, *see* Washington State Library, Aberdeen WA p. 2545

Stafford J W & Lois Library, *see* Columbia College, Columbia MO p. 1324

Stafford Library, Stafford CT p. 369

Stafford R H, *see* Washington County Library, Woodbury MN p. 1290

Stahl John A Library, West Point NE p. 1423

Stahler Helen Library, *see* Christ United Methodist Church Library, Akron OH p. 1853

Staiger Ralph C Library, *see* International Reading Association Library, Newark DE p. 385

Stair Public Library, Morenci MI p. 1210

Stake Family History Center, *see* Church of Jesus Christ of Latter-Day Saints, Broomall PA p. 2038

Staley Library, *see* Millikin University, Decatur IL p. 634

Stallo Francis J Memorial, *see* Auglaize County Public District Library, Minster OH p. 1944

Stamats Herbert S Library, *see* Cedar Rapids Museum of Art, Cedar Rapids IA p. 800

Stamford Carnegie Library, Stamford TX p. 2389

Stamford Community Library, Stamford VT p. 2436

Stamford Historical Society Library, Stamford CT p. 370

Stamford Hospital, Stamford CT p. 370

Stamford Law Library, *see* Connecticut Judicial Branch Law Libraries, Stamford CT p. 344

Stamford Village Library, Stamford NY p. 1747

Stamps H B Memorial Library, Rogersville TN p. 2264

Standard Municipal Library, Standard AB p. 2718

Standardbred Canada Library, Mississauga ON p. 2823

Standards Council of Canada, Ottawa ON p. 2833

Standish J Spencer & Patricia Library, *see* Siena College, Loudonville NY p. 1655

Standley Lake Library, *see* Jefferson County Public Library, Arvada CO p. 315

Stanfield Public Library, Stanfield OR p. 2020

Stanford Comprehensive Cancer Center, *see* Stanford Health Library, Stanford CA p. 205

Stanford Free Library, Stanfordville NY p. 1747

Stanford Health Library, Palo Alto CA p. 205

Stanford Hospital, *see* Stanford Health Library, Palo Alto CA p. 205

Stanford Linear Accelerator Center Research Library, *see* Stanford University Libraries, Menlo Park CA p. 271

Stanford University Libraries, Stanford CA p. 270

Stanhope Public Library, Stanhope IA p. 845

Stanislaus County Free Library, Modesto CA p. 188

Stanislaus County Law Library, Modesto CA p. 189

Stanley Community Public Library, Stanley ID p. 584

Stanley Correctional Institution Library, Stanley WI p. 2639

Stanley Dean F MD Memorial Library, *see* Decatur Memorial Hospital, Decatur IL p. 633

Stanley Doris Memorial Library, Moody AL p. 31

Stanley Edmund Library, *see* Friends University, Wichita KS p. 900

Stanley Public Library, Stanley ND p. 1848

Stanley Thomas Library, *see* Ferrum College, Ferrum VA p. 2463

Stanley Tubbs Memorial Library, Sallisaw OK p. 1977

Stanly Community College, Albemarle NC p. 1773

Stanly County Public Library, Albemarle NC p. 1773

Stansel Horace Memorial, *see* Sunflower County Library System, Ruleville MS p. 1302

Stanstead College, Stanstead QC p. 2913

Stantec Architecture Inc Library, San Francisco CA p. 247

Stanton Community Library, Stanton IA p. 845

Stanton County Library, Johnson KS p. 874

Stanton Public Library, Stanton NE p. 1420

Stanton W H Memorial Library, *see* Uncle Remus Regional Library System, Social Circle GA p. 542

Stanwood Community Library, *see* Sno-Isle Libraries, Stanwood WA p. 2542

Stanwood Public Library, Stanwood IA p. 845

Staples Public Library, *see* Great River Regional Library, Staples MN p. 1276

Stapleton Library, *see* Indiana University of Pennsylvania, Indiana PA p. 2071

Star Academy Center Library, *see* Department of Corrections, Custer SD p. 2112

Star City Public Library, *see* Wapiti Regional Library, Star City SK p. 2922

Star of the Republic Museum Library, Washington TX p. 2398

Star Tribune, Minneapolis MN p. 1261

Stark County District Library, Canton OH p. 1864

Stark County Law Library, Canton OH p. 1865

Starke County Public Library System, Knox IN p. 757

Starksboro Public Library, Starksboro VT p. 2436

Starkville-Oktibbeha County Public, Starkville MS p. 1315

Starr C V East Asian Library, *see* Columbia University, New York NY p. 1675

Starr C V Library, *see* Japan Society, New York NY p. 1683

Starr County Public Library, Larosita TX p. 2354

Starr County Public Library, Roma TX p. 2377

Starr Dorothy C S Civil War Research Library, *see* Fort Ward Museum, Alexandria VA p. 2445

Starr Library, Rhinebeck NY p. 1727

STARRT (Skilled Trades & Apprenticeship Research, Resources & Training), *see* Mohawk College Library, Stoney Creek ON p. 2810

Starsmore Center for Local History Library, *see* Colorado Springs Pioneers Museum, Colorado Springs CO p. 295

Start-Kilgour Memorial Library, *see* Simpson University, Redding CA p. 214

State Assisted Academic Library Council of Kentucky (N), Cincinnati OH p. 2952

State Botanical Garden of Georgia Library, Athens GA p. 509

State Capital Museum & Outreach Center, *see* Washington State Historical Society, Olympia WA p. 2523

State Correctional Institution, Albion PA p. 2026

State Correctional Institution, Bellefonte PA p. 2032

State Correctional Institution, Camp Hill PA p. 2041

State Correctional Institution, Frackville PA p. 2058

State Correctional Institution, Houtzdale PA p. 2070

State Correctional Institution, Hunlock Creek PA p. 2070

State Correctional Institution, Huntingdon PA p. 2070

State Correctional Institution, Indiana PA p. 2071

State Correctional Institution, Somerset PA p. 2141

State Correctional Institution, Waymart PA p. 2152

State Education Resource Center Library, Middletown CT p. 352

Stettenheim Ivan M Library, *see* Congregation Emanu-El of the City of New York, New York NY p. 1676

Stettler Public Library, Stettler AB p. 2718

Stevens Ash Inc Library, Detroit MI p. 1172

Stevens Charles E American Atheist Library & Archives, Inc, Cranford NJ p. 1480

Stevens County Library, Hugoton KS p. 872

Stevens-German Library, *see* Hartwick College, Oneonta NY p. 1710

Stevens Henager College Library, Ogden UT p. 2408

Stevens Institute of Technology, Hoboken NJ p. 1491

Stevens Library, *see* Connecticut River Museum, Essex CT p. 338

Stevens Memorial Community Library, Attica NY p. 1575

Stevens Memorial Library, Ashburnham MA p. 1050

Stevens Memorial Library, North Andover MA p. 1112

Stevens Museum - The John Hay Center, *see* Washington County Historical Society Library, Salem IN p. 777

Stevenson Community Library, *see* Fort Vancouver Regional Library District, Stevenson WA p. 2546

Stevenson George B Library, *see* Lock Haven University of Pennsylvania, Lock Haven PA p. 2082

Stevenson-Ives Library, *see* McLean County Museum of History, Bloomington IL p. 595

Stevenson Library, *see* Bard College, Annandale-on-Hudson NY p. 1574

Stevenson Public Library, Stevenson AL p. 36

Stevenson Robert L, *see* Los Angeles Public Library System, Los Angeles CA p. 174

Stevenson University Library, Stevenson MD p. 1043

Stevensville Library, *see* North Valley Public Library, Stevensville MT p. 1388

Stewart Charles B, *see* Montgomery County Memorial Library System, Montgomery TX p. 2301

Stewart County Public Library, Dover TN p. 2233

Stewart David M Library, *see* Stewart Museum, Montreal QC p. 2901

Stewart David Memorial Library, *see* Southfield Public Library, Southfield MI p. 1228

Stewart Ewell Sale Library, *see* Academy of Natural Sciences of Philadelphia, Philadelphia PA p. 2102

Stewart Free Library, Corinna ME p. 982

Stewart John Memorial Library, *see* Wilson College, Chambersburg PA p. 2043

Stewart-Lakewood Library, *see* Atlanta-Fulton Public Library System, Atlanta GA p. 512

Stewart Library, *see* North Georgia College & State University, Dahlonega GA p. 527

Stewart Library, *see* Weber State University, Ogden UT p. 2409

Stewart Memorial Library, *see* Coe College, Cedar Rapids IA p. 800

Stewart Museum, Montreal QC p. 2901

Stewart Public Library, North Anson ME p. 993

Stewart Public Library, Stewart BC p. 2738

Stewart Resource Centre, *see* Saskatchewan Teachers' Federation, Saskatoon SK p. 2926

Stewart S Walter, *see* Toronto Public Library, Toronto ON p. 2863

Stewart-Swift Research Center, Middlebury VT p. 2428

Stewartsville Library, *see* Bedford Public Library System, Vinton VA p. 2451

Stewartville Public Library, Stewartville MN p. 1285

Stey-Nevant Public Library, Farrell PA p. 2057

Stickney Crossing Library, *see* Great River Regional Library, Clearwater MN p. 1276

Stickney-Forest View Public Library District, Stickney IL p. 707

Stiern Walter W Library, *see* California State University, Bakersfield CA p. 123

Stigler Public Library, Stigler OK p. 1978

Still A T Memorial Library, *see* A T Still University of Health Sciences, Kirksville MO p. 1342

Stillman College, Tuscaloosa AL p. 38

Stillman Library, *see* Tobey Hospital, Wareham MA p. 1133

Stillwater County Library, Columbus MT p. 1377

Stillwater Free Library, Stillwater NY p. 1749

Stillwater Public Library, Stillwater MN p. 1285

Stillwater Public Library, Stillwater OK p. 1978

Stilwell Public Library, Stilwell OK p. 1979

Stimley Sherman E Blue Ridge Neighborhood Library, *see* Houston Public Library, Houston TX p. 2340

Stimson Library, *see* United States Army, Fort Sam Houston TX p. 2321

Stine Laboratory Library, *see* E I Du Pont De Nemours & Co, Inc, Newark DE p. 385

Stinson Memorial Public Library District, Anna IL p. 589

Stinson, Morrison, Hecker Library, Kansas City MO p. 1341

Stirling Municipal Library, Stirling AB p. 2718

Stirling-Randon Public Library, Stirling ON p. 2845

Stites & Harbison, Louisville KY p. 926

Stitt David L & Jane Library, *see* Austin Presbyterian Theological Seminary, Austin TX p. 2278

Stockbridge Library, *see* Capital Area District Libraries, Stockbridge MI p. 1200

Stockbridge Library Association, Stockbridge MA p. 1129

Stockmen's Memorial Foundation Library, Cochrane AB p. 2695

Stockport Public Library, Stockport IA p. 846

Stockton Public Library, Stockton KS p. 895

Stockton-San Joaquin County Public Library, Stockton CA p. 272

Stockton Springs Community Library, Stockton Springs ME p. 1003

Stockton Township Public Library, Stockton IL p. 708

Stockwell-Mudd Libraries, *see* Albion College, Albion MI p. 1148

Stoel, Rives, Boley, Jones & Grey, Seattle WA p. 2532

Stoel Rives LLP, Portland OR p. 2014

Stohlman Library, *see* Caritas St Elizabeth's Medical Center, Boston MA p. 1059

Stokely Memorial Library, Newport TN p. 2262

Stokes Donald E Library, *see* Princeton University, Princeton NJ p. 1524

Stokes Louis Health Sciences Library, *see* Howard University Libraries, Washington DC p. 404

Stokes Rembert Learning Resources Center Library, *see* Wilberforce University, Wilberforce OH p. 1948

Stoll Keenon Ogden PLLC, Lexington KY p. 921

Stone Charles H Memorial Library, Pilot Mountain NC p. 1814

Stone Child College, Box Elder MT p. 1375

Stone County Library, Mountain View AR p. 110

Stone County Library, Galena MO p. 1329

Stone George G Center for Children's Books, *see* Claremont Graduate University, Claremont CA p. 134

Stone Memorial Library, Conneautville PA p. 2047

Kellogg Sue, *see* DeKalb County Public Library, Stone Mountain GA p. 530

Stone Olive Clifford Library, *see* Clymer Rolla A Research Library, El Dorado KS p. 865

Stone Ralph & Co, Inc, Los Angeles CA p. 177

Stone Ridge Public Library, Stone Ridge NY p. 1749

Stone-Robinson Library, *see* Selma University, Selma AL p. 36

Stone School Museum Collections Library, *see* Newmarket Historical Society, Newmarket NH p. 1460

Stone Science Library, *see* Boston University Libraries, Boston MA p. 1059

Stoneham Public Library, Stoneham MA p. 1129

Stonehenge Study Group, Santa Barbara CA p. 261

Stonehenge Viewpoint Library, *see* Stonehenge Study Group, Santa Barbara CA p. 261

Stonehill College, Easton MA p. 1086

Stones River Regional Library, Murfreesboro TN p. 2255

Stonewall County Library, Aspermont TX p. 2277

Stonewall Library, *see* Stonewall National Museum & Archives, Fort Lauderdale FL p. 444

Stonewall National Museum & Archives, Fort Lauderdale FL p. 444

Stonewall Public, *see* East Mississippi Regional Library System, Stonewall MS p. 1313

Stonington Free Library, Stonington CT p. 370

Stonington Historical Society, Stonington CT p. 370

Stonington Public Library, Stonington ME p. 1003

Stonington Township Public Library, Stonington IL p. 708

Stony Brook University, Stony Brook NY p. 1749

Stony Creek Free Library, Stony Creek NY p. 1750

Stony Plain Public Library, Stony Plain AB p. 2718

Storey County Public Library, Virginia City NV p. 1435

Storm Lake Public Library, Storm Lake IA p. 846

Stormont, Dundas & Glengarry County Library, Cornwall ON p. 2801

Stormont-Vail Healthcare, Topeka KS p. 897

Storms Douglas Memorial Library, *see* York Central Hospital, Richmond Hill ON p. 2839

Storrowton Village Museum Library, West Springfield MA p. 1137

Storrs Richard Salter Library, Longmeadow MA p. 1100

Stott Explorers Library, *see* Johnson Martin & Osa Safari Museum, Chanute KS p. 860

Stottman Dorothea, *see* Bullitt County Public Library, Louisville KY p. 935

Stoughton Public Library, Stoughton MA p. 1129

Stoughton Public Library, Stoughton WI p. 2640

Stout Reference Library, *see* Indianapolis Museum of Art, Indianapolis IN p. 754

Stow-Munroe Falls Public Library, Stow OH p. 1937

Stowe Free Library, Stowe VT p. 2436

Stowe Harriet Beecher Center Library, Hartford CT p. 347

Stowe Lyman Maynard Library, *see* University of Connecticut Health Center, Farmington CT p. 340

Stowell George H Free Library, Cornish Flat NH p. 1444

Stoxen Library, *see* Dickinson State University, Dickinson ND p. 1840

Stradling, Yocca, Carlson & Rauth, Newport Beach CA p. 194

Strasburg Community, *see* Shenandoah County Library, Strasburg VA p. 2460

Strasburg-Heisler Library, Strasburg PA p. 2143

Strasburger & Price LLP Library, Dallas TX p. 2310

Stratford Free Public Library, Stratford NJ p. 1532

Stratford Historical Society Library, Stratford CT p. 371

Stratford Library Association, Stratford CT p. 371

Stratford Public, *see* Prince Edward Island Public Library Service, Stratford PE p. 2876

Stratford Public Library, Stratford IA p. 846

Stratford Public Library, North Stratford NH p. 1461

Stratford Public Library, Stratford ON p. 2845

Strathcona County Library, Sherwood Park AB p. 2716

Strathmore Municipal Library, Strathmore AB p. 2718

Stratton Free Library, West Swanzey NH p. 1467

Stratton Leslie M Medical Library, *see* Methodist Healthcare, Memphis TN p. 2250

Stratton Public Library, Stratton CO p. 323

Stratton Public Library, Stratton ME p. 1003

Stratton Public Library, Stratton NE p. 1420

Stratton Samuel S VA Medical Center, *see* VA Healthcare Network - Upstate New York, Albany NY p. 1571

Straub Clinic & Hospital, Honolulu HI p. 565

Strauss G Robert Jr Memorial Library, *see* Albright-Knox Art Gallery, Buffalo NY p. 1596

Strawberry Point Public Library, Strawberry Point IA p. 846

Strawbery Banke, Inc, Portsmouth NH p. 1463

Strayer University, Washington DC p. 416

Strazzeri Medical Library, *see* Providence Holy Cross Medical Center, Mission Hills CA p. 187

Streator Public Library, Streator IL p. 708

Street John L Library, Cadiz KY p. 909

Streeter Centennial Library, Streeter ND p. 1848

Strickler Richard Lee Research Center, *see* Ocean County Historical Society, Toms River NJ p. 1534

Stroke Recovery Association, Barrie ON p. 2794

Stromberg Joseph G Library of the Health Sciences, *see* Swedish Covenant Hospital, Chicago IL p. 625

Stromsburg Public Library, Stromsburg NE p. 1420

Strong B Elizabeth Memorial Library, Turin NY p. 1757

Strong Dr Joseph M Memorial Library, *see* EMH Regional Healthcare System, Elyria OH p. 1898

Strong Kate Historical Library, *see* Long Island Museum of American Art, History & Carriages, Stony Brook NY p. 1749

Strong Museum Library, Rochester NY p. 1732

Strong Public, *see* Barton Library, Strong AR p. 98

Strong Public Library, Strong ME p. 1003

Stroock & Lavan, Los Angeles CA p. 178

Stroock & Stroock & Lavan Library, New York NY p. 1700

Strosacker Library, *see* Northwood University, Midland MI p. 1208

Stroud Public Library, Stroud OK p. 1979

Strozier Robert Manning Library, *see* Florida State University Libraries, Tallahassee FL p. 494

Struckman-Baatz Public Library, Western NE p. 1423

Strum Public Library, Strum WI p. 2640

Stuart Public Library, Stuart IA p. 846

Stuart Township Library, Stuart NE p. 1420

Stubblefield Helen Law Library, *see* Laboure College, Boston MA p. 1062

Stubbs Memorial Library, Holstein IA p. 821

Stuck Medical Library, *see* Mount Clemens Regional Medical Center, Mount Clemens MI p. 1210

Studebaker National Museum Archives, South Bend IN p. 779

Stuhr Museum of the Prairie Pioneer, Grand Island NE p. 1400

Sturdivant Public Library, East Machias ME p. 984

Sturdy Memorial Hospital, Attleboro MA p. 1050

Sturgeon Lake Public Library, *see* Wapiti Regional Library, Shellbrook SK p. 2922

Sturgis District Library, Sturgis MI p. 1229

Sturgis Horace W Library, *see* Kennesaw State University, Kennesaw GA p. 537

Sturgis Library, Barnstable MA p. 1051

Sturgis Public Library, Sturgis SD p. 2220

Sturgis Public Library, *see* Starkville-Oktibbeha County Public, Sturgis MS p. 1315

Sturgis Roy & Christine Library, Rison AR p. 113

Sturm Elizabeth Library, *see* Truckee Meadows Community College, Reno NV p. 1432

Sturm Memorial Library, Manawa WI p. 2611

Stutsman County Library, Jamestown ND p. 1844

Stuttgart Public Library, Stuttgart AR p. 116

STV Inc Library, Douglassville PA p. 2049

Styles Mary Riley Public Library, Falls Church VA p. 2463

Sublette County Library, Pinedale WY p. 2658

Substance Abuse Librarians & Information Specialists (N), Berkeley CA p. 2939

Suburban Hospital, Bethesda MD p. 1022

Suburban Library League (N), Sterling Heights MI p. 2946

Suburban Temple, Beachwood OH p. 1858

Sucker Creek First Nations Public Library, Little Current ON p. 2816

Suckow Ruth Memorial Library, Earlville IA p. 813

Sudbury Rock & Lapidary Society Library, Sudbury ON p. 2847

Sueltenfuss Library, *see* Our Lady of the Lake University, San Antonio TX p. 2380

Suffern Free Library, Suffern NY p. 1750

Suffolk Cooperative Library System, Bellport NY p. 1580

Suffolk County Community College, Brentwood NY p. 1584

Suffolk County Community College, Riverhead NY p. 1728

Suffolk County Community College, Selden NY p. 1742

Suffolk County Historical Society Library, Riverhead NY p. 1728

Suffolk County Vanderbilt Museum Library, Centerport NY p. 1604

Suffolk Public Library System, Suffolk VA p. 2497

Suffolk University, Boston MA p. 1067

Sugar Grove Free Library, Sugar Grove PA p. 2144

Sugar Grove Public Library District, Sugar Grove IL p. 708

Sugar-Salem School Community Library, Sugar City ID p. 584

Sugden Richard Library, Spencer MA p. 1126

Suhr Charles L Library, *see* Clarion University of Pennsylvania, Oil City PA p. 2100

Suisun City Library, *see* Solano County Library, Suisun City CA p. 148

Sul Ross State University, Alpine TX p. 2273

Sulligent Public Library, *see* Northwest Regional Library, Sulligent AL p. 40

Sullivan & Cromwell LLP, Washington DC p. 416

Sullivan & Cromwell LLP, New York NY p. 1700

Sullivan & Worcester LLP, Boston MA p. 1067

Sullivan City Public Library, Sullivan IL p. 708

Sullivan Correctional Facility Library, Fallsburg NY p. 1621

Sullivan County Community College, Loch Sheldrake NY p. 1653

Sullivan County Law Library, Laporte PA p. 2078

Sullivan County Library, Dushore PA p. 2051

Sullivan County Public Library, Sullivan IN p. 780

Sullivan County Public Library, Milan MO p. 1345

Sullivan County Public Library, Blountville TN p. 2224

Sullivan Family Library, *see* Chaminade University of Honolulu, Honolulu HI p. 560

Sullivan Free Library, Chittenango NY p. 1606

Sullivan Lilly Pike Municipal Library, Enfield NC p. 1792

Sullivan Public Library, Sullivan MO p. 1368

Sullivan Public Library, Sullivan NH p. 1466

Sullivan Richard C Public Library of Wilton Manors, Wilton Manors FL p. 504

Sullivan University Library, Louisville KY p. 926

SullivanMunce Cultural Center, Zionsville IN p. 789

Sully Area Library, Onida SD p. 2216

Sully Community Library, Sully IA p. 846

Sulphur Regional, *see* Calcasieu Parish Public Library, Sulphur LA p. 954

Sulphur Springs Public Library, Sulphur Springs AR p. 116

Sulphur Springs Public Library, Sulphur Springs TX p. 2389

Sultan Community Library, *see* Sno-Isle Libraries, Sultan WA p. 2542

Sulzbacher Memorial Staff Library, *see* Spring Grove Hospital Center, Catonsville MD p. 1023

Sulzer Conrad Regional, *see* Chicago Public Library, Chicago IL p. 609

Sumiton Public Library, Sumiton AL p. 36

Summa Barberton Citizens Hospital, Barberton OH p. 1857

Summa Health System, Akron OH p. 1853

Summar Emma Waters Library, *see* Union University, Jackson TN p. 2238

Summerfield Public Library, Summerfield KS p. 895

Summerlin Library, *see* Las Vegas-Clark County Library District, Las Vegas NV p. 1430

Summers County Public Library, Hinton WV p. 2560

Summerside Rotary Library, *see* Prince Edward Island Public Library Service, Summerside PE p. 2876

Summersville Public Library, Summersville WV p. 2572

Summerville Public Library, Summerville PA p. 2144

Summit Christian College Library, Gering NE p. 1399

Summit County Library, Frisco CO p. 308

Summit County Library, Park City UT p. 2410

Summit Free Public Library, Summit NJ p. 1532

Summit Pacific College, Abbotsford BC p. 2724

Summit Public Library District, Summit IL p. 709

Sumner Public Library, Sumner IA p. 847

Sump Memorial Library, Papillion NE p. 1416

Sumpter Township Library, Toledo IL p. 710

Sumrall Public - L R Boyer Memorial Library, *see* Lamar County Library System, Sumrall MS p. 1313

Sumter Correctional Institution Library, *see* Florida Department of Corrections, Bushnell FL p. 431

Sumter County Library, Sumter SC p. 2206

Sumter County Library System, Livingston AL p. 24

Sumter County Library System, Wildwood FL p. 504

Sun City Library, *see* Riverside County Library System, Sun City CA p. 218

Sun City West Library, *see* Johnson R H Library, Sun City West AZ p. 82

Sun Life Assurance Company of Canada, Toronto ON p. 2858

Sun Media, Toronto ON p. 2858

Sun Prairie Public Library, Sun Prairie WI p. 2641

Sun-Times News Group, Merrillville IN p. 764

Sunbright Public Library, Sunbright TN p. 2266

Sunbury Shores Arts & Nature Centre, Inc Library, Saint Andrews NB p. 2766

Suncor Energy Library, Calgary AB p. 2693

Sunder Ram Library, *see* Environmental Protection Agency, Dallas TX p. 2308

Sunderland Public Library, Sunderland MA p. 1130

Sunderland Public Library, *see* Brock Township Public Library, Sunderland ON p. 2795

Sundquist Research Library, *see* Yakima Valley Museum Archives, Yakima WA p. 2551

Sundre Municipal Library, Sundre AB p. 2718

Sundridge-Strong Union Public Library, Sundridge ON p. 2847

Sunfield District Library, Sunfield MI p. 1230

Sunflower County Library System, Indianola MS p. 1302

Sunkist Library, *see* County of Los Angeles Public Library, La Puente CA p. 143

Sunland Park Community Library, Sunland Park NM p. 1565

Sunland Training Center, Marianna FL p. 462

Sunnybrook Health Sciences Centre, Toronto ON p. 2858, 2859

Sunnybrook Library Services, *see* Sunnybrook Health Sciences Centre, Toronto ON p. 2859

Sunnyside Community Library, *see* Queens Borough Public Library, Long Island City NY p. 1645

Sunnyside Regional, *see* Fresno County Public Library, Fresno CA p. 152

Sunnyvale Public Library, Sunnyvale CA p. 273

Sunnyvale Public Library, Sunnyvale TX p. 2389

Pearl Dan, *see* Broward County Division of Libraries, Sunrise FL p. 442

Sunrise Hospital & Medical Center, Las Vegas NV p. 1430

Sunrise Library, *see* Las Vegas-Clark County Library District, Las Vegas NV p. 1430

Sunshine City Library, Prairie View KS p. 891

Sunshine Hall Free Library, Eldred NY p. 1618

Sunshine Township Library, Mason City NE p. 1408

Sunsites Community Library, *see* Cochise County Library District, Pearce AZ p. 58

Suntree/Viera Public Library, Melbourne FL p. 463

SUNY Cortland, Cortland NY p. 1611

SUNY Upstate Medical University, Syracuse NY p. 1753

SUNY Westchester Community College, Valhalla NY p. 1760

SUNYConnect (N), Albany NY p. 2950

Superior Court Law Library, Phoenix AZ p. 77

Superior Public Library, Superior AZ p. 82

Superior Public Library, Superior NE p. 1420

Superior Public Library, Superior WI p. 2641

Supplee Memorial Presbyterian Church Library, Maple Glen PA p. 2084

Supreme Court Law Library, Honolulu HI p. 565

Supreme Court Library, Staten Island NY p. 1748

Supreme Court Library At Saratoga Springs, Saratoga Springs NY p. 1739

Supreme Court Library of Puerto Rico, San Juan PR p. 2676

Supreme Court of Canada Library, Ottawa ON p. 2833

Supreme Court of Illinois Library, Springfield IL p. 707

Supreme Court of Ohio, Columbus OH p. 1890

Supreme Court of the United States Library, Washington DC p. 416

Supreme Court, Appellate Division, New York NY p. 1700

Surf-Bal-Bay Library, Surfside FL p. 492

Surface Transportation Board Library, Washington DC p. 416

Surgoinsville Public Library, Surgoinsville TN p. 2266

Suring Area Public Library, Suring WI p. 2641

Surrey Public Library, Surrey BC p. 2739

Surrey Township Public Library, Farwell MI p. 1178

Surry Community College, Dobson NC p. 1787

Surry Public, *see* Blackwater Regional Library, Surry VA p. 2458

Surveyors Historical Society Library, Lawrenceburg IN p. 761

Survival Research Foundation Library, Miami FL p. 468

Susquehanna County Historical Society & Free Library Association, Montrose PA p. 2092

Susquehanna County Law Library, Montrose PA p. 2092

Susquehanna Health Medical Library, Williamsport PA p. 2157

Susquehanna Library Cooperative (N), Lock Haven PA p. 2955

Susquehanna University, Selinsgrove PA p. 2138

Sussex County Community College Library, Newton NJ p. 1513

Sussex County Department of Libraries, Georgetown DE p. 383

Sussex County Historical Society Library, Newton NJ p. 1514

Sussex County Law Library, Newton NJ p. 1514

Sussex County Library System, Newton NJ p. 1514

Sussman Albert Library, *see* International Council of Shopping Centers, New York NY p. 1683

Sutherland, Asbill & Brennan LLP Library, Washington DC p. 416

Sutherland Public Library, Sutherland NE p. 1420

Sutin, Thayer & Browne, Albuquerque NM p. 1550

Sutro Library, *see* California State Library, San Francisco CA p. 241

Sutter Coast Hospital Library, Crescent City CA p. 138

Sutter County Free Library, Yuba City CA p. 286

Sutter Medical Center of Santa Rosa, Santa Rosa CA p. 268

Sutter Roseville Medical Center Library, Roseville CA p. 220

Suttle Dr William M Medical Library, *see* Central Mississippi Medical Center, Jackson MS p. 1303

Sutton County Library, Sonora TX p. 2388

Sutton Free Library, Sutton Mills NH p. 1466

Sutton Free Public Library, Sutton MA p. 1130

Sutton Memorial Library, Sutton NE p. 1420

Sutton Public Library, Sutton AK p. 54

Sutton Public Library, Sutton WV p. 2572

Suttons Bay-Bingham District Library, Suttons Bay MI p. 1230

Suwannee River Regional Library, Live Oak FL p. 461

SVLN (N), *see* Southside Virginia Library Network, Farmville VA p. 2957

Swain Hall Library, *see* Indiana University Bloomington, Bloomington IN p. 728

Swain Library of Chemistry & Chemical Engineering, *see* Stanford University Libraries, Stanford CA p. 271

Swain Robert S Natural History Library, East Sandwich MA p. 1086

Swaledale Public Library, Swaledale IA p. 847

Swampscott Public Library, Swampscott MA p. 1130

SWAN (N), *see* System Wide Automated Network, Burr Ridge IL p. 2942

Swan Hills Municipal Library, Swan Hills AB p. 2719

Swan Lake Public Library, Swan Lake MT p. 1389

Swan Library, Albion NY p. 1571

Swan Paul Library, *see* Becker College, Leicester MA p. 1098

Swaney Memorial Library, New Cumberland WV p. 2567

Swans Island Educational Society, Swans Island ME p. 1003

Swans Island Public Library, *see* Swans Island Educational Society, Swans Island ME p. 1003

Swansea Free Public Library, Swansea MA p. 1130

Swansea Memorial, *see* Toronto Public Library, Toronto ON p. 2863

Swanson W Clarke, *see* Omaha Public Library, Omaha NE p. 1414

Swanton Local School District Public Library, Swanton OH p. 1937

Swanton Public Library, Swanton VT p. 2437

Swanville Library, *see* Great River Regional Library, Swanville MN p. 1276

Swarthmore College, Swarthmore PA p. 2144

Swarthmore Public Library, Swarthmore PA p. 2145

Swarthout Minor Memorial Library, *see* Curtiss Glenn H Museum of Local History, Hammondsport NY p. 1633

Perkins Library, *see* Genesee District Library, Swartz Creek MI p. 1180

Swasey Ambrose Library, *see* Colgate Rochester Crozer Divinity School, Rochester NY p. 1729

Swayze Gordon & Ruby Health Resource Centre, Toronto ON p. 2859

Swayzee Public Library, Swayzee IN p. 780

Swea City Public Library, Swea City IA p. 847

Swedburg Loren T & Melva M Library, *see* Nebraska Christian College, Papillion NE p. 1416

Swedenborg Foundation Library, West Chester PA p. 2153

Swedenborg Library, *see* Bryn Athyn College, Bryn Athyn PA p. 2038

Swedenborg Memorial Library, *see* Urbana University, Urbana OH p. 1942

Swedenborgian Library & Archives, Berkeley CA p. 127

Swedish-American Archives of Greater Chicago, *see* North Park University, Chicago IL p. 620

Swedish American Health System, Rockford IL p. 698

Swedish Covenant Hospital, Chicago IL p. 625

Swedish Historical Society of Rockford, Rockford IL p. 698

Swedish Medical Center Library, Englewood CO p. 306

Swedish Medical Center Library, Seattle WA p. 2532

Sween Jane C Library, *see* Montgomery County Historical Society Library, Rockville MD p. 1038

Sweet Briar College, Sweet Briar VA p. 2497

Sweet Corrine & Jack, *see* Salt Lake City Public Library, Salt Lake City UT p. 2413

Sweet Home Public Library, Sweet Home OR p. 2020

Sweet Joseph L Memorial Library, *see* Attleboro Public Library, Attleboro MA p. 1050

Sweet Springs Public Library, Sweet Springs MO p. 1368

Sweetser Children's Services, Saco ME p. 999

Sweetwater County-City Library, Sweetwater TX p. 2390

Sweetwater County Library, *see* Sweetwater County Library System, Green River WY p. 2655

Sweetwater County Library System, Green River WY p. 2655

Sweetwater Public Library, Sweetwater TN p. 2266

Swem Earl Gregg Library, *see* College of William & Mary in Virginia, Williamsburg VA p. 2502

Swenson Robert E Library, *see* Cabrillo College, Aptos CA p. 121

Swenson Swedish Immigration Research Center, Rock Island IL p. 696

Swett Morris J Technical Library, *see* United States Army, Fort Sill OK p. 1964

SWFLN (N), *see* Southwest Florida Library Network, Fort Myers FL p. 2940

Swigart Museum Library, Huntingdon PA p. 2070

Swilley Monroe F Jr Library, *see* Mercer University Atlanta, Atlanta GA p. 516

Swindle Harold S Public Library, *see* Piedmont Regional Library, Nicholson GA p. 557

Swinkin Esther Memorial Library, *see* Temple Beth Sholom, Hamden CT p. 344

Swirbul Library, *see* Adelphi University Libraries, Garden City NY p. 1625

Swisher Carl S Library, *see* Jacksonville University, Jacksonville FL p. 454

Swisher Carl S Library, *see* Bethune-Cookman College, Daytona Beach FL p. 435

Swisher County Library, Tulia TX p. 2393

SWITCH (N), *see* Southeastern Wisconsin Information Technology Exchange, Inc, Milwaukee WI p. 2958

Switzerland County Public Library, Vevay IN p. 784

SWON (N), *see* SouthWest Ohio & Neighboring Libraries, Blue Ash OH p. 2952

SwRI Library, *see* Slick Thomas Baker Memorial Library, San Antonio TX p. 2382

SWVAHILI (N), *see* Southwestern Virginia Health Information Librarians, Roanoke VA p. 2957

Sycamore Public Library, Sycamore IL p. 709

Sykesville Public Library, Sykesville PA p. 2145

Sylvan Grove Public Library, Sylvan Grove KS p. 895

Sylvan Lake Municipal Library, Sylvan Lake AB p. 2719

Sylvan Oaks Community Library, *see* Sacramento Public Library, Citrus Heights CA p. 225

Sylvester Memorial Wellston Public Library, Wellston OH p. 1946

Sylvia Public Library, Sylvia KS p. 895

Synergy Medical Education Alliance, Saginaw MI p. 1224

Syngenta Crop Protection Library, Greensboro NC p. 1797

Syosset Public Library, Syosset NY p. 1751

Syracuse Public Library, Syracuse NE p. 1420

Syracuse Supreme Court Law Library, *see* New York State Unified Court System, Syracuse NY p. 1752

Syracuse Turkey Creek Township Public Library, Syracuse IN p. 780

Syracuse University, Syracuse NY p. 2970

Syracuse University College of Law, Syracuse NY p. 1753

Syracuse University Library, Syracuse NY p. 1754

System Wide Automated Network (N), Burr Ridge IL p. 2942

T O H P Burnham Public Library, Essex MA p. 1087

TABAMLN (N), *see* Tampa Bay Medical Library Network, Orlando FL p. 2941

Tabb Library, *see* York County Public Library, Yorktown VA p. 2505

Taber Elizabeth Library, Marion MA p. 1102

Taber Emily Public Library, Macclenny FL p. 461

Taber Lloyd, *see* County of Los Angeles Public Library, Marina del Rey CA p. 143

Taber Public Library, Taber AB p. 2719

Tabernacle Baptist Church Library, Carrollton GA p. 523

Tabo Juan, *see* Albuquerque-Bernalillo County Library System, Albuquerque NM p. 1548

Tabor City Public, *see* Columbus County Public Library, Tabor City NC p. 1829

Tabor College Library, Hillsboro KS p. 872

Tabor Public Library, Tabor IA p. 847

Tacoma Art Museum, Tacoma WA p. 2540

Tacoma Community College Library, Tacoma WA p. 2540

Tacoma Family History Center, Tacoma WA p. 2540

Tacoma Public Library, Tacoma WA p. 2540

Taft College Library, Taft CA p. 274

Taft Museum of Art Library, Cincinnati OH p. 1873

Taft Public Library, Mendon MA p. 1105

Taft Public Library, Taft TX p. 2390

Taft, Stettinius & Hollister Library, Cincinnati OH p. 1873

Taggart Law Library, *see* Ohio Northern University, Ada OH p. 1851

Tahlequah Public Library, Tahlequah OK p. 1980

Taitano Richard F Micronesian Area Research Center, *see* University of Guam, Mangilao GU p. 2667

Temple Adath Israel, Merion Station PA p. 2088
Temple Am Echad, Lynbrook NY p. 1655
Temple Arthur Sr Memorial Library, Pineland TX p. 2370
Temple Benjamin/Ryan House, see Ewing Township Historical Preservation Society Library, Ewing NJ p. 1485
Temple Beth El, Hollywood FL p. 451
Temple Beth El, Fall River MA p. 1088
Temple Beth El, Bloomfield Hills MI p. 1159
Temple Beth El Congregation Sons of Israel & David, Providence RI p. 2175
Temple Beth El Library, Rochester NY p. 1733
Temple Beth Israel Library, Fresno CA p. 153
Temple Beth Sholom, Hamden CT p. 344
Temple Beth Sholom, Cherry Hill NJ p. 1478
Temple Beth Sholom Library, Miami Beach FL p. 469
Temple Beth Torah Library, Upper Nyack NY p. 1758
Temple Beth Tzedek, Amherst NY p. 1573
Temple Beth Zion Library, Buffalo NY p. 1599
Temple B'Nai Israel Library, Parkersburg WV p. 2568
Temple B'Rith Kodesh Library, Rochester NY p. 1733
Temple College, Temple TX p. 2391
Temple - Congregation Shomer Emunim Library, Sylvania OH p. 1938
Temple Daily Telegram Library, Temple TX p. 2391
Temple De Hirsch Sinai Library, Seattle WA p. 2532
Temple Emanu-El, Birmingham AL p. 9
Temple Emanu-El, Long Beach NY p. 1654
Temple Emanu-El, Dallas TX p. 2310
Temple Emanu-El Library, Providence RI p. 2175
Temple Emanuel Library, Tucson AZ p. 88
Temple Emanuel Library, Worcester MA p. 1144
Temple Emanuel Library, Cherry Hill NJ p. 1478
Temple Isaiah, Lafayette CA p. 163
Temple Israel, Sharon MA p. 1123
Temple Israel, Columbus OH p. 1891
Temple Israel Libraries & Media Center, West Bloomfield MI p. 1236
Temple Israel Library, Boston MA p. 1067
Temple Israel Library, Minneapolis MN p. 1261
Temple Israel Library, Vestal NY p. 1761
Temple Israel Library, Dayton OH p. 1894
Temple Israel of New Rochelle, New Rochelle NY p. 1667
Temple Jeremiah, Northfield IL p. 683
Temple Judah Library, Cedar Rapids IA p. 801
Temple Judea, Coral Gables FL p. 434
Temple Judea Mizpah Library, Skokie IL p. 703
Temple Library, see Laurel University Library, High Point NC p. 1802
Temple on the Heights, Pepper Pike OH p. 1929
Temple Public Library, Temple TX p. 2391
Temple Sharey Tefilo-Israel, South Orange NJ p. 1531
Temple Sholom of Broomall Library, Broomall PA p. 2038
Temple Sinai, Dresher PA p. 2050
Temple Sinai Library, Washington DC p. 416
Temple Sinai Library, Brookline MA p. 1072
Temple Sinai Library, Rochester NY p. 1733
Temple Sinai Library, Roslyn Heights NY p. 1736
Temple Sinai of North Dade, North Miami Beach FL p. 473
Temple Terrace Public Library, Temple Terrace FL p. 500
Temple University Health System, Philadelphia PA p. 2117
Temple University Hospital, Philadelphia PA p. 2117
Temple University Libraries, Ambler PA p. 2028
Temple University Libraries, Philadelphia PA p. 2117
Temple University School of Podiatric Medicine, Philadelphia PA p. 2117
Templeton Anna, see College of the North Atlantic, St. John's NL p. 2771
Tenafly Public Library, Tenafly NJ p. 1533
Tenenbaum Abe & Esther Library, Savannah GA p. 551
Tener John K Library, Charleroi PA p. 2044

Tennessean Library & Archives, Nashville TN p. 2258
Tennessee Correction Academy Library, Tullahoma TN p. 2268
Tennessee Department of Corrections, Nashville TN p. 2258
Tennessee Department of Corrections, Pikeville TN p. 2263
Tennessee General Assembly, Nashville TN p. 2258
Tennessee Health Science Library Association (N), Kingsport TN p. 2955
Tennessee Prison for Women Library, see Tennessee Department of Corrections, Nashville TN p. 2258
Tennessee Regional Library for the Blind & Physically Handicapped, Nashville TN p. 2258
Tennessee State Law Library, Jackson TN p. 2238
Tennessee State Law Library, Nashville TN p. 2259
Tennessee State Library & Archives, Nashville TN p. 2259
Tennessee State Museum Library, Nashville TN p. 2259
Tennessee State University, Nashville TN p. 2259
Tennessee Technological University, Cookeville TN p. 2231, 2974
Tennessee Temple University, Chattanooga TN p. 2228
Tennessee Valley Authority, Chattanooga TN p. 2228
Tennessee Valley Authority, Knoxville TN p. 2243
Tennessee Wesleyan College, Athens TN p. 2224
Tenney Memorial Library Inc, Newbury VT p. 2430
Tensas Parish Library, Saint Joseph LA p. 967
Terence Cardinal Cooke, see New York Public Library - Astor, Lenox & Tilden Foundations, New York NY p. 1693
Terra Alta Public Library, Terra Alta WV p. 2572
Terra State Community College Library, Fremont OH p. 1900
Terrace Bay Public Library, Terrace Bay ON p. 2847
Terrace Heights Library, see Yakima Valley Libraries, Yakima WA p. 2551
Terrace Public Library, Terrace BC p. 2739
Terrebonne Parish Library, Houma LA p. 951
Terrell County Library, see Kinchafoonee Regional Library System, Dawson GA p. 528
Terrell County Public Library, Sanderson TX p. 2385
Terrell State Hospital, Terrell TX p. 2391
Terrey John N Library, see Everett Community College, Everett WA p. 2515
Terril Community Library, Terril IA p. 847
Terry Adolphine Fletcher, see Central Arkansas Library System, Little Rock AR p. 106
Terry Mattie Public Library, Valliant OK p. 1984
Terry Mildred L Branch, see Chattahoochee Valley Libraries, Columbus GA p. 526
Terry Robert James Library, see Texas Southern University, Houston TX p. 2342
Terryville Public Library, Terryville CT p. 372
Terteling N L Library, see College of Idaho, Caldwell ID p. 572
Terwilliger Nature Education & Wildlife Rehabilitation, see WildCare, San Rafael CA p. 257
Tescott Public Library, Tescott KS p. 896
Testing Engineers International, Inc, South Salt Lake UT p. 2416
Teszler Sandor Library, see Wofford College, Spartanburg SC p. 2206
Teton County Library, Jackson WY p. 2656
Teton Science School Library, Kelly WY p. 2656
Tetra-Tech Em Inc, Chicago IL p. 625
Teva Pharmaceuticals, Frazer PA p. 2059
Tewksbury Public Library, Tewksbury MA p. 1131
Tewksbury Township Public Library, Oldwick NJ p. 1516
Texarkana College, Texarkana TX p. 2391
Texarkana Museums System, Texarkana TX p. 2392
Texarkana Public Library, Texarkana TX p. 2392
Texas A & M University - Commerce, Commerce TX p. 2974
Texas A&M International University, Laredo TX p. 2354

Texas A&M University at Galveston, Galveston TX p. 2326
Texas A&M University Central Texas, Killeen TX p. 2350
Texas A&M University-Commerce, Commerce TX p. 2300
Texas A&M University-Corpus Christi, Corpus Christi TX p. 2302
Texas A&M University-Kingsville, Kingsville TX p. 2351
Texas A&M University Libraries, College Station TX p. 2298
Texas A&M University-Texarkana, Texarkana TX p. 2392
Texas Baptist Historical Museum Library, see Baptist General Convention of Texas, Brenham TX p. 2291
Texas Biomedical Research Institute, San Antonio TX p. 2383
Texas Children's Hospital, Houston TX p. 2342
Texas Chiropractic College, Pasadena TX p. 2369
Texas Christian University, Fort Worth TX p. 2323
Texas College, Tyler TX p. 2393
Texas Commission on Environment Quality Library, Austin TX p. 2281
Texas Council of Academic Libraries (N), Victoria TX p. 2956
Texas County Library, Houston MO p. 1331
Texas Department of Health & Human Services, Big Spring TX p. 2290
Texas Department of State Health Services, Austin TX p. 2282
Texas Education Agency, Austin TX p. 2282
Texas General Land Office, Austin TX p. 2282
Texas Health Harris Methodist Fort Worth Hospital, Fort Worth TX p. 2324
Texas Health Presbyterian Hospital Library, Dallas TX p. 2311
Texas Historical Commission Library, Austin TX p. 2282
Texas Legislative Reference Library, Austin TX p. 2282
Texas Lutheran University, Seguin TX p. 2386
Texas Medical Association, Austin TX p. 2282
Texas Medical Center Library, see Houston Academy of Medicine, Houston TX p. 2337
Texas Natural Resources Information System, Austin TX p. 2282
Texas Navigator Group (N), Austin TX p. 2956
Texas Ranger Hall of Fame & Museum, Waco TX p. 2397
Texas Ranger Research Center, see Texas Ranger Hall of Fame & Museum, Waco TX p. 2397
Texas School for the Blind, Austin TX p. 2282
Texas Scottish Rite Hospital, Dallas TX p. 2311
Texas Southern University, Houston TX p. 2342
Texas State Court of Appeals, Eastland TX p. 2315
Texas State Law Library, Austin TX p. 2282
Texas State Library & Archives Commission, Austin TX p. 2282, 2283
Texas State Museum of Asian Cultures, Corpus Christi TX p. 2302
Texas State Technical College, Harlingen TX p. 2331
Texas State Technical College, Waco TX p. 2397
Texas State Technical College Library, Sweetwater TX p. 2390
Texas State University-San Marcos, San Marcos TX p. 2385
Texas Tech University, Lubbock TX p. 2357
Texas Tech University Health Sciences, Lubbock TX p. 2357
Texas Tech University Health Sciences Center, Amarillo TX p. 2274
Texas Tech University Libraries, Lubbock TX p. 2358
Texas Trans-Pecos Regional Library System, El Paso TX p. 2317
Texas Wesleyan University, Fort Worth TX p. 2324
Texas Woman's University Libraries, Denton TX p. 2312
Texas Woman's University, Dallas TX p. 2311
Texas Woman's University, Denton TX p. 2974
Texhoma Public Library, Texhoma OK p. 1980
Texline Public Library, Texline TX p. 2392

Thrivent Financial for Lutherans, Minneapolis MN p. 1261

Throckmorton John L Library, *see* United States Army, Fort Bragg NC p. 1794

Thunder Bay Historical Museum Society Library, Thunder Bay ON p. 2849

Thunder Bay Law Association Library, Thunder Bay ON p. 2849

Thunder Bay Public Library, Thunder Bay ON p. 2849

Thunderbird School of Global Management, Glendale AZ p. 64

Thunderchild Library, Turtleford SK p. 2929

Thurber Engineering Library, Vancouver BC p. 2742

TIAX LLC Library, Lexington MA p. 1099

Tibetan Buddhist Resource Center, Inc, New York NY p. 1701

Ticasuk Library, Unalakleet AK p. 54

Ticonderoga Historical Society Library, Ticonderoga NY p. 1755

Tidewater Community College, Chesapeake VA p. 2456

Tidewater Community College, Portsmouth VA p. 2485

Tidewater Community College, Virginia Beach VA p. 2500

Tidewater Community College Learning Resources Center, Norfolk VA p. 2483

Tidioute Public Library, Tidioute PA p. 2145

Tifereth Israel Synagogue Library, Lincoln NE p. 1406

Tiffin-Seneca Public Library, Tiffin OH p. 1938

Tiffin University, Tiffin OH p. 1938

Tifton-Tift County Public, *see* Coastal Plain Regional Library, Tifton GA p. 554

Tigard Public Library, Tigard OR p. 2021

Tigerton Public, *see* Shawano City-County Library, Tigerton WI p. 2637

Tignish Public, *see* Prince Edward Island Public Library Service, Tignish PE p. 2876

Tillamook Bay Community College Library, Tillamook OR p. 2021

Tillamook County Library, Tillamook OR p. 2021

Tillamook County Pioneer Museum, Tillamook OR p. 2021

Tiller Community Library, Tiller OR p. 2021

Tilley Public Library, Tilley AB p. 2719

Tillinghast Dolores Memorial Library, Harpers Ferry IA p. 820

Tills Goldie & Joe Library, *see* Congregation Agudas Achim, San Antonio TX p. 2379

Tillsonburg Public Library, Tillsonburg ON p. 2849

Tilton Library, South Deerfield MA p. 1124

Timberland Regional Library, Tumwater WA p. 2543

Times Publishing Co, Saint Petersburg FL p. 488

Timken Co, North Canton OH p. 1923

Timmerman L H Library, *see* Lake Area Technical Institute Library, Watertown SD p. 2221

Timmins Public Library, Timmins ON p. 2849

Timmonsville Public Library, *see* Florence County Library System, Timmonsville SC p. 2193

Timpanogos Cave National Monument Library, *see* National Park Service, American Fork UT p. 2403

Timrod Library, Summerville SC p. 2206

Tingley Memorial Library, Bradenton Beach FL p. 430

Tinian Public, *see* Joeten-Kiyu Public Library, Tinian MP p. 2669

Tinicum Memorial Public Library, Essington PA p. 2056

Tinley Park Public Library, Tinley Park IL p. 709

Tinmouth Public Library, Tinmouth VT p. 2437

Tinton Falls Public Library, Tinton Falls NJ p. 1533

Tioga County Historical Society Museum Library, Owego NY p. 1713

Tipp City Public Library, Tipp City OH p. 1938

Tippecanoe County Historical Association, Lafayette IN p. 759

Tippecanoe County-Ivy Tech Library, Lafayette IN p. 759

Tippecanoe County Public Library, Lafayette IN p. 759

Tippitt Mary E Memorial Library, Townsend TN p. 2267

Tipton County Public Library, Tipton IN p. 782

Tipton County Public Library, Covington TN p. 2232

Tipton Library, Tipton KS p. 896

Tipton Public Library, Tipton IA p. 847

Tiptonville Public Library, Tiptonville TN p. 2267

TIRR Memorial Hermann, Houston TX p. 2343

Tisch Family Library, *see* Gunnery, Washington CT p. 374

Tisch Library, *see* Tufts University, Medford MA p. 1104

Tisdale Charles Library, *see* Jackson/Hinds Library System, Jackson MS p. 1303

Tisdale T Terrell Library, *see* Jones County Junior College, Ellisville MS p. 1298

Tishman Learning Center Health Sciences Library, *see* Montefiore Medical Center, Bronx NY p. 1588

Tishomingo Library, *see* Northeast Regional Library, Tishomingo MS p. 1298

Tiskilwa Public Library, Tiskilwa IL p. 709

Titanium Metals Corporation of America (Laboratory), Henderson NV p. 1428

Titonka Public Library, Titonka IA p. 847

Titus Elizabeth Memorial Library, *see* Sullivan City Public Library, Sullivan IL p. 708

Titusville Public Library, Titusville FL p. 500

Tiverton Library Services, Tiverton RI p. 2176

Tivoli Free Library, Tivoli NY p. 1755

TLL Temple Memorial Library, Diboll TX p. 2313

TLN (N), *see* Library Network, Novi MI p. 2946

TMC HealthCare, Tucson AZ p. 88

Tobacco Merchants Association of the United States, Princeton NJ p. 1524

Tobey Hospital, Wareham MA p. 1133

Tobias Public Library, Tobias NE p. 1421

Tobin Edith & Jack Medical Library, *see* Deborah Heart & Lung Center, Browns Mills NJ p. 1475

Tobin James Edward Library, *see* Molloy College, Rockville Centre NY p. 1734

Toccoa Falls College, Toccoa Falls GA p. 554

Toccoa-Stephens County Public Library, Toccoa GA p. 554

Williams Avis G, *see* DeKalb County Public Library, Decatur GA p. 530

Todd County Public Library, Elkton KY p. 912

Todd James S Memorial Library, *see* American Medical Association, Chicago IL p. 606

Todd L O Library Resource Center, *see* Meridian Community College, Meridian MS p. 1308

Todd Library, *see* Waubonsee Community College, Sugar Grove IL p. 708

Todd Wehr Library, St Norbert College, De Pere WI p. 2587

Tofthagen A M Library & Museum, *see* Lakota City Library, Lakota ND p. 1845

Tohono Chul Park Library, Tucson AZ p. 88

Tohono O'odham Community College Library, Sells AZ p. 81

Tok Community Library, Tok AK p. 54

Toledo Blade-Library, Toledo OH p. 1939

Toledo Hospital, Toledo OH p. 1939

Toledo-Lucas County Public Library, Toledo OH p. 1939

Toledo Museum of Art, Toledo OH p. 1940

Toledo Public Library, Toledo IA p. 848

Toledo Public Library, Toledo OR p. 2021

Toledo Zoological Society, Toledo OH p. 1940

Tolland Public Library, Tolland CT p. 372

Tolland Public Library, Tolland MA p. 1131

Tolleson Public Library, Tolleson AZ p. 84

Tolono Public Library District, Tolono IL p. 710

Alexandra Tolstoy Memorial Library, *see* Tolstoy Foundation, Inc, Valley Cottage NY p. 1760

Tolstoy Foundation, Inc, Valley Cottage NY p. 1760

Toluca Public Library, Toluca IL p. 710

Tomah Public Library, Tomah WI p. 2642

Tomahawk Public Library, Tomahawk WI p. 2642

Tomahawk Public Library, Tomahawk AB p. 2719

Tomball College Library, *see* Lone Star College System, Tomball TX p. 2340

Tombigbee Regional Library System, West Point MS p. 1317

Tombstone Reading Station-Tombstone City Library, Tombstone AZ p. 85

Tomkins Cove Public Library, Tomkins Cove NY p. 1755

Tomlinson Library, *see* Colorado Mesa University, Grand Junction CO p. 310

Tommaney Library, *see* Haskell Indian Nations University, Lawrence KS p. 877

Tomoka Correctional Institution Library, *see* Florida Department of Corrections, Daytona Beach FL p. 436

Tompkins Cortland Community College, Dryden NY p. 1615

Tompkins County Public Library, Ithaca NY p. 1643

Tompkins-McCaw Library, *see* Virginia Commonwealth University Libraries, Richmond VA p. 2492

Tompkins Memorial, *see* Cape Breton Regional Library, Reserve Mines NS p. 2785

Tompkins Memorial Library, Edgefield SC p. 2193

Tonasket Community, *see* North Central Regional Library, Tonasket WA p. 2549

Tonganoxie Public Library, Tonganoxie KS p. 896

Tongass Historical Museum, Ketchikan AK p. 50

Tonkawa Public Library, Tonkawa OK p. 1980

Tonkon Torp LLP, Portland OR p. 2014

Tonopah Library District, Tonopah NV p. 1435

Tonto Basin Public Library, Tonto Basin AZ p. 85

Tooele City Public Library, Tooele UT p. 2416

Toole County Library, Shelby MT p. 1388

Topeka & Shawnee County Public Library, Topeka KS p. 897

Topeka Genealogical Society Library, Topeka KS p. 897

Topeka Juvenile Correctional Facility Library, *see* Kansas Department of Corrections, Topeka KS p. 896

Topeka Zoological Park Library, Topeka KS p. 897

Topinabee Public Library, Topinabee MI p. 1231

Toponas Public Library, Toponas CO p. 324

Toppan Rare Books Library, *see* American Heritage Center, Laramie WY p. 2657

Topsfield Town Library, Topsfield MA p. 1131

Topsham Public Library, Topsham ME p. 1003

Torbay Public Library, Torbay NL p. 2773

Toronto Botanical Garden, Toronto ON p. 2859

Toronto Catholic District School Board, Toronto ON p. 2859

Toronto District School Board, North York ON p. 2825

Toronto Dominion Bank, Toronto ON p. 2859

Toronto General Hospital, *see* University Health Network, Toronto ON p. 2864

Toronto Health Libraries Association (N), Toronto ON p. 2960

Toronto International Film Festival Group, Toronto ON p. 2859

Toronto Jewish Library, Toronto ON p. 2859

Toronto Lawyers Association Library, Toronto ON p. 2859

Toronto Mendelssohn Choir Library, Toronto ON p. 2859

Toronto Monthly Meeting of the Religious Society of Friends (Quakers), Toronto ON p. 2859

Toronto Public Health Library, Toronto ON p. 2859

Toronto Public Library, Toronto KS p. 898

Toronto Public Library, Toronto ON p. 2860

Toronto Real Estate Board Library, Don Mills ON p. 2802

Toronto Rehab, Toronto ON p. 2864

Toronto Star Newspapers Ltd Library, Toronto ON p. 2864

Toronto Urban Development Services, Toronto ON p. 2864

Torrance Memorial Medical Center, Torrance CA p. 276

Torrance Public Library, Torrance CA p. 276

Torreyson Library, *see* University of Central Arkansas, Conway AR p. 97

Torrington Historical Society Library, Torrington CT p. 372

Torrington Library, Torrington CT p. 372

Torys Law Library, New York NY p. 1701

Torys LLP Library, Toronto ON p. 2864

Totman Albert F Public Library, Phippsburg ME p. 995

Tougaloo College, Tougaloo MS p. 1315

Trinity Presbyterian Church, East Brunswick NJ p. 1482

Trinity Presbyterian Church Library, Cherry Hill NJ p. 1478

Trinity United Presbyterian Church Library, Santa Ana CA p. 260

Trinity University, Washington DC p. 417

Trinity University, San Antonio TX p. 2383

Trinity Valley Community College Library, Athens TX p. 2277

Trinity Western University, Langley BC p. 2731

Triodyne Inc, Glenview IL p. 651

Trion Public Library, Trion GA p. 554

Tripler Army Medical Center, Honolulu HI p. 565

Triplett Andrew Library, see NAS Meridian Library, Meridian MS p. 1308

Tripoli Public Library, Tripoli IA p. 848

Tripp County Library-Grossenburg Memorial, Winner SD p. 2222

Triton College Library, River Grove IL p. 695

Triton Environmental Consultants Ltd Library, Richmond BC p. 2737

Triton Museum of Art Library, Santa Clara CA p. 263

Trocaire College Library, Buffalo NY p. 1599

Trochu Municipal Library, Trochu AB p. 2719

Troke Margaret K, see Stockton-San Joaquin County Public Library, Stockton CA p. 273

Tronox LLC, Oklahoma City OK p. 1975

Troup-Harris Regional Library System, La Grange GA p. 537

Trouton Earl & Marion Library, see Kingswood University, Sussex NB p. 2767

Troutman Sanders LLP, Atlanta GA p. 518

Troutman Sanders LLP, Richmond VA p. 2490

Trowbridge Research Library, see Wyandotte County Museum, Bonner Springs KS p. 858

Troxler Memorial, see Blackwater Regional Library, Wakefield VA p. 2458

Troy & Gould, Los Angeles CA p. 178

Troy-Miami County Public Library, Troy OH p. 1941

Troy Public Library, Troy AL p. 37

Troy Public Library, Troy MI p. 1232

Troy Public Library, Troy NY p. 1757

Troy University, Dothan AL p. 15

Troy University Library, Troy AL p. 37

Troy University, Montgomery Campus, Montgomery AL p. 31

Truax Library, see Madison Area Technical College, Madison WI p. 2606

Truchas Community Library, Truchas NM p. 1566

Truckee Meadows Community College, Reno NV p. 1432

Trudeau Institute Library, Saranac Lake NY p. 1738

Truett-McConnell College, Cleveland GA p. 525

Truett Memorial Library, see First Baptist Church of Dallas, Dallas TX p. 2308

Truman College, Chicago IL p. 625

Truman Harry S Memorial Hospital Library, see Department of Veterans Affairs, Columbia MO p. 1324

Truman Harry S Presidential Library & Museum, see National Archives & Records Administration, Independence MO p. 1333

Truman State University, Kirksville MO p. 1342

Trumann Public Library, Trumann AR p. 116

Trumbull Correctional Institution Library, see State of Ohio Department of Corrections, Leavittsburg OH p. 1909

Trumbull County Law Library, Warren OH p. 1944

Trumbull Jonathan Library, Lebanon CT p. 349

Trumbull Library, Trumbull CT p. 373

Trumbull Memorial Hospital, Warren OH p. 1944

Truro Public Library, Truro IA p. 848

Truro Public Library, North Truro MA p. 1113

Trussville Public Library, Trussville AL p. 38

Truth or Consequences Public Library, Truth or Consequences NM p. 1566

Truth Sojourner Library, see State University of New York College at New Paltz, New Paltz NY p. 1666

Truth Sojourner Library, see University of Iowa, Iowa City IA p. 823

Truxal Andrew G Library, see Anne Arundel Community College, Arnold MD p. 1011

TRW Automotive Library, Livonia MI p. 1204

Tryon Lucia M Library, see West Florida Public Library, Pensacola FL p. 483

Tryon Palace, New Bern NC p. 1812

Tryon Public Library, Tryon OK p. 1980

Tsawwassen Library, see Fraser Valley Regional Library, Delta BC p. 2724

Tualatin Public Library, Tualatin OR p. 2022

Tuality Health Information Resource Center, see Tuality Healthcare, Hillsboro OR p. 2000

Tuality Healthcare, Hillsboro OR p. 2000

Tuba City Public Library, see Flagstaff City-Coconino County Public Library System, Tuba City AZ p. 62

Tubb-May Memorial Library, see East Mississippi Community College, Scooba MS p. 1314

Tuck Museum Library, see Hampton Historical Society, Hampton NH p. 1449

Tuckahoe Area Library, see Henrico County Public Library, Henrico VA p. 2471

Tuckahoe Public Library, Tuckahoe NY p. 1757

Tucker Ellis LLP, Cleveland OH p. 1881

Tucker Free Library, Henniker NH p. 1451

Tucker Gerald Memorial Medical Library, see National Jewish Health, Denver CO p. 302

Tucker Memorial Public Library, Alexandria NE p. 1391

Tucson Electric Power Co Library, Tucson AZ p. 88

Tucson Museum of Art, Tucson AZ p. 88

Tucumcari Public Library, Tucumcari NM p. 1566

Tuftonboro Free Library, Center Tuftonboro NH p. 1441

Tufts Library, Weymouth MA p. 1139

Tufts University, Boston MA p. 1068

Tufts University, Medford MA p. 1104

Tulane University, New Orleans LA p. 963

Tulare County Library, Visalia CA p. 280

Tulare County Office of Education, Visalia CA p. 281

Tulare County Public Law Library, Visalia CA p. 281

Tulare Public Library, Tulare CA p. 276

Tullis R B, see Montgomery County Memorial Library System, New Caney TX p. 2301

Tully Community, see San Jose Public Library, San Jose CA p. 251

Tully Free Library, Tully NY p. 1757

Tulsa City-County Library, Tulsa OK p. 1982

Tulsa Community College Learning Resources Center, Tulsa OK p. 1983

Tulsa County Law Library, Tulsa OK p. 1984

Tulsa World, Tulsa OK p. 1984

Tulsa Zoo & Living Museum, Tulsa OK p. 1984

Tuluksak School-Community Library, Tuluksak AK p. 54

Tumbler Ridge Public Library, Tumbler Ridge BC p. 2739

Tunbridge Public Library, Tunbridge VT p. 2437

Tunkhannock Public Library, Tunkhannock PA p. 2147

Tunxis Community College Library, Farmington CT p. 340

Tuolumne County Free Library, Sonora CA p. 269

Tuolumne County Genealogical Society Library, Sonora CA p. 269

Lightfoot Tupper Memorial Library, Brundidge AL p. 11

Turchin Library, see Tulane University, New Orleans LA p. 963

Turcotte Library, see Southern Alberta Art Gallery Library, Lethbridge AB p. 2710

Turgeson John Public Library, Belmont WI p. 2581

Turin Library, see Strong B Elizabeth Memorial Library, Turin NY p. 1757

Turkey Public Library, Turkey TX p. 2393

Turnbow Walter Library, see Northwest Technical Institute, Springdale AR p. 115

Turner Alice, see Saskatoon Public Library, Saskatoon SK p. 2926

Turner Arthur F Community, see Yolo County Library, West Sacramento CA p. 285

Turner County-Victoria Evans Memorial, see Coastal Plain Regional Library, Ashburn GA p. 554

Turner Free Library, Randolph MA p. 1120

Turner Isabel, see Kingston Frontenac Public Library, Kingston ON p. 2813

Turner J A Professional Library, see Peel District School Board, Mississauga ON p. 2823

Turner Mark & Emily Memorial Library, Presque Isle ME p. 998

Turner Public Library, Turner ME p. 1004

Turon Community Library, Turon KS p. 898

Turpin Library, see Dallas Theological Seminary, Dallas TX p. 2307

Turtle Bay Music School Library, New York NY p. 1701

Turtle Lake Public Library, Turtle Lake WI p. 2642

Turtle Lake Public Library, see McLean-Mercer Regional Library, Turtle Lake ND p. 1848

Turtle Mountain Community College Library, Belcourt ND p. 1837

Tuscaloosa Public Library, Tuscaloosa AL p. 38

Tuscarawas County Law Library Association, New Philadelphia OH p. 1921

Tuscarawas County Public Library, New Philadelphia OH p. 1921

Tuscola Public Library, Tuscola IL p. 710

Tusculum College, Greeneville TN p. 2236

Tuskegee University, Tuskegee AL p. 39

Tutt Charles Learning Library, see Colorado College, Colorado Springs CO p. 294

Tutt Virginia M, see Saint Joseph County Public Library, South Bend IN p. 779

Tuttle Cliff Neighborhood Library, see Houston Public Library, Houston TX p. 2340

Tuttle James A Library, Antrim NH p. 1437

Tuttleman Library, see Gratz College, Melrose Park PA p. 2088

Tutwiler Julia Library, see University of West Alabama, Livingston AL p. 24

Tuxedo Park Library, Tuxedo Park NY p. 1757

Tuzzy Consortium Library, Barrow AK p. 46

TVA Research Library-Knoxville, see Tennessee Valley Authority, Knoxville TN p. 2243

Twain Mark, see Hartford Public Library, Hartford CT p. 346

Twain Mark, see Long Beach Public Library, Long Beach CA p. 167

Twain Mark, see Los Angeles Public Library System, Los Angeles CA p. 174

Twain Mark Home Foundation, Hannibal MO p. 1330

Twain Mark Library, Redding CT p. 365

Twain Mark Museum Library, see Twain Mark Home Foundation, Hannibal MO p. 1330

Twentieth Century Club Library, Almond NY p. 1572

Twentieth Century Fox Film Corp, Los Angeles CA p. 178

Twiggs County Public, see Middle Georgia Regional Library System, Jeffersonville GA p. 541

Twin Bridges Public Library, Twin Bridges MT p. 1389

Twin Cities Biomedical Consortium (N), Minneapolis MN p. 2947

Twin Falls Public Library, Twin Falls ID p. 584

Twin Hickory Area Library, see Henrico County Public Library, Glen Allen VA p. 2471

Twin Lakes Library System, Milledgeville GA p. 545

Twin Mountain Public Library, Carrol NH p. 1440

Twin Valley Behavioral Healthcare, Columbus OH p. 1891

Twinbrook Library, see Montgomery County Public Libraries, Rockville MD p. 1039

Twinsburg Public Library, Twinsburg OH p. 1941

Twisp Community, see North Central Regional Library, Twisp WA p. 2549

Two Harbors Public Library, Two Harbors MN p. 1286

Two Hills Public Library, see Melnyk Alice Public Library, Two Hills AB p. 2720

Two Rivers Correctional Institute Library, Umatilla OR p. 2022

Tycher Library, see Mankoff Resource Center, Dallas TX p. 2309

Tyco Electronics, Harrisburg PA p. 2066

Tydings & Rosenberg LLP, Baltimore MD p. 1018

United States Agency for International Development, Washington DC p. 417

United States Air Force, Maxwell AFB AL p. 24

United States Air Force, Eielson AFB AK p. 47

United States Air Force, Elmendorf AFB AK p. 47

United States Air Force, Davis Monthan AFB AZ p. 61

United States Air Force, Luke AFB AZ p. 68

United States Air Force, Little Rock AFB AR p. 108

United States Air Force, Beale AFB CA p. 125

United States Air Force, Edwards AFB CA p. 144

United States Air Force, Travis AFB CA p. 276

United States Air Force, Vandenberg AFB CA p. 279

United States Air Force, Peterson AFB CO p. 320

United States Air Force, Dover AFB DE p. 383

United States Air Force, Washington DC p. 417

United States Air Force, Eglin AFB FL p. 439

United States Air Force, Hurlburt Field FL p. 452

United States Air Force, MacDill AFB FL p. 462

United States Air Force, Patrick AFB FL p. 481

United States Air Force, Tyndall AFB FL p. 501

United States Air Force, Moody AFB GA p. 545

United States Air Force, Hickam AFB HI p. 559

United States Air Force, Mountain Home AFB ID p. 580

United States Air Force, Scott AFB IL p. 701

United States Air Force, Wichita KS p. 900

United States Air Force, Barksdale AFB LA p. 941

United States Air Force, Andrews AFB MD p. 1009

United States Air Force, Hanscom AFB MA p. 1093

United States Air Force, Columbus AFB MS p. 1297

United States Air Force, Keesler AFB MS p. 1306

United States Air Force, Whiteman AFB MO p. 1372

United States Air Force, Malmstrom AFB MT p. 1385

United States Air Force, Offutt AFB NE p. 1411

United States Air Force, Nellis AFB NV p. 1431

United States Air Force, McGuire AFB NJ p. 1500

United States Air Force, Cannon AFB NM p. 1552

United States Air Force, Holloman AFB NM p. 1557

United States Air Force, Kirtland AFB NM p. 1557

United States Air Force, Rome NY p. 1735

United States Air Force, Seymour Johnson AFB NC p. 1823

United States Air Force, Grand Forks AFB ND p. 1843

United States Air Force, Minot AFB ND p. 1846

United States Air Force, Wright-Patterson AFB OH p. 1951

United States Air Force, Altus Air Force Base OK p. 1956

United States Air Force, Tinker AFB OK p. 1980

United States Air Force, Vance AFB OK p. 1984

United States Air Force, Charleston AFB SC p. 2185

United States Air Force, Shaw AFB SC p. 2204

United States Air Force, Ellsworth AFB SD p. 2212

United States Air Force, Arnold AFB TN p. 2223

United States Air Force, Brooks AFB TX p. 2292

United States Air Force, Goodfellow AFB TX p. 2328

United States Air Force, Laughlin AFB TX p. 2354

United States Air Force, Randolph AFB TX p. 2373

United States Air Force, San Antonio TX p. 2383

United States Air Force, Sheppard AFB TX p. 2386

United States Air Force, Hill AFB UT p. 2406

United States Air Force, Langley AFB VA p. 2473

United States Air Force, Fairchild AFB WA p. 2515

United States Air Force, F E Warren AFB WY p. 2655

United States Air Force, APO AP GU p. 2667

United States Air Force Academy Libraries, USAF Academy CO p. 324

United States Armed Forces, Falls Church VA p. 2463

United States Armed Forces School of Music, Virginia Beach VA p. 2500

United States Army, Fort Rucker AL p. 18

United States Army, Redstone Arsenal AL p. 34

United States Army, Elmendorf AFB AK p. 47

United States Army, Fort Wainwright AK p. 48

United States Army, Yuma AZ p. 91

United States Army, Fort Irwin CA p. 148

United States Army, Jolon CA p. 161

United States Army, Sacramento CA p. 225

United States Army, Fort Carson CO p. 307

United States Army, Jacksonville FL p. 455

United States Army, Fort Benning GA p. 532

United States Army, Fort Gordon GA p. 533

United States Army, Fort McPherson GA p. 533

United States Army, Fort Stewart GA p. 533

United States Army, Fort Shafter HI p. 559

United States Army, Honolulu HI p. 565

United States Army, Schofield Barracks HI p. 567

United States Army, Rock Island IL p. 696

United States Army, Fort Leavenworth KS p. 867

United States Army, Fort Riley KS p. 867

United States Army, Fort Campbell KY p. 912

United States Army, Fort Knox KY p. 913

United States Army, Fort Polk LA p. 949

United States Army, New Orleans LA p. 963

United States Army, Aberdeen Proving Ground MD p. 1009

United States Army, Fort George G Meade MD p. 1028

United States Army, Frederick MD p. 1029

United States Army, Concord MA p. 1083

United States Army, Natick MA p. 1108

United States Army, Saint Paul MN p. 1282

United States Army, Vicksburg MS p. 1317

United States Army, Fort Leonard Wood MO p. 1328

United States Army, Saint Louis MO p. 1361

United States Army, Omaha NE p. 1414

United States Army, Hanover NH p. 1450

United States Army, White Sands Missile Range NM p. 1566

United States Army, Brooklyn NY p. 1595

United States Army, Buffalo NY p. 1599

United States Army, Fort Drum NY p. 1623

United States Army, West Point NY p. 1767

United States Army, Fort Bragg NC p. 1794

United States Army, Fort Sill OK p. 1963

United States Army, McAlester OK p. 1968

United States Army, Philadelphia PA p. 2118

United States Army, Tobyhanna PA p. 2146

United States Army, Fort Jackson SC p. 2194

United States Army, Memphis TN p. 2252

United States Army, El Paso TX p. 2317

United States Army, Fort Bliss TX p. 2320

United States Army, Fort Hood TX p. 2320

United States Army, Fort Sam Houston TX p. 2320

United States Army, Fort Worth TX p. 2324

United States Army, Galveston TX p. 2326

United States Army, Alexandria VA p. 2446

United States Army, Fort Belvoir VA p. 2464

United States Army, Fort Eustis VA p. 2464

United States Army, Fort Lee VA p. 2465

United States Army, Fort Monroe VA p. 2465

United States Army, Fort Myer VA p. 2465

United States Army, Fort Story VA p. 2465

United States Army, Joint Base Lewis McChord WA p. 2518

United States Army, Tacoma WA p. 2540

United States Army, Walla Walla WA p. 2547

United States Army, Fort McCoy WI p. 2593

United States Army, Fort Buchanan PR p. 2672

United States Army Corps of Engineers, Mobile AL p. 26

United States Army Corps of Engineers, Champaign IL p. 603

United States Army Corps of Engineers, Portland OR p. 2014

United States Army Corps of Engineers, Norfolk VA p. 2483

United States Army Corps of Engineers, Seattle WA p. 2533

United States Army Corps of Engineers Library, Pittsburgh PA p. 2128

United States Army Dugway Proving Ground, Dugway UT p. 2404

United States Army Heritage & Education Center, Carlisle PA p. 2042

United States Army Medical Research Institute, Aberdeen Proving Ground MD p. 1009

United States Army Military History Institute, see United States Army Heritage & Education Center, Carlisle PA p. 2042

United States Army, RDECOM-ARDEC, Picatinny Arsenal NJ p. 1520

United States Army Research Laboratory, Adelphi MD p. 1009

United States Army Research Office, Research Triangle Park NC p. 1820

United States Army Training & Doctrine Command (N), Fort Monroe VA p. 2957

United States Army Transportation Museum Library, Fort Eustis VA p. 2465

United States Army War College Library, Carlisle PA p. 2042

United States Attorney's Office Library, see United States Department of Justice, Grand Rapids MI p. 1186

United States Attorney's Office Library, Newark NJ p. 1513

United States Book Exchange Library, Cleveland OH p. 1881

United States Botanic Garden Library, Washington DC p. 417

United States Bureau of Alcohol, Tobacco, Firearms & Explosives, Beltsville MD p. 1020

United States Bureau of Land Management, Roswell NM p. 1561

United States Bureau of the Census, Atlanta GA p. 518

United States Bureau of the Census, Kansas City KS p. 875

United States Cavalry Association, Fort Riley KS p. 867

United States Cavalry Memorial Research Library, see United States Cavalry Association, Fort Riley KS p. 867

United States Cavalry Museum, Fort Riley KS p. 867

United States Coast Guard Academy Library, New London CT p. 360

United States Commission on Civil Rights, Washington DC p. 417

United States Committee for Refugees & Immigrants Library, Washington DC p. 417

United States Conference of Catholic Bishops Library, Washington DC p. 417

United States Consumer Product Safety Commission, Bethesda MD p. 1022

United States Court Library - Eighth Circuit, Kansas City MO p. 1341

United States Court Library - Eighth Circuit, Omaha NE p. 1414

United States Court of Appeals, Little Rock AR p. 107

United States Court of Appeals, Wilmington DE p. 389

United States Court of Appeals, Des Moines IA p. 810

United States Court of Appeals, New Orleans LA p. 964

United States Court of Appeals, Minneapolis MN p. 1261

United States Court of Appeals, Camden NJ p. 1477

United States Court of Appeals, Newark NJ p. 1513

United States Court of Appeals, Tulsa OK p. 1984

United States Court of Appeals, Philadelphia PA p. 2118

United States Court of Appeals, Richmond VA p. 2491

United States Court of Appeals, Hato Rey PR p. 2673

United States Court of Appeals, Providence RI p. 2175

United States Court of Appeals, Washington DC p. 417, 418

United States Court of Appeals, Nashville TN p. 2260

United States Court of Appeals, Cincinnati OH p. 1873

United States Court of Appeals, Saint Louis MO p. 1361

United States Court of Appeals Library, Portland OR p. 2015

United States Court of Appeals, Pasadena CA p. 207

United States Court of International Trade, New York NY p. 1702

United States Courts, Kansas City KS p. 875

United States Marine Corps, Beaufort SC p. 2181

United States Marine Corps, Parris Island SC p. 2202

United States Merchant Marine Academy, Kings Point NY p. 1649

United States Merit Systems Protection Board Library, Washington DC p. 420

United States Military Academy Library, West Point NY p. 1767

United States National Arboretum Library, Washington DC p. 420

United States National Library of Medicine (N), Bethesda MD p. 2945

United States National Oceanic & Atmospheric, Miami FL p. 468

United States National Park Service, Skagway AK p. 53

United States National Park Service, Ganado AZ p. 64

United States National Park Service, Willcox AZ p. 89

United States National Park Service, Garfield AR p. 101

United States National Park Service, Point Reyes Station CA p. 211

United States National Park Service, San Diego CA p. 238

United States National Park Service, Twentynine Palms CA p. 277

United States National Park Service, La Junta CO p. 314

United States National Park Service, Washington DC p. 420

United States National Park Service, Savannah GA p. 551

United States National Park Service, Lincoln City IN p. 761

United States National Park Service, Harpers Ferry IA p. 820

United States National Park Service, Larned KS p. 877

United States National Park Service, Glen Echo MD p. 1030

United States National Park Service, Brookline MA p. 1072

United States National Park Service, Salem MA p. 1122

United States National Park Service, Wellfleet MA p. 1135

United States National Park Service, Grand Portage MN p. 1253

United States National Park Service, Diamond MO p. 1327

United States National Park Service, Beatrice NE p. 1393

United States National Park Service, Capulin NM p. 1552

United States National Park Service, Currie NC p. 1786

United States National Park Service, Chillicothe OH p. 1868

United States National Park Service, King of Prussia PA p. 2074

United States National Park Service, Sullivan's Island SC p. 2206

United States National Park Service, Gatlinburg TN p. 2235

United States National Park Service-Fort Vancouver Library, Vancouver WA p. 2546

United States National Ski Hall of Fame, Ishpeming MI p. 1194

United States Naval Academy, Annapolis MD p. 1011

United States Naval Observatory, Washington DC p. 421

United States Naval War College Library, Newport RI p. 2169

United States Navy, Camp Pendleton CA p. 131

United States Navy, China Lake CA p. 133

United States Navy, El Centro CA p. 146

United States Navy, Monterey CA p. 190

United States Navy, San Diego CA p. 238

United States Navy, Groton CT p. 342

United States Navy, Jacksonville FL p. 455

United States Navy, Pensacola FL p. 482

United States Navy, Albany GA p. 507

United States Navy, Great Lakes IL p. 652

United States Navy, Indian Head MD p. 1033

United States Navy, Patuxent River MD p. 1036

United States Navy, Stennis Space Center MS p. 1315

United States Navy, Camp Lejeune NC p. 1779

United States Navy, Philadelphia PA p. 2118

United States Navy, Newport RI p. 2170

United States Navy, Beaufort SC p. 2182

United States Navy, Charleston SC p. 2185

United States Navy, Corpus Christi TX p. 2302

United States Navy, Kingsville TX p. 2351

United States Navy, Dahlgren VA p. 2459

United States Navy, Norfolk VA p. 2483

United States Navy, Portsmouth VA p. 2485

United States Navy, Bremerton WA p. 2511

United States Navy, Oak Harbor WA p. 2522

United States Navy, Sugar Grove WV p. 2572

United States Nuclear Regulatory Commission, Rockville MD p. 1040

United States Olympic Committee, Colorado Springs CO p. 296

United States Patent & Trademark Office, Alexandria VA p. 2446

United States Postal Service Library, Washington DC p. 421

United States Railroad Retirement Board Library, Chicago IL p. 626

United States Securities & Exchange Commission Library, Washington DC p. 421

United States Senate Library, Washington DC p. 421

United States Sentencing Commission Library, Washington DC p. 421

United States Space & Rocket Center, Huntsville AL p. 22

United States Sports Academy Library, Daphne AL p. 14

United States Tax Court Library, Washington DC p. 421

United States Trademark Office Law Library, Alexandria VA p. 2446

United States Veterans Affairs Medical Center, Dayton OH p. 1894

United Steelworkers of America Library, Toronto ON p. 2864

United Technologies Corp, Windsor Locks CT p. 379

United Theological Seminary Library, Trotwood OH p. 1941

United Theological Seminary of the Twin Cities, New Brighton MN p. 1267

United Tribes Technical College Library, Bismarck ND p. 1838

Unity College, Unity ME p. 1004

Unity Free Public Library, Charlestown NH p. 1441

Unity Hospital, see Allina Health Library Services, Fridley MN p. 1258

Unity Hospital Medical Library, see Interlakes Oncology Medical Library, Rochester NY p. 1729

Unity Library & Archives, Unity Village MO p. 1370

Universal City Public Library, Universal City TX p. 2394

Universidad Adventista de las Antillas, Mayaguez PR p. 2674

Universidad Central De Bayamon Library, Bayamon PR p. 2672

Universidad Central Del Caribe, Bayamon PR p. 2672

Universidad del este Library, Carolina PR p. 2672

Universidad del Turabo, Gurabo PR p. 2673

Universite de Moncton, Moncton NB p. 2766

Universite de Moncton, Shippagan NB p. 2767

Universite de Montreal, Montreal QC p. 2979

Universite de Sherbrooke Service des Bibliotheques et Archives, Sherbrooke QC p. 2912

Universite du Quebec, Montreal QC p. 2902

Universite du Quebec a Chicoutimi Bibliotheque, Chicoutimi QC p. 2881

Universite du Quebec a Montreal Bibliotheque, Montreal QC p. 2902

Universite du Quebec a Rimouski - Bibliotheque, Rimouski QC p. 2907

Universite du Quebec a Trois-Rivieres - Service de la Bibliotheque, Trois-Rivieres QC p. 2914

Universite du Quebec en Outaouais, Gatineau QC p. 2884

Universite Laval Bibliotheque, Quebec QC p. 2906

Universite Sainte-Anne, Church Point NS p. 2778

University at Albany, State University of New York, Albany NY p. 1570, 2970

University at Buffalo Libraries-State University of New York, Buffalo NY p. 1599

University at Buffalo, State University of New York, Buffalo NY p. 2970

University Baptist Church Library, Baton Rouge LA p. 945

University Center of Greenville Library, see University of South Carolina Upstate Library, Greenville SC p. 2206

University Center Rochester, Rochester MN p. 1273

University City Public Library, University City MO p. 1370

University Club Library, Washington DC p. 421

University Club Library, New York NY p. 1702

University College of the North, Norway House MB p. 2750

University College of the North Libraries, The Pas MB p. 2753

University de Moncton, Edmundston NB p. 2762

University Health Network, Toronto ON p. 2864

University Hospital, Augusta GA p. 520

University Hospitals Case Medical Center, Cleveland OH p. 1881

University Libraries, University of Memphis, Memphis TN p. 2252

University Library of Columbus, Columbus IN p. 733

University Medical Center of Southern Nevada, Las Vegas NV p. 1430

University of Akron Libraries, Akron OH p. 1853

University of Alabama, Tuscaloosa AL p. 38, 39, 2961

University of Alabama at Birmingham, Birmingham AL p. 9

University of Alabama in Huntsville, Huntsville AL p. 22

University of Alaska Anchorage, Anchorage AK p. 45

University of Alaska Anchorage, Matanuska-Susitna, Palmer AK p. 52

University of Alaska Fairbanks, Fairbanks AK p. 48

University of Alaska Fairbanks, Kotzebue AK p. 51

University of Alaska Fairbanks, School of Fisheries & Ocean Sciences, Seward AK p. 53

University of Alaska Southeast, Juneau AK p. 50

University of Alaska Southeast, Ketchikan AK p. 51

University of Alberta, Camrose AB p. 2694

University of Alberta, Edmonton AB p. 2702, 2977

University of Arizona, Tucson AZ p. 88, 2962

University of Arkansas at Little Rock, Little Rock AR p. 107

University of Arkansas at Monticello, Crossett AR p. 97

University of Arkansas Community College at Hope, Hope AR p. 103

University of Arkansas Community College at Morrilton, Morrilton AR p. 110

University of Arkansas for Medical Sciences, Texarkana AR p. 116

University of Arkansas for Medical Sciences Library, Little Rock AR p. 107

University of Arkansas for Medical Sciences, El Dorado AR p. 98

University of Arkansas Fort Smith, Fort Smith AR p. 101

University of Arkansas Libraries, Fayetteville AR p. 99

University of Arkansas-Monticello, Monticello AR p. 110

University of Arkansas-Pine Bluff, Pine Bluff AR p. 112

University of Baltimore, Baltimore MD p. 1018

University of Bridgeport, Bridgeport CT p. 332

University of British Columbia, Vancouver BC p. 2977

University of British Columbia Library, Vancouver BC p. 2742

University of Montana Helena, Helena MT p. 1383
University of Montana Western, Dillon MT p. 1378
University of Montevallo, Montevallo AL p. 27
University of Nebraska at Kearney, Kearney NE p. 1403
University of Nebraska at Omaha, Omaha NE p. 1414, 2969
University of Nebraska-Lincoln, Lincoln NE p. 1407
University of Nebraska Medical Center, Omaha NE p. 1415
University of Nevada, Las Vegas Libraries, Las Vegas NV p. 1430
University of Nevada-Reno, Reno NV p. 1433
University of New Brunswick Libraries, Fredericton NB p. 2763
University of New Brunswick, Saint John Campus, Saint John NB p. 2767
University of New England Libraries, Biddeford ME p. 978
University of New Hampshire at Manchester Library, Manchester NH p. 1456
University of New Hampshire Library, Durham NH p. 1445
University of New Hampshire School of Law, Concord NH p. 1443
University of New Haven, West Haven CT p. 377
University of New Mexico, Albuquerque NM p. 1550
University of New Mexico, Gallup NM p. 1556
University of New Mexico, Los Alamos NM p. 1559
University of New Mexico, Albuquerque NM p. 2969, 1550
University of New Orleans, New Orleans LA p. 964, 2967
University of North Alabama, Florence AL p. 17
University of North Carolina at Asheville, Asheville NC p. 1775
University of North Carolina at Chapel Hill, Chapel Hill NC p. 1780, 2971
University of North Carolina at Charlotte, Charlotte NC p. 1784
University of North Carolina at Greensboro, Greensboro NC p. 1797, 2971
University of North Carolina at Pembroke, Pembroke NC p. 1814
University of North Carolina School of the Arts, Winston-Salem NC p. 1833
University of North Dakota, Grand Forks ND p. 1842, 1843
University of North Florida, Jacksonville FL p. 455
University of North Texas, Denton TX p. 2975
University of North Texas Health Science Center at Fort Worth, Fort Worth TX p. 2324
University of North Texas Libraries, Denton TX p. 2313
University of Northern British Columbia Library, Prince George BC p. 2736
University of Northern Colorado, Greeley CO p. 2963
University of Northern Colorado Libraries, Greeley CO p. 312
University of Northern Iowa, Cedar Falls IA p. 2965
University of Northern Iowa Library, Cedar Falls IA p. 799
University of Notre Dame, Notre Dame IN p. 771
University of Oklahoma, Norman OK p. 1971
University of Oklahoma, Tulsa OK p. 1984
University of Oklahoma, Norman OK p. 2972
University of Oklahoma Health Sciences Center, Oklahoma City OK p. 1975
University of Ontario Institute of Technology Library, Oshawa ON p. 2827
University of Oregon, Charleston OR p. 1993
University of Oregon Libraries, Eugene OR p. 1997
University of Ottawa Libraries, Ottawa ON p. 2834
University of Pennsylvania Libraries, Philadelphia PA p. 2118
University of Pittsburgh, Pittsburgh PA p. 2128, 2129, 2973
University of Pittsburgh at Bradford, Bradford PA p. 2037
University of Pittsburgh at Greensburg, Greensburg PA p. 2062
University of Pittsburgh at Titusville, Titusville PA p. 2146

University of Pittsburgh, Johnstown PA p. 2073
University of Pittsburgh Medical Center Shadyside, Pittsburgh PA p. 2129
University of Portland, Portland OR p. 2015
University of Prince Edward Island, Charlottetown PE p. 2876
University of Puerto Rico, Arecibo PR p. 2671
University of Puerto Rico, Bayamon PR p. 2672
University of Puerto Rico, Mayaguez PR p. 2674
University of Puerto Rico, San Juan PR p. 2676
University of Puerto Rico Library, San Juan PR p. 2676
University of Puerto Rico Library, Cayey Campus, Cayey PR p. 2672
University of Puerto Rico Library System, San Juan PR p. 2676
University of Puerto Rico, Rio Piedras Campus, San Juan PR p. 2977
University of Puget Sound, Tacoma WA p. 2540
University of Redlands, Redlands CA p. 215
University of Regina, Regina SK p. 2925
University of Rhode Island, Narragansett RI p. 2168
University of Rhode Island, Providence RI p. 2175
University of Rhode Island, Kingston RI p. 2973
University of Richmond, Richmond VA p. 2491
University of Rio Grande, Rio Grande OH p. 1931
University of Rochester, Rochester NY p. 1733
University of Rochester Medical Center, Rochester NY p. 1734
University of Saint Francis, Fort Wayne IN p. 742
University of Saint Mary, Leavenworth KS p. 879
University of Saint Mary of the Lake - Mundelein Seminary, Mundelein IL p. 678
University of Saint Thomas, Saint Paul MN p. 1282
University of Saint Thomas, Houston TX p. 2344
University of San Diego, San Diego CA p. 239
University of San Francisco, San Francisco CA p. 248
University of Saskatchewan Libraries, Saskatoon SK p. 2927
University of Science & Arts of Oklahoma, Chickasha OK p. 1959
University of Scranton, Scranton PA p. 2138
University of Sioux Falls, Sioux Falls SD p. 2219
University of South Alabama, Mobile AL p. 26, 2961
University of South Carolina, Allendale SC p. 2180
University of South Carolina, Columbia SC p. 2189, 2973
University of South Carolina Aiken, Aiken SC p. 2180
University of South Carolina at Beaufort Library, Bluffton SC p. 2182
University of South Carolina at Union Library, Union SC p. 2207
University of South Carolina Sumter, Sumter SC p. 2206
University of South Carolina Upstate Library, Spartanburg SC p. 2205
University of South Dakota, Vermillion SD p. 2220
University of South Florida, Tampa FL p. 498, 2964
University of South Florida Saint Petersburg, Saint Petersburg FL p. 488
University of Southern California Libraries, Los Angeles CA p. 179
University of Southern Indiana, Evansville IN p. 739
University of Southern Maine, Lewiston ME p. 990
University of Southern Maine, Portland ME p. 998
University of Southern Mississippi, Long Beach MS p. 1307
University of Southern Mississippi, Hattiesburg MS p. 2968
University of Southern Mississippi Library, Hattiesburg MS p. 1300
University of Saint Francis, Joliet IL p. 660
University of Sudbury Library, Sudbury ON p. 2847
University of Tampa, Tampa FL p. 499
University of Tennessee, Knoxville TN p. 2243
University of Tennessee at Chattanooga Library, Chattanooga TN p. 2228
University of Tennessee at Martin, Martin TN p. 2246
University of Tennessee College of Social Work Library at Nashville, Nashville TN p. 2260

University of Tennessee Graduate School of Medicine, Knoxville TN p. 2243
University of Tennessee, Knoxville, Knoxville TN p. 2243
University of Tennessee-Memphis, Memphis TN p. 2252
University of Tennessee Space Institute Library, Tullahoma TN p. 2268
University of Tennessee, Knoxville, Knoxville TN p. 2974
University of Texas, Houston TX p. 2344
University of Texas at Arlington Library, Arlington TX p. 2277
University of Texas at Austin, Austin TX p. 2283, 2975
University of Texas at Austin, Round Top TX p. 2377
University of Texas at Brownsville, Brownsville TX p. 2292
University of Texas at Dallas, Richardson TX p. 2374
University of Texas at El Paso Library, El Paso TX p. 2317
University of Texas at San Antonio Libraries, San Antonio TX p. 2383
University of Texas at Tyler Library, Tyler TX p. 2394
University of Texas Health Science Center, San Antonio TX p. 2383
University of Texas Health Science Center at Tyler, Tyler TX p. 2394
University of Texas-Houston Health Science Center, Houston TX p. 2344
University of Texas Libraries, Austin TX p. 2283
University of Texas Medical Branch, Galveston TX p. 2326
University of Texas of the Permian Basin, Odessa TX p. 2366
University of Texas-Pan American Library, Edinburg TX p. 2315
University of Texas Southwestern Medical Center Library, Dallas TX p. 2311
University of the Arts University Libraries, Philadelphia PA p. 2119
University of the Cumberlands/Cumberland College, Williamsburg KY p. 937
University of the District of Columbia, Washington DC p. 421
University of the Fraser Valley, Abbotsford BC p. 2724
University of the Incarnate Word, San Antonio TX p. 2384
University of the Ozarks, Clarksville AR p. 96
University of the Pacific Library, Stockton CA p. 273
University of the Pacific - McGeorge School of Law, Sacramento CA p. 226
University of the Sacred Heart, Santurce PR p. 2678
University of the Sciences in Philadelphia, Philadelphia PA p. 2120
University of the South, Sewanee TN p. 2265
University of the Southwest, Hobbs NM p. 1557
University of the Virgin Islands, Kingshill VI p. 2679
University of the Virgin Islands, Saint Thomas VI p. 2679
University of Toledo, Toledo OH p. 1940, 1941
University of Toronto, Toronto ON p. 2978
University of Toronto Libraries, Toronto ON p. 2865, 2867
University of Tulsa Libraries, Tulsa OK p. 1984
University of Utah, Salt Lake City UT p. 2414
University of Vermont Libraries, Burlington VT p. 2421
University of Victoria Libraries, Victoria BC p. 2746
University of Virginia, Charlottesville VA p. 2454
University of Virginia's College at Wise, Wise VA p. 2504
University of Washington, Seattle WA p. 2976
University of Washington Botanic Gardens, Seattle WA p. 2533
University of Washington Libraries, Seattle WA p. 2533
University of Waterloo Library, Waterloo ON p. 2869

VA-Northern Indiana Health Care System, Fort Wayne IN p. 743

VA Northern Indiana Healthcare Systems, Marion IN p. 763

VA Pittsburgh Healthcare System, Pittsburgh PA p. 2129

VA Puget Sound Health Care System, Tacoma WA p. 2541

VA San Diego Healthcare System Medical Library, San Diego CA p. 239

Vacaville Public Library, *see* Solano County Library, Vacaville, *see* Solano County Library CA p. 148

Vaiden Public Library, Vaiden MS p. 1317

Vairo John D Library, *see* Pennsylvania State University, Media PA p. 2088

Val Verde County Library, Del Rio TX p. 2312

Valatie Free Library, Valatie NY p. 1760

Valdes Juan Library, *see* Evangelical Seminary of Puerto Rico, San Juan PR p. 2676

Valdez Consortium Library, Valdez AK p. 55

Valdez Joel D, *see* Pima County Public Library, Tucson AZ p. 87

Valdosta-Lowndes County Public, *see* South Georgia Regional Library System, Valdosta GA p. 555

Valdosta State Prison, *see* Georgia Department of Corrections, Office of Library Services, Valdosta GA p. 554

Valdosta State University, Valdosta GA p. 555, 2964

VALE (N), *see* Virtual Academic Library Environment, Wayne NJ p. 2949

Vale Canada Limited, Mississauga ON p. 2823

Vale Inco Ltd, Toronto ON p. 2867

Valemount Public Library, Valemount BC p. 2740

Valencia Community College, Kissimmee FL p. 456

Valencia Community College, Orlando FL p. 478

Valencia Community College, Winter Park FL p. 505

Valentine H A Memorial Library, *see* High Street Christian Church, Akron OH p. 1853

Valentine Public Library, Valentine NE p. 1422

Valentine Richmond History Center, Richmond VA p. 2491

Valerie Merrick Memorial Library, Fort Totten ND p. 1842

Valhalla Public Library, Valhalla Centre AB p. 2720

Validata Computer & Research Corp Library, Montgomery AL p. 31

Valier Public Library, Valier MT p. 1389

Valle Vista Community Library, *see* Mohave County Library District, Kingman AZ p. 67

Valle Vista Library, *see* Riverside County Library System, Hemet CA p. 218

Vallejo Naval & Historical Museum, Vallejo CA p. 278

Valley City Barnes County Public Library, Valley City ND p. 1848

Valley City State University, Valley City ND p. 2971

Valley City State University Library, Valley City ND p. 1848

Valley Community Library, Peckville PA p. 2102

Valley Cottage Free Library, Valley Cottage NY p. 1760

Valley District Public Library, Fairview IL p. 645

Valley Falls Free Library, Valley Falls NY p. 1760

Valley Forge Christian College, Phoenixville PA p. 2120

Valley Forge Military Academy & College, Wayne PA p. 2152

Willcox Horace Memorial Library, *see* United States National Park Service, King of Prussia PA p. 2074

Valley Head Public Library, Valley Head WV p. 2573

Valley Hi-North Laguna Library, *see* Sacramento Public Library, Sacramento CA p. 225

Valley Hospital, Ridgewood NJ p. 1526

Valley Library, *see* Oregon State University Libraries, Corvallis OR p. 1994

Valley Library Consortium (N), Saginaw MI p. 2946

Valley Medical Center Library, Renton WA p. 2526

Valley Mills Public Library, Valley Mills TX p. 2394

Valley of the Tetons District Library, Victor ID p. 585

Valley Park Community Library, Valley Park MO p. 1370

Valley Presbyterian Hospital, Van Nuys CA p. 279

Valley Public Library, Valley NE p. 1422

Valley Regional Hospital, Claremont NH p. 1442

Valley Regional Library, South Morris MB p. 2752

Valley State Prison for Women, *see* California Department of Corrections Library System, Chowchilla CA p. 222

Valley Stream Public Library, *see* Waldinger Henry Memorial Library, Valley Stream NY p. 1760

Valley View Library, *see* King County Library System, SeaTac WA p. 2517

ValleyCare Health Library & Ryan Comer Cancer Resource Center, *see* ValleyCare Health System, Pleasanton CA p. 211

ValleyCare Health System, Pleasanton CA p. 211

Valleyview Municipal Library, Valleyview AB p. 2720

Valparaiso Community Library, Valparaiso FL p. 501

Valparaiso Public (Central), *see* Porter County Public Library System, Valparaiso IN p. 783

Valparaiso Public Library, Valparaiso NE p. 1422

Valparaiso University, Valparaiso IN p. 783

Value Line Publishing, Inc, New York NY p. 1702

Valve Manufacturers Association of America, Washington DC p. 421

Van Alstyne Public Library, Van Alstyne TX p. 2395

Van Buren District Library, Decatur MI p. 1168

Van Buren Library, *see* Carter County Library District, Van Buren MO p. 1370

Van Buren Public Library, Van Buren AR p. 116

Van Buren Public Library, Van Buren IN p. 784

Van Cleave Kevin Poole Memorial Library, *see* Natchez Adams Wilkinson Library Service, Centreville MS p. 1310

Van Doren Dorris, *see* El Paso Public Library, El Paso TX p. 2316

Van Dyke Grace Bird Library, *see* Bakersfield College, Bakersfield CA p. 123

Van Etten Library, *see* Chemung County Library District, Van Etten NY p. 1619

Van Gorden-Williams Library & Archives, *see* Scottish Rite Masonic Museum & Library, Inc, Lexington MA p. 1099

Van Hoof Gerard H Library, *see* Kimberly Public Library, Little Chute WI p. 2602

Van Horn City County Library, Van Horn TX p. 2395

Van Horn Public Library, Pine Island MN p. 1270

Van Horne Public Library, Van Horne IA p. 848

Van Houten Robert W Library, *see* New Jersey Institute of Technology, Newark NJ p. 1511

Van Meter Public Library, Van Meter IA p. 848

Van Ness Feldman Library, Washington DC p. 422

Van Noy Library, *see* United States Army, Fort Belvoir VA p. 2464

Van Oosten John Library, *see* United States Geological Survey, Ann Arbor MI p. 1151

Van Pelt J Robert & John & Ruanne Opie Library, *see* Michigan Technological University, Houghton MI p. 1191

Van Pelt Library, *see* University of Pennsylvania Libraries, Philadelphia PA p. 2118

Van Rensselaer - Rankin Family Historic Cherry Hill Museum & Library, Albany NY p. 1571

Van Trump James D Library, *see* Pittsburgh History & Landmarks Foundation, Pittsburgh PA p. 2127

Van Tyne Josselyn Memorial Library, *see* Wilson Ornithological Society, Ann Arbor MI p. 1153

Van Wagenen Library, *see* State University of New York College of Agriculture & Technology, Cobleskill NY p. 1608

Van Wert County Law Library Association, Van Wert OH p. 1943

Van Wyck Homestead Museum Library, *see* Fishkill Historical Society, Fishkill NY p. 1622

Van Wylen Library, *see* Hope College, Holland MI p. 1190

Van Zandt County Library, Canton TX p. 2294

Vance-Granville Community College, Henderson NC p. 1800

Vance Memorial Library, *see* Dallas Baptist University, Dallas TX p. 2305

Vance Township Library, Fairmount IL p. 645

Vanceboro Public Library, Vanceboro NC p. 1827

Vancleave Public Library, *see* Jackson-George Regional Library System, Vancleave MS p. 1311

VanCott Stuart Memorial Library, *see* Congregational Church of Patchogue, Patchogue NY p. 1715

Vancouver Aquarium Marine Science Centre, Vancouver BC p. 2743

Vancouver Art Gallery Library, Vancouver BC p. 2743

Vancouver Coastal Health, North Vancouver BC p. 2735

Vancouver Community College, Vancouver BC p. 2743

Vancouver Community Library, *see* Fort Vancouver Regional Library District, Vancouver WA p. 2546

Vancouver Holocaust Education Centre Library & Archives, Vancouver BC p. 2743

Vancouver Island Health Authority Medical Libraries, Victoria BC p. 2746

Vancouver Island Regional Library, Nanaimo BC p. 2732

Vancouver Mall Community Library, *see* Fort Vancouver Regional Library District, Vancouver WA p. 2546

Vancouver Public Library, Vancouver BC p. 2744

Vancouver School of Theology Library, Vancouver BC p. 2744

Vandalia Correctional Center Library, Vandalia IL p. 714

Vanderbilt University, Nashville TN p. 2260

Vandercook College of Music, Chicago IL p. 627

Vandergrift Public Library Association, Vandergrift PA p. 2149

Vanderhoof Public Library, Vanderhoof BC p. 2744

VanDusen Botanical Gardens Association, Vancouver BC p. 2744

Vanguard College Library, Edmonton AB p. 2703

Vanguard University of Southern California, Costa Mesa CA p. 137

Vanier College Library, Saint Laurent QC p. 2909

Vankleek Hill Public Library, VanKleek Hill ON p. 2868

Vann Lee & Jim Library, *see* University of Saint Francis, Fort Wayne IN p. 742

Varey Vida B Library, *see* Plymouth Congregational Church, Seattle WA p. 2529

Varnum Memorial Library, Jeffersonville VT p. 2426

Vassalboro Public Library, East Vassalboro ME p. 984

Vassar Brothers Medical Center, Poughkeepsie NY p. 1723

Vassar College Library, Poughkeepsie NY p. 1723

Vaughan John Library-Learning Resource Center, *see* Northeastern State University, Tahlequah OK p. 1979

Vaughan Memorial Library, *see* Acadia University, Wolfville NS p. 2786

Vaughan Public Libraries, Thornhill ON p. 2847

Vaughn College Library, Flushing NY p. 1623

Vaughn Library, *see* Tyler Junior College, Tyler TX p. 2393

Vaughn Public Library, Vaughn NM p. 1566

Vaughn Public Library, Ashland WI p. 2579

Vaught Fred A Memorial Public Library, Hartsville TN p. 2237

Vauxhall Public Library, Vauxhall AB p. 2720

Vedder, Price, Chicago IL p. 627

Vedder Research Library, *see* Greene County Historical Society, Coxsackie NY p. 1612

Veedersburg Public, *see* Covington-Veedersburg Public Library, Veedersburg IN p. 734

Vegreville Centennial Library, Vegreville AB p. 2720

Velva School & Public Library, Velva ND p. 1848

Venable LLP Library, Los Angeles CA p. 180

Venable LLP Library, Washington DC p. 422

Venable LLP Library, Baltimore MD p. 1019

Venable, LLP Library, Vienna VA p. 2498

Venango County Law Library, Franklin PA p. 2059

Venice-Abbot Kinney Memorial, *see* Los Angeles Public Library System, Venice CA p. 174

Venice Public Library, Venice FL p. 501

Venice Public Library, Venice IL p. 714

Ventress Memorial Library, Marshfield MA p. 1103

Ventura College, Ventura CA p. 279

Ventura County Law Library, Ventura CA p. 279

Ventura County Library, Ventura CA p. 279

Virginia State Police Academy Library, Richmond VA p. 2493

Virginia State University, Petersburg VA p. 2484

Virginia Theological Seminary, Alexandria VA p. 2446

Virginia Tidewater Consortium for Higher Education (N), Norfolk VA p. 2957

Virginia Transportation Research Council Library, Charlottesville VA p. 2455

Virginia Union University, Richmond VA p. 2493

Virginia University of Lynchburg, Lynchburg VA p. 2476

Virginia War Museum, Newport News VA p. 2480

Virginia Wesleyan College, Norfolk VA p. 2483

Virginia Western Community College, Roanoke VA p. 2495

Virginian-Pilot Library, Norfolk VA p. 2483

Viroqua Public Library, see McIntosh Memorial Library, Viroqua WI p. 2643

Virtua Health System, Voorhees Division, Voorhees NJ p. 1539

Virtua Memorial Hospital Of Burlington County, Mount Holly NJ p. 1506

Virtual Academic Library Environment (N), Wayne NJ p. 2949

Virtual Library of Virginia (N), Fairfax VA p. 2957

Vise Doris & Harry Library, see Cumberland University, Lebanon TN p. 2244

Visidyne, Inc Library, Burlington MA p. 1072

Vista Grande Library, see Casa Grande Public Library, Casa Grande AZ p. 59

Vista Grande Public Library, Santa Fe NM p. 1564

Vista Health Systems, East Site, Waukegan IL p. 716

Vista Hermosa Library, see Walla Walla County Rural Library District, Prescott WA p. 2547

Viterbo University, La Crosse WI p. 2603

VIVA (N), see Virtual Library of Virginia, Fairfax VA p. 2957

Vivian Robert A, see Monroe County Library System, Monroe MI p. 1210

Vogel Library, see Wartburg College Library, Waverly IA p. 850

Vogel Marylee, see Spencer County Public Library, Richland IN p. 776

Voice Library, see Michigan State University Library, East Lansing MI p. 1175

Volga Public Library, Volga IA p. 849

Volpe Angelo & Jennette Library, see Tennessee Technological University, Cookeville TN p. 2231

Volpe John A National Transportation Systems Center, Cambridge MA p. 1078

Volta Bureau Library, see Bell Alexander Graham Association for the Deaf & Hard of Hearing, Washington DC p. 394

Volunteer Manitoba, Winnipeg MB p. 2759

Volunteer State Community College Library, Gallatin TN p. 2235

Voluntown Public Library, Voluntown CT p. 373

Volusia County Law Library, Daytona Beach FL p. 436

Volusia County Public Library, Daytona Beach FL p. 436

Von Braun Library & Archives, see United States Space & Rocket Center, Huntsville AL p. 22

Von Canon Library, see Southern Virginia University, Buena Vista VA p. 2453

Von Riesen Library, see McCook Community College, McCook NE p. 1408

Vonda Public Library, see Wapiti Regional Library, Vonda SK p. 2922

Vonore Public Library, Vonore TN p. 2268

Voorhees College, Denmark SC p. 2192

Voorheesville Public Library, Voorheesville NY p. 1761

Voorhies Charles Fine Art Library, see Pacific Northwest College of Art, Portland OR p. 2013

Vorys, Sater, Seymour & Pease Library, Washington DC p. 422

Vose Library, Union ME p. 1004

Voskuyl Roger John Library, see Westmont College, Santa Barbara CA p. 262

Voyer Bertha Memorial Library, see Hall-Voyer Foundation, Honey Grove TX p. 2333

VSE Corporation Library-BAV Division, Alexandria VA p. 2446

VTC (N), see Virginia Tidewater Consortium for Higher Education, Norfolk VA p. 2957

Vues & Voix, Montreal QC p. 2902

Vulcan Municipal Library, Vulcan AB p. 2721

Wabamun Public Library, Wabamun AB p. 2721

Wabasca Public Library, Wabasca AB p. 2721

Wabash Carnegie Public Library, Wabash IN p. 785

Wabash College, Crawfordsville IN p. 734

Wabash Valley College, Mount Carmel IL p. 676

Wabash Valley Correctional Facility, Carlisle IN p. 731

Wabasha Public Library, Wabasha MN p. 1287

Wabasso Public Library, Wabasso MN p. 1287

Wabeno Public Library, Wabeno WI p. 2643

Wachtell, Lipton, Rosen & Katz, New York NY p. 1702

Wachute Joseph W & Emma L Memorial, see Prairie du Chien Memorial Library, Prairie du Chien WI p. 2631

Wacker Silicones Corp, Adrian MI p. 1148

Waco-McLennan County Library System, Waco TX p. 2397

Waco Tribune-Herald Library, Waco TX p. 2398

Wade David Correctional Center, Homer LA p. 951

Wade Marion E Center, see Wheaton College, Wheaton IL p. 718

Wade Richard & Glen Vyck McKinney Library, see Rio Grande Bible Institute & Language School, Edinburg TX p. 2315

Wadena City Library, Wadena MN p. 1287

Wadena Public Library, Wadena IA p. 849

Wadewitz E H Memorial Library, see Printing Industries of America, Sewickley PA p. 2139

Wadhams Free Library, Wadhams NY p. 1762

Wadleigh Library, see Chester College of New England, Chester NH p. 1441

Wadleigh Memorial Library, Milford NH p. 1457

Wadley Helen, see Monroe County Public Library, Islamorada FL p. 456

Wadley Public, see Jefferson County Library System, Wadley GA p. 540

Wadsworth Atheneum, Hartford CT p. 348

Wadsworth Library, Geneseo NY p. 1627

Wadsworth Library, see Mount Ida College, Newton MA p. 1110

Wadsworth Public Library, see Everhard Ella M Public Library, Wadsworth OH p. 1943

Wadsworth-Rittman Community Hospital Library, Wadsworth OH p. 1944

Waelder Public Library, Waelder TX p. 2398

Waggoner Frances Banta Community Library, DeWitt IA p. 810

Waggoner Library, see Trevecca Nazarene University, Nashville TN p. 2259

Wagnalls Memorial Library, Lithopolis OH p. 1910

Wagner Albert C Youth Correctional Facility Library, Bordentown NJ p. 1474

Wagner Charles A, see Jefferson Parish Library, Metairie LA p. 957

Wagner College, Staten Island NY p. 1748

Wagner Community Library, Falls City OR p. 1998

Wagner Free Institute of Science Library, Philadelphia PA p. 2120

Wagner Lois Memorial Library, Richmond MI p. 1221

Wagner Public Library, Wagner SD p. 2221

Wagoner City Public Library, Wagoner OK p. 1985

Wahab Public Law Library, see Virginia Beach Public Library Department, Virginia Beach VA p. 2500

Wahiawa Public Library, see Hawaii State Public Library System, Wahiawa HI p. 563

Wahl Rosalie E, see Washington County Library, Lake Elmo MN p. 1290

Wahlstrom Magnus Library, see University of Bridgeport, Bridgeport CT p. 332

Wahoo Public Library, Wahoo NE p. 1422

Wahta Mohawks, Bala ON p. 2793

Waialua Public Library, see Hawaii State Public Library System, Waialua HI p. 563

Waianae Public Library, see Hawaii State Public Library System, Waianae HI p. 563

Waidner-Spahr Library, see Dickinson College, Carlisle PA p. 2041

Waikiki-Kapahulu Public Library, see Hawaii State Public Library System, Honolulu HI p. 563

Wailuku Public Library, see Hawaii State Public Library System, Wailuku HI p. 563

Waimanalo Public & School Library, see Hawaii State Public Library System, Waimanalo HI p. 563

Waimea Public Library, see Hawaii State Public Library System, Waimea HI p. 563

Wainfleet Township Public Library, Wainfleet ON p. 2869

Wainwright Jonathan M Memorial Library, see Veterans Affairs Medical Center, Walla Walla WA p. 2547

Wainwright Public Library, Wainwright AB p. 2721

Waipahu Public Library, see Hawaii State Public Library System, Waipahu HI p. 563

Wakarusa-Olive & Harrison Township Public Library, see Wakarusa Public Library, Wakarusa IN p. 785

Wakarusa Public Library, Wakarusa IN p. 785

Wakaw Public Library, see Wapiti Regional Library, Wakaw SK p. 2922

Wake County Public Library System, Raleigh NC p. 1817

Wake Forest University, Winston-Salem NC p. 1834

Wake Technical Community College, Raleigh NC p. 1818

WaKeeney Public Library, WaKeeney KS p. 899

Wakefield Jesse Memorial Library, Port Lions AK p. 52

Wakefield June Memorial Library, see Northwestern Medical Center Library, Saint Albans VT p. 2434

Wakefield Library Association, Wakefield NH p. 1466

Wakefield Public Library, Wakefield KS p. 899

Wakefield Public Library, Wakefield MI p. 1233

Wakulla County Public Library, Crawfordville FL p. 434

Walden Community Library, West Danville VT p. 2439

Walden University Library, Minneapolis MN p. 1262

Waldinger Henry Memorial Library, Valley Stream NY p. 1760

Waldmann John & Bertha E Memorial Dental Library, see New York University School of Medicine, New York NY p. 1696

Waldo Community, see Kansas City Public Library, Kansas City MO p. 1338

Waldo County General Hospital, Belfast ME p. 977

Waldo County Law Library, Belfast ME p. 977

Waldo Dwight B Library, see Western Michigan University, Kalamazoo MI p. 1198

Waldoboro Public Library, Waldoboro ME p. 1004

Waldorf College, Forest City IA p. 816

Waldport Public Library, Waldport OR p. 2022

Waldron District Library, Waldron MI p. 1233

Waldrop Frances N Health Sciences Library, see Department of Mental Health, Saint Elizabeths Hospital, Washington DC p. 397

Waldwick Public Library, Waldwick NJ p. 1539

Wales Public Library, Wales MA p. 1132

Walford Lionel A Library, see NOAA, National Marine Fisheries Service, Highlands NJ p. 1491

Walhalla Public Library, Walhalla ND p. 1849

Walker E F Memorial Library, see First Baptist Church, Luling TX p. 2358

Walker Elisha Staff Library, see New York Downtown Hospital, New York NY p. 1689

Walker J B Memorial Library, see Hickman County Public Library, Centerville TN p. 2226

Walker Jackson Law Library, Houston TX p. 2345

Walker James E Library, see Middle Tennessee State University, Murfreesboro TN p. 2254

Walker Management Library, see Vanderbilt University, Nashville TN p. 2261

Walker Memorial Library, Westbrook ME p. 1006

Walker Memorial Library, see Howard Payne University, Brownwood TX p. 2292

Walker Nott Dragicevic Associates Ltd Library, Toronto ON p. 2867

Walker Public Library, Walker MN p. 1287

Walkerton-Lincoln Township Public Library, Walkerton IN p. 785

Warren Public Library, *see* Warren Library Association, Warren PA p. 2150

Warren Rick Memorial Public Library District, Elkville IL p. 642

Warren Stanford L, *see* Durham County Library, Durham NC p. 1788

Warren State Hospital, North Warren PA p. 2099

Warren Township Public Library, Warren IL p. 715

Warren-Trumbull County Public Library, Warren OH p. 1944

Warren Wilson College, Swannanoa NC p. 1826

Warrenton Community Library, Hammond OR p. 2000

Warrenville Library, *see* Illinois Youth Center, Warrenville IL p. 715

Warrenville Public Library District, Warrenville IL p. 715

Warrior Run Area Public Library, *see* Montgomery House, McEwensville PA p. 2085

Warroad Public Library, *see* Northwest Regional Library, Warroad MN p. 1286

Warsaw Community Public Library, Warsaw IN p. 785

Warsaw-Kornegay, *see* Duplin County Library, Warsaw NC p. 1804

Warsaw Public Library, Warsaw IL p. 715

Warsaw Public Library, Warsaw NY p. 1762

Warsham Hoyt, *see* Gadsden Public Library, Gadsden AL p. 18

Warshaw, Burstein, Cohen, Schlesinger & Kuh, New York NY p. 1702

Wartburg College Library, Waverly IA p. 850

Wartburg Public Library, Wartburg TN p. 2268

Wartburg Theological Seminary, Dubuque IA p. 812

Warwick Free Public Library, Warwick MA p. 1133

Warwick Public Library, Warwick RI p. 2177

Wasaga Beach Public Library, Wasaga Beach ON p. 2869

Wasatch County Library, Heber City UT p. 2406

Wasco City/Community Library, Wasco OR p. 2022

Wasco State Prison, *see* California Department of Corrections Library System, Wasco CA p. 222

Waseca County Historical Society Library, Waseca MN p. 1287

Waseca-Le Sueur Regional Library, Waseca MN p. 1287

Washakie County Library System, Worland WY p. 2661

Washburn County Law Library, Shell Lake WI p. 2638

Washburn Memorial Library, Washburn ME p. 1005

Washburn Public Library, Washburn TN p. 2268

Washburn Public Library, Washburn WI p. 2644

Washburn University, Topeka KS p. 897

Washington & Jefferson College Library, Washington PA p. 2151

Washington & Lee University, Lexington VA p. 2474

Washington Adventist Hospital, Takoma Park MD p. 1043

Washington Adventist University, Takoma Park MD p. 1043

Washington Art Association Library, Washington Depot CT p. 374

Washington Bible College, Lanham MD p. 1034

Washington Carnegie Public Library, Washington IN p. 786

Washington-Centerville Public Library, Centerville OH p. 1866

Washington Charles B, *see* Omaha Public Library, Omaha NE p. 1414

Washington College, Chestertown MD p. 1023

Washington Correction Center, *see* Washington State Library, Shelton WA p. 2545

Washington Correctional Facility Library, Comstock NY p. 1609

Washington Correctional Institution Library, *see* Florida Department of Corrections, Chipley FL p. 431

Washington Corrections Center for Women, *see* Washington State Library, Gig Harbor WA p. 2545

Washington County COMMUNITY College Library, Calais ME p. 980

Washington County Cooperative Library Services, Hillsboro OR p. 2000

Washington County Cooperative Library Services (N), Hillsboro OR p. 2953

Washington County Free Library, Hagerstown MD p. 1031

Washington County Historical Association, Fort Calhoun NE p. 1398

Washington County Historical Society, Hagerstown MD p. 1031

Washington County Historical Society, Portland OR p. 2015

Washington County Historical Society Library, Salem IN p. 777

Washington County Historical Society Library, Washington PA p. 2151

Washington County - Jonesborough Library, Jonesborough TN p. 2240

Washington County Law Library, Marietta OH p. 1913

Washington County Law Library, Hillsboro OR p. 2001

Washington County Law Library, Washington PA p. 2151

Washington County Law Library, *see* Washington County Library, Stillwater MN p. 1290

Washington County Library, Chipley FL p. 431

Washington County Library, Woodbury MN p. 1290

Washington County Library, Potosi MO p. 1350

Washington County Library, Plymouth NC p. 1814

Washington County Library, *see* University of Wisconsin, West Bend WI p. 2648

Washington County Library System, Fayetteville AR p. 100

Washington County Library System, Greenville MS p. 1298

Washington County Library System, Saint George UT p. 2412

Washington County Museum of Fine Arts Library, Hagerstown MD p. 1032

Washington County Public Library, Chatom AL p. 12

Washington County Public Library, Springfield KY p. 935

Washington County Public Library, Marietta OH p. 1913

Washington County Public Library, Abingdon VA p. 2443

Washington District Library, Washington IL p. 715

Washington Group International, Denver CO p. 304

Washington Harold Library Center, *see* Chicago Public Library, Chicago IL p. 610

Washington Hebrew Congregation Libraries, Washington DC p. 422

Washington Hospital, Washington PA p. 2151

Washington Hospital Center, Washington DC p. 422

Washington Hospital Healthcare System, Fremont CA p. 150

Washington Idaho Network (N), Spokane WA p. 2957

Washington Leon H Jr Memorial, *see* Los Angeles Public Library System, Los Angeles CA p. 174

Washington Library Resource Center, *see* Johns Hopkins University Libraries, Washington DC p. 405

Washington Martha, *see* Fairfax County Public Library, Alexandria VA p. 2461

Washington Mary Hospital, Fredericksburg VA p. 2466

Washington Memorial Library, *see* Middle Georgia Regional Library System, Macon GA p. 540

Washington Metropolitan Area Transit Authority, Washington DC p. 422

Washington Municipal Library, Washington LA p. 971

Washington National Cathedral, Washington DC p. 422

Washington Parish Library System, Franklinton LA p. 950

Washington Park-Annie McPheeters Library, *see* Atlanta-Fulton Public Library System, Atlanta GA p. 513

Washington Park Library, *see* Providence Community Library, Providence RI p. 2173

Washington Park Public Library, Washington Park IL p. 715

Washington Phyllis J College of Education & Human Sciences, *see* University of Montana, Missoula MT p. 2969

Washington Post, Washington DC p. 422

Washington Public Library, Washington IA p. 849

Washington Public Library, Washington KS p. 899

Washington Public Library, Washington MO p. 1371

Washington Public Library, Washington NJ p. 1539

Washington Research Library Consortium (N), Upper Marlboro MD p. 2945

Washington School for the Deaf, Vancouver WA p. 2546

Washington State Community College, Marietta OH p. 1914

Washington State Department of Natural Resources, Olympia WA p. 2522

Washington State Historical Society, Olympia WA p. 2523

Washington State Historical Society Research Center, Tacoma WA p. 2541

Washington State Law Library, Olympia WA p. 2523

Washington State Library, Tumwater WA p. 2544

Washington State Office of Secretary of State, Olympia WA p. 2523

Washington State Penitentiary-Main Institution, *see* Washington State Library, Walla Walla WA p. 2545

Washington State Penitentiary-Medium, *see* Washington State Library, Walla Walla WA p. 2545

Washington State Prison, *see* Georgia Department of Corrections, Davisboro GA p. 528

Washington State Reformatory, *see* Washington State Library, Monroe WA p. 2545

Washington State University, Spokane WA p. 2538

Washington State University Extension, Olympia WA p. 2523

Washington State University Libraries, Pullman WA p. 2525

Washington State University Libraries, Vancouver WA p. 2546

Washington State University Tri-Cities, Richland WA p. 2526

Washington Talking Book & Braille Library, Seattle WA p. 2535

Washington Theological Consortium (N), Washington DC p. 2940

Washington Times Corp, Washington DC p. 422

Washington Township Free Public Library, Long Valley NJ p. 1497

Washington Township Historical Society Library, Long Valley NJ p. 1497

Washington Township Public Library, Lynn IN p. 762

Washington University Libraries, Saint Louis MO p. 1362

Washington's Headquarters State Historic Site Library, *see* New York State Office of Parks, Recreation & Historic Preservation, Newburgh NY p. 1705

Washoe County Law Library, Reno NV p. 1433

Washoe County Library System, Reno NV p. 1433

Washoe Health System, Reno NV p. 1434

Washougal Community Library, *see* Fort Vancouver Regional Library District, Washougal WA p. 2546

Washta Public Library, Washta IA p. 849

Washtenaw Community College, Ann Arbor MI p. 1153

Washtenaw County Metropolitan Planning Commission Library, Ann Arbor MI p. 1153

Washtenaw Library for the Blind & Physically Disabled, *see* Ann Arbor District Library, Ann Arbor MI p. 1150

Wasilla Meta-Rose Public Library, Wasilla AK p. 55

Waskom Public Library, Waskom TX p. 2398

Wasserman Public Affairs Library, *see* University of Texas Libraries, Austin TX p. 2285

Watanabe Family Library, *see* Eiteljorg Museum of American Indians & Western Art, Indianapolis IN p. 750

Watauga County Public Library, Boone NC p. 1777

Watauga Public Library, Watauga TX p. 2398

Weaver-Bolden Library, *see* Tuscaloosa Public Library, Tuscaloosa AL p. 38

Sprinkle Memorial Library, *see* Buncombe County Public Libraries, Weaverville NC p. 1774

Webb City Public Library, Webb City MO p. 1372

Webb County Library, Mirando City TX p. 2363

Webb Del E Memorial Library, *see* Loma Linda University, Loma Linda CA p. 165

Webb Institute, Glen Cove NY p. 1628

Webb Joe W Memorial, *see* Claiborne Parish Library, Haynesville LA p. 951

Webb Lillian Memorial, *see* Letcher County Public Libraries, Neon KY p. 937

Webb Memorial Library, *see* Penrose-Saint Francis Health Services, Colorado Springs CO p. 296

Webb Public Library, Webb IA p. 851

Webb Shadle Memorial Library, Pleasantville IA p. 839

Webber International University, Babson Park FL p. 426

Webberville Library, *see* Capital Area District Libraries, Webberville MI p. 1200

Webbwood Public, *see* Massey & Township Public Library, Webbwood ON p. 2820

Weber Center for Learning Resources, *see* Arapahoe Community College, Littleton CO p. 316

Weber County Library System, Ogden UT p. 2408

Weber E C Fraser Public Library, Fraser MI p. 1181

Weber Memorial Library, *see* San Antonio Community Hospital, Upland CA p. 278

Weber State University, Ogden UT p. 2409

Webermeier Memorial Public Library, Milford NE p. 1408

Webster-Addison Public Library, Webster Springs WV p. 2573

Webster County Historical Museum Library, Red Cloud NE p. 1418

Webster County Library, *see* Kinchafoonee Regional Library System, Preston GA p. 529

Webster County Public Library, Dixon KY p. 911

Webster County Public Library, *see* Tombigbee Regional Library System, Eupora MS p. 1318

Webster Free Library, Kingfield ME p. 989

Webster Free Public Library, Webster NH p. 1467

Webster Groves Public Library, Webster Groves MO p. 1372

Webster Institute for the History of Astronomy, *see* Adler Planetarium & Astronomy Museum, Chicago IL p. 604

Webster John P Library, *see* First Church of Christ Congregational, West Hartford CT p. 376

Webster Memorial Library, Wentworth NH p. 1467

Webster Memorial Library, *see* Van Buren District Library, Decatur MI p. 1168

Webster Noah House & West Hartford Historical Society, West Hartford CT p. 376

Webster Noah Memorial Library, *see* West Hartford Public Library, West Hartford CT p. 376

Webster Parish Library, Minden LA p. 957

Webster Public Library, Webster NY p. 1765

Webster Public Library, Webster SD p. 2222

Webster University, Saint Louis MO p. 1363

Wedemeyer Marlin R Staff Library, *see* Twin Valley Behavioral Healthcare, Columbus OH p. 1891

Wedsworth Memorial Library, Cascade MT p. 1376

Weed Army Community Hospital, Medical Library, *see* United States Army, Fort Irwin CA p. 149

Weed Memorial, *see* Ferguson Library, Stamford CT p. 369

Weedsport Library, Weedsport NY p. 1765

Weehawken Free Public Library, Weehawken NJ p. 1540

Weeks Marta & Austin Music Library, *see* University of Miami Libraries, Coral Gables FL p. 434

Weeks Public Library, Greenland NH p. 1449

Weeks-Townsend Memorial Library, *see* Union College, Barbourville KY p. 906

Weeks William D Memorial Library, Lancaster NH p. 1453

Weeping Water Public Library, Weeping Water NE p. 1423

Wegner Health Science Information Center, Sioux Falls SD p. 2219

Wegner Health Science Information Center, *see* University of South Dakota, Vermillion SD p. 2221

Wehr Todd Library, *see* Medical College of Wisconsin Libraries, Milwaukee WI p. 2619

Wehr Todd Memorial Library, *see* Carroll College, Waukesha WI p. 2644

Wehr Todd Memorial Library, *see* Viterbo University, La Crosse WI p. 2603

Wehrle A T Memorial Library, *see* Pontifical College Josephinum, Columbus OH p. 1890

Weigel Paul Library of Architecture, Planning & Design, *see* Kansas State University Libraries, Manhattan KS p. 881

Weil, Gotshal & Manges Library, New York NY p. 1702

Weil, Gotshal & Manges LLP, Washington DC p. 422

Weil, Gotshal & Manges LLP, Houston TX p. 2345

Weil Journalism Library, *see* Indiana University Bloomington, Bloomington IN p. 728

Weill Joan Adirondack Library, *see* Paul Smiths College of Arts & Sciences, Paul Smiths NY p. 1715

Weimar Public Library, Weimar TX p. 2399

Weinberg Harry & Jeanette Memorial Library, *see* University of Scranton, Scranton PA p. 2138

Weinberg Nature Center Library, Scarsdale NY p. 1739

Weiner, Brodsky, Sidman & Kider PC, Washington DC p. 422

Weiner Library, *see* Fairleigh Dickinson University, Teaneck NJ p. 1532

Weinlos Library, *see* Misericordia Community Hospital - Caritas Health Group, Edmonton AB p. 2701

Weintraub, Genshlea, Chediak & Sproul, Sacramento CA p. 226

Weippe Public Library, *see* Clearwater County Free Library District, Weippe ID p. 585

Weir John Alexander Memorial Law Library, *see* University of Alberta, Edmonton AB p. 2703

Weir Mary H Public Library, Weirton WV p. 2573

Weir Public Library, Weir KS p. 899

Weir Public Library, *see* Tombigbee Regional Library System, Weir MS p. 1318

WeirFoulds Library, Toronto ON p. 2867

Weis Library, *see* Washington Adventist University, Takoma Park MD p. 1043

Weisberg Alex F Library, *see* Temple Emanu-El, Dallas TX p. 2310

Weiser Public Library, Weiser ID p. 585

Weiss Louis A Memorial Hospital, Chicago IL p. 627

Weiss Samuel A Community Library, Glassport PA p. 2061

Weiss Sherman & Ruth Community Library, Hayward WI p. 2597

Welch Jenna & Laura Busch Community Library, *see* El Paso Community College Library, El Paso TX p. 2316

Welch Library, *see* Free Will Baptist Bible College, Nashville TN p. 2256

Welch Library, *see* McDowell Public Library, Welch WV p. 2573

Welch Margaret Memorial Library, Longville MN p. 1256

Welchs, Billerica MA p. 1054

Weld Free Public Library, Weld ME p. 1006

Welder Library, *see* University of Mary, Bismarck ND p. 1838

Welder Rob & Bessie Wildlife Foundation Library, Sinton TX p. 2387

Weldon C E Public Library, Martin TN p. 2246

Weldon D B Library, *see* Western University - Libraries, London ON p. 2819

Weldon Mary Wood Memorial Library, Glasgow KY p. 915

Weldon Memorial, *see* Halifax County Library, Weldon NC p. 1800

Weldon Public Library, *see* Wapiti Regional Library, Weldon SK p. 2922

Weldon Public Library District, Weldon IL p. 717

Welhausen Carl & Mary Library, Yoakum TX p. 2402

Welland Public Library, Welland ON p. 2870

Wellehan Library, *see* Saint Joseph's College, Standish ME p. 1002

Weller Geoffrey R Library, *see* University of Northern British Columbia Library, Prince George BC p. 2736

Weller Public Library, Mohawk NY p. 1662

Weller Public Library, Waitsburg WA p. 2546

Welles Lucy Robbins Library, Newington CT p. 361

Welles-Turner Memorial Library, Glastonbury CT p. 340

Wellesley College, Wellesley MA p. 1135

Wellesley Free Library, Wellesley MA p. 1135

Wellesley Hills Congregational Church Library, Wellesley Hills MA p. 1135

Wellfleet Public Library, Wellfleet MA p. 1135

Wellington County Library, Fergus ON p. 2805

Wellington County Museum & Archives, Fergus ON p. 2805

Wellington Law Association Library, Guelph ON p. 2807

Wellington Management Co, LLP, Radnor PA p. 2132

Wellington Public Library, Wellington CO p. 325

Wellington Public Library, Wellington KS p. 899

Wellman, Inc Library, *see* Florence-Darlington Technical College Libraries, Florence SC p. 2193

Wellman Scofield Public Library, Wellman IA p. 851

Wells Branch Community Library, Austin TX p. 2285

Wells College, Aurora NY p. 1576

Wells County Public Library, Bluffton IN p. 728

Wells David G MD Memorial Library, *see* Verde Valley Medical Center, Cottonwood AZ p. 61

Wells Fargo Bank Library, San Francisco CA p. 249

Wells Herman B Library, *see* Indiana University Bloomington, Bloomington IN p. 727

Wells Memorial Library, Upper Jay NY p. 1758

Wells Public Library, Wells ME p. 1006

Wells Public Library, Wells MN p. 1288

Wells Reserve Library, *see* Fish Dorothy Coastal Resource Library at Wells Reserve, Wells ME p. 1006

Wells Village Library, Wells VT p. 2438

Wellsburg Public Library, Wellsburg IA p. 851

Wellspan Health at York Hospital, York PA p. 2159

Wellspring Community Health Library, *see* North Colorado Medical Center, Greeley CO p. 312

Wellspring Health & Resource Library, *see* McKee Medical Center, Loveland CO p. 318

WellStar Library Services, Marietta GA p. 544

Wellsville Carnegie Public Library, Wellsville OH p. 1946

Wellsville City Library, Wellsville KS p. 899

Wellsville Public Library, Wellsville MO p. 1372

Welsch Erwin Memorial Research Library, *see* San Diego Model Railroad Museum, San Diego CA p. 235

Welsh W Keith Library, *see* North York General Hospital, Toronto ON p. 2856

Welshimer P H Memorial Library, *see* Milligan College, Milligan College TN p. 2253

Welter Donald R Library, *see* Three Rivers Community College, Norwich CT p. 363

Weltner Philip Library, *see* Oglethorpe University, Atlanta GA p. 517

Welty Eudora Library, *see* Jackson/Hinds Library System, Jackson MS p. 1303

Welty Hope Public Library District, Cerro Gordo IL p. 602

Wenatchee Public, *see* North Central Regional Library, Wenatchee WA p. 2549

Wenatchee Valley College, Wenatchee WA p. 2549

Wende Correctional Facility Library, Alden NY p. 1572

Wendell Free Library, Wendell MA p. 1135

Wendell Public Library, Wendell ID p. 585

Wendt Kurt Engineering Library, *see* University of Wisconsin-Madison, Madison WI p. 2610

Wenham Museum, Wenham MA p. 1136

Wenonah Free Public Library, Wenonah NJ p. 1540

Wenrich Memorial Library, *see* Landmark Society of Western New York, Inc, Rochester NY p. 1730

West Virginia Northern Community College Library, Wheeling WV p. 2575

West Virginia School for the Blind Library, Romney WV p. 2570

West Virginia School for the Deaf & Blind Library, Romney WV p. 2570

West Virginia School of Osteopathic Medicine Library, Lewisburg WV p. 2564

West Virginia State University, Institute WV p. 2562

West Virginia Supreme Court of Appeals, Charleston WV p. 2557

West Virginia University, Charleston WV p. 2557

West Virginia University, Parkersburg WV p. 2568

West Virginia University Institute of Technology, Montgomery WV p. 2565

West Virginia University Libraries, Morgantown WV p. 2566

West Virginia Wesleyan College, Buckhannon WV p. 2555

West Warren Library, West Warren MA p. 1138

West Warwick Public Library, West Warwick RI p. 2177

West Wilma L Occupational Therapy Library, see American Occupational Therapy Foundation, Bethesda MD p. 1021

West Winfield Library, West Winfield NY p. 1767

West Woodstock Library, Woodstock CT p. 380

West Yellowstone Public Library, West Yellowstone MT p. 1390

Westat, Inc Library, Rockville MD p. 1040

Westbank Community Library District, Austin TX p. 2285

Westboro Public Library, Westboro WI p. 2648

Westborough Public Library, Westborough MA p. 1138

Westbrook Carl O Library, see Connors State College, Warner OK p. 1985

Westbrook Public Library, Westbrook CT p. 377

Westbrook Public Library, Westbrook MN p. 1288

Westbury Memorial Public Library, Westbury NY p. 1767

Westchester County Department of Parks, Recreation & Conservation, Cross River NY p. 1612

Westchester County Historical Society Library, Elmsford NY p. 1620

Westchester Library System, Tarrytown NY p. 1755

Westchester Public Library, Westchester IL p. 717

Westchester Public Library, Chesterton IN p. 732

Westchester Reform Temple Library, Scarsdale NY p. 1739

Westergard Johanna W Library, see Piscataway Township Free Public Library, Piscataway NJ p. 1520

Westerlo Public Library, Westerlo NY p. 1767

Westerly Hospital, Westerly RI p. 2178

Westerly Public Library, Westerly RI p. 2178

Western Allegheny Community Library, Oakdale PA p. 2100

Western Archeological & Conservation Center Library, see National Park Service, Tucson AZ p. 86

Western Baptist Bible College Memorial Library, Kansas City MO p. 1341

Western Baptist Hospital Library, Paducah KY p. 932

Western Canada Aviation Museum Library, Winnipeg MB p. 2759

Western Canadian Universities, Bamfield BC p. 2724

Western Carolina University, Cullowhee NC p. 1786

Western College Memorial Archives, see Miami University Libraries, Oxford OH p. 1926

Western College of Veterinary Medicine, see University of Saskatchewan Libraries, Saskatoon SK p. 2927

Western Connecticut State University, Danbury CT p. 335

Western Correctional Institution Library, Cumberland MD p. 1026

Western Costume Co, North Hollywood CA p. 195

Western Council of State Libraries, Inc (N), Boise ID p. 2941

Western Counties Regional Library, Yarmouth NS p. 2786

Western Dakota Technical Institute Library, Rapid City SD p. 2217

Western Development Museum, Saskatoon SK p. 2927

Western District Library, Orion IL p. 686

Western Fairs Association Library, Sacramento CA p. 226

Western Hemisphere Institute for Security Cooperation, Fort Benning GA p. 533

Western Illinois Area Agency on Aging, Rock Island IL p. 696

Western Illinois Correctional Center Library, Mount Sterling IL p. 677

Western Illinois University Libraries, Macomb IL p. 668

Western Iowa Technical Community College, Sioux City IA p. 844

Western Kentucky University Libraries, Bowling Green KY p. 907

Western Kentucky University, School of Teacher Education, Bowling Green KY p. 2966

Western Libraries, see Western Washington University, Bellingham WA p. 2509

Western Manitoba Regional Library, Brandon MB p. 2748

Western Maryland Public Libraries, Hagerstown MD p. 1032

Western Massachusetts Health Information Consortium (N), Springfield MA p. 2946

Western Medical Center, Santa Ana CA p. 260

Western Memorial Regional Hospital, Corner Brook NL p. 2770

Western Michigan University, Kalamazoo MI p. 1198

Western Missouri Mental Health Center, Kansas City MO p. 1341

Western Museum of Mining & Industry Library, Colorado Springs CO p. 297

Western Nebraska Community College Library, Scottsbluff NE p. 1418

Western Nebraska Veterans Home Library, Scottsbluff NE p. 1419

Western Nevada Community College, Carson City NV p. 1426

Western New England University, Springfield MA p. 1128

Western New Mexico Correctional Facility Library, see New Mexico Corrections Department, Grants NM p. 1556

Western New Mexico University, Silver City NM p. 1565

Western New York Library Resources Council (N), Buffalo NY p. 2951

Western North Carolina Library Network (N), Boone NC p. 2951

Western Oklahoma State College, Altus OK p. 1956

Western Oregon University, Monmouth OR p. 2006, 2972

Western Organization of Resource Councils Library, Billings MT p. 1375

Western Pennsylvania Hospital, Pittsburgh PA p. 2129

Western Philatelic Library, Sunnyvale CA p. 274

Western Piedmont Community College, Morganton NC p. 1811

Western Plains Library System, Clinton OK p. 1960

Western Pocono Community Library, Brodheadsville PA p. 2038

Western Reception & Diagnostic Correctional Center, see Missouri Department of Corrections, Saint Joseph MO p. 1335

Western Reserve Historical Society Research Library, Cleveland OH p. 1881

Western Seminary, Portland OR p. 2015

Western State College, Gunnison CO p. 312

Western State Hospital, Hopkinsville KY p. 918

Western State Hospital, see Washington State Library, Tacoma WA p. 2545

Western State University, Fullerton CA p. 154

Western Sullivan Public Library, Callicoon NY p. 1600

Western Sullivan Public Library, Jeffersonville NY p. 1647

Western Sullivan Public Library, Narrowsburg NY p. 1664

Western Taylor County Public Library, Gilman WI p. 2594

Western Technical College Library, La Crosse WI p. 2604

Western Texas College, Snyder TX p. 2388

Western Theological Seminary, Holland MI p. 1191

Western Town Library, Westernville NY p. 1767

Western University - Libraries, London ON p. 2819

Western University of Health Sciences, Pomona CA p. 211

Western Wake Library, see Wake Technical Community College, Cary NC p. 1819

Western Washington University, Bellingham WA p. 2509

Western Wyoming Community College, Rock Springs WY p. 2659

Western Yearly Meeting of Friends, Plainfield IN p. 773

Western Youth Institution Library, see North Carolina Department of Correction, Morganton NC p. 1811

Westerners International Library, Oklahoma City OK p. 1975

Westerville Public Library, Westerville OH p. 1946

Westfield Athenaeum, Westfield MA p. 1138

Westfield Memorial Library, Westfield NJ p. 1543

Westfield Public Library, Westfield PA p. 2155

Westfield Public Library, Westfield WI p. 2648

Westfield State University, Westfield MA p. 1138

Westfield Washington Public Library, Westfield IN p. 787

Westfir City Library, Westfir OR p. 2022

Westford Library, Westford VT p. 2439

Westgate Public Library, Westgate IA p. 852

Westhampton Free Library, Westhampton Beach NY p. 1768

Westhampton Public Library, Westhampton MA p. 1139

Westlake Community Hospital Library, Melrose Park IL p. 673

Westlake Porter Public Library, Westlake OH p. 1947

Westland Public Library, Westland MI p. 1236

Westlock Municipal Library, Westlock AB p. 2721

Westminster Presbyterian Church Library, Greensboro NC p. 1798

Westminster Abbey Library, Seminary of Christ The King, Mission BC p. 2732

Westminster College, Fulton MO p. 1328

Westminster College, New Wilmington PA p. 2097

Westminster College, Salt Lake City UT p. 2415

Westminster Historical Society Library, Westminster MA p. 1139

Westminster Law Library, see University of Denver, Denver CO p. 304

Westminster Presbyterian Church Library, Upper St Clair PA p. 2149

Westminster Presbyterian Church Library, Alexandria VA p. 2447

Westminster Public Library, Westminster CO p. 326

Westminster Public Library, see Forbush Memorial Library, Westminster MA p. 1139

Westminster Seminary California Library, Escondido CA p. 147

Westminster Theological Seminary, Glenside PA p. 2062

Westmont College, Santa Barbara CA p. 262

Westmont Public Library, Westmont IL p. 717

Westmoreland County Community College, Youngwood PA p. 2160

Westmoreland County Federated Library System, Greensburg PA p. 2062

Westmoreland County Historical Society, Greensburg PA p. 2063

Westmoreland County Law Library, Greensburg PA p. 2063

Westmoreland Hospital Library, see Excela Health, Greensburg PA p. 2062

Westmoreland Institution Library, see Correctional Services of Canada, Dorchester NB p. 2762

Westmoreland Public Library, Westmoreland NH p. 1468

Westmoreland Public Library, Westmoreland TN p. 2268

Westmoreland Reading Center, Westmoreland NY p. 1768

Whitehead Charles Wewahitchka Public Library, *see* Northwest Regional Library System, Wewahitchka FL p. 481

Whitehead Elizabeth Augustus Library, *see* Whitehead Institute for Biomedical Research, Cambridge MA p. 1079

Whitehead Institute for Biomedical Research, Cambridge MA p. 1079

Whitehorse Public, *see* Department of Community Services, Government of Yukon, Whitehorse YT p. 2933

Whitehouse Community Library, Inc, Whitehouse TX p. 2400

Whiteriver Public Library, Whiteriver AZ p. 89

Whitesboro Public Library, Whitesboro TX p. 2400

Whitesburg Public Library, *see* West Georgia Regional Library, Whitesburg GA p. 524

Whitestone Community Library, *see* Queens Borough Public Library, Whitestone NY p. 1645

Whitesville Public Library, Whitesville NY p. 1769

Whitetop Public, *see* Wythe-Grayson Regional Library, Whitetop VA p. 2472

Whitewater Memorial Library, Whitewater KS p. 900

Whitewater Region, Beachburg ON p. 2794

Whitewater Region Public Library, Forester's Falls ON p. 2805

Whitewright Public Library, Whitewright TX p. 2400

Whitfield Bryan W Jr, *see* Harlan County Public Library, Harlan KY p. 916

Whitfield Henry State Museum Research Library, Guilford CT p. 343

Whitfield-Murray Historical Society, Dalton GA p. 528

Whiting Forensic Institute Library, Middletown CT p. 352

Whiting Library, Chester VT p. 2421

Whiting Public Library, Whiting IN p. 788

Whiting Public Library, Whiting IA p. 852

Whiting-Robertsdale Historical Society, Whiting IN p. 788

Whitingham Free Public Library, Jacksonville VT p. 2426

Whitinsville Social Library, Inc, Whitinsville MA p. 1140

Whitley County Library, Williamsburg KY p. 937

Whitman Alice E Memorial Library, *see* Frontier Nursing Service Library, Hyden KY p. 918

Whitman College, Walla Walla WA p. 2547

Whitman County Rural Library District, Colfax WA p. 2512

Whitman Memorial Library, Bryant Pond ME p. 980

Whitman Public Library, Whitman MA p. 1140

Whitman Stanley House Library, Farmington CT p. 340

Whitman Walt Birthplace Association, Huntington Station NY p. 1639

Whitman Walt, *see* Brooklyn Public Library, Brooklyn NY p. 1592

Whitmire Memorial, *see* Newberry County Library, Whitmire SC p. 2201

Whitney Edwina Library of The Storrs Congregational Church, Storrs CT p. 371

Whitney Knowledge Center, *see* General Electric Global Research, Niskayuna NY p. 1706

Whitney Library, *see* Las Vegas-Clark County Library District, Las Vegas NV p. 1430

Whitney Library, *see* New Haven Museum & Historical Society, New Haven CT p. 356

Whitney Museum of American Art, New York NY p. 1702

Whitneyville Library Association, Inc, Whitneyville ME p. 1007

Whittaker Miller F Library, *see* South Carolina State University, Orangeburg SC p. 2202

Whittemore Henry Library, *see* Framingham State College, Framingham MA p. 1090

Whittemore Howard Memorial Library, Naugatuck CT p. 353

Whittemore Public Library, Whittemore IA p. 853

Whittier College, Costa Mesa CA p. 137

Whittier College, Whittier CA p. 283

Whittier N Paul Historical Aviation Library, *see* San Diego Aero-Space Museum, Inc, San Diego CA p. 232

Whittier Public Library, Whittier CA p. 283

Whitwer Raymond A Tilden Public Library, Tilden NE p. 1421

Whitworth University, Spokane WA p. 2538

WHOI Data Library & Archives, *see* Marine Biological Laboratory Woods Hole Oceanographic Institution Library, Woods Hole MA p. 1142

Whole World Books, *see* Friends of the Third World, Inc, Fort Wayne IN p. 741

Whorton John L Media Center Library, *see* First Baptist Church, Longview TX p. 2356

Whyte Museum of the Canadian Rockies, Banff AB p. 2684

Wibaux Public Library, Wibaux MT p. 1390

Wichita Art Museum, Wichita KS p. 901

Wichita Center for the Arts, Wichita KS p. 901

Wichita County Library, Leoti KS p. 879

Wichita Falls Public Library, Wichita Falls TX p. 2401

Wichita Public Library, Wichita KS p. 901

Wichita Sedgwick County Historical Museum Library, Wichita KS p. 901

Wichita State University Libraries, Wichita KS p. 902

Wickenburg Public Library, Wickenburg AZ p. 89

Wickes Ruth Brady Library, *see* Public Libraries of Saginaw, Saginaw MI p. 1224

Wickliffe Public Library, Wickliffe OH p. 1947

Wickson James E Memorial Library, Frankenmuth MI p. 1181

Wicomico Public Library, Salisbury MD p. 1040

Wide Awake Club Library, Fillmore NY p. 1622

Widener University, Wilmington DE p. 389

Widener University, Chester PA p. 2044

Wider Church Ministries Library, *see* United Church of Christ, Cleveland OH p. 1881

Wien Noel Library, *see* Fairbanks North Star Borough Public Library & Regional Center, Fairbanks AK p. 47

Wiener Gabe M Music & Arts Library, *see* Columbia University, New York NY p. 1675

Weiner-Rogers Law Library, *see* University of Nevada, Las Vegas Libraries, Las Vegas NV p. 1431

Wiggans Health Sciences Library, *see* Norwalk Hospital, Norwalk CT p. 362

Wiggin & Dana LLP, New Haven CT p. 356

Wiggin Memorial Library, Stratham NH p. 1465

Wiggins Memorial Library, *see* Campbell University, Buies Creek NC p. 1778

Wiggins Norman Adrian School of Law Library, *see* Campbell University, Raleigh NC p. 1778

Wightman Dorothy Library, *see* Duplin County Library, Kenansville NC p. 1804

Wilberforce University, Wilberforce OH p. 1948

Wilbour Library of Egyptology, *see* Brooklyn Museum of Art, Brooklyn NY p. 1590

Wilbraham Public Library, Wilbraham MA p. 1140

Wilbur Wright College, Chicago IL p. 2965

Wilbur Wright College North, Chicago IL p. 627

Wilcox County Library, Camden AL p. 11

Wilcox County Library, *see* Ocmulgee Regional Library System, Abbeville GA p. 532

Wilcox John J Jr LGBT Library of Philadelphia, Philadelphia PA p. 2120

Wilcox Library, *see* William Penn University, Oskaloosa IA p. 837

Wilcox Mary Memorial Library, Whitney Point NY p. 1769

Wilcox Memorial Hospital, Lihue HI p. 567

Wilcox Public Library, Wilcox NE p. 1423

Wilcox Public Library, Wilcox PA p. 2155

Wilcox S W II Learning Resource Center, *see* Kauai Community College, Lihue HI p. 567

WildCare, San Rafael CA p. 257

Wildenthal Bryan Memorial Library, *see* Sul Ross State University, Alpine TX p. 2273

Wilder L Douglas Library & Learning Resource Center, *see* Virginia Union University, Richmond VA p. 2493

Wilder Laura Ingalls Library, *see* Wright County Library, Mansfield MO p. 1330

Wilder Library, *see* Northeast Iowa Community College, Calmar IA p. 798

Wilder Memorial Library, Weston VT p. 2439

Wilder Public Library District, Wilder ID p. 585

Wilderness Coast Public Libraries, Monticello FL p. 470

Wildlife Conservation Society Library, Bronx NY p. 1588

Wildlife Information Center, Slatington PA p. 2140

Wildlife Information Service Library, Las Cruces NM p. 1558

Wildman, Harrold, Allen & Dixon LLP, Chicago IL p. 628

Wildwood Correctional Complex Library, Kenai AK p. 50

Wildwood Heritage Museum & Library, Village Mills TX p. 2395

Wildwood Pre-Trial Facility Library, Kenai AK p. 50

Wildwood Public Library, Wildwood AB p. 2722

Wilentz, Goldman & Spitzer, Woodbridge NJ p. 1545

Wiley College, Marshall TX p. 2360

Wiley Morrison & Mary Library District, Elmwood IL p. 642

Wiley Rein LLC Library, Washington DC p. 423

Wilford Hall Medical Center Library, Lackland AFB TX p. 2352

Wilhite Kate Stamper Library, *see* Moberly Area Community College, Moberly MO p. 1346

Wilhite Thomas Memorial Library, Perkins OK p. 1976

Wilhoit Public Library, Wilhoit AZ p. 89

Wilkens Library, *see* Cape Cod Community College, West Barnstable MA p. 1136

Wilkes-Barre Law & Library Association, Wilkes-Barre PA p. 2156

Wilkes Community College, Wilkesboro NC p. 1830

Wilkes County Public Library, North Wilkesboro NC p. 1813

Wilkes Library, *see* Strayer University, Washington DC p. 416

Wilkes Memorial Library, Hubbard TX p. 2345

Wilkes University, Wilkes-Barre PA p. 2156

Wilkes-Barre General Hospital, Wilkes-Barre PA p. 2156

Wilkin County Museum Library, Breckenridge MN p. 1243

Wilkinsburg Public Library, Pittsburgh PA p. 2130

Wilkinson Barker Knauer LLP Library, Washington DC p. 423

Wilkinson Charles B MD Memorial Library, *see* Western Missouri Mental Health Center, Kansas City MO p. 1341

Wilkinson Margaret & John Library, *see* Museum of Arts & Sciences, Daytona Beach FL p. 436

Wilkinson Public Library, *see* San Miguel County Public Library District 1, Telluride CO p. 323

Will County Law Library, Joliet IL p. 660

Will Grinton I, *see* Yonkers Public Library, Yonkers NY p. 1772

Will Grinton I Library, *see* Yonkers Historical Society, Yonkers NY p. 1771

Willacoochee Public Library, *see* Satilla Regional Library, Willacoochee GA p. 531

Willamette Falls Hospital, Oregon City OR p. 2009

Willamette University, Salem OR p. 2018

Willamina Public Library, Willamina OR p. 2023

Willard-Cybulski Correctional Institution Library, Enfield CT p. 338

Willard Elmo, *see* Beaumont Public Library System, Beaumont TX p. 2287

Willard Frances E Memorial Library, *see* National Woman's Christian Temperance Union, Evanston IL p. 643

Willard Library, Battle Creek MI p. 1155

Willard Library of Evansville, Evansville IN p. 739

Willard Memorial Library, Willard OH p. 1948

Willet Memorial Library, *see* Wesleyan College, Macon GA p. 541

Willett Free Library, Saunderstown RI p. 2175

William Carey University Libraries, New Orleans LA p. 964

WIN (N), *see* Washington Idaho Network, Spokane WA p. 2957
Winchester Community Library, Winchester IN p. 788
Winchester Engineering & Analytical Center Library, *see* United States Food & Drug Administration Department of Health & Human Services, Winchester MA p. 1141
Winchester Historical Society Library, Winsted CT p. 380
Winchester Hospital, Winchester MA p. 1141
Winchester Public Library, Winchester IL p. 720
Winchester Public Library, Winchester KS p. 902
Winchester Public Library, Winchester MA p. 1141
Winchester Public Library, Winchester WI p. 2649
Wind Cave Library, *see* National Park Service, Hot Springs SD p. 2213
Wind River Tribal College Library, Ethete WY p. 2654
Windber Medical Center, Windber PA p. 2157
Windber Public Library, Windber PA p. 2157
Windels Marx Lane & Mittendorf, LLP Library, New York NY p. 1703
Windham Community Memorial Hospital, Willimantic CT p. 378
Windham Free Library Association, Windham CT p. 379
Windham Public Library, Windham ME p. 1007
Windham Public Library, Windham NY p. 1770
Windham Textile & History Museum, Willimantic CT p. 378
Windham Town Library, Windham VT p. 2440
Winding Rivers Library System, La Crosse WI p. 2604
Windom Public Library, Windom MN p. 1289
Windsor Community Museum, Windsor ON p. 2871
Windsor Dorothy Hull Township Library, Dimondale MI p. 1174
Windsor Free Public Library, Windsor MA p. 1142
Windsor Historical Society Library, Windsor CT p. 379
Windsor Locks Public Library, Windsor Locks CT p. 379
Windsor Park Community Library, *see* Queens Borough Public Library, Bayside NY p. 1645
Windsor Public, *see* Blackwater Regional Library, Windsor VA p. 2458
Windsor Public Library, Windsor CT p. 379
Windsor Public Library, Windsor VT p. 2440
Windsor Public Library, Windsor ON p. 2872
Windsor Public Library, *see* Windsor Community Museum, Windsor ON p. 2871
Windsor Regional, *see* Sonoma County Library, Windsor CA p. 268
Windsor Regional Hospital, Windsor ON p. 2872
Windsor-Severance Library, Windsor CO p. 326
Windsor Star Library, Windsor ON p. 2872
Windsor Storm Memorial Public Library District, Windsor IL p. 720
Windward Community College Library, Kaneohe HI p. 566
Windwood Presbyterian Church Library, Houston TX p. 2345
Wine Institute Library, San Francisco CA p. 249
Winebrenner Theological Seminary Library, Findlay OH p. 1899
Winedale Historical Center Library, *see* University of Texas at Austin, Round Top TX p. 2377
Winfield Library, Winfield TN p. 2269
Winfield Public Library, Winfield IL p. 720
Winfield Public Library, Winfield IA p. 853
Winfield Public Library, Winfield KS p. 903
Winfield Public Library, Winfield AB p. 2722
Winfield Public Library, *see* Northwest Regional Library, Winfield AL p. 41
Wingate Baptist Church Library, Wingate NC p. 1832
Wingate University, Wingate NC p. 1832
Winhall Memorial Library, Bondville VT p. 2419
Winkelpleck Odon Public Library, Odon IN p. 771
Winkler County Library, Kermit TX p. 2349
Winkler Henry R, *see* University of Cincinnati Libraries, Cincinnati OH p. 1874
Winn Army Community Hospital Medical Library, *see* United States Army, Fort Stewart GA p. 533

Winn Correctional Center Library, Winnfield LA p. 971
Winn Parish Library, Winnfield LA p. 972
Winnebago County Court House, Oshkosh WI p. 2628
Winnebago County Law Library, Rockford IL p. 698
Winnebago Public Library, Winnebago IL p. 720
Winneconne Public Library, Winneconne WI p. 2649
Winnefox Library System, Oshkosh WI p. 2628
Winner Bette Public Library, Gillam MB p. 2748
Winnetka-Northfield Public Library District, Winnetka IL p. 720
Winnett School Library, *see* Petroleum County Community Library, Winnett MT p. 1390
Winnipeg Art Gallery, Winnipeg MB p. 2759
Winnipeg Free Press Library, Winnipeg MB p. 2760
Winnipeg Public Library, Winnipeg MB p. 2760
Winnipeg School Division, Winnipeg MB p. 2760
Winona County Historical Society, Winona MN p. 1290
Winona Public Library, Winona MN p. 1290
Winona State University, Winona MN p. 1290
Winooski Memorial Library, Winooski VT p. 2440
Winslow Medical Library, *see* Meadville Medical Center, Meadville PA p. 2086
Winslow Public Library, Winslow AZ p. 90
Winslow Public Library, Winslow ME p. 1007
Winsted Public Library, Winsted MN p. 1290
Winston & Strawn Library, New York NY p. 1703
Winston & Strawn Library, Houston TX p. 2345
Winston & Strawn LLP, Washington DC p. 423
Winston & Strawn LLP Library, Chicago IL p. 628
Winston-Salem Journal Library, Winston-Salem NC p. 1834
Winston-Salem State University, Winston-Salem NC p. 1834
Winter Harbor Public Library, Winter Harbor ME p. 1007
Winter Haven Hospital, Winter Haven FL p. 505
Winter Haven Public Library, Winter Haven FL p. 505
Winter Park Public Library, Winter Park FL p. 505
Winter Public Library, Winter WI p. 2650
Wintermann Eula & David Library, Eagle Lake TX p. 2314
Winterport Memorial Library, Winterport ME p. 1007
Winters-Bellbrook Community Library, *see* Greene County Public Library, Bellbrook OH p. 1951
Winters Public Library, Winters TX p. 2401
Winterset Public Library, Winterset IA p. 853
Winterthur Library, Winterthur DE p. 389
Winterton Public Library, Winterton NL p. 2773
Winthrop & Weinstine, Minneapolis MN p. 1263
Winthrop Community, *see* North Central Regional Library, Winthrop WA p. 2549
Winthrop Public Library, Winthrop IA p. 853
Winthrop Public Library, Winthrop MN p. 1290
Winthrop Public Library & Museum, Winthrop MA p. 1142
Winthrop University, Rock Hill SC p. 2202
Winthrop University Hospital, Mineola NY p. 1661
WIPP Technical Library, *see* SM Stoller Corp, Carlsbad NM p. 1553
Wire Association International Library, Guilford CT p. 343
Wiregrass Georgia Technical College, Douglas GA p. 531
Wiregrass Georgia Technical College, Fitzgerald GA p. 532
Wiregrass Georgia Technical College Library, Sparks GA p. 552
Wiregrass Georgia Technical College Library, Valdosta GA p. 555
Wirt Alice & Jack Public Library, *see* Bay County Library System, Bay City MI p. 1156
Wirtz Labor Library, *see* United States Department of Labor, Washington DC p. 419
Wiscasset Public Library, Wiscasset ME p. 1008
Wisconsin Center for Film & Theater, *see* University of Wisconsin-Madison, Madison WI p. 2610
Wisconsin Center for the Blind & Visually Impaired, Janesville WI p. 2600
Wisconsin Conference United Methodist Church, Sun Prairie WI p. 2641

Wisconsin Conservatory Music Library, Milwaukee WI p. 2622
Wisconsin Department of Employee Trust Funds Library, Madison WI p. 2610
Wisconsin Department of Justice, Madison WI p. 2610
Wisconsin Department of Public Instruction, Madison WI p. 2610
Wisconsin Department of Veterans Affairs, Madison WI p. 2610
Wisconsin Historical Society Library, Madison WI p. 2610
Wisconsin Indianhead Technical College, Ashland WI p. 2579
Wisconsin Indianhead Technical College, New Richmond WI p. 2625
Wisconsin Indianhead Technical College, Rice Lake WI p. 2634
Wisconsin Indianhead Technical College, Superior WI p. 2641
Wisconsin Legislative Reference Bureau, Madison WI p. 2611
Wisconsin Library Services (N), Madison WI p. 2958
Wisconsin Lutheran College Library, Milwaukee WI p. 2622
Wisconsin Lutheran Seminary Library, Mequon WI p. 2615
Wisconsin Maritime Museum, Manitowoc WI p. 2612
Wisconsin Medical Society Library, Madison WI p. 2611
Wisconsin Public Library Consortium (N), Madison WI p. 2958
Wisconsin School for the Deaf, Delavan WI p. 2588
Wisconsin School for the Visually Handicapped Library, *see* Wisconsin Center for the Blind & Visually Impaired, Janesville WI p. 2600
Wisconsin Secure Program Facility Library, Boscobel WI p. 2583
Wisconsin State Department of Transportation Library, Madison WI p. 2611
Wisconsin State Journal - Capital Times Library, Madison WI p. 2611
Wisconsin State Law Library, Madison WI p. 2611
Wisconsin Talking Book & Braille Library, Milwaukee WI p. 2622
Wisconsin Valley Library Service, Wausau WI p. 2647
Wisconsin Valley Library Service (N), Wausau WI p. 2958
Wisconsin Veterans Museum, *see* Wisconsin Department of Veterans Affairs, Madison WI p. 2610
Wisconsin Veterans' Home Library, King WI p. 2602
Wisconsin's Water Library, *see* University of Wisconsin-Madison, Madison WI p. 2610
Wisdom Library, *see* Southwest Baptist University Libraries, Salem MO p. 1320
Wise A J, *see* Shelby County Libraries, Fort Loramie OH p. 1935
Wise County Public, *see* Lonesome Pine Regional Library, Wise VA p. 2504
Wise Isaac M Temple Library, Cincinnati OH p. 1875
Wise Stephen Free Synagogue, New York NY p. 1703
Wise Stephen S Temple Library, Los Angeles CA p. 180
Wise Watson W Medical Research Library, *see* University of Texas Health Science Center at Tyler, Tyler TX p. 2394
Wise William A Law Library, *see* University of Colorado Boulder, Boulder CO p. 292
Wiseburn Library, *see* County of Los Angeles Public Library, Hawthorne CA p. 144
Wisewood Library, Buffalo Narrows SK p. 2917
Wishart Arthur A Library, *see* Algoma University College, Sault Ste. Marie ON p. 2840
Wisner Albert Public Library, Warwick NY p. 1762
Wisner Public Library, Wisner NE p. 1423
WISPALS Library Consortium (N), Kenosha WI p. 2958

Woodward Biomedical Library, *see* University of British Columbia Library, Vancouver BC p. 2743

Woodward-Clyde International Library, *see* URS Corp, San Diego CA p. 239

Woodward Felix G Library, *see* Austin Peay State University, Clarksville TN p. 2228

Woodward Memorial Library, LeRoy NY p. 1651

Woodward Park Regional, *see* Fresno County Public Library, Fresno CA p. 153

Woodward Public Library, Woodward IA p. 854

Woodward Public Library, Woodward OK p. 1986

Woodworth Consolidated Library, *see* United States Army, Fort Gordon GA p. 533

Woodyard Dora Bee Memorial Library, Elizabeth WV p. 2558

Woolaroc Museum Library, Bartlesville OK p. 1958

Woolfolk Margaret Library, *see* Crittenden County Library, Marion AR p. 109

Woolmarket Library, *see* Harrison County Library System, Biloxi MS p. 1300

Woolworth Community Library, Jal NM p. 1557

Woolworth Richard W Library & Research Center, *see* Stonington Historical Society, Stonington CT p. 370

Woonsocket Community Library, Woonsocket SD p. 2222

Woonsocket Harris Public Library, Woonsocket RI p. 2178

Wor-Wic Community College, Salisbury MD p. 1041

Worcester Art Museum Library, Worcester MA p. 1145

Worcester County Horticultural Society, Boylston MA p. 1069

Worcester County Jail, West Boylston MA p. 1136

Worcester County Library, Snow Hill MD p. 1042

Worcester Free Library, Worcester NY p. 1771

Worcester Historical Museum, Worcester MA p. 1145

Worcester Law Library, *see* Massachusetts Trial Court, Worcester MA p. 1144

Worcester Polytechnic Institute, Worcester MA p. 1145

Worcester Public Library, Worcester MA p. 1145

Worcester State College, Worcester MA p. 1145

Worcester State Hospital, Worcester MA p. 1146

Worcester Talking Book Library, *see* Worcester Public Library, Worcester MA p. 1145

Worcester Telegram & Gazette Library, Worcester MA p. 1146

Worch Memorial Public Library, Versailles OH p. 1943

Word Cecil B Learning Resources Center, *see* Northeast Alabama Community College, Rainsville AL p. 34

Worden Memorial Library, *see* Barclay College, Haviland KS p. 870

Worden Public Library District, Worden IL p. 721

Workers' Compensation Board of British Columbia Library, Richmond BC p. 2737

Workingmen's Institute Library, New Harmony IN p. 768

Workman & Temple Family Homestead Museum Library, City of Industry CA p. 134

Workplace Safety & Insurance Board, Toronto ON p. 2868

WorkSafeBC Library, *see* Workers' Compensation Board of British Columbia Library, Richmond BC p. 2737

World & I Magazine Library, *see* Washington Times Corp, Washington DC p. 422

World Archaeological Society, Hollister MO p. 1331

World Bank Group Library, Washington DC p. 423

World Book Publishing, Chicago IL p. 628

World Data Center Glaciology, Boulder CO p. 292

World Evangelism Bible College, Baton Rouge LA p. 945

World Food Logistics Organization Library, Alexandria VA p. 2447

World Forest Institute Library, *see* World Forestry Center, Portland OR p. 2015

World Forestry Center, Portland OR p. 2015

World Jewish Genealogy Organization Library, Brooklyn NY p. 1595

World Life Research Institute Library, Colton CA p. 135

World Research Foundation Library, Sedona AZ p. 81

World Resources Institute, Washington DC p. 423

WW II PT Boats Museum & Library, *see* PT Boats, Inc, Memphis TN p. 2250

World Wildlife Fund, Washington DC p. 423

Worley David Library, *see* Austin Graduate School of Theology, Austin TX p. 2278

Wornstaff Memorial Public Library, Ashley OH p. 1855

Worsley & District Public Library, Worsley AB p. 2722

Worth Pinkham Memorial Library, Ho-Ho-Kus NJ p. 1491

Worth Public Library District, Worth IL p. 721

Worthington Biochemical Corp Library, Lakewood NJ p. 1494

Worthington Historical Society Library, Worthington OH p. 1950

Worthington-Jefferson Township Public Library, Worthington IN p. 789

Worthington Libraries, Worthington OH p. 1950

Worthington Library, Worthington MA p. 1146

Worthington Scranton Commonwealth College Library, *see* Pennsylvania State University, Dunmore PA p. 2051

Worthington West Franklin Community Library, Worthington PA p. 2157

WPLC (N), *see* Wisconsin Public Library Consortium, Madison WI p. 2958

Wray Public Library, Wray CO p. 326

Wregie Memorial Library, Oxford Junction IA p. 837

Wren Memorial Library, *see* Chatham County Public Libraries, Siler City NC p. 1823

Wren Public Library, *see* Tombigbee Regional Library System, Aberdeen MS p. 1318

Wright & Greenhill PC, Austin TX p. 2285

Wright & Talisman, Washington DC p. 423

Wright Cliff, *see* Saskatoon Public Library, Saskatoon SK p. 2926

Wright County Library, Hartville MO p. 1330

Wright Extension Library, *see* Metropolitan Library System in Oklahoma County, Oklahoma City OK p. 1973

Wright Frank Lloyd Preservation Trust, Oak Park IL p. 684

Wright Henry Howard Research Center Library, *see* SI Group, Inc, Schenectady NY p. 1741

Wright Hillman, *see* Montmorency County Public Libraries, Hillman MI p. 1154

Wright Institute Library, Berkeley CA p. 128

Wright John J Library, *see* La Roche College, Pittsburgh PA p. 2126

Wright John Shepard Memorial Library, *see* Indiana Academy of Science, Indianapolis IN p. 751

Wright Library, *see* Vernon College, Vernon TX p. 2395

Wright Memorial Public Library, Oakwood OH p. 1924

Wright-Potts Library, *see* Voorhees College, Denmark SC p. 2192

Wright Richard Library, *see* Jackson/Hinds Library System, Jackson MS p. 1303

Wright Shirley M Memorial Library, Trempealeau WI p. 2642

Wright Solomon Library, Pownal VT p. 2432

Wright State University, Celina OH p. 1866

Wright State University, Dayton OH p. 2972

Wright State University Libraries, Dayton OH p. 1894

Wright Vassie D Memorial, *see* Los Angeles Public Library System, Los Angeles CA p. 174

WRLC (N), *see* Washington Research Library Consortium, Upper Marlboro MD p. 2945

WVLS (N), *see* Wisconsin Valley Library Service, Wausau WI p. 2958

Wyalusing Public Library, Wyalusing PA p. 2158

Wyandanch Public Library, Wyandanch NY p. 1771

Wyandotte County Law Library, Kansas City KS p. 876

Wyandotte County Museum, Bonner Springs KS p. 858

Wyckoff Heights Medical Center, Brooklyn NY p. 1595

Wyckoff Public Library, Wyckoff NJ p. 1546

Wyeth Canada, Scientific Information, Saint Laurent QC p. 2909

Wyeth Ola, *see* Live Oak Public Libraries, Savannah GA p. 550

WYLD Network (N), Cheyenne WY p. 2958

Wyle Laboratories, El Segundo CA p. 146

Wylie Zula Bryant Public Library, Cedar Hill TX p. 2296

Wyllie John Cook Library, *see* University of Virginia's College at Wise, Wise VA p. 2504

Wylliesburg Community, *see* Charlotte County Library, Wylliesburg VA p. 2453

Wymore Public Library, Wymore NE p. 1424

Wyner Center, Hebrew College, *see* American Jewish Historical Society, New England Branch, Newton Centre MA p. 1110

Wynnewood Public Library, Wynnewood OK p. 1986

Wyocena Public Library, Wyocena WI p. 2650

Wyoming Correctional Facility General Library, Attica NY p. 1575

Wyoming County Public Library, Pineville WV p. 2569

Wyoming Department of Corrections, Riverton WY p. 2659

Wyoming Free Circulating Library, Wyoming NY p. 1771

Wyoming Free Library, Wyoming PA p. 2159

Wyoming Game & Fish Department Library, Casper WY p. 2652

Wyoming Honor Farm Library, *see* Wyoming Department of Corrections, Riverton WY p. 2659

Wyoming Pioneer Home Library, Thermopolis WY p. 2661

Wyoming Public Library, Wyoming IA p. 854

Wyoming Public Library District, Wyoming IL p. 722

Wyoming Seminary, Kingston PA p. 2074

Wyoming State Archives, Cheyenne WY p. 2653

Wyoming State Hospital Library, Evanston WY p. 2655

Wyoming State Law Library, *see* Wyoming Supreme Court, Cheyenne WY p. 2653

Wyoming State Library, Cheyenne WY p. 2653

Wyoming State Penitentiary Library, Rawlins WY p. 2659

Wyoming State Training School Medical Library, Lander WY p. 2657

Wyoming Supreme Court, Cheyenne WY p. 2653

Wyoming Women's Center Library, Lusk WY p. 2658

Wyomissing Public Library, Wyomissing PA p. 2159

Wyotech Library (Wyoming Technical Institute), Blairsville PA p. 2035

Wysox Township Library, Milledgeville IL p. 674

Wythe County Public, *see* Wythe-Grayson Regional Library, Wytheville VA p. 2472

Wythe George Law Library, *see* Hampton Public Library, Hampton VA p. 2468

Wythe-Grayson Regional Library, Independence VA p. 2472

Wytheville Community College Library, Wytheville VA p. 2505

X L Global Services Corporate Library, Stamford CT p. 370

Xavier Society for the Blind, New York NY p. 1703

Xavier University, Cincinnati OH p. 1875

Xavier University of Louisiana Library, New Orleans LA p. 964

Xenia Community Library, *see* Greene County Public Library, Xenia OH p. 1951

Xerox Corp, Norwalk CT p. 362

Xerox Corporation, Webster NY p. 1765

Xerox Research Centre of Canada Library, Mississauga ON p. 2823

Xwi7xwa Library, *see* University of British Columbia Library, Vancouver BC p. 2743

Yachats Public Library, Yachats OR p. 2023

Yadkin County Public Library, Yadkinville NC p. 1835

Yakama Nation Library, Toppenish WA p. 2541

Abdoo, Marianne, Head, Tech Serv, Bloomfield Township Public Library, 1099 Lone Pine Rd, Bloomfield Township, MI, 48302-2410. Tel: 248-642-5800. Fax: 248-258-2555. p. 1159

Abdullah, Cheryl, Dir, Dover Town Library, 56 Dedham St, Dover, MA, 02030-2214. Tel: 508-785-8113. Fax: 508-785-0138. p. 1084

Abdullah, Taliah, Sr Librn, Youth Serv, Denver Public Library, Pauline Robinson Branch, 5575 E 33rd Ave, Denver, CO, 80207-2027. Tel: 303-370-1530. Fax: 303-370-1541. p. 301

Abdullahi, Ismail, Assoc Prof, North Carolina Central University, 1801 Fayetteville St, Durham, NC, 27707. Tel: 919-530-6485. Fax: 919-530-6402. p. 2971

Abed, Donna M, Dir, Delaware Technical & Community College, 333 Shipley St, Wilmington, DE, 19801. Tel: 302-573-5431. Fax: 302-577-2038. p. 387

Abed, Shireen, YA Serv, West Hempstead Public Library, 500 Hempstead Ave, West Hempstead, NY, 11552. Tel: 516-481-6591. Fax: 516-481-2608. p. 1766

Abeita, Jan A, Mgr, Access Serv, Oregon Institute of Technology Library, 3201 Campus Dr, Klamath Falls, OR, 97601-8801. Tel: 541-885-1772. Fax: 541-885-1777. p. 2002

Abel, Bev, ILL Librn, Purchasing, Pocono Mountain Public Library, 5540 Memorial Blvd, Tobyhanna, PA, 18466. Tel: 570-894-8860. Fax: 570-894-8852. p. 2146

Abel, Jocelyn, Head, Tech Serv, Lancaster Bible College Library, 901 Eden Rd, Lancaster, PA, 17601-5036. Tel: 717-560-8250. Fax: 717-560-8265. p. 2076

Abel, Patty, Librn, Champion Municipal Library, Two Ave South, Champion, AB, T0L 0R0, CANADA. Tel: 403-897-3099. Fax: 403-897-3099. p. 2695

Abele, Susan D, Curator, Newton History Museum at The Jackson Homestead, 527 Washington St, Newton, MA, 02458. Tel: 617-796-1462. Fax: 617-552-7228. p. 1110

Abell, Donna, Dir of Libr Serv, Owensboro Community & Technical College, 4800 New Hartford Rd, Owensboro, KY, 42303. Tel: 270-686-4575. Fax: 270-686-4594. p. 931

Abell, Russel, Interim Dir, Pratt Institute Libraries, 200 Willoughby Ave, Brooklyn, NY, 11205-3897. Tel: 718-399-4223. Fax: 718-399-4401. p. 1594

Abella, Elisa, Dir, Miami Dade College, Medical Center Campus Library & Information Resource Center, 950 NW 20th St, Miami, FL, 33127. Tel: 305-237-4498. Fax: 305-237-4301. p. 466

Abels, Eileen G, PhD, Assoc Dean, Acad Affairs, Prof, Drexel University, Rush Bldg, Rm 306, 30 N 33rd St, Philadelphia, PA, 19104-2875. Tel: 215-895-2474. Fax: 215-895-2494. p. 2972

Abelson, Steve, Res, Kirkland & Ellis LLP Library, 300 N LaSalle St, 11th Flr, Chicago, IL, 60654. Tel: 312-862-3246. Fax: 312-862-2200. p. 616

Abend, Susan, Ch, Sierra Vista Public Library, 2600 E Tacoma, Sierra Vista, AZ, 85635-1399. Tel: 520-458-4225. Fax: 520-458-5377. p. 82

Aberamowitz, Ellen, Mgr, Libr Serv, Mercy Fitzgerald Hospital, 1500 Lansdowne Ave, MS No 0127, Darby, PA, 19023-1295. Tel: 610-237-4150. Fax: 610-237-4830. p. 2049

Aberman, Nancy, Sr Librn, Ad Serv, Reading Public Library, 64 Middlesex Ave, Reading, MA, 01867-2550. Tel: 781-944-0840. Fax: 781-942-9106. p. 1120

Abernathy, Bobbie, Br Mgr, Cherokee Regional Library System, Chickamauga Public, 306 Cove Rd, Chickamauga, GA, 30707-1410. Tel: 706-375-3004. Fax: 706-375-7034. p. 538

Abernathy, Karling, Cat, Buffalo Bill Historical Center, 720 Sheridan Ave, Cody, WY, 82414. Tel: 307-578-4059. Fax: 307-527-6042. p. 2653

Abernathy, Mary Jo, Dir, Chilton Clanton Library, 100 First Ave, Clanton, AL, 35045. Tel: 205-755-1768. Fax: 205-755-1374. p. 12

Abeyta, Kateri, IT Mgr, Network Serv, Denver Public Library, Ten W 14th Ave Pkwy, Denver, CO, 80204-2731. Tel: 720-865-1111. Fax: 720-865-2087. p. 300

Abilock, Debbie, Pres, Bay Area Library & Information Network, 1462 Cedar St, Berkeley, CA, 94702. Tel: 415-355-2826. p. 2938

Abinanti, Annie, Circ Mgr, University of Nevada-Reno, Savitt Medical Library & IT Department, Pennington Medical Education Bldg, 1664 N Virginia St, Mail Stop 306, Reno, NV, 89557. Tel: 775-784-4625. Fax: 775-784-4489. p. 1433

Abing, Kevin, Asst Curator, Milwaukee County Historical Society, 910 N Old World Third St, Milwaukee, WI, 53203. Tel: 414-273-8288. Fax: 414-273-3268. p. 2619

Abini, Sandra, Librn III/Youth Serv, Beverly Hills Public Library, 444 N Rexford Dr, Beverly Hills, CA, 90210-4877. Tel: 310-288-2220. Fax: 310-278-3387. p. 129

Abini, Sandra, Mgr, Pasco County Library System, Centennial Park, 5740 Moog Rd, Holiday, FL, 34690. Tel: 727-834-3204. Fax: 727-834-3225. p. 451

Ables, Sharron, Coordr, Copper Valley Community Library, Mile 186 Glenn Hwy, Glennallen, AK, 99588. Tel: 907-822-5427. Fax: 907-822-5427. p. 49

Ables, Venita Ann, Librn, Calhoun County Library, Thornton Public Library, 220 Second St, Rte 1, Thornton, AR, 71766. Tel: 870-352-7619. p. 102

Abma, Christine, ILL, Herrick District Library, 300 S River Ave, Holland, MI, 49423-3290. Tel: 616-355-3100. p. 1190

Abney, Steven P, Assoc Prof, University of Michigan, 304 West Hall, 1085 S University, Ann Arbor, MI, 48109-1107. Tel: 734-763-2285. Fax: 734-764-2475. p. 2967

Abood, Jill, Head, Pub Serv, East Lansing Public Library, 950 Abbott Rd, East Lansing, MI, 48823-3105. Tel: 517-319-6939. Fax: 517-351-9536. p. 1175

Abouelaziz, Cheryl, Dir, Tiverton Library Services, Union Public Library, 3832 Main Rd, Tiverton, RI, 02878-1321. Tel: 401-625-6799. p. 2177

Abraham, Andi, Tech Serv Coordr, East Baton Rouge Parish Library, 7711 Goodwood Blvd, Baton Rouge, LA, 70806-7625. Tel: 225-231-3700. Fax: 225-231-3718. p. 942

Abraham, Catherine, Ref, MassBay Community College, 50 Oakland St, Wellesley, MA, 02481. Tel: 781-239-2617. Fax: 781-239-3621. p. 1134

Abraham, Deborah, Dir, Everett Public Libraries, Shute Memorial, 781 Broadway, Everett, MA, 02149. Tel: 617-394-2308. Fax: 617-394-2354. p. 1087

Abraham, Deborah V, Dir, Everett Public Libraries, 410 Broadway, Everett, MA, 02149. Tel: 617-394-2303. Fax: 617-389-1230. p. 1087

Abraham, Latecia, Pub Info Coordr, Medical University of South Carolina Library, 171 Ashley Ave, Ste 300, Charleston, SC, 29425-0001. Tel: 843-792-9211. Fax: 843-792-7947. p. 2184

Abraham, Lawrence, Head, Instrul Serv, Fordham University School of Law, 140 W 62nd St, New York, NY, 10023-7485. Tel: 212-636-6900. Fax: 212-930-8818. p. 1678

Abraham, Lila J, Ref, Nutter McClennen & Fish LLP, World Trade Center W, 155 Seaport Blvd, Boston, MA, 02210. Tel: 617-439-2000. Fax: 617-310-9000. p. 1066

Abraham, Lorraine, Chief Info Officer, Libr Dir, Emory & Henry College, 30480 Armbrister Dr, Emory, VA, 24327. Tel: 276-944-6808. Fax: 276-944-4592. p. 2460

Abraham, Vanessa, Asst Dir, Bedford Free Public Library, Seven Mudge Way, Bedford, MA, 01730-2168. Tel: 781-275-9440. Fax: 781-275-3590. p. 1052

Abraham, Vanessa, Dir, Groton Public Library, 99 Main St, Groton, MA, 01450. Tel: 978-448-8000. Fax: 978-448-1169. p. 1093

Abrahamson, Sue, Youth Serv Librn, Waupaca Area Public Library, 107 S Main St, Waupaca, WI, 54981-1521. Tel: 715-258-4414. p. 2645

Abramo, Marisa, Head of Libr, National City Public Library, 1401 National City Blvd, National City, CA, 91950-4401. Tel: 619-336-4350. Fax: 619-336-4368. p. 193

Abramov, Michael, Libr Dir, Austin Public Library, St John, 7500 Blessing Ave, Austin, TX, 78752. Tel: 512-974-7570. Fax: 512-380-7055. p. 2279

Abramovitz, Louis C, Librn, Wilkinson Barker Knauer LLP Library, 2300 N St NW, Ste 700, Washington, DC, 20037. Tel: 202-383-3420. Fax: 202-783-5851. p. 423

Abrams, Ann, Librn, Temple Israel Library, 477 Longwood Ave, Boston, MA, 02215. Tel: 617-566-3960. Fax: 617-731-3711. p. 1067

Abrams, Cooky, Dir, Garden Home Community Library, 7475 SW Oleson Rd, Portland, OR, 97223-7474. Tel: 503-245-9932. p. 2010

Abrams, Faye, Projects Officer, Ontario Council of University Libraries, 130 Saint George St, Toronto, ON, M5S 1A5, CANADA. Tel: 416-946-0578. Fax: 416-978-6755. p. 2960

Abrams, Harvey Lee, Pres, International Institute for Sport History Library, PO Box 175, State College, PA, 16804-0175. Tel: 814-321-4018. p. 2143

Abrams, Israela, Head, Ch, Swampscott Public Library, 61 Burrill St, Swampscott, MA, 01907. Tel: 781-596-8867. Fax: 781-596-8826. p. 1130

Abrams, Laura, Asst Dir, Coll Develop, Cohasset Historical Society Library, 106 S Main St, Cohasset, MA, 02025. Tel: 781-383-1434. Fax: 781-383-1190. p. 1082

Abrams, Leslie, Head of Libr, University of California, San Diego, The Arts Library, 9500 Gilman Dr, 0175Q, La Jolla, CA, 92093-0175. p. 162

Abrams, Vera M, Dir, Fallon County Library, Six W Fallon Ave, Baker, MT, 59313. Tel: 406-778-7160. Fax: 406-778-7116. p. 1373

Abramson, Anne, Foreign & Intl Law Librn, The John Marshall Law School, 315 S Plymouth Ct, Chicago, IL, 60604. Tel: 312-427-2737. Fax: 312-427-8307. p. 618

Abreu, Sara, Dir, Inter-American University of Puerto Rico, Barrio San Daniel, Sector Las Canelas, Arecibo, PR, 00614-4050. Tel: 787-878-5475, Ext 2321. Fax: 787-880-1624. p. 2671

Abreu, Victoria, Tech Serv, Flagler County Public Library, 2500 Palm Coast Pkwy NW, Palm Coast, FL, 32137. Tel: 386-446-6763. Fax: 386-446-6773. p. 479

Abreu-Baez, Nancy, Actg Circ Supvr, University of Puerto Rico Library System, Circulation & Reserve Collection, Rio Piedras Campus, San Juan, PR, 00931. Tel: 787-764-0000, Ext 3335, 787-764-0000, Ext 5116. Fax: 787-772-1479. p. 2677

Abromeit, Kathleen, Pub Serv Librn, Oberlin College Library, Mary M Vial Music Library, Oberlin Conservatory of Music, 77 W College St, Oberlin, OH, 44074-1588. Tel: 440-775-8280. Fax: 440-775-8203. p. 1925

Abruzzi, Amy, Ref, Lafayette College, 710 Sullivan Rd, Easton, PA, 18042-1797. Tel: 610-330-5631. Fax: 610-252-0370. p. 2052

Abruzzo, Paul, Ref & Instrul Serv, Instr Coordr, New School, Raymond Fogelman Library, 55 W 13th St, New York, NY, 10011. Tel: 212-229-5307, Ext 3055. Fax: 212-229-5306. p. 1688

Absalom, Kelli, Dir, Info Resources & Res, Orillia Public Library, 36 Mississaga St W, Orillia, ON, L3V 3A6, CANADA. Tel: 705-325-2338. Fax: 705-327-1744. p. 2826

Abshagen, Janet, ILL, Van Buren District Library, 200 N Phelps St, Decatur, MI, 49045-1086. Tel: 269-423-4771. Fax: 269-423-8373. p. 1168

Absher, Linda, Humanities Librn, Portland State University Library, 1875 SW Park Ave, Portland, OR, 97201-3220. Tel: 503-725-4713. Fax: 503-725-4524. p. 2014

Abshier, Dana G, Dir, Liberty Municipal Library, 1710 Sam Houston Ave, Liberty, TX, 77575-4741. Tel: 936-336-8901. Fax: 936-336-2414. p. 2355

Abston, Deborah, Soc Sci Librn, Arizona State University Libraries, Downtown Phoenix Campus Library, UCENT Bldg, Ste L1-62, 411 N Central Ave, Phoenix, AZ, 85004-1213. Tel: 602-496-0307. Fax: 602-496-0312. p. 83

Abu-Zeid, Barbara, Info Serv Coordr, Emory University Libraries, Woodruff Health Sciences Center Library, 1462 Clifton Rd NE, Atlanta, GA, 30322. Tel: 404-727-8727. Fax: 404-727-9821. p. 514

Abuzeit, Farouqua, Ch, Wellesley Free Library, 530 Washington St, Wellesley, MA, 02482. Tel: 781-235-1610, Ext 1109. Fax: 781-235-0495. p. 1135

Abzinger, Sue, Librn, Royal Columbian Hospital, 330 E Columbia St, New Westminster, BC, V3L 3W7, CANADA. Tel: 604-520-4755. Fax: 604-520-4804. p. 2734

Acampora, Susan, Syst Librn, The College of New Rochelle, 29 Castle Pl, New Rochelle, NY, 10805-2308. Tel: 914-654-5345. Fax: 914-654-5884. p. 1666

Accardi, Maria, Coordr, Libr Instruction, Indiana University Southeast Library, 4201 Grant Line Rd, New Albany, IN, 47150. Tel: 812-941-2551. Fax: 812-941-2656. p. 767

Accardo, Janet, Dir, Skadden, Arps, Slate, Meagher & Flom Library, Four Times Sq, New York, NY, 10036. Tel: 212-735-3000. Fax: 212-735-3244. p. 1700

Accorsi, Kathleen, Cat, Eatontown Library, 33 Broad St, Eatontown, NJ, 07724-1594. Tel: 732-389-2665. Fax: 732-389-7665. p. 1482

Acerro, Heather, Head, Ch, Rochester Public Library, 101 Second St SE, Rochester, MN, 55904-3776. Tel: 507-328-2339. Fax: 507-328-2384. p. 1273

Acevedo, Leslie, Adult Serv, Teen Serv, Flint Public Library, 1026 E Kearsley St, Flint, MI, 48502-1994. Tel: 810-249-2046. Fax: 810-249-2635. p. 1179

Acevedo, Pat, Youth Serv Librn, Madison County Public Library, Berea Branch, 319 Chestnut St, Berea, KY, 40403. Tel: 859-986-7112. Fax: 859-986-7208. p. 934

Acfalle, Marie, Libr Tech, United States Army, Grant Library, 1637 Flint St, Fort Carson, CO, 80913-4105. Tel: 719-526-2350. Fax: 719-524-0070. p. 307

Acheson, David, Tech Serv, California Academy of Sciences Library, Golden Gate Park, 55 Music Concourse Dr, San Francisco, CA, 94118. Tel: 415-379-5496. Fax: 415-379-5729. p. 240

Achipa, Joshua, Bibliog Instr, Ref, Southern Nazarene University, 4115 N College, Bethany, OK, 73008. Tel: 405-491-6350. Fax: 405-491-6355. p. 1958

Achterman, Douglas, Dir, Gavilan College Library, 5055 Santa Teresa Blvd, Gilroy, CA, 95020. Tel: 408-848-4809. Fax: 408-846-4927. p. 154

Acierno, Lou, Dir, LIM College Library, 216 E 45th St, 2nd Flr, New York, NY, 10017. Tel: 646-218-4126. Fax: 212-750-3453. p. 1685

Acierno, Lou, Dir, Metropolitan College of New York Library, 431 Canal St, 12th Flr, New York, NY, 10013. Tel: 212-343-1234, Ext 2001. Fax: 212-343-7398. p. 1686

Ackel, Alexis, Electronic Res Librn, University of North Texas Health Science Center at Fort Worth, 3500 Camp Bowie Blvd, Fort Worth, TX, 76107-2699. Tel: 817-735-2070. Fax: 817-763-0325. p. 2324

Acker, Connie, Dir, Cedar Grove Public Library, 131 Van Altena Ave, Cedar Grove, WI, 53013. Tel: 920-668-6834. Fax: 920-668-8744. p. 2585

Acker, Jennifer, ILL, Hudson Valley Community College, 80 Vandenburgh Ave, Troy, NY, 12180. Tel: 518-629-7336. Fax: 518-629-7509. p. 1756

Acker, Robert, Instrul Serv Librn, Ref Serv, DePaul University Libraries, Naperville, 150 W Warrenville Rd, Naperville, IL, 60563. Tel: 312-476-4867. p. 612

Ackerly, Jean, Asst Dir, Newbury Town Library, 0 Lunt St, Byfield, MA, 01922-1232. Tel: 978-465-0539. Fax: 978-465-1071. p. 1072

Ackerman, Amy, Ref Serv, Saint Johns County Public Library System, Bartram Trail, 60 Davis Pond Blvd, Fruit Cove, FL, 32259-4390. Tel: 904-827-6963. Fax: 904-827-6965. p. 487

Ackerman, Cathy, Circ, Pine Bluff & Jefferson County Library System, Redfield Public Library, 310 Brodie St, Redfield, AR, 72132. Tel: 501-397-5070. Fax: 501-397-5070. p. 112

Ackerman, Daniel, Assoc Curator, Old Salem Museums & Gardens Library, Frank L Horton Museum Center, 924 S Main St, Winston-Salem, NC, 27101. Tel: 336-721-7365, 336-721-7372. Fax: 336-721-7367. p. 1833

Ackerman, David, Audio Engineer, Harvard Library, Eda Kuhn Loeb Music Library, Music Bldg, Harvard University, Cambridge, MA, 02138. Tel: 617-495-2794. Fax: 617-496-4636. p. 1076

Ackerman, Linda, Asst Dir, Ch, Portland Public Library, 301 Portland Blvd, Portland, TN, 37148-1229. Tel: 615-325-2279. Fax: 615-325-7061. p. 2263

Ackerman, Mark, Assoc Prof, University of Michigan, 304 West Hall, 1085 S University, Ann Arbor, MI, 48109-1107. Tel: 734-763-2285. Fax: 734-764-2475. p. 2967

Ackerman, Rachel, Librn, Northwest Arkansas Community College Library, One College Dr, Bentonville, AR, 72712-5091. Tel: 479-619-4244. Fax: 479-619-4115. p. 95

Ackerman, Shirley, Adminr, Tech Serv, Kentucky Historical Society, 100 W Broadway, Frankfort, KY, 40601. Tel: 502-564-1792. Fax: 502-564-4701. p. 913

Ackerman, Wendi, Dep Dir, SUNY Upstate Medical University, 766 Irving Ave, Syracuse, NY, 13210-1602. Tel: 315-464-8141. Fax: 315-464-4584. p. 1753

Ackerson, Christine, Academy Librn, Valley Forge Military Academy & College, 1001 Eagle Rd, Wayne, PA, 19087-3695. Tel: 610-989-1438. Fax: 610-975-9642. p. 2152

Ackerson, Kay, Media Spec, Independence Community College Library, 1057 W College Ave, Independence, KS, 67301. Tel: 620-331-4100. Fax: 620-331-6821. p. 873

Ackerson, Lynda, Mgr, Libr Serv, Oregon City Public Library, 362 Warner Milne Rd, Oregon City, OR, 97045. Tel: 503-657-8269. Fax: 503-657-3702. p. 2009

Ackland, Susan, In Charge, Schreiner Memorial Library, Potosi Branch, 103 N Main St, Potosi, WI, 53820. Tel: 608-763-2115. p. 2605

Ackroyd, Anne, Br Mgr, Camden County Library System, Blackwood Rotary Library - Gloucester Township, 15 S Black Horse Pike, Blackwood, NJ, 08012. Tel: 856-228-0022. Fax: 856-228-9085. p. 1538

Ackroyd, Margaret A, Asst Satellite Librn, United States Courts Library, Sandra Day O'Connor United States Courthouse, Ste 410, 401 W Washington St, SPC16, Phoenix, AZ, 85003-2135. Tel: 602-322-7295. Fax: 602-322-7299. p. 77

Ackroyd-Kelly, Elaine, Instrul Support/Educ Res Librn, East Stroudsburg University, 216 Normal St, East Stroudsburg, PA, 18301-2999. Tel: 570-422-3760. Fax: 570-422-3151. p. 2051

Acland, Francis Oliver, Assoc Librn, Graceland University, One University Pl, Lamoni, IA, 50140. Tel: 641-784-5301. Fax: 641-784-5497. p. 826

Acosta, Ana, Adult Ref, Menasha Public Library, 440 First St, Menasha, WI, 54952-3191. Tel: 920-967-3660. Fax: 920-967-5159. p. 2614

Acosta, Kellie, Librn, Ward County Library, Grandfalls Public, 209 Ave D, Grandfalls, TX, 79742. Tel: 432-547-2861. Fax: 432-547-2861. p. 2363

Acosta, Lydia, Univ Librn, VPres for Info Serv, Nova Southeastern University Libraries, 3100 Ray Ferrero Jr Blvd, Fort Lauderdale, FL, 33314. Tel: 954-262-4600. Fax: 954-262-3805. p. 443

Acosta, Migell, Chief Info Officer, Interim Asst Dir, Info Syst, County of Los Angeles Public Library, 7400 E Imperial Hwy, Downey, CA, 90242-3375. Tel: 562-940-8418. Fax: 562-803-3032. p. 140

Acosta, Omar, Acq, Artesia Public Library, 306 W Richardson Ave, Artesia, NM, 88210-2499. Tel: 575-746-4252. Fax: 575-746-3075. p. 1551

Acosta, Ray, Libr Tech, Oxnard College Library, 4000 S Rose Ave, Oxnard, CA, 93033-6699. Tel: 805-986-5800, Ext 1971. Fax: 805-986-5888. p. 202

Acquaviva, Melissa, Dir, Ohio County Public Library, 413 Main St, Hartford, KY, 42347. Tel: 270-298-3790. Fax: 270-298-4214. p. 916

Acree, Eric Kofi, Head of Libr, Cornell University Library, John Henrik Clarke Africana Library, 310 Triphammer Rd, Ithaca, NY, 14850. Tel: 607-255-5229. Fax: 607-255-2493. p. 1641

Acree, Pam, Tech Serv Adminr, Dickstein Shapiro LLP, Research Services, 1825 Eye St NW, Washington, DC, 20006. Tel: 202-420-4999. Fax: 202-420-2201. p. 398

Acres, Renelle, Circ Supvr, Port Moody Public Library, 100 Newport Dr, Port Moody, BC, V3H 3E1, CANADA. Tel: 604-469-4575, 604-469-4577. Fax: 604-469-4576. p. 2735

Acsbok, Michael, Info Tech Mgr, Westchester Public Library, 200 W Indiana Ave, Chesterton, IN, 46304-3122. Tel: 219-926-7696. Fax: 219-926-6424. p. 732

Acton, Anne M, Dir, New England School of Law Library, 154 Stuart St, Boston, MA, 02116-5687. Tel: 617-422-7290. Fax: 617-422-7303. p. 1065

Acton, Cindy, Ref Librn, Cargill, Inc, 15407 McGinty Rd W, Wayzata, MN, 55391. Tel: 952-742-6498. Fax: 952-742-6062. p. 1287

Acton, Lori, District Dir, Laurel County Public Library District, 120 College Park Dr, London, KY, 40741. Tel: 606-864-5759. Fax: 606-862-8057. p. 922

Acton, Susan, Access Serv, Electronic Res, Ser, Northland Pioneer College Libraries, PO Box 610, Holbrook, AZ, 86025. Tel: 928-532-6123. p. 65

Adair, Galina, Ch, Kinnelon Public Library, 132 Kinnelon Rd, Kinnelon, NJ, 07405-2393. Tel: 973-838-1321. Fax: 973-838-0741. p. 1493

Adair, Michele, Br Mgr, Northeast Missouri Library Service, Lewis County Branch-LaGrange, 114 S Main, LaGrange, MO, 63448. Tel: 573-655-2288. Fax: 573-655-2288. p. 1336

Adair, Tem, Libr Asst/ILL, Nebraska Methodist College, 720 N 87th St, Omaha, NE, 68114. Tel: 402-354-7251. Fax: 402-354-7250. p. 1413

Adair Williams, Catherine, Ref & Info Serv, Verona Public Library, 17 Gould St, Verona, NJ, 07044-1928. Tel: 973-857-4848. Fax: 973-857-4851. p. 1537

Adalian, Paul, Dean, Univ Libr, Southern Oregon University, 1250 Siskiyou Blvd, Ashland, OR, 97520-5076. Tel: 541-552-6833. Fax: 541-552-6429. p. 1990

Adam, Fay, Librn, Southeast Regional Library, Bengough Branch, 301 Main St, Bengough, SK, S0C 0K0, CANADA. Tel: 306-268-2022. p. 2929

Adam, Gaelen, Librn, Tobey Hospital, 43 High St, Wareham, MA, 02571. Tel: 508-273-4037. Fax: 508-295-0910. p. 1133

Adam, Jodi, Circ, Libr Spec, Lake Wales Public Library, 290 Cypress Garden Lane, Lake Wales, FL, 33853. Tel: 863-678-4004. Fax: 863-678-4051. p. 458

Adam, Marilyn, Ser Librn, Viterbo University, 900 Viterbo Dr, La Crosse, WI, 54601. Tel: 608-796-3268. Fax: 608-796-3275. p. 2603

Adam-Turner, Nancy, Info Literacy, Ref, Bluefield State College, 219 Rock St, Bluefield, WV, 24701. Tel: 304-327-4052. Fax: 304-327-4203. p. 2554

Adamcyk, William, Dir, Milton Public Library, 476 Canton Ave, Milton, MA, 02186-3299. Tel: 617-698-5757. Fax: 617-698-0441. p. 1106

Adamczyk, Nancy S, Dir, Madison Public Library, 39 Keep St, Madison, NJ, 07940. Tel: 973-377-0722. Fax: 973-377-3142. p. 1498

Adamczyk, Will, Circ, Thomas Crane Public Library, 40 Washington St, Quincy, MA, 02269-9164. Tel: 617-376-1300. Fax: 617-376-1313. p. 1119

Adami, Donna, Librn, Illinois Prairie District Public Library, Washburn Branch, 112 W Magnolia, Washburn, IL, 61570. Tel: 309-248-7429..Fax: 309-248-7429. p. 673

Adamic, Lada A, Asst Prof, University of Michigan, 304 West Hall, 1085 S University, Ann Arbor, MI, 48109-1107. Tel: 734-763-2285. Fax: 734-764-2475. p. 2967

Adamich, Thomas A, Head, Metadata Serv, Muskingum University Library, 163 Stormont St, New Concord, OH, 43762-1199. Tel: 740-826-8015. Fax: 740-826-8404. p. 1920

Adamkiewicz, Pat, Tech Serv, DeKalb Public Library, 309 Oak St, DeKalb, IL, 60115-3369. Tel: 815-756-9568. Fax: 815-756-7837. p. 635

Adamo, Clare, Dir, Holy Apostles College & Seminary Library, 33 Prospect Hill Rd, Cromwell, CT, 06416-2005. Tel: 860-632-3009. Fax: 860-632-3090. p. 334

Adamo, Jo, Circ Librn, Merrill Memorial Library, 215 Main St, Yarmouth, ME, 04096. Tel: 207-846-4763. Fax: 207-846-2422. p. 1008

Adamo, Lisa, Br Mgr, United States Geological Survey Library, National Ctr, Rm 1D100, 12201 Sunrise Valley Dr, Reston, VA, 20192. Fax: 703-648-6373. p. 2487

Adamo, Richard, Head Law Librn, Essex Law Library, J Michael Ruane Judicial Ctr, 56 Federal St, Salem, MA, 01970. Tel: 978-741-0674. Fax: 978-745-7224. p. 1121

Adamovic, Carol, Info Res Coordr, Delaware River Basin Commission Library, 25 State Police Dr, Ewing, NJ, 08628. Tel: 609-883-9500, Ext 249. Fax: 609-883-9522. p. 1484

Adamowski, Elizabeth, Dir, Itasca Community Library, 500 W Irving Park Rd, Itasca, IL, 60143. Tel: 630-773-1699. Fax: 630-773-1707. p. 658

Adamowski, Mary, Head, Youth Serv, Orland Park Public Library, 14921 Ravinia Ave, Orland Park, IL, 60462. Tel: 708-428-5100. Fax: 708-349-8322. p. 686

Adams, A Lee, Pub Serv, John A Burns School of Medicine, 651 Ilalo St, MEB, Honolulu, HI, 96813. Tel: 808-692-0824. Fax: 808-692-1244. p. 564

Adams, A Lee, Chair, Hawaii-Pacific Chapter of the Medical Library Association, Health Sciences Library, 651 Ilalo St MEB, Honolulu, HI, 96813. Tel: 808-692-0810. Fax: 808-692-1244. p. 2941

Adams, Alma, Ch, Dowagiac District Library, 211 Commercial St, Dowagiac, MI, 49047-1728. Tel: 269-782-3826. Fax: 269-782-9798. p. 1174

Adams, Amanda, Law Librn, Nipissing District Law Association Library, 360 Plouffe St, North Bay, ON, P1B 9L5, CANADA. Tel: 705-495-3271. Fax: 705-495-3487. p. 2825

Adams, Amy J, Head, Ref, Southeastern University, 1000 Longfellow Blvd, Lakeland, FL, 33801. Tel: 863-667-5089. Fax: 863-669-4160. p. 460

Adams, Anna, Adult Serv Coordr, Edgecombe County Memorial Library, 909 Main St, Tarboro, NC, 27886. Tel: 252-823-1141. Fax: 252-823-7699. p. 1826

Adams, Beatrice, In Charge, Western Counties Regional Library, Pubnico Branch, 35 Hwy, No 335, Pubnico Head, NS, B0W 2W0, CANADA. Tel: 902-762-2204. Fax: 902-762-3208. p. 2787

Adams, Benita, Asst Librn, Arapahoe Public Library, 302 Nebraska Ave, Arapahoe, NE, 68922. Tel: 308-962-7806. Fax: 308-962-3806. p. 1391

Adams, Bertha, Project Archivist, Philadelphia Museum of Art Library, Ruth & Raymond G Perelman Bldg, 2525 Pennsylvania Ave, Philadelphia, PA, 19130. Tel: 215-684-7643. Fax: 215-236-0534. p. 2114

Adams, Bonnie, Dir, Kasson Public Library, 16 NW First Ave, Kasson, MN, 55944-1471. Tel: 507-634-7615. Fax: 507-634-7630. p. 1255

Adams, Brenda, Head, Tech Serv, Morris County Library, 30 E Hanover Ave, Whippany, NJ, 07981. Tel: 973-285-6955. Fax: 973-285-6960. p. 1544

Adams, Brenda, Fiscal Officer, Ramapo Catskill Library System, 619 Rte 17M, Middletown, NY, 10940-4395. Tel: 845-343-1131, Ext 223. Fax: 845-343-1205. p. 1660

Adams, Brinda Franceine, Dir, Coalmont Public Library, 7426 State Rte 56, Coalmont, TN, 37313-0334. Tel: 931-592-9373. Fax: 931-592-9373. p. 2230

Adams, Bruce, Assoc Dir, Coll Mgt, King County Library System, 960 Newport Way NW, Issaquah, WA, 98027. Tel: 425-369-3203. Fax: 425-369-3255. p. 2516

Adams, Carolann, ILL, Collier County Public Library, 2385 Orange Blossom Dr, Naples, FL, 34109. Tel: 239-593-0334. Fax: 239-254-8167. p. 471

Adams, Carole, Dir, Runnells Community Library, 6575 SE 116th St, Runnells, IA, 50237-1193. Tel: 515-966-2068. p. 841

Adams, Carolyn, Access Serv, University of Nevada-Reno, 1664 N Virginia St, Mailstop 0322, Reno, NV, 89557-0322. Tel: 775-682-5715. Fax: 775-784-4529. p. 1433

Adams, Catherine, Asst Librn, Mariposa County Library, 4978 Tenth St, Mariposa, CA, 95338. Tel: 209-966-2140. Fax: 209-742-7527. p. 183

Adams, Catherine E, Acq Librn, Law Library of Montgomery County, Court House, Swede & Airy Streets, Norristown, PA, 19404. Tel: 610-278-3805. Fax: 610-278-5998. p. 2098

Adams, Cathy, Mgr, Libr Serv, MRA Laboratories Library, Information Services, 15 Print Works Dr, Adams, MA, 01220. Tel: 413-743-3927. Fax: 413-743-0305. p. 1048

Adams, Cathy, ILL, Century College Library, 3300 N Century Ave, White Bear Lake, MN, 55110. Tel: 651-779-3968. Fax: 651-779-3963. p. 1288

Adams, Cathy, Br Mgr, Pioneer Library System, Noble Public, 204 N Fifth St, Noble, OK, 73068. Tel: 405-872-5713. Fax: 405-872-8329. p. 1970

Adams, Celeste, Dir, Grand Rapids Art Museum, 101 Monroe Center, Grand Rapids, MI, 49503. Tel: 616-831-1000, 616-831-2901, 616-831-2909 (appt number). Fax: 616-559-0422. p. 1184

Adams, Chase, Admin Serv, Nashville Public Library, 615 Church St, Nashville, TN, 37219-2314. Tel: 615-862-5760. Fax: 615-862-5771. p. 2257

Adams, Cheryl, Head, Cat, Utah State University, 3000 Old Main Hill, Logan, UT, 84322-3000. Tel: 435-797-2667. Fax: 435-797-2880. p. 2407

Adams, Christina, Mrs, Br Mgr, Davidson County Public Library System, Denton Public, 310 W Salisbury St, Denton, NC, 27239-6944. Tel: 336-859-2215. Fax: 336-859-5006. p. 1806

Adams, Christine, Bus & Econ Librn, Youngstown State University, One University Plaza, Youngstown, OH, 44555-0001. Tel: 330-941-3680. Fax: 330-941-3734. p. 1953

Adams, Christine, ILL, College of Physicians & Surgeons of British Columbia, 100-1383 W Eighth Ave, Vancouver, BC, V6H 4C4, CANADA. Tel: 604-733-6671. Fax: 604-737-8582. p. 2740

Adams, Cindy, Librn, McKenna Long & Aldridge, 303 Peachtree St, Ste 5300, Atlanta, GA, 30308. Tel: 404-527-4057. Fax: 404-527-8474. p. 516

Adams, David, Asst Prof, Missouri State University, Duane G Meyer Library, 901 S National Ave, Springfield, MO, 65897. Tel: 417-836-4525. Fax: 417-836-4764. p. 2968

Adams, David L, Head, Syst, Missouri State University, 850 S John Q Hammons Pkwy, Springfield, MO, 65807. Tel: 417-836-6211. Fax: 417-836-4764. p. 1367

Adams, Dawn, Currahee Campus Librn, North Georgia Technical College Library, 1500 Hwy 197 N, Clarkesville, GA, 30523. Tel: 706-779-8104. Fax: 706-754-7777. p. 524

Adams, Debbie, Access Serv, ILL, Agnes Scott College, 141 E College Ave, Decatur, GA, 30030-3770. Tel: 404-471-6339. Fax: 404-471-5037. p. 529

Adams, Deborah L, Dir, Botsford Hospital, 28050 Grand River Ave, Farmington Hills, MI, 48336-5919. Tel: 248-471-8434. Fax: 248-471-8060. p. 1177

Adams, Debra, Dir, Teton County Library, 125 Virginian Lane, Jackson, WY, 83001. Tel: 307-733-2164, Ext 128. Fax: 307-733-4568. p. 2656

Adams, Diane, Dir, International Falls Public Library, 750 Fourth St, International Falls, MN, 56649. Tel: 218-283-8051. Fax: 218-283-4379. p. 1254

Adams, Eveann, In Charge, Tingley Memorial Library, 111 Second St N, Bradenton Beach, FL, 34217-2465. Tel: 941-779-1208. Fax: 941-779-1304. p. 430

Adams, Faith, Librn, Nyssa Public Library, 319 Main St, Nyssa, OR, 97913-3845. Tel: 541-372-2978. Fax: 541-372-3278. p. 2008

Adams, Gaynell, Librn, Bridge City Correctional Center for Youth Library, 3225 River Rd, Bridge City, LA, 70094. Tel: 504-436-4253. Fax: 504-342-8208. p. 946

Adams, Heidi Sue, Lead Med Librn, Kalispell Regional Medical Center, 310 Sunnyview Lane, Kalispell, MT, 59901. Tel: 406-752-1739. Fax: 406-752-8771. p. 1384

Adams, Hildreth, Asst Dir, Mount Sterling Montgomery County Library, 241 W Locust St, Mount Sterling, KY, 40353. Tel: 859-498-2404. Fax: 859-498-7477. p. 930

Adams, Jackie, Dir, Kent County Public Library, 408 High St, Chestertown, MD, 21620-1312. Tel: 410-778-3636. Fax: 410-778-6756. p. 1023

Adams, Jacqueline, Libr Dir, Yarmouth Town Libraries, 312 Old Main St, South Yarmouth, MA, 02664. Tel: 508-760-4820. Fax: 508-760-2699. p. 1126

Adams, Jacqueline, Libr Dir, Yarmouth Town Libraries, South Yarmouth Branch, 312 Old Main St, South Yarmouth, MA, 02664. Tel: 508-760-4822. Fax: 508-760-2699. p. 1126

Adams, Jacqueline, Libr Dir, Yarmouth Town Libraries, West Yarmouth Branch, 391 Main St, Rte 28, West Yarmouth, MA, 02673. Tel: 508-775-5206. Fax: 508-778-4812. p. 1126

Adams, James, Dir of Tech Serv, Metal Powder Industries Federation-APMI International Library, 105 College Rd E, Princeton, NJ, 08540-6692. Tel: 609-452-7700. Fax: 609-987-8523. p. 1522

Adams, James, Librn, Hanover Juvenile Correctional Center, 7093 Broad Neck Rd, Hanover, VA, 23069. Tel: 804-537-6682. Fax: 804-537-5491. p. 2469

Adams, January, Dir, Libr Serv, Franklin Township Free Public Library, 485 DeMott Lane, Somerset, NJ, 08873. Tel: 732-873-8700. Fax: 732-873-0746. p. 1529

Adams, Jean, Libr Dir, The Amargosa Valley Library, 829 E Farm Rd, HCR 69, Box 401T, Amargosa Valley, NV, 89020. Tel: 775-372-5340. Fax: 775-372-1188. p. 1425

Adams, Jean, Librn, Public Library of Johnston County & Smithfield, James Bryan Creech Public Library, Black Creek Rd, Four Oaks, NC, 27524. Tel: 919-963-6013. p. 1824

Adams, Jean H, Exec Dir, Walla Walla County Rural Library District, 37 Jade Ave, Walla Walla, WA, 99362-1628. Tel: 509-527-3284. Fax: 509-527-3740. p. 2547

Adams, Jeanine, Commun Br Supvr, Pierce County Library System, Tillicum Branch, 14916 Washington Ave SW, Lakewood, WA, 98498. Tel: 253-548-3314. Fax: 253-588-2095. p. 2540

Adams, Jennifer, Mgr, Ch Serv, Manhattan Public Library, 629 Poyntz Ave, Manhattan, KS, 66502-6086. Tel: 785-776-4741. Fax: 785-776-1545. p. 881

Adams, Jennifer, Br Mgr, Public Library Association of Annapolis & Anne Arundel County, Inc, Mountain Road, 4730 Mountain Rd, Pasadena, MD, 21122. Tel: 410-222-6699. Fax: 410-222-6705. p. 1010

Adams, John L, Librn, Jones Day, 2727 N Harwood St, Dallas, TX, 75201-1515. Tel: 214-969-4823. Fax: 214-969-5100. p. 2308

Adams, Judie, Asst Dir, Tyrone-Snyder Public Library, 1000 Pennsylvania Ave, Tyrone, PA, 16686. Tel: 814-684-1133, Ext 4. Fax: 814-684-1878. p. 2147

Adams, Julie, Librn, New York Mills Public Library, 30 N Main Ave, New York Mills, MN, 56567-4318. Tel: 218-385-2436. Fax: 218-385-2508. p. 1268

Adams, Julie, Assoc Dir, Tennessee Wesleyan College, 23 Coach Farmer Dr, Athens, TN, 37303. Tel: 423-746-5250. Fax: 423-746-5272. p. 2224

Adams, K, Dir, University of Manitoba Libraries, Elizabeth Dafoe Libr, Rm 156, Winnipeg, MB, R3T 2N2, CANADA. Tel: 204-474-9881. Fax: 204-474-7583. p. 2758

Adams, Karlene, ILL, Saint Johns County Public Library System, 6670 US 1 South, Saint Augustine, FL, 32086. Tel: 904-827-6934. p. 486

Adams, Kate, Coordr, Distance Educ & Undergrad Serv, University of Nebraska-Lincoln, 1248 R St, Lincoln, NE, 68588-4100. Tel: 402-472-2526. p. 1407

Adams, Kathy, Online Serv, Tech Serv, Macon State College Library, 100 College Station Dr, Macon, GA, 31206-5144. Tel: 478-471-2042. Fax: 478-471-2869. p. 540

Adams, Kathy, Dir, Lanesborough Public Library, 83 N Main St, Lanesborough, MA, 01237. Tel: 413-442-0222. Fax: 413-443-5811. p. 1097

Adams, Kellie, Sr Law Librn, Queens County Supreme Court Library, General Court House, 88-11 Sutphin Blvd, Jamaica, NY, 11435. Tel: 718-298-1206. Fax: 718-298-1189. p. 1646

Adams, Keri, Head, YA, Johnson Free Public Library, 274 Main St, Hackensack, NJ, 07601-5797. Tel: 201-343-4169. Fax: 201-343-1395. p. 1489

Adams, Keri, YA Serv, Catawba County Library, Maiden Branch, 11 S A Ave, Maiden, NC, 28650. Tel: 828-428-2712. Fax: 828-428-3845. p. 1813

Adams, Keri Lynn, YA Serv, Malden Public Library, 36 Salem St, Malden, MA, 02148-5291. Tel: 781-324-0218. Fax: 781-324-4467. p. 1102

Adams, Kerry, Head, Info Res, Emerson College Library, 120 Boylston St, Boston, MA, 02116-4624. Tel: 617-824-8338. Fax: 617-824-7817. p. 1060

Adams, Kimberly D, Ref Librn, Library of the Marine Corps, Gray Research Ctr, 2040 Broadway St, Quantico, VA, 22134-5107. Tel: 703-784-4409. Fax: 703-784-4306. p. 2486

Adams, Laura, Acq Tech, Bridgewater College, 402 E College St, Bridgewater, VA, 22812. Tel: 540-828-5411. Fax: 540-828-5482. p. 2452

Adams, Laurie, Librn, Carnegie-Schuyler Library, 303 E Second St, Pana, IL, 62557. Tel: 217-562-2326. Fax: 217-562-2343. p. 688

Adams, Leslee, Librn, Saint Maries Public Library, 822 College Ave, Saint Maries, ID, 83861-1720. Tel: 208-245-3732. Fax: 208-245-7102. p. 583

Adams, Linda, Dir, Dickens Public Library, 210 Main, Dickens, IA, 51333. Tel: 712-836-2217. p. 811

Adams, Linda, Dir, Webb Public Library, 124 Main St, Webb, IA, 51366. Tel: 712-838-7719. p. 851

Adams, Linda, Dir, Andover Free Library, 40 Main St, Andover, NY, 14806. Tel: 607-478-8442. Fax: 607-478-5056. p. 1574

Adams, Linda, Dir, Shackelford County Library, 402 N Second St, Albany, TX, 76430. Tel: 325-762-2672. Fax: 325-762-2672. p. 2272

Adams, Linda K, Dir, Arlington Public Library, 711 Main St, Arlington, IA, 50606. Tel: 563-633-3475. Fax: 563-633-3475. p. 794

Adams, Linda K, Dir, Fayette Community Library, 104 W State St, Fayette, IA, 52142. Tel: 563-425-3344. Fax: 563-425-3344. p. 816

Adams, Louise, Ref, Kilpatrick Stockton, 1100 Peachtree St, Ste 2800, Atlanta, GA, 30309. Tel: 404-815-6261. Fax: 404-815-6555. p. 516

Adams, Luanna, Br Mgr, Harris County Public Library, Fairbanks Branch, 7122 N Gessner, Houston, TX, 77040. Tel: 713-466-4438. Fax: 281-466-9757. p. 2336

Adams, Mararia, Asst Dir, Syst, Louisiana State University Health Sciences Center, 1501 Kings Hwy, Shreveport, LA, 71130. Tel: 318-675-5448. Fax: 318-675-5442. p. 968

Adams, Mark, Communications Coordr, College Center for Library Automation, 1753 W Paul Dirac Dr, Tallahassee, FL, 32310. Tel: 850-922-6044. Fax: 850-922-4869. p. 2940

Adams, Mary, Br Mgr, Hopkins County-Madisonville Public Library, Dawson Springs Branch, 103 W Ramsey St, Dawson Springs, KY, 42408. Tel: 270-797-8990. Fax: 270-797-8990. p. 927

Adams, Mary, Librn, Louisiana Department of Justice, Office of the Attorney General, 1885 N Third St, 4th Flr, Baton Rouge, LA, 70802. Tel: 225-326-6422. Fax: 225-326-6495. p. 943

Adams, Mazie, Exec Dir, Lakewood Historical Society Library, 14710 Lake Ave, Lakewood, OH, 44107. Tel: 216-221-7343. p. 1908

Adams, Michael, Ref, City University of New York, 365 Fifth Ave, New York, NY, 10016-4309. Tel: 212-817-7055. Fax: 212-817-2982. p. 1673

Adams, Michael, Pres, Faith Evangelical Seminary Library, 3504 N Pearl St, Tacoma, WA, 98407-2607. Tel: 253-752-2020. Fax: 253-759-1790. p. 2538

Adams, Nancy, Assoc Dir & Coordr of Educ & Instruction, Pennsylvania State University, College of Medicine, Penn State Hershey, Harrell Health Sciences Library, 500 University Dr, Hershey, PA, 17033. Tel: 717-531-8989. Fax: 717-531-8635. p. 2069

Adams, Nancy J, Dir, Whitehall Township Public Library, 3700 Mechanicsville Rd, Whitehall, PA, 18052-3399. Tel: 610-432-4339. Fax: 610-432-9387. p. 2155

Adams, Nancy R, Tech Serv Librn, Palmer Theological Seminary, Six Lancaster Ave, Wynnewood, PA, 19096. Tel: 610-645-9317. p. 2158

Adams, Nicole, Br Supvr, Oshawa Public Library, Jess Hann Branch, Lake Vista Sq, 199 Wentworth St W, Oshawa, ON, L1J 6P4, CANADA. Tel: 905-579-6111, Ext 5862. p. 2827

Adams, Owen E, Jr, Cat/Ref Librn, Northwest Florida State College, 100 College Blvd, Niceville, FL, 32578. Tel: 850-729-5392. Fax: 850-729-5295. p. 472

Adams, Pansy, Libr Tech, Tech Serv, Southeast Kentucky Area Health Education Center, 100 Medical Center Dr, Hazard, KY, 41701-9429. Tel: 606-439-6796. Fax: 606-439-6798. p. 917

Adams, Paul, Libr Dir, Oklahoma Library for the Blind & Physically Handicapped, 300 NE 18th St, Oklahoma City, OK, 73105. Tel: 405-521-3514. Fax: 405-521-4582. p. 1974

Adams, Paula, Head, User Serv, Columbus State University Libraries, 4225 University Ave, Columbus, GA, 31907. Tel: 706-565-3616. Fax: 706-568-2084. p. 526

Adams, Phyllis, Pub Serv, Oklahoma Historical Society, 2401 N Laird Ave, Oklahoma City, OK, 73105-4997. Tel: 405-522-5225. Fax: 405-522-0644. p. 1974

Adams, Rebecca, Librn, Atchison County Library, 200 S Main St, Rock Port, MO, 64482-1532. Tel: 660-744-5404. Fax: 660-744-2861. p. 1351

Adams, Robert, Coordr, Acq, Reserves, Boston Architectural College, 320 Newbury St, Boston, MA, 02115. Tel: 617-585-0155. Fax: 617-585-0151. p. 1055

Adams, Sabrena, Br Mgr, Phoenix Public Library, Yucca Library, 5648 N 15th Ave, Phoenix, AZ, 85015-2512. p. 76

Adams, Sarah, Actg Head, Libr, Harvard Library, Eda Kuhn Loeb Music Library, Music Bldg, Harvard University, Cambridge, MA, 02138. Tel: 617-495-2794. Fax: 617-496-4636. p. 1076

Adams, Sarah, Spec Coll Librn, Harvard Library, Eda Kuhn Loeb Music Library, Music Bldg, Harvard University, Cambridge, MA, 02138. Tel: 617-495-2794. Fax: 617-496-4636. p. 1076

Adams, Sarah, Dir, St Croix Falls Public Library, 230 S Washington St, Saint Croix Falls, WI, 54024. Tel: 715-483-1777. Fax: 715-483-1777. p. 2635

Adams, Sheila, Circ Mgr, Glenwood-Lynwood Public Library District, 19901 Stony Island Ave, Glenwood, IL, 60411. Tel: 708-758-0090. Fax: 708-758-0106. p. 651

Adams, Sheryll, Br Mgr, Chicago Public Library, McKinley Park, 1915 W 35th St, Chicago, IL, 60609. Tel: 312-747-6082. Fax: 312-747-1982. p. 609

Adams, Shirley R, Acq, Erskine College & Theological Seminary, One Depot St, Due West, SC, 29639. Tel: 864-379-8898. Fax: 864-379-2900. p. 2193

Adams, Stephanie J, Info Tech, Instruction Librn, Syst Adminr, Cecil College, One Seahawk Dr, North East, MD, 21901-1904. Tel: 410-287-1005. Fax: 410-287-1607. p. 1035

Adams, Steve, Fiction/Media Coordr, Duluth Public Library, 520 W Superior St, Duluth, MN, 55802. Tel: 218-730-4212. Fax: 218-723-3815, 218-723-3822. p. 1247

Adams, Steven, Librn, Princeton University, Biology, Fine Hall Library, McDonnell Hall, One Washington Ave, Princeton, NJ, 08544. Tel: 609-258-3235. Fax: 609-258-2627. p. 1523

Adams, Steven, Librn, Princeton University, Fine Hall Library-Mathematics, Physics & Statistics, One Washington Rd, Princeton, NJ, 08544-0001. Tel: 609-258-5484. Fax: 609-258-2627. p. 1523

Adams, Steven, Interim Librn, Princeton University, Psychology, Green Hall, Princeton, NJ, 08544-1010. Tel: 609-258-3239. Fax: 609-258-1113. p. 1524

Adams, Suellen, Dr, Asst Prof, University of Rhode Island, Rodman Hall, 94 W Alumni Ave, Ste 2, Kingston, RI, 02881-0815. Tel: 401-874-4740. Fax: 401-874-4964. p. 2973

Adams, Susan, Youth Serv Mgr, Wake County Public Library System, Southeast Regional Library, 908 Seventh Ave, Garner, NC, 27529. Tel: 919-662-2265. Fax: 919-662-2270. p. 1818

Adams, Tammie, Asst Librn, Marmora & Lake Public Library, 37 Forsyth St, Marmora, ON, K0K 2M0, CANADA. Tel: 613-472-3122. p. 2820

Adams, Valarie, Coordr, Cat, University of Tennessee at Chattanooga Library, 615 McCallie Ave, Dept 6456, Chattanooga, TN, 37403-2598. Tel: 423-425-4501. Fax: 423-425-4775. p. 2228

Adams, Virginia, Librn, Ider Public Library, 10808 Alabama Hwy 75, Ider, AL, 35981. Tel: 256-657-2170. Fax: 256-657-3178. p. 22

Adams, Virginia, Ch, Dickinson County Library, 401 Iron Mountain St, Iron Mountain, MI, 49801-3435. Tel: 906-774-1218. Fax: 906-774-4079. p. 1193

Adams, Virginia, Supvr, ILL, Mount Hood Community College Library, 26000 SE Stark St, Gresham, OR, 97030. Tel: 503-491-7161. Fax: 503-491-7389. p. 1999

Adams, Virginia, Circ Mgr, Vancouver Community College, 250 W Pender St, Vancouver, BC, V6B 1S9, CANADA. Tel: 604-871-7497. Fax: 604-443-8588. p. 2743

Adams, Vivian, Head Librn, Yakama Nation Library, Yakama Nation Cultural Ctr, Hwy 97 at Fort Rd, Toppenish, WA, 98948. Tel: 509-865-2800, Ext 6, 509-865-5121, Ext 4721, 509-865-5121, Ext 4747. Fax: 509-865-6101. p. 2541

Adams, Wanda, Ref, Leavenworth Public Library, 417 Spruce St, Leavenworth, KS, 66048. Tel: 913-682-5666. Fax: 913-682-1248. p. 879

Adams, Warren, Dir, Cumberland County Historical Society Library, 981 Great St, Greenwich, NJ, 08323. Tel: 856-455-4055, 856-455-8580. p. 1488

Adams Wendt, Kris, Pub Libr Consult, Wisconsin Valley Library Service, 300 N First St, Wausau, WI, 54403. Tel: 715-261-7250. Fax: 715-261-7259. p. 2647

Adams, William R, Dir, Saint Augustine Preservation Department Library, Government House, PO Box 210, Saint Augustine, FL, 32085-0210. Tel: 904-825-5033. Fax: 904-825-5096. p. 486

Adams, CRM, Tony, Dir, Wyoming State Archives, Barrett Bldg, 2301 Central Ave, Cheyenne, WY, 82002. Tel: 307-777-7826. Fax: 307-777-7044. p. 2653

Adams-Cook, Vicki, Br Mgr, Cuyahoga County Public Library, Middleburg Heights Branch, 15600 E Bagley Rd, Middleburg Heights, OH, 44130-4830. Tel: 440-234-3600. Fax: 440-234-0849. p. 1927

Adams-O'Brien, Frances, Info Res Mgr, Municipal Technical Advisory Service Library, Univ Tennessee Conference Ctr Bldg, 600 Henley St, Ste 120, Knoxville, TN, 37996-4105. Tel: 865-974-9842. Fax: 865-974-0423. p. 2242

Adams-Walker, Norvel, Senior Mgr, East Region, Memphis Public Library & Information Center, 3030 Poplar Ave, Memphis, TN, 38111-3527. Tel: 901-415-2700. Fax: 901-323-7108. p. 2249

Adamski, Julie, Syst Support Spec, Helen M Plum Memorial Public Library District, 110 W Maple St, Lombard, IL, 60148-2594. Tel: 630-627-0316. Fax: 630-627-0336. p. 667

Adamski, Rosemary, Asst Mgr, Washington Talking Book & Braille Library, 2021 Ninth Ave, Seattle, WA, 98121-2783. Tel: 206-615-0400. Fax: 206-615-0437. p. 2535

Adamson, Anne, IT Dept Head, Caldwell Public Library, 1010 Dearborn, Caldwell, ID, 83605-4195. Tel: 208-459-3242. Fax: 208-459-7344. p. 572

Adamson, Dianne, Br Mgr, Martin County Library, Trimont Branch, 190 W Main St, Trimont, MN, 56176. Tel: 507-639-2571. p. 1250

Adamson, Gwenyth, Daytona Beach Campus Libr Dir, Keiser University Library System, 1500 NW 49th St, Fort Lauderdale, FL, 33309. Tel: 954-351-4035. Fax: 954-351-4051. p. 443

Adamson, Jennifer, Ch, Olathe Public Library, 201 E Park St, Olathe, KS, 66061. Tel: 913-971-6869. Fax: 913-971-6809. p. 886

Adamson, Margaret, Librn, Kansas Department of Corrections, 1737 SE Hwy 54, El Dorado, KS, 67042. Tel: 316-321-7284. Fax: 316-322-2018. p. 865

Adamson, Shane, Media Coordr, Loveland Public Library, 300 N Adams Ave, Loveland, CO, 80537-5754. Tel: 970-962-2598. Fax: 970-962-2905. p. 317

Adamson, Stephanie, Dir, Aberdeen District Library, 76 E Central, Aberdeen, ID, 83210-1930. Tel: 208-397-4427. Fax: 208-397-4427. p. 569

Adan, Joan, Curator, Forest Lawn Museum Library, 1712 S Glendale Ave, Glendale, CA, 91205. Tel: 323-340-4707. p. 155

Adarkwa, Joshua, Dir, Patten University, 2433 Coolidge Ave, Oakland, CA, 94601. Tel: 510-261-8500, Ext 7775. p. 198

Adasiak, Paul, Metadata Coordr, University of Alaska Fairbanks, 310 Tanana Dr, Fairbanks, AK, 99775. Tel: 907-474-5354. Fax: 907-474-6841. p. 48

Adcock, Ann, Pub Serv, Aiken Technical College Library, 2276 Jefferson Davis Hwy, Graniteville, SC, 29829. Tel: 803-593-9954, Ext 1312. Fax: 803-593-2169. p. 2195

Adcock, Chris, Dir, Talbot Belmond Public Library, 440 E Main St, Belmond, IA, 50421-1224. Tel: 641-444-4160. Fax: 641-444-3457. p. 796

Adcock, June, Librn, Claude Public Library, 100 Trice St, Claude, TX, 79019. Tel: 806-226-7881. Fax: 806-226-7881. p. 2297

Adcock, Margaret, Br Mgr, Granville County Library System, Berea Branch, 1211 Hwy 158, Berea, NC, 27565. Tel: 919-693-1231. Fax: 919-693-1231. p. 1814

Addington, Jennifer, Mgr, Br Serv, Palos Verdes Library District, 701 Silver Spur Rd, Rolling Hills Estates, CA, 90274. Tel: 310-377-9584, Ext 552. Fax: 310-541-6807. p. 219

Addington, Jennifer, Br Mgr, Palos Verdes Library District, Malaga Cove, 2400 Via Campesina, Palos Verdes Estates, CA, 90274-3662. Tel: 310-377-9584, Ext 552. Fax: 310-373-7594. p. 220

Addington, Jennifer, Br Operations Mgr, Palos Verdes Library District, Miraleste, 29089 Palos Verdes Dr E, Rancho Palos Verdes, CA, 90275. Tel: 310-377-9584, Ext 453. Fax: 310-547-4067. p. 220

Addis, Clara Elizabeth, Librn, AnMed Health Medical Library, 800 N Fant St, Anderson, SC, 29621-5708. Tel: 864-512-1253. Fax: 864-512-1552. p. 2181

Addison, Andra, Dir of Communications, The Seattle Public Library, 1000 Fourth Ave, Seattle, WA, 98104-1109. Tel: 206-386-4103. p. 2531

Addison, David, In Charge, Santa Cruz City-County Library System Headquarters, Aptos Branch, 7695 Soquel Dr, Aptos, CA, 95003-3899. Tel: 831-427-7702, Ext 7671. Fax: 831-427-7722. p. 264

Addison, Sunny, Ref, Public Library of Anniston-Calhoun County, 108 E Tenth St, Anniston, AL, 36201. Tel: 256-237-8501, 256-237-8503. Fax: 256-238-0474. p. 4

Addleman, Jayanti, County Librn, Monterey County Free Libraries, 188 Seaside Ctr, Marina, CA, 93933-2500. Tel: 831-883-7573. Fax: 831-883-7574. p. 182

Addleman, Kelly, ILL, Pub Serv, Seton Hill University, One Seton Hill Dr, Greensburg, PA, 15601. Tel: 724-838-4291. Fax: 724-838-4203. p. 2062

Addlesperger, Elisa, Instrul Serv Librn, Ref Serv, DePaul University Libraries, Loop, One E Jackson Blvd, 10th Flr, Chicago, IL, 60604. Tel: 312-362-5045. Fax: 312-362-6186. p. 612

Addlesperger, Elisa, Instrul Serv Librn, Ref Serv, DePaul University Libraries, O'Hare, 3166 S River Rd, Des Plaines, IL, 60018. Tel: 312-362-5045. Fax: 847-296-4381. p. 612

Addo, Wilson, Res Spec, Orrick, Herrington & Sutcliffe, 666 Fifth Ave, New York, NY, 10103. Tel: 212-506-5340. Fax: 212-506-5151. p. 1696

Ade, Pam, YA Librn, Rossford Public Library, 720 Dixie Hwy, Rossford, OH, 43460-1289. Tel: 419-666-0924. Fax: 419-666-1989. p. 1932

Adebonojo, Leslie, Student Serv Librn, East Tennessee State University, Sherrod Library, Seehorn Dr & Lake St, Johnson City, TN, 37614-0204. Tel: 423-439-4308. Fax: 423-439-5222. p. 2239

Adelberg, Janet H, Librn, Cary Memorial Library, 17 Old Winthrop Rd, Wayne, ME, 04284. Tel: 207-685-3612. p. 1006

Adelson, Robin, Exec Dir, Children's Book Council Library, 12 W 37th St, 2nd Flr, New York, NY, 10018-7480. Tel: 212-966-1990. Fax: 212-966-2073. p. 1672

Adema, Liz, Supvr, Middlesex County Library, Parkhill Branch, 233 Main St, Parkhill, ON, N0M 2K0, CANADA. Tel: 519-294-6583. p. 2845

Ademodi, Olugbenga, Res Librn, Saint Thomas University Library, Law Library, 16401 NW 37th Ave, Miami Gardens, FL, 33054. Tel: 305-623-2330. Fax: 305-623-2337. p. 469

Aden, Abdul, Govt Doc, Pub Serv, Cheyney University, 1837 University Circle, Cheyney, PA, 19319. Tel: 610-399-2203. Fax: 610-399-2491. p. 2044

Aden, Sara, Asst Dir, North Platte Public Library, 120 W Fourth St, North Platte, NE, 69101-3993. Tel: 308-535-8036. Fax: 308-535-8296. p. 1410

Adermann, Anna, Dir, Assumption Public Library District, 205 N Oak St, Assumption, IL, 62510. Tel: 217-226-3915. Fax: 217-226-3915. p. 590

Adeyemon, Earnestine, Electronic Res, Case Western Reserve University, 11055 Euclid Ave, Cleveland, OH, 44106. Tel: 216-368-4248. Fax: 216-368-6950. p. 1876

Adinolfi, Susan, Dir, Bank of America Merrill Lynch & Co, 250 Vesey St, 24th Flr, New York, NY, 10080. Tel: 212-449-3814. Fax: 212-449-1379. p. 1669

Adkins, Andrea, Mgr, Info Serv, Washington County Public Library, 615 Fifth St, Marietta, OH, 45750-1973. Tel: 740-373-1057. p. 1913

Adkins, Bev, Br Mgr, Piedmont Regional Library, Braselton Branch, 132 W Broadway, Braselton, GA, 30517. Tel: 706-654-1992. p. 557

Adkins, Cookie, Cat, Bastrop Public Library, 1100 Church St, Bastrop, TX, 78602. Tel: 512-321-5441. Fax: 512-321-3163. p. 2286

Adkins, Dawn, Supvr, Govt Docs, University of Tennessee, Taylor Law Center, 1505 W Cumberland Ave, Knoxville, TN, 37996-1800. Tel: 865-974-6724. Fax: 865-974-6571, 865-974-6595. p. 2243

Adkins, Delania, Head Librn, Pike County Public Library District, Belfry Public, 24371 US Hwy 119 N, Belfry, KY, 41514. Tel: 606-353-9429. Fax: 606-257-4138. p. 932

Adkins, Delania, Head Librn, Pike County Public Library District, Elkhorn City Public, 150 E Main St, Elkhorn City, KY, 41522. Tel: 606-754-5451. Fax: 606-766-0025. p. 932

Adkins, Delania, Head Librn, Pike County Public Library District, Vesta Roberts-Johnson Memorial Library, 180 Hwy 610 W, Virgie, KY, 41572. Tel: 606-639-9839. Fax: 606-766-0024. p. 932

Adkins, Delania, Librn, Pike County Public Library District, Pikeville Public, 119 College St, Pikeville, KY, 41501-1787. Tel: 606-432-1285. Fax: 606-766-0027. p. 932

Adkins, Denice, Assoc Prof, University of Missouri-Columbia, 303 Townsend Hall, Columbia, MO, 65211. Tel: 573-882-4546. Fax: 573-884-2917. p. 2968

Adkins, Diane S, Dir, Pittsylvania County Public Library, 24 Military Dr, Chatham, VA, 24531. Tel: 434-432-3271. Fax: 434-432-1405. p. 2455

Adkins, Elaine, Tech Serv, Carroll County Public Library, 115 Airport Dr, Westminster, MD, 21157. Tel: 410-386-4500. Fax: 410-386-4509. p. 1045

Adkins, John, Ref & Instrul Serv, Instr Coordr, University of Charleston, 2300 MacCorkle Ave SE, Charleston, WV, 25304-1099. Tel: 304-357-4779. Fax: 304-357-4715. p. 2556

Adkins, Kimberly, Librn, Jackson Kelly, 1600 Laidley Tower, Charleston, WV, 25322. Tel: 304-340-1260. Fax: 304-340-1261. p. 2556

Adkins, Lissa, Ser, University of Charleston, 2300 MacCorkle Ave SE, Charleston, WV, 25304-1099. Tel: 304-357-4780. Fax: 304-357-4715. p. 2556

Adkins, Rosemarie, Librn, Department of Veterans Affairs, Colmery O'Neil VA Medical Ctr, 2200 SW Gage Blvd, Topeka, KS, 66622. Tel: 785-350-3111, Ext 2779. Fax: 785-350-4421. p. 896

Adkins, Thomas S, Dir, Garnet A Wilson Public Library of Pike County, 207 N Market St, Waverly, OH, 45690-1176. Tel: 740-947-4921. Fax: 740-947-2918. p. 1945

Ahmad, Basil, Librn, Muslim Education & Welfare Foundation of Canada, 14175 Kindersley Dr, Surrey, BC, V3R 5P6, CANADA. Tel: 604-255-9941. Fax: 604-255-9941. p. 2738

Ahmadi, Narges, Librn, Lee Memorial Health System Library, PO Box 2218, Fort Myers, FL, 33902-2218. Tel: 239-334-5410. Fax: 239-332-6422. p. 446

Ahman, Cindy, Br Mgr, Carroll County Public Library, North Carroll, 2255 Hanover Pike, Greenmount, MD, 21074. Tel: 410-386-4480. Fax: 410-386-4486. p. 1046

Ahmed, Aftab, Info Tech Mgr, Durham County Library, 300 N Roxboro St, Durham, NC, 27701. Tel: 919-560-0100. Fax: 919-560-0137. p. 1788

Ahmed, Khalil, Ref, J Sargeant Reynolds Community College Library, Downtown Campus-Library & Information Services, 700 E Jackson St, 2nd Flr, Richmond, VA, 23219-1543. Tel: 804-523-5211. Fax: 804-786-6200. p. 2488

Ahmed, Rebecca, Libr Tech, VA Medical Center, 1400 Veterans of Foreign Wars Pkwy, West Roxbury, MA, 02132. Tel: 617-323-7700, Ext 35142. Fax: 857-203-5532. p. 1137

Aho, Kristine, Spec Coll & Archives Librn, Duluth Public Library, 520 W Superior St, Duluth, MN, 55802. Tel: 218-730-4209. Fax: 218-723-3815, 218-723-3822. p. 1247

Aho, Mary, Asst Librn, Michigan Department of Corrections, 13924 Wadaga Rd, Baraga, MI, 49908. Tel: 906-353-7070, Ext 1321. Fax: 906-353-7957. p. 1155

Aho, Stacia, Virtual Libr Mgr, Arlington County Department of Libraries, 1015 N Quincy St, Arlington, VA, 22201. Tel: 703-228-5968. Fax: 703-228-3354. p. 2448

Ahola, Scott, Ref Librn, Black Hills State University, 1200 University St, Unit 9676, Spearfish, SD, 57799-9676. Tel: 605-642-6359. Fax: 605-642-6298. p. 2220

Ahola, Scott, Assoc Dir, Black Hills State University, E Y Berry Library Learning Ctr, 1200 University St, Unit 9676, Spearfish, SD, 57799-9676. Tel: 605-642-6359. Fax: 605-642-6298. p. 2973

Ahrens, Callie, Principal Librn, Carlsbad City Library, Library Learning Center, 3368 Eureka Pl, Carlsbad, CA, 92008. Tel: 760-931-4520. Fax: 760-729-8335. p. 132

Ahrens, Carol, Dir, Hicksville Public Library, 169 Jerusalem Ave, Hicksville, NY, 11801. Tel: 516-931-1417. Fax: 516-822-5672. p. 1636

Ahrens, Cheryl, Dir, Arapahoe Public Library, 302 Nebraska Ave, Arapahoe, NE, 68922. Tel: 308-962-7806. Fax: 308-962-3806. p. 1391

Ahrens, Debra, Head of Libr, Free Library of Philadelphia, Oak Lane Branch, 6614 N 12th St, Philadelphia, PA, 19126-3299. Tel: 215-685-2848. Fax: 215-685-2847. p. 2108

Ahrens, Debra, Access Serv, University of Wisconsin-Madison, Business Library, Grainger Hall, Rm 2200, 975 University Ave, Madison, WI, 53706. Tel: 608-262-5935. Fax: 608-262-9001. p. 2608

Ahrens, Jeff, Head, Tech Serv, Round Lake Area Public Library District, 906 Hart Rd, Round Lake, IL, 60073. Tel: 847-546-7060, Ext 134. Fax: 847-546-7104. p. 699

Ahrens, Tracy, Asst Dir, Comfort Public Library, 701 High St, Comfort, TX, 78013. Tel: 830-995-2398. Fax: 830-995-5574. p. 2299

Aicher, Boniface, Librn, Westminster Abbey Library, Seminary of Christ The King, Mission, BC, V2V 4J2, CANADA. Tel: 604-826-8975. p. 2732

Aicher, Teresa, Dir, Belvidere Free Public Library, 301 Second St, Belvidere, NJ, 07823-1517. Tel: 908-475-3941. Fax: 908-475-3893. p. 1471

Aiello, Helen, Ser, Wesleyan University, 252 Church St, Middletown, CT, 06459-3199. Tel: 860-685-3844. Fax: 860-685-2661. p. 352

Aiello, Kira, Tech Serv, New Rochelle Public Library, One Library Plaza, New Rochelle, NY, 10801. Tel: 914-632-7878, Ext 1000. Fax: 914-632-0262. p. 1666

Aiello, Pauline, Ref Librn, Massasoit Community College Library, One Massasoit Blvd, Brockton, MA, 02302. Tel: 508-588-9100, Ext 1948. Fax: 508-427-1265. p. 1071

Aigner, Lois A, Librn, Boonville-Warrick County Public Library, 611 W Main St, Boonville, IN, 47601-1544. Tel: 812-897-1500. Fax: 812-897-1508. p. 729

Aigner, Lorna, Dir, Muscoda Public Library, 206 N Wisconsin Ave, Muscoda, WI, 53569. Tel: 608-739-3182. Fax: 608-739-3183. p. 2623

Aikau, Fredericka P, Libr Tech, Hawaii State Archives, Iolani Palace Grounds, 364 S King St, Honolulu, HI, 96813. Tel: 808-586-0329. Fax: 808-586-0330. p. 561

Aiken, Corine, Libr Mgr, Timberland Regional Library, Vernetta Smith Chehalis Timberland Library, 400 N Market Blvd, Chehalis, WA, 98532. Tel: 360-748-3301. Fax: 360-748-2169. p. 2544

Aiken, Jennie, Asst Librn, Sweet Springs Public Library, 217 Turner St, Sweet Springs, MO, 65351. Tel: 660-335-4314. p. 1368

Aiken, Julian, Circ, Yale University Library, Lillian Goldman Library Yale Law School, 127 Wall St, New Haven, CT, 06511. Tel: 203-432-1600. Fax: 203-432-2112. p. 358

Aiken, Julian, Head, Circ, Wallingford Public Library, 200 N Main St, Wallingford, CT, 06492-3791. Tel: 203-265-6754. Fax: 203-269-5698. p. 373

Aiken, Mike, Regional Mgr, Cobb County Public Library System, Mountain View, 3320 Sandy Plains Rd, Marietta, GA, 30066. Tel: 770-509-2725. Fax: 770-509-2726. p. 543

Ailey, Coneen H, Dir, Parrott-Wood Memorial Library, 3133 W Old Andrew Johnson Hwy, Strawberry Plains, TN, 37871. Tel: 865-933-1311. Fax: 865-932-3718. p. 2266

Aimone, Alan, Ref Librn, United States Military Academy Library, Jefferson Hall Library & Learning Center, 758 Cullum Rd, West Point, NY, 10996. Tel: 845-938-3833. Fax: 845-938-4000. p. 1767

Ain, Terry, YA Serv, Rockville Centre Public Library, 221 N Village Ave, Rockville Centre, NY, 11570. Tel: 516-766-6257. Fax: 516-766-6090. p. 1734

Ainslie, Donna, Circ Supvr, Lake Oswego Public Library, 706 Fourth St, Lake Oswego, OR, 97034-2399. Tel: 503-675-3996. Fax: 503-635-4171. p. 2003

Ainsworth, Donna, Evening Librn, Copiah-Lincoln Community College, 151 Colin Dr, Mendenhall, MS, 39111. Tel: 601-849-0118. Fax: 601-849-0160. p. 1308

Ainsworth, Sally, County Librn, Tehama County Library, 645 Madison St, Red Bluff, CA, 96080-3383. Tel: 530-527-0607. Fax: 530-527-1562. p. 214

Ainsworth, Sally, County Librn, Tehama County Library, Corning Branch, 740 Third St, Corning, CA, 96021-2517. Tel: 530-824-7050. Fax: 530-824-7051. p. 214

Ainsworth-Mahaney, Lee, Dir, Aurora Town Public Library, 550 Main St, East Aurora, NY, 14052. Tel: 716-652-4440. Fax: 716-655-5875. p. 1616

Airoldi, Joan, Dir, Whatcom County Library System, 5205 Northwest Dr, Bellingham, WA, 98226-9050. Tel: 360-384-3150, Ext 201. Fax: 360-384-4947. p. 2509

Airoldi, Melissa, Automation Syst Adminr, Austin Community College, 1212 Rio Grande, Austin, TX, 78701. Tel: 512-223-8683. Fax: 512-223-8611. p. 2278

Airth-Kindree, Martha, Librn, Mile Bluff Medical Center, 1050 Division St, Mauston, WI, 53948. Tel: 608-847-6161. Fax: 608-847-6017. p. 2613

Aitchison, Jada, Acq, Ser, University of Arkansas at Little Rock, Pulaski County Law Library, 1203 McMath Ave, Little Rock, AR, 72202-5142. Tel: 501-324-9444. Fax: 501-324-9447. p. 107

Aitken, Elizabeth, Librn, Calgary Health Region, 7007 14th St SW, Calgary, AB, T2V 1P9, CANADA. Tel: 403-943-3373. Fax: 403-943-3486. p. 2688

Aitken, Elizabeth, Librn, Rock View Gen Hospital Knowlege Ctr, University of Calgary Library, Health Sciences Library, Health Sci Ctr, 3330 Hospital Dr NW, Calgary, AB, T2N 4N1, CANADA. Tel: 403-943-3488. Fax: 403-210-9847. p. 2693

Aitken, Laurie, Ref, Islip Public Library, 71 Monell Ave, Islip, NY, 11751-3999. Tel: 631-581-5933. Fax: 631-277-8429. p. 1641

Aitken, Nancy, Acq, Vermont Technical College, Main St, Randolph Center, VT, 05061. Tel: 802-728-1237. Fax: 802-728-1506. p. 2433

Ajala, Mabel, Dir, Ch Serv, Passaic Public Library, 195 Gregory Ave, Passaic, NJ, 07055. Tel: 973-779-0474. Fax: 973-779-0889. p. 1518

Akaka, Puanani, Librn, Chaminade University of Honolulu, 3140 Waialae Ave, Honolulu, HI, 96816-1578. Tel: 808-735-4725. Fax: 808-735-4891. p. 560

Akao, Pamela, Br Mgr, Hawaii State Public Library System, Thelma Parker Memorial Public & School Library, 67-1209 Mamalahoa Hwy, Kamuela, HI, 96743-8429. Tel: 808-887-6067. Fax: 808-887-6066. p. 563

Aked, Michael, Acq, Owens Community College Library, 30335 Oregon Rd, Perrysburg, OH, 43551. Tel: 567-661-7031. Fax: 567-661-7021. p. 1929

Aker, Julia, Dir, Jackson County Public Library, 303 W Second St, Seymour, IN, 47274-2147. Tel: 812-522-3412, Ext 223. Fax: 812-522-5456. p. 777

Akerman, Patricia, Librn, Saint Cloud Technical College Library, 1540 Northway Dr, Saint Cloud, MN, 56303-1240. Tel: 320-308-5966. Fax: 320-308-5960. p. 1276

Akers, Carla, Mgr, Charlestown-Clark County Public Library, Borden Branch, 117 W Main St, Borden, IN, 47106. Tel: 812-967-3440. Fax: 812-967-3440. p. 731

Akers, Cynthia, Head, Instrul Serv, Emporia State University, 1200 Commercial St, Box 4051, Emporia, KS, 66801. Tel: 620-341-5480. Fax: 620-341-5997. p. 866

Akers, Cynthia, Chair, Kansas Regents Library Database Consortium, c/o Emporia State University, William Allen White Library, 1200 Commercial St, Emporia, KS, 66801. Tel: 620-341-5480. p. 2943

Akers, Judith, Dir, First Presbyterian Church, 1427 Chicago Ave, Evanston, IL, 60201. Tel: 847-864-1472. Fax: 847-864-1494. p. 643

Akes, Pat, Ch, Friendswood Public Library, 416 S Friendswood Dr, Friendswood, TX, 77546-3897. Tel: 281-482-7135. Fax: 281-482-2685. p. 2325

Akhter, Khaver, Asst Admin, Saddleback College, 28000 Marguerite Pkwy, Mission Viejo, CA, 92692. Tel: 949-582-4516. Fax: 949-364-0284. p. 187

Aki, Maxine, Br Mgr, Hawaii State Public Library System, Keaau Public & School Library, 16-571 Keaau-Pahoa Rd, Keaau, HI, 96749-8106. Tel: 808-982-4281. Fax: 808-982-4242. p. 562

Akinniyi, Angela Reaux, Dir, Libr Serv, Louisiana Association of Business & Industry Library, 3113 Valley Creek Dr, Baton Rouge, LA, 70808. Tel: 225-928-5388. Fax: 225-929-6054. p. 943

Akins, Diana F, Chief, Libr Serv, Bay Pines Veterans Affairs Healthcare System, 10000 Bay Pines Blvd, Bay Pines, FL, 33744. Tel: 727-398-6561. Fax: 727-398-9367. p. 427

Akins, John, Librn, Victor Valley Community College Library, 18422 Bear Valley Rd, Victorville, CA, 92395-5850. Tel: 760-245-4271, Ext 2262. Fax: 760-245-4373. p. 280

Akiti, Andrea, Br Mgr, Atlanta-Fulton Public Library System, Stewart-Lakewood Library, 2893 Lakewood Ave SW, Atlanta, GA, 30315. Tel: 404-762-4054. Fax: 404-762-4056. p. 512

Akkerman, Karen, Br Mgr, Harris County Public Library, Clear Lake City-County Freeman Branch, 16616 Diana Lane, Houston, TX, 77062. Tel: 281-488-1906. Fax: 281-286-3931. p. 2335

Aklus, Sue, AV, Moore County Library, 101 Saunders St, Carthage, NC, 28327. Tel: 910-947-5335. Fax: 910-947-3660. p. 1779

Akram, Zakkiyya, Actg Sr Librn, Los Angeles Public Library System, Wilshire, 149 N Saint Andrew Pl, Los Angeles, CA, 90004. Tel: 323-957-4550. Fax: 323-957-4555. p. 174

Akulich, Helen, Head Librn, Holland & Knight LLP, 31 W 52nd St, New York, NY, 10019. Tel: 212-513-3581. Fax: 212-385-9010. p. 1681

Al, Kearson, Librn, First Baptist Church, 99 N Main St, Marion, NC, 28752. Tel: 828-652-6030. Fax: 828-659-9111. p. 1808

Al-Buhaisi, Dawn, Librn, South University, 9801 Belvedere Rd, Royal Palm Beach, FL, 33411-3640. Tel: 561-273-6401. Fax: 561-273-6420. p. 485

Al-Shabibi, Amy, Tech Mgr, Champaign Public Library, 200 W Green St, Champaign, IL, 61820-5193. Tel: 217-403-2050. Fax: 217-403-2053. p. 602

Alabre, Cheryl, Ser, Princeton University, Biology, Fine Hall Library, McDonnell Hall, One Washington Ave, Princeton, NJ, 08544. Tel: 609-258-3235. Fax: 609-258-2627. p. 1523

Alan, Robert, Head of Ser & Acq Serv, Pennsylvania State University Libraries, 510 Paterno Library, University Park, PA, 16802. Tel: 814-865-0401. Fax: 814-865-3665. p. 2148

Alaniz, B J, Librn Dir, Duval County-San Diego Public Library, 315 S Dr Dunlap St, San Diego, TX, 78384. Tel: 361-279-8201. Fax: 361-279-8212. p. 2384

Alarcon, Myra, Librn, Wyle Laboratories, 128 Maryland St, El Segundo, CA, 90245-4100. Tel: 310-322-1763, Ext 6730. Fax: 310-322-9799. p. 146

Alaverdova, Liana, Neighborhood Librn Supvr, Brooklyn Public Library, Ryder, 5902 23rd Ave, Brooklyn, NY, 11204. Tel: 718-331-2962. Fax: 718-331-3445. p. 1592

Albacete, M J, Exec Dir, Canton Museum of Art Library, 1001 Market Ave N, Canton, OH, 44702. Tel: 330-453-7666. Fax: 330-453-1034. p. 1863

Albair, Catherine, Dir, Middlesex County Adult Correction Center Library, Rte 130, Apple Orchard Lane, North Brunswick, NJ, 08902. Tel: 732-297-3636, Ext 6224. p. 1514

Albanese, Holly, Dir, Flagler County Public Library, 2500 Palm Coast Pkwy NW, Palm Coast, FL, 32137. Tel: 904-446-6764. Fax: 386-446-6773. p. 479

Albano, Carol, Librn Dir, Harborfields Public Library, 31 Broadway, Greenlawn, NY, 11740-1382. Tel: 631-757-4200. Fax: 631-757-7216. p. 1631

Albarelli, Gary R, Dir, Florida Institute of Phosphate Research, 1855 W Main St, Bartow, FL, 33830-4338. Tel: 863-534-7160. Fax: 863-534-7165. p. 426

Albarracin, Ignacio, Mgr, San Antonio Public Library, Cortez, 2803 Hunter Blvd, San Antonio, TX, 78224. Tel: 210-922-7372. Fax: 210-932-1495. p. 2382

Albaugh, Carrie, Asst Librn, Mechanicsville Public Library, 218 E First St, Mechanicsville, IA, 52306. Tel: 563-432-7135. Fax: 563-432-7135. p. 831

Albee, Deborah, Circ Supvr, Fort Madison Public Library, 1920 Avenue E, Fort Madison, IA, 52627. Tel: 319-372-5721. Fax: 319-372-5726. p. 817

Albee, Tina Maura, Supvr, Coll Develop, West Palm Beach Public Library, 411 Clematis St, West Palm Beach, FL, 33401. Tel: 561-868-7765. Fax: 561-868-7706. p. 504

Alben, Jonah, Librn, Wyoming Free Library, 358 Wyoming Ave, Wyoming, PA, 18644-1822. Tel: 570-693-1364. Fax: 570-693-0189. p. 2159

Alberico, Ralph, Dean of Libr & Educ Tech, James Madison University Libraries & Educational Technologies, 800 S Main St, Harrisonburg, VA, 22807-0001. Tel: 540-568-3828. Fax: 540-568-6339. p. 2470

Albers, Jan, Exec Dir, The Stewart-Swift Research Center at the Henry Sheldon Museum of Vermont History, One Park St, Middlebury, VT, 05753. Tel: 802-388-2117. Fax: 802-388-2112. p. 2428

Albers, Kate, Actg Mgr, Children's Programmer, Upper Arlington Public Library, Miller Park Branch, 1901 Arlington Ave, Upper Arlington, OH, 43212. Tel: 614-488-5710. Fax: 614-487-2032. p. 1891

Albers, Marian, Dir, Mascoutah Public Library, Three W Church St, Mascoutah, IL, 62258. Tel: 618-566-2562. Fax: 618-566-2563. p. 671

Albert, Asita, Acq, Cat, University of Maine at Fort Kent, 23 University Dr, Fort Kent, ME, 04743. Tel: 207-834-7525. Fax: 207-834-7518. p. 986

Albert, Christina, Asst Librn, Eldon Public Library, 608 W Elm St, Eldon, IA, 52554. Tel: 641-652-7517. Fax: 641-652-7517. p. 813

Albert, Julie, Info Spec, Columbus Dispatch Editorial Library, 34 S Third St, Columbus, OH, 43215. Tel: albertj@dispatch.com. Fax: 614-469-6165. p. 1884

Albert, Karen M, Dir, Philadelphia University, 4201 Henry Ave, Philadelphia, PA, 19144-5497. Tel: 215-951-2847. Fax: 215-951-2574. p. 2115

Albert, Paul, Assoc Dir, Res Digital Serv, Cornell University Library, The Samuel J Wood Library & The C V Starr Biomedical Information Center, 1300 York Ave, C115, Box 67, New York, NY, 10065-4896. Tel: 212-746-6050. Fax: 212-746-6494. p. 1642

Albert, Renea, Res Librn, Rolla A Clymer Research Library, 383 E Central, El Dorado, KS, 67042. Tel: 316-321-9333. Fax: 316-321-3619. p. 865

Albert, Sharon, Cat Mgr, Linden Free Public Library, 31 E Henry St, Linden, NJ, 07036. Tel: 908-298-3830. Fax: 908-486-2636. p. 1495

Alberts, Cathy, Dir, River Grove Public Library District, 8638 W Grand Ave, River Grove, IL, 60171. Tel: 708-453-4484. Fax: 708-453-4517. p. 694

Alberts, Fay, Librn, Parkland Regional Library, Preeceville Branch, PO Box 663, Preeceville, SK, S0A 3B0, CANADA. Tel: 306-547-3444. p. 2932

Albertson, Chris, City Librn, Tyler Public Library, 201 S College Ave, Tyler, TX, 75702-7381. Tel: 903-593-7323. Fax: 903-531-1329. p. 2394

Albertson, Dan, Asst Prof, University of Alabama, 514 Main Library, Tuscaloosa, AL, 35487. Tel: 205-348-4610. Fax: 205-348-3746. p. 2961

Albertson, Linda, Librn, Neosho Public Library, Hwy 67, Neosho, WI, 53059. Tel: 920-625-3086. p. 2625

Albertson, Lois, Mgr, Staff Develop, SEFLIN - Southeast Florida Library Information Network, Inc, Wimberly Library, Office 452, Florida Atlantic University, 777 Glades Rd, Boca Raton, FL, 33431. Tel: 561-208-0984. Fax: 561-208-0995. p. 2940

Albertson, Luci, Dir, Ch Serv, Bedford Public Library, Three Meetinghouse Rd, Bedford, NH, 03110-5406. Tel: 603-472-2300, 603-472-3023. Fax: 603-472-2978. p. 1438

Albertz, Sally, Dir, Fond du Lac County Historical Society, Blakely Museum, 336 Old Pioneer Rd, Fond du Lac, WI, 54935-6126. Tel: 920-922-0991. p. 2592

Albiges, Jeanine, Ch, Boyertown Community Library, 29 E Philadelphia Ave, Boyertown, PA, 19512-1124. Tel: 610-369-0496. Fax: 610-369-0542. p. 2036

Albin, Tom, Dean, Upper Room Devotional Library, 1908 Grand Ave, Nashville, TN, 37212. Tel: 615-340-7110. Fax: 615-340-7257. p. 2260

Albrecht, Amy, Pub Serv, McKinney Memorial Public Library, 101 E Hunt St, McKinney, TX, 75069. Tel: 972-547-7323. Fax: 972-542-0868. p. 2361

Albrecht, Cheryl, Assoc Dean, Libr Serv, University of Cincinnati Libraries, PO Box 210033, Cincinnati, OH, 45221-0033. Tel: 513-556-1784. Fax: 513-556-0325. p. 1874

Albrecht, Debbie, Exec Dir, Lansing Public Library, 2750 Indiana Ave, Lansing, IL, 60438. Tel: 708-474-2447, Ext 100. Fax: 708-474-9466. p. 664

Albrecht, Rhonda Kay, Bus Mgr, Rushville Public Library, 130 W Third St, Rushville, IN, 46173-1899. Tel: 765-932-3496. Fax: 765-932-4528. p. 776

Albrecht, Susan, Acq Mgr, Wabash College, PO Box 352, Crawfordsville, IN, 47933. Tel: 765-361-6216. Fax: 765-361-6295. p. 734

Albrecht, Tim, Circ, Normandale Community College Library, 9700 France Ave S, Bloomington, MN, 55431. Tel: 952-487-8444. Fax: 952-487-8101. p. 1242

Albrecht, Val, Librn, McLean-Mercer Regional Library, Hazen Branch, Main St, Hazen, ND, 58545. Tel: 701-748-2977. p. 1848

Albright, Eric, Dir, Tufts University, 145 Harrison Ave, Boston, MA, 02111-1843. Fax: 617-636-4039. p. 1068

Albright, Hyesoo, Circ Supvr, Centralia College, 600 Centralia College Blvd, Centralia, WA, 98531. Tel: 360-736-9391, Ext 242. Fax: 360-330-7502. p. 2511

Albright, Janet, Assoc Dean, Libr Serv, Shasta College Library, 11555 Old Oregon Trail, Redding, CA, 96003-7692. Tel: 530-242-7555. p. 214

Albright, Julie, Youth Serv, Ventura County Library, Ojai Library, 111 E Ojai Ave, Ojai, CA, 93023. Tel: 805-646-1639. Fax: 805-646-4693. p. 280

Albright, Katie, Librn Dir, Rossland Public Library Association, 2180 Columbia Ave, Rossland, BC, V0G 1Y0, CANADA. Tel: 250-362-7611. Fax: 250-362-7138. p. 2737

Albright, Margaret, ILL, Rodman Public Library, 215 E Broadway St, Alliance, OH, 44601-2694. Tel: 330-821-2665. Fax: 330-821-5053. p. 1854

Albright, Wava, Librn, Joyce Public Library, 9490 W State Rd 120, Orland, IN, 46776-6329. Tel: 260-829-6329. p. 771

Albritton, Henry L, Head, Libr Syst, Norfolk State University Library, 700 Park Ave, Norfolk, VA, 23504-8010. Tel: 757-823-8517. Fax: 757-823-2431. p. 2482

Albritton, Rosie, Dr, Dir, Libr Serv, Prairie View A&M University, PO Box 519, MS 1040, Prairie View, TX, 77446-0519. Tel: 936-261-1500. Fax: 936-261-1539. p. 2372

Albro, Mary, Assoc Librn, Adult Learning Serv, Hartford Public Library, 500 Main St, Hartford, CT, 06103-3075. Tel: 860-695-6284. Fax: 860-722-6900. p. 346

Albury, Karen, Dep Dir, Westerville Public Library, 126 S State St, Westerville, OH, 43081-2095. Tel: 614-882-7277, Ext 2168. Fax: 614-882-5369. p. 1946

Alcade, Carmen, Health Sci Librn, Humber River Regional Hospital, 200 Church St, Weston, ON, M9N 1N8, CANADA. Tel: 416-243-4597. Fax: 416-243-4236. p. 2870

Alcala, Rebecca, Br Mgr, San Francisco Public Library, Excelsior Branch Library, 4400 Mission St (at Cotter), San Francisco, CA, 94112-1927. Tel: 415-355-2868. Fax: 415-337-4738. p. 246

Alcamo, Thomas, Curator, Aurora Historical Society, 363 Oakwood Ave, East Aurora, NY, 14052-2319. Tel: 716-655-1321. p. 1616

Alcantara, Agnes, Librn, Blaney McMurtry LLP, Maritime Life Tower, Two Queen St E, Ste 1500, Toronto, ON, M5C 3G5, CANADA. Tel: 416-593-1221, Ext 3550. Fax: 416-593-5437. p. 2850

Alcock, Arlette, Libr Tech, First Nations University of Canada, Northern Campus Library, 1301 Central Ave, Prince Albert, SK, S6V 4W1, CANADA. Tel: 306-765-3333, Ext 7430. Fax: 306-765-3330. p. 2922

Alcock, Crystal, Ch, Kenora Public Library, 24 Main St S, Kenora, ON, P9N 1S7, CANADA. Tel: 807-467-2081. Fax: 807-467-2085. p. 2812

Alcock, Tara, Librn, Petersburg Public Library, 12 Nordic Dr, Petersburg, AK, 99833. Tel: 907-772-3349. Fax: 907-772-3759. p. 52

Alcook, Barb, Librn, Huron Law Association, One The Square, Goderich, ON, N7A 1M2, CANADA. Tel: 519-524-7962. Fax: 519-524-1065. p. 2806

Alcorn, Barbara, Libr Mgr, Albert-Westmorland-Kent Regional Library, Hillsborough Public, 2849 Main St, Unit 2, Hillsborough, NB, E4H 2X7, CANADA. Tel: 506-734-3722. Fax: 506-734-3711. p. 2765

Alcorn, Cynthia, Librn, Grand Lodge of Masons in Massachusetts, 186 Tremont St, Boston, MA, 02111. Tel: 617-426-6040, Ext 4221. Fax: 617-426-6115. p. 1061

Alcorn, JoAnne, Ser Librn, Brazosport College Library, 500 College Dr, Lake Jackson, TX, 77566. Tel: 979-230-3259. Fax: 979-230-3185. p. 2352

Alcorn, Patricia, Ref Librn, United States Army, Fort Stewart Main Post Library, 316 Lindquist Rd, Fort Stewart, GA, 31314-5126. Tel: 912-767-2260, 912-767-2828. Fax: 912-767-3794. p. 533

Alcorn, Shodie, Ch, Bedford Free Library, On the Village Green, Bedford, NY, 10506. Tel: 914-234-3570. Fax: 914-234-0546. p. 1579

Alcott, Martha, Asst Libr Dir, Head, Ref Serv, Chappaqua Public Library, 195 S Greeley Ave, Chappaqua, NY, 10514. Tel: 914-238-4779. Fax: 914-238-3597. p. 1605

Aldahl, Sharon, Br Mgr, La Crosse County Library, Hazel Brown Leicht Memorial Library, 201 Neshonoc Rd, West Salem, WI, 54669. Tel: 608-786-1505. Fax: 608-786-0036. p. 2598

Aldana, Lynda, Head, Tech Serv, University of Maryland, Baltimore County, 1000 Hilltop Circle, Baltimore, MD, 21250. Tel: 410-455-2356. Fax: 410-455-1598. p. 1018

Alder, Connie, Dir, Manti Public Library, Two S Main St, Manti, UT, 84642-1349. Tel: 435-835-2201. Fax: 435-835-2202. p. 2407

Alder, Nancy, ILL, Brigham Young University, Harold B Lee Library, 2060 HBLL, Provo, UT, 84602. Tel: 801-422-2927. Fax: 801-422-0466. p. 2411

Alder, Sheridan Lynne, Librn, Agriculture & Agri-Food Canada, 4902 Victorian Ave N, Vineland Station, ON, L0R 2E0, CANADA. Tel: 905-562-4113, Ext 212. Fax: 905-562-4335. p. 2868

Alderdice, Sally, Dir, Claverack Free Library, 629 Rte 23B, Claverack, NY, 12513. Tel: 518-851-7120. Fax: 518-851-7120. p. 1607

Alderfer, Amy, Cat, United States Holocaust Memorial Museum Library, 100 Raoul Wallenberg Pl SW, Washington, DC, 20024. Tel: 202-479-9717. Fax: 202-479-9726. p. 420

Alderfer, Joel D, Librn, Mennonite Historians of Eastern Pennsylvania, 565 Yoder Rd, Harleysville, PA, 19438. Tel: 215-256-3020. Fax: 215-256-3023. p. 2064

Alderman, Barbara, Librn, Brevard Community College, 250 Community College Pkwy, Palm Bay, FL, 32909. Tel: 321-433-7997. Fax: 321-433-5309. p. 479

Alderman, Marlene, Libr Dir, Boston University Libraries, Pappas Law Library, 765 Commonwealth Ave, Boston, MA, 02215. Tel: 617-353-8870. Fax: 617-353-5995. p. 1058

Alderman, Nanette, Mgr, Salt Lake County Library Services, West Jordan Branch, 1970 W 7800 South, West Jordan, UT, 84088-4025. Tel: 801-944-7633. Fax: 801-562-8761. p. 2414

Alderman, Patricia, Chief, Info Archit Div, US Department of Defense, Fort McNair, Marshall Hall, Washington, DC, 20319-5066. Tel: 202-685-3511. Fax: 202-685-3733. p. 418

Alderson, Craig, Operations Mgr, University of California, Berkeley, Social Welfare, 227 Haviland Hall, Berkeley, CA, 94720-6000. Tel: 510-642-4432. Fax: 510-643-1476. p. 128

Alderson, Julia, Librn, Oklahoma Library for the Blind & Physically Handicapped, 300 NE 18th St, Oklahoma City, OK, 73105. Tel: 405-521-3514. Fax: 405-521-4582. p. 1974

Aldous, Mary, Librn, United States Navy, Naval Health Research Center, Wilkins Biomedical Library, Gate 4, Barracks Bldg 333, McClelland & Patterson Rds, San Diego, CA, 92152. Tel: 619-553-8425. Fax: 619-553-0213. p. 238

Aldred, Richard, Cat Librn, Haverford College, 370 Lancaster Ave, Haverford, PA, 19041-1392. Tel: 610-896-1175. Fax: 610-896-1102. p. 2067

Aldred, Susan, Librn, Annapolis Valley Regional Library, Middleton Branch, 45 Gates Ave, Middleton, NS, B0S 1P0, CANADA. Tel: 902-825-4835. p. 2778

Aldrich, Alan, Instruction Librn, University of South Dakota, 414 E Clark St, Vermillion, SD, 57069. Tel: 605-677-5371. Fax: 605-677-6834. p. 2220

Aldrich, Duncan, Media & Data Serv, University of Nevada-Reno, 1664 N Virginia St, Mailstop 0322, Reno, NV, 89557-0322. Tel: 775-682-5669. Fax: 775-784-4529. p. 1433

Aldrich, Elaine, Librn, Cooley Dickinson Hospital, 30 Locust St, Northampton, MA, 01060. Tel: 413-582-2291. Fax: 413-582-2985. p. 1113

Aldrich, Jane, Archivist, South Carolina Historical Society Library, Fireproof Bldg, 100 Meeting St, Charleston, SC, 29401-2299. Tel: 843-723-3225, Ext 21. Fax: 843-723-8584. p. 2185

Aldrich, Kathy, Prog Coordr, Big Bend Community College Library, 7662 Chanute St, Moses Lake, WA, 98837. Tel: 509-793-2350. Fax: 509-762-2402. p. 2521

Aldrich, Mark, Media Spec, Garner Correctional Institution Library, 50 Nunnawauk Rd, Newtown, CT, 06470. Tel: 203-270-2897. Fax: 203-270-1826. p. 361

Aldrich, Michael, Instrul Serv Librn, Irvine Sullivan Ingram Library, University of West Georgia, 1601 Maple St, Carrollton, GA, 30118. Tel: 678-839-6498. Fax: 678-839-6511. p. 523

Aldrich, Michael, Univ Librn, Brigham Young University-Hawaii, 55-220 Kulanui St, BYU-Hawaii, No 1966, Laie, HI, 96762-1294. Tel: 808-675-3851. Fax: 808-675-3877. p. 567

Aldrich, Nina, Libr Tech II, Colorado Department of Corrections, Skyline Correctional Center Library, PO Box 300, Canon City, CO, 81215. Tel: 719-269-5420, Ext 3351. Fax: 719-269-5404. p. 294

Aldrich, Stacey A, State Librn, California State Library, 900 N St, Sacramento, CA, 95814. Tel: 916-654-0188. Fax: 916-376-5310. p. 223

Aldridge, Amity, Dir, Weathersfield Proctor Library, 5181 Rte 5, Ascutney, VT, 05030. Tel: 802-674-2863. p. 2417

Aldridge, Betsy, Sr Res Spec, Paccar, Inc, 12479 Farm to Market Rd, Mount Vernon, WA, 98273. Tel: 360-757-5234. Fax: 360-757-5201. p. 2521

Aleba, Juanita, Dir, Mary Wilcox Memorial Library, 2630 Main St, Whitney Point, NY, 13862. Tel: 607-692-3159. Fax: 607-692-3159. p. 1769

Aleccia, Jan, Dir, The Joint Commision, One Renaissance Blvd, Oakbrook Terrace, IL, 60181. Tel: 630-792-5474. Fax: 630-792-4474. p. 684

Alef, Julie, Br Mgr, Saint Clair County Library System, Saint Clair Public, 310 S Second St, Saint Clair, MI, 48079. Tel: 810-329-3951. Fax: 810-329-7142. p. 1220

Alegria, Sara, Dr, Assoc Dir, Miami Dade College, North Campus Learning Resources, 11380 NW 27th Ave, Miami, FL, 33167. Tel: 305-237-1777. Fax: 305-237-8276. p. 466

Aleksandravicius, Regina, Mgr, Ch Serv, Wethersfield Public Library, 515 Silas Deane Hwy, Wethersfield, CT, 06109. Tel: 860-529-2665. Fax: 860-257-2822. p. 378

Aleksic, Olha, Bibliographer, Harvard Library, Ukrainian Research Institute Reference Library, 34 Kirkland St, Cambridge, MA, 02138. Tel: 617-496-5891. Fax: 617-495-8097. p. 1077

Aleman, Karla, Distance Instruction Librn, Morehead State University, 150 University Blvd, Morehead, KY, 40351. Tel: 606-783-5114. Fax: 606-783-5037. p. 929

Aleman, Stephanie, Dir, President Millard Fillmore Library, 25 S 100 W, Fillmore, UT, 84631. Tel: 435-743-5314. Fax: 435-743-6710. p. 2406

Alen, Louis, Br Mgr, Memphis Public Library, East Shelby Branch, 7200 E Shelby Dr, Memphis, TN, 38125. Tel: 901-751-7360. p. 2250

Aleshire, Anne, Fiscal Officer, University of Alaska Fairbanks, 310 Tanana Dr, Fairbanks, AK, 99775. Tel: 907-474-6696. Fax: 907-474-6841. p. 48

Alessi, Paula, Librn, Courier Library, 701 W Sandusky St, Findlay, OH, 45840-2325. Tel: 419-422-5151. Fax: 419-427-8480. p. 1899

Alewine, Michael, Distance Educ & Outreach Librn, University of North Carolina at Pembroke, Faculty Row, Pembroke, NC, 28372. Tel: 910-521-6516. Fax: 910-521-6547. p. 1814

Alex, Dvornyak, Sr Web Developer, University of Toronto Libraries, Faculty of Information Inforum, 140 Saint George St, 4th Flr, Toronto, ON, M5S 3G6, CANADA. Tel: 416-978-6120. Fax: 416-978-5769. p. 2866

Alexander, Ann, Br Mgr, Johnson County Public Library, 401 State St, Franklin, IN, 46131-2545. Tel: 317-738-2833. Fax: 317-738-9635. p. 744

Alexander, Barbara, Br Mgr, Stanislaus County Free Library, Newman Branch, 1305 Kern St, Newman, CA, 95360-1603. Tel: 209-862-2010. Fax: 209-862-2010. p. 188

Alexander, Ben, Asst Prof, Queens College of the City University of New York, Benjamin Rosenthal Library, Rm 254, 65-30 Kissena Blvd, Flushing, NY, 11367. Tel: 718-997-3790. Fax: 718-997-3797. p. 2970

Alexander, Cari, Music & Media Librn, Texas Christian University, 2913 Lowden St, TCU Box 298400, Fort Worth, TX, 76129. Tel: 817-257-7106. Fax: 817-257-7282. p. 2323

Alexander, Carita, Pharm Librn, University of Louisiana at Monroe Library, 700 University Ave, Monroe, LA, 71209-0720. Tel: 318-342-3042. Fax: 318-342-1075. p. 958

Alexander, Channette, Librn, University of Kansas Libraries, Spahr Engineering Library, 1532 W 15th St, Lawrence, KS, 66045-7611. Tel: 785-864-3866. Fax: 785-864-5755. p. 878

Alexander, Cherry, Dir, Tallahassee Community College Library, 444 Appleyard Dr, Tallahassee, FL, 32304-2895. Tel: 850-201-8396. Fax: 850-201-8380. p. 495

Alexander, David, Digital Access Mgr, Librn, University of South Dakota, 414 E Clark St, Vermillion, SD, 57069. Tel: 605-677-5371. Fax: 605-677-6834. p. 2220

Alexander, Dennice B, Admin Librn, Arkansas Department of Correction Library System, 6814 Princeton Pike, Pine Bluff, AR, 71611. Tel: 870-267-6277. Fax: 870-267-6363. p. 112

Alexander, Donna M, Librn, Saint Mary's Regional Medical Center, 235 W Sixth St, Reno, NV, 89520-0108. Tel: 775-770-3108. Fax: 775-770-3685. p. 1432

Alexander, Donna S, Head, ILL, Purchasing, Blue Ridge Community College, One College Lane, Weyers Cave, VA, 24486. Tel: 540-453-2247. Fax: 540-234-9598. p. 2502

Alexander, Gail, Librn, Centennial College of Applied Arts & Technology, Centre for Creative Communications Library, 951 Carlaw Ave, Toronto, ON, M4K 3M2, CANADA. Tel: 416-289-5000, Ext 8600. Fax: 416-289-5118. p. 2840

Alexander, Gail, Librn, Centennial College of Applied Arts & Technology, Morningside Campus Library, 755 Morningside Ave, Rm 160, Scarborough, ON, M1C 5J9, CANADA. Tel: 416-289-5000, Ext 8000. Fax: 416-289-5156. p. 2840

Alexander, Gary, Coll Mgt, University of Denver, Westminster Law Library, 2255 E Evans Ave, Denver, CO, 80208. Tel: 303-871-6188. Fax: 303-871-6999. p. 304

Alexander, Gwen, Dean, Emporia State University, 1200 Commercial St, Campus Box 4025, Emporia, KS, 66801-4025. Tel: 800-552-4770, Ext 5203. Fax: 620-341-5233. p. 2965

Alexander, Janet, Access Serv, Sarah Lawrence College, One Mead Way, Bronxville, NY, 10708. Tel: 914-395-2432. Fax: 914-395-2473. p. 1588

Alexander, Janet, Archivist, Ref, Widener University, One University Pl, Chester, PA, 19013-5792. Tel: 610-449-4591. Fax: 610-499-4588. p. 2044

Alexander, Jayne, Br Mgr, Great Neck Library, Parkville, Ten Campbell St, New Hyde Park, NY, 11040. Tel: 516-466-8055, Ext 235. Fax: 516-437-1929. p. 1630

Alexander, Jean, Head, Ref, Carnegie Mellon University, Hunt Library, 4909 Frew St, Pittsburgh, PA, 15213-3890. Tel: 412-268-6809. Fax: 412-268-2793. p. 2123

Alexander, Jeannie, Br Librn, Bucks County Free Library, Yardley-Makefield Branch, 1080 Edgewood Rd, Yardley, PA, 19067-1648. Tel: 215-493-9020. Fax: 215-493-0279. p. 2050

Alexander, Jennie, Dir, Mount Zion District Library, 115 W Main, Mount Zion, IL, 62549. Tel: 217-864-3622. Fax: 217-864-5708. p. 678

Alexander, Jessica, Ref Serv, South Texas College of Law, 1303 San Jacinto St, Houston, TX, 77002-7000. Tel: 713-646-1711. Fax: 713-659-2217. p. 2342

Alexander, Johanna, Librn, Ref Serv Coordr, California State University, 9001 Stockdale Hwy, Bakersfield, CA, 93311-1022. Tel: 661-664-3256. Fax: 661-654-3238. p. 123

Alexander, Karen, Circ Librn, Luther Seminary Library, Gullixson Hall, 2375 Como Ave, Saint Paul, MN, 55108. Tel: 651-641-3301. Fax: 651-641-3280. p. 1278

Alexander, Karla, Dir of Libr Serv, University of Saint Francis, 201 Pope John Paul II Ctr, 2701 Spring St, Fort Wayne, IN, 46808. Tel: 260-399-7700, Ext 6060. Fax: 260-399-8166. p. 742

Alexander, Kathy, Tech Serv, Cleveland County Library System, 104 Howie Dr, Shelby, NC, 28150. Tel: 704-487-9069. Fax: 704-487-4856. p. 1823

Alexander, Kimberly, PhD, Curator, Strawbery Banke, Inc, 454 Court St, Portsmouth, NH, 03802-4603. Tel: 603-422-7526. Fax: 603-422-7527, 603-433-1115. p. 1463

Alexander, Laurie, Assoc Univ Librn, Learning & Teaching, University of Michigan, 818 Hatcher Graduate Library, Ann Arbor, MI, 48109-1205. Tel: 734-764-9356. Fax: 734-763-5080. p. 1152

Alexander, Laurie, Dir, University of Michigan, Shapiro Undergraduate Library, 919 S University Ave, Ann Arbor, MI, 48109-1185. Tel: 734-764-7490. Fax: 734-764-6849. p. 1153

Alexander, Laurie, Interim Head, Ref & Instruction, University of Michigan, Harlan Hatcher Graduate Library, 209 Hatcher N, 920 N University, Ann Arbor, MI, 48109-1205. Tel: 734-763-1539. p. 1153

Alexander, Lea Ann, Spec Coll Librn, Henderson State University, 1100 Henderson, Arkadelphia, AR, 71999-0001. Tel: 870-230-5258. Fax: 870-230-5365. p. 93

Alexander, Linda, Info Serv, Old Lyme, Two Library Lane, Old Lyme, CT, 06371. Tel: 860-434-1684. Fax: 860-434-9547. p. 363

Alexander, Linda, Instr, University of South Florida, 4202 Fowler Ave, CIS 1040, Tampa, FL, 33620-7800. Tel: 813-974-3520. p. 2964

Alexander, Marcia M, Ser Coll Mgr & Acq, Centenary College of Louisiana, 2834 Woodlawn St, Shreveport, LA, 71104-3335. Tel: 318-869-5047. Fax: 318-869-5004. p. 967

Alexander, Margaret, Veterinary Med Librn, Tuskegee University, Hollis Burke Frissell Bldg, 1200 W Old Montgomery Rd, Tuskegee, AL, 36088. Tel: 334-727-8780. Fax: 334-727-8442. p. 39

Alexander, Margaret, Librn, Santa Fe Institute Library, 1399 Hyde Park Rd, Santa Fe, NM, 87501. Tel: 505-946-2707. Fax: 505-982-0565. p. 1563

Alexander, Michael, Br Mgr, Harrison County Library System, Gulfport Library, 1708 25th Ave, Gulfport, MS, 39501. Tel: 228-871-7171. Fax: 228-871-7067. p. 1299

Alexander, Rebecca, Libr Spec, San Francisco Art Institute, 800 Chestnut St, San Francisco, CA, 94133. Tel: 415-749-4562. p. 244

Alexander, Rebecca, Cat, Washburn University, School of Law Library, 1700 SW College Ave, Topeka, KS, 66621. Tel: 785-670-1088. Fax: 785-670-3194. p. 897

Alexander, Richard, Dir, Cumberland County Public Library, 114 W Hill St, Burkesville, KY, 42717. Tel: 270-864-2207. Fax: 270-864-5937. p. 908

Alexander, Rose, Libr Mgr, Thorhild Library, 210 Seventh Ave, Thorhild, AB, T0A 3J0, CANADA. Tel: 780-398-3502. Fax: 780-398-3504. p. 2719

Alexander, Ruby, Librn, First Baptist Church of Highland Park Library, 6801 Sheriff Rd, Landover, MD, 20785. Tel: 301-773-6655, Ext 236. Fax: 301-773-1347. p. 1034

Alexander, Shawna, Br Mgr, Forest Public Library, 210 S Raleigh St, Forest, MS, 39074. Tel: 601-469-1481. Fax: 601-469-5903. p. 1298

Alexander, Shelia, Circ Librn, Hardin County Library, 1365 Pickwick St, Savannah, TN, 38372. Tel: 731-925-4314, 731-925-6848. Fax: 731-925-7132. p. 2264

Alexander, Shelly, Librn, North Las Vegas Library District, Alexander Library, 1755 W Alexander Rd, North Las Vegas, NV, 89032. Tel: 702-633-2880. Fax: 702-399-9813. p. 1432

Alexander, Ted, Librn, National Park Service, PO Box 158, Sharpsburg, MD, 21782. Tel: 301-432-8674. Fax: 301-432-4590. p. 1041

Alexander, Teri, Head, Circ, Clemson University Libraries, Box 343001, Clemson, SC, 29634-3001. Tel: 864-656-5172. Fax: 864-656-0758. p. 2186

Alexander, Victor, Tech Coordr, Off of Distance Learning, Chicago State University, 9501 S Martin Luther King Jr Dr, LIB 440, Chicago, IL, 60628-1598. Tel: 773-995-2955. Fax: 773-995-3772. p. 610

Alexander, Wendy, Dir, Rosendale Library, 264 Main St, Rosendale, NY, 12472. Tel: 845-658-9013. Fax: 845-658-3752. p. 1735

Alexander, Whitney, Dir of Tech Serv, Santa Clara University, Heafey Law Library, School of Law, 500 El Camino Real, Santa Clara, CA, 95053-0430. Tel: 408-554-2733. Fax: 408-554-5318. p. 263

Alexander-East, Jessie, Mgr, Youth Serv, Mid-Continent Public Library, 15616 E US Hwy 24, Independence, MO, 64050-2098. Tel: 816-836-5200. Fax: 816-521-7253. p. 1332

Alexandre, Ritza, Tech Serv, Trinitas Hospital, 225 Williamson St, Elizabeth, NJ, 07207. Tel: 908-994-5371. Fax: 908-994-5099. p. 1483

Alexandria, Graziela, Pres, Toronto Health Libraries Association, 3409 Yonge St, Toronto, ON, M4N 2L0, CANADA. Tel: 905-828-3231. Fax: 416-485-6877. p. 2960

Alexenko, Natasha, Dir, Long Island Maritime Museum Library, 86 West Ave, West Sayville, NY, 11796-1908. Tel: 631-447-8679, 631-854-4974. Fax: 631-854-4979. p. 1767

Alfano, Elissa, Mrg, Admin Serv, Sonoma County Library, 211 E St, Santa Rosa, CA, 95404. Tel: 707-545-0831. Fax: 707-575-0437. p. 267

Alfano, Louis F, Sr, Dr, Pres, American Society of Abdominal Surgeons, 824 Main St, 2nd Flr, Ste 1, Melrose, MA, 02176. Tel: 781-665-6102. Fax: 781-665-4127. p. 1104

Alfarone, Charles, Dr, Pub Serv Coordr, Canizaro Library at Ave Maria University, 5251 Avila Ave, Ave Maria, FL, 34142. Tel: 239-280-2548. p. 426

Alfgren, Drew, Ref Librn, University of Maryland, Baltimore County, 1000 Hilltop Circle, Baltimore, MD, 21250. Tel: 410-455-2356. p. 1018

Alfonzo, Paige, Ref Serv, Ser, University of Mary Hardin-Baylor, 900 College St, UMHB Sta, Box 8016, Belton, TX, 76513-2599. Tel: 254-295-5011. Fax: 254-295-4642. p. 2289

Alford, Angela, Adult Ref Librn, DeSoto Public Library, 211 E Pleasant Run Rd, Ste C, DeSoto, TX, 75115-3939. Tel: 972-230-9656. Fax: 972-230-5797. p. 2313

Alford, Becky, Ref Librn, Clarke University, 1550 Clarke Dr, Dubuque, IA, 52001. Tel: 563-588-6320. Fax: 563-588-8160. p. 811

Alford, Diane, Mgr, First Presbyterian Church of Gadsden Library, 530 Chestnut St, Gadsden, AL, 35901. Tel: 256-547-5747. Fax: 256-547-5789. p. 18

Alford, Duncan, Dir, University of South Carolina, Coleman Karesh Law Library, USC Law Ctr, 701 Main St, Columbia, SC, 29208. Tel: 803-777-5942. Fax: 803-777-9405. p. 2190

Alford, Heidi, Librn, Toole County Library, 229 Second Ave S, Shelby, MT, 59474. Tel: 406-424-8345. Fax: 406-424-8346. p. 1388

Alford, Larry, Dean, Univ Libr, Temple University Libraries, 1210 W Berks St, Philadelphia, PA, 19122-6088. Tel: 215-204-8231. Fax: 215-204-5201. p. 2117

Alford, Marsha, Human Res Mgr, Kanawha County Public Library, 123 Capitol St, Charleston, WV, 25301. Tel: 304-343-4646. Fax: 304-348-6530. p. 2556

Alford, Richard, Coll Develop, Southeastern Baptist Theological Seminary Library, 114 N Wingate St, Wake Forest, NC, 27587. Tel: 919-863-8255. Fax: 919-863-8150. p. 1827

Alford, Rodney, Tech Serv, Dyersburg State Community College, 1510 Lake Rd, Dyersburg, TN, 38024. Tel: 731-286-3272. Fax: 731-286-3228. p. 2233

Algee, Scarlett, Dir, Tiptonville Public Library, 126 Tipton St, Tiptonville, TN, 38079-1133. Tel: 731-253-7391. Fax: 731-253-7391. p. 2267

Alger, Adrienne, Cataloger, Scappoose Public Library, 52469 SE Second St, Scappoose, OR, 97056. Tel: 503-543-7123. Fax: 503-543-7161. p. 2019

Alger, Dale R, Dir, Roundup Community Library, 601 Sixth Ave W, Roundup, MT, 59072. Tel: 406-323-1802. Fax: 406-323-1346. p. 1388

Alger, Donna, Asst Dir, Malden Public Library, 36 Salem St, Malden, MA, 02148-5291. Tel: 781-324-0218. Fax: 781-324-4467. p. 1102

Alger, Sallie, Head, Bibliog Serv, Andrews University, 1400 Library Rd, Berrien Springs, MI, 49104-1400. Tel: 269-471-6215. Fax: 269-471-6166. p. 1157

Ali, Farooq, Dr, Cat, Govt Doc, East Central University, 1100 E 14th St, Ada, OK, 74820-6999. Tel: 580-310-5298. Fax: 580-436-3242. p. 1955

Ali, Insaf M, Supvr, Columbia University, Philip L Milstein Family College Library, 208 Butler Library, 535 W 114th St, New York, NY, 10027. Tel: 212-854-5327. Fax: 212-854-0089. p. 1675

Ali, Khalil, Libr Commun Serv Mgr, Richmond Public Library, Hull Street, 1400 Hull St, Richmond, VA, 23224. Tel: 804-646-8699. Fax: 804-646-8276. p. 2490

Ali, Sadiq Omowali, Librn, Sojourner-Douglass College, 500 N Caroline St, Baltimore, MD, 21205. Tel: 410-276-0306, Ext 269. Fax: 410-675-1810. p. 1017

Alibrando, Dorothy McLaughlin, Mgr, New Jersey Department of Environmental Protection, 432 E State St, 1st Flr, Trenton, NJ, 08608. Tel: 609-984-2249. Fax: 609-292-3298. p. 1535

Alie, Bernie, Head, Youth Serv, Kennebunk Free Library, 112 Main St, Kennebunk, ME, 04043. Tel: 207-985-2173. Fax: 207-985-4730. p. 988

Alifano, Alison F, Assoc Dir, Info Res, Sullivan & Cromwell LLP, 125 Broad St, New York, NY, 10004. Tel: 212-558-4896. Fax: 212-558-3346. p. 1700

Alimena, Diane, Ref, Pequannock Township Public Library, 477 Newark Pompton Tpk, Pompton Plains, NJ, 07444. Tel: 973-835-7460. Fax: 973-835-1928. p. 1521

Alire, Wilifred Louise, Librn, Reedley College Library, 995 N Reed Ave, Reedley, CA, 93654. Tel: 559-638-0352. Fax: 559-638-0384. p. 216

Alison, Gibson, Dir, Union Township Public Library, Russellville Branch Library, 280 W Main St, Russellville, OH, 45168-8730. Tel: 937-392-4871. Fax: 937-377-1302. p. 1932

Alita, John, Asst Dir, San Bruno Public Library, 701 Angus Ave W, San Bruno, CA, 94066-3490. Tel: 650-616-7078. Fax: 650-876-0848. p. 230

Alix, Valarie, Librn, Chinook Regional Library, Gravelbourg Branch, Box 568, Gravelbourg, SK, S0H 1X0, CANADA. Tel: 306-648-3177. p. 2928

Alkalimat, Abdul, Prof, University of Illinois at Urbana-Champaign, Library & Information Science Bldg, 501 E Daniel St, Champaign, IL, 61820-6211. Tel: 217-333-3280. Fax: 217-244-3302. p. 2965

Allain, Denise, Libr Dir, Clayton Town & County Library, 45 N Midway St, Clayton, AL, 36016. Tel: 334-775-3506. Fax: 334-775-3538. p. 12

Allaire, Daniel, Dir, Info Resources & Res, Assemblee Nationale du Quebec Bibliotheque, 1035 Rue des Parlementaires, Edifice Pamphile-Lemay, Quebec, QC, G1A 1A3, CANADA. Tel: 418-644-5536. Fax: 418-646-3207. p. 2903

Allaire, Lucie, Coordr, Doc, Canada Agriculture & Agri-Food Canada, 3600 Blvd Casavant W, Saint-Hyacinthe, QC, J2S 8E3, CANADA. Tel: 450-768-3247, 450-773-1105. Fax: 450-773-8461. p. 2910

Allan, Bonnie, In Charge, Pictou - Antigonish Regional Library, Pictou Library, Water St, Pictou, NS, B0K 1H0, CANADA. Tel: 902-485-5021. p. 2784

Allan, Kenneth, Mgr, Libr Serv, Vegreville Centennial Library, 4709 50th St, Vegreville, AB, T9C 1R1, CANADA. Tel: 780-632-3491. Fax: 780-603-2338. p. 2720

Allan, Mark, Asst Dir, Ref & Instruction Serv, Angelo State University Library, 2025 S Johnson, San Angelo, TX, 76904-5079. Tel: 325-486-6535. Fax: 325-942-2198. p. 2378

Allard, Amber, Cataloger, Syst Adminr, Spies Public Library, 940 First St, Menominee, MI, 49858-3296. Tel: 906-863-3911. Fax: 906-863-5000. p. 1208

Allard, Andre, Librn, Centre Hospitalier de l'Universite de Montreal, 1058 rue Saint Denis, Montreal, QC, H2X 3J4, CANADA. Tel: 514-890-8000, Ext 35867. Fax: 514-412-7317. p. 2893

Allard, Elaine S, Coordr, Tech Serv & Electronic Res, Plymouth State University, Highland St, Plymouth, NH, 03264-1595. Tel: 603-535-2258. Fax: 603-535-2445. p. 1462

Allard, Ginette, Prof, College de Maisonneuve, 3800, rue Sherbrooke Est, Montreal, QC, H1X 2A2, CANADA. Tel: 514-254-7131. Fax: 514-251-9741. p. 2978

Allard, Jessica, Libr Dir, Burlington College Library, 351 North Ave, Burlington, VT, 05401. Tel: 802-862-9616. Fax: 802-864-8408. p. 2420

Allard, Paula, Admin Supvr, The Record Library, 530 E Market St, Stockton, CA, 95202. Tel: 209-546-8271. Fax: 209-547-8186. p. 272

Allard, Rhonda, Consumer Health Librn, Cornell University Library, The Samuel J Wood Library & The C V Starr Biomedical Information Center, 1300 York Ave, C115, Box 67, New York, NY, 10065-4896. Tel: 212-746-6050. Fax: 212-746-6494. p. 1642

Allbee, Robbyn, Admin Mgr, Round Lake Area Public Library District, 906 Hart Rd, Round Lake, IL, 60073. Tel: 847-546-7060, Ext 105. Fax: 847-546-7104. p. 699

Allcorn, Linda, Dir, Boonslick Regional Library, 219 W Third St, Sedalia, MO, 65301-4347. Tel: 660-827-7111. Fax: 660-827-4668. p. 1364

Allee, Nancy, Dep Dir, University of Michigan, A Alfred Taubman Health Sciences Library, 1135 E Catherine, Ann Arbor, MI, 48109-2038. Tel: 734-764-1210. p. 1153

Allegrini, Julia, Br Librn, Kenton County Public Library, 502 Scott Blvd, Covington, KY, 41011. Tel: 859-962-4074. Fax: 859-962-4096. p. 910

Alleman, Angela, Acq & Cat, Louisiana State University Libraries, LSU School of Veterinary Medicine Library, Skip Bertman Dr, Baton Rouge, LA, 70803-8414. Tel: 225-578-9794. Fax: 225-578-9798. p. 944

Alleman, Kathryn, Br Mgr, Fairfax County Public Library, John Marshall Branch, 6209 Rose Hill Dr, Alexandria, VA, 22310-6299. Tel: 703-971-0010. p. 2461

Alleman, Sheryl, Tech Serv, Lincoln County Library, 519 Emerald, Kemmerer, WY, 83101. Tel: 307-877-6961. Fax: 307-877-4147. p. 2656

Alleman, Steve, Head, Coll, University of Missouri-Kansas City Libraries, 800 E 51st St, Kansas City, MO, 64110. Tel: 816-235-1580. Fax: 816-333-5584. p. 1341

Allen, Amy, Univ Archivist, University of Arkansas Libraries, 365 N McIlroy Ave, Fayetteville, AR, 72701-4002. Tel: 479-575-6370. Fax: 479-575-6656. p. 99

Allen, Angela, Coll Develop, Head, Info Serv, Salina Public Library, 301 W Elm St, Salina, KS, 67401. Tel: 785-825-4624. Fax: 785-823-0706. p. 893

Allen, Angela A, Dir, Libr & Info Serv, Kansas Wesleyan University, 100 E Claflin Ave, Salina, KS, 67401-6100. Tel: 785-827-5541, Ext 4120. Fax: 785-827-0927. p. 893

Allen, Barbara, Bibliographer, Ref Serv, University of Northern Iowa Library, 1227 W 27th St, Cedar Falls, IA, 50613-3675. Tel: 319-273-3715. Fax: 319-273-2913. p. 799

Allen, Barbara Mcfadden, Dir, Committee on Institutional Cooperation, 1819 S Neil St, Ste D, Champaign, IL, 61820-7271. Tel: 217-244-9240. Fax: 217-244-7127. p. 2942

Allen, Betty, Adminr, British Columbia Genealogical Society, 12837 76th Ave, No 211, Surrey, BC, V3W 2V3, CANADA. Tel: 604-888-7870. p. 2738

Allen, Bev, Archivist, Colorado State University Pueblo Library, 2200 Bonforte Blvd, Pueblo, CO, 81001-4901. Tel: 719-549-2475. Fax: 719-549-2738. p. 320

Allen, Beverley, VPres, Cinema Arts, Inc, 207 Lincoln Green Lane, Newfoundland, PA, 18445. Tel: 570-676-4145. Fax: 570-676-9194. p. 2097

Allen, Bob, Res Librn, Faegre & Benson, LLP, 2200 Wells Fargo Ctr, 90 South Seventh St, Minneapolis, MN, 55402-3901. Tel: 612-766-7000. Fax: 612-766-1600. p. 1259

Allen, Bonnie, Dean of Libr, University of Montana, Maureen & Mike Mansfield Library, 32 Campus Dr, No 9936, Missoula, MT, 59812-9936. Tel: 406-243-6866. Fax: 406-243-4067. p. 1386

Allen, Bonnie, Librn, Churchill Public Library, 181 Laverendrye Ave, Churchill, MB, R0B 0E0, CANADA. Tel: 204-675-2731. p. 2748

Allen, Brad, Exec Dir, Lawrence Public Library, 707 Vermont St, Lawrence, KS, 66044-2371. Tel: 785-843-3833, Ext 102. Fax: 785-843-3368. p. 877

Allen, Brett, Libr Dir, Fairfield/Teton Public Library, 14 North Fourth St, Fairfield, MT, 59436. Tel: 406-467-2477. Fax: 406-467-2477. p. 1378

Allen, Carolyn Henderson, Dean, University of Arkansas Libraries, 365 N McIlroy Ave, Fayetteville, AR, 72701-4002. Tel: 479-575-4101. Fax: 479-575-6656. p. 99

Allen, Catharine, Dir, Lima Public Library, 1872 Genesee St, Lima, NY, 14485. Tel: 585-582-1311. Fax: 585-582-1701. p. 1652

Allen, Cathy, Dir, Hurt-Battelle Memorial Library of West Jefferson, 270 Lily Chapel Rd, West Jefferson, OH, 43162-1202. Tel: 614-879-8448. Fax: 614-879-8668. p. 1946

Allen, Connie, Br Mgr, Cass County Public Library, Drexel Branch, 211 E Main St, Drexel, MO, 64742. Tel: 816-657-4740. p. 1330

Allen, Darla, Dir, Charles & Joann Lester Library, 100 Park St, Nekoosa, WI, 54457. Tel: 715-886-7879. p. 2624

Allen, David, Ad, Johnson County Public Library, White River Library, 1664 Library Blvd, Greenwood, IN, 46142. Tel: 317-885-1330. Fax: 317-882-4117. p. 744

Allen, David, Cat, Cuyahoga Falls Library, 2015 Third St, Cuyahoga Falls, OH, 44221-3294. Tel: 330-928-2117, Ext 111. Fax: 330-928-2535. p. 1892

Allen, Debbie, Head, Youth Serv, Round Lake Area Public Library District, 906 Hart Rd, Round Lake, IL, 60073. Tel: 847-546-7060, Ext 120. Fax: 847-546-7104. p. 699

Allen, Deborah, Dir, Bowerston Public Library, 200 Main St, Bowerston, OH, 44695. Tel: 740-269-8531. Fax: 740-269-8503. p. 1860

Allen, Debra C, Asst Dir, Orangeburg County Library, 510 Louis St, Orangeburg, SC, 29115-5030. Tel: 803-531-4636. Fax: 803-533-5860. p. 2201

Allen, Delene H, Dir of Libr Serv, Quitman Public Library, 202 East Goode St, Quitman, TX, 75783-2533. Tel: 903-763-4191. Fax: 903-763-2532. p. 2373

Allen, Denise, Asst Librn, Emery County Library, Emery Branch, 100 N Center, Emery, UT, 84522. Tel: 435-286-2474. Fax: 435-286-2434. p. 2404

Allen, Don, Chief Librn, Canada Department of National Defence, Base Borden Public & Military Library, CFB BORDEN, 41 Kapyong Rd, Borden, ON, L0M 1C0, CANADA. Tel: 705-424-1200, Ext 2273. p. 2796

Allen, Don, Br Serv Librn, Department of Community Services, Government of Yukon, 1171 First Ave, Whitehorse, YT, Y1A 0G9, CANADA. Tel: 867-667-5448. Fax: 867-393-6333. p. 2933

Allen, Don, Br Serv Librn, Department of Community Services, Government of Yukon, Whitehorse Public, 2071 Second Ave, Whitehorse, YT, Y1A 2C6, CANADA. Tel: 867-667-5448. Fax: 867-393-6333. p. 2933

Allen, Donna, Dir, Dennis Joos Memorial Library, 888 Washington St, West Stewartstown, NH, 03597. Tel: 603-246-3329. Fax: 603-246-3329. p. 1467

Allen, Elaine, Dir, Fulton Public Library, 312 Main St, Fulton, KY, 42041. Tel: 270-472-3439. Fax: 270-472-6241. p. 914

Allen, Elizabeth, Ref & Instrul Serv Librn, Lesley University, 89 Brattle St, Cambridge, MA, 02138-2790. Tel: 617-349-8840. Fax: 617-349-8849. p. 1077

Allen, Elizabeth, Dir, Schlow Centre Region Library, 211 S Allen St, State College, PA, 16801-4806. Tel: 814-237-6236. Fax: 814-238-8508. p. 2143

Allen, Ethan, Librn, Detroit Symphony Orchestra Library, 3711 Woodward Ave, Detroit, MI, 48201. Tel: 313-576-5100, 313-576-5172. Fax: 313-576-5593. p. 1170

Allen, Ethan J, Jr, Dir, Florida Atlantic University, 5353 Parkside Dr, Jupiter, FL, 33458. Tel: 561-799-8030. Fax: 561-799-8587. p. 455

Allen, Fern, Librn, City of Kawartha Lakes Public Library, Burnt River Branch, 186 Burnt River Rd, Burnt River, ON, K0M 1C0, CANADA. Tel: 705-454-9646. Fax: 705-454-8465. p. 2816

Allen, Frances, Ch, Susquehanna County Historical Society & Free Library Association, Two Monument Sq, Montrose, PA, 18801-1115. Tel: 570-278-1881. Fax: 570-278-9336. p. 2092

Allen, Frank R, Assoc Dir, Admin Serv, University of Central Florida Libraries, 4000 Central Florida Blvd, Bldg 2, Orlando, FL, 32816-2666. Tel: 407-823-2892. Fax: 407-823-2529. p. 477

Allen, Fredrick, Digital Serv, Kapiolani Community College Library, 4303 Diamond Head Rd, Honolulu, HI, 96816. Tel: 808-734-9599. Fax: 808-734-9453. p. 564

Allen, Gary, Adult Serv, Hazel Park Memorial Library, 123 E Nine Mile Rd, Hazel Park, MI, 48030. Tel: 248-542-0940, 248-546-4095. Fax: 248-546-4083. p. 1189

Allen, Ginger, Br Mgr, Dallas Public Library, Skyline, 6006 Everglade, Dallas, TX, 75227-2799. Tel: 214-670-0938. Fax: 214-670-0321. p. 2307

Allen, Jacqueline, Librn, Melvin Public Library, 102 S Center St, Melvin, IL, 60952. Tel: 217-388-2421. Fax: 217-388-2421. p. 673

Allen, Jacqueline, Dir, Libr & Imaging Serv, Dallas Museum of Art, 1717 N Harwood, Dallas, TX, 75201. Tel: 214-922-1276. Fax: 214-954-0174. p. 2306

Allen, Jan, Dir, Marshall County Memorial Library, 310 Old Farmington Rd, Lewisburg, TN, 37091. Tel: 931-359-3335. Fax: 931-359-5866. p. 2245

Allen, Janice E, Acq, Cinema Arts, Inc, 207 Lincoln Green Lane, Newfoundland, PA, 18445. Tel: 570-676-4145. Fax: 570-676-9194. p. 2097

Allen, Jaylyn, Librn, Pine Forest Regional Library, Jane Blain Brewer Memorial, 102 S Fifth St, Mount Olive, MS, 39119. Tel: 601-797-4955. Fax: 601-797-4955. p. 1314

Allen, Jen, Asst Librn, Ossipee Public Library, 74 Main St, Center Ossipee, NH, 03814. Tel: 603-539-6390. Fax: 603-539-5758. p. 1440

Allen, Jenny, In Charge, Stanly County Public Library, Badin Branch, 62 Pine St, Badin, NC, 28009. Tel: 704-422-3218. p. 1773

Allen, Jim, Asst Dir, Cap Projects & Fac Serv, County of Los Angeles Public Library, 7400 E Imperial Hwy, Downey, CA, 90242-3375. Tel: 562-940-4145. Fax: 562-803-3032. p. 140

Allen, Jim, Dir, River Valley Community College, One College Dr, Claremont, NH, 03743. Tel: 603-542-7744, Ext 465. Fax: 603-543-1844. p. 1442

Allen, Joseph Lee, Sr, Dir, Libr Serv, Bob Jones University, 1700 Wade Hampton Blvd, Greenville, SC, 29614. Tel: 864-242-5100, Ext 6000. Fax: 864-232-1729. p. 2195

Allen, Joyce, Asst Librn, Robertsdale Public Library, 18301 Pennsylvania St, Robertsdale, AL, 36567. Tel: 251-947-8960. Fax: 251-947-5521. p. 35

Allen, Julia, Dir, United States Army, Fort Wainwright Post Library, Santiago Ave, Bldg 3700, Fort Wainwright, AK, 99703-6600. Tel: 907-353-2642. Fax: 907-353-2609. p. 48

Allen, Karen, Br Mgr, Cass County Public Library, Garden City Branch, 201 C Date St, Garden City, MO, 64747-9211. Tel: 816-862-6611. p. 1330

Allen, Karen, Youth Serv Mgr, Greenville County Library System, 25 Heritage Green Pl, Greenville, SC, 29601-2034. Tel: 864-242-5000, Ext 2249. Fax: 864-235-8375. p. 2196

Allen, Karen-Marie, Br Mgr, Wake County Public Library System, Olivia Raney Local History Library, 4016 Carya Dr, Raleigh, NC, 27610. Tel: 919-250-1229. Fax: 919-212-0476. p. 1818

Allen, Katherine, Librn, University of Minnesota Libraries-Twin Cities, Andersen Horticultural Library, 3675 Arboretum Dr, Chaska, MN, 55318. Tel: 952-443-1405. Fax: 952-443-2521. p. 1262

Allen, Kathy, Librn, Clare Public Library, 119 E Front St, Clare, IA, 50524. Tel: 515-546-6222. Fax: 515-546-6222. p. 802

Allen, Keith, Principal Librn, Tampa-Hillsborough County Public Library System, Charles J Fendig Public Library, 3909 W Neptune St, Tampa, FL, 33629. Fax: 813-276-8561. p. 497

Allen, Keith, Principal Librn, Tampa-Hillsborough County Public Library System, Town 'N Country Regional Public Library, 7606 Paula Dr, Tampa, FL, 33615-4116. Fax: 813-554-5121. p. 498

Allen, Kelly, Youth Serv Librn, Oregon Public Library, 256 Brook St, Oregon, WI, 53575. Tel: 608-835-3656. Fax: 608-835-2856. p. 2627

Allen, Kiersten, Dir, Louisburg Public Library, 206 S Broadway, Louisburg, KS, 66053. Tel: 913-837-2217. Fax: 913-837-2218. p. 880

Allen, Kim, ILL, University of Medicine & Dentistry of New Jersey, 30 12th Ave, Newark, NJ, 07103-2706. Tel: 973-972-4580. p. 1513

Allen, Kimberly, Dir of Develop, Linda Hall Library, 5109 Cherry St, Kansas City, MO, 64110-2498. Tel: 816-926-8792. Fax: 816-926-8790. p. 1337

Allen, Laurie, Libr Mgr, Rockwell Scientific Co, 1049 Camino Dos Rios, Thousand Oaks, CA, 91360. Tel: 805-373-4722. Fax: 805-373-4296. p. 275

Allen, Laurie, Coordr, Digital Scholarship & Serv, Haverford College, 370 Lancaster Ave, Haverford, PA, 19041-1392. Tel: 610-896-4226. Fax: 610-896-1102. p. 2067

Allen, Leean L, Dir, Pike County Public Library District, 119 College St, Pikeville, KY, 41502-1787. Tel: 606-432-9977. Fax: 606-432-9908. p. 932

Allen, Lychelle, Librn, Georgia Department of Corrections, Office of Library Services, Rte 2, Upper River Rd, Hawkinsville, GA, 31036. Tel: 478-783-6102. Fax: 478-783-6008. p. 536

Allen, Lynn, Librn, Vose Library, 343 Common Rd, Union, ME, 04862-4252. Tel: 207-785-4733. p. 1004

Allen, Marcia, Coll Develop, North Central Kansas Libraries System, 629 Poyntz Ave, Manhattan, KS, 66502-6086. Tel: 785-776-4741. Fax: 785-776-1545. p. 881

Allen, Marcy, Coll Develop, Manhattan Public Library, 629 Poyntz Ave, Manhattan, KS, 66502-6086. Tel: 785-776-4741. Fax: 785-776-1545. p. 881

Allen, Margaret, Circ Supvr, Cumberland County Library, 800 E Commerce St, Bridgeton, NJ, 08302-2295. Tel: 856-453-2210. Fax: 856-451-1940. p. 1474

Allen, Marion, Librn, New Hampshire Hospital, 36 Clinton St, Concord, NH, 03301-3861. Tel: 603-271-5420. Fax: 603-271-5415. p. 1442

Allen, Marion, Admin Coordr, Health Sciences Libraries of New Hampshire & Vermont, Breene Memorial Library, New Hampshire Hospital, 36 Clinton St, Concord, NH, 03246. Tel: 603-271-5420. Fax: 603-527-7197. p. 2948

Allen, Mark, Librn, American Electric Power Service Corp, Legal Library, One Riverside Plaza, Flr 29, Columbus, OH, 43215. Tel: 614-716-2981. Fax: 614-716-1687. p. 1883

Allen, Martha, Coordr, Info Serv, Saint Louis University, 3650 Lindell Blvd, Saint Louis, MO, 63108-3302. Tel: 314-977-3596. Fax: 314-977-3108. p. 1360

Allen, Mary, Librn, Graham County Public Library, 414 N West St, Hill City, KS, 67642-1646. Tel: 785-421-2722. Fax: 785-421-5583. p. 871

Allen, Mary, Youth Serv Librn, Southwest Public Libraries, Westland Area Library, 4740 W Broad St, Columbus, OH, 43228. Tel: 614-878-1301. Fax: 614-878-3454. p. 1903

Allen, Mary Beth, Librn, University of Illinois Library at Urbana-Champaign, Applied Health Sciences Library, 146 Main Library, 1408 W Gregory St, Urbana, IL, 61801. Tel: 217-244-1870. Fax: 217-333-8384. p. 711

Allen, Mary Beth, Librn, University of Illinois Library at Urbana-Champaign, Social Sciences, Health & Education Library, 100 Main Library, MC-522, 1408 W Gregory Dr, Urbana, IL, 61801. Tel: 217-244-1870. Fax: 217-333-2214. p. 713

Allen, Maureen, Dep Librn, New Westminster Public Library, 716 Sixth Ave, New Westminster, BC, V3M 2B3, CANADA. Tel: 604-527-4669. Fax: 604-527-4674. p. 2734

Allen, Maxine, Librn, McCune Osage Township Library, 509 Sixth St, McCune, KS, 66753. Tel: 620-632-4112. p. 882

Allen, Meg, Circ, Baraboo Public Library, 230 Fourth Ave, Baraboo, WI, 53913. Tel: 608-356-6166. Fax: 608-355-2779. p. 2580

Allen, Megan, Asst Dir, Thomas Crane Public Library, 40 Washington St, Quincy, MA, 02269-9164. Tel: 617-376-1331. Fax: 617-376-1313. p. 1119

Allen, Megan, Electronic Res, Case Western Reserve University, School of Law Library, 11075 East Blvd, Cleveland, OH, 44106-7148. Tel: 216-368-5223. Fax: 216-368-1002. p. 1876

Allen, Melanie, Br Mgr, Alma Public Library, 624 Fayetteville Ave, Alma, AR, 72921. Tel: 479-632-4140. Fax: 479-632-6099. p. 93

Allen, Michael, Libr Asst, Shaw University, 118 E South St, Raleigh, NC, 27601. Tel: 919-546-8526. Fax: 919-831-1161. p. 1817

Allen, Michelle, Youth Serv Librn, Memphis Public Library, Poplar-White Station, 5094 Poplar, Memphis, TN, 38117-7629. Tel: 901-415-2777. Fax: 901-682-8975. p. 2250

Allen, Misty, ILL, Media Coordr, Weber State University, 2901 University Circle, Ogden, UT, 84408-2901. Tel: 801-626-7820. Fax: 801-626-7045. p. 2409

Allen, Mitchell, Fiscal Officer, Avery-Mitchell-Yancey Regional Library System, 289 Burnsville School Rd, Burnsville, NC, 28714. Tel: 828-682-4476. Fax: 828-682-6277. p. 1779

Allen, Nancy, Dean, Libr Dir, University of Denver, 2150 E Evans Ave, Denver, CO, 80208-2007. Tel: 303-871-3441. Fax: 303-871-2290. p. 303

Allen, Nancy, Ref, New College of Florida University of South Florida Sarasota Manatee, 5800 Bay Shore Rd, Sarasota, FL, 34243-2109. Tel: 941-487-4405. Fax: 941-487-4307. p. 490

Allen, Norma A, Coll Develop, Tech Serv, Social Security Administration Library, Annex Bldg 1520, Baltimore, MD, 21235-6401. Tel: 410-965-6027. Fax: 410-966-2027. p. 1017

Allen, Pat, In Charge, Tipton Library, Main St, Tipton, KS, 67485. Tel: 785-373-6975. p. 896

Allen Patterson, Katherine, Br Mgr, Greece Public Library, Barnard Crossing, 2780 Dewey Ave, Rochester, NY, 14616. Tel: 585-663-3357. Fax: 585-663-5587. p. 1631

Allen, Penny, Mgr, Vulcan Municipal Library, 303 Centre St, Vulcan, AB, T0L 2B0, CANADA. Tel: 403-485-2571. Fax: 403-485-2571. p. 2721

Allen, Rhonda, Circ Supvr, Bethel University, 325 Cherry Ave, McKenzie, TN, 38201. Tel: 731-352-4083. Fax: 731-352-4070. p. 2247

Allen, Richard, Ref Serv, Middlesex Community College, Bldg 1-ARC, Springs Rd, Bedford, MA, 01730. Tel: 781-280-3708. Fax: 781-280-3771. p. 1052

Allen, Richard, Tech Serv, Winthrop Public Library & Museum, Two Metcalf Sq, Winthrop, MA, 02152-3157. Tel: 617-846-1703. Fax: 617-846-7083. p. 1142

Allen, Rita M, Dir, Cannon County Library System, 212 College St, Woodbury, TN, 37190. Tel: 615-563-5861. Fax: 615-563-2140. p. 2269

Allen, Rita M, Dir, Cannon County Library System, Aburntown Branch Library, 73 E Main St, Auburntown, TN, 37016. Tel: 615-464-2622. Fax: 615-464-2623. p. 2269

Allen, Robbie, Pub Serv, Saint Johns River State College, 5001 St Johns Ave, Palatka, FL, 32177-3897. Tel: 386-312-4200. Fax: 386-325-4292. p. 478

Allen, Robert B, PHD, Assoc Prof, Drexel University, Rush Bldg, Rm 306, 30 N 33rd St, Philadelphia, PA, 19104-2875. Tel: 215-895-2474. Fax: 215-895-2494. p. 2972

Allen, Roberta, Archivist, Ref, Danville Public Library, 319 N Vermilion St, Danville, IL, 61832. Tel: 217-477-5220. Fax: 217-477-5230. p. 633

Allen, Ron, Dir, Washington University Libraries, Kopolow Business Library, One Brookings Dr, Campus Box 1133, Saint Louis, MO, 63130-4899. Tel: 314-935-6739. Fax: 314-935-4970. p. 1363

Allen, Ruby, Ref Librn, Atlanta-Fulton Public Library System, Sandy Springs Regional Library, 395 Mount Vernon Hwy, Sandy Springs, GA, 30328. Tel: 404-303-6130. Fax: 404-303-6133. p. 512

Allen, Sammie, Mgr, Dayton Metro Library, Northtown-Shiloh, 35 Bennington Dr, Dayton, OH, 45405. Tel: 937-496-8954. Fax: 937-496-4354. p. 1893

Allen, Sandra, Mgr, Suwannee River Regional Library, Jennings Public Library, 1322 Plum St, Jennings, FL, 32053-2221. Tel: 386-938-1143. Fax: 386-938-1153. p. 461

Allen, Sandra, Br Mgr, Saint Petersburg Public Library, South, 2300 Roy Hanna Dr S, Saint Petersburg, FL, 33712. Tel: 727-893-7244. Fax: 727-864-2470. p. 488

Allen, Selicia, Archivist/Librn, Spec Coll, Virginia Union University, 1500 N Lombardy St, Richmond, VA, 23220. Tel: 804-257-4117. Fax: 804-257-5818. p. 2493

Allen, Shannon, Outreach Serv Librn, Gadsden County Public Library, 7325 Pat Thomas Pkwy, Quincy, FL, 32351. Tel: 850-627-7106. Fax: 850-627-7775. p. 485

Allen, Sharon, Dir, Humboldt County Library, 85 E Fifth St, Winnemucca, NV, 89445. Tel: 775-623-6388. Fax: 775-623-6438. p. 1435

Allen, Sheila, Acad Computing Coordr, Synergy Medical Education Alliance, Covenant Houghton Bldg, 2nd Flr, 1000 Houghton Ave, Ste 2000, Saginaw, MI, 48602-5398. Tel: 989-583-6846. Fax: 989-583-6898. p. 1224

Allen, Sherry, Coordr, Riverside County Regional Medical Center Library, 26520 Cactus Ave, Moreno Valley, CA, 92555. Tel: 951-486-5101. Fax: 951-486-5045. p. 191

Allen, Stacey, Chief of Operations, National Park Service, 1055 Pittsburg Landing Rd, Shiloh, TN, 38376. Tel: 731-689-5275. Fax: 731-689-5450. p. 2265

Allen, Thea, Head, Tech Serv, Environmental Protection Agency Library - RTP, MD C267-01, 109 Alexander Dr, Research Triangle Park, NC, 27711. Tel: 919-541-2777. Fax: 919-541-1405. p. 1819

Allen, Theresa, Financial Serv, Bossier Parish Central Library, Benton Branch, 115 Courthouse Dr, Benton, LA, 71006. Tel: 318-965-2751. Fax: 318-965-4379. p. 946

Allen, Tracy, Adult Serv, Finkelstein Memorial Library, 24 Chestnut St, Spring Valley, NY, 10977-5594. Tel: 845-352-5700. Fax: 845-352-2319. p. 1746

Allen, Travis, Librn, White County Regional Library System, Baldwin Memorial, 612 Van Buren, Judsonia, AR, 72081. Tel: 501-729-3995. Fax: 501-729-5994. p. 114

Allen, Wendy, Circ, Pub Serv Librn, Roanoke Public Libraries, 706 S Jefferson St, Roanoke, VA, 24016-5191. Tel: 540-853-2473. Fax: 540-853-1781. p. 2494

Allen, Wilda, Chief Exec Officer, Grey Highlands Public Library, 101 Highland Dr, Flesherton, ON, N0C 1E0, CANADA. Tel: 519-924-2241. Fax: 519-924-2562. p. 2805

Allen, Yvonne T, Br Mgr, Wake County Public Library System, Wake Forest Community Library, 400 E Holding Ave, Wake Forest, NC, 27587. Tel: 919-554-3308. Fax: 919-554-8499. p. 1818

Allen-Hart, Joan, Asst Dir, Br Serv, San Diego County Public Law Library, 1105 Front St, San Diego, CA, 92101-3904. Tel: 619-531-3904. Fax: 619-238-7716. p. 234

Allen-Hart, Joan, Librn, San Diego County Public Law Library, North County, 325 S Melrose, Ste 300, Vista, CA, 92081-6697. Tel: 760-940-4386. Fax: 760-724-7694. p. 234

Allender, Rex, Librn, Central United Methodist Church Library, 201 University Blvd NE, Albuquerque, NM, 87106-4596. Tel: 505-243-7834. Fax: 505-242-6986. p. 1549

Allerton, Elizabeth, Libr Mgr, Alachua County Library District, Micanopy Branch, Micanopy Town Hall, 706 NE Cholokka Blvd, Micanopy, FL, 32667-4113. Tel: 352-466-3122. Fax: 352-466-3124. p. 448

Allerton, Sarah, Ch, Saint Albans Free Library, 11 Maiden Lane, Saint Albans, VT, 05478. Tel: 802-524-1507. Fax: 802-524-1514. p. 2434

Alley, Teresa A, Coordr, Libr Serv, Southwest Virginia Community College Library, Russell Hall, 599 Community College Rd, Cedar Bluff, VA, 24609. Tel: 276-964-7265. Fax: 276-964-7259. p. 2453

Alleyne, Jennifer, Cataloger/Ref Librn, Per, Florida Hospital College of Health Sciences, 671 Winyah Dr, Orlando, FL, 32803. Tel: 407-303-7747, Ext 5273. Fax: 407-303-9622. p. 475

Allgaier, Anne, Librn, Prince George Regional Hospital, 1475 Edmonton St, Prince George, BC, V2M 1S2, CANADA. Tel: 250-565-2219. Fax: 250-565-2787. p. 2736

Alligood, Elaine, Chief, Libr Serv, VA Medical Center, 1400 Veterans of Foreign Wars Pkwy, West Roxbury, MA, 02132. Tel: 617-323-7700, Ext 35142. Fax: 857-203-5532. p. 1137

Allin, Elizabeth, Librn, NPR Library, 635 Massachusetts Ave NW, Washington, DC, 20001. Tel: 202-513-3056. p. 412

Alling, Emily, Libr Dir, Marlboro College, 64 Dalrymple Rd, Marlboro, VT, 05344-0300. Tel: 802-258-9221. Fax: 802-451-7550. p. 2428

Allision, Virginia, Asst Librn, Watkins College of Art & Design Library, 2298 Rosa L Parks Blvd (MetroCenter), Nashville, TN, 37228. Tel: 615-383-4848. Fax: 615-383-4849. p. 2261

Allison, Andrea, Librn, Quetico Park, Quetico Park, Atikokan, ON, P0T 1C0, CANADA. Tel: 807-929-2571, Ext 224. Fax: 807-929-2123. p. 2793

Allison, Celia, Mgr, Coll Serv, Wethersfield Public Library, 515 Silas Deane Hwy, Wethersfield, CT, 06109. Tel: 860-529-2665. Fax: 860-257-2822. p. 378

Allison, Crystal, Asst Librn, Hale County Public Library, 1103 Main St, Greensboro, AL, 36744. Tel: 334-624-3409. Fax: 334-624-3409. p. 19

Allison, Debby, Head Librn, Kiowa County Library, 320 S Main, Ste 120, Greensburg, KS, 67054. Tel: 620-723-1118. p. 869

Allison, DeeAnn, Dir, Computing Operations & Research Serv, University of Nebraska-Lincoln, 1248 R St, Lincoln, NE, 68588-4100. Tel: 402-472-2526. p. 1407

Allison, Elizabeth, Librn, Episcopal Church Center, Five Rock Point Rd, Burlington, VT, 05408. Tel: 802-863-3431. Fax: 802-860-1562. p. 2420

Allison, Flora, Pub Serv, Barber Scotia College, 145 Cabarrus Ave W, Concord, NC, 28025. Tel: 704-789-2953. Fax: 704-789-2955. p. 1785

Allison, James M, Dir, Bexar County Law Library, Bexar County Courthouse, 5th Flr, 100 Dolorosa, San Antonio, TX, 78205. Tel: 210-227-8822. Fax: 210-271-9614. p. 2379

Allison, Jason, Librn, Cecil County Circuit Court Library, Courthouse, 2nd Flr, 129 E Main St, Elkton, MD, 21921. Tel: 410-996-5325. Fax: 410-996-5120. p. 1027

Allison, Jennifer, Asst Librn, Hale County Public Library, 1103 Main St, Greensboro, AL, 36744. Tel: 334-624-3409. Fax: 334-624-3409. p. 19

Allison, Jennifer, Ref, Pepperdine University Libraries, School of Law-Jerene Appleby Harnish Law Library, 24255 Pacific Coast Hwy, Malibu, CA, 90263. Tel: 310-506-4643. Fax: 310-506-4836. p. 182

Allison, Johanna, Librn, Gore Bay Union Public Library, 15 Water St, Gore Bay, ON, P0P 1H0, CANADA. Tel: 705-282-2221. Fax: 705-282-3076. p. 2806

Allison, Joy, Online Serv, Pub Serv, Mount Saint Mary's University, 16300 Old Emmitsburg Rd, Emmitsburg, MD, 21727-7799. Tel: 301-447-5244. Fax: 301-447-5099. p. 1027

Allison, Julia D, Libr Coordr, Texas Children's Hospital, 6621 Fannin St, MC-W16277, Houston, TX, 77030. Tel: 832-826-1619. Fax: 832-825-1601. p. 2342

Allison, Peter, Coll Develop Mgr, University of Connecticut Library, 369 Fairfield Rd, Storrs, CT, 06269-1005. Tel: 860-486-2219. Fax: 860-486-0584. p. 370

Allison, Rhonda, Asst Librn, Scottdale Public Library, 235 Pittsburgh St, Scottdale, PA, 15683-1796. Tel: 724-887-6140. Fax: 724-887-6140. p. 2137

Allison, Susan, Asst Dir, Richardson Public Library, 900 Civic Center Dr, Richardson, TX, 75080. Tel: 972-744-4350. Fax: 972-744-5806. p. 2374

Allison, Terri, Info Serv, Carrollton Public Library, 1700 Keller Springs Rd, Carrollton, TX, 75006. Tel: 972-466-4800. Fax: 972-466-4265. p. 2295

Allison, Theodore R, Dir, New Carlisle Public Library, 111 E Lake Ave, New Carlisle, OH, 45344-1418. Tel: 937-845-3601. Fax: 937-845-0908. p. 1920

Allman, Janice, Tech Serv Librn, East Bridgewater Public Library, 32 Union St, East Bridgewater, MA, 02333-1598. Tel: 508-378-1616. Fax: 508-378-1617. p. 1085

Allmon, Warren, Dr, Dir, Paleontological Research Institution Library, 1259 Trumansburg Rd, Ithaca, NY, 14850. Tel: 607-273-6623, Ext 20. Fax: 607-273-6620. p. 1643

Allocco, Claudia, Librn, Valley Hospital, 223 N Van Dien Ave, Ridgewood, NJ, 07450. Tel: 201-447-8285. Fax: 201-447-8602. p. 1526

Allred, Betty, Librn, Lilbourn Memorial Library, 210 E Lewis Ave, Lilbourn, MO, 63862. Tel: 573-688-2622. p. 1343

Allred, Cynthia, Librn, Jonesville Public Library, 150 W Main St, Jonesville, NC, 28642. Tel: 336-835-7604. Fax: 336-526-4226. p. 1804

Allred, Martha, Evening/Weekend Librn, West Texas A&M University, University Dr & 26th St, Canyon, TX, 79016. Tel: 806-651-2229. Fax: 806-651-2213. p. 2294

Allred, Nora, Copyright Librn, Ref & ILL Librn, Michigan Technological University, 1400 Townsend Dr, Houghton, MI, 49931-1295. Tel: 906-487-3208. p. 1191

Allred, Zachary, Pub Serv Librn, Snow College, 141 E Center St, Ephraim, UT, 84627. Tel: 435-283-7363. Fax: 435-283-7369. p. 2405

Allshouse, Lucinda, Librn, Presbyterian Intercommunity Hospital, 12401 E Washington Blvd, Whittier, CA, 90602. Tel: 562-698-0811, Ext 2583. Fax: 562-698-9002. p. 283

Alltmont, Shea, Communications Mgr, Delaware County District Library, 84 E Winter St, Delaware, OH, 43015. Tel: 740-362-3861. Fax: 740-369-0196. p. 1895

Allwine, Jamie, Libr Mgr, Timberland Regional Library, Winlock Branch, 322 First St, Winlock, WA, 98596. Tel: 360-785-3461. Fax: 360-785-3800. p. 2544

Allyn, Jill, Librn, Garvey, Schubert & Barer, 1191 Second Ave, Ste 1800, Seattle, WA, 98101-2939. Tel: 206-464-3939. Fax: 206-464-0125. p. 2527

Alm, Janet, Dr, Dir of Libr, Kalamazoo Valley Community College Libraries, 6767 West O Ave, Kalamazoo, MI, 49003. Tel: 269-488-4328, 269-488-4380. Fax: 269-488-4488. p. 1197

Alman, Susan, Asst Prof, University of Pittsburgh, 135 N Bellefield Ave, Pittsburgh, PA, 15260. Tel: 412-624-5230. Fax: 412-624-5231. p. 2973

Almand, Nancy, Librn, Fresno City College Library, 1101 E University Ave, Fresno, CA, 93741. Tel: 559-442-8204. Fax: 559-265-5758. p. 151

Almasi, Stephen M, Sr Librn, Coxsackie Correctional Facility Library, Rte 9W, Coxsackie, NY, 12051-0200. Tel: 518-731-2781, Ext 4602. Fax: 518-731-2099. p. 1612

Almberg, Jackie, Librn, Czar Municipal Library, PO Box 127, Czar, AB, T0B 0Z0, CANADA. Tel: 780-857-3740. Fax: 780-857-2223. p. 2696

Almeida, Larry, Asst Dir, Kootenai-Shoshone Area Libraries, 8385 N Government Way, Hayden, ID, 83835-9280. Tel: 208-772-5612, Ext 12. Fax: 208-772-2498. p. 575

Almeida, larry, Coordr, Cooperative Information Network, 8385 N Government Way, Hayden, ID, 83835-9280. Tel: 208-772-5612. Fax: 208-772-2498. p. 2941

Almendarez, Monica, Pres, Greater Philadelphia Law Library Association, Wolf, Block, Schorr & Solis-Cohen LLP Library, 25th fl, 1650 Arch St, Philadelphia, PA, 19103. p. 2954

Almendarez, Val, Coll Archivist, Academy of Motion Picture Arts & Sciences, 333 S La Cienega Blvd, Beverly Hills, CA, 90211. Tel: 310-247-3000, Ext 2224. Fax: 310-657-5193. p. 129

Almeyda, Brenda, Info Literacy, Ref Librn, Johnson C Smith University, 100 Beatties Ford Rd, Charlotte, NC, 28216. Tel: 704-371-6740. Fax: 704-378-1191. p. 1783

Almgren, Shelley, Per, Syst Librn, Texas Wesleyan University, 1201 Wesleyan St, Fort Worth, TX, 76105. Tel: 817-531-4816. Fax: 817-531-4806. p. 2324

Almodovar, Milton David, Head, Syst Support & Serv, Pace University Library, New York Civic Ctr, One Pace Plaza, New York, NY, 10038-1502. Tel: 212-346-1331. Fax: 212-346-1615. p. 1696

Almoite, Benjamin T, Librn, Virginia State Law Library, Supreme Court Bldg, 2nd Flr, 100 N Ninth St, Richmond, VA, 23219-2335. Tel: 804-786-2075. Fax: 804-786-4542. p. 2493

Almon, Margaret, Librn, Montgomery Hospital, 1301 Powell St, Norristown, PA, 19404. Tel: 610-270-2232. p. 2099

Almonar, Schmid, Br Mgr, Brooklyn Public Library, DeKalb Branch, 790 Bushwick Ave, Brooklyn, NY, 11221. Tel: 718-455-3898. Fax: 718-455-4071. p. 1591

Almquist, Arne J, PhD, Assoc Provost, Northern Kentucky University, University Dr, Highland Heights, KY, 41099. Tel: 859-572-5483. Fax: 859-572-6181. p. 917

Almquist, Deborah, Dir, NSMC, 500 Lynnfield St, Lynn, MA, 01904. Tel: 781-581-9200, Ext 4123. Fax: 781-581-0720. p. 1101

Almquist, Deborah, Dir, Libr Serv, North Shore Medical Center, Salem Hospital, 81 Highland Ave, Salem, MA, 01970. Tel: 978-354-4950. Fax: 978-744-9110. p. 1121

Alms, Mary Lynn, Dir, Town & Country Public Library District, 320 E North St, Elburn, IL, 60119. Tel: 630-365-2244. Fax: 630-365-2358. p. 640

Almy, Mary, Dir, Dermott O'Toole Memorial Library, PO Box 35, Tenakee Springs, AK, 99841-0035. Tel: 907-736-2248. Fax: 907-736-2249. p. 54

Aloi, Michael, Cat, Tech Serv, Dowling College Library, 150 Idle Hour Blvd, Oakdale, NY, 11769-1999. Tel: 631-244-3219. Fax: 631-244-3374. p. 1709

Aloia, Danielle, Spec Projects Librn, New York Academy of Medicine Library, 1216 Fifth Ave, New York, NY, 10029-5293. Tel: 212-822-7323. Fax: 212-423-0266. p. 1688

Aloisa, Francine A, Dir, Somers Public Library, 51 Ninth District Rd, Somers, CT, 06071-0368. Tel: 860-763-3501. Fax: 860-763-1718. p. 367

Aloisi, John, Acq Librn, Detroit Baptist Theological Seminary Library, 4801 Allen Rd, Allen Park, MI, 48101. Tel: 313-381-0111. Fax: 313-381-0798. p. 1149

Alomia, Sharyn, In Charge, Tuolumne County Free Library, Twain Harte Branch, 18701 Tiffeni Rd, Ste 1F, Twain Harte, CA, 95383. Tel: 209-586-4501. p. 269

Alonso, Carmen, Cat, United States Air Force, 437 SVS/SVMG, 106 W McCaw St, Bldg 215, Charleston AFB, SC, 29404-4700. Tel: 843-963-3320. Fax: 843-963-3840. p. 2185

Alpaugh, Amy, Dir, Salem Public Library, 562 Easton Tpk, Hamlin, PA, 18427-9720. Tel: 570-689-0903. Fax: 570-689-4432. p. 2064

Alpert, Phyllis Sue, Asst Dir, Miami-Dade Public Library System, 101 W Flagler St, Miami, FL, 33130-1523. Tel: 305-375-5184. Fax: 305-375-3048. p. 466

Alpert, Zalman, Per, Yeshiva University Libraries, Mendel Gottesman Library of Hebraica-Judaica, 2520 Amsterdam Ave, New York, NY, 10033. Tel: 212-960-5382. Fax: 212-960-0066. p. 1704

Alpi, Kristine, Head of Libr, North Carolina State University Libraries, Kenan Veterinary Medical Library, 1060 William Moore Dr, Campus Box 8401, Raleigh, NC, 27607. Tel: 919-513-6219. Fax: 919-513-6400. p. 1816

AlSaffar, Jackie, Ref/Outreach Coordr, Buena Vista University Library, 610 W Fourth St, Storm Lake, IA, 50588. Tel: 712-749-2089. Fax: 712-749-2059. p. 846

Alsagoff, Rachel, Mgr, Heald College, 1500 Kapiolani Blvd, Honolulu, HI, 96814. Tel: 808-628-5525. Fax: 808-955-6964. p. 564

Alsbury, Susan, Librn, Copiah-Jefferson Regional Library System, Longie Dale Hamilton Memorial Library, 1012 Spring St, Wesson, MS, 39191. Tel: 601-643-5725. Fax: 601-643-5725. p. 1301

Alsdorf, Judy, ILL, Lynn University Library, 3601 N Military Trail, Boca Raton, FL, 33431-5598. Tel: 561-237-7055. Fax: 561-237-7074. p. 428

Alsobrook, Anne, Cat, H Grady Bradshaw Chambers County Library, 3419 20th Ave, Valley, AL, 36854. Tel: 334-768-2161. Fax: 334-768-7272. p. 39

Alsop, Nancy, Pub Libr Consult, Viking Library System, 204 N Cascade St, Fergus Falls, MN, 56537. Tel: 218-739-5286. Fax: 218-739-5287. p. 1251

Alspaugh, Nancy, Librn, Selover Public Library, 31 State Rte 95, Chesterville, OH, 43317-0025. Tel: 419-768-3431. Fax: 419-768-2249. p. 1867

Alstadt, Nancy A, Librn, Bayer Corp Library, 100 Bayer Rd, Pittsburgh, PA, 15205-9741. Tel: 412-777-2783. Fax: 412-777-7470. p. 2121

Alston, Barbara, Br Mgr, Elmont Public Library, Stewart Manor Branch, 100 Covert Ave, Stewart Manor, NY, 11530. Tel: 516-354-8026. Fax: 516-358-1962. p. 1620

Alston, Paula, Dir, Montgomery-Floyd Regional Library System, 125 Sheltman St, Christiansburg, VA, 24073. Tel: 540-382-6965. Fax: 540-382-6964. p. 2457

Alston-Reeder, Lizzie, Coordr, Evening-Weekend Serv, Winston-Salem State University, 601 Martin Luther King Jr Dr, Winston-Salem, NC, 27110. Tel: 336-750-2447. Fax: 336-750-2459. p. 1834

Alsup, Kathleen, Asst Dir, Saint John's Mercy Medical Center, Tower B, 621 S New Ballas Rd, Ste 1000, Saint Louis, MO, 63141. Tel: 314-251-6340. Fax: 314-251-4299. p. 1357

Alt, Laura, Dir, Shelby Public Library, 255 Walnut, Shelby, NE, 68662-0146. Tel: 402-527-5181. Fax: 402-527-5181. p. 1419

Alt, Margaret, Asst Librn, Scribner Public Library, 504 Main St, Scribner, NE, 68057. Tel: 402-664-3540. Fax: 402-664-3540. p. 1419

Altamirano, Felipe, Head, Lending Serv, Maywood Public Library District, 121 S Fifth Ave, Maywood, IL, 60153. Tel: 708-343-1847, Ext 11. Fax: 708-343-2115. p. 672

Altan, A, Ser & ILL Tech, Prairie State College Library, 202 S Halsted St, Chicago Heights, IL, 60411-8200. Tel: 708-709-3550. Fax: 708-709-3940. p. 628

Altas, Sandra, Circ Supvr, Smithtown Library, One N Country Rd, Smithtown, NY, 11787. Tel: 631-265-2072. Fax: 631-265-2044. p. 1744

Altenhofen, Mary Clare, Head, Pub Serv, Head, Res Serv, Harvard Library, Fine Arts Library, Fogg Art Museum, 32 Quincy St, Cambridge, MA, 02138. Tel: 617-495-3374. Fax: 617-496-4889. p. 1075

Alter, Patricia, Coll Develop, Arlington County Department of Libraries, 1015 N Quincy St, Arlington, VA, 22201. Tel: 703-228-5985. Fax: 703-228-3354. p. 2448

Altftadt, Lynn, Ch, Crestline Public Library, 324 N Thoman St, Crestline, OH, 44827-1410. Tel: 419-683-3909. Fax: 419-683-3022. p. 1892

Althoff, Diane, Librn, Gregory Public Library, 112 E Fifth, Gregory, SD, 57533-1463. Tel: 605-835-8858. Fax: 605-835-9575. p. 2212

Althoff, Dixie, Asst Librn, Lena Community District Library, 300 W Mason St, Lena, IL, 61048. Tel: 815-369-3180. Fax: 815-369-3181. p. 665

Althoff, Emily, Br Mgr, Saint Louis County Library, Oak Bend Branch, 842 S Holmes Ave, Saint Louis, MO, 63122. Tel: 314-822-0051. p. 1359

Altieri, Marylene, Curator, Harvard Library, Arthur & Elizabeth Schlesinger Library on the History of Women in America, Three James St, Cambridge, MA, 02138-3766. Tel: 617-495-8651. Fax: 617-496-8340. p. 1076

Altis, Judy Jean, Dir, Mountain State University Library, 609 S Kanawha St, Beckley, WV, 25801. Tel: 304-929-1368. Fax: 304-929-1665. p. 2553

Altman, Gretchen, Br Mgr, Morgan County Public Library, Eminence Branch, Eminence Lion's Club, Waher's Rd, Eminence, IN, 46125. Tel: 765-528-2117. p. 763

Altman, Karen D, Br Librn, Berkeley County Library System, Sangaree, 595 Sangaree Pkwy, Summerville, SC, 29483. Tel: 843-695-1208. p. 2200

Altman, Mary, Librn, United States Air Force, Medical Center Library, 81st Medical Group/SGGMEL, 301 Fisher St, Rm 1A132, Keesler AFB, MS, 39534-2519. Tel: 228-376-4949. Fax: 228-377-6127. p. 1306

Altmann, Robert, Archivist, Diocese of La Crosse Archives, PO Box 4004, La Crosse, WI, 54602-4004. Tel: 608-788-7700. Fax: 608-788-8413. p. 2602

Altmeyer, Sue, Electronic Serv Librn, Cleveland State University, Cleveland-Marshall Law Library, Cleveland-Marshall College of Law, 1801 Euclid Ave, Cleveland, OH, 44115-2223. Tel: 216-687-4894. Fax: 216-687-6881. p. 1878

Altomara, Rita, Dir, Free Public Library of the Borough of Fort Lee, 320 Main St, Fort Lee, NJ, 07024. Tel: 201-592-3614. Fax: 201-585-0375. p. 1486

Alton, Doug, Media Serv Tech, Housatonic Community College Library, 900 Lafayette Blvd, Bridgeport, CT, 06604. Tel: 203-332-5077. Fax: 203-332-5252. p. 331

Altschuler, Jean, Tech Serv, Arnold & Porter Library, 555 12th St NW, Washington, DC, 20004-1206. Tel: 202-942-5000. Fax: 202-942-5999. p. 393

Altstatt, Lynne, Librn, Smithsonian Libraries, Vine DeLoria, Jr Library, National Museum of the American Indian, Cultural Resources Ctr, MRC 538, 4220 Silver Hill Rd, Suitland, DC, 20746-0537. Tel: 301-238-1376. Fax: 301-238-3038. p. 414

Aluri, Rao, Dr, Instr, Appalachian State University, RCOE, Dept of LES, 311 Edwin Duncan Hall, Boone, NC, 28608. Tel: 828-262-7236. Fax: 828-262-6035. p. 2971

Aluzzo, Adrienne, Digital Projects Librn, Lawrence Technological University Library, 21000 W Ten Mile Rd, Southfield, MI, 48075-1058. Tel: 248-204-2821. Fax: 248-204-3005. p. 1228

Alvarado, Gloria, Asst Librn, Utica Public Library District, Mill & Grove Sts, Utica, IL, 61373. Tel: 815-667-4509. Fax: 815-667-4140. p. 713

Alvardo, Jane, Per, Philadelphia College of Osteopathic Medicine, 4170 City Ave, Philadelphia, PA, 19131-1694. Tel: 215-871-6470. Fax: 215-871-6478. p. 2114

Alvare, Luz, Head Librn, International Food Policy Research Institute Library, 2033 K St NW, Washington, DC, 20006-1002. Tel: 202-862-5600, 202-862-5614. Fax: 202-467-4439. p. 405

Alvarez, Alma, Dir, Town of Chester Public Library, 6307 State Rte 9, Chestertown, NY, 12817. Tel: 518-494-5384. Fax: 518-491-5171. p. 1606

Alvarez, Manuel, Info Tech Dir, Texas State Library & Archives Commission, 1201 Brazos St, Austin, TX, 78701. Tel: 512-463-5481. p. 2282

Alvarez, Miguel, Circ, Ref, Pontifical Catholic University Of Puerto Rico, Monseignor Fremiot Torres Oliver Legal Information & Research Center, 2250 Avenida Las Americas, Ste 544, Ponce, PR, 00717-9997. Tel: 787-841-2000, Ext 1850, 1851. Fax: 787-841-5354. p. 2675

Alvarez, Minerva, Librn, South Texas College Library, 3201 W Pecan Blvd, McAllen, TX, 78501-6661. Tel: 956-872-3442. Fax: 956-872-7202. p. 2361

Alvarez, Patricia, Per, Palm Beach State College, 4200 Congress Ave, Mail Sta 17, Lake Worth, FL, 33461. Tel: 561-868-3800. Fax: 561-868-3708. p. 459

Alvarez, Rebecca A, Mgr, San Antonio Public Library, Las Palmas, 515 Castroville, San Antonio, TX, 78237. Tel: 210-434-6394. Fax: 210-435-5479. p. 2382

Alvarez, Rosaura, Ref, Speer Memorial Library, 801 E 12th St, Mission, TX, 78572. Tel: 956-580-8750. Fax: 956-580-8756. p. 2363

Alvarez, Sam, Br Librn, Catskill Public Library, Palenville Branch, 3335 Rte 23A, Palenville, NY, 12463. Tel: 518-678-3357. Fax: 518-678-9251. p. 1603

Alvarez, Sam, Mgr, Catskill Public Library, One Franklin St, Catskill, NY, 12414-1407. Tel: 518-943-4230. Fax: 518-943-1439. p. 1603

Alvarez, Shaunta, Archives Librn, Elon University, 308 N O'Kelly Ave, Elon, NC, 27244-0187. Tel: 336-278-6531. Fax: 336-278-6637. p. 1791

Alvarez-Cleary, Suzet, Asst Dir, Miami-Dade Public Library System, 101 W Flagler St, Miami, FL, 33130-1523. Tel: 305-375-5034. Fax: 305-375-3048. p. 466

Alvarez-Lenda, Alina, Librn, Hunton & Williams, 200 Park Ave, New York, NY, 10166. Tel: 212-309-1078. Fax: 212-309-1100. p. 1682

Alver, Tiffany, Librn, WLC Architects Library, 10470 Foothill Blvd, Rancho Cucamonga, CA, 91730-3754. Tel: 909-987-0909. Fax: 909-980-9980. p. 213

Alves, Catherine Mello, Librn, Massachusetts Trial Court, Superior Court House, 360 Gorham St, Lowell, MA, 01852. Tel: 978-452-9301. Fax: 978-970-2000. p. 1100

Alves, Persephone, Circ, Swansea Free Public Library, 69 Main St, Swansea, MA, 02777. Tel: 508-674-9609. Fax: 508-675-5444. p. 1130

Alvey, Patty, Pub Serv, Brescia University, 717 Frederica St, Owensboro, KY, 42301. Tel: 270-686-4212. Fax: 270-686-4266. p. 931

Alvia, Manuel, Supvr, Pub Serv, Iona College, Helen T Arrigoni Library-Technology Center, 715 North Ave, New Rochelle, NY, 10801-1890. Tel: 914-633-2000, Ext 4165. Fax: 914-633-2136. p. 1666

Alvin, Glenda, Asst Dir, Coll Develop, Tennessee State University, 3500 John A Merritt Blvd, Nashville, TN, 37209. Tel: 615-963-5230. Fax: 615-963-1368. p. 2259

Alvin, Shipley B, Admin Dir, Valparaiso Community Library, 459 Valparaiso Pkwy, Valparaiso, FL, 32580. Tel: 850-729-5406. Fax: 850-729-1120. p. 501

Alvis, Donna, Br Mgr, West Georgia Regional Library, Ephesus Public, 200 Rogers St, Roopville, GA, 30170. Tel: 770-854-7323. Fax: 770-854-7326. p. 524

Alward, Allan, Libr Mgr, Albert-Westmorland-Kent Regional Library, Sackville Public, 66 Main St, Sackville, NB, E4L 4A7, CANADA. Tel: 506-364-4915. Fax: 506-364-4915. p. 2765

Alward, Donna J, Dir, Houghton Lake Public Library, 4431 W Houghton Lake Dr, Houghton Lake, MI, 48629-8713. Tel: 989-366-9230. Fax: 989-366-0063. p. 1192

Alward, Judy, Info Spec, University of Alaska Anchorage, Environment & Natural Resources Institute Arctic Environment & Data Information Center Library, 707 A St, Anchorage, AK, 99501. Tel: 907-257-2732. Fax: 907-257-2707. p. 45

Alyea, Betty, Adult Serv, Libr Asst, Barry-Lawrence Regional Library, Monett Branch, 213 Sixth St, Monett, MO, 65708. Tel: 417-235-6646. Fax: 417-235-6799. p. 1346

Alzo, Michael G, Actg Univ Librn, Assoc Librn, Syst Librn, St Lawrence University, 23 Romoda Dr, Canton, NY, 13617. Tel: 315-229-5424. Fax: 315-229-7446. p. 1602

Alzo, Nancy, Ref Serv Coordr, State University of New York College at Potsdam, 44 Pierrepont Ave, Potsdam, NY, 13676-2294. Tel: 315-267-3317. Fax: 315-267-2744. p. 1722

Alzofon, Sammy, Dir, The Palm Beach Post Library, 2751 S Dixie Hwy, West Palm Beach, FL, 33405. Tel: 561-820-4495. Fax: 561-837-8409. p. 503

Amack, April, Dir, Morgan Community College Library, 920 Barlow Rd, Fort Morgan, CO, 80701-4399. Tel: 970-542-3187. Fax: 970-542-3114. p. 308

Amadife, Nkechi, Coordr, Libr Instruction, Head, Pub Serv, Kentucky State University, 400 E Main St, Frankfort, KY, 40601-2355. Tel: 502-597-6817. Fax: 502-597-5068. p. 914

Amador, Cindy, Libr Serv Mgr, Mohave County Library District, Lake Havasu City Branch Library, 1770 McCulloch Blvd N, Lake Havasu City, AZ, 86403-8847. Tel: 928-453-0718. Fax: 928-453-0720. p. 67

Amalong, Rebecca, Tech Serv Librn, Jasper County Public Library, 208 W Susan St, Rensselaer, IN, 47978. Tel: 219-866-5881. Fax: 219-866-7378. p. 774

Aman, Timothy, Ref, Spokane Community College Library, Mailstop 2160, Learning Resources Ctr, Bldg 16, 1810 N Greene St, Spokane, WA, 99217-5399. Tel: 509-533-7054. Fax: 509-533-8818. p. 2536

Amar, Alex, Libr Asst, Allan Memorial Institute of Psychiatry, Royal Victoria Hospital, 1025 Pine Ave W, Montreal, QC, H3A 1A1, CANADA. Tel: 514-934-1934, Ext 34528. Fax: 514-843-1731. p. 2887

Amaral, Jean, Ref Serv, Antioch University New England Library, 40 Avon St, Keene, NH, 03431-3516. Tel: 603-283-2400. Fax: 603-357-7345. p. 1452

Amaral, Jean, Emerging Tech Librn, Queensborough Community College, City University of New York, 222-05 56th Ave, Bayside, NY, 11364-1497. Tel: 718-631-5795. Fax: 718-281-5012. p. 1579

Amare, Marjanneke, Bibliog Serv Librn, Wayland Free Public Library, Five Concord Rd, Wayland, MA, 01778. Tel: 508-358-2311. Fax: 508-358-5249. p. 1134

Amato, Sara, Digital Assets Librn, Willamette University, 900 State St, Salem, OR, 97301. Tel: 503-370-6719. Fax: 503-370-6141. p. 2019

Amavizca, Omar, Mgr, Tech Serv, Merced College, 3600 M St, Merced, CA, 95348. Tel: 209-384-6145. Fax: 209-384-6084. p. 185

Amaya, Angela, Ref, Las Positas College Library, 3000 Campus Hill Dr, Livermore, CA, 94551-7623. Tel: 925-424-1150. Fax: 925-606-7249. p. 164

Amaya, Guadalupe, Asst Librn, Virgil & Josephine Gordon Memorial Library, 917 N Circle Dr, Sealy, TX, 77474. Tel: 979-885-7469. Fax: 979-885-7469. p. 2385

Ambelang, Richard, Info Res & Tech Librn, Goddard College, 123 Pitkin Rd, Plainfield, VT, 05667. Tel: 802-322-1608. p. 2432

Amber, Lynn, Access Serv Librn, Dartmouth College Library, Baker-Berry Library, 6025 Baker-Berry Library, Hanover, NH, 03755-3525. Tel: 603-646-2560. Fax: 603-646-2167. p. 1450

Amberg, Kathleen, Supvr, Johnson & Johnson Pharmaceutical Research & Development, 1003 US Hwy 202 P, Raritan, NJ, 08869-0602. Tel: 908-704-4919, 908-704-8998. Fax: 908-707-9860. p. 1525

Ambler, Betty, Librn, ConnDot Library & Information Center, 2800 Berlin Tpk, Newington, CT, 06111-4113. Tel: 860-594-3035. Fax: 860-594-3039. p. 360

Ambler, Judith F, Circuit Librn, United States Court of Appeals, Burn Courthouse, 1st Flr, 601 Market St, Room 1609, Philadelphia, PA, 19106. Tel: 267-299-4300. Fax: 267-299-4328. p. 2118

Ambra, Stephen P, Dir, Learning Res, NHTI, Concord's Community College, 31 College Dr, Concord, NH, 03301-7425. Tel: 603-271-7185. Fax: 603-271-7189. p. 1443

Ambrosait, Denise, Librn, Sea Cliff Village Library, Sea Cliff & Central Ave, Sea Cliff, NY, 11579-0280. Tel: 516-671-4290. Fax: 516-759-6613. p. 1742

Ambrose, Diane L, Dir, Citizens Library, 55 S College St, Washington, PA, 15301. Tel: 724-222-2400. Fax: 724-222-2606. p. 2151

Ambrose, Jan, Dir, Marseilles Public Library, 155 E Bluff St, Marseilles, IL, 61341-1499. Tel: 815-795-4437. Fax: 815-795-5137. p. 671

Ambrose, Ric, Curator, Dir, The Clay Center for the Arts & Sciences of West Virginia, 300 Leon Sullivan Way, Charleston, WV, 25301. Tel: 304-561-3526. p. 2556

Ambrosi, Tom, Archivist, University of Minnesota Duluth Library, 416 Library Dr, Duluth, MN, 55812. Tel: 218-726-7681. Fax: 218-726-8019. p. 1248

Ambrosini, Lynne, Chief Curator, Taft Museum of Art Library, 316 Pike St, Cincinnati, OH, 45202-4293. Tel: 513-241-0343. Fax: 513-241-2266. p. 1873

Ambrosino, Maureen, Libr Dir, Westborough Public Library, 55 W Main St, Westborough, MA, 01581. Tel: 508-366-3050. Fax: 508-366-3049. p. 1138

Ambroziak, Marta, Circ, New York Medical College, Basic Science Bldg, 95 Grasslands Rd, Valhalla, NY, 10595. Tel: 914-594-4204. Fax: 914-594-3171. p. 1760

Ambrus, Andre, Asst Prof, Res & Instruction Librn, University of La Verne, 2040 Third St, La Verne, CA, 91750. Tel: 909-593-3511, Ext 4305. Fax: 909-392-2733. p. 162

Ambruso, Diane, Dir, Thaddeus Stevens College of Technology, 750 E King St, Lancaster, PA, 17602-3198. Tel: 717-299-7754. Fax: 717-396-7186. p. 2078

Amburgey, Joyce, Head Librn, Letcher County Public Libraries, Lillian Webb Memorial, 1049 Hwy 317, Neon, KY, 41840. Tel: 606-855-7913. Fax: 606-855-4565. p. 937

Ameduri, Christine, Asst Archivist, Gettysburg College, 300 N Washington St, Gettysburg, PA, 17325. Tel: 717-337-7006. Fax: 717-337-7001. p. 2059

Ameen, Joe, Night/Weekend Serv Coordr, University of California, Merced Library, 5200 N Lake Rd, Merced, CA, 95343-5001. Tel: 209-201-5013. Fax: 209-228-4271. p. 186

Ameling, Linda S, Asst Dir, Adult Serv, Grande Prairie Public Library District, 3479 W 183rd St, Hazel Crest, IL, 60429. Tel: 708-798-5563. Fax: 708-798-5874. p. 654

Amelung, Richard C, Assoc Dir, Saint Louis University, Omer Poos Law Library, Morrissey Hall, 3700 Lindell Blvd, Saint Louis, MO, 63108-3478. Tel: 314-977-2743. Fax: 314-977-3966. p. 1361

Amemasor, James, Ref Librn, New Jersey Historical Society Library, 52 Park Pl, Newark, NJ, 07102-4302. Tel: 973-596-8500, Ext 249. Fax: 973-596-6957. p. 1511

Amen, Kathy, Govt Doc, Saint Mary's University, Louis J Blume Library, One Camino Santa Maria, San Antonio, TX, 78228-8608. Tel: 210-436-3441. Fax: 210-436-3782. p. 2381

Amendolea, Jennifer, Asst Librn, Ardmore Higher Education Center Library, 611 Veterans Blvd, Ardmore, OK, 73401. Tel: 580-220-2871. Fax: 580-223-5611. p. 1956

Amerson, Robert, Circ Mgr, University of South Carolina Aiken, 471 University Pkwy, Aiken, SC, 29801. Tel: 803-641-3485. Fax: 803-641-3302. p. 2180

Ames, Barbara, Admin/Personnel Mgr, Twin Falls Public Library, 201 Fourth Ave E, Twin Falls, ID, 83301-6397. Tel: 208-733-2964. Fax: 208-733-2965. p. 584

Ames, Becky, Dir, Simpson Memorial Library, Eight Plymouth Rd, Carmel, ME, 04419. Tel: 207-848-7145. Fax: 207-848-7145. p. 981

Ames, Debra, Librn, State University of New York College at Brockport, 350 New Campus Dr, Brockport, NY, 14420-2997. Tel: 585-395-2142. Fax: 585-395-5651. p. 1585

Ames, Gregg, Curator, Saint Louis Mercantile Library at the University of Missouri-St Louis, Thomas Jefferson Library Bldg, One University Blvd, Saint Louis, MO, 63121-4400. Tel: 314-516-7253. Fax: 314-516-7241. p. 1359

Ames, Kathryn S, Dir, Athens Regional Library System, 2025 Baxter St, Athens, GA, 30606-6331. Tel: 706-613-3650. Fax: 706-613-3660. p. 508

Ames, Kim, Extn Serv, Marion Public Library, Prospect Branch, 116 N Main, Prospect, OH, 43342. Tel: 740-494-2684. p. 1914

Ames, Lucile, Librn, North Central Regional Library, Okanogan Community, 228 Pine St, Okanogan, WA, 98840. Tel: 509-422-2609. Fax: 509-422-2609. p. 2549

Ames, Mark, Librn, Muskegon Area District Library, Norton Shores Jacob O Funkhouser Branch, 705 Seminole Rd, Muskegon, MI, 49441-4797. Tel: 231-780-8844. Fax: 231-780-5436. p. 1213

Amesse, Robert, Ref, Quinte West Public Library, Seven Creswell Dr, Trenton, ON, K8V 6X5, CANADA. Tel: 613-394-3381. Fax: 613-394-2079. p. 2868

Amey, Tracey, Librn, Digital Initiatives, Roger & Peggy Madigan Library, 999 Hagan Way, Williamsport, PA, 17701. Tel: 570-327-4523. Fax: 570-327-4503. p. 2156

Amici, Heidi, Info Tech, Mem Serv Librn, Monmouth County Library, 125 Symmes Dr, Manalapan, NJ, 07726. Tel: 732-431-7220. Fax: 732-308-2955. p. 1498

Amick, Alison, Curator of Coll, Oklahoma City Museum of Art, 415 Couch Dr, Oklahoma City, OK, 73102. Tel: 405-236-3100. Fax: 405-236-3122. p. 1974

Amick, Betty, Librn, Platte County Public Library, Glendo Branch, 213 Second St, Glendo, WY, 82213. Tel: 307-735-4480. p. 2661

Amill, Ileana, Ref, Pontifical Catholic University Of Puerto Rico, Encarnacion Valdes Library, 2250 Avenida Las Americas, Ste 509, Ponce, PR, 00717-0777. Tel: 787-841-2000, Ext 1801, 787-841-2000, Ext 1802. Fax: 787-284-0235. p. 2675

Amilowski, Janine, Dir, Res, Korn Ferry International, 233 S Wacker Dr, Ste 3300, Chicago, IL, 60606. Tel: 312-466-1834. Fax: 312-466-0451. p. 616

Amjadi, Hadi, Syst Librn, Golden Gate University, 536 Mission St, San Francisco, CA, 94105-2967. Tel: 415-442-7242. Fax: 415-543-6779. p. 242

Amjadi, Prano, Head, Ref, Santa Clara University, Heafey Law Library, School of Law, 500 El Camino Real, Santa Clara, CA, 95053-0430. Tel: 408-554-5320. Fax: 408-554-5318. p. 263

Amling, Jennifer, Mkt & Graphics Coordr, Helen M Plum Memorial Public Library District, 110 W Maple St, Lombard, IL, 60148-2594. Tel: 630-627-0316. Fax: 630-627-0336. p. 667

Ammerman, Jackie, Assoc Univ Librn, Digital Initiatives & Open Access, Boston University Libraries, Mugar Memorial Library, 771 Commonwealth Ave, Boston, MA, 02215. Tel: 617-353-3710. Fax: 617-353-2084. p. 1058

Ammon, Bette, Dir, Coeur d'Alene Public Library, 702 E Front Ave, Coeur d'Alene, ID, 83814-2373. Tel: 208-769-2315. Fax: 208-769-2381. p. 573

Ammons, Connie, Ref, Bossier Parish Central Library, 2206 Beckett St, Bossier City, LA, 71111. Tel: 318-746-1693. Fax: 318-746-7768. p. 945

Ammons, Denise, Coordr, Acq, Loyola University New Orleans, 6363 Saint Charles Ave, New Orleans, LA, 70118-6195. Tel: 504-864-7111. Fax: 504-864-7247. p. 961

Ammons, Doug, Librn, Clover Park Technical College Library, 4500 Steilacoom Blvd SW, Bldg 15, Lakewood, WA, 98499-4098. Tel: 253-589-6067. Fax: 253-589-5726. p. 2519

Amo, David, Librn, Michigan Department of Corrections, 2400 S Sheridan Dr, Muskegon, MI, 49442. Tel: 231-773-3201, Ext 271. Fax: 616-773-3657. p. 1212

Amodeo, Marian, Chief, Pub Serv, Hartford Public Library, 500 Main St, Hartford, CT, 06103-3075. Tel: 860-695-6296. Fax: 860-722-6900. p. 345

Amokomowo, Donna, Libr Asst Supvr, Montgomery College, Germantown Campus Library, 20200 Observation Dr, Germantown, MD, 20876. Tel: 240-567-7137. Fax: 301-353-7859. p. 1037

Amokomowo, Donna, Libr Asst Supvr, Montgomery College, Technical Services, 51 Mannakee St, Rockville, MD, 20850. Tel: 240-567-7137. Fax: 301-251-7141. p. 1037

Amon, Carolyn, Law Librn, Greenbaum, Rowe, Smith & Davis LLP, 99 Wood Ave S, Woodbridge, NJ, 07095. Tel: 732-549-5600. Fax: 732-549-1881. p. 1545

Amon, Tammy, Circ Librn, Falmouth Public Library, 300 Main St, Falmouth, MA, 02540. Tel: 508-457-2555. Fax: 508-457-2559. p. 1088

Amore, Shirley, City Librn, Denver Public Library, Ten W 14th Ave Pkwy, Denver, CO, 80204-2731. Tel: 720-865-1111. Fax: 720-865-2087. p. 300

Amores, Michelle, Sr Librn, San Jose Public Library, Santa Teresa, 290 International Circle, San Jose, CA, 95119-1132. Tel: 408-808-3068. Fax: 408-365-5787. p. 251

Amores, Michelle, Sr Librn, San Jose Public Library, Tully Community, 880 Tully Rd, San Jose, CA, 95111. Tel: 408-808-3030. Fax: 408-977-3113. p. 251

Amory, Dita, Actg Curator, Metropolitan Museum of Art, Robert Lehman Collection Library, 1000 Fifth Ave, New York, NY, 10028. Tel: 212-570-3915. Fax: 212-650-2542. p. 1686

Amos, Anita, Adult Serv, Essex Library Association, Inc, 33 West Ave, Essex, CT, 06426-1196. Tel: 860-767-1560. Fax: 860-767-2500. p. 338

Amos, Craig S, Bibliog Instr, Norfolk State University Library, 700 Park Ave, Norfolk, VA, 23504-8010. Tel: 757-823-8183. Fax: 757-823-2431. p. 2482

Amos, Jeanne, Dir, El Dorado County Library, 345 Fair Lane, Placerville, CA, 95667. Tel: 530-621-5546. Fax: 530-622-3911. p. 208

Amos, Kathy, Adult Serv, Outreach Librn, Alexandria-Monroe Public Library, 117 E Church St, Alexandria, IN, 46001-2005. Tel: 765-724-2196. Fax: 765-724-2204. p. 723

Amos, Kay, Dir, Ralls County Library, 100 N Public, Center, MO, 63436-1000. Tel: 573-267-3200. Fax: 573-267-3200. p. 1322

Amoura, Hakima, Librn, Lakeshore General Hospital, 160 Stillview Rd, Pointe-Claire, QC, H9R 2Y2, CANADA. Tel: 514-630-2225, Ext 6499. Fax: 514-630-5111. p. 2903

Amoyaw, Sandy, Adminr, Yonkers Public Library, Crestwood, 16 Thompson St, Yonkers, NY, 10707. Tel: 914-779-3774. p. 1772

Amoyaw, Sandy, Adminr, Yonkers Public Library, Grinton I Will Branch, 1500 Central Park Ave, Yonkers, NY, 10710. Tel: 914-337-1500. Fax: 914-337-9114. p. 1772

Ampol, Linda, Librn, Martin Correctional Institution Library, 1150 SW Allapattah Rd, Indiantown, FL, 34956-4310. Tel: 772-597-3705, Ext 224. Fax: 772-597-4529. p. 452

Amrhein, John, AV, Stony Brook University, Music, Melville Library, Rm W1530, Stony Brook, NY, 11794-3333. Tel: 631-632-7097. Fax: 631-632-7116. p. 1750

Amrhein, Kathleen, Br Mgr, West Lauri Ann Memorial Library, Sharpsburg Branch, 200 Linden Ave, Pittsburgh, PA, 15215-2322. Tel: 412-781-0783. Fax: 412-781-3504. p. 2129

Amsberry, Dan, Libr Mgr, Sweetwater County Library System, Rock Springs Library, 400 C St, Rock Springs, WY, 82901-6221. Tel: 307-352-6667, Ext 2410. Fax: 307-352-6657. p. 2655

Amsberry, Dawn, Ref Librn, Pennsylvania State University Libraries, Library Learning Services, 305 Pattee Library, Tower, University Park, PA, 16802-1803. Tel: 814-865-5093. Fax: 814-865-3665. p. 2148

Amschl, Tiffany, Adult Serv, Crete Public Library District, 1177 N Main St, Crete, IL, 60417. Tel: 708-672-8017. Fax: 708-672-3529. p. 632

Amstadt, Mary, Circ, McHenry Public Library District, 809 N Front St, McHenry, IL, 60050. Tel: 815-385-0036. Fax: 815-385-7085. p. 672

Amstutz, Sharon, ILL, Bedford Public Library System, 321 N Bridge St, Bedford, VA, 24523-1924. Tel: 540-586-8911, Ext 2113. Fax: 540-586-8875. p. 2450

Amstutz, Tim, Circ, Bethel College, 1001 W McKinley Ave, Mishawaka, IN, 46545. Tel: 574-257-3347. Fax: 574-257-3499. p. 765

Amulung, Johnene, Librn, Rolling Hills Public Library, 302 Fourth St, Rolling Hills, AB, T0J 2S0, CANADA. Tel: 403-964-2186. Fax: 403-964-3659. p. 2715

Amundson, Roseann, Ch, Montgomery Memorial Library, 711 Main St, Jewell, IA, 50130. Tel: 515-827-5112. Fax: 515-827-5112. p. 824

Amy, Osborne, Pres, Southeastern Chapter of the American Association of Law Libraries, c/o University of Kentucky, Law Library, 620 S Limestone St, Lexington, KY, 40506-0048. Tel: 859-257-8347. Fax: 859-323-4906. p. 2944

Amy, Swartz, Asst Cat Librn, Berklee College of Music Library, 150 Massachusetts Ave, Boston, MA, 02115. Tel: 617-747-3194. Fax: 617-747-2050. p. 1055

An, Yuan, PhD, Asst Prof, Drexel University, Rush Bldg, Rm 306, 30 N 33rd St, Philadelphia, PA, 19104-2875. Tel: 215-895-2474. Fax: 215-895-2494. p. 2972

Anaka, Patricia, Br Head, Toronto Public Library, Port Union, 5450 Lawrence Ave E, Toronto, ON, M1C 3B2, CANADA. Tel: 416-396-8885. Fax: 416-396-3558. p. 2863

Anasiewicz, Leona, Librn, Postal Rate Commission Library, 901 New York Ave NW, Ste 200, Washington, DC, 20268. Tel: 202-789-6877. Fax: 202-789-6861. p. 413

Anastos, Sophia, Dir, River Forest Public Library, 735 Lathrop Ave, River Forest, IL, 60305-1883. Tel: 708-366-5205, Ext 303. Fax: 708-366-8699. p. 694

Anaya, Amy, Head, Borrower Serv, Jones Library, Inc, 43 Amity St, Amherst, MA, 01002-2285. Tel: 413-259-3132. Fax: 413-256-4096. p. 1048

Anca, Meret, Librn, New York Orthopaedic Hospital-Columbia University College of Physicians & Surgeons, 622 W 168th St, PH11-1139, New York, NY, 10032. Tel: 212-305-3294. Fax: 212-305-6193. p. 1690

Ancell, Jack, Dir, Southside Virginia Community College Libraries, 109 Campus Dr, Alberta, VA, 23821. Tel: 434-949-1066. Fax: 434-949-0013. p. 2444

Ancell, Jack, Dir, Learning Res, Southside Virginia Community College, 200 Daniel Rd, Keysville, VA, 23947. Tel: 434-949-1066. Fax: 434-736-2079. p. 2472

Andel, Beatrice, Librn, Dallas Public Library, Main St, Dallas, WI, 54733. Tel: 715-837-1186. p. 2587

Anderegg, Peter, Librn, Massachusetts Trial Court, Superior Court House, 84 Elm St, Fitchburg, MA, 01420-3296. Tel: 978-345-6726. Fax: 978-345-7334. p. 1089

Anderies, John, Head, Spec Coll, Haverford College, 370 Lancaster Ave, Haverford, PA, 19041-1392. Tel: 610-896-2948. Fax: 610-896-1102. p. 2067

Anderman, Lynea, Dir of Libr Serv, Pennsylvania Institute of Technology Library, 800 Manchester Ave, Media, PA, 19063-4098. Tel: 610-892-1524. Fax: 610-892-1523. p. 2087

Anderman, Paul, Librn, North Central Regional Library, Peshastin Community, 8396 Main St, Peshastin, WA, 98847-9734. Tel: 509-548-7821. Fax: 509-548-7821. p. 2549

Andersen, Deborah Lines, Dr, Assoc Prof, University at Albany, State University of New York, Draper 116, 135 Western Ave, Albany, NY, 12222. Tel: 518-442-5122. Fax: 518-442-5367. p. 2970

Andersen, Jeff, Dir, Lyme Historical Society Library, 96 Lyme St, Old Lyme, CT, 06371. Tel: 860-434-5542. Fax: 860-434-9778. p. 363

Andersen, Judy, Librn, Olympic College, Poulsbo Campus, 1000 Olympic College Pl NW, Poulsbo, WA, 98370. Tel: 360-394-2720. Fax: 360-394-2721. p. 2511

Andersen, Julie, YA Librn, Casa Grande Public Library, Vista Grande Library, 1556 N Arizola Rd, Casa Grande, AZ, 85122. Tel: 520-421-8652. Fax: 520-836-0819. p. 59

Andersen, Kimberly, Br Mgr, Indianapolis-Marion County Public Library, West Indianapolis, 1216 S Kappes St, Indianapolis, IN, 46221-1540. Tel: 317-275-4540. p. 754

Andersen, Linda, Libr Asst, Inland Library System, 555 W Sixth St, San Bernardino, CA, 92140. Tel: 909-381-8257. Fax: 909-888-3171. p. 227

Andersen, Mark, Div Chief, Chicago Public Library, Business-Science-Technology Division, 400 S State St, Chicago, IL, 60605. Tel: 312-747-4470. p. 608

Andersen, Michael, Head, Ref, Butte-Silver Bow Public Library, 226 W Broadway St, Butte, MT, 59701-9297. Tel: 406-723-3361. Fax: 406-782-1825. p. 1376

Andersen, Patricia, Pub Serv Librn, Colorado School of Mines, 1400 Illinois St, Golden, CO, 80401-1887. Tel: 303-273-3652. Fax: 303-273-3199. p. 309

Andersen, Patricia A, Librn, Montgomery County Historical Society Library, 111 W Montgomery Ave, Rockville, MD, 20850. Tel: 301-340-2974. Fax: 301-340-2871. p. 1038

Andersen, Patricia M, Dir, South Dakota School of Mines & Technology, 501 E Saint Joseph St, Rapid City, SD, 57701-3995. Tel: 605-394-2418. Fax: 605-394-1256. p. 2217

Andersen, Pia, Tech Serv, Volusia County Public Library, 1290 Indian Lake Rd, Daytona Beach, FL, 32124. Tel: 386-248-1745. Fax: 386-248-1746. p. 436

Andersen, Susan, Mgr, Bow Island Municipal Library, 510 Centre St, Bow Island, AB, T0K 0G0, CANADA. Tel: 403-545-2828. Fax: 403-545-6642. p. 2686

Andersen, Torris, Assoc Prof, Ref Librn, Ocean County College Library, College Dr, Toms River, NJ, 08754. Tel: 732-255-0400, Ext 2250. Fax: 732-255-0421. p. 1533

Andersen, Valerie, Librn, Western Nevada Community College, 2201 W College Pkwy, Carson City, NV, 89703. Tel: 775-445-3229. Fax: 775-445-3363. p. 1426

Andersen-Kopczyk, Dana, Ch, Brown Deer Public Library, 5600 W Bradley Rd, Brown Deer, WI, 53223-3510. Tel: 414-357-0106. Fax: 414-354-8081. p. 2583

Anderson, Alan, Br Mgr, Washington County Library System, Washington Branch, 220 N 300 E, Washington City, UT, 84780. Tel: 435-627-2706. Fax: 435-627-2776. p. 2412

Anderson, Allison H, Dir, Pickens County Library System, 304 Biltmore Rd, Easley, SC, 29640. Tel: 864-850-7077. Fax: 864-850-7088. p. 2193

Anderson, Amy, Br Mgr, Wayne County Public Library, Creston Branch, 116 S Main St, Creston, OH, 44217. Tel: 330-435-4204. Fax: 330-435-6279. p. 1950

Anderson, Amy, Head, Per, Southwestern University, 1100 E University Ave, Georgetown, TX, 78626. Tel: 512-863-1561. Fax: 512-863-8198. p. 2327

Anderson, Angie, Youth Serv, Hyrum Library, 50 W Main, Hyrum, UT, 84319. Tel: 435-245-6411. Fax: 435-245-0180. p. 2406

Anderson, Anita, Dir, Minnesota Attorney General Library, Bremer Tower, Ste 1050, 445 Minnesota St, Saint Paul, MN, 55101-2109. Tel: 651-757-1050, 651-757-1055. Fax: 651-296-7000. p. 1279

Anderson, Ara, Ref, Campbell County Public Library System, 2101 S 4-J Rd, Gillette, WY, 82718-5205. Tel: 307-687-0009. Fax: 307-686-4009. p. 2655

Anderson, Audrey, Info Spec, PPG Industries, Inc, Chemicals Technical Information Center, 440 College Park Dr, Monroeville, PA, 15146. Tel: 724-325-5221. Fax: 724-325-5289. p. 2128

Anderson, Audrey, Info Spec, PPG Industries, Inc, Glass Technology Center, Guys Run Rd, Harmar Township, PA, 15238. Tel: 412-820-8517. Fax: 412-820-8696. p. 2128

Anderson, Autumn, Br Supvr, Wythe-Grayson Regional Library, Fries Public, 105 W Main St, Fries, VA, 24330. Tel: 276-744-3160. Fax: 276-744-3160. p. 2472

Anderson, Autumn, Br Supvr, Wythe-Grayson Regional Library, Whitetop Public, 16309 Highlands Pkwy, Whitetop, VA, 24292. Tel: 276-388-2873. Fax: 276-388-2873. p. 2472

Anderson, Barb, Br Mgr, Clark County Public Library, Park Branch, 1119 Bechtle Ave, Springfield, OH, 45504. Tel: 937-322-2498. p. 1935

Anderson, Barbara, Asst Dir, Spring Lake District Library, 123 E Exchange St, Spring Lake, MI, 49456-2018. Tel: 616-846-5770. Fax: 616-844-2129. p. 1229

Anderson, Barbara, Circ, Albright College, 13th & Exeter Sts, Reading, PA, 19604. Tel: 610-921-7200. Fax: 610-921-7509. p. 2132

Anderson, Bette, Dir, Renton Public Library, 100 Mill Ave S, Renton, WA, 98057. Tel: 425-430-6610. Fax: 425-430-6833. p. 2525

Anderson, Bette, Dir, Renton Public Library, Highlands, 2902 NE 12th St, Renton, WA, 98056. Tel: 425-430-6790. p. 2526

Anderson, Bianca, Foreign & Intl Law Librn, Ref Librn, University of Miami, 1311 Miller Dr, Coral Gables, FL, 33146. Tel: 305-284-2251. Fax: 305-284-3554. p. 434

Anderson, Bonnie, Adult Serv, ILL, Seneca Public Library District, 210 N Main St, Seneca, IL, 61360. Tel: 815-357-6566. Fax: 815-357-6568. p. 701

Anderson, Bonnie, Mgr, Youth Serv, Puyallup Public Library, 324 S Meridian, Puyallup, WA, 98371. Tel: 253-770-3334. Fax: 253-841-5483. p. 2525

Anderson, Brenda, Acq, Tech Serv, North Platte Public Library, 120 W Fourth St, North Platte, NE, 69101-3993. Tel: 308-535-8036. Fax: 308-535-8296. p. 1410

Anderson, Carol, Adult Ref Librn, Leesburg Public Library, 100 E Main St, Leesburg, FL, 34748. Tel: 352-728-9790. Fax: 352-728-9794. p. 461

Anderson, Carol, Tech Serv, Teaneck Public Library, 840 Teaneck Rd, Teaneck, NJ, 07666. Tel: 201-837-4171. Fax: 201-837-0410. p. 1533

Anderson, Carol, Dir, Spring Green Community Library, 230 E Monroe St, Spring Green, WI, 53588-8035. Tel: 608-588-2276. p. 2639

Anderson, Carrie, Libr Tech, Colorado Department of Corrections, 12101 Hwy 61, Sterling, CO, 80751. Tel: 970-521-3404. Fax: 970-521-8905. p. 323

Anderson, Carrie, Asst Librn, North Valley Public Library, 208 Main St, Stevensville, MT, 59870. Tel: 406-777-5061. Fax: 406-777-5061. p. 1388

Anderson, Catherine, Curator, Dir, Miami County Museum, 51 N Broadway, Peru, IN, 46970. Tel: 765-473-9183. Fax: 765-473-3880. p. 772

Anderson, Chela, Libr Serv Mgr, Daly City Public Library, 40 Wembley Dr, Daly City, CA, 94015-4399. Tel: 650-991-8023. Fax: 650-991-5726. p. 138

Anderson, Cheryl, Ch, Stromsburg Public Library, 230 Central St, Stromsburg, NE, 68666. Tel: 402-764-7681. Fax: 402-764-7681. p. 1420

Anderson, Cheryl, Librn, Arlington Community Library, 306 S Main St, Arlington, SD, 57212. Tel: 605-983-5741, Ext 230. p. 2210

Anderson, Cheryl, Dr, Dean, University of the Incarnate Word, 4301 Broadway, UPO Box 297, San Antonio, TX, 78209-6397. Tel: 210-829-6010. Fax: 210-829-6041. p. 2384

Anderson, Christine, Librn, Fluvanna Free Library, 3532 Fluvanna Ave Ext, Jamestown, NY, 14701. Tel: 716-487-1773. Fax: 716-487-2311. p. 1646

Anderson, Christopher, Pub Serv, Miles College, 5500 Myron Massey Blvd, Fairfield, AL, 35064. Tel: 205-929-1712. Fax: 205-929-1635. p. 16

Anderson, Christopher J, PhD, Methodist Librn, Drew University Library, 36 Madison Ave, Madison, NJ, 07940. Tel: 973-408-3910. Fax: 973-408-3770. p. 1497

Anderson, Christopher J, PhD, Dir, United Methodist Church, 36 Madison Ave, Madison, NJ, 07940. Tel: 973-408-3590. Fax: 973-408-3836. p. 1498

Anderson, Clifford, Curator, Spec Coll, Princeton Theological Seminary, Mercer St & Library Pl, Princeton, NJ, 08542. Tel: 609-497-7940. p. 1522

Anderson, Cokie G, Digitization Librn, Oklahoma State University Libraries, Oklahoma State University, Athletic Ave, Stillwater, OK, 74078-1071. Tel: 405-744-6316. Fax: 405-744-4515. p. 1978

Anderson, Connie, Head, Ref, Southern Oregon University, 1250 Siskiyou Blvd, Ashland, OR, 97520-5076. Tel: 541-552-6820. Fax: 541-552-6429. p. 1990

Anderson, Connie, Assess Serv Spec, Clark College, Information Commons @ Columbia Tech Center, Information Commons - CTC 245, 18700 SE Mill Plain Blvd, Vancouver, WA, 98683. Tel: 360-992-6137. p. 2545

Anderson, Craig, Librn, Kean University, 1000 Morris Ave, Union, NJ, 07083. Tel: 908-737-4600. Fax: 908-737-4620. p. 1537

Anderson, Dale, Libr Dir, VPres, AMG International Library, 6815 Shallowford Rd, Chattanooga, TN, 37421-1755. Tel: 423-894-6060, Ext 238. Fax: 423-894-9511. p. 2226

Anderson, Dave, Br Mgr, Campbell County Public Library District, 3920 Alexandria Pike, Cold Spring, KY, 41076. Tel: 859-781-6166. Fax: 859-572-5032. p. 909

Anderson, David, Dir, Crossett Public Library, 1700 Main St, Crossett, AR, 71635. Tel: 870-364-2230. Fax: 870-364-2231. p. 97

Anderson, Dawn, Librn, Northwest Regional Library, Godel Memorial Library, 314 E Johnson Ave, Warren, MN, 56762-1235. Tel: 218-745-5465. Fax: 218-745-8807. p. 1286

Anderson, Debbie, Librn, Estrella Mountain Community College Library, 3000 N Dysart Rd, Avondale, AZ, 85323-1000. Tel: 623-935-8091. Fax: 623-935-8060. p. 57

Anderson, Deborah, Youth Serv Adminr, County of Los Angeles Public Library, 7400 E Imperial Hwy, Downey, CA, 90242-3375. Tel: 562-940-8522. Fax: 562-803-3032. p. 140

Anderson, Deborah, Librn, Ozark Regional Library, Fredericktown Branch, 115 S Main St, Fredericktown, MO, 63645. Tel: 573-783-2120. p. 1333

Anderson, Deborah, Dr, Dir, Clovis Community College Library, 417 Schepps Blvd, Clovis, NM, 88101. Tel: 575-769-4080. Fax: 575-769-4190. p. 1553

Anderson, Deborah F, Librn, Brevard Community College, 250 Community College Pkwy, Palm Bay, FL, 32909. Tel: 321-433-5260. Fax: 321-433-5309. p. 479

Anderson, Debra, Br Mgr, Louisville Free Public Library, Jeffersontown Branch, 10635 Watterson Trail, Jeffersontown, KY, 40299. Tel: 502-267-5713. Fax: 502-266-6569. p. 924

Anderson, Debra, Univ Archivist, University of Wisconsin-Green Bay, 2420 Nicolet Dr, Green Bay, WI, 54311-7001. Tel: 920-465-2539. Fax: 920-465-2136. p. 2596

Anderson, Delores, Br Supvr, Saint John the Baptist Parish Library, Garyville Branch, 111 Historic Front St, Garyville, LA, 70051. Tel: 985-535-6868. Fax: 985-535-6868. p. 955

Anderson, Diana, Ch, McMinnville Public Library, 225 NW Adams St, McMinnville, OR, 97128-5425. Tel: 503-435-5569. Fax: 503-435-5560. p. 2005

Anderson, Diana B, Dir, Walter E Olson Memorial Library, 203 N Main St, Eagle River, WI, 54521. Tel: 715-479-8070, Ext 21. Fax: 715-479-2435. p. 2589

Anderson, Diane, Adult Serv, Shelby County Public Library, 57 W Broadway, Shelbyville, IN, 46176. Tel: 317-398-7121, 317-835-2653. Fax: 317-398-4430. p. 778

Anderson, Dixie, Dir, Libr Serv, Alberta Health Services, Red Deer Regional Hospital Centre Medical Library Services, 3942 50A Ave, Red Deer, AB, T4N 4E7, CANADA. Tel: 403-343-4557. Fax: 403-343-4910. p. 2714

Anderson, Dody, Principal Librn, Watsonville Public Library, 310 Union St, Watsonville, CA, 95076. Tel: 831-768-3400. Fax: 831-763-4015. p. 282

Anderson, Donna, Dir, Gila County Historical Museum Library, 1330 N Broad St, Globe, AZ, 85501. Tel: 928-425-7385. p. 64

Anderson, Donna, Exec Dir, Swedish Historical Society of Rockford, 404 S Third St, Rockford, IL, 61104. Tel: 815-963-5559. Fax: 815-963-5559. p. 698

Anderson, Dottie, Dir, United States Department of Commerce, David Skaggs Research Center, 325 Broadway, Rm 2C407, Boulder, CO, 80305. Tel: 303-497-6742. Fax: 303-497-3894. p. 291

Anderson, Douglas, Head, Ref, Ashtabula County District Library, 335 W 44th St, Ashtabula, OH, 44004-6897. Tel: 440-997-9341, Ext 225. Fax: 440-992-7714. p. 1855

Anderson, Douglas, Dr, Dir, Marietta College, 220 Fifth St, Marietta, OH, 45750. Tel: 740-376-4757. Fax: 740-376-4843. p. 1913

Anderson, Edgar, Dir, James E Whalley Museum & Library, 351 Middle St, Portsmouth, NH, 03801. Tel: 603-436-3712. p. 1463

Anderson, Elizabeth, Libr Dir, Preston Public Library, 101 St Paul St NW, Preston, MN, 55965. Tel: 507-765-4511. p. 1271

Anderson, Elizabeth, Br Librn, Bucks County Free Library, Samuel Pierce Branch, 491 Arthur Ave, Perkasie, PA, 18944-1033. Tel: 215-257-9718. Fax: 215-257-0759. p. 2050

Anderson, Eloise, Asst Librn, St Croix Falls Public Library, 230 S Washington St, Saint Croix Falls, WI, 54024. Tel: 715-483-1777. Fax: 715-483-1777. p. 2635

Anderson, Emma J, Dir, Clairton Public Library, 616 Miller Ave, Clairton, PA, 15025-1497. Tel: 412-233-7966. Fax: 412-233-2536. p. 2044

Anderson, Eric, Br Dir, Settlement Music School, Germantown Library, 6128 Germantown Ave, Philadelphia, PA, 19144. Tel: 215-320-2610. Fax: 215-438-7133. p. 2117

Anderson, Eric, Dir, Settlement Music School, 416 Queen St, Philadelphia, PA, 19147-3094. Tel: 215-320-2602. Fax: 215-551-0483. p. 2117

Anderson, Fiona, Dir of Libr Serv, Vancouver Island Regional Library, 6250 Hammond Bay Rd, Nanaimo, BC, V9R 5N3, CANADA. Tel: 250-753-1154, Ext 243. Fax: 250-758-2482. p. 2732

Anderson, Fred, Acq, Librn, Virginia Baptist Historical Society & the Center for Baptist Heritage & Studies Library, PO Box 34, University of Richmond, Richmond, VA, 23173. Tel: 804-289-8434. Fax: 804-289-8953. p. 2492

Anderson, Freya, Head, Info Serv, Librn, Alaska State Library, 333 Willoughby Ave, State Office Bldg, 8th Flr, Juneau, AK, 99801. Tel: 907-465-2910. Fax: 907-465-2151. p. 49

Anderson, Gayle, Librn, De Soto Trail Regional Library, Lucy Maddox Memorial, 11880 Columbia St, Blakely, GA, 39823. Tel: 229-723-3079. Fax: 229-723-6429. p. 522

Anderson, Gerald, Librn, Joliet Junior College, J-Bldg, 3rd Flr, 1215 Houbolt Rd, Joliet, IL, 60431-8938. Tel: 815-729-9020, Ext 2350. Fax: 815-744-2465. p. 659

Anderson, Glenn, Asst Dean, Coll Develop, Auburn University, Ralph Brown Draughon Library, 231 Mell St, Auburn, AL, 36849. Tel: 334-844-4500. Fax: 334-844-4424. p. 5

Anderson, Grace, Dir, Online Serv, Regional Medical Center, 1001 Towson Ave, Fort Smith, AR, 72901-4915. Tel: 479-441-5337. Fax: 479-441-5339. p. 101

Anderson, Grace, Dir, Arkansas Area Health Education Center Consortium, Sparks Regional Medical Ctr, 1001 Tawson Ave, Fort Smith, AR, 72901-4992. Tel: 479-441-5337. Fax: 479-441-5339. p. 2937

Anderson, Greg, Archives Librn, University of Nebraska at Kearney, 2508 11th Ave, Kearney, NE, 68849-2240. Tel: 308-865-8593. Fax: 308-865-8722. p. 1403

Anderson, Helen, Coll Develop, University of Rochester, River Campus Libraries, 755 Library Rd, Rochester, NY, 14627-0055. Tel: 585-275-4461. Fax: 585-273-5309. p. 1733

Anderson, Hope, Ch, Morrill Memorial Library, 33 Walpole St, Norwood, MA, 02062-1206. Tel: 781-769-0200. Fax: 781-769-6083. p. 1115

Anderson, J Theodore, Dir, Libr & Archives, The National Presbyterian Church & Center, Administration Bldg, 4101 Nebraska Ave NW, Washington, DC, 20016-2793. Tel: 202-537-7529. Fax: 202-686-0031. p. 410

Anderson, Jaime, Mat Mgt Mgr, Sonoma County Library, 211 E St, Santa Rosa, CA, 95404. Tel: 707-545-0831. Fax: 707-575-0437. p. 267

Anderson, James D, Librn, Good Samaritan Church Library, 6085 Park Blvd, Pinellas Park, FL, 33781. Tel: 727-544-8558. Fax: 727-544-8558. p. 483

Anderson, James D, Prof, Rutgers, The State University of New Jersey, Four Huntington St, New Brunswick, NJ, 08901-1071. Tel: 732-932-7500, Ext 8955. Fax: 732-932-2644. p. 2969

Anderson, Jane, Managing Librn, Bay County Library System, Alice & Jack Wirt Public Library, 500 Center Ave, Bay City, MI, 48708-5989. Tel: 989-893-9566. Fax: 989-893-9799. p. 1156

Anderson, Jane, Dir, Chesterfield Public Library, 524 Rte 63, Chesterfield, NH, 03443-0158. Tel: 603-363-4621. Fax: 603-363-4958. p. 1441

Anderson, Janice, Curator, Concordia University Libraries, Faculty of Fine Arts Slide Library, 1395 Rene Levesque Blvd W, Montreal, QC, H3G 2M5, CANADA. Tel: 514-848-2424, Ext 4274. Fax: 514-848-8627. p. 2894

Anderson, Janice L, ILL, Ref Librn, Malone University, 2600 Cleveland Ave NW, Canton, OH, 44709-3897. Tel: 330-471-8317. Fax: 330-454-6977. p. 1863

Anderson, Jean, Br Mgr, North Las Vegas Library District, Aliante Library, 2400 Deer Springs Way, North Las Vegas, NV, 89084. Tel: 702-839-2980. Fax: 702-839-5707. p. 1432

Anderson, Jean, Circ, Ref, Columbia-Greene Community College Library, 4400 Rte 23, Hudson, NY, 12534. Tel: 518-828-4181, Ext 3287. Fax: 518-828-4396. p. 1638

Anderson, Jennifer, Head, Coll Presv, San Diego State University Library & Information Access, 5500 Campanile Dr, San Diego, CA, 92182-8050. Tel: 619-594-4962. Fax: 619-594-3270. p. 237

Anderson, Jewell, Ref & Instruction Librn, Armstrong Atlantic State University, 11935 Abercorn St, Savannah, GA, 31419. Tel: 912-344-3027. Fax: 912-344-3457. p. 549

Anderson, Joann, Libr Assoc, Rushville Public Library, 207 Sprague St, Rushville, NE, 69360. Tel: 308-327-2740. Fax: 308-327-2740. p. 1418

Anderson, Joanna, Distance Educ Librn, East Tennessee State University, Sherrod Library, Seehorn Dr & Lake St, Johnson City, TN, 37614-0204. Tel: 423-439-4714. Fax: 423-439-5222. p. 2239

Anderson, John, Dir, Maps Librn, Louisiana State University Libraries, Cartographic Information Center, Dept of Geography & Anthropology, Howe-Russell Geoscience Complex, Rm 313, Baton Rouge, LA, 70803-4100. Tel: 225-578-6247. Fax: 225-578-4420. p. 943

Anderson, John, Cat, Saint Bonaventure University, 3261 W State Rd, Saint Bonaventure, NY, 14778. Tel: 716-375-2340. Fax: 716-375-2389. p. 1737

Anderson, John W, Libr Spec, Big Bend Community College Library, 7662 Chanute St, Moses Lake, WA, 98837. Tel: 509-793-2350. Fax: 509-762-2402. p. 2521

Anderson, Joleen, Dir, Rembrandt Public Library, Main St & Broadway, Rembrandt, IA, 50576. Tel: 712-286-6801. Fax: 712-286-6801. p. 840

Anderson, Jon R, Dir, Marian J Mohr Memorial Library, One Memorial Ave, Johnston, RI, 02919-3221. Tel: 401-231-4980. Fax: 401-231-4984. p. 2167

Anderson, Joseph, Head of Libr, American Institute of Physics, One Physics Ellipse, College Park, MD, 20740-3843. Tel: 301-209-3177. Fax: 301-209-3144. p. 1024

Anderson, Joyce, Dir, Fullerton Public Library, 903 Broadway, Fullerton, NE, 68638. Tel: 308-536-2382. Fax: 308-536-2382. p. 1399

Anderson, Jude, Managing Librn I, Sno-Isle Libraries, Granite Falls Community Library, 815 E Galena St, Granite Falls, WA, 98252. Tel: 360-691-6087. Fax: 360-691-5533. p. 2542

Anderson, Judith, Dir, Longmont Public Library, 409 Fourth Ave, Longmont, CO, 80501-6006. Tel: 303-651-8470. Fax: 303-651-8911. p. 317

Anderson, Judy, Pub Serv, Tech Serv, Sauk Valley Community College, 173 IL Rte 2, Dixon, IL, 61021-9112. Tel: 815-288-5511, Ext 316. Fax: 815-288-5651. p. 637

Anderson, Judy, Head, Ref, Concordia University Library, 2811 NE Holman St, Portland, OR, 97211-6067. Tel: 503-493-6453. Fax: 503-280-8697. p. 2010

Anderson, Julie, Asst Dir, Cumberland Public Library, 1305 Second Ave, Cumberland, WI, 54829. Tel: 715-822-2767. p. 2587

Anderson, Karen, Librn, Perkins Coie Library, 2901 N Central Ave, Ste 2000, Phoenix, AZ, 85012. Tel: 602-351-8213. p. 75

Anderson, Karen, Dir, Clarkia District Library, 377 Poplar St, Clarkia, ID, 83812. Tel: 208-245-2908. Fax: 208-245-2908. p. 573

Anderson, Karen, Dir, Trinity Health, 20 Burdick Expressway W, Health Center E, Minot, ND, 58701. Tel: 701-857-5435. p. 1846

Anderson, Karen, Librn, Hudson's Hope Public Library, 9905 Dudley Dr, Hudson's Hope, BC, V0C 1V0, CANADA. Tel: 250-783-9414. Fax: 250-783-5272. p. 2729

Anderson, Karen, Dir, Pub Serv, Hamilton Public Library, 55 York Blvd, Hamilton, ON, L8R 3K1, CANADA. Tel: 905-546-3200, Ext 3497. Fax: 905-546-3202. p. 2808

Anderson, Karen L, Actg Dir, Glasgow City-County Library, 408 Third Ave S, Glasgow, MT, 59230. Tel: 406-228-2731. Fax: 406-228-8193. p. 1379

Anderson, Kari, Ref Coordr, University of Washington Libraries, Natural Sciences, Allen Library S, Ground & First Flrs, Box 352900, Seattle, WA, 98195-2900. Tel: 206-685-2789. Fax: 206-685-1665. p. 2534

Anderson, Katherine, Pub Serv Librn, South Plains College Library, 1401 S College Ave, Box E, Levelland, TX, 79336. Tel: 806-716-2303. Fax: 806-894-5274. p. 2355

Anderson, Katie, Ref, Rutgers University Libraries, Paul Robeson Library, Camden, 300 N Fourth St, Camden, NJ, 08102-1404. Tel: 856-225-2830. Fax: 856-225-6428. p. 1477

Anderson, Katrina, Exec Dir, Manheim Township Public Library, 595 Granite Run Dr, Lancaster, PA, 17601. Tel: 717-509-4604, Ext 303. Fax: 717-560-0570. p. 2077

Anderson, Kaycee, Circ, North Platte Public Library, 120 W Fourth St, North Platte, NE, 69101-3993. Tel: 308-535-8036. Fax: 308-535-8296. p. 1410

Anderson, Kim, In Charge, Multnomah County Library, Northwest, 2300 NW Thurman St, Portland, OR, 97210. Tel: 503-988-5560. Fax: 503-988-3486. p. 2012

Anderson, Kirsten, Librn, O'Melveny & Myers LLP, 610 Newport Center Dr, Newport Beach, CA, 92660-6429. Tel: 949-760-9600. Fax: 949-823-6994. p. 194

Anderson, Kris, Coll Develop Officer, University of Hawaii at Manoa Library, 2550 McCarthy Mall, Honolulu, HI, 96822. Tel: 808-956-7203. Fax: 808-956-5968. p. 565

Anderson, Kristi Susan, Librn, Parker Hannifin Corp, 16666 Von Karman Ave, M/S A-17, Irvine, CA, 92606-4997. Tel: 949-851-3352. Fax: 949-851-3571. p. 160

Anderson, Kristina, Electronic Res/Institutional Repository/Ref Librn, Seton Hall University, One Newark Ctr, Newark, NJ, 07102. Tel: 973-642-8764. p. 1513

Anderson, Lajmar, Acad Projects Librn, Earlham College, 801 National Rd W, Richmond, IN, 47374-4095. Tel: 765-983-1360. Fax: 765-983-1304. p. 774

Anderson, Larry, Librn, South Dakota State Penitentiary, 1600 N Dr, Sioux Falls, SD, 57104-0915. Tel: 605-367-5170, 605-367-5171. p. 2219

Anderson, Laura, Circ, Rice Lake Public Library, Two E Marshall St, Rice Lake, WI, 54868. Tel: 715-234-4861. Fax: 715-234-5026. p. 2633

Anderson, Lawrence, Librn, Houston Community College Northeast College, Northline Library, 8001 Fulton St, Houston, TX, 77022. Tel: 713-718-8045. Fax: 713-718-8063. p. 2338

Anderson, Leah, Circ & ILL Mgr, Concordia College, 901 S Eighth St, Moorhead, MN, 56562. Tel: 218-299-4640. Fax: 218-299-4253. p. 1265

Anderson, Len, Reader Serv Mgr, Tigard Public Library, 13500 SW Hall Blvd, Tigard, OR, 97223-8111. Tel: 503-684-6537, Ext 2511. Fax: 503-598-7515, 503-718-2797. p. 2021

Anderson, Leona, Vols Librn, Maine Education Center for the Deaf & Hard of Hearing, One Mackworth Island, Falmouth, ME, 04105-1951. Tel: 207-781-6237. Fax: 207-781-6240. p. 985

Anderson, Linda, Ref, Austin Public Library, 323 Fourth Ave NE, Austin, MN, 55912-3370. Tel: 507-433-2391. Fax: 507-433-8787. p. 1240

Anderson, Linda, Head, Circ, Kenosha Public Library, 812 56th St, Kenosha, WI, 53140-3735. Tel: 262-564-6134. Fax: 262-564-6370. p. 2601

Anderson, Lisa, Ch, Burlington Public Library, 820 E Washington, Burlington, WA, 98233. Tel: 360-755-0760. Fax: 360-755-0717. p. 2511

Anderson, Lois, Interim Dir, Montgomery College, 51 Mannakee St, Rockville, MD, 20850. Tel: 240-567-7101. p. 1037

Anderson, Lorea, Mgr, Crossfield Municipal Library, 1026 Chisholm Ave, Crossfield, AB, T0M 0S0, CANADA. Tel: 403-946-4232. Fax: 403-946-4212. p. 2696

Anderson, Lynn, Dir, Central Bible College, 3000 N Grant Ave, Springfield, MO, 65803. Tel: 417-833-2551, Ext 1165. Fax: 417-833-5478. p. 1366

Anderson, Lynn, Tech Serv Librn, Snow College, 141 E Center St, Ephraim, UT, 84627. Tel: 435-283-7366. Fax: 435-283-7369. p. 2405

Anderson, Marcia, Head, Bibliog & Metadata Serv, Arizona State University Libraries, 300 E Orange Mall Dr, Tempe, AZ, 85287-1006. Tel: 480-965-9392. Fax: 480-965-1043. p. 83

Anderson, Marcia, Head, Bibliog & Metadata Serv, Arizona State University Libraries, Bibliographic & Metadata Services, PO Box 871006, Tempe, AZ, 85287-1006. Tel: 480-965-5889. Fax: 480-965-1043. p. 83

Anderson, Marcia, Dir, Grand Rapids Area Library, 140 NE Second St, Grand Rapids, MN, 55744-2601. Tel: 218-327-8826. Fax: 218-326-7644. p. 1253

Anderson, Margaret, Asst Dir, R H Johnson Library, 13801 W Meeker Blvd, Sun City West, AZ, 85375-4406. Tel: 623-544-6130. Fax: 623-544-6131. p. 82

Anderson, Margaret, Asst Archivist, Worcester Polytechnic Institute, 100 Institute Rd, Worcester, MA, 01609-2280. Tel: 508-831-5410. Fax: 508-831-5829. p. 1145

Anderson, Margrete, Circ Supvr, Belmont Abbey College, 100 Belmont-Mt Holly Rd, Belmont, NC, 28012. Tel: 704-461-6565. Fax: 704-461-6743. p. 1776

Anderson, Marian, In Charge, Huntington Beach Public Library System, Helen Murphy Branch, 15882 Graham St, Huntington Beach, CA, 92649-1724. Tel: 714-375-5006. Fax: 714-373-3088. p. 159

Anderson, Marjorie, Admin Dir, Stevens Henager College Library, 1890 S 1350 W, Ogden, UT, 84401. Tel: 801-622-1567. Fax: 801-621-0853. p. 2408

Anderson, Mark, Govt Doc, University of Northern Colorado Libraries, 501 20th St, Greeley, CO, 80639. Tel: 970-351-1474. Fax: 970-351-2963. p. 312

Anderson, Mark, Head, Reader Serv, Morris County Library, 30 E Hanover Ave, Whippany, NJ, 07981. Tel: 973-285-6972. p. 1544

Anderson, Marlene, Coll Develop, Dir of Libr Serv, Bismarck State College Library, 1500 Edwards Ave, Bismarck, ND, 58501. Tel: 701-224-5578. Fax: 701-224-5551. p. 1837

Anderson, Marleta, Dir, Berkshire Free Library, 12519 State Rte 38, Berkshire, NY, 13736-1908. Tel: 607-657-4418. Fax: 607-657-4418. p. 1581

Anderson, Mary, Circ Librn, Caribou Public Library, 30 High St, Caribou, ME, 04736. Tel: 207-493-4214. Fax: 207-493-4654. p. 981

Anderson, Mary, Sr Librn, Hennepin County Library, Golden Valley, 830 Winnetka Ave N, Golden Valley, MN, 55427-4532. Tel: 612-543-6378. Fax: 612-543-6377. p. 1263

Anderson, Mary, Head, Circ Serv, University of Missouri-Kansas City Libraries, 800 E 51st St, Kansas City, MO, 64110. Tel: 816-235-1678. Fax: 816-333-5584. p. 1341

Anderson, Mary Ann, Tech Serv, Norfolk Library, Nine Greenwoods Rd E, Norfolk, CT, 06058-1320. Tel: 860-542-5075. Fax: 860-542-1795. p. 361

Anderson, Mary Ann, Ch, Valley City-Barnes County Public Library, 410 N Central Ave, Valley City, ND, 58072-2949. Tel: 701-845-3821. Fax: 701-845-4884. p. 1848

Anderson, Mary Kay, Br Supvr, Spokane County Library District, Moran Prairie Library, 6004 S Regal St, Spokane, WA, 99223-6949. Tel: 509-893-8340. Fax: 509-893-8480. p. 2537

Anderson, Matt, Libr Syst Spec, Mount Hood Community College Library, 26000 SE Stark St, Gresham, OR, 97030. Tel: 503-491-7616. Fax: 503-491-7389. p. 1999

Anderson, Maureen, Access Serv Librn, ILL, Lebanon Valley College, 101 N College Ave, Annville, PA, 17003-1400. Tel: 717-867-6977. Fax: 717-867-6979. p. 2029

Anderson, Maureen H, Access Serv Librn, University of Dayton School of Law, 300 College Park, Dayton, OH, 45469-2780. Tel: 937-229-2314. Fax: 937-229-2555. p. 1894

Anderson, Megan, Coordr, Coll Serv, University of Winnipeg Library, 515 Portage Ave, Winnipeg, MB, R3B 2E9, CANADA. Tel: 204-786-9124. Fax: 204-783-8910. p. 2759

Anderson, Megan, Media Spec, Fanshawe College, 1001 Fanshawe College Blvd, London, ON, N5Y 5R6, CANADA. Tel: 519-452-4240. Fax: 519-452-4473. p. 2817

Anderson, Missy, Prog Coordr, Medical University of South Carolina Library, 171 Ashley Ave, Ste 300, Charleston, SC, 29425-0001. Tel: 843-792-9211. Fax: 843-792-7947. p. 2184

Anderson, Molly, Dir, Nantucket Atheneum, One India St, Nantucket, MA, 02554-3519. Tel: 508-228-1974. Fax: 508-228-1973. p. 1107

Anderson, Nancy, Dean of Libr, Howard Payne University, 1000 Fisk Ave, Brownwood, TX, 76801. Tel: 325-649-8610. Fax: 325-649-8904. p. 2292

Anderson, Nancy D, Head Librn, Gordon College Library, 419 College Dr, Barnesville, GA, 30204. Tel: 770-358-5078. Fax: 770-358-5240. p. 521

Anderson, Noel, Asst Librn, Chinook Regional Library, Hazlet Branch, Railway Ave, Hazlet, SK, S0N 1E0, CANADA. Tel: 306-678-2155. p. 2928

Anderson, Olivia, Br Head, Greater Victoria Public Library Board, Bruce Hutchison Branch, 4636 Elk Lake Dr, Victoria, BC, V8Z 7K2, CANADA. Tel: 250-727-0104. p. 2745

Anderson, Olivia, Br Head, Greater Victoria Public Library Board, Central Saanich, 1209 Clarke Rd, Victoria, BC, V8M 1P8, CANADA. Tel: 250-727-0104. Fax: 250-652-6224. p. 2745

Anderson, Otis, Instrul Serv Librn, University of Montana Western, 710 S Atlantic St, Dillon, MT, 59725. Tel: 406-683-7163. Fax: 406-683-7493. p. 1378

Anderson, Pamalla, Archivist, Southern Methodist University, DeGolyer Library of Special Collections, 6404 Robert S Hyer Lane, Dallas, TX, 75275. Tel: 214-768-0829. Fax: 214-768-1565. p. 2310

Anderson, Pat A, Dir, Adams County Library, 103 N Sixth St, Hettinger, ND, 58639-7015. Tel: 701-567-2741. Fax: 701-567-2741. p. 1844

Anderson, Patricia, Dir, Maryland Historical Society Library, 201 W Monument St, Baltimore, MD, 21201. Tel: 410-685-3750. Fax: 410-385-0487. p. 1015

Anderson, Patricia, Dir, Clark Public Library, 303 Westfield Ave, Clark, NJ, 07066. Tel: 732-388-5999. Fax: 732-388-7866. p. 1479

Anderson, Patricia K, Dir, Montville Township Public Library, 90 Horseneck Rd, Montville, NJ, 07045-9626. Tel: 973-402-0900. Fax: 973-402-0592. p. 1504

Anderson, Patti, Acq, Parkland Regional Library, Hwy 52 W, Yorkton, SK, S3N 3Z4, CANADA. Tel: 306-783-7022. Fax: 306-782-2844. p. 2931

Anderson, Paul, Assoc Univ Librn, Admin Serv, University of Delaware Library, 181 S College Ave, Newark, DE, 19717-5267. Tel: 302-831-2231. Fax: 302-831-1046. p. 386

Anderson, Paul, Mgr, Tufts University, 145 Harrison Ave, Boston, MA, 02111-1843. Tel: 617-636-2961. Fax: 617-636-4039. p. 1068

Anderson, Paul J, Curator, North Saint Paul Historical Society, 2666 E Seventh Ave, North Saint Paul, MN, 55109. Tel: 651-777-8965. p. 1268

Anderson, Peggy, Acq, Govt Doc, Southwest Minnesota State University Library, 1501 State St, Marshall, MN, 56258. Tel: 507-537-6148. Fax: 507-537-6200. p. 1258

Anderson, Rebekah, Dir, Fredrikson & Bryon, 200 S Sixth St, Ste 4000, Minneapolis, MN, 55402. Tel: 612-492-7842. Fax: 612-492-7077. p. 1259

Anderson, Richita, Librn, Aesthetic Realism Foundation, Eli Siegel Collection, 141 Greene St, New York, NY, 10012-3201. Tel: 212-777-4490. Fax: 212-777-4426. p. 1667

Anderson, Richita, Librn, Aesthetic Realism Foundation, Library, 141 Greene St, New York, NY, 10012-3201. Tel: 212-777-4490. Fax: 212-777-4426. p. 1667

Anderson, Rick, Assoc Dean, Scholarly Res & Coll, University of Utah, Marriott Library, 295 S 1500 East, Salt Lake City, UT, 84112-0860. Tel: 801-587-9989. Fax: 801-585-7185. p. 2415

Anderson, Roz, Pres, Columbia Area Medical Librarians' Association, University of South Carolina, School of Medicine Library, 6311 Garner's Ferry Rd, Columbia, SC, 29209. Tel: 803-733-3361. Fax: 803-733-1509. p. 2955

Anderson, Rozalynd, Asst Dir, Educ & Outreach, University of South Carolina, School of Medicine, 6311 Garners Ferry Rd, Columbia, SC, 29209. Tel: 803-733-3344. Fax: 803-733-1509. p. 2190

Anderson, Ruth, Archivist, Rock County Historical Society, 933 Mineral Point Ave, Janesville, WI, 53545. Tel: 608-756-4509. Fax: 608-741-9596. p. 2600

Anderson, Ruth, Asst Librn, Mayerthorpe Public Library, 4911 52nd St, Mayerthorpe, AB, T0E 1N0, CANADA. Tel: 780-786-2404. Fax: 780-786-4590. p. 2711

Anderson, Ruth Ann, Tech Serv, Baraboo Public Library, 230 Fourth Ave, Baraboo, WI, 53913. Tel: 608-356-6166. Fax: 608-355-2779. p. 2580

Anderson, Sandra, Ref Librn, Atlanta-Fulton Public Library System, Northside Library, 3295 Northside Pkwy NW, Atlanta, GA, 30327. Tel: 404-814-3508. Fax: 404-814-3511. p. 512

Anderson, Sandra, Librn, Alberta Teachers' Association Library, 11010 142 St, Edmonton, AB, T5N 2R1, CANADA. Tel: 780-447-9442. Fax: 780-455-6481. p. 2699

Anderson, Sandy, In Charge, Schenectady County Public Library, Duane, 1331 State St, Schenectady, NY, 12304. Tel: 518-386-2242. Fax: 518-386-2242. p. 1741

Anderson, Sarah, Dir, North Park University, Brandel Library, 5114 N Christiana Ave, Chicago, IL, 60625. Tel: 773-244-5584. Fax: 773-244-4891. p. 620

Anderson, Scott, Asst Archivist, Prescott Historical Society, 415 W Gurley St, Prescott, AZ, 86301. Tel: 928-445-3122. Fax: 928-776-9053. p. 78

Anderson, Sean, Tech Librn, Texas A&M University-Commerce, 2600 S Neal St, Commerce, TX, 75429. Tel: 903-468-8661. Fax: 903-886-5434. p. 2300

Anderson, Shannon, Archivist, Chilliwack Museum & Historical Society, 45820 Spadina Ave, Chilliwack, BC, V2P 1T3, CANADA. Tel: 604-795-5210, 604-795-9255. Fax: 604-795-5291. p. 2726

Anderson, Sharon, Coordr, Hearst San Simeon State Historical Monument, 750 Hearst Castle Rd, San Simeon, CA, 93452-9741. Tel: 805-927-2076. Fax: 805-927-2117. p. 257

Anderson, Sharon, Br Mgr, Polk County Library, Humansville Branch, 101 S Ohio St, Humansville, MO, 65674. Tel: 417-754-2455. Fax: 417-754-2455. p. 1320

Anderson, Sharon, Commun Libr Mgr, Queens Borough Public Library, Far Rockaway Community Library, 1637 Central Ave, Far Rockaway, NY, 11691. Tel: 718-327-2549. Fax: 718-337-4184. p. 1644

Anderson, Shawn, Librn, South Texas College Library, 3201 W Pecan Blvd, McAllen, TX, 78501-6661. Tel: 956-872-8330. Fax: 956-872-7202. p. 2361

Anderson, Shelley, Br Librn, Library District Number One, Doniphan County, Wathena Branch, 206 St Joseph, Wathena, KS, 66090. Tel: 785-989-4711. p. 898

Anderson, Shelley, Dir, Ellsworth Public Library, 312 W Main, Ellsworth, WI, 54011. Tel: 715-273-3209. Fax: 715-273-3209. p. 2591

Anderson, Shelly, Coordr, Iowa Western Community College-Clarinda Campus, 923 E Washington, Clarinda, IA, 51632. Tel: 712-542-5117, Ext 234. Fax: 712-542-3604. p. 802

Anderson, Sheridan Cash, Librn, South Dakota Supreme Court, 500 E Capitol Ave, Pierre, SD, 57501-5070. Tel: 605-773-4899. p. 2217

Anderson, Sherry, Sr Librn, Hennepin County Library, Brooklyn Park, 8600 Zane Ave N, Brooklyn Park, MN, 55443-1897. Tel: 612-543-6228. Fax: 612-543-6247. p. 1263

Anderson, Sherry, Dir, Ricks Memorial Library (Yazoo Library Association), 310 N Main St, Yazoo City, MS, 39194-4253. Tel: 662-746-5557. Fax: 662-746-7309. p. 1318

Anderson, Siow Lee, Asst Librn, Macsherry Library, 112 Walton St, Alexandria Bay, NY, 13607. Tel: 315-482-2241. Fax: 315-482-2241. p. 1572

Anderson, Stacey, Dir, Corfu Free Library, Seven Maple Ave, Corfu, NY, 14036. Tel: 585-599-3321. Fax: 585-599-3821. p. 1610

Anderson, Stacy, Distance Educ, Ferris State University Library, 1010 Campus Dr, Big Rapids, MI, 49307-2279. Tel: 231-591-3500. Fax: 231-591-3724. p. 1158

Anderson, Stacy, Head, Ref, Martins Ferry Public Library, 20 James Wright Pl, Martins Ferry, OH, 43935. Tel: 740-633-0314. Fax: 740-633-6242. p. 1914

Anderson, Steven Paul, Dir, Maryland State Law Library, Courts of Appeal Bldg, 361 Rowe Blvd, Annapolis, MD, 21401-1697. Tel: 410-260-1430. Fax: 410-260-1572, 410-974-2063. p. 1010

Anderson, Steven W, Dir, Allen Community College Library, 1801 N Cottonwood, Iola, KS, 66749-1648. Tel: 620-365-5116, Ext 235. Fax: 620-365-3284. p. 873

Anderson, Sue, Info Serv Librn, Illinois Wesleyan University, One Ames Plaza, Bloomington, IL, 61701-7188. Tel: 309-556-3350. Fax: 309-556-3706. p. 595

Anderson, Sue, Librn, Tulsa City-County Library, Maxwell Park, 1313 N Canton, Tulsa, OK, 74112. Tel: 918-669-6055. Fax: 981-669-6057. p. 1983

Anderson, Sufa, Br Mgr, Las Vegas-Clark County Library District, Rainbow Library, 3150 N Buffalo Dr, Las Vegas, NV, 89128. Tel: 702-507-3710. Fax: 702-507-3730. p. 1429

Anderson, Susan, Commun Libr Mgr, County of Los Angeles Public Library, West Hollywood Library, 625 N San Vicente Blvd, West Hollywood, CA, 90069-5020. Tel: 310-652-5340. Fax: 310-652-2580. p. 143

Anderson, Susan, Librn, Provena Saint Joseph Hospital, 77 N Airlite St, Elgin, IL, 60123. Tel: 847-695-3200, Ext 5385. Fax: 847-888-3532. p. 641

Anderson, Susan, Dir, El Progreso Memorial Library, 301 W Main St, Uvalde, TX, 78801. Tel: 830-278-2017. Fax: 830-278-4940. p. 2394

Anderson, Susan, Dir, D R Moon Memorial Library, 154 Fourth Ave, Stanley, WI, 54768. Tel: 715-644-2004. Fax: 715-644-2941. p. 2639

Anderson, Susan, Mgr, Calgary Public Library, Country Hills, 11950 Country Village Link NE, Calgary, AB, T3K 6E3, CANADA. p. 2689

Anderson, Susan K, Martha Hamilton Morris Archivist, Philadelphia Museum of Art Library, Ruth & Raymond G Perelman Bldg, 2525 Pennsylvania Ave, Philadelphia, PA, 19130. Tel: 215-684-7659. Fax: 215-236-0534. p. 2114

Anderson, Susie, Dir, Horseshoe Bend Regional Library, 207 N West St, Dadeville, AL, 36853. Tel: 256-825-9232. Fax: 256-825-4314. p. 14

Anderson, Tamara, Pub Serv, Middlesex Community College, Bldg 1-ARC, Springs Rd, Bedford, MA, 01730. Tel: 781-280-3708. Fax: 781-280-3771. p. 1052

Anderson, Tamara, Chair, Niagara County Community College, 3111 Saunders Settlement Rd, Sanborn, NY, 14132. Tel: 716-614-6788. Fax: 716-614-6816, 716-614-6828. p. 1737

Anderson, Tami L, Dir, Hartington Public Library, 106 S Broadway, Hartington, NE, 68739. Tel: 402-254-6245. Fax: 402-254-6245. p. 1401

Anderson, Tara, Br Support, Stormont, Dundas & Glengarry County Library, Lancaster Branch, (Main St) 195 Military St, Lancaster, ON, K0C 1N0, CANADA. Tel: 613-347-2311. Fax: 613-347-9088. p. 2801

Anderson, Ted, Curator, Illinois Railway Museum, 7000 Olson Rd, Union, IL, 60180. Tel: 815-923-2020. Fax: 815-923-2006. p. 711

Anderson, Terri, ILL, Ref, Chippewa Falls Public Library, 105 W Central, Chippewa Falls, WI, 54729-2397. Tel: 715-723-1146. Fax: 715-720-6922. p. 2585

Anderson, Terry Ann, Doc Delivery Supvr, The Kansas City Public Library, 14 W Tenth St, Kansas City, MO, 64105. Tel: 806-701-3564. Fax: 816-701-3401. p. 1338

Anderson, Theressa, Mgr, Okefenokee Regional Library, Alma-Bacon County Public, 201 N Pierce St, Alma, GA, 31510. Tel: 912-632-4710. Fax: 912-632-4512. p. 557

Anderson, Thomas, Coll Develop Librn, Head, Tech Serv, Montgomery City-County Public Library System, 245 High St, Montgomery, AL, 36104. Tel: 334-240-4975. Fax: 334-240-4977. p. 29

Anderson, Timothy, Head, Tech Serv, Florence County Library System, 509 S Dargan St, Florence, SC, 29506. Tel: 843-662-8424. Fax: 843-661-7544. p. 2193

Anderson, Vera, Librn, White River Regional Library, Sharp County - Evening Shade Branch, 222 Main St, Evening Shade, AR, 72532. Tel: 870-266-3873. p. 94

Anderson, Vicki, Dir, Northwest Regional Library, 410 Ramstand St, Buffalo, SD, 57720. Tel: 605-375-3835. p. 2211

Anderson, Vicky, Res Serv Spec, Otter Tail County Historical Society, 1110 Lincoln Ave W, Fergus Falls, MN, 56537. Tel: 218-736-6038. Fax: 218-739-3075. p. 1251

Anderson, Wendy, Br Mgr, Omaha Public Library, Bess Johnson Elkhorn Public Library, 2100 Reading Plaza, Elkhorn, NE, 68022. Tel: 402-289-4367. Fax: 402-289-0420. p. 1414

Anderson-Story, Janet, Dir, Flint Hills Technical College Library, 3301 W 18th Ave, Emporia, KS, 66801. Tel: 620-341-1323. Fax: 620-343-4610. p. 866

Anderton, Joy, Asst Dir, Willard Library, Seven W Van Buren St, Battle Creek, MI, 49017-3009. Tel: 269-968-8166. Fax: 269-968-3284. p. 1155

Andes, Barbara, Br Mgr, Br Operations Coordr, Massanutten Regional Library, Village Library, 113 S Central Ave, Broadway, VA, 22815. Tel: 540-896-1646. Fax: 540-896-9260. p. 2470

Andes, Eileen, Coordr, Theodore Roosevelt National Park Library, PO Box 7, Medora, ND, 58645-0007. Tel: 701-623-4466. Fax: 701-623-4840. p. 1846

Andes, Ellen, Asst Dir, Springdale Public Library, 405 S Pleasant St, Springdale, AR, 72764. Tel: 479-750-8180. Fax: 479-750-8182. p. 115

Andes, Tina, Br Mgr, Bushnell Public Library, 402 N Florida St, Bushnell, FL, 33513. Tel: 352-793-8274. Fax: 352-793-1608. p. 431

Andrade, Brooke P, ILL, Ref, National Humanities Center Library, Seven Alexander Dr, Research Triangle Park, NC, 27709. Tel: 919-549-0661. Fax: 919-990-8535. p. 1819

Andrade, Martha, Br Mgr, El Paso Public Library, Armijo, 620 E Seventh Ave, El Paso, TX, 79901. Tel: 915-533-1333. Fax: 915-532-1758. p. 2316

Andre, Deborah, Circ, Smiths Falls Public Library, 81 Beckwith St N, Smiths Falls, ON, K7A 2B9, CANADA. Tel: 613-283-2911. Fax: 613-283-9834. p. 2842

Andrea, Jackie, Dir, Alta Vista Public Library, 203 S White Ave, Alta Vista, IA, 50603. Tel: 641-364-6009. Fax: 641-364-6009. p. 792

Andrea, Ryce, Librn, Group Health Cooperative, 201 16th Ave E, Seattle, WA, 98112. Tel: 206-326-3392. Fax: 206-326-2629. p. 2527

Andreadis, Debby, Asst Dir, Educ & Res Serv, Denison University Libraries, 400 W Loop, Granville, OH, 43023. Tel: 740-587-7625. Fax: 740-587-6285. p. 1902

Andreeff, Tania, Librn, United States Tax Court Library, 400 Second St NW, Washington, DC, 20217. Tel: 202-521-4585. Fax: 202-521-4574. p. 421

Andreen, Cathy, Librn, Johnson County Library, Linch Branch, PO Box 160, Linch, WY, 82640-0160. Tel: 307-437-6424. p. 2651

Andreoli, Emma, ILL, Hanson Bridgett LLP, 425 Market St, 26th Flr, San Francisco, CA, 94105. Tel: 415-995-5855. Fax: 415-541-9366. p. 242

Andreou, Constantinos, Head, Circ, Nova Southeastern University Libraries, 3100 Ray Ferrero Jr Blvd, Fort Lauderdale, FL, 33314. Tel: 954-262-4682. Fax: 954-262-3805. p. 444

Andres, Agnes, Br Librn, Community District Library, New Lothrop-Hazelton Township, 9387 Genesee St, New Lothrop, MI, 48460. Tel: 810-638-7575. Fax: 810-638-7575. p. 1166

Andres, Anne, Assoc Librn, Columbia Bible College Library, 2940 Clearbrook Rd, Abbotsford, BC, V2T 2Z8, CANADA. Tel: 604-853-3567. Fax: 604-853-3063. p. 2723

Andres, Kelly, Librn, Donalda Public Library, 5001 Main St, Donalda, AB, T0B 1H0, CANADA. Tel: 403-883-2345. Fax: 403-883-2022. p. 2696

Andres, Patricia, Dir, Neoga Public Library District, 550 Chestnut St, Neoga, IL, 62447. Tel: 217-895-3944. Fax: 217-895-3944. p. 679

Andresen, Judy, Ref Librn, Western State Law Library, 1111 N State College Blvd, Fullerton, CA, 92831-3014. Tel: 714-459-1113. Fax: 714-871-4806. p. 154

Andresen, Julie, Dir, Hannibal-LaGrange University, 2800 Palmyra Rd, Hannibal, MO, 63401-1999. Tel: 573-221-3675, Ext 3130. Fax: 573-248-0294. p. 1329

Andreski, Marie, Automation Syst Coordr, Levittown Public Library, One Bluegrass Lane, Levittown, NY, 11756-1292. Tel: 516-731-5728. Fax: 516-735-3168. p. 1652

Andrew, Aletha, Dr, Dir of Libr Serv, Wayne Community College Library, 3000 Wayne Memorial Dr, Goldsboro, NC, 27533. Tel: 919-735-5151, Ext 292. Fax: 919-736-3204. p. 1795

Andrew, Lynn, Dir, Mary Wood Weldon Memorial Library, 107 W College St, Glasgow, KY, 42141. Tel: 270-651-2824. Fax: 270-651-2824. p. 915

Andrew, Rea, Vols Serv Coordr, Newberg Public Library, 503 E Hancock St, Newberg, OR, 97132-2899. Tel: 503-538-7323. Fax: 503-538-9720. p. 2007

Andrews, Alice K, Supvr, Acq, Supvr, Tech Serv, Roanoke Bible College, 715 N Poindexter St, Elizabeth City, NC, 27909-4054. Tel: 252-334-2027. Fax: 252-334-2071. p. 1791

Andrews, Ann, Children's Coll Develop, Memphis Public Library & Information Center, 3030 Poplar Ave, Memphis, TN, 38111-3527. Tel: 901-415-2712. Fax: 901-323-7108. p. 2249

Andrews, Anna, Librn, Everest College Library, 14280 E Jewell Ave, Ste 100, Aurora, CO, 80012-5692. Tel: 303-745-6244. p. 288

Andrews, Anna, Librn, Everest College Library, 9065 Grant St, Thornton, CO, 80229. Tel: 303-457-2757. p. 324

Andrews, Becky, Br Head, East Baton Rouge Parish Library, Baker Branch, 3501 Groom Rd, Baker, LA, 70714. Tel: 225-778-5940. Fax: 225-778-5949. p. 942

Andrews, Beth, Librn, Park Cities Baptist Church, 3933 Northwest Pkwy, Dallas, TX, 75225-3333. Tel: 214-860-3993. Fax: 214-860-1538. p. 2309

Andrews, Carl, ILL, Medgar Evers College, 1650 Bedford Ave, Brooklyn, NY, 11225-2010. Tel: 718-270-4873. Fax: 718-270-5182. p. 1593

Andrews, Christine, Ref, Whitehall Township Public Library, 3700 Mechanicsville Rd, Whitehall, PA, 18052-3399. Tel: 610-432-4339. Fax: 610-432-9387. p. 2155

Andrews, David, Ref Serv, Ad, Wallingford Public Library, 200 N Main St, Wallingford, CT, 06492-3791. Tel: 203-265-6754. Fax: 203-269-5698. p. 373

Andrews, Deb, Librn, Parkland Regional Library, Englefeld Branch, PO Box 22, Englefeld, SK, S0K 1N0, CANADA. Tel: 306-287-3497. p. 2932

Andrews, Debbie, Dir, Faith Memorial Library, 122 N Garrison Ave, Wallace, NE, 69169. Tel: 308-387-4537. p. 1422

Andrews, Debra, Juv Coll Develop Librn, Kokomo-Howard County Public Library, 220 N Union St, Kokomo, IN, 46901-4614. Tel: 765-457-3242. Fax: 765-457-3683. p. 758

Andrews, Diane, Asst Librn, Elkford Public Library, 816 Michele Rd, Elkford, BC, V0B 1H0, CANADA. Tel: 250-865-2912. Fax: 250-865-2460. p. 2728

Andrews, Dianne, ILL, Meredith College, 3800 Hillsborough St, Raleigh, NC, 27607-5298. Tel: 919-760-8531. Fax: 919-760-2830. p. 1815

Andrews, Elizabeth, Archivist for Coll & Assoc Head, Massachusetts Institute of Technology Libraries, Institute Archives & Special Collections, Bldg 14N-118, Hayden Library, 160 Memorial Dr, Cambridge, MA, 02139-4307. Tel: 617-253-4323. Fax: 617-258-7305. p. 1078

Andrews, Emily, Libr Dir, William H & Lucy F Rand Memorial Library, 160 Railroad St, North Troy, VT, 05859-9492. Tel: 802-988-4741. p. 2431

Andrews, Evelyn F, Librn, Senate Library of Pennsylvania, Main Capitol Bldg, Rm 157, Harrisburg, PA, 17120-0030. Tel: 717-787-6120. Fax: 717-772-2366. p. 2066

Andrews, James, Dr, Assoc Prof, University of South Florida, 4202 Fowler Ave, CIS 1040, Tampa, FL, 33620-7800. Tel: 813-974-3520. Fax: 813-974-6840. p. 2964

Andrews, James E, PhD, Dir, University of South Florida, 4202 Fowler Ave, CIS 1040, Tampa, FL, 33620-7800. Tel: 813-974-2108. Fax: 813-974-6840. p. 2964

Andrews, Janet, Syst Librn, Maitland Public Library, 501 S Maitland Ave, Maitland, FL, 32751-5672. Tel: 407-647-7700. p. 462

Andrews, Jay, Asst Librn, Chewelah Public Library, 307 E Clay Ave, Chewelah, WA, 99109. Tel: 509-935-6805. Fax: 509-935-4564. p. 2512

Andrews, Jeanette, Ref Serv Librn, Urbandale Public Library, 3520 86th St, Urbandale, IA, 50322-4056. Tel: 515-278-3945. Fax: 515-278-3918. p. 848

Andrews, Joan, Mgr, College of Registered Nurses of British Columbia Library, 2855 Arbutus St, Vancouver, BC, V6J 3Y8, CANADA. Tel: 604-736-7331. Fax: 604-738-2272. p. 2740

Andrews, Judy, Asst Dir, Youth Serv, York Public Library, 520 Nebraska Ave, York, NE, 68467-3095. Tel: 402-363-2620. Fax: 402-363-2627. p. 1424

Andrews, Judy, Libr Tech 1, Farmville Public Library, 4276 W Church St, Farmville, NC, 27828. Tel: 252-753-3355. Fax: 252-753-2855. p. 1792

Andrews, Kathy, Coordr, Ch Serv, Lena Community District Library, 300 W Mason St, Lena, IL, 61048. Tel: 815-369-3180. Fax: 815-369-3181. p. 665

Andrews, Lara, Librn, Canadian War Museum, One Vimy Pl, Ottawa, ON, K1A 0M8, CANADA. Tel: 819-776-8652. Fax: 819-776-8623. p. 2830

Andrews, Leila, Librn, Helper City Library, 19 S Main, Helper, UT, 84526. Tel: 435-472-5601. Fax: 435-472-3064. p. 2406

Andrews, Linda R, Dir, Hoover Public Library, 200 Municipal Dr, Hoover, AL, 35216. Tel: 205-444-7810. Fax: 205-444-7878. p. 20

Andrews, Marie, Librn, Bureau of Land Management, 455 Emerson St, Craig, CO, 81625-1129. Tel: 970-826-5000. Fax: 970-826-5002. p. 297

Andrews, Marsha, Librn, Homewood Public Library, 17917 Dixie Hwy, Homewood, IL, 60430-1703. Tel: 708-798-0121. Fax: 708-798-0662. p. 657

Andrews, Mary, Grand Rapids Satellite Librn, US Court of Appeals for the Sixth Circuit Library, 312 Potter Stewart US Courthouse, Cincinnati, OH, 45202. Tel: 616-456-2068. Fax: 513-564-7329. p. 1873

Andrews, Ron, Head, Tech, Chelsea District Library, 221 S Main St, Chelsea, MI, 48118-1267. Tel: 734-475-8732. Fax: 734-475-6190. p. 1163

Andrews, Sandi, Head, Circ, Weber State University, 2901 University Circle, Ogden, UT, 84408-2901. Tel: 801-626-6546. Fax: 801-626-7045. p. 2409

Andrews, Sandra D, PhD, Dr, Asst Prof, University of North Carolina at Greensboro, School of Education, 349 Curry Bldg, Greensboro, NC, 27402. Tel: 336-334-5738. Fax: 336-334-5060. p. 2971

Andrews, Sara, ILL, University of Nebraska Medical Center, 600 S 42nd St, Omaha, NE, 68198-6705. Tel: 402-559-7079. Fax: 402-559-5498. p. 1415

Andrews, Sarah, Br Librn, London Public Library, Byron Memorial, 1295 Commissioners Rd W, London, ON, N6K 1C9, CANADA. Tel: 519-471-4000. p. 2817

Andrews, Sarah, Br Librn, London Public Library, Glanworth, 2950 Glanworth Dr, London, ON, N6N 1N6, CANADA. Tel: 519-681-6797. p. 2818

Andrews, Sarah, Br Librn, London Public Library, Lambeth Branch, 7112 Beattie St, Lambeth, ON, N6P 1A2, CANADA. Tel: 519-652-2951. p. 2818

Andrews, Shannah, Tech Serv, Williams & Connolly Library, 725 12th St NW, Washington, DC, 20005. Tel: 202-434-5376. Fax: 202-434-5029. p. 423

Andrews, Shelley, Br Mgr, Sacramento Public Library, Carmichael Regional Library, 5605 Marconi Ave, Carmichael, CA, 95608. p. 224

Andrews, Susan, Head, Ser, Texas A&M University-Commerce, 2600 S Neal St, Commerce, TX, 75429. Tel: 903-886-5733. Fax: 903-886-5434. p. 2300

Andrews, Susan, City Librn, Hurst Public Library, 901 Precinct Line Rd, Hurst, TX, 76053. Tel: 817-788-7300. Fax: 817-590-9515. p. 2345

Andrews, Wanda, Libr Asst, Pennsylvania State University, N Atherton St, State College, PA, 16801. Tel: 814-863-9940. Fax: 814-863-5568. p. 2143

Andrews-Jotham, Julie, Br Mgr, Brampton Library, South Fletcher's Branch, 500 Ray Lawson Blvd, Brampton, ON, L6Y 5B3, CANADA. Tel: 905-793-4636, Ext 4505. Fax: 905-453-8425. p. 2796

Andrews-Jotham, Julie, Chief Exec Officer, The Municipality of Hastings Highlands Library, 33011 Hwy 62 N, Maynooth, ON, K0L 2S0, CANADA. Tel: 613-338-2262. Fax: 613-338-3292. p. 2821

Andreychuk, Eric D, Libr Dir, Bullard Sanford Memorial Library, 520 W Huron Ave, Vassar, MI, 48768. Tel: 989-823-2171. Fax: 989-823-8573. p. 1233

Andreyo, Sara, Law Librn, Somerset County Law Library, Court House, 111 E Union St, Ste 60, Somerset, PA, 15501. Tel: 814-445-1508, 814-445-1510. Fax: 814-445-1455. p. 2141

Andrick, Annita, Dir, Libr & Archives, Erie County Historical Society, Erie County History Ctr, 419 State St, Erie, PA, 16501. Tel: 814-454-1813, Ext 26. Fax: 814-454-6890. p. 2055

Andrick, Silda, Tech Serv, University of Illinois Library at Urbana-Champaign, Latin American & Caribbean, 324 University of Illinois Library MC 522, 1408 W Gregory Dr, Urbana, IL, 61801. Tel: 217-333-2786. Fax: 217-333-2214. p. 712

Andrilli, Ene, Pub Serv, Anthony Cardinal Bevilacqua Theological Research Center, 100 E Wynnewood Rd, Wynnewood, PA, 19096. Tel: 610-785-6274. Fax: 610-664-7913. p. 2158

Androulidakis, Pam, Supvr, Circ, Berthoud Public Library, 236 Welch Ave, Berthoud, CO, 80513. Tel: 970-532-2757. Fax: 970-532-4372. p. 289

Andrulli, Avis, Libr Tech, Truckee Meadows Community College, Nell J Redfield Learning Resource Center, Technical Institute, 475 Edison Way, Reno, NV, 89502-4103. Tel: 775-857-4990. Fax: 775-857-4976. p. 1433

Andrus, Kay L, Dir, Creighton University, Klutznick Law Library - McGrath, North, Mullin & Kratz Legal Research Center, School of Law, 2500 California Plaza, Omaha, NE, 68178-0340. Tel: 402-280-2251, 402-280-2875. Fax: 402-280-2244. p. 1412

Andrus, Sue, Instrul Serv Librn, Tri-County Technical College Library, 7900 Hwy 76, Pendleton, SC, 29670. Tel: 864-646-1750. Fax: 864-646-1543. p. 2202

Andrushkiw, Svitlana, Dir, Shevchenko Scientific Society Inc, 63 Fourth Ave, New York, NY, 10003. Tel: 212-254-5130. Fax: 212-254-5239. p. 1699

Andrusko, Diane, Mgr, Ad Serv, St Catharines Public Library, 54 Church St, St. Catharines, ON, L2R 7K2, CANADA. Tel: 905-688-6103, Ext 228. Fax: 905-688-6292. p. 2843

Andry, Belinda, Mgr, Libr Serv, American College of Surgeons Library, 633 N St Clair St, Chicago, IL, 60611. Tel: 312-202-5239. Fax: 312-202-5011. p. 605

Andrykowski, Jeremy, Customer Serv Coordr, Arlington Heights Memorial Library, 500 N Dunton Ave, Arlington Heights, IL, 60004-5966. Tel: 847-870-4311. Fax: 847-506-2650. p. 589

Andrysiak, Vera, Admin Coordr, Cent Libr Serv, Winnipeg Public Library, Millennium, 251 Donald St, Winnipeg, MB, R3C 3P5, CANADA. Tel: 204-986-6440. Fax: 204-942-5671. p. 2760

Aneja, Kusum, Tech Serv, Valencia Community College, Raymer Maguire Jr Learning Resources Center, West Campus, 1800 S Kirkman Rd, Orlando, FL, 32811. Tel: 407-582-1210. Fax: 407-582-1686. p. 478

Anello, Karen, Librn, Dechert Library, Cira Ctr, 2929 Arch St, Philadelphia, PA, 19104. Tel: 215-994-4000. Fax: 215-994-2222. p. 2105

Anfenson-Comeau, Shelby, Ref, Louisiana State University, 2048 Johnson Hwy, Eunice, LA, 70535. Tel: 337-550-1380. Fax: 337-550-1455. p. 949

Ang, Vince, Operations Mgr, Hayward Public Library, 835 C St, Hayward, CA, 94541-5120. Tel: 510-881-7987. p. 157

Angall, Mary Faith, Asst Curator, Mineral Point Public Library, 137 High St, Mineral Point, WI, 53565. Tel: 608-987-2447. Fax: 608-987-2447. p. 2622

Angel, Christine, PhD, Asst Prof, Saint John's University, Saint Augustine Hall, Rm 408, 8000 Utopia Pkwy, Jamaica, NY, 11439. Tel: 718-990-1452. Fax: 718-990-2071. p. 2970

Angel, Jeanne Schultz, Dir, Lombard Historical Society Library, 23 W Maple St, Lombard, IL, 60148. Tel: 630-629-1885. Fax: 630-629-9927. p. 667

Angela, Craig, YA Serv, Charlotte Mecklenburg Library, 310 N Tryon St, Charlotte, NC, 28202-2176. Tel: 704-416-0101. Fax: 704-416-0130. p. 1782

Angelesco, Nancy, Dir, Langlois Public Library, 48234 Hwy 101, Langlois, OR, 97450. Tel: 541-348-2066. Fax: 541-348-2066. p. 2003

Angelini, Mary Frances, Librn, Harvard Library, Grossman Library for University Extension, Sever Hall, Rm 311, Harvard Yard, Cambridge, MA, 02138. Tel: 617-495-4163. Fax: 617-495-9438. p. 1075

Angell, Allison, Head, Ch, Benicia Public Library, 150 East L St, Benicia, CA, 94510-3281. Tel: 707-746-4343. Fax: 707-747-8122. p. 126

Angelloz, Anna, Br Mgr, Iberville Parish Library, Grosse Tete Branch, 18135 Willow Rd, Grosse Tete, LA, 70740. Tel: 225-648-2667. Fax: 225-648-2667. p. 966

Angelo, Alice, Access Serv, Trinity College Library, 300 Summit St, Hartford, CT, 06106. Tel: 860-297-2247. Fax: 860-297-2251. p. 347

Angelo, F Michael, Archivist, Thomas Jefferson University, 1020 Walnut St, Philadelphia, PA, 19107. Tel: 215-503-8097. Fax: 215-923-3203. p. 2118

Angelo, Kathryn, Outreach & Publicity, Long Branch Free Public Library, 328 Broadway, Long Branch, NJ, 07740. Tel: 732-222-3900. Fax: 732-222-3799. p. 1496

Angelo, Thomas, Br Mgr, Brooklyn Public Library, Walt Whitman Branch, 93 Saint Edwards St, Brooklyn, NY, 11205. Tel: 718-935-0244. Fax: 718-935-0284. p. 1592

Angeloni, Denise, Sci Res Spec, Ontario Ministry of the Environment, 40 Saint Clair Ave W, 11th Flr, Toronto, ON, M4V 1M2, CANADA. Tel: 416-327-1241. Fax: 416-327-2936. p. 2856

Angelos, Ruth, Circ Coordr, Westmont College, 955 La Paz Rd, Santa Barbara, CA, 93108-1099. Tel: 805-565-6000, 805-565-6147. Fax: 805-565-6220. p. 262

Angelotti, Mary, Doc Delivery Mgr, Yale University Library, Harvey Cushing/John Hay Whitney Medical Library, Sterling Hall of Medicine, 333 Cedar St, L110 SHM, New Haven, CT, 06520. Tel: 203-785-5352. Fax: 203-785-5636. p. 358

Angelovich, Peggy, Info Res & Serv Support Spec, Pennsylvania State University, One Campus Dr, Mont Alto, PA, 17237-9703. Tel: 717-749-6040. Fax: 717-749-6059. p. 2091

Angelow, Susan, Br Mgr, Brunswick County Library, G V Barbee Sr Branch, 8200 E Oak Island Dr, Oak Island, NC, 28465. Tel: 910-278-4283. Fax: 910-278-4049. p. 1824

Angert, Carol, Head, Circ, Greenburgh Public Library, 300 Tarrytown Rd, Elmsford, NY, 10523. Tel: 914-721-8208. Fax: 914-721-8201. p. 1620

Anghel, Elisabeth, Librn, Mount San Jacinto College, 1499 N State St, San Jacinto, CA, 92583-2399. Tel: 951-487-6752, Ext 1580. Fax: 951-654-8387. p. 249

Anghelescu, Hermina G B, Dr, Assoc Prof, Wayne State University, 106 Kresge Library, Detroit, MI, 48202. Tel: 313-577-1825. Fax: 313-577-7563. p. 2967

Angione, Pauline V, Dir, Dorcas Library, 28 Main St, Prospect Harbor, ME, 04669. Tel: 207-963-2023. Fax: 800-851-1374. p. 998

Angle, Laurie, Head, Adult Serv, Albert Wisner Public Library, Two Colonial Ave, Warwick, NY, 10990-1191. Tel: 845-986-1047. Fax: 845-987-1228. p. 1763

Anglestad, Judy, Libr Tech, La Ronge Public Library, 1212 Hildebrand Dr, La Ronge, SK, S0J 1L0, CANADA. Tel: 306-425-2160. Fax: 306-425-3883. p. 2918

Anglim, Christopher, Ref/Archives Librn, University of the District of Columbia, Learning Resources Division, 4200 Connecticut Ave NW, Washington, DC, 20008. Tel: 202-274-6370. Fax: 202-274-6012. p. 421

Anglim, Suzy, Br Supvr, Youth Serv, Barry-Lawrence Regional Library, Shell Knob Branch, 24931 State Hwy 39, Shell Knob, MO, 65747. Tel: 417-858-3618. Fax: 417-858-3618. p. 1347

Anglin, Emily, Br Head, Williamson County Public Library, Leiper's Fork, 5333 Old Hwy 96, Franklin, TN, 37064-9357. Tel: 615-794-7019. Fax: 615-591-6976. p. 2234

Anglin, Judith L, Dir, Ketchikan Public Library, 629 Dock St, Ketchikan, AK, 99901. Tel: 907-225-3331. Fax: 907-225-0153. p. 50

Angry-Smith, Evelyn, Ref Serv, Manchester Community College Library, Great Path, Manchester, CT, 06040. Tel: 860-512-2874. Fax: 860-512-2871. p. 350

Angstman, Jodi, Asst Librn, Dumont Community Library, 602 Second St, Dumont, IA, 50625. Tel: 641-857-3304. Fax: 641-857-3304. p. 812

Angus, Carolyn, Dir, Claremont Graduate University, 740 N College Ave, Claremont, CA, 91711-5913. Tel: 909-607-1186. p. 134

Angus, Janet, Dir, Merrimack Public Library, 470 Daniel Webster Hwy, Merrimack, NH, 03054-3694. Tel: 603-424-5021. Fax: 603-424-7312. p. 1457

Anhalt, Joy, Tech Serv, Tinley Park Public Library, 7851 Timber Dr, Tinley Park, IL, 60477-3398. Tel: 708-532-0160, Ext 7. Fax: 708-532-2981. p. 709

Anilao-Herron, Dawn D, Librn, Burnsville Library, 235 Kanawha Ave, Burnsville, WV, 26335. Tel: 304-853-2338. p. 2555

Ankem, Kalyani, Assoc Prof, North Carolina Central University, 1801 Fayetteville St, Durham, NC, 27707. Tel: 919-530-6485. Fax: 919-530-6402. p. 2971

Ankeny, Connie, Librn, Dalton Public Library, 306 Main St, Dalton, NE, 69131. Tel: 308-377-2413. p. 1397

Ann Smith, Mary, Coordr, Acq, Edgewood College Library, 1000 Edgewood College Dr, Madison, WI, 53711-1997. Tel: 608-663-3300. Fax: 608-663-6778. p. 2606

Annaballi, Karen, Ch, Coatesville Area Public Library, 501 E Lincoln Hwy, Coatesville, PA, 19320-3413. Tel: 610-384-4115. Fax: 610-384-7551. p. 2046

Annan, Isaac, Head, Per, Johnson Free Public Library, 274 Main St, Hackensack, NJ, 07601-5797. Tel: 201-343-4169. Fax: 201-343-1395. p. 1489

Anne, Barnard, ILS Coordr, Orion Township Public Library, 825 Joslyn Rd, Lake Orion, MI, 48362. Tel: 248-693-3000, Ext 339. Fax: 248-693-3009. p. 1199

Annesi, Lori, Spec Coll, Monroe Community College, LeRoy V Good Library, 1000 E Henrietta Rd, Rochester, NY, 14692. Tel: 585-292-2338. p. 1730

Annett, Susan, Principal Librn, Pub Serv, Santa Monica Public Library, 601 Santa Monica Blvd, Santa Monica, CA, 90401. Tel: 310-458-8640. Fax: 310-394-8951. p. 266

Annie, Rochfort, Archivist, Marlborough Gallery Library, 40 W 57th St, New York, NY, 10019. Tel: 212-541-4900. Fax: 212-541-4948. p. 1685

Annif, Ethan, Head, Circ Serv, Dominican University of California, 50 Acacia Ave, San Rafael, CA, 94901-2298. Tel: 415-482-1837. Fax: 415-459-2309. p. 256

Anning, Chris, Librn, Minnesota Department of Revenue Library, 600 N Robert St, Saint Paul, MN, 55101. Tel: 651-556-6134. Fax: 651-556-3103. p. 1279

Annino, Jeanne, Literacy Coordr, Plymouth Public Library, 132 South St, Plymouth, MA, 02360-3309. Tel: 508-830-4260. Fax: 508-830-4258. p. 1118

Annis, Eleanor, Cat Librn, University of Northern British Columbia Library, 333 University Way, Prince George, BC, V2N 4Z9, CANADA. Tel: 250-960-6617. Fax: 250-960-6610. p. 2736

Annis, Nicole, Libr Dir, Keosauqua Public Library, 608 First St, Keosauqua, IA, 52565. Tel: 319-293-3766. Fax: 319-293-3766. p. 825

Annis, Valerie G, Dir, Minor Memorial Library, 23 South St, Roxbury, CT, 06783. Tel: 860-350-2181. Fax: 860-350-6882. p. 366

Anoud, Dana, Librn, Masaryk Memorial Institute Inc, 450 Scarborough Golf Club Rd, Scarborough, ON, M1G 1H1, CANADA. Tel: 416-439-0792. Fax: 416-439-6473. p. 2840

Ansel-McCabe, Erynne, Dir, Iroquois Indian Museum Library, 324 Caverns Rd, Howes Cave, NY, 12092. Tel: 518-296-8949. Fax: 518-296-8955. p. 1638

Ansell, Donna, Head, Circ, Blackstone Public Library, 86 Main St, Blackstone, MA, 01504-2277. Tel: 508-883-1931. Fax: 508-883-1531. p. 1054

Ansley, John, Head, Archives & Spec Coll, Marist College, 3399 North Rd, Poughkeepsie, NY, 12601-1387. Tel: 845-575-3199. Fax: 845-575-3150. p. 1722

Anslinger, Eileen, Prog Spec, Department of Veterans Affairs, 2907 Pleasant Valley Blvd, Altoona, PA, 16602-4305. Tel: 814-943-8164, Ext 7156. Fax: 814-940-7895. p. 2028

Ansnes, Cristina M, Dir, North Castle Public Library, 19 Whippoorwill Rd E, Armonk, NY, 10504. Tel: 914-273-3887. Fax: 914-273-5572. p. 1575

Ansnes, Cristina M, Dir, North Castle Public Library, North White Plains Branch, Ten Clove Rd, North White Plains, NY, 10603. Tel: 914-948-6359. Fax: 914-948-6359. p. 1575

Anspach, Judith Ford, Dir, Indiana University, Ruth Lilly Law Library, 530 W New York St, Indianapolis, IN, 46202-3225. Tel: 317-274-3884, 317-274-4028. Fax: 317-274-8825. p. 752

Anstead, Chris, Librn, Smiths Falls Railway Museum Library & Archives, 90 William St W, Smiths Falls, ON, K7A 5A5, CANADA. Tel: 613-283-5696. Fax: 613-283-7211. p. 2842

Anstey, Gayle, Ad, Corning Public Library, 603 Ninth St, Corning, IA, 50841-1304. Tel: 641-322-3866. Fax: 641-322-3491. p. 804

Anstine, Rebecca C, Libr Tech, Harrisburg Area Community College, 2010 Pennsylvania Ave, York, PA, 17404. Tel: 717-718-0328, Ext 3520. Fax: 717-718-8967. p. 2159

Ansty, Maggie, Librn for Blind & Physically Handicapped, Indiana State Library, 315 W Ohio St, Indianapolis, IN, 46202. Tel: 317-232-3738. Fax: 317-232-0002. p. 752

Antaramia, Bob, Access Serv, Circ, University of Hartford Libraries, 200 Bloomfield Ave, West Hartford, CT, 06117. Tel: 860-768-4264. p. 376

Anteau, Joseph B, Asst Librn, Consumers Energy, Corporate Library, One Energy Plaza, EP1-244, Jackson, MI, 49201. Tel: 517-788-2520. Fax: 517-768-3804. p. 1195

Antell, Karen, Head, Ref, University of Oklahoma, 401 W Brooks, Norman, OK, 73019. Tel: 405-325-2611. Fax: 405-325-7550. p. 1971

Antelman, Kristin, Assoc Dir, Digital Libr, North Carolina State University Libraries, Two Broughton Dr, Raleigh, NC, 27695. Tel: 919-515-7188. Fax: 919-515-3628. p. 1816

Antes, Sue, Librn, Syracuse Public Library, 480 Fifth St, Syracuse, NE, 68446. Tel: 402-269-2336. p. 1420

Anthony, Annette, Regional Librn, Fisheries & Oceans Canada, 80 E White Hills Rd, St. John's, NL, A1C 5X1, CANADA. Tel: 709-772-2020, 709-772-2022. Fax: 709-772-2575. p. 2772

Anthony, Carolyn A, Dir, Skokie Public Library, 5215 Oakton St, Skokie, IL, 60077-3680. Tel: 847-673-7774. Fax: 847-673-7797. p. 703

Anthony, Charlotte, Librn, Yavapai County Law Library, Yavapai County Courthouse, 120 S Cortez St, Rm 112, Prescott, AZ, 86303. Tel: 928-771-3309. Fax: 928-771-3503. p. 79

Anthony, Mark, Tech Serv, Fort McMurray Public Library, 151 MacDonald Dr, Fort McMurray, AB, T9H 5C5, CANADA. Tel: 780-743-7800. Fax: 780-743-7938. p. 2704

Anthony, Meg, Ch, Deerfield Public Library, 920 Waukegan Rd, Deerfield, IL, 60015. Tel: 847-945-3311. Fax: 847-945-3402. p. 634

Anthony, Theresa M, Head, Virtual Libr Br, Library of the Marine Corps, Gray Research Ctr, 2040 Broadway St, Quantico, VA, 22134-5107. Tel: 703-784-4409. Fax: 703-784-4306. p. 2486

Anthony, Valarie, Supvr, Access Serv, Georgia Southwestern State University, 800 Georgia Southwestern State University Dr, Americus, GA, 31709. Tel: 229-931-2259. Fax: 229-931-2265. p. 508

Anthony, Vivienne, Circ/ILL Asst, Assumption College, 500 Salisbury St, Worcester, MA, 01609. Tel: 508-767-7291. Fax: 508-767-7374. p. 1143

Anthonyson, Deborah, Sr Librn, Palo Alto City Library, Mitchell Park, 3700 Middlefield Rd, Palo Alto, CA, 94303. Fax: 650-856-7925. p. 204

Antipa, Susan, Ad, Carson City Library, 900 N Roop St, Carson City, NV, 89701. Tel: 775-887-2244. Fax: 775-887-2273. p. 1425

Antle, Carol, Ref, Shelby County Public Library, 57 W Broadway, Shelbyville, IN, 46176. Tel: 317-398-7121, 317-835-2653. Fax: 317-398-4430. p. 778

Antle, Judy A, Archivist, Missisquoi Historical Society, Two River St, Stanbridge East, QC, J0J 2H0, CANADA. Tel: 450-248-3153. Fax: 450-248-0420. p. 2913

Antle, Rachael, Dir, Russell County Public Library, 94 N Main, Jamestown, KY, 42629. Tel: 270-343-3545. Fax: 270-343-2019. p. 919

Antoline, Jean, Librn, Youngwood Area Public Library, 17 S Sixth St, Youngwood, PA, 15697-1623. Tel: 724-925-9350. Fax: 724-925-9350. p. 2160

Anton, Bette, Head Librn, University of California, Berkeley, Fong Optometry & Health Sciences Library, 490 Minor Hall, Berkeley, CA, 94720-6000. Tel: 510-642-1020. Fax: 510-643-8600. p. 128

Anton, Laurie, Sr Exec Coordr, Nevada Medical Library Group, Barton Memorial Hospital Library, 2170 South Ave, South Lake Tahoe, CA, 96150. Tel: 530-543-5844. Fax: 530-541-4697. p. 2938

Antonacci, Delia, Prof, Seneca College of Applied Arts & Technology, 1750 Finch Ave E, Toronto, ON, M2J 2X5, CANADA. Tel: 416-491-5050, Ext 6733. Fax: 416-491-4606. p. 2978

Antonaccio, Carolyn, Circ, Kemmerer Library Harding Township, 19 Blue Mill Rd, New Vernon, NJ, 07976. Tel: 973-267-2665. p. 1510

Antonaccio, Emil, Pres, Somers Historical Society Library, Elephant Hotel, 335 Rte 202, Somers, NY, 10589-3204. Tel: 914-277-4977. p. 1745

Antonelli, Pat, Librn, Bowling Green State University, One University Dr, 2nd Flr, Huron, OH, 44839-9791. Tel: 419-433-5560, Ext 20739. Fax: 419-433-9696. p. 1905

Antonetti, Martin, Curator, Smith College Libraries, Mortimer Rare Book Room, Northampton, MA, 01063. Tel: 413-585-2907. Fax: 413-585-4486. p. 1114

Antonie, Renee, Librn, Wapiti Regional Library, Blaine Lake Public Library, CNR Station, Blaine Lake, SK, S0J 0J0, CANADA. Tel: 306-497-3130. p. 2921

Antonitis, Victoria, Ch, North Providence Union Free Library, 1810 Mineral Spring Ave, North Providence, RI, 02904. Tel: 401-353-5600. p. 2170

Antoniuk, Donna, Librn, Rio Grande Bible Institute & Language School, 4300 US Hwy 281, Edinburg, TX, 78539-9650. Tel: 956-380-8100. Fax: 956-380-8101. p. 2315

Antonnucio, Steve, Supv Librn, Pueblo City-County Library District, Frank & Marie Barkman Branch, 1300 Jerry Murphy Rd, Pueblo, CO, 81001-1858. Tel: 719-562-5682. Fax: 719-562-5685. p. 321

Antonoff, Jeff, Exec Dir, Long Beach Jewish Community Center - The Alpert JCC, 3801 E Willow St, Long Beach, CA, 90815. Tel: 562-426-7601. Fax: 562-424-3915. p. 166

Antonov, Yelena, Br Mgr, Riverside County Library System, Calimesa Library, 974 Calimesa Blvd, Calimesa, CA, 92320. Tel: 909-795-9807. Fax: 909-795-3198. p. 217

Antonowicz, Shearin, Ref, Greensboro Public Library, 219 N Church St, Greensboro, NC, 27402-3178. Tel: 336-373-2466. Fax: 336-333-6781. p. 1796

Antonucci, Carl, Dir, Capital Community College Library, 950 Main St, Hartford, CT, 06103. Tel: 860-906-5027. Fax: 860-906-5255. p. 344

Antonucci, Carl, Libr Dir, Central Connecticut State University, 1615 Stanley St, New Britain, CT, 06050. Tel: 860-832-2097. Fax: 860-832-3409. p. 353

Antonucci, Carl, Ref, Utica Public Library, 303 Genesee St, Utica, NY, 13501. Tel: 315-735-2279. Fax: 315-734-1034. p. 1760

Antonucci, Dana, Librn, Stony Brook University, Science & Engineering Library, N-1000 Melville Library, Stony Brook, NY, 11794-3301. Tel: 631-632-7148. Fax: 631-632-7186. p. 1750

Antonucci, Ron, Br Mgr, Cleveland Public Library, Brooklyn, 3706 Pearl Rd, Cleveland, OH, 44109. Tel: 216-623-6920. Fax: 216-623-6970. p. 1878

Antonucci-Durgan, Dana, Head Librn, Stony Brook University, Chemistry, Chemistry Bldg, C-299, Stony Brook, NY, 11794-3425. Tel: 631-632-7150. Fax: 631-632-9191. p. 1750

Antony, Deb, Asst Dir, Horicon Public Library, 404 E Lake St, Horicon, WI, 53032-1297. Tel: 920-485-3535. Fax: 920-485-3536. p. 2598

Antony, Tammy, Librn, Parkland Regional Library, MacNutt Branch, PO Box 150, MacNutt, SK, S0A 2K0, CANADA. p. 2932

Antorietto, Joyce, Asst Librn, San Diego Museum of Man, Balboa Park, 1350 El Prado, San Diego, CA, 92101. Tel: 619-239-2001. Fax: 619-239-2749. p. 235

Antram, Nancy, Ch, Annie Halenbake Ross Library, 232 W Main St, Lock Haven, PA, 17745-1241. Tel: 570-748-3321. Fax: 570-748-1050. p. 2082

Antrim, Brenda, Ref, Santa Monica College Library, 1900 Pico Blvd, Santa Monica, CA, 90405-1628. Tel: 310-434-4334, 310-434-4692. Fax: 310-434-4387. p. 266

Antrim, Patricia, Dr, Chair, Coordr, Prof, University of Central Missouri, Dept of Educational Leadership & Human Development, Lovinger 4101, Warrensburg, MO, 64093. Tel: 660-543-8633. Fax: 660-543-4164. p. 2968

Antunes, Lynne, Actg Dir, Dartmouth Public Libraries, North Dartmouth, 1383 Tucker Rd, Dartmouth, MA, 02747. Tel: 508-999-0728. Fax: 508-999-0795. p. 1084

Antuns, Lynne, Actg Dir, Dartmouth Public Libraries, 732 Dartmouth St, Dartmouth, MA, 02748. Tel: 508-999-0726. Fax: 508-992-9914. p. 1084

Anway, Vickie, Tech Serv, Botetourt County Library, 28 Avery Row, Roanoke, VA, 24012. Tel: 540-977-3433. Fax: 540-977-2407. p. 2493

Anyadike, Barna, In Charge, Dillwyn Correctional Center, 1522 Prison Rd, Dillwyn, VA, 23936. Tel: 434-983-4200, Ext 4883. Fax: 434-983-1821. p. 2460

Anzalone, Filippa Marullo, Prof of Law & Assoc Dean, Libr & Tech Serv, Boston College, 885 Centre St, Newton Centre, MA, 02459. Tel: 617-552-6809. Fax: 617-552-2889. p. 1110

Aoki, Jodi, Archivist, Trent University, Archives, Thomas J Bata Library, 1st Flr, 1600 W Bank Dr, Peterborough, ON, K9J 7B8, CANADA. Tel: 705-748-1011, Ext 7413. p. 2836

Aperto, Sharon, Head, Ref, The Nyack Library, 59 S Broadway, Nyack, NY, 10960. Tel: 845-358-3370, Ext 29. p. 1708

Apicella, Doug, Ref Serv, Wiggin & Dana LLP, 265 Church St, New Haven, CT, 06510. Tel: 203-498-4400. Fax: 203-782-2889. p. 356

Apollo, Francine, Bibliog Instr, Coordr of Ref Serv, State University of New York College of Agriculture & Technology, 142 Schenectady Ave, Cobleskill, NY, 12043. Tel: 518-255-5858. Fax: 518-255-5843. p. 1608

Aponte, Carmen L, Cat, University of the Sacred Heart, Rosales St, PO Box 12383, Santurce, PR, 00914-0383. Tel: 787-728-1515, Ext 4353. Fax: 787-268-8868. p. 2678

Aponte, Jose A, Dir, San Diego County Library, 5560 Overland Ave, Ste 110, San Diego, CA, 92123. Tel: 858-694-2389. Fax: 858-495-5658. p. 233

Aponte, Sarah, Librn, City College of the City University of New York, Dominican Studies Institute Research Library & Archives, NAC 2/204, 160 Convent Ave, New York, NY, 10031-0198. Tel: 212-650-7170, 212-650-7496. Fax: 212-650-7489. p. 1673

Apostola, Elaine, Dep Dir, Maine State Law & Legislative Reference Library, 43 State House Sta, Augusta, ME, 04333-0043. Tel: 207-287-1600. Fax: 207-287-6467. p. 974

Apostolos, Erin, Dir, Meredith Public Library, 91 Main St, Meredith, NH, 03253. Tel: 603-279-4303. Fax: 603-279-5352. p. 1457

Appel, Howard, Educ Coordr, Anvil Mountain Correctional Center Library, PO Box 730, Nome, AK, 99762-0730. Tel: 907-443-2241. Fax: 907-443-5195. p. 52

Appel, Maryland, Circ Supvr, Allegany County Library System, 31 Washington St, Cumberland, MD, 21502. Tel: 301-777-1200. Fax: 301-777-7299. p. 1026

Appel, Myra, Head, Humanities & Soc Sci, University of California, Davis, 100 NW Quad, Davis, CA, 95616-5292. Tel: 530-752-6561. Fax: 530-752-3148. p. 139

Appelbaum, Elliot, Br Mgr, Lexington Public Library, Eagle Creek, 101 N Eagle Creek Dr, Lexington, KY, 40509. Tel: 859-231-5560. Fax: 859-422-6868. p. 921

Appelbaum, Elliot, Br Mgr, Lexington Public Library, Tates Creek, 3628 Walden Dr, Lexington, KY, 40517. Tel: 859-231-5500. Fax: 859-422-6888. p. 921

Appelbaum, Lee, Librn, Stamford Community Library, 986 Main Rd, Stamford, VT, 05352. Tel: 802-694-1379. Fax: 802-694-1636. p. 2436

Appelt, Kristina Marie, Lead Info Literacy Librn, Prairie State College Library, 202 S Halsted St, Chicago Heights, IL, 60411-8200. Tel: 708-709-3550. Fax: 708-709-3940. p. 628

Appelt, Lisa, Pub Serv Dir, Dauphin County Library System, 101 Walnut St, Harrisburg, PA, 17101. Tel: 717-234-4961, Ext 105. Fax: 717-234-7479. p. 2064

Appelt, Susan, Tech Serv, Oakland Community College, Library Systems, 2900 Featherstone Rd, MTEC A210, Auburn Hills, MI, 48326. Tel: 248-232-4480. Fax: 248-232-4089. p. 1154

Apperson, Carolee, Librn, Camden County Library District, Climax Springs Branch, 14157 N State Hwy 7, Climax Springs, MO, 65324. Tel: 573-347-2722. Fax: 573-347-2722. p. 1321

Apperson, Diane, Sr Librn, Denver Public Library, Bear Valley, 5171 W Dartmouth, Denver, CO, 80236-2006. Tel: 303-935-0616. Fax: 303-934-9403. p. 301

Apple, Andrea, Head, Pub Serv, Kern County Library, 701 Truxtun Ave, Bakersfield, CA, 93301-4816. Tel: 661-868-0700. Fax: 661-868-0799. p. 124

Apple, Ellen, Ref, Southern Nazarene University, 4115 N College, Bethany, OK, 73008. Tel: 405-491-6350. Fax: 405-491-6355. p. 1958

Appleby, Barbara, Media Serv, Saint John's University Library, 8000 Utopia Pkwy, Queens, NY, 11439. Tel: 718-990-6735. Fax: 718-380-0353. p. 1725

Appleby, Barbara, Br Mgr, Montgomery County Memorial Library System, Malcolm Purvis Library, 510 Melton St, Magnolia, TX, 77354. Tel: 936-788-8324. Fax: 936-788-8304. p. 2300

Appleby, Rachel, Law Librn, Alberta Law Libraries, Judicial, Calgary Courts Ctr, 2001-N, 601 - 5 St SW, Calgary, AB, T2P 5P7, CANADA. Tel: 403-592-4796. Fax: 403-297-2981. p. 2687

Appleby, Rayola, Acq, Saint Bonaventure University, 3261 W State Rd, Saint Bonaventure, NY, 14778. Tel: 716-375-2339. Fax: 716-375-2389. p. 1737

Applegate, Carolyn J, Br Mgr, Mansfield-Richland County Public Library, Bellville Branch, 97 Bell St, Bellville, OH, 44813. Tel: 419-886-3811. Fax: 419-886-3791. p. 1912

Applegate, Jeff, Br Mgr, Colusa County Free Library, Stonyford Branch, 5080 Stonyford-Lodoga Rd, Stonyford, CA, 95979. Tel: 530-963-3722. p. 136

Applegate, Loretta, Dir, Noonday Community Library Inc, 16662 CR 196, Tyler, TX, 75703. Tel: 903-939-0540. Fax: 903-939-0540. p. 2393

Applegate, Susan, ILL, Boston Public Library, 700 Boylston St, Boston, MA, 02117-0286. Tel: 617-536-5400. Fax: 617-236-4306. p. 1056

Applegate, Tamara, Libr Mgr, Apache County Library District, Vernon Public, 10 County Rd 3142, Vernon, AZ, 85940. Tel: 928-532-5005. Fax: 928-532-5005. p. 80

Appleton, Betsy, Electronic Res Librn, George Mason University Libraries, 4400 University Dr, MSN 2FL, Fairfax, VA, 22030-4444. Tel: 703-993-2250. Fax: 703-993-2200. p. 2462

Appleton, Brenda, Coll Develop, Vancouver Community College, 250 W Pender St, Vancouver, BC, V6B 1S9, CANADA. Tel: 604-443-8641. Fax: 604-443-8588. p. 2743

Applin, Mary Beth, Dr, Dean, Learning Res, Hinds Community College, 505 E Main St, Raymond, MS, 39154. Tel: 601-857-3255. Fax: 601-857-3293. p. 1313

Applin, Peter, Head, Cat, Lone Star College System, 20515 State Hwy 249, Bldg 11, Rm 11437, Houston, TX, 77070-2607. Tel: 281-290-3717. Fax: 281-290-2979. p. 2340

Appling, Cenie, Asst Librn, North Central Regional Library, Quincy Community, 108 B St SW, Quincy, WA, 98848-1203. Tel: 509-787-2359. p. 2549

Appling, Jane, Regional Mgr, Seattle Public Library, Deldridge, 5423 Deldridge Way SW, Seattle, WA, 98106. p. 2531

Appling, Jane, Regional Mgr, Seattle Public Library, High Point, 3411 SW Raymond St, Seattle, WA, 98126. Tel: 206-684-7454. p. 2531

Appling, Jane, Regional Mgr, Seattle Public Library, South Park, 8604 Eighth Ave S, Seattle, WA, 98108. Tel: 206-615-1688. Fax: 206-615-0539. p. 2531

Appling, Jane, Regional Mgr, Seattle Public Library, Southwest, 9010 35th Ave SW, Seattle, WA, 98126. Tel: 206-684-7455. p. 2532

Appling, Jane, Regional Mgr, Seattle Public Library, West Seattle Branch, 2306 42nd Ave SW, Seattle, WA, 98116. Tel: 206-684-7444. p. 2532

Appling, Pauline, Ref Serv, Kelley, Drye & Warren, Washington Harbour, 3050 K St, Ste 400, Washington, DC, 20007-5108. Tel: 202-342-8613. Fax: 202-342-8451. p. 406

Appling, Sherryl, Cat, Logan County Public Library, 201 W Sixth St, Russellville, KY, 42276. Tel: 270-726-6129. Fax: 270-726-6127. p. 934

Apps, Michelle, Coll Develop, Ref, Broward College, 3501 SW Davie Rd, Davie, FL, 33314. Tel: 954-201-6648. Fax: 954-201-6490. p. 435

Apt, Robbie, Outreach Serv Mgr, Delaware County District Library, 84 E Winter St, Delaware, OH, 43015. Tel: 740-362-3861. Fax: 740-369-0196. p. 1895

Apulu, Ruth, Librn, American Samoa Office of Library Services, Taufuna High School - Community, Taufuna Village, AS, 96799. Tel: 684-699-1303. Fax: 684-633-4240. p. 2665

Aquila, Natalie, Circ Supvr, University of Saint Thomas, 1100 W Main, Houston, TX, 77006. Tel: 713-525-2192. Fax: 713-525-3886. p. 2344

Aquila, Sam, Coordr, Cat, University of Victoria Libraries, McPherson Library, PO Box 1800, Victoria, BC, V8W 3H5, CANADA. Tel: 250-721-8211. Fax: 250-721-8215. p. 2746

Arabadjief, Mark, Ref Librn, Joliet Junior College, J-Bldg, 3rd Flr, 1215 Houbolt Rd, Joliet, IL, 60431-8938. Tel: 815-729-9020, Ext 2350. Fax: 815-744-2465. p. 660

Arabadjis, Chris, Dir, Pratt Institute Libraries, Multi-Media Services, 200 Willoughby Ave, Brooklyn, NY, 11205. Tel: 718-399-4356. Fax: 718-399-4428. p. 1594

Arabian, Nina, Ser Tech & PT Librn, Vanier College Library, 821 Ave Sainte-Croix, Saint Laurent, QC, H4X 3L9, CANADA. Tel: 514-744-7500, Ext 7540. Fax: 514-744-7545. p. 2909

Aragon, Ruben, Pres, New Mexico Consortium of Academic Libraries, Dean's Office, University Libraries MSC 053020, Albuquerque, NM, 87131-0001. p. 2949

Aragon, Ruben F, Dir, Libr & Info Serv, New Mexico Highlands University, Ninth & National Ave, Las Vegas, NM, 87701. Tel: 505-454-3401. Fax: 505-454-0026. p. 1559

Aragon, Sonia, Supvr, El Paso Community College Library, Mission del Paso Campus Library, 10700 Gateway East, Rm C-102, El Paso, TX, 79927. Fax: 915-831-7041. p. 2316

Aragon, Tova, Coll, Poudre River Public Library District, 201 Peterson St, Fort Collins, CO, 80524-2990. Tel: 970-221-6740. Fax: 970-221-6398. p. 308

Arakelian, Sylvia, Head Librn, Jaffe Raitt Heuer & Weiss, 27777 Franklin Rd, Ste 2500, Southfield, MI, 48034-8214. Tel: 248-351-3000, 248-727-1470. Fax: 248-351-3082. p. 1228

Aramburo, Clemencia, Coordr, Tech Serv, Mount Ida College, Wadsworth Library, 777 Dedham St, Newton, MA, 02459. Tel: 617-928-4552. Fax: 617-928-4038. p. 1110

Aranas, Pauline, Assoc Dean, Dep Dir, University of Southern California Libraries, Asa V Call Law Library, 699 Exposition Blvd, LAW 202, MC 0072, Los Angeles, CA, 90089-0072. Tel: 213-740-6482. Fax: 213-740-7179. p. 179

Arand, Betsy, Managing Librn, Sno-Isle Libraries, Freeland Branch, 5495 Harbor Ave, Freeland, WA, 98249. Tel: 360-331-7323. Fax: 360-331-1572. p. 2542

Arango, Xiomara, Div Head, Morehouse School of Medicine Library, 720 Westview Dr SW, Atlanta, GA, 30310-1495. Tel: 404-752-1532. Fax: 404-752-1049. p. 517

Arata, Barbara, Chairperson, First Congregational Church Library, Walton Pl, Stamford, CT, 06901. Tel: 203-323-6511. Fax: 203-348-2270. p. 369

Arata, Jayne, Librn, Hubbardston Public Library, Seven Main St, Hubbardston, MA, 01452. Tel: 978-928-4775. Fax: 978-928-1273. p. 1096

Arata, Jayne, Dir, Petersham Memorial Library, 23 Common St, Petersham, MA, 01366. Tel: 978-724-3405. Fax: 978-724-0089. p. 1117

Araujo, Sonia, Asst Dir, Jersey City Free Public Library, 472 Jersey Ave, Jersey City, NJ, 07302-3499. Tel: 201-547-4549. Fax: 201-547-5936. p. 1492

Araya, Beth, Coordr, Saint Francis Medical Center, 3630 E Imperial Hwy, Lynwood, CA, 90262. Tel: 310-900-8671. Fax: 310-639-5936. p. 181

Arbaugh, Linda E, Commun Librn, Santa Clara County Library District, Milpitas Public, 160 N Main St, Milpitas, CA, 95035-4323. Tel: 408-262-1171. Fax: 408-262-5806. p. 181

Arbeeny, Pam, Coll Mgt Librn, Fort Lewis College Library, 1000 Rim Dr, Durango, CO, 81301-3999. Tel: 970-247-7250. Fax: 970-247-7149. p. 305

Arbogast, Gia, Asst Dir, Outreach, Communications & Prog, Miami-Dade Public Library System, 101 W Flagler St, Miami, FL, 33130-1523. Tel: 305-375-5184. Fax: 305-375-3048. p. 466

Arbour, Cara, Asst Librn, Hay Lakes Municipal Library, PO Box 69, Hay Lakes, AB, T0B 1W0, CANADA. Tel: 780-878-2665. p. 2706

Arbuckle, Katheryn, Interim Chief Librn, University of Alberta, University Library, 5-02 Cameron Libr, Edmonton, AB, T6G 2J8, CANADA. Tel: 780-492-3790. Fax: 780-492-8302. p. 2702

Arbuckle, Stef, Dir, Weir Public Library, 612 S Jefferson, Weir, KS, 66781. Tel: 620-396-8899. Fax: 620-356-8899. p. 899

Arcand, Daniel, Librn, Ecole Nationale de Police du Quebec, 350 rue Marguerite d'Youville, Nicolet, QC, J3T 1X4, CANADA. Tel: 819-293-8631, Ext 6256. Fax: 819-293-8625. p. 2902

Arcand, Renaud, Libr Spec, Tech Serv, Bibliothèques de Montrèal, 801, rue Brennan, 5e Etage, Bureau 5206, Montreal, QC, H3C 0G4, CANADA. Tel: 514-872-1892. Fax: 514-872-0530. p. 2889

Arcangelie, Dottie, Sr Libr Asst, Feather River College Library, 570 Golden Eagle Ave, Quincy, CA, 95971-9124. Tel: 530-283-0202, Ext 236. Fax: 530-283-4097. p. 212

Arce, Carlos, Exec Dir, City College - Miami Library, 9300 S Dadeland Blvd, Ste PH, Miami, FL, 33156. Tel: 305-666-9242. Fax: 305-666-9243. p. 465

Arce, Patty, Br Mgr, San Diego County Library, Campo-Morena Village Branch, 31356 Hwy 94, Campo, CA, 91906-3112. Tel: 619-478-5945. Fax: 619-478-2446. p. 233

Arce, Teri, Head Librn, Plano Public Library System, W O Haggard Jr Library, 2501 Coit Rd, Plano, TX, 75075. Tel: 972-769-4250. Fax: 972-769-4256. p. 2370

Arceneaux, Keisa, Acq Librn, Terrebonne Parish Library, 151 Library Dr, Houma, LA, 70360. Tel: 985-876-5861. Fax: 985-917-0582. p. 951

Arceneaux, Pamela D, Curator, Rare Bks, Sr Librn, Historic New Orleans Collection, 410 Chartres St, New Orleans, LA, 70130-2102. Tel: 504-598-7118. Fax: 504-598-7168. p. 960

Arceo, Merly M, ILL, Mount Sinai Hospital Medical Center, California Ave at 15th St, Chicago, IL, 60608. Tel: 773-257-6240. Fax: 773-257-6135. p. 619

Arch, Xan, Coll Develop Librn, Reed College, 3203 SE Woodstock Blvd, Portland, OR, 97202-8199. Tel: 503-777-7702. Fax: 503-777-7786. p. 2014

Archambault, Andre, Librn, Canada Department of Justice Montreal Headquarters Library, East Tower, 9th flr, No 200 Quest boul Rene-Levesque W, Montreal, QC, H2Z 1X4, CANADA. Tel: 514-283-6674, 514-283-8739. Fax: 514-283-6425. p. 2892

Archambault, Brian J, Librn, Lawrence Law Library, Two Appleton St, Lawrence, MA, 01840-1525. Tel: 978-687-7608. Fax: 978-688-2346. p. 1097

Archambault, Caroline, Librn, HEC Montreal, 3000, chemin de la Cote-Sainte-Catherine, Montreal, QC, H3T 2A7, CANADA. Tel: 514-340-6221. Fax: 514-340-5639. p. 2896

Archambault, Christine, Head, Tech Serv, Western New England University, 1215 Wilbraham Rd, Springfield, MA, 01119-2689. Tel: 413-782-1474. Fax: 413-782-1745. p. 1128

Archambault, Sharon, Adult Serv & Outreach Coordr, Langley-Adams Library, 185 Main St, Groveland, MA, 01834-1314. Tel: 978-372-1732. Fax: 978-374-6590. p. 1093

Archambault, Susan, Bus Librn, Chesterfield Township Library, 50560 Patricia Ave, Chesterfield, MI, 48051-3804. Tel: 586-598-4900. Fax: 586-598-7900. p. 1163

Archdale, Gloria, ILL, Miles City Public Library, One S Tenth St, Miles City, MT, 59301-3398. Tel: 406-234-1496. Fax: 406-234-2095. p. 1386

Archdale, Michelle, Libr Tech, Agricultural Research Service, Midwest Area, 1815 N University St, Peoria, IL, 61604. Tel: 309-681-6526. Fax: 309-681-6681. p. 689

Archer, Bonita, Libr Asst, University of Rochester Medical Center, Basil G Bibby Library, Eastman Dental, 625 Elmwood Ave, Rochester, NY, 14620. Tel: 585-275-5010. Fax: 585-273-1230. p. 1734

Archer, Carolyn, Dir, Moorhead Public Library, PO Box 33, Moorhead, IA, 51558-0033. Tel: 712-886-5211. p. 833

Archer, Carolyn, Info Res Mgr, Workplace Safety & Insurance Board, 200 Front St W, 17th Flr, Toronto, ON, M5V 3J1, CANADA. Tel: 416-344-5660. Fax: 416-344-4050. p. 2868

Archer, Cynthia, Univ Librn, York University Libraries, 4700 Keele St, Toronto, ON, M3J 1P3, CANADA. Tel: 416-736-5935. Fax: 416-736-5451. p. 2868

Archer, David, Asst Dir, Pub Serv, Cook Memorial Public Library District, 413 N Milwaukee Ave, Libertyville, IL, 60048-2280. Tel: 847-362-2330. Fax: 847-362-2354. p. 665

Archer, Doris, Pub Serv, Christopher Newport University, One Avenue of the Arts, Newport News, VA, 23606. Tel: 757-594-7245. Fax: 757-594-7717. p. 2479

Archer, Elaine, Librn, Hepburn Library of Edwards, 205 Main St, Edwards, NY, 13635. Tel: 315-562-3521. Fax: 315-562-2600. p. 1618

Archer, Florence, Principal Librn, Ref, Danville Public Library, 511 Patton St, Danville, VA, 24541. Tel: 434-799-5195. Fax: 434-792-5172. p. 2459

Archer, Marilyn, Dir, Libr Serv, Cossatot Community College of the University of Arkansas, 183 Hwy 399, DeQueen, AR, 71832. Tel: 870-584-4471. Fax: 870-642-3320. p. 97

Archer, Mary, Youth Serv Librn, Princeton Public Library, 698 E Peru St, Princeton, IL, 61356. Tel: 815-875-1331. Fax: 815-872-1376. p. 692

Archer, Sandra, Head, Ref Serv, Academy of Motion Picture Arts & Sciences, 333 S La Cienega Blvd, Beverly Hills, CA, 90211. Tel: 310-247-3000, Ext 2205. Fax: 310-657-5193. p. 128

Archibald, Louise, Asst Librn, Fisheries & Oceans Canada, 401 Burrard St, Ste 200, Vancouver, BC, V6C 3S4, CANADA. Tel: 604-666-3851. Fax: 604-666-3145. p. 2741

Archibald, Sylvia, Dir of Libr Serv, Coalinga-Huron USD Library District, 305 N Fourth St, Coalinga, CA, 93210. Tel: 559-935-1676. Fax: 559-935-1058. p. 135

Archibeque, Orlando, Soc Sci Coll Develop Librn, Auraria Library, 1100 Lawrence St, Denver, CO, 80204-2095. Tel: 303-556-3482. Fax: 303-556-3528. p. 298

Archiere, Jean, Asst Librn, Bridgewater Library Association, 62 Main St S, Bridgewater, CT, 06752-9998. Tel: 860-354-6937. Fax: 860-354-4583. p. 332

Archuletta, Susan, Asst Librn, Nesbitt Memorial Library, 529 Washington St, Columbus, TX, 78934-2326. Tel: 979-732-3392. Fax: 979-732-3392. p. 2299

Arcuria, Janice, Asst Dir, Youth Serv, Clayton County Library System, 865 Battlecreek Rd, Jonesboro, GA, 30236. Tel: 770-473-3850. Fax: 770-473-3858. p. 536

Ardan, Brian, Electronic Coll Librn, Lock Haven University of Pennsylvania, 401 N Fairview Ave, Lock Haven, PA, 17745-2390. Tel: 570-484-2312. Fax: 570-484-2506. p. 2082

Ardeleanu-Ionita, Mihaela, Librn, Commission de Toponymie du Quebec Bibliotheque, 750, boul Charest Est, RC, Quebec, QC, G1K 9M1, CANADA. Tel: 418-646-9609. Fax: 418-528-1373. p. 2904

Arden, Michael, AV Librn, United States Military Academy Library, Jefferson Hall Library & Learning Center, 758 Cullum Rd, West Point, NY, 10996. Tel: 845-938-3833. Fax: 845-938-4000. p. 1767

Ardis, Susan, Head Librn, University of Texas Libraries, McKinney Engineering Library, One University Sta S5435, ECJ 1.300, Austin, TX, 78712. Tel: 512-495-4511. Fax: 512-495-4507. p. 2284

Ardoin, Paul, Automation Librn, Ref Librn, Saint Martin Parish Library, 201 Porter St, Saint Martinville, LA, 70582. Tel: 337-394-2207, Ext 23. Fax: 337-394-2248. p. 967

Aregbesola, Emmanuel Bayo, Libr Mgr, Natural Resources Canada Library, PO Box 960, Corner Brook, NL, A2H 6J3, CANADA. Tel: 709-637-4900. Fax: 709-637-4910. p. 2769

Arehart, Carrick, Mgr, Info Serv, Louisville Free Public Library, 301 York St, Louisville, KY, 40203-2205. Tel: 502-574-1712. Fax: 502-574-1666, 502-574-1693. p. 924

Arellano Douglas, Veronica I, Ref, Saint Mary's College of Maryland Library, 18952 E Fisher Rd, Saint Mary's City, MD, 20686-3001. Tel: 240-895-4265. Fax: 240-895-4914. p. 1040

Arellano, Jose, Supvr, Libr & Info Serv, Brooklyn Public Library, Brownsville, 61 Glenmore Ave, Brooklyn, NY, 11212. Tel: 718-498-9721. Fax: 718-498-4071. p. 1591

Arellano, Marcos, Head, Tech Serv, Stickney-Forest View Public Library District, 6800 W 43rd St, Stickney, IL, 60402. Tel: 708-749-1050. Fax: 708-749-1054. p. 707

Arellano, Oscar, Head, Adult Serv, Stickney-Forest View Public Library District, 6800 W 43rd St, Stickney, IL, 60402. Tel: 708-749-1050. Fax: 708-749-1054. p. 707

Arena, Albert, Dir, The Waltham Museum Inc Library, 25 Lexington St, Waltham, MA, 02452. Tel: 781-893-8017, 781-893-9020. p. 1133

Arena, Elizabeth, Ch, North Babylon Public Library, 815 Deer Park Ave, North Babylon, NY, 11703-3812. Tel: 631-669-4020. Fax: 631-669-3432. p. 1706

Arena, Francesco, Dir, Res Serv, Conseil Superieur de l'Education, 1175 ave Lavigerie, Bureau 180, Sainte-Foy, QC, G1V 5B2, CANADA. Tel: 418-643-2845, 418-644-0753. Fax: 418-644-2530. p. 2910

Arend, Mark, Asst Dir, Winnefox Library System, 106 Washington Ave, Oshkosh, WI, 54901-4985. Tel: 920-236-5220. Fax: 920-236-5228. p. 2628

Arends, Katherine, Br Mgr, Alamance County Public Libraries, Mebane Public Library, 101 S First St, Mebane, NC, 27302. Tel: 919-563-6431. Fax: 919-563-5098. p. 1779

Arends, Phyllis, Asst.Librn, Kothe Memorial Library, 309 Third St, Parkersburg, IA, 50665-1030. Tel: 319-346-2442. Fax: 319-346-2442. p. 838

Arendt, Nancy, Exec Dir, Eisenhower Medical Center, 39000 Bob Hope Dr, Rancho Mirage, CA, 92270. Tel: 760-837-3782. Fax: 760-837-8581. p. 213

Arenivar, Becky, Programming Spec, Prescott Public Library, 800 Borner St N, Prescott, WI, 54021-1703. Tel: 715-262-5555. Fax: 715-262-4229. p. 2631

Arens, Layne, Br Mgr, Chicago Public Library, Roosevelt, 1101 W Taylor St, Chicago, IL, 60607. Tel: 312-746-5656. Fax: 312-746-5667. p. 609

Arensdorf, Julie, Instrul Serv Librn, Loras College Library, 1450 Alta Vista St, Dubuque, IA, 52004-4327. Tel: 563-588-7917. Fax: 563-588-7147. p. 812

Areson, Sue, In Charge, Providence Journal Co, 75 Fountain St, Providence, RI, 02902. Tel: 401-277-7391. Fax: 401-277-7665. p. 2173

Arfe, Arlene, Librn, JBI International, 110 E 30th St, New York, NY, 10016. Tel: 212-889-2525. Fax: 212-689-3692. p. 1683

Argáez, Diego, Res Officer, Canadian Association of Research Libraries, 350 Albert St, Ste 600, Ottawa, ON, K1R 1B1, CANADA. Tel: 613-562-5800, Ext 2427. Fax: 613-562-5297. p. 2959

Argast, Deborah, Mgr, Ch Serv, Eckhart Public Library, 603 S Jackson St, Auburn, IN, 46706-2298. Tel: 260-925-2414. Fax: 260-925-9376. p. 725

Argentati, Carolyn, Dep Dir, North Carolina State University Libraries, Two Broughton Dr, Raleigh, NC, 27695. Tel: 919-515-7188. Fax: 919-515-3628. p. 1816

Argo, Greg, Cat, Electronic Res, Ref, Concordia University, 1282 Concordia Ave, Saint Paul, MN, 55104. Tel: 651-641-6315. Fax: 651-641-8782. p. 1278

Argo, Suzanne, Br Mgr, First Regional Library, B J Chain Public Library, 6619 Hwy 305 N, Olive Branch, MS, 38654. Tel: 662-895-5900. Fax: 662-895-9171. p. 1301

Argov, Sharon R, Dir, Libr & Info Res, American InterContinental University, 2250 N Commerce Pkwy, Weston, FL, 33326. Tel: 954-446-6100, Ext 6325. Fax: 954-660-4147. p. 504

Arguimbau, Ellie, Sr Archivist, Montana Historical Society, 225 N Roberts St, Helena, MT, 59601-4514. Tel: 406-444-4774. Fax: 406-444-5297. p. 1382

Arhin, G, Supvr, Arizona Department of Corrections - Adult Institutions, 4374 Butte Ave, Florence, AZ, 85232. Tel: 520-868-0201. Fax: 520-868-8556. p. 63

Arhipov, Sergei, Librn, Saint Tikhon's Orthodox Theological Seminary, St Tikhon's Rd, South Canaan, PA, 18459. Tel: 570-937-4411, Ext 121. Fax: 570-937-3100. p. 2142

Aris, Michelle, Librn, El Centro Public Library, El Centro Community Center, 375 S First St, El Centro, CA, 92243. Tel: 760-336-8977. p. 145

Arjona, Josie, Ref Serv, Travis County Law Library, Travis City Admin Bldg, 314 W 11th, Rm 140, Austin, TX, 78701-2112. Tel: 512-854-4569. Fax: 512-854-9887. p. 2283

Arkenberg, Christine, Pub Serv Mgr, Milwaukee Public Library, 814 W Wisconsin Ave, Milwaukee, WI, 53233-2385. Tel: 414-286-3000. Fax: 414-286-2794. p. 2620

Arkwright, Patti, Dir, Maury Loontjens Memorial Library, 35 Kingstown Rd, Narragansett, RI, 02882. Tel: 401-789-9507. Fax: 401-782-0677. p. 2168

Arledge, Genni, Admin Librn, Navy Personnel Research, Studies & Technology, 5761 Commitment Loop, Bldg 785, Millington, TN, 38055. Tel: 901-874-2115. Fax: 901-874-2720. p. 2253

Arlequeeuw, Beverley, Dir, Port Byron Library, 12 Mentz Dr, Port Byron, NY, 13140. Tel: 315-776-5694. Fax: 315-776-5693. p. 1720

Arlequeeuw, Beverly, Dir, Port Jervis Free Library, 138 Pike St, Port Jervis, NY, 12771. Tel: 845-856-7313, 845-856-9154. Fax: 845-858-8710. p. 1721

Arling, Jennifer, Br Librn, Preble County District Library, West Manchester Branch, 212 S High St, West Manchester, OH, 45382. Tel: 937-678-8503. Fax: 937-678-4030. p. 1898

Arlitsch, Kenning, Dean of Libr, Montana State University Libraries, Centennial Mall, Bozeman, MT, 59717. Tel: 406-994-6978. Fax: 406-994-2851. p. 1375

Armacost, Andrew, Head, Coll Develop & Curator of Coll, RBMSCL, Duke University Libraries, 411 Chapel Dr, Durham, NC, 27708. Tel: 919-660-5835. Fax: 919-660-5934. p. 1787

Armantrout, Judy, Mgr, Three Rivers Regional Library System, St Mary's Library, 100 Herb Bauer Dr, Saint Marys, GA, 31558-3300. Tel: 912-882-4800. Fax: 912-882-2453. p. 522

Armas, Cecilia, Mgr, Mary Kay Inc, 16251 Dallas Pkwy, Addison, TX, 75001. Tel: 972-687-6300. Fax: 972-687-1613. p. 2272

Armato, Lisa, Librn, Allen County Public Library, Georgetown, 6600 E State Blvd, Fort Wayne, IN, 46815. Tel: 260-421-1320. Fax: 260-749-8513. p. 740

Armbrister, Ann, Dep Exec Dir, College Center for Library Automation, 1753 W Paul Dirac Dr, Tallahassee, FL, 32310. Tel: 850-922-6044. Fax: 850-922-4869. p. 2940

Armbruster, Carol, Dir, Stanton Public Library, 1009 Jackpine St, Stanton, NE, 68779. Tel: 402-439-2230. Fax: 402-439-2248. p. 1420

Armbruster, Michelle, Libr Dir, Morrison & Mary Wiley Library District, 206 W Main St, Elmwood, IL, 61529-9641. Tel: 309-742-2431. Fax: 309-742-8298. p. 642

Arment, Donna, Tech Serv & Syst Librn Supvr, Durango Public Library, 1900 E Third Ave, Durango, CO, 81301. Tel: 970-375-3386. Fax: 970-375-3398. p. 304

Arment, Shirley, Asst Dir, Alexander Mitchell Public Library, 519 S Kline St, Aberdeen, SD, 57401-4495. Tel: 605-626-7097. Fax: 605-626-3506. p. 2209

Armentrout, Kim, Dir, Powhatan County Public Library, 2270 Mann Rd, Powhatan, VA, 23139-5748. Tel: 804-598-5670. Fax: 804-598-5671. p. 2485

Armentrout, Philip, Tech Serv Librn, Union Institute & University, 62 Ridge St, Ste 2, Montpelier, VT, 05602. Tel: 802-828-8747. Fax: 802-828-8748. p. 2429

Armieri, Christina, Br Mgr, Brooklyn Public Library, Mill Basin, 2385 Ralph Ave, Brooklyn, NY, 11234. Tel: 718-241-3973. Fax: 718-241-1957. p. 1591

Armington, Shawn, Dir, Flemington Free Public Library, 118 Main St, Flemington, NJ, 08822. Tel: 908-782-5733. Fax: 908-782-3875. p. 1486

Arminio, Roberta Y, Exec Dir, Ossining Historical Society Museum, 196 Croton Ave, Ossining, NY, 10562. Tel: 914-941-0001. Fax: 914-941-0001. p. 1712

Armison, Bernie, Asst Librn, Rushford Free Library, 9012 Main St, Rushford, NY, 14777-9700. Tel: 585-437-2533. Fax: 585-437-9940. p. 1736

Armond, David, Info Tech, Brigham Young University, Howard W Hunter Law Library, 256 JRCB, Provo, UT, 84602-8000. Tel: 801-422-3593. Fax: 801-422-0404. p. 2411

Armour, Annie, Head, Spec Coll & Archives, University of the South, 735 University Ave, Sewanee, TN, 37383-1000. Tel: 931-598-3213. Fax: 931-598-1702. p. 2265

Armour, Hedy, Info Mgt Spec, Librn, Parks Canada, Historic Properties, 1869 Upper Water St, Halifax, NS, B3J 1S9, CANADA. Tel: 902-426-7266. Fax: 902-426-7012. p. 2782

Armour, Jane K, Distance Educ, Electronic Res, Volunteer State Community College Library, 1480 Nashville Pike, Gallatin, TN, 37066-3188. Tel: 615-230-3400, Ext 3406. Fax: 615-230-3410. p. 2235

Armour, Keith, Mgr, Public Library of Cincinnati & Hamilton County, Homework Central, North Bldg, 1st Flr, 800 Vine St, Cincinnati, OH, 45202. Tel: 513-369-6962. Fax: 513-369-4412. p. 1872

Arms, Michele, Asst Dir, Cherry Valley Public Library District, 755 E State St, Cherry Valley, IL, 61016-9699. Tel: 815-332-5161, Ext 35. Fax: 815-332-2441. p. 604

Arms, Wendi, Music Librn, Converse College, 580 E Main St, Spartanburg, SC, 29302. Tel: 864-596-9074. Fax: 864-596-9075. p. 2204

Armstrong, Alison, Head of Instruction & Info Serv, University of Vermont Libraries, 538 Main St, Burlington, VT, 05405-0036. Tel: 802-656-2020. Fax: 802-656-4038. p. 2421

Armstrong, Andrew, Librn, Christendom College, 263 St Johns Way, Front Royal, VA, 22630. Tel: 540-636-2900, Ext 231. Fax: 540-636-6569. p. 2466

Armstrong, Angela, Youth Serv Librn, Ardmore Public Library, 320 E St NW, Ardmore, OK, 73401. Tel: 580-223-8290. Fax: 580-221-3240. p. 1956

Armstrong, Annette T, Libr Dir, Green Hills Public Library District, 8611 W 103rd St, Palos Hills, IL, 60465. Tel: 708-598-8446, Ext 11. Fax: 708-598-0856. p. 687

Armstrong, Beth, Asst Circ Mgr, Giles County Public Library, 122 S Second St, Pulaski, TN, 38478-3285. Tel: 931-363-2720. Fax: 931-424-7032. p. 2264

Armstrong, Betty Joe, Tech Serv, Oregon City Public Library, 362 Warner Milne Rd, Oregon City, OR, 97045. Tel: 503-657-8269. Fax: 503-657-3702. p. 2009

Armstrong, Brenda, Acq, William G Squires Library, 260 11th St NE, Cleveland, TN, 37311. Tel: 423-614-8550. Fax: 423-614-8555. p. 2230

Armstrong, Bruce, Asst Archivist, National Archives of The Christian & Missionary Alliance, 8595 Explorer Dr, Colorado Springs, CO, 80920-1012. Tel: 719-265-2172. Fax: 719-599-8234. p. 295

Armstrong, Carol, Librn, Tall Timbers Research Station Library, 13093 Henry Beadel Dr, Tallahassee, FL, 32312-0918. Tel: 850-893-4153, Ext 234. Fax: 850-668-7781. p. 495

Armstrong, Carolyn, Libr Tech, Nova Scotia Community College, 236 Belcher St, Kentville, NS, B4N 0A6, CANADA. Tel: 902-679-7380. Fax: 902-679-5187. p. 2783

Armstrong, Christi, Librn, Houston Love Memorial Library, Division for the Blind & Physically Handicapped, PO Box 1369, Dothan, AL, 36302. Tel: 334-793-9767. p. 15

Armstrong, Christi, Reader Serv, Houston Love Memorial Library, 212 W Burdeshaw St, Dothan, AL, 36303. Tel: 334-793-9767. Fax: 334-793-6645. p. 15

Armstrong, Christine, Asst Dir, Bellevue University, 1000 Galvin Rd S, Bellevue, NE, 68005. Tel: 402-557-7301. Fax: 402-557-5427. p. 1393

Armstrong, Jason, Network Serv Coordr, Allegany County Library System, 31 Washington St, Cumberland, MD, 21502. Tel: 301-777-1200. Fax: 301-777-7299. p. 1026

Armstrong, Jeanne, Ref Librn, Western Washington University, 516 High St, MS 9103, Bellingham, WA, 98225. Tel: 360-650-7667. Fax: 360-650-3044. p. 2509

Armstrong, Jennifer, Ref, National Semiconductor Corp, 2900 Semiconductor Dr, MS-DT-05, Santa Clara, CA, 95052-8090. Tel: 408-721-3810. Fax: 408-721-7060. p. 262

Armstrong, Jody, Assoc Dir, Columbia University, Arthur W Diamond Law Library, 435 W 116th St, New York, NY, 10027. Tel: 212-854-3922. Fax: 212-854-3295. p. 1674

Armstrong, John, Librn, Tech Proc, Gulf Coast State College Library, 5230 W Hwy 98, Panama City, FL, 32401. Tel: 850-872-3893. Fax: 850-872-3861. p. 480

Armstrong, Jolene, Librn, Connors State College, 1000 College Rd, Warner, OK, 74469-9700. Tel: 918-463-6210. Fax: 918-463-6314. p. 1985

Armstrong, Joyce, Dir, Hamilton County Library, 102 W Ave C, Syracuse, KS, 67878. Tel: 620-384-5622. Fax: 620-384-5623. p. 895

Armstrong, Judy, Homebound Serv, Sheridan County Public Library System, 335 W Alger St, Sheridan, WY, 82801-3899. Tel: 307-674-8585, Ext 5. p. 2660

Armstrong, Judy, Pres, Ontario Library Consortium, Owen Sound & North Grey Union Public Library, 824 First Ave W, Owen Sound, ON, N4K 4K4, CANADA. Tel: 519-376-6623. p. 2960

Armstrong, Kacie, Dir, Euclid Public Library, 631 E 222nd St, Euclid, OH, 44123-2091. Tel: 216-261-5300, Ext 111. Fax: 216-261-0575. p. 1898

Armstrong, Kathleen, Dir, Cahokia Public Library District, 140 Cahokia Park Dr, Cahokia, IL, 62206-2129. Tel: 618-332-1491. Fax: 618-332-1104. p. 599

Armstrong, Kay, Librn, Mary Berry Brown Memorial Library, 1318 Hinton Waters, Midland City, AL, 36350. Tel: 334-983-3511. p. 25

Armstrong, Leslie, Ref Serv, Ad, Ref Serv, YA, Locust Valley Library, 170 Buckram Rd, Locust Valley, NY, 11560-1999. Tel: 516-671-1837. Fax: 516-676-8164. p. 1654

Armstrong, Lorraine, Librn, Chinook Regional Library, Eastend Branch, Eastend Memorial Hall, Eastend, SK, S0N 0T0, CANADA. Tel: 306-295-3788. p. 2928

Armstrong, Mary, Ref, Bracebridge Public Library, 94 Manitoba St, Bracebridge, ON, P1L 2B5, CANADA. Tel: 705-645-4171. Fax: 705-645-6551. p. 2796

Armstrong, Maureen, Br Mgr, Hamden Public Library, Whitneyville, 125 Carleton St, Hamden, CT, 06517. Tel: 203-287-2677. Fax: 203-287-2677. p. 343

Armstrong, Nancy, Dir, Mount Juliet-Wilson County Public, 2765 N Mount Juliet Rd, Mount Juliet, TN, 37122. Tel: 615-758-7051. Fax: 615-758-2439. p. 2254

Armstrong, Nancy A, Dir, Ohio Northern University, Taggart Law Library, 525 S Main St, Ada, OH, 45810. Tel: 419-772-2250. Fax: 419-772-1875. p. 1851

Armstrong, Nicky, Librn, Youngstown Municipal Library, PO Box 39, Youngstown, AB, T0J 3P0, CANADA. Tel: 403-779-3864. Fax: 403-779-3828. p. 2722

Armstrong, Nora, Info Serv Mgr, Cumberland County Public Library & Information Center, 300 Maiden Lane, Fayetteville, NC, 28301-5000. Tel: 910-483-7727. Fax: 910-486-5372. p. 1792

Armstrong, Oriana B, Librn, United States Army, 701 San Marco Blvd, Rm 430-W, Jacksonville, FL, 32207. Tel: 904-232-3643. Fax: 904-232-1838. p. 455

Armstrong, Pamela, Cat Mgr, Saint Joseph County Public Library, 304 S Main, South Bend, IN, 46601-2125. Tel: 574-282-4646. Fax: 574-280-2763. p. 779

Armstrong, Rhonda, Dean, Indiana University Kokomo Library, 2300 S Washington St, Kokomo, IN, 46904. Tel: 765-455-9265. Fax: 765-455-9276. p. 758

Armstrong, Robin, Cat Librn, Madison Library District, 73 N Center, Rexburg, ID, 83440-1539. Tel: 208-356-3461. p. 582

Armstrong, Rosalee, Librn, Lincoln Library, 201 N Main St, Medicine Lodge, KS, 67104. Tel: 620-886-5746. Fax: 620-886-9985. p. 883

Armstrong, Ruth Carter, Dir, White & Case Law Library, 1155 Avenue of the Americas, New York, NY, 10036. Tel: 212-819-8200. Fax: 212-354-8113. p. 1702

Armstrong, Sandra, Asst Librn, Odon Winkelpleck Public Library, 202 W Main St, Odon, IN, 47562. Tel: 812-636-4949. Fax: 812-636-4949. p. 771

Armstrong, Susan, Ref, Superior Court Law Library, 101 W Jefferson, Phoenix, AZ, 85003. Tel: 602-506-3461. Fax: 602-506-3677. p. 77

Armstrong, Val, Br Mgr, Dallas Public Library, Bachman Lake, 9480 Webb Chapel Rd, Dallas, TX, 75220-4496. Tel: 214-670-6376. Fax: 214-670-6614. p. 2306

Armstrong, Vicki, Libr Tech, Phoenix VA Health Care System, 650 E Indian School Rd, Phoenix, AZ, 85012. Tel: 602-222-6411. Fax: 602-222-6472. p. 77

Armstrong, Vicki, Br Mgr, Tacoma Public Library, Moore Branch, 215 S 56th St, Tacoma, WA, 98408. p. 2540

Armstrong, Vicki, Br Mgr, Tacoma Public Library, Mottet Branch, 3523 East G St, Tacoma, WA, 98404. p. 2540

Armstrong, William, Coll Develop Coordr, Louisiana State University Libraries, 295 Middleton Library, Baton Rouge, LA, 70803. Tel: 225-578-2738. Fax: 225-578-9432. p. 943

Arn, Nancy, Dir, Barton Library, 200 E Fifth St, El Dorado, AR, 71730-3897. Tel: 870-863-5447. Fax: 870-862-3944. p. 98

Arnason, Laurie, Librn, Pauline Johnson Library, 23 Main St, Lundar, MB, R0C 1Y0, CANADA. Tel: 204-762-5367. Fax: 204-762-5367. p. 2749

Arnaudin, Edwin, Br Mgr, Andrews Public Library, 871 Main St, Andrews, NC, 28901. Tel: 828-321-5956. Fax: 828-321-3256. p. 1773

Arnaudin, Edwin, Access Serv Librn, Transylvania County Library, 212 S Gaston, Brevard, NC, 28712. Tel: 828-884-3151, Ext 223. Fax: 828-877-4230. p. 1777

Arndell, Bettie, Per, Grayson County Public Library, 130 E Market St, Leitchfield, KY, 42754-1439. Tel: 270-259-5455. Fax: 270-259-4552. p. 920

Arndt, Glenda, Libr Asst, Watonwan County Library, Madelia Branch, 23 First St NW, Madelia, MN, 56062-1411. Tel: 507-642-3511. Fax: 507-642-8144. p. 1277

Arndt, Regina, Youth Serv, Altoona Public Library, 1303 Lynn Ave, Altoona, WI, 54720-0278. Tel: 715-839-5029. Fax: 715-830-5119. p. 2577

Arndt, Robert, Ref Serv Librn, University of North Carolina at Pembroke, Faculty Row, Pembroke, NC, 28372. Tel: 910-521-6516. Fax: 910-521-6547. p. 1814

Arndt, Sharon, Librn, Ogemaw District Library, Ogemaw East, 200 Washington, Prescott, MI, 48756. Tel: 989-873-5807. p. 1223

Arndt, Theresa, Assoc Dir, Libr Res & Admin, Dickinson College, 333 W High St, Carlisle, PA, 17013-2896. Tel: 717-245-1397. Fax: 717-245-1439.- p. 2042

Arne, Debbie, Librn, Western Dakota Technical Institute Library, 800 Mickelson Dr, Rapid City, SD, 57703. Tel: 605-718-2904. Fax: 605-718-2537. p. 2217

Arnelien, Heather, Asst Librn, Chinook Regional Library, Cabri Branch, PO Box 18, Cabri, SK, S0N 0J0, CANADA. Tel: 306-587-2911. p. 2928

Arneson, Bess, Pub Relations & Prog Serv Mgr, L E Phillips Memorial Public Library, 400 Eau Claire St, Eau Claire, WI, 54701. Tel: 715-839-5094. Fax: 715-839-5310. p. 2590

Arneson, Rosemary, Univ Librn, University of Mary Washington, 1801 College Ave, Fredericksburg, VA, 22401-4665. Tel: 540-654-1147. Fax: 540-654-1067. p. 2466

Arneson, Rosemary H, Dir, University of Montevallo, Station 6100, Montevallo, AL, 35115-6100. Tel: 205-665-6100. Fax: 205-665-6112. p. 27

Arnett, Anna, Br Mgr, La Porte County Public Library, Union Mills Branch, 3727 W 800 South, Union Mills, IN, 46382-9672. Tel: 219-767-2604. Fax: 219-767-2604. p. 759

Arnett, Earlene Hawkins, Dir, Scott County Public Library, 104 S Bradford Lane, Georgetown, KY, 40324-2335. Tel: 502-863-3566. Fax: 502-863-9621. p. 915

Arnett, Kathy, Mgr, Harrison Regional Library System, 50 Lester St, Columbiana, AL, 35051. Tel: 205-669-3910. Fax: 205-669-3940. p. 13

Arnett, Kristen, ILL, Maitland Public Library, 501 S Maitland Ave, Maitland, FL, 32751-5672. Tel: 407-647-7700. p. 462

Arnett, Ray, Dir, Fremont Area District Library, 104 E Main, Fremont, MI, 49412. Tel: 231-924-3480. Fax: 231-924-2355. p. 1182

Arnette, Sharon, Tech Serv, Henderson County Public Library, 301 N Washington St, Hendersonville, NC, 28739. Tel: 828-697-4725. Fax: 828-692-8449, 828-697-4700. p. 1801

Arney, Chad, Head, Tech Strategy & Innovation, Michigan Technological University, 1400 Townsend Dr, Houghton, MI, 49931-1295. Tel: 906-487-4321. p. 1191

Arney, Chris, Cat Librn, Center for Creative Leadership Library, One Leadership Pl, Greensboro, NC, 27410. Tel: 336-286-4083. Fax: 336-286-4087. p. 1795

Arnheim, Juliette, Librn, Princeton University, Chemistry, Frick Laboratory, One Washington Rd, Princeton, NJ, 08544. Tel: 609-258-8601. p. 1523

Arnold, Alexandria, Asst Dir, Summit Free Public Library, 75 Maple St, Summit, NJ, 07901-9984. Tel: 908-273-0350. Fax: 908-273-0031. p. 1532

Arnold, Allison, Asst Dir, Saint Clair County Library System, 210 McMorran Blvd, Port Huron, MI, 48060-4098. Tel: 810-987-7323, Ext 122. Fax: 810-987-7874. p. 1219

Arnold, Angela, Circ Supvr, University of California, Berkeley, Jean Gray Hargrove Music Library, Hargrove Music Library, Berkeley, CA, 94720-6000. Tel: 510-643-6196. Fax: 510-642-8237. p. 128

Arnold, Barb, Libr Assoc, Craig Public Library, 504 Third St, Craig, AK, 99921. Tel: 907-826-3281. Fax: 907-826-3280. p. 46

Arnold, Bonnie, Mgr, Adventist Hinsdale Hospital, 120 N Oak St, Hinsdale, IL, 60521. Tel: 630-856-7230. Fax: 630-856-7239. p. 656

Arnold, Bonnie, Mgr, Libr Serv, La Grange Memorial Hospital, 5101 Willow Springs Rd, La Grange, IL, 60525. Tel: 708-245-7236. Fax: 708-245-5613. p. 662

Arnold, Brenda, Libr Mgr, Tilley District & Public Library, 148 First St E, Tilley, AB, T0J 3K0, CANADA. Tel: 403-377-2233, Ext 150. Fax: 403-377-2097. p. 2719

Arnold, Carol, Access Serv, University of Tulsa Libraries, Mabee Legal Information Center, 3120 E Fourth Pl, Tulsa, OK, 74104-3189. Tel: 918-631-2404. Fax: 918-631-3556. p. 1984

Arnold, Carole, Dir, Dolores Library District, 1002 Railroad Ave, Dolores, CO, 81323. Tel: 970-882-4127. Fax: 970-882-2224. p. 304

Arnold, Cassandra, Dir, Carlsbad Public Library, 101 S Halagueno St, Carlsbad, NM, 88220. Tel: 575-885-6776. Fax: 575-887-7706. p. 1552

Arnold, Diane, Per, Chestnut Hill College, 9601 Germantown Ave, Philadelphia, PA, 19118-2695. Tel: 215-248-7054. Fax: 215-248-7056. p. 2104

Arnold, Eric, Supvr, University of Tennessee, Knoxville, Map Library, 15 Hoskins Bldg, Knoxville, TN, 37996-4006. Tel: 865-974-4315. Fax: 865-974-3925. p. 2244

Arnold, George, Ref Librn, American University Library, 4400 Massachusetts Ave NW, Washington, DC, 20016-8046. Tel: 202-885-3237. Fax: 202-885-3226. p. 393

Arnold, Gretchen, Dir, University of Virginia, Claude Moore Health Sciences Library, Univ Va Health System, 1300 Jefferson Park Ave, Charlottesville, VA, 22908. Tel: 434-924-5444. Fax: 434-924-0379. p. 2455

Arnold, J, Dir, Libr Serv, Stockton Township Public Library, 140 W Benton Ave, Stockton, IL, 61085. Tel: 815-947-2030. Fax: 815-947-2030. p. 708

Arnold, Jan, Libr Dir, Springfield Art Association, 700 N Fourth St, Springfield, IL, 62702-5232. Tel: 217-523-2631. Fax: 217-523-3866. p. 706

Arnold, Jana, Circ Coordr, Community Library Association, 415 Spruce Ave N, Ketchum, ID, 83340. Tel: 208-726-3493. p. 577

Arnold, Jennifer, Dir, Central Piedmont Community College Library, 1201 Elizabeth Ave, Charlotte, NC, 28235. Tel: 704-330-6635. Fax: 704-330-6887. p. 1781

Arnold, Jessie B, Dean, Univ Libr, Alcorn State University, 1000 ASU Dr, Alcorn State, MS, 39096-7500. Tel: 601-877-6350. Fax: 601-877-3885. p. 1293

Arnold, Joanna, Librn, Georgia Power Co-Southern Co, 241 Ralph McGill Blvd NE, Bin 10044, Atlanta, GA, 30308. Tel: 404-506-6633. Fax: 404-506-6652. p. 515

Arnold, Joanne, ILL, Colchester District Library, 203 Macomb St, Colchester, IL, 62326. Tel: 309-776-4861. Fax: 309-776-4099. p. 630

Arnold, Karla, Circ Supvr, London Public Library, 20 E First St, London, OH, 43140. Tel: 740-852-9543. Fax: 740-852-3691. p. 1911

Arnold, Kim, Archivist, Presbyterian Church in Canada Archives, 50 Wynford Dr, Toronto, ON, M3C 1J7, CANADA. Tel: 416-441-1111, Ext 310. Fax: 416-441-2825. p. 2857

Arnold, Lee, Sr Dir, Libr & Coll, Historical Society of Pennsylvania, 1300 Locust St, Philadelphia, PA, 19107-5699. Tel: 215-732-6200. Fax: 215-732-2680. p. 2110

Arnold, Mark, Exec Dir, The Art Center of Waco Library, 1300 College Dr, Waco, TX, 76708. Tel: 254-752-4371. Fax: 254-752-3506. p. 2395

Arnold, Melissa D, Curator, Peninsula Library & Historical Society, Cuyahoga Valley Historical Museum, 1775 Main St, Second Flr, Peninsula, OH, 44264. Tel: 330-657-2892. p. 1929

Arnold, Michelle, Govt Doc, Clearwater Public Library System, 100 N Osceola Ave, Clearwater, FL, 33755. Tel: 727-562-4970. Fax: 727-562-4975. p. 432

Arnold, Pabby, Children's Serv Coordr, East Baton Rouge Parish Library, 7711 Goodwood Blvd, Baton Rouge, LA, 70806-7625. Tel: 225-231-3760. Fax: 225-231-3788. p. 942

Arnold, Patricia, Librn, United States Department of the Air Force, Bldg 7445, Rm 105, 2230 Andrews Ave, Lackland AFB, TX, 78236. Tel: 210-671-2767. Fax: 210-671-1014. p. 2352

Arnold, Patsy, Mgr, Grand Island Public Library, 211 N Washington St, Grand Island, NE, 68801-5855. Tel: 308-385-5333, Ext 153. Fax: 308-385-5339. p. 1400

Arnold, Richard, Pub Serv Librn, Sullivan County Community College, 112 College Rd, Loch Sheldrake, NY, 12759-5108. Tel: 845-434-5750, Ext 4227. p. 1653

Arnold, Roberta, Asst Dir, Publications, Radiological Society of North America, 820 Jorie Blvd, Oak Brook, IL, 60523-2251. Tel: 630-571-2670. Fax: 630-571-7837. p. 683

Arnold, Ruth S, Dir, Staunton Public Library, One Churchville Ave, Staunton, VA, 24401. Tel: 540-332-3902. Fax: 540-332-3906. p. 2496

Arnold, Sandi, Cat, Circ, Williamsburg County Library, 215 N Jackson, Kingstree, SC, 29556-3319. Tel: 843-355-9486. Fax: 843-355-9991. p. 2198

Arnold, Sharmain, Ch, Riviera Beach Public Library, 600 W Blue Heron Blvd, Riviera Beach, FL, 33404-4398. Tel: 561-845-4195. Fax: 561-881-7308. p. 485

Arnold, Susan, Dir, West Virginia University Libraries, Health Sciences Library, Robert C Byrd Health Sciences Ctr N, One Medical Center Dr, Morgantown, WV, 26506. Tel: 304-293-2113. Fax: 304-293-5995. p. 2567

Arnold, Suzanne, Librn, Park Synagogue, 27500 Shaker Blvd, Pepper Pike, OH, 44124-5050. Tel: 216-371-2244, Ext 223. Fax: 216-321-0639. p. 1929

Arnold, Suzanne, Librn, Park Synagogue, Zehman Library, 27575 Shaker Blvd, Pepper Pike, OH, 44124. Tel: 216-371-2244, Ext 223, 216-831-5363, Ext 223. Fax: 216-321-0639. p. 1929

Arnold-Friend, Louise A, Coll Mgr, United States Army Heritage & Education Center, 950 Soldiers Dr, Carlisle, PA, 17013-5021. Tel: 717-245-3103. Fax: 717-245-3067. p. 2042

Arnold-Robbins, Ellen, Dir, Takoma Park Maryland Library, 101 Philadelphia Ave, Takoma Park, MD, 20912. Tel: 301-891-7259. Fax: 301-270-0814. p. 1043

Arnold-Yergel, Kathleen, Exec Dir, Montgomery County-Norristown Public Library, 1001 Powell St, Norristown, PA, 19401-3817. Tel: 610-278-5100, Ext 140. p. 2098

Arnott, Lesley, Dir, Libr Serv, LSU Health Sciences Center, 4864 Jackson St, Monroe, LA, 71202. Tel: 318-330-7644. Fax: 318-330-7649. p. 957

Arns, Jennifer, Asst Prof, University of South Carolina, 1501 Greene St, Columbia, SC, 29208. Tel: 803-777-3858. Fax: 803-777-7938. p. 2973

Aro, Carlene, Ser, South Dakota State University, 1300 N Campus Dr, Box 2115, Brookings, SD, 57007-1098. Tel: 605-688-5567. Fax: 605-688-6133. p. 2211

Aromire, Lami, Coordr, Tech Support, Baltimore County Public Library, 320 York Rd, Towson, MD, 21204-5179. Tel: 410-887-4656. Fax: 410-887-6103. p. 1044

Aronoff, Shelley, Coll Develop, Glendale Community College Library, 1500 N Verdugo Rd, Glendale, CA, 91208-2894. Tel: 818-240-1000, Ext 5574. Fax: 818-246-5107. p. 155

Aronoff, Vera, Cat Librn, Loyola Law School, 919 S Albany St, Los Angeles, CA, 90015-1211. Tel: 213-736-1419. Fax: 213-487-2204. p. 175

Aronson, Jan, Librn, Weeping Water Public Library, 206 West H St, Weeping Water, NE, 68463. Tel: 402-267-3050. p. 1423

Aronson, Mimi, Br Mgr, Phoenix Public Library, Desert Broom Library, 29710 N Cave Creek Rd, Phoenix, AZ, 85331. p. 76

Aronson, Shirley, Govt Doc, Maryland State Law Library, Courts of Appeal Bldg, 361 Rowe Blvd, Annapolis, MD, 21401-1697. Tel: 410-260-1430. Fax: 410-260-1572, 410-974-2063. p. 1010

Arora, Parneet, Ref Librn, Southern New Hampshire University, 2500 N River Rd, Manchester, NH, 03106-1045. Tel: 603-645-9605. Fax: 603-645-9685. p. 1456

Arpen, Audrey, Asst Librn, Chief Dull Knife College, One College Dr, Lame Deer, MT, 59043. Tel: 406-477-8293. Fax: 406-477-6575. p. 1384

Arps, Joyce, Dir of Libr Serv, Texas College, 2404 N Grand Ave, Tyler, TX, 75702-4500. Tel: 903-593-8311, Ext 2237. Fax: 903-526-4426. p. 2393

Arquette, Andrea S, Librn, Clifton Community Library, 7171 Rte 3, Cranberry Lake, NY, 12927. Tel: 315-848-3256. Fax: 315-848-3554. p. 1612

Arras, Marlena, Dir, Finance & Gen Serv, Charlotte Community Library, 226 S Bostwick St, Charlotte, MI, 48813-1801. Tel: 517-543-8859. Fax: 517-543-8868. p. 1162

Arredondo, Faythe, Librn III, YA Serv, Tulare County Library, Visalia Headquarters Branch, 200 W Oak Ave, Visalia, CA, 93291. Tel: 559-713-2706. Fax: 559-737-4586. p. 281

Arredondo, Gloria, Dir, Libr Serv, Arrowhead Regional Medical Center, 400 N Pepper Ave, Colton, CA, 92324-1819. Tel: 909-580-1385. Fax: 909-580-1310. p. 135

Arriaga, Joaquin, Ref, University of Miami, Louis Calder Memorial Library, Miller School of Medicine, 1601 NW Tenth Ave, Miami, FL, 33136. Tel: 305-243-6648. Fax: 305-325-8853. p. 469

Arrighetti, Julie, MERLN Librn, US Department of Defense, Fort McNair, Marshall Hall, Washington, DC, 20319-5066. Tel: 202-685-3470. Fax: 202-685-3733. p. 418

Arrigo, Paul A, Libr Dir, Lee College Library, 150 Lee Dr, Baytown, TX, 77520. Tel: 281-425-6447. Fax: 281-425-6557. p. 2286

Arrington, Carol, Librn, Tanner Medical Center, 705 Dixie St, Carrollton, GA, 30117. Tel: 770-836-9540. Fax: 770-836-9870. p. 523

Arrington, Todd, Librn, US National Park Service, 8523 W State Hwy 4, Beatrice, NE, 68310. Tel: 402-223-3514. Fax: 402-228-4231. p. 1393

Arrivee, Sally, Head Ref Librn, Madison Heights Public Library, 240 W 13 Mile Rd, Madison Heights, MI, 48071-1894. Tel: 248-588-7763. Fax: 248-588-2470. p. 1205

Arroyo, Tony, Dir, Pima Community College, Desert Vista, 5901 S Calle Santa Cruz, Tucson, AZ, 85709-6055. Tel: 520-206-5068. Fax: 520-206-5090. p. 86

Arsenault, Catherine, Libr Tech, Prince Edward Island Public Library Service, Kinkora Public, 45 Anderson St, Kinkora, PE, C0B 1N0, CANADA. Tel: 902-887-2172. p. 2876

Arsenault, Clement, Assoc Prof, Universite de Montreal, 3150, rue Jean-Brillant, bur C-2004, Montreal, QC, H3T 1N8, CANADA. Tel: 514-343-6044. Fax: 514-343-5753. p. 2979

Arsenault, Cora, Ref, Hudson Public Library, Three Washington St at The Rotary, Hudson, MA, 01749-2499. Tel: 978-568-9644. Fax: 978-568-9646. p. 1096

Arsenault, Corinne, ILL, Universite Sainte-Anne, 1695, Rte 1, Church Point, NS, B0W 1M0, CANADA. Tel: 902-769-2114, Ext 161. Fax: 902-769-0137. p. 2778

Arsenault, Debbie, Libr Tech, Lakeridge Health, One Hospital Ct, Oshawa, ON, L1G 2B9, CANADA. Tel: 905-576-8711, Ext 3754. Fax: 905-721-4759. p. 2827

Arsenault, Doris, Libr Tech, Prince Edward Island Public Library Service, Abram Village Public, a/s ecole Evangeline RR3, Wellington, Abram Village, PE, C0B 2E0, CANADA. Tel: 902-854-2491. Fax: 902-854-2981. p. 2876

Arsenault, Lorraine, Archivist, Rivier College, 420 S Main St, Nashua, NH, 03060-5086. Tel: 603-897-8278. Fax: 603-897-8889. p. 1459

Arsenault, Paul, Tech Serv, Pawtucket Public Library, 13 Summer St, Pawtucket, RI, 02860. Tel: 401-725-3714. Fax: 401-728-2170. p. 2171

Arsenault, Shannon, Sr Libr Tech, Northern College of Applied Arts & Technology Library, 4715 Hwy 101 E, South Porcupine, ON, PON 1HO, CANADA. Tel: 705-235-7150. Fax: 705-235-7279. p. 2842

Arseneau, Catherine, Mgr, Cape Breton University Library, Beaton Institute, 1250 Grand Lake Rd, Sydney, NS, B1P 6L2, CANADA. Tel: 902-563-1326. Fax: 902-562-8899. p. 2785

Arseneau, Christina Hirn, Curator, The Heritage Museum & Cultural Center, Priscilla U Byrns Heritage Ctr, 708 Market St, Saint Joseph, MI, 49085. Tel: 269-983-1191. Fax: 269-983-1274. p. 1225

Arseneau, Helene, Dir, Centre Regional de Services aux Bibliotheques Publiques, 3125 rue Girard, Trois-Rivieres, QC, G8Z 2M4, CANADA. Tel: 819-375-9623. Fax: 819-375-0132. p. 2914

Arseneault, Celine, Librn, Jardin Botanique de Montreal Bibliotheque, 4101 Sherbrooke St E, Montreal, QC, H1X 2B2, CANADA. Tel: 514-872-1440, 514-872-1824. Fax: 514-872-5167. p. 2897

Artabane, Lynn, Tech Info Spec, Pension Benefit Guaranty Corporation, 1200 K St NW, Ste 360, Washington, DC, 20005-4026. Tel: 202-326-4000, Ext 6061. Fax: 202-326-4011. p. 412

Arteaga, Adela, Mgr, Circ Serv, Frisco Public Library, 6101 Frisco Square Blvd, Ste 3000, Frisco, TX, 75034-3000. Tel: 972-292-5669. Fax: 972-292-5699. p. 2325

Arthen, Leona, Dir, Worthington Library, One Huntington Rd, Worthington, MA, 01098. Tel: 413-238-5565. p. 1146

Arthur, Gwen, Dir, Clark University, 950 Main St, Worcester, MA, 01610-1477. Tel: 508-793-7384. Fax: 508-793-8871. p. 1143

Arthur, Joyce, Acq, Wofford College, 429 N Church St, Spartanburg, SC, 29303-3663. Tel: 864-597-4300. Fax: 864-597-4329. p. 2206

Arthur, Mary, Librn, United States Air Force, 71 FTW/CSC-CSSL, 446 McAffrey Ave, Bldg 314, Ste 24, Vance AFB, OK, 73705-5710. Tel: 580-213-7368. Fax: 580-237-8106. p. 1984

Arthur, Michael A, Head, Acq & Coll Serv, University of Central Florida Libraries, 4000 Central Florida Blvd, Bldg 2, Orlando, FL, 32816-2666. Tel: 407-882-0143. Fax: 407-823-2529. p. 477

Arthur, Steve, Librn, Ellis Public Library, 907 Washington St, Ellis, KS, 67637. Tel: 785-726-3464. Fax: 785-726-3900. p. 865

Artiglia, Susan Weart, Ref Librn, United States Army, Keith A Campbell Memorial Library, 2601 Harney Rd, Ste 29, Fort Sam Houston, TX, 78234-5029. Tel: 210-221-4387, 210-221-4702. Fax: 210-227-5921. p. 2320

Artiola, Cara, Youth Serv, Joseph & Elizabeth Shaw Public Library, One S Front St, Clearfield, PA, 16830. Tel: 814-765-3271. Fax: 814-765-6316. p. 2046

Artist, Thomas, Asst Librn, Chapmanville Public Library, 299 Vance St, Chapmanville, WV, 25508. Tel: 304-855-3405. Fax: 304-855-8590. p. 2555

Artley, Kathleen Ann, Admin Dir, Northern Cambria Public Library, 1030 Philadelphia Ave, Northern Cambria, PA, 15714-1399. Tel: 814-948-8222. Fax: 814-948-2813. p. 2100

Artman, Julie, Chair, Coll Mgt, Chapman University, One University Dr, Orange, CA, 92866-1099. Tel: 714-532-7756. Fax: 714-532-7743. p. 200

Artola, Adele, Head, Tech Serv, Pace University Library, New York Civic Ctr, One Pace Plaza, New York, NY, 10038-1502. Tel: 212-346-1331. Fax: 212-346-1615. p. 1696

Arts, Regina, Librn, Food & Drug Administration, 60 Eighth St NE, Atlanta, GA, 30309. Tel: 404-253-1160, Ext 1261. Fax: 404-253-1206. p. 515

Artz, Joanne, Asst Dir, Head, Ref Serv, University of Southern Indiana, 8600 University Blvd, Evansville, IN, 47712. Tel: 812-465-1056. Fax: 812-465-1693. p. 739

Aruja, Endel, Librn, Tartu Institute Library, 310 Bloor St W, Toronto, ON, M5S 1W4, CANADA. Tel: 416-447-8958. p. 2859

Arvesen, Nancy, In Charge, Multnomah County Library, St Johns, 7510 N Charleston Ave, Portland, OR, 97203-3709. Tel: 503-988-5397. Fax: 503-988-5176. p. 2012

Arvig, Gabrielle, Cat, Los Angeles Southwest College, Cox Bldg, 1600 W Imperial Hwy, Los Angeles, CA, 90047-4899. Tel: 323-241-5235. Fax: 323-241-5221. p. 174

Arvin, Karen J, Tech Serv, Western Seminary, 5511 SE Hawthorne Blvd, Portland, OR, 97215-3367. Tel: 503-517-1841. Fax: 503-517-1801. p. 2015

Arvin, Shelley, Ref/Instruction Librn, Indiana State University, 510 North 6 1/2 St, Terre Haute, IN, 47809. Tel: 812-237-2605. Fax: 812-237-3376. p. 781

Arvizu, Norma, Interim City Librn, Monterey Park Bruggemeyer Library, 318 S Ramona Ave, Monterey Park, CA, 91754-3399. Tel: 626-307-1418. Fax: 626-288-4251. p. 190

Arwood, Katie, Dir, White Pine Library, 106 E Walnut, Stanton, MI, 48888-9294. Tel: 989-831-4327. Fax: 989-831-4976. p. 1229

Arzola, Ruth, Circ, Pontifical Catholic University Of Puerto Rico, Encarnacion Valdes Library, 2250 Avenida Las Americas, Ste 509, Ponce, PR, 00717-0777. Tel: 787-841-2000, Ext 1801, 787-841-2000, Ext 1802. Fax: 787-284-0235. p. 2675

Asad, Afroz, Info Tech, Bellwood Public Library, 600 Bohland Ave, Bellwood, IL, 60104-1896. Tel: 708-547-7393. Fax: 708-547-9352. p. 593

Asadi, Fatemeh, Dr, Pub Serv Dir, Chicago State University, 9501 S Martin Luther King Jr Dr, LIB 440, Chicago, IL, 60628-1598. Tel: 773-995-2558. Fax: 773-995-3772. p. 610

Asamoah, Carol, Tech Serv, Indiana University of Pennsylvania, Punxsutawney Campus Library, 1012 Winslow St, Punxsutawney, PA, 15767. Tel: 814-938-4870. Fax: 814-938-5900. p. 2071

Asato, Noriko, Asst Prof, University of Hawaii, 2550 The Mall, Honolulu, HI, 96822. Tel: 808-956-7321. Fax: 808-956-5835. p. 2964

Asbell, John, Coll Develop Librn, The University of Texas-Pan American Library, 1201 W University Dr, Edinburg, TX, 78541-2999. Tel: 956-665-5282. Fax: 956-665-5396. p. 2315

Asbury, Edie, Librn, Holy Spirit Hospital, 503 N 21st St, Camp Hill, PA, 17011. Tel: 717-763-2664. Fax: 717-763-2136. p. 2040

Asbury, Peggy, Assoc Archivist, University of Alaska Fairbanks, 310 Tanana Dr, Fairbanks, AK, 99775. Tel: 907-474-6595. Fax: 907-474-6841. p. 48

Ascencio, Mario A, Dir, Corcoran Gallery of Art/College of Art & Design Library, 500 17th St NW, Washington, DC, 20006. Tel: 202-478-1543. Fax: 202-628-7908. p. 396

Ascenzo, Sally Ellen, Co-Dir, Marrowbone Public Library District, 216 W Main St, Bethany, IL, 61914. Tel: 217-665-3014. Fax: 217-665-3246. p. 594

Asch, Emily J, Head, Tech Serv, Saint Catherine University, 2004 Randolph Ave, Mail F-10, Saint Paul, MN, 55105-1794. Tel: 651-690-6653. Fax: 651-690-8636. p. 1281

Aschenbrenner, Angela, Dir, United States Air Force, 437 SVS/SVMG, 106 W McCaw St, Bldg 215, Charleston AFB, SC, 29404-4700. Tel: 843-963-3320. Fax: 843-963-3840. p. 2185

Ascher, Marie, Ref, New York Medical College, Basic Science Bldg, 95 Grasslands Rd, Valhalla, NY, 10595. Tel: 914-594-3168. Fax: 914-594-3171. p. 1760

Aschim, Mary Jo, Librn, Toole County Library, Sunburst Branch, 105 First St N, Sunburst, MT, 59482. Tel: 406-937-6980. Fax: 406-937-6980. p. 1388

Aschkenasy, Linda, Cat, Yeshiva University Libraries, Dr Lillian & Dr Rebecca Chutick Law Library, Benjamin N Cardozo School of Law, 55 Fifth Ave, New York, NY, 10003-4301. Tel: 212-790-0223. Fax: 212-790-0236. p. 1703

Aschkenes, Anna, Exec Dir, Middlesex County Cultural & Heritage Commission, 703 Jersey Ave, New Brunswick, NJ, 08901. Tel: 732-745-4489. Fax: 732-745-4524. p. 1508

Asencio-Toro, Doris, Libr Dir, Inter-American University of Puerto Rico, San German Campus, Ave Inter-American University, Rd 102, K 30 6, San German, PR, 00683-9801. Tel: 787-892-5115. Fax: 787-264-2544. p. 2675

Asfeld, Carla, Br Mgr, Great River Regional Library, Annandale Public Library, 30 Cedar St E, Annandale, MN, 55302-1113. Tel: 320-274-8448. Fax: 320-274-8448. p. 1274

Asfeld, Carla, Br Mgr, Great River Regional Library, Kimball Library, Five Main St N, Kimball, MN, 55353. Tel: 320-398-3915. Fax: 320-398-3915. p. 1275

Ash, Cathy, Librn, Doddridge County Public Library, Center Point Branch, General Delivery, Center Point, WV, 26339. Tel: 304-782-2461. Fax: 304-782-2461. p. 2574

Ash, Cathy J, Librn, Doddridge County Public Library, 117 Court St, West Union, WV, 26456. Tel: 304-873-1941. Fax: 304-873-1324. p. 2574

Ash, Daniel, Dr, Exec Dir, Kentuckiana Metroversity, Inc, 109 E Broadway, Louisville, KY, 40202. Tel: 502-897-3374. Fax: 502-895-1647. p. 2944

Ash, Jane, Ch, E C Scranton Memorial Library, 801 Boston Post Rd, Madison, CT, 06443. Tel: 203-245-8722, Ext 15. Fax: 203-245-7821. p. 349

Ash, John, Circ Mgr, Gainesville State College, 3820 Mundy Mill Rd, Oakwood, GA, 30566. Tel: 678-717-3662. Fax: 770-718-3657. p. 547

Ash, Karl W, Fr, Librn, William McKinley Presidential Library & Museum, 800 McKinley Monument Dr NW, Canton, OH, 44708. Tel: 330-455-7043. Fax: 330-455-1137. p. 1864

Ash, Kathleen, Dir, Frost Free Library, 28 Jaffrey Rd, Marlborough, NH, 03455. Tel: 603-876-4479. Fax: 603-876-4479. p. 1457

Ash, Mary Ellen, Ref & Instruction, Saint Bonaventure University, 3261 W State Rd, Saint Bonaventure, NY, 14778. Tel: 716-375-2343. Fax: 716-375-2389. p. 1737

Ash, Ruth, Archivist, Allegheny College Library, 555 N Main St, Meadville, PA, 16335. Tel: 814-332-2398. Fax: 814-337-5673. p. 2086

Ash, Scott, Circ Serv Supvr, Pearl Public Library, 2416 Old Brandon Rd, Pearl, MS, 39208-4601. Tel: 601-932-2562. Fax: 601-932-3535. p. 1311

Ash, Susan, Dir, Twin Falls Public Library, 201 Fourth Ave E, Twin Falls, ID, 83301-6397. Tel: 208-733-2964. Fax: 208-733-2965. p. 584

Ash, Viki, Children's Coordr, San Antonio Public Library, Children's Department, 600 Soledad, San Antonio, TX, 78205-2786. Tel: 210-207-2621. Fax: 210-207-2555. p. 2382

Ash, Viki, Coordr, Ch Serv, San Antonio Public Library, 600 Soledad, San Antonio, TX, 78205-2786. Tel: 210-207-2620. Fax: 210-207-2603. p. 2382

Ashbridge, Candy, Libr Mgr, Vancouver Island Regional Library, Qualicum Beach Branch, 101-660 Primrose St, Qualicum Beach, BC, V9K 1S9, CANADA. Tel: 250-752-6121. Fax: 250-752-6630. p. 2733

Ashbrook, Laura, Librn, Readsboro Community Library, 301 Phelps Lane, Readsboro, VT, 05350. Tel: 802-423-5460. Fax: 802-423-9914. p. 2433

Ashbrook, Leslie, Res Librn, University of Virginia, Arthur J Morris Law Library, 580 Massie Rd, Charlottesville, VA, 22903-1789. Tel: 434-243-2493. Fax: 434-982-2232. p. 2455

Ashbrook, Pamela, Ch, Nantahala Regional Library, 11 Blumenthal St, Murphy, NC, 28906. Tel: 828-837-2025. Fax: 828-837-6416. p. 1812

Ashby, Andrea, Libr Tech, National Park Service Independence National Historical Park, Merchants Exchange Bldg, 3rd Flr, 143 S Third St, Philadelphia, PA, 19106. Tel: 215-597-8047. Fax: 215-597-3969. p. 2113

Ashby, Cathy A, Dir, Ruth Enlow Library of Garrett County, Six N Second St, Oakland, MD, 21550-1393. Tel: 301-334-3996, Ext 102. Fax: 301-334-4152. p. 1035

Ashby, Deborah, Librn, Sandhills Community College, 3395 Airport Rd, Pinehurst, NC, 28374. Tel: 910-695-3821. Fax: 910-695-3947. p. 1814

Ashby, Jennifer, Dir, Asotin County Library, 417 Sycamore St, Clarkston, WA, 99403-2666. Tel: 509-758-5454. Fax: 509-751-1460. p. 2512

Ashby, Jennifer, Dir, Asotin County Library, Heights Branch, 2036 Fourth Ave, Clarkston, WA, 99403-1322. Tel: 509-758-4601. p. 2512

Ashby, Judy, Coordr, Putnam Northern Westchester BOCES, 200 BOCES Dr, Yorktown Heights, NY, 10598. Tel: 914-248-2392. Fax: 914-248-2419. p. 1772

Ashby, Michael, Circ Serv Coordr, University of Saint Francis, 201 Pope John Paul II Ctr, 2701 Spring St, Fort Wayne, IN, 46808. Tel: 260-399-7700, Ext 6058. Fax: 260-399-8166. p. 742

Ashby, Michael, Youth Serv Librn, Samuels Public Library, 538 Villa Ave, Front Royal, VA, 22630. Tel: 540-635-3153. Fax: 540-635-7229. p. 2466

Ashby, Patti, Asst Libr Dir, Hillsdale Free Will Baptist College Library, 3701 S I-35, Moore, OK, 73160. Tel: 405-912-9025. Fax: 405-912-9050. p. 1969

Ashby, Susan DiRenzo, Head, Libr Syst, University of Akron Libraries, 315 Buchtel Mall, Akron, OH, 44325-1701. Tel: 330-972-7240. Fax: 330-972-5106. p. 1853

Ashcraft, Carolyn, State Librn, Arkansas State Library, 900 W Capitol, Ste 100, Little Rock, AR, 72201-3108. Tel: 501-682-1526. Fax: 501-682-1529. p. 105

Ashcroft, Megan, Librn, Saskatchewan Genealogical Society Library, 110 - 1514 11th Ave, Regina, SK, S4P 0H2, CANADA. Tel: 306-780-9207. Fax: 306-780-3615. p. 2924

Ashcroft, Susan, Coll Develop, Douglas College Library, 700 Royal Ave, New Westminster, BC, V3M 5Z5, CANADA. Tel: 604-527-5189. Fax: 604-527-5193. p. 2734

Ashdown, Maryn, Actg Dep Dir, Port Moody Public Library, 100 Newport Dr, Port Moody, BC, V3H 3E1, CANADA. Tel: 604-469-4575, 604-469-4577. Fax: 604-469-4576. p. 2735

Ashe, Casey, Supvr, Tulsa Community College Learning Resources Center, Metro Campus, 909 S Boston Ave, Tulsa, OK, 74119-2011. Tel: 918-595-7285. Fax: 918-595-7179. p. 1983

Ashe, Kathleen, Cat, Syst Librn, Southwest Minnesota State University Library, 1501 State St, Marshall, MN, 56258. Tel: 507-537-6142. Fax: 507-537-6200. p. 1258

Ashe, Kathleen, Univ Librn, Southwest Minnesota State University Library, 1501 State St, Marshall, MN, 56258. Tel: 507-537-6372. Fax: 507-537-6200. p. 1258

Ashenfelter, Martha, Youth Serv Librn, Jefferson County Rural Library District, 620 Cedar Ave, Port Hadlock, WA, 98339-9514. Tel: 360-385-6544. Fax: 360-385-7921. p. 2524

Asher, Curt, Interim Dean, California State University, 9001 Stockdale Hwy, Bakersfield, CA, 93311-1022. Tel: 661-654-3172. Fax: 661-654-3238. p. 123

Asher, Darla, Online Res Coordr/Ref Librn, Saint Leo University, 33701 State Rd 52, Saint Leo, FL, 33574. Tel: 352-588-8475. Fax: 352-588-8484. p. 487

Asher, Dorothy, Dir, Lizzadro Museum of Lapidary Art Library, 220 Cottage Hill Ave, Elmhurst, IL, 60126. Tel: 630-833-1616. Fax: 630-833-1225. p. 642

Asher, Rhonda, Tech Serv, Perry County Public Library, 289 Black Gold Blvd, Hazard, KY, 41701. Tel: 606-436-2475, 606-436-4747. Fax: 606-436-0191. p. 917

Ashford, Lenora, Tech Serv Librn, Long Beach Public Library, 111 W Park Ave, Long Beach, NY, 11561-3326. Tel: 516-432-7201. Fax: 516-889-4641. p. 1654

Ashford, Robin, Ref/Distance Learning Librn, George Fox University, Portland Center Library, Hampton Plaza, 12753 SW 68th Ave, Portland, OR, 97223. Tel: 503-554-6136. Fax: 503-554-6134. p. 2007

Ashkar, Carolyn, Dir, Knoxville College, 901 Knoxville College Dr, Knoxville, TN, 37921. Tel: 865-524-6554. Fax: 865-524-6549. p. 2242

Ashley, Cheryl, Dir, Little Ferry Free Public Library, 239 Liberty St, Little Ferry, NJ, 07643. Tel: 201-641-3721. Fax: 201-641-8575. p. 1496

Ashley, Cheryl, Ch, Verona Public Library, 17 Gould St, Verona, NJ, 07044-1928. Tel: 973-857-4848. Fax: 973-857-4851. p. 1537

Ashley, Jeannie R, Libr Mgr, Ref, Fulton County Law Library, Justice Center Tower, Ste 7000, 185 Central Ave, Atlanta, GA, 30303. Tel: 404-730-4544. Fax: 404-730-4565. p. 515

Ashley, Jon, Bus Res Librn, University of Virginia, Arthur J Morris Law Library, 580 Massie Rd, Charlottesville, VA, 22903-1789. Tel: 434-924-4730. Fax: 434-982-2232. p. 2455

Ashley, Peggy, Librn, Post Public Library, 105 E Main St, Post, TX, 79356-3299. Tel: 806-990-2149. p. 2372

Ashley, Rich, Interim Dir, Fossil Ridge Public Library, 386 W Kennedy Rd, Braidwood, IL, 60408. Tel: 815-458-2187. Fax: 815-458-2042. p. 597

Ashley, Teresa, Ref Librn, Austin Community College, Northridge Campus Library, 11928 Stone Hollow Dr, Austin, TX, 78758. Tel: 512-223-4742. Fax: 512-223-4902. p. 2278

Ashlin, Scott, Libr Tech, Maryland State Law Library, Courts of Appeal Bldg, 361 Rowe Blvd, Annapolis, MD, 21401-1697. Tel: 410-260-1430. Fax: 410-260-1572, 410-974-2063. p. 1010

Ashman, Mary Ellen, Librn, Sedgwick Library Association, 45 Main St, Sedgwick, ME, 04676. Tel: 207-359-2177. p. 1000

Ashmore, Ann, Ref, Delta State University, Laflore Circle at Fifth Ave, Cleveland, MS, 38733-2599. Tel: 662-846-4440. Fax: 662-846-4443. p. 1296

Ashmore, Chris, Dir, Jacksonville Public Library, 201 W College Ave, Jacksonville, IL, 62650-2497. Tel: 217-243-5435. Fax: 217-243-2182. p. 659

Ashmore, Nancy K, Dir, Prairie du Chien Memorial Library, 125 S Wacouta Ave, Prairie du Chien, WI, 53821-1632. Tel: 608-326-6211. Fax: 608-326-7069. p. 2631

Ashton, Cherylon, Ch, Amherst Public Library, 221 Spring St, Amherst, OH, 44001. Tel: 440-988-4230. Fax: 440-988-4115. p. 1854

Ashton, Jean W, Dir, New York Historical Society Library, 170 Central Park W, New York, NY, 10024. Tel: 212-873-3400. Fax: 212-875-1591. p. 1689

Ashton, Kelsey, Circ Serv, Town of Vail Public Library, 292 W Meadow Dr, Vail, CO, 81657. Tel: 970-479-2190. Fax: 970-479-2192. p. 325

Ashton-Pritting, Randi Lynn, Dir, University of Hartford Libraries, 200 Bloomfield Ave, West Hartford, CT, 06117. Tel: 860-768-4264. p. 376

Ashwill, Cindy, Asst Dean, University of Illinois at Urbana-Champaign, Library & Information Science Bldg, 501 E Daniel St, Champaign, IL, 61820-6211. Tel: 217-333-3280. Fax: 217-244-3302. p. 2965

Ashwill, Jane, Librn, Prof, Erie Community College-North, 6205 Main St, Williamsville, NY, 14221-7095. Tel: 716-851-1265. Fax: 716-851-1277. p. 1769

Ashworth, Deborah, Br Head, Fort Erie Public Library, Stevensville Branch, 2508 Stevensville Rd, Stevensville, ON, L0S 1S0, CANADA. Tel: 905-382-2051. Fax: 905-382-4683. p. 2806

Ashworth, Sandra, Dir, Boundary County District Library, 6370 Kootenai St, Bonners Ferry, ID, 83805. Tel: 208-267-3750. Fax: 208-267-5231. p. 572

Asik, Linda, Libr Assoc, Northrop Grumman Norden Systems, 10000 Norden Pl, Norwalk, CT, 06854-2807. Tel: 203-852-5886. Fax: 203-852-4579. p. 362

Asimakopulos, Marika, Librn, McGill University Libraries, Edward Rosenthall Mathematics & Statistics Library, Burnside Hall, Rm 1105, 805 Sherbrooke St W, Montreal, QC, H3A 2K6, CANADA. Tel: 514-398-7430. Fax: 514-398-3899. p. 2899

Askew, Consuella, Dr, Assoc Dean, Pub Serv, Florida International University, 11200 SW Eighth St, Miami, FL, 33199. Tel: 305-348-2463. Fax: 305-348-3408. p. 465

Askew, Consuella, Dr, Assoc Dean, Pub Serv, Florida International University, 3000 NE 151st St, North Miami, FL, 33181-3600. Tel: 305-919-5726. Fax: 305-919-5914. p. 472

Askew, Matisha, Libr Tech, Elizabeth City State University, 1704 Weeksville Rd, Elizabeth City, NC, 27909. Tel: 252-335-8511. Fax: 252-335-3446. p. 1790

Askey, Dale, Assoc Univ Librn, McMaster University Library, 1280 Main St W, Hamilton, ON, L8S 4L6, CANADA. Tel: 905-525-9140, Ext 21880. Fax: 905-524-9850. p. 2810

Asleson, Fay, Head Librn, Chetwynd Public Library, 5012 46th St, Chetwynd, BC, V0C 1J0, CANADA. Tel: 250-788-2559. Fax: 250-788-2186. p. 2726

Aslett, Kimberley, Librn, Sault Area Hospital, 750 Great Northern Rd, Sault Ste. Marie, ON, P6B 0A8, CANADA. Tel: 705-759-3434, Ext 4368. Fax: 705-759-3847. p. 2840

Asmuth, Gretchen, Law Librn, Kirkpatrick & Lockhart, Preston, Gates, Ellis, 1601 K St NW, Washington, DC, 20006-1600. Tel: 202-778-9000 (main), 202-778-9160. Fax: 202-778-9100. p. 406

Asmuth, Gretchen W, Law Librn, K&L Gates LLP, 1601 K St NW, L-3, Washington, DC, 20006. Tel: 202-661-3715. Fax: 202-778-9100. p. 406

Aspatore, Robert, Circ, DeKalb Public Library, 309 Oak St, DeKalb, IL, 60115-3369. Tel: 815-756-9568. Fax: 815-756-7837. p. 635

Aspelin, Jackie, Librn, Sully Area Library, PO Box 205, Onida, SD, 57564-0205. Tel: 605-258-2133. Fax: 605-258-2361. p. 2216

Asplund, Susan, Ser Librn, Eastern New Mexico University, 1300 S Ave K, Sta 32, Portales, NM, 88130-7402. Tel: 575-562-2629. Fax: 575-562-2647. p. 1560

Aspri, Jo-Anne, Librn, Kent County Memorial Hospital, 455 Toll Gate Rd, Warwick, RI, 02886. Tel: 401-737-7000, Ext 1309. Fax: 401-736-1000. p. 2177

Asquith, April, Head, Ref, Needham Free Public Library, 1139 Highland Ave, Needham, MA, 02494-3298. Tel: 781-455-7559. Fax: 781-455-7591. p. 1108

Assar, Sabina, Bus & Intelligence Librn, Thompson Coburn LLP, One US Bank Plaza, Saint Louis, MO, 63101. Tel: 314-552-6424. Fax: 314-552-7472. p. 1361

Asselin, Ange-Aimee, Librn, Bibliotheque Jean-Charles Magnan, 510 boul de la Montagne, Saint-Casimir, QC, G0A 3L0, CANADA. Tel: 418-339-2543. Fax: 418-339-3105. p. 2909

Asselin, Paule, Librn, Centre Jeunesse de Montreal - Institut universitaire, 1001 boul de Maisonneuve est, 5ieme etage, Montreal, QC, H2L 4R5, CANADA. Tel: 514-896-3396. Fax: 514-896-3483. p. 2893

Asselin, Sylvie, Dir, Bibliotheque Municipale de Saint-Simeon, 502 St-Laurent, Saint-Simeon, QC, G0T 1X0, CANADA. Tel: 418-638-2691. p. 2911

Astengo, Be, Youth Serv Sr Libr Mgr, Alachua County Library District, 401 E University Ave, Gainesville, FL, 32601-5453. Tel: 352-334-3947. Fax: 352-334-1256. p. 448

Asteris, Mark, Coordr, Media Serv, Lamar University, 211 Redbird Lane, Beaumont, TX, 77705. Tel: 409-880-8064. Fax: 409-880-2318. p. 2287

Asthana, Maneet, Librn, Army Times Publishing Co Library, 6883 Commercial Dr, Springfield, VA, 22159. Tel: 703-642-7319. Fax: 703-750-8622. p. 2496

Astifidis, Maria, Dir, Beth Israel Medical Center, 317 E 17th, New York, NY, 10003. Tel: 212-420-2855. Fax: 212-420-4640. p. 1670

Astika, Tanya, Librn, Yukon Public Law Library, Yukon Law Courts, 2134 Second Ave, Whitehorse, YT, Y1A 2C6, CANADA. Tel: 867-667-3086. Fax: 867-393-6212. p. 2934

Astleford, Sandra, Dir of Tech Serv, Bellevue Public Library, 1003 Lincoln Rd, Bellevue, NE, 68005-3199. Tel: 402-293-3157. Fax: 402-293-3163. p. 1393

Aston, Don, Librn, North American Radio Archives, 33888 Farm Rd, Wildomar, CA, 92595. Tel: 951-244-5242. Fax: 951-244-0022. p. 284

Aston, Rollah, Dir, Eastern New Mexico University - Roswell, 52 University Blvd, Roswell, NM, 88203. Tel: 575-624-7282. Fax: 575-624-7479. p. 1561

Astrinsky, Aviva E, Head Librn, YIVO Institute for Jewish Research, 15 W 16th St, New York, NY, 10011. Tel: 212-294-6134. Fax: 212-292-1892. p. 1704

Astuto, Becky, ILL, Summit County Library, 0037 Peak One Dr, Frisco, CO, 80443. Tel: 970-668-4135. Fax: 970-668-5556. p. 309

Asu, Glynis, Ref Librn, Hamilton College, 198 College Hill Rd, Clinton, NY, 13323-1299. Tel: 315-859-4482. Fax: 315-859-4578. p. 1607

Asuquo, Rose, Circ Coordr, DC Regional Library for the Blind & Physically Handicapped, Adaptive Services Division, Rm 215, 901 G St NW, Washington, DC, 20001. Tel: 202-559-5368 (videophone), 202-727-2142. Fax: 202-727-0322. p. 397

Atabaev, John, Univ Archivist, Texas A&M University-Commerce, 2600 S Neal St, Commerce, TX, 75429. Tel: 903-886-5717. Fax: 903-886-5434. p. 2300

Atchinson, Cadence, Pub Serv Librn, University of New England Libraries, 11 Hills Beach Rd, Biddeford, ME, 04005. Tel: 207-602-2497. Fax: 207-602-5922. p. 978

Atchison, Karlyne, Librn, McDonald Public Library, PO Box 89, McDonald, KS, 67745-0089. Tel: 785-538-2441. p. 882

Atchley, Cathy, Br Mgr, Prince William Public Library System, Central, 8601 Mathis Ave, Manassas, VA, 20110-5229. Tel: 703-361-8211. Fax: 703-335-2956. p. 2486

Atchley, Kathy, Librn, Western Plains Library System, Clinton Public Library, 721 Frisco, Clinton, OK, 73601-3320. Tel: 580-323-2165. Fax: 580-323-7884. p. 1960

Athanas, Ryan, Asst Dir, Harborfields Public Library, 31 Broadway, Greenlawn, NY, 11740-1382. Tel: 631-757-4200. Fax: 631-757-7216. p. 1631

Athanasov, Martha, Per, Reformed Theological Seminary Library, 5422 Clinton Blvd, Jackson, MS, 39209-3099. Tel: 601-923-1623. Fax: 601-923-1621. p. 1305

Athas, George, Cat, Chelsea Public Library, 569 Broadway, Chelsea, MA, 02150-2991. Tel: 617-466-4350. Fax: 617-466-4359. p. 1080

Atherton, Alicia, Circ Mgr, Thomas County Public Library System, 201 N Madison St, Thomasville, GA, 31792-5414. Tel: 229-225-5252. Fax: 229-225-5258. p. 553

Athey, Jan, Librn, Train Collectors Association, 300 Paradise Lane, Strasburg, PA, 17579. Tel: 717-687-8623. Fax: 717-687-0742. p. 2143

Atik, Shifra, Dir, Long Island Jewish Medical Center, 270-05 76th Ave, New Hyde Park, NY, 11040. Tel: 718-470-7070. Fax: 718-470-6150. p. 1665

Atik, Shifra, Dir, Long Island Jewish Medical Center, The Zucker-Hillside Hospital, 75-59 263rd St, Glen Oaks, NY, 11004. Tel: 718-470-8090. Fax: 718-962-1718. p. 1665

Atkin, Evette, Dir, Branch District Library, Ten E Chicago St, Coldwater, MI, 49036-1615. Tel: 517-278-2341, Ext 16. Fax: 517-279-7134. p. 1164

Atkins, Cynthia, Dir, Hopkinsville Community College Library, 720 North Dr, Hopkinsville, KY, 42240. Tel: 270-707-3760. Fax: 270-885-6048. p. 918

Atkins, Dan, Br Supvr, Guelph Public Library, Bull Frog Mall Branch, 380 Eramosa Rd, Guelph, ON, N1E 6R2, CANADA. Tel: 519-829-4401. p. 2807

Atkins, Daniel, Prof, University of Michigan, 304 West Hall, 1085 S University, Ann Arbor, MI, 48109-1107. Tel: 734-763-2285. Fax: 734-764-2475. p. 2967

Atkins, Darlene, Serv Delivery Tech, Stormont, Dundas & Glengarry County Library, Alexandria Branch, 170A MacDonald Blvd, Alexandria, ON, K0C 1A0, CANADA. Tel: 613-525-3241. Fax: 613-525-2034. p. 2801

Atkins, David, Access Serv, University of Tennessee, Knoxville, 1015 Volunteer Blvd, Knoxville, TN, 37996-1000. Tel: 865-974-6866. Fax: 865-974-4259. p. 2243

Atkins, David R, Libr Dir, Montgomery County Public Library, 215 W Main, Troy, NC, 27371. Tel: 910-572-1311. Fax: 910-576-5565. p. 1827

Atkins, Jackie, Coordr, Outreach Serv, Cherokee Regional Library System, North Georgia Talking Books Center, 305 S Duke St, LaFayette, GA, 30728-2936. Tel: 706-638-1958. Fax: 706-638-4913. p. 538

Atkins, Janet, Librn, Edwina Whitney Library of The Storrs Congregational Church, Two N Eagleville Rd, Storrs, CT, 06268. Tel: 860-423-5930. Fax: 860-429-9693. p. 371

Atkins, Lenetta, Mgr, Mercy Medical Center, 1111 Sixth Ave, Des Moines, IA, 50314-2611. Tel: 515-247-4189. Fax: 515-643-8809. p. 810

Atkins, Mary Ann, Digital Coll Librn, Libr Syst Coordr, Lewis University Library, One University Pkwy, Unit 300, Romeoville, IL, 60446-2200. Tel: 815-836-5665. Fax: 815-838-9456. p. 698

Atkins, Priscilla, Head, Ref & Instruction, Hope College, Van Wylen Library, 53 Graves Pl, Holland, MI, 49422. Tel: 616-395-7986. Fax: 616-395-7965. p. 1190

Atkins, Sherry, ILL, Western Seminary, 5511 SE Hawthorne Blvd, Portland, OR, 97215-3367. Tel: 503-517-1840. Fax: 503-517-1801. p. 2015

Atkins, Stephanie, Head, Access Serv, Washington University Libraries, One Brookings Dr, Campus Box 1061, Saint Louis, MO, 63130-4862. Tel: 314-935-8235. Fax: 314-935-4045. p. 1362

Atkins, Sue, Librn, Northwest Regional Library, Millport Public Library, 480 Columbus St, Millport, AL, 35576. Tel: 205-662-4286. p. 40

Atkins, Susan Q, Dir, Media Serv, Nazareth College of Rochester Library, 4245 East Ave, Rochester, NY, 14618-3790. Tel: 585-389-2134. Fax: 585-389-2145. p. 1730

Atkins, Winston, Presv Officer, Duke University Libraries, 411 Chapel Dr, Durham, NC, 27708. Tel: 919-660-5843. Fax: 919-684-2855. p. 1787

Atkinson, Calberta O, Librn, Birmingham Public Library, Wylam Branch, 4300 Seventh Ave, Wylam, Birmingham, AL, 35224. Tel: 205-785-0349. Fax: 205-781-6571. p. 8

Atkinson, Donna, Supvr, Haliburton County Public Library, Wilberforce Branch, 2307 Loop Rd, Wilberforce, ON, K0L 3C0, CANADA. Tel: 705-448-2510. p. 2808

Atkinson, Elmer, Pres, Grand Army of the Republic Museum & Library, 4278 Griscom St, Philadelphia, PA, 19124-3954. Tel: 215-289-6484. p. 2110

Atkinson, Eric, Head, Info Serv, Orange County Library District, 101 E Central Blvd, Orlando, FL, 32801. Tel: 407-835-7323. p. 476

Atkinson, Jan, Librn, Shawano City-County Library, Birnamwood Public, 337 S Main St, Birnamwood, WI, 54414-9259. Tel: 715-449-3120. p. 2637

Atkinson, Janet, Br Mgr, Great River Regional Library, Melrose Library, 225 East First St N, Melrose, MN, 56352-1153. Tel: 320-256-3885. Fax: 320-256-3885. p. 1275

Atkinson, Jenny, Dir, Charlestown Boys' & Girls' Club, 15 Green St, Charlestown, MA, 02129. Tel: 617-242-1775. Fax: 617-241-3847. p. 1079

Atkinson, Kathryn, Libr Board of Trustees Pres, Ozark County Library, 200 Elm St, Gainesville, MO, 65655. Tel: 417-679-4442. p. 1329

Atkinson, Lee, ILL Librn, Weeks Public Library, 36 Post Rd, Greenland, NH, 03840-2312. Tel: 603-436-8548. Fax: 603-427-0913. p. 1449

Atkinson, Lorrie, Chief Librn, Wainfleet Township Public Library, 19M9 Park St, Wainfleet, ON, L0S 1V0, CANADA. Tel: 905-899-1277. Fax: 905-899-2495. p. 2869

Atkinson, Rebecca, Readers' Advisory & Ref Serv, Pueblo City-County Library District, 100 E Abriendo Ave, Pueblo, CO, 81004-4290. Tel: 719-562-5624. Fax: 719-562-5619. p. 320

Atkinson, Sandy, Coordr, North Dakota Vision Services-School for the Blind, 500 Stanford Rd, Grand Forks, ND, 58203. Tel: 701-795-2700. Fax: 701-795-2727. p. 1842

Atkinson, Susan, Dir, Gilmer Public Library, 214 Walnut St, Glenville, WV, 26351. Tel: 304-462-5620. Fax: 304-462-5620. p. 2559

Atkinson, Susan, Syst Mgr, Southeast Regional Library, 49 Bison Ave, Weyburn, SK, S4H 0H9, CANADA. Tel: 306-848-3104. Fax: 306-842-2665. p. 2929

Atlas, Michelle Cohen, Prof, Ref Librn, University of Louisville Libraries, Kornhauser Health Sciences Library, Health Sciences Ctr, 500 S Preston St, Louisville, KY, 40202. Tel: 502-852-8534. Fax: 502-852-1631. p. 927

Ator-James, Carrie Susan, Dir, Hocking College Library, 3301 Hocking Pkwy, Nelsonville, OH, 45764. Tel: 740-753-6336. Fax: 740-753-6341. p. 1920

Atson, Elsa B, Dir, Libr Serv, Donald F & Mildred Topp Othmer Library of Chemical History, 315 Chestnut St, Philadelphia, PA, 19106. Tel: 215-873-8205. Fax: 215-629-5205. p. 2113

Attanasio, Lisa, Ref Serv, Free Public Library of Bayonne, 697 Avenue C, Bayonne, NJ, 07002. Tel: 201-858-6970. Fax: 201-437-6928. p. 1470

Attebery, Barbara, Librn, Res, Pub & Coll Support, Ochsner Clinic Foundation, 1st Flr Hospital, 1514 Jefferson Hwy, New Orleans, LA, 70121-2429. Tel: 504-842-3760. Fax: 504-842-5339. p. 962

Attebury, Ramirose, Head, Govt Doc, University of Idaho Library, Rayburn St, Moscow, ID, 83844. Tel: 208-885-2503. Fax: 208-885-6817. p. 579

Attia, Audrey, Chief Librn, Institut Universitaire de Geriatrie de Montreal, 4565 Chemin Queen Mary, Montreal, QC, H3W 1W5, CANADA. Tel: 514-340-2800, Ext 3266. Fax: 514-340-2815. p. 2897

Attig, Ann M, Dir, Nazarene Bible College, 1111 Academy, Park Loop, Colorado Springs, CO, 80910-3717. Tel: 719-884-5000, Ext 5071. Fax: 719-884-5119. p. 296

Atwater, Amanda, YA Librn, North Indian River County Library, 1001 Sebastian Blvd, CR 512, Sebastian, FL, 32958. Tel: 772-589-1355. Fax: 772-388-3697. p. 491

Atwater, Beth, Br Mgr, Mid-Continent Public Library, Lee's Summit Branch, 150 NW Oldham Pkwy, Lee's Summit, MO, 64081-1501. Tel: 816-524-0567. Fax: 816-246-5342. p. 1332

Atwater, James, Asst Curator, US Army Transportation Museum Library, Besson Hall, 300 Washington Blvd, Fort Eustis, VA, 23604-5260. Tel: 757-878-1115. Fax: 757-878-5656. p. 2465

Atwater, Stephanie, Dir, Friend Memorial Public Library, One Reach Rd, Brooklin, ME, 04616. Tel: 207-359-2276. p. 979

Atwater, William F, Dir, United States Army, Ordnance Center & Ordnance Museum Library, Bldg 2601, USAOC&S, Aberdeen Proving Ground, MD, 21005-5201. Tel: 410-278-2396, 410-278-3602. Fax: 410-278-7473. p. 1009

Atwater-Singer, Meg, Coll Mgt Librn, University of Evansville, 1800 Lincoln Ave, Evansville, IN, 47722. Tel: 812-488-2487. Fax: 812-488-6996. p. 739

Atwill, Jade, Librn, Pennsylvania State University Libraries, George & Sherry Middlemas Arts & Humanities Library, Pennsylvania State University, W 202 Pattee Library, University Park, PA, 16802-1801. Tel: 814-863-0738. Fax: 814-863-7502. p. 2148

Atwood, Beth, Mgr, Greenville County Library System, Taylors (Burdette) Branch, 316 W Main St, Taylors, SC, 29687. Tel: 864-268-5955. Fax: 864-268-4275. p. 2196

Atwood, Candace, Circ, Sampson-Clinton Public Library, Bryan Memorial, 302 W Weeksdale St, Newton Grove, NC, 28366. Tel: 910-594-1260. p. 1784

Atwood, Gail R, Librn, Cornerstone University, 1001 E Beltline Ave NE, Grand Rapids, MI, 49525. Tel: 616-949-5300. Fax: 616-222-1405. p. 1184

Atwood, Julie, Acq, Jones County Junior College, 900 S Court St, Ellisville, MS, 39437. Tel: 601-477-4055. Fax: 601-477-2600. p. 1298

Atwood, Michael E, PhD, Assoc Dean, Res & Undergrad Educ, Prof, Drexel University, Rush Bldg, Rm 306, 30 N 33rd St, Philadelphia, PA, 19104-2875. Tel: 215-895-2474. Fax: 215-895-2494. p. 2972

Atzberger, Christine, Head, Ref, Bexley Public Library, 2411 E Main St, Bexley, OH, 43209. Tel: 614-231-9709. p. 1860

Au, Ka-Neng, Head, Tech Serv, Rutgers University Libraries, John Cotton Dana Library, 185 University Ave, Newark, NJ, 07102. Tel: 973-353-5222. Fax: 973-353-1133. p. 1512

Au, Karen, ILL, University of Hawaii Center, West Hawaii, 81-964 Halekii St, Kealakekua, HI, 96750. Tel: 808-322-4858, 808-322-4862. Fax: 808-322-4859. p. 566

Au, Marcia Learned, Dir/Chief Exec Officer, Evansville Vanderburgh Public Library, 200 SE Martin Luther King Jr Blvd, Evansville, IN, 47713-1604. Tel: 812-428-8200. p. 738

Au, Rita, Br Head, Toronto Public Library, Steeles, Bamburgh Gardens Shopping Plaza, 375 Bamburgh Circle, Toronto, ON, M1W 3Y1, CANADA. Tel: 416-396-8975. Fax: 416-396-3602. p. 2863

Au, Saleena, Digital Content Spec, University of Bridgeport, 126 Park Ave, Bridgeport, CT, 06604-5620. Tel: 203-576-4507. Fax: 203-576-4791. p. 332

Auberry, Kendra, Head, Ref, Greenwood Public Library, 310 S Meridian St, Greenwood, IN, 46143-3135. Tel: 317-881-1953. Fax: 317-881-1963. p. 747

Aubin, Danielle, Dir, Musee de la Civilisation - Bibliotheque du Seminaire de Quebec, Nine rue de l'Universite, Quebec, QC, G1R 5K1, CANADA. Tel: 418-643-2158. Fax: 418-692-5206. p. 2906

Aubin, Tina, Asst Dir, Ch, Putnam Public Library, 225 Kennedy Dr, Putnam, CT, 06260-1691. Tel: 860-963-6826. Fax: 860-963-6828. p. 365

Auble, Colleen, Admin Mgr, Pend Oreille County Library District, 109 S Union St, Newport, WA, 99156. Tel: 509-447-2111. Fax: 509-447-2806. p. 2521

Aubrey, Elizabeth, Access Serv Mgr, School of the Art Institute of Chicago, 37 S Wabash Ave, Chicago, IL, 60603-3103. Tel: 312-899-5097. Fax: 312-899-1851. p. 624

Aubry, John, Dir, New School, Raymond Fogelman Library, 55 W 13th St, New York, NY, 10011. Tel: 212-229-5307. Fax: 212-229-5306. p. 1688

Aubry, Mike, Tech Serv, Illinois School for the Deaf, 125 Webster, Jacksonville, IL, 62650. Tel: 217-479-4240. Fax: 217-479-4244. p. 658

Auchstetter, Rosann, Cat, Nova Southeastern University Libraries, Shepard Broad Law Center Library, 3305 College Ave, Fort Lauderdale, FL, 33314. Tel: 954-262-6100. p. 444

Aucoim, Alicia, Br Mgr, Assumption Parish Library, Pierre Part Branch, 2800 Hwy 70 S, Pierre Part, LA, 70390. Tel: 985-252-4220. Fax: 985-252-1476. p. 958

Aude, Sabrina, ILL, Ashford University Library, 400 N Bluff Blvd, Clinton, IA, 52732. Tel: 563-242-4023, Ext 3211. Fax: 563-242-2003. p. 803

Audet, Nicole, Chief Exec Officer, Kapuskasing Public Library, 24 Mundy Ave, Kapuskasing, ON, P5N 1P9, CANADA. Tel: 705-335-3363. Fax: 705-335-2464. p. 2812

Audoma, Olivia, Br Mgr, City of Commerce Public Library, Greenwood Branch, 6134 Greenwood Ave, Commerce, CA, 90040. Tel: 562-927-1516. Fax: 562-927-2076. p. 136

Audrain, Glenda, Dir, Washington County Library System, 1080 W Clydesdale Dr, Fayetteville, AR, 72701. Tel: 479-442-6253. Fax: 479-442-6812. p. 100

Audrain, Glenda, Dir, Washington County Library System, Winslow Branch Library, 351 South Hwy 71, Winslow, AR, 72959. Tel: 479-634-5405. p. 100

Auel, Lisa, Dir, Alachua County Historic Trust, 513 E University Ave, Gainesville, FL, 32601. Tel: 352-378-2280. Fax: 352-378-1246. p. 448

Auensen, Don, Cataloger, Chattahoochee Technical College Library, 980 S Cobb Dr SE, Marietta, GA, 30060-3300. Tel: 770-528-6466. Fax: 770-528-4454. p. 542

Auer, Margaret E, Dean, Univ Librn/Instrul Design Studio, University of Detroit Mercy Library, 4001 W McNichols Rd, Detroit, MI, 48221-3038. Tel: 313-993-1071. Fax: 313-993-1780. p. 1172

Auerbach, Marsha, Ref Librn, Nashua Public Library, Two Court St, Nashua, NH, 03060. Tel: 603-589-4600. Fax: 603-594-3457. p. 1458

Auerbach, Stevanne, Dir, Institute for Childhood Resources, 268 Bush St, San Francisco, CA, 94104. Tel: 510-540-0111. p. 243

Aufderhaar, Kathleen, Syst Librn, Bluffton University, One University Dr, Bluffton, OH, 45817-2104. Tel: 419-358-3414. Fax: 419-358-3384. p. 1860

Augelli, John, Exec Dir, Rosenberg Library, 2310 Sealy Ave, Galveston, TX, 77550. Tel: 409-763-8854, Ext 114. Fax: 409-763-0275. p. 2326

Augello, Laura, Mgr, ILL, Tangipahoa Parish Library, Administration Office, 200 E Mulberry St, Amite, LA, 70422. Tel: 985-748-7559. Fax: 985-748-2812. p. 941

Auger, Bernard, Dir, Libr Serv, Bibliotheque du Seminaire de Saint-Hyacinthe, 650 rue Girouard Est, Saint-Hyacinthe, QC, J2S 2Y2, CANADA. Tel: 450-774-8977. Fax: 450-774-7101. p. 2910

Auger, Brian, Dir, Somerset County Library System, One Vogt Dr, Bridgewater, NJ, 08807-2136. Tel: 908-526-4016, Ext 129. p. 1475

Auger, Henriette, Acq, Bibliothèques de Montrèal, 801, rue Brennan, 5e Etage, Bureau 5206, Montreal, QC, H3C 0G4, CANADA. Tel: 514-872-1539. Fax: 514-872-0530. p. 2889

Auger, Sylvie, Tech Serv, College LaSalle, Bureau 4100, 2000 Saint Catherine St W, Montreal, QC, H3H 2T2, CANADA. Tel: 514-939-2006, Ext 4407. Fax: 514-939-7292. p. 2894

August, Kimberly, Tech Serv, Bryan Cave LLP, 1290 Avenue of the Americas, New York, NY, 10104. Tel: 212-541-2032. Fax: 212-541-1465. p. 1671

August, Roberta Z, Youth Serv Coordr, Saint John the Baptist Parish Library, 2920 New Hwy 51, LaPlace, LA, 70068. Tel: 985-652-2225, 985-652-6857. Fax: 985-652-8005. p. 954

Augustine, Janis C, Dir, Salem Public Library, 28 E Main St, Salem, VA, 24153. Tel: 540-375-3089. Fax: 540-389-7054. p. 2496

Augustine, Marleah, Adult Serv, Hays Public Library, 1205 Main, Hays, KS, 67601-3693. Tel: 785-625-9014. Fax: 785-625-8683. p. 871

Augustine, Matthew, Automation Syst Coordr, Euclid Public Library, 631 E 222nd St, Euclid, OH, 44123-2091. Tel: 216-261-5300, Ext 126. Fax: 216-261-0575. p. 1898

Augustniak, Ashley, Ref Librn/Fel Coordr, Donald F & Mildred Topp Othmer Library of Chemical History, 315 Chestnut St, Philadelphia, PA, 19106. Tel: 215-873-8205. Fax: 215-629-5205. p. 2113

Aukeman, Sharon, Mgr, Highland County District Library, Leesburg Branch, 240 E Main, Leesburg, OH, 45135. Tel: 937-780-7295. Fax: 937-780-7295. p. 1904

Aulisio, George, Outreach Serv, Pub Serv, University of Scranton, Monroe & Linden, Scranton, PA, 18510-4634. Tel: 570-941-4000, 570-941-4008. Fax: 570-941-7817. p. 2138

Aull, Kylah, Librn, North Dakota Legislative Council Library, 600 E Boulevard Ave, Bismarck, ND, 58505-0660. Tel: 701-328-4900. Fax: 701-328-3615. p. 1838

Ault, Jeffrey, Adult/Ref Serv, Dir, Dobbs Ferry Public Library, 55 Main St, Dobbs Ferry, NY, 10522. Tel: 914-231-3051. Fax: 914-693-4671. p. 1615

Ault, Robert D, Micro, Ser, Youngstown State University, One University Plaza, Youngstown, OH, 44555-0001. Tel: 330-941-1719. Fax: 330-941-3734. p. 1953

Ault, Sherry Lynn, Dir, Hubbard Public Library, 436 W Liberty St, Hubbard, OH, 44425. Tel: 330-534-3512. Fax: 330-534-7836. p. 1905

Aultz, Kathy, Exec Dir, Douglas County Historical Society, 5730 N 30th St, No 11A, Omaha, NE, 68111. Tel: 402-451-1013. Fax: 402-453-9448. p. 1412

Aurand, Martin, Head, Spec Coll, Carnegie Mellon University, Hunt Library, 4909 Frew St, Pittsburgh, PA, 15213-3890. Tel: 412-268-2446. Fax: 412-268-2793. p. 2123

Aure, Tina, Asst Librn, Pierce County Law Library, County-City Bldg, 930 Tacoma Ave S, Rm 1A - 105, Tacoma, WA, 98402-2174. Tel: 253-798-7494. Fax: 253-798-2989. p. 2539

Aurelio, Trisha, Tech Serv Supvr, University of Redlands, 1200 E Colton Ave, Redlands, CA, 92374-3758. Tel: 909-748-8022. Fax: 909-335-5392. p. 215

Aurini-Onderwater, Paula, Archivist, City of Edmonton, Archives, 10440 - 108 Ave, 2nd Flr, Prince of Wales Armouries Heritage Centre, Edmonton, AB, T5H 3Z9, CANADA. Tel: 780-496-8723. Fax: 780-496-8732. p. 2699

Auris, Barbara, Circ, Lower Providence Community Library, 50 Parklane Dr, Eagleville, PA, 19403-1171. Tel: 610-666-6640. Fax: 610-666-5109. p. 2051

Ausanio, Holly, Adminr, Clearwater Public Library System, 100 N Osceola Ave, Clearwater, FL, 33755. Tel: 727-562-4970. Fax: 727-562-4977. p. 432

Ausborn, Scot, Dir, Libr Serv, Institute for Psychoanalysis, Chicago, 122 S Michigan Ave, Ste 1300, Chicago, IL, 60603-6107. Tel: 312-922-7474. Fax: 312-922-5656. p. 615

Ausel, Jill, Dir, Chatham College, Woodland Rd, Pittsburgh, PA, 15232. Tel: 412-365-1244. Fax: 412-365-1465. p. 2124

Ausen, Orrin, Dir, Libr Serv, Bethany Lutheran College Memorial Library, 700 Luther Dr, Mankato, MN, 56001-4490. Tel: 507-344-7000. Fax: 507-344-7376. p. 1257

Ausman-Dhatt, Nancy, Dir, Barron Public Library, Ten N Third St, Barron, WI, 54812-1119. Tel: 715-537-3881. Fax: 715-537-5080. p. 2580

Ausmus, Pat, Mgr, Northwest Georgia Regional Library System, Chatsworth-Murray County Library, 706 Old Dalton-Ellijay Rd, Chatsworth, GA, 30705. Tel: 706-695-4200. Fax: 706-695-7381. p. 528

Aust, Karen, Pub Serv, Gulfport Public Library, 5501 28th Ave S, Gulfport, FL, 33707. Tel: 727-893-1074. Fax: 727-893-1072. p. 450

Austad, Julie, Ref Librn (Info Serv), Clark College, Mail Stop LIB 112, 1933 Fort Vancouver Way, Vancouver, WA, 98663-3598. Tel: 360-992-2426. Fax: 360-992-2869. p. 2545

Austen, Barbara, Archivist, Connecticut Historical Society Research Center, One Elizabeth St, Hartford, CT, 06105. Tel: 860-236-5621, Ext 251. Fax: 860-236-2664. p. 344

Austiff, Gerald, Librn, Metropolitan Water Reclamation District of Greater Chicago Library, 100 E Erie St, Chicago, IL, 60611. Tel: 312-751-6658, 312-751-6659. Fax: 312-751-6635. p. 619

Austin, Amanda, Librn, Tri-Valley School - Community Library, Suntrana Rd, Healy, AK, 99743. Tel: 907-683-2507. Fax: 907-683-2517. p. 49

Austin, Brice, Dir of Circ, University of Colorado Boulder, 1720 Pleasant St, 184 UCB, Boulder, CO, 80309-0184. Tel: 303-492-3975. Fax: 303-492-3340. p. 291

Austin, Cheryl, Dir, Weedsport Library, 2795 E Brutus St, Weedsport, NY, 13166-8720. Tel: 315-834-6222. Fax: 315-834-8621. p. 1765

Austin, David, User Serv, Northwest University, 5520 108th Ave NE, Kirkland, WA, 98083-0579. Tel: 425-889-5302. Fax: 425-889-7801. p. 2519

Austin, Diane, Asst Dir, Instr, University of South Florida, 4202 Fowler Ave, CIS 1040, Tampa, FL, 33620-7800. Tel: 813-974-3520. Fax: 813-974-6840. p. 2964

Austin, Gary, Distance Learning/Bus Librn, University of South Florida Saint Petersburg, 140 Seventh Ave S, POY118, Saint Petersburg, FL, 33701. Tel: 727-873-4401. Fax: 727-873-4196. p. 489

Austin, Gary, Instrul & Ref Librn, Georgia College & State University, 320 N Wayne St, Milledgeville, GA, 31061-3397. Tel: 478-445-4047. Fax: 478-445-6847, p. 544

Austin, Gary, Pres, Amelia County Historical Society Library, Jackson Bldg, 16501 Church St, Amelia, VA, 23002. Tel: 804-561-3180. p. 2447

Austin, Glenda, In Charge, Stanly County Public Library, Oakboro Branch, 214 S Main St, Oakboro, NC, 28129. Tel: 704-485-4310. p. 1773

Austin, Javii, Res Librn, Finnegan, Henderson, Farabow, Garrett & Dunner, 901 New York Ave NW, Washington, DC, 20001-4413. Tel: 202-408-4373. Fax: 202-408-4400. p. 400

Austin, Jeanne, Ref, Chili Public Library, 3333 Chili Ave, Rochester, NY, 14624-5494. Tel: 585-889-2200. Fax: 585-889-5819. p. 1729

Austin, Jill, Circ Supvr, Portage District Library, 300 Library Lane, Portage, MI, 49002. Tel: 269-329-4542, Ext 706. Fax: 269-324-9222. p. 1220

Austin, Jim, Dir, Info Tech, Washington Research Library Consortium, 901 Commerce Dr, Upper Marlboro, MD, 20774. Tel: 301-390-2000. Fax: 301-390-2020. p. 2945

Austin, Joanne, Supvr, Osterhout Free Library, North, 28 Oliver St, Wilkes-Barre, PA, 18705. Tel: 570-822-4660. Fax: 570-822-4660. p. 2155

Austin, John R, Dir, Northern Illinois University Libraries, David C Shapiro Memorial Law Library, Normal Rd, DeKalb, IL, 60115-2890. Tel: 815-753-9493. Fax: 815-753-9499. p. 636

Austin, Joyce, Archivist, Rossland Historical Museum Association Archives, PO Box 26, Rossland, BC, V0G 1Y0, CANADA. Tel: 250-362-7722. Fax: 250-362-5379. p. 2737

Austin, Kit, Asst Admin, University of Iowa, 3087 Main Library, Iowa City, IA, 52242-1420. Tel: 319-335-5707. Fax: 319-335-5374. p. 2965

Austin, Kurt, Pub Div Dir, National Council of Teachers of English Library, 1111 W Kenyon Rd, Urbana, IL, 61801-1096. Tel: 217-278-3619. Fax: 217-328-0977. p. 711

Austin, LaVerne, Per, Otterbein University, 138 W Main St, Westerville, OH, 43081. Tel: 614-823-1264. Fax: 614-823-1921. p. 1946

Austin, Mary, Libr Dir, Little Priest Tribal College Library, 601 E College Dr, Winnebago, NE, 68071. Tel: 402-878-3334. Fax: 402-878-2319. p. 1423

Austin, Michelle, Mgr, Toccoa-Stephens County Public Library, 121 W Savannah St, PO Box Drawer L, Toccoa, GA, 30577. Tel: 706-886-6082. Fax: 706-886-2134. p. 554

Austin, Nathan, Dir, Allegany Public Library, 90 W Main St, Allegany, NY, 14706-1204. Tel: 716-373-1056. Fax: 716-373-1056. p. 1572

Austin, Pat, Assoc Prof, University of New Orleans, College of Education, Rm 342, New Orleans, LA, 70148. Tel: 504-280-6251, 504-280-6528. Fax: 504-280-1120. p. 2967

Austin, Peggy, Coordr, Acq & Per, Cypress College Library, 9200 Valley View St, Cypress, CA, 90630-5897. Tel: 714-484-7066. Fax: 714-826-6723. p. 138

Austin, Peter, Tech Serv, Salem College, 626 S Church St, Winston-Salem, NC, 27108. Tel: 336-917-5422. Fax: 336-917-5339. p. 1833

Austin, Richard, Instr, University of South Florida, 4202 Fowler Ave, CIS 1040, Tampa, FL, 33620-7800. Tel: 813-974-3520. Fax: 813-974-6840. p. 2964

Austin, Terry, Ch, Sherburne Memorial Library, PO Box 73, Killington, VT, 05751. Tel: 802-422-4251, 802-422-9765. Fax: 802-422-4323. p. 2427

Austin, Whitney, Br Mgr, Springfield-Greene County Library District, Fair Grove Branch, 81 S Orchard Blvd, Fair Grove, MO, 65648-8421. Tel: 417-759-2637. Fax: 417-759-2638. p. 1368

Austin, Whitney, Br Mgr, Springfield-Greene County Library District, Strafford Branch, 101 S State Hwy 125, Strafford, MO, 65757-8998. Tel: 417-736-9233. p. 1368

Austin-Halsey, Patrisha, Dir, Betty Anne Jolly Norris Community Library, One Norris Sq, Norris, TN, 37828. Tel: 865-494-6800. p. 2262

Austin-Scaff, Jessica, Br Head, Charleston County Public Library, Edgar Allan Poe Branch, 1921 I'On St, Sullivan's Island, SC, 29482. Tel: 843-883-3914. p. 2183

Auston, Anthony, Asst Dir, Palatine Public Library District, 700 N North Ct, Palatine, IL, 60067-8159. Tel: 847-358-5881. p. 686

Auston, Geri, Br Mgr, Calaveras County Library, West Point Branch, 291 Main St, Ste B, West Point, CA, 95255. Tel: 209-293-7020. p. 227

Austrino, Kathleen, Br Mgr, Public Library of Youngstown & Mahoning County, Poland Branch, 311 S Main St, Poland, OH, 44514. p. 1953

Austrino, Kathleen, Br Mgr, Public Library of Youngstown & Mahoning County, Springfield Branch, 10418 Main St, New Middletown, OH, 44442. p. 1953

Auten, Timothy, ILL, Cabarrus County Public Library, 27 Union St N, Concord, NC, 28025-4793. Tel: 704-920-2050. Fax: 704-784-3822. p. 1785

Autio, Lisa, Libr Tech, The Learning Center, 500 W Broadway, Missoula, MT, 59802-4587. Tel: 406-329-5712. Fax: 406-329-5688. p. 1386

Autrey, LeAnn, Asst Dir, Humboldt County Library, 85 E Fifth St, Winnemucca, NV, 89445. Tel: 775-623-6388. Fax: 775-623-6438. p. 1435

Autry, Doris, Librn, Raymond Jordan Boyd Public Library, 101 W Rock Island Ave, Boyd, TX, 76023-3001. Tel: 940-433-5580. Fax: 940-433-8253. p. 2290

Auvil, Phyllis, Librn, Alderson Library, RR 1, Box 147, Alderson, WV, 24910-0147. Tel: 304-445-7221. Fax: 304-445-7221. p. 2553

Auwen, Joan, Librn, United States Army, Nye Library, 1640 Randolph Rd, Fort Sill, OK, 73503-9022. Tel: 580-442-2048, 580-442-3806. Fax: 580-442-7346. p. 1963

Auxier, Tiffany, Youth Serv Mgr, Hinsdale Public Library, 20 E Maple St, Hinsdale, IL, 60521. Tel: 630-986-1976. Fax: 630-986-9654. p. 656

Auyong, Dorothy, Cat, Huntington Library, 1151 Oxford Rd, San Marino, CA, 91108. Tel: 626-405-2188. Fax: 626-449-5720. p. 255

Auzenne, Shirley, In Charge, Lafayette Public Library, Chenier Center, 220-B W Willow St, Lafayette, LA, 70501. Tel: 337-291-2941. p. 952

Avalos, Francisco, Librn, University of Arizona, James E Rogers College of Law Library, PO Box 210176, Tucson, AZ, 85721-0176. Tel: 520-621-1413. Fax: 520-621-3138. p. 89

Avalos, Mary Helen, Dep Librn, Globe Public Library, 339 S Broad St, Globe, AZ, 85501-1744. Tel: 928-425-6111. Fax: 928-425-3357. p. 65

Avasthi, Smita, Electronic Res, Southwestern Oregon Community College Library, 1988 Newmark Ave, Coos Bay, OR, 97420-2956. Tel: 541-888-7431. Fax: 541-888-7605. p. 1993

Avdette, JoAnn, Head, Circ, Gale Free Library, 23 Highland St, Holden, MA, 01520-2599. Tel: 508-210-5560. Fax: 508-829-0232. p. 1095

Aveline, Helen, Dir, Berlin-Peck Memorial Library, 234 Kensington Rd, Berlin, CT, 06037. Tel: 860-828-7125. Fax: 860-829-1848. p. 330

Avellino, Denise, Ref Serv Librn, Holy Family University Library, 9801 Frankford Ave, Philadelphia, PA, 19114. Tel: 267-341-3315, 267-341-3316. Fax: 215-632-8067. p. 2111

Aven, Lauralee, Health Sci, Ref & Instrul Librn, University of Saint Francis, 201 Pope John Paul II Ctr, 2701 Spring St, Fort Wayne, IN, 46808. Tel: 260-399-7700, Ext 6057. Fax: 260-399-8166. p. 742

Aven, Lauralee, Coordr, Northeast Indiana Health Science Libraries Consortium, Univ Saint Francis Vann Library, 2701 Spring St, Fort Wayne, IN, 46808. Tel: 260-399-7700, Ext 6065. Fax: 260-399-8166. p. 2943

Averett, Lewis Hobgood, Pub Serv, George M Jones Library Association, 2311 Memorial Ave, Lynchburg, VA, 24501. Tel: 434-846-0501. Fax: 434-846-1572. p. 2475

Averett, Steve, Ref, Brigham Young University, Howard W Hunter Law Library, 256 JRCB, Provo, UT, 84602-8000. Tel: 801-422-3593. Fax: 801-422-0404. p. 2411

Averette, Kim, Ser, Sheppard Memorial Library, 530 S Evans St, Greenville, NC, 27858-2308. Tel: 252-329-4376. Fax: 252-329-4587. p. 1799

Averre, Amy, Dir, Husson University, One College Circle, Bangor, ME, 04401-2999. Tel: 207-941-7187, 207-941-7188. Fax: 207-941-7989. p. 976

Avers, Kathy, Asst Librn, Council Grove Public Library, 829 W Main St, Council Grove, KS, 66846. Tel: 620-767-5716. Fax: 620-767-7312. p. 862

Aversa, Elizabeth, Prof, University of Alabama, 514 Main Library, Tuscaloosa, AL, 35487. Tel: 205-348-4610. Fax: 205-348-3746. p. 2961

Aversano, Gloria, Librn, National Oceanic & Atmospheric Administration, 4301 Rickenbacker Causeway, Miami, FL, 33149. Tel: 305-361-4428. Fax: 305-361-4448. p. 468

Aversano, Gloria, Librn, United States National Oceanic & Atmospheric, National Hurricane Center/Tropical Prediction Center Library, 11691 SW 17 St, Miami, FL, 33165-2149. Tel: 305-229-4406. Fax: 305-553-9879. p. 468

Avery, Amanda, Outreach & Assessment Librn, Marywood University Library, 2300 Adams Ave, Scranton, PA, 18509-1598. Tel: 570-961-4707. Fax: 570-961-4769. p. 2137

Avery, Arianne, ILL, Virginia Wesleyan College, 1584 Wesleyan Dr, Norfolk, VA, 23502-5599. Tel: 757-455-3224. Fax: 757-455-2129. p. 2483

Avery, Audrey, Head, Ch, Dover Public Library, 45 S State St, Dover, DE, 19901. Tel: 302-736-7030. Fax: 302-736-5087. p. 382

Avery, Barbara, Ch, Cove City Public Library, 102 N Main St, Cove City, NC, 28523. Tel: 252-638-6363. Fax: 252-638-4639. p. 1785

Avery, Barbara, Librn, Marshall & Melhorn, Four SeaGate, 8th Flr, Toledo, OH, 43604. Tel: 419-249-7100. Fax: 419-249-7151. p. 1939

Avery, Brian, Ref Serv, Clearwater Public Library System, Countryside, 2741 State Rd 580, Clearwater, FL, 33761. Tel: 727-562-4970. Fax: 727-669-1289. p. 432

Avery, Connie, Ch, Flagg-Rochelle Public Library District, 619 Fourth Ave, Rochelle, IL, 61068. Tel: 815-562-3431. Fax: 815-562-3432. p. 695

Avery, Connie, Librn, Solomon Public Library, 108 N Walnut, Solomon, KS, 67480. Tel: 785-655-3521. p. 894

Avery, Ernest, Tech Serv Librn, Piedmont Community College, 1715 College Dr, Roxboro, NC, 27573. Tel: 336-599-1181, Ext 231. Fax: 336-599-9146. p. 1821

Avery, Galen, Dir, Lucas County Law Library, Lucas County Family Court Center, 905 Jackson St, Toledo, OH, 43604-5512. Tel: 419-213-4747. Fax: 419-213-4287. p. 1939

Avery, Glen, Tech Librn, Houghton College, One Willard Ave, Houghton, NY, 14744. Tel: 585-567-9615. Fax: 585-567-9248. p. 1638

Avery, Kim, Curator, Guysborough Historical Society, 106 Church St, Guysborough, NS, B0H 1N0, CANADA. Tel: 902-533-4008. Fax: 902-533-2258. p. 2780

Avery, Louise, Curator, Kitimat Museum & Archives, 293 City Centre, Kitimat, BC, V8C 1T6, CANADA. Tel: 250-632-8950. Fax: 250-632-7429. p. 2731

Avery, Robert, Dir, Rome Historical Society, 200 Church St, Rome, NY, 13440. Tel: 315-336-5870. Fax: 315-336-5912. p. 1735

Avery, Sharon, Archivist, State Historical Society of Iowa-Des Moines Library, 600 E Locust, Des Moines, IA, 50319-0290. Tel: 515-281-6200. Fax: 515-282-0502. p. 810

Avery-Sublett, Anet, Dir, Angelina College Library, 3500 S First St, Lufkin, TX, 75904. Tel: 936-633-5219. Fax: 936-633-5442. p. 2358

Avigdor, Rita, Operations Mgr, Public Library InterLINK, c/o Burnaby Public Library-Kingsway Branch, 7252 Kingsway, Burnaby, BC, V5E 1G3, CANADA. Tel: 604-517-8441. Fax: 604-517-8410. p. 2959

Avila, Grace, Mgr, Circ & Reserves, York College Library, 94-20 Guy R Brewer Blvd, Jamaica, NY, 11451. Tel: 718-262-2072. Fax: 718-262-2027, 718-262-2997. p. 1646

Avila, Salvador, Br Mgr, Las Vegas-Clark County Library District, Enterprise Library, 25 E Shelbourne Ave, Las Vegas, NV, 89123. Tel: 702-507-3760. Fax: 702-507-3779. p. 1429

Avin, Shirley, Chief Librn, Atlanta VA Medical Center Library, 1670 Clairmont Rd, Decatur, GA, 30033-4004. Tel: 404-321-6111, Ext 7672. Fax: 404-728-7781. p. 529

Avoine, Dominique, Asst Univ Librn, Pub Serv, Tele-Universite, 455 rue du Parvis, Quebec, QC, G1K 9H6, CANADA. Tel: 418-657-2747. Fax: 418-657-2094. p. 2906

Avrett, Robert, III, Ch, Gilpin County Public Library District, 15131 Hwy 119, Black Hawk, CO, 80422. Tel: 303-582-5777. Fax: 303-582-3938. p. 289

Avrin, Judy, Coordr, Virtual Academic Library Environment, William Paterson University Library, 300 Pompton Rd, Wayne, NJ, 07470-2103. Tel: 973-720-3179. Fax: 973-720-3171. p. 2949

Awadalla, Maggie, Electronic Res, Old Bridge Public Library, One Old Bridge Plaza, Old Bridge, NJ, 08857-2498. Tel: 732-721-5600, Ext 5039. Fax: 732-679-0556. p. 1516

Awe, Susan C, Dir of Outreach, University of New Mexico, William J Parish Memorial Business & Economics Library, One University of New Mexico, MSC05 3020, Albuquerque, NM, 87131-1496. Tel: 505-277-5912. Fax: 505-277-9813. p. 1551

Awilda, Reyes, Govt Doc, Maps Librn, West Chester University, 25 W Rosedale Ave, West Chester, PA, 19383. Tel: 610-436-3206. p. 2153

Ax-Fultz, Laura J, Asst Law Librn, Ref, Circ/ILL, Pennsylvania State University - Dickinson School of Law (University Libraries), 1170 Harrisburg Pike, Carlisle, PA, 17013-1617. Tel: 717-241-3541. Fax: 717-240-5127. p. 2042

Axel-Lute, Paul, Dep Dir, Rutgers University Library for the Center for Law & Justice, 123 Washington St, Newark, NJ, 07102-3094. Tel: 973-353-3151. Fax: 973-353-1356. p. 1513

Axelrod, Adelina, Cat, John Carter Brown Library, Brown University, George & Brown Sts, Providence, RI, 02912. Tel: 401-863-2725. Fax: 401-863-3477. p. 2171

Axelsen, Shari, Libr Assoc, La Crosse County Library, John Bosshard Memorial, 1720 Henry Johns Blvd, Bangor, WI, 54614. Tel: 608-486-4408. Fax: 608-486-4408. p. 2598

Axford, Paul, Coordr, Br Serv, Clarington Public Library, Newcastle Village Branch, 150 King Ave E, Newcastle, ON, L1B 1L5, CANADA. Tel: 905-987-4844. p. 2796

Axtman, Steve, Coordr, Training Prog, North Dakota State Library, Library Memorial Bldg, 604 East Blvd Ave, Dept 250, Bismarck, ND, 58505-0800. Tel: 701-328-3495. Fax: 701-328-2040. p. 1838

Ayad, Farid, Dr, Pres, Canadian Arab Federation Library, 1057 McNicoll Ave, Scarborough, ON, M1W 3W6, CANADA. Tel: 416-493-8635. Fax: 416-493-9239. p. 2840

Ayala, Kevin, Asst Dir, Bay County Library System, 500 Center Ave, Bay City, MI, 48708. Tel: 989-894-2837. Fax: 989-894-2021. p. 1155

Ayala, Robert, Dir, Converse Public Library, 601 S Seguin Rd, Converse, TX, 78109. Tel: 210-659-4160. Fax: 210-659-4160. p. 2301

Ayanbiola, Felicia, ILL, Howard University Libraries, Law Library, 2929 Van Ness St NW, Washington, DC, 20008. Tel: 202-806-8045. Fax: 202-806-8400. p. 404

Ayars, Tom, Ref, Cumberland County Library, 800 E Commerce St, Bridgeton, NJ, 08302-2295. Tel: 856-453-2210. Fax: 856-451-1940. p. 1474

Aycock, Anthony, Librn, North Carolina Justice Academy, 200 W College St, Salemburg, NC, 28385. Tel: 910-525-4158, Ext 267. Fax: 910-525-4491. p. 1821

Aycock, Laurie, Govt Doc Assoc, Irvine Sullivan Ingram Library, University of West Georgia, 1601 Maple St, Carrollton, GA, 30118. Tel: 678-839-6498. Fax: 678-839-6511. p. 523

Aycock, Mary, Head, Cat, Curtis Laws Wilson Library, 400 W 14th St, Rolla, MO, 65409-0060. Tel: 573-341-7826. Fax: 573-341-4233. p. 1351

Aycrigg, Gloria C, Pub Serv Asst, Florida Southern College, 111 Lake Hollingsworth Dr, Lakeland, FL, 33801-5698. Tel: 863-616-6452. Fax: 863-680-4126. p. 459

Ayer, Carol A, Dir, National Forest Service Library, 240 W Prospect Rd, Fort Collins, CO, 80526. Tel: 970-498-1310. Fax: 970-498-1059. p. 307

Ayer, Caroline, In Charge, OPIRG Guelph Library, University of Guelph, One Trent Lane, Guelph, ON, N1G 2W1, CANADA. Tel: 519-824-2091. Fax: 519-824-8990. p. 2807

Ayer, H D, Dir of Libr Serv, Ambrose Library, 150 Ambrose Circle SW, Calgary, AB, T3H 0L5, CANADA. Tel: 403-310-2947. Fax: 403-571-2556. p. 2687

Ayers, Amy, Interim Dir, Mount Kisco Public Library, 100 E Main St, Mount Kisco, NY, 10549. Tel: 914-666-8041. Fax: 914-666-3899. p. 1663

Ayers, Carolyn, Head, Tech Serv, Manhasset Public Library, 30 Onderdonk Ave, Manhasset, NY, 11030. Tel: 516 627-2300, Ext 320. Fax: 516-627-4339. p. 1657

Ayers, Dawn, Dir, Cameron Public Library, 506 Main St, Cameron, WI, 54822. Tel: 715-458-2267. Fax: 715-458-2267. p. 2584

Ayers, Donna, Instruction & Ref Librn, Los Angeles Mission College Library, 13356 Eldridge Ave, Sylmar, CA, 91342-3200. Tel: 818-364-7750. Fax: 818-364-7749. p. 274

Ayers, Lynn, Cat Librn, Wilberforce University, 1055 N Bickett Rd, Wilberforce, OH, 45384-5801. Tel: 937-708-5278. Fax: 937-708-5771. p. 1948

Ayers, Micaela, Dir, Butler Community College Libraries, 901 S Haverhill Rd, El Dorado, KS, 67042-3280. Tel: 316-322-3235. Fax: 316-322-3315. p. 864

Ayers, Michelle, Head, Res Serv, United States Court of Appeals, Burn Courthouse, 1st Flr, 601 Market St, Room 1609, Philadelphia, PA, 19106. Tel: 267-299-4300. Fax: 267-299-4328. p. 2118

Ayers, Rachel, Libr Dir, Towanda Public Library, 620 Highland, Towanda, KS, 67144-9042. Tel: 316-536-2464. Fax: 316-536-2847. p. 898

Ayers, Ryan M, Mgr, Libr Serv, Saint Francis Hospital & Health Centers, 1600 Albany, Beech Grove, IN, 46107. Tel: 317-783-8106. Fax: 317-782-6934. p. 726

Ayers, Susan, Dir, Clyde-Savannah Public Library, 204 Glasgow St, Clyde, NY, 14433. Tel: 315-923-7767. Fax: 315-923-9315. p. 1608

Ayers, Tia Jah Wynne, Br Mgr, Indianapolis-Marion County Public Library, Decatur, 5301 Kentucky Ave, Indianapolis, IN, 46221-6540. Tel: 317-275-4330. p. 754

Aylward, Emily, ILL Supvr, Connecticut College, 270 Mohegan Ave, New London, CT, 06320-4196. Tel: 860-439-2650. Fax: 860-439-2871. p. 359

Aylward, James F, Dir, United States Navy, Academic Resources Information Center (ARIC), 440 Meyerkord Rd, Newport, RI, 02841. Tel: 401-841-4352, 401-841-6631. Fax: 401-841-2805. p. 2170

Aynedjian, Amy, Ch, Englewood Public Library, 31 Engle St, Englewood, NJ, 07631. Tel: 201-568-2215. Fax: 201-568-6895. p. 1484

Aynes, Sharon, Asst Librn, Henry County Library, 172 Eminence Terrace, Eminence, KY, 40019-1146. Tel: 502-845-5682. Fax: 502-845-4807. p. 912

Ayotte, Andrea, Info Coordr, Canadian Music Centre, National Library/Ontario Region, 20 St Joseph St, Toronto, ON, M4Y 1J9, CANADA. Tel: 416-961-6601, Ext 204. Fax: 416-961-7198. p. 2851

Ayotte, Jackie, Dir, Louis B Goodall Memorial Library, 952 Main St, Sanford, ME, 04073. Tel: 207-324-4714. Fax: 207-324-5982. p. 999

Ayotte-Zarelski, Louise, Dir, College Universitaire de Saint-Boniface, 200 Ave de la Cathedrale, Winnipeg, MB, R2H 0H7, CANADA. Tel: 204-233-0210, Ext 403. Fax: 204-233-9472. p. 2755

Ayotte-Zaretski, Louise, Head, Ref (Info Serv), Legislative Library of Manitoba, 200 Vaughan St, Rm 100, Winnipeg, MB, R3C 1T5, CANADA. Tel: 204-945-4330. Fax: 204-948-1312. p. 2756

Ayre, Ann, Actg Librn, Union Congregational Church, 176 Cooper Ave, Montclair, NJ, 07043. Tel: 973-744-7424. Fax: 973-744-1364. p. 1503

Ayres, Barbara, Asst Librn, Warren Public Library, 15 Sackett Hill Rd, Warren, CT, 06754. Tel: 860-868-2195. p. 374

Ayres, Laura-Ellen, Asst Dir, Direct Serv, Rapides Parish Library, 411 Washington St, Alexandria, LA, 71301-8338. Tel: 318-445-6436, Ext 1002. Fax: 318-445-6478. p. 940

Ayres, Mary, Mgr, Libr Serv, Southern State Community College, 100 Hobart Dr, Hillsboro, OH, 45133-9487. Tel: 937-695-0307, Ext 3681. Fax: 937-393-9370, 937-695-8093. p. 1904

Ayres, Mary, Mgr, Rural Ohio Valley Health Sciences Library Network, Southern State Community College- South, 12681 US Rte 62, Sardinia, OH, 45171. Tel: 937-695-0307, Ext 3681. Fax: 937-695-1440. p. 2952

Ayres, Melissa, Libr Assoc, Windsor Public Library, 43 State St, Windsor, VT, 05089. Tel: 802-674-2556. Fax: 802-674-5767. p. 2440

Ayres, Michael, Libr Serv Mgr-Tech Serv, Irving Public Library, 801 W Irving Blvd, Irving, TX, 75015. Tel: 972-721-2439. Fax: 972-721-2329. p. 2346

Ayzenberg, Marina, Br Mgr, Brooklyn Public Library, Brighton Beach, 16 Brighton First Rd, Brooklyn, NY, 11235. Tel: 718-946-2917. Fax: 718-946-6176. p. 1591

Azaria, Jill, Libr Assoc, Dallas Public Library, 1515 Young St, Dallas, TX, 75201-5499. Tel: 214-670-1400. Fax: 214-670-7839. p. 2306

Azarian, Helen, Head, Customer Serv Supvr, Evansville Vanderburgh Public Library, Central, 200 SE Martin Luther King Jr Blvd, Evansville, IN, 47713. Tel: 812-428-8200. Fax: 812-428-8397. p. 738

Azukas, Mary Ann, Tech Serv, Chicago Ridge Public Library, 10400 S Oxford Ave, Chicago Ridge, IL, 60415. Tel: 708-423-7753. Fax: 708-423-2758. p. 628

Azzopardi, Alexa, Librn, Washtenaw Community College, 4800 E Huron River Dr, Ann Arbor, MI, 48105-4800. Tel: 734-677-5294. Fax: 734-973-3446. p. 1153

Azzoto, Judy, ILL, Ref Serv, Cazenovia College, Lincklaen St, Cazenovia, NY, 13035. Tel: 315-655-7132. Fax: 315-655-8675. p. 1603

Baaden, Bea, Dr, Dir, Sch Media Prog, Long Island University, C W Post Campus, 720 Northern Blvd, Brookville, NY, 11548-1300. Tel: 516-299-3818. Fax: 516-299-4168. p. 2969

Baader, Joan, Circ Mgr, Bensenville Community Public Library, 200 S Church Rd, Bensenville, IL, 60106. Tel: 630-766-4642, Ext 415. Fax: 630-766-0788. p. 594

Baalman, Pat, Dir, Moore Family Library, 95 S Adams, Grinnell, KS, 67738. Tel: 785-824-3885. p. 870

Baardsen, Jean, Dir, Carteret Community College Library, 201 College Circle, Morehead City, NC, 28557. Tel: 252-222-6216. Fax: 252-222-6219. p. 1810

Baars, Bill, Dir, Lake Oswego Public Library, 706 Fourth St, Lake Oswego, OR, 97034-2399. Tel: 503-636-7628. Fax: 503-635-4171. p. 2003

Baas, Mark, Assoc Dean for Instruction & Educ Tech, Saint Cloud State University, 112 Miller Ctr, 720 Fourth Ave S, Saint Cloud, MN, 56301-4498. Tel: 320-308-2022. Fax: 320-308-4778. p. 1276

Baas, Mark, Assoc Dean for Instruction & Educ Tech, Saint Cloud State University, Learning Resources & Technology Services, 720 Fourth Ave S, Saint Cloud, MN, 56301-4498. Tel: 320-308-2084. Fax: 320-308-4778. p. 2968

Babajide, John, Librn, State of Ohio Department of Corrections, State Rd 545 N, 1150 N Main St, Mansfield, OH, 44903. Tel: 419-526-2000, Ext 3050. Fax: 419-526-1763. p. 1913

Babanoury, Betty, Dir, Niagara Falls Public Library, 1425 Main St, Niagara Falls, NY, 14305. Tel: 716-286-4881. Fax: 716-286-4912. p. 1705

Babanoury, Betty, Dir, Niagara Falls Public Library, LaSalle, 8728 Buffalo Ave, Niagara Falls, NY, 14304. Tel: 716-283-8309. p. 1705

Babatunde, Olusola, Govt Doc, Texas Southern University, Thurgood Marshall School of Law Library, 3100 Cleburne Ave, Houston, TX, 77004. Tel: 713-313-1978. Fax: 713-313-4483. p. 2342

Babay, J A, Br Mgr, Centre County Library & Historical Museum, Centre Hall Area Branch, 109 W Beryl St, Centre Hall, PA, 16828. Tel: 814-364-2580. Fax: 814-364-2598. p. 2032

Babb, Deborah, Electronic Serv Librn, Christian Brothers University, 650 E Pkwy South, Memphis, TN, 38104. Tel: 901-321-3432. Fax: 901-321-3219. p. 2248

Babbit, Jan R, Assoc Dir, Cleveland State University, Cleveland-Marshall Law Library, Cleveland-Marshall College of Law, 1801 Euclid Ave, Cleveland, OH, 44115-2223. Tel: 216-687-6913. Fax: 216-687-6881. p. 1878

Babbitt, Deborah, Pub Serv Dir, Nampa Public Library, 101 11th Ave S, Nampa, ID, 83651. Tel: 208-468-5814. Fax: 208-318-0530. p. 580

Babbitt, Jane G, Tech Serv, Rockport Public Library, One Limerock St, Rockport, ME, 04856-6141. Tel: 207-236-3642. Fax: 207-236-3642. p. 999

Babbitt, Susan, Librn, Tulsa City-County Library, Collinsville Branch, 1223 Main, Collinsville, OK, 74021. Tel: 918-596-2840. Fax: 918-596-2841. p. 1982

Babchak, Paulette, Ch, Johnsburg Public Library District, 3000 N Johnsburg Rd, Johnsburg, IL, 60051. Tel: 815-344-0077. Fax: 815-344-3524. p. 659

Babcock, Audrey, Dir, Deposit Free Library, 159 Front St, Deposit, NY, 13754. Tel: 607-467-2577. p. 1614

Babcock, Beverlee, Dir, Macomb County Library, Macomb Library for the Blind & Physically Handicapped, 16480 Hall Rd, Clinton Township, MI, 48038-1132. Tel: 586-412-5976. Fax: 586-286-0634. p. 1164

Babcock, Beverlee, Head, Spec Serv, Macomb County Library, 16480 Hall Rd, Clinton Township, MI, 48038-1132. Tel: 586-286-6660. Fax: 586-412-5958. p. 1164

Babcock, Elizabeth, Curator of Hist, Maturango Museum, 100 E Las Flores Ave, Ridgecrest, CA, 93555. Tel: 760-375-6900. Fax: 760-375-0479. p. 216

Babcock, Jane, Dir, Goodwin Memorial Library, 50 Middle St, Hadley, MA, 01035-9544. Tel: 413-584-7451. Fax: 413-584-9137. p. 1093

Babcock, Sandra, Librn, Paradise Valley Municipal Library, PO Box 60, Paradise Valley, AB, T0B 3R0, CANADA. Tel: 780-745-2277. Fax: 780-745-2641. p. 2713

Babcock, Wally, Ref Librn, Finger Lakes Community College, 4355 Lakeshore Dr, Canandaigua, NY, 14424-8395. Tel: 585-394-3500, Ext 7371. Fax: 585-394-8708. p. 1601

Babec, Christine, Assoc Librn, Justice Institute of British Columbia Library, 715 McBride Blvd, New Westminster, BC, V3L 5T4, CANADA. Tel: 604-528-5595. Fax: 604-528-5593. p. 2734

Baber, David, Adminr, Broward County Historical Commission Library, 301 SW 13th Ave, Fort Lauderdale, FL, 33312. Tel: 954-357-5553. Fax: 954-357-5522. p. 442

Babin, Bryan, IT Dept Head, State Library of Louisiana, 701 N Fourth St, Baton Rouge, LA, 70802-5232. Tel: 225-342-4923. Fax: 225-219-4804. p. 945

Babin, Danielle, Tech Serv, Borden Ladner Gervais LLP Library, 1000 de la Gauchetiere W, Ste 900, Montreal, QC, H3B 5H4, CANADA. Tel: 514-954-3159. Fax: 514-954-1905. p. 2892

Babin, Leisha, Br Mgr, Saint Mary Parish Library, Bayou Vista Branch, 1325 Bellview Dr, Bayou Vista, LA, 70380. Tel: 985-399-9866. Fax: 985-399-4232. p. 950

Babin, Leisha, Interim Br Mgr, Saint Mary Parish Library, Amelia Branch, 625 Lake Palourde, Amelia, LA, 70360. Tel: 985-631-2262. Fax: 985-631-2632. p. 950

Babineaux, Tori, Br Mgr, Vermilion Parish Library, Erath Branch, 111 W Edwards St, Erath, LA, 70533-4027. Tel: 337-937-5628. Fax: 337-937-5656. p. 939

Babirye-Alibatya, Rebecca, Commun Libr Mgr, Queens Borough Public Library, Woodhaven Community Library, 85-41 Forest Pkwy, Woodhaven, NY, 11421. Tel: 718-849-1010. p. 1645

Babish, Jo Ann, Head, Libr Serv, Moses Taylor Hospital Medical Library, 700 Quincy Ave, Scranton, PA, 18510. Tel: 570-340-2125. Fax: 570-963-8994. p. 2137

Babiy, Sofiya, Br Mgr, Brooklyn Public Library, Sheepshead Bay, 2636 E 14th St, Brooklyn, NY, 11235. Tel: 718-368-1815. Fax: 718-368-1872. p. 1592

Babli, Linda, Ref & Info Serv Librn, Winter Haven Public Library, 325 Ave A NW, Winter Haven, FL, 33881. Tel: 863-291-5880. Fax: 863-298-7708. p. 505

Babou, Robin, Librn, Rio Hondo Community College Library, 3600 Workman Mill Rd, Whittier, CA, 90601. Tel: 562-908-3417. Fax: 562-463-4642. p. 283

Baca, David, Interim Dir, Texas A&M University at Galveston, 200 Seawolf Pkwy, Galveston, TX, 77553. Tel: 409-740-4560. Fax: 409-740-4702. p. 2326

Baca, Margaret G, Dir of Tech Serv, Santa Fe Public Library, 145 Washington Ave, Santa Fe, NM, 87501. Tel: 505-955-6786. Fax: 505-955-6676. p. 1563

Baca, Olivia, Ref Librn, Central New Mexico Community College Libraries, 525 Buena Vista SE, Albuquerque, NM, 87106-4023. Tel: 505-224-3292. Fax: 505-224-3321. p. 1548

Bacani, Gail, Med Librn, Arizona State Hospital Library, 2500 E Van Buren St, Phoenix, AZ, 85008. Tel: 602-220-6045. Fax: 602-629-7285. p. 72

Bacchiocchi, Donna, Head, Tech Serv, Bentley College, 175 Forest St, Waltham, MA, 02452-4705. Tel: 781-891-2168. Fax: 781-891-2830. p. 1132

Baccus, Janet G, Mgr, Nixon & Baccus Family Association Clearinghouse, 5817 144th St E, Puyallup, WA, 98375-5221. Tel: 253-537-8288. p. 2525

Bach, Cathy, Br Mgr, Pamunkey Regional Library, Richard S Gillis Jr - Ashland Branch, 201 S Railroad Ave, Ashland, VA, 23005. Tel: 804-798-4072. Fax: 804-798-6276. p. 2469

Bach, Cheryl, Librn, Ozark Regional Library, Recklein Memorial, 305 N Smith St, Cuba, MO, 65453. Tel: 573-885-3431. p. 1333

Bach, Jeanette, Dir, Pigeon District Library, 7236 Nitz St, Pigeon, MI, 48755. Tel: 989-453-2341. Fax: 989-453-2266. p. 1217

Bach, Kathy, Br Mgr, Public Library of Cincinnati & Hamilton County, Westwood, 3345 Epworth Ave, Cincinnati, OH, 45211. Tel: 513-369-4474. Fax: 513-369-4475. p. 1873

Bach, Maria, Br Mgr, Public Library of Cincinnati & Hamilton County, Harrison Branch, 10398 New Haven Rd, Harrison, OH, 45030. Tel: 513-369-4442. Fax: 513-369-4443. p. 1872

Bachand, Denise, Dir, Preston Public Library, 389 Rt 2, Preston, CT, 06365. Tel: 860-886-1010. Fax: 860-886-4952. p. 364

Bache, Arlene, Br Mgr, Middle Georgia Regional Library System, East Wilkinson County Public Library, 154 E Main St, Irwinton, GA, 31042-2602. Tel: 478-946-2778. Fax: 478-946-2778. p. 541

Bachman, Ann, Dir, House Memorial Public Library, 220 Thurston Ave, Pender, NE, 68047. Tel: 402-385-2521. Fax: 402-385-2521. p. 1416

Bachman, Joan, Librn, West Fork Public Library, 198 Main St, West Fork, AR, 72774. Tel: 479-839-2626. Fax: 479-839-2626. p. 117

Bachman, Steven J, Dir, Your Home Public Library, 107 Main St, Johnson City, NY, 13790. Tel: 607-797-4816. Fax: 607-798-8895. p. 1647

Bachmann, Donna, Soc Sci Librn, University of Puget Sound, 1500 N Warner St, Campus Mail Box 1021, Tacoma, WA, 98416-1021. Tel: 253-879-3619. Fax: 253-879-3670. p. 2541

Bachmann, Sandra, Circ, North Indian River County Library, 1001 Sebastian Blvd, CR 512, Sebastian, FL, 32958. Tel: 772-589-1355. Fax: 772-388-3697. p. 491

Bachor, Kathy, Ch, New City Free Library, 220 N Main St, New City, NY, 10956. Tel: 845-634-4997. p. 1664

Bachowski, Donna, Mgr, Ref Serv, Orange County Library District, Talking Books Section, 101 E Central Blvd, Orlando, FL, 32801. Tel: 407-835-7464. Fax: 407-835-7645. p. 476

Bachtell, Deanna, Circ, Evening/Weekend Supvr, Ohio State University LIBRARIES, Marion Campus Library, 1469 Mount Vernon Ave, Marion, OH, 43302. Tel: 740-725-6327. Fax: 740-725-6309. p. 1888

Bachtold, Matthew, Dir, Upton Town Library, Two Main St, Upton, MA, 01568-1608. Tel: 508-529-6272. Fax: 508-529-2453. p. 1131

Bachus, Jill, Librn, Curtis Memorial Library, 116 S Main, Wheatland, IA, 52777. Tel: 563-374-1534. Fax: 563-374-1534. p. 852

Bacig, Maribeth, Dir, Bus Knowledge Serv, Cargill, Inc, 15407 McGinty Rd W, Wayzata, MN, 55391. Tel: 952-742-6498. Fax: 952-742-6062. p. 1287

Bacigalupo, Kathy J, Cat, Libr Supvr, Arkansas State University, 322 University Loop West Circle, State University, AR, 72401. Tel: 870-972-3077. Fax: 870-972-3199. p. 115

Bacino, Janice C, Dir of Libr Serv, University of Montana-Helena, 1115 N Roberts St, Helena, MT, 59601. Tel: 406-444-2743. Fax: 406-444-6892. p. 1383

Back, Mary Constance, Dir, Reader Serv, Rolling Meadows Library, 3110 Martin Lane, Rolling Meadows, IL, 60008. Tel: 847-259-6050. Fax: 847-259-5319. p. 698

Backenstose, Sharon, Tech Serv, United States Army, Fort Jackson Main Post Library, Thomas Lee Hall Main Post Library, Bldg 4679, Fort Jackson, SC, 29207. Tel: 803-751-4816, 803-751-5589. Fax: 803-751-1065. p. 2194

Backers, Patricia, In Charge, Merced County Library, Cressey Branch, 9257 N Cressey Way, Cressey, CA, 95312. Tel: 209-394-1456. p. 185

Backhus, Diane, Mgr, San Antonio Public Library, Johnston, 6307 Sun Valley, San Antonio, TX, 78237. Tel: 210-674-8410. p. 2382

Backlund, Doug, Database Mgr, South Dakota Department of Game, Fish & Parks Division of Wildlife, 523 E Capitol, Pierre, SD, 57501. Tel: 605-773-4345. Fax: 605-773-6245. p. 2216

Backman, Deborah, Ch, Hudson Public Library, Three Washington St at The Rotary, Hudson, MA, 01749-2499. Tel: 978-568-9645. Fax: 978-568-9646. p. 1096

Backman, Estelle, Librn, Greenberg Families Library, 21 Nadolny Sachs PR, Ottawa, ON, K2A 1R9, CANADA. Tel: 613-798-9818. Fax: 613-798-9839. p. 2831

Backs, Steve, Mgr, Ad Serv, Monroe County Public Library, 303 E Kirkwood Ave, Bloomington, IN, 47408. Tel: 812-349-3050. Fax: 812-349-3051. p. 728

Backstrom, Priscilla, Dir, Maddock Community Library, Second & Dakota Ave, Maddock, ND, 58348. Tel: 701-438-2235. Fax: 701-438-2202. p. 1845

Backus, Linda, Librn, Medical College of Wisconsin Libraries, Froedtert Hospital Library, Froedtert Specialty Clinics Bldg, 2nd Flr, 9200 W Wisconsin Ave, Milwaukee, WI, 53226. Tel: 414-805-4311. Fax: 414-805-4313. p. 2619

Bacon, Carol, Dir, Tyngsborough Public Library, 25 Bryant Lane, Tyngsboro, MA, 01879-1003. Tel: 978-649-7361. Fax: 978-649-2578. p. 1131

Bacon, Gale, Dir, Belgrade Community Library, 106 N Broadway, Belgrade, MT, 59714. Tel: 406-388-4346. Fax: 406-388-6586. p. 1373

Bacon, Jessica, YA Serv, Marlborough Public Library, 35 W Main St, Marlborough, MA, 01752-5510. Tel: 508-460-3796. Fax: 508-485-1494. p. 1103

Bacon, Kelli, Librn, Hemenway & Barnes, 60 State St, Boston, MA, 02109. Tel: 617-227-7940. Fax: 617-227-0781. p. 1062

Bacon, Maggie, Dir, Northwestern Michigan College, 1701 E Front St, Traverse City, MI, 49686-3061. Tel: 231-995-1063. Fax: 231-995-1056. p. 1231

Bacon, Tammee, Tech Serv, Northwest Regional Library, 210 LaBree Ave N, Thief River Falls, MN, 56701. Tel: 218-681-1066. Fax: 218-681-1095. p. 1286

Badal, Lala, Asst Dir, California Lutheran University, 60 W Olsen Rd, Thousand Oaks, CA, 91360-2787. Tel: 805-493-3250. Fax: 805-493-3842. p. 274

Badalamente, Stephen, Ref Serv, Columbia Basin College Library, 2600 N 20th Ave, Pasco, WA, 99301. Tel: 509-542-4553. Fax: 509-546-0401. p. 2523

Badarak, Mary, Dir, Cochiti Lake Public Library, 6515 Hoochaneetsa Blvd, Cochiti Lake, NM, 87083. Tel: 505-465-2561. Fax: 505-465-3009. p. 1553

Bade, Cristi W, Adult Serv, Ref Librn, Kershaw County Library, 1304 Broad St, Camden, SC, 29020-3595. Tel: 803-425-1508. Fax: 803-425-7180. p. 2182

Bade, Katherine, Automation Librn, Library Connection, Inc, 599 Matianuck Ave, Windsor, CT, 06095-3567. Tel: 860-298-5322. Fax: 860-298-5328. p. 2939

Baden, Diane, Head, Cat, Boston College Libraries, Thomas P O'Neill Jr Library (Central Library), 140 Commonwealth Ave, Chestnut Hill, MA, 02467. Tel: 617-552-3210. Fax: 617-552-0599. p. 1081

Baden, Marla, Head, Tech Serv & Libr Technology Serv, Indiana University-Purdue University Fort Wayne, 2101 E Coliseum Blvd, Fort Wayne, IN, 46805-1499. Tel: 260-481-6086. Fax: 260-481-6509. p. 741

Baden, Mary Kay, Tech Serv Coordr, Scott County Library System, 13090 Alabama Ave S, Savage, MN, 55378-1479. Tel: 952-707-1760. Fax: 952-707-1775. p. 1283

Bader, David, Supvr, Haynes & Boone LLP, 2323 Victory Ave, Ste 700, Dallas, TX, 75219. Tel: 214-651-5709. Fax: 214-200-0801. p. 2308

Bader, Susan Gerding, Dir, Baylor University Libraries, Mabel Peters Caruth Learning Resource Center, Louise Herrington School of Nursing, 3700 Worth St, Dallas, TX, 75246. Tel: 214-820-2100. Fax: 214-820-4770. p. 2396

Badertscher, Amy E, Dir of Libr Serv, Kenyon College Library & Information Services, 103 College Dr, Gambier, OH, 43022-9624. Tel: 740-427-5186. Fax: 740-427-5272. p. 1901

Badger, Audrey, Cat, Palmer Public Library, 655 S Valley Way, Palmer, AK, 99645. Tel: 907-745-4690. Fax: 907-746-3570. p. 52

Badger, Celeste, Head, Youth Serv, Centerville-Center Township Public Library, 126 E Main St, Centerville, IN, 47330-1206. Tel: 765-855-5223. Fax: 765-855-2009. p. 731

Badger, Terry S, Acq, Washington State Office of Secretary of State, 1129 Washington St SE, Olympia, WA, 98504-2283. Tel: 360-586-1602. Fax: 360-664-8814. p. 2523

Badgett, Adrian, Br Mgr, Pittsylvania County Public Library, Gretna Branch Library, 207 Coffey St, Gretna, VA, 24557. Tel: 434-656-2579. Fax: 434-656-9030. p. 2456

Badgley, Susan, Librn, Genesee District Library, Mount Morris Area, 685 Van Buren Ave, Mount Morris, MI, 48458. Tel: 810-686-6120. Fax: 810-686-0661. p. 1180

Badics, Joe, ILL, Eastern Michigan University, 955 W Circle Dr Library, Rm 200, Ypsilanti, MI, 48197. Tel: 734-487-0020, Ext 2053. Fax: 734-487-5399. p. 1238

Badillo, Tonya, Literacy & Diversity, Long Branch Free Public Library, 328 Broadway, Long Branch, NJ, 07740. Tel: 732-222-3900. Fax: 732-222-3799. p. 1496

Badillo, Tonya, Mgr, Ad Serv, Long Branch Free Public Library, 328 Broadway, Long Branch, NJ, 07740. Tel: 732-222-3900. Fax: 732-222-3799. p. 1496

Badiuk, Barb, Librn, Southeast Regional Library, Fort Qu'Appelle Branch, 140 Company Ave S, Fort Qu'Appelle, SK, S0G 1S0, CANADA. Tel: 306-332-6411. p. 2929

Badon, Sheila, Ch, Vermilion Parish Library, 405 E Saint Victor, Abbeville, LA, 70510-5101. Tel: 337-893-2655. Fax: 337-898-0526. p. 939

Badoud, Helen, In Charge, Pike County Public Library, Lackawaxen Township, 223 Rte 590, Greeley, PA, 18425-9718. Tel: 570-685-3100. Fax: 570-685-9450. p. 2090

Badry, Freda, Exec Dir, Edmonton Autism Society Library, 11720 Kingsway Ave, No 101, Edmonton, AB, T5G 0X5, CANADA. Tel: 780-453-3971. Fax: 780-447-4948. p. 2700

Baechler, Christine, Asst Br Supvr, Region of Waterloo Library, Baden Branch, 115 Snyder's Rd E, Baden, ON, N3A 2V4, CANADA. Tel: 519-634-8933. p. 2793

Baeckler, Virginia, Dir, Plainsboro Free Public Library, 9 Van Doren St, Plainsboro, NJ, 08536. Tel: 609-275-2899. Fax: 609-799-5883. p. 1521

Baele, Connie, Librn, Mineral-Gold Public Library District, 120 E Main St, Mineral, IL, 61344. Tel: 309-288-3971. Fax: 309-288-3971. p. 674

Baen, Karen, Dir, Libr Serv, Southwest Texas Junior College, 2401 Garner Field Rd, Uvalde, TX, 78801. Tel: 830-591-7367. Fax: 830-591-4186. p. 2394

Baenthaler, Dorothea, Head, Youth Serv, Tiverton Library Services, 238 Highland Rd, Tiverton, RI, 02878. Tel: 401-625-6796, Ext 16. Fax: 401-625-5499. p. 2176

Baenthaler, Dorothea, Head, Youth Serv, Tiverton Library Services, Union Public Library, 3832 Main Rd, Tiverton, RI, 02878-1321. Tel: 401-625-6796, Ext 16. p. 2177

Baer, Andrea, Dr, Instruction & Ref Librn, King's College, 14 W Jackson St, Wilkes-Barre, PA, 18711-0850. Tel: 570-208-5840. Fax: 570-208-6022. p. 2155

Baer, Carol, ILL, Belmont Public Library, 336 Concord Ave, Belmont, MA, 02478-0904. Tel: 617-489-2000, 617-993-2850. Fax: 617-993-2893. p. 1052

Baer, Catherine, Youth Serv Coordr, Rosemary Garfoot Public Library, 2107 Julius St, Cross Plains, WI, 53528-9499. Tel: 608-798-3881. Fax: 608-798-0196. p. 2587

Baer, D Richard, Dir, Hollywood Film Archive Library, PMB 321, 8391 Beverly Blvd, Hollywood, CA, 90048. Tel: 323-655-4968. p. 158

Baer, Eileen, Asst Dir, Bedford Hills Free Library, 26 Main St, Bedford Hills, NY, 10507-1832. Tel: 914-666-6472. Fax: 914-666-6473. p. 1579

Baer, Katherine, Govt Doc, Maryland State Law Library, Courts of Appeal Bldg, 361 Rowe Blvd, Annapolis, MD, 21401-1697. Tel: 410-260-1430. Fax: 410-260-1572, 410-974-2063. p. 1010

Baer, Margaret, Ref, Cooley Godward Kronish LLP Library, 101 California St, 5th Flr, San Francisco, CA, 94111. Tel: 415-693-2000. Fax: 415-693-2222. p. 241

Baer, Nancy, Dir, Wales Public Library, 77 Main St, Wales, MA, 01081. Tel: 413-245-9072. Fax: 413-245-9098. p. 1132

Baer, Richard, Chair, Camosun College Library, 3100 Foul Bay Rd, Victoria, BC, V8P 5J2, CANADA. Tel: 250-370-3604. Fax: 250-370-3624. p. 2745

Baer, Robert, Dir, Enumclaw Public Library, 1700 First St, Enumclaw, WA, 98022. Tel: 360-825-2938. Fax: 360-825-0825. p. 2515

Baer, Sam, Dir, E M Cooper Memorial Public Library, 5751 Rte 86, Wilmington, NY, 12997. Tel: 518-946-7701. Fax: 518-946-7701. p. 1770

Baer, Susan, Dir, Regina Qu'Appelle Health Region, 1440 14th Ave, Regina, SK, S4P 0W5, CANADA. Tel: 306-766-3830. Fax: 306-766-3839. p. 2923

Baer, William, Dir, Dixie State College of Utah, 225 S 700 E, Saint George, UT, 84770. Tel: 435-652-7711. Fax: 435-656-4169. p. 2411

Baerg, Brenda, AV, Canmore Public Library, 950 Eighth Ave, Canmore, AB, T1W 2T1, CANADA. Tel: 403-678-2468. Fax: 403-678-2165. p. 2694

Baerwald, Susan, Res Librn, Hellmuth, Obata & Kassabaum, Inc, 211 N Broadway, Ste 700, Saint Louis, MO, 63102. Tel: 314-754-4217. Fax: 314-421-6073. p. 1355

Baetz, Tracy L, Exec Dir, The Brick Store Museum, 117 Main St, Kennebunk, ME, 04043. Tel: 207-985-4802. Fax: 207-985-6887. p. 988

Baeza, Victor, Dir of Libr Grad & Res Serv, Oklahoma State University Libraries, Oklahoma State University, Athletic Ave, Stillwater, OK, 74078-1071. Tel: 405-744-1241. Fax: 405-744-5183. p. 1978

Baffigo, Carlos, Support Serv Mgr, Glendora Public Library & Cultural Center, 140 S Glendora Ave, Glendora, CA, 91741. Tel: 626-852-4827. Fax: 626-852-4899. p. 156

Bagby, Pam, Librn, Hart County Library, 150 Benson St, Hartwell, GA, 30643. Tel: 706-376-4655. Fax: 706-376-1157. p. 536

Bagby, Pamela, Asst Dir, Tech Serv, Henry County Public Library System, 1001 Florence McGarity Blvd, McDonough, GA, 30252. Tel: 678-432-5909. Fax: 678-432-6153. p. 544

Bagdasarian, Armine, ILL, Regis College Library, 235 Wellesley St, Weston, MA, 02493. Tel: 781-768-7300. Fax: 781-768-7323. p. 1139

Bagga, Purnima, Cat, Ref Serv, Gwynedd-Mercy College, 1325 Sumneytown Pike, Gwynedd Valley, PA, 19437. Tel: 215-646-7300, Ext 493. Fax: 215-641-5596. p. 2063

Baggerley, Roberta, Dir, Bayfield Carnegie Library, 37 N Broad St, Bayfield, WI, 54814-9620. Tel: 715-779-3953. Fax: 715-779-5094. p. 2580

Baggett, Judy, Librn, Edward Ward Carmack Sumner County Public Library, 658 Hartsville Pike, Gallatin, TN, 37066-2509. Tel: 615-452-1722. Fax: 615-451-3319. p. 2235

Baggett, Kelly, Actg Commun Libr Mgr, County of Los Angeles Public Library, South Whittier Library, 14433 Leffingwell Rd, Whittier, CA, 90604-2966. Tel: 562-946-4415. Fax: 562-941-6138. p. 143

Baggett, Kevin, Circ Librn, Louisiana State University Libraries, Paul M Hebert Law Center, One E Campus Dr, Baton Rouge, LA, 70803-1000. Tel: 225-578-4042. Fax: 225-578-5773. p. 944

Baggett-Heuser, Lorraine, Circ Serv, Tech Serv, Camden County College Library, College Dr, Blackwood, NJ, 08012. Tel: 856-227-7200, Ext 4417. Fax: 856-374-4897. p. 1473

Bagh, Charlotte, Govt Doc, Dallas Public Library, 1515 Young St, Dallas, TX, 75201-5499. Tel: 214-670-1400. Fax: 214-670-7839. p. 2306

Baginski, Mary Pat, Circ, ILL, Ironwood Carnegie Public Library, 235 E Aurora St, Ironwood, MI, 49938-2178. Tel: 906-932-0203. Fax: 906-932-2447. p. 1194

Bagley, Art, Coll Develop, Ref, University of Tampa, 401 W Kennedy Blvd, Tampa, FL, 33606-1490. Tel: 813-253-6231. Fax: 813-258-7426. p. 499

Bagley, Caitlin, Res & Instruction Librn, Murray State University, 205 Waterfield Library, Dean's Office, Murray, KY, 42071-3307. Tel: 270-809-6221. Fax: 270-809-3736. p. 930

Bagley, Carol Lynne, Sr Ref Librn, Chicopee Public Library, 449 Front St, Chicopee, MA, 01013. Tel: 413-594-1800, Ext 125. Fax: 413-594-1819. p. 1081

Bagley, Elizabeth Leslie, Dir, Agnes Scott College, 141 E College Ave, Decatur, GA, 30030-3770. Tel: 404-471-6339. Fax: 404-471-5037. p. 529

Bagley, Laurie, Librn, Alta Bates Medical Center, Ashby Health Sciences Library, 2450 Ashby Ave, Berkeley, CA, 94705. Tel: 510-204-4444. Fax: 510-204-4091. p. 126

Bagley, Laurie, Librn, Alta Bates Medical Center, Herrick Health Sciences Library, 2001 Dwight Way, Berkeley, CA, 94704. Tel: 510-204-4444. Fax: 510-204-3521. p. 126

Bagley, Michelle, Dean, Libr Serv, eLearning, Tutoring & Fac Develop, Clark College, Mail Stop LIB 112, 1933 Fort Vancouver Way, Vancouver, WA, 98663-3598. Tel: 360-992-2151. Fax: 360-992-2869. p. 2545

Bagnall, Anne, Commun Libr Mgr, Queens Borough Public Library, Sunnyside Community Library, 43-06 Greenpoint Ave, Long Island City, NY, 11104. Tel: 718-784-3033. p. 1645

Bagnato, Halle, Ch, Hudson Library & Historical Society, 96 Library St, Hudson, OH, 44236-5122. Tel: 330-653-6658. Fax: 330-650-3373. p. 1905

Bagwell, Millie, Librn, Crossville Public Library, 80 Gaines St, Crossville, AL, 35962-3455. Tel: 256-528-2628. Fax: 256-528-2628. p. 13

Bagwell, Paula, Librn, Saint Petersburg College, Clearwater Campus Library, 2465 Drew St, Clearwater, FL, 33765. Tel: 727-791-2415. Fax: 727-791-2601. p. 483

Bagwell, Rhonda, Librn, Barton Library, Strong Public, 246 Second Ave, Strong, AR, 71765. Tel: 870-797-2165. Fax: 870-797-2165. p. 98

Bahi, Zineb, Asst Librn, Laboratoire de Sciences Judiciaires et de Medicine Legale, Ministere de la Securite Publique Edifice Wilfrid Derome, 1701 rue Parthenais, 12th Flr, Montreal, QC, H2K 3S7, CANADA. Tel: 514-873-3301, Ext 61565. Fax: 514-873-4847. p. 2897

Bahlinger, Thomas, Coll Develop Librn, Instrul Serv Librn, San Antonio College, 1001 Howard St, San Antonio, TX, 78212. Tel: 210-486-0554. Fax: 210-486-0568. p. 2381

Bahmanyar, Suzie, Med Librn, O'Connor Hospital Medical Library, 2105 Forest Ave, San Jose, CA, 95128. Tel: 408-947-2647. Fax: 408-947-3428. p. 250

Bahn, Gilbert S, Dr, In Charge, Schuyler Technical Library, 4519 N Ashtree St, Moorpark, CA, 93021. Tel: 805-529-7922. p. 191

Bahnaman, Steve, Electronic Res Librn, Ref, Campbell University, 113 Main St, Buies Creek, NC, 27506. Tel: 910-893-1460. Fax: 910-893-1470. p. 1778

Bahner, Jean, Ref Serv, Bosler Free Library, 158 W High St, Carlisle, PA, 17013-2988. Tel: 717-243-4642. Fax: 717-243-8281. p. 2041

Bahner, Jean, Librn, State Correctional Institution, 1111 Altamont Blvd, Frackville, PA, 17931. Tel: 570-874-4516. p. 2058

Bahr, Cindy, Dir, Forreston Public Library, 204 First Ave, Forreston, IL, 61030. Tel: 815-938-2624. Fax: 815-938-2152. p. 646

Bahr, Ellen, Info Syst, Alfred University, Herrick Memorial Library, One Saxon Dr, Alfred, NY, 14802. Tel: 607-871-2976. Fax: 607-871-2299. p. 1572

Bahre, Dorothy, Asst Librn, Nashville Public Library, 219 E Elm St, Nashville, IL, 62263-1711. Tel: 618-327-3827. Fax: 618-327-4820. p. 679

Bahret, Karla, Circ Librn, Silver Lake Library, 203 Railroad St, Silver Lake, KS, 66539. Tel: 785-582-5141. Fax: 785-582-4282. p. 894

Bahringer, Annie, Adult Serv, W J Niederkorn Library, 316 W Grand Ave, Port Washington, WI, 53074-2293. Tel: 262-284-5031. Fax: 262-284-7680. p. 2631

Bahu, Rebecca, Br Coordr, Saint Joseph County Public Library, 304 S Main, South Bend, IN, 46601-2125. Tel: 574-282-4646. Fax: 574-280-2763. p. 779

Bai, Sheryl, Network Serv, University of Connecticut Health Center, 263 Farmington Ave, Farmington, CT, 06034. Tel: 860-679-8371. Fax: 860-679-4046. p. 340

Baier, Susan, Youth & Extn Serv Div Mgr, Santa Clara City Library, 2635 Homestead Rd, Santa Clara, CA, 95051. Tel: 408-615-2921. Fax: 408-247-9657. p. 262

Baikie, Dee, Ch, Homewood Public Library, 17917 Dixie Hwy, Homewood, IL, 60430-1703. Tel: 708-798-0121. Fax: 708-798-0662. p. 657

Bailen, Linda, ILL, Northern Waters Library Service, 3200 E Lakeshore Dr, Ashland, WI, 54806-2510. Tel: 715-682-2365. Fax: 715-685-2704. p. 2579

Bailey, Alicia, Libr Asst I, Montgomery City-County Public Library System, Juliette Hampton Morgan Memorial Library (Main Library), 245 High St, Montgomery, AL, 36104. Tel: 334-240-4999. Fax: 334-240-4980. p. 30

Bailey, Alvin R, Dir, Denison Public Library, 300 W Gandy St, Denison, TX, 75020-3153. Tel: 903-465-1797. Fax: 903-465-1130. p. 2312

Bailey, Amanda, Ch, Washington County Public Library, 205 Oak Hill St, Abingdon, VA, 24210. Tel: 276-676-6382. Fax: 276-676-6235. p. 2443

Bailey, Amy, Librn, Missouri State Court of Appeals, University Plaza, 300 Hammons Pkwy, Springfield, MO, 65806. Tel: 417-895-6813. Fax: 417-895-6817. p. 1366

Bailey, Ann, Asst Librn, Watertown Regional Library, 160 Sixth St NE, Watertown, SD, 57201-2778. Tel: 605-882-6220. Fax: 605-882-6221. p. 2221

Bailey, Anne, Dir, Br Libr, Toronto Public Library, 789 Yonge St, Toronto, ON, M4W 2G8, CANADA. Tel: 416-393-7131. Fax: 416-393-7229. p. 2860

Bailey, Barbara, Circ, Chester County Library System, 450 Exton Square Pkwy, Exton, PA, 19341-2496. Tel: 610-280-2600. Fax: 610-280-2688. p. 2056

Bailey, Barbara J, Dir, Welles-Turner Memorial Library, 2407 Main St, Glastonbury, CT, 06033. Tel: 860-652-7719. Fax: 860-652-7721. p. 340

Bailey, Barry, Ref/Digital Librn, Johnson County Community College, 12345 College Blvd, Box 21, Overland Park, KS, 66210. Tel: 913-469-8500, Ext 4841. Fax: 913-469-3816. p. 888

Bailey, Becky, Dir, Red River Regional Library, 1753A Alpine Dr, Clarksville, TN, 37040-6729. Tel: 931-645-9531. Fax: 931-645-6695. p. 2229

Bailey, Becky, Regional Mgr, Tennessee State Library & Archives, 403 Seventh Ave N, Nashville, TN, 37243-0312. Tel: 615-741-2764. Fax: 615-532-2472, 615-741-6471. p. 2259

Bailey, Bernadette, Librn, American Federation of Teachers Library, 555 New Jersey Ave NW, Washington, DC, 20001-2079. Tel: 202-879-4481. Fax: 202-879-4406. p. 392

Bailey, Billy, Librn, Lebanon Correctional Institution Library, 3791 State Rd 63, PO Box 56, Lebanon, OH, 45036. Tel: 513-932-1211, Ext 3728. Fax: 513-932-5803. p. 1909

Bailey, Camilla, Tech Serv, Elbert County Public Library, 345 Heard St, Elberton, GA, 30635. Tel: 706-283-5375. Fax: 706-283-5456. p. 532

Bailey, Carla, ILL, University of Mary Washington, 1801 College Ave, Fredericksburg, VA, 22401-4665. Tel: 540-654-1147. Fax: 540-654-1067. p. 2466

Bailey, Carol, Br Mgr, Jacksonville Public Library, Pablo Creek, 13295 Beach Blvd, Jacksonville, FL, 32246-7259. Tel: 904-992-7101. Fax: 904-992-3987. p. 454

Bailey, Carol, Librn, Kaplan University Hagerstown Library, 18618 Crestwood Dr, Hagerstown, MD, 21742. Tel: 301-766-3701. Fax: 301-791-7661. p. 1031

Bailey, Cheryl M, Dir, University of Mary, 7500 University Dr, Bismarck, ND, 58504-9652. Tel: 701-355-8070. Fax: 701-355-8255. p. 1838

Bailey, Chris H, Curator, American Clock & Watch Museum, Inc, 100 Maple St, Bristol, CT, 06010-5092. Tel: 860-583-6070. Fax: 860-583-1862. p. 332

Bailey, Christina, ILL, Smyrna Public Library, 100 Village Green Circle, Smyrna, GA, 30080-3478. Tel: 770-431-2860. Fax: 770-431-2862. p. 551

Bailey, Cindy, Br Mgr, Lancaster Public Library, Lancaster Public Library East - Leola Branch, 46 Hillcrest Ave, Leola, PA, 17540. Tel: 717-656-7920. p. 2077

Bailey, Clare, Tech Serv, Bureau of National Affairs, Inc Library, 1801 S Bell St, Rm 3200, Arlington, VA, 22202. Tel: 703-341-3306. Fax: 703-341-1636. p. 2449

Bailey, Crystal, Br Mgr, Whitman County Rural Library District, Garfield Branch, 109 N Third, Garfield, WA, 99130. Tel: 509-635-1490. p. 2513

Bailey, Deborah, Librn, Richards Memorial Library, 44 Richards Ave, Paxton, MA, 01612. Tel: 508-754-0793. Fax: 508-754-0793. p. 1116

Bailey, Delphine, Librn, Reese Unity District Library, 2065 Gates St, Reese, MI, 48757-9580. Tel: 989-868-4120. Fax: 989-868-4123. p. 1221

Bailey, Diane, Asst Librn, Mooneyham Public Library, 240 E Main St, Forest City, NC, 28043. Tel: 828-248-5224. Fax: 828-248-5224. p. 1794

Bailey, Donna, Ad, Richton Park Public Library District, 4045 Sauk Trail, Richton Park, IL, 60471. Tel: 708-481-5333. Fax: 708-481-4343. p. 694

Bailey, Ellen, Librn, Pope & McGlamry, 3455 Peachtree Rd NE, Ste 925, Atlanta, GA, 30326. Tel: 404-523-7706. Fax: 404-524-1648. p. 518

Bailey, Eric, Dir, Lake Bluff Public Library, 123 E Scranton Ave, Lake Bluff, IL, 60044. Tel: 847-234-2540. Fax: 847-234-2649. p. 663

Bailey, Gwen, Syst Librn, Malaspina University-College Library, 900 Fifth St, Nanaimo, BC, V9R 5S5, CANADA. Tel: 250-753-3245, Ext 2444. Fax: 250-740-6473. p. 2732

Bailey, Gwen Putnam, Ad, Rye Public Library, 581 Washington Rd, Rye, NH, 03870. Tel: 603-964-8401. Fax: 603-964-7065. p. 1464

Bailey, Heather, Br Mgr, Stanislaus County Free Library, Empire Branch, 18 S Abbie, Empire, CA, 95319. Tel: 209-524-5505. Fax: 209-524-5505. p. 188

Bailey, Jane Marie, Dir, Columbiana Public Library, 50 Lester St, Columbiana, AL, 35051. Tel: 205-669-5812. Fax: 205-669-5803. p. 13

Bailey, Janet, Access Serv, Curric Center Librn, Oklahoma Baptist University, 500 W University, OBU Box 61310, Shawnee, OK, 74804-2504. Tel: 405-878-2249. Fax: 405-878-2256. p. 1977

Bailey, Janet, Operations Mgr, Manheim Township Public Library, 595 Granite Run Dr, Lancaster, PA, 17601. Tel: 717-560-6441. Fax: 717-560-0570. p. 2077

Bailey, Janet, Head, Tech Serv, ILL, Abilene Public Library, 202 Cedar St, Abilene, TX, 79601-5793. Tel: 352-676-6063. p. 2271

Bailey, Janice, Librn, Stockton-San Joaquin County Public Library, Maya Angelou Branch, 2324 Pock Lane, Stockton, CA, 95205. Tel: 209-937-7701. Fax: 209-937-7702. p. 273

Bailey, Jeff, Head, Pub Serv, Interim Dean, Arkansas State University, 322 University Loop West Circle, State University, AR, 72401. Tel: 870-972-2724. Fax: 870-972-3199. p. 115

Bailey, JoAnn, Tech Serv Supvr, Lake City Community College, 149 SE College Pl, Lake City, FL, 32025-2006. Tel: 386-754-4338. Fax: 386-754-4837. p. 457

Bailey, Joanna, Dir, Neill Public Library, 210 N Grand Ave, Pullman, WA, 99163-2693. Tel: 509-334-3595. Fax: 509-334-6051. p. 2524

Bailey, Joanna M, Dir, Libr Serv, Bay Minette Public Library, 205 W Second St, Bay Minette, AL, 36507. Tel: 251-580-1648. Fax: 251-937-0339. p. 6

Bailey, Kathy, Asst Dir, Pub Serv, Tuscaloosa Public Library, 1801 Jack Warner Pkwy, Tuscaloosa, AL, 35401-1027. Tel: 205-345-5820, Ext 201. Fax: 205-752-8300. p. 38

Bailey, Kathy, ILL/Circ Supvr, Alverno College Library, 3401 S 39th St, Milwaukee, WI, 53215. Tel: 414-382-6397. Fax: 414-382-6354. p. 2617

Bailey, Kimberly, Ref & Instruction Librn, University of Pittsburgh at Bradford, 300 Campus Dr, Bradford, PA, 16701. Tel: 814-362-7610. Fax: 814-362-7688. p. 2037

Bailey, Larry, Librn, Parkland Regional Library, Earl Grey Branch, Main St, Earl Grey, SK, S0A 1J0, CANADA. Tel: 306-939-2212. p. 2931

Bailey, Linda, Curator, Photog & Prints, Cincinnati Museum Center At Union Terminal, 1301 Western Ave, Cincinnati, OH, 45203. Tel: 513-287-7094. Fax: 513-287-7095. p. 1869

Bailey, Lisa, Br Mgr, McKinney Memorial Public Library, John & Judy Gay Library, 6861 W Eldorado Pkwy, McKinney, TX, 75070-5637. Tel: 972-547-2020. p. 2361

Bailey, Lisa B, Tech Serv, Brown McCarroll, LLP Library, 111 Congress Ave, Ste 1400, Austin, TX, 78701-4043. Tel: 512-370-3377. Fax: 512-479-1101. p. 2279

Bailey, Lois A, Dir, Fleetwood Area Public Library, 110 W Arch St, Ste 209, Fleetwood, PA, 19522-1301. Tel: 610-944-0146. Fax: 610-944-9064. p. 2057

Bailey, Lori, Circ, Wanaque Public Library, 616 Ringwood Ave, Wanaque, NJ, 07465. Tel: 973-839-4434, Ext 104. Fax: 973-839-8904. p. 1539

Bailey, Louise, Dir, Mansfield Public Library, 54 Warrenville Rd, Mansfield Center, CT, 06250. Tel: 860-423-2501. Fax: 860-423-9856. p. 350

Bailey, Lugene, Per, Ref, Central State University, 1400 Brush Row Rd, Wilberforce, OH, 45384. Tel: 937-376-6394. Fax: 937-376-6132. p. 1948

Bailey, M Linda, Librn, Porterville College Library, 100 E College Ave, Porterville, CA, 93257-5901. Tel: 559-791-2293. Fax: 559-791-2289. p. 212

Bailey, Mara, Tech Serv, Franklin T Degroodt Library, 6475 Minton Rd SW, Palm Bay, FL, 32908. Tel: 321-952-6317. Fax: 321-952-6320. p. 479

Bailey, Marilyn, Asst Dir, Lester Public Library of Rome, 1157 Rome Center Dr, Nekoosa, WI, 54457. Tel: 715-325-8990. Fax: 715-325-8993. p. 2624

Bailey, Marjorie, Librn, Doyle Public Library District, 109 S O'Bannon, Raymond, IL, 62560-5190. Tel: 217-229-4471. p. 694

Bailey, Marnie, Librn, Fasken Martineau DuMoulin LLP Library, 2900-550 Burrard St, Vancouver, BC, V6C 0A3, CANADA. Tel: 604-631-3131. Fax: 604-631-3232. p. 2741

Bailey, Mary W, Ref Serv Coordr, Virginia State University, One Hayden Dr, Petersburg, VA, 23806-0001. Tel: 804-524-6821. Fax: 804-524-6959. p. 2484

Bailey, Nancy, Dir, Byron-Bergen Public Library, 13 S Lake Ave, Bergen, NY, 14416-9420. Tel: 585-494-1120. Fax: 585-494-2339. p. 1581

Bailey, Patricia, Adult Serv, Circ, Meadville Public Library, 848 N Main St, Meadville, PA, 16335-2689. Tel: 814-336-1773. Fax: 814-333-8173. p. 2086

Bailey, Patty M, Librn, Coffeeville Public Library, 714 Main St, Coffeeville, MS, 38922-2590. Tel: 662-675-8822. Fax: 662-675-2001. p. 1296

Bailey, Peggy, Youth Serv, Ashe County Public Library, 148 Library Dr, West Jefferson, NC, 28694. Tel: 336-846-2041. Fax: 336-846-7503. p. 1829

Bailey, Peter, Libr Dir, St Albert Public Library, Five Saint Anne St, St. Albert, AB, T8N 3Z9, CANADA. Tel: 780-459-1530. Fax: 780-458-5772. p. 2717

Bailey, Ray, Coordr, Instrul Tech, Interim Dir, Instrul Serv, Morehead State University, 150 University Blvd, Morehead, KY, 40351. Tel: 606-783-5106. Fax: 606-783-5037. p. 929

Bailey, Rebecca, Res & Instruction Librn, Northeastern University Libraries, Snell Library, 360 Huntington Ave, Boston, MA, 02115. Tel: 617-373-2344. p. 1065

Bailey, Sally, Early Childhood Librn, Akron-Summit County Public Library, North Hill, 183 E Cuyahoga Falls Ave, Akron, OH, 44310-3078. Tel: 330-535-9423. Fax: 330-376-5661. p. 1852

Bailey, Sandra, Tech Serv Librn, San Marcos Public Library, 625 E Hopkins, San Marcos, TX, 78666. Tel: 512-393-8200. p. 2384

Bailey, Scott, Managing Librn, Squire, Sanders & Dempsey Library, 1201 Pennsylvania Ave NW, Ste 500, Washington, DC, 20044. Tel: 202-626-6708. Fax: 202-626-6780. p. 416

Bailey, Sena, Govt Doc, Colby Community College, 1255 S Range Ave, Colby, KS, 67701. Tel: 785-462-3984, Ext 5494. Fax: 785-460-4600. p. 861

Bailey, Sherryl, Ref Serv, YA, Derry Public Library, 64 E Broadway, Derry, NH, 03038-2412. Tel: 603-432-6140. Fax: 603-432-6128. p. 1444

Bailey, Steve, Syst Librn, William Jewell College, 500 College Hill, Liberty, MO, 64068-1843. Tel: 816-415-7609. Fax: 816-415-5021. p. 1343

Bailey, Tim, Automation Librn, Auburn University, 7440 East Dr, Montgomery, AL, 36117. Tel: 334-244-3200. Fax: 334-244-3720. p. 28

Bailey, Tracey, Exec Dir, Health Law Institute Library, University of Alberta, Law Centre, Edmonton, AB, T6G 2H5, CANADA. Tel: 780-248-1175. Fax: 780-492-9575. p. 2701

Bailey, Virginia, Ref, Abilene Christian University, 221 Brown Library, ACU Box 29208, Abilene, TX, 79699-9208. Tel: 325-674-2344. Fax: 325-674-2202. p. 2271

Bailey, Vivian, Asst Librn, Adelphi University, 55 Kennedy Dr, Hauppauge, NY, 11788-4001. Tel: 516-237-8610. Fax: 516-237-8613. p. 1634

Bailie, Coleen, Head, Tech Serv, West Haven Public Library, 300 Elm St, West Haven, CT, 06516-4692. Tel: 203-937-4233. p. 377

Bailie, Cynthia, Dir, Foundation Center-Cleveland Library, 1422 Euclid Ave, Ste 1600, Cleveland, OH, 44115-2001. Tel: 216-861-1934. Fax: 216-861-1936. p. 1880

Baillargeon, Daniele, Coll Develop, Dir, Ref, Cegep de Trois-Rivieres Bibliotheque, 3175 Laviolette, Trois-Rivieres, QC, G9A 5E6, CANADA. Tel: 819-376-1721, Ext 2609. Fax: 819-693-3844. p. 2914

Baillie, Barbara, Librn, Mullan Public Library, 117 Hunter Ave, Mullan, ID, 83846. Tel: 208-744-1220. Fax: 208-744-1220. p. 580

Bailon, Kathy, Libr Dir, Fashion Institute of Design & Merchandising Library, 55 Stockton St, 5th Flr, San Francisco, CA, 94108-5829. Tel: 415-675-5200. Fax: 415-989-5312. p. 242

Baily, Scott, Dir, Acad Computing & Networking Serv, Colorado State University Libraries, Morgan Library, 1201 Center Avenue Mall, Fort Collins, CO, 80523-. Tel: 970-491-1838. Fax: 970-491-1195. p. 307

Baima, Thomas, Chair, Association of Chicago Theological Schools, Univ of St Mary of the Lake, 1000 E Maple Ave, Mundelein, IL, 60060. Tel: 847-970-4860. p. 2942

Bain, Allison, Ch, Nicholas P Sims Library, 515 W Main, Waxahachie, TX, 75165-3235. Tel: 972-937-2671. Fax: 972-937-4409. p. 2398

Bain, June, Librn, Hunter Public Library, 7965 Main St, Hunter, NY, 12442. Tel: 518-263-4655. Fax: 518-263-4655. p. 1639

Bain, Larry, Dir, Fort Scott Community College Library, 2108 S Horton, Fort Scott, KS, 66701. Tel: 620-223-2700, Ext 401. Fax: 620-223-6530. p. 867

Bain, Laurel, Librn, Gunnison Public Library of the Gunnison County Library District, 307 N Wisconsin, Gunnison, CO, 81230-2627. Tel: 970-641-3485. Fax: 970-641-4653. p. 312

Bain, Michael, Dir, Atlanta Christian College, 2605 Ben Hill Rd, East Point, GA, 30344-1999. Tel: 404-669-2097. Fax: 404-669-4009. p. 531

Bain, Paul, Ref Serv, Harvard Library, Francis A Countway Library of Medicine, Boston Med Libr-Harvard Med Libr, Ten Shattuck St, Boston, MA, 02115. Tel: 617-432-4807. p. 1074

Bain, Tim, Br Mgr, Broward County Division of Libraries, Dania Beach-Paul DeMaio Library, One Park Ave E, Dania Beach, FL, 33004. Tel: 954-357-7073. p. 441

Bainbridge, Joanne, Br Head, Toronto Public Library, Malvern, 30 Sewells Rd, Toronto, ON, M1B 3G5, CANADA. Tel: 416-396-8969. Fax: 416-396-3560. p. 2862

Baines, Florence, Circ Media, Tidewater Community College Learning Resources Center, 300 Granby St, Norfolk, VA, 23510. Tel: 757-822-1124. Fax: 757-822-1106. p. 2483

Bains, Sneh P, Dir, Free Public Library of Bayonne, 697 Avenue C, Bayonne, NJ, 07002. Tel: 201-858-6970. Fax: 201-437-6928. p. 1470

Bainum, Bobbie, Assoc Librn, Mount Ayr Public Library, 121 W Monroe St, Mount Ayr, IA, 50854. Tel: 641-464-2159. Fax: 641-464-2159. p. 833

Baione, Tom, Harold Boeschenstein Dir, American Museum of Natural History Library, 79th St & Central Park W, New York, NY, 10024-5192. Tel: 212-769-5417. Fax: 212-769-5009. p. 1668

Bair, Brinda, Librn, Garfield County-Panguitch City Library, 25 S 200 E, Panguitch, UT, 84759. Tel: 435-676-2431. Fax: 435-676-2758. p. 2410

Bair, David, Cat, Brookings Institution Library, 1775 Massachusetts Ave NW, Washington, DC, 20036. Tel: 202-797-6240. Fax: 202-797-2970. p. 394

Bair, Jeannette, Librn, Rochester Public Library, PO Box 256, Rochester, VT, 05767. Tel: 802-767-3927. p. 2434

Bair, Sherrilynn, Dir, Snake River School Community Library, 924 W Hwy 39, Blackfoot, ID, 83221. Tel: 208-684-3063. Fax: 208-684-3141. p. 569

Baird, Candy, Asst Dir, Delta Public Library, 402 Main St, Delta, OH, 43515-1304. Tel: 419-822-3110. Fax: 419-822-5310. p. 1896

Baird, Caroline, Librn, Waynoka Public Library, 113 E Cecil St, Waynoka, OK, 73860. Tel: 580-824-6181. Fax: 580-824-6181. p. 1985

Baird, Caryn, Res, Times Publishing Co, 490 First Ave S, Saint Petersburg, FL, 33701-4223. Tel: 727-893-8111. Fax: 727-893-8107. p. 488

Baird, Joanne, Librn, Montreal Children's Hospital, 2300 Tupper St, Montreal, QC, H3H 1P3, CANADA. Tel: 514-412-4400, Ext 22054. Fax: 514-412-4345. p. 2899

Baird, Laura, Br Supvr, Spokane County Library District, Medical Lake Library, 321 E Herb, Medical Lake, WA, 99022. Tel: 509-893-8330. Fax: 509-893-8479. p. 2537

Baird, Lynn, Dr, Dean, Libr Serv, University of Idaho Library, Rayburn St, Moscow, ID, 83844. Tel: 208-885-6534. Fax: 208-885-7070. p. 579

Baird, Robin, Ref Serv, United States Department of the Army, CEHEC-ZL Casey Bldg, 7701 Telegraph Rd, Alexandria, VA, 22315-3860. Tel: 703-428-6388. Fax: 703-428-6310. p. 2446

Baird, Sandy, Coordr, Archives & Spec Coll, Georgetown College, 400 E College St, Georgetown, KY, 40324. Tel: 502-863-8410. Fax: 502-868-7740. p. 915

Baird, Sara, Head, Access & Licensing Serv, San Diego State University Library & Information Access, 5500 Campanile Dr, San Diego, CA, 92182-8050. Tel: 619-594-2530. Fax: 619-594-3270. p. 237

Baird, Stephanie Ann, Mgr, Ch Serv, Tuscarawas County Public Library, 121 Fair Ave NW, New Philadelphia, OH, 44663-2600. Tel: 330-364-4474. Fax: 330-364-8217. p. 1921

Baird-Adams, Jan, Mgr, Montgomery County Public Libraries, White Oak Library, 11701 New Hampshire Ave, Silver Spring, MD, 20904-2898. Tel: 240-777-9558. Fax: 301-989-1921. p. 1039

Bairefoot, Elanya K, Ref & ILL Librn, Eau Gallie Public Library, 1521 Pineapple Ave, Melbourne, FL, 32935-6594. Tel: 321-255-4304. Fax: 321-255-4323. p. 463

Baisley, Caroline, Dir, Greenwich Department of Health Library, 101 Field Point Rd, Greenwich, CT, 06836. Tel: 203-622-6488. Fax: 203-622-7770. p. 341

Baize, Christine, Libr Asst III, Kings County Library, Lemoore Branch, 457 C St, Lemoore, CA, 93245. Tel: 559-924-2188. Fax: 559-924-1521. p. 156

Bajjaly, Stephen T, Dr, Assoc Dean, Wayne State University, 106 Kresge Library, Detroit, MI, 48202. Tel: 313-577-0350. Fax: 313-577-7563. p. 2967

Bajrami, Ericka, Ch, Licia & Mason Beekley Community Library, Ten Central Ave, New Hartford, CT, 06057. Tel: 860-379-7235. Fax: 860-379-5806. p. 355

Bajus, Tamara, Librn, Border Regional Library, Elkhorn Branch, 110 Richhill Ave, Elkhorn, MB, R0M 0N0, CANADA. Tel: 204-845-2292. p. 2753

Bajwa, Zaheer, Librn, Ahmadiyya Movement In Islam Inc, 2141 LeRoy Pl NW, Washington, DC, 20008. Tel: 202-232-3737. Fax: 202-232-8181. p. 391

Baker, Alison, Dir, Kelley Library, 234 Main St, Salem, NH, 03079-3190. Tel: 603-898-7064. Fax: 603-898-8583. p. 1464

Baker, Amia, Dir, Fayette County Memorial Library, 326 Temple Ave N, Fayette, AL, 35555. Tel: 205-932-6625. Fax: 205-932-4152. p. 17

Baker, Amy, Cat Tech, Central New Mexico Community College Libraries, 525 Buena Vista SE, Albuquerque, NM, 87106-4023. Tel: 505-224-3292. Fax: 505-224-3321. p. 1548

Baker, Angela, Dir, Gerontological Society of America, 1220 L St NW, No 901, Washington, DC, 20005. Tel: 202-289-9806, Ext 125. Fax: 202-289-9824. p. 403

Baker, Ann, Head, Med Libr, Captain James A Lovell Federal Health Care Center, 3001 Green Bay Rd, North Chicago, IL, 60064. Tel: 224-610-3757. p. 681

Baker, Anne, Electronic Res & Ref Librn, Rosalind Franklin University of Medicine & Science, 3333 Green Bay Rd, North Chicago, IL, 60064. Tel: 847-578-8642. Fax: 847-578-3401. p. 682

Baker, Ariana, Dir, Libr Serv, Warren County Community College Library, 475 Rte 57 W, Washington, NJ, 07882-4343. Tel: 908-835-2339. Fax: 908-835-1283. p. 1539

Baker, Barbara, AV, Lima Public Library, 650 W Market St, Lima, OH, 45801. Tel: 419-228-5113. Fax: 419-224-2669. p. 1910

Baker, Barry, Info Tech, North Chicago Public Library, 2100 Argonne Dr, North Chicago, IL, 60064. Tel: 847-689-0125. Fax: 847-689-9117. p. 682

Baker, Barry B, Dir of Libr, University of Central Florida Libraries, 4000 Central Florida Blvd, Bldg 2, Orlando, FL, 32816-2666. Tel: 407-823-2564. Fax: 407-823-2529. p. 477

Baker, Becky, Dir, Seward Memorial Library, 233 S Fifth St, Seward, NE, 68434. Tel: 402-643-3318. p. 1419

Baker, Benjamin, Libr Asst, Manchester Historic Association Library, 129 Amherst St, Manchester, NH, 03101. Tel: 603-622-7531. p. 1456

Baker, Beth, Dir, Dickinson County Library, 401 Iron Mountain St, Iron Mountain, MI, 49801-3435. Tel: 906-774-1218. Fax: 906-774-4079. p. 1193

Baker, Betsy, Dir, Milton Free Public Library, 13 Main St, Milton Mills, NH, 03852. Tel: 603-473-8535. p. 1458

Baker, Betty, Br Operations Coordr, University of New Mexico, 200 College Rd, Gallup, NM, 87301. Tel: 505-863-7656. Fax: 505-863-7624. p. 1556

Baker, Betty, Circ, Chillicothe & Ross County Public Library, Bainbridge Paxton Township, 204 N Quarry St, Bainbridge, OH, 45612. Tel: 740-702-4185. Fax: 740-702-4186. p. 1867

Baker, Bo, Ref & Instruction Librn, University of Tennessee at Chattanooga Library, 615 McCallie Ave, Dept 6456, Chattanooga, TN, 37403-2598. Tel: 423-425-4501. Fax: 423-425-4775. p. 2228

Baker, Brad, Libr Tech, Colorado Mountain College, 3000 County Rd 114, Glenwood Springs, CO, 81601. Tel: 970-947-8271. Fax: 970-947-8288. p. 309

Baker, Bradley, Circ Mgr, Belmont Abbey College, 100 Belmont-Mt Holly Rd, Belmont, NC, 28012. Tel: 704-461-6748. Fax: 704-461-6743. p. 1776

Baker, Brandon, II, Ref Librn, California Western School of Law Library, 290 Cedar St, San Diego, CA, 92101. Tel: 619-525-1425. Fax: 619-685-2918. p. 231

Baker, Caitlin, Ref Librn, Flagler College, 44 Sevilla St, Saint Augustine, FL, 32084-4302. Tel: 904-819-6206. Fax: 904-823-8511. p. 486

Baker, Camilla, Instrul Serv Librn, Augusta State University, 2500 Walton Way, Augusta, GA, 30904-2200. Tel: 706-737-1745. Fax: 706-667-4415. p. 518

Baker, Carole, Mgr, Saint Elizabeth Medical Center, 20 Medical Village Dr, Ste 201, Edgewood, KY, 41017. Tel: 859-301-2248. Fax: 859-301-2655. p. 911

Baker, Carolyn, Head of Libr, Margaret Clark Gilbreath Library, 9601 Interstate 630, Exit 7, Little Rock, AR, 72205. Tel: 501-202-2671. Fax: 501-202-1318. p. 107

Baker, Carolyn, Librn, Missouri Department of Corrections, Ozark Correctional Center, 929 Honor Camp Lane, Fordland, MO, 65652-9700. Tel: 417-767-4491. Fax: 417-738-2400. p. 1335

Baker, Carolyn, Ch, Beatrice Public Library, 100 N 16th St, Beatrice, NE, 68310-4100. Tel: 402-223-3584. Fax: 402-223-3913. p. 1393

Baker, Carolyn, Coordr, Acq, East Carolina University, William E Laupus Health Sciences Library, 600 Moye Blvd, Health Sciences Bldg, Greenville, NC, 27834. Tel: 252-744-2221. Fax: 252-744-2672. p. 1799

Baker, Cheryl, County Librn, Modoc County Library, 212 W Third St, Alturas, CA, 96101. Tel: 530-233-6340. Fax: 530-233-3375. p. 120

Baker, Cheryl, Librn, South China Public Library, 247 Village St, South China, ME, 04358. Tel: 207-445-3094. p. 1001

Baker, Christine, Cataloger/Ref Librn, Colorado School of Mines, 1400 Illinois St, Golden, CO, 80401-1887. Tel: 303-273-3446. Fax: 303-273-3199. p. 309

Baker, Christine, Librn, FDA Biosciences Library, 5100 Paint Branch Pkwy, College Park, MD, 20740. Tel: 240-402-1878. Fax: 301-436-2653. p. 1024

Baker, Clara, Dir, Bass Harbor Memorial Library, 89 Bernard Rd, Bernard, ME, 04612. Tel: 207-244-3798. p. 977

Baker, Claudia, Dir of Develop, The Kansas City Public Library, 14 W Tenth St, Kansas City, MO, 64105. Tel: 816-701-3518. Fax: 816-701-3401. p. 1338

Baker, Colleen, Br Mgr, San Diego County Library, Julian Branch, 1850 Hwy 78, Julian, CA, 92036. Tel: 760-765-0370. Fax: 760-765-2748. p. 234

Baker, Courtney, Libr Asst II, Montgomery City-County Public Library System, Hampstead Branch Library, 5251 Hampstead High St, Ste 107, Montgomery, AL, 36116. Tel: 334-244-5770. Fax: 334-244-5773. p. 29

Baker, Darlene, Supvr, Essex County Library, Cottam Branch, 122 Fox St, Cottam, ON, N0R 1B0, CANADA. Tel: 226-946-1529, Ext 212. p. 2804

Baker, Deana, In Charge, Beth Sholom Congregation, 8231 Old York Rd, Elkins Park, PA, 19027. Tel: 215-887-1342. Fax: 215-887-6605. p. 2053

Baker, Deborah, Adminr, University of Georgia, 225 Herty Dr, Athens, GA, 30602-6018. Tel: 706-542-1922. Fax: 706-542-5001. p. 510

Baker, Debra, Dir, Wolfe County Library, 176 Kentucky Hwy 15 N, Campton, KY, 41301. Tel: 606-668-6571. Fax: 606-668-6561. p. 909

Baker, Diana, Tech Serv, Coalinga-Huron USD Library District, 305 N Fourth St, Coalinga, CA, 93210. Tel: 559-935-1676. Fax: 559-935-1058. p. 135

Baker, Diane, Ref Librn, Lake Michigan College, 2755 E Napier Ave, Benton Harbor, MI, 49022. Tel: 269-927-8605. Fax: 269-927-6656. p. 1156

Baker, Donna, Head, Spec Coll & Archives, Morehead State University, 150 University Blvd, Morehead, KY, 40351. Tel: 606-783-5122. Fax: 606-783-5037. p. 929

Baker, Doris, Acq, Asst Dir, Grundy County-Jewett Norris Library, 1331 Main St, Trenton, MO, 64683. Tel: 660-359-3577. Fax: 660-359-6220. p. 1368

Baker, Doris, Spec Coll Librn, Ector County Library, 321 W Fifth St, Odessa, TX, 79761-5066. Tel: 432-332-0633, Ext 4015. Fax: 432-377-6502. p. 2366

Baker, Douglas, Dir, Kenosha Public Library, 812 56th St, Kenosha, WI, 53140-3735. Tel: 262-564-6324. Fax: 262-564-6370. p. 2601

Baker, Dylan, Info Tech Coordr, Ada Community Library, 10664 W Victory Rd, Boise, ID, 83709. Tel: 208-362-0181, Ext 132. Fax: 208-362-0303. p. 570

Baker, Elaine, Pub Serv Dir, Mid-Columbia Libraries, 405 S Dayton, Kennewick, WA, 99336. Tel: 509-582-4745. Fax: 509-737-6349. p. 2518

Baker, Elizabeth, Asst Libr Dir, Ref Serv, Sampson-Clinton Public Library, 217 Graham St, Clinton, NC, 28328. Tel: 910-592-4153. Fax: 910-590-3504. p. 1784

Baker, Emily F, Dir, Olathe Public Library, 201 E Park St, Olathe, KS, 66061. Tel: 913-971-6880. Fax: 913-971-6809. p. 886

Baker, Eric, Res & Instruction Librn, Auraria Library, 1100 Lawrence St, Denver, CO, 80204-2095. Tel: 303-556-8192. Fax: 303-556-3528. p. 298

Baker, Francia, In Charge, District of Columbia Public Library, Parklands-Turner Community, The Shops at Park Village, 1547-49 Alabama Ave, SE, Washington, DC, 20020. Tel: 202-698-1103. p. 398

Baker, George, Dir, Trumbull County Law Library, 120 High St NW, Warren, OH, 44481. Tel: 330-675-2525. Fax: 330-675-2527. p. 1944

Baker, Gordon N, Dr, Dean of Libr, Clayton State University, 2000 Clayton State Blvd, Morrow, GA, 30260. Tel: 678-466-4325. Fax: 678-466-4349. p. 545

Baker, Grover, Librn, Middle Tennessee State University, Center for Popular Music, John Bragg Mass Communication Bldg, Rm 140, 1301 E Main St, Murfreesboro, TN, 37132. Tel: 615-898-5512. Fax: 615-898-5829. p. 2254

Baker, Gwendolyn, Dir, Baltimore International College, 17 Commerce St, Baltimore, MD, 21202-3230. Tel: 410-752-4710, Ext 137 or 138. Fax: 410-752-6720. p. 1011

Baker, Heather, Librn, Lallouise Florey McGraw Public Library, 42860 Hwy 25, Vincent, AL, 35178-6156. Tel: 205-672-2749. Fax: 205-672-2749. p. 39

Baker, Heather, Ch, Harwinton Public Library, 80 Bentley Dr, Harwinton, CT, 06791. Tel: 860-485-9113. Fax: 860-485-2713. p. 348

Baker, Heather, Children's & Teen Serv Coordr, Grove City Community Library, 125 W Main St, Grove City, PA, 16127-1569. Tel: 724-458-7320. Fax: 724-458-7332. p. 2063

Baker, Holly, Ch, Park County Public Library, 1500 Heart Mountain St, Cody, WY, 82414. Tel: 307-527-1884. Fax: 307-527-1888. p. 2653

Baker, Ilene, Coordr, Great Lakes Colleges Association, 121 S Broad St, 7th Flr, Philadelphia, PA, 19107. Tel: 215-735-7300. Fax: 215-735-7373. p. 2110

Baker, Jacci, Dir, Albany Public Library, 200 N Water St, Albany, WI, 53502. Tel: 608-862-3491. p. 2577

Baker, James, Tech Serv, Oak Lawn Public Library, 9427 S Raymond Ave, Oak Lawn, IL, 60453-2434. Tel: 708-422-4990. Fax: 708-422-5061. p. 683

Baker, Jane, Communications Mgr, Spokane County Library District, 4322 N Argonne Rd, Spokane, WA, 99212-1868. Tel: 509-893-8205. Fax: 509-893-8472. p. 2536

Baker, Janet, Exec Dir, SullivanMunce Cultural Center, 225 W Hawthorne St, Zionsville, IN, 46077. Tel: 317-873-4900. p. 789

Baker, Janet, Head, Circ, Township of Washington Public Library, 144 Woodfield Rd, Washington Township, NJ, 07676. Tel: 201-664-4586. Fax: 201-664-7331. p. 1539

Baker, Jeff, Asst Dir, Info Res, Purdue Pharma LP & Associated Companies, One Stamford Forum, 201 Tresser Blvd, Stamford, CT, 06901. Tel: 203-566-7577. Fax: 203-588-6212. p. 369

Baker, Jeff, Dir, Chili Public Library, 3333 Chili Ave, Rochester, NY, 14624-5494. Tel: 585-889-2200. Fax: 585-889-5819. p. 1729

Baker, Jenny, Info Literacy Librn, Res Asst, Wisconsin Lutheran College Library, 8800 W Bluemound Rd, Milwaukee, WI, 53226. Tel: 414-443-8864. Fax: 414-443-8505. p. 2622

Baker, Jill, AV Spec, San Diego Mesa College Library, 7250 Mesa College Dr, San Diego, CA, 92111-4998. Tel: 619-388-2655. Fax: 619-388-2922. p. 235

Baker, Jill, Librn, St Lawrence College Library, Two Saint Lawrence Dr, Cornwall, ON, K6H 4Z1, CANADA. Tel: 613-933-6080, Ext 2701. p. 2801

Baker, Jill, Librn, St Lawrence College Library, 100 Portsmouth Ave, Kingston, ON, K7L 5A6, CANADA. Tel: 613-544-5400, Ext 1705. Fax: 613-545-3914. p. 2814

Baker, Joan, Tech Serv, Brown, Rudnick, Berlack, Israels LLP, One Financial Ctr, Boston, MA, 02111. Tel: 617-856-8213. Fax: 617-856-8201. p. 1059

Baker, Jodie, Coordr of Ref Serv, Tarleton State University Library, 201 Saint Felix, Stephenville, TX, 76401. Tel: 254-968-9987. Fax: 254-968-9467. p. 2389

Baker, Joyce, Libr Mgr, Coolidge Public Library, 160 W Central Ave, Coolidge, AZ, 85128. Tel: 520-723-6030. Fax: 520-723-7026. p. 61

Baker, Joyce, Dir, Operations, Belmont Technical College, 120 Fox-Shannon Pl, Saint Clairsville, OH, 43950-9735. Tel: 740-695-9500, Ext 1019. Fax: 740-695-2247. p. 1933

Baker, Kathy, ILL, Louisburg Public Library, 206 S Broadway, Louisburg, KS, 66053. Tel: 913-837-2217. Fax: 913-837-2218. p. 880

Baker, Kathy, Asst Dir, Head, Tech Serv, Marshfield Public Library, 211 E Second St, Marshfield, WI, 54449. Tel: 715-387-8494, Ext 213. Fax: 715-387-6909. p. 2613

Baker, Kathy M, Tech Serv Librn, National Steel & Shipbuilding Co, 7470 Mission Valley Rd, San Diego, CA, 92108. Tel: 619-544-8644. Fax: 619-544-3543. p. 232

Baker, Kelly Daniels, Youth Serv, Sunderland Public Library, 20 School St, Sunderland, MA, 01375. Tel: 413-665-2642. Fax: 413-665-1435. p. 1130

Baker, Kimberly, Dir, Leavenworth Public Library, 417 Spruce St, Leavenworth, KS, 66048. Tel: 913-682-5666. Fax: 913-682-1248. p. 879

Baker, Larry L, Exec Dir, San Juan County Archaeological Research Center & Library at Salmon Ruins, 6131 US Hwy 64, Bloomfield, NM, 87413. Tel: 505-632-2013. Fax: 505-632-8633. p. 1552

Baker, Laura, Doc Delivery, Furman University Libraries, 3300 Poinsett Hwy, Greenville, SC, 29613-4100. Tel: 864-294-2277. Fax: 864-294-3004. p. 2195

Baker, Laura, Pub Serv, Midlands Technical College Library, 1260 Lexington Dr, West Columbia, SC, 29170-2176. Tel: 803-822-3533. Fax: 803-822-3670. p. 2207

Baker, Laura, Govt Doc, Abilene Christian University, 221 Brown Library, ACU Box 29208, Abilene, TX, 79699-9208. Tel: 325-674-2344. Fax: 325-674-2202. p. 2271

Baker, Lesli, Asst Dir, Pub Serv, Utah Valley University Library, 800 W University Pkwy, Orem, UT, 84058-5999. Tel: 801-863-8286. Fax: 801-863-7065. p. 2409

Baker, Linda, Coordr, Ch Serv, Burton Public Library, 14588 W Park St, Burton, OH, 44021. Tel: 440-834-4466. Fax: 440-834-0128. p. 1862

Baker, Linda, Ref Librn, Dallas County Community College District, 1402 Corinth St, Dallas, TX, 75215. Tel: 214-860-5779. p. 2305

Baker, Linda, Librn, El Centro College, 801 Main St, Dallas, TX, 75202-3605. Tel: 214-860-2174. Fax: 214-860-2440. p. 2307

Baker, Lisa L, Librn, Musick, Peeler & Garrett Library, One Wilshire Bldg, 624 S Grand Ave, Ste 2000, Los Angeles, CA, 90017. Tel: 213-629-7600. Fax: 213-624-1376. p. 176

Baker, Lois, Librn, Lewis & Clark Trail Heritage Foundation, Inc, PO Box 3434, Great Falls, MT, 59403-3434. Tel: 406-761-3950. p. 1380

Baker, Maggie, Head, Adult Serv, Olathe Public Library, 201 E Park St, Olathe, KS, 66061. Tel: 913-971-6849. Fax: 913-971-6809. p. 886

Baker, Malinda, Librn, Yolo County Library, Esparto Branch, 17065 Yolo Ave, Esparto, CA, 95627. Tel: 530-787-3426. Fax: 530-787-4874. p. 285

Baker, Martha, Librn, Bayfront Medical Center, 701 Sixth St S, Saint Petersburg, FL, 33701. Tel: 727-893-6136. Fax: 727-893-6819. p. 487

Baker, Martha A, Mgr, Libr Serv, Hobart Institute of Welding Technology, 400 Trade Sq E, Troy, OH, 45373-2400. Tel: 937-332-5603. Fax: 937-332-5220. p. 1941

Baker, Mary Beth, Exec Dir, Stonington Historical Society, 40 Palmer St, Stonington, CT, 06378. Tel: 860-535-8445. p. 370

Baker, Matthew, Coll Serv Librn, Columbia University, The Burke Library at Union Theological Seminary, 3041 Broadway, New York, NY, 10027. Tel: 212-851-5607. Fax: 212-851-5613. p. 1674

Baker, Megan W, Dir, Bolton Free Library, 4922 Lakeshore Dr, Bolton Landing, NY, 12814. Tel: 518-644-2233. Fax: 518-644-2233. p. 1584

Baker, Melissa, Media Librn, Wilton Library Association, 137 Old Ridgefield Rd, Wilton, CT, 06897-3019. Tel: 203-762-3950. Fax: 203-834-1166. p. 378

Baker, Melissa, Mkt & Prog Coordr, Montgomery County Memorial Library System, 104 I-45 N, Conroe, TX, 77301-2720. Tel: 936-788-8377, Ext.266. Fax: 936-788-8398. p. 2300

Baker, Michael, Dir, Chicago Public Library, Carter G Woodson Regional, 9525 S Halsted St, Chicago, IL, 60628. Tel: 312-747-6900. Fax: 312-747-6947. p. 610

Baker, Michael, Media Spec, Jackson-Madison County Library, 433 E Lafayette St, Jackson, TN, 38301-6386. Tel: 731-425-8600. Fax: 731-425-8609. p. 2238

Baker, Michelle, Head, Circ, Pub Serv Coordr, Meriden Public Library, 105 Miller St, Meriden, CT, 06450. Tel: 203-630-6351. Fax: 203-238-3647. p. 350

Baker, Miriam, Br Mgr, Uncle Remus Regional Library System, Morgan County Library, 1131 East Ave, Madison, GA, 30650. Tel: 706-342-1206. Fax: 706-342-0883. p. 542

Baker, Mona, Adult Serv, Sierra Vista Public Library, 2600 E Tacoma, Sierra Vista, AZ, 85635-1399. Tel: 520-458-4225. Fax: 520-458-5377. p. 82

Baker, Nancy, Head, Tech Serv, Mokena Community Public Library District, 11327 W 195th St, Mokena, IL, 60448. Tel: 708-479-9663. Fax: 708-479-9684. p. 674

Baker, Nancy L, Univ Librn, University of Iowa Libraries, 125 W Washington St, Iowa City, IA, 52242-1420. p. 823

Baker, Neal, Libr Dir, Earlham College, 801 National Rd W, Richmond, IN, 47374-4095. Tel: 765-983-1355. Fax: 765-983-1304. p. 774

Baker, Nettie L, Assoc Dir, University of Dallas, 1845 E Northgate Dr, Irving, TX, 75062-4736. Tel: 972-721-4031. Fax: 972-721-4010. p. 2347

Baker, Nola, Ref Serv, Supvr, Ad Serv, Branch District Library, Ten E Chicago St, Coldwater, MI, 49036-1615. Tel: 517-278-2341, Ext 28. Fax: 517-279-7134. p. 1164

Baker, Pam, Coordr, Libr Instruction, California State University-Monterey Bay, 100 Campus Ctr, Seaside, CA, 93955-8001. Tel: 831-582-3887. Fax: 831-582-3875. p. 268

Baker, Paula J, Dir, Rutland Free Library, Ten Court St, Rutland, VT, 05701-4058. Tel: 802-773-1860. Fax: 802-773-1825. p. 2434

Baker, Penny, Dept Head, Tech Serv, Sterling & Francine Clark Art Institute Library, 225 South St, Williamstown, MA, 01267. Tel: 413-458-0531. Fax: 413-458-9542. p. 1140

Baker, Phyllis, Librn, Stateville Correctional Center Libraries, PO Box 112, Joliet, IL, 60434-0112. Tel: 815-727-3607, Ext 5613. p. 660

Baker, Phyllis, Circ Asst, Longwood University, Redford & Race St, Farmville, VA, 23909. Tel: 434-395-2743. Fax: 434-395-2453. p. 2463

Baker, Quincee, Dir, Fort Berthold Library, 220 Eighth Ave N, New Town, ND, 58763. Tel: 701-627-4738. Fax: 701-627-4677. p. 1847

Baker, Richard A, Librn, Guernsey County Law Library, Guernsey County Court House, 801 Wheeling Ave, Rm D 301, Cambridge, OH, 43725. Tel: 740-432-9258. p. 1863

Baker, Robert, Dr, Dir, Pima Community College, District Library Services, 4905B E Broadway Blvd, Tucson, AZ, 85709-1140. Tel: 520-206-6485. Fax: 520-206-6542. p. 86

Baker, Rochelle, Tech Serv Coordr, Burton Public Library, 14588 W Park St, Burton, OH, 44021. Tel: 440-834-4466. Fax: 440-834-0128. p. 1862

Baker, Rosalie, Tech Serv Mgr, Bernardsville Public Library, One Anderson Hill Rd, Bernardsville, NJ, 07924. Tel: 908-766-0118. Fax: 908-766-2464. p. 1472

Baker, Roxanne, Libr Dir, Wide Awake Club Library, 46 W Main St, Fillmore, NY, 14735-8706. Tel: 585-567-8301. Fax: 585-567-8301. p. 1622

Baker, Ruth, Ser, Community College of Philadelphia Library, 1700 Spring Garden St, Philadelphia, PA, 19130. Tel: 215-751-8388. Fax: 215-751-8762. p. 2104

Baker, Ryan, City Librn, Irwindale Public Library, 5050 N Irwindale Ave, Irwindale, CA, 91706. Tel: 626-430-2229. p. 160

Baker, Sally, Res Librn, DLA Piper US LLP, 203 N LaSalle St, Ste 1900, Chicago, IL, 60601. Tel: 312-984-2615. Fax: 312-251-5845. p. 612

Baker, Sandra L, Law Librn, Venango County Law Library, Venango County Court House, 1168 Liberty St, Franklin, PA, 16323. Tel: 814-432-9612. Fax: 814-432-3149. p. 2059

Baker, Sarah, Tech Serv, Granville Public Library, 217 E Broadway, Granville, OH, 43023-1398. Tel: 740-587-0196. Fax: 740-587-0197. p. 1903

Baker, Sharon, Dir, Perry Cook Memorial Public Library, 7406 County Rd 242, Shauck, OH, 43349. Tel: 419-362-7181. Fax: 419-362-1518. p. 1934

Baker, Sharon, Pub Serv Asst, Lutheran Theological Seminary, 7301 Germantown Ave, Philadelphia, PA, 19119-1794. Tel: 215-248-6329. Fax: 215-248-6327. p. 2112

Baker, Sherri, Ref, Panola College, 1109 W Panola St, Carthage, TX, 75633. Tel: 903-693-2052. Fax: 903-693-1115. p. 2295

Baker, Steven, Dean of Libr, Palm Beach Atlantic University, 300 Pembroke Pl, West Palm Beach, FL, 33401-6503. Tel: 561-803-2223. Fax: 561-803-2235. p. 503

Baker, Steven, Dir, Kewaskum Public Library, 206 First St, Kewaskum, WI, 53040-8929. Tel: 262-626-4312. Fax: 262-626-4861. p. 2602

Baker, Stewart, Ref Librn, Web Serv, California State University Dominguez Hills, 1000 E Victoria St, Carson, CA, 90747. Tel: 310-243-2062. Fax: 310-516-4219. p. 132

Baker, Stuart, Assoc Univ Librn, Libr Tech, Northwestern University Library, 1970 Campus Dr, Evanston, IL, 60208-2300. Tel: 847-491-7658. p. 644

Baker, Susan, Dir, Chiniak Public Library, 42650 Chiniak Hwy, Chiniak, AK, 99615. Tel: 907-486-3022. Fax: 907-486-3022. p. 46

Baker, Susan, Presch Outreach Plus Mgr, Rapides Parish Library, Westside Regional, 5416 Provine Pl, Alexandria, LA, 71303. Tel: 318-442-2483, Ext 1905. Fax: 318-442-7678. p. 940

Baker, Susan, Ref Librn, Durham Technical Community College, 1637 Lawson St, Durham, NC, 27703. Tel: 919-536-7211. Fax: 919-686-3471. p. 1788

Baker, Terri, Art Librn, Western Kentucky University Libraries, Helm-Cravens Library Complex, 1906 College Heights Blvd, No 11067, Bowling Green, KY, 42101-1067. Tel: 270-745-2905. Fax: 270-745-6422. p. 907

Baker, Tracey, Ref Serv, Minnesota Historical Society Library, 345 Kellogg Blvd W, Saint Paul, MN, 55102-1906. Tel: 651-259-3300. Fax: 651-297-7436. p. 1280

Baker, Vicky, Regional Mgr, North Region, Mid-Continent Public Library, 15616 E US Hwy 24, Independence, MO, 64050-2098. Tel: 816-836-5200. Fax: 816-521-7253. p. 1332

Baker, Warren Patrick, Dr, Libr Mgr, AMG International Library, 6815 Shallowford Rd, Chattanooga, TN, 37421-1755. Tel: 423-894-6060, Ext 254. Fax: 423-510-8074. p. 2226

Baker Wilkinson, Maureen, Dir, Warren County Library, 189 Route 519, Belvidere, NJ, 07823. Tel: 908-475-6322. Fax: 908-475-6359. p. 1472

Baker, William, Bibliographer, Northern Illinois University Libraries, DeKalb, IL, 60115-2868. Tel: 815-753-1857. p. 635

Baker, Zachary, Dr, Asst Univ Librn for Coll Develop (Humanities & Soc Sci), Stanford University Libraries, 557 Escondido Mall, Stanford, CA, 94305-6004. Tel: 650-725-1064. p. 270

Baker-Receniello, Deborah, Br Mgr, Timberland Regional Library, Oakville Branch, 204 Main St, Oakville, WA, 98568. Tel: 360-273-5305. Fax: 360-273-7446. p. 2543

Baker-Walker, Vonni, Mgr, Lake Blackshear Regional Library System, Dooly County, 1200 E Union St, Vienna, GA, 31092-7545. Tel: 229-268-4687. Fax: 229-268-4687. p. 508

Baker-Wood, Mary, Dir, Richard Sugden Library, Eight Pleasant St, Spencer, MA, 01562. Tel: 508-885-7513. Fax: 508-885-7523. p. 1126

Bakewell, Maureen, Librn, The Town of Laurentian Hills Public Library, 34465 Hwy 17, RR 1, Hwy 17, Deep River, ON, K0J 1P0, CANADA. Tel: 613-584-2714. Fax: 613-584-9145. p. 2802

Bakke, Celia, Digital Repository & Scholarly Communications Librn, San Jose State University, One Washington Sq, San Jose, CA, 95192-0028. Tel: 408-808-2469. Fax: 408-808-2141. p. 252

Bakke, Dan, Dir, Altoona Public Library, 700 Eighth St SW, Altoona, IA, 50009. Tel: 515-967-3881. Fax: 515-967-6934. p. 792

Bakker, Connie, Dean, College of Lake County, 19351 W Washington St, Grayslake, IL, 60030. Tel: 847-543-2464. Fax: 847-223-7690. p. 652

Bakos, Judith, Dir, Monmouth Beach Library, 18 Willow Ave, Monmouth Beach, NJ, 07750. Tel: 732-229-1187. p. 1502

Bakos, Stephanie, Dir, Berkeley Heights Public Library, 290 Plainfield Ave, Berkeley Heights, NJ, 07922. Tel: 908-464-9333. Fax: 908-464-7098. p. 1472

Baksa, Diane, Supvr, Vale Canada Limited, 2060 Flavelle Blvd, Mississauga, ON, L5K 1Z9, CANADA. Tel: diane.baksa@vale.com. Fax: 905-403-2401. p. 2823

Baksh, Fazana, Ch, Altamonte Springs City Library, 281 N Maitland Ave, Altamonte Springs, FL, 32701. Tel: 407-571-8830. Fax: 407-571-8834. p. 425

Baksh, Fazia, Libr Tech, Royal Alexandra Hospital, 10240 Kingsway, Edmonton, AB, T5H 3V9, CANADA. Tel: 780-735-5832. Fax: 780-735-4136. p. 2702

Baksic, Sharon, Librn, Bessemer Public Library, 411 S Sophie St, Bessemer, MI, 49911. Tel: 906-667-0404. Fax: 906-667-0442. p. 1157

Baky, John S, Dir, La Salle University, 1900 W Olney Ave, Philadelphia, PA, 19141-1199. Tel: 215-951-1286. Fax: 215-951-1595. p. 2111

Bala, Beth, Tech Serv Librn/Syst Adminr, Illinois College, 245 Park St, Jacksonville, IL, 62650. Tel: 217-245-3020. Fax: 217-245-3082. p. 658

Balas, Barbara, Ref, Lehigh Carbon Community College Library, 4525 Education Park Dr, Schnecksville, PA, 18078-9372. Tel: 610-799-1770. Fax: 610-779-1159. p. 2136

Balas, Janet L, Automation Syst Librn, Monroeville Public Library, 4000 Gateway Campus Blvd, Monroeville, PA, 15146-3381. Tel: 412-372-0500. Fax: 412-372-1168. p. 2091

Balas, Jennifer, Pres, Berks County Library Association, Reading Public Library, 100 S Fifth St, Reading, PA, 19602. Tel: 610-478-9035, 610-655-6350. p. 2953

Balassie, Kate, Librn, New York State Legislative Library, State Capitol, Rm 337, Albany, NY, 12224-0345. Tel: 518-455-2468. Fax: 518-426-6901. p. 1569

Balch, Kim, Librn, Slaton City Library, 200 W Lynn, Slaton, TX, 79364-4136. Tel: 806-828-2008. Fax: 806-828-2029. p. 2387

Balch, Timothy, Ref Serv Librn, Marshall University Libraries, One John Marshall Dr, Huntington, WV, 25755-2060. Tel: 304-696-2335. Fax: 304-696-5858. p. 2561

Balcom, Jennifer, Dir, DeWitt Public Library, 13101 Schavey Rd, DeWitt, MI, 48820-9008. Tel: 517-669-3156. Fax: 517-669-6408. p. 1173

Balcom, Karen, Dr, Web Coordr, San Antonio College, 1001 Howard St, San Antonio, TX, 78212. Tel: 210-486-0554. p. 2381

Balcom, Lesley, Assoc Dir of Libr/Learning & Res Serv, University of New Brunswick Libraries, Five Macaulay Dr, Fredericton, NB, E3B 5H5, CANADA. Tel: 506-458-7056. Fax: 506-453-4595. p. 2763

Balcos, Kimberley, Asst Dir, Tech Serv, Central Piedmont Community College Library, 1201 Elizabeth Ave, Charlotte, NC, 28235. Tel: 704-330-6023. Fax: 704-330-6887. p. 1781

Balcziunas, Adam, Electronic Res & Syst Librn, King's College, 14 W Jackson St, Wilkes-Barre, PA, 18711-0850. Tel: 570-208-5840. Fax: 570-208-6022. p. 2155

Baldauf, Brenda, Dir, Spiceland Town-Township Public Library, 106 W Main St, Spiceland, IN, 47385. Tel: 765-987-7472. p. 780

Balderson, Donna, Circ, Morgantown Public Library System, 373 Spruce St, Morgantown, WV, 26505. Tel: 304-291-7425. Fax: 304-291-7427. p. 2566

Baldi, LynnAnn, Circ, Lyme Public Library, 482 Hamburg Rd, Lyme, CT, 06371-3110. Tel: 860-434-2272. Fax: 860-434-9972. p. 349

Baldini, Don Francis, Asst Dir, New York Public Library - Astor, Lenox & Tilden Foundations, New York Public Library for the Performing Arts, Library for the Performing Arts, 40 Lincoln Center Plaza, New York, NY, 10023-7498. Tel: 212-870-1644. Fax: 212-870-1860. p. 1692

Baldini, Lois D, Dir, Libr Serv, North Haven Memorial Library, 17 Elm St, North Haven, CT, 06473. Tel: 203-239-5803. Fax: 203-234-2130. p. 362

Baldino, Bernadette, Dir, Easton Public Library, 691 Morehouse Rd, Easton, CT, 06612. Tel: 203-261-0134. Fax: 203-261-0708. p. 338

Baldo, Marie, Dir, Hermiston Public Library, 235 E Gladys Ave, Hermiston, OR, 97838-1827. Tel: 541-567-2882. Fax: 541-667-5055. p. 2000

Baldock, Joie, Youth Serv Dir, Kiel Public Library, 511 Third St, Kiel, WI, 53042. Tel: 920-894-7122. Fax: 920-894-4023. p. 2602

Balduff, Edith, Librn, Saint Stephen United Church of Christ, 905 E Perkins Ave, Sandusky, OH, 44870. Tel: 419-626-1612. Fax: 419-626-1617. p. 1934

Baldwin, Candice, Librn, Metropolitan Community College, Longview Campus Library, 500 SW Longview Rd, Lee's Summit, MO, 64081-2105. Tel: 816-604-2080. Fax: 816-604-2087. p. 1339

Baldwin, Charlene, Dean of Libr, Chapman University, One University Dr, Orange, CA, 92866-1099. Tel: 714-532-7756. Fax: 714-532-7743. p. 200

Baldwin, Claudette, Dir, Jolys Regional Library, 505 Herbert Ave N, Saint Pierre Jolys, MB, R0A 1V0, CANADA. Tel: 204-433-7729. Fax: 204-433-7412. p. 2751

Baldwin, Conner, Ref Librn, Schreiner University, 2100 Memorial Blvd, Kerrville, TX, 78028-5697. Tel: 830-792-7314. Fax: 830-792-7448. p. 2350

Baldwin, Douglas, Librn, Syst Adminr, Cranbury Public Library, 23 N Main St, Cranbury, NJ, 08512. Tel: 609-655-0555. Fax: 609-655-2858. p. 1480

Baldwin, Elaine, Librn, St Mary's General Hospital, 911 Queen's Blvd, Kitchener, ON, N2M 1B2, CANADA. Tel: 519-749-6549. Fax: 519-749-6526. p. 2815

Baldwin, Jennifer, Ref, Temple University Libraries, 1210 W Berks St, Philadelphia, PA, 19122-6088. Tel: 215-204-4585. Fax: 215-204-5201. p. 2117

Baldwin, Joyce, Libr Mgr, Nassau County Public Library System, Callahan Branch, 450077 State Rd 200, Callahan, FL, 32011-3767. Tel: 904-879-3434. Fax: 904-879-0636. p. 440

Baldwin, Laura, Coll Develop Coordr, Anchorage Public Library, 3600 Denali St, Anchorage, AK, 99503. Tel: 907-343-2980. Fax: 907-343-2930. p. 44

Baldwin, Leeann, Tech Serv, Hermiston Public Library, 235 E Gladys Ave, Hermiston, OR, 97838-1827. Tel: 541-567-2882. Fax: 541-667-5055. p. 2000

Baldwin, Linda B, Circ Mgr, Longwood University, Redford & Race St, Farmville, VA, 23909. Tel: 434-395-2082. Fax: 434-395-2453. p. 2463

Baldwin, Lora K, Assoc Librn, Info Tech Serv, Indiana University East Campus Library, 2325 Chester Blvd, Richmond, IN, 47374. Tel: 765-973-8326. Fax: 765-973-8315. p. 775

Baldwin, Lydia, Librn, Inyo County Free Library, Big Pine Branch, 500 S Main St, Big Pine, CA, 93513. Tel: 760-938-2420. p. 159

Baldwin, Lynne, Br Mgr, Jacksonville Public Library, Mandarin, 3330 Kori Rd, Jacksonville, FL, 32257-5454. Tel: 904-262-5201. Fax: 904-292-1029. p. 453

Baldwin, Margaret, Dr, Dir, Antioch University Library, 2326 Sixth Ave, Seattle, WA, 98121-1814. Tel: 206-268-4109. Fax: 206-441-3307. p. 2527

Baldwin, Mark, Mgr, Raytheon Co, 1847 W Main Rd, Portsmouth, RI, 02871-1087. Tel: 401-842-4372. Fax: 401-842-5206. p. 2171

Baldwin, Martha R, Cat, Tech Serv, Carl Elliott Regional Library System, 98 E 18th St, Jasper, AL, 35501. Tel: 205-221-2568. p. 23

Baldwin, Mason, Mgr, The Hamner Institutes for Health Sciences, Six Davis Dr, Research Triangle Park, NC, 27709. Tel: 919-558-1402. Fax: 919-558-1300. p. 1819

Baldwin, Michael, Dir, Benbrook Public Library, 1065 Mercedes, Benbrook, TX, 76126. Tel: 817-249-6632. Fax: 817-249-3326. p. 2289

Baldwin, Patty, Ref, Guilford Free Library, 67 Park St, Guilford, CT, 06437. Tel: 203-453-8282. Fax: 203-453-8288. p. 342

Baldwin, Robert, Dir, Learning Res, Allegany College of Maryland Library, 12401 Willowbrook Rd SE, Cumberland, MD, 21502-2596. Tel: 301-784-5268. Fax: 301-784-5017. p. 1026

Baldwin, Sandy, Interim Dir, Tonopah Library District, 167 S Central St, Tonopah, NV, 89049. Tel: 775-482-3374. Fax: 775-482-5143. p. 1435

Baldwin, Susan, Supvr, Ferguson Library, Harry Bennett Branch, 115 Vine Rd, Stamford, CT, 06905. Tel: 203-964-1000, Ext 8290. Fax: 203-968-2728. p. 369

Baldwin, Susan, Supvr, Ferguson Library, Weed Memorial & Hollander, 1143 Hope St, Stamford, CT, 06907. Tel: 203-964-1000, Ext 8284. p. 369

Baldwin, Suzie, Dir, Waveland-Brown Township Public Library, 115 E Green, Waveland, IN, 47989. Tel: 765-435-2700. Fax: 765-435-2434. p. 786

Baldwin, Ted, Head of Libr, University of Cincinnati Libraries, College of Engineering & Applied Science Library, 850 Baldwin Hall, Cincinnati, OH, 45221. Tel: 513-556-4211. Fax: 513-556-2654. p. 1874

Baldwin, Toby, Dir, Mountain View College, 4849 W Illinois, Dallas, TX, 75211-6599. Tel: 214-860-8669. Fax: 214-860-8667. p. 2309

Baldwin, Tonya, Librn, Western Plains Library System, Hazel Cross Library, 111 W Broadway, Thomas, OK, 73669. Tel: 580-661-3532. Fax: 580-661-3532. p. 1960

Baldwin, Tracy, Librn, Dowl HKM Library, 222 N 32nd, Ste 700, Billings, MT, 59101-1976. Tel: 406-656-6399. Fax: 406-656-6398. p. 1374

Bale, John, Pres, New Providence Historical Society Library, c/o Memorial Library, 377 Elkwood Ave, New Providence, NJ, 07974. Tel: 908-665-1034. p. 1510

Balemian, Victoria, Dir, Clyde Public Library, 222 W Buckeye St, Clyde, OH, 43410. Tel: 419-547-7174. Fax: 419-547-0480. p. 1882

Balentine, Kim, Ch, Lincoln Public Library, 145 Old River Rd, Lincoln, RI, 02865. Tel: 401-333-2422. Fax: 401-333-4154. p. 2168

Balentine, Kimmerle, Ch, Groton Public Library, 52 Newtown Rd, Groton, CT, 06340. Tel: 860-441-6750. Fax: 860-448-0363. p. 342

Bales, Jack, Ref & Instrul Serv Librn, University of Mary Washington, 1801 College Ave, Fredericksburg, VA, 22401-4665. Tel: 540-654-1780. Fax: 540-654-1067. p. 2466

Bales, John, Dir, Libr Serv, Westminster Seminary California Library, 1725 Bear Valley Pkwy, Escondido, CA, 92027. Tel: 760-480-8474. Fax: 760-480-0252. p. 147

Bales, Linda Lee, Commun Libr Supvr, Yakima Valley Libraries, Mabton Library, 415 B St, Mabton, WA, 98935. Tel: 509-894-4128. Fax: 509-894-4128. p. 2550

Balez, Rachel, Dir, Meade County Public Library, 400 Library Pl, Brandenburg, KY, 40108-1045. Tel: 270-422-2094. Fax: 270-422-3133. p. 908

Balf, Ruth E, Pub Serv, College of the Albemarle Library, 1208 N Road St, Elizabeth City, NC, 27906. Tel: 252-335-0821, Ext 2371. Fax: 252-335-0649. p. 1790

Bali, Lomi, Librn, American Samoa Office of Library Services, Pago Pago Branch, PO Box 272, Pago Pago, AS, 96799. Tel: 684-633-5651. Fax: 684-633-4240. p. 2665

Balint, Mary, Br Mgr, Walton County Public Library System, Freeport Public, 76 Hwy 20 W, Freeport, FL, 32439. Tel: 850-835-2040. Fax: 850-835-2154. p. 437

Balis, Michelle, Librn, Corpus Christi Public Libraries, Parkdale, 1230 Carmel Pkwy, Corpus Christi, TX, 78411. Tel: 361-853-9961. p. 2302

Balistreri, JoAnn, Ref Serv Coordr, Saint Petersburg Public Library, 3745 Ninth Ave N, Saint Petersburg, FL, 33713. Tel: 727-893-7724. Fax: 727-892-5432. p. 488

Balius, Angela, Librn, Mississippi Gulf Coast Community College, 2300 Hwy 90, Gautier, MS, 39553. Tel: 228-497-7642. Fax: 228-497-7643. p. 1298

Balk, Karolyn, Ch, Garnavillo Public Library, 122 Main St, Garnavillo, IA, 52049. Tel: 563-964-2119. Fax: 563-964-2119. p. 817

Balkam, Susan, Libr Tech, Nova Scotia Community College, 1575 Lake Rd, Shelburne, NS, B0T 1W0, CANADA. Tel: 902-543-0690. Fax: 902-875-8669. p. 2784

Balko, Patricia, Coll Mgt Librn, University of Pittsburgh, Johnstown Campus, 450 Schoolhouse Rd, Johnstown, PA, 15904. Tel: 814-269-7290. Fax: 814-269-7286. p. 2073

Ball, Benna, Archivist, Baylor University Libraries, W R Poage Legislative Library, Baylor Collections of Political Materials, 201 Baylor Ave, Waco, TX, 76706. Tel: 247-710-3767. Fax: 254-710-3059. p. 2396

Ball, Betty, YA Serv, Youth Serv, Franklin County Library, 906 N Main St, Louisburg, NC, 27549-2199. Tel: 919-496-2111. Fax: 919-496-1339. p. 1807

Ball, Christine, ILL, Finkelstein Memorial Library, 24 Chestnut St, Spring Valley, NY, 10977-5594. Tel: 845-352-5700. Fax: 845-352-2319. p. 1746

Ball, Corinne, Ch, Britt Public Library, 132 Main Ave S, Britt, IA, 50423-1628. Tel: 641-843-4245. Fax: 641-843-4245. p. 797

Ball, Dannie J, Dir, Iberville Parish Library, 24605 J Gerald Berret Blvd, Plaquemine, LA, 70764. Tel: 225-687-2520, 225-687-4397. Fax: 225-687-9719. p. 965

Ball, Eileen Annie, Dir, Franklin County Public Library, Point Mall, 29 Island Dr, Eastpoint, FL, 32328-3265. Tel: 850-670-8151. Fax: 850-670-8151. p. 438

Ball, Geri, Asst Librn, Chinook Regional Library, Chaplin Branch, Second Ave Hall Complex, Chaplin, SK, S0H 0V0, CANADA. Tel: 306-395-2524. p. 2928

Ball, Jaime, Librn III, Apache County Library District, Round Valley Public, 179 S Main St, Eagar, AZ, 85925. Tel: 928-333-4694. Fax: 928-333-5682. p. 80

Ball, Jeanne, Instruction & Outreach, Thiel College, 75 College Ave, Greenville, PA, 16125-2183. Tel: 724-589-2124, 724-589-2205. Fax: 724-589-2122. p. 2063

Ball, Jonelle, Dir, Home Township Library, 329 E Main St, Edmore, MI, 48829. Tel: 989-427-5241. Fax: 989-427-3233. p. 1176

Ball, Juanita, ILL, Richland Community College, One College Park, Decatur, IL, 62521. Tel: 217-875-7200, Ext 328. Fax: 217-875-6961. p. 634

Ball, Juanita, Asst Librn, Darwin R Barker Library, Seven Day St, Fredonia, NY, 14063. Tel: 716-672-8051. Fax: 716-679-3547. p. 1624

Ball, Julie, Asst Librn, Sandown Public Library, 305 Main St, Sandown, NH, 03873. Tel: 603-887-3428. Fax: 603-887-0590. p. 1465

Ball, Justin, Tech Serv Coordr, Derby Public Library, 1600 E Walnut Grove, Derby, KS, 67037. Tel: 316-788-0760. Fax: 316-788-7313. p. 863

Ball, Karen, Ch, Mason Library, 231 Main St, Great Barrington, MA, 01230. Tel: 413-528-2403. p. 1092

Ball, Marti, Librn, Birmingham Public Library, Inglenook, 4100 N 40th Terrace, Birmingham, AL, 35217. Tel: 205-849-8739. Fax: 205-841-2551. p. 7

Ball, Mary Kay, Ref Serv & Bk Discussions, Barberton Public Library, 602 W Park Ave, Barberton, OH, 44203-2458. Tel: 330-745-1194. Fax: 330-745-8261. p. 1857

Ball, Patricia, Mgr, Cobb County Public Library System, Stratton, 1100 Powder Springs Rd, Marietta, GA, 30064. Tel: 770-528-2522. Fax: 770-528-2595. p. 543

Ball, Rick, Dir, Lincoln County Public Libraries, 220 W Sixth St, Libby, MT, 59923-1898. Tel: 406-293-2778. Fax: 406-293-4235. p. 1385

Ball, Robin, Circ Serv, Per, Sadie Pope Dowdell Library of South Amboy, 100 Harold G Hoffman Plaza, South Amboy, NJ, 08879. Tel: 732-721-6060. Fax: 732-721-1054. p. 1530

Ball, Sandy, Br Mgr, Morgan County Public Library, Morgantown Branch, 39 Washington St, Morgantown, IN, 46160. Tel: 812-597-0889. p. 763

Ball, Shirlene D, Lead, Info Spec/Analyst, United States Department of Transportation, National Highway Traffic Safety Administration-Technical Information Services, NPO-400, 1200 New Jersey Ave SE, Washington, DC, 20590. Fax: 202-493-2833. p. 420

Ball, Thom, Mgr, San Mateo County Library, Pacifica Sanchez Library, 1111 Terra Nova Blvd, Pacifica, CA, 94044. Tel: 650-359-3397. Fax: 650-359-3808. p. 256

Ball, Thom, Mgr, San Mateo County Library, Pacifica Sharp Park Library, 104 Hilton Way, Pacifica, CA, 94044. Tel: 650-355-5196. Fax: 650-355-6658. p. 256

Ball-Pyatt, Karen, Librn, Kitchener Public Library, Grace Schmidt Room, 85 Queen St N, Kitchener, ON, N2H 2H1, CANADA. Tel: 519-743-0271, Ext 252. Fax: 519-743-1261. p. 2815

Balla-Boudreau, Naomi, Libr Dir, McBride & District Public Library, 241 Dominion St, McBride, BC, V0J 2E0, CANADA. Tel: 250-569-2411. Fax: 250-569-2411. p. 2731

Ballada, Radmila, Head, Tech Serv/Tech Serv Librn, Clark College, Mail Stop LIB 112, 1933 Fort Vancouver Way, Vancouver, WA, 98663-3598. Tel: 360-992-2443. Fax: 360-992-2869. p. 2545

Ballain, Craig, Dir, University of Alaska Anchorage, Matanuska-Susitna College, 8295 E College Dr, Palmer, AK, 99645. Tel: 907-745-9740. Fax: 907-745-9777. p. 52

Ballam, Anne Marie, Ch, Haverhill Library Association, 67 Court St, Haverhill, NH, 03765. Tel: 603-989-5578. p. 1451

Ballangee, Matthew, Asst Dir, Info Tech, East Carolina University, William E Laupus Health Sciences Library, 600 Moye Blvd, Health Sciences Bldg, Greenville, NC, 27834. Tel: 252-744-2253. Fax: 252-744-2672. p. 1799

Ballanik, Alla, Libr Tech, University of Maryland Libraries, White Memorial Chemistry Library, 1526 Chemistry Bldg, College Park, MD, 20742-7011. Tel: 301-405-9081. Fax: 301-405-9164. p. 1025

Ballard, Cheri, Librn, Newton Town Library, 51 South Center St, Newton, UT, 84327. Tel: 435-563-9283. p. 2408

Ballard, Denise, Dir, Horse Cave Free Public Library, 111 Higbee St, Horse Cave, KY, 42749-1110. Tel: 270-786-1130. p. 918

Ballard, Donna, District Librn, East Mississippi Community College, 1527 Kemper, Scooba, MS, 39358. Tel: 662-476-5054. Fax: 662-476-5053. p. 1314

Ballard, Donna S, District Librn, East Mississippi Community College, Golden Triangle Campus Library, 8731 S Frontage Rd, Mayhew, MS, 39753. Tel: 662-243-1914. Fax: 662-243-1952. p. 1314

Ballard, Jan, Archivist, Moravian College & Moravian Theological Seminary, 1200 Main St, Bethlehem, PA, 18018-6650. Tel: 610-861-1594. Fax: 610-861-1577. p. 2034

Ballard, Jennifer, Librn, Arkansas State University, 7648 Victory Blvd, Newport, AR, 72112-8912. Tel: 870-512-7861. Fax: 870-512-7870. p. 111

Ballard, Judy, Circ Mgr, Gloucester County Library System, 389 Wolfert Station Rd, Mullica Hill, NJ, 08062. Tel: 856-223-6000. Fax: 856-223-6039. p. 1507

Ballard, Linda, Head, Circ, Interim Dir, Chelsea District Library, 221 S Main St, Chelsea, MI, 48118-1267. Tel: 734-475-8732. Fax: 734-475-6190. p. 1163

Ballard, Marilyn, Librn, Camas County District Library, 607 Soldier Rd, Fairfield, ID, 83327. Tel: 208-764-2553. Fax: 208-764-2553. p. 574

Ballard, Marsha, Tech Serv Librn, Scottsdale Community College Library, 9000 E Chaparral Rd, Scottsdale, AZ, 85256. Tel: 480-423-6638. Fax: 480-423-6666. p. 80

Ballard, Matthew, Libr Syst Adminr, Programming, Otis College of Art & Design Library, 9045 Lincoln Blvd, Westchester, CA, 90045. Tel: 310-665-6800, Ext 6930. Fax: 310-665-6998. p. 283

Ballard, Patricia, Head, Monograph & AV Cat, Winthrop University, 824 Oakland Ave, Rock Hill, SC, 29733. Tel: 803-323-2179. Fax: 803-323-2215. p. 2203

Ballard, Randall, Br Librn, Fayette County Public Libraries, Patrick C Graney Jr Library, 500 Main St, Mount Hope, WV, 25880. Tel: 304-877-3260. Fax: 304-877-3260. p. 2568

Ballard, Robert M, Prof, North Carolina Central University, 1801 Fayetteville St, Durham, NC, 27707. Tel: 919-530-6485. Fax: 919-530-6402. p. 2971

Ballard, Sharon, Br Mgr, Riverside County Library System, Thousand Palms Library, 72-715 La Canada Way, Thousand Palms, CA, 92276. Tel: 760-343-1556. Fax: 760-343-0957. p. 218

Ballard, Terry, Automation Librn, Quinnipiac University, 275 Mount Carmel Ave, Hamden, CT, 06518. Tel: 203-582-8945. Fax: 203-582-3451. p. 343

Ballard-Thrower, Rhea, Dir, Howard University Libraries, Law Library, 2929 Van Ness St NW, Washington, DC, 20008. Tel: 202-806-8047. Fax: 202-806-8400. p. 404

Ballenger, Norma, Head Librn, El Paso Community College Library, Mission del Paso Campus Library, 10700 Gateway East, Rm C-102, El Paso, TX, 79927. Tel: 915-831-7052. Fax: 915-831-7041. p. 2316

Ballester, Yvonne, Tech Mgr, Emporia State University, 1200 Commercial St, Campus Box 4025, Emporia, KS, 66801-4025. Tel: 800-552-4770, Ext 5271. Fax: 620-341-5233. p. 2965

Ballhagen, Valerie, Dir, Elizabeth Rasmussen Martin Memorial Library, 406 Packwaukee, New Hartford, IA, 50660. Tel: 319-983-2533. Fax: 319-983-2533. p. 835

Balliett, Kristy, Br Asst, Marathon County Public Library, Hatley Branch, 435 Curtis Ave, Hatley, WI, 54440. Tel: 715-446-3537. Fax: 715-446-3537. p. 2646

Ballinger, Jennie, Tech Serv, Fort Smith Public Library, 3201 Rogers Ave, Fort Smith, AR, 72903. Tel: 479-783-0229. Fax: 479-782-8571. p. 100

Ballinger, Rosalia, User Experience Librn, Cardinal Stritch University Library, 6801 N Yates Rd, Milwaukee, WI, 53207-3985. Tel: 414-410-4272. Fax: 414-410-4268. p. 2617

Balliot, Nanette Kelley, Reader Serv, Roger Williams University, Ten Metacom Ave, Bristol, RI, 02809-5171. Tel: 401-254-4542. Fax: 401-254-4543. p. 2163

Balliot, Robert L, Dir, Libr Serv, Middletown Public Library, 700 W Main Rd, Middletown, RI, 02842-6391. Tel: 401-846-1573. Fax: 401-846-3031. p. 2168

Ballmer, Amy, Ref, City University of New York, 365 Fifth Ave, New York, NY, 10016-4309. Tel: 212-817-7059. Fax: 212-817-2982. p. 1673

Ballock, Tracie, Head, Coll Mgt, Duquesne University, 600 Forbes Ave, Pittsburgh, PA, 15282. Tel: 412-396-4560. Fax: 412-396-5639. p. 2125

Ballou, Barbara, Ch, Whipple Free Library, Two Central Sq, New Boston, NH, 03070. Tel: 603-487-3391. Fax: 603-487-2886. p. 1459

Ballou, Jill, Ad, Computer Serv Librn, West Babylon Public Library, 211 Rte 109, West Babylon, NY, 11704. Tel: 631-669-5445. Fax: 631-669-6539. p. 1765

Ballou, Julie, Mgr, Metropolitan Library System in Oklahoma County, Northwest Library, 5600 NW 122nd St, Oklahoma City, OK, 73142-4204. Tel: 405-606-3580. Fax: 405-606-3570. p. 1973

Ballou, Marlene, Coll Develop Librn, Norfolk State University Library, 700 Park Ave, Norfolk, VA, 23504-8010. Tel: 757-823-8517. Fax: 757-823-2431. p. 2482

Balls, Jennifer, Ch, Soda Springs Public Library, 149 S Main, Soda Springs, ID, 83276-1496. Tel: 208-547-2606. Fax: 208-547-2606. p. 584

Balog, Mary, Youth Serv, Hudson Library & Historical Society, 96 Library St, Hudson, OH, 44236-5122. Tel: 330-653-6658. Fax: 330-650-3373. p. 1905

Balough, Sandra A, Dean of Libr Serv, Saint Francis University, 106 Franciscan Way, Loretto, PA, 15940. Tel: 814-472-3153. Fax: 814-472-3154. p. 2083

Baloun, Betty, Librn, Redfield Carnegie Library, Five E Fifth Ave, Redfield, SD, 57469-1243. Tel: 605-472-4555. Fax: 605-472-4559. p. 2217

Balsamello, Rick, Dir, Westville Public Library District, 233 S State St, Westville, IL, 61883-1461. Tel: 217-267-3170. Fax: 217-267-3468. p. 718

Balsbaugh, J Dale, Dir, Libr & Info Serv, Payne Theological Seminary, 1230 Wilberforce-Clifton Rd, Wilberforce, OH, 45384. Tel: 937-376-2946, Ext 203, 937-376-2947, Ext 203. Fax: 937-376-2888. p. 1948

Balsley, Arrin, Dir, Duncombe Public Library, 621 Prince St, Duncombe, IA, 50532. Tel: 515-543-4646. Fax: 515-543-8186. p. 812

Baltes, Janet, Cat, Tech Serv, University of Wisconsin-Superior, PO Box 2000, Belknap & Catlin, Superior, WI, 54880-2000. Tel: 715-394-8136. Fax: 715-394-8462. p. 2641

Balthis, Charles, Cat, University of Mary Washington, 1801 College Ave, Fredericksburg, VA, 22401-4665. Tel: 540-654-1772. Fax: 540-654-1067. p. 2466

Baltrusch, Linda, Head Librn, United States Sentencing Commission Library, One Columbus Circle NE, Ste 2-500 S Lobby, Washington, DC, 20002-8002. Tel: 202-502-4500. Fax: 202-502-4699. p. 421

Baltzer-Kom, Stephanie, Coordr, Digital Mat, North Dakota State Library, Library Memorial Bldg, 604 East Blvd Ave, Dept 250, Bismarck, ND, 58505-0800. Tel: 701-328-1860. Fax: 701-328-2040. p. 1838

Balz, Deborah, Br Coordr, Marathon County Public Library, Athens Branch, 221 Caroline St, Athens, WI, 54411-0910. Tel: 715-257-7292. Fax: 715-257-7292. p. 2646

Balzekas, Stanley, Jr, Pres, Balzekas Museum of Lithuanian Culture, 6500 S Pulaski Rd, Chicago, IL, 60629. Tel: 773-582-6500. Fax: 773-582-5133. p. 606

Bambrick, Jane, Ref, William Paterson University of New Jersey, 300 Pompton Rd, Wayne, NJ, 07470. Tel: 973-720-2290. Fax: 973-720-3171. p. 1540

Banach, Patricia S, Dir, Libr Serv, Eastern Connecticut State University, 83 Windham St, Willimantic, CT, 06226-2295. Tel: 860-465-4466. Fax: 860-465-5521. p. 378

Banarjee, Rina, Br Mgr, Mercer County Library System, West Windsor, 333 N Post Rd, Princeton Junction, NJ, 08550. Tel: 609-799-0462. Fax: 609-936-9511. p. 1494

Banas, Carol, Librn, United States Air Force, 341 SVS/SVMG, 7356 Fourth Ave N, Malmstrom AFB, MT, 59402-7506. Tel: 406-731-4638. Fax: 406-727-6104. p. 1385

Banasek, Megan, Libr Syst & Applications Librn, Pacific University Library, 2043 College Way, Forest Grove, OR, 97116. Tel: 503-352-1407. Fax: 503-352-1416. p. 1998

Banbor, Marianne, In Charge, Free Library of Philadelphia, Independence Branch, 18 S Seventh St, Philadelphia, PA, 19106-2314. Tel: 215-685-1633. Fax: 215-685-1844. p. 2108

Bancone, Mary-Lynne, Res Librn, O'Melveny & Myers LLP, Times Square Tower, Seven Times Sq, New York, NY, 10036. Fax: 212-326-2061. p. 1696

Band, Richard A, Dir, Lancaster County Library, 313 S White St, Lancaster, SC, 29720. Tel: 803-285-1502. Fax: 803-285-6004. p. 2198

Bandelier, Celia, Dir, Roanoke Public Library, 126 N Main St, Roanoke, IN, 46783. Tel: 260-672-2989. Fax: 260-676-2239. p. 775

Bandelin, Janis M, Dr, Dir, Furman University Libraries, 3300 Poinsett Hwy, Greenville, SC, 29613-4100. Tel: 864-294-2190. Fax: 864-294-3004. p. 2195

Bandhold, Sharon, Ch, Plattsburgh Public Library, 19 Oak St, Plattsburgh, NY, 12901-2810. Tel: 518-563-0921. Fax: 518-563-1681. p. 1719

Bandlow, Barbara, Adult Serv/Circ Librn, Keene Memorial Library, 1030 N Broad St, Fremont, NE, 68025-4199. Tel: 402-727-2694. Fax: 402-727-2693. p. 1399

Bandoni, Lawrence, Chair, John Curtis Free Library, 534 Hanover St, Hanover, MA, 02339-2228. Tel: 781-826-2972. Fax: 781-826-3130. p. 1093

Bandy, Margaret, Mgr, Libr Serv, Exempla-Saint Joseph Hospital, 1835 Franklin St, Denver, CO, 80218-1191. Tel: 303-837-7375. Fax: 303-837-7977. p. 301

Bandyopadhyay, Aditi, Ref Librn, Adelphi University Libraries, One South Ave, Garden City, NY, 11530. Tel: 516-877-4166. Fax: 516-877-3592. p. 1625

Bane, Adele, Dr, Assoc Dir, West Chester University, 25 W Rosedale Ave, West Chester, PA, 19383. Tel: 610-436-2263. p. 2153

Bane, Janice, Libr & Licensing Mgr, Barbershop Harmony Society, 110 Seventh Ave N, Nashville, TN, 37203. Tel: 615-823-3993. Fax: 615-313-7619. p. 2255

Bane, Linda, Asst Librn, Potomac State College of West Virginia University, 101 Fort Ave, Keyser, WV, 26726. Tel: 304-788-6901. Fax: 304-788-6946. p. 2563

Banes, Kim, Dir, Elberon Public Library, 106 Main St, Elberon, IA, 52225. Tel: 319-439-5476. Fax: 319-439-5476. p. 813

Banfield, Jacqueline, Dir, Sherman Public Library, 421 N Travis, Sherman, TX, 75090-5975. Tel: 903-892-7240. Fax: 903-892-7101. p. 2387

Banfield, Janet, Chief Exec Officer, Ramara Township Public Library, 5482 Hwy 12 S, Orillia, ON, L3V 6H7, CANADA. Tel: 705-325-5776. Fax: 705-325-8176. p. 2826

Bang, Marit, Ref, Shook, Hardy & Bacon, 2555 Grand Blvd, 3rd Flr, Kansas City, MO, 64108-2613. Tel: 816-474-6550. Fax: 816-421-5547. p. 1341

Bangilan, Joel, Br Serv Coordr, San Antonio Public Library, 600 Soledad, San Antonio, TX, 78205-2786. Tel: 210-207-2560. Fax: 210-207-2603. p. 2382

Bangle, Ricci, Head Librn, Bette Winner Public Library, Recreation Ctr, Gillam, MB, R0B 0L0, CANADA. Tel: 204-652-2617. Fax: 204-652-2617. p. 2748

Banick, Cheryl R, Dir of Libr Serv, Department of Veterans Affairs, Library Service, 830 Chalkstone Ave, Providence, RI, 02908-4799. Tel: 401-457-3001. Fax: 401-457-3097. p. 2172

Banick, Michael, Dir, Mountainside Public Library, Constitution Plaza, Mountainside, NJ, 07092. Tel: 908-233-0115. Fax: 908-232-7311. p. 1506

Banister, Amy, Mkt, Programming, Public Library of Cincinnati & Hamilton County, 800 Vine St, Cincinnati, OH, 45202-2009. Tel: 513-369-6961. Fax: 513-369-6993. p. 1871

Banitt, Nick, Info Spec, Minnesota Library Information Network, University of Minnesota-Twin Cities, 15 Andersen Library, 222 21st Ave S, Minneapolis, MN, 55455-0439. Tel: 612-624-8096. Fax: 612-624-4508. p. 2947

Bankart, Henry, Fac Mgr, Kitsap Regional Library, 1301 Sylvan Way, Bremerton, WA, 98310-3498. Tel: 360-405-9153. Fax: 360-405-9128. p. 2510

Bankes, Cryder H, III, Mgr, CBS News Reference Library, 524 W 57th St, Ste 533/2, New York, NY, 10019. Tel: 212-975-2877. p. 1671

Bankhead, Detrice, Assoc Univ Librn, Human Res, University of California, Santa Barbara, Santa Barbara, CA, 93106-9010. Tel: 805-893-3841. Fax: 805-893-7010. p. 261

Bankhead, Henry, Interim Librn, Los Gatos Public Library, 100 Villa Ave, Los Gatos, CA, 95030-6981. Tel: 408-354-6891. Fax: 408-399-6008. p. 180

Bankhead, Sheila, Ref, Northwest Regional Library System, 898 W 11 St, Panama City, FL, 32401. Tel: 850-522-2100. Fax: 850-522-2138. p. 480

Bankman, Lisa, Events & Seminars Mgr, Howard County Library System, 6600 Cradlerock Way, Columbia, MD, 21045-4912. Tel: 410-313-7750. Fax: 410-313-7742. p. 1026

Banks, Acklen J, Jr, Br Mgr, Milwaukee Public Library, Capitol, 3969 N 74th St, Milwaukee, WI, 53216. Tel: 414-286-3006. Fax: 414-286-8432. p. 2620

Banks, Ann, Librn, Fishers Island Library, 988 Oriental Ave, Fishers Island, NY, 06390. Tel: 631-788-7362. Fax: 631-788-7362. p. 1622

Banks, Bonnie, Youth Serv, Shelby County Libraries, 230 E North St, Sidney, OH, 45365-2785. Tel: 937-492-8354. Fax: 937-492-9229. p. 1934

Banks, Curtis G, Asst Librn, Gill Memorial Library, 145 E Broad St, Paulsboro, NJ, 08066. Tel: 856-423-5155. Fax: 856-423-9162. p. 1519

Banks, Dorinne, Ref & Instruction Librn, George Washington University, Virginia Science & Technology Campus Library, 44983 Knoll Sq, Ste 179, Ashburn, DC, 20147-2604. Tel: 703-726-8230. Fax: 703-726-8237. p. 402

Banks, Jan J, Dir, Casey County Public Library, 238 Middleburg St, Liberty, KY, 42539. Tel: 606-787-9381. Fax: 606-787-7720. p. 922

Banks, Jeff, Head, Human Res Dept, University of Arkansas Libraries, 365 N McIlroy Ave, Fayetteville, AR, 72701-4002. Tel: 479-575-4769. Fax: 479-575-6656. p. 99

Banks, Joy, Librn, Bok Tower Gardens, 1151 Tower Blvd, Lake Wales, FL, 33853-3412. Tel: 863-734-1227. Fax: 863-676-6770. p. 458

Banks, Justin, Archivist, Austin College, 900 N Grand Ave, Ste 6L, Sherman, TX, 75090-4402. Tel: 903-813-2557. Fax: 903-813-2297. p. 2387

Banks, Marcus, Mgr, Educ & Info Serv, University of California San Francisco, 530 Parnassus Ave, San Francisco, CA, 94143-0840. Tel: 415-476-4926. p. 248

Banks, Melissa A, Dir, Somerville Library, 35 West End Ave, Somerville, NJ, 08876. Tel: 908-725-1336. Fax: 908-231-0608. p. 1530

Banks, Robert, Dep Dir, Operations, Topeka & Shawnee County Public Library, 1515 SW Tenth Ave, Topeka, KS, 66604-1374. Tel: 785-580-4400. Fax: 785-580-4496. p. 897

Banks, Roland, Dir, El Centro Public Library, 1140 N Imperial Ave, El Centro, CA, 92243. Tel: 760-337-4565. Fax: 760-352-1384. p. 145

Banks, Sandi, Sr City Librn, Ventura County Library, Simi Valley Library, 2969 Tapo Canyon Rd, Simi Valley, CA, 93063. Tel: 805-526-1735. Fax: 805-526-1738. p. 280

Banks, Sharon, Commun Libr Mgr, Queens Borough Public Library, Pomonok Community Library, 158-21 Jewel Ave, Flushing, NY, 11365. Tel: 718-591-4343. p. 1645

Banks, Susan, Dep Dir, Carnegie Library of Pittsburgh, 4400 Forbes Ave, Pittsburgh, PA, 15213-4080. Tel: 412-622-1911. Fax: 412-622-6278. p. 2122

Banks, Susan, Librn, Bastyr University Library, 14500 Juanita Dr NE, Kenmore, WA, 98028. Tel: 425-602-3022. Fax: 425-602-3188. p. 2518

Banks, Theresa, Librn, Hudson County Law Library, Hudson County Admin Bldg, 595 Newark Ave, Jersey City, NJ, 07306. Tel: 201-795-6629. Fax: 201-795-6603. p. 1492

Banks, William, Dir, Washington Bible College-Capital Bible Seminary, 6511 Princess Garden Pkwy, Lanham, MD, 20706. Tel: 301-552-1400, Ext 1231. Fax: 301-552-2775. p. 1034

Bankson, John, Librn, United States Environmental Protection Agency, 6201 Congdon Blvd, Duluth, MN, 55804-2595. Tel: 218-529-5000. Fax: 218-529-5418. p. 1248

Bannen, Carol, Dir, Reinhart Boerner Van Deuren SC, 1000 N Water St, Ste 2100, Milwaukee, WI, 53203-3400. Tel: 414-298-8253. Fax: 414-298-8097. p. 2621

Banner, Susan, Pub Serv, Sherman Public Library, 421 N Travis, Sherman, TX, 75090-5975. Tel: 903-892-7240. Fax: 903-892-7101. p. 2387

Bannerman-Williams, Fred, Dep Dir, Memphis Public Library & Information Center, 3030 Poplar Ave, Memphis, TN, 38111-3527. Tel: 901-415-2700. Fax: 901-323-7108. p. 2249

Bannister, Cathy, Mgr, Wayne County Public Library, Fremont Public, 202 N Goldsboro St, Fremont, NC, 27830. Tel: 919-705-1893. p. 1795

Bannister, Lois, Librn, Garland Smith Public Library, 407 W Seminole, Marlow, OK, 73055. Tel: 580-658-5354. Fax: 580-658-9110. p. 1967

Bannister, Sharon, Automated Serv Coordr, Glen Ellyn Public Library, 400 Duane St, Glen Ellyn, IL, 60137-4508. Tel: 630-469-0879. Fax: 630-469-1086. p. 650

Bannister, Shelly, Actg Dir, Betty Foster Public Library, 405 Shaffner St, Ponder, TX, 76259. Tel: 940-479-2683. Fax: 940-479-2314. p. 2371

Bannon, Brian, Commissioner, Chicago Public Library, 400 S State St, Chicago, IL, 60605. Tel: 312-747-4090. Fax: 312-747-4968. p. 608

Bannon, Sue, Ch, Hartland Public Library, 110 E Park Ave, Hartland, WI, 53029. Tel: 262-367-3350. Fax: 262-369-2251. p. 2597

Bannon, Susan H, Assoc Prof, Auburn University, 4036 Haley Ctr, Auburn, AL, 36849-5221. Tel: 334-844-4460. Fax: 334-844-3072. p. 2961

Bannwart, Susan, Ch Mgr, La Porte County Public Library, 904 Indiana Ave, La Porte, IN, 46350-3435. Tel: 219-362-6156. Fax: 219-362-6158. p. 758

Bans, Jason, Automation Coordr, Hancock County Library System, 312 Hwy 90, Bay Saint Louis, MS, 39520-3595. Tel: 228-467-5282. Fax: 228-467-5503. p. 1293

Bansley, Judith, Librn, Parkland Regional Library, Invermay Branch, 301 Fourth Ave N, Invermay, SK, S0A 1M0, CANADA. Tel: 306-593-4990. p. 2932

Banta, Brady, PhD, Dr, Head, Archives, Arkansas State University, 322 University Loop West Circle, State University, AR, 72401. Tel: 870-972-3077. Fax: 870-972-3199. p. 115

Banta, Linda, Asst Librn, Mendes & Mount, LLP, 750 Seventh Ave, New York, NY, 10019-6829. Tel: 212-261-8000, 212-261-8338. Fax: 212-261-8750. p. 1686

Banta, Mykal, Asst Dir, Syst Coordr, Delray Beach Public Library, 100 W Atlantic Ave, Delray Beach, FL, 33444. Tel: 561-266-0198. Fax: 561-266-9757. p. 437

Banta, Rita, Asst Dir, W A Rankin Memorial Library, 502 Indiana St, Neodesha, KS, 66757-1532. Tel: 620-325-3275. Fax: 620-325-3275. p. 884

Banta, Wendy, Libr Asst, Smithers Public Library, 3817 Alfred Ave, Box 55, Smithers, BC, V0J 2N0, CANADA. Tel: 250-847-3043. Fax: 250-847-1533. p. 2737

Bantam, Rita, Dir, Woodbine Public Library, 58 Fifth St, Woodbine, IA, 51579. Tel: 712-647-2750. Fax: 712-647-2750. p. 853

Banter, Hugh, Acq, University of Texas Libraries, Serials Acquisitions Unit, PO Box P, Austin, TX, 78713-8916. Tel: 512-495-4222. Fax: 512-495-4296. p. 2285

Banush, David, Assoc Univ Librn, Access Serv, Brown University, Ten Prospect St, Box A, Providence, RI, 02912. Tel: 401-863-2167. Fax: 401-863-1272. p. 2172

Banwart, Gail, Librn, Peninsula College Library, 1502 E Lauridsen Blvd, Port Angeles, WA, 98362-6698. Tel: 360-417-6284. Fax: 360-417-6295. p. 2524

Banzhaf, Troy, In Charge, US National Park Service, 15930 Hyw 62, Garfield, AR, 72732. Tel: 479-451-8122. Fax: 479-451-8639. p. 101

Bapiran, Loretto, Customer Serv Supvr, Parsippany-Troy Hills Free Public Library, 449 Halsey Rd, Parsippany, NJ, 07054. Tel: 973-887-5150. Fax: 973-887-0062. p. 1517

Baqqi, Joanna, Tech Serv Librn, Bedford Public Library, Three Meetinghouse Rd, Bedford, NH, 03110-5406. Tel: 603-472-2300, 603-472-3023. Fax: 603-472-2978. p. 1438

Bar, Karen, Tech Serv Mgr, Oak Park Public Library, 834 Lake St, Oak Park, IL, 60301. Tel: 708-383-8200. Fax: 708-697-6900. p. 684

Bara, Stefanie, Children's & YA Librn, Azle Memorial Library, 333 W Main St, Azle, TX, 76020. Tel: 817-444-7216. Fax: 817-444-7064. p. 2285

Barabe, Dee, Libr Tech, Wisconsin Indianhead Technical College, 2100 Beaser Ave, Ashland, WI, 54806. Tel: 715-682-4591, Ext 3108. Fax: 715-682-8040. p. 2579

Barahona, Philip, Res, Weil, Gotshal & Manges Library, 767 Fifth Ave, New York, NY, 10153. Tel: 212-310-8626. Fax: 212-310-8007. p. 1702

Barajas, Donna, Dept Supvr, Klamath County Library Services District, 126 S Third St, Klamath Falls, OR, 97601-6394. Tel: 541-882-8894. Fax: 541-882-6166. p. 2001

Barajas, Ramon, Ref Serv, Munger, Tolles & Olson LLP, 355 S Grand Ave, 35th Flr, Los Angeles, CA, 90071-1560. Tel: 213-683-9100. Fax: 213-683-5173. p. 176

Barak, Barbara, Coordr, Toronto Jewish Library, 4600 Bathurst St, 4th Flr, Toronto, ON, M2R 3V3, CANADA. Tel: 416-631-5843. Fax: 416-849-1005. p. 2859

Barak, Esti, Pres, Temple Beth Israel Library, 6622 N Maroa Ave, Fresno, CA, 93704. Tel: 559-432-3600. Fax: 559-432-3685. p. 153

Baram-Clothier, Evelyn, Dr, Dir, American Medical Foundation for Peer Review & Education Library, The Barclay on Rittenhouse Sq, 237 S 18th St, Ste 11-D, Philadelphia, PA, 19103-6164. Tel: 215-545-6363. Fax: 215-545-2163. p. 2102

Baran, Terri K, Law Librn, Sullivan County Law Library, Court House, Main & Muncy St, Laporte, PA, 18626. Tel: 570-946-4053. Fax: 570-946-4609. p. 2078

Baranieski, Melinda, Head, Libr & Info Serv, Vancouver Community College, 250 W Pender St, Vancouver, BC, V6B 1S9, CANADA. Tel: 604-871-7319. Fax: 604-443-8588. p. 2743

Barannik, Halyna, Sr Librn, Shawangunk Correctional Facility Library, Quick Rd, Wallkill, NY, 12589. Tel: 845-895-2081, Ext 4600. p. 1762

Baranowski, Bernice, Libr Coordr, Canadian Centre for Ecumenism Library, 1819, René-Lévesque ouest, Bureau No 003, Montreal, QC, H3H 2P5, CANADA. Tel: 514-937-9176. Fax: 514-937-4986. p. 2892

Baranowski, Richard, Hist Coll Librn, Way Public Library, 101 E Indiana Ave, Perrysburg, OH, 43551. Tel: 419-874-3135, Ext 110. Fax: 419-874-6129. p. 1929

Baratko, David, Sr Media Serv Tech, Connecticut College, 270 Mohegan Ave, New London, CT, 06320-4196. Tel: 860-439-2693. Fax: 860-439-2871. p. 359

Baratta, Maria, Asst Dir, New Jersey State Library, Talking Book & Braille Center, 2300 Stuyvesant Ave, Trenton, NJ, 08618. Tel: 609-406-7179, Ext 803. Fax: 609-406-7181. p. 1536

Baratta, Paula, Supv Librn, Eastern Region, Newark Public Library, Five Washington St, Newark, NJ, 07101. Tel: 973-733-7760. Fax: 973-733-5648. p. 1511

Baratta, Paula, Supv Librn-in-Charge, Eastern Region, Newark Public Library, North End, 722 Summer Ave, Newark, NJ, 07104. Tel: 973-733-7766. Fax: 973-733-7835. p. 1512

Barbanell, Robert, Br Serv Mgr, Elizabeth Public Library, Elizabeth Port, 102-110 Third St, Elizabeth, NJ, 07206-1717. Tel: 908-353-4820. Fax: 908-289-5663. p. 1483

Barbanell, Robert, Br Serv Mgr, Elizabeth Public Library, Elmora, 740 W Grand St, Elizabeth, NJ, 07202. Tel: 908-353-4820. Fax: 908-353-6877. p. 1483

Barbanell, Robert, Br Serv Mgr, Elizabeth Public Library, Lacorte, 408 Palmer St, Elizabeth, NJ, 07202. Tel: 908-353-4820. Fax: 908-820-4764. p. 1483

Barbara, Miles, Br Librn, Sweetwater County Library System, Bairoil Branch Library, 101 Blue Bell St, Bairoil, WY, 82322. Tel: 307-328-0239. Fax: 307-328-0239. p. 2655

Barbara, Stith, Commun Serv Coordr, Seymour Public Library District, 176-178 Genesee St, Auburn, NY, 13021. Tel: 315-252-2571. Fax: 315-252-7985. p. 1576

3271

Barbarena, Corine, Sr Librn, Irving Public Library, East, 440 S Nursery Rd, Irving, TX, 75060. Tel: 972-721-3722. Fax: 972-721-3724. p. 2347

Barbari, Debra, Head, Tech Serv, Russell Library, 123 Broad St, Middletown, CT, 06457. Tel: 860-347-2528, Ext 151. p. 352

Barbarito, Mary Ellen, Acq Mgr, Yale University Library, Divinity School Library, 409 Prospect St, New Haven, CT, 06511-2108. Tel: 203-432-5294. Fax: 203-432-3906. p. 357

Barbee, Diane, Interim Dir, Saint Helens Public Library, 375 S 18th St, Ste A, Saint Helens, OR, 97051-2022. Tel: 503-397-4544, Ext 1. Fax: 503-366-3020. p. 2017

Barbee, Janet S, Acq, Cabarrus County Public Library, 27 Union St N, Concord, NC, 28025-4793. Tel: 704-920-2050. Fax: 704-784-3822. p. 1785

Barbee, Kathy, Asst Librn, Utica Public Library District, Mill & Grove Sts, Utica, IL, 61373. Tel: 815-667-4509. Fax: 815-667-4140. p. 713

Barbee, Luanne, Head, Circ, Wingate University, PO Box 219, Wingate, NC, 28174-1202. Tel: 704-233-8089. Fax: 704-233-8254. p. 1832

Barber, Alan, Tech Serv, Jackson County Public Library System, 2929 Green St, Marianna, FL, 32446. Tel: 850-482-9631. Fax: 850-482-9632. p. 462

Barber, Bonnie, Chair, Department of Community Services, Government of Yukon, Dawson City Community, Robert Service School, Dawson City, YT, Y0B 1G0, CANADA. Tel: 867-993-5571. Fax: 867-993-6770. p. 2933

Barber, Danita, Libr Mgr, Plano Public Library System, Gladys Harrington Library, 1501 E 18th St, Plano, TX, 75074. Tel: 972-941-7175. Fax: 972-941-7292. p. 2370

Barber, Elsa, Libr Asst, Edison Community College Library, 1973 Edison Dr, Piqua, OH, 45356. Tel: 937-778-7953. Fax: 937-778-7958. p. 1930

Barber, Genora F, Info Spec, US Bureau of the Census, 101 Marietta St NW, Ste 3200, Atlanta, GA, 30303-2700. Tel: 404-730-3833. Fax: 404-730-3964. p. 518

Barber, Holly, Cat, Doane College, 1014 Boswell Ave, Crete, NE, 68333-2421. Tel: 402-826-8565. Fax: 402-826-8199. p. 1396

Barber, Jeff, Chief Exec Officer, Libr Dir, Regina Public Library, Library Directors Office, 2311 12th Ave, Regina, SK, S4P 0N3, CANADA. Tel: 306-777-6099. Fax: 306-949-7263. p. 2923

Barber, Jessica, YA Librn, Giles County Public Library, 122 S Second St, Pulaski, TN, 38478-3285. Tel: 931-363-2720. Fax: 931-424-7032. p. 2263

Barber, Joseph R, Librn, Orange County Community College Library, 115 South St, Middletown, NY, 10940. Tel: 845-562-4542. Fax: 845-341-4424. p. 1660

Barber, Judith, Librn, Belfast Public Library, 75 S Main St, Belfast, NY, 14711-8605. Tel: 585-365-2072. Fax: 585-365-2072. p. 1579

Barber, Kay, Librn, Lenawee Health Alliance, 818 Riverside Ave, Adrian, MI, 49221. Tel: 517-265-0961. Fax: 517-265-0884. p. 1147

Barber, Kyle, Br Mgr, Nashville Public Library, Thompson Lane, 380 Thompson Lane, Nashville, TN, 37211-2485. Tel: 615-862-5873. Fax: 615-862-5898. p. 2258

Barber, Laura, Principal Law Librn, New York State Supreme Court Library-Troy, Court House Second St Annex, 86 Second St, Troy, NY, 12180-4098. Tel: 518-285-6183. Fax: 518-274-0590. p. 1756

Barber, Mary Lou, Librn, Montmorency County Public Libraries, Lewiston Public, 2851 Kneeland St, Lewiston, MI, 49756. Tel: 989-786-2985. p. 1154

Barber, Mary Lou, Librn, Lewiston Public Library, 2851 Kneeland, Lewiston, MI, 49756. Tel: 989-786-2985. Fax: 989-786-2985. p. 1203

Barber, Maryke, Outreach Librn, Hollins University, 7950 E Campus Dr, Roanoke, VA, 24020-1000. Tel: 540-362-6328. Fax: 540-362-6756. p. 2493

Barber, Susie, Librn, Arley Public Library, 6788 Hwy 41, Arley, AL, 35541. Tel: 205-387-0129. Fax: 205-387-0129. p. 4

Barber White, Linda, Budget & Coll Develop Mgr, LeRoy Collins Leon County Public Library System, 200 W Park Ave, Tallahassee, FL, 32301-7720. Tel: 850-606-2665. Fax: 850-606-2601. p. 492

Barber-Grenier, Peggy, Librn, Wapiti Regional Library, Marcelin Public Library, 100 First Ave, Marcelin, SK, S0J 1R0, CANADA. Tel: 306-226-2110. p. 2921

Barbera, Christine, Asst Librn, Hubbardston Public Library, Seven Main St, Hubbardston, MA, 01452. Tel: 978-928-4775. Fax: 978-928-1273. p. 1096

Barbero, Linda, Circ Mgr, Contra Costa County Library, 1750 Oak Park Blvd, Pleasant Hill, CA, 94523-4497. Tel: 925-646-6434. Fax: 925-646-6461. p. 208

Barbero, Linda, Circ Mgr, Contra Costa County Library, Pleasant Hill Library, 1750 Oak Park Blvd, Pleasant Hill, CA, 94523-4497. Tel: 925-646-6434. Fax: 925-646-6040. p. 209

Barbie, Robert Joe, Syst Operational Analyst II, Richmond Public Library, 101 E Franklin St, Richmond, VA, 23219-2193. Tel: 804-646-4256. Fax: 804-646-7685. p. 2489

Barbier, Pat, Librn, Saint Petersburg College, Clearwater Campus Library, 2465 Drew St, Clearwater, FL, 33765. Tel: 727-791-2603. Fax: 727-791-2601. p. 483

Barbieri, Dawn, Tech Serv, Ramsdell Public Library, 1087 Main St, Housatonic, MA, 01236-9730. Tel: 413-274-3738. p. 1096

Barbieri, Eileen, Br Supvr, Southside Regional Library, Clarksville Area Public Library, 914 Virginia Ave, Clarksville, VA, 23927. Tel: 434-374-8692. Fax: 434-374-8200. p. 2452

Barbone, Patricia E, Dir, Libr Serv, Hughes, Hubbard & Reed Library, One Battery Park Plaza, 16th Flr, New York, NY, 10004. Tel: 212-837-6594. Fax: 212-422-4726. p. 1681

Barbosa-Jerez, Mary, Head, Coll Develop, Saint Olaf College, Rolvaag Memorial Library, Glasoe Science Library, Halvorson Music Library, 1510 Saint Olaf Ave, Northfield, MN, 55057-1097. Tel: 507-786-3634. Fax: 507-786-3734. p. 1269

Barbour, Dan, YA Librn, Shrewsbury Public Library, 609 Main St, Shrewsbury, MA, 01545. Tel: 508-841-8537. Fax: 508-841-8540. p. 1124

Barbour, Wendell, Dean of Libr, Longwood University, Redford & Race St, Farmville, VA, 23909. Tel: 434-395-2083. Fax: 434-395-2453. p. 2463

Barboza, Calida, Electronic Res Librn, Ithaca College Library, 953 Danby Rd, Ithaca, NY, 14850-7060. Tel: 607-274-1892. Fax: 607-274-1539. p. 1643

Barcel, Ellen, In Charge, Incorporated Long Island Chapter of the New York State Archaeological Association, Southold Indian Museum, 1080 Main Bayview Rd, Southold, NY, 11971. Tel: 631-765-5577. Fax: 631-765-5577. p. 1746

Barchie, Debbie, Dir, Barrington Public Library, 281 County Rd, Barrington, RI, 02806. Tel: 401-247-1920. Fax: 401-247-3763. p. 2163

Barciauskas, Jonas, Dir, Coll Serv, Boston College Libraries, 140 Commonwealth Ave, Chestnut Hill, MA, 02467. Tel: 617-552-3195. Fax: 617-552-8828. p. 1080

Barciauskas, Jonas, Head, Coll Develop, Boston College Libraries, Thomas P O'Neill Jr Library (Central Library), 140 Commonwealth Ave, Chestnut Hill, MA, 02467. Tel: 617-552-4447. Fax: 617-552-0599. p. 1081

Barckley, Darlene, Librn, Ecosystems International Inc Library, 1107 Dicus Mill Rd, Millersville, MD, 21108. Tel: 410-987-4976. Fax: 410-729-1960. p. 1035

Barclay, Bella, Commun Libr Mgr, Queens Borough Public Library, Baisley Park Community Library, 117-11 Sutphin Blvd, Jamaica, NY, 11436. Tel: 718-529-1590. p. 1644

Barclay, Donald, Dep Univ Librn, University of California, Merced Library, 5200 N Lake Rd, Merced, CA, 95343-5001. Tel: 209-201-9724. Fax: 209-228-4271. p. 186

Barclay, Kim, Bibliog Instruction Librn, Long Beach City College, 4901 E Carson St, Long Beach, CA, 90808. Tel: 562-938-4708. Fax: 562-938-3062, 562-938-4777. p. 166

Barclay, Sandra, Librn/Cat, Kennesaw State University, 1000 Chastain Rd, Kennesaw, GA, 30144. Tel: 770-423-4445. Fax: 770-423-6185. p. 537

Barcus, Carol, Teen Serv, Huron Public Library, 333 Williams St, Huron, OH, 44839. Tel: 419-433-5009. Fax: 419-433-7228. p. 1906

Barczyk, Ewa, Dir, University of Wisconsin-Milwaukee Libraries, 2311 E Hartford Ave, Milwaukee, WI, 53211. Tel: 414-229-4785, 414-229-6202. Fax: 414-229-6766. p. 2622

Bard, Corey, Dir, Ruidoso Public Library, 107 Kansas City Rd, Ruidoso, NM, 88345. Tel: 505-258-3704. Fax: 505-258-4619. p. 1561

Bard, Corey, Dir, Curry Public Library, 94341 Third St, Gold Beach, OR, 97444. Tel: 541-247-7246. Fax: 541-247-4411. p. 1999

Bardeen, Marjorie R, Interim Dir, Libr Serv, LancasterHistory.org Library, 230 N President Ave, Lancaster, PA, 17603-3125. Tel: 717-392-4633. Fax: 717-293-2739. p. 2077

Barden, Cheryl A, Coop Librn, Meritor, Inc, 2135 W Maple Rd, Troy, MI, 48084-7186. Tel: 248-435-1668. Fax: 248-435-1670. p. 1232

Barden, Daniel, Tech Serv Adminr, Alachua County Library District, 401 E University Ave, Gainesville, FL, 32601-5453. Tel: 352-334-3960. Fax: 352-334-3999. p. 448

Barden, John R, Dir, Maine State Law & Legislative Reference Library, 43 State House Sta, Augusta, ME, 04333-0043. Tel: 207-287-1600. Fax: 207-287-6467. p. 974

Barden, Kathryn, Head, Pub Serv, Westminster College, Reeves Memorial Library, 501 Westminster Ave, Fulton, MO, 65251-1299. Tel: 573-592-5245. Fax: 573-642-6356. p. 1328

Barden, Susan, Dir, Carpenter-Carse Library, 69 Ballards Corner Rd, Hinesburg, VT, 05461. Tel: 802-482-2878. p. 2425

Bardi, Gina, Ref Librn, San Francisco Maritime Library, Fort Mason Ctr, Bldg E, 3rd Flr, San Francisco, CA, 94123. Tel: 415-561-7030. Fax: 415-556-1624. p. 245

Bardis, Gail, Cat, United States Army, 1794 Walker Ave SW, Fort McPherson, GA, 30330-1013. Tel: 404-464-2644. Fax: 404-464-3801. p. 533

Bardolph, Anne D, Acq, Florida State University Libraries, College of Law Library, 425 W Jefferson St, Tallahassee, FL, 32306. Tel: 850-644-4578. Fax: 850-644-5216. p. 494

Bardwell, Gail, Dir, Gilsum Public Library, 650 Rte 10, Gilsum, NH, 03448-7502. Tel: 603-357-0320. Fax: 603-352-0845. p. 1448

Barefoot, Gary, Curator, Mount Olive College, 634 Henderson St, Mount Olive, NC, 28365-1699. Tel: 919-658-7869, Ext 1416. Fax: 919-658-8934. p. 1811

Barefoot, Maria, Health Sci Librn, Youngstown State University, One University Plaza, Youngstown, OH, 44555-0001. Tel: 330-941-3681, Fax: 330-941-3734. p. 1953

Barefoot, Ruth, Sr Librn, Innovation, San Jose Public Library, 150 E San Fernando St, San Jose, CA, 95112-3580. Tel: 408-808-2131. p. 250

Bareither, Sandy, Librn, North Central Regional Library, Waterville Community, 105 N Chelan St, Waterville, WA, 98858. Tel: 509-745-8354. Fax: 509-745-8354. p. 2549

Barelos, Deb, Circ Mgr, Omaha Public Library, 215 S 15th St, Omaha, NE, 68102-1629. Tel: 402-444-4800. Fax: 402-444-4504. p. 1413

Bares, Joan, Dir, Medcenter One, 622 Ave A East, Bismarck, ND, 58501. Tel: 701-323-5390. Fax: 701-323-6967. p. 1838

Bares, Joan, Ref, United States Army, Stimson Library, Medical Department Center & School, 3630 Stanley Rd, Bldg 2840, Ste 106, Fort Sam Houston, TX, 78234-6100. Tel: 210-221-6900. Fax: 210-221-8264. p. 2321

Barette, Isabelle, Libr Tech, Hopital Riviere-Des-Prairies, 7070 boul Perras, Montreal, QC, H1E 1A4, CANADA. Tel: 514-323-7260, Ext 2316. Fax: 514-323-3512. p. 2896

Barfell, Brenda, Librn, Calhoun County Library, 109 Second St, Hampton, AR, 71744. Tel: 870-798-4492. Fax: 870-798-4492. p. 102

Barfield, Angela, Acq, Winebrenner Theological Seminary Library, 950 N Main St, Findlay, OH, 45840-3652. Tel: 419-434-4261. Fax: 419-434-4267. p. 1899

Barfield, Laura, Syst, Trident Technical College, Main Campus Learning Resources Center, LR-M, PO Box 118067, Charleston, SC, 29423-8067. Tel: 843-574-6089. Fax: 843-574-6484. p. 2185

Barfield, William, Media Spec, Presbyterian Hospital, 200 Hawthorne Lane, Charlotte, NC, 28204-2528. Tel: 704-384-4258. Fax: 704-384-5058. p. 1783

Bargar, Arthur, Media Spec, Milford Public Library, 57 New Haven Ave, Milford, CT, 06460. Tel: 203-783-3290. Fax: 203-877-1072. p. 352

Bargar, Polly, Librn, Dr Earl S Sloan Library, 2817 Sandusky St, Zanesfield, OH, 43360. Tel: 937-592-8343. Fax: 937-592-6474. p. 1953

Barge, Al, Librn, Georgia Department of Corrections, Office of Library Services, 27823 Main St, Morgan, GA, 31766. Tel: 229-849-5058. Fax: 229-849-5017. p. 545

Barger, Angela, Per, Fort Hays State University, 600 Park St, Hays, KS, 67601-4099. Tel: 785-628-4529. Fax: 785-628-4096. p. 871

Barger, Deborah, YA Librn, Bradford Public Library, 138 E Main St, Bradford, OH, 45308-1108. Tel: 937-448-2612. Fax: 937-448-2615. p. 1861

Barger, Renae, Exec Dir, National Network of Libraries of Medicine Middle Atlantic Region, University of Pittsburgh, 3550 Terrace St, 200 Scaife Hall, Pittsburgh, PA, 15261. p. 2954

Bargmann, Lesa, Asst Librn, Bancroft Public Library, 104 E Poplar St, Bancroft, NE, 68004. Tel: 402-648-3350. p. 1392

Bargmann, Ruthann, Chief Librn, Bancroft Public Library, 104 E Poplar St, Bancroft, NE, 68004. Tel: 402-648-3350. p. 1392

Barham, Anne, Circ, Sampson-Clinton Public Library, Bryan Memorial, 302 W Weeksdale St, Newton Grove, NC, 28366. Tel: 910-594-1260. p. 1784

Barham, Cecilia Hurt, Dir, Decatur Public Library, 1700 Hwy 51 S, Decatur, TX, 76234-9292. Tel: 940-627-5512. Fax: 940-627-2905. p. 2311

Barham, James, Coordr, Media Serv, Lambuth University, 705 Lambuth Blvd, Jackson, TN, 38301. Tel: 731-425-3293. Fax: 731-425-3200. p. 2238

Barham, Sharon, ILL, Queens University of Charlotte, 1900 Selwyn Ave, Charlotte, NC, 28274-0001. Tel: 704-337-2401. Fax: 704-337-2517. p. 1784

Barhorst, Sheila, Br Coordr, Shelby County Libraries, Russia Branch, 200 Raider St, Russia, OH, 45363. Tel: 937-526-4300. Fax: 937-526-4300. p. 1935

Baria, D K, Outreach Coordr, Mississippi Delta Community College, 414 Hwy 3 South, Moorhead, MS, 38761. Tel: 662-246-6353. Fax: 662-246-8627. p. 1309

Barich, Phyllis, Coll Develop & Off-Campus Serv Coordr, Red River College Library, 2055 Notre Dame Ave, Winnipeg, MB, R3H 0J9, CANADA. Tel: 204-949-8372. Fax: 204-949-9173. p. 2757

Baril, Charlotte, Dir, Libr Serv, Bibliotheque Municipale de Rouyn-Noranda, 201 Ave Dallaire, Rouyn-Noranda, QC, J9X 4T5, CANADA. Tel: 819-762-0944. Fax: 819-797-7136. p. 2908

Baril, Kathleen, Coll & Electronic Res Librn, Ohio Northern University, 525 S Main St, Ada, OH, 45810. Tel: 419-772-2188. Fax: 419-772-1927. p. 1851

Bariola, Kristy Aust, Dir of Libr Serv, Mississippi Delta Community College, 414 Hwy 3 South, Moorhead, MS, 38761. Tel: 662-246-6378. Fax: 662-246-8627. p. 1309

Barkan, Steven, Dir, University of Wisconsin-Madison, Law School, 975 Bascom Mall, Madison, WI, 53706. Tel: 608-262-1151. Fax: 608-262-2775. p. 2609

Barkauskas, Eleanor, In Charge, Macdermid, Inc Library, 245 Freight St, Waterbury, CT, 06702. Tel: 203-575-5700. Fax: 203-575-5630. p. 374

Barkema, Bonnie, Dir, Stubbs Memorial Library, 207 E Second St, Holstein, IA, 51025. Tel: 712-368-4563. Fax: 712-368-4483. p. 821

Barker, Andrew, Libr Tech, College of the North Atlantic, Grand Falls-Windsor Campus, Five Cromer Ave, Grand Falls-Windsor, NL, A2A 1X3, CANADA. Tel: 709-292-5637. Fax: 709-489-5765. p. 2771

Barker, Anne, Humanities Librn, University of Missouri-Columbia, Elmer Ellis Library, Ellis Library Bldg, Rm 104, Columbia, MO, 65201-5149. Tel: 573-882-6324. Fax: 573-882-8044. p. 1325

Barker, Anne, Dir, Nacogdoches Public Library, 1112 North St, Nacogdoches, TX, 75961-4482. Tel: 936-559-2970. Fax: 936-569-8282. p. 2364

Barker, Bessie, Br Mgr, Boone-Madison Public Library, Coal River, 494 John Slack Circle, Racine, WV, 25165. Tel: 304-837-8437. Fax: 304-834-8437. p. 2564

Barker, Deborah, Librn, US Army Corps of Engineers Library, Pittsburgh District, 1000 Liberty Ave, Pittsburgh, PA, 15222-4186. Tel: 412-395-7422. Fax: 412-644-2811. p. 2128

Barker, Diane, Librn, Harris County Public Library, Crosby Branch, 135 Hare Rd, Crosby, TX, 77532. Tel: 281-328-3535. Fax: 281-328-5590. p. 2336

Barker, Elizabeth, Dir, Wornstaff Memorial Public Library, 302 E High St, Ashley, OH, 43003-9703. Tel: 740-747-2085. Fax: 740-747-2085. p. 1855

Barker, Gloria, Dir, Commun & Tech Serv, Wheaton College Library, 26 E Main St, Norton, MA, 02766-2322. Tel: 508-286-3723. p. 1115

Barker, Janice, Dir, Osawatomie Public Library, 527 Brown Ave, Osawatomie, KS, 66064-1367. Tel: 913-755-2136. Fax: 913-755-2335. p. 886

Barker, Jody, Head, Circ Serv, Nazareth College of Rochester Library, 4245 East Ave, Rochester, NY, 14618-3790. Tel: 585-389-2160. Fax: 585-389-2145. p. 1730

Barker, John, Archivist, Librn, Hawaiian Mission Children's Society Library, 553 S King St, Honolulu, HI, 96813. Tel: 808-531-0481. Fax: 808-545-2280. p. 564

Barker, Kate, Mgr, Richmond Hill Public Library, 9607 Ford Ave, Richmond Hill, GA, 31324. Tel: 912-756-3580. Fax: 912-756-2976. p. 548

Barker, Lorie, Librn, Porterville College Library, 100 E College Ave, Porterville, CA, 93257-5901. Tel: 559-791-2370. Fax: 559-791-2289. p. 212

Barker, Marian, Ch, Coll Mgr, Jackson County Library Services, 205 S Central Ave, Medford, OR, 97501-2730. Tel: 541-774-6554. Fax: 541-774-6748. p. 1909

Barker, Marlene, Br Mgr, San Diego County Library, Borrego Springs Branch, 587 Palm Canyon Dr, Ste 125, Borrego Springs, CA, 92004. Tel: 760-767-5761. Fax: 760-767-3619. p. 233

Barker, Mary, Dir, Coffey County Library, Lebo Branch, 327 S Ogden St, Lebo, KS, 66856-9306. Tel: 620-256-6452. Fax: 620-256-6301. p. 859

Barker, Melissa, Asst Librn, ILL, Murphy Public Library, Nine Blumenthal St, Murphy, NC, 28906. Tel: 828-837-2417. Fax: 828-837-6416. p. 1812

Barker, Patty, Librn, Sheridan Public Library, 103 W First St, Sheridan, IN, 46069. Tel: 317-758-5201. Fax: 317-758-0045. p. 778

Barker, Peggie, Head, Tech Serv, Ferrum College, 150 Wiley Dr, Ferrum, VA, 24088. Tel: 540-365-4426. Fax: 540-365-4423. p. 2463

Barker, Rachael, Youth Serv Prog Coordr, Gallia County District Library, Seven Spruce St, Gallipolis, OH, 45631. Tel: 740-446-7323. Fax: 740-446-1701. p. 1901

Barker, Robin, Syst Design/Coll Mgr, Whatcom County Library System, 5205 Northwest Dr, Bellingham, WA, 98226-9050. Tel: 360-384-3150. Fax: 360-384-4947. p. 2509

Barker, Scott, Dir, Info Tech, Sr Lecturer, University of Washington, Mary Gates Hall, Ste 370, Campus Box 352840, Seattle, WA, 98195-2840. Tel: 206-685-9937. Fax: 206-616-3152. p. 2976

Barker, Susanne, Librn, British Columbia Ministry of Forests Library, 722 Johnson St, 4th Flr, Victoria, BC, V8W 9C2, CANADA. Tel: 250-387-3628. Fax: 250-953-3079. p. 2745

Barker, Wendy, Exec Dir, Escondido History Center, 321 N Broadway, Escondido, CA, 92025. Tel: 760-743-8207. Fax: 760-743-8267. p. 146

Barkett, Gina, Asst Dir, Kirtland Public Library, 9267 Chillicothe Rd, Kirtland, OH, 44094. Tel: 440-256-7323. Fax: 440-256-1372. p. 1908

Barkley, Donna, Br Mgr, Public Library of Cincinnati & Hamilton County, Mount Healthy, 7608 Hamilton Ave, Cincinnati, OH, 45231. Tel: 513-369-4469. Fax: 513-369-4470. p. 1872

Barkley, Hellena, Br Mgr, Killeen City Library System, 205 E Church Ave, Killeen, TX, 76541. Tel: 254-501-7875. Fax: 254-501-7704. p. 2350

Barkley, James, Librn, Mt Cuba Astronomical Observatory Memorial Library, Hillside Mill Rd, Greenville, DE, 19807. Tel: 302-654-6407. p. 383

Barkley, Shelley, Librn, Crop Diversification Centre South Library, 301 Horticultural Sta Rd E, Brooks, AB, T1R 1E6, CANADA. Tel: 403-362-1350. Fax: 403-362-1306. p. 2686

Barkley, Terry W, Dir, Church of the Brethren, 1451 Dundee Ave, Elgin, IL, 60120-1694. Tel: 847-429-4368. Fax: 847-429-4378. p. 640

Barkman, LeRoy, Librn, Steinbach Bible College Library, 50 PTH 12 N, Steinbach, MB, R5G 1T4, CANADA. Tel: 204-326-6451. Fax: 204-326-6908. p. 2752

Barksdale, Iain, Head, Ref (Info Serv), University of Alabama, School of Law Library, 101 Paul Bryant Dr, Tuscaloosa, AL, 35487. Tel: 205-348-5925. Fax: 205-348-1112. p. 38

Barksdale, Mary, Head, Ref & Acq, The Brentwood Library, 8109 Concord Rd, Brentwood, TN, 37027. Tel: 615-371-0090, Ext 8130. Fax: 615-371-2238. p. 2225

Barksdale, Renita, Mgr, Greenville County Library System, Anderson Road (West) Branch, 2625 Anderson Rd, Greenville, SC, 29611. Tel: 864-269-5210. Fax: 864-269-3986. p. 2196

Barksdale, Terry, Head Librn, Austin Community College, Cypress Creek Campus Library, 1555 Cypress Creek Rd, Cedar Park, TX, 78613. Tel: 512-223-2135. Fax: 512-223-2035. p. 2278

Barlett, Paula, Libr Spec, Cecil College, One Seahawk Dr, North East, MD, 21901-1904. Tel: 410-287-1005. Fax: 410-287-1607. p. 1035

Barlin, Maria, Head, Ch, Smithtown Library, One N Country Rd, Smithtown, NY, 11787. Tel: 631-265-2072. Fax: 631-265-2044. p. 1744

Barlous, Jaye, Ref Librn, University of Oregon Libraries, John E Jaqua Law Library, William W Knight Law Ctr, 2nd Flr, 1515 Agate St, Eugene, OR, 97403-1221. Tel: 541-346-1901. Fax: 541-346-1669. p. 1997

Barlow, Amy, Ref & Instruction Librn, Quinebaug Valley Community College Library, 742 Upper Maple St, Danielson, CT, 06239. Tel: 860-412-7272. Fax: 860-412-7277. p. 335

Barlow, Barbara, Br Supvr, Jackson/Hinds Library System, Evelyn T Majure Library, 217 W Main St, Utica, MS, 39175-0340. Tel: 601-885-8381. Fax: 601-885-2612. p. 1303

Barlow, Cathy, Acq Mgr, Principia College, One Maybeck Pl, Elsah, IL, 62028-9703. Tel: 618-374-5235. Fax: 618-374-5107. p. 643

Barlow, Don W, Exec Dir, Westerville Public Library, 126 S State St, Westerville, OH, 43081-2095. Tel: 614-882-7277, Ext 2140. Fax: 614-882-5369. p. 1946

Barlow, Donna, Dir, Saint Francis Medical Center, 601 Hamilton Ave, Trenton, NJ, 08629-1986. Tel: 609-599-5068. Fax: 609-599-5773. p. 1536

Barlow, Helen, Librn, Jackson-George Regional Library System, East Central Public Library, 21801 Slider Rd, Moss Point, MS, 39562. Tel: 228-588-6263. Fax: 228-588-0145. p. 1310

Barlow, Jennifer, Mgr, Borgess Medical Center Library, 1521 Gull Rd, Kalamazoo, MI, 49048-1666. Tel: 269-226-7360. Fax: 269-226-6881. p. 1196

Barmer, Theresa, Br Mgr, Jacksonville Public Library, Southeast Regional, 10599 Deerwood Park Blvd, Jacksonville, FL, 32256-0507. Tel: 904-996-0325. Fax: 904-996-0340. p. 454

Barmer, Theresa, Br Mgr, Jacksonville Public Library, Webb Wesconnett Regional, 6887 103rd St, Jacksonville, FL, 32210-6897. Tel: 904-778-7305. Fax: 904-777-2262. p. 454

Barna, Mary, Dir, Valley Community Library, 739 River St, Peckville, PA, 18452. Tel: 570-489-1765. p. 2102

Barnabas, Heather, Circ, Montefiore Medical Center, 111 E 210th St, Bronx, NY, 10467. Tel: 718-920-4666. Fax: 718-920-4658. p. 1588

Barnaby, Bruce, Tech Serv, Canada Department of Fisheries & Oceans, 1190 Westmount Rd, Sydney, NS, B1P 6L1, CANADA. Tel: 902-564-3660, Ext 1164. Fax: 902-564-3672. p. 2784

Barnard, Ann, Tech Serv, Samuel Merritt College, 400 Hawthorne Ave, Oakland, CA, 94609. Tel: 510-869-8693. Fax: 510-869-6633. p. 199

Barnard, Brianna, Librn, Lauren Rogers Museum of Art Library, 565 N Fifth Ave, Laurel, MS, 39440-3410. Tel: 601-649-6374. Fax: 601-428-8601, 601-649-6379. p. 1307

Barnard, Diana, Archivist, Saint Joseph College, 1678 Asylum Ave, West Hartford, CT, 06117-2791. Tel: 860-231-5740. Fax: 860-523-4356. p. 376

Barnard, Madelene, Br Mgr, Manatee County Public Library System, South Manatee County, 6081 26th St N, Bradenton, FL, 34207. Tel: 941-755-3892. Fax: 941-751-7098. p. 430

Barnard, Melissa, Dir, Grace A Dow Memorial Library, 1710 W St Andrews Ave, Midland, MI, 48640-2698. Tel: 989-837-3430. Fax: 989-837-3468. p. 1208

Barnard, Phyllis, Youth Serv, Lincoln Library, 326 S Seventh St, Springfield, IL, 62701. Tel: 217-753-4900, Ext 215. Fax: 217-753-5329. p. 706

Barnard, Rebecca, Archivist, St Philip's College, 1801 Martin Luther King Dr, San Antonio, TX, 78203-2098. Tel: 210-486-2330. Fax: 210-486-2335. p. 2381

Barnard, Terri, Med Librn, Via Christi Libraries, North Saint Francis Street, 929 N Saint Francis St, Wichita, KS, 67214-1315. Tel: 316-268-5979. Fax: 316-268-8694. p. 901

Barnello, Inga H, Pub Serv Librn, Le Moyne College, 1419 Salt Springs Rd, Syracuse, NY, 13214-1301. Tel: 315-445-4326. Fax: 315-445-4642. p. 1751

Barnes, Barbara, Instruction & Outreach, Librn, Lewis-Clark State College Library, 500 Eighth Ave, Lewiston, ID, 83501. Tel: 208-792-2235. Fax: 208-792-2831. p. 578

Barnes, Barbara, Librn, Tulsa City-County Library, Owasso Branch, 103 W Broadway, Owasso, OK, 74055. Tel: 918-591-4566. Fax: 918-591-4568. p. 1983

Barnes, Brenda, Librn, Dyess Public Library, 101 E Fourth St, Dyess, AR, 72330. Tel: 870-764-2101 (city hall). p. 98

Barnes, Brenda, Head, Ref, Texas Christian University, 2913 Lowden St, TCU Box 298400, Fort Worth, TX, 76129. Tel: 817-257-5430. Fax: 817-257-7282. p. 2323

Barnes, Brian, Circ Librn, Instrul Serv Librn, Res Librn, Mississippi College, 151 E Griffith St, Jackson, MS, 39201-1391. Tel: 601-925-7120. Fax: 601-925-7112. p. 1304

Barnes, Bruce, Coll Develop, Head, Tech Serv, University of Massachusetts Dartmouth Library, 285 Old Westport Rd, North Dartmouth, MA, 02747-2300. Tel: 508-999-8666. Fax: 508-999-8987. p. 1112

Barnes, Caroline, Tech Serv, Black Hawk College, 6600 34th Ave, Moline, IL, 61265. Tel: 309-796-5700. Fax: 309-796-0393. p. 674

Barnes, Cathy, Res, Fayetteville Publishing Co, 458 Whitfield St, Fayetteville, NC, 28306. Tel: 910-486-3584. Fax: 910-486-3545. p. 1793

Barnes, Connie, Pub Serv, Watauga Public Library, 7109 Whitley Rd, Watauga, TX, 76148-2024. Tel: 817-514-5855. Fax: 817-581-3910. p. 2398

Barnes, Debra, Librn, New Mexico Corrections Department, 1983 Joe R Silva Blvd, Las Cruces, NM, 88004. Tel: 575-523-3200. Fax: 575-523-3337. p. 1558

Barnes, Donna L, Librn, James J Lunsford (Hillsborough County) Law Library, 701 E Twiggs St, Tampa, FL, 33602. Tel: 813-272-5818. Fax: 813-272-5226. p. 497

Barnes, Dorothy, Librn, Bailey Memorial Library, 111 Moulton Ave, North Clarendon, VT, 05759-9327. Tel: 802-747-7743. p. 2430

Barnes, Fatima, Libr Dir, Meharry Medical College Library, 1005 Dr D B Todd Jr Blvd, Nashville, TN, 37208. Tel: 615-327-5770. Fax: 615-327-6448. p. 2257

Barnes, Houston, Tech Serv, Lindsey Wilson College, 210 Lindsey Wilson St, Columbia, KY, 42728. Tel: 270-384-8252. Fax: 270-384-4188. p. 910

Barnes, Jana, Dir, Winchester Community Library, 125 N East St, Winchester, IN, 47394-1698. Tel: 765-584-4824. Fax: 765-584-3624. p. 788

Barnes, Joseph W, Dr, Dir, Georgia Perimeter College, Dunwoody Campus Library, 2101 Womack Rd, Dunwoody, GA, 30338-4497. Tel: 770-274-5084. Fax: 770-274-5090. p. 525

Barnes, Joyce, Circ, Sampson-Clinton Public Library, 217 Graham St, Clinton, NC, 28328. Tel: 910-592-4153. Fax: 910-590-3504. p. 1784

Barnes, Judy, Med Librn, Ingham Regional Medical Center, 401 W Greenlawn Ave, Lansing, MI, 48910-2819. Tel: 517-334-2270. Fax: 517-334-2939. p. 1201

Barnes, Kelli, Tech Serv, Sumter County Library System, 7375 Powell Rd, Ste 150, Wildwood, FL, 34785. Tel: 352-689-4560. Fax: 352-689-4561. p. 504

Barnes, Kris, Br Supvr, Spokane County Library District, Deer Park Library, 208 S Forest, Deer Park, WA, 99006. Tel: 509-893-8300. Fax: 509-893-8476. p. 2537

Barnes, Kristen, Youth Serv Librn, Winter Haven Public Library, 325 Ave A NW, Winter Haven, FL, 33881. Tel: 863-291-5880. Fax: 863-298-7708. p. 505

Barnes, Laura, Inst Librn, University of Illinois Library at Urbana-Champaign, Prairie Research Institute Library, 1816 S Oak St, Champaign, IL, 61820. Tel: 217-333-8957. Fax: 217-333-8944. p. 712

Barnes, Lauren, Mountain View Campus Librn, Chattahoochee Technical College Library, 980 S Cobb Dr SE, Marietta, GA, 30060-3300. Tel: 770-509-6320. Fax: 770-528-4454. p. 542

Barnes, Lauren, Librn, Appalachian Technical College, 8371 Main St, Woodstock, GA, 30188. Tel: 678-454-1800. Fax: 678-454-1899. p. 558

Barnes, Lee Ann, Dir, Okeene Public Library, 215 N Main, Okeene, OK, 73763. Tel: 580-822-3306. Fax: 580-822-3309. p. 1971

Barnes, Linda, Dep Dir, Rockland Public Library, 80 Union St, Rockland, ME, 04841. Tel: 207-594-0310. Fax: 207-594-0333. p. 999

Barnes, Lisa, Ch, Wilkinsburg Public Library, 605 Ross Ave, Pittsburgh, PA, 15221-2195. Tel: 412-244-2944. Fax: 412-243-6943. p. 2130

Barnes, Lori Ann, Dir, Town of Vail Public Library, 292 W Meadow Dr, Vail, CO, 81657. Tel: 970-479-2184. Fax: 970-479-2192. p. 325

Barnes, Lynn, Br Supvr II, Pend Oreille County Library District, Ione Public Library, 210 Blackwell, Ste 1, Ione, WA, 99139. Tel: 509-442-3030. Fax: 509-442-3248. p. 2522

Barnes, Lynn, Br Supvr II, Pend Oreille County Library District, Metalines Community Library, Cutter Bldg, 302 Park St, Metaline Falls, WA, 99153. Tel: 509-446-3232. Fax: 509-446-2302. p. 2522

Barnes, Margaret, Dir of Libr Serv, Tigard Public Library, 13500 SW Hall Blvd, Tigard, OR, 97223-8111. Tel: 503-684-6537, Ext 2501. Fax: 503-598-7515, 503-718-2797. p. 2021

Barnes, Marlene, Br Mgr, Broward County Division of Libraries, Galt Ocean Mile Reading Center, 3403 Galt Ocean Dr, Fort Lauderdale, FL, 33308. Tel: 954-537-2877. Fax: 954-537-2879. p. 441

Barnes, Mary C, Cataloger, Girard Free Library, 105 E Prospect St, Girard, OH, 44420-1899. Tel: 330-545-2508. Fax: 330-545-8213. p. 1902

Barnes, Patricia, Dir, Cynthiana-Harrison County Public Library, 104 N Main St, Cynthiana, KY, 41031. Tel: 859-234-4881. Fax: 859-234-0059. p. 911

Barnes, Paula Simpson, Dir, North Olympic Library System, 2210 S Peabody St, Port Angeles, WA, 98362-6536. Tel: 360-417-8500, Ext 7715. Fax: 360-457-3125. p. 2523

Barnes, Rebecca, Asst Librn, Western Town Library, 9172 Main St, Westernville, NY, 13486. Tel: 315-827-4118. Fax: 315-827-4118. p. 1767

Barnes, Rhonda Lee, Dir, Le Roy Public Library, 605 N Broadway, Le Roy, MN, 55951. Tel: 507-324-5641. Fax: 507-324-5641. p. 1256

Barnes, Robert W, Librn, Christ Episcopal Church, 141 East Ave, Rochester, NY, 14604. Tel: 585-454-3878. Fax: 585-730-5646. p. 1729

Barnes, Roger L, Archivist, Per, Ref Librn, Piedmont Baptist College & Graduate School, 420 S Broad St, Winston-Salem, NC, 27101. Tel: 336-725-8344, Ext 7952. Fax: 336-725-5522. p. 1833

Barnes, Sharon, Tech Consult, South Central Kansas Library System, 321 N Main St, South Hutchinson, KS, 67505-1146. Tel: 620-663-3211. Fax: 620-663-9797. p. 895

Barnes, Sharon, Asst Dir, Watonga Public Library, 301 N Prouty, Watonga, OK, 73772. Tel: 580-623-7748. Fax: 580-623-7747. p. 1985

Barnes, Sheron, Spec Coll Librn, University of Houston, 2602 N Ben Jordan St, Victoria, TX, 77901-5699. Tel: 361-570-4177. Fax: 361-570-4155. p. 2395

Barnes, Sybil, Tech Serv, National Park Service, 1000 Hwy 36, Estes Park, CO, 80517-8397. Tel: 970-586-1362. Fax: 970-586-4702. p. 306

Barnes, Tamika, Dir, Environmental Protection Agency Library - RTP, MD C267-01, 109 Alexander Dr, Research Triangle Park, NC, 27711. Tel: 919-541-2777. Fax: 919-541-1405. p. 1819

Barnes, Thelma, Ser, Cincinnati State Technical & Community College, 3520 Central Pkwy, Cincinnati, OH, 45223-2612. Tel: 513-569-1610. Fax: 513-559-1527. p. 1869

Barnes, Wayne, Soc Sci Librn, University of Missouri-Columbia, Elmer Ellis Library, Ellis Library Bldg, Rm 104, Columbia, MO, 65201-5149. Tel: 573-882-3310. Fax: 573-882-8044. p. 1325

Barnes, Windie, Tech Serv Supvr, Sandhills Community College, 3395 Airport Rd, Pinehurst, NC, 28374. Tel: 910-695-3818. Fax: 910-695-3947. p. 1814

Barnes-Long, Judith, Coordr, Access Serv, University of Massachusetts Lowell Libraries, Lydon Library, 84 University Ave, Lowell, MA, 01854-2896. Tel: 978-934-3552. Fax: 978-934-3014. p. 1101

Barnett, Andrew, Asst Dir, McMillan Memorial Library, 490 E Grand Ave, Wisconsin Rapids, WI, 54494-4898. Tel: 715-423-1040. Fax: 715-423-2665. p. 2650

Barnett, Caroline, Librn, First Regional Library, M R Davis Public Library, 8554 Northwest Dr, Southaven, MS, 38671. Tel: 662-342-0102. Fax: 662-342-0556. p. 1301

Barnett, Catharine, Young Adult Serv & Family/Adult Serv, Chillicothe Public Library District, 430 N Bradley Ave, Chillicothe, IL, 61523-1920. Tel: 309-274-2719. Fax: 309-274-3000. p. 628

Barnett, Deborah, Librn, Russellville Public Library, 110 E Lawrence St, Russellville, AL, 35653. Tel: 256-332-1535. p. 35

Barnett, Debra, Assoc Librn, Mayland Community College, 200 Mayland Dr, Spruce Pine, NC, 28777. Tel: 828-765-7351, Ext 243. Fax: 828-765-0728. p. 1825

Barnett, Kristen, Librn, Northeast Mississippi Community College, 101 Cunningham Blvd, Booneville, MS, 38829. Tel: 662-720-7237, 662-728-7751. Fax: 662-728-2428. p. 1294

Barnett, Laurie, Clinical Med Librn, United States Department of Veterans Affairs, Library Service (142D), 13000 Bruce B Downs Blvd, Tampa, FL, 33612. Tel: 813-972-2000, Ext 6570. Fax: 813-978-5917. p. 498

Barnett, Leecy, Bibliog Instr, Lynn University Library, 3601 N Military Trail, Boca Raton, FL, 33431-5598. Tel: 561-237-7072. Fax: 561-237-7074. p. 428

Barnett, Linda, Head, Pub Serv, Memorial University of Newfoundland, Health Sciences Library, Memorial University, 300 Prince Philip Dr, St. John's, NL, A1B 3V6, CANADA. Tel: 709-777-6676. Fax: 709-777-6866. p. 2772

Barnett, Lynette, Circ Mgr, Kendallville Public Library, 221 S Park Ave, Kendallville, IN, 46755-2248. Tel: 260-343-2010. Fax: 260-343-2011. p. 756

Barnett, Marie M, Librn, Grand Lodge of Virginia AF&AM Library & Museum Historical Foundation, 4115 Nine Mile Rd, Richmond, VA, 23223-4926. Tel: 804-222-3110. Fax: 804-222-4253. p. 2488

Barnett, Mary Anne, Asst Librn, Gale Library, 16 S Main St, Newton, NH, 03858-3310. Tel: 603-382-4691. Fax: 603-382-2528. p. 1460

Barnett, Mertis, Librn, Dillon County Library, Lake View Branch, 207 S Main St, Lake View, SC, 29563. Tel: 843-759-2692. Fax: 843-759-0061. p. 2193

Barnett, Molly, Tech Serv, Wake Forest University, Coy C Carpenter School of Medicine Library, Medical Center Blvd, Winston-Salem, NC, 27157-1069. Tel: 336-716-4691. Fax: 336-716-2186. p. 1834

Barnett, Pat, Asst Dir, Mary H Weir Public Library, 3442 Main St, Weirton, WV, 26062. Tel: 304-797-8510. Fax: 304-797-8526. p. 2573

Barnett, Philip, Librn, City College of the City University of New York, Science-Engineering, Marshak Bldg, Rm 29, 160 Convent Ave, New York, NY, 10031. Tel: 212-650-8243. Fax: 212-650-7626. p. 1673

Barnett, Roberta, Dir, Lane County Library, Healy Extension, 2009 W Hwy 4, Healy, KS, 67850-5088. Tel: 620-398-2267. p. 863

Barnett, Sheila, Br Mgr, Fort Worth Library, Shamblee, 1062 Evans Ave, Fort Worth, TX, 76104-5135. Tel: 817-392-5580. Fax: 817-392-5583. p. 2322

Barnett, Steven, Mat Mgr, New Mexico State Library, Library for the Blind & Physically Handicapped, 1209 Camino Carlos Rey, Santa Fe, NM, 87507-5166. Tel: 505-476-9775. Fax: 505-476-9776. p. 1563

Barnett-Ellis, Paula, Ref Librn, Jacksonville State University Library, 700 Pelham Rd N, Jacksonville, AL, 36265. Tel: 256-782-5255. Fax: 256-782-5872. p. 22

Barnette, Lynne, Interim Mgr, Durham County Library, East Regional, 211 Lick Creek Lane, Durham, NC, 27703-6746. Tel: 919-560-0128. Fax: 919-598-8673. p. 1788

Barney, Anita, Dir, The Brookfield Library, 182 Whisconier Rd, Brookfield, CT, 06804. Tel: 203-775-6241. Fax: 203-740-7723. p. 332

Barney, Beth, Librn, Los Angeles County Counsel Law Library, 500 W Temple St, Rm 610, Los Angeles, CA, 90012. Tel: 213-974-1982. Fax: 213-626-7446. p. 171

Barney, Emily, Web Technologist, Illinois Institute of Technology, Chicago-Kent College of Law Library, 565 W Adams St, Chicago, IL, 60661. Tel: 312-906-5600. Fax: 312-906-5679. p. 615

Barney, Jean, Librn, Deutsch, Kerrigan & Stiles, 755 Magazine St, New Orleans, LA, 70130-3672. Tel: 504-593-0779. Fax: 504-566-1201. p. 960

Barney, Marilyn, Librn, Swanton Public Library, One First St, Swanton, VT, 05488. Tel: 802-868-7656. p. 2437

Barney, Melanie, Librn, Aiso Library, 543 Lawton Rd, Ste 617A, Monterey, CA, 93944-3214. Tel: 831-242-5572. Fax: 831-242-5816. p. 189

Barney, Nancy D, Dir, Laura E Richards Library, 863 Five Islands Rd, Georgetown, ME, 04548-3306. Tel: 207-371-2134. Fax: 207-371-2134. p. 986

Barnfield, Ann, Circ, Wheaton Public Library, 225 N Cross St, Wheaton, IL, 60187-5376. Tel: 630-868-7512. Fax: 630-668-8950. p. 719

Barnhardt, Jeff, Circ Supvr, Warner Pacific College, 2219 SE 68th Ave, Portland, OR, 97215-4099. Tel: 503-517-1037. Fax: 503-517-1351. p. 2015

Barnhart, Anne, Head, Instrul Serv, Irvine Sullivan Ingram Library, University of West Georgia, 1601 Maple St, Carrollton, GA, 30118. Tel: 678-839-6498. Fax: 678-839-6511. p. 523

Barnhart, Audrey, Dir, Texas County Library, 117 W Walnut, Houston, MO, 65483. Tel: 417-967-0058. Fax: 417-967-2262. p. 1331

Barnhart, Audrey, Dir, Texas County Library, Cabool Branch, Main & Walnut St, Cabool, MO, 65689-0072. Tel: 417-962-3722. Fax: 417-962-3722. p. 1331

Barnhart, Audrey, Dir, Texas County Library, Licking Branch, 126 S Main St, Licking, MO, 65542. Tel: 573-674-2038. Fax: 573-674-2038. p. 1331

Barnhart, Fred, Asst Dean, Libr Serv & Coll, Loyola University Chicago Libraries, 1032 W Sheridan Rd, Chicago, IL, 60660. Tel: 773-508-2620. Fax: 773-508-2993. p. 617

Barnhart, Linda, Head, Metadata & Content Mgt, University of California, San Diego, 9500 Gilman Dr, Mail Code 0175G, La Jolla, CA, 92093-0175. Tel: 858-534-3307. Fax: 858-822-0349. p. 162

Barnhart, Mary, Br Mgr, Trails Regional Library, Warrensburg Branch, 432 N Holden, Warrensburg, MO, 64093. Tel: 660-747-9177. Fax: 660-747-7928. p. 1371

Barnhart, Sue, Br Mgr, Putnam County District Library, Pandora-Riley Branch, 118 E Main St, Pandora, OH, 45877-0478. Tel: 419-384-3232. p. 1926

Barnhart, Teresa, Dir, Wayne Public Library, 137 E Main St, Wayne, OH, 43466. Tel: 419-288-2708. Fax: 419-288-3766. p. 1945

Barnickel, Chris, Asst Dir, Kansas City, Kansas Public Library, 625 Minnesota Ave, Kansas City, KS, 66101. Tel: 913-279-2223. Fax: 913-279-2033. p. 875

Barnicle, Susan, AV, Morse Institute Library, 14 E Central St, Natick, MA, 01760. Tel: 508-647-6522. Fax: 508-647-6527. p. 1107

Barnidge, Janys, Ref, Tallahassee Community College Library, 444 Appleyard Dr, Tallahassee, FL, 32304-2895. Tel: 850-201-8396. Fax: 850-201-8380. p. 495

Barnish, Ann, Presv Spec, University of Wisconsin-Milwaukee Libraries, American Geographical Society Library, Golda Meir Library, 2311 E Hartford Ave, Milwaukee, WI, 53211. Tel: 414-229-3984, 414-229-6282. Fax: 414-229-3624. p. 2622

Barniskis, Shannon, Youth Serv Librn, Horicon Public Library, 404 E Lake St, Horicon, WI, 53032-1297. Tel: 920-485-3535. Fax: 920-485-3536. p. 2598

Barnum, Florence, Librn, Brookfield Free Public Library, 40 Ralph Rd, Brookfield, VT, 05036. Tel: 802-276-3358. Fax: 802-276-3926. p. 2420

Barnwell, Jane, Dir, Pacific Resources for Education & Learning, 900 Fort Street Mall, Ste 1300, Honolulu, HI, 96813. Tel: 808-441-1320. Fax: 808-441-1385. p. 565

Baroco, Maria, Adult Serv, Ref Serv, Orange Beach Public Library, 26267 Canal Rd, Orange Beach, AL, 36561-3917. Tel: 251-981-2923. Fax: 251-981-2920. p. 33

Baroff, Deborah, Curator, Museum of the Great Plains, 601 NW Ferris Ave, Lawton, OK, 73507. Tel: 580-581-3460. Fax: 580-581-3458. p. 1967

Baron, Brenda, Librn, Duffield Public Library, PO Box 479, Duffield, AB, T0E 0N0, CANADA. Tel: 780-892-2644. Fax: 780-892-3344. p. 2697

Baron, Desiree, Br Head, Vancouver Public Library, Kerrisdale, 2112 W 42nd Ave, Vancouver, BC, V6M 2B6, CANADA. Tel: 604-665-3974. Fax: 604-606-2788. p. 2744

Baron, Krystyna, Librn, Polish Institute of Arts & Sciences in America, Inc, 208 E 30th St, New York, NY, 10016. Tel: 212-686-4164. Fax: 212-545-1130. p. 1697

Baron, Sally, Youth Serv Mgr, Wake County Public Library System, North Regional Library, 7009 Harps Mill Rd, Raleigh, NC, 27615. Tel: 919-870-4020. Fax: 919-870-4007. p. 1818

Baron, Sara, Dean of Libr, Regent University Library, 1000 Regent University Dr, Virginia Beach, VA, 23464. Tel: 757-352-4185. Fax: 757-352-4167. p. 2499

Barone, Armanda, Asst Dir, Tech Serv, University of California, Berkeley, Technical Services, 250 Moffit Library, Berkeley, CA, 94720-6000. Tel: 510-643-8239. Fax: 510-642-8331. p. 128

Barone, Deborah, Acq, United States Air Force, Air University - Muir S Fairchild Research Information Center, 600 Chennault Circle, Maxwell AFB, AL, 36112-6010. Tel: 334-953-2410. p. 24

Barone, Patti, In Charge, Delaware Township Library Association, PO Box 303, Dingmans Ferry, PA, 18328-0303. Tel: 570-828-2626. p. 2049

Baroudi, Tonya, Librn, Prince George's County, 14735 Main St, M4100, Upper Marlboro, MD, 20772. Tel: 301-952-3438. Fax: 301-952-2770. p. 1045

Baroza, Hilda, Circ, John A Burns School of Medicine, 651 Ilalo St, MEB, Honolulu, HI, 96813. Tel: 808-692-0816. Fax: 808-692-1244. p. 564

Barr, Ashley, Med Librn, MacNeal Hospital, 3249 S Oak Park Ave, Berwyn, IL, 60402. Tel: 708-783-3089. Fax: 708-783-3369. p. 594

Barr, Belinda, Asst Dean, Assessment & Access Serv, Miami University Libraries, 225 King Library, Oxford, OH, 45056. Tel: 513-529-7096. Fax: 513-529-3110. p. 1926

Barr, Daniel J, Dir, Murray Public Library, 166 E 5300 South, Murray, UT, 84107-6075. Tel: 801-264-2585. Fax: 801-264-2586. p. 2408

Barr, Leslie, Asst Dir, Mengle Memorial Library, 324 Main St, Brockway, PA, 15824-0324. Tel: 814-265-8245. Fax: 814-265-1125. p. 2037

Barr, Linda Robinson, Managing Librn, University of the Virgin Islands, Two John Brewers Bay, Saint Thomas, VI, 00802-9990. Tel: 340-693-1361, 340-693-1367. Fax: 340-693-1365. p. 2679

Barr, Ray, Develop Officer, Winter Park Public Library, 460 E New England Ave, Winter Park, FL, 32789-4493. Tel: 407-623-3300. Fax: 407-623-3489. p. 505

Barr, Rick, Dir, Dean College, 99 Main St, Franklin, MA, 02038-1994. Tel: 508-541-1771. Fax: 508-541-1918. p. 1090

Barr, Robb, Regional Br Mgr, Phoenix Public Library, Cholla Library, 10050 Metro Pkwy E, Phoenix, AZ, 85051. p. 76

Barraclough, Jeffrey, Asst Exec Dir, Manchester Historic Association Library, 129 Amherst St, Manchester, NH, 03101. Tel: 603-622-7531. p. 1456

Barraclough, Pat, Outreach & Children's Serv, Unicoi County Public Library, 201 Nolichucky Ave, Erwin, TN, 37650-1237. Tel: 423-743-6533. Fax: 423-743-0275. p. 2234

Barrasso, Beata, Head, Tech Serv, Springfield Free Public Library, 66 Mountain Ave, Springfield, NJ, 07081-1786. Tel: 973-376-4930, Ext 225. Fax: 973-376-1334. p. 1532

Barratsingh, Felicia, Spec Asst, Budget & Payment Proc, New York State Supreme Court, First Judicial District Criminal Law Library, 100 Centre St, 17th Flr, New York, NY, 10013. Tel: 646-386-3889. Fax: 212-748-7908. p. 1695

Barratt, Donna, Head, Tech Serv, Thompson Coburn LLP, One US Bank Plaza, Saint Louis, MO, 63101. Tel: 314-552-6347. Fax: 314-552-7347. p. 1361

Barratt, Elizabeth, Ser, College of Physicians & Surgeons of British Columbia, 100-1383 W Eighth Ave, Vancouver, BC, V6H 4C4, CANADA. Tel: 604-733-6671. Fax: 604-737-8582. p. 2740

Barratt, Karen, Mgr, British Columbia Securities Commission, 701 W Georgia St, Vancouver, BC, V7Y 1L2, CANADA. Tel: 604-899-6524. Fax: 604-899-6506. p. 2740

Barravecchia, Mary N, Librn, United States Navy, Naval Undersea Warfare Center Division, Newport Technical Library, 1176 Howell St, Bldg 101, Newport, RI, 02841. Tel: 401-832-4338. Fax: 401-832-3699. p. 2170

Barree, Adele, Head, Tech Serv, Somerset County Library System, One Vogt Dr, Bridgewater, NJ, 08807-2136. Tel: 908-526-4016, Ext 107. p. 1475

Barreiro, Elena, Librn, McCarthy Tetrault Library, 777 Dunsmuir St, No 1300, Vancouver, BC, V7Y 1K2, CANADA. Tel: 604-643-7178. Fax: 604-643-7900. p. 2741

Barrera, Amanda, Asst Dir, Amarillo Public Library, 413 E Fourth Ave, Amarillo, TX, 79101. Tel: 806-378-9330. Fax: 806-378-9327. p. 2274

Barrera, Jennifer, Asst Dir, User Serv, Tarleton State University Library, 201 Saint Felix, Stephenville, TX, 76401. Tel: 254-968-9248. Fax: 254-968-9467. p. 2389

Barresi, Patricia, Dir, John C Hart Memorial Library, 1130 Main St, Shrub Oak, NY, 10588. Tel: 914-245-1598. Fax: 914-245-5936. p. 1743

Barrett, Ann, Coordr, Ref (Info Serv), Dalhousie University, W K Kellogg Health Sciences Library, Tupper Medical Bldg, 5850 College St, Halifax, NS, B3H 1X5, CANADA. Tel: 902-494-1649. p. 2780

Barrett, Ariella, Librn, Coll & Access Serv, The National Academies, 500 Fifth St NW, Keck 304, Washington, DC, 20001-2721. Tel: 202-334-2125. Fax: 202-334-1651. p. 409

Barrett, Ava, Admin Supvr, Main Libr, Jacksonville Public Library, 303 N Laura St, Jacksonville, FL, 32202-3505. Tel: 904-630-1968. Fax: 904-630-2431. p. 453

Barrett, Barbara, Head, Ch, Jericho Public Library, One Merry Lane, Jericho, NY, 11753. Tel: 516-935-6790. Fax: 516-433-9581. p. 1647

Barrett, Beth, Dir, Louisville Public Library, 951 Spruce St, Louisville, CO, 80027. Tel: 303-335-4849. Fax: 303-335-4833. p. 317

Barrett, Betty, Br Mgr, Bradshaw H Grady Chambers County Library, Lafayette Pilot Public Library, 198 First St SE, Lafayette, AL, 36862. Tel: 334-864-0012. p. 39

Barrett, Edward, Admin Serv, United States Food & Drug Administration Department of Health & Human Services, 109 Holton St, Winchester, MA, 01890. Tel: 781-729-5700. Fax: 781-729-3593. p. 1141

Barrett, Eileen, Ref Librn, Reading Public Library, 64 Middlesex Ave, Reading, MA, 01867-2550. Tel: 781-944-0840. Fax: 781-942-9106. p. 1120

Barrett, Elinor, Assoc Dir, Daniel Boone Regional Library, 100 W Broadway, Columbia, MO, 65203. Tel: 573-443-3161. Fax: 573-443-3281. p. 1324

Barrett, Elizabeth, Br Mgr, Onslow County Public Library, Sneads Ferry Branch, 242 Sneads Ferry Rd, Sneads Ferry, NC, 28460. Tel: 910-327-6471. Fax: 910-327-0284. p. 1803

Barrett, Heather, Ch, Willow Branch Township Library, 330 N Eldon, Cisco, IL, 61830. Tel: 217-669-2312. Fax: 217-669-2312. p. 629

Barrett, Jan, Librn, Gardiner Roberts LLP Library, Scotia Plaza, Ste 3100, 40 King St W, Toronto, ON, M5H 3Y2, CANADA. Tel: 416-865-6600. Fax: 416-865-6636. p. 2853

Barrett, Karen, Dir, Helen Keller Services for the Blind, One Helen Keller Way, Hempstead, NY, 11550. Tel: 516-485-1234, Ext 246. Fax: 516-538-6785. p. 1635

Barrett, Kayla, Cat, Mgr, Georgia Archives, 5800 Jonesboro Rd, Morrow, GA, 30260. Tel: 678-364-3781. Fax: 678-364-3856. p. 545

Barrett, Laura, Dir, Educ Serv, Dir of Outreach, Dartmouth College Library, Baker-Berry Library, 6025 Baker-Berry Library, Hanover, NH, 03755-3525. Tel: 603-646-2560. Fax: 603-646-2167. p. 1450

Barrett, Liz, Asst Dir, Pittsford Community Library, 24 State St, Pittsford, NY, 14534. Tel: 585-248-6275. Fax: 585-248-6259. p. 1718

Barrett, Mary Ellin, Dir, Polk City Community Library, 215 S Bougainvillea Ave, Polk City, FL, 33868. Tel: 863-984-4340. Fax: 863-965-6385. p. 484

Barrett, Matthew, Adminr, Librn, Los Angeles County Metropolitan Transportation Authority, One Gateway Plaza, 15th Flr, Mail Stop 99-15-1, Los Angeles, CA, 90012-2952. Tel: 213-922-4859. p. 172

Barrett, Meschelyn, Dir, Stokely Memorial Library, 383 E Broadway, Newport, TN, 37821-3105. Tel: 423-623-3832. Fax: 423-623-3832. p. 2262

Barrett, Patricia, ILL, Broome County Public Library, 185 Court St, Binghamton, NY, 13901-3503. Tel: 607-778-3571. Fax: 607-778-6429. p. 1582

Barrett, Peg, Libr Dept Fac Chair, Keene State College, 229 Main St, Keene, NH, 03435-3201. Tel: 603-358-2714. Fax: 603-358-2745. p. 1453

Barrett, Ramona, Ch, Carnegie Public Library, 114 Delta Ave, Clarksdale, MS, 38614-4212. Tel: 662-624-4461. Fax: 662-627-4344. p. 1295

Barrett, Steve, Archivist, Idaho State Historical Society, Idaho History Ctr, 2205 Old Penitentiary Rd, Boise, ID, 83712. Tel: 208-334-3356. Fax: 208-334-3198. p. 571

Barrett, Timothy, Dir, Ctr for the Bk, University of Iowa, 3087 Main Library, Iowa City, IA, 52242-1420. Tel: 319-335-5707. Fax: 319-335-5374. p. 2965

Barrett, Walt, Supvr, Tech Serv, Meridian-Lauderdale County Public Library, 2517 Seventh St, Meridian, MS, 39301. Tel: 601-693-6771. Fax: 601-486-2260. p. 1308

Barrette, Josee, Circ, Cegep de Saint-Laurent Bibliotheque, 625 Boul Ste-Croix, Saint Laurent, QC, H4L 3X7, CANADA. Tel: 514-747-6521. Fax: 514-748-1249, 514-855-1942. p. 2909

Barrette, Olivier, Chef de Section, Bibliothèques de Montréal, Haut-Anjou, 7070, rue Jarry Est, Montreal, QC, H1J 1G4, CANADA. Tel: 514-493-8270. Fax: 514-493-8273. p. 2889

Barrette, Olivier, Chef de Section, Bibliothèques de Montrèal, Jean-Corbeil, 7500, avenue Goncourt, Montreal, QC, H1K 3X9, CANADA. Tel: 514-493-8270. Fax: 514-493-8273. p. 2890

Barretto, Joao, Acq Librn, City College of San Francisco, 50 Phelan Ave, San Francisco, CA, 94112. Tel: 415-452-5454. Fax: 415-452-5588. p. 241

Barricelli, Roberta, Head, YA, Chelmsford Public Library, 25 Boston Rd, Chelmsford, MA, 01824-3088. Tel: 978-256-5521. Fax: 978-256-8511. p. 1079

Barrie, Dale, Calgary Librn, Alberta Law Libraries, Edmonton, Law Courts Bldg, 2nd Flr, 1A Sir Winston Churchill Sq, Edmonton, AB, T5J 0R2, CANADA. Tel: 403-297-7355. Fax: 780-427-0397. p. 2699

Barrie, John, Dir, Dominican College Library, 480 Western Hwy, Blauvelt, NY, 10913-2000. Tel: 845-848-7505. Fax: 845-359-2525. p. 1583

Barringer, Catherine, Dean, Southeast Community College Library, 4771 W Scott Rd, Beatrice, NE, 68310-7042. Tel: 402-228-3468. Fax: 402-228-2218. p. 1393

Barringer, Loretta, Circ, Cabarrus County Public Library, 27 Union St N, Concord, NC, 28025-4793. Tel: 704-920-2050. Fax: 704-784-3822. p. 1785

Barrington, Connie, Br Mgr, Imperial County Free Library, Calipatria Branch, 105 S Lake, Calipatria, CA, 92233. Tel: 760-348-2630. Fax: 760-348-5575. p. 145

Barrington, Connie, County Librn, Imperial County Free Library, 1331 S Clark Rd, Bldg 24, El Centro, CA, 92243. Tel: 760-339-6460. Fax: 760-339-6465. p. 145

Barrins, P C, In Charge, Edward F Barrins Memorial Library, 2023 E Adams St, Tucson, AZ, 85719-4320. Tel: 520-327-7956. p. 85

Barrionuevo, Marcela, Librn, El Rito Public Library, 182 Placitas Rd, El Rito, NM, 87530. Tel: 575-581-4608. Fax: 575-581-9591. p. 1554

Barrish, Alan, Dir, Ethelbert B Crawford Public Library, 393 Broadway, Monticello, NY, 12701. Tel: 845-794-4660. Fax: 845-794-4602. p. 1662

Barron, Daniel, Dr, Dir, Avery-Mitchell-Yancey Regional Library System, 289 Burnsville School Rd, Burnsville, NC, 28714. Tel: 828-682-4476. Fax: 828-682-6277. p. 1779

Barron, Edwina T, Librn, Preformed Line Products Co, 660 Beta Dr, Mayfield Village, OH, 44143. Tel: 440-473-9149. Fax: 440-473-9103. p. 1916

Barron, Elizabeth, Govt Doc, Ref, University of Tampa, 401 W Kennedy Blvd, Tampa, FL, 33606-1490. Tel: 813-253-6231. Fax: 813-258-7426. p. 499

Barron, Heather, Dir, Bourbon Public Library, 307 N Main St, Bourbon, IN, 46504-1596. Tel: 574-342-5655. Fax: 574-342-5001. p. 729

Barron, Joy, Asst Librn, Towanda Public Library, 620 Highland, Towanda, KS, 67144-9042. Tel: 316-536-2464. Fax: 316-536-2847. p. 898

Barron, Kevin D, Asst Dir, Mississippi County Library System, Osceola Public, 320 West Hale Ave, Osceola, AR, 72370-2530. Tel: 870-563-2721. Fax: 870-563-6550. p. 96

Barron, Pamela P, PhD, Dr, Assoc Prof, University of North Carolina at Greensboro, School of Education, 349 Curry Bldg, Greensboro, NC, 27402. Tel: 336-334-3476. Fax: 336-334-5060. p. 2971

Barron, Paul B, Dir, Libr & Archives, George C Marshall Foundation Research Library, 1600 VMI Parade, Lexington, VA, 24450-1600. Tel: 540-463-7103, Ext 129. Fax: 540-464-5229. p. 2474

Barron, Sandra, Dir, Guttenberg Public Library, 603 S Second St, Guttenberg, IA, 52052. Tel: 563-252-3108. p. 820

Barron, Shelley, Dir, Le Grand Pioneer Heritage Library, 206 N Vine St, Le Grand, IA, 50142. Tel: 641-479-2122. Fax: 641-479-2122. p. 827

Barron, Virginia, Librn, Reber Memorial Library, 193 N Fourth, Raymondville, TX, 78580-1994. Tel: 956-689-2930. Fax: 956-689-6476. p. 2373

Barron, Viviana, Libr Tech, United States Army, Grant Library, 1637 Flint St, Fort Carson, CO, 80913-4105. Tel: 719-526-2350. Fax: 719-524-0070. p. 307

Barrow, Brad, In Charge, Amador County Library, Pine Grove Branch, 19889 Hwy 88, Pine Grove, CA, 95665. Tel: 209-296-3111. p. 161

Barrow, Brad, Libr Asst, Amador County Library, Pioneer Branch, 25070 Buckhorn Ridge Rd, Pioneer, CA, 95666. Tel: 209-295-7330. p. 161

Barrow, Christene, Librn, Lone Oak Area Public Library, 102 Jones St, Lone Oak, TX, 75453. Tel: 903-662-4565. Fax: 903-662-0955. p. 2356

Barrow, Deborah, Libr Dir, San Diego Public Library, 820 E St, San Diego, CA, 92101-6478. Tel: 619-236-5830. Fax: 619-238-6639. p. 235

Barrow, Phyllis, Dir, Finance & Operations, Georgetown University, 37th & N St NW, Washington, DC, 20057-1174. Tel: 202-687-7454. Fax: 202-687-7501. p. 402

Barrow, William, Spec Coll Librn, Cleveland State University, University Library, Rhodes Tower, 2121 Euclid Ave, Cleveland, OH, 44115-2214. Tel: 216-687-6998. Fax: 216-687-9380. p. 1879

Barrows, Marcella, Librn, Mary L Blood Memorial Library, 41 Brownsville-Hartland Rd, West Windsor, VT, 05037. Tel: 802-484-7205. p. 2439

Barry, Alan, Br Mgr, Mississauga Library System, Port Credit, 20 Lakeshore Rd E, Mississauga, ON, L5G 1C8, CANADA. Tel: 905-615-4835. Fax: 905-615-4751. p. 2823

Barry, Alan, Mgr, Mississauga Library System, Lakeview, 1110 Atwater Ave, Mississauga, ON, L5E 1M9, CANADA. Tel: 905-615-4805. Fax: 905-615-3625. p. 2823

Barry, Alison, Coordr, Libr User Serv, Endicott College Library, 376 Hale St, Beverly, MA, 01915. Tel: 978-232-2276. Fax: 978-232-2700. p. 1054

Barry, Angela, Ref, Faulkner University, 5345 Atlanta Hwy, Montgomery, AL, 36109-3398. Tel: 334-386-7207. Fax: 334-386-7481. p. 28

Barry, Becky, Head, Circ, Blount County Public Library, 508 N Cusick St, Maryville, TN, 37804-5714. Tel: 865-982-0981. Fax: 865-977-1142. p. 2246

Barry, Carol, Dr, Assoc Prof, Louisiana State University, 267 Coates Hall, Baton Rouge, LA, 70803. Tel: 225-578-3158. Fax: 225-578-4581. p. 2966

Barry, Joette, Librn, North Central Regional Library, Grand Coulee Community, 225 Federal St, Grand Coulee, WA, 99133. Tel: 509-633-0972. Fax: 509-633-0972. p. 2548

Barry, Jud B, Dir, Bristol Public Library, 701 Goode St, Bristol, VA, 24201-4199. Tel: 276-645-8782. Fax: 276-669-5593. p. 2452

Barry, Kevin, Res Analyst, Plunkett & Cooney, 38585 Woodward Ave, Bloomfield Hills, MI, 48304. Tel: 248-901-4094. Fax: 248-901-4040. p. 1159

Barry, Kevin, Res, J P Morgan Chase & Co, 277 Park Ave, New York, NY, 10172. Tel: 212-622-4900. p. 1687

Barry, Lezlie, Dir, Maynard Community Library, 225 Main St W, Maynard, IA, 50655. Tel: 563-637-2330. Fax: 563-637-2330. p. 831

Barry, Lita, Chief Librn, Grimsby Public Library, 18 Carnegie Lane, Grimsby, ON, L3M 1Y1, CANADA. Tel: 905-945-5142. Fax: 905-945-4442. p. 2806

Barry, Lorraine, Head, Info Serv, Reading Public Library, 64 Middlesex Ave, Reading, MA, 01867-2550. Tel: 781-942-6703. Fax: 781-942-9106. p. 1120

Barry, Marilyn, Dir, Dekalb Medical Center, 2701 N Decatur Rd, Decatur, GA, 30033. Tel: 404-501-5638. Fax: 404-501-1052. p. 530

Barry, Maureen, Chief Exec Officer, Burlington Public Library, 2331 New St, Burlington, ON, L7R 1J4, CANADA. Tel: 905-639-3611, Ext 100. Fax: 905-681-7277. p. 2797

Barry, Peggy, Commun Serv Mgr, Naperville Public Library, 200 W Jefferson Ave, Naperville, IL, 60540-5374. Tel: 630-961-4100, Ext 2234. Fax: 630-637-6389. p. 679

Barry, Richard, Librn, American Nurses Association, 8515 Georgia Ave, Ste 400, Silver Spring, MD, 20910. Tel: 301-628-5143. Fax: 301-628-5008. p. 1041

Barry, Simon, Tech Serv Librn, National Theatre School of Canada Library, 5030 Rue Saint Denis, Montreal, QC, H2J 2L8, CANADA. Tel: 514 842-7954, Ext 112. Fax: 514-842-5661. p. 2900

Barry, Therese M, Syst Adminr, Greene County Library System, 107 Hatfield St, Jefferson, PA, 15344. Tel: 724-883-2107. Fax: 724-883-2378. p. 2072

Barsevich, Linda, Dir of Finance, Carnegie Library of Pittsburgh, 4400 Forbes Ave, Pittsburgh, PA, 15213-4080. Tel: 412-622-3104. Fax: 412-622-6278. p. 2122

Barsky, Mairi, Br Mgr, Sonoma County Library, Occidental Branch, 73 Main St, Occidental, CA, 95465. Tel: 707-874-3080. p. 267

Barsky, Mairi, Mgr, Sonoma County Library, Guerneville Regional, 14107 Armstrong Woods Rd, Guerneville, CA, 95446. Tel: 707-869-9004. Fax: 707-869-1267. p. 267

Barsom, Michelle, Asst Librn, Early County Site, Bainbridge College Library, 2500 E Shotwell St, Bainbridge, GA, 39818. Tel: 229-248-2590. Fax: 229-248-2589. p. 521

Barsotti, Jean Ann, Dir, Carnegie Free Library, 1301 Seventh Ave, Beaver Falls, PA, 15010-4219. Tel: 724-846-4340. Fax: 724-846-0370. p. 2031

Barstow, Sandra, Head, Coll Develop, University of Wyoming Libraries, 13th & Ivinson, Laramie, WY, 82071. Tel: 307-766-5621. Fax: 307-766-2510. p. 2658

Bart, Sharon, In Charge, Multnomah County Library, Sellwood-Moreland, 7860 SE 13th Ave, Portland, OR, 97202-6300. Tel: 503-988-5398. Fax: 503-988-5175. p. 2012

Barta, Carol R, Asst Dir, North Central Kansas Libraries System, 629 Poyntz Ave, Manhattan, KS, 66502-6086. Tel: 785-776-4741, Ext 140. Fax: 785-776-1545. p. 881

Barta, Carol R, Asst Dir, North Central Kansas Libraries System, Subregional Talking Books, Manhattan Public Library, 629 Poyntz Ave, Manhattan, KS, 66502-6131. Tel: 785-776-4741, Ext 140. Fax: 785-776-1545. p. 882

Barta, Penny, Libr Assoc, Brown County Library, Wrightstown Branch, 615 Main St, Wrightstown, WI, 54180. Tel: 920-532-4011. Fax: 920-532-4199. p. 2595

Barta Weidner, Carol, Head of Libr, Free Library of Philadelphia, Holmesburg Branch, 7810 Frankford Ave, Philadelphia, PA, 19136-3013. Tel: 215-685-8756. Fax: 215-685-8757. p. 2108

Barta-Norton, Nancy, Libr Dir, Pearle L Crawford Memorial Library, 40 Schofield Ave, Dudley, MA, 01571. Tel: 508-949-8021. Fax: 508-949-8026. p. 1085

Bartee, Clark, Librn, United States Army, 2000 Fort Point Rd, Rm 308, Galveston, TX, 77553. Tel: 409-766-3196. Fax: 409-766-3905. p. 2326

Bartel, Alexa, Libr Dir, Coker College, 300 E College Ave, Hartsville, SC, 29550. Tel: 843-383-8125. Fax: 843-383-8129. p. 2198

Bartel, Barbara, Dir, West Iron District Library, 116 W Genesee St, Iron River, MI, 49935-1437. Tel: 906-265-2831. Fax: 906-265-2062. p. 1194

Bartel, Patricia, Librn, Ontario Ministry of Transportation Library, 301 Saint Paul St, Ground Flr, Saint Catharines, ON, L2R 7R4, CANADA. Tel: 905-704-2171. p. 2839

Bartel, Susan, Spec Serv, Newton Public Library, 720 N Oak, Newton, KS, 67114. Tel: 316-283-2890. Fax: 316-283-2916. p. 884

Bartell, Patricia, Asst Dir, Seminole Community Library, 9200 113th St N, Seminole, FL, 33772. Tel: 727-394-6905. Fax: 727-398-3113. p. 491

Bartell, Sandra, Br Mgr, Hamden Public Library, Brundage Community, 91 Circular Ave, Hamden, CT, 06514. Tel: 203-287-2675. Fax: 203-287-2675. p. 343

Bartelt, Roxane, Head, Ch, Kenosha Public Library, 812 56th St, Kenosha, WI, 53140-3735. Tel: 262-564-6151. Fax: 262-564-6370. p. 2601

Bartenfelder, Tom, Ch, Glenside Public Library District, 25 E Fullerton Ave, Glendale Heights, IL, 60139-2697. Tel: 630-260-1550. Fax: 630-260-1433. p. 650

Bartenhagen, Lynn, Coordr, Muscatine Art Center, 1314 Mulberry Ave, Muscatine, IA, 52761. Tel: 563-263-8282. Fax: 563-263-4702. p. 834

Bartens, Helen, Curator, Norfolk Historical Society, 109 Norfolk St S, Simcoe, ON, N3Y 2W3, CANADA. Tel: 519-426-1583. Fax: 519-426-1584. p. 2841

Barth, Candace, Ref, New Milford Public Library, 24 Main St, New Milford, CT, 06776. Tel: 860-355-1191, Ext 206. Fax: 860-350-9579. p. 360

Barth, Candace E, Head, Pub Serv, Wolcott Public Library, 469 Bound Line Rd, Wolcott, CT, 06716. Tel: 203-879-8110. Fax: 203-879-8109. p. 380

Barth, Christopher, Assoc Dean, Librn, United States Military Academy Library, Jefferson Hall Library & Learning Center, 758 Cullum Rd, West Point, NY, 10996. Tel: 845-938-3833. Fax: 845-938-4000. p. 1767

Barth, Paul, Librn, Roosevelt Hospital, 1000 Tenth Ave, New York, NY, 10019. Tel: 212-523-6100. Fax: 212-523-6108. p. 1698

Barth, Taylor, Asst Br Mgr, Ch, Librn I, Montgomery City-County Public Library System, Hampstead Branch Library, 5251 Hampstead High St, Ste 107, Montgomery, AL, 36116. Tel: 334-244-5770. Fax: 334-244-5773. p. 29

Barthe, Margaret R, Dir, Haines City Public Library, 303 Ledwith Ave, Haines City, FL, 33844-5507. Tel: 863-421-3633. p. 450

Barthelemy, Shermaine, Br Librn, Plaquemines Parish Library, Port Sulphur Branch, 139 Delta St, Port Sulphur, LA, 70083. Tel: 504-564-3681, 985-564-3682. Fax: 504-564-3274. p. 945

Barthol, Sue, Br Mgr, Morehouse Parish Library, Bonita Branch, 15004 Henry St, Bonita, LA, 71223. Tel: 318-823-2154. p. 941

Barthol, Sue, Br Mgr, Morehouse Parish Library, Mer Rouge Branch, 107 S 16th St, Mer Rouge, LA, 71261. Tel: 318-647-5639. p. 942

Bartholomew, Audra, Br Mgr, Bossier Parish Central Library, Haughton Branch, 116 E McKinley Ave, Haughton, LA, 71037. Tel: 318-949-0196. Fax: 318-949-0195. p. 946

Bartholomew, Jennifer, Electronic Serv, Luther Seminary Library, Gullixson Hall, 2375 Como Ave, Saint Paul, MN, 55108. Tel: 651-641-3458. Fax: 651-641-3280. p. 1278

Bartholomew, Malik, Access Serv Asst, Dillard University, 2601 Gentilly Blvd, New Orleans, LA, 70122-3097. Tel: 504-816-4784. Fax: 504-816-4787. p. 960

Bartholomew, Maryann, Ref, Plainsboro Free Public Library, 9 Van Doren St, Plainsboro, NJ, 08536. Tel: 609-275-2899. Fax: 609-799-5883. p. 1521

Bartkowiak, Barbara, Ref Librn, Marshfield Clinic, 1000 N Oak Ave, Marshfield, WI, 54449-5777. Tel: 715-389-4285. Fax: 715-389-5366. p. 2613

Bartle, Erin Gail, Librn, Huron County Law Library Association, Court House, 3rd Flr, Two E Main St, Norwalk, OH, 44857. Tel: 419-668-5127. Fax: 419-663-5026. p. 1924

Bartle, Lisa, Coord, Coll Develop, California State University, San Bernardino, 5500 University Pkwy, San Bernardino, CA, 92407-2318. Tel: 909-537-5104. Fax: 909-537-7048. p. 227

Bartles, John D, Tech Serv, Prince George's Community College Library, 301 Largo Rd, Largo, MD, 20774-2199. Tel: 301-322-0469. Fax: 301-808-8847. p. 1034

Bartles, Maryanne, Dir of Libr, Dearborn Public Library, 16301 Michigan Ave, Dearborn, MI, 48126. Tel: 313-943-2330. Fax: 313-943-2853. p. 1167

Bartlett, Alan E, Syst Coordr, Allegheny College Library, 555 N Main St, Meadville, PA, 16335. Tel: 814-332-3768. Fax: 814-337-5673. p. 2086

Bartlett, Barbara, Mgr, New York State Division for Historic Preservation, 17 Rippleton Rd, Cazenovia, NY, 13035. Tel: 315-655-3200. Fax: 315-655-4304. p. 1604

Bartlett, Bernadette, Mich Doc, Library of Michigan, 702 W Kalamazoo St, Lansing, MI, 48915. Tel: 517-373-2971. Fax: 517-373-5700. p. 1201

Bartlett, Diane, Br Mgr, Stanislaus County Free Library, Turlock Branch, 550 Minaret Ave, Turlock, CA, 95380-4198. Tel: 209-664-8100. Fax: 209-664-8101. p. 188

Bartlett, Helen, Asst Librn, Tech Serv, Yale University Library, Irving S Gilmore Music Library, 120 High St, New Haven, CT, 06520. Tel: 203-432-0492. Fax: 203-432-7339. p. 357

Bartlett, Joan, Asst Prof, McGill University, 3661 Peel St, Montreal, QC, H3A 1X1, CANADA. Tel: 514-398-6976. Fax: 514-398-7193. p. 2979

Bartlett, Liz, Br Mgr, Wake County Public Library System, Cary Community Library, 310 S Academy St, Cary, NC, 27511. Tel: 919-460-3350. Fax: 919-460-3362. p. 1817

Bartlett, Lorraine, Br Mgr, Hampton Public Library, Willow Oaks, 227 Fox Hill Rd, Hampton, VA, 23669. Tel: 757-850-5114. Fax: 757-850-5239. p. 2468

Bartlett, Lyndy, Ser Librn, YA Librn, Missoula Public Library, 301 E Main, Missoula, MT, 59802-4799. Tel: 406-721-2665. Fax: 406-728-5900. p. 1386

Bartlett, Lynne, Electronic Res Librn, Bluefield College, 3000 College Dr, Bluefield, VA, 24605. Tel: 276-326-4238. Fax: 276-326-4288. p. 2451

Bartlett, Margaret, Mgr, Instruction & Educ Serv, Rochester Institute of Technology, 90 Lomb Memorial Dr, Rochester, NY, 14623-5604. Tel: 585-475-2559. Fax: 585-475-7007. p. 1731

Bartlett, Mark, Head Librn, The New York Society Library, 53 E 79th St, New York, NY, 10075. Tel: 212-288-6900, Ext 201. Fax: 212-744-5832. p. 1694

Bartlett, Mike, Libr Dir, Meeker Regional Library District, 490 Main St, Meeker, CO, 81641. Tel: 970-878-5911. Fax: 970-878-5495. p. 318

Bartlett, Pamela, Head, Tech Serv, Thomas M Cooley Law School Libraries, 300 S Capitol Ave, Lansing, MI, 48901. Tel: 517-371-5140, Ext 3410. Fax: 517-334-5715, 517-334-5717. p. 1202

Bartlett, Pernell, Libr Tech, Elizabeth City State University, 1704 Weeksville Rd, Elizabeth City, NC, 27909. Tel: 252-335-8537. Fax: 252-335-3446. p. 1790

Bartlett, Rebecca, Head, Tech Serv, La Grange Public Library, Ten W Cossitt Ave, La Grange, IL, 60525. Tel: 708-352-0576, Ext 14. p. 662

Bartlett, Rhonda, Br Mgr, Lake Blackshear Regional Library System, Elizabeth Harris Library, 312 Harman St, Unadilla, GA, 31091. Tel: 478-627-9303. Fax: 478-627-9303. p. 508

Bartlett, Robin, Dir, Richwood Public Library, Eight White Ave, Richwood, WV, 26261. Tel: 304-846-6099. Fax: 304-846-9290. p. 2570

Bartlett, Sally, Head, Circ, Amherst Town Library, 14 Main St, Amherst, NH, 03031-2930. Tel: 603-673-2288. Fax: 603-672-6063. p. 1437

Bartlett, Susan, Librn, Cambrian College of Applied Arts & Technology Library, 1400 Barrydowne Rd, Sudbury, ON, P3A 3V8, CANADA. Tel: 705-524-7333. Fax: 705-566-6163. p. 2846

Bartlett, Valerie, Dir, Teinert Memorial Public Library, 337 N Dalton St, Bartlett, TX, 76511. Tel: 254-527-3208. Fax: 254-527-0217. p. 2286

Bartley, Barbara, Pub Serv Librn, Kennebec Valley Community College, 92 Western Ave, Fairfield, ME, 04937-1367. Tel: 207-453-5004. Fax: 207-453-5194. p. 985

Bartley, Linda, Youth Serv Mgr, McCracken County Public Library, 555 Washington St, Paducah, KY, 42003-1735. Tel: 270-442-2510, Ext 13. Fax: 270-443-9322. p. 932

Bartley, Margaret, Exec Dir, The Seattle Metaphysical Library (As-You-Like-It Library), 2220 NW Market St, Rm L-05, Ballard, WA, 98107. Tel: 206-329-1794. p. 2507

Bartley, Tara, Ch, Benson Memorial Library, 213 N Franklin St, Titusville, PA, 16354-1788. Tel: 814-827-2913. Fax: 814-827-9836. p. 2145

Bartnik, Linda, Head, Ref, Murray State University, 205 Waterfield Library, Dean's Office, Murray, KY, 42071-3307. Tel: 270-809-4151. Fax: 270-809-3736. p. 930

Bartolotto, Jullie, Exec Dir, Historical Society of Long Beach, 4260 Atlantic Ave, Long Beach, CA, 90807. Tel: 562-424-2220. Fax: 562-424-2262. p. 166

Bartolucci, Maureen, Asst Dir, Pequannock Township Public Library, 477 Newark Pompton Tpk, Pompton Plains, NJ, 07444. Tel: 973-835-7460. Fax: 973-835-1928. p. 1521

Barton, Alice, Dir, Hawn Memorial Library, 220 John St, Clayton, NY, 13624-1107. Tel: 315-686-3762. Fax: 315-686-6028. p. 1607

Barton, Barbara, Br Mgr, Fort Bend County Libraries, Mamie George Branch, 320 Dulles Ave, Stafford, TX, 77477-4799. Tel: 281-242-7398. Fax: 281-242-5793. p. 2375

Barton, Brenda, Youth Serv, Albany County Public Library, 310 S Eighth St, Laramie, WY, 82070-3969. Tel: 307-721-2580. Fax: 307-721-2584. p. 2657

Barton, Brian J, Exec Dir, Braille Circulating Library, Inc, 2700 Stuart Ave, Richmond, VA, 23220. Tel: 804-359-3743. Fax: 804-359-4777. p. 2488

Barton, Carolina, Dir, Libr Serv, Concordia University Library, 1530 Concordia W, Irvine, CA, 92612. Tel: 949-214-3093. p. 160

Barton, David, Libr Dir, Ivy Tech Community College, 8000 S Education Dr, Terre Haute, IN, 47802. Tel: 812-298-2307. Fax: 812-299-5723. p. 781

Barton, David, Dean, Libr Serv, Metropolitan State University, 645 E Seventh St, Saint Paul, MN, 55106. Tel: 651-793-1619. Fax: 651-793-1615. p. 1279

Barton, Deborah, Librn, Baptist Health Systems, 1225 N State St, Jackson, MS, 39202-2002. Tel: 601-968-4187. Fax: 601-292-4201. p. 1302

Barton, Dixie, Circ, Ohio State University LIBRARIES, Louis Bromfield Library - Mansfield Campus, 1660 University Dr, Mansfield, OH, 44906-1599. Tel: 419-755-4324. Fax: 419-755-4327. p. 1887

Barton, Gary, Br Mgr, Dougherty County Public Library, Northwest, 2507 Dawson Rd, Albany, GA, 31707. Tel: 229-420-3270. p. 507

Barton, Hope, Assoc Univ Librn & Dir, Serv, University of Iowa Libraries, 125 W Washington St, Iowa City, IA, 52242-1420. p. 823

Barton, Jackie, Asst Dir, Cleve J Fredricksen Library, 100 N 19th St, Camp Hill, PA, 17011-3900. Tel: 717-761-3900. Fax: 717-761-5493. p. 2040

Barton, Janet, Libr Dir, Litchfield District Library, 108 N Chicago St, Litchfield, MI, 49252-9738. Tel: 517-542-3887. Fax: 517-542-3887. p. 1203

Barton, Kathryn, Local Hist/Genealogy, Guernsey Memorial Library, Three Court St, Norwich, NY, 13815. Tel: 607-334-4034. Fax: 607-336-3901. p. 1708

Barton, Maureen, Dir, Ivy Tech Community College, 3501 First Ave, Evansville, IN, 47710-3398. Tel: 812-429-1412. Fax: 812-429-9802. p. 738

Barton, Nancy, Patron Serv, Starke County Public Library System, 152 W Culver Rd, Knox, IN, 46534-2220. Tel: 574-772-7323. p. 757

Barton, Nancy, Circ Supvr, Davis County Library, Centerville Branch, 45 S 400 West, Centerville, UT, 84014. Tel: 801-294-4054. p. 2405

Barton, Nancy, Adult Serv, Circ, ILL, Hot Springs County Library, 344 Arapahoe, Thermopolis, WY, 82443-0951. Tel: 307-864-3104. Fax: 307-864-5416. p. 2661

Barton, Nona, Ser, Fort Hays State University, 600 Park St, Hays, KS, 67601-4099. Tel: 785-628-5262. Fax: 785-628-4096. p. 871

Barton, Roberta, Pub Info Officer, Fresno County Public Library, 2420 Mariposa St, Fresno, CA, 93721-2285. Tel: 559-488-1922. p. 151

Bartone, Caryn, Head, Youth Serv, Salem-South Lyon District Library, 9800 Pontiac Trail, South Lyon, MI, 48178-1307. Tel: 248-437-6431. Fax: 248-437-6593. p. 1227

Bartosz, Kimberly, Ref Serv Coordr, University of Wisconsin-Parkside Library, 900 Wood Rd, Kenosha, WI, 53141. Tel: 262-595-2356. Fax: 262-595-2545. p. 2602

Bartow, Lisa, Dir, Stony Creek Free Library, 37 Harrisburg Rd, Stony Creek, NY, 12878-1622. Tel: 518-696-5911. Fax: 518-696-5911. p. 1750

Bartram, Dawn, Libr Assoc, Richland Correctional Institution Library, 1001 Olivesburg Rd, Mansfield, OH, 44905-1228. Tel: 419-526-2100, Ext 2215. Fax: 419-521-2814. p. 1913

Bartus, Bonnae, Br Supvr, Gaston County Public Library, Mount Holly Branch, 245 W Catawba Ave, Mount Holly, NC, 28120. Tel: 704-827-3581. Fax: 704-827-8573. p. 1794

Bartz, Laurie, YA Serv, Hedberg Public Library, 316 S Main St, Janesville, WI, 53545. Tel: 608-758-6600. Fax: 608-758-6583. p. 2600

Barua, Suparna, Librn, NYS Supreme Court, Orange County Govt Ctr, 255-275 Main St, Goshen, NY, 10924. Tel: 845-291-3138. Fax: 845-291-2595. p. 1629

Barus, Lisa, Asst Librn, Whitingham Free Public Library, 2948 Vt Rte 100, Jacksonville, VT, 05342. Tel: 802-368-7506. p. 2426

Baruth, Christopher, PhD, Adminr, Curator, University of Wisconsin-Milwaukee Libraries, American Geographical Society Library, Golda Meir Library, 2311 E Hartford Ave, Milwaukee, WI, 53211. Tel: 414-229-3984, 414-229-6282. Fax: 414-229-3624. p. 2622

Barvoets, Peter, Ser & Syst, State University of New York College of Agriculture & Technology, 142 Schenectady Ave, Cobleskill, NY, 12043. Tel: 518-255-5894. Fax: 518-255-5843. p. 1608

Barwis, Eleanor, Librn, Abington Presbyterian Church Library, 1082 Old York Rd, Abington, PA, 19001. Tel: 215-887-4530. Fax: 215-887-5988. p. 2025

Bary, Thomas, Digital Media Spec, Northeastern University Libraries, Snell Library, 360 Huntington Ave, Boston, MA, 02115. Tel: 617-373-3399. p. 1065

Barzilai-Nahon, Karine, Asst Prof, University of Washington, Mary Gates Hall, Ste 370, Campus Box 352840, Seattle, WA, 98195-2840. Tel: 206-685-9937. Fax: 206-616-3152. p. 2976

Basbas, Sarah, Br Mgr, Manchester City Library, West Community Branch Library, 76 N Main St, Manchester, NH, 03102-4084. Tel: 603-624-6560. Fax: 603-628-6216. p. 1455

Bascle, Brenda, Br Mgr, Lafourche Parish Public Library, Lockport Branch, 518 Sixth St, Lockport, LA, 70374. Tel: 985-532-3158. Fax: 985-532-0270. p. 971

Basel, William, Ref, Cheshire Public Library, 104 Main St, Cheshire, CT, 06410-2499. Tel: 203-272-2245. Fax: 203-272-7714. p. 333

Baselice, Gail, Media Spec, Baldwin Public Library, 2385 Grand Ave, Baldwin, NY, 11510-3289. Tel: 516-223-6228. Fax: 516-623-7991. p. 1577

Bases, Grace, Cat, Martin Luther College Library, 1995 Luther Ct, New Ulm, MN, 56073-3965. Tel: 507-354-8221, Ext 364. Fax: 507-233-9107. p. 1268

Bash, Marianne, Ref Librn, Washington State University Libraries, 14204 NE Salmon Creek Ave, Vancouver, WA, 98686. Tel: 360-546-9681. Fax: 360-546-9039. p. 2546

Bashaw, Debra, Dir, McMullen Memorial Library, 906 N Main St, Huntington, TX, 75949. Tel: 936-876-4516. Fax: 936-876-4516. p. 2345

Bashforth, Chris, Exec Dir, Santa Ynez Valley Historical Society, 3596 Sagunto St, Santa Ynez, CA, 93460. Tel: 805-688-7889. Fax: 805-688-1109. p. 268

Bashore, Mathew, Network Serv, Ref, Brighton Memorial Library, 2300 Elmwood Ave, Rochester, NY, 14618. Tel: 585-784-5300. Fax: 585-784-5333. p. 1728

Basile, Anne, Librn, First United Methodist Church Library, 7000 Erie St, Sylvania, OH, 43560-1920. Tel: 419-882-2205. Fax: 419-882-2205. p. 1938

Basilone, Leigh, Circ Asst, Chester Public Library, 21 W Main St, Chester, CT, 06412. Tel: 860-526-0018. p. 334

Basinger, Andrea, Adult Serv, Garrett Public Library, 107 W Houston St, Garrett, IN, 46738. Tel: 260-357-5485. Fax: 260-357-5170. p. 744

Basinger, Jeannie, Br Mgr, Bienville Parish Library, Saline Branch, 1434 Fourth St, Saline, LA, 71070. Tel: 318-576-8990. Fax: 318-576-8780. p. 941

Basioli, Maja, Ref Librn, Seton Hall University, One Newark Ctr, Newark, NJ, 07102. p. 1513

Baskett, Georgia I, Cat, University of Tennessee at Martin, Ten Wayne Fisher Dr, Martin, TN, 38238. Tel: 731-881-7079. Fax: 731-881-7074. p. 2246

Baskin, Jeffrey L, Dir, William F Laman Public Library, 2801 Orange St, North Little Rock, AR, 72114-2296. Tel: 501-758-1720. Fax: 501-753-0524. p. 111

Baskin, Kathryn A, Managing Dir, Southern States Energy Board, 6325 Amherst Ct, Norcross, GA, 30092. Tel: 770-242-7712. Fax: 770-242-0421. p. 547

Baskin, Sandra C, Dir, Sherman County Public Library, 719 N Main, Stratford, TX, 79084. Tel: 806-366-2200. Fax: 806-366-7551. p. 2389

Baskins, Linda, Asst Librn, Killen Public Library, 325 J C Malden Hwy, Killen, AL, 35645. Tel: 256-757-5471. Fax: 256-757-5471. p. 23

Basler, Patricia, Dir, Stoughton Public Library, 84 Park St, Stoughton, MA, 02072-2974. Tel: 781-344-2711. Fax: 781-344-7340. p. 1129

Basler, Thomas G, Dir, Medical University of South Carolina Library, 171 Ashley Ave, Ste 300, Charleston, SC, 29425-0001. Tel: 843-792-9211. Fax: 843-792-7947. p. 2184

Basnight, Jane W, Ref Librn, North Carolina Legislative Library, 500 Legislative Office Bldg, 300 N Salisbury St, Raleigh, NC, 27603-5925. Tel: 919-733-9390. Fax: 919-715-5460. p. 1815

Bass, April, Libr Spec, Johnston Community College Library, Learning Resource Ctr, 245 College Rd, Smithfield, NC, 27577. Tel: 919-464-2251. p. 1824

Bass, Barbera, Br Mgr, Sacramento Public Library, Arcade Community Library, 2443 Marconi Ave, Sacramento, CA, 95821. p. 224

Bass, Beverly, Br Mgr, Collins LeRoy Leon County Public Library System, Dr B L Perry Jr Branch, 2817 S Adams St, Tallahassee, FL, 32301. Tel: 850-606-2950. Fax: 850-606-2951. p. 492

Bass, Brittany, Dir, Olney Central College, 305 N West St, Olney, IL, 62450. Tel: 618-395-7777, Ext 2260. Fax: 618-392-3293. p. 685

Bass, Clayton, Pres, Huntsville Museum of Art Library, 300 Church St S, Huntsville, AL, 35801. Tel: 256-535-4350, Ext 232. Fax: 256-532-1743, 256-533-6748. p. 21

Bass, David E, III, Dir, Franklin County Public Library, 355 Franklin St, Rocky Mount, VA, 24151. Tel: 540-483-3098. Fax: 540-483-6652. p. 2495

Bass, Erica, Librn, Department of Veterans Affairs, 11201 Benton St, Loma Linda, CA, 92357. Tel: 909-422-3000, Ext 2970. Fax: 909-422-3164. p. 165

Bass, Jae, Tech Serv Adminr, Saint Johns County Public Library System, 6670 US 1 South, Saint Augustine, FL, 32086. Tel: 904-827-6924. Fax: 904-827-6905. p. 486

Bass, James, Cat, University of Saint Mary, 4100 S Fourth St Trafficway, Leavenworth, KS, 66048-5082. Tel: 913-758-6306. Fax: 913-758-6200. p. 879

Bass, Jimmy, Dir, Coweta Public Library System, 85 Literary Lane, Newnan, GA, 30265. Tel: 770-683-2052. Fax: 770-683-0065. p. 546

Bass, Karen, Circ Supvr, Davis County Library, Kaysville Branch, 44 N Main St, Kaysville, UT, 84037. Tel: 801-544-2826. Fax: 801-544-5646. p. 2405

Bass, Kim, Libr Spec I, Okeechobee County Public Library, 206 SW 16th St, Okeechobee, FL, 34974. Tel: 863-763-3536. Fax: 863-763-5368. p. 474

Bass, Marcia, Ref, Lower Merion Library System, 75 E Lancaster Ave, Ardmore, PA, 19003-2388. Tel: 610-645-6110. Fax: 610-649-8835. p. 2029

Bass, Marcia, Head, Ref, Ludington Public Library, Five S Bryn Mawr Ave, Bryn Mawr, PA, 19010-3471. Tel: 610-525-1776. Fax: 610-525-1783. p. 2039

Bass, Marlene, YA Librn, Wayne County Public Library, 150 S Main St, Monticello, KY, 42633. Tel: 606-348-8565. Fax: 606-348-3829. p. 929

Bass, Rhonda J, Libr Dir, Groesbeck Maffett Public Library, 601 W Yeagua St, Groesbeck, TX, 76642-1658. Tel: 254-729-3667. Fax: 254-729-2345. p. 2330

Bass, Royce, Pub Serv, Saint John's River State College, Saint Augustine Center Library, 2990 College Dr, Saint Augustine, FL, 32084. Tel: 904-808-7474. Fax: 904-808-7478. p. 479

Bass, Sheryl, Head Librn, Capital Area District Libraries, Mason Library, 145 W Ash St, Mason, MI, 48854. Tel: 517-676-9088. Fax: 517-676-3780. p. 1200

Bassanese, Lynn A, Dir, National Archives & Records Administration, 4079 Albany Post Rd, Hyde Park, NY, 12538. Tel: 845-486-7741. Fax: 845-486-1147. p. 1640

Bassermann, Cloudagh, Pres, Bibliotheque Municipale de La Baie d'Urfe, 20551 chemin du Bord du Lac, Baie d'Urfe, QC, H9X 1R3, CANADA. Tel: 514-457-3274. p. 2879

Bassett, Christine, Librn, The Hospital of Central Connecticut, 100 Grand St, New Britain, CT, 06050. Tel: 860-224-5900, Ext 2570, 860-224-5900, Ext 2571. Fax: 860-224-5970. p. 354

Bassett, Christine, Assoc Dir, Syst Mgt, United States Military Academy Library, Jefferson Hall Library & Learning Center, 758 Cullum Rd, West Point, NY, 10996. Tel: 845-938-3833. Fax: 845-938-4000. p. 1767

Bassett, Dawn, Coordr, Libr Serv, Canadian Grain Commission Library, 801-303 Main St, Winnipeg, MB, R3C 3G8, CANADA. Tel: 204-984-6336. Fax: 204-983-6098. p. 2754

Bassett, Hilary, Exec Dir, Greater Portland Landmarks, Inc, 93 High St, Portland, ME, 04101. Tel: 207-774-5561. Fax: 207-774-2509. p. 996

Bassett, Pegeen, Doc Librn, Northwestern University, Chicago, Pritzker Legal Research Center, 375 E Chicago Ave, Chicago, IL, 60611. Tel: 312-503-7344. Fax: 312-503-9230. p. 621

Bassett, Ruth, Librn, Brandywine Conservancy, Inc, US Rte 1, Box 141, Chadds Ford, PA, 19317. Tel: 610-388-2700. Fax: 610-388-1197. p. 2043

Bassett, Steven, Web Developer, Northeastern University Libraries, Snell Library, 360 Huntington Ave, Boston, MA, 02115. Tel: 617-373-7082. p. 1065

Bassham, Mia Wang, Dir, Learning Res, Luzerne County Community College Library, 1333 S Prospect St, Nanticoke, PA, 18634-3899. Tel: 800-377-5222, Ext 7420. Fax: 570-735-6130. p. 2094

Bassler, Terri, Ch, Belleville Public Library, 121 E Washington St, Belleville, IL, 62220. Tel: 618-234-0441, Ext 17. Fax: 618-234-9474. p. 593

Basso, Joe, IT Mgr, Park Ridge Public Library, 20 S Prospect, Park Ridge, IL, 60068-4188. Tel: 847-720-3205. Fax: 847-825-0001. p. 688

Basso, Mary, Librn, Georgian Court University, 900 Lakewood Ave, Lakewood, NJ, 08701-2697. Tel: 732-987-2427. Fax: 732-987-2017. p. 1493

Basso, Travis, ILL, Reserves, Concordia College, 171 White Plains Rd, Bronxville, NY, 10708. Tel: 914-337-9300, Ext 2202. Fax: 914-395-4893. p. 1588

Bastian, Jeannette, Assoc Prof, Simmons College, 300 The Fenway, Boston, MA, 02115. Tel: 617-521-2800. Fax: 617-521-3192. p. 2967

Bastien, Cyrene, Br Mgr, Great River Regional Library, Stickney Crossing Library, 822 Clearwater Center, Clearwater, MN, 55320. Tel: 320-558-6001. Fax: 320-558-6001. p. 1276

Bastin, Judy, Ref & Instruction Librn, Butler Community College Libraries, 901 S Haverhill Rd, El Dorado, KS, 67042-3280. Tel: 316-322-3234. Fax: 316-322-3315. p. 864

Basu, Geetali, Ref Serv Coordr, County College of Morris, 214 Center Grove Rd, Randolph, NJ, 07869-2086. p. 1525

Batchelder, Karen, AV, Clinton-Essex-Franklin Library System, 33 Oak St, Plattsburgh, NY, 12901-2810. Tel: 518-563-5190, Ext 20. Fax: 518-563-0421. p. 1718

Batchelor, Carolyn, Libr Supvr-Popular Libr, Skagit Valley College, Whidbey Island Campus Library, 1900 SE Pioneer Way, Oak Harbor, WA, 98277-3099. Tel: 360-679-5221. Fax: 360-679-5341. p. 2521

Batchelor, Lori, Adult Serv, Benbrook Public Library, 1065 Mercedes, Benbrook, TX, 76126. Tel: 817-249-6632. Fax: 817-249-3326. p. 2289

Batchen, Joan, Sr Dir for Libr Serv, Kirkland & Ellis LLP Library, 300 N LaSalle St, 11th Flr, Chicago, IL, 60654. Tel: 312-862-2399. Fax: 312-862-2200. p. 616

Batchler, Lee Anne, Ch, Cherokee County Public Library, Blacksburg Branch, 201 S Rutherford St, Blacksburg, SC, 29702. Tel: 864-839-2630. Fax: 864-839-2572. p. 2194

Batdorf, Cindy, Mgr, Libr Serv, Montgomery House, 20 Church St, McEwensville, PA, 17749. Tel: 570-538-1381. Fax: 570-538-1381. p. 2085

Bateman, Andre L, Librn, Georgia Department of Corrections, Rogers State Prison, 1978 Georgia Hwy 147, Reidsville, GA, 30453. Tel: 912-557-7019. Fax: 912-557-7051. p. 547

Bateman, Anne, Mgr, Ernst & Young, Ernst & Young Tower, 222 Bay St, Toronto, ON, M5K 1J7, CANADA. Tel: 416-943-3471. Fax: 416-943-2954. p. 2853

Bateman, Joyce Davenport, ILL, Motlow State Community College Libraries, Ledford Mill Rd, Tullahoma, TN, 37388. Tel: 931-393-1660. Fax: 931-393-1516. p. 2267

Bateman, Kimberly, Ref Librn, Tidewater Community College, 1700 College Crescent, Virginia Beach, VA, 23453. Fax: 757-427-0327. p. 2500

Bateman, Patti, Dir, Libr & Cultural Serv, Aurora Public Library, 14949 E Alameda Pkwy, Aurora, CO, 80012. Tel: 303-739-6594. Fax: 303-739-6579. p. 288

Batemarco, Diane, Ref Serv, Fordham University Westchester Library, 400 Westchester Ave, West Harrison, NY, 10604. Tel: 914-367-3426. p. 1766

Bates, Amy, Ch, Talbot Belmond Public Library, 440 E Main St, Belmond, IA, 50421-1224. Tel: 641-444-4160. Fax: 641-444-3457. p. 796

Bates, Andy, Br Mgr, Seattle Public Library, Lake City, 12501 28th Ave NE, Seattle, WA, 98125. Tel: 206-684-7518. p. 2531

Bates, Andy, Regional Mgr, Seattle Public Library, Madrona-Sally Goldmark Branch, 1134 33rd Ave, Seattle, WA, 98122. Tel: 206-684-4705. p. 2531

Bates, Avis C, Librn, Polsinelli Shughart PC, 700 W 47th St, Ste 1000, Kansas City, MO, 64112. Tel: 816-753-1000. Fax: 816-753-1536. p. 1340

Bates, Brenda, Librn, Texas County Library, Summersville Branch, On the Square, 139 Rogers Ave, Summersville, MO, 65571. Tel: 417-932-5261. Fax: 417-932-5261. p. 1331

Bates, Connie G, Dir, Gibson County Memorial Library, 303 S High St, Trenton, TN, 38382-2027. Tel: 731-855-1991. Fax: 731-855-1991. p. 2267

Bates, Daniel, Bibliog Mgt, Louisiana Tech University, Everett St at The Columns, Ruston, LA, 71272. Tel: 318-257-3555. Fax: 318-257-2579. p. 966

Bates, Douglas, Dr, Dean of Libr & Learning Assistance, Tennessee Technological University, 1100 N Peachtree Ave, Cookeville, TN, 38505. Tel: 931-372-3408. Fax: 931-372-6112. p. 2231

Bates, Jocelyn, Info Tech Librn, Arizona Western College & NAU Yuma Branch Campus, 2020 S Ave 8E, Yuma, AZ, 85366. Tel: 928-344-7777. Fax: 928-344-7751. p. 90

Bates, Karla, Asst Dir, Cent Libr Serv, Muskegon Area District Library, 4845 Airline Rd, Unit 5, Muskegon, MI, 49444-4503. Tel: 231-737-6248. Fax: 231-737-6307. p. 1212

Bates, Karla, Librn, Muskegon Area District Library, Holton Branch, 8776 Holton Duck Lake Rd, Holton, MI, 49425. Tel: 231-821-0268. Fax: 231-724-6675. p. 1213

Bates, Katheryn, Br Mgr, Lawrence County Library, Driftwood, 28 Hwy 25, Lynn, AR, 72440. Tel: 870-528-3506. Fax: 870-528-3506. p. 116

Bates, Kim, Commun Librn, Edmonton Public Library, Riverbend, 460 Riverbend Sq, Rabbit Hill Rd & Terwillegar Dr, Edmonton, AB, T6R 2X2, CANADA. Tel: 780-944-5311. Fax: 780-944-5327. p. 2700

Bates, Mary, Mgr, Southeast Arkansas Regional Library, Eudora Branch, 161 N Cherry St, Eudora, AR, 71640. Tel: 870-355-2450. Fax: 870-355-2450. p. 110

Bates, Peta, Librn, Law Society of Saskatchewan Libraries, Saskatoon Court House, 520 Spadina Crescent E, Saskatoon, SK, S7K 3G7, CANADA. Tel: 306-933-5141. Fax: 306-933-5166. p. 2922

Bates, Rachel, Tech Serv Supvr, Northeastern University School of Law Library, 400 Huntington Ave, Boston, MA, 02115. Tel: 617-373-3553. Fax: 617-373-8705. p. 1066

Bates, Robin, Ref Serv, Essex Law Library, J Michael Ruane Judicial Ctr, 56 Federal St, Salem, MA, 01970. Tel: 978-741-0674. Fax: 978-745-7224. p. 1121

Bates, S Mabell, Spec Coll Librn, Bridgewater State College, Ten Shaw Rd, Bridgewater, MA, 02325. Tel: 508-531-1756. Fax: 508-531-1349, 508-531-6103. p. 1070

Bates, Tom, Dir, Alvin Community College Library, 3110 Mustang Rd, Alvin, TX, 77511. Tel: 281-756-3559. Fax: 281-756-3854. p. 2273

Bates-Ulibarri, Mary, Ref Librn, Central New Mexico Community College Libraries, Westside Campus Library, WS 1-101, 10549 Universe Blvd NM, Albuquerque, NM, 87105. Tel: 505-224-5426. p. 1549

Batesel, Sarah, Dir, Mayville State University, 330 Third St NE, Mayville, ND, 58257. Tel: 701-788-4814. Fax: 701-788-4846. p. 1846

Bateson, Peggy, Head, Circ, Cary Memorial Library, 1874 Massachusetts Ave, Lexington, MA, 02420. Tel: 781-862-6288, Ext 212. Fax: 781-862-7355. p. 1099

Batey, Deborah, Chief Librn, VA San Diego Healthcare System Medical Library, 3350 La Jolla Village Dr, San Diego, CA, 92161. Tel: 858-552-8585. Fax: 858-552-7537. p. 239

Bath, Linda, Circ, Mayville Public Library, 111 N Main St, Mayville, WI, 53050. Tel: 920-387-7910. Fax: 920-387-7917. p. 2613

Bath, Raman P, Librn, Fresno County Public Library, Fowler Branch, 306 S Seventh St, Fowler, CA, 93625. Tel: 559-600-9281. p. 152

Bathe-Schine, Marita, Ch, Lawrence Memorial Library, 40 North St, Bristol, VT, 05443. Tel: 802-453-2366. p. 2420

Batista, David, Head, Ref & Res Serv, Rutgers University Libraries, Camden Law Library, 217 N Fifth St, Camden, NJ, 08102-1203. Tel: 856-225-6469. p. 1477

Batkin, Jonathan, Dir, Wheelwright Museum of the American Indian, 704 Camino Lejo, Santa Fe, NM, 87505. Tel: 505-982-4636. Fax: 505-989-7386. p. 1565

Batman, Autumn, Head, Ref, Harrison County Public Library, 105 N Capitol Ave, Corydon, IN, 47112. Tel: 812-738-4110. Fax: 812-738-5408. p. 734

Batra, Gurvinder, Librn, The Gordon & Ruby Swayze Health Resource Centre, 825 Coxwell Ave, Toronto, ON, M4C 3E7, CANADA. Tel: 416-469-6580, Ext 6010. Fax: 416-469-6106. p. 2859

Batson, Darrell, Dir, Frederick County Public Libraries, 110 E Patrick St, Frederick, MD, 21701. Tel: 301-600-1613. Fax: 301-600-3789. p. 1028

Batson, Debra L, Dir, Plympton Public Library, 248 Main St, Plympton, MA, 02367-1114. Tel: 781-585-4551. Fax: 781-585-7660. p. 1118

Batson, Lill, Dir, Viola Public Library District, 1705 14th St, Viola, IL, 61486-9462. Tel: 309-596-2620. Fax: 309-596-2822. p. 714

Batson, Pamela Bea, Libr Dir, Haynie Public Library, 1619 W Main St, Prague, OK, 74864. Tel: 405-567-4013. Fax: 405-567-4732. p. 1976

Batson, Rebecca E, Div Head of Ref & Pub Serv, Head Librn, Delaware State University, 1200 N Dupont Hwy, Dover, DE, 19901-2277. Tel: 302-857-7887. Fax: 302-857-6177. p. 382

Batt, Carol, Dep Dir-Chief Operating Officer, Buffalo & Erie County Public Library System, One Lafayette Sq, Buffalo, NY, 14203-1887. Tel: 716-858-8900. Fax: 716-858-6211. p. 1596

Battad, Maria Teresa, Circ, Milford Public Library, 57 New Haven Ave, Milford, CT, 06460. Tel: 203-783-3290. Fax: 203-877-1072. p. 352

Battaglia, Margie, Head, Access Serv, Boston College Libraries, Thomas P O'Neill Jr Library (Central Library), 140 Commonwealth Ave, Chestnut Hill, MA, 02467. Tel: 617-552-4834. Fax: 617-552-0599. p. 1081

Battaglia, Nancy W, Librn, Children's Hospitals & Clinics, 345 N Smith Ave, Saint Paul, MN, 55102. Tel: 651-220-6145. Fax: 651-220-6408. p. 1277

Battcher, Ray, Curator, Librn, Bristol Historical Preservation Society Library, 48 Court St, Bristol, RI, 02809-2208. Tel: 401-253-7223. p. 2163

Battel, Andrea, Librn, United States Court of Appeals, King Courthouse, Rm 5007, 50 Walnut St, Newark, NJ, 07102. Tel: 973-645-3034. p. 1513

Battis, Cynthia J, Coll Develop, Public Library of Brookline, 361 Washington St, Brookline, MA, 02445. Tel: 617-730-2370. Fax: 617-730-2160. p. 1071

Battista, Annmarie, Head, Circ, Bloomfield College Library, Liberty St & Oakland Ave, Bloomfield, NJ, 07003. Tel: 973-748-9000, Ext 332. Fax: 973-743-3998. p. 1473

Battistoni, Janet, Ch, Hyde Park Free Library, Two Main St, Hyde Park, NY, 12538. Tel: 845-229-7791. Fax: 845-229-6521. p. 1640

Battles, Barbara, Outreach Serv Librn, South Brunswick Public Library, 110 Kingston Lane, Monmouth Junction, NJ, 08852. Tel: 732-329-4000, Ext 7637. Fax: 732-329-0573. p. 1502

Battles De Ramos, Stacey, Access Serv Librn, Boston University Libraries, School of Theology Library, 745 Commonwealth Ave, 2nd Flr, Boston, MA, 02215. Tel: 617-353-3034. Fax: 617-358-0699. p. 1058

Battleson, Brenda, Asst Prof, University at Buffalo, State University of New York, 534 Baldy Hall, Buffalo, NY, 14260. Tel: 716-645-2412. Fax: 716-645-3775. p. 2971

Battley, Joan, Dir, North Chicago Public Library, 2100 Argonne Dr, North Chicago, IL, 60064. Tel: 847-689-0125, Ext 110. Fax: 847-689-9117. p. 682

Batts, Coretta, Mgr, Southeast Arkansas Regional Library, Lake Village Branch, 108 Church St, Lake Village, AR, 71653. Tel: 870-265-6116. Fax: 870-265-6116. p. 110

Batuang, Rebecca, Br Mgr, Brooklyn Public Library, Rugby, 1000 Utica Ave, Brooklyn, NY, 11203. Tel: 718-566-0054. Fax: 718-566-0059. p. 1592

Baty, Linda, Cat, Tech Serv Librn, Canby Public Library, 292 N Holly St, Canby, OR, 97013-3732. Tel: 503-266-3394. Fax: 503-266-1709. p. 1993

Baty, Melinda, Outreach Coordr, Youth Serv Coordr, Birchard Public Library of Sandusky County, 423 Croghan St, Fremont, OH, 43420. Tel: 419-334-7101. Fax: 419-334-4788. p. 1900

Baty, Will, Ref Librn, Santa Rosa Junior College, 1501 Mendocino Ave, Santa Rosa, CA, 95401. Tel: 707-524-1664. Fax: 707-527-4545. p. 267

Bauchspies, Robert, Librn, United States International Trade Commission, National Library of International Trade, 500 E St SW, Rm 300, Washington, DC, 20436. Tel: 202-205-2636. Fax: 202-205-2316. p. 420

Bauder, Julia, Data Serv Librn, Grinnell College Libraries, 1111 Sixth Ave, Grinnell, IA, 50112-1770. Tel: 641-269-4431. Fax: 641-269-4283. p. 819

Baudino, Frank, Head, Info Serv, Northwest Missouri State University, 800 University Dr, Maryville, MO, 64468-6001. Tel: 660-562-1192. Fax: 660-562-1049. p. 1344

Baudouin, Eleanor, Ref Librn, Air Force Research Laboratory, Technical Library, 203 W Eglin Blvd, Ste 300, Eglin AFB, FL, 32542-6843. Tel: 850-882-3212, 850-882-5586. Fax: 850-882-3214. p. 439

Baudouin, Karen, Ref Librn, Smithtown Library, One N Country Rd, Smithtown, NY, 11787. Tel: 631-265-2072. Fax: 631-265-2044. p. 1744

Bauer, Abi, Librn, Oxford Municipal Library, 411 Ogden St, Oxford, NE, 68967. Tel: 308-824-3381. Fax: 308-824-3381. p. 1416

Bauer, Carole, Br Mgr, Peoples Library, Lower Burrell, 3052 Wachter Ave, Lower Burrell, PA, 15068-3543. Tel: 724-339-1565. Fax: 724-339-2027. p. 2097

Bauer, Douglas, Sr Librn, Orleans Correctional Facility Library, 3531 Gaines Basin Rd, Albion, NY, 14411. Tel: 585-589-6820, Ext 4600. Fax: 585-589-6820, Ext 3199. p. 1571

Bauer, Elizabeth, Circ Supvr, Middleton Public Library, 7425 Hubbard Ave, Middleton, WI, 53562-3117. Tel: 608-827-7404. Fax: 608-836-5724. p. 2616

Bauer, Ellen, Asst Br Mgr, Pine Bluff & Jefferson County Library System, White Hall Public Library, 300 Anderson St, White Hall, AR, 71602. Tel: 870-247-5064. Fax: 870-247-2613. p. 112

Bauer, Evelyn, Mgr, Union Beach Memorial Library, 810 Union Ave, Union Beach, NJ, 07735. Tel: 732-264-3792. p. 1537

Bauer, Francie, Asst Dir, Roosevelt University, Robert R McCormick Tribune Foundation Library, 1400 N Roosevelt Blvd, Schaumburg, IL, 60173. Tel: 847-619-7980. Fax: 847-619-7983. p. 623

Bauer, Frankie, Asst Admin, Talbot County Free Library, 100 W Dover St, Easton, MD, 21601-2620. Tel: 410-822-1626. Fax: 410-820-8217. p. 1027

Bauer, Hella, Librn, Raymond A Whitwer Tilden Public Library, 202 S Center St, Tilden, NE, 68781. Tel: 402-368-5306. Fax: 402-368-5515. p. 1421

Bauer, Jacky, Mgr, Lakeland Library Region, 1302 100 St, North Battleford, SK, S9A 0V8, CANADA. Tel: 306-445-6108. Fax: 306-445-5717. p. 2919

Bauer, Jo Ann, Supv Librn, Humboldt County Library, 1313 Third St, Eureka, CA, 95501-0553. Tel: 707-269-1918. p. 147

Bauer, JoAnn, Supv Librn, Ch, Humboldt County Library, Eureka (Main Library), 1313 Third St, Eureka, CA, 95501. Tel: 707-269-1900. p. 147

Bauer, Kate, Exec Dir, American Association of Birth Centers Library, 3123 Gottschall Rd, Perkiomenville, PA, 18074-9604. Tel: 215-234-8068. Fax: 215-234-8829. p. 2102

Bauer, Lisa, Asst Dir, Iola Village Library, 180 S Main St, Iola, WI, 54945-9689. Tel: 715-445-4330. Fax: 715-445-2917. p. 2599

Bauer, Melissa, Online Learning Librn, Kent State University, 6000 Frank Ave NW, North Canton, OH, 44720-7548. Tel: 330-494-3320. Fax: 330-494-6212. p. 1923

Bauer, Melissa, Asst Librn, Electronic Res, Walsh University, 2020 E Maple St NW, North Canton, OH, 44720-3336. Tel: 330-244-4658. Fax: 330-490-7270. p. 1923

Bauer, Miranda, Youth Serv, Benbrook Public Library, 1065 Mercedes, Benbrook, TX, 76126. Tel: 817-249-6632. Fax: 817-249-3326. p. 2289

Bauer, Nancy E, Dir, Palmer Public Library, 1455 N Main St, Palmer, MA, 01069. Tel: 413-283-3330. Fax: 413-283-9970. p. 1116

Bauer, Peggy, Sr Librn, Hennepin County Library, Excelsior, 343 Third St, Excelsior, MN, 55331-1878. Tel: 612-543-6353. Fax: 612-543-6352. p. 1263

Bauer, Peggy, Sr Librn, Hennepin County Library, Minnetonka, 17524 Excelsior Blvd, Minnetonka, MN, 55345-1099. Tel: 612-543-5728. Fax: 612-543-5727. p. 1264

Bauer, Peggy, Ch, Glenolden Library, 211 S Llanwellyn Ave, Glenolden, PA, 19036-2118. Tel: 610-583-1010. Fax: 610-583-7610. p. 2061

Bauer, Sandra, Dir, Exira Public Library, 114 W Washington St, Exira, IA, 50076. Tel: 712-268-5489. Fax: 712-268-5489. p. 815

Bauer, Veronica, Librn, Geneseo Public Library, 725 Main St, Geneseo, KS, 67444-9702. Tel: 620-824-6140. p. 868

Bauersfeld, Diane, Pub Serv, Wyoming Supreme Court, Supreme Court Bldg, 2301 Capitol Ave, Cheyenne, WY, 82002-0450. Tel: 307-777-8564. Fax: 307-777-7240. p. 2653

Baues, Susan, Librn, Innisfil Public Library, 20 Church St, Cookstown, ON, L0L 1L0, CANADA. Tel: 705-458-1273. Fax: 705-458-1294. p. 2801

Baugh, Alicia, Librn, Grand Meadow Public Library, 125 Grand Ave E, Grand Meadow, MN, 55936. Tel: 507-754-5859. Fax: 507-754-5859. p. 1253

Baugh, Dave, Archivist, Philadelphia City Archives, 3101 Market St, 1st Flr, Philadelphia, PA, 19104. Tel: 215-685-9400. Fax: 215-685-9409. p. 2114

Baugh, Elizabeth, Dir, Free Library of Northampton Township, 25 Upper Holland Rd, Richboro, PA, 18954-1514. Tel: 215-357-3050. p. 2134

Baugh, Georgia, Electronic Res & Ref Librn, Saint Louis University, 3650 Lindell Blvd, Saint Louis, MO, 63108-3302. Tel: 314-977-3598. Fax: 314-977-3108. p. 1360

Baugh, Jane Roth, Info Serv, Woods Rogers PLC, Wells Fargo Tower, Ste 1400, Ten S Jefferson St, Roanoke, VA, 24011. Tel: 540-983-7531. Fax: 540-983-7711. p. 2495

Baugh, Mick, Librn, Vorys, Sater, Seymour & Pease Library, 1909 K St, Washington, DC, 20036-5109. Tel: 202-467-8800. Fax: 202-467-8900. p. 422

Baugh, Ned, Mgr, Info Sys, Monroe County Public Library, 303 E Kirkwood Ave, Bloomington, IN, 47408. Tel: 812-349-3050. Fax: 812-349-3051. p. 728

Baughan, Betty, In Charge, Charlotte County Library, Keysville Branch, 300 King St, Keysville, VA, 23947. Tel: 434-736-0083. p. 2453

Baughan, Betty, Librn, Charlotte County Library, Wylliesburg Community, Hwy 15, Wylliesburg, VA, 23976. Tel: 434-735-8812. p. 2453

Baugher, Phil, Dir, Westchester Public Library, 200 W Indiana Ave, Chesterton, IN, 46304-3122. Tel: 219-926-7696. Fax: 219-926-6424. p. 732

Baughman, Amanda, Asst Librn, East Mississippi Regional Library System, Bay Springs Municipal, 815 S Court St, Bay Springs, MS, 39422. Tel: 601-764-2291. Fax: 601-764-2291. p. 1313

Baughman, Autumn, Mgr, Outreach Serv, Bedford Public Library, 1323 K St, Bedford, IN, 47421. Tel: 812-275-4471. Fax: 812-278-5244. p. 726

Baughman, Carol, Br Mgr, Gloucester County Library System, East Greenwich Library, 535 Kings Hwy, Mickleton, NJ, 08056-1412. Tel: 856-423-1149. Fax: 856-423-3036. p. 1507

Baughman, Monica, Dep Dir, Worthington Libraries, 820 High St, Worthington, OH, 43085. Tel: 614-807-2602. Fax: 614-807-2642. p. 1950

Baughman, Vesta, Librn, Allen University Library, 1530 Harden St, Columbia, SC, 29204. Tel: 803-376-5719. Fax: 803-765-6009. p. 2186

Baughman, Walter, Evening Circ Spec, Mount Vernon Nazarene University, 800 Martinsburg Rd, Mount Vernon, OH, 43050-9500. Tel: 740-397-9000, Ext 4240. Fax: 740-397-8847. p. 1919

Baughn, Robert, Librn/Exec Ed, AFI Cat, American Film Institute, 2021 N Western Ave, Los Angeles, CA, 90027. Tel: 323-856-7661. Fax: 323-856-7803. p. 168

Baum, Christina, Dir, Southern Connecticut State University, 501 Crescent St, New Haven, CT, 06515. Tel: 203-392-5750. Fax: 203-392-5775. p. 356

Baum, Kathleen, Mgr, Portage County District Library, Windham Branch, 9647 E Center St, Windham, OH, 44288. Tel: 330-326-3145. Fax: 330-326-2490. p. 1901

Baum, Nathan, Asst Dir, Electronic Res & Serv, Stony Brook University, W-1502 Melville Library, John S Toll Rd, Stony Brook, NY, 11794-3300. Tel: 631-632-7100. Fax: 631-632-7116. p. 1749

Baum, Patricia, Dir, Wanatah Public Library, 101 N Main St, Wanatah, IN, 46390. Tel: 219-733-9303. Fax: 219-733-2763. p. 785

Bauman, Anne, Ref Librn, Island Trees Public Library, 38 Farmedge Rd, Island Trees, NY, 11756-5200. Tel: 516-731-2211. Fax: 516-731-2395, 516-731-3798. p. 1640

Bauman, Debbie, Access Serv, Acq, Dir, Moore Public Library, 403 Fergus Ave, Moore, MT, 59464. Tel: 406-374-2364. Fax: 406-374-2364. p. 1387

Bauman, Janet, Ch, Back Mountain Memorial Library, 96 Huntsville Rd, Dallas, PA, 18612. Tel: 570-675-1182. Fax: 570-674-5863. p. 2048

Bauman, Kay, Dep Exec Dir, Libr Operations, Metropolitan Library System in Oklahoma County, 300 Park Ave, Oklahoma City, OK, 73102. Tel: 405-606-3725. Fax: 405-606-3722. p. 1972

Bauman, Kurt R, Mgr, Northeastern Pennsylvania Alliance, 1151 Oak St, Pittston, PA, 18640-3795. Tel: 570-655-5581, Ext 237. Fax: 570-654-5137. p. 2130

Bauman, Linda, Ch, Watertown Regional Library, 160 Sixth St NE, Watertown, SD, 57201-2778. Tel: 605-882-6220. Fax: 605-882-6221. p. 2221

Bauman, Marian R, Dir, Neptune Public Library, 25 Neptune Blvd, Neptune, NJ, 07753-1125. Tel: 732-775-8241. Fax: 732-774-1132. p. 1507

Bauman, Stephen, Circ, Bourbonnais Public Library District, 250 W John Casey Rd, Bourbonnais, IL, 60914. Tel: 815-933-1727. Fax: 815-933-1961. p. 596

Baumann, Kari, Dir, Elbert County Library District, 651 Beverly St, Elizabeth, CO, 80107-7560. Tel: 303-646-3416. Fax: 303-646-0315. p. 305

Baumann, Lynne, Librn, Chinook Regional Library, Tompkins Branch, Main St, Tompkins, SK, S0N 2S0, CANADA. Tel: 306-622-2255. p. 2929

Baumann, Mauri, Ref Serv, Ad, Melbourne Public Library, 540 E Fee Ave, Melbourne, FL, 32901. Tel: 321-952-4514. Fax: 321-952-4518. p. 463

Baumann, Patrick, AV, Automation Librn, East Central University, 1100 E 14th St, Ada, OK, 74820-6999. Tel: 580-310-5373. Fax: 580-436-3242. p. 1955

Baumann, Walter, Cat, Doc, DePaul University Libraries, Vincent G Rinn Law Library, 25 E Jackson Blvd, 5th Flr, Chicago, IL, 60604-2287. Tel: 312-362-5225. Fax: 312-362-6908. p. 612

Baumbach, Gary, Chief Librn, Woodstock Public Library, 445 Hunter St, Woodstock, ON, N4S 4G7, CANADA. Tel: 519-539-4801. Fax: 519-539-5246. p. 2872

Baumbach, Joyce, Interim Dir, Rowlett Public Library, 3900 Main St, Rowlett, TX, 75088-5075. Tel: 972-412-6161. Fax: 972-412-6153. p. 2377

Baumgartner, Leah, Ref Serv, YA, Wells County Public Library, 200 W Washington St, Bluffton, IN, 46714-1999. Tel: 260-824-1612. Fax: 260-824-3129. p. 728

Baumgartner, Rachel, Ch, Local Hist Librn, Reading Public Library, 64 Middlesex Ave, Reading, MA, 01867-2550. Tel: 781-944-0840. Fax: 781-942-9106. p. 1120

Baunach, Vicky, Coll Develop, Tech Serv, Carbon County Library System, 215 W Buffalo St, Rawlins, WY, 82301. Tel: 307-328-2618. Fax: 307-328-2615. p. 2659

Baures, Lisa, Ref Librn, Minnesota State University, Mankato, ML3097, Mankato, MN, 56001. Tel: 507-389-5952. Fax: 507-389-5155. p. 1257

Bausch, Claire, Dir of Libr, Nicholson Memorial Library System, 625 Austin St, Garland, TX, 75040-6365. Tel: 972-205-2543. Fax: 972-205-2523. p. 2327

Bauserman, Tara, Librn, Pocahontas County Free Libraries, Durbin Branch, Main St, Durbin, WV, 26264. Tel: 304-456-3142. Fax: 304-456-3142. p. 2565

Bautista, Christine, Govt Pub & Info Supvr, Laredo Community College, West End Washington St, Laredo, TX, 78040. Tel: 956-721-5841. Fax: 956-721-5447. p. 2353

Bautz, Travis, Head Librn, Greene County Public Library, Xenia Community Library, 76 E Market St, Xenia, OH, 45385-0520. Tel: 937-352-4000. Fax: 937-376-5523. p. 1951

Bavido, Mary, Patron Serv Mgr, Bartlett Public Library District, 800 S Bartlett Rd, Bartlett, IL, 60103. Tel: 630-837-2855. Fax: 630-837-2669. p. 592

Bavin, Ann, Dir, Marvin Memorial Library, 29 W Whitney Ave, Shelby, OH, 44875-1252. Tel: 419-347-5576. Fax: 419-347-7285. p. 1934

Bavlinka, Joyce, Librn, State University of New York, 111 Livingston St, Ste 306, Brooklyn, NY, 11201. Tel: 718-802-3300, 718-802-3314. Fax: 718-802-3332. p. 1595

Baxendale, Betsy, Supvr, N Region Libr, Aurora Public Library, Martin Luther King Jr Library, 9898 E Colfax Ave, Aurora, CO, 80010. Tel: 303-739-1940. p. 288

Baxley, Wanda, Br Mgr, Williamsburg County Library, 215 N Jackson, Kingstree, SC, 29556-3319. Tel: 843-558-7679. Fax: 843-558-0743. p. 2198

Baxley, Wanda, Br Mgr, Williamsburg County Library, Hemingway Branch, 306 N Main St, Hemingway, SC, 29554. Tel: 843-558-7679. Fax: 843-558-0743. p. 2198

Baxstrom, Donnalee, Dir, Pine River Public Library District, 395 Bayfield Center Dr, Bayfield, CO, 81122. Tel: 970-884-2222. Fax: 970-884-7155. p. 289

Baxter, Barbara, Coll Develop, Alameda County Library, 2450 Stevenson Blvd, Fremont, CA, 94538-2326. Tel: 510-745-1550. Fax: 510-793-2987. p. 149

Baxter, Belle, Adult Serv, Elwood Public Library, 1929 Jericho Tpk, East Northport, NY, 11731. Tel: 631-499-3722. Fax: 631-499-0057. p. 1617

Baxter, Brenda, Libr Mgr, Washoe County Library System, Duncan-Traner Community Library, 1650 Carville Dr, Reno, NV, 89512. Tel: 775-333-5134. Fax: 775-333-5076. p. 1434

Baxter, Brenda, Libr Mgr, Washoe County Library System, Verdi Community Library, 270 Bridge St, Verdi, NV, 89439. Tel: 775-345-8104. Fax: 775-345-8106. p. 1434

Baxter, Brenda, Mgr, Washoe County Library System, Senior Center Library, 1155 E Ninth St, Reno, NV, 89512. Tel: 775-328-2586. Fax: 775-785-4610. p. 1434

Baxter, Charlene, Pub Serv, Tech Serv, La Grange College, 601 Broad St, La Grange, GA, 30240-2999. Tel: 706-880-8311. Fax: 706-880-8040. p. 537

Baxter, Jill, Br Mgr, Las Vegas-Clark County Library District, Clark County Library, 1401 E Flamingo Rd, Las Vegas, NV, 89119. Tel: 702-507-3400. Fax: 702-507-3482. p. 1429

Baxter, Jill, Asst Librn, Hyrum Library, 50 W Main, Hyrum, UT, 84319. Tel: 435-245-6411. Fax: 435-245-0180. p. 2406

Baxter, Jim, Asst Dir, Libr Serv, Tarrant County College, Northwest Campus Walsh Library, 4801 Marine Creek Pkwy, Fort Worth, TX, 76179. Tel: 817-515-7725. Fax: 817-515-7720. p. 2323

Baxter, Judy, Libr Mgr, Vancouver Island Regional Library, South Cowichan, 310-2720 Mill Bay Rd, Mill Bay, BC, V0R 2P0, CANADA. Tel: 250-743-5436. Fax: 250-743-5506. p. 2733

Baxter, Julie, Dir, Moffat Library of Washingtonville, Six W Main St, Washingtonville, NY, 10992. Tel: 845-496-5483. Fax: 845-496-6854. p. 1763

Baxter, Karen, Visual Arts Librn, California Institute of the Arts, 24700 McBean Pkwy, Valencia, CA, 91355. Tel: 661-253-7880. Fax: 661-254-4561. p. 278

Baxter, Karen, Librn, Roosevelt County Library, Culbertson Public, 202 Broadway Ave S, Culbertson, MT, 59218. Tel: 406-787-5275. p. 1390

Baxter, Mariellen, Mgr, Enoch Pratt Free Library, Canton, 1030 S Ellwood Ave, Baltimore, MD, 21224-4930. Tel: 410-396-8548. Fax: 410-396-7491. p. 1013

Baxter, Rebecca, Head of Libr, Free Library of Philadelphia, Frankford Branch, 4634 Frankford Ave, Philadelphia, PA, 19124-5804. Tel: 215-685-1473, 215-685-1474. Fax: 215-289-6914. p. 2107

Baxter, Sandy, Libr Mgr, Department of Veterans Affairs, 76 Veterans Ave, Bath, NY, 14810. Tel: 607-664-4000, 607-664-4813. Fax: 607-664-4814. p. 1578

Baxter, Sandy, Librn, Veterans Administration Medical Center, 400 Fort Hill Ave, Canandaigua, NY, 14424. Tel: 585-393-7995. Fax: 585-393-8356. p. 1601

Baxter, William, Librn, Smithsonian Libraries, National Air & Space Museum Library, National Air & Space Museum, Rm 3100, MRC 314, Sixth St & Independence Ave SW, Washington, DC, 20560-0314. Tel: 202-633-2324. Fax: 202-786-2835. p. 415

Baxter-Cooke, Cynthia, Head, Info Serv, Norfolk State University Library, 700 Park Ave, Norfolk, VA, 23504-8010. Tel: 757-823-2166. Fax: 757-823-2431. p. 2482

Bay, Ann, Ref & Libr Instruction, Blinn College Library, 800 Blinn Blvd, Brenham, TX, 77833. Tel: 979-830-4250. Fax: 979-830-4222. p. 2291

Bayer, Barbara Ann, Dir, Seneca East Public Library, 14 N Main St, Attica, OH, 44807. Tel: 419-426-8205. Fax: 419-426-3701. p. 1856

Bayer, Lee, Head, ILL, California State University, San Bernardino, 5500 University Pkwy, San Bernardino, CA, 92407-2318. Tel: 909-537-3498. Fax: 909-537-7048. p. 227

Bayer, Mandy, Outreach Med Librn, Northeast Georgia Health System, 743 Spring St NE, Gainesville, GA, 30501-3899. Tel: 770-538-7630. Fax: 770-535-3463. p. 534

Bayer, Marc Dewey, ILL Librn, Syst, State University of New York College at Buffalo, 1300 Elmwood Ave, Buffalo, NY, 14222-1095. Tel: 716-878-6314. Fax: 716-878-6335. p. 1599

Bayer, Vicki, Libr Mgr, Debevoise & Plimpton, 555 13th St NW, Ste 1100 E, Washington, DC, 20004. Tel: 202-383-8055, 202-383-8075. Fax: 202-383-8118. p. 397

Bayes, Amy, Ch, Newton Public Library, 720 N Oak, Newton, KS, 67114. Tel: 316-283-2890. Fax: 316-283-2916. p. 884

Baykan, Mary C, Dir, Western Maryland Public Libraries, 100 S Potomac St, Hagerstown, MD, 21740. Tel: 301-739-3250, Ext 140. Fax: 301-739-7603. p. 1032

Baykan, Mary Catherine, Dir, Washington County Free Library, 100 S Potomac St, Hagerstown, MD, 21740. Tel: 301-739-3250. Fax: 301-739-7603. p. 1031

Baykoucheva, Svetla, Head Librn, University of Maryland Libraries, White Memorial Chemistry Library, 1526 Chemistry Bldg, College Park, MD, 20742-7011. Tel: 301-405-9078. Fax: 301-405-9164. p. 1025

Bayles, Mark S, Asst Dir, Chapel Hill Public Library, 100 Library Dr, Chapel Hill, NC, 27514. Tel: 919-969-2036. Fax: 919-968-2838. p. 1780

Bayless, Lyn, Cat, ILL, Columbia State Community College, 1665 Hampshire Pike, Columbia, TN, 38401. Tel: 931-540-2559. Fax: 931-540-2565. p. 2231

Bayless, Paul, Br Mgr, Saint Louis County Library, Grand Glaize Branch, 1010 Meramec Sta Rd, Manchester, MO, 63021. Tel: 636-225-6454. Fax: 314-225-6072. p. 1358

Bayley, Douglas, Asst Librn, Monell Chemical Senses Center, 3500 Market St, Philadelphia, PA, 19104-3308. Tel: 215-898-6666. Fax: 215-898-2084. p. 2112

Bayley, Liz, Dir, McMaster University Library, Health Sciences Library, 1280 Main St W, Hamilton, ON, L8S 4K1, CANADA. Tel: 905-525-9140, Ext 22545. Fax: 905-528-3733. p. 2810

Baylis, Janet, Head, Tech Serv, Patchogue-Medford Library, 54-60 E Main St, Patchogue, NY, 11772. Tel: 631-654-4700, Ext 280. Fax: 631-289-3999. p. 1715

Baylis, Lisa, Head, Circ, Bedford Free Public Library, Seven Mudge Way, Bedford, MA, 01730-2168. Tel: 781-275-9440. Fax: 781-275-3590. p. 1052

Baylor, Arthur, Asst Librn, American Standards Testing Bureau, Inc, 40 Wall St, 28th Flr, New York, NY, 10005-2672. Tel: 212-943-3160. Fax: 212-825-2250. p. 1669

Bayne, Cathy, Dir, Fairfax Public Library, 313 Vanderbilt St, Fairfax, IA, 52228. Tel: 319-846-2994. Fax: 319-846-2889. p. 815

Bayne, Jamie, Info Serv Supvr, Boyd County Public Library, 1740 Central Ave, Ashland, KY, 41101. Tel: 606-329-0090. Fax: 606-329-0578. p. 905

Bayne, Pauline, Asst Dean, University of Tennessee, Knoxville, 1015 Volunteer Blvd, Knoxville, TN, 37996-1000. Tel: 865-974-4465. Fax: 865-974-4259. p. 2243

Bayne, Pauline S, Librn, University of Tennessee, Knoxville, George F DeVine Music Library, 301 Music Bldg, 1741 Volunteer Blvd, Knoxville, TN, 37996-2600. Tel: 865-974-3474. Fax: 865-974-0564. p. 2244

Bayne, Virginia, Circ, Oak Ridge Public Library, 1401 Oak Ridge Tpk, Oak Ridge, TN, 37830-6224. Tel: 865-425-3455. Fax: 865-425-3429. p. 2262

Baynes, Patricia, Dir, Palmyra Community Library, 127 Cuyler St, Palmyra, NY, 14522. Tel: 315-597-5276. Fax: 315-597-1375. p. 1714

Baynham, Robert, Dean, Western Baptist Bible College Memorial Library, 2119 Tracy, Kansas City, MO, 64108. Tel: 816-842-4195. Fax: 816-842-3050. p. 1341

Bayonet, Megan, ILL, Mary Baldwin College, 109 E Frederick St, Staunton, VA, 24401. Tel: 540-887-7085. Fax: 540-887-7137. p. 2496

Bayonne, Phara, Dir, University of Connecticut at Stamford, One University Pl, Stamford, CT, 06901-2315. Tel: 203-251-8523. Fax: 203-251-8526. p. 370

Bayorgeon, Mary M, Dir, Libr Serv, Saint Elizabeth Hospital, 1506 S Oneida St, Appleton, WI, 54915. Tel: 920-738-2324. Fax: 920-831-1265. p. 2579

Bayrd, Venice, Librn, Longwood Gardens Library, 409 Conservatory Rd, Kennett Square, PA, 19348-1805. Tel: 610-388-1000, Ext 510. Fax: 610-388-2078. p. 2074

Bayrer, Rebecca, Mgr, Libr Serv, Kaiser Permanente Health Sciences Library, 1200 El Camino Real, South San Francisco, CA, 94080. Tel: 650-742-2540. Fax: 650-742-2239. p. 270

Bays, Karen, County Coordr, Pioneer Library System, Shawnee Public, 101 N Philadelphia, Shawnee, OK, 74801. Tel: 405-275-6353. Fax: 405-273-0590. p. 1970

Baysinger, Grace, Bibliographer, Head Librn, Stanford University Libraries, Swain Library of Chemistry & Chemical Engineering, Organic Chemistry Bldg, 364 Lomita Dr, Stanford, CA, 94305-5080. Tel: 650-723-9237. Fax: 650-725-2274. p. 271

Baysinger, Richard, Media Librn, Eastern New Mexico University, 1300 S Ave K, Sta 32, Portales, NM, 88130-7402. Tel: 575-562-2602. Fax: 575-562-2647. p. 1560

Bazan, Christine, Br Mgr, Cheektowaga Public Library, Reinstein Memorial, 2580 Harlem Rd, Cheektowaga, NY, 14225. Tel: 716-892-8089. Fax: 716-892-3370. p. 1606

Bazemore, Trudy, Asst Dir, Georgetown County Library, 405 Cleland St, Georgetown, SC, 29440-3200. Tel: 843-545-3300. Fax: 843-545-3395. p. 2194

Bazile, Grace, Ref Serv, DeVry College of New York Library, 180 Madison Ave, 16th Flr, New York, NY, 10016-5267. Tel: 212-312-4414. p. 1677

Bazile, Richard, Chair, Wilbur Wright College North, 4300 N Narragansett Ave, Chicago, IL, 60634-1500. Tel: 773-481-8408. Fax: 773-481-8407. p. 627

Bazile, Richard, Coordr, Wilbur Wright College, 4300 N Narragansett, Chicago, IL, 60634. Tel: 773-481-8400, 773-777-7900. Fax: 773-481-8407. p. 2965

Bazinet, Jeanne, Librn, Centre Jeunesse de Montreal - Institut universitaire, 1001 boul de Maisonneuve est, 5ieme etage, Montreal, QC, H2L 4R5, CANADA. Tel: 514-896-3396. Fax: 514-896-3483. p. 2893

Bazirjian, Rosann, Dean, University of North Carolina at Greensboro, 320 Spring Garden St, Greensboro, NC, 27402. Tel: 336-334-5880. Fax: 336-334-5399. p. 1797

Bazzano, Rody, Asst Librn, St Thomas Seminary & Archdiocesan Center, 467 Bloomfield Ave, Bloomfield, CT, 06002. Tel: 860-242-5573, Ext 2609. Fax: 860-242-4886, Library. p. 331

Beaber, Patricia A, Head, ILL, Head, Ref, The College of New Jersey Library, 2000 Pennington Rd, Ewing, NJ, 08628-0718. Tel: 609-771-2405. Fax: 609-637-5177. p. 1484

Beach, Amber, Br Mgr, Tulare County Library, Ivanhoe Branch, 15964 Heather, Ivanhoe, CA, 93235. Tel: 559-798-1264. Fax: 559-798-5634. p. 281

Beach, Audrey H, Librn, Mississippi Delta Community College, Drew Library, 153 N Mail St, Drew, MS, 38737. Tel: 662-745-6322. Fax: 662-745-0194. p. 1309

Beach, Audrey H, Res Librn, Mississippi Delta Community College, 414 Hwy 3 South, Moorhead, MS, 38761. Tel: 662-246-6376. Fax: 662-246-8627. p. 1309

Beach, Audrey Horn, Librn, Mississippi Delta Community College, Greenwood Library, 207 West Park Ave, Greenwood, MS, 38930. Tel: 662-453-7377. Fax: 662-453-2043. p. 1309

Beach, Elizabeth, Human Res Officer, Missouri River Regional Library, 214 Adams St, Jefferson City, MO, 65101-3244. Tel: 573-634-6064, Ext 261. p. 1335

Beach, Gretchen, Cat & Digital Serv Librn, Marshall University Libraries, One John Marshall Dr, Huntington, WV, 25755-2060. Tel: 304-696-2312. Fax: 304-696-5858. p. 2561

Beach, Jackie, Dir, Craven-Pamlico-Carteret Regional Library System, 400 Johnson St, New Bern, NC, 28560. Tel: 252-638-7800. Fax: 252-638-7817. p. 1812

Beach, Jane, Dir, Cooperstown Public Library, 182 N Main St, Cooperstown, PA, 16317. Tel: 814-374-4605. Fax: 814-374-4606. p. 2047

Beach, Jennifer, Br Mgr, Alamance County Public Libraries, Graham Public Library, 211 S Main St, Graham, NC, 27253. Tel: 336-570-6730. Fax: 336-570-6732. p. 1779

Beach, Kevin, Coll Develop, Manatee County Public Library System, 1301 Barcarrota Blvd W, Bradenton, FL, 34205. Tel: 941-748-5555. Fax: 941-749-7191. p. 429

Beach, LaVonne M, Dir, La Crescent Public Library, 321 Main St, La Crescent, MN, 55947. Tel: 507-895-4047. Fax: 507-895-7153. p. 1255

Beach, Natalie, Dir, Chemeketa Community College Library, Bldg 9, 2nd Flr, 4000 Lancaster Dr NE, Salem, OR, 97305-1500. Tel: 503-399-5105. Fax: 503-399-5214. p. 2017

Beach, Pauline, Dir, Parnell Memorial Library, 277 Park Dr, Montevallo, AL, 35115-3882. Tel: 205-665-9207. Fax: 205-665-9214. p. 27

Beach, Regina, Dir, Georgia Perimeter College, Decatur Learning Resources Center, 3251 Panthersville Rd, Decatur, GA, 30034. Tel: 678-891-2590. Fax: 678-891-2866. p. 525

Beach, Sherry, Dir, Will Rogers Library, 1515 N Florence Ave, Claremore, OK, 74017. Tel: 918-341-1564. Fax: 918-342-0362. p. 1960

Beacham, Karen, Asst Librn, Echo Public Library, 20 S Bonanza, Echo, OR, 97826. Tel: 541-376-8411. Fax: 541-376-8218. p. 1995

Beacock, Bruce James, Archives Mgr, Archivist, Simcoe County Archives, 1149 Hwy 26, RR 2, Minesing, ON, L0L 1Y2, CANADA. Tel: 705-726-9300, Ext 1287, 705-726-9331. Fax: 705-725-5341. p. 2822

Beacom, Natalie, Adult Ref, New Berlin Public Library, 15105 Library Lane, New Berlin, WI, 53151. Tel: 262-785-4980. Fax: 262-785-4984. p. 2625

Beadle, Betty, Supvr, Somerset County Library System, Washington Valley, Washington Valley Rd, Martinsville, NJ, 08836. Tel: 732-356-2363. p. 1475

Beadle, Joe, Librn, Anamosa State Penitentiary, 406 N High St, Anamosa, IA, 52205. Tel: 319-462-3504, Ext 2237. Fax: 319-462-3013. p. 793

Beadles, Pam, Acq, Mount Union College Library, 1972 Clark Ave, Alliance, OH, 44601-3993. Tel: 330-823-3844. Fax: 330-823-3963. p. 1854

Beadsby, Caroline, Librn, Hyder Public Library, 50 Main St, Hyder, AK, 99923. Tel: 250-636-2637. Fax: 250-636-2714. p. 49

Beagle, Donald, Dir, Libr & Info Serv, Belmont Abbey College, 100 Belmont-Mt Holly Rd, Belmont, NC, 28012. Tel: 704-461-6748. Fax: 704-461-6743. p. 1776

Beagle, Pamela, Ref Librn, Barry University, 11300 NE Second Ave, Miami, FL, 33161. Tel: 305-899-3760. Fax: 305-899-4792. p. 464

Beaird, Catherine, Br Mgr, Shreve Memorial Library, Hamilton/South Caddo Branch, 2111 Bert Kouns Industrial Loop, Shreveport, LA, 71118. Tel: 318-687-6824. Fax: 318-686-0971. p. 969

Beaird, Kathy, Ref Mgr, Norman Williams Public Library, Ten S Park St, Woodstock, VT, 05091. Tel: 802-457-2295. Fax: 802-457-5181. p. 2440

Beal, Billy C, Dean, Meridian Community College, 910 Hwy 19 N, Meridian, MS, 39307. Tel: 601-484-8760. Fax: 601-482-3936. p. 1308

Beal, Joanne, Librn, Dayton Law Library, 41 N Perry St, Rm 505, Dayton, OH, 45402. Tel: 937-225-4496. Fax: 937-225-5056. p. 1892

Beal, Linda, Librn, Fayette County Public Libraries, Montgomery Branch, 507 Ferry St, Montgomery, WV, 25136. Tel: 304-442-5665. Fax: 304-442-5665. p. 2568

Beal, Susan, Bus Off Mgr, Indian Trails Public Library District, 355 S Schoenbeck Rd, Wheeling, IL, 60090. Tel: 847-459-4100. Fax: 847-459-4760. p. 719

Beale, Elizabeth, Pres, Atlantic Provinces Economic Council Library, 5121 Sackville St, Ste 500, Halifax, NS, B3J 1K1, CANADA. Tel: 902-422-6516. Fax: 902-429-6803. p. 2780

Beale, Leslie, Circuit Librn, Lewis County General Hospital, 7785 N State St, Lowville, NY, 13367. Tel: 315-376-5065, 315-376-5610. Fax: 315-376-5848. p. 1655

Beale, Leslie, Circuit Librn, Claxton-Hepburn Medical Center Library, 214 King St, Ogdensburg, NY, 13669. Tel: 315-393-3600, Ext 5632. Fax: 315-393-8506. p. 1709

Bealer, Anita, Sr Librn, Hennepin County Library, Southdale, 7001 York Ave S, Edina, MN, 55435-4287. Tel: 612-543-5971. Fax: 612-543-5976. p. 1264

Bealer, Rebecca, Ser, Louisiana State University Health Sciences Center, 433 Bolivar St, Box B3-1, New Orleans, LA, 70112-2223. Tel: 504-568-6108. Fax: 504-568-7718. p. 961

Beales, Donna, Dir, Lowell General Hospital, 295 Varnum Ave, Lowell, MA, 01854. Tel: 978-937-6247. Fax: 978-937-6855. p. 1100

Beales, Donna, Librn, Northeastern Consortium for Health Information, Lowell General Hospital Health Science Library, 295 Varnum Ave, Lowell, MA, 01854. Tel: 978-937-6247. Fax: 978-937-6855. p. 2945

Beall, Jeffrey, Scholarly Initiatives Librn, Auraria Library, 1100 Lawrence St, Denver, CO, 80204-2095. Tel: 303-556-5936. Fax: 303-556-3528. p. 298

Beall, Mary, Dep Librn, Southfield Public Library, 26300 Evergreen Rd, Southfield, MI, 48076. Tel: 248-796-4302. Fax: 248-796-4305. p. 1228

Bealle, Penny J, Dr, Coll Develop, Info Literacy, Suffolk County Community College, 121 Speonk Riverhead Rd, Riverhead, NY, 11901-9990. Tel: 631-548-2541. Fax: 631-369-2641. p. 1728

Beals, Brynn, Librn, St Joseph Medical Center Library, 1717 South J St, Tacoma, WA, 98405. Tel: 253-426-6778. Fax: 253-426-6260. p. 2540

Beals, Penny, Ch, El Reno Carnegie Library, 215 E Wade, El Reno, OK, 73036-2753. Tel: 405-262-2409. Fax: 405-422-2136. p. 1962

Beam, Daniel, Ref Librn, United States Department of Health & Human Services, Rm 4541, Cohen Bldg, 330 Independence Ave SW, Washington, DC, 20201. Tel: 202-619-2700. Fax: 202-619-3719. p. 419

Beam, Terry, Librn, Pennsylvania Legislative Budget & Finance Committee Library, Finance Bldg, Rm 400, Harrisburg, PA, 17105-8737. Tel: 717-783-1600. Fax: 717-787-5487. p. 2066

Beam-Ingram, Alicia, Br Mgr, Harrisville Public Library, 1767 Simpson Hwy 469, Harrisville, MS, 39082-4005. Tel: 601-847-1268. p. 1300

Beaman, Patricia, Per, Southern Adventist University, 4851 Industrial Dr, Collegedale, TN, 37315. Tel: 423-236-2789. Fax: 423-236-1788. p. 2230

Beamer, Michele B, Br Librn, Orange County Library, Wilderness, 6421 Flat Run Rd, Locust Grove, VA, 22508. Tel: 540-854-5310, 540-972-1675. Fax: 540-854-5402. p. 2483

Beamguard, Julie, Principal Librn, Tampa-Hillsborough County Public Library System, Bloomingdale Regional Pulbic, 1906 Bloomingdale Ave, Valrico, FL, 33594-6206. Fax: 813-635-1646. p. 497

Beamon, Lennie, Br Mgr, Madison County Library System, Camden Public Library, 116 Parkside Ave, Camden, MS, 39045. Tel: 662-468-0309. Fax: 662-468-0309. p. 1295

Bean, Alice, Librn, Gilmanton Iron Works Public Library, Ten Elm St, Gilmanton Iron Works, NH, 03837. p. 1448

Bean, Barbara, Ref, Michigan State University, 115 Law College Bldg, East Lansing, MI, 48824-1300. Tel: 517-432-6878. Fax: 517-432-6861. p. 1175

Bean, Benjamin, Youth Serv, Salinas Public Library, Cesar Chavez Library, 615 Williams Rd, Salinas, CA, 93905. Tel: 831-758-7345. Fax: 831-758-9172. p. 226

Bean, Christopher A, Dir, Shenandoah University, 1460 University Dr, Winchester, VA, 22601. Tel: 540-665-4553. Fax: 540-665-4609. p. 2503

Bean, Elaine, Tech Serv, Rivier College, 420 S Main St, Nashua, NH, 03060-5086. Tel: 603-897-8672. Fax: 603-897-8889. p. 1459

Bean, Ethelle S, Acq/Syst Librn, Assoc VPres/Dir, Dakota State University, 820 N Washington Ave, Madison, SD, 57042-1799. Tel: 605-256-5207. Fax: 605-256-5208. p. 2214

Bean, Jeannette, Per, Spec, Southeast Community College-Lincoln Campus, 8800 O St, Lincoln, NE, 68520. Tel: 402-437-2589. Fax: 402-437-2404. p. 1406

Bean, Lawrence, Br Mgr, Potter Justin Public Library, Liberty Branch, PO Box 116, Liberty, TN, 37095. Tel: 615-536-6116. p. 2266

Bean, Margaret, Head of Libr, University of Oregon Libraries, Science, Onyx Bridge, Lower Level, University of Oregon, Eugene, OR, 97403. Tel: 541-346-1876. Fax: 541-346-3012. p. 1997

Bean, Nancy, Dir, Warren General Hospital, Two Crescent Park W, Warren, PA, 16365. Tel: 814-723-4973, Ext 1825. Fax: 814-723-3785. p. 2150

Bean, Norma, Interim Dir, Texas Southern University, 3100 Cleburne Ave, Houston, TX, 77004. Tel: 713-313-7402. Fax: 713-313-1080. p. 2342

Bean, Sally, Br Mgr, Oakland Public Library, Temescal, 5205 Telegraph Ave, Oakland, CA, 94609. Tel: 510-597-5049. Fax: 510-597-5062. p. 198

Bean, Steven, Librn, Itasca Community College Library, 1851 E Hwy 169, Grand Rapids, MN, 55744. Tel: 218-327-4147. Fax: 218-327-4299. p. 1253

Beane, Joel W, Bibliog Instr, Coll Develop, Dir, Kingwood Public Library, 205 W Main St, Kingwood, WV, 26537-1418. Tel: 304-329-1499. Fax: 304-329-1499. p. 2563

Beane, Kathie, Librn, United States Department of Agriculture, National Agricultural Library, 1052 South Bldg, 14th & Independence Ave SW, Washington, DC, 20250. Tel: 202-720-3434. Fax: 202-720-0342. p. 418

Bear, Suzy, Librn, Prince Albert Parkland Health Region Library, 1200 24th St W, Prince Albert, SK, S6V 5T4, CANADA. Tel: 306-765-6026. Fax: 306-765-6062. p. 2921

Bear, Vikijane, Dir, Palacios Library, Inc, 326 Main St, Palacios, TX, 77465. Tel: 361-972-3234. Fax: 361-972-2142. p. 2368

Bearce, Lisa, Ch, Peterborough Town Library, Two Concord St, Peterborough, NH, 03458. Tel: 603-924-8040. Fax: 603-924-8041. p. 1462

Beard, Barbara S, Br Mgr, Beaumont Public Library System, Literacy Depot, 1205 Franklin St, Beaumont, TX, 77701. Tel: 409-835-7924. Fax: 409-838-6734. p. 2287

Beard, Craig, Ref Librn, University of Alabama at Birmingham, Mervyn H Sterne Library, 917 13th St S, Birmingham, AL, 35205. Tel: 205-934-6364. p. 10

Beard, Denise, Asst Dir, Truth or Consequences Public Library, Downtown, 401 N Foch St, Truth or Consequences, NM, 87901. Tel: 505-894-7821. p. 1566

Beard, Evelyn, Cat, Tech Serv, Texas Southern University, Thurgood Marshall School of Law Library, 3100 Cleburne Ave, Houston, TX, 77004. Tel: 713-313-1005. Fax: 713-313-4483. p. 2342

Beard, Faydra, Libr Mgr, Gleichen & District Library, 404 Main St, Gleichen, AB, T0J 1N0, CANADA. Tel: 403-734-2390. Fax: 403-734-2390. p. 2705

Beard, Johnsy, Tech Serv Mgr, Jefferson Community & Technical College, Southwest Campus Library, 1000 Community College Dr, Louisville, KY, 40272. Tel: 502-213-7229. Fax: 502-935-8653. p. 924

Beard, Patricia H, Dir, Washington County - Jonesborough Library, 200 Sabin Dr, Jonesborough, TN, 37659-1306. Tel: 423-753-1800. Fax: 423-753-1802. p. 2240

Beard, Renee, Br Mgr, Ohio Township Public Library System, 4111 Lakeshore Dr, Newburgh, IN, 47630-2274. Tel: 812-853-5468. Fax: 812-853-0509. p. 768

Beard, Wannell, Dir, Benton Public Library, PO Box 128, Benton, TN, 37307-0128. Tel: 423-338-4536. p. 2224

Bearden, Rick, Automation Librn, Ferris State University Library, 1010 Campus Dr, Big Rapids, MI, 49307-2279. Tel: 231-591-3500. Fax: 231-591-3724. p. 1158

Bearden, Tracy, Mgr, Irving Public Library, Northwest, 2928 N Beltline Rd, Irving, TX, 75062. Tel: 972-721-2691. Fax: 972-721-3637. p. 2347

Bearden, William, Assoc Dir, Tech Serv, Richard Stockton College of New Jersey Library, 101 Vera King Farris Dr, Galloway, NJ, 08205-9441. Tel: 609-652-4343. Fax: 609-652-4964. p. 1487

Beardmore, Elizabeth, Dean, ITT Technical Institute, 2810 Dupont Commerce Ct, Fort Wayne, IN, 46825. Tel: 260-497-6260. Fax: 260-484-0860. p. 742

Beards, Tarshel, Publ & Develop Coordr, Chicago State University, 9501 S Martin Luther King Jr Dr, LIB 440, Chicago, IL, 60628-1598. Tel: 773-995-4414. Fax: 773-995-3772. p. 610

Beardsley, Amy, Asst Librn, Mary Wilcox Memorial Library, 2630 Main St, Whitney Point, NY, 13862. Tel: 607-692-3159. Fax: 607-692-3159. p. 1769

Beardsley, Jennifer, Librn, Bastyr University Library, 14500 Juanita Dr NE, Kenmore, WA, 98028. Tel: 425-602-3029. Fax: 425-602-3188. p. 2518

Beardsley, Renee, Libr Mgr, New Woodstock Free Library, 2106 Main St, New Woodstock, NY, 13122-8718. Tel: 315-662-3134. p. 1667

Bearly, Sean, Info Syst Coordr, Newport Beach Public Library, 1000 Avocado Ave, Newport Beach, CA, 92660-6301. Tel: 949-717-3820. Fax: 949-640-5681. p. 194

Bearman, Alan, Dr, Dean of Libr, Washburn University, 1700 SW College Ave, Topeka, KS, 66621. Tel: 785-670-1179. Fax: 785-670-3223. p. 897

Bearre, Denise, Librn, Michigan Department of Corrections, 7401 Walton Rd, Kingsley, MI, 49649. Tel: 231-263-5253. Fax: 231-263-3944, 231-263-7606. p. 1198

Bearss, Daniel, Sr Librn, The National Academies, 500 Fifth St NW, Keck 304, Washington, DC, 20001-2721. Tel: 202-334-2125. Fax: 202-334-1651. p. 409

Beary, Camille, Asst Dir, Lyon College, 2300 Highland Rd, Batesville, AR, 72501-3699. Tel: 870-307-7444. Fax: 870-307-7279. p. 93

Beasecker, Robert, Dir, Spec Coll & Univ Archives, Grand Valley State University Libraries, One Campus Dr, Allendale, MI, 49401-9403. Tel: 616-331-8556. p. 1149

Beasley, Allison, Adult Serv, Kankakee Public Library, 201 E Merchant St, Kankakee, IL, 60901. Tel: 815-939-4564. Fax: 815-939-9057. p. 661

Beasley, Barbara, Mgr, Metropolitan Library System in Oklahoma County, Warr Acres Library, 5901 NW 63, Warr Acres, OK, 73132-7502. Tel: 405-721-2616. Fax: 405-606-3534. p. 1973

Beasley, Bernadine, Head, Ser Acq, Jackson State University, 1325 J R Lynch St, Jackson, MS, 39217. Tel: 601-979-2123. Fax: 601-979-2239. p. 1303

Beasley, Carla, Asst Dir, Mat Mgr, Forsyth County Public Library, 585 Dahlonega Rd, Cumming, GA, 30040-2109. Tel: 770-781-9840. Fax: 770-781-8089. p. 527

Beasley, Deborah, Youth Serv, Blue Island Public Library, 2433 York St, Blue Island, IL, 60406-2011. Tel: 708-388-1078, Ext 22. Fax: 708-388-1143. p. 596

Beasley, Gerald, Univ Librn, Concordia University Libraries, 1400 de Maisonneuve Blvd W, LB 209, Montreal, QC, H3G 1M8, CANADA. Tel: 514-848-2424, Ext 7695. Fax: 514-848-2882. p. 2894

Beasley, Glen, Strategic Planning, Newtown Library Co, 114 Centre Ave, Newtown, PA, 18940. Tel: 215-968-7659. p. 2098

Beasley, Gloria, Circ, University of Montevallo, Station 6100, Montevallo, AL, 35115-6100. Tel: 205-665-6100. Fax: 205-665-6112. p. 27

Beasley, Jonathan, Tech Serv, Eastern University, 1300 Eagle Rd, Saint Davids, PA, 19087. Tel: 610-341-5981. Fax: 610-341-1375. p. 2135

Beasley, Kathleen, Mgr, San Mateo County Library, Belmont Library, 1110 Alameda de las Pulgas, Belmont, CA, 94002. Tel: 650-591-8286. Fax: 650-591-2763. p. 255

Beasley, Linda, Acq, Harrison County Library System, 2600 24th Ave, No 6, Gulfport, MS, 39501-2081. Tel: 228-868-1383. Fax: 228-863-7433. p. 1299

Beasley, Nancy, ILL, Bracebridge Public Library, 94 Manitoba St, Bracebridge, ON, P1L 2B5, CANADA. Tel: 705-645-4171. Fax: 705-645-6551. p. 2796

Beasley, Sarah, Humanities & Soc Sci Librn, Scholarly Communication Coordr, Portland State University Library, 1875 SW Park Ave, Portland, OR, 97201-3220. Tel: 503-725-3688. Fax: 503-725-4524. p. 2014

Beason, Ed, Media Spec, Tennessee Technological University, 1100 N Peachtree Ave, Cookeville, TN, 38505. Tel: 931-372-3326. Fax: 931-372-6112. p. 2231

Beathard, Lana, Bus Mgr, Montgomery County Memorial Library System, 104 I-45 N, Conroe, TX, 77301-2720. Tel: 936-788-8377, Ext 238. Fax: 936-788-8398. p. 2300

Beaton, Brenda, Br Head, Toronto Public Library, Runnymede, 2178 Bloor St W, Toronto, ON, M6S 1M8, CANADA. Tel: 416-393-7697. Fax: 416-393-7574. p. 2863

Beaton, Brenda, Br Head, Toronto Public Library, Swansea Memorial, 95 Lavinia Ave, Toronto, ON, M6S 3H9, CANADA. Tel: 416-393-7695. Fax: 416-393-7552. p. 2863

Beaton, Rebecca, Br Mgr, Thompson-Nicola Regional District Library System, Blue River Branch, 829 Cedar St, Blue River, BC, V0E 1J0, CANADA. Tel: 250-673-8235. Fax: 250-673-8235. p. 2729

Beatrice, Hodgson, In Charge, City of Kawartha Lakes Public Library, Coboconk Branch, Nine Grandy Rd, Coboconk, ON, K0M 1K0, CANADA. Tel: 705-454-3322. Fax: 705-454-2392. p. 2816

Beatson, Joan, Ch, Granby Public Library, 15 N Granby Rd, Granby, CT, 06035. Tel: 860-844-5275. Fax: 860-653-0241. p. 341

Beatson, Leigh, Tech Serv, Fried, Frank, Harris, Shriver & Jacobson LLP, 1001 Pennsylvania Ave NW, Ste 800, Washington, DC, 20004. Tel: 202-639-7103. Fax: 202-639-7008. p. 401

Beattie, Lyn, Law Librn, Alberta Law Libraries, Judicial, Calgary Courts Ctr, 2001-N, 601 - 5 St SW, Calgary, AB, T2P 5P7, CANADA. Tel: 403-297-8234. Fax: 403-297-2981. p. 2687

Beattie, Margaret J, Br Mgr, Central Rappahannock Regional Library, 1201 Caroline St, Fredericksburg, VA, 22401-3761. Tel: 540-372-1144. Fax: 540-373-9411. p. 2465

Beattie, Norman, Pub Serv Coordr, Red River College Library, 2055 Notre Dame Ave, Winnipeg, MB, R3H 0J9, CANADA. Tel: 204-632-2470. Fax: 204-697-4791. p. 2757

Beatty, Gretchen, Dir, Nederland Community Library, 200 Hwy 72 N, Nederland, CO, 80466. Tel: 303-258-1101. p. 319

Beatty, John, Media Serv, Saint Thomas University Library, Law Library, 16401 NW 37th Ave, Miami Gardens, FL, 33054. Tel: 305-474-2428. Fax: 305-623-2337. p. 469

Beatty, Stacey, Librn, Arkansas River Valley Regional Library System, Yell County, 904 Atlanta St, Danville, AR, 72833. Tel: 479-495-2911. Fax: 479-495-2822. p. 97

Beatty, Virginia L, Archivist/Librn, National Woman's Christian Temperance Union, 1730 Chicago Ave, Evanston, IL, 60201-4585. Tel: 847-864-1397. Fax: 847-864-9497. p. 644

Beaty, Devon, Libr Asst I, Montgomery City-County Public Library System, Juliette Hampton Morgan Memorial Library (Main Library), 245 High St, Montgomery, AL, 36104. Tel: 334-240-4999. Fax: 334-240-4980. p. 30

Beaty, Kelly, Asst Dir, Westbrook Public Library, 556 First Ave, Westbrook, MN, 56183. Tel: 507-274-6174. Fax: 507-274-6174. p. 1288

Beaubier, Aidan, Librn, Agriculture & Agri-Food Canada, RR No 1 Government Rd, Indian Head, SK, S0G 2K0, CANADA. Tel: 306-695-2274, 306-695-5220. Fax: 306-695-3445. p. 2918

Beaubier, Aidan, Librn, Agriculture & Agri-Food Canada, One Airport Rd, Swift Current, SK, S9H 3X2, CANADA. Tel: 306-778-7260. Fax: 306-778-3188. p. 2927

Beaucage, Lorrayne, Librn, Ref, College Jesus-Marie de Sillery Bibliotheque, 2047 Chemin Saint-Louis, Sillery, QC, G1T 1P3, CANADA. Tel: 418-687-9250, Ext 19. Fax: 418-687-9847. p. 2912

Beauchamp, Anna, ILL, Southern Oregon University, 1250 Siskiyou Blvd, Ashland, OR, 97520-5076. Tel: 541-552-6441. Fax: 541-552-6429. p. 1990

Beauchamp, R Mitchel, Librn, Beauchamp Botanical Library, 1434 E 24th St, National City, CA, 91950-6010. Tel: 619-477-0295. Fax: 619-477-5380. p. 193

Beauchemin, Lisette, Head, Adult Serv, Head, Ch, Bibliotheques de Trois-Rivieres, 1425 Place de l'Hotel de Ville, CP 1713, Trois-Rivieres, QC, G9A 5L9, CANADA. Tel: 819-372-4645. Fax: 819-693-1892. p. 2913

Beauchesne, Marie-Hélène, Tech Serv, Department of Fisheries & Oceans Canada, 850 route de la Mer, Mont-Joli, QC, G5H 3Z4, CANADA. Tel: 418-775-0552. Fax: 418-775-0538. p. 2887

Beauclair, Rene, Librn, Cinematheque Quebecoise, 335 boul de Maisonneuve est, Montreal, QC, H2X 1K1, CANADA. Tel: 514-842-9768, Ext 262. Fax: 514-842-1816. p. 2893

Beaudet, Normand, Librn, Institute Philippe Pinel de Montreal Bibliotheque, 10905 Henri Bourassa Blvd E, Montreal, QC, H1C 1H1, CANADA. Tel: 514-648-8461, Ext 557. Fax: 514-881-3706. p. 2897

Beaudim, Carol, Dir, College Saint-Charles-Garnier Bibliotheque, 1150 Blvd Rene Levesque W, Quebec, QC, G1S 1V7, CANADA. Tel: 418-681-0107. Fax: 418-681-0118. p. 2904

Beaudoin, Cathleen C, Dir, Dover Public Library, 73 Locust St, Dover, NH, 03820-3785. Tel: 603-516-6050. Fax: 603-516-6053. p. 1445

Beaudoin, Joan, Dr, Asst Prof, Wayne State University, 106 Kresge Library, Detroit, MI, 48202. Tel: 313-577-1825. Fax: 313-577-7563. p. 2968

Beaudoin, Lise, In Charge, Bibliotheque Gabrielle-Roy, Collège-des-Jésuites, 1120 Blvd Rene-Levesques Ouest, Quebec, QC, G1S 4W4, CANADA. Tel: 418-641-6792. p. 2903

Beaudoin, Lise, In Charge, Bibliotheque Gabrielle-Roy, Saint-Jean-Baptiste, 755 rue Saint-Jean, Quebec, QC, G1R 1R1, CANADA. Tel: 418-641-6798. p. 2903

Beaudoin, Lucie, Admin Officer, Soquem, Inc, 600, ave Centrale, Val-d'Or, QC, J9P 1P8, CANADA. Tel: 819-874-3773. Fax: 819-874-3770. p. 2914

Beaudoin, Shauna, Head of Libr, Spina Bifida & Hydrocephalus Association of Ontario, 555 Richmond St W, Ste 1006, Toronto, ON, M5V 3B1, CANADA. Tel: 416-214-1056. Fax: 416-214-1446. p. 2858

Beaudoin, Sylvie, Pub Serv, Bibliotheques Publiques de Longueuil, St-Jean-Baptiste Branch, 700, rue Duvernay, Longueuil, QC, J4K 4L1, CANADA. p. 2887

Beaudoin, Sylvie, Tech Librn, Bibliotheques Publiques de Longueuil, Succursale Fatima, 2130 rue Jean-Louis, Longueuil, QC, J4H 1M1, CANADA. Tel: 450-463-7180. p. 2887

Beaudry, Guylaine, Dr, Dir, Webster Libr, Concordia University Libraries, 1400 de Maisonneuve Blvd W, LB 209, Montreal, QC, H3G 1M8, CANADA. Tel: 514-848-2424, Ext 7699. Fax: 514-848-2882. p. 2894

Beaulieu, Chantal, Chef de Div, Bibliothèques de Montrèal, Georges-Vanier, 2450, rue Workman, Montreal, QC, H3J 1L8, CANADA. Tel: 514-872-3067. Fax: 514-872-0511. p. 2889

Beaulieu, Chantal, Chef de Div, Bibliothèques de Montrèal, Marie-Uguay, 6052, rue Monk, Montreal, QC, H4E 3H6, CANADA. Tel: 514-872-3067. Fax: 514-872-0513. p. 2890

Beaulieu, Chantal, Chef de Div, Bibliothèques de Montrèal, Saint-Charles, 2333, rue Mullins (adultes), 1050, rue Hibernia (jeunes), Montreal, QC, H3K 3E3, CANADA. Tel: 514-872-3067. p. 2891

Beaulieu, Chantal, Chef de Div, Bibliothèques de Montrèal, Saint-Henri, 4707, rue Notre-Dame Ouest, Montreal, QC, H4C 1S9, CANADA. Tel: 514-872-3067. Fax: 514-872-0512. p. 2891

Beaulieu, Daniel, Dir, Pub Serv, College Universitaire de Saint-Boniface, 200 Ave de la Cathedrale, Winnipeg, MB, R2H 0H7, CANADA. Tel: 204-233-0210, Ext 403. Fax: 204-233-9472. p. 2755

Beaulieu-Couture, Louise, Pub Serv Mgr, Bibliotheque Municipale de Gatineau, Édifice Pierre Papin, CP 1970 Succ. Hull, Gatineau, QC, J8X 3Y9, CANADA. p. 2882

Beaupre, Anne, Res Sharing Tech, Algoma University College, 1520 Queen St E, Sault Ste. Marie, ON, P6A 2G4, CANADA. Tel: 705-949-2101. Fax: 705-949-6583. p. 2840

Beauregard, Jennifer, Librn, Harvard Library, Development Office Library, University Pl, 4th Flr, 124 Mount Auburn St, Cambridge, MA, 02138-5762. Tel: 617-495-9750. Fax: 617-496-9140. p. 1074

Beauregard, John, Archivist, Gordon College, 255 Grapevine Rd, Wenham, MA, 01984-1899. Tel: 978-867-4140. Fax: 978-867-4660. p. 1136

Beauregard, Louise, Tech Serv, Norton Rose Canada LLP Library, One Place Ville Marie, Ste 2500, Montreal, QC, H3B 1R1, CANADA. Tel: 514-847-4701. Fax: 514-286-5474. p. 2900

Beauregard, Susan, YA Serv, Reading Public Library, 64 Middlesex Ave, Reading, MA, 01867-2550. Tel: 781-944-0840. Fax: 781-942-9106. p. 1120

Beaven, Emma, Res Sharing Spec, Enoch Pratt Free Library, 400 Cathedral St, Baltimore, MD, 21201-4484. Tel: 410-396-5498. Fax: 410-396-5837. p. 1012

Beaven, Emma E, Mgr, Maryland Interlibrary Loan Organization, c/o Enoch Pratt Free Library, 400 Cathedral St, Baltimore, MD, 21201-4484. Tel: 410-396-5498. Fax: 410-396-5837. p. 2944

Beaver, Ann, Br Mgr, Dallas Public Library, Hampton-Illinois, 2951 S Hampton Rd, Dallas, TX, 75224. Tel: 214-670-7646. Fax: 214-670-7652. p. 2306

Beaver, Dianna, Acq, Archivist, University of Pittsburgh at Bradford, 300 Campus Dr, Bradford, PA, 16701. Tel: 814-362-7610. Fax: 814-362-7688. p. 2037

Beaver, Fern, Asst Librn, Rolette Public Library, 1015 First Ave, Rolette, ND, 58366. Tel: 701-246-3849. p. 1848

Beaver, Maxine, Asst Librn, Kuskokwim Consortium Library, 420 State Hwy, Bethel, AK, 99559. Tel: 907-543-4516. Fax: 907-543-4503. p. 46

Beaver, Natalie, Br Mgr, Sacramento Public Library, Isleton Neighborhood Library, 412 Union St, Isleton, CA, 95641. p. 225

Beaver, Ramarie, Ch, Plano Public Library System, W O Haggard Jr Library, 2501 Coit Rd, Plano, TX, 75075. Tel: 972-769-4250. Fax: 972-769-4256. p. 2370

Beaver, Sarah Beth, Ch, Spencer Public Library, 21 E Third St, Spencer, IA, 51301-4188. Tel: 712-580-7290. Fax: 712-580-7468. p. 845

Beaver, Vicki, Circ, Putnam County Library, 4219 State Rte 34, Hurricane, WV, 25526. Tel: 304-757-7308. Fax: 304-757-7384. p. 2562

Beavers, Janet H, Librn, Northern Lights College Library, 11401 Eighth St, Dawson Creek, BC, V1G 4G2, CANADA. Tel: 250-784-7533. Fax: 250-784-7567. p. 2727

Beavers, Paul, Assessment Officer, Wayne State University Libraries, Office of the Dean, 3100 Undergraduate Library, 5155 Gullen Mall, Detroit, MI, 48202. Tel: 313-577-2360. Fax: 313-577-5525. p. 1173

Beavers, Rachel, Br Mgr, Wyoming County Public Library, Hanover Public, 5556 Interstate Hwy, Hanover, WV, 24839. Tel: 304-664-5580. Fax: 304-664-5580. p. 2570

Beazer, Donna, Libr Mgr, Jim & Mary Kearl Library of Cardston, 25 Third Ave W, Cardston, AB, T0K 0K0, CANADA. Tel: 403-653-4775. Fax: 403-653-4716. p. 2694

Beazley, Mike, Acad Librn, Acadia University, 50 Acadia St, Wolfville, NS, B4P 2R6, CANADA. Tel: 902-585-1249. Fax: 902-585-1748. p. 2786

Bebbington, Clare, ILL, Atlantic County Library System, 40 Farragut Ave, Mays Landing, NJ, 08330-1750. Tel: 609-625-2776. Fax: 609-625-8143. p. 1500

Bebbington, George, Librn, Somerset County Historical Society, Nine Van Veghten Dr, Bridgewater, NJ, 08807-3259. Tel: 908-218-1281. p. 1475

Bebej, Cheryl, Youth Serv Librn, Princeton Public Library, 698 E Peru St, Princeton, IL, 61356. Tel: 815-875-1331. Fax: 815-872-1376. p. 692

Beccaria, Mike, Syst Librn, Paul Smiths College of Arts & Sciences, Rte's 30 & 86, Paul Smiths, NY, 12970. Tel: 518-327-6376. Fax: 518-327-6350. p. 1715

Bechard, Marjo, Librn, Cegep de Victoriaville, E'cole Quebecoise du Meuble et du Bois Ouvre, 765 Est Notre Dame, Victoriaville, QC, G6P 4B3, CANADA. Tel: 819-758-6401, Ext 2621. Fax: 819-758-2729. p. 2915

Bechard, Marjolaine, Librn, Cegep de Victoriaville, 475 rue Notre Dame E, Victoriaville, QC, G6P 4B3, CANADA. Tel: 819-758-6401, Ext 2486. Fax: 819-758-2729. p. 2915

Bechard, Mary Ellen, Coordr, Librn, Windsor Regional Hospital, Metropolitan Campus, 1995 Lens Ave, Windsor, ON, N8W 1L9, CANADA. Tel: 519-254-5577, Ext 52706. p. 2872

Bechard, Staci, Librn, Montana School for the Deaf & Blind Library, 3911 Central Ave, Great Falls, MT, 59405-1697. Tel: 406-771-6051. Fax: 406-771-6164. p. 1380

Becho, Arnold, Dir, Mayor Joe V Sanchez Public Library, 525 S Kansas Ave, Weslaco, TX, 78596-6215. Tel: 956-968-4533. Fax: 956-973-1641. p. 2399

Becht, Cynthia, Head, Archives & Spec Coll, Loyola Marymount University, One LMU Dr, MS 8200, Los Angeles, CA, 90045-2659. Tel: 310-338-2780. Fax: 310-338-4366. p. 175

Bechtel, Beth, Tech Serv Mgr, Waukesha Public Library, 321 Wisconsin Ave, Waukesha, WI, 53186-4786. Tel: 262-522-7283. Fax: 262-524-3677. p. 2645

Beck, Alison M, Assoc Dir, University of Texas Libraries, Center for American History, SRH 2-101, D1100, University of Texas at Austin, Austin, TX, 78712. Tel: 512-495-4515. Fax: 512-495-4542. p. 2284

Beck, Allisa, Coll Develop, University of Southern Mississippi, 730 E Beach Blvd, Long Beach, MS, 39560-2698. Tel: 228-214-3468. Fax: 228-865-4544. p. 1307

Beck, Charles, Perkins Mail Ctr Mgr, Duke University Libraries, 411 Chapel Dr, Durham, NC, 27708. Tel: 919-660-5869. Fax: 919-660-5923. p. 1787

Beck, Connie, Librn, Indiana Law Enforcement Academy, 5402 Sugar Grove Rd, Plainfield, IN, 46168. Tel: 317-837-3236. Fax: 317-839-9741. p. 773

Beck, Dana, Head, Per, Arkansas State University, 322 University Loop West Circle, State University, AR, 72401. Tel: 870-972-3077. Fax: 870-972-3199. p. 115

Beck, Darlene, Mgr, Halifax Public Libraries, Spring Garden Road Memorial, 5381 Spring Garden Rd, Halifax, NS, B3J 1E9, CANADA. Tel: 902-490-5804. Fax: 902-490-5747. p. 2779

Beck, Donna, Eng Librn, Carnegie Mellon University, Engineering & Science Library, 4400 Wean Hall, Pittsburgh, PA, 15213-3890. Tel: 412-268-2426. Fax: 412-681-1998. p. 2123

Beck, Donna, Dir, Burritt Memorial Library, 427 College St, Spencer, TN, 38585-0314. Tel: 931-946-2575. Fax: 931-946-2575. p. 2266

Beck, Elizabeth, Cat Librn, Coordr, Cat & Acq, Millsaps College, 1701 N State St, Jackson, MS, 39210-0001. Tel: 601-974-1076. Fax: 601-974-1082. p. 1304

Beck, Ellen, Librn, Randolph Free Library, 26 Jamestown St, Randolph, NY, 14772. Tel: 716-358-3712. Fax: 716-358-2039. p. 1726

Beck, Erika, Ref, Emory University School of Law, 1301 Clifton Rd, Atlanta, GA, 30322. Tel: 404-727-0321. Fax: 404-727-2202. p. 514

Beck, Gloria, Govt Doc, Virginia State University, One Hayden Dr, Petersburg, VA, 23806-0001. Tel: 804-524-6945. Fax: 804-524-6959. p. 2484

Beck, Jamie, Syst Adminr, High Point Public Library, 901 N Main St, High Point, NC, 27262. Tel: 336-883-3660. Fax: 336-883-3636. p. 1802

Beck, Jan, Br Mgr, Davidson County Public Library System, West Davidson Public, 246 Tyro School Rd, Lexington, NC, 27295-6006. Tel: 336-853-4800. Fax: 336-853-4803. p. 1806

Beck, Jeannie, Ser, Southeastern Baptist Theological Seminary Library, 114 N Wingate St, Wake Forest, NC, 27587. Tel: 919-556-3104. Fax: 919-863-8150. p. 1827

Beck, Jeff, Ref Librn, Wabash College, PO Box 352, Crawfordsville, IN, 47933. Tel: 765-361-6346. Fax: 765-361-6295. p. 734

Beck, Jennie, Ch, Aiken-Bamberg-Barnwell-Edgefield Regional Library System, Aiken County, 314 Chesterfield St SW, Aiken, SC, 29801. Tel: 803-642-2020. Fax: 803-642-7570. p. 2179

Beck, Linda, Br Mgr, East Central Georgia Regional Library, Jeff Maxwell Branch, 1927 Lumpkin Rd, Augusta, GA, 30906. Tel: 706-793-2020. Fax: 706-790-1023. p. 520

Beck, Linda, Acq, Owensboro Community & Technical College, 4800 New Hartford Rd, Owensboro, KY, 42303. Tel: 270-686-4657. Fax: 270-686-4594. p. 931

Beck, Linda, Dir, Indian Valley Public Library, 100 E Church Ave, Telford, PA, 18969. Tel: 215-723-9109. Fax: 215-723-0583. p. 2145

Beck, Lori, Dir, Onawa Public Library, 707 Iowa Ave, Onawa, IA, 51040. Tel: 712-423-1733. Fax: 712-433-4622. p. 836

Beck, Mary Ellen, Dir, Douglas Library of Hebron, 22 Main St, Hebron, CT, 06248. Tel: 860-228-9312. Fax: 860-228-4372. p. 348

Beck, Maureen Anne, Dir, Libr Serv, Stevenson University Library, 1525 Greenspring Valley Rd, Stevenson, MD, 21153. Tel: 443-334-2231. Fax: 410-486-7329. p. 1043

Beck, Melissa, Sr Cat Librn, University of California Los Angeles Library, Hugh & Hazel Darling Law Library, 112 Law Bldg, Box 951458, 385 Charles E Young Dr E, Los Angeles, CA, 90095-1458. Tel: 310-825-7826. Fax: 310-825-1372. p. 178

Beck, Michael, Adult Serv Coordr, Scottsdale Public Library, 3839 N Drinkwater Blvd, Scottsdale, AZ, 85251-4467. Tel: 480-312-7323. Fax: 480-312-7993. p. 81

Beck, Mike, Pub Serv Mgr, High Point Public Library, 901 N Main St, High Point, NC, 27262. Tel: 336-883-3643. Fax: 336-883-3636. p. 1802

Beck, Patti, Ch, Whittier Public Library, Whittwood Branch, 10537 Santa Gertrudes Ave, Whittier, CA, 90603-2760. Tel: 562-567-9950. Fax: 562-567-2881. p. 283

Beck, Paul, Spec Coll & Archives Librn, University of Wisconsin-La Crosse, 1631 Pine St, La Crosse, WI, 54601-3748. Tel: 608-785-8511. Fax: 608-785-8639. p. 2603

Beck, Sheila, Acq, Coordr, Tech Serv, Queensborough Community College, City University of New York, 222-05 56th Ave, Bayside, NY, 11364-1497. Tel: 718-631-5711. Fax: 718-281-5012. p. 1579

Beck, Stephanie, Dir, Van Buren Public Library, 115 S First St, Van Buren, IN, 46991. Tel: 765-934-2171. Fax: 765-934-4926. p. 784

Beck, Susan, Head, Access Serv, New Mexico State University Library, 2911 McFie Circle, Las Cruces, NM, 88003. Tel: 575-646-5091. Fax: 575-646-6940. p. 1558

Beck, Susan J, Pub Serv, Ref, Rutgers University Libraries, Paul Robeson Library, Camden, 300 N Fourth St, Camden, NJ, 08102-1404. Tel: 856-225-6033. Fax: 856-225-6428. p. 1477

Beck, Thomas J, Coll Develop & Res Librn, Auraria Library, 1100 Lawrence St, Denver, CO, 80204-2095. Tel: 303-556-8371. Fax: 303-556-3528. p. 298

Beck, Tom, Head, Spec Coll, University of Maryland, Baltimore County, 1000 Hilltop Circle, Baltimore, MD, 21250. Tel: 410-455-2356. Fax: 410-455-1567. p. 1018

Beck, Tracey Rae, Exec Dir, American Swedish Historical Museum Library, 1900 Pattison Ave, Philadelphia, PA, 19145. Tel: 215-389-1776. Fax: 215-389-7701. p. 2103

Beckendorf, Andrea, Dr, Dept Head, Res Support & Instruction Librn, Luther College, 700 College Dr, Decorah, IA, 52101. Tel: 563-387-1227. Fax: 563-387-1657. p. 807

Becker, Amy, Tech Serv, Peter White Public Library, 217 N Front St, Marquette, MI, 49855. Tel: 906-228-9510. Fax: 906-226-1783. p. 1207

Becker, Ann, Dir, Barrett Memorial Library, 65 W Geneva St, Williams Bay, WI, 53191-0190. Tel: 262-245-2709. p. 2649

Becker, Bethry J, Librn, United States Air Force, 976 Cannon Dr, FL 4460, Little Rock AFB, AR, 72099-5289. Tel: 501-987-6979. p. 108

Becker, Brooke, Ref Librn, University of Alabama at Birmingham, Mervyn H Sterne Library, 917 13th St S, Birmingham, AL, 35205. Tel: 205-934-6364. p. 10

Becker, Cathy, Dir, Atkins Public Library, 84 Main Ave, Atkins, IA, 52206. Tel: 319-446-7676. Fax: 319-446-7676. p. 795

Becker, Cecelia, Ref, Somers Public Library, 51 Ninth District Rd, Somers, CT, 06071-0368. Tel: 860-763-3501. Fax: 860-763-1718. p. 367

Becker, Charles, Dir, Pima Community College, District Library Services, 4905B E Broadway Blvd, Tucson, AZ, 85709-1140. Tel: 520-206-7693. Fax: 520-206-7690. p. 86

Becker, Charles, Dir, Pima Community College, East, 8181 E Irvington Rd, Tucson, AZ, 85709-4000. Tel: 520-206-7693. Fax: 520-206-7690. p. 86

Becker, Danielle, Web Librn, Hunter College Libraries, 695 Park Ave, New York, NY, 10065. Tel: 212-772-4172. Fax: 212-772-4142. p. 1682

Becker, Dorothy, In Charge, Passaic County Historical Society, Lambert Castle, Three Valley Rd, Paterson, NJ, 07503-2932. Tel: 973-247-0085. Fax: 973-881-9434. p. 1518

Becker, Edward A, Ref Serv, Massachusetts School of Law Library, 500 Federal St, Andover, MA, 01810. Tel: 978-681-0800. Fax: 978-681-6330. p. 1049

Becker, Greg, Ref Mgr, Carroll County Public Library, 115 Airport Dr, Westminster, MD, 21157. Tel: 410-386-4500. Fax: 410-386-4509. p. 1045

Becker, Jo-Anne, Br Mgr, Thompson-Nicola Regional District Library System, Chase Branch, 614 Shuswap Ave, Chase, BC, V0E 1M0, CANADA. Tel: 250-679-3331. p. 2729

Becker, Joseph, Head, Ser, George Mason University Libraries, 4400 University Dr, MSN 2FL, Fairfax, VA, 22030-4444. Tel: 703-993-2250. Fax: 703-993-2200. p. 2462

Becker, Joshua, Info Literacy Librn, Western New England University, 1215 Wilbraham Rd, Springfield, MA, 01119. Tel: 413-782-1537. Fax: 413-796-2011. p. 1128

Becker, Karen, Ref Librn, Kankakee Community College, 100 College Dr, Kankakee, IL, 60901-6505. Tel: 815-802-8400. Fax: 815-802-8101. p. 660

Becker, Leslie, Circ, Curry College, 1071 Blue Hill Ave, Milton, MA, 02186-9984. Tel: 617-333-2102. Fax: 617-333-2164. p. 1106

Becker, Linda, Dir, Libr Serv, Pillsbury Winthrop Shaw Pittman LLP, 1540 Broadway, New York, NY, 10036-4039. Tel: 212-858-1000. Fax: 212-858-1500. p. 1697

Becker, Marie, Librn, St Vincent Health, 1907 W Sycamore St, Kokomo, IN, 46901-4113. Tel: 765-456-5499. Fax: 765-456-5823. p. 758

Becker, Marsha, Circ, Taylor University, 236 W Reade Ave, Upland, IN, 46989-1001. Tel: 765-998-5266. Fax: 765-998-5569. p. 783

Becker, Millie, Asst Librn, Josiah Carpenter Library, 41 Main St, Pittsfield, NH, 03263. Tel: 603-435-8406. p. 1462

Becker, Patricia, Librn, Saginaw County Law Library, 111 S Michigan Ave, Rm LL007, Saginaw, MI, 48602. Tel: 989-790-5533. Fax: 989-790-5248. p. 1224

Becker, Patti, Dr, Head, Ref, University of Wisconsin-Stevens Point, 900 Reserve St, Stevens Point, WI, 54481-1985. Tel: 715-346-4443. Fax: 715-346-3857. p. 2640

Becker, Ronald L, Head, Spec Coll & Univ Archives, Rutgers University Libraries, Special Collections & University Archives, 169 College Ave, New Brunswick, NJ, 08901-1163. Tel: 848-932-6155. Fax: 732-932-7012. p. 1509

Beckerman, Shari, In Charge, Warshaw, Burstein, Cohen, Schlesinger & Kuh, 555 Fifth Ave, 11th Flr, New York, NY, 10017. Tel: 212-984-7700. Fax: 212-972-9150. p. 1702

Beckert, Harriet, Curator, Newtown Historic Association, Inc, Court St & Centre Ave, Newtown, PA, 18940. Tel: 215-968-4004. p. 2098

Beckert, Helen V, Asst Dir, Glen Ridge Free Public Library, 240 Ridgewood Ave, Glen Ridge, NJ, 07028. Tel: 973-748-5482. Fax: 973-748-9350. p. 1488

Beckett, Debra, ILS Syst Mgr, Lawrenceburg Public Library District, 150 Mary St, Lawrenceburg, IN, 47025-1995. Tel: 812-537-2775. Fax: 812-537-2810. p. 760

Beckett, George, Assoc Univ Librn, Memorial University of Newfoundland, Health Sciences Library, Memorial University, 300 Prince Philip Dr, St. John's, NL, A1B 3V6, CANADA. Tel: 709-777-6670. Fax: 709-777-6866. p. 2772

Beckett, Mary, Youth Serv, Edythe L Dyer Community Library, 269 Main Rd N, Hampden, ME, 04444. Tel: 207-862-3550. p. 987

Beckett, Michael, Adminr, Missouri Department of Natural Resources, 26600 Park Rd N, Lawson, MO, 64062. Tel: 816-580-3387. Fax: 816-580-3782. p. 1343

Beckett, Russell, Circ Mgr, Glendale Community College Library, 1500 N Verdugo Rd, Glendale, CA, 91208-2894. Tel: 818-240-1000, Ext 5574. Fax: 818-246-5107. p. 155

Beckett, Vivienne, Asst Dir, Scenic Regional Library of Franklin, Gasconade & Warren Counties, 308 Hawthorne Dr, Union, MO, 63084. Tel: 636-583-3224. p. 1369

Beckham, Carol, Ref Serv, Woodland Public Library, 250 First St, Woodland, CA, 95695-3411. Tel: 530-661-5980. Fax: 530-666-5408. p. 284

Beckham, Sharon, Circ, Texas Tech University Health Sciences Center, 3601 Fourth St, Lubbock, TX, 79430-7781. Tel: 806-743-2200. Fax: 806-743-2218. p. 2357

Beckman, Amy, Br Mgr, Boone County Public Library, Scheben Branch, 8899 US 42, Union, KY, 41091. Fax: 856-384-5557. p. 909

Beckman, Andrew, Archivist, Studebaker National Museum Archives, 201 S Chapin St, South Bend, IN, 46601. Tel: 574-235-9714, 574-235-9983. Fax: 574-235-5522. p. 779

Beckman, April, Ch, Charlestown-Clark County Public Library, 51 Clark Rd, Charlestown, IN, 47111. Tel: 812-256-3337. Fax: 812-256-3890. p. 731

Beckman, Kristina, Libr Asst, El Segundo Public Library, 111 W Mariposa Ave, El Segundo, CA, 90245-2299. Tel: 310-524-2722. Fax: 310-648-7560. p. 146

Beckman, Patricia, Br Supvr, Boonslick Regional Library, Cole Camp Branch, 701 W Main St, Cole Camp, MO, 65325. Tel: 660-668-3887. Fax: 660-668-3852. p. 1365

Beckman, Rachel, Circ, Maryland Institute College of Art, 1401 Mount Royal Ave, Baltimore, MD, 21217. Tel: 410-225-2304, 410-225-2311. Fax: 410-225-2316. p. 1015

Beckman, Roger, Head of Libr, Indiana University Bloomington, Chemistry Library, Chemistry C003, 800 E Kirkwood Ave, Bloomington, IN, 47405-7102. Tel: 812-855-9452. p. 727

Beckman, Roger, Head of Libr, Indiana University Bloomington, Life Sciences Library, Jordan Hall A304, 1001 E Third St, Bloomington, IN, 47405-7005. Tel: 812-855-8947. p. 727

Beckstead, Jenn, Young Adult Serv Coordr, Natrona County Public Library, 307 E Second St, Casper, WY, 82601. Tel: 307-237-4935. Fax: 307-266-3734. p. 2652

Beckstrom, Carol, Libr Assoc, Carlton Public Library, 310 Chestnut Ave, Carlton, MN, 55718. Tel: 218-384-3322. Fax: 218-384-4229. p. 1244

Beckstrom, Matthew A, Info Tech, Lewis & Clark Library, 120 S Last Chance Gulch, Helena, MT, 59601. Tel: 406-447-1690, Ext 111. Fax: 406-447-1687. p. 1382

Beckum, Erope, Mgr, Circ Serv, Rockford Public Library, 215 N Wyman St, Rockford, IL, 61101-1023. Tel: 815-965-7606. Fax: 815-965-0866. p. 697

Beckwith, Joy, Ch, Weston Public Library, 56 Norfield Rd, Weston, CT, 06883-2225. Tel: 203-222-2665. Fax: 203-222-2560. p. 377

Beckwith, LeAnn, Dir, Hillsdale Community Library, 11 E Bacon St, Hillsdale, MI, 49242. Tel: 517-437-6470. Fax: 517-437-6477. p. 1190

Beckwith, Marcia, Mrs, Cir & Fac Mgr, Manheim Township Public Library, 595 Granite Run Dr, Lancaster, PA, 17601. Tel: 717-560-6441. Fax: 717-560-0570. p. 2077

Beckwith, Rachel, Bibliog Instr, Ref, Hampshire College Library, 893 West St, Amherst, MA, 01002-5001. Tel: 413-559-5440. Fax: 413-559-5419. p. 1048

Beckwith, Vera, Head Librn, East Saint Louis Public Library, 5300 State St, East Saint Louis, IL, 62203. Tel: 618-397-0991. Fax: 618-397-1260. p. 639

Becote, Linda D, Tech Serv, Francis Marion University, 4822 East Palmetto St, Florence, SC, 29506. Tel: 843-661-1308. Fax: 843-661-1309. p. 2194

Beda, Sandra, Head, Ref & Res Serv, Warren-Newport Public Library District, 224 N O'Plaine Rd, Gurnee, IL, 60031. Tel: 847-244-5150, Ext 3025. Fax: 847-244-3499. p. 653

Bedard, Amy T, Dir, William H Miner Agricultural Research Institute, 596 Ridge Rd, Chazy, NY, 12921. Tel: 518-846-7121, Ext 149. Fax: 518-846-7774. p. 1606

Bedard, Anne Marie, ILL, Saint Clair County Library System, 210 McMorran Blvd, Port Huron, MI, 48060-4098. Tel: 810-987-7323, Ext 143. Fax: 810-987-7874. p. 1219

Bedard, Kami, Mgr, Libr Serv, Pierce Atwood LLP, 254 Commercial St, Portland, ME, 04101. Tel: 207-791-1100. Fax: 207-791-1350. p. 996

Bedard, Martha A, Dean, Univ Libr, University of New Mexico-University Libraries, 1900 Roma NE, Albuquerque, NM, 87131-0001. p. 1550

Bedard, Roxanne, Librn, Chinook Regional Library, Ponteix Branch, 130 First Ave E, Ponteix, SK, S0N 1Z0, CANADA. Tel: 306-625-3353. p. 2928

Beddingfield, Connie, Asst Librn, Attalla-Etowah County Public Library, 604 N Fourth St, Attalla, AL, 35954. Tel: 256-538-9266. Fax: 256-538-9223. p. 5

Beddow, Lucinda M, Head Librn, Calhoun Community College, Hwy 31 N, Decatur, AL, 35609. Tel: 256-306-2784. Fax: 256-306-2780. p. 14

Bede, Gilbert, Syst Librn, Okanagan College Library, 1000 KLO Rd, Kelowna, BC, V1Y 4X8, CANADA. p. 2730

Bedel, Julianne, Dir, Barberton Public Library, 602 W Park Ave, Barberton, OH, 44203-2458. Tel: 330-745-1194. Fax: 330-745-8261. p. 1857

Bedenbaugh, Dee, Dep Dir, Lexington County Public Library System, 5440 Augusta Rd, Lexington, SC, 29072. Tel: 803-785-2643. Fax: 803-785-2601. p. 2199

Bedford, Dale, Principal Librn, Clifton Public Library, 292 Piaget Ave, Clifton, NJ, 07011. Tel: 973-772-5500. p. 1479

Bedford-Dean, LaTina, Youth Serv Librn, Yeadon Public Library, 809 Longacre Blvd, Yeadon, PA, 19050-3398. Tel: 610-623-4090. Fax: 610-394-9374. p. 2159

Bedi, Param, VPres, Libr & Info Tech, Bucknell University, Library & Information Technology, 221 Ellen Clarke Bertrand Library, Lewisburg, PA, 17837. Tel: 570-577-1557. Fax: 570-577-3313. p. 2080

Bedi, Shailoo, Dir, Pub Serv, University of Victoria Libraries, McPherson Library, PO Box 1800, Victoria, BC, V8W 3H5, CANADA. Tel: 250-721-8211. Fax: 250-721-8215. p. 2746

Bedinger, Helen, Librn, Arizona Department of Corrections - Adult Institutions, 7125 E Juan Sanchez Blvd, San Luis, AZ, 85349. Tel: 928-627-8871. Fax: 928-627-6503. p. 80

Bednarski, Diane, Principal Librn, Info Mgt, Santa Monica Public Library, 601 Santa Monica Blvd, Santa Monica, CA, 90401. Tel: 310-458-8625. Fax: 310-394-8951. p. 266

Bedry, Donna, Mgr, Calgary Public Library, Fish Creek, 11161 Bonaventure Dr SE, Calgary, AB, T2J 6S1, CANADA. p. 2689

Bedry, Donna, Mgr, Calgary Public Library, Glenmore Square, Glenmore Sq Shopping Ctr, 7740 18th St SE, Calgary, AB, T2C 2N5, CANADA. p. 2689

Bedwell, Lois, Librn, Oyen Municipal Library, 105 Third Ave W, Oyen, AB, T0J 2J0, CANADA. Tel: 403-664-3580. Fax: 403-664-2520. p. 2713

Bee, Christine, Dir, Murphy Memorial Library, 111 N Page, Monona, IA, 52159-0430. Tel: 563-539-2356. Fax: 563-539-2306. p. 832

Bee Lynn, Sandy, Circ Mgr, Ella M Everhard Public Library, 132 Broad St, Wadsworth, OH, 44281-1897. Tel: 330-334-5761. Fax: 330-334-6605. p. 1943

Beebe, Anne, Ref & Instruction Librn, Northern Virginia Community College Libraries, Woodbridge Library, 15200 Neabsco Mills Rd, Seefeldt 427, Woodbridge, VA, 22191. Tel: 703-878-5727. Fax: 703-670-8433. p. 2448

Beebe, Jane, Head, Cat, Amherst College, Amherst, MA, 01002. Fax: 413-542-2662. p. 1048

Beebe, Jane, Music Librn, Amherst College, Vincent Morgan Music Library, Amherst, MA, 01002. Tel: 413-542-2667. p. 1048

Beebe, Marla, Ref, Brewton-Parker College, 201 David-Eliza Fountain Circle, Mount Vernon, GA, 30445. Tel: 912-583-3235. Fax: 912-583-3454. p. 546

Beecher, Brian, Assoc Dean, Elgin Community College, 1700 Spartan Dr, Elgin, IL, 60123. Tel: 847-214-7337. Fax: 574-241-7595. p. 640

Beecher, Brian, Dir, University of Wisconsin-Rock County Library, 2909 Kellogg Ave, Janesville, WI, 53546-5606. Tel: 608-758-6531. Fax: 608-758-6560. p. 2600

Beechler Bergendorf, Yvonne Rae, Dir, Wood Dale Public Library District, 520 N Wood Dale Rd, Wood Dale, IL, 60191. Tel: 630-766-6762. Fax: 630-766-5715. p. 721

Beecroft, Veronica, Assoc Dir, Circ, Capital Area District Libraries, 401 S Capitol Ave, Lansing, MI, 48933. Tel: 517-367-0810. Fax: 517-374-1068. p. 1200

Beeker, Jonathan, Librn, ECPI University, 10021 Balls Ford Rd, Manassas, VA, 20109. Tel: 703-330-5300, Ext 212. Fax: 703-369-0530. p. 2477

Beekman, Lois, Circ, Fremont Area District Library, 104 E Main, Fremont, MI, 49412. Tel: 231-924-3480. Fax: 231-924-2355. p. 1182

Beeko, Stephen, Tech Serv, Southwest Tennessee Community College, George Freeman Library, 5983 Macon Cove, Memphis, TN, 38134. Tel: 901-333-4732. Fax: 901-333-4566. p. 2251

Beeler, Linda, Ref Serv, Thomas Crane Public Library, 40 Washington St, Quincy, MA, 02269-9164. Tel: 617-376-1310. Fax: 617-376-1308. p. 1119

Beem, Joan, Dir, The Church of Jesus Christ of Latter-Day Saints, 76 Saint Paul Dr, Ventura, CA, 93003. Tel: 805-643-5607. p. 279

Beene, Lonnie, Acq Librn, Asst Prof, McNeese State University, 4205 Ryan St, Lake Charles, LA, 70609. Tel: 337-475-5724. Fax: 337-475-5719, 337-475-5727. p. 954

Beene, Lonnie, Dir, Northeast Texas Community College, Farm-to-Market Rd 1735, Mount Pleasant, TX, 75456. Tel: 903-572-1911, Ext 454. Fax: 903-572-7017. p. 2364

Beer, Donna, Computer Serv, Highland Park Public Library, 494 Laurel Ave, Highland Park, IL, 60035-2690. Tel: 847-432-0216. Fax: 847-432-9139. p. 655

Beer, Lillian, Chairperson, Beth David Congregation, 2625 SW Third Ave, Miami, FL, 33129. Tel: 305-854-3911. Fax: 305-285-5841. p. 464

Beere, Elizabeth, Electronic Res, Carroll Community College, 1601 Washington Rd, Westminster, MD, 21157-6944. Tel: 410-386-8333. Fax: 410-386-8331. p. 1045

Beerens, Pamela, Libr Tech II, Pinal County Library District, 92 W Butte Ave, Florence, AZ, 85132. Tel: 520-866-6457. Fax: 520-866-6533. p. 63

Beermann, William, Cataloger, Lutheran School of Theology at Chicago & McCormick Theological Seminary, 1100 E 55th St, Chicago, IL, 60615-5199. Tel: 773-256-0736. Fax: 773-256-0737. p. 618

Beers, Carol, ILL, Tulare County Library, 200 W Oak Ave, Visalia, CA, 93291-4993. Tel: 559-733-6954. Fax: 559-730-2524. p. 280

Beers, Carol, Librn II, Tulare County Library, Visalia Headquarters Branch, 200 W Oak Ave, Visalia, CA, 93291. Tel: 559-713-2707. Fax: 559-737-4586. p. 281

Beers, Stacie, Dir, Smyrna Public Library, Seven E Main St, Smyrna, NY, 13464-1932. Tel: 607-627-6271. Fax: 607-627-6271. p. 1744

Beers, Tammie, Youth Serv Librn, Mechanicsburg Public Library, 60 S Main St, Mechanicsburg, OH, 43044. Tel: 937-834-2004. Fax: 937-834-3396. p. 1916

Bees, Mary, Supvr, Circ, Pickaway County District Public Library, 1160 N Court St, Circleville, OH, 43113-1725. Tel: 740-477-1644, Ext 225. Fax: 740-474-2855. p. 1875

Beesinger, Cheryl, Dir, Archer Public Library, 105 N Center, Archer City, TX, 76351. Tel: 940-574-4954. p. 2276

Beesley, Marie, Head, Circ/ILL, Charlton Public Library, 40 Main St, Charlton, MA, 01507. Tel: 508-248-0452. Fax: 508-248-0456. p. 1079

Beesley, Sally, Dir, Jefferson County Library District, 241 SE Seventh St, Madras, OR, 97741-1611. Tel: 541-475-3351. Fax: 541-475-7434. p. 2004

Beeson, Julie, Circ Serv Mgr, Kaubisch Memorial Public Library, 205 Perry St, Fostoria, OH, 44830-2265. Tel: 419-435-2813. Fax: 419-435-5350. p. 1900

Beeson, Sandra J, Coordr, Tech Serv, Northern Virginia Community College Libraries, 8333 Little River Tpk, Annandale, VA, 22003. Tel: 703-323-3096. Fax: 703-323-3831. p. 2447

Beeson, Sandra J, Coordr, Northern Virginia Community College Libraries, Media Processing Services, 8333 Little River Tpk, Annandale, VA, 22003-3796. Tel: 703-323-3096. Fax: 703-323-3831. p. 2447

Beestrum, Molly, Syst Librn, Dominican University, 7900 W Division St, River Forest, IL, 60305-1066. Tel: 708-524-6875. Fax: 708-366-5360. p. 694

Beetham, Michael, Law Librn, Connecticut Judicial Branch Law Libraries, Stamford Law Library, Stamford Courthouse, 123 Hoyt St, Stamford, CT, 06905. Tel: 203-965-4521. Fax: 203-965-5784. p. 344

Beets, Kimberly, Dir, Bonner Springs City Library, 200 E Third St, Bonner Springs, KS, 66012-1047. Tel: 913-441-2665. Fax: 913-441-2660. p. 858

Beetz, Connie, Dir, Graves-Hume Public Library District, 1401 W Main, Mendota, IL, 61342. Tel: 815-538-5142. Fax: 815-538-3816. p. 673

Beezley, JoAnne, Govt Doc, Pittsburg State University, 1605 S Joplin St, Pittsburg, KS, 66762-5889. Tel: 620-235-4889. Fax: 620-235-4090. p. 890

Beffa, Lisa, Mgr, SRI International, 333 Ravenswood Ave, Menlo Park, CA, 94025. Tel: 650-859-5506. Fax: 650-859-2757. p. 185

Begay, Derek H, Librn, Dine College, Junction Hwy 371, Rte 9, Crownpoint, NM, 87313. Tel: 505-786-7391. Fax: 505-786-5240. p. 1554

Begay, Melissa, Librn, Kaibab Paiute Public Library, 250 N Pipe Springs Rd, Fredonia, AZ, 86022. Tel: 928-643-6004. Fax: 928-643-7260. p. 64

Begg, Debra, Dir, University of Ottawa Libraries, Music, Perez Hall, 50 University, Ottawa, ON, K1N 6N5, CANADA. Tel: 613-562-5209. p. 2834

Begg, Robert T, Dir, Albany Law School, 80 New Scotland Ave, Albany, NY, 12208. Tel: 518-445-2336. Fax: 518-472-5842. p. 1568

Beggs, Dace, Br Mgr, Richmond Public Library, Ironwood Branch, Ironwood Plaza, 8200-11688 Steveston Hwy, Richmond, BC, V7A 1N6, CANADA. Tel: 604-231-6468. Fax: 604-274-0454. p. 2736

Begin, Diane, Librn, HEC Montreal, 3000, chemin de la Cote-Sainte-Catherine, Montreal, QC, H3T 2A7, CANADA. Tel: 514-340-6223. Fax: 514-340-5639. p. 2896

Begley, Angela, Br Mgr, Martin County Public Library, Rufus M Reed Public, 1442 Riverfront Rd, Lovely, KY, 41231. Tel: 606-395-6500. Fax: 606-395-6001. p. 918

Begley, Candace, Dir, Windham Public Library, Church & Main Sts, Windham, NY, 12496. Tel: 518-734-4405. Fax: 518-734-4405. p. 1770

Beglo, Jo, Bibliographer, National Gallery of Canada Library, 380 Sussex Dr, Ottawa, ON, K1N 9N4, CANADA. Tel: 613-990-3285. Fax: 613-990-9818. p. 2832

Begolka, Carol, Librn, Atlanta Public Library District, 100 Race St, Atlanta, IL, 61723. Tel: 217-648-2112. Fax: 217-648-5269. p. 590

Begue, Jean, Ref Librn, Louis Bay 2nd Library, 345 Lafayette Ave, Hawthorne, NJ, 07506-2599. Tel: 973-427-5745, Ext 17. Fax: 973-427-5269. p. 1490

Beh-Zahn, Lynn, Asst Dir, Everest Institute, 1630 Portland Ave, Rochester, NY, 14621. Tel: 585-266-0430, Ext 108. Fax: 585-266-8243. p. 1729

Beharriell, Rick, Coordr, Western Counties Regional Library, 405 Main St, Yarmouth, NS, B5A 1G3, CANADA. Tel: 902-742-2486. Fax: 902-742-6920. p. 2786

Beharriell, Terri, Chief Librn, Huron Shores Public Library, Ten John St, Iron Bridge, ON, P0R 1H0, CANADA. Tel: 705-843-2192. Fax: 705-843-2035. p. 2812

Behee, Jodi, Br Librn, Kiowa County Library, Mullinville Branch, 115 N Main, Mullinville, KS, 67109. Tel: 620-548-2630. p. 870

Beheshti, Jamshid, Assoc Prof, McGill University, 3661 Peel St, Montreal, QC, H3A 1X1, CANADA. Tel: 514-398-3366. Fax: 514-398-7193. p. 2979

Behle, Kelly, Coordr, Youth Serv, Santa Clarita Public Library, 18601 Soledad Canyon Rd, Santa Clarita, CA, 91351. Tel: 661-251-2720. Fax: 661-298-7137. p. 263

Behler, Anne, Info Literacy Librn, Pennsylvania State University Libraries, Library Learning Services, 305 Pattee Library, Tower, University Park, PA, 16802-1803. Tel: 814-863-3832. Fax: 814-865-3665. p. 2148

Behles, Pat, Govt Doc, University of Baltimore, Law Library, 1415 Maryland Ave, Baltimore, MD, 21201. Tel: 410-837-4554. Fax: 410-837-4570. p. 1018

Behling, Erika, Ref/Instruction Librn, College of Lake County, 19351 W Washington St, Grayslake, IL, 60030. Tel: 847-543-2892. Fax: 847-223-7690. p. 652

Behling, Erika, Instrul Serv Librn, University of Wisconsin-Parkside Library, 900 Wood Rd, Kenosha, WI, 53141. Tel: 262-595-2642. Fax: 262-595-2545. p. 2601

Behling, Ruth, Librn, AECOM Library, 515 S Flower, 9th Flr, Los Angeles, CA, 90071. Tel: 213-593-8556. p. 168

Behling, Ruth, Coop Librn, Economics Research Associates Library, 1101 Connecticut Ave NW, Ste 750, Washington, DC, 20036. Tel: 202-496-9877. p. 399

Behm, Anna, Librn, Westmont Public Library, 428 N Cass, Westmont, IL, 60559-1502. Tel: 630-969-5625. Fax: 630-969-6490. p. 717

Behm, Joan, Dir, Cambridge Community Library, 200 Spring St, Cambridge, WI, 53523-9218. Tel: 608-423-3900. Fax: 608-423-7330. p. 2584

Behm, Kaylene, Access Serv, University of Southern Mississippi Library, 118 College Dr, No 5053, Hattiesburg, MS, 39406. Tel: 601-266-4251. Fax: 601-266-6033. p. 1300

Behm, Lynda, Librn, Atwater Public Library, 322 Atlantic Ave W, Atwater, MN, 56209. Tel: 320-974-3363. p. 1240

Behn, Ken, Tech Coordr, Southern Tier Library System, 9424 Scott Rd, Painted Post, NY, 14870-9598. Tel: 607-962-3141. Fax: 607-962-5356. p. 1714

Behney, Nancy L, Asst Dir, Milanof-Schock Library, 1184 Anderson Ferry Rd, Mount Joy, PA, 17552. Tel: 717-653-1510. Fax: 717-653-6590. p. 2093

Behnfeldt, Sue, Librn, Fulton County Association, Court House, 210 S Fulton, Wauseon, OH, 43567. Tel: 419-337-9260. Fax: 419-337-9293. p. 1945

Behnke, Janet, Circ Supvr, Loyola University Chicago Libraries, Health Sciences Library, Bldg 101, Rm 1717, 2160 S First Ave, Maywood, IL, 60153-5585. Tel: 708-216-9192. Fax: 708-216-8115. p. 617

Behnke, John, Dir, Saint Lawrence Catholic Church, 1203 Fifth St SE, Minneapolis, MN, 55414. Tel: 612-331-7941. Fax: 612-378-1771. p. 1261

Behnke, Lori, Coordr, Acq, Loras College Library, 1450 Alta Vista St, Dubuque, IA, 52004-4327. Tel: 563-588-7826. Fax: 563-588-7147. p. 812

Behr, Jeanette, Mgr, Res, League of Minnesota Cities Library, 145 University Ave W, Saint Paul, MN, 55103-2044. Tel: 651-281-1200. Fax: 651-281-1299. p. 1278

Behrens, Beth, Asst Dir, Tech Serv, The University of Memphis, One N Front St, Memphis, TN, 38103. Tel: 901-678-2749. Fax: 901-678-5293. p. 2252

Behrens, Elizabeth, Assoc Univ Librn, Memorial University of Newfoundland, Ferriss Hodgett Library, University Dr, Corner Brook, NL, A2H 6P9, CANADA. Tel: 709-637-6267. Fax: 709-637-6273, 709-639-8125. p. 2772

Behrens, Jennifer L, Ref Librn, Duke University Libraries, School of Law Library, 210 Science Dr, Durham, NC, 27708. Tel: 919-613-7198. Fax: 919-613-7237. p. 1788

Behrens, Kathie, Librn, Canby Public Library, 110 Oscar Ave N, Canby, MN, 56220-1332. Tel: 507-223-5738. Fax: 507-223-5738. p. 1244

Behrens, Kathie, Librn, Madison Public Library, 401 Sixth Ave, Madison, MN, 56256-1236. Tel: 320-598-7938. p. 1257

Behring, Susan, Ref, Brigham City Library, 26 E Forest, Brigham City, UT, 84302-2198. Tel: 435-723-5850. Fax: 435-723-2813. p. 2403

Behringer, Ken, Dir, Dakota County Library System, 1340 Wescott Rd, Eagan, MN, 55123-1099. Tel: 615-450-2930. Fax: 651-450-2915. p. 1249

Behringer, Ken, Dir, Pleasant Hill Library, 1490 S Frontage Rd, Hastings, MN, 55033. Tel: 651-438-0200. Fax: 651-480-4944. p. 1253

Behringer, Mary E, Dir, Blauvelt Free Library, 541 Western Hwy, Blauvelt, NY, 10913. Tel: 845-359-2811. Fax: 845-398-0017. p. 1583

Behrje, Rolfe, Libr Syst Adminr, Portage District Library, 300 Library Lane, Portage, MI, 49002. Tel: 269-329-4542, Ext 704. Fax: 269-324-9222. p. 1220

Behroozi, Cy, Dir, Brookings Institution Library, 1775 Massachusetts Ave NW, Washington, DC, 20036. Tel: 202-797-6240. Fax: 202-797-2970. p. 394

Behroozi, Leslie, Instrul Serv/Ref Librn, Marquette University, Sensenbrenner Hall, 1103 W Wisconsin Ave, Milwaukee, WI, 53233-2313. Tel: 414-288-7092. Fax: 414-288-5914. p. 2618

Beidl, Mary Beth, Asst Dir, Nassau Library System, 900 Jerusalem Ave, Uniondale, NY, 11553-3039. Tel: 516-292-8920, Ext 273. Fax: 516-565-0950. p. 1758

Beidler, Susan K, Head, Coll Mgt, Lycoming College, 700 College Pl, Williamsport, PA, 17701-5192. Tel: 570-321-4084. Fax: 570-321-4090. p. 2156

Beier, Michael, Dir, United States Army Dugway Proving Ground, 5124 Kister Ave, IMWE-DUG-MWL MS1, Dugway, UT, 84022-1097. Tel: 435-831-2178. Fax: 435-831-3543. p. 2404

Beiermann, Jennifer J, YA Serv, Cumberland Public Library, 1464 Diamond Hill Rd, Cumberland, RI, 02864-5510. Tel: 401-333-2552, Ext 203. Fax: 401-334-0578. p. 2165

Beikert, Brenda, Dir, Foxburg Free Library, 31 Main St, Foxburg, PA, 16036. Tel: 724-659-3431. Fax: 724-659-3214. p. 2058

Beil, Jamie L, Asst Librn, John Mosser Public Library District, 106 W Meek St, Abingdon, IL, 61410-1451. Tel: 309-462-3129. Fax: 309-462-3129. p. 587

Beile, Penny M, Assoc Dir, Info Serv & Scholarly Communication, University of Central Florida Libraries, 4000 Central Florida Blvd, Bldg 2, Orlando, FL, 32816-2666. Tel: 407-823-5488. Fax: 407-823-2529. p. 477

Bein, Miriam, Dir, Hillside Public Library, John F Kennedy Plaza, Hillside & Liberty Aves, Hillside, NJ, 07205-1893. Tel: 973-923-4413. p. 1491

Beinhoff, Lisa, Coordr, Sauk Valley Community College, 173 IL Rte 2, Dixon, IL, 61021-9112. Tel: 815-288-5511, Ext 306. Fax: 815-288-5651. p. 637

Beinhoff, Lisa, Dir, New Mexico Institute of Mining & Technology, 801 Leroy Pl, Socorro, NM, 87801. Tel: 575-835-5030. Fax: 575-835-6666. p. 1565

Beining, Shirley, Br Coordr, Putnam County District Library, The Educational Service Ctr, 124 Putnam Pkwy, Ottawa, OH, 45875-1471. Tel: 419-523-3747. Fax: 419-523-6477. p. 1926

Beining, Shirley, Br Mgr, Putnam County District Library, Columbus Grove Branch, 317 N Main St, Columbus Grove, OH, 45830. Tel: 419-659-2355. p. 1926

Beinkampen, Karen, Circ, Philmont Public Library, 101 Main St, Philmont, NY, 12565-1001. Tel: 518-672-5010. Fax: 518-672-5010. p. 1717

Beins, Linda, ILL, Ref, Finger Lakes Library System, 119 E Green St, Ithaca, NY, 14850. Tel: 607-273-4074. Fax: 607-273-3618. p. 1642

Beintema, William J, Dir, University of Tennessee, Taylor Law Center, 1505 W Cumberland Ave, Knoxville, TN, 37996-1800. Tel: 865-974-4381. Fax: 865-974-6571, 865-974-6595. p. 2243

Beise, Susan, Asst Dir, Newton Public Library, 100 N Third Ave W, Newton, IA, 50208. Tel: 641-792-4108. Fax: 641-791-0729. p. 835

Beisenherz, Nona, Foreign & Intl Law Librn, Loyola University New Orleans, Loyola Law Library, School of Law, 7214 St Charles Ave, New Orleans, LA, 70118. Tel: 504-861-5539. Fax: 504-861-5895. p. 961

Beisswenger, Drew, Head Music Libr, Missouri State University, 850 S John Q Hammons Pkwy, Springfield, MO, 65807. Tel: 417-836-5499. Fax: 417-836-4764. p. 1367

Beisswenger, Drew, Head of Libr, Missouri State University, Music Library, Ellis Hall, Rm 209, 901 S National, Springfield, MO, 65804-0095. Tel: 417-836-5499. p. 1367

Beisswenger, Drew, Assoc Prof, Missouri State University, Duane G Meyer Library, 901 S National Ave, Springfield, MO, 65897. Tel: 417-836-4525. Fax: 417-836-4764. p. 2968

Beiter, Karen, Cat, Belleville Public Library, 121 E Washington St, Belleville, IL, 62220. Tel: 618-234-0441, Ext 20. Fax: 618-234-9474. p. 593

Bejcek, Nicole, Supvr, Libr Ref, United States Air Force, Bldg 214, 7205 Randall Ave, F E Warren AFB, WY, 82005-2988. Tel: 307-773-3416. Fax: 307-773-4515. p. 2655

Bejune, Matthew, Ref & Instruction Librn, Quinsigamond Community College, 670 W Boylston St, Worcester, MA, 01606-2092. Tel: 508-854-4210. Fax: 508-854-4204. p. 1144

Beke-Harrigan, Heidi, Asst Librn, Tech Serv, Walsh University, 2020 E Maple St NW, North Canton, OH, 44720-3336. Tel: 330-490-7186. Fax: 330-490-7270. p. 1923

Bekele, Araya-Yohannes, Libr Dir, Chaleur Library Region, Mgr Robichaud Public Library, 855 Principale St, Local 3, Beresford, NB, E8K 1T3, CANADA. Tel: 506-542-2704. Fax: 506-542-2714. p. 2761

Bekele, Metasebia, Head, Circ, Florida Hospital College of Health Sciences, 671 Winyah Dr, Orlando, FL, 32803. Tel: 407-303-7747, Ext 9809. Fax: 407-303-9622. p. 475

Bekker, Jennifer, Ref & Adult Serv Supvr, Lewisville Public Library System, 1197 W Main at Civic Circle, Lewisville, TX, 75067. Tel: 972-219-3721. Fax: 972-219-5094. p. 2355

Belanger, Annie, Head, Info Serv & Res, University of Waterloo Library, 200 University Ave W, Waterloo, ON, N2L 3G1, CANADA. Tel: 519-888-4567, Ext 32282. Fax: 519-888-4320. p. 2869

Belanger, Arthur, Mgr, Libr Syst, Yale University Library, Harvey Cushing/John Hay Whitney Medical Library, Sterling Hall of Medicine, 333 Cedar St, L110 SHM, New Haven, CT, 06520. Tel: 203-785-6928. Fax: 203-785-5636. p. 358

Belanger, Cynthia, Adult Serv, Red Deer Public Library, 4818 49th St, Red Deer, AB, T4N 1T9, CANADA. Tel: 403-346-4576. Fax: 403-341-3110. p. 2714

Belanger, David L, Dir, Delaware County Library System, 340 N Middletown Rd, Bldg 19, Media, PA, 19063-5597. Tel: 610-891-8622. Fax: 610-891-8641. p. 2087

Bélanger, France, Actg Librn, Hydro Quebec Bibliotheque, 800, De Maisonneuve E, blvd, 2nd Flr, Montreal, QC, H2L 4M8, CANADA. Tel: 514-840-3000, Ext 5939. Fax: 514-840-5044. p. 2896

Belanger, Janice, Ref Serv, Dawson College Library, 3040 Sherbrooke St W, Westmount, QC, H3Z 1A4, CANADA. Tel: 514-931-8731, Ext 1733. Fax: 514-931-3567. p. 2915

Belanger, Maria, Libr Tech, Fisheries & Oceans Canada, 80 E White Hills Rd, St. John's, NL, A1C 5X1, CANADA. Tel: 709-772-2020, 709-772-2022. Fax: 709-772-2575. p. 2772

Belanger, Marie, Br Head, Toronto Public Library, Kennedy-Eglinton, Liberty Square Shopping Plaza, 2380 Eglinton Ave E, Toronto, ON, M1K 2P3, CANADA. Tel: 416-396-8924. Fax: 416-396-8928. p. 2862

Belanger, Mary Elizabeth, Ch, Taunton Public Library, 12 Pleasant St, Taunton, MA, 02780. Tel: 508-821-1410. Fax: 508-821-1414. p. 1131

Belanger Morrow, Janet, Head, Res Mgt, Northeastern University Libraries, Snell Library, 360 Huntington Ave, Boston, MA, 02115. Tel: 617-373-4959. Fax: 617-373-8396. p. 1065

Belanger, Pascal, Tech Serv, College de l'Assomption, 270 boul l'Ange-Gardien, L'Assomption, QC, J5W 1R7, CANADA. Tel: 450-589-5621, Ext 258. Fax: 450-589-2910. p. 2885

Belbin, Nicole, Head, Access Serv, Western New England University, 1215 Wilbraham Rd, Springfield, MA, 01119-2689. Tel: 413-782-1484. Fax: 413-782-1745. p. 1128

Belbin, Ron, Libr Support Spec, Western Nevada Community College, Beck Library & Media Services (Fallon Campus), 160 Campus Way, Fallon, NV, 89406. Tel: 775-423-5330. p. 1426

Belch, Ella, AV, Thomas Nelson Community College Library, Wythe Hall 228, 99 Thomas Nelson Dr, Hampton, VA, 23666. Tel: 757-825-2875. Fax: 757-825-2870. p. 2468

Belcher, Cassandra, Libr Mgr, United States Army, PO Box 896, Jolon, CA, 93928-0896. Tel: 831-386-2719. Fax: 831-386-2002. p. 161

Belcher, Dana, Dir, Fleming County Public Library, 202 Bypass Blvd, Flemingsburg, KY, 41041-7934. Tel: 606-845-7851. Fax: 606-845-7045. p. 912

Belcher, Dana, Acq/Per Librn, Asst Libr Dir, East Central University, 1100 E 14th St, Ada, OK, 74820-6999. Tel: 580-310-5564. Fax: 580-436-3242. p. 1955

Belcher, Ellen, Archives, Spec Coll Librn, John Jay College of Criminal Justice, 899 Tenth Ave, New York, NY, 10019. Tel: 212-237-8238. Fax: 212-237-8221. p. 1684

Belcher, Jim, Dir of Libr Serv, South Plains College Library, 1401 S College Ave, Box E, Levelland, TX, 79336. Tel: 806-716-2300, 806-716-2330. Fax: 806-894-5274. p. 2355

Belcher, Peggy, Circ, Pope County Library System, 116 E Third St, Russellville, AR, 72801. Tel: 479-968-4368. Fax: 479-968-3222. p. 114

Belcher, Rebecca, Access Serv, Appalachian School of Law Library, 1221 Edgewater Dr, Grundy, VA, 24614-7062. Tel: 276-935-6688, Ext 1311. Fax: 276-935-7138. p. 2467

Belcher, Roxanne, Mgr, Johnson County Library, Shawnee Branch, 13811 Johnson Dr, Shawnee, KS, 66216. Tel: 913-962-3806. Fax: 913-962-3809. p. 888

Belden, Dreanna, Asst Dean, External Relations, University of North Texas Libraries, PO Box 305190, Denton, TX, 76203-5190. Tel: 940-369-8740. Fax: 940-369-8760. p. 2313

Belden, Pam, Dir, Waterford Public Library, 101 N River St, Waterford, WI, 53185-4149. Tel: 262-534-3988. Fax: 262-534-9624. p. 2644

Belderis, I, Ref, Theosophical University Library, 2416 N Lake Ave, Altadena, CA, 91001. Tel: 626-798-8020. Fax: 626-798-4749. p. 120

Belderis, James T, Head of Libr, Theosophical University Library, 2416 N Lake Ave, Altadena, CA, 91001. Tel: 626-798-8020. Fax: 626-798-4749. p. 120

Beleu, Steve, US Govt Doc Librn, Oklahoma Department of Libraries, 200 NE 18th St, Oklahoma City, OK, 73105. Tel: 405-521-2502. Fax: 405-525-7804. p. 1974

Belew, Beth, Spec Pop Librn, Johnson County Public Library, White River Library, 1664 Library Blvd, Greenwood, IN, 46142. Tel: 317-885-1330. Fax: 317-882-4117. p. 744

Belew, Reese, Tech Serv & Automation, Dallas County Law Library, George Allen Courts Bldg, 600 Commerce St, Ste 292, Dallas, TX, 75202-4606. Tel: 214-653-6013. Fax: 214-653-6103. p. 2305

Belfont, Lew, Head, Customer Serv, Howard County Library System, 6600 Cradlerock Way, Columbia, MD, 21045-4912. Tel: 410-313-7750. Fax: 410-313-7742. p. 1026

Belgard, Titus, Ser, Louisiana State University at Alexandria, 8100 Hwy 71 S, Alexandria, LA, 71302. Tel: 318-473-6440. Fax: 318-473-6556. p. 940

Belhumeur, Marilyn, Librn, Gabriel Dumont Institute Library, College West, Rm 218, 3737 Wascana Pkwy, Regina, SK, S4S 0A2, CANADA. Tel: 306-347-4124. Fax: 306-565-0809. p. 2922

Belin, Elvie, Mgr, Southeast Arkansas Regional Library, Hermitage Branch, PO Box 98, Hermitage, AR, 71647-0098. Tel: 870-463-8962. Fax: 870-463-8962. p. 110

Belina, Aniela, Doc, Centre International de Criminologie Comparee, 3150 Jean-Brillant, Local C-4110, Montreal, QC, H3T 1N8, CANADA. Tel: 514-343-6534. Fax: 514-343-2269. p. 2893

Beline, Jayne, Dir, Parsippany-Troy Hills Free Public Library, 449 Halsey Rd, Parsippany, NJ, 07054. Tel: 973-887-5150. Fax: 973-887-0062. p. 1517

Belisle, Barbara, Circ, University of Montevallo, Station 6100, Montevallo, AL, 35115-6100. Tel: 205-665-6100. Fax: 205-665-6112. p. 27

Belisle, Georgette, Head, Ref, Midlothian Public Library, 14701 S Kenton Ave, Midlothian, IL, 60445-4122. Tel: 708-535-2027. Fax: 708-535-2053. p. 674

Belisle, Gisele, Chief Librn, Bibliotheque Publique de Moonbeam, 53 St-Aubin Ave, CP 370, Moonbeam, ON, P0L 1V0, CANADA. Tel: 705-367-2462. Fax: 705-367-2120. p. 2823

Belk, Julie, ILL Mgr, Hayner Public Library District, 326 Belle St, Alton, IL, 62002. Tel: 618-462-0677. Fax: 618-462-0665. p. 588

Belkin, Betsey, Dir, Ursuline College, 2550 Lander Rd, Pepper Pike, OH, 44124-4398. Tel: 440-449-4202. Fax: 440-449-3180. p. 1929

Belkin, Nicholas, Chairperson, Prof, Rutgers, The State University of New Jersey, Four Huntington St, New Brunswick, NJ, 08901-1071. Tel: 732-932-7500, Ext 8955. Fax: 732-932-2644. p. 2969

Bell, Aisha, Ch, Scarsdale Public Library, 54 Olmsted Rd, Scarsdale, NY, 10583. Tel: 914-722-1300. Fax: 914-722-1305. p. 1739

Bell, Alice, Circ/AV, Ohio State University LIBRARIES, Michael E Moritz Law Library, 55 W 12th Ave, Columbus, OH, 43210-1391. Tel: 614-292-9417. Fax: 614-292-3202. p. 1888

Bell, Alicia, Ch, Belvedere-Tiburon Library, 1501 Tiburon Blvd, Tiburon, CA, 94920. Tel: 415-789-2665. Fax: 415-789-2650. p. 275

Bell, Audrey, Br Mgr, East Central Georgia Regional Library, Audio Visual & Talking Book Center, James Brown Blvd, Augusta, GA, 30901. Tel: 706-821-2625. Fax: 706-724-5403. p. 519

Bell, Beth, Br Mgr, Charleston County Public Library, West Ashley, 45 Windermere Blvd, Charleston, SC, 29407. Tel: 843-766-6635. p. 2183

Bell, Beverly, Librn, Florence County Library System, Timmonsville Public Library, 111 S Warren St, Timmonsville, SC, 29161-1743. Tel: 843-346-2941. Fax: 843-346-2931. p. 2193

Bell, Brandy, Librn, Georgia Department of Corrections, Office of Library Services, Laying Farm Rd, Hardwick, GA, 31034. Tel: 478-445-4175. Fax: 478-453-6507. p. 536

Bell, Brian, Br Mgr, Richmond Hill Public Library, Richvale Library, 40 Pearson Ave, Richmond Hill, ON, L4C 6T7, CANADA. Tel: 905-889-2847. Fax: 905-889-2435. p. 2839

Bell, Brittany, Asst Librn, Spiro Public Library, 208 S Main, Spiro, OK, 74959. Tel: 918-962-3461. Fax: 918-962-5320. p. 1978

Bell, Burnette, Ref Librn, Wake Technical Community College, Health Sciences, 2901 Holston Lane, Raleigh, NC, 27610-2092. Tel: 919-747-0016. p. 1818

Bell, Carol, Cat Supvr, Lee County Library System, Processing Center, 881 Gunnery Rd N, Ste 2, Lehigh Acres, FL, 33971-1246. Tel: 239-461-7327. Fax: 239-461-7373. p. 446

Bell, Christine L, Dir, Libr Serv, Newton-Wellesley Hospital, 2014 Washington St, Newton Lower Falls, MA, 02462-1699. Tel: 617-243-6279. Fax: 617-243-6595. p. 1111

Bell, Daniel, Ref & Info Serv, Web Coordr, University of Tulsa Libraries, Mabee Legal Information Center, 3120 E Fourth Pl, Tulsa, OK, 74104-3189. Tel: 918-631-2404. Fax: 918-631-3556. p. 1984

Bell, David, Ref Librn, Eastern Illinois University, 600 Lincoln Ave, Charleston, IL, 61920. Tel: 217-581-7547. p. 603

Bell, Dawn M, Dir, Fredericktown Area Public Library, 38 Water St, Fredericktown, PA, 15333. Tel: 724-377-0017. Fax: 724-377-2924. p. 2059

Bell, Don C, Cat, Ref Serv, Shelton State Community College, 9500 Old Greensboro Rd, Tuscaloosa, AL, 35405. Tel: 205-391-2245. Fax: 205-391-3926. p. 38

Bell, Dorothy, Br Mgr, Saint Petersburg Public Library, West Saint Petersburg Community Library, 750 66th St N, Saint Petersburg, FL, 33710. Tel: 727-341-7199. p. 488

Bell, Elloise S, Pub Serv, Sunflower County Library System, Inverness Public, City Hall, 802 E Grand Ave, Inverness, MS, 38753. Tel: 662-265-6009. Fax: 662-265-5502. p. 1302

Bell, Ervin, Librn, Michigan Department of Corrections, 9625 Pierce Rd, Freeland, MI, 48623. Tel: 989-695-9880. Fax: 989-695-6345. p. 1182

Bell, Evangeline, In Charge, City of Houston, 900 Bagby, 4th Flr, Houston, TX, 77002. Tel: 832-393-6354. Fax: 713-247-1017. p. 2334

Bell, Fran, Librn, Poinsett County Public Library, Marked Tree Branch, 102 Locust St, Marked Tree, AR, 72365-2255. Tel: 870-358-3190. Fax: 870-358-2244. p. 102

Bell, Geraldine, Dr, Dir, Miles College, 5500 Myron Massey Blvd, Fairfield, AL, 35064. Tel: 205-929-1000. Fax: 205-929-1635. p. 16

Bell, Gladys, Peabody Librn, Hampton University, 130 E Tyler St, Hampton, VA, 23668. Tel: 757-727-5371. Fax: 757-727-5952. p. 2468

Bell, Gretchen, Dir, Nanuet Public Library, 149 Church St, Nanuet, NY, 10954. Tel: 845-623-4281. Fax: 845-623-2415. p. 1664

Bell, Gretchen M, Dean of Libr, Piedmont Community College, 1715 College Dr, Roxboro, NC, 27573. Tel: 336-599-1181, Ext 267. Fax: 336-599-9146. p. 1821

Bell, Hazel L, Ser Librn, Alcorn State University, 1000 ASU Dr, Alcorn State, MS, 39096-7500. Tel: 601-877-6362. Fax: 601-877-3885. p. 1293

Bell, Jane, Librn, North Lake College Library, 5001 N MacArthur Blvd, Irving, TX, 75062. Tel: 972-273-3400. Fax: 972-273-3431. p. 2347

Bell, Janice, Head, Pub Serv, Southern University, 167 Roosevelt Steptoe Ave, Baton Rouge, LA, 70813-0001. Tel: 225-771-2844. Fax: 225-771-4113. p. 944

Bell, Jo Ann, Librn, Church of the Incarnation, 3966 McKinney Ave, Dallas, TX, 75204-2099. Tel: 214-521-5101, Ext 25. Fax: 214-528-7209. p. 2305

Bell, Kate, Ch, Flint Memorial Library, 147 Park St, North Reading, MA, 01864. Tel: 978-664-4942. Fax: 978-664-0812. p. 1113

Bell, Kathie, Asst Curator, Boot Hill Museum, Front St, Dodge City, KS, 67801. Tel: 620-227-8188. Fax: 620-227-7673. p. 863

Bell, Kathy, Librn, Worcester County Horticultural Society, 11 French Dr, Boylston, MA, 01505. Tel: 508-869-6111, Ext 116. Fax: 508-869-0314. p. 1069

Bell, Kim, Dir, Hampton Public Library, Four Federal St S, Hampton, IA, 50441-1934. Tel: 641-456-4451. Fax: 641-456-2377. p. 820

Bell, Kris, Ch, Paso Robles Public Library, 1000 Spring St, Paso Robles, CA, 93446-2207. Tel: 805-237-3870. Fax: 805-238-3665. p. 207

Bell, Kristi, Sr Librn, Tech Serv, San Jose Public Library, 150 E San Fernando St, San Jose, CA, 95112-3580. Tel: 408-808-2468. Fax: 408-808-2423. p. 250

Bell, Laurie M, Dir, Pomfret Public Library, 449 Pomfret St, Pomfret, CT, 06258. Tel: 860-928-3475. p. 364

Bell, Lisa, Acq, North Central Regional Library, 16 N Columbia St, Wenatchee, WA, 98801-8103. Tel: 509-663-1117, Ext 108. Fax: 509-662-8060. p. 2548

Bell, Marcia, Dir, San Francisco Law Library, Financial District, Monadnock Bldg, 685 Market St, Ste 420, San Francisco, CA, 94105. Tel: 415-882-9310. Fax: 415-882-9594. p. 245

Bell, Marcia R, Dir, San Francisco Law Library, 401 Van Ness Ave, Rm 400, San Francisco, CA, 94102-4672. Tel: 415-554-6821. Fax: 415-554-6820. p. 245

Bell, Marcia R, Dir, San Francisco Law Library, Courthouse Reference Room, 400 McAllister St, Rm 512, San Francisco, CA, 94102. Tel: 415-551-3647. Fax: 415-551-3787. p. 245

Bell, Margaret A, Admin Librn, Hinds Community College, Vicksburg Learning Resources/Library, 755 Hwy 27, Vicksburg, MS, 39180-8699. Tel: 601-629-6846. Fax: 601-629-6862. p. 1313

Bell, Maureen, Br Mgr, Dakota County Library System, Wentworth, 199 E Wentworth Ave, West Saint Paul, MN, 55118. Tel: 651-554-6805. Fax: 651-451-1914. p. 1249

Bell, Michael, Asst Dean, Head, Mat Proc, University of Tennessee at Chattanooga Library, 615 McCallie Ave, Dept 6456, Chattanooga, TN, 37403-2598. Tel: 423-425-4501. Fax: 423-425-4775. p. 2228

Bell, Olga, Ref, West Nyack Free Library, 65 Strawtown Rd, West Nyack, NY, 10994. Tel: 845-358-6081. Fax: 845-358-4071. p. 1766

Bell, Pat, Dir, Arthur Public Library, 224 S Main St, Arthur, IA, 51431-8054. Tel: 712-367-2240. Fax: 712-367-2240. p. 794

Bell, Regina, Librn, Georgia Department of Corrections, Office of Library Services, 2023 Gainesville Hwy S, Alto, GA, 30510. Tel: 706-776-4700. Fax: 706-776-4710. p. 508

Bell, Regina, Ref, Atlantic County Library System, 40 Farragut Ave, Mays Landing, NJ, 08330-1750. Tel: 609-625-2776. Fax: 609-625-8143. p. 1500

Bell, Richard, Dir, Fortville-Vernon Township Public Library, 625 E Broadway, Fortville, IN, 46040-1549. Tel: 317-485-6402. Fax: 317-485-4084. p. 743

Bell, Robert David, Curric Mat Librn, Ref Librn, Oklahoma State University - Tulsa Library, 700 N Greenwood Ave, Tulsa, OK, 74106-0700. Tel: 918-594-8136. Fax: 918-594-8145. p. 1981

Bell, Sherry, Ref Archivist, City of Edmonton, Archives, 10440 - 108 Ave, 2nd Flr, Prince of Wales Armouries Heritage Centre, Edmonton, AB, T5H 3Z9, CANADA. Tel: 780-496-8711. Fax: 780-496-8732. p. 2699

Bell, Stacy, Mgr, Res, Deere & Co Library, One John Deere Pl, Moline, IL, 61265. Tel: 309-765-4733. Fax: 309-765-4088. p. 674

Bell, Steven, Assoc Univ Librn, Temple University Libraries, 1210 W Berks St, Philadelphia, PA, 19122-6088. Tel: 215-204-8231. Fax: 215-204-5201. p. 2117

Bell, Susan K, Adminr, American Museum of Natural History Library, Henry Fairfield Osborn Library, Central Park W at 79th St, New York, NY, 10024. Tel: 212-769-5803. Fax: 212-769-5842. p. 1668

Bell, Suzanne T, Govt Doc Librn, University of Guam, UOG Sta, Mangilao, GU, 96923. Tel: 671-735-2316. Fax: 671-734-6882. p. 2667

Bell, Valerie, Asst Dir, Pub Serv, Ocean County Library, 101 Washington St, Toms River, NJ, 08753. Tel: 732-914-5404. p. 1534

Bell, Wanda, Asst Dir, Bienville Parish Library, 2768 Maple St, Arcadia, LA, 71001-3699. Tel: 318-263-7410. Fax: 318-263-7428. p. 941

Bell-Garrison, Eileen, Dean, Libr Serv, Gonzaga University, 502 E Boone Ave, Spokane, WA, 99258-0095. Tel: 509-323-6535. Fax: 509-323-5904. p. 2536

Bell-Garrison, Eileen, Pres, Washington Idaho Network, Gonzaga University, Foley Center Library, 502 E Boone Ave, AD 95, Spokane, WA, 99258. Tel: 509-313-6535. Fax: 509-313-5904. p. 2957

Bell-Harney, Kathy, Ref, Boyden Library, Ten Bird St, Foxborough, MA, 02035. Tel: 508-543-1245. Fax: 508-543-1193. p. 1089

Bell-Johnson, Mary Fran, Electronic Res Asst, Longwood University, Redford & Race St, Farmville, VA, 23909. Tel: 434-395-2450. Fax: 434-395-2453. p. 2463

Bellafante, Nancy, Evening Ref Librn, Drexel University Libraries, Hagerty Library, 33rd & Market Sts, Philadelphia, PA, 19104-2875. Tel: 215-895-2750. Fax: 215-895-2070. p. 2105

Bellafiore, Ken, Media Spec, Nassau Community College, One Education Dr, Garden City, NY, 11530-6793. Tel: 516-572-7400. Fax: 516-572-7846. p. 1626

Bellaire, Nancy, Dir, Monroe County Library System, 840 S Roessler St, Monroe, MI, 48161. Tel: 734-241-5770. Fax: 734-241-4722. p. 1209

Bellamy, Yetra, Dir, IT, Fac Dir, American InterContinental University, Dunwoody Campus-Media Center, 6600 Peachtree-Dunwoody Rd, 500 Embassy Row, Atlanta, GA, 30328. Tel: 404-965-6533. p. 510

Bellanca, Patricia, Access Serv, Circ Mgr, Rutgers University Libraries, Center of Alcohol Studies, Brinkley & Adele Smithers Hall, 607 Allison Rd, Piscataway, NJ, 08854-8001. Tel: 732-445-3803. Fax: 732-445-5944. p. 1508

Bellar, Patricia, Ch, Gorham-Macbane Public Library, 405 White St, Springfield, TN, 37172-2340. Tel: 615-384-5123. Fax: 615-384-0106. p. 2266

Bellard, Eloise, Ref Librn, Adelphi University Libraries, One South Ave, Garden City, NY, 11530. Tel: 516-877-3584. Fax: 516-877-3592. p. 1625

Bellas, Susan, Br Mgr, Clermont County Public Library, Bethel Branch, 611 W Plane St, Bethel, OH, 45106-1302. Tel: 513-734-2619. Fax: 513-734-1321. p. 1858

Bellavia, Rand, Dir, D'Youville College, 320 Porter Ave, Buffalo, NY, 14201-1084. Tel: 716-829-7616. Fax: 716-829-7770. p. 1597

Belle-Isle, Lynn, Chief Exec Officer, Hawkesbury Public Library, 550 Higginson St, Hawkesbury, ON, K6A 1H1, CANADA. Tel: 613-632-0106, Ext 2253. Fax: 613-636-2097. p. 2811

Belleau, Suzanne, Dir, Krotz Springs Municipal Public Library, 216 Park St, Krotz Springs, LA, 70570. Tel: 337-566-8190. Fax: 337-566-2233. p. 952

Bellefeuille, Carol, Commun Serv, New Bedford Free Public Library, 613 Pleasant St, New Bedford, MA, 02740-6203. Tel: 508-991-6275. Fax: 508-991-6368. p. 1108

Belleh, Ene, Ref Librn, Christiana Hospital Library, Christiana Hospital, 4755 Ogletown Stanton Rd, Newark, DE, 19718-0002. Tel: 302-733-1115. Fax: 302-733-1365. p. 385

Bellel, Agnes H, Dr, Coordr, Alabama State University, College of Education, 915 S Jackson St, Montgomery, AL, 36104. Tel: 334-229-6829, 334-229-8801. Fax: 334-229-6831. p. 2961

Bellemare, Chantale, City Librn, Albert-Westmorland-Kent Regional Library, Moncton Public, 644 Main St, Ste 101, Moncton, NB, E1C 1E2, CANADA. Tel: 506-869-6000. Fax: 506-869-6040. p. 2765

Bellemare, Jocelyne, Chief Librn, Institut Universitaire de Cardiologie et de Pneumologie de Québec Bibliotheque, 2725 Chemin Ste-Foy, Quebec, QC, G1V 4G5, CANADA. Tel: 418-656-4563. Fax: 418-656-4720. p. 2905

Beller, Joanne, Ref Coordr, Worcester Polytechnic Institute, 100 Institute Rd, Worcester, MA, 01609-2280. Tel: 508-831-5410. Fax: 508-831-5829. p. 1145

Beller, Michael, Ref, Mills College, 5000 MacArthur Blvd, Oakland, CA, 94613. Tel: 510-430-2051. Fax: 510-430-2278. p. 197

Belleville, Matthew, Libr Spec I, Okeechobee County Public Library, 206 SW 16th St, Okeechobee, FL, 34974. Tel: 863-763-3536. Fax: 863-763-5368. p. 474

Belley, Johanne, Dir, Universite du Quebec a Chicoutimi Bibliotheque, 555 Blvd de l'Universite E, Chicoutimi, QC, G7H 2B1, CANADA. Tel: 418-545-5011, Ext 5631. Fax: 418-693-5896. p. 2881

Belli, Reilly, Circ Supvr, Tech Mgr, Wood River Public Library, 326 E Ferguson Ave, Wood River, IL, 62095-2098. Tel: 618-254-4832. Fax: 618-254-4836. p. 721

Bellimer, Mary Ellen, Dir, Unity Free Public Library, 13 Center Rd, Charlestown, NH, 03603. Tel: 603-543-3253. Fax: 603-542-9736. p. 1441

Bellin, Bernie, Interim Dir, Muskego Public Library, S73 W16663 Janesville Rd, Muskego, WI, 53150. Tel: 262-971-2100. Fax: 262-971-2115. p. 2623

Bellin, Matt, Chief Operating Officer, James J Hill Reference Library, 80 W Fourth St, Saint Paul, MN, 55102-1669. Tel: 651-265-5442. Fax: 651-265-5520. p. 1278

Belling, Christine, Syst Adminr, Syosset Public Library, 225 S Oyster Bay Rd, Syosset, NY, 11791-5897. Tel: 516-921-7161. Fax: 516-921-8771. p. 1751

Belling, Sharon, Dir, Oakfield Public Library, 130 N Main St, Oakfield, WI, 53065-9563. Tel: 920-583-4552. Fax: 920-583-2544. p. 2626

Bellinger, Christina, Head, Tech Serv, University of New Hampshire Library, 18 Library Way, Durham, NH, 03824. Tel: 603-862-0073. Fax: 603-862-0085. p. 1445

Bellinger, Margaret A, Dir, Integrated Libr Tech Serv, Yale University Library, Sterling Memorial Library, 120 High St, New Haven, CT, 06520. Tel: 203-432-2068. Fax: 203-432-1294. p. 359

Bellinger, Randy, Dir, Monroe Public Library, 416 S Buchanan St, Monroe, IA, 50170. Tel: 641-259-3065. Fax: 641-259-3065. p. 832

Belliston, Jeff, Chair, Brigham Young University, Harold B Lee Library, 2060 HBLL, Provo, UT, 84602. Tel: 801-422-2927. Fax: 801-422-0466. p. 2411

Bellistri, Joan, Librn, Anne Arundel County Circuit Court, Seven Church Circle, Ste 303, Annapolis, MD, 21401. Tel: 410-222-1387. Fax: 410-268-9762. p. 1009

Belliveau, Gerard J, Jr, Head Librn, Racquet & Tennis Club Library, 370 Park Ave, New York, NY, 10022-5968. Tel: 212-753-9700. p. 1698

Bellmany, Robin, Circ, Putnam County Library System, 601 College Rd, Palatka, FL, 32177-3873. Tel: 386-329-0126. Fax: 386-329-1240. p. 478

Bello, Maria, Librn, National Marine Fisheries Service, 301 Research Ct, Kodiak, AK, 99615-7400. Tel: 907-481-1712. Fax: 907-481-1702. p. 51

Bello, Maria, Librn, National Marine Fisheries Service, 75 Virginia Beach Dr, Miami, FL, 33149. Tel: 305-361-4229. Fax: 305-365-4104. p. 468

Bellofatto, Vince, Pub Relations, Tuscaloosa Public Library, 1801 Jack Warner Pkwy, Tuscaloosa, AL, 35401-1027. Tel: 205-345-5820, Ext 210. Fax: 205-752-8300. p. 38

Bellos, Alexander, Automation Syst Coordr, Tech Serv, Glen Cove Public Library, Four Glen Cove Ave, Glen Cove, NY, 11542-2885. Tel: 516-676-2130. Fax: 516-676-2788. p. 1628

Bellot, Cindy, Mgr, Dixie County Public Library, 16328 SE Hwy 19, Cross City, FL, 32628. Tel: 352-498-1219. Fax: 352-498-1408. p. 435

Bellovin, Joanne, Dean, Central Florida Community College, 3001 SW College Rd, Ocala, FL, 34474-4415. Tel: 352-237-2111, Ext 1344. Fax: 352-873-5818. p. 473

Bellows, Susan, Cat Librn, Midlands Technical College Library, 1260 Lexington Dr, West Columbia, SC, 29170-2176. Tel: 803-822-3616. Fax: 803-822-3670. p. 2207

Bellu, Annette, Asst Dir, Chadron Public Library, 507 Bordeaux, Chadron, NE, 69337. Tel: 308-432-0531. Fax: 308-432-0534. p. 1395

Bellucci, Anthony, Acq, United States Air Force, 744 Douhet Dr, Bldg 4244, Barksdale AFB, LA, 71110. Tel: 318-456-2093. Fax: 318-752-0509. p. 941

Belluscio, Lynne, Dir, LeRoy Historical Society Library, 23 E Main St, LeRoy, NY, 14482-1210. Tel: 585-768-7433. Fax: 585-768-7579. p. 1651

Belmar, Cynthia, Librn, Houston Community College - Northwest College, Katy Campus Library, 1550 Foxlake Dr, Houston, TX, 77084-6029. Tel: 713-718-5849. Fax: 281-492-6075. p. 2338

Belmonte, Karen, Librn, Virginia Memorial Public Library, 100 N Main St, Virginia, IL, 62691-1364. Tel: 217-452-3846. Fax: 217-452-3846. p. 714

Belongia, Lori, Dir, Marshfield Public Library, 211 E Second St, Marshfield, WI, 54449. Tel: 715-387-8494, Ext 214. Fax: 715-387-6909. p. 2613

Beloungy, Julie, Dir, Thorp Public Library, 401 S Conway Dr, Thorp, WI, 54771. Tel: 715-669-5953. Fax: 715-669-7319. p. 2642

Below, Eileen, Libr Supvr, Brown County Library, Weyers-Hilliard Branch, 2680 Riverview Dr, Green Bay, WI, 54313. Tel: 920-448-4405. Fax: 920-448-4404. p. 2595

Belt, Gordon, Dir, Pub Serv, Tennessee State Library & Archives, 403 Seventh Ave N, Nashville, TN, 37243-0312. Tel: 615-253-6468. Fax: 615-532-2472, 615-741-6471. p. 2259

Belter, Phyllis, Head, Automation & Vols, Coronado Public Library, 640 Orange Ave, Coronado, CA, 92118-1526. Tel: 619-522-2474. Fax: 619-435-4205. p. 137

Belton, Keith, Sr Librn/e-Br Mgr, Lee County Library System, 2345 Union St, Fort Myers, FL, 33901-3917. Tel: 239-533-4813. Fax: 239-485-1100. p. 445

Belton, Marsha, ILL Mgr, Mississippi Valley State University, 14000 Hwy 82 W, Itta Bena, MS, 38941. Tel: 662-254-3494. Fax: 662-254-3499. p. 1302

Beltran, Cherie, Librn, Ranger College, 1100 College Circle, Ranger, TX, 76470-3298. Tel: 254-647-1414. Fax: 254-647-1656. p. 2373

Beltran, Dana, Librn, Northern Virginia Community College Libraries, Loudoun Campus, 1000 Harry Flood Byrd Hwy, Sterling, VA, 20164-8699. Tel: 703-450-2641. Fax: 703-404-7374. p. 2447

Beltz, Nicola V, Prog Mgr, Virginia Tidewater Consortium for Higher Education, 4900 Powhatan Ave, Norfolk, VA, 23529. Tel: 757-683-3183. Fax: 757-683-4515. p. 2957

Belvin, Diana, Acq, Moore County Library, 101 Saunders St, Carthage, NC, 28327. Tel: 910-947-5335. Fax: 910-947-3660. p. 1779

Belvin, Robert, Dir, New Brunswick Free Public Library, 60 Livingston Ave, New Brunswick, NJ, 08901-2597. Tel: 732-745-5721. Fax: 732-846-0226. p. 1508

Belvins, Sally, Ch Serv Librn, Bitterroot Public Library, 306 State St, Hamilton, MT, 59840-2759. Tel: 406-363-1670. Fax: 406-363-1678. p. 1380

Belway, Liane, Librn, Holland College Library Services, 140 Weymouth St, Charlottetown, PE, C1A 4Z1, CANADA. Tel: 902-888-6752. Fax: 902-566-9522. p. 2875

Belyeu, Elizabeth, Libr Asst I, Montgomery City-County Public Library System, Juliette Hampton Morgan Memorial Library (Main Library), 245 High St, Montgomery, AL, 36104. Tel: 334-240-4999. Fax: 334-240-4980. p. 30

Belz, Sue, Br Mgr, Reading Public Library, Southeast, 1426 Perkiomen Ave, Reading, PA, 19602-2136. Tel: 610-655-6362. Fax: 610-655-6669. p. 2134

Belzile, Sylvie, Dir, Universite de Sherbrooke Service des Bibliotheques et Archives, Cite Universitaire, Sherbrooke, QC, J1K 2R1, CANADA. Tel: 819-821-7550. Fax: 819-821-7096. p. 2912

Belzowski, Nora, Res Serv Librn, Valparaiso University, 1410 Chapel Dr, Valparaiso, IN, 46383-6493. Tel: 219-464-5023. p. 783

Bemben, Debra, Br Mgr, San Bernardino Public Library, Dorothy Inghram Branch, 1505 W Highland Ave, San Bernardino, CA, 92411. Tel: 909-887-4494. Fax: 909-887-6594. p. 229

Ben-Reuven, Lisa, Librn, California State Board of Equalization, 450 N St, Sacramento, CA, 95814. Tel: 916-445-7356. Fax: 916-323-3387. p. 222

Ben-Simon, Julie, Mgr, Acq Serv, King County Library System, 960 Newport Way NW, Issaquah, WA, 98027. Tel: 425-369-3205. Fax: 425-369-3255. p. 2516

Bena, Amanda L, Access Serv Librn, Frostburg State University, One Stadium Dr, Frostburg, MD, 21532. Tel: 301-687-7012. Fax: 301-687-7069. p. 1029

Benac, Maria J, Br Mgr, Beaufort County Library, Saint Helena Branch, 1025 Sea Island Pkwy, Saint Helena Island, SC, 29920. Tel: 843-255-6486. p. 2181

Benamati, Dennis C, Dir, Jamestown Community College, 525 Falconer St, Jamestown, NY, 14702-0020. Tel: 716-338-1125. Fax: 716-338-1464. p. 1647

Benard, Paula, Operations Mgr, Warren County-Vicksburg Public Library, 700 Veto St, Vicksburg, MS, 39180-3595. Tel: 601-636-6411. Fax: 601-634-4809. p. 1317

Benavides, Marilyn, Dir, Smithfield Public Library, 25 N Main St, Smithfield, UT, 84335-1957. Tel: 435-563-3555. p. 2416

Benavides, Ray, Head, Circ, Coastal Bend College, 3800 Charco Rd, Beeville, TX, 78102-2110. Tel: 361-354-2737, 361-354-2740. Fax: 361-354-2719. p. 2288

Benavides, Roxana, Br Mgr, Brooklyn Public Library, Sunset Park, 5108 Fourth Ave, Brooklyn, NY, 11220. Tel: 718-567-2806. Fax: 718-567-2810. p. 1592

Bend, Evan, Electronic Res Librn, Outagamie Waupaca Library System, 225 N Oneida, Appleton, WI, 54911-4780. Tel: 920-832-6190. Fax: 920-832-6422. p. 2578

Benda, Chris, Ref & Info Serv, Vanderbilt University, Divinity Library, 419 21st Ave S, Nashville, TN, 37203-2427. Tel: 615-322-2865. Fax: 615-343-8279. p. 2260

Bendall, Teresa, Head Librn, Alberta Government Library, South Tower, 3rd Flr, 10030 107th St, Edmonton, AB, T5J 3E4, CANADA. Tel: 780-427-7272. Fax: 780-422-3980. p. 2698

Bender, Andrea, Head, Tech Serv, Williams & Connolly Library, 725 12th St NW, Washington, DC, 20005. Tel: 202-434-5319. Fax: 202-434-5029. p. 423

Bender, Carla, Librn, NASA Dryden Flight Research Center, 4825 Lilly Ave M/S 2412, Edwards AFB, CA, 93523. Tel: 661-276-3702. Fax: 661-276-2244. p. 144

Bender, Elizabeth, Ch, Leonia Public Library, 227 Fort Lee Rd, Leonia, NJ, 07605. Tel: 201-592-5777. Fax: 201-592-5775. p. 1495

Bender, Helen, Librn, Boston Public Library, West End, 151 Cambridge St, Boston, MA, 02114-2704. Tel: 617-523-3957. Fax: 617-723-1621. p. 1057

Bender, Nathan E, Tech Serv Librn, Albany County Public Library, 310 S Eighth St, Laramie, WY, 82070-3969. Tel: 307-721-2580. Fax: 307-721-2584. p. 2657

Bender, Sandra, Librn, Wapiti Regional Library, Archerwill Public Library, First Ave, Archerwill, SK, S0E 0B0, CANADA. Tel: 306-323-2128. p. 2921

Bender, Thomas B, IV, Ref Outreach Librn, Xavier University of Louisiana, One Drexel Dr, New Orleans, LA, 70125-1098. Tel: 504-520-5292. Fax: 504-520-7940. p. 964

Bender, Trudy, Head Librn, Northland Pioneer College Libraries, PO Box 610, Holbrook, AZ, 86025. Tel: 928-524-7324. p. 65

Bendix, Linda, Dir, Frank L Weyenberg Library of Mequon-Thiensville, 11345 N Cedarburg Rd, Mequon, WI, 53092-1998. Tel: 262-242-2593. Fax: 262-478-3200. p. 2615

Bendixon, Conrad w, Evening Ref (Info Serv), Saint Ambrose University Library, 518 W Locust St, Davenport, IA, 52803. Tel: 563-333-6473. Fax: 563-333-6248. p. 807

Bendlin, Chrissy, Dir, Hot Springs County Library, 344 Arapahoe, Thermopolis, WY, 82443-0951. Tel: 307-864-3104. Fax: 307-864-5416. p. 2661

Bendroth, Margaret Lamberts, Dr, Exec Dir, American Congregational Association, 14 Beacon St, 2nd Flr, Boston, MA, 02108-9999. Tel: 617-523-0470. Fax: 617-523-0491. p. 1054

Benedetti, Jo-Ann, Adult Serv, Info Serv, Outreach Serv Librn, Upper Hudson Library System, 28 Essex St, Albany, NY, 12206. Tel: 518-437-9880, Ext 225. Fax: 518-437-9884. p. 1571

Benedetto Beals, Jennifer, Dept Head, University of Tennessee, Knoxville, Special Collections, 121 Hodges Library, 1015 Volunteer Blvd, Knoxville, TN, 37996-1000. Tel: 865-974-4480. p. 2244

Benedetto, Robert, Dir, Graduate Theological Union Library, 2400 Ridge Rd, Berkeley, CA, 94709. Tel: 510-649-2540. Fax: 510-649-2508. p. 126

Benedict, Debbie A, Dir, Meagher County City Library, 15 First Ave SE, White Sulphur Springs, MT, 59645. Tel: 406-547-2250. Fax: 406-547-3691. p. 1390

Benedict, Jeanne, Dir, Henry D Moore Library, 22 Village Rd, Steuben, ME, 04680. Tel: 207-546-7301. p. 1003

Benedict, Kay, Archivist, Casa Grande Valley Historical Society, 110 W Florence Blvd, Casa Grande, AZ, 85122. Tel: 520-836-2223. p. 59

Benedict, Leann, Asst Dir, Tech Serv, Saint Charles Parish Library, 160 W Campus Dr, Destrehan, LA, 70047. Tel: 985-764-2366. Fax: 985-764-0447. p. 948

Benedict, Mary Jane, Librn, Speed Art Museum Library, 2035 S Third St, Louisville, KY, 40208. Tel: 502-634-2710. Fax: 502-636-2899. p. 925

Benedicta, Amanda, Dir, Watervliet Public Library, 1501 Broadway, Watervliet, NY, 12189-2895. Tel: 518-274-4471. Fax: 518-271-0667. p. 1764

Benefiel, Edward, Librn, Gordon, Arata, McCollam, Duplantis & Egan LLP, 201 Saint Charles Ave, Ste 4000, New Orleans, LA, 70170. Tel: 504-582-1111, Ext 4039. Fax: 504-582-1121. p. 960

Benekin, Vanessa, Br Mgr, Jersey City Free Public Library, Lafayette, 307 Pacific Ave, Jersey City, NJ, 07304. Tel: 201-547-5017. Fax: 201-547-5878. p. 1492

Benetz, E Steven, Dept Head, Dir, Div Head, Eustis Memorial Library, 120 N Center St, Eustis, FL, 32726-3598. Tel: 352-357-5686. Fax: 352-357-5450. p. 439

Benford, Heidi, Acq Asst, Clayton State University, 2000 Clayton State Blvd, Morrow, GA, 30260. Tel: 678-466-4328. Fax: 678-466-4349. p. 545

Benford, Jennie, Univ Archivist, Carnegie Mellon University, Hunt Library, 4909 Frew St, Pittsburgh, PA, 15213-3890. Tel: 412-268-7402. Fax: 412-268-2793. p. 2123

Bengel, Tricia, Emerging Technologies Adminr, Nashville Public Library, 615 Church St, Nashville, TN, 37219-2314. Tel: 615-862-5760. Fax: 615-862-5771. p. 2257

Benggio, Leesa, Dir, Organizational Res, South Carolina State Library, 1430-1500 Senate St, Columbia, SC, 29201. Tel: 803-734-8668. Fax: 803-734-8676. p. 2189

Bengston, Carl, Dean, Libr/Learning Res Ctr, Cerritos College Library, 11110 Alondra Blvd, Norwalk, CA, 90650. Tel: 562-860-2451, Ext 2430. Fax: 562-467-5002. p. 195

Bengston, Marge, Head, Ch, Emma S Clark Memorial Library, 120 Main St, Setauket, NY, 11733-2868. Tel: 631-941-4080. Fax: 631-941-4541. p. 1742

Bengtson, Ardell, Tech Serv, Dakota County Library System, 1340 Wescott Rd, Eagan, MN, 55123-1099. Tel: 651-450-2937. Fax: 651-450-2915. p. 1249

Bengtson, Jason, Pres, Linn County Library Consortium, Russell D Cole Library, 620 3rd St SW, Mount Vernon, IA, 52314-1012. Tel: 319-895-4259. p. 2943

Bengtson, Jonathan, Dir, Libr & Archives, University of Toronto Libraries, John M Kelly Library, University of Saint Michael's College, 113 Saint Joseph St, Toronto, ON, M5S 1J4, CANADA. Tel: 416-926-7114. Fax: 416-926-7262. p. 2866

Bengtson, Jonathan, Dir, Libr & Archives, University of Toronto Libraries, Pontifical Institute for Mediaeval Studies, 113 Saint Joseph St, Toronto, ON, M5S 1J4, CANADA. Tel: 416-926-7146. Fax: 416-926-7262. p. 2867

Benham, Virginia, Br Librn, Moundsville-Marshall County Public Library, Benwood-McMechen Public, 201 Marshall St, McMechen, WV, 26040. Tel: 304-232-9720. Fax: 304-232-9720. p. 2567

Benitez-Sharpless, Mercedes, Br Librn, Cataloger/Ref Librn, Coll Develop, Lafayette College, Kirby Library of Government & Law, Kirby Hall of Civil Rights, 716 Sullivan Rd, Easton, PA, 18042-1780. Tel: 610-330-5398. Fax: 610-330-5397. p. 2052

Benjamin, Audrey, Dir, Devon Public Library, 101, 17 Athabasca Ave, Devon, AB, T9G 1G5, CANADA. Tel: 780-987-3720. p. 2696

Benjamin, Carolyn, Head, Tech Serv, Wilton Library Association, 137 Old Ridgefield Rd, Wilton, CT, 06897-3019. Tel: 203-762-3950. Fax: 203-834-1166. p. 378

Benjamin, Elfrieda, Asst Librn, Windham Public Library, Church & Main Sts, Windham, NY, 12496. Tel: 518-734-4405. Fax: 518-734-4405. p. 1770

Benjamin, Harriet, Commun Libr Mgr, Queens Borough Public Library, Jackson Heights Community Library, 35-51 81st St, Jackson Heights, NY, 11372. Tel: 718-899-2500. Fax: 718-899-7003. p. 1644

Benjamin, Marian, Tech Serv, Mansfield-Richland County Public Library, 43 W Third St, Mansfield, OH, 44902-1295. Tel: 419-521-3134. Fax: 419-525-4750. p. 1912

Benjamin, Marianne, Librn, Anti-Defamation League, 605 Third Ave, New York, NY, 10158. Tel: 212-885-5844, 212-885-7823. Fax: 212-885-5882. p. 1669

Benjaminsen, Linda, Tech Serv, Framingham Public Library, 49 Lexington St, Framingham, MA, 01702-8278. Tel: 508-879-5570, Ext 4319. Fax: 508-820-7210. p. 1090

Benke, Robin P, Dir, Libr Serv, University of Virginia's College at Wise, One College Ave, Wise, VA, 24293. Tel: 276-328-0151. Fax: 276-328-0105. p. 2504

Benko, Karen, Cat Librn, Williams College, 55 Sawyer Library Dr, Williamstown, MA, 01267. Tel: 413-597-4322. Fax: 413-597-4106. p. 1141

Bennedsen, Karin, Pub Serv, Georgia Highlands College Libraries, 3175 Cedartown Hwy SE, Rome, GA, 30161. Tel: 706-295-6318. Fax: 706-295-6365. p. 548

Benner, Ellyn, Ch, Horsham Township Library, 435 Babylon Rd, Horsham, PA, 19044-1224. Tel: 215-443-2609, Ext 206. Fax: 215-443-2697. p. 2069

Benner, Merry Jane, Ch, Shelby Township Library, 51680 Van Dyke, Shelby Township, MI, 48316-4448. Tel: 586-739-7414. Fax: 586-726-0535. p. 1227

Benner, Nancy, Mgr, Montgomery County Public Libraries, Rockville Library, 21 Maryland Ave, Rockville, MD, 20850-2371. Tel: 240-777-0140. Fax: 240-777-0157. p. 1039

Benner, Vickie, Ch, Epsom Public Library, 1775 Dover Rd, Epsom, NH, 03234. Tel: 603-736-9920. Fax: 603-736-9920. p. 1446

Bennet, Hannah, Librn, Princeton University, School of Architecture Library, Architecture Bldg, 2nd Flr, S-204, One Washington Rd, Princeton, NJ, 08544. Tel: 609-258-3256. p. 1524

Bennett, Amanda, Dir, Ada Public Library, 320 N Main St, Ada, OH, 45810-1199. Tel: 419-634-5246. Fax: 419-634-9747. p. 1851

Bennett, Anita, Circ/Reserves Coordr, Northeastern University Libraries, Snell Library, 360 Huntington Ave, Boston, MA, 02115. Tel: 617-373-4646. p. 1065

Bennett, Bernice, Archives, Elizabethtown Community & Technical College Library, 600 College Street Rd, Elizabethtown, KY, 42701. Tel: 270-706-8442. Fax: 270-769-1618. p. 912

Bennett, Carolyn, Info Serv, Tech Coordr, Beatrice Public Library, 100 N 16th St, Beatrice, NE, 68310-4100. Tel: 402-223-3584. Fax: 402-223-3913. p. 1393

Bennett, Cathy, Assoc Dean, Belmont Technical College, 120 Fox-Shannon Pl, Saint Clairsville, OH, 43950-9735. Tel: 740-695-9500, Ext 1019. Fax: 740-695-2247. p. 1933

Bennett, Christopher, Dir, Lake Erie College, 391 W Washington St, Painesville, OH, 44077-3309. Tel: 440-375-7400. p. 1926

Bennett, Connie J, Libr Serv Dir, Eugene Public Library, 100 W Tenth Ave, Eugene, OR, 97401. Tel: 541-682-5450. Fax: 541-682-5898. p. 1996

Bennett, Deborah A, Dir, Caroline County Public Library, 100 Market St, Denton, MD, 21629. Tel: 410-479-1343. Fax: 410-479-1443. p. 1027

Bennett, Delain, Mgr, Huxford Genealogical Society Inc, 101 College Ave, Homerville, GA, 31634. Tel: 912-487-2310. Fax: 912-487-3881. p. 536

Bennett, Diane, Dir, Graves County Public Library, 601 N 17th St, Mayfield, KY, 42066. Tel: 270-247-2911. Fax: 270-247-2991. p. 928

Bennett, Donna S, Head, Pub Serv, Northern Kentucky University, Nunn Dr, Highland Heights, KY, 41099. Tel: 859-572-5715. Fax: 859-572-6529, 859-572-6664. p. 917

Bennett, Dorothee, Libr Tech, Mkt, United States Air Force, 305 W F St, Bldg 278, Eglin AFB, FL, 32542-6842. Tel: 850-882-3462. Fax: 850-882-2621. p. 439

Bennett, Erica, Syst Librn, Fullerton College, 321 E Chapman Ave, Fullerton, CA, 92832-2095. Tel: 714-992-7375. Fax: 714-992-9961. p. 153

Bennett, Faris, Head, Info Serv, Head, Ref, Haverhill Public Library, 99 Main St, Haverhill, MA, 01830-5092. Tel: 978-373-1586. Fax: 978-372-8508. p. 1094

Bennett, Geneva, Asst Librn, Northwest Georgia Regional Library System, Calhoun-Gordon County Library, 100 N Park Ave, Calhoun, GA, 30701. Tel: 706-624-1456. Fax: 706-624-1458. p. 528

Bennett, Jackie, Librn, Bristol Area Library, 619 Old County Rd, Rte 130, Pemaquid, ME, 04558. Tel: 207-677-2115. p. 995

Bennett, Jean E, ILL, Ref Serv, Weatherford Public Library, 1014 Charles St, Weatherford, TX, 76086-5098. Tel: 817-598-4150. Fax: 817-598-4161. p. 2399

Bennett, Jennifer, Mgr, Info Res N Am, National Economic Research Associates, Inc, 360 Hamilton Ave, 10th Flr, White Plains, NY, 10601. Tel: 212-345-2993. Fax: 914-448-4040. p. 1768

Bennett, Jodi, Circ Supvr, Cardinal Stritch University Library, 6801 N Yates Rd, Milwaukee, WI, 53207-3985. Tel: 414-410-4262. Fax: 414-410-4268. p. 2617

Bennett, Jolene, Asst Librn, Elgin Public Library, 214 Main St, Elgin, IA, 52141. Tel: 563-426-5313. Fax: 563-426-5999. p. 814

Bennett, Joseph W, Asst Librn, Library Company of the Baltimore Bar, 100 N Calvert St, Rm 618, Baltimore, MD, 21202-1723. Tel: 410-727-0280. Fax: 410-685-4791. p. 1015

Bennett, Karen, Tech Asst, ILL, Weston Public Library, 56 Norfield Rd, Weston, CT, 06883-2225. Tel: 203-222-2665. Fax: 203-222-2560. p. 377

Bennett, Kathy, Librn, National Automobile, Aerospace & General Workers Union of Canada, 205 Placer Ct, Willowdale, ON, M2H 3H9, CANADA. Tel: 416-497-4110. Fax: 416-495-6552. p. 2871

Bennett, Kay, Br Mgr, Smith County Public Library, Gordonsville Branch, 63 E Main St, Gordonsville, TN, 38563-0217. Tel: 615-683-8063. Fax: 615-683-8063. p. 2226

Bennett, Kelli, Admin Librn, Pike-Amite-Walthall Library System, 1022 Virginia Ave, McComb, MS, 39648. Tel: 601-684-7034, Ext 15. Fax: 601-250-1213. p. 1307

Bennett, Kristen, Head of Libr, Volusia County Public Library, Edgewater Public, 103 Indian River Blvd, Edgewater, FL, 32132. Tel: 386-424-2916. Fax: 386-424-2918. p. 436

Bennett, Laura, Dir, Blanding Public Library, 124 Bay State Rd, Rehoboth, MA, 02769. Tel: 508-252-4236. Fax: 508-252-5834. p. 1120

Bennett, Linda, Dir, Phillips-Lee-Monroe Regional Library, 623 Pecan St, Helena, AR, 72342. Tel: 870-338-3537. Fax: 870-338-8855. p. 103

Bennett, Linda, Chief Librn, Department of Veterans Affairs, 1481 W Tenth St, Indianapolis, IN, 46202. Tel: 317-554-0000. Fax: 317-988-4846. p. 750

Bennett, Linda, Br Mgr, Stark County District Library, DeHoff Memorial Branch, 216 Hartford Ave SE, Canton, OH, 44707. Tel: 330-452-9014. Fax: 330-452-8224. p. 1864

Bennett, Linda, Libr Dir, Grove City Community Library, 125 W Main St, Grove City, PA, 16127-1569. Tel: 724-458-7320. Fax: 724-458-7332. p. 2063

Bennett, Linda L, Dir, Roy Row, Sr & Imogene Row Johns Library, 2005 White Dr, Batesville, AR, 72501. Tel: 870-612-2020. p. 94

Bennett, Mary, Spec Coll Librn, State Historical Society of Iowa, 402 Iowa Ave, Iowa City, IA, 52240-1806. Tel: 319-335-3916. Fax: 319-335-3935. p. 823

Bennett, Melissa, Legis Librn, Saskatchewan Legislative Library, 234-2405 Legislative Dr, Regina, SK, S4S 0B3, CANADA. Tel: 306-787-2276. Fax: 306-787-5856. p. 2924

Bennett, Michelle, Br Mgr, Atlanta-Fulton Public Library System, Adamsville-Collier Heights, 3424 Martin Luther King Dr, Atlanta, GA, 30331. Tel: 404-699-4206. Fax: 404-699-6380. p. 511

Bennett, Miranda, Prog Dir, Coll, University of Houston, M D Anderson Library, 114 University Libraries, Houston, TX, 77204-2000. Tel: 713-743-9800. Fax: 713-743-9811. p. 2343

Bennett, Nancy, Bus & Human Res Mgr, Brandon Township Public Library, 304 South St, Ortonville, MI, 48462. Tel: 248-627-1460. Fax: 248-627-9880. p. 1215

Bennett, Nancy, Br Mgr, Camden County Library System, South County Regional Branch, 35 Coopers Folly Rd, Atco, NJ, 08004. Tel: 856-753-2537, Ext 4404. Fax: 856-753-7289. p. 1539

Bennett, Pamela D, Ch, Laurens County Library, 1017 W Main St, Laurens, SC, 29360. Tel: 864-681-7323. Fax: 864-681-0598. p. 2199

Bennett, Pamela S, Dep Dir, Pub Serv Librn, United States Army, Combined Arms Research Library, US Army Command & General Staff College, Eisenhower Hall, 250 Gibbon Ave, Fort Leavenworth, KS, 66027-2314. Tel: 913-758-3058. Fax: 913-758-3014. p. 867

Bennett, Pat, Tech Serv Mgr, Everett Public Library, 2702 Hoyt Ave, Everett, WA, 98201-3556. Tel: 425-257-8019. Fax: 425-257-8017. p. 2515

Bennett, Phyllis, Librn, Preble County District Library, Brooke-Gould Memorial, 301 N Barron St, Eaton, OH, 45320-1705. Tel: 937-456-4331. Fax: 937-456-4774. p. 1897

Bennett, Regina, Circ, Satilla Regional Library, 200 S Madison Ave, Ste D, Douglas, GA, 31533. Tel: 912-384-4667. Fax: 912-389-4365. p. 530

Bennett, Rich, Chair, Spec & Area Studies Coll, University of Florida Libraries, 535 Library W, Gainesville, FL, 32611-7000. Tel: 352-273-2592. Fax: 352-846-2746. p. 449

Bennett, Ricki, ILL, Gadsden County Public Library, 7325 Pat Thomas Pkwy, Quincy, FL, 32351. Tel: 850-627-7106. Fax: 850-627-7775. p. 485

Bennett, Roxane, Dir, Fox River Valley Public Library District, 555 Barrington Ave, Dundee, IL, 60118-1496. Tel: 847-428-3661. Fax: 847-428-0521. p. 637

Bennett, Sarah, Mgr, Libr Serv, Sullivan & Worcester, LLP, One Post Office Sq, Boston, MA, 02109. Tel: 617-338-2800. Fax: 617-338-2880. p. 1067

Bennett, Sherry, Tech Serv Supvr, California State University, 9001 Stockdale Hwy, Bakersfield, CA, 93311-1022. Tel: 661-654-3254. Fax: 661-654-6910. p. 123

Bennett, Shirley, Libr Mgr, Clearfield County Public Library, Curwensville Branch, 601 Beech St, Curwensville, PA, 16833. Tel: 814-236-0355. Fax: 814-236-3620. p. 2048

Bennett, Sonia, Dir, Saint Joseph's University, Campbell Library, Mandeville Hall, 5600 City Ave, Philadelphia, PA, 19131. Tel: 610-660-1195. Fax: 610-660-1604. p. 2116

Bennett, Stacey, Librn, East Central Arkansas Regional Library, Cherry Valley Branch, 166 Hwy 1B, Cherry Valley, AR, 72324-8704. Tel: 870-588-3323. Fax: 870-588-4311. p. 117

Bennett, Steven, II, Law Librn, Vandalia Correctional Center Library, Rte 51 N, Vandalia, IL, 62471. Tel: 618-283-4170. p. 714

Bennett, Sue, Coordr, Texas Navigator Group, PO Box 12927, Austin, TX, 78711. Tel: 512-463-5406. Fax: 512-936-2306. p. 2956

Bennett, Susan, Dir, Lexington Historical Society, Inc, 1332 Massachusetts Ave, Lexington, MA, 02420-3809. Tel: 781-862-1703. Fax: 781-862-4920. p. 1099

Bennett, Swannee, Curator, Dep Dir, Historic Arkansas Museum Library, 200 E Third St, Little Rock, AR, 72201-1608. Tel: 501-324-9395. Fax: 501-324-9345. p. 106

Bennett, Theresa, Dir, Webster Public Library, Webster Plaza, 980 Ridge Rd, Webster, NY, 14580. Tel: 585-872-7075. p. 1765

Bennett, Thomas C, Dir, Prince Memorial Library, 266 Main St, Cumberland, ME, 04021-9754. Tel: 207-829-2216. Fax: 207-829-2221. p. 982

Bennett, Tom D, Curator, Alaska Heritage Museum & Library at Wells Fargo, 301 W Northern Lights Blvd, K3212-051, Anchorage, AK, 99503. Tel: 907-265-2834. Fax: 907-265-2860. p. 43

Bennett, Valerie, Curator, O Henry Museum Library, 409 E Fifth St, Austin, TX, 78701. Tel: 512-472-1903. Fax: 512-472-7102. p. 2280

Bennett, Vivian, Librn, Snow Lake Community Library, PO Box 760, Snow Lake, MB, R0B 1M0, CANADA. Tel: 204-358-2322. Fax: 204-358-2116. p. 2752

Bennett, Wanda, Dir, Ladoga-Clark Township Public Library, 128 E Main St, Ladoga, IN, 47954. Tel: 765-942-2456. Fax: 765-942-2457. p. 759

Bennett-Brown, Mary, Dir, Human Res, Public Library of Cincinnati & Hamilton County, 800 Vine St, Cincinnati, OH, 45202-2009. Tel: 513-369-6968. Fax: 513-369-6993. p. 1871

Bennick, Walter, Archivist, Winona County Historical Society, 160 Johnson St, Winona, MN, 55987. Tel: 507-454-2723. Fax: 507-454-0006. p. 1290

Bennin, Cheryl, Dir, Sarah Hull Hallock Free Library, 56-58 Main St, Milton, NY, 12547. Tel: 845-795-2200. Fax: 845-795-1005. p. 1661

Benning, Susan, Br Mgr, Alamance County Public Libraries, May Memorial Library, 342 S Spring St, Burlington, NC, 27215. Tel: 336-229-3588. Fax: 336-229-3592. p. 1779

Benninger, Fran, Asst Librn, Pamlico County Library, 603 Main St, Bayboro, NC, 28515. Tel: 252-745-3515. Fax: 252-745-3847. p. 1776

Benninger, Lynda, Br Coordr, Bruce County Public Library, Teeswater Branch, Two Clinton St S, Teeswater, ON, N0G 2S0, CANADA. Tel: 519-392-6801. Fax: 519-392-6801. p. 2837

Benningfield, Rose, Ch, Powell County Public Library, 725 Breckenridge St, Stanton, KY, 40380. Tel: 606-663-4511. Fax: 606-663-4346. p. 936

Beno, Henry, Res, Fox Valley Technical College, 1825 N Bluemound Dr, Appleton, WI, 54914. Tel: 920-735-5747. Fax: 920-735-4870. p. 2578

Beno, Julie, Br Supvr, Lincoln City Libraries, South Branch, 2675 South St, Lincoln, NE, 68502-3099. Tel: 402-441-8535. Fax: 402-441-8572. p. 1405

Benoit, Emilie, Fac Serv, Ref, Roger Williams University, Ten Metacom Ave, Bristol, RI, 02809-5171. Tel: 401-254-4687. Fax: 401-254-4543. p. 2163

Benoit, Gerald, Assoc Prof, Simmons College, 300 The Fenway, Boston, MA, 02115. Tel: 617-521-2800. Fax: 617-521-3192. p. 2967

Benoit, Greg, Libr Dir, Gates Public Library, 902 Elmgrove Rd, Rochester, NY, 14624. Tel: 585-247-6446. Fax: 585-426-5733. p. 1729

Benoit, Greg, Adult Serv, Webster Public Library, Webster Plaza, 980 Ridge Rd, Webster, NY, 14580. Tel: 585-872-7075. p. 1765

Benoit, Katrina, Librn, Acadia Parish Library, Estherwood Branch, 116 N LeBlanc St, Estherwood, LA, 70534. Tel: 337-785-1090. p. 948

Benoit, Katrina, Librn, Acadia Parish Library, Mermentau Branch, 107 Second St, Mermentau, LA, 70556. Tel: 318-824-0690. Fax: 318-824-0690. p. 948

Benoit, Kristine, Ch, Saint Johns County Public Library System, 6670 US 1 South, Saint Augustine, FL, 32086. Tel: 904-827-6912. p. 486

Benoit, Manon, Circ, Cegep St Jean Sur Richelieu Bibliotheque, 30 boul du Seminaire, CP 1018, Saint-Jean-Sur-Richelieu, QC, J3B 7B1, CANADA. Tel: 450-347-5301, Ext 2333. Fax: 450-347-3329, 450-358-9350. p. 2911

Benoit, Margaret, Tech Serv, Holmes Public Library, 470 Plymouth St, Halifax, MA, 02338. Tel: 781-293-2271. Fax: 781-294-8518. p. 1093

Benoit, Robin, Ch, Fairport Public Library, One Fairport Village Landing, Fairport, NY, 14450. Tel: 585-223-9091, Fax: 585-223-3998. p. 1621

Benolken, Julie, Ref, Inver Hills Community College Library, 2500 80th St E, Inver Grove Heights, MN, 55076-3209. Tel: 651-450-8622. Fax: 651-450-3679. p. 1254

Benoun, Kathleen, Libr Assoc, Washington State Library, Western State Hospital Branch, 9601 Steilacoom Blvd SW, WSH 08-300, W27-19, Tacoma, WA, 98498-7213. Tel: 253-756-2593. Fax: 253-756-3970. p. 2545

Benoy, Eric, Coll Develop Librn, Media Librn, Ref Librn, New Orleans Baptist Theological Seminary, 4110 Seminary Pl, New Orleans, LA, 70126. Tel: 504-282-4455, Ext 3336. Fax: 504-816-8429. p. 961

Benoy, Eric, Dir, New Orleans Baptist Theological Seminary, Martin Music Library, 4110 Seminary Pl, New Orleans, LA, 70126. Tel: 504-282-4455, Ext 3289. Fax: 504-816-8429. p. 961

Benrubi, Deborah, Cat, University of San Francisco, 2130 Fulton St, San Francisco, CA, 94117-1080. Tel: 415-422-5672. Fax: 415-422-5949. p. 248

Bensen, Donna, Br Mgr, Gloucester County Library System, 389 Wolfert Station Rd, Mullica Hill, NJ, 08062. Tel: 856-223-6014. Fax: 856-223-6039. p. 1507

Bensen, Mary Lynne, Head, Ref & Instruction, State University of New York, College at Oneonta, 108 Ravine Pkwy, Oneonta, NY, 13820. Tel: 607-436-2729. Fax: 607-436-3081. p. 1711

Benshoff, Kristine, Adult Serv, Cabarrus County Public Library, 27 Union St N, Concord, NC, 28025-4793. Tel: 704-920-2050. Fax: 704-784-3822. p. 1785

Bensing, Karen McNally, Librn, Benjamin Rose Library, 11900 Fairhill Rd, Cleveland, OH, 44120. Tel: 216-373-1682. Fax: 216-373-1813. p. 1881

Bensinger, Gina, ILL, Pottsville Free Public Library, 215 W Market St, Pottsville, PA, 17901-4304. Tel: 570-622-8105, 570-622-8880. Fax: 570-622-2157. p. 2131

Bensinger, Susanne, Librn, Elsie Public Library, 145 W Main St, Elsie, MI, 48831. Tel: 989-862-4633. Fax: 989-862-4633. p. 1176

Benskin, Sheryl, Libr Asst, North Valley Public Library, 208 Main St, Stevensville, MT, 59870. Tel: 406-777-5061. Fax: 406-777-5061. p. 1388

Bensley, Ruth, Circ, The Morristown & Morris Township Library, One Miller Rd, Morristown, NJ, 07960. Tel: 973-538-6161. Fax: 973-267-4064. p. 1505

Benson, Allen, Dr, Libr Dir, United States Naval War College Library, 686 Cushing Rd, Newport, RI, 02841-1207. Tel: 401-841-2641. Fax: 401-841-6491. p. 2169

Benson, Bill, Ref, United States Air Force, Air Force Research Laboratory, Wright Research Site Technical Library, Det 1 AFRL/WSC, Bldg 642, Rm 1300, 2950 Hobson Way, Wright-Patterson AFB, OH, 45433-7765. Tel: 937-255-5511, Ext 4267. Fax: 937-656-7746. p. 1951

Benson, Carol, Librn, Ref, Oakland Community College, 739 S Washington, Bldg C, Royal Oak, MI, 48067-3898. Tel: 248-246-2528. Fax: 248-246-2520. p. 1223

Benson, Cecilia, Librn, Bull Shoals Library, 1218 Central Blvd, Bull Shoals, AR, 72619. Tel: 870-445-4265. p. 96

Benson, Cherese, Assoc Librn, PPG Industries, Inc, Technical Information Center, 4325 Rosanna Dr, Allison Park, PA, 15101. Tel: 412-492-5443. Fax: 412-492-5509. p. 2128

Benson, James, Dean of Libr, Saint John's University Library, 8000 Utopia Pkwy, Queens, NY, 11439. Tel: 718-990-6735. Fax: 718-380-0353. p. 1725

Benson, Joseph Fred, Archivist, Missouri Supreme Court Library, Supreme Court Bldg, 207 W High St, Jefferson City, MO, 65101. Tel: 573-751-8752. Fax: 573-751-2573. p. 1335

Benson, Karl, Dir, Boyle County Public Library, 1857 S Danville Bypass, Danville, KY, 40422. Tel: 859-236-8466. Fax: 859-236-7692. p. 911

Benson, Kathryn, Dir, Maxwell Memorial Library, 14 Genesee St, Camillus, NY, 13031. Tel: 315-672-3661. Fax: 315-672-5514. p. 1600

Benson, Mandy, Dir, First Baptist Church Library, 1021 Hennepin Ave, Minneapolis, MN, 55403. Tel: 612-332-3651. Fax: 612-332-3661. p. 1259

Benson, Mary, Librn, Pearl River Community College, Forest County Center Library, 5448 US Hwy 49 S, Hattiesburg, MS, 39401. Tel: 601-554-5522. Fax: 601-554-5470. p. 1312

Benson, Mary Ellen, Dept Head, Librn, Community College of Allegheny County, 595 Beatty Rd, Monroeville, PA, 15146. Tel: 724-325-6713. Fax: 724-325-6696. p. 2091

Benson, Mary Margaret, Coll Develop, Tech Serv, Linfield College, 900 S Baker St, McMinnville, OR, 97128. Tel: 503-883-2263. Fax: 503-883-2566. p. 2005

Benson, Paula, Mgr, Edmonton Public Library, Capilano, 201 Capilano Mall, 5004-98 Ave, Edmonton, AB, T6A 0A1, CANADA. Tel: 780-496-1802. Fax: 780-496-7009. p. 2700

Benson, Peter, Dir, Saranac Lake Free Library, 109 Main St, Saranac Lake, NY, 12983. Tel: 518-891-4190. Fax: 518-891-5931. p. 1738

Benson, Robert, Ref, Roane State Community College Library, 276 Patton Lane, Harriman, TN, 37748. Tel: 865-354-4254. Fax: 865-882-4562. p. 2236

Benson, Sarah, Head Librn, Saskatoon Theol Union Libr, College of Emmanuel & St Chad Library, 114 Seminary Crescent, Saskatoon, SK, S7N 0X3, CANADA. Tel: 306-975-1554. Fax: 306-934-2683. p. 2925

Benson, Sarah, Head Librn, Saskatoon Theol Union Libr, Saint Andrew's College Library, 1121 College Dr, Saskatoon, SK, S7N 0W3, CANADA. Tel: 306-966-8983. Fax: 306-966-8981. p. 2926

Benson, Sheryl, Libr Tech - ILL, Alamosa Public Library, 300 Hunt Ave, Alamosa, CO, 81101. Tel: 719-589-6592, Ext 2538. Fax: 719-589-3786. p. 287

Benson, Steve, Dir of Libr Serv, Richardson Public Library, 900 Civic Center Dr, Richardson, TX, 75080. Tel: 972-744-4350. Fax: 972-744-5806. p. 2374

Benson, Toni, Genealogy Librn, Local Hist Librn, Van Buren District Library, 200 N Phelps St, Decatur, MI, 49045-1086. Tel: 269-423-4771. Fax: 269-423-8373. p. 1168

Bent, Jeff, ILL, Sonnenschein, Nath & Rosenthal, 8000 Sears Tower, 233 S Wacker Dr, Ste 7800, Chicago, IL, 60606-6404. Tel: 312-876-8000. Fax: 312-876-7934. p. 625

Bent, Nancy, Ref, La Grange Public Library, Ten W Cossitt Ave, La Grange, IL, 60525. Tel: 708-352-0576. p. 662

Bente, Heather, Dir, Waterville Public Library, 82 Main St, Waterville, IA, 52170. Tel: 563-535-7295. Fax: 563-535-7030. p. 850

Bentley, Barbara J, Mgr, Cummings & Lockwood, Six Landmark Sq, Stamford, CT, 06901. Tel: 203-351-4375. Fax: 203-708-3847. p. 369

Bentley, Chantelle, Br Mgr, Campbell County Public Library District, Newport Branch, 901 E Sixth St, Newport, KY, 41071. Tel: 859-572-5035. Fax: 859-572-5036. p. 909

Bentley, Chantelle, Br Mgr, Clermont County Public Library, Felicity Branch, 209 Prather Rd, Felicity, OH, 45120. Tel: 513-876-4134. Fax: 513-876-3619. p. 1858

Bentley, Chantelle, Br Mgr, Clermont County Public Library, Williamsburg Branch, 594 Main St, Williamsburg, OH, 45176. Tel: 513-724-1070. Fax: 513-724-5549. p. 1858

Bentley, Cynthia, Coordr, Circ, George Mason University Libraries, Johnson Center, 4400 University Dr, MSN 1A6, Fairfax, VA, 22030-4444. Tel: 703-993-9057. Fax: 703-993-9063. p. 2462

Bentley, Dona, Prof, User Serv Librn, University of La Verne, 2040 Third St, La Verne, CA, 91750. Tel: 909-593-3511, Ext 4305. Fax: 909-392-2733. p. 162

Bentley, Jane, Librn, San Diego Museum of Man, Balboa Park, 1350 El Prado, San Diego, CA, 92101. Tel: 619-239-2001. Fax: 619-239-2749. p. 235

Bentley, Lynne, Dir, Humber College, 205 Humber College Blvd, Toronto, ON, M9W 5L7, CANADA. Tel: 416-675-4574. Fax: 416-675-7439. p. 2854

Bentley, Margaret, Librn, Moretown Memorial Library, 897 Rte 100-B, Moretown, VT, 05660-9120. Tel: 802-496-9728. p. 2429

Bentley, Margaret Ann, Adult Serv, Asst Dir, Shiawassee District Library, 502 W Main St, Owosso, MI, 48867-2607. Tel: 989-725-5134. Fax: 989-723-5444. p. 1216

Bentley, Peggy, Librn, Letcher County Public Libraries, Jenkins Public, 9543 Hwy 805, Jenkins, KY, 41537. Tel: 606-832-4101. Fax: 606-832-0040. p. 937

Bentley, Sara A, Ch, Field Library of Peekskill, Four Nelson Ave, Peekskill, NY, 10566-2138. Tel: 914-737-1212. Fax: 914-862-9710. p. 1716

Benton, Bleue J, Coll Develop Mgr, Oak Park Public Library, 834 Lake St, Oak Park, IL, 60301. Tel: 708-383-8200. Fax: 708-697-6900. p. 684

Benton, Chad, Syst Adminr, Columbus County Public Library, 407 N Powell Blvd, Whiteville, NC, 28472. Tel: 910-642-3116. Fax: 910-642-3839. p. 1829

Benton, Chris, Circ Serv Librn, Elon University, 308 N O'Kelly Ave, Elon, NC, 27244-0187. Tel: 336-278-6593. Fax: 336-278-6637. p. 1791

Benton, Kimshiro, Youth Serv, James Kennedy Public Library, 320 First Ave E, Dyersville, IA, 52040. Tel: 563-875-8912. Fax: 563-875-6162. p. 812

Benton, Susan, Asst Librn, Avon Park Public Library, 100 N Museum Ave, Avon Park, FL, 33825. Tel: 863-452-3803. Fax: 863-452-3809. p. 426

Bents, Stephanie, Digital Librn, Emerging Tech Librn, Rapid City Public Library, 610 Quincy St, Rapid City, SD, 57701-3630. Tel: 605-394-6139. Fax: 605-394-4064. p. 2217

Benzing, Matt, Info Tech Librn, Rensselaer Libraries, Rensselaer Polytechnic Inst, 110 Eighth St, Troy, NY, 12180-3590. Tel: 518-276-8300. Fax: 518-276-2044. p. 1756

Beppu, Suzanne, Coordr, Libr Serv, McMinnville Public Library, 225 NW Adams St, McMinnville, OR, 97128-5425. Tel: 503-435-5557. Fax: 503-435-5560. p. 2005

Bequillard, Lisa, Acq of New Ser, ILL, Licia & Mason Beekley Community Library, Ten Central Ave, New Hartford, CT, 06057. Tel: 860-379-7235. Fax: 860-379-5806. p. 355

Berard, Carole A, Asst Libr Dir, Canton Free Library, Eight Park St, Canton, NY, 13617. Tel: 315-386-3712. Fax: 315-386-4131. p. 1602

Berard, G Lynn, Principal Librn, Carnegie Mellon University, Engineering & Science Library, 4400 Wean Hall, Pittsburgh, PA, 15213-3890. Tel: 412-268-2426. Fax: 412-681-1998. p. 2123

Berard, Sue Ann, Dir, Northwood University, 2600 N Military Trail, West Palm Beach, FL, 33409-2911. Tel: 561-478-5537. Fax: 561-697-3138. p. 502

Berberette, Pamela, Libr Assoc, Mississippi State University, Jackson Architecture, 509 E Capitol St, Jackson, MS, 39201. Tel: 601-354-6184. Fax: 601-354-6481. p. 1309

Berberian, Kristine, Dir, Vernon Free Public Library, 567 Governor Hunt Rd, Vernon, VT, 05354-9484. Tel: 802-257-0150. Fax: 802-257-4949. p. 2437

Berberich, Jeremy, Librn, Gateway Community & Technical College, Boone Campus Library, 500 Technology Way, Rm 125, Florence, KY, 41042. Tel: 859-442-1682. p. 911

Bercier, Carolyn, Dep Dir, Gallier House Library, 1132 Royal St, New Orleans, LA, 70116. Tel: 504-525-5661. Fax: 504-568-9735. p. 960

Bercier, Carolyn, Dep Dir, Hermann-Grima House Library, 820 Saint Louis St, New Orleans, LA, 70112. Tel: 504-525-5661. Fax: 504-568-9735. p. 960

Berdish, Laura, Ref Serv Librn, University of Michigan, Kresge Business Administration Library, Stephen M Ross School of Business, 701 Tappan St, K3330, Ann Arbor, MI, 48109-1234. Tel: 734-763-9360. Fax: 734-764-3839. p. 1152

Berecka, Alan, Ref Librn, Del Mar College, 101 Baldwin Blvd, Corpus Christi, TX, 78404. Tel: 361-698-1310. Fax: 361-698-1182. p. 2302

Berenbaum, Maria A, Acq, Florida Atlantic University, 777 Glades Rd, Boca Raton, FL, 33431. Tel: 561-297-2134. Fax: 561-297-2189. p. 428

Berent, Cheryl, Ref, Mount Vernon Public Library, 28 S First Ave, Mount Vernon, NY, 10550. Tel: 914-668-1840. Fax: 914-668-1018. p. 1664

Berent, Joanne, Ref Librn/Trainer, Gowling Lafleur Henderson LLP, One First Canadian Pl, 100 King St W, Ste 1600, Toronto, ON, M5X 1G5, CANADA. Tel: 416-862-4354. Fax: 416-862-7661. p. 2854

Bereolos, Demetrius, Libr Spec, Tulsa Community College Learning Resources Center, West Campus Library, 7505 W 41st St, Tulsa, OK, 74107-8633. Tel: 918-595-8093. Fax: 918-595-8016. p. 1984

Berescik, Susan, Dir, East Hampton Public Library, 105 Main St, East Hampton, CT, 06424. Tel: 860-267-6621. Fax: 860-267-4427. p. 337

Berezansky, Stephen, Automation Librn, Syst Adminr, Haverhill Public Library, 99 Main St, Haverhill, MA, 01830-5092. Tel: 978-373-1586. Fax: 978-372-8508. p. 1094

Bereznay, Lucinda, Br Mgr, Cuyahoga County Public Library, Brooklyn Branch, 4480 Ridge Rd, Brooklyn, OH, 44144-3353. Tel: 216-398-4600. Fax: 216-398-1545. p. 1927

Berezovsky, Lori, Head, Outreach Serv, Salina Public Library, 301 W Elm St, Salina, KS, 67401. Tel: 785-825-4624. Fax: 785-823-0706. p. 893

Berezovsky, Nick, Head of Acq/Cataloging, Salina Public Library, 301 W Elm St, Salina, KS, 67401. Tel: 785-825-4624. Fax: 785-823-0706. p. 893

Berg, Barbara, Dir, Juneau Public Libraries, 292 Marine Way, Juneau, AK, 99801. Tel: 907-586-5324. Fax: 907-586-3419. p. 50

Berg, Chanell, Dir, World Evangelism Bible College Library, 8919 World Ministry Ave, Baton Rouge, LA, 70810-9000. Tel: 225-768-3890. Fax: 225-768-4533. p. 945

Berg, Cora, Archivist, Saint Mary's University of Minnesota, 700 Terrace Heights, No 26, Winona, MN, 55987-1399. Tel: 507-457-1563. Fax: 507-457-1565. p. 1289

Berg, Dolores, Circ, Cambria County Library System & District Center, 248 Main St, Johnstown, PA, 15901. Tel: 814-536-5131. Fax: 814-536-6905. p. 2073

Berg, Elaine W, Access Serv Coordr, Austin Peay State University, 601 E College St, Clarksville, TN, 37044. Tel: 931-221-6405. Fax: 931-221-7296. p. 2228

Berg, Heidi, Br Mgr, Nashville Public Library, Bellevue, 650 Colice Jeanne Rd, Nashville, TN, 37221-2811. Tel: 615-862-5854. Fax: 615-862-5758. p. 2257

Berg, Jacob, ILL, Monograms & Journals Acq, Trinity University, 125 Michigan Ave NE, Washington, DC, 20017. Tel: 202-884-9350. Fax: 202-884-9241. p. 417

Berg, Jan, Dir, DeForest Area Public Library, 203 Library St, DeForest, WI, 53532. Tel: 608-846-5482. Fax: 608-846-6875. p. 2588

Berg, Jeanne, Head, Tech Serv, Branch District Library, Ten E Chicago St, Coldwater, MI, 49036-1615. Tel: 517-278-2341. Fax: 517-279-7134. p. 1164

Berg, Jenny, Sr Librn, Ref, McMinnville Public Library, 225 NW Adams St, McMinnville, OR, 97128-5425. Tel: 503-435-5562. Fax: 503-435-5560. p. 2005

Berg, John, Head, Circ & Ref, University of Wisconsin - Platteville, One University Plaza, Platteville, WI, 53818. Tel: 608-342-1355. Fax: 608-342-1645. p. 2630

Berg, Kathy, Librn, Lakeland Library Region, Lashburn Branch, 95 Main St E, Lashburn, SK, S0M 1H0, CANADA. Tel: 306-285-4144. p. 2920

Berg, Lynn, Cat, Tech Serv, New Brunswick Theological Seminary, 21 Seminary Pl, New Brunswick, NJ, 08901-1159. Tel: 732-247-5243. Fax: 732-249-5412. p. 1508

Berg, Peter, Assoc Dir, Spec Coll & Presv, Michigan State University Library, 100 Library, East Lansing, MI, 48824-1048. Tel: 517-884-6396. Fax: 517-532-0487. p. 1175

Berg, Rebecca, Br Mgr, Chicago Public Library, Canaryville, 642 W 43rd St, Chicago, IL, 60609. Tel: 312-747-0644. Fax: 312-747-4167. p. 608

Berg, Richard R, Archivist, The Evangelical & Reformed Historical Society, 555 W James St, Lancaster, PA, 17603. Tel: 717-290-8704. Fax: 717-735-8157. p. 2076

Berg, Richard R, Dir, Lancaster Theological Seminary, 555 W James St, Lancaster, PA, 17603-9967. Tel: 717-290-8704. Fax: 717-393-4254. p. 2077

Berg, Sally, Head Librn, Arizona Department of Corrections - Adult Institutions, 10000 S Wilmot Rd, Tucson, AZ, 85734. Tel: 520-574-0024, Ext 37919. Fax: 520-574-7308. p. 85

Berg, Susan, Dir, Library at the Mariners' Museum, 100 Museum Dr, Newport News, VA, 23606-3759. Tel: 757-581-7780. Fax: 757-591-7310. p. 2480

Berg, Susan, Dir, Libr Media Prog, Wright State University, 421 Allyn Hall, 3640 Colonel Glenn Hwy, Dayton, OH, 45435-0001. Tel: 937-775-4148. Fax: 937-775-4855. p. 2972

Bergamo, Helen, Art Coll Coordr, Wells College, 170 Main St, Aurora, NY, 13026-0500. Tel: 315-364-3351. Fax: 315-364-3412. p. 1576

Bergann, Heinz, Dir, Alamosa Public Library, 300 Hunt Ave, Alamosa, CO, 81101. Tel: 719-589-2105, Ext 2524. Fax: 719-587-3541. p. 287

Bergdorf, Randolph S, Dir, Peninsula Library & Historical Society, 6105 Riverview Rd, Peninsula, OH, 44264. Tel: 330-657-2291. Fax: 330-657-2311. p. 1928

Bergen, Jerri, Pres, American Aviation Historical Society, 15211 Springdale St, Huntington Beach, CA, 92649-1156. Tel: 714-549-4818. Fax: 714-549-3657. p. 158

Bergen, Katrina, Ch, Youth Serv Librn, Dixon Public Library, 230 N First St, Dixon, CA, 95620-3028. Tel: 707-678-5447. Fax: 707-678-3515. p. 140

Berger, Angela, Bus Mgr, Commun Network Mgr, Park Ridge Public Library, 20 S Prospect, Park Ridge, IL, 60068-4188. Tel: 847-720-3202. Fax: 847-825-0001. p. 688

Berger, Annette, Mgr, Libr Serv, National Renewable Energy Laboratory Library, 15013 Denver West Pkwy, Golden, CO, 80401-3305. Tel: 303-275-3023. Fax: 303-275-4222. p. 310

Berger, Cheryl, Libr Tech, Harrington College of Design Library, 200 W Madison St, Chicago, IL, 60606. Tel: 312-697-3318. Fax: 312-697-8115. p. 614

Berger, David O, Dir of Libr Serv, Concordia Seminary Library, 801 Seminary Pl, Saint Louis, MO, 63105-3199. Tel: 314-505-7040. Fax: 314-505-7046. p. 1353

Berger, Edward, Assoc Dir, Rutgers University Libraries, Institute of Jazz Studies, John Cotton Dana Library, 185 University Ave, 4th Flr, Newark, NJ, 07102. Tel: 973-353-5595. Fax: 973-353-5944. p. 1513

Berger, Jane, Ref, Owens Community College Library, 30335 Oregon Rd, Perrysburg, OH, 43551. Tel: 567-661-7223. Fax: 567-661-7021. p. 1929

Berger, Jim, Librn, Pima Community College, 2202 W Anklam Rd, Tucson, AZ, 85709-0001. Tel: 520-206-6821. Fax: 520-206-3059. p. 86

Berger, Joyce, Librn, Survival Research Foundation Library, 1000 Island Blvd, Ste 512, Miami, FL, 33160. Tel: 305-936-1408. p. 468

Berger, Judy, Br Coordr, Marathon County Public Library, Spencer Branch, 105 Park St, Spencer, WI, 54479-0398. Tel: 715-659-3996. Fax: 715-659-3996. p. 2646

Berger, June, Dir, Stroock & Stroock & Lavan Library, 180 Maiden Lane, New York, NY, 10038. Tel: 212-806-5700. Fax: 212-806-6006. p. 1700

Berger, Kathleen M, Asst Librn, Info Serv, Boston University Libraries, Frederic S Pardee Management Library, Boston University School of Management, 595 Commonwealth Ave, Boston, MA, 02215. Tel: 617-353-4312. Fax: 617-353-4307. p. 1058

Berger, Leslie A, Electronic Res Librn, East Stroudsburg University, 216 Normal St, East Stroudsburg, PA, 18301-2999. Tel: 570-422-3597. Fax: 570-422-3151. p. 2051

Berger, Marianne, Ref, College of DuPage Library, 425 Fawell Blvd, Glen Ellyn, IL, 60137-6599. Tel: 630-942-2338. Fax: 630-858-8757. p. 649

Berger, Marilyn, Librn, McGill University Libraries, Blackader-Lauterman Library of Architecture & Art, Redpath Library Bldg, 3459 McTavish St, Montreal, QC, H3A 1Y1, CANADA. Tel: 514-398-4742. Fax: 514-398-6695. p. 2898

Berger, Pearl, Dean of Libr, Yeshiva University Libraries, 500 W 185th St, New York, NY, 10033. Tel: 212-960-5363. Fax: 212-960-0066. p. 1703

Berger, Rebecca N, Dir, Door County Library, 107 S Fourth Ave, Sturgeon Bay, WI, 54235. Tel: 920-743-6578. Fax: 920-743-6697. p. 2640

Berger, Sharon, Ser, Messiah College, One College Ave, Ste 3002, Mechanicsburg, PA, 17055. Tel: 717-691-6006, Ext 7017. Fax: 717-691-2356. p. 2087

Berger, Sidney E, Dir, Peabody Essex Museum, East India Sq, 161 Essex St, Salem, MA, 01970-3783. Tel: 978-745-9500. Fax: 978-741-9012. p. 1121

Berger, Susan, ILL, Butler University Libraries, 4600 Sunset Ave, Indianapolis, IN, 46208. Tel: 317-940-9227. Fax: 317-940-9711. p. 749

Berger, Toby, Librn, Pepperdine University Libraries, Irvine Center Library, Lakeshore Towers III, 18111 Von Karman Ave, Irvine, CA, 92715. Tel: 949-223-2520. Fax: 949-223-2559. p. 182

Berger, Youshin, Commun Libr Mgr, Queens Borough Public Library, Glen Oaks Community Library, 256-04 Union Tpk, Glen Oaks, NY, 11004. Tel: 718-831-8636. Fax: 718-831-8635. p. 1644

Bergeris, Callie, Ref & Instrul Serv Librn, Iona College, 715 North Ave, New Rochelle, NY, 10801-1890. Tel: 914-633-2227. Fax: 914-633-2136. p. 1666

Bergeron, Cheri, Librn, Montana Office of Public Instruction, 1300 11th Ave, Helena, MT, 59601-3916. Tel: 406-444-2082. Fax: 406-444-3924. p. 1382

Bergeron, Cheryl, Br Mgr, Vermilion Parish Library, Maurice Branch, 100 E Joseph St, Maurice, LA, 70555. Tel: 337-893-5583. Fax: 337-893-5583. p. 939

Bergeron, Corine, Dir, Dummer Public Library, 63 Hill Rd, Milan, NH, 03588-9711. Tel: 603-449-0995. p. 1457

Bergeron, Judy, Dir, Smithville Public Library, 507 Main St, Smithville, TX, 78957. Tel: 512-237-3282, Ext 2401. Fax: 512-237-4549. p. 2388

Bergeron, Linda, Br Mgr, Baker County Public Library, Halfway Branch, 260 Gover Lane, Halfway, OR, 97834. Tel: 541-742-5279. p. 1991

Bergeron, Marcel, Dir, Seminaire De Chicoutimi Bibliotheque, 679 rue Chabanel, Chicoutimi, QC, G7H 1Z7, CANADA. Tel: 418-693-8448. Fax: 418-693-8449. p. 2881

Bergeron, Nancy, Dir, Madbury Public Library, Nine Town Hall Rd, Madbury, NH, 03823. Tel: 603-743-1400. p. 1455

Bergeron, Pierrette, Assoc Prof, Universite de Montreal, 3150, rue Jean-Brillant, bur C-2004, Montreal, QC, H3T 1N8, CANADA. Tel: 514-343-6044. Fax: 514-343-5753. p. 2979

Bergeron, Sherry, Br Mgr, Evangeline Parish Library, Basile Branch, 3036 Stagg Ave, Basile, LA, 70515. Tel: 337-432-6794. Fax: 337-432-6794. p. 971

Bergeron, Sue, Children's & Teen Programmer, North Grenville Public Library, Norenberg Bldg, One Water St, Kemptville, ON, K0G 1J0, CANADA. Tel: 613-258-4711, Ext 4. Fax: 613-258-4134. p. 2812

Bergeron, Tangella, Br Mgr, Lafourche Parish Public Library, Bayou Blue Branch, 198 Mazerac St, Houma, LA, 70364. Tel: 985-580-0634. Fax: 985-580-0634. p. 971

Bergeron, Wendy, Curator, American Independence Museum Library, One Governors Lane, Exeter, NH, 03833. Tel: 603-772-2622. Fax: 603-772-0861. p. 1447

Bergerone, Rose, Asst Librn, Allenstown Public Library, 59 Main St, Allenstown, NH, 03275-1716. Tel: 603-485-7651. p. 1437

Bergerson, Ellen, ILL, Des Moines University, 3300 Grand Ave, Des Moines, IA, 50312. Tel: 515-271-1537. Fax: 515-271-1625. p. 808

Berges, Cherry, Dir, Madisonville Community College, 2000 College Dr, Madisonville, KY, 42431. Tel: 270-824-8677. Fax: 270-825-8553. p. 927

Bergfeld, Emily, Ref Librn, Bernard E Witkin Alameda County Law Library, 12th & Oak St Bldg, 125 Twelfth St, Oakland, CA, 94607-4912. Tel: 510-272-6486. Fax: 510-208-4823. p. 199

Berggren, Karen, Librn, Arizona State Parks, Homolovi Ruins Visitor Center, SR 87 one mile N of I-40, Winslow, AZ, 86047. Tel: 928-289-4106. Fax: 928-289-2021. p. 90

Berggren, Kathy, Dir, Matteson Public Library, 801 S School St, Matteson, IL, 60443-1897. Tel: 708-748-4431. Fax: 708-748-0510. p. 671

Berggren-Thomas, Priscilla, Dir, Phillips Free Library, 37 S Main St, Homer, NY, 13077-1323. Tel: 607-749-4616. Fax: 607-749-4616. p. 1637

Bergheger, Brian F, Dir, Elmhurst Historical Museum Library, 120 E Park Ave, Elmhurst, IL, 60126. Tel: 630-833-1457. Fax: 630-833-1326. p. 642

Berghuis, Shara, Dir, Wray Public Library, 621 Blake St, Wray, CO, 80758-1619. Tel: 970-332-4744. Fax: 970-332-4784. p. 326

Bergjord, Judi, Outreach Serv Librn, Creighton University, Health Sciences Library-Learning Resource Center, 2770 Webster St, Omaha, NE, 68178-0210. Tel: 402-280-5199. Fax: 402-280-5134. p. 1412

Berglund, Edean, Chief Librn, United States Army, Bldg 9040 Fitzsimmons Dr, 2nd Flr, Tacoma, WA, 98431. Tel: 253-968-0118. Fax: 253-968-0958. p. 2540

Berglund, Kara, Web Coordr, Canterbury Public Library, One Municipal Dr, Canterbury, CT, 06331-1453. Tel: 860-546-9022. Fax: 860-546-1142. p. 333

Bergman, Barbara, Media Librn, Minnesota State University, Mankato, ML3097, Mankato, MN, 56001. Tel: 507-389-5952. Fax: 507-389-5155. p. 1257

Bergman, Becky, Coordr, Libr Serv, Ear Falls Township Library, Two Willow Crescent, Ear Falls, ON, P0V 1T0, CANADA. Tel: 807-222-3209. Fax: 807-222-3432. p. 2803

Bergman, Edward, Adult Serv, Leominster Public Library, 30 West St, Leominster, MA, 01453. Tel: 978-534-7522. Fax: 978-840-3357. p. 1098

Bergman, Emily, Head, Coll & Tech Serv, Occidental College Library, 1600 Campus Rd, Los Angeles, CA, 90041. Tel: 323-259-2935. Fax: 323-341-4991. p. 176

Bergman, Jerry, Dr, Librn, Society for the Study of Male Psychology & Physiology Library, 321 Iuka, Montpelier, OH, 43543. Tel: 419-485-3602. p. 1918

Bergman, Mary, ILL, Public Library of Brookline, 361 Washington St, Brookline, MA, 02445. Tel: 617-730-2370. Fax: 617-730-2160. p. 1071

Bergman, Sherrie, Librn, Bowdoin College Library, 3000 College Sta, Brunswick, ME, 04011-8421. p. 979

Bergmann, Mary Jo, Br Coordr, Circ, Iowa State University Library, 302 Parks Library, Ames, IA, 50011-2140. Tel: 515-294-1442, 515-294-1443. Fax: 515-294-5525. p. 793

Bergmann, Susan, Ref Coordr, Riverhead Free Library, 330 Court St, Riverhead, NY, 11901-2885. Tel: 631-727-3228. Fax: 631-727-4762. p. 1728

Bergquist, Amy, Librn, Bowman Regional Public Library, 18 E Divide St, Bowman, ND, 58623. Tel: 701-523-3797. p. 1839

Bergquist, Christine, Dir, Wilbraham Public Library, 25 Crane Park Dr, Wilbraham, MA, 01095-1799. Tel: 413-596-6141. Fax: 413-596-5090. p. 1140

Bergquist, Donald, Mgr Fac, Rockford Public Library, 215 N Wyman St, Rockford, IL, 61101-1023. Tel: 815-965-7606. Fax: 815-965-0866. p. 697

Bergquist, Vi, Chief Info Officer, Saint Cloud Technical College Library, 1540 Northway Dr, Saint Cloud, MN, 56303-1240. Tel: 320-308-5966. Fax: 320-308-5960. p. 1276

Bergstein, Brenda Sislen, Librn, OHR Kodesh Congregation, 8300 Meadowbrook Dr, Chevy Chase, MD, 20815. Tel: 301-589-3880. Fax: 301-495-4801. p. 1024

Bergstrom, Bev, Br Supvr, Spokane County Library District, Fairfield Library, 305 E Main, Fairfield, WA, 99012. Tel: 509-893-8320. Fax: 509-893-8477. p. 2537

Bergstrom, Beverly, Br Supvr, Spokane County Library District, Otis Orchards Library, 22324 E Wellesley Ave, Otis Orchards, WA, 99027-9336. Tel: 509-893-8390. Fax: 509-893-8482. p. 2537

Bergstrom, Dennis, Br Mgr, Spokane Public Library, East Side, 524 S Stone Ave, Spokane, WA, 99202. Tel: 509-444-5376. Fax: 509-444-5369. p. 2537

Bergstrom, Dennis, Br Mgr, Spokane Public Library, Hillyard, 4005 N Cook Ave, Spokane, WA, 99207. Tel: 509-444-5381. Fax: 509-444-5370. p. 2538

Bergstrom, Dennis, Br Mgr, Spokane Public Library, Indian Trail, 4909 W Barnes Rd, Spokane, WA, 99208. Tel: 509-444-5396. Fax: 509-444-5399. p. 2538

Bergstrom, John, ILL, University of Iowa Libraries, Law Library, 200 Boyd Law Bldg, Iowa City, IA, 52242-1166. Tel: 319-335-9015. Fax: 319-335-9039. p. 824

Bergstrom, Mary Linn, Head of Libr, University of California, San Diego, Science & Engineering, 9500 Gilman Dr, Dept 0175E, La Jolla, CA, 92093-0175. Tel: 858-534-4579. Fax: 858-534-5583. p. 162

Berhanu, Aslaku, Librn, Temple University Libraries, Blockson Afro-American Collection, Sullivan Hall, 1st Flr, 1330 W Berks St, Philadelphia, PA, 19122. Tel: 215-204-6632. Fax: 215-204-5197. p. 2117

Berhe-Hunt, Annette C, Coll Develop, Dir, LeMoyne-Owen College, 807 Walker Ave, Memphis, TN, 38126. Tel: 901-435-1351. Fax: 901-435-1374. p. 2249

Bering, Jane, Libr Dir, Gaines County Library, 704 Hobbs Hwy, Seminole, TX, 79360. Tel: 432-758-4007. Fax: 432-758-4024. p. 2386

Berish, Dolores, Dir, Libr Serv, Chatfield College Library, 20918 State Rte 251, Saint Martin, OH, 45118. Tel: 513-875-3344. Fax: 513-875-3912. p. 1933

Berk, Ellen, Youth Ref Librn, Fruitville Public Library, 100 Coburn Rd, Sarasota, FL, 34240. Tel: 941-861-2500. Fax: 941-861-2528. p. 489

Berk, Josh, Dir, Memorial Library of Nazareth & Vicinity, 295 E Center St, Nazareth, PA, 18064-2298. Tel: 610-759-4932. Fax: 610-759-9513. p. 2095

Berk, Rita, Dir, Moravian College & Moravian Theological Seminary, 1200 Main St, Bethlehem, PA, 18018-6650. Tel: 610-861-1541. Fax: 610-861-1577. p. 2034

Berke, Sheila E, Coll Mgmt & Tech Serv Adminr, Miami-Dade Public Library System, 101 W Flagler St, Miami, FL, 33130-1523. Tel: 305-375-5590. Fax: 305-375-3048. p. 466

Berkes, Anna Louisa, Ref, Thomas Jefferson Foundation Inc, 1329 Kenwood Farm Lane, Charlottesville, VA, 22902. Tel: 434-984-7544. Fax: 434-984-7546. p. 2454

Berkes, Mary Jo, Br Mgr, Beaufort County Library, Hilton Head Island Branch, 11 Beach City Rd, Hilton Head Island, SC, 29926. Tel: 843-255-6500. Fax: 843-255-9495. p. 2181

Berkey, Swee Lian, Info Tech, Ref, University of Hawaii, 2525 Dole St, Honolulu, HI, 96822-2328. Tel: 808-956-5581, 808-956-7583. Fax: 808-956-4615. p. 565

Berkman, Virginia, Circ Supvr, Ocean County Library, Bay Head Reading Center, 136 Meadow Ave, Bay Head, NJ, 08742-5080. Tel: 732-892-0662. Fax: 732-892-0647. p. 1534

Berkowitz, Daniel, Dr, Interim Dir, University of Iowa, 3087 Main Library, Iowa City, IA, 52242-1420. Tel: 319-335-5707. Fax: 319-335-5374. p. 2965

Berkowitz, MaryGrace, Cataloger/Ref Librn, Oklahoma City Community College, 7777 S May Ave, Oklahoma City, OK, 73159. Tel: 405-682-1611, Ext 7229. Fax: 405-682-7585. p. 1973

Berkowitz, Nancy, Dir, Town of Indian Lake Public Library, 113 Pelon Rd, Indian Lake, NY, 12842. Tel: 518-648-5444. Fax: 518-648-6227. p. 1640

Berliner, Mary Ann, Dir, Los Angeles County Harbor UCLA Medical Center, 1000 W Carson St, Torrance, CA, 90509-2910. Tel: 310-222-2372. Fax: 310-533-5146. p. 275

Berman, Ellen, Head, Ref, Rockville Centre Public Library, 221 N Village Ave, Rockville Centre, NY, 11570. Tel: 516-766-6257. Fax: 516-766-6090. p. 1734

Berman, Joan, Spec Coll & Archives Librn, Humboldt State University Library, One Harpst St, Arcata, CA, 95521-8299. Tel: 707-826-4939. Fax: 707-826-3440. p. 122

Berman, Pat, Finance Mgr, Arlington Heights Memorial Library, 500 N Dunton Ave, Arlington Heights, IL, 60004-5966. Tel: 847-506-2615. Fax: 847-506-2650. p. 589

Berman, Susan F, Dir, Libr Serv, Baltimore Hebrew Congregation, 7401 Park Heights Ave, Baltimore, MD, 21208. Tel: 410-764-1587. Fax: 410-764-7948. p. 1011

Bermel, Elizabeth, Dir, Scarsdale Public Library, 54 Olmsted Rd, Scarsdale, NY, 10583. Tel: 914-722-1300. Fax: 914-722-1305. p. 1739

Bermel, Nichole, Librn, Sutherland Public Library, 900 Second St, Sutherland, NE, 69165. Tel: 308-386-2228. p. 1420

Bermudez, Nathalia, ILL, Sr Librn, YA Serv, East Orange Public Library, 21 S Arlington Ave, East Orange, NJ, 07018-3892. Tel: 973-266-5600. Fax: 973-674-1991. p. 1482

Bernad, Manny, Librn, Coleman College Library, 8888 Balba Ave, San Diego, CA, 92123. Tel: 619-465-3990. p. 231

Bernal, Megan, Assoc Dir, Libr Info & Discovery Syst, DePaul University Libraries, 2350 N Kenmore, Chicago, IL, 60614. Tel: 773-325-3725, 773-325-7862. Fax: 773-325-7870. p. 612

Bernal, Rebecca, ILL, Colorado Mesa University, 1200 College Pl, Grand Junction, CO, 81501. Tel: 970-248-1862. Fax: 970-248-1930. p. 310

Bernard, Brenda, Admin Officer, National Archives & Records Administration, 900 Market St, Philadelphia, PA, 19107-4292. Tel: 215-606-0100. Fax: 215-606-0116. p. 2113

Bernard, Francine, Dir, Agriculture & Agri-Food Canada, 2560 Hochelaga Blvd, Sainte-Foy, QC, G1V 2J3, CANADA. Tel: 418-657-7985, Ext 239. Fax: 418-648-2402. p. 2910

Bernard, Latrisha, Access Serv Asst, Dillard University, 2601 Gentilly Blvd, New Orleans, LA, 70122-3097. Tel: 504-816-4784. Fax: 504-816-4787. p. 960

Bernard, Lenore, Librn, Ivy Tech Community College, 3501 First Ave, Evansville, IN, 47710-3398. Tel: 812-429-1412. Fax: 812-429-9802. p. 738

Bernard, Michele, Librn, Raymond Chabot Grant Thornton Library, 600 de la Gauchetiere W, Ste 1900, Montreal, QC, H3B 4L8, CANADA. Tel: 514-878-2691. Fax: 514-878-2127. p. 2900

Bernard, Rosemary, Libr Dir, Middleport Free Library, Nine Vernon St, Middleport, NY, 14105. Tel: 716-735-3281. Fax: 716-735-3281. p. 1660

Bernard, Sara, Dir, Pittsfield Public Library, 205 N Memorial, Pittsfield, IL, 62363-1406. Tel: 217-285-2200. Fax: 217-285-9423. p. 691

Bernard, Sharon A, Dir, Fitchburg Public Library, 610 Main St, Fitchburg, MA, 01420-3146. Tel: 978-345-9635. Fax: 978-345-9631. p. 1089

Bernard, Yvon, Dir, Libr Serv, Cegep Beauce-Appalaches Bibliotheque, 1055 116e rue, Saint-Georges de Beauce, QC, G5Y 3G1, CANADA. Tel: 418-228-8896, Ext 220. Fax: 418-228-0562. p. 2910

Bernardi, Kathleen, Ch, Tech Serv, Haddon Heights Public Library, 608 Station Ave, Haddon Heights, NJ, 08035-1907. Tel: 856-547-7132. Fax: 856-547-2867. p. 1489

Bernardi, Nancy, Media Spec, Gettysburg College, 300 N Washington St, Gettysburg, PA, 17325. Tel: 717-337-7022. Fax: 717-337-7001. p. 2059

Bernardi, Toni, Dir, Ch Serv, San Francisco Public Library, 100 Larkin St, San Francisco, CA, 94102-4733. Tel: 415-557-4270. Fax: 415-557-4424. p. 246

Bernardis, Tim, Dir, Little Big Horn College Library, One Forestry Lane, Crow Agency, MT, 59022. Tel: 406-638-3113. Fax: 406-638-3170. p. 1377

Bernardo, Anne R, Dir, Tulare County Public Law Library, 221 S Mooney Blvd, Rm 1, County Courthouse, Visalia, CA, 93291. Tel: 559-636-4600. p. 281

Bernardo, Karen, Dir, Coburn Free Library, 275 Main St, Owego, NY, 13827. Tel: 607-687-3520. Fax: 607-687-5628. p. 1713

Bernardo, Mario, Asst Dir, Libr Computing & Tech Syst, Florida Gulf Coast University Library, 10501 FGCU Blvd S, Fort Myers, FL, 33965-6501. Tel: 239-590-7621. p. 444

Bernardo, Sonia, Librn, Capuchin College Library, 4121 Harewood Rd NE, Washington, DC, 20017. Tel: 202-529-2188. Fax: 202-526-6664. p. 395

Bernards, Dennis, Ser, Brigham Young University, Harold B Lee Library, 2060 HBLL, Provo, UT, 84602. Tel: 801-422-2927. Fax: 801-422-0466. p. 2411

Bernat, Mary, Ref Serv, Palmer Public Library, 1455 N Main St, Palmer, MA, 01069. Tel: 413-283-3330. Fax: 413-283-9970. p. 1116

Bernath, Tina, Spec Coll & Archives Librn, Troy University, 502 University Dr, Dothan, AL, 36304. Tel: 334-983-6556, Ext 1324. Fax: 334-983-6327. p. 15

Bernau, Brent, Law Ref Librn/Taxation & Doc Spec, University of San Diego, Katherine M & George M Pardee Jr Legal Research Center, 5998 Alcala Park, San Diego, CA, 92110-2492. Tel: 619-260-7557. Fax: 619-260-4616. p. 239

Bernau, Karen, Dir, Knutson Memorial Library, 500 Central Ave, Coon Valley, WI, 54623. Tel: 608-452-3757. Fax: 608-452-2090. p. 2586

Bernbeck, Melanie, Librn, Utica Library Association, 249 N Ohio, Utica, KS, 67584-0146. Tel: 785-391-2419. p. 898

Berner, Andrew J, Curator, Dir, University Club Library, One W 54th St, New York, NY, 10019. Tel: 212-572-3418. Fax: 212-572-3452. p. 1702

Berner Harris, Cynthia, Dir of Libr, Wichita Public Library, 223 S Main St, Wichita, KS, 67202. Tel: 316-261-8520. Fax: 316-219-6320. p. 901

Berner, Mark, Librn, Fresno County Public Library, Clovis Regional, 1155 Fifth St, Clovis, CA, 93612-1391. Tel: 559-600-9531. p. 152

Bernero, Cheryl, Br Mgr, El Paso Public Library, Westside, 125 Belvidere, El Paso, TX, 79912. Tel: 915-581-2024. Fax: 915-833-4785. p. 2317

Bernhardt, Beth, Electronic Res Librn, University of North Carolina at Greensboro, 320 Spring Garden St, Greensboro, NC, 27402. Tel: 336-256-1210. Fax: 336-334-5399. p. 1798

Bernhardt, Marcia, Curator, Iron County Historical Museum, 100 Brady, Caspian, MI, 49915. Tel: 906-265-2617. p. 1161

Bernhardt, Sharon, Area Res Mgr, N Region, Indianapolis-Marion County Public Library, 2450 N Meridian St, Indianapolis, IN, 46208. Tel: 317-275-4475. Fax: 317-269-5300. p. 753

Bernhardt, Sharon, Br Mgr, Indianapolis-Marion County Public Library, Nora, 8625 Guilford Ave, Indianapolis, IN, 46240-1835. Tel: 317-275-4470. p. 754

Bernheim, Laura, Ref, Waltham Public Library, 735 Main St, Waltham, MA, 02451. Tel: 781-314-3435. Fax: 781-314-3426. p. 1133

Bernheisel, Nancy, Coordr, Air & Waste Management Association Library, One Gateway Ctr, 3rd Flr, 420 Fort Duquesne Blvd, Pittsburgh, PA, 15222. Tel: 412-232-3444. Fax: 412-232-3450. p. 2121

Bernier, Guy, Pres, Societe Genealogique de l'Est du Quebec Bibliotheque, 110 Rue de L'Eveche EST, Rimouski, QC, G5L 1X9, CANADA. Tel: 418-723-5323. Fax: 418-724-3242. p. 2907

Bernier, Jennifer, Librn, Connecticut Legislative Library, Legislative Office Bldg, Rm 5400, 300 Capitol Ave, Hartford, CT, 06106-1591. Tel: 860-240-8888. Fax: 860-240-8881. p. 344

Bernier, Lucie, Chef de Section, Bibliothèques de Montréal, Ahuntsic, 10300, rue Lajeunesse, Montreal, QC, H3L 2E5, CANADA. Tel: 514-872-6993. Fax: 514-872-0518. p. 2889

Bernier, Marion, In Charge, Bibliotheque Gabrielle-Roy, Bibliothèque Chrystine-Brouillet, 264 rue Racine, Quebec, QC, G2B 1E6, CANADA. Tel: 418-641-6120. p. 2903

Berning, Robert, Dir, Carlisle Public Library, 135 School St, Carlisle, IA, 50047-8702. Tel: 515-989-0909. Fax: 515-989-4328. p. 798

Berninger, Martha, Supvr, ILL & Ref Serv, Wisconsin Department of Public Instruction, Reference & Loan Library, 2109 S Stoughton Rd, Madison, WI, 53716-2899. Tel: 608-224-6168. Fax: 608-224-6168. p. 2610

Bernini, Charlotte, ILL, Howe Library, 13 South St, Hanover, NH, 03755. Tel: 603-643-4120. Fax: 603-643-0725. p. 1450

Bernnard, Deborah, Head of Libr, University at Albany, State University of New York, Thomas E Dewey Graduate Library, 135 Western Ave, Albany, NY, 12222. Tel: 518-442-3699. Fax: 518-442-3474. p. 1571

Berns, Cindy, Dir, Postville Public Library, 235 W Tilden, Postville, IA, 52162. Tel: 563-864-7600. Fax: 563-864-7600. p. 839

Berns, Jeffrey J, Librn, Spiegel & McDiarmid LLP, 1333 New Hampshire Ave NW, 2nd Flr, Washington, DC, 20036. Tel: 202-879-4055. Fax: 202-393-2866. p. 416

Bernstein, Alan, Univ Librn, Valdosta State University, 1500 N Patterson St, Valdosta, GA, 31698-0150. Tel: 229-333-5860. Fax: 229-259-5055. p. 555

Bernstein, Alan M, Dir, Heritage Public Library, 9001 Blvd, Providence Forge, VA, 23140-0008. Tel: 804-966-2480. Fax: 804-966-5982. p. 2486

Bernstein, Bernice, Acq Librn, Maryland State Law Library, Courts of Appeal Bldg, 361 Rowe Blvd, Annapolis, MD, 21401-1697. Tel: 410-260-1430. Fax: 410-260-1572, 410-974-2063. p. 1010

Bernstein, Beth, Librn, Seyfarth Shaw Library, 2029 Century Park E, Ste 3300, Los Angeles, CA, 90067. Tel: 310-277-7200. Fax: 310-201-5219. p. 177

Bernstein, Elaine, Dir, Libr Serv, North York General Hospital, 4001 Leslie St, Toronto, ON, M2K 1E1, CANADA. Tel: 416-756-6142. Fax: 416-756-6605. p. 2856

Bernstein, Jay, ILL, Reader Serv, Kingsborough Community College, 2001 Oriental Blvd, Brooklyn, NY, 11235. Tel: 718-368-6548. Fax: 718-368-5482. p. 1592

Bernstein, Kelly, Mgr, Info Serv, Region of Waterloo Library, 2017 Nafziger Rd, Baden, ON, N3A 3H4, CANADA. Tel: 519-575-4590. Fax: 519-634-5371. p. 2793

Bernstein, Lee S, Br Head, Pub Serv, FDA Biosciences Library, 5100 Paint Branch Pkwy, College Park, MD, 20740. Tel: 240-402-1882. Fax: 301-436-2653. p. 1024

Bernstein, Melissa, Dir, University of Utah, S J Quinney Law Library, 332 S 1400 East, Salt Lake City, UT, 84112-0731. Tel: 801-581-3386. Fax: 801-585-3033. p. 2415

Bernstein, Mildred, Head, Youth Serv, South Huntington Public Library, 145 Pidgeon Hill Rd, Huntington Station, NY, 11746. Tel: 631-549-4411. Fax: 631-549-1266. p. 1639

Bernstein, Noreen, Youth Serv Dir, Williamsburg Regional Library, 7770 Croaker Rd, Williamsburg, VA, 23188-7064. Tel: 757-259-4045. Fax: 757-259-4079, 757-259-7798. p. 2503

Bernstein, Pamela, Asst Dir, Irvington Public Library, 12 S Astor St, Irvington, NY, 10533. Tel: 914-591-7840. Fax: 914-591-0347. p. 1640

Bernstein, Pat, Librn, Burns & Roe Enterprises, Inc, 800 Kinderkamack Rd, Oradell, NJ, 07649. Tel: 201-986-4224. Fax: 201-986-4418. p. 1516

Bernstein, Robin R, Sr Dir for Libr Serv, Bellevue University, 1000 Galvin Rd S, Bellevue, NE, 68005. Tel: 402-557-7300. Fax: 402-557-5427. p. 1393

Bernstein, Toby, Asst Head, Metadata Mgt, Northeastern University Libraries, Snell Library, 360 Huntington Ave, Boston, MA, 02115. Tel: 617-373-4791. p. 1065

Berntsen, Willow, Cat Supvr, University of Puget Sound, 1500 N Warner St, Campus Mail Box 1021, Tacoma, WA, 98416-1021. Tel: 253-879-3107. Fax: 253-879-3670. p. 2541

Berntson, Shirley, Librn, Southeast Regional Library, Oxbow Branch, 516 Prospect Ave, Oxbow, SK, S0C 2B0, CANADA. Tel: 306-483-5175. p. 2930

Bernuetz, Oliver D, Info Spec/Librn, Canada/Manitoba Business Service Centre Library, 240 Graham Ave, Ste 250, Winnipeg, MB, R3C 0J7, CANADA. Tel: 204-983-6182. Fax: 204-983-3852. p. 2754

Bero, Margaret, Ref Librn, Nashua Community College, 505 Amherst St, Nashua, NH, 03063-1026. Tel: 603-882-6923, Ext 1565. Fax: 603-882-8690. p. 1458

Bero, Stephen, Dir, Warren-Newport Public Library District, 224 N O'Plaine Rd, Gurnee, IL, 60031. Tel: 847-244-5150, Ext 3101. Fax: 847-244-3499. p. 653

Berona, David, Dean, Plymouth State University, Highland St, Plymouth, NH, 03264-1595. Tel: 603-535-2258. Fax: 603-535-2445. p. 1462

Beronja, Debra N, Curric Res Ctr Librn, Youngstown State University, One University Plaza, Youngstown, OH, 44555-0001. Tel: 330-941-2511. Fax: 330-941-3734. p. 1953

Berquist, Linda, Circ Supvr, Orange Public Library & History Center, 407 E Chapman Ave, Orange, CA, 92866-1509. Tel: 714-288-2400. Fax: 714-771-6126. p. 201

Berret, Barbara, Coll Develop, Bethel Park Public Library, 5100 W Library Ave, Bethel Park, PA, 15102. Tel: 412-831-6800, Ext 262, 412-851-2465. Fax: 412-835-9360. p. 2033

Berreth, Sheila, Bkmobile/Outreach Serv Dir, Morton Mandan Public Library, 609 W Main St, Mandan, ND, 58554. Tel: 701-667-5365. Fax: 701-667-5368. p. 1845

Berrios, Ilianet, Libr Tech, McDonald Army Health Center Library, Bldg 576, Jefferson Ave, Fort Eustis, VA, 23604-5548. Tel: 757-314-7857. Fax: 757-314-7773. p. 2464

Berrios, Juan Jose, Dir, Commun & Tech Serv, University of Puerto Rico Library, Cayey Campus, 205 Ave Antonio R Barcelo, Cayey, PR, 00736. Tel: 787-738-2161, Ext 2447. Fax: 787-263-2108. p. 2672

Berrish, Karen, Assoc Dir, Digital Serv, University of Houston - Clear Lake, 2700 Bay Area Blvd, Houston, TX, 77058-1098. Tel: 281-283-3919. Fax: 281-283-3937. p. 2343

Berro, Christine A, Dir, Portage District Library, 300 Library Lane, Portage, MI, 49002. Tel: 269-329-4542, Ext 700. Fax: 269-324-9222. p. 1220

Berry, Anita, Ch, Librn I, Montgomery City-County Public Library System, Governors Square Branch Library, 2885-B East South Blvd, Montgomery, AL, 36111. Tel: 334-284-7929. Fax: 334-240-4839. p. 29

Berry, Ann, Dir, Pilgrim Society, 75 Court St, Plymouth, MA, 02360-3891. Tel: 508-746-1620. Fax: 508-746-3396. p. 1118

Berry, Barbara, Circ Mgr, Plain City Public Library, 305 W Main St, Plain City, OH, 43064-1148. Tel: 614-873-4912. Fax: 614-873-8364. p. 1930

Berry, Carol, Circ Mgr, Eagle Public Library, 100 N Stierman Way, Eagle, ID, 83616-5162. Tel: 208-939-6814. Fax: 208-939-1359. p. 574

Berry, Carol, Dir, Dormann Library, 101 W Morris St, Bath, NY, 14810. Tel: 607-776-4613. Fax: 607-776-6693. p. 1578

Berry, Carol Lepzelter, Sr Electronic Res Librn, Argonne National Laboratory, 9700 S Cass Ave, Bldg 240, Argonne, IL, 60439-4801. Tel: 630-252-3876. Fax: 630-252-5024. p. 589

Berry, Charlotte, Asst Librn, Hill Library, 1151 Parker Mountain Rd, Center Strafford, NH, 03815. Tel: 603-664-2800. Fax: 603-664-2800. p. 1440

Berry, Coleen, Pub Relations Librn, Monmouth County Library, 125 Symmes Dr, Manalapan, NJ, 07726. Tel: 732-431-7220. Fax: 732-308-2955. p. 1498

Berry, Dale, Br Mgr, Franklin Parish Library, Wisner Branch, 129 Fort Scott St, Wisner, LA, 71378. Tel: 318-724-7399. Fax: 318-724-7399. p. 972

Berry, Dave, Instrul Serv/Ref Librn, Taft College Library, 29 Emmons Park Dr, Taft, CA, 93268-2317. Tel: 661-763-7707. Fax: 661-763-7778. p. 274

Berry, Dhyana, Circ/ILL Asst, Berklee College of Music Library, 150 Massachusetts Ave, Boston, MA, 02115. Tel: 617-747-2258. Fax: 617-747-2050. p. 1055

Berry, Diane, Dir, Echo Public Library, 20 S Bonanza, Echo, OR, 97826. Tel: 541-376-8411. Fax: 541-376-8218. p. 1995

Berry, Elizabeth Black, Dir, Weil, Gotshal & Manges LLP, 700 Louisiana St, Ste 1600, Houston, TX, 77002. Tel: 713-546-5055. Fax: 713-224-9511. p. 2345

Berry, Esther, Asst Librn, Tinicum Memorial Public Library, 620 Seneca St, Essington, PA, 19029-1199. Tel: 610-521-9344. Fax: 610-521-3463. p. 2056

Berry, Evette, Circ, Calgary Public Library, W R Castell Central Library, 616 Macleod Trail SE, Calgary, AB, T2G 2M2, CANADA. Tel: 403-260-2600. Fax: 403-237-5393. p. 2689

Berry, Gayle C, Coll Mgt Librn, Clarkson University Libraries, Andrew S Schuler Educational Resources Center, CU Box 5590, Eight Clarkson Ave, Potsdam, NY, 13699-5590. Tel: 315-268-4452. Fax: 315-268-7655. p. 1721

Berry, Glenda, Br Mgr, Hawaii State Public Library System, Makawao Public Library, 1159 Makawao Ave, Makawao, HI, 96768. Tel: 808-573-8785. Fax: 808-573-8787. p. 563

Berry, Jane D, Asst Dir, Glenview Public Library, 1930 Glenview Rd, Glenview, IL, 60025-2899. Tel: 847-729-7500. Fax: 847-729-7558. p. 650

Berry, Janelle, Dir, Crosby County Library, 114 W Aspen St, Crosbyton, TX, 79322. Tel: 806-675-2673. Fax: 806-675-2673. p. 2303

Berry, John D, Librn, University of California, Berkeley, Ethnic Studies, 30 Stephens Hall, MC 2360, Berkeley, CA, 94720-2360. Tel: 510-642-0941. Fax: 510-643-8433. p. 128

Berry, Judy, Dir, Berrien Springs Community Library, 215 W Union St, Berrien Springs, MI, 49103-1077. Tel: 269-471-7074. Fax: 269-471-4433. p. 1157

Berry, Karen, Tech Serv, Collingwood Public Library, 55 St Marie St, Collingwood, ON, L9Y 0W6, CANADA. Tel: 705-445-1571, Ext 6231. Fax: 705-445-3704. p. 2800

Berry, Kathleen, Asst Librn, Ch, Wissahickon Valley Public Library, 650 Skippack Pike, Blue Bell, PA, 19422. Tel: 215-643-1320, Ext 14. Fax: 215-643-6611. p. 2036

Berry, Kathleen, Info Tech Librn, Bennington College, One College Dr, Bennington, VT, 05201-6001. Tel: 802-440-4610. Fax: 802-440-4580. p. 2418

Berry, Kathryn, Br Mgr, Richland Parish Library, Mangham Branch, 302 Hixon St, Mangham, LA, 71259. Tel: 318-248-2493. Fax: 318-248-3912. p. 966

Berry, Kenneth, Dir, Hill Library, 1151 Parker Mountain Rd, Center Strafford, NH, 03815. Tel: 603-664-2800. Fax: 603-664-2800. p. 1440

Berry, Lisa M, Assoc Dir, Ref & Outreach, Houston Academy of Medicine, 1133 John Freeman Blvd, Houston, TX, 77030. Tel: 713-799-7164. Fax: 713-790-7052. p. 2337

Berry, Louise Parker, Dir, Darien Library, 1441 Post Rd, Darien, CT, 06820-5419. Tel: 203-655-1234. Fax: 203-655-1547. p. 336

Berry, Marie, Head, Access Serv, Campbell University, 113 Main St, Buies Creek, NC, 27506. Tel: 910-893-1460. Fax: 910-893-1470. p. 1778

Berry, Marshelle, Br Mgr, Jacksonville Public Library, Brentwood, 3725 Pearl St, Jacksonville, FL, 32206-6401. Tel: 904-630-0924. Fax: 904-630-0441. p. 453

Berry, Marshelle, Br Mgr, Jacksonville Public Library, Raiford A Brown Eastside Branch, 1390 Harrison St, Jacksonville, FL, 32206-5324. Tel: 904-630-5466. Fax: 904-630-5463. p. 453

Berry, Marshelle, Br Mgr, Jacksonville Public Library, Westbrook, 2809 Commonwealth Ave, Jacksonville, FL, 32254-2599. Tel: 904-384-7424. Fax: 904-381-1107. p. 454

Berry, Mary A, Dr, Chair, Prof, Sam Houston State University, 1921 Ave J, Huntsville, TX, 77340. Tel: 936-294-1150. Fax: 936-294-1153. p. 2974

Berry, Mary Wallace, Librn, Presbyterian Hospital, 200 Hawthorne Lane, Charlotte, NC, 28204-2528. Tel: 704-384-4258. Fax: 704-384-5058. p. 1783

Berry, Maxine, Dir, Loomis Public Library, 301 Commercial St, Loomis, NE, 68958. Tel: 308-876-2334. Fax: 308-876-2334. p. 1407

Berry, Maya, Acq & Pub Serv Librn, Christian Brothers University, 650 E Pkwy South, Memphis, TN, 38104. Tel: 901-321-3432. Fax: 901-321-3219. p. 2248

Berry, Michael D, Archivist, Ref Librn, Lander University, 320 Stanley Ave, Greenwood, SC, 29649-2099. Tel: 864-388-8435. Fax: 864-388-8816. p. 2197

Berry, Myna, Acq Mgr, Drury University, 900 N Benton Ave, Springfield, MO, 65802. Tel: 417-873-7425. Fax: 417-873-7432. p. 1366

Berry, Nancy C, Asst Dir, Lancaster County Library, 313 S White St, Lancaster, SC, 29720. Tel: 803-285-1502. Fax: 803-285-6004. p. 2198

Berry, Paul L, Librn, Calvert Marine Museum Library, 14150 Solomons Island Rd, Solomons, MD, 20688. Tel: 410-326-2042, Ext 14. Fax: 410-326-6691. p. 1042

Berry, Robert H, Soc Sci Librn, Sacred Heart University, 5151 Park Ave, Fairfield, CT, 06825-1000. Tel: 203-365-4842. Fax: 203-374-9968. p. 339

Berry, Sandra S, Asst Br Mgr, Ch, Librn I, Montgomery City-County Public Library System, Pintlala Branch Library, 255 Federal Rd, Pintlala, AL, 36043-9781. Tel: 334-281-8069. Fax: 334-240-4860. p. 30

Berry, Sarha, Librn, Hansen District Library, 120 Maple Ave W, Hansen, ID, 83334-4975. Tel: 208-423-4122. p. 575

Berry, Solomon K, Libr Spec, Bryan Cave LLP, 1290 Avenue of the Americas, New York, NY, 10104. Tel: 212-541-2165. Fax: 212-541-1465. p. 1671

Berry, Timothy E, Head Librn, Librn IV, Mgr, Montgomery City-County Public Library System, Juliette Hampton Morgan Memorial Library (Main Library), 245 High St, Montgomery, AL, 36104. Tel: 334-240-4996. Fax: 334-240-4980. p. 30

Berryhill, Carisse, Spec Coll & Archives Librn, Abilene Christian University, 221 Brown Library, ACU Box 29208, Abilene, TX, 79699-9208. Tel: 325-674-2344. Fax: 325-674-2202. p. 2271

Berryhill, Heidi, Circ, Johnson Bible College, 7900 Johnson Dr, Knoxville, TN, 37998. Tel: 865-251-2277. Fax: 865-251-2278. p. 2241

Berryman, Deborah Lynne, Asst Librn, Buchanan District Library, 128 E Front St, Buchanan, MI, 49107. Tel: 269-695-3681. Fax: 269-695-0004. p. 1160

Berryman, Donna, Asst Dir, University of Rochester Medical Center, 601 Elmwood Ave, Rochester, NY, 14642. Tel: 585-275-3361. Fax: 585-756-7762. p. 1734

Bersche, Karen Scott, Dir, Towanda District Library, 301 S Taylor St, Towanda, IL, 61776. Tel: 309-728-2176. Fax: 309-728-2139. p. 710

Bert, Nancy L, Librn, Alexander Hamilton Memorial Free Library, 13676 Monterey Lane, Blue Ridge Summit, PA, 17214. Tel: 717-794-2240. Fax: 717-794-5929. p. 2036

Bertalan, Bejamin, Acq, Allentown Public Library, 1210 Hamilton St, Allentown, PA, 18102. Tel: 610-820-2400. Fax: 610-820-0640. p. 2026

Bertalmio, Lynne, Dir, Stillwater Public Library, 224 N Third St, Stillwater, MN, 55082. Tel: 651-275-4338. Fax: 651-275-4342. p. 1285

Berteaux, Susan, Dir, Massachusetts Maritime Academy, 101 Academy Dr, Buzzards Bay, MA, 02532. Tel: 508-830-5034. Fax: 508-830-5074. p. 1072

Bertelli, Mariella, Br Head, Toronto Public Library, Spadina Road, Ten Spadina Rd, Toronto, ON, M5R 2S7, CANADA. Tel: 416-393-7666. Fax: 416-393-7415. p. 2863

Bertels, Nancy, Librn, Sutton Public Library, 11317 N Jonesville Mine Rd, Sutton, AK, 99674. Tel: 907-745-4467. Fax: 907-745-1057. p. 54

Berthiaume, Dennis, Tech Serv, Wentworth Institute of Technology, 550 Huntington Ave, Boston, MA, 02115-5998. Tel: 617-989-4040. Fax: 617-989-4091. p. 1068

Berthiaume, Guy, Pres & Chief Exec Officer, Bibliotheque et Archives nationales du Quebec, 475 de Maisonneuve E, Montreal, QC, H2L 5C4, CANADA. Tel: 514-873-1101, Ext 3250. Fax: 514-864-3818. p. 2888

Bertholf, Nancy, Librn, Chandler Public Library, 900 E Hwy 31, Chandler, TX, 75758. Tel: 903-849-4122. Fax: 903-849-4122. p. 2296

Berthot, Sherry, Libr Tech, Bull Shoals Library, 1218 Central Blvd, Bull Shoals, AR, 72619. Tel: 870-445-4265. p. 96

Bertke, Heather, Acq Asst, Washtenaw Community College, 4800 E Huron River Dr, Ann Arbor, MI, 48105-4800. Tel: 734-973-3402. Fax: 734-973-3446. p. 1153

Bertoia, James, Librn, Sparwood Public Library, 110 Pine Ave, Sparwood, BC, V0B 2G0, CANADA. Tel: 250-425-2299. Fax: 250-425-0229. p. 2737

Bertoldi, Robert, Circ, Pub Serv, Everett Community College, 2000 Tower St, Everett, WA, 98201-1352. Tel: 425-388-9492. Fax: 425-388-9144. p. 2515

Bertollini, Barry, Dir, South Routt Library District, 227 Dodge Ave, Oak Creek, CO, 80467. Tel: 970-736-8371. Fax: 970-736-8371. p. 319

Bertolucci, Ysabel, Librn, Kaiser-Permanente Medical Center, 280 W MacArthur Blvd, Oakland, CA, 94611-5693. Tel: 510-752-6158. Fax: 510-752-1500. p. 197

Bertram, Dorie, Dir, Pub Serv, Washington University Libraries, Law Library, Washington Univ Sch Law, Anheuser-Busch Hall, One Brookings Dr, Campus Box 1171, Saint Louis, MO, 63130. Tel: 314-935-6484. Fax: 314-935-7125. p. 1363

Bertram, Marcia, Librn, Frances E Kennard Public Library, Auburn & Canal Sts, Meshoppen, PA, 18630. Tel: 570-833-5060. Fax: 570-833-4238. p. 2088

Bertrand, Brian, Br Head, Toronto Public Library, High Park, 228 Roncesvalles Ave, Toronto, ON, M6R 2L7, CANADA. Tel: 416-393-7671. Fax: 416-393-7411. p. 2861

Bertrand, Gord, Syst Coordr, Saint Francis Xavier University, West St, Antigonish, NS, B2G 2W5, CANADA. Tel: 902-867-2334. Fax: 902-867-5153. p. 2777

Bertrand, Gordon, Coordr of Libr Tech, Grant MacEwan University Library, 10700 104th Ave, Edmonton, AB, T5J 4S2, CANADA. Tel: 780-497-5850. Fax: 780-497-5895. p. 2701

Bertrand, Leonard, Dir, Tulane University, Music & Media Library, 7001 Freret St, New Orleans, LA, 70118-5682. Tel: 504-865-5642. Fax: 504-865-6773. p. 963

Bertrand, Mary, Circ Asst, Clinton Public Library, Lyons, 105 Main St, Clinton, IA, 52732. Tel: 563-242-5355. Fax: 563-243-6553. p. 803

Bertrand, Stephen, Dir, Kankakee Public Library, 201 E Merchant St, Kankakee, IL, 60901. Tel: 815-939-4564. Fax: 815-939-9057. p. 661

Bertrand, Sylvie, Asst Librn, Canada Aviation Museum, 11 Aviation Pkwy, Ottawa, ON, K1K 4R3, CANADA. Tel: 613-993-2303. Fax: 613-990-3655. p. 2828

Bertrand, Sylvie, Reader Serv, Canada Science & Technology Museum, 2380 Lancaster Rd, Ottawa, ON, K1B 3W9, CANADA. Tel: 613-991-2982. Fax: 613-990-3636. p. 2829

Bertsch, Christine, Librn, Bernstein, Shur, Sawyer & Nelson, 100 Middle St, Portland, ME, 04104. Tel: 207-228-7281. Fax: 207-774-1127. p. 996

Bertschmann, Mary, In Charge, Huguenot Society of America Library, 20 W 44th St, Ste 510, New York, NY, 10036. Tel: 212-755-0592. Fax: 212-317-0676. p. 1682

Beru, Tsegaye, Pub Serv, Duquesne University, Center for Legal Information, 900 Locust St, Pittsburgh, PA, 15282. Tel: 412-396-4423. Fax: 412-396-6294. p. 2125

Berube, David, Circ Librn, Barrington Public Library, 105 Ramsdell Lane, Barrington, NH, 03825. Tel: 603-664-9715. Fax: 603-664-5219. p. 1438

Berube, Lucy, Librn, Lakeland Library Region, Loon Lake Branch, Box 216, Loon Lake, SK, S0M 1L0, CANADA. Tel: 306-837-2186. p. 2920

Berube, Matthew, Head, Info Serv, Jones Library, Inc, 43 Amity St, Amherst, MA, 01002-2285. Tel: 413-259-3195. Fax: 413-256-4096. p. 1048

Berube, Michael, Adult Serv, Southington Public Library & Museum, 255 Main St, Southington, CT, 06489. Tel: 860-628-0947. Fax: 860-628-0488. p. 368

Berube, Penny, Ch, Moses Greeley Parker Memorial Library, 28 Arlington St, Dracut, MA, 01826. Tel: 978-454-5474. Fax: 978-454-9120. p. 1085

Berube, Serge, Librn, Cegep de Saint Felicien, 1105 boul Hamel, Saint Felicien, QC, G8K 2R8, CANADA. Tel: 418-679-5412, Ext 284. Fax: 418-679-1040. p. 2908

Berude, Lucy, Librn, Lakeland Library Region, Makwa Branch, 111 Main St, Makwa, SK, S0M 1N0, CANADA. Tel: 306-236-3995. p. 2920

Berwick, Phillip, Assoc Dean, Washington University Libraries, Law Library, Washington Univ Sch Law, Anheuser-Busch Hall, One Brookings Dr, Campus Box 1171, Saint Louis, MO, 63130. Tel: 314-935-6440. Fax: 314-935-7125. p. 1363

Berza, Marielynn, Ref, The Morristown & Morris Township Library, One Miller Rd, Morristown, NJ, 07960. Tel: 973-538-6161. Fax: 973-267-4064. p. 1505

Berzinsky, Judy, Circ, NASA, 21000 Brookpark Rd, MS 60-3, Cleveland, OH, 44135. Fax: 216-433-5777. p. 1880

Besancon, Russ, Ref Serv, Iosco-Arenac District Library, 120 W Westover St, East Tawas, MI, 48730. Tel: 989-362-2651. Fax: 989-362-6056. p. 1175

Besant, Michele, Dir, University of Wisconsin-Madison, School of Library & Information Studies Library, 600 N Park St, Rm 4191, Madison, WI, 53706. Tel: 608-263-2963. Fax: 608-263-4849. p. 2609

Beschorner, Jane, Dir, J J Hands Library, 609 Second St, Lohrville, IA, 51453. Tel: 712-465-4115. Fax: 712-465-4115. p. 828

Besel, Jane, Dir, Carnegie Public Library, 202 N Animas St, Trinidad, CO, 81082. Tel: 719-846-6841, 719-846-7517. Fax: 719-846-0885. p. 324

Beseres, Peggi, Head Librn, Jesse F Hallett Memorial Library, 101 First St SE, Crosby, MN, 56441. Tel: 218-546-8005. Fax: 218-546-7287. p. 1247

Beshara, Dick, Ref Serv, Spec Coll & Archives Librn, South Dakota School of Mines & Technology, 501 E Saint Joseph St, Rapid City, SD, 57701-3995. Tel: 605-394-2418. Fax: 605-394-1256. p. 2217

Beshears, Lonetta, Dir, Sunbright Public Library, 142 Melton Dr, Sunbright, TN, 37872. Tel: 423-628-2439. Fax: 423-628-2439. p. 2266

Beske, Venice, Spec Projects Librn, Wyoming State Library, 2800 Central Ave, Cheyenne, WY, 82002. Tel: 307-777-6333. Fax: 307-777-6289. p. 2653

Besnoy, Amy, Sci, University of San Diego, Helen K & James S Copley Library, 5998 Alcala Park, San Diego, CA, 92110. Fax: 619-260-4617. p. 239

Beson, Kathy, Head, Ch, Menasha Public Library, 440 First St, Menasha, WI, 54952-3191. Tel: 920-967-3671. Fax: 920-967-5159. p. 2614

Bespalec, Judy, Per, Doane College, 1014 Boswell Ave, Crete, NE, 68333-2421. Tel: 402-826-8565. Fax: 402-826-8199. p. 1396

Bess, Bennett A, Librn, Pawnee Public Library, 613 Douglas St, Pawnee, IL, 62558. Tel: 217-625-7716. Fax: 217-625-7716. p. 689

Bess, Dorcas, Head, Circ Serv, East Central Georgia Regional Library, 902 Greene St, Augusta, GA, 30901. Tel: 706-821-2600. Fax: 706-724-6762. p. 519

Bess, Kathy, Circ Coordr, Holy Family University Library, 9801 Frankford Ave, Philadelphia, PA, 19114. Tel: 267-341-3315, 267-341-3316. Fax: 215-632-8067. p. 2111

Bess, Peter, Youth Serv Librn, Butler Area Public Library, 218 N McKean St, Butler, PA, 16001-4971. Tel: 724-287-1715, Ext 109. Fax: 724-285-5090. p. 2039

Besser, Brenda, Instr, Librn, Inver Hills Community College Library, 2500 80th St E, Inver Grove Heights, MN, 55076-3209. Tel: 651-450-3798. Fax: 651-450-3679. p. 1254

Bessette, Audrey, Librn, Bibliotheque Somerset Library, 289 Carlton Ave, Somerset, MB, R0G 2L0, CANADA. Tel: 204-744-2170. Fax: 204-744-2170. p. 2752

Bessler, Cindy, Tech Serv, Whittier College, Bonnie Bell Wardman Library, 7031 Founders Hill Rd, Whittier, CA, 90608-9984. Tel: 562-907-4247. Fax: 562-698-7168. p. 283

Best, Laurel, Exec Dir, Huntsville-Madison Public Library, 915 Monroe St, Huntsville, AL, 35801. Tel: 256-532-5940. Fax: 256-532-5997. p. 21

Best, Lynn, Acq, Tech Serv Librn, College of Southern Nevada, 6375 W Charleston Blvd, W10I, Las Vegas, NV, 89146. Tel: 702-651-5527. Fax: 702-651-5718. p. 1429

Best, Rae Ellen, Librn, United States House of Representatives Library, Cannon House Office Bldg, B-106, Legislative Resource Ctr, Washington, DC, 20515-6606. Tel: 202-226-5200. Fax: 202-226-4874. p. 420

Best, Reba A, Head, Cat, University of Tennessee, Taylor Law Center, 1505 W Cumberland Ave, Knoxville, TN, 37996-1800. Tel: 865-974-6728. Fax: 865-974-6571, 865-974-6595. p. 2243

Best, Rickey D, Coll Develop Librn, Auburn University, 7440 East Dr, Montgomery, AL, 36117. Tel: 334-244-3276. Fax: 334-244-3720. p. 28

Bester, Greg, Br Mgr, Cambridge Libraries & Galleries, Clemens Mill, 50 Saginaw Pkwy, Cambridge, ON, N1T 1W2, CANADA. Tel: 519-740-6294. Fax: 519-621-2080. p. 2798

Bestwick, Sandy, Dir, New Vineyard Public Library, 20 Lake St, New Vineyard, ME, 04956. Tel: 207-652-2250. p. 993

Beswick, Alexandra, Mgr, Cobb County Public Library System, Gritters, 880 Shaw Pk Rd, Marietta, GA, 30066. Tel: 770-528-2524. Fax: 770-528-2533. p. 543

Beswick, Laura, Libr Mgr, Vancouver Island Regional Library, Gold River Branch, 396 Nimpkish Dr, Gold River, BC, V0P 1G0, CANADA. Tel: 250-283-2502. Fax: 250-283-2552. p. 2732

Beswick, Laura, Libr Mgr, Vancouver Island Regional Library, Port Hardy Branch, 7110 Market, Port Hardy, BC, V0N 2P0, CANADA. Tel: 250-949-6661. Fax: 250-949-6600. p. 2733

Beswick, Laura, Libr Mgr, Vancouver Island Regional Library, Port McNeill Branch, Broughton Plaza, No 4, Port McNeill, BC, V0N 2R0, CANADA. Tel: 250-956-3669. Fax: 250-956-3669. p. 2733

Beswick, Laura, Libr Mgr, Vancouver Island Regional Library, Sayward Branch, Sayward Centre Mall, 641C Kelsey Way, Sayward, BC, V0P 1R0, CANADA. Tel: 250-282-5551. Fax: 250-282-5533. p. 2733

Beswick, Laura, Libr Mgr, Vancouver Island Regional Library, Sointula Branch, 280 First St, Sointula, BC, V0N 3E0, CANADA. Tel: 250-973-6493. Fax: 250-973-6493. p. 2733

Beswick, Laura, Libr Mgr, Vancouver Island Regional Library, Tahsis Branch, 977 S Maquinna, Tahsis, BC, V0P 1X0, CANADA. Tel: 250-934-6621. Fax: 250-934-6621. p. 2733

Betancourt, Ingrid, Supv Librn, Multilingual Serv, Newark Public Library, Five Washington St, Newark, NJ, 07101. Tel: 973-733-3637. Fax: 973-733-5648. p. 1511

Betcher, Audrey, Libr Dir, Rochester Public Library, 101 Second St SE, Rochester, MN, 55904-3776. Tel: 507-328-2344. Fax: 507-328-2384. p. 1273

Betchik, Kari, Dept Head, Tech Serv, Perry Public Library, 3753 Main St, Perry, OH, 44081-9501. Tel: 440-259-3300. Fax: 440-259-3977. p. 1929

Beteck, Ellis B, Dean of Libr, University of Maryland-Eastern Shore, 11868 Academic Oval, Princess Anne, MD, 21853. Tel: 410-651-2200, 410-651-6621. Fax: 410-651-6269. p. 1036

Beteilho, Amy, Librn, Consumer Health Information Program & Services, 12350 Imperial Hwy, Norwalk, CA, 90650. Tel: 562-868-4003. Fax: 562-868-4065. p. 2938

Beth, Amy, Dean, Libr Serv, Springfield Technical Community College Library, One Armory Sq, Ste 1, Springfield, MA, 01105-1685. Tel: 413-755-4531. Fax: 413-755-6315. p. 1128

Beth, Falenski, Ch, Huntington Woods Public Library, 26415 Scotia, Huntington Woods, MI, 48070-1198. Tel: 248-543-9720. Fax: 248-543-2559. p. 1193

Beth, Hoeffgen, YA Serv, Public Library of Mount Vernon & Knox County, 201 N Mulberry St, Mount Vernon, OH, 43050-2413. Tel: 740-392-2665. Fax: 740-397-3866. p. 1919

Beth, Sandy, ILL, Saint Mary's University of Minnesota, 700 Terrace Heights, No 26, Winona, MN, 55987-1399. Tel: 507-457-1561. Fax: 507-457-1565. p. 1289

Bethke, Sherri, Head, Continuing Coll, University of Iowa Libraries, Law Library, 200 Boyd Law Bldg, Iowa City, IA, 52242-1166. Tel: 319-335-9002. Fax: 319-335-9039. p. 823

Bethurem, Kip, Fac Mgr, Sheridan County Public Library System, 335 W Alger St, Sheridan, WY, 82801-3899. Tel: 307-674-8585, Ext 5. p. 2660

Betlejewski, Karen, Coordr, Del Norte County Historical Society Museum Library, 577 H St, Crescent City, CA, 95531. Tel: 707-464-3922. Fax: 707-464-7186. p. 137

Betsy, Erickson, Dir, Ephraim Public Library, 30 S Main St, Ephraim, UT, 84627. Tel: 435-283-4544. p. 2405

Bett, Bruce, Syst Librn, Macomb Community College Libraries, J-Bldg, 14500 E 12 Mile Rd, Warren, MI, 48088-3896. Tel: 586-445-7880. Fax: 586-445-7157. p. 1234

Bettag, Megan, Libr Asst, Indianapolis Museum of Art, 4000 Michigan Rd, Indianapolis, IN, 46208-3326. Tel: 317-920-2647. Fax: 317-926-8931. p. 754

Bettelyoun, Theresa, Outreach Coordr, Oglala Lakota College, Three Mile Creek Rd, Kyle, SD, 57752. Tel: 605-455-6069. Fax: 605-455-6070. p. 2213

Bettencourt, Patrick, Actg Dean, Modesto Junior College Library, 435 College Ave, Modesto, CA, 95350. Tel: 209-575-6062. Fax: 209-575-6669. p. 188

Bettig, Allen, Tech Spec, Glenview Public Library, 1930 Glenview Rd, Glenview, IL, 60025-2899. Tel: 847-729-7500. Fax: 847-729-7558. p. 651

Bettineski, Mari, Acq, Ser, Warner Pacific College, 2219 SE 68th Ave, Portland, OR, 97215-4099. Tel: 503-517-1023. Fax: 503-517-1351. p. 2015

Bettinger, Sheila, Dir, Ellisburg Free Library, 12117 State Rte 193, Ellisburg, NY, 13636. Tel: 315-846-5087. Fax: 315-846-5087. p. 1619

Betts, Joyce, Ch, Churchill County Library, 553 S Maine St, Fallon, NV, 89406-3387. Tel: 775-423-7581. Fax: 775-423-7766. p. 1427

Betts, Karen, AV, Cambria County Library System & District Center, 248 Main St, Johnstown, PA, 15901. Tel: 814-536-5131. Fax: 814-536-6905. p. 2073

Betts, Samantha, Mgr, Tech Serv, Fairfield County District Library, Northwest Branch, 2855 Helena Dr NW, Carroll, OH, 43112. Tel: 740-756-4391. p. 1909

Betts, Vicki, Cat/Ref Librn, University of Texas at Tyler Library, 3900 University Blvd, Tyler, TX, 75799. Tel: 905-566-7344. Fax: 903-566-2513. p. 2394

Betty, Claudia Michelle, Asst Dir, Ref Serv Librn, Art Center College of Design, 1700 Lida St, Pasadena, CA, 91103. Tel: 626-396-2231. Fax: 626-568-0428. p. 205

Betty, Jan, Coordr, Ch & Youth Serv, Milanof-Schock Library, 1184 Anderson Ferry Rd, Mount Joy, PA, 17552. Tel: 717-653-1510. Fax: 717-653-6590. p. 2093

Beturne, Cheryl, Ref, Enfield Public Library, 104 Middle Rd, Enfield, CT, 06082. Tel: 860-763-7510. Fax: 860-763-7514. p. 338

Betz, Margaret, Librn, New Florence Community Library, 122 Ligonier St, New Florence, PA, 15944. Tel: 724-235-2249. Fax: 724-235-2249. p. 2096

Betz, Pat, Dir, Glenn A Jones Memorial Library, 400 S Parish Ave, Johnstown, CO, 80534. Tel: 970-587-2459. Fax: 970-587-2352. p. 314

Beuch, Beth, Librn, Scott County Library System, New Market Public Library, 110 J Roberts Way, Elko New Market, MN, 55054. Tel: 952-496-8030. Fax: 952-496-8030. p. 1284

Beulah, Shauna, Head of Libr, Talbot County Free Library, Saint Michaels Branch, 106 N Fremont St, Saint Michaels, MD, 21663. Tel: 410-745-5877. Fax: 410-745-6937. p. 1027

Beutel, Eileen, Hub Supvr, Lake Agassiz Regional Library, Crookston Public Library, 110 N Ash St, Crookston, MN, 56716-1702. Tel: 218-281-4522. Fax: 218-281-4523. p. 1266

Beutler, Joan, Mgr, Foremost Municipal Library, 103 First Ave E, Foremost, AB, T0K 0X0, CANADA. Tel: 403-867-3855. Fax: 403-867-3856. p. 2704

Beutow, Geruth, Ref, Concordia University, 1282 Concordia Ave, Saint Paul, MN, 55104. Tel: 651-641-8244. Fax: 651-641-8782. p. 1278

Beutter Manus, Sara J, Educ & Outreach Music Librn, Vanderbilt University, Anne Potter Wilson Music Library, Blair School of Music, 2400 Blakemore Ave, Nashville, TN, 37212. Tel: 615-322-8686. Fax: 615-343-0050. p. 2261

Bevans, Marquita, Tech Serv, Parkland Regional Library, 5404 56th Ave, Lacombe, AB, T4L 1G1, CANADA. Tel: 403-782-3850. Fax: 403-782-4650. p. 2709

Bevecqua, Joanna, Head, Coll Develop, Borough of Manhattan Community College Library, 199 Chambers St, New York, NY, 10007. Tel: 212-220-1446. Fax: 212-748-7466. p. 1671

Bever, Diane J, Ref/Info Serv Librn, Indiana University Kokomo Library, 2300 S Washington St, Kokomo, IN, 46904. Tel: 765-455-9265. Fax: 765-455-9276. p. 758

Bever, Greta M, Asst Commissioner, Cent Libr Serv, Chicago Public Library, 400 S State St, Chicago, IL, 60605. Tel: 312-747-4300. Fax: 312-747-4968. p. 608

Bever, Greta M, Asst Commissioner, Cent Libr Serv, Chicago Public Library, Harold Washington Library Center, 400 S State St, Chicago, IL, 60605. Tel: 312-747-4070. Fax: 312-747-4077. p. 610

Beverage, Stephanie, Dir, Libr Serv, Huntington Beach Public Library System, 7111 Talbert Ave, Huntington Beach, CA, 92648. Tel: 714-842-4481. Fax: 714-375-5180. p. 158

Beveridge, Marguerite, Principal Librn, California Department of Justice, Attorney General's Law Library, 1300 I St, Sacramento, CA, 95814. Tel: 916-324-5312. Fax: 916-323-5342. p. 222

Beverley, Heather, Librn, Samson Public Library, 200 N Johnson St, Samson, AL, 36477-2006. Tel: 334-898-7806. Fax: 334-898-7806. p. 35

Beverly, Emily, Cat, Nottoway County Public Libraries, 414 Tyler St, Crewe, VA, 23930. Tel: 434-645-9310. Fax: 434-645-8513. p. 2458

Bevilacqua, Louise, Circ, Northern Essex Community College, 100 Elliott St, Haverhill, MA, 01830. Tel: 978-556-3422. Fax: 978-556-3738. p. 1094

Bevill, Gwen, Dir, Kennedale Public Library, 316 W Third St, Kennedale, TX, 76060-2202. Tel: 817-985-2136. Fax: 817-483-0660. p. 2349

Bevington, Mary Ann, Ch, Huron Public Library, 333 Williams St, Huron, OH, 44839. Tel: 419-433-5009. Fax: 419-433-7228. p. 1906

Bevins, Angela, Circ Serv, United States Air Force, 437 SVS/SVMG, 106 W McCaw St, Bldg 215, Charleston AFB, SC, 29404-4700. Tel: 843-963-3320. Fax: 843-963-3840. p. 2185

Bevins, Susan, Acq, Fletcher Free Library, 235 College St, Burlington, VT, 05401. Tel: 802-865-7221. Fax: 802-865-7227. p. 2420

Bevis, Mary, Acq, Periodicals Librn, Jacksonville State University Library, 700 Pelham Rd N, Jacksonville, AL, 36265. Tel: 256-782-5255. Fax: 256-782-5872. p. 22

Beyea, Marion, Dir, Provincial Archives of New Brunswick, 23 Dineen Dr, Fredericton, NB, E3B 5A3, CANADA. Tel: 506-453-2122. Fax: 506-453-3288. p. 2763

Beyeler, Jeri Ann, Libr Dir, Leadore Community Library, 202 S Railroad St, Leadore, ID, 83464-5022. Tel: 208-768-2640. p. 577

Beyer, Cindy, Ch, W J Niederkorn Library, 316 W Grand Ave, Port Washington, WI, 53074-2293. Tel: 262-284-5031. Fax: 262-284-7680. p. 2631

Beyer, Hope Elizabeth, Tech Serv Librn, South Plains College Library, 1401 S College Ave, Box E, Levelland, TX, 79336. Tel: 806-716-2302. Fax: 806-894-5274. p. 2355

Beyer, Laura, Head, Circ, Matawan-Aberdeen Public Library, 165 Main St, Matawan, NJ, 07747. Tel: 732-583-9100. Fax: 732-583-9360. p. 1500

Beyer, Marianne, Dir, South Hills School of Business & Technology Library, 508 58th St, Altoona, PA, 16602. Tel: 814-944-6134. Fax: 814-944-4684. p. 2028

Beyer, Robyn L, Dir, Libr & Res Serv, Pepper Hamilton LLP, 3000 Two Logan Sq, 18th & Arch Sts, Philadelphia, PA, 19103-2799. Tel: 215-981-4100, 215-981-4636. Fax: 215-981-4750. p. 2114

Beyer, Susan, Tech Serv Dir, Midwestern Baptist Theological Seminary Library, 5001 N Oak Trafficway, Kansas City, MO, 64118-4620. Tel: 816-414-3725. Fax: 816-414-3790. p. 1339

Beyerl, Christine, Head Librn, Willmar Public Library, 410 Fifth St SW, Willmar, MN, 56201-3298. Tel: 320-235-3162. Fax: 320-235-3169. p. 1289

Beynon, Susie, Pub Serv, Lambton County Library, 787 Broadway St, Wyoming, ON, N0N 1T0, CANADA. Tel: 519-337-3291. Fax: 519-845-0700. p. 2872

Bezanson, Debbie, Assoc Univ Librn, Res & User Serv, The George Washington University, 2130 H St NW, Ste 201, Washington, DC, 20052. Tel: 202-994-6455. Fax: 202-994-6464. p. 401

Bezio, Lynn, Librn, New York State Supreme Court Fourth District, 72 Clinton St, Plattsburgh, NY, 12901. Tel: 518-565-4808. Fax: 518-562-1193. p. 1719

Bezkorowajny, Carol, Automation Syst Coordr, Circ, Monroe Free Library, 44 Millpond Pkwy, Monroe, NY, 10950. Tel: 845-783-4411. Fax: 845-782-4707. p. 1662

Bhagwandin, John, Libr Mgr, New York Public Library - Astor, Lenox & Tilden Foundations, 58th Street Branch, 127 E 58th St, (Between Park & Lexington Aves), New York, NY, 10022-1211. Tel: 212-759-7358. Fax: 212-758-6858. p. 1691

Bhaskaran, Shanti, Supvr, Literacy Serv, Santa Clara City Library, 2635 Homestead Rd, Santa Clara, CA, 95051. Tel: 408-615-2957. Fax: 408-247-9657. p. 262

Bhaskaran, Shanti, Br Mgr, Head, Literacy, Santa Clara City Library, Mission Library Family Reading Center, 1098 Lexington St, Santa Clara, CA, 95050. Tel: 408-615-2957. Fax: 408-249-2486. p. 263

Bhatt, Anjana, Univ Librn, E-Res, Florida Gulf Coast University Library, 10501 FGCU Blvd S, Fort Myers, FL, 33965-6501. Tel: 239-590-7634. p. 444

Bhatt, Jay, Ref Librn, Drexel University Libraries, Hagerty Library, 33rd & Market Sts, Philadelphia, PA, 19104-2875. Tel: 215-895-1873. Fax: 215-895-2070. p. 2105

Bhattacharya, Rakhi, Br Mgr, Brooklyn Public Library, Highlawn, 1664 W 13th St, Brooklyn, NY, 11223. Tel: 718-234-7208. Fax: 718-234-7238. p. 1591

Bhogal, Surinder, Br Mgr, Surrey Public Library, Strawberry Hill, 7399- 122nd St, Surrey, BC, V3W 5J2, CANADA. Tel: 604-501-5841. Fax: 604-501-5846. p. 2739

Bhogal, Surinder, Dep Chief Librn, Surrey Public Library, 10350 University Dr, Surrey, BC, V3T 4B8, CANADA. Tel: 604-598-7304. Fax: 604-598-7310. p. 2739

Bhowal, Indira, Coll Mgt Serv Dir, Mississippi Library Commission, 3881 Eastwood Dr, Jackson, MS, 39211. Tel: 601-432-4119. Fax: 601-432-4480. p. 1304

Bhullar, Goodie, Coordr, Libr Instruction, University of Missouri-Columbia, Elmer Ellis Library, Ellis Library Bldg, Rm 104, Columbia, MO, 65201-5149. Tel: 573-882-9163. Fax: 573-882-8044. p. 1325

Biagi, Damian, Cat Librn, Western New England University, 1215 Wilbraham Rd, Springfield, MA, 01119. Tel: 413-782-1635. Fax: 413-796-2011. p. 1128

Biagini, Mary Kay, Assoc Dean, Prof, University of Pittsburgh, 135 N Bellefield Ave, Pittsburgh, PA, 15260. Tel: 412-624-5230. Fax: 412-624-5231. p. 2973

Biagiotti, Joseph L, Asst Dir, Cadwalader, Wickersham & Taft Library, One World Financial Ctr, New York, NY, 10281. Tel: 212-504-6767. Fax: 212-993-3351. p. 1671

Biaja, Christie, Librn, Putnam County Public Library District, Standard Branch, 128 First St, Standard, IL, 61363. Tel: 815-339-2471. Fax: 815-339-2471. p. 655

Bianchi, June, ILL, Ser, Cape Cod Hospital, 27 Park St, Hyannis, MA, 02601-5230. Tel: 508-862-5867. Fax: 774-552-6904. p. 1096

Bianchi, Marcia, Cat, Reed College, 3203 SE Woodstock Blvd, Portland, OR, 97202-8199. Tel: 503-777-7702. Fax: 503-777-7786. p. 2014

Bianchi, Terra, Univ Archivist, University of Texas at Tyler Library, 3900 University Blvd, Tyler, TX, 75799. Tel: 903-565-5849. Fax: 903-566-2513. p. 2394

Bianco, Elena, Tech Serv, Skagit Valley College, 2405 E College Way, Mount Vernon, WA, 98273-5899. Tel: 360-416-7624. Fax: 360-416-7698. p. 2521

Bianco, Mary, Ch, Hyannis Public Library Association, 401 Main St, Hyannis, MA, 02601-3019. Tel: 508-775-2280. Fax: 508-790-0087. p. 1096

Bias, Peggy, Dir, Bedford Public Library System, 321 N Bridge St, Bedford, VA, 24523-1924. Tel: 540-586-8911, Ext 1112. Fax: 540-586-8875. p. 2450

Bias, Randolph, Assoc Prof, University of Texas at Austin, One University Sta, D7000, Austin, TX, 78712-0390. Tel: 512-471-3821. Fax: 512-471-3971. p. 2975

Bibb, David, Dir, University of Great Falls Library, 1301 20th St S, Great Falls, MT, 59405-4948. Tel: 406-791-5315. Fax: 406-791-5395. p. 1380

Bibbins, Roberta F, Dir, Orangeburg County Library, 510 Louis St, Orangeburg, SC, 29115-5030. Tel: 803-533-5854. Fax: 803-533-5860. p. 2201

Bibbs, Brenda, Br Mgr, Aiken-Bamberg-Barnwell-Edgefield Regional Library System, Mobley Library/Johnston Branch, 407 Calhoun St, Johnston, SC, 29832. Tel: 803-275-5157. Fax: 803-275-2754. p. 2179

Biberman, Caren, Dir, Libr Serv, Cahill, Gordon & Reindel Library, 80 Pine St, New York, NY, 10005. Tel: 212-701-3542. Fax: 212-269-5420. p. 1671

Bible, Ann, Dir, Defiance College, 201 College Pl, Defiance, OH, 43512-1667. Tel: 419-783-2490. Fax: 419-783-2594. p. 1895

Bible, Mitzi, Asst Librn, The T Elmer Cox Library, 229 N Main St, Greeneville, TN, 37745. Tel: 423-638-9866. p. 2236

Bibler, Helen A, Dir, Ravalli County Museum, 205 Bedford, Hamilton, MT, 59840. Tel: 406-363-3338. Fax: 406-363-6588. p. 1381

Biblo, Herbert, Dir, Long Island Library Resources Council, 627 N Sunrise Service Rd, Bellport, NY, 11713. Tel: 631-675-1570. p. 2950

Bichan, Renee, Ch, Auburn Public Library, 369 Southbridge St, Auburn, MA, 01501. Tel: 508-832-7790. Fax: 508-832-7792. p. 1051

Bichel, Rebecca, Dean of Libr, University of Texas at Arlington Library, 702 Planetarium Pl, Arlington, TX, 76019. Tel: 817-272-0368. Fax: 817-272-5797. p. 2277

Bicicchi, Rachel, Coordr, Educ Tech, Millikin University, 1184 W Main, Decatur, IL, 62522. Tel: 217-424-6214. Fax: 217-424-3992. p. 634

Bick, Israel, Exec Dir, International Stamp Collectors Society Library, PO Box 854, Van Nuys, CA, 91408-0854. Tel: 818-997-6496. p. 279

Bickers, Patrick, Head, ILL & Grad Student Serv, University of Missouri-Kansas City Libraries, 800 E 51st St, Kansas City, MO, 64110. Tel: 816-235-2225. Fax: 816-333-5584. p. 1341

Bickerstaff, Rhonda, Librn, New Madrid County Library, New Madrid Memorial, 431 Mill St, New Madrid, MO, 63869. Tel: 573-748-2378. Fax: 573-748-7637. p. 1350

Bickford, Jane, Br Librn, Boston Public Library, Connolly, 433 Centre St, Jamaica Plain, MA, 02130-1895. Tel: 617-522-1960. Fax: 617-971-0695. p. 1057

Bickford, Louella, Dir, Lawrence Public Library, 33 Lawrence Ave, Fairfield, ME, 04937. Tel: 207-453-6867. Fax: 207-453-6867. p. 985

Bickford, Nancy, Acq & Per Mgr, The University of Findlay, 1000 N Main St, Findlay, OH, 45840-3695. Tel: 419-434-4617. p. 1899

Bickle, Carol, Librn, Heritage Christian Reformed Church Library, 2857 S 11th, Kalamazoo, MI, 49009. Tel: 269-372-3830. Fax: 269-372-5939. p. 1197

Bickley, Sally, Head, Ref Serv, Del Mar College, 101 Baldwin Blvd, Corpus Christi, TX, 78404. Tel: 361-698-1310. Fax: 361-698-1182. p. 2302

Bicknell, Kenneth, Digital Res Librn, Los Angeles County Metropolitan Transportation Authority, One Gateway Plaza, 15th Flr, Mail Stop 99-15-1, Los Angeles, CA, 90012-2952. Tel: 213-933-4861. p. 172

Bicknell-Holmes, Tracy, Prof, University of Nebraska-Lincoln, Engineering Library, Nebraska Hall, Rm W204, City Campus 0516, Lincoln, NE, 68588-0516. Tel: 402-472-3411. Fax: 402-472-0663. p. 1407

Bicknese, Douglas, Archivist, National Archives & Records Administration, 7358 S Pulaski Rd, Chicago, IL, 60629-5898. Tel: 773-948-9001. Fax: 773-948-9050. p. 619

Bidding, Patricia, Dir, Ralpho Township Public Library, 32B Market St, Elysburg, PA, 17824. Tel: 570-672-9449. p. 2054

Biddinger, Edith, Asst Dir, Oelwein Public Library, 201 E Charles St, Oelwein, IA, 50662-1939. Tel: 319-283-1515. Fax: 319-283-6646. p. 836

Biddle, Cori, Info Literacy Librn, Bridgewater College, 402 E College St, Bridgewater, VA, 22812. Tel: 540-828-5415. Fax: 540-828-5482. p. 2452

Biddle, Daniel, Supvr, New York University, Institute of Fine Arts Conservation Center Library, 14 E 78th St, New York, NY, 10075. Tel: 212-992-5854. Fax: 212-992-5851. p. 1695

Biddle, Joan, Ch, Holmes County Public Library, 303 N J Harvey Etheridge, Bonifay, FL, 32425. Tel: 850-547-3573. Fax: 850-547-2801. p. 429

Biddle, Nina, Br Mgr, Sacramento Public Library, Central Library, 828 I St, Sacramento, CA, 95814. p. 224

Biden, Ann-Marie, Youth Serv Librn, Upland Public Library, 450 N Euclid Ave, Upland, CA, 91786-4732. Tel: 909-931-4215. Fax: 909-931-4209. p. 278

Bidney, Marcy, Head, Map Coll, Pennsylvania State University Libraries, The Donald W Hamer Maps Library, 001 Pattee Library, B-level, Curtin Rd, University Park, PA, 16802-1807. Tel: 814-863-0094. p. 2148

Bidwell, Lynne, Electronic Res, Librn, Lewis-Clark State College Library, 500 Eighth Ave, Lewiston, ID, 83501. Tel: 208-792-2438. Fax: 208-792-2831. p. 578

Bidwell, Mary, Dir, Henderson Free Library, 8939 New York State Rte 178, Henderson, NY, 13650. Tel: 315-938-7169. Fax: 315-938-7038. p. 1635

Bieber, Annemarie, In Charge, Eastern Counties Regional Library, Cyril Ward Memorial, 27 Pleasant St, Guysborough, NS, B0H 1N0, CANADA. Tel: 902-533-3586. p. 2784

Bieber, Ashley, Youth Serv Mgr, Rice Lake Public Library, Two E Marshall St, Rice Lake, WI, 54868. Tel: 715-234-4861. Fax: 715-234-5026. p. 2633

Bieber, Karla, Libr Dir, A H Brown Public Library, 521 N Main St, Mobridge, SD, 57601-2130. Tel: 605-845-2808. p. 2216

Biederman, Sue, Dir, Everly Public Library, 308 N Main St, Everly, IA, 51338-0265. Tel: 712-834-2390. Fax: 712-834-2390. p. 815

Biegun, Teresa, Info Serv Librn, Macomb Community College Libraries, Center Campus, C-Bldg, 44575 Garfield Rd, Clinton Township, MI, 48038-1139. Tel: 586-286-2233. Fax: 586-286-2002. p. 1234

Biehl, Brenda, Mgr, Sequoyah Regional Library System, Rose Creek Public, 4476 Towne Lake Pkwy, Woodstock, GA, 30189. Tel: 770-591-1491. Fax: 770-591-1693. p. 523

Biehl, Vicki, Head, Adult Serv, Pearl River Public Library, 80 Franklin Ave, Pearl River, NY, 10965. Tel: 845-735-4084. Fax: 845-735-4041. p. 1716

Biel, Sally, Librn, Pennsylvania Historical & Museum Commission, 400 North St, Plaza Level, Harrisburg, PA, 17120-0053. Tel: 717-783-9898. Fax: 717-214-2989. p. 2066

Bielanski, Ruth, Ch, Manville Public Library, 100 S Tenth Ave, Manville, NJ, 08835. Tel: 908-722-9722. Fax: 908-722-0631. p. 1499

Bielavitz, Tom, Asst Univ Librn, Admin Serv & Planning, Portland State University Library, 1875 SW Park Ave, Portland, OR, 97201-3220. Tel: 503-725-4576. Fax: 503-725-4524. p. 2014

Bielawa, Michael, Commun Relations Librn, Bridgeport Public Library, 925 Broad St, Bridgeport, CT, 06604. Tel: 203-576-7413. Fax: 203-576-8255. p. 331

Bielawa, Michael, Head Librn, Bridgeport Public Library, Newfield, 1230 Stratford Ave, Bridgeport, CT, 06607. Tel: 203-576-7828. p. 331

Bielawski, Marvin F, Dep Univ Librn, Syst Coordr, Princeton University, One Washington Rd, Princeton, NJ, 08544-2098. Tel: 609-258-3190. Fax: 609-258-0441. p. 1523

Bielefield, Arlene, Dr, Assoc Prof, Southern Connecticut State University, 501 Crescent St, New Haven, CT, 06515. Tel: 203-392-5708. Fax: 203-392-5780. p. 2963

Bielman, Paul Francis, Librn, Kaiser-Permanente Medical Center, 4647 Zion Ave, San Diego, CA, 92120. Tel: 619-528-7323. Fax: 619-528-3444. p. 231

Bielot, Alixe M, Dir, Mayville Public Library, 111 N Main St, Mayville, WI, 53050. Tel: 920-387-7910. Fax: 920-387-7917. p. 2613

Bielsen, Heidi, Archivist, Plymouth Historical Museum Archives, 155 S Main St, Plymouth, MI, 48170-1635. Tel: 734-455-8940. Fax: 734-455-7797. p. 1218

Bielskas, Amanda, Librn, Columbia University, Geology, 601 Schermerhorn, 1190 Amsterdam Ave, New York, NY, 10027. Tel: 212-854-6767. Fax: 212-854-4716. p. 1674

Bielskas, Amanda, Librn, Columbia University, Lamont-Doherty Geoscience Library, Lamont-Doherty Earth Observatory, 61 Rte 9 W, PO Box 1000, Palisades, NY, 10964-8000. Tel: 845-365-8809. Fax: 845-365-8151. p. 1674

Bieniek, Cynthia, Archivist, Saint Clair Shores Public Library, 22500 11 Mile Rd, Saint Clair Shores, MI, 48081-1399. Tel: 586-771-9020. Fax: 586-771-8935. p. 1224

Bierbauer, Charles, Dean, University of South Carolina, 1501 Greene St, Columbia, SC, 29208. Tel: 803-777-4105. Fax: 803-777-4103. p. 2973

Bierman, James, Eng Librn, University of Oklahoma, Engineering, Engineering Library, 222FH, 865 Asp Ave, Norman, OK, 73019. Tel: 405-325-2941. Fax: 405-325-0345. p. 1971

Biermann, Sandra, Mkt, Strategic Planning, Battelle Energy Alliance, LLC, 1776 Science Center Dr, MS 2300, Idaho Falls, ID, 83415-2300. Tel: 208-526-1185. Fax: 208-526-0211. p. 576

Biermann, Sandra, Strategic Planning, Tech Enhancement, Idaho National Laboratory, 1765 N Yellowstone Hwy, Idaho Falls, ID, 83415-2300. Tel: 208-526-8126. Fax: 208-526-0211. p. 576

Biesterfeld, Brenda, Br Mgr, Tulare County Library, Lindsay Branch, 157 N Mirage St, Lindsay, CA, 93247. Tel: 559-562-3021. Fax: 559-562-5066. p. 281

Biesterfeld, Patricia, Interim Exec Dir, Traverse Des Sioux Library System, 1400 Madison Ave, Ste 622, Mankato, MN, 56001-5488. Tel: 507-625-6169. Fax: 507-625-4049. p. 1257

Bieterman, Karen, Librn, American Society of Anesthesiologists, 520 N Northwest Hwy, Park Ridge, IL, 60068-2573. Tel: 847-825-5586, Ext 58. Fax: 847-825-1692. p. 688

Bifolco, Pat, Tech Serv, Franklin Square Public Library, 19 Lincoln Rd, Franklin Square, NY, 11010. Tel: 516-488-3444. Fax: 516-354-3368. p. 1624

Bigam, Joyce, Ch, Cuyahoga Falls Library, 2015 Third St, Cuyahoga Falls, OH, 44221-3294. Tel: 330-928-2117, Ext 122. Fax: 330-928-2535. p. 1892

Bigard, Lydia, Br Mgr, Clayton County Library System, Forest Park Branch, 696 Main St, Forest Park, GA, 30297. Tel: 404-366-0850. Fax: 404-366-0884. p. 537

Bigelow, Deborah, Dir, Leonia Public Library, 227 Fort Lee Rd, Leonia, NJ, 07605. Tel: 201-592-5776. Fax: 201-592-5775. p. 1495

Bigelow, Jan, Librn, Westview Christian Reformed Church Library, 2929 Leonard St NW, Grand Rapids, MI, 49504. Tel: 616-453-3105. Fax: 616-453-8891. p. 1186

Bigelow, Lynne, Ch, Youth Serv, Iosco-Arenac District Library, 120 W Westover St, East Tawas, MI, 48730. Tel: 989-362-2651. Fax: 989-362-6056. p. 1175

Bigelow, Risha, Librn, Alamance County Public Libraries, North Park, North Park Community Ctr, 849 Sharpe Rd, Burlington, NC, 27217. Tel: 336-226-7185. Fax: 336-513-5425. p. 1779

Bigelow, Rosemary, Tech Serv, Rockport Public Library, 17 School St, Rockport, MA, 01966. Tel: 978-546-6934. Fax: 978-546-1011. p. 1121

Biger, Jackie, Head, Ch, Amherst Town Library, 14 Main St, Amherst, NH, 03031-2930. Tel: 603-673-2288. Fax: 603-672-6063. p. 1437

Biggar, George, Sr Syst Adminr, Rensselaer Libraries, Rensselaer Polytechnic Inst, 110 Eighth St, Troy, NY, 12180-3590. Tel: 518-276-8300. Fax: 518-276-2044. p. 1756

Bigger, Jean, Tech Serv, Illinois Mathematics & Science Academy, 1500 W Sullivan Rd, Aurora, IL, 60506-1000. Tel: 630-907-5920. Fax: 630-907-5004. p. 591

Bigger, Samantha, Libr Tech Spec, Boulder City Library, 701 Adams Blvd, Boulder City, NV, 89005-2697. Tel: 702-293-1281. Fax: 702-293-0239. p. 1425

Biggerstaff, Marilyn, Librn, Nowata City-County Library, 224 S Pine, Nowata, OK, 74048. Tel: 918-273-3363. Fax: 918-273-1818. p. 1971

Biggerstaff, Vicki, Tech Serv Librn, Siouxland Libraries, 200 N Dakota Ave, Sioux Falls, SD, 57104. Tel: 605-367-8703. Fax: 605-367-4312. p. 2218

Biggins, Shelia, Br Mgr, Faulkner-Van Buren Regional Library System, Vilonia Branch, Three Bise Dr, Vilonia, AR, 72173. Tel: 501-796-8520. Fax: 501-796-8753. p. 97

Biggs, Eric, Pub Serv, Saint John's River State College, Orange Park Center Library, 283 College Dr, Orange Park, FL, 32065-6751. Tel: 904-276-6831. Fax: 904-276-6796. p. 479

Biggs, Joyce, Librn, Selover Public Library, 31 State Rte 95, Chesterville, OH, 43317-0025. Tel: 419-768-3431. Fax: 419-768-2249. p. 1867

Bigham, Jacquelyn, Res, International Brotherhood of Teamsters, 25 Louisiana Ave NW, Washington, DC, 20001. Tel: 202-624-6929. Fax: 202-624-6910. p. 405

Bighetty, Merle, Head Librn, Tawowikamik Public Library, PO Box 100, Pelican Narrows, SK, S0P 0E0, CANADA. Tel: 306-632-2161. Fax: 306-632-2022. p. 2920

Bigley, Kathy, Br Mgr, Mid-Continent Public Library, Parkville Branch, 8815 Tom Watson Pkwy, Parkville, MO, 64152-3522. Tel: 816-741-4721. Fax: 816-741-6215. p. 1333

Bigley, Nikki, Mat Mgr, Cecil County Public Library, 301 Newark Ave, Elkton, MD, 21921-5441. Tel: 410-996-5600. Fax: 410-996-5604. p. 1027

Biglin, Karen, Coll Develop, Scottsdale Community College Library, 9000 E Chaparral Rd, Scottsdale, AZ, 85256. Tel: 480-423-6434. Fax: 480-423-6666. p. 80

Biglow, Carolyn, Librn, National Institute for Occupational Safety & Health, Cochrans Mill Rd, Pittsburgh, PA, 15236. Tel: 412-386-4431. Fax: 412-386-4592. p. 2126

Bigman, Deanna, Acq, Cat, Page Public Library, 479 S Lake Powell Blvd, Page, AZ, 86040. Tel: 928-645-4270. Fax: 928-645-5804. p. 70

Bignotti, Ken, YA Serv, Livonia Public Library, Alfred Noble Branch, 32901 Plymouth Rd, Livonia, MI, 48150-1793. Tel: 734-421-6600. Fax: 734-421-6606. p. 1203

Bigwood, David, Tech Serv, Lunar & Planetary Institute, 3600 Bay Area Blvd, Houston, TX, 77058-1113. Tel: 281-486-2134. Fax: 281-486-2186. p. 2341

Bihl, Elisabeth, Exec Dir, Canadian Music Centre, 20 St Joseph St, Toronto, ON, M4Y 1J9, CANADA. Tel: 416-961-6601, Ext 204. Fax: 416-961-7198. p. 2851

Bikman, Margaret, Instruction & Ref Librn, Whatcom Community College Library, 237 W Kellogg Rd, Bellingham, WA, 98226. Tel: 360-383-3300. p. 2509

Bilal, Dania, Prof, University of Tennessee, Knoxville, 451 Communications Bldg, 1345 Circle Park Dr, Knoxville, TN, 37996-0341. Tel: 865-974-2148. Fax: 865-974-4967. p. 2974

Bilby, Sean, Coll Develop Librn, Norfolk Public Library, 235 E Plume St, Norfolk, VA, 23510-1706. Tel: 757-664-7323. Fax: 757-441-5863. p. 2481

Bildon, Vanessa, Br Mgr, Dillon County Library, Latta Branch, 101 N Marion St, Latta, SC, 29565-3597. Tel: 843-752-5389. Fax: 843-752-7457. p. 2193

Bildstein, Keith, Dir, Acopian Center for Conservation Learning, 410 Summer Valley Rd, Orwigsburg, PA, 17961. Tel: 570-943-3411, Ext 101. Fax: 570-943-2284. p. 2101

Biles, William, Br Mgr, Lexington Public Library, Beaumont, 3080 Fieldstone Way, Lexington, KY, 40513. Tel: 859-231-5500. Fax: 859-422-6878. p. 921

Bilger, Stephanie Marie, Med Libr Tech, Lewistown Hospital, 400 Highland Ave, Lewistown, PA, 17044-9983. Tel: 717-242-7242, 717-248-5411. Fax: 717-242-7245. p. 2081

Bilinsky, Marcia, Acq of Monographs, College of Physicians & Surgeons of British Columbia, 100-1383 W Eighth Ave, Vancouver, BC, V6H 4C4, CANADA. Tel: 604-733-6671. Fax: 604-737-8582. p. 2740

Bilka, Hazel A, Librn, Bellwood-Antis Public Library, 526 Main St, Bellwood, PA, 16617-1910. Tel: 814-742-8234. Fax: 814-742-8235. p. 2032

Bilko, Kathy, Librn, Banner Desert Medical Center, 1400 S Dobson Rd, Mesa, AZ, 85202. Tel: 480-512-3024. Fax: 480-512-8720. p. 68

Bill, Jon, Archivist, Auburn Cord Duesenberg Museum, 1600 S Wayne St, Auburn, IN, 46706-3509. Tel: 260-925-1444, Ext 19. Fax: 260-925-6266. p. 725

Bill, Julie, YA Serv, Lee County Library System, East County Regional, 881 Gunnery Rd N, Lehigh Acres, FL, 33971. Tel: 239-461-7307. Fax: 239-461-7321. p. 445

Bill, Leah, Asst Dir, Coal City Public Library District, 85 N Garfield St, Coal City, IL, 60416. Tel: 815-634-4552. Fax: 815-634-2950. p. 630

Billbrough, Dorothy, Dir, Colby Memorial Library, Seven Colby Rd, Danville, NH, 03819-5104. Tel: 603-382-6733. Fax: 603-382-0487. p. 1444

Billerbeck, Ann Rae, Asst Librn, Reinbeck Public Library, 501 Clark St, Reinbeck, IA, 50669. Tel: 319-788-2652. Fax: 319-788-2826. p. 840

Billesberger, Valerie, Archivist, Mission Community Archives, 33215 Second Ave, Mission, BC, V2V 4L1, CANADA. Tel: 604-820-2621. p. 2732

Billhartz, Joe, Asst Librn, Trenton Public Library, 118 E Indiana, Trenton, IL, 62293. Tel: 618-224-7662. Fax: 618-224-7671. p. 710

Billiar, Joanne, Librn, Saint Vincent Charity Hospital, 2351 E 22nd St, Cleveland, OH, 44115-3197. Tel: 216-241-5118. Fax: 216-363-3337. p. 1881

Billings, Cathy, Librn Spec, Glendale Public Library, Brand Library & Art Center, 1601 W Mountain St, Glendale, CA, 91201-1209. Tel: 818-548-2713. Fax: 818-548-5079. p. 155

Billings, Christy, Circ Asst, Russell Library, 123 Broad St, Middletown, CT, 06457. Tel: 860-347-2528, Ext 159. p. 352

Billings, Joann, Ser, Henry Ford Community College, 5101 Evergreen Rd, Dearborn, MI, 48128-1495. Tel: 313-845-6371. Fax: 313-845-9795. p. 1167

Billings, Julie, Librn, Silver Bay Public Library, Nine Davis Dr, Silver Bay, MN, 55614-1318. Tel: 218-226-4331. p. 1284

Billings, Marilyn, Scholarly Communication/Spec Initiatives Librn, University of Massachusetts Amherst, 154 Hicks Way, Amherst, MA, 01003-9275. Tel: 413-545-6891. Fax: 413-545-6873. p. 1049

Billings, Marilyn, Supvr, Haliburton County Public Library, Gooderham Branch, 1032 Gooderham St, Gooderham, ON, K0M 1R0, CANADA. Tel: 705-447-3163. p. 2808

Billings, Mary, Assoc Librn, Reader Serv, Hartford Public Library, 500 Main St, Hartford, CT, 06103-3075. Tel: 860-695-6335. Fax: 860-722-6870. p. 346

Billings, Melinda, Dir, Adult Ministries, Westminster Presbyterian Church Library, 3906 W Friendly Ave, Greensboro, NC, 27410. Tel: 336-299-3785. Fax: 336-299-5837. p. 1798

Billings, Shane Malcolm, Ad, Charles M Bailey Public Library, 39 Bowdoin St, Winthrop, ME, 04364. Tel: 207-377-8673. p. 1007

Billings, Victoria A, Tech Serv, Portage County Public Library, Charles M White Library Bldg, 1001 Main St, Stevens Point, WI, 54481-2860. Tel: 715-346-1544. Fax: 715-346-1239. p. 2640

Billington, James H, Dr, Librn of Congress, Library of Congress, 101 Independence Ave at First St SE, Washington, DC, 20540. Tel: 202-707-5205. Fax: 202-707-1925. p. 406

Billinsky, Christyn G, Sr Instr, University of South Carolina, 1501 Greene St, Columbia, SC, 29208. Tel: 803-777-3858. Fax: 803-777-7938. p. 2973

Billman, Brooke, AZHIN Librn, University of Arizona, Arizona Health Sciences Library, 1501 N Campbell Ave, Tucson, AZ, 85724. Tel: 520-626-1544. Fax: 520-626-2922. p. 88

Billops, Camille, Archivist, Hatch-Billops Collection, Inc Library, 491 Broadway, 7th Flr, New York, NY, 10012. Tel: 212-966-3231. Fax: 212-966-3231. p. 1681

Bills, Linda Gail, Dir, Allegheny College Library, 555 N Main St, Meadville, PA, 16335. Tel: 814-332-3362. Fax: 814-337-5673. p. 2086

Billson, Virginia, Br Mgr, Willoughby-Eastlake Public Library, Eastlake Branch, 36706 Lake Shore Blvd, Eastlake, OH, 44095. Tel: 440-942-7880. Fax: 440-942-4095. p. 1949

Billy, George J, Dr, Dir, United States Merchant Marine Academy, 300 Steamboat Rd, Kings Point, NY, 11024-1699. Tel: 516-726-5747. Fax: 516-726-5900. p. 1649

Bilobeau, Justine, In Charge, Hopital L'Hotel-Dieu de Quebec, 11 Cote du Palais, Quebec, QC, G1R 2J6, CANADA. Tel: 418-525-4444. Fax: 418-691-5468. p. 2905

Bilodeau, Guy, Head Librn, Universite Laval Bibliotheque, Bibliotheque Scientifique, Pavillon Alexandre-Vachon, 1045 rue de la Médecine, Quebec, QC, G1V 0A6, CANADA. Tel: 418-656-2131, Ext 2948. Fax: 418-656-7699. p. 2907

Bilodeau, Nancy, Mgr, Ch Serv, Bibliotheque Municipale de Gatineau, Édifice Pierre Papin, CP 1970 Succ. Hull, Gatineau, QC, J8X 3Y9, CANADA. p. 2882

Bilsky, Tammy, Librn, Palliser Regional Library, Holdfast Branch, 125 Roberts St, Holdfast, SK, S0G 2H0, CANADA. Tel: 306-488-2140. p. 2918

Bilsland, Mary Jane, Mgr, Edmonton Public Library, Strathcona, 8331 104th St, Edmonton, AB, T6E 4E9, CANADA. Tel: 780-496-1828. Fax: 780-496-1451. p. 2700

Biltz, Michael, Dir, Pub Serv, Dodge City Public Library, 1001 N Second Ave, Dodge City, KS, 67801-4484. Tel: 620-225-0248. Fax: 620-225-2761. p. 863

Bilyeu, Barbara, Ref, Paso Robles Public Library, 1000 Spring St, Paso Robles, CA, 93446-2207. Tel: 805-237-3870. Fax: 805-238-3665. p. 207

Bilyeu, Crystal, Ch, Cedar City Public Library in the Park, 303 N 100 East, Cedar City, UT, 84720. Tel: 435-586-6661. Fax: 435-865-7280. p. 2404

Bilyeu, David, Col Librn, Central Oregon Community College Barber Library, 2600 NW College Way, Bend, OR, 97701-5998. Tel: 541-383-7563. Fax: 541-383-7406. p. 1991

Bilyeu, Jennifer, Adult Serv, Cat, Seneca Public Library District, 210 N Main St, Seneca, IL, 61360. Tel: 815-357-6566. Fax: 815-357-6568. p. 701

Bilyj, Diane, Coordr, Manitoba School for the Deaf Multimedia Center, 242 Stradford St, Winnipeg, MB, R2Y 2C9, CANADA. Tel: 204-945-8934. Fax: 204-945-1767. p. 2757

Bindeman, Marie E, Dir, Lockport Public Library, 23 East Ave, Lockport, NY, 14094. Tel: 716-433-5935. Fax: 716-439-0198. p. 1653

Bindeman, Thomas C, Exec Dir, Nioga Library System, 6575 Wheeler Rd, Lockport, NY, 14094. Tel: 716-434-6167, Ext 24. Fax: 716-434-8231. p. 1653

Binder, Amanda, Instrul Serv, University of Illinois at Springfield, One University Plaza, MS BRK-140, Springfield, IL, 62703-5407. Tel: 217-206-8458. Fax: 217-206-6354. p. 707

Binder, Carley, Libr Mgr, Blackfalds Public Library, 5018 Waghorn St, Blackfalds, AB, T0M 0J0, CANADA. Tel: 403-885-2343. Fax: 403-885-4353. p. 2685

Binderman, Mary, Dir, Libr & Info Serv, American Occupational Therapy Foundation, 4720 Montgomery Lane, Bethesda, MD, 20814-5385. Tel: 301-652-6611, Ext 2557. Fax: 301-656-3620. p. 1021

Bindler, Elaine, Librn, West Milford Township Library, 1490 Union Valley Rd, West Milford, NJ, 07480. Tel: 973-728-2820. Fax: 973-728-2106. p. 1541

Bindman, Rachel, Br Mgr, Los Angeles Public Library System, Venice-Abbot Kinney Memorial, 501 S Venice Blvd, Venice, CA, 90291-3440. Tel: 310-821-2065. Fax: 310-756-9283. p. 174

Bineault, Marc, Librn, Bois-Des-Filion Library, 60, 36 ie'me Ave S, Bois-des-Filion, QC, J6Z 2J6, CANADA. Tel: 450-621-2041. Fax: 450-621-8483. p. 2880

Bineault, Marc, Dir, Bibliotheque H J Hemens, 339 Chemin Grande-Cote, Rosemere, QC, J7A 1K2, CANADA. Tel: 450-621-6132. Fax: 450-621-6131. p. 2907

Binford, Marilyn, Bus Mgr, Ouachita Parish Public Library, 1800 Stubbs Ave, Monroe, LA, 71201. Tel: 318-327-1490. Fax: 318-327-1373. p. 957

Bing, Meagan, Circ, YA Serv, Orange Beach Public Library, 26267 Canal Rd, Orange Beach, AL, 36561-3917. Tel: 251-981-2923. Fax: 251-981-2920. p. 33

Bingel, Laurie, Dean, Southwestern Illinois College Library, 2500 Carlyle Ave, Belleville, IL, 62221. Tel: 618-235-2700, Ext 5204. Fax: 618-222-8964. p. 593

Bingham, Betty L, Dir, Jackson County Public Library, 118 US Hwy, 421 N, McKee, KY, 40447. Tel: 606-287-8113. Fax: 606-287-7774. p. 928

Bingham, Sherree, Ser/Gifts/Acq, Allegheny College Library, 555 N Main St, Meadville, PA, 16335. Tel: 814-332-2968. Fax: 814-337-5673. p. 2086

Bingham-Green, Erica, Libr Spec, Stephentown Memorial Library, 472 State Rte 43, Stephentown, NY, 12168. Tel: 518-733-5750. p. 1748

Bingham-Harper, Pat, Cat, Spec Coll Librn, Florida State University Libraries, College of Law Library, 425 W Jefferson St, Tallahassee, FL, 32306. Tel: 850-644-4578. Fax: 850-644-5216. p. 494

Binkholder, Mary Ann, Pres, Gerald Area Library, 357 S Main St, Gerald, MO, 63037. Tel: 573-764-7323. p. 1329

Binkley, Glennys, Librn, Wapiti Regional Library, Hudson Bay Public Library, 130 Main St, Hudson Bay, SK, S0E 0Y0, CANADA. Tel: 306-865-3110. p. 2921

Binkley, Timothy, Archivist, United Theological Seminary Library, 4501 Denlinger Rd, Trotwood, OH, 45426. Tel: 937-529-2201, Ext 3400. Fax: 937-529-2292. p. 1941

Binkley, Veta, Head, Tech Serv, Valley Cottage Free Library, 110 Rte 303, Valley Cottage, NY, 10989. Tel: 845-268-7700. Fax: 845-268-7760. p. 1760

Binkley, Yildiz Barlas, Dr, Dean, Libr & Media Ctr, Tennessee State University, 3500 John A Merritt Blvd, Nashville, TN, 37209. Tel: 615-963-5211. Fax: 615-963-5216. p. 2259

Binkowski, Kraig, Dir, Ref Libr & Archives, Yale University Library, Center for British Art, 1080 Chapel St, New Haven, CT, 06520. Tel: 203-432-2846. Fax: 203-432-9613. p. 357

Binnendyk, Myra, Libr Mgr, Penhold & District Public Library, Penhold Regional Multi-Plex, One Waskasoo Ave, Penhold, AB, T0M 1R0, CANADA. Tel: 403-886-2636. Fax: 403-886-2638. p. 2713

Binoniemi, Amanda, Ref & Instruction Librn, Michigan Technological University, 1400 Townsend Dr, Houghton, MI, 49931-1295. Tel: 906-487-1814. p. 1191

Binsfeld, Carrie, Dir, Finance & Gen Serv, Williamsburg Regional Library, 7770 Croaker Rd, Williamsburg, VA, 23188-7064. Tel: 757-259-4047. Fax: 757-259-4079, 757-259-7798. p. 2503

Bintner, Leslie, Dir, AIB College of Business Library, 2500 Fleur Dr, Des Moines, IA, 50321-1749. Tel: 515-244-4221. Fax: 515-288-4366. p. 808

Biondi, Michala, Project Archivist, Columbia University, The Burke Library at Union Theological Seminary, 3041 Broadway, New York, NY, 10027. Tel: 212-851-5607. Fax: 212-851-5613. p. 1674

Biondi, Priscilla, Evening/Weekend Librn, Wentworth Institute of Technology, 550 Huntington Ave, Boston, MA, 02115-5998. Tel: 617-989-4040. Fax: 617-989-4091. p. 1068

Biorn, Wendy, Dir, Carver County Historical Society Library, 555 W First St, Waconia, MN, 55387. Tel: 952-442-4234. Fax: 952-442-3025. p. 1287

Bir, Katie, Asst Dir, Colon Township Library, 128 S Blackstone Ave, Colon, MI, 49040. Tel: 269-432-3958. Fax: 269-432-4554. p. 1165

Birch, Cynthia, Supvr, University of Miami, Mary & Edward Norton Library of Ophthalmology, Bascom Palmer Eye Inst, 900 NW 17th St, Miami, FL, 33136. Tel: 305-326-6078. Fax: 305-326-6066. p. 469

Birch, Paul M, Info Tech, University of Richmond, William T Muse Law Library, 28 Westhampton Way, Richmond, VA, 23173. Tel: 804-289-8222. Fax: 804-289-8683. p. 2491

Birch, Rodney, Ref Librn, George Fox University, 416 N Meridian St, Newberg, OR, 97132. Tel: 503-554-2410. Fax: 503-554-3599. p. 2007

Birch, Rodney, VPres, Association of Christian Librarians, PO Box 4, Cedarville, OH, 45314. Tel: 937-766-2255. Fax: 937-766-5499. p. 2951

Birch, Rodney G, Ref Librn, Mid-America Nazarene University, 2030 E College Way, Olathe, KS, 66062-1899. Tel: 913-971-3563. Fax: 913-971-3285. p. 886

Birch, Thomas H, Head of Libr, Public Libraries of Saginaw, Zauel Memorial Library, 3100 N Center Rd, Saginaw, MI, 48603. Tel: 989-799-2771. Fax: 989-799-1771. p. 1224

Birch, Thomas H, Jr, Dir, Bay County Library System, 500 Center Ave, Bay City, MI, 48708. Tel: 989-894-2837. Fax: 989-894-2021. p. 1155

Birch, Tobeylynn, Assoc Dean, Loyola Marymount University, One LMU Dr, MS 8200, Los Angeles, CA, 90045-2659. Tel: 310-338-3088. Fax: 310-338-4366. p. 175

Birchard, Charles, Libr Tech, Department of Veterans Affairs, PO Box 5000-142D, Hines, IL, 60141-5142. Tel: 708-202-2000. Fax: 708-202-2719. p. 656

Birchenall, Martha, Mgr, Newark Free Library, 750 Library Ave, Newark, DE, 19711-7146. Tel: 302-731-7550. Fax: 302-731-4019. p. 385

Birchfield, Margaret, Dir, Windsor Free Public Library, 1890 Rte 9, Windsor, MA, 01270. Tel: 413-684-3811. Fax: 413-684-3806. p. 1142

Birck, Gwen, Ref, Cocoa Beach Public Library, 550 N Brevard Ave, Cocoa Beach, FL, 32931. Tel: 321-868-1104. Fax: 321-868-1107. p. 433

Birckhead, Janet, Adult Serv, Long Branch Free Public Library, 328 Broadway, Long Branch, NJ, 07740. Tel: 732-222-3900. Fax: 732-222-3799. p. 1496

Bird, Amanda, Info Spec, Hickory Public Library, 375 Third St NE, Hickory, NC, 28601-5126. Tel: 828-304-0500, Ext 7282. Fax: 828-304-0023. p. 1801

Bird, Beverly, Commun Relations, Atlantic County Library System, 40 Farragut Ave, Mays Landing, NJ, 08330-1750. Tel: 609-625-2776. Fax: 609-625-8143. p. 1500

Bird, Christine, Access Serv, ILL, University of Hartford Libraries, 200 Bloomfield Ave, West Hartford, CT, 06117. Tel: 860-768-4264. p. 376

Bird, Debra, Tech Serv, Sun Prairie Public Library, 1350 Linnerud Dr, Sun Prairie, WI, 53590-2631. Tel: 608-825-7323. Fax: 608-825-3936. p. 2641

Bird, Jason, Mgr, Libr Serv, Sault College Library, 443 Northern Ave, Sault Ste. Marie, ON, P6A 5L3, CANADA. Tel: 705-759-2554, Ext 2711. Fax: 705-759-1319. p. 2840

Bird, Jim, Ref, University of Maine, 5729 Fogler Library, Orono, ME, 04469-5729. Fax: 207-581-1653. p. 994

Bird, Kathryn, Librn, Pacific Newspaper Group Library, 200 Granville St, Vancouver, BC, V6C 3N3, CANADA. Tel: 604-605-2699. Fax: 604-605-2353. p. 2742

Bird, Nicole, Dir of Libr Serv, DeVry University, 901 Corporate Center Dr, Pomona, CA, 91768. Tel: 909-868-4227. p. 211

Bird, Nora, Instr, University of North Carolina at Greensboro, School of Education, 349 Curry Bldg, Greensboro, NC, 27402. Tel: 336-256-0162. Fax: 336-334-5060. p. 2971

Bird, Sean, Dir, Rossville Community Library, 407 Main St, Rossville, KS, 66533. Tel: 785-584-6454. Fax: 785-584-6454. p. 892

Bird, Sean, Asst Dean, Univ Libr, Washburn University, 1700 SW College Ave, Topeka, KS, 66621. Tel: 785-670-1550. Fax: 785-670-3223. p. 897

Bird, Sherilyn, Dean of Libr, Texas Woman's University Libraries, 304 Administration Dr, Denton, TX, 76204. Tel: 940-898-3701. Fax: 940-898-3764. p. 2312

Bird, Virginia K, Dir, New River Public Library Cooperative, 110 N Lake Ave, Lake Butler, FL, 32054. Tel: 386-496-2526. Fax: 386-496-3394. p. 457

Bird, William, Exec Dir, Lorain County Historical Society, 509 Washington Ave, Elyria, OH, 44035. Tel: 440-322-3341. Fax: 440-322-2817. p. 1898

Birden, Cindy, Tech Serv Supvr, West Florida Public Library, 200 W Gregory, Pensacola, FL, 32502. Tel: 850-436-5060. p. 482

Birden, Sofia, Assoc Dir, Ref Librn, University of Maine at Fort Kent, 23 University Dr, Fort Kent, ME, 04743. Tel: 207-834-7525. Fax: 207-834-7518. p. 986

Birdsall, Amelia, Web Coordr, NYS Small Business Development Center Research Network, 22 Corporate Woods Blvd, 3rd Flr, Albany, NY, 12211. Tel: 518-641-0650. Fax: 518-443-5275. p. 1570

Birdsall, Annette, Ch, Finger Lakes Library System, 119 E Green St, Ithaca, NY, 14850. Tel: 607-273-4074. Fax: 607-273-3618. p. 1642

Birdsell, Mary, Actg Exec Dir, Canadian Foundation for Children, Youth & the Law, 415 Yonge St, Ste 1203, Toronto, ON, M5B 2E7, CANADA. Tel: 416-920-1633. Fax: 416-920-5855. p. 2851

Birdsey, Vanessa J, Dir, Scott County Library System, 13090 Alabama Ave S, Savage, MN, 55378-1479. Tel: 952-707-1761. Fax: 952-707-1775. p. 1283

Birdseye, Catherine, Dir, Garrett Public Library, 107 W Houston St, Garrett, IN, 46738. Tel: 260-357-5485. Fax: 260-357-5170. p. 744

Birdseye, Martha, Librn, Andrews & Kurth LLP Library, 3500 I St, Ste 1100, Washington, DC, 20005. Tel: 202-662-2700. Fax: 202-662-2739. p. 393

Birdsong, Joy, Mgr, Sports Illustrated Library, 1271 Ave of the Ameicas, Rm 32-319, New York, NY, 10020. Tel: 212-522-3046. Fax: 212-522-1719. p. 1700

Birdwhistell, Terry, Dr, Dean of Libr, University of Kentucky Libraries, I-85, 401 Hilltop Ave, Lexington, KY, 40506-0456. Tel: 859-257-0500, Ext 2087. p. 921

Birk, Janet, Dir, Coffey County Library, Gridley Branch, 512 Main St, Gridley, KS, 66852. Tel: 620-836-3905. Fax: 620-836-3401. p. 859

Birkam, Anne, Cat, Govt Doc, Public Libraries of Saginaw, 505 Janes Ave, Saginaw, MI, 48607. Tel: 989-755-0904. Fax: 989-755-9829. p. 1223

Birkeland, Paddy, Libr Mgr, Spruce View Public Library, Hwy 54, Spruce View, AB, T0M 1V0, CANADA. Tel: 403-728-0012. Fax: 403-728-3155. p. 2717

Birkenmeir, Wendy, Head, Ch, Fountaindale Public Library District, 300 W Briarcliff Rd, Bolingbrook, IL, 60440-2844. Tel: 630-759-2102, Ext 4198. Fax: 630-759-9519. p. 596

Birkenseer, Susan, Ref & Instruction Librn, Saint Mary's College Library, 1928 Saint Mary's Rd, Moraga, CA, 94575. Tel: 925-631-4229. Fax: 925-376-6097. p. 191

Birkett, Shirley, Asst Mgr, Gulf Gate Public Library, 7112 Curtiss Ave, Sarasota, FL, 34231. Tel: 941-861-1230. Fax: 941-316-1221. p. 489

Birkhead, Paul, Librn, Rowan Public Library, East Branch, 110 Broad St, Rockwell, NC, 28138. Tel: 704-279-5014. Fax: 704-216-7838. p. 1823

Birkhead, Wendi, Campus Librn, Mohave Community College Library, Lake Havasu City Campus, 1977 W Acoma Blvd, Lake Havasu City, AZ, 86403-2999. Tel: 928-453-5809. Fax: 928-453-8335. p. 66

Birkholz, Tina, Ref Librn, Elgin Community College, 1700 Spartan Dr, Elgin, IL, 60123. Tel: 847-214-7337. p. 641

Birkinshaw, Elaine, Mgr, Spec Proj, Saint Petersburg Public Library, 3745 Ninth Ave N, Saint Petersburg, FL, 33713. Tel: 727-893-7724. Fax: 727-892-5432. p. 488

Birkmeyer, Carl, Media Support Serv Mgr, Baltimore County Public Library, 320 York Rd, Towson, MD, 21204-5179. Tel: 410-887-2082. Fax: 410-887-6103. p. 1044

Birmingham, Cara, Librn, Genesee District Library, Flint Township (McCarty Public Library), 2071 S Graham Rd, Flint, MI, 48532. Tel: 810-732-9150. Fax: 810-732-0878. p. 1180

Birmingham, Laura, Asst Dir, Indian Prairie Public Library District, 401 Plainfield Rd, Darien, IL, 60561-4207. Tel: 630-887-8760. Fax: 630-887-8801. p. 633

Birmingham, Sean, Asst Dir, Head, Adult Serv, Villa Park Public Library, 305 S Ardmore Ave, Villa Park, IL, 60181-2698. Tel: 630-834-1164, Ext 109. Fax: 630-834-0489. p. 714

Birnbaum, Jonathan A, Dean, McHenry County College Library, 8900 US Hwy 14, Crystal Lake, IL, 60012-2738. Tel: 815-479-7545. Fax: 815-455-3999. p. 632

Birnbaum, Kerry, Ref, Cheltenham Township Library System, Elkins Park Free Library, 563 E Church Rd, Elkins Park, PA, 19027-2499. Tel: 215-635-5000. Fax: 215-635-5844. p. 2061

Birney, Kathryn, Librn, Puskarich Public Library, Scio Branch, 331 W Main St, Scio, OH, 43988. Tel: 740-945-6811. Fax: 740-945-9515. p. 1862

Birney, Sue, Adult Serv, Winfield Public Library, 605 College St, Winfield, KS, 67156-3199. Tel: 620-221-4470. Fax: 620-221-6135. p. 903

Birnie, K Joan, Dir, Broken Bow Public Library, 626 South D St, Broken Bow, NE, 68822. Tel: 308-872-2927. Fax: 308-872-2927. p. 1394

Biro, Sarah, Br Librn, Pine City Public Library, 300 Fifth St SE, Pine City, MN, 55063-1799. Tel: 320-629-6403. Fax: 320-629-6403. p. 1270

Biron, Carmen, Librn, Centennial College of Applied Arts & Technology, Progress Campus Library, 941 Progress Ave, Scarborough, ON, M1G 3T8, CANADA. Tel: 416-289-5000, Ext 2600. Fax: 416-289-5242. p. 2840

Biros, Panagiota, Br Head, Toronto Public Library, Barbara Frum, 20 Covington Rd, Toronto, ON, M6A 3C1, CANADA. Tel: 416-395-5440. Fax: 416-395-5447. p. 2861

Birr, Caroline, Interim Dir, Merri-Hill-Rock Library Cooperative, c/o Kimball Library, Three Academy Ave, Atkinson, NH, 03811-2299. Tel: 603-362-5234. Fax: 603-362-4791. p. 2948

Birrer, Monica Anne, Dir, Spanish Peaks Library District, 415 Walsen Ave, Walsenburg, CO, 81089. Tel: 719-738-2774. Fax: 719-738-2468. p. 325

Birsinger, Marcia, Librn, Saint Luke the Evangelist Catholic Church, 11011 Hall Rd, Houston, TX, 77089. Tel: 281-481-4251. Fax: 281-481-8780. p. 2342

Birtalan, Mary, Cat, Kent State University, 6000 Frank Ave NW, North Canton, OH, 44720-7548. Tel: 330-244-3323. Fax: 330-494-6212. p. 1923

Birtcher, Martha L, Dir, Public Library of Catasauqua, 302 Bridge St, Catasauqua, PA, 18032-2510. Tel: 610-264-4151. Fax: 610-264-4593. p. 2043

Birtell, Amy, Dir, Clinton Public Library, 306 Eighth Ave S, Clinton, IA, 52732. Tel: 563-242-8441. Fax: 563-242-8162. p. 803

Birtell Parker, Amy Beth, Dir, Tripoli Public Library, 101 Fourth Ave SW, Tripoli, IA, 50676. Tel: 319-882-4807. Fax: 319-882-3580. p. 848

Birzenieks, Michael, Librn, New York State Supreme Court, 285 Wall St, Kingston, NY, 12401. Tel: 845-340-3053. Fax: 845-340-3773. p. 1650

Bisbee, Eamon, Ch, Goodwin Library, 422 Main St, Farmington, NH, 03835-1519. Tel: 603-755-2944. Fax: 603-755-2944. p. 1447

Bisch, Steve, Circ Supvr, Washington State University Tri-Cities, 2770 University Dr, Richland, WA, 99354. Tel: 509-372-7313. Fax: 509-372-7281. p. 2526

Bischoff, Beverly, Librn, Hope Lutheran Church Library, 1115 N 35th St, Milwaukee, WI, 53208. Tel: 414-342-0471. p. 2618

Bischoff, Helen E, Ref Librn, Georgetown College, 400 E College St, Georgetown, KY, 40324. Tel: 502-863-8405. Fax: 502-868-7740. p. 915

Bischoff, Jean B, Univ Archivist, Elizabeth City State University, 1704 Weeksville Rd, Elizabeth City, NC, 27909. Tel: 252-335-3647. Fax: 252-335-3446. p. 1791

Biser, Gloria, Circ Mgr, DeSales University, 2755 Station Ave, Center Valley, PA, 18034. Tel: 610-282-1100, Ext 1266. Fax: 610-282-2342. p. 2043

Bish, Dianne, City Librn, Roseville Public Library, 225 Taylor St, Roseville, CA, 95678-2681. Tel: 916-774-5221. Fax: 916-773-5594. p. 220

Bish, Linda, Librn, Kennedy Free Library, Church St, Kennedy, NY, 14747. Tel: 716-267-4265. Fax: 716-267-2049. p. 1649

Bish, Lucille, Dir, Region of Waterloo Library, 2017 Nafziger Rd, Baden, ON, N3A 3H4, CANADA. Tel: 519-575-4570. Fax: 519-634-5371. p. 2793

Bishoff, Dave, Mgr, Libr Tech Serv, University of Denver, 2150 E Evans Ave, Denver, CO, 80208-2007. Tel: 303-871-2604. Fax: 303-871-2290. p. 303

Bishop, Amelia, Br Librn, Autauga-Prattville Public Library, Autaugaville Public, 207 N Taylor St, Autaugaville, AL, 36003. Tel: 334-365-9322. p. 34

Bishop, Amelia, Librn, Autauga-Prattville Public Library, Marbury Community, 205 County Rd 20 E, Marbury, AL, 36051. Tel: 205-755-8575. p. 34

Bishop, Ann, Human Res Mgr, Greenville County Library System, 25 Heritage Green Pl, Greenville, SC, 29601-2034. Tel: 864-242-5000, Ext 2262. Fax: 864-235-8375. p. 2196

Bishop, Betsy, Ch, Somers Library, 80 Primrose St, Rte 139 & Reis Park, Somers, NY, 10589. Tel: 914-232-5717. Fax: 914-232-1035. p. 1745

Bishop, Bradley Wade, Dr, Asst Prof, University of Kentucky, 320 Little Library Bldg, Lexington, KY, 40506-0224. Tel: 859-257-3970. Fax: 859-257-4205. p. 2966

Bishop, Carrie, Ref Librn, Pennsylvania State University, College Pl, Hiller Bldg, Rm 113, 301 E DuBois Ave, Du Bois, PA, 15801. Tel: 814-375-4756. Fax: 814-375-4784. p. 2051

Bishop, Celina, Human Res Mgr, Mid-Columbia Libraries, 405 S Dayton, Kennewick, WA, 99336. Tel: 509-582-4745. Fax: 509-737-6349. p. 2518

Bishop, Chris, Mgr, Community Health Network Library, 1500 N Ritter Ave, Indianapolis, IN, 46219. Tel: 317-355-3600. Fax: 317-351-7816. p. 750

Bishop, Dorothy, Librn, Sheridan Public Library, 103 W First St, Sheridan, IN, 46069. Tel: 317-758-5201. Fax: 317-758-0045. p. 778

Bishop, Francesca, Commun Libr Mgr, Queens Borough Public Library, Court Square Community Library, 25-01 Jackson Ave, Long Island City, NY, 11101. Tel: 718-937-2790. p. 1644

Bishop, Francesca, Commun Libr Mgr, Queens Borough Public Library, South Hollis Community Library, 204-01 Hollis Ave, South Hollis, NY, 11412. Tel: 718-465-6779. p. 1645

Bishop, Genie, Librn, Allen County Public Library, Woodburn Branch, 4701 State Rd 101 N, Woodburn, IN, 46797. Tel: 260-421-1370. Fax: 260-632-0101. p. 741

Bishop, Henry, Curator, Black Cultural Centre for Nova Scotia Library, No 7 Hwy at Cherry Brook Rd, 1149 Main St, Dartmouth, NS, B2Z 1A8, CANADA. Tel: 902-434-6223. Fax: 902-434-2306. p. 2778

Bishop, Janet, Coordr, Archives, Colorado State University Libraries, Morgan Library, 1201 Center Avenue Mall, Fort Collins, CO, 80523-. Tel: 970-491-1838. Fax: 970-491-1195. p. 307

Bishop, Kay, Assoc Prof, University at Buffalo, State University of New York, 534 Baldy Hall, Buffalo, NY, 14260. Tel: 716-645-2412. Fax: 716-645-3775. p. 2971

Bishop, Lesa, Br Librn, Reynolds County Library District, Bunker Branch, 203 N Main St, Bunker, MO, 63629. Tel: 573-689-2718. Fax: 573-689-2718. p. 1323

Bishop, Lisa, Ser, J Sargeant Reynolds Community College Library, Parham Campus-Library & Information Services, 1651 E Parham Rd, Richmond, VA, 23228. Tel: 804-523-5328. Fax: 804-371-3086. p. 2489

Bishop, Lorraine, Br Librn, Wapiti Regional Library, Bjorkdale Public Library, 105 Hara Ave, Bjorkdale, SK, S0E 0E0, CANADA. Tel: 308-886-2119. p. 2921

Bishop, Mari, Tech Serv, Troutman Sanders LLP, 600 Peachtree St NE, Ste 5200, Atlanta, GA, 30308-2216. Tel: 404-885-3780. Fax: 404-962-6783. p. 518

Bishop, Marlene, Head, Acq, Head, Coll Develop, Louisiana State University Health Sciences Center, 433 Bolivar St, Box B3-1, New Orleans, LA, 70112-2223. Tel: 504-568-6109. Fax: 504-568-7718. p. 961

Bishop, Marlene, Pres, Health Sciences Library Association of Louisiana, LSUHSC-New Orleans Library, 433 Bolivar St, Box B3-1, New Orleans, LA, 70112. Tel: 504-568-6109. Fax: 504-568-7718. p. 2944

Bishop, Marsha, Head Librn, National Radio Astronomy Observatory Library, 520 Edgemont Rd, Charlottesville, VA, 22903-2475. Tel: 434-296-0254. Fax: 434-296-0278. p. 2454

Bishop, Mary, Librn, Carlos Albizu University Library, 2173 NW 99 Ave, Miami, FL, 33172. Tel: 305-593-1223, Ext 131. Fax: 305-593-8318. p. 464

Bishop, Mary, Ref Librn, Defiance College, 201 College Pl, Defiance, OH, 43512-1667. Tel: 419-783-2483. Fax: 419-783-2594. p. 1895

Bishop, Melissa, Dir, Flora-Monroe Township Public Library, 109 N Center St, Flora, IN, 46929-1004. Tel: 574-967-3912. Fax: 574-967-3671. p. 740

Bishop, Michelle, First Year Experience Librn, State University of New York at Oswego, SUNY Oswego, 7060 State Rte 104, Oswego, NY, 13126-3514. Tel: 315-312-3564. Fax: 315-312-3194. p. 1713

Bishop, Pat, Tech Serv, Eastern Maine Medical Center, 489 State St, Bangor, ME, 04402. Tel: 207-973-8228. Fax: 207-973-8233. p. 976

Bishop, Pearlie, Bus Mgr, Kinchafoonee Regional Library System, Terrell County Library, 913 Forrester Dr SE, Dawson, GA, 39842-2106. Tel: 229-995-2902. Fax: 229-995-5989. p. 528

Bishop, Rachel, Ref & Instrul Serv Librn, Hope College, Van Wylen Library, 53 Graves Pl, Holland, MI, 49422. Tel: 616-395-7299. Fax: 616-395-7965. p. 1190

Bishop, Sasha, Librn, Technical College of the Lowcountry, 921 Ribaut Rd, Beaufort, SC, 29902-5441. Tel: 843-525-8304. Fax: 843-525-8346. p. 2181

Bishop, Sheila K, Dir, Niceville Public Library, 206 N Partin Dr, Niceville, FL, 32578. Tel: 850-729-4070. Fax: 850-729-4093. p. 472

Bishop, Shelley, Acq, United States Forest Service, One Gifford Pinchot Dr, Madison, WI, 53726-2398. Tel: 608-231-9312. Fax: 608-231-9311. p. 2608

Bishop, Shiwanda, Asst Librn, Albemarle Regional Library, Ahoskie Public Library, 210 E Church St, Ahoskie, NC, 27910. Tel: 252-332-5500. Fax: 252-332-6435. p. 1835

Bishop, Teresa, Sr Librn, New Hanover County Public Library, Myrtle Grove, 5155 S College Rd, Wilmington, NC, 28412. Tel: 910-798-6390. Fax: 910-452-6417. p. 1830

Bishop, Tim, Tech Serv Librn, Lake Michigan College, 2755 E Napier Ave, Benton Harbor, MI, 49022. Tel: 269-927-8100, Ext 5027. Fax: 269-927-6656. p. 1156

Bishop, Wanda, Librn, Sebastopol Public Library, PO Box 173, Sebastopol, MS, 39359-0173. Tel: 601-625-8826. Fax: 601-625-8826. p. 1314

Bishr, Tarek, Ref, Bank of America Merrill Lynch & Co, 250 Vesey St, 24th Flr, New York, NY, 10080. Tel: 212-449-3814. Fax: 212-449-1379. p. 1669

Bisko, Lynne, Non-Print Librn, Elon University, 308 N O'Kelly Ave, Elon, NC, 27244-0187. Tel: 336-278-6587. Fax: 336-278-6637. p. 1791

Bisnett, Sandra, Librn, Fresno County Public Library, West Fresno Branch, 188 E California Ave, Fresno, CA, 93706. Tel: 559-455-6066. p. 153

Bisom, Diane, Assoc Univ Librn, Info Tech & Syst, University of California, Riverside Libraries, 900 University Ave, Riverside, CA, 92521. Tel: 951-827-2080. p. 218

Biss, Catherine, Chief Exec Officer, Markham Public Library, Central Admin, 6031 Hwy 7, Markham, ON, L3P 3A7, CANADA. Tel: 905-513-7977. Fax: 905-471-6015. p. 2820

Bisschop, K, Adult Serv, Peterborough Public Library, 345 Aylmer St N, Peterborough, ON, K9H 3V7, CANADA. Tel: 705-745-5382. Fax: 705-745-8958. p. 2836

Bissell, Ann, Bibliog Instr, Coll Develop, Ref, Bay De Noc Community College, 2001 N Lincoln Rd, Escanaba, MI, 49829-2511. Tel: 906-217-4055, 906-217-4076. Fax: 906-217-1682. p. 1177

Bissell, Maxine, Pub Serv, Yakima Valley Genealogical Society Library, 1901 S 12th Ave, Union Gap, WA, 98903. Tel: 509-248-1328. p. 2545

Bissen, Barbara, Dir, Hokah Public Library, 57 Main, Hokah, MN, 55941. Tel: 507-894-2665. Fax: 507-894-2665. p. 1254

Bissett, Jan, Ref Serv, Res, Dickinson Wright PLLC Library, 38525 Woodward Ave, Ste 2000, Bloomfield Hills, MI, 48304-2970. Tel: 248-433-7200. Fax: 248-433-7274. p. 1159

Bissett, John P, Head, Tech Serv, Washington & Lee University, Wilbur C Hall Law Library, Lewis Hall, E Denny Circle, Lexington, VA, 24450. Tel: 540-458-8546. Fax: 540-458-8967. p. 2474

Bissett, Susan, Instrul Serv Librn, Union County College Libraries, 1033 Springfield Ave, Cranford, NJ, 07016. Tel: 908-709-7623. Fax: 908-709-7589. p. 1480

Bissey, Mary, Asst Dir, Champaign Public Library, 200 W Green St, Champaign, IL, 61820-5193. Tel: 217-403-2050. Fax: 217-403-2053. p. 602

Bisson, Aurelien, Dir, Centre Regional de Service aux Bibliotheque Publique de Pret Gaspesie Isle de la Madelene, 31 Rue des Ecoliers, CP 430, Cap-Chat, QC, G0J 1E0, CANADA. Tel: 418-786-5597. Fax: 418-786-2024. p. 2880

Bisson, Jacques, Head, Info Serv, Centre de Reference Technique, 700 Leigh Capreol St, NAI-CRT, Rm 0135, Dorval, QC, H4Y 1G7, CANADA. Tel: 514-633-3589. Fax: 514-420-5801. p. 2881

Bissonnette, Bette, Librn, Saints Memorial Medical Center, Hospital Dr, Lowell, MA, 01852-1389. Tel: 978-934-8308. Fax: 978-934-8241. p. 1100

Bissonnette, Sheila, Dir, Pere Marquette District Library, 185 E Fourth St, Clare, MI, 48617. Tel: 989-386-7576. Fax: 989-386-3576. p. 1163

Bissonnette, Susan, Distance Learning Serv, Info Literacy, Herkimer County Community College Library, 100 Reservoir Rd, Herkimer, NY, 13350. Tel: 315-866-0300, Ext 8270. Fax: 315-866-1806. p. 1635

Bistyga, H, Coordr, Prog, Anderson County Library, 300 N McDuffie St, Anderson, SC, 29621-5643. Tel: 864-260-4500. Fax: 864-260-4510. p. 2180

Biswas, Shukla, Tech Serv, Massachusetts School of Law Library, 500 Federal St, Andover, MA, 01810. Tel: 978-681-0800. Fax: 978-681-6330. p. 1049

Bitetti, Bronwen, Assoc Librn, Bard College, Center for Curatorial Studies, PO Box 5000, Annandale-on-Hudson, NY, 12504-5000. Tel: 845-752-2395. Fax: 845-758-2442. p. 1574

Bitner, Hannah, Librn, Calvary Bible College & Theological Seminary, 15800 Calvary Rd, Kansas City, MO, 64147-1341. Tel: 816-322-0110, Ext 1205. Fax: 816-331-4474. p. 1337

Bitner, Joseph, County Librn, Annie Halenbake Ross Library, 232 W Main St, Lock Haven, PA, 17745-1241. Tel: 570-748-3321. Fax: 570-748-1050. p. 2082

Bitney, Lisa, Dir, Coll Serv, Pierce County Library System, 3005 112th St E, Tacoma, WA, 98446-2215. Tel: 253-548-3397. Fax: 253-537-4600. p. 2539

Bitove, Miragh, Archivist, Hockey Hall of Fame, 400 Kipling Ave, Toronto, ON, M8V 3L1, CANADA. Tel: 419-933-8224. Fax: 416-251-5770. p. 2854

Bitten, Loretta, Br Mgr, Birmingham Public Library, Powderly, 3301 Jefferson Ave SW, Birmingham, AL, 35221. Tel: 205-925-6178. Fax: 205-923-3630. p. 7

Bitter, Jane, E-Libr Mgr, Emerson Process Management eLibrary, 1100 W Louis Henna Blvd, Round Rock, TX, 78681. Tel: 512-834-7255. p. 2377

Bitters, Victoria, Asst Head, Ref Serv, Eisenhower Public Library District, 4613 N Oketo Ave, Harwood Heights, IL, 60706. Tel: 708-867-7828. Fax: 708-867-1535. p. 654

Bittle, Carolyn Theresa, Dean, Learning Res, Richmond Community College Library, 1042 W Hamlet Ave, Hamlet, NC, 28345. Tel: 910-582-7000, 910-582-7043. Fax: 910-582-7045. p. 1800

Bittle, Catherine, Dir, Ridley Township Public Library, 100 E MacDade Blvd, Folsom, PA, 19033-2592. Tel: 610-583-0593. Fax: 610-583-9505. p. 2057

Bittle, Catherine, Dir, Ridley Park Public Library, 107 E Ward St, Ridley Park, PA, 19078-3097. Tel: 610-583-7207. Fax: 610-583-2160. p. 2134

Bittle, Kevin, Br Mgr, Charlotte Mecklenburg Library, Sugar Creek, 4045 N Tryon St, Charlotte, NC, 28206. Tel: 704-416-7000. Fax: 704-416-7100. p. 1782

Bittman, Lana, Electronic Res & Per Librn, Fashion Institute of Technology-SUNY, Seventh Ave at 27th St, New York, NY, 10001-5992. Tel: 212-217-4382. Fax: 212-217-4371. p. 1678

Bittner, Anne, Cat Librn, Northampton Community College, 3835 Green Pond Rd, Bethlehem, PA, 18020-7599. Tel: 610-861-5360. Fax: 610-861-5373. p. 2034

Bittner, Debbie, Br Mgr, Prince William Public Library System, Dumfries Neighborhood, 18007 Dumfries Shopping Plaza, Dumfries, VA, 22026-2411. Tel: 703-792-5678. Fax: 703-221-7814. p. 2486

Bitunjac, Robert, Br Mgr, Chicago Public Library, Clearing, 6423 W 63rd Pl, Chicago, IL, 60638. Tel: 312-747-5657. Fax: 312-747-7658. p. 608

Bivens, Judy, Coordr, Instrul Res Ctr, Trevecca Nazarene University, 73 Lester Ave, Nashville, TN, 37210-4227. Tel: 615-248-1206. Fax: 615-248-1452. p. 2259

Bivens, Judy, Prog Coordr, Trevecca Nazarene University, School of Education, 333 Murfreesboro Rd, Nashville, TN, 37210-2877. Tel: 615-248-1206. Fax: 615-248-1597. p. 2974

Bivens, Lynn, Head, Ref, Info Literacy, Saint Joseph's College, 278 Whites Bridge Rd, Standish, ME, 04084-5263. Tel: 207-893-7724. Fax: 207-893-7883. p. 1002

Bivins, Hulen E, Dr, State Librn, North Dakota State Library, Library Memorial Bldg, 604 East Blvd Ave, Dept 250, Bismarck, ND, 58505-0800. Tel: 701-328-2492. Fax: 701-328-2040. p. 1838

Bixby, Gwen, Librn, Delevan-Yorkshire Public Library, 28 School St, Delevan, NY, 14042. Tel: 716-492-1961. Fax: 716-492-3398. p. 1613

Bixby, Jayanne, Children & Teen Librn, Sno-Isle Libraries, Freeland Branch, 5495 Harbor Ave, Freeland, WA, 98249. Tel: 360-331-7323. Fax: 360-331-1572. p. 2542

Bixel, Lisa L, Circ, Bremen Public Library, 304 N Jackson St, Bremen, IN, 46506. Tel: 574-546-2849. Fax: 574-546-4938. p. 729

Biza, Jillah, Librn, St Joseph Mercy Hospital, 5301 E Huron River Dr, Rm 1712, Ann Arbor, MI, 48106. Tel: 734-712-3045. Fax: 734-712-2679. p. 1151

Bizik, Michael, Librn, Cahill, Gordon & Reindel Library, 1990 K St NW, Ste 950, Washington, DC, 20006. Tel: 202-862-8953. Fax: 202-862-8958. p. 395

Bizimana, Bernard, Librn, Ecole de Technologie Superieure (Service de la bibliotheque), 1100 rue Notre-Dame Ouest, Montreal, QC, H3C 1K3, CANADA. Tel: 514-396-8946. Fax: 514-396-8633. p. 2895

Bizimana, Bernard, Head, Tech Serv, HEC Montreal, 3000, chemin de la Cote-Sainte-Catherine, Montreal, QC, H3T 2A7, CANADA. Tel: 514-340-6217. Fax: 514-340-5639. p. 2896

Bizonet, Rebecca, Archivist, The Henry Ford, 20900 Oakwood Blvd, Dearborn, MI, 48124-5029. Tel: 313-982-6100, Ext 2284. Fax: 313-982-6244. p. 1167

Bizub, Johanna C, Dir, Libr Serv, Prudential Financial, Prudential Insurance Law Library, Four Plaza, 751 Broad St, Newark, NJ, 07102-3714. Tel: 973-367-3175. Fax: 973-802-2298. p. 1512

Bjartmarsdottir, Anna, Ref & Instruction, University of Alaska Anchorage, Consortium Library, 3211 Providence Dr, Anchorage, AK, 99508-8176. Tel: 907-786-1871. Fax: 907-786-1834. p. 45

Bjerke, Cheryl, Librn, Library of the US Courts, 400 S Virginia St, Rm 1001, Reno, NV, 89501. Tel: 775-686-5776. Fax: 775-686-5779. p. 1432

Bjerken, Lisa, Sr Librn, Hennepin County Library, Hopkins, 22 11th Ave N, Hopkins, MN, 55343-7575. Tel: 612-543-6403. Fax: 612-543-6402. p. 1263

Bjoin, Cheryl, Dir, Saint James Library, 125 5th St S, Saint James, MN, 56081-1736. Tel: 507-375-1278. Fax: 507-375-5415. p. 1276

Bjoin, Cheryl, Dir, Watonwan County Library, 125 Fifth St S, Saint James, MN, 56081. Tel: 507-375-1278. Fax: 507-375-5415. p. 1276

Bjork, Janet, Govt Doc, Ser, Gordon College, 255 Grapevine Rd, Wenham, MA, 01984-1899. Tel: 978-867-4345. Fax: 978-867-4660. p. 1136

Bjork, Johanna, Bibliog Instr, Ref Serv, Bismarck State College Library, 1500 Edwards Ave, Bismarck, ND, 58501. Tel: 701-224-5738. Fax: 701-224-5551. p. 1837

Bjork, Karen, Digital Initiatives Coordr, Portland State University Library, 1875 SW Park Ave, Portland, OR, 97201-3220. Tel: 503-725-5874. Fax: 503-725-4524. p. 2014

Bjorklund, Dana M, Tech Serv Librn, Cleveland Institute of Art, 11141 East Blvd, Cleveland, OH, 44106. Tel: 216-421-7446. Fax: 216-421-7439. p. 1877

Bjorklund, Lori, Librn, Bureau of Land Management, 1206 S Challis St, Salmon, ID, 83467. Tel: 208-756-5400. Fax: 208-756-5151. p. 583

Bjorn, Arik, Librn, South Carolina Commission on Higher Education Library, 1122 Lady St, Ste 300, Columbia, SC, 29201-3240. Tel: 803-737-2293. Fax: 803-737-2297. p. 2189

Bjornson, Bonita, ILL, Ser, The King's University College, 9125 50th St, Edmonton, AB, T6B 2H3, CANADA. Tel: 780-465-8304. Fax: 780-465-3534. p. 2701

Bjornstad, Jill, Librn, Cashton Memorial Library, 809 Main St, Cashton, WI, 54619. Tel: 608-654-5465. Fax: 608-654-7383. p. 2584

Black, Alistair, Prof, University of Illinois at Urbana-Champaign, Library & Information Science Bldg, 501 E Daniel St, Champaign, IL, 61820-6211. Tel: 217-333-3280. Fax: 217-244-3302. p. 2965

Black, Andrea, Dir, Dillsburg Area Public Library, 17 S Baltimore St, Dillsburg, PA, 17019. Tel: 717-432-5613. Fax: 717-432-7641. p. 2049

Black, Barb, Tech Serv Mgr, Ella M Everhard Public Library, 132 Broad St, Wadsworth, OH, 44281-1897. Tel: 330-334-5761. Fax: 330-334-6605. p. 1943

Black, Barbara, Tech Serv Coordr, Iowa City Public Library, 123 S Linn St, Iowa City, IA, 52240. Tel: 319-887-6006. Fax: 319-356-5494. p. 823

Black, Barbara, Librn, Wadsworth-Rittman Community Hospital Library, 195 Wadsworth Rd, Wadsworth, OH, 44281. Tel: 330-334-1504. Fax: 330-336-0107. p. 1944

Black, Bettye, Curator, Langston University, PO Box 1600, Langston, OK, 73050-1600. Tel: 405-466-3293. Fax: 405-466-3459. p. 1967

Black, Christine, Lead Librn, Data Contracts, Board of Governors of The Federal Reserve System, Research Library, 20th & C St NW, MS 102, Washington, DC, 20551. Tel: 202-452-3333. Fax: 202-530-6222. p. 394

Black, Diane, Acq, Cat, Augusta Richmond County Historical Society Library, c/o Reese Library, Augusta State University, 2500 Walton Way, Augusta, GA, 30904-2200. Tel: 706-737-1532. Fax: 706-667-4415. p. 518

Black, Douglas, Coll Develop, Northern Michigan University, 1401 Presque Isle, Marquette, MI, 49855. Tel: 906-227-1208. Fax: 906-227-1333. p. 1207

Black, Fiona, Dr, Dir, Dalhousie University, 6100 University Ave, Halifax, NS, B3H 3J5, CANADA. Tel: 902-494-3656. Fax: 902-494-2451. p. 2978

Black, Jack, Mgr, El Camino Hospital Library & Information Center, 2500 Grant Rd, Mountain View, CA, 94039. Tel: 650-940-7210. Fax: 650-940-7299. p. 192

Black, Janet, Tech Serv Technician, Southwestern Oklahoma State University, 100 Campus Dr, Weatherford, OK, 73096-3002. Tel: 580-774-3089. Fax: 580-774-3112. p. 1985

Black, Jennifer S, Communications Dir, Glenview Public Library, 1930 Glenview Rd, Glenview, IL, 60025-2899. Tel: 847-729-7500. Fax: 847-729-7558. p. 650

Black, Kimberly, Commun Serv, Prevention Pathways, 504 Prospect Ave, Norfolk, NE, 68701-4022. Tel: 402-370-3113. Fax: 402-370-3444. p. 1410

Black, Kimberly, Assoc Prof, University of Tennessee, Knoxville, 451 Communications Bldg, 1345 Circle Park Dr, Knoxville, TN, 37996-0341. Tel: 865-974-2148. Fax: 865-974-4967. p. 2974

Black, Kristey, Cataloger, Washington County Library System, Springdale Branch, 126 Lion Blvd, Springdale, UT, 84767. Tel: 435-772-3676. Fax: 435-772-3124. p. 2412

Black, Lawrence, Librn, New York State Office of Mental Retardation & Developmental Disabilities, 1050 Forest Hill Rd, Staten Island, NY, 10314. Tel: 718-494-5119. Fax: 718-494-6660. p. 1748

Black, Linda, Br Librn, Lake Agassiz Regional Library, Fertile Public Library, 101 S Mill St, Fertile, MN, 56540. Tel: 218-945-6137. Fax: 218-945-3236. p. 1266

Black, Linda, Ref, Bellevue University, 1000 Galvin Rd S, Bellevue, NE, 68005. Tel: 402-557-7315. Fax: 402-557-5427. p. 1393

Black, Lois, Dir, Moore Memorial Library District, 509 Main St, Hillsdale, IL, 61257-0325. Tel: 309-658-2666. Fax: 309-658-2666. p. 656

Black, Meg, Librn, Metropolitan Museum of Art, Robert Lehman Collection Library, 1000 Fifth Ave, New York, NY, 10028. Tel: 212-570-3915. Fax: 212-650-2542. p. 1686

Black, Myretta, Asst Dir, Knox County Public Library System, 500 W Church Ave, Knoxville, TN, 37902-2505. Tel: 865-215-8750. Fax: 865-215-8742. p. 2241

Black, Patricia, Dir, Universite du Quebec, CP 8889, Succ Centre-Ville, 1255 Rue St Denis, Locale-A-1200, Montreal, QC, H3C 3P3, CANADA. Tel: 514-987-6134. Fax: 514-987-0262. p. 2902

Black, Richard E, Dir, Godfrey Memorial Library, 134 Newfield St, Middletown, CT, 06457-2534. Tel: 860-346-4375. Fax: 860-347-9874. p. 351

Black, Robert, Ser, Missouri Southern State University, 3950 E Newman Rd, Joplin, MO, 64801-1595. Tel: 417-625-9386. Fax: 417-625-9734. p. 1336

Black, Robert E, Libr Dir, Natchitoches Parish Library, 450 Second St, Natchitoches, LA, 71457-4649. Tel: 318-357-3280. Fax: 318-357-7073. p. 958

Black, Robin, Dir, Museum of Independent Telephony Library, 412 S Campbell, Abilene, KS, 67410. Tel: 785-263-2681. Fax: 785-263-0380. p. 855

Black, Ruth, Tech Serv, Rockville Centre Public Library, 221 N Village Ave, Rockville Centre, NY, 11570. Tel: 516-766-6257. Fax: 516-766-6090. p. 1734

Black, Sharon, Dir, Sumiton Public Library, Town Hall, 416 State St, Sumiton, AL, 35148. Tel: 205-648-7451. Fax: 205-648-7451. p. 36

Black, Sharon, Head of Libr, University of Pennsylvania Libraries, Annenberg School of Communication, 3620 Walnut, Philadelphia, PA, 19104-6220. Tel: 215-898-6106. Fax: 215-898-5388. p. 2119

Black, Sherry, Dir, Auburn Memorial Library, 1810 Courthouse Ave, Auburn, NE, 68305-2323. Tel: 402-274-4023. Fax: 402-274-4433. p. 1392

Black, Steve, Ref, Ser, College of Saint Rose, 392-396 Western Ave, Albany, NY, 12203. Tel: 518-458-5494. Fax: 518-454-2897. p. 1568

Black, William, Admin Librn, Interim Dir, Middle Tennessee State University, MTSU, PO Box 13, Murfreesboro, TN, 37132. Tel: 615-898-2817. p. 2254

Black-Dorward, Alissa, Ref Librn, Fordham University School of Law, 140 W 62nd St, New York, NY, 10023-7485. Tel: 212-636-7694. Fax: 212-930-8818. p. 1678

Black-Howell, Richard, Ref Librn, Howard Community College Library, 10901 Little Patuxent Pkwy, Columbia, MD, 21044. Tel: 443-518-4812. Fax: 443-518-4993. p. 1025

Black-Junttonen, Mary, Head Librn, Michigan State University Library, Fine Arts-Music, W 403 Library, East Lansing, MI, 48824. Tel: 517-884-6469. Fax: 517-432-3532. p. 1175

Blackaby, Dan, Cat, Mgr, Bibliog Serv, Ref, Western State Law Library, 1111 N State College Blvd, Fullerton, CA, 92831-3014. Tel: 714-459-1113. Fax: 714-871-4806. p. 154

Blackard, Janice, Tech Serv, University of the Ozarks, 415 N College Ave, Clarksville, AR, 72830. Tel: 479-979-1382. Fax: 479-979-1477. p. 96

Blackbourn, Belinda, Tech Serv, Grande Prairie Public Library, 101-9839 103 Ave, Grande Prairie, AB, T8V 6M7, CANADA. Tel: 780-357-7460. Fax: 780-538-4983. p. 2705

Blackburn, Barbara, Libr Serv Dir, Duncan Public Library, 122 N Hwy 75, Duncan, AZ, 85534. Tel: 928-359-2094. Fax: 928-359-2094. p. 61

Blackburn, Cassie, Asst Librn, Kiowa County Library, 320 S Main, Ste 120, Greensburg, KS, 67054. Tel: 620-723-1118. p. 869

Blackburn, Clayton Edwin, Chief Librn, United States Army, 1794 Walker Ave SW, Fort McPherson, GA, 30330-1013. Tel: 404-464-2640, 404-464-2665. Fax: 404-464-3801. p. 533

Blackburn, Jane, Asst Dir, Braswell Memorial Public Library, 727 N Grace St, Rocky Mount, NC, 27804-4842. Tel: 252-442-1951. Fax: 252-442-7366. p. 1820

Blackburn, Jean, Ref, Malaspina University-College Library, 900 Fifth St, Nanaimo, BC, V9R 5S5, CANADA. Tel: 250-753-3245, Ext 2091. Fax: 250-740-6473. p. 2732

Blackburn, Joseph, Ser, Texas Tech University Health Sciences Center, 3601 Fourth St, Lubbock, TX, 79430-7781. Tel: 806-743-2200. Fax: 806-743-2218. p. 2357

Blackburn, Kourtney, Circ Supvr, Saint John Fisher College, 3690 East Ave, Rochester, NY, 14618-3599. Tel: 585-385-8165. Fax: 585-385-8445. p. 1732

Blackburn, Monica, Ch, Dep Chief Librn, Mississippi Mills Libraries, 155 High St, Almonte, ON, K0A 1A0, CANADA. Tel: 613-256-1037. Fax: 613-256-4887. p. 2792

Blackburn, Paula, Adult Serv, Gates Public Library, 902 Elmgrove Rd, Rochester, NY, 14624. Tel: 585-247-6446. Fax: 585-426-5733. p. 1729

Blackburn, Steven Peter, PhD, Dir, Hartford Seminary Library, 77 Sherman St, Hartford, CT, 06105-2260. Tel: 860-509-9561. Fax: 860-509-9509. p. 346

Blacker, Joan, ILL, Everett Public Library, 2702 Hoyt Ave, Everett, WA, 98201-3556. Tel: 425-257-8020. Fax: 425-257-8017. p. 2515

Blackerby, Nyma, Actg Br Mgr, Jackson/Hinds Library System, Quisenberry Library, 605 E Northside Dr, Clinton, MS, 39056-5121. Tel: 601-924-5684. Fax: 601-924-1953. p. 1303

Blackledge, David, Br Mgr, Extn Serv Librn, Librn IV, Montgomery City-County Public Library System, Hampstead Branch Library, 5251 Hampstead High St, Ste 107, Montgomery, AL, 36116. Tel: 334-240-4843. Fax: 334-240-4839. p. 29

Blackledge, David, Coordr, Extn Serv, Librn IV, Montgomery City-County Public Library System, 245 High St, Montgomery, AL, 36104. Tel: 334-240-4843. Fax: 334-240-4839. p. 29

Blackledge, David, Br Mgr, Extended Serv Librn, Librn IV, Montgomery City-County Public Library System, Pike Road Branch Library, 9585 Vaughn Rd, Pike Road, AL, 36064. Tel: 334-240-4843. Fax: 334-240-4839. p. 30

Blackledge, David, Br Mgr, Extn Serv Librn, Librn IV, Montgomery City-County Public Library System, Pine Level Branch Library, 20 Kohn Dr, Pine Level, AL, 36065. Tel: 334-240-4843. Fax: 334-240-4839. p. 30

Blackledge, David, Br Mgr, Extn Serv Librn, Librn IV, Montgomery City-County Public Library System, Pintlala Branch Library, 255 Federal Rd, Pintlala, AL, 36043-9781. Tel: 334-240-4843. Fax: 334-240-4839. p. 30

Blackledge, Jayne, Dir, North Wales Area Library, 233 S Swartley St, North Wales, PA, 19454. Tel: 215-699-5410. Fax: 215-699-5901. p. 2099

Blackman, Andrea, Spec Coll Librn, Nashville Public Library, 615 Church St, Nashville, TN, 37219-2314. Tel: 615-862-5760. Fax: 615-862-5771. p. 2257

Blackman, Christine, Cat Librn, Williams College, 55 Sawyer Library Dr, Williamstown, MA, 01267. Tel: 413-597-4403. Fax: 413-597-4106. p. 1141

Blackman, Deborah, Circ Librn, Douglas County Public Library, 1625 Library Lane, Minden, NV, 89423-4420. Tel: 775-782-9841. Fax: 775-782-5754. p. 1431

Blackman, Deborah, Circ Librn, ILL, Douglas County Public Library, Lake Tahoe, 233 Warrior Way, Zephyr Cove, NV, 89448. Tel: 775-588-6411. Fax: 775-588-6464. p. 1431

Blackman, Dorothy, Dir, Libr Mgr, Edmeston Free Library & Museum, Six West St, Edmeston, NY, 13335. Tel: 607-965-8208. Fax: 607-965-8208. p. 1618

Blackman, Ivy, Asst Librn, Cataloger, Whitney Museum of American Art, 945 Madison Ave, New York, NY, 10021. Tel: 212-570-3682. p. 1702

Blackman, Joni, Dir, Fenton History Center-Library, 67 Washington St, Jamestown, NY, 14701-6697. Tel: 716-664-6256. Fax: 716-483-7524. p. 1646

Blackman, Marcia, Reader Serv, East Meadow Public Library, 1886 Front St, East Meadow, NY, 11554-1705. Tel: 516-794-2570. Fax: 516-794-1272. p. 1617

Blackman, Michelle, Librn, El Cajon First Presbyterian Church Library, 500 Farragut Circle, El Cajon, CA, 92020. Tel: 619-442-2583. Fax: 619-442-2588. p. 145

Blackman, Shelley, Librn, Evergreen Valley College Library, 3095 Yerba Buena Rd, San Jose, CA, 95135. Tel: 408-274-7900, Ext 6660. Fax: 408-532-1925. p. 249

Blackman, Sue, Librn, Valparaiso Public Library, 300 W Second St, Valparaiso, NE, 68065. Tel: 402-784-6141. Fax: 402-784-6141. p. 1422

Blackmer Reyes, Kathryn, Cultural Heritage Ctr Librn, San Jose State University, One Washington Sq, San Jose, CA, 95192-0028. Tel: 408-808-2097. Fax: 408-808-2141. p. 251

Blackmon, Monique, In Charge, Runnells Specialized Hospital, 40 Watchung Way, Berkeley Heights, NJ, 07922. Tel: 908-771-5757. Fax: 908-771-5820. p. 1472

Blackmon, Paul, Head Librn, H Councill Trenholm State Technical College Library, 3086 Mobile Hwy, Montgomery, AL, 36108. Tel: 334-420-4457. Fax: 334-420-4458. p. 28

Blackmore, Dorothy, Mgr, Kootenai-Shoshone Area Libraries, Harrison Public, 111 Coeur d'Alene Ave, Harrison, ID, 83833. Tel: 208-689-3976. Fax: 208-689-3976. p. 575

Blackmore, Elodie E, Dir, East Smithfield Public Library, 50 Esmond St, Smithfield, RI, 02917-3016. Tel: 401-231-5150. Fax: 401-231-2940. p. 2176

Blackmore, Gail, Librn, Public Utilities Commission of Ohio Library, 180 E Broad St, 11th Flr, Columbus, OH, 43215. Tel: 614-466-8054. Fax: 614-728-8373. p. 1890

Blackmore, Heide, Adult Serv Mgr, Strathcona County Library, 401 Festival Lane, Sherwood Park, AB, T8A 5P7, CANADA. Tel: 780-410-8600. Fax: 780-467-6861. p. 2716

Blackmore, Lenora, Br Mgr, Henry County Library, 123 E Green St, Clinton, MO, 64735-1462. Tel: 660-885-2612. Fax: 660-885-8953. p. 1323

Blackstock, Margaret, Libr Mgr, Millet Public Library, 5031 49th Ave, Millet, AB, T0C 1Z0, CANADA. Tel: 780-387-5222. p. 2711

Blackwelder, Carolyn, Dir, Olive Warner Memorial Library, 111 S Broadway, Hooker, OK, 73945. Tel: 580-652-2835. Fax: 580-652-2831. p. 1965

Blackwelder, Mary B, Dir, Medical College of Wisconsin Libraries, Health Research Ctr, 3rd Flr, 8701 Watertown Plank Rd, Milwaukee, WI, 53226-0509. Tel: 414-955-8323. Fax: 414-955-6532. p. 2619

Blackwell, Cheryl, Ref & Instrul Serv Librn, Albion College, 602 E Cass St, Albion, MI, 49224-1879. Tel: 517-629-0447. Fax: 517-629-0504. p. 1148

Blackwell, Marvin, Br Mgr, Chicago Public Library, Chicago Lawn, 6120 S Kedzie Ave, Chicago, IL, 60629. Tel: 312-747-0639. Fax: 312-747-6182. p. 608

Blackwell, Michael, Br Mgr, Columbus Metropolitan Library, Dublin Branch, 75 N High St, Dublin, OH, 43017. Tel: 614-645-2275. Fax: 614-479-4179. p. 1884

Blackwell, Randall, ILL, Philadelphia College of Osteopathic Medicine, 4170 City Ave, Philadelphia, PA, 19131-1694. Tel: 215-871-6470. Fax: 215-871-6478. p. 2114

Blackwell, Robin, Librn, Citronelle Memorial Library, 7855 State St, Citronelle, AL, 36522. Tel: 251-866-7319. Fax: 251-866-5210. p. 12

Blackwell, Sara, In Charge, Department of Veterans Affairs, 921 NE 13th St 142D, Oklahoma City, OK, 73104. Tel: 405-270-0501, Ext 3688. Fax: 405-270-5145. p. 1971

Blackwell, Scott, Mgr, User Serv, Florida Institute of Technology, 150 W University Blvd, Melbourne, FL, 32901-6988. Tel: 321-674-8021. Fax: 321-724-2559. p. 463

Blackwell, Tamara, Adult/Ref Serv, Bolivar County Library System, 104 S Leflore Ave, Cleveland, MS, 38732. Tel: 662-843-2774. Fax: 662-843-4701. p. 1295

Blackwell, Tammy, YA Librn, Marshall County Public Library System, 1003 Poplar St, Benton, KY, 42025. Tel: 270-527-9969. Fax: 270-527-0506. p. 907

Blackwell, Terri, Asst Coordr, Big Country Library System, 202 Cedar St, Abilene, TX, 79601-5793. Tel: 325-676-6022. Fax: 325-676-6028. p. 2272

Blaczczok, Nadin, Asst Librn, Chinook Regional Library, Chaplin Branch, Second Ave Hall Complex, Chaplin, SK, S0H 0V0, CANADA. Tel: 306-395-2524. p. 2928

Blades, Valerie, Librn, Parkland Regional Library, Theodore Branch, PO Box 448, Theodore, SK, S0A 4C0, CANADA. Tel: 306-647-2315. p. 2932

Bladzinski, Dawn, Ch Serv Librn, South River Public Library, 55 Appleby Ave, South River, NJ, 08882-2499. Tel: 732-254-2488. Fax: 732-254-4116. p. 1531

Blaga, Nicholas, Ft Lauderdale Campus Libr Dir, Keiser University Library System, 1500 NW 49th St, Fort Lauderdale, FL, 33309. Tel: 954-351-4035. Fax: 954-351-4051. p. 443

Blagrave, Kathleen, Acq of New Ser, Ser, Web Coordr, Sir Mortimer B Davis Jewish General Hospital, 3755 Cote Ste Catherine Rd, A-200, Montreal, QC, H3T 1E2, CANADA. Tel: 514-340-8222, Ext 5927. Fax: 514-340-7552. p. 2901

Blaho, Brian, Info Spec, Kaye Scholer LLP, 425 Park Ave, New York, NY, 10022. Tel: 212-836-8550. Fax: 212-836-6613. p. 1684

Blaho, Jean, Info Spec, UOP Knowledge & Library Services, 25 E Algonquin Rd, Des Plaines, IL, 60016. Tel: 847-391-2306. Fax: 847-391-3330. p. 636

Blain, Jessica, Libr Dir, Evans Public Library District, 215 S Fifth St, Vandalia, IL, 62471-2703. Tel: 618-283-2824. Fax: 618-283-4705. p. 713

Blaine, Barry Richard, Law Librn, Fayette County Law Library, Court House, 61 E Main St, Ste D, Uniontown, PA, 15401-3514. Tel: 724-430-1228. Fax: 724-430-4886. p. 2147

Blaine, Billie, Librn, Florida Supreme Court Library, 500 S Duval St, Tallahassee, FL, 32399-1926. Tel: 850-488-8919. Fax: 850-922-5219. p. 495

Blaine, Glenda, In Charge, Northeastern Junior College, 100 College Ave, Sterling, CO, 80751-2399. Tel: 970-521-6612. Fax: 970-521-6759. p. 323

Blair, Alma, Librn, Hickman County Memorial Library, 209 Mayfield Rd, Clinton, KY, 42031-1427. Tel: 270-653-2225. Fax: 270-653-2225. p. 909

Blair, Barbara, Br Librn, Tombigbee Regional Library System, Evans Memorial Library, 105 N Long St, Aberdeen, MS, 39730. Tel: 662-369-4601. Fax: 662-369-2971. p. 1318

Blair, Charles, Dir, Digital Libr Develop Ctr, University of Chicago Library, 1100 E 57th St, Chicago, IL, 60637-1502. Tel: 773-702-8459. Fax: 773-702-6623. p. 626

Blair, David, Dir, Mariposa Museum Library, 26 Main St, Peterborough, NH, 03458. Tel: 603-924-4555. Fax: 603-924-3212. p. 1461

Blair, Donna, Librn, North Jersey Media Group Library, 150 River St, Hackensack, NJ, 07601. Tel: 201-646-4000. Fax: 201-646-4737. p. 1489

Blair, Jennifer, Adult Serv, Covina Public Library, 234 N Second Ave, Covina, CA, 91723-2198. Tel: 626-384-5293. Fax: 626-384-5315. p. 137

Blair, Jo, Librn, Houston Community College - Southwest College, Alief Center, 2811 Hayes Rd, Houston, TX, 77082. Tel: 713-718-6941. Fax: 713-718-6932. p. 2338

Blair, Julia, Strategic Initiatives Librn, Michigan Technological University, 1400 Townsend Dr, Houghton, MI, 49931-1295. Tel: 906-487-3168. p. 1191

Blair, Leigh, Br Mgr, Jackson County Library Services, Phoenix Branch, 510 W First St, Phoenix, OR, 97535. Tel: 541-535-7090. Fax: 541-535-7090. p. 2005

Blair, Linda, Asst Librn, Lake Placid Public Library, 2471 Main St, Lake Placid, NY, 12946. Tel: 518-523-3200. Fax: 518-523-3200. p. 1650

Blair, Maxine G, Librn, Saint Joseph's-Candler, Candler Medical Library, 5353 Reynolds St, Savannah, GA, 31405. Tel: 912-819-6011. Fax: 912-819-6031. p. 550

Blair, Maxine G, Librn, Saint Joseph's-Candler, Health Sciences Library, 11705 Mercy Blvd, Savannah, GA, 31419. Tel: 912-819-4472. Fax: 912-819-3390. p. 551

Blair, Patricia, Asst Br Mgr, Ch, Librn I, Montgomery City-County Public Library System, Rufus A Lewis Regional Branch Library, 3095 Mobile Hwy, Montgomery, AL, 36108. Tel: 334-240-4848. Fax: 334-240-4847. p. 29

Blair, Robin, ILL, Elizabethtown Community & Technical College Library, 600 College Street Rd, Elizabethtown, KY, 42701. Tel: 270-706-8445. Fax: 270-769-1618. p. 912

Blair, Rose, Chair, Department of Community Services, Government of Yukon, Burwash Landing Community, Kluane First Nation Bldg, 1093 Alaska Hwy, Burwash Landing, YT, Y0B 1V0, CANADA. Tel: 867-841-4707. Fax: 867-841-5904. p. 2933

Blair, Susan, Asst Youth Serv, Dorothy Alling Memorial Library, 21 Library Lane, Williston, VT, 05495. Tel: 802-878-4918. Fax: 802-878-3964. p. 2440

Blair, Thea, Mgr, Support & Cultural Serv, Mission Viejo Library, 100 Civic Ctr, Mission Viejo, CA, 92691. Tel: 949-830-7100, Ext 5123. Fax: 949-586-8447. p. 187

Blair, Tracy, Ch, Corry Public Library, 117 W Washington St, Corry, PA, 16407. Tel: 814-664-4404, 814-664-7611. Fax: 814-663-0742. p. 2047

Blair, Valle, Ch, James Prendergast Library Association, 509 Cherry St, Jamestown, NY, 14701. Tel: 716-484-7135. Fax: 716-487-1148. p. 1647

Blair-Sheldon, Pamela, Youth Serv Mgr, Maricopa County Library District, 2700 N Central Ave, Ste 700, Phoenix, AZ, 85004. Tel: 602-652-3052. Fax: 602-652-3071. p. 74

Blais, Carole, ILL/Doc Delivery Serv, Ref Serv, Canadian Nuclear Safety Commission Library, 280 Slater St, Ottawa, ON, K1P 1C2, CANADA. Tel: 613-995-2060. Fax: 613-995-5086. p. 2829

Blais, Marie-Josee, Head of Libr, Centre de Pedopsychiatrie du CHUQ, One Ave Du-Sacre Coeur, Quebec, QC, G1N 2W1, CANADA. Tel: 418-529-6851, Ext 278. Fax: 418-691-0751. p. 2904

Blais, Naomi, Coordr, Canadian Dental Association Resource Centre, 1815 Alta Vista Dr, Ottawa, ON, K1G 3Y6, CANADA. Tel: 613-520-5025. Fax: 613-523-7736. p. 2829

Blaisdell, Judith, Ch, Jonathan Bourne Public Library, 19 Sandwich Rd, Bourne, MA, 02532-3699. Tel: 508-759-0644, Ext 106. Fax: 508-759-0647. p. 1069

Blaise-Cote, Louis, Librn, Cegep de Saint-Hyacinthe Bibliotheque, 3000 rue Boulle, Saint-Hyacinthe, QC, J2S 1H9, CANADA. Tel: 450-773-6800. Fax: 450-773-9971. p. 2910

Blake, Amy, Supvr, Youth Serv, Knox County Public Library, 502 N Seventh St, Vincennes, IN, 47591-2119. Tel: 812-886-4380. Fax: 812-886-0342. p. 784

Blake, Barbara, Asst Coordr, Librn II, West Texas Library System, 1306 Ninth St, Lubbock, TX, 79401-2798. Tel: 806-775-2858. Fax: 806-775-2856. p. 2358

Blake, Ben, Head, Archives & Spec Coll, Univ Archivist, Youngstown State University, One University Plaza, Youngstown, OH, 44555-0001. Tel: 330-941-3788. Fax: 330-941-3734. p. 1953

Blake, Catherine, Assoc Prof, University of Illinois at Urbana-Champaign, Library & Information Science Bldg, 501 E Daniel St, Champaign, IL, 61820-6211. Tel: 217-333-3280. Fax: 217-244-3302. p. 2965

Blake, Joni, Exec Dir, Greater Western Library Alliance, 5109 Cherry St, Kansas City, MO, 64110. Tel: 816-926-8765. Fax: 816-926-8790. p. 2947

Blake, Marsha, Ref Serv, Westminster Theological Seminary, 2960 W Church Rd, Glenside, PA, 19038. Tel: 215-572-3821. Fax: 215-887-3412. p. 2062

Blake, Mary, Dir, Sloatsburg Public Library, One Liberty Rock Rd, Sloatsburg, NY, 10974-2392. Tel: 845-753-2001. Fax: 845-753-2144. p. 1744

Blake, Michael R, Asst Librn, Digital Res Librn, Harvard-Smithsonian Center for Astrophysics Library, 60 Garden St, MS-56, Cambridge, MA, 02138. Tel: 617-496-7601. Fax: 617-495-7199. p. 1077

Blake, Miriam, Dir, Los Alamos National Laboratory, MS-P362, PO Box 1663, Los Alamos, NM, 87544-7113. Tel: 505-667-4448. Fax: 505-665-6452. p. 1559

Blake, Richard, Pub Serv, Columbia Theological Seminary, 701 Columbia Dr, Decatur, GA, 30030. Tel: 404-687-4549. Fax: 404-687-4687. p. 529

Blake, Ruth A, Dir, Waterboro Public Library, 187 Main St, East Waterboro, ME, 04030. Tel: 207-247-3363. Fax: 207-247-3363. p. 984

Blake, Tim, Satellite Librn, United States Courts Library, Sandra Day O'Connor United States Courthouse, Ste 410, 401 W Washington St, SPC16, Phoenix, AZ, 85003-2135. Tel: 602-322-7295. Fax: 602-322-7299. p. 77

Blake, Tom, Digital Serv Mgr, Boston Public Library, 700 Boylston St, Boston, MA, 02117-0286. Tel: 617-536-5400. Fax: 617-236-4306. p. 1056

Blakeley, Loretta, Admin Support Coordr, California State University, Stanislaus, One University Circle, Turlock, CA, 95382. p. 277

Blakely, Ann, Ref, University of Tulsa Libraries, 2933 E Sixth St, Tulsa, OK, 74104-3123. Tel: 918-631-3061. Fax: 918-631-3791. p. 1984

Blakely, Jeannie, Tech Serv, Georgia Highlands College Libraries, 3175 Cedartown Hwy SE, Rome, GA, 30161. Tel: 706-295-6318. Fax: 706-295-6365. p. 548

Blakely, Jennifer, Circ, Cambridge Public Library, 449 Broadway, Cambridge, MA, 02138. Tel: 617-349-4040. Fax: 617-349-4028. p. 1073

Blaker, Laura, Dir, Independence Public Library, 805 First St E, Independence, IA, 50644. Tel: 319-334-2470. Fax: 319-332-0306. p. 822

Blakeslee, Julie, ILL, Ellinwood School & Community Library, 210 N Schiller Ave, Ellinwood, KS, 67526-1651. Tel: 620-564-2306. Fax: 620-564-2848. p. 865

Blakeslee, Rena, Circ, Rider University, Katharine Houk Talbott Library, Westminster Choir College, 101 Walnut Lane, Princeton, NJ, 08540-3899. Tel: 609-921-7100, Ext 8335. Fax: 609-497-0243. p. 1494

Blakeslee, Sarah, Interim Univ Librn, California State University, Chico, 400 W First St, Chico, CA, 95929-0295. Tel: 530-898-4244. Fax: 530-898-4443. p. 133

Blakesley, Beth, Assoc Dean, Washington State University Libraries, 100 Dairy Rd, Pullman, WA, 99164. Tel: 509-335-6134. Fax: 509-335-6721. p. 2525

Blakesley, Beth, Head, Res Serv, Washington State University Libraries, Holland & Terrell Libraries, 100 Dairy Rd, Pullman, WA, 99164. Tel: 509-335-6134. Fax: 509-335-0934. p. 2525

Blakesley, Beth, Head, Res Serv, Washington State University Libraries, Owen Science & Engineering, PO Box 643200, Pullman, WA, 99164-3200. Tel: 509-335-6134. Fax: 509-335-2534. p. 2525

Blakley, Alma, Br Mgr, Jackson State University, Information Services Library, 3825 Ridgewood Rd, Jackson, MS, 39211. Tel: 601-432-6313. Fax: 601-432-6144. p. 1303

Blakney, Sandi, Dir, Allen Park Public Library, 8100 Allen Rd, Allen Park, MI, 48101. Tel: 313-381-2425. Fax: 313-381-2124. p. 1149

Blalock, Beverly, Head, Circ, Presbyterian College, 211 E Maple St, Clinton, SC, 29325. Tel: 864-833-8299. Fax: 864-833-8315. p. 2186

Blalock, Docia, Dir, Winslow Public Library, 420 W Gilmore St, Winslow, AZ, 86047. Tel: 928-289-4982. Fax: 928-289-4182. p. 90

Blalock, Joan, Br Librn, Spartanburg County Public Libraries, Cowpens Library, 181 School St, Cowpens, SC, 29330. Tel: 864-463-0430. p. 2205

Blalock, Renee C, Dir, Birmingham Public Library, 2100 Park Pl, Birmingham, AL, 35203. Tel: 205-226-3614. Fax: 205-226-3743. p. 7

Blalock-Koral, Molly, Mgr, Access Serv, Portland State University Library, 1875 SW Park Ave, Portland, OR, 97201-3220. Tel: 503-725-4234. Fax: 503-725-4524. p. 2014

Blanchard, Barbara, Mgr, San Mateo County Library, Foster City Library, 1000 E Hillsdale Blvd, Foster City, CA, 94404. Tel: 650-574-4842. Fax: 650-572-1875. p. 255

Blanchard, Brittany, Res & Instruction Librn, Embry-Riddle Aeronautical University, 3700 Willow Creek Rd, Prescott, AZ, 86301-3720. Tel: 928-777-6656. p. 78

Blanchard, Cheryl, Librn, Paine Memorial Free Library, Two Gilliland Ln, Willsboro, NY, 12996. Tel: 518-963-4478. p. 1770

Blanchard, Debra, Dir, Athol Public Library, 568 Main St, Athol, MA, 01331. Tel: 978-249-9515. Fax: 978-249-7636. p. 1050

Blanchard, Edith, Dir, Charles H MacNider Museum Library, 303 Second St SE, Mason City, IA, 50401-3925. Tel: 641-421-3666. Fax: 641-422-9612. p. 830

Blanchard, J, Ref, University of Manitoba Libraries, Elizabeth Dafoe Libr, Rm 156, Winnipeg, MB, R3T 2N2, CANADA. Tel: 204-474-9881. Fax: 204-474-7583. p. 2758

Blanchard, Jim, Head Librn, University of Manitoba Libraries, Father Harold Drake Library - St Pauls College, 70 Dysart Rd, Winnipeg, MB, R3T 2M6, CANADA. Tel: 204-474-6882. Fax: 204-474-7615. p. 2758

Blanchard, Jim, Head, Ref, University of Manitoba Libraries, Elizabeth Dafoe Library, 25 Chancellor's Circle, Winnipeg, MB, R3T 2N2, CANADA. Tel: 204-474-6846. Fax: 204-474-7577. p. 2758

Blanchard, Jim, Head of Libr, University of Manitoba Libraries, St John's College Library, 92 Dysart Rd, Winnipeg, MB, R3T 2M5, CANADA. Tel: 204-474-8542. Fax: 204-474-7614. p. 2759

Blanchard, JoElla, Dir, Cantwell Community-School Library, Mile 133-5 Denali Hwy, Cantwell, AK, 99729. Tel: 907-768-2372. Fax: 907-768-2500. p. 46

Blanchard, Laura, Exec Dir, Philadelphia Area Consortium of Special Collections Libraries, c/o The Historical Society of Pennsylvania, 1300 Locust St, Philadelphia, PA, 19107. Tel: 215-985-1445. Fax: 215-985-1446. p. 2954

Blanchard, Lauren, Asst Librn, Maine Maritime Academy, Pleasant St, Box C-1, Castine, ME, 04420. Tel: 207-326-2263. Fax: 207-326-2261. p. 981

Blanchard, Laurie, Long Term Care Librn, University of Manitoba Libraries, J W Crane Memorial Library, 2109 Portage Ave, Winnipeg, MB, R3J 0L3, CANADA. Tel: 204-831-2943. Fax: 204-888-1805. p. 2758

Blanchard, Laurie, Outreach Librn, University of Manitoba Libraries, Riverview Health Centre Virtual Library, One Morley St, Winnipeg, MB, R3L 2P4, CANADA. Tel: 204-478-6873. Fax: 204-478-6121. p. 2759

Blanchard, Leslie, Br Mgr, Central Arkansas Library System, Adolphine Fletcher Terry Branch, 2015 Napa Valley Dr, Little Rock, AR, 72212. Tel: 501-228-0129. p. 106

Blanchard, Linda, Head, Coll Develop, York County Public Library, 100 Long Green Blvd, Yorktown, VA, 23693. Tel: 757-890-5104. Fax: 757-890-5127. p. 2505

Blanchard, Linda C, In Charge, Bayliss Public Library, Curtis Public, N 9220 Portage Ave, Curtis, MI, 49820. Tel: 906-586-9411. Fax: 906-586-6166. p. 1226

Blanchard, Michael S, Automation Syst Coordr, Metropolitan Community College Library, 30th & Fort Sts, Omaha, NE, 68103. Tel: 402-457-2521. Fax: 402-457-2655. p. 1413

Blanchard, Monica, Dr, Curator, Catholic University of America, Semitics/ICOR Library, 620 Michigan Ave NE, 18 Mullen Library, Washington, DC, 20064. Tel: 202-319-5084. Fax: 202-319-4735. p. 396

Blanchard, Ruth, Chief Exec Officer, Head Librn, Elizabethtown-Kitley Township Public Library, 6544 New Dublin Rd, Addison, ON, K0E 1A0, CANADA. Tel: 613-498-3338. p. 2791

Blanchard, Sandy, Circ, Coe College, 1220 First Ave NE, Cedar Rapids, IA, 52402-5092. Tel: 319-399-8595. Fax: 319-399-8019. p. 800

Blanchard, Sudie, Asst Dir, York Public Library, 15 Long Sands Rd, York, ME, 03909. Tel: 207-363-2818. Fax: 207-363-7250. p. 1008

Blanchard, Tammi, Br Mgr, Lafourche Parish Public Library, South Lafourche Public Library, 16241 East Main St, CutOff, LA, 70345. Tel: 985-632-7140. Fax: 985-632-4963. p. 971

Blanchette, Christy, Adult Serv, Valley Cottage Free Library, 110 Rte 303, Valley Cottage, NY, 10989. Tel: 845-268-7700. Fax: 845-268-7760. p. 1760

Blanchette, Gaetan, Fr, In Charge, The Abbey of Gethsemani Library, 3642 Monks Rd, Trappist, KY, 40051. Tel: 502-549-3117, Ext 152. Fax: 502-549-4124. p. 936

Blanchette, Hollie, Circ, Valemount Public Library, 1090A Main St, Valemount, BC, V0E 2Z0, CANADA. Tel: 250-566-4367. Fax: 250-566-4278. p. 2740

Blanchette, Lynn H, Dir, Coventry Public Library, 1672 Flat River Rd, Coventry, RI, 02816. Tel: 401-822-9101. Fax: 401-822-9133. p. 2164

Blanchette, Mona, Ch, Ayer Library, 26 E Main St, Ayer, MA, 01432. Tel: 978-772-8250. Fax: 978-772-8251. p. 1051

Blanck, Dag, PhD, Dr, Dir, Swenson Swedish Immigration Research Center, Augustana College, 3520 Seventh Ave, Rock Island, IL, 61201. Tel: 309-794-7204. Fax: 309-794-7443. p. 696

Blanco-Rivera, Joel, Asst Prof, Simmons College, 300 The Fenway, Boston, MA, 02115. Tel: 617-521-2800. Fax: 617-521-3192. p. 2967

Bland, Annette, Asst Dir, Columbia Public Library, 106 N Metter, Columbia, IL, 62236-2299. Tel: 618-281-4237. Fax: 618-281-6977. p. 631

Bland, Dianne, Librn, Tolono Public Library District, 111 E Main St, Tolono, IL, 61880. Tel: 217-485-5558. Fax: 217-485-3088. p. 710

Bland, Kim, Adult Serv, Hardin County Public Library, 100 Jim Owen Dr, Elizabethtown, KY, 42701. Tel: 270-769-6337. Fax: 270-769-0437. p. 912

Bland, Robert, Automation Syst Coordr, University of North Carolina at Asheville, One University Heights, CPO 1500, Asheville, NC, 28804-8504. Tel: 828-251-6543. p. 1775

Bland, Rodney, Dir, Burleson Public Library, 248 SW Johnson Ave, Burleson, TX, 76028. Tel: 817-426-9210. Fax: 817-426-9371. p. 2293

Bland, Rose, Syst Coordr, University of South Florida, Hinks & Elaine Shimberg Health Sciences Library, 12901 Bruce B Downs Blvd, MDC Box 31, Tampa, FL, 33612-4799. Tel: 813-974-2399. Fax: 813-974-3605, 813-974-4930. p. 498

Bland, Sally, Librn, Brighton Memorial Library, 110 N Main, Brighton, IL, 62012. Tel: 618-372-8450. Fax: 618-372-7450. p. 597

Blandford, Linda, Info Consult, ILL, Spalding University Library, 853 Library Lane, Louisville, KY, 40203-9986. Tel: 502-585-7130. Fax: 502-585-7156. p. 925

Blaney, Jackie, ILL, Pope County Library System, 116 E Third St, Russellville, AR, 72801. Tel: 479-968-4368. Fax: 479-968-3222. p. 114

Blaney, Janice, Librn, Holy Trinity Lutheran Church Library, 11709 W Cleveland Ave, West Allis, WI, 53227-2901. Tel: 414-321-0700. Fax: 414-321-5530. p. 2647

Blanford, Rita, Ref Librn, Lorain County Community College, 1005 Abbe Rd N, North Elyria, OH, 44035-1691. Tel: 440-366-7289. Fax: 440-366-4127. p. 1924

Blank, Myra, ILL, Rhode Island College, 600 Mt Pleasant Ave, Providence, RI, 02908-1924. Tel: 401-456-8126. Fax: 401-456-9646. p. 2174

Blank, Pam, Circ, Middlesborough-Bell County Public Library, 126 S 20th St, Middlesboro, KY, 40965-1212. Tel: 606-248-4812. Fax: 606-248-8766. p. 929

Blank, Peter, Head Librn, Stanford University Libraries, Art & Architecture Library, 102 Cummings Art Bldg, Main Flr, Stanford, CA, 94305-2018. Tel: 650-723-3408, 650-725-1037. Fax: 650-725-0140. p. 271

Blank, Sharon L, Pub Serv, Ref Serv, Screven-Jenkins Regional Library, 106 S Community Dr, Sylvania, GA, 30467. Tel: 912-564-7526. Fax: 912-564-7580. p. 553

Blanke, Henry, Head, Ref, Marymount Manhattan College, 221 E 71st St, New York, NY, 10021. Tel: 212-774-4806. Fax: 212-458-8207. p. 1685

Blankemeyer, Sue A, Head Librn, United States Air Force, 201 Mitchell Blvd, Bldg 223, Laughlin AFB, TX, 78843-2125. Tel: 830-298-5119. p. 2354

Blankenburg, Julie, Cat, Head of Libr, Ref Serv, United States Forest Service, One Gifford Pinchot Dr, Madison, WI, 53726-2398. Tel: 608-231-9313. Fax: 608-231-9311. p. 2608

Blankenship, Betsy L, Dir, Ohio State University LIBRARIES, Marion Campus Library, 1469 Mount Vernon Ave, Marion, OH, 43302. Tel: 740-725-6254. Fax: 740-725-6309. p. 1888

Blankenship, Brandi, Br Mgr, Mid-Continent Public Library, Weston Branch, 18204 Library Dr, Weston, MO, 64098. Tel: 816-640-2874. Fax: 816-640-2688. p. 1333

Blankenship, Cheryl, Ch, Briggs Lawrence County Public Library, 321 S Fourth St, Ironton, OH, 45638. Tel: 740-532-1124. Fax: 740-532-4948. p. 1906

Blankenship, Donna, Br Librn, Mingo County Library, Matewan Branch, Warm Hollow Rd, Matewan, WV, 25678. Tel: 304-426-6306. Fax: 304-426-6306. p. 2558

Blankenship, Frances, Dir, War Public Library, Bldg 701, Berwind Lake Rd, War, WV, 24892. Tel: 304-875-4622. Fax: 304-875-4622. p. 2573

Blankenship, James, Curator, United States Department of the Interior, 5001 Siege Rd, Petersburg, VA, 23803. Tel: 804-732-3531. Fax: 804-732-0835. p. 2484

Blankenship, Karen, Dir, Libr Serv, San Jacinto College, 8060 Spencer Hwy, Pasadena, TX, 77505. Tel: 281-476-1850. Fax: 281-478-2734. p. 2369

Blankenship, Rebecca, Dir, Logan Area Public Library, 16 Wildcat Way, Logan, WV, 25601. Tel: 304-752-6652. Fax: 304-752-2684. p. 2564

Blankenship, Rosemary, Coordr, Libr Serv, Germanna Community College, 10000 Germanna Point Dr, Fredericksburg, VA, 22408-9543. Tel: 540-891-3015. Fax: 540-891-3060. p. 2466

Blankenship, Stefanie, Youth Serv Librn, Cranston Public Library, Auburn Branch, 396 Pontiac Ave, Cranston, RI, 02910-3322. Tel: 401-781-6116. p. 2165

Blankenship, Terry, Dir, Rob & Bessie Welder Wildlife Foundation Library, 10620 Hwy 77 N, Sinton, TX, 78387. Tel: 361-364-2643. Fax: 361-364-2650. p. 2387

Blankespoor, Wendy, Archivist, Calvin College & Calvin Theological Seminary, 1855 Knollcrest Circle SE, Grand Rapids, MI, 49546-4402. Tel: 616-526-6919. Fax: 616-526-6470. p. 1184

Blankvoort, Antoinette, Librn, North Norfolk MacGregor Regional Library, 35 Hampton E, MacGregor, MB, R0H 0R0, CANADA. Tel: 204-685-2796. Fax: 204-685-2478. p. 2749

Blansett, Betty, Circ, Ada Public Library, 124 S Rennie, Ada, OK, 74820. Tel: 580-436-8121. Fax: 580-436-0534. p. 1955

Blanton, Brigette, Asst Dir, Greensboro Public Library, 219 N Church St, Greensboro, NC, 27402-3178. Tel: 336-373-2471. Fax: 336-333-6781. p. 1796

Blanton, James, Dir, Daviess County Public Library, 2020 Frederica St, Owensboro, KY, 42301. Tel: 270-684-0211. Fax: 270-684-0218. p. 931

Blanton, James, Cent Libr Mgr, Chesapeake Public Library, 298 Cedar Rd, Chesapeake, VA, 23322-5512. Tel: 757-410-7120. Fax: 757-410-7112. p. 2456

Blanton, Libby, Supvr, Southside Virginia Community College, 200 Daniel Rd, Keysville, VA, 23947. Tel: 434-736-2044. Fax: 434-736-2079. p. 2472

Blanton, Linda Heck, Cat Librn, Johnson City Public Library, 100 W Millard St, Johnson City, TN, 37604. Tel: 423-434-4462. Fax: 423-434-4469. p. 2240

Blare, Cheryl, Managing Librn, United States Courts for the Ninth Circuit Library, 95 Seventh St, San Francisco, CA, 94103. Tel: 415-556-9500. Fax: 415-556-9927. p. 247

Blas, Elise, Info Literacy Librn, Washburn University, 1700 SW College Ave, Topeka, KS, 66621. Tel: 785-670-2507. Fax: 785-670-3223. p. 897

Blasco, Martin, Ref, Field Library of Peekskill, Four Nelson Ave, Peekskill, NY, 10566-2138. Tel: 914-737-1212. Fax: 914-862-9710. p. 1716

Blasier, Charlotte, Ch, Hudson Library & Historical Society, 96 Library St, Hudson, OH, 44236-5122. Tel: 330-653-6658. Fax: 330-650-3373. p. 1905

Blasingame, Laurie, PRN Med Librn, Kalispell Regional Medical Center, 310 Sunnyview Lane, Kalispell, MT, 59901. Tel: 406-752-1739. Fax: 406-752-8771. p. 1384

Blatherwick, Cynthia, Pub Serv Librn, Joe Barnhart Bee County Public Library, 110 W Corpus Christi St, Beeville, TX, 78102-5604. Tel: 361-362-4901. Fax: 361-358-8694. p. 2288

Blatt, Hanna, Coll Develop, Paramus Public Library, E 116 Century Rd, Paramus, NJ, 07652-4398. Tel: 201-599-1300. Fax: 201-599-0059. p. 1517

Blatti, Mary, Teen Serv Mgr, Manhattan-Elwood Public Library District, 240 Whitson St, Manhattan, IL, 60442. Tel: 815-478-3987. Fax: 815-478-3988. p. 669

Blattner, Bettina, Dir, Lost Rivers District Library, 126 S Front St, Arco, ID, 83213. Tel: 208-527-8511. p. 569

Blau-McDonald, Melanie A, Exec Dir, SouthWest Ohio & Neighboring Libraries, 10901 Reed Hartman Hwy, Ste 120, Blue Ash, OH, 45242. Tel: 513-751-4422. Fax: 513-751-0463. p. 2952

Blauet, Doris, Librn, Genesys Regional Medical Center, One Genesys Pkwy, Grand Blanc, MI, 48439-1477. Tel: 810-606-5260. Fax: 810-606-5270. p. 1183

Blauvelt, Thomas, Head, Bibliog Serv, Syst Mgr, Northern New York Library Network, 6721 US Hwy 11, Potsdam, NY, 13676. Tel: 315-265-1119. Fax: 315-265-1881. p. 2950

Blaylock, James C, Dir, Baptist Missionary Association Theological Seminary, 1530 E Pine St, Jacksonville, TX, 75766-5407. Tel: 903-586-2501, Ext 232. Fax: 903-586-0378. p. 2347

Blaylock, Jan, Dir, Lindsay Community Library, 112 W Choctaw, Lindsay, OK, 73052. Tel: 405-756-3449. Fax: 405-756-2268. p. 1967

Blaze, Suzi, Pub Serv Adminr, Alachua County Library District, 401 E University Ave, Gainesville, FL, 32601-5453. Tel: 352-334-3968. Fax: 352-334-3918. p. 448

Blazecka, Christina, Chief Exec Officer, Cochrane Public Library, 178 Fourth Ave, Cochrane, ON, P0L 1C0, CANADA. Tel: 705-272-4178. Fax: 705-272-4165. p. 2800

Blazek, Jesse, Head, Circ Serv, Stickney-Forest View Public Library District, 6800 W 43rd St, Stickney, IL, 60402. Tel: 708-749-1050. Fax: 708-749-1054. p. 707

Blean, Irene, Cluster Coordr, Hartford Public Library, Ropkins Branch, 1750 Main St, Hartford, CT, 06120. Tel: 860-695-7520. Fax: 860-722-6906. p. 346

Bleattler, Mercedes, Ch, Largo Public Library, 120 Central Park Dr, Largo, FL, 33771. Tel: 727-587-6715. Fax: 727-586-7353. p. 460

Bleau, Sharon, Ref, Mountain State University Library, 609 S Kanawha St, Beckley, WV, 25801. Tel: 304-929-1368. Fax: 304-929-1665. p. 2553

Blechl, Sue, Dir, Emporia Public Library, 110 E Sixth Ave, Emporia, KS, 66801-3960. Tel: 620-340-6462. Fax: 620-340-6444. p. 865

Blecker, Marian, Librn, Alamance Regional Medical Center, 1240 Huffman Mill Rd, Burlington, NC, 27216. Tel: 336-538-7574. Fax: 336-538-7571. p. 1779

Bledsoe, Carole, Asst County Librn, Pub Serv, Spartanburg County Public Libraries, 151 S Church St, Spartanburg, SC, 29306-3241. Tel: 864-596-3500. Fax: 864-596-3518. p. 2205

Bledsoe, Cynthia, Dep Dir, Charleston County Public Library, 68 Calhoun St, Charleston, SC, 29401. Tel: 843-805-6801. p. 2183

Bledsoe, Debra, Team Mgr, Eastman Chemical Co, Research Library, Bldg 150B, Kingsport, TN, 37662. Tel: 423-229-4290. Fax: 423-224-0519. p. 2240

Bledsoe, Jenny, Librn, Gladbrook Public Library, 301 Second St, Gladbrook, IA, 50635. Tel: 641-473-3236. Fax: 641-473-3236. p. 818

Bledsoe, Jenny, Dir, Toledo Public Library, 206 E High St, Toledo, IA, 52342-1617. Tel: 641-484-3362. Fax: 641-484-2058. p. 848

Bledsoe, Kathleen, Spec Coll Librn, Marshall University Libraries, One John Marshall Dr, Huntington, WV, 25755-2060. Tel: 304-696-3174. Fax: 304-696-5858. p. 2562

Bledsoe, Luci, Dir, Johnson Creek Public Library, 125 Lincoln St, Johnson Creek, WI, 53038. Tel: 920-699-3741. Fax: 920-699-3741. p. 2600

Bledsoe, Martha, Head, Circ, Villa Park Public Library, 305 S Ardmore Ave, Villa Park, IL, 60181-2698. Tel: 630-834-1164. Fax: 630-834-0489. p. 714

Bledsoe, Stephanie, Dir, Mississippi County Library District, Mitchell Memorial, 204 E Washington St, East Prairie, MO, 63845. Tel: 573-649-2131. Fax: 573-649-2131. p. 1323

Bledsoe, Stephanie R, Dir, Mississippi County Library District, 105 E Marshall St, Charleston, MO, 63834. Tel: 573-683-6748. Fax: 573-683-2761. p. 1323

Bleecker, Jeanne, Dir, Smoky Valley Library District, 73 Hadley Circle, Round Mountain, NV, 89045. Tel: 775-377-2215. Fax: 775-377-2699. p. 1434

Bleier, Karen, Coop Librn, Burns & McDonnell Engineering Co, 9400 Ward Pkwy, Kansas City, MO, 64114. Tel: 816-822-3550. Fax: 816-822-3409. p. 1337

Bleil, Katie, Educ Dir, Michigan Maritime Museum, 91 Michigan Ave, South Haven, MI, 49090. Tel: 269-637-9156. Fax: 269-637-1594. p. 1227

Bleiler, Jennifer, Head, Acq & Electronic Res, Curtis Laws Wilson Library, 400 W 14th St, Rolla, MO, 65409-0060. Tel: 573-341-4015. Fax: 573-341-4233. p. 1351

Bleistein, Stacey, Ref Librn, Post University, 800 Country Club Rd, Waterbury, CT, 06723-2540. Tel: 203-596-4560. Fax: 203-575-9691. p. 375

Bleiweis, Maxine, Dir, Westport Library Association, 20 Jesup Rd, Westport, CT, 06880. Tel: 203-291-4801. Fax: 203-227-3829. p. 377

Blend, L, Ch, North Shore Public Library, 250 Rte 25A, Shoreham, NY, 11786-9677. Tel: 631-929-4488. Fax: 631-929-4551. p. 1743

Blenke, Christina, Electronic Serv Librn, Pace University, 861 Bedford Rd, Pleasantville, NY, 10570-2799. Tel: 914-773-3222. Fax: 914-773-3508. p. 1719

Bleskin, Suzanne, Dir, Crestwood Public Library District, 4955 W 135th St, Crestwood, IL, 60445. Tel: 708-371-4090. Fax: 708-371-4127. p. 631

Blessing, Marilyn, Libr Dir, Brookston - Prairie Township Public Library, 111 W Second St, Brookston, IN, 47923. Tel: 765-563-6511. Fax: 765-563-6833. p. 730

Blessing, Matt, Head, Spec Coll & Archives, Marquette University Libraries, 1355 W Wisconsin Ave, Milwaukee, WI, 53233. Tel: 414-288-5901. Fax: 414-288-6709. p. 2618

Blessing, Toni, Adult Serv Mgr, Kanawha County Public Library, 123 Capitol St, Charleston, WV, 25301. Tel: 304-343-4646. Fax: 304-348-6530. p. 2556

Blessman, Jill, Acq, Illinois Historic Preservation Agency, 112 N Sixth St, Springfield, IL, 62701. Tel: 217-785-7943. Fax: 217-785-6250. p. 705

Blevens, Cheryl, Ref/Instruction Mgr, Indiana State University, 510 North 6 1/2 St, Terre Haute, IN, 47809. Tel: 812-237-8986. Fax: 812-237-3376. p. 781

Blevins, Cheryl, Br Mgr, Nelsonville Public Library, The Plains Public, 14 S Plains Rd, The Plains, OH, 45780. Tel: 740-797-4579. Fax: 740-797-4579. p. 1920

Blevins, George, Libr Tech, Gilpin County Public Library District, 15131 Hwy 119, Black Hawk, CO, 80422. Tel: 303-582-5777. Fax: 303-582-3938. p. 289

Blevins, Jane, Coll Develop, Palm Beach County Library System, 3650 Summit Blvd, West Palm Beach, FL, 33406-4198. Tel: 561-233-2709. Fax: 561-233-2622. p. 503

Blevins, Jean, Asst Librn, Bracken County Public Library, 310 W Miami St, Brooksville, KY, 41004. Tel: 606-735-3620. Fax: 606-735-3378. p. 908

Blevins, Kim, Youth Serv, Carnegie Public Library, 219 E Fourth St, East Liverpool, OH, 43920-3143. Tel: 330-385-2048. Fax: 330-385-7600. p. 1897

Blewett, Daniel, Ref, College of DuPage Library, 425 Fawell Blvd, Glen Ellyn, IL, 60137-6599. Tel: 630-942-2279. Fax: 630-858-8757. p. 649

Bley, Vonna, Ch, Danville Public Library, 319 N Vermilion St, Danville, IL, 61832. Tel: 217-477-5225. Fax: 217-477-5230. p. 633

Bleyl, Sarah, Br Mgr, Kern County Library, Southwest Branch, 8301 Ming Ave, Bakersfield, CA, 93311-2020. Tel: 661-664-7716. Fax: 661-664-7717. p. 125

Blick, William, Electronic Res/Web Librn, Queensborough Community College, City University of New York, 222-05 56th Ave, Bayside, NY, 11364-1497. Tel: 718-281-5778. Fax: 718-281-5012. p. 1579

Bliese, Mark, Coordr of Libr Tech, Concordia Seminary Library, 801 Seminary Pl, Saint Louis, MO, 63105-3199. Tel: 314-505-7036. Fax: 314-505-7046. p. 1353

Bligh, Kevin, Ref Serv, Ad, Ocean City Free Public Library, 1735 Simpson Ave, Ste 4, Ocean City, NJ, 08226. Tel: 609-399-2434, Ext 5226. Fax: 609-398-0751. p. 1516

Blinn, Joanne, Ref Librn, Foley & Hoag LLP Library, 155 Seaport Blvd, Boston, MA, 02210. Tel: 617-832-7070. Fax: 617-832-7000. p. 1061

Blinn, Karen E, Tech Serv, Marion Public Library, 600 S Washington St, Marion, IN, 46953-1992. Tel: 765-668-2900. Fax: 765-668-2911. p. 763

Blinn, Kate, Academic Outreach Librn, Earlham College, 801 National Rd W, Richmond, IN, 47374-4095. Tel: 765-983-1408. Fax: 765-983-1304. p. 774

Blinn, Pat, Ref, Lincoln Library, 326 S Seventh St, Springfield, IL, 62701. Tel: 217-753-4900, Ext 232. Fax: 217-753-5329. p. 706

Bliss, Elizabeth, Librn, Atlantic County Library System, Brigantine Branch, 201 15th St S, Brigantine, NJ, 08203. Tel: 609-266-0110. Fax: 609-266-0040. p. 1500

Bliss, Heide-Marie, Br Mgr, O'Melveny & Myers LLP, Times Square Tower, Seven Times Sq, New York, NY, 10036. Fax: 212-326-2061. p. 1696

Bliss, Ross, Br Head, Vancouver Public Library, Renfrew, 2969 E 22nd Ave, Vancouver, BC, V5M 2Y3, CANADA. Tel: 604-257-8705. Fax: 604-257-8704. p. 2744

Blobaum, Paul, Ref, Governors State University Library, One University Pkwy, University Park, IL, 60466-0975. Tel: 708-534-4139. Fax: 708-534-4564. p. 711

Bloch, Ania, Br Mgr, Los Angeles Public Library System, Sunland-Tujunga Branch, 7771 Foothill Blvd, Tujunga, CA, 91042-2197. Tel: 818-352-4481. Fax: 818-352-2501. p. 174

Bloch, Judith, Coop Librn, Shannon & Wilson, Inc, 400 N 34th St, Ste 100, Seattle, WA, 98103-8636. Tel: 206-695-6821. Fax: 206-695-6777. p. 2532

Bloch, Kathleen, Coll Mgr, Spertus Institute of Jewish Studies, 610 S Michigan Ave, Chicago, IL, 60605. Tel: 312-322-1712. Fax: 312-922-0455. p. 625

Blocher, Carolyn, Asst Dir, Stillwater Public Library, 224 N Third St, Stillwater, MN, 55082. Tel: 651-275-4338. Fax: 651-275-4342. p. 1285

Block, Darla, Tech Serv Mgr, Westchester Public Library, 200 W Indiana Ave, Chesterton, IN, 46304-3122. Tel: 219-921-0964. Fax: 219-926-6424. p. 732

Block, Glenda, Mgr, Westworth Village City Library, 101 Seymour Ave, Fort Worth, TX, 76114. Tel: 817-738-2248. p. 2324

Block, Grace, Lead Libr Tech, University of Washington Libraries, Social Work, 252 Social Work Bldg, Box 354900, 15th Ave NE, Seattle, WA, 98195-4900. Tel: 206-685-2180. Fax: 206-685-7647. p. 2535

Block, Jane, Librn, University of Illinois Library at Urbana-Champaign, Architecture & Art Library, 208 Architecture, 608 E Lorado Taft Dr, Urbana, IL, 61801. Tel: 217-333-7073. Fax: 217-244-5169, p. 711

Block, Jennifer, ILL, Princeton University, Biology, Fine Hall Library, McDonnell Hall, One Washington Ave, Princeton, NJ, 08544. Tel: 609-258-3235. Fax: 609-258-2627. p. 1523

Block, Joanne, Librn, Littler Mendelson Library, 650 California St, 20th Flr, San Francisco, CA, 94108-2693. Tel: 415-399-8441. Fax: 415-399-8490. p. 243

Block, Julia, Acq Librn, Long Island University, One University Plaza, Brooklyn, NY, 11201-9926. Tel: 718-488-1081. Fax: 718-780-4057. p. 1593

Block, Karla, Librn, Tompkins Cortland Community College, 170 North St, Dryden, NY, 13053-8504. Tel: 607-844-8222. Fax: 607-844-6540. p. 1615

Block, Laura, Chief Operations Officer, Laramie County Library System, 2200 Pioneer Ave, Cheyenne, WY, 82001-3610. Tel: 307-773-7223. Fax: 307-634-2082. p. 2652

Block, Lisa, Med Librn, Atlanta Medical Center, 303 Parkway Dr NE, Box 415, Atlanta, GA, 30312-1212. Tel: 404-265-4605. Fax: 404-265-3559. p. 513

Block, Ron, Circ Supvr, Jacksonville Public Library, 303 N Laura St, Jacksonville, FL, 32202-3505. Tel: 904-630-2962. Fax: 904-630-1435. p. 453

Blocker, LouAnn, Electronic Res/Ser Librn, Augusta State University, 2500 Walton Way, Augusta, GA, 30904-2200. Tel: 706-737-1745. Fax: 706-667-4415. p. 518

Blocklyn, Philip D, Archivist, Librn, Oyster Bay Historical Society Library, 20 Summit St, Oyster Bay, NY, 11771. Tel: 516-922-5032. Fax: 516-922-6892. p. 1714

Blocksidge, Katie, Ref Librn, Ohio State University LIBRARIES, Newark Campus Library, Warner Library & Student Center, 1179 University Dr, Newark, OH, 43055-1797. Tel: 740-366-9307. Fax: 740-366-9264. p. 1889

Blodgett, Gini, Dir, American Physical Therapy Association, 1111 N Fairfax St, 4th Flr, Alexandria, VA, 22314-1484. Tel: 703-706-8534. Fax: 703-838-8910. p. 2445

Blodgett, Jan, Dr, Col Archivist & Rec Mgt Coordr, Davidson College, 209 Ridge Rd, Davidson, NC, 28035-0001. Tel: 704-894-2632. Fax: 704-894-2625. p. 1786

Blodgett, Jayne, Metadata Coordr, University of Minnesota-Morris, 600 E Fourth St, Morris, MN, 56267. Tel: 320-589-6174. Fax: 320-589-6168. p. 1267

Blodgett, Peter, Curator, Huntington Library, 1151 Oxford Rd, San Marino, CA, 91108. Tel: 626-405-2207. Fax: 626-449-5720. p. 255

Blodgett, Peter W, In Charge, Thetford Town Library, George Peabody Branch, PO Box 190, Post Mills, VT, 05058-0190. Tel: 802-333-9724. p. 2437

Blodgett, Peter W, Librn, Thetford Town Library, 16 Library Lane, Thetford, VT, 05074. Tel: 802-785-4361. Fax: 802-785-4361. p. 2437

Bloechle, Brent, Libr Mgr, Plano Public Library System, Maribelle M Davis Library, 7501-B Independence Pkwy, Plano, TX, 75025. Tel: 972-208-8000. Fax: 972-208-8037. p. 2370

Bloemker, LaVerne, Archivist, Madison County Historical Museum & Archival Library, 715 N Main St, Edwardsville, IL, 62025-1111. Tel: 618-656-7562, 618-656-7569. Fax: 618-659-3457. p. 639

Blom, Madlyn, Libr Assoc, Lee Memorial Health System Library, PO Box 2218, Fort Myers, FL, 33902-2218. Tel: 239-334-5410. Fax: 239-332-6422. p. 446

Blome, Pamela, Monograph Cat Librn, Colorado School of Mines, 1400 Illinois St, Golden, CO, 80401-1887. Tel: 303-273-3691. Fax: 303-273-3199. p. 309

Blomeley, Sherry, Regional Mgr, Cobb County Public Library System, West Cobb Regional, 1750 Dennis Kemp Lane, Kennesaw, GA, 30152. Tel: 770-528-4699. Fax: 770-528-4619. p. 543

Blomquist, Carol, Br Mgr, Stanislaus County Free Library, Florence L Gondring Library, 2250 Magnolia, Ceres, CA, 95307-3209. Tel: 209-537-8938. Fax: 209-537-8939. p. 188

Blomquist, Donna, Youth Serv, LaSalle Public Library, 305 Marquette St, LaSalle, IL, 61301. Tel: 815-223-2341. Fax: 815-223-2353. p. 664

Blomquist, Donna, Dir, Bethlehem Lutheran Church Library, 1145 N Fifth Ave, Saint Charles, IL, 60174-1230. Tel: 630-584-2199. Fax: 630-584-2674. p. 699

Blomquist, Randall, Presv Spec, Missouri History Museum, 225 S Skinker Blvd, Saint Louis, MO, 63105. Tel: 314-746-4500. Fax: 314-746-4548. p. 1356

Blondeau, Karen, Dir, Valencia Community College, Raymer Maguire Jr Learning Resources Center, West Campus, 1800 S Kirkman Rd, Orlando, FL, 32811. Tel: 407-582-1601. Fax: 407-582-1686. p. 478

Blondo, Darla, Asst Librn, Swanton Public Library, One First St, Swanton, VT, 05488. Tel: 802-868-7656. p. 2437

Blood, Bettina, Adult Serv, Morrill Memorial Library, 33 Walpole St, Norwood, MA, 02062-1206. Tel: 781-769-0200. Fax: 781-769-6083. p. 1115

Blood, Esther, Head, Circ/ILL, Louisiana State University at Alexandria, 8100 Hwy 71 S, Alexandria, LA, 71302. Tel: 318-473-6438. Fax: 318-473-6556. p. 939

Blood, Janet, Assoc Dean, Libr Serv, Eastern Maine Community College Library, Katahdin Hall, 354 Hogan Rd, Bangor, ME, 04401-4280. Tel: 207-974-4640. Fax: 207-974-4641. p. 975

Bloom, Beth, Instruction Librn, Seton Hall University Libraries, Walsh Library Bldg, 400 S Orange Ave, South Orange, NJ, 07079. Tel: 973-275-2035. Fax: 973-761-9432. p. 1530

Bloom, Cathy, Ch, Irvin L Young Memorial Library, 431 W Center St, Whitewater, WI, 53190-1915. Tel: 262-473-0530. Fax: 262-473-0539. p. 2649

Bloom, Debbie, Dir, Ida Public Library, 320 N State St, Belvidere, IL, 61008-3299. Tel: 815-544-3838. Fax: 815-544-8909. p. 594

Bloom, Jason, Assoc Dir, Head, Tech & User Experience, Ames Free Library, 53 Main St, North Easton, MA, 02356. Tel: 508-238-2000. Fax: 508-238-2980. p. 1112

Bloom, Laura, Head, Cat, Thomas Beaver Free Library, 205 Ferry St, Danville, PA, 17821-1939. Tel: 570-275-4180. Fax: 570-275-8480. p. 2049

Bloom, Leah Massar, Head, Ref, State University of New York, 735 Anderson Hill Rd, Purchase, NY, 10577-1400. Tel: 914-251-6413. Fax: 914-251-6437. p. 1724

Bloom, Myra, Bibliog Instr, Ref, Oral Roberts University Library, 7777 South Lewis Ave, Tulsa, OK, 74171. Tel: 918-495-7174. Fax: 918-495-6893. p. 1981

Bloom, Polly, Dir, Douglass Public Library, 319 S Forrest St, Douglass, KS, 67039. Tel: 316-746-2600. Fax: 316-746-3936. p. 864

Bloom, Susan, Head, Tech Serv, Deerfield Public Library, 920 Waukegan Rd, Deerfield, IL, 60015. Tel: 847-945-3311. Fax: 847-945-3402. p. 634

Bloom, Vickey, Dir, Grosse Pointe Public Library, Ten Kercheval at Fisher Rd, Grosse Pointe Farms, MI, 48236-3693. Tel: 313-343-2074. Fax: 313-343-2437. p. 1187

Bloom, Vicki, Dean, Libr Serv, Indiana University South Bend, 1700 Mishawaka Ave, South Bend, IN, 46615. Tel: 574-520-4448. Fax: 574-520-4472. p. 778

Bloom, Wendy B, Dir, Ramsey Free Public Library, 30 Wyckoff Ave, Ramsey, NJ, 07446. Tel: 201-327-1445. Fax: 201-327-3687. p. 1525

Bloomberg, Kathleen, Assoc Dir, Libr Operations, Illinois State Library, Gwendolyn Brooks Bldg, 300 S Second St, Springfield, IL, 62701-9713. Tel: 217-785-0052. Fax: 217-524-0041. p. 705

Bloomberg, Micheal, Circ, Syst Librn, Augsburg College, 2211 Riverside Ave, Minneapolis, MN, 55454. Tel: 612-330-1604. Fax: 612-330-1436. p. 1259

Bloomfield, Christopher, Info Tech Coordr, Springfield Town Library, 43 Main St, Springfield, VT, 05156. Tel: 802-885-3108. Fax: 802-885-4906. p. 2436

Bloomfield, Pat, Librn, Clifton Public Library, 104 E Parallel, Clifton, KS, 66937. Tel: 785-455-2222. p. 861

Bloomfield, Ron, Curator, Bay County Historical Society, 321 Washington Ave, Bay City, MI, 48708. Tel: 989-893-5733. Fax: 989-893-5741. p. 1155

Bloomfield, Susan, Health Sci Librn, Southern Maine Medical Center, One Medical Center Dr, Biddeford, ME, 04005. Tel: 207-283-7289. Fax: 207-283-7063. p. 978

Bloomgarden, Carol, Head, Adult Serv, Harborfields Public Library, 31 Broadway, Greenlawn, NY, 11740-1382. Tel: 631-757-4200. Fax: 631-757-7216. p. 1631

Bloomquist, Mary Jane, Asst Prof, Circ Librn, McNeese State University, 4205 Ryan St, Lake Charles, LA, 70609. Tel: 337-475-5718. Fax: 337-475-5719, 337-475-5727. p. 954

Bloomquist, Pam, Acq/ILL Librn, Warner University, 13895 Hwy 27, Lake Wales, FL, 33859. Tel: 863-638-7674. Fax: 863-638-7675. p. 458

Bloomstone, Ajaye, Acq Librn, Louisiana State University Libraries, Paul M Hebert Law Center, One E Campus Dr, Baton Rouge, LA, 70803-1000. Tel: 225-578-4044. Fax: 225-578-5773. p. 944

Bloor, Bernice, Librn, Southeast Regional Library, Lake Alma Branch, Hwy 18, Lake Alma, SK, S0C 1M0, CANADA. Tel: 306-447-2061. p. 2930

Bloos, Susan, Librn, Kitchener Public Library, Forest Heights, 251 Fischer-Hallman Rd, Kitchener, ON, N2H 2H1, CANADA. Tel: 519-743-0644. Fax: 519-743-0644. p. 2815

Blose, Denise, Head, Circ, Peoples Library, 880 Barnes St, New Kensington, PA, 15068. Tel: 724-339-1021. Fax: 724-339-2027. p. 2097

Blossic, Audrey, Dir, Springfield Township Library, 70 Powell Rd, Springfield, PA, 19064-2446. Tel: 610-543-2113. Fax: 610-543-1356. p. 2142

Blossom, Amy, Br Mgr, Jackson County Library Services, Ashland Branch, 410 Siskiyou Blvd, Ashland, OR, 97520-2196. Tel: 541-774-6980. p. 2005

Blosveren, Barbara, Libr Dir, Stratford Library Association, 2203 Main St, Stratford, CT, 06615. Tel: 203-385-4161. Fax: 203-381-2079. p. 371

Blotner, Linda Solow, Dir, University of Hartford Libraries, Mildred P Allen Memorial, 200 Bloomfield Ave, West Hartford, CT, 06117-0395. Tel: 860-768-4492. Fax: 860-768-5295. p. 376

Blough, Kathy, Cat Librn, Music, Saint Olaf College, Rolvaag Memorial Library, Glasoe Science Library, Halvorson Music Library, 1510 Saint Olaf Ave, Northfield, MN, 55057-1097. Tel: 507-786-3794. Fax: 507-786-3734. p. 1269

Blough, Keith, Dir, Columbus Law Library Association, 369 S High St, 10th Flr, Columbus, OH, 43215-4518. Tel: 614-221-4181. Fax: 614-221-2115. p. 1884

Blouin, France, Cat, Ministere des Finances Bibliotheque, 12 rue St Louis, Bureau 2-12, Quebec, QC, G1R 5L3, CANADA. Tel: 418-644-7297. Fax: 418-643-9911. p. 2906

Blouin, Francis, Prof, University of Michigan, 304 West Hall, 1085 S University, Ann Arbor, MI, 48109-1107. Tel: 734-763-2285. Fax: 734-764-2475. p. 2967

Blouin, Francis X, Jr, Dir, University of Michigan, Bentley Historical Library, 1150 Beal Ave, Ann Arbor, MI, 48109-2113. Tel: 734-764-3482. Fax: 734-936-1333. p. 1151

Blount, Evelyn, Head, Ref (Info Serv), Guilford College, 5800 W Friendly Ave, Greensboro, NC, 27410-4175. Tel: 336-316-2312. Fax: 336-316-2950. p. 1796

Blount, Patti, Adult Serv, Dir, Durand Public Library, 604 Seventh Ave E, Durand, WI, 54736. Tel: 715-672-8730. p. 2589

Blount, Rosetta, Circ Mgr, North Chicago Public Library, 2100 Argonne Dr, North Chicago, IL, 60064. Tel: 847-689-0125. Fax: 847-689-9117. p. 682

Bloustein, David, Librn, New Jersey Office of the Public Defender, 31 Clinton St, 10th Flr, Newark, NJ, 07102. Tel: 973-877-1264. Fax: 973-877-1239. p. 1511

Blower, Kevin, Head, Tech Serv, Bethel College, 1001 W McKinley Ave, Mishawaka, IN, 46545. Tel: 574-257-3334. Fax: 574-257-3499. p. 765

Blower, Paul, Head, Adult Serv, St Thomas Public Library, 153 Curtis St, St. Thomas, ON, N5P 3Z7, CANADA. Tel: 519-631-6050. Fax: 519-631-1987. p. 2844

Blowers, Carolyn, Dir, Dixon Homestead Library, 180 Washington Ave, Dumont, NJ, 07628. Tel: 201-384-2030. Fax: 201-384-5878. p. 1481

Bloy, Jonathan, Web Librn, Edgewood College Library, 1000 Edgewood College Dr, Madison, WI, 53711-1997. Tel: 608-663-3300. Fax: 608-663-6778. p. 2606

Bloyd, Alison, Dir, Thomas-Wilhite Memorial Library, 101 E Thomas, Perkins, OK, 74059. Tel: 405-547-5185. Fax: 405-547-1040. p. 1976

Blubaugh, Penny, Commun Serv, Mgr, YA Serv, Eisenhower Public Library District, 4613 N Oketo Ave, Harwood Heights, IL, 60706. Tel: 708-867-7828. Fax: 708-867-1535. p. 654

Blue, Amy, Ref, Antioch Public Library District, 757 Main St, Antioch, IL, 60002. Tel: 847-395-0874, Ext 227. Fax: 847-395-5399. p. 589

Blue, Ana Rosa, Ref Serv, Workers' Compensation Board of British Columbia Library, 6951 Westminster Hwy, Richmond, BC, V7C 1C6, CANADA. Tel: 604-231-8450. Fax: 604-279-7608. p. 2737

Blue, Christal, Ch, East Orange Public Library, 21 S Arlington Ave, East Orange, NJ, 07018-3892. Tel: 973-266-5600. Fax: 973-674-1991. p. 1482

Blue, Jerry, Sr Librn, Hennepin County Library, Sumner, 611 Van White Memorial Blvd, Minneapolis, MN, 55411-4196. Tel: 612-543-6878. Fax: 612-543-6877. p. 1265

Blue, JoAnne, Br Mgr, Dixie Regional Library System, Edmondson Memorial, 109 Stovall St, Vardaman, MS, 38878-0174. Tel: 662-682-7333. Fax: 662-682-7333. p. 1312

Blue, Lisa, Teen Serv, Winter Park Public Library, 460 E New England Ave, Winter Park, FL, 32789-4493. Tel: 407-623-3300. Fax: 407-623-3489. p. 505

Blue, Michael, Librn, Florida Department of Corrections, 5850 E Milton Rd, Milton, FL, 32583. Tel: 850-983-5876. Fax: 850-983-4523. p. 470

Blue, Myra, Dean, Pamlico Community College, 5049 Hwy 306 S, Grantsboro, NC, 28529. Tel: 252-249-1851, Ext 3033. Fax: 252-249-2377. p. 1795

Blue, Wendy, Info Spec, Novartis Pharmaceuticals Canada, Inc, 385 Bouchard Blvd, Dorval, QC, H9F 1A9, CANADA. Tel: 514-631-6775, Ext 3302. Fax: 514-631-8851. p. 2881

Bluedorn, Victoria, Dir, Rock Island County Law Library, Courthouse, 210 15th St, Rock Island, IL, 61201. Tel: 309-786-4451, Ext 3259. Fax: 309-558-3263. p. 696

BlueEyes, Sharon, Tech Serv Supvr, Farmington Public Library, 2101 Farmington Ave, Farmington, NM, 87401. Tel: 505-599-1274. Fax: 505-599-1257. p. 1555

Bluemle, Stefanie, Ref, Augustana College Library, 3435 9 1/2 Ave, Rock Island, IL, 61201-2296. Tel: 309-794-7266. Fax: 309-794-7640. p. 696

Bluestone, Ronald, Div Mgr, Library of Congress, Science, Technology & Business Division, Sci Reading Rm, John Adams Bldg, Rm 508, Washington, DC, 20540-4750. Tel: 202-707-5664. Fax: 202-707-1925. p. 408

Bluh, Pamela, Assoc Dir, University of Maryland, Baltimore, Thurgood Marshall Law Library, 501 W Fayette St, Baltimore, MD, 21201-1768. Tel: 410-706-2736. Fax: 410-706-2372. p. 1019

Bluhm, Pat, Access Serv, Frank L Weyenberg Library of Mequon-Thiensville, 11345 N Cedarburg Rd, Mequon, WI, 53092-1998. Tel: 262-242-2593. Fax: 262-478-3200. p. 2615

Bluhm, Sarina, Ch, Ref Serv, Ch, Norfolk Public Library, 139 Main St, Norfolk, MA, 02056. Tel: 508-528-3380. Fax: 508-528-6417. p. 1111

Bluhm-Stieber, Hella, Med Librn, Santa Clara Valley Medical Center, 751 S Bascom Ave, Rm 2E063, San Jose, CA, 95128. Tel: 408-885-5654. Fax: 408-885-5655. p. 252

Blum, Cynthia, Cat, Holdrege Area Public Library, 604 East Ave, Holdrege, NE, 68949. Tel: 308-995-6556. Fax: 308-995-5732. p. 1402

Blum, David, Online Serv, Battelle Memorial Institute, 505 King Ave, Columbus, OH, 43201. Tel: 614-424-5138. Fax: 614-458-6302. p. 1883

Blum, Jennifer, Circ Supvr, Owens Community College Library, 30335 Oregon Rd, Perrysburg, OH, 43551. Tel: 567-661-7016. Fax: 567-661-7021. p. 1929

Blum, Jo Ann, Asst Librn, Lawton Public Library, 125 S Main St, Lawton, MI, 49065. Tel: 269-624-5481. Fax: 269-624-1909. p. 1203

Blume, Jane E, Dir, Bellingham Technical College Library, 3028 Lindbergh Ave, Bellingham, WA, 98225-1599. Tel: 360-752-8383. Fax: 360-752-8384. p. 2508

Blume, Scott, Instruction & Ref Librn, Whatcom Community College Library, 237 W Kellogg Rd, Bellingham, WA, 98226. Tel: 360-383-3300. p. 2509

Blumenthal, Jane, Dir, University of Michigan, A Alfred Taubman Health Sciences Library, 1135 E Catherine, Ann Arbor, MI, 48109-2038. Tel: 734-764-1210. p. 1153

Blumhoefer, Jane, Asst Librn, Fairfax Public Library, 124 SE First St, Fairfax, MN, 55332. Tel: 507-426-7269. Fax: 507-426-7269. p. 1250

Blundon, Brenda, Librn, Department of Justice, East Block, Confederation Bldg, 5th Flr, 100 Prince Philip Dr, St. John's, NL, A1B 4J6, CANADA. Tel: 709-729-0285. Fax: 709-729-1370. p. 2772

Blundy, Necia, Ch, Marlborough Public Library, 35 W Main St, Marlborough, MA, 01752-5510. Tel: 508-624-6994. Fax: 508-485-1494. p. 1103

Blunk, Ann, Asst Curator, Indiana Medical History Museum Collection, 3045 W Vermont St, Indianapolis, IN, 46222-4943. Tel: 317-635-7329. Fax: 317-635-7349. p. 752

Blustain, Malinda, Dir, Phillips Academy, c/o Phillips Acad, 180 Main St, Andover, MA, 01810. Tel: 978-749-4490. Fax: 978-749-4495. p. 1049

Bly, Joanne, Librn, McKean County Law Library, 500 W Main St, Smethport, PA, 16749-1149. Tel: 814-887-3325. Fax: 814-887-2712. p. 2141

Blyberg, John, Asst Dir, Innovation & UX, Darien Library, 1441 Post Rd, Darien, CT, 06820-5419. Tel: 203-669-5222. Fax: 203-655-1547. p. 336

Blye, Marlene V, Pub Serv, Eustis Memorial Library, 120 N Center St, Eustis, FL, 32726-3598. Tel: 352-357-5686. Fax: 352-357-5450. p. 439

Blyth, Irene, Librn, Southeast Regional Library, Whitewood Branch, 731 Lalonde St, Whitewood, SK, S0G 5C0, CANADA. Tel: 306-735-4233. Fax: 306-735-4233. p. 2931

Blyth, Krista, Libr Mgr, York Library Region, Chipman Branch, Eight King St, Chipman, NB, E4A 2H3, CANADA. Tel: 506-339-5852. Fax: 506-339-9804. p. 2764

Blythe, Lois J, Info Tech Supvr, Burlington Public Library, 210 Court St, Burlington, IA, 52601. Tel: 319-753-1647. Fax: 319-753-0789. p. 797

Blythe, Susan, Dir, Conrad Public Library, 114 N Main Ave, Conrad, IA, 50621. Tel: 641-366-2583. Fax: 641-366-3105. p. 804

Boak, Jean, Dr, Dir, International Graduate University Library, Capitol Hill Campus, 1325 D St SE, Washington, DC, 22003. Tel: 202-544-1555. Fax: 202-547-8819. p. 405

Boardman, Richard C, Curator, Free Library of Philadelphia, Map Collection, 1901 Vine St, Philadelphia, PA, 19103-1189. Tel: 215-686-5397. p. 2108

Boast, Deanne, Librn, Southeast Regional Library, Moosomin Branch, 701 Main St, Moosomin, SK, S0G 3N0, CANADA. Tel: 306-435-2107. p. 2930

Boatman, Patricia, Br Mgr, Lafourche Parish Public Library, Martha Sowell Utley Memorial (Main Library), 314 St Mary St, Thibodaux, LA, 70301-2620. Tel: 985-447-4119. Fax: 985-449-4128. p. 971

Boatman, Sarah, Ch, Iberia Parish Library, 445 E Main St, New Iberia, LA, 70560-3710. Tel: 337-364-7134. Fax: 337-364-7042. p. 959

Boatright, Christine, Coordr, Libr Res, Lake City Community College, 149 SE College Pl, Lake City, FL, 32025-2006. Tel: 386-754-4337. Fax: 386-754-4837. p. 457

Boatright, Joshua, Librn, Berkeley City College Library, 2050 Center St, Rm 131, Berkeley, CA, 94704. Tel: 510-981-2991. p. 126

Boatright, Kathleen M, Adminr, Denison Public Library, 300 W Gandy St, Denison, TX, 75020-3153. Tel: 903-465-1797. Fax: 903-465-1130. p. 2312

Boatright, Linda, Ref & Circ Librn, Oklahoma City Community College, 7777 S May Ave, Oklahoma City, OK, 73159. Tel: 405-682-1611, Ext 7468. Fax: 405-682-7585. p. 1973

Boatright, Susanne, Librn, Metropolitan Community College, Blue River Library, 20301 E 78 Hwy, Independence, MO, 64057. Tel: 816-220-6649. Fax: 816-220-6751. p. 1339

Boatright-Rerat, Cari, Teen Librn, Joplin Public Library, 300 S Main, Joplin, MO, 64801. Tel: 417-623-7953. Fax: 417-625-4728. p. 1335

Boaz, Judy, Librn, George Coon Public Library, 114 S Harrison St, Princeton, KY, 42445-1946. Tel: 270-365-2884. Fax: 270-365-2892. p. 933

Bob, Conrad, Dir of Libr, Oak Ridge National Laboratory, Bldg 4500N, MS-6191, Bethel Valley Rd, Oak Ridge, TN, 37830. Tel: 865-574-4872. Fax: 865-574-6915. p. 2262

Boback, Mary, In Charge, New York State Supreme Court, Family Court House, Ninth Judicial District, 50 Market St, Poughkeepsie, NY, 12601-3203. Tel: 845-486-2215. Fax: 212-401-9102. p. 1723

Bobak, Michael, Ref/Instruction Librn, Bellevue University, 1000 Galvin Rd S, Bellevue, NE, 68005. Tel: 402-557-7303. Fax: 402-557-5427. p. 1393

Bobal, Sharon, Dir, Reynoldsville Public Library, 460 Main St, Reynoldsville, PA, 15851-1251. Tel: 814-653-9471. Fax: 814-653-9471. p. 2134

Bobbit, Phyllis, Br Mgr, Wythe-Grayson Regional Library, 147 S Independence Ave, Independence, VA, 24348-2800. Tel: 276-773-2761. Fax: 276-773-3289. p. 2472

Bobbitt, Romaine Chase, Br Mgr, Enoch Pratt Free Library, Washington Village, 856 Washington Blvd, Baltimore, MD, 21230. Tel: 410-396-1099. Fax: 410-396-1115. p. 1013

Bobbs, Lynne, Pub Serv, Miles College, 5500 Myron Massey Blvd, Fairfield, AL, 35064. Tel: 205-929-1710. Fax: 205-929-1635. p. 16

Bobby, Ana, Libr Operations, Mgr, Access Serv, Youngstown State University, One University Plaza, Youngstown, OH, 44555-0001. Tel: 330-941-1717. Fax: 330-941-3734. p. 1953

Bobeen, Jeanette E, Ch, Sioux City Public Library, 529 Pierce St, Sioux City, IA, 51101-1203. Tel: 712-255-2933. p. 844

Bobis, Lisa, Tech Serv Mgr, Downers Grove Public Library, 1050 Curtiss St, Downers Grove, IL, 60515. Tel: 630-960-1200. Fax: 630-960-9374. p. 637

Bobish, Michael, Br Mgr, Ocean County Library, Berkeley Branch, 30 Station Rd, Bayville, NJ, 08721-2198. Tel: 732-269-2144. Fax: 732-237-2955. p. 1534

Bobka, Marlene S, VPres, FOI Services Inc Library, 704 Quince Orchard Rd, Ste 275, Gaithersburg, MD, 20878-1751. Tel: 301-975-9400. Fax: 301-975-0702. p. 1030

Bobo, Janice, Br Head, Williamson County Public Library, College Grove Community, 8607 Horton Hwy, College Grove, TN, 37046. Tel: 615-776-5490. p. 2234

Bobo, Janice, Br Head, Williamson County Public Library, Nolensville Branch, 915 Oldham Dr, Nolensville, TN, 37135. Tel: 615-776-5490. Fax: 615-776-3626. p. 2234

Bobo, Susan, Archit Librn, Oklahoma State University Libraries, Oklahoma State University, Athletic Ave, Stillwater, OK, 74078-1071. Tel: 405-744-6034. Fax: 405-744-5183. p. 1978

Bobo, Susan, Librn, Oklahoma State University Libraries, Architecture, 210 Advanced Technology Research Ctr, Stillwater, OK, 74078-5019. Tel: 405-744-6047. Fax: 405-744-5183. p. 1978

Bobotek, Bea, Librn, Inova Mount Vernon Hospital, 2501 Parker's Lane, Alexandria, VA, 22306. Tel: 703-664-7269. Fax: 703-664-7523. p. 2445

Bobowicz, Steven, Cat Librn, Western New England University, 1215 Wilbraham Rd, Springfield, MA, 01119-2689. Tel: 413-782-1309. Fax: 413-782-1745. p. 1128

Bobrofsky, Judith, Dir, Loyal Public Library, 214 N Main St, Loyal, WI, 54446. Tel: 715-255-8189. Fax: 715-255-8348. p. 2605

Bobrowsky, Tammy, Acq, Ser, Bemidji State University, 1500 Birchmont Dr NE, Box 4, Bemidji, MN, 56601-2600. Tel: 218-755-4110. Fax: 218-755-2051. p. 1241

Boccia, Philip, Tech Librn, Long Beach Public Library, 111 W Park Ave, Long Beach, NY, 11561-3326. Tel: 516-432-7201. Fax: 516-889-4641. p. 1654

Boccia, Terri, Acq, Sterling & Francine Clark Art Institute Library, 225 South St, Williamstown, MA, 01267. Tel: 413-458-0437. Fax: 413-458-9542. p. 1140

Bochicchio, Nicholas A, Jr, Admin Dir, The Ferguson Library, One Public Library Plaza, 96 Broad St, Stamford, CT, 06904. Tel: 203-964-1000, Ext 8202. Fax: 203-357-9098. p. 369

Bochin, Janet, Cataloger, California State University, Fresno, Henry Madden Library, 5200 N Barton Ave, Mail Stop ML-34, Fresno, CA, 93740-8014. Tel: 559-278-2158. Fax: 559-278-6952. p. 150

Bochinski, Elise, Access Serv, Archivist, Fairfield University, 1073 N Benson Rd, Fairfield, CT, 06430-5195. Tel: 203-254-4044. Fax: 203-254-4135. p. 339

Bock, David, Librn, New Melleray Library, 6632 Melleray Circle, Peosta, IA, 52068. Tel: 563-588-2319, Ext 426. Fax: 563-588-4117. p. 838

Bock, Debbie, Head, Ref, Johnson Free Public Library, 274 Main St, Hackensack, NJ, 07601-5797. Tel: 201-343-4169. Fax: 201-343-1395. p. 1489

Bock, Gail, Asst Librn, Chinook Regional Library, Eastend Branch, Eastend Memorial Hall, Eastend, SK, S0N 0T0, CANADA. Tel: 306-295-3788. p. 2928

Bock, Melanie, Coordr, Andrew McFarland Mental Health Center, 901 Southwind Rd, Springfield, IL, 62703. Tel: 217-786-6983. Fax: 217-786-6803. p. 706

Bock, Susie, Spec Coll Librn, University of Southern Maine, 314 Forest Ave, Portland, ME, 04104. Tel: 207-780-4269. Fax: 207-780-4042. p. 998

Bockman, Glenda, Dir, Ancilla College, 9601 S Union Rd, Donaldson, IN, 46513. Tel: 574-936-8898, Ext 323. Fax: 574-935-1773. p. 736

Bockrath, Christine, Libr Mgr, Clarian Health Partners, 1701 N Senate Blvd, Rm D1422, Indianapolis, IN, 46206-1367. Tel: 317-962-8021. Fax: 317-962-8397. p. 750

Bockus, Deborah, Mgr, Access Serv, Worcester Polytechnic Institute, 100 Institute Rd, Worcester, MA, 01609-2280. Tel: 508-831-5410. Fax: 508-831-5829. p. 1145

Bockwoldt, Becky, Librn, La Moure School & Public Library, PO Box 656, La Moure, ND, 58458-0656. Tel: 701-883-5396. Fax: 701-883-5144. p. 1845

Bocnuk, Debby, Librn, Babbitt Public Library, 71 South Dr, Babbitt, MN, 55706-1232. Tel: 218-827-3345. Fax: 218-827-3345. p. 1240

Bodas, Carol, Mgr, Salk Institute for Biological Studies, 10010 N Torrey Pines Rd, La Jolla, CA, 92037-1099. Tel: 858-453-4100, Ext 1235. Fax: 858-452-7472. p. 161

Bodden, Elizabeth, Ch, Theresa Public Library, 290 Mayville St, Theresa, WI, 53091-0307. Tel: 920-488-2342. Fax: 920-488-2342. p. 2642

Bodden, Evelyn, ILL, City College of the City University of New York, North Academic Ctr, 160 Convent Ave, New York, NY, 10031. Tel: 212-650-7155. Fax: 212-650-7604. p. 1672

Bodden, Mary Alice, Dir, Theresa Public Library, 290 Mayville St, Theresa, WI, 53091-0307. Tel: 920-488-2342. Fax: 920-488-2342. p. 2642

Boddy, Pamela D, Dir, Titusville Public Library, 2121 S Hopkins Ave, Titusville, FL, 32780. Tel: 321-264-5026. Fax: 321-264-5030. p. 500

Bodenheimer, Lisa, Head, Cat, Clemson University Libraries, Box 343001, Clemson, SC, 29634-3001. Tel: 864-656-1769. Fax: 864-656-0758. p. 2186

Bodenmiller, Elizabeth, Syst Mgr, Madonna University Library, 36600 Schoolcraft Rd, Livonia, MI, 48150-1173. Tel: 734-432-5702. Fax: 734-432-5687. p. 1204

Bodensteiner, Chris, Dir, Fort Atkinson Public Library, 302 Third St NW, Fort Atkinson, IA, 52144. Tel: 563-534-2222. Fax: 563-534-2222. p. 816

Boder, Eilenne, Br Mgr, Ramsey County Library, Shoreview Branch, 4570 N Victoria St, Shoreview, MN, 55126. Tel: 651-486-2300. Fax: 651-486-2313. p. 1284

Bodewes, Ted, Head, Circ, River Forest Public Library, 735 Lathrop Ave, River Forest, IL, 60305-1883. Tel: 708-366-5205. Fax: 708-366-8699. p. 694

Bodick, Patricia, Chief Exec Officer, Librn, Larder Lake Public Library, 69 Fourth Ave, Larder Lake, ON, P0K 1L0, CANADA. Tel: 705-643-2222. Fax: 705-643-2222. p. 2815

Bodie, Mathew, Librn, Saint Petersburg College, Tarpon Springs Campus Library, 600 Klosterman Rd, Tarpon Springs, FL, 34689. Tel: 727-712-5240. Fax: 727-712-5706. p. 483

Bodine, Kristen, Ch, Librn I, Louisville Public Library, 951 Spruce St, Louisville, CO, 80027. Tel: 303-335-4849. Fax: 303-335-4833. p. 317

Bodle, Sharon, Admin Coordr, The College of Wooster Libraries, 1140 Beall Ave, Wooster, OH, 44691-2364. Tel: 330-263-2442. Fax: 330-263-2253. p. 1949

Bodnar, Marilyn, Librn, Instrul Initiatives, Roger & Peggy Madigan Library, 999 Hagan Way, Williamsport, PA, 17701. Tel: 570-327-4523. Fax: 570-327-4503. p. 2156

Bodnar, Russ, Chief of Interpretation, USDI National Park Service, PO Box 220, Nageezi, NM, 87037-0220. Tel: 505-786-7014. Fax: 505-786-7061. p. 1560

Bodnar, Tracey, In Charge, National Park Service, 84 County Rd 2900, Aztec, NM, 87410. Tel: 505-334-6174, Ext 232. Fax: 505-334-6372. p. 1552

Bodner, Deb, Head, Ch, Clinton-Macomb Public Library, 40900 Romeo Plank Rd, Clinton Township, MI, 48038-2955. Tel: 586-226-5031. Fax: 586-226-5008. p. 1164

Bodrero-Hoggan, Danielle, Ref Serv, The Scripps Research Institute, 10550 N Torrey Pines Rd, La Jolla, CA, 92037. Tel: 858-784-8705. Fax: 858-784-2035. p. 161

Bodson, Phillipe, Librn, Correctional Service of Canada, 400 Montee Saint Francois, Laval, QC, H7C 1S7, CANADA. Tel: 450-664-1320, Ext 5505. Fax: 450-664-6719. p. 2886

Bodwell, Martha, ILL Librn, Sanbornton Public Library, 27 Meetinghouse Hill Rd, Sanbornton, NH, 03269. Tel: 603-286-8288. Fax: 603-286-9544. p. 1464

Bodycomb, Aphrodite, Asst Dir, Bus Develop & Operations, University of Maryland, Baltimore, Health Sciences & Human Services Library, 601 W Lombard St, Baltimore, MD, 21201. Tel: 410-706-8853. Fax: 410-706-3101. p. 1019

Bodziock, Pam, Teen Librn, Monroeville Public Library, 4000 Gateway Campus Blvd, Monroeville, PA, 15146-3381. Tel: 412-372-0500. Fax: 412-372-1168. p. 2091

Bodzioney, Judy, Fac Coordr, Pima Medical Institute Library, 3350 E Grant Rd, Tucson, AZ, 85716. Tel: 520-326-1600. Fax: 520-795-3463. p. 87

Boe, Michael, Sr Librn, Hennepin County Library, Brookdale, 6125 Shingle Creek Pkwy, Brooklyn Center, MN, 55430-2110. Tel: 612-543-5627. Fax: 612-543-5602. p. 1263

Boe, Paige, Br Mgr, Dallas Public Library, Preston Royal Branch, 5626 Royal Lane, Dallas, TX, 75229-5599. Tel: 214-670-7128. Fax: 214-670-7135. p. 2307

Boe, Patricia Renee, Dir, Dike Public Library, 133 E Elder, Dike, IA, 50624-9612. Tel: 319-989-2608. Fax: 319-989-2984. p. 811

Boeckman, Alice, Ch, Bellevue Public Library, 1003 Lincoln Rd, Bellevue, NE, 68005-3199. Tel: 402-293-3157. Fax: 402-293-3163. p. 1393

Boedeker, Mary, Co-Dir, Real County Public Library, 225 Main St, Leakey, TX, 78873. Tel: 830-232-5199. Fax: 830-232-5913. p. 2354

Boedicker, Michael, AV, Danville Public Library, 319 N Vermilion St, Danville, IL, 61832. Tel: 217-477-5224. Fax: 217-477-5230. p. 633

Boeg, Nigel, Mgr, Mat Serv, Frisco Public Library, 6101 Frisco Square Blvd, Ste 3000, Frisco, TX, 75034-3000. Tel: 972-292-5669. Fax: 972-292-5699. p. 2325

Boegel, Roberta, Ref Serv, Woodland Public Library, 250 First St, Woodland, CA, 95695-3411. Tel: 530-661-5980. Fax: 530-666-5408. p. 284

Boeger, Teresa, Dir, Phoenix Children's Hospital, 1919 E Thomas Rd, Phoenix, AZ, 85016. Tel: 602-933-1400. Fax: 602-933-1409. p. 76

Boehm, Alan, Spec Coll Librn, Middle Tennessee State University, MTSU, PO Box 13, Murfreesboro, TN, 37132. Tel: 615-904-8501. p. 2254

Boehm, Beth, Cat, Waynesburg College, 93 Locust Ave, Waynesburg, PA, 15370-1242. Tel: 724-852-7640. Fax: 724-627-4188. p. 2152

Boehm, Lenore, Acq Mgr, DePaul University Libraries, Vincent G Rinn Law Library, 25 E Jackson Blvd, 5th Flr, Chicago, IL, 60604-2287. Tel: 312-362-5224. Fax: 312-362-6908. p. 612

Boehm, Sarah, Dir, Bradford Public Library District, 111 S Peoria St, Bradford, IL, 61421. Tel: 309-897-8400. Fax: 309-897-8314. p. 597

Boehme, Doro, Spec Coll Librn, School of the Art Institute of Chicago, 37 S Wabash Ave, Chicago, IL, 60603-3103. Tel: 312-899-5097. Fax: 312-899-1851. p. 624

Boehning, Karen, Automation Syst Coordr, Oshkosh Public Library, 106 Washington Ave, Oshkosh, WI, 54901-4985. Tel: 920-236-5201, 920-236-5205. Fax: 920-236-5228. p. 2628

Boehning, Karen, Tech Coordr, Winnefox Library System, 106 Washington Ave, Oshkosh, WI, 54901-4985. Tel: 920-236-5220. Fax: 920-236-5228. p. 2628

Boehnke, Barbara, Assoc Libr Dir, Canisius College, 2001 Main St, Buffalo, NY, 14208-1098. Tel: 716-888-2900. Fax: 716-888-8420. p. 1597

Boehnke, Marquita, Supvr, Youth Serv, Central Kansas Library System, 1409 Williams St, Great Bend, KS, 67530-4020. Tel: 620-792-4865. Fax: 620-792-5495. p. 869

Boerboom, Pat, Ch, Saint Peter Public Library, 601 S Washington Ave, Saint Peter, MN, 56082-1447. Tel: 507-934-7420. Fax: 507-934-1204. p. 1283

Boerdoom, Deborah, Librn, Central Louisiana State Hospital, Distefano Memorial Library, 242 W Shamrock St, Pineville, LA, 71361. Tel: 318-484-6363. Fax: 318-484-6284. p. 965

Boerdoom, Deborah, Librn, Central Louisiana State Hospital, Forest Glen Patient's Library, 242 W Shamrock St, Pineville, LA, 71361. Tel: 318-484-6364. Fax: 318-484-6284. p. 965

Boersma, Dianne C, Librn, Berkeley County Library System, Goose Creek Branch, 325 Old Moncks Corner Rd, Goose Creek, SC, 29445. Tel: 843-572-1376. Fax: 843-572-1376. p. 2200

Boersma, Ignacia, Ch, New Glarus Public Library, 319 Second St, New Glarus, WI, 53574. Tel: 608-527-2003. Fax: 608-527-5126. p. 2625

Boes, Aimee, Adult Outreach/Prog Coordr, Upper Sandusky Community Library, 301 N Sandusky Ave, Upper Sandusky, OH, 43351-1139. Tel: 419-294-1345. Fax: 419-294-4499. p. 1942

Boes, Kanjana, ILL Tech, Alliant International University, 10455 Pomerado Rd, San Diego, CA, 92131-1799. Tel: 858-635-4511. Fax: 858-635-4599. p. 230

Boesch, Mary Pat, Asst Librn, Cedar Rapids Public Library, 423 W Main St, Cedar Rapids, NE, 68627. Tel: 308-358-0603. Fax: 308-358-0117. p. 1395

Boese, Aimee, Ref, Pender County Public Library, 103 S Cowan St, Burgaw, NC, 28425. Tel: 910-259-1234. Fax: 910-259-0656. p. 1778

Boese, Bob, Interim Dir, Marshall-Lyon County Library, 301 W Lyon St, Marshall, MN, 56258. Tel: 507-537-7003. p. 1258

Boese, Bonnie, Librn, Anoka-Ramsey Community College, 300 Spirit River Dr S, Cambridge, MN, 55008. Tel: 763-433-1807. p. 1243

Boetcher, Martha M, Dir, Saugatuck-Douglas District Library, Ten Mixer St, Douglas, MI, 49406. Tel: 269-857-8241. Fax: 269-857-3005. p. 1174

Boetcker, Ruth, Head, Instruction & Extn Serv, Marist College, 3399 North Rd, Poughkeepsie, NY, 12601-1387. Tel: 845-575-3199. Fax: 845-575-3150. p. 1722

Boettcher, Bonna, Librn, Cornell University Library, Sidney Cox Library of Music & Dance, Lincoln Hall, Ithaca, NY, 14853-4101. Tel: 607-255-7126. Fax: 607-254-2877. p. 1641

Boettger, Rose, Acq, Lehigh Carbon Community College Library, 4525 Education Park Dr, Schnecksville, PA, 18078-9372. Tel: 610-799-1196. Fax: 610-779-1159. p. 2136

Boff, Colleen, Assoc Dean, Bowling Green State University Libraries, 204 Wm T Jerome Library, Bowling Green, OH, 43403-0170. p. 1861

Boff, Colleen, Interim Coordr, Info Tech, Bowling Green State University Libraries, 204 Wm T Jerome Library, Bowling Green, OH, 43403-0170. p. 1861

Bogage, Alan, Dir, Libr Serv, Carroll Community College, 1601 Washington Rd, Westminster, MD, 21157-6944. Tel: 410-386-8339. Fax: 410-386-8331. p. 1045

Bogan, Kelliann, Archivist, Colby-Sawyer College, 541 Main St, New London, NH, 03257-4648. Tel: 603-526-3360. Fax: 603-526-3777. p. 1459

Bogan, Mary E, Info Serv, Emporia State University, 1200 Commercial St, Box 4051, Emporia, KS, 66801. Tel: 620-341-5037. Fax: 620-341-5997. p. 866

Bogan, Sharon, Libr Assoc, Desoto Parish Library, Stonewall Branch, 808 Hwy 171, Stonewall, LA, 71078. Tel: 318-925-9191. Fax: 318-915-1694. p. 956

Bogan, Terri L, Assoc Librn, Ref & Instrul Serv Librn, Hope International University, 2500 E Nutwood Ave, Fullerton, CA, 92831. Tel: 714-879-3901, Ext 1261. Fax: 714-681-7515. p. 154

Bogard, Sherry, Ch, Shelby County Public Library, 309 Eighth St, Shelbyville, KY, 40065. Tel: 502-633-3803. Fax: 502-633-4025. p. 935

Bogardus, Carolyn, Br Mgr, Charles County Public Library, Potomac Branch, 3225 Ruth B Swann Dr, Indian Head, MD, 20640-3038. Tel: 301-375-7375. p. 1034

Bogardus, Carolyn, Libr Dir, Port Isabel Public Library, 213 Yturria St, Port Isabel, TX, 78578. Tel: 956-943-1822. Fax: 956-943-4638. p. 2371

Bogart, Debra, Tampa Campus Libr Dir, Keiser University Library System, 1500 NW 49th St, Fort Lauderdale, FL, 33309. Tel: 954-351-4035. Fax: 954-351-4051. p. 443

Bogart, Jim, Develop, Saint Louis County Library, 1640 S Lindbergh Blvd, Saint Louis, MO, 63131-3598. Tel: 314-994-3300, Ext 2156. Fax: 314-997-7602. p. 1358

Bogart, Lisa, Head of Mkt, Somerset County Library System, One Vogt Dr, Bridgewater, NJ, 08807-2136. Tel: 908-526-4016, Ext 136. p. 1475

Bogart, Ramona, Libr Mgr, Afton Free Library, 105A Main St, Afton, NY, 13730. Tel: 607-639-1212. Fax: 607-639-1557. p. 1567

Bogaski, Doug, Tech Support, City of Winnipeg Water & Waste Department, 1199 Pacific Ave, Winnipeg, MB, R3E 3S8, CANADA. Tel: 204-986-3880. Fax: 204-224-0032. p. 2755

Bogda, Neal, Digital Res Librn, Web Librn, Cardinal Stritch University Library, 6801 N Yates Rd, Milwaukee, WI, 53207-3985. Tel: 414-410-4263. Fax: 414-410-4268. p. 2617

Boge, Patricia, Commun Relations Coordr, La Crosse Public Library, 800 Main St, La Crosse, WI, 54601. Tel: 608-789-7100. Fax: 608-789-7106. p. 2603

Bogel, Gayle, Asst Prof, Southern Connecticut State University, 501 Crescent St, New Haven, CT, 06515. Tel: 203-392-5704. Fax: 203-392-5780. p. 2963

Bogel, Steven, Ref Librn, Drexel University Health Sciences Libraries, 245 N 15th St MS 449, Philadelphia, PA, 19102-1192. Fax: 215-762-8180. p. 2105

Bogel, Steven, Evening Ref Librn, Drexel University Libraries, Hagerty Library, 33rd & Market Sts, Philadelphia, PA, 19104-2875. Tel: 215-895-2750. Fax: 215-895-2070. p. 2105

Bogel, Steven, Librn, Pennsylvania Hospital, Medical Library, Three Pine Ctr, 800 Spruce St, Philadelphia, PA, 19107-6192. Tel: 215-829-3370. Fax: 215-829-7155. p. 2113

Bogenschutz, Debbie, Coll Develop, Instrul Serv Librn, Ref, Cincinnati State Technical & Community College, 3520 Central Pkwy, Cincinnati, OH, 45223-2612. Tel: 513-569-1611. Fax: 513-559-1527. p. 1869

Bogey, Daniel, Dir, Clearfield County Public Library, 601 Beech St, Curwensville, PA, 16833. Tel: 814-236-0589. Fax: 814-236-3620. p. 2048

Bogger, Tommy L, Actg Libr Dir, Norfolk State University Library, 700 Park Ave, Norfolk, VA, 23504-8010. Tel: 757-823-8517. Fax: 757-823-2431. p. 2482

Boggess, Karen, Mgr, Kanawha County Public Library, Nitro Public, 1700 Park Ave, Nitro, WV, 25143. Tel: 304-755-4432. Fax: 304-755-5130. p. 2556

Boggs, Chrystie, Asst Librn, Steinbach Bible College Library, 50 PTH 12 N, Steinbach, MB, R5G 1T4, CANADA. Tel: 204-326-6451. Fax: 204-326-6908. p. 2752

Boggs, Jacqueline, Dir, Glenolden Library, 211 S Llanwellyn Ave, Glenolden, PA, 19036-2118. Tel: 610-583-1010. Fax: 610-583-7610. p. 2061

Boggs, John, Database Mgr, Peninsula Libraries Automated Network, 2471 Flores St, San Mateo, CA, 94403-4000. Tel: 650-349-5538. Fax: 650-349-5089. p. 2938

Boggs, Lauren, Cataloger, Suburban Library Cooperative, 44750 Delco Blvd, Sterling Heights, MI, 48313. Tel: 586-685-5750. Fax: 586-685-3010. p. 2946

Boggs, Marlene, Adult Serv Mgr, Mid-Continent Public Library, 15616 E US Hwy 24, Independence, MO, 64050-2098. Tel: 816-836-5200. Fax: 816-521-7253. p. 1332

Boggs, Paula, Librn, Piedmont Public Library, One Child Ave, Piedmont, WV, 26750. Tel: 304-355-2757. Fax: 304-355-2757. p. 2569

Boggs, Sheri, Youth Coll Develop Librn, Spokane County Library District, 4322 N Argonne Rd, Spokane, WA, 99212-1868. Tel: 509-893-8200. Fax: 509-893-8472. p. 2536

Boggs, Stephen J, Dir, New Carlisle & Olive Township Public Library, 408 S Bray St, New Carlisle, IN, 46552. Tel: 574-654-3046. Fax: 574-654-8260. p. 768

Boggs, Sue, Cat, Libr Tech, University of Puget Sound, 1500 N Warner St, Campus Mail Box 1021, Tacoma, WA, 98416-1021. Tel: 253-879-2667. Fax: 253-879-3670. p. 2541

Bogie, Sally, Dir, C C Mellor Memorial Library, One Pennwood Ave, Edgewood, PA, 15218-1627. Tel: 412-731-0909. Fax: 412-731-8969. p. 2053

Bogin, Michael, Asst Dir, Huntington Public Library, 338 Main St, Huntington, NY, 11743. Tel: 631-427-5165. Fax: 631-421-7131. p. 1639

Bogino, Jeannie, Libr Dir, New Lebanon Library, 550 State Rte 20, New Lebanon, NY, 12125. Tel: 518-794-8844. p. 1665

Bognanni, Kathy, Br Mgr, Carver County Library, Chanhassen Branch, 7711 Kerber Blvd, Chanhassen, MN, 55317-9634. Tel: 952-227-1500. Fax: 952-227-1510. p. 1245

Bogner, Irene, Librn, Beverly Hospital, 309 W Beverly Blvd, Montebello, CA, 90640. Tel: 323-725-4305. Fax: 323-889-2424. p. 189

Bogorff, Bob, Univ Archivist, Nova Southeastern University Libraries, 3100 Ray Ferrero Jr Blvd, Fort Lauderdale, FL, 33314. Tel: 954-262-4641. Fax: 954-262-3805. p. 444

Bograd, Michael, Dir, Mississippi Department of Environmental Quality Library, 700 N State St, Jackson, MS, 39202. Tel: 601-961-5501. p. 1304

Bogstad, Janice, Dr, Head, Tech Serv, University of Wisconsin-Eau Claire, 105 Garfield Ave, Eau Claire, WI, 54702-4004. Tel: 715-836-6032. Fax: 715-836-2949. p. 2590

Bogue, Mary A, Tech Serv Librn, Earlham College, 801 National Rd W, Richmond, IN, 47374-4095. Tel: 765-983-1363. Fax: 765-983-1304. p. 774

Bogue, Patricia, Br Mgr, Mid-Continent Public Library, Claycomo Branch, 309 NE US Hwy 69, Claycomo, MO, 64119-3116. Tel: 816-455-5030. Fax: 816-455-6987. p. 1332

Bogun, Joan, Librn, Beaufort, Hyde & Martin County Regional Library, Belhaven Public, 333 E Main St, Belhaven, NC, 27810. Tel: 252-943-2993. Fax: 252-943-2606. p. 1828

Bogusch, Linda, Ch, Waco-McLennan County Library System, 1717 Austin Ave, Waco, TX, 76701-1794. Tel: 254-750-5942. Fax: 254-750-5940. p. 2397

Bohall, Rob, Ref Librn, George Fox University, 416 N Meridian St, Newberg, OR, 97132. Tel: 503-554-2410. Fax: 503-554-3599. p. 2007

Bohan, Colleen, Mgr, Battelle Energy Alliance, LLC, 1776 Science Center Dr, MS 2300, Idaho Falls, ID, 83415-2300. Tel: 208-526-1185. Fax: 208-526-0211. p. 576

Bohannon, Vicki, Dir, Belle Plaine City Library, 222 W Fifth Ave, Belle Plaine, KS, 67013. Tel: 620-488-3431. p. 857

Bohl, Phillip, Assoc Dir, Pepperdine University Libraries, School of Law-Jerene Appleby Harnish Law Library, 24255 Pacific Coast Hwy, Malibu, CA, 90263. Tel: 310-506-4643. Fax: 310-506-4836. p. 182

Bohlar, Sally, Librn, Lovett Memorial Library, 302 N Main, McLean, TX, 79057. Tel: 806-779-2851. Fax: 806-779-3241. p. 2361

Bohleke, B, Dr, Archivist, Libr Dir, Lutheran Theological Seminary, 66 Seminary Ridge, Gettysburg, PA, 17325. Tel: 717-338-3014. Fax: 717-337-1611. p. 2060

Bohlen, James, Librn, Rush-Copley Medical Center, 2000 Ogden Ave, Aurora, IL, 60504. Tel: 630-978-4917. Fax: 630-978-6854. p. 592

Bohman, Sherry, Tech Serv, Cedar City Public Library in the Park, 303 N 100 East, Cedar City, UT, 84720. Tel: 435-586-6661. Fax: 435-865-7280. p. 2404

Bohme, Carol, Circ Supvr, Pioneer Memorial Library, 375 W Fourth St, Colby, KS, 67701-2197. Tel: 785-460-4470. Fax: 785-460-4472. p. 861

Bohmfalk, Pam P, Asst Dir, Hastings Public Library, 517 W Fourth St, Hastings, NE, 68901-7560. Tel: 402-461-2346. Fax: 402-461-2359. p. 1401

Bohmfalk, Rachel, South Campus Librn (1), Laredo Community College, Senator Judith Zaffirini Library (South Library), 5500 S Zapata Hwy, Laredo, TX, 78046. Fax: 956-794-4375. p. 2353

Bohne, David R, Dir, San Leandro Public Library, 300 Estudillo Ave, San Leandro, CA, 94577. Tel: 510-577-3940. Fax: 510-577-3967. p. 252

Bohr, Darsi, Dir, Speedway Public Library, 5633 W 25th St, Speedway, IN, 46224-3899. Tel: 317-243-8959. Fax: 317-243-9373. p. 780

Bohrer, Clara Nalli, Dir, West Bloomfield Township Public Library, 4600 Walnut Lake Rd, West Bloomfield, MI, 48323. Tel: 248-682-2120. Fax: 248-232-2291. p. 1236

Boice, Daniel, Dir, Divine Word College, 102 Jacoby Dr SW, Epworth, IA, 52045-0380. Tel: 563-876-3353, Ext 207. p. 814

Boies, Laurie Ellen, Dir, Ruth Suckow Memorial Library, 122 Northern Ave, Earlville, IA, 52041. Tel: 563-923-5235. Fax: 563-923-5235. p. 813

Boiko, Robert, Sr Lecturer, University of Washington, Mary Gates Hall, Ste 370, Campus Box 352840, Seattle, WA, 98195-2840. Tel: 206-685-9937. Fax: 206-616-3152. p. 2976

Boileau, Linda, Chef de Div, Bibliothèques de Montrèal, Benny, 3465, avenue Benny, Montreal, QC, H4B 2R9, CANADA. Tel: 514-868-4021. Fax: 514-872-4585. p. 2889

Boileau, Linda, Chef de Div, Bibliothèques de Montrèal, Côte-des-Neiges, 5290, chemin de la Côte-des-Neiges, Montreal, QC, H3T 1Y2, CANADA. Tel: 514-868-4021. Fax: 514-872-0516. p. 2889

Boileau, Linda, Chef de Div, Bibliothèques de Montrèal, Interculturelle, 6767, chemin de la Côte-des-Neiges, Montréal, QC, H3S 2T6, CANADA. Tel: 514-868-4021. p. 2890

Boileau, Linda, Chef de Div, Bibliothèques de Montrèal, Notre-Dame-de-Grâce, 3755, rue Botrel, Montreal, QC, H4A 3G8, CANADA. Tel: 514-868-4021. Fax: 514-872-0517. p. 2890

Boire, Jennilyn, Librn, High Level Municipal Library, 10601 103 St, High Level, AB, T0H 1Z0, CANADA. Tel: 780-926-2097. Fax: 780-926-4268. p. 2706

Boisclair, Charlotte, Librn, Greene Public Library, 179 Hopkins Hollow Rd, Greene, RI, 02827. Tel: 401-397-3873. Fax: 401-385-9190. p. 2166

Boisjoli, Madeleine, Librn, Bibliothèque Allard Regional Library, 104086 PTH 11, Saint Georges, MB, R0E 1V0, CANADA. Tel: 204-367-8443. Fax: 204-367-1780. p. 2751

Boisselle, Vincent, Head Librn, Hobart & William Smith Colleges, 334 Pulteney St, Geneva, NY, 14456. Tel: 315-781-3549. Fax: 315-781-3560. p. 1627

Boisvert, Andrew D, Archivist, Old Colony Historical Society, 66 Church Green, Taunton, MA, 02780. Tel: 508-822-1622. Fax: 508-880-6317. p. 1130

Boisvert, Danielle, Coll Develop Librn, Ref Librn, Universite du Quebec en Outaouais, 283, Blvd Alexandre-Tache, Case postale 1250, succ Hull, Gatineau, QC, J8X 3X7, CANADA. Tel: 819-595-3900, Ext 2374. Fax: 819-773-1669. p. 2884

Boisvert, Denis, Dir, Universite du Quebec a Rimouski - Bibliotheque, 300 Allee des Ursulines, Rimouski, QC, G5L 3A1, CANADA. Tel: 418-723-1986, Ext 1470. Fax: 418-724-1621. p. 2907

Boisvert, Mary Ellen, Circ Librn, Aldrich Public Library, Six Washington St, Barre, VT, 05641-4227. Tel: 802-476-7550. Fax: 802-479-0450 (Call before sending fax). p. 2418

Boitnott, Pat, Br Tech, Monroe County Library System, Robert A Vivian Branch, 2664 Vivian Rd, Monroe, MI, 48162-9212. Tel: 734-241-1430. Fax: 734-241-1430. p. 1210

Boito, Scott C, Mgr, Info Serv, Rhodia Inc, 350 George Patterson Blvd, Bristol, PA, 19007. Tel: 215-781-6229. Fax: 215-781-6002. p. 2037

Boivin, Amy, Circ, Taunton Public Library, 12 Pleasant St, Taunton, MA, 02780. Tel: 508-821-1410. Fax: 508-821-1414. p. 1131

Boivin, Martine, Cat, Ministere de la Justice, 1200 route de l'Eglise, 4th Flr, Quebec, QC, G1V 4M1, CANADA. Tel: 418-643-8409. Fax: 418-643-9749. p. 2905

Bojanowski, Laura, Librn, National Forest Service Library, 240 W Prospect Rd, Fort Collins, CO, 80526. Tel: 970-498-1284. Fax: 970-498-1059. p. 307

Bojda, Jan, Ch, Evanston Public Library, 1703 Orrington, Evanston, IL, 60201. Tel: 847-448-8601. Fax: 847-866-0313. p. 643

Bokay, Kevin Patrick, Actg Dir, United States Army, Grant Library, 1637 Flint St, Fort Carson, CO, 80913-4105. Tel: 719-526-8144. Fax: 719-524-0070. p. 307

Bokka, Rohini, Tech Serv Mgr, Naperville Public Library, 200 W Jefferson Ave, Naperville, IL, 60540-5374. Tel: 630-961-4100. Fax: 630-637-6389. p. 679

Boksenbaum, Howard, Chief Libr Officer, State of Rhode Island Office of Library & Information Services, One Capitol Hill, 4th Flr, Providence, RI, 02908. Tel: 401-574-9301. Fax: 401-574-9320. p. 2175

Boksenbaum, Howard, Libr Serv Dir, Library of Rhode Island Network, c/o Office of Library & Info Services, One Capitol Hill, 2nd Flr, Providence, RI, 02908-5870. Tel: 401-574-9300. Fax: 401-574-9320. p. 2955

Bolan, Pamela, Librn, Seneca College of Applied Arts & Technology, Seneca @ York, 70 The Pond Rd, North York, ON, M3J 3M6, CANADA. Tel: 416-491-5050, Ext 33040. p. 2813

Boland, Amy, Br Mgr, Trails Regional Library, Waverly Branch, 203 E Kelling, Waverly, MO, 64096. Tel: 660-493-2987. Fax: 660-747-5774. p. 1371

Boland, Arlene, Head, Ref, Ruth L Rockwood Memorial Library, Ten Robert Harp Dr, Livingston, NJ, 07039. Tel: 973-992-4600. Fax: 973-994-2346. p. 1496

Boland, Bruce, Librn, Newfoundland Department of Natural Resources Library, Herald Bldg, Four Herald Ave, Corner Brook, NL, A2H 6J8, CANADA. Tel: 709-637-2307. Fax: 709-637-2403. p. 2770

Boland, Corrine, Adult Serv, Hazel Park Memorial Library, 123 E Nine Mile Rd, Hazel Park, MI, 48030. Tel: 248-542-0940, 248-546-4095. Fax: 248-546-4083. p. 1189

Boland, Lucy, Librn, Bridgeport Public Library, North, 3455 Madison Ave, Bridgeport, CT, 06606. Tel: 203-576-7423. Fax: 203-576-7752. p. 331

Boland, Susan, Assoc Dir, Pub & Res Serv, University of Cincinnati, 2540 Clifton Ave, Cincinnati, OH, 45219. Tel: 513-556-4407. Fax: 513-556-6265. p. 1874

Bolar, Rita, Mgr, Industry Canada, 50 Victoria St, C229, Place du Portage Phase I, Gatineau, QC, K1A 0C9, CANADA. Tel: 819-953-1886. Fax: 819-997-5585. p. 2883

Bolch, Leona, Br Mgr, Atlanta-Fulton Public Library System, Alpharetta Library, 238 Canton St, Alpharetta, GA, 30004. Tel: 770-740-2425. Fax: 770-740-2427. p. 511

Bolden, Mary Jane, Librn, Atlantic County Library System, Somers Point Branch, 801 Shore Rd, Somers Point, NJ, 08244. Tel: 609-927-7113. Fax: 609-926-3062. p. 1500

Bolden, Rachael, Circ Supvr, Washington & Jefferson College Library, 60 S Lincoln St, Washington, PA, 15301. Tel: 724-223-6070. Fax: 724-223-5272. p. 2151

Bolden, Yolanda F, Br Mgr, Outreach Serv Librn, Forsyth County Public Library, Malloy/Jordon East Winston Heritage Center, 1110 E Seventh St, Winston-Salem, NC, 27101. Tel: 336-703-2950. Fax: 336-727-8498. p. 1832

Bolds, Edwin, Librn, Los Medanos College Library, 2700 E Leland Rd, Pittsburg, CA, 94565. Tel: 925-439-2181, Ext 3219. p. 208

Bolds, Scarlette, Dir of Circ, Winn Parish Library, 205 W Main St, Winnfield, LA, 71483-2718. Tel: 318-628-4478. Fax: 318-628-9820. p. 972

Boldt, Kimberly M, Syst Librn, Todd Wehr Library, St Norbert College, 301 Third St, De Pere, WI, 54115. Tel: 920-403-3282. Fax: 920-403-4064. p. 2587

Bolduc, Janet, Interim Dir, Central Maine Medical Center, 300 Main St, Lewiston, ME, 04240. Tel: 207-795-2560. Fax: 207-795-2569. p. 989

Bolduc, Karen L, ILL, Groton Public Library, 99 Main St, Groton, MA, 01450. Tel: 978-448-8000. Fax: 978-448-1169. p. 1093

Bole, Mary, Librn, Manitoba Genealogical Society Inc Library, 1045 St James St, Unit E, Winnipeg, MB, R3H 1B1, CANADA. Tel: 204-783-9139. p. 2756

Bolek, Barbara, Cat, Sr Assoc Librn, University of Michigan-Dearborn, 4901 Evergreen Rd, Dearborn, MI, 48128-2406. Tel: 313-593-5401. Fax: 313-593-5478. p. 1168

Boleman, Marie, Dir, Westfield Public Library, 117 E Third St, Westfield, WI, 53964-9107. Tel: 608-296-2544. Fax: 608-296-2622. p. 2648

Boleman, Teresa, Circ, Cocoa Beach Public Library, 550 N Brevard Ave, Cocoa Beach, FL, 32931. Tel: 321-868-1104. Fax: 321-868-1107. p. 433

Boles, Ann, Tech Serv, Yavapai County Free Library District, 172 E Merritt St, Ste E, Prescott, AZ, 86301. Tel: 928-771-3191. Fax: 928-771-3113. p. 79

Boles, Ann, Head Librn, Wickenburg Public Library, 164 E Apache St, Wickenburg, AZ, 85390. Tel: 928-684-2665. p. 89

Boles, Frank, Dir, Central Michigan University, Clarke Historical Library, 250 E Preston, Mount Pleasant, MI, 48859. Tel: 989-774-3965. Fax: 989-774-2160. p. 1211

Boles, Gloria, ILL, Faulkner University, 5345 Atlanta Hwy, Montgomery, AL, 36109-3398. Tel: 334-386-7207. Fax: 334-386-7481. p. 28

Boles, Quetha, Coordr, Tech Serv, Union College, 310 College St, Campus Box D-21, Barbourville, KY, 40906-1499. Tel: 606-546-1627. Fax: 606-546-1239. p. 906

Bolfing, Trina, Pub Relations Librn, Westbank Community Library District, 1309 Westbank Dr, Austin, TX, 78746. Tel: 512-327-3045. Fax: 512-327-3074. p. 2285

Bolger, Dorita F, Ref, Westminster College, S Market St, New Wilmington, PA, 16172-0001. Tel: 724-946-7330. Fax: 724-946-6220. p. 2097

Bolger, Eileen, Regional Archives Dir, National Archives & Records Administration, Denver Federal Ctr, Bldg 48, W Sixth Ave & Kipling St, Denver, CO, 80225-0307. Tel: 303-407-5740. Fax: 303-407-5707. p. 302

Bolger, Gina, ILL/Doc Delivery/CMC Librn, Cornerstone University, 1001 E Beltline Ave NE, Grand Rapids, MI, 49525. Tel: 616-949-5300. Fax: 616-222-1405. p. 1184

Bolger, Laurie, Librn, University Club Library, One W 54th St, New York, NY, 10019. Tel: 212-572-3418. Fax: 212-572-3452. p. 1702

Bolger, Taffy, Asst Librn, Hinsdale County Library District, 221 Silver St, Lake City, CO, 81235. Tel: 970-944-2615. Fax: 970-944-4102. p. 314

Bolgert, Sarah E, Info Spec, Michael Best & Friedrich LLP, 100 E Wisconsin Ave, Milwaukee, WI, 53202-4108. Tel: 414-271-6560. Fax: 414-277-0656. p. 2619

Bolich, Cecelia, ILL Asst, Saint Leo University, 33701 State Rd 52, Saint Leo, FL, 33574. Tel: 352-588-8328. Fax: 352-588-8484. p. 487

Bolin, Benjamin, Info Literacy Librn, The California Maritime Academy Library, 200 Maritime Academy Dr, Vallejo, CA, 94590. Tel: 707-654-1091. Fax: 707-654-1094. p. 278

Bolin, Carolyn, Librn, Miami County Law Library, 201 W Main St, Troy, OH, 45373. Tel: 937-440-5994. p. 1941

Bolin, Julie, Dir, Scott & White Healthcare, 2401 S 31st, MS-AG-302, Temple, TX, 76508. Tel: 254-724-2228. Fax: 254-724-4229. p. 2390

Bolin, Mary, Chair, Tech Serv, University of Nebraska-Lincoln, 1248 R St, Lincoln, NE, 68588-4100. Tel: 402-472-2526. p. 1407

Bolin, Matthew, Asst Dir, Acq, American Museum of Natural History Library, 79th St & Central Park W, New York, NY, 10024-5192. Tel: 212-769-5409. Fax: 212-769-5009. p. 1668

Bolin, Ruth, Dir, Suffern Free Library, 210 Lafayette Ave, Suffern, NY, 10901. Tel: 845-357-1237. Fax: 845-357-3156. p. 1750

Boling, Amy, YA Librn, Saint Charles Parish Library, 160 W Campus Dr, Destrehan, LA, 70047. Tel: 985-764-2366. Fax: 985-764-0447. p. 948

Boling, Charles, Actg Coordr, Libr & Instrul Serv, Virginia Highlands Community College Library, 100 VHCC Dr, Abingdon, VA, 24210. Tel: 276-739-2514. Fax: 276-739-2593. p. 2443

Boling, Jeff, Ref Serv, United States Air Force, 15 SVS/SVMG, 990 Mills Blvd, Bldg 595, Hickam AFB, HI, 96853-5316. Tel: 808-449-8299. Fax: 808-449-8298. p. 559

Boling, Karen, Br Mgr, West Georgia Regional Library, Tallapoosa Public Library, 388 Bowden St, Tallapoosa, GA, 30176. Tel: 770-574-3124. Fax: 770-574-3124. p. 524

Bolis, Christine, Ch, Brown County Public Library, 205 Locust Lane, Nashville, IN, 47448. Tel: 812-988-2850. Fax: 812-988-8119. p. 767

Boll, Jackie, Dean, Libr/Learning Res Ctr, Fullerton College, 321 E Chapman Ave, Fullerton, CA, 92832-2095. Tel: 714-992-7040. Fax: 714-992-9961. p. 153

Bollar, Maggie, Ch, New Carlisle Public Library, 111 E Lake Ave, New Carlisle, OH, 45344-1418. Tel: 937-845-3601. Fax: 937-845-0908. p. 1920

Bollard, Joyce, Librn, Cabot Performance Materials Library, County Line Rd, Boyertown, PA, 19512. Tel: 610-369-8414. Fax: 610-367-2068. p. 2037

Bollenbacher, Beverly, Dir, Sweetwater Public Library, 210 Mayes Ave, Sweetwater, TN, 37874. Tel: 423-337-5274. Fax: 423-337-0552. p. 2266

Bollenback, Mark, ILL, Ref Serv, Valencia Community College, East Campus, 701 N Econlockhatchee Trail, Orlando, FL, 32825. Tel: 407-582-2467. Fax: 407-582-8914. p. 478

Boller, Gerry, Librn, Dorchester Public Library, Sixth & Washington, Dorchester, NE, 68343. Tel: 402-946-3891. p. 1397

Boller, Mary, Children's Consult, Northwest Kansas Library System, Two Washington Sq, Norton, KS, 67654-1615. Tel: 785-877-5148. Fax: 785-877-5697. p. 885

Bollerman, Matthew, Dir, Hauppauge Public Library, 601 Veterans Memorial Hwy, Hauppauge, NY, 11788. Tel: 631-979-1600. Fax: 631-979-5457. p. 1634

Bollerman, Matthew, Libr Dir, Westhampton Free Library, Seven Library Ave, Westhampton Beach, NY, 11978-2697. Tel: 631-288-3335. Fax: 631-288-5715. p. 1768

Bolley, Jean S, Head Librn, Capital Area District Libraries, Foster Community Library, 200 N Foster Ave, Lansing, MI, 48912. Tel: 517-485-5185. Fax: 517-485-5239. p. 1200

Bolliger, Becky L, Librn, Halliburton Energy Services, 3000 N Sam Houston Pkwy E, Houston, TX, 77032. Tel: 281-871-4544. Fax: 281-871-4575. p. 2335

Bollman, Karen, Br Supvr, Palatine Public Library District, Rand Road, 1585 N Rand Rd, Palatine, IL, 60074. Tel: 847-202-1194. p. 686

Bollman, Karen, Supvr, Palatine Public Library District, North Hoffman Branch, 3600 Lexington Dr, Hoffman Estates, IL, 60192. Tel: 847-934-0220. p. 686

Bolluyt, Linda, Dir, Spirit Lake Public Library, 702 16th St, Spirit Lake, IA, 51360. Tel: 712-336-2667. Fax: 712-336-0511. p. 845

Bolm, George C, Dir, Vicksburg & Warren County Historical Society, Old Court House Museum, 1008 Cherry St, Vicksburg, MS, 39183. Tel: 601-636-0741. p. 1317

Bologna, Vincent, Dir, Library Association of Warehouse Point, 107 Main St, East Windsor, CT, 06088. Tel: 860-623-5482. Fax: 860-627-6823. p. 337

Bolom, Jeremy, Head, Pub Serv, Lincoln Parish Library, 910 N Trenton St, Ruston, LA, 71270-3328. Tel: 318-513-6412. Fax: 318-251-5045. p. 966

Bolon, Jill, Youth Serv, Spokane Public Library, Shadle, 2111 W Wellesley Ave, Spokane, WA, 99205. Tel: 509-444-5392. Fax: 509-444-5372. p. 2538

Bolshaw, Cynthia, Tech Serv, Gordon-Conwell Theological Seminary, 130 Essex St, South Hamilton, MA, 01982-2317. Tel: 978-646-4079. Fax: 978-646-4567. p. 1125

Bolster, Norma, Chief Librn, Eaglesham Public Library, PO Box 206, Eaglesham, AB, T0H 1H0, CANADA. Tel: 780-359-3792. Fax: 780-359-3745. p. 2697

Bolt, Norine, Asst Dir, East Ridge City Library, 1517 Tombras Ave, East Ridge, TN, 37412-2716. Tel: 423-867-7323. p. 2233

Bolt, Stephanie, Librn, Midway Public Library, 612 Sixth Ave, Midway, BC, V0H 1M0, CANADA. Tel: 250-449-2620. Fax: 250-449-2389. p. 2731

Bolte, Jacqueline, Ref Serv Coordr, La Roche College, 9000 Babcock Blvd, Pittsburgh, PA, 15237. Tel: 412-536-1063. Fax: 412-536-1062. p. 2126

Bolthouse, Jon-Mark, Dir, Fond Du Lac Public Library, 32 Sheboygon St, Fond du Lac, WI, 54935. Tel: 920-929-7080. Fax: 920-929-7082. p. 2592

Bolton, Karen, Ref & Ser Librn, Milwaukee School of Engineering, 500 E Kilbourn Ave, Milwaukee, WI, 53202. Tel: 414-277-7183. Fax: 414-277-7186. p. 2620

Bolton, Kathy E, Ch, Nashua Public Library, Two Court St, Nashua, NH, 03060. Tel: 603-589-4630. Fax: 603-594-3457. p. 1458

Bolton, Mary, Br Mgr, Stone County Library, Crane Area Branch, 111 Main St, Crane, MO, 65633. Tel: 417-723-8261. Fax: 417-723-8851. p. 1329

Bolton, Michael, Digital Initiatives, Texas A&M University Libraries, 5000 TAMU, College Station, TX, 77843-5000. Tel: 979-845-5751. Fax: 979-845-6238. p. 2298

Bolton, Stephen B, Dir, North Country Library System, 22072 County Rte 190, Watertown, NY, 13601-1066. Tel: 315-782-5540. Fax: 315-782-6883. p. 1763

Bolzon, Henry, Head Librn, Encyclopaedia Britannica Inc, 331 N LaSalle, Chicago, IL, 60654. Tel: 312-347-7429. Fax: 312-294-2162. p. 613

Bomba-Lewandoski, Vickie Marie, Info Officer, The Connecticut Agricultural Experiment Station, 123 Huntington St, New Haven, CT, 06511-2000. Tel: 203-974-8447. Fax: 203-974-8502. p. 355

Bombard, Agnes, Asst Dir, Au Sable Forks Free Library, Nine Church Lane, Au Sable Forks, NY, 12912-4400. Tel: 518-647-5596. Fax: 518-647-5753. p. 1575

Bombard, Janet, Libr Dir, Harrison Memorial Library, Ocean Ave & Lincoln St, Carmel, CA, 93921. Tel: 831-624-1366. Fax: 831-624-0407. p. 132

Bombardier, Patricia, Dir, College of Our Lady of the Elms, 291 Springfield St, Chicopee, MA, 01013-2839. Tel: 413-265-2281. Fax: 413-594-7418. p. 1082

Bombardo, Chris, Info Tech Supvr, Mercer University, Walter F George School of Law, Furman Smith Law Library, 1021 Georgia Ave, Macon, GA, 31201-1001. Tel: 478-301-2182. Fax: 478-301-2284. p. 540

Bombaro, Christine, Assoc Dir, Info Literacy & Res Serv, Dickinson College, 333 W High St, Carlisle, PA, 17013-2896. Tel: 717-245-1397. Fax: 717-245-1439. p. 2042

Bombeld, Madeleine, ILL, William Madison Randall Library, 601 S College Rd, Wilmington, NC, 28403-5616. Tel: 910-962-3000. Fax: 910-962-3078. p. 1831

Bon, Adolfo, Libr Syst Spec, Teachers College, Columbia University, 525 W 120th St, New York, NY, 10027-6696. Tel: 212-678-3819. p. 1701

Bona, Diamond, Librn, St John & Wayne, One Riverfront Plaza, 1037 Raymond Blvd, 16th Fl, Newark, NJ, 07102. Tel: 973-491-3300. Fax: 973-491-3555. p. 1513

Bona, Jay, Circ Coordr, Lyndon State College, 1001 College Rd, Lyndonville, VT, 05851. Tel: 802-626-6366. Fax: 802-626-6331. p. 2427

Bonadurer, Ellen, Circ, Dixie State College of Utah, 225 S 700 E, Saint George, UT, 84770. Tel: 435-652-7713. Fax: 435-656-4169. p. 2411

Bonamici, Andrew R, Assoc Univ Librn, University of Oregon Libraries, 1501 Kincaid St, Eugene, OR, 97403-1299. Tel: 541-346-3056. Fax: 541-346-3485. p. 1997

Bonamico, Lee Aura, Network Tech, Ref & ILL Librn, Aldrich Public Library, Six Washington St, Barre, VT, 05641-4227. Tel: 802-476-7550. Fax: 802-479-0450 (Call before sending fax). p. 2418

Bonanno, Rosemary, Exec Dir, Vancouver Island Regional Library, 6250 Hammond Bay Rd, Nanaimo, BC, V9R 5N3, CANADA. Tel: 250-729-2313. Fax: 250-758-2482. p. 2732

Bonanza, Dennis, Librn, Marble Valley Regional Correctional Facility, 167 State St, Rutland, VT, 05701. Tel: 802-747-4608. Fax: 802-786-5843. p. 2434

Bonaro, Cindy, Br Mgr, Pierce County Library System, University Place Branch, 3609 Market Pl W, University Place, WA, 98466. Tel: 253-548-3307. Fax: 253-565-2913. p. 2540

Bonasso, Karen, Mgr, Windsor Public Library, Central Library, 850 Ouellette Ave, Windsor, ON, N9A 4M9, CANADA. Tel: 519-255-6770. p. 2872

Bonath, Gail J, Assoc Librn, Grinnell College Libraries, 1111 Sixth Ave, Grinnell, IA, 50112-1770. Tel: 641-269-3358. Fax: 641-269-4283. p. 819

Bonaventure, Bonnie, Asst Br Mgr, Pointe Coupee Parish Library, Julian Poydras Branch, 4985 Poydras Lane, Rougon, LA, 70773. Tel: 225-627-5846. Fax: 225-627-5846. p. 965

Bond, Amy, Dir, Lonesome Pine Regional Library, 124 Library Rd SW, Wise, VA, 24293-5907. Tel: 276-328-8325. Fax: 276-328-1739. p. 2504

Bond, Anita, Librn, East Parker County Library, 201 FM 1187 N, Aledo, TX, 76008. Tel: 817-441-6545. Fax: 817-441-5787. p. 2273

Bond, Betty, ILL, Bethel University Library, 3900 Bethel Dr, Saint Paul, MN, 55112. Tel: 651-638-6222. Fax: 651-638-6001. p. 1277

Bond, Carol, Librn, Penfield Public Library, 1985 Baird Rd, Penfield, NY, 14526. Tel: 585-340-8720. Fax: 585-340-8748. p. 1716

Bond, Carolyn, Circ Supvr, Port Moody Public Library, 100 Newport Dr, Port Moody, BC, V3H 3E1, CANADA. Tel: 604-469-4575, 604-469-4577. Fax: 604-469-4576. p. 2735

Bond, Emily, Instruction & Outreach, Pub Serv, Cosumnes River College Library, 8401 Center Pkwy, Sacramento, CA, 95823. Tel: 916-691-7249. Fax: 916-691-7349. p. 223

Bond, Jenifer, Asst Libr Dir, Bryant University, 1150 Douglas Pike, Smithfield, RI, 02917-1284. Tel: 401-232-6125. Fax: 401-232-6126. p. 2176

Bond, Kate, Asst Head, Ch Serv, Russell Library, 123 Broad St, Middletown, CT, 06457. Tel: 860-347-2528, Ext 161. p. 352

Bond, Paul, Coordr, Libr Instruction, University of Pittsburgh, Johnstown Campus, 450 Schoolhouse Rd, Johnstown, PA, 15904. Tel: 814-269-7287. Fax: 814-269-7286. p. 2073

Bond, Ruth, Br Mgr, Kitsap Regional Library, Sylvan Way Branch, 1301 Sylvan Way, Bremerton, WA, 98310-3466. Tel: 360-415-6727. Fax: 360-405-9128. p. 2510

Bond, Ruth, Dir, Libr Serv, Kitsap Regional Library, 1301 Sylvan Way, Bremerton, WA, 98310-3498. Tel: 360-415-6727. Fax: 360-405-9128. p. 2510

Bond, Trevor James, Head, Ms, Archives & Spec Coll, Washington State University Libraries, 100 Dairy Rd, Pullman, WA, 99164. Tel: 509-335-6693. Fax: 509-335-6721. p. 2525

Bondar, Audrey, Coll Develop, Henry Ford Hospital, 2799 W Grand Blvd, Detroit, MI, 48202. Tel: 313-916-2550. Fax: 313-874-4730. p. 1171

Bondareff, Hyla, Electronic Res, Washington University Libraries, Law Library, Washington Univ Sch Law, Anheuser-Busch Hall, One Brookings Dr, Campus Box 1171, Saint Louis, MO, 63130. Tel: 314-935-6434. Fax: 314-935-7125. p. 1363

Bondi, Joseph, Pub Serv, Broadview Public Library District, 2226 S 16th Ave, Broadview, IL, 60155-4000. Tel: 708-345-1325. Fax: 708-345-5024. p. 597

Bondy, Amy, Interim Circ Librn, Elizabeth City State University, 1704 Weeksville Rd, Elizabeth City, NC, 27909. Tel: 252-335-8741. Fax: 252-335-3446. p. 1790

Bondy, Christie, Ch, Person County Public Library, 319 S Main St, Roxboro, NC, 27573. Tel: 336-597-7881. Fax: 336-597-5081. p. 1821

Bondy, Jennifer L, Acad Serv Officer III, Wayne State University, 106 Kresge Library, Detroit, MI, 48202. Tel: 313-577-2523. Fax: 313-577-7563. p. 2967

Bone, Jennifer, Asst Dir, Tech Serv Librn, Keene Public Library, 60 Winter St, Keene, NH, 03431-3360. Tel: 603-352-0157. Fax: 866-743-0446. p. 1452

Bone, Patricia, Asst Librn, Indiana Tech, 1600 E Washington Blvd, Fort Wayne, IN, 46803. Tel: 260-422-5561, Ext 2215. Fax: 260-422-3189. p. 741

Bonelli, Deborah, Dir, Libr Serv, Saint Barnabas Hospital, Third Ave & 83rd St, Bronx, NY, 10457-2594. Tel: 718-960-6113. Fax: 718-960-3050. p. 1588

Bonelli, Vicky, Dir, Lincoln Trail College, 11220 State Hwy 1, Robinson, IL, 62454-5707. Tel: 618-544-8657, Ext 1427. Fax: 618-544-3957. p. 695

Bonello, Elizabeth, ILL Tech, Scott County Library System, 13090 Alabama Ave S, Savage, MN, 55378-1479. Tel: 952-707-1760. Fax: 952-707-1775. p. 1283

Bonesteel, Dinah, Admin Coordr, Cobb County Public Library System, 266 Roswell St, Marietta, GA, 30060-2004. Tel: 770-528-2320. Fax: 770-528-2349. p. 542

Bonet, Maria M, Govt Doc, Pontifical Catholic University Of Puerto Rico, Encarnacion Valdes Library, 2250 Avenida Las Americas, Ste 509, Ponce, PR, 00717-0777. Tel: 787-841-2000, Ext 1806. Fax: 787-284-0235. p. 2675

Bonetti, Paula, Dir, Ashland Public Library, 66 Front St, Ashland, MA, 01721-1606. Tel: 508-881-0134. Fax: 508-881-0135. p. 1050

Bonetti, Susanna, Dir, San Francisco Center for Psychoanalysis, 2340 Jackson St, 4th Flr, San Francisco, CA, 94115. Tel: 415-563-4477. Fax: 415-563-8406. p. 245

Boney, Glendoria, Br Librn, Duplin County Library, Florence Gallier Library, 104 W Main St, Magnolia, NC, 28453. Tel: 910-289-7056. Fax: 910-289-7056. p. 1804

Bonfield, Brett, Dir, Collingswood Public Library, 771 Haddon Ave, Collingswood, NJ, 08108-3714. Tel: 856-858-0649. Fax: 856-858-5016. p. 1480

Bongard, Nancy, Librn, Uxbridge Township Public Library, Zephyr Branch, 13000 Concession 39, Zephyr, ON, L0E 1T0, CANADA. Tel: 905-473-2375. Fax: 905-473-2375. p. 2868

Bonge, Pat, Dir, McCook Community College, 1205 E Third St, McCook, NE, 69001-2631. Tel: 308-345-6303, Ext 8127. Fax: 308-345-8193. p. 1408

Bongers, Desiree M, Dir, Ripon Public Library, 120 Jefferson St, Ripon, WI, 54971-1395. Tel: 920-748-6160. Fax: 920-748-6298. p. 2634

Bongers, Joe, Acq, Head, Adult Serv, Ref Serv, Menasha Public Library, 440 First St, Menasha, WI, 54952-3191. Tel: 920-967-3660. Fax: 920-967-5159. p. 2614

Bonholzer, Gordon, Tech Info Spec, NASA, Library, Bldg 21, Code 272, Greenbelt, MD, 20771. Tel: 301-286-6244. Fax: 301-286-1755. p. 1030

Boni, Bethyn A, Dir, New York Chiropractic College Library, 2360 State Rte 89, Seneca Falls, NY, 13148-9460. Tel: 315-568-3244. Fax: 315-568-3119. p. 1742

Boni-Awotwi, Sekum, Assoc Librn, Howard University Libraries, Louis Stokes Health Sciences Library, 501 W St NW, Washington, DC, 20059. Tel: 202-884-1533. Fax: 202-884-1733. p. 404

Bonifacic, Lisa, Asst Librn, Andrew W Mellon Foundation, 140 E 62nd St, New York, NY, 10065. Tel: 212-838-8400. Fax: 212-888-4172. p. 1685

Bonilla-Mangual, Luis, Cat, Supreme Court Library of Puerto Rico, Munoz Rivera Ave, Puerta de Tierra, San Juan, PR, 00902. Tel: 787-723-6033, Ext 2163. Fax: 787-724-5090. p. 2676

Bonini, Margo, Dir, Sebewaing Township Library, 41 N Center St, Sebewaing, MI, 48759-1406. Tel: 989-883-3520. Fax: 989-883-3520. p. 1227

Bonitz, Faith E, ILL, University of Saint Thomas, 2115 Summit Ave, Mail Box 5004, Saint Paul, MN, 55105. Tel: 651-962-5001. Fax: 651-962-5406. p. 1282

Bonk, Sharon B, Dir, Libr Serv, Benjamin Franklin Institute of Technology, Franklin Union Blg., Rm. 114, 41 Berkeley St, Boston, MA, 02116. Tel: 617-423-4630, Ext 123. p. 1055

Bonnard, Michael, Cat Librn, Georgia College & State University, 320 N Wayne St, Milledgeville, GA, 31061-3397. Tel: 478-445-4047. Fax: 478-445-6847. p. 544

Bonne, Nancy, Ch, Beverly Public Library, 32 Essex St, Beverly, MA, 01915-4561. Tel: 978-921-6062. Fax: 978-922-8329. p. 1053

Bonneau, Solange, Sr, Librn, Grand Seminaire des Saints Apotres Library, Archeveche de Sherbrooke Cathedrale, 130 rue de la Cathedrale, Sherbrooke, QC, J1H 4M1, CANADA. Tel: 819-563-9934, Ext 217. Fax: 819-562-0125. p. 2912

Bonnell, Colleen, Dir, Payette Public Library, 24 S Tenth St, Payette, ID, 83661-2861. Tel: 208-642-6029. Fax: 208-642-6046. p. 581

Bonnema, Clare, Dir, Health Sci Libr, Ingalls Memorial Hospital Medical Library, One Ingalls Dr, Harvey, IL, 60426. Tel: 708-915-6881, 708-915-6882. Fax: 708-915-3109. p. 654

Bonner, Amanda, Ch, Hoover Public Library, 200 Municipal Dr, Hoover, AL, 35216. Tel: 205-444-7810. Fax: 205-444-7878. p. 20

Bonner, Barbara, In Charge, Danforth Public Library, 46 Central St, Danforth, ME, 04424. Tel: 207-448-2055. p. 983

Bonner, Candy, Br Mgr, San Diego County Library, Potrero Branch, 24883 Potrero Valley Rd, Potrero, CA, 91963-0051. Tel: 619-478-5978. Fax: 619-478-2695. p. 234

Bonner, Christina, Head, Ref & Instruction, Ohio Dominican University Library, 1216 Sunbury Rd, Columbus, OH, 43219. Tel: 614-251-4585. Fax: 614-252-2650. p. 1886

Bonner, Elaine D, Mgr, Access Serv, Lutheran School of Theology at Chicago & McCormick Theological Seminary, 1100 E 55th St, Chicago, IL, 60615-5199. Tel: 773-256-0732. Fax: 773-256-0737. p. 618

Bonner, Pat, Br Mgr, Spokane Public Library, Shadle, 2111 W Wellesley Ave, Spokane, WA, 99205. Tel: 509-444-5391. Fax: 509-444-5372. p. 2538

Bonner, Sarah, Instruction Coordr, Ref Librn, Chowan University, One University Pl, Murfreesboro, NC, 27855. Tel: 252-398-6533. Fax: 252-398-1301. p. 1811

Bonner, Scott, Ad, Richmond Heights Memorial Library, 8001 Dale Ave, Richmond Heights, MO, 63117. Tel: 314-645-6202. Fax: 314-781-3434. p. 1350

Bonnet, Alice, Asst City Librn, Leola Public Library, 802 Main St, Leola, SD, 57456. Tel: 605-439-3383. p. 2214

Bonnett, Marilyn, Dir, Utah State Hospital, 1300 E Center St, Provo, UT, 84606-3554. Tel: 801-344-4400. Fax: 801-344-4225. p. 2411

Bonnett, Polly, Br Coordr, Mesa Public Library, Dobson Ranch Branch, 2425 S Dobson Rd, Mesa, AZ, 85202. Tel: 480-644-3448. Fax: 602-644-3445. p. 69

Bonney, Heather, Dir, Sampson-Clinton Public Library, 217 Graham St, Clinton, NC, 28328. Tel: 910-592-4153. Fax: 910-590-3504. p. 1784

Bonney, John, Ref, Neptune Public Library, 25 Neptune Blvd, Neptune, NJ, 07753-1125. Tel: 732-775-8241. Fax: 732-774-1132. p. 1507

Bonney, Zipporah, Libr Asst I, Montgomery City-County Public Library System, Governors Square Branch Library, 2885-B East South Blvd, Montgomery, AL, 36111. Tel: 334-284-7929. Fax: 334-240-4839. p. 29

Bonnici, Laurie, Asst Prof, University of Alabama, 514 Main Library, Tuscaloosa, AL, 35487. Tel: 205-348-4610. Fax: 205-348-3746. p. 2961

Bonnie, Paparella, Dir, West Lawn-Wyomissing Hills Library, 101 Woodside Ave, West Lawn, PA, 19609. Tel: 610-678-4888. Fax: 610-678-9210. p. 2154

Bonomo, April, Librn, Rockville Correctional Facility Library, 811 W 50 N, Rockville, IN, 47872. Tel: 765-569-3178. Fax: 765-569-0149. p. 776

Bonous-Smit, Barbara, Head, Ref & Ser, Queensborough Community College, City University of New York, 222-05 56th Ave, Bayside, NY, 11364-1497. Tel: 718-281-5010. Fax: 718-281-5012. p. 1579

Bonsett, Steve, Librn, Henryville Correctional Facility Library, PO Box 148, Henryville, IN, 47126. Tel: 812-294-4372. p. 748

Bonsteel, Sue, ILL, Ref Serv, Stevenson University Library, 1525 Greenspring Valley Rd, Stevenson, MD, 21153. Tel: 410-486-7000, 443-334-2233. Fax: 410-486-7329. p. 1043

Bontekoe, Karen, Librn, Kaweah Delta Health Care District Library, 400 W Mineral King Ave, Visalia, CA, 93291-6263. Tel: 559-624-2000. Fax: 559-635-4051. p. 280

Bontenbal, Kevin, Info Tech Librn, Cuesta College Library, Hwy 1, San Luis Obispo, CA, 93401. Tel: 805-546-3117. Fax: 805-546-3109. p. 253

Bontrager, Bridget, Tech Serv, Mashpee Public Library, 64 Steeple St, Mashpee, MA, 02649. Tel: 508-539-1435. Fax: 508-539-1437. p. 1103

Bontrager, Jason, Ref & Circ Librn, Blinn College Library, 800 Blinn Blvd, Brenham, TX, 77833. Tel: 979-830-4250. Fax: 979-830-4222. p. 2291

Bontrager, Margi, Dir, Greentown Public Library, 421 S Harrison St, Greentown, IN, 46936-1496. Tel: 765-628-3534. Fax: 765-628-3759. p. 747

Bonvillain, Shanna, Asst Librn, Louisiana Universities Marine Consortium, 8124 Hwy 56, Chauvin, LA, 70344-2124. Tel: 985-851-2806. Fax: 985-851-2874. p. 947

Booch, Lisa, Tech Serv, A Holmes Johnson Memorial Library, 319 Lower Mill Bay Rd, Kodiak, AK, 99615. Tel: 907-486-8684. Fax: 907-486-8681. p. 51

Boock, Michael, Head, Tech Serv, Oregon State University Libraries, 121 The Valley Library, Corvallis, OR, 97331-4501. Tel: 541-737-9155. Fax: 541-737-8267. p. 1994

Boodee, Bonnie, In Charge, Sharon Hospital, 50 Hospital Hill Rd, Sharon, CT, 06069. Tel: 860-364-4008. p. 367

Boodram, Radika, ILL, Long Beach Public Library, 111 W Park Ave, Long Beach, NY, 11561-3326. Tel: 516-432-7201. Fax: 516-889-4641. p. 1654

Booe, Kevin Wayne, Dir, Boise Public Library, 715 S Capitol Blvd, Boise, ID, 83702. Tel: 208-384-4029. p. 570

Booe, Kevin Wayne, Dir, Boise Public Library, Library! at Cole & Ustick, 7557 W Ustick Rd, Boise, ID, 83704. Tel: 208-384-4029. Fax: 208-376-1043. p. 570

Booher, Dustin, Relig Studies Librn, Catholic University of America, Religious Studies-Philosophy & Humanities Libraries, 620 Michigan Ave NE, 312 Mullen Library, Washington, DC, 20064. Tel: 202-319-5091. Fax: 202-319-4735. p. 396

Booher, Mary, Librn, Glades County Public Library, 201 Riverside Dr SW, Moore Haven, FL, 33471. Tel: 863-946-0744. Fax: 863-946-1661. p. 470

Book, Andrea, Dir, Lasalle Parish Library, 3108 N First St, Jena, LA, 71342. Tel: 318-992-5675. Fax: 318-992-7374, 318-992-7394. p. 951

Book, Kent, Libr Dir, Greeley County Library, 517 Broadway, Tribune, KS, 67879. Tel: 620-376-4801. Fax: 620-376-4077. p. 898

Book, Kent, Librn, Union League Club Library, 38 E 37th St, New York, NY, 10016. Tel: 212-685-3800. Fax: 212-545-0130. p. 1701

Booker, Carolyn, Pub Serv Mgr, Keller Public Library, 640 Johnson Rd, Keller, TX, 76248. Tel: 817-743-4800. Fax: 817-743-4890. p. 2349

Booker, Edward, Br Mgr, Orange County Library District, Herndon, 4324 E Colonial Dr, Orlando, FL, 32803. p. 476

Booker, Glenn, Asst Teaching Prof, Drexel University, Rush Bldg, Rm 306, 30 N 33rd St, Philadelphia, PA, 19104-2875. Tel: 215-895-2474. Fax: 215-895-2494. p. 2973

Booker, Jan, Librn/Mgr, Lakeland Regional Medical Center, 1324 Lakeland Hills Blvd, Lakeland, FL, 33805. Tel: 863-687-1176. Fax: 863-687-1488. p. 459

Booker, Latrice, Coordr, Libr Instruction, Ref Serv, Indiana University Northwest Library, 3400 Broadway, Gary, IN, 46408. Tel: 219-980-6547. Fax: 219-980-6558. p. 745

Bookheim, Bill, Evening/Weekend Ref Librn, California Western School of Law Library, 290 Cedar St, San Diego, CA, 92101. Tel: 619-515-1584. Fax: 619-685-2918. p. 231

Boon, Belinda, Dr, Asst Prof, Kent State University, 314 Library, Kent, OH, 44242-0001. Tel: 330-672-2782. Fax: 330-672-7965. p. 2972

Boone, Beth, Ref Serv, Ad, Neuse Regional Library, 510 N Queen St, Kinston, NC, 28501. Tel: 252-527-7066, Ext 122. Fax: 252-527-8220. p. 1805

Boone, Diana, Dept Head, Creighton University, Health Sciences Library-Learning Resource Center, 2770 Webster St, Omaha, NE, 68178-0210. Tel: 402-280-5175. Fax: 402-280-5134. p. 1412

Boone, Kimball, Ser Librn, Brigham Young University-Hawaii, 55-220 Kulanui St, BYU-Hawaii, No 1966, Laie, HI, 96762-1294. Tel: 808-675-3880. Fax: 808-675-3877. p. 567

Boone, Sharon, Br Mgr, Trinity County Library, Hayfork Branch, Hympom Rd, Hayfork, CA, 96041. Tel: 530-628-5427. Fax: 530-628-5304. p. 282

Boone, Susan, Ref Archivist, Smith College Libraries, Sophia Smith Collection, Seven Neilson Dr, Northampton, MA, 01063. Tel: 413-585-2974. Fax: 413-585-2886. p. 1114

Boone, Thomas, Ref Librn, Loyola Law School, 919 S Albany St, Los Angeles, CA, 90015-1211. Tel: 213-736-1329. Fax: 213-487-2204. p. 175

Boonstra, Connie, Dir, Odell Public Library, 307 S Madison St, Morrison, IL, 61270-2724. Tel: 815-772-7323. Fax: 815-772-7323. p. 676

Boos, Heather, In Charge, Morris, Manning & Martin Library LLP, 1333 H St NW, Ste 820, Washington, DC, 20005. Tel: 202-408-5153. Fax: 202-408-5146. p. 408

Boos, JoEllen, Youth Serv Mgr, Bellevue Public Library, 224 E Main St, Bellevue, OH, 44811-1467. Tel: 419-483-4769. Fax: 419-483-0158. p. 1859

Boosalis, Vicki, Mgr, Porterville Developmental Center, Residents' Resource Center, 26501 Ave 140, Porterville, CA, 93258-9109. Tel: 559-782-2021. p. 212

Boote, Beverley, Head Librn, Manitou Regional Library, 418 Main St, Manitou, MB, R0G 1G0, CANADA. Tel: 204-242-3134. Fax: 204-242-3184. p. 2749

Booth, Angela, Librn, Pepper, Hamilton LLP, 4000 Town Ctr, Ste 1800, Southfield, MI, 48075. Tel: 248-359-7300. Fax: 248-359-7700. p. 1228

Booth, Ann, Librn, Weber County Library System, North Branch, 475 E 2600 North, North Ogden, UT, 84414-2833. Tel: 801-782-8800. Fax: 801-782-8801. p. 2409

Booth, Brenda, Br Mgr, Manatee County Public Library System, Rocky Bluff, 7016 US Hwy 301 N, Ellenton, FL, 34222. Tel: 941-723-4821. Fax: 941-723-4825. p. 430

Booth, Debbie, Coordr, University of Delaware Library, Marine Studies, 700 Pilotown Rd, Lewes, DE, 19958. Tel: 302-645-4290. p. 386

Booth, Germaine, Ch, Massapequa Public Library, Central Avenue, 523 Central Ave, Massapequa, NY, 11758. Tel: 516-798-4607, Ext 320. Fax: 516-798-2804. p. 1658

Booth, Heather, Teen Serv, Thomas Ford Memorial Library, 800 Chestnut Ave, Western Springs, IL, 60558. Tel: 708-246-0520. Fax: 708-246-0403. p. 717

Booth, Janet C, Chief Exec Officer, Welland Public Library, 50 The Boardwalk, Welland, ON, L3B 6J1, CANADA. Tel: 905-734-6210. Fax: 905-734-8955. p. 2870

Booth, Judy, Sr Librn, Fullerton Public Library, Hunt Branch, 201 S Basque Ave, Fullerton, CA, 92833-3372. Tel: 714-738-5364. p. 154

Booth, Maureen, Law Librn, United States Department of the Interior Library, 1849 C St NW, Rm 1151, Washington, DC, 20240. Tel: 202-208-3686. Fax: 202-208-6773. p. 419

Booth, Pat, Sr Libr Tech, College of Central Florida Citrus Campus Learning Resources Center, 3800 S Lecanto Hwy, C2-202, Lecanto, FL, 34461. Tel: 352-249-1205. Fax: 352-249-1212. p. 460

Booth, Sarah, Asst Dir, Montgomery County Memorial Library System, 104 I-45 N, Conroe, TX, 77301-2720. Tel: 936-788-8377, Ext 236. Fax: 936-788-8398. p. 2300

Booth, Todd, Ref Serv, Saint Johns County Public Library System, 6670 US 1 South, Saint Augustine, FL, 32086. Tel: 904-827-6913. p. 486

Booth-Moyle, Gillian, Tech Serv, Caledon Public Library, Caledon East Branch, 6500 Old Church Rd, Caledon East, ON, L0N 1E0, CANADA. Tel: 905-584-1456. p. 2795

Booth-Poor, Elizabeth, Dir, Bartholomew County Public Library, 536 Fifth St, Columbus, IN, 47201-6225. Tel: 812-379-1254. Fax: 812-379-1275. p. 733

Booth-Riley, Gail, Librn, Richmond Community College Library, 1042 W Hamlet Ave, Hamlet, NC, 28345. Tel: 910-410-1752. Fax: 910-582-7045. p. 1800

Boothe, Elizabeth, Info Serv, Central Virginia Community College Library, Amherst Hall, Rm 2506, 3506 Wards Rd, Lynchburg, VA, 24502-2498. Tel: 434-832-7750. Fax: 434-386-4677. p. 2475

Bootle, Ina, Libr Spec, Clemson University Libraries, Gunnin Architecture Library, 112 Lee Hall, Clemson University, Clemson, SC, 29634-0501. Tel: 864-656-3933. Fax: 864-656-3932. p. 2186

Boots, Margie, Circ, Portland Public Library, 301 Portland Blvd, Portland, TN, 37148-1229. Tel: 615-325-2279. Fax: 615-325-7061. p. 2263

Boozer, Rhonda, ILL & Reserves Asst, Clayton State University, 2000 Clayton State Blvd, Morrow, GA, 30260. Tel: 678-466-4325. Fax: 678-466-4349. p. 545

Boragine, Becky A, Dir, Lincoln Public Library, 145 Old River Rd, Lincoln, RI, 02865. Tel: 401-333-2422. Fax: 401-333-4154. p. 2168

Borah, Eloisa, Head, Pub Serv, University of California Los Angeles Library, Eugene & Maxine Rosenfeld Management Library, 110 Westwood Plaza, E-302, Los Angeles, CA, 90095. Tel: 310-825-3138. Fax: 310-825-6632. p. 179

Boraks, Heidi, Ref Asst, International Development Research Centre Library, 150 Kent St, Ottawa, ON, K1G 3H9, CANADA. Tel: 613-236-6163. Fax: 613-563-3858. p. 2831

Boras, David, Head, Circ, Blue Island Public Library, 2433 York St, Blue Island, IL, 60406-2011. Tel: 708-388-1078, Ext 15. Fax: 708-388-1143. p. 596

Borawski, Chris, Mgr, Montgomery County Public Libraries, Poolesville Library, 19633 Fisher Ave, Poolesville, MD, 20837-2071. Tel: 240-773-9552. p. 1039

Borbon, Sharon E, Dir, Fresno County Public Law Library, Fresno County Courthouse, Rm 600, 1100 Van Ness Ave, Fresno, CA, 93721-2017. Tel: 559-237-2227. Fax: 559-442-4960. p. 151

Borchardt, Conie, Circ Mgr, University of Saint Thomas, Archbishop Ireland Memorial Library, 2260 Summit Ave, Mail No IRL, Saint Paul, MN, 55105. Tel: 651-962-5453. Fax: 651-962-5460. p. 1282

Borchers, Joan, AV, Riverdale Presbyterian Church Library, 6513 Queens Chapel Rd, Hyattsville, MD, 20782-2197. Tel: 301-927-0477. Fax: 301-699-2156. p. 1033

Borchers, Margaret, Dir, Edith Wheeler Memorial Library, 733 Monroe Tpk, Monroe, CT, 06468. Tel: 203-452-2850. Fax: 203-261-3359. p. 353

Borchert, James, Br Librn, Siouxland Libraries, Oak View, 3700 E Third St, Sioux Falls, SD, 57103. Tel: 605-367-8060. Fax: 605-367-4343. p. 2219

Borchert, Theresa, Electronic Res, Concordia College, 901 S Eighth St, Moorhead, MN, 56562. Tel: 218-299-3235. Fax: 218-299-4253. p. 1265

Borck, Cathy Jean, Dir, Kilbourn Public Library, 620 Elm St, Wisconsin Dells, WI, 53965. Tel: 608-254-2146. p. 2650

Borck, Patricia, Dir, Macon State College Library, 100 College Station Dr, Macon, GA, 31206-5144. Tel: 478-471-2865. Fax: 478-471-2869. p. 540

Bordea, Diana, Asst Librn, Price City Library, 159 E Main St, Price, UT, 84501-3046. Tel: 435-636-3188. Fax: 435-637-2905. p. 2410

Bordeau, Jamie, Asst Librn, Union Institute & University, 62 Ridge St, Ste 2, Montpelier, VT, 05602. Tel: 802-828-8747. Fax: 802-828-8748. p. 2429

Bordeaux, Michele, Br Mgr, Monmouth County Library, Oceanport Branch, Monmouth Blvd & Myrtle Ave, Oceanport, NJ, 07757. Tel: 732-229-2626. Fax: 732-571-0661. p. 1499

Bordelon, Denise, Asst Librn, Rapides Regional Medical Center, 211 Fourth St, Alexandria, LA, 71301-8421. Tel: 318-769-5341. Fax: 318-473-3489. p. 940

Borden, Charmaine, Regional Librn, Nova Scotia Community College, 39 Acadia Ave, Stellarton, NS, B0K 1S0, CANADA. Tel: 902-755-7201. Fax: 902-755-7289. p. 2784

Borden, Charmaine, Regional Librn, Nova Scotia Community College, 36 Arthur St, Truro, NS, B2N 1X5, CANADA. Tel: 902-893-5326. Fax: 902-893-6693. p. 2786

Borden, Margaret, Librn, Falmouth Public Library, East Falmouth Branch, 310 E Falmouth Hwy, East Falmouth, MA, 02536. Tel: 508-548-6340. Fax: 508-543-6340. p. 1089

Borden, Pam, Librn, Law Society of Prince Edward Island Library, 42 Water St, Charlottetown, PE, C1A 1A4, CANADA. Tel: 902-368-6099. Fax: 902-368-7557. p. 2875

Borden, Sara, Tech Serv Mgr, Logansport-Cass County Public Library, 616 E Broadway, Logansport, IN, 46947-3187. Tel: 574-753-6383. Fax: 574-722-5889. p. 761

Border, Peggy, Ref Librn, Fruitville Public Library, 100 Coburn Rd, Sarasota, FL, 34240. Tel: 941-861-2500. Fax: 941-861-2528. p. 489

Border, Sue, Dir, Woodward Memorial Library, Seven Wolcott St, LeRoy, NY, 14482. Tel: 585-768-8300. Fax: 585-768-4768. p. 1651

Borders, Susan, Dir, Darby Free Library, 1001 Main St, Darby, PA, 19023-0169. Tel: 610-586-7310. Fax: 610-586-2781. p. 2049

Borders, Willie Ruth, Dir, Westmoreland Public Library, 2305 Epperson Springs Rd, Westmoreland, TN, 37186. Tel: 615-644-2026. Fax: 615-644-2026. p. 2268

Bordinaro, Caroline, Bibliog Instruction Coordr, California State University Dominguez Hills, 1000 E Victoria St, Carson, CA, 90747. Tel: 310-243-2084. Fax: 310-516-4219. p. 132

Bordner, Christine, Ch, Western Allegheny Community Library, 8042 Steubenville Pike, Oakdale, PA, 15071-9375. Tel: 724-695-8150. Fax: 724-695-2860. p. 2100

Bordner, Eldyne, Asst Librn, Bethel-Tulpehocken Public Library, 8601 Lancaster Ave, Bethel, PA, 19507. Tel: 717-933-4060. Fax: 717-933-9655. p. 2033

Bordner, Georgianne, Head, Tech Serv, Librn, Regent University Library, 1000 Regent University Dr, Virginia Beach, VA, 23464. Tel: 757-352-4493. Fax: 757-352-4167. p. 2499

Bordner, Vicki, Head, ILL, Head, Media Serv, Head, Ref, Scott County Public Library, 108 S Main St, Scottsburg, IN, 47170. Tel: 812-752-2751. Fax: 812-752-2878. p. 777

Bordonaro, Frances, Tech Serv Librn, Falmouth Public Library, 300 Main St, Falmouth, MA, 02540. Tel: 508-457-2555. Fax: 508-457-2559. p. 1088

Bordonaro, Salvatore, Dir, Cheektowaga Public Library, 1030 Losson Rd, Cheektowaga, NY, 14227. Tel: 716-668-4991. Fax: 716-668-4806. p. 1606

Bordone, James D, Sr Librn, Ref, Passaic Public Library, 195 Gregory Ave, Passaic, NJ, 07055. Tel: 973-779-0474. Fax: 973-779-0889. p. 1518

Borehan, Theresa, Br Mgr, Caledon Public Library, Caledon Village, 18313 Hurontario St, Caledon Village, ON, L7K 0X7, CANADA. Tel: 519-927-5800. p. 2795

Borejdo, Judy, Librn, Mankoff Resource Center, 7900 Northaven Rd, Dallas, TX, 75230. Tel: 214-739-2737. Fax: 214-750-6473. p. 2309

Borelli, Karen, Ch, Rock Falls Public Library District, 1007 Seventh Ave, Rock Falls, IL, 61071. Tel: 815-626-3958. Fax: 815-626-8750. p. 696

Borello, Maryellen, Commun Libr Mgr, Queens Borough Public Library, Ozone Park Community Library, 92-24 Rockaway Blvd, Ozone Park, NY, 11417. Tel: 718-845-3127. Fax: 718-848-1082. p. 1645

Borer, Ann, Librn, Douglas County District Court, Hall of Justice, 1701 Farnam St, 1st Flr, Omaha, NE, 68183. Tel: 402-444-7174. Fax: 402-444-3927. p. 1412

Borer, Annette C, Librn, Felhaber, Larson, Fenlon & Vogt, 220 S Sixth St, Ste 2200, Minneapolis, MN, 55402-4302. Tel: 612-373-8441. Fax: 612-338-0535. p. 1259

Borg, Betty, Pres, Eagle Public Library, Second & Amundsen, Eagle, AK, 99738. Tel: 907-547-2334. p. 47

Borger, Kirk A, Ch, Dir, Riverview Public Library, 14300 Sibley Rd, Riverview, MI, 48193. Tel: 734-283-1250. Fax: 734-283-6843. p. 1221

Borger, Shauna, Coordr, Evergreen Indiana Consortium, Indiana State Library, 315 W Ohio St, Indianapolis, IN, 46202. Tel: 317-605-4518. Fax: 317-232-0002. p. 2943

Borgert, Diane, Br Mgr, Great River Regional Library, Swanville Library, 213 DeGraff St, Swanville, MN, 56382. Tel: 320-547-2346. p. 1276

Borges, Timothy L, Dir, Portuguese Union of the State of California, 1120 E 14th St, San Leandro, CA, 94577. Tel: 510-351-4972. Fax: 510-483-5015. p. 252

Borgfelt, Susan, Circ, Normandale Community College Library, 9700 France Ave S, Bloomington, MN, 55431. Tel: 952-487-8437. Fax: 952-487-8101. p. 1242

Borgman, Stephanie, Ch Serv Spec, Harris County Public Library, 8080 El Rio, Houston, TX, 77054. Tel: 713-749-9036. Fax: 713-749-9090. p. 2335

Borgstede, Arlene, Libr Dir, Alberta Genealogical Society Library & Research Centre, No 162-14315-118 Ave, Edmonton, AB, T5L 4S6, CANADA. Tel: 780-424-4429. Fax: 780-423-8980. p. 2698

Borin, Jacqueline M, Coordr, Pub Serv, California State University, 333 S Twin Oaks Valley Rd, San Marcos, CA, 92096-0001. Tel: 760-750-4336. Fax: 760-750-3287. p. 254

Borio, Gail, Librn, National College of Business & Technology, 8415 Kingston Pike, Knoxville, TN, 37919. Tel: 865-539-2011. Fax: 865-539-2049. p. 2243

Boris, Charry D, Librn, Financial Accounting Foundation Library, 401 Merritt 7, Norwalk, CT, 06856-5116. Tel: 203-956-5238. Fax: 203-956-3492. p. 362

Borisovets, Natalie, Head, Ref & Pub Serv, Rutgers University Libraries, John Cotton Dana Library, 185 University Ave, Newark, NJ, 07102. Tel: 973-353-5222. Fax: 973-353-1133. p. 1512

Bork, Harry J, Dir, Fox Lake Public District Library, 255 E Grand Ave, Fox Lake, IL, 60020-1697. Tel: 847-587-0198. Fax: 847-587-9493. p. 646

Borkenhagen, Jennifer, Circ, ILL, Ref, Concordia University, 1282 Concordia Ave, Saint Paul, MN, 55104. Tel: 651-641-8770. Fax: 651-641-8782. p. 1278

Borkholder, Audrey, Dir, Burr Oak Township Library, 220 S Second St, Burr Oak, MI, 49030-5133. Tel: 269-489-2906. Fax: 269-489-2906. p. 1160

Borland, Jane, Med Librn, Mary Washington Hospital, 1001 Sam Perry Blvd, Fredericksburg, VA, 22401-9523. Tel: 540-741-1597. Fax: 540-741-1514. p. 2466

Bormet, Noreen, Ad, Manhattan-Elwood Public Library District, 240 Whitson St, Manhattan, IL, 60442. Tel: 815-478-3987. Fax: 815-478-3988. p. 669

Born, Judy, Coll Develop, Head, Pub Serv, Manatee Community College Library, 5840 26th St W, Bradenton, FL, 34207. Tel: 941-752-5262. Fax: 941-752-5308. p. 429

Borne, Bobbie, Head, Teen Serv, Wallingford Public Library, 200 N Main St, Wallingford, CT, 06492-3791. Tel: 203-265-6754. Fax: 203-269-5698. p. 373

Borneman, Dea, Media Spec, Missouri State University, Haseltine Library, Greenwood Laboratory School, 901 S National, Rm 3, Springfield, MO, 65897. Tel: 417-836-8563. p. 1367

Borneman, Dea, Asst Prof, Missouri State University, Duane G Meyer Library, 901 S National Ave, Springfield, MO, 65897. Tel: 417-836-4525. Fax: 417-836-4764. p. 2968

Bornhauser, Kathryn, Literacy Serv, Blanchard-Santa Paula Public Library District, 119 N Eighth St, Santa Paula, CA, 93060-2709. Tel: 805-525-2384. Fax: 805-933-2324. p. 266

Bornhoft, Kathy, Asst Dir, Wellington Public Library, 3800 Wilson Ave, Wellington, CO, 80549. Tel: 970-568-3040. Fax: 970-568-9713. p. 325

Bornstein, Paula, Circ, Lindenhurst Memorial Library, One Lee Ave, Lindenhurst, NY, 11757-5399. Tel: 631-957-7755. Fax: 631-957-7114. p. 1652

Borntrager, Conrad, Archivist, Order of Servants of Mary (Servites), USA Province, 3121 W Jackson Blvd, Chicago, IL, 60612-2729. Tel: 773-533-0360. Fax: 773-533-8307. p. 622

Borntrager, Conrad, Archivist, Our Lady of Sorrows Basilica, 3121 W Jackson Blvd, Chicago, IL, 60612-2729. Tel: 773-638-5800, Ext 31. p. 622

Borock, Freddie, Mrs, Med Librn, North Shore LIJ Health System, 301 E Main St, Bay Shore, NY, 11706-8458. Tel: 631-968-3026. Fax: 631-968-3978. p. 1578

Borovic, Gail, Human Res Mgr, Mentor Public Library, 8215 Mentor Ave, Mentor, OH, 44060. Tel: 440-255-8811. Fax: 440-255-0520. p. 1917

Borow, Rena, Pub Serv Librn, Jewish Theological Seminary Library, 3080 Broadway, New York, NY, 10027. Tel: 212-678-8970. Fax: 212-678-8891, 212-678-8998. p. 1683

Borowske, Kate, Ref, Hamline University, Bush Memorial Library, 1536 Hewitt, Saint Paul, MN, 55104. Tel: 651-523-2375. Fax: 651-523-2199. p. 1278

Borowski, Lorraine, Dir, Decorah Public Library, 202 Winnebago St, Decorah, IA, 52101. Tel: 563-382-3717. Fax: 563-382-4524. p. 807

Borque, Alan, Head, Circ, Head, Coll Mgt, Harvard Library, History of Science Library - Cabot Science Library, Science Center, One Oxford St, Cambridge, MA, 02138. Tel: 617-495-5355. Fax: 617-495-5324. p. 1075

Borrego, Paulina, Ref Serv Librn, University of Massachusetts Amherst, Science & Engineering Library, A273 Lederle Graduate Research Ctr Lowrise, Amherst, MA, 01003. Tel: 413-545-1370. Fax: 413-577-1534. p. 1049

Borrelli, Virginia, Br Mgr, Coordr, Ch Serv, Sevier County Public Library System, 321 Court Ave, Sevierville, TN, 37862. Tel: 865-453-3532. Fax: 865-908-6108. p. 2265

Borsch, Lydia, Circ Mgr, Norman Williams Public Library, Ten S Park St, Woodstock, VT, 05091. Tel: 802-457-2295. Fax: 802-457-5181. p. 2440

Borsody, Rosemarie, Pub Serv, Lee Library Association, 100 Main St, Lee, MA, 01238-1688. Tel: 413-243-0385. Fax: 413-243-0381. p. 1098

Borst, Barbara, Instrul Serv Librn, Colorado Mesa University, 1200 College Pl, Grand Junction, CO, 81501. Tel: 970-248-1872. Fax: 970-248-1930. p. 310

Bortles, Elaine P, Supvr, Circ, Mount Hood Community College Library, 26000 SE Stark St, Gresham, OR, 97030. Tel: 503-352-1403. Fax: 503-491-7389. p. 1999

Bortz, Merry, Automation Syst Coordr, Del Mar College, 101 Baldwin Blvd, Corpus Christi, TX, 78404. Tel: 361-698-1310. Fax: 361-698-1182. p. 2302

Borum, Rachel, Libr Assoc, Mendocino County Library District, Round Valley, 23925 Howard St, Covelo, CA, 95428. Tel: 707-983-6738. p. 278

Bos, Donna, Circ, Acorn Public Library District, 15624 S Central Ave, Oak Forest, IL, 60452-3204. Tel: 708-687-3700. Fax: 708-687-3712. p. 683

Bos, Donna, Dir, Inwood Public Library, 103 S Main, Inwood, IA, 51240. Tel: 712-753-4814. p. 822

Bos, Jeannette, Ch, William E Dermody Free Public Library, 420 Hackensack St, Carlstadt, NJ, 07072. Tel: 201-438-8866. Fax: 201-438-2733. p. 1477

Bos, Joy, Circ, Allendale Township Library, 6175 Library Ln, Allendale, MI, 49401. Tel: 616-895-4178. Fax: 616-895-5178. p. 1149

Bosanko, Ruby, Librn, Marcus P Beebe Memorial Library, 120 Main St, Ipswich, SD, 57451. Tel: 605-426-6707. p. 2213

Bosben, Pam, Dir, Rosemary Garfoot Public Library, 2107 Julius St, Cross Plains, WI, 53528-9499. Tel: 608-798-3881. Fax: 608-798-0196. p. 2587

Bosca, David, Head Librn, South University, 9801 Belvedere Rd, Royal Palm Beach, FL, 33411-3640. Tel: 561-273-6402. Fax: 561-273-6420. p. 485

Bosch, Elaine, Circ Supvr, Grand Rapids Public Library, 111 Library St NE, Grand Rapids, MI, 49503-3268. Tel: 616-988-5402, Ext 5452. Fax: 616-988-5419. p. 1185

Bosch, Jean, Libr Mgr, Poudre River Public Library District, 201 Peterson St, Fort Collins, CO, 80524-2990. Tel: 970-221-6740. Fax: 970-221-6398. p. 307

Bosch, Sheila, Head Librn, New London Public Library, 15 Ash St, New London, MN, 56273-9567. Tel: 320-354-2943. p. 1268

Bosch, Sheila, Librn, Spicer Library, 198 Manitoba St, Spicer, MN, 56288-9629. Tel: 320-796-5560. Fax: 320-796-3013. p. 1285

Bosco, David, Head, Circ, Todd Wehr Library, St Norbert College, 301 Third St, De Pere, WI, 54115. Tel: 920-403-3293. Fax: 920-403-4064. p. 2587

Bose, Deborah, Dir, Grant Area District Library, 122 Elder St, Grant, MI, 49327. Tel: 231-834-5713, Ext 103. Fax: 231-834-9705. p. 1186

Bose, Marcia, Head, Ref & Adult Serv, Roselle Public Library District, 40 S Park St, Roselle, IL, 60172-2020. Tel: 630-529-1641, Ext 212. Fax: 630-529-7579. p. 699

Bose, Mathew, Asst Libr Dir, Ref Librn, Oak Bluffs Public Library, 56R School St, Oak Bluffs, MA, 02557. Tel: 508-693-9433. Fax: 508-693-5377. p. 1116

Bose, Willa, Dir, Waskom Public Library, 103 Waskom Ave, Waskom, TX, 75692-9281. Tel: 903-687-3041. p. 2398

Bosh, Jeffrey V, Dir, Sidley Austin LLP, 1501 K St NW, Washington, DC, 20005. Tel: 202-736-8525. Fax: 202-736-8711. p. 414

Bosken, Sally, Dir, United States Naval Observatory, 3450 Massachusetts Ave NW, Washington, DC, 20392-5420. Tel: 202-762-1463. Fax: 202-762-1516. p. 421

Bosler, Gerald, Dean, Libr & Learning Res, Macomb Community College Libraries, Center Campus, C-Bldg, 44575 Garfield Rd, Clinton Township, MI, 48038-1139. Tel: 586-286-2104, Ext 2. Fax: 586-286-2002. p. 1234

Bosler, Gerald, Dean, Libr & Learning Res, Macomb Community College Libraries, J-Bldg, 14500 E 12 Mile Rd, Warren, MI, 48088-3896. Tel: 586-445-7309. Fax: 586-445-7157. p. 1234

Bosler, Sarah, Head, Ref, Citrus College, 1000 W Foothill Blvd, Glendora, CA, 91741-1899. Tel: 626-914-8640. Fax: 626-963-2531. p. 156

Bosley, Janet, Tech Serv Librn, West Virginia Supreme Court of Appeals, Bldg 1, Rm E-404, 1900 Kanawha Blvd E, Charleston, WV, 25305-0833. Tel: 304-558-2607. Fax: 304-558-3673. p. 2557

Bosley, Katie, Youth Serv, Pierson Library, 5376 Shelburne Rd, Shelburne, VT, 05482. Tel: 802-985-5124. Fax: 802-985-5129. p. 2435

Bosma, Janice M, Assoc Dean, Cedarville University, 251 N Main St, Cedarville, OH, 45314-0601. Tel: 937-766-7842. Fax: 937-766-2337. p. 1865

Bosman, Ellen, Head, Tech Serv, New Mexico State University Library, 2911 McFie Circle, Las Cruces, NM, 88003. Tel: 575-646-1723. Fax: 575-646-6940. p. 1558

Bosnell, Sharon, ILL, Trent University, 1600 West Bank Dr, Peterborough, ON, K9J 7B8, CANADA. Tel: 705-748-1011, Ext 5196. Fax: 705-748-1126. p. 2836

Boss, Catherine Mary, Coordr, Jersey Shore University Medical Center, 1945 Rte 33, Neptune, NJ, 07754-0397. Tel: 732-776-4266. Fax: 732-776-4530. p. 1507

Boss, Georgiana, Br Mgr, Jackson County Public Library, Crothersville Branch, 120 E Main St, Crothersville, IN, 47229. Tel: 812-793-2927. Fax: 812-793-3721. p. 778

Boss, Georgiana, Br Mgr, Jackson County Public Library, Medora Branch, 27 Main St, Medora, IN, 47260. Tel: 812-966-2278. Fax: 812-966-2229. p. 778

Boss O'Hagan, Keydi, Managing Librn, Holy Name Medical Center, 718 Teaneck Rd, Teaneck, NJ, 07666. Tel: 201-833-3395. Fax: 201-833-3006. p. 1533

Bossaller, Jenny, Asst Prof, University of Missouri-Columbia, 303 Townsend Hall, Columbia, MO, 65211. Tel: 573-882-4546. Fax: 573-884-2917. p. 2969

Bosse, David C, Librn, Historic Deerfield Inc & Pocumtuck Valley Memorial Association Libraries, Six Memorial St, Deerfield, MA, 01342-9736. Tel: 413-775-7125. Fax: 413-775-7223. p. 1084

Bossenga, Susanna, Electronic Res & Ser Mgt Librn, Northeastern Illinois University, 5500 N Saint Louis Ave, Chicago, IL, 60625-4699. Tel: 773-442-4474. Fax: 773-442-4531. p. 620

Bossler, Joshua, Ref & Instruction Librn, Coastal Carolina University, 755 Hwy 544, Conway, SC, 29526. Tel: 843-349-2650. Fax: 843-349-2412. p. 2191

Bossman, Daria, Asst State Librn, Develop Serv, South Dakota State Library, 800 Governors Dr, Pierre, SD, 57501-2294. Tel: 605-773-3131. p. 2216

Bosso, Bruce, Dir, New York State Supreme Court, 45 Monroe Pl, Brooklyn, NY, 11201. Tel: 718-722-6356. Fax: 718-722-6302. p. 1594

Bosso, Lynn, Dir, Prog & Youth Serv, Kirkwood Public Library, 140 E Jefferson Ave, Kirkwood, MO, 63122. Tel: 314-821-5770, Ext 1011. Fax: 314-822-3755. p. 1342

Bost, Kay, Head, Spec Coll & Archives, Oklahoma State University Libraries, Oklahoma State University, Athletic Ave, Stillwater, OK, 74078-1071. Tel: 405-744-6311. Fax: 405-744-5183. p. 1978

Bost, Kay, Head, Spec Coll & Archives, Oklahoma State University Libraries, Special Collections & University Archives, Library 204, Stillwater, OK, 74078-1071. Tel: 405-744-6311. Fax: 405-744-7579. p. 1978

Bosteels, Mary Jo, Coordr, Cat, Tech Serv, Santa Clara City Library, 2635 Homestead Rd, Santa Clara, CA, 95051. Tel: 408-615-2941. Fax: 408-247-9657. p. 262

Bostelle, Timothy, Head, Librn Info Tech, University of Washington Libraries, Tacoma Library, 1900 Commerce St, Box 358460, Tacoma, WA, 98402-3100. Tel: 253-692-4650. Fax: 253-692-4445. p. 2535

Boster, Alda, Dir, Sam T Wilson Public Library, 11968 Walker St, Arlington, TN, 38002. Tel: 901-867-1943. p. 2223

Bostian, Laini, Ch, Culpeper County Library, 271 Southgate Shopping Ctr, Culpeper, VA, 22701-3215. Tel: 540-825-8691. Fax: 540-825-7486. p. 2459

Bostic, Donna, Librn, Strasburger & Price LLP Library, 901 Main St, Ste 4300, Dallas, TX, 75202. Tel: 214-651-4300. Fax: 214-651-4330. p. 2310

Bostick, Sharon, Dean, Univ Libr, University of Missouri-Kansas City Libraries, 800 E 51st St, Kansas City, MO, 64110. Tel: 816-235-1531. Fax: 816-333-5584. p. 1341

Boston, Joseph, Ref Librn, Sullivan & Cromwell LLP, 125 Broad St, New York, NY, 10004. Tel: 212-558-3780. Fax: 212-558-3346. p. 1700

Boston, Susie, Librn, Albany Public Library District, 302 S Main St, Albany, IL, 61230. Tel: 309-887-4193. p. 587

Bostrom, Laura, Br Mgr, Woodford County Library, Midway Branch, 400 Northside Dr, Midway, KY, 40347. Tel: 859-846-4014. Fax: 859-846-4035. p. 936

Bostrom, Nancy, Youth Serv, Lewistown Public Library, 701 W Main St, Lewistown, MT, 59457. Tel: 406-538-5212. Fax: 406-538-3920. p. 1384

Bostwick, Dawn S, Dir, Pub Libr Serv, Nassau County Public Library System, 25 N Fourth St, Fernandina Beach, FL, 32034-4123. Tel: 904-548-4862. Fax: 904-277-7366. p. 439

Bostwick, Jona, Libr Dir, Veterans Affairs Medical Center Library, 718 Smyth Rd, No 142D, Manchester, NH, 03104-7004. Tel: 603-624-4366, Ext 6030. Fax: 603-626-6503. p. 1456

Bosveld, Jennifer, Dir, Pudding House Innovative Writers Programs, Pudding House, 81 Shadymere Lane, Columbus, OH, 43213. Tel: 614-986-1881. p. 1890

Boswell, Catherine, ILL & Distance Libr Serv Spec, Syst Serv, Antioch University New England Library, 40 Avon St, Keene, NH, 03431-3516. Tel: 603-283-2400. Fax: 603-357-7345. p. 1452

Boswell, Susan, Dir of Communications, Alexander Graham Bell Association for the Deaf & Hard of Hearing, 3417 Volta Pl NW, Washington, DC, 20007. Tel: 202-337-5220. Fax: 202-337-8314. p. 394

Boswell, Tracey, Cat, Ref, Nelson-Atkins Museum of Art, 4525 Oak St, Kansas City, MO, 64111-1873. Tel: 816-751-1231. Fax: 816-751-0498. p. 1340

Bosworth, LaKeisha, Children's Coordr, Ouachita Parish Public Library, 1800 Stubbs Ave, Monroe, LA, 71201. Tel: 318-327-1490. Fax: 318-327-1373. p. 957

Boteilho, Amy, Actg Commun Libr Mgr, County of Los Angeles Public Library, Hacienda Heights Library, 16010 La Monde St, Hacienda Heights, CA, 91745-4299. Tel: 626-968-9356. Fax: 626-336-3126. p. 141

Botero, Cecilia, Assoc Dean, Dir, Health Sci Ctr Libr, University of Florida Libraries, 535 Library W, Gainesville, FL, 32611-7000. Tel: 352-273-8400. Fax: 352-392-2565. p. 449

Bothmer, James, Dir, Creighton University, Health Sciences Library-Learning Resource Center, 2770 Webster St, Omaha, NE, 68178-0210. Tel: 402-280-5120. Fax: 402-280-5134. p. 1412

Botke, Deborah, Treas, Greater Philadelphia Law Library Association, Wolf, Block, Schorr & Solis-Cohen LLP Library, 25th fl, 1650 Arch St, Philadelphia, PA, 19103. Tel: 215-979-1715. p. 2954

Botkin, Gwen, Librn, Missouri Department of Corrections, Potosi Correctional Center, 11593 State Hwy O, Mineral Point, MO, 63660. Tel: 573-438-6000, Ext 560. Fax: 573-438-6006. p. 1335

Botkin, Karin, Res Info Spec, Buck Consultants LLC, 500 Plaza Dr, Secaucus, NJ, 07096. Tel: 201-902-2575. Fax: 201-902-2726. p. 1529

Botsford, Jane, Coordr, Ref Serv-Adult, Santa Clara City Library, 2635 Homestead Rd, Santa Clara, CA, 95051. Tel: 408-615-2907. Fax: 408-247-9657. p. 262

Bott, David, Mgr, Info Tech, Network Serv, St Catharines Public Library, 54 Church St, St. Catharines, ON, L2R 7K2, CANADA. Tel: 905-688-6103, Ext 212. Fax: 905-688-6292. p. 2843

Botta, Gail, Coll Develop, Albany Medical College, 47 New Scotland Ave, MC 63, Albany, NY, 12208. Tel: 518-262-5971. Fax: 518-262-5820. p. 1568

Bottar, David, Dir, Central New York Regional Planning & Development Board, 126 N Salina St, Ste 200, Syracuse, NY, 13202. Tel: 315-422-8276, Ext 207. Fax: 315-422-9051. p. 1751

Botticelli, Jill, Dir, Arlington Baptist College, 3001 W Division, Arlington, TX, 76012-3425. Tel: 817-461-8741, Ext 127. Fax: 817-274-1138. p. 2276

Botticelli, Peter, Asst Prof, University of Arizona, 1515 E First St, Tucson, AZ, 85719. Tel: 520-621-3565. Fax: 520-621-3279. p. 2962

Bottino, Bob, Libr Mgr, Department of Veterans Affairs, 200 Springs Rd, Bedford, MA, 01730. Tel: 781-687-2504, Ext 2077. Fax: 781-687-2507. p. 1052

Bottoms, Laura, Acq, Assoc Dir, Rogers State University Library, 1701 W Will Rogers Blvd, Claremore, OK, 74017-3252. Tel: 918-343-7719. Fax: 918-343-7897. p. 1960

Bottorrf, Timothy, Head, Hospitality (UOF) Librn, University of Central Florida Libraries, 4000 Central Florida Blvd, Bldg 2, Orlando, FL, 32816-2666. Tel: 407-903-8004. Fax: 407-903-8101. p. 477

Botts, Laura, Head, Spec Coll, Mercer University, Jack Tarver Library, 1300 Edgewood Ave, Macon, GA, 31207. Tel: 478 301 2968. Fax: 478-301-2111. p. 540

Botzenhardt, Rita, Youth Serv Librn, Henderson District Public Libraries, James I Gibson Library, 100 W Lake Mead Pkwy, Henderson, NV, 89015. Tel: 702-565-8402. Fax: 702-565-8832. p. 1428

Bouchard, Audrey, Librn, Centre d'Archives du Saguenay-Lac-Saint-Jean, 930 rue Jacques Cartier E Bureau C-103, Chicoutimi, QC, G7H 7K9, CANADA. Tel: 418-698-3516. Fax: 418-698-3758. p. 2881

Bouchard, Carol Ann, Circ Supvr, Concord Public Library, 45 Green St, Concord, NH, 03301-4294. Tel: 603-225-8670. Fax: 603-230-3693. p. 1442

Bouchard, Jane A, Dir, Schroon Lake Public Library, 15 Leland Ave, Schroon Lake, NY, 12870. Tel: 518-532-7737. Fax: 518-532-9474. p. 1741

Bouchard, Joseph, Librn, Michigan Department of Corrections, 13924 Wadaga Rd, Baraga, MI, 49908. Tel: 906-353-7070, Ext 1321. Fax: 906-353-7957. p. 1155

Bouchard, Katherine O, Librn, North Memorial Health Care, 3300 Oakdale N, Robbinsdale, MN, 55422. Tel: 763-520-5673. Fax: 763-520-1453. p. 1272

Bouchard, Kerry, Dir, Libr Syst, Texas Christian University, 2913 Lowden St, TCU Box 298400, Fort Worth, TX, 76129. Tel: 817-257-7106. Fax: 817-257-7282. p. 2323

Bouchard, Martin, Dir, Bibliotheque Municipale d'Alma, 500 Collard, Alma, QC, G8B 1N2, CANADA. Tel: 418-669-5139. Fax: 418-669-5089. p. 2879

Bouchard, Maryse, Chef de Div, Bibliothèques de Montrèal, Robert-Bourassa, 41, avenue Saint-Just, Montreal, QC, H2V 4T7, CANADA. Tel: 514-495-6270. Fax: 514-495-6287. p. 2891

Bouchard, Nicole, Pub Serv, Bibliotheque Municipale de Sainte-Therese, 150 Boul du Seminaire, Sainte Therese, QC, J7E 1Z2, CANADA. Tel: 450-434-1442. Fax: 450-434-6070. p. 2909

Bouchard, Rita P, Law Librn, Preti Flaherty Beliveau & Pachios, One City Ctr, Portland, ME, 04112. Tel: 207-791-3000. Fax: 207-791-3111. p. 997

Bouche, Nichole, Dir, University of Virginia, Albert & Shirley Small Special Collections Library, PO Box 400113, Charlottesville, VA, 22904-4110. Tel: 434-243-1776. Fax: 434-924-4968. p. 2455

Boucher, Anne-Marie, Librn, McGarry Public Library, One 27th St, Virginiatown, ON, P0K 1X0, CANADA. Tel: 705-634-2312. Fax: 705-634-2312. p. 2869

Boucher, Denise, Acq, Cegep St Jean Sur Richelieu Bibliotheque, 30 boul du Seminaire, CP 1018, Saint-Jean-Sur-Richelieu, QC, J3B 7B1, CANADA. Tel: 450-347-5301, Ext 2333. Fax: 450-347-3329, 450-358-9350. p. 2911

Boucher, Geo, Mgr, The Shore Line Trolley Museum Library, 17 River St, East Haven, CT, 06512. Tel: 203-467-6927. Fax: 203-467-7635. p. 337

Boucher, Janet, Ch, Blue Ridge Regional Library, 310 E Church St, Martinsville, VA, 24112-2999. Tel: 276-403-5444. Fax: 276-632-1660. p. 2477

Boucher, K, ILL, Alice Baker Memorial Public Library, 820 E Main, Eagle, WI, 53119. Tel: 262-594-2800. Fax: 262-594-5126. p. 2589

Boucher, Marc, Dir, Nicolet Area Technical College, 5364 College Dr, Rhinelander, WI, 54501. Tel: 715-365-4489. Fax: 715-365-4404. p. 2633

Boucher, Marc, Dir, University of Wisconsin, 400 University Dr, West Bend, WI, 53095-3619. Tel: 262-335-5214. Fax: 262-335-5220. p. 2648

Boucher, Nancy, Acq, Mount Wachusett Community College Library, 444 Green St, Gardner, MA, 01440. Tel: 978-630-9125. Fax: 978-630-9556. p. 1090

Boucher, Nell, Dir, Gardiner Library, 133 Farmer's Tpk, Gardiner, NY, 12525-5517. Tel: 845-255-1255. Fax: 845-255-1265. p. 1626

Boucher, Raymond, Dir, Dawson College Library, 3040 Sherbrooke St W, Westmount, QC, H3Z 1A4, CANADA. Tel: 514-931-8731, Ext 1204. Fax: 514-931-3567. p. 2915

Boucher-Tabor, Stacey, Tech Serv, Oakland County Library for the Visually & Physically Impaired, 1200 N Telegraph Rd, Pontiac, MI, 48341-0482. Tel: 248-858-5050. Fax: 248-858-9313. p. 1218

Boucouvalas, Mary Lou, Dir, Louis T Graves Memorial Public Library, 18 Maine St, Kennebunkport, ME, 04046-6173. Tel: 207-967-2778. p. 989

Bouda, Georgia, Dir, Bloomington Public Library, 205 E Olive St, Bloomington, IL, 61701. Tel: 309-828-6091. Fax: 309-828-7312. p. 595

Boudakian, Jessica, Circ Asst, Carlow University, 3333 Fifth Ave, Pittsburgh, PA, 15213. Tel: 412-578-2048. Fax: 412-578-6242. p. 2122

Boudet, Janet R, Assoc Dir, Roddenbery Memorial Library, 320 N Broad St, Cairo, GA, 39828-2109. Tel: 229-377-3632. Fax: 229-377-7204. p. 522

Boudinot, David, Adult Prog/Ref, Henry Carter Hull Library, Inc, Ten Killingworth Tpk, Clinton, CT, 06413. Tel: 860-669-2342. Fax: 860-669-8318. p. 334

Boudreau, Erica, Librn, National Archives & Records Administration, Columbia Point, Boston, MA, 02125. Tel: 617-514-1600. Fax: 617-514-1593. p. 1064

Boudreau, Janice, Dir, Universite Sainte-Anne, 1695, Rte 1, Church Point, NS, B0W 1M0, CANADA. Tel: 902-769-2114, Ext 161. Fax: 902-769-0137. p. 2778

Boudreau, Julie, In Charge, Universite de Moncton, Centre de Ressources Pédagogiques, 68, rue Notre-Dame-du-Sacré-Coeur, Pavillon Jeanne-de-Valois, local B-010, Moncton, NB, E1A 3E9, CANADA. Tel: 506-858-4356. Fax: 506-858-4317. p. 2766

Boudreau, Julienne, Ref, Cinematheque Quebecoise, 335 boul de Maisonneuve est, Montreal, QC, H2X 1K1, CANADA. Tel: 514-842-9768, Ext 262. Fax: 514-842-1816. p. 2893

Boudreau, Marianne, Tech Serv, National Theatre School of Canada Library, 5030 Rue Saint Denis, Montreal, QC, H2J 2L8, CANADA. Tel: 514-842-7954, Ext 125. Fax: 514-842-5661. p. 2900

Boudreau, Mary, Librn, Morrison, Mahoney LLP, 250 Summer St, Boston, MA, 02210. Tel: 617-439-7507. Fax: 617-439-7590. p. 1064

Boudreau, Shelley, Asst Librn, Red Rock Public Library Board, 42 Salls St, Red Rock, ON, P0T 2P0, CANADA. Tel: 807-886-2558. Fax: 807-886-2558. p. 2838

Boudreau, Suzanne, Coll Develop, Schaumburg Township District Library, 130 S Roselle Rd, Schaumburg, IL, 60193. Tel: 847-923-3336. Fax: 847-923-3131. p. 701

Boudreau, Tanya, Librn, Cold Lake Public Library, Harbor View, 1301 Eighth Ave, Cold Lake, AB, T9M 1J7, CANADA. Tel: 780-639-3967. Fax: 780-639-3963. p. 2695

Boudreau-Henry, Kathy, Prof, Middle Tennessee State University, PO Box 91, Murfreesboro, TN, 37132. Tel: 615-898-2804. Fax: 615-898-2859. p. 2974

Boudreault, Danielle, Libr Tech, Cegep de Baie-Comeau, 537 boul Blanche, Baie Comeau, QC, G5C 2B2, CANADA. Tel: 418-589-5707, Ext 325. Fax: 418-589-9842. p. 2879

Boudreaux, Edie, IT Spec, Iberia Parish Library, 445 E Main St, New Iberia, LA, 70560-3710. Tel: 337-364-7024, 337-364-7074. Fax: 337-364-7042. p. 959

Boudreaux, Tina, Financial Admin Officer, Cameron Parish Library, 501 Marshall St, Cameron, LA, 70631. Tel: 337-775-5421. Fax: 337-775-5346. p. 946

Bougard, Renée, Assoc Dir, National Network of Libraries of Medicine South Central Region, c/o HAM-TMC Library, 1133 John Freeman Blvd, Houston, TX, 77030-2809. Tel: 713-799-7880. Fax: 713-790-7030. p. 2956

Bough, Ingrid, Territorial Dir of Libr, Archives & Mus, Virgin Islands Division of Libraries, Archives & Museums, 23 Dronningens Gade, Saint Thomas, VI, 00802. Tel: 340-774-3407. Fax: 340-775-1887. p. 2679

Bough, Ingrid, Territorial Dir of Libr, Archives & Mus, Vilinet, c/o Division of Libraries, Archives & Museums, 23 Dronningens Gade, Saint Thomas, VI, 00802. Tel: 340-773-5715. Fax: 340-773-3257. p. 2958

Bough, LaVonda, Asst Librn, Odon Winkelpleck Public Library, 202 W Main St, Odon, IN, 47562. Tel: 812-636-4949. Fax: 812-636-4949. p. 771

Boughey, Karin, Head, Adult Serv, Milford Public Library, 330 Family Dr, Milford, MI, 48381-2000. Tel: 248-684-0845. Fax: 248-684-2923. p. 1209

Boughida, Karim, Assoc Univ Librn, Digital Initiatives & Content Mgt, The George Washington University, 2130 H St NW, Ste 201, Washington, DC, 20052. Tel: 202-994-6455. Fax: 202-994-6464. p. 401

Boughner, Kay, In Charge, Dickinson County Library, Solomonson Branch, 620 Section St, Norway, MI, 49870. Tel: 906-563-8617. Fax: 906-563-7224. p. 1194

Boughner, Martin, Head, Syst, Head, Tech Serv, Port Moody Public Library, 100 Newport Dr, Port Moody, BC, V3H 3E1, CANADA. Tel: 604-469-4575, 604-469-4577. Fax: 604-469-4576. p. 2735

Boughton, Kimberly, Librn, Lands End, One Lands End Lane, Dodgeville, WI, 53595. Tel: 608-935-4175. Fax: 608-935-4260. p. 2588

Boughton, Lesley, State Librn, Wyoming State Library, 2800 Central Ave, Cheyenne, WY, 82002. Tel: 307-777-5911. Fax: 307-777-6289. p. 2653

Boughton, Lesley, State Librn, WYLD Network, c/o Wyoming State Library, 516 S Greeley Hwy, Cheyenne, WY, 82002-0060. Tel: 307-777-5911. Fax: 307-777-6289. p. 2958

Boughton, Toni, Access Serv, University of Wyoming Libraries, Library Annex, Dept 3262, 1000 E University Ave, Laramie, WY, 82071. Tel: 307-766-6535. p. 2658

Bouisset, Simon, Coll Develop Librn, Ref Librn, Universite du Quebec en Outaouais, 283, Blvd Alexandre-Tache, Case postale 1250, succ Hull, Gatineau, QC, J8X 3X7, CANADA. Tel: 819-595-3900, Ext 2373. Fax: 819-773-1669. p. 2884

Boulanger, Danny, Dir, Bibliotheque et Archives nationales du Quebec, 475 de Maisonneuve E, Montreal, QC, H2L 5C4, CANADA. Tel: 514-873-1101, Ext 3241. Fax: 514-873-9312. p. 2888

Boulay, Martine, In Charge, Bibliotheque Municipale, 220 rue du Pont, Saint Nicolas, QC, G7A 1T7, CANADA. Tel: 418-835-8588. Fax: 418-835-5297. p. 2909

Bouldin, Lucy W, Dir, Storey County Public Library, 95 S R St, Virginia City, NV, 89440. Tel: 775-847-0956. Fax: 775-847-0998. p. 1435

Boulet, Edith, Br Head, Winnipeg Public Library, St Boniface, 100-131 Provencher Blvd, Winnipeg, MB, R2H 0G2, CANADA. Tel: 204-986-4331. Fax: 204-986-6827. p. 2760

Boulet, Richard, Dir, Blue Hill Public Library, Five Parker Point Rd, Blue Hill, ME, 04614-0821. Tel: 207-374-5515, Ext 13. Fax: 207-374-5254. p. 978

Boulie, Lee, Info Serv Librn, Rhodes College, 2000 North Pkwy, Memphis, TN, 38112-1694. Tel: 901-843-3900. Fax: 901-843-3404. p. 2251

Boulos, Valerie E, Coll Officer, Florida International University, 11200 SW Eighth St, Miami, FL, 33199. Tel: 305-348-6447. Fax: 305 348-0122. p. 465

Boulrice, Melissa-Renee, Asst Admin, Canada Council for the Arts, 350 Albert St, Ottawa, ON, K1P 5V8, CANADA. Tel: 613-566-4414. Fax: 613-566-4390. p. 2828

Bouman, Judith, Head, Adult Serv, North Bay Public Library, 271 Worthington St E, North Bay, ON, P1B 1H1, CANADA. Tel: 705-474-4830. Fax: 705-495-4010. p. 2825

Boumil, Donna, Librn, Dodge Memorial Library, 144 Lake St, Rouses Point, NY, 12979. Tel: 518-297-6242. p. 1736

Bounds, Linda, Librn, Mid-Mississippi Regional Library System, Walnut Grove Public, 146 Main St, Walnut Grove, MS, 39189. Tel: 601-253-2483. Fax: 601-253-9374. p. 1306

Bourassa, Cindy, Cat, Southeast Regional Library, 49 Bison Ave, Weyburn, SK, S4H 0H9, CANADA. Tel: 306-848-3108. Fax: 306-842-2665. p. 2929

Bourassa, Claire, Chief, Documentation Serv, Translation Bureau Documentation Centre, 70 Crémazie St, 8th Flr, Gatineau, QC, K1A 0S5, CANADA. Tel: 819-997-0858. Fax: 819-994-3735. p. 2884

Bourassa, Denis, Asst Admin, Mediatheque Maskoutaine, 2720 rue Dessaulles, Saint-Hyacinthe, QC, J2S 2V7, CANADA. Tel: 450-773-1830. Fax: 450-773-3398. p. 2910

Bourassa, Julie, Chair, Taylor Memorial Library, Main St, Hancock, MA, 01237. Tel: 413-738-5326. p. 1093

Bouray, Shari, Dir, Pecatonica Public Library District, 400 W 11th St, Pecatonica, IL, 61063. Tel: 815-239-2616. Fax: 815-239-2250. p. 689

Bourbeau, Marie, Tech Serv, Cegep Riviere du-Loup-Bibliotheque, 80 rue Frontenac, Riviere-du-Loup, QC, G5R 1R1, CANADA. Tel: 418-862-6903, Ext 2325. Fax: 418-862-4959. p. 2907

Bourdages, Josette, Pub Serv, INRS - Institut Armand-Frappier - Bibliotheque, 531 blvd des Prairies, Laval, QC, H7V 1B7, CANADA. Tel: 450-687-5010, Ext 4267. Fax: 450-686-5501. p. 2886

Bourdon, Brenda, Dir, Learning Support Serv, Baker College of Muskegon Library, 1903 Marquette Ave, Muskegon, MI, 49442-3404. Tel: 231-777-5330. Fax: 231-777-5334. p. 1212

Bourdon, Jesse, Access Serv & Syst, Croton Free Library, 171 Cleveland Dr, Croton-on-Hudson, NY, 10520. Tel: 914-271-6612. Fax: 914-271-0931. p. 1612

Bouret, Lucie, Per, Cegep St Jean Sur Richelieu Bibliotheque, 30 boul du Seminaire, CP 1018, Saint-Jean-Sur-Richelieu, QC, J3B 7B1, CANADA. Tel: 450-347-5301, Ext 2333. Fax: 450-347-3329, 450-358-9350. p. 2911

Bourg, Chris, Dr, Asst Univ Librn, Pub Serv, Stanford University Libraries, 557 Escondido Mall, Stanford, CA, 94305-6004. Tel: 650-725-1064. p. 270

Bourg, Sarah, Head, YA, Lebanon Public Library, 104 E Washington St, Lebanon, IN, 46052. Tel: 765-482-3460. Fax: 317-873-5059. p. 761

Bourgault, Jean-Daniel, Libr Mgr, Institut National de la Recherche Scientifique, Universite du Quebec, 490 de la Couronne, local 1401, Quebec, QC, G1K 9A9, CANADA. Tel: 418-654-2577. Fax: 418-654-2660. p. 2905

Bourgeois, Robin, Br Supvr, Saint Charles Parish Library, Hahnville Branch, 14996 River Rd, Hahnville, LA, 70057-2100. Tel: 985-783-2341. p. 949

Bourgeois, Tina, Dir, Albert-Westmorland-Kent Regional Library, 644 Main St, Ste 201, Moncton, NB, E1C 1E2, CANADA. Tel: 506-869-6032. Fax: 506-869-6022. p. 2765

Bourget, Dominique, Tech Serv, Bibliotheque Municipale de Sainte-Therese, 150 Boul du Seminaire, Sainte Therese, QC, J7E 1Z2, CANADA. Tel: 450-434-1442. Fax: 450-434-6070. p. 2909

Bourgoin, Loree, Dir, Lyme Academy College of Fine Arts, 84 Lyme St, Old Lyme, CT, 06371-2333. Tel: 860-434-5232, Ext 132. Fax: 860-434-2095. p. 363

Bourke, Rosanne, Circ, Cayuga County Community College, 197 Franklin St, Auburn, NY, 13021. Tel: 315-294-8596. Fax: 315-255-2050. p. 1576

Bourke, Thomas, Pub Serv, Gulfport Public Library, 5501 28th Ave S, Gulfport, FL, 33707. Tel: 727-893-1074. Fax: 727-893-1072. p. 450

Bourlet, Debra, Operations Mgr, University of Richmond, William T Muse Law Library, 28 Westhampton Way, Richmond, VA, 23173. Tel: 804-289-8225. Fax: 804-289-8683. p. 2491

Bourne, Brandy, Web Serv Librn, University of North Carolina at Asheville, One University Heights, CPO 1500, Asheville, NC, 28804-8504. Tel: 828-251-6639. p. 1775

Bourne, Cynthia, Libr Tech, Colorado Department of Corrections, 30999 County Rd 15, Fort Lyon, CO, 81038. Tel: 719-456-2288, Ext 4252. Fax: 719-456-3211. p. 308

Bourne, Jill, Dep City Librn, San Francisco Public Library, 100 Larkin St, San Francisco, CA, 94102-4733. Tel: 415-557-4400. Fax: 415-557-4424. p. 246

Bourque, Allen, Circ, Tech Serv, Harvard Library, Godfrey Lowell Cabot Science Library, Science Center, One Oxford St, Cambridge, MA, 02138. Tel: 617-496-8805. Fax: 617-495-5324. p. 1074

Bourque, Kevin, Adult Serv Mgr, Wake County Public Library System, North Regional Library, 7009 Harps Mill Rd, Raleigh, NC, 27615. Tel: 919-870-4022. Fax: 919-870-4007. p. 1818

Bourque, Lisa, Archives Mgr, Hist Coll Dir, Ref, Lynn Public Library, Five N Common St, Lynn, MA, 01902. Tel: 781-595-0567. Fax: 781-592-5050. p. 1101

Bourque, Michelle, Pub Serv Librn, Haut-Saint-Jean Regional Library, 15, rue de l'Église St, Ste 102, Edmundston, NB, E3V 1J3, CANADA. Tel: 506-735-2074. Fax: 506-735-2193. p. 2762

Bourque, Sylvie, Actg Libr Mgr, Albert-Westmorland-Kent Regional Library, Richibouctou Public, 9376 Main St, Richibouctou, NB, E4W 4C9, CANADA. Tel: 506-523-7851. Fax: 506-523-7851. p. 2765

Boutain, Judy, Dir, Sprague Public Library, 119 W Second St, Sprague, WA, 99032. Tel: 509-257-2662. Fax: 509-257-2691. p. 2538

Boutang, Lisbeth, Ch, Cloquet Public Library, 320 14th St, Cloquet, MN, 55720-2100. Tel: 218-879-1531. Fax: 218-879-6531. p. 1246

Boutaugh, Alison, Dir, Thompson Public Library, 934 Riverside Dr, North Grosvenordale, CT, 06255. Tel: 860-923-9779. Fax: 860-923-3705. p. 361

Boutet, Nancy, Youth Serv, J V Fletcher Library, 50 Main St, Westford, MA, 01886-2599. Tel: 978-399-2307. Fax: 978-692-4418. p. 1138

Boutet, Nicole, Acq of New Ser, Tele-Universite, 455 rue du Parvis, Quebec, QC, G1K 9H6, CANADA. Tel: 418-657-2747. Fax: 418-657-2094. p. 2906

Bouthillier, France, Assoc Prof, Dir, McGill University, 3661 Peel St, Montreal, QC, H3A 1X1, CANADA. Tel: 514-398-3362. Fax: 514-398-7193. p. 2979

Boutilier, Brian G, Dir, Medford Public Library, 111 High St, Medford, MA, 02155. Tel: 781-395-7950. Fax: 781-391-2261. p. 1104

Boutilier, Carol, Dir, Sparta Public Library, 22 Woodport Rd, Sparta, NJ, 07871. Tel: 973-729-3101. Fax: 973-729-1755. p. 1531

Boutilier, Sandra, Librn, Pacific Newspaper Group Library, 200 Granville St, Vancouver, BC, V6C 3N3, CANADA. Tel: 604-605-2653. Fax: 604-605-2353. p. 2742

Boutin, Jay-Lynn, Librn, Carbon Municipal Library, 401 Bruce Ave, Carbon, AB, T0M 0L0, CANADA. Tel: 403-572-3440. p. 2694

Boutin, Louise, Dir, Bibliotheque et Archives nationales du Quebec, 475 de Maisonneuve E, Montreal, QC, H2L 5C4, CANADA. Tel: 514-873-1101, Ext 3129. Fax: 514-873-9312. p. 2888

Boutros, David, Assoc Dir, University of Missouri, 302 Newcomb Hall, 5100 Rockhill Rd, Kansas City, MO, 64110-2499. Tel: 816-235-1544. Fax: 816-235-5500. p. 1341

Boutwell, Kaci, Asst Dir, Flomaton Public Library, 436 Houston St, Flomaton, AL, 36441. Tel: 251-296-3552. Fax: 251-296-3355. p. 17

Bouvier, Cindi, Youth Serv, Escondido Public Library, 239 S Kalmia St, Escondido, CA, 92025. Tel: 760-839-4827. Fax: 760-741-4255. p. 146

Bouvy, Rita, Dep Dir, Bullard Sanford Memorial Library, 520 W Huron Ave, Vassar, MI, 48768. Tel: 989-823-2171. Fax: 989-823-8573. p. 1233

Bova, Katie, Dir, ProLiteracy, 104 Marcellus St, Syracuse, NY, 13204. Tel: 315-422-9121, Ext 2459. Fax: 315-422-6369. p. 1753

Bova, Linda, Librn, Sachem Public Library, 150 Holbrook Rd, Holbrook, NY, 11741. Tel: 631-588-5024. Fax: 631-588-5064. p. 1637

Bove, Timothy, Asst Mgr, Harvard Library, John F Kennedy School of Government Library, 79 John F Kennedy St, Cambridge, MA, 02138. Tel: 617-495-1300. Fax: 617-495-1972. p. 1075

Bovino, William, Cat, University of Pennsylvania Libraries, 3420 Walnut St, Philadelphia, PA, 19104-6206. Tel: 215-898-0315. Fax: 215-898-0559. p. 2118

Bowcutt, Kristen, Dir, Wasatch County Library, 465 E 1200 South, Heber City, UT, 84032-3943. Tel: 435-654-1511. Fax: 435-654-6456. p. 2406

Bowden, David, Libr Spec, Dartmouth College Library, Paddock Music Library, 6245 Hopkins Ctr, Hanover, NH, 03755. Tel: 603-646-3234. Fax: 603-646-1219. p. 1450

Bowden, Francine, Librn, Maine Department of Corrections, 17 Mallison Falls Rd, Windham, ME, 04062. Tel: 207-893-7000. Fax: 207-893-7001. p. 1007

Bowden, Jane, Libr Assoc, Faegre & Benson, LLP, 2200 Wells Fargo Ctr, 90 South Seventh St, Minneapolis, MN, 55402-3901. Tel: 612-766-7000. Fax: 612-766-1600. p. 1259

Bowden, Katherine, Circ, East Brunswick Public Library, Two Jean Walling Civic Center, East Brunswick, NJ, 08816-3599. Tel: 732-390-6950. Fax: 732-390-6796. p. 1481

Bowden, Kerri, Circ, ILL, Danville Area Community College Library, 2000 E Main St, Danville, IL, 61832-5199. Tel: 217-443-8734. Fax: 217-554-1623. p. 632

Bowden, Laurie, Ch, Burlington County Library, Evesham Branch, Evesham Municipal Complex, 984 Tuckerton Rd, Marlton, NJ, 08053. Tel: 856-983-1444. Fax: 856-983-4939. p. 1543

Bowden, Linda, Librn, Central Community College, 3134 W Hwy 34, Grand Island, NE, 68802. Tel: 308-398-7395, 308-398-7396. Fax: 308-398-7397. p. 1400

Bowden, Lorinda, Commun Libr Supvr, Yakima Valley Libraries, Union Gap Library, 3104 S First St, Union Gap, WA, 98903. Tel: 509-452-4252. Fax: 509-249-9299. p. 2551

Bowden, Michael L, Automation Syst Coordr, Harrisburg Area Community College, 735 Cumberland St, Lebanon, PA, 17042. Tel: 717-780-1936. p. 2079

Bowden, Ronald, Librn, Northeast Texas Community College, Farm-to-Market Rd 1735, Mount Pleasant, TX, 75456. Tel: 903-572-1911, Ext 452. Fax: 903-572-7017. p. 2364

Bowden, Russ, Mgr, Libr Media Serv, Santa Rosa Junior College, 1501 Mendocino Ave, Santa Rosa, CA, 95401. Tel: 707-527-4261 (Media Servs), 707-527-4391. Fax: 707-527-4545. p. 267

Bowdes, Gayle, Dir, Kiowa Public Library, 123 N Seventh St, Kiowa, KS, 67070. Tel: 620-825-4630. Fax: 620-825-4630. p. 876

Bowdle, Amy, Dir, Belle Center Free Public Library, 103 S Elizabeth St, Belle Center, OH, 43310. Tel: 937-464-3611. Fax: 937-464-3611. p. 1858

Bowdoin, Sally, Ser, Brooklyn College Library, 2900 Bedford Ave, Brooklyn, NY, 11210-2889. Tel: 718-951-5339. Fax: 718-951-4540. p. 1589

Bowe, Jane O, Librn, Christian & Barton, LLP Attorneys At Law, 909 E Main St, Richmond, VA, 23219. Tel: 804-697-6305. Fax: 804-697-6155. p. 2488

Bowe, Martin, Ref Serv, Garden City Public Library, 60 Seventh St, Garden City, NY, 11530-2891. Tel: 516-742-8405. Fax: 516-742-2675. p. 1626

Bowell, Daniel J, Univ Librn, Taylor University, 236 W Reade Ave, Upland, IN, 46989-1001. Tel: 765-998-5241. Fax: 765-998-5569. p. 783

Bowen, Amanda, Head, Coll, Harvard Library, Fine Arts Library, Fogg Art Museum, 32 Quincy St, Cambridge, MA, 02138. Tel: 617-495-3374. Fax: 617-496-4889. p. 1075

Bowen, Anne H, Dir, Ocmulgee Regional Library System, 535 Second Ave, Eastman, GA, 31023. Tel: 478-374-4711. Fax: 478-374-5646. p. 531

Bowen, Annie, Circ, Columbus County Public Library, 407 N Powell Blvd, Whiteville, NC, 28472. Tel: 910-642-3116. Fax: 910-642-3839. p. 1829

Bowen, Arneice, Cat Mgr, North Carolina Agricultural & Technical State University, 1601 E Market St, Greensboro, NC, 27411-0002. Tel: 336-334-7669, Ext 3228. Fax: 336-334-7783. p. 1797

Bowen, Carol, Dir, Bement Public Library District, 349 S Macon, Bement, IL, 61813. Tel: 217-678-7101. Fax: 217-678-7034. p. 594

Bowen, Christopher, Dir, Downers Grove Public Library, 1050 Curtiss St, Downers Grove, IL, 60515. Tel: 630-960-1200. Fax: 630-960-9374. p. 637

Bowen, Coy, Asst Admin, Circ, Head, ILL, Texas Health Harris Methodist Fort Worth Hospital, 1301 Pennsylvania Ave, Fort Worth, TX, 76104. Tel: 817-250-2118. Fax: 817-250-5119. p. 2324

Bowen, Jeffrey T, Head, Cat, University of North Florida, Bldg 12-Library, One UNF Dr, Jacksonville, FL, 32224-2645. Tel: 904-620-1502. Fax: 904-620-2719. p. 455

Bowen, Jennifer, Cat, University of Rochester, River Campus Libraries, 755 Library Rd, Rochester, NY, 14627-0055. Tel: 585-275-4461. Fax: 585-273-5309. p. 1733

Bowen, Jessica, Dir, Dennis P McHugh Piermont Public Library, 25 Flywheel Park W, Piermont, NY, 10968. Tel: 845-359-4595. p. 1717

Bowen, Kathy, Head, Youth Serv, Thorntown Public Library, 124 N Market St, Thorntown, IN, 46071-1144. Tel: 765-436-7348. Fax: 765-436-7011. p. 782

Bowen, Marvin, Br Mgr, Chicago Public Library, Chicago Bee, 3647 S State St, Chicago, IL, 60609. Tel: 312-747-6872. Fax: 312-747-7095. p. 608

Bowen, Pamela, Dir, Seneca Nation Library, 830 Broad St, Salamanca, NY, 14779. Tel: 716-945-3157. Fax: 716-945-9770. p. 1737

Bowen, Patricia, Librn, Kentucky Mountain Bible College, 855 Hwy 541, Jackson, KY, 41339-9433. Tel: 606-693-5000. Fax: 606-693-4884. p. 919

Bowen, Sara, Ch, Arcade Free Library, 365 W Main St, Arcade, NY, 14009. Tel: 585-492-1297. Fax: 585-492-3305. p. 1574

Bowen, Sharon, Doc, Paccar, Inc, 12479 Farm to Market Rd, Mount Vernon, WA, 98273. Tel: 360-757-5234. Fax: 360-757-5201. p. 2521

Bowen, Sheila, Librn, Wayne County Public Library, Fort Gay Public, 8608 Rear Broadway, Fort Gay, WV, 25514. Tel: 304-648-5338. Fax: 304-648-5338. p. 2563

Bowen, Tammara, Libr Asst, Spokane County Law Library, Gardner Center Bldg, 1033 W Gardner, Spokane, WA, 99201. Tel: 509-477-3680. p. 2536

Bowen, Tammy, Asst Librn, White Pine Library, 106 E Walnut, Stanton, MI, 48888-9294. Tel: 989-831-4327. Fax: 989-831-4976. p. 1229

Bower, Ann, Ch, Brooks Free Library, 739 Main St, Harwich, MA, 02645. Tel: 508-430-7562. Fax: 508-430-7564. p. 1094

Bower, Bridget, Archivist, Ithaca College Library, 953 Danby Rd, Ithaca, NY, 14850-7060. Tel: 607-274-3096. Fax: 607-274-1539. p. 1643

Bower, Cheryl, Dir, Delton District Library, 330 N Grove St, Delton, MI, 49046. Tel: 269-623-8040. Fax: 269-623-6740. p. 1169

Bower, Edith, In Charge, Western Counties Regional Library, McKay Memorial Library, 254 Water St, Shelburne, NS, B0T 1W0, CANADA. Tel: 902-875-3615. Fax: 902-875-1015. p. 2787

Bower, Judy, Librn, Parents Helping Parents Library, 1400 Parkmoor Ave, Ste 100, San Jose, CA, 95126. Tel: 408-727-5775, Ext 110. Fax: 408-286-1116. p. 250

Bower, Margarete, Head, Ref, University of Pittsburgh, Langley Library, 217 Langley Hall, Pittsburgh, PA, 15260. Tel: 412- 624-3714. Fax: 412-624-1809. p. 2129

Bower, Margarete, Librn, University of Pittsburgh, Chemistry, 200 Eberly Hall, Pittsburgh, PA, 15260. Tel: 412-624-3714. Fax: 412-624-8296. p. 2129

Bower, Margarete, Librn, University of Pittsburgh, Computer Science, 200 Eberly Hall, Pittsburgh, PA, 15260. Tel: 412-624-3714. p. 2129

Bower, Mary McNamee, Curator of Coll, Evansville Museum of Arts, History & Science Library, 411 SE Riverside Dr, Evansville, IN, 47713. Tel: 812-425-2406. Fax: 812-421-7509. p. 738

Bower Peterson, Kathi, Librn, Library Association of La Jolla, 1008 Wall St, La Jolla, CA, 92037. Tel: 858-454-5872. Fax: 858-454-5835. p. 161

Bower, Rick, Ref Serv, Pellissippi State Technical Community College, 10915 Harding Valley Rd, Knoxville, TN, 37933. Tel: 865-539-7106. Fax: 865-694-6625. p. 2243

Bower, Sandra, Br Librn, Claiborne Parish Library, Joe W Webb Memorial, 1919 Main St, Haynesville, LA, 71038. Tel: 318-624-0364. Fax: 318-624-2624. p. 951

Bower, Shirley, Mgr, Digital Assets, Rochester Institute of Technology, 90 Lomb Memorial Dr, Rochester, NY, 14623-5604. Tel: 585-475-2028. Fax: 585-475-7007. p. 1731

Bower, Theresa, Sister, Dir, Assumption College for Sisters Library, Mallinckrodt Convent, 350 Bernardsville Rd, Mendham, NJ, 07945. Tel: 973-543-6528, Ext 234. Fax: 973-543-1738. p. 1501

Bower, William, Librn, Pleasant Mount Public Library, 375 Great Bend Tpk, Pleasant Mount, PA, 18453-9801. Tel: 570-448-2573. Fax: 570-448-9713. p. 2130

Bowering, Doris, Librn, Placentia Resource Center, 14 Atlantic Ave, Placentia, NL, A0B 2Y0, CANADA. Tel: 709-227-3621. Fax: 709-227-3621. p. 2770

Bowers, Andy, Asst Mgr, Circ, Duke University Libraries, Divinity School Library, Gray Bldg, 102 Chapel Dr, Durham, NC, 27708. Tel: 919-660-3546. Fax: 919-681-7594. p. 1787

Bowers, Ashley, Asst State Librn, Admin, Tennessee State Library & Archives, 403 Seventh Ave N, Nashville, TN, 37243-0312. Tel: 615-532-2398. Fax: 615-532-2472, 615-741-6471. p. 2259

Bowers, Brandon, Librn, Bureau of Prisons, PO Box 1000, El Reno, OK, 73036. Tel: 405-262-4875. Fax: 405-262-6266. p. 1962

Bowers, Donnie, Web Developer, Holland College Library Services, 140 Weymouth St, Charlottetown, PE, C1A 4Z1, CANADA. Tel: 902-566-9558. Fax: 902-566-9522. p. 2875

Bowers, Jean M, Dir, United States Department of Labor, 200 Constitution Ave NW, Rm N-2445, Washington, DC, 20210-0002. Tel: 202-693-6610. Fax: 202-693-6644. p. 419

Bowers, Joyce, Br Mgr, Cleveland Public Library, East 131st Street, 3830 E 131st St, Cleveland, OH, 44120. Tel: 216-623-6941. Fax: 216-623-6978. p. 1878

Bowers, Joyce, Br Mgr, Cleveland Public Library, Mount Pleasant, 14000 Kinsman Rd, Cleveland, OH, 44120. Tel: 216-623-7032. Fax: 216-623-7035. p. 1878

Bowers, Karen, Br Librn, Community District Library, Byron Community-Burns Township George Vince Library, 312 W Maple St, Byron, MI, 48418. Tel: 810-266-4620, Ext 445. Fax: 810-266-5010. p. 1166

Bowers, Karen, Librn, Germanna Community College, 2130 Germanna Hwy, Locust Grove, VA, 22508-2102. Tel: 540-423-9163. Fax: 540-423-9159. p. 2475

Bowers, Matt, Ch, Wakarusa Public Library, 124 N Elkhart St, Wakarusa, IN, 46573. Tel: 574-862-2465. Fax: 574-862-4156. p. 785

Bowers, Nan, Chief Librn, Nevada Legislative Counsel Bureau, 401 S Carson St, Carson City, NV, 89701-4747. Tel: 775-684-6827. Fax: 775-684-6400. p. 1426

Bowers, Sandy, Adminr, Licking County Law Library Association, 65 E Main St, Newark, OH, 43055. Tel: 740-349-6561. Fax: 740-349-6561. p. 1922

Bowers, Sharon, Dir, Wilton Public Library, 106 E Fourth St, Wilton, IA, 52778. Tel: 563-732-2583. Fax: 563-732-2593. p. 853

Bowers, Stacey, Interim Asst Dir, Outreach & Instrul Coordr, University of Denver, Westminster Law Library, 2255 E Evans Ave, Denver, CO, 80208. Tel: 303-871-6188. Fax: 303-871-6999. p. 304

Bowers, Steven K, Exec Dir, Detroit Area Library Network, 5048 Gullen Mall, 6th Flr SEL, Detroit, MI, 48202. Tel: 313-577-6789. Fax: 313-577-1231. p. 2946

Bowers-Sharpe, Krista, Ref Librn, Western Illinois University Libraries, One University Circle, Macomb, IL, 61455. Tel: 309-298-2785, Ext 1. Fax: 309-298-2791. p. 669

Bowersox, Judy A, Asst Librn, West End Library, 1724 State Rte 235, Laurelton, PA, 17835. Tel: 570-922-4773. Fax: 570-922-1162. p. 2079

Bowie, Cathryn, Electronic Serv Librn, Law Librn, State of Oregon Law Library, Supreme Court Bldg, 1163 State St, Salem, OR, 97301-2563. Tel: 503-986-5921. Fax: 503-986-5623. p. 2018

Bowie, Lucille, In Charge, Southern University, Art & Architecture Library, School of Architecture, Engineering West Bldg, 2nd Flr, Baton Rouge, LA, 70813. Tel: 225-771-3290. Fax: 225-771-4113, 225-771-4709. p. 944

Bowie, Ruby, Librn, Tombigbee Regional Library System, Choctaw County Public Library, 511 Louisville St, Ackerman, MS, 39735. Tel: 662-285-6348. Fax: 662-285-3042. p. 1318

Bowie, Vicky, Br Mgr, Hawaii State Public Library System, Pearl City Public Library, 1138 Waimano Home Rd, Pearl City, HI, 96782. Tel: 808-453-6566. Fax: 808-453-6570. p. 563

Bowitz, Margaret, Tech Serv Dir, Metropolitan Milwaukee Fair Housing Council Library, 600 E Mason St, Ste 200, Milwaukee, WI, 53202. Tel: 414-278-1240. Fax: 414-278-8033. p. 2619

Bowker, Danielle, Dir, Middleborough Public Library, 102 N Main St, Middleborough, MA, 02346. Tel: 508-946-2470. Fax: 508-946-2473. p. 1105

Bowker, Jean, Dir, Riverside Public Library Association, Inc, Ten Zurbrugg Way, Riverside, NJ, 08075. Tel: 856-461-6922. p. 1527

Bowlby, Joan, Sr Librn, San Jose Public Library, Pearl Avenue, 4270 Pearl Ave, San Jose, CA, 95136-1899. Tel: 408-808-3053. Fax: 408-723-6930. p. 251

Bowlby, Joan, Sr Librn, San Jose Public Library, Vineland, 1450 Blossom Hill Rd, San Jose, CA, 95118. Tel: 408-808-3000. Fax: 408-978-1080. p. 251

Bowle, Suzanne, Dir, Grand Ledge Area District Library, Wacousta Branch, 13080 Wacousta Rd, Grand Ledge, MI, 48837. Tel: 517-626-6577. Fax: 517-626-6577. p. 1183

Bowler, Maryann, Head, Circ, Glenview Public Library, 1930 Glenview Rd, Glenview, IL, 60025-2899. Tel: 847-729-7500. Fax: 847-729-7558. p. 650

Bowler, Meagan, Coll Coordr, Mount Royal University Library, 4825 Mount Royal Gate SW, Calgary, AB, T3E 6K6, CANADA. Tel: 403-440-6126. Fax: 403-440-6758. p. 2692

Bowles, Beverly, Evening Librn, Maryland Correctional Institution for Women Library, Rte 175, Box 535, Jessup, MD, 20794. Tel: 410-379-3828. Fax: 410-799-8867. p. 1033

Bowles, Pamela, Managing Librn, Austin Public Library, Milwood, 12500 Amherst Dr, Austin, TX, 78727. Tel: 512-974-9880. Fax: 512-974-9884. p. 2279

Bowles, Suzanne E, Dir, Grand Ledge Area District Library, 131 E Jefferson St, Grand Ledge, MI, 48837-1534. Tel: 517-627-7014. Fax: 517-627-6276. p. 1183

Bowles, Vickery, Dir, Coll Mgt & City-Wide Serv, Toronto Public Library, 789 Yonge St, Toronto, ON, M4W 2G8, CANADA. Tel: 416-393-7131. Fax: 416-393-7229. p. 2860

Bowley, Cathleen, Coordr, Ch Serv, Burbank Public Library, 110 N Glenoaks Blvd, Burbank, CA, 91502-1203. Tel: 818-238-5610. Fax: 818-238-5553. p. 130

Bowlin, Cindy, Libr Assoc, Norris Public Library, 132 N Main, Rutherfordton, NC, 28139. Tel: 828-287-4981. Fax: 828-287-0660. p. 1821

Bowling, Adam, Head, Syst, Indiana State Library, 315 W Ohio St, Indianapolis, IN, 46202. Tel: 317-232-3290. Fax: 317-232-0002. p. 752

Bowling, Carol, Libr Mgr, Lane Public Libraries, 300 N Third St, Hamilton, OH, 45011-1629. Tel: 513-894-7156, Ext 110. Fax: 513-894-2718. p. 1903

Bowling, Karen, Asst Librn, Smithfield Public Library, 25 N Main St, Smithfield, UT, 84335-1957. Tel: 435-563-3555. p. 2416

Bowling, Rebekah, Br Supvr, Smyth-Bland Regional Library, Bland County, 697 Main St, Bland, VA, 24315. Tel: 276-688-3737. Fax: 276-688-9820. p. 2477

Bowling, Seth, Circ, Orange Beach Public Library, 26267 Canal Rd, Orange Beach, AL, 36561-3917. Tel: 251-981-2923. Fax: 251-981-2920. p. 33

Bowling, Stephen, Librn, Breathitt County Public Library, 1024 College Ave, Jackson, KY, 41339. Tel: 606-666-5541. Fax: 606-666-8166. p. 919

Bowling, Zachary, Br Mgr, Defiance Public Library, Johnson Memorial, 116 W High St, Hicksville, OH, 43526. Tel: 419-542-6200. Fax: 419-542-1015. p. 1895

Bowman, Andrea, Dir, Boswell & Grant Township Public Library, 101 E Main St, Boswell, IN, 47921. Tel: 765-869-5428. Fax: 765-869-5428. p. 729

Bowman, Betsy, Librn, Phillips-Lee-Monroe Regional Library, Lee County Library, 77 W Main St, Marianna, AR, 72360-2297. Tel: 870-295-2688. p. 103

Bowman, Cheryl, Head, Tech Serv, Thorold Public Library, 14 Ormond St N, Thorold, ON, L2V 1Y8, CANADA. Tel: 905-227-2581. Fax: 905-227-2311. p. 2848

Bowman, Colleen, Supvr, Bicknell Vigo Township Public Library, Sandborn Branch, 112 Anderson St, Sandborn, IN, 47578. Tel: 812-694-8403. p. 726

Bowman, Deborah A, Dir, Chebeague Island Library, 247 South Rd, Unit 3, Chebeague Island, ME, 04017-3200. Tel: 207-846-4351. Fax: 207-846-4358. p. 982

Bowman, Elizabeth, Coll Develop Librn, Outreach Librn, Santa Barbara City College, 721 Cliff Dr, Santa Barbara, CA, 93109-2394. Tel: 805-965-0581, Ext 2633. Fax: 805-965-0771. p. 260

Bowman, Jesse, Digital Serv Librn, Outreach Librn, Valparaiso University, School of Law Library, 656 S Greenwich St, Valparaiso, IN, 46383. Tel: 219-465-7911. Fax: 219-465-7917. p. 784

Bowman, Jimmie, Dir, Putnamville Correctional Facility, 1946 W US 40, Greencastle, IN, 46135-9275. Tel: 765-653-8441. Fax: 765-653-4157. p. 746

Bowman, Joanne, Mat Mgt Coordr, Henrico County Public Library, 1001 N Laburnum Ave, Henrico, VA, 23223-2705. Tel: 804-290-9000. Fax: 804-222-5566. p. 2471

Bowman, Kathleen, Ref, North Indian River County Library, 1001 Sebastian Blvd, CR 512, Sebastian, FL, 32958. Tel: 772-589-1355. Fax: 772-388-3697. p. 491

Bowman, Kay, Br Mgr, Montgomery County Public Libraries, Bethesda Library, 7400 Arlington Rd, Bethesda, MD, 20814. Tel: 240-773-0934. Fax: 301-657-0841. p. 1038

Bowman, Lee, Cataloger, Librn, Wilmington College, Pyle Ctr 1227, 1870 Quaker Way, Wilmington, OH, 45177-2473. Tel: 937-382-6661, Ext 394. Fax: 937-383-8571. p. 1949

Bowman, Leslie, Coordr, Instruction, University of the Sciences in Philadelphia, 4200 Woodland Ave, Philadelphia, PA, 19104-4491. Tel: 215-596-8964. Fax: 215-596-8760. p. 2120

Bowman, Lois B, Spec Coll Librn, Eastern Mennonite University, 1200 Park Rd, Harrisonburg, VA, 22802-2462. Tel: 540-432-4175. Fax: 540-432-4977. p. 2470

Bowman, Lynne, Asst Dir, Coll & Tech Serv, University of Kentucky Libraries, Medical Center Library, 800 Rose St, Lexington, KY, 40536-0298. Tel: 859-323-8919. Fax: 859-323-1040. p. 922

Bowman, Marilyn, Br Head, Charleston County Public Library, Edisto Branch, Thomas Hall, Hwy 174, Edisto Island, SC, 29438. Tel: 843-869-2355. Fax: 843-869-2355. p. 2183

Bowman, Mary, Dir, Little Wood River District Library, 16 Panther Ave, Carey, ID, 83320-5063. Tel: 208-823-4510. p. 572

Bowman, Mary Anne, Br Mgr, Saint Mary's County Memorial Library, Charlotte Hall Branch, 37600 New Market Rd, Charlotte Hall, MD, 20622. Tel: 301-884-2211. Fax: 301-884-2113. p. 1035

Bowman, Mary Ellen, Librn, Newport Beach Public Library, Mariners, 1300 Irvine Ave, Newport Beach, CA, 92660. Tel: 949-717-3800. Fax: 949-642-4848. p. 194

Bowman, Michael, Eng Librn, Ref & Info Serv Coordr, Portland State University Library, 1875 SW Park Ave, Portland, OR, 97201-3220. Tel: 503-725-3690. Fax: 503-725-4524. p. 2014

Bowman, Randall, Ref & Instruction Librn, Elon University, 308 N O'Kelly Ave, Elon, NC, 27244-0187. Tel: 336-278-6571. Fax: 336-278-6637. p. 1791

Bowman, Sonya, Head, ILL, Tennessee Technological University, 1100 N Peachtree Ave, Cookeville, TN, 38505. Tel: 931-372-3326. Fax: 931-372-6112. p. 2231

Bowman, Terri, Br Mgr, Clark County Public Library, Enon Branch, 209 E Main St, Enon, OH, 45323. Tel: 937-864-2502. p. 1935

Bowman, Vivian, Ref Serv, Rutgers University Libraries, Paul Robeson Library, Camden, 300 N Fourth St, Camden, NJ, 08102-1404. Tel: 856-225-6033. Fax: 856-225-6428. p. 1477

Bowra, Richard, Exec Dir, Dauphin County Library System, 101 Walnut St, Harrisburg, PA, 17101. Tel: 717-234-4961, Ext 102. Fax: 717-234-7479. p. 2064

Bowser, Anita, Dir, Ford City Public Library, 1136 Fourth Ave, Ford City, PA, 16226-1202. Tel: 724-763-3591. Fax: 724-763-2705. p. 2058

Bowser, Bonnie W, Circ Mgr, Eastern Mennonite University, 1200 Park Rd, Harrisonburg, VA, 22802-2462. Tel: 540-432-4175. Fax: 540-432-4977. p. 2470

Bowyer, Dennis, Res, Pratt & Whitney Rocketdyne, Inc, 6633 Canoga Ave, Canoga Park, CA, 91309. Tel: 818-586-2575. Fax: 818-586-9150. p. 131

Bowyer, Marsha, Ref Libr Tech, Winnipeg School Division, 1075 Wellington Ave, Winnipeg, MB, R3E 0J7, CANADA. Tel: 204-788-0203. Fax: 204-783-9628. p. 2760

Box, Krista, Sr Res Librn, Board of Governors of The Federal Reserve System, Research Library, 20th & C St NW, MS 102, Washington, DC, 20551. Tel: 202-452-3333. Fax: 202-530-6222. p. 394

Boxer, Molly, Exec Dir, Berkshire Botanical Garden Library, PO Box 826, Stockbridge, MA, 01262-0826. Tel: 413-298-3926. Fax: 413-298-4897. p. 1128

Boyajian, Joanne, Adult Serv, Ontario City Library, 215 East C St, Ontario, CA, 91764. Tel: 909-395-2233. Fax: 909-395-2043. p. 200

Boyce, Barbara, Dir, Tufts University, Edwin Ginn Library, Mugar Bldg, 1st Flr, 160 Packard St, Medford, MA, 02155-7082. Tel: 617-627-2175. Fax: 617-627-3736. p. 1104

Boyce, Carol, Dir, Vestal Public Library, 320 Vestal Pkwy E, Vestal, NY, 13850-1632. Tel: 607-754-4243. Fax: 607-754-7936. p. 1761

Boyce, Helen E, Head, Doc Serv, University of Houston, The O'Quinn Law Library, 12 Law Library, Houston, TX, 77204-6054. Tel: 713-743-2300. Fax: 713-743-2296. p. 2343

Boyce, Judy, Youth Serv Librn, West Baton Rouge Parish Library, 830 N Alexander Ave, Port Allen, LA, 70767-2327. Tel: 225-342-7920. Fax: 225-342-7918. p. 966

Boycik, Stacey, Br Mgr, Cuyahoga County Public Library, Parma-Snow Branch, 1700 Snow Rd, Parma, OH, 44134-2728. Tel: 216-661-4240. Fax: 216-661-1019. p. 1928

Boyd, Alan, Assoc Dir, Oberlin College Library, 148 W College St, Oberlin, OH, 44074. Tel: 440-775-8285. Fax: 440-775-6586. p. 1924

Boyd, Ali, Br Mgr, Cleveland Public Library, Rice, 11535 Shaker Blvd, Cleveland, OH, 44120. Tel: 216-623-7046. Fax: 216-623-7049. p. 1878

Boyd, Allison, Libr Asst, Nashville State Technical Community College, 120 White Bridge Rd, Nashville, TN, 37209-4515. Tel: 615-353-3472. Fax: 615-353-3558. p. 2258

Boyd, Betty, Admin Serv, Asst Admin, Cat, Liberty Municipal Library, 1710 Sam Houston Ave, Liberty, TX, 77575-4741. Tel: 936-336-8901. Fax: 936-336-2414. p. 2355

Boyd, Chandra, Educ Curator, Oklahoma City Museum of Art, 415 Couch Dr, Oklahoma City, OK, 73102. Tel: 405-236-3100. Fax: 405-236-3122. p. 1974

Boyd, Christopher, Acq, Mercer County Community College Library, 1200 Old Trenton Rd, West Windsor, NJ, 08550. Tel: 609-570-3559. Fax: 609-570-3845. p. 1542

Boyd, Cornelia, Ref Librn, New River Community College, 226 Martin Hall, Dublin, VA, 24084. Tel: 540-674-3600, Ext 4303. Fax: 540-676-3626. p. 2460

Boyd, Darian, Media Serv Tech, Provena Saint Joseph Medical Center, 333 N Madison St, Joliet, IL, 60435. Tel: 815-725-7133, Ext 3530. Fax: 815-773-7755. p. 660

Boyd, Dolly, Br Mgr, Calhoun County Public Library, Hugh Creek Park, 11442 SE CR 69, Blountstown, FL, 32424. Tel: 850-674-3334. Fax: 850-674-3334. p. 427

Boyd, Doreen, Asst Librn, Fort Worth Library, Seminary South, 501 E Bolt St, Fort Worth, TX, 76110. Tel: 817-926-0215. Fax: 817-926-1703. p. 2322

Boyd, Doug, Dir, Louis B Nunn Ctr for Oral Hist, University of Kentucky Libraries, Special Collections, King Bldg, Lexington, KY, 40506-0039. Tel: 859-257-9672. Fax: 859-257-6311. p. 922

Boyd, Erin, Cat Librn, Troy University, Montgomery Campus, 252 Montgomery St, Montgomery, AL, 36104-3425. Tel: 334-241-9576. Fax: 334-241-9590. p. 31

Boyd, Glenda, Supvr, Pub Serv, Western Texas College, 6200 S College Ave, Snyder, TX, 79549. Tel: 325-574-7678. Fax: 325-573-9321. p. 2388

Boyd, Jarrett, Dir, Carroll County Public Library, 136 Court St, Carrollton, KY, 41008. Tel: 502-732-7020. Fax: 502-732-7122. p. 909

Boyd, John, Ref & ILL Librn, Bellarmine University, 2001 Newburg Rd, Louisville, KY, 40205-0671. Tel: 502-272-8140. Fax: 502-272-8038. p. 923

Boyd, Kate, Head Librn, University of South Carolina, Digital Collections, 1322 Greene St, Columbia, SC, 29208. Tel: 803-777-2249. p. 2190

Boyd, Kathleen, Dir, Salve Regina University, 100 Ochre Point Ave, Newport, RI, 02840-4192. Tel: 401-341-2374. Fax: 401-341-2951. p. 2169

Boyd, Ken, Dir, Info Res, Theological Education Association of Mid America, Southern Baptist Theological Seminary, 2825 Lexington Rd, Louisville, KY, 40280. Tel: 502-897-4807. Fax: 502-897-4600. p. 2944

Boyd, Ken, Dr, Dean, Info Serv, Asbury Theological Seminary, 204 N Lexington Ave, Wilmore, KY, 40390-1199. Tel: 859-858-2233. Fax: 859-858-2330. p. 938

Boyd, Leann, Info Serv Librn, South Georgia College, 100 W College Park Dr, Douglas, GA, 31533-5098. Tel: 912-260-4323. Fax: 912-260-4452. p. 531

Boyd, Lynne, Managing Librn, Canadian Agriculture Library - Summerland, 4200 Hwy 97, Summerland, BC, V0H 1Z0, CANADA. Tel: 250-494-2100. Fax: 250-494-0755. p. 2738

Boyd, Marie, Bibliog Instr, Ref, Chaffey College Library, 5885 Haven Ave, Rancho Cucamonga, CA, 91737-3002. Tel: 909-652-6800. Fax: 909-466-2821. p. 212

Boyd, Marsha, Dir, West Branch Public Library, 119 N Fourth St, West Branch, MI, 48661. Tel: 989-345-2235. Fax: 989-345-8735. p. 1236

Boyd, Mary, Circ Supvr, Ligonier Valley Library Association, Inc, 120 W Main St, Ligonier, PA, 15658-1243. Tel: 724-238-6451. Fax: 724-238-6989. p. 2081

Boyd, Nancy, Dir, Commun Engagement, Tuscaloosa Public Library, 1801 Jack Warner Pkwy, Tuscaloosa, AL, 35401-1027. Tel: 205-345-5820. Fax: 205-752-8300. p. 38

Boyd, Patricia D, Dir, Waldwick Public Library, 19-21 E Prospect St, Waldwick, NJ, 07463-2099. Tel: 201-652-5104. Fax: 201-652-6233. p. 1539

Boyd, Randolph, Archives Librn, Spec Coll Librn, Chapman University, One University Dr, Orange, CA, 92866-1099. Tel: 714-532-7756. Fax: 714-532-7743. p. 200

Boyd, Raylyn, Librn, Phillips Community College of the University of Arkansas, 1210 Ricebelt Ave, DeWitt, AR, 72042. Tel: 870-946-3506, Ext 1621. Fax: 870-946-2644. p. 98

Boyd, Roberta, ILL, Lied Scottsbluff Public Library, 1809 Third Ave, Scottsbluff, NE, 69361-2493. Tel: 308-630-6250. Fax: 308-630-6293. p. 1418

Boyd, Sarah J, Br Supvr, Gaston County Public Library, Bessemer City Branch, 207 N 12th St, Bessemer City, NC, 28016. Tel: 704-629-3321. Fax: 704-629-3321. p. 1794

Boyd, Susan, Assoc Librn, Santa Clara University, 500 El Camino Real, Santa Clara, CA, 95053-0500. Tel: 408-554-6830. Fax: 408-554-6827. p. 263

Boyd, Sylvia, Tech Coordr, Bridgeport Public Library, 925 Broad St, Bridgeport, CT, 06604. Tel: 203-576-8284. Fax: 203-576-8255. p. 331

Boyd, Trenton, Head Librn, University of Missouri-Columbia, Zalk Veterinary Medical Library, W-218 Veterinary-Medicine Bldg, Columbia, MO, 65211. Tel: 573-882-2461. Fax: 573-882-2950. p. 1326

Boyd, Tristan, Coll Develop, Head, Tech Serv, Westbank Community Library District, 1309 Westbank Dr, Austin, TX, 78746. Tel: 512-314-3590. Fax: 512-327-3074. p. 2285

Boydston, Becky, Syst Coordr, Mount Laurel Library, 100 Walt Whitman Ave, Mount Laurel, NJ, 08054. Tel: 856-234-7319. Fax: 856-234-6916. p. 1506

Boydstun, Betty, Circ, Phillips Community College of the University of Arkansas, 1000 Campus Dr, Helena, AR, 72342. Tel: 870-338-6474. Fax: 870-338-2783. p. 103

Boye, Gary, Music Librn, Appalachian State University, 218 College St, Boone, NC, 28608. Tel: 828-262-2389. Fax: 828-262-3001. p. 1776

Boye, Gary R, Dr, Music Librn, Appalachian State University, Music Library, 813 Rivers St, Boone, NC, 28608-2097. Tel: 828-262-2389. Fax: 828-265-8642. p. 1777

Boyens, Kathryn R, Dir, Olivet Nazarene University, One University Ave, Bourbonnais, IL, 60914-2271. Tel: 815-939-5354. Fax: 815-939-5170. p. 596

Boyer, Allison, Youth Serv, Loutit District Library, 407 Columbus Ave, Grand Haven, MI, 49417. Tel: 616-842-5560, Ext 219. Fax: 616-847-0570. p. 1183

Boyer, Clif, Dir, Horry County Memorial Library, 1008 Fifth Ave, Conway, SC, 29526. Tel: 843-248-1544. Fax: 843-248-1548. p. 2191

Boyer, Daniel, Civil Law Librn, McGill University Libraries, Nahum Gelber Law Library, 3660 Peel St, Montreal, QC, H3A 1W9, CANADA. Tel: 514-398-4715. Fax: 514-398-3585. p. 2898

Boyer, Donnelle R, Ch, Big Horn County Public Library, 419 N Custer Ave, Hardin, MT, 59034. Fax: 406-665-1804. p. 1381

Boyer, Ellen, Libr Dir, Greenfield Public Library, 402 Main St, Greenfield, MA, 01301. Tel: 413-772-1544. Fax: 413-772-1589. p. 1092

Boyer, Harold, Pub Serv Mgr, Springfield Township Library, 70 Powell Rd, Springfield, PA, 19064-2446. Tel: 610-543-2113. Fax: 610-543-1356. p. 2142

Boyer, Jason, Info Tech Dir, Jackson County Public Library, 303 W Second St, Seymour, IN, 47274-2147. Tel: 812-522-3412, Ext 227. Fax: 812-522-5456. p. 777

Boyer, Jean, Info Serv Librn, Cumberland County Public Library & Information Center, Bordeaux, 3711 Village Dr, Fayetteville, NC, 28304-1530. Tel: 910-424-4008. Fax: 910-423-1456. p. 1792

Boyer, Jessica, In Charge, Elko-Lander-Eureka County Library System, Wells Branch, 208 Baker St, Wells, NV, 89835. Tel: 775-752-3856. p. 1427

Boyer, Larry, Dr, Dean, Acad Libr & Learning Res, East Carolina University, J Y Joyner Library, E Fifth St, Greenville, NC, 27858-4353. Tel: 252-328-6518. Fax: 252-328-6892. p. 1798

Boyer, Lois, Librn, Trinity United Presbyterian Church Library, 13922 Prospect Ave, Santa Ana, CA, 92705. Tel: 714-544-7850, Ext 121. Fax: 714-544-6837. p. 260

Boyer, Yvonne, Mgr, Cooley Godward Kronish LLP Library, 101 California St, 5th Flr, San Francisco, CA, 94111. Tel: 415-693-2000. Fax: 415-693-2222. p. 241

Boyer, Yvonne, Bibliographer, Vanderbilt University, Central Library, 419 21st Ave S, Nashville, TN, 37203-2427. Tel: 615-322-6284. Fax: 615-343-7451. p. 2260

Boyes, Martha, Ch, Clear Lake Public Library, 200 N Fourth St, Clear Lake, IA, 50428-1698. Tel: 641-357-6133, 641-357-6134. Fax: 641-357-4645. p. 802

Boyett, Jan, Librn, Fish & Wildlife Research Institute, 100 Eighth Ave SE, Saint Petersburg, FL, 33701-5095. Tel: 727-896-8626. Fax: 727-823-0166. p. 488

Boykin, Amy, Instruction Librn, Christopher Newport University, One Avenue of the Arts, Newport News, VA, 23606. Tel: 757-594-7244. Fax: 757-594-7717. p. 2479

Boykin, Dianne, Cat, Charleston Southern University, 9200 University Blvd, Charleston, SC, 29406. Tel: 843-863-7925. Fax: 843-863-7947. p. 2183

Boykins, Ruby, Librn, Lakeview Public Library, 1120 Woodfield Rd, Rockville Centre, NY, 11570. Tel: 516-536-3071. Fax: 516-536-6260. p. 1734

Boyko, Oleksandr, Asst Mgr, Coll Develop, Hamtramck Public Library, 2360 Caniff St, Hamtramck, MI, 48212. Tel: 313-365-7050. Fax: 313-365-0160. p. 1187

Boyle, Brian, Head, Ref Serv, Kramer, Levin, Naftalis & Frankel LLP, 1177 Avenue of the Americas, New York, NY, 10036. Tel: 212-715-9321. Fax: 212-715-8000. p. 1684

Boyle, Christina-Anne, Head, Coll Develop, Government of Canada, Federal Courts & Tax Court of Canada, Courts Administration Service-Library Services, 90 Sparks St, Ottawa, ON, K1A 0H9, CANADA. Tel: 613-947-3906. Fax: 613-943-5303. p. 2831

Boyle, Dylan, Librn, Grundy County-Jewett Norris Library, 1331 Main St, Trenton, MO, 64683. Tel: 660-359-3577. Fax: 660-359-6220. p. 1368

Boyle, Faith, Head, Youth Serv, West Orange Free Public Library, 46 Mount Pleasant Ave, West Orange, NJ, 07052-4903. Tel: 973-736-0198. Fax: 973-736-1655. p. 1541

Boyle, Jeanne, Assoc Univ Librn, Planning & Organizational Res, Rutgers University Libraries, 169 College Ave, New Brunswick, NJ, 08901-1163. Tel: 732-932-7505. Fax: 732-932-7637. p. 1508

Boyle, Jennifer, Ch, Rockaway Borough Free Public Library, 82 E Main St, Rockaway, NJ, 07866. Tel: 973-627-5709. Fax: 973-627-5796. p. 1527

Boyle, Judy, Mgr Fac, Hudson Library & Historical Society, 96 Library St, Hudson, OH, 44236-5122. Tel: 330-653-6658. Fax: 330-650-3373. p. 1905

Boyle, Katie, Dir, Cedar Vale Memorial Library, 608 Cedar St, Cedar Vale, KS, 67024. Tel: 620-758-2598. Fax: 620-758-2598. p. 859

Boyle, Kenneth J, Media Spec, Indiana State Prison, One Park Row St, Michigan City, IN, 46360-6597. Tel: 219-874-7256, Ext 6100. Fax: 219-874-0335. p. 764

Boyle, Lois, Pres, Richmond Museum of History, 400 Nevin Ave, Richmond, CA, 94801-3017. Tel: 510-235-7387. Fax: 510-235-4345. p. 216

Boyle, Marion, Chair, Wesley United Methodist Church Library, 721 King St, La Crosse, WI, 54601. Tel: 608-782-3018. Fax: 608-782-3018. p. 2604

Boyle, Robert, Head, Ref, Field Library of Peekskill, Four Nelson Ave, Peekskill, NY, 10566-2138. Tel: 914-737-1212. Fax: 914-862-9710. p. 1716

Boyle, Sean, Tech Serv Librn, Gainesville State College, 1201 Bishop Farms Pkwy, Watkinsville, GA, 30677. Tel: 706-310-6297. Fax: 706-310-6237. p. 556

Boyle, Thomas, Dir, Midland Lutheran College, 900 N Clarkson, Fremont, NE, 68025. Tel: 402-941-6250. Fax: 402-727-6223. p. 1399

Boyle, Wendy, Actg Librn, Stratton Public Library, 88 Main St, Stratton, ME, 04982. Tel: 207-246-4401. Fax: 207-246-3267. p. 1003

Boyles, Christina, Asst Dir, Mineral County Public Library, 110 First St, Hawthorne, NV, 89415. Tel: 775-945-2778. Fax: 775-945-0703. p. 1428

Boyles, Edith, Librn, Anglican Church of Canada, Church Army in Canada Taylor College, 105 Mountianview Dr, Saint John, NB, E2J 5B5, CANADA. Tel: 506-693-8975. Fax: 506-657-8217. p. 2767

Boylston, Susanna, Asst Dir, Libr Instructions & Coll Develop, Davidson College, 209 Ridge Rd, Davidson, NC, 28035-0001. Tel: 704-894-2331. Fax: 704-894-2625. p. 1786

Boyne, Alice, Exec Dir, English-Speaking Union, 144 E 39th St, New York, NY, 10016. Tel: 212-818-1200. Fax: 212-867-4177. p. 1677

Boynton, Brittany, Circ, Wake Technical Community College, Health Sciences, 2901 Holston Lane, Raleigh, NC, 27610-2092. Tel: 919-747-0002. p. 1818

Boynton, Chris, Coordr, Outreach Serv, Maine State Library, LMA Bldg, 230 State St, Augusta, ME, 04333. Tel: 207-287-5653. Fax: 207-287-5615. p. 974

Boynton, Chris Ranney, Librn, Maine Regional Library for the Blind & Physically Impaired, c/o Maine State Library, 64 State House Sta, Augusta, ME, 04333-0064. Tel: 207-287-5653. Fax: 207-287-5654. p. 974

Boynton, Laura, Youth Serv, Smyrna Public Library, 100 Village Green Circle, Smyrna, GA, 30080-3478. Tel: 770-431-2860. Fax: 770-431-2862. p. 551

Boynton, Mia, Librn, Monhegan Memorial Library, One Library Lane, Monhegan, ME, 04852. Tel: 207-596-0549. p. 992

Boyse, Carol, Head, Syst, New Mexico State University Library, 2911 McFie Circle, Las Cruces, NM, 88003. Tel: 575-646-6421. Fax: 575-646-6940. p. 1558

Boysen, Alysia, ILL, Siouxland Libraries, 200 N Dakota Ave, Sioux Falls, SD, 57104. Tel: 605-367-8700. Fax: 605-367-4312. p. 2218

Boyte-Hawryluk, Serena, Head, Children's/Youth Serv, Grande Prairie Public Library, 101-9839 103 Ave, Grande Prairie, AB, T8V 6M7, CANADA. Tel: 780-357-7454. Fax: 780-538-4983. p. 2705

Bozarth, Sandra, Sr Asst Librn, California State University, 9001 Stockdale Hwy, Bakersfield, CA, 93311-1022. Tel: 661-654-6230. Fax: 661-654-3238. p. 123

Bozek, Wendy, Librn, Castor Municipal Library, 5103 51 St, Castor, AB, T0C 0X0, CANADA. Tel: 403-882-3999. Fax: 403-882-3915. p. 2694

Bozeman, Pat, Spec Coll Librn, University of Houston, M D Anderson Library, 114 University Libraries, Houston, TX, 77204-2000. Tel: 713-743-9800. Fax: 713-743-9811. p. 2343

Bozz, Rita, Br Mgr, Hamilton Public Library, Binbrook Branch, 2641 Hwy 56, Binbrook, ON, L0R 1C0, CANADA. Tel: 905-546-3200, Ext 1046. p. 2808

Bozz, Rita, Br Mgr, Hamilton Public Library, Concession, 565 Concession St, Hamilton, ON, L8V 1A8, CANADA. Tel: 905-546-3200, Ext 1046. p. 2809

Bozz, Rita, Br Mgr, Hamilton Public Library, Mount Hope, 3027 Homestead Dr, Mount Hope, ON, L0R 1W0, CANADA. Tel: 905-546-3200, Ext 1046. p. 2809

Braack, Craig, Historian, Allegany County Historical Museum Library, Seven Courthouse, Court St, Belmont, NY, 14813-1089. Tel: 585-268-9293. Fax: 585-268-9446. p. 1580

Braaten, Carrie, Librn, Anoka County Library, Centennial, 100 Civic Heights Circle, Circle Pines, MN, 55014-1786. Tel: 763-717-3294. Fax: 763-717-3297. p. 1241

Brabble, Peggy, Ch, Pasquotank-Camden Library, 100 E Colonial Ave, Elizabeth City, NC, 27909. Tel: 252-335-2473, 252-335-7536. Fax: 252-331-7449. p. 1791

Brabham, Robin, Spec Coll Librn, University of North Carolina at Charlotte, 9201 University City Blvd, Charlotte, NC, 28223-0001. Tel: 704-687-2369. Fax: 704-687-3050. p. 1784

Braccia, Dana, Adult Serv Sr Libr Mgr, Scottsdale Public Library, 3839 N Drinkwater Blvd, Scottsdale, AZ, 85251-4467. Tel: 480-312-7323. Fax: 480-312-7993. p. 81

Braccia, Dana, Br Coordr, Scottsdale Public Library, Mustang Library, 10101 N 90th St, Scottsdale, AZ, 85258-4404. Tel: 480-312-6031. Fax: 480-312-6884. p. 81

Brace, Bethany, Dir, Fremont Public Library, Seven Jackie Bernier Dr, Fremont, NH, 03044. Tel: 603-895-9543. Fax: 603-895-0549. p. 1448

Brace, Patti, Coll Develop, Dir, Pretty Prairie Public Library, 119 W Main St, Pretty Prairie, KS, 67570. Tel: 620-459-6392. Fax: 620-459-7354. p. 891

Bracey, Linda Gail, Dir, South Mississippi Regional Library, 900 Broad St, Columbia, MS, 39429. Tel: 601-736-5516. Fax: 601-736-1379. p. 1296

Bracey, Renee M, Circ Serv Coordr, Siena Heights University Library, 1247 E Siena Heights Dr, Adrian, MI, 49221-1796. Tel: 517-264-7150. Fax: 517-264-7711. p. 1148

Brach, Carol A, Br Librn, Hesburgh Libraries, Engineering, 149 Fitzpatrick Hall, Notre Dame, IN, 46556. Tel: 574-631-6665. Fax: 574-631-9208. p. 770

Bracher, Thomas, Libr Tech, United States Army, Basset Army Hospital Medical Library, 1060 Gaffney Rd, No 7440, Fort Wainwright, AK, 99703-7440. Tel: 907-361-5194. Fax: 907-361-4845. p. 48

Brack, Amanda, Tech Serv Spec, Louisville Presbyterian Theological Seminary, 1044 Alta Vista Rd, Louisville, KY, 40205-1798. Tel: 502-895-3411, Ext 420. Fax: 502-895-1096. p. 925

Brack, Lillie, Dir, Cent Libr, The Kansas City Public Library, 14 W Tenth St, Kansas City, MO, 64105. Tel: 816-701-3543. Fax: 816-701-3401. p. 1338

Bracke, Paul J, Assoc Dean, Digital Prog & Info Access, Purdue University Libraries, 504 W State St, West Lafayette, IN, 47907-2058. Tel: 765-496-3606. Fax: 765-494-0156. p. 786

Brackeen, Susan, Libr Asst, Northeast Mississippi Community College, 101 Cunningham Blvd, Booneville, MS, 38829. Tel: 662-720-7407. Fax: 662-728-2428. p. 1294

Bracken, Darla, Dir, Friona Public Library, 109 W Seventh St, Friona, TX, 79035-2548. Tel: 806-250-3200. Fax: 806-250-2185. p. 2325

Bracken, Enda, Dep Dir, Willoughby-Eastlake Public Library, 263 E 305th St, Willowick, OH, 44095. Tel: 440-943-2203. Fax: 440-943-2383. p. 1948

Bracken, James K, Dean, Kent State University Libraries, 1125 Risman Dr, Kent, OH, 44242. Tel: 330-672-2962. Fax: 330-672-4811. p. 1907

Bracken, Jeanne Munn, Ref Librn, Lincoln Public Library, Three Bedford Rd, Lincoln, MA, 01773. Tel: 781-259-8465. Fax: 781-259-1056. p. 1099

Bracken, Karen, Circ Coordr, Riverside Public Library, 3581 Mission Inn Ave, Riverside, CA, 92501. Tel: 951-826-5201. Fax: 951-788-1528. p. 218

Bracken, Lee, Asst Head, Res Mgt, Northeastern University Libraries, Snell Library, 360 Huntington Ave, Boston, MA, 02115. Tel: 617-373-2748. p. 1065

Brackett, Janet, Access Serv, University of Maine at Farmington, 116 South St, Farmington, ME, 04938-1990. Tel: 207-778-7210. Fax: 207-778-7223. p. 985

Brackett, Susan, ILL Librn, Meredith Public Library, 91 Main St, Meredith, NH, 03253. Tel: 603-279-4303. Fax: 603-279-5352. p. 1457

Brackins, Kay, Dep Dir, American Helicopter Society International Library, 217 N Washington St, Alexandria, VA, 22314. Tel: 703-684-6777. Fax: 703-739-9279. p. 2445

Bracy, Pauletta B, Assoc Prof, North Carolina Central University, 1801 Fayetteville St, Durham, NC, 27707. Tel: 919-530-6485. Fax: 919-530-6402. p. 2971

Bradbeer, Gayle, User Support/Sci & Eng Coll Develop Librn, Auraria Library, 1100 Lawrence St, Denver, CO, 80204-2095. Tel: 303-556-2791. Fax: 303-556-3528. p. 298

Bradberry, Richard, Dir of Libr Serv, Morgan State University, 1700 E Cold Spring Lane, Baltimore, MD, 21251. Tel: 443-885-3488. p. 1016

Bradberry, Richard, Dr, Dean of Libr, Bowie State University, 14000 Jericho Park Rd, Bowie, MD, 20715. Tel: 301-860-3850. Fax: 301-860-3848. p. 1022

Bradburd, Nancy M, Librn, Philadelphia Orchestra Library, 300 S Broad St, Philadelphia, PA, 19102-4297. Tel: 215-670-2342. Fax: 215-985-0746. p. 2115

Bradbury, Gale F, Dir, Ledyard Public Libraries, 718 Colonel Ledyard Hwy, Ledyard, CT, 06339. Tel: 860-464-9917. Fax: 860-464-9927. p. 349

Bradbury, Gale F, Dir, Ledyard Public Libraries, Gales Ferry Library, 18 Hurlbutt Rd, Gales Ferry, CT, 06335. Tel: 860-464-6943. p. 349

Bradbury, John F, Interim Assoc Dir, University of Missouri, G-3 Curtis Laws Wilson Library, MS&T, 400 W 14th St, Rolla, MO, 65409-1420. Tel: 573-341-4874. p. 1351

Bradbury, Stacey, Asst Dir, Hart County Public Library, 500 E Union St, Munfordville, KY, 42765. Tel: 270-524-1953. Fax: 270-524-7323. p. 930

Bradby, Sherida, Supv Librn, Pamunkey Regional Library, 7527 Library Dr, Hanover, VA, 23069. Tel: 804-537-6211. Fax: 804-537-6389. p. 2469

Bradd, Ida, Syst Coordr, College of Physicians & Surgeons of British Columbia, 100-1383 W Eighth Ave, Vancouver, BC, V6H 4C4, CANADA. Tel: 604-733-6671. Fax: 604-737-8582. p. 2740

Brade, Angela, Chief Operating Officer, Support Serv, Howard County Library System, 6600 Cradlerock Way, Columbia, MD, 21045-4912. Tel: 410-313-7750. Fax: 410-313-7742. p. 1026

Brade, Carol, ILL, Scott Community College Library, 500 Belmont Rd, Bettendorf, IA, 52722. Tel: 563-441-4150. Fax: 563-441-4154. p. 796

Bradekamp, Carolyn, Co-Dir, Preston Public Library, One W Gillet, Preston, IA, 52069. Tel: 563-689-3581. Fax: 563-689-3581. p. 839

Braden, Darren, Teen Serv Librn, Monterey Park Bruggemeyer Library, 318 S Ramona Ave, Monterey Park, CA, 91754-3399. Tel: 626-307-1368. Fax: 626-288-4251. p. 190

Braden, Deborah, Circ Supvr, Saint Johns County Public Library System, Anastasia Island Branch, 124 Seagrove Main St, Saint Augustine Beach, FL, 32080. Tel: 904-209-3734. Fax: 904-209-3735. p. 487

Braden, Jim W, Jr, Librn, AT&T Southeast, 675 W Peachtree St NW, Ste 4200, Atlanta, GA, 30375. Tel: 404-335-0746. Fax: 404-614-4054. p. 511

Braden, Lise, Br Mgr, San Francisco Public Library, Ocean View Branch Library, 345 Randolph St, San Francisco, CA, 94132-3119. Tel: 415-355-5615. Fax: 415-452-8584. p. 246

Braden, Mark, Cat Librn, Occidental College Library, 1600 Campus Rd, Los Angeles, CA, 90041. Tel: 323-259-2668. Fax: 323-341-4991. p. 176

Braden, Patty, Dir, Romulus Public Library, 11121 Wayne Rd, Romulus, MI, 48174. Tel: 734-942-7589. Fax: 734-941-3575. p. 1222

Braden, Patty, Dir, Fall Creek Public Library, 122 E Lincoln Ave, Fall Creek, WI, 54742-9425. Tel: 715-877-3334. Fax: 715-877-2392. p. 2591

Braden, Rita, Dir, Wakefield Public Library, 205 Third St, Wakefield, KS, 67487-0348. Tel: 785-461-5510. Fax: 785-461-5510. p. 899

Bradford, Barry, Dir, Tangipahoa Parish Library, Administration Office, 200 E Mulberry St, Amite, LA, 70422. Tel: 985-748-7559. Fax: 985-748-2812. p. 941

Bradford, Charlene, Br Mgr, First Regional Library, Sardis Public Library, 101 McLaurin St, Sardis, MS, 38666. Tel: 662-487-2126. Fax: 662-487-2126. p. 1302

Bradford, Debra, Librn, Webster County Public Library, Providence Branch, 230 Willow St, Providence, KY, 42450. Tel: 270-667-5658. Fax: 270-667-6368. p. 911

Bradford, Gary, Electronic & Multimedia Spec, Tennessee Technological University, 1100 N Peachtree Ave, Cookeville, TN, 38505. Tel: 931-372-3326. Fax: 931-372-6112. p. 2231

Bradford, Jane, Instrul Serv & Res Librn, Stetson University, 421 N Woodland Blvd, Unit 8418, DeLand, FL, 32723. Tel: 386-822-7190. p. 437

Bradford, Jane, ILL, Per, Thomas Beaver Free Library, 205 Ferry St, Danville, PA, 17821-1939. Tel: 570-275-4180. Fax: 570-275-8480. p. 2049

Bradford, Joanie, Mgr, Baltimore County Public Library, North Point, 1716 Merritt Blvd, Baltimore, MD, 21222-3295. Tel: 410-887-7255. Fax: 410-282-3272. p. 1044

Bradford, John, Head, Automation & Tech Serv, Villa Park Public Library, 305 S Ardmore Ave, Villa Park, IL, 60181-2698. Tel: 630-834-1164. Fax: 630-834-0489. p. 714

Bradford, Kristi, Managing Librn, Pima County Public Library, Nanini, 7300 N Shannon Rd, Tucson, AZ, 85741. Tel: 520-594-5365. Fax: 520-594-5366. p. 87

Bradford, Margaret, Asst Br Mgr, Atlanta-Fulton Public Library System, Roswell Regional Library, 115 Norcross St, Roswell, GA, 30075. Tel: 770-640-3075. Fax: 770-640-3077. p. 512

Bradford, Patrice, In Charge, Apollo Group, 8000 E Maplewood Ave, Ste 200, Greenwood Village, CO, 80111. Tel: 303-220-4862. Fax: 303-220-4811. p. 312

Bradford, Tamara, Dir, OSHA, 200 Constitution Ave NW, Rm N-2625, Washington, DC, 20210-2001. Tel: 202-693-2350. Fax: 202-693-1648. p. 412

Bradford, William, Br Mgr, Cleveland Public Library, Hough, 1566 Crawford Rd, Cleveland, OH, 44106. Tel: 216-623-6997. Fax: 216-623-6999. p. 1878

Bradford, William, Br Mgr, Cleveland Public Library, Langston Hughes Branch, 10200 Superior Ave, Cleveland, OH, 44106. Tel: 216-623-6975. Fax: 216-623-6974. p. 1878

Bradigan, Pamela S, Assoc Dir, Ohio State University LIBRARIES, John A Prior Health Sciences Library, 376 W Tenth Ave, Columbus, OH, 43210-1240. Tel: 614-292-4866. Fax: 614-292-1920. p. 1889

Bradlee, Marcia, In Charge, Northern Illinois University Libraries, Faraday Library, Faraday Hall, Rm 212, DeKalb, IL, 60115. Tel: 815-753-1257. p. 635

Bradley, Ann E, Sr Librn, Lee County Library System, Captiva Memorial Library, 11560 Chapin Lane, Captiva, FL, 33924. Tel: 239-472-2133. Fax: 239-472-0272. p. 445

Bradley, Anne, Access Serv & Syst, Acq, College Bourget Bibliotheque, 65 rue Saint Pierre, Rigaud, QC, J0P 1P0, CANADA. Tel: 450-451-0815. Fax: 450-451-4171. p. 2907

Bradley, Arnold R, Archivist, University of Colorado Boulder, Archives & Special Collections, 1720 Pleasant St, Boulder, CO, 80309-0184. Tel: 303-492-6144, 303-492-7242. Fax: 303-492-1881. p. 291

Bradley, Barbara, Head, Acq, Oklahoma State University Libraries, Oklahoma State University, Athletic Ave, Stillwater, OK, 74078-1071. Tel: 405-744-9729. Fax: 405-744-5183. p. 1978

Bradley, Bridget, Exec Officer, District of Columbia Public Library, 901 G St NW, Washington, DC, 20001-4599. Tel: 202-727-1101. Fax: 202-727-1129. p. 398

Bradley, Bruce, Librn, Hist of Sci/Spec Coll, Linda Hall Library, 5109 Cherry St, Kansas City, MO, 64110-2498. Tel: 816-926-8737. Fax: 816-926-8790. p. 1337

Bradley, Caroline, Sr Ref Librn, Westerly Public Library, 44 Broad St, Westerly, RI, 02891. Tel: 401-596-2877, Ext 312. Fax: 401-596-5600. p. 2178

Bradley, Cheryl, Ref Serv, Fairhope Public Library, 501 Fairhope Ave, Fairhope, AL, 36532. Tel: 251-928-7483. Fax: 251-928-9717. p. 16

Bradley, Cheryl, Dir, Stevens Memorial Library, 20 Memorial Dr, Ashburnham, MA, 01430. Tel: 978-827-4115. Fax: 978-827-4116. p. 1050

Bradley, Christine, Dir, Norwalk Public Library, One Belden Ave, Norwalk, CT, 06850. Tel: 203-899-2780. Fax: 203-857-4410. p. 362

Bradley, Connie, Ch, Miami Public Library, 200 N Main, Miami, OK, 74354. Tel: 918-541-2292. Fax: 918-542-9363. p. 1968

Bradley, Darlene, Mgr, Libr Serv, Arcadia Public Library, 20 W Duarte Rd, Arcadia, CA, 91006. Tel: 626-821-5570. Fax: 626-447-8050. p. 121

Bradley, Eric, Assoc Dir, Tech Serv, Cornerstone University, 1001 E Beltline Ave NE, Grand Rapids, MI, 49525. Tel: 616-949-5300. Fax: 616-222-1405. p. 1184

Bradley, Grace, Librn, Calhoun County Library, Point Comfort Branch, One Lamar St, Point Comfort, TX, 77978. Tel: 361-987-2954. Fax: 361-987-2954. p. 2372

Bradley, Jaime M, Col Archivist, Berea College, 100 Campus Dr, Berea, KY, 40404. Tel: 859-985-3272. Fax: 859-985-3912. p. 907

Bradley, James, Info Literacy, Instruction & Outreach, Wilmington University Library, 320 DuPont Hwy, New Castle, DE, 19720. Tel: 302-328-9401. Fax: 302-328-0914. p. 385

Bradley, Jana, Dr, Dir, Prof, University of Arizona, 1515 E First St, Tucson, AZ, 85719. Tel: 520-621-3565. Fax: 520-621-3279. p. 2962

Bradley, Jeronell W, Dir of Libr, Florence-Darlington Technical College Libraries, 2715 W Lucas St, Florence, SC, 29501. Tel: 843-661-8032. Fax: 843-661-8266. p. 2193

Bradley, Jeronell W, Dir, Florence-Darlington Technical College Libraries, Segars Library Health Sciences Campus, 320 W Cheves St, Florence, SC, 29501. Tel: 843-676-8575. p. 2194

Bradley, JoAnn, Head, ILL, California State University, Chico, 400 W First St, Chico, CA, 95929-0295. Tel: 530-898-5862. Fax: 530-898-4443. p. 133

Bradley, Kate, Librn, Bellevue College, 3000 Landerholm Circle SE, Bellevue, WA, 98007-6484. Tel: 425-564-2262. Fax: 425-564-6186. p. 2508

Bradley, Katherine R, Ref Asst, K&L Gates LLP, State Street Financial Ctr, One Lincoln St, Boston, MA, 02111-2950. Tel: 617-951-9048. Fax: 617-261-3175. p. 1062

Bradley, Kathy, Asst Librn, Licking Memorial Hospital, 1320 W Main St, Newark, OH, 43055-3699. Tel: 740-348-4130. Fax: 740-348-4012. p. 1922

Bradley, Laura, Ref Librn, Cadwalader, Wickersham & Taft, 700 Sixth St NW, Suite 300, Washington, DC, 20001. Tel: 202-862-2217. Fax: 202-862-2400. p. 395

Bradley, Lola, Pub Serv Librn, University of South Carolina Upstate Library, 800 University Way, Spartanburg, SC, 29303. Tel: 864-503-5006. Fax: 864-503-5601. p. 2205

Bradley, Lola, Pub Serv Librn, University of South Carolina Upstate Library, University Center of Greenville Library, 225 S Pleasantburg Dr, Greenville, SC, 29607-2544. Tel: 864-503-5006. Fax: 864-250-8905. p. 2206

Bradley, Marianne, Admin Coordr, Archives Mgr, Agnes Scott College, 141 E College Ave, Decatur, GA, 30030-3770. Tel: 404-471-6090. Fax: 404-471-5037. p. 529

Bradley, Michelle, Dir, Frankfort Community Public Library, 208 W Clinton St, Frankfort, IN, 46041. Tel: 765-654-8746. Fax: 765-654-8747. p. 743

Bradley, Nancy, Dir, Dallas County Library, 219 W Main, Buffalo, MO, 65622. Tel: 417-345-2647. Fax: 417-345-2647. p. 1321

Bradley, Paula, Circ, Lebanon Public Library, 101 S Broadway, Lebanon, OH, 45036. Tel: 513-932-2665. Fax: 513-932-7323. p. 1909

Bradley, Rebecca, Ref, Lone Star College System, Kingwood College Library, 20000 Kingwood Dr, Kingwood, TX, 77339. Tel: 281-312-1691. Fax: 281-312-1456. p. 2340

Bradley, Sarah, Br Head, Toronto Public Library, Lillian H Smith Branch, 239 College St, Toronto, ON, M5T 1R5, CANADA. Tel: 416-393-7746. Fax: 416-393-7609. p. 2863

Bradley, Sharon A, Spec Coll Librn, University of Georgia, 225 Herty Dr, Athens, GA, 30602-6018. Tel: 706-542-5083. Fax: 706-542-5001. p. 510

Bradley, Shelley J, Adminr, Gable & Gotwals, Inc, 1100 Oneok Plaza, 100 W Fifth St, Tulsa, OK, 74103-4217. Tel: 918-595-4938. Fax: 918-595-4990. p. 1980

Bradley, Stuart V, Jr, VPres, Gen Counsel & Secy of the Corp, Railway Mail Service Library, Inc, 117 E Main St, Boyce, VA, 22620-9639. Tel: 540-837-9090. p. 2452

Bradley, Tina, Ref Librn, Arkansas State University-Mountain Home, 1600 S College St, Mountain Home, AR, 72653-5326. Tel: 870-508-6112. Fax: 870-508-6291. p. 110

Bradley, Tina, Asst Librn, Emery County Library, Cleveland Branch, 45 W Main, Cleveland, UT, 84518. Tel: 435-653-2204. Fax: 435-653-2104. p. 2403

Bradley, Vera, Libr Serv Mgr, Magee Rehabilitation Hospital, 1513 Race St, Philadelphia, PA, 19102. Tel: 215-587-3423. Fax: 215-568-3533. p. 2112

Bradley, Vera, Programmer, Beaufort County Library, Saint Helena Branch, 1025 Sea Island Pkwy, Saint Helena Island, SC, 29920. Tel: 843-255-6486. p. 2181

Bradley, Winifred, District Dept Head of Libr, Pensacola State College, 1000 College Blvd, Pensacola, FL, 32504-8998. Tel: 850-484-1393. Fax: 850-484-1991. p. 482

Bradley-Sanders, Colleen, Archivist, New York University School of Medicine, Medical Science Bldg 195, 550 First Ave, New York, NY, 10016-6450. Tel: 212-263-5397. Fax: 212-263-6534. p. 1695

Bradshaw, Beth, Head, Ref, Hickory Public Library, 375 Third St NE, Hickory, NC, 28601-5126. Tel: 828-304-0500, Ext 7278. Fax: 828-304-0023. p. 1801

Bradshaw, Christine, Cat Librn, La Crosse County Library, Administration Ctr, 103 State St, Holmen, WI, 54636. Tel: 608-526-9600. Fax: 608-526-3299. p. 2598

Bradshaw, Connie, Dir, Glenwood & Souris Regional Library, 18-114 Second St S, Souris, MB, R0K 2C0, CANADA. Tel: 204-483-2757. p. 2752

Bradshaw, David O, Electronic Res, Warren Wilson College, 701 Warren Wilson Rd, Swannanoa, NC, 28778. Tel: 828-771-3059. Fax: 828-771-7085. p. 1826

Bradshaw, Debra, Dir of Libr Serv, Nazarene Theological Seminary, 1700 E Meyer Blvd, Kansas City, MO, 64131. Tel: 816-268-5472. Fax: 816-822-9025. p. 1340

Bradshaw, Elizabeth, Weekend Coordr/Pub Serv Librn, Clayton State University, 2000 Clayton State Blvd, Morrow, GA, 30260. Tel: 678-466-4338. Fax: 678-466-4349. p. 545

Bradshaw, Graham, Head, Coll Develop, University of Toronto Libraries, 130 St George St, Toronto, ON, M5S 1A5, CANADA. Tel: 416-978-2289. Fax: 416-978-1608. p. 2865

Bradshaw, Jennifer, Dir, Woodbury Public Library, 23 Smith Clove Rd, Central Valley, NY, 10917. Tel: 845-928-2114. Fax: 845-928-8867. p. 1605

Bradshaw, Jennifer, Dir, Woodbury Public Library, 16 County Rte 105, Highland Mills, NY, 10930-9802. Tel: 845-928-6162. Fax: 845-928-3079. p. 1636

Bradshaw, Kathy, Human Res Librn, University of North Carolina at Greensboro, 320 Spring Garden St, Greensboro, NC, 27402. Tel: 336-334-3741. Fax: 336-334-5399. p. 1798

Bradshaw, Kayla, Cataloger, Green County Public Library, 112 W Court St, Greensburg, KY, 42743. Tel: 270-932-7081. Fax: 270-932-7081. p. 915

Bradshaw, Ken, Libr Dir, West Kentucky Community & Technical College, 4810 Alben Barkley Dr, Paducah, KY, 42001. Tel: 270-534-3169. Fax: 270-554-6218. p. 932

Bradshaw, Marlys, Tech Serv Mgr, Supreme Court of Ohio, 65 S Front St, 11th Flr, Columbus, OH, 43215-3431. Tel: 614-387-9661. Fax: 614-387-9689. p. 1890

Bradshaw, Pamela, Prog Supvr, Idaho Commission for Libraries, 325 W State St, Boise, ID, 83702-6072. Tel: 208-334-2150. Fax: 208-334-4016. p. 571

Bradshaw, Patricia, Dir, Malheur County Library, 388 SW Second Ave, Ontario, OR, 97914. Tel: 541-889-6371. Fax: 541-889-4279. p. 2008

Bradshaw, Ruth, Dir, Human Res, Public Library of Youngstown & Mahoning County, 305 Wick Ave, Youngstown, OH, 44503-1079. Tel: 330-744-8636. Fax: 330-744-3355. p. 1952

Bradshaw, Sharon K, Dir, Lawrence County Law Library Association, Lawrence County Courthouse, 4th Flr Annex, 111 S Fourth St, Ironton, OH, 45638-1586. Tel: 740-533-0582. Fax: 740-533-1084. p. 1906

Bradshaw, Sue, Tech Serv, Voorhees College, 5480 Voorhees Rd, Denmark, SC, 29042. Tel: 803-793-3351, Ext 7095. Fax: 803-793-0471. p. 2192

Bradshaw, Susan, Librn, Central Florida Community College, 3001 SW College Rd, Ocala, FL, 34474-4415. Tel: 352-237-2111, Ext 1344. Fax: 352-873-5818. p. 473

Bradt, Kay, Dir, Libr Serv, Baker University, 518 Eighth St, Baldwin City, KS, 66006-0065. Tel: 785-594-8390. Fax: 785-594-6721. p. 857

Brady, Althea H, Ch, Sr Librn, James White Memorial Library, Five Washburn Rd, East Freetown, MA, 02717-1220. Tel: 508-763-5344. p. 1086

Brady, Althea H, Librn, White James Memorial Library, G H Hathaway Library, Six N Main St, Assonet, MA, 02702. Tel: 508-644-2385. p. 1086

Brady, Cathy, Asst Librn, Wyalusing Public Library, 202 Church St, Wyalusing, PA, 18853. Tel: 570-746-1711. Fax: 570-746-1671. p. 2158

Brady, Eileen, Spec Coll & Archives Librn, University of North Florida, Bldg 12-Library, One UNF Dr, Jacksonville, FL, 32224-2645. Tel: 904-620-1533. Fax: 904-620-2719. p. 455

Brady, Fayth, Br Mgr, Harris County Public Library, Octavia Fields Memorial, 1503 S Houston Ave, Humble, TX, 77338. Tel: 281-446-3377. Fax: 281-446-4203. p. 2336

Brady, Florence, Asst Dir, Tuxedo Park Library, 227 Rte 17, Tuxedo Park, NY, 10987-4405. Tel: 845-351-2207. Fax: 845-351-2213. p. 1757

Brady, Francine, Ref, Havre Hill County Library, 402 Third St, Havre, MT, 59501. Tel: 406-265-2123. Fax: 406-262-1091. p. 1381

Brady, Jane, Sister, Circ, ILL, Christ the King Seminary Library, 711 Knox Rd, East Aurora, NY, 14052. Tel: 716-652-8959. Fax: 716-652-8903. p. 1616

Brady, John, Dir, Reader Serv, Newberry Library, 60 W Walton St, Chicago, IL, 60610-3305. Tel: 312-943-9090. Fax: 312-255-3527. p. 620

Brady, Kathleen M, Dir, United States Air Force, 8102 Condor St, MacDill AFB, FL, 33621-5408. Tel: 813-828-0424. Fax: 813-828-4416. p. 462

Brady, Kelly, Br Mgr, Washington County Public Library, New Matamoras Branch, 100 Merchant St, New Matamoras, OH, 45767. Tel: 740-865-3386. Fax: 740-865-2054. p. 1914

Brady, Lee Ann, Asst Librn, Clyde Public Library, 101 S Green St, Clyde, KS, 66938. Tel: 785-446-3563. p. 861

Braffet, Holly, Br Mgr, Hawaii State Public Library System, Hana Public & School Library, 4111 Hana Hwy, Hana, HI, 96713. Tel: 808-248-4848. Fax: 808-248-4849. p. 561

Bragdon, Heather, Spec Projects, Bingham McCutchen LLP, 150 Federal St, Boston, MA, 02110. Tel: 617-951-8313. Fax: 617-951-8543. p. 1055

Bragdon, Lynn, Librn, Department of Veterans Affairs, 2121 North Ave, Grand Junction, CO, 81501-6428. Tel: 970-242-0731, Ext 2254. Fax: 970-244-1309. p. 310

Brager, Kelly, Head, Tech Serv, Mayville State University, 330 Third St NE, Mayville, ND, 58257. Tel: 701-788-4815. Fax: 701-788-4846. p. 1846

Bragg, Anne, Librn, Errol Public Library, 67 Main St, Errol, NH, 03579. Tel: 603-482-7720. p. 1447

Bragg, Laura, Librn, Pouch Cove Public Library, PO Box 40, Pouch Cove, NL, A0A 3L0, CANADA. Tel: 709-335-2652. Fax: 709-335-2652. p. 2770

Bragg, Melody, Tech Info Spec, United States Department of Labor, 1301 Airport Rd, Beaver, WV, 25813-9426. Tel: 304-256-3556. Fax: 304-256-3372. p. 2553

Bragg, Millie, Br Mgr, Chesterfield County Library, Pageland Community Library, 109 W Blakeney St, Pageland, SC, 29728. Tel: 843-672-6930. Fax: 843-672-6670. p. 2186

Bragg, Sheila, Asst Dir, Bellevue Public Library, 106 N Third St, Bellevue, IA, 52031. Tel: 563-872-4991. Fax: 563-872-4094. p. 796

Bragg, Tina, Mgr, Screven-Jenkins Regional Library, Jenkins County Memorial Library, 223 Daniel St, Millen, GA, 30442. Tel: 478-982-4244. Fax: 478-982-2192. p. 553

Braham, Brenda, Digital Initiatives Librn, Montgomery College, Technical Services, 51 Mannakee St, Rockville, MD, 20850. Tel: 240-567-8033. Fax: 301-251-7141. p. 1037

Brahm, Suzanne, Dir, Highland Falls Library, 298 Main St, Highland Falls, NY, 10928. Tel: 845-446-3113. Fax: 845-446-1109. p. 1636

Brahme, Maria, Ref, Pepperdine University Libraries, West Los Angeles Graduate Campus Library, 6100 Center Dr, Los Angeles, CA, 90045. Tel: 310-568-5717. Fax: 310-568-5789. p. 182

Brahms, William, Br Mgr, Camden County Library System, 203 Laurel Rd, Voorhees, NJ, 08043. Tel: 856-772-1636, Ext 3308. Fax: 856-772-6105. p. 1538

Brain, Barbara, Asst Dir, Adult & Support Serv, Saint Louis County Library, 1640 S Lindbergh Blvd, Saint Louis, MO, 63131-3598. Tel: 314-994-3300, Ext 2153. Fax: 314-997-7602. p. 1358

Brain, Connie, Br Mgr, Palm Beach County Library System, Jupiter Branch, 705 N Military Trail, Jupiter, FL, 33458. Tel: 561-744-2301. Fax: 561-744-6297. p. 503

Brainard, Blair, Head, Ref & Instruction, Radford University, 801 E Main St, Radford, VA, 24142-0001. Tel: 540-831-5688. Fax: 540-831-6138. p. 2487

Brainard, Lisa, Librn, Wellesley College, Science Library, Science Ctr, 106 Central St, Wellesley, MA, 02481. Tel: 781-283-3084. Fax: 781-283-3642. p. 1135

Brainard, Lisa, Access Serv Librn, The Sage Colleges, 140 New Scotland Ave, Albany, NY, 12208. Tel: 518-292-1959. Fax: 518-292-1904. p. 1570

Brainard, Lisa, Access Serv Librn, The Sage Colleges, 45 Ferry St, Troy, NY, 12180. Tel: 518-292-1959. Fax: 518-292-1904. p. 1756

Brainerd, Jubilee, Sr Librn, Lee County Library System, Dunbar Jupiter Hammon Public Library, 3095 Blount St, Fort Myers, FL, 33916-2032. Tel: 239-334-3602. Fax: 239-334-7940. p. 445

Brainerd, Mildred, Mgr, Massillon Public Library, Barry Askren Memorial Branch, 1200 Market St NE, Navarre, OH, 44662. Tel: 330-879-2113. Fax: 330-879-5574. p. 1915

Braithwaite, Elaine, Br Mgr, West Haven Public Library, Ora B Mason Branch, 260 Benham Hill Rd, West Haven, CT, 06516-6541. Tel: 203-933-9381. Fax: 203-931-7149. p. 377

Brajcich, Jennifer, Br Mgr, Surrey Public Library, Ocean Park, 12854 17th Ave, Surrey, BC, V4A 1T5, CANADA. Tel: 604-502-6448. Fax: 604-502-6468. p. 2739

Brajcich, Jennifer, Mgr, Surrey Public Library, Newton, 13795 70th Ave, Surrey, BC, V3W 0E1, CANADA. Tel: 604-598-7400. Fax: 604-598-7401. p. 2739

Brake, Amy, Ref & Instruction Librn, North Carolina Wesleyan College, 3400 N Wesleyan Blvd, Rocky Mount, NC, 27804. Tel: 252-985-5233. Fax: 252-985-5235. p. 1821

Brake, Marion, Tech Serv, Central Regional Integrated Health Authority, 125 Trans Canada Hwy, Gander, NL, A1V 1P7, CANADA. Tel: 709-256-5760. Fax: 709-256-4308. p. 2770

Brake, Sandy, Asst Dir, Stewart County Public Library, 102 Natcor Dr, Dover, TN, 37058. Tel: 931-232-3127. Fax: 931-232-3159. p. 2233

Brakebill, Eva, Dir, Niota Public Library, 11 E Main St, Niota, TN, 37826. Tel: 423-568-2613. Fax: 423-568-3026. p. 2262

Braker, Marge, Librn, Illinois Prairie District Public Library, Roanoke Branch, 123 Broad St, Roanoke, IL, 61561. Tel: 309-923-7686. Fax: 309-923-7601. p. 673

Braks, Mary Ellen, Youth Serv, Spokane County Library District, Spokane Valley Library, 12004 E Main Ave, Spokane Valley, WA, 99206-5114. Tel: 509-893-8400. Fax: 509-893-8483. p. 2537

Bramble, Antonia, Br Librn, Brooklyn Public Library, Flatbush, 22 Linden Blvd, Brooklyn, NY, 11226. Tel: 718-856-0813. Fax: 718-856-0899. p. 1591

Bramblett Barr, Anne, Dir, West Pittston Library, 200 Exeter Ave, West Pittston, PA, 18643-2442. Tel: 570-654-9847. Fax: 570-654-8037. p. 2154

Brambley, Jamie, Dir, Fulton County Library, 227 N First St, McConnellsburg, PA, 17233-1003. Tel: 717-485-5327. Fax: 717-485-5646. p. 2085

Brambley, Jamie, Dir, Fulton County Library, Hustontown Branch, 313 Pitt St, Ste B, Hustontown, PA, 17229. Tel: jbrambley@fclspa.org. Fax: 717-987-3606. p. 2085

Brame, Thomas, Librn, Century Correctional Institution Library, 400 Tedder Rd, Century, FL, 32535-3659. Tel: 850-256-2600, Ext 401. Fax: 850-256-2335. p. 431

Bramhill, Sylvia, Asst Librn, ILL, Fort Nelson Public Library, 5315-50th Ave S, Box 330, Fort Nelson, BC, V0C 1R0, CANADA. Tel: 250-774-6777. Fax: 250-774-6777. p. 2728

Bramlett, Judy, Ref, Chester County Library, 100 Center St, Chester, SC, 29706. Tel: 803-377-8145. Fax: 803-377-8146. p. 2185

Bramlett, Loretta, Dir, Libr Serv, Florida State Hospital, Main Library Bldg 1260, Chattahoochee, FL, 32324. Tel: 850-663-7671. Fax: 850-663-7303. p. 431

Bramlett, Rene, Dir, Clover Public Library District, 440 N Division St, Woodhull, IL, 61490. Tel: 309-334-2680. Fax: 309-334-2378. p. 721

Bramson, Rosemary, Dir, Temple - Congregation Shomer Emunim Library, 6453 Sylvania Ave, Sylvania, OH, 43560-3999. Tel: 419-885-3341. Fax: 419-882-2778. p. 1938

Bramwell, Victoria, Circ, ILL & Ser, Hanover College, 121 Scenic Dr, Hanover, IN, 47243. Tel: 812-866-7169. Fax: 812-866-7172. p. 748

Branam, Linda, Dir, Hobart Public Library, 200 S Main St, Hobart, OK, 73651. Tel: 580-726-2535. Fax: 580-726-3600. p. 1965

Brancato, Gale, Cat, Hartford Seminary Library, 77 Sherman St, Hartford, CT, 06105-2260. Tel: 860-509-9563. Fax: 860-509-9509. p. 346

Brancato, Jennifer, Archivist, Stephen F Austin State University, 1936 North St, Nacogdoches, TX, 75962. Tel: 936-468-1841. Fax: 936-468-7610. p. 2364

Branch, Brenda, Dir, Austin Public Library, 800 Guadalupe St, Austin, TX, 78701. Tel: 512-974-7444. p. 2278

Branch, Lynn W, Bus & Finance Mgr, Sheppard Memorial Library, 530 S Evans St, Greenville, NC, 27858-2308. Tel: 252-329-4580. Fax: 252-329-4587. p. 1799

Branch, Mariana, Dir, Kingsville Public Library, 6006 Academy St, Kingsville, OH, 44048-0057. Tel: 440-224-0239. Fax: 440-224-0029. p. 1907

Branch, Nell, Librn, Holmes Community College, Goodman Campus, 178 Hill St, Goodman, MS, 39079. Tel: 662-472-9018. Fax: 662-472-9155. p. 1298

Branch, Robert, Dr, Dept Head/Prof, University of Georgia, College of Education, 224 River's Crossing, Athens, GA, 30602-7144. Tel: 706-542-4110. Fax: 706-542-4032. p. 2964

Branch, Sharon, Br Mgr, East Providence Public Library, Fuller, 260 Dover Ave, East Providence, RI, 02914. Tel: 401-434-1136. Fax: 401-434-3896. p. 2166

Branch, Virginia C, Ref, Appalachian State University, 218 College St, Boone, NC, 28608. Tel: 828-262-4966. Fax: 828-262-3001. p. 1777

Branciforte, Eileen, Dir, Cromwell Belden Public Library, 39 West St, Cromwell, CT, 06416. Tel: 860-632-3460. Fax: 860-632-3484. p. 334

Branciforte, Jessica, Head, Children's & Young Adult Serv, Essex Library Association, Inc, 33 West Ave, Essex, CT, 06426-1196. Tel: 860-767-1560. Fax: 860-767-2500. p. 338

Branciforti, Mary Ann, Asst Dir, Linwood Public Library, 301 Davis Ave, Linwood, NJ, 08221. Tel: 609-926-7991. Fax: 609-927-6147. p. 1495

Branco, Susan R, Dir, Westport Free Public Library, 408 Old County Rd, Westport, MA, 02790. Tel: 508-636-1100. Fax: 508-636-1102. p. 1139

Branco, Tina, Dir, South Thomaston Public Library, Eight Dublin Rd, South Thomaston, ME, 04858. Tel: 207-596-0022. Fax: 207-596-7529. p. 1002

Brancoli-Monchicourt, Cara, Circ Supvr, Mill Valley Public Library, 375 Throckmorton Ave, Mill Valley, CA, 94941-2698. Tel: 415-389-4292, Ext 112. Fax: 415-388-8929. p. 186

Brancolini, Kristine R, Dean of Libr, Loyola Marymount University, One LMU Dr, MS 8200, Los Angeles, CA, 90045-2659. Tel: 310-338-2788. Fax: 310-338-4366. p. 175

Brand, Beth, Librn, Desert Botanical Garden Library, 1201 N Galvin Pkwy, Phoenix, AZ, 85008. Tel: 480-481-8133. Fax: 480-481-8124. p. 72

Brand, Carol A, Asst Dir, Sachem Public Library, 150 Holbrook Rd, Holbrook, NY, 11741. Tel: 631-588-5024. Fax: 631-588-5064. p. 1637

Brand, Joseph, Librn, Monell Chemical Senses Center, 3500 Market St, Philadelphia, PA, 19104-3308. Tel: 215-898-6666. Fax: 215-898-2084. p. 2112

Brand Wallace, Julie, Commun Relations & Mkt Mgr, King County Library System, 960 Newport Way NW, Issaquah, WA, 98027. Tel: 425-369-3273. Fax: 425-369-3255. p. 2516

Brandao, John, In Charge, Tulane University, Turchin Library, Goldring/Woldenberg Hall I, 3rd Flr, Seven McAlister Dr, New Orleans, LA, 70118. Tel: 504-865-5376. Fax: 504-862-8953. p. 963

Brandau, Susan, Dir, Windber Public Library, 1909 Graham Ave, Windber, PA, 15963-2011. Tel: 814-467-4950. Fax: 814-467-0960. p. 2157

Brandeis, Robert, Dr, Chief Librn, University of Toronto Libraries, Victoria University Library, 71 Queens Park Crescent E, Toronto, ON, M5S 1K7, CANADA. Tel: 416-585-4472. Fax: 416-585-4591. p. 2867

Brandel, Sara, Campus Librn, Mohave Community College Library, Bullhead City Campus, 3400 Hwy 95, Bullhead City, AZ, 86442-8204. Tel: 928-758-2420. Fax: 928-758-4436. p. 66

Branden, Shirley, Head, Instrul Serv, Head, Ref Serv, University of Delaware Library, 181 S College Ave, Newark, DE, 19717-5267. Tel: 302-831-2231. Fax: 302-831-1046. p. 386

Brandenberg, Teresa, Young Adult Serv Coordr, Russell Public Library, 126 E Sixth St, Russell, KS, 67665-2041. Tel: 785-483-2742. Fax: 785-483-6254. p. 892

Brandenburg, Lorraine, In Charge, Woodford County Historical Society Library, 121 Rose Hill, Versailles, KY, 40383-1221. Tel: 859-873-6786. p. 936

Brandes, Jay, Global Campus Librn, Troy University Library, 309 Wallace Hall, 501 University Ave, Troy, AL, 36082. Tel: 334-670-6344. Fax: 334-670-3694. p. 37

Brandler, Sherry, Circ Supvr, Orange Beach Public Library, 26267 Canal Rd, Orange Beach, AL, 36561-3917. Tel: 251-981-2923. Fax: 251-981-2920. p. 33

Brandon, Barbara, Ref/Fac Serv Librn, University of Miami, 1311 Miller Dr, Coral Gables, FL, 33146. Tel: 305-284-2251. Fax: 305-284-3554. p. 434

Brandon, Carl, Dir, Media Serv, Cedarville University, 251 N Main St, Cedarville, OH, 45314-0601. Tel: 937-766-7840. Fax: 937-766-2337. p. 1865

Brandon, Carol, Head, Outreach Serv, Warren-Newport Public Library District, 224 N O'Plaine Rd, Gurnee, IL, 60031. Tel: 847-244-5150. Fax: 847-244-3499. p. 653

Brandon, Valerie, Adminr, Mid-Illinois Talking Book Center, 600 Highpoint Lane, East Peoria, IL, 61611. Tel: 309-694-9200. Fax: 309-694-9230. p. 639

Brandreth, Elizabeth A, Sister, Dir, Libr Serv, Mercy Hospital, 746 Jefferson Ave, Scranton, PA, 18501. Tel: 570-348-7800. Fax: 570-340-4871. p. 2137

Brandriff, Maria, Asst Libr Dir, Cheshire Public Library, 104 Main St, Cheshire, CT, 06410-2499. Tel: 203-272-2245. Fax: 203-272-7714. p. 333

Brands, Lisa, City Librn, Edgerton Public Library, 811 First Ave, Edgerton, MN, 56128. Tel: 507-442-7071. Fax: 507-442-7071. p. 1249

Brandsma, Terry, Info Tech Librn, University of North Carolina at Greensboro, 320 Spring Garden St, Greensboro, NC, 27402. Tel: 336-256-1218. Fax: 336-334-5399. p. 1798

Brandt, Barbara, Dir, Bangor Public Library, 39 S Main St, Bangor, PA, 18013-2690. Tel: 610-588-4136. Fax: 610-588-1931. p. 2031

Brandt, Catherine, Head, Circ, Menasha Public Library, 440 First St, Menasha, WI, 54952-3191. Tel: 920-967-3660. Fax: 920-967-5159. p. 2614

Brandt, Cathy, Head, Circ, Tiffin-Seneca Public Library, 77 Jefferson St, Tiffin, OH, 44883. Tel: 419-447-3751. Fax: 419-447-3045. p. 1938

Brandt, D Scott, Assoc Dean, Res, Purdue University Libraries, 504 W State St, West Lafayette, IN, 47907-2058. Tel: 765-494-2889. Fax: 765-494-0156. p. 786

Brandt, Esther, Librn, Lincoln County Public Libraries, Eureka Branch, 318 Dewey Ave, Eureka, MT, 59917. Tel: 406-296-2613. Fax: 406-296-2613. p. 1385

Brandt, Janet, Acq, Cat Mgr, Dept Head, Tech Serv, Red Wing Public Library, 225 East Ave, Red Wing, MN, 55066-2298. Tel: 651-385-3673. Fax: 651-385-3644. p. 1272

Brandt, Jill, ILL, North Hampton Public Library, 237A Atlantic Ave, North Hampton, NH, 03862-2341. Tel: 603-964-6326. Fax: 603-964-1107. p. 1461

Brandt, John, Electronic Res Librn, California State University, Stanislaus, One University Circle, Turlock, CA, 95382. Tel: 209-664-6563. p. 277

Brandt, Maria, Ref Coordr, Southwest Minnesota State University Library, 1501 State St, Marshall, MN, 56258. Tel: 507-537-6165. Fax: 507-537-6200. p. 1258

Brandt, Mary, Dir, Baker College Library of Owosso, 1020 S Washington St, Owosso, MI, 48867-4400. Tel: 989-729-3325. Fax: 989-729-3429. p. 1216

Brandt, Ronna, Dir, Savoy Hollow Library, Town Off Bldg, 720 Main St, Savoy, MA, 01256-9387. Tel: 413-743-4290. Fax: 413-743-4292. p. 1123

Brandt-Riske, Kris, Librn, American Federation of Astrologers, Inc Library, 6535 S Rural Rd, Tempe, AZ, 85283-3746. Tel: 480-838-1751. Fax: 480-838-8293. p. 83

Brandvold, Cathy S, Dir, Valier Public Library, 400 Teton Ave, Valier, MT, 59486. Tel: 406-279-3366. Fax: 406-279-3368. p. 1389

Brandyburg, Tyrone, Superintendent, US National Park Service, 40 Patriots Hall Dr, Currie, NC, 28435. Tel: 910-283-5591. Fax: 910-283-5351. p. 1786

Branget, Ruth, AV, Collingwood Public Library, 55 St Marie St, Collingwood, ON, L9Y 0W6, CANADA. Tel: 705-445-1571, Ext 6224. Fax: 705-445-3704. p. 2800

Branham, Howard, Dir, Camden Archives & Museum Library, 1314 Broad St, Camden, SC, 29020-3535. Tel: 803-425-6050. Fax: 803-424-4021. p. 2182

Brank, Jennifer, Asst Libr Dir, Duane Morris LLP Library, 30 S 17th St, Philadelphia, PA, 19103-4196. Tel: 215-979-1720. Fax: 215-979-1020. p. 2106

Brankovich, Beverly, Coordr, Cat, Albion College, 602 E Cass St, Albion, MI, 49224-1879. Tel: 517-629-0285. Fax: 517-629-0504. p. 1148

Brann, Lesley, Ref Serv, Colchester - East Hants Regional Library, 754 Prince St, Truro, NS, B2N 1G9, CANADA. Tel: 902-895-0235, 902-895-1625, 902-895-4183. Fax: 902-895-7149. p. 2786

Brann, Marge, Librn, First United Methodist Church, Nine N Almansor St, Alhambra, CA, 91801-2699. Tel: 626-289-4258. Fax: 626-289-4316. p. 120

Brannak, Cindy, Br Librn, Dobson Community Library, 205 S Main St, Dobson, NC, 27017. Tel: 336-386-8208. Fax: 336-386-4086. p. 1786

Branning, Katharine, Dir, French Institute-Alliance Francaise Library, 22 E 60th St, New York, NY, 10022-1077. Tel: 646-388-6614. Fax: 212-935-4119. p. 1679

Brannock, Jennifer, Spec Coll Librn, University of Southern Mississippi Library, 118 College Dr, No 5053, Hattiesburg, MS, 39406. Tel: 601-266-4347. Fax: 601-266-6033. p. 1300

Brannock, Jennifer, Spec Coll Librn, University of Southern Mississippi Library, William David McCain Library & Archives, 118 College Dr, No 5148, Hattiesburg, MS, 39406. Tel: 601-266-4347. Fax: 601-226-6269. p. 1301

Brannon, Christopher, Info Serv, Coeur d'Alene Public Library, 702 E Front Ave, Coeur d'Alene, ID, 83814-2373. Tel: 208-769-2315. Fax: 208-769-2381. p. 573

Brannon, Debbie, Tech Serv, Hardin County Library, 1365 Pickwick St, Savannah, TN, 38372. Tel: 731-925-4314, 731-925-6848. Fax: 731-925-7132. p. 2264

Brannon, Kathy, Tech Serv, Upper Dublin Public Library, 805 Loch Alsh Ave, Fort Washington, PA, 19034. Tel: 215-628-8744. p. 2058

Brannon, Page, Head, Ref & Instruction, University of Alaska Anchorage, Consortium Library, 3211 Providence Dr, Anchorage, AK, 99508-8176. Tel: 907-786-1873. Fax: 907-786-1834. p. 45

Brannon, RaShauna, Electronic Res Librn, University Libraries, University of Memphis, 126 Ned R McWherter Library, Memphis, TN, 38152-3250. Tel: 901-678-8226. p. 2252

Brannon, Sian, Asst Dean for Coll Mgt, University of North Texas Libraries, PO Box 305190, Denton, TX, 76203-5190. Tel: 940-891-6945. Fax: 940-369-8760. p. 2313

Branscum, Jill, Govt Doc, ILL, Ref, Anderson University, Robert A Nicholson Library, 1100 E Fifth St, Anderson, IN, 46012-3495. Tel: 765-641-4280. Fax: 765-641-3850. p. 724

Branson, Cathy, Dir of Libr Serv, Hazard Community & Technical College Library, One Community College Dr, Hazard, KY, 41701. Tel: 606-487-3145. Fax: 606-439-1657. p. 916

Branson, Cathy, Dir of Libr Serv, Hazard Community & Technical College, 601 Jefferson Ave, Jackson, KY, 41339. Tel: 606-666-7521. Fax: 606-666-8910. p. 919

Branson, Colleen, Dir, Mannford Public Library, 101 Green Valley Park Rd, Mannford, OK, 74044. Tel: 918-865-2665. Fax: 918-865-3429. p. 1967

Branson, Gary, Dir, Marion Public Library, 445 E Church St, Marion, OH, 43302-4290. Tel: 740-387-0992. Fax: 740-382-9954. p. 1914

Branson, Khristi, Asst Librn, Ashland City Library, 604 Main St, Ashland, KS, 67831. Tel: 620-635-2589. Fax: 620-635-2931. p. 856

Brantley, Brenda, Head, Pub Serv, Bossier Parish Community College Library, 6220 E Texas St, Bossier City, LA, 71111. Tel: 318-678-6068. Fax: 318-678-6400. p. 946

Brantley, Cammie, Mgr, San Antonio Public Library, McCreless, 1023 Ada St, San Antonio, TX, 78223. Tel: 210-207-9170. Fax: 210-207-9175. p. 2382

Brantley, Rebecca, Electronic Serv Librn, Louisiana Tech University, Everett St at The Columns, Ruston, LA, 71272. Tel: 318-257-3555. Fax: 318-257-2579. p. 966

Brantley, Teresa, Mgr, Chatham County Public Libraries, Pittsboro Memorial Library, 158 West St, Pittsboro, NC, 27312. Tel: 919-542-3524. Fax: 919-542-3860. p. 1823

Branton, Ann, Bibliog Serv, University of Southern Mississippi Library, 118 College Dr, No 5053, Hattiesburg, MS, 39406. Tel: 601-266-4350. Fax: 601-266-6033. p. 1300

Branton, Beverly A, Reader Serv, University of Toronto Libraries, Victoria University Library, 71 Queens Park Crescent E, Toronto, ON, M5S 1K7, CANADA. Tel: 416-585-4471. Fax: 416-585-4591. p. 2867

Brantz, Malcolm, Dir, Arapahoe Community College, 5900 S Santa Fe Dr, Littleton, CO, 80160. Tel: 303-797-5739. Fax: 303-798-4173. p. 316

Brase, Beth, Dir, Strawberry Point Public Library, 401 Commercial St, Strawberry Point, IA, 52076-9657. Tel: 563-933-4340. Fax: 563-933-4340. p. 846

Brashear, Pat, Cat, Midland County Public Library, 301 W Missouri, Midland, TX, 79701. Tel: 432-688-4320. Fax: 432-688-4939. p. 2363

Brashear, Patricia, Asst Librn, Letcher County Public Libraries, Lillian Webb Memorial, 1049 Hwy 317, Neon, KY, 41840. Tel: 606-855-7913. Fax: 606-855-4565. p. 937

Brashear, Ronald, Arnold Thackray Dir, Donald F & Mildred Topp Othmer Library of Chemical History, 315 Chestnut St, Philadelphia, PA, 19106. Tel: 215-873-8205. Fax: 215-629-5205. p. 2113

Brasher, David, Info Serv, Columbus-Lowndes Public Library, 314 N Seventh St, Columbus, MS, 39701. Tel: 662-329-5300. Fax: 662-329-5156. p. 1297

Brasher, Jeannette, Librn, Chilton Clanton Library, Jemison Public Library, 14 Padgett Lane, Jemison, AL, 35085. Tel: 205-688-4492. Fax: 205-688-1109. p. 12

Brasher, Lisa, Dir, Levy County Public Library System, 612 E Hathaway Ave, Bronson, FL, 32621. Tel: 352-486-5552. Fax: 352-486-5553. p. 430

Brasile, Frank, Tech Serv & Syst Librn, Pierce College Library, Puyallup Campus, 1601 39th Ave SE, Puyallup, WA, 98374. Tel: 253-840-8306. Fax: 253-840-8316. p. 2520

Brassard, Carole, Asst Dir, Human Res & Phys Plant, Bibliotheque Publique de Chicoutimi, 155, rue Racine Est, Chicoutimi, QC, G7H 1R5, CANADA. Tel: 418-698-3000, Ext 4177. Fax: 418-698-5359. p. 2880

Brassard, Janice, Librn, Tangent Community Library, PO Box 63, Tangent, AB, T0H 3J0, CANADA. Tel: 780-837-6443. p. 2719

Brassaw, Lori, Dir, College of Eastern Utah Library, 451 E & 400 N, Price, UT, 84501. Tel: 435-613-5328. Fax: 435-613-5863. p. 2410

Brassel, Beth, YA Librn, Pollard Memorial Library, 401 Merrimack St, Lowell, MA, 01852. Tel: 978-970-4120. Fax: 978-970-4117. p. 1100

Brassell, Sally, Librn, Nixon Public Library, 401 N Nixon Ave, Nixon, TX, 78140. Tel: 830-582-1913. Fax: 830-582-1713. p. 2366

Brassil, Ellen, Librn, Baystate Medical Center, 759 Chestnut St, Springfield, MA, 01199. Tel: 413-794-1865. Fax: 413-794-1974. p. 1127

Braswell, Ashley, Sr Libr Assoc, Nashville Public Library, 114 W Church St, Nashville, NC, 27856. Tel: 252-459-2106. Fax: 252-459-8819. p. 1812

Braswell, Elizabeth, Dir, Quartzsite Public Library, 465 N Plymouth Ave, Quartzsite, AZ, 85346. Tel: 928-927-6593. Fax: 928-927-3593. p. 79

Braswell, Heather, Tech Serv, Mount Olive College, 634 Henderson St, Mount Olive, NC, 28365-1699. Tel: 919-658-7869. Fax: 919-658-8934. p. 1811

Braswell, Toni, Br Mgr, Memphis Public Library, Whitehaven, 4120 Mill Branch Rd, Memphis, TN, 38116. Tel: 901-396-9700. Fax: 901-332-6150. p. 2250

Bratcher, Cassie, Tech Serv Librn, Filson Historical Society Library, 1310 S Third St, Louisville, KY, 40208. Tel: 502-635-5083. Fax: 502-635-5086. p. 923

Bratcher, Perry, Syst Mgr, Northern Kentucky University, University Dr, Highland Heights, KY, 41099. Tel: 859-572-5456. Fax: 859-572-5390. p. 917

Bratsch, Kris, Asst Librn, Renville City Library, 221 N Main, Renville, MN, 56284. Tel: 320-329-8193. p. 1272

Brattin, Barbara, Dir, San Miguel County Public Library District 1, 100 W Pacific Ave, Telluride, CO, 81435-2189. Tel: 970-728-4519. Fax: 970-728-3340. p. 323

Bratton, Diane, Circ, Millburn Free Public Library, 200 Glen Ave, Millburn, NJ, 07041. Tel: 973-376-1006, Ext 28. Fax: 973-376-0104. p. 1502

Bratton, Karen, Res, Douglas County Museum, 123 Museum Dr, Roseburg, OR, 97470. Tel: 541-957-7007. Fax: 541-957-7017. p. 2016

Bratton, Melissa, Syst Adminr, Harrison County Library System, 2600 24th Ave, No 6, Gulfport, MS, 39501-2081. Tel: 228-868-1383. Fax: 228-863-7433. p. 1299

Bratton, Phyllis Ann K, Dir, Jamestown College, 6070 College Lane, Jamestown, ND, 58405-0001. Tel: 701-252-3467. Fax: 701-253-4446. p. 1844

Bratz, Robin, In Charge, Covenant United Methodist Church Library, 212 W Springfield Rd, Springfield, PA, 19064-2402. Tel: 610-544-1400. Fax: 610-544-2862. p. 2142

Braucht, Karen, Librn, Perkins Coie Library, 1201 Third Ave, Ste 4900, Seattle, WA, 98101. Tel: 206-359-8444. Fax: 206-359-9444. p. 2529

Braud, Cheryl, Asst Dir, Iberia Parish Library, 445 E Main St, New Iberia, LA, 70560-3710. Tel: 337-364-7024, 337-364-7074. Fax: 337-364-7042. p. 959

Braud, John, Br Mgr, Iberia Parish Library, Jeanerette Branch, 411 Kentucky St, Jeanerette, LA, 70544. Tel: 337-276-4014. Fax: 337-276-9595. p. 959

Brauer, Bonnie, Libr Tech, Summit Pacific College, 35235 Straiton Rd, Abbotsford, BC, V2S 7Z1, CANADA. Tel: 604-851-7230. Fax: 604-853-8951. p. 2724

Brauer, Lorraine, Chairperson, Hines Creek Municipal Library, 212-10 St, Hines Creek, AB, T0H 2A0, CANADA. Tel: 780-494-3879. Fax: 780-494-3605. p. 2707

Braughler, Jim, ILL, L D Fargo Public Library, 120 E Madison St, Lake Mills, WI, 53551-1644. Tel: 920-648-2166. Fax: 920-648-5561. p. 2604

Braught, Laura, Libr Mgr, Piedmont Regional Library, Maysville Public, 9247 Gillsville Rd, Maysville, GA, 30558. Tel: 706-652-2323. Fax: 706-652-2323. p. 557

Brault, Charles, Dir, Chamberlin Free Public Library, 46 Main St, Greenville, NH, 03048. Tel: 603-878-1105. Fax: 603-878-4092. p. 1449

Brault, Valerie, Tech Serv, American Scientific Corp Library, 3250 Holly Way, Chula Vista, CA, 91910-3217. Tel: 619-422-1754. Fax: 619-426-1280. p. 134

Braun, Dan, Head, YA, Worth Public Library District, 6917 W 111th St, Worth, IL, 60482. Tel: 708-448-2855. Fax: 708-448-9174. p. 721

Braun, Janice, Spec Coll & Archives Librn, Mills College, 5000 MacArthur Blvd, Oakland, CA, 94613. Tel: 510-430-2047. Fax: 510-430-2278. p. 197

Braun, Ken, Librn, Pioneer Hi-Bred International, Inc, 7300 NW 62nd Ave, Johnston, IA, 50131. Tel: 515-535-4818. Fax: 515-535-2184. p. 824

Braun, Marcia, Librn, Houston Community College Central College, Central Campus Library, 1300 Holman, Houston, TX, 77004. Tel: 713-718-6133. Fax: 713-718-6154. p. 2337

Braun, Pam, ILL, Ela Area Public Library District, 275 Mohawk Trail, Lake Zurich, IL, 60047. Tel: 847-438-3433. Fax: 847-438-9290. p. 663

Braun, Pat, Librn, Greenwood Public Library, 102 N Main St, Greenwood, WI, 54437. Tel: 715-267-7103. Fax: 715-267-6636. p. 2597

Braun, Phyllis, Asst Librn, Baldwin City Library, 800 Seventh St, Baldwin City, KS, 66006. Tel: 785-594-3411. Fax: 785-594-3411. p. 857

Braund-Allen, Juli, Librn, Alaska Resources Library & Information Services, Library Bldg, 3211 Providence Dr, Ste 111, Anchorage, AK, 99508-4614. Tel: 907-786-7666. Fax: 907-786-7652. p. 43

Braund-Allen, Juli, Ref & Instruction, University of Alaska Anchorage, Consortium Library, 3211 Providence Dr, Anchorage, AK, 99508-8176. Tel: 907-786-1871. Fax: 907-786-1834. p. 45

Braunstein, Mark, Visual Res Librn, Connecticut College, 270 Mohegan Ave, New London, CT, 06320-4196. Tel: 860-439-2729. Fax: 860-439-2871. p. 359

Brautigam, Colette, Visual Res, Lawrence University, 113 S Lawe St, Appleton, WI, 54911-5683. Fax: 920-832-6967. p. 2578

Brautigan, Faith, Dir, Kokomo-Howard County Public Library, 220 N Union St, Kokomo, IN, 46901-4614. Tel: 765-457-3242. Fax: 765-457-3683. p. 758

Brautigarm, David K, Per, Westminster College, S Market St, New Wilmington, PA, 16172-0001. Tel: 724-946-7330. Fax: 724-946-6220. p. 2097

Bravo, Kim, Curator, Free Library of Philadelphia, Automobile Reference Collection, 1901 Vine St, Philadelphia, PA, 19103-1189. Tel: 215-686-5404. p. 2107

Bravo, Phil, Br Head, Winnipeg Public Library, St James-Assiniboia, 1910 Portage Ave, Winnipeg, MB, R3J 0J2, CANADA. Tel: 204-986-5583. Fax: 204-986-3798. p. 2760

Bravos, Angelica, Ref Librn, Tech Serv, United States Geological Survey Library, 345 Middlefield Rd, Bldg 15 (MS-955), Menlo Park, CA, 94025-3591. Tel: 650-329-5025. Fax: 650-329-5132. p. 185

Brawley, Edith M, Archivist, Cat, Erskine College & Theological Seminary, One Depot St, Due West, SC, 29639. Tel: 864-379-8763. Fax: 864-379-2900. p. 2193

Brawn, Kari, Mgr, Calgary Public Library, Louise Riley Branch, 1904 14th Ave NW, Calgary, AB, T2N 1M5, CANADA. p. 2690

Brawner, Linda, Coordr, Educ Tech, Online Serv Coordr, Marygrove College Library, 8425 W McNichols Rd, Detroit, MI, 48221-2599. Tel: 313-927-1300. Fax: 313-927-1366. p. 1171

Brax, Jennifer, Adult Serv, H Leslie Perry Memorial Library, 205 Breckenridge St, Henderson, NC, 27536. Tel: 252-438-3316. Fax: 252-438-3744. p. 1800

Braxton, Susan M, Head Inst Librn, University of Illinois Library at Urbana-Champaign, Prairie Research Institute Library, 1816 S Oak St, Champaign, IL, 61820. Tel: 217-333-5856. Fax: 217-244-0802. p. 712

Bray, Angela, Br Mgr, Eugene Public Library, Bethel Branch, 1990 Echo Hollow Rd, Eugene, OR, 97402-7004. Tel: 541-682-5450. Fax: 541-682-5898. p. 1996

Bray, Angela, Br Mgr, Eugene Public Library, Sheldon Branch, 1566 Coburg Rd, Eugene, OR, 97401-4802. Tel: 541-682-5450. Fax: 541-682-5898. p. 1996

Bray, Angie, Br Serv Mgr, Eugene Public Library, 100 W Tenth Ave, Eugene, OR, 97401. Tel: 541-682-5450. Fax: 541-682-5898. p. 1996

Bray, Barbara, Librn, US Department of Labor, Curtis Bldg, Ste 740 W, 170 S Independence Mall W, Philadelphia, PA, 19106-3309. Tel: 215-861-4912. Fax: 215-861-4904. p. 2118

Bray, Brian W, Mgr, Sterne-Hoya House Museum & Library, 211 S Lanana St, Nacogdoches, TX, 75961-0012. Tel: 936-560-5426. Fax: 936-569-9813. p. 2365

Bray, Debbie Lamm, Dean, Salem Bible College Library, 12234 River Rd NE, Gervais, OR, 97026. Tel: 503-304-0092. Fax: 503-304-0899. p. 1999

Bray, Honore, Dir, Missoula Public Library, 301 E Main, Missoula, MT, 59802-4799. Tel: 406-721-2665. Fax: 406-728-5900. p. 1386

Bray, Katie, Pub Serv Librn, Bellingham Public Library, 210 Central Ave, CS-9710, Bellingham, WA, 98227-9710. Tel: 360-778-7323. p. 2508

Bray, Linda M, Dir, Libr & Archives, Unity Library & Archives, 1901 NW Blue Pkwy, Unity Village, MO, 64065-0001. Tel: 816-524-3550, Ext 2010. p. 1370

Bray, Nancy Davis, Interim Dir, Georgia College & State University, 320 N Wayne St, Milledgeville, GA, 31061-3397. Tel: 478-445-0991. Fax: 478-445-6847. p. 544

Bray, Sharon, Ch, Tumbler Ridge Public Library, 340 Front St, Tumbler Ridge, BC, V0C 2W0, CANADA. Tel: 250-242-4778. Fax: 250-242-4707. p. 2739

Bray, Vicki, Dir, Flewellin Memorial Library, 108 W Comanche Ave, Shabbona, IL, 60550. Tel: 815-824-2079. Fax: 815-824-2708. p. 701

Brayden, Rodger, Dir, Forest Park Public Library, 7555 Jackson Blvd, Forest Park, IL, 60130. Tel: 708-366-7171, Ext 102. Fax: 708-366-7293. p. 646

Brayford, Susan, Mgr, Southern Alberta Institute of Technology Library, 1301 16th Ave NW, Calgary, AB, T2M 0L4, CANADA. Tel: 403-210-4477. Fax: 403-284-8619. p. 2693

Brayford, Susan, Libr Mgr, SAIT Polytechnic, 1301 - 16 Ave NW, Calgary, AB, T2M 0L4, CANADA. Tel: 403-284-7231, 403-284-8897. Fax: 403-284-7238. p. 2977

Braz, Zoltan, YA Librn, North Brunswick Free Public Library, 880 Hermann Rd, North Brunswick, NJ, 08902. Tel: 732-246-3545. Fax: 732-246-1341. p. 1514

Brazeau, Linda, Asst Dir, Stockbridge Library Association, 46 Main St, Stockbridge, MA, 01262. Tel: 413-298-5501. Fax: 413-298-0218. p. 1129

Brazeau, Lyne, Librn, Plantagenet Village Library System, 550 Albert St, Plantagenet, ON, K0B 1L0, CANADA. Tel: 613-673-2051. Fax: 613-673-2051. p. 2836

Brazeau, Lyne, Librn, Plantagenet Village Library System, Lefaivre Branch, 1963 Hotel de Ville St, Lefaivre, ON, K0B 1J0, CANADA. Tel: 613-679-4928. Fax: 613-679-4928. p. 2836

Brazer, Susan, Ref, Salisbury University, 1101 Camden Ave, Salisbury, MD, 21801-6863. Tel: 410-543-6130. Fax: 410-543-6203. p. 1040

Brazil, Joanna, Youth Serv Librn, Winfield Public Library, 605 College St, Winfield, KS, 67156-3199. Tel: 620-221-4470. Fax: 620-221-6135. p. 903

Brazile, Orella, Dr, Univ Librn, Southern University at Shreveport, 3050 Martin Luther King Jr Dr, Shreveport, LA, 71107. Tel: 318-670-6401. Fax: 318-674-3403. p. 970

Brazill, Dan, Coordr, Lancaster County Prison Library, 625 E King St, Lancaster, PA, 17602-3199. Tel: 717-299-7814. p. 2076

Brazill, Mia, Assoc Dir, Coll Develop, Smith College Libraries, Northampton, MA, 01063. Tel: 413-585-2922. Fax: 413-585-2904. p. 1113

Brazin, Lillian, Dir, Libr Serv, Albert Einstein Healthcare Network, 5501 Old York Rd, Philadelphia, PA, 19141. Tel: 215-456-6345. Fax: 215-456-8267. p. 2106

Brazzale, Melinda, Mgr, Commun & Media Relations, Laramie County Library System, 2200 Pioneer Ave, Cheyenne, WY, 82001-3610. Tel: 307-773-7225. Fax: 307-634-2082. p. 2652

Bread, Monica, Librn, Saint Anthony Hospital, 1000 N Lee St, Oklahoma City, OK, 73102-1080. Tel: 405-272-6284. Fax: 405-272-7075. p. 1975

Breakenridge-Fink, Susan, Coordr, Admin Serv, Drake University, 2725 University Ave, Des Moines, IA, 50311. Tel: 515-271-3994. Fax: 515-271-3933. p. 809

Breaster, Steve, Librn, Riverside Community College District, 4800 Magnolia Ave, Riverside, CA, 92506-1299. Tel: 951-222-8651. Fax: 951-328-3679. p. 217

Breau, Kenneth, Mgr, Universite de Moncton, Centre d'études Acadiennes, 18, Ave Antonine-Maillet, Moncton, NB, E1A 3E9, CANADA. Tel: 506-858-4085. Fax: 506-858-4530. p. 2766

Breault, Laurel, Acq, Gladwin County District Library, 402 James Robertson Dr, Gladwin, MI, 48624. Tel: 989-426-8221. Fax: 989-426-6958. p. 1183

Breault, Liz, Dir, Abbott Memorial Library, One Church St, Dexter, ME, 04930. Tel: 207-924-7292. p. 983

Breaux, Stephanie, Dir, Whittier College, Fairchild Aerial Photography Collection, Fairchild Collection, Whittier College, Whittier, CA, 90608. Tel: 562-907-4220. Fax: 562-693-6117. p. 283

Brecht, Albert, Assoc Dean, Chief Info Officer, Prof, University of Southern California Libraries, Asa V Call Law Library, 699 Exposition Blvd, LAW 202, MC 0072, Los Angeles, CA, 90089-0072. Tel: 213-740-6482. Fax: 213-740-7179. p. 179

Brecht, Rae, Commun Serv, Brookings Public Library, 515 Third St, Brookings, SD, 57006. Tel: 605-692-9407. Fax: 605-692-9386. p. 2210

Breckbill, Anita, Head of Libr, University of Nebraska-Lincoln, Music Library, Westbrook Music Bldg 30, Lincoln, NE, 68588-0101. Tel: 402-472-6300. Fax: 402-472-1592. p. 1407

Breda, Karen S, Legal Info Librn, Boston College, 885 Centre St, Newton Centre, MA, 02459. Tel: 617-552-4407. Fax: 617-552-2889. p. 1110

Bredberg, Leann, Dir, Andalusia Township Library, 503 W Second St, Andalusia, IL, 61232. Tel: 309-798-2542. Fax: 309-798-2310. p. 588

Bredemeyer, Carol, Fac Serv Librn, Northern Kentucky University, Nunn Dr, Highland Heights, KY, 41099. Tel: 859-572-5395. Fax: 859-572-6529, 859-572-6664. p. 917

Bredhoff, Stacey, Curator, National Archives & Records Administration, Columbia Point, Boston, MA, 02125. Tel: 617-514-1600. Fax: 617-514-1593. p. 1064

Breece, Nancy, Br Mgr, Burlington County Library, Pemberton Community Library, 16 Broadway, Browns Mills, NJ, 08015. Tel: 609-893-8262. Fax: 609-893-7547. p. 1543

Breed, Liz, Mkt Dir, Capital Area District Libraries, 401 S Capitol Ave, Lansing, MI, 48933. Tel: 517-367-6348. Fax: 517-374-1068. p. 1200

Breed, Luellen, Automation Librn, University of Wisconsin-Parkside Library, 900 Wood Rd, Kenosha, WI, 53141. Tel: 262-595-2274. Fax: 262-595-2545. p. 2601

Breed, Scotty, Asst Librn, Stonington Historical Society, 40 Palmer St, Stonington, CT, 06378. Tel: 860-535-1131. p. 370

Breeden, Carolyn, VPres, Acad Affairs, Santa Ana College, 1530 W 17th St, Santa Ana, CA, 92706-3398. Tel: 714-564-6080. Fax: 714-564-6729. p. 259

Breeden, Kathy, Dir, Libr Serv, Columbia State Community College, 1665 Hampshire Pike, Columbia, TN, 38401. Tel: 931-540-2555. Fax: 931-540-2565. p. 2231

Breeden-Johnson, Cynthia, Literacy Prog Coordr, Hayward Public Library, 835 C St, Hayward, CA, 94541-5120. Tel: 510-881-7911. Fax: 510-293-5093. p. 157

Breedlove, Anne, Outreach Serv Librn, LeRoy Collins Leon County Public Library System, 200 W Park Ave, Tallahassee, FL, 32301-7720. Tel: 850-606-2665. Fax: 850-606-2601. p. 492

Breedlove, Janet, Libr Mgr, Rusk County Library, Tatum Public, 335 Hood, Tatum, TX, 75691. Tel: 903-947-2211. Fax: 903-947-3215. p. 2332

Breems, Jennifer, Ref, Dordt College, 498 Fourth Ave NE, Sioux Center, IA, 51250. Tel: 712-722-6040. Fax: 712-722-1198. p. 843

Breen, Jane, Ch, West Hartford Public Library, Julia Faxon Branch, 1073 New Britain Ave, West Hartford, CT, 06110. Tel: 860-561-8200. p. 376

Breen, Kate, ILL, Long Island University, 100 Second Ave, Brentwood, NY, 11717. Tel: 631-273-5112. Fax: 631-273-5198. p. 1584

Breen, Maribeth, Dir, Henry Carter Hull Library, Inc, Ten Killingworth Tpk, Clinton, CT, 06413. Tel: 860-669-2342. Fax: 860-669-8318. p. 334

Breen, Marty J, Ref Librn, Concordia University, 7400 Augusta St, River Forest, IL, 60305-1499. Tel: 708-209-3181. Fax: 708-209-3175. p. 694

Breen, Richard, Dir, Willamette University, J W Long Law Library, 245 Winter St SE, Salem, OR, 97301. Tel: 503-370-6386. Fax: 503-375-5426. p. 2019

Breen, Violet Allison, Head, Ref, Midwestern State University, 3410 Taft Ave, Wichita Falls, TX, 76308-2099. Tel: 940-397-4171. Fax: 940-397-4689. p. 2400

Breeze, Jerry, Govt Doc Librn, Columbia University, Lehman Library, 420 W 118th St, New York, NY, 10027. Tel: 212-854-3794. Fax: 212-854-2495. p. 1675

Breezeel, Brenda, Syst Librn, Harding University, 915 E Market St, Searcy, AR, 72149-2267. Tel: 501-279-5387. p. 114

Bregman, Adeane, Librn, Boston College Libraries, Bapst Art Library, 140 Commonwealth Ave, Chestnut Hill, MA, 02467-3810. Tel: 617-552-3136. Fax: 617-552-0510. p. 1080

Bregoli, Marilyn, Dir, Pine Manor College, 400 Heath St, Chestnut Hill, MA, 02467. Tel: 617-731-7083. Fax: 617-731-7045. p. 1081

Brehio, Janice, Ch, Richards Free Library, 58 N Main St, Newport, NH, 03773-1597. Tel: 603-863-3430. Fax: 603-863-3022. p. 1460

Brehm-Heeger, Paula, Operations Mgr, Public Library of Cincinnati & Hamilton County, 800 Vine St, Cincinnati, OH, 45202-2009. Tel: 513-369-6941. Fax: 513-369-6993. p. 1871

Breidenbach, Susan, Tech Serv Mgr, Bedford Public Library, 1323 K St, Bedford, IN, 47421. Tel: 812-275-4471. Fax: 812-278-5244. p. 726

Breier, Elisabeth, Ser, Sir Mortimer B Davis Jewish General Hospital, 3755 Cote Ste Catherine Rd, A-200, Montreal, QC, H3T 1E2, CANADA. Tel: 514-340-8222, Ext 5927. Fax: 514-340-7552. p. 2901

Breiner, Arlene, Cat, Albright College, 13th & Exeter Sts, Reading, PA, 19604. Tel: 610-921-7204. Fax: 610-921-7509. p. 2132

Breitenbach, Kathleen, Teen Serv Librn, Hamilton Township Public Library, One Justice Samuel A Alito, Jr Way, Hamilton, NJ, 08619. Tel: 609-581-4060. Fax: 609-581-4071. p. 1490

Breiter, Jane, Librn, Frankfort Career Development Center Library, 380 Coffee Tree Rd, Frankfort, KY, 40601. Tel: 502-564-2120. p. 913

Breithaupt, Lisa, Br Mgr, Clermont County Public Library, Owensville Branch, 2548 US Rte 50, Owensville, OH, 45160. Tel: 513-732-6084. Fax: 513-732-9168. p. 1858

Breithaupt, Richard H, Jr, Libr Dir, American Heritage Library & Museum, 600 S Central Ave, Glendale, CA, 91204-2009. Tel: 818-240-1775. p. 154

Breithut, Kathy, Youth Serv Mgr, Worcester County Library, 307 N Washington St, Snow Hill, MD, 21863. Tel: 443-235-5597. Fax: 410-632-1159. p. 1042

Breithut, Kathy, Youth Serv Mgr, Worcester County Library, Ocean Pines Branch, 11107 Cathell Rd, Berlin, MD, 21811. Tel: 410-208-4014. p. 1042

Breitmeyer, Alane, Instrul Designer, St Charles Community College, 4601 Mid Rivers Mall Dr, Cottleville, MO, 63376. Tel: 636-922-8647. Fax: 636-922-8433. p. 1326

Breitsch, Jamie, Ref Serv, Ad, Kirtland Public Library, 9267 Chillicothe Rd, Kirtland, OH, 44094. Tel: 440-256-7323. Fax: 440-256-1372. p. 1908

Brekhus, Rachel, Humanities Librn, University of Missouri-Columbia, Elmer Ellis Library, Ellis Library Bldg, Rm 104, Columbia, MO, 65201-5149. Tel: 573-882-7563. Fax: 573-882-8044. p. 1325

Brekke, Tanya, Tech Serv, Crook County Library, 414 Main St, Sundance, WY, 82729. Tel: 307-283-1006, 307-283-1008. Fax: 307-283-1006. p. 2660

Breland, Joyce, Librn, Pine Forest Regional Library, William Estes Powell Memorial, 1502 Bolton Ave, Beaumont, MS, 39423. Tel: 601-784-3471. Fax: 601-784-3471. p. 1314

Breland, Mary-Louise, Dir, Laurel-Jones County Library System, Inc, 530 Commerce St, Laurel, MS, 39440. Tel: 601-428-4313. Fax: 601-428-0597. p. 1306

Bremer, Carrie, Dir, Athena Public Library, 418 E Main St, Athena, OR, 97813. Tel: 541-566-2470. Fax: 541-566-2470. p. 1990

Bremer, Glenda L, Dir, Rock County Community Library, 201 W Main, Luverne, MN, 56156. Tel: 507-449-5040. Fax: 507-449-5034. p. 1256

Bremer, Lynn, Dir, Santa Barbara Mission, 2201 Laguna St, Santa Barbara, CA, 93105. Tel: 805-682-4713, Ext 152. Fax: 805-682-9323. p. 261

Bremer, Marian, Mgr, Massachusetts Institute of Technology, 244 Wood St, Lexington, MA, 02420-9176. Tel: 781-981-7171. Fax: 781-981-0345. p. 1099

Bremer, Nolan, Cat Librn, Concordia University Library, 2811 NE Holman St, Portland, OR, 97211-6067. Tel: 503-493-6210. Fax: 503-280-8697. p. 2010

Bremer, Peter, Ref Coordr, University of Minnesota-Morris, 600 E Fourth St, Morris, MN, 56267. Tel: 320-589-6173. Fax: 320-589-6168. p. 1267

Bremer, Robert, User Serv Librn, Louisiana Tech University, Everett St at The Columns, Ruston, LA, 71272. Tel: 318-257-3555. Fax: 318-257-2579. p. 966

Bremer, Thomas, Dean, Winona State University, 175 W Mark St, Winona, MN, 55987-5838. Tel: 507-457-5146. p. 1290

Bremigen, Jean, Operations Mgr, Roger & Peggy Madigan Library, 999 Hagan Way, Williamsport, PA, 17701. Tel: 570-327-4523. Fax: 570-327-4503. p. 2156

Bremner, Patricia E, Doc, United States Army, AMSRD-NSC-OC-T, 20 Kansas St, Natick, MA, 01760-5056. Tel: 508-233-4306. Fax: 508-233-4248. p. 1108

Bremner, Sally, Med Ref Librn, University of Alaska Anchorage, Consortium Library, 3211 Providence Dr, Anchorage, AK, 99508-8176. Tel: 907-786-1871. Fax: 907-786-1834. p. 45

Bren, Barbara, Head, Doc Serv, Head, Ref, University of Wisconsin-Whitewater Library, 800 W Main St, Whitewater, WI, 53190. Tel: 262-472-5521. Fax: 262-472-5727. p. 2649

Brenan, Amy, Access Serv, Duke University Libraries, Ford Library, One Towerview Rd, Durham, NC, 27708. Tel: 919-660-7873. Fax: 919-660-7950. p. 1787

Brendel, Rebecca, Librn, Yuma County Library District, 2951 S 21st Dr, Yuma, AZ, 85364. Tel: 928-373-2453. Fax: 928-782-9420. p. 91

Brenden, Sheri, Res Librn, Faegre & Benson, LLP, 2200 Wells Fargo Ctr, 90 South Seventh St, Minneapolis, MN, 55402-3901. Tel: 612-766-7000. Fax: 612-766-1600. p. 1259

Brendle, Mary Sue, Librn, Mountain Regional Library System, Union County Public Library, PO Box 1029, Blairsville, GA, 30514-1029. Tel: 706-745-7491. Fax: 706-745-5652. p. 558

Breneman, Mary Jo, Head, Circ, Coal City Public Library District, 85 N Garfield St, Coal City, IL, 60416. Tel: 815-634-4552. Fax: 815-634-2950. p. 630

Brenenson, Stephanie, Bibliog Instr, Ref Serv, Florida International University, 11200 SW Eighth St, Miami, FL, 33199. Tel: 305-348-1843. Fax: 305-348-3408. p. 465

Brenion, Frederick, Sr Librn, Patton State Hospital, Patients' Library, 3102 E Highland Ave, Patton, CA, 92369. Tel: 909-425-6039. Fax: 909-425-6162. p. 207

Brennan, Adam, Ref Librn, Tulsa Community College Learning Resources Center, Metro Campus, 909 S Boston Ave, Tulsa, OK, 74119-2011. Tel: 918-595-7330. Fax: 918-595-7179. p. 1983

Brennan, Bernadette, Libr Serv Librn, Bedford Public Library System, 321 N Bridge St, Bedford, VA, 24523-1924. Tel: 540-586-8911, Ext 2115. Fax: 540-586-8875. p. 2450

Brennan, Cathy, Librn, Alberta Beach Municipal Library, PO Box 186, Alberta Beach, AB, T0E 0A0, CANADA. Tel: 780-924-3491. Fax: 780-924-3491. p. 2683

Brennan, Christopher, Dir, New Brunswick Theological Seminary, 21 Seminary Pl, New Brunswick, NJ, 08901-1159. Tel: 732-246-5604. Fax: 732-249-5412. p. 1508

Brennan, David, Coll Develop & Digital Res Mgt, Pennsylvania State University, College of Medicine, Penn State Hershey, Harrell Health Sciences Library, 500 University Dr, Hershey, PA, 17033. Tel: 717-531-0003, Ext 285323. Fax: 717-531-8635. p. 2069

Brennan, Deirdre, Exec Dir, Oak Park Public Library, 834 Lake St, Oak Park, IL, 60301. Tel: 708-697-6911. Fax: 708-697-6900. p. 684

Brennan, Laura, Ch, Northborough Free Library, 34 Main St, Northborough, MA, 01532-1942. Tel: 508-393-5025. Fax: 508-393-5027. p. 1114

Brennan, Linda, Media Spec, Hamilton College, Media, Christian Johnson Bldg, 198 College Hill Rd, Clinton, NY, 13323-1299. Tel: 315-859-4923. p. 1608

Brennan, M E, Mgr, Integrated Information Solutions, 600 Mountain Ave, Rm 1B 202, Murray Hill, NJ, 07974. Tel: 908-582-4840. Fax: 908-582-3146. p. 2949

Brennan, Mary Ann, Cat, Warren County-Vicksburg Public Library, 700 Veto St, Vicksburg, MS, 39180-3595. Tel: 601-636-6411. Fax: 601-634-4809. p. 1317

Brennan, Patricia Flately, Prof, University of Wisconsin-Madison, 4217 H C White Hall, 600 N Park St, Madison, WI, 53706. Tel: 608-263-5251. Fax: 608-263-4849. p. 2976

Brennan, Ray, Ref, Cross' Mills Public Library, 4417 Old Post Rd, Charlestown, RI, 02813. Tel: 401-364-6211. Fax: 401-364-0609. p. 2164

Brennan, Susan, Dir, Weston Public Library, 87 School St, Weston, MA, 02493. Tel: 781-893-3312. Fax: 781-529-0174. p. 1139

Brennan, Theresa, Asst Librn, Stirling-Randon Public Library, 43 Front St W, Stirling, ON, K0K 3E0, CANADA. Tel: 613-395-2837. p. 2845

Brennan, Tish, Head, Ref, Rhode Island College, 600 Mt Pleasant Ave, Providence, RI, 02908-1924. Tel: 401-456-8126. Fax: 401-456-9646. p. 2174

Brennecke, Adrienne, Ref/Data Acq Librn, Federal Reserve Bank of Saint Louis, One Federal Reserve Bank Plaza, Saint Louis, MO, 63102-2005. Tel: 314-444-7479. Fax: 314-444-8694. p. 1354

Brenneise, Harvey, Librn, Rancho Santa Ana Botanic Garden Library, 1500 N College Ave, Claremont, CA, 91711. Tel: 909-625-8767, Ext 236. Fax: 909-626-7670. p. 135

Brenneman, Betsey J, Sr Librn, Electronic Res, Worcester State College, 486 Chandler St, Worcester, MA, 01602-2597. Tel: 508-929-8801. Fax: 508-929-8198. p. 1145

Brenneman, Martha, Librn, Memorial Public Library of the Borough of Alexandria, 313 Main St, Ste 1, Alexandria, PA, 16611. Tel: 814-669-4313. p. 2026

Brenner, Anji, City Librn, Mill Valley Public Library, 375 Throckmorton Ave, Mill Valley, CA, 94941-2698. Tel: 415-389-4292, Ext 115. Fax: 415-388-8929. p. 186

Brenner, Candace, Br Mgr, Mansfield-Richland County Public Library, Madison Branch, 1395 Grace St, Mansfield, OH, 44905. Tel: 419-589-7050. Fax: 419-589-7108. p. 1913

Brenner, Eric, Ref, Skyline College Library, 3300 College Dr, San Bruno, CA, 94066-1698. Tel: 650-738-4311. Fax: 650-738-4149. p. 230

Brenner, Terry, Libr Asst I, Missouri Supreme Court Library, Supreme Court Bldg, 207 W High St, Jefferson City, MO, 65101. Tel: 573-751-7331. Fax: 573-751-2573. p. 1335

Breno, Patricia, Libr Mgr, Owens Community College Library, 30335 Oregon Rd, Perrysburg, OH, 43551. Tel: 567-661-7020. Fax: 567-661-7021. p. 1929

Brenoel, Dorothy, ILL, Tech Serv, Thiel College, 75 College Ave, Greenville, PA, 16125-2183. Tel: 724-589-2124, 724-589-2205. Fax: 724-589-2122. p. 2063

Brenot, Nancy L, Acq, Allegheny College Library, 555 N Main St, Meadville, PA, 16335. Tel: 814-332-3768. Fax: 814-337-5673. p. 2086

Brent, Katherine, Circ & ILL, State University of New York College of Agriculture & Technology, 142 Schenectady Ave, Cobleskill, NY, 12043. Tel: 518-255-5851. Fax: 518-255-5843. p. 1608

Brent, Roberta, Acq, Lutheran Theological Seminary, 66 Seminary Ridge, Gettysburg, PA, 17325. Tel: 717-334-6286, Ext 2102. Fax: 717-337-1611. p. 2060

Brenton, Janelle, Libr Asst, Nova Scotia Department of Natural Resources Library, Founders Sq, 1701 Hollis St, 3rd Flr, Halifax, NS, B3J 3M8, CANADA. Tel: 902 424 3179. Fax: 902-424-7735. p. 2782

Brents, Jessica, Head Librn, Mattie Terry Public Library, 311 N Johnson, Valliant, OK, 74764. Tel: 580-933-4883. Fax: 580-933-5532. p. 1984

Breolini, Ann, Mgr, Libr & Info Serv, Vancouver Aquarium Marine Science Centre, 845 Avison Way, Stanley Park, Vancouver, BC, V6G 3E2, CANADA. Tel: 604-659-3404. Fax: 604-659-3515. p. 2743

Brereton, Rudy, Asst Librn, Hatton School & Public Library, 503 Fourth St, Hatton, ND, 58240. Tel: 701-543-3456. Fax: 701-543-3459. p. 1844

Bresett, Ardyce, Dir, Pember Library & Museum of Natural History, 33 W Main St, Granville, NY, 12832. Tel: 518-642-2525. Fax: 518-642-2525. p. 1630

Bresette, Jae Lynn, Tech Serv, Jackson County Library Services, 205 S Central Ave, Medford, OR, 97501-2730. Tel: 541-774-6553. Fax: 541-774-6748. p. 2005

Breska, Bret, Circ & Tech Serv Mgr, Lyons Public Library, 4209 Joliet Ave, Lyons, IL, 60534-1597. Tel: 708-447-3577. Fax: 708-447-3589. p. 668

Bresler, Barbara, Head of Libr, Adath Israel Congregation, 3201 E Galbraith Rd, Cincinnati, OH, 45236. Tel: 513-793-1800. Fax: 513-792-5085. p. 1868

Bresler, Carey, Dir, Atglen Public Library, 413 Valley Ave, Atglen, PA, 19310-1402. Tel: 610-593-6848. Fax: 610-593-6848. p. 2030

Breslin, Ellen, Librn, New York State Legislative Library, State Capitol, Rm 337, Albany, NY, 12224-0345. Tel: 518-455-2468. Fax: 518-426-6901. p. 1569

Breslin, Lenore, Evening Ref Librn, Helen Kate Furness Free Library, 100 N Providence Rd, Wallingford, PA, 19086. Tel: 610-566-9331. Fax: 610-566-9337. p. 2150

Breslow, Phyllis, Ch, Medford Public Library, 111 High St, Medford, MA, 02155. Tel: 781-395-7950. Fax: 781-391-2261. p. 1104

Bresnahan, Kimberly, Coordr, Libr Serv, Missouri Department of Corrections, 2729 Plaza Dr, Jefferson City, MO, 65109-1146. Tel: 573-526-6540. Fax: 573-751-4099. p. 1334

Bresnahan, Kimberly, Libr Serv Coordr, Missouri Department of Corrections, Western Reception & Diagnostic Correctional Center, 3401 Faraon St, Saint Joseph, MO, 64506-5101. Tel: 816-387-2158. Fax: 816-387-2217. p. 1335

Bresnahan, Kimberly, Librn, Missouri Department of Corrections, Western Missouri Correctional Center, 609 E Pence Rd, Cameron, MO, 64429-8823. Tel: 816-632-1390, Ext 421. Fax: 816-632-7882. p. 1335

Bresnahan, Megan, Librn, Bibliogr for Computer Sci & Math, University of Colorado Boulder, Gemmill Library of Engineering, Mathematics & Physics, Mathematics Bldg, Rm 135, 184 UCB, Boulder, CO, 80309-0184. Tel: 303-492-4679. Fax: 303-492-6488. p. 291

Bressler, Darla, Res Librn, Bloomsburg University of Pennsylvania, 400 E Second St, Bloomsburg, PA, 17815-1301. Tel: 570-389-4224. Fax: 570-389-3066. p. 2035

Bressman, Anne S, Librn, Temple Emanuel Library, 1101 Springdale Rd, Cherry Hill, NJ, 08003. Tel: 856-489-0035. Fax: 856-489-0032. p. 1478

Brestel, Mary Beth, Br Mgr, Public Library of Cincinnati & Hamilton County, Delhi Township, 5095 Foley Rd, Cincinnati, OH, 45238. Tel: 513-369-6019. Fax: 513-369-4453. p. 1871

Bretell, Cynthia, Prog Head, Siast Kelsey Campus, 107 Fourth Ave S, Saskatoon, SK, S7K 5X2, CANADA. Tel: 306-659-3850. Fax: 306-933-6490. p. 2979

Bretscher, Susan, Librn, Our Lady of Lourdes Memorial Hospital Library, 169 Riverside Dr, Binghamton, NY, 13905. Tel: 607-798-5290. Fax: 607-798-5989. p. 1582

Bretschneider, Kathy, Dir, Lied Battle Creek Public Library, 100 S Fourth St, Battle Creek, NE, 68715. Tel: 402-675-6934. Fax: 402-675-3911. p. 1392

Brett, Lorraine, Asst Librn, Union Hospital, 1606 N Seventh St, Terre Haute, IN, 47804. Tel: 812-238-7641. Fax: 812-238-7595. p. 781

Bretvold, Geri, In Charge, New Town Public Library, PO Box 309, New Town, ND, 58763-0309. Tel: 701-627-4812. Fax: 701-627-4316. p. 1847

Bretz Wallace, Cinda S, Dir, Willard Memorial Library, Six W Emerald St, Willard, OH, 44890-1498. Tel: 419-933-8564. Fax: 419-933-4783. p. 1948

Bretzin, Charles F, Dir, Portville Free Library, Two N Main St, Portville, NY, 14770-9530. Tel: 716-933-8441. Fax: 716-933-7020. p. 1721

Breuer, Jennifer, Dir, Glen Ridge Free Public Library, 240 Ridgewood Ave, Glen Ridge, NJ, 07028. Tel: 973-748-5482. Fax: 973-748-9350. p. 1488

Brevig, Charlotte, Asst Librn, Chatfield Public Library, 314 S Main St, Chatfield, MN, 55923. Tel: 507-867-3480. Fax: 507-867-3480. p. 1245

Brew, Charlar, Dir, Saint Martin Parish Library, 201 Porter St, Saint Martinville, LA, 70582. Tel: 337-394-2207, Ext 23. Fax: 337-394-2248. p. 967

Brewer, Barbara, Dir, Monroe Public Library, 925 16th Ave, Monroe, WI, 53566-1497. Tel: 608-328-7010. Fax: 608-329-4657. p. 2623

Brewer, Becky, Head, Info Serv, Jackson County Public Library, 303 W Second St, Seymour, IN, 47274-2147. Tel: 812-522-3412, Ext 239. Fax: 812-522-5456. p. 777

Brewer, Debra, Librn, Alleghany County Public Library, 122 N Main St, Sparta, NC, 28675. Tel: 336-372-5573. Fax: 336-372-4912. p. 1824

Brewer, Gayla, Acq, Cherokee Regional Library System, 305 S Duke St, LaFayette, GA, 30728-2936. Tel: 706-638-2064. Fax: 706-638-3979. p. 538

Brewer, Gayla, Br Mgr, Cherokee Regional Library System, Dade County Public Library, 102 Court St, Trenton, GA, 30752. Tel: 706-657-7857. Fax: 706-657-7860. p. 538

Brewer, Gayla C, Librn, Electronic Computer Programming College Inc Library, 3805 Brainerd Rd, Chattanooga, TN, 37411. Tel: 423-624-0077. Fax: 423-624-1575. p. 2227

Brewer, Jan, Ref, Stillwater Public Library, 224 N Third St, Stillwater, MN, 55082. Tel: 651-275-4338. Fax: 651-275-4342. p. 1285

Brewer, Janet L, Dr, Dir, Anderson University, Robert A Nicholson Library, 1100 E Fifth St, Anderson, IN, 46012-3495. Tel: 765-641-4280. Fax: 765-641-3850. p. 724

Brewer, Jenny, Ad, Helen Hall Library, 100 W Walker, League City, TX, 77573-3899. Tel: 281-554-1108. Fax: 281-554-1118. p. 2354

Brewer, Johnette, Libr Asst II, Central Carolina Technical College Library, 506 N Guignard Dr, Sumter, SC, 29150. Tel: 803-778-6647. Fax: 803-778-7889. p. 2206

Brewer, Julie, Mrg, Admin Serv, Mgr, Libr Human Res, University of Delaware Library, 181 S College Ave, Newark, DE, 19717-5267. Tel: 302-831-2231. Fax: 302-831-1046. p. 386

Brewer, Karen, Dir, New York University School of Medicine, Medical Science Bldg 195, 550 First Ave, New York, NY, 10016-6450. Tel: 212-263-5397. Fax: 212-263-6534. p. 1695

Brewer, Kathryn, Librn, Post & Schell, PC, Four Penn Center, 1600 JFK Blvd, 15th Flr, Philadelphia, PA, 19103-2808. Tel: 215-587-1100. Fax: 215-587-1444. p. 2115

Brewer, Kathy, Ch, Youth Serv, Sedro-Woolley Public Library, 802 Ball Ave, Sedro-Woolley, WA, 98284-2008. Tel: 360-855-1166. p. 2535

Brewer, Kristina, Libr Dir, Trine University, 720 Park Ave, Angola, IN, 46703. Tel: 260-665-4162. Fax: 260-665-4283. p. 724

Brewer, Linda, Librn, Southport Memorial Library, 1032 Hendricks Hill Rd, Southport, ME, 04576-3309. Tel: 207-633-2741. p. 1002

Brewer, Maggie, Fiction & Readers' Advisor Coordr, North Kingstown Free Library, 100 Boone St, North Kingstown, RI, 02852-5176. Tel: 401-294-3306. Fax: 401-294-1690. p. 2170

Brewer, Marvin, Librn, John Portman & Associates Library, 303 Peachtree St NE, Ste 4600, Atlanta, GA, 30308. Tel: 404-614-5555. Fax: 404-614-5553. p. 518

Brewer, Mary, Div Mgr of Info Res, Arkansas State Library, 900 W Capitol, Ste 100, Little Rock, AR, 72201-3108. Tel: 501-682-2326. Fax: 501-682-1529. p. 105

Brewer, Patsy, Dir, Waynesboro-Wayne County Library System, 1103A Mississippi Dr, Waynesboro, MS, 39367. Tel: 601-735-2268. Fax: 601-735-6407. p. 1317

Brewer, Rick, Asst Dir, Res, Educ & Clinical Serv, University of Kentucky Libraries, Medical Center Library, 800 Rose St, Lexington, KY, 40536-0298. Tel: 859-323-5296. Fax: 859-323-1040. p. 922

Brewer, Rosy, Managing Librn I, Sno-Isle Libraries, Mountlake Terrace Community Library, 23300 58th Ave W, Mountlake Terrace, WA, 98043. Tel: 425-776-8722. Fax: 425-776-3411. p. 2542

Brewer, Roxane, Cat Supvr, McDaniel College, Two College Hill, Westminster, MD, 21157-4390. Tel: 410-857-2847. Fax: 410-857-2748. p. 1046

Brewer, Sharon, Br Mgr, Chatham County Public Libraries, Goldston Public Library, 9235 Pittsboro-Goldston Rd, Goldston, NC, 27252-0040. Tel: 919-898-4522. p. 1823

Brewer, Shasta, Br Coordr, Tech Serv, York County Library, 138 E Black St, Rock Hill, SC, 29731. Tel: 803-981-5832. Fax: 803-981-5866. p. 2203

Brewer, Shirley, Dir, Oglala Lakota College, Pine Ridge College Center, PO Box 439, Pine Ridge, SD, 57770. Tel: 605-867-5893. Fax: 605-867-1241. p. 2214

Brewer, Tony, Br Mgr, High Plains Library District, Erie Community Library, 400 Powers St, Erie, CO, 80516. Tel: 720-685-5202. Fax: 720-685-5201. p. 312

Brewerton, Colleen, ILL, Tech Serv, Madison Library District, 73 N Center, Rexburg, ID, 83440-1539. Tel: 208-356-3461. p. 582

Brewster, Cythia, Asst Librn, Frost Free Library, 28 Jaffrey Rd, Marlborough, NH, 03455. Tel: 603-876-4479. Fax: 603-876-4479. p. 1457

Brewster, Jay, Acq Spec, Portland Community College Library, 12000 SW 49th AV, Portland, OR, 97219. Tel: 971-722-4633. Fax: 971-722-8397. p. 2013

Brewster, Mary, Dir, Bethalto Public Library District, 321 S Prairie St, Bethalto, IL, 62010-1525. Tel: 618-377-8141. Fax: 618-377-3520. p. 594

Brewster, Nancy, Asst Dir, Edward U Demmer Memorial Library, 6961 W School St, Three Lakes, WI, 54562. Tel: 715-546-3391. Fax: 715-546-2930. p. 2642

Brey, Mary, Tech Serv, Spring Green Community Library, 230 E Monroe St, Spring Green, WI, 53588-8035. Tel: 608-588-2276. p. 2639

Breyer, Gail, Circ, Loyola-Notre Dame Library, Inc, 200 Winston Ave, Baltimore, MD, 21212. Tel: 410-617-6800. Fax: 410-617-6895. p. 1015

Breyer, Jack, Dr, Dir, United States Navy, 1002 Balch Blvd, Bldg 1003, Stennis Space Center, MS, 39522-5001. Tel: 228-688-4597. Fax: 228-688-4191. p. 1315

Breyfogle, D, Assoc Dir, Coll, University of Manitoba Libraries, Elizabeth Dafoe Libr, Rm 156, Winnipeg, MB, R3T 2N2, CANADA. Tel: 204-474-9881. Fax: 204-474-7583. p. 2758

Breza, Jeanna, Acq, Community Service, Inc Library, 114 E Whiteman St, Yellow Springs, OH, 45387. Tel: 937-767-2161. Fax: 937-767-2826. p. 1952

Breznau, Adrienne, Librn II, Colorado Department of Corrections, 3600 Havana St, Denver, CO, 80239. Tel: 303-307-2500, Ext 3608. Fax: 303-307-2674. p. 299

Breznay, Ann Marie, Assoc Dean, Budget & Planning, University of Utah, Marriott Library, 295 S 1500 East, Salt Lake City, UT, 84112-0860. Tel: 801-581-3852. Fax: 801-585-7185. p. 2415

Brhel, Richard, Dir, Myers University, 3921 Chester Ave, Cleveland, OH, 44114. Tel: 216-432-8990. Fax: 216-426-9296. p. 1880

Briand, Mary B, Head Librn, Harris Corporation-GCS, Library 62A-130, 1650 Robert J Conlan Blvd NE, Palm Bay, FL, 32905-3378. Tel: 321-724-7733. Fax: 321-729-1019. p. 479

Briand, Simone, Asst Dir, Cleveland Chiropractic College, 10850 Lowell Ave, Overland Park, KS, 66210. Tel: 913-234-0810. Fax: 913-234-0901. p. 887

Briant, Cathy, Adult Serv, Somerset County Library System, Hillsborough Public, Hillsborough Municipal Complex, 379 S Branch Rd, Hillsborough, NJ, 08844. Tel: 908-369-2200. Fax: 908-369-8242. p. 1475

Briant, Susan, Dir, Haddonfield Public Library, 60 Haddon Ave, Haddonfield, NJ, 08033-2422. Tel: 856-429-1304. Fax: 856-429-3760. p. 1489

Bricault, Camille, Head Librn, Bibliothéques municipales de Saint-Jean-sur-Richelieu, 180, rue Laurier, CP 1025, Saint-Jean-sur-Richelieu, QC, J3B 7B2, CANADA. Tel: 450-357-2112. Fax: 450-359-2457. p. 2911

Bricco, Ellen, Circ, Northeast Wisconsin Technical College Library, 2740 W Mason St, Green Bay, WI, 54303-4966. Tel: 920-498-6812. Fax: 920-498-6910. p. 2596

Brice, Donna, Circ, Manchester Community College Library, Great Path, Manchester, CT, 06040. Tel: 860-512-2878. Fax: 860-512-2871. p. 350

Brice, Donna, Dir, Eastern Lancaster County Library, 11 Chestnut Dr, New Holland, PA, 17557-9437. Tel: 717-354-0525. Fax: 717-354-7787. p. 2096

Brice, Elizabeth, Asst Dean, Tech Serv, Head, Spec Coll & Archives, Miami University Libraries, 225 King Library, Oxford, OH, 45056. Tel: 513-529-4140. Fax: 513-529-3110. p. 1926

Brice, Heather, Librn, Windber Medical Center, 600 Somerset Ave, Windber, PA, 15963. Tel: 814-467-3000. Fax: 814-266-8230. p. 2157

Brice, John, Syst Adminr, Crawford County Federated Library System, 848 N Main St, Meadville, PA, 16335-2689. Tel: 814-336-1773. Fax: 814-333-8173. p. 2086

Brice, John J, III, Exec Dir, Meadville Public Library, 848 N Main St, Meadville, PA, 16335-2689. Tel: 814-336-1773. Fax: 814-333-8173. p. 2086

Brick, Gale, Librn, Parkland Regional Library, Ituna Branch, 317 Fourth Ave N, Ituna, SK, S0A 1N0, CANADA. Tel: 306-795-2672. p. 2932

Brickhouse, Veronica, Mgr, Dare County Library, 700 N Hwy 64-264, Manteo, NC, 27954. Tel: 252-473-2372. Fax: 252-473-6034. p. 1808

Brickley, Loretta, Ch, Anamosa Public Library & Learning Center, 600 E First St, Anamosa, IA, 52205. Tel: 319-462-2183. Fax: 319-462-5349. p. 793

Brickner-Schulz, Elise, Dir, Libr Serv, Miller Nash LLP Library, 111 SW Fifth Ave, 3400 US Bancorp Tower, Portland, OR, 97204-3699. Tel: 503-205-2427. Fax: 503-224-0155. p. 2011

Bridge, Frank, Pub Serv Adminr, Chesterfield County Public Library, 9501 Lori Rd, Chesterfield, VA, 23832. Tel: 804-748-1980. Fax: 804-751-4679. p. 2457

Bridges, Abbie, Librn, Mono County Free Library, Bridgeport, 94 N School St, Bridgeport, CA, 93517. Tel: 760-932-7482. Fax: 760-932-7539. p. 182

Bridges, Emily, Librn, Advocates for Youth, 2000 M St NW, Ste 750, Washington, DC, 20036. Tel: 202-419-3420, Ext 43. Fax: 202-419-1448. p. 391

Bridges, Ginny, Mgr, Brown County Public Library, Sardinia Branch, 13309 Purdy Rd, Sardinia, OH, 45171. Tel: 937-446-1565. Fax: 937-445-1506. p. 1919

Bridges, Jane, Mgr, Memorial Health University Medical Center, 4700 Waters Ave, Savannah, GA, 31403. Tel: 912-350-8345. p. 550

Bridges, Jo, Youth Serv, Oakland Park City Library, 1298 NE 37th St, Oakland Park, FL, 33334. Tel: 954-630-4372. Fax: 954-561-6146. p. 473

Bridges, Kimberly, Tech Serv, Bryan College Station Public Library System, 201 E 26th St, Bryan, TX, 77803-5356. Tel: 979-209-5600. Fax: 979-209-5610. p. 2292

Bridges, Peggy, Dir, Harcourt Inc, 6277 Sea Harbor Dr, Orlando, FL, 32887. Tel: 407-345-3113. Fax: 407-351-9906. p. 476

Bridges, Pepre, Libr Dir, Macon County-Tuskegee Public Library, 302 S Main St, Tuskegee, AL, 36083-1894. Tel: 334-727-5192. Fax: 334-727-5989. p. 39

Bridges, Rex, Pub Serv, Jackson-George Regional Library System, 3214 Pascagoula St, Pascagoula, MS, 39567. Tel: 228-769-3130. Fax: 228-769-3146. p. 1310

Bridges, Ruth, Dir, Schiff, Hardin LLP Library, 233 S Wacker Dr, Ste 6600, Chicago, IL, 60606. Tel: 312-258-5500. Fax: 312-258-5600. p. 624

Bridges, Shirley, Libr Asst I, Montgomery City-County Public Library System, Bertha Pleasant Williams Library - Rosa L Parks Avenue Branch, 1276 Rosa L Parks Ave, Montgomery, AL, 36108. Tel: 334-240-4979. Fax: 334-240-4925. p. 31

Bridgewater, Carolyn, Ref, Louisiana State University Health Sciences Center, 433 Bolivar St, Box B3-1, New Orleans, LA, 70112-2223. Tel: 504-568-6100. Fax: 504-568-7718. p. 961

Bridgewater, Gera J, Head, Pub Serv, Ref, Delgado Community College, Bldg 10, Rm 116, 615 City Park Ave, New Orleans, LA, 70119. Tel: 504-671-5316. p. 959

Bridgewood, Bobbie, Mgr, Tulsa City-County Library, Nathan Hale Library, 6038 E 23rd St, Tulsa, OK, 74114. Tel: 918-669-6060. Fax: 918-669-6062. p. 1983

Bridgforth, Don, Dir, Human Res, Mid-Continent Public Library, 15616 E US Hwy 24, Independence, MO, 64050-2098. Tel: 816-836-5200. Fax: 816-521-7253. p. 1332

Bridgman, Susan, Br Head, Vancouver Public Library, Dunbar, 4515 Dunbar St, Vancouver, BC, V6S 2G7, CANADA. Tel: 604-665-3968. Fax: 604-665-3550. p. 2744

Bridle, Jane, Br Head, Winnipeg Public Library, Fort Garry, 1360 Pembina Hwy, Winnipeg, MB, R3T 2B4, CANADA. Tel: 204-986-4910. Fax: 204-986-3399. p. 2760

Bridwell, Barbara, Br Mgr, West Georgia Regional Library, Warren P Sewell Memorial Library of Bowdon, 450 West Ave, Bowdon, GA, 30108. Tel: 770-258-8991. Fax: 770-258-8990. p. 524

Bridwell, Joy, Asst Librn, Stone Child College, 8294 Upper Box Elder Rd, Box Elder, MT, 59521. Tel: 406-395-4875. p. 1375

Briedis, Liga L, Coordr, Access Serv, ILL Supvr, Drake University, 2725 University Ave, Des Moines, IA, 50311. Tel: 515-271-3908. Fax: 515-271-3933. p. 809

Briese, LeeAnn, Dir, Community Library, 24615 89th St, Salem, WI, 53168. Tel: 262-843-3348. Fax: 262-843-3144. p. 2636

Brigandi, Carmen E, Asst Dir, Tech & Admin Serv, California Western School of Law Library, 290 Cedar St, San Diego, CA, 92101. Tel: 619-525-1418. Fax: 619-685-2918. p. 231

Brigante, Cheryl, Cat, Stonehill College, 320 Washington Ave, Easton, MA, 02357-4015. Tel: 505-565-1151. Fax: 508-565-1424. p. 1086

Brigantino, Maria, Bus Mgr, Fort Erie Public Library, 136 Gilmore Rd, Fort Erie, ON, L2A 2M1, CANADA. Tel: 905-871-2546, Ext 307. Fax: 905-871-9884. p. 2806

Brigell, Bruce, Ref, Skokie Public Library, 5215 Oakton St, Skokie, IL, 60077-3680. Tel: 847-673-7774. Fax: 847-673-7797. p. 703

Briggler, Gregory, Head, Circ, New School, Harry Scherman Library, 150 W 85th St, New York, NY, 10024-4499. Tel: 212-580-0210, Ext 4803. Fax: 212-580-1738. p. 1688

Briggs, Amanda, Asst Dir, Waterville Public Library, 206 White St, Waterville, NY, 13480. Tel: 315-841-4651. Fax: 315-841-4258. p. 1764

Briggs, Amanda, Librn, Petersburg Public Library, A P Hill Branch, 1237 Halifax St, Petersburg, VA, 23803. Tel: 804-733-2391. Fax: 804-733-2391. p. 2484

Briggs, Amber W, Asst Librn, Yancey County Public Library, 321 School Circle, Burnsville, NC, 28714. Tel: 828-682-2600. Fax: 828-682-3060. p. 1779

Briggs, Carol, Dir, Roeliff Jansen Community Library Association, Inc, 9091 Rte 22, Hillsdale, NY, 12529. Tel: 518-325-4101. Fax: 518-325-4105. p. 1636

Briggs, Celia, Librn, Friendship Public Library, Three Main St, Friendship, ME, 04547-0039. Tel: 207-832-5332. p. 986

Briggs, Christie O, Supvr, Montana Talking Bk Libr Serv, Montana State Library, 1515 E Sixth Ave, Helena, MT, 59620-1800. Tel: 406-444-5399. Fax: 406-444-0266. p. 1383

Briggs, Gay Lynn, Circ, Forsyth Technical Community College Library, 2100 Silas Creek Pkwy, Winston-Salem, NC, 27103. Tel: 336-734-7219. Fax: 336-761-2465. p. 1833

Briggs, Irene, Asst Dir, Pub Serv, Baltimore County Public Library, 320 York Rd, Towson, MD, 21204-5179. Tel: 410-887-6122. Fax: 410-887-6103. p. 1044

Briggs, John, Media Spec, Forsyth Technical Community College Library, 2100 Silas Creek Pkwy, Winston-Salem, NC, 27103. Tel: 336-734-7378. Fax: 336-761-2465. p. 1833

Briggs, Krista, Young Adult Serv Coordr, Canton Free Library, Eight Park St, Canton, NY, 13617. Tel: 315-386-3712. Fax: 315-386-4131. p. 1602

Briggs, Lea, Dir, Presentation College Library, 1500 N Main, Aberdeen, SD, 57401-1299. Tel: 605-229-8468. Fax: 605-229-8430. p. 2209

Briggs, Melinda, Ref Librn, Latham & Watkins, 600 W Broadway, Ste 1800, San Diego, CA, 92101. Tel: 619-236-1234. Fax: 619-696-7419. p. 231

Briggs, Nola, Librn, Walthill Public Library, PO Box 466, Walthill, NE, 68067. Tel: 402-846-5051. p. 1422

Briggs, Randy, Sr Librn, Lee County Library System, Pine Island Public Library, 10700 Russell Rd NW, Bokeelia, FL, 33922-3110. Tel: 239-461-3188. Fax: 239-283-7711. p. 446

Briggs, Robert, Circ, Roswell Public Library, 301 N Pennsylvania Ave, Roswell, NM, 88201. Tel: 575-622-7101. Fax: 575-622-7107. p. 1561

Briggs, Sharon, Acq, University of Rochester, River Campus Libraries, 755 Library Rd, Rochester, NY, 14627-0055. Tel: 585-275-4461. Fax: 585-273-5309. p. 1733

Briggs, Sharon, Dir, Monticello Public Library, 512 E Lake Ave, Monticello, WI, 53570-9658. Tel: 608-938-4011. Fax: 608-938-1772. p. 2623

Briggs-Erickson, Carol, Libr Coordr, Muskegon Community College, 221 S Quarterline Rd, Muskegon, MI, 49442. Tel: 231-777-0269. Fax: 231-777-0279. p. 1213

Brigham, Jeffrey, Co-Dir, Tech Serv Librn, Andover Newton Theological School, 169 Herrick Rd, Newton Centre, MA, 02459. Tel: 617-831-2417. Fax: 617-831-1643. p. 1110

Bright, Alice, Ser Librn, Carnegie Mellon University, Hunt Library, 4909 Frew St, Pittsburgh, PA, 15213-3890. Tel: 412-268-2446. Fax: 412-268-2793. p. 2123

Bright, Donna, Chief Exec Officer, Ajax Public Library, 55 Harwood Ave S, Ajax, ON, L1S 2H8, CANADA. Tel: 905-683-4000, Ext 8825. Fax: 905-683-6960. p. 2791

Bright, Sherry, Acq, Per, Ref, Buchanan County Public Library, Rte 2, Poetown Rd, Grundy, VA, 24614-9613. Tel: 276-935-6581. Fax: 276-935-6292. p. 2467

Bright, Velma, Dir, Akron Carnegie Public Library, 205 E Rochester St, Akron, IN, 46910. Tel: 574-893-4113. Fax: 574-893-4113. p. 723

Brightbill, Kathryn, Supvr, Pub Serv, Mars Hill College, 124 Cascade St, Mars Hill, NC, 28754. Tel: 828-689-1492. p. 1809

Brightly, Patricia, Chief Librn, Ch, ILL Librn, Whitneyville Library Association, Inc, 51 School St, Whitneyville, ME, 04654. Tel: 207-255-8077. p. 1007

Brightly, Renee, Asst Cat Librn, Asst Librn, Whitneyville Library Association, Inc, 51 School St, Whitneyville, ME, 04654. Tel: 207-255-8077. p. 1007

Brighton, Debra F, Dir, El Segundo Public Library, 111 W Mariposa Ave, El Segundo, CA, 90245-2299. Tel: 310-524-2730. Fax: 310-648-7560. p. 146

Brigl, Ursula, Chief Librn, Cranbrook Public Library, 1212 Second St N, Cranbrook, BC, V1C 4T6, CANADA. Tel: 250-426-4063. Fax: 250-426-2098. p. 2727

Brigman, Stacy, Br Mgr, Lompoc Public Library, Village, 3755 Constellation Rd, Lompoc, CA, 93436. Tel: 805-733-3323. Fax: 805-733-3323. p. 165

Bril, Patricia, Electronic Res, Paulina June & George Pollak Library, 800 N State College Blvd, Fullerton, CA, 92834. Tel: 714-278-2714. Fax: 714-278-2439. p. 154

Brill, Carol, Dir, Alverno College Library, 3401 S 39th St, Milwaukee, WI, 53215. Tel: 414-382-6054. Fax: 414-382-6354. p. 2617

Brill, Pamela, Dir, Saluda County Library, 101 S Main St, Saluda, SC, 29138. Tel: 864-445-2267, 864-445-9586. Fax: 864-445-2725. p. 2204

Brillant, Clothilde, Acq, Cegep de Chicoutimi, 534 Jacques-Cartier, Est, Chicoutimi, QC, G7H 1Z6, CANADA. Tel: 418-549-9520, Ext 337. Fax: 418-549-1315. p. 2881

Brillant, Susanne, Head, Ref, Universite Laval Bibliotheque, Bibliotheque des Sciences Humaines et Sociales, Pavillon Jean-Charles-Bonenfant, 2345, allée des Bibliothèques, Quebec, QC, G1V 0A6, CANADA. Fax: 418-656-3048. p. 2906

Briller, Karin, Ref, Franklin Square Public Library, 19 Lincoln Rd, Franklin Square, NY, 11010. Tel: 516-488-3444. Fax: 516-354-3368. p. 1624

Briller, Karin, Ref, Malverne Public Library, 61 Saint Thomas Pl, Malverne, NY, 11565. Tel: 516-599-0750. Fax: 516-599-3320. p. 1657

Brilliant, Billie Jean, Libr Asst, Millinocket Memorial Library, Five Maine Ave, Millinocket, ME, 04462. Tel: 207-723-7020. Fax: 207-723-7020. p. 992

Brillon, Alicia, Ref Librn, University of Colorado Boulder, The William A Wise Law Library, 2450 Kittredge Loop Dr, 402 UCB, Boulder, CO, 80309-0402. Tel: 303-492-2704. Fax: 303-492-2707. p. 292

Brim-Jones, Shirley, Libr Asst, Rockingham County Public Library, Madison Branch, 140 E Murphy St, Madison, NC, 27025. Tel: 336-548-6553. Fax: 336-548-2010. p. 1790

Brimmage, Darlene, Libr Assoc, Dallas Public Library, 1515 Young St, Dallas, TX, 75201-5499. Tel: 214-670-1400. Fax: 214-670-7839. p. 2306

Brimmer, Tara, Ch & Youth Librn, Schreiner Memorial Library, 113 W Elm St, Lancaster, WI, 53813-1202. Tel: 608-723-7304. Fax: 608-723-7304. p. 2605

Briner, Vicki, Dir, City College Library - Fort Lauderdale, 2000 W Commercial Blvd, Ste 200, Fort Lauderdale, FL, 33309-3001. Tel: 954-492-5353, Ext 2239. Fax: 954-491-1965. p. 443

Bringard, Celeste, Circ Supvr, Eustis Memorial Library, 120 N Center St, Eustis, FL, 32726-3598. Tel: 352-357-5686. Fax: 352-357-5450. p. 439

Brink, Barbara, Dir of Develop, University of California, San Diego, 9500 Gilman Dr, Mail Code 0175G, La Jolla, CA, 92093-0175. Tel: 858-534-3336. Fax: 858-534-4970. p. 162

Brink, Jan, Dir, Hedrick Public Library, 109 N Main St, Hedrick, IA, 52563. Tel: 641-653-2211. Fax: 641-653-2487. p. 820

Brink, Judith Ann, Head Librn, University of Pittsburgh, Bevier Engineering Library, 126 Benedum Hall, Pittsburgh, PA, 15261. Tel: 412-624-0859. Fax: 412-624-8103. p. 2128

Brinkerhoff, Carolyn, Librn, St John's Westminster Union Church, 1085 Neeb Rd, Cincinnati, OH, 45233. Tel: 513-347-4613. Fax: 513-347-4615. p. 1873

Brinkerhoff, Celia, Pub Serv Librn, Kwantlen Polytechnic University Library, 12666 72 Ave., Surrey, BC, V3W 2M8, CANADA. Tel: 604-599-3235. Fax: 604-599-2106. p. 2738

Brinkerhoff, Kathie, Dir, Pershing County Library, 1125 Central, Lovelock, NV, 89419. Tel: 775-273-2216. Fax: 775-273-0421. p. 1431

Brinkley, Bruce, Ref Librn, Indiana Wesleyan University, 4201 S Washington St, Marion, IN, 46953. Tel: 765-677-2179. Fax: 765-677-2676. p. 762

Brinkley, Cheryl, Br Mgr, Charleston County Public Library, John L Dart Branch, 1067 King St, Charleston, SC, 29403. Tel: 843-722-7550. Fax: 843-727-6784. p. 2183

Brinkley, Lydia, Tech Serv, Bolivar County Library System, 104 S Leflore Ave, Cleveland, MS, 38732. Tel: 662-843-2774. Fax: 662-843-4701. p. 1295

Brinkley, Patricia, Youth Serv, Gulfport Public Library, 5501 28th Ave S, Gulfport, FL, 33707. Tel: 727-893-1074. Fax: 727-893-1072. p. 450

Brinkman, Bernadette, Dir, Penfield Public Library, 1985 Baird Rd, Penfield, NY, 14526. Tel: 585-340-8720. Fax: 585-340-8748. p. 1716

Brinkman, Bernadette, Br Mgr, Rochester Public Library, Monroe, 809 Monroe Ave, Rochester, NY, 14607. Tel: 585-428-8202. p. 1732

Brinkman, Carol, Outreach Librn, Prof, University of Louisville Libraries, Kornhauser Health Sciences Library, Health Sciences Ctr, 500 S Preston St, Louisville, KY, 40202. Tel: 502-852-1008. Fax: 502-852-1631. p. 927

Brinkman, Dana, Dir, Kent County Library, 156 W Fourth St, Jayton, TX, 79528. Tel: 806-237-3287. Fax: 806-237-2511. p. 2348

Brinkman, Jodi, Br Mgr, Great River Regional Library, Cold Spring Library, 27 Red River Rd, Cold Spring, MN, 56320. Tel: 320-685-8281. p. 1275

Brinkman, Stacy, Archit/Art Librn, Miami University Libraries, 225 King Library, Oxford, OH, 45056. Tel: 513-529-6650. Fax: 513-529-3110. p. 1926

Brinkman, Stacy, Archit/Art Librn, Miami University Libraries, Wertz Art-Architecture Library, Alumni Hall, Oxford, OH, 45056. Tel: 513-529-6650. Fax: 513-529-4159. p. 1926

Brinkmeyer, Ann, Coll Develop, Nevada State Library & Archives, 100 N Stewart St, Carson City, NV, 89701-4285. Tel: 775-684-3309. Fax: 775-684-3330. p. 1426

Brinton, Kevin, Librn, Logan Correctional Center Library, 1096 1350th St, Box 1000, Lincoln, IL, 62656. Tel: 217-735-5581, Ext 329. Fax: 217-735-4381. p. 666

Briody, Michael, Circ, Goodnow Library, 21 Concord Rd, Sudbury, MA, 01776-2383. Tel: 978-443-1035. Fax: 978-443-1047. p. 1129

Brior, Raymond, Tech Serv Librn, Johnson State College Library, 337 College Hill, Johnson, VT, 05656. Tel: 802-635-1495. Fax: 802-635-1294. p. 2427

Brisbee, Laura, Mgr, International Data Corp Library, 155 Bovet Rd, Ste 800, San Mateo, CA, 94402. Tel: 650-653-7000. Fax: 650-653-7077. p. 255

Brisbin, John A, Dir, Bacon Free Library, 58 Eliot St, Natick, MA, 01760. Tel: 508-653-6730. p. 1107

Briscoe, Georgia K, Assoc Dir, Head, Tech Serv, University of Colorado Boulder, The William A Wise Law Library, 2450 Kittredge Loop Dr, 402 UCB, Boulder, CO, 80309-0402. Tel: 303-492-7312. Fax: 303-492-2707. p. 292

Briscoe, Wayne, Head Librn, Fort St James Public Library, 425 Manson St, Fort St. James, BC, V0J 1P0, CANADA. Tel: 250-996-7431. Fax: 250-996-7484. p. 2728

Briseno, Alexandra, Librn, Michigan Department of Transportation Library, 425 W Ottawa, Lansing, MI, 48909. Tel: 517-373-8548. Fax: 517-241-3194. p. 1201

Brisk, Adam, Libr Tech, Wisconsin Indianhead Technical College, 600 N 21st St, Superior, WI, 54880-5296. Tel: 715-394-6677, Ext 6276. Fax: 715-394-3771. p. 2641

Brisson, Carole, Head, Libr Syst & Cat, Supreme Court of Canada Library, 301 Wellington St, Ottawa, ON, K1A 0J1, CANADA. Tel: 613-947-0628. Fax: 613-952-2832. p. 2833

Brisson, Caroline, Tech Serv, Norton Rose Canada LLP Library, One Place Ville Marie, Ste 2500, Montreal, QC, H3B 1R1, CANADA. Tel: 514-847-4701. Fax: 514-286-5474. p. 2900

Brisson, Janice M, Libr Tech, British Columbia Ministry of Energy & Mines, 1810 Blanshard St, Victoria, BC, V8W 9N3, CANADA. Tel: 250-952-0583. Fax: 250-952-0581. p. 2745

Brisson, Ruth Ann, Circ Mgr, ILL, Learning Res Ctr Spec, Western Piedmont Community College, 1001 Burkemont Ave, Morganton, NC, 28655-4504. Tel: 828-448-6195. Fax: 828-448-6173. p. 1811

Bristah, Pamela, Librn, Wellesley College, Music Library, Jewett Arts Ctr, Rm 208, 106 Central St, Wellesley, MA, 02481-8203. Tel: 781-283-2075. Fax: 781-283-2869. p. 1135

Brister, Linda, Librn, Pike-Amite-Walthall Library System, Alpha Center, 414 McComb Ave, McComb, MS, 39648. Tel: 601-685-8312. p. 1308

Brister, Ron, Coll Develop, Memphis Pink Palace Museum Library, 3050 Central Ave, Memphis, TN, 38111-3399. Tel: 901-320-6322. Fax: 901-320-6391. p. 2249

Bristol, Arlen, Sr Librn, Rutan & Tucker Library, 611 Anton, Ste 1400, Costa Mesa, CA, 92626. Tel: 714-641-5100. Fax: 714-546-9035. p. 137

Bristow, Robert, Dir, Allendale Township Library, 6175 Library Ln, Allendale, MI, 49401. Tel: 616-895-4178, Ext 10. Fax: 616-895-5178. p. 1149

Brit, Brenda, Vols Librn, East Millinocket Public Library, 53 Main St, East Millinocket, ME, 04430-1199. Tel: 207-746-3554. Fax: 207-746-3550. p. 984

Britain, Annette, Network Adminr, Wichita Falls Public Library, 600 11th St, Wichita Falls, TX, 76301-4604. Tel: 940-767-0868, Ext 246. Fax: 940-720-6672. p. 2401

Britain, Karla, Tech Serv, Union College Library, 3800 S 48th St, Lincoln, NE, 68506-4386. Tel: 402-486-2514. Fax: 402-486-2678. p. 1406

Brite, Christopher, Automation Serv, Cat, Mgr, Per, Conception Abbey & Seminary Library, 37174 State Hwy W, Conception, MO, 64433. Tel: 660-944-2803. Fax: 660-944-2833. p. 1326

Britski, April, Exec Dir, Canadian Artists' Representation, Two Daly Ave, Ste 250, Ottawa, ON, K1N 6E2, CANADA. Tel: 613-233-6161. Fax: 613-233-6162. p. 2829

Britt, Betty, Dir, Human Res, Blackwater Regional Library, 22511 Main St, Courtland, VA, 23837. Tel: 757-653-2821. Fax: 757-653-9374. p. 2458

Britt, Rob, Coordr, East Asian Libr Serv, University of Washington Libraries, Marian Gould Gallagher Law Library, William H Gates Hall, Box 353025, Seattle, WA, 98195-3025. Tel: 206-543-7447. Fax: 206-685-2165. p. 2534

Britt-Wernke, Lisa, Coll & Access Serv Librn, University of Cincinnati, 2540 Clifton Ave, Cincinnati, OH, 45219. Tel: 513-556-0156. Fax: 513-556-6265. p. 1874

Brittain, Dana, Br Mgr, Fort Bend County Libraries, Bob Lutts Fulshear Simonton Branch, 8100 FM 359 S, Fulshear, TX, 77441. Tel: 281-346-2384. Fax: 281-346-1265. p. 2375

Brittain, Leslie, Ref, Winfield Public Library, OS-291 Winfield Rd, Winfield, IL, 60190. Tel: 630-653-7599. Fax: 630-653-7781. p. 720

Brittain, Rebecca, Dir, Blakesburg Public Library, 109 Cass St, Blakesburg, IA, 52536. Tel: 641-938-2834. Fax: 641-938-2834. p. 797

Britten, Nancy, Circ, Neenah Public Library, 240 E Wisconsin Ave, Neenah, WI, 54956-3010. Tel: 920-886-6315. Fax: 920-886-6324. p. 2624

Britten, William, Syst Coordr, University of Tennessee, Knoxville, 1015 Volunteer Blvd, Knoxville, TN, 37996-1000. Tel: 865-974-4304. Fax: 865-974-4259. p. 2243

Brittingham, June, Librn, Eastern Correctional Institution, West Library, 30420 Revells Neck Rd, Westover, MD, 21890-3358. Tel: 410-845-4000, Ext 6423. Fax: 410-845-4206. p. 1046

Brittingham, Mary, Librn, Millsboro Public Library, 217 W State St, Millsboro, DE, 19966. Tel: 302-934-8743. Fax: 302-934-8623. p. 384

Britto, Veronica, Br Mgr, Free Library of Philadelphia, David Cohen Ogontz Branch, 6017 Ogontz Ave, Philadelphia, PA, 19141-1311. Tel: 215-685-3566, 215-685-3567. Fax: 215-685-3568. p. 2107

Britton, Constance, Head Librn, Ohio Agricultural Research & Development Center Library, 1680 Madison Ave, Wooster, OH, 44691-4096. Tel: 330-263-3773. Fax: 330-263-3689. p. 1950

Britton, Deanna, Dir, Lucius E & Elsie C Burch Library, 501 Poplar View Pkwy, Collierville, TN, 38017. Tel: 901-457-2600. Fax: 901-854-5893. p. 2230

Britton, James, III, Ref, Okefenokee Regional Library, 401 Lee Ave, Waycross, GA, 31501. Tel: 912-287-4978. Fax: 912-284-2533. p. 557

Britton, Ona, Coordr, Ref & Instrul Serv, University of Central Oklahoma, 100 N University Dr, Edmond, OK, 73034. Tel: 405-974-2979. Fax: 405-974-3806, 405-974-3874. p. 1962

Britton, Sharon, Dir, Bowling Green State University, One University Dr, 2nd Flr, Huron, OH, 44839-9791. Tel: 419-433-5560, Ext 20739. Fax: 419-433-9696. p. 1905

Britton, Toi, Mgr, The News Tribune Library, 1950 S State St, Tacoma, WA, 98405-2860. Tel: 253-597-8626, 253-597-8629. Fax: 253-597-8274. p. 2539

Britton, Valerie, Head, Circ, Pleasant Valley Free Library, 1584 Main St, Pleasant Valley, NY, 12569. Tel: 845-635-8460. Fax: 845-635-9556. p. 1719

Britz, Johannes J, Dr, Dean, Prof, University of Wisconsin-Milwaukee, 510 Bolton Hall, 3120 N Maryland Ave, Milwaukee, WI, 53211. Tel: 414-229-4707. Fax: 414-229-6699. p. 2976

Brixius, Mike, In Charge, Iowa State Penitentiary, John Bennett Correctional Center Library, Three John Bennett Dr, Fort Madison, IA, 52627. Tel: 319-372-5432, Ext 439. p. 817

Brlas, Celeste, AV, Elyria Public Library System, 320 Washington Ave, Elyria, OH, 44035-5199. Tel: 440-323-5747. Fax: 440-323-5788. p. 1898

Brnik, Julie, Prog & PR Spec, Hershey Public Library, 701 Cocoa Ave, Hershey, PA, 17033. Tel: 717-533-6555. Fax: 717-534-1666. p. 2069

Broad, Kathryn, Syst Librn, Oklahoma City University, Law Library, 2501 N Blackwelder, Oklahoma City, OK, 73106. Tel: 405-208-5271. Fax: 405-208-5172. p. 1974

Broad, Shannon, ILL, Dixie State College of Utah, 225 S 700 E, Saint George, UT, 84770. Tel: 435-652-7720. Fax: 435-656-4169. p. 2412

Broad, Shannon, Ser, Dixie State College of Utah, 225 S 700 E, Saint George, UT, 84770. Tel: 435-652-2720. Fax: 435-656-4169. p. 2412

Broadley, Louise, Mgr, Pub Serv, North Vancouver District Public Library, 1277 Lynn Valley Rd, North Vancouver, BC, V7J 2A1, CANADA. Tel: 604-990-5800. Fax: 604-984-7600. p. 2734

Broadnax, Zenora, Bibliog Instr, Fernbank Science Center Library, 156 Heaton Park Dr NE, Atlanta, GA, 30307-1398. Tel: 678-874-7116. Fax: 678-874-7110. p. 515

Broadus, Joyce, Mgr, Carnegie Library of Pittsburgh, Hill District, 2177 Centre Ave, Pittsburgh, PA, 15219-3396. Tel: 412-281-3753. p. 2123

Broadus, LaQuita, Asst Librn, Pine Forest Regional Library, Stone County, 242 Second St SE, Wiggins, MS, 39577. Tel: 601-928-4993. Fax: 601-928-4993. p. 1314

Broadway, Marsha, Ch, Brigham Young University, Harold B Lee Library, 2060 HBLL, Provo, UT, 84602. Tel: 801-422-2927. Fax: 801-422-0466. p. 2411

Broberg, Lori, Head, Circ, Pierce College Library, Puyallup Campus, 1601 39th Ave SE, Puyallup, WA, 98374. Tel: 253-840-8300. Fax: 253-840-8316. p. 2520

Brobst, Helen, Ref Librn, Hanson Bridgett LLP, 425 Market St, 26th Flr, San Francisco, CA, 94105. Tel: 415-995-5855. Fax: 415-541-9366. p. 242

Brobst, Tom, Sr Librn, California Department of Corrections Library System, San Quentin State Prison Library, 100 Main St, San Quentin, CA, 94964. Tel: 415-454-1460, Ext 3384. Fax: 415-455-5049. p. 222

Broch, Elana, Asst Population Res Librn, Princeton University, Donald E Stokes Library - Public & International Affairs & Population Research, Wallace Hall, Princeton, NJ, 08544. Tel: 609-258-5517. Fax: 609-258-6844. p. 1524

Brock, Amber, Circ, Tallahassee Community College Library, 444 Appleyard Dr, Tallahassee, FL, 32304-2895. Tel: 850-201-8396. Fax: 850-201-8380. p. 495

Brock, Andre, Dr, Asst Prof, University of Iowa, 3087 Main Library, Iowa City, IA, 52242-1420. Tel: 319-335-5707. Fax: 319-335-5374. p. 2965

Brock, Ann, Dir, Joanne Cole-Mitte Memorial Library, 170 N Gabriel St, Bertram, TX, 78605. Tel: 512-355-2113. Fax: 512-355-3323. p. 2289

Brock, Bonnie, Tech Serv Mgr, University of South Carolina Upstate Library, 800 University Way, Spartanburg, SC, 29303. Tel: 864-503-5639. Fax: 864-503-5601. p. 2205

Brock, Carol, Dir, George Holmes Bixby Memorial Library, 52 Main St, Francestown, NH, 03043-3025. Tel: 603-547-2730. Fax: 603-547-2730. p. 1447

Brock, Charlene, ILL, United States Department of Health & Human Services, National Center for Health Statistics Staff Research Library, 3311 Toledo Rd, Rm 2403, Hyattsville, MD, 20782. Tel: 301-458-4775. Fax: 301-458-4019. p. 1039

Brock, Irene, Acq Asst, Washtenaw Community College, 4800 E Huron River Dr, Ann Arbor, MI, 48105-4800. Tel: 734-973-3399. Fax: 734-973-3446. p. 1153

Brock, Judy, Br Supvr, Scenic Regional Library of Franklin, Gasconade & Warren Counties, New Haven Branch, 901 Maupin, New Haven, MO, 63068. Tel: 573-237-2189. p. 1369

Brock, Lindsey, Dir, Info Serv, Middlesex County Library, 34B Frank St, Strathroy, ON, N7G 2R4, CANADA. Tel: 519-245-8237, Ext 4022. Fax: 519-245-8238. p. 2845

Brock, Lynn Alan, Dean, Libr Serv, Cedarville University, 251 N Main St, Cedarville, OH, 45314-0601. Tel: 937-766-7846. Fax: 937-766-2337. p. 1865

Brock, Meagan, Libr Spec, Ill & Tech Serv, Bluegrass Community & Technical College, Oswald Bldg, 470 Cooper Dr, Lexington, KY, 40506-0235. Tel: 859-246-6380. Fax: 859-246-4675. p. 920

Brock, Monica, Librn, Johnson County Library, Kaycee Branch, 231 Ritter Ave, Kaycee, WY, 82639. Tel: 307-738-2473. Fax: 307-738-2473. p. 2651

Brock, Rebecca, Dir, Sweetwater County-City Library, 206 Elm St, Sweetwater, TX, 79556. Tel: 325-235-4978. Fax: 325-235-4979. p. 2390

Brock, Rebecca, Librn, Chapmanville Public Library, 299 Vance St, Chapmanville, WV, 25508. Tel: 304-855-3405. Fax: 304-855-8590. p. 2555

Brock, Verna, Circ Serv Coordr, LeRoy Collins Leon County Public Library System, 200 W Park Ave, Tallahassee, FL, 32301-7720. Tel: 850-606-2665. Fax: 850-606-2601. p. 492

Brockman, Liz, Ch, North Richland Hills Public Library, 9015 Grand Ave, North Richland Hills, TX, 76180. Tel: 817-427-6818. Fax: 817-427-6808. p. 2366

Brockman, Terry, Cataloger, Marion County Public Library, 201 E Main St, Lebanon, KY, 40033-1133. Tel: 270-692-4698. Fax: 270-692-9555. p. 920

Brockman, William, Paterno Family Librn for Lit, Pennsylvania State University Libraries, George & Sherry Middlemas Arts & Humanities Library, Pennsylvania State University, W 202 Pattee Library, University Park, PA, 16802-1801. Tel: 814-865-9718. Fax: 814-863-7502. p. 2148

Brockmeyer, Carol, Librn, Daugherty Public Library District, 220 S Fifth St, Dupo, IL, 62239. Tel: 618-286-4444. Fax: 618-286-3636. p. 638

Brockmeyer, Donna, Dr, Dir, Saint Thomas More College-University of Saskatchewan, 1437 College Dr, Saskatoon, SK, S7N 0W6, CANADA. Tel: 306-966-8962. Fax: 306-966-8909. p. 2926

Brocleur, Chantal, Coll Develop, Bibliotheque de Repentigny, One Place d'Evry, Repentigny, QC, J6A 8H7, CANADA. Tel: 450-470-3001, Ext 3427. Fax: 450-470-3079. p. 2907

Brodbeck, Jeanne, Info Tech, Palm Beach County Library System, 3650 Summit Blvd, West Palm Beach, FL, 33406-4198. Tel: 561-233-2738. Fax: 561-233-2692. p. 503

Broderick, Amber, Curator, American Morgan Horse Institute, 34 Main St, Middlebury, VT, 05482. Tel: 802-985-8665. Fax: 802-985-5242. p. 2428

Broderick, Anita M, Coordr, Info Serv, Saint Clare's Health Systems, 375 E McFarlan St, Dover, NJ, 07801. Tel: 973-989-1122. Fax: 973-989-1159. p. 1481

Broderick, Jackie, Br Mgr, Uncle Remus Regional Library System, Monroe - Walton County Library, 217 W Spring St, Monroe, GA, 30655. Tel: 770-267-4630. Fax: 770-267-6682. p. 542

Broderson, Diane, ILL, Colorado College, 1021 N Cascade Ave, Colorado Springs, CO, 80903-3252. Tel: 719-389-6658. Fax: 719-389-6082. p. 294

Brodeur, Jacques, Head, Cat, Syst Adminr, Department of Canadian Heritage, 15 Eddy St, 2nd Flr, Gatineau, QC, K1A 0M5, CANADA. Tel: 819-994-5915. Fax: 819-953-7988. p. 2883

Brodhead, Heather, Librn, Santa Barbara Museum of Art, 1130 State St, Santa Barbara, CA, 93101. Tel: 805-884-6451. Fax: 805-966-6840. p. 261

Brodie, Carolyn, Dr, Prof, Kent State University, 314 Library, Kent, OH, 44242-0001. Tel: 330-672-2782. Fax: 330-672-7965. p. 2971

Brodie, Lois, Supvr, Ch Serv, Ridgewood Public Library, 125 N Maple Ave, Ridgewood, NJ, 07450-3288. Tel: 201-670-5600. Fax: 201-670-0293. p. 1526

Brodin, Jared, Dir of Tech Serv, American Institute for Biosocial & Medical Research Inc Library, 4117 S Meridian St, Puyallup, WA, 98373. Tel: 253-286-2888. Fax: 253-286-2451. p. 2525

Brodle, Gloria, Adult Serv, Br Mgr, Fremont County Library System, Riverton Branch, 1330 W Park, Riverton, WY, 82501. Tel: 307-856-3556. Fax: 307-857-3722. p. 2657

Brodosi, David, Coordr, Distance Learning & Instrul Media Serv, University of South Florida Saint Petersburg, 140 Seventh Ave S, POY118, Saint Petersburg, FL, 33701. Tel: 727-873-4401. Fax: 727-873-4196. p. 489

Brodsky, Karen, Instrul Serv Librn, Pub Relations, Sonoma State University Library, 1801 E Cotati Ave, Rohnert Park, CA, 94928-3609. Tel: 707-664-4240. Fax: 707-664-2090. p. 219

Brodsky, Karen, Exec Dir, Bernardsville Public Library, One Anderson Hill Rd, Bernardsville, NJ, 07924. Tel: 908-766-0659. Fax: 908-766-2464. p. 1472

Brodt, Kristin, Mgr, ILL, Muhlenberg College, 2400 Chew St, Allentown, PA, 18104-5586. Tel: 484-664-3500. Fax: 484-664-3511. p. 2027

Brody, Fern, Assoc Univ Librn, University of Pittsburgh, 3960 Forbes Ave, Pittsburgh, PA, 15260. Tel: 412-648-7710. Fax: 412-648-7887. p. 2128

Brody, Jeff, Dir, Commun Relations, Kitsap Regional Library, 1301 Sylvan Way, Bremerton, WA, 98310-3498. Tel: 360-475-9032. Fax: 360-405-9128. p. 2510

Brody, Lynne M, Dean of Libr, Southwestern University, 1100 E University Ave, Georgetown, TX, 78626. Tel: 512-863-1214. Fax: 512-863-8198. p. 2327

Brody, Roberta, Assoc Prof, Queens College of the City University of New York, Benjamin Rosenthal Library, Rm 254, 65-30 Kissena Blvd, Flushing, NY, 11367. Tel: 718-997-3790. Fax: 718-997-3797. p. 2970

Broekemeier, Jean, Librn, Morgan Public Library, 210 Vernon Ave, Morgan, MN, 56266. Tel: 507-249-3153. Fax: 507-249-3839. p. 1267

Broere, Heather, Br Mgr, Watsonville Public Library, Freedom Branch, 2021 Freedom Blvd, Freedom, CA, 95019. Tel: 831-768-3420. Fax: 831-763-4143. p. 282

Broering, Amy, Ch, Mercer County District Library, 303 N Main St, Celina, OH, 45822. Tel: 419-586-4442. Fax: 419-586-3222. p. 1866

Broestl, Mary K, Librn, Terra State Community College Library, 2830 Napoleon Rd, Fremont, OH, 43420-9670. Tel: 419-559-2318. Fax: 419-334-3667. p. 1901

Brogan, Chris, Chief Financial Officer, Pueblo City-County Library District, 100 E Abriendo Ave, Pueblo, CO, 81004-4290. Tel: 719-562-5652. Fax: 719-562-5619. p. 320

Brogan, Loona, Librn, Cutler Memorial Library, 151 High St, Plainfield, VT, 05667. Tel: 802-454-8504. p. 2432

Brogan, Martha, Coll Mgt & Develop Dir, University of Pennsylvania Libraries, 3420 Walnut St, Philadelphia, PA, 19104-6206. Tel: 215-746-3418. Fax: 215-898-0559. p. 2118

Brogan, Tom, Br Mgr, Brooklyn Public Library, Greenpoint, 107 Norman Ave, Brooklyn, NY, 11222. Tel: 718-349-8504. Fax: 718-349-8790. p. 1591

Brogden, Stephen R, Libr Serv Dir, Thousand Oaks Library, 1401 E Janss Rd, Thousand Oaks, CA, 91362-2199. Tel: 805-449-2660, Ext 7300. Fax: 805-373-6858. p. 275

Brogdon, Debbie, Br Mgr, Lake Blackshear Regional Library System, Cordele-Crisp Carnegie, 115 E 11th Ave, Cordele, GA, 31015-4232. Tel: 229-276-1300. Fax: 229-276-1151. p. 508

Brogdon, Dennise, Librn, Hughston Foundation Library, 6262 Veterans Pkwy, Columbus, GA, 31909-3540. Tel: 706-494-3390. Fax: 706-494-3379. p. 526

Brogran, Annie, Col Librn, College of Physicians of Philadelphia, 19 S 22nd St, Philadelphia, PA, 19103-3097. Tel: 215-399-2304. Fax: 215-561-6477. p. 2104

Brokke, Harris, Exec Dir, Maturango Museum, 100 E Las Flores Ave, Ridgecrest, CA, 93555. Tel: 760-375-6900. Fax: 760-375-0479. p. 216

Brokopp, Barbara, Circ, Hamline University, Bush Memorial Library, 1536 Hewitt, Saint Paul, MN, 55104. Tel: 651-523-2375. Fax: 651-523-2199. p. 1278

Broll, Lisa, Br Mgr, Allegany County Library System, South Cumberland, 100 Seymour St, Cumberland, MD, 21502. Tel: 301-724-1607. Fax: 301-724-1504. p. 1026

Broman, Elizabeth, Ref Librn, Smithsonian Libraries, Cooper-Hewitt, National Design Museum Library, Two E 91st St, 3rd Flr, New York City, DC, 10128. Tel: 212-633-8336. Fax: 212-849-8339. p. 414

Bromberg, Peter, Asst Dir, Princeton Public Library, 65 Witherspoon St, Princeton, NJ, 08542. Tel: 609-924-8822, Ext 223. Fax: 609-924-6109. p. 1522

Bromley, Jennifer, Music Librn, NPR Library, 635 Massachusetts Ave NW, Washington, DC, 20001. Fax: 202-513-3056. p. 412

Bromley, Marilyn M, Dir, Bureau of National Affairs, Inc Library, 1801 S Bell St, Rm 3200, Arlington, VA, 22202. Tel: 703-341-3307. Fax: 703-341-1636. p. 2449

Brommer, Colleen, Dir, Harlem Public Library, 37 First Ave S, Harlem, MT, 59526. Tel: 406-353-2712. Fax: 406-353-2616. p. 1381

Bromser-Kloeden, Leah, Mgr, Loudoun County Public Library, Purcellville Branch, 220 E Main St, Purcellville, VA, 20132-3167. Tel: 540-338-7235. Fax: 540-338-2629. p. 2474

Brondfield, Ellen, Dir, Steptoe & Johnson Library, 1330 Connecticut Ave NW, Washington, DC, 20036. Tel: 202-429-6429. Fax: 202-429-3902. p. 416

Bronkar, Cherie, Outreach Librn, Muskingum University Library, 163 Stormont St, New Concord, OH, 43762-1199. Tel: 740-826-8017. Fax: 740-826-8404. p. 1920

Bronner, Nancy, Head, Automated Libr Serv, Clapp Memorial Library, 19 S Main St, Belchertown, MA, 01007-0627. Tel: 413-323-0417. Fax: 413-323-0453. p. 1052

Bronski, Kevin, Exec Dir, Southern Regional Council, Inc, 1201 W Peachtree St, Ste 2000, Atlanta, GA, 30309. Tel: 404-817-8597. Fax: 404-817-8791. p. 518

Bronson, Diane, Coll Develop Librn, Live Oak Public Libraries, 2002 Bull St, Savannah, GA, 31401. Tel: 912-652-3600. Fax: 912-652-3638. p. 550

Bronson, Madelyn, Br Mgr, Granite Falls Public Library, 155 Seventh Ave, Granite Falls, MN, 56241. Tel: 320-564-3738. Fax: 320-564-4666. p. 1253

Bronson, Mark C, Dir, Cheboygan Area Public Library, 100 S Bailey St, Cheboygan, MI, 49721-1661. Tel: 231-627-2381. Fax: 231-627-9172. p. 1162

Brooks, Sharon, Evening Librn, Eastern Correctional Institution, East Library, 30420 Revells Neck Rd, Westover, MD, 21890-3358. Tel: 410-845-4000, Ext 6227. Fax: 410-845-4208. p. 1046

Brooks, Sherry, Librn, Griffin Technical College Library, 501 Varsity Rd, Griffin, GA, 30223. Tel: 770-412-4755. Fax: 770-229-3006. p. 535

Brooks, Stephen L, Libr Tech, USACE Baltimore District Library, Ten S Howard St, Baltimore, MD, 21201. Tel: 410-962-3423. Fax: 410-962-1889. p. 1019

Brooks, Terrence, Assoc Prof, University of Washington, Mary Gates Hall, Ste 370, Campus Box 352840, Seattle, WA, 98195-2840. Tel: 206-685-9937. Fax: 206-616-3152. p. 2976

Brooks, Theresa, Libr Assoc, Hampton University, Nursing, 130 E Tyler St, Hampton, VA, 23668. Tel: 757-727-5353. Fax: 757-727-5423. p. 2468

Brooks, Tina M, Dir, Rainbow City Public Library, 3702 Rainbow Dr, Rainbow City, AL, 35906. Tel: 256-442-8477. Fax: 256-442-4128. p. 34

Brooks, Wendy, Dean, Learning Res, Media Serv, Alpena Community College, The Center Bldg, Rm 111, 665 Johnson St, Alpena, MI, 49707. Tel: 989-358-7249. Fax: 989-358-7556. p. 1150

Brooks-Reese, Karen, Mgr, Carnegie Library of Pittsburgh, Lawrenceville, 279 Fisk St, Pittsburgh, PA, 15201-2898. Tel: 412-682-3668. p. 2123

Broom, Bridgette, Br Mgr, Lamar County Library System, Sumrall Public - L R Boyer Memorial Library, 103 Poplar St, Sumrall, MS, 39482. Tel: 601-758-4711. Fax: 601-758-4711. p. 1313

Broom, Diane, Br Supvr, Boise Public Library, Library! at Hillcrest, 5246 W Overland Rd, Boise, ID, 83705. Tel: 208-562-4931. p. 570

Broome, Gail E, Dir, Degenstein Community Library, 40 S Fifth St, Sunbury, PA, 17801. Tel: 570-286-2461. Fax: 570-286-4203. p. 2144

Broome, Rhonda, Mgr, Sequoyah Regional Library System, Hickory Flat Public, 2740 E Cherokee Dr, Canton, GA, 30115. Tel: 770-345-7565. Fax: 770-345-7660. p. 523

Broome, Susan G, Assoc Dir, Tech Serv, Spec Coll & Archives Librn, Mercer University, Jack Tarver Library, 1300 Edgewood Ave, Macon, GA, 31207. Tel: 478-301-2193. Fax: 478-301-2111. p. 540

Broomfield, Sandy, Dir, Berwick Public Library, 103 Old Pine Hill Rd, Berwick, ME, 03901. Tel: 207-698-5737. Fax: 207-698-5737. p. 977

Brophy, Denise M, Adult Serv, Providence Community Library, Rochambeau Library, 708 Hope St, Providence, RI, 02906. Tel: 401-272-3780. p. 2173

Brophy, Judy, Educ Tech Support Spec, Daniel Webster College, 20 University Dr, Nashua, NH, 03063-1300. Tel: 603-577-6411. Fax: 603-577-6199. p. 1458

Brophy, Linda, Circ & Ref, Pompton Lakes Public Library, 333 Wanaque Ave, Pompton Lakes, NJ, 07442. Tel: 973-835-0482. Fax: 973-835-4767. p. 1521

Brophy, Mary Jill, Automation Librn, Tech Serv, Lorain County Community College, 1005 Abbe Rd N, North Elyria, OH, 44035-1691. Tel: 440-366-7285. Fax: 440-366-4127. p. 1924

Brosamer, Laura, Librn, Saint Mary's Hospital, 1800 E Lake Shore Dr, Decatur, IL, 62521-3883. Tel: 217-464-2182. Fax: 217-464-1674. p. 634

Brose, Bonnie, Librn, Logan County Libraries, West Mansfield Branch, 127 N Main, West Mansfield, OH, 43358. Tel: 937-355-0033. p. 1859

Brose, Christopher, Head, Computer Serv, Tiffin-Seneca Public Library, 77 Jefferson St, Tiffin, OH, 44883. Tel: 419-447-3751. Fax: 419-447-3045. p. 1938

Brose, Pat, Extn Serv, Campbell County Public Library System, 2101 S 4-J Rd, Gillette, WY, 82718-5205. Tel: 307-687-9228. Fax: 307-686-4009. p. 2655

Brosek, Jennifer, Coordr, WISPALS Library Consortium, c/o Gateway Technical College, 3520 30th Ave, Kenosha, WI, 53144-1690. Tel: 262-564-2602. Fax: 262-564-2787. p. 2958

Brosey, Barbara A, Dir, Manheim Community Library, 15 E High St, Manheim, PA, 17545-1505. Tel: 717-665-6700. Fax: 717-665-2470. p. 2084

Brosius, Karen, Dir, Columbia Museum of Art, Main & Hampton, Columbia, SC, 29201. Tel: 803-799-2810. Fax: 803-343-2150. p. 2187

Brosk, Carol, Librn, Barack, Ferrazzano, Kirshbaum & Nagelberg Library, 200 W Madison St, Ste 3900, Chicago, IL, 60606. Tel: 312-984-3100. Fax: 312-984-3150. p. 607

Broskey, Lorelei A, Dir, Lehigh County Law Library, County Court House, 455 W Hamilton St, Allentown, PA, 18101-1614. Tel: 610-782-3385. Fax: 610-820-3311. p. 2027

Brosnan, Eileen, Ser & Acq Tech, Justice Institute of British Columbia Library, 715 McBride Blvd, New Westminster, BC, V3L 5T4, CANADA. Tel: 604-528-5599. Fax: 604-528-5593. p. 2734

Brosnan, Susan, Asst Dir, Preston Public Library, 389 Rt 2, Preston, CT, 06365. Tel: 860-886-1010. Fax: 860-886-4952. p. 364

Brosnan, Susan H, Archivist, Librn, Knights of Columbus Supreme Council Archives, One State St, New Haven, CT, 06511-6702. Tel: 203-752-4578. Fax: 203-865-0351. p. 355

Brosowsky, Anne K, Librn, Planned Parenthood of Wisconsin, Inc, 302 N Jackson St, Milwaukee, WI, 53202. Tel: 414-289-3704. Fax: 414-271-1935. p. 2621

Brossard, Katherine, Dir, Info Res, Mitchell College Library, 437 Pequot Ave, New London, CT, 06320-4498. Tel: 860-701-5156, Ext 7789. Fax: 860-701-5099. p. 360

Brosseau, Esther, Librn, Phillips County Library, Saco Branch, PO Box 74, Saco, MT, 59261. p. 1386

Brosseau, Hollie, Teen Librn, Westminster Public Library, 3705 W 112th Ave, Westminster, CO, 80031. Tel: 303-658-2606. Fax: 303-404-5135. p. 326

Brosseau, Joyce, Librn, Roxbury Free Library, 1491 Roxbury Rd, Roxbury, VT, 05669. Tel: 802-485-6860. p. 2434

Brosseau, Lise, Div Mgr, Libr & Culture, Bibliotheque de Dollard-des-Ormeaux, 12001 Blvd de Salaberry, Dollard-des-Ormeaux, QC, H9B 2A7, CANADA. Tel: 514-684-1012, Ext 402. Fax: 514-684-9569. p. 2881

Brossette, Carol, Financial Serv Assoc, Shreve Memorial Library, 424 Texas St, Shreveport, LA, 71101. Tel: 318-226-5873. Fax: 318-226-4780. p. 969

Brostrom, Vicki, Children's Serv Supvr, Brookfield Public Library, 1900 N Calhoun Rd, Brookfield, WI, 53005. Tel: 262-782-4140. Fax: 262-796-6670. p. 2583

Brostuen, Lori, Head, Tech Serv, Syst Coordr, Redwood Library & Athenaeum, 50 Bellevue Ave, Newport, RI, 02840-3292. Tel: 401-847-0292. Fax: 401-847-0192. p. 2169

Brothers, Kelly, Br Mgr, Louisville Free Public Library, Westport Community, 8100 Westport Rd, Ste B, Louisville, KY, 40222. Tel: 502-394-0379. Fax: 502-394-0377. p. 925

Brothers, Lesley, In Charge, Eastern Counties Regional Library, Sherbrooke Branch, 11 Main St, Sherbrooke, NS, B0J 3C0, CANADA. Tel: 902-522-2180. Fax: 902-522-2180. p. 2783

Brothers, Nancy, Prog Coordr, Pub Relations Coordr, Morton Grove Public Library, 6140 Lincoln Ave, Morton Grove, IL, 60053-2989. Tel: 847-929-5122. Fax: 847-965-7903. p. 676

Brothers, Vicky, Librn, Hepburn Library of Norfolk, One Hepburn St, Norfolk, NY, 13667. Tel: 315-384-3052. Fax: 315-384-3841. p. 1706

Brotherton, Lise, Prof, College de Maisonneuve, 3800, rue Sherbrooke Est, Montreal, QC, H1X 2A2, CANADA. Tel: 514-254-7131. Fax: 514-251-9741. p. 2978

Brott, Judith, Mgr, California Institute of Technology, 1200 E California Blvd, M/C 1-32, Pasadena, CA, 91125-3200. Tel: 626-395-6834. Fax: 626-792-7540. p. 205

Broude, Jeff, Ref Librn, California State University Dominguez Hills, 1000 E Victoria St, Carson, CA, 90747. Tel: 310-243-3709. Fax: 310-516-4219. p. 132

Brougden, Kathlyeen, Ch, Putnam County Library System, 601 College Rd, Palatka, FL, 32177-3873. Tel: 386-329-0126. Fax: 386-329-1240. p. 478

Brough, Marianna, Br Coordr, Indiana University Bloomington, Neal-Marshall Black Culture Center Library, Neal-Marshall Ctr, Rm A113, 275 N Jordan, Bloomington, IN, 47405. Tel: 812-855-3237. Fax: 812-856-4558. p. 728

Brough, Randy, Dir, Laconia Public Library, 695 Main St, Laconia, NH, 03246-2780. Tel: 603-524-4775. Fax: 603-527-1277. p. 1453

Broughman, Adrian, Circ, Randolph College, 2500 Rivermont Ave, Lynchburg, VA, 24503. Tel: 434-947-8133. Fax: 434-947-8134. p. 2476

Broughman, Lisa, Coll Develop, Randolph College, 2500 Rivermont Ave, Lynchburg, VA, 24503. Tel: 434-947-8133. Fax: 434-947-8134. p. 2476

Broughton, Boyd, Access Serv Librn, Mount Mercy University, 1330 Elmhurst Dr NE, Cedar Rapids, IA, 52402-4797. Tel: 319-368-6465. Fax: 319-363-9060. p. 801

Broughton, Boyd, VPres, Linn County Library Consortium, Russell D Cole Library, 620 3rd St SW, Mount Vernon, IA, 52314-1012. Tel: 319-895-4259. p. 2943

Broughton, Dettye, Librn, White River Regional Library, Sharp County - Cave City Branch, 120 Spring St, Cave City, AR, 72521. Tel: 870-283-6947. p. 94

Broughton, Leslie, Head, Coll/Instruction Div, New Mexico Highlands University, Ninth & National Ave, Las Vegas, NM, 87701. Tel: 505-454-3408. Fax: 505-454-0026. p. 1559

Broussard, Camille, Librn, New York Law School Library, 185 W Broadway, New York, NY, 10013. Tel: 212-431-2332. Fax: 212-965-8839. p. 1689

Broussard, Carmen, Librn, Quemado Public Library, 19791 N Hwy 277, Quemado, TX, 78877. Tel: 830-757-1313. Fax: 830-757-3322. p. 2373

Broussard, Linda, Lead Librn, United States Geological Survey, 700 Cajundome Blvd, Lafayette, LA, 70506-3152. Tel: 337-266-8692. Fax: 337-266-8841. p. 953

Broussard, Mary, Instrul Serv Librn & Coordr of Ref & Assessment, Lycoming College, 700 College Pl, Williamsport, PA, 17701-5192. Tel: 570-321-4068. Fax: 570-321-4090. p. 2156

Brousseau, Ginny, Ch, Tolland Public Library, 21 Tolland Green, Tolland, CT, 06084. Tel: 860-871-3620. Fax: 860-871-3626. p. 372

Brousseau, Julie, Acq, Borden Ladner Gervais LLP Library, 1000 de la Gauchetiere W, Ste 900, Montreal, QC, H3B 5H4, CANADA. Tel: 514-954-3159. Fax: 514-954-1905. p. 2892

Brousseau, Mary, Res, Alamance Community College, 1247 Jimmie Kerr Rd, Graham, NC, 27253. Tel: 336-506-4116. Fax: 336-578-5561. p. 1795

Brouwer, Carol H, Dir, North Smithfield Public Library, 20 Main St, Slatersville, RI, 02876. Tel: 401-767-2780. Fax: 401-767-2782. p. 2176

Broverman, Janice, Librn, Edmonton Police, 9620 103A Ave, 2nd flr, Edmonton, AB, T5H 0H7, CANADA. Tel: 780-421-3459. p. 2700

Browar, Lisa, Pres, Linda Hall Library, 5109 Cherry St, Kansas City, MO, 64110-2498. Tel: 816-926-8781. Fax: 816-926-8790. p. 1337

Browder, Greg, Librn, Dallas Public Library, 1515 Young St, Dallas, TX, 75201-5499. Tel: 214-670-1400. Fax: 214-670-7839. p. 2306

Browder, Tonya, Dir, Tompkins Memorial Library, 104 Courthouse Sq, Edgefield, SC, 29824. Tel: 803-637-4010. Fax: 803-637-2116. p. 2193

Brower, Cecil, Ser Tech, University of Washington Libraries, Tacoma Library, 1900 Commerce St, Box 358460, Tacoma, WA, 98402-3100. Tel: 253-692-5746. Fax: 253-692-4445. p. 2535

Brower, Karen, Circ, Dorr Township Library, 1804 Sunset Dr, Dorr, MI, 49323. Tel: 616-681-9678. Fax: 616-681-5650. p. 1174

Brower, Matthew, Bus Ref & Instruction Librn, University of Colorado Boulder, William M White Business Library, Koelbel Bldg, Leeds College of Business, Boulder, CO, 80309. Tel: 303-492-7156. Fax: 303-735-0333. p. 292

Brower, Pauline, YA Serv, Suffern Free Library, 210 Lafayette Ave, Suffern, NY, 10901. Tel: 845-357-1237. Fax: 845-357-3156. p. 1750

Brower, Stewart, Dir, University of Oklahoma, Schusterman Ctr, 4502 E 41st St, Tulsa, OK, 74135. Tel: 918-660-3222. Fax: 918-660-3215. p. 1984

Brower, Susan, Coordr, Media Serv, Loyola University New Orleans, 6363 Saint Charles Ave, New Orleans, LA, 70118-6195. Tel: 504-864-7111. Fax: 504-864-7247. p. 961

Browman, Gwyneth, Neighborhood Libr Supvr, Brooklyn Public Library, Spring Creek, 12143 Flatlands Ave, Brooklyn, NY, 11207. Tel: 718-257-6571. Fax: 718-257-6588. p. 1592

Brown, Aimee, Archives & Spec Coll Librn, Colorado Mesa University, 1200 College Pl, Grand Junction, CO, 81501. Tel: 970-248-1864. Fax: 970-248-1930. p. 310

Brown, Alice, Mgr, Libr Serv, Shalimar Public Library, Six Tenth Ave, Shalimar, FL, 32579. Tel: 850-609-1515. p. 491

Brown, Amanda H, Spec Coll Instruction Librn, University of Colorado Boulder, Archives & Special Collections, 1720 Pleasant St, Boulder, CO, 80309-0184. Tel: 303-492-7582. Fax: 303-492-1881. p. 291

Brown, Amy, Libr Mgr, Worthington Libraries, Worthington Park Library, 1389 Worthington Centre Dr, Worthington, OH, 43085. Tel: 614-807-2642. Fax: 614-807-2676. p. 1951

Brown, Andrea, Mgr, Henrico County Public Library, Glen Allen Branch Library, 10501 Staples Mill Rd, Glen Allen, VA, 23060-3242. Tel: 804-290-9500. Fax: 804-501-2341. p. 2471

Brown, Ann, Dir, Duncan Public Library, 2211 N Hwy 81, Duncan, OK, 73533. Tel: 580-255-0636. Fax: 580-255-6136. p. 1961

Brown, Annette, Libr Tech, Department of Veterans Affairs, 142D/JC, 915 N Grand Blvd, Saint Louis, MO, 63106. Tel: 314-289-6421. Fax: 314-289-6321. p. 1354

Brown, Barbara, Libr Tech/Ser & Doc Delivery, Department of Mental Health, St Elizabeths Hospital, 1100 Alabama Ave SE, Washington, DC, 20032. Tel: 202-299-5997. p. 397

Brown, Barbara, Librn, Granby Town Library, 8960 Granby Rd, Granby, VT, 05840. Tel: 802-328-4494. p. 2424

Brown, Barbara Jean, Sr, Exec Dir, Interfaith Resource Center, 913 Wilson Rd, Wilmington, DE, 19803. Tel: 302-477-0910. Fax: 302-477-0911. p. 388

Brown, Barry, Head, Access & Coll Serv, University of Montana, Maureen & Mike Mansfield Library, 32 Campus Dr, No 9936, Missoula, MT, 59812-9936. Tel: 406-243-6811. Fax: 406-243-4067. p. 1386

Brown, Belinda, Librn, Victor Public Library, 124 S Third St, Victor, CO, 80860. Tel: 719-689-2011. Fax: 719-689-3157. p. 325

Brown, Belva, Libr Mgr, York Library Region, Doaktown Community Library, 430 Main St, Doaktown, NB, E9C 1E8, CANADA. Tel: 506-365-2018. Fax: 506-365-2019. p. 2764

Brown, Betty, Adult Serv, Ref Librn, Middleborough Public Library, 102 N Main St, Middleborough, MA, 02346. Tel: 508-946-2470. Fax: 508-946-2473. p. 1105

Brown, Bettye, Coordr, Pub Serv, Harris-Stowe State University Library, 3026 Laclede Ave, Saint Louis, MO, 63103-2199. Tel: 314-340-3621. Fax: 314-340-3630. p. 1355

Brown, Beverly C, Dir, Rockland Memorial Library, 20 Belmont St, Rockland, MA, 02370-2232. Tel: 781-878-1236. Fax: 781-878-4013. p. 1120

Brown, Blois, ILL, Ecorse Public Library, 4184 W Jefferson Ave, Ecorse, MI, 48229. Tel: 313-389-2030. Fax: 313-389-2032. p. 1176

Brown, Blondel, Circ, Metropolitan College of New York Library, 431 Canal St, 12th Flr, New York, NY, 10013. Tel: 212-343-1234, Ext 2002. Fax: 212-343-7398. p. 1686

Brown, Brenda, Mgr, Chandler Public Library, 22 S Delaware, Chandler, AZ, 85225. Tel: 480-782-2817. Fax: 480-782-2823. p. 59

Brown, Brenda, Br Mgr, Northeast Missouri Library Service, H E Sever Memorial, 207 W Chestnut, Kahoka, MO, 63445. Tel: 660-727-3262. Fax: 660-727-1055. p. 1336

Brown, Brenda, Spec Coll Librn, Washington County Library System, 88 West 100 South, Saint George, UT, 84770-3490. Tel: 435-256-6328. Fax: 435-634-5741. p. 2412

Brown, Buzz, Pres, Greater West Bloomfield Historical Society, 3951 Orchard Lake Rd, Orchard Lake, MI, 48324. Tel: 248-682-2279. p. 1215

Brown, Camille, Ser, Spertus Institute of Jewish Studies, 610 S Michigan Ave, Chicago, IL, 60605. Tel: 312-322-1751. Fax: 312-922-0455. p. 625

Brown, Candice, Dir, Clifton Public Library, 292 Piaget Ave, Clifton, NJ, 07011. Tel: 973-772-5500. p. 1479

Brown, Caris, Local Hist Librn, Helen Hall Library, 100 W Walker, League City, TX, 77573-3899. Tel: 281-554-1105. Fax: 281-554-1118. p. 2354

Brown, Carlletta, Acq, Thomas-Wilhite Memorial Library, 101 E Thomas, Perkins, OK, 74059. Tel: 405-547-5185. Fax: 405-547-1040. p. 1976

Brown, Carlton, Syst Librn, Duke University Libraries, Ford Library, One Towerview Rd, Durham, NC, 27708. Tel: 919-660-7871. Fax: 919-660-7950. p. 1787

Brown, Carol, Dir, Tillamook County Pioneer Museum, 2106 Second St, Tillamook, OR, 97141. Tel: 503-842-4553. Fax: 503-842-4553. p. 2021

Brown, Carol, Dir, Western Wyoming Community College, 2500 College Dr, Rock Springs, WY, 82902. Tel: 307-382-1701. Fax: 307-382-7665. p. 2659

Brown, Carole, Dir, Reese Unity District Library, 2065 Gates St, Reese, MI, 48757-9580. Tel: 989-868-4120. Fax: 989-868-4123. p. 1221

Brown, Caroline, Fac Serv, Spec Projects, Montclair Free Public Library, 50 S Fullerton Ave, Montclair, NJ, 07042. Tel: 973-744-0500, Ext 2226. Fax: 973-744-5268. p. 1503

Brown, Caryn, Librn, Tehama County Library, Los Molinos Branch, 7881 Hwy 99E, Los Molinos, CA, 96055-9701. Tel: 530-384-2772. Fax: 530-384-9826. p. 214

Brown, Catherine M, Ref, University of California Los Angeles Library, College Library, Powell Library Bldg, Los Angeles, CA, 90095. Tel: 310-825-5756. Fax: 310-206-9312. p. 178

Brown, Cathy, Ch, Louisville Public Library, 700 Lincoln Ave, Louisville, OH, 44641-1474. Tel: 330-875-1696. Fax: 330-875-3530. p. 1912

Brown, Cecelia, Librn, Adams County Law Library, Court House, 111-117 Baltimore St, Gettysburg, PA, 17325. Tel: 717-337-9812. Fax: 717-334-1625. p. 2059

Brown, Cecelia M, PhD, Dr, Dir, Prof, University of Oklahoma, Bizzell Memorial Library, 401 W Brooks, Rm 120, Norman, OK, 73019-6032. Tel: 405-325-3921. Fax: 405-325-7648. p. 2972

Brown, Charlene, Librn, Willow Branch Township Library, 330 N Eldon, Cisco, IL, 61830. Tel: 217-669-2312. Fax: 217-669-2312. p. 629

Brown, Charles, Univ Librn, Sullivan University Library, 3101 Bardstown Rd, Louisville, KY, 40205. Tel: 502-456-6773. Fax: 502-456-0016. p. 926

Brown, Charles, Exec Dir, New Orleans Public Library, 219 Loyola Ave, New Orleans, LA, 70112-2044. Tel: 504-529-7323, 504-596-2570. Fax: 504-596-2609. p. 962

Brown, Charles E, Asst Dir, Saint Louis Mercantile Library at the University of Missouri-St Louis, Thomas Jefferson Library Bldg, One University Blvd, Saint Louis, MO, 63121-4400. Tel: 314-516-7243. Fax: 314-516-7241. p. 1359

Brown, Charlotte, Librn, Ozark Regional Library, Annapolis Branch, 204 N Allen St, Annapolis, MO, 63620. Tel: 573-598-3706. p. 1333

Brown, Charlotte, Dir, Fayetteville-Lincoln County Public Library, 306 Elk Ave N, Fayetteville, TN, 37334. Tel: 931-433-3286. Fax: 931-433-0063. p. 2234

Brown, Chris, Ser, Fresno Pacific University, 1717 S Chestnut Ave, Fresno, CA, 93702. Tel: 559-453-2087. Fax: 559-453-2124. p. 153

Brown, Chris, Commun Libr Mgr, Contra Costa County Library, Pittsburg Library, 80 Power Ave, Pittsburg, CA, 94565-3842. Tel: 925-427-8390. Fax: 925-427-8137. p. 209

Brown, Chris, Ref, University of Denver, 2150 E Evans Ave, Denver, CO, 80208-2007. Tel: 303-871-3441. Fax: 303-871-2290. p. 303

Brown, Chris, Archivist, Res, Centenary College of Louisiana, 2834 Woodlawn St, Shreveport, LA, 71104-3335. Tel: 318-869-5462. Fax: 318-869-5462. p. 967

Brown, Chris, Br Coordr, Scenic Regional Library of Franklin, Gasconade & Warren Counties, 308 Hawthorne Dr, Union, MO, 63084. Tel: 636-583-3224. p. 1369

Brown, Chrisanne, Tech Serv Mgr, Boise Public Library, 715 S Capitol Blvd, Boise, ID, 83702. Tel: 208-384-4464. p. 570

Brown, Christine, Head of Libr, University of Alberta, Rutherford (Humanities & Social Sciences) Library, 1-01 Rutherford South, Edmonton, AB, T6G 2J8, CANADA. Tel: 780-492-1405. Fax: 780-492-5083. p. 2702

Brown, Christopher, Dir, Williamsport-Washington Township Public Library, 28 E Second St, Williamsport, IN, 47993-1299. Tel: 765-762-6555. Fax: 765-762-6588. p. 788

Brown, Christopher, Asst Dir, Pella Public Library, 603 Main St, Pella, IA, 50219-1592. Tel: 641-628-4268. Fax: 641-628-1735. p. 838

Brown, Christopher, Adminr, Arlington Public Library System, 101 E Abram St, MS 10-0100, Arlington, TX, 76010-1183. Tel: 817-459-6914. Fax: 817-459-6936. p. 2276

Brown, Chuck, Circ, Chattanooga-Hamilton County Bicentennial Library, 1001 Broad St, Chattanooga, TN, 37402-2652. Tel: 423-757-5310. Fax: 423-757-4994. p. 2226

Brown, Cindy, Dir, Bekkum Memorial Library, 206 N Main St, Westby, WI, 54667-1108. Tel: 608-634-4419. Fax: 608-634-6429. p. 2648

Brown, Clifford, Dir, Washington Park Public Library, 5103 Bunkum Rd, No 2, Washington Park, IL, 62204. Tel: 618-271-5103. Fax: 618-271-7511. p. 715

Brown, Connie, Dir, Glenwood Resource Center, 711 S Vine St, Glenwood, IA, 51534. Tel: 712-527-2438. Fax: 712-527-2280. p. 818

Brown, Corinne, Dir, Hanska Community Library, 201 W Second St, Hanska, MN, 56041. Tel: 507-439-6294. p. 1253

Brown, Dale, In Charge, Florida Department of Corrections, 128 Yelvington Rd, East Palatka, FL, 32131-2100. Tel: 386-326-6829. Fax: 386-312-2219. p. 438

Brown, Darmae, Cataloger, Saline County Public Library, 1800 Smithers Dr, Benton, AR, 72015. Tel: 501-778-4766. Fax: 501-778-0536. p. 95

Brown, Darren, Curator of Coll, Beverly Historical Society, 117 Cabot St, Beverly, MA, 01915-5107. Tel: 978-922-1186. Fax: 978-922-7387. p. 1053

Brown, Dave, Cat Librn, Fullerton College, 321 E Chapman Ave, Fullerton, CA, 92832-2095. Tel: 714-992-7376. Fax: 714-992-9961. p. 153

Brown, David, Tech Serv, Alhambra Public Library, 101 S First St, Alhambra, CA, 91801-3432. Tel: 626-570-5008. Fax: 626-457-1104. p. 120

Brown, David, Ref/Instruction Librn, Dalton State College, 650 College Dr, Dalton, GA, 30720-3778. Tel: 706-272-4585. Fax: 706-272-4511. p. 528

Brown, David, Adult Serv, Murray Public Library, 166 E 5300 South, Murray, UT, 84107-6075. Tel: 801-264-2580. Fax: 801-264-2586. p. 2408

Brown, Dawn M, Asst Dir, Springvale Public Library, 443 Main St, Springvale, ME, 04083. Tel: 207-324-4624. p. 1002

Brown, Deana, Ref & Instruction Librn, Santa Fe Community College Library, 6401 Richards Ave, Santa Fe, NM, 87508-4887. Tel: 505-428-1213. Fax: 505-428-1288. p. 1563

Brown, Deborah, Res Serv, Harvard Library, Dumbarton Oaks Research Library, 1703 32nd St NW, Washington, MA, 20007. Tel: 202-339-6400. Fax: 202-625-0279. p. 1074

Brown, Deborah, Circ, Piedmont Community College, 1715 College Dr, Roxboro, NC, 27573. Tel: 336-599-1181, Ext 446. Fax: 336-599-9146. p. 1821

Brown, Deborah, Sr Librn, Irving Public Library, Northwest, 2928 N Beltline Rd, Irving, TX, 75062. Tel: 972-721-2691. Fax: 972-721-3637. p. 2347

Brown, Dennis, Distance Educ, Info Literacy, Elizabeth City State University, 1704 Weeksville Rd, Elizabeth City, NC, 27909. Tel: 252-335-3577. Fax: 252-335-3469. p. 1790

Brown, Derek, Dir, Info Tech, Rochester Hills Public Library, 500 Olde Towne Rd, Rochester, MI, 48307-2043. Tel: 248-650-7123. Fax: 248-650-7121. p. 1222

Brown, Diana, Interim Mgr, Hockessin Public Library, 1023 Valley Rd, Hockessin, DE, 19707. Tel: 302-239-5160. Fax: 302-239-1519. p. 384

Brown, Diana M, Dir, St Charles Public Library District, One S Sixth Ave, Saint Charles, IL, 60174-2105. Tel: 630-584-0076, Ext 228. Fax: 630-584-3448. p. 699

Brown, Diane M, Dep State Librn, State Library of Louisiana, 701 N Fourth St, Baton Rouge, LA, 70802-5232. Tel: 225-342-4923. Fax: 225-219-4804. p. 945

Brown, Dianna, Head, Circ, Hutchinson Public Library, 901 N Main, Hutchinson, KS, 67501-4492. Tel: 620-663-5441. Fax: 620-663-9506. p. 873

Brown, Don, Music Librn, El Camino College, 16007 S Crenshaw Blvd, Torrance, CA, 90506. Tel: 310-660-3525. Fax: 310-660-3513. p. 275

Brown, Donald C, Librn, Vermont Grand Lodge Library, 49 East Rd - Berlin, Barre, VT, 05641-5390. Tel: 802-223-1883. Fax: 802-223-2187. p. 2418

Brown, Donna, Sr Mgr, Content Mgt, Aventis Pharmaceuticals Library, Scientific Information & Library Services, 1041 Rt 202-206, Mail Stop: BRW K-303A, Bridgewater, NJ, 08807-6800. Tel: 908-231-4952. Fax: 908-231-2802. p. 1474

Brown, Donna, Mgr, Dayton Metro Library, Northmont, 333 W National Rd, Englewood, OH, 45322. Tel: 937-496-8950. p. 1893

Brown, Doris, Libr Asst I, Montgomery City-County Public Library System, 245 High St, Montgomery, AL, 36104. Tel: 334-240-4300. Fax: 334-240-4977. p. 29

Brown, Dorothy, Librn, Florida Department of Corrections, Santa Rosa Correctional Annex, 5850 E Milton Rd, Milton, FL, 32583. Tel: 850-981-7810. Fax: 850-983-5907. p. 470

Brown, Eileen, Doc, William Madison Randall Library, 601 S College Rd, Wilmington, NC, 28403-5616. Tel: 910-962-3000. Fax: 910-962-3078. p. 1831

Brown, Eleanor, Dir, Institute of Design & Construction, 141 Willoughby St, Brooklyn, NY, 11201. Tel: 718-855-3661. Fax: 718-852-5889. p. 1592

Brown, Eli, Head, Spec Coll, North Carolina State University Libraries, Two Broughton Dr, Raleigh, NC, 27695. Tel: 919-515-2273. Fax: 919-515-3628. p. 1816

Brown, Elizabeth, Dir, Saint Joseph Health System, 2700 Dolbeer St, Eureka, CA, 95501. Tel: 707-445-8121, Ext 7514. Fax: 707-269-3836. p. 147

Brown, Ellen, Dir, Mercer County Library System, 2751 Brunswick Pike, Lawrenceville, NJ, 08648-4132. Tel: 609-882-9246. Fax: 609-538-9238. p. 1494

Brown, Ellen, Dir, Mercer County Library System, Lawrence Headquarters, 2751 Brunswick Pike, Lawrenceville, NJ, 08648. Tel: 609-989-6920. Fax: 609-538-9238. p. 1494

Brown, Elmita, Commun Libr Mgr, County of Los Angeles Public Library, Hermosa Beach Library, 550 Pier Ave, Hermosa Beach, CA, 90254-3892. Tel: 310-379-8475. Fax: 310-374-0746. p. 141

Brown, Erica S, Libr Assoc, University of New Hampshire Library, David G Clark Memorial Physics Library, DeMeritt Hall, Nine Library Way, Durham, NH, 03824-3568. Tel: 603-862-2348. Fax: 603-862-2998. p. 1446

Brown, Evan, Librn, Florida Department of Corrections, 20706 US Hwy 90 W, Sanderson, FL, 32087. Tel: 386-719-4614. Fax: 386-719-4516. p. 489

Brown, Evan J, Librn, Florida Department of Corrections, Union Correctional Institution Library, 7819 NW 228th St, Raiford, FL, 32026-4040. Tel: 386-431-2000, Ext 2173. Fax: 386-431-2016. p. 485

Brown, Eve, Librn, Merchantville Public Library, 130 S Centre St, Merchantville, NJ, 08109-2201. Tel: 856-665-3128. Fax: 856-665-4296. p. 1501

Brown, Eve, Mgr, Camden County Library System, Merchantville Public Library, 130 S Centre St, Merchantville, NJ, 08109. Tel: 856-665-3128. Fax: 856-665-4296. p. 1538

Brown, Falvia, In Charge, First United Methodist Church Library, 6201 Belcrest Rd, Hyattsville, MD, 20782. Tel: 301-927-6133. Fax: 301-927-7368. p. 1032

Brown, Frances, Mgr, Pitney Bowes Management Services, 3333 Hwy 6 S, Houston, TX, 77082. Tel: 281-544-9156. Fax: 281-544-8121. p. 2341

Brown, Fred, Ref Librn, Johnson & Wales University Library, Culinary Library, 321 Harborside Blvd, Providence, RI, 02905. Tel: 401-598-1466. p. 2172

Brown, Fredriatta, Ch, Librn II, Montgomery City-County Public Library System, Juliette Hampton Morgan Memorial Library (Main Library), 245 High St, Montgomery, AL, 36104. Tel: 334-240-4991. Fax: 334-240-4980. p. 30

Brown, Gail, Librn, Middlesex Law Association, Ground Flr, Unit N, 80 Dundas St, London, ON, N6A 6A1, CANADA. Tel: 519-679-7046. Fax: 519-672-5917. p. 2818

Brown, Genny, Librn, Charles Evans Community Library, 299 Antoski Dr, Galena, AK, 99741. Tel: 907-656-1883, Ext 127. Fax: 907-656-1769. p. 48

Brown, George, Asst Dir, Shrewsbury Public Library, 609 Main St, Shrewsbury, MA, 01545. Tel: 508-841-8537. Fax: 508-841-8540. p. 1124

Brown, Gertrude, Asst Librn, Community United Methodist Church Library, 20 N Center St, Naperville, IL, 60540-4611. Tel: 630-355-1483. Fax: 630-778-2011. p. 678

Brown, Gina, Ch, Robert L Williams Public Library, 323 W Beech, Durant, OK, 74701. Tel: 580-924-3486. Fax: 580-924-8843. p. 1962

Brown, Glenna, Br Mgr, Wyoming County Public Library, Oceana Public, 101 Cook Pkwy, Oceana, WV, 24870. Tel: 304-682-6784. Fax: 304-682-6784. p. 2570

Brown, Holly, Dir, Gilman Public Library, 100 Main St, Alton, NH, 03809. Tel: 603-875-2550. Fax: 603-875-2550. p. 1437

Brown, Irmgarde, Br Mgr, Harford County Public Library, Havre de Grace Branch, 120 N Union Ave, Havre de Grace, MD, 21078-3000. Tel: 410-939-6700. Fax: 410-939-6702. p. 1020

Brown, Jack Perry, Dir, Art Institute of Chicago, 111 S Michigan Ave, Chicago, IL, 60603. Tel: 312-443-3671. Fax: 312-443-0849. p. 606

Brown, Jackie, Commun Relations Spec, King County Library System, 960 Newport Way NW, Issaquah, WA, 98027. Tel: 425-369-3275. Fax: 425-369-3255. p. 2516

Brown, Jacqueline, Cat, West Baton Rouge Parish Library, 830 N Alexander Ave, Port Allen, LA, 70767-2327. Tel: 225-342-7920. Fax: 225-342-7918. p. 966

Brown, Jacqueline Y, Dir, Archives, Wilberforce University, 1055 N Bickett Rd, Wilberforce, OH, 45384-5801. Tel: 937-708-5630. Fax: 937-708-5771. p. 1948

Brown, James, Info Tech Coordr, Lebanon Public Library, 104 E Washington St, Lebanon, IN, 46052. Tel: 765-482-3460. Fax: 317-873-5059. p. 761

Brown, Jan, Br Librn, Pottawatomie Wabaunsee Regional Library, Eskridge Branch, 115 S Main St, Eskridge, KS, 66423. Tel: 785-449-2296. Fax: 785-449-2296. p. 893

Brown, Jan, Acq, Lord Fairfax Community College, 173 Skirmisher Lane, Middletown, VA, 22645-1745. Tel: 540-868-7155. Fax: 540-868-7171. p. 2479

Brown, Jane, Br Mgr, Mesquite Public Library, 300 W Grubb Dr, Mesquite, TX, 75149. Tel: 972-216-6220. Fax: 972-216-6740. p. 2362

Brown, Jane, Br Mgr, Mesquite Public Library, North Branch, 2600 Oates Dr, Mesquite, TX, 75150. Tel: 972-681-0465. Fax: 972-681-0467. p. 2362

Brown, Janet, Info & Res Serv, Wichita State University Libraries, 1845 Fairmount, Wichita, KS, 67260-0068. Tel: 316-978-5075. Fax: 316-978-3048. p. 902

Brown, Janis, Assoc Dir, Syst & Info Tech, University of Southern California Libraries, Norris Medical Library, 2003 Zonal Ave, Los Angeles, CA, 90089-9130. Tel: 323-442-1113. Fax: 323-221-1235. p. 179

Brown, Jean, ILL, Otsego County Library, 700 S Otsego Ave, Gaylord, MI, 49735-1723. Tel: 989-732-5841. Fax: 989-732-9401. p. 1182

Brown, Jeanette, Dir, USA Today Library, 7950 Jones Branch Dr, McLean, VA, 22108. Tel: 703-854-5588. Fax: 703-854-2112. p. 2478

Brown, Jeanne, Head of Libr, University of Nevada, Las Vegas Libraries, Architecture Studies, Paul B Sogg Architecture Bldg, Box 454049, Las Vegas, NV, 89154-4049. Tel: 702-895-1959. Fax: 702-895-1975. p. 1431

Brown, Jene, Mgr, Los Angeles Public Library System, Western Area, 1246 Glendon Ave, Los Angeles, CA, 90024. Tel: 310-470-3060. Fax: 310-470-3504. p. 174

Brown, Jennifer, Outreach Serv Librn, University of Alaska Southeast, 11120 Glacier Hwy, Juneau, AK, 99801-8676. Tel: 907-796-6285. Fax: 907-796-6249. p. 50

Brown, Jennifer, Asst Librn, Marlow Town Library, 12 Church St, Marlow, NH, 03456. Tel: 603-446-3466. Fax: 603-446-3466. p. 1457

Brown, Jennifer, Cat Librn, Mars Hill College, 124 Cascade St, Mars Hill, NC, 28754. Tel: 828-689-1448. p. 1809

Brown, Jess, Ref, Wauwatosa Public Library, 7635 W North Ave, Wauwatosa, WI, 53213-1718. Tel: 414-471-8486. Fax: 414-479-8484. p. 2647

Brown, Jill, Divinity Cataloger, Vanderbilt University, Divinity Library, 419 21st Ave S, Nashville, TN, 37203-2427. Tel: 615-322-2865. Fax: 615-343-8279. p. 2260

Brown, Jill, Acq, J Sargeant Reynolds Community College Library, Parham Campus-Library & Information Services, 1651 E Parham Rd, Richmond, VA, 23228. Tel: 804-523-5327. Fax: 804-371-3086. p. 2489

Brown, Jim, Dir, Saint Charles City County Library District, 77 Boone Hills Dr, Saint Peters, MO, 63376-0529. Tel: 636-441-2300. Fax: 636-441-3132. p. 1363

Brown, Joanne, Tech Serv, University of Wisconsin-Madison, Primate Center - Lawrence Jacobsen Library, 1220 Capitol Ct, Madison, WI, 53715. Tel: 608-263-3512. Fax: 608-263-4031. p. 2609

Brown, JoAnne M, Br Mgr, Coastal Plain Regional Library, Turner County-Victoria Evans Memorial, 605 North St, Ashburn, GA, 31714. Tel: 229-567-4027. Fax: 229-567-4027. p. 554

Brown, John, Tech Serv, Monroe County Public Library, 700 Fleming St, Key West, FL, 33040. Tel: 305-292-3595. Fax: 305-295-3626. p. 456

Brown, Juanita, Libr Asst I, Montgomery City-County Public Library System, Juliette Hampton Morgan Memorial Library (Main Library), 245 High St, Montgomery, AL, 36104. Tel: 334-240-4999. Fax: 334-240-4980. p. 30

Brown, Judy, Libr Mgr, San Luis Obispo County Library, San Miguel Branch, 254 13th St, San Miguel, CA, 93451. Tel: 805-467-3224. p. 254

Brown, Judy, Br Mgr, Middle Georgia Regional Library System, Gordon Public Library, 284 Milledgeville Hwy W, Gordon, GA, 31031. Tel: 478-628-5352. Fax: 478-628-5352. p. 541

Brown, Judy, Br Mgr, Cumberland County Public Library & Information Center, East Regional, 4809 Clinton Rd, Fayetteville, NC, 28301-8992. Tel: 910-485-2955. Fax: 910-485-5492. p. 1792

Brown, Judy, ILL, Ref, Cherokee County Public Library, 300 E Rutledge Ave, Gaffney, SC, 29340-2227. Tel: 864-487-2711. Fax: 864-487-2752. p. 2194

Brown, Julie, Br Mgr, Palm Beach County Library System, Southwest County Regional, 20701 95th Ave S, Boca Raton, FL, 33434. Tel: 561-482-4554. Fax: 561-483-9679. p. 503

Brown, Julie, Libr Mgr, Bowden Public Library, PO Box 218, Bowden, AB, T0M 0K0, CANADA. Tel: 403-224-3688. Fax: 403-224-3735. p. 2686

Brown, Julie G, Automated Syst Coordr, Cataloger, ILL Librn, Volunteer State Community College Library, 1480 Nashville Pike, Gallatin, TN, 37066-3188. Tel: 615-230-3400, Ext 3438. Fax: 615-230-3410. p. 2235

Brown, June, Librn, Horseshoe Bend District Library, 392 Hwy 55, Horseshoe Bend, ID, 83629-9701. Tel: 208-793-2460. Fax: 208-793-2871. p. 576

Brown, Karen, Youth Serv, Monterey Public Library, 625 Pacific St, Monterey, CA, 93940-2866. Tel: 831-646-3744. Fax: 831-646-5618. p. 190

Brown, Karen, Libr Tech, Smithsonian Libraries, Warren M Robbins Library, National Museum of African Art, Nat Museum of African Art, Rm 2138, MRC 708, 950 Independence Ave SW, Washington, DC, 20560. Tel: 202-633-4682. Fax: 202-357-4879. p. 415

Brown, Karen, Asst Dir, Cambridge Public Library, 449 Broadway, Cambridge, MA, 02138. Tel: 617-349-4040. Fax: 617-349-4028. p. 1073

Brown, Karen, Head, Circ, Winchester Public Library, 80 Washington St, Winchester, MA, 01890. Tel: 781-721-7171, Ext 16. Fax: 781-721-7170. p. 1142

Brown, Karen, Librn, Nute Library, 22 Elm St, Milton, NH, 03851. Tel: 603-652-7829. Fax: 603-652-4793. p. 1458

Brown, Karen, Librn, Hondros College Resource Center, 4140 Executive Pkwy, Westerville, OH, 43081-3855. Tel: 800-783-0095, Ext 6258. Fax: 614-508-6269. p. 1946

Brown, Karen, Coll Develop, Indiana University of Pennsylvania, 431 S 11th St, Indiana, PA, 15705-1096. Tel: 724-357-2344. Fax: 724-357-4891. p. 2071

Brown, Karen, Curator, Racine Heritage Museum, 701 S Main St, Racine, WI, 53403-1211. Tel: 262-636-3926. Fax: 262-636-3940. p. 2632

Brown, Kate, Librn, Boston Public Library, Adams Street, 690 Adams St, Dorchester, MA, 02122-1907. Tel: 617-436-6900. Fax: 617-288-7703. p. 1056

Brown, Katherine Skinner, City Librn, Sterling Municipal Library, Mary Elizabeth Wilbanks Ave, Baytown, TX, 77520. Tel: 281-427-7331. Fax: 281-420-5347. p. 2286

Brown, Kathryn, Librn, Daleville Public Library, 200 Warhawk Dr, Daleville, AL, 36322. Tel: 334-503-9119. Fax: 334-503-9119. p. 14

Brown, Kathryn, Acq, Ocean City Free Public Library, 1735 Simpson Ave, Ste 4, Ocean City, NJ, 08226. Tel: 609-399-2434, Ext 5223. Fax: 609-398-0751. p. 1516

Brown, Katie, Fac Serv, Saint Thomas University Library, Law Library, 16401 NW 37th Ave, Miami Gardens, FL, 33054. Tel: 305-623-2339. Fax: 305-623-2337. p. 469

Brown, Katrina, Dir, Northern Wyoming Community College District, 3059 Coffeen Ave, Sheridan, WY, 82801-1500. Tel: 307-674-6446. Fax: 307-674-3350. p. 2660

Brown, Keisha, Circ Serv, Fresno County Public Law Library, Fresno County Courthouse, Rm 600, 1100 Van Ness Ave, Fresno, CA, 93721-2017. Tel: 559-237-2227. Fax: 559-442-4960. p. 151

Brown, Kelly, Dir, University of Science & Arts of Oklahoma, 1901 S 17th St, Chickasha, OK, 73018. Tel: 405-574-1262. Fax: 405-574-1220. p. 1960

Brown, Kris, Dir, Solon Public Library, 320 W Main St, Solon, IA, 52333-9504. Tel: 319-624-2678. Fax: 319-624-5034. p. 845

Brown, Krista, ILL, Norwin Public Library Association Inc, 100 Caruthers Ln, Irwin, PA, 15642. Tel: 724-863-4700. Fax: 724-863-6195. p. 2072

Brown, Krystal, Ch, Attleboro Public Library, 74 N Main St, Attleboro, MA, 02703. Tel: 508-222-0157, 508-222-0159. Fax: 508-226-3326. p. 1050

Brown, Larry, Financial Dir, Williamson Public Library, 101 Logan St, Williamson, WV, 25661. Tel: 304-235-6029. Fax: 304-235-6029. p. 2575

Brown, Laura, Clinical Librn, City of Hope, 1500 East Duarte Rd, Duarte, CA, 91010. Tel: 626-301-8497. Fax: 909-357-1929. p. 144

Brown, Laverne, Mgr, Dallas Public Library, 1515 Young St, Dallas, TX, 75201-5499. Tel: 214-670-1400. Fax: 214-670-7839. p. 2306

Brown, Laverne, Br Mgr, Dallas Public Library, Renner Frankford Branch, 6400 Frankford Rd, Dallas, TX, 75252-5747. Tel: 214-670-6100. Fax: 214-670-6090. p. 2307

Brown, Leslie, Ref Librn, North Greenville University, 7801 N Tigerville Rd, Tigerville, SC, 29688. Tel: 864-977-7091. Fax: 864-977-2126. p. 2206

Brown, Linda, Asst Dir/Ch, Kendall Young Library, 1201 Willson Ave, Webster City, IA, 50595-2294. Tel: 515-832-9101. Fax: 515-832-9102. p. 851

Brown, Linda, In Charge, Dunn Center Public Library, PO Box 14, Dunn Center, ND, 58626-0014. Tel: 701-548-8400. p. 1840

Brown, Linda, Chair, Coll & Tech Serv, Bowling Green State University Libraries, 204 Wm T Jerome Library, Bowling Green, OH, 43403-0170. p. 1861

Brown, Linda, Asst Br Mgr, Washington County Public Library, Damascus Branch, 126 E Laurel Ave, Damascus, VA, 24236. Tel: 276-475-3820. Fax: 276-475-5081. p. 2443

Brown, Linda, Head, Support Serv, Muskego Public Library, S73 W16663 Janesville Rd, Muskego, WI, 53150. Tel: 262-971-2100. Fax: 262-971-2115. p. 2624

Brown, Linda, Librn, Chinook Regional Library, Consul Branch, PO Box 121, Consul, SK, S0N 0P0, CANADA. Tel: 306-299-2118. p. 2928

Brown, Lisa, Genealogy Serv, Libr Tech, Surry Community College, 630 S Main St, Dobson, NC, 27017-8432. Tel: 336-386-3350. Fax: 336-386-3692. p. 1787

Brown, Lisle, Curator, Marshall University Libraries, One John Marshall Dr, Huntington, WV, 25755-2060. Tel: 304-696-2344. Fax: 304-696-5858. p. 2562

Brown, Lois, Br Mgr, Claymont Public Library, Dennison Branch, 15 N Fourth St, Dennison, OH, 44621. Tel: 740-922-5851. Fax: 740-922-6391. p. 1942

Brown, Lorie, Youth Serv, Southern Tier Library System, 9424 Scott Rd, Painted Post, NY, 14870-9598. Tel: 607-962-3141. Fax: 607-962-5356. p. 1714

Brown, Lynn, Digital Serv & Syst, Roberts Wesleyan College & Northeastern Seminary, 2301 Westside Dr, Rochester, NY, 14624-1997. Tel: 585-594-6064. Fax: 585-594-6543. p. 1731

Brown, Lynn, Acq, Messiah College, One College Ave, Ste 3002, Mechanicsburg, PA, 17055. Tel: 717-691-6006, Ext 7073. Fax: 717-691-2356. p. 2087

Brown, Maggie, Librn, Chinook Regional Library, Mankota Branch, Village Office Complex, First Ave, Mankota, SK, S0H 2W0, CANADA. Tel: 306-478-2401. p. 2928

Brown, Marcy, Librn, Forbes Regional Hospital, 2570 Haymaker Rd, Monroeville, PA, 15146. Tel: 412-858-2422. Fax: 412-858-2532. p. 2091

Brown, Margaret, YA Serv, Cyrenius H Booth Library, 25 Main St, Newtown, CT, 06470. Tel: 203-270-4535. Fax: 203-426-2196. p. 361

Brown, Margaret, Div Chief, Cent Serv, Arlington County Department of Libraries, 1015 N Quincy St, Arlington, VA, 22201. Tel: 703-228-5952. Fax: 703-228-3354. p. 2448

Brown, Margaret, Div Chief, Arlington County Department of Libraries, Central Library, 1015 N Quincy St, Arlington, VA, 22201-4661. Tel: 703-228-5952. Fax: 703-228-5962. p. 2448

Brown, Margaret, Ser & Pub Serv Librn, Kwantlen Polytechnic University Library, 12666 72 Ave., Surrey, BC, V3W 2M8, CANADA. Tel: 604-599-2087. Fax: 604-599-2106. p. 2738

Brown, Margo L, Ref Serv, Art Circle Public Library, Cumberland County, 154 E First St, Crossville, TN, 38555-4696. Tel: 931-484-6790. Fax: 931-484-2350. p. 2232

Brown, Marie, Instrul Serv Librn, Mesa Community College Library, 1833 W Southern Ave, Mesa, AZ, 85202. Tel: 480-461-7663. Fax: 480-461-7681. p. 68

Brown, Marie, Mgr, Br Serv, Camden County Library District, Stoutland Branch, 132 Starling Ave, Stoutland, MO, 65567. Tel: 417-286-3611. Fax: 417-286-3611. p. 1321

Brown, Marie, Asst Librn, Polk Public Library, 180 N Main St, Polk, NE, 68654. Tel: 402-765-7266. Fax: 402-765-7266. p. 1417

Brown, Marilyn, Youth Serv, Herrick District Library, 300 S River Ave, Holland, MI, 49423-3290. Tel: 616-355-3100. p. 1190

Brown, Marilyn, Cat, Ref Serv, Wingate University, PO Box 219, Wingate, NC, 28174-1202. Tel: 704-233-8089. Fax: 704-233-8254. p. 1832

Brown, Marilyn, Librn, Saint John Law Society Library, 110 Charlotte St, Saint John, NB, E2L 4Y9, CANADA. Tel: 506-658-2542. Fax: 506-634-7556. p. 2767

Brown, Marthe, Archivist, Laurentian University, 935 Ramsey Lake Rd, Sudbury, ON, P3E 2C6, CANADA. Tel: 705-675-1151, Ext 3329. Fax: 705-675-4877. p. 2846

Brown, Marvilean, ILL, Barry University, 11300 NE Second Ave, Miami, FL, 33161. Tel: 305-899-3760. Fax: 305-899-4792. p. 464

Brown, Mary, Archivist, Marymount Manhattan College, 221 E 71st St, New York, NY, 10021. Tel: 212-774-4817. Fax: 212-458-8207. p. 1685

Brown, Mary, Archivist, Center for Migration Studies Archives, 209 Flagg Pl, Staten Island, NY, 10304. Tel: 718-351-8800. Fax: 718-667-4596. p. 1747

Brown, Mary C, Dir, Union County Public Library, 175 W Main St, Lake Butler, FL, 32054-1639. Tel: 386-496-3432. Fax: 386-496-1285. p. 457

Brown, Mary, Dr, Prof, Southern Connecticut State University, 501 Crescent St, New Haven, CT, 06515. Tel: 203-392-5772. Fax: 203-392-5780. p. 2963

Brown, Mary Louise, Curator of Objects & Textiles, Madison County Historical Museum & Archival Library, 715 N Main St, Edwardsville, IL, 62025-1111. Tel: 618-656-7562, 618-656-7569. Fax: 618-659-3457. p. 639

Brown, Mary O, ILL, Warren Wilson College, 701 Warren Wilson Rd, Swannanoa, NC, 28778. Tel: 828-771-3062. Fax: 828-771-7085. p. 1826

Brown, Mason, Instrul Librn, Instr, Hunter College Libraries, Health Professions Library, Hunter College Brookdale Campus, 425 E 25th St, New York, NY, 10010. Tel: 212-481-5117. Fax: 212-772-5116. p. 1682

Brown, Maureen, Adult Serv, Ref, Bethlehem Public Library, 451 Delaware Ave, Delmar, NY, 12054-3042. Tel: 518-439-9314. Fax: 518-478-0901. p. 1614

Brown, Maxine, Div Chief, United States Patent & Trademark Office, 400 Dulany St, Rm 1D58, Alexandria, VA, 22314. Tel: 571-272-3547. Fax: 571-273-0048. p. 2446

Brown, Megan, Librn, Genesee District Library, Goodrich Area, 10237 Hegel Rd, Goodrich, MI, 48438. Tel: 810-636-2489. Fax: 810-636-3304. p. 1180

Brown, Melinda, Instruction Coordr, Vanderbilt University, Central Library, 419 21st Ave S, Nashville, TN, 37203-2427. Tel: 615-322-6285. Fax: 615-343-7451. p. 2260

Brown, Melvyn, Supvr, Ser, Philadelphia University, 4201 Henry Ave, Philadelphia, PA, 19144-5497. Tel: 215-951-2572. Fax: 215-951-2574. p. 2115

Brown, Merrikay, Br Mgr, Forsyth County Public Library, Lewisville Branch, 6490 Shallowford Rd, Lewisville, NC, 27023. Tel: 336-703-2940. Fax: 336-945-9745. p. 1832

Brown, Michael D, Cataloger, University of Chicago Library, D'Angelo Law Library, 1121 E 60th St, Chicago, IL, 60637-2786. Tel: 773-702-9620. Fax: 773-702-2889. p. 626

Brown, Michele, Head, Ref Serv, Central Rappahannock Regional Library, 1201 Caroline St, Fredericksburg, VA, 22401-3761. Tel: 540-372-1144. Fax: 540-373-9411. p. 2465

Brown, Michele, Head Librn, Central Rappahannock Regional Library, Fredericksburg Subregional for the Blind-Physically Handicapped, 1201 Caroline St, Fredericksburg, VA, 22401. Tel: 540-372-1144, Ext 234, 540-372-1160. p. 2466

Brown, Michelle, Adult Serv, Brockway Memorial Library, 10021 NE Second Ave, Miami Shores, FL, 33138. Tel: 305-758-8107. p. 470

Brown, Mildred, Chair, Tech Serv, Southern University, 167 Roosevelt Steptoe Ave, Baton Rouge, LA, 70813-0001. Tel: 225-771-2862. Fax: 225-771-4113. p. 944

Brown, Miriam J, Coordr, Central Louisiana Medical Center Library Consortium, 2495 Shreveport Hwy, 142D, Alexandria, LA, 71306. Tel: 318-619-9102. Fax: 318-619-9144. p. 2944

Brown, Molly, Coordr, Pub Serv & Outreach, Wells College, 170 Main St, Aurora, NY, 13026-0500. Tel: 315 364-3354. Fax: 315-364-3412. p. 1576

Brown, Nancy, Ref Spec for Acq, Columbia International University, 7435 Monticello Rd, Columbia, SC, 29203-1599. Tel: 803-807-5103. Fax: 803-744-1391. p. 2187

Brown, Nellie M, Librn, Ipnatchiaq Public Library, 59 Main St, Deering, AK, 99736. Tel: 907-363-2136. Fax: 907-363-2156. p. 46

Brown, Pamela, Dep Exec Dir, Four County Library System, 304 Clubhouse Rd, Vestal, NY, 13850-3713. Tel: 607-723-8236, Ext 303. Fax: 607-723-1722. p. 1761

Brown, Pat, Librn, San Diego County Public Law Library, North County, 325 S Melrose, Ste 300, Vista, CA, 92081-6697. Tel: 760-940-4386. Fax: 760-724-7694. p. 234

Brown, Pat, Dir, Hoisington Public Library, 169 S Walnut, Hoisington, KS, 67544. Tel: 620-653-4128. Fax: 620-653-4128. p. 872

Brown, Pat, Coord, Coll Develop, Spartanburg County Public Libraries, 151 S Church St, Spartanburg, SC, 29306-3241. Tel: 864-596-3500. Fax: 864-596-3518. p. 2205

Brown, Patricia, Dir, Haines Borough Public Library, PO Box 1089, Haines, AK, 99827-1089. Tel: 907-766-2545. Fax: 907-766-2551. p. 49

Brown, Patricia, Dir, Sussex County Department of Libraries, Greenwood Public, 100 Mill St, Greenwood, DE, 19950. Tel: 302-349-5309. Fax: 302-349-5284. p. 383

Brown, Patricia, Librn, Christopher Public Library, 204 E Market St, Christopher, IL, 62822-1759. Tel: 618-724-7534. Fax: 618-724-7534. p. 629

Brown, Patricia, Br Librn, Community District Library, Bentley Memorial/Perry, 135 S Main St, Perry, MI, 48872-0017. Tel: 517-625-3166. Fax: 517-625-7214. p. 1166

Brown, Patty May, Periodicals Librn, Marion County Public Library, 201 E Main St, Lebanon, KY, 40033-1133. Tel: 270-692-4698. Fax: 270-692-9555. p. 920

Brown, Paul, Dir, McCormick County Library, 201 Railroad Ave, McCormick, SC, 29835. Tel: 864-852-2821. Fax: 864-852-2821. p. 2200

Brown, Paula, Asst Dir, Spencer Public Library, 21 E Third St, Spencer, IA, 51301-4188. Tel: 712-580-7290. Fax: 712-580-7468. p. 845

Brown, Paula, Acq, Mississippi College, 101 W College St, Clinton, MS, 39058. Tel: 601-925-3232. Fax: 601-925-3435. p. 1296

Brown, Peggy, Virtual Res Librn, Hampton University, 130 E Tyler St, Hampton, VA, 23668. Tel: 757-637-2096. Fax: 757-727-5952. p. 2468

Brown, Penny, ILL, Palm Beach State College, 4200 Congress Ave, Mail Sta 17, Lake Worth, FL, 33461. Tel: 561-868-3800. Fax: 561-868-3708. p. 459

Brown, Penny, Librn, Livermore Public Library, 22 Church St, Livermore, ME, 04253-3699. Tel: 207-897-7173. p. 990

Brown, Ray, Med Librn, Griffin Memorial Hospital, Bldg 54W, Rm 221, 900 E Main St, Norman, OK, 73071. Tel: 405-321-4880, Ext 2141. Fax: 405-573-6684. p. 1970

Brown, Rebecca, Pub Serv Coordr, Takoma Park Maryland Library, 101 Philadelphia Ave, Takoma Park, MD, 20912. Tel: 301-891-7259. Fax: 301-270-0814. p. 1043

Brown, Rebecca, Head, Access Serv & Doc Delivery, University of North Carolina School of the Arts, 1533 S Main St, Winston-Salem, NC, 27127. Tel: 336-770-3270. Fax: 336-770-3271. p. 1833

Brown, Richard, Personnel Adminr, Richland County Public Library, 1431 Assembly St, Columbia, SC, 29201-3101. Tel: 803-799-9084. Fax: 803-929-3448. p. 2188

Brown, Richard RG, Actg Dir General, Strategic Res, Library & Archives Canada, 550 De la Cité Blvd, Gatineau, QC, K1A 0N4, CANADA. Tel: 819-934-5808. Fax: 819-934-7539. p. 2883

Brown, Richard W, Tech Libr Spec, Pennsylvania State University, N Atherton St, State College, PA, 16801. Tel: 814-863-9940. Fax: 814-863-5568. p. 2143

Brown, Ricki V, City Librn, Abilene Public Library, 202 Cedar St, Abilene, TX, 79601-5793. Tel: 325-676-6025. p. 2271

Brown, Rob, Syst Coordr, Hamilton East Public Library, One Library Plaza, Cumberland Rd, Noblesville, IN, 46060-5639. Tel: 317-770-3231. Fax: 317-776-6936. p. 769

Brown, Robert, Ref Librn, Laredo Public Library, 1120 E Calton Rd, Laredo, TX, 78041. Tel: 956-795-2400. Fax: 956-795-2403. p. 2353

Brown, Robin, Info Literacy Librn, Instruction Coordr, Borough of Manhattan Community College Library, 199 Chambers St, New York, NY, 10007. Tel: 212-220-1445. Fax: 212-748-7466. p. 1671

Brown, Ron, Assoc Dir, Coll Serv, New York University School of Law, 40 Washington Sq S, New York, NY, 10012-1099. Tel: 212-998-6300. Fax: 212-995-4559. p. 1695

Brown, Ronald, Ref Mgr, Atlanta-Fulton Public Library System, South Fulton Regional Library, 4055 Flatshoals Rd SW, Union City, GA, 30291. Tel: 770-306-3092. Fax: 770-306-3127. p. 512

Brown, Rosanna, Dir, Lassen Community College Library, 478-200 Hwy 139, Susanville, CA, 96130. Tel: 530-251-8830. Fax: 530-257-8964. p. 274

Brown, Ruby, Libr Tech, Department of Veterans Affairs, 3701 Loop Rd E, Tuscaloosa, AL, 35404. Tel: 205-554-2000, Ext 2355. Fax: 205-554-2033. p. 38

Brown, S C, Dir, Northeastern Oklahoma A&M College, 200 I NE, Miami, OK, 74354. Tel: 918-540-6381. Fax: 918-542-7065. p. 1968

Brown, Sally, Dir, Lowville Free Library, 5387 Dayan St, Lowville, NY, 13367. Tel: 315-376-2131. Fax: 315-376-2131. p. 1655

Brown, Sally, Librn, Main Line Reform Temple, 410 Montgomery Ave, Wynnewood, PA, 19096. Tel: 610-649-7800. Fax: 610-642-6338. p. 2158

Brown, Samantha, Librn, Georgia Department of Corrections, Office of Library Services, 3178 Mt Zion Church Rd, Pelham, GA, 31779. Tel: 229-294-2940. Fax: 229-294-6691. p. 547

Brown, Sammy Jo, Asst Librn, Anita Public Library, 812 Third St, Anita, IA, 50020. Tel: 712-762-3639. Fax: 712-762-3178. p. 793

Brown, Samuel R, Dir, Naugatuck Valley Community College, 750 Chase Pkwy, Waterbury, CT, 06708. Tel: 203-575-8024. Fax: 203-575-8062. p. 375

Brown, Sandra, Librn, United States Army, 7400 Leake Ave, Rm 108, New Orleans, LA, 70118. Tel: 504-862-2559. Fax: 504-862-1721. p. 963

Brown, Sandra, Ref Serv Librn, Southwest Baptist University Libraries, 1600 University Ave, Bolivar, MO, 65613. Tel: 417-328-1604, 417-328-1621. Fax: 417-328-1652. p. 1320

Brown, Sandra, Dir, Mount Marty College Library, 1105 W Eighth St, Yankton, SD, 57078-3724. Tel: 605-668-1555. Fax: 605-668-1357. p. 2222

Brown, Sara, Govt Doc, Pub Serv Librn, Ashland Community & Technical College, 1400 College Dr, Ashland, KY, 41101. Tel: 606-326-2015. Fax: 606-326-2186. p. 905

Brown, Sarah B, Dir, Mason Public Library, 200 Reading Rd, Mason, OH, 45040-1694. Tel: 513-398-2711. Fax: 513-398-9342. p. 1915

Brown, Sarah M, Libr Dir, Everest University, 9200 Southpark Center Loop, Orlando, FL, 32819. Tel: 407-608-5078. Fax: 407-345-8671. p. 475

Brown, Sharon, Librn, Bristol Regional Medical Center Library, One Medical Park Blvd, Bristol, TN, 37621-8964. Tel: 423-844-4440. Fax: 423-844-4443. p. 2225

Brown, Sharon, Chief Librn, Wilfrid Laurier University Library, 75 University Ave W, Waterloo, ON, N2L 3C5, CANADA. Tel: 519-884-0710, Ext 3380. Fax: 519-884-3209. p. 2869

Brown, Sharon M, Librn, Holston Valley Medical Center, 130 W Ravine Rd, Kingsport, TN, 37660. Tel: 423-224-6870. Fax: 423-224-6014. p. 2240

Brown, Sharon M, Coordr, Libr Serv, Tennessee Health Science Library Association, Holston Valley Med Ctr Health Sciences Library, 130 W Ravine Rd, Kingsport, TN, 37660. Tel: 423-224-6870. Fax: 423-224-6014. p. 2955

Brown, Sheila, Ch, Townsend Public Library, 276 Main St, Townsend, MA, 01469-1513. Tel: 978-597-1714. Fax: 978-597-2779. p. 1131

Brown, Sheila, Adminr, Butler County Federated Library System, 218 N McKean St, Butler, PA, 16001. Tel: 724-283-1880. Fax: 724-841-0433. p. 2040

Brown, Shelley, Circ, University of Alberta, John Alexander Weir Memorial Law Library, Law Centre, 111 St & 89 Ave, Edmonton, AB, T6G 2H5, CANADA. Tel: 780-492-1445. Fax: 780-492-7546. p. 2703

Brown, Sheri, Ref, Florida State College at Jacksonville, Downtown Campus, 101 W State St, Jacksonville, FL, 32202-3056. Tel: 904-633-8368. Fax: 904-633-8328. p. 453

Brown, Sherie L, Dir, Massillon Public Library, 208 Lincoln Way E, Massillon, OH, 44646-8416. Tel: 330-832-9831. Fax: 330-830-2182. p. 1915

Brown, Stacy, Pub Serv, Georgia Highlands College Libraries, 3175 Cedartown Hwy SE, Rome, GA, 30161. Tel: 706-295-6318. Fax: 706-295-6365. p. 548

Brown, Stan, Libr Syst Officer, Miami University Libraries, 225 King Library, Oxford, OH, 45056. Tel: 513-529-2351. Fax: 513-529-3110. p. 1926

Brown, Stephen, Tech Serv Librn, Indiana Wesleyan University, 4201 S Washington St, Marion, IN, 46953. Tel: 765-677-2197. Fax: 765-677-2676. p. 762

Brown, Steve, Librn, Traffic Injury Research Foundation of Canada, 171 Nepean St, Ste 200, Ottawa, ON, K2P 0B4, CANADA. Tel: 613-238-5235. Fax: 613-238-5292. p. 2834

Brown, Steven L, Dir, North Richland Hills Public Library, 9015 Grand Ave, North Richland Hills, TX, 76180. Tel: 817-427-6800. Fax: 817-427-6808. p. 2366

Brown, Sue, Tech Serv Mgr, Brookfield Public Library, 1900 N Calhoun Rd, Brookfield, WI, 53005. Tel: 262-782-4140. Fax: 262-796-6670. p. 2583

Brown, Susan, Asst Dir, Derry Public Library, 64 E Broadway, Derry, NH, 03038-2412. Tel: 603-432-6140. Fax: 603-432-6128. p. 1444

Brown, Susan, Head, Circ, Ashland Public Library, 224 Claremont Ave, Ashland, OH, 44805. Tel: 419-289-8188. Fax: 419-281-8552. p. 1855

Brown, Susan, Asst Dean, Admin, University of Toronto, 140 St George St, Toronto, ON, M5S 3G6, CANADA. Tel: 416-978-8588. Fax: 416-978-5762. p. 2978

Brown, Susan M, Dir, Transylvania University Library, 300 N Broadway, Lexington, KY, 40508. Tel: 859-246-5008. Fax: 859-233-8779. p. 921

Brown, Suzanne, Librn, Clearfield Public Library, 401 Broadway, Ste 200, Clearfield, IA, 50840-0028. Tel: 641-336-2939. p. 802

Brown, Suzanne, Circ, National American University, 321 Kansas City St, Rapid City, SD, 57701-3692. Tel: 605-394-4943. Fax: 605-394-4871. p. 2217

Brown, Sylvia, Librn, Woodland Public Library, 169 Main St, Baileyville, ME, 04694. Tel: 207-427-3235. Fax: 207-427-3673. p. 975

Brown, Taryn, Youth Serv & Commun Relations Librn, Southwest Georgia Regional Library, 301 S Monroe St, Bainbridge, GA, 39819. Tel: 229-248-2665. Fax: 229-248-2670. p. 521

Brown, Terrence Neal, Dir, Libr Serv, Mid-America Baptist Theological Seminary, 2095 Appling Rd, Cordova, TN, 38016. Tel: 901-751-3007. Fax: 901-751-8454. p. 2232

Brown, Terry, Circ Mgr, Darlington County Library, Society Hill Branch, 473 S Main St, Society Hill, SC, 29593. Tel: 843-378-0026. Fax: 843-378-0026. p. 2192

Brown, Timothy, Cat, Wofford College, 429 N Church St, Spartanburg, SC, 29303-3663. Tel: 864-597-4300. Fax: 864-597-4329. p. 2206

Brown, Tom, Dir, Libr Serv, Donnelly College, 608 N 18th St, Kansas City, KS, 66102. Tel: 913-621-8735. Fax: 913-621-8719. p. 875

Brown, Valerie, Librn, Andes Public Library, 242 Main St, Andes, NY, 13731. Tel: 845-676-3333. Fax: 845-676-3333. p. 1574

Brown, Vandella, Mgr, Diversity Prog, Illinois State Library, Gwendolyn Brooks Bldg, 300 S Second St, Springfield, IL, 62701-9713. Tel: 217-785-9075. Fax: 217-785-4326. p. 705

Brown, Vik G, Dept Chair, Southern Utah University, 351 W University Blvd, Cedar City, UT, 84720. Tel: 435-586-7952. Fax: 435-865-8152. p. 2404

Brown, Virginia, ILL, Ref Serv, Hinshaw & Culbertson Library, 222 N LaSalle, Ste 300, Chicago, IL, 60601-1081. Tel: 312-704-3000. Fax: 312-704-3951. p. 614

Brown, Virginia, Acq, Northern Wyoming Community College District, 3059 Coffeen Ave, Sheridan, WY, 82801-1500. Tel: 307-674-6446. Fax: 307-674-3350. p. 2660

Brown, Walter, Br Mgr, Clay County Public Library System, Orange Park Public Library, 2054 Plainfield Ave, Orange Park, FL, 32073-5498. Tel: 904-278-4750. Fax: 904-278-3618. p. 475

Brown, Wanda, Assoc Dean, Wake Forest University, PO Box 7777, Winston-Salem, NC, 27109-7777. Tel: 336-758-5094. Fax: 336-758-3694, 336-758-8831. p. 1834

Brown, Yvonne, Librn, Lapeer District Library, Goodland, 2370 N Van Dyke Rd, Imlay City, MI, 48444. Tel: 810-724-1970. Fax: 810-724-5612. p. 1202

Brown, Zack, Librn, Midstate College, 411 W Northmoor Rd, Peoria, IL, 61614. Tel: 800-251-4299, Ext 1200. Fax: 309-692-3918. p. 690

Brown, Zella'Ques S, Head, Circ Serv, Librn II, Montgomery City-County Public Library System, Juliette Hampton Morgan Memorial Library (Main Library), 245 High St, Montgomery, AL, 36104. Tel: 334-240-4999. Fax: 334-240-4980. p. 30

Brown-Carman, Vivian, Dir, Libr Serv, The Edward Waters College Library, 1658 Kings Rd, Jacksonville, FL, 32209. Tel: 904-470-8080. Fax: 904-470-8032. p. 452

Brown-Epstein, Helen-Ann, Clinical Librn, Cornell University Library, The Samuel J Wood Library & The C V Starr Biomedical Information Center, 1300 York Ave, C115, Box 67, New York, NY, 10065-4896. Tel: 212-746-6050. Fax: 212-746-6494. p. 1642

Brown-Eustis, Sandra, Librn, Mechanic Falls Public Library, 15 Elm St, Mechanic Falls, ME, 04256. Tel: 207-345-9450. p. 991

Brown-Lindsay, Opal, Dir, Mount Vernon Public Library, 28 S First Ave, Mount Vernon, NY, 10550. Tel: 914-668-1840. Fax: 914-668-1018. p. 1664

Brown-Petteway, Diane, Br Mgr, New Haven Free Public Library, Stetson Branch, 200 Dixwell Ave, New Haven, CT, 06511. Tel: 203-946-8119. Fax: 203-946-6782. p. 356

Brown-Salazar, Margaret, Ref & Instruction Librn, Saint Mary's College Library, 1928 Saint Mary's Rd, Moraga, CA, 94575. Tel: 925-631-4229. Fax: 925-376-6097. p. 191

Brown-Seeley, Pamela, Archives Mgr, Circ, Saint Joseph's College, Hwy 231 S, Rensselaer, IN, 47978. Tel: 219-866-6209. Fax: 219-866-6135. p. 774

Brown-Sica, Margaret, Assoc Dir, Tech Strategy & Learning Spaces, Auraria Library, 1100 Lawrence St, Denver, CO, 80204-2095. Tel: 303-556-6762. Fax: 303-556-3528. p. 298

Brownback, Lisa, Ref, Cape May County Library, 30 Mechanic St, Cape May Court House, NJ, 08210. Tel: 609-463-6350. Fax: 609-465-3895. p. 1477

Browndorf, Megan, Soc Sci Librn, North Dakota State University Libraries, 1201 Albrecht Blvd, Fargo, ND, 58108. Tel: 701-231-8817. Fax: 701-231-6128. p. 1841

Browne, Cynthia, Adminr, Deutschheim State Historic Site Library, 107 W Second St, Hermann, MO, 65041. Tel: 573-486-2200. Fax: 573-486-2249. p. 1330

Browne, Diane, Tech Serv, Needham Free Public Library, 1139 Highland Ave, Needham, MA, 02494-3298. Tel: 781-455-7559. Fax: 781-455-7591. p. 1108

Browne, Diane, Asst Dir, Stoughton Public Library, 84 Park St, Stoughton, MA, 02072-2974. Tel: 781-344-2711. Fax: 781-344-7340. p. 1129

Browne, Gretchen, Dir, Plainview-Old Bethpage Public Library, 999 Old Country Rd, Plainview, NY, 11803-4995. Tel: 516-938-0077. Fax: 516-433-4645. p. 1718

Browne, Kelly, Asst Dir, Sacramento County Public Law Library, 813 Sixth St, 1st Flr, Sacramento, CA, 95814-2403. Tel: 916-874-6011. Fax: 916-874-5691. p. 224

Browne, Kelly, VPres, Northern California Association of Law Libraries, 268 Bush St, No 4006, San Francisco, CA, 94104. Tel: 916-874-7427. p. 2938

Browne, Lianne, Br Supvr, Whitby Public Library, Rossland Branch, 701 Rossland Rd E, Whitby, ON, L1N 8Y9, CANADA. Tel: 905-668-1886. p. 2871

Browne, Nona, Adminr, Menaul Historical Library of the Southwest, 301 Menaul Blvd NE, Albuquerque, NM, 87107. Tel: 505-343-7480. p. 1549

Browne, Sarah P, Chief, Law Libr Serv, New York State Department of Law Library, The Capitol, Albany, NY, 12224. Tel: 518-474-3840. Fax: 518-473-1822. p. 1569

Browne, Wynne, Libr Serv Dir, Downs Rachlin Martin PLLC, 90 Prospect St, Saint Johnsbury, VT, 05819. Tel: 802-748-8324. Fax: 802-748-4394. p. 2434

Brownell, Audrey, Fund-Raising Officer, Maricopa County Library District, 2700 N Central Ave, Ste 700, Phoenix, AZ, 85004. Tel: 602-652-3047. Fax: 602-652-3071. p. 74

Brownell, Cathy, Pub Serv & IT, Sierra Vista Public Library, 2600 E Tacoma, Sierra Vista, AZ, 85635-1399. Tel: 520-458-4225. Fax: 520-458-5377. p. 82

Brownell, Diane, Asst Librn, Riceville Public Library, 307 Woodland Ave, Riceville, IA, 50466. Tel: 641-985-2273. Fax: 641-985-4002. p. 840

Brownell, Helen C, Dir, Easton Library, 1074 State Rte 40, Greenwich, NY, 12834. Tel: 518-692-2253. Fax: 518-692-2253. p. 1631

Brownfield, Molly, Head, Ref Serv, Duke University Libraries, School of Law Library, 210 Science Dr, Durham, NC, 27708. Tel: 919-613-77123. Fax: 919-613-7237. p. 1788

Browning, Barbara, Cat/Ref/Libr Instruction, Allegany College of Maryland Library, 12401 Willowbrook Rd SE, Cumberland, MD, 21502-2596. Tel: 301-784-5240. Fax: 301-784-5017. p. 1026

Browning, Bruno, Dir, University of Wisconsin-Madison, L & S Learning Support Services, Van Hise Hall, 1220 Linden Dr, Madison, WI, 53706. Tel: 608-262-1408. Fax: 608-262-7579. p. 2609

Browning, Greta, Ref, Appalachian State University, William Leonard Eury Appalachian Collection, Belk Library, 4th Flr, 218 College St, Boone, NC, 28608. Tel: 828-262-7974. Fax: 828-262-2553. p. 1777

Browning, Kathleen, Adult Serv Coordr, Farmington Public Library, 2101 Farmington Ave, Farmington, NM, 87401. Tel: 505-566-2210. Fax: 505-599-1257. p. 1555

Browning, Nancye, Asst Dir, Louisville Free Public Library, 301 York St, Louisville, KY, 40203-2205. Tel: 502-574-1743. Fax: 502-574-1666, 502-574-1693. p. 924

Browning, Rita, Dir, Cresskill Public Library, 53 Union Ave, Cresskill, NJ, 07626. Tel: 201-567-5067. Fax: 201-567-5067. p. 1480

Browning, Sandy, Circ Mgr, Lewes Public Library, 111 Adams Ave, Lewes, DE, 19958. Tel: 302-645-2733. Fax: 302-645-6235. p. 384

Browning, Somer, Cat, State University of New York Maritime College, Six Pennyfield Ave, Fort Schuyler, Bronx, NY, 10465. Tel: 718-409-7232. Fax: 718-409-7256. p. 1588

Browning, Tim, Librn, Theological Education Association of Mid America, Southern Baptist Theological Seminary, 2825 Lexington Rd, Louisville, KY, 40280. Tel: 502-897-4807. Fax: 502-897-4600. p. 2944

Browning, Vicki, Circ Librn, Bath County Memorial Library, 24 W Main St, Owingsville, KY, 40360. Tel: 606-674-2531. Fax: 606-674-2531. p. 931

Browning, Wes, Info Tech Mgr, University of Texas, M D Anderson Cancer Center Research Medical Library, 1400 Pressler St, Houston, TX, 77030-3722. Tel: 713-745-1545. Fax: 713-563-3650. p. 2344

Brownlee, Julie, Supvr, Circ, Northborough Free Library, 34 Main St, Northborough, MA, 01532-1942. Tel: 508-393-5025. Fax: 508-393-5027. p. 1114

Brownlee, Rachell, Ch, Pere Marquette District Library, 185 E Fourth St, Clare, MI, 48617. Tel: 989-386-7576. Fax: 989-386-3576. p. 1163

Brownlow, Jennifer, Ref, Malaspina University-College Library, 900 Fifth St, Nanaimo, BC, V9R 5S5, CANADA. Tel: 250-740-6335. Fax: 250-740-6473. p. 2732

Brownson, Ann, Ref Librn, Eastern Illinois University, 600 Lincoln Ave, Charleston, IL, 61920. Tel: 217-581-6099. p. 603

Broxterman, Audrey, Librn, Vermillion Public Library, 102 Main St, Vermillion, KS, 66544. Tel: 785-382-6227. p. 899

Broxton, Larry, Chief, PR & Mkt, Prince George's County Memorial Library System, 6532 Adelphi Rd, Hyattsville, MD, 20782-2098. Tel: 301-699-3500. Fax: 301-927-0887. p. 1032

Broyles, Kathy, Ref Librn, University of North Texas Health Science Center at Fort Worth, 3500 Camp Bowie Blvd, Fort Worth, TX, 76107-2699. Tel: 817-735-2070. Fax: 817-763-0325. p. 2324

Broyles, Linda, Cataloger, Coll Develop, Database Mgr, Pensacola State College, 1000 College Blvd, Pensacola, FL, 32504-8998. Tel: 850-484-1107. Fax: 850-484-1991. p. 482

Brozovich, Kimberly, Dir of Tech Serv, Rock Island Public Library, 401 19th St, Rock Island, IL, 61201. Tel: 309-732-7323. Fax: 309-732-7342. p. 696

Brubacher, Ryan, Visual Res Curator, Occidental College Library, 1600 Campus Rd, Los Angeles, CA, 90041. Tel: 323-259-2714. Fax: 323-341-4991. p. 176

Brubaker, Beryl H, Libr Dir, Eastern Mennonite University, 1200 Park Rd, Harrisonburg, VA, 22802-2462. Tel: 540-432-4175. Fax: 540-432-4977. p. 2470

Brubaker, Grace, Dir, Shenandoah County Library, New Market Area, 9417 S Congress St, New Market, VA, 22844. Tel: 540-740-8650. Fax: 540-740-2956. p. 2460

Brubaker, Jana, Head, Tech Serv, Northern Illinois University Libraries, DeKalb, IL, 60115-2868. Tel: 815-753-5914. p. 635

Brubaker, Jerome P, Curator, Old Fort Niagara Association Library & Archives, Old Fort Niagara, Fort Niagara State Park, Youngstown, NY, 14174. Tel: 716-745-9667. Fax: 716-745-9141. p. 1772

Brubaker, Noah, Computer Serv, University of Indianapolis, 1400 E Hanna Ave, Indianapolis, IN, 46227-3697. Tel: 317-788-3268. Fax: 317-788-3275. p. 755

Brubaker, Ronald D, Librn, Minneapolis Public Library, 519 Delia Ave, Minneapolis, KS, 67467. Tel: 785-392-3205. Fax: 785-392-2934. p. 883

Bruce, Boyd, Asst Libr Serv Mgr/Regional Br Mgr, Lake County Library System, 2401 Woodlea Rd, Tavares, FL, 32778. Tel: 352-536-2275. Fax: 352-253-6184. p. 499

Bruce, Boyd, Regional Br Mgr, Lake County Library System, Cooper Memorial Library, 2525 Oakley Seaver Dr, Clermont, FL, 34711. Tel: 352-536-2275. Fax: 352-536-2259. p. 500

Bruce, Dot, Dir, Mildred G Fields Memorial Library, 1075 E Van Hook St, Milan, TN, 38358-2892. Tel: 731-686-8268, 731-723-3747. Fax: 731-686-3207. p. 2253

Bruce, Eugene, Tec Data Librn, United States Navy, Albert T Camp Technical Library, Naval Surface Warfare Ctr, 4171 Fowler Rd, Bldg 299, Ste 101, Indian Head, MD, 20640-5110. Tel: 301-744-4742. Fax: 301-744-4192. p. 1033

Bruce, Harry, Prof & Dean, University of Washington, Mary Gates Hall, Ste 370, Campus Box 352840, Seattle, WA, 98195-2840. Tel: 206-685-9937. Fax: 206-616-3152. p. 2976

Bruce, Jen, Librn, University Center Rochester, 851 30 Ave SE, Rochester, MN, 55904. Tel: 507-285-7233. Fax: 507-281-7772. p. 1273

Bruce, Jim, Librn, Nicola Valley Institute of Technology Library, 4155 Belshaw St, Merritt, BC, V1K 1R1, CANADA. Tel: 250-378-3303. Fax: 250-378-3332. p. 2731

Bruce, Judy, Dir, Br Serv, Saint Louis Public Library, 1415 Olive St, Saint Louis, MO, 63103-2315. Tel: 314-539-0300. Fax: 314-241-3840. p. 1359

Bruce, Lorne, Spec Coll & Archives Librn, University of Guelph, 50 Stone Rd E, Guelph, ON, N1G 2W1, CANADA. Tel: 519-824-4120, Ext 52089. Fax: 519-824-6931. p. 2807

Bruce, Lorraine, Sr Lecturer, University of Washington, Mary Gates Hall, Ste 370, Campus Box 352840, Seattle, WA, 98195-2840. Tel: 206-685-9937. Fax: 206-616-3152. p. 2976

Bruce, Malcolm, Libr Assoc, Buncombe County Public Libraries, East Asheville, 902 Tunnel Rd, Asheville, NC, 28805. Tel: 828-250-4738. p. 1774

Bruce, Maureen, Mgr, Moundview Memorial Hospital, 402 W Lake St, Friendship, WI, 53934. Tel: 608-339-3331. Fax: 608-339-9385. p. 2593

Bruce, William P, Dir, John A Gupton College, 1616 Church St, Nashville, TN, 37203. Tel: 615-327-3927. Fax: 615-321-4518. p. 2256

Bruch, Courtney, Coordr, Instruction & Ref, Front Range Community College, 3705 W 112th Ave, Westminster, CO, 80031-2140. Tel: 303-404-5133. Fax: 303-404-5144. p. 326

Bruchis, Wanda, Exec Dir, Mid-York Library System, 1600 Lincoln Ave, Utica, NY, 13502. Tel: 315-735-8328. Fax: 315-735-0943. p. 1758

Bruck, Ingrid, Dir, Long Branch Free Public Library, 328 Broadway, Long Branch, NJ, 07740. Tel: 732-222-3900. Fax: 732-222-3799. p. 1496

Brucker, Patricia, Head Librn, Augusta Technical College, 3200 Augusta Tech Dr, Augusta, GA, 30906. Tel: 706-771-4165. Fax: 706-771-4169. p. 519

Brucker, Wonja, Asst Dir, Br Coordr, Schenectady County Public Library, 99 Clinton St, Schenectady, NY, 12305-2083. Tel: 518-388-4545. Fax: 518-386-2241. p. 1740

Bruckner, Nancy, Cat, Otis Library, Two Cliff St, Norwich, CT, 06360. Tel: 860-889-2365. Fax: 860-886-4744. p. 362

Bruder, Connie, Assoc Dir, Pub Serv, Indiana State Library, 315 W Ohio St, Indianapolis, IN, 46202. Tel: 317-232-3734. Fax: 317-232-0002. p. 752

Bruder, Connie, Asst Dir, Head Audio/Visual, Lebanon Public Library, 104 E Washington St, Lebanon, IN, 46052. Tel: 765-482-3460. Fax: 317-873-5059. p. 761

Brudno, Roger, Dir, Oroville Hospital, 2767 Olive Hwy, Oroville, CA, 95966. Tel: 530-554-1309. p. 202

Brudvig, Karen L, Sr Med Librn, Saint Joseph's Hospital, 69 W Exchange St, Saint Paul, MN, 55102. Tel: 651-232-3193. Fax: 651-326-8095. p. 1281

Brueck, Lora, Asst Dir, Coll Develop, Worcester Polytechnic Institute, 100 Institute Rd, Worcester, MA, 01609-2280. Tel: 508-831-5410. Fax: 508-831-5829. p. 1145

Brueckner, Amanda, Ch, Karl Junginger Memorial Library, 625 N Monroe St, Waterloo, WI, 53594-1183. Tel: 920-478-3344. Fax: 920-478-2351. p. 2644

Brueggemann, Louise, Children's Serv Supvr, Naperville Public Library, 95th Street, 3015 Cedar Glade Dr, Naperville, IL, 60564. Tel: 630-961-4100, Ext 4960. Fax: 630-637-4870. p. 679

Bruegging, Carol, Ref Librn, Govt Doc, The Kansas City Public Library, 14 W Tenth St, Kansas City, MO, 64105. Tel: 816-701-3653. Fax: 816-701-3401. p. 1338

Bruemmer, Bruce, Archivist, Cargill, Inc, 15407 McGinty Rd W, Wayzata, MN, 55391. Tel: 952-742-6498. Fax: 952-742-6062. p. 1287

Bruen, Deborah, Librn, Sacred Heart Academy, c/o Sacred Heart Academy, 265 Benham St, Hamden, CT, 06514. Tel: 203-288-2309. Fax: 203-230-9680. p. 343

Bruenderman, Jason, Head, Syst & Tech Support, Southeast Missouri State University, One University Plaza, Mail Stop 4600, Cape Girardeau, MO, 63701. Tel: 573-986-6833. Fax: 573-651-2666. p. 1322

Brueschoff, Sara, Youth Serv Librn, Ocean City Free Public Library, 1735 Simpson Ave, Ste 4, Ocean City, NJ, 08226. Tel: 609-399-2434, Ext 5235. Fax: 609-398-0751. p. 1516

Bruestle, Beth, Dir, McLean-Mercer Regional Library, Downtown Plaza, Second St, Riverdale, ND, 58565. Tel: 701-654-7652. Fax: 701-654-7526. p. 1847

Bruggenthies, Cindy, Br Mgr, Great River Regional Library, Albany Public Library, 400 Railroad Ave, Albany, MN, 56307. Tel: 320-845-4843. Fax: 320-845-4843. p. 1274

Brugger, Arden, Librn, Riverside Presbyterian Church, 849 Park St, Jacksonville, FL, 32204. Tel: 904-355-4585. Fax: 904-355-4508. p. 454

Brugman, Ardys, In Charge, Douglas Public Library, Main St, Douglas, NE, 68344. Tel: 402-799-3175. p. 1397

Brugman, Ron, Educ Supvr, Arizona Department of Corrections - Adult Institutions, Arizona State Prison Complex - Phoenix Library, 2500 E Van Buren St, Phoenix, AZ, 85008. Tel: 602-685-3100, Ext 3758. Fax: 602-685-3129. p. 71

Bruguier, Elsa, Librn, Union County College Libraries, Plainfield Campus, 232 E Second St, Plainfield, NJ, 07060-1308. Tel: 908-412-3545. p. 1480

Bruinsma, Alison, Young Adult Serv Coordr, Brookings Public Library, 515 Third St, Brookings, SD, 57006. Tel: 605-692-9407. Fax: 605-692-9386. p. 2210

Brule, Laura, Ref Librn, Atlanta-Fulton Public Library System, Roswell Regional Library, 115 Norcross St, Roswell, GA, 30075. Tel: 770-640-3075. Fax: 770-640-3077. p. 512

Bruley, Jeannine, Librn, Isle La Motte Library, 2238 Main St, Isle La Motte, VT, 05463. Tel: 802-928-4113. p. 2426

Brum, Janice, Archivist, The City of Calgary, Corporate Records, Archives, 313 Seventh Ave SE, Calgary, AB, T2G 0J1, CANADA. Tel: 403-268-8180. Fax: 403-268-6731. p. 2691

Brumbach, Kristin, Youth Serv Librn, Mifflin Community Library, Six Philadelphia Ave, Shillington, PA, 19607. Tel: 610-777-3911. Fax: 610-777-5516. p. 2139

Brumback, Sheri, Head of Libr, Volusia County Public Library, DeBary Public, 200 N Charles R Beall Blvd, DeBary, FL, 32713. Tel: 386-668-3835. Fax: 386-668-3837. p. 436

Brumbaugh, Darlene, Dir, Brumbaugh Public Library, 202 Fink, Glenvil, NE, 68941. Tel: 402-771-2215. p. 1400

Brumbaugh, Lee, Curator of Photog, Nevada Department of Cultural Affairs Division of Museums & History, 1650 N Virginia St, Reno, NV, 89503. Tel: 775-688-1191, Ext 226. Fax: 775-688-2917. p. 1432

Brumbelow, Dana L, Asst Dir, Culpeper County Library, 271 Southgate Shopping Ctr, Culpeper, VA, 22701-3215. Tel: 540-825-8691. Fax: 540-825-7486. p. 2459

Brumberg, Esther, Coll, Sr Curator, Museum of Jewish Heritage, 36 Battery Pl, New York, NY, 10280. Tel: 646-437-4248. Fax: 646-437-4372. p. 1687

Brumett, Renee, Electronic Res Librn, Springfield-Greene County Library District, 4653 S Campbell, Springfield, MO, 65810-1723. Tel: 417-882-0714. Fax: 417-883-9348. p. 1367

Brumfield, Dawn, Dir, Learning Res Ctr, Southwest Mississippi Community College, Lakeside Dr, Summit, MS, 39666. Tel: 601-276-2004. Fax: 601-276-3748. p. 1315

Brumit, Melanie, Dir, Cameron J Jarvis Troup Municipal Library, 102 S Georgia, Troup, TX, 75789-2020. Tel: 903-842-3101. Fax: 903-842-2890. p. 2393

Brummett, Frances, Circ Mgr, Salt Lake City Public Library, 210 E 400 S, Salt Lake City, UT, 84111-3280. Tel: 801-322-8110. Fax: 801-322-8194. p. 2413

Brun, Nathalie, Libr Dir, Albert-Westmorland-Kent Regional Library, Dieppe Public, 333 Acadie Ave, Dieppe, NB, E1A 1G9, CANADA. Tel: 506-877-5015, 506-877-7945. Fax: 506-877-7897. p. 2765

Brunal-Perry, Omaira, Spanish Doc Coll, University of Guam, Guam & Micronesia Collection, UOG Sta, Mangilao, GU, 96923. Tel: 671-735-2157, 671-735-2160. Fax: 671-734-7403. p. 2667

Brundage, Ken, Dir, Gannon University, 109 University Sq, Erie, PA, 16541. Tel: 814-871-7557. Fax: 814-871-5666. p. 2055

Brundy, Curtis, Ref Librn/Sci Liaison, Creighton University, 2500 California Plaza, Omaha, NE, 68178-0209. Tel: 402-280-3369. Fax: 402-280-2435. p. 1412

Bruneau, Andre, Head, Adult Serv, Bibliotheque Municipale Eva-Senecal, 450 Marquette St, Sherbrooke, QC, J1H 1M4, CANADA. Tel: 819-821-5861. Fax: 819-822-6110. p. 2912

Bruneau, Deborah G, Dir, Adams Free Library, 92 Park St, Adams, MA, 01220-2096. Tel: 413-743-8345. Fax: 413-743-8344. p. 1047

Bruneau, Michel, Dr, Chairperson, Bibliotheque Somerset Library, 289 Carlton Ave, Somerset, MB, R0G 2L0, CANADA. Tel: 204-744-2170. Fax: 204-744-2170. p. 2752

Brunelle, Mary, Head, Libr Syst & Tech, Assumption College, 500 Salisbury St, Worcester, MA, 01609. Tel: 508-767-7002. Fax: 508-767-7374. p. 1143

Bruner, Christal, Br Mgr, Info Tech Dir, Mexico-Audrain County Library District, 305 W Jackson St, Mexico, MO, 65265. Tel: 573-581-4939. Fax: 573-581-7510. p. 1345

Bruner, Scott A, Dir, Chino Valley Public Library, 1020 W Palomino Rd, Chino Valley, AZ, 86323-5500. Tel: 928-636-2687. Fax: 928-636-9129. p. 60

Brunet, Denis, In Charge, Services Documentaires Multimedia, Inc, 5650 Iberville, Ste 620, Montreal, QC, H2G 2B3, CANADA. Tel: 514-382-0895. Fax: 514-384-9139. p. 2901

Brunet, Jocelyne, Cat, Chateauguay Municipal Library, 25 Maple Blvd, Chateauguay, QC, J6J 3P7, CANADA. Tel: 450-698-3085. Fax: 450-698-3109. p. 2880

Brunet, Mélanie, Librn, International Development Research Centre Library, 150 Kent St, Ottawa, ON, K1G 3H9, CANADA. Tel: 613-236-6163. Fax: 613-563-3858. p. 2831

Brunette, Dottie, County Librn, Jackson County Public Library, 310 Keener St, Sylva, NC, 28779-3241. Tel: 828-586-2016, Ext 303. Fax: 828-586-3423. p. 1826

Brungard, Charlene, Dir, Jersey Shore Public Library, 110 Oliver St, Jersey Shore, PA, 17740. Tel: 570-398-9891. Fax: 570-398-9897. p. 2073

Bruni, Marie, Dir, Huntington Memorial Library, 62 Chestnut, Oneonta, NY, 13820-2498. Tel: 607-432-1980. p. 1711

Bruni, Sharon Jean, Dir, South Park Township Library, 2575 Brownsville Rd, South Park, PA, 15129-8527. Tel: 412-833-5585. Fax: 412-833-7368. p. 2142

Brunick, Lisa, Bibliog Instruction/Ref, Augustana College, 2001 S Summit Ave, Sioux Falls, SD, 57197-0001. Tel: 605-274-4921. Fax: 605-274-5447. p. 2218

Brunjes, Kathy, Chairperson, Health Science Library Information Consortium, 211 Marginal Way, No 245, Portland, ME, 04101. Tel: 207-795-2561. Fax: 207-795-2569. p. 2944

Brunk, Angie, Ref & Instrul Serv, Instr Coordr, East Central University, 1100 E 14th St, Ada, OK, 74820-6999. Tel: 580-310-5308. Fax: 580-436-3242. p. 1955

Brunken, Joyce, Circ, Sr Libr Asst, Yankton Community Library, 515 Walnut, Yankton, SD, 57078-4042. Tel: 605-668-5275. Fax: 605-668-5277. p. 2222

Brunnemann, Wendy, Libr Dir, Wall Community Library, 407 Main St, Wall, SD, 57790. Tel: 605-279-2929. p. 2221

Brunner, Aimee, Tech Serv Mgr, Barton County Library, 300 W Tenth St, Lamar, MO, 64759. Tel: 417-682-5355. Fax: 417-682-3206. p. 1343

Brunner, Jeffery, Electronic Res Librn, University of Wisconsin Oshkosh, 801 Elmwood Ave, Oshkosh, WI, 54901. Tel: 920-424-0371. Fax: 920-424-7734. p. 2628

Brunner, Karen, Dir of Libr Serv, Riker, Danzig, Scherer, Hyland & Perretti, Headquarters Plaza, One Speedwell Ave, Morristown, NJ, 07962. Tel: 973-538-0800. Fax: 973-538-1984. p. 1505

Brunner, Pat, Librn, Antigo Public Library, Elcho Branch, Hwy 45 N, Elcho, WI, 54428. Tel: 715-275-3225. p. 2578

Bruno, Amy, Librn, Dacono Public Library, 512 Cherry St, Dacono, CO, 80514-9382. Tel: 303-833-2317, Ext 129. Fax: 303-833-5528. p. 297

Bruno, Coleen, Dir, Kim Yerton Indian Action Library, 2905 Hubbard Ln, Ste C, Eureka, CA, 95501. Tel: 707-443-8401. Fax: 707-443-9281. p. 147

Bruno, Frank A, Dr, Dir, Dorchester County Library, 506 N Parler Ave, Saint George, SC, 29477-2297. Tel: 843-563-9189. Fax: 843-563-7823. p. 2204

Bruno, Jean, Librn, Child Custody Evaluation Services, Inc, PO Box 202, Glenside, PA, 19038-0202. Tel: 215-576-0177. p. 2062

Bruno, Kathy, Asst Librn, Greenbaum, Rowe, Smith & Davis LLP, 99 Wood Ave S, Woodbridge, NJ, 07095. Tel: 732-549-5600. Fax: 732-549-1881. p. 1545

Bruno, Thomas, Br Mgr, Henrico County Public Library, Gayton Branch Library, 10600 Gayton Rd, Henrico, VA, 23238-4117. Tel: 804-290-9600. Fax: 804-750-2685. p. 2471

Bruns, Anni, Circ Serv Supvr, Eckhart Public Library, 603 S Jackson St, Auburn, IN, 46706-2298. Tel: 260-925-2414. Fax: 260-925-9376. p. 725

Bruns, Clara, Dir, Info Access, Goddard College, 123 Pitkin Rd, Plainfield, VT, 05667. Tel: 802-322-1603. p. 2432

Bruns, Gayle L, Dir, Larchwood Public Library, 1020 Broadway, Larchwood, IA, 51241. Tel: 712-477-2583. Fax: 712-477-2366. p. 827

Bruns, Linda, Br Mgr, Franklin County Public Library District, Laurel Public Library, 200 N Clay St, Laurel, IN, 47024. Tel: 765-698-2582. Fax: 765-698-2626. p. 730

Bruns, Linda Spillman, Ch, Ohio Township Public Library System, 4111 Lakeshore Dr, Newburgh, IN, 47630-2274. Tel: 812-853-5468. Fax: 812-853-0509. p. 768

Bruns, Todd, Institutional Repository Librn, Eastern Illinois University, 600 Lincoln Ave, Charleston, IL, 61920. Tel: 217-581-8381. p. 603

Brunscheen, Sandi, Librn, Edna Zybell Memorial Library, 309 Sixth Ave, Box P, Clarence, IA, 52216. Tel: 563-452-3734. Fax: 563-452-3520. p. 802

Brunskill, Annie, Dir, Haakon County Public Library, 140 S Howard Ave, Philip, SD, 57567. Tel: 605-859-2442. p. 2216

Brunsma, Kathy, Tech Serv, Lincoln Memorial University, Cumberland Gap Pkwy, Box 2012, Harrogate, TN, 37752. Tel: 423-869-6221. Fax: 423-869-6426. p. 2236

Brunson, Carmel Chaille, Circ, Info Tech, Georgia Perimeter College, Dunwoody Campus Library, 2101 Womack Rd, Dunwoody, GA, 30338-4497. Tel: 770-274-5092. Fax: 770-274-5090. p. 525

Brunson, Esther, Head Librn, Northeastern Technical College Library, 1201 Chesterfield Hwy, Cheraw, SC, 29520-7015. Tel: 843-921-6954. Fax: 843-537-6148. p. 2185

Brunson, Gene, Syst Adminr, Berkeley County Library System, 1003 Hwy 52, Moncks Corner, SC, 29461. Tel: 843-719-4241. p. 2200

Brunson, Neal E, Dir, Afro-American Historical Society Museum Library, 1841 Kennedy Blvd, Jersey City, NJ, 07305. Tel: 201-547-5262. Fax: 201-547-5392. p. 1492

Brunsting, Marlys, Automation Coordr, University of Wisconsin-Green Bay, 2420 Nicolet Dr, Green Bay, WI, 54311-7001. Tel: 920-465-2333. Fax: 920-465-2136. p. 2596

Brunton, Becky, Dir, Roane State Community College Library, 276 Patton Lane, Harriman, TN, 37748. Tel: 865-882-4551. Fax: 865-882-4562. p. 2236

Brunton, Margaret, Head of Libr, Free Library of Philadelphia, Chestnut Hill Branch, 8711 Germantown Ave, Philadelphia, PA, 19118-2716. Tel: 215-685-9290. Fax: 215-685-9291. p. 2107

Bruser, Deborah, Mgr, Yellowknife Public Library, Centre Square Mall, 5022 49th St, 2nd Flr, Yellowknife, NT, X1A 2N5, CANADA. Tel: 867-669-3401. Fax: 867-920-5671. p. 2776

Brush, Ed, Assoc Librn, Merced College, 3600 M St, Merced, CA, 95348. Tel: 209-384-6283. Fax: 209-384-6084. p. 185

Brush, Peter, Bibliographer, Vanderbilt University, Central Library, 419 21st Ave S, Nashville, TN, 37203-2427. Tel: 615-343-4838. Fax: 615-343-7451. p. 2260

Brusha, Don, Librn, Avon Park Public Library, 100 N Museum Ave, Avon Park, FL, 33825. Tel: 863-452-3803. Fax: 863-452-3809. p. 426

Brusik, Susan, ILL, University of Utah, Marriott Library, 295 S 1500 East, Salt Lake City, UT, 84112-0860. Tel: 801-581-8558. Fax: 801-585-3464. p. 2415

Brusilovsky, Peter, Asst Prof, University of Pittsburgh, 135 N Bellefield Ave, Pittsburgh, PA, 15260. Tel: 412-624-5230. Fax: 412-624-5231. p. 2973

Bruss, Heidi, Coll Mgt Librn, Illinois College of Optometry Library, 3241 S Michigan Ave, Chicago, IL, 60616-3878. Tel: 312-949-7143. Fax: 312-949-7337. p. 614

Bruss, Michelle, Ref Serv, Belleville Public Library, 121 E Washington St, Belleville, IL, 62220. Tel: 618-234-0441. Fax: 618-234-9474. p. 593

Brussow, Michele, Head Librn, Capital Area District Libraries, South Lansing Library, 3500 S Cedar St, Ste 108, Lansing, MI, 48910. Tel: 517-272-9840. Fax: 517-272-9901. p. 1200

Brust, Eric W, Ref Librn, Jackson County Law Library, Inc, 1125 Grand Blvd, Ste 1050, Kansas City, MO, 64106. Tel: 816-221-2221. Fax: 816-221-6607. p. 1337

Brustman, Mary Jane, Assoc Dir, Pub Serv, University at Albany, State University of New York, 1400 Washington Ave, Albany, NY, 12222-0001. Tel: 518-442-3540. Fax: 518-442-3088. p. 1570

Bruton, Ben, Bibliog Instr, Ref, Minot State University, 500 University Ave W, Minot, ND, 58707. Tel: 701-858-3200. Fax: 701-858-3581. p. 1846

Bruton, Tammy, Asst Librn, Horse Cave Free Public Library, 111 Higbee St, Horse Cave, KY, 42749-1110. Tel: 270-786-1130. p. 918

Bruwelheide, Janis, Dr, Dir, Montana State University, Library Media, 213 Reid Hall, Bozeman, MT, 59717. Tel: 406-994-3120. Fax: 406-994-3261. p. 2969

Bruxvoort, Barbara, Ch, San Bruno Public Library, 701 Angus Ave W, San Bruno, CA, 94066-3490. Tel: 650-616-7078. Fax: 650-876-0848. p. 230

Bruxvoort, Diane, Assoc Dean, Scholarly Res & Research Serv, University of Florida Libraries, 535 Library W, Gainesville, FL, 32611-7000. Tel: 352-273-2505. Fax: 352-392-7251. p. 449

Bruynell, Laura, Head, Youth Serv, Lynnfield Public Library, 18 Summer St, Lynnfield, MA, 01940-1837. Tel: 781-334-5411. Fax: 781-334-2164. p. 1101

Bruzzese, Christine, Supv Librn, City of New York Department of Records & Information Services, 31 Chambers St, Rm 112, New York, NY, 10007. Tel: 212-788-8590. Fax: 212-788-8589. p. 1673

Bryan, Bonita, Coordr, Coll Serv, Emory University Libraries, Woodruff Health Sciences Center Library, 1462 Clifton Rd NE, Atlanta, GA, 30322. Tel: 404-727-8727. Fax: 404-727-9821. p. 514

Bryan, Carla Wolf, Librn, Duncanville Public Library, 201 James Collins Blvd, Duncanville, TX, 75116. Tel: 972-780-5050. Fax: 972-780-4958. p. 2314

Bryan, Charles F, Jr, Pres, Virginia Historical Society Library, 428 North Blvd, Richmond, VA, 23220. Tel: 804-358-4901. Fax: 804-355-2399. p. 2492

Bryan, Cheryl, Dir, Eastham Public Library, 190 Samoset Rd, Eastham, MA, 02642. Tel: 508-240-5950. Fax: 508-240-0786. p. 1086

Bryan, Jackie, Ref & Instrul Serv Librn, Saint Leo University, 33701 State Rd 52, Saint Leo, FL, 33574. Tel: 352-588-7437. Fax: 352-588-8484. p. 487

Bryan, Jami, Br Librn, University of Mary Washington, 1801 College Ave, Fredericksburg, VA, 22401-4665. Tel: 540-286-8057. Fax: 540-654-1067. p. 2466

Bryan, Jami L, Assoc Dean, Tech & Learning Res, Northern Virginia Community College Libraries, Annandale Campus, 8333 Little River Turnpike, Godwin 300, Annandale, VA, 22003. Tel: 703-323-3867. Fax: 703-323-3005. p. 2447

Bryan, Jaxie, Librn, Johnston Community College Library, Learning Resource Ctr, 245 College Rd, Smithfield, NC, 27577. Tel: 919-464-2251. p. 1824

Bryan, Jennifer A, Head, Spec Coll & Archives, United States Naval Academy, 589 McNair Rd, Annapolis, MD, 21402-5029. Tel: 410-293-6900. Fax: 410-293-6909. p. 1011

Bryan, Karla, Ref, Trinity Valley Community College Library, 100 Cardinal Dr, Athens, TX, 75751-2765. Tel: 903-675-6260. Fax: 903-675-6207. p. 2277

Bryan, Katheleene, Head, Circ, Daytona Beach College Library, 1200 W International Speedway Blvd, Daytona Beach, FL, 32114. Tel: 386-506-3521. Fax: 386-506-3008. p. 435

Bryan, Michael, Dir, Seminole Community Library, 9200 113th St N, Seminole, FL, 33772. Tel: 727-394-6905. Fax: 727-398-3113. p. 491

Bryan, Peggy, Assoc Dir, Whitman County Rural Library District, 102 S Main St, Colfax, WA, 99111-1863. Tel: 509-397-4366. Fax: 509-397-6156. p. 2512

Bryan, Rose, Br Mgr, Adams Public Library System, Geneva Branch, 305 E Line St, Geneva, IN, 46740-1026. Tel: 260-368-7270. Fax: 260-368-9776. p. 735

Bryan, Virginia, Dean, Learning Res, Bossier Parish Community College Library, 6220 E Texas St, Bossier City, LA, 71111. Tel: 318-678-6077. Fax: 318-678-6400. p. 946

Bryan, Virginia, Actg Librn, Washington County Museum of Fine Arts Library, City Park, 91 Key St, Hagerstown, MD, 21741. Tel: 301-739-5727. Fax: 301-745-3741. p. 1032

Bryant, Amy, Assoc Libr Dir, Head, Ref, Earlham College, 801 National Rd W, Richmond, IN, 47374-4095. Tel: 765-983-1302. Fax: 765-983-1304. p. 774

Bryant, Ann, Librn, Huddleston Bolen, LLP, 611 Third Ave, Huntington, WV, 25722-1308. Tel: 304-529-6181. Fax: 304-522-4312. p. 2561

Bryant, Barbara, Supvr, Circ, Whitman Public Library, 100 Webster St, Whitman, MA, 02382. Tel: 781-447-7613. Fax: 781-447-7678. p. 1140

Bryant, Chase, Blanche R Solomon Memorial Library, 17 Park St, Headland, AL, 36345. Tel: 334-693-2706. Fax: 334-693-5023. p. 20

Bryant, Darcel, Assoc Librn, Howard University Libraries, Louis Stokes Health Sciences Library, 501 W St NW, Washington, DC, 20059. Tel: 202-884-1535. Fax: 202-884-1733. p. 404

Bryant, David, Dir, Rancho Mirage Public Library, 71-100 Hwy 111, Rancho Mirage, CA, 92270. Tel: 760-341-7323. Fax: 760-341-5213. p. 213

Bryant, Donna, Pub Serv, Sherborn Library, Four Sanger St, Sherborn, MA, 01770-1499. Tel: 508-653-0770. Fax: 508-650-9243. p. 1123

Bryant, Ed, ILL Spec, Oklahoma City University, Dulaney-Browne Library, 2501 N Blackwelder, Oklahoma City, OK, 73106. Tel: 405-208-5068. Fax: 405-208-5291. p. 1974

Bryant, Gary, Circ Mgr, New River Community College, 226 Martin Hall, Dublin, VA, 24084. Tel: 540-674-3600, Ext 4334. Fax: 540-676-3626. p. 2460

Bryant, Jan, Head Librn, Muskogee Public Library, 801 W Okmulgee, Muskogee, OK, 74401. Tel: 918-682-6657. Fax: 918-682-9466. p. 1969

Bryant, Jennifer, Outreach Serv Librn, North Miami Public Library, 835 NE 132nd St, North Miami, FL, 33161. Tel: 305-891-5535. Fax: 305-892-0843. p. 473

Bryant, Jennifer, Youth Serv Dir, Sandown Public Library, 305 Main St, Sandown, NH, 03873. Tel: 603-887-3428. Fax: 603-887-0590. p. 1465

Bryant, Jessica, Br Supvr, Jackson/Hinds Library System, Fannie Lou Hamer Library, 3450 Albermarle Rd, Jackson, MS, 39213-6513. Tel: 601-362-3012. Fax: 601-362-1505. p. 1303

Bryant, Jimmy, Archivist, University of Central Arkansas, 201 Donaghey Ave, Conway, AR, 72035. Tel: 501-450-3174. Fax: 501-450-5208. p. 97

Bryant, Karen, Tech Serv, Calhoun County Public Library, 17731 NE Pear St, Blountstown, FL, 32424. Tel: 850-674-8773. Fax: 850-674-2843. p. 427

Bryant, Kelli, Librn, Grand Saline Public Library, 201 E Pacific Ave, Grand Saline, TX, 75140. Tel: 903-962-5516. Fax: 903-962-6866. p. 2329

Bryant, Kelly, Asst Librn, Andrews Public Library, 871 Main St, Andrews, NC, 28901. Tel: 828-321-5956. Fax: 828-321-3256. p. 1773

Bryant, Kim, Ch, Idaho Falls Public Library, 457 W Broadway, Idaho Falls, ID, 83402. Tel: 208-612-8460. Fax: 208-612-8467. p. 576

Bryant, Kris, Dir, Thelma Dingus Bryant Library, 409 W Main St, Wallace, NC, 28466. Tel: 910-285-3796. Fax: 910-285-8224. p. 1827

Bryant, Kristi, Ref/Tech Support Librn, Wells Public Library, 1434 Post Rd, Wells, ME, 04090-4508. Tel: 207-646-8181, Ext. 205. Fax: 207-646-5636. p. 1006

Bryant, Laura A, Dir, Galax-Carroll Regional Library, 610 W Stuart Dr, Galax, VA, 24333. Tel: 276-236-2042, 276-236-2351. Fax: 276-236-5153. p. 2466

Bryant, Llewann, Dir, Keck Memorial Library, 119 N Second St, Wapello, IA, 52653-1501. Tel: 319-523-5261. Fax: 319-523-5261. p. 849

Bryant, Marion, Regional Mgr, Tennessee State Library & Archives, 403 Seventh Ave N, Nashville, TN, 37243-0312. Tel: 931-388-9282. Fax: 615-532-2472, 615-741-6471. p. 2259

Bryant, Marion K, Dir, Buffalo River Regional Library, 104 E Sixth St, Columbia, TN, 38401-3359. Tel: 931-388-9282. Fax: 931-388-1762. p. 2231

Bryant, Maureen, Librn, United States International Trade Commission, Law Library, 500 E St SW, Rm 614, Washington, DC, 20436. Tel: 202-205-3287. Fax: 202-205-3111. p. 420

Bryant, Melissa Lynn, Librn, Satre Memorial Library, 528 Fifth St, Milnor, ND, 58060. Tel: 701-427-5295. p. 1846

Bryant, Michael, Br Mgr, Broward County Division of Libraries, Tyrone Bryant Branch, 2230 NW 21st Ave, Fort Lauderdale, FL, 33311. Tel: 954-497-1675. Fax: 954-497-1677. p. 441

Bryant, Nancy Lynn, Libr Dir, Gas City-Mill Township Public Library, 135 E Main St, Gas City, IN, 46933-1496. Tel: 765-674-4718. Fax: 765-674-5176. p. 745

Bryant, Penny L, Libr Dir, Bertolet Memorial Library District, 705 S Main St, Leaf River, IL, 61047. Tel: 815-738-2742. Fax: 815-738-2742. p. 664

Bryant, Prudence, Head, Ref, Alabama A&M University, 4900 Meridian St, Huntsville, AL, 35762. Tel: 256-372-4729. Fax: 256-372-5768. p. 21

Bryant, Robyn, Ch, Eagle Valley Library District, 600 Broadway, Eagle, CO, 81631. Tel: 970-328-8800. Fax: 970-328-6901. p. 305

Bryant, Robyn, ILL, Taunton Public Library, 12 Pleasant St, Taunton, MA, 02780. Tel: 508-821-1410. Fax: 508-821-1414. p. 1131

Bryant, Ron, Asst Dir, Arizona State Braille & Talking Book Library, 1030 N 32nd St, Phoenix, AZ, 85008. Tel: 602-255-5578. Fax: 602-286-0444. p. 72

Bryant, Sally, Access Serv Librn, Pepperdine University Libraries, 24255 Pacific Coast Hwy, Malibu, CA, 90263. Tel: 310-506-4252. Fax: 310-506-7225. p. 182

Bryant, Sheila, Pres, Michigan Health Sciences Libraries Association, 1407 Rensen St, Ste 4, Lansing, MI, 48910. Tel: 517-394-2774. Fax: 517-394-2675. p. 2946

Bryant, Teresa, Br Mgr, Macon County Public Library, Nantahala Community, 128 Nantahala School Rd, Topton, NC, 28781. Tel: 828-321-3020. Fax: 828-488-9857. p. 1794

Bryant, Virginia, Asst Dir, Tech Serv, George Washington University, Jacob Burns Law Library, 716 20th St NW, Washington, DC, 20052. Tel: 202-994-1378. Fax: 202-994-2874. p. 402

Bryant, Vonda, Mgr, Learning Serv, Broward County Division of Libraries, 100 S Andrews Ave, Fort Lauderdale, FL, 33301. Tel: 954-357-5976. Fax: 954-357-5733. p. 440

Bryars, Paula, Librn, Louisiana Economic Development Library, 1051 N Third St, Baton Rouge, LA, 70802. Tel: 225-342-3071. Fax: 225-342-5349. p. 943

Bryce, Alan L, Libr Assoc, University of New Hampshire Library, Engineering, Mathematics & Computer Science, Kingsbury Hall, 33 Academic Way, Durham, NH, 03824. Tel: 603-862-1740. Fax: 603-862-4112. p. 1446

Bryce, Nancy, Ref Serv, Williams County Public Library, 107 E High St, Bryan, OH, 43506-1702. Tel: 419-636-6734. Fax: 419-636-3970. p. 1862

Bryce, Richard, Ch, Denville Free Public Library, 121 Diamond Spring Rd, Denville, NJ, 07834. Tel: 973-627-6555. Fax: 973-627-1913. p. 1481

Bryden, David L, Dir, High Point University, 833 Montlieu Ave, High Point, NC, 27262-4221. Tel: 336-841-9215. Fax: 336-841-5123. p. 1802

Bryn, Amy, Dir, Heart of America Library, 201 Third St SW, Rugby, ND, 58368-1793. Tel: 701-776-6223. Fax: 701-776-6897. p. 1848

Bryner, Jan, Librn, York County Law Library, Judicial Ctr, York, PA, 17401-1583. Tel: 717-854-0754. Fax: 717-843-7394. p. 2160

Bryniak, Carrie, Mgr, Ch Serv, Mgr, Outreach Serv, Ella M Everhard Public Library, 132 Broad St, Wadsworth, OH, 44281-1897. Tel: 330-335-1296. Fax: 330-334-6605. p. 1943

Brynjulson, Jennifer, In Charge, Siouxland Libraries, Colton Branch, 325 E Fourth, Colton, SD, 57018. Tel: 605-446-3519. Fax: 605-446-3519. p. 2219

Brynteson, Susan, Vice Provost & May Morris Univ Librn, University of Delaware Library, 181 S College Ave, Newark, DE, 19717-5267. Tel: 302-831-2231. Fax: 302-831-1046. p. 386

Bryson, Albert, Asst Prof, Cat Librn, Lincoln University, 1570 Old Baltimore Pike, Lincoln University, PA, 19352. Tel: 484-365-7358. Fax: 610-932-1206. p. 2082

Bryson, Keneitha, Libr Asst III, Haywood County Public Library, Canton Branch, 11 Pennsylvania Ave, Canton, NC, 28716. Tel: 828-648-2924. Fax: 828-648-0377. p. 1829

Brzoska, Ellen, Librn, Yakima Valley Genealogical Society Library, 1901 S 12th Ave, Union Gap, WA, 98903. Tel: 509-248-1328. p. 2545

Brzozowski, Nancy, Web Coordr, Walsh College, 3838 Livernois Rd, Troy, MI, 48083-5066. Tel: 248-823-1254. Fax: 248-689-9066. p. 1232

Buadoo, Joseph, Mgr, Cobb County Public Library System, Sibley Branch Library, 1539 S Cobb Dr, Marietta, GA, 30060. Tel: 770-528-2520. Fax: 770-528-2594. p. 543

Buban, Chris, AV, Coordr, Instrul Tech, Mgr, Monmouth College, 700 E Broadway, Monmouth, IL, 61462-1963. Tel: 309-457-2193. Fax: 309-457-2226. p. 675

Buban, Julie, Circ Librn, Drake Public Library, 115 Drake Ave, Centerville, IA, 52544. Tel: 641-856-6676. Fax: 641-856-6135. p. 801

Bubolz, Jocelyn, Dir, Jefferson Public Library, 321 S Main St, Jefferson, WI, 53549-1772. Tel: 920-674-7733. Fax: 920-674-7735. p. 2600

Bubrick, Marlene, Head, Tech Serv, University of California, 200 McAllister St, San Francisco, CA, 94102-4978. Tel: 415-565-4757. Fax: 415-581-8849. p. 248

Bucci, John, Br Librn, Cranston Public Library, William H Hall Free Library, 1825 Broad St, Cranston, RI, 02905-3599. Tel: 401-781-2450. Fax: 401-781-2494. p. 2165

Buccilli, Lina, Librn, Ontario Energy Board, 2300 Yonge St, Ste 2700, Toronto, ON, M4P 1E4, CANADA. Tel: 416-440-7655. Fax: 416-440-7656. p. 2856

Buccola, Victor L, Librn, United States Court of Appeals, 600 Camp St, Rm 106, New Orleans, LA, 70130. Tel: 504-310-7797. Fax: 504-310-7578. p. 964

Buch, Jennifer, Children's Serv Supvr, Ida Rupp Public Library, 310 Madison St, Port Clinton, OH, 43452. Tel: 419-732-3212. Fax: 419-734-9867. p. 1930

Buchalter, Ann, Media/Instruction Librn, Laney College, 900 Fallon St, Oakland, CA, 94607. Tel: 510-464-3493. Fax: 510-464-3264. p. 197

Buchanan, Bob, Librn, Auburn University, Veterinary Medical, 101 Greene Hall, Auburn, AL, 36849-5606. Tel: 334-844-1749. Fax: 334-844-1758. p. 6

Buchanan, Diana, Librn, Gannett Co Inc, 120 E Lenawee, Lansing, MI, 48919. Tel: 517-377-1008. Fax: 517-377-1298. p. 1201

Buchanan, Frances, AV, R H Johnson Library, 13801 W Meeker Blvd, Sun City West, AZ, 85375-4406. Tel: 623-544-6130. Fax: 623-544-6131. p. 82

Buchanan, Francie, Dir, Info Resources & Res, Cabell County Public Library, 455 Ninth Street Plaza, Huntington, WV, 25701. Tel: 304-528-5700. Fax: 304-528-5701. p. 2561

Buchanan, Heidi, Ref Librn/Info Literacy Coordr, Western Carolina University, 176 Central Dr, Cullowhee, NC, 28723. Tel: 828-227-3408. Fax: 828-227-7015. p. 1786

Buchanan, Jane, Head, Borrower Serv, Greenfield Public Library, 402 Main St, Greenfield, MA, 01301. Tel: 413-772-1544. Fax: 413-772-1589. p. 1092

Buchanan, Jane, Dir, MN Spear Memorial Library, Ten Cooleyville Rd, Shutesbury, MA, 01072-9766. Tel: 413-259-1213. Fax: 413-259-1107. p. 1124

Buchanan, Janet, Librn, Illinois Appellate Court, 14th & Main Sts, Mount Vernon, IL, 62864. Tel: 618-242-6414. Fax: 618-242-9133. p. 678

Buchanan, June, Cat, Database Mgr, Saint Thomas University Library, Law Library, 16401 NW 37th Ave, Miami Gardens, FL, 33054. Tel: 305-623-2336. Fax: 305-623-2337. p. 469

Buchanan, Kathy, Librn, Corning Public Library, 613 Pine St, Corning, AR, 72422. Tel: 870-857-3453. Fax: 870-857-3453. p. 97

Buchanan, Kay A, Head of Libr, University of Virginia, Education, Ruffner Hall, 3rd Flr, 405 Emmet St S, Charlottesville, VA, 22904-4278. Tel: 434-982-2664. Fax: 434-924-3886. p. 2455

Buchanan, Lori E, Libr Assessment Coordr, Austin Peay State University, 601 E College St, Clarksville, TN, 37044. Tel: 931-221-7017. Fax: 931-221-7296. p. 2228

Buchanan, Madeleine, Br Mgr, Hawaii State Public Library System, Lahaina Public Library, 680 Wharf St, Lahaina, HI, 96761. Tel: 808-662-3950. Fax: 808-662-3951. p. 562

Buchanan, Mandy, Curator, Lauren Rogers Museum of Art Library, 565 N Fifth Ave, Laurel, MS, 39440-3410. Tel: 601-649-6374. Fax: 601-428-8601, 601-649-6379. p. 1307

Buchanan, Mary, Ref & Info Literacy Librn, Clarion University of Pennsylvania, 840 Wood St, Clarion, PA, 16214. Tel: 814-393-1811. Fax: 814-393-2344. p. 2045

Buchanan, Stephanie, Br Mgr, Willard Memorial Library, Greenwich Public Library, Four New St, Greenwich, OH, 44837. Tel: 419-752-7331. Fax: 419-752-6801. p. 1948

Buchanan-Taylor, Deborah, Librn, National Employment Law Project Library, 80 Maiden lane, New York, NY, 10038. Tel: 212-285-3025, Ext 100. Fax: 212-285-3044. p. 1688

Buchanio, Vicki, Ref, Franklin Public Library, 118 Main St, Franklin, MA, 02038. Tel: 508-520-4940. p. 1090

Buchar, Merilee, Circ Mgr, Lewis University Library, One University Pkwy, Unit 300, Romeoville, IL, 60446-2200. Tel: 815-836-5300. Fax: 815-838-9456. p. 698

Buchel, Deborah, Librn, Degolyer & MacNaughton Library, 5001 Spring Valley Rd, Ste 800 East, Dallas, TX, 75244. Tel: 214-368-6391. Fax: 214-369-4061. p. 2307

Bucher, Debra, Coll Develop Librn, Vassar College Library, 124 Raymond Ave, Maildrop 20, Poughkeepsie, NY, 12604-0020. Tel: 845-437-5760. Fax: 845-437-5864. p. 1723

Bucher, Eric M, Librn, Roxborough Memorial Hospital, 5800 Ridge Ave, Philadelphia, PA, 19128. Tel: 215-487-4345. Fax: 215-487-4350. p. 2116

Buchholz, Gail W, Dir, LIMRA International InfoCenter, 300 Day Hill Rd, Windsor, CT, 06095-4761. Tel: 860-688-3358. Fax: 860-298-9555. p. 379

Buchholz, Marjorie, Librn, Park County Public Library, 1500 Heart Mountain St, Cody, WY, 82414. Tel: 307-527-1883. Fax: 307-527-1888. p. 2653

Buchler, Dorothy, Bus Mgr, South Haven Memorial Library, 314 Broadway St, South Haven, MI, 49090. Tel: 269-637-2403. Fax: 269-639-1685. p. 1227

Buchman, Farilyn, Chief Financial Officer, North Canton Public Library, 185 N Main St, North Canton, OH, 44720-2595. Tel: 330-499-4712. Fax: 330-499-7356. p. 1923

Buchmiller, Carol Dee, Librn, International Society Daughters of Utah Pioneers, 300 N Main St, Salt Lake City, UT, 84103-1699. Tel: 801-532-6479. Fax: 801-538-1119. p. 2412

Buchsbaum, Kathy, Commun Libr Mgr, Queens Borough Public Library, Cambria Heights Community Library, 218-13 Linden Blvd, Cambria Heights, NY, 11411. Tel: 718-528-3535. p. 1644

Buchtel, John, Head, Spec Coll Res Ctr, Georgetown University, 37th & N St NW, Washington, DC, 20057-1174. Tel: 202-687-7475. Fax: 202-687-7501. p. 402

Buchwald, Norman I, Bibliog Instr, Info Tech, Chabot College Library, 25555 Hesperian Blvd, Hayward, CA, 94545. Tel: 510-723-6993. p. 157

Buck, Alan, Librn, Cat, Roger & Peggy Madigan Library, 999 Hagan Way, Williamsport, PA, 17701. Tel: 570-327-4523. Fax: 570-327-4503. p. 2156

Buck, Amy, Ch, Cornwall Free Library, 30 Pine St, Cornwall, CT, 06753. Tel: 860-672-6874. Fax: 860-672-6398. p. 334

Buck, BebeAnna, Circ Serv Supvr, University of Wisconsin-Eau Claire, 105 Garfield Ave, Eau Claire, WI, 54702-4004. Tel: 715-836-3715. Fax: 715-836-2949. p. 2590

Buck, Doug, Bus Mgr, Pioneer Library System, 225 N Webster Ave, Norman, OK, 73069-7133. Tel: 405-701-2644. Fax: 405-701-2649. p. 1970

Buck, Jeanne, Dir, Reed Memorial Library, 1733 Rte 6, Carmel, NY, 10512. Tel: 845-225-2439. Fax: 845-225-1436. p. 1603

Buck, Karen, Librn, Parkland Regional Library, Elfros Branch, Nackra St, Elfros, SK, S0A 0V0, CANADA. Tel: 306-328-2175. p. 2932

Buck, Laura, Info Spec I, University of Missouri-Columbia, Zalk Veterinary Medical Library, W-218 Veterinary-Medicine Bldg, Columbia, MO, 65211. Tel: 573-882-2461. Fax: 573-882-2950. p. 1326

Buck, Marguerite, Ser, Immaculata University, 1145 King Rd, Immaculata, PA, 19345-0705. Tel: 610-647-4400, Ext 3833. Fax: 610-640-5828. p. 2071

Buck, Maryanne, Head Librn, Cheltenham Township Library System, Glenside Free Library, 215 S Keswick Ave, Glenside, PA, 19038-4420. Tel: 215-885-0455. Fax: 215-885-1019. p. 2061

Buck, Maryanne, Librn, University of Pennsylvania Libraries, Morris Arboretum Library, 100 Northwestern Ave, Philadelphia, PA, 19118-2697. Tel: 215-247-5777, Ext 115. Fax: 215-248-4439. p. 2119

Buck, Stephanie, Archivist/Librn, Cape Ann Museum Library/Archives, 27 Pleasant St, Gloucester, MA, 01930. Tel: 978-283-0455. Fax: 978-283-4141. p. 1091

Buck, Sylvia G, Librn, Warren Public Library, 934 Main St, Warren, MA, 01083-0937. Tel: 413-436-7690. Fax: 413-436-7690. p. 1133

Buck, Teresa, Head, Tech Serv, University of Mary Hardin-Baylor, 900 College St, UMHB Sta, Box 8016, Belton, TX, 76513-2599. Tel: 254-295-4640. Fax: 254-295-4642. p. 2289

Buck, Tina, Acq, Cat, Tech Serv, Saint Edwards University, 3001 S Congress Ave, Austin, TX, 78704-6489. Tel: 512-464-8825. Fax: 512-448-8737. p. 2281

Buckardt, Kate, Librn, Adult Serv, Lake Forest Library, 360 E Deerpath Ave, Lake Forest, IL, 60045-2252. Tel: 847-810-4612. Fax: 847-234-1453. p. 663

Buckborough, Karla, Librn, The Cavan Monaghan Libraries, One Dufferin St, Millbrook, ON, L0A 1G0, CANADA. Tel: 705-932-2919. Fax: 705-932-4019. p. 2821

Buckett, James, Head, Coll, Access & Tech Serv, University of Wisconsin-Madison, Steenbock Memorial Agricultural Library, 550 Babcock Dr, Madison, WI, 53706. Tel: 608-262-9635. Fax: 608-263-3221. p. 2610

Buckholz, Maggie, Dir, Burlington Public Library, 820 E Washington, Burlington, WA, 98233. Tel: 360-755-0760. Fax: 360-755-0717. p. 2511

Buckingham, Marilyn, Librn, Newfoundland & Labrador Oil & Gas Industries Association, Atlantic Pl, Ste 602, 215 Water St, Box 44, St. John's, NL, A1C 6C9, CANADA. Tel: 709-758-6610. Fax: 709-758-6611. p. 2773

Buckingham, Teresa R, Ad, Glenwood Public Library, 109 N Vine St, Glenwood, IA, 51534-1516. Tel: 712-527-5252. Fax: 712-527-3619. p. 818

Buckles, Brandi, In Charge, Pennsylvania Department of Transportation, Law Library, 400 North St, 9th Flr, Harrisburg, PA, 17120-0096. Tel: 717-787-5473. Fax: 717-772-2741. p. 2065

Buckley, Angela, Head Librn, Cheltenham Township Library System, East Cheltenham Free Library, 400 Myrtle Ave, Cheltenham, PA, 19012-2038. Tel: 215-379-2077. Fax: 215-379-1275. p. 2061

Buckley, Barbara, Ch, Oceanside Library, 30 Davison Ave, Oceanside, NY, 11572-2299. Tel: 516-766-2360. Fax: 516-766-1895. p. 1709

Buckley, Don, City Librn, Cerritos Library, 18025 Bloomfield Ave, Cerritos, CA, 90703. Tel: 562-916-1350. Fax: 562-916-1375. p. 133

Buckley, Eugennie, ILL Coordr, Georgetown University, Dahlgren Memorial Library, Preclinical Science Bldg GM-7, 3900 Reservoir Rd NW, Washington, DC, 20007. Tel: 202-687-1448. Fax: 202-687-1862. p. 402

Buckley, Janet, Head, Cat, Greenwood Public Library, 310 S Meridian St, Greenwood, IN, 46143-3135. Tel: 317-883-4246. Fax: 317-881-1963. p. 747

Buckley, Keith, Coll Develop Librn, Indiana University, School of Law Library, Maurer School of Law, 211 S Indiana Ave, Bloomington, IN, 47405. Tel: 812-855-7216. Fax: 812-855-7099. p. 727

Buckley, Kerry W, Exec Dir, Historic Northampton, 46 Bridge St, Northampton, MA, 01060. Tel: 413-584-6011. Fax: 413-584-7956. p. 1113

Buckley, Lily Mae, Librn, Sulphur Springs Public Library, 512 S Black Ave, Sulphur Springs, AR, 72768. Tel: 479-298-3753. Fax: 479-298-3963. p. 116

Buckley, Lynell, Ref, Louisiana Tech University, Everett St at The Columns, Ruston, LA, 71272. Tel: 318-257-3555. Fax: 318-257-2579. p. 966

Buckley, Mary Alice, Cat/ILL Librn, Argonne National Laboratory, 9700 S Cass Ave, Bldg 240, Argonne, IL, 60439-4801. Tel: 630-252-0007. Fax: 630-252-5024. p. 589

Buckley, Pamela, Coordr, Ch Serv, Minor Memorial Library, 23 South St, Roxbury, CT, 06783. Tel: 860-350-2181. Fax: 860-350-6882. p. 366

Buckley, Steven, Curator, New Jersey Scout Museum Library, 705 Ginesi Dr, 2nd Flr, Morganville, NJ, 07751. Tel: 732-862-1282. Fax: 732-536-2850. p. 1504

Buckley, Steven F, Med Librn, Interlakes Oncology Medical Library, 1555 Long Pond Rd, Rochester, NY, 14626. Tel: 585-723-7755. Fax: 585-723-7078. p. 1729

Buckley, Tammy, Librn, UPMC Horizon, Greenville Campus Medical Library, 110 N Main St, Greenville, PA, 16125. Tel: 724-589-6672. Fax: 724-589-6631. p. 2057

Buckman, Kathie, Cat Librn, Ref Librn, Henderson State University, 1100 Henderson, Arkadelphia, AR, 71999-0001. Tel: 870-230-5307. Fax: 870-230-5365. p. 93

Bucknall, Tim, Asst Dean, Info Tech & Electronic Res, University of North Carolina at Greensboro, 320 Spring Garden St, Greensboro, NC, 27402. Tel: 336-334-5880. Fax: 336-334-5399. p. 1797

Buckner, Bill, Genealogy Serv, Waco-McLennan County Library System, 1717 Austin Ave, Waco, TX, 76701-1794. Tel: 254-750-5945. Fax: 254-750-5940. p. 2397

Buckner, Cindy, Assoc Curator, Grand Rapids Art Museum, 101 Monroe Center, Grand Rapids, MI, 49503. Tel: 616-831-1000, 616-831-2901, 616-831-2909 (appt number). Fax: 616-559-0422. p. 1184

Buckner, Melinda, Librn, Mississippi Department of Corrections, PO Box 1057, Parchman, MS, 38738. Tel: 662-745-6611, Ext 3101. p. 1310

Buckner, Regina, Dir, Operational Serv, Western Michigan University, Arcadia at Vande Giessen St, Kalamazoo, MI, 49008-5353. Tel: 269-387-5204. Fax: 269-387-5077. p. 1198

Buckner, Terry, Circ Librn, Bluegrass Community & Technical College, Oswald Bldg, 470 Cooper Dr, Lexington, KY, 40506-0235. Tel: 859-246-6397. Fax: 859-246-4675. p. 920

Buckner, William, Mgr, Waco-McLennan County Library System, R B Hoover Library, 1428 Wooded Acres Dr, Waco, TX, 76710. Tel: 254-750-5945. Fax: 254-745-6019. p. 2398

Buckrham, Gail, Ch, Sampson-Clinton Public Library, 217 Graham St, Clinton, NC, 28328. Tel: 910-592-4153. Fax: 910-590-3504. p. 1784

Bucks, Carol, In Charge, Irish-American Cultural Institute Library, One Lackawanna Pl, Morristown, NJ, 07960. Tel: 973-605-1991. Fax: 973-605-8875. p. 1505

Bucks, Susan, Govt Doc, Monmouth University, 400 Cedar Ave, West Long Branch, NJ, 07764. Tel: 732-263-5591. Fax: 732-263-5124. p. 1541

Buckson, Kate, Mkt Coordr, Westmont Public Library, 428 N Cass, Westmont, IL, 60559-1502. Tel: 630-969-5625. Fax: 630-969-6490. p. 717

Buckstead, Jonathan, Ref Librn, Austin Community College, Cypress Creek Campus Library, 1555 Cypress Creek Rd, Cedar Park, TX, 78613. Tel: 512-223-2132. Fax: 512-223-2035. p. 2278

Buckwalter, Heather, Acq, Ser, Creighton University, Klutznick Law Library - McGrath, North, Mullin & Kratz Legal Research Center, School of Law, 2500 California Plaza, Omaha, NE, 68178-0340. Tel: 402-280-2251, 402-280-2875. Fax: 402-280-2244. p. 1412

Bucky, Karen, Dept Head, User Serv, Sterling & Francine Clark Art Institute Library, 225 South St, Williamstown, MA, 01267. Tel: 413-458-9545. Fax: 413-458-9542. p. 1140

Bucsit, Dolly, Asst Librn, Sharp HealthCare, 7901 Frost St, San Diego, CA, 92123. Tel: 858-939-3242. Fax: 858-939-3248. p. 238

Bucy, Mary L, Dir, Hudson Public Library, 401 Fifth St, Hudson, IA, 50643. Tel: 319-988-4217. p. 821

Buda, Janet, Br Librn, Boston Public Library, North End, 25 Parmenter St, Boston, MA, 02113-2306. Tel: 617-227-8135. Fax: 617-723-1617. p. 1057

Budaker, Diane, Acq, University of New Brunswick Libraries, Five Macaulay Dr, Fredericton, NB, E3B 5H5, CANADA. Tel: 506-453-3529. Fax: 506-453-4595. p. 2763

Budd, John M, Prof, University of Missouri-Columbia, 303 Townsend Hall, Columbia, MO, 65211. Tel: 573-882-4546. Fax: 573-884-2917. p. 2968

Budd, Luann, Dir, Admin Serv, San Jose State University, One Washington Sq, San Jose, CA, 95192-0028. Tel: 408-808-2050. Fax: 408-808-2141. p. 251

Budd, Nancy, Librn, Wapiti Regional Library, Nipawin Public Library, 501 Second St E, Nipawin, SK, S0E 1E0, CANADA. Tel: 306-862-4867. p. 2921

Budde, Mitzi J, Head Librn, Virginia Theological Seminary, 3737 Seminary Rd, Alexandria, VA, 22304-5201. Tel: 703-461-1731. Fax: 703-370-0935. p. 2446

Budell, Lynn, Asst Dir, Pub Serv, Conyers-Rockdale Library System, 864 Green St, Conyers, GA, 30012. Tel: 770-388-5040. Fax: 770-388-5043. p. 527

Budenz, Jennifer, Syst Coordr, Kokomo-Howard County Public Library, 220 N Union St, Kokomo, IN, 46901-4614. Tel: 765-457-3242. Fax: 765-457-3683. p. 758

Budin, Miriam, Head, Ch, Chappaqua Public Library, 195 S Greeley Ave, Chappaqua, NY, 10514. Tel: 914-238-4779. Fax: 914-238-3597. p. 1605

Budler, Joanne, State Librn, State Library of Kansas, State Capitol Bldg, Topeka, KS, 66612. Tel: 785-296-3296. Fax: 785-296-6650. p. 896

Budlong, Leslee, Regional Dir, Baker & McKenzie LLP Library, 815 Connecticut Ave NW, Ste 900, Washington, DC, 20006-4078. Tel: 202-452-7070. Fax: 202-452-7074. p. 394

Budlong, Leslee I, Dir, Libr Serv, Baker & McKenzie LLP, 114 Avenue of the Americas, New York, NY, 10036. Tel: 212-626-4100. Fax: 212-310-1600. p. 1669

Budman, Galina, Libr Asst, DLA Piper US LLP, 2000 University Ave, East Palo Alto, CA, 94303. Tel: 650-833-2000. Fax: 650-833-2001. p. 144

Budris, Danguole, Libr Dir, Oak Bluffs Public Library, 56R School St, Oak Bluffs, MA, 02557. Tel: 508-693-9433. Fax: 508-693-5377. p. 1116

Budzik, Joanne, Head, Tech Serv, Coatesville Area Public Library, 501 E Lincoln Hwy, Coatesville, PA, 19320-3413. Tel: 610-384-4115. Fax: 610-384-7551. p. 2046

Budzko, Ellie, In Charge, Palermo Community Library, Rte 3, Palermo, ME, 04354. Tel: 207-993-6088. p. 995

Buechner, Deborah, Ch, Garrett Public Library, 107 W Houston St, Garrett, IN, 46738. Tel: 260-357-5485. Fax: 260-357-5170. p. 744

Bueckert, Debbie, Librn/Mgr, Fort Vermilion Community Library, 5103 River Rd, Fort Vermilion, AB, T0H 1N0, CANADA. Tel: 780-927-4279. Fax: 780-927-4746. p. 2704

Buehler, Marianne, Head, Publ & Scholarship Support Serv, Rochester Institute of Technology, 90 Lomb Memorial Dr, Rochester, NY, 14623-5604. Tel: 585-475-5589. Fax: 585-475-7007. p. 1731

Buehner, Cathy, Head, Adult Serv, Highland Township Public Library, 444 Beach Farm Circle, Highland, MI, 48357. Tel: 248-887-2218. Fax: 248-887-5179. p. 1189

Buehner, Pauline, Circ, Jefferson County Library, Northwest, 5680 State Rd PP, High Ridge, MO, 63049. Tel: 636-677-8186. Fax: 636-677-8243. p. 1331

Buehrer, Ellen, Ch, Galion Public Library Association, 123 N Market St, Galion, OH, 44833. Tel: 419-468-3203. Fax: 419-468-7298. p. 1901

Buelke, Virginia, Pres, Citrus Springs Memorial Library, 1826 W Country Club Blvd, Citrus Springs, FL, 34434. Tel: 352-489-2313. p. 431

Buell, Arthur, Ref Coordr, California State University, Stanislaus, One University Circle, Turlock, CA, 95382. Tel: 209-664-6557. p. 277

Buelow, Mary, Head, Info Serv, Hedberg Public Library, 316 S Main St, Janesville, WI, 53545. Tel: 608-758-5808. Fax: 608-758-6615. p. 2599

Buenaventura, Nenita, Access Serv & Electronic Res Librn, Long Beach City College, 4901 E Carson St, Long Beach, CA, 90808. Tel: 562-938-3028 (PCC Campus), 562-938-4232 (LAC Campus). Fax: 562-938-3062, 562-938-4777. p. 166

Buendia, Veronica, Learning Res Spec, Palo Alto College, 1400 W Villaret St, San Antonio, TX, 78224-2499. Tel: 210-486-3564. Fax: 210-486-9184. p. 2380

Buendtner, Joanne Marie, Dir, Bullard Community Library, 211 W Main, Bullard, TX, 75757. Tel: 903-894-6125. Fax: 903-894-6125. p. 2293

Bueno, Catherine, Commun Libr Mgr, County of Los Angeles Public Library, Avalon Library, 215 Sumner Ave, Avalon, CA, 90704. Tel: 310-510-1050. Fax: 310-510-1645. p. 140

Bueno, Olivia, Libr Asst, Town of Bernalillo Public Library, 124 Calle Malinche, Bernalillo, NM, 87004. Tel: 505-867-1440. Fax: 505-867-8040. p. 1552

Buerkle, Korie, Ch, Newberg Public Library, 503 E Hancock St, Newberg, OR, 97132-2899. Tel: 503-538-7323. Fax: 503-538-9720. p. 2007

Buesking, Debbie, Cataloger, Evangel University, 1111 N Glenstone Ave, Springfield, MO, 65802. Tel: 417-865-2815, Ext 7268. p. 1366

Bueti, Teresa, Ch, Chappaqua Public Library, 195 S Greeley Ave, Chappaqua, NY, 10514. Tel: 914-238-4779. Fax: 914-238-3597. p. 1605

Buetow, Tamara, Ref Librn, Concordia University, 1282 Concordia Ave, Saint Paul, MN, 55104. Tel: 651-641-8278. Fax: 651-641-8782. p. 1278

Buettner, Debbie, Ch, Lima Public Library, 650 W Market St, Lima, OH, 45801. Tel: 419-228-5113. Fax: 419-224-2669. p. 1910

Buffalo, Dee, Br Mgr, Delaware County Library, 429 S Ninth St, Jay, OK, 74346. Tel: 918-253-8521. Fax: 918-253-8726. p. 1966

Buffaloe, Don, Ref, Pepperdine University Libraries, School of Law-Jerene Appleby Harnish Law Library, 24255 Pacific Coast Hwy, Malibu, CA, 90263. Tel: 310-506-4643. Fax: 310-506-4836. p. 182

Buffington, Sarah, Curator, Pennsylvania Historical & Museum Commission, 270 16th St, Ambridge, PA, 15003-2298. Tel: 724-266-4500. Fax: 724-266-3010. p. 2029

Buffleben, Kathleen, Librn, Stockton-San Joaquin County Public Library, Mountain House Branch, 579 Wicklund Crossing, Mountain House, CA, 95391. Tel: 209-831-5661. Fax: 209-831-5665. p. 273

Bufford, Mandrell, ILL Coordr, Baylor Health Sciences Library, 3302 Gaston Ave, Dallas, TX, 75246. Tel: 214-828-8151. Fax: 214-820-2095. p. 2304

Buford, Renee, Head, Circ, Pearl River County Library System, 900 Goodyear Blvd, Picayune, MS, 39466. Tel: 601-798-5081. Fax: 601-798-5082. p. 1311

Buford, Terrence, Dir, Irondequoit Public Library, 45 Cooper Rd, Rochester, NY, 14617. Tel: 585-336-6062. Fax: 585-336-6066. p. 1729

Bugee, Jenna, Youth Serv Librn, Gibbon Public Library, 116 LaBarre, Gibbon, NE, 68840. Tel: 308-468-5889. Fax: 308-468-5501. p. 1399

Bugg, Kimberly, Librn, Carver Bible College Library, 3870 Cascade Rd, Atlanta, GA, 30331. Tel: 404-527-4520. Fax: 404-527-4524. p. 514

Bugg, Sharon, Asst Librn, Brighton Public Library, 35 Alice St, Brighton, ON, K0K 1H0, CANADA. Tel: 613-475-2511. p. 2797

Buggs, Lisa, Commun Educ & Enrichment Prog Supvr, Jacksonville Public Library, 303 N Laura St, Jacksonville, FL, 32202-3505. Tel: 904-630-4655. Fax: 904-630-2450. p. 453

Bugnone, Cheryl, Dir, Kinsman Free Public Library, 6420 Church St, Kinsman, OH, 44428-9702. Tel: 330-876-2461. Fax: 330-876-3335. p. 1907

Buhay, Diane, Head, Access & Res Serv, University of New Brunswick, Saint John Campus, 100 Tucker Park Rd, Saint John, NB, E2L 4L5, CANADA. Tel: 506-648-5710. Fax: 506-648-5701. p. 2767

Buhl, Howard, Br Mgr, Mid-Continent Public Library, Dearborn Branch, 206 Maple Leaf Ave, Dearborn, MO, 64439-9085. Tel: 816-450-3502. Fax: 816-450-3502. p. 1332

Buhl, Maria, ILL, Guilderland Public Library, 2228 Western Ave, Guilderland, NY, 12084-9701. Tel: 518-456-2400. Fax: 518-456-0923. p. 1632

Buhler, Diane, Exec Dir, Parent Action on Drugs Library, Seven Hawksdale Rd, Rm 121, Toronto, ON, M3K 1W3, CANADA. Tel: 416-395-4970. p. 2857

Buhler, Jeremy, Assessment Librn, University of British Columbia Library, 1961 East Mall, Vancouver, BC, V6T 1Z1, CANADA. Tel: 604-827-3510. p. 2742

Buhler, Mary Ann, Dir of Libr Serv, Manhattan Christian College Library, 1415 Anderson Ave, Manhattan, KS, 66502-4081. Tel: 785-539-3571, Ext 110. Fax: 785-539-0832. p. 881

Buhne, Cindy, Ch, Youth Serv, Bracebridge Public Library, 94 Manitoba St, Bracebridge, ON, P1L 2B5, CANADA. Tel: 705-645-4171. Fax: 705-645-6551. p. 2796

Buhr, Denise, Ref Serv, Indiana University-Purdue University Fort Wayne, 2101 E Coliseum Blvd, Fort Wayne, IN, 46805-1499. Tel: 260-481-6512. Fax: 260-481-6509. p. 741

Buhr, Mary, Dir, Iroquois County Genealogical Society Library, Old Courthouse Museum, 103 W Cherry St, Watseka, IL, 60970-1524. Tel: 815-432-3730. Fax: 815-432-3730. p. 716

Buhrow, Paula J, Tech Serv Mgr, Burlington Public Library, 210 Court St, Burlington, IA, 52601. Tel: 319-753-1647. Fax: 319-753-0789. p. 797

Bui-Burton, Kim, Dir, Monterey Public Library, 625 Pacific St, Monterey, CA, 93940-2866. Tel: 831-646-5601. Fax: 831-646-5618. p. 190

Buick, Stacey, Dir, Malvern Public Library, 502 Main St, Malvern, IA, 51551. Tel: 712-624-8554. Fax: 712-624-8245. p. 829

Buie, Delinda, Curator of Rare Bks & Ms, Head, Spec Coll, University of Louisville Libraries, Special Collections/Photographic Archives, Belknap Campus, 2215 S Third St, Louisville, KY, 40208. Tel: 502-852-6762. Fax: 502-852-8734. p. 927

Buie, Delinda Stephens, Head, Spec Coll, University of Louisville Libraries, William F Ekstrom Library, Belknap Campus, 2215 S Third St, Louisville, KY, 40292. Tel: 502-852-6762. Fax: 502-852-7394. p. 927

Buitron, C Monica, Asst Librn, Sutton County Library, 306 E Mulberry St, Sonora, TX, 76950. Tel: 325-387-2111. Fax: 325-387-9044. p. 2388

Buja, L Maximillian, Dir, National Network of Libraries of Medicine South Central Region, c/o HAM-TMC Library, 1133 John Freeman Blvd, Houston, TX, 77030-2809. Tel: 713-799-7177. Fax: 713-790-7030. p. 2956

Buja, Maximilian, Exec Dir, Houston Academy of Medicine, 1133 John Freeman Blvd, Houston, TX, 77030. Tel: 713-795-4200. Fax: 713-790-7052. p. 2337

Bujalski, Eileen, Acq, Albertus Magnus College Library, 700 Prospect St, New Haven, CT, 06511. Tel: 203-773-8594. Fax: 203-773-8588. p. 355

Bujdd-Plouffe, Michelle, Prof, College Lionel-Groulx, 100, rue Duquet, Sainte-Therese, QC, J7E 3G6, CANADA. Tel: 450-430-3120, Ext 407. Fax: 450-971-7883. p. 2979

Buker, Kathleen M, Archives Chief, United States Army, Combined Arms Research Library, US Army Command & General Staff College, Eisenhower Hall, 250 Gibbon Ave, Fort Leavenworth, KS, 66027-2314. Tel: 913-758-3161. Fax: 913-758-3014. p. 867

Bukovac, Jamie, Dir, Indian Prairie Public Library District, 401 Plainfield Rd, Darien, IL, 60561-4207. Tel: 630-887-8760. Fax: 630-887-8801. p. 633

Bukowski, Ivone, Ref Librn, YA Serv, Val Verde County Library, 300 Spring St, Del Rio, TX, 78840. Tel: 830-774-7595. Fax: 830-774-7607. p. 2312

Bukralia, Rajeev, Dir, Black Hills State University, 1200 University St, Unit 9676, Spearfish, SD, 57799-9676. Tel: 605-642-6360. Fax: 605-642-6298. p. 2220

Bukrey, Sarah, Circ, Stoughton Public Library, 304 S Fourth St, Stoughton, WI, 53589-0191. Tel: 608-873-6281. Fax: 608-873-0108. p. 2640

Bulaong, Grace F, Dir, New Jersey City University, 2039 Kennedy Blvd, Jersey City, NJ, 07305-1597. Tel: 201-200-3027. Fax: 201-200-2330, 201-200-2331. p. 1492

Bulfer, Margaret J, Dir, Mountain Lakes Free Public Library, Nine Elm Rd, Mountain Lakes, NJ, 07046-1316. Tel: 973-334-5095. Fax: 973-299-1622. p. 1506

Bulgarelli, Nancy, Dir, Med Libr, Oakland University Library, 2200 N Squirrel Rd, Rochester, MI, 48309-4402. Tel: 248-370-2481. Fax: 248-370-2474. p. 1221

Bulger, Jim, Mgr, Allina Health Library Services, 800 E 28th St, No 14001, Minneapolis, MN, 55407. Tel: 612-863-4312. Fax: 612-863-5695. p. 1258

Bulger, Jim, Mgr, Allina Health Library Services, Mercy Hospital, 4050 Coon Rapids Blvd, Coon Rapids, MN, 55433. Tel: 612-863-4312. p. 1258

Bulger, Jim, Mgr, Allina Health Library Services, Unity Hospital, 550 Osborne Rd, Fridley, MN, 55432. Tel: 612-863-4312. p. 1258

Bulger, Jim, Team Leader, Allina Health Library Services, Abbott Northwestern Hospital, 800 E 28th St, Minneapolis, MN, 55407. Tel: 612-863-4312. Fax: 612-863-5695. p. 1258

Bulger, Lois, Ch, David A Howe Public Library, 155 N Main St, Wellsville, NY, 14895. Tel: 585-593-3410. Fax: 585-593-4176. p. 1765

Bulgin, David, Archivist, LandMark Communications, 200 E Market St, Greensboro, NC, 27401-2910. Tel: 336-373-5215. Fax: 336-373-4437. p. 1797

Bull, Capers, Jr, Adult Serv, Orangeburg County Library, 510 Louis St, Orangeburg, SC, 29115-5030. Tel: 803-531-4636. Fax: 803-533-5860. p. 2201

Bull, Ellen, Librn, Society of Actuaries Library, 475 N Martingale Rd, Ste 600, Schaumburg, IL, 60173-2226. Tel: 847-706-3500. Fax: 847-706-3599. p. 701

Bull, Jennifer, Head, Tech Serv, Ashland Public Library, 224 Claremont Ave, Ashland, OH, 44805. Tel: 419-289-8188, Ext 19. Fax: 419-281-8552. p. 1855

Bull, Jennifer Wells, Head, Tech Serv, Hammond Public Library, 564 State St, Hammond, IN, 46320-1532. Tel: 219-931-5100, Ext 320. Fax: 219-931-3474. p. 747

Bull, Jonathan, Res Serv Librn, Valparaiso University, 1410 Chapel Dr, Valparaiso, IN, 46383-6493. Tel: 219-464-5771. p. 783

Bull, Millard Barry, Tech Serv Librn, Savannah River Site, Bldg 773A, Aiken, SC, 29808. Tel: 803-725-0069, 803-725-2940. Fax: 803-725-5367. p. 2179

Bull, Sharon, Dr, Dir, Libr & Archives, Northwest Nazarene University, 623 University Blvd, Nampa, ID, 83686. Tel: 208-467-8609. Fax: 208-467-8610. p. 580

Bull, Sue, Librn, Britton Public Library, 759 Seventh St, Britton, SD, 57430. Tel: 605-448-2800. Fax: 605-448-2497. p. 2210

Bullard, Deborah, Asst Librn, Lewis Dana Hill Memorial Library, 2079 Main St, Center Lovell, ME, 04231-9702. Tel: 207-928-2301. p. 982

Bullard, K Ellen, Assoc Dir, Providence Public Library, 150 Empire St, Providence, RI, 02903-3283. Tel: 401-455-8060. Fax: 401-455-8065, 401-455-8080. p. 2173

Bullard, Karen, Asst Dir, Troy Public Library, 300 N Three Notch St, Troy, AL, 36081. Tel: 334-566-1314. Fax: 334-566-4392. p. 37

Bullard, Linda, Mgr, Newberry County Library, Whitmire Memorial, 1510 Church St, Whitmire, SC, 29178. Tel: 803-694-3961. Fax: 803-694-9945. p. 2201

Bullard, Mary, Librn, Monroe County Community College, 1555 S Raisinville Rd, Monroe, MI, 48161. Tel: 734-384-4204. Fax: 734-384-4160. p. 1209

Bullard, Mary Kay, Dir, Rosebud County Library, Bicentennial Library of Colstrip, 419 Willow Ave, Colstrip, MT, 59323. Tel: 406-748-3040. Fax: 406-748-2133. p. 1379

Bullard, Mary Kay, Reader Serv, Deadwood Public Library, 435 Williams St, Deadwood, SD, 57732-1113. Tel: 605-578-2821. Fax: 605-578-2071. p. 2211

Bullard, Sandy, Asst Librn, Rushville Public Library, 104 N Monroe St, Rushville, IL, 62681-1364. Tel: 217-322-3030. Fax: 217-322-3030. p. 699

Bullen, Andrew, Info Tech, Illinois State Library, Gwendolyn Brooks Bldg, 300 S Second St, Springfield, IL, 62701-9713. Tel: 312-814-4386. Fax: 217-785-4326. p. 705

Bullene, Kathy, Managing Librn I, Sno-Isle Libraries, Arlington Community Library, 135 N Washington Ave, Arlington, WA, 98223. Tel: 360-435-3033. Fax: 360-435-3854. p. 2542

Buller, Mildred, Libr Dir, Peabody Township Library, 214 Walnut St, Peabody, KS, 66866. Tel: 620-983-2502. p. 889

Bullian, Jeremy, Librn, Hillsborough Community College, Brandon Campus Learning Resources Center, 10414 E Columbus Dr, Tampa, FL, 33619-9640. Tel: 813-253-7803. p. 496

Bullian, Lana, Dir, Safety Harbor Public Library, 101 Second St N, Safety Harbor, FL, 34695. Tel: 727-724-1525. Fax: 727-724-1533. p. 486

Bullied, Jane, Tech Serv, Canada/Manitoba Business Service Centre Library, 240 Graham Ave, Ste 250, Winnipeg, MB, R3C 0J7, CANADA. Tel: 204-984-2272. Fax: 204-983-3852. p. 2754

Bullington, Edgar, Ch, Glendale Public Library, Grandview, 1535 Fifth St, Glendale, CA, 91201-1985. Tel: 818-548-2049. Fax: 818-549-0678. p. 155

Bullington, Jeff, Coordr, Col Liaisons, Colorado State University Libraries, Morgan Library, 1201 Center Avenue Mall, Fort Collins, CO, 80523-. Tel: 970-491-1838. Fax: 970-491-1195. p. 307

Bullis, Brad, Pub Serv Adminr, Adult Serv, New Haven Free Public Library, 133 Elm St, New Haven, CT, 06510. Tel: 203-946-8130. Fax: 203-946-8140. p. 355

Bulloch, Kris, Librn, Asphodel-Norwood Public Library, 2363 County Rd 45, Norwood, ON, K0L 2V0, CANADA. Tel: 705-639-2228. Fax: 705-639-1880. p. 2825

Bulloch, Kris, Librn, Asphodel-Norwood Public Library, Westwood Branch, 312 Centre Line, Westwood, ON, K0L 3B0, CANADA. Tel: 705-696-2744. Fax: 705-639-1880. p. 2825

Bullock, Andrea, Ref & Instruction Librn, Portland State University Library, 1875 SW Park Ave, Portland, OR, 97201-3220. Tel: 503-725-4504. Fax: 503-725-4524. p. 2014

Bullock, Connie, Dir, Cambridge Springs Public Library, 158 McClellan St, Cambridge Springs, PA, 16403-1018. Tel: 814-398-2123. Fax: 814-398-2123. p. 2040

Bullock, Ednita, Head, Coll Mgt, North Carolina Agricultural & Technical State University, 1601 E Market St, Greensboro, NC, 27411-0002. Tel: 336-334-7668, Ext 3232. Fax: 336-334-7783. p. 1797

Bullock, Lois, Asst Librn, Frost, Brown & Todd LLC, 400 W Market St, 32nd Flr, Louisville, KY, 40202-3363. Tel: 502-589-5400. Fax: 502-581-1087. p. 923

Bullock, Lynn, Archivist, The City of Calgary, Corporate Records, Archives, 313 Seventh Ave SE, Calgary, AB, T2G 0J1, CANADA. Tel: 403-268-8180. Fax: 403-268-6731. p. 2691

Bullock, Mary, Outreach & Youth Serv Librn, Warren County Memorial Library, 119 South Front St, Warrenton, NC, 27589. Tel: 252-257-4990. Fax: 252-257-4089. p. 1828

Bullock, Susan, Dir, Simsbury Public Library, 725 Hopmeadow St, Simsbury, CT, 06070. Tel: 860-658-7663. Fax: 860-658-6732. p. 367

Bullock, Wanda, Librn, Pulaski County Public Library, Shopville Branch, 144 Old Shopville Rd, Somerset, KY, 42503. Tel: 606-274-1671. Fax: 606-274-1671. p. 935

Bulmer, Cindy, Dir, Whitefish Township Community Library, 7247 North M Hwy 123, Paradise, MI, 49768. Tel: 906-492-3500. Fax: 906-492-3500. p. 1216

Bulmer, Kathy, Librn, Boyle Public Library, PO Box 450, Boyle, AB, T0A 0M0, CANADA. Tel: 780-689-4161. Fax: 780-689-5660. p. 2686

Bulow, Karen, Pub Serv, Texas Chiropractic College, 5912 Spencer Hwy, Pasadena, TX, 77505. Tel: 281-998-6049. Fax: 281-487-4168. p. 2369

Bultron-Griffith, Carmen, Circ Asst, Beaufort County Library, Saint Helena Branch, 1025 Sea Island Pkwy, Saint Helena Island, SC, 29920. Tel: 843-255-6486. p. 2181

Bumbera, Alice N, Librn, The Crosswicks Library Co, 483 Main St, Crosswicks, NJ, 08515. Tel: 609-298-6271. Fax: 609-298-0510. p. 1481

Bumgarner, Elizabeth, Main Libr Coordr, Aurora Public Library, One E Benton St, Aurora, IL, 60505-4299. Tel: 630-264-4120. Fax: 630-896-3209. p. 591

Bumgarner, Steve, Dir, Eagle Public Library, 100 N Stierman Way, Eagle, ID, 83616-5162. Tel: 208-939-6814. Fax: 208-939-1359. p. 574

Bumpus, Sandy, Asst Librn, Abington Public Library, 600 Gliniewicz Way, Abington, MA, 02351. Tel: 781-982-2139. Fax: 781-878-7361. p. 1047

Bumstead, Ann, Head, Ch, Woodbury Public Library, 269 Main St S, Woodbury, CT, 06798. Tel: 203-263-3502. Fax: 203-263-0571. p. 380

Bumstead, Linda, Librn & Ref Supvr, Alberta Government Library, 10025 Jasper Ave, 15th Flr, Edmonton, AB, T5J 2N3, CANADA. Tel: 780-415-0224. Fax: 780-422-9694. p. 2698

Bunal, Jane, Librn/Mgr, Horry County Memorial Library, Conway Branch, 801 Main St, Conway, SC, 29526. Tel: 843-915-7323. p. 2191

Bunch, Craig, Asst Librn, McNay Art Museum Library, 6000 N New Braunfels Ave, San Antonio, TX, 78209. Tel: 210-805-1727. Fax: 210-824-0218. p. 2380

Bunch, Gena, Br Librn, Lapeer District Library, Otter Lake Branch, 6361 Detroit St, Otter Lake, MI, 48464-9104. Tel: 810-793-6300. Fax: 810-793-7040. p. 1203

Bunch, Ruby, In Charge, Eldon Public Library, 308 E First St, Eldon, MO, 65026. Tel: 573-392-6657. Fax: 573-392-4071. p. 1327

Bunch, Wilma, Dean, Info Serv, CoxHealth Libraries, Cox Medical Ctr N, 1423 N Jefferson Ave, J-200, Springfield, MO, 65802. Tel: 417-269-3460. Fax: 417-269-3492. p. 1366

Bundy, Diane, Br Mgr, Bossier Parish Central Library, Henry L Aulds Memorial, 3950 Wayne Ave, Bossier City, LA, 71112. Tel: 318-742-2337. Fax: 318-752-4034. p. 946

Bundy, Gene, Spec Coll Librn, Eastern New Mexico University, 1300 S Ave K, Sta 32, Portales, NM, 88130-7402. Tel: 575-562-2636. Fax: 575-562-2647. p. 1560

Bundy, Hal, Network Adminr, Ottawa Library, 105 S Hickory St, Ottawa, KS, 66067-2306. Tel: 785-242-3080. Fax: 785-242-8789. p. 887

Bundy, John, Superintendent, Russell Cave National Monument Library, 3729 County Rd 98, Bridgeport, AL, 35740. Tel: 256-495-2672. Fax: 256-495-9220. p. 11

Bundy, Lanham, Br Librn, Providence Community Library, Washington Park Library, 1316 Broad St, Providence, RI, 02905. Tel: 401-781-3136, Ext 1201. Fax: 401-781-3148. p. 2173

Bundy, Marlene, Coll Develop, Ref, Sinclair Community College Library, 444 W Third St, Dayton, OH, 45402-1460. Tel: 937-512-3003. Fax: 937-512-4564. p. 1894

Bundy, Rebecca, Br Mgr, Chippewa River District Library, Faith Johnston Memorial, 4035 N Mission, Rosebush, MI, 48878. Tel: 989-433-0006. Fax: 989-433-0006. p. 1211

Bundy, Suzanne, Librn for Blind & Physically Handicapped, Topeka & Shawnee County Public Library, Subregional Library for the Blind & Physically Handicapped, 1515 SW Tenth Ave, Topeka, KS, 66604-1374. Tel: 785-580-4530. p. 897

Bunge, Rosalie, Head, Acq, Head, Coll Develop, Head, Coll Serv, Normandale Community College Library, 9700 France Ave S, Bloomington, MN, 55431. Tel: 952-487-8296. Fax: 952-487-8101. p. 1242

Bunger, Ron, Assoc Dir of Libr, Richmont Graduate University, 1815 McCallie Ave, Chattanooga, TN, 37404-3026. Tel: 423-648-2408. Fax: 423-265-7375. p. 2228

Bunker, Andrea, YA Serv, Newburyport Public Library, 94 State St, Newburyport, MA, 01950-6619. Tel: 978-465-4428, Ext 228. Fax: 978-463-0394. p. 1109

Bunker, Donna, Librn, Chesley Memorial Library, Eight Mountain Ave, Northwood, NH, 03261. Tel: 603-942-5472. Fax: 603-942-5132. p. 1461

Bunker, Janet, Ch, Cambridge Community Library, Superior St, Cambridge, ID, 83610. Tel: 208-257-3434. p. 572

Bunker, Nancy A, Coordr of Ref Serv, Whitworth University, 300 W Hawthorne Rd, Spokane, WA, 99251-0001. Tel: 509-777-4481. Fax: 509-777-3221. p. 2538

Bunker, Patricia, Ref Serv, Trinity College Library, 300 Summit St, Hartford, CT, 06106. Tel: 860-297-2254. Fax: 860-297-2251. p. 347

Bunkley, Anita, Mgr, Okefenokee Regional Library, Blackshear Memorial Library, 600 S Main St, Blackshear, GA, 31516. Tel: 912-449-7040. Fax: 912-449-2265. p. 557

Bunn, Dumont C, Dr, Dir of Libr Serv, Middle Georgia Technical College, 80 Cohen Walker Dr, Warner Robins, GA, 31088-2730. Tel: 478-988-6863. Fax: 478-988-6813. p. 556

Bunn, Silvia, Br Mgr, Chattahoochee Valley Libraries, Mildred L Terry Branch, 640 Veterans Pkwy, Columbus, GA, 31901. Tel: 706-748-2851. Fax: 706-748-2853. p. 526

Bunnell, Laura, Actg Head of Ref, Morley Library, 184 Phelps St, Painesville, OH, 44077-3926. Tel: 440-352-3383, Ext 302. Fax: 440-352-9097. p. 1927

Bunnelle, Jim, Acq & Coll Develop Librn, Lewis & Clark College, Aubrey R Watzek Library, 0615 SW Palatine Hill Rd, Portland, OR, 97219-7899. Tel: 503-768-7274. Fax: 503-768-7282. p. 2011

Bunner, Kim, Tech Dir, Parlin Ingersoll Public Library, 205 W Chestnut St, Canton, IL, 61520. Tel: 309-647-0328. Fax: 309-647-8117. p. 599

Bunner, Mary, Tech Serv, Buncombe County Public Libraries, 67 Haywood St, Asheville, NC, 28801. Tel: 828-250-4700. Fax: 828-250-4746. p. 1774

Bunnett, Brian, Dir, University of New Mexico, Health Sciences Library & Informatics Center, MSC09-5100, One University of New Mexico, Albuquerque, NM, 87131-0001. Tel: 505-272-4688. Fax: 505-272-5350. p. 1551

Bunt, Betty, Cataloger, Ref Librn, Houghton College, One Willard Ave, Houghton, NY, 14744. Tel: 585-567-9252. Fax: 585-567-9248. p. 1638

Buntin, Bill, Media Spec, Palm Beach State College, 4200 Congress Ave, Mail Sta 17, Lake Worth, FL, 33461. Tel: 561-868-3800. Fax: 561-868-3708. p. 459

Bunting, Christine, Head, Spec Coll, University of California, 1156 High St, Santa Cruz, CA, 95064. Tel: 831-459-4425. Fax: 831-459-5856. p. 264

Bunton, Glenn, Head, Syst Develop, Old Dominion University Libraries, 4427 Hampton Blvd, Norfolk, VA, 23529-0256. Tel: 757-683-5952. Fax: 757-683-5767. p. 2482

Bunyan, Emily Cooper, Dir, Knox County Public Library, 502 N Seventh St, Vincennes, IN, 47591-2119. Tel: 812-886-4380. Fax: 812-886-0342. p. 784

Bunyan, Linda, Mgr, Summa Health System, 55 N Arch, Ste G-3, Akron, OH, 44304. Tel: 330-375-3081. Fax: 330-375-3978. p. 1853

Bunyan, Linda, Librn, Affinity Medical Center, 875 Eighth St NE, Massillon, OH, 44646. Tel: 330-832-8761, Ext 1635. Fax: 330-834-4784. p. 1915

Bunyatova, Lyudmila, Dir, Wyckoff Heights Medical Center, 374 Stockholm St, Brooklyn, NY, 11237. Tel: 718-963-7198. Fax: 718-497-7649. p. 1595

Buonanno, Gillian, Dir, Wanaque Public Library, 616 Ringwood Ave, Wanaque, NJ, 07465. Tel: 973-839-4434, Ext 101. Fax: 973-839-8904. p. 1539

Buono-Gaimari, Maria, Acq, Tech Serv, Cumberland County Law Library, Cumberland County Courthouse, 1st Flr, Broad & Fayette Sts, Bridgeton, NJ, 08302. Tel: 856-451-8000, 856-453-4530, 856-853-3539. p. 1474

Burall, Timothy, Br Mgr, Public Library Association of Annapolis & Anne Arundel County, Inc, Riviera Beach, 1130 Duvall Hwy, Pasadena, MD, 21122. Tel: 410-222-6285. Fax: 410-222-6287. p. 1011

Burazer, Mary, Cat, Belmont Abbey College, 100 Belmont-Mt Holly Rd, Belmont, NC, 28012. Tel: 704-461-6745. Fax: 704-461-6743. p. 1776

Burbank, Elizabeth, Asst Librn, Madbury Public Library, Nine Town Hall Rd, Madbury, NH, 03823. Tel: 603-743-1400. p. 1455

Burbank, Joyce, Librn, South Congregational Church, 242 Salmon Brook St, Granby, CT, 06035. Tel: 860-653-7289. Fax: 860-653-7952. p. 341

Burbank, Scott, Financial Serv, Alabama Public Library Service, 6030 Monticello Dr, Montgomery, AL, 36130. Tel: 334-213-3629. Fax: 334-213-3993. p. 27

Burch, David, Head, Libr Computing Serv, Loyola Law School, 919 S Albany St, Los Angeles, CA, 90015-1211. Tel: 213-736-1115. Fax: 213-487-2204. p. 175

Burch, James, Dir, Libr & Info Serv, Savannah Technical College, 100 Technology Dr, Hinesville, GA, 31313. Tel: 912-443-5874. Fax: 912-408-3038. p. 536

Burch, James, Dir, Libr & Info Serv, Savannah Technical College, 5717 White Bluff Rd, Savannah, GA, 31405-5521. Tel: 912-443-5874. Fax: 912-443-5875. p. 551

Burch, John R, Jr, Dir of Libr Serv, Campbellsville University, One University Dr, Campbellsville, KY, 42718-2799. Tel: 270-789-5015. Fax: 270-789-5336. p. 909

Burch, Julie, Asst Admin, Sturgis District Library, 255 North St, Sturgis, MI, 49091. Tel: 269-659-7224. Fax: 269-651-4534. p. 1229

Burch, Nan, Librn, Houghton International, Madison & Van Buren Aves, Valley Forge, PA, 19482. Tel: 610-666-4121. Fax: 610-666-7354. p. 2149

Burch, Nancy, Dir, Vernonia Public Library, 701 Weed Ave, Vernonia, OR, 97064-1102. Tel: 503-429-1818. Fax: 503-429-0729. p. 2022

Burch, Paul, Mgr, Public Library of Cincinnati & Hamilton County, Circulation Services, 800 Vine St, Cincinnati, OH, 45202-2009. Tel: 513-369-6996. Fax: 513-369-6902. p. 1871

Burchard, Patricia, Coordr, ILL, Ref Serv, Utica College, 1600 Burrstone Rd, Utica, NY, 13502-4892. Tel: 315-792-3388. Fax: 315-792-3361. p. 1759

Burchard, Shannon S, Head, Tech Serv, Interim Dir, University of San Francisco, Zief Law Library, 2101 Fulton St, San Francisco, CA, 94117-1004. Tel: 415-422-6679. Fax: 415-422-2345. p. 249

Burchell, Stankeisha, Librn, GEO Corporation, 1282 E State Rd 78, Moore Haven, FL, 33471. Tel: 863-946-2420, Ext 140. Fax: 863-946-2393. p. 470

Burchett, Melissa, Br Mgr, Kanawha County Public Library, Dunbar Public, 301 12th Street Mall, Dunbar, WV, 25064. Tel: 304-766-7161. Fax: 304-766-7242. p. 2556

Burchfield, Amy, Access & Fac Serv Librn, Cleveland State University, Cleveland-Marshall Law Library, Cleveland-Marshall College of Law, 1801 Euclid Ave, Cleveland, OH, 44115-2223. Tel: 216-687-6885. Fax: 216-687-6881. p. 1878

Burchfield, Jessie, Circ, University of Arkansas at Little Rock, Pulaski County Law Library, 1203 McMath Ave, Little Rock, AR, 72202-5142. Tel: 501-324-9444. Fax: 501-324-9447. p. 107

Burchfield, Scarlett, Dir, Texas Health Harris Methodist Fort Worth Hospital, 1301 Pennsylvania Ave, Fort Worth, TX, 76104. Tel: 817-250-2916. Fax: 817-250-5119. p. 2324

Burchill, Jean, Mgr, Henrico County Public Library, Varina Branch Library, 2001 Library Rd, Henrico, VA, 23231-5826. Tel: 804-290-9800. Fax: 804-222-4244. p. 2471

Burd, Barbara, Dir, Libr Serv, College of Misericordia, 301 Lake St, Dallas, PA, 18612-1098. Tel: 570-674-6231. Fax: 570-674-6342. p. 2048

Burd, Barbara, Dean, Coastal Carolina University, 755 Hwy 544, Conway, SC, 29526. Tel: 843-349-2402. Fax: 843-349-2412. p. 2191

Burd, Karen, Dir, Priestley Forsyth Memorial Library, 100 King St, Northumberland, PA, 17857-1670. Tel: 570-473-8201. Fax: 570-473-8807. p. 2100

Burdayron, Linda, Supvr, Bibliotheque de Dorval, 1401 Chemin du Bord du Lac, Dorval, QC, H9S 2E5, CANADA. Tel: 514-633-4170. Fax: 514-633-4177. p. 2881

Burden, Cathy, Youth Serv, Pickerington Public Library, 201 Opportunity Way, Pickerington, OH, 43147-1296. Tel: 614-837-4104. Fax: 614-837-8425. p. 1930

Burden, Elizabeth, Access Serv, University of Arkansas Fort Smith, 5210 Grand Ave, Fort Smith, AR, 72903. Tel: 479-788-7245. Fax: 479-788-7209. p. 101

Burden, Paul, Dir, Libr Serv, DeVry University, 18624 W Creek Dr, Tinley Park, IL, 60477. Tel: 708-342-3360, 708-342-3361. Fax: 708-342-3315. p. 709

Burden, Shirley, Br Head, Cullman County Public Library System, Hanceville Public, 108 S Main St, Hanceville, AL, 35077. Tel: 256-352-0685. Fax: 256-352-1111. p. 13

Burden, Wyvonne, Bus Mgr, Greenwood-Leflore Public Library System, 405 W Washington St, Greenwood, MS, 38930-4297. Tel: 662-453-3634. Fax: 662-453-0683. p. 1299

Burdett, Danny, Head, Circ, Glencoe Public Library, 320 Park Ave, Glencoe, IL, 60022-1597. Tel: 847-835-5056. Fax: 847-835-5648. p. 650

Burdett, Pamela, Assoc Dir, Head, Pub Serv, Stetson University College of Law Library, 1401 61st St S, Gulfport, FL, 33707. Tel: 727-562-7824. Fax: 727-345-8973. p. 450

Burdette, Ilona, Dir of Libr Serv, St Catharine College Library, 2735 Bardstown Rd, Saint Catharine, KY, 40061. Tel: 859-336-5082, Ext 1260. Fax: 859-336-5031. p. 934

Burdette, Linda, Circ, College of Lake County, 19351 W Washington St, Grayslake, IL, 60030. Tel: 847-543-2438. Fax: 847-223-7690. p. 652

Burdge, Claudia A, Librn, Akron Department of Planning & Urban Development Library, 403 Municipal Bldg, 166 S High St, Akron, OH, 44308. Tel: 330-375-2084. Fax: 330-375-2387. p. 1851

Burdge, Edsel, Jr, Chair, Eastern Mennonite Associated Libraries & Archives, 2215 Millstream Rd, Lancaster, PA, 17602. Tel: 717-393-9745. Fax: 717-393-8751. p. 2954

Burdick, Carla, Br Mgr, Middletown Public Library, Bayshore, 180 Main St, Port Monmouth, NJ, 07758. Tel: 732-787-1568. p. 1501

Burdick, Faith, Ref Librn, Galesburg Public Library, 40 E Simmons St, Galesburg, IL, 61401-4591. Tel: 309-343-6118. Fax: 309-343-4877. p. 648

Burdick, Patricia, Asst Dir, Digital & Spec Coll, Spec Coll Librn, Colby College Libraries, 5100 Mayflower Hill, Waterville, ME, 04901. Tel: 207-859-5151. Fax: 207-859-5105. p. 1005

Burdick, Susan, Circ & ILL Mgr, Yale University Library, Divinity School Library, 409 Prospect St, New Haven, CT, 06511-2108. Tel: 203-432-5288. Fax: 203-432-3906. p. 357

Burdick, Terri, Librn, Soldotna Public Library, 235 N Binkley St, Soldotna, AK, 99669. Tel: 907-262-4227. Fax: 907-262-6856. p. 54

Burdiss, Angela, Head, Tech Serv & Syst, Marietta College, 220 Fifth St, Marietta, OH, 45750. Tel: 740-376-4537. Fax: 740-376-4843. p. 1913

Burds, Jason, Info Tech Supvr, Carnegie-Stout Public Library, 360 W 11th St, Dubuque, IA, 52001. Tel: 563-589-4225, Ext 2229. Fax: 563-589-4217. p. 811

Bureau, Michelle, Librn, Supvr, Saint Joseph's Hospital, 350 N Wilmot Rd, Tucson, AZ, 85711. Tel: 520-873-3925. Fax: 520-873-6554. p. 87

Burelle, Sylvie, Chef de Section, Bibliothèques de Montrèal, Hochelaga, 1870, rue Davidson, Montreal, QC, H1W 2Y6, CANADA. Tel: 514-872-6733. Fax: 514-872-0522. p. 2890

Bures, Loran, Librn, SCS Engineers Library, 3900 Kilroy Airport Way, Ste 100, Long Beach, CA, 90806-6816. Tel: 562-426-9544. Fax: 562-427-0805. p. 167

Burford, Mary, Indexer, Alternative Press Center Library, 2040 N Milwaukee Ave, 2nd Flr, Chicago, IL, 60647. Tel: 312-451-8133. Fax: 773-772-4180. p. 605

Burg, Eileen, Dir, Arkansas State University-Mountain Home, 1600 S College St, Mountain Home, AR, 72653-5326. Tel: 870-508-6112. Fax: 870-508-6291. p. 110

Burg, Patricia, Head Librn, Illinois State Museum Library, 502 S Spring St, Springfield, IL, 62706-5000. Tel: 217-524-0496, 217-782-6623. Fax: 217-782-1254, 217-785-2857. p. 705

Burgalassi, Anthony J, Librn, Katten Muchin Rosenman LLP, 575 Madison Ave, New York, NY, 10022. Tel: 212-940-8800. Fax: 212-894-5598. p. 1684

Burgamy, Pam, Br Mgr, Chattahoochee Valley Libraries, Cusseta-Chattahoochee Public Library, 262 Broad St, Cusseta, GA, 31805. Tel: 706-989-3700. Fax: 706-989-1850. p. 526

Burgard, Daniel, Dir, South Central Academic Medical Libraries Consortium, c/o Lewis Library-UNTHSC, 3500 Camp Bowie Blvd, Fort Worth, TX, 76107. Tel: 817-735-2380. Fax: 817-735-5158. p. 2956

Burgard, Daniel E, Libr Dir, University of North Texas Health Science Center at Fort Worth, 3500 Camp Bowie Blvd, Fort Worth, TX, 76107-2699. Tel: 817-735-2589. Fax: 817-763-0325. p. 2324

Burge, Peggy, Librn, University of Puget Sound, 1500 N Warner St, Campus Mail Box 1021, Tacoma, WA, 98416-1021. Tel: 253-879-3512. Fax: 253-879-3670. p. 2541

Burge, Tom, Librn, Sequoia & Kings Canyon National Parks, 47050 Generals Hwy, Three Rivers, CA, 93271. Tel: 559-565-3139. Fax: 559-565-3730. p. 275

Burge, Vera, Librn, Rae Hobson Memorial Library, PO Box 3, Republic, KS, 66964-0003. Tel: 785-361-2481. p. 891

Burgener, Marsha, Librn, Atwood-Hammond Public Library, 123 N Main St, Atwood, IL, 61913. Tel: 217-578-2727. Fax: 217-578-2727. p. 591

Burger, John, Exec Dir, Association of Southeastern Research Libraries, c/o SOLINET, 1438 W Peachtree St NW, Ste 200, Atlanta, GA, 30309-2955. Tel: 404-892-0943. Fax: 404-892-7879. p. 2941

Burger, Leslie, Dir, Princeton Public Library, 65 Witherspoon St, Princeton, NJ, 08542. Tel: 609-924-8822, Ext 253. Fax: 609-924-6109. p. 1522

Burger, Linda, ILL, Harlan Community Library, 718 Court St, Harlan, IA, 51537. Tel: 712-755-5934. Fax: 712-755-3952. p. 820

Burger-Martindale, Gerry, Cent Libr Mgr, Calgary Public Library, W R Castell Central Library, 616 Macleod Trail SE, Calgary, AB, T2G 2M2, CANADA. Tel: 403-260-2600. Fax: 403-237-5393. p. 2689

Burgers, Clarene, Asst Dir, Inwood Public Library, 103 S Main, Inwood, IA, 51240. Tel: 712-753-4814. p. 822

Burgeson, Diane, Asst Dir, Shelby Township Library, 51680 Van Dyke, Shelby Township, MI, 48316-4448. Tel: 586-739-7414. Fax: 586-726-0535. p. 1227

Burgess, Alexis, Commun Serv Librn, Meriden Public Library, 105 Miller St, Meriden, CT, 06450. Tel: 203-630-6349. Fax: 203-238-3647. p. 350

Burgess, Carol, Dir, Arkoma Public Library, 1101 Main St, Arkoma, OK, 74901. Tel: 918-875-3971. Fax: 918-875-3013. p. 1957

Burgess, Cynthia, Librn/Curator of Bks & Printed Mat, Baylor University Libraries, Armstrong Browning Library, 710 Speight Ave, Waco, TX, 76798-7152. Tel: 254-710-4959. Fax: 254-710-3552. p. 2396

Burgess, Dorothy, Cat, Gadsden State Community College, 1001 George Wallace Dr, Gadsden, AL, 35902. Tel: 256-549-8496. Fax: 256-549-8401. p. 18

Burgess, Edwin B, Dir, United States Army, Combined Arms Research Library, US Army Command & General Staff College, Eisenhower Hall, 250 Gibbon Ave, Fort Leavenworth, KS, 66027-2314. Tel: 913-758-3001. Fax: 913-758-3014. p. 867

Burgess, Jim, Mus Spec, Manassas National Battlefield Park Library, 6511 Sudley Rd, Manassas, VA, 20109-2005. Tel: 703-361-1339. Fax: 703-361-7106. p. 2477

Burgess, Joanna, Digital Assets Librn, Reed College, 3203 SE Woodstock Blvd, Portland, OR, 97202-8199. Tel: 503-777-7702. Fax: 503-777-7786. p. 2014

Burgess, Jodi, ILL, St Mary's Hospital Medical Center, 700 S Park St, Madison, WI, 53715. Tel: 608-258-6535. Fax: 608-258-6119. p. 2607

Burgess, John, Dir, Libr & Educ Res, Keyano College Library, 8115 Franklin Ave, Fort McMurray, AB, T9H 2H7, CANADA. Tel: 780-791-8927. Fax: 780-791-1555. p. 2704

Burgess, Judy, Dir, Abilene Public Library, 209 NW Fourth, Abilene, KS, 67410-2690. Tel: 785-263-3082. Fax: 785-263-2274. p. 855

Burgess, Larry E, Dir, A K Smiley Public Library, 125 W Vine St, Redlands, CA, 92373. Tel: 909-798-7565. Fax: 909-798-7566. p. 215

Burgess, Lynn, Dir, Boaz Public Library, 404 Thomas Ave, Boaz, AL, 35957. Tel: 256-593-8056. Fax: 256-593-8153. p. 10

Burgess, Markesha, Librn, Holley A G State Hospital, Benjamin L Brock Medical Library, 1199 W Lantana Rd, Lantana, FL, 33462. Tel: 561-582-5666. Fax: 561-540-3710. p. 460

Burgess, Michele, In Charge, Vermont Veterans Home Library, 325 North St, Bennington, VT, 05201. Tel: 802-447-6520. Fax: 802-447-2757. p. 2419

Burgess, Pam, Circ, Albertville Public Library, 200 Jackson St, Albertville, AL, 35950. Tel: 256-891-8290. Fax: 256-891-8295. p. 3

Burgess, Sherri, Librn, Burchell Campbell Memorial Library, 11075 Hwy 101, Lexington, AL, 35648-0459. Tel: 256-229-5579. Fax: 256-229-5579. p. 23

Burgest, Loretta, Adult Serv, University Park Public Library District, 1100 Blackhawk Dr, University Park, IL, 60466. Tel: 708-534-2580. Fax: 708-534-2583. p. 711

Burgett, Shelley Wood, Dir, Libr Serv, Somerset Community College Library, Harold B Strunk Learning Resource Ctr, 808 Monticello St, Somerset, KY, 42501. Tel: 606-451-6710. Fax: 606-679-5139. p. 935

Burgh, Scott G, Librn, City of Chicago, 30 N LaSalle, Ste 800, Chicago, IL, 60602. Tel: 312-744-7632. Fax: 312-744-1974. p. 611

Burgher, Rosalie, Asst Dir, Olive Free Library Association, 4033 Rte 28A, West Shokan, NY, 12494. Tel: 845-657-2482. Fax: 845-657-2664. p. 1767

Burgin, Robert E, Assoc Dean, Prof, North Carolina Central University, 1801 Fayetteville St, Durham, NC, 27707. Tel: 919-530-6485. Fax: 919-530-6402. p. 2971

Burgio, Cindy, Br Mgr, Horry County Memorial Library, Little River Branch, Ralph H Ellis County Complex Bldg, 107 Hwy 57 N, Little River, SC, 29566. Tel: 843-399-5541. Fax: 843-399-5542. p. 2191

Burgmeier, Michael, Ref, Northern Michigan University, 1401 Presque Isle, Marquette, MI, 49855. Tel: 906-227-2187. Fax: 906-227-1333. p. 1207

Burgos, Eddie, Tech Coordr, University of Puerto Rico Library, Cayey Campus, 205 Ave Antonio R Barcelo, Cayey, PR, 00736. Tel: 787-738-2161, Ext 2021, 787-738-5651. Fax: 787-263-2108. p. 2672

Burgos, Mary, Head, Tech Serv, Columbia University, Arthur W Diamond Law Library, 435 W 116th St, New York, NY, 10027. Tel: 212-854-3922. Fax: 212-854-3295. p. 1674

Burgoyne, Cathi, Tech Serv Supvr, Carroll College, 1601 N Benton Ave, Helena, MT, 59625. Tel: 406-447-4342. Fax: 406-447-4525. p. 1381

Burhanna, Ken, Head, Instrul Serv, Kent State University Libraries, 1125 Risman Dr, Kent, OH, 44242. Tel: 330-672-1660. Fax: 330-672-4811. p. 1907

Burhop, Kimberly, Mgr, Libr Human Res, Duke University Libraries, 411 Chapel Dr, Durham, NC, 27708. Tel: 919-660-5937. Fax: 919-660-5923. p. 1787

Burhop, Nancy, Mgr, Lesueur County Historical Society Museum Library, 301 Second St NE, Elysian, MN, 56028-2008. Tel: 507-267-4620. p. 1250

Buri, Darin, Br Mgr, University of North Dakota, F D Holland Jr Geology Library, 81 Cornell St, Stop 8358, Grand Forks, ND, 58202-8358. Tel: 701-777-2408. Fax: 701-777-4449. p. 1843

Buri, Gertrude, Asst Librn, Wissahickon Valley Public Library, 650 Skippack Pike, Blue Bell, PA, 19422. Tel: 215-643-1320, Ext 12. Fax: 215-643-6611. p. 2036

Buri, Maura, Circ, Villanova University, Law Library, Garey Hall, 299 N Spring Mill Rd, Villanova, PA, 19085. Tel: 610-519-7020. Fax: 610-519-7033. p. 2150

Burington, Peg, Dir, Waupaca Area Public Library, 107 S Main St, Waupaca, WI, 54981-1521. Tel: 715-258-4414. p. 2645

Burk, Martha, Mgr, Coll Mgt, Babson College, 231 Forest St, Babson Park, MA, 02457-0310. Tel: 781-239-4988. Fax: 781-239-5226. p. 1051

Burk, Teresa, Dir, ACA Library of Savannah College of Art & Design, 1600 Peachtree St NW, Atlanta, GA, 30309. Tel: 404-253-3196. Fax: 404-253-3278. p. 510

Burk, William, Librn, University of North Carolina at Chapel Hill, Couch Biology (Botany Section), 301 Coker Hall, CB No 3280, Chapel Hill, NC, 27599. Tel: 919-962-4785. Fax: 919-843-8393. p. 1780

Burkart, Martha, Curric Coll, Juv Coll, Ser, Concordia University, 1282 Concordia Ave, Saint Paul, MN, 55104. Tel: 651-606-6309. Fax: 651-641-8782. p. 1278

Burkart, Stacy, Head, Ch, Verona Public Library, 500 Silent St, Verona, WI, 53593. Tel: 608-845-7180. Fax: 608-845-8917. p. 2643

Burke, Adam, Librn, Waubonsee Community College, State Rte 47 at Waubonsee Dr, Sugar Grove, IL, 60554. Tel: 630-466-2396. Fax: 630-466-7799. p. 708

Burke, Alison, ILL, Yale University Library, Lillian Goldman Library Yale Law School, 127 Wall St, New Haven, CT, 06511. Tel: 203-432-1600. Fax: 203-432-2112. p. 358

Burke, Ann, Ch, Babylon Public Library, 24 S Carll Ave, Babylon, NY, 11702. Tel: 631-669-1624. Fax: 631-669-7826. p. 1577

Burke, Anne, Dir, Peace College, 15 E Peace St, Raleigh, NC, 27604-1194. Tel: 919-508-2303. Fax: 919-508-2769. p. 1816

Burke, Art, Librn, Grand Tower Public Library, 111 Walnut St, Grand Tower, IL, 62942. Tel: 618-565-2181. Fax: 618-565-2181. p. 651

Burke, Brigid, Tech Serv & Digital Projects Librn, Fairleigh Dickinson University, 285 Madison Ave, M-LAO-03, Madison, NJ, 07940. Tel: 973-443-8514. Fax: 973-443-8525. p. 1497

Burke, Carol, Commun Libr Mgr, County of Los Angeles Public Library, George Nye Jr Library, 6600 Del Amo Blvd, Lakewood, CA, 90713-2206. Tel: 562-421-8497. Fax: 562-496-3943. p. 143

Burke, Dale, Tech Serv Librn, Edmonds Community College Library, 20000 68th Ave W, Lynnwood, WA, 98036. Tel: 425-640-1529. p. 2520

Burke, Debbie, Librn, Patrick Henry School District Public Library, 208 NE Ave, Deshler, OH, 43516. Tel: 419-278-3616. Fax: 419-278-3616. p. 1896

Burke, Derva, Dir, Meehan Memorial Lansing Public Library, 515 Main St, Lansing, IA, 52151. Tel: 563-538-4693. Fax: 563-538-4693. p. 827

Burke, Ethel, Librn, Sally Stretch Keen Memorial Library, 94 Main St, Vincentown, NJ, 08088. Tel: 609-859-3598. Fax: 609-859-4029. p. 1537

Burke, Heather L, Librn, DeVry University, 3880 Kilroy Airport Way, Long Beach, CA, 90806. Tel: 562-997-5581. Fax: 562-997-5389. p. 166

Burke, Helen, Sr Librn, Hennepin County Library, Minneapolis Central, 300 Nicollet Mall, Minneapolis, MN, 55401. Tel: 612-543-8079. Fax: 612-543-8173. p. 1264

Burke, Jane H, Dir, Alden-Ewell Free Library, 13280 Broadway, Alden, NY, 14004. Tel: 716-937-7082. Fax: 716-937-7082. p. 1571

Burke, Janet, Ch, Mashpee Public Library, 64 Steeple St, Mashpee, MA, 02649. Tel: 508-539-1435. Fax: 508-539-1437. p. 1103

Burke, Jeanne, Educ Coordr, Creighton University, Health Sciences Library-Learning Resource Center, 2770 Webster St, Omaha, NE, 68178-0210. Tel: 402-280-5108. Fax: 402-280-5134. p. 1412

Burke, Jennifer, Ch, DeWitt Community Library, Shoppingtown Mall, 3649 Erie Blvd E, DeWitt, NY, 13214. Tel: 315-446-3578. Fax: 315-446-1955. p. 1614

Burke, Jennifer A, Dir, Sandwich District Library, 107 E Center St, Sandwich, IL, 60548-1603. Tel: 815-786-8308. Fax: 815-786-9231. p. 700

Burke, Jo, Librn, Oblon, Spivak, 1940 Duke St, Alexandria, VA, 22314-3454. Tel: 703-412-6391. Fax: 703-413-2220. p. 2446

Burke, John, Dir, Miami University-Middletown, 4200 N University Blvd, Middletown, OH, 45042-3497. Tel: 513-727-3293. p. 1917

Burke, Joseph, Ref, United States Air Force, National Air & Space Intelligence Center Research Center, NASIC/GXKA, 4180 Watson Way, Wright-Patterson AFB, OH, 45433-5648. Tel: 937-257-3531. Fax: 937-257-0122. p. 1951

Burke, Joseph, III, Exec Dir, Wilkes-Barre Law & Library Association, Luzerne County, Court House, Rm 23, 200 N River St, Wilkes-Barre, PA, 18711-1001. Tel: 570-822-6712. Fax: 570-822-8210. p. 2156

Burke, Lauri, Commun Serv, Barrington Public Library, 281 County Rd, Barrington, RI, 02806. Tel: 401-247-1920. Fax: 401-247-3763. p. 2163

Burke, Leslie, Coll Develop & Digital Integration Librn, Kalamazoo College, 1200 Academy St, Kalamazoo, MI, 49006-3285. Tel: 269-337-7144. Fax: 269-337-7143. p. 1197

Burke, Linda, Circ, North Babylon Public Library, 815 Deer Park Ave, North Babylon, NY, 11703-3812. Tel: 631-669-4020. Fax: 631-669-3432. p. 1706

Burke, Linda M, Chairperson, Davidson County Community College, 297 DCCC Rd, Lexington, NC, 27295. Tel: 336-249-8186, Ext 270. Fax: 336-248-8135. p. 1806

Burke, Lynne, Dir of Tech Serv, New England Historic Genealogical Society Library, 99-101 Newbury St, Boston, MA, 02116-3007. Tel: 617-226-1225. Fax: 617-536-7307. p. 1065

Burke, Marianne, Dir, University of Vermont Libraries, Dana Medical Library, 81 Colchester Ave, Burlington, VT, 05405. Tel: 802-656-3483. Fax: 802-656-0762. p. 2421

Burke, Marianne, Chair, North Atlantic Health Sciences Libraries, Inc, University of Vermont Medical School, Dana Medical Library, Medical Education Center, Burlington, CT, 05405. Tel: 508-656-3483. Fax: 508-656-0762. p. 2939

Burke, Nita, Libr Dir, Johnson Public Library, 131 E Catherine St, Darlington, WI, 53530. Tel: 608-776-4171. p. 2587

Burke, Sandra, Outreach Serv Librn, Palmer Public Library, 1455 N Main St, Palmer, MA, 01069. Tel: 413-283-3330. Fax: 413-283-9970. p. 1116

Burke, Shannon, Asst Dir, Deer Park Public Library, 3009 Center St, Deer Park, TX, 77536-5099. Tel: 281-478-7208. Fax: 281-478-7212. p. 2311

Burke, Sheila, Librn, Chouteau County Library, Geraldine Branch, 603 Main St, Geraldine, MT, 59446. Tel: 406-737-4331. p. 1379

Burke, Stephanie, Dir, North Arlington Free Public Library, 210 Ridge Rd, North Arlington, NJ, 07031. Tel: 201-955-5640. Fax: 201-991-7850. p. 1514

Burke, Susan, PhD, Dr, Assoc Prof, University of Oklahoma, Bizzell Memorial Library, 401 W Brooks, Rm 120, Norman, OK, 73019-6032. Tel: 405-325-3921. Fax: 405-325-7648. p. 2972

Burke, Ted, Instrul Tech, Dean College, 99 Main St, Franklin, MA, 02038-1994. Tel: 508-541-1771. Fax: 508-541-1918. p. 1090

Burke, Timothy, Asst Dir, Albany Public Library, 161 Washington Ave, Albany, NY, 12210. Tel: 518-427-4378. Fax: 518-449-3386. p. 1568

Burke, Timothy, Exec Dir, Upper Hudson Library System, 28 Essex St, Albany, NY, 12206. Tel: 518-437-9880, Ext 222. Fax: 518-437-9884. p. 1571

Burke, Wendy, Dir, Colusa County Free Library, 738 Market St, Colusa, CA, 95932. Tel: 530-458-7671. Fax: 530-458-7358. p. 135

Burke-Foret, Frances, Head, Coll Mgt, Tufts University, 145 Harrison Ave, Boston, MA, 02111-1843. Tel: 617-636-0319. Fax: 617-636-4039. p. 1068

Burke-Urr, Fran, Coll Mgr, Fauquier County Public Library, 11 Winchester St, Warrenton, VA, 20186-2825. Tel: 540-349-1928. Fax: 540-349-3278. p. 2500

Burkenroad, Andrea, Br Mgr, Los Angeles Public Library System, Hyde Park, 2205 Florence Ave, Los Angeles, CA, 90043. Tel: 323-750-7241. Fax: 213-612-0436. p. 173

Burkett, Phyllis, Dir, Crowley Ridge Regional Library, 315 W Oak Ave, Jonesboro, AR, 72401. Tel: 870-935-5133. Fax: 870-935-7987. p. 104

Burkett, Phyllis G, Dir & Chief Exec of the Br Libr, Craighead County Jonesboro Public Library, 315 W Oak Ave, Jonesboro, AR, 72401-3513. Tel: 870-935-5133, Ext 29. Fax: 870-935-7987. p. 104

Burkett, Rod, Regional Librn, Providence Community Library, Knight Memorial Library, 275 Elmwood Ave, Providence, RI, 02907. Tel: 401-467-2625. p. 2173

Burkett-Pederson, Karen, Dir, Bondurant Community Library, 104 Second St NE, Bondurant, IA, 50035. Tel: 515-967-4790. Fax: 515-967-2668. p. 797

Burkey, Ramona, Dir, Cheshire Public Library, 104 Main St, Cheshire, CT, 06410-2499. Tel: 203-272-2245. Fax: 203-272-7714. p. 333

Burkhalter, Harris, Cat Librn, Bethany Lutheran College Memorial Library, 700 Luther Dr, Mankato, MN, 56001-4490. Tel: 507-344-7850. Fax: 507-344-7376. p. 1257

Burkhalter, Walter, Dir, Mid-Wisconsin Federated Library System, 112 Clinton St, Horicon, WI, 53032. Tel: 920-485-0833. Fax: 920-485-0899. p. 2598

Burkhardsmeier, Cathy, Librn, Minnewaukan Public Library, 130 Main St, Minnewaukan, ND, 58351. Tel: 701-473-5735. Fax: 701-473-5377. p. 1846

Burkhardt, Andy, Emerging Tech Librn, Champlain College Library, 163 S Willard St, Burlington, VT, 05401. Tel: 802-860-2717. p. 2420

Burkhardt, Diane, Fac Serv Librn, University of Denver, Westminster Law Library, 2255 E Evans Ave, Denver, CO, 80208. Tel: 303-871-6188. Fax: 303-871-6999. p. 304

Burkhardt, Diane, Head, Tech Serv, North Merrick Public Library, 1691 Meadowbrook Rd, North Merrick, NY, 11566. Tel: 516-378-7474. Fax: 516-378-0876. p. 1706

Burkhardt, Joanna M, Chair, Tech Serv & CMO, Robert L Carothers Library & Learning Commons, 15 Lippitt Rd, Kingston, RI, 02881. Tel: 401-874-2666. Fax: 401-874-4608. p. 2168

Burkhardt, Joanna M, Dir, University of Rhode Island, 80 Washington St, Providence, RI, 02903-1803. Tel: 401-277-5130. Fax: 401-277-5148. p. 2175

Burkhardt, Odilo, Fr, Librn, Blue Cloud Abbey Library, 46561 147th St, Marvin, SD, 57251. Tel: 605-398-9200. Fax: 605-398-9201. p. 2215

Burkhardt, Robert, Dr, Dir, Athens State University Library, 407 E Pryor St, Athens, AL, 35611. Tel: 256-233-8218. Fax: 256-233-6547. p. 5

Burkhardt, Sue Ann, Librn, Levy County Public Library System, Luther Callaway Public, 104 NE Third St, Chiefland, FL, 32626-0937. Tel: 352-493-2758. Fax: 352-493-2758. p. 430

Burkhart, Don, Librn, Illinois Department of Corrections, 1300 W Locust St, Canton, IL, 61520-8791. Tel: 309-647-7030, Ext 549, 309-647-7030, Ext 550. Fax: 309-647-0353. p. 599

Burkhart, Linda, Dir, Sanford Museum & Planetarium, 117 E Willow, Cherokee, IA, 51012. Tel: 712-225-3922. Fax: 712-225-0446. p. 802

Burkhart, Linda, Dir, Franklin Free Library, 334 Main St, Franklin, NY, 13775. Tel: 607-829-2941. Fax: 607-829-5017. p. 1624

Burkhart, Monica, Librn, Patton Public Library, 444 Magee Ave, Patton, PA, 16668-1210. Tel: 814-674-8231. Fax: 814-674-6188. p. 2101

Burkhart, Sara, Librn, Wright County Library, Mountain Grove Branch, 206 Green St, Mountain Grove, MO, 65711. Tel: 417-926-4453. Fax: 417-926-6240. p. 1330

Burkhead, Keith, Extn Serv, Guilford Technical Community College, 601 High Point Rd, Jamestown, NC, 27282. Tel: 336-334-4822, Ext 2292. Fax: 336-841-4350. p. 1803

Burkholder, Chris, Libr Mgr, Fairview Public Library, 10209 109th St, Fairview, AB, T0H 1L0, CANADA. Tel: 780-835-2613. Fax: 780-835-2613. p. 2704

Burkholder, Debra, Outreach Serv Librn, Platteville Public Library, 65 S Elm, Platteville, WI, 53818. Tel: 608-348-7441. Fax: 608-348-9923. p. 2630

Burkholder, Jenny, Ch, Maplewood Memorial Library, Hilton, 1688 Springfield Ave, Maplewood, NJ, 07040-2923. Tel: 973-762-1688. p. 1499

Burkholder, Karen, Outreach Librn, Clay County Public Library, 211 Bridge St, Manchester, KY, 40962. Tel: 606-598-2617. Fax: 606-598-4671. p. 928

Burkholder, Kristen, PhD, Access Serv Librn, Oklahoma City University, Dulaney-Browne Library, 2501 N Blackwelder, Oklahoma City, OK, 73106. Tel: 405-208-5068. Fax: 405-208-5291. p. 1974

Burkholder, Lynn, Dir, Lower Providence Community Library, 50 Parklane Dr, Eagleville, PA, 19403-1171. Tel: 610-666-6640. Fax: 610-666-5109. p. 2051

Burkholder, Marie, Librn, Iosco-Arenac District Library, Whittemore Branch, 483 Bullock St, Whittemore, MI, 48770-5134. Tel: 989-756-3186. Fax: 989-756-3186. p. 1176

Burkos, Rivka, Head Librn, Bramson Ort College, 69-30 Austin St, Forest Hills, NY, 11375. Tel: 718-261-5800. Fax: 718-301-1976. p. 1623

Burks, China, Evening Supvr, Libr Tech III, Lamar State College-Orange Library, 410 Front St, Orange, TX, 77630-5796. Tel: 409-882-3081. Fax: 409-883-7552. p. 2367

Burks, Delena, Br Mgr, Hutchinson County Library, Fritch Branch, 205 N Cornell, Fritch, TX, 79036. Tel: 806-857-3752. Fax: 806-857-0940. p. 2290

Burks, Meredith, Librn, Good Shepherd Medical Center, 700 E Marshall Ave, Longview, TX, 75601. Tel: 903-315-2165. Fax: 903-315-2034. p. 2356

Burks, Paula, Tech Serv Librn, Santa Rosa Junior College, 1501 Mendocino Ave, Santa Rosa, CA, 95401. Tel: 707-527-4261 (Media Servs), 707-527-4391. Fax: 707-527-4545. p. 267

Burks, Rhonda, Br Mgr, Oldham County Public Library, Mahan Oldham County Public, 12505 Harmony Landing Lane, Goshen, KY, 40026. Tel: 502-228-1852. Fax: 502-228-1852. p. 919

Burks, Steven, Ref & Info Serv, Web Coordr, Saint Michael's College, One Winooski Park, Box L, Colchester, VT, 05439-2525. Tel: 802-654-2354. Fax: 802-654-2630. p. 2422

Burks, Violet, Dir, Halls Public Library, 110 N Church St, Halls, TN, 38040-1502. Tel: 731-836-5302. p. 2236

Burleson, Cynthia, Asst Librn, Mitchell County Public Library, 18 N Mitchell Ave, Bakersville, NC, 28705. Tel: 828-688-2511. p. 1775

Burlew, Liberty, Librn, Reading Community Library, 104 N Main St, Reading, MI, 49274. Tel: 517-283-3916. Fax: 517-283-2510. p. 1220

Burley, Cheryl, Circ, Euclid Public Library, 631 E 222nd St, Euclid, OH, 44123-2091. Tel: 216-261-5300, Ext 153. Fax: 216-261-0575. p. 1898

Burley, Lisa, E-Learning & Instruction, Harding University, 915 E Market St, Searcy, AR, 72149-2267. Tel: 501-279-4185. p. 114

Burley, Paul R, Tech Serv Librn, Northwestern University Library, Transportation Library, 1970 Campus Dr, Evanston, IL, 60208. Tel: 847-491-5274. Fax: 847-491-8601. p. 644

Burling, Tina, Coordr, Saint Vincent Health Center, 232 W 25th St, Erie, PA, 16544. Tel: 814-452-5736. Fax: 814-452-7131. p. 2056

Burlingame, Ann, Dep Dir, Wake County Public Library System, 4020 Carya Dr, Raleigh, NC, 27610-2900. Tel: 919-212-7820. p. 1817

Burlingame, Suzette, Assoc Dir, Tech, Stark County District Library, 715 Market Ave N, Canton, OH, 44702-1018. Tel: 330-458-2720. Fax: 330-455-9596. p. 1864

Burlingham, Bronwyn, Commun Librn, Edmonton Public Library, Mill Woods, 601 Mill Woods Town Centre, 2331 66 St, Edmonton, AB, T6K 4B5, CANADA. Tel: 780-442-4534. Fax: 780-496-1450. p. 2700

Burlingham, Merry, Librn, University of Texas Libraries, South Asian Library Program, PCL 3 313, Austin, TX, 78713. Tel: 512-495-4329. Fax: 512-495-4397. p. 2285

Burnam, Paul, Dir, Methodist Theological School in Ohio Library, 3081 Columbus Pike, Delaware, OH, 43015. Tel: 740-362-3435. Fax: 740-362-3456. p. 1895

Burnett, Alex, Assoc Law Librn, Maine State Law & Legislative Reference Library, 43 State House Sta, Augusta, ME, 04333-0043. Tel: 207-287-1600. Fax: 207-287-6467. p. 974

Burnett, Anne E, Foreign & Intl Law Librn, University of Georgia, 225 Herty Dr, Athens, GA, 30602-6018. Tel: 702-542-5298. Fax: 706-542-5001. p. 510

Burnett, Beth, Head, Tech Serv, Armstrong Atlantic State University, 11935 Abercorn St, Savannah, GA, 31419. Tel: 912-344-3027. Fax: 912-344-3457. p. 549

Burnett, Daniel, Dr, Dir, Libr Serv, Wesley Biblical Seminary Library, 787 E Northside Dr, Jackson, MS, 39206. Tel: 601-366-8880. Fax: 601-366-8832. p. 1305

Burnett, Denise, Dir, Portales Public Library, 218 S Ave B, Portales, NM, 88130. Tel: 505-356-3940. Fax: 505-356-3964. p. 1560

Burnett, Dorothy, Dr, Dir, Tougaloo College, Tougaloo College, 500 W County Line Rd, Tougaloo, MS, 39174-9799. Tel: 601-977-7706. Fax: 601-977-7714. p. 1315

Burnett, Heidi, Dir, Human Res, Maynard Cronin Erickson Curran & Reiter, PLC, 3200 N Central, Ste 1800, Phoenix, AZ, 85012. Tel: 602-279-8500. Fax: 602-263-8185. p. 75

Burnett, Heidi, Libr Mgr, Oakland Park City Library, 1298 NE 37th St, Oakland Park, FL, 33334. Tel: 954-630-4370. Fax: 954-561-6146. p. 473

Burnett, John C, Tech Serv Librn, Albright-Knox Art Gallery, 1285 Elmwood Ave, Buffalo, NY, 14222-1096. Tel: 716-270-8240. Fax: 716-882-6213. p. 1596

Burnett, Kristina, Circ, Howe Library, 13 South St, Hanover, NH, 03755. Tel: 603-643-4120. Fax: 603-643-0725. p. 1450

Burnett, Laura, Libr Mgr, High Plains Library District, Centennial Park, 2227 23rd Ave, Greeley, CO, 80634-6632. Tel: 970-506-8626. Fax: 970-506-8601. p. 312

Burnett, Marian, Librn, College of the North Atlantic, Corner Brook Campus, PO Box 822, Corner Brook, NL, A2H 6H6, CANADA. Tel: 709-637-8528. Fax: 709-634-2126. p. 2771

Burnett, Michael S, Dir, Northville Public Library, 341 S Third St, Northville, NY, 12134-4231. Tel: 518-863-6922. Fax: 518-863-6922. p. 1708

Burnett, Sandy, Mgr, Kootenai-Shoshone Area Libraries, Rathdrum Branch, 16780 N Hwy 41, Rathdrum, ID, 83858. Tel: 208-687-1029. Fax: 208-687-1029. p. 575

Burnett, Vickie, Dir, Brenizer Public Library, 430 W Center Ave, Merna, NE, 68856. Tel: 308-643-2268. Fax: 308-643-2268. p. 1408

Burnette, Brandon, Govt Doc Librn, Southeastern Oklahoma State University, 1405 N Fourth Ave, PMB 4105, Durant, OK, 74701-0609. Tel: 580-745-2795. Fax: 580-745-7463. p. 1961

Burnette, Cheryl, Webmaster, Homewood Public Library, 1721 Oxmoor Rd, Homewood, AL, 35209-4085. Tel: 205-332-6600. Fax: 205-802-6424. p. 20

Burnette, Mark, Librn, National Louis University Library & Learning Support, North Shore, 5202 Old Orchard Rd, Skokie, IL, 60077. Tel: 224-233-2520. Fax: 224-233-2520. p. 619

Burney, Chana, Adult Serv, Ref, Page Public Library, 479 S Lake Powell Blvd, Page, AZ, 86040. Tel: 928-645-4270. Fax: 928-645-5804. p. 70

Burney, Doris, Head Librn, Waelder Public Library, 310 North Ave E, Waelder, TX, 78959. Tel: 830-788-7167. Fax: 830-788-7541. p. 2398

Burney, Jan, Libr Mgr, Sheep River Library, 129 Main St NE, Turner Valley, AB, T0L 2A0, CANADA. Tel: 403-933-3278. Fax: 403-933-3298. p. 2719

Burnham, Carol, Dir, Calhoun Memorial Library, 321 Moore St, Chetek, WI, 54728. Tel: 715-924-3195. Fax: 715-925-2052. p. 2585

Burnham, Elizabeth, Librn, Shelburne Free Public Library, 233 Shelburne Center Rd, Shelburne Falls, MA, 01370. Tel: 413-625-0307. Fax: 413-625-0307. p. 1123

Burnham, Judy, Dir, University of South Alabama, Biomedical Library, Biomedical Library Bldg, 5791 USA Dr N, Mobile, AL, 36688-0002. Tel: 251-460-6885. Fax: 251-460-6958. p. 26

Burnham, Leigh, Ch, Grapevine Public Library, 1201 Municipal Way, Grapevine, TX, 76051. Tel: 817-410-3405. Fax: 817-410-3084. p. 2329

Burnham, Maribe, Dir, Linden Public Library, 131 S Main, Linden, IA, 50146. Tel: 641-744-2124. p. 828

Burniston, Daniel J, Libr Dir, Chartiers-Houston Community Library, 730 W Grant St, Houston, PA, 15342. Tel: 724-745-4300. Fax: 724-745-4233. p. 2070

Burnk, Patricia, Pres, Warren County Historical Society & Genealogy, 313 Mansfield St, Belvidere, NJ, 07823-1828. Tel: 908-475-4246. p. 1471

Burnley, Alesia, Dir, Lebanon-Wilson County Library, 108 S Hatton Ave, Lebanon, TN, 37087-3590. Tel: 615-444-0632. Fax: 615-444-0535. p. 2245

Burnley, Sharon, Ch, Canal Fulton Public Library, 154 Market St NE, Canal Fulton, OH, 44614-1196. Tel: 330-854-4148. Fax: 330-854-9520. p. 1863

Burno, LaTanya C, Exec Dir, J Lewis Crozer Library, 620 Engle St, Chester, PA, 19013-2199. Tel: 610-494-3454. Fax: 610-494-8954. p. 2044

Burns, Amanda, Dir, Suring Area Public Library, 604 E Main St, Suring, WI, 54174. Tel: 920-842-4451. p. 2641

Burns, Amy, Sr Librn, Central Piedmont Community College Library, 1201 Elizabeth Ave, Charlotte, NC, 28235. Tel: 704-330-4212. Fax: 704-330-6887. p. 1781

Burns, Brian T, Media Librn, Hampden Sydney College, 257 Via Sacra, HSC Box 7, Hampden Sydney, VA, 23943. Tel: 434-223-7225. Fax: 434-223-6351. p. 2468

Burns, Bridget, Acq, NASA, Library, Bldg 21, Code 272, Greenbelt, MD, 20771. Tel: 301-286-6245. Fax: 301-286-1755. p. 1030

Burns, Cathie, Ch, Stoughton Public Library, 304 S Fourth St, Stoughton, WI, 53589-0191. Tel: 608-873-6281. Fax: 608-873-0108. p. 2640

Burns, Chris, Res Support & Data Serv Librn, Kwantlen Polytechnic University Library, 12666 72 Ave., Surrey, BC, V3W 2M8, CANADA. Tel: 604-599-3198. Fax: 604-599-2106. p. 2738

Burns, Chris R, Interim Dir, Mineral Area College, 5270 Flat River Rd, Park Hills, MO, 63601. Tel: 573-518-2243. Fax: 573-518-2162. p. 1349

Burns, Christa, Spec Projects Librn, Nebraska Library Commission, The Atrium, 1200 N St, Ste 120, Lincoln, NE, 68508-2023. Tel: 402-471-3107. Fax: 402-471-2083. p. 1406

Burns, Cindy C, Asst Dir, Albuquerque-Bernalillo County Library System, 501 Copper Ave NW, Albuquerque, NM, 87102. Fax: 505-768-5191. p. 1548

Burns, Dale, Cat, Orem Public Library, 58 N State St, Orem, UT, 84057-5596. Tel: 801-229-7050. Fax: 801-229-7130. p. 2409

Burns, David, Tech Serv, Spring Arbor University, 106 E Main St, Spring Arbor, MI, 49283. Tel: 800-968-9103, Ext 1443. Fax: 517-750-2108. p. 1229

Burns, Diane, Dir, Beech Grove Public Library, 1102 Main St, Beech Grove, IN, 46107. Tel: 317-788-4203. Fax: 317-788-0489. p. 726

Burns, Elizabeth, Dir, Department of Veterans Affairs Medical Library, 4801 E Linwood Blvd, Kansas City, MO, 64128-2295. Tel: 816-922-2315. Fax: 816-922-3340. p. 1337

Burns, Elizabeth, Head, Ch, YA Serv, New Jersey State Library, Talking Book & Braille Center, 2300 Stuyvesant Ave, Trenton, NJ, 08618. Tel: 609-406-7179, Ext 804. Fax: 609-406-7181. p. 1536

Burns, Elizabeth, Acq, Dir, Ohio State University LIBRARIES, Louis Bromfield Library - Mansfield Campus, 1660 University Dr, Mansfield, OH, 44906-1599. Tel: 419-755-4324. Fax: 419-755-4327. p. 1887

Burns, Emily, Ch, Van Buren District Library, 200 N Phelps St, Decatur, MI, 49045-1086. Tel: 269-423-4771. Fax: 269-423-8373. p. 1168

Burns, Jackie, Ref, Missouri Western State University, 4525 Downs Dr, Saint Joseph, MO, 64507-2294. Tel: 816-271-4368. Fax: 816-271-4574. p. 1352

Burns, Jacqueline, Cat, Libr Tech, Normandale Community College Library, 9700 France Ave S, Bloomington, MN, 55431. Tel: 952-487-8293. Fax: 952-487-8101. p. 1242

Burns, Jeanne, Head, Outreach Serv, Alexandrian Public Library, 115 W Fifth St, Mount Vernon, IN, 47620. Tel: 812-838-3286. Fax: 812-838-9639. p. 766

Burns, Jeffrey M, Dr, Dir, Archdiocese of San Francisco, 320 Middlefield Rd, Menlo Park, CA, 94025. Tel: 650-328-6502. p. 184

Burns, Joyce S, Ref Librn, Coweta Public Library System, 85 Literary Lane, Newnan, GA, 30265. Tel: 770-683-2052. Fax: 770-683-0065. p. 546

Burns, Jurate S, Dir, Destin Library, 150 Sibert Ave, Destin, FL, 32541-1523. Tel: 850-837-0199. Fax: 850-837-5248. p. 438

Burns, Kathleen, Br Mgr, Currituck County Public Library, Corolla Branch, 1123 Ocean Trail, Corolla, NC, 27927-9998. Tel: 252-453-0496. Fax: 252-453-6960. p. 1776

Burns, Kathy, Br Mgr, Palatine Public Library District, North Hoffman Branch, 3600 Lexington Dr, Hoffman Estates, IL, 60192. Tel: 847-934-0220. p. 686

Burns, Kathy, Br Mgr, Palatine Public Library District, Rand Road, 1585 N Rand Rd, Palatine, IL, 60074. Tel: 847-202-1194. p. 686

Burns, Kelly, Youth Serv, Carrollton Public Library, 1700 Keller Springs Rd, Carrollton, TX, 75006. Tel: 972-466-4717. Fax: 972-466-4265. p. 2295

Burns, Kerry, Interim Dir, Daly City Public Library, 40 Wembley Dr, Daly City, CA, 94015-4399. Tel: 650-991-8023. Fax: 650-991-5726. p. 138

Burns, Kim, Tech Serv, Southeast Kansas Library System, 218 E Madison Ave, Iola, KS, 66749. Tel: 620-365-5136. Fax: 620-365-5137. p. 874

Burns, Linda, Head, Reader Serv, Glenview Public Library, 1930 Glenview Rd, Glenview, IL, 60025-2899. Tel: 847-729-7500. Fax: 847-729-7558. p. 650

Burns, Linda, Dir, Cross Plains Public Library, 149 N Main St, Cross Plains, TX, 76443. Tel: 254-725-7722. Fax: 254-725-6629. p. 2303

Burns, Liz, Asst Dir, Lewis & Clark Community College, 5800 Godfrey Rd, Godfrey, IL, 62035. Tel: 618-468-4320. Fax: 618-468-4301. p. 651

Burns, Liz, Dir, Rogers Memorial Library, 91 Coopers Farm Rd, Southampton, NY, 11968. Tel: 631-283-0774, Ext 501. Fax: 631-287-6539. p. 1745

Burns, Marie T, Dir, Advocate Lutheran General Hospital, 1775 Dempster St, Park Ridge, IL, 60068. Tel: 847-723-5494. Fax: 847-692-9576. p. 688

Burns, Marilyn, Librn, Grace Lutheran Church Library, 200 N Catherine Ave, La Grange, IL, 60525-1826. Tel: 708-352-0730. Fax: 708-352-0737. p. 662

Burns, Marla, Librn, Caledonia Public Library, 231 E Main St, Caledonia, MN, 55921-1321. Tel: 507-725-2671. Fax: 507-725-5258. p. 1243

Burns, Martha, Youth Serv Coordr, Scott County Public Library, 108 S Main St, Scottsburg, IN, 47170. Tel: 812-752-2751. Fax: 812-752-2878. p. 777

Burns, Mary-Frances, Dir, Morley Library, 184 Phelps St, Painesville, OH, 44077-3926. Tel: 440-352-3383. Fax: 440-352-2653. p. 1927

Burns, Nancy O, Dir, Stevens Memorial Community Library, 146 Main St, Attica, NY, 14011-1243. Tel: 585-591-2733. Fax: 585-591-3855. p. 1575

Burns, Patrick, Dr, Dean of Libr, VPres, Info Tech, Colorado State University Libraries, Morgan Library, 1201 Center Avenue Mall, Fort Collins, CO, 80523-. Tel: 970-491-1838. Fax: 970-491-1195. p. 307

Burns, Patti, Adult Serv, Georgetown County Library, 405 Cleland St, Georgetown, SC, 29440-3200. Tel: 843-545-3300. Fax: 843-545-3395. p. 2194

Burns, Rebecca, Librn, Southwest Arkansas Regional Library, Ashdown Branch, 160 E Commerce, Ashdown, AR, 71822. Tel: 870-898-3233. Fax: 870-898-3233. p. 103

Burns, Richard, State Librn, Hawaii State Public Library System, Office of the State Librarian, 44 Merchant St, Honolulu, HI, 96813. Tel: 808-586-3704. Fax: 808-586-3715. p. 561

Burns, Ross, Dir of Tech Serv, Sul Ross State University, PO Box C-109, Alpine, TX, 79832-0001. Tel: 432-837-8123. Fax: 432-837-8400. p. 2273

Burns, Summer-Lee, Libr Tech, Aberdeen Hospital, 835 E River Rd, New Glasgow, NS, B2H 3S6, CANADA. Tel: 902-752-7600, Ext 2130. Fax: 902-752-2507. p. 2784

Burns, Susan, Cataloger, Coll Mgt Librn, Palmer College of Chiropractic-Davenport Campus, 1000 Brady St, Davenport, IA, 52803-5287. Tel: 563-884-5467. Fax: 563-884-5897. p. 806

Burns, Tim, In Charge, Grand River Hospital, 835 King St W, Kitchener, ON, N2G 1G3, CANADA. Tel: 519-749-4300, Ext 2235. Fax: 519-749-4208. p. 2815

Burns, Virginia, Libr Mgr, Timberland Regional Library, Centralia Timberland Library, 110 S Silver St, Centralia, WA, 98531-4218. Tel: 360-736-0183. Fax: 360-330-7530. p. 2543

Burns, W James, PhD, Exec Dir, Desert Caballeros Western Museum, 21 N Frontier St, Wickenburg, AZ, 85390. Tel: 928-684-2272. Fax: 928-684-5794. p. 89

Burns-Feyl, Sarah K, Asst Univ Librn, Pace University, 861 Bedford Rd, Pleasantville, NY, 10570-2799. Tel: 914-773-3220. Fax: 914-773-3508. p. 1719

Burnsides, Patti, Ad, Scott County Public Library, 104 S Bradford Lane, Georgetown, KY, 40324-2335. Tel: 502-863-3566. Fax: 502-863-9621. p. 915

Burnsworth, Micky, Ref, Warren-Trumbull County Public Library, 444 Mahoning Ave NW, Warren, OH, 44483. Tel: 330-399-8807. Fax: 330-395-3988. p. 1944

Burnweit, Richard, ILL Mgr, Westmont College, 955 La Paz Rd, Santa Barbara, CA, 93108-1099. Tel: 805-565-6000, 805-565-6147. Fax: 805-565-6220. p. 262

Burpoe, Laurie, Librn, Delaware County Supreme Court Law Library, Three Court St, Delhi, NY, 13753-9990. Tel: 607-746-3959. Fax: 607-746-8198. p. 1613

Burr, Barbara, Dir, Human Res, Mesa County Public Library District, 443 North 6th St, Grand Junction, CO, 81501. Tel: 970-243-4442. p. 310

Burr, Donna, Dir, Brooks Institute Library, 27 E Cota St, Santa Barbara, CA, 93101. Tel: 805-690-7627, 805-966-3888. Fax: 805-564-1475. p. 260

Burr, Donna, Dir, Brooks Ventura Library, 5301 N Ventura Ave, Ventura, CA, 93001. Tel: 805-585-8000. p. 279

Burr, Jennifer S, Bibliog Instr, Ref & Info Serv, Team Leader, Nazareth College of Rochester Library, 4245 East Ave, Rochester, NY, 14618-3790. Tel: 585-389-2133. Fax: 585-389-2145. p. 1730

Burr, Jill, Librn, Virginia Beach Public Library Department, Pungo-Blackwater Library, 916 Princess Anne Rd, Virginia Beach, VA, 23457. Tel: 757-426-5194. p. 2500

Burr, Linda, Dir of Develop, University of North Carolina at Greensboro, 320 Spring Garden St, Greensboro, NC, 27402. Tel: 336-256-0184. Fax: 336-334-5399. p. 1798

Burr, Robert, Tech Serv Librn, Holy Family University Library, 9801 Frankford Ave, Philadelphia, PA, 19114. Tel: 267-341-3315, 267-341-3316. Fax: 215-632-8067. p. 2111

Burr-Wilken, Bernie, ILL, Albany County Public Library, 310 S Eighth St, Laramie, WY, 82070-3969. Tel: 307-721-2580. Fax: 307-721-2584. p. 2657

Burrell, Angie, Librn, Mid-Mississippi Regional Library System, West Public, 24843 Hwy 51, West, MS, 39192. Tel: 662-967-2510. Fax: 662-967-2510. p. 1306

Burrell, Carolyn, Electronic Res & Ref Librn, Antelope Valley College Library, 3041 W Ave K, Lancaster, CA, 93536-5426. Tel: 661-722-6533. Fax: 661-722-6456. p. 163

Burrell, Graham, Librn, Schoolcraft College, Radcliff Library, 1751 Radcliff St, Rm RC355, Garden City, MI, 48135. Tel: 734-462-4400, Ext 6019. Fax: 734-462-4743. p. 1204

Burrell, Pam, Ref Librn, Laredo Public Library, 1120 E Calton Rd, Laredo, TX, 78041. Tel: 956-795-2400. Fax: 956-795-2403. p. 2353

Burrell, Shannon, Archivist, Amistad Research Center, Tulane University, Tilton Hall, 6823 St Charles Ave, New Orleans, LA, 70118. Tel: 504-862-3222. Fax: 504-862-8961. p. 959

Burress, Debra, Asst Librn, K&L Gates Library, 1717 Main St, Ste 2800, Dallas, TX, 75201. Tel: 214-939-5510. Fax: 214-939-5849. p. 2309

Burrier, Carrie, Coordr, Youth Serv, Akron-Summit County Public Library, 60 S High St, Akron, OH, 44326. Tel: 330-643-9000. Fax: 330-643-9160. p. 1852

Burrill, Susan, Mgr, Coop Serv, Ajax Public Library, 55 Harwood Ave S, Ajax, ON, L1S 2H8, CANADA. Tel: 905-683-4000, Ext 8822. Fax: 905-683-6960. p. 2791

Burris, Ashley, Dir, Lawrence County Library, 1315 W Main St, Walnut Ridge, AR, 72476. Tel: 870-886-3222. Fax: 870-886-9520. p. 116

Burris, Karen, Legis Librn, Reed Smith LLP, 1301 K St NW, Ste 1100, E Tower, Washington, DC, 20005-3317. Tel: 202-414-9200. Fax: 202-414-9299. p. 413

Burris, Kathy, Res Serv Librn, Landmark College Library, River Rd S, Putney, VT, 05346. Tel: 802-387-1648. Fax: 802-387-6896. p. 2432

Burris, Leatha, ILL Spec, Kalamazoo College, 1200 Academy St, Kalamazoo, MI, 49006-3285. Tel: 269-337-7153. Fax: 269-337-7143. p. 1197

Burris, Michael, Dir, Harlan Community Library, 718 Court St, Harlan, IA, 51537. Tel: 712-755-5934. Fax: 712-755-3952. p. 820

Burriss, Victoria, Librn, Macon County Law Library, Macon County Courthouse, 253 E Wood St, Rm 303, Decatur, IL, 62523. Tel: 217-424-1372. p. 634

Burritt, Devin, Assoc Dir, Jackson Memorial Library, 38 Main St, Tenants Harbor, ME, 04860. Tel: 207-372-8961. p. 1003

Burritt, Devin, Asst Libr Dir, Youth Serv Librn, Wells Public Library, 1434 Post Rd, Wells, ME, 04090-4508. Tel: 207-646-8181, Ext. 202. Fax: 207-646-5636. p. 1006

Burroughs, Catherine, Assoc Dir, National Network of Libraries of Medicine Pacific Northwest Region, T-344 Health Sciences Bldg, University of Washington, Seattle, WA, 98195. Tel: 206-543-9261. Fax: 206-543-2469. p. 2957

Burroughs, Joanne, Supvr, Haliburton County Public Library, Highland Grove Branch, 5373 Loop Rd, Highland Grove, ON, K0L 2A0, CANADA. Tel: 705-448-2652. p. 2808

Burroughs Kelly, Angela, Cataloger, St Charles Community College, 4601 Mid Rivers Mall Dr, Cottleville, MO, 63376. Tel: 636-922-8000. Fax: 636-922-8433. p. 1326

Burroughs, Phyllis, Head Librn, Avery County Morrison Public Library, 150 Library Pl, Newland, NC, 28657. Tel: 828-733-9393. Fax: 828-682-6277. p. 1813

Burrous, Kay, Dir, South Macon Public Library District, 451 W Glenn St, Macon, IL, 62544. Tel: 217-764-3356. Fax: 217-764-5490. p. 669

Burrow, Gale, Asst Dir, Educ Serv, Claremont Colleges Library, 800 Dartmouth Ave, Claremont, CA, 91711. Tel: 909-621-8014. p. 134

Burrows, Barbara, Br Mgr, Wellington County Library, Palmerston Branch, 265 Bell St, Palmerston, ON, N0G 2P0, CANADA. Tel: 519-343-2142. p. 2805

Burrows, Charlotte, Prov Libr Serv Supvr, Thousand Oaks Library, 1401 E Janss Rd, Thousand Oaks, CA, 91362-2199. Tel: 805-449-2660, Ext 7338. Fax: 805-373-6858. p. 275

Burrows, Muriel E, Dir, Johnston Public Library, 210 W Tenth St, Baxter Springs, KS, 66713-1611. Tel: 620-856-5591. p. 857

Burrows, Susan M, Dir, Libr Serv, Cleary, Gottlieb, Steen & Hamilton LLP Library, One Liberty Plaza, New York, NY, 10006. Tel: 212-225-3444. Fax: 212-225-3999. p. 1673

Burrows, Suzetta, Dir, University of Miami, Louis Calder Memorial Library, Miller School of Medicine, 1601 NW Tenth Ave, Miami, FL, 33136. Tel: 305-243-6441. Fax: 305-325-8853. p. 469

Burry, Paul, Support Serv Coordr, Prince George Public Library, 887 Dominion St, Prince George, BC, V2L 5L1, CANADA. Tel: 250-563-9251. Fax: 250-563-0892. p. 2736

Burshteyn, Dina, Librn, Baptist Hospital East, 4000 Kresge Way, Louisville, KY, 40207-4676. Tel: 502-897-8183. Fax: 502-897-8020. p. 923

Burshtin, Lynn, Chief Librn, National Railway Historical Society Library, 100 N 17th St, Ste 1203, Philadelphia, PA, 19103-2783. Tel: 215-557-6606. Fax: 215-557-6740. p. 2113

Bursi, Amy Moore, Coll Mgt, Georgia Perimeter College, Dunwoody Campus Library, 2101 Womack Rd, Dunwoody, GA, 30338-4497. Tel: 770-274-5093. Fax: 770-274-5090. p. 525

Bursi, Peter, Bibliog Instr, Georgia Perimeter College, Dunwoody Campus Library, 2101 Womack Rd, Dunwoody, GA, 30338-4497. Tel: 770-274-5086. Fax: 770-274-5090. p. 525

Bursk, Mary Ann, Br Librn, Youth Serv, Bucks County Free Library, Levittown Branch, 7311 New Falls Rd, Levittown, PA, 19055-1006. Tel: 215-949-2324. Fax: 215-949-0643. p. 2050

Burson, Max M, Dir, Pub Serv Librn, Friends University, 2100 W University St, Wichita, KS, 67213-3397. Tel: 316-295-5521. Fax: 316-295-5080. p. 900

Burson, Patricia, Tech Serv, Santa Monica College Library, 1900 Pico Blvd, Santa Monica, CA, 90405-1628. Tel: 310-434-4334, 310-434-4692. Fax: 310-434-4387. p. 266

Burson, Wilford, Genealogy Info Spec, Danville Public Library, 511 Patton St, Danville, VA, 24541. Tel: 434-799-5195. Fax: 434-792-5172. p. 2459

Burstein, Alvin, Librn, New Orleans-Birmingham Psychoanalytic Center Library, 3624 Coliseum St, New Orleans, LA, 70115. Tel: 504-899-5815. Fax: 504-899-5886. p. 962

Burstein, Miriam, Circ, Harcum College Library, 750 Montgomery Ave, Bryn Mawr, PA, 19010-3476. Tel: 610-526-6085. Fax: 610-526-6086. p. 2039

Burstein, Nancy, Curator, Dir, Williamstown House of Local History, 1095 Main St, Williamstown, MA, 01267. Tel: 413-458-2160. p. 1141

Bursten, Julie, Br Mgr, Toledo-Lucas County Public Library, West Toledo, 1320 Sylvania Ave, Toledo, OH, 43612. Tel: 419-259-5290. Fax: 419-476-0892. p. 1940

Burt, Angela, Br Mgr, Chesterfield County Public Library, Meadowdale, 4301 Meadowdale Blvd, Richmond, VA, 23234. Tel: 804-318-8755. p. 2457

Burt, Laura, Bibliog Instr, Database Mgt, Ref Serv, North Park University, Brandel Library, 5114 N Christiana Ave, Chicago, IL, 60625. Tel: 773-244-5587. Fax: 773-244-4891. p. 620

Burt, Neal, Info Tech, Helen Hall Library, 100 W Walker, League City, TX, 77573-3899. Tel: 281-554-1125. Fax: 281-554-1118. p. 2354

Burt, Patricia, Dir, Red River College Library, 2055 Notre Dame Ave, Winnipeg, MB, R3H 0J9, CANADA. Tel: 204-632-2382. Fax: 204-697-4791. p. 2757

Burt, Patricia, Chair, Manitoba Library Consortium, Inc, c/o Library Administration, University of Winnipeg, 515 Portage Ave, Winnipeg, MB, R3B 2E9, CANADA. Tel: 204-632-2382. Fax: 204-697-4791. p. 2959

Burtle, Laura, Assoc Univ Librn, Learning & Tech Initiatives, Georgia State University Library, 100 Decatur St SE, Atlanta, GA, 30303-3202. Tel: 404-413-2706. Fax: 404-413-2701. p. 516

Burton, Betty, Adult Prog, Vineyard Haven Public Library, 200 Main St, Vineyard Haven, MA, 02568-9710. Tel: 508-696-4211, Ext 16. Fax: 508-696-7495. p. 1132

Burton, Brenda, Res, Kirkland & Ellis LLP Library, 300 N LaSalle St, 11th Flr, Chicago, IL, 60654. Tel: 312-862-3270. Fax: 312-862-2200. p. 616

Burton, Brenda, Circ Supvr, Public Library of Johnston County & Smithfield, 305 E Market St, Smithfield, NC, 27577-3919. Tel: 919-934-8146. Fax: 919-934-8084. p. 1824

Burton, Cara, Dir, Solvay Public Library, 615 Woods Rd, Solvay, NY, 13209-1697. Tel: 315-468-2441. Fax: 315-468-0373. p. 1745

Burton, Carla, Br Mgr, Atlanta-Fulton Public Library System, Northeast-Spruill Oaks Regional Library, 9560 Spruill Rd, Alpharetta, GA, 30022. Tel: 770-360-8820. Fax: 770-360-8823. p. 512

Burton, Curtis, Dir, Bicentennial City-County Public Library, County Courthouse, Eighth St, Paducah, TX, 79248. Tel: 806-492-2006. Fax: 806-492-2006. p. 2367

Burton, Cynthia, Ref, Allegheny College Library, 555 N Main St, Meadville, PA, 16335. Tel: 814-332-2982. Fax: 814-337-5673. p. 2086

Burton, Donna, Dir, Ontario Legislative Library, Legislative Bldg, Queen's Park, Toronto, ON, M7A 1A9, CANADA. Tel: 416-325-3945. Fax: 416-314-8541. p. 2856

Burton, Ellen, Customer Serv Supvr, University of Richmond, 28 Westhampton Way, Richmond, VA, 23173. Tel: 804-289-8454. Fax: 804-289-8757. p. 2491

Burton, Jametoria, Head Librn, Florida State College at Jacksonville, Deerwood Center Library, 9911 Old Baymeadows Rd, Jacksonville, FL, 32256. Tel: 904-997-2563. Tel: 904-997-2571. p. 452

Burton, Jean, Cat, West Chester University, 25 W Rosedale Ave, West Chester, PA, 19383. Tel: 610-436-2917. p. 2153

Burton, Jeannie, Dir, Benton County Library System, 247 Court St, Ashland, MS, 38603. Tel: 662-224-6400. Fax: 662-224-6304. p. 1293

Burton, John, Ref Serv, Albany Public Library, 1390 Waverly Dr SE, Albany, OR, 97322. Tel: 541-917-7580, Ext 4702. Fax: 541-917-7586. p. 1989

Burton, Karen, Assoc Dir, Weber County Library System, 2464 Jefferson Ave, Ogden, UT, 84401-2464. Tel: 801-337-2617. Fax: 801-337-2615. p. 2408

Burton, Karen, Librn, Weber County Library System, Ogden Valley Branch, 131 S 7400 East, Huntsville, UT, 84317-9309. Tel: 801-745-2220. Fax: 801-745-2221. p. 2409

Burton, Kari, Libr Asst I, Montgomery City-County Public Library System, Juliette Hampton Morgan Memorial Library (Main Library), 245 High St, Montgomery, AL, 36104. Tel: 334-240-4999. Fax: 334-240-4980. p. 30

Burton, Marcia, Head, Computer Dept, Maywood Public Library District, 121 S Fifth Ave, Maywood, IL, 60153. Tel: 708-343-1847, Ext 13. Fax: 708-343-2115. p. 672

Burton, Mary, Supv Librn, Madison Public Library, Monroe, 1705 Monroe St, Madison, WI, 53711. Tel: 608-224-7103. Fax: 608-224-7102. p. 2607

Burton, Mary, Supv Librn, Madison Public Library, Pinney Branch, 204 Cottage Grove Rd, Madison, WI, 53716. Tel: 608-224-7103. Fax: 608-224-7102. p. 2607

Burton, Melody, Chief Librn, University of British Columbia Library, Okanagan Library, 3333 University Way, Kelowna, BC, V1V 1V7, CANADA. p. 2743

Burton, Michele, Libr Dir, Tumbler Ridge Public Library, 340 Front St, Tumbler Ridge, BC, V0C 2W0, CANADA. Tel: 250-242-4778. Fax: 250-242-4707. p. 2739

Burton, Rose, ILL, Ref, Elyria Public Library System, 320 Washington Ave, Elyria, OH, 44035-5199. Tel: 440-323-5747. Fax: 440-323-5788. p. 1898

Burton, Rose, Asst Librn, United States Air Force, 75 MSG/SVMG, Bldg 440, 7415 Eighth St, Hill AFB, UT, 84056-5006. Tel: 801-777-2533, 801-777-3833. Fax: 801-777-6667. p. 2406

Burton, Shonn, Adult Serv, Circ, Paterson Free Public Library, 250 Broadway, Paterson, NJ, 07501. Tel: 973-321-1223. Fax: 973-321-1205. p. 1518

Burton, Steve, Music Librn, Kennesaw State University, 1000 Chastain Rd, Kennesaw, GA, 30144. Tel: 770-499-3167. Fax: 770-423-6185. p. 537

Burton, Susan, Exec Dir, Mid-America Library Alliance/Kansas City Metropolitan Library & Information Network, 15624 E 24 Hwy, Independence, MO, 64050. Tel: 816-521-7257. Fax: 816-461-0966. p. 2948

Burton, Tonia, Ch, Prog Coordr, Brighton Memorial Library, 2300 Elmwood Ave, Rochester, NY, 14618. Tel: 585-784-5300. Fax: 585-784-5333. p. 1728

Burton, Wayne, Dir, Church of Jesus Christ of Latter-Day Saints-Philadelphia, 721 Paxon Hollow Rd, Broomall, PA, 19008. Tel: 610-356-8507. p. 2038

Burts, Lenora, Ref Serv, Web Serv, National Library of Medicine, Bldg 38, Rm 2E-17B, 8600 Rockville Pike, Bethesda, MD, 20894. Tel: 301-496-6308. Fax: 301-496-4450. p. 1022

Burwash, Janice, Info Res, Burlington Public Library, 820 E Washington, Burlington, WA, 98233. Tel: 360-755-0760. Fax: 360-755-0717. p. 2511

Burwell, Cathy, Ref Serv, Cape Fear Community College, 415 N Second St, Wilmington, NC, 28401-3993. Tel: 910-362-7456. Fax: 910-362-7005. p. 1830

Burwell, Susan, Fiscal Officer, Loudonville Public Library, 122 E Main St, Loudonville, OH, 44842-1267. Tel: 419-994-5531. Fax: 419-994-4321. p. 1911

Bury, Robert, Exec Dir, Dossin Great Lakes Museum, 100 Strand Dr on Belle Isle, Detroit, MI, 48207. Tel: 313-852-4051. Fax: 313-833-5342. p. 1171

Bury, Stephen, Chief Librn, The Frick Collection, Ten E 71st St, New York, NY, 10021. Tel: 212-288-8700. Fax: 212-879-2091. p. 1679

Busboom, Vel, ILL, Crete Public Library, 305 E 13th St, Crete, NE, 68333. Tel: 402-826-3809. Fax: 402-826-4199. p. 1396

Busby, Jane, Ser, Griffin Technical College Library, 501 Varsity Rd, Griffin, GA, 30223. Tel: 770-412-4755. Fax: 770-229-3006. p. 535

Busby, Lorraine A, Univ Librn, Memorial University of Newfoundland, Queen Elizabeth II Library, 234 Elizabeth Ave, St. John's, NL, A1B 3Y1, CANADA. Tel: 709-737-7428. Fax: 709-737-2153. p. 2773

Busby, Sharol, Librn, Clayton Public Library District, 211 E Maine St, Clayton, IL, 62324. Tel: 217-894-6519. Fax: 217-894-6519. p. 629

Busch, Ann, Media Librn, YA Serv, Roseville Public Library, 29777 Gratiot Ave, Roseville, MI, 48066. Tel: 586-445-5407. Fax: 586-445-5499. p. 1223

Busch, Barbara, Dir, United States Navy, SPAWAR Systems Center San Diego Technical Library, Code 84300, 53560 Hull St, San Diego, CA, 92152-5001. Tel: 619-553-4890. Fax: 619-553-4893. p. 239

Busch, Francesca, Dir, University of Indianapolis, 1400 E Hanna Ave, Indianapolis, IN, 46227-3697. Tel: 317-788-3268. Fax: 317-788-3275. p. 755

Busch, Michael, Acq Librn, The Master's Seminary Library, 13248 Roscoe Blvd, Sun Valley, CA, 91352. Tel: 818-909-5634. Fax: 818-909-5680. p. 273

Busch, Nancy, Dr, Assoc Dean, University of Nebraska-Lincoln, 1248 R St, Lincoln, NE, 68588-4100. Tel: 402-472-2526. p. 1407

Busch, Trudi, Dir, Oppenheimer Wolff & Donnelly Library, 45 S Seventh St, Minneapolis, MN, 55402. Tel: 612-607-7290. Fax: 612-607-7100. p. 1261

Busch, Valerie, Circ, ILL, Libr Spec, Grays Harbor College, 1620 Edward P Smith Dr, Aberdeen, WA, 98520-7599. Tel: 360-538-4050. Fax: 360-538-4294. p. 2507

Buschman, Debbie, Doc Delivery, Ref, Group Technology Library & Information Services, 150 W Warrenville Rd, MC F1, Naperville, IL, 60563. Tel: 630-420-4850. Fax: 630-420-3697. p. 678

Buschman, John, Dean, Univ Libr, Seton Hall University Libraries, Walsh Libary Bldg, 400 S Orange Ave, South Orange, NJ, 07079. Tel: 973-761-9005. Fax: 973-761-9432. p. 1530

Buscholl, Cindy, Asst Librn, Chinook Regional Library, Leader Branch, 151 First St W, Leader, SK, S0N 1H0, CANADA. Tel: 306-628-3830. p. 2928

Busco, Linda, Librn, First Presbyterian Church Library, 21 Firelands Blvd, Norwalk, OH, 44857. Tel: 419-668-1923. Fax: 419-663-5115. p. 1924

Busgith, Sabrina, ILL, Kaye Scholer LLP, 425 Park Ave, New York, NY, 10022. Tel: 212-836-8000, 212-836-8312. Fax: 212-836-6613. p. 1684

Bush, Ann, Principal Librn, Tampa-Hillsborough County Public Library System, Hillsborough Talking Book Library, 3910 S Manhattan Ave, Tampa, FL, 33611. Tel: 813-272-6024. Fax: 813-272-6072. p. 497

Bush, Belle, Ref, Houston County Public Library System, Nola Brantley Memorial Library, 721 Watson Blvd, Warner Robins, GA, 31093. Tel: 478-923-0128. Fax: 478-929-8611. p. 547

Bush, Cheryl, Pub Relations, Warren-Trumbull County Public Library, 444 Mahoning Ave NW, Warren, OH, 44483. Tel: 330-399-8807, Fax: 330-395-3988. p. 1944

Bush, Clesson S, Cataloger, Greene County Historical Society, 90 County Rd 42, Coxsackie, NY, 12051-3022. Tel: 518-731-1033, 518-731-6822. p. 1612

Bush, Emily, Instruction Librn, Nashville State Technical Community College, 120 White Bridge Rd, Nashville, TN, 37209-4515. Tel: 615-353-3559. Fax: 615-353-3558. p. 2258

Bush, Evan, Ch, Derry Public Library, 64 E Broadway, Derry, NH, 03038-2412. Tel: 603-432-6140. Fax: 603-432-6128. p. 1444

Bush, Fay, Assoc Dir, Access Serv, Cornerstone University, 1001 E Beltline Ave NE, Grand Rapids, MI, 49525. Tel: 616-949-5300. Fax: 616-222-1405. p. 1184

Bush, Gary, Actg Dean, Alabama A&M University, 4900 Meridian St, Huntsville, AL, 35762. Tel: 256-372-4747. Fax: 256-372-5768. p. 21

Bush, Janice, ILL Asst, Indiana University Southeast Library, 4201 Grant Line Rd, New Albany, IN, 47150. Tel: 812-941-2487. Fax: 812-941-2656. p. 767

Bush, Joe, Librn, North Central Correctional Facility, 313 Lanedale, Rockwell City, IA, 50579. Tel: 712-297-7521, Ext 229. Fax: 712-297-9316. p. 841

Bush, Karen, Asst Librn, Sutton Public Library, 450 Fourth St, No C, Sutton, WV, 26601. Tel: 304-765-7224. Fax: 304-765-7224. p. 2572

Bush, Keith, Dir, Oak Hills Christian College, 1600 Oak Hills Rd SW, Bemidji, MN, 56601-8832. Tel: 218-751-8670, Ext 1299. Fax: 218-751-8825. p. 1241

Bush, Leanna, Libr Tech, United States Army Medical Research Institute of Chemical Defense, 3100 Ricketts Point Rd, Aberdeen Proving Ground, MD, 21010-5400. Tel: 410-436-4135. Fax: 410-436-3176. p. 1009

Bush, Loretta, In Charge, United States Department of Energy, PO Box 98518, Las Vegas, NV, 89193-8518. Tel: 702-295-1274. Fax: 702-295-0109. p. 1430

Bush, Martha M, Libr Dir, Franklin-Springboro Public Library, 44 E Fourth St, Franklin, OH, 45005. Tel: 937-746-2665. Fax: 937-746-2846. p. 1900

Bush, Renee, Youth Serv, Clark County Public Library, 370 S Burns Ave, Winchester, KY, 40391-1876. Tel: 859-744-5661. Fax: 859-744-5993. p. 938

Bush, Sandra, Librn, Buffalo & Erie County Public Library System, Frank E Merriweather Jr Library, 1324 Jefferson Ave, Buffalo, NY, 14208. Tel: 716-883-4418. Fax: 716-883-4418. p. 1596

Bush, Stephanie D, Instrul Serv Librn, Eastern Mennonite University, 1200 Park Rd, Harrisonburg, VA, 22802-2462. Tel: 540-432-4175. Fax: 540-432-4977. p. 2470

Bush-Tomio, Kim, Dir, Tyler Museum of Art Library, 1300 S Mahon, Tyler, TX, 75701-3499. Tel: 903-595-1001. Fax: 903-595-1055. p. 2393

Bushallow, Lara, Syst Librn, George Mason University Libraries, 4400 University Dr, MSN 2FL, Fairfax, VA, 22030-4444. Tel: 703-993-2250. Fax: 703-993-2200. p. 2462

Bushbaum, Michael, Assoc Law Librn, Valparaiso University, School of Law Library, 656 S Greenwich St, Valparaiso, IN, 46383. Tel: 219-465-7827. Fax: 219-465-7917. p. 784

Bushel, Anne, Local Hist Librn, Ref Librn, Rossford Public Library, 720 Dixie Hwy, Rossford, OH, 43460-1289. Tel: 419-666-0924. Fax: 419-666-1989. p. 1932

Bushey, Donna, Asst Librn, Cavendish-Fletcher Community Library, 573 Main St, Proctorsville, VT, 05153. Tel: 802-226-7503. Fax: 802-226-7858. p. 2432

Bushey, Helen, Asst Librn, H F Brigham Free Public Library, 104 Main St, Bakersfield, VT, 05441. Tel: 802-827-4414. p. 2417

Bushey, Mary, Dir, Res, United States Army, Center for Army Analysis, Bldg 1839, 6001 Goethals Rd, Fort Belvoir, VA, 22060-5230. Tel: 703-806-5191. Fax: 703-806-5724. p. 2464

Bushfield, Debra, Librn, Hand County Library, 402 N Broadway, Miller, SD, 57362-1438. Tel: 605-853-3693. Fax: 605-853-2201. p. 2215

Bushman, Catherine, Head, Circ, West Haven Public Library, 300 Elm St, West Haven, CT, 06516-4692. Tel: 203-937-4233. p. 377

Bushman, Eileen, Supvr, Essex County Library, Kingsville Branch, 40 Main W, Kingsville, ON, N9Y 1H3, CANADA. Tel: 226-946-1529, Ext 270. p. 2804

Bushman, Linda, Dir, Gibbon Public Library, 116 LaBarre, Gibbon, NE, 68840. Tel: 308-468-5889. Fax: 308-468-5501. p. 1399

Bushong, Sara A, Dean, Bowling Green State University Libraries, 204 Wm T Jerome Library, Bowling Green, OH, 43403-0170. p. 1861

Bushta, Linda, Br Mgr, Lake County Library, Upper Lake Branch, 310 Second St, Upper Lake, CA, 95485. Tel: 707-275-2049. p. 163

Bushway, Colleen, Librn, Grand Isle Free Library, Ten Hyde Rd, Grand Isle, VT, 05458. Tel: 802-372-4797. p. 2425

Bushway, David, Instrul Tech, Mendocino College Library, 1000 Hensley Creek Rd, Ukiah, CA, 95482-7821. Tel: 707-468-3053. Fax: 707-468-3056. p. 277

Buske, Don H, Archivist, Archdiocese of Cincinnati Archives, 212 E Eighth St, Cincinnati, OH, 45202. Tel: 513-621-2086. Fax: 513-621-2695. p. 1868

Busko, Robert, Dir, Scotland County Memorial Library, 312 W Church St, Laurinburg, NC, 28352-3720. Tel: 910-276-0563. Fax: 910-276-4032. p. 1805

Busko, Robert, Dir, Haywood County Public Library, 678 S Haywood St, Waynesville, NC, 28786-4398. Tel: 828-452-5169, Ext 2505. Fax: 828-452-6746. p. 1828

Busquets, Carmen L, Librn, University of Puerto Rico Library System, Zenobia & Juan Ramon Jimenez Room, Rio Piedras Campus, Edif Jose M Lazaro, San Juan, PR, 00931. Tel: 787-764-0000, Ext 5170. Fax: 787-772-1479. p. 2677

Busroe, Andrew, Dir, Alice Lloyd College, 100 Purpose Rd, Pippa Passes, KY, 41844. Tel: 606-368-6132. Fax: 606-368-6212. p. 933

Buss, Carmen, Dir, Cresco Public Library, 320 N Elm St, Cresco, IA, 52136-1452. Tel: 563-547-2540. Fax: 563-547-1769. p. 805

Buss, Crystal, Circ Serv Librn, University of Wisconsin Oshkosh, 801 Elmwood Ave, Oshkosh, WI, 54901. Tel: 920-424-7315. Fax: 920-424-7338. p. 2628

Buss, DeAnn, Dir, Info Syst, Syracuse University Library, 222 Waverly Ave, Syracuse, NY, 13244-2010. Tel: 315-443-2573. p. 1754

Buss, Elizabeth, Asst Librn, Elizabeth Rasmussen Martin Memorial Library, 406 Packwaukee, New Hartford, IA, 50660. Tel: 319-983-2533. Fax: 319-983-2533. p. 835

Buss, Erica, Librn, Altadena Library District, Bob Lucas Memorial Library & Literacy Center, 2659 N Lincoln Ave, Altadena, CA, 91001-4963. Tel: 626-798-8338. Fax: 626-798-3968. p. 120

Buss, Greg, Chief Librn, Richmond Public Library, 100-7700 Minoru Gate, Richmond, BC, V6Y 1R9, CANADA. Tel: 604-231-6418. Fax: 604-273-0459. p. 2736

Buss, Mary Aileen, Adult Serv, Long Beach Public Library, 111 W Park Ave, Long Beach, NY, 11561-3326. Tel: 516-432-7201. Fax: 516-889-4641. p. 1654

Bussart, Barbara, Head, Ref, Woonsocket Harris Public Library, 303 Clinton St, Woonsocket, RI, 02895. Tel: 401-769-9044. Fax: 401-767-4120. p. 2178

Bussell, Melba, Librn, Barton Library, Smackover Public, 700 N Broadway, Smackover, AR, 71762. Tel: 870-725-3741. Fax: 870-725-3798. p. 98

Bussey, Dawn A, Dir, Glen Ellyn Public Library, 400 Duane St, Glen Ellyn, IL, 60137-4508. Tel: 630-469-0879. Fax: 630-469-1086. p. 650

Bussey, Ginny, Circ, Kinnelon Public Library, 132 Kinnelon Rd, Kinnelon, NJ, 07405-2393. Tel: 973-838-1321. Fax: 973-838-0741. p. 1493

Bussey, Karen W, Law Libr Asst, Jefferson County Law Library, Jefferson County Court House, 716 Richard Arrington Jr Blvd N, Ste 530, Birmingham, AL, 35203. Tel: 205-325-5628. Fax: 205-322-5915. p. 8

Bussey, Tosha, Youth/Young Adult Librn, Atlanta-Fulton Public Library System, Ponce de Leon Library, 980 Ponce de Leon Ave NE, Atlanta, GA, 30306. Tel: 404-885-7820. Fax: 404-885-7822. p. 512

Bussey, Tosha L, Librn, Carver Bible College Library, 3870 Cascade Rd, Atlanta, GA, 30331. Tel: 404-527-4520. Fax: 404-527-4524. p. 514

Bussie, Robert, Circ Supvr, Calumet College of Saint Joseph, 2400 New York Ave, Whiting, IN, 46394. Tel: 219-473-4332. Fax: 219-473-4259. p. 788

Bussiere, Linda, Head, Tech Serv, Goodrich Memorial Library, 202 Main St, Newport, VT, 05855. Tel: 802-334-7902. Fax: 802-334-3890. p. 2430

Bussio, Hillary, Br Mgr, Monterey County Free Libraries, Aromas Branch, 389-D Blohm Ave, Aromas, CA, 95004. Tel: 831-726-3240. Fax: 831-726-0102. p. 183

Bussy, Nancy, Mgr, Charlestown-Clark County Public Library, New Washington Branch, 210 S Poplar St, New Washington, IN, 47162. Tel: 812-967-4577. Fax: 812-967-4577. p. 731

Busta, Heather, ILL, Northeast Iowa Community College, 1625 Hwy 150, Calmar, IA, 52132. Tel: 563-562-3263. Fax: 563-562-4361. p. 798

Bustamante, Yolanda, Libr Dir, Sinton Public Library, 100 N Pirate Blvd, Sinton, TX, 78387. Tel: 361-364-4545. Fax: 361-364-5711. p. 2387

Bustos, Albert, Ref/ILL Supvr, Laredo Community College, West End Washington St, Laredo, TX, 78040. Tel: 956-721-5845. Fax: 956-721-5447. p. 2353

Bustos, Rod, Head, Digital Libr Serv, Georgia State University Library, 100 Decatur St SE, Atlanta, GA, 30303-3202. Tel: 404-413-2770. Fax: 404-413-2701. p. 516

Bustos, Rod, Automation Librn, Augusta State University, 2500 Walton Way, Augusta, GA, 30904-2200. Tel: 706-737-1745. Fax: 706-667-4415. p. 518

Bustos, Tom, Tech Mgr, University of California, Merced Library, 5200 N Lake Rd, Merced, CA, 95343-5001. Tel: 209-337-8710. Fax: 209-228-4271. p. 186

Butch, Barbara, Dir, Sleeper Public Library, 2236 Main St, Ubly, MI, 48475-9726. Tel: 989-658-8901. Fax: 989-658-8788. p. 1232

Butch, Serena, Head, Youth Serv, Schenectady County Public Library, 99 Clinton St, Schenectady, NY, 12305-2083. Tel: 518-388-4513. Fax: 518-386-2241. p. 1740

Butchart, Lorraine, Tech Serv Coordr, Jackson District Library, 290 W Michigan Ave, Jackson, MI, 49201. Tel: 517-788-4673. Fax: 517-788-9987. p. 1195

Butcher, Cindy, Mgr, Dayton Metro Library, East, 2008 Wyoming St, Dayton, OH, 45410. Tel: 937-496-8930. Fax: 937-496-4330. p. 1893

Butcher, Jill, Asst Dir, ILL, Warren County Library, 189 Route 519, Belvidere, NJ, 07823. Tel: 908-475-6322. Fax: 908-475-6359. p. 1472

Butcher, Jill, Ref, Warren County Library, 189 Route 519, Belvidere, NJ, 07823. Tel: 908-475-6322. Fax: 908-475-6359. p. 1472

Butcher, Linda, Asst Librn, Yale Public Library, 213 N Main, Yale, OK, 74085. Tel: 918-387-2135. Fax: 918-387-2616. p. 1986

Butcher, Mikki, ILL, James Madison University Libraries & Educational Technologies, 800 S Main St, Harrisonburg, VA, 22807-0001. Tel: 340-568-6807. Fax: 540-568-6339. p. 2470

Butcher, Patti, Dir, State Library of Kansas, 300 SW Tenth Ave, Rm 343 N, Topeka, KS, 66612-1593. Tel: 785-296-3875. Fax: 785-368-7291. p. 2944

Butcher, Robyn, Librn, University of Toronto Libraries, Family & Community Medicine Library, 500 University Ave, Toronto, ON, M5G 1V7, CANADA. Tel: 416-978-5606. Fax: 416-978-3912. p. 2866

Butcher, Sharon, Ref, United States Air Force, FL 2804, 100 Kindel Dr, Ste C212, Arnold AFB, TN, 37389-3212. Tel: 931-454-4430. Fax: 931-454-5421. p. 2223

Butera, Mary, Dir, South Londonderry Free Library, 15 Old School St, South Londonderry, VT, 05155. Tel: 802-824-3371. Fax: 802-824-3371. p. 2435

Buth, Karen, Libr Serv Mgr/Access Serv, Beverly Hills Public Library, 444 N Rexford Dr, Beverly Hills, CA, 90210-4877. Tel: 310-288-2220. Fax: 310-278-3387. p. 129

Buthod, Craig, Dir, Louisville Free Public Library, 301 York St, Louisville, KY, 40203-2205. Tel: 502-574-1611. Fax: 502-574-1666, 502-574-1693. p. 924

Buti, Debbie, Cataloger, Syst, Chabot College Library, 25555 Hesperian Blvd, Hayward, CA, 94545. Tel: 510-723-6768. p. 157

Butkovic, Margaret, Dir, Canadian Memorial Chiropractic College, 6100 Leslie St, Toronto, ON, M2H 3J1, CANADA. Tel: 416-482-2340, Ext 159. Fax: 416-482-4816. p. 2851

Butkovich, Nancy J, Librn, Pennsylvania State University Libraries, Physical & Mathematical Sciences, 201 Davey Lab, University Park, PA, 16802-6301. Tel: 814-865-3716. Fax: 814-865-2565. p. 2148

Butler, A Hays, Head, Govt Doc & Micro, Ref & Instrul Serv Librn, Rutgers University Libraries, Camden Law Library, 217 N Fifth St, Camden, NJ, 08102-1203. Tel: 856-225-6496. p. 1477

Butler, Adior, Curator, Alan Wofsy Fine Arts Reference Library, 1109 Geary Blvd, San Francisco, CA, 94109. Tel: 415-292-6500. Fax: 415-292-6594. p. 249

Butler, Amy, Electronic Res, Head, Acq, University of North Alabama, One Harrison Plaza, Box 5028, Florence, AL, 35632-0001. Tel: 256-765-4266. Fax: 256-765-4438. p. 17

Butler, Amy, Librn, Stetson Public Library, 70 Village Rd, Stetson, ME, 04488. Tel: 207-296-2020. p. 1003

Butler, Ann, Dir, Libr & Archives, Bard College, Center for Curatorial Studies, PO Box 5000, Annandale-on-Hudson, NY, 12504-5000. Tel: 845-758-7566. Fax: 845-758-2442. p. 1574

Butler, Ann, Librn, Buncombe County Public Libraries, Black Mountain Branch, 105 Dougherty St, Black Mountain, NC, 28711. Tel: 828-250-4756. p. 1774

Butler, Barbara, Dean, Sonoma State University Library, 1801 E Cotati Ave, Rohnert Park, CA, 94928-3609. Tel: 707-664-2397. Fax: 707-664-2090. p. 219

Butler, Barbara, Dir, Tolland Public Library, 21 Tolland Green, Tolland, CT, 06084. Tel: 860-871-3620. Fax: 860-871-3626. p. 372

Butler, Barbara, Librn, University of Oregon, Institute of Marine Biology, 63466 Boat Basin Dr, Charleston, OR, 97420-1221. Tel: 541-888-2581, Ext 219. Fax: 541-888-3391. p. 1993

Butler, Becky, Tech Serv Mgr, Salt Lake City Public Library, 210 E 400 S, Salt Lake City, UT, 84111-3280. Tel: 801-524-8521. Fax: 801-322-8185. p. 2413

Butler, Brooke, Youth Serv Librn, George F Johnson Memorial Library, 1001 Park St, Endicott, NY, 13760. Tel: 607-757-5350. Fax: 607-757-2491. p. 1620

Butler, Carol, Librn, Salvador Dali Foundation Inc, 1000 Third St S, Saint Petersburg, FL, 33701. Tel: 727-823-3767. Fax: 727-823-8532. p. 487

Butler, Cathy, Br Mgr, Public Library Association of Annapolis & Anne Arundel County, Inc, West County Area, 1325 Annapolis Rd, Odenton, MD, 21113. Tel: 410-222-6277. Fax: 410-222-6279. p. 1011

Butler, Chris, Dir, In-Sight Library, 43 Jefferson Blvd, Warwick, RI, 02888-9961. Tel: 401-941-3322. Fax: 401-941-3356. p. 2177

Butler, Clifford, Librn, Sunland Training Center, 3700 Williams Dr, Marianna, FL, 32446. Tel: 850-482-9378. Fax: 850-482-9236. p. 462

Butler, Craig, Librn, Leaf Rapids Public Library, Town Center Complex, Leaf Rapids, MB, R0B 1W0, CANADA. Tel: 204-473-2742. p. 2749

Butler, Darin, Mgr, Salt Lake County Library Services, Sandy Branch, 10100 S Petunia Way, 1450 East, Sandy, UT, 84092-4380. Tel: 801-944-7600. Fax: 801-572-8247. p. 2414

Butler, Darryl, Curator, Kings Landing Library, 5804 Rte 102, Prince William, NB, E6K 0A5, CANADA. Tel: 506-363-4999. Fax: 506-363-4989. p. 2766

Butler, David, Teen Serv, Salem Public Library, 28 E Main St, Salem, VA, 24153. Tel: 540-375-3089. Fax: 540-389-7054. p. 2496

Butler, Diane, Asst Univ Librn, Libr Core Syst & Serv, Rice University, 6100 Main, MS-44, Houston, TX, 77005. Tel: 713-348-4400. Fax: 713-348-5258. p. 2341

Butler, Doug, Head, Tech Serv, Asbury University, One Macklem Dr, Wilmore, KY, 40390-1198. Tel: 859-858-3511, Ext 2522. Fax: 859-858-3921. p. 938

Butler, Douglas A, Assoc Dir, Pasco-Hernando Community College, 10230 Ridge Rd, New Port Richey, FL, 34654-5199. Tel: 727-816-3418. Fax: 727-816-3346. p. 472

Butler, Ed, Br Mgr, San Bernardino County Law Library, 8401 N Haven Ave, Rancho Cucamonga, CA, 91730-3893. Tel: 909-944-5106. p. 213

Butler, Elizabeth M, Dir, Centerville Public Library Association, Inc, 585 Main St, Centerville, MA, 02632. Tel: 508-790-6220. Fax: 508-790-6218. p. 1079

Butler, Emily, Cat Librn, Milton L Rock Resource Center, 1720 Locust St, Philadelphia, PA, 19103. Tel: 215-717-3123. Fax: 215-717-3170. p. 2116

Butler, H Julene, Assoc Univ Librn, Brigham Young University, Harold B Lee Library, 2060 HBLL, Provo, UT, 84602. Tel: 801-422-2927. Fax: 801-422-0466. p. 2411

Butler, Jennifer, Ref Serv, Sidley Austin LLP, 1501 K St NW, Washington, DC, 20005. Tel: 202-736-8525. Fax: 202-736-8711. p. 414

Butler, Jennifer, Assoc Dean, Dir, Libr & Tech, Morton College Library, 3801 S Central Ave, Cicero, IL, 60804. Tel: 708-656-8000, Ext 322. Fax: 708-656-3297. p. 629

Butler, JoAnn, Mgr, Literacy Serv, Boston Public Library, 700 Boylston St, Boston, MA, 02117-0286. Tel: 617-536-5400. Fax: 617-236-4306. p. 1056

Butler, JoAnn E, Coordr, Boston Public Library, Dudley Literacy Center, 65 Warren St, Roxbury, MA, 02119-3206. Tel: 617-859-2446. Fax: 617-859-2447. p. 1057

Butler, John, Assoc Univ Librn, Info Tech, University of Minnesota Libraries-Twin Cities, 499 O Meredith Wilson Library, 309 19th Ave S, Minneapolis, MN, 55455-0414. Tel: 612-625-9148. Fax: 612-626-9353. p. 1262

Butler, John, Principal Librn, Jersey City Free Public Library, 472 Jersey Ave, Jersey City, NJ, 07302-3499. Tel: 201-547-4500. Fax: 201-547-4584. p. 1492

Butler, Karen, Mgr, District of Columbia Public Library, Northeast, 330 Seventh St NE, Washington, DC, 20002. Tel: 202-698-3320. p. 398

Butler, Kate, Tech Librn, George H & Ella M Rodgers Memorial Library, 194 Derry Rd, Hudson, NH, 03051. Tel: 603-886-6030. Fax: 603-816-4501. p. 1452

Butler, Kathy, Librn, Virginia Hospital Center, 1701 N George Mason Dr, Arlington, VA, 22205. Tel: 703-558-6524. Fax: 703-558-5343. p. 2450

Butler, Kim, Archivist/Assoc Dir of Archives, North Central College, 320 E School St, Naperville, IL, 60540. Tel: 630-637-5714. Fax: 630-637-5716. p. 679

Butler, Kimberly, Ch, Newburyport Public Library, 94 State St, Newburyport, MA, 01950-6619. Tel: 978-465-4428, Ext 235. Fax: 978-463-0394. p. 1109

Butler, Kristen, ILL, Salve Regina University, 100 Ochre Point Ave, Newport, RI, 02840-4192. Tel: 401-341-2330. Fax: 401-341-2951. p. 2169

Butler, Linda K, Dr, Acq, University of Tennessee at Martin, Ten Wayne Fisher Dr, Martin, TN, 38238. Tel: 731-881-7096. Fax: 731-881-7074. p. 2246

Butler, Maria, Exec Dir, Pensacola Museum of Art, 407 S Jefferson St, Pensacola, FL, 32502-5901. Tel: 850-432-6247. Fax: 850-469-1532. p. 482

Butler, Maria, Commun Relations Coordr, Lawrence Public Library, 707 Vermont St, Lawrence, KS, 66044-2371. Tel: 785-843-3833, Ext 123. Fax: 785-843-3368. p. 877

Butler, Martha, Dir, Back Mountain Memorial Library, 96 Huntsville Rd, Dallas, PA, 18612. Tel: 570-675-1182. Fax: 570-674-5863. p. 2048

Butler, Mary Edith, Dean, Waubonsee Community College, State Rte 47 at Waubonsee Dr, Sugar Grove, IL, 60554. Tel: 630-466-2854. Fax: 630-466-7799. p. 708

Butler, Mary Edith, Dir, Libr Serv, Eastern Oklahoma State College Library, 1301 W Main St, Wilburton, OK, 74578. Tel: 918-465-1779. Fax: 918-465-0112. p. 1986

Butler, Mary Jane, Mgr, Robeson County Public Library, Annie Hubbard McEachern Public, 221 W Broad St, Saint Pauls, NC, 28384. Tel: 910-865-4002. Fax: 910-865-4002. p. 1808

Butler, Michael P, Exec Officer, OHIONET, 1500 W Lane Ave, Columbus, OH, 43221-3975. Tel: 614-486-2966. Fax: 614-486-1527. p. 2952

Butler, Michelle, Librn, Natrona County Public Library, Mark J Davis Jr Memorial - Edgerton Branch, 935 Cottonwood, Edgerton, WY, 82635. Tel: 307-437-6617. Fax: 307-437-6617. p. 2652

Butler, Nancy, Librn, Haynes Library, 33 Washburn Rd, Alexandria, NH, 03222-6532. Tel: 603-744-6529. p. 1437

Butler, Rachel, ILL/Ref Librn, Oklahoma City Community College, 7777 S May Ave, Oklahoma City, OK, 73159. Tel: 405-682-1611, Ext 7643. Fax: 405-682-7585. p. 1973

Butler, Shirley, Coordr of Libr Tech, Trinity University, 125 Michigan Ave NE, Washington, DC, 20017. Tel: 202-884-9353. Fax: 202-884-9241. p. 417

Butler, Stanley, Br Mgr, Enoch Pratt Free Library, Walbrook, 3203 W North Ave, Baltimore, MD, 21216-3015. Tel: 410-396-0935. Fax: 410-396-0256. p. 1013

Butler, Sue, Admin Serv Mgr, Eastern Monroe Public Library, 1002 N Ninth St, Stroudsburg, PA, 18360. Tel: 570-421-0800. Fax: 570-421-0212. p. 2143

Butler, Suzanne, Ref, Vernon College, 4400 College Dr, Vernon, TX, 76384. Tel: 940-552-6291, Ext 2220. Fax: 940-552-0288. p. 2395

Butler, Tabetha, Librn, Ashville Free Library, 2200 N Maple St, Ashville, NY, 14710-9679. Tel: 716-763-9906. Fax: 716-763-9906. p. 1575

Butler, Thomas A, Jr, Dir, Hinsdale Public Library, 58 Maple St, Hinsdale, MA, 01235. Tel: 413-655-2303. Fax: 413-655-2303. p. 1095

Butler, Timothy, Info Spec, ILL, Kenyon & Kenyon LLP, One Broadway, 10th Flr, New York, NY, 10004-1007. Tel: 212-425-7200. Fax: 212-908-6113. p. 1684

Butler, Todd, Ser, Saint Edwards University, 3001 S Congress Ave, Austin, TX, 78704-6489. Tel: 512-233-1679. Fax: 512-448-8737. p. 2281

Butler, William J, In Charge, American Association for the International Commission of Jurists Library, 280 Madison Ave, Ste 1102, New York, NY, 10016. Tel: 212-972-0883. Fax: 212-972-0888. p. 1667

Butler-Smith, Roseanne, Dir, Amherst Public Library, 350 John James Audubon Pkwy, Amherst, NY, 14228. Tel: 716-688-4919, 716-689-4922. Fax: 716-689-6116. p. 1573

Butler-Smith, Roseanne, Dir, Amherst Public Library, Clearfield, 770 Hopkins Rd, Williamsville, NY, 14221. Tel: 716-688-4955. Fax: 716-688-0281. p. 1573

Butler-Smith, Roseanne, Dir, Amherst Public Library, Eggertsville-Snyder Branch, 4622 Main St, Synder, NY, 14226. Tel: 716-839-0700. Fax: 716-839-4277. p. 1573

Butman, Megan C, Res Librn, DLA Piper US LLP, 203 N LaSalle St, Ste 1900, Chicago, IL, 60601. Tel: 312-849-8668. Fax: 312-251-5845. p. 612

Butrico, Evelyn, Dir, East Greenbush Community Library, Ten Community Way, East Greenbush, NY, 12061. Tel: 518-477-7476. Fax: 518-477-6692. p. 1616

Butson, Patricia L, Librn, United States Courts Library, 300 Ala Moana Blvd C-341, Honolulu, HI, 96850. Tel: 808-541-1797. Fax: 808-541-3667. p. 565

Butt, Francis Bernard, Sister, Asst Archivist, Sisters, Servants of the Immaculate Heart of Mary Archives, Villa Maria House of Studies, 1140 King Rd, Immaculata, PA, 19345. Tel: 610-647-2160. Fax: 610-889-4874. p. 2071

Butter, Karen, Asst Vice Chancellor, Univ Librn, University of California San Francisco, 530 Parnassus Ave, San Francisco, CA, 94143-0840. Tel: 415-476-8293. p. 248

Butter, Karen, Univ Librn, University of California San Francisco, Mission Bay FAMRI Library, William J Rutter Conference Ctr, Rm 150, 1675 Owens St, San Francisco, CA, 94143-2119. Tel: 415-514-4060. p. 248

Butterfield, Elizabeth, Monographs & Acq Mgr, Willamette University, 900 State St, Salem, OR, 97301. Tel: 503-370-6616. Fax: 503-370-6141. p. 2019

Butterfield, George, Ref, Creighton University, Klutznick Law Library - McGrath, North, Mullin & Kratz Legal Research Center, School of Law, 2500 California Plaza, Omaha, NE, 68178-0340. Tel: 402-280-2251, 402-280-2875. Fax: 402-280-2244. p. 1412

Butterfield, Kevin, Head, Tech Serv, College of William & Mary in Virginia, The Wolf Law Library, 613 S Henry St, Williamsburg, VA, 23187. Tel: 757-221-3255. Fax: 757-221-3051. p. 2502

Butterfield, Robert, Dir, Instrul Res Serv, University of Wisconsin-Stout Library, 315 Tenth Ave, Menomonie, WI, 54751-0790. Tel: 715-232-2617. Fax: 715-232-1783. p. 2615

Butterman, Sandy, Extn Serv, Marion Public Library, Caledonia Branch, 112 E Marion St, Caledonia, OH, 43314. Tel: 419-845-3666. p. 1914

Butterworth, Don, Tech Serv Mgr, Asbury Theological Seminary, 204 N Lexington Ave, Wilmore, KY, 40390-1199. Tel: 859-858-2233. Fax: 859-858-2330. p. 938

Butterworth, Linda, Ref & Instruction Librn, Prescott College Library, 217 Garden St, Prescott, AZ, 86301. Tel: 928-350-1300. p. 78

Butterworth, Terry, Electronic Res Librn, OCLC Library, 6565 Kilgour Pl, Dublin, OH, 43017. Tel: 614-764-4300. Fax: 614-793-8707. p. 1896

Buttleman, Dennis P, Curator, The Masonic Library & Museum of Pennsylvania, Masonic Temple, One N Broad St, Philadelphia, PA, 19107-2520. Tel: 215-988-1485. Fax: 215-988-1953. p. 2112

Buttler, Laura, Circ, University of Winnipeg Library, 515 Portage Ave, Winnipeg, MB, R3B 2E9, CANADA. Tel: 204-786-9801. Fax: 204-783-8910. p. 2759

Button, Elizabeth M, Librn, McNeil & Foster Library, 630 Central Ave, New Providence, NJ, 07974. Tel: 908-219-0278. Fax: 908-219-0192. p. 1510

Button, Eric, Head, Commun Serv, Saint Louis County Library, 1640 S Lindbergh Blvd, Saint Louis, MO, 63131-3598. Tel: 314-994-3300, Ext 3253. Fax: 314-997-7602. p. 1358

Button, Leslie Horner, Assoc Dir, Libr Serv, University of Massachusetts Amherst, 154 Hicks Way, Amherst, MA, 01003-9275. Tel: 413-545-6845. Fax: 413-545-6873. p. 1049

Button, Melissa S, Bus Mgr, University of Maryland, Baltimore County, 1000 Hilltop Circle, Baltimore, MD, 21250. Tel: 410-455-2356. p. 1018

Buttram, Connie, Br Mgr, Pulaski County Library District, Waynesville Branch, 306 Historic 66 W, Waynesville, MO, 65536. Tel: 573-774-2965. Fax: 573-774-6429. p. 1350

Buttram, Janet, Br Mgr, Botetourt County Library, Buchanan Branch, 19795 Main St, Buchanan, VA, 24066. Tel: 540-254-2538. Fax: 540-254-1793. p. 2493

Buttram, Janet, ILL, Botetourt County Library, 28 Avery Row, Roanoke, VA, 24012. Tel: 540-977-3433. Fax: 540-977-2407. p. 2493

Butts, Adam, Br Mgr, Mansfield-Richland County Public Library, Lucas Branch, 34 W Main St, Lucas, OH, 44843. Tel: 419-892-2576. Fax: 419-892-2576. p. 1913

Butts, Kay, Asst Librn, Oneonta Public Library, 221 Second St S, Oneonta, AL, 35121. Tel: 205-274-7641. Fax: 205-274-7643. p. 32

Butts, Lewis, Asst Librn, Pennsylvania Department of Conservation & Natural Resources, 3240 Schoolhouse Rd, Middletown, PA, 17057-3534. Tel: 717-702-2018. Fax: 717-702-2065. p. 2089

Butts, Lynette, Automation Supvr, Chinook Regional Library, 1240 Chaplin St W, Swift Current, SK, S9H 0G8, CANADA. Tel: 306-773-3186. Fax: 306-773-0434. p. 2927

Butts, Vicki, Cat, Oneonta Public Library, 221 Second St S, Oneonta, AL, 35121. Tel: 205-274-7641. Fax: 205-274-7643. p. 32

Buttura, Nancy, Asst Circ Librn, Aldrich Public Library, Six Washington St, Barre, VT, 05641-4227. Tel: 802-476-7550. Fax: 802-479-0450 (Call before sending fax). p. 2418

Butz, Debra, Spec Coll & Archives Librn, Tech Serv, Alverno College Library, 3401 S 39th St, Milwaukee, WI, 53215. Tel: 414-382-6202, Ext 2080. Fax: 414-382-6354. p. 2617

Butz, Hildergarde, Librn, Wapiti Regional Library, Canwood Public Library, 660 Main St, Canwood, SK, S0J 0K0, CANADA. p. 2921

Butzel, Steve, Asst Dir, Portsmouth Public Library, 175 Parrott Ave, Portsmouth, NH, 03801-4452. Tel: 603-766-1711. Fax: 603-433-0981. p. 1463

Buus, Linda, Info Spec, Northern Wyoming Community College District - Gillette College, 300 W Sinclair, Gillette, WY, 82718. Tel: 307-686-0254. Fax: 307-686-0339. p. 2655

Buxton, Ann, Mgr, Franklin Memorial Library, 331 W Main, Swainsboro, GA, 30401. Tel: 478-237-7791. Fax: 478-237-3553. p. 552

Buxton, Barbara, Head, Adult Serv, Port Moody Public Library, 100 Newport Dr, Port Moody, BC, V3H 3E1, CANADA. Tel: 604-469-4575, 604-469-4577. Fax: 604-469-4576. p. 2735

Buxton, Vicky, Libr Asst, Forrest County General Hospital, 6051 Hwy 49 S, Hattiesburg, MS, 39402. Tel: 601-288-4260. Fax: 601-288-4209. p. 1300

Buys, Cunera, Librn, Northwestern University Library, Ralph P Boas Mathematics Library, Lunt Bldg, Rm 130, 2033 Sheridan Rd, Evanston, IL, 60208. Tel: 847-491-7627. p. 644

Buysse, Mary, Librn, Minneota Public Library, 103 N Jefferson St, Minneota, MN, 56264-0217. Tel: 507-872-5473. Fax: 507-872-6144. p. 1263

Buzard, Brian L, Librn, Winnebago County Law Library, Courthouse Bldg, Ste 301, Rockford, IL, 61101-1221. Tel: 815-319-4967. Fax: 815-319-4801. p. 698

Buzas, John, Librn, Department of Correctional Education, 1954 State Farm Rd, State Farm, VA, 23160-9998. Tel: 804-784-3551, Ext 2259. Fax: 804-784-2480. p. 2496

Buzza, Jane, Develop Officer, University of Victoria Libraries, McPherson Library, PO Box 1800, Victoria, BC, V8W 3H5, CANADA. Tel: 250-721-8211. Fax: 250-721-8215. p. 2746

Buzzell, Heather, Dir, Grand Forks & District Public Library, 7342 Fifth St, Grand Forks, BC, V0H 1H0, CANADA. Tel: 250-442-3944. Fax: 250-442-2645. p. 2728

Byard, Kim, Librn, Berwyn Municipal Library, 5105 51st St, Berwyn, AB, T0H 0E0, CANADA. Tel: 780-338-3616. Fax: 780-338-3616. p. 2685

Byard, Kim, Asst Librn, Grimshaw Municipal Library, 5007 47th Ave, Grimshaw, AB, T0H 1W0, CANADA. Tel: 780-332-4553. Fax: 780-332-1250. p. 2706

Byars, David, Circ/Reserves, De Anza College, 21250 Stevens Creek Blvd, Cupertino, CA, 95014-5793. Tel: 408-864-8759. Fax: 408-864-8603. p. 138

Bybell, Betsy, Outreach Serv Librn, Latah County Library District, 110 S Jefferson, Moscow, ID, 83843-2833. Tel: 208-882-3925. Fax: 208-882-5098. p. 579

Byce, Debbie, Librn, Whitewater Region Public Library, 2022 Forester's Fall Rd, Forester's Falls, ON, K0J 1V0, CANADA. Tel: 613-646-2543. p. 2805

Byerly, Christine, Librn, Frederic Public Library, 127 Oak St W, Frederic, WI, 54837. Tel: 715-327-4979. Fax: 715-327-4455. p. 2593

Byerly, Dustin, Libr Asst, Goddard College, 123 Pitkin Rd, Plainfield, VT, 05667. Tel: 802-322-1601. p. 2432

Byerly, Greg, Dr, Assoc Prof, Kent State University, 314 Library, Kent, OH, 44242-0001. Tel: 330-672-2782. Fax: 330-672-7965. p. 2972

Byerly, Jim, Electronic Res Librn, Minnesota Department of Transportation Library, 395 John Ireland Blvd, MS 155, Saint Paul, MN, 55155. Tel: 651-366-3739. Fax: 651-366-3789. p. 1279

Byerly, Tracy, Chief Communications & Membership Develop Officer, Amigos Library Services, Inc, 14400 Midway Rd, Ste 200, Dallas, TX, 75244-3509. Tel: 972-340-2893. Fax: 972-991-6061. p. 2955

Byers, Kathy, Ref Serv, Bosler Free Library, 158 W High St, Carlisle, PA, 17013-2988. Tel: 717-243-4642. Fax: 717-243-8281. p. 2041

Byers, Marie P, Archivist, Lipscomb University, One University Park Dr, Nashville, TN, 37204-3951. Tel: 615-966-6031. Fax: 615-966-5874. p. 2257

Byers, Ruth, Librn, Community College of Allegheny County, 808 Ridge Ave, Pittsburgh, PA, 15212-6003. Tel: 412-237-2585. Fax: 412-237-6563. p. 2124

Byford, Mary Ellen, Tech Serv Mgr, Manhattan-Elwood Public Library District, 240 Whitson St, Manhattan, IL, 60442. Tel: 815-478-3987. Fax: 815-478-3988. p. 669

Byland, Tom, Mgr, Appalachian State University, Music Library, 813 Rivers St, Boone, NC, 28608-2097. Tel: 828-262-2388. Fax: 828-265-8642. p. 1777

Byler, Anne Meyer, Ref & Instruction Librn, Goshen College, Harold & Wilma Good Library, 1700 S Main, Goshen, IN, 46526-4794. Tel: 574-535-7424. Fax: 574-535-7438. p. 745

Bylica, Shelley, Pub Serv Librn, Marvin Memorial Library, 29 W Whitney Ave, Shelby, OH, 44875-1252. Tel: 419-347-5576. Fax: 419-347-7285. p. 1934

Bynagle, Hans E, Dr, Dir, Whitworth University, 300 W Hawthorne Rd, Spokane, WA, 99251-0001. Tel: 509-777-3260. Fax: 509-777-3221. p. 2538

Bynum, Brenda, Dir, Mount Pleasant Public Library, 213 N Madison, Mount Pleasant, TX, 75455. Tel: 903-575-4180. Fax: 903-577-8000. p. 2364

Bynum, Kizzy, Dir, Madison Parish Library, 403 N Mulberry St, Tallulah, LA, 71282. Tel: 318-574-4308. Fax: 318-574-4312. p. 970

Byram, Sandra, Asst Librn, Keyser-Mineral County Public Library, Burlington Public, PO Box 61, Burlington, WV, 26710-0061. Tel: 304-289-3690. Fax: 304-289-3233. p. 2563

Byram, Sandy, Asst Librn, Burlington Library, Patterson Creek Rd, Burlington, WV, 26710. Tel: 304-289-3690. Fax: 304-289-3233. p. 2555

Byrd, Caroline, Assoc Dir, Saint Mary's University, Louis J Blume Library, One Camino Santa Maria, San Antonio, TX, 78228-8608. Tel: 210-436-3441. Fax: 210-436-3782. p. 2381

Byrd, Carolyn, Dir, Patrick Henry Community College, 645 Patriot Ave, Martinsville, VA, 24115. Tel: 276-656-0211. Fax: 276-656-0327. p. 2478

Byrd, Carrie, Ref & Instruction Librn, University of the Cumberlands/Cumberland College, 821 Walnut St, Williamsburg, KY, 40769. Tel: 606-539-4160. Fax: 606-539-4317. p. 937

Byrd, Denise, Assoc Librn, National Institute on Drug Abuse, 5500 Nathan Shock Dr, Baltimore, MD, 21224-6823. Tel: 410-550-1488. Fax: 410-550-1438. p. 1016

Byrd, Fay, Dir, Wilkes Community College, 1328 Collegiate Dr, Wilkesboro, NC, 28697. Tel: 336-838-6289. Fax: 336-838-6515. p. 1830

Byrd, James C, Spec Projects, Avery-Mitchell-Yancey Regional Library System, 289 Burnsville School Rd, Burnsville, NC, 28714. Tel: 828-682-4476. Fax: 828-682-6277. p. 1779

Byrd, Jeannie, Ser/Electronic Res Librn, Union University, 1050 Union University Dr, Jackson, TN, 38305-3697. Tel: 731-661-5339. Fax: 731-661-5175. p. 2238

Byrd, John, Head, Cat, Kansas City, Kansas Public Library, 625 Minnesota Ave, Kansas City, KS, 66101. Tel: 913-279-2108. Fax: 913-279-2033. p. 875

Byrd, Karen, In Charge, Dwight Library, 637 Main, Dwight, KS, 66849. Tel: 785-482-3804. p. 864

Byrd, Lois, Br Mgr, Allendale-Hampton-Jasper Regional Library, Hampton, 12 Locust St, East Hampton, SC, 29924. Tel: 803-943-7528. Fax: 803-943-3261. p. 2180

Byrd, Melissa, Asst Univ Librn, Pub Serv, Lincoln Memorial University, Cumberland Gap Pkwy, Box 2012, Harrogate, TN, 37752. Tel: 423-869-7079. Fax: 423-869-6426. p. 2236

Byrd, Robert, Assoc Univ Librn, Coll & User Serv, Dir, Rare Bk, Ms & Spec Coll Libr, Duke University Libraries, 411 Chapel Dr, Durham, NC, 27708. Tel: 919-660-5821. Fax: 919-660-5923. p. 1787

Byrd, Sara, Librn, Vanderbilt University, Walker Management Library, Owen Graduate School of Management, 401 21st Ave S, Nashville, TN, 37203. Tel: 615-322-2546. Fax: 615-343-0061. p. 2261

Byrd, Sharon H, Spec Coll Outreach Librn, Davidson College, 209 Ridge Rd, Davidson, NC, 28035-0001. Tel: 704-894-2331. Fax: 704-894-2625. p. 1786

Byrd, Wendy, Librn, Rains County Public Library, 150 Doris Briggs Pkwy, Emory, TX, 75440-3012. Tel: 903-473-5000, Ext 283. Fax: 903-473-1703. p. 2318

Byrne, Allan, In Charge, Newfoundland Historical Society Library, Colonial Bldg, Military Rd, St. John's, NL, A1C 2C9, CANADA. Tel: 709-722-3191. Fax: 709-729-0578. p. 2773

Byrne, Amy, Adult Serv Supvr, Naperville Public Library, 200 W Jefferson Ave, Naperville, IL, 60540-5374. Tel: 630-961-4100, Ext 6312. Fax: 630-637-6389. p. 679

Byrne, Christina A, Asst Head Librn, University of Washington Libraries, Engineering Library, Engineering Library Bldg, Box 352170, Seattle, WA, 98195-2170. Tel: 206-685-8371. Fax: 206-543-3305. p. 2533

Byrne, Christopher, Instrul Serv Librn, Ref, Res, College of William & Mary in Virginia, The Wolf Law Library, 613 S Henry St, Williamsburg, VA, 23187. Tel: 757-221-3255. Fax: 757-221-3051. p. 2502

Byrne, Colleen, Libr Dir, New Providence Memorial Library, 377 Elkwood Ave, New Providence, NJ, 07974-1837. Tel: 908-665-0311. Fax: 908-665-2319. p. 1510

Byrne, Donna, Law Librn, Hancock Estabrook, LLP, 1500 AXA Tower One, 100 Madison St, Syracuse, NY, 13202. Tel: 315-565-4706. Fax: 315-565-4806. p. 1751

Byrne, Elizabeth D, Head Librn, University of California, Berkeley, Environmental Design, 210 Wurster Hall, Berkeley, CA, 94720-6000. Tel: 510-643-7323. Fax: 510-642-8266. p. 127

Byrne, Ellen, Librn, Sierra Club, 85 Second St, 2nd Flr, San Francisco, CA, 94105-3441. Tel: 415-977-5506. Fax: 415-977-5799. p. 247

Byrne, Frances, Circ, Northport-East Northport Public Library, 151 Laurel Ave, Northport, NY, 11768. Tel: 631-261-6930. Fax: 631-261-6718. p. 1707

Byrne, Joe, Fac Mgr, Bartow County Public Library System, Cartersville Main Street, 429 W Main St, Cartersville, GA, 30120. Tel: 770-382-4203. Fax: 770-386-3056. p. 524

Byrne, Leslie, Spec Coll, Daviess County Public Library, 2020 Frederica St, Owensboro, KY, 42301. Tel: 270-684-0211. Fax: 270-684-0218. p. 931

Byrne, Louise, Libr Coordr, Alberta Law Libraries - St Albert, Courthouse, Three Saint Anne St, St. Albert, AB, T8N 2E8, CANADA. Tel: 780-458-7300. Fax: 780-460-2963. p. 2717

Byrne, Michelle, Ch, Williamson Free Public Library, 6380 Rte 21, Ste 1, Williamson, NY, 14589. Tel: 315-589-2048. Fax: 315-589-5077. p. 1769

Byrne, Roseanne, Dep Dir, Dakota County Library System, 1340 Wescott Rd, Eagan, MN, 55123-1099. Tel: 651-450-2931. Fax: 651-450-2915. p. 1249

Byrne, Shane, Dir, University of Arizona, Space Imagery Center, 1629 E University Blvd, Tucson, AZ, 85721-0092. Tel: 520-621-4861. Fax: 520-621-4933. p. 89

Byrne, Susan Simmons, Dir, Clinch River Regional Library, 130 N Main St, Ste 2, Clinton, TN, 37716-3691. Tel: 865-457-0931. Fax: 865-457-8546. p. 2230

Byrne, Susan Simmons, Regional Mgr, Tennessee State Library & Archives, 403 Seventh Ave N, Nashville, TN, 37243-0312. Tel: 865-457-0931. Fax: 615-532-2472, 615-741-6471. p. 2259

Byrnes, Gloria, Cataloger, Palmer Public Library, 1455 N Main St, Palmer, MA, 01069. Tel: 413-283-3330. Fax: 413-283-9970. p. 1116

Byrnes, Linda, Dir, Jordan Bramley Library, 15 Mechanic St, Jordan, NY, 13080. Tel: 315-689-3296. Fax: 315-689-1231. p. 1648

Byrnes, Mike, Pub Serv Mgr, Yavapai College Library, 1100 E Sheldon St, Bldg 19, Prescott, AZ, 86301. Tel: 928-771-6124. Fax: 928-776-2275. p. 78

Byrns, Alice, Dir of Libr Serv, Northeast Wisconsin Masonic Library & Museum, 525 N Taylor St, Green Bay, WI, 54303. Tel: 920-491-8374. p. 2596

Byro, Laurie, Circ Supvr, Lee Memorial Library, 500 W Crescent Ave, Allendale, NJ, 07401-1799. Tel: 201-327-4338. Fax: 201-327-5838. p. 1469

Byro, Shari, Br Mgr, Watonwan County Library, Madelia Branch, 23 First St NW, Madelia, MN, 56062-1411. Tel: 507-642-3511. Fax: 507-642-8144. p. 1277

Byron, Debby, Asst Dir, Bus Operations, Jefferson County Library, 5678 State Rd PP, High Ridge, MO, 63049-2216. Tel: 636-677-8689. Fax: 636-677-1769. p. 1330

Bzdel, Joanne, Librn, Wapiti Regional Library, Birch Hills Public Library, 126 McCallum Ave, Birch Hills, SK, S0J 0G0, CANADA. Tel: 306-749-3281. p. 2921

Caballero, Cesar, Dean & Univ Librn, California State University, San Bernardino, 5500 University Pkwy, San Bernardino, CA, 92407-2318. Tel: 909-537-5084, 909-537-5092. Fax: 909-537-7048. p. 227

Cabanas -Malave, Eva, Supvry Librn, United States Army, Post Library, Bldg 518, 518 Depot Rd, Fort Buchanan, PR, 00934-4559. Tel: 787-707-3208. Fax: 787-707-3480. p. 2672

Cabanas, Marcy, Ref Librn, Fried, Frank, Harris, Shriver & Jacobson Library, One New York Plaza, New York, NY, 10004. Tel: 212-859-4886. Fax: 212-859-8000. p. 1679

Cabellon, Ken, Librn, CH2M Hill Inc Library, 2020 SW Fourth Ave, 3rd Flr, Portland, OR, 97201. Tel: 503-235-5000. Fax: 503-736-2000. p. 2010

Cabibi, Lee, Librn, McCormick, Barstow, Sheppard, Wayte & Carruth, Five River Park Pl E, Fresno, CA, 93720. Tel: 559-433-1300. Fax: 559-433-2300. p. 153

Cable, Susan, Ref Librn, Grand Canyon University, 3300 W Camelback Rd, Phoenix, AZ, 85017-3030. Tel: 602-639-6641. Fax: 602-639-7835. p. 73

Cable, Terri, Acq, Nicolet Area Technical College, 5364 College Dr, Rhinelander, WI, 54501. Tel: 715-365-4436. Fax: 715-365-4551. p. 2633

Cabral, Beverlee S, Head Librn, Fashion Institute of Design & Merchandising, 350 Tenth Ave, 3rd Flr, San Diego, CA, 92101. Tel: 619-235-2049. p. 231

Cabral, Jeff, Dir, McArthur Public Library, 270 Main St, Biddeford, ME, 04005. Tel: 207-284-4181. Fax: 207-284-6761. p. 977

Cabral, Mary K, Ref & Instruction Librn, Clarkson University Libraries, Andrew S Schuler Educational Resources Center, CU Box 5590, Eight Clarkson Ave, Potsdam, NY, 13699-5590. Tel: 315-268-4462. Fax: 315-268-7655. p. 1721

Cabral, Samantha, Educ Res Ctr/Ref Librn, Rivier College, 420 S Main St, Nashua, NH, 03060-5086. Tel: 603-897-8463. Fax: 603-897-8889. p. 1459

Cabrales, Arthur V, Br Mgr, Las Vegas-Clark County Library District, Windmill Library, 7060 W Windmill Lane, Las Vegas, NV, 89113. Tel: 702-507-6030. Fax: 702-507-6064. p. 1430

Cabrera-Kennard, Mary, Dir of Educ, Mansfield Fine Arts Guild, Inc, 700 Marion Ave, Mansfield, OH, 44903. Tel: 419-756-1700. Fax: 419-756-0860. p. 1912

Cabrera-Luna, Ana, Sr LTA, ILL/ICL, Florida International University, 3000 NE 151st St, North Miami, FL, 33181-3600. Tel: 305-919-5726. Fax: 305-919-5914. p. 472

Cabus, Michael, Syst Librn, Philadelphia University, 4201 Henry Ave, Philadelphia, PA, 19144-5497. Tel: 215-951-5365. Fax: 215-951-2574. p. 2115

Caccavale, Jennifer, Ch, Penfield Public Library, 1985 Baird Rd, Penfield, NY, 14526. Tel: 585-340-8720. Fax: 585-340-8748. p. 1716

Cacciavillani, Stephanie, Pub Serv Librn, Gering Public Library, 1055 P St, Gering, NE, 69341. Tel: 308-436-7433. Fax: 308-436-6869. p. 1399

Caddell, Bill, Interim Dir, Monticello Union Township Public Library, 321 W Broadway, Monticello, IN, 47960-2047. Tel: 574-583-2665, 574-583-5643. Fax: 574-583-2782. p. 766

Cadden, Pam, Ch, Charleston County Public Library, 68 Calhoun St, Charleston, SC, 29401. Tel: 843-805-6902. p. 2183

Cade, Bob, Librn, Florida Department of Corrections, 8784 US Hwy 27 W, Mayo, FL, 32066-3456. Tel: 386-294-4728. p. 463

Cade, Leslie, Archivist, Rec Mgr, Cleveland Museum of Art, 11150 East Blvd, Cleveland, OH, 44106-1797. Tel: 216-707-2530. Fax: 216-421-0921. p. 1877

Cadell, Lynda, Br Mgr, Allendale-Hampton-Jasper Regional Library, Hardeeville Branch, Main St, Hardeeville, SC, 29927. Tel: 843-784-3426. Fax: 843-784-5277. p. 2180

Cadena, Cara, Ref Librn, Missoula Public Library, 301 E Main, Missoula, MT, 59802-4799. Tel: 406-721-2665. Fax: 406-728-5900. p. 1386

Cadiente, Jessica, ILL, Flagstaff City-Coconino County Public Library System, 300 W Aspen, Flagstaff, AZ, 86001. Tel: 928-213-2331. Fax: 928-774-9573. p. 62

Cadieux, Joe, Commun Serv, West Hartford Public Library, 20 S Main St, West Hartford, CT, 06107-2432. Tel: 860-561-6950. Fax: 860-561-6976. p. 376

Cadieux, Lyne, Br Librn, Prince Edward Island Public Library Service, Bibliotheque Dr J Edmond Arsenault, Hillsborough Parc, 5 rue Acadienne, Charlottetown, PE, C1C 1M2, CANADA. Tel: 902-368-6092. p. 2876

Cadigan, Peggy, Dir, Libr Devlop Bur, New Jersey State Library, 185 W State St, Trenton, NJ, 08618. Tel: 609-278-2640, Ext 113. Fax: 609-278-2650. p. 1536

Cadiz Ocasio, Lourdes, Chief Librn, University of Puerto Rico Library System, Business Administration Library, Rio Piedras Campus, San Juan, PR, 00931. Tel: 787-764-0000, Ext 3150, 787-764-0000, Ext 5175. Fax: 787-772-1479. p. 2677

Cadmus, Femi, Assoc Law Librn, George Mason University Libraries, School of Law, 3301 N Fairfax Dr, Arlington, VA, 22201-4426. Tel: 703-993-8107. Fax: 703-993-8113. p. 2462

Cadra, Laura, Head, Ref, Loyola Law School, 919 S Albany St, Los Angeles, CA, 90015-1211. Tel: 213-736-1141. Fax: 213-487-2204. p. 175

Cadwallader, Darlene, Circ, ILL, Oldsmar Library, 400 St Petersburg Dr E, Oldsmar, FL, 34677. Tel: 813-749-1178. Fax: 813-854-1881. p. 474

Cadwell, Tammy, In Charge, Elko-Lander-Eureka County Library System, Carlin Branch, 811 Main St, Carlin, NV, 89822. Tel: 775-754-6766. Fax: 775-754-6621. p. 1427

Cady, Carol, Maps Librn, Saint Lawrence University, Launders Science Library, Park St, Canton, NY, 13617. Tel: 315-229-5824. Fax: 315-229-7291. p. 1602

Cady, Carol, Maps Librn, St Lawrence University, 23 Romoda Dr, Canton, NY, 13617. Tel: 315-229-5824. Fax: 315-229-7291. p. 1602

Cady, June, Librn, New Mexico School for the Blind & Visually Impaired Library, 1900 N White Sands Blvd, Alamogordo, NM, 88310. Tel: 575-437-3505, Ext 4510. Fax: 575-439-4454. p. 1547

Cady, Priscilla C, Dir, North Woodstock Library, 1286 Rte 169, Woodstock, CT, 06281. Tel: 860-928-2629. p. 380

Cady, Vicki, In Charge, Supreme Court Library at Saratoga Springs, Fourth Judicial District, 474 Broadway, Ste 10, Saratoga Springs, NY, 12866-2297. Tel: 518-584-4862. p. 1739

Caesar, Janye, Mgr, Marion County Library, Mullins Branch, 210 N Main St, Mullins, SC, 29574. Tel: 843-464-9621. Fax: 843-464-5215. p. 2200

Caesar, Roselyn, In Charge, International City-County Management Association Library, 777 N Capitol St NE, Ste 500, Washington, DC, 20002-4201. Tel: 202-289-4262. Fax: 202-962-3510. p. 405

Caetano, Vincent, Libr Tech, Royal Victoria Hospital, Medical Library, 687 Pine Ave W, Rm H4-01, Montreal, QC, H3A 1A1, CANADA. Tel: 514-934-1934, Ext 35290. Fax: 514-843-1483. p. 2901

Cafarella, Karen, Info Serv, Guelph Public Library, 100 Norfolk St, Guelph, ON, N1H 4J6, CANADA. Tel: 519-824-6220. Fax: 519-824-8342. p. 2807

Caffee, Ray, Dir, Hand County Library, 402 N Broadway, Miller, SD, 57362-1438. Tel: 605-853-3693. Fax: 605-853-2201. p. 2215

Caffeo, Mandy, Asst Dir, Pahrump Community Library, 701 E St, Pahrump, NV, 89048-2164. Tel: 775-727-5930. Fax: 775-727-6209. p. 1432

Caffey, Barbara, Libr Dir, Myrtle Point Library, 435 Fifth St, Myrtle Point, OR, 97458-1113. Tel: 541-572-2591. Fax: 541-572-5168. p. 2007

Caffey, Debbie, Tech Serv, United States Air Force, 23 FSS/FSDL, 3010 Robinson Rd, Bldg 328, Moody AFB, GA, 31699-1594. Tel: 229-257-3018, 229-257-3539. Fax: 229-257-4119. p. 545

Caffrey, Alex, Tech Serv, Cumberland County Library, 800 E Commerce St, Bridgeton, NJ, 08302-2295. Tel: 856-453-2210. Fax: 856-451-1940. p. 1474

Caffrey, Carolyn, Instruction & Ref Librn, University of Wisconsin-Superior, PO Box 2000, Belknap & Catlin, Superior, WI, 54880-2000. Tel: 715-394-8343. Fax: 715-394-8462. p. 2641

Cage, Kimberly, Librn, Locke Reynolds LLP, 1000 Capital Center S, 201 N Illinois St, Ste 1000, Indianapolis, IN, 46204-4210. Tel: 317-237-3800, 317-237-3831. Fax: 317-237-3900. p. 755

Cage, Kimberly, Librn, Frost, Brown & Todd LLC, 400 W Market St, 32nd Flr, Louisville, KY, 40202-3363. Tel: 502-237-3831. Fax: 502-581-1087. p. 923

Cagle, Christy, Extn Serv, Carl Elliott Regional Library System, 98 E 18th St, Jasper, AL, 35501. Tel: 205-221-2568. p. 23

Cagna, Robert, Dir, West Virginia University, 3110 MacCorkle Ave SE, Charleston, WV, 25304. Tel: 304-347-1287. Fax: 304-347-1288. p. 2557

Cagni, Karen, Dir, Providence Presbyterian Church Library, 5497 Providence Rd, Virginia Beach, VA, 23464. Tel: 757-420-6159. Fax: 757-420-7553. p. 2499

Cahalan, Sarah Burke, Ref/Spec Projects Librn, Harvard Library, Dumbarton Oaks Research Library, 1703 32nd St NW, Washington, MA, 20007. Tel: 202-339-6400. Fax: 202-625-0279. p. 1074

Cahill, Betty, Sister, Archivist, St Walburg Monastery Archives, 2500 Amsterdam Rd, Villa Hills, KY, 41017. Tel: 859-331-6324. Fax: 859-331-2136. p. 936

Cahill, Darcy, Mgr, Baltimore County Public Library, Cockeysville Branch, 9833 Greenside Dr, Cockeysville, MD, 21030-2188. Tel: 410-887-7750. Fax: 410-666-0325. p. 1044

Cahill, James J, Jr, Dir, Margate City Public Library, 8100 Atlantic Ave, Margate City, NJ, 08402. Tel: 609-822-4700. Fax: 609-823-0064. p. 1499

Cahill, Joanne, ILL, Haverford Township Free Library, 1601 Darby Rd, Havertown, PA, 19083-3798. Tel: 610-446-3082. Fax: 610-853-3090. p. 2067

Cahill, Kathleen, Librn, Giner Electrochemical Systems LLC Library, 89 Rumford Ave, Newton, MA, 02466. Tel: 781-529-0500, Ext 511. p. 1109

Cahill, Linda, Coordr, Libr Serv, Piedmont Virginia Community College, 501 College Dr, Charlottesville, VA, 22902. Tel: 434-961-5308. Fax: 434-977-6842. p. 2454

Cahill, Maureen, Student Serv Librn, University of Georgia, 225 Herty Dr, Athens, GA, 30602-6018. Tel: 706-542-3825. Fax: 706-542-5001. p. 510

Cahill, Sandra, Circ Serv Mgr, Alexandria Library, Kate Waller Barrett Branch, 717 Queen St, Alexandria, VA, 22314. Tel: 703-746-1703. Fax: 703-746-1709. p. 2444

Cahill-Aylward, Susan, Dir, American Society of Landscape Architects, 636 I St NW, Washington, DC, 20001-3736. Tel: 202-216-2320. Fax: 202-898-1185. p. 393

Cahillane, Sandra, Syst, Ref & Instruction Librn, Bay Path College, 539 Longmeadow St, Longmeadow, MA, 01106. Tel: 413-565-1376. Fax: 413-567-8345. p. 1100

Cahn, Mary, Librn, Cahill, Gordon & Reindel Library, 80 Pine St, New York, NY, 10005. Tel: 212-701-3542. Fax: 212-269-5420. p. 1671

Cahoon, Andrea R, Dir, Ringwood Public Library, 30 Cannici Dr, Ringwood, NJ, 07456. Tel: 973-962-6256. Fax: 973-962-7799. p. 1526

Cahoy, Ellysa Stern, Asst Head, Learning Serv, Educ & Behav Sci Librn, Pennsylvania State University Libraries, Education & Behavioral Sciences, 501 Paterno Library, University Park, PA, 16802-1812. Tel: 814-865-2842. p. 2148

Cai, Wei, Br Mgr, Seattle Public Library, Beacon Hill, 2821 Beacon Ave S, Seattle, WA, 98144. Tel: 206-684-4711. p. 2531

Cai, Wei, Regional Mgr, Seattle Public Library, Columbia, 4721 Rainier Ave S, Seattle, WA, 98118. Tel: 206-386-1908. p. 2531

Cai, Wei, Regional Mgr, Seattle Public Library, International District/Chinatown, 713 Eighth Ave S, Seattle, WA, 98104. Tel: 206-386-1300. p. 2531

Cai, Wei, Regional Mgr, Seattle Public Library, NewHolly, 7058 32nd Ave S, Seattle, WA, 98118. Tel: 206-386-1905. p. 2531

Caiazzo, Catherine, Dir, Schoharie Free Association Library, 103 Knower Ave, Schoharie, NY, 12157. Tel: 518-295-7127. Fax: 518-295-7127. p. 1741

Caiazzo, Ralph, Ref, New York Law Institute Library, 120 Broadway, Rm 932, New York, NY, 10271-0043. Tel: 212-732-8720. Fax: 212-406-1204. p. 1689

Cain, Adrienne, Br Mgr, Chambers County Library System, West Chambers Branch, 10616 Eagle Dr, Mont Belvieu, TX, 77580-1289. Tel: 281-576-2245, 409-576-2550. Fax: 281-576-2496. p. 2275

Cain, Anne, Interim Dir, San Jose Public Library, 150 E San Fernando St, San Jose, CA, 95112-3580. Tel: 408-808-2150. p. 250

Cain, Asante, Librn, Grand Rapids Public Library, Seymour, 2350 Eastern Ave SE, Grand Rapids, MI, 49507. Tel: 616-988-5413. Fax: 616-241-1445. p. 1185

Cain, Belinda, Librn, Lerch, Early & Brewer, Three Bethesda Metro Ctr, Ste 460, Bethesda, MD, 20814. Tel: 301-986-1300. Fax: 301-986-0332. p. 1021

Cain, Beverly, State Librn, State Library of Ohio, 274 E First Ave, Ste 100, Columbus, OH, 43201. Tel: 614-644-7061. Fax: 614-466-3584. p. 1890

Cain, Beverly L, Dir, Portsmouth Public Library, 1220 Gallia St, Portsmouth, OH, 45662-4185. Tel: 740-353-5990. Fax: 740-353-1249. p. 1930

Cain, Carmen, Dir, Carmen Public Library, 421 W Main St, Carmen, OK, 73726. Tel: 580-987-2301. Fax: 580-987-2303. p. 1959

Cain, Charlene, Head, Access Serv, Louisiana State University Libraries, Paul M Hebert Law Center, One E Campus Dr, Baton Rouge, LA, 70803-1000. Tel: 225-578-4957. Fax: 225-578-5773. p. 944

Cain, Cori, Circ, Libr Tech, Ref Serv, Minneapolis Community & Technical College Library, Wheelock Whitney Hall, 1501 Hennepin Ave, Minneapolis, MN, 55403. Tel: 612-659-6297. Fax: 612-659-6295. p. 1261

Cain, Dominique, Head Librn, Holland & Knight Law Library, 2099 Pennsylvania Ave NW, Ste 100, Washington, DC, 20006. Tel: 202-955-3000. Fax: 202-955-5564. p. 403

Cain, Elizabeth, Dir, Halstead Public Library, 264 Main St, Halstead, KS, 67056-0285. Tel: 316-835-2170. Fax: 316-835-2170. p. 870

Cain, Gay, Br Mgr, Memphis Public Library, Bartlett Branch, 5884 Stage Rd, Bartlett, TN, 38134. Tel: 901-386-8968. Fax: 901-386-2358. p. 2249

Cain, Glenda, Circ, Houston Love Memorial Library, 212 W Burdeshaw St, Dothan, AL, 36303. Tel: 334-793-9767. Fax: 334-793-6645. p. 15

Cain, Glenda, Librn, Houston Love Memorial Library, Division for the Blind & Physically Handicapped, PO Box 1369, Dothan, AL, 36302. Tel: 334-793-9767. p. 15

Cain, Hope, Dir, Sulphur Springs Public Library, 611 N Davis St, Sulphur Springs, TX, 75482. Tel: 903-885-4926. Fax: 903-439-1052. p. 2389

Cain, Joanne, Tech Serv Coordr, Modoc County Library, 212 W Third St, Alturas, CA, 96101. Tel: 530-233-6340. Fax: 530-233-3375. p. 120

Cain, Linda, Ref Librn, Jacksonville State University Library, 700 Pelham Rd N, Jacksonville, AL, 36265. Tel: 256-782-5255. Fax: 256-782-5872. p. 22

Cain, Melanie, Dir, Magoffin County Library, 141 Church St, Salyersville, KY, 41465. Tel: 606-349-2411. Fax: 606-349-1120. p. 934

Cain, Robert, IT Spec, Tipp City Public Library, 11 E Main St, Tipp City, OH, 45371. Tel: 937-667-3826. Fax: 937-667-7968. p. 1938

Cain, Sheena, Librn, Faulkner-Van Buren Regional Library System, Twin Groves Branch, Ten Twin Groves Lane, Twin Groves, AR, 72039. Tel: 501-335-8088. Fax: 501-335-8088. p. 96

Cain, Susie, Children's & Youth Serv, Graves County Public Library, 601 N 17th St, Mayfield, KY, 42066. Tel: 270-247-2911. Fax: 270-247-2991. p. 928

Caine, Shari, Exec Dir, Des Plaines Historical Society Library, 781 Pearson St, Des Plaines, IL, 60016. Tel: 847-391-5399. Fax: 847-297-4741. p. 636

Caines, Kathye, Dir, Hemet Public Library, 300 E Latham, Hemet, CA, 92543. Tel: 951-765-2447. Fax: 951-765-2446. p. 158

Cairney, Pam, Tech Serv, Mount Horeb Public Library, 105 Perimeter Rd, Mount Horeb, WI, 53572. Tel: 608-437-5021. Fax: 608-437-6264. p. 2623

Cairns, Bridget, Exec Dir, Prince Edward Island Association for Community Living, 158 Belvedere Ave, Ste 1, Charlottetown, PE, C1A 2Z1, CANADA. Tel: 902-566-4844. Fax: 902-368-8057. p. 2875

Cairns, Jacob, Br Mgr, Kern County Library, Wanda Kirk Branch, 3611 Rosamond Blvd, Rosamond, CA, 93560-7653. Tel: 661-256-3236. Fax: 661-256-2906. p. 124

Cairns, Jacob, Br Supvr, Kern County Library, Mojave Branch, 16916 1/2 Hwy 14 Sp D-2, Mojave, CA, 93501-1226. Tel: 661-824-2243. p. 124

Cairns, Virginia, Head, Ref, University of Tennessee at Chattanooga Library, 615 McCallie Ave, Dept 6456, Chattanooga, TN, 37403-2598. Tel: 423-425-4501. Fax: 423-425-4775. p. 2228

Cairo, Christine, Dir, Prog Develop, Indianapolis-Marion County Public Library, 2450 N Meridian St, Indianapolis, IN, 46208. Tel: 317-275-4080. Fax: 317-269-5300. p. 753

Caisse, Jo, Mgr, Deschutes Public Library District, Bend Branch, 601 NW Wall St, Bend, OR, 97701. Tel: 541-617-7087. Fax: 541-617-7044. p. 1992

Caisse, Linda, Ref & Non-Fiction Serv Coordr, North Kingstown Free Library, 100 Boone St, North Kingstown, RI, 02852-5176. Tel: 401-294-3306. Fax: 401-294-1690. p. 2170

Caithamer, Joel, Ch, Kenton County Public Library, William E Durr Branch, 1992 Walton-Nicholson Rd, Independence, KY, 41051. Tel: 859-962-4034. Fax: 859-962-4037. p. 910

Caitlin, Pereira, Visual Res, Massachusetts College of Art & Design, 621 Huntington Ave, Boston, MA, 02115-5882. Tel: 617-879-7116. Fax: 617-879-7110. p. 1063

Caitlin, Swift, Ref Librn, Campbell University, Norman Adrian Wiggins School of Law Library, 225 Hillsborough St, Ste 203, Raleigh, NC, 27603. Tel: 919-865-5869. Fax: 919-865-5995. p. 1778

Cal, Daria, Br Mgr, Seattle Public Library, Rainier Beach, 9125 Rainier Ave S, Seattle, WA, 98118. Tel: 206-386-1906. p. 2531

Calabrese, August, Br Mgr, Orange County Library District, Winter Garden Branch, 805 E Plant St, Winter Garden, FL, 34787. p. 477

Calahan, Lady, Librn, Dunklin County Library, Senath Branch, 108 N Main St, Senath, MO, 63876. Tel: 573-738-2363. p. 1342

Calametti, Jeffrey D, Dir of Libr Serv, University of Mobile, 5735 College Pkwy, Mobile, AL, 36613-2842. Tel: 251-442-2243. Fax: 251-442-2515. p. 26

Calandra, Linda, Develop Officer, Fresno County Public Library, 2420 Mariposa St, Fresno, CA, 93721-2285. Tel: 559-600-7323. p. 151

Calandro, Daniel, Ref Spec, Mercer County Community College Library, 1200 Old Trenton Rd, West Windsor, NJ, 08550. Tel: 609-570-3554, 609-570-3560. Fax: 609-570-3845. p. 1542

Calantone, Susan, Dir, Roselle Park, 404 Chestnut St, Roselle Park, NJ, 07204-1506. Tel: 908-245-2456. Fax: 908-245-9204. p. 1528

Calarco, Pascal, Assoc Univ Librn, Digital & Discovery Serv, University of Waterloo Library, 200 University Ave W, Waterloo, ON, N2L 3G1, CANADA. Tel: 519-888-4567, Ext 38215. Fax: 519-888-4320. p. 2869

Calbow, Marilyn, Librn, Putnam County Public Library District, McNabb Branch, 322 W Main St, McNabb, IL, 61335. Tel: 815-882-2378. Fax: 815-882-2378. p. 655

Calcagno, Ellie, Adminr, Ewing Township Historical Preservation Society Library, 27 Federal City Rd, Ewing, NJ, 08638. Tel: 609-883-2455. Fax: 609-883-2455. p. 1485

Calcagno, Eva, Mgr, Washington County Cooperative Library Services, 111 NE Lincoln St, No 230-L MS58, Hillsboro, OR, 97124-3036. Tel: 503-846-3233. Fax: 503-846-3220. p. 2000

Calcagno, Eva, Mgr, Washington County Cooperative Library Services, 111 NE Lincoln St, MS No 58, Hillsboro, OR, 97124-3036. Tel: 503-846-3222. Fax: 503-846-3220. p. 2953

Caldara, Tara, Admin Serv, Zion-Benton Public Library District, 2400 Gabriel Ave, Zion, IL, 60099. Tel: 847-872-4680, Ext 109. Fax: 847-872-4942. p. 722

Caldararo, Liz, Asst Dir, Commack Public Library, 18 Hauppauge Rd, Commack, NY, 11725-4498. Tel: 631-499-0888. Fax: 631-499-0591. p. 1609

Caldararo, Michael, Dir, Norfolk Public Library, 308 Prospect Ave, Norfolk, NE, 68701-4138. Tel: 402-844-2100. Fax: 402-844-2102. p. 1410

Caldarello, Beth Ann, Dir of Libr Serv, DeVry University, 11224 Holmes Rd, Second Flr, Kansas City, MO, 64131. Tel: 816-941-0430, Ext 5392. p. 1337

Calder, Mary Lee, Librn, San Saba County Library, 103 S Live Oak, San Saba, TX, 76877. Tel: 325-372-3079. Fax: 325-372-3079. p. 2385

Calderelli, Leatrice, ILL, New Cumberland Public Library, One Benjamin Plaza, New Cumberland, PA, 17070-1597. Tel: 717-774-7820. Fax: 717-774-7824. p. 2096

Calderon, Andres, Ch, Banning Library District, 21 W Nicolet St, Banning, CA, 92220. Tel: 951-849-3192. p. 125

Calderon, Maggie, Librn, Columbus Village Public Library, 222 W Broadway Ave, Columbus, NM, 88029. Tel: 575-531-2612. p. 1554

Calderon-Solis, S, Librn, California Department of Corrections Library System, Pleasant Valley State Prison, 24863 W Jayne Ave, Coalinga, CA, 93210. Tel: 559-935-4900, Ext 6765. p. 222

Calderone, Sandy, ILL, Montville Township Public Library, 90 Horseneck Rd, Montville, NJ, 07045-9626. Tel: 973-402-0900. Fax: 973-402-0592. p. 1504

Caldow, Rebecca, Librn, Fort Worth Library, Ridglea, 3628 Bernie Anderson Ave, Fort Worth, TX, 76116-5403. Tel: 817-737-6619. Fax: 817-763-8404. p. 2322

Caldrone, Sally, Librn, Community College of Allegheny County, 1750 Clairton Rd, West Mifflin, PA, 15122-3097. Tel: 412-469-6295. Fax: 412-469-6370. p. 2154

Caldwell, Angela, Info Res & Serv Support Spec, Penn State University York, 1031 Edgecomb Ave, York, PA, 17403-3398. Tel: 717-771-4020. Fax: 717-771-4022. p. 2159

Caldwell, Anita, Asst Librn, Museum of Western Colorado, 462 Ute Ave, Grand Junction, CO, 81501. Tel: 970-242-0971, Ext 209. Fax: 970-242-3960. p. 311

Caldwell, Christine, Assoc Librn, Bibliographer, University of California, 1156 High St, Santa Cruz, CA, 95064. Tel: 831-459-1287. Fax: 831-459-8206. p. 264

Caldwell, Cora, Librn, Idaho School for the Deaf & Blind Library, 1450 Main St, Gooding, ID, 83330. Tel: 208-934-4457, Ext 341. Fax: 208-934-8352. p. 574

Caldwell, Deborah, Cat, Ref, Naval Surface Warfare Center, 110 Vernon Ave, Panama City, FL, 32407-7001. Tel: 850-234-4848. Fax: 850-234-4844. p. 480

Caldwell, Eliz, Sr Ref Librn, Florence County Library System, 509 S Dargan St, Florence, SC, 29506. Tel: 843-662-8424. Fax: 843-661-7544. p. 2193

Caldwell, Jane, Asst Dir, Ref Librn, Emory & Henry College, 30480 Armbrister Dr, Emory, VA, 24327. Tel: 276-944-6208. Fax: 276-944-4592. p. 2460

Caldwell, Janet, Curator, Dir, Bedford Historical Society Library, 30 S Park St, Bedford, OH, 44146-3635. Tel: 440-232-0796. p. 1858

Caldwell, Jody, Head, Ref, Drew University Library, 36 Madison Ave, Madison, NJ, 07940. Tel: 973-408-3481. Fax: 973-408-3770. p. 1497

Caldwell, Kathryn, Tech Serv, University of Oklahoma, Physics & Astronomy, Physics & Astronomy, 219NH, 440 W Brooks, Norman, OK, 73019. Tel: 405-325-2887. Fax: 405-325-3640. p. 1971

Caldwell, Kathy, Dir, Ellis Memorial Library, 700 W Ave A, Port Aransas, TX, 78373. Tel: 361-749-4116. Fax: 361-749-5679. p. 2371

Caldwell, Kay, Dir, Oneida County Free Library, 31 N 100 W, Malad City, ID, 83252-1234. Tel: 208-766-2229. Fax: 208-766-2229. p. 578

Caldwell, Lisa, Automated Serv Coordr, Springdale Public Library, 405 S Pleasant St, Springdale, AR, 72764. Tel: 479-750-8180. Fax: 479-750-8182. p. 115

Caldwell, Liz, Librn, The Alliance for Children & Families, 11700 W Lake Park Dr, Milwaukee, WI, 53224. Tel: 414-359-1040, Ext 3615. Fax: 414-359-1074. p. 2616

Caldwell, Marlene, Info Tech Mgr, University of Texas, M D Anderson Cancer Center Research Medical Library, 1400 Pressler St, Houston, TX, 77030-3722. Tel: 713-745-5158. Fax: 713-563-3650. p. 2344

Caldwell, Martha, Br Mgr, Clayton County Library System, Jonesboro Branch, 124 Smith St, Jonesboro, GA, 30236. Tel: 770-478-7120. Fax: 770-473-3846. p. 537

Caldwell, Michele, Circ Mgr, Tech Serv Mgr, Beaverton City Library, 12375 SW Fifth St, Beaverton, OR, 97005-2883. Tel: 503-526-2209. Fax: 503-526-2636. p. 1991

Caldwell, Naomi, Dr, Assoc Prof, University of Rhode Island, Rodman Hall, 94 W Alumni Ave, Ste 2, Kingston, RI, 02881-0815. Tel: 401-874-2278. Fax: 401-874-4964. p. 2973

Caldwell, Patricia, Br Head, Saskatoon Public Library, Cliff Wright Branch, Lakewood Civic Center, 1635 McKercher Dr, Saskatoon, SK, S7H 5J9, CANADA. Tel: 306-975-7545. Fax: 306-975-7632. p. 2926

Caldwell, Patricia, Br Head, Saskatoon Public Library, J S Wood Branch, 1801 Lansdowne Ave, Saskatoon, SK, S7H 2C4, CANADA. Tel: 306-975-7595. Fax: 306-975-7636. p. 2926

Caldwell, Rea, Librn, Robert A Frost Memorial Library, 42 Main St, Limestone, ME, 04750-1399. Tel: 207-325-4706. Fax: 207-325-3035. p. 990

Caldwell, Sally, Dir, Egremont Free Library, One Buttonball Lane, South Egremont, MA, 01258. Tel: 413-528-1474. Fax: 413-528-6416. p. 1125

Caldwell, Vicki, Librn, Mitchell Community College, 500 W Broad St, Statesville, NC, 28677. Tel: 704-878-3271. p. 1826

Caldwell, Waynette, Librn, Greater West Central Public Library District, Littleton Branch, 110 S Center, Littleton, IL, 61452. Tel: 309-257-2202. Fax: 309-257-2202. p. 591

Cale, Sandy, Asst Dir, Jefferson Township Public Library, 1031 Weldon Rd, Oak Ridge, NJ, 07438. Tel: 973-208-6244. Fax: 973-697-7051. p. 1515

Calease, Patricia, Asst Librn, Clarksville Public Library, 103 W Greene St, Clarksville, IA, 50619-0039. Tel: 319-278-1168. Fax: 319-278-1168. p. 802

Caleb, Peter, Dir, Manhattan School of Music, 120 Claremont Ave, New York, NY, 10027. Tel: 917-493-4507, 917-493-4511. Fax: 212-749-5471. p. 1685

Calef, Dan C, Dir, Adams County Library, 569 N Cedar St, Ste 1, Adams, WI, 53910-9800. Tel: 608-339-4250. Fax: 608-339-4575. p. 2577

Cales, Joan, Dir, Winfield Public Library, 605 College St, Winfield, KS, 67156-3199. Tel: 620-221-4470. Fax: 620-221-6135. p. 903

Caley, Lynn, Bus Mgr, Lucy Robbins Welles Library, 95 Cedar St, Newington, CT, 06111-2645. Tel: 860-665-8728. Fax: 860-667-1255. p. 361

Calhoun, Anne, Cat, Missouri Baptist University, One College Park Dr, Saint Louis, MO, 63141-8698. Tel: 314-434-1115. Fax: 314-392-2343. p. 1356

Calhoun, Ansley, Librn, Kirkland & Ellis Library, 655 15th St NW, Ste 1200, Washington, DC, 20005-5793. Tel: 202-879-5009, 202-879-5113. Fax: 202-879-5200. p. 406

Calhoun, Chip, Archivist, American Institute of Physics, One Physics Ellipse, College Park, MD, 20740-3843. Tel: 301-209-3177. Fax: 301-209-3144. p. 1024

Calhoun, Gary D, Adminr, Arizona Department of Corrections - Adult Institutions, 2100 S Hwy 87, Winslow, AZ, 86047. Tel: 928-289-9551, Ext 6538. Fax: 928-289-9551, Ext 6553. p. 90

Calhoun, John, Head, Acq & Coll Develop, California State University Dominguez Hills, 1000 E Victoria St, Carson, CA, 90747. Tel: 310-243-2830. Fax: 310-516-4219. p. 132

Calhoun, John, Coll Develop, Louisiana Tech University, Everett St at The Columns, Ruston, LA, 71272. Tel: 318-257-3555. Fax: 318-257-2579. p. 966

Calhoun, Katharine, Head, Info Delivery, Georgia Institute of Technology Library, 704 Cherry St, Atlanta, GA, 30332-0900. Tel: 404-894-4501. Fax: 404-894-6084. p. 515

Calhoun, Laurie, Sr Info Spec, International Center for Research on Women Library, 1120 20th St NW, Ste 500 N, Washington, DC, 20036. Tel: 202-742-1226, 202-797-0007. Fax: 202-797-0020. p. 405

Calhoun, Shawn, Head, Access Serv, University of San Francisco, 2130 Fulton St, San Francisco, CA, 94117-1080. Tel: 415-422-2048. Fax: 415-422-5949. p. 248

Calkins, Larry, Librn, Western Nevada Community College, 2201 W College Pkwy, Carson City, NV, 89703. Tel: 775-445-3229. Fax: 775-445-3363. p. 1426

Call, Anna, Head, Ref, Boxford Town Library, Ten Elm St, Boxford, MA, 01921. Tel: 978-887-7323. Fax: 978-887-6352. p. 1069

Call, Elizabeth, Spec Coll Librn, Brooklyn Historical Society Othmer Library, 128 Pierrepont St, Brooklyn, NY, 11201-2711. Tel: 718-222-4111. Fax: 718-222-3794. p. 1590

Call, Sylvia, ILL, Hutchinson Community College, 1300 N Plum St, Hutchinson, KS, 67501. Tel: 620-665-3418. Fax: 620-665-3392. p. 873

Callaghan, Cathy, Info Serv, University of Prince Edward Island, 550 University Ave, Charlottetown, PE, C1A 4P3, CANADA. Tel: 902-566-0343. Fax: 902-628-4305. p. 2876

Callaghan, Claire, Chief Librn, King's University College at the University of Western Ontario, 266 Epworth Ave, London, ON, N6A 2M3, CANADA. Tel: 519-433-3491, Ext 4390. Fax: 519-963-0307. p. 2817

Callaghan, Claire, Chief Librn, Saint Peter's Seminary, 1040 Waterloo St N, London, ON, N6A 3Y1, CANADA. Tel: 519-433-3491, Ext 4390. Fax: 519-963-0307. p. 2818

Callaghan, Jean, Ser/Electronic Res Librn, Wheaton College Library, 26 E Main St, Norton, MA, 02766-2322. Tel: 508-286-3715. p. 1115

Callaghan, Richard, Dir, Bedford Free Public Library, Seven Mudge Way, Bedford, MA, 01730-2168. Tel: 781-275-9440. Fax: 781-275-3590. p. 1052

Callaghan, Susan, Acq, Hudson Library & Historical Society, 96 Library St, Hudson, OH, 44236-5122. Tel: 330-653-6658. Fax: 330-650-3373. p. 1905

Callahan, Ann, In Charge, Jackson County Law Library, 226 E Main St, Jackson, OH, 45640-1764. Tel: 740-286-8054. p. 1906

Callahan, Carmen, Librn, Ropers, Majeski, Kohn & Bentley, 1001 Marshall St, Redwood City, CA, 94063. Tel: 650-364-8200. Fax: 650-780-1701. p. 215

Callahan, Catherine M, Sr Librn, Acq, New York State Department of Law Library, The Capitol, Albany, NY, 12224. Tel: 518-474-3840. Fax: 518-473-1822. p. 1569

Callahan, D Gregory, Dir, Hyde Park Free Library, Two Main St, Hyde Park, NY, 12538. Tel: 845-229-7791. Fax: 845-229-6521. p. 1640

Callahan, Greg, Libr Spec, Lenoir-Rhyne University Library, 625 7th Ave NE, Hickory, NC, 28601. Tel: 828-328-7236. Fax: 828-328-7338. p. 1801

Callahan, Jane E, Librn, New Bedford Law Library, Superior Courthouse, 441 County St, New Bedford, MA, 02740. Tel: 508-992-8077. Fax: 508-991-7411. p. 1108

Callahan, John, Dir, Palm Beach County Library System, 3650 Summit Blvd, West Palm Beach, FL, 33406-4198. Tel: 561-233-2600. Fax: 561-233-2692. p. 503

Callahan, John, Media Serv, University of Massachusetts Lowell Libraries, 61 Wilder St, Lowell, MA, 01854-3098. Tel: 978-934-4571. Fax: 978-934-3015. p. 1100

Callahan, Patrick F, Dir, State University of New York, 735 Anderson Hill Rd, Purchase, NY, 10577-1400. Tel: 914-251-6436. Fax: 914-251-6437. p. 1724

Callahan, Peggy, Principal Librn, Tampa-Hillsborough County Public Library System, North Tampa Branch, 8916 North Blvd, Tampa, FL, 33604-1299. Fax: 813-975-2057. p. 498

Callan, Doris, Dir, Pine Bush Area Library, 227 Maple Ave, Pine Bush, NY, 12566. Tel: 845-744-3375. Fax: 845-744-3375. p. 1717

Callanan, Ellen, Br Coordr, Extn Serv, Sussex County Library System, 125 Morris Tpk, Newton, NJ, 07860-0076. Tel: 973-948-3660. Fax: 973-948-2071. p. 1514

Callas, Anne, Archivist, Librn, Rec Mgr, American Society of Health-System Pharmacists, 7272 Wisconsin Ave, Bethesda, MD, 20814. Tel: 301-657-3000. p. 1021

Callegari, Catherine, Dir, Gay-Kimball Library, 10 S Main St, Troy, NH, 03465. Tel: 603-242-7743. Fax: 603-242-7743. p. 1466

Callegari, Peggy, Br Librn, Plaquemines Parish Library, Belle Chasse Branch, 8442 Hwy 23, Belle Chasse, LA, 70037. Tel: 504-394-3570. Fax: 504-394-6102. p. 945

Calleja, Linda, Adult Serv, Vermillion Public Library, 18 Church St, Vermillion, SD, 57069-3093. Tel: 605-677-7060. Fax: 605-677-7160. p. 2221

Callery, Bernadette G, Archivist/Librn, Carnegie Museum of Natural History Library, 4400 Forbes Ave, Pittsburgh, PA, 15213-4080. Tel: 412-622-3264, 412-622-8870. Fax: 412-622-8837. p. 2124

Callicoat, Sharon, Ch, Milton-Union Public Library, 560 S Main St, West Milton, OH, 45383. Tel: 937-698-5515. Fax: 937-698-3774. p. 1946

Callihan, Denise, Dir, Libr Serv, PPG Industries, Inc, Technical Information Center, 4325 Rosanna Dr, Allison Park, PA, 15101. Tel: 724-325-5221. Fax: 412-492-5509. p. 2128

Callihan, Denise, Mgr, Libr Serv, PPG Industries, Inc, Glass Technology Center, Guys Run Rd, Harmar Township, PA, 15238. Tel: 412-820-8568. Fax: 412-820-8696. p. 2128

Callihan, Denise, Mgr, PPG Industries, Inc, Chemicals Technical Information Center, 440 College Park Dr, Monroeville, PA, 15146. Tel: 724-325-5221. Fax: 724-325-5289. p. 2128

Callihoe, Christine, Libr Mgr, Forestburg Municipal Library, 4901 50th St, Forestburg, AB, T0B 1N0, CANADA. Tel: 780-582-4110. Fax: 780-582-4127. p. 2704

Callihoe, Christine, Libr Mgr, Galahad Public Library, PO Box 58, Galahad, AB, T0B 1R0, CANADA. Tel: 780-583-3917. Fax: 780-583-3917. p. 2705

Callis, Malcolm, Asst Librn, Clayton Public Library, 17 Chestnut St, Clayton, NM, 88415. Tel: 575-374-9423. Fax: 575-374-9423. p. 1553

Callis, Peggy, Dir, Owensville Carnegie Public Library, 110 S Main St, Owensville, IN, 47665. Tel: 812-724-3335. Fax: 812-724-3336. p. 772

Callison, Becky, Exec Dir, East Albemarle Regional Library, 100 E Colonial Ave, Elizabeth City, NC, 27909-0303. Tel: 252-335-2511. Fax: 252-335-2386. p. 1790

Callison, Becky, Dir, Wilson County Public Library, 249 Nash St W, Wilson, NC, 27893-3801. Tel: 252-237-5355, Ext 5024. p. 1831

Callison, Joan, Dir, Murray Public Library, 416 Maple St, Murray, IA, 50174. Tel: 641-447-2711. p. 834

Callison, Lorianne, Sr Librn, Pierce County Library System, Summit, 5107 112th St E, Tacoma, WA, 98446. Tel: 253-548-3321. Fax: 253-536-6009. p. 2540

Callison, Rachel, Ref Librn, Carnegie Mellon University, Software Engineering Institute Library, 4500 Fifth Ave, Pittsburgh, PA, 15213-2612. Tel: 412-268-7733. Fax: 412-268-1340. p. 2124

Calloni, Rodrigo, Syst/Electronic Info Res Librn, Inter-American Development Bank Library, 1300 New York Ave NW, Stop W-0102, Washington, DC, 20577. Tel: 202-623-2952. Fax: 202-623-3183. p. 405

Calman, Doug, Librn Spec, Florida Department of Environmental Protection, 3000 Commonwealth Blvd, Tallahassee, FL, 32399. Tel: 850-617-0316. Fax: 850-412-0500, 850-617-0341. p. 493

Calmes, Amy, Librn, Genesee District Library, Burton Memorial, G-4012 E Atherton Rd, Burton, MI, 48519. Tel: 810-742-0674. Fax: 810-742-2928. p. 1179

Calmes, Vicky, Dir, Colby Public Library, 211 W Spence St, Colby, WI, 54421. Tel: 715-223-2000. p. 2586

Calo, Andrew M, Dir, Laboure College, 2120 Dorchester Ave, Boston, MA, 02124. Tel: 617-296-8300, Ext 4012. Fax: 617-296-7947. p. 1062

Caltabiano, Anne, Circ Serv Mgr, Youth Serv Mgr, Glendale Public Library, 5959 W Brown St, Glendale, AZ, 85302-1248. Tel: 623-930-3569. Fax: 623-842-4209. p. 64

Calunas, Marianne, Tech Serv, Oakland Community College, Library Systems, 2900 Featherstone Rd, MTEC A210, Auburn Hills, MI, 48326. Tel: 248-232-4478. Fax: 248-232-4089. p. 1154

Caluori, Rob, Mgr, Info Tech, Westchester Library System, 540 White Plains Rd, Ste 200, Tarrytown, NY, 10591-5110. Tel: 914-231-8642. Fax: 914-674-4185. p. 1755

Calvani, Patricia, Pres, York County Library System, 159 E Market St, 3rd Flr, York, PA, 17401. Tel: 717-846-5300. Fax: 717-849-6999. p. 2160

Calvanico, David, Head, Adult Serv, Mount Laurel Library, 100 Walt Whitman Ave, Mount Laurel, NJ, 08054. Tel: 856-234-7319. Fax: 856-234-6916. p. 1506

Calvaruso, Marie, Coll Develop, Harris, Beach PLLC, 99 Garnsey Rd, Pittsford, NY, 14534. Tel: 585-419-8800, Ext 8917. Fax: 585-419-8814. p. 1718

Calvello, Carol, Librn, Bucks County Courier Times Library, 8400 Rte 13, Levittown, PA, 19057-5198. Tel: 215-949-4000. Fax: 215-949-4177. p. 2080

Calvert, Anne, Asst Dir, Portland Library, 20 Freestone Ave, Portland, CT, 06480. Tel: 860-342-6770. Fax: 860-342-6778. p. 364

Calvert, Donna, Spec Serv Dir, West Virginia Library Commission, State Capitol Complex, 1900 Kanawha Blvd E, Charleston, WV, 25305-0620. Tel: 304-558-4061. Fax: 304-558-6016. p. 2557

Calvert, Hilde M, Head, Coll Develop, Ball State University Libraries, 2000 W University Ave, Muncie, IN, 47306-1099. Tel: 765-285-8033. Fax: 765-285-2008. p. 766

Calvin, Diane L, Head, Info Serv, Ball State University Libraries, 2000 W University Ave, Muncie, IN, 47306-1099. Tel: 765-285-3327. Fax: 765-285-2008. p. 766

Calvo, Jane, Asst Admin, Monmouth University, 400 Cedar Ave, West Long Branch, NJ, 07764. Tel: 732-571-3450. Fax: 732-263-5124. p. 1541

Calzonetti, Jo Ann, Head Librn, University of Akron Libraries, Science & Technology, Auburn Science Engineering Center, No 104, Akron, OH, 44325-3907. Tel: 330-972-8323. Fax: 330-972-7033. p. 1853

Camacho, Frank, Prog Mgr, Info Tech, San Diego Public Library, 820 E St, San Diego, CA, 92101-6478. Tel: 619-236-5808. Fax: 619-238-6639. p. 235

Camacho, Gerinaldo, Ref Serv, Pontifical Catholic University of Puerto Rico, Ramon Emeterio Betances St 482, Mayaguez, PR, 00680. Tel: 787-834-5151, Ext 5008. Fax: 787-831-7155. p. 2673

Camacho, Leticia, Bus Librn, Brigham Young University, Harold B Lee Library, 2060 HBLL, Provo, UT, 84602. Tel: 801-422-2927. Fax: 801-422-0466. p. 2411

Camack, Angela, Ref Serv, Sussex County Community College Library, One College Hill Rd, Newton, NJ, 07860. Tel: 973-300-2164. Fax: 973-300-2276. p. 1513

Camadeco, Barbara, Assoc Dir, Middletown Public Library, 700 W Main Rd, Middletown, RI, 02842-6391. Tel: 401-846-1573. Fax: 401-846-3031. p. 2168

Camara, David, Br Mgr, Brooklyn Public Library, Washington Irving Branch, 360 Irving Ave, Brooklyn, NY, 11237. Tel: 718-628-8378. Fax: 718-628-8439. p. 1591

Camarata, Corinne, Asst Dir, Port Washington Public Library, One Library Dr, Port Washington, NY, 11050. Tel: 516-883-4400. Fax: 516-883-7927. p. 1721

Camarata, Jean, Librn, Northeast Iowa Medical Education Foundation Library, 2055 Kimball Ave, Waterloo, IA, 50702. Tel: 319-272-2525. Fax: 319-272-2527. p. 850

Camarda, Jan, Head, Circ, Westhampton Free Library, Seven Library Ave, Westhampton Beach, NY, 11978-2697. Tel: 631-288-3335. Fax: 631-288-5715. p. 1768

Camarena, Janet, Dir, Foundation Center-San Francisco Library, 312 Sutter St, No 606, San Francisco, CA, 94108. Tel: 415-397-0902. Fax: 415-397-7670. p. 242

Camarillo, Angie, Tech Serv, United States Army, 201 N Third, Walla Walla, WA, 99362-1876. Tel: 509-527-7427. Fax: 509-527-7816. p. 2547

Camarillo, Josephine, Head, Ch, Ref Serv, Ch, Ref Serv, YA, Ellensburg Public Library, 209 N Ruby St, Ellensburg, WA, 98926-3397. Tel: 509-962-7218. Fax: 509-962-7295. p. 2514

Camejo, Joanne, Librn, Loeb & Loeb LLP, 345 Park Ave, 18th flr, New York, NY, 10154-0037. Tel: 212-407-4000, 212-407-4961. Fax: 212-407-4990. p. 1685

Camenga, Carol, Evening Librn, ECPI University, 4800 Airport Center Pkwy, Charlotte, NC, 28208. Tel: 704-399-1010, Ext 244. Fax: 704-399-9144. p. 1783

Camenga, John, ILL, Charlotte Mecklenburg Library, 310 N Tryon St, Charlotte, NC, 28202-2176. Tel: 704-416-0101. Fax: 704-416-0130. p. 1782

Camerio, Zack, Ser, Alabama Supreme Court & State Law Library, Heflin-Torbert Judicial Bldg, 300 Dexter Ave, Montgomery, AL, 36104. Tel: 334-229-0578. Fax: 334-229-0543. p. 28

Cameron, Agnes, Librn, Mercy College Libraries, Yorktown Campus, 2651 Strang Blvd, Yorktown Heights, NY, 10598. Tel: 914-245-6100, Ext 2222. Fax: 914-962-1042. p. 1615

Cameron, Benoit, Chief Librn, Douglas Mental Health University Institute, 6875 LaSalle Blvd, Perry Pavilion, Rm E4501, Montreal, QC, H4H 1R3, CANADA. Tel: 514-762-3029. Fax: 514-762-3039. p. 2895

Cameron, Cara, City Librn, Casa Grande Public Library, 449 N Dry Lake, Casa Grande, AZ, 85222. Tel: 520-421-8710. Fax: 520-421-8701. p. 59

Cameron, Donna, Librn, Atlantic County Library System, Mays Landing Branch, 40 Farragut Ave, Mays Landing, NJ, 08330. Tel: 609-625-2776. Fax: 609-625-8143. p. 1500

Cameron, Jacqueline, Circ Supvr, Department of Community Services, Government of Yukon, 1171 First Ave, Whitehorse, YT, Y1A 0G9, CANADA. Tel: 867-667-5413. Fax: 867-393-6333. p. 2933

Cameron, Jane, Cat, Pellissippi State Technical Community College, 10915 Harding Valley Rd, Knoxville, TN, 37933. Tel: 865-694-6520. Fax: 865-694-6625. p. 2243

Cameron, Jessica Ford, Dir, Tyrone-Snyder Public Library, 1000 Pennsylvania Ave, Tyrone, PA, 16686. Tel: 814-684-1133, Ext 3. Fax: 814-684-1878. p. 2147

Cameron, Joanne, Ref, Palm Beach State College, 3160 PGA Blvd, Palm Beach Gardens, FL, 33410-2893. Tel: 561-207-5800. Fax: 561-207-5805. p. 479

Cameron, Kathleen, Mgr, Digital Content Develop, University of California San Francisco, 530 Parnassus Ave, San Francisco, CA, 94143-0840. Tel: 415-502-9580. p. 248

Cameron, Margaret C, Info Res Coordr, Alzheimer Society of Toronto, 20 Eglinton Ave W, Ste 1600, Toronto, ON, M4R 1K8, CANADA. Tel: 416-322-6560. Fax: 416-322-6656. p. 2849

Cameron, Maria, Adult Serv, Southlake Public Library, 1400 Main St, Ste 130, Southlake, TX, 76092-7640. Tel: 817-748-8243. p. 2388

Cameron, Mary, Libr Tech, Prince Edward Island Public Library Service, Georgetown Public, 36 Kent St, Georgetown, PE, C0A 1L0, CANADA. Tel: 902-652-2832. p. 2876

Cameron, Mary Ann, Librn, Sisseton Memorial Library, 305 E Maple St, Sisseton, SD, 57262-1524. Tel: 605-698-7391. p. 2219

Cameron-Klugh, Druet, Bibliographer, Sr Ref Librn, University of Iowa Libraries, Law Library, 200 Boyd Law Bldg, Iowa City, IA, 52242-1166. Tel: 319-335-9002. Fax: 319-335-9039. p. 823

Cameron-Vedros, Crystal, Head, Copyright Compliance & Doc Delivery, University of Kansas Medical Center, 2100 W 39th Ave, Kansas City, KS, 66160-7180. Tel: 913-588-7916. Fax: 913-588-7304. p. 876

Camillus, Kerwin, Br Mgr, Sacramento Public Library, Franklin Community Library, 10055 Franklin High Rd, Elk Grove, CA, 95757. p. 225

Camino, Holly, Mgr, Medina County District Library, Buckeye Library, 6625 Wolff Rd, Medina, OH, 44256-6211. Tel: 330-725-4415. Fax: 330-722-4548. p. 1916

Camizzi, Patricia, Circ, Valparaiso Community Library, 459 Valparaiso Pkwy, Valparaiso, FL, 32580. Tel: 850-729-5406. Fax: 850-729-1120. p. 501

Cammack, Bruce, Rare Bks, Texas Tech University Libraries, 18th & Boston Ave, Lubbock, TX, 79409-0002. Tel: 806-742-2261. Fax: 806-742-0737. p. 2358

Cammack, Nancy, Br Mgr, Lubbock Public Library, Groves, 5520 19th St, Lubbock, TX, 79416. Tel: 806-767-3734. Fax: 806-795-9641. p. 2357

Cammarata, Clo, Prog & Partnerships Mgr, Richland County Public Library, 1431 Assembly St, Columbia, SC, 29201-3101. Tel: 803-799-9084. Fax: 803-929-3448. p. 2188

Cammarata, Paula, Circ/Reserves, Tufts University, Edwin Ginn Library, Mugar Bldg, 1st Flr, 160 Packard St, Medford, MA, 02155-7082. Tel: 617-627-3273. Fax: 617-627-3736. p. 1104

Cammenga, Cheryl, Br Mgr, Kent District Library, Kentwood Branch, 4950 Breton SE, Kentwood, MI, 49508. Tel: 616-784-2007. Fax: 616-647-3914. p. 1166

Cammon, Laura W, In Charge, University of Georgia, Sapelo Island, GA, 31327. Tel: 912-485-2276. Fax: 912-485-2133. p. 549

Camp, Aimee, Br Mgr, El Paso Public Library, Ysleta, 9321 Alameda, El Paso, TX, 79907. Tel: 915-858-0905. Fax: 915-860-8017. p. 2317

Camp, Dawn, Asst Librn, Washington County Historical Society Library, 307 E Market St, Salem, IN, 47167. Tel: 812-883-6495. p. 777

Camp, Jan, Pres, Decatur Genealogical Society Library, 1255 W South Side Dr, Decatur, IL, 62521-4024. Tel: 217-429-0135. p. 633

Camp, Mark, Coordr, Cultural Survival Inc, Library, 215 Prospect St, Cambridge, MA, 02139. Tel: 617-441-5400, Ext 11. Fax: 617-441-5417. p. 1073

Camp, Mary, Dir, Texas Legislative Reference Library, State Capitol Bldg, 1100 N Congress Ave, Rm 2N-3, Austin, TX, 78701. Tel: 512-463-1252. Fax: 512-475-4626. p. 2282

Camp, Sheila, Tech Serv, US Courts Library, 2305 US Courthouse, 200 NW Fourth St, Oklahoma City, OK, 73102. Tel: 405-609-5463. Fax: 405-609-5461. p. 1975

Campa, Tiffany, Librn, United States Army, Military Occupational Specialty Library, Bldg 2110, Fort Wainwright, AK, 99703. Tel: 907-353-7297. Fax: 907-353-7472. p. 48

Campagna, Denise, Librn, Van Buren District Library, Lawrence Community, 212 N Paw Paw St, Lawrence, MI, 49064. Tel: 269-674-3200. Fax: 269-674-3200. p. 1168

Campagna, Jane, Dir, Scott Community College Library, 500 Belmont Rd, Bettendorf, IA, 52722. Tel: 563-441-4150. Fax: 563-441-4154. p. 796

Campagna, Jane, Librn, Clinton Community College Library, 1000 Lincoln Blvd, Clinton, IA, 52732. Tel: 563-244-7046. Fax: 563-244-7107. p. 803

Campagna, Marcy, Head, Tech Serv, Elmwood Park Public Library, One Conti Pkwy, Elmwood Park, IL, 60707. Tel: 708-395-1205. Fax: 708-453-4671. p. 643

Campagna, Rosemary, Govt Doc, Ref, Brooklyn Law School Library, 250 Joralemon St, Brooklyn, NY, 11201. Tel: 718-780-7580. Fax: 718-780-0369. p. 1590

Campana, Claire, Coll Develop, Horry County Memorial Library, 1008 Fifth Ave, Conway, SC, 29526. Tel: 843-248-1550. Fax: 843-248-1549. p. 2191

Campana, Deborah, Librn, Oberlin College Library, Mary M Vial Music Library, Oberlin Conservatory of Music, 77 W College St, Oberlin, OH, 44074-1588. Tel: 440-775-8280. Fax: 440-775-8203. p. 1925

Campanella, Judith, Librn, Cayuga County Community College, 197 Franklin St, Auburn, NY, 13021. Tel: 315-294-8596. Fax: 315-255-2050. p. 1576

Campanella, Judy, Librn, Cayuga Community College, 806 W Broadway, Fulton, NY, 13069. Tel: 315-294-9019. Fax: 315-592-5055. p. 1625

Campanella, Vinise, Ch, Richmond Memorial Library, 19 Ross St, Batavia, NY, 14020. Tel: 585-343-9550. Fax: 585-344-4651. p. 1578

Campanelli, Mary, Managing Librn, Columbus Metropolitan Library, Gahanna Branch, 310 Granville St, Gahanna, OH, 43230. Tel: 614-645-2275. Fax: 614-479-4279. p. 1884

Campbell, Alice, ILL, Youth Serv, Redwood Library & Athenaeum, 50 Bellevue Ave, Newport, RI, 02840-3292. Tel: 401-847-0292. Fax: 401-847-0192. p. 2169

Campbell, Amber, Syst Adminr, Orange County Public Library, 137 W Margaret Lane, Hillsborough, NC, 27278. Tel: 919-245-2525. Fax: 919-644-3003. p. 1802

Campbell, Amy, Ref Librn, Marshall Public Library, 113 S Garfield, Pocatello, ID, 83204-5722. Tel: 208-232-1263. Fax: 208-232-9266. p. 582

Campbell, Angela, Br Mgr, Hightower Sara Regional Library, Cedartown Branch, 245 East Ave, City Complex, Cedartown, GA, 30125-3001. Tel: 770-748-5644. Fax: 770-748-4399. p. 549

Campbell, Angela, Dir, Glenwood Public Library, 109 N Vine St, Glenwood, IA, 51534-1516. Tel: 712-527-5252. Fax: 712-527-3619. p. 818

Campbell, Angela, Tech Serv Librn, Central Texas College, Bld 102, 6200 W Central Texas Expressway, Killeen, TX, 76549. Tel: 254-526-1237. Fax: 254-526-1878. p. 2350

Campbell, Ann, In Charge, Eastern Counties Regional Library, Port Hawkesbury Branch, 304 Pitt St (SAERC), Unit 3, Port Hawkesbury, NS, B9A 2T9, CANADA. Tel: 902-625-2729. Fax: 902-625-2729. p. 2783

Campbell, Anne, Dir, National City Public Library, 1401 National City Blvd, National City, CA, 91950-4401. Tel: 619-336-4350. Fax: 619-336-4368. p. 193

Campbell, Anne, Br Head, Toronto Public Library, New Toronto, 110 Eleventh St, Toronto, ON, M8V 3G5, CANADA. Tel: 416-394-5350. Fax: 416-394-5358. p. 2862

Campbell, Anne S, YA Librn, Groton Public Library, 52 Newtown Rd, Groton, CT, 06340. Tel: 860-441-6750. Fax: 860-448-0363. p. 342

Campbell, Annette, Librn, Naples Community Hospital, 350 Seventh St N, Naples, FL, 34102-5730. Tel: 239-436-5384. Fax: 239-436-5058. p. 471

Campbell, Barbara, Dir, Milford Free Library, S Main St, Milford, NY, 13807. Tel: 607-286-9076. Fax: 607-286-3461. p. 1661

Campbell, Barbara, Dir, Libr & Info Serv, Nova Scotia Barristers' Society, 1815 Upper Water St, 7th Flr, Halifax, NS, B3J 1S7, CANADA. Tel: 902-425-2665. Fax: 902-422-1697. p. 2781

Campbell, Bonnie L, Ref Serv, New Haven Museum & Historical Society, 114 Whitney Ave, New Haven, CT, 06510-1025. Tel: 203-562-4183. Fax: 203-562-2002. p. 356

Campbell, Carol, Librn, St Thomas Episcopal Church Library, 231 Sunset Ave, Sunnyvale, CA, 94086-5938. Tel: 408-736-4155. Fax: 408-733-7054. p. 273

Campbell, Catherine, Dir, Craven Community College, 800 College Ct, New Bern, NC, 28562. Tel: 252-638-7271. Fax: 252-672-5091. p. 1812

Campbell, Cathy, Ch, Otsego County Library, 700 S Otsego Ave, Gaylord, MI, 49735-1723. Tel: 989-732-5841. Fax: 989-732-9401. p. 1182

Campbell, Christine M, Asst Libr Dir, Henrico County Public Library, 1001 N Laburnum Ave, Henrico, VA, 23223-2705. Tel: 804-290-9000. Fax: 804-222-5566. p. 2471

Campbell, Cindy, Circ Librn, Prescott Public Library, 215 E Goodwin St, Prescott, AZ, 86303. Tel: 928-777-1508. Fax: 928-771-5829. p. 78

Campbell, Cindy, Acq, Edison State College, 8099 College Pkwy SW, Bldg J, Fort Myers, FL, 33919. Tel: 239-433-8026. Fax: 239-489-9095. p. 444

Campbell, Colleen, Circ Mgr, Baltimore County Public Library, Loch Raven, 1046 Taylor Ave, Towson, MD, 21286. Tel: 410-887-4444. Fax: 410-296-4339. p. 1044

Campbell, Craig, Archives, Res Ctr Mgr, Hockey Hall of Fame, 400 Kipling Ave, Toronto, ON, M8V 3L1, CANADA. Tel: 416-933-8224. Fax: 416-251-5770. p. 2854

Campbell, Crystal, Librn, Parkland Regional Library, Neudorf Branch, 103 Main St, Neudorf, SK, S0A 2T0, CANADA. Tel: 306-748-2553. p. 2932

Campbell, Cyndie, Head, Archives, Documentation & Visual Res, National Gallery of Canada Library, 380 Sussex Dr, Ottawa, ON, K1N 9N4, CANADA. Tel: 613-990-0597. Fax: 613-990-9818. p. 2832

Campbell, Cynthia, Actg Adminr, Bristol Law Library, Superior Court House, Nine Court St, Taunton, MA, 02780. Tel: 508-824-7632. Fax: 508-824-4723. p. 1130

Campbell, Daniel, Dir, United States Court of International Trade, One Federal Plaza, New York, NY, 10278. Tel: 212-264-2816. Fax: 212-264-3242. p. 1702

Campbell, David, In Charge, Lynn Lake Library, PO Box 1127, Lynn Lake, MB, R0B 0W0, CANADA. Tel: 204-356-8222. p. 2749

Campbell, David, Syst Librn, New Brunswick Public Library Service, 250 King St, Fredericton, NB, E3B 9M9, CANADA. Tel: 506-453-2354. Fax: 506-444-4064. p. 2763

Campbell, Deas, Librn, El Paso Community College Library, Transmountain Campus Library, 9570 Gateway Blvd N, El Paso, TX, 79924. Tel: 915-831-5092. p. 2316

Campbell, Debbie, Coordr, Instrul Serv & ILL, Millikin University, 1184 W Main, Decatur, IL, 62522. Tel: 217-424-6214. Fax: 217-424-3992. p. 634

Campbell, Debbie, Dep Dir, Owen County Public Library, Ten S Montgomery St, Spencer, IN, 47460-1713. Tel: 812-829-3392. Fax: 812-829-6165. p. 780

Campbell, Deirdre, Cat, Sierra Joint Community College District, 5000 Rocklin Rd, Rocklin, CA, 95677. Tel: 916-660-7230. Fax: 916-630-4539. p. 219

Campbell, Deirdre, Pub Serv, Hazard Community & Technical College Library, One Community College Dr, Hazard, KY, 41701. Tel: 606-487-3145. Fax: 606-439-1657. p. 916

Campbell, Donna, Tech Serv & Syst Librn, Westminster Theological Seminary, 2960 W Church Rd, Glenside, PA, 19038. Tel: 215-935-3872. Fax: 215-887-3412. p. 2062

Campbell, Francis D, Librn, American Numismatic Society Library, 75 Varick St, New York, NY, 10013. Tel: 212-571-4470. Fax: 212-571-4479. p. 1668

Campbell, Gillian, Ref, Coquitlam Public Library, 575 Poirier St, Coquitlam, BC, V3J 6A9, CANADA. Tel: 604-937-4147. Fax: 604-931-1460. p. 2727

Campbell, James W, Librn, New Haven Museum & Historical Society, 114 Whitney Ave, New Haven, CT, 06510-1025. Tel: 203-562-4183. Fax: 203-562-2002. p. 356

Campbell, Janet, Dir, Mansfield Public Library, 255 Hope St, Mansfield, MA, 02048-2353. Tel: 508-261-7380. Fax: 508-261-7422. p. 1102

Campbell, Janice, Asst Dir, Coll Develop, Youth Serv, Eagle Public Library, 100 N Stierman Way, Eagle, ID, 83616-5162. Tel: 208-939-6814. Fax: 208-939-1359. p. 574

Campbell, Janis, Head Librn, Oregon County Library District, Myrtle Public, General Delivery, State Hwy V, Myrtle, MO, 65778. Tel: 417-938-4350. Fax: 417-938-4350. p. 1319

Campbell, Jay, Supvr, Tech Serv, Milford Town Library, 80 Spruce St, Milford, MA, 01757. Tel: 508-473-0651, 508-473-2145. Fax: 508-473-8651. p. 1105

Campbell, Jayne, Assoc Dir, Johns Hopkins University Libraries, Carol J Gray Nursing Information Resource Center, 525 N Wolfe St, Rm 313, Baltimore, MD, 21202. Tel: 410-955-7559. p. 1014

Campbell, Jean, Dir, Forsyth Public Library, 268 S Elwood, Forsyth, IL, 62535. Tel: 217-877-8174. Fax: 217-877-3533. p. 646

Campbell, Jeff, IT Mgr, Okanagan Regional Library, 1430 KLO Rd, Kelowna, BC, V1W 3P6, CANADA. Tel: 250-860-4033. Fax: 250-861-8696. p. 2730

Campbell, Jennifer, Libr Serv Mgr, The Hospital of Central Connecticut, 100 Grand St, New Britain, CT, 06050. Tel: 860-224-5900, Ext 2570, 860-224-5900, Ext 2571. Fax: 860-224-5970. p. 354

Campbell, Jill, Librn, Lincoln Land Community College Library, 5250 Shepherd Rd, Springfield, IL, 62794. Tel: 217-786-2354. Fax: 217-786-2251. p. 705

Campbell, Jill, Ref, Anderson City, Anderson, Stony Creek & Union Townships Public Library, 111 E 12th St, Anderson, IN, 46016-2701. Tel: 765-641-2454. Fax: 765-641-2197. p. 723

Campbell, Joan, Librn, Urban Land Institute, 1025 Thomas Jefferson St NW, Ste 500W, Washington, DC, 20007. Tel: 202-624-7137. Fax: 202-624-7140. p. 421

Campbell, Joan, Coll Librn, Bowdoin College Library, 3000 College Sta, Brunswick, ME, 04011-8421. Tel: 207-725-3285. p. 979

Campbell, Jonathan, Coordr, Pike County Public Library District, Phelps Public, 38575 State Hwy 194 E, Phelps, KY, 41553. Tel: 606-456-7860. Fax: 606-766-0026. p. 932

Campbell, Jonathan, Dr, Assoc VPres, Acad Admin, Libr Dir, Walsh College, 3838 Livernois Rd, Troy, MI, 48083-5066. Tel: 248-823-1229. Fax: 248-689-9066. p. 1232

Campbell, Joseph A, Ref Librn, Bethune-Cookman College, 640 Mary McLeod Bethune Blvd, Daytona Beach, FL, 32114. Tel: 386-481-2186. Fax: 386-481-2182. p. 435

Campbell, Joyce, Head Librn, Arthur E Pomeroy Public Library, 912A Tilbury Rd, Kearny, AZ, 85237. Tel: 520-363-5861. Fax: 520-363-5214. p. 66

Campbell, Judith, Dean, Libr Serv, Holyoke Community College Library, Donahue Bldg, 2nd Flr, 303 Homestead Ave, Holyoke, MA, 01040-1099. Tel: 413-552-2260. Fax: 413-552-2729. p. 1095

Campbell, Karen, Spec Coll & Archives Librn, Mary L Cook Public Library, 381 Old Stage Rd, Waynesville, OH, 45068. Tel: 513-897-4826. Fax: 513-897-9215. p. 1945

Campbell, Kathy, Head, Ref, East Tennessee State University, Sherrod Library, Seehorn Dr & Lake St, Johnson City, TN, 37614-0204. Tel: 423-439-5629. Fax: 423-439-5222. p. 2239

Campbell, Kelly, Dir, Libr Serv, Golden Gate Baptist Theological Seminary Library, 201 Seminary Dr, Mill Valley, CA, 94941. Tel: 415-380-1678. Fax: 415-380-1652. p. 186

Campbell, Laura, Assoc Librn, Strategic Initiatives, Library of Congress, 101 Independence Ave at First St SE, Washington, DC, 20540. Tel: 202-707-5000. Fax: 202-707-1925. p. 406

Campbell, LaVerne, Br Mgr, Pittsylvania County Public Library, Brosville Cascade, 11948 Martinsville Hwy, Danville, VA, 24541. Tel: 434-685-1285. Fax: 434-685-3347. p. 2455

Campbell, Laverne, Head, Coll & Acq, Pittsylvania County Public Library, 24 Military Dr, Chatham, VA, 24531. Tel: 434-685-1285. Fax: 434-685-3347. p. 2455

Campbell, Lisa, Librn, National Sporting Library, Inc, 102 The Plains Rd, Middleburg, VA, 20118. Tel: 540-687-6542. Fax: 540-687-8540. p. 2479

Campbell, Liz, Br Mgr, Kershaw County Library, 1304 Broad St, Camden, SC, 29020-3595. Tel: 803-425-1508. Fax: 803-425-7180. p. 2182

Campbell, Lynne, Ch, John Curtis Free Library, 534 Hanover St, Hanover, MA, 02339-2228. Tel: 781-826-2972. Fax: 781-826-3130. p. 1093

Campbell, Marianne, Librn, Blue Ridge Community College Library, 180 W Campus Dr, Flat Rock, NC, 28731. Tel: 828-694-1879. Fax: 828-694-1692. p. 1793

Campbell, Martha, Asst Dir, Croton Free Library, 171 Cleveland Dr, Croton-on-Hudson, NY, 10520. Tel: 914-271-6612. Fax: 914-271-0931. p. 1612

Campbell, Mary, Ch, Teen Librn, Akron Public Library, 350 Reed St, Akron, IA, 51001. Tel: 712-568-2601. Fax: 712-568-2601. p. 791

Campbell, Mary, Br Mgr, Cumberland County Public Library & Information Center, North Regional, 855 McArthur Rd, Fayetteville, NC, 28311-1961. Tel: 910-822-1998. Fax: 910-480-0030. p. 1792

Campbell, Mary, Managing Librn II, Sno-Isle Libraries, Oak Harbor Community Library, 1000 SE Regatta Dr, Oak Harbor, WA, 98277. Tel: 360-675-5115. Fax: 360-679-3761. p. 2542

Campbell, Mary L, Librn, Ryerss Museum & Library, Burholme Park, 7370 Central Ave, Philadelphia, PA, 19111-3055. Tel: 215-685-0544, 215-685-0599. p. 2116

Campbell, MaryAnn, Dir, Oregon Historical Society Research Library, 1200 SW Park Ave, Portland, OR, 97205. Tel: 503-306-5243. Fax: 503-219-2040. p. 2013

Campbell, Megan, Librn, Talladega County Law Library, Talladega County Judicial Bldg, Northeast St, Talladega, AL, 35161. Tel: 256-761-2116. Fax: 256-480-5293. p. 37

Campbell, Melissa M, Dir, Plainville Public Library, 198 South St, Plainville, MA, 02762-1512. Tel: 508-695-1784. Fax: 508-695-6359. p. 1118

Campbell, Melodye, Ref Librn, Keuka College, 141 Central Ave, Keuka Park, NY, 14478-0038. Tel: 315-279-5219. Fax: 315-279-5334. p. 1649

Campbell, Michael, Cataloger, Dillard University, 2601 Gentilly Blvd, New Orleans, LA, 70122-3097. Tel: 504-816-4246. Fax: 504-816-4787. p. 960

Campbell, Michelle, Mgr, Libr Serv, Upper Grand District School Board, 500 Victoria Rd N, Guelph, ON, N1E 6K2, CANADA. Tel: 519-822-4420. Fax: 519-763-6870. p. 2807

Campbell, Mike, In Charge, Mackenzie, Hughes LLP, 101 S Salina St, Ste 600, Syracuse, NY, 13202-1399. Tel: 315-474-7571. Fax: 315-474-6409. p. 1752

Campbell, Neil A, Assoc Prof, Assoc Univ Librn, University of Victoria Libraries, Diana M Priestly Law Library, PO Box 2300, STN CSC, Victoria, BC, V8W 3B1, CANADA. Tel: 250-721-8565. Fax: 250-472-4174. p. 2746

Campbell, Nicole, Head, Ref & Electronic Serv, Washington State University Libraries, 14204 NE Salmon Creek Ave, Vancouver, WA, 98686. Tel: 360-546-9687. Fax: 360-546-9039. p. 2546

Campbell, Pamela, Digital Projects Librn, Federal Reserve Bank of Saint Louis, One Federal Reserve Bank Plaza, Saint Louis, MO, 63102-2005. Tel: 314-444-8907. Fax: 314-444-8694. p. 1354

Campbell, Patrica, Dir, Conant Public Library, Four Meetinghouse Hill Rd, Sterling, MA, 01564. Tel: 978-422-6409. Fax: 978-422-6643. p. 1128

Campbell, Patricia, Managing Librn, Austin Public Library, Old Quarry, 7051 Village Center Dr, Austin, TX, 78731. Tel: 512-345-4435. Fax: 512-794-0459. p. 2279

Campbell, Rachel, Dir, Eccles-Lesher Memorial Library, 673 Main St, Rimersburg, PA, 16248-4817. Tel: 814-473-3800. Fax: 814-473-8200. p. 2134

Campbell, Robert, Dir, Cape Breton University Library, 1250 Grand Lake Rd, Sydney, NS, B1P 6L2, CANADA. Tel: 902-563-1698. Fax: 902-563-1177. p. 2785

Campbell, Roger, Librn, Pike-Amite-Walthall Library System, Crosby Branch, Hwy 33, Crosby, MS, 39633. Tel: 601-639-4633. p. 1308

Campbell, Rose, Chief, Libr Serv, Portland VA Medical Center Library, 3710 SW US Veterans Hospital Rd, P6LIB, Portland, OR, 97239-2964. Tel: 503-220-8262, Ext 55955. Fax: 503-721-7816. p. 2014

Campbell, Sandra, Dir, University of Arkansas-Monticello Library, 514 University Dr, Monticello, AR, 71656. Tel: 870-460-1180. Fax: 870-460-1980. p. 110

Campbell, Sarah, Circ, Syst Tech, Tech Serv, Portland Public Library, Five Monument Sq, Portland, ME, 04101. Tel: 207-871-1700, Ext 736. Fax: 207-871-1703. p. 997

Campbell, Sarah, Asst Archivist, College of the Holy Cross, One College St, Worcester, MA, 01610. Tel: 508-793-2575. Fax: 508-793-2372. p. 1143

Campbell, Scott, Tech Serv Librn, University of Louisville Libraries, Brandeis School of Law Library, 2301 S Third St, Louisville, KY, 40208. Tel: 502-852-6074. Fax: 502-852-8906. p. 926

Campbell, Scott, Dir of Libr, Langdon Library, 328 Nimble Hill Rd, Newington, NH, 03801. Tel: 603-436-5154. Fax: 603-436-5154. p. 1460

Campbell, Sherie, Libr Mgr, Trochu Municipal Library, 317 Main St, Trochu, AB, T0M 2C0, CANADA. Tel: 403-442-2458. p. 2719

Campbell, Shirley, Librn, Department of Veterans Affairs North Texas Health Care System, 4500 S Lancaster Rd, Dallas, TX, 75216. Tel: 214-857-1251. p. 2307

Campbell, Shirley, Librn, Oak Cliff Presbyterian Church Library, 6000 S Hampton Rd, Dallas, TX, 75232. Tel: 214-339-2211. Fax: 214-339-3500. p. 2309

Campbell, Stan, Head, Commun Relations, Alexandrian Public Library, 115 W Fifth St, Mount Vernon, IN, 47620. Tel: 812-838-3286. Fax: 812-838-9639. p. 766

Campbell, Stanley R, Dir, Libr Serv, Centre College of Kentucky, 600 W Walnut St, Danville, KY, 40422. Tel: 859-238-5271. Fax: 859-236-7925. p. 911

Campbell, Stephanie, Br Librn, Prince Edward Island Public Library Service, Kensington Public, 55 Victoria St, Kensington, PE, C0B 1M0, CANADA. Tel: 902-836-3721. p. 2876

Campbell, Susan, Dir, York College of Pennsylvania, 441 Country Club Rd, York, PA, 17403-3651. Tel: 717-815-1305. Fax: 717-849-1608. p. 2160

Campbell, Susie, Librn, Lewis Public Library, 506 W Main St, Lewis, IA, 51544. Tel: 712-769-2228. Fax: 712-769-2228. p. 828

Campbell, Suzanne, Librn, Government Printing Office, 732 N Capitol NW, Rm C-818, MS GCL, Washington, DC, 20401. Tel: 202-512-0064. Fax: 202-512-0076. p. 403

Campbell, Suzanne, Chief Exec Officer, Orillia Public Library, 36 Mississaga St W, Orillia, ON, L3V 3A6, CANADA. Tel: 705-325-2338. Fax: 705-327-1744. p. 2826

Campbell, Suzanne O, Head, Spec Coll & Programming, Angelo State University Library, 2025 S Johnson, San Angelo, TX, 76904-5079. Tel: 325-486-6553. Fax: 325-942-2198. p. 2378

Campbell, Tanya E, Dir, Dayton Public Library, 22 First St NW, Dayton, IA, 50530. Tel: 515-547-2700. Fax: 515-547-2700. p. 807

Campbell, Ted T, Dir, Stuttgart Public Library, 2002 S Buerkle St, Stuttgart, AR, 72160-6508. Tel: 870-673-1966. Fax: 870-673-4295. p. 116

Campbell, Theresa, Ch, Killeen City Library System, 205 E Church Ave, Killeen, TX, 76541. Tel: 254-501-8959. Fax: 254-501-7704. p. 2350

Campbell, Victoria, Youth Serv Mgr, Beaverton City Library, 12375 SW Fifth St, Beaverton, OR, 97005-2883. Tel: 503-526-2599. Fax: 503-526-2636. p. 1991

Campbell, Zandra, Br Mgr, Enoch Pratt Free Library, Cherry Hill, 606 Cherry Hill Rd, Baltimore, MD, 21225. Tel: 410-396-1168. Fax: 410-396-1174. p. 1013

Campbell-Meier, Jennifer, Asst Prof, University of Alabama, 514 Main Library, Tuscaloosa, AL, 35487. Tel: 205-348-4610. Fax: 205-348-3746. p. 2961

Campe, Mary Beth, Dir, Elmhurst Public Library, 125 S Prospect, Elmhurst, IL, 60126-3298. Tel: 630-530-6300. Fax: 630-516-1364. p. 642

Campeau, Kathy, Br Asst, Middlesex County Library, Dorchester Branch, 2123 Dorchester Rd, Dorchester, ON, N0L 1G0, CANADA. Tel: 519-268-3451. Fax: 519-268-1047. p. 2845

Campeau, Nicole, Librn, Institut de Recherches Cliniques de Montreal Library, 110 Pine Ave W, Rm 2340, Montreal, QC, H2W 1R7, CANADA. Tel: 514-987-5599. Fax: 514-987-5675. p. 2896

Campen, Cathy, Ch, Andover Public Library, 355 Rte 6, Andover, CT, 06232. Tel: 860-742-7428. Fax: 860-742-7428. p. 329

Campenella, Linda, Asst Librn, Du Quoin Public Library, 28 S Washington St, Du Quoin, IL, 62832. Tel: 618-542-5045. Fax: 618-542-4735. p. 637

Campi, Joseph, ILL, University of San Francisco, 2130 Fulton St, San Francisco, CA, 94117-1080. Tel: 415-422-6167. Fax: 415-422-5949. p. 248

Campion, Jowanda, Libr Coordr, Trinidad State Junior College, 600 Prospect St, Trinidad, CO, 81082. Tel: 719-846-5593. p. 324

Campo, Charles A, Chief Librn, Bangor Daily News Library, 491 Main St, Bangor, ME, 04401-6296. Tel: 207-990-8160. Fax: 207-990-8081. p. 975

Campo, Susan, Librn, Lewis Dana Hill Memorial Library, 2079 Main St, Center Lovell, ME, 04231-9702. Tel: 207-928-2301. p. 982

Campos, Ana, Actg Sr Librn, Los Angeles Public Library System, Leon H Washington Jr Memorial-Vernon Branch, 4504 S Central Ave, Los Angeles, CA, 90011-9623. Tel: 213-234-9106. Fax: 213-485-8155. p. 174

Campos, Denise, Br Mgr, Monterey County Free Libraries, Soledad Branch, 401 Gabilan Dr, Soledad, CA, 93960. Tel: 831-678-2430. Fax: 831-678-3087. p. 183

Campos, Jesus, Dir of Tech Serv, South Texas College Library, 3201 W Pecan Blvd, McAllen, TX, 78501-6661. Tel: 956-872-8330. Fax: 956-872-7202. p. 2361

Campos, Josie O, Dir, Superior Public Library, 99 Kellner Ave, Superior, AZ, 85273. Tel: 520-689-2327. Fax: 520-689-5809. p. 82

Campoy, Rene, Dr, Asst Dean, Murray State University, 3201 Alexander Hall, Murray, KY, 42071-3309. Tel: 270-809-2500. Fax: 270-809-3799. p. 2966

Canaan, Sibyl, Dir, Field Library of Peekskill, Four Nelson Ave, Peekskill, NY, 10566-2138. Tel: 914-737-1212. Fax: 914-862-9710. p. 1716

Canada, Charlyn, Dir, Eagle Valley Library District, 600 Broadway, Eagle, CO, 81631. Tel: 970-328-8800. Fax: 970-328-6901. p. 305

Canada, Nancy, Dir, Chester County Public Library, 1012 East Main St, Henderson, TN, 38340-0323. Tel: 731-989-4673. Fax: 731-989-4673. p. 2237

Canada, Sally, In Charge, Titanium Metals Corporation of America (Laboratory), PO Box 2128, Henderson, NV, 89009. Tel: 702-564-2544, Ext 396. Fax: 702-564-9038. p. 1428

Canada, Waltrene M, Dean, Libr Serv, North Carolina Agricultural & Technical State University, 1601 E Market St, Greensboro, NC, 27411-0002. Tel: 336-334-7782, Ext 3202. Fax: 336-334-7783. p. 1797

Canady, Denise, Ch, Cambridge City Public Library, 33 W Main St, Cambridge City, IN, 47327. Tel: 765-478-3335. Fax: 765-478-6144. p. 731

Canady, Terry, Br Supvr, Barry-Lawrence Regional Library, Pierce City Branch, 101 N Walnut St, Pierce City, MO, 65723. Tel: 417-476-5110. Fax: 417-476-5110. p. 1347

Canales, Esmeralda, Br Mgr, Duval County-San Diego Public Library, Freer Branch, 608 Carolyn St, Freer, TX, 78357. Tel: 361-394-5350. Fax: 361-394-5350. p. 2384

Canales, Guadalupe, Br Mgr, Los Angeles Public Library System, Sun Valley Branch, 7935 Vineland Ave, Sun Valley, CA, 91352-4498. Tel: 818-764-1138. Fax: 818-764-2245. p. 174

Canapary, Andrea, Br Head, Mariposa County Library, El Portal Branch, 9670 Rancheria Flat Rd, 1st Flr, El Portal, CA, 95318. Tel: 209-379-2401. p. 184

Canavan, M J, Head, Syst, University of Massachusetts Amherst, 154 Hicks Way, Amherst, MA, 01003-9275. Tel: 413-545-6824. Fax: 413-545-6873. p. 1049

Cancellare, Andrea, Access Serv, Sul Ross State University, PO Box C-109, Alpine, TX, 79832-0001. Tel: 432-837-8123. Fax: 432-837-8400. p. 2273

Cancienne, Julie, Br Librn, Saint Charles Parish Library, West Regional Branch, 105 Lakewood Dr, Luling, LA, 70070. Tel: 985-785-8471. Fax: 985-785-8499. p. 949

Cancilla, Bron, Br Mgr, Placer County Library, Granite Bay Branch, 6475 Douglas Blvd, Granite Bay, CA, 95746. Tel: 916-791-5590. Fax: 916-791-1837. p. 123

Candee, Alan, Br Mgr, Sacramento Public Library, Walnut Grove Neighborhood Library, 14177 Market St, Walnut Grove, CA, 95690. p. 225

Candela, Jane W, VPres, Packer Engineering Inc, 1950 N Washington St, Naperville, IL, 60563-1366. Tel: 630-577-1953. Fax: 630-577-1989. p. 679

Candelaria, J Randel, Dean, Forsyth Technical Community College Library, 2100 Silas Creek Pkwy, Winston-Salem, NC, 27103. Tel: 336-734-7216. Fax: 336-761-2465. p. 1833

Candiloro, Cyndi, Commun Librn, Readsboro Community Library, 301 Phelps Lane, Readsboro, VT, 05350. Tel: 802-423-5460. Fax: 802-423-9914. p. 2433

Canelli, Charlotte, Dir, Morrill Memorial Library, 33 Walpole St, Norwood, MA, 02062-1206. Tel: 781-769-0200, Ext 101. Fax: 781-769-6083. p. 1115

Canepa, Laurie, Librn, Legislative Council Service Library, 411 State Capitol, Santa Fe, NM, 87501. Tel: 505-986-4600. Fax: 505-986-4680. p. 1562

Canevit, Debbie, Librn, Valley District Public Library, 515 Carter St, Fairview, IL, 61432. Tel: 309-778-2240. Fax: 309-778-2240. p. 645

Canfield, Cheryl, Head, ILL, Head, Ref, Hutchinson Public Library, 901 N Main, Hutchinson, KS, 67501-4492. Tel: 620-663-5441. Fax: 620-663-9506. p. 873

Canfield, Francine, Dir, Hollis & Helen Baright Public Library, 5555 S 77th St, Ralston, NE, 68127-2899. Tel: 402-331-7636. Fax: 402-331-1168. p. 1417

Canfield, Sally, Dir, Normal Memorial Library, 301 N Eagle St, Fayette, OH, 43521. Tel: 419-237-2115. Fax: 419-237-2002. p. 1899

Canfield, Toni, Librn, Argosy University, 1515 Central Pkwy, Eagan, MN, 55121. Tel: 651-846-3351. Fax: 651-994-0105. p. 1249

Canfora, Alan, Dir, Akron Law Library, 209 S High St, 4th Flr, Akron, OH, 44308-1675. Tel: 330-643-2804. Fax: 330-535-0077. p. 1851

Cangelosi, Daniel, Br Mgr, Jefferson Parish Library, Edith S Lawson Library (Westwego Branch), 635 Fourth St, Westwego, LA, 70094. Tel: 504-349-5912. Fax: 504-349-5920. p. 956

Cangialosi, Carmela, Dir, DDB Worldwide, 437 Madison Ave, New York, NY, 10022. Tel: 212-415-2546. p. 1677

Cangiano, Barbara, Assoc Librn, Pub Serv, James Blackstone Memorial Library, 758 Main St, Branford, CT, 06405-3697. Tel: 203-488-1441. Fax: 203-481-6077. p. 331

Canham, Robin, Serv Assessment Librn, SIAST-Saskatchewan Institute of Applied Science & Technology, 4500 Wascana Pkwy, Regina, SK, S4P 3S7, CANADA. Tel: 306-665-7409. Fax: 306-798-0560. p. 2924

Cani, Lindita, Head, Tech Serv, South Orange Public Library, 65 Scotland Rd, South Orange, NJ, 07079. Tel: 973-762-0230. Fax: 973-762-1469. p. 1531

Canick, Simon, Assoc Dean, Info Res & Scholarly Communications, William Mitchell College of Law, 871 Summit Ave, Saint Paul, MN, 55105. Tel: 651-290-6333. Fax: 651-290-6318. p. 1283

Canino, Sarah, Music Librn, Vassar College Library, 124 Raymond Ave, Maildrop 20, Poughkeepsie, NY, 12604-0020. Tel: 845-437-5760. Fax: 845-437-5864. p. 1723

Canino, Sarah, Music Librn, Vassar College Library, George Sherman Dickinson Music Library, Poughkeepsie, NY, 12604-0038. Tel: 845-437-7492. Fax: 845-437-7335. p. 1724

Cann, Cheryle, Head of Libr, University of Missouri-Saint Louis Libraries, Ward E Barnes Library, One University Blvd, Saint Louis, MO, 63121. Tel: 314-516-5576. Fax: 314-516-6468. p. 1362

Cann, Mary Ellen, ILL, Guelph Public Library, 100 Norfolk St, Guelph, ON, N1H 4J6, CANADA. Tel: 519-824-6220. Fax: 519-824-8342. p. 2807

Cannady, Bernadette, Circ Mgr, Wicomico Public Library, 122 S Division St, Salisbury, MD, 21801. Tel: 410-749-3612, Ext 133. Fax: 410-548-2968. p. 1040

Cannan, Gwynedd, Archivist, Trinity Church Archives, 74 Trinity Pl, 4th Flr, New York, NY, 10006-2088. Tel: 212-602-9652, 212-602-9687. Fax: 212-602-9641. p. 1701

Cannard, Kristin, Mgr, Washoe County Library System, Sierra View Library, Reno Town Mall, 4001 S Virginia St, Reno, NV, 89502. Tel: 775-827-0327. Fax: 775-827-8792. p. 1434

CannCasciato, Daniel, Head, Cat, Central Washington University, 400 E University Way, Ellensburg, WA, 98926-7548. Tel: 509-963-1901. Fax: 509-963-3684. p. 2514

Cannell, Karen T, Head, Spec Coll & Archives, Fashion Institute of Technology-SUNY, Seventh Ave at 27th St, New York, NY, 10001-5992. Tel: 212-217-4386. Fax: 212-217-4371. p. 1678

Canney, Kara, Head, Ch, Trumbull Library, 33 Quality St, Trumbull, CT, 06611. Tel: 203-452-5197. Fax: 203-452-5125. p. 373

Canning, Vivien, Br Head, Toronto Public Library, Humberwood, 850 Humberwood Blvd, Toronto, ON, M9W 7A6, CANADA. Tel: 416-394-5210. Fax: 416-394-5215. p. 2862

Cannizzaro, Regina, Coordr, Tech Serv, County College of Morris, 214 Center Grove Rd, Randolph, NJ, 07869-2086. p. 1525

Cannon, Anita, Pub Serv Librn, Mount Allison University Libraries & Archives, 49 York St, Sackville, NB, E4L 1C6, CANADA. Tel: 506-364-2572. Fax: 506-364-2617. p. 2766

Cannon, Ann D, Ref Librn, Norfolk State University Library, 700 Park Ave, Norfolk, VA, 23504-8010. Tel: 757-823-2417. Fax: 757-823-2431. p. 2482

Cannon, Chelsi, Ref, Spec Coll Librn, La Sierra University Library, 4500 Riverwalk Pkwy, Riverside, CA, 92505-3344. Tel: 951-785-2397. Fax: 951-785-2445. p. 217

Cannon, Deborah, Librn, Linowes & Blocher LLP, 7200 Wisconsin Ave, Ste 800, Bethesda, MD, 20814. Tel: 301-961-5163. Fax: 301-654-2801. p. 1021

Cannon, Geoffrey, Dep Dir, Halton Hills Public Library, Nine Church St, Georgetown, ON, L7G 2A3, CANADA. Tel: 905-873-2681. Fax: 905-873-6118. p. 2806

Cannon, Heather, Tech Serv Librn, Adler School of Professional Psychology, 17 N Dearborn St, Chicago, IL, 60602. Tel: 312-261-4070. Fax: 312-201-8756. p. 605

Cannon, Kat J, Asst Librn, Bryant & Stratton College Library, 301 Centre Pointe Dr, Virginia Beach, VA, 23462. Tel: 757-499-7900. Fax: 757-499-9977. p. 2498

Cannon, Kelly, Outreach & Scholarly Communication Librn, Muhlenberg College, 2400 Chew St, Allentown, PA, 18104-5586. Tel: 484-664-3602. Fax: 484-664-3511. p. 2027

Cannon, Laurie, Librn, Carlow-Mayo Public Library, c/o Hermon Public School, 124 Fort Stewart Rd, RR 4, Bancroft, ON, K0L 1C0, CANADA. Tel: 613-332-2544. Fax: 613-223-2544. p. 2793

Cannon, Linda, Coll Develop Librn, Joplin Public Library, 300 S Main, Joplin, MO, 64801. Tel: 417-623-7953. Fax: 417-625-4728. p. 1335

Cannon, Marcia, Ch, Abbot Public Library, 235 Pleasant St, Marblehead, MA, 01945. Tel: 781-631-1481. Fax: 781-639-0558. p. 1102

Cannon, Regina W, Librn, University of Georgia Libraries, 1109 Experiment St, Griffin, GA, 30223-1797. Tel: 770-228-7238. Fax: 770-229-3213. p. 535

Cannon, Rhonda, Dir, Admin Serv, University of Oklahoma, 401 W Brooks, Norman, OK, 73019. Tel: 405-325-2611. Fax: 405-325-7550. p. 1971

Cannon, Robert E, Dir, Libr Div, Broward County Division of Libraries, 100 S Andrews Ave, Fort Lauderdale, FL, 33301. Tel: 954-357-7376. Fax: 954-357-6542. p. 440

Cannon, Shirron, Asst Librn, Gadsden County Public Library, Havana Public, 203 E Fifth Ave, Havana, FL, 32333. Tel: 850-539-2844. p. 485

Cannon, Susan, Mgr, Access Serv, Saint Mary's University, 5429 Inglis St, Halifax, NS, B3H 3C3, CANADA. Tel: 902-420-5656. Fax: 902-420-5561. p. 2782

Cannon, Twana, Asst Br Mgr, Atlanta-Fulton Public Library System, East Point Library, 2757 Main St, East Point, GA, 30344. Tel: 404-762-4842. Fax: 404-762-4844. p. 512

Cannon, Tyrone, Dean, University of San Francisco, 2130 Fulton St, San Francisco, CA, 94117-1080. Tel: 415-422-6167. Fax: 415-422-5949. p. 248

Canny, Roseann, Librn, Connecticut Judicial Branch Law Libraries, Rockville Law Library, Rockville Courthouse, 69 Brooklyn St, Rockville, CT, 06066. Tel: 860-896-4955. Fax: 860-875-3213. p. 344

Cano, Maria E, Librn, Rio Grande Bible Institute & Language School, 4300 US Hwy 281, Edinburg, TX, 78539-9650. Tel: 956-380-8100. Fax: 956-380-8101. p. 2315

Canon, Charles H, III, Archivist, Coll Serv, Roberts Wesleyan College & Northeastern Seminary, 2301 Westside Dr, Rochester, NY, 14624-1997. Tel: 585-594-6016. Fax: 585-594-6543. p. 1731

Canonaco, Gail, Head Librn, Oshawa Public Library, Legends, 1661 Harmony Rd N, Oshawa, ON, L1H 7K5, CANADA. Tel: 905-436-5461. p. 2827

Canora, Edward, Adult Serv, Circ Supvr, Librn II, Dobbs Ferry Public Library, 55 Main St, Dobbs Ferry, NY, 10522. Tel: 914-693-6614. Fax: 914-693-4671. p. 1615

Canosa-Albano, Jean, Mgr, Pub Serv, Springfield City Library, 220 State St, Springfield, MA, 01103. Tel: 413-263-65828, Ext 291. Fax: 413-263-6817. p. 1127

Canose, Joe, Sr VPres, Christopher & Dana Reeve Foundation, 636 Morris Tpk, Ste 3A, Short Hills, NJ, 07078. Tel: 973-467-8270, Ext 7206. Fax: 973-467-9845. p. 1529

Cansler, Kristi, ILL, California State University, 9001 Stockdale Hwy, Bakersfield, CA, 93311-1022. Tel: 661-654-2218. Fax: 661-654-3238. p. 123

Canter, Brandi, Regional Supvr, Great River Regional Library, 1300 W St Germain St, Saint Cloud, MN, 56301-3667. Tel: 320-650-2530. Fax: 320-650-2501. p. 1274

Canter, Brandi, Br Mgr, Great River Regional Library, Royalton Library, 12 N Birch St, Royalton, MN, 56373. Tel: 320-584-8151. Fax: 320-584-8151. p. 1275

Canterbury, Les, Acq Librn, Natural Sci Librn, University of Redlands, 1200 E Colton Ave, Redlands, CA, 92374-3758. Tel: 909-748-8022. Fax: 909-335-5392. p. 215

Cantillon, Angela, Assoc Dir for Operations, Christopher & Dana Reeve Foundation, 636 Morris Tpk, Ste 3A, Short Hills, NJ, 07078. Tel: 973-467-8270, Ext 7214. Fax: 973-467-9845. p. 1529

Cantin, Sylvie, Chef de Section, Bibliothèques de Montréal, Cartierville, 5900, rue De Salaberry, Montreal, QC, H4J 1J1, CANADA. Tel: 514-868-5916. Fax: 514-872-0510. p. 2889

Cantin, Sylvie, Chef de Section, Bibliothèques de Montréal, Salaberry, 4170, rue De Salaberry, Montreal, QC, H4J 1H1, CANADA. Tel: 514-868-5916. Fax: 514-872-0519. p. 2891

Cantley, Shelby D, Dir, Anderson University, Instructional Materials Center, Decker Hall, 1100 E Fifth St, Anderson, IN, 46012-3495. Tel: 765-641-4290. Fax: 765-641-3878. p. 724

Cantor, Laurence, Head, Tech Serv, Jericho Public Library, One Merry Lane, Jericho, NY, 11753. Tel: 516-935-6790. Fax: 516-433-9581. p. 1647

Cantrell, Chely, Br Mgr, Ouachita Parish Public Library, Ouachita Valley Branch, 581 McMillian Rd, West Monroe, LA, 71294. Tel: 318-327-1471. Fax: 318-327-1473. p. 957

Cantrell, Gary, Ref Librn, Adelphi University Libraries, One South Ave, Garden City, NY, 11530. Tel: 516-877-3562. Fax: 516-877-3592. p. 1625

Cantrell, Sarah, Educ Serv Librn, Georgetown University, Dahlgren Memorial Library, Preclinical Science Bldg GM-7, 3900 Reservoir Rd NW, Washington, DC, 20007. Tel: 202-687-8874. Fax: 202-687-1862. p. 402

Cantrell, Wanda, Mgr, Off of the Dean of Libr & Info Serv, Andrews University, 1400 Library Rd, Berrien Springs, MI, 49104-1400. Tel: 269-471-3264, 269-471-3275. Fax: 269-471-6166. p. 1157

Cantu, Eliama, Librn, Starr County Public Library, 1705 N Athens, Roma, TX, 78584. Tel: 956-849-0072. p. 2377

Cantwell, Jacqueline, Sr Librn, New York State Supreme Court Library, Brooklyn, Supreme Court Bldg, Rm 349, 360 Adams St, Brooklyn, NY, 11201-3782. Tel: 347-296-1144. Fax: 718-643-2412. p. 1594

Cantwell, Mary Louise, Br Mgr, Central Arkansas Library System, Roosevelt Thompson Branch, 38 Rahling Circle, Little Rock, AR, 72223. Tel: 501-821-3060. p. 106

Cantwell, Patricia Keene, Assoc Dir, College of the Atlantic, 109 Eden St, Bar Harbor, ME, 04609-1198. Tel: 207-288-5015, Ext 211. Fax: 207-288-2328. p. 976

Canup, Shirley G, Head, Pub Serv, Thompson Coburn LLP, One US Bank Plaza, Saint Louis, MO, 63101. Tel: 314-552-6260. Fax: 314-552-7260. p. 1361

Canzano, Deborah, Ref Librn, Orange County Community College Library, 115 South St, Middletown, NY, 10940. Tel: 845-341-4542. Fax: 845-341-4424. p. 1660

Canzano, Deborah, Ref Librn, Orange County Community College Library, Newburgh Campus, One Washington Ctr, Newburgh, NY, 12550. Tel: 845-562-4542. p. 1660

Cao, Tanya, Cat Librn, Chapman University School of Law, 370 N Glassell St, Rm 325, Orange, CA, 92866. Tel: 714-628-2537. p. 201

Caouette, Martine, In Charge, Bibliotheque Gabrielle-Roy, Bibliotheque Aliette-Marchand, 233 Pierre-Bertrand Blvd, Quebec, QC, G1M 2C7, CANADA. Tel: 418-641-6223. p. 2903

Caparrelli, Fran, ILL, Bud Werner Memorial Library, 1289 Lincoln Ave, Steamboat Springs, CO, 80487. Tel: 970-879-0240. Fax: 970-879-3476. p. 323

Capdevielle, Helen, Librn, Lewis, Rice & Fingersh Law Library, 500 N Broadway, Ste 2000, Saint Louis, MO, 63102-2147. Tel: 314-444-7600. Fax: 314-612-7681. p. 1355

Cape, Angela, Per, Southern Nazarene University, 4115 N College, Bethany, OK, 73008. Tel: 405-491-6350. Fax: 405-491-6355. p. 1958

Cape, Brad, Curator, Embroiderers Guild of America Inc Library, 426 W Jefferson St, Louisville, KY, 40202-3202. Tel: 502-589-6956. Fax: 502-584-7900. p. 923

Capeci, James, Doc Delivery, Missouri Southern State University, 3950 E Newman Rd, Joplin, MO, 64801-1595. Tel: 417-625-9386. Fax: 417-625-9734. p. 1336

Capell, Sandy, Libr Tech, Sutter County Free Library, Pleasant Grove Branch, 3075 Howsley Rd, Pleasant Grove, CA, 95668-9723. Tel: 916-655-3484. p. 286

Capellen, Donna, Librn, Big Horn County Library, Lovell Branch Library, 300 Oregon Ave, Lovell, WY, 82431. Tel: 307-548-7228. Fax: 307-548-7228. p. 2651

Capen, Peggy, Librn, Orrington Public Library, 15 School St, Orrington, ME, 04474. Tel: 207-825-4938. p. 995

Capezzuto, Donna, Ref & Instrul Serv, Instr Coordr, Ref Serv, Ohio University, Shannon Hall, 1st Flr, 45425 National Rd, Saint Clairsville, OH, 43950-9724. Tel: 740-695-1720, 740-699-2519. Fax: 740-695-7075. p. 1933

Capitanio, E Renee, Head, Tech Serv, Sachem Public Library, 150 Holbrook Rd, Holbrook, NY, 11741. Tel: 631-588-5024. Fax: 631-588-5064. p. 1637

Capizzo, Louise, Youth Serv Librn, Scarborough Public Library, 48 Gorham Rd, Scarborough, ME, 04074. Tel: 207-883-4723. Fax: 207-883-9728. p. 1000

Caplan, Cassandra, Bus Planning Officer, West Virginia University Libraries, WVU Libraries, 1549 University Ave, Morgantown, WV, 26506. Tel: 304-293-4040. Fax: 304-293-6638. p. 2566

Caplan, Ellen, Head, Cat, Stephen F Austin State University, 1936 North St, Nacogdoches, TX, 75962. Tel: 936-468-1762. Fax: 936-468-7610. p. 2364

Caplan, Frances, Dean of Libr, Robert Morris University Library, 6001 University Blvd, Moon Township, PA, 15108-1189. Tel: 412-397-6868. Fax: 412-397-4288. p. 2092

Caplan, Phyllis, Asst Dir, Digital Serv, Florida Center for Library Automation, 5830 NW 39th Ave, Gainesville, FL, 32606. Tel: 352-392-9020, Ext 324. Fax: 352-392-9185. p. 2940

Caplis, Dennis, Libr Dir, Newaygo Area District Library, 44 N State Rd, Newaygo, MI, 49337-8969. Tel: 231-652-6723. Fax: 231-652-6616. p. 1214

Caplow, Julie, Assoc Prof, University of Missouri-Columbia, 303 Townsend Hall, Columbia, MO, 65211. Tel: 573-882-4546. Fax: 573-884-2917. p. 2968

Capobianco, Margaret, Youth Serv, Long Beach Public Library, 111 W Park Ave, Long Beach, NY, 11561-3326. Tel: 516-432-7201. Fax: 516-889-4641. p. 1654

Capobianco, Sarah, Br Mgr, East Providence Public Library, Riverside, 475 Bullocks Point Ave, East Providence, RI, 02915. Tel: 401-433-4877. Fax: 401-433-4820. p. 2166

Capodagli, James, Ref Librn, SUNY Upstate Medical University, 766 Irving Ave, Syracuse, NY, 13210-1602. Tel: 315-464-7193. Fax: 315-464-4584. p. 1753

Capone, Catherine, Circ Supvr, John C Hart Memorial Library, 1130 Main St, Shrub Oak, NY, 10588. Tel: 914-245-5262. Fax: 914-245-2216. p. 1743

Capone, Mary Ann, Asst Dir, Ansonia Library, 53 S Cliff St, Ansonia, CT, 06401-1909. Tel: 203-734-6275. Fax: 203-732-4551. p. 329

Caporale, Karin, Ref, Wixom Public Library, 49015 Pontiac Trail, Wixom, MI, 48393-2567. Tel: 248-624-2512. Fax: 248-624-0862. p. 1237

Capozzella, Michele, Asst Dir, Danbury Public Library, 170 Main St, Danbury, CT, 06810. Tel: 203-797-4505. Fax: 203-797-4501. p. 335

Capozzi, Maria Angela, Curator, United States National Park Service, 5801 Oxford Rd, Glen Echo, MD, 20812. Tel: 301-320-1411. Fax: 301-320-1415. p. 1030

Cappadonna, Mary, Cat, Oceanside Public Library, 330 N Coast Hwy, Oceanside, CA, 92054-2824. Tel: 760-435-5608. Fax: 760-435-9614. p. 199

Cappel, Lisa, Br Mgr, Public Library of Cincinnati & Hamilton County, Miami Township, Eight N Miami Ave, Cleves, OH, 45002. Tel: 513-369-6050. Fax: 513-369-4487. p. 1872

Cappelli, Cybele, Dir, Astor Home for Children, 6339 Mill St, Rhinebeck, NY, 12572-1427. Tel: 845-871-1013. Fax: 845-876-2020. p. 1727

Cappellini, Nancy, Dir, Hanson Public Library, 132 Maquan St, Hanson, MA, 02341. Tel: 781-293-2151. Fax: 781-293-6801. p. 1093

Cappelson, Sharon, Sr Res Librn, Parade Publications, Inc, 711 Third Avenue, 7th Flr, New York, NY, 10017-4014. Tel: 212-450-7000. Fax: 212-450-7283. p. 1697

Capper, Susan, Librn, Briggs Lawrence County Public Library, Eastern, 410 Elizabeth St, Proctorville, OH, 45669. Tel: 740-886-6697. Fax: 740-886-7175. p. 1906

Cappeta, Pat, Coordr, Ch Serv, Penn Area Library, 2001 Municipal Court, Harrison City, PA, 15636. Tel: 724-744-4414. Fax: 724-744-0226. p. 2066

Capponi, Debra, Br Mgr, Prince George's County Memorial, Bladensburg Branch, 4820 Annapolis Rd, Bladensburg, MD, 20710-1250. Tel: 301-927-4916. Fax: 301-454-0324. p. 1032

Capps, Larry, Exec Dir, US Space & Rocket Center, One Tranquility Base, Huntsville, AL, 35805-3399. Tel: 256-721-7148. Fax: 256-722-5600. p. 22

Caprio, Katie, Assoc Librn, Rensselaerville Library, 1459 County Rte 351, Rensselaerville, NY, 12147. Tel: 518-797-3949. Fax: 518-797-5211. p. 1727

Caprio, Mark, Digital & Tech Serv, Providence College, One Cunningham Sq, Providence, RI, 02918-0001. Tel: 401 865-1996. Fax: 401-865-2823. p. 2173

Capron, Patricia M, Librn, Wells Village Library, Five E Wells Rd, Wells, VT, 05774-9791. Tel: 802-645-0611. p. 2438

Capron, Rhoda, Librn, Blaisdell Memorial Library, 129 Stage Rd, Nottingham, NH, 03290. Tel: 603-679-8484. Fax: 603-679-6774. p. 1461

Capron, Shirley L, Archives Coordr, SIT Graduate Institute/SIT Study Abroad, One Kipling Rd, Brattleboro, VT, 05302. Tel: 802-258-3354. Fax: 802-258-3248. p. 2420

Capuano, James, Supv Librn, Newark Public Library, Five Washington St, Newark, NJ, 07101. Tel: 973-733-7784, 973-733-7800. Fax: 973-733-5648. p. 1511

Capurso, Judith, Instrul Serv Librn, Ulster County Community College, Stone Ridge, NY, 12484. Tel: 845-687-5213. Fax: 845-687-5220. p. 1749

Capute, Virginia, Librn, Chesapeake College, PO Box 8, Wye Mills, MD, 21679. Tel: 410-827-5860. Fax: 410-827-5257. p. 1046

Caputo, Corinne, Head, Tech Serv, Syst Coordr, Westminster College, Reeves Memorial Library, 501 Westminster Ave, Fulton, MO, 65251-1299. Tel: 573-592-5245. Fax: 573-642-6356. p. 1328

Caputo, Lisa, Asst Dir, Head, Adult Serv, Syosset Public Library, 225 S Oyster Bay Rd, Syosset, NY, 11791-5897. Tel: 516-921-7161. Fax: 516-921-8771. p. 1751

Caputo, Maria, In Charge, Congregation Shearith Israel Archives, Eight W 70th St, New York, NY, 10023. Tel: 212-873-0300. Fax: 212-724-6165. p. 1676

Caputo, Victor, Pub Relations, Bryant Library, Two Paper Mill Rd, Roslyn, NY, 11576-2193. Tel: 516-621-2240. Fax: 516-621-7211. p. 1735

Cara, Cass, Librn, Santa Barbara News Press Library, 715 Anacapa St, Santa Barbara, CA, 93101-2203. Tel: 805-564-5200, Ext 251. Fax: 805-966-6258. p. 261

Carabba, Katrina, Br Mgr, Whatcom County Library System, Deming Branch, 5044 Mount Baker Hwy, Deming, WA, 98244. Tel: 360-592-2422. Fax: 360-592-2422. p. 2509

Caradine, Mary L, Librn, Media Spec, Coahoma Community College, 3240 Friars Point Rd, Clarksdale, MS, 38614. Tel: 662-621-4289. Fax: 662-627-9530. p. 1295

Caraher, Michael, Dir, Seneca Falls Library, 47 Cayuga St, Seneca Falls, NY, 13148. Tel: 315-568-8265, Ext 3. Fax: 315-568-1606. p. 1742

Caraluzzo, TerriAnne, Circ Supvr, Citrus County Library System, Floral City Library, 8360 E Orange Ave, Floral City, FL, 34436-3200. Tel: 352-726-3671. Fax: 352-726-1159. p. 427

Caran, Elizabeth, Readers' Serv Manager, Wake County Public Library System, Eva H Perry Regional Library, 2100 Shepherd's Vineyard Dr, Apex, NC, 27502. Tel: 919-387-4304. Fax: 919-387-4320. p. 1818

Carangelo, Martha, Librn, Rio Abajo Community Library, 28 Calle de Centros Sur, La Joya, NM, 87028. Tel: 505-861-8289. p. 1557

Caras, Sally, Librn, Verrill Dana Library, One Portland Sq, Portland, ME, 04112. Tel: 207-253-4964. Fax: 207-774-7499. p. 998

Caravello, A, Circ, North Shore Public Library, 250 Rte 25A, Shoreham, NY, 11786-9677. Tel: 631-929-4488. Fax: 631-929-4551. p. 1743

Caraway, Antoinette, Librn, Saint Petersburg College, Clearwater Campus Library, 2465 Drew St, Clearwater, FL, 33765. Tel: 727-791-2416. Fax: 727-791-2601. p. 483

Caraway, Beatrice, Head, Coll Develop, Acq & Res Sharing, Trinity University, One Trinity Pl, San Antonio, TX, 78212-7200. Tel: 210-999-7292. Fax: 210-999-8182. p. 2383

Carbo, Maryjane, Dir, Beaufort, Hyde & Martin County Regional Library, Old Court House, 158 N Market St, Washington, NC, 27889. Tel: 252-946-6401. Fax: 252-946-0352. p. 1828

Carbo, Maryjane, Dir, Martin Memorial Library, 200 N Smithwick St, Williamston, NC, 27892. Tel: 252-946-6401. Fax: 252-792-8964. p. 1830

Carbo, Toni, Prof, University of Pittsburgh, 135 N Bellefield Ave, Pittsburgh, PA, 15260. Tel: 412-624-5230. Fax: 412-624-5231. p. 2973

Carbo, Toni, PhD, iSchool Prog Leader, DU Univ Ctr for Grad Studies, Sacramento, Teaching Prof, Drexel University, Rush Bldg, Rm 306, 30 N 33rd St, Philadelphia, PA, 19104-2875. Tel: 215-895-2474. Fax: 215-895-2494. p. 2973

Carbone, Christopher, Libr Dir, South Brunswick Public Library, 110 Kingston Lane, Monmouth Junction, NJ, 08852. Tel: 732-329-4000, Ext 7287. Fax: 732-329-0573. p. 1502

Carbone, Denise, Conservator, American Philosophical Society Library, 105 S Fifth St, Philadelphia, PA, 19106-3386. Tel: 215-440-3413. Fax: 215-440-3423. p. 2103

Carbone, Jerry J, Dir, Brooks Memorial Library, 224 Main St, Brattleboro, VT, 05301. Tel: 802-254-5290. Fax: 802-257-2309. p. 2420

Carbone, Kathy, Performing Arts Librn, California Institute of the Arts, 24700 McBean Pkwy, Valencia, CA, 91355. Tel: 661-253-7882. Fax: 661-254-4561. p. 278

Carbone, Marie, ILL, Auburn Public Library, 369 Southbridge St, Auburn, MA, 01501. Tel: 508-832-7790. Fax: 508-832-7792. p. 1051

Carbonell, Marilyn, Coll Develop, Nelson-Atkins Museum of Art, 4525 Oak St, Kansas City, MO, 64111-1873. Tel: 816-751-1381. Fax: 816-751-0498. p. 1340

Carbonell, Marilyn, Head Librn, Nelson-Atkins Museum of Art, 4525 Oak St, Kansas City, MO, 64111-1873. Tel: 816-751-1381. Fax: 816-751-0498. p. 1340

Card, Judy, Youth Serv Coordr, First Regional Library, 370 W Commerce St, Hernando, MS, 38632. Tel: 662-429-4439. Fax: 662-429-8853. p. 1301

Card, Nan, Archivist, Rutherford B Hayes Presidential Center Library, Spiegel Grove, Fremont, OH, 43420-2796. Tel: 419-332-2081, Ext 239. Fax: 419-332-4952. p. 1900

Carda, Mary, Librn, Lake Andes Carnegie Public Library, Fifth & Main St, Lake Andes, SD, 57356. Tel: 605-487-7524. p. 2214

Cardea, Barbara, Librn, Trinity Presbyterian Church Library, 499 Rte 70E, Cherry Hill, NJ, 08034. Tel: 856-428-2050. Fax: 856-795-8471. p. 1478

Cardello, Margaret, Dir, Marlborough Public Library, 35 W Main St, Marlborough, MA, 01752-5510. Tel: 508-624-6901. Fax: 508-485-1494. p. 1103

Carden, Barbara, Circ, Whitworth University, 300 W Hawthorne Rd, Spokane, WA, 99251-0001. Tel: 509-777-3767. Fax: 509-777-3221. p. 2538

Carden, Virginia, Admin Res Librn, Duke University Libraries, Medical Center Library, DUMC Box 3702, Ten Bryan-Searle Dr, Durham, NC, 27710-0001. Tel: 919-660-1184. Fax: 919-681-7599. p. 1788

Cardenas-Dow, Melissa, Behav Sci Librn, Outreach Librn, University of Redlands, 1200 E Colton Ave, Redlands, CA, 92374-3758. Tel: 909-748-8022. Fax: 909-335-5392. p. 215

Cardenas-Parra, Yolanda, Circ, City of Commerce Public Library, 5655 Jillson St, Commerce, CA, 90040-1485. Tel: 323-722-6660. Fax: 323-724-1978. p. 136

Carder, Rachel, Head, Circ, Lucius E & Elsie C Burch Library, 501 Poplar View Pkwy, Collierville, TN, 38017. Tel: 901-457-2600. Fax: 901-854-5893. p. 2230

Cardillo, Maryann, Circ Supvr, Thiel College, 75 College Ave, Greenville, PA, 16125-2183. Tel: 724-589-2118. Fax: 724-589-2122. p. 2063

Cardinal, Darlene, Libr Assoc/Testing Serv Coordr, Edison Community College Library, 1973 Edison Dr, Piqua, OH, 45356. Tel: 937-778-7954. Fax: 937-778-7958. p. 1930

Cardinal, Julia White, Dir, Beals Memorial Library, 50 Pleasant St, Winchendon, MA, 01475. Tel: 978-297-0300. Fax: 978-297-2018. p. 1141

Cardinal, Nancy, Ch, Fort Walton Beach Library, 185 Miracle Strip Pkwy SE, Fort Walton Beach, FL, 32548. Tel: 850-833-9590. Fax: 850-833-9659. p. 447

Cardinale, Salvatore, Info Res Mgr, Day Pitney LLP, 200 Campus Dr, Florham Park, NJ, 07932. Tel: 973-966-6300. Fax: 973-966-1015. p. 1486

Cardo, Ines, Ref Librn, Security Public Library, 715 Aspen Dr, Security, CO, 80911-1807. Tel: 719-391-3191. Fax: 719-392-7641. p. 322

Cardon, Denise, Circ, Coordr, Access Serv, ILL, Northeastern Ohio Universities College of Medicine, 4209 State Rd 44, Rootstown, OH, 44272. Tel: 330-325-6600. Fax: 330-325-0522. p. 1932

Cardona, Maria, Cat, Inter-American University of Puerto Rico, School of Law Library, PO Box 70351, Hato Rey, PR, 00936. Tel: 787-751-1912. Fax: 787-753-6851. p. 2673

Cardoza, Fran, Ref Librn, Rogue Community College, Wiseman Ctr, 3345 Redwood Hwy, Grants Pass, OR, 97527. Tel: 541-956-7153. Fax: 541-471-3588. p. 1999

Cardoza, Jaime, Automation Librn, Dustin Michael Sekula Memorial Library, 1906 S Closner Blvd, Edinburg, TX, 78539. Tel: 956-383-6246. Fax: 956-318-3123. p. 2315

Cardoza, Sandy, Media Spec, De Anza College, 21250 Stevens Creek Blvd, Cupertino, CA, 95014-5793. Tel: 408-864-8771. Fax: 408-864-8603. p. 138

Cardwell, Dorisanne, Libr Asst, Wiregrass Georgia Technical College Library, 4089 Val Tech Rd, Valdosta, GA, 31602. Tel: 229-259-5177. Fax: 229-259-5179. p. 555

Cardwell, Glenda, Librn, Rockford Public Library, 110 Main St, Rockford, AL, 35136. Tel: 256-377-4911. Fax: 256-377-4489. p. 35

Cardwell, Karen, Mgr, Sandia National Laboratories, 7011 East Ave, Livermore, CA, 94550. Tel: 925-294-1029. Fax: 925-294-2355. p. 164

Cardwell-Copenhefer, Carolyn, Instrul Tech Adminr, Louisville Presbyterian Theological Seminary, 1044 Alta Vista Rd, Louisville, KY, 40205-1798. Tel: 502-895-3411, Ext 422. Fax: 502-895-1096. p. 925

Cardy, Eileen, Med Libr Tech, Alberta Health Services, Alberta Hospital-Edmonton Library, 17480 Fort Rd, Edmonton, AB, T5J 2J7, CANADA. Tel: 780-342-5268. Fax: 780-342-5608. p. 2714

Careaga, Greg, Head, Res, Outreach & Instruction, Librn, University of California, 1156 High St, Santa Cruz, CA, 95064. Tel: 831-459-3687. Fax: 831-459-8206. p. 264

Careaga, Juana, Dir of Libr, Florida Keys Community College Library, Bldg A, 2nd Fl, 5901 College Rd, Key West, FL, 33040. Tel: 305-809-3501. Fax: 305-292-5162. p. 456

Career, Suzane, Adminr, Societe de Genealogie de l'Outaouais Bibliotheque, 855, boul de la Gappe, Gatineau, QC, J8T 8H9, CANADA. Tel: 819-686-0291. Fax: 819-568-5933. p. 2884

Cares, Erlene, Patron Serv, Labette Community College Library, 200 S 14th St, Parsons, KS, 67357. Tel: 620-820-1167. Fax: 620-421-1469. p. 889

Caretta, Angela, Br Mgr, Cambridge Libraries & Galleries, Hespeler, Five Tannery St E, Cambridge, ON, N3C 2C1, CANADA. Tel: 519-658-4412. Fax: 519-621-2080. p. 2798

Caretto, Carla, Librn, Rochester College, 800 W Avon Rd, Rochester Hills, MI, 48307. Tel: 248-218-2260. Fax: 248-218-2265. p. 1222

Carew, Colonel John E, Dir, The Salvation Army Archives, 26 Howden Rd, Scarborough, ON, M1R 3E4, CANADA. Tel: 416-285-4344, Ext 25. Fax: 416-285-7763. p. 2841

Carey, Barbara, Librn, Saint Joseph's Seminary, 201 Seminary Ave, Yonkers, NY, 10704. Tel: 914-367-8262. Fax: 914-968-8787. p. 1771

Carey, Cathy, Cat, Ref Serv, Ser, Alverno College Library, 3401 S 39th St, Milwaukee, WI, 53215. Tel: 414-382-6180. Fax: 414-382-6354. p. 2617

Carey, Elizabeth, Dir, Shorewood Public Library, 3920 N Murray Ave, Shorewood, WI, 53211-2385. Tel: 414-847-2670. p. 2638

Carey, Frank, Dir, Daemen College Library, Research & Information Commons, 4380 Main St, Amherst, NY, 14226-3592. Tel: 716-839-8243. Fax: 716-839-8475. p. 1573

Carey, Janice, Supvr, Canadian Centre for Occupational Health & Safety, 135 Hunter St E, Hamilton, ON, L8N 1M5, CANADA. Tel: 905-572-2981, Ext 4454. Fax: 905-572-4500. p. 2808

Carey, John E, Pres, FOI Services Inc Library, 704 Quince Orchard Rd, Ste 275, Gaithersburg, MD, 20878-1751. Tel: 301-975-9400. Fax: 301-975-0702. p. 1030

Carey, Judith, Develop Dir, Cuyahoga County Public Library, 2111 Snow Rd, Parma, OH, 44134-2728. Tel: 216-398-1800. Fax: 216-398-1748. p. 1927

Carey, Karen, Circ Asst, Russell Library, 123 Broad St, Middletown, CT, 06457. Tel: 860-347-2528, Ext 158. p. 352

Carey, Lynne, Asst Libr Dir, Ames Public Library, 515 Douglas Ave, Ames, IA, 50010. Tel: 515-239-5640. Fax: 515-233-9001. p. 792

Carey, Mercedes, Adult, Tech & Media Serv Coordr, LeRoy Collins Leon County Public Library System, 200 W Park Ave, Tallahassee, FL, 32301-7720. Tel: 850-606-2665. Fax: 850-606-2601. p. 492

Carey, Nancy, Librn, New York Mills Public Library, 399 Main St, New York Mills, NY, 13417. Tel: 315-736-5391. p. 1704

Carey Nevin, Judy, Ref Serv Coordr, Otterbein University, 138 W Main St, Westerville, OH, 43081. Tel: 614-823-1366. Fax: 614-823-1921. p. 1946

Carey Nevin, Judy, Ref & Instruction Librn, Piedmont Virginia Community College, 501 College Dr, Charlottesville, VA, 22902. Tel: 434-961-5308. Fax: 434-977-6842. p. 2454

Carey, Paula, Ref Librn, Boston University Libraries, Science & Engineering Library, 38 Cummington St, Boston, MA, 02215. Tel: 617-358-3963. Fax: 617-353-3470. p. 1059

Carey, Rachel, Cataloger, Fontana Regional Library, 33 Fryemont St, Bryson City, NC, 28713. Tel: 828-488-2382. Fax: 828-488-2638. p. 1778

Carey, Susanna O, Dir, Au Sable Forks Free Library, Nine Church Lane, Au Sable Forks, NY, 12912-4400. Tel: 518-647-5596. Fax: 518-647-5753. p. 1575

Carey, Sybil, Asst Dir, ILL Librn, Abbie Greenleaf Library, 439 Main St, Franconia, NH, 03580. Tel: 603-823-8424. Fax: 603-823-5581. p. 1447

Carey, Theresa, Head, Youth Serv, Morton Grove Public Library, 6140 Lincoln Ave, Morton Grove, IL, 60053-2989. Tel: 847-929-5113. Fax: 847-965-7903. p. 676

Carey, Tracy, Dir, Pub Serv, Centre County Library & Historical Museum, 200 N Allegheny St, Bellefonte, PA, 16823-1601. Tel: 814-355-1516. Fax: 814-355-2700. p. 2032

Carey-Robinson, Jennifer, Ch, Leicester Public Library, 1136 Main St, Leicester, MA, 01524-0389. Tel: 508-892-7020. Fax: 508-892-7045. p. 1098

Cargill, Jennifer, Dean of Libr, Louisiana State University Libraries, 295 Middleton Library, Baton Rouge, LA, 70803. Tel: 225-578-2217. Fax: 225-578-9432. p. 943

Cargo, John, Tech Coordr, Iosco-Arenac District Library, 120 W Westover St, East Tawas, MI, 48730. Tel: 989-362-2651. Fax: 989-362-6056. p. 1175

Carhart, Jo-Ann, Head, Adult Serv, East Islip Public Library, 381 E Main St, East Islip, NY, 11730-2896. Tel: 631-581-9200. Fax: 631-581-2245. p. 1617

Carichner, Lena, Librn, Hughesville Area Public Library, 146 S Fifth St, Hughesville, PA, 17737. Tel: 570-584-3762. Fax: 570-584-2689. p. 2070

Carideo, Jean, Br Mgr, Chesapeake Public Library, Greenbrier, 1214 Volvo Pkwy, Chesapeake, VA, 23320-7600. Tel: 757-410-7058. Fax: 757-410-7071. p. 2456

Carignan, Tracie, Br Mgr, Riverside County Library System, Glen Avon Library, 9244 Galena St, Riverside, CA, 92509. Tel: 951-685-8121. Fax: 951-685-7158. p. 217

Carini, Peter, Col Archivist, Dartmouth College Library, Rauner Special Collections Library, 6065 Webster Hall, Hanover, NH, 03755-3519. Tel: 603-646-0538. Fax: 603-646-0447. p. 1450

Carkeek, Richard, Supvr, Circ, University of Washington Libraries, East Asia, 322 Gowen Hall, 3rd Flr, Box 353527, Seattle, WA, 98195-3527. Tel: 206-543-4490. Fax: 206-221-5298. p. 2533

Carl, Cherie, Interim Coordr, Tidewater Community College Learning Resources Center, 300 Granby St, Norfolk, VA, 23510. Tel: 757-822-1772. Fax: 757-822-1106. p. 2483

Carl, Cherie, Ref Librn, Tidewater Community College, 1700 College Crescent, Virginia Beach, VA, 23453. Fax: 757-427-0327. p. 2500

Carl, Patti, Librn, Missouri Department of Corrections, Farmington Correctional Center, 1012 W Columbia St, Farmington, MO, 63640-2902. Tel: 573-218-7100, Ext 346. Fax: 573-218-7106. p. 1334

Carl, Vicky, Asst Librn, ILL Librn, Richards Free Library, 58 N Main St, Newport, NH, 03773-1597. Tel: 603-863-3430. Fax: 603-863-3022. p. 1460

Carla, Waldrup, Librn, Haleyville Public Library, 913 20th St, Haleyville, AL, 35565. Tel: 205-486-7450. Fax: 205-486-7450. p. 19

Carlan, Amy, Libr Mgr, Piedmont Regional Library, Jefferson Public, 379 Old Pendergrass Rd, Jefferson, GA, 30549-2780. Tel: 706-367-8012. p. 557

Carlblom, Sheila, Treas, Association of Christian Librarians, PO Box 4, Cedarville, OH, 45314. Tel: 937-766-2255. Fax: 937-766-5499. p. 2951

Carlblom, Sheila O, Dir, Indiana Wesleyan University, 4201 S Washington St, Marion, IN, 46953. Tel: 765-677-2191. Fax: 765-677-2676. p. 762

Carle, Ann, Cat, George H & Ella M Rodgers Memorial Library, 194 Derry Rd, Hudson, NH, 03051. Tel: 603-886-6030, Ext 4512. Fax: 603-816-4501. p. 1452

Carle, Daria, Ref & Instruction, University of Alaska Anchorage, Consortium Library, 3211 Providence Dr, Anchorage, AK, 99508-8176. Tel: 907-786-1871. Fax: 907-786-1834. p. 45

Carle, Jane R, Dir, Kirtland Public Library, 9267 Chillicothe Rd, Kirtland, OH, 44094. Tel: 440-256-7323. Fax: 440-256-1372. p. 1908

Carle, Mary-Jane, Ch, Bill Memorial Library, 240 Monument St, Groton, CT, 06340. Tel: 860-445-0392. Fax: 860-449-8971. p. 342

Carles, Pam, Access Serv Coordr, The University of Findlay, 1000 N Main St, Findlay, OH, 45840-3695. Tel: 419-434-4612. p. 1899

Carles, Pam, Circ, Winebrenner Theological Seminary Library, 950 N Main St, Findlay, OH, 45840-3652. Tel: 419-434-4263. Fax: 419-434-4267. p. 1899

Carless, Jennifer, Orlando Campus Libr Dir, Keiser University Library System, 1500 NW 49th St, Fort Lauderdale, FL, 33309. Tel: 954-351-4035. Fax: 954-351-4051. p. 443

Carleton, Don E, Dir, University of Texas Libraries, Center for American History, SRH 2-101, D1100, University of Texas at Austin, Austin, TX, 78712. Tel: 512-495-4515. Fax: 512-495-4542. p. 2284

Carleton, Don E, Dr, Dir, University of Texas at Austin Center for American History, 3738 FM 2714, Round Top, TX, 78954. Tel: 979-278-3530. Fax: 979-278-3531. p. 2377

Carleton, Patty, Dir, Youth Serv, Saint Louis Public Library, 1415 Olive St, Saint Louis, MO, 63103-2315. Tel: 314-539-0300. Fax: 314-241-3840. p. 1359

Carli, Melinda, Mgr, Lamar County Library System, Lumberton Public, 106 W Main Ave, Lumberton, MS, 39455. Tel: 601-796-4227. Fax: 601-796-4227. p. 1312

Carlin, Anna, Info Literacy Librn, Florida Gulf Coast University Library, 10501 FGCU Blvd S, Fort Myers, FL, 33965-6501. Tel: 239-590-7663. p. 445

Carlin, Beth, Mgr, Libr Serv, Saint Francis Hospital, 355 Ridge Ave, Evanston, IL, 60202. Tel: 847-316-2460. Fax: 847-316-5816. p. 644

Carlin, Beth, Librn, Westlake Community Hospital Library, 1225 Lake St, Melrose Park, IL, 60160-4000. Tel: 708-999-8406. Fax: 708-316-5816, 708-938-7496. p. 673

Carlin, Jane A, Dir, University of Puget Sound, 1500 N Warner St, Campus Mail Box 1021, Tacoma, WA, 98416-1021. Tel: 253-879-3118. Fax: 253-879-3670. p. 2540

Carlin, Jennifer, Ch, Kemmerer Library Harding Township, 19 Blue Mill Rd, New Vernon, NJ, 07976. Tel: 973-267-2665. p. 1510

Carlin, Sarah, Ref Serv Librn, YA Librn, Scott County Library System, 200 N Sixth Ave, Eldridge, IA, 52748. Tel: 563-285-4794. Fax: 563-285-4743. p. 813

Carlisle, Lisa, Librn, State of Ohio Department of Corrections, 5900 Bis Rd, Lancaster, OH, 43130. Tel: 740-653-4324, Ext 2728. Fax: 740-654-4511. p. 1909

Carlisle, Maeleah, Mgr, Springfield City Library, Brightwood Branch, 359 Plainfield St, Springfield, MA, 01107. Tel: 413-263-6805. Fax: 413-263-6810. p. 1127

Carlisle, Molly, Supvr, Youth Serv, Tigard Public Library, 13500 SW Hall Blvd, Tigard, OR, 97223-8111. Tel: 503-684-6537, Ext 2519. Fax: 503-598-7515, 503-718-2797. p. 2021

Carlisle, Pam, Outreach/Educ, Bossier Parish Central Library, Bossier Parish Historical Center, 2206 Beckett St, Bossier City, LA, 71111. Tel: 318-746-7717. p. 946

Carlisle, Scott, Asst Head, Electronic Res Mgt, Northeastern University Libraries, Snell Library, 360 Huntington Ave, Boston, MA, 02115. Tel: 617-373-2726. p. 1065

Carlisle, Scott, Cat, Princeton University, Department of Rare Books, One Washington Rd, Princeton, NJ, 08544. Tel: 609-258-3184. p. 1523

Carlisle, Tara, Info Literacy Librn, Scottsdale Community College Library, 9000 E Chaparral Rd, Scottsdale, AZ, 85256. Tel: 480-423-6651. Fax: 480-423-6666. p. 80

Carlito, Delores, Ref Librn, Instruction & Outreach, University of Alabama at Birmingham, Mervyn H Sterne Library, 917 13th St S, Birmingham, AL, 35205. Tel: 205-934-6364. p. 10

Carlo, Donna, Libr Asst, Youth Serv, Barry-Lawrence Regional Library, Purdy Branch, 403 Hwy C, Purdy, MO, 65734. Tel: 417-442-7314. Fax: 417-442-7314. p. 1347

Carlock, Barbara, Mgr, Sheridan County Public Library System, Clearmont Branch, 1254 Front St, Clearmont, WY, 82835. Tel: 307-758-4331. Fax: 307-758-4331. p. 2660

Carlock, Ruth, Dir, York College, 1125 E Eighth St, York, NE, 68467-2699. Tel: 402-363-5703. Fax: 402-363-5685. p. 1424

Carlock, Sherry, Asst Librn, Sallie Logan Public Library, 1808 Walnut St, Murphysboro, IL, 62966. Tel: 618-684-3271. Fax: 618-684-2392. p. 678

Carlow, Jennifer, Libr Coordr, Cary Medical Center, 163 Van Buren Rd, Ste 1, Caribou, ME, 04736-2599. Tel: 207-498-3111, Ext 1365. Fax: 207-498-1272. p. 981

Carlquist, Donita, Dir, Wells Branch Community Library, 15001 Wells Port Dr, Austin, TX, 78728. Tel: 512-989-3188. Fax: 512-989-3533. p. 2285

Carlquist, Victoria, Ref, Ridgefield Library Association Inc, 472 Main St, Ridgefield, CT, 06877-4585. Tel: 203-438-2282. Fax: 203-438-4558. p. 365

Carlson, Alexis, Ref/Outreach Librn, Indian River State College, 2229 NW Ninth Ave, Okeechobee, FL, 34972. Tel: 772-462-7600, 863-824-6000. p. 474

Carlson, Amy, Dept Head, University of Hawaii at Manoa Library, Serials Department, 2550 McCarthy Mall, Honolulu, HI, 96822. Tel: 808-956-7692. Fax: 808-956-5968. p. 566

Carlson, Barbara L, Ch, Lyme Public Library, 482 Hamburg Rd, Lyme, CT, 06371-3110. Tel: 860-434-2272. Fax: 860-434-9972. p. 349

Carlson, Beth, Dir, Shell Lake Public Library, 501 First St, Shell Lake, WI, 54871. Tel: 715-468-2074. Fax: 715-468-7638. p. 2638

Carlson, Cindy, ILL Supvr, Northwestern College, 3003 Snelling Ave N, Saint Paul, MN, 55113. Tel: 651-631-5241. Fax: 651-631-5598. p. 1280

Carlson, Coleen, Dir, Converse Jackson Township Public Library, 108 S Jefferson St, Converse, IN, 46919. Tel: 765-395-3344. Fax: 765-395-3733. p. 734

Carlson, Debra, Ch, Lied Scottsbluff Public Library, 1809 Third Ave, Scottsbluff, NE, 69361-2493. Tel: 308-630-6284. Fax: 308-630-6293. p. 1418

Carlson, Erin, Tech Serv Librn, Pepperdine University Libraries, 24255 Pacific Coast Hwy, Malibu, CA, 90263. Tel: 310-506-4252. Fax: 310-506-7225. p. 182

Carlson, Gayle B, Dir, East Hanover Township Free Public Library, 415 Ridgedale Ave, East Hanover, NJ, 07936. Tel: 973-428-3075. Fax: 973-428-7253. p. 1482

Carlson, George, Librn, Santa Clara University, 500 El Camino Real, Santa Clara, CA, 95053-0500. Tel: 408-554-5436. Fax: 408-554-6827. p. 263

Carlson, Greg, Libr Mgr, Frances T Bourne Jacaranda Public Library, 4143 Woodmere Park Blvd, Venice, FL, 34293. Tel: 941-861-1277. Fax: 941-486-2725. p. 501

Carlson, Jane, Youth Serv Librn, Indianola Public Library, 207 North B St, Indianola, IA, 50125. Tel: 515-961-9418. Fax: 515-961-9419. p. 822

Carlson, Jim, Acq, Cat, Coll Develop, UMC Library, 2900 University Ave, Crookston, MN, 56716-0801. Tel: 218-281-8399. Fax: 218-281-8080. p. 1246

Carlson, Joe, Dir, Ironwood Carnegie Public Library, 235 E Aurora St, Ironwood, MI, 49938-2178. Tel: 906-932-0203. Fax: 906-932-2447. p. 1194

Carlson, John, Dir, University of Wisconsin-Madison, Center for Demography & Ecology Library, 4471 Social Science Bldg, 1180 Observatory Dr, Madison, WI, 53706-1393. Tel: 608-262-4879. Fax: 608-262-8400. p. 2608

Carlson, Jolene, Asst Dir, Downers Grove Public Library, 1050 Curtiss St, Downers Grove, IL, 60515. Tel: 630-960-1200. Fax: 630-960-9374. p. 637

Carlson, Jonathan, Sci Librn, Saint John's University, 2835 Abbey Plaza, Collegeville, MN, 56321. Tel: 320-363-2579. Fax: 320-363-2126. p. 1246

Carlson, Jonathan, Sci Librn, College of Saint Benedict, 37 S College Ave, Saint Joseph, MN, 56374. Tel: 320-363-2579. Fax: 320-363-5197. p. 1277

Carlson, Joshua, Youth Serv Dir, Utica Public Library, 303 Genesee St, Utica, NY, 13501. Tel: 315-735-2279. Fax: 315-734-1034. p. 1760

Carlson, Judith, Head, Archives, Head, Tech Serv, Westfield State University, 577 Western Ave, Westfield, MA, 01085-2580. Tel: 413-572-5252. Fax: 413-572-5520. p. 1138

Carlson, Julie, Br Mgr, Cameron Parish Library, Johnson Bayou, 4586 Gulf Beach Hwy, Cameron, LA, 70631. Tel: 337-569-2892. Fax: 337-569-2905. p. 946

Carlson, Kathleen, Dir, Wyoming Supreme Court, Supreme Court Bldg, 2301 Capitol Ave, Cheyenne, WY, 82002-0450. Tel: 307-777-7509. Fax: 307-777-7240. p. 2653

Carlson, Kathy, Asst Dir, Wellman Scofield Public Library, 711 Fourth St, Wellman, IA, 52356. Tel: 319-646-6858. Fax: 319-646-6561. p. 851

Carlson, Kristin, Br Mgr, Winnetka-Northfield Public Library District, Northfield, 1785 Orchard Ln, Winnetka, IL, 60093. Tel: 847-446-5990. Fax: 847-446-6586. p. 720

Carlson, Kristin, Ch, Williamsburg Public Library, 214 W State St, Williamsburg, IA, 52361. Tel: 319-668-1195. Fax: 319-668-9621. p. 853

Carlson, Linda, Reader Serv, Johns Hopkins University School of Advanced International Studies, 1740 Massachusetts Ave NW, Washington, DC, 20036. Tel: 202-663-5903. Fax: 202-663-5916. p. 405

Carlson, Margaret, Ch, Saint John the Baptist Parish Library, 2920 New Hwy 51, LaPlace, LA, 70068. Tel: 985-652-2225, 985-652-6857. Fax: 985-652-8005. p. 954

Carlson, Marilyn Kay, Librn, Little River Community Library, 125 Main St, Little River, KS, 67457. Tel: 620-897-6610. p. 880

Carlson, Mark, Librn, Tulsa City-County Library, Skiatook Branch, 316 E Rogers Blvd, Skiatook, OK, 74073. Tel: 918-596-2830. Fax: 918-596-2831. p. 1983

Carlson, Mary B, Librn, Fairview-Southdale Hospital, 6401 France Ave S, Edina, MN, 55435. Tel: 952-924-5005. Fax: 952-924-5933. p. 1249

Carlson, Michael, Br Mgr, Frederick County Public Libraries, Brunswick Branch, 915 N Maple Ave, Brunswick, MD, 21716. Tel: 301-600-7251. Fax: 301-834-8763. p. 1029

Carlson, Nancy, Librn, Novartis Consumer Health Library, 10401 Hwy 6, Lincoln, NE, 68517. Tel: 402-464-6311, Ext 68915. p. 1406

Carlson, Neal, Assoc Prof, Ser Librn, Lincoln University, 1570 Old Baltimore Pike, Lincoln University, PA, 19352. Tel: 484-365-7262. Fax: 610-932-1206. p. 2082

Carlson, Pat, Librn, Department of Veterans Affairs, 1898 Fort Rd, Sheridan, WY, 82801. Tel: 307-672-1661. Fax: 307-672-1652. p. 2660

Carlson, Patricia, Town Librn, Stamford Community Library, 986 Main Rd, Stamford, VT, 05352. Tel: 802-694-1379. Fax: 802-694-1636. p. 2436

Carlson, Penny, Br Librn, Cadillac-Wexford Public Library, Mesick Branch, 117 Eugene St, Mesick, MI, 49668. Tel: 231-885-1120. Fax: 231-885-1120. p. 1160

Carlson, Robert, Br Mgr, San Francisco Public Library, North Beach Branch Library, 2000 Mason St, San Francisco, CA, 94133-2337. Tel: 415-355-5626. Fax: 415-772-8251. p. 246

Carlson, Ronnie, Media Serv Supvr, Saint Catherine University, Minneapolis Campus, 601 25th Ave S, Minneapolis, MN, 55454. Tel: 651-690-7792. p. 1281

Carlson, Ruth, In Charge, Northern Illinois University Libraries, Hoffman Estates Education Center, NIU HEEC, 5555 Trillium Blvd, Hoffman Estates, IL, 60192. Tel: 815-753-8830. Fax: 815-752-8980. p. 635

Carlson, Sarah, Pub Serv, Stoughton Public Library, 304 S Fourth St, Stoughton, WI, 53589-0191. Tel: 608-873-6281. Fax: 608-873-0108. p. 2640

Carlson, Sharon, Dr, Dir, Western Michigan University, Archives & Regional History Collection, 111 East Hall, 1903 W Michigan Ave, Kalamazoo, MI, 49008-5307. Tel: 269-387-8496. Fax: 269-387-8484. p. 1198

Carlson, Susan, Ref Serv, Ad, Georgetown Charter Township Library, 1525 Baldwin St, Jenison, MI, 49428. Tel: 616-457-9620. Fax: 616-457-3666. p. 1196

Carlson, Susan, Asst Dir, Mason County District Library, 217 E Ludington Ave, Ludington, MI, 49431-2118. Tel: 231-843-8465. Fax: 231-843-1491. p. 1204

Carlson, Terry, Br Mgr, San Francisco Public Library, West Portal Branch Library, 190 Lenox Way, San Francisco, CA, 94127-1113. Tel: 415-355-2886. Fax: 415-731-3269. p. 247

Carlson, Trudy, Assoc Dir, Libr Admin Serv, Tarleton State University Library, 201 Saint Felix, Stephenville, TX, 76401. Tel: 254-968-9455. Fax: 254-968-9467. p. 2389

Carlson, Vicki, Cat Mgr, Wegner Health Science Information Center, 1400 W 22nd St, Ste 100, Sioux Falls, SD, 57105. Tel: 605-357-1400. Fax: 605-357-1490. p. 2219

Carlsson, Ann D, Dir, Simon Fairfield Public Library, 290 Main St, East Douglas, MA, 01516. Tel: 508-476-2695. Fax: 508-476-2695. p. 1086

Carlstrom, Judith, Tech Serv, The State Library of Massachusetts, State House, Rm 341, 24 Beacon St, Boston, MA, 02133. Tel: 617-727-2590, Ext 272. Fax: 617-727-5819. p. 1067

Carlyle, Allyson, Assoc Prof, University of Washington, Mary Gates Hall, Ste 370, Campus Box 352840, Seattle, WA, 98195-2840. Tel: 206-685-9937. Fax: 206-616-3152. p. 2976

Carlzen, Stella, Commun Libr Mgr, Mohave County Library District, 3269 N Burbank St, Kingman, AZ, 86402-7000. Tel: 928-692-5714. Fax: 928-757-0458. p. 66

Carmack, Cynthia, Dir, Millard Oakley Library, 107 E Main St, Livingston, TN, 38570. Tel: 931-823-1888. Fax: 931-403-0798. p. 2245

Carmack, Joyce, Dir, Martin Township Public Library, 132 W Main St, Colfax, IL, 61728. Tel: 309-723-2541. Fax: 309-723-5037. p. 630

Carmack, Nan, Dir, Campbell County Public Library, 684 Village Hwy, Lower Level, Rustburg, VA, 24588. Tel: 434-332-9658. Fax: 434-332-9697. p. 2495

Carman, Carol, Ref, Maryland State Law Library, Courts of Appeal Bldg, 361 Rowe Blvd, Annapolis, MD, 21401-1697. Tel: 410-260-1430. Fax: 410-260-1572, 410-974-2063. p. 1010

Carman, Debbie, Info Spec, E I Du Pont De Nemours & Co, Inc, Elkton Rd, Newark, DE, 19714. Tel: 302-366-5353. p. 385

Carman, Deborah, Ref Librn, Res Librn, University of Kansas Medical Center, 2100 W 39th Ave, Kansas City, KS, 66160-7180. Tel: 913-588-7118. Fax: 913-588-7304. p. 876

Carman, Tonya, Bus Mgr, Anderson City, Anderson, Stony Creek & Union Townships Public Library, 111 E 12th St, Anderson, IN, 46016-2701. Tel: 765-641-2198. Fax: 765-641-2197. p. 723

Carmelita, Mary, Sister, Librn, Saint Joseph's Hospital, 16th St & Girard Ave, Philadelphia, PA, 19130-1615. Tel: 215-787-9000, 215-787-9156. p. 2116

Carmical, Ethel, Dir, Humphreys County Public Library, 201 Pavo Ave, Waverly, TN, 37185-1529. Tel: 931-296-2143. Fax: 931-296-6520. p. 2268

Carmichael, Beverly, Librn, Windham Town Library, Town Hall, 26 Harrington Rd, Windham, VT, 05359. Tel: 802-875-2244. p. 2440

Carmichael, Chris, Tech Serv & Syst Mgr, Owen Sound & North Grey Union Public Library, 824 First Ave W, Owen Sound, ON, N4K 4K4, CANADA. Tel: 519-376-6623. Fax: 519-376-7170. p. 2834

Carmichael, Christine, Ref, Webmaster, Creighton University, 2500 California Plaza, Omaha, NE, 68178-0209. Tel: 402-280-1757. Fax: 402-280-2435. p. 1412

Carmichael, James V, Jr, Dr, Prof, University of North Carolina at Greensboro, School of Education, 349 Curry Bldg, Greensboro, NC, 27402. Tel: 336-334-3478. Fax: 336-334-5060. p. 2971

Carmichael, Lisandra, Head, Circ, University of West Florida, 11000 University Pkwy, Pensacola, FL, 32514-5750. Tel: 850-474-2412. Fax: 850-474-3338. p. 482

Carmichael, Thomas, Dr, Dean, University of Western Ontario, Faculty of Information & Media Studies, North Campus Bldg, Rm 240, London, ON, N6A 5B7, CANADA. Tel: 519-661-4017. Fax: 519-661-3506. p. 2978

Carmichael, Wendy, Tech Serv, British Columbia Legislative Library, Parliament Bldgs, Victoria, BC, V8V 1X4, CANADA. Tel: 250-356-9186. Fax: 250-356-7216. p. 2745

Carmichael, Yvonne, Asst Dir, Tech Serv, Clayton County Library System, 865 Battlecreek Rd, Jonesboro, GA, 30236. Tel: 770-473-3850. Fax: 770-473-3858. p. 536

Carmody, Deb, Libr Asst, Monmouth County Historical Association Library & Archives, 70 Court St, Freehold, NJ, 07728. Tel: 732-462-1466. Fax: 732-462-8346. p. 1487

Carmona, Yann, Lit Develop Assoc, French Institute-Alliance Francaise Library, 22 E 60th St, New York, NY, 10022-1077. Tel: 646-388-6639. Fax: 212-935-4119. p. 1679

Carnahan, Jennifer, Tech Serv Librn, Wartburg Theological Seminary, 333 Wartburg Pl, Dubuque, IA, 52003. Tel: 563-589-0267. Fax: 563-589-0333. p. 812

Carnahan, Kinney, Ch, Johnston Public Library, 6700 Merle Hay Rd, Johnston, IA, 50131-0327. Tel: 515-278-5233. Fax: 515-278-4975. p. 824

Carnahan, Paul A, Librn, Vermont Historical Society Library, Vermont History Ctr, 60 Washington St, Barre, VT, 05641-4209. Tel: 802-479-8509. Fax: 802-479-8510. p. 2418

Carnahan, Sally Ann, Libr Tech, Mount Hope-Funks Grove Townships Library District, 111 S Hamilton St, McLean, IL, 61754-7624. Tel: 309-874-2291. Fax: 309-874-2291. p. 672

Carneal, Tom, Curator, Nodaway County Historical Society/Mary H Jackson Research Center, 110 N Walnut St, Maryville, MO, 64468-2251. Tel: 660-582-8176. Fax: 660-562-3377. p. 1344

Carner, Dorothy, Librn, University of Missouri-Columbia, Columbia Missourian Newspaper Library, School of Journalism, 315 Lee Hills Hall, Columbia, MO, 65205. Tel: 573-882-6591. Fax: 573-882-5702. p. 1325

Carner, Dorothy J, Head, Journalism Libr, University of Missouri-Columbia, Frank Lee Martin Memorial Journalism Library, 449 S Ninth St, 102 Reynolds Journalism Institute, Columbia, MO, 65211. Tel: 573-882-7502. Fax: 573-884-4963. p. 1326

Carnes, Abbie, YA Serv, York County Library, 138 E Black St, Rock Hill, SC, 29731. Tel: 803-981-5830. Fax: 803-981-5866. p. 2203

Carnes, Lee Elliott, Libr Mgr, K&L Gates Law Library, Hearst Tower, 214 N Tryon St, 47th Flr, Charlotte, NC, 28202. Tel: 704-331-7553. Fax: 704-353-3253. p. 1783

Carnes, Michelle D, Br Mgr, Atlanta-Fulton Public Library System, Fairburn Hobgood-Palmer Library, 60 Valley View Dr, Fairburn, GA, 30213. Tel: 770-306-3138. Fax: 770-306-3140. p. 512

Carnes, Vanda, Dir, Knightstown Public Library, Five E Main St, Knightstown, IN, 46148-1248. Tel: 765-345-5095. Fax: 765-345-5377. p. 757

Carnevale, Ellen, Librn, Population Reference Bureau Library, 1875 Connecticut Ave NW, Ste 520, Washington, DC, 20009-5728. Fax: 202-328-3937. p. 413

Carney, Amy, Coll Coordr, Seward Community Library Museum, 239 Six Ave, Seward, AK, 99664. Tel: 907-224-4010. Fax: 907-224-3521. p. 53

Carney, Barbara, Asst Dir, Vigo County Historical Museum Library, 1411 S Sixth St, Terre Haute, IN, 47802. Tel: 812-235-9717. Fax: 812-235-4998. p. 781

Carney, Colleen, Dir, York County Library, 138 E Black St, Rock Hill, SC, 29731. Tel: 803-981-5858. Fax: 803-981-5866. p. 2203

Carney, Kathleen, Assoc Univ Librn, Boston College Libraries, 140 Commonwealth Ave, Chestnut Hill, MA, 02467. Tel: 617-552-4470. Fax: 617-552-8828. p. 1080

Carney, Kathleen, Assoc Univ Librn, Instrul Serv Librn, Res, Boston College Libraries, Thomas P O'Neill Jr Library (Central Library), 140 Commonwealth Ave, Chestnut Hill, MA, 02467. Tel: 617-552-8709. Fax: 617-552-0599. p. 1081

Carney, Kathleen, Dir of Libr Serv, College of the Holy Cross, One College St, Worcester, MA, 01610. Tel: 508-793-3372. Fax: 508-793-2372. p. 1143

Carney, Marilyn, Health Sci Librn, Ser, Wake Technical Community College, Health Sciences, 2901 Holston Lane, Raleigh, NC, 27610-2092. Tel: 919-747-0003. p. 1818

Carney, Marilyn, Ser, Wake Technical Community College, 9101 Fayetteville Rd, Raleigh, NC, 27603-5696. Tel: 919-866-5642. Fax: 919-662-3575. p. 1818

Carney, Neal, Ref Librn, Massasoit Community College Library, One Massasoit Blvd, Brockton, MA, 02302. Tel: 508-588-9100, Ext 1941. Fax: 508-427-1265. p. 1071

Carney, Shirley, Dir, Western District Library, 1111 Fourth St, Orion, IL, 61273. Tel: 309-526-8375. Fax: 309-526-8375. p. 686

Carney-Smith, Jessie, PhD, Dr, Dean, Univ Libr, Fisk University, Fisk University, 1000 17th Ave N, Nashville, TN, 37208-3051. Tel: 615-329-8730. Fax: 615-329-8761. p. 2256

Carns, Paula, Interim Librn, University of Illinois Library at Urbana-Champaign, Latin American & Caribbean, 324 University of Illinois Library

MC 522, 1408 W Gregory Dr, Urbana, IL, 61801. Tel: 217-244-1902. Fax: 217-333-2214. p. 712

Carns, Paula, Lit & Lang Librn, University of Illinois Library at Urbana-Champaign, Literatures & Languages, 225 Main Libr, 1408 W Gregory Dr, Urbana, IL, 61801. Tel: 217-333-0076. Fax: 217-333-2214. p. 712

Carol, Edquist, Librn, Beauval Public Library, Bag Service, No 9000, Beauval, SK, S0M 0G0, CANADA. Tel: 306-288-2022, Ext 3304. Fax: 306-288-2222. p. 2917

Carol-Ricks, Sally, Electronic Res, Syst Librn, Texas Lutheran University, 1000 W Court St, Seguin, TX, 78155-5978. Tel: 830-372-8100. Fax: 830-372-8156. p. 2386

Carolan, Mary Lou, Dir, Wallkill Public Library, Seven Bona Ventura Ave, Wallkill, NY, 12589-4422. Tel: 845-895-3707. Fax: 845-895-8659. p. 1762

Caroleo, Linn, Dir, Cundy's Harbor Library, 935 Cundy's Harbor Rd, Harpswell, ME, 04079-4511. Tel: 207-725-1461. p. 987

Caroli, Carlo, Ser/Circ Coordr, Supvr (Weekend), A T Still University of Health Sciences, Kirksville Campus, 800 W Jefferson St, Kirksville, MO, 63501. Tel: 660-626-2886. Fax: 660-626-2031, 660-626-2333. p. 1342

Carolyn, Oldt, Br Mgr, Gloucester County Library System, Logan Township, 498 Beckett Rd, Logan Township, NJ, 08085. Tel: 856-241-0202. Fax: 856-241-0491. p. 1507

Caron, Daniel J, PhD, Dep Head & Librn & Archivist of Can, Library & Archives Canada, 550 De la Cité Blvd, Gatineau, QC, K1A 0N4, CANADA. Tel: 819-934-5800. Fax: 819-934-5888. p. 2883

Caron, Francoise, Librn, York Library Region, Bibliotheque Dre-Marguerite-Michaud, 715 Priestman St, Fredericton, NB, E3B 5W7, CANADA. Tel: 506-453-7100. Fax: 506-453-3958. p. 2764

Caron, Gilbert, Chief Financial Officer, University of Ottawa Libraries, 65 University, Ottawa, ON, K1N 6N5, CANADA. Tel: 613-562-5800, Ext 3646. Fax: 613-562-5195. p. 2834

Caron, Jenny, Ch, Watertown Free Public Library, 123 Main St, Watertown, MA, 02472. Tel: 617-972-6435. Fax: 617-926-4375. p. 1134

Caron, Josée, Librn, Bibliotheque Municipale de Sainte-Anne-de-Bellevue, 40, rue Saint-Pierre, Sainte-Anne-de-Bellevue, QC, H9X 1Y6, CANADA. Tel: 514-457-5248. Fax: 514-457-7146. p. 2909

Caron, Josephine, Br Mgr, Long Beach Public Library, Los Altos, 5614 E Britton Dr, Long Beach, CA, 90815. Tel: 562-570-1045. p. 167

Carosella, Paula, Outreach Librn, Schenectady County Public Library, 99 Clinton St, Schenectady, NY, 12305-2083. Tel: 518-388-4521. Fax: 518-386-2241. p. 1740

Carotenuto, Gwen, Dir, Westville Public Library, 1035 Broadway, Westville, NJ, 08093. Tel: 856-456-0357. Fax: 856-742-8190. p. 1543

Carpenter, Abby, Info Serv Supvr, Florence-Lauderdale Public Library, 350 N Wood Ave, Florence, AL, 35630. Tel: 256-764-6564. Fax: 256-764-6629. p. 17

Carpenter, Anne, Librn, Autism Society of Michigan Library, 2178 Commons Pkwy, Okemos, MI, 48864. Tel: 517-882-2800. Fax: 517-882-2816. p. 1215

Carpenter, Beth, Web Coordr, Outagamie Waupaca Library System, 225 N Oneida, Appleton, WI, 54911-4780. Tel: 920-832-6190. Fax: 920-832-6422. p. 2578

Carpenter, Beth, Dir, Kimberly Public Library, 515 W Kimberly Ave, Kimberly, WI, 54136. Tel: 920-788-7515. Fax: 920-788-7516. p. 2602

Carpenter, Betty, Librn, Public Library of Mount Vernon & Knox County, Gambier Public, 115 Meadow Lane, Gambier, OH, 43022. Tel: 740-427-2665. Fax: 740-427-2665. p. 1919

Carpenter, Betty, Mgr, Public Library of Mount Vernon & Knox County, Danville Public, 512 S Market St, Danville, OH, 43014-9609. Tel: 740-599-2665. Fax: 740-599-2665. p. 1919

Carpenter, Brian, Ref & Instruction Librn, Blinn College Library, 800 Blinn Blvd, Brenham, TX, 77833. Tel: 979-830-4250. Fax: 979-830-4222. p. 2291

Carpenter, Cathy, Head, Archit Libr, Georgia Institute of Technology Library, 704 Cherry St, Atlanta, GA, 30332-0900. Tel: 404-894-4501. Fax: 404-894-6084. p. 515

Carpenter, Cathy, Head, Archit Libr, Georgia Institute of Technology, College of Architecture Library, 245 Fourth St, Rm 152, Atlanta, GA, 30332-0900. Tel: 404-894-4877. p. 515

Carpenter, Cheryl, Br Mgr, Mansfield-Richland County Public Library, Plymouth Branch, 29 W Broadway, Plymouth, OH, 44865. Tel: 419-687-5655. Fax: 419-687-5655. p. 1913

Carpenter, David, Assoc Dir, Head, Ref, Vanderbilt University, Central Library, 419 21st Ave S, Nashville, TN, 37203-2427. Tel: 615-322-3618. Fax: 615-343-7451. p. 2260

Carpenter, Frances, Asst Librn, Sedan Public Library, 115 N Chautauqua St, Sedan, KS, 67361-1301. Tel: 620-725-3405. Fax: 620-725-3405. p. 894

Carpenter, Gail, Circ Mgr, Tech Serv Mgr, Brandon Township Public Library, 304 South St, Ortonville, MI, 48462. Tel: 248-627-1472. Fax: 248-627-9880. p. 1215

Carpenter, Jennifer, Ser, Ohio State University LIBRARIES, Lima Campus Library, 4240 Campus Dr, Lima, OH, 45804. Tel: 419-995-8401. Fax: 419-995-8138. p. 1888

Carpenter, Judy, Ch, Penfield Public Library, 1985 Baird Rd, Penfield, NY, 14526. Tel: 585-340-8720. Fax: 585-340-8748. p. 1716

Carpenter, Kathryn, Asst Univ Librn, Health Sci, University of Illinois at Chicago, MC 234, 801 S Morgan St, Chicago, IL, 60607. Tel: 312-996-2227. Fax: 312-996-9584. p. 627

Carpenter, Kathryn, Asst Univ Librn, University of Illinois at Chicago, Library of the Health Sciences, Chicago, 1750 W Polk St, Chicago, IL, 60612. Tel: 312-996-8966. Fax: 312-996-9584. p. 627

Carpenter, Kathryn, Dir, National Network of Libraries of Medicine Greater Midwest Region, c/o Library of Health Sci, Univ Illinois at Chicago, 1750 W Polk St, M/C 763, Chicago, IL, 60612-4330. Tel: 312-996-2464. Fax: 312-996-2226. p. 2942

Carpenter, Kell, Ref Librn, Twin Lakes Library System, 151 S Jefferson St SE, Milledgeville, GA, 31061-3419. Tel: 478-452-0677. Fax: 478-452-0680. p. 545

Carpenter, Laurie, Dir, Orono Public Library, 39 Pine St, Orono, ME, 04473. Tel: 207-866-5060. p. 994

Carpenter, Lorenza, In Charge, Imperial County Free Library, Holtville Branch, 101 E Sixth St, Holtville, CA, 92250-1228. Tel: 760-356-2385. Fax: 760-356-2437. p. 145

Carpenter, Maria, Dir, Somerville Public Library, 79 Highland Ave, Somerville, MA, 02143. Tel: 617-623-5000. Fax: 617-628-4052. p. 1124

Carpenter, Mary, Support Serv Mgr, Council Bluffs Public Library, 400 Willow Ave, Council Bluffs, IA, 51503-4269. Tel: 712-323-7553, Ext 127. Fax: 712-323-1269. p. 805

Carpenter, Mary, In Charge, Alcona County Library System, Mikado Township, 2291 S F-41, Mikado, MI, 48745. Tel: 989-736-8389. Fax: 989-736-8389. p. 1188

Carpenter, Mary, Dir, Fred A Vaught Memorial Public Library, 211 White Oak St, Hartsville, TN, 37074-1420. Tel: 615-374-3677. Fax: 615-374-4553. p. 2237

Carpenter, Mary, Regional Mgr, Tennessee State Library & Archives, 403 Seventh Ave N, Nashville, TN, 37243-0312. Tel: 731-587-2347. Fax: 615-532-2472, 615-741-6471. p. 2259

Carpenter, Mary Vaughan, Dir, University of Tennessee at Martin, Ten Wayne Fisher Dr, Martin, TN, 38238. Tel: 731-881-7070. Fax: 731-881-7074. p. 2246

Carpenter, Mildred, Acq, Allan Hancock College, 800 S College Dr, Santa Maria, CA, 93454. Tel: 805-922-6966, Ext 3637. Fax: 805-922-3763. p. 265

Carpenter, Monica, Head Librn, La Harpe Carnegie Public Library District, 209 E Main St, La Harpe, IL, 61450. Tel: 217-659-7729. Fax: 217-659-7735. p. 662

Carpenter, Pat, Asst Dir, Nineveh Public Library of Colesville Township, 3029 NY State Hwy 7, Nineveh, NY, 13813. Tel: 607-693-1858. Fax: 607-693-1858. p. 1706

Carpenter, Pat, Librn, Platte County Public Library, Guernsey Branch, 108 S Wyoming Ave, Guernsey, WY, 82214. Tel: 307-836-2816. p. 2661

Carpenter, Peggy, Librn, Zeigler Public Library, 102 E Maryland St, Zeigler, IL, 62999. Tel: 618-596-2041. Fax: 618-596-2041. p. 722

Carpenter, Robert, Dir, Hampton Public Library, 4207 Victoria Blvd, Hampton, VA, 23669-4243. Tel: 757-727-1154. Fax: 757-727-1152. p. 2468

Carpenter, Stewart, Head, Cat, First Regional Library, 370 W Commerce St, Hernando, MS, 38632. Tel: 662-429-4439. Fax: 662-429-8853. p. 1301

Carpenter, Van, Dir, Northland International University Library, W10085 Pike Plains Rd, Dunbar, WI, 54119. Tel: 715-324-6999, Ext 5500. Fax: 715-324-6133. p. 2588

Carpenter, Wyvonia, Dir, Centreville Public Library, 701 S 47th St, Centreville, IL, 62207. Tel: 618-271-2040. Fax: 618-271-6893. p. 602

Carper, John, In Charge, John Snow, Inc, 44 Farnsworth St, Boston, MA, 02210-1211. Tel: 617-482-9485. Fax: 617-482-0617. p. 1067

Carr, Alan, Assoc Dir, National Network of Libraries of Medicine Pacific Southwest Region, Louise M Darling Biomedical Library, 12-077 Ctr for Health Science, Box 951798, Los Angeles, CA, 90095-1798. Tel: 310-825-7263. Fax: 310-825-5389. p. 2938

Carr, Allison, Soc Sci Librn, California State University, 333 S Twin Oaks Valley Rd, San Marcos, CA, 92096-0001. Tel: 760-750-4340. Fax: 760-750-3287. p. 254

Carr, Allison, Ref & Instruction Librn, Central Georgia Technical College Library, 3300 Macon Tech Dr, Macon, GA, 31206-3628. Tel: 478-757-3547. Fax: 478-757-3545. p. 540

Carr, Amber, Pub Serv, Missouri Southern State University, 3950 E Newman Rd, Joplin, MO, 64801-1595. Tel: 417-625-9386. Fax: 417-625-9734. p. 1336

Carr, Anna, Asst Dir, Northeast Harbor Library, One Joy Rd, Northeast Harbor, ME, 04662. Tel: 207-276-3333. Fax: 207-276-3315. p. 994

Carr, Annette, Bus Librn, Touro College Libraries, 43 W 23rd St, Fifth Fl, New York, NY, 10010. Tel: 212-463-0400, Ext 5321. Fax: 212-627-3696. p. 1701

Carr, Ashley, Ref Librn, Austin Community College, Northridge Campus Library, 11928 Stone Hollow Dr, Austin, TX, 78758. Tel: 512-223-4869. Fax: 512-223-4902. p. 2278

Carr, Barbara, Cat, Johnson C Smith University, 100 Beatties Ford Rd, Charlotte, NC, 28216. Tel: 704-371-6740. Fax: 704-378-1191. p. 1783

Carr, Barbara, Librn, Grant County Library, 18 Mountain View St, Petersburg, WV, 26847-1524. Tel: 304-257-4122. Fax: 304-257-4122. p. 2569

Carr, Brenda, Tech Librn, Dighton Public Library, 395 Main St, Dighton, MA, 02715. Tel: 508-669-6421. Fax: 508-669-6963. p. 1084

Carr, Coleen, Acq, Rider University, 2083 Lawrenceville Rd, Lawrenceville, NJ, 08648-3099. Tel: 609-896-5111. Fax: 609-896-8029. p. 1494

Carr, Curtis, Syst Coordr, Virginia Polytechnic Institute & State University Libraries, Drill Field Dr, Blacksburg, VA, 24062-9001. Tel: 540-231-6617. Fax: 540-231-3946. p. 2451

Carr, Dana, Br Librn, Grant County Library, Allegheny-Mountain Top, PO Box 161, Mount Storm, WV, 26739-0161. Tel: 304-693-7504. Fax: 304-693-7504. p. 2569

Carr, Ericka, Interim County Librn, Merced County Library, 2100 O St, Merced, CA, 95340-3637. Tel: 209-385-7484. Fax: 209-726-7912. p. 185

Carr, Gabrielle, Coordr, Access Serv, Indiana University Southeast Library, 4201 Grant Line Rd, New Albany, IN, 47150. Tel: 812-941-2262. Fax: 812-941-2656. p. 767

Carr, Gayle, Dir, Greenup Township Public Library, 101 N Franklin St, Greenup, IL, 62428. Tel: 217-923-3616. Fax: 217-923-3616. p. 652

Carr, Gregory C, Br Mgr, Las Vegas-Clark County Library District, Sunmerlin Library & Performing Arts Center, 1771 Inner Circle Dr, Las Vegas, NV, 89134. Tel: 702-507-3860. Fax: 702-507-3880. p. 1430

Carr, Jane, Head, Ref, Mgr, Tech Serv, Lake Oswego Public Library, 706 Fourth St, Lake Oswego, OR, 97034-2399. Tel: 503-636-7628. Fax: 503-635-4171. p. 2003

Carr, Jean, Ch, Vernon Free Public Library, 567 Governor Hunt Rd, Vernon, VT, 05354-9484. Tel: 802-257-0150. Fax: 802-257-4949. p. 2437

Carr, Jerome B, Pres, Carr Research Laboratory, Inc Library, 251 W Central St, Ste D-36, Natick, MA, 01760. Tel: 508-651-7027. Fax: 508-647-4737. p. 1107

Carr Jeter, Crystal, Br Mgr, Cleveland Public Library, Lorain, 8216 Lorain Ave, Cleveland, OH, 44102. Tel: 216-623-7011. Fax: 216-623-7014. p. 1878

Carr, John, Dir, Brumback Library, 215 W Main St, Van Wert, OH, 45891-1695. Tel: 419-238-2168. Fax: 419-238-3180. p. 1943

Carr, Karen, Dir, Wilton Public Library, 400 East St, Wilton, WI, 54670. Tel: 608-435-6710. Fax: 608-435-6190. p. 2649

Carr, Kathy, Madison County Library System, Flora Public Library, 168 Carter St No C, Flora, MS, 39071. Tel: 601-879-8835. Fax: 601-879-8835. p. 1295

Carr, Lee, Circ/Ser Asst, Holy Family University Library, 9801 Frankford Ave, Philadelphia, PA, 19114. Tel: 267-341-3315, 267-341-3316. Fax: 215-632-8067. p. 2111

Carr, Lisa, Dir, Seymour Public Library District, 176-178 Genesee St, Auburn, NY, 13021. Tel: 315-252-2571. Fax: 315-252-7985. p. 1576

Carr, Lisa, Chief Librn, Watertown Daily Times Library, 260 Washington St, Watertown, NY, 13601. Tel: 315-782-1000, Ext 345. Fax: 315-661-2523. p. 1764

Carr, Marcia, Br Mgr, Door County Library, Washington Island Branch, Main & Lakeview Rds, Washington Island, WI, 54246. Tel: 920-847-2323. p. 2641

Carr, Marie Therese, Sister, Archives, Neumann College Library, One Neumann Dr, Aston, PA, 19014-1298. Tel: 610-361-5206. Fax: 610-459-1370. p. 2030

Carr, Marjorie, Dir, Enfield Free Public Library, 23 Main St, Enfield, NH, 03748. Tel: 603-632-7145. Fax: 603-632-4055. p. 1446

Carr, Mary, Mgr, Mount Clemens Regional Medical Center, 1000 Harrington Blvd, Mount Clemens, MI, 48043. Tel: 586-493-8047. Fax: 586-493-8739. p. 1210

Carr, Mary M, Dean, Instrul Serv & Telecommunications, Spokane Community College Library, Mailstop 2160, Learning Resources Ctr, Bldg 16, 1810 N Greene St, Spokane, WA, 99217-5399. Tel: 509-533-7045. Fax: 509-533-7276. p. 2536

Carr, Meagan, Librn, Franklin Memorial Hospital, 111 Franklin Health Commons, Farmington, ME, 04938. Tel: 207-779-2554. Fax: 207-779-2749. p. 985

Carr, Melissa, Dir, Daniel Boone Regional Library, 100 W Broadway, Columbia, MO, 65203. Tel: 573-443-3161. Fax: 573-443-3281. p. 1324

Carr, Richard, Head, Ref, University of New Mexico, Health Sciences Library & Informatics Center, MSC09-5100, One University of New Mexico, Albuquerque, NM, 87131-0001. Tel: 505-272-2311. Fax: 505-272-5350. p. 1551

Carr, Shannon, Web Serv Mgr, Oregon Health & Science University Library, 3181 SW Sam Jackson Park Rd, Portland, OR, 97239-3098. Tel: 503 494-3484. Fax: 503-494-3227. p. 2013

Carr Stanley, Beverly, Ref Librn, Salem County Historical Society, 79-83 Market St, Salem, NJ, 08079. Tel: 856-935-5004. Fax: 856-935-0728. p. 1528

Carr, Steven, Br Mgr, Arlington County Department of Libraries, Glenclaryn, 300 S Kensington St, Arlington, VA, 22204. Tel: 703-228-6547. Fax: 703-824-3529. p. 2448

Carr, Susan, Asst Dir, Edwardsville Public Library, 112 S Kansas St, Edwardsville, IL, 62025. Tel: 618-692-7556. Fax: 618-692-9566. p. 639

Carr, Susan, Librn, Cape Cod Museum of Natural History, 869 Main St, Brewster, MA, 02631. Tel: 508-896-3867. Fax: 508-896-8844. p. 1070

Carr, Verna, Br Mgr, Putnam County Library, Poca Branch, PO Box 606, Poca, WV, 25159-0606. Tel: 304-755-3241. Fax: 304-755-3241. p. 2562

Carr-Payne, Ella, Res Libr Adminr, AREVA NP, Inc, 3315 Old Forest Rd, Lynchburg, VA, 24501. Tel: 434-832-2476. Fax: 434-832-2475. p. 2475

Carr-Wiggin, Anne, Mgr, NEOS Library Consortium, Cameron Library, 5th Flr, University of Alberta, Edmonton, AB, T6G 2J8, CANADA. Tel: 780-492-0075. Fax: 780-492-8302. p. 2958

Carrai, Sherry, Acq Tech, Alameda Free Library, 1550 Oak St, Alameda, CA, 94501-2932. Tel: 510-747-7725. p. 119

Carrano, Paula Marie, Mgr, Brooklyn Public Library, Paerdegat, 850 E 59th St, Brooklyn, NY, 11234. Tel: 718-241-3994. Fax: 718-241-1335. p. 1592

Carrasquillo, Denise, Dep Dir, East Chicago Public Library, 2401 E Columbus Dr, East Chicago, IN, 46312-2998. Tel: 219-397-2453. Fax: 219-397-6715. p. 736

Carrasquillo, Denise, Dep Dir, East Chicago Public Library, Robert A Pastrick Branch, 1008 W Chicago Ave, East Chicago, IN, 46312. Tel: 219-397-2453. Fax: 219-397-6715. p. 736

Carratura, Karen, Bus Mgr, Westwood Free Public Library, 49 Park Ave, Westwood, NJ, 07675. Tel: 201-664-0583. Fax: 201-664-6088. p. 1543

Carraway, Shawn, Tech Coordr, Midlands Technical College Library, Beltline Library, 316 S Beltline Blvd, 2nd Flr, Columbia, SC, 29205. Tel: 803-738-7734. Fax: 803-738-7719. p. 2207

Carreiro, Lynne, Asst Dir, Falmouth Public Library, 300 Main St, Falmouth, MA, 02540. Tel: 508-457-2555. Fax: 508-457-2559. p. 1088

Carrell, Jacqueline, Pub Serv/Ref Librn, Richard Bland College Library, 11301 Johnson Rd, Petersburg, VA, 23805. Tel: 804-862-6226. Fax: 804-862-6125. p. 2484

Carreno, Lisa Guedea, Dir, Goshen College, Harold & Wilma Good Library, 1700 S Main, Goshen, IN, 46526-4794. Tel: 574-535-7425. Fax: 574-535-7438. p. 745

Carreon, Martha, Ch, El Progreso Memorial Library, 301 W Main St, Uvalde, TX, 78801. Tel: 830-278-2017. Fax: 830-278-4940. p. 2394

Carreras-Hubbard, Karen, Coordr, Libr Serv, Berkshire Community College, 1350 West St, Pittsfield, MA, 01201. Tel: 413-236-2153. Fax: 413-448-2700. p. 1117

Carrere, Ernest, Ref, Fresno Pacific University, 1717 S Chestnut Ave, Fresno, CA, 93702. Tel: 559-453-2131. Fax: 559-453-2124. p. 153

Carrick, Kathleen M, Dir, Case Western Reserve University, School of Law Library, 11075 East Blvd, Cleveland, OH, 44106-7148. Tel: 216-368-6357. Fax: 216-368-1002. p. 1876

Carrico, Deborah, Br Mgr, Public Library of Cincinnati & Hamilton County, Elmwood Place, 6120 Vine St, Cincinnati, OH, 45216. Tel: 513-369-4452. Fax: 513-369-4534. p. 1871

Carrico, Jeff, Assoc Dean, Scholarly Communications & Access, Georgia Institute of Technology Library, 704 Cherry St, Atlanta, GA, 30332-0900. Tel: 404-894-4501. Fax: 404-894-6084. p. 515

Carrico, Kent, Instruction & Off-Campus Serv Librn, Benedictine University Library, 5700 College Rd, Lisle, IL, 60532-0900. Tel: 630-829-6055. Fax: 630-960-9451. p. 666

Carrico, Steven, Head, Acq & Licensing, University of Florida Libraries, 535 Library W, Gainesville, FL, 32611-7000. Tel: 352-273-2675. Fax: 352-392-4788. p. 449

Carrier, Helene, Dir, University of Ottawa Libraries, Morisset Library (Arts & Sciences), 65 University, Ottawa, ON, K1N 9A5, CANADA. Tel: 613-562-5882. Fax: 613-562-5133. p. 2834

Carrier, Nancy, Head Librn, Red Rock Public Library Board, 42 Salls St, Red Rock, ON, P0T 2P0, CANADA. Tel: 807-886-2558. Fax: 807-886-2558. p. 2838

Carrier, Paul, Acq, Doc, Ref, Government of Quebec - Agriculture Fisheries & Foods, 96 Montee de Sandy-Beach, No 205, Gaspe, QC, G4X 2V6, CANADA. Tel: 418-368-7615. Fax: 418-360-8211. p. 2882

Carrier, Timothy, YA Serv, Jefferson-Madison Regional Library, 201 E Market St, Charlottesville, VA, 22902-5287. Tel: 434-979-7151, Ext 206, 434-979-7151, Ext 207. Fax: 434-971-7035. p. 2453

Carriera, Danielle, Ref Serv, Ad, Spec Coll Librn, Pequot Library, 720 Pequot Ave, Southport, CT, 06890-1496. Tel: 203-259-0346, Ext 17. Fax: 203-259-5602. p. 368

Carriere, Joan, Librn, Wapiti Regional Library, Paddockwood Public Library, First St N, Paddockwood, SK, S0J 1Z0, CANADA. Tel: 306-989-4522. p. 2921

Carriere, Joyce, Librn, Wapiti Regional Library, Spiritwood Public Library, 200 Main St, Spiritwood, SK, S0J 2M0, CANADA. Tel: 306-883-2337. p. 2922

Carrigan, Mildred, ILL, Eastern Counties Regional Library, 390 Murray St, Mulgrave, NS, B0E 2G0, CANADA. Tel: 902-747-2597. Fax: 902-747-2500. p. 2783

Carringer, Barbara, Circ, Hiwassee College, 225 Hiwassee College Dr, Madisonville, TN, 37354. Tel: 423-442-2001, Ext 1267. Fax: 423-420-1896. p. 2246

Carrington, Brad, Head of Libr, University of Kentucky Libraries, Education, 205 Dickey Hall, Lexington, KY, 40506-0017. Tel: 859-257-7977. Fax: 859-323-1976. p. 922

Carriveau, Ane, Ser, Syst Coordr, Ripon College, 300 Seward St, Ripon, WI, 54971. Tel: 920-748-8750. Fax: 920-748-7243. p. 2634

Carriveau, Ken, Access Serv Unit Leader, Baylor University Libraries, Moody Memorial Library, 1312 S Third, Waco, TX, 76798. p. 2396

Carrlo, Donald, Librn III, New Jersey Department of Labor Library, John Fitch Plaza, 5th Flr, Trenton, NJ, 08611. Tel: 609-292-2035. Fax: 609-984-5456. p. 1535

Carroccio, Chaundra, Commun Prog & Outreach Serv, East Baton Rouge Parish Library, 7711 Goodwood Blvd, Baton Rouge, LA, 70806-7625. Tel: 225-939-3896. Fax: 225-231-3788. p. 942

Carroccio, Chaundra, Br Mgr, East Baton Rouge Parish Library, Scotlandville, 7373 Scenic Hwy, Baton Rouge, LA, 70807. Tel: 225-354-7580. Fax: 225-354-7551. p. 943

Carrol, William F, Archivist, Worcester Historical Museum, 30 Elm St, Worcester, MA, 01605. Tel: 508-753-8278, Ext 105. Fax: 508-753-9070. p. 1145

Carroll, Anita, Dir, Middletown Public Library, 125 S Broad St, Middletown, OH, 45044. Tel: 513-424-1251. Fax: 513-424-6585. p. 1917

Carroll, Anita G, Libr Dir, Franklin-Springboro Public Library, Springboro Branch, 125 Park Lane, Springboro, OH, 45066-9801. Tel: 937-748-3200. Fax: 937-748-4831. p. 1900

Carroll, Aubrey, Head, Ref, Florence County Library System, 509 S Dargan St, Florence, SC, 29506. Tel: 843-662-8424. Fax: 843-661-7544. p. 2193

Carroll, Barbara, Acq, Libr Spec II, Northern Virginia Community College Libraries, Medical Education Campus, 6699 Springfield Center Dr, Rm 341, Springfield, VA, 22150. Tel: 703-822-0014. Fax: 703-822-6612. p. 2447

Carroll, Celia, Br Mgr, Santa Monica Public Library, Ocean Park, 2601 Main St, Santa Monica, CA, 90405-4001. Tel: 310-392-3804. Fax: 310-399-6739. p. 266

Carroll, Chris, Circ Mgr, Irvine Sullivan Ingram Library, University of West Georgia, 1601 Maple St, Carrollton, GA, 30118. Tel: 678-839-6498. Fax: 678-839-6511. p. 523

Carroll, Christine, Ch, Co-Dir, Berlin Public Library, 121 W Park Ave, Berlin, WI, 54923. Tel: 920-361-5420. Fax: 920-361-5424. p. 2582

Carroll, Dale, Librn, Centralia College, 600 Centralia College Blvd, Centralia, WA, 98531. Tel: 360-736-9391, Ext 259. Fax: 360-330-7502. p. 2511

Carroll, Daniel, Adult Serv, YA Serv, Blue Island Public Library, 2433 York St, Blue Island, IL, 60406-2011. Tel: 708-388-1078, Ext 30. Fax: 708-388-1143. p. 596

Carroll, David, Dir, Western Museum of Mining & Industry Library, 225 N Gate Blvd, I-25 Exit 156-A, Colorado Springs, CO, 80921. Tel: 719-495-2182. Fax: 719-488-9261. p. 297

Carroll, David, Dir of Libr Serv, Lamar University, 211 Redbird Lane, Beaumont, TX, 77705. Tel: 409-880-8159. Fax: 409-880-2318. p. 2287

Carroll, Donna, Br Mgr, Jacksonville Public Library, Willowbranch, 2875 Park St, Jacksonville, FL, 32205-8099. Tel: 904-381-8490. Fax: 904-381-8495. p. 454

Carroll, Douglas T, Dir, Libr Serv, Distance Educ, Electronic Res, George Washington University, Virginia Science & Technology Campus Library, 44983 Knoll Sq, Ste 179, Ashburn, DC, 20147-2604. Tel: 703-726-3780. Fax: 703-726-8237. p. 402

Carroll, Edward W, Dir, Hennepin County Law Library, C-2451 Government Ctr, 300 S Sixth St, Minneapolis, MN, 55487. Tel: 612-348-8860. Fax: 612-348-4230. p. 1260

Carroll, Holly, Dir, Poudre River Public Library District, 201 Peterson St, Fort Collins, CO, 80524-2990. Tel: 970-221-6670. Fax: 970-221-6398. p. 307

Carroll, Hyecha, Libr Tech, United States Court of Appeals for the Armed Forces Library, 450 E St NW, Washington, DC, 20442-0001. Tel: 202-761-1466. p. 417

Carroll, Iris, Ref Serv Librn, Modesto Junior College Library, 435 College Ave, Modesto, CA, 95350. Tel: 209-575-6082. Fax: 209-575-6669. p. 188

Carroll, Jean, Dir, Tupper Lightfoot Memorial Library, 164 S Main St, Brundidge, AL, 36010. Tel: 334-735-2145. Fax: 334-735-2145. p. 11

Carroll, Jennifer, Coll Develop Librn, University of New Hampshire Library, 18 Library Way, Durham, NH, 03824. Tel: 603-862-4049. Fax: 603-862-0294. p. 1445

Carroll, Kris, Mgr, Geauga County Public Library, Bainbridge Library, 17222 Snyder Rd, Chagrin Falls, OH, 44023. Tel: 440-543-5611. Fax: 440-543-4734. p. 1867

Carroll, LeighAnn, Automation Spec, Lawson State Community College Library, 1100 Ninth Ave SW, Bessemer, AL, 35022. Tel: 205-929-3434, 205-929-6333. Fax: 205-925-3716. p. 6

Carroll, Linda, Admin Dir, Alameda County Library, 2450 Stevenson Blvd, Fremont, CA, 94538-2326. Tel: 510-745-1509. Fax: 510-793-2987. p. 149

Carroll, Mary Kay, Asst Dir, Caestecker Public Library, 518 Hill St, Green Lake, WI, 54941-8828. Tel: 920-294-3572. Fax: 920-294-6055. p. 2596

Carroll, Shirley, Librn, Snyder County Libraries, Middleburg Community Library, 13 N Main St, Middleburg, PA, 17842. Tel: 570-837-5931. Fax: 570-837-5931. p. 2138

Carroll, Susan, Info Tech Spec, Longwood University, Redford & Race St, Farmville, VA, 23909. Tel: 434-395-2873. Fax: 434-395-2453. p. 2463

Carroll, Terri, Dir, Carl Albert State College, 1507 S McKenna, Poteau, OK, 74953. Tel: 918-647-1310. Fax: 918-647-1314. p. 1976

Carroll-Mann, Robin, Prog Head, Pub Relations Coordr, Summit Free Public Library, 75 Maple St, Summit, NJ, 07901-9984. Tel: 908-277-9452. Fax: 908-273-0031. p. 1532

Carron, Amanda, Spec Serv, Bonne Terre Memorial Library, Five SW Main St, Bonne Terre, MO, 63628. Tel: 573-358-2260. Fax: 573-358-5941. p. 1320

Carrothers, Jackie, Librn, Cutler Public Library, Civic Ctr, 409 S Main, Cutler, IL, 62238. Tel: 618-497-2961. Fax: 618-497-8818. p. 632

Carrothers, Kevin, Librn Supvr, Coppell Public Library, 177 N Hertz Rd, Coppell, TX, 75019. Tel: 972-304-3655. Fax: 972-304-3622. p. 2301

Carrubba, Nicole, Ch, Portsmouth Free Public Library, 2658 E Main Rd, Portsmouth, RI, 02871. Tel: 401-683-9457. Fax: 401-683-5013. p. 2171

Carruthers, Cindy, Circ, Tech Serv, Huron Public Library, 333 Williams St, Huron, OH, 44839. Tel: 419-433-5009. Fax: 419-433-7228. p. 1906

Carruthers, Hilda, Librn, Iosco-Arenac District Library, Mary Johnston Memorial Library - Standish Branch, 114 N Court, Standish, MI, 48658-9416. Tel: 989-846-6611. Fax: 989-846-6611. p. 1176

Carruthers, Lia, Youth Serv Mgr, Bernardsville Public Library, One Anderson Hill Rd, Bernardsville, NJ, 07924. Tel: 908-766-0118. Fax: 908-766-2464. p. 1472

Carson, Bryan, Dr, Instrul Serv Librn, Ref Serv, Western Kentucky University Libraries, Helm-Cravens Library Complex, 1906 College Heights Blvd, No 11067, Bowling Green, KY, 42101-1067. Tel: 270-745-2905. Fax: 270-745-6422. p. 908

Carson, C Herbert, Dr, Asst Dir, Prof, University of Rhode Island, Rodman Hall, 94 W Alumni Ave, Ste 2, Kingston, RI, 02881-0815. Tel: 401-874-4646. Fax: 401-874-4964. p. 2973

Carson, Curtis, Asst Librn, Saint John's Episcopal Hospital-South Shore Division, 327 Beach 19th St, Far Rockaway, NY, 11691. Tel: 718-869-7699. Fax: 718-869-8528. p. 1621

Carson, Denise, Dir, Bethany College, 235 E Swensson Ave, Lindsborg, KS, 67456-1896. Tel: 785-227-3380, Ext 8342. p. 880

Carson, Edward, Librn, Cape May County Library, Lower Cape Branch, 2600 Bayshore Rd, Villas, NJ, 08251. Tel: 609-886-8999. p. 1477

Carson, Jacquelyn, Librn, Mobile County Public Law Library, Mobile Government Plaza, 205 Government St, Mobile, AL, 36644-2308. Tel: 251-574-8436. Fax: 251-574-4757. p. 25

Carson, Joyce, Br Mgr, Perry County District Library, Somerset Branch, 103 Public Sq, Somerset, OH, 43783. Tel: 740-743-1161. Fax: 740-743-9139. p. 1921

Carson, Kim, Coll & Syst Coordr, Orangeville Public Library, One Mill St, Orangeville, ON, L9W 2M2, CANADA. Tel: 519-941-0610, Ext 5226. Fax: 519-941-4698. p. 2826

Carson, Linda, Extn Serv, Wilderness Coast Public Libraries, 1180 W Washington St, Monticello, FL, 32344. Tel: 850-926-9204. Fax: 850-997-7403. p. 470

Carson, Mari, Librn, Muskoka Lakes Library Board, Bala Public, Community Centre, 1008 Maple St, Bala, ON, P0C 1A0, CANADA. Tel: 705-762-1086. p. 2837

Carson, Marjorie, Cat, Bay City Public Library, 1100 Seventh St, Bay City, TX, 77414. Tel: 979-245-6931. Fax: 979-245-2614. p. 2286

Carson, Outi, ILL, Pinellas Park Public Library, 7770 52nd St, Pinellas Park, FL, 33781-3498. Tel: 727-541-0718. Fax: 727-541-0818. p. 483

Carson, Susan, Br Mgr, Buffalo & Erie County Public Library System, East Clinton, 1929 Clinton, Buffalo, NY, 14206-3214. Tel: 716-823-5626. Fax: 716-823-5626. p. 1596

Carson, Tom J, Head, Ref Serv, Kenosha Public Library, 812 56th St, Kenosha, WI, 53140-3735. Tel: 262-564-6132. Fax: 262-564-6370. p. 2601

Carstarphen, Minnie, Dir, Wallace Community College, 3000 Earl Goodwin Pkwy, Selma, AL, 36701. Tel: 334-876-9344, 334-876-9345. Fax: 334-876-9314. p. 36

Carstens, Cathy, Internet Serv, Gates Public Library, 902 Elmgrove Rd, Rochester, NY, 14624. Tel: 585-247-6446. Fax: 585-426-5733. p. 1729

Carstens, Timothy, Head, Cat, Western Carolina University, 176 Central Dr, Cullowhee, NC, 28723. Tel: 828-227-7188. Fax: 828-227-7015. p. 1786

Carstensen, Nancy, Youth Serv, Oceanside Public Library, 330 N Coast Hwy, Oceanside, CA, 92054-2824. Tel: 760-435-5594. Fax: 760-435-9614. p. 199

Carswell, Alanna, Librn, Wapiti Regional Library, Shellbrook Public Library, 105 Railway Ave W, Shellbrook, SK, S0J 2E0, CANADA. Tel: 306-747-3419. p. 2922

Carswell, Roberta, Supvr, Ch Serv, Ridgewood Public Library, 125 N Maple Ave, Ridgewood, NJ, 07450-3288. Tel: 201-670-5600. Fax: 201-670-0293. p. 1526

Carswell, Roger L, Dir, Iola Public Library, 218 E Madison Ave, Iola, KS, 66749. Tel: 620-365-3262. Fax: 620-365-5137. p. 874

Carswell, Roger L, Dir, Southeast Kansas Library System, 218 E Madison Ave, Iola, KS, 66749. Tel: 620-365-5136. Fax: 620-365-5137. p. 874

Cartaina, Liz, Br Mgr, Jersey City Free Public Library, The Heights, 14 Zabriskie St, Jersey City, NJ, 07307. Tel: 201-547-4556. Fax: 201-876-0092. p. 1492

Cartelli, Ann, Head, Ref Serv, Free Library of Springfield Township, 1600 Paper Mill Rd, Wyndmoor, PA, 19038. Tel: 215-836-5300. Fax: 215-836-2404. p. 2158

Carter, Adela B, Dir, Flint Public Library, One S Main St, Middleton, MA, 01949. Tel: 978-774-8132. Fax: 978-777-3270. p. 1105

Carter, Amber, Med Librn, Sunrise Hospital & Medical Center, 3186 S Maryland Pkwy, Las Vegas, NV, 89109. Tel: 702-731-8210. Fax: 702-731-8674. p. 1430

Carter, Amy, Ch, Cook Memorial Library, 93 Main St, Tamworth, NH, 03886. Tel: 603-323-8510. Fax: 603-323-2077. p. 1466

Carter, Ann, Ch, Coordr, Dennysville-Lincoln Memorial Library, 17 King St, Dennysville, ME, 04628. Tel: 207-726-4750. p. 983

Carter, Anna, Br Mgr, Scott-Sebastian Regional Library, Mansfield Library, 200 N Sebascott Ave, Mansfield, AR, 72944. p. 102

Carter, Barbara, Genealogy Librn, Bartlett-Carnegie Sapulpa Public Library, 27 W Dewey, Sapulpa, OK, 74066. Tel: 918-224-5624. Fax: 918-224-3546. p. 1977

Carter, Ben, Ch, Conyers-Rockdale Library System, 864 Green St, Conyers, GA, 30012. Tel: 770-388-5040. Fax: 770-388-5043. p. 527

Carter, Beverly, Mgr, John A H Murphree Law Library, Alachua County Courthouse, Rm 413, 201 E University Ave, Gainesville, FL, 32601. Tel: 352-374-3659. Fax: 352-381-0136. p. 449

Carter, Bonnie, Libr Tech, United States Department of Labor, 1301 Airport Rd, Beaver, WV, 25813-9426. Tel: 304-256-3266. Fax: 304-256-3372. p. 2553

Carter, Bruce, DTS Libr Mgr, Mohave County Library District, 3269 N Burbank St, Kingman, AZ, 86402-7000. Tel: 928-692-5744. p. 66

Carter, Camille, Br Mgr, Los Angeles Public Library System, John Muir Branch, 1005 W 64th St, Los Angeles, CA, 90044-3715. Tel: 323-789-4800. Fax: 323-789-5758. p. 174

Carter, Carolyn, Br Supvr, Jackson/Hinds Library System, Willie Morris Branch, 4912 Old Canton Rd, Jackson, MS, 39211-5404. Tel: 601-987-8181. Fax: 601-987-8212. p. 1303

Carter, Catherine J, Dir, DeVry University, 3300 N Campbell Ave, Chicago, IL, 60618. Tel: 773-697-2215. Fax: 773-697-2714. p. 612

Carter, Cathy, Dir, Benzie Shores District Library, 630 Main St, Frankfort, MI, 49635. Tel: 231-352-4671. Fax: 231-352-4671. p. 1181

Carter, Charmia, Librn, Columbus Regional Healthcare System, 710 Center St, Columbus, GA, 31902. Tel: 706-571-1178. Fax: 706-660-2674. p. 526

Carter, Christina, Ref & Instruction, University of Alaska Anchorage, Consortium Library, 3211 Providence Dr, Anchorage, AK, 99508-8176. Tel: 907-786-1871. Fax: 907-786-1834. p. 45

Carter, Christina, Libr Adminr, Imperial Public Library, 200 W Ninth St, Imperial, CA, 92251. Tel: 760-355-1332. Fax: 760-355-4857. p. 159

Carter, Craig, Circ Mgr, Tigard Public Library, 13500 SW Hall Blvd, Tigard, OR, 97223-8111. Tel: 503-684-6537, Ext 2509. Fax: 503-598-7515, 503-718-2797. p. 2021

Carter, Cynthia, Cat, Indian River County Library System, 1600 21st St, Vero Beach, FL, 32960. Tel: 772-770-5060. Fax: 772-770-5066. p. 501

Carter, David, Dir, Saint Mary's Seminary & University, 5400 Roland Ave, Baltimore, MD, 21210-1994. Tel: 410-864-3621. Fax: 410-435-8571. p. 1017

Carter, David, Librn, University of Michigan, Art, Architecture & Engineering Library, Duderstadt Ctr, 2281 Bonnisteel Blvd, Ann Arbor, MI, 48109-2094. Tel: 734-647-5747. Fax: 734-764-4487. p. 1152

Carter, Denise, Dir, Lake Whitney Public Library, 106 N Colorado St, Whitney, TX, 76692-2213. Tel: 254-694-4639. Fax: 254-694-0896. p. 2400

Carter, Destiny, Libr Dir, University of Arkansas for Medical Sciences, 300 E Sixth St, Texarkana, AR, 71854. Tel: 870-779-6023. Fax: 870-779-6050. p. 116

Carter, Dianna, Head of Libr, Kinchafoonee Regional Library System, Calhoun County Library, 19379 E Hartford St, Edison, GA, 39846-5626. Tel: 229 835-2012. Fax: 229 835-2012. p. 528

Carter, Donna, Br Librn, McDowell Public Library, Northfork Branch, Rte 52, Northfork, WV, 24868. Tel: 304-862-4541. Fax: 304-862-4541. p. 2574

Carter, Edd, Libr Tech, Colorado Department of Corrections, 0200 County Rd 219, Rifle, CO, 81650. Tel: 970-625-1700, Ext 3064. Fax: 970-625-7565. p. 321

Carter, Elizabeth, Br Supvr, Bruce County Public Library, Southampton Branch, 215 High St, Southampton, ON, N0H 2L0, CANADA. Tel: 519-797-3586. Fax: 519-797-3586. p. 2837

Carter, Elizabeth, Librn, Bruce County Public Library, Port Elgin Branch, 708 Goderich St, Port Elgin, ON, N0H 2C0, CANADA. Tel: 519-832-2201. p. 2837

Carter, Ellen, Head, Circ, Rutherford Public Library, 150 Park Ave, Rutherford, NJ, 07070. Tel: 201-939-8600. Fax: 201-939-4108. p. 1528

Carter, Estell, Acq, Asst Dir, Onslow County Public Library, 58 Doris Ave E, Jacksonville, NC, 28540. Tel: 910-455-7350, Ext 227. Fax: 910-455-1661. p. 1803

Carter, Genevieve, Cat, Huronia Museum, 549 Little Lake Park Rd, Midland, ON, L4R 4P4, CANADA. Tel: 705-526-2844. Fax: 705-527-6622. p. 2821

Carter, Gwen, Circ, Great Falls Public Library, 301 Second Ave N, Great Falls, MT, 59401-2593. Tel: 406-453-0349, Ext 213. Fax: 406-453-0181. p. 1380

Carter, Gwendolyn, Librn, Mississippi Gulf Coast Community College, 2300 Hwy 90, Gautier, MS, 39553. Tel: 228-497-7642. Fax: 228-497-7643. p. 1298

Carter, J Drusilla, Dir, Chesterfield County Library, 119 W Main St, Chesterfield, SC, 29709-1512. Tel: 843-623-7489. Fax: 843-623-3295. p. 2186

Carter, Jami, Dir, Tooele City Public Library, 128 W Vine St, Tooele, UT, 84074-2059. Tel: 435-882-2182. Fax: 435-882-6843. p. 2416

Carter, Janice, Dir of Libr Serv, Golden Gate University, 536 Mission St, San Francisco, CA, 94105-2967. Tel: 415-442-7248. Fax: 415-543-6779. p. 242

Carter, Janie, Adminr, University of Arkansas at Monticello, 1326 Hwy 52 W, Crossett, AR, 71635. Tel: 870-364-6414. Fax: 870-364-5707. p. 97

Carter, Janie, Br Head, Info Literacy, University of Arkansas-Monticello Library, 514 University Dr, Monticello, AR, 71656. Tel: 870-460-1080. Fax: 870-460-1980. p. 110

Carter, Jay, Dir, Conway County Library Headquarters, 101 W Church St, Morrilton, AR, 72110-3399. Tel: 501-354-5204. Fax: 501-354-5206. p. 110

Carter, Jean, Br Mgr, Jersey City Free Public Library, Marion, 1017 West Side Ave, Jersey City, NJ, 07306. Tel: 201-547-4552. Fax: 201-547-5888. p. 1492

Carter, Jennifer Lynne, Dir, Warren Township Public Library, 210 Burnett Ave, Warren, IL, 61087. Tel: 815-745-2076. Fax: 815-745-2076. p. 715

Carter, Joanne, Libr Asst/Circ Serv Spec, Mechanicsburg Public Library, 60 S Main St, Mechanicsburg, OH, 43044. Tel: 937-834-2004. Fax: 937-834-3396. p. 1916

Carter, Jocklyn, Ch, West Hempstead Public Library, 500 Hempstead Ave, West Hempstead, NY, 11552. Tel: 516-481-6591. Fax: 516-481-2608. p. 1766

Carter, Jonathan, Circ, Guilford College, 5800 W Friendly Ave, Greensboro, NC, 27410-4175. Tel: 336-316-2450. Fax: 336-316-2950. p. 1796

Carter, Judith, Head, Tech Serv, Marquette University Libraries, 1355 W Wisconsin Ave, Milwaukee, WI, 53233. Tel: 414-288-7214. Fax: 414-288-7813. p. 2618

Carter, Julie, Instrul & Access Serv Librn, Whitman College, 345 Boyer Ave, Walla Walla, WA, 99362. Tel: 509-527-5915. Fax: 509-527-5900. p. 2547

Carter, Kathleen, Ramirez Librn, University of Texas Health Science Center at San Antonio Libraries, 7703 Floyd Curl Dr, MSC 7940, San Antonio, TX, 78229-3900. Tel: 210-567-2400. Fax: 210-567-2490. p. 2383

Carter, Kay, Asst Curator, Medical University of South Carolina Library, Waring Historical Library, 175 Ashley Ave, Charleston, SC, 29425-0001. Tel: 843-792-2288. Fax: 843-792-8619. p. 2185

Carter, Kerri, Instruction & Outreach, Westminster College, 1840 S 1300 East, Salt Lake City, UT, 84105-3697. Tel: 801-832-2250. Fax: 801-832-3109. p. 2415

Carter, Kimberly A, Sr Librn, Midwest Research Institute, 425 Volker Blvd, Kansas City, MO, 64110. Tel: 816-360-5188. Fax: 816-753-8420. p. 1339

Carter, Krissie, Youth Serv, Clovis-Carver Public Library, 701 N Main, Clovis, NM, 88101. Tel: 505-769-7840. Fax: 505-769-7842. p. 1553

Carter, Laura, Dir, Auburn Public Library, 338 W Jefferson, Auburn, IL, 62615. Tel: 217-438-6211. Fax: 217-438-9317. p. 591

Carter, Laura, Br Mgr, Kingston Frontenac Public Library, Arden Branch, 5998 Arden Rd, Arden, ON, K0H 1B0, CANADA. Tel: 613-335-2570. p. 2813

Carter, Laura, Br Mgr, Kingston Frontenac Public Library, Calvin Park Branch, 88 Wright Crescent, Kingston, ON, K7L 4T9, CANADA. Tel: 613-546-2582. p. 2813

Carter, Laura, Br Mgr, Kingston Frontenac Public Library, Cloyne Branch, 1011 Little Pond Rd, Cloyne, ON, K0H 1K0, CANADA. Tel: 613-336-8744. p. 2813

Carter, Laura, Br Mgr, Kingston Frontenac Public Library, Hartington Branch, 5597 Hwy 38, Hartington, ON, K0H 1W0, CANADA. Tel: 613-372-2524. p. 2813

Carter, Laura, Br Mgr, Kingston Frontenac Public Library, Howe Island Branch, 50 Baseline Rd, Howe Island, ON, K7G 2V6, CANADA. Tel: 613-549-7972. p. 2813

Carter, Laura, Br Mgr, Kingston Frontenac Public Library, Isabel Turner Branch, 935 Gardiners Rd, Kingston, ON, K7M 9A9, CANADA. Tel: 613-389-2611. p. 2813

Carter, Laura, Br Mgr, Kingston Frontenac Public Library, Kingscourt Branch, 115 Kirkpatrick St, Kingston, ON, K7K 2P4, CANADA. Tel: 613-546-0698. p. 2813

Carter, Laura, Br Mgr, Kingston Frontenac Public Library, Mountain Grove Branch, 1455 Mountain Grove Rd, Mountain Grove, ON, K0H 2E0, CANADA. Tel: 613-335-5360. p. 2813

Carter, Laura, Br Mgr, Kingston Frontenac Public Library, Parham Branch, 1021 Long Lake Rd, Parham, ON, K0H 2K0, CANADA. Tel: 613-375-6400. p. 2813

Carter, Laura, Br Mgr, Kingston Frontenac Public Library, Pittsburgh Branch, 80 Gore Rd, Kingston, ON, K7K 6X6, CANADA. Tel: 613-542-8222. p. 2813

Carter, Laura, Br Mgr, Kingston Frontenac Public Library, Plevna Branch, 6638 Buckshot Lake Rd, Plevna, ON, K0H 2M0, CANADA. Tel: 613-479-2542. p. 2813

Carter, Laura, Br Mgr, Kingston Frontenac Public Library, Sharbot Lake Branch, 1037 Robert St, Sharbot Lake, ON, K0H 2P0, CANADA. Tel: 613-279-2583. p. 2813

Carter, Laura, Br Mgr, Kingston Frontenac Public Library, Storrington Branch, 3910 Battersea Rd, Battersea, ON, K0H 1H0, CANADA. Tel: 613-353-6333. p. 2813

Carter, Laura, Br Mgr, Kingston Frontenac Public Library, Sydenham Branch, 4432 George St, Sydenham, ON, K0H 2TO, CANADA. Tel: 613-376-3437. p. 2813

Carter, Laura, Br Mgr, Kingston Frontenac Public Library, Wolfe Island Branch, Ten Hwy 95, Wolfe Island, ON, K0H 2Y0, CANADA. Tel: 613-385-2112. p. 2813

Carter, Laura, Br Operations Mgr, Kingston Frontenac Public Library, 130 Johnson St, Kingston, ON, K7L 1X8, CANADA. Tel: 613-549-8888, Ext 1330. Fax: 613-549-8476. p. 2813

Carter, Lenore, Br Mgr, Assumption Parish Library, Labadieville Branch, 105 Cherry St, Labadieville, LA, 70372. Tel: 985-526-7055. Fax: 985-526-0278. p. 958

Carter, Linda, Dir, Metropolitan Community College, Maple Woods Community College Library, 2601 NE Barry Rd, Kansas City, MO, 64156. Tel: 816-604-3080. Fax: 816-437-3082. p. 1339

Carter, Lisa, Clinical Librn, Hartford Hospital, ERC Bldg-3, 80 Seymour St, Hartford, CT, 06102. Tel: 860-545-2425. Fax: 860-545-2572. p. 345

Carter, Mae, In Charge, International Joint Commission, 100 Ouellette Ave, 8th Flr, Windsor, ON, N9A 6T3, CANADA. Tel: 519-257-6703. Fax: 519-257-6740. p. 2871

Carter, Marie, Libr Mgr, VA Long Beach Health Care System, 5901 E Seventh St, Bldg 2, Rm 345, Long Beach, CA, 90822-5201. Tel: 562-826-8000, ext 5463. Fax: 562-826-5447. p. 167

Carter, Michael K, Librn, Metropolitan Museum of Art, Cloisters Library, Fort Tryon Park, New York, NY, 10040. Tel: 212-396-5365. Fax: 212-795-3640. p. 1686

Carter, Michelle, Ref, College of Lake County, 19351 W Washington St, Grayslake, IL, 60030. Tel: 847-543-2891. Fax: 847-223-7690. p. 652

Carter, Michelle, Br Mgr, Huron County Library, Clinton Branch, 27 Albert St, Clinton, ON, N0M 1L0, CANADA. Tel: 519-482-3673. p. 2799

Carter, Michelle, Br Mgr, Huron County Library, Zurich Branch, 50 Main St, Zurich, ON, N0M 2T0, CANADA. Tel: 519-236-4965. p. 2800

Carter, Paula, Br Mgr, Fayette County Public Libraries, Oak Hill Branch, 611 Main St, Oak Hill, WV, 25901. Tel: 304-469-9890. Fax: 304-469-9890. p. 2568

Carter, Peggy, Head, Spec Coll, Ms & Archives, Louisiana Tech University, Everett St at The Columns, Ruston, LA, 71272. Tel: 318-257-3555. Fax: 318-257-2579. p. 966

Carter, Peggy, Asst Dir, Iredell County Public Library, 201 N Tradd St, Statesville, NC, 28677. Tel: 704-878-3098. Fax: 704-878-5449. p. 1825

Carter, Quentin, Pub Serv, Solano Community College Library, 4000 Suisun Valley Rd, Fairfield, CA, 94534. Tel: 707-864-7132. Fax: 707-864-7231. p. 148

Carter, Richard, Ref Librn, University of Toronto Libraries, John M Kelly Library, University of Saint Michael's College, 113 Saint Joseph St, Toronto, ON, M5S 1J4, CANADA. Tel: 416-926-7114. Fax: 416-926-7262. p. 2866

Carter, Sandra B, Libr Mgr, Chaleur Library Region, Dalhousie Centennial Library, 403 rue Adelaïde, Dalhousie, NB, E8C 1B6, CANADA. Tel: 506-684-7370. Fax: 506-684-7374. p. 2761

Carter, Sarah, Info & Res Serv, Ringling College of Art & Design, 2700 N Tamiami Trail, Sarasota, FL, 34234. Tel: 941-359-7671. Fax: 941-359-7632. p. 490

Carter, Shirley, Br Mgr, Richland County Public Library, Blythewood Branch, 218 McNulty Rd, Blythewood, SC, 29016. Tel: 803-691-9806. p. 2188

Carter, Stephanie, Mrs, Asst Br Librn, Ref Librn, Brazoria County Library System, Angleton Branch, 401 E Cedar St, Angleton, TX, 77515-4652. Tel: 979-864-1513. Fax: 979-864-1518. p. 2275

Carter, Steve T, ILL, Internal Revenue Service, 1111 Constitution Ave NW, Rm 4324, Washington, DC, 20224. Tel: 202-622-8050. Fax: 202-622-5844. p. 405

Carter, Sue, Librn, St John's Hospital, 800 E Carpenter, Springfield, IL, 62769. Tel: 217-544-6464, Ext 45566. Fax: 217-525-2895. p. 706

Carter, Tammy, Dir, South Arkansas Film Coop, c/o Malvern-Hot Spring County Library, 202 E Third St, Malvern, AR, 72104. Tel: 501-332-5441. Fax: 501-332-6679. p. 2938

Carter, Tom, Dean of Libr, Saint Mary's College Library, 1928 Saint Mary's Rd, Moraga, CA, 94575. Tel: 925-631-4229. Fax: 925-376-6097. p. 191

Carter, Tonya, Ch, Lancaster Community Library, 235 School St, Kilmarnock, VA, 22482-3830. Tel: 804-435-1729. Fax: 804-435-0255. p. 2472

Carter, Vern, Cat, Tech Serv, Fresno Pacific University, 1717 S Chestnut Ave, Fresno, CA, 93702. Tel: 559-453-7124. Fax: 559-453-2124. p. 153

Carter, Wade, Webmaster, Stephen F Austin State University, 1936 North St, Nacogdoches, TX, 75962. Tel: 936-468-1444. Fax: 936-468-7610. p. 2364

Cartinas, Melda, Supvr, Webb County Library, Hwy 359, Mirando City, TX, 78369. Tel: 361-586-4626. Fax: 361-586-5060. p. 2363

Cartmell, D, Librn, Washington Correctional Facility Library, PO Box 180, Comstock, NY, 12821-0180. Tel: 518-639-4486. Fax: 518-639-3299. p. 1609

Cartmill, Lee, Assoc Univ Librn, Cornell University Library, 201 Olin Library, Ithaca, NY, 14853-5301. Tel: 607-255-5181. Fax: 607-255-6788. p. 1641

Cartnel, Lynn, In Charge, US National Park Service, 46 Volcano Rd, Capulin, NM, 88414. Tel: 575-278-2201, Ext 231. Fax: 575-278-2211. p. 1552

Cartner, Peggy, Sr Librn, Center for Creative Leadership Library, One Leadership Pl, Greensboro, NC, 27410. Tel: 336-286-4083. Fax: 336-286-4087. p. 1795

Cartolano, Rob, Dir, Libr Info Tech, Columbia University, Butler Library, Rm 517, 535 W 114th St, New York, NY, 10027. Tel: 212-854-7309. Fax: 212-854-9099. p. 1674

Carton, Ninette, Dir, Atkinson Public Library District, 109 S State, Atkinson, IL, 61235. Tel: 309-936-7606. Fax: 309-936-7606. p. 590

Carton, Ruthann, Asst Dir, Atkinson Public Library District, 109 S State, Atkinson, IL, 61235. Tel: 309-936-7606. Fax: 309-936-7606. p. 590

Carton, Stacy, Librn, Rutgers University Libraries, Media Center-Douglass Library, Eight Chapel Dr, New Brunswick, NJ, 08901. Tel: 732-932-9783. Fax: 732-445-0290. p. 1509

Cartularo, Teresa, Ref, Widener University, One University Pl, Chester, PA, 19013-5792. Tel: 610-499-4084. Fax: 610-499-4588. p. 2044

Cartwright, Erin, Libr Coordr, Parents, Let's Unite for Kids, 516 N 32nd St, Billings, MT, 59101. Tel: 406-255-0540. Fax: 406-255-0523. p. 1374

Caruso, Agnese, Res Spec, PricewaterhouseCoopers, National Tax Research Services, Royal Trust Tower, 77 King St W, Ste 3000, Toronto, ON, M5K 1G8, CANADA. Tel: 416-815-5103. Fax: 416-814-3200. p. 2857

Caruso, Arlene, Ref Librn, Henderson District Public Libraries, 280 S Green Valley Pkwy, Henderson, NV, 89012. Tel: 702-492-7252. Fax: 702-492-1711. p. 1428

Caruso, Carl J, Dir, Broadview Public Library District, 2226 S 16th Ave, Broadview, IL, 60155-4000. Tel: 708-345-1325. Fax: 708-345-5024. p. 597

Caruso, Janet, Librn, Mental Health America Library, 230 North Rd, Poughkeepsie, NY, 12601. Tel: 845-486-2896. Fax: 845-486-2897. p. 1723

Caruso, Monica, County Librn, Watauga County Public Library, 140 Queen St, Boone, NC, 28607. Tel: 828-264-8784. Fax: 828-264-1794. p. 1777

Caruso, Yuusuf, Librn, Columbia University, African Studies, 308 International Affairs Bldg, 420 W 118th St, New York, NY, 10027. Tel: 212-854-8045. Fax: 212-854-3834. p. 1674

Caruth, Janet, Acq, Coll Develop, Ref Serv, Cleveland State Community College Library, 3535 Adkisson Dr, Cleveland, TN, 37312-2813. Tel: 423-478-6209. Fax: 423-478-6255. p. 2229

Caruthers, Janet, Dir, Columbia College, 1001 Rogers St, Columbia, MO, 65216. Tel: 573-875-7376. Fax: 573-875-7379. p. 1324

Caruthers, Melecia, Mgr, ILL, Oklahoma Department of Libraries, 200 NE 18th St, Oklahoma City, OK, 73105. Tel: 405-521-2502. Fax: 405-525-7804. p. 1974

Carvajal, Jane, Dir, Libr Serv, DeVry University, 2450 Crystal Dr, Arlington, VA, 22202. Tel: 703-414-4095. Fax: 703-414-4104. p. 2449

Carvajal, Joan, Dir, Greenwood Lake Public Library, 79 Waterstone Rd, Greenwood Lake, NY, 10925-2146. Tel: 845-477-8377. Fax: 845-477-8397. p. 1632

Carvalho, Diane, Librn, New Haven Free Public Library, Mitchell, 37 Harrison St, New Haven, CT, 06515. Tel: 203-946-8117. p. 356

Carvalho, Joseph, Exec Dir, Pres, Connecticut Valley Historical Museum, The Quadrangle, Edwards St, Springfield, MA, 01103. Tel: 413-263-6800, Ext 230. Fax: 413-263-6875. p. 1127

Carvalho, Kathy, Head, Circ, Westwood Free Public Library, 49 Park Ave, Westwood, NJ, 07675. Tel: 201-664-0583. Fax: 201-664-6088. p. 1543

Carver, Charlotte, Asst Dir, Cat, Lilly Library, 19 Meadow St, Florence, MA, 01062. Tel: 413-587-1500. Fax: 413-587-1504. p. 1089

Carver, Christy, Asst Librn, Greenbrier County Public Library, 152 Robert W McCormick Dr, Lewisburg, WV, 24901. Tel: 304-647-7568. Fax: 304-647-7569. p. 2563

Carver, Deborah, Dean of Libr, University of Oregon Libraries, 1501 Kincaid St, Eugene, OR, 97403-1299. Tel: 541-346-3056. Fax: 541-346-3485. p. 1997

Carver, Donna J, Coordr, Ref, Valencia Community College, Raymer Maguire Jr Learning Resources Center, West Campus, 1800 S Kirkman Rd, Orlando, FL, 32811. Tel: 407-582-1210. Fax: 407-582-1686. p. 478

Carver, Jan, Sci Librn, University of Kentucky Libraries, Science Library, 211 King Bldg, Lexington, KY, 40506-0039. Tel: 859-257-4074. Fax: 859-323-4988. p. 922

Carver, Linda, Admin Serv, University of Mary Washington, 1801 College Ave, Fredericksburg, VA, 22401-4665. Tel: 540-654-1147. Fax: 540-654-1067. p. 2466

Carver, Molly, Dir, Bellevue Public Library, 224 E Main St, Bellevue, OH, 44811-1467. Tel: 419-483-4769. Fax: 419-483-0158. p. 1859

Carver, Nancy, Head, Pub Serv, East Central Georgia Regional Library, 902 Greene St, Augusta, GA, 30901. Tel: 706-821-2600. Fax: 706-724-6762. p. 519

Carver, Sandra, Librn, Breckinridge County Public Library, Cloverport Community, 101 Fourth St, Cloverport, KY, 40111. Tel: 270-788-3388, Ext 228. Fax: 270-788-6640. p. 916

Carver, Stephanie, Librn, New Hanover County Public Library, 201 Chestnut St, Wilmington, NC, 28401. Tel: 910-798-6352. Fax: 910-798-6312. p. 1830

Carwile, Marti, Acq Mgr, Monmouth College, 700 E Broadway, Monmouth, IL, 61462-1963. Tel: 309-457-2191. Fax: 309-457-2226. p. 675

Cary, Diane, Ch, Shenandoah County Library, 514 Stoney Creek Blvd, Edinburg, VA, 22824. Tel: 540-984-8200. Fax: 540-984-8207. p. 2460

Cary, Marna, Librn, Riverdale Presbyterian Church Library, 6513 Queens Chapel Rd, Hyattsville, MD, 20782-2197. Tel: 301-927-0477. Fax: 301-699-2156. p. 1033

Cary, Paul, Dir, Baldwin Wallace University, Jones Music Library, 49 Seminary St, Berea, OH, 44017-1905. Tel: 440-826-2375. p. 1859

Carzon, Eric, Bus & Finance Mgr, Montgomery County Public Libraries, 21 Maryland Ave, Ste 310, Rockville, MD, 20850. Tel: 240-777-0048. Fax: 240-777-0047. p. 1038

Casaccio, Ellen, Dir of Circ, Richards Memorial Library, 118 N Washington St, North Attleboro, MA, 02760. Tel: 508-699-0122. Fax: 508-699-8075. p. 1112

Casalaspi, Paul, Dir, Info Tech Serv Div, The Library of Virginia, 800 E Broad St, Richmond, VA, 23219-8000. Tel: 804-692-3756. Fax: 804-692-3594. p. 2489

Casale, Joseph, Asst Dir, Finance & Develop, Newark Public Library, Five Washington St, Newark, NJ, 07101. Tel: 973-733-7841. Fax: 973-733-5648. p. 1511

Casamer, Sandy, Asst Dir, Macomb County Library, 16480 Hall Rd, Clinton Township, MI, 48038-1132. Tel: 586-412-5954. Fax: 586-412-5958. p. 1164

Casari, William, Instruction & Archives, Hostos Community College Library, 475 Grand Concourse, A-207, Bronx, NY, 10451. Tel: 718-518-4220. Fax: 718-518-4206. p. 1587

Casart, Gabrielle, Br Mgr, Hawaii State Public Library System, Laupahoehoe Public & School Library, 35-2065 Old Mamalahoa Hwy, Laupahoehoe, HI, 96764. Tel: 808-962-2229. Fax: 808-962-2230. p. 562

Cascanet, Valerie, Dir, Annie Porter Ainsworth Memorial Library, 6064 S Main St, Sandy Creek, NY, 13145. Tel: 315-387-3732. Fax: 315-387-2005. p. 1738

Casci, Gail, Asst Librn, Hinckley, Allen & Snyder LLP, 50 Kennedy Plaza, Providence, RI, 02903. Tel: 401-274-2000. Fax: 401-277-9600. p. 2172

Casciero, Albert J, Dean of Libr, University of the District of Columbia, Learning Resources Division, 4200 Connecticut Ave NW, Washington, DC, 20008. Tel: 202-274-6370. Fax: 202-274-6012. p. 421

Cascio, Keri, Dir, Innovative Tech & Libr Res Mgt, Linda Hall Library, 5109 Cherry St, Kansas City, MO, 64110-2498. Tel: 816-363-4600. Fax: 816-926-8790. p. 1337

Casco, Martha Patricia, In Charge, Hialeah-John F Kennedy Library, North Hialeah e-Library, 7400 W Tenth Ave, Hialeah, FL, 33014. Tel: 305-816-4470. Fax: 305-816-4473. p. 451

Case, Amber Brock, Libr Dir, Seattle Genealogical Society Library, 6200 Sand Point Way NE, Seattle, WA, 98115. Tel: 206-522-8658. p. 2530

Case, Bonnie N, Dir, Highland Park Library, 4700 Drexel Dr, Highland Park, TX, 75205-3198. Tel: 214-559-9400. Fax: 214-559-9335. p. 2333

Case, Carol, Librn, Henderson County Public Library, Green River, 50 Green River Rd, Zirconia, NC, 28790. Tel: 828-697-4969. Fax: 828-697-4969. p. 1801

Case, Donald, Dr, Prof, University of Kentucky, 320 Little Library Bldg, Lexington, KY, 40506-0224. Tel: 859-257-8415. Fax: 859-257-4205. p. 2966

Case, Jackie, Dir, Libr Serv, Wake Technical Community College, 9101 Fayetteville Rd, Raleigh, NC, 27603-5696. Tel: 919-662-3607. Fax: 919-662-3575. p. 1818

Case, Linda, Commun Br Supvr, Pierce County Library System, Milton/Edgewood Branch, 900 Meridian Ave E, Milton, WA, 98354. Tel: 253-548-3725. Fax: 253-927-2581. p. 2539

Case, Mary, Univ Librn, University of Illinois at Chicago, MC 234, 801 S Morgan St, Chicago, IL, 60607. Tel: 312-996-2716. Fax: 312-413-0424. p. 627

Case, Maureen, Head, Tech Serv, Upper St Clair Township Library, 1820 McLaughlin Run Rd, Upper St Clair, PA, 15241-2397. Tel: 412-835-5540. Fax: 412-835-6763. p. 2149

Casebier, Diane, Bibliog Instr, Ser, Houston Baptist University, 7502 Fondren Rd, Houston, TX, 77074-3298. Tel: 281-649-3178. Fax: 281-649-3489. p. 2337

Casella, Darla, Ch, Abilene Public Library, Mockingbird Branch, 1214 N Mockingbird, Abilene, TX, 79603. Tel: 325-437-7323. p. 2272

Casella, Jessie, Med Librn, Brattleboro Memorial Hospital, 17 Belmont Ave, Brattleboro, VT, 05301. Tel: 802-257-8357. Fax: 802-257-8822. p. 2419

Caserotti, Gretchen, Head, Children's & Teen Serv, Darien Library, 1441 Post Rd, Darien, CT, 06820-5419. Tel: 203-669-5223. Fax: 203-655-1547. p. 336

Casey, Anne Marie, Libr Dir, Embry-Riddle Aeronautical University, 600 S Clyde Morris Blvd, Daytona Beach, FL, 32114-3900. Tel: 386-226-6593. Fax: 386-226-6368. p. 436

Casey, Christopher, Electronic Res Librn, Ohio Dominican University Library, 1216 Sunbury Rd, Columbus, OH, 43219. Tel: 614-251-4752. Fax: 614-252-2650. p. 1886

Casey, Diane Dates, Dean, Governors State University Library, One University Pkwy, University Park, IL, 60466-0975. Tel: 708-534-4110. Fax: 708-534-4564. p. 711

Casey, Evelyn, Br Mgr, Prince William Public Library System, Lake Ridge Neighborhood, 12964 Harbor Dr, Woodbridge, VA, 22192-2930. Tel: 703-792-5675. Fax: 703-491-6661. p. 2486

Casey, Ilean, Acq, Flagstaff City-Coconino County Public Library System, 300 W Aspen, Flagstaff, AZ, 86001. Tel: 928-213-2331. Fax: 928-774-9573. p. 62

Casey, Jean, Dir, Clear Lake Public Library, 200 N Fourth St, Clear Lake, IA, 50428-1698. Tel: 641-357-6133, 641-357-6134. Fax: 641-357-4645. p. 802

Casey, Jeanette, Dir, University of Wisconsin-Madison, Mills Music Library, 728 State St, Madison, WI, 53706. Tel: 608-263-1884. Fax: 608-265-2754. p. 2609

Casey, Judy Faye, Dir, Rogers Public Library, 711 S Dixieland Rd, Rogers, AR, 72758. Tel: 479-621-1152, Ext 11. Fax: 479-621-1165. p. 113

Casey, Kathleen, Govt Doc, Saint Louis University, Omer Poos Law Library, Morrissey Hall, 3700 Lindell Blvd, Saint Louis, MO, 63108-3478. Tel: 314-977-2742. Fax: 314-977-3966. p. 1361

Casey, Kristie, Youth Serv, New Port Richey Public Library, 5939 Main St, New Port Richey, FL, 34652. Tel: 727-853-1279. Fax: 727-853-1280. p. 472

Casey, Michael, Div Dir, Info Tech, Gwinnett County Public Library, 1001 Lawrenceville Hwy NW, Lawrenceville, GA, 30046-4707. Tel: 770-822-5334. p. 538

Casey, Tom, Syst Adminr, Public Library of Youngstown & Mahoning County, 305 Wick Ave, Youngstown, OH, 44503-1079. Tel: 330-744-8636. Fax: 330-744-3355. p. 1952

Casey, William F, Dir, Nassau University Medical Center, 2201 Hempstead Tpk, East Meadow, NY, 11554. Tel: 516-572-8742. Fax: 516-572-5788. p. 1617

Cash, Amanda, Br Mgr, East Central Georgia Regional Library, Harlem Branch, 375 N Louisville St, Harlem, GA, 30814. Tel: 706-556-9795. Fax: 706-556-2576. p. 520

Cash, Brenda, ILL, Southeast Kansas Library System, 218 E Madison Ave, Iola, KS, 66749. Tel: 620-365-5136. Fax: 620-365-5137. p. 874

Cash, Brenda L, Dir, Pennville Township Public Library, 195 N Union, Pennville, IN, 47369. Tel: 260-731-3333. Fax: 260-731-3333. p. 772

Cash, Debbie, Coordr, Northern Va Center Libr & Res & Instrul Serv, Virginia Polytechnic Institute & State University Libraries, Drill Field Dr, Blacksburg, VA, 24062-9001. Tel: 703-538-8341. Fax: 540-231-3946. p. 2451

Cash, Debbie, Librn, Virginia Polytechnic Institute & State University Libraries, Northern Virginia Resource Center, 7054 Haycock Rd, Falls Church, VA, 22043-2311. Tel: 703-538-8340. Fax: 703-538-8342. p. 2451

Cash, Derek, Dr, Dir of Libr Serv, Blue Mountain College, 201 W Main St, Blue Mountain, MS, 38610. Tel: 662-685-4771, Ext 147. Fax: 662-685-9519. p. 1294

Cash, Diana, Asst Dir, Kingston Public Library, 10004 Bradford Way, Kingston, TN, 37763. Tel: 865-376-9905. Fax: 865-376-2301. p. 2241

Cash, Eunice, Dir, AARP, 601 E St NW, B3-400, Washington, DC, 20049. p. 391

Cash, Greg, Asst Dir, Lewis & Clark Community College, 5800 Godfrey Rd, Godfrey, IL, 62035. Tel: 618-468-4340. Fax: 618-468-4301. p. 651

Cashell, Elizabeth A, Dir of Libr Serv, Henry County Library, 123 E Green St, Clinton, MO, 64735-1462. Tel: 660-885-2612. Fax: 660-885-8953. p. 1323

Cashen, Terry, Tech Coordr, McHenry Public Library District, 809 N Front St, McHenry, IL, 60050. Tel: 815-385-0036. Fax: 815-385-7085. p. 672

Casiano-Torres, Luis O, Dr, Head Librn, University of Puerto Rico Library System, Library & Information Sciences, Rio Piedras Campus, Edif Jose M Lazaro, San Juan, PR, 00931. Tel: 787-764-0000, Ext 5112. Fax: 787-772-1479. p. 2677

Casias, Helen, Managing Librn, Pikes Peak Community College Library, Rampart Range Campus, 11195 Hwy 83, Box R-7, Colorado Springs, CO, 80921-3602. Tel: 719-502-2440. Fax: 719-502-3431. p. 296

Casino, Joseph J, Dir, Philadelphia Archdiocesan Historical Research Center, 100 E Wynnewood Rd, Wynnewood, PA, 19096-3001. Tel: 610-667-2125. Fax: 610-667-2730. p. 2158

Caskey, Kendra, Dir, Goodall City Library, 203 West A St, Ogallala, NE, 69153-2544. Tel: 308-284-4354. Fax: 308-284-6390. p. 1411

Casler, Carla Long, Assoc Dir, University of Arizona, College of Agriculture & Life Sciences Arid Lands Information Center, 1955 E Sixth St, Tucson, AZ, 85719-5224. Tel: 520-621-8571. Fax: 520-621-3816. p. 89

Cason, Charles, Chief Financial Officer, Amigos Library Services, Inc, 14400 Midway Rd, Ste 200, Dallas, TX, 75244-3509. Tel: 972-340-2846. Fax: 972-991-6061. p. 2956

Cason, James, Acq, Lake-Sumter Community College Library, 9501 US Hwy 441, Leesburg, FL, 34788-8751. Tel: 352-435-5030. Fax: 352-365-3590. p. 461

Casper, Chris, Librn, Broward College, South Campus Library LRC, 7300 Hollywood, Pembroke Pines, FL, 33024. Tel: 954-201-8827. Fax: 954-201-0282. p. 435

Casper, Harriet, Media Spec, Temple Sinai of North Dade, 18801 NE 22nd Ave, North Miami Beach, FL, 33180. Tel: 305-932-9010, 305-932-9011. Fax: 305-932-5153. p. 473

Casper, Kristine, Ch, Huntington Public Library, 338 Main St, Huntington, NY, 11743. Tel: 631-427-5165. Fax: 631-421-7131. p. 1639

Casper, Nicole, Spec Coll & Archives Librn, Stonehill College, 320 Washington St, Easton, MA, 02357-4015. Tel: 508-565-1396. Fax: 508-565-1424. p. 1087

Casper, Susan, Dir, Marianna Community Public Library, 247 Jefferson Ave, Marianna, PA, 15345. Tel: 724-267-3888. Fax: 724-267-3888. p. 2084

Casper, Vicki, Librn, Hildreth Public Library, 248 Commercial Ave, Hildreth, NE, 68947. Tel: 308-938-2471. Fax: 308-938-2545. p. 1402

Caspers, Jean, Librn, Linfield College, 900 S Baker St, McMinnville, OR, 97128. Tel: 503-883-2262. Fax: 503-883-2566. p. 2005

Caspers-Graper, Mary, Head, Tech Serv, South Dakota State University, 1300 N Campus Dr, Box 2115, Brookings, SD, 57007-1098. Tel: 605-688-5565. Fax: 605-688-6133. p. 2210

Casperson, Jeanette, Dir, Ute Public Library, 130 Main St, Ute, IA, 51060. Tel: 712-885-2237. Fax: 712-885-2237. p. 848

Cassady, Dawn, Circ Serv Mgr, The Urbana Free Library, 210 W Green St, Urbana, IL, 61801-5326. Tel: 217-367-4057. Fax: 217-367-4061. p. 713

Cassagne, Susan S, Dir, Natchez Adams Wilkinson Library Service, 220 S Commerce St, Natchez, MS, 39120-3502. Tel: 601-445-8862. Fax: 601-446-7795. p. 1309

Cassano, Rocco, Asst Dir, East Meadow Public Library, 1886 Front St, East Meadow, NY, 11554-1705. Tel: 516-794-2570. Fax: 516-794-1272. p. 1617

Cassanova, Belinda, Dir, Ingleside Public Library, 2775 Waco St, Ingleside, TX, 78362. Tel: 361-776-5355. Fax: 361-776-2264. p. 2346

Cassaro, James P, Head of Libr, University of Pittsburgh, Frick Fine Arts Library, Frick Fine Arts Bldg, 1st Flr, Pittsburgh, PA, 15260. Tel: 412-648-2410. Fax: 412-648-7568. p. 2129

Cassaro, James P, Head of Libr, University of Pittsburgh, Theodore M Finney Music Library, Music Bldg B28, Pittsburgh, PA, 15260. Tel: 412-624-4131. Fax: 412-624-4180. p. 2129

Cassavant, Judith, Mgr, Cat Dept, Worcester Public Library, Three Salem Sq, Worcester, MA, 01608. Tel: 508-799-1655. Fax: 508-799-1652. p. 1145

Cassedy, Karen, Automation Syst Coordr, National Gallery of Art Library, Fourth St & Constitution Ave NW, Washington, DC, 20565. Tel: 202-842-6511. Fax: 202-789-3068. p. 409

Cassel, Nancy, Asst Librn, Orford Social Library, 573 NH Rte 10, Orford, NH, 03777. Tel: 603-353-9756. p. 1461

Cassell, Kay Ann, Assoc Prof, Rutgers, The State University of New Jersey, Four Huntington St, New Brunswick, NJ, 08901-1071. Tel: 732-932-7500, Ext 8955. Fax: 732-932-2644. p. 2969

Cassella, Teresa, Law Librn, A Max Brewer Memorial Law Library, Harry T & Harriette V Moore Justice Ctr, 2825 Judge Fran Jamieson Way, Viera, FL, 32940. Tel: 321-617-7295. Fax: 321-617-7303. p. 502

Cassens, David, Interim Univ Librn, Saint Louis University, 3650 Lindell Blvd, Saint Louis, MO, 63108-3302. Tel: 314-977-3095. Fax: 314-977-3108. p. 1360

Cassens, Treisa, Dir, Pub Serv, Golden West College, 15744 Golden West St, Huntington Beach, CA, 92647. Tel: 714-895-8741, Ext 51214. Fax: 714-895-8926. p. 158

Casseo, Jessica, Supvr, Lafourche Parish Public Library, Raceland Branch, 177 Recreation Dr, Raceland, LA, 70394-2915. Tel: 985-537-6875. Fax: 985-537-6875. p. 971

Casserley, Sean, County Librn, Johnson County Library, 9875 W 87th St, Overland Park, KS, 66212. Tel: 913-495-2400. Fax: 913-495-2460. p. 888

Casserly, Mary Frances, Dr, Dean, Libr Dir, University at Albany, State University of New York, 1400 Washington Ave, Albany, NY, 12222-0001. Tel: 518-442-3568. Fax: 518-442-3088. p. 1570

Casserly, Thomas, Assoc Univ Librn, Undergrad & Distance Serv, Boston University Libraries, Mugar Memorial Library, 771 Commonwealth Ave, Boston, MA, 02215. Tel: 617-353-3710. Fax: 617-353-2084. p. 1058

Cassidy, Brenda, Dir, J A Tarbell Library, 136 Forest Rd, Lyndeborough, NH, 03082. Tel: 603-654-6790. Fax: 603-654-6790. p. 1454

Cassidy, Diane, Ch, Gafney Library, Inc, 14 High St, Sanbornville, NH, 03872. Tel: 603-522-9735. Fax: 603-522-7123. p. 1464

Cassidy, Gwen, Ch, Lancaster Public Library, 5466 Broadway, Lancaster, NY, 14086. Tel: 716-683-1120. Fax: 716-686-0749. p. 1651

Cassidy, James, Librn, Adelphi University, 55 Kennedy Dr, Hauppauge, NY, 11788-4001. Tel: 516-237-8611. Fax: 516-237-8613. p. 1634

Cassidy, Jo, Librn, Big Lake Public Library, 3140 S Big Lake Rd, Big Lake, AK, 99652. Tel: 907-892-6475. Fax: 907-892-6546. p. 46

Cassidy, Karen, Librn, Saint Stephen United Church of Christ, 905 E Perkins Ave, Sandusky, OH, 44870. Tel: 419-626-1612. Fax: 419-626-1617. p. 1934

Cassidy, Lisa, Circ Supvr, Belmont Public Library, 336 Concord Ave, Belmont, MA, 02478-0904. Tel: 617-489-2000, 617-993-2850. Fax: 617-993-2893. p. 1052

Cassidy, Lori, Online Serv, Orange Coast College Library, 2701 Fairview Rd, Costa Mesa, CA, 92628. Tel: 714-432-5885. Fax: 714-432-6850. p. 137

Cassidy, Lori, AV, Per, Saddleback College, 28000 Marguerite Pkwy, Mission Viejo, CA, 92692. Tel: 949-582-4875. Fax: 949-364-0284. p. 187

Cassidy, Margot, Dir of Libr Serv, DeVry University Library, 2149 W Dunlap Ave, Phoenix, AZ, 85021-2982. Fax: 602-734-1999. p. 72

Cassidy, Mary, Librn, Toluca Public Library, 102 N Main St, Toluca, IL, 61369. Tel: 815-452-2211. Fax: 815-452-2211. p. 710

Cassidy, Suzanne L, Dir, Mercer University, Walter F George School of Law, Furman Smith Law Library, 1021 Georgia Ave, Macon, GA, 31201-1001. Tel: 478-301-2612. Fax: 478-301-2284. p. 540

Cassisi, Patricia, Adult Ref Librn, Yarmouth Town Libraries, South Yarmouth Branch, 312 Old Main St, South Yarmouth, MA, 02664. Tel: 508-760-4820. Fax: 508-760-2699. p. 1126

Cassler, Courtney, Dir, Westville-New Durham Township Public Library, 153 Main St, Westville, IN, 46391. Tel: 219-785-2015. Fax: 219-785-2015. p. 787

Casson, Ed, Cat, Tech Serv, Los Angeles Mission College Library, 13356 Eldridge Ave, Sylmar, CA, 91342-3200. Tel: 818-364-7750. Fax: 818-364-7749. p. 274

Casstevens, Susie, Librn, A H Meadows Library, 921 S Ninth St, Midlothian, TX, 76065-3636. Tel: 972-775-3417. Fax: 972-775-5630. p. 2363

Castaing, Linda, Circ, Calumet City Public Library, 660 Manistee Ave, Calumet City, IL, 60409. Tel: 708-862-6220, Ext 240. Fax: 708-862-0872. p. 599

Castaldi, Mary Louise, Ref Librn, University of the Arts University Libraries, Anderson Hall, 1st Flr, 333 S Broad St, Philadelphia, PA, 19102. Tel: 215-717-6280. Fax: 215-717-6287. p. 2119

Castaldo, Anthony, ANSER Mgr & Network Adminr, Ramapo Catskill Library System, 619 Rte 17M, Middletown, NY, 10940-4395. Tel: 845-343-1131, Ext 228. Fax: 845-343-1205. p. 1660

Castaneda, Margi, Librn, Yuma County Law Library, 168 S Second Ave, Ste L, Yuma, AZ, 85364-2364. Tel: 928-329-2255. p. 91

Castanon, Dorothea, Br Mgr, Corpus Christi Public Libraries, Ben F McDonald Branch, 4044 Greenwood Dr, Corpus Christi, TX, 78416. Tel: 361-826-2356. p. 2301

Castanteen, Sharon, Dir, Johnson Free Public Library, 274 Main St, Hackensack, NJ, 07601-5797. Tel: 201-343-4169. Fax: 201-343-1395. p. 1489

Casteel, Janie, Asst Dir, Adult Serv, Atlantic Public Library, 507 Poplar St, Atlantic, IA, 50022. Tel: 712-243-5466. Fax: 712-243-5011. p. 795

Casteel, Shannon, Cat, Lewis-Clark State College Library, 500 Eighth Ave, Lewiston, ID, 83501. Tel: 208-792-2229. Fax: 208-792-2831. p. 578

Casteel, Theresa, Librn, Illinois Department of Corrections, 6665 State Rte 146E, Vienna, IL, 62995. Tel: 618-658-8331, Ext 2120. p. 714

Castellana, Kristen, Librn, University of Michigan, Music Library, School of Music, 3239 Moore Bldg, Ann Arbor, MI, 48109-2085. Tel: 734-764-2512. Fax: 734-764-5097. p. 1153

Castellani, Jo Nell, Dir, Chadwick Public Library District, 110 Main St, Chadwick, IL, 61014. Tel: 815-684-5215. Fax: 815-684-5215. p. 602

Castellani, Margaret, Head Cataloger, Cleveland Museum of Art, 11150 East Blvd, Cleveland, OH, 44106-1797. Tel: 216-707-2530. Fax: 216-421-0921. p. 1877

Castellanos, Nicolas, Generalist Librn, University of Saint Thomas, Cardinal Beran Library at Saint Mary's Seminary, 9845 Memorial Dr, Houston, TX, 77024-3498. Tel: 713-686-4345, Ext 248, 713-686-4345, Ext 265. Fax: 713-681-7550. p. 2344

Castelli, Dave, Librn, Intermountain Health Care, Eighth Ave & C St, Salt Lake City, UT, 84143-0001. Tel: 801-507-5142. Fax: 801-408-5287. p. 2412

Castelli, Patricia, Ch, Orem Public Library, 58 N State St, Orem, UT, 84057-5596. Tel: 801-229-7050. Fax: 801-229-7130. p. 2409

Castelluzzo, Julie, Electronic Res, Cooper Union for Advancement of Science & Art Library, Seven E Seventh St, New York, NY, 10003. Tel: 212-353-4178. Fax: 212-353-4017. p. 1676

Caster, Kathleen J, Dir, Riley City Library, 206 S Broadway, Riley, KS, 66531. Tel: 785-485-2978. p. 892

Castile, Ron, Head, Ref, Somerville Public Library, 79 Highland Ave, Somerville, MA, 02143. Tel: 617-623-5000, Ext 2969. Fax: 617-628-4052. p. 1124

Castillo, Amy, Periodicals Librn, Tarleton State University Library, 201 Saint Felix, Stephenville, TX, 76401. Tel: 254-968-9868. Fax: 254-968-9467. p. 2389

Castillo, Judy, ILL, Notre Dame de Namur University Library, 1500 Ralston Ave, Belmont, CA, 94002-1908. Tel: 650-508-3746. Fax: 650-508-3697. p. 126

Castillo, Mateo, Tech Serv Mgr, Elsa Public Library, 711 N Hidalgo St, Elsa, TX, 78543. Tel: 956-262-3061. Fax: 956-262-3066. p. 2318

Castillo, Naomi, In Charge, United States Geological Survey, 520 N Park Ave, Ste 221, Tucson, AZ, 85719-6644. Tel: 520-670-6671, Ext 244. Fax: 520-670-5592. p. 88

Castillo, Sally J, ILL, Oakwood Hospital Medical Library, 18101 Oakwood Blvd, Dearborn, MI, 48124-2500. Tel: 313-593-7685. Fax: 313-436-2699. p. 1167

Castillo, Sara M, Tech Serv Librn, Neal, Gerber & Eisenberg LLP, Two N La Salle St, Ste 1700, Chicago, IL, 60602. Tel: 312-269-5294. Fax: 312-578-1793. p. 620

Castillo-Speed, Lillian, Head Librn, University of California, Berkeley, Ethnic Studies, 30 Stephens Hall, MC 2360, Berkeley, CA, 94720-2360. Tel: 510-642-3947. Fax: 510-643-8433. p. 128

Castine, Carole McDowell, Dir, Bessemer Public Library, 701 Ninth Ave N, Bessemer, AL, 35020-5305. Tel: 205-428-7868. Fax: 205-428-7885. p. 6

Castle, Cindy, Dir, Roane County Public Library, 110 Parking Plaza, Spencer, WV, 25276. Tel: 304-927-1130. Fax: 304-927-1196. p. 2572

Castle, Elaine, Librn, Logan County Libraries, Lakeview Branch, 130 N Main, Lakeview, OH, 43331. Tel: 937-842-4144. p. 1859

Castle, Emma, Br Mgr, Martin County Library System, Cummings-Palm City Branch, 2551 SW Matheson Ave, Palm City, FL, 34990. Tel: 772-288-2551. Fax: 772-288-5563. p. 492

Castle, Mary, Br Coordr, Blinn College Library, 800 Blinn Blvd, Brenham, TX, 77833. Tel: 979-830-4250. Fax: 979-830-4222. p. 2291

Castle, Pamela, Librn, Artesia Public Library, 306 W Richardson Ave, Artesia, NM, 88210-2499. Tel: 575-746-4252. Fax: 575-746-3075. p. 1551

Castle, Sara, Asst Dir, Youth/Young Adult Librn, Pinckney Community Public Library, 350 Mower Rd, Pinckney, MI, 48169. Tel: 734-878-3888. Fax: 734-878-2907. p. 1217

Castleberry, Crata, Librn, United States Court of Appeals, 600 W Capitol Ave, Rm 224, Little Rock, AR, 72201. Tel: 501-604-5215. Fax: 501-604-5217. p. 107

Castleberry, Sharon, Syst Coordr, DeSoto Public Library, 211 E Pleasant Run Rd, Ste C, DeSoto, TX, 75115-3939. Tel: 972-230-9656. Fax: 972-230-5797. p. 2313

Castleman, John, Dir, Syracuse Turkey Creek Township Public Library, 115 E Main St, Syracuse, IN, 46567. Tel: 574-457-3022. Fax: 574-457-8971. p. 780

Casto, Jane, Mgr, Cumberland County Public Library & Information Center, 300 Maiden Lane, Fayetteville, NC, 28301-5000. Tel: 910-483-7727. Fax: 910-486-5372. p. 1792

Casto, Jill, Coordr, Circ, Flesh Public Library, 124 W Greene St, Piqua, OH, 45356-2399. Tel: 937-773-6753. Fax: 937-773-5981. p. 1930

Casto, Joanna, Dir, Paden City Public Library, 114 S Fourth Ave, Paden City, WV, 26159. Tel: 304-337-9333. Fax: 304-337-9333. p. 2568

Casto, Lisa, Dir, Libr Serv, The Art Institute of Dallas, Two North Park E, 8080 Park Lane, Ste 100, Dallas, TX, 75231-5993. Tel: 469-587-1246. Fax: 214-692-8106. p. 2304

Casto, Mitch, Head, Access Serv, Staff Librn, West Virginia University Institute of Technology, 405 Fayette Pike, Montgomery, WV, 25136-2436. Tel: 304-442-3230. Fax: 304-442-3091. p. 2565

Caston, Richard, Dir, Mississippi Department of Corrections, 3794 Hwy 468, Pearl, MS, 39288. Tel: 601-932-2880, Ext 6343. Fax: 601-932-2880, Ext 6202. p. 1311

Castor, Elizabeth, Circ, Calaveras County Library, 891 Mountain Ranch Rd, San Andreas, CA, 95249. Tel: 209-754-6510. Fax: 209-754-6512. p. 226

Castro, David, Ser Coll Dir, University of Puerto Rico Library, Cayey Campus, 205 Ave Antonio R Barcelo, Cayey, PR, 00736. Tel: 787-738-5651, Ext 2024. Fax: 787-263-2108. p. 2672

Castro, Janice, In Charge, Community Hospital of San Bernardino, 1805 Medical Center Dr, San Bernardino, CA, 92411-1288. Tel: 909-887-6333, Ext 1488. Fax: 909-806-1062. p. 227

Castro, Rick L, Cat & Tech Serv Librn, University of Guam, UOG Sta, Mangilao, GU, 96923. Tel: 671-735-2307. Fax: 671-734-6882. p. 2667

Castro, Rodrigo, Mgr, Pub Serv, Barry University, 11300 NE Second Ave, Miami, FL, 33161. Tel: 305-899-3768. Fax: 305-899-4792. p. 464

Castro, Rosa I, Libr Tech, Department of Veterans Affairs, Library Service 142D, Ten Calle Casia, San Juan, PR, 00921-3201. Tel: 787-641-7582, Ext 12165, 787-641-7582, Ext 12226. Fax: 787-641-4550. p. 2676

Castro, Sandra, Dir, Commonwealth of Puerto Rico, Cesar Gonzalez Ave, San Juan, PR, 00919. Tel: 787-759-2000, Ext 2822. Fax: 787-753-6945. p. 2675

Castro, Yoshira, Br Mgr, Manatee County Public Library System, Palmetto Branch, 923 Sixth St W, Palmetto, FL, 34221. Tel: 941-722-3333. Fax: 941-749-7193. p. 430

Castro-Reino, Pilar, Br Mgr, Denver Public Library, Ford-Warren Branch, 2825 High St, Denver, CO, 80205-4545. Tel: 720-865-0920. Fax: 720-865-0925. p. 301

Castro-Reino, Pilar, Br Mgr, Denver Public Library, Hadley, 1890 S Grove St, Denver, CO, 80219-4618. Tel: 303-935-4267. Fax: 303-934-1294. p. 301

Castro-Reino, Pilar, Br Mgr, Denver Public Library, Hampden, 9755 E Girard Ave, Denver, CO, 80231-5003. Tel: 303-750-3885. Fax: 303-751-4878. p. 301

Castro-Reino, Pilar, Br Mgr, Denver Public Library, Montbello, 12955 Albrook Dr, Denver, CO, 80239-4704. Tel: 303-373-0767. Fax: 303-371-3542. p. 301

Castro-Reino, Pilar, Br Mgr, Denver Public Library, Ross-Barnum Branch, 3570 W First Ave, Denver, CO, 80219-1346. Tel: 303-935-1891. Fax: 303-934-9324. p. 301

Castro-Reino, Pilar, Br Mgr, Denver Public Library, Woodbury, 3265 Federal Blvd, Denver, CO, 80211-3211. Tel: 720-865-0930. Fax: 720-865-0933. p. 301

Castro-Santos, Jocelyn, Librn, Slate Memorial Library, 332 Main Rd, Gill, MA, 01376. Tel: 413-863-2591. Fax: 413-863-9347. p. 1091

Castrogiovanni, Andrea, In Charge, Doctors Community Hospital, 8118 Good Luck Rd, Lanham, MD, 20706. Tel: 301-552-8072. p. 1034

Castrogiovanni, Andrea, Librn, Montgomery County Public Libraries, Montgomery County Correctional Facility, 22880 Whelan Lane, Boyds, MD, 20841. Tel: 240-773-9914. Fax: 240-773-9939. p. 1038

Castronovo, Danielle, Archivist, Digital Coll Librn, California Academy of Sciences Library, Golden Gate Park, 55 Music Concourse Dr, San Francisco, CA, 94118. Tel: 415-379-5484. Fax: 415-379-5729. p. 240

Caswell, Erika, Br Mgr, Los Angeles Public Library System, Felipe deNeve Branch, 2820 W Sixth St, Los Angeles, CA, 90057-3204. Tel: 213-384-7676. Fax: 213-368-7667. p. 173

Caswell, Jerry, Head, Info Tech, University of Northern Iowa Library, 1227 W 27th St, Cedar Falls, IA, 50613-3675. Tel: 319-273-7059. Fax: 319-273-2913. p. 799

Caswell, Mariah, Librn, Mississippi Mills Libraries, 128 MacFarlane St, Pakenham, ON, K0A 2X0, CANADA. Tel: 613-624-5306. p. 2835

Caswell, Meriah, Chief Exec Officer, Librn, Greater Madawaska Public Library, 4984 Calabogie Rd, Calabogie, ON, K0J 1H0, CANADA. Tel: 613-752-2317. Fax: 613-752-2617. p. 2798

Caswell, Roberta, Ref Librn, James Prendergast Library Association, 509 Cherry St, Jamestown, NY, 14701. Tel: 716-484-7135. Fax: 716-487-1148. p. 1647

Caswell, Theresa, Dir, Gale Library, 16 S Main St, Newton, NH, 03858-3310. Tel: 603-382-4691. Fax: 603-382-2528. p. 1460

Catahan, Margie, Libr Coordr, Saint Joseph Library, 480 S Batavia St, Orange, CA, 92868-3907. Tel: 714-633-8121, Ext 7765. p. 201

Cataio, Joe, Acq, Actg Archivist, ILL, Moody Bible Institute, 820 N La Salle Blvd, Chicago, IL, 60610-3284. Tel: 312-329-4136. Fax: 312-329-8959. p. 619

Catalfio, Maria, Librn, International Union of United Automobile, Aerospace & Agricultural Implement Workers of America, 8731 E Jefferson Ave, Detroit, MI, 48214. Tel: 313-926-5000, 313-926-5386. Fax: 313-926-5871. p. 1171

Catan, Rachel, Children's & Parents' Serv, Mastics-Moriches-Shirley Community Library, 407 William Floyd Pkwy, Shirley, NY, 11967. Tel: 631-399-1511. Fax: 631-281-4442. p. 1743

Catanese, Lynn, Curator, Hagley Museum & Library, 298 Buck Rd E, Wilmington, DE, 19807. Tel: 302-658-2400. Fax: 302-658-0568. p. 388

Catano, Rachel, Ser/Archives, NHTI, Concord's Community College, 31 College Dr, Concord, NH, 03301-7425. Tel: 603-271-7186. Fax: 603-271-7189. p. 1443

Cate, Carol, Dir, Poy Sippi Public Library, W2251 Commercial St, Poy Sippi, WI, 54967-8423. Tel: 920-987-5737. Fax: 920-987-5737. p. 2631

Cate, Janet, Asst Dir, Head, Adult Serv, Kennebunk Free Library, 112 Main St, Kennebunk, ME, 04043. Tel: 207-985-2173. Fax: 207-985-4730. p. 988

Cate, Linda, ILL, Gateway Technical College, 3520 30th Ave, Kenosha, WI, 53144-1690. Tel: 262-564-2786. Fax: 262-564-2787. p. 2601

Cate, Selena, Dir, Thornton Public Library, 1886 NH Rte 175, Thornton, NH, 03223-6227. Tel: 603-726-8981. Fax: 603-726-3801. p. 1466

Catena, Dawn, Librn, Matrix Solutions Library, 150-13 Ave SW, Ste 200, Calgary, AB, T2R 0V2, CANADA. Tel: 403-237-0606. Fax: 403-263-2493. p. 2692

Cater, Judy J, Chair, Palomar College, 1140 W Mission Rd, San Marcos, CA, 92069-1487. Tel: 760-744-1150. Fax: 760-761-3500. p. 2962

Cater, Kathy, Res, Schnader, Harrison, Segal & Lewis Library, 1600 Market St, Ste 3600, Philadelphia, PA, 19103. Tel: 215-751-2111. Fax: 215-751-2205. p. 2116

Caterson-Beazley, Martha, Librn, United States Environmental Protection Agency, 27 Tarzwell Dr, Narragansett, RI, 02882-1198. Tel: 401-782-3025. Fax: 401-782-3140. p. 2168

Cates, Joyce, Head Librn, Oregon County Library District, Thomasville Public, Rte HC3, Box 62, Birch Tree, MO, 65438. Tel: 417-764-3603. Fax: 417-764-3603. p. 1319

Cates, Juana, Librn, First Baptist Church Library, 200 E Main St, Murfreesboro, TN, 37130. Tel: 615-893-2514. Fax: 615-895-5804. p. 2254

Cates, Larry, Genealogy Serv, High Point Public Library, 901 N Main St, High Point, NC, 27262. Tel: 336-883-3637. Fax: 336-883-3636. p. 1802

Cates, Patrick, Tech Serv, General Theological Seminary, 440 West 21st St, New York, NY, 10011. Tel: 212-243-5150. Fax: 212-924-6304. p. 1679

Cates, Wyatt, Head, Media Serv, Evergreen State College, Library Bldg, Rm 2300, 2700 Evergreen Pkwy NW, Olympia, WA, 98505-0002. Tel: 360-867-6271. Fax: 360-867-6790. p. 2522

Cathcart, Cynthia, Dir, Conde Nast Publications Library, Four Times Sq, New York, NY, 10036. Tel: 212-286-8245. Fax: 212-286-6763. p. 1675

Cathcart, Laura M, Res, United Daughters of the Confederacy, 328 North Blvd, Richmond, VA, 23220-4009. Tel: 804-355-1636. Fax: 804-353-1396. p. 2491

Cathcart, Rachael, Librn, South Florida Water Management District, 3301 Gun Club Rd, West Palm Beach, FL, 33406. Tel: 561-682-6076. Fax: 561-682-2093. p. 503

Cathel, Elke, Mgt Analyst, Glendora Public Library & Cultural Center, 140 S Glendora Ave, Glendora, CA, 91741. Tel: 626-852-4895. Fax: 626-852-4899. p. 156

Cathers, Erica, Ref, Gloucester City Library, 50 N Railroad Ave, Gloucester City, NJ, 08030. Tel: 856-456-4181. Fax: 856-456-6724. p. 1488

Cathey, Gail, Cat, Chestnut Hill College, 9601 Germantown Ave, Philadelphia, PA, 19118-2695. Tel: 215-248-7053. Fax: 215-248-7056. p. 2104

Cathi, Carmack, Dir of Archival Tech Serv, Tennessee State Library & Archives, 403 Seventh Ave N, Nashville, TN, 37243-0312. Tel: 615-253-3468. Fax: 615-532-2472, 615-741-6471. p. 2259

Cathy, East, Librn, Yakima Valley Libraries, White Swan Library, 391 First St, White Swan, WA, 98952. Tel: 509-874-2060. Fax: 509-874-2060. p. 2551

Catledge, Kim, Br Mgr, Chicago Public Library, South Chicago, 9055 S Houston Ave, Chicago, IL, 60617. Tel: 312-747-8065. Fax: 312-747-8491. p. 609

Catlett, Stephen, Archivist, Greensboro Historical Museum Archives Library, 130 Summit Ave, Greensboro, NC, 27401-3004. Tel: 336-373-2043, 336-373-2976. Fax: 336-373-2204. p. 1796

Catron, Donna, Adult Serv, Muncie Public Library, John F Kennedy Branch, 1700 W McGalliard Rd, Muncie, IN, 47304. Tel: 765-747-8215. Fax: 765-747-8225. p. 767

Catron, Mia, Br Mgr, Pulaski County Public Library System, Charles & Ona B Free Memorial, 300 Giles Ave, Dublin, VA, 24084. Tel: 540-674-2856. Fax: 540-674-2907. p. 2486

Catron, Steve, Br Supvr, Cass County Public Library, Harrisonville Branch, 400 E Mechanic, Harrisonville, MO, 64701. Tel: 816-884-3483. p. 1330

Catrone, Deborah, Br Mgr, Akron-Summit County Public Library, Goodyear, 60 Goodyear Blvd, Akron, OH, 44305-4487. Tel: 330-784-7522. Fax: 330-784-6599. p. 1852

Catrone, Rick, Circ Mgr, Columbus Metropolitan Library, Main Library, 96 S Grant Ave, Columbus, OH, 43215-4781. Tel: 614-645-2275. Fax: 614-849-1389. p. 1885

Catt, Ann, Librn, Latah County Historical Society Library, 327 E Second St, Moscow, ID, 83843. Tel: 208-882-1004. Fax: 208-882-0759. p. 579

Catt, Cathy, Ch, Andover Public Library, 1511 E Central Ave, Andover, KS, 67002. Tel: 316-558-3500. Fax: 316-558-3503. p. 856

Catt, Martha E, Dir, Hussey-Mayfield Memorial Public Library, 250 N Fifth St, Zionsville, IN, 46077-1324. Tel: 317-873-3149. Fax: 317-873-8339. p. 789

Catt, Susan L, Dir, Ivy Tech Community College of Indiana, 200 Daniels Way, Bloomington, IN, 47404. Tel: 812-330-6079. Fax: 812-330-6082. p. 728

Catterall, Susan, Res, Fredrikson & Bryon, 200 S Sixth St, Ste 4000, Minneapolis, MN, 55402. Tel: 612-492-7086. Fax: 612-492-7077. p. 1259

Cattrell, Betty, Dir, Haysville Community Library, 210 S Hays, Haysville, KS, 67060. Tel: 316-524-5242. Fax: 316-524-0142. p. 871

Cauce, Rita, Head, Res Develop, Florida International University, 11200 SW Eighth St, Miami, FL, 33199. Tel: 305-348-0547, 919-4052. Fax: 305-348-1798. p. 465

Cauce, Rita, Head, Res Develop, Florida International University, 3000 NE 151st St, North Miami, FL, 33181-3600. Tel: 305-919-4052. Fax: 305-919-5914. p. 472

Caudell, Alexis, Dir, Mitchell Community Public Library, 804 Main St, Mitchell, IN, 47446. Tel: 812-849-2412. Fax: 812-849-2665. p. 765

Caudill, Mitchell, Libr Spec, Southeast Kentucky Community & Technical College, Two Long Ave, Whitesburg, KY, 41858. Tel: 606-589-3334. p. 937

Caudle, Debra, Dir, Ellsworth Public Library, 1549 Dewitt St, Ellsworth, IA, 50075. Tel: 515-836-4852. Fax: 515-836-2162. p. 814

Caudle, Debra, Dir, Plainfield Public Library, 723 Main St, Plainfield, IA, 50666. Tel: 319-276-4461. Fax: 319-276-4461. p. 838

Caudle, Janet, Circ, Orange County Public Library, Carrboro Branch, McDougle Middle School, 900 Old Fayetteville Rd, Chapel Hill, NC, 27516. Tel: 919-969-3006. Fax: 919-969-3008. p. 1802

Caufield, Daniel, Institutional Serv Mgr, Buffalo & Erie County Public Library System, Erie County Correctional Facility, 11581 Walden Ave, Alden, NY, 14004-0300. Tel: 716-858-7159. Fax: 716-858-7162. p. 1596

Caufield, Daniel, Mgr, Buffalo & Erie County Public Library System, Erie County Holding Center, 40 Delaware Ave, Buffalo, NY, 14202-3999. p. 1596

Caughlin, Amy, Chief Librn, Scugog Memorial Public Library, 231 Water St, Port Perry, ON, L9L 1A8, CANADA. Tel: 905-985-7686. p. 2838

Caulder, Susan Wong, Librn, United States District Court, 450 Golden Gate Ave, Box 36060, San Francisco, CA, 94102. Tel: 415-436-8130. Fax: 415-436-8134. p. 248

Cauldwell, Norma Jean, Asst Dir, Tech Serv, Walpole Public Library, 65 Common St, Walpole, MA, 02081. Tel: 508-660-7369. Fax: 508-660-2714. p. 1132

Cauley, Heidi, Tech Serv, Attleboro Public Library, 74 N Main St, Attleboro, MA, 02703. Tel: 508-222-0157, 508-222-0159. Fax: 508-226-3326. p. 1050

Cauley, Phyllis, Br Coordr, Circ, Calhoun County Public Library, 17731 NE Pear St, Blountstown, FL, 32424. Tel: 850-674-8773. Fax: 850-674-2843. p. 427

Caulfield, Ann, Asst Librn, Kelley Drye & Warren, 101 Park Ave, New York, NY, 10178. Tel: 212-808-7800. Fax: 212-808-7897. p. 1684

Cauntay, Robin, Br Mgr, Monterey County Free Libraries, King City Branch, 402 Broadway, King City, CA, 93930. Tel: 831-385-3677. Fax: 831-385-0918. p. 183

Cauntay, Robin, Librn, California Department of Corrections Library System, Correctional Training Facility, Hwy 101 N, Soledad, CA, 93960. Tel: 831-678-3951. Fax: 831-678-5910. p. 221

Cause, Cheryl, Librn, Newfield Village Library & Reading Room, 637 Water St, West Newfield, ME, 04095. Tel: 207-793-4348. Fax: 207-793-2162. p. 1006

Causey, Enid, Archivist, Charleston Southern University, 9200 University Blvd, Charleston, SC, 29406. Tel: 843-863-7940. Fax: 843-863-7947. p. 2183

Causey, Melissa, Youth Serv, Bartow Public Library, 2150 S Broadway Ave, Bartow, FL, 33830. Tel: 863-534-0131. Fax: 863-534-0913. p. 426

Cauthen, Paul, Asst Music Librn, University of Cincinnati Libraries, College-Conservatory of Music, 600 Blegen Library, Cincinnati, OH, 45221. Tel: 513-556-1965. Fax: 513-556-3777. p. 1874

Cauthen, Rosalie, Librn, Harnett County Public Library, Coats Branch, 243 S McKinley St, Coats, NC, 27521. Tel: 910-230-1944. p. 1807

Cauthon, Debbie, Asst Dir, Hutchinson County Library, 625 N Weatherly, Borger, TX, 79007-3621. Tel: 806-273-0126. Fax: 806-273-0128. p. 2290

Cava, Heidi, Librn, Rush City Public Library, 240 W Fourth St, Rush City, MN, 55069. Tel: 320-358-3948. p. 1273

Cavacco, Julie, Ch, Tilton Library, 75 N Main St, South Deerfield, MA, 01373. Tel: 413-665-4683. Fax: 413-665-9118. p. 1124

Cavada, Jean, Asst Librn, Tiskilwa Public Library, 119 E Main, Tiskilwa, IL, 61368. Tel: 815-646-4511. Fax: 815-646-4247. p. 709

Cavallo, Richard J, Chief Financial Officer, Mercer County Library System, 2751 Brunswick Pike, Lawrenceville, NJ, 08648-4132. Tel: 609-989-6918. Fax: 609-538-9238. p. 1494

Cavanagh, Jane, Edmonton Librn, Alberta Law Libraries, Edmonton, Law Courts Bldg, 2nd Flr, 1A Sir Winston Churchill Sq, Edmonton, AB, T5J 0R2, CANADA. Tel: 780-415-8584. Fax: 780-427-0397. p. 2699

Cavanagh, Moira, Ref Serv, Thayer Public Library, 798 Washington St, Braintree, MA, 02184. Tel: 781-848-0405, Ext 4434. Fax: 781-356-5447. p. 1069

Cavanagh, Shirley, Access Serv, Southern Connecticut State University, 501 Crescent St, New Haven, CT, 06515. Tel: 203-392-5768. Fax: 203-392-5775. p. 356

Cavanaugh, Amy C, Bibliog Instr, Ref, Grove City College, 300 Campus Dr, Grove City, PA, 16127-2198. Tel: 724-458-2148. Fax: 724-458-2181. p. 2063

Cavanaugh, Candace, Ref Librn, Riverside County Law Library, Larson Justice Ctr, 46-200 Oasis St, Indio, CA, 92201. Tel: 760-863-8316. Fax: 760-342-2581. p. 159

Cavanaugh, Jane, Sr Acad Librn, University of Wisconsin Colleges, 1500 University Dr, Waukesha, WI, 53188. Tel: 262-521-5473. Fax: 262-521-5116. p. 2645

Cavanaugh, Jason, Ref Librn, Forbush Memorial Library, 118 Main St, Westminster, MA, 01473. Tel: 978-874-7416. Fax: 978-874-7424. p. 1139

Cavanaugh, Jerome, Dr, Dir, Far Eastern Research Library, Nine First Ave NE, Plato, MN, 55370-0181. Tel: 320-238-2591, 612-926-6887. p. 1271

Cavanaugh, Karen, Actg Commun Libr Mgr, County of Los Angeles Public Library, Hawaiian Gardens Library, 11940 Carson St, Hawaiian Gardens, CA, 90716-1137. Tel: 562-496-1212. Fax: 562-425-0410. p. 141

Cavanaugh, Laurie, Head, Ref Serv, Wareham Free Library, 59 Marion Rd, Wareham, MA, 02571. Tel: 508-295-2343. Fax: 508-295-2678. p. 1133

Cavanaugh, Linda, Dir, Clyde Public Library, 125 Oak St, Clyde, TX, 79510-4702. Tel: 325-893-5315. Fax: 325-893-5315. p. 2298

Cavanaugh, Marianne L, Head Librn, Saint Louis Art Museum, One Fine Arts Dr, Forest Park, Saint Louis, MO, 63110-1380. Tel: 314-655-5255. Fax: 314-721-6172. p. 1357

Cavazos, Leo, Librn, Houston Community College Central College, Central Campus Library, 1300 Holman, Houston, TX, 77004. Tel: 713-718-6133. Fax: 713-718-6154. p. 2337

Cave, Mark, Curator of Manuscripts, Historic New Orleans Collection, 410 Chartres St, New Orleans, LA, 70130-2102. Tel: 504-598-7132. Fax: 504-598-7168. p. 960

Cave-Davis, Carol, Dir, Brookdale University Medical Center, One Brookdale Plaza, Brooklyn, NY, 11212. Tel: 718-240-5312. Fax: 718-240-5030. p. 1589

Cave-Davis, Carol, Dir, Jamaica Hospital Medical Center, 8900 Van Wyck Expressway, Jamaica, NY, 11418-2832. Tel: 718-206-8450. Fax: 718-206-8460. p. 1643

Cavelier, Jeffrey, Circ Supvr, Pacific Oaks College, 55 Eureka St, Pasadena, CA, 91103. Tel: 626-529-8451. p. 206

Caverlee, Ellen, Librn, First United Methodist Church, 500 Common St, Shreveport, LA, 71101. Tel: 318-865-4706. Fax: 318-429-6888. p. 968

Cavicchi, Jon R, IP Librn, University of New Hampshire School of Law, Two White St, Concord, NH, 03301. Tel: 603-228-1541, Ext 1130. Fax: 603-228-0388. p. 1443

Cavill, Melissa, ILL Spec, Cotuit Library, 871 Main St, Cotuit, MA, 02635. Tel: 508-428-8141. Fax: 508-428-4636. p. 1083

Cavin, Karen, Asst Librn, Albemarle Regional Library, Elizabeth Sewell Parker Memorial Library, 213 E Main, Murfreesboro, NC, 27855. Tel: 252-398-4494. Fax: 252-398-5724. p. 1835

Caviness, Amy, Automation Mgr, Mid-Continent Public Library, 15616 E US Hwy 24, Independence, MO, 64050-2098. Tel: 816-836-5200. Fax: 816-521-7253. p. 1332

Caviness, Todd, Libr Syst Mgr, Mid-Continent Public Library, 15616 E US Hwy 24, Independence, MO, 64050-2098. Tel: 816-836-5200. Fax: 816-521-7253. p. 1332

Caviston, Melissa, ILL, Cheltenham Township Library System, Glenside Free Library, 215 S Keswick Ave, Glenside, PA, 19038-4420. Tel: 215-885-0455. Fax: 215-885-1019. p. 2061

Caw, Thomas S, Pub Serv, University of Hartford Libraries, Mildred P Allen Memorial, 200 Bloomfield Ave, West Hartford, CT, 06117-0395. Tel: 860-768-4770. Fax: 860-768-5295. p. 376

Cawley, Amy, Exec Dir, Roselle Public Library District, 40 S Park St, Roselle, IL, 60172-2020. Tel: 630-529-1641, Ext 321. Fax: 630-529-7579. p. 699

Cawley, Bob, Librn, Tri-City Jewish Center Library, 2715 30th St, Rock Island, IL, 61201. Tel: 309-788-3426. p. 696

Cawley, Elizabeth, Info Tech, Bard College, One Library Rd, Annandale-on-Hudson, NY, 12504. Tel: 845-758-7064. Fax: 845-758-5801. p. 1574

Cawley, Kristine, Dir, Ref, Rock Island Public Library, 401 19th St, Rock Island, IL, 61201. Tel: 309-732-7326. Fax: 309-732-7342. p. 696

Cawley, Kristine, Librn, Tri-City Jewish Center Library, 2715 30th St, Rock Island, IL, 61201. Tel: 309-788-3426. p. 696

Cawrse, Elizabeth, Asst Librn, Montgomery County Circuit Court, Judicial Ctr, 50 Maryland Ave, Ste 326, Rockville, MD, 20850. Tel: 240-777-9120. Fax: 240-777-9126. p. 1038

Caws-Elwitt, Hilary, Pub Serv, Susquehanna County Historical Society & Free Library Association, Two Monument Sq, Montrose, PA, 18801-1115. Tel: 570-278-1881. Fax: 570-278-9336. p. 2092

Cawthron, Lillie, Br Mgr, Huntsville-Madison Public Library, R Showers Center, 4600 Blue Spring Rd, Huntsville, AL, 35810. Tel: 256-851-7492. p. 21

Cayabyab, Luz, Br Mgr, Anaheim Public Library, Elva L Haskett Branch, 2650 W Broadway, Anaheim, CA, 92804. Tel: 714-765-5075. Fax: 714-765-5076. p. 120

Cayce, Daniel, Access Serv, Del Mar College, 101 Baldwin Blvd, Corpus Christi, TX, 78404. Tel: 361-698-1310. Fax: 361-698-1182. p. 2302

Cayer, Danielle, In Charge, Centre Hospitalier Jacques Viger, 1051 rue St Hubert, Montreal, QC, H2L 3Y5, CANADA. Tel: 514-842-7180, Ext 2104. Fax: 514-842-1212. p. 2893

Cayer, John, ILL, Fairfield University, 1073 N Benson Rd, Fairfield, CT, 06430-5195. Tel: 203-254-4044. Fax: 203-254-4135. p. 339

Cayer, Judith Graeter, Ref Librn, Rosemont College Library, 1400 Montgomery Ave, Rosemont, PA, 19010-1631. Tel: 610-527-0200, Ext 2990. Fax: 610-525-2930. p. 2135

Cayne, Claudia E, Dir, Scoville Memorial Library, 38 Main St, Salisbury, CT, 06068. Tel: 860-435-2838. Fax: 860-435-8136. p. 366

Cayouette, Nathalie, Info Officer, Lafarge Canada, Inc, 334 Avro Ave, Pointe-Claire, QC, H9R 5W5, CANADA. Tel: 514-428-7277. Fax: 514-428-0049. p. 2903

Cayouette, Veronique, Librn, Revenu Quebec Bibliotheque, 3800 rue de Marly, Secteur 6-2-9, Quebec, QC, G1X 4A5, CANADA. Tel: 418-652-5765. Fax: 418-577-5039. p. 2906

Cayton, Debra, Librn, Beaufort, Hyde & Martin County Regional Library, Old Court House, 158 N Market St, Washington, NC, 27889. Tel: 252-946-6401. Fax: 252-946-0352. p. 1828

Caywood, Carolyn, Dir, Virginia Beach Public Library Department, Subregional Library for the Blind & Handicapped, Bayside Special Library Services, 936 Independence Blvd, Virginia Beach, VA, 23455. Tel: 757-385-2680. p. 2500

Caywood, Carolyn, Librn, Virginia Beach Public Library Department, Bayside Area, 936 Independence Blvd, Virginia Beach, VA, 23455. Tel: 757-385-2680. p. 2500

Caza, Andrea, Ref, National Energy Board Library, 444 Seventh Ave SW, Calgary, AB, T2P 0X8, CANADA. Tel: 403-299-3561. Fax: 403-292-5576. p. 2692

Cazanave, Brian, Ch, Cliffside Park Free Public Library, 505 Palisade Ave, Cliffside Park, NJ, 07010. Tel: 201-945-2867. Fax: 201-945-1016. p. 1479

Cazares, Len, Librn, Houston Community College Central College, Central Campus Library, 1300 Holman, Houston, TX, 77004. Tel: 713-718-6133. Fax: 713-718-6154. p. 2337

Cazares, Theresa, Commun Libr Mgr, County of Los Angeles Public Library, Los Nietos Library, 11644 E Slauson Ave, Whittier, CA, 90606-3396. Tel: 562-695-0708. Fax: 562-699-3876. p. 142

Cease, Jennifer, Cat, Pfeiffer University, 48380 US Hwy 52 N, Misenheimer, NC, 28109. Tel: 704-463-3351. Fax: 704-463-3356. p. 1809

Cebelak, Pat, Head, Adult Serv, Oxford Public Library, 530 Pontiac Rd, Oxford, MI, 48371-4844. Tel: 248-628-3034. Fax: 248-628-5008. p. 1216

Cebula, Emily, Dir, Yates Community Library, 15 N Main St, Lyndonville, NY, 14098. Tel: 585-765-9041. Fax: 585-765-9527. p. 1656

Ceccarelli, Joyce, Dir, Ansonia Library, 53 S Cliff St, Ansonia, CT, 06401-1909. Tel: 203-734-6275. Fax: 203-732-4551. p. 329

Ceci, Vicki, Ref Librn, Lorain County Community College, 1005 Abbe Rd N, North Elyria, OH, 44035-1691. Tel: 440-366-7289. Fax: 440-366-4127. p. 1924

Cecil, Brad, Circ, ILL, Ser, Ohio University, Shannon Hall, 1st Flr, 45425 National Rd, Saint Clairsville, OH, 43950-9724. Tel: 740-695-1720, 740-699-2519. Fax: 740-695-7075. p. 1933

Cecil, Cheryl, Chair, Circ, Samford University Library, 800 Lakeshore Dr, Birmingham, AL, 35229. Tel: 205-726-2699. Fax: 205-726-4009. p. 9

Cecil, Sharon, Cat Tech, Indiana Wesleyan University, 4201 S Washington St, Marion, IN, 46953. Tel: 765-677-2982. Fax: 765-677-2676. p. 762

Cecil, Vicki, Dir, Hartford City Public Library, 314 N High St, Hartford City, IN, 47348-2143. Tel: 765-348-1720. Fax: 765-348-5000. p. 748

Cecillia, Shearron-Hawkins, Br Mgr, Fort Bend County Libraries, Missouri City Branch, 1530 Texas Pkwy, Missouri City, TX, 77489-2170. Tel: 281-261-3044. Fax: 281-261-5829. p. 2375

Cedar-Face, Mary Jane, Coll Develop, Southern Oregon University, 1250 Siskiyou Blvd, Ashland, OR, 97520-5076. Tel: 541-552-6836. Fax: 541-552-6429. p. 1990

Cedeno, Maribel, Ref Serv, Universidad Adventista de las Antillas, Carr 106 Km 2 Interior, Bo La Quinta, Mayaguez, PR, 00680. Tel: 787-834-9595, Ext 2274. Fax: 787-834-6015. p. 2674

Cederquist, Jan, Dir, Enterprise Public Library, 101 E Grubbs St, Enterprise, AL, 36330. Tel: 334-347-2636. Fax: 334-393-6477. p. 15

Ceglia, Leona, Head, Tech Serv, Harborfields Public Library, 31 Broadway, Greenlawn, NY, 11740-1382. Tel: 631-757-4200. Fax: 631-757-7216. p. 1631

Celata, Stacy, Circ Coordr, Saint John Fisher College, 3690 East Ave, Rochester, NY, 14618-3599. Tel: 585-385-8165. Fax: 585-385-8445. p. 1732

Celentano, Carrie, Ch, Hodgkins Public Library District, 6500 Wenz Ave, Hodgkins, IL, 60525. Tel: 708-579-1844. Fax: 708-579-1896. p. 657

Celestin, Charlotte, Br Mgr, Terrebonne Parish Library, Gibson Branch, 6363 S Bayou Black Dr, Gibson, LA, 70356. Tel: 985-575-2639. Fax: 985-575-3069. p. 951

Celio, Rose, Ch, Beaver County Library System, One Campus Dr, Monaca, PA, 15061-2523. Tel: 724-728-3737. Fax: 724-728-8024. p. 2090

Cella, Mary, Reader Serv Librn, St Charles Public Library District, One S Sixth Ave, Saint Charles, IL, 60174-2105. Tel: 630-584-0076, Ext 248. Fax: 630-584-3448. p. 699

Celle, Deborah, Ref, United States Courts for the Ninth Circuit Library, 95 Seventh St, San Francisco, CA, 94103. Tel: 415-556-9500. Fax: 415-556-9927. p. 247

Cellini, Jacqueline, Head, Ref, Librn, Northwestern Memorial Hospital, 250 E Superior-Prentice Women's Hospital, First Floor, Room 2104, Chicago, IL, 60611. Tel: 312-472-3640. Fax: 312-472-3836. p. 621

Celsie, Mary Jane, Dir, Pub Serv, Richmond Hill Public Library, One Atkinson St, Richmond Hill, ON, L4C 0H5, CANADA. Tel: 905-884-9288. Fax: 905-770-0312, 905-884-6544. p. 2839

Cemper, R, Mrs, Dir, O'Neill Public Library, 601 E Douglas, O'Neill, NE, 68763. Tel: 402-336-3110. Fax: 402-336-3268. p. 1415

Cen, Luozhu, Dr, Dir, Libr Serv, Butte College Library, 3536 Butte Campus Dr, Oroville, CA, 95965-8399. Tel: 530-879-4050. Fax: 530-895-2849. p. 201

Cen, Wei, Emerging Tech Librn, Gulf Coast State College Library, 5230 W Hwy 98, Panama City, FL, 32401. Tel: 850-872-3893. Fax: 850-872-3861. p. 480

Center, Clark, Curator, University of Alabama, University Libraries, University of Alabama Campus, Capstone Dr, Tuscaloosa, AL, 35487. Tel: 205-348-0513. Fax: 205-348-1699. p. 38

Center, Jim, Ref, Jones Day, 555 S Flower St, 50th Flr, Los Angeles, CA, 90013-90071. Tel: 213-489-3939. Fax: 213-243-2539. p. 171

Center, Judy B, Dir, Cambridge Public Library, 21 W Main St, Cambridge, NY, 12816. Tel: 518-677-2443. Fax: 518-677-2443. p. 1600

Centi, Debbie, Br Mgr, Placer County Library, Meadow Vista Branch, 16981 Placer Hills Rd, Ste B6, Meadow Vista, CA, 95722. Tel: 530-878-2647. Fax: 530-878-4983. p. 123

Cepeda, Geraldine Amparo, Exec Dir/Librn, Guam Law Library, 141 San Ramon St, Hagatna, GU, 96910-4333. Tel: 671-472-8062, 671-477-7623. Fax: 671-472-1246. p. 2667

Ceppaglia, Deborah, Ref & Instruction Librn, Medaille College Library, 18 Agassiz Circle, Buffalo, NY, 14214. Tel: 716-880-2283. Fax: 716-884-9638. p. 1598

Cerame, Rebekah, Mgr, Northrop Grumman Corp, PO Box 1693, MS-1138, Baltimore, MD, 21203-1693. Tel: 410-765-5565. Fax: 410-993-7675. p. 1017

Ceravolo, Teresa, Librn, Birmingham Public Library, Southside, 1814 11th Ave S, Birmingham, AL, 35205. Tel: 205-933-7776. Fax: 205-918-0723. p. 7

Cerian, Martin, Assoc Dean for Libr & Tech Serv, Saint John's University Library, Rittenberg Law Library, 8000 Utopia Pkwy, Queens, NY, 11439. Tel: 718-990-6651, 718-990-6659. Fax: 718-990-6649. p. 1725

Cerjan, Martin, Asst Dean, Vanderbilt University, Alyne Queener Massey Law Library, 131 21st Ave S, Nashville, TN, 37203. Tel: 615-322-0020. Fax: 615-343-1265. p. 2261

Cerling, Teresa, Dir, Chatfield Brass Band, Inc, 81 Library Lane, Chatfield, MN, 55923. Tel: 507-867-3275. p. 1245

Cernieux, Debra, Reader Serv, South Huntington Public Library, 145 Pidgeon Hill Rd, Huntington Station, NY, 11746. Tel: 631-549-4411. Fax: 631-549-1266. p. 1639

Cerniglia, Lauren, Asst Dir, Circ & Tech Serv, Cook Memorial Public Library District, 413 N Milwaukee Ave, Libertyville, IL, 60048-2280. Tel: 847-362-2330. Fax: 847-362-2354. p. 665

Cernile, Carol, Librn, Stelco, Inc, 386 Wilcox St, Hamilton, ON, L8P 1A2, CANADA. Tel: 905-528-2511, Ext 2076. Fax: 905-308-7012. p. 2811

Cerny, Jessica, Asst Br Mgr, Chesterfield County Public Library, Clover Hill, 6701 Deer Run Rd, Midlothian, VA, 23112. Tel: 804-318-8406. p. 2457

Ceron-Flores, Stephanie, Med Staff Spec, Wilcox Memorial Hospital, 3-3420 Kuhio Hwy, Lihue, HI, 96766-1099. Tel: 808-245-1173. Fax: 808-246-2918. p. 567

Cervantes, Maria, Libr Asst, Wickenburg Public Library, 164 E Apache St, Wickenburg, AZ, 85390. Tel: 928-684-2665. p. 89

Cervantes, Melinda, Dir, Pima County Public Library, 101 N Stone Ave, Tucson, AZ, 85701. Tel: 520-564-5600. Fax: 520-594-5621. p. 86

Cervantes, Michelle, Libr Mgr, Round Rock Public Library, 216 E Main St, Round Rock, TX, 78664. Tel: 512-218-7000, 512-218-7003. Fax: 512-218-7061. p. 2377

Cervantes-Squires, Michaelene, Head, YA, Mokena Community Public Library District, 11327 W 195th St, Mokena, IL, 60448. Tel: 708-479-9663. Fax: 708-479-9684. p. 674

Cervelli, Kara, Ch, Perry Public Library, 3753 Main St, Perry, OH, 44081-9501. Tel: 440-259-3300. Fax: 440-259-3977. p. 1929

Cervenka, Patricia, Dir, Marquette University, Sensenbrenner Hall, 1103 W Wisconsin Ave, Milwaukee, WI, 53233-2313. Tel: 414-288-7092. Fax: 414-288-5914. p. 2618

Cerveny, June, Coll Develop, Patchogue-Medford Library, 54-60 E Main St, Patchogue, NY, 11772. Tel: 631-654-4700, Ext 231. Fax: 631-289-3999. p. 1715

Cesena, Danielle, Ch, Belleville Public Library & Information Center, 221 Washington Ave, Belleville, NJ, 07109-3189. Tel: 973-450-3434. Fax: 973-450-9518, 973-759-6731. p. 1471

Cespo, Barbara, Ch, Warner Library, 121 N Broadway, Tarrytown, NY, 10591. Tel: 914-631-7734. Fax: 914-631-2324. p. 1754

Cessna, Jennifer, Info Spec, Hershey Foods Corp, 1025 Reese Ave, Hershey, PA, 17033-2272. Tel: 717-534-5106. Fax: 717-534-5069. p. 2069

Cesta, Jennifer, Pub Serv, Public Library of Steubenville & Jefferson County, 407 S Fourth St, Steubenville, OH, 43952-2942. Tel: 740-282-9782. Fax: 740-282-2919. p. 1937

Cetina, Judith G, PhD, Archives, Cuyahoga County Archives Library, The Robert Russell Rhodes House, 2905 Franklin Blvd NW, Cleveland, OH, 44113. Tel: 216-443-7250. Fax: 216-443-3636. p. 1879

Cetwinski, Tom, Dir, Admin Serv, University of South Florida, Tampa Campus Library, 4101 USF Apple Dr, LIB122, Tampa, FL, 33620. Tel: 813-974-4592. Fax: 813-974-5153. p. 499

Chaberek, Guna K, Dir, Mineral County Public Library, 301 Second Ave E, Superior, MT, 59872. Tel: 406-822-3563. Fax: 406-822-3569. p. 1389

Chabot, Jean, Librn, Centre Regional de Services aux Bibliotheques Publiques du Bas-Saint-Laurent, 465 St Pierre, Riviere-du-Loup, QC, G5R 4T6, CANADA. Tel: 418-867-1682. Fax: 418-867-3434. p. 2907

Chabot, Jean-Pierre, Prof, College Lionel-Groulx, 100, rue Duquet, Sainte-Therese, QC, J7E 3G6, CANADA. Tel: 450-430-3120, Ext 407. Fax: 450-971-7883. p. 2979

Chabot, Lisabeth, Col Librn, Ithaca College Library, 953 Danby Rd, Ithaca, NY, 14850-7060. Tel: 607-274-3821. Fax: 607-274-1211. p. 1643

Chacon, Katherine, Teen Librn, New Britain Public Library, 20 High St, New Britain, CT, 06051-4226. Tel: 860-224-3155. Fax: 860-223-6729. p. 354

Chacon, Lorraine, Circ Mgr, Pueblo City-County Library District, 100 E Abriendo Ave, Pueblo, CO, 81004-4290. Tel: 719-562-5621. Fax: 719-562-5619. p. 320

Chacon, Lorraine, Circ, Pueblo City-County Library District, 100 E Abriendo Ave, Pueblo, CO, 81004-4290. Tel: 719-562-5621. Fax: 719-562-5619. p. 320

Chadderton, Phyllis, Circ, Alberta Health Services, PO Box 1000, Ponoka, AB, T4J 1R8, CANADA. Tel: 403-783-7691. Fax: 403-783-7695. p. 2713

Chadsey, Kathy, Ch, Tillamook County Library, 1716 Third St, Tillamook, OR, 97141. Tel: 503-842-4792. Fax: 503-815-8194. p. 2021

Chadwell, Faye, Univ Librn/OSU Press Dir, Oregon State University Libraries, 121 The Valley Library, Corvallis, OR, 97331-4501. Tel: 541-737-3331. Fax: 541-737-3453. p. 1994

Chadwick, Cindy, Dep County Librn, Alameda County Library, Extension Services, 2450 Stevenson Blvd, Fremont, CA, 94538-2326. Tel: 510-745-1510. Fax: 510-745-1494. p. 149

Chadwick, Gayle, Br Librn, Lincoln County Library, Cokeville Branch, 240 E Main St, Cokeville, WY, 83114. Tel: 307-279-3213. Fax: 307-279-3263. p. 2656

Chadwick, Georgia, Dir, Law Libr, Law Library of Louisiana, Louisiana Supreme Court, 2nd Flr, 400 Royal St, New Orleans, LA, 70130-2104. Tel: 504-310-2402. Fax: 504-310-2419. p. 960

Chadwick, Linda, Chief Librn, Brockville Public Library, 23 Buell St, Brockville, ON, K6V 5T7, CANADA. Tel: 613-342-3936. Fax: 613-342-9598. p. 2797

Chadwick, Peggy, Cat, Williams Baptist College, 91 W Fulbright, Walnut Ridge, AR, 72476. Tel: 870-759-4139. p. 116

Chadwick, Tracie, Tech Serv, Idaho Falls Public Library, 457 W Broadway, Idaho Falls, ID, 83402. Tel: 208-612-8460. Fax: 208-612-8467. p. 576

Chae, Hui Soo, Assoc Dir, Head Knowledge Ctr, Teachers College, Columbia University, 525 W 120th St, New York, NY, 10027-6696. Tel: 212-678-3448. p. 1701

Chafetz, Danielle, Libr Dir, Haut-Saint-Jean Regional Library, Grand Sault Public, 131 Rue Pleasant, Ste 201, Grand Sault, NB, E3Z 1G6, CANADA. Tel: 506-475-7781. Fax: 506-475-7783. p. 2762

Chaff, Sandra L, Archivist, Librn, Germantown Historical Society, 5501 Germantown Ave, Philadelphia, PA, 19144-2291. Tel: 215-844-1683. Fax: 215-844-2831. p. 2110

Chaffee, Joanne, Br Mgr, Milan-Berlin Township Public Library, Berlin Township Public, Four E Main St, Berlin Heights, OH, 44814-9602. Tel: 419-588-2250. Fax: 419-588-0025. p. 1918

Chaffee, Lance, Dir, Olean Public Library, 134 N Second St, Olean, NY, 14760-2583. Tel: 716-372-0200. Fax: 716-372-8651. p. 1710

Chaffin, Debbie, Dir, Media Serv, University of North Alabama, One Harrison Plaza, Box 5028, Florence, AL, 35632-0001. Tel: 256-765-4208. Fax: 256-765-4438. p. 17

Chaffin, Sharon, Br Mgr, Perry County District Library, Thornville Branch, 99 E Columbus St, Thornville, OH, 43076. Tel: 740-246-5133. Fax: 740-246-3994. p. 1921

Chaffin, Walker, Libr Mgr, K&L Gates LLP, 1601 K St NW, L-3, Washington, DC, 20006. Tel: 202-778-9162. Fax: 202-778-9100. p. 406

Chaffin, Walker, Libr Mgr, Kirkpatrick & Lockhart, Preston, Gates, Ellis, 1601 K St NW, Washington, DC, 20006-1600. Tel: 202-778-9000 (main), 202-778-9160. Fax: 202-778-9100. p. 406

Chaffin, William J, Reader Serv, Washington College, 300 Washington Ave, Chestertown, MD, 21620-1197. Tel: 410-778-7292. Fax: 410-778-7288. p. 1023

Chafin, Karen S, Dir, Pikeville College, 147 Sycamore St, Pikeville, KY, 41501-9118. Tel: 606-218-5606. Fax: 606-218-5613. p. 933

Chafin, Sandra, Ch, Mims/Scottsmoor Public Library, 3615 Lionel Rd, Mims, FL, 32754. Tel: 321-264-5080. Fax: 321-264-5081. p. 470

Chagat, Jonathan, Sr Res Librn, Ohio Attorney General, 30 E Broad St, 15th Flr, Columbus, OH, 43215. Tel: 614-466-2465, 614-466-4534. Fax: 614-752-9867. p. 1886

Chahal, Jasbir, Br Mgr, Boone County Public Library, Florence Branch, 7425 US 42, Florence, KY, 41042. Fax: 859-371-0037. p. 909

Chaillez, Lise, Librn, College Edouard-Montpetit Bibliotheque, Ecole Nationale d'Aerotechnique Bibliotheque, 5555 Place de la Savane, Saint Hubert, QC, J3Y 8Y9, CANADA. Tel: 450-678-3560, Ext 4254. Fax: 450-678-3240. p. 2887

Chaippetta, Tina, Dir, International Personnel Management Association, 1617 Duke St, Alexandria, VA, 22314. Tel: 703-549-7100. Fax: 703-684-0948. p. 2446

Chajes, Susan, Head, Ch, Mount Pleasant Public Library, 350 Bedford Rd, Pleasantville, NY, 10570-3099. Tel: 914-769-0548. Fax: 914-769-6149. p. 1719

Chakraborty, Moushumi, Dir, Pub Serv, Salisbury University, 1101 Camden Ave, Salisbury, MD, 21801-6863. Tel: 410-543-6130. Fax: 410-543-6203. p. 1040

Chalaron, Peggy, Dept Head, Louisiana State University Libraries, Education Resources, 227 Middleton Library, Baton Rouge, LA, 70803-3300. Tel: 225-578-2349. Fax: 225-578-6992. p. 944

Chalfant, Kate, Tech Serv, Wright Memorial Public Library, 1776 Far Hills Ave, Oakwood, OH, 45419-2598. Tel: 937-294-7171. Fax: 937-294-8578. p. 1924

Chalick, David, Librn, Collier County Public Library, Golden Gate, 2432 Lucerne Rd, Naples, FL, 34116. Tel: 239-455-1441. Fax: 239-455-8921. p. 471

Chaliff, Pamela, Dir, Rockcastle County Library, 60 Ford Dr, Mount Vernon, KY, 40456. Tel: 606-256-2388. Fax: 606-256-5460. p. 930

Challacombe, Elaine, Curator, University of Minnesota Libraries-Twin Cities, Wangensteen Historical Library of Biology & Medicine, 568 Diehl Hall, 505 Essex St SE, Minneapolis, MN, 55455. Tel: 612-626-6881. Fax: 612-626-6500. p. 1262

Challis, Donna, Dir, Lakeland Library Region, 1302 100 St, North Battleford, SK, S9A 0V8, CANADA. Tel: 306-445-6108. Fax: 306-445-5717. p. 2919

Chalmers, Judy, Tech Serv Librn, Washoe County Law Library, 75 Courth St, Rm 101, Reno, NV, 89501. Tel: 775-328-3250. Fax: 775-328-3441. p. 1433

Chalmers, Patricia L, Asst Librn, Ref Serv, University of King's College Library, 6350 Coburg Rd, Halifax, NS, B3H 2A1, CANADA. Tel: 902-422-1271. Fax: 902-423-3357. p. 2783

Chalone, Craig, Libr Asst I, University of Maine at Machias, 116 O'Brien Ave, Machias, ME, 04654-1397. Tel: 207-255-1362. Fax: 207-255-1356. p. 991

Chalungsooth, Apichart, Libr Tech & Syst Spec, Howard Community College Library, 10901 Little Patuxent Pkwy, Columbia, MD, 21044. Tel: 443-518-4683. Fax: 443-518-4993. p. 1025

Chamberlain, Beth, Head, Tech Serv, Touro College, 225 Eastview Dr, Central Islip, NY, 11722-4539. Tel: 631-761-7000, 631-761-7150. Fax: 631-761-7159. p. 1605

Chamberlain, Deborah, Librn, Russell Memorial Library, 4333 State Prison Hollow Rd, Monkton, VT, 05469. Tel: 802-453-4471. p. 2429

Chamberlain, Deeda, Youth Serv, Woodburn Public Library, 280 Garfield St, Woodburn, OR, 97071-4698. Tel: 503-980-2413. Fax: 503-982-2808. p. 2023

Chamberlain, Eileen, Librn, Sanford Health Library, 801 Broadway N, Fargo, ND, 58102. Tel: 701-234-5571. Fax: 701-234-5927. p. 1841

Chamberlain, Ellen E, Distinguished Univ Prof, Libr Dir, University of South Carolina at Beaufort Library, One University Blvd, Bluffton, SC, 29909-6085. Tel: 843-208-8022. Fax: 843-208-8296. p. 2182

Chamberlain, Enrique, Dr, Head Librn, North Lake College Library, 5001 N MacArthur Blvd, Irving, TX, 75062. Tel: 972-273-3400. Fax: 972-273-3431. p. 2347

Chamberlain, Jane, Adult Serv, Bloomington Public Library, 205 E Olive St, Bloomington, IL, 61701. Tel: 309-828-6091. Fax: 309-828-7312. p. 595

Chamberlain, Marion, Circ Supvr, Seminole Community Library, 9200 113th St N, Seminole, FL, 33772. Tel: 727-394-6905. Fax: 727-398-3113. p. 491

Chamberlain, Martin, Librn, Bibliotheque de l'Abbaye Saint-Benoit, Saint Benoit-du-Lac, QC, J0B 2M0, CANADA. Tel: 819-843-4080. Fax: 819-868-1861. p. 2908

Chamberland, Fayth, Ch, YA Librn, Concord Free Public Library, 129 Main St, Concord, MA, 01742-2494. Tel: 978-318-3300. Fax: 978-318-3344. p. 1082

Chamberlin, Charles E, Sr Assoc Dean, Univ Libr, University of Washington Libraries, Allen Library, 4th Flr, Rm 482, Box 352900, Seattle, WA, 98195-2900. Tel: 206-685-1978. Fax: 206-685-8727. p. 2533

Chamberlin, Leslie, Dir, The University of New Mexico, Travelstead Hall, MSC 05 3040, Tireman Library, 119 COE UNM, Albuquerque, NM, 87131-0001. Tel: 505-277-6384, 505-277-7260. Fax: 505-277-8427. p. 2969

Chamberlin, Mark Lincoln, Brother, Librn, Lynn Museum & Historical Society Library, 590 Washington St, Lynn, MA, 01901. Tel: 781-581-6200. Fax: 781-581-6202. p. 1101

Chamberot, Robert, Chef de Section, Bibliothèques de Montrèal, Côte-des-Neiges, 5290, chemin de la Côte-des-Neiges, Montreal, QC, H3T 1Y2, CANADA. Tel: 514-872-2935. Fax: 514-872-0516. p. 2889

Chamberot, Robert, Chef de Section, Bibliothèques de Montrèal, Notre-Dame-de-Grâce, 3755, rue Botrel, Montreal, QC, H4A 3G8, CANADA. Tel: 514-872-2935. Fax: 514-872-0517. p. 2890

Chambers, Betty, Librn, Dorion Public Library, 170 Dorion Loop Rd, Dorion, ON, P0T 1K0, CANADA. Tel: 807-857-2289. Fax: 807-857-2203. p. 2802

Chambers, Billie Jean, Dir, Dandridge Memorial Library, 1235 Circle Dr, Dandridge, TN, 37725-4750. Tel: 865-397-9758. Fax: 865-397-0950. p. 2232

Chambers, Cathy, Cat Librn, Otis College of Art & Design Library, 9045 Lincoln Blvd, Westchester, CA, 90045. Tel: 310-665-6800, Ext 6930. Fax: 310-665-6998. p. 283

Chambers, Coleen, Exec Dir, Historical & Genealogical Society of Indiana County, 621 Wayne Ave, Indiana, PA, 15701-3042. Tel: 724-463-9600. Fax: 724-463-9899. p. 2071

Chambers, Cynthia, Head, Cat, Saint John's University Library, 8000 Utopia Pkwy, Queens, NY, 11439. Tel: 718-990-6735. Fax: 718-380-0353. p. 1725

Chambers, Frances, Tech Serv, Central Virginia Community College Library, Amherst Hall, Rm 2506, 3506 Wards Rd, Lynchburg, VA, 24502-2498. Tel: 434-832-7754. Fax: 434-386-4677. p. 2475

Chambers, Holly, Distance Educ, State University of New York College at Potsdam, 44 Pierrepont Ave, Potsdam, NY, 13676-2294. Tel: 315-267-3312. Fax: 315-267-2744. p. 1722

Chambers, Judith, Dir, Shelby Township Library, 51680 Van Dyke, Shelby Township, MI, 48316-4448. Tel: 586-726-2344. Fax: 586-726-0535. p. 1227

Chambers, Karen, Dir, Woodville Public Library, 26 Venson St, Woodville, AL, 35776. Tel: 256-776-2796. Fax: 256-776-3294. p. 41

Chambers, Kathy, Libr Spec, Inyo County Free Library, Lone Pine Branch, 127 Bush St, Lone Pine, CA, 93545. Tel: 760-876-5031. p. 159

Chambers, Margaret, Asst Dir, Communications, Consortium of Academic & Research Libraries in Illinois, 100 Trade Ctr Dr, Ste 303, Champaign, IL, 61820. Tel: 217-333-2618. Fax: 217-244-7596. p. 2942

Chambers, Rhonda J, Dir, Missouri Valley Public Library, 420 E Huron St, Missouri Valley, IA, 51555. Tel: 712-642-4111. Fax: 712-642-4172. p. 832

Chambers, Sandra, Librn, Melanee Smith Memorial Library, 2103 Main St, Waller, TX, 77484. Tel: 936-372-3961. p. 2398

Chambers, Stephanie, News Res Librn, The Globe & Mail Library, 444 Front St W, Toronto, ON, M5V 2S9, CANADA. Tel: 416-585-5060. p. 2853

Chambers, Stephen, Exec Dir, Western Fairs Association Library, 1776 Tribute Rd, Ste 210, Sacramento, CA, 95815-4410. Tel: 916-927-3100. Fax: 916-927-6397. p. 226

Chambers, Stephen, Br Mgr, Monroe County Public Library, Big Pine Key Branch, 213 Key Deer Blvd, Big Pine Key, FL, 33043. Tel: 305-872-0992. Fax: 305-289-6304. p. 456

Chambers, Steve, Librn, Center on Education & Training for Employment, 1900 Kenny Rd, Columbus, OH, 43210-1016. Tel: 614-292-6991. Fax: 614-292-1260. p. 1883

Chambers, Sydney, Cat Librn, Gonzaga University, 502 E Boone Ave, Spokane, WA, 99258-0095. Tel: 509-313-6537. Fax: 509-323-5904. p. 2536

Chambers, Victoria, Librn, Hamilton Health Sciences, 286 Victoria Ave N, Hamilton, ON, L8L 5G4, CANADA. Tel: 905-527-4322, Ext 44247, 905-527-4322, Ext 44248. Fax: 905-577-1453. p. 2808

Chamblee, Pat, Dir, Petros Public Library, 208 Main St, Petros, TN, 37845. Tel: 423-324-2825. p. 2263

Chameides, Emily, Libr Dir, Hudson Area Library, 400 State St, Hudson, NY, 12534. Tel: 518-828-1792. Fax: 518-822-0567. p. 1638

Chamis, William, Sr Assoc, Info Res N Am, National Economic Research Associates, Inc, 360 Hamilton Ave, 10th Flr, White Plains, NY, 10601. Tel: 212-345-9304. Fax: 914-448-4040. p. 1768

Chamness, Berry, Coordr, Info Access & Delivery, Bryn Mawr College, 101 N Merion Ave, Bryn Mawr, PA, 19010-2899. Tel: 610-526-5295. Fax: 610-526-7480. p. 2039

Chamness, Christine, ILL, Ref Serv, University of Wisconsin-Fox Valley Library, 1478 Midway Rd, Menasha, WI, 54952-1297. Tel: 920-832-2672. Fax: 920-832-2874. p. 2614

Champ, Debra, Info Tech Dir, Indianapolis-Marion County Public Library, 2450 N Meridian St, Indianapolis, IN, 46208. Tel: 317-275-4910. Fax: 317-269-5300. p. 753

Champagne, Anne, Tech Serv Librn, Art Institute of Chicago, 111 S Michigan Ave, Chicago, IL, 60603. Tel: 312-443-3671. Fax: 312-443-0849. p. 606

Champagne, Carol, Youth Serv Coordr, Plymouth District Library, 223 S Main St, Plymouth, MI, 48170-1687. Tel: 734-453-0750, Ext 237. Fax: 734-453-0733. p. 1218

Champagne, Guy, Prof, College de Maisonneuve, 3800, rue Sherbrooke Est, Montreal, QC, H1X 2A2, CANADA. Tel: 514-254-7131. Fax: 514-251-9741. p. 2978

Champagne, Julie, Dir, Saint Mary Parish Library, 206 Iberia St, Franklin, LA, 70538-4906. Tel: 337-828-1624. Fax: 337-828-2329. p. 949

Champagne, Louise, Info Serv, Southington Public Library & Museum, 255 Main St, Southington, CT, 06489. Tel: 860-628-0947. Fax: 860-628-0488. p. 368

Champagne, Michelle, Librn, HEC Montreal, 3000, chemin de la Cote-Sainte-Catherine, Montreal, QC, H3T 2A7, CANADA. Tel: 514-340-6224. Fax: 514-340-5639. p. 2896

Champagne, Sylvain, Head, User Serv, HEC Montreal, 3000, chemin de la Cote-Sainte-Catherine, Montreal, QC, H3T 2A7, CANADA. Tel: 514-340-6211. Fax: 514-340-5639. p. 2896

Champion, Brian, Librn, Brigham Young University, Harold B Lee Library, 2060 HBLL, Provo, UT, 84602. Tel: 801-422-2927. Fax: 801-422-0466. p. 2411

Champion, Eric, Asst Librn, Art Institute of Indianapolis Library, 3500 Depauw Blvd, Indianapolis, IN, 46268. Tel: 317-613-4800, 317-613-4803. Fax: 317-613-4808. p. 749

Champion, Kathy, Tech Serv, American River College Library, 4700 College Oak Dr, Sacramento, CA, 95841. Tel: 916-484-8455. Fax: 916-484-8018, 916-484-8657. p. 220

Champion, Virginia, Head, Access Serv, University of South Florida Saint Petersburg, 140 Seventh Ave S, POY118, Saint Petersburg, FL, 33701. Tel: 727-873-4843. Fax: 727-873-4196. p. 489

Chan, Alice, Br Mgr, San Francisco Public Library, Visitacion Valley Branch Library, 201 Leland Ave, San Francisco, CA, 94134-2829. Tel: 415-355-2848. Fax: 415-333-1027. p. 247

Chan, Allan, Librn, Fillmore Riley, 1700-360 Main St, Winnipeg, MB, R3C 3Z3, CANADA. Tel: 204-956-2970. Fax: 204-957-0516. p. 2755

Chan, Carl C, Chamberlin Librn, Aiso Library, 543 Lawton Rd, Ste 617A, Monterey, CA, 93944-3214. Tel: 831-242-7680. Fax: 831-242-5816. p. 189

Chan, Co-Ming, Head, Cat, Oklahoma State University Libraries, Oklahoma State University, Athletic Ave, Stillwater, OK, 74078-1071. Tel: 405-744-9729. Fax: 405-744-5183. p. 1978

Chan, Connie, Ref, Alhambra Public Library, 101 S First St, Alhambra, CA, 91801-3432. Tel: 626-570-5008. Fax: 626-457-1104. p. 120

Chan, Cynthia, Librn, Toronto Dominion Bank, 55 King St W, Toronto, ON, M5K 1A2, CANADA. Tel: 416-982-8068. p. 2859

Chan, Frederick, Cat, University of Arkansas Libraries, Robert A & Vivian Young Law Library, School of Law, Waterman Hall 107, Fayetteville, AR, 72701-1201. Tel: 479-575-3682. Fax: 479-575-2053. p. 100

Chan, Jeanny, Tech Serv, Cerritos Library, 18025 Bloomfield Ave, Cerritos, CA, 90703. Tel: 562-916-1345. Fax: 562-916-1375. p. 133

Chan, Karen, Per, City College of San Francisco, 50 Phelan Ave, San Francisco, CA, 94112. Tel: 415-452-4354. Fax: 415-452-5588. p. 241

Chan, Lawrence, Sr Col Lab Tech, Queensborough Community College, City University of New York, 222-05 56th Ave, Bayside, NY, 11364-1497. Tel: 718-281-5595. Fax: 718-281-5012. p. 1579

Chan, Michelle, Commun Libr Mgr, Queens Borough Public Library, Bellerose Community Library, 250-06 Hillside Ave, Bellerose, NY, 11426. Tel: 718-831-8644. p. 1644

Chan, Phan Thi Ngoc, Librn, Harvard Library, Harvard-Yenching Library, Two Divinity Ave, Cambridge, MA, 02138. Tel: 617-495-2756. Fax: 617-496-6008. p. 1075

Chan, Polly, Librn, Marine Corps Base Hawaii Libraries, Camp Smith Branch, Bldg 1, Rm 201, Camp H M Smith, HI, 96861-4123. Tel: 808-477-6348. p. 566

Chan, Stephen S, Asst Dir, Info Serv, Educ Tech Librn, Campbell University, Norman Adrian Wiggins School of Law Library, 225 Hillsborough St, Ste 203, Raleigh, NC, 27603. Tel: 919-865-5869. Fax: 919-865-5995. p. 1778

Chan, Steve, Circ, Sheridan College Library, Davis Campus, 7899 McLaughlin Rd, Brampton, ON, L6V 1G6, CANADA. Tel: 905-459-7533. Fax: 905-874-4345. p. 2826

Chan, Susanna, Head, Children's Dept, South Brunswick Public Library, 110 Kingston Lane, Monmouth Junction, NJ, 08852. Tel: 732-329-4000, Ext 7285. Fax: 732-329-0573. p. 1502

Chan, Tony, Mgr, Quarles & Brady, 411 E Wisconsin Ave, Milwaukee, WI, 53202-4491. Tel: 414-277-5000. Fax: 414-271-3552. p. 2621

Chan, Wing, Br Mgr, San Francisco Public Library, Sunset Branch Library, 1305 18th Ave, San Francisco, CA, 94122-1807. Tel: 415-355-2808. Fax: 415-665-2461. p. 247

Chan, Yolanda, Br Mgr, Markham Public Library, Markham Village Branch, 6031 Hwy 7 E, Markham, ON, L3P 3A7, CANADA. Tel: 905-513-7977, Ext 4277. Fax: 905-294-7586. p. 2820

Chance, Rosemary, Dr, Assoc Prof, Sam Houston State University, 1921 Ave J, Huntsville, TX, 77340. Tel: 936-294-1151. Fax: 936-294-1153. p. 2974

Chand, Carmen, ILL, Pan American Health Organization Headquarters Library, 525 23rd St NW, Washington, DC, 20037. Tel: 202-974-3734. p. 412

Chandler, Amy, Br Mgr, San Diego County Library, Encinitas Branch, 540 Cornish Dr, Encinitas, CA, 92024-4599. Tel: 760-634-6451. Fax: 760-753-0582. p. 233

Chandler, Bertha, Asst Dir, Cambridge Public Library, 449 Broadway, Cambridge, MA, 02138. Tel: 617-349-4040. Fax: 617-349-4028. p. 1073

Chandler, Cindy, Dir, Blaine Public Library, 220 Indian Ridge Rd, Blaine, TN, 37709. Tel: 865-933-0845. Fax: 865-933-0845. p. 2224

Chandler, Dan, Asst Librn, Integris Baptist Medical Center, 3300 Northwest Expressway, Oklahoma City, OK, 73112. Tel: 405-949-3766. Fax: 405-949-3883. p. 1972

Chandler, Dana, Univ Archivist, Tuskegee University, Hollis Burke Frissell Bldg, 1200 W Old Montgomery Rd, Tuskegee, AL, 36088. Tel: 334-727-8892, 334-727-8894. Fax: 334-727-9282. p. 39

Chandler, Donna, Bibliog Instruction Librn, Fresno City College Library, 1101 E University Ave, Fresno, CA, 93741. Tel: 559-442-8204. Fax: 559-265-5758. p. 151

Chandler, Elisa, Librn, Nunavut Court of Justice Library, PO Box 297, Iqaluit, NU, X0A 0H0, CANADA. Tel: 867-975-6134. Fax: 867-975-6168. p. 2789

Chandler, Janis, Cataloger, Rockland Memorial Library, 20 Belmont St, Rockland, MA, 02370-2232. Tel: 781-878-1236. Fax: 781-878-4013. p. 1120

Chandler, Jenny, In Charge, Ledger-Enquirer, PO Box 711, Columbus, GA, 31902-0711. Tel: 706-324-5526, 706-571-8525. Fax: 706-576-6290. p. 526

Chandler, Kathleen, Dir, Pitkin County Library, 120 N Mill St, Aspen, CO, 81611. Tel: 970-925-4025. Fax: 970-925-3935. p. 288

Chandler, Sandra, Br Mgr, Knox County Public Library System, Murphy Branch, L T Ross Bldg, 2247 Western Ave, Knoxville, TN, 37921-5756. Tel: 865-521-7812. Fax: 865-521-0962. p. 2242

Chandler, Simone, Librn, Northeast Regional Library, Anne Spencer Cox Library, 303 N Third St, Baldwyn, MS, 38824-1517. Tel: 662-365-3305. Fax: 662-365-3305. p. 1297

Chandler, Susan, Coordr, Extn Serv, Sterling Municipal Library, Mary Elizabeth Wilbanks Ave, Baytown, TX, 77520. Tel: 281-427-7331. Fax: 281-420-5347. p. 2286

Chandler, Theresa, Dir, Elgin Public Library, 1699 Division St, Elgin, OR, 97827. Tel: 541-437-2860. Fax: 541-437-2860. p. 1995

Chandler, Trudy, In Charge, First Christian Church Library, 23 W Washington St, New Castle, PA, 16101. Tel: 724-652-6657. p. 2096

Chandler, Vivian, Br Mgr, Clayton County Library System, Riverdale Branch, 420 Valley Hill Rd, Riverdale, GA, 30274. Tel: 770-472-8100. Fax: 770-472-8106. p. 537

Chandler, Yvonne J, Dr, Assoc Prof, Dir, Ga, Nev, SWIM, LEAP Cohorts, University of North Texas, 1155 Union Circle, Denton, TX, 76203-5017. Tel: 940-565-2445. Fax: 940-565-3101. p. 2975

Chandonnet, Denise, Access Serv, University of Massachusetts Lowell Libraries, Lydon Library, 84 University Ave, Lowell, MA, 01854-2896. Tel: 978-934-3215. Fax: 978-934-3014. p. 1101

Chandra, Yasmin, Mgr, PricewaterhouseCoopers, National Tax Research Services, Royal Trust Tower, 77 King St W, Ste 3000, Toronto, ON, M5K 1G8, CANADA. Tel: 416-815-5103. Fax: 416-814-3200. p. 2857

Chandrasekar, Suseela, Chief Librn, United States Army, RDECOM-ARDEC, Bldg 59, Phipps Rd, AMSRD-AAR-EMK, Picatinny Arsenal, NJ, 07806-5000. Tel: 973-724-4712. Fax: 973-724-3044. p. 1520

Chaney, Cassandra, Librn, Oshkosh Correctional Institution Library, 1730 W Snell Rd, Oshkosh, WI, 54903. Tel: 920-231-4010, Ext 2220. Fax: 920-236-2626. p. 2628

Chaney, Jacquelin S, Dir, Putnam County Library, 4219 State Rte 34, Hurricane, WV, 25526. Tel: 304-757-7308. Fax: 304-757-7384. p. 2562

Chaney, Jeanne, Circ, Ripon College, 300 Seward St, Ripon, WI, 54971. Tel: 920-748-8747. Fax: 920-748-7243. p. 2634

Chaney, Linda M, Dir, Parker Public Library, 115 N Main Ave, Parker, SD, 57053. Tel: 605-297-5552. p. 2216

Chaney, Robin, Cat, Blinn College Library, 800 Blinn Blvd, Brenham, TX, 77833. Tel: 979-830-4250. Fax: 979-830-4222. p. 2291

Chaney, Robin, Dir, Southwest Area Multicounty Multitype Interlibrary Exchange, 109 S Fifth St, Ste 30, Marshall, MN, 56258-1240. Tel: 507-532-9013. Fax: 507-532-2039. p. 2947

Chaney, Will, Dir, Info Tech Dept, University of Florida Libraries, 535 Library W, Gainesville, FL, 32611-7000. Tel: 352-273-2801. Fax: 352-392-2354. p. 449

Chang, Ching, Acq, Medgar Evers College, 1650 Bedford Ave, Brooklyn, NY, 11225-2010. Tel: 718-270-4865. Fax: 718-270-4908. p. 1593

Chang, Helen, Librn, Saint Mark's Hospital, 1200 E 3900 South, Salt Lake City, UT, 84124. Tel: 801-268-7004. Fax: 801-270-3417. p. 2413

Chang, Henry C, Dr, Dir, Libr Serv, Braille Institute Library Services, 741 N Vermont Ave, Los Angeles, CA, 90029-3514. Tel: 323-663-1111, Ext 3185. Fax: 323-662-2440. p. 168

Chang, Hillary, Br Mgr, Hawaii State Public Library System, McCully-Moiliili Public Library, 2211 S King St, Honolulu, HI, 96826. Tel: 808-973-1099. Fax: 808-973-1095. p. 563

Chang, Jennifer, Head of Libr, Free Library of Philadelphia, Northeast Regional, 2228 Cottman Ave, Philadelphia, PA, 19149-1297. Tel: 215-685-0500. Fax: 215-742-3225. p. 2108

Chang, Kerrie, Acq, Todd Wehr Library, St Norbert College, 301 Third St, De Pere, WI, 54115. Tel: 920-403-3271. Fax: 920-403-4064. p. 2587

Chang, Lena, Head, Ref, De Anza College, 21250 Stevens Creek Blvd, Cupertino, CA, 95014-5793. Tel: 408-864-8728. Fax: 408-864-8603. p. 138

Chang, May, Ast Dir, Libr Tech & Digital Initiatives, East Carolina University, J Y Joyner Library, E Fifth St, Greenville, NC, 27858-4353. Tel: 252-328-2780. Fax: 252-328-6892. p. 1798

Chang, Sheau-Hwang, Syst Coordr, Bridgewater State College, Ten Shaw Rd, Bridgewater, MA, 02325. Tel: 508-531-1766. Fax: 508-531-1349, 508-531-6103. p. 1070

Chang, Sherry, Assoc Dir, Pub Serv, Stony Brook University, W-1502 Melville Library, John S Toll Rd, Stony Brook, NY, 11794-3300. Tel: 631-632-7100. Fax: 631-632-7116. p. 1749

Chang, Sherry, Head Librn, Stony Brook University, Mathematics-Physics-Astronomy, Physics Bldg C-124, Stony Brook, NY, 11794-3855. Tel: 631-632-7145. Fax: 631-632-9192. p. 1750

Chang, Stella, Head, Cat, Weber State University, 2901 University Circle, Ogden, UT, 84408-2901. Tel: 801-626-6869. Fax: 801-626-7045. p. 2409

Chang, Susan, Dir, DeVry University, 1221 Swift Rd, Addison, IL, 60101. Tel: 630-652-8360. Fax: 630-953-9665. p. 587

Chang, T T, Mrs, In Charge, Chinatown Building & Education Foundation, 125 N Tenth St, Philadelphia, PA, 19107. Tel: 215-923-6767. Fax: 610-623-6775. p. 2104

Chang, Teresa, Ch, North Castle Public Library, 19 Whippoorwill Rd E, Armonk, NY, 10504. Tel: 914-273-3887. Fax: 914-273-5572. p. 1575

Chang, Tony, Librn, Washington University Libraries, East Asian, One Brookings Dr, Campus Box 1061, Saint Louis, MO, 63130-4862. Tel: 314-935-4816. Fax: 314-935-7505. p. 1363

Chang, Yee Ching, Info Res Spec, Workplace Safety & Insurance Board, 200 Front St W, 17th Flr, Toronto, ON, M5V 3J1, CANADA. Tel: 416-344-4052. Fax: 416-344-4050. p. 2868

Chanse, Andrew, Br Operations Adminr, Maricopa County Library District, 2700 N Central Ave, Ste 700, Phoenix, AZ, 85004. Tel: 602-652-3005. Fax: 602-652-3079. p. 74

Chantmon, Catherine, Res Serv, Piedmont Baptist College & Graduate School, 420 S Broad St, Winston-Salem, NC, 27101. Tel: 336-725-8344, Ext 7953. Fax: 336-725-5522. p. 1833

Chao, Gloria, Head, Tech Serv, Rutgers University Libraries, Camden Law Library, 217 N Fifth St, Camden, NJ, 08102-1203. Tel: 856-225-6457. p. 1477

Chao, Kenny, Ref Serv, Ad, Fort Bend County Libraries, 1001 Golfview Dr, Richmond, TX, 77469-5199. Tel: 281-341-2653. Fax: 281-341-2688. p. 2375

Chapa, Angie, Librn, Hidalgo County Law Library, Courthouse, 100 N Closner, Edinburg, TX, 78539. Tel: 956-318-2155. Fax: 956-381-4269. p. 2315

Chapa, Corinna, Tech Serv, Brownsville Public Library System, 2600 Central Blvd, Brownsville, TX, 78520-8824. Tel: 956-548-1055. Fax: 956-548-0684. p. 2292

Chapa, Esmeralda, Acq, Supvr, Laredo Community College, West End Washington St, Laredo, TX, 78040. Tel: 956-721-5277. Fax: 956-721-5447. p. 2353

Chapa, Laura, Ref Librn, Youth Serv, Nueces County Keach Family Library, 100 Terry Shamsie Blvd, Robstown, TX, 78380. Tel: 361-387-3431. Fax: 361-387-7964. p. 2376

Chapa-Domercq, Monica, Mgr, Ad Serv, Oceanside Public Library, 330 N Coast Hwy, Oceanside, CA, 92054-2824. Tel: 760-435-5586. Fax: 760-435-9614. p. 199

Chaparro, Luis, Dir of Tech Serv, El Paso Community College Library, PO Box 20500, El Paso, TX, 79998-0500. Fax: 915-831-2484. p. 2315

Chaparro, Luis, Head Librn, El Paso Community College Library, Valle Verde Campus Library, 919 Hunter St, El Paso, TX, 79915. Tel: 915-831-2132. p. 2316

Chapedos, Gislain, Circ, Per, Government of Quebec - Agriculture Fisheries & Foods, 96 Montee de Sandy-Beach, No 205, Gaspe, QC, G4X 2V6, CANADA. Tel: 418-368-7615. Fax: 418-360-8211. p. 2882

Chaperon, Johanne, Acq, Hopital Hotel-Dieu du CHUM, 3840 rue St-Urbain, Montreal, QC, H2W 1T8, CANADA. Tel: 514-890-8000, Ext 14355. p. 2896

Chapin, Caroline D, Dir, First Parish Church of Norwell, 24 West St, Norwell, MA, 02061. Tel: 781-659-7100. p. 1115

Chapin, Jean, Head, Ref, Harrison Memorial Library, Ocean Ave & Lincoln St, Carmel, CA, 93921. Tel: 831-624-4629. Fax: 831-624-0407. p. 132

Chapin, Jean, Dir, Gunn Memorial Library, Inc, Five Wykeham Rd, Washington, CT, 06793-1308. Tel: 860-868-7586. Fax: 860-868-7247. p. 374

Chapin, Linda, Librn, Field Library, 243 Millers Falls Rd, Northfield, MA, 01360. Tel: 413-498-0220. p. 1114

Chapin, Marcia L, Head Librn, Harvard Library, Chemistry & Chemical Biology, Department of Chemistry & Chemical Biology, 12 Oxford St, Cambridge, MA, 02138. Tel: 617-495-4076. Fax: 617-495-0788. p. 1074

Chapin, Norman, Dr, Dir, Columbia Memorial Hospital, Columbia Memorial Hospital, 71 Prospect Ave, Hudson, NY, 12534. Tel: 518-697-3230, 518-828-7601. Fax: 518-822-2178. p. 1638

Chapkin, Joshua, Computer Serv, Valencia Community College, East Campus, 701 N Econlockhatchee Trail, Orlando, FL, 32825. Tel: 407-582-2467. Fax: 407-582-8914. p. 478

Chaplin, Bradley, Dir, Kalkaska County Library, 247 S Cedar St, Kalkaska, MI, 49646. Tel: 231-258-9411. p. 1198

Chaplinsky, Paula, Adminr, Clearwater Public Library System, 100 N Osceola Ave, Clearwater, FL, 33755. Tel: 727-562-4970. Fax: 727-562-4977. p. 432

Chapma, Liane, Asst Librn, Gibbs Library, 40 Old Union Rd, Washington, ME, 04574. Tel: 207-845-2663. p. 1005

Chapman, Ann, Head Librn, Capital Area District Libraries, Haslett Library, 1590 Franklin St, Haslett, MI, 48840. Tel: 517-339-2324. Fax: 517-339-0349. p. 1200

Chapman, Anna Mae, Asst Librn, Meriden Library, 22 Bean Rd, Meriden, NH, 03770. Tel: 603-469-3252. p. 1457

Chapman, Carol, Adult Literacy Coordr, Ventura County Library, 5600 Everglades St, Ste A, Ventura, CA, 93003. Tel: 805-677-7159. Fax: 805-677-7173. p. 279

Chapman, Carol, Chief Librn, Lakeland Regional Library, 318 Williams Ave, Killarney, MB, R0K 1G0, CANADA. Tel: 204-523-4949. Fax: 204-523-7460. p. 2749

Chapman, Christopher, Circ Mgr, Clemson University Libraries, Gunnin Architecture Library, 112 Lee Hall, Clemson University, Clemson, SC, 29634-0501. Tel: 864-656-3933. Fax: 864-656-3932. p. 2186

Chapman, Dale, Ref, Fordham University Library at Lincoln Center, Leon Lowenstein Bldg, 113 W 60th St, New York, NY, 10023-7480. Tel: 212-636-6050. Fax: 212-636-6766. p. 1678

Chapman, Darlene, Librn, IWK Health Centre for Children, Women & Families, 5980 University Ave, Halifax, NS, B3H 4N1, CANADA. Tel: 902- 470-6729. Fax: 902-470-7122. p. 2781

Chapman, Donna, Dir, Woodbury County Library, 825 Main St, Moville, IA, 51039. Tel: 712-873-3322. Fax: 712-873-3744. p. 834

Chapman, Donna, Asst Dir, Darlington County Library, Society Hill Branch, 473 S Main St, Society Hill, SC, 29593. Tel: 843-378-0026. Fax: 843-378-0026. p. 2192

Chapman, Eileen, Cat, Tech Serv Supvr, West Springfield Public Library, 200 Park St, West Springfield, MA, 01089. Tel: 413-736-4561. Fax: 413-736-6469. p. 1137

Chapman, Elizabeth, Br Head, Lompoc Public Library, Buellton Branch, 140 W Hwy 246, Buellton, CA, 93427. Tel: 805-688-3115. Fax: 805-688-3115. p. 165

Chapman, Elwynda, Cataloger/Ref Librn, US Customs & Border Protection Library, 90 K St NE, 9th Flr, Washington, DC, 20004. Tel: 202-325-0168. Fax: 202-325-0170. p. 418

Chapman, Greta, Dir, Rapid City Public Library, 610 Quincy St, Rapid City, SD, 57701-3630. Tel: 605-394-6139. Fax: 605-394-4064. p. 2217

Chapman, Janis, Asst Librn, White Hall Township Library, 119 E Sherman St, White Hall, IL, 62092. Tel: 217-374-6014. Fax: 217-374-6554. p. 719

Chapman, Jonathan P, Librn, Minnesota Department of Corrections, 7600 - 525th St, Rush City, MN, 55069. Tel: 320-358-0400, Ext 373. Fax: 763-689-7555. p. 1273

Chapman, Julie, Coordr, Libr Instruction, Northeast Wisconsin Technical College Library, 2740 W Mason St, Green Bay, WI, 54303-4966. Tel: 920-498-5487. Fax: 920-498-6910. p. 2596

Chapman, Karena, Circ, Charles A Ransom District Library, 180 S Sherwood Ave, Plainwell, MI, 49080-1896. Tel: 269-685-8024. Fax: 269-685-2266. p. 1218

Chapman, Kendall P, Dir, Libr Serv, Copiah-Lincoln Community College, 1028 J C Redd Dr, Wesson, MS, 39191. Tel: 601-643-8364. Fax: 601-643-8212. p. 1317

Chapman, Kimbre, Ch, Caldwell Public Library, 1010 Dearborn, Caldwell, ID, 83605-4195. Tel: 208-459-3242. Fax: 208-459-7344. p. 572

Chapman, Kristin, Librn, MedStar Franklin Square Medical Center, 9000 Franklin Square Dr, Baltimore, MD, 21237. Tel: 443-777-7363. Fax: 410-687-1742. p. 1016

Chapman, Linda, Librn, Hale Center Public Library, 609 Main St, Hale Center, TX, 79041. Tel: 806-839-2055. Fax: 806-839-2055. p. 2330

Chapman, Louella, Librn, Selover Public Library, 31 State Rte 95, Chesterville, OH, 43317-0025. Tel: 419-768-3431. Fax: 419-768-2249. p. 1867

Chapman, Marcella, Dir, Coffey County Library, Waverly Branch, 608 Pearson, Waverly, KS, 66871-9688. Tel: 785-733-2400. Fax: 785-733-2474. p. 859

Chapman, Merrilee, Librn, Stockton-San Joaquin County Public Library, Tracy Branch, 20 E Eaton Ave, Tracy, CA, 95376. Fax: 209-831-4252. p. 273

Chapman, Ophelia, Syst Librn, Morehead State University, 150 University Blvd, Morehead, KY, 40351. Tel: 606-783-5119. Fax: 606-783-5037. p. 929

Chapman, Patricia, Dir, Park County Public Library, 350 Bulldogger Rd, Bailey, CO, 80421-2379. Tel: 303-838-5539. Fax: 303-838-2351. p. 289

Chapman, Patricia, Dir, Park County Public Library, Fairplay Branch, Old Park County Court House, 418 Main St, Fairplay, CO, 80440. Tel: 719-836-2848, 719-836-4297. Fax: 719-836-0863. p. 289

Chapman, Paula J, Librn, Aurora Public Library, 14 W Second Ave N, Aurora, MN, 55705-1314. Tel: 218-229-2021. p. 1240

Chapman, Rebecca, Ref Serv, Midwestern University Library, 555 31st St, Downers Grove, IL, 60515. Tel: 630-515-6200. Fax: 630-515-6195. p. 637

Chapman, Rebecca, Dir, United States Air Force, McBride Library, 81 FSS/FSDL McBride Library, 512 Larcher Blvd Bldg 2222, Keesler AFB, MS, 39534-2345. Tel: 228-377-2181. Fax: 228-435-0203. p. 1306

Chapman, Roberta, Br Coordr, Haldimand County Public Library, Caledonia Branch, 100 Haddington St, Unit 2, Caledonia, ON, N3W 2N4, CANADA. Tel: 905-768-5941. Fax: 905-765-2634. p. 2802

Chapman, Roberta, Br Coordr, Haldimand County Public Library, Hagersville Branch, 13 Alma St N, Hagersville, ON, N0A 1H0, CANADA. Tel: 905-768-5941. Fax: 905-768-5941. p. 2803

Chapman, Roberta, Br Coordr, Haldimand County Public Library, Jarvis Branch, Two Monson St, Jarvis, ON, N0A 1J0, CANADA. Tel: 519-587-4746. Fax: 519-587-3470. p. 2803

Chapman, Ronald F, Dr, Head Librn, Honolulu Academy of Arts, 900 S Beretania St, Honolulu, HI, 96814-1495. Tel: 808-532-8755. Fax: 808-532-3683. p. 564

Chapman, Sammy, Coll Develop, Ref, Lambuth University, 705 Lambuth Blvd, Jackson, TN, 38301. Tel: 731-425-3270. Fax: 731-425-3200. p. 2238

Chapman, Sarah, Dir, Whipple Free Library, Two Central Sq, New Boston, NH, 03070. Tel: 603-487-3391. Fax: 603-487-2886. p. 1459

Chapman, Sharon, Libr Dir, University of South Carolina Sumter, 200 Miller Rd, Sumter, SC, 29150-2498. Tel: 803-775-8727. Fax: 803-938-3811. p. 2206

Chapman, Shelly, Human Res Mgr, Salt Lake City Public Library, 210 E 400 S, Salt Lake City, UT, 84111-3280. Tel: 801-524-8225. Fax: 801-322-8194. p. 2413

Chapman-Smith, V, Regional Adminr, National Archives & Records Administration, 900 Market St, Philadelphia, PA, 19107-4292. Tel: 215-606-0102. Fax: 215-606-0116. p. 2113

Chapmin, Curtis, Dir, Libr Serv, Hiwassee College, 225 Hiwassee College Dr, Madisonville, TN, 37354. Tel: 423-442-2001, Ext 1266. Fax: 423-420-1896. p. 2246

Chappell, Cyndi, Mgr, Johnson County Library, Blue Valley, 9000 W 151st, Overland Park, KS, 66221. Tel: 913-495-3826. Fax: 913-495-3821. p. 888

Chappell, Leanna, Head, Ch, Swanton Local School District Public Library, 305 Chestnut St, Swanton, OH, 43558. Tel: 419-826-2760. Fax: 419-826-1020. p. 1937

Chappell, Linda, Dir, Grand Marais Public Library, 104 Second Ave W, Grand Marais, MN, 55604. Tel: 218-387-1140. Fax: 218-387-2562. p. 1252

Chappell, Patti, Br Mgr, Cannon County Library System, Aburntown Branch Library, 73 E Main St, Auburntown, TN, 37016. Tel: 615-464-2622. Fax: 615-464-2623. p. 2269

Chappell, Raymond, Pres, Wallingford Historical Society Inc, Library, 180 S Main St, Wallingford, CT, 06492. Tel: 203-294-1996. p. 373

Chappell, Shirien, Head, Access Serv, University of Oregon Libraries, 1501 Kincaid St, Eugene, OR, 97403-1299. Tel: 541-346-3056. Fax: 541-346-3485. p. 1997

Chapple, Melinda, Reader Serv Librn, Simpson University, 2211 College View Dr, Redding, CA, 96003-8606. Tel: 530-226-4117. Fax: 530-226-4858. p. 214

Chapuis, Audrey, Access Serv Librn, Northwestern University, Chicago, Pritzker Legal Research Center, 375 E Chicago Ave, Chicago, IL, 60611. Tel: 312-503-0314. Fax: 312-503-9230. p. 621

Chaput, Elaine Marie, Librn, Ste Rose Regional Library, 580 Central Ave, Ste Rose du Lac, MB, R0L 1S0, CANADA. Tel: 204-447-2527. Fax: 204-447-2527. p. 2752

Chaput, Johanne, Dir, Bibliotheque Municipale de Deux-Montagnes, 200 rue Henri-Dunant, Ville de Deux-Montagnes, QC, J7R 4W6, CANADA. Tel: 450-473-2702. Fax: 450-473-2816. p. 2915

Chaput, Louise, Pub Serv, Northwest Community College Library, 5331 McConnell Ave, Terrace, BC, V8G 4X2, CANADA. Tel: 250-638-5407. Fax: 250-635-1594. p. 2739

Charbonneau, Darline, Human Res Dir, Yakima Valley Libraries, 102 N Third St, Yakima, WA, 98901-2759. Tel: 509-452-8541. Fax: 509-575-2093. p. 2550

Charbonneau, Deborah, Dr, Asst Prof, Wayne State University, 106 Kresge Library, Detroit, MI, 48202. Tel: 313-577-1825. Fax: 313-577-7563. p. 2968

Charbonneau, Helen, Asst Dir, Wellesley Free Library, 530 Washington St, Wellesley, MA, 02482. Tel: 781-235-1610, Ext 1130. Fax: 781-235-0495. p. 1135

Charbonneau, Lisa, Coordr, Bibliotheque Municipale et Scolaire de Sutton, 19 Highland St, Sutton, QC, J0E 2K0, CANADA. Tel: 450-538-5843. Fax: 450-538-4286. p. 2913

Charbonneau, Louise, Electronic Res, ILL & Ser, Mohawk Valley Community College Library, 1101 Sherman Dr, Utica, NY, 13501-5394. Tel: 315-731-5793. Fax: 315-792-5666. p. 1759

Charbonneau, Normand, Dir, Bibliotheque et Archives nationales du Quebec, 475 de Maisonneuve E, Montreal, QC, H2L 5C4, CANADA. Tel: 514-873-1101, Ext 6408. Fax: 514-873-9312. p. 2888

Charest, Claire, Ref, University de Moncton, 165 boul Hebert, Edmundston, NB, E3V 2S8, CANADA. Tel: 506-737-5058. Fax: 506-737-5373. p. 2762

Charest, Claude, Librn, Bibliotheque Louis-Ange-Santerre, 500, ave Jolliet, Sept Iles, QC, G4R 2B4, CANADA. Tel: 418-964-3355. Fax: 418-964-3353. p. 2911

Charest, Ronald, Head Librn, Borden Ladner Gervais LLP Library, 1000 de la Gauchetiere W, Ste 900, Montreal, QC, H3B 5H4, CANADA. Tel: 514-954-3159. Fax: 514-954-1905. p. 2892

Charette, Rachel, Br Librn, Livonia Public Library, Alfred Noble Branch, 32901 Plymouth Rd, Livonia, MI, 48150-1793. Tel: 734-421-6600. Fax: 734-421-6606. p. 1203

Charis, Erica, Outreach Librn, Berklee College of Music Library, 150 Massachusetts Ave, Boston, MA, 02115. Tel: 617-747-8465. Fax: 617-747-2050. p. 1055

Charland, Molly, Dir, Libr & Educ, The Society of the Four Arts, Three Four Arts Plaza, Palm Beach, FL, 33480. Tel: 561-659-8519. Fax: 561-832-6779. p. 479

Charlebois, Claire, Dir, Viola Township Library, 100 N Grice, Viola, KS, 67149. Tel: 620-584-6679. p. 899

Charlebois, George, Librn, Royal Canadian Mounted Police Training Academy, 5600 11th Ave W, Regina, SK, S4P 3J7, CANADA. p. 2923

Charlebois, Pierre, Librn, Reader's Digest Magazines Ltd, 1100 Ouest Boul Rene-Levesque, Montreal, QC, H3B 5H5, CANADA. Tel: 514-940-7229. Fax: 514-940-7337. p. 2901

Charlefour, Stephanie, Youth Librn, Garden City Public Library, 31735 Maplewood Rd, Garden City, MI, 48135. Tel: 734-793-1830. Fax: 734-793-1831. p. 1182

Charles, Cynthia, Asst Dean, Pub Serv, Dillard University, 2601 Gentilly Blvd, New Orleans, LA, 70122-3097. Tel: 504-816-4263. Fax: 504-816-4787. p. 960

Charles, Jane V, Ref, Edison State College, 8099 College Pkwy SW, Bldg J, Fort Myers, FL, 33919. Tel: 239-489-9300. Fax: 239-489-9095. p. 444

Charles, Leslin, Assoc Dir, Libr Serv, Berkeley College, 44 Rifle Camp Rd, Woodland Park, NJ, 07424. Tel: 973-278-5400. Fax: 973-278-9141. p. 1545

Charles, Mario A, Librn, College of New Rochelle, Rosa Parks Campus, 144 W 125th St, New York, NY, 10027. Tel: 212-662-7500. Fax: 212-864-9469. p. 1666

Charles, Ouida, Mgr, Ref Serv, Palo Alto City Library, 1213 Newell Rd, Palo Alto, CA, 94303-2907. Tel: 650-329-2620. Fax: 650-327-2033. p. 204

Charles, Pam, Circ Supvr, Shreve Memorial Library, Hamilton/South Caddo Branch, 2111 Bert Kouns Industrial Loop, Shreveport, LA, 71118. Tel: 318-687-6824. Fax: 318-686-0971. p. 969

Charles, Richelle, Librn - Cafritz Art Libr, Montgomery College, Takoma Park Campus Library, 7600 Takoma Ave, Takoma Park, MD, 20912. Tel: 240-567-5833. Fax: 240-567-5820. p. 1037

Charles, Sharon, Div Mgr, Commun & Patron Serv, Hennepin County Library, 12601 Ridgedale Dr, Minnetonka, MN, 55305-1909. Tel: 612-543-8558. Fax: 612-543-8600. p. 1263

Charlot, Beverly D, Syst Librn, Delaware State University, 1200 N Dupont Hwy, Dover, DE, 19901-2277. Tel: 302-857-6195. Fax: 302-857-6177. p. 382

Charlson, Kim L, Dir, Perkins School for the Blind, 175 N Beacon St, Watertown, MA, 02472. Tel: 617-972-7240. Fax: 617-972-7363. p. 1133

Charlton, Joyce, Librn, Naples Public Library, 103 Walnut St, Naples, TX, 75568. Tel: 903-897-2964. Fax: 903-897-2964. p. 2365

Charlton, Sara, Dir, Tillamook County Library, 1716 Third St, Tillamook, OR, 97141. Tel: 503-842-4792. Fax: 503-815-8194. p. 2021

Charnes, Alan, Exec Dir, Colorado Alliance of Research Libraries, 3801 E Florida Ave, Ste 515, Denver, CO, 80210. Tel: 303-759-3399, Ext 104. Fax: 303-759-3363. p. 2939

Charney, Patricia, Dir, Mendham Borough Library,
Ten Hilltop Rd, Mendham, NJ, 07945. Tel:
973-543-4152. Fax: 973-543-9096. p. 1501

Charnigo, Laurie, Ref Librn, Jacksonville State
University Library, 700 Pelham Rd N,
Jacksonville, AL, 36265. Tel: 256-782-5255.
Fax: 256-782-5872. p. 22

Charnov, Elaine, Dir, Educ, Programming &
Exhibitions, The New York Public Library -
Astor, Lenox & Tilden Foundations, 476 Fifth
Ave, (@ 42nd St), New York, NY, 10018-2788.
Tel: 212-642-0115. Fax: 212-869-3567, p. 1690

Charny, Rachel, Info Spec, Mount Vernon Public
Library, 28 S First Ave, Mount Vernon, NY,
10550. Tel: 914-668-1840. Fax: 914-668-1018.
p. 1664

Charoenpanitkul, Chantana, Govt Doc, Shippensburg
University, 1871 Old Main Dr, Shippensburg,
PA, 17257-2299. Tel: 717-477-1634. Fax:
717-477-1389. p. 2140

Charpentier, Debbie, Archivist, Millicent Library,
45 Centre St, Fairhaven, MA, 02719. Tel:
508-992-5342. Fax: 508-993-7288. p. 1087

Charpentier, Richard, Pres, Franco-American Centre
Bibliotheque, 52 Concord St, Manchester, NH,
03101. Tel: 603-669-4045. Fax: 603-669-0644.
p. 1455

Charron, Connie, Ch, Plano Public Library System,
Christopher A Parr Library, 6200 Windhaven
Pkwy, Plano, TX, 75093. Tel: 972-769-4300.
Fax: 972-769-4304. p. 2371

Charron, Virginia, Libr Dir, Kitimat Public Library
Association, 940 Wakashan Ave, Kitimat, BC,
V8C 2G3, CANADA. Tel: 250-632-8985. Fax:
250-632-2630. p. 2731

Charte, Martha, Tech Serv, J Robert Jamerson
Memorial Library, 106 Main St, Appomattox,
VA, 24522. Tel: 434-352-5340. Fax:
434-352-0933. p. 2448

Charter, Gwendolyn, Ref, Peabody Institute Library,
82 Main St, Peabody, MA, 01960-5592. Tel:
978-531-0100. Fax: 978-532-1797. p. 1116

Chartier, Heather, Membership Serv Supvr,
Edmonton Public Library, Lois Hole Library,
17650-69 Ave NW, Edmonton, AB, T5T
3X9, CANADA. Tel: 780-442-0885. Fax:
780-442-0887. p. 2700

Chartier, Lynette, Dir, Direction des Ressources
Educatives Francaises, Dept of Educ, 0140-200
Ave de la Cathedrale, Saint Boniface, MB,
R2H 0H7, CANADA. Tel: 204-945-8594. Fax:
204-945-0092. p. 2751

Chartier, Mary, Ch, San Bernardino Public
Library, 555 W Sixth St, San Bernardino,
CA, 92410-3001. Tel: 909-381-8215. Fax:
909-381-8229. p. 229

Chartier, Mary, Ser, Gateway Technical College,
3520 30th Ave, Kenosha, WI, 53144-1690. Tel:
262-564-2380. Fax: 262-564-2787. p. 2601

Chartier, Michelle, Tech Serv, College
Edouard-Montpetit Bibliotheque, 945 Chemin
de Chambly, Longueuil, QC, J4H 3M6,
CANADA. Tel: 450-679-2631, Ext 2609. Fax:
450-677-2945. p. 2887

Chartier, Paulita, Dir, Communications, State Library
of Louisiana, 701 N Fourth St, Baton Rouge,
LA, 70802-5232. Tel: 225-342-9713. Fax:
225-219-4804. p. 945

Chartrand, Danielle, ILL & Distance Libr Serv Spec,
INRS - Institut Armand-Frappier - Bibliotheque,
531 blvd des Prairies, Laval, QC, H7V 1B7,
CANADA. Tel: 450-687-5010, Ext 4340. Fax:
450-686-5501. p. 2886

Chartrand, Michael, Tech Serv, Samaritan Medical
Center, 830 Washington St, Watertown, NY,
13601. Tel: 315-785-4191. Fax: 315-779-5173.
p. 1764

Chartrand, Richard, Dir, East Alton Public
Library District, 250 Washington, East Alton,
IL, 62024-1547. Tel: 618-259-0787. Fax:
618-259-0788. p. 638

Charvat, Betty, Ch, East Rockaway Public Library,
477 Atlantic Ave, East Rockaway, NY, 11518.
Tel: 516-599-1664. Fax: 516-596-0154. p. 1617

Chase, Allison, Dir, Alice Baker Memorial Public
Library, 820 E Main, Eagle, WI, 53119. Tel:
262-594-2800. Fax: 262-594-5126. p. 2589

Chase, Anita, Circ, ILL, New England School
of Law Library, 154 Stuart St, Boston,
MA, 02116-5687. Tel: 617-422-7307. Fax:
617-422-7303. p. 1065

Chase, Anne, Dir, Berea College, 100 Campus Dr,
Berea, KY, 40404. Tel: 859-985-3364. Fax:
859-985-3912. p. 907

Chase, Brian, Dir, Normal Public Library, 206
W College Ave, Normal, IL, 61761. Tel:
309-452-1757. Fax: 309-452-5312. p. 681

Chase, Carla, Circ Mgr, Westerly Public Library,
44 Broad St, Westerly, RI, 02891. Tel:
401-596-2877, Ext 305. Fax: 401-596-5600.
p. 2178

Chase, Carolyn, Dir, Plains Community Library,
500 Grand Ave, Plains, KS, 67869. Tel:
620-563-7326. Fax: 620-563-6114. p. 890

Chase, David, Co-Dir, Pat Parker-Vito Russo Center
Library, Lesbian & Gay Community Serv Ctr,
208 W 13th St, New York, NY, 10011. Tel:
212-620-7310. p. 1697

Chase, Eleanor L, Head, Govt Doc, University of
Washington Libraries, Allen Library, 4th Flr, Rm
482, Box 352900, Seattle, WA, 98195-2900. Tel:
206-543-1937. Fax: 206-685-8727. p. 2533

Chase, Janice L, Ch, Stoneham Public Library,
431 Main St, Stoneham, MA, 02180. Tel:
781-438-1324. Fax: 781-279-3836. p. 1129

Chase, Julie Anne, Dir, Dane County Library
Service, 201 W Mifflin St, Madison, WI,
53703-2597. Tel: 608-266-6388. p. 2606

Chase, Karla, Dir, Orange City Public Library, 112
Albany Ave SE, Orange City, IA, 51041-1730.
Tel: 712-707-4302. Fax: 712-707-4431. p. 837

Chase, Karlen, Digital Serv & Circuit Librn,
Western New York Library Resources Council,
4455 Genesee St, Buffalo, NY, 14225. Tel:
716-633-0705. Fax: 716-633-1736. p. 2951

Chase, LeeAnn, Circ Librn, ILL Librn, Hooksett
Public Library, 1701B Hooksett Rd, Hooksett,
NH, 03106-1852. Tel: 603-485-6092. Fax:
603-485-6193. p. 1451

Chase, Nancy, Librn, Cove City Public Library,
102 N Main St, Cove City, NC, 28523. Tel:
252-638-6363. Fax: 252-638-4639. p. 1785

Chase, Peter F, Dir, Plainville Public Library,
56 E Main St, Plainville, CT, 06062. Tel:
860-793-1446. Fax: 860-793-2241. p. 364

Chase-Williams, Janet, Head Librn, Mariposa
County Law Library, 4978 10th St, Mariposa,
CA, 95338. p. 183

Chase-Williams, Janet, Librn, Mariposa County
Library, 4978 Tenth St, Mariposa, CA, 95338.
Tel: 209-966-2140. Fax: 209-742-7527. p. 183

Chasky, Abby, Sarasota Campus Libr Dir, Keiser
University Library System, 1500 NW 49th St,
Fort Lauderdale, FL, 33309. Tel: 954-351-4035.
Fax: 954-351-4051. p. 443

Chasse, Emily, Online Serv, Central Connecticut
State University, 1615 Stanley St, New
Britain, CT, 06050. Tel: 860-832-2063. Fax:
860-832-3409. p. 353

Chasseur, Mary, Librn, James E Wickson Memorial
Library, 359 S Franklin St, Frankenmuth, MI,
48734. Tel: 989-652-8323. Fax: 989-652-3450.
p. 1181

Chastain-Warheit, Christine, Dir, Christiana Hospital
Library, Christiana Hospital, 4755 Ogletown
Stanton Rd, Newark, DE, 19718-0002. Tel:
302-733-1115. Fax: 302-733-1365. p. 385

Chasteen-Futch, Rivanne, Asst Dir, Lakeland
Public Library, 100 Lake Morton Dr, Lakeland,
FL, 33801-5375. Tel: 863-834-4280. Fax:
863-834-4293. p. 459

Chatelain, Milton, Circ, Louisiana State University
Libraries, LSU School of Veterinary Medicine
Library, Skip Bertman Dr, Baton Rouge,
LA, 70803-8414. Tel: 225-578-9795. Fax:
225-578-9798. p. 944

Chaterjee, Jay, Head, Ref, Joint Free Public Library
of the Chathams, 214 Main St, Chatham, NJ,
07928. Tel: 973-635-0603. Fax: 973-635-7827.
p. 1478

Chatham, Dave, Dir, Presbyterian College,
211 E Maple St, Clinton, SC, 29325. Tel:
864-833-8299. Fax: 864-833-8315. p. 2186

Chatham, Debra, ILL, Sierra Vista Public Library,
2600 E Tacoma, Sierra Vista, AZ, 85635-1399.
Tel: 520-458-4225. Fax: 520-458-5377. p. 82

Chatlak, Nancy, Librn, Ohio County Law Library,
City-County Bldg, Rm 406, 1500 Chapline St,
Wheeling, WV, 26003. Tel: 304-234-3780. Fax:
304-234-6437. p. 2574

Chatman, Notre, Tech & Learning Res Prog Develop
Officer, Chicago State University, 9501 S
Martin Luther King Jr Dr, LIB 440, Chicago,
IL, 60628-1598. Tel: 773-995-4412. Fax:
773-995-3772. p. 610

Chatman, Wendy, Librn, Parkland Regional Library,
Quill Lake Branch, PO Box 638, Quill Lake,
SK, S0A 3E0, CANADA. Tel: 306-383-2242.
p. 2932

Chatt, Molly, Head, Ch, East Greenbush Community
Library, Ten Community Way, East Greenbush,
NY, 12061. Tel: 518-477-7476. Fax:
518-477-6692. p. 1616

Chatterjee, Judy, Br Mgr, San Diego County Library,
Poway Branch, 13137 Poway Rd, Poway,
CA, 92064-4687. Tel: 858-513-2900. Fax:
858-513-2922. p. 234

Chatterjee, Sheila, Dir of Libr Serv, The Salvation
Army College for Officer Training at Crestmont,
30840 Hawthorne Blvd, Rancho Palos
Verdes, CA, 90275. Tel: 310-544-6475. Fax:
310-265-6514. p. 213

Chatterley, Trish, Coll Mgr, University of Alberta,
John W Scott Health Sciences Library, Walter
C Mackenzie Health Sciences Ctr 2K3 28,
Edmonton, AB, T6G 2R7, CANADA. Tel:
780-492-7933. Fax: 780-492-6960. p. 2702

Chattin, Jim, Dir, Lake Region Public Library, 423
Seventh St NE, Devils Lake, ND, 58301-2529.
Tel: 701-662-2220. Fax: 701-662-2281. p. 1839

Chattoo, Calmer, Electronic Res/Spec Formats Cat
Librn, University of Miami, 1311 Miller Dr,
Coral Gables, FL, 33146. Tel: 305-284-2251.
Fax: 305-284-3554. p. 434

Chaudhary, Niraj, Mgr, Info Tech, Auraria Library,
1100 Lawrence St, Denver, CO, 80204-2095.
Tel: 303-556-4351. Fax: 303-556-3528. p. 298

Chaudhuri, Liene, Ref Librn, Valley Cottage Free
Library, 110 Rte 303, Valley Cottage, NY,
10989. Tel: 845-268-7700. Fax: 845-268-7760.
p. 1760

Chaudry, Amin, Librn, Stockton-San Joaquin County
Public Library, Weston Ranch Branch, 1453 W
French Camp Rd, Stockton, CA, 95206. Tel:
209-937-8540. Fax: 209-937-8660. p. 273

Chavez, Ashlee, Dir, Lompoc Public Library, 501
E North Ave, Lompoc, CA, 93436-3498. Tel:
808-875-8789. Fax: 805-736-6440. p. 165

Chavez, David, Fac Planning, Fresno County
Public Library, 2420 Mariposa St, Fresno, CA,
93721-2285. Tel: 559-488-3125. p. 151

Chavez, Joan, Dir, Moise Memorial Library, 208 S
Fifth St, Santa Rosa, NM, 88435-2329. Tel:
575-472-3101. Fax: 575-472-4101. p. 1565

Chavez, John U, Electronic Res, Ref Serv, Paradise
Valley Community College Library, 18401
N 32nd St, Phoenix, AZ, 85032-1200. Tel:
602-787-7222. Fax: 602-787-7205. p. 75

Chavez, Leroy, Libr Tech, New Mexico State
Library, 356-D E Ninth St, Cimarron, NM,
87714. Tel: 575-376-2474. Fax: 575-376-2433.
p. 1553

Chavez, Lillian, Dir, Mescalero Community Library,
148 Cottonwood Dr, Mescalero, NM, 88340.
Tel: 505-464-5010. Fax: 505-464-5011. p. 1560

Chavez, Lyena, Head, Instruction & Outreach,
Merrimack College, 315 Turnpike St, North
Andover, MA, 01845. Tel: 978-837-5215. Fax:
978-837-5434. p. 1111

Chavez, Maria, Libr Mgr, Ungaretti & Harris Library, 3500 Three First National Plaza, Chicago, IL, 60602-4283. Tel: 312-977-4378. Fax: 312-977-4405. p. 625

Chavez, Sandra, Dir, Laingsburg Public Library, 255 E Grand River, Laingsburg, MI, 48848-8601. Tel: 517-651-6282. Fax: 517-651-6371. p. 1199

Chavez, Todd A, Dir, Acad Res, University of South Florida, Tampa Campus Library, 4101 USF Apple Dr, LIB122, Tampa, FL, 33620. Tel: 813-974-7905. Fax: 813-974-5153. p. 499

Chavis, Joanie D, Dean, Learning Res, Baton Rouge Community College, 201 Community College Dr, Baton Rouge, LA, 70806. Tel: 225-216-8303. Fax: 225-216-8712. p. 942

Chayes, Marion, Dir, Abington Memorial Hospital, 1200 York Rd, Abington, PA, 19001. Tel: 215-481-2096. p. 2025

Chayes, Marion, Dir, Libr Serv, Abington Memorial Hospital, 2500 Maryland Rd, Willow Grove, PA, 19090-1284. Tel: 215-481-5591. Fax: 215-481-5550. p. 2157

Cheadle, Anne, Dir, Latah County Library District, 110 S Jefferson, Moscow, ID, 83843-2833. Tel: 208-882-3925. Fax: 208-882-5098. p. 579

Cheairs, Susan, Dir, Tipton County Public Library, 300 W Church Ave, Covington, TN, 38019-2729. Tel: 901-476-8289. Fax: 901-476-0008. p. 2232

Cheatham, Brenda, Librn, Mae S Bruce Library, 13302 Sixth, Santa Fe, TX, 77510-9148. Tel: 409-925-5540. Fax: 409-925-8697. p. 2385

Cheatham, Cheryl, Ref, Case Western Reserve University, School of Law Library, 11075 East Blvd, Cleveland, OH, 44106-7148. Tel: 216-368-1611. Fax: 216-368-1002. p. 1876

Cheatham, Jim, Ref, Lexington County Public Library System, Cayce-West Columbia Branch, 1500 Augusta Rd W, Columbia, SC, 29169. Tel: 803-794-6791. Fax: 803-926-5383. p. 2199

Cheatham, Judy, Hist Coll Librn, Shelby County Public Library, 57 W Broadway, Shelbyville, IN, 46176. Tel: 317-398-7121, 317-835-2653. Fax: 317-398-4430. p. 778

Cheatham, Richard, Dir, Whittier College, Media Center, 13406 Philadelphia St, Whittier, CA, 90601-4413. Tel: 562-907-4846. Fax: 562-907-4922. p. 283

Chebaro, Kaoukab, Librn, Columbia University, Area Studies, 307 International Affairs Bldg, 420 W 118th St, New York, NY, 10027. Tel: 212-854-3630. Fax: 212-854-3834. p. 1674

Chebaro, Kaoukab, Librn, Columbia University, Middle East & Islamic Studies/Area Studies, 303 International Affairs, 420 W 118th St, New York, NY, 10027. Tel: 212-854-3995. Fax: 212-854-3834. p. 1675

Chebatarev, Tanya, Curator, Bakhmeteff Archives, Columbia University, Rare Book & Manuscript, Butler Library, 6th Flr E, 535 W 114th St, New York, NY, 10027. Tel: 212-854-3986. Fax: 212-854-1365. p. 1675

Checkai, Peg, Asst Dir, Ch, Watertown Public Library, 100 S Water St, Watertown, WI, 53094-4320. Tel: 920-262-4090, Ext 24. Fax: 920-261-8943. p. 2644

Checkley, Catherine, Br Supvr, Prince George Public Library, Nechako Branch, 6547 Hart Hwy, Prince George, BC, V2K 3A4, CANADA. Tel: 250-962-9710. Fax: 250-962-7394. p. 2736

Chee, Kathleen, Univ Librn, Hawaii Pacific University Libraries, 1060 Bishop St, Honolulu, HI, 96813-3192. Tel: 808-544-0210. Fax: 808-544-0880. p. 560

Chee, Kathleen, Univ Librn, Hawaii Pacific University Libraries, Atherton Library, 45-045 Kamehameha Hwy, Kaneohe, HI, 96744-5297. Tel: 808-544-0292. Fax: 808-544-0880. p. 561

Chee, Lorna, Br Mgr, San Francisco Public Library, Chinatown/Him Mark Lai Branch Library, 1135 Powell St, San Francisco, CA, 94108. Tel: 415-355-2888. Fax: 415-274-0277. p. 246

Cheek, Anna, Ref Asst, Golden Gate Baptist Theological Seminary Library, 3200 NE 109th Ave, Vancouver, WA, 98682-7749. Tel: 360-882-2171. Fax: 360-882-2275. p. 2546

Cheek, Belinda, Coordr, Access Serv, North Central College, 320 E School St, Naperville, IL, 60540. Tel: 630-637-5703. Fax: 630-637-5716. p. 679

Cheek, Richard O, Dean, Libr Serv, Oklahoma Baptist University, 500 W University, OBU Box 61310, Shawnee, OK, 74804-2504. Tel: 405-878-2249. Fax: 405-878-2256. p. 1977

Cheesman, Ruby, Mgr, Salt Lake County Library Services, Bingham Creek, 4834 W 9000 South, West Jordan, UT, 84088-2213. Tel: 801-944-7688. Fax: 801-282-0943. p. 2414

Cheikhi, Ikram, Ref Librn, Alberta Government Library, Capital Blvd, 11th Flr, 10044 - 108 St, Edmonton, AB, T5J 5E6, CANADA. Tel: 780-427-6249. Fax: 780-427-5927. p. 2698

Chekhovskiy, Kim, Access Serv, Samuel Roberts Noble Foundation, Inc, 2510 Sam Noble Pkwy, Ardmore, OK, 73401. Tel: 580-224-6260. Fax: 580-224-6265. p. 1957

Chekijian, Berj, Librn, Armenian Library & Museum of America, Inc, 65 Main St, Watertown, MA, 02472. Tel: 617-926-2562, Ext 22. Fax: 617-926-0175. p. 1133

Chelton, Mary K, Prof, Queens College of the City University of New York, Benjamin Rosenthal Library, Rm 254, 65-30 Kissena Blvd, Flushing, NY, 11367. Tel: 718-997-3790. Fax: 718-997-3797. p. 2970

Chemay, Connie, Head, Pub Serv, River Parishes Community College Library, 7384 John LeBlanc Blvd (Hwy 22), Sorrento, LA, 70778. Tel: 225-675-0218, 225-675-0231. Fax: 225-675-8595. p. 970

Chemero, Andrea J, Adjunct Fac Librn, Harrisburg Area Community College, 1641 Old Philadelphia Pike, Lancaster, PA, 17602. Tel: 717-358-2986. Fax: 717-358-2952. p. 2076

Chen, Ai-Hua, Commun Libr Mgr, Queens Borough Public Library, Queensboro Hill Community Library, 60-05 Main St, Flushing, NY, 11355. Tel: 718-359-8332. p. 1645

Chen, Barbara, ILL/Ser Spec, University of Saint Francis, 201 Pope John Paul II Ctr, 2701 Spring St, Fort Wayne, IN, 46808. Tel: 260-399-7700, Ext 6061. Fax: 260-399-8166. p. 743

Chen, Bess, Br Mgr, Sacramento Public Library, Martin Luther King Jr Regional Library, 7340 24th St Bypass, Sacramento, CA, 95822. p. 225

Chen, Chaichin, Web Serv, State of Rhode Island Office of Library & Information Services, One Capitol Hill, 4th Flr, Providence, RI, 02908. Tel: 401-574-9307. Fax: 401-574-9320. p. 2175

Chen, Chaomei, PhD, Assoc Prof, Drexel University, Rush Bldg, Rm 306, 30 N 33rd St, Philadelphia, PA, 19104-2875. Tel: 215-895-2474. Fax: 215-895-2494. p. 2972

Chen, Ching-jung, Dr, Librn, City College of the City University of New York, Architecture Visual Resources Library, Spitzer 104, 160 Convent Ave, New York, NY, 10031. Tel: 212-650-8754. Fax: 212-650-7604. p. 1673

Chen, Denise, Broadcast Librn, NPR Library, 635 Massachusetts Ave NW, Washington, DC, 20001. Fax: 202-513-3056. p. 412

Chen, Dung Lam, Acq Librn, Skidmore College, 815 N Broadway, Saratoga Springs, NY, 12866. Tel: 518-580-5000. Fax: 518-580-5541. p. 1738

Chen, Freda, Head, Tech Serv & Cat, Oklahoma Department of Libraries, 200 NE 18th St, Oklahoma City, OK, 73105. Tel: 405-521-2502. Fax: 405-525-7804. p. 1974

Chen, Gwen, Sr Librn, California Environmental Protection Agency Public Library, 1001 I St, Sacramento, CA, 95812. Tel: 916-327-0635. p. 222

Chen, Gwen, Sr Librn, California Environmental Protection Agency Public Library, Department of Toxic Substances Control - Technical Reference, 1001 I St, Sacramento, CA, 95814. Tel: 916-324-5898. Fax: 916-327-4494. p. 222

Chen, Helen, Dr, Coordr, Tennessee State University, 3500 John A Merritt Blvd, Nashville, TN, 37209. Tel: 615-963-7185. Fax: 615-963-7193. p. 2259

Chen, Hong, Br Mgr, Manchester Public Library, 586 Main St, Manchester, CT, 06040. Tel: 860-643-6892. Fax: 860-643-9453. p. 350

Chen, Hsien-min, Ref Serv, New Brunswick Free Public Library, 60 Livingston Ave, New Brunswick, NJ, 08901-2597. Tel: 732-745-5108. Fax: 732-846-0226. p. 1508

Chen, Hsin-Liang, Asst Prof, University of Texas at Austin, One University Sta, D7000, Austin, TX, 78712-0390. Tel: 512-471-3821. Fax: 512-471-3971. p. 2975

Chen, Jiangping, Dr, Assoc Prof, University of North Texas, 1155 Union Circle, Denton, TX, 76203-5017. Tel: 940-565-2445. Fax: 940-565-3101. p. 2975

Chen, Letty, Librn, Oregon College of Oriental Medicine Library, 10525 SE Cherry Blossom Dr, Portland, OR, 97216. Tel: 503-253-3443, Ext 121. Fax: 503-253-2701. p. 2013

Chen, Li, Syst Librn, Southern Polytechnic State University, 1100 S Marietta Pkwy, Marietta, GA, 30060-2896. Tel: 678-915-7467. Fax: 678-915-4944. p. 543

Chen, Lynn, Head Librn, Skidmore, Owings & Merrill, 14 Wall St, New York, NY, 10005. Tel: 212-298-9300. Fax: 212-298-9500. p. 1700

Chen, Manxue, Coll & Res Librn, Sir Mortimer B Davis Jewish General Hospital, 3755 Cote Ste Catherine Rd, A-200, Montreal, QC, H3T 1E2, CANADA. Tel: 514-340-8222, Ext 2453. Fax: 514-340-7552. p. 2901

Chen, Meghan, Dean, Libr & Learning Res, Mt San Antonio College Library, 1100 N Grand Ave, Walnut, CA, 91789. Tel: 909-274-4260. Fax: 909-468-4011. p. 282

Chen, Min-Jing, In Charge, Catholic University of America, Physics Library, 101 Hannan Hall, 620 Michigan Ave NE, Washington, DC, 20064. Tel: 202-319-5167. Fax: 202-319-4485. p. 396

Chen, Mun Hwa, Adult Serv, Somerset County Library System, One Vogt Dr, Bridgewater, NJ, 08807-2136. Tel: 908-526-4016, Ext 137. p. 1475

Chen, Nora, Commun Libr Mgr, County of Los Angeles Public Library, Rivera Library, 7828 S Serapis Ave, Pico Rivera, CA, 90660-4600. Tel: 562-949-5485. Fax: 562-948-3455. p. 143

Chen, Pingsheng, Electronic Res Librn, Ref Supvr, Worcester Public Library, Three Salem Sq, Worcester, MA, 01608. Tel: 508-799-1655. Fax: 508-799-1652. p. 1145

Chen, Qi, Dir, Libr Serv, Argosy University of Chicago Library, 225 N Michigan Ave, Chicago, IL, 60601. Tel: 312-777-7650. Fax: 312-777-7749. p. 606

Chen, Sandy, Per Coordr, Clarion University of Pennsylvania, 840 Wood St, Clarion, PA, 16214. Tel: 814-393-2748. Fax: 814-393-2344. p. 2045

Chen, Si, Br Mgr, Chicago Public Library, Chinatown, 2353 S Wentworth Ave, Chicago, IL, 60616. Tel: 312-747-8013. Fax: 312-747-5820. p. 608

Chen, Stacey, Acq, Stanislaus County Free Library, 1500 I St, Modesto, CA, 95354-1166. Tel: 209-558-7800. Fax: 209-529-4779. p. 188

Chen, Stacey, Br Mgr, Stanislaus County Free Library, Salida Branch, 4835 Sisk Rd, Salida, CA, 95368-9445. Tel: 209-543-7353. Fax: 209-543-7318. p. 188

Chen, Su, Dir, University of California Los Angeles Library, Richard C Rudolph East Asian Library, 21617 Research Library YRL, Los Angeles, CA, 90095-1575. Tel: 310-825-1401. Fax: 310-206-4960. p. 179

Chen, Suzy, Instrul Serv Librn, Glendale Community College Library, 1500 N Verdugo Rd, Glendale, CA, 91208-2894. Tel: 818-240-1000, Ext 5574. Fax: 818-246-5107. p. 155

Chen, Tina, Supv Librn, Torrance Public Library, El Retiro, 126 Vista Del Parque, Redondo Beach, CA, 90277. Tel: 310-375-0922. Fax: 310-375-6588. p. 276

Chen, Wenhui, Ref Librn, Molloy College, 1000 Hempstead Ave, Rockville Centre, NY, 11571. Tel: 516-678-5000, Ext 6461. Fax: 516-678-8908. p. 1734

Chen, Xiaotian, Electronic Serv Librn, Bradley University, 1501 W Bradley Ave, Peoria, IL, 61625. Tel: 309-677-2850. Fax: 309-677-2558. p. 690

Chen, Yan, Prof, University of Michigan, 304 West Hall, 1085 S University, Ann Arbor, MI, 48109-1107. Tel: 734-763-2285. Fax: 734-764-2475. p. 2967

Chen, Yao, Head of Libr, University of Minnesota Libraries-Twin Cities, East Asian, S-75 Wilson Library, 309 19th Ave S, Minneapolis, MN, 55455. Tel: 612-624-9833. p. 1262

Chen, Yueh-Lin, Assoc Librn, Seattle Art Museum, McCaw Foundation Library of Asian Art, Seattle Asian Art Museum, 1400 E Prospect St, Seattle, WA, 98112. Tel: 206-654-3202. Fax: 206-654-3191. p. 2530

Chen-Gaffey, Aiping, Tech Serv Librn, Slippery Rock University of Pennsylvania, Slippery Rock, PA, 16057-9989. Tel: 724-738-2660. Fax: 724-738-2661. p. 2140

Chen-Knapp, Liana, Librn, Weintraub, Genshlea, Chediak & Sproul, 400 Capitol Mall, Ste 1100, Sacramento, CA, 95814. Tel: 916-558-6000. Fax: 916-446-1611. p. 226

Chen-Wood, Hwai-Min, Commun Libr Mgr, Queens Borough Public Library, Forest Hills Community Library, 108-19 71st Ave, Forest Hills, NY, 11375. Tel: 718-268-7934. Fax: 718-268-1614. p. 1644

Chenault, John, Assoc Prof, Ref Librn, University of Louisville Libraries, Kornhauser Health Sciences Library, Health Sciences Ctr, 500 S Preston St, Louisville, KY, 40202. Tel: 502-852-1631. p. 927

Chenault, Nell, Head, Media Serv, Reserves, Virginia Commonwealth University Libraries, James Cabell Branch Library, Monroe Park Campus, 901 Park Ave, Richmond, VA, 23284-2033. Tel: 804-828-2070. Fax: 804-828-0151. p. 2492

Chenault, Rachel, Actg Br Mgr, Ch, Librn I, Montgomery City-County Public Library System, Bertha Pleasant Williams Library - Rosa L Parks Avenue Branch, 1276 Rosa L Parks Ave, Montgomery, AL, 36108. Tel: 334-240-4979. Fax: 334-240-4925. p. 31

Chenever, Roye, Br Mgr, Pointe Coupee Parish Library, Livonia Branch, 3100 Hwy 78, Livonia, LA, 70755. Tel: 225-637-2987. Fax: 225-637-2987. p. 964

Chenevert, Marie, Adult Serv, South Portland Public Library, 482 Broadway, South Portland, ME, 04106. Tel: 207-767-7660. Fax: 207-767-7626. p. 1002

Chenevert, Tina, Br Mgr, San Bernardino County Library, James S Thalman Branch, 14020 City Center Dr, Chino Hills, CA, 91709-5442. Tel: 909-590-5380. Fax: 909-591-5267. p. 229

Cheney, Brannigan, Circ Mgr, Weber County Library System, 2464 Jefferson Ave, Ogden, UT, 84401-2464. Tel: 801-337-2617. Fax: 801-337-2615. p. 2408

Cheney, Debora, Head, Libr Serv, Pennsylvania State University Libraries, 510 Paterno Library, University Park, PA, 16802. Tel: 814-863-1345. Fax: 814-865-3665. p. 2148

Cheney, Felicia, Dir, Edgartown Free Public Library, 58 N Water St, Edgartown, MA, 02539. Tel: 508-627-1373. p. 1087

Cheney, Kristin, Dir, Seattle University, School of Law Library, Sullivan Hall, 901 12th Ave, Seattle, WA, 98122-4411. Tel: 206-398-4221. Fax: 206-398-4194. p. 2532

Cheney, Marcia, Ch, Campbell County Public Library System, 2101 S 4-J Rd, Gillette, WY, 82718-5205. Tel: 307-687-9225. Fax: 307-686-4009. p. 2655

Cheney, Philip Mathews, Dir, Oconee County Public Library, 501 W South Broad St, Walhalla, SC, 29691. Tel: 864-638-4133. Fax: 864-638-4132. p. 2207

Cheney, Susan, Cat & Syst Adminr, Saint Joseph's University, Francis A Drexel Library, 5600 City Ave, Philadelphia, PA, 19131-1395. Tel: 610-660-1976. Fax: 610-660-1916. p. 2116

Cheng, Hong, Cat, University of California Los Angeles Library, Richard C Rudolph East Asian Library, 21617 Research Library YRL, Los Angeles, CA, 90095-1575. Tel: 310-206-9606. Fax: 310-206-4960. p. 179

Cheng, Hong, Instruction Librn, Fiorello H LaGuardia Community College Library, 31-10 Thomson Ave, Long Island City, NY, 11101. Tel: 720-482-6019. Fax: 718-482-5444, 718-609-2011. p. 1654

Cheng, Hung-Ming, Circ Serv Mgr, Braille Institute Library Services, 741 N Vermont Ave, Los Angeles, CA, 90029-3514. Tel: 323-663-1111, Ext 1317. Fax: 323-662-2440. p. 168

Cheng, James, Head of Libr, Harvard Library, Harvard-Yenching Library, Two Divinity Ave, Cambridge, MA, 02138. Tel: 617-495-2756. Fax: 617-496-6008. p. 1075

Cheng, Jenny, Commun Libr Mgr, County of Los Angeles Public Library, Walnut Library, 21155 La Puente Rd, Walnut, CA, 91789-2017. Tel: 909-595-0757. Fax: 909-595-7553. p. 143

Cheng, Jim, Dir, Columbia University, C V Starr East Asian Library, 300 Kent Hall, MC 3901, 1140 Amsterdam Ave, New York, NY, 10027. Tel: 212-854-4318. Fax: 212-662-6286. p. 1675

Cheng, Kirby, Head, Info Tech, Indiana University South Bend, 1700 Mishawaka Ave, South Bend, IN, 46615. Tel: 574-520-4421. Fax: 574-520-4472. p. 778

Cheng, Lawrence, Coordr, Media Serv, Shoreline Community College, 16101 Greenwood Ave N, Shoreline, WA, 98133-5696. Tel: 206-546-4592. Fax: 206-546-4604. p. 2535

Cheng, Rachel, Univ Librn, Eastern Michigan University, 955 W Circle Dr Library, Rm 200, Ypsilanti, MI, 48197. Tel: 734-487-0020, Ext 2202. p. 1238

Cheng, Rawdon, Syst Adminr, Upper Hudson Library System, 28 Essex St, Albany, NY, 12206. Tel: 518-437-9880, Ext 233. Fax: 518-437-9884. p. 1571

Cheng, Sam Catherine, Microcomputers & AV Equip Librn, Douglas College Library, 700 Royal Ave, New Westminster, BC, V3M 5Z5, CANADA. Tel: 604-527-5181. Fax: 604-527-5193. p. 2734

Cheng, Steven, Br Mgr, Los Angeles Public Library System, La Biblioteca del Pueblo de Lincoln Heights, 2530 Workman St, Los Angeles, CA, 90031-2202. Tel: 323-226-1692. Fax: 323-226-1691. p. 173

Cheng, Yaoming, Sr Librn, California Department of Corrections Library System, California Medical Facility, 1600 California Dr, Vacaville, CA, 95696. Tel: 707-448-6841, Ext 2603. Fax: 707-449-6541. p. 221

Cheng, Yungrang Laura, Dr, Asst Prof, Kent State University, 314 Library, Kent, OH, 44242-0001. Tel: 330-672-2782. Fax: 330-672-7965. p. 2972

Chenique, Maria, Ch, Highlands County Library System, 319 W Center Ave, Sebring, FL, 33870-3109. Tel: 863-402-6716. Fax: 863-385-2883. p. 491

Chenoweth, Brian, Mgr, Sr Info Spec, Novelis Global Technology Centre, 945 Princess St, Kingston, ON, K7L 5L9, CANADA. Tel: 613-541-2071. Fax: 613-541-2134. p. 2814

Chenoweth, Carol, Bibliog Instr, Tallahassee Community College Library, 444 Appleyard Dr, Tallahassee, FL, 32304-2895. Tel: 850-201-8396. Fax: 850-201-8380. p. 495

Chenoweth, Linda, Asst Dir, West Texas A&M University, University Dr & 26th St, Canyon, TX, 79016. Tel: 806-651-2212. Fax: 806-651-2213. p. 2294

Chenoweth, Rose, Dir, Mid-Illinois Talking Book Center, 600 Highpoint Lane, East Peoria, IL, 61611. Tel: 309-694-9200. Fax: 309-694-9230. p. 639

Chenoweth, Susan, Mgr, Federal Reserve Bank of Chicago, 230 S LaSalle St, Chicago, IL, 60604-1413. Tel: 312-322-5824. Fax: 312-322-5091. p. 613

Chenu-Campbell, Catherine, Acq Librn, Sacramento City College, 3835 Freeport Blvd, Sacramento, CA, 95822. Tel: 916-558-2253. Fax: 916-558-2114. p. 224

Cherepon, Lois, Ref, Saint John's University, Staten Island Campus, 300 Howard Ave, Staten Island, NY, 10301. Tel: 718-390-4521, Fax: 718-390-4290. p. 1748

Cheresnowski, Linda, Distance Educ Librn, Clarion University of Pennsylvania, 1801 W First St, Oil City, PA, 16301. Tel: 814-676-6591, Ext 1247. Fax: 814-677-3987. p. 2100

Cheri, Eckholt, Libr Tech, Nevada County Library, Bear River Station, 11130 Magnolia Rd, Grass Valley, CA, 95949. p. 193

Cherico, Florence, Br Mgr, Jersey City Free Public Library, West Bergen, 476 West Side Ave, Jersey City, NJ, 07304. Tel: 201-547-4554. Fax: 201-547-5887. p. 1492

Cherkaoui, Tuskasa, Music, Lynn University Library, 3601 N Military Trail, Boca Raton, FL, 33431-5598. Tel: 561-237-7214. Fax: 561-237-7074. p. 428

Cherniak, Ann, Dept Chair, College of Lake County, 19351 W Washington St, Grayslake, IL, 60030. Tel: 847-543-2469. Fax: 847-223-7690. p. 2965

Cherniak, Anne, Ref, College of Lake County, 19351 W Washington St, Grayslake, IL, 60030. Tel: 847-543-2460. Fax: 847-223-7690. p. 652

Chernevych, Andrew, Archivist, Sir Alexander Galt Museum & Archives, West End of Fifth Ave S, Lethbridge, AB, T1J 0P6, CANADA. Tel: 403-329-7302. Fax: 403-329-4958. p. 2710

Cherney, Jane, Pub Serv, United States Army, Bldg 2109, Joint Base Lewis McChord, WA, 98433-9500. Tel: 253-966-1309. Fax: 253-967-3922. p. 2518

Cherney, John, Head Librn, Webmaster, Wisconsin State Department of Transportation Library, 4802 Sheboygan Ave, Rm 100A, Madison, WI, 53707. Tel: 608-264-8142. Fax: 608-261-6306. p. 2611

Chernykh, Galina, Dir, Harrison Public Library, Bruce Ave, Harrison, NY, 10528. Tel: 914-835-0324. Fax: 914-835-1564. p. 1634

Cheromcha, Kate, Librn, Windham Community Memorial Hospital, 112 Mansfield Ave, Willimantic, CT, 06226. Tel: 860-456-6807. Fax: 860-456-6883. p. 378

Cherpak, Evelyn M, Dr, Archivist, Naval Hist Coll, United States Naval War College Library, 686 Cushing Rd, Newport, RI, 02841-1207. Tel: 401-841-2435. Fax: 401-841-7790. p. 2169

Cherrier, Mireille, Per, Cegep de Saint-Laurent Bibliotheque, 625 Boul Ste-Croix, Saint Laurent, QC, H4L 3X7, CANADA. Tel: 514-747-6521. Fax: 514-748-1249, 514-855-1942. p. 2909

Cherry, Alissa, Dir, Union of British Columbia Indian Chiefs, 342 Water St, 4th Flr, Vancouver, BC, V6B 1B6, CANADA. Tel: 604-684-0231. Fax: 604-684-5726. p. 2742

Cherry, Deborah, Librn, Tennessee Valley Authority, Legal Research Center, 400 W Summit Hill Dr, Knoxville, TN, 37922. Tel: 865-632-6613. Fax: 865-632-6718. p. 2243

Cherry, Ed, Automation Syst Coordr, Online Serv, Samford University Library, 800 Lakeshore Dr, Birmingham, AL, 35229. Tel: 205-726-2506. Fax: 205-726-4009. p. 9

Cherry, Megan, Librn, National Park Service, PO Box 6, Interior, SD, 57750. Tel: 605-433-5361. Fax: 605-433-5248. p. 2213

Cherry, Philip, Dir, Onslow County Public Library, 58 Doris Ave E, Jacksonville, NC, 28540. Tel: 910-455-7350, Ext 221. Fax: 910-455-1661. p. 1803

Chertok, Elena, Ser Spec, University of Oregon Libraries, John E Jaqua Law Library, William W Knight Law Ctr, 2nd Flr, 1515 Agate St, Eugene, OR, 97403-1221. Tel: 541-346-1659. Fax: 541-346-1669. p. 1997

Chery, Marc, Librn IV, San Diego Public Library, 820 E St, San Diego, CA, 92101-6478. Tel: 619-236-5830. Fax: 619-238-6639. p. 235

Chesbro, Melinda, Content Mgt Dir, Fort Vancouver Regional Library District, 1007 E Mill Plain Blvd, Vancouver, WA, 98663. Tel: 360-695-1561. Fax: 360-693-2681. p. 2546

Chesham, Jane, Ref Serv, Hillside Public Library, 405 N Hillside Ave, Hillside, IL, 60162-1295. Tel: 708-449-7510. Fax: 708-449-6119. p. 656

Chesher, Cathy, Youth Serv, Adrian Public Library, 143 E Maumee St, Adrian, MI, 49221-2773. Tel: 517-265-2265. Fax: 517-265-8847. p. 1147

Cheski, Patricia F, Dir, Menominee County Library, S319 Railroad St, Stephenson, MI, 49887. Tel: 906-753-6923. Fax: 906-753-4678. p. 1229

Chesley, Ed Arnold, Librn, John Van Puffelen Library of the Appalachian Bible College, 161 College Dr, Mount Hope, WV, 25880-1040. Tel: 304-877-6428, Ext 3271. Fax: 304-877-5983. p. 2567

Chesling, Gina, Ch, Scott County Library System, Blue Grass Branch, 114 N Mississippi St, Blue Grass, IA, 52726. Tel: 563-381-2868. Fax: 563-381-2868. p. 813

Chesmelewski, John C, Librn, Department of Veterans Affairs, 142D/JC, 915 N Grand Blvd, Saint Louis, MO, 63106. Tel: 314-289-6421. Fax: 314-289-6321. p. 1354

Chesner, Michelle, Librn, Columbia University, Area Studies, 307 International Affairs Bldg, 420 W 118th St, New York, NY, 10027. Tel: 212-854-3630. Fax: 212-854-3834. p. 1674

Chesnes, Wendy, Dir, Norway Public Library, 108 Railroad St, Norway, IA, 52318. Tel: 319-227-7487. Fax: 319-227-7487. p. 836

Chesnut, Mary, Res & Instruction Librn, Northern Kentucky University, University Dr, Highland Heights, KY, 41099. Tel: 859-572-5826. Fax: 859-572-5390. p. 917

Chesnut, Patricia J, Dir, Nevada County Historical Society, 214 Church St, Nevada City, CA, 95959. Tel: 530-265-5910. p. 193

Chesson, Brent, Mgr, Libr Serv, Principal Financial Group, 711 High St, S006 W80, Des Moines, IA, 50392. Tel: 515-247-5893. Fax: 515-248-3011. p. 810

Chester, Carol, Cat, Tech Serv Mgr, North Georgia College & State University, 238 Georgia Circle, Dahlonega, GA, 30597-3001. Tel: 706-867-2810. p. 527

Chester, Claudia, Interim Univ Librn, John F Kennedy University Libraries, 100 Ellinwood Way, Pleasant Hill, CA, 94523. Tel: 925-969-3108. Fax: 925-969-3101. p. 210

Chester, Karene, Bibliog Instr, Delaware Technical & Community College, 333 Shipley St, Wilmington, DE, 19801. Tel: 302-573-5431. Fax: 302-577-2038. p. 387

Chester, Len, Chair, Ontario Genealogical Society Library, 5120 Yonge St, North York, ON, M2N 5N9, CANADA. Tel: 416-395-5623. Fax: 416-489-9803. p. 2825

Chester, Stacey, Youth Serv Mgr, Cherry Valley Public Library District, 755 E State St, Cherry Valley, IL, 61016-9699. Tel: 815-332-5161, Ext 33. Fax: 815-332-2441. p. 604

Chester, Stephanie, Tech Serv, State Transportation Library, Ten Park Plaza, Boston, MA, 02116. Tel: 617-973-8000. Fax: 617-973-7153. p. 1067

Chester-Fangman, Christina, Instruction Librn, Austin Peay State University, 601 E College St, Clarksville, TN, 37044. Tel: 931-221-1267. Fax: 931-221-7296. p. 2228

Chestnut, Lisa, Ch, Big Horn County Library, 430 West C St, Basin, WY, 82410. Tel: 307-568-2388. Fax: 307-568-2011. p. 2651

Chetwynd, Margo, In Charge, Western Counties Regional Library, Barrington Municipal, 3533 Hwy No 3, Barrington Passage, NS, B0W 1G0, CANADA. Tel: 902-637-3348. p. 2787

Cheung, Cecilia, Head Librn, San Diego City College, 1313 Park Blvd, San Diego, CA, 92101-4712. Tel: 619-388-3873. Fax: 619-388-3410. p. 232

Cheung, Sylvia, Br Head, Toronto Public Library, Goldhawk Park, 295 Alton Towers Circle, Toronto, ON, M1V 4P1, CANADA. Tel: 416-396-8964. Fax: 416-396-3561. p. 2861

Chevalier, Dana, Librn, Peavey Memorial Library, 26 Water St, Eastport, ME, 04631. Tel: 207-853-4021. Fax: 207-853-4021. p. 984

Chevalier, Sharon K, Circ, Doc Delivery, ILL, Centenary College of Louisiana, 2834 Woodlawn St, Shreveport, LA, 71104-3335. Tel: 318-869-5047. Fax: 318-869-5004. p. 967

Chevere, Elizabeth, In Charge, National Association for Visually Handicapped, 22 West 21st St, 6th Flr, New York, NY, 10010. Tel: 212-889-3141. Fax: 212-727-2931. p. 1687

Chevere, Maria Isabel, Librn, Universidad Central Del Caribe, Avenida Laurel, Santa Juanita, Bayamon, PR, 00956. Tel: 787-798-3001, Ext 2306. Fax: 787-785-3425. p. 2672

Cheverie, Joan, Head, Copyright & Digital Rights Mgt, Georgetown University, 37th & N St NW, Washington, DC, 20057-1174. Tel: 202-687-1870. Fax: 202-687-7501. p. 402

Cheverton, Sarah, Assoc Dean of Libr & Educ Tech, James Madison University Libraries & Educational Technologies, 800 S Main St, Harrisonburg, VA, 22807-0001. Tel: 540-568-3393. Fax: 540-568-6339. p. 2470

Chevrette, Marc-André, Acq, Librn, Pub Serv, Cegep de La Pocatiere, 140 Fourth Ave, La Pocatiere, QC, G0R 1Z0, CANADA. Tel: 418-856-1525. Fax: 418-856-4589. p. 2885

Chevrier, David, Librn, Montreal Association for the Blind, 7005 de Maisonneuve Blvd W, Montreal, QC, H4B 1T3, CANADA. Tel: 514-487-1891, Ext 220. Fax: 514-487-5494. p. 2899

Chew, Jean-Marie, Law Librn, Rhode Island Department of Corrections, Medium Price Security Library, PO Box 20983, Cranston, RI, 02920-0983. Tel: 401-464-1903. Fax: 401-464-1198. p. 2165

Chew, Jean-Marie, Law Librn, Rhode Island Department of Corrections, Minimum Security Library, PO Box 8212, Cranston, RI, 02920-0212. Tel: 401-462-2168. Fax: 401-462-2161. p. 2165

Chew, Jean-Marie, Law Librn, Rhode Island Department of Corrections, Women's Dix Library, PO Box 8312, Cranston, RI, 02920-0312. Tel: 401-462-3134. p. 2165

Chew, Jean-Marie, Law Librn, Rhode Island Department of Corrections, Women's Gloria MacDonald Library, 1311 Wilma Schlesser Lane, Cranston, RI, 02920. Tel: 401-462-2364. Fax: 401-462-1842. p. 2165

Chew, Joan, Law Librn, Rhode Island Department of Corrections, High Security Center Library, PO Box 8200, Cranston, RI, 02920-0200. Tel: 401-462-2125. Fax: 401-462-1112. p. 2165

Chew, Marynelle, Head, Tech Serv, Brigham Young University-Hawaii, 55-220 Kulanui St, BYU-Hawaii, No 1966, Laie, HI, 96762-1294. Tel: 808-675-3863. Fax: 808-675-3877. p. 567

Chewning, Barbara, Libr Tech, South Piedmont Community College, Cyber Center, 680 Hwy 74 W, Polkton, NC, 28135. Tel: 704-272-5387. Fax: 704-272-5384. p. 1814

Chewning, Vonnie, Librn, Southwest Arkansas Regional Library, Winthrop Branch, 720 High St, Winthrop, AR, 71866. Tel: 870-381-7580. Fax: 870-381-7580. p. 103

Cheyne, Catherine, Asst Dir, Delanco Public Library, M Joan Pearson School, 1303 Burlington Ave, Delanco, NJ, 08075. Tel: 856-461-6850. Fax: 856-461-6850. p. 1481

Chhina, Amrit, Libr Asst, University of Manitoba Libraries, St John's College Library, 92 Dysart Rd, Winnipeg, MB, R3T 2M5, CANADA. Tel: 204-474-8542. Fax: 204-474-7614. p. 2759

Chi, Pingfeng, Dir, Center For Chinese Research Materials, 10415 Willow Crest Ct, Vienna, VA, 22182-1852. Tel: 703-715-2688. Fax: 703-715-7913. p. 2498

Chiaffone, Steve, Doc Delivery Mgr, New York Academy of Medicine Library, 1216 Fifth Ave, New York, NY, 10029-5293. Tel: 212-822-7327. Fax: 212-423-0266. p. 1688

Chianese, Scott, Ref Librn, Hamilton Township Public Library, One Justice Samuel A Alito, Jr Way, Hamilton, NJ, 08619. Tel: 609-581-4060. Fax: 609-581-4067. p. 1490

Chiang, Art, Librn, Florida State College at Jacksonville, 3939 Roosevelt Blvd, C-100, Jacksonville, FL, 32205. Tel: 904-381-3522. Fax: 904-381-3579. p. 452

Chiappetta, Joyce, Dir, Baldwin Borough Public Library, Wallace Bldg, 41 Macek Dr, Pittsburgh, PA, 15227-3638. Tel: 412-885-2255. Fax: 412-885-5255. p. 2121

Chiaramonte, Carrie, Br Mgr, Niagara Falls Public Library, Chippawa, 3763 Main St, Niagara Falls, ON, L2G 6B3, CANADA. Tel: 905-295-4391. p. 2824

Chiaramonte, Carrie, Br Mgr, Niagara Falls Public Library, Community Center, 7150 Montrose Rd, Niagara Falls, ON, O2H 3N3, CANADA. Tel: 905-371-1200. p. 2824

Chiaramonte, Carrie, Br Mgr, Niagara Falls Public Library, Stamford Centre, Town & Country Plaza, 3643 Portage Rd N, Niagara Falls, ON, L2J 2K8, CANADA. Tel: 905-357-0410. p. 2824

Chiasson, Christine, In Charge, Mohawk College Library, Brantford Library, 411 Elgin St, Brantford, ON, N3T 5V2, CANADA. Tel: 519-759-7200, Ext 6020. Fax: 519-758-6008. p. 2810

Chiavaroli, Melissa, Adult Serv, Seekonk Public Library, 410 Newman Ave, Seekonk, MA, 02771. Tel: 508-336-8230. Fax: 508-336-6437. p. 1123

Chiavetta, Vicki, Dir, Coppell Public Library, 177 N Hertz Rd, Coppell, TX, 75019. Tel: 972-304-3655. Fax: 972-304-3622. p. 2301

Chiba, Toru, Electronic Serv Librn, Fairmont State University, 1201 Locust Ave, Fairmont, WV, 26554. Tel: 304-367-4594. Fax: 304-367-4677. p. 2559

Chibnal, Daniel, User Serv & Instruction Design Librn, Grand View University Library, 1350 Morton Ave, Des Moines, IA, 50316-1494. Tel: 515-263-2879. Fax: 515-263-2998. p. 809

Chibnik, Kitty, Assoc Dir, Head, Access Serv, Columbia University, Avery Architectural & Fine Arts Library, 1172 Amsterdam Ave, MC 0301, New York, NY, 10027. Tel: 212-854-3506. Fax: 212-854-8904. p. 1674

Chichester, Christina, Ad, Burlington County Library, Cinnaminson Branch, 1619 Riverton Rd, Cinnaminson, NJ, 08077. Tel: 856-829-9340. Fax: 856-829-2243. p. 1543

Chick, Cathy, Ref, University of Arkansas Libraries, Robert A & Vivian Young Law Library, School of Law, Waterman Hall 107, Fayetteville, AR, 72701-1201. Tel: 479-575-5835. Fax: 479-575-2053. p. 100

Chick, Kathy, Dir, East Owyhee County Library District, 520 Boise Ave, Grand View, ID, 83624. Tel: 208-834-2785. p. 575

Chick-Gravel, Shelley, Br Mgr, Central Rappahannock Regional Library, Snow Branch, 8740 Courthouse Rd, Spotsylvania, VA, 22553-2513. Tel: 540-507-7565. p. 2466

Chickering, F William, Dean of Libr, Rider University, 2083 Lawrenceville Rd, Lawrenceville, NJ, 08648-3099. Tel: 609-896-5111. Fax: 609-896-8029. p. 1494

Chidester, John, Dir, Mount Vernon Nazarene University, 800 Martinsburg Rd, Mount Vernon, OH, 43050-9500. Tel: 740-397-9000, Ext 4240. Fax: 740-397-8847. p. 1919

Chidester, John K, Dir, Public Library of Mount Vernon & Knox County, 201 N Mulberry St, Mount Vernon, OH, 43050-2413. Tel: 740-392-2665. Fax: 740-397-3866. p. 1919

Chien, Lori, Chief Ref Librn, Jervis Public Library Association, Inc, 613 N Washington St, Rome, NY, 13440-4296. Tel: 315-336-4570. p. 1734

Chien, Peter, Chief Librn, Automation, Jervis Public Library Association, Inc, 613 N Washington St, Rome, NY, 13440-4296. Tel: 315-336-4570. p. 1734

Chiesi, Charles, Electronic Res & Syst Librn, Hilbert College, 5200 S Park Ave, Hamburg, NY, 14075. Tel: 716-649-7900, Ext 239. Fax: 716-648-6530. p. 1632

Chifari, Elizabeth, Librn, Holland & Knight LLP, 701 Brickell Ave, Ste 3000, Miami, FL, 33131. Tel: 305-789-7420. Fax: 305-789-7799. p. 465

Chiknas, Coralyn, Ch, Kelley Library, 234 Main St, Salem, NH, 03079-3190. Tel: 603-898-7064. Fax: 603-898-8583. p. 1464

Chilcoat, Jennifer, Assoc Dir, Central Arkansas Library System, 100 Rock St, Little Rock, AR, 72201-4698. Tel: 501-918-3031. p. 106

Childers, Libby, Adult Serv Mgr, McCracken County Public Library, 555 Washington St, Paducah, KY, 42003-1735. Tel: 270-442-2510, Ext 13. Fax: 270-443-9322. p. 932

Childers, Marsha, Mgr, Cabell County Public Library, Cox Landing Branch, Rt 1, Box 75, 6363 Cox Lane, Lesage, WV, 25537. Tel: 304-733-3022. Fax: 304-733-3022. p. 2561

Childers, Scott, Dir, York Public Library, 520 Nebraska Ave, York, NE, 68467-3095. Tel: 402-363-2620. Fax: 402-363-2627. p. 1424

Childres, Betty, Libr Dir, Kennesaw State University, 1000 Chastain Rd, Kennesaw, GA, 30144. Tel: 770-423-6199. Fax: 770-423-6185. p. 537

Childress, Boyd, Librn, Auburn University, The Library of Architecture, Design & Construction, Dudley Hall Commons, Auburn, AL, 36849. Tel: 334-844-1752. Fax: 334-844-1756. p. 6

Childress, C Dawn, Humanities Librn, Pennsylvania State University Libraries, George & Sherry Middlemas Arts & Humanities Library, Pennsylvania State University, W 202 Pattee Library, University Park, PA, 16802-1801. Tel: 814-865-0660. Fax: 814-863-7502. p. 2148

Childress, Jack D, In Charge, Price-Pottenger Nutrition Foundation Library, 7890 Broadway, Lemon Grove, CA, 91945. Tel: 619-462-7600. Fax: 619-433-3136. p. 163

Childress, Novella, In Charge, Florida Department of Corrections, 6901 State Rd 62, Bowling Green, FL, 33834-9505. Tel: 863-767-4500,Ext 4716. Fax: 863-767-4504. p. 429

Childrey, Cynthia, Dean & Univ Librn, Northern Arizona University, Bldg 028, Knoles Dr, Flagstaff, AZ, 86011. Tel: 928-523-2173. Fax: 928-523-3770. p. 62

Childs, Carolyn, Librn, Gunnison Civic Library, 38 W Center St, Gunnison, UT, 84634. Tel: 435-528-3104. Fax: 435-528-3145. p. 2406

Childs, Deirdre, Head, Access Serv, Drexel University Libraries, Hagerty Library, 33rd & Market Sts, Philadelphia, PA, 19104-2875. Tel: 215-895-6785. Fax: 215-895-2070. p. 2105

Childs, Gary, Educ Librn, Drexel University Health Sciences Libraries, 245 N 15th St MS 449, Philadelphia, PA, 19102-1192. Fax: 215-762-8180. p. 2105

Childs, Mary, Br Librn, Lincoln-Lawrence-Franklin Regional Library, Franklin County Public Library, 38 First St, Meadville, MS, 39653. Tel: 601-384-2997. Fax: 601-384-3003. p. 1295

Childs, Miriam, Head, Tech Serv, Law Library of Louisiana, Louisiana Supreme Court, 2nd Flr, 400 Royal St, New Orleans, LA, 70130-2104. Tel: 504-310-2400. Fax: 504-310-2419. p. 960

Childs, Mona, Librn, West Virginia School for the Blind Library, 301 E Main St, Romney, WV, 26757. Tel: 304-822-4656, 304-822-4894. Fax: 304-822-4896. p. 2570

Childs, Sarah, Cat Librn, Hussey-Mayfield Memorial Public Library, 250 N Fifth St, Zionsville, IN, 46077-1324. Tel: 317-873-3149, Ext 13330. Fax: 317-873-8339. p. 789

Childs, Ward J, Archivist, Philadelphia City Archives, 3101 Market St, 1st Flr, Philadelphia, PA, 19104. Tel: 215-685-9400. Fax: 215-685-9409. p. 2114

Childs-Helton, Sally, Spec Coll & Archives Librn, Butler University Libraries, 4600 Sunset Ave, Indianapolis, IN, 46208. Tel: 317-940-9265. Fax: 317-940-9711. p. 749

Chileen, Carol, Br Librn, Fulton County Public Library, Aubbee, 7432 Olson Rd, Leiters Ford, IN, 46945. Tel: 574-542-4859. Fax: 574-542-4859. p. 776

Chilenski, Karlyn, Libr Assoc II, Lorain Public Library System, Columbia Branch, 13824 W River Rd N, Columbia Station, OH, 44028. Tel: 440-236-8751. Fax: 440-236-8956. p. 1911

Chiller, Vanessa, Supvr, Essex County Library, Stoney Point Branch, 6720 Tecumseh Rd, Stoney Point, ON, N0R 1N0, CANADA. Tel: 226-946-1529, Ext 232. p. 2804

Chilton, Galadriel, Electronic Res, University of Wisconsin-La Crosse, 1631 Pine St, La Crosse, WI, 54601-3748. Tel: 608-785-8738. Fax: 608-785-8639. p. 2603

Chilton, Sarah, Archives, Ref Serv, Brookings Institution Library, 1775 Massachusetts Ave NW, Washington, DC, 20036. Tel: 202-797-6240. Fax: 202-797-2970. p. 394

Chimato, Mary Carmen, Asst Dean, University of the Pacific Library, 3601 Pacific Ave, Stockton, CA, 95211. Tel: 209-946-2939. Fax: 209-946-2805. p. 273

Chin, Judy, Libr Coordr, Alberta Law Libraries - Edson, Provincial Bldg, 205, 111-54th St, Edson, AB, T7E 1T2, CANADA. Tel: 780-723-8283. Fax: 780-723-8909. p. 2703

Chin, Kristen, Dir, Foster Public Library, 184 Howard Hill Rd, Foster, RI, 02825. Tel: 401-397-4801. Fax: 401-392-3101. p. 2166

Chin, Siew-Ben, Tech Serv Librn, Richard J Daley College, 7500 S Pulaski Rd, Chicago, IL, 60652-1200. Tel: 773-838-7979. Fax: 773-838-7670. p. 623

Chinault, Sue, Mgr, Michigan Commission for the Blind - Braille & Talking Book Library, Michigan Library & Historical Ctr, 702 W Kalamazoo St, Lansing, MI, 48915-1703. Tel: 517-373-5353. Fax: 517-373-5865. p. 1201

Chinery, Kristine, Librn, Wayne State University Libraries, Walter P Reuther Library of Labor & Urban Affairs, 5401 Cass Ave, Detroit, MI, 48202. Tel: 313-577-4024. Fax: 313-577-4300. p. 1173

Ching, Cathy, Br Librn, South Central Regional Library, Morden Branch, 514 Stephen St, Morden, MB, R6M 1T7, CANADA. Tel: 204-822-4092. p. 2753

Ching, Tina, Ref, Seattle University, School of Law Library, Sullivan Hall, 901 12th Ave, Seattle, WA, 98122-4411. Tel: 206-398-4221. Fax: 206-398-4194. p. 2532

Chinnaswamy, Sainath, Dean, Learning Res, Bristol Community College, 777 Elsbree St, Fall River, MA, 02720. Tel: 508-678-2811, Ext 2675. Fax: 508-730-3270. p. 1088

Chinoransky, Susan, Head, Ser, George Washington University, Jacob Burns Law Library, 716 20th St NW, Washington, DC, 20052. Tel: 202-994-8902. Fax: 202-994-2874. p. 402

Chiofalo, Maureen, Dir, Rockville Centre Public Library, 221 N Village Ave, Rockville Centre, NY, 11570. Tel: 516-766-6257. Fax: 516-766-6090. p. 1734

Chiorazzi, Michael G, Dir, University of Arizona, James E Rogers College of Law Library, PO Box 210176, Tucson, AZ, 85721-0176. Tel: 520-621-1413. Fax: 520-621-3138. p. 89

Chiota, Anna, Br Mgr, Saint Catharines Public Library, Grantham Branch, 425 Carlton St, St. Catharines, ON, L2M 4W8, CANADA. Tel: 905-688-6103, Ext 345. Fax: 905-688-6292. p. 2843

Chiota, Anna, Br Mgr, Saint Catharines Public Library, Port Dalhousie Branch, 23 Brock St, St. Catharines, ON, L2N 5E1, CANADA. Tel: 905-688-6103, Ext 245. Fax: 905-688-6292. p. 2843

Chiota, Anna, Br Mgr, Saint Catharines Public Library, William Hamilton Merritt Branch, 149 Hartzel Rd, St. Catharines, ON, L2P 1N6, CANADA. Tel: 905-688-6103, Ext 245. Fax: 905-688-6292. p. 2843

Chiota, Anna, Mgr, Br Serv, St Catharines Public Library, 54 Church St, St. Catharines, ON, L2R 7K2, CANADA. Tel: 905-688-6103. Fax: 905-688-6292. p. 2843

Chipps, Dawn, Info Assoc, Towers Perrin, 1800 McGill College Ave, Ste 2200, Montreal, QC, H3A 3J6, CANADA. Tel: 514-982-2172. Fax: 514-982-9269. p. 2902

Chipps, Laura, ILL, University of California, San Diego, 9500 Gilman Dr, Mail Code 0175G, La Jolla, CA, 92093-0175. Tel: 858-534-3336. Fax: 858-534-4970. p. 162

Chipps, Susan, Br Mgr, Washington County Public Library, Lyman-Pomeroy Beverly Branch, MacIntosh St, Beverly, OH, 45715. Tel: 740-984-4060. Fax: 740-984-2083. p. 1914

Chirgwin, Jane, Libr Dir, Rensselaer Public Library, 676 East St, Rensselaer, NY, 12144. Tel: 518-462-1193. Fax: 518-462-2819. p. 1726

Chirinos, Joel, Librn, University of Texas at Brownsville & Texas Southmost College Library, 80 Fort Brown St, Brownsville, TX, 78521. Tel: 956-882-7465. Fax: 956-882-5495. p. 2292

Chisaki, Jane, Dir, Alameda Free Library, 1550 Oak St, Alameda, CA, 94501-2932. p. 119

Chisholm, Carol, Librn, Sun-Times News Group, 1433 E 83rd Ave, Merrillville, IN, 46410. Tel: 219-648-3135. Fax: 219-648-3026. p. 764

Chisholm, Cathy, Librn, Cape Breton University Library, 1250 Grand Lake Rd, Sydney, NS, B1P 6L2, CANADA. Tel: 902-563-1993. Fax: 902-563-1826. p. 2785

Chisholm, Faye, Circ, Vancouver School of Theology, 6000 Iona Dr, Vancouver, BC, V6T 1L4, CANADA. Tel: 604-822-9430. Fax: 604-822-9212. p. 2744

Chisholm, Kathryn R, Dir, James A Tuttle Library, 45 Main St, Antrim, NH, 03440-3906. Tel: 603-588-6786. p. 1437

Chisholm, Margaret, Ref Librn, Yale University Library, Lillian Goldman Library Yale Law School, 127 Wall St, New Haven, CT, 06511. Tel: 203-432-1600. Fax: 203-432-2112. p. 358

Chislett, Pam, Adult Serv, Dep Dir, Head, Info Serv, Grande Prairie Public Library, 101-9839 103 Ave, Grande Prairie, AB, T8V 6M7, CANADA. Tel: 780-357-7474. Fax: 780-538-4983. p. 2705

Chism, Kahlil, Educ Spec, National Archives & Records Administration, 441 Freedom Pkwy, Atlanta, GA, 30307. Tel: 404-865-7126. Fax: 404-865-7102. p. 517

Chism, Stephen J, Gen Ref/Composition Librn, University of Arkansas Libraries, 365 N McIlroy Ave, Fayetteville, AR, 72701-4002. Tel: 479-575-8420. Fax: 479-575-6656. p. 99

Chism, Valerie, YA Librn, Baldwinsville Public Library, 33 E Genesee St, Baldwinsville, NY, 13027-2575. Tel: 315-635-5631. Fax: 315-635-6760. p. 1577

Chisum, Tyvon, ILL, Argosy University, Bldg 2, Ste 400, 980 Hammond Dr, Atlanta, GA, 30328. Tel: 770-407-1033. Fax: 770-671-0418. p. 510

Chittenden, Carolyn F, Dir, Camden County Library District, 89 Rodeo Rd, Camdenton, MO, 65020. Tel: 573-346-5954. Fax: 573-346-1263. p. 1321

Chittenden, Lloyd, Tech Serv Librn, Fort Lewis College Library, 1000 Rim Dr, Durango, CO, 81301-3999. Tel: 970-247-7250. Fax: 970-247-7149. p. 305

Chitty, A Ben, Syst Coordr, Queens College, Benjamin S Rosenthal Library, 65-30 Kissena Blvd, Flushing, NY, 11367-0904. Tel: 718-997-3700. Fax: 718-997-3753. p. 1623

Chitwood, Rosie, Br Mgr, Athens Regional Library System, Royston Branch, 684 Franklin Springs St, Royston, GA, 30662. Tel: 706-245-6748. Fax: 706-245-6748. p. 509

Chiu, Cathy, Br Head, University of California, Santa Barbara, Santa Barbara, CA, 93106-9010. Tel: 805-893-2478. Fax: 805-893-7010. p. 261

Chiu, Kuei, Interim Head, Coll Develop, University of California, Riverside Libraries, 900 University Ave, Riverside, CA, 92521, Tel: 951-827-3703. p. 218

Chlebanowski, Lise, Libr Mgr, Avondale Public Library, 495 E Western Ave, Avondale, AZ, 85323. Tel: 623-478-3100. Fax: 623-478-3809. p. 57

Chlebo, Dawn, Head, Circ, Milford Public Library, 330 Family Dr, Milford, MI, 48381-2000. Tel: 248-684-0845. Fax: 248-684-2923. p. 1209

Chlysta, Cheryl, Mgr, Portage County District Library, Aurora Memorial, 115 E Pioneer Trail, Aurora, OH, 44202-9349. Tel: 330-562-6502. Fax: 330-562-2084. p. 1901

Chmiel, Mary Faith, Dir, Spotswood Public Library, 548 Main St, Spotswood, NJ, 08884. Tel: 732-251-1515. Fax: 732-251-8151. p. 1531

Chmielewski, Denise, Syst Coordr, Franklin & Marshall College, 450 College Ave, Lancaster, PA, 17603-3318. Tel: 717-358-7192. Fax: 717-291-4160. p. 2076

Chmielewski, Jeanne, Acq, Pub Relations, Southington Public Library & Museum, 255 Main St, Southington, CT, 06489. Tel: 860-628-0947. Fax: 860-628-0488. p. 368

Chmilar, Linda, Libr Mgr, Grimshaw Municipal Library, 5007 47th Ave, Grimshaw, AB, T0H 1W0, CANADA. Tel: 780-332-4553. Fax: 780-332-1250. p. 2706

Chmura, Joseph J, Head, Pub Serv, Hobart & William Smith Colleges, 334 Pulteney St, Geneva, NY, 14456. Tel: 315-781-3550. Fax: 315-781-3560. p. 1627

Cho, Esther, Foreign & Intl Law Ref, Georgetown University, Georgetown Law Library (John Wolff & Edward Bennett Williams Libraries), 111 G St NW, Washington, DC, 20001. Fax: 202-662-9168. p. 403

Cho, Jung, Cataloger, Queensborough Community College, City University of New York, 222-05 56th Ave, Bayside, NY, 11364-1497. Tel: 718-631-6218. Fax: 718-281-5012. p. 1579

Cho, Leon, Br Mgr, Oakland Public Library, Montclair, 1687 Mountain Blvd, Oakland, CA, 94611. Tel: 510-482-7810. Fax: 510-482-7865. p. 198

Cho, Michael, Tech Serv Librn, Sullivan & Cromwell LLP, 125 Broad St, New York, NY, 10004. Tel: 212-558-3780. Fax: 212-558-3346. p. 1700

Choate, Celeste, Assoc Dir, Serv, Coll & Access, Ann Arbor District Library, 343 S Fifth Ave, Ann Arbor, MI, 48104. Tel: 734-327-4241. Fax: 734-327-8309. p. 1150

Choate, Filomena, Youth Serv, Winfield Public Library, OS-291 Winfield Rd, Winfield, IL, 60190. Tel: 630-653-7599. Fax: 630-653-7781. p. 720

Chobot, Karen M, Dir, North Dakota State College of Science, 800 Sixth St N, Wahpeton, ND, 58076-0001. Tel: 701-671-2298, 701-671-2618. Fax: 701-671-2674. p. 1849

Chodakowsky, Joshua, Res Spec, Global Intelligence Group, 285 Madison Ave, 10th Flr, New York, NY, 10017. Tel: 212-210-3983. Fax: 212-210-3918. p. 1680

Chodoba, Nick, ILL, Ref Serv, The Brookfield Library, 182 Whisconier Rd, Brookfield, CT, 06804. Tel: 203-775-6241. Fax: 203-740-7723. p. 332

Chodock, Ted, Ref & Instruction, College of Southern Nevada, 6375 W Charleston Blvd, W10I, Las Vegas, NV, 89146. Tel: 702-651-5509. Fax: 702-651-5718. p. 1429

Choi, Christy, Tech Serv Librn, Nyack College Library, One South Blvd, Nyack, NY, 10960-3698. Fax: 845-353-0817. p. 1708

Choi, Eunice, Head Librn, Illinois Department of Employment Security, 33 S State St, Chicago, IL, 60603. Tel: 312-793-6202. Fax: 312-793-6292. p. 615

Choi, Helen, Cataloger, Pace University, 78 N Broadway, White Plains, NY, 10603. Tel: 914-422-4648. Fax: 914-422-4139. p. 1769

Choi, Ikeson, PhD, Assoc Prof, University of Georgia, College of Education, 224 River's Crossing, Athens, GA, 30602-7144. Tel: 706-542-4110. Fax: 706-542-4032. p. 2964

Choi, Kunwoo, Br Mgr, Beaumont Public Library System, Elmo Willard Branch, 3590 E Lucas, Beaumont, TX, 77708. Tel: 409-892-4988. Fax: 409-898-4088. p. 2287

Choi, Lan, Ref Librn, Bureau of National Affairs, Inc Library, 1801 S Bell St, Rm 3200, Arlington, VA, 22202. Tel: 703-341-3313. Fax: 703-341-1636. p. 2449

Choi, Namjoo, Dr, Asst Prof, University of Kentucky, 320 Little Library Bldg, Lexington, KY, 40506-0224. Tel: 859-257-4113. Fax: 859-257-4205. p. 2966

Choi, Sylvia, Coll Mgt Librn, School of the Art Institute of Chicago, 37 S Wabash Ave, Chicago, IL, 60603-3103. Tel: 312-899-5097. Fax: 312-899-1851. p. 624

Choice, Nancy J, Chief, Pub Serv, Public Library Association of Annapolis & Anne Arundel County, Inc, Five Harry S Truman Pkwy, Annapolis, MD, 21401. Tel: 410-222-7287. Fax: 410-222-7188. p. 1010

Choiniere, Kathy, Ch, Slater Library, 26 Main St, Jewett City, CT, 06351. Tel: 860-376-0024. Fax: 860-376-0024. p. 348

Choinski, Elizabeth M, Head of Libr, University of Mississippi, Science, 1031 Natural Products Ctr, University, MS, 38677. Tel: 662-915-7910. Fax: 662-915-7549. p. 1316

Chojecki, Randolph, Tech Serv Librn, Daemen College Library, Research & Information Commons, 4380 Main St, Amherst, NY, 14226-3592. Tel: 716-839-8243. Fax: 716-839-8475. p. 1573

Cholach, Barb, Librn, Grassland Public Library, PO Box 150, Grassland, AB, T0A 1V0, CANADA. Tel: 780-525-3733. Fax: 780-525-3750. p. 2706

Cholewiek, Linda, Br Mgr, Mercer County Library System, Hightstown Memorial, 114 Franklin St, Hightstown, NJ, 08520. Tel: 609-448-1474. Fax: 609-490-0279. p. 1494

Choma, Stephanie, Librn, Brandon Free Public Library, Four Franklin St, Brandon, VT, 05733. Tel: 802-247-8230. Fax: 802-247-1212. p. 2419

Chomel, Susan, Br Mgr, Westchester Public Library, Hageman, 100 Francis St, Porter, IN, 46304. Tel: 219-926-9080. p. 732

Chomel, Suzanne, Br Mgr, Westchester Public Library, 200 W Indiana Ave, Chesterton, IN, 46304-3122. Tel: 219-926-9080. Fax: 219-926-6424. p. 732

Chomsky, Herschel, Libr Asst, Perth Amboy Free Public Library, 196 Jefferson St, Perth Amboy, NJ, 08861. Tel: 732-826-2600. Fax: 732-324-8079. p. 1519

Chong, Jean, Mgr, Borden Ladner Gervais LLP Library, 1200 Waterfront Centre, 200 Burrard St, Vancouver, BC, V7X 1T2, CANADA. Tel: 604-640-4012. Fax: 604-662-5347. p. 2740

Chong, Laurie Whitehill, Spec Coll Librn, Rhode Island School of Design Library, 15 Westminster St, Providence, RI, 02903. Tel: 401-709-5927. Fax: 401-709-5932. p. 2174

Chong, Paula, Coordr, Louisiana Correctional Institute for Women Library, Hwy 74, Saint Gabriel, LA, 70776. Tel: 225-642-5529. Fax: 225-319-2757. p. 967

Chong, Simon, Syst Mgr, Newmarket Public Library, 438 Park Ave, Newmarket, ON, L3Y 1W1, CANADA. Tel: 905-953-5110. Fax: 905-953-5104. p. 2824

Chonko, Doreen, Tech Serv, Dunedin Public Library, 223 Douglas Ave, Dunedin, FL, 34698. Tel: 727-298-3080, Ext 237. Fax: 727-298-3088. p. 438

Chopra, Mahinder, Prof, Ref Librn, Lincoln University, 1570 Old Baltimore Pike, Lincoln University, PA, 19352. Tel: 484-365-7371. Fax: 610-932-1206. p. 2082

Chopra, Swaran, Dir, Children's Hospital of Philadelphia, 34th & Civic Center Blvd, Philadelphia, PA, 19104. Tel: 215-590-2317. Fax: 215-590-1470. p. 2104

Chops, Michel, Librn, Cegep du Vieux Montreal Library, 255 Ontario St E, Montreal, QC, H2X 1X6, CANADA. Tel: 514-982-3437. Fax: 514-982-3448. p. 2892

Choquette, Keith, Asst Dir, Brockton Public Library System, 304 Main St, Brockton, MA, 02301-5390. Tel: 508-580-7890. Fax: 508-580-7898. p. 1070

Choquette, Mary Beth, Ch, Wadleigh Memorial Library, 49 Nashua St, Milford, NH, 03055-3753. Tel: 603-673-2408. Fax: 603-672-6064. p. 1457

Choquette-Poulin, Guyane, Tech Spec, Hopital Louis-H Lafontaine, 7401 Hochelaga, Montreal, QC, H1N 3M5, CANADA. Tel: 514-251-4000, Ext 3291. Fax: 514-251-0270. p. 2896

Choromanski, Mary, Dir, Libr Serv, Bacharach Institute for Rehabilitation, 61 W Jim Leeds Rd, Pomona, NJ, 08240. Tel: 609-652-7000. p. 1521

Choszczyk, Annette, Dir, Delta County Libraries, 149 E Main St, Hotchkiss, CO, 81419. p. 313

Chotikavanic, Walee, Circ, University of Oklahoma Health Sciences Center, 1000 Stanton L Young Blvd, Oklahoma City, OK, 73117-1213. Tel: 405-271-2285, Ext 48751. Fax: 405-271-3297. p. 1975

Chou, Marcia, Head, Pub Serv, Upper Dublin Public Library, 805 Loch Alsh Ave, Fort Washington, PA, 19034. Tel: 215-628-8744. p. 2058

Choudhury, Sayeed, Assoc Dean, Johns Hopkins University Libraries, The Sheridan Libraries, 3400 N Charles St, Baltimore, MD, 21218. Tel: 410-516-8325. Fax: 410-516-5080. p. 1014

Chouinard, Denys, Archivist, Montreal City Hall, 275 Notre Dame St E, R-113, Montreal, QC, H2Y 1C6, CANADA. Tel: 514-872-3496. Fax: 514-872-3475. p. 2899

Chouinard, Jayne, Ch Serv Librn, Yarmouth Town Libraries, South Yarmouth Branch, 312 Old Main St, South Yarmouth, MA, 02664. Tel: 508-760-4820. Fax: 508-760-2699. p. 1126

Chouinard, Jeanne Marie, Chief, Libr Serv, Oscar G Johnson Veterans Affairs Medical Center, 325 East H St, Iron Mountain, MI, 49801. Tel: 906-774-3300, Ext 32450, 906-779-3172. Fax: 906-779-3107. p. 1194

Chow, Anthony S, PhD, Instr, University of North Carolina at Greensboro, School of Education, 349 Curry Bldg, Greensboro, NC, 27402. Tel: 336-334-3411. Fax: 336-334-5060. p. 2971

Chow, Connie, Br Mgr, Huntsville-Madison Public Library, Eleanor E Murphy Library, 7910 Charlotte Dr SW, Huntsville, AL, 35802. Tel: 256-881-5620. Fax: 256-881-9181. p. 21

Chow, Cynthia, Br Mgr, Hawaii State Public Library System, Kaneohe Public Library, 45-829 Kamehameha Hwy, Kaneohe, HI, 96744. Tel: 808-233-5676. Fax: 808-233-5672. p. 562

Chow, Donna Stambaugh, Dir, South University Library, 5355 Vaughn Rd, Montgomery, AL, 36116-1120. Tel: 334-395-8800. Fax: 334-395-8859. p. 31

Chow, Helen, Cir/Check-In Supvr, Naperville Public Library, 200 W Jefferson Ave, Naperville, IL, 60540-5374. Tel: 630-961-4100, Ext 6372. Fax: 630-637-6389. p. 679

Chow, Judy, Chair, West Los Angeles College Library, 9000 Overland Ave, Culver City, CA, 90230. Tel: 310-287-4408. Fax: 310-287-4366. p. 138

Chow, Mei Ling, Cat Librn, Montclair State University, One Normal Ave, Montclair, NJ, 07043-1699. Tel: 973-655-4422. Fax: 973-655-7780. p. 1503

Chown, Deborah S, Libr Dir, Greenfield Community College Library, One College Dr, Greenfield, MA, 01301-9739. Tel: 413-775-1830. Fax: 413-775-1838. p. 1092

Choy, Louisa, Digital Serv Librn, Wheelock College Library, 132 The Riverway, Boston, MA, 02215-4815. Tel: 617-879-2213. Fax: 617-879-2408. p. 1068

Chrapkiewiz, Stascia, Asst Librn, Ottawa County Law Library Association, 315 Madison St, Port Clinton, OH, 43452. Tel: 419-734-6763. p. 1930

Chrazstowski, Tina, Librn, University of Illinois Library at Urbana-Champaign, Chemistry, 170 Noyes Lab, MC-712, 505 S Matthews, Urbana, IL, 61801. Tel: 217-333-3737. p. 712

Chrey, Bonnie, Res Coordr, Kitsap County Historical Society, 280 Fourth St, Bremerton, WA, 98337-1813. Tel: 360-479-6226. Fax: 360-415-9294. p. 2510

Chrils, Geraldine, Dir, Patchogue-Medford Library, 54-60 E Main St, Patchogue, NY, 11772. Tel: 631-654-4700, Ext 300. Fax: 631-289-3999. p. 1715

Chrisinske, Julie, Asst Dir, Community District Library, 231 N Shiawassee St, Corunna, MI, 48817. Tel: 989-743-3287. Fax: 989-743-5496. p. 1166

Chrisinske, Julie, Head Librn, Capital Area District Libraries, Williamston Library, 201 School St, Williamston, MI, 48895-1449. Tel: 517-655-1191. Fax: 517-655-5243. p. 1200

Christ, Marian, Cat Librn, American Philosophical Society Library, 105 S Fifth St, Philadelphia, PA, 19106-3386. Tel: 215-440-3407. Fax: 215-440-3423. p. 2103

Christel, Mark A, Dir, The College of Wooster Libraries, 1140 Beall Ave, Wooster, OH, 44691-2364. Tel: 330-263-2483. Fax: 330-263-2253. p. 1949

Christeleit, Lorna Mae, Dir, Volga Public Library, 505 Washington St, Volga, IA, 52077. Tel: 563-767-3511. Fax: 563-767-3511. p. 849

Christenberry, Faye, Head Librn, University of Washington Libraries, Mathematics Research Library, C-306 Padelford Hall, Seattle, WA, 98195. Tel: 206-543-7296. p. 2534

Christensen, Andrew, Ref Librn, Georgetown University, Georgetown Law Library (John Wolff & Edward Bennett Williams Libraries), 111 G St NW, Washington, DC, 20001. Fax: 202-662-9168. p. 403

Christensen, Arlene, Librn, Stanford Free Library, 14 Creamery Rd, Stanfordville, NY, 12581. Tel: 845-868-1341. Fax: 845-868-7482. p. 1747

Christensen, Beth, Music Librn, Saint Olaf College, Rolvaag Memorial Library, Glasoe Science Library, Halvorson Music Library, 1510 Saint Olaf Ave, Northfield, MN, 55057-1097. Tel: 507-786-3362. Fax: 507-786-3734. p. 1269

Christensen, Bret N, Pub Serv Librn, Riverside County Law Library, 3989 Lemon St, Riverside, CA, 92501-4203. Tel: 951-368-0379. Fax: 951-368-0185. p. 217

Christensen, Cecily, Ref Serv, Bellingham Public Library, 100 Blackstone St, Bellingham, MA, 02019. Tel: 508-966-1660. Fax: 508-966-3189. p. 1052

Christensen, Charlynn, Evening/Weekend Supvr, Snow College, 141 E Center St, Ephraim, UT, 84627. Tel: 435-283-7363. Fax: 435-283-7369. p. 2405

Christensen, Delise, Librn, Arizona City Community Library, 13254 S Sunland Gin Rd, Arizona City, AZ, 85223. Tel: 520-466-5565. Fax: 520-466-6050. p. 57

Christensen, Diane, Br Mgr, Sacramento Public Library, Galt Neighborhood Library, 1000 Caroline Ave, Galt, CA, 95632. p. 225

Christensen, Gail, Librn, Dyckman Free Library, 345 Main St W, Sleepy Eye, MN, 56085-1331. Tel: 507-794-7655. p. 1284

Christensen, Heather, Cat, Eastern New Mexico University, 1300 S Ave K, Sta 32, Portales, NM, 88130-7402. Tel: 575-562-2300. Fax: 575-562-2647. p. 1560

Christensen, Jean, Dir, Belleville Public Library, 130 S Vine St, Belleville, WI, 53508-9102. Tel: 608-424-1812. Fax: 608-424-3545. p. 2581

Christensen, Jennifer, Tech Serv Mgr, Upper Arlington Public Library, 2800 Tremont Rd, Columbus, OH, 43221. Tel: 614-486-9621. Fax: 614-486-4530. p. 1891

Christensen, Jessica, Ch, Rock County Community Library, 201 W Main, Luverne, MN, 56156. Tel: 507-449-5040. Fax: 507-449-5034. p. 1256

Christensen, John, Sci, Brigham Young University, Harold B Lee Library, 2060 HBLL, Provo, UT, 84602. Tel: 801-422-2927. Fax: 801-422-0466. p. 2411

Christensen, John E, Dir, Washburn University, School of Law Library, 1700 SW College Ave, Topeka, KS, 66621. Tel: 785-670-1088. Fax: 785-670-3194. p. 897

Christensen, Kay, Cat, Govt Doc, Augustana College, 2001 S Summit Ave, Sioux Falls, SD, 57197-0001. Tel: 605-274-5357. Fax: 605-274-5447. p. 2218

Christensen, Laurie, Mgr, Arapahoe Library District, Castlewood Xpress Library, 6739 S Uinta St, Centennial, CO, 80112. Fax: 303-771-3264. p. 305

Christensen, Laurie, Mgr, Arapahoe Library District, Koelbel Library, 5955 S Holly St, Centennial, CO, 80121. Tel: 303-220-1651. p. 306

Christensen, Laurie, Mgr, Arapahoe Library District, Southglenn Public, 6972 S Vine, Ste 2000, Centennial, CO, 80122-3270. Fax: 303-740-8356. p. 306

Christensen, Leslie A, Head of Libr, St Mary's Hospital Medical Center, 700 S Park St, Madison, WI, 53715. Tel: 608-258-6532. Fax: 608-258-6119. p. 2607

Christensen, Marlayna, Outreach Serv, University of California, San Diego, Social Science & Humanities Library, 9500 Gilman Dr, Mail Code 0175R, La Jolla, CA, 92093-0175. Tel: 858-822-3943. Fax: 858-534-7548. p. 162

Christensen, Monique, Circ Mgr, Siouxland Libraries, 200 N Dakota Ave, Sioux Falls, SD, 57104. Tel: 605-367-8723. Fax: 605-367-4312. p. 2218

Christensen, Pamela R, Dir, Peter White Public Library, 217 N Front St, Marquette, MI, 49855. Tel: 906-228-9510. Fax: 906-226-1783. p. 1207

Christensen, Robyn L, Librn, Worcester Historical Museum, 30 Elm St, Worcester, MA, 01605. Tel: 508-753-8278, Ext 105. Fax: 508-753-9070. p. 1145

Christensen, Susan, Coordr, Bldg Mgt, California State University, Fresno, Henry Madden Library, 5200 N Barton Ave, Mail Stop ML-34, Fresno, CA, 93740-8014. Tel: 559-278-5792. Fax: 559-278-6952. p. 150

Christensen, Tamara, Libr Asst, Burlington Public Library, 34 Library Lane, Burlington, CT, 06013. Tel: 860-673-3331. Fax: 860-673-0897. p. 333

Christensen, Vicki, Dir, Anita Public Library, 812 Third St, Anita, IA, 50020. Tel: 712-762-3639. Fax: 712-762-3178. p. 793

Christenson, Bridget, Dir, Hatch Public Library, 111 W State St, Mauston, WI, 53948-1344. Tel: 608-847-4454. Fax: 608-847-2306. p. 2613

Christerson, Julie H, Supvr, Acq, Supvr, Govt Docs, Mount Hood Community College Library, 26000 SE Stark St, Gresham, OR, 97030. Tel: 503-352-1412. Fax: 503-491-7389. p. 1999

Christian, Betty, Librn, Tallahatchie County Library System, 102 N Walnut, Charleston, MS, 38921. Tel: 662-647-2638. Fax: 662-647-0975. p. 1295

Christian, Diane, Youth Serv Coordr, Aurora Public Library, One E Benton St, Aurora, IL, 60505-4299. Tel: 630-264-4100. Fax: 630-896-3209. p. 591

Christian, George, Exec Dir, Library Connection, Inc, 599 Matianuck Ave, Windsor, CT, 06095-3567. Tel: 860-298-5322. Fax: 860-298-5328. p. 2939

Christian, Mariel, Dir, RTI International, 3040 Cornwallis Rd, Research Triangle Park, NC, 27709. Tel: 919-541-6303. Fax: 919-541-1221. p. 1820

Christian, Michael A, Librn, National Society of the Sons of the American Revolution, 809 W Main St, Louisville, KY, 40202. Tel: 502-588-6138. Fax: 502-585-7674. p. 925

Christian, Patricia, Librn, Squire, Sanders & Dempsey, 1300 Huntington Ctr, 41 S High St, Ste 1300, Columbus, OH, 43215. Tel: 614-365-2700. Fax: 614-365-2499. p. 1890

Christian, Raymond, Br Mgr, Garfield County-Panguitch City Library, Escalante Branch, 90 N 100 West, Escalante, UT, 84726. Tel: 435-826-4220. p. 2410

Christian, Sharon, YA Serv, Springdale Public Library, 405 S Pleasant St, Springdale, AR, 72764. Tel: 479-750-8180. Fax: 479-750-8182. p. 115

Christians, Corey, Network Serv, Syst Coordr, Prescott Public Library, 215 E Goodwin St, Prescott, AZ, 86303. Tel: 928-777-1520. Fax: 928-771-5829. p. 78

Christiansen, Bernyce, Coordr, Saint Louis Regional Library Network, 341 Sappington Rd, Saint Louis, MO, 63122. Tel: 314-395-1305. p. 2948

Christiansen, Jeff, Librn, Inland Hospital, 200 Kennedy Memorial Dr, Waterville, ME, 04901. Tel: 207-861-3018. Fax: 207-861-3025. p. 1005

Christiansen, Karen, Adult Serv, Paso Robles Public Library, 1000 Spring St, Paso Robles, CA, 93446-2207. Tel: 805-237-3870. Fax: 805-238-3665. p. 207

Christiansen, Laura, Librn, Chrysler Museum of Art, 245 W Olney Rd, Norfolk, VA, 23510-1587. Tel: 757-965-2035. Fax: 757-664-6201. p. 2481

Christiansen, Margaret L, Dir, Regent University, 1000 Regent University Dr, Virginia Beach, VA, 23464-9800. Tel: 757-352-4463. Fax: 757-352-4451. p. 2499

Christiansen, Marilyn, Librn, Trinity Lutheran Parish Library, 511 S Fifth St, Saint Peter, MN, 56082. Tel: 507-934-4786. Fax: 507-934-4562. p. 1283

Christiansen, Ray, Dir, Kaneville Public Library, 2S101 Harter Rd, Kaneville, IL, 60144. Tel: 630-557-2441. Fax: 630-557-2553. p. 660

Christiansen, Renee, Youth Serv Mgr, Library System of Lancaster County, 1866 Colonial Village Lane, Ste 107, Lancaster, PA, 17601. Tel: 717-207-0500. Fax: 717-207-0504. p. 2077

Christianson, Chris, Mgr, Masonic Grand Lodge Library, 201 14th Ave N, Fargo, ND, 58102. Tel: 701-235-8321. Fax: 701-235-8323. p. 1841

Christianson, Darla, Librn, Wapiti Regional Library, Naicam Public Library, 109 Centre St, Naicam, SK, S0K 2Z0, CANADA. Tel: 306-874-2156. p. 2921

Christianson, Elin, Archivist, Curator, Hobart Historical Society, Inc, 706 E Fourth St, Hobart, IN, 46342-4411. Tel: 219-942-0970. p. 748

Christianson, John, Br Mgr, Humboldt County Library, Garberville Branch, 715 Cedar St, Garberville, CA, 95542-3201. Tel: 707-923-2230. Fax: 707-923-2230. p. 147

Christianson, Kimberly, Libr Tech, Per, Normandale Community College Library, 9700 France Ave S, Bloomington, MN, 55431. Tel: 952-487-8291. Fax: 952-487-8101. p. 1242

Christianson, Leslie, User Serv Librn, Marywood University Library, 2300 Adams Ave, Scranton, PA, 18509-1598. Tel: 570-961-4707. Fax: 570-961-4769. p. 2137

Christie, Anne, Bioscience Librn, University of Alaska Fairbanks, 310 Tanana Dr, Fairbanks, AK, 99775. Tel: 907-474-7442. Fax: 907-474-6841. p. 48

Christie, Deborah, Dir, Head Librn, Goodwin Library, 422 Main St, Farmington, NH, 03835-1519. Tel: 603-755-2944. Fax: 603-755-2944. p. 1447

Christie, H, Head, Pub Serv, Flagstaff City-Coconino County Public Library System, 300 W Aspen, Flagstaff, AZ, 86001. Tel: 928-213-2331. Fax: 928-774-9573. p. 62

Christie, James, Dr, Prof, Arizona State University, Farmer Bldg 434, Tempe, AZ, 85287. Tel: 480-965-2314. Fax: 480-965-1863. p. 2961

Christie, Jean, Br Mgr, Fort Erie Public Library, Crystal Ridge, 89 Ridge Rd, Ridgeway, ON, L0S 1N0, CANADA. Tel: 905-894-1281. Fax: 905-894-9248. p. 2806

Christie, Julian, Actg Libr Serv Mgr, York Library Region, McAdam Public Library, 146 Saunders Rd, McAdam, NB, E6J 1L2, CANADA. Tel: 506-784-1403. p. 2764

Christie, Kesha, Storyhour Coordr, Collins Public Library, 212 Main St, Collins, IA, 50055. Tel: 641-385-2464. Fax: 641-385-2205. p. 803

Christie, Laurie, Literacy Serv, Morse Institute Library, 14 E Central St, Natick, MA, 01760. Tel: 508-647-6400, Ext 1583. Fax: 508-647-6527. p. 1107

Christie, Lori, Acq, Tech Serv & Automation, Scott County Public Library, 108 S Main St, Scottsburg, IN, 47170. Tel: 812-752-2751. Fax: 812-752-2878. p. 777

Christie-Milley, D Kim, Archivist, City of Edmonton, Archives, 10440 - 108 Ave, 2nd Flr, Prince of Wales Armouries Heritage Centre, Edmonton, AB, T5H 3Z9, CANADA. Tel: 780-496-8716. Fax: 780-496-8732. p. 2699

Christin, Sylvain, Dir, College Bourget Bibliotheque, 65 rue Saint Pierre, Rigaud, QC, J0P 1P0, CANADA. Tel: 450-451-0815. Fax: 450-451-4171. p. 2907

Christine, Erin, Coll Serv Assoc, The College of Wooster Libraries, 1140 Beall Ave, Wooster, OH, 44691-2364. Tel: 330-263-2467. Fax: 330-263-2253. p. 1949

Christine, Todd, Ref Spec, State Historical Society of Missouri Library, 1020 Lowry St, Columbia, MO, 65201-7298. Tel: 573-882-7083. Fax: 573-884-4950. p. 1324

Christman, Andrea, Tech Serv & Syst Librn, Sinclair Community College Library, 444 W Third St, Dayton, OH, 45402-1460. Tel: 937-512-4513. Fax: 937-512-4564. p. 1894

Christman, Christopher, Librn, Placer County Law Library, 1523 Lincoln Way, Auburn, CA, 95603. Tel: 530-823-2573. Fax: 530-823-9470. p. 122

Christman, Inese, ILS Adminr, Wisconsin Valley Library Service, 300 N First St, Wausau, WI, 54403. Tel: 715-261-7250. Fax: 715-261-7259. p. 2647

Christman, Inese, Asst Dir, ILS Adminr, Wisconsin Valley Library Service, 300 N First St, Wausau, WI, 54403. Tel: 715-261-7257. Fax: 715-261-7259. p. 2958

Christman, Michele, Adult Serv, Faulkner-Van Buren Regional Library System, 1900 Tyler St, Conway, AR, 72032. Tel: 501-327-7482. Fax: 501-327-9098. p. 96

Christman, Vanessa, Librn, El Dorado County Law Library, 550 Main St, Ste A, Placerville, CA, 95667-5699. Tel: 530-621-6423. p. 208

Christmann, Catherine, Youth Serv Mgr, Thomas Branigan Memorial Library, 200 E Picacho Ave, Las Cruces, NM, 88001-3499. Tel: 575-528-4085. Fax: 575-528-4030. p. 1557

Christmas, Erin, Mgr, Santa Clarita Public Library, 18601 Soledad Canyon Rd, Santa Clarita, CA, 91351. Tel: 661-251-2720. Fax: 661-298-7137. p. 263

Christner, Terry, Ch, Hutchinson Public Library, 901 N Main, Hutchinson, KS, 67501-4492. Tel: 620-663-5441. Fax: 620-663-9506. p. 873

Christoff, Suzanne, Assoc Dir, Spec Coll & Archives, United States Military Academy Library, Jefferson Hall Library & Learning Center, 758 Cullum Rd, West Point, NY, 10996. Tel: 845-938-3833. Fax: 845-938-4000. p. 1767

Christofferson, Jo, Dir, Elk Horn Public Library, 2027 Washington St, Elk Horn, IA, 51531. Tel: 712-764-2013. Fax: 712-764-5515. p. 814

Christofferson, Rolane, Dir, Prairie County Library, 309 Garfield Ave, Terry, MT, 59349. Tel: 406-635-5546. Fax: 406-635-5546. p. 1389

Christolon, Blair, Coll Develop, Prince William Public Library System, 13083 Chinn Park Dr, Prince William, VA, 22192-5073. Tel: 703-792-6100. Fax: 703-792-4875. p. 2485

Christopher, Beverly, Br Mgr, Montgomery County Memorial Library System, Charles B Stewart - West Branch, 202 Bessie Price Owen Dr, Montgomery, TX, 77356. Tel: 936-442-7718, 936-788-8314. Fax: 936-788-8349. p. 2301

Christopher, Carol, Asst Librn, Ashaway Free Library, 15 Knight St, Ashaway, RI, 02804-1410. Tel: 401-377-2770. Fax: 401-377-2770. p. 2163

Christopher, Clara, Circ Mgr, West Baton Rouge Parish Library, 830 N Alexander Ave, Port Allen, LA, 70767-2327. Tel: 225-342-7920. Fax: 225-342-7918. p. 966

Christopher, Conway, Asst Librn, Rhine Research Center, 2741 Campus Walk Ave, Bldg 500, Durham, NC, 27705-3707. Tel: 919-309-4600, Ext 204. Fax: 919-309-4700. p. 1790

Christopher, Gary Jay, Dir, Libr Serv, Aria Health, Health Sciences Libraries, Red Lion & Knights Rds, Philadelphia, PA, 19114-1436. Tel: 215-949-5160. Fax: 215-949-7821. p. 2103

Christopher, Kerri, Head, Ref, Louisiana State University Health Sciences Center, 1501 Kings Hwy, Shreveport, LA, 71130. Tel: 318-675-5393. Fax: 318-675-5442. p. 968

Christopher, Lynn, Librn, Hill Public Library, 30 Crescent St, Hill, NH, 03243. Tel: 603-934-9712. Fax: 603-934-9712. p. 1451

Christopher, Margaret, AV, Gardner-Webb University, 110 S Main St, Boiling Springs, NC, 28017. Tel: 704-406-4291. Fax: 704-406-4623. p. 1776

Christopherson, Gary, Circ, Algonquin Area Public Library District, 2600 Harnish Dr, Algonquin, IL, 60102-5900. Tel: 847-458-6060, 847-658-4343. Fax: 847-458-9370. p. 588

Christopoulos-Nutting, Suellen, Media & Digital Res Librn, New York Chiropractic College Library, 2360 State Rte 89, Seneca Falls, NY, 13148-9460. Tel: 315-568-3244. Fax: 315-568-3119. p. 1742

Christos, Lauren, Ref Librn, Florida International University, 3000 NE 151st St, North Miami, FL, 33181-3600. Tel: 305-919-5721. Fax: 305-919-5914. p. 472

Christy, Arthur, Computer Spec, Texas A&M University-Texarkana, 7101 University Ave, Texarkana, TX, 75503. Tel: 903-223-3159. Fax: 903-334-6695. p. 2392

Christy, Denise, Mgr, Oklahoma Department of Career & Technology Education, 1500 W Seventh Ave, Stillwater, OK, 74074-4364. Tel: 405-377-2000, Ext 161. Fax: 405-743-5142, 743-6809. p. 1978

Christy, Jan, Tech Serv, Johnson Bible College, 7900 Johnson Dr, Knoxville, TN, 37998. Tel: 865-251-2277. Fax: 865-251-2278. p. 2241

Christy, Kathleen, Mgr, Ref Serv, Blount County Public Library, 508 N Cusick St, Maryville, TN, 37804-5714. Tel: 865-982-0981. Fax: 865-977-1142. p. 2246

Christy, Matthew, Asst Dir, Tech Serv, Baylor Health Sciences Library, 3302 Gaston Ave, Dallas, TX, 75246. Tel: 214-828-8151. Fax: 214-820-2095. p. 2304

Christy, Rebecca, Br Mgr, Colusa County Free Library, Williams Branch, 901 E St, Williams, CA, 95987. Tel: 530-473-5955. Fax: 530-473-5955. p. 136

Christy, Silvia DeLourdes, Asst Libr Dir, Seguin-Guadalupe County Public Library, 707 E College St, Seguin, TX, 78155-3217. Tel: 830-401-2426. Fax: 830-401-2477. p. 2386

Chronister, Helen, Librn, Minnie Cobey Memorial Library, 1354 E Broad St, Columbus, OH, 43205. Tel: 614-253-8523. Fax: 614-253-6323. p. 1884

Chronopoulos, Corrine, Dir, Pelham Public Library, 24 Village Green, Pelham, NH, 03076. Tel: 603-635-7581. Fax: 603-635-6952. p. 1461

Chrysler, John, Exec Dir, Masonry Institute of America Library, 22815 Frampton Ave, Torrance, CA, 90501-5034. Tel: 310-257-9000. Fax: 310-257-1942. p. 275

Chrystian, Annette, Librn, Holden Municipal Library, 4912-50 St, Holden, AB, T0B 2C0, CANADA. Tel: 780-688-3838. Fax: 780-688-3838. p. 2707

Chrzan, Carolyn J, Asst Dir, Presque Isle District Library, 181 E Erie St, Rogers City, MI, 49779-1709. Tel: 989-734-2477, Ext 223. Fax: 989-734-4899. p. 1222

Chu, Barbara, Librn, University of Toronto Libraries, Department of Physics, McLennan Physical Laboratories, 60 St George St, Rm 211C, Toronto, ON, M5S 1A1, CANADA. Tel: 416-978-5188. Fax: 416-978-5919. p. 2865

Chu, Felix, Cat, Western Illinois University Libraries, One University Circle, Macomb, IL, 61455. Tel: 309-298-2739. Fax: 309-298-2791. p. 669

Chu, Heting, Dr, Assoc Prof, Long Island University, C W Post Campus, 720 Northern Blvd, Brookville, NY, 11548-1300. Tel: 516-299-2177. Fax: 516-299-4168. p. 2970

Chu, Melanie, Outreach Librn, California State University, 333 S Twin Oaks Valley Rd, San Marcos, CA, 92096-0001. Tel: 760-750-4340. Fax: 760-750-3287. p. 254

Chuah, Sally, Cat, Ref, Santa Barbara City College, 721 Cliff Dr, Santa Barbara, CA, 93109-2394. Tel: 805-965-0581, Ext 2643. Fax: 805-965-0771. p. 260

Chuang, Felicia S, Dir, University of Texas-Houston Health Science Center, 2800 S McGregor Way, Houston, TX, 77021. Tel: 713-741-6043. Fax: 713-741-6050. p. 2344

Chubb, Elaine, Asst Librn, Wayne County Public Library, Clifton Branch, 300 E Water St, Clifton, TN, 38425-0501. Tel: 931-676-3678. Fax: 931-676-3678. p. 2268

Chubb, Jelain, State Archivist, Texas State Library & Archives Commission, 1201 Brazos St, Austin, TX, 78701. Tel: 512-463-5467. p. 2282

Chubon, Jeannine, Dir, Salina Free Library, 100 Belmont St, Mattydale, NY, 13211. Tel: 315-454-4524. Fax: 315-454-3466. p. 1659

Chudnoff, Leslie, Br Mgr, Los Angeles Public Library System, Northridge Branch, 9051 Darby Ave, Northridge, CA, 91325-2708. Tel: 818-886-3640. Fax: 818-886-6850. p. 174

Chuk, Denise, Librn, Windsor Star Library, 167 Ferry St, Windsor, ON, N9A 4M5, CANADA. Tel: 519-255-5711. Fax: 519-255-5515. p. 2872

Chukumah, Vincent, Ch, Atlanta-Fulton Public Library System, Dogwood Library, 1838 Donald L Hollowell Pkwy NW, Atlanta, GA, 30318. Tel: 404-792-4961. Fax: 404-792-4963. p. 512

Chukwurah, Omaa, Librn, Housatonic Community College Library, 900 Lafayette Blvd, Bridgeport, CT, 06604. Tel: 203-332-5179. Fax: 203-332-5252. p. 331

Chulka, Sandra, Bibliog Instr, College of New Caledonia Library, 3330 22nd Ave, Prince George, BC, V2N 1P8, CANADA. Tel: 250-562-2131, Ext 298. Fax: 250-561-5845. p. 2736

Chun, Laurianne, Librn, Hawaii Center for the Deaf & Blind Library, 3440 Leahi Ave, Honolulu, HI, 96815. Tel: 808-733-4831. Fax: 808-733-4824. p. 560

Chung, Barbara, Ch, Carlsbad City Library, 1775 Dove Lane, Carlsbad, CA, 92011-4048. Tel: 760-602-2064. Fax: 760-602-7942. p. 132

Chung, Hai-Chin, Tech Serv, South Brunswick Public Library, 110 Kingston Lane, Monmouth Junction, NJ, 08852. Tel: 732-329-4000, Ext 7284. Fax: 732-329-0573. p. 1502

Chung, Hsi Hsi, Ref, Metuchen Public Library, 480 Middlesex Ave, Metuchen, NJ, 08840. Tel: 732-632-8526. Fax: 732-632-8535. p. 1501

Chung, Lucy, Dr, Interim Dir, The United Library, 2121 Sheridan Rd, Evanston, IL, 60201. Tel: 847-866-3911. Fax: 847-866-3957. p. 644

Chung, Nakhoh Thomas, Dr, Pres, Korean Scientists & Engineers Association in America Library, 1952 Gallows Rd, Ste 300, Vienna, VA, 22182. Tel: 703-748-1221. Fax: 703-748-1331. p. 2498

Chupela, Dolores, Ch, Edison Township Free Public Library, 340 Plainfield Ave, Edison, NJ, 08817. Tel: 732-287-2298. Fax: 732-819-9134. p. 1483

Church, Gary, Ref, Lone Star College System, Montgomery College Library, 3200 College Park Dr, Conroe, TX, 77384. Tel: 936-273-7389. Fax: 936-273-7395. p. 2340

Church, James, In Charge, Metropolitan State Hospital, Staff Library, 11401 S Bloomfield Ave, Norwalk, CA, 90650. Tel: 562-651-2295. Fax: 562-651-4439. p. 195

Church, James, Sr Librn, Metropolitan State Hospital, Staff Library, 11401 Bloomfield Ave, Norwalk, CA, 90650. Tel: 562-651-3274. Fax: 562-651-4439. p. 195

Church, Jill, Per, D'Youville College, 320 Porter Ave, Buffalo, NY, 14201-1084. Tel: 716-829-8107. Fax: 716-829-7770. p. 1597

Church, Martha, ILL, West Hartford Public Library, 20 S Main St, West Hartford, CT, 06107-2432. Tel: 860-561-6950. Fax: 860-561-6976. p. 376

Church, Rachel, Br Head, Muskegon Area District Library, Fruitport Branch, Park & Third Sts, Fruitport, MI, 49415-0911. Tel: 231-865-3461. Fax: 231-737-6307. p. 1213

Church, Sue Ellen, Info Spec, Ref Serv, Tech Serv, Blue Ridge Community College, One College Lane, Weyers Cave, VA, 24486. Tel: 540-453-2247. Fax: 540-234-9598. p. 2502

Churchill, Amy, YA Serv, Public Libraries of Saginaw, 505 Janes Ave, Saginaw, MI, 48607. Tel: 989-755-0904. Fax: 989-755-9829. p. 1223

Churchill, Charlene, Dir, Heath Public Library, One E Main St, Heath, MA, 01346. Tel: 413-337-4934. Fax: 413-337-8542. p. 1095

Churchill, Charlene E, Dir, Ellsworth Public Library, 20 State St, Ellsworth, ME, 04605. Tel: 207-667-6363. Fax: 207-667-4901. p. 984

Churchill, Craig, Librn, Abilene Christian University, 221 Brown Library, ACU Box 29208, Abilene, TX, 79699-9208. Tel: 325-674-2344. Fax: 325-674-2202. p. 2271

Churchill, Richard, Govt Doc, Central Connecticut State University, 1615 Stanley St, New Britain, CT, 06050. Tel: 860-832-2066. Fax: 860-832-3409. p. 353

Churley, Margaret, Ref, River Edge Free Public Library, 685 Elm Ave, River Edge, NJ, 07661. Tel: 201-261-1663. Fax: 201-986-0214. p. 1526

Chute, Cheryl, Librn, London Free Press, 369 York St, London, ON, N6A 4G1, CANADA. Tel: 519-667-4559. Fax: 519-667-4528. p. 2817

Chute, Mary, State Librn, New Jersey State Library, 185 W State St, Trenton, NJ, 08618. Tel: 609-278-2640. Fax: 609-278-2652. p. 1536

Chute, Tamar, Archivist, Ohio State University LIBRARIES, Archives, 2700 Kenny Rd, Columbus, OH, 43210. Tel: 614-292-3271. Fax: 614-688-4150. p. 1887

Chwialkowski, Mary, Br Mgr, Toledo-Lucas County Public Library, Maumee Branch, 501 River Rd, Maumee, OH, 43537. Tel: 419-259-5360. Fax: 419-259-5203. p. 1940

Chwialkowski, Mary, Br Mgr, Toledo-Lucas County Public Library, Toledo Heights, 423 Shasta Dr, Toledo, OH, 43609. Tel: 419-259-5220. Fax: 419-385-9297. p. 1940

Chyun, Mi-Hye, Chair, Rider University, Katharine Houk Talbott Library, Westminster Choir College, 101 Walnut Lane, Princeton, NJ, 08540-3899. Tel: 609-921-7100, Ext 8304. Fax: 609-497-0243. p. 1494

Ciampa-Lauria, Donna, Dir, Queens Borough Public Library, Flushing Library, 41-17 Main St, Flushing, NY, 11355. Tel: 718-661-1219. Fax: 718-661-1290. p. 1644

Ciancibelli, Molly, Asst Librn, Kalama Public Library, 312 First St, Kalama, WA, 98625. Tel: 360-673-4568. Fax: 360-673-4560. p. 2518

Ciannella, Adeline, Dir, Haverford Township Free Library, 1601 Darby Rd, Havertown, PA, 19083-3798. Tel: 610-446-3082, Ext 213. Fax: 610-853-3090. p. 2067

Cibic, Luidmila, Br Head, Toronto Public Library, Weston, Two King St, Toronto, ON, M9N 1K9, CANADA. Tel: 416-394-1016. Fax: 416-394-1037. p. 2863

Ciborowski, Elzbieta, Dir of Libr Serv, Kaplan University, 1751 Madison Ave, Ste 750, Council Bluffs, IA, 51503. Tel: 712-328-4212. Fax: 712-328-4061. p. 805

Cicchini, Deborah R, Librn, Saint John North Shores Hospital, 26755 Ballard Rd, Harrison Township, MI, 48045. Tel: 586-465-5501, Ext 45858. Fax: 586-466-5370. p. 1188

Cicciari, Karla, Sr Info Spec, Unilever Bestfoods Information Center, 800 Sylvan Ave, Englewood Cliffs, NJ, 07632-3201. Tel: 201-894-7568. Fax: 201-871-8265. p. 1484

Ciccone, Karen, Head of Libr, North Carolina State University Libraries, Natural Resources Library, Jordan Hall, Rm 1102, 2800 Faucette Dr, Campus Box 7114, Raleigh, NC, 27695-7114. Tel: 919-515-3513. Fax: 919-515-3687. p. 1816

Ciccone, Michael, Dir of Coll, Hamilton Public Library, 55 York Blvd, Hamilton, ON, L8R 3K1, CANADA. Tel: 905-546-3200. Fax: 905-546-3202. p. 2808

Cichewicz, Joy, Br Mgr, Ypsilanti District Library, West Michigan Avenue, 229 W Michigan Ave, Ypsilanti, MI, 48197-5485. Tel: 734-482-4110. Fax: 734-482-0047. p. 1238

Cichowski, Kristine, Dir, Rehabilitation Institute of Chicago, 345 E Superior St, 1st Flr, Chicago, IL, 60611. Tel: 312-238-5433. Fax: 312-238-2860. p. 622

Cicola, William, Dir, Rio Rancho Public Library, 755 Loma Colorado Dr NE, Rio Rancho, NM, 87124. Tel: 505-896-8817. Fax: 502-892-4782. p. 1561

Ciejka, Patricia, Assoc Dir, University of Texas Medical Branch, 301 University Blvd, Galveston, TX, 77555-1035. Tel: 409-772-8745. Fax: 409-762-9782. p. 2327

Cierocki, Anna, Adult Serv, ILL, Essex Library Association, Inc, 33 West Ave, Essex, CT, 06426-1196. Tel: 860-767-1560. Fax: 860-767-2500. p. 338

Cieslak, Ken, Br Mgr, Saint Louis County Library, Indian Trails Branch, 8400 Delport Dr, Saint Louis, MO, 63114. Tel: 314-428-5424. Fax: 314-428-8863. p. 1359

Cieslik, Bob, Admin Serv, Cleveland State University, University Library, Rhodes Tower, 2121 Euclid Ave, Cleveland, OH, 44115-2214. Tel: 216-687-2256. Fax: 216-687-9380. p. 1879

Cieszynski, Izabela M, Dir, Newport News Public Library System, 700 Town Center Dr, Ste 300, Newport News, VA, 23606. Tel: 757-926-1350. Fax: 757-926-1365. p. 2480

Cieszynski, Jasmine, Instrul Serv Librn, Olivet Nazarene University, One University Ave, Bourbonnais, IL, 60914-2271. Tel: 815-928-5449. Fax: 815-939-5170. p. 596

Cifarelli, Donna, Ch, Plano Public Library System, L E R Schimelpfenig Library, 5024 Custer Rd, Plano, TX, 75023. Tel: 972-769-4200. Fax: 972-769-4210. p. 2371

Cifelli, Anne, Librn, Yarmouth Port Library, 297 Main St, Rte 6A, Yarmouth Port, MA, 02675. Tel: 508-362-3717. Fax: 508-362-6739. p. 1146

Cifelli, Linda, Librn, Kean University, 1000 Morris Ave, Union, NJ, 07083. Tel: 908-737-4600. Fax: 908-737-4620. p. 1537

Cifferelli, Michael, Cataloger/Ref Librn, Gateway Community College, 20 Church St, New Haven, CT, 06510. Tel: 203-285-2052. Fax: 203-285-2055. p. 355

Cigliano, Flavia, Exec Dir, Nichols House Museum Inc Library, 55 Mount Vernon, Boston, MA, 02108. Tel: 617-227-6993. Fax: 617-723-8026. p. 1065

Cigrand, Carol, Libr Asst, Cascade Public Library, 310 First Ave W, Cascade, IA, 52033. Tel: 563-852-3201. Fax: 563-852-6011. p. 799

Cihak, Herb, Assoc Dean, Libr & Info Serv, Pepperdine University Libraries, School of Law-Jerene Appleby Harnish Law Library, 24255 Pacific Coast Hwy, Malibu, CA, 90263. Tel: 310-506-4643. Fax: 310-506-4836. p. 182

Cihak, LaRaine, Librn, Gilbert Public Library, 628 Second St, Friend, NE, 68359-1308. Tel: 402-947-5081. p. 1399

Cilenti, Jeanne, Br Mgr, Cuyahoga County Public Library, North Royalton Branch, 14600 State Rd, North Royalton, OH, 44133-5120. Tel: 440-237-3800. Fax: 440-237-6149. p. 1927

Ciliberti, Anne, Dean, William Paterson University of New Jersey, 300 Pompton Rd, Wayne, NJ, 07470. Tel: 973-720-2113. Fax: 973-720-3171. p. 1540

Cimasi, Robert James, Pres, Health Capital Consultants, LLC Library, 1143 Olivette Executive Pkwy, Saint Louis, MO, 63132. Tel: 314-994-7641. Fax: 314-991-3435. p. 1355

Cimino, Rachel, Tech Serv, Oxford Public Library, 48 S Second St, Oxford, PA, 19363-1377. Tel: 610-932-9625. Fax: 610-932-9251. p. 2101

Cina, Gregory, Archivist, Library of the Marine Corps, Gray Research Ctr, 2040 Broadway St, Quantico, VA, 22134-5107. Tel: 703-784-4685. Fax: 703-784-4306. p. 2486

Cinnamon, Wendy, Librn, Valemount Public Library, 1090A Main St, Valemount, BC, V0E 2Z0, CANADA. Tel: 250-566-4367. Fax: 250-566-4278. p. 2740

Cinque, Deborah G, Dir, Weil, Gotshal & Manges Library, 767 Fifth Ave, New York, NY, 10153. Tel: 212-310-8626. Fax: 212-310-8007. p. 1702

Cintron, Linnae, Head, Tech Serv, Eastern Monroe Public Library, 1002 N Ninth St, Stroudsburg, PA, 18360. Tel: 570-421-0800. Fax: 570-421-0212. p. 2143

Ciocci, Ginny, Ref & Instrul Serv Supvr, Sr Team Leader, Cherry Hill Public Library, 1100 Kings Hwy N, Cherry Hill, NJ, 08034-1911. Tel: 856-903-1222. Fax: 856-667-9503. p. 1478

Ciocco, Ronalee, Head, User Serv, Gettysburg College, 300 N Washington St, Gettysburg, PA, 17325. Tel: 717-337-6994. Fax: 717-337-7001. p. 2059

Ciofu, Monique, Dir, Baker College of Cadillac Library, 9600 E 13th St, Cadillac, MI, 49601-9169. Tel: 231-876-3112. Fax: 231-775-6187. p. 1160

Ciparelli, Peter, Dir, Killingly Public Library, 25 Westcott Rd, Danielson, CT, 06239. Tel: 860-779-5383. Fax: 860-779-1823. p. 335

Ciparelli, Peter F, Exec Dir, New London Public Library, 63 Huntington St, New London, CT, 06320. Tel: 860-447-1411. Fax: 860-443-2083. p. 360

Ciphery, Cathy, Asst Librn, Sangudo Public Library, 5131 53rd Ave, Sangudo, AB, T0E 2A0, CANADA. Tel: 780-785-3431. Fax: 780-785-3179. p. 2716

Cipkowski, Pam, Cataloger, Loyola University Chicago Libraries, Law School Library, 25 E Pearson St, 3rd Flr, Chicago, IL, 60611. Tel: 312-915-7191. Fax: 312-915-6797. p. 617

Cipollari, Marilyn, Youth Serv - Coll Develop, Sadie Pope Dowdell Library of South Amboy, 100 Harold G Hoffman Plaza, South Amboy, NJ, 08879. Tel: 732-721-6060. Fax: 732-721-1054. p. 1530

Ciraco, Christina, Policy Publ & Info Res Coordr, Workplace Safety & Insurance Board, 200 Front St W, 17th Flr, Toronto, ON, M5V 3J1, CANADA. Tel: 416-344-4335. Fax: 416-344-4050. p. 2868

Cirar, Tracy, Librn, Colonel Robert R McCormick Research Center, One S 151 Winfield Rd, Wheaton, IL, 60189-6097. Tel: 630-260-8186. Fax: 630-260-9298. p. 718

Cirasella, Jill, Bibliog Serv, Brooklyn College Library, 2900 Bedford Ave, Brooklyn, NY, 11210-2889. Tel: 718-951-5336. Fax: 718-951-4540. p. 1589

Cirenza, Donna, Asst Dir, Tennessee Regional Library for the Blind & Physically Handicapped, 403 Seventh Ave N, Nashville, TN, 37243-0313. Tel: 615-741-6748. Fax: 615-532-8856. p. 2258

Cirillo, Jerry, Dir, Boyden Library, Ten Bird St, Foxborough, MA, 02035. Tel: 508-543-1245. Fax: 508-543-1193. p. 1089

Cirillo, Margaret, Librn, The Kingston Hospital Medical Library, 396 Broadway, Kingston, NY, 12401. Tel: 845-334-2786. Fax: 845-338-0527. p. 1649

Cirillo, Mimi, Librn, United States Air Force, 2603 Tuskegee Airmen Ave, McGuire AFB, NJ, 08641-5016. Tel: 609-754-2079. Fax: 609-754-5108. p. 1500

Cirillo, Susan E, Dr, Dean, Libr & Acad Support, Salem State University Library, 352 Lafayette St, Salem, MA, 01970-5353. Tel: 978-542-6230. Fax: 978-542-6596. p. 1122

Cirilo, Victor, Circ Librn, Circ Supvr, Val Verde County Library, 300 Spring St, Del Rio, TX, 78840. Tel: 830-774-7595. Fax: 830-774-7607. p. 2312

Cirona, Peter, YA Serv, Massapequa Public Library, Central Avenue, 523 Central Ave, Massapequa, NY, 11758. Tel: 516-798-4607, Ext 305. Fax: 516-798-2804. p. 1658

Cirone, Cynthia, Cat, Mount Union College Library, 1972 Clark Ave, Alliance, OH, 44601-3993. Tel: 330-823-3844. Fax: 330-823-3963. p. 1854

Cirone, Patricia, Dir, Beverly Public Library, 32 Essex St, Beverly, MA, 01915-4561. Tel: 978-921-6062. Fax: 978-922-8329. p. 1053

Cirrincione, Tammy, Sr Pub Serv Librn, Washoe County Library System, 301 S Center St, Reno, NV, 89501-2102. Tel: 775-327-8345. Fax: 775-327-8392. p. 1433

Cirrincione, Tammy, Mgr, Washoe County Library System, South Valleys Library, 15650A Wedge Pkwy, Reno, NV, 89511. Tel: 775-851-8540. Fax: 775-851-5188. p. 1434

Cirrito, Marianne, Asst Dir, Libr Operations, Purdue Pharma LP & Associated Companies, One Stamford Forum, 201 Tresser Blvd, Stamford, CT, 06901. Tel: 203-588-8498. Fax: 203-588-6212. p. 369

Cisco, Dan, Supvry Librn, Marine Corps Recruit Depot Library, 3800 Chosin Ave, Bldg 7 W, San Diego, CA, 92140-5196. Tel: 619-524-1850. Fax: 619-524-8243. p. 231

Cisin, Fred, Librn, Berkeley City College Library, 2050 Center St, Rm 131, Berkeley, CA, 94704. Tel: 510-981-2964. p. 126

Cisna, Alice, Librn, Arthur Public Library, 225 S Walnut, Arthur, IL, 61911. Tel: 217-543-2037. Fax: 217-543-4081. p. 590

Cisna-Mills, Jennifer, Head, Adult Serv, Fountaindale Public Library District, 300 W Briarcliff Rd, Bolingbrook, IL, 60440-2844. Tel: 630-759-2102, Ext 4201. Fax: 630-759-9519. p. 596

Cisneros, Debbie, Circ, ILL, Lake County Public Library, 1115 Harrison Ave, Leadville, CO, 80461-3398. Tel: 719-486-0569. Fax: 719-486-3544. p. 316

Cisneros, Donna, Cat, Danville Public Library, 511 Patton St, Danville, VA, 24541. Tel: 434-799-5195. Fax: 434-792-5172. p. 2459

Cisneros, Donna, Supvr, Danville Public Library, Westover, 94 Clifton St, Danville, VA, 24541. Tel: 434-799-5152. p. 2460

Cisneros, Stacey L, Head, Adult Serv, Batavia Public Library District, Ten S Batavia Ave, Batavia, IL, 60510-2793. Tel: 630-879-1393. Fax: 630-879-9118. p. 592

Cisney, Doug, Br Mgr, Sonoma County Library, Petaluma Regional, 100 Fairgrounds Dr, Petaluma, CA, 94952. Tel: 707-763-9801. Fax: 707-763-0288. p. 267

Ciszek, Matthew, Head Librn, Pennsylvania State University, 177 Vine Ave, Sharon, PA, 16146. Tel: 724-983-2880. Fax: 724-983-2881. p. 2139

Citizen, Angela, Head of Br Serv, Head, Children's/Youth Serv, Inglewood Public Library, 101 W Manchester Blvd, Inglewood, CA, 90301-1771. Tel: 310-412-5397. Fax: 310-412-8848. p. 159

Citro, Kathleen, Assoc Dir, Ref/Worldwide Libr Serv, Embry-Riddle Aeronautical University, 600 S Clyde Morris Blvd, Daytona Beach, FL, 32114-3900. Tel: 386-226-6596. Fax: 386-226-6368. p. 436

Citro, Lynda L, Librn Supvr, Charlotte County Library System, Englewood Charlotte Public, 3450 North Access Rd, Englewood, FL, 34224. Tel: 941-681-3739. Fax: 941-681-3740. p. 484

Citro, Paul, Librn, Broward County Division of Libraries, Cybrary Center, 100 S Andrews Ave, 7th Flr, Fort Lauderdale, FL, 33301. Tel: 954-357-7485. Fax: 954-357-7792. p. 441

Civieta-Gaskell, Carmen, Head, Monographic Ordering & Database Maintenance, University of Miami Libraries, 1300 Memorial Dr, Coral Gables, FL, 33146. Tel: 305-284-3233. Fax: 305-284-4027. p. 434

Cizek, Kathleen, Pub Serv Adminr, Nicholson Memorial Library System, 625 Austin St, Garland, TX, 75040-6365. Tel: 972-205-2546. Fax: 972-205-2523. p. 2327

Claar, Rebecca, Asst Dir/Ch, Bedford County Library, 240 S Wood St, Bedford, PA, 15522. Tel: 814-623-5010. p. 2031

Claassen, Lynda C, Head of Libr, Spec Coll & Archives Librn, University of California, San Diego, Mandeville Special Collections, UCSD Libraries 0175S, 9500 Gilman Dr, La Jolla, CA, 92093-0175. Tel: 858-534-2533. Fax: 858-534-5950. p. 162

Claes, Jane, Asst Prof, University of Houston-Clear Lake, 2700 Bay Area Blvd, Houston, TX, 77058-1098. Tel: 281-283-3577. Fax: 281-283-3630. p. 2974

Claggett, Laura, Mgr, UOP Knowledge & Library Services, 25 E Algonquin Rd, Des Plaines, IL, 60016. Tel: 847-391-2265. Fax: 847-391-3330. p. 636

Clague, Debbie, Br Head, Winnipeg Public Library, Windsor Park, 955 Cottonwood Rd, Winnipeg, MB, R2J 1G3, CANADA. Tel: 204-986-4945. Fax: 204-986-7122. p. 2760

Claiborne, Dawn, Dir, Scott County Public Library, 290 S Main St, Oneida, TN, 37841-2605. Tel: 423-569-8634. Fax: 423-569-3062. p. 2262

Claiborne, Mary Pomeroy, Communications Adminr, Pub Relations, Knox County Public Library System, 500 W Church Ave, Knoxville, TN, 37902-2505. Tel: 865-215-8767. Fax: 865-215-8742. p. 2241

Clair, Cathy, Librn, Debra S Fish Early Childhood Resource Library, Ten Yorkton Ct, Saint Paul, MN, 55117-1065. Tel: 651-641-3544. Fax: 651-645-0990. p. 1278

Clair, Joan, Coordr, Hamilton College, Music, McEwen Hall, 198 College Hill Rd, Clinton, NY, 13323-1299. Tel: 315-859-4349. p. 1608

Clair, Kathy, Dir, Reddick Library, 1010 Canal St, Ottawa, IL, 61350. Tel: 815-434-0509. Fax: 815-434-2634. p. 686

Clairmont-Schmidt, Cynthia, Asst State Librn, North Dakota State Library, Library Memorial Bldg, 604 East Blvd Ave, Dept 250, Bismarck, ND, 58505-0800. Tel: 701-328-4652. Fax: 701-328-2040. p. 1838

Clambor, Barbara, Outreach Librn, Rochester Regional Library Council, 390 Packetts Landing, Fairport, NY, 14450. Tel: 585-223-7570. Fax: 585-223-7712. p. 2950

Clamme, Rosalie, Dir, Jay County Public Library, 315 N Ship St, Portland, IN, 47371. Tel: 260-726-7890. Fax: 260-726-7317. p. 773

Clampitt, Patty, Acq, Southeast Regional Library, 49 Bison Ave, Weyburn, SK, S4H 0H9, CANADA. Tel: 306-848-3107. Fax: 306-842-2665. p. 2929

Clancy, Catherine, Librn, Boston Public Library, Roslindale Branch, 4238 Washington St, Roslindale, MA, 02131-2517. Tel: 617-323-2343. Fax: 617-325-1664. p. 1057

Clancy, Jeanne, Youth Serv, Chester County Library System, 450 Exton Square Pkwy, Exton, PA, 19341-2496. Tel: 610-280-2600. Fax: 610-280-2688. p. 2056

Clancy, Meg, Youth Serv, South Hadley Public Library, 27 Bardwell St, South Hadley, MA, 01075. Tel: 413-538-5045. Fax: 413-539-9250. p. 1125

Clanton, Kay, Dir, Washington County Library System, 341 Main St, Greenville, MS, 38701-4097. Tel: 662-335-2331. Fax: 662-390-4758. p. 1298

Clanton, Kevin, Dir, Clark County Law Library, 309 S Third St, Ste 400, Las Vegas, NV, 89155. Tel: 702-455-4696. Fax: 702-455-5120. p. 1428

Clanton-Green, Kim, Br Mgr, Las Vegas-Clark County Library District, Sahara West Library, 9600 W Sahara Ave, Las Vegas, NV, 89117. Tel: 702-507-3630. Fax: 702-507-3673. p. 1429

Clapp, Alison, Mgr, Libr & Info Serv, Children's Hospital Boston Library, Fegan Plaza, 300 Longwood Ave, Boston, MA, 02115. Tel: 617-355-7232. Fax: 617-730-0983. p. 1059

Clapp, Carol, Archivist, Librn, Torrington Historical Society Library, 192 Main St, Torrington, CT, 06790. Tel: 860-482-8260. p. 372

Clapp, Joyce, Librn, Marceline Carnegie Library, 119 E California Ave, Marceline, MO, 64658. Tel: 660-376-3223. Fax: 660-376-3577. p. 1344

Clapp, Lee, Head, Tech Serv, New London Public Library, 63 Huntington St, New London, CT, 06320. Tel: 860-447-1411. Fax: 860-443-2083. p. 360

Clapp, Sharon, Web Serv, Connecticut State Library, 231 Capitol Ave, Hartford, CT, 06106. Tel: 860-757-6500. Fax: 860-757-6503. p. 345

Clapperton, Maureen, Dir, HEC Montreal, 3000, chemin de la Cote-Sainte-Catherine, Montreal, QC, H3T 2A7, CANADA. Tel: 514-340-6689. Fax: 514-340-5639. p. 2896

Clapperton, Shannon, Br Mgr, Prairie-River Library District, Kamiah Community, 505 Main St, Kamiah, ID, 83536-9702. Tel: 208-935-0428. Fax: 208-935-0428. p. 577

Clarage, Elizabeth, Dir, Coll Serv, Consortium of Academic & Research Libraries in Illinois, 100 Trade Ctr Dr, Ste 303, Champaign, IL, 61820. Tel: 217-753-9168. Fax: 217-244-7596. p. 2942

Clarchick, Lynn Maidment, Dir, Avella Area Public Library, 11 School Ct, Avella, PA, 15312-2356. Tel: 724-587-5688. Fax: 724-587-3432. p. 2030

Clare, Gayle P, Dir, Opp Public Library, 1604 N Main St, Opp, AL, 36467. Tel: 334-493-6423. Fax: 334-493-6423. p. 32

Clare, Richard, Tech Serv, Framingham State College, 100 State St, Framingham, MA, 01701. Tel: 508-626-4656. Fax: 508-626-4649. p. 1090

Clariday, Sandra, Assoc Dean, Libr & Info Serv, Tennessee Wesleyan College, 23 Coach Farmer Dr, Athens, TN, 37303. Tel: 423-746-5249. Fax: 423-746-5272. p. 2224

Claris, Nancy, Librn, Epsom Public Library, 1775 Dover Rd, Epsom, NH, 03234. Tel: 603-736-9920. Fax: 603-736-9920. p. 1446

Clarius, Norman, ILL, Hunter College Libraries, 695 Park Ave, New York, NY, 10065. Tel: 212-772-4146. Fax: 212-772-4140. p. 1682

Clark, Aileen, Circ Mgr, Emma S Clark Memorial Library, 120 Main St, Setauket, NY, 11733-2868. Tel: 631-941-4080. Fax: 631-941-4541. p. 1742

Clark, Angela, Asst Librn, University of Miami, 4600 Rickenbacker Causeway, Miami, FL, 33149-1098. Tel: 305-421-4020. Fax: 305-361-9306. p. 468

Clark, Ann Marie, Dir, Fred Hutchinson Cancer Research Center, 1100 Fairview Ave N, B1-010, Seattle, WA, 98109. Tel: 206-667-2992. Fax: 206-667-4737. p. 2528

Clark, Anne, Ch, Shiawassee District Library, 502 W Main St, Owosso, MI, 48867-2607. Tel: 989-725-5134. Fax: 989-723-5444. p. 1216

Clark, Annette, Youth Serv Mgr, Norwalk Easter Public Library, 1051 North Ave, Norwalk, IA, 50211. Tel: 515-981-0217. Fax: 515-981-4346. p. 836

Clark, Annette, Librn, Vance-Granville Community College, State Rd 1126, Poplar Creek Rd, Exit 209, Henderson, NC, 27536. Tel: 252-492-2061. Fax: 252-738-3372. p. 1800

Clark, Barbara, Support Serv Sr Mgr, National Automobile Museum, Ten S Lake St, Reno, NV, 89501-1558. Tel: 775-333-9300. Fax: 775-333-9309. p. 1432

Clark, Barbara J, Patron Serv, United States Department of the Army, CEHEC-ZL Casey Bldg, 7701 Telegraph Rd, Alexandria, VA, 22315-3860. Tel: 703-428-6388. Fax: 703-428-6310. p. 2446

Clark, Becky, Libr Assoc, University of Guelph, 120 Main St E, Ridgetown, ON, N0P 2C0, CANADA. Tel: 519-674-1540. Fax: 519-674-1539. p. 2839

Clark, Betsy, Pub Serv, Georgia Highlands College Libraries, 3175 Cedartown Hwy SE, Rome, GA, 30161. Tel: 706-295-6318. Fax: 706-295-6365. p. 548

Clark, Betty, Libr Tech, New Hampshire State Library, Gallen State Office Park, Dolloff Bldg, 117 Pleasant St, Concord, NH, 03301-3852. Tel: 603-271-2417, 603-271-3429. Fax: 603-271-8370. p. 1443

Clark, Betty, Dir, Mabel D Blodgett Memorial Library, 35 S Main St, Rushville, NY, 14544-9648. Tel: 585-554-3939. p. 1736

Clark, Betty, Libr Assoc, ILL Serv, West Virginia University Institute of Technology, 405 Fayette Pike, Montgomery, WV, 25136-2436. Tel: 304-442-3230. Fax: 304-442-3091. p. 2565

Clark, Brenda, Librn, Revere Memorial Library, Revere Memorial Hall, Ten Main St, Isle Au Haut, ME, 04645. Tel: 207-335-2979. Fax: 207-335-5001. p. 988

Clark, Brian, Instrul Serv Librn, Western Illinois University Libraries, One University Circle, Macomb, IL, 61455. Tel: 309-298-2785, Ext 2. Fax: 309-298-2791. p. 669

Clark, Brian, Tech Coordr, Martinsburg-Berkeley County Public Library, 101 W King St, Martinsburg, WV, 25401. Tel: 304-267-8933. Fax: 304-267-9720. p. 2565

Clark, Caren, Circ, Regis University, 3333 Regis Blvd, Denver, CO, 80221-1099. Tel: 303-458-4030. Fax: 303-964-5497. p. 303

Clark, Carla, Librn, Miami Dade College, Medical Center Campus Library & Information Resource Center, 950 NW 20th St, Miami, FL, 33127. Tel: 305-237-4342. Fax: 305-237-4301. p. 466

Clark, Carmella, Br Mgr, Cherokee Regional Library System, Rossville Public, 504 McFarland Ave, Rossville, GA, 30741-1253. Tel: 706-866-1368. Fax: 706-858-9251. p. 538

Clark, Carol, Circ Mgr, ILL, Marengo-Union Library District, 200 S State St, Marengo, IL, 60152. Tel: 815-568-8236. Fax: 815-568-5209. p. 670

Clark, Carol, Br Mgr, Lexington County Public Library System, Gaston Branch, 214 S Main St, Gaston, SC, 29053. Tel: 803-791-3208. Fax: 803-791-3208. p. 2199

Clark, Carolyn, Ref Librn, Atlanta-Fulton Public Library System, Auburn Avenue Research Library on African-American Culture & History, 101 Auburn Ave NE, Atlanta, GA, 30303. Tel: 404-730-4001, Ext 199. Fax: 404-730-5879. p. 511

Clark, Carolyn, Tech Serv, Moultrie-Colquitt County Library, 204 Fifth St SE, Moultrie, GA, 31768. Tel: 229-985-6540. Fax: 229-985-0936. p. 545

Clark, Carolyn, Instr, Web Coordr, North Platte Public Library, 120 W Fourth St, North Platte, NE, 69101-3993. Tel: 308-535-8036. Fax: 308-535-8296. p. 1410

Clark, Carolyn Craycraft, Instruction Librn, Baker University, 518 Eighth St, Baldwin City, KS, 66006-0065. Tel: 785-594-4543. Fax: 785-594-6721. p. 857

Clark, Chad, Distance Educ, Lamar State College, 317 Stilwell Blvd, Port Arthur, TX, 77640. Tel: 409-984-6224. Fax: 409-984-6008. p. 2371

Clark, Charles M, Sr Librn, Mississippi Gulf Coast Community College, 2226 Switzer Rd, Gulfport, MS, 39507. Tel: 228-897-3809. Fax: 228-896-2521. p. 1300

Clark, Cheryl, Dir, Adams Free Library, Two N Main St, Adams, NY, 13605. Tel: 315-232-2265. Fax: 315-232-2265. p. 1567

Clark, Christy, Tech Mgr, Muskingum County Library System, 220 N Fifth St, Zanesville, OH, 43701-3587. Tel: 740-453-0391, Ext 122. Fax: 740-455-6937. p. 1953

Clark, Cindy, Dir of Develop, Westport Library Association, 20 Jesup Rd, Westport, CT, 06880. Tel: 203-291-4820. Fax: 203-227-3829. p. 377

Clark, Craig B, Libr Dir, Boynton Beach City Library, 208 S Seacrest Blvd, Boynton Beach, FL, 33435. Tel: 561-742-6390. Fax: 561-742-6381. p. 429

Clark, Cynthia, Br Mgr, Shreve Memorial Library, Mooringsport Branch, 603 Latimer St, Mooringsport, LA, 71060. Tel: 318-996-6720. Fax: 318-996-6720. p. 969

Clark, Cynthia, Assoc Dean, Libr for Tech & Automated Serv, Adelphi University Libraries, One South Ave, Garden City, NY, 11530. Tel: 516-877-3531. Fax: 516-877-3592. p. 1625

Clark, Cynthia, Co-Dir, Coll & Circ Operations, The New York Public Library - Astor, Lenox & Tilden Foundations, 476 Fifth Ave, (@ 42nd St), New York, NY, 10018-2788. Tel: 212-930-9201. Fax: 212-869-3567. p. 1690

Clark, Dalene, Asst Dir, Bennington Public Library, 15505 Warehouse St, Bennington, NE, 68007. Tel: 402-238-2201. Fax: 402-238-2218. p. 1394

Clark, Dana, Libr Syst Tech II, Keene State College, 229 Main St, Keene, NH, 03435-3201. Tel: 603-358-2755. Fax: 603-358-2745. p. 1453

Clark, Daniel, Computer Serv, North Indian River County Library, 1001 Sebastian Blvd, CR 512, Sebastian, FL, 32958. Tel: 772-589-1355. Fax: 772-388-3697. p. 491

Clark, David, Dir, Ilsley Public Library, 75 Main St, Middlebury, VT, 05753. Tel: 802-388-4098. Fax: 802-388-4367. p. 2428

Clark, Deborah, Interim Dir, San Bernardino Public Library, 555 W Sixth St, San Bernardino, CA, 92410-3001. Tel: 909-381-8215. Fax: 909-381-8229. p. 229

Clark, Demetria, Admin Serv, Venable LLP Library, 575 Seventh St, NW, Washington, DC, 20004-1601. Tel: 202-344-4942. Fax: 202-344-8300. p. 422

Clark, Diane M, Mgr, Stepan Co, 22 W Frontage Rd, Northfield, IL, 60093. Tel: 847-441-1434. Fax: 847-501-2466. p. 633

Clark, Dianna, Dir, State Library of Ohio, SEO Library Center, 40780 Marietta Rd, Caldwell, OH, 43724. Tel: 877-552-4262. p. 1890

Clark, Donna, Dir, Cedar Springs Public Library, 43 W Cherry St, Cedar Springs, MI, 49319. Tel: 616-696-1910. Fax: 616-696-1910. p. 1161

Clark, Donna, Pub Serv Dir, Odessa College, 201 W University Blvd, Odessa, TX, 79764. Tel: 432-335-6640. Fax: 432-335-6610. p. 2366

Clark, Ellen, Asst Dir, Acton Memorial Library, 486 Main St, Acton, MA, 01720. Tel: 978-264-9641. Fax: 978-635-0073. p. 1047

Clark, Ellen Boates, Dir, Wilmette Public Library District, 1242 Wilmette Ave, Wilmette, IL, 60091-2558. Tel: 847-256-6924. Fax: 847-256-6911. p. 719

Clark, Ellen McCallister, Dir, Society of the Cincinnati Library, 2118 Massachusetts Ave NW, Washington, DC, 20008. Tel: 202-785-2040, Ext 411. Fax: 202-785-0729. p. 416

Clark, Fran, Circ Serv Dir, Highline Community College Library, 2400 S 240th St, MS 25-4, Des Moines, WA, 98198. Tel: 206-878-3710, Ext 3610. Fax: 206-870-3776. p. 2514

Clark, Genetta, Br Coordr, Siskiyou County Public Library, Scott Bar Branch, 27233 Scott River Rd, Scott Bar, CA, 96085-9998. Tel: 530-496-3248. p. 286

Clark, George, Environ Res Librn/Govt Info Serv Mgr, Harvard Library, Social Sciences Program, Lamont Library, Level B, Harvard University, Cambridge, MA, 02138. Tel: 617-495-2106. Fax: 617-496-5570. p. 1076

Clark, Gerard, Access Serv, Florida Department of State, Division of Library & Information Services, R A Gray Bldg, 500 S Bronough St, Tallahassee, FL, 32399-0250. Tel: 850-245-6639. Fax: 850-245-6735. p. 493

Clark, Ginger, Librn, Saint Mark's Parish Library, 680 Calder, Beaumont, TX, 77701-2398. Tel: 409-832-3405. Fax: 409-832-8045. p. 2287

Clark, Hailey, Asst Librn, Chinook Regional Library, Vanguard Branch, Library/Musem Bldg, Dominion St, Vanguard, SK, S0N 2V0, CANADA. Tel: 306-582-2244. p. 2929

Clark, J Dee, ILL, Ashland Public Library, 66 Front St, Ashland, MA, 01721-1606. Tel: 508-881-0134. Fax: 508-881-0135. p. 1050

Clark, James M, Librn, First Judicial District of Pennsylvania Law Library, Rm 600, City Hall, Philadelphia, PA, 19107. Tel: 215-686-3799. Fax: 215-686-3737. p. 2106

Clark, Jamie, Circ, Mountain Empire Community College, 3441 Mountain Empire Rd, Big Stone Gap, VA, 24219. Tel: 276-523-2400, Ext 305. Fax: 276-523-8220. p. 2451

Clark, Janice, Br Coordr, Branch District Library, Algansee, 580-B S Ray Quincy Rd, Quincy, MI, 49082-9530. Tel: 517-639-9830. Fax: 517-639-9830. p. 1164

Clark, Janice, Dir, Yale Public Library, 213 N Main, Yale, OK, 74085. Tel: jclark@yale.lib.ok.us. Fax: 918-387-2616. p. 1986

Clark, Jean, Tech Serv, Pioneerland Library System, 410 Fifth St SW, Willmar, MN, 56201. Tel: 320-235-6106, Ext 30. Fax: 320-214-0187. p. 1288

Clark, Jessica, Mgr, Carnegie Library of Pittsburgh, Brookline, 708 Brookline Blvd, Pittsburgh, PA, 15226. Tel: 412-561-1003. p. 2122

Clark, Joan, State Librn, Arizona State Library, Archives & Public Records, 1700 W Washington, Rm 200, Phoenix, AZ, 85007. Tel: 602-926-3805. Fax: 602-256-7983. p. 72

Clark, Joe, Librn, Kent State University Libraries, Performing Arts, D-004 Music & Speech Ctr, 1325 Theatre Dr, Kent, OH, 44242-0001. Tel: 330-672-1667. Fax: 330-672-4482. p. 1907

Clark, John, Asst Librn, Lincoln College of New England, 2279 Mount Vernon Rd, Southington, CT, 06489-1057. Tel: 860-628-4751, Ext 149. Fax: 860-628-6444. p. 368

Clark, John R, IV, Librn, Hartland Public Library, 16 Mill St, Hartland, ME, 04943-3736. Tel: 207-938-4702. p. 987

Clark, Jonathan, ILL, Libr Tech, Wilson College, 1015 Philadelphia Ave, Chambersburg, PA, 17201-1285. Tel: 717-264-4141, Ext 3380. Fax: 717-263-7194. p. 2043

Clark, Juleigh, Pub Serv, Colonial Williamsburg Foundation, 313 First St, Williamsburg, VA, 23185-4306. Tel: 757-565-8511. Fax: 757-565-8508. p. 2502

Clark, Julie, Asst Librn, Conway Data, Inc Library, 6625 The Corners Pkwy, Ste 200, Norcross, GA, 30092. Tel: 770-446-6996. Fax: 770-263-8825. p. 547

Clark, Karen, Acq, Logan Library, 255 N Main, Logan, UT, 84321-3914. Tel: 435-716-9123. Fax: 435-716-9145. p. 2407

Clark, Kenna, Dir, Carnegie Library of Ballinger, 204 N Eighth St, Ballinger, TX, 76821. Tel: 325-365-3616. Fax: 325-365-5004. p. 2286

Clark, Kimball, Cataloger, Harvard Library, Dumbarton Oaks Research Library, 1703 32nd St NW, Washington, MA, 20007. Tel: 202-339-6400. Fax: 202-625-0279. p. 1074

Clark, Kimberly, Br Mgr, Saint Louis County Library, Lewis & Clark Branch, 9909 Lewis-Clark Blvd, Saint Louis, MO, 63136-5322. Tel: 314-994-3300. p. 1359

Clark, Kristen, Operations Mgr, Mill Valley Public Library, 375 Throckmorton Ave, Mill Valley, CA, 94941-2698. Tel: 415-389-4292, Ext 113. Fax: 415-388-8929. p. 186

Clark, Kristen, Dir, Clarksville Public Library, 103 W Greene St, Clarksville, IA, 50619-0039. Tel: 319-278-1168. Fax: 319-278-1168. p. 802

Clark, Lana, Dir, Montrose Public Library, 202 Main St, Montrose, IA, 52639-0100. Tel: 319-463-5532. Fax: 319-463-5532. p. 833

Clark, Larry, Genealogy Librn, Porter County Public Library System, 103 Jefferson St, Valparaiso, IN, 46383-4820. Tel: 219-462-0524. Fax: 219-477-4866. p. 783

Clark, Laura, Dir of Circ, Gail Borden Public Library District, 270 N Grove Ave, Elgin, IL, 60120-5596. Tel: 847-429-4681. Fax: 847-742-0485. p. 640

Clark, Laurel, Asst Admin, Fall River Public Library, 104 N Main St, Fall River, MA, 02720. Tel: 508-324-2700. Fax: 508-324-2707. p. 1088

Clark, Linda, Circ, South Windsor Public Library, 1550 Sullivan Ave, South Windsor, CT, 06074. Tel: 860-644-1541. Fax: 860-644-7645. p. 368

Clark, Linda, Dir, Lynn Murray Memorial Library, 601 Railroad St, Chester, WV, 26034. Tel: 304-387-1010. Fax: 304-387-1010. p. 2557

Clark, Linda, Librn, Victoria Municipal Library, 102 Stewart Ave, Holland, MB, R0G 0X0, CANADA. Tel: 204-526-2011. p. 2749

Clark, Linda J, Ch, Bay Shore-Brightwaters Public Library, One S Country Rd, Brightwaters, NY, 11718-1517. Tel: 631-665-4350. Fax: 631-665-4958. p. 1585

Clark, M, ILL, North Shore Public Library, 250 Rte 25A, Shoreham, NY, 11786-9677. Tel: 631-929-4488. Fax: 631-929-4551. p. 1743

Clark, Maeve, Coordr, Info Serv, Iowa City Public Library, 123 S Linn St, Iowa City, IA, 52240. Tel: 319-887-6004. Fax: 319-356-5494. p. 822

Clark, Margaret, Ref, Florida State University Libraries, College of Law Library, 425 W Jefferson St, Tallahassee, FL, 32306. Tel: 850-644-9244. Fax: 850-644-5216. p. 494

Clark, Margaret, Head, Ch, Parsippany-Troy Hills Free Public Library, Lake Hiawatha Branch, 68 Nokomis Ave, Lake Hiawatha, NJ, 07034. Tel: 973-335-0952. Fax: 973-335-8610. p. 1518

Clark, Marjorie, Mgr, Wilson Free Library, 265 Young St, Wilson, NY, 14172-9500. Tel: 716-751-6070. Fax: 716-751-6526. p. 1770

Clark, Mark, Dr, Prof, University of Wisconsin-Eau Claire, 105 Garfield Ave, Eau Claire, WI, 54702. Tel: 715-836-2635. Fax: 715-836-5099. p. 2976

Clark, Mary, Br Mgr, Chicago Public Library, Uptown, 929 W Buena Ave, Chicago, IL, 60613. Tel: 312-744-8400. Fax: 312-744-8453. p. 610

Clark, Mary Marshall, Dir, Columbia Ctr for Oral Hist, Columbia University, Rare Book & Manuscript, Butler Library, 6th Flr E, 535 W 114th St, New York, NY, 10027. Tel: 212-854-2231, 212-854-5590. Fax: 212-854-1365. p. 1675

Clark, Melanie, Librn, Chinook Regional Library, Vanguard Branch, Library/Musem Bldg, Dominion St, Vanguard, SK, S0N 2V0, CANADA. Tel: 306-582-2244. p. 2929

Clark, Melissa, Info Serv, South Dakota State University, 1300 N Campus Dr, Box 2115, Brookings, SD, 57007-1098. Tel: 605-688-5955. Fax: 605-688-6133. p. 2210

Clark, Mia Y, Circ Mgr, Talbot County Free Library, 100 W Dover St, Easton, MD, 21601-2620. Tel: 410-822-1626. Fax: 410-820-8217. p. 1027

Clark, Midori, Commun Relations Mgr, Pueblo City-County Library District, 100 E Abriendo Ave, Pueblo, CO, 81004-4290. Tel: 719-562-5605. Fax: 719-562-5619. p. 320

Clark, Nancy, Adult Serv, Anchorage Public Library, 3600 Denali St, Anchorage, AK, 99503. Tel: 907-343-2972. Fax: 907-343-2930. p. 44

Clark, Nancy, Head, Circ, Napa City-County Library, 580 Coombs St, Napa, CA, 94559-3396. Tel: 707-253-4072. Fax: 707-253-4615. p. 192

Clark, Nathan R E, Dir, Emmetsburg Public Library, 707 N Superior St, Emmetsburg, IA, 50536. Tel: 712-852-4009. Fax: 712-852-3785. p. 814

Clark, Nathan R E, Dir, Ruthven Public Library, 1301 Gowrie St, Ruthven, IA, 51358. Tel: 712-837-4820. Fax: 712-837-4820. p. 841

Clark, Nina A, Librn, Fulbright & Jaworski LLP, 555 S Flower St, 41st Flr, Los Angeles, CA, 90071. Tel: 213-892-9262. Fax: 213-892-9494. p. 170

Clark, Oliver, Mgr, Kansas City Public Library, Lucile H Bluford Branch, 3050 Prospect Ave, Kansas City, MO, 64128. Tel: 816-701-3582. Fax: 816-701-3492. p. 1338

Clark, Patricia, Dir, All Childrens' Hospital, 501 Sixth Ave S, Saint Petersburg, FL, 33701. Tel: 727-767-4278. Fax: 727-767-8557. p. 487

Clark, Patty, In Charge, Manufacturers Association of Central New York Library, 5788 Widewaters Pkwy, Syracuse, NY, 13214. Tel: 315-474-4201. Fax: 315-474-0524. p. 1752

Clark, Patty, Res Librn, Virginia Wesleyan College, 1584 Wesleyan Dr, Norfolk, VA, 23502-5599. Tel: 757-455-2100. Fax: 757-455-2129. p. 2483

Clark, Paul, Mgr, Libr Serv, Dr Everett Chalmers Hospital, 700 Priestman St, Fredericton, NB, E3B 5N5, CANADA. Tel: 506-452-5432. Fax: 506-452-5585. p. 2763

Clark, Penny, Univ Archivist, Lamar University, 211 Redbird Lane, Beaumont, TX, 77705. Tel: 409-880-8660. Fax: 409-880-2318. p. 2287

Clark, Rachel, Librn, Edward K Baxter Memorial Library, 5114 Rte 14, Sharon, VT, 05065. Tel: 802-763-2875. p. 2435

Clark, Rae, Cat, New York State Department of Health, Empire State Plaza, Albany, NY, 12201. Tel: 518-474-6172. Fax: 518-474-3933. p. 1569

Clark, Richard, Librn/Asst Ed, Christian Record Services for the Blind, 4444 S 52nd St, Lincoln, NE, 68516. Tel: 402-488-0981. Fax: 402-488-7582. p. 1404

Clark, Richard, Youth & Teen Serv, Pasadena Public Library, 1201 Jeff Ginn Memorial Dr, Pasadena, TX, 77506-4895. Tel: 713-477-0276. Fax: 713-475-7005. p. 2368

Clark, Robert, Supvry Archivist, National Archives & Records Administration, 4079 Albany Post Rd, Hyde Park, NY, 12538. Tel: 845-486-7770. Fax: 845-486-1147. p. 1640

Clark, Robin R, Dir, Sump Memorial Library, 222 N Jefferson St, Papillion, NE, 68046. Tel: 402-597-2040. Fax: 402-339-8019. p. 1416

Clark, Ruth C, Dr, Assoc Prof, East Carolina University, 101 Umstead Residence Hall, Greenville, NC, 27858-4353. Tel: 252-328-6621. Fax: 252-328-4368. p. 2971

Clark, Sandra, Dir, Historian, Michigan Department of History, Arts & Libraries - Michigan Historical Center, 702 W Kalamazoo St, Lansing, MI, 48909-8240. Tel: 517-373-6362. Fax: 517-241-3647. p. 1201

Clark, Sarah, Access Serv & Distance Learning, Rogers State University Library, 1701 W Will Rogers Blvd, Claremore, OK, 74017-3252. Tel: 918-343-7719. Fax: 918-343-7897. p. 1960

Clark, Scott, Ad, Asst Dir, Vestal Public Library, 320 Vestal Pkwy E, Vestal, NY, 13850-1632. Tel: 607-754-4243. Fax: 607-754-7936. p. 1761

Clark, Sheila, Ref & Circ Librn, Canadian University College Library, 5410 Ramona Ave, Lacombe, AB, T4L 2B7, CANADA. Tel: 403-782-3381, Ext 4101. Fax: 403-782-3977. p. 2708

Clark, Sherry, Pres, South Londonderry Free Library, 15 Old School St, South Londonderry, VT, 05155. Tel: 802-824-3371. Fax: 802-824-3371. p. 2435

Clark, Sheryl, Circ Supvr, Bartlesville Public Library, 600 S Johnstone, Bartlesville, OK, 74003. Tel: 918-338-4162. Fax: 918-337-5338. p. 1957

Clark, Shirley, Mgr, Suwannee River Regional Library, Branford Public Library, 703 NW Suwannee Ave, Branford, FL, 32008-3279. Tel: 386-935-1556. Fax: 386-935-6351. p. 461

Clark, Stephanie, Dir, Planning & Assessment, Georgetown University, 37th & N St NW, Washington, DC, 20057-1174. Tel: 202-687-1601. Fax: 202-687-7501. p. 402

Clark, Stephen D, Head, Acq, College of William & Mary in Virginia, Earl Gregg Swem Library, One Landrum Dr, Williamsburg, VA, 23187. Tel: 757-221-3107. Fax: 757-221-3645. p. 2502

Clark, Summer, Asst Dir, Surrey Township Public Library, 105 E Michigan, Farwell, MI, 48622. Tel: 989-588-9782. Fax: 989-588-4488. p. 1178

Clark, Susan, Dir, Ivy Tech Community College, 104 W 53rd St, Anderson, IN, 46013. Tel: 765-289-2291, Ext 1321. Fax: 765-643-3294. p. 724

Clark, Susan, Acq, Cataloger, University of Kansas School of Medicine-Wichita, 1010 N Kansas, Wichita, KS, 67214-3199. Tel: 316-293-2629. Fax: 316-293-2608. p. 901

Clark, Susan, Dir, University of Mississippi Medical Center, 2500 N State St, Jackson, MS, 39216-4505. Tel: 601-984-1290. Fax: 601-984-1251. p. 1305

Clark, Susan G, Head, Adult Serv, Zion-Benton Public Library District, 2400 Gabriel Ave, Zion, IL, 60099. Tel: 847-872-4680, Ext 111. Fax: 847-872-4942. p. 722

Clark, Suzanne, Circ, Enterprise Public Library, 101 E Grubbs St, Enterprise, AL, 36330. Tel: 334-347-2636. Fax: 334-393-6477. p. 15

Clark, T Michele, Archivist, US National Park Service, 99 Warren St, Brookline, MA, 02445. Tel: 617-566-1689. Fax: 617-232-4073. p. 1072

Clark, Teresa, Libr Dir, Garland Public Library, 86 W Factory St, Garland, UT, 84312. Tel: 435-257-3117. Fax: 435-257-1217. p. 2406

Clark, Terri, Acq Mgr, Mid-Continent Public Library, 15616 E US Hwy 24, Independence, MO, 64050-2098. Tel: 816-836-5200. Fax: 816-521-7253. p. 1332

Clark, Terry, Ch, Jefferson Public Library, 200 W Lincolnway, Jefferson, IA, 50129-2185. Tel: 515-386-2835. Fax: 515-386-8163. p. 824

Clark, Tony, Pub Affairs, National Archives & Records Administration, 441 Freedom Pkwy, Atlanta, GA, 30307. Tel: 404-865-7109. Fax: 404-865-7102. p. 517

Clark, Twila, ILL Coordr, Herbert Wescoat Memorial Library, 120 N Market St, McArthur, OH, 45651-1218. Tel: 740-596-5691. Fax: 740-596-2477. p. 1916

Clark, Valerie, Ref, Niles Public Library District, 6960 Oakton St, Niles, IL, 60714. Tel: 847-663-1234. Fax: 847-663-1350. p. 680

Clark, Valerie, Dir, Bracken County Public Library, 310 W Miami St, Brooksville, KY, 41004. Tel: 606-735-3620. Fax: 606-735-3378. p. 908

Clark, Yvonne, Librn, Mid-Mississippi Regional Library System, Tchula Public, 105 Mercer St, Tchula, MS, 39169-5235. Tel: 662-235-5235. Fax: 662-235-4925. p. 1306

Clark-Dawe, Cathryn, Librn, Webster Free Public Library, 947 Battle St, Webster, NH, 03303. Tel: 603-648-2706. Fax: 603-648-2889. p. 1467

Clark-Gorey, Kenda, Legis Librn, New Brunswick Legislative Library, Legislative Bldg, 706 Queen St, Fredericton, NB, E3B 1C5, CANADA. Tel: 506-453-2338. Fax: 506-444-5889. p. 2763

Clark-Greene, Barbara, Ref Librn, Groton Public Library, 52 Newtown Rd, Groton, CT, 06340. Tel: 860-441-6750. Fax: 860-448-0363. p. 342

Clarke Arado, Therese, Assoc Dir, Admin & Pub Serv, Res Librn, Northern Illinois University Libraries, David C Shapiro Memorial Law Library, Normal Rd, DeKalb, IL, 60115-2890. Tel: 815-753-9497. Fax: 815-753-9499. p. 636

Clarke, Barbara, Head, Teacher Educ Res Ctr, State University of New York College at Geneseo, SUNY Geneseo, One College Circle, Geneseo, NY, 14454-1498. Tel: 585-245-5592. p. 1627

Clarke, Barbara, Librn, Temple Sholom of Broomall Library, 55 N Church Lane, Broomall, PA, 19008. Tel: 610-356-5165. Fax: 610-356-6713. p. 2038

Clarke, Betsy, Librn, Boston Public Library, Jamaica Plain Branch, 12 Sedgwick St, Jamaica Plain, MA, 02130-2897. Tel: 617-524-2053. Fax: 617-983-0661. p. 1057

Clarke, Dee, Teen Librn, Bedford Free Public Library, Seven Mudge Way, Bedford, MA, 01730-2168. Tel: 781-275-9440. Fax: 781-275-3590. p. 1052

Clarke, Helen, Asst Vice-Provost - Coll/Librn, University of Calgary Library, 2500 University Dr NW, Calgary, AB, T2N 1N4, CANADA. Tel: 403-220-3796. Fax: 403-282-1218. p. 2693

Clarke, Janet, Bibliog Instr, Stony Brook University, W-1502 Melville Library, John S Toll Rd, Stony Brook, NY, 11794-3300. Tel: 631-632-7100. Fax: 631-632-7116. p. 1749

Clarke, Jennifer, Asst Dir, Libr Coll Develop & Access Serv, Bucknell University, Acquisitions, Library & Information Technology, Lewisburg, PA, 17837. Tel: 570-577-3252. p. 2080

Clarke, Jennifer, Asst Dir, Libr Coll Develop & Access Serv, Bucknell University, Cataloging, 117 Bertrand Library, Lewisburg, PA, 17837. Tel: 570-577-3252. p. 2080

Clarke, Jennifer, Asst Dir, Libr Coll Develop & Access Serv, Bucknell University, Library & Information Technology, 221 Ellen Clarke Bertrand Library, Lewisburg, PA, 17837. Tel: 570-577-3252. Fax: 570-577-3313. p. 2080

Clarke, Joanne R, Br Mgr, Kinchafoonee Regional Library System, Randolph County Library, 200 E Pearl St, Cuthbert, GA, 39840-1474. Tel: 229-732-2566. Fax: 229-732-6824. p. 528

Clarke, Judith, Circ, Co-Dir, Tech Serv, University of Maine at Augusta Libraries, 46 University Dr, Augusta, ME, 04330-9410. Tel: 207-621-3349. Fax: 207-621-3311. p. 975

Clarke, Karen, Br Supvr, Jackson/Hinds Library System, Beverley J Brown Library, 7395 South Siwell Rd, Byram, MS, 39272-8741. Tel: 601-372-0954. Fax: 601-373-7164. p. 1303

Clarke, Kim, Assoc Vice-Provost - Res/Librarian, University of Calgary Library, 2500 University Dr NW, Calgary, AB, T2N 1N4, CANADA. Tel: 403-220-5953. Fax: 403-282-1218. p. 2693

Clarke, Kim, Dir, University of Calgary Library, Law Library, 2500 University Dr NW, Calgary, AB, T2N 1N4, CANADA. Tel: 403-220-6702. Fax: 403-282-3000. p. 2693

Clarke, Leslie, Ch, Ocean City Free Public Library, 1735 Simpson Ave, Ste 4, Ocean City, NJ, 08226. Tel: 609-399-2434, Ext 5241. Fax: 609-398-0751. p. 1516

Clarke, Linda Berry, Dir, Chatham County Public Libraries, 500 N Second Ave, Siler City, NC, 27344. Tel: 919-742-2016. Fax: 919-742-5546. p. 1823

Clarke, Lois, Librn, Bell Island Public Library, 20 Bennett St, Bell Island, NL, A0A 4H0, CANADA. Tel: 709-488-2413. Fax: 709-488-2413. p. 2769

Clarke, Margot, Br Head, Toronto Public Library, Richview, 1806 Islington Ave, Toronto, ON, M9P 3N3, CANADA. Tel: 416-394-5120. Fax: 416-394-5158. p. 2863

Clarke, Marilyn, Librn, Bay Roberts Public Library, PO Box 610, Bay Roberts, NL, A0A 1G0, CANADA. Tel: 709-786-9629. Fax: 709-786-9674. p. 2769

Clarke, Nancy, Br Supvr, Guelph Public Library, East Side Branch, One Starwood Dr, Guelph, ON, N1E 0H5, CANADA. Tel: 519-829-4405. p. 2807

Clarke, Patrick, Exec Dir, James Buchanan Foundation for the Preservation of Wheatland Library, 1120 Marietta Ave, Lancaster, PA, 17603. Tel: 717-392-8721. Fax: 717-295-8825. p. 2076

Clarke, Patti, Libr Tech, Buena Vista Correctional Complex Library, 15125 Hwys 24 & 285, Buena Vista, CO, 81211. Tel: 719-395-7254. Fax: 719-395-7214. p. 293

Clarke, Patti, In Charge, Colorado Department of Corrections, PO Box 2005, Buena Vista, CO, 81211-2005. Tel: 719-395-2404, Ext 3177. Fax: 719-395-7362. p. 293

Clarke, Robert, Univ Librn, Trent University, 1600 West Bank Dr, Peterborough, ON, K9J 7B8, CANADA. Tel: 705-748-1011, Ext 1324. Fax: 705-748-1126. p. 2836

Clarke, Sarah, Asst Librn, Milton Free Public Library, 13 Main St, Milton Mills, NH, 03852. Tel: 603-473-8535. p. 1458

Clarke, Sharon, Youth Serv, Seekonk Public Library, 410 Newman Ave, Seekonk, MA, 02771. Tel: 508-336-8230, Ext 140. Fax: 508-336-6437. p. 1123

Clarke, Susan, Med Ed/Libr Mgr, Doheny Eye Institute, 1450 San Pablo St, DEI3400, Los Angeles, CA, 90033. Tel: 323-442-7139. p. 170

Clarke, Susan, Head, Ref, Stephen F Austin State University, 1936 North St, Nacogdoches, TX, 75962. Tel: 936-468-1459. Fax: 936-468-7610. p. 2364

Clarke, Tim, Head, Libr Syst & Info Transfer Serv, Muhlenberg College, 2400 Chew St, Allentown, PA, 18104-5586. Tel: 484-664-3520. Fax: 484-664-3511. p. 2027

Clarke, Tom, Divinity Sch Librn, Shaw University, 118 E South St, Raleigh, NC, 27601. Tel: 919-716-5518. Fax: 919-831-1161. p. 1817

Clarkson, Anna, Project Archivist, Baltimore Museum of Art, Ten Art Museum Dr, Baltimore, MD, 21218-3898. Tel: 443-573-1782. Fax: 443-573-1781. p. 1012

Clarkson, Bev, Asst Dir, Pittsburg Public Library, 308 N Walnut, Pittsburg, KS, 66762-4732. Tel: 620-231-8110. Fax: 620-232-2258. p. 890

Clarkson, Wendy, Head, Automation, Somerset County Library System, One Vogt Dr, Bridgewater, NJ, 08807-2136. p. 1475

Clary, Lara, Mgr, Acad Res, California State University, Northridge, 18111 Nordhoff St, Northridge, CA, 91330. Tel: 818-677-2205. Fax: 818-677-2676. p. 195

Clary, Nanci, Pub Serv Adminr, Chesterfield County Public Library, 9501 Lori Rd, Chesterfield, VA, 23832. Tel: 804-717-6412. Fax: 804-751-4679. p. 2457

Clasby, Nathan, Circ, NHTI, Concord's Community College, 31 College Dr, Concord, NH, 03301-7425. Tel: 603-271-7186. Fax: 603-271-7189. p. 1443

Claspell, Barbara, Asst Dir, Nicholas P Sims Library, 515 W Main, Waxahachie, TX, 75165-3235. Tel: 972-937-2671. Fax: 972-937-4409. p. 2398

Clasper, James, Asst Eng & Applied Sci Librn, University of Cincinnati Libraries, College of Engineering & Applied Science Library, 850 Baldwin Hall, Cincinnati, OH, 45221. Tel: 513-556-1452. Fax: 513-556-2654. p. 1874

Claspy, William, Coll Develop, Case Western Reserve University, 11055 Euclid Ave, Cleveland, OH, 44106. Tel: 216-368-3595. Fax: 216-368-6950. p. 1876

Claspy, William, Librn, Case Western Reserve University, Astronomy, Sears Bldg, 10900 Euclid Ave, Cleveland, OH, 44106. Tel: 216-368-6701. Fax: 216-368-5406. p. 1876

Class, Mary P, Adult Serv, Dir, William Fogg Library, 116 Old Rd, Eliot, ME, 03903. Tel: 207-439-9437. Fax: 207-439-9437. p. 984

Classon, Emily, Commun Serv Librn, Memorial Hall Library, Two N Main St, Andover, MA, 01810. Tel: 978-623-8401. Fax: 978-623-8407. p. 1049

Claudel-Simoneaux, Jeanne, Librn, Sessions, Fishman, Nathan & Israel LLP Library, 201 St Charles Ave, Ste 3500, New Orleans, LA, 70170-3500. Tel: 504-582-1563. Fax: 504-582-1555. p. 963

Claudine, Sarah, Librn, George Kurian Reference Books, 3689 Campbell Ct, Yorktown Heights, NY, 10598-1808. Tel: 914-962-3287. Fax: 914-962-3287. p. 1772

Claudnic, Irene, Librn, Oglesby Public Library, 111 S Woodland St, Oglesby, IL, 61348. Tel: 815-883-3619. Fax: 815-883-3615. p. 685

Claus, Cindy, Law Libr Operations Mgr, University of Nevada, Las Vegas Libraries, Wiener-Rogers Law Library, William S Boyd School of Law, 4505 Maryland Pkwy, Las Vegas, NV, 89154-1080. Tel: 702-895-2400. Fax: 702-895-2410. p. 1431

Clausen, Beth, Head, ILL, Head, Multimedia Ctr, Head, Res Sharing & Reserve Coll, Northwestern University Library, 1970 Campus Dr, Evanston, IL, 60208-2300. Tel: 847-491-7658. p. 644

Clausen, Jane, Dir, Lubbock Public Library, 1306 Ninth St, Lubbock, TX, 79401. Tel: 806-775-2834. Fax: 806-775-2827. p. 2357

Clausen, Robin, Managing Librn, Pierce County Library System, Buckley Branch, 123 S River Ave, Buckley, WA, 98321. Tel: 360-548-3710. Fax: 360-829-2874. p. 2539

Clausen, Robin, Managing Librn, Pierce County Library System, DuPont Branch, 1540 Wilmington Dr, DuPont, WA, 98327. Tel: 253-548-3326. Fax: 253-964-4010. p. 2539

Clausen, Robin, Managing Librn, Pierce County Library System, Eatonville Branch, 205 Center St W, Eatonville, WA, 98328-9488. Tel: 253-548-3311. Fax: 360-832-7201. p. 2539

Clausen, Robin, Managing Librn, Pierce County Library System, Key Center, 8905 Key Peninsula Hwy N, Lakebay, WA, 98349. Tel: 253-548-3309. Fax: 253-884-3706. p. 2539

Clausen, Robin, Managing Librn, Pierce County Library System, Milton/Edgewood Branch, 900 Meridian Ave E, Milton, WA, 98354. Tel: 253-548-3725. Fax: 253-927-2581. p. 2539

Clausen, Robin, Managing Librn, Pierce County Library System, Orting Branch, 202 Washington Ave S, Orting, WA, 98360. Tel: 253-548-3312. Fax: 360-893-4149. p. 2539

Clausen, Robin, Managing Librn, Pierce County Library System, Steilacoom Branch, 2950 Steilacoom Blvd SW, Steilacoom, WA, 98388-5107. Tel: 253-548-3313. Fax: 253-589-7095. p. 2540

Clausen, Robin, Managing Librn, Pierce County Library System, Tillicum Branch, 14916 Washington Ave SW, Lakewood, WA, 98498. Tel: 253-548-3314. Fax: 253-588-2095. p. 2540

Clauson, Ingrid, Librn, Fairbanks North Star Borough Public Library & Regional Center, North Pole Branch, 601 Snowman Lane, North Pole, AK, 99705. Tel: 907-488-6101. Fax: 907-488-8465. p. 48

Clauson Krull, Judy, Dir, Libr Serv, University of Sioux Falls, 1101 W 22nd St, Sioux Falls, SD, 57105-1699. Tel: 605-331-6661. p. 2219

Claveau, Michel, Coordr, Tech Serv, Bibliothèques de Montréal, 801, rue Brennan, 5e Etage, Bureau 5206, Montreal, QC, H3C 0G4, CANADA. Tel: 514-872-6563. Fax: 514-872-0530. p. 2889

Clawson, Janet, Asst Librn, Colfax Public Library, 207 S Clark St, Colfax, IN, 46035. Tel: 765-324-2915. Fax: 765-324-2689. p. 732

Clawson, Nicole, Youth Serv, Saint Louis County Library, 1640 S Lindbergh Blvd, Saint Louis, MO, 63131-3598. Tel: 314-994-3300, Ext 2230. Fax: 314-997-7602. p. 1358

Clawson, Stacey, Librn, DeWitt Public Library, Cleon Collier Memorial Library, 211 Main St, Gillett, AR, 72055. Tel: 870-548-2821. Fax: 870-548-2821. p. 98

Claxton, Janice, Asst Librn, Trinity Baptist College Library, 800 Hammond Blvd, Jacksonville, FL, 32221-1342. Tel: 904-596-2508. Fax: 904-596-2531. p. 455

Claxton, Jean, Br Mgr, Audubon Regional Library, St Helena Branch, Oak Plaza Shopping Ctr, Hwy 10, Greensburg, LA, 70441. Tel: 225-222-4328. Fax: 504-222-4335. p. 947

Clay, Causie, Mrs, Head, Tech Proc, Greenwood-Leflore Public Library System, 405 W Washington St, Greenwood, MS, 38930-4297. Tel: 662-453-3634. Fax: 662-453-0683. p. 1299

Clay, Debra, Librn, Chevron Global Library Houston, 3901 Briarpark Dr, Houston, TX, 77042. Tel: 713-954-6007. Fax: 713-954-6907. p. 2334

Clay, Edwin S, III, Dir, Fairfax County Public Library, 12000 Government Center Pkwy, Ste 324, Fairfax, VA, 22035-0012. Tel: 703-324-3100. Fax: 703-324-8365. p. 2461

Clay, JoAnn, Br Co-Mgr, Iberia Parish Library, Lydia Branch, 4800 Freyou Rd, New Iberia, LA, 70560. Tel: 337-364-7808. Fax: 337-364-7808. p. 959

Clay, Karen, Dir, Eastern Oregon University, One University Blvd, La Grande, OR, 97850. Tel: 541-962-3792. Fax: 541-962-3335. p. 2003

Clay, Kathy, Br Mgr, Stark County District Library, Madge Youtz Branch, 2921 Mahoning Rd NE, Canton, OH, 44705. Tel: 330-452-2618. Fax: 330-580-1807. p. 1865

Clay, Rudolph, Head, Libr Outreach, Washington University Libraries, One Brookings Dr, Campus Box 1061, Saint Louis, MO, 63130-4862. Tel: 314-935-5400. Fax: 314-935-4045. p. 1362

Clay, Wendy, Librn, Southwest Arkansas Regional Library, Lockesburg Branch, PO Box 46, Lockesburg, AR, 71846. Tel: 870-289-2233. Fax: 870-289-2233. p. 103

Claybaugh, Amy, Coll Develop, Saint Luke's Health System Libraries, 190 E Bannock St, Boise, ID, 83712-6297. Tel: 208-381-2276. Fax: 208-381-4317. p. 572

Claybaugh, Amy, Treas, Idaho Health Information Association, c/o Eastern Idaho Regional Medical Center, PO Box 2077, Idaho Falls, ID, 83403. Tel: 208-529-6077. Fax: 208-529-7014. p. 2941

Claypool, Nancy, Dir, Marshall Public Library, 612 Archer Ave, Marshall, IL, 62441. Tel: 217-826-2535. Fax: 217-826-5529. p. 671

Clayton, Barbara, Br Mgr, Giles County Public Library, Lynnville Branch, 105 Mill St, Lynnville, TN, 38472. Tel: 931-527-0707. p. 2264

Clayton, Carla, Librn, Waters Corp, 34 Maple St, Milford, MA, 01757. Tel: 508-478-2000. Fax: 508-482-2417. p. 1106

Clayton, Christine, Asst Librn, Worcester Art Museum Library, 55 Salisbury St, Worcester, MA, 01609-3196. Tel: 508-799-4406, Ext 3070. Fax: 508-798-5646. p. 1145

Clayton, Debra, Acq, Lee County Library, 219 N Madison St, Tupelo, MS, 38804-3899. Tel: 662-841-9027. Fax: 662-840-7615. p. 1316

Clayton, Diane, Dir, Hamline University, Bush Memorial Library, 1536 Hewitt, Saint Paul, MN, 55104. Tel: 651-523-2375. Fax: 651-523-2199. p. 1278

Clayton, Kathy, Libr Mgr, Timberland Regional Library, Amanda Park Timberland Library, 6118 US Hwy 101, Amanda Park, WA, 98526-0089. Tel: 360-288-2725. Fax: 360-288-2376. p. 2543

Clayton, Lesley, Mgr, Ch Serv, Mamie Doud Eisenhower Public Library, Three Community Park Rd, Broomfield, CO, 80020-3781. Tel: 720-887-2318. Fax: 720-887-1384. p. 292

Clayton, Russell, In Charge, Avoyelles Correctional Center Library, 1630 Prison Rd, Cottonport, LA, 71327. Tel: 318-876-2891, Ext 350. Fax: 318-876-4220. p. 947

Clayton, Sharon, Assoc Librn, Knox College, Two E South St, Galesburg, IL, 61401. Tel: 309-341-7249. Fax: 309-341-7799. p. 648

Clayton, Shirley, Mgr, Sequoyah Regional Library System, Ball Ground Public, 435 Old Canton Rd, Ball Ground, GA, 30107. Tel: 770-735-2025. Fax: 770-735-6050. p. 523

Clayton, Susan Jean, County Librn, Lake County Library, 1425 N High St, Lakeport, CA, 95453-3800. Tel: 707-263-8816. Fax: 707-263-6796. p. 163

Clayton, Tricia, Ref, Oglethorpe University, 4484 Peachtree Rd NE, Atlanta, GA, 30319. Tel: 404-364-8511. Fax: 404-364-8517. p. 517

Clayton, Vickie, Ref Serv, Person County Public Library, 319 S Main St, Roxboro, NC, 27573. Tel: 336-597-7881. Fax: 336-597-5081. p. 1821

Clayton, William, Asst Univ Librn, University of Georgia Libraries, Athens, GA, 30602-1641. Tel: 706-542-0472. Fax: 706-542-4144. p. 510

Claytor, Alisa, Computer Spec, Athens Regional Library System, Madison County, 1315 Hwy 98 W, Danielsville, GA, 30633. Tel: 706-795-5597. Fax: 706-795-0830. p. 509

Clear, Nancy Renner, Dir of Educ, All Souls Unitarian Church, 5805 E 56th St, Indianapolis, IN, 46226-1526. Tel: 317-545-6005. Fax: 317-545-4662. p. 749

Cleary, Cindy, Dir, Libr Serv, Glendale Public Library, 222 E Harvard St, Glendale, CA, 91205-1075. Tel: 818-548-2043. Fax: 818-548-7225. p. 155

Cleary, Daniel E, Head, Ser, Sci Librn, York College Library, 94-20 Guy R Brewer Blvd, Jamaica, NY, 11451. Tel: 718-262-2037. Fax: 718-262-2027, 718-262-2997. p. 1646

Cleary, Heather, Librn, Visual Res, Otis College of Art & Design Library, 9045 Lincoln Blvd, Westchester, CA, 90045. Tel: 310-665-6800, Ext 6930. Fax: 310-665-6998. p. 283

Cleary, Joan, Asst Librn, Richmond Free Library, 201 Bridge St, Richmond, VT, 05477. Tel: 802-434-3036. Fax: 802-434-3223. p. 2434

Cleary, Susan M, Dir, Libr Serv, Nutter McClennen & Fish LLP, World Trade Center W, 155 Seaport Blvd, Boston, MA, 02210. Tel: 617-439-2000. Fax: 617-310-9000. p. 1066

Cleary, William, Br Coordr, Martins Ferry Public Library, 20 James Wright Pl, Martins Ferry, OH, 43935. Tel: 740-633-0314. Fax: 740-633-6242. p. 1914

Cleaveland, Marsha, Tech Serv Librn, American Indian College, 10020 N 15th Ave, Phoenix, AZ, 85021-2199. Tel: 602-944-3335. p. 71

Cleaveland, Nichola, Librn, Prince Edward Island Public Library Service, Government Services Library, Basement, Jones Bldg, 11 Kent St, Charlottetown, PE, C1A 7N8, CANADA. Tel: 902-368-4653. p. 2876

Cleaver, Susie, Br Mgr, Mishawaka-Penn-Harris Public Library, Harris, 51446 Elm Rd, Granger, IN, 46530-7171. Tel: 574-271-3179, Ext 311. Fax: 574-271-3183. p. 765

Cleborne, Diana, Town Librn, South Hero Community Library, 75 South St, South Hero, VT, 05486. Tel: 802-372-6209. Fax: 802-372-5188. p. 2435

Clegg, Michael, Pub Serv Mgr, Allen County Public Library, 900 Library Plaza, Fort Wayne, IN, 46802. Tel: 260-421-1301. Fax: 260-421-1386. p. 740

Cleghorn, Joanne, ILL, Fisheries & Oceans Canada, 531 Brandy Cove Rd, Saint Andrews, NB, E5B 2L9, CANADA. Tel: 506-529-5909. Fax: 506-529-5862. p. 2766

Cleland, Alyssa, Dir, Angie Williams Cox Public Library, 119 N Main St, Pardeeville, WI, 53954-0370. Tel: 608-429-2354. Fax: 608-429-4308. p. 2629

Cleland, Becky, Evening Librn, Isothermal Community College Library, 286 ICC Loop Rd, Spindale, NC, 28160. Tel: 828-286-3636, Ext 309. Fax: 828-286-8208. p. 1825

Cleland, Camille, Tech Serv, Skokie Public Library, 5215 Oakton St, Skokie, IL, 60077-3680. Tel: 847-673-7774. Fax: 847-673-7797. p. 703

Cleland, Marsha, Br Mgr, Allendale-Hampton-Jasper Regional Library, Pratt Memorial, 123-A E Wilson St, Ridgeland, SC, 29936-3602. Tel: 843-726-7744. Fax: 843-726-7813. p. 2180

Cleland-Sipfle, Kate, Coordr, Cat, Southern Oregon University, 1250 Siskiyou Blvd, Ashland, OR, 97520-5076. Tel: 541-552-6839. Fax: 541-552-6429. p. 1990

Clem, Judy, Br Mgr, Indianapolis-Marion County Public Library, Garfield Park, 2502 Shelby St, Indianapolis, IN, 46203-4236. Tel: 317-275-4490. p. 754

Clemens, Carol, Dir, Ventura Public Library, Seven W Ventura St, Ventura, IA, 50482. Tel: 641-829-4410. Fax: 641-829-4410. p. 848

Clemens, David, Dir, Longwood Public Library, 800 Middle Country Rd, Middle Island, NY, 11953. Tel: 631-924-6400. Fax: 631-924-7538. p. 1660

Clemens, Lawrence E, Head, Coll Develop & Media Serv, United States Naval Academy, 589 McNair Rd, Annapolis, MD, 21402-5029. Tel: 410-293-6900. Fax: 410-293-6909. p. 1011

Clemens, Mary, Circ, Carol Stream Public Library, 616 Hiawatha Dr, Carol Stream, IL, 60188. Tel: 630-653-0755. Fax: 630-653-6809. p. 601

Clemens, Muriel, Circ Evening Coordr, Saint Leo University, 33701 State Rd 52, Saint Leo, FL, 33574. Tel: 352-588-8476. Fax: 352-588-8484. p. 487

Clemens, Nick, Librn, Chelsea Public Library, 296 Rte 110, Chelsea, VT, 05038. Tel: 802-685-2188. p. 2421

Clement, Alison, Librn, Marshall Community Health Library, 681 Main St, Ste 103, Placerville, CA, 95667. Tel: 530-626-5459. Fax: 530-626-2779. p. 208

Clement, Amber, Ref Serv, Bayliss Public Library, 541 Library Dr, Sault Sainte Marie, MI, 49783. Tel: 906-632-9331. Fax: 906-635-0210. p. 1226

Clement, Elaine, Ref, Harvard Library, Godfrey Lowell Cabot Science Library, Science Center, One Oxford St, Cambridge, MA, 02138. Tel: 617-496-8442. Fax: 617-495-5324. p. 1074

Clement, Ellie, Head, Ref & Res Serv, Harvard Library, History of Science Library - Cabot Science Library, Science Center, One Oxford St, Cambridge, MA, 02138. Tel: 617-495-5355. Fax: 617-495-5324. p. 1075

Clement, Emily, Ref, Baker & Botts LLP, One Shell Plaza, 910 Louisiana St, Houston, TX, 77002. Tel: 713-229-1643. Fax: 713-229-1522. p. 2334

Clement, Heather, Librn, Nordegg Public Library, General Delivery, Nordegg, AB, T0M 2H0, CANADA. Tel: 403-800-3667. Fax: 403-721-3930. p. 2712

Clement, Karen, Circ, Finger Lakes Community College, 4355 Lakeshore Dr, Canandaigua, NY, 14424-8395. Tel: 585-394-3500, Ext 7371. Fax: 585-394-8708. p. 1601

Clement, Kevin, Ref Serv, Chesapeake Public Library, Indian River, 2320 Old Greenbrier Rd, Chesapeake, VA, 23325-4916. Tel: 757-410-7008. Fax: 757-410-7014. p. 2456

Clement, Kevin T, Dir, Libr & Archives, Dir, Libr Serv, Baltimore County Historical Society Library, 9811 Van Buren Lane, Hunt Valley, MD, 21030. Tel: 410-666-1976, Ext 102. Fax: 410-666-5276. p. 1032

Clement, Linda, Ref Librn, Austin Community College, Cypress Creek Campus Library, 1555 Cypress Creek Rd, Cedar Park, TX, 78613. Tel: 512-223-2033. Fax: 512-223-2035. p. 2278

Clement, Mercedes, Head Librn, Daytona Beach College Library, 1200 W International Speedway Blvd, Daytona Beach, FL, 32114. Tel: 386-506-3440. Fax: 386-506-3008. p. 435

Clement, Pat, Dir, Pittsburg Public Library, 308 N Walnut, Pittsburg, KS, 66762-4732. Tel: 620-231-8110. Fax: 620-232-2258. p. 890

Clement, Richard, Dean of Libr, Utah State University, 3000 Old Main Hill, Logan, UT, 84322-3000. Tel: 435-797-2631. Fax: 435-797-2880. p. 2407

Clement, Russell, Art Librn, Northwestern University Library, 1970 Campus Dr, Evanston, IL, 60208-2300. Tel: 847-491-7658. p. 644

Clemente, F, Head, Info Serv, Public Safety Canada, 340 Laurier Ave W, 10A, Ottawa, ON, K1A 0P8, CANADA. Tel: 613-991-2780. Fax: 613-941-6171. p. 2832

Clemente, Nancy, Librn/Unit Coordr, Clarion University of Pennsylvania, 1801 W First St, Oil City, PA, 16301. Tel: 814-676-6591, Ext 1245. Fax: 814-677-3987. p. 2100

Clements, Andrea, ILL, Brigham Young University-Hawaii, 55-220 Kulanui St, BYU-Hawaii, No 1966, Laie, HI, 96762-1294. Tel: 808-675-3850. Fax: 808-675-3877. p. 567

Clements, Angela, Electronic Res Librn, Crawfordsville District Public Library, 205 S Washington St, Crawfordsville, IN, 47933. Tel: 765-362-2242. Fax: 765-362-7986. p. 734

Clements, Anne, Dir, Central Baptist College, 1501 College Ave, Conway, AR, 72034. Tel: 501-329-6872. Fax: 501-329-2941. p. 96

Clements, Betty, Ref, Claremont School of Theology Library, 1325 N College Ave, Claremont, CA, 91711. Tel: 909-447-2589. p. 134

Clements, Catherine, Br Mgr, Akron-Summit County Public Library, Norton Branch, 3930 S Cleveland-Massillon Rd, Norton, OH, 44203-5563. Tel: 330-825-7800. Fax: 330-825-5155. p. 1852

Clements, Charlotte, Libr Mgr, Florida State College at Jacksonville, South Campus, 11901 Beach Blvd, Jacksonville, FL, 32246-6624. Tel: 904-646-2173. Fax: 904-646-2155. p. 453

Clements, Cynthia, Coll Develop, Richland College Library, 12800 Abrams Rd, Dallas, TX, 75243-2199. Tel: 972-238-6081. p. 2309

Clements, D A, Lecturer, University of Washington, Mary Gates Hall, Ste 370, Campus Box 352840, Seattle, WA, 98195-2840. Tel: 206-685-9937. Fax: 206-616-3152. p. 2976

Clements, Elaine, Exec Dir, Andover Historical Society Library, 97 Main St, Andover, MA, 01810. Tel: 978-475-2236. Fax: 978-470-2741. p. 1049

Clements, Maureen, Broadcast Librn, NPR Library, 635 Massachusetts Ave NW, Washington, DC, 20001. Fax: 202-513-3056. p. 412

Clemmer, Angie B, Access Serv/Ser Coordr, Kansas City University of Medicine & Biosciences D'Angelo Library, 1750 Independence Ave, Kansas City, MO, 64106-1453. Tel: 816-654-7263. Fax: 816-654-7261. p. 1338

Clemmer, Melissa, Evening Librn, Northeast Mississippi Community College, 101 Cunningham Blvd, Booneville, MS, 38829. Tel: 662-720-7237, 662-728-7751. Fax: 662-728-2428. p. 1294

Clemons, Cassie, Dir, Libr Serv, Okefenokee Technical College, 426 W 12th St, Alma, GA, 31510. Tel: 912-287-5834. p. 507

Clemons, Cassie, Dir, Libr Serv, Okefenokee Technical College, 1701 Carswell Ave, Waycross, GA, 31503. Tel: 912-287-5834. Fax: 912-287-4865. p. 557

Clemons, Charlene, Asst Dir, Ellsworth Public Library, 20 State St, Ellsworth, ME, 04605. Tel: 207-667-6363. Fax: 207-667-4901. p. 984

Clemons, Cheryl, Youth Serv, Grant County Public Library District, 201 Barnes Rd, Williamstown, KY, 41097-9482. Tel: 859-824-2080. Fax: 859-824-2083. p. 937

Clemons, Constance, Supvr, Cuyahoga Community College, Metropolitan Campus Library, 2900 Community College Ave, Cleveland, OH, 44115. Tel: 216-987-4296. Fax: 216-987-4404. p. 1879

Clemons, Jessica, Sci Librn, The College of Wooster Libraries, 1140 Beall Ave, Wooster, OH, 44691-2364. Tel: 330-263-2280. Fax: 330-263-2253. p. 1949

Clemons, Kysh, Br Mgr, Atlanta-Fulton Public Library System, Perry Homes Library, 2011 Bolton Rd, Ste 100, Atlanta, GA, 30318. Tel: 404-792-4994. Fax: 404-792-4996. p. 512

Clemons, Theodosia, Librn, Thirty Sixth District Court Law Library, 421 Madison Ave, Detroit, MI, 48226. Tel: 313-965-2792. Fax: 313-965-4057. p. 1172

Clendenning, Cynthia, Ch, Central Brevard Library & Reference Center, 308 Forrest Ave, Cocoa, FL, 32922. Tel: 321-633-1795. Fax: 321-633-1806. p. 433

Clendineng, Sarah, Dir, Fort Madison Public Library, 1920 Avenue E, Fort Madison, IA, 52627. Tel: 319-372-5721. Fax: 319-372-5726. p. 817

Clendinning, David, Dir, West Virginia State University, Campus Box L17, Institute, WV, 25112. Tel: 304-766-3116. Fax: 304-766-4103. p. 2562

Clennon, Cindy, Dir, Electronic Res, Consortium of Academic & Research Libraries in Illinois, 100 Trade Ctr Dr, Ste 303, Champaign, IL, 61820. Tel: 217-333-4895. Fax: 217-244-7596. p. 2942

Cleo, Marmion, Coordr, University of Arizona, Film Collection, 1510 E University Blvd, Tucson, AZ, 85721. Tel: 520-307-2801. Fax: 520-621-9733. p. 89

Cler, Janet, Dir, Tolono Public Library District, 111 E Main St, Tolono, IL, 61880. Tel: 217-485-5558. Fax: 217-485-3088. p. 710

Clerkin, Laura, Dir, Bethlehem Public Library, 2155 Main St, Bethlehem, NH, 03574. Tel: 603-869-2409. Fax: 603-869-2280. p. 1439

Clerkin, Rebecca, Libr Dir, Media Serv, Great Bay Community College, 277 Portsmouth Ave, Stratham, NH, 03885-2297. Tel: 603-427-7618, 603-772-2210. Fax: 603-772-0216. p. 1465

Cleveland, Ana D, Dr, Prof & Dir, Houston Prog, University of North Texas, 1155 Union Circle, Denton, TX, 76203-5017. Tel: 940-565-2445. Fax: 940-565-3101. p. 2975

Cleveland, Debbie, Head, Ch, Auburn Public Library, 49 Spring St, Auburn, ME, 04210. Tel: 207-333-6640. Fax: 207-333-6644. p. 974

Cleveland, Donald, Dr, Prof Emeritus, University of North Texas, 1155 Union Circle, Denton, TX, 76203-5017. Tel: 940-565-2445. Fax: 940-565-3101. p. 2975

Cleveland, Donarae, Dir, Field-Carnegie Library, 200 Walnut St, Odebolt, IA, 51458. Tel: 712-668-2718. Fax: 712-668-4380. p. 836

Cleveland, Laura, Librn, Lafayette County Library, 219 E Third St, Lewisville, AR, 71845. Tel: 870-921-4757. Fax: 870-921-4756. p. 105

Cleveland, Laura, Dir, Columbia County Library, 2057 N Jackson St, Box 668, Magnolia, AR, 71753. Tel: 870-234-1991. Fax: 870-234-5077. p. 108

Cleveland, Laura, Ch, Watauga Public Library, 7109 Whitley Rd, Watauga, TX, 76148-2024. Tel: 817-514-5855. Fax: 817-581-3910. p. 2398

Cleveland, Susan, Dir, Our Lady of Lourdes, Medical Center Library, 1600 Haddon Ave, Camden, NJ, 08103. Tel: 856-757-3548. Fax: 856-757-3215. p. 1476

Cleveland, Susannah, Head Librn, Bowling Green State University Libraries, Music Library & Sound Recordings Archives, Jerome Library, 3rd Flr, Bowling Green, OH, 43403. Tel: 419-372-9929. Fax: 419-372-2499. p. 1861

Cleveland, Trudy, Librn, Houston Community College - Southwest College, Stafford Campus Library, 9910 Cash Rd, Stafford, TX, 77477-4405. Tel: 713-718-7823. Fax: 713-718-6723. p. 2338

Clevenger, Judy Beth, Dir, Scott-Sebastian Regional Library, 18 N Adair, Greenwood, AR, 72936. Tel: 479-996-2856. Fax: 479-996-2236. p. 101

Clever, Jill, Asst Mgr, Toledo-Lucas County Public Library, Holland Branch, 1032 S McCord Rd, Holland, OH, 43528. Tel: 419-259-5240. Fax: 419-865-6706. p. 1939

Clever, Jill, Genealogy Mgr, Local Hist Mgr, Toledo-Lucas County Public Library, 325 N Michigan St, Toledo, OH, 43604-6614. Tel: 419-259-5233. Fax: 419-255-1334. p. 1939

Clever, Shannon, Librn, Department of Veterans Affairs, 510 Butler Ave, Martinsburg, WV, 25405-9809. Tel: 304-263-0811, Ext 3826. Fax: 304-262-4847. p. 2565

Clevesy, Sandra R, Dir, Metrowest Medical Center, 115 Lincoln St, Framingham, MA, 01702. Tel: 508-383-1591. Fax: 508-879-0471. p. 1090

Clevidence, Sarah, Adult Serv, Findlay-Hancock County District Public Library, 206 Broadway, Findlay, OH, 45840-3382. Tel: 419-422-1712. Fax: 419-422-0638. p. 1899

Clewell, Natalie, Librn, West Georgia Technical College, Douglas Campus, 4600 Timber Ridge Dr, Douglasville, GA, 30135. Tel: 770-947-7330. Fax: 770-947-7239. p. 556

Clewell, Natalie, ELI Librn/Distance Educ Librn, Northern Virginia Community College Libraries, Extended Learning Institute, 8000 Forbes Pl, Springfield, VA, 22151. Tel: 703-764-5083. p. 2447

Clexton, John, Librn, Grosse Pointe Public Library, Ewald, 15175 E Jefferson, Grosse Pointe Park, MI, 48230. Tel: 313-343-2071. Fax: 313-821-8356. p. 1187

Cliche, Mireille, Chef de Div, Bibliothèques de Montrèal, Parc-Extension, 421, rue Saint-Roch, Montreal, QC, H3N 1K2, CANADA. Tel: 514-868-3444. Fax: 514-872-6152. p. 2890

Cliche, Mireille, Chef de Div, Bibliothèques de Montrèal, Saint-Michel, 7601, rue François-Perrault, Montreal, QC, H2A 3L6, CANADA. Tel: 514-868-3444. Fax: 514-872-0528. p. 2891

Clifford, Anne, Head, Adult Serv, Principal Librn, Coronado Public Library, 640 Orange Ave, Coronado, CA, 92118-1526. Tel: 619-522-2470. Fax: 619-435-4205. p. 137

Clifford, Cynthia, Tech Serv, Greenfield Public Library, 402 Main St, Greenfield, MA, 01301. Tel: 413-772-1544. Fax: 413-772-1589. p. 1092

Clifford, Jerie, Librn, Nye County Law Library, 101 Radar Rd, Tonopah, NV, 89049. Tel: 775-482-8141. Fax: 775-482-8198. p. 1435

Clifford, Lois E, Librn, Renison University College Library, 240 Westmount Rd N, Waterloo, ON, N2L 3G4, CANADA. Tel: 519-884-4400, 519-884-4404, Ext 28646. Fax: 519-884-5135. p. 2869

Clift, Clifford, Exec Dir, Mutual UFO Network, Inc, 2619 W 11th St Rd, Ste 21, Greeley, CO, 80634. p. 312

Clift, Terry, Mgr, United Health Services, 33-57 Harrison St, Johnson City, NY, 13790. Tel: 607-763-6030. Fax: 607-763-5992. p. 1647

Clifton, Cathey, Tech Serv, Harnett County Public Library, 601 S Main St, Lillington, NC, 27546-6107. Tel: 910-893-3446. Fax: 910-893-3001. p. 1806

Clifton, Christine, Dir, Quogue Library, 90 Quogue St, Quogue, NY, 11959. Tel: 631-653-4224. Fax: 631-653-6151. p. 1725

Clifton, Deborah J, PhD, Dr, Coll Curator, Librn, Lafayette Natural History Museum & Planetarium, 433 Jefferson St, Lafayette, LA, 70501-7013. Tel: 337-291-5415. Fax: 337-291-5464. p. 952

Clifton, Felecia, Br Mgr, University of North Dakota, Gordon Erickson Music Library, Hughes Fine Arts Ctr 170, 3350 Campus Rd, Stop 7125, Grand Forks, ND, 58202-7125. Tel: 701-777-2817. Fax: 701-777-3319. p. 1843

Clifton, Jennifer, LSTA Coordr, Indiana State Library, 315 W Ohio St, Indianapolis, IN, 46202. Tel: 317-234-6550. Fax: 317-232-0002. p. 752

Clifton, Sarah, Asst Librn, Columbus County Public Library, East Columbus Library, 103 Church Rd, Riegelwood, NC, 28456. Tel: 910-655-4157. Fax: 910-655-9414. p. 1829

Clifton, Shari, Bibliographer, University of Oklahoma Health Sciences Center, 1000 Stanton L Young Blvd, Oklahoma City, OK, 73117-1213. Tel: 405-271-2285. Fax: 405-271-3297. p. 1975

Cline, Andrea, Dir, Oaklyn Memorial Library, 602 Newton Ave, Oaklyn, NJ, 08107. Tel: 856-858-8226. p. 1515

Cline, Carrie, Dir, McDonald County Library, 808 Bailey Rd, Pineville, MO, 64856. Tel: 417-223-4489. Fax: 417-223-4011. p. 1349

Cline, Claire, Br Mgr, Central Manitoulin Public Libraries, Providence Bay Branch, 11 Mutchmor St, Providence Bay, ON, P0P 1T0, CANADA. Tel: 705-377-4503. p. 2822

Cline, Claire, Head Librn, Central Manitoulin Public Libraries, 6020 Hwy 542, Mindemoya, ON, P0P 1S0, CANADA. Tel: 705-377-5334. Fax: 705-377-5334. p. 2822

Cline, Consuela, Coordr, Libr Instruction, Coordr, Ref (Info Serv), Mercer University, Jack Tarver Library, 1300 Edgewood Ave, Macon, GA, 31207. Tel: 478 301 5334. Fax: 478-301-2111. p. 540

Cline, James D, Dir, Porter County Public Library System, 103 Jefferson St, Valparaiso, IN, 46383-4820. Tel: 219-462-0524, Ext 126. Fax: 219-477-4866. p. 783

Cline, John, Chief Librn, Department of Veterans Affairs, PO Box 5000-142D, Hines, IL, 60141-5142. Tel: 708-202-2000. Fax: 708-202-2719. p. 656

Cline, Jonathan, Br Mgr, Dayton Metro Library, Electra C Doren Branch, 701 Troy St, Dayton, OH, 45404. Tel: 937-496-8928. Fax: 937-496-4328. p. 1893

Cline, Kent, Ser, Clackamas Community College, 19600 S Molalla Ave, Oregon City, OR, 97045. Tel: 503-657-6958, Ext 2289. Fax: 503-655-8925. p. 2009

Cline, LaVerne, Asst Librn, Young Public Library, 150 Community Center Rd, Young, AZ, 85554. Tel: 928-462-3588. Fax: 928-462-3588. p. 90

Cline, Lee Ann, Archives, Cat Librn, Tech Serv Librn, Dalton State College, 650 College Dr, Dalton, GA, 30720-3778. Tel: 706-272-4585. Fax: 706-272-4511. p. 528

Cline, Lynn S, Head, Acq & Coll Develop, Missouri State University, 850 S John Q Hammons Pkwy, Springfield, MO, 65807. Tel: 417-836-4658. Fax: 417-836-4764. p. 1367

Cline, Lynn S, Prof, Missouri State University, Duane G Meyer Library, 901 S National Ave, Springfield, MO, 65897. Tel: 417-836-4525. Fax: 417-836-4764. p. 2968

Cline, Suzanne, Dir, Shelby County Libraries, 230 E North St, Sidney, OH, 45365-2785. Tel: 937-492-8354. Fax: 937-492-9229. p. 1934

Cline, Virginia, YA Serv, Atlanta-Fulton Public Library System, Dr Robert E Fulton Regional at Ocee, 5090 Abbotts Bridge Rd, Alpharetta, GA, 30005-4601. Tel: 770-360-8897. Fax: 770-360-8892. p. 512

Clinger, Melinda, Dir, Fulton County Historical Society, Inc, 37 E 375 N, Rochester, IN, 46975-8384. Tel: 574-223-4436. Fax: 574-224-4436. p. 776

Clini, Judith M, Dir, Agawam Public Library, 750 Cooper St, Agawam, MA, 01001. Tel: 413-789-1550. Fax: 413-789-1552. p. 1048

Clink, Kellian, Instrul Serv Librn, Ref Librn, Minnesota State University, Mankato, ML3097, Mankato, MN, 56001. Tel: 507-389-5952. Fax: 507-389-5155. p. 1257

Clinkscales, Geneen, Educ Tech Librn, Johnson C Smith University, 100 Beatties Ford Rd, Charlotte, NC, 28216. Tel: 704-371-6740. Fax: 704-378-1191. p. 1783

Clinkscales, Joyce, Media Spec, Music, Emory University Libraries, Robert W Woodruff Library, 540 Asbury Circle, Atlanta, GA, 30322-2870. Tel: 404-727-1066. Fax: 404-727-2257. p. 514

Clinton, Beth, Chief Librn, Cumberland Public Libraries, 21 Acadia St, 2nd Flr, Amherst, NS, B4H 4W3, CANADA. Tel: 902-667-1767. Fax: 902-667-1360. p. 2777

Clinton, Greg, Lecturer, University of Georgia, College of Education, 224 River's Crossing, Athens, GA, 30602-7144. Tel: 706-542-4110. Fax: 706-542-4032. p. 2964

Clinton, Karen, Children & Teen Librn, Redford Township District Library, 25320 W Six Mile, Redford, MI, 48240. Tel: 313-531-5960. Fax: 313-531-1721. p. 1220

Clinton, Marshall, Dir, Tech & Info Serv, University of Toronto Libraries, 130 St George St, Toronto, ON, M5S 1A5, CANADA. Tel: 416-978-7649. Fax: 416-978-1608. p. 2865

Clintworth, William A, Dir, University of Southern California Libraries, Norris Medical Library, 2003 Zonal Ave, Los Angeles, CA, 90089-9130. Tel: 323-442-1116. Fax: 323-221-1235. p. 179

Clipp, Jane, Per, Martinsburg-Berkeley County Public Library, 101 W King St, Martinsburg, WV, 25401. Tel: 304-267-8933. Fax: 304-267-9720. p. 2565

Clipperton, Celeste, Ch & Youth Librn, Watonwan County Library, 125 Fifth St S, Saint James, MN, 56081. Tel: 507-375-1278. Fax: 507-375-5415. p. 1276

Clive, Myndi, Ref Librn, Washoe County Law Library, 75 Courth St, Rm 101, Reno, NV, 89501. Tel: 775-328-3250. Fax: 775-328-3441. p. 1433

Clontz, Marcia Joyner, Dir, Nantahala Regional Library, 11 Blumenthal St, Murphy, NC, 28906. Tel: 828-837-2025. Fax: 828-837-6406. p. 1812

Cloonan, Ann, Dir, Bedford Free Library, On the Village Green, Bedford, NY, 10506. Tel: 914-234-3570. Fax: 914-234-0546. p. 1579

Cloonan, Michele V, Dean, Prof, Simmons College, 300 The Fenway, Boston, MA, 02115. Tel: 617-521-2800. Fax: 617-521-3192. p. 2967

Clooney, Amber, Electronic Ref Librn, Chicopee Public Library, 449 Front St, Chicopee, MA, 01013. Tel: 413-594-1800, Ext 114. Fax: 413-594-1819. p. 1081

Cloran, Jane, Dir, Abbie Greenleaf Library, 439 Main St, Franconia, NH, 03580. Tel: 603-823-8424. Fax: 603-823-5581. p. 1447

Close, Heather, Ref & Res Coordr, Alberta Legislature Library, 216 Legislature Bldg, 10800-97 Ave, Edmonton, AB, T5K 2B6, CANADA. Tel: 780-427-0204. Fax: 780-427-6016. p. 2699

Closson, Carol, Librn, Parkland Regional Library, Stockholm Branch, PO Box 173, Stockholm, SK, S0A 3Y0, CANADA. Tel: 306-793-2102. p. 2932

Closson, Michael, Exec Dir, Acterra Environmental Library, 3921 E Bayshore Rd, Palo Alto, CA, 94303. Tel: 650-962-9876, Ext 303. Fax: 650-962-8234. p. 204

Closz, Jean, Ch, Blount County Public Library, 508 N Cusick St, Maryville, TN, 37804-5714. Tel: 865-982-0981. Fax: 865-977-1142. p. 2246

Clotfelter, Jennifer, Ref, Atlanta Christian College, 2605 Ben Hill Rd, East Point, GA, 30344-1999. Tel: 404-669-2097. Fax: 404-669-4009. p. 531

Clotworthy, Christopher B, Librn, Resources for the Future Inc Library, 1616 P St NW, Rm B-6, Washington, DC, 20036-1400. Tel: 202-328-5089. Fax: 202-939-3460. p. 413

Cloud, Scott, Librn, Dick Conner Correctional Center Leisure Library, PO Box 220, Hominy, OK, 74035. Tel: 918-594-1300, Ext 4416. Fax: 918-594-1324. p. 1965

Cloud, Susan, ILL Coordr, Lake Forest College, 555 N Sheridan, Lake Forest, IL, 60045. Tel: 847-735-5062. Fax: 847-735-6297. p. 663

Clough, Spencer, Assoc Dir, The State Library of Massachusetts, State House, Rm 341, 24 Beacon St, Boston, MA, 02133. Tel: 617-727-2403. Fax: 617-727-5819. p. 1067

Clough, Spencer, Dir, Southern New England School of Law Library, 333 Faunce Corner Rd, North Dartmouth, MA, 02747. Tel: 508-998-9888. p. 1112

Clougherty, Leo, Head Librn, University of Iowa Libraries, Biological Sciences, 120 Iowa Ave, Iowa City, IA, 52242-1325. Tel: 319-335-3083. Fax: 319-335-2698. p. 823

Clougherty, Leo, Librn, University of Iowa Libraries, Chemistry, 400 Chemistry Bldg, Iowa City, IA, 52242. Tel: 319-335-3085. Fax: 319-335-1193. p. 823

Clougherty, Leo, Librn, University of Iowa Libraries, Geoscience, 136 Trowbridge Hall, Iowa City, IA, 52242. Tel: 319-335-3084. Fax: 319-335-3419. p. 823

Clouse, Bev, Libr Serv Mgr, Mohave County Library District, Kingman Branch, 3269 N Burbank St, Kingman, AZ, 86401. Tel: 928-692-2665. Fax: 928-692-5788. p. 67

Clouse, Linda, Head, Reader Serv, Almont District Library, 213 W St Clair St, Almont, MI, 48003-8476. Tel: 810-798-3100. Fax: 810-798-2208. p. 1149

Clouser, Christopher, Sci, Indiana University of Pennsylvania, 431 S 11th St, Indiana, PA, 15705-1096. Tel: 724-357-5697. Fax: 724-357-4891. p. 2071

Clouser, Marilyn, Librn, Mount Angel Public Library, 290 E Charles St, Mount Angel, OR, 97362. Tel: 503-845-6401. Fax: 503-845-6261. p. 2007

Clouthier, Richard, Librn, Greater Sudbury Public Library, Valley East, 4100 Elmview Dr, Hanmer, ON, P3P 1J7, CANADA. Tel: 705-688-3961. Fax: 705-969-7787. p. 2846

Cloutier, Bryan, Dir, Oxford Public Library, 530 Pontiac Rd, Oxford, MI, 48371-4844. Tel: 248-628-3034. Fax: 248-628-5008. p. 1216

Cloutier, Cathy, Ch, Kelley Library, 234 Main St, Salem, NH, 03079-3190. Tel: 603-898-7064. Fax: 603-898-8583. p. 1464

Cloutier, Claudette, Assoc Vice-Provost - Learning/Librn, University of Calgary Library, 2500 University Dr NW, Calgary, AB, T2N 1N4, CANADA. Tel: 403-220-3447. Fax: 403-282-1218. p. 2693

Cloutier, Russell, Asst Dir, Warren Free Public Library, 282 Main St, Warren, ME, 04864. Tel: 207-273-2900. p. 1004

Clover, Carol, Dir, Info Serv, Maywood Public Library District, 121 S Fifth Ave, Maywood, IL, 60153. Tel: 708-343-1847, Ext 21. Fax: 708-343-2115. p. 672

Clover, Linda, Librn, New Hanover County Public Library, Northeast Regional Library, 1241 Military Cutoff Rd, Wilmington, NC, 28403. Tel: 910-798-6370. Fax: 910-256-1238. p. 1830

Clover-Owens, Ryan, Dir, Durland Alternatives Library, Cornell University, 127 Anabel Taylor Hall, Rm 127, Ithaca, NY, 14853-1001. Tel: 607-255-6486. Fax: 607-255-9985. p. 1642

Clow, Pamela, Coll & Delivery Serv Mgr, Quincy Public Library, 526 Jersey St, Quincy, IL, 62301-3996. Tel: 217-223-1309, Ext 243. Fax: 217-222-5672. p. 693

Clowers, John E, Cat, Circ Supvr, Arkansas State University, Palm & Iowa Sts, Beebe, AR, 72012. Tel: 501-882-8808. Fax: 501-882-8833. p. 94

Clowers, Katherine, Librn, Pamlico County Library, 603 Main St, Bayboro, NC, 28515. Tel: 252-745-3515. Fax: 252-745-3847. p. 1776

Cloyd, Kathleen, Librn, DeKoven Foundation, 600 21st St, Racine, WI, 53403. Tel: 262-633-6401. Fax: 262-633-6401. p. 2632

Cloyd, Steve, Librn, University of Wisconsin-Madison, Plant Pathology Memorial, 1630 Linden Dr, Rm 584, Madison, WI, 53706. Tel: 608-262-8698. Fax: 608-263-2626. p. 2609

Clubb, Warren, Curator, Western Development Museum, 2935 Melville St, Saskatoon, SK, S7J 5A6, CANADA. Tel: 306-934-1400, Ext 228. Fax: 306-934-4467. p. 2927

Cluchey, Marilyn, Dir, Pentwater Township Library, 402 E Park, Pentwater, MI, 49449. Tel: 231-869-8581. Fax: 231-869-4000. p. 1217

Cluchey, Phyllis, Br Mgr, Mid-Continent Public Library, Camden Point Branch, 401 Hardesty St, Camden Point, MO, 64018-2528. Tel: 816-280-3384. Fax: 816-280-3384. p. 1332

Clum, Linda L, Dir, Fair Haven Public Library, 14426 Richmond Ave, Fair Haven, NY, 13064. Tel: 315-947-5851. Fax: 315-947-5851. p. 1621

Clumpner, Krista, Head, Tech Serv, Northern Michigan University, 1401 Presque Isle, Marquette, MI, 49855. Tel: 906-227-1205. Fax: 906-227-1333. p. 1206

Clymer, Denna, Libr Spec, Crowder College, 601 Laclede Ave, Neosho, MO, 64850. Tel: 417-455-5610. Fax: 417-451-4280. p. 1347

Clymer, Frances Backus, Dir, Park County Public Library, 1500 Heart Mountain St, Cody, WY, 82414. Tel: 307-527-1881. Fax: 307-527-1888. p. 2653

Clyne, Christine, Genealogy & Hist Librn, Cook Memorial Library, 93 Main St, Tamworth, NH, 03886. Tel: 603-323-8510. Fax: 603-323-2077. p. 1466

Clyne, Dawn, Info Tech, Minnesota State University, Mankato, ML3097, Mankato, MN, 56001. Tel: 507-389-5952. Fax: 507-389-5155. p. 1257

Coady, Marie, Ch, Holmes Public Library, 470 Plymouth St, Halifax, MA, 02338. Tel: 781-293-2271. Fax: 781-294-8518. p. 1093

Coakley, Gail, Adult Serv, Head, Ref, Easton Area Public Library & District Center, 515 Church St, Easton, PA, 18042-3587. Tel: 610-258-2917. Fax: 610-253-2231. p. 2052

Coakley, Lynn, Coordr, Tech Serv, Springfield Technical Community College Library, One Armory Sq, Ste 1, Springfield, MA, 01105-1685. Tel: 413-755-4565. Fax: 413-755-6315. p. 1128

Coakley, Lynn, Coordr, Cooperating Libraries of Greater Springfield, Springfield Technical Community College, One Armory Sq, Springfield, MA, 01102. Tel: 413-755-4565. Fax: 413-755-6315. p. 2945

Coakley-Welch, Kevin, Law Librn, Commonwealth of Massachusetts, One Ashburton Pl, Boston, MA, 02108. Tel: 617-693-2060, 617-693-2098. Fax: 617-727-6016. p. 1059

Coale, Kim, Tech Serv, Jefferson Davis Community College, 220 Alco Dr, Brewton, AL, 36426. Tel: 251-809-1582. Fax: 251-809-1548. p. 11

Coalson, Marianne, Br Mgr, Cedar Mill Community Library, Bethany Branch, 15325 NW Central Dr, Ste J-8, Portland, OR, 97229. Tel: 503-617-7323. p. 2010

Coalter, Harriet H, Dir, Richmond Public Library, 38 W Main, Richmond, UT, 84333-1409. Tel: 435-258-5525. Fax: 435-258-3604. p. 2411

Coalter, Harriet H, Libr Dir, Richmond Public Library, 101 E Franklin St, Richmond, VA, 23219-2193. Tel: 804-646-4550. Fax: 804-646-7685. p. 2489

Coalter, Milton J, Jr, Dr, Dir, Union Theological Seminary & Presbyterian School of Christian Education, 3401 Brook Rd, Richmond, VA, 23227. Tel: 804-278-4311. Fax: 804-278-4375. p. 2490

Coalwell, Mickey, Libr Develop Consult, Northeast Kansas Library System, 4317 W Sixth St, Lawrence, KS, 66049. Tel: 785-838-4090. Fax: 785-838-3989. p. 878

Coard, Eric, Chief Business Officer, District of Columbia Public Library, 901 G St NW, Washington, DC, 20001-4599. Tel: 202-727-1103. Fax: 202-727-1129. p. 398

Coate, Carol Netzley, Dir, Milton-Union Public Library, 560 S Main St, West Milton, OH, 45383. Tel: 937-698-5515. Fax: 937-698-3774. p. 1946

Coates, Carolyn, Acq Librn, Eastern Connecticut State University, 83 Windham St, Willimantic, CT, 06226-2295. Tel: 860-465-5557. Fax: 860-465-5523. p. 378

Coates, Charlene, ILL, Coatesville Area Public Library, 501 E Lincoln Hwy, Coatesville, PA, 19320-3413. Tel: 610-384-4115. Fax: 610-384-7551. p. 2046

Coates, Jean, Asst Dir, Access & Acq, Davidson College, 209 Ridge Rd, Davidson, NC, 28035-0001. Tel: 704-894-2332. Fax: 704-894-2625. p. 1786

Coates, Joe, Archives, Calumet College of Saint Joseph, 2400 New York Ave, Whiting, IN, 46394. Tel: 219-473-4376. Fax: 219-473-4259. p. 788

Coates, Kevin, Adult Serv, Lambton County Library, 787 Broadway St, Wyoming, ON, N0N 1T0, CANADA. Tel: 519-845-3324, Ext 5233. Fax: 519-845-0700. p. 2872

Coates, Kit, Ch, Cedar Park Public Library, 550 Discovery Blvd, Cedar Park, TX, 78613. Tel: 512-401-5634. Fax: 512-259-5236. p. 2296

Coatney, Lou, ILL, Carl Sandburg College, 2400 Tom L Wilson Blvd, Galesburg, IL, 61401. Tel: 309-341-5257. Fax: 309-344-3526. p. 647

Coats, Laurie, Coordr, East Texas Medical Center, 100 S Beckham Ave, Tyler, TX, 75701. Tel: 903-531-8685. Fax: 903-535-6464. p. 2393

Cobane, Marjorie, Youth Serv, Utica Public Library, 303 Genesee St, Utica, NY, 13501. Tel: 315-735-2279. Fax: 315-734-1034. p. 1760

Cobaugh, Carol, Circ, Bala-Cynwyd Library, 131 Old Lancaster Rd, Bala Cynwyd, PA, 19004-3037. Tel: 610-664-1196. Fax: 610-664-5534. p. 2030

Cobb, Adrienne, Publ & Ref Librn, South Texas College of Law, 1303 San Jacinto St, Houston, TX, 77002-7000. Tel: 713-646-1711. Fax: 713-659-2217. p. 2342

Cobb, Becky, Dep Dir, Multnomah County Library, 205 NE Russell St, Portland, OR, 97212-3796. Tel: 503-988-5403. Fax: 503-988-5441. p. 2011

Cobb, Betty, Youth Serv Mgr, Johnson City Public Library, 100 W Millard St, Johnson City, TN, 37604. Tel: 423-434-4350. Fax: 423-434-4469. p. 2240

Cobb, Christopher, Libr Dir, Monterey County Law Library, 100 W Alisal, Ste 144, Salinas, CA, 93901. Tel: 831-755-5046. Fax: 831-422-9593. p. 226

Cobb, Christopher, Libr Dir, Monterey County Law Library, Monterey Branch, Monterey County Court House, 1200 Aguajito Rd, Rm 202, Monterey, CA, 93940. Tel: 831-647-7746. Fax: 831-372-6036. p. 226

Cobb, David, Head, Map Coll, Harvard Library, Social Sciences Program, Lamont Library, Level B, Harvard University, Cambridge, MA, 02138. Tel: 617-495-2106. Fax: 617-496-5570. p. 1076

Cobb, Elizabeth, Ref Serv, Jefferson County Library, Windsor, 7479 Metropolitian Blvd, Barnhart, MO, 63012. Tel: 636-461-1914. Fax: 636-461-1915. p. 1331

Cobb, Jannie R, Librn, The George Meany Memorial Archives Library, National Labor College, 10000 New Hampshire Ave, Silver Spring, MD, 20903. Tel: 301-431-5447. Fax: 301-628-0161. p. 1041

Cobb, Joyce, Sr Librn, Hennepin County Library, Minneapolis Central, 300 Nicollet Mall, Minneapolis, MN, 55401. Tel: 612-543-8179. Fax: 612-543-8173. p. 1264

Cobb, Margaret, Mgr, Forsyth Medical Center, 3333 Silas Creek Pkwy, Winston-Salem, NC, 27103-3090. Tel: 336-718-5995. p. 1833

Cobb, Tee, Br Librn, York County Library, Clover Public, 107 Knox St, Clover, SC, 29710. Tel: 803-222-3474. Fax: 803-222-6695. p. 2203

Cobbs, Carol, Dir, Fiscal Officer, Columbiana Public Library, 332 N Middle St, Columbiana, OH, 44408. Tel: 330-482-5509. Fax: 330-482-9669. p. 1883

Cobbs, Chris, Ch, Dunlap Public Library District, 302 S First St, Dunlap, IL, 61525. Tel: 309-243-5716. Fax: 309-243-5874. p. 638

Cobell, Mary, Circ, Kinnelon Public Library, 132 Kinnelon Rd, Kinnelon, NJ, 07405-2393. Tel: 973-838-1321. Fax: 973-838-0741. p. 1493

Coberly, William, Dir of Libr Serv, Shepherds Theological Seminary Library, 6051 Tryon Rd, Cary, NC, 27518. Tel: 919-573-1556. Fax: 919-573-1438. p. 1780

Cobham, Jude, LTA Supvr, Circ, Florida International University, 3000 NE 151st St, North Miami, FL, 33181-3600. Tel: 305-919-5797. Fax: 305-919-5914. p. 472

Coble, Carol, Librn, Texhoma Public Library, PO Box 647, Texhoma, OK, 73949-0647. Tel: 580-423-7150. p. 1980

Coble, Crystal, Librn, White River Regional Library, Sharp County - Williford Branch, 232 Main St, Williford, AR, 72482. Tel: 870-966-4227. p. 94

Coble, Jim, Head, Core Serv, IT, Duke University Libraries, 411 Chapel Dr, Durham, NC, 27708. Tel: 919-660-5974. Fax: 919-660-5923. p. 1787

Coblish, Denise Lynn, Dir, Round Lake Library, 31 Wesley Ave, Round Lake, NY, 12151. Tel: 518-899-2285. Fax: 518-899-0006. p. 1736

Cobon, Linda, Archivist, Canadian National Exhibition Archives, Exibition Pl, Two Manitoba Dr, Toronto, ON, M6K 3C3, CANADA. Tel: 416-263-3658. Fax: 416-263-3591. p. 2852

Cobos, Ana Maria, Circ, Saddleback College, 28000 Marguerite Pkwy, Mission Viejo, CA, 92692. Tel: 949-528-4542. Fax: 949-364-0284. p. 187

Coburn, Angie, Circ, Gardendale Martha Moore Public Library, 995 Mt Olive Rd, Gardendale, AL, 35071. Tel: 205-631-6639. Fax: 205-631-0146. p. 18

Coburn, Carrie, Br Mgr, Saint Louis County Library, Cliff Cave Branch, 5430 Telegraph Rd, Saint Louis, MO, 63129. Tel: 314-487-6003. p. 1358

Coburn, Oakley H, Dean, Wofford College, 429 N Church St, Spartanburg, SC, 29303-3663. Tel: 864-597-4300. Fax: 864-597-4329. p. 2206

Cocchia, Anita, Exec Dir, BC Electronic Library Network, WAC Bennett Library, 7th Flr, Simon Fraser University, 8888 University Dr, Burnaby, BC, V5A 1S6, CANADA. Tel: 778-782-7004. Fax: 778-782-3023. p. 2959

Cocciolo, Anthony, Head, Tech, Teachers College, Columbia University, 525 W 120th St, New York, NY, 10027-6696. Tel: 212-678-3769. p. 1701

Cochet, Joan, Libr Mgr, National Center for State Courts Library, 300 Newport Ave, Williamsburg, VA, 23185-4147. Tel: 757-259-1826. Fax: 757-259-2096. p. 2503

Cochran, Cathy, Electronic Res, University of Tennessee, Taylor Law Center, 1505 W Cumberland Ave, Knoxville, TN, 37996-1800. Tel: 865-974-0236. Fax: 865-974-6571, 865-974-6595. p. 2243

Cochran, Christine, ILL, Mount Union College Library, 1972 Clark Ave, Alliance, OH, 44601-3993. Tel: 330-823-3844. Fax: 330-823-3963. p. 1854

Cochran, Elissa, Librn, Provena Covenant Medical Center Library, 1400 W Park St, Urbana, IL, 61801. Tel: 217-337-2283. Fax: 217-337-2299. p. 711

Cochran, Jennifer, Br Supvr, Youth Serv, Barry-Lawrence Regional Library, Eagle Rock Branch, 27824 State Hwy 86, Eagle Rock, MO, 65641. Tel: 417-271-3186. Fax: 417-271-3186. p. 1346

Cochran, Keith, Assoc Dir, Indiana University Bloomington, William & Gayle Cook Music Library, Simon Music Library & Recital Ctr M160, 200 S Jordan Ave, Bloomington, IN, 47405. Tel: 812-855-2970. Fax: 812-855-3843. p. 727

Cochran, Lori A, Dir, Powers Library, 29 Church St, Moravia, NY, 13118. Tel: 315-497-1955. Fax: 315-497-3284. p. 1663

Cochran, Mable, Librn, Pine Forest Regional Library, McLain Public, 117 Church Ave, McLain, MS, 39456. Tel: 601-753-2364. Fax: 601-753-2364. p. 1314

Cochran, Marilyn, Dir, Orland Free Library, 333 Mill St, Orland, CA, 95963. Tel: 530-865-1640. p. 201

Cochran, Richard M, Assoc Dean of Libr, Central Michigan University, Park 407, Mount Pleasant, MI, 48859. Tel: 989-774-6421. Fax: 989-774-2179. p. 1211

Cochran, Sheree, Dir, Alexandria Technical College Library, 1601 Jefferson St, Rm 305, Alexandria, MN, 56308. Tel: 320-762-4465. p. 1239

Cochran, William M, Dir, Parmly Billings Library, 510 N Broadway, Billings, MT, 59101-1196. Tel: 406-657-8292. Fax: 406-657-8293. p. 1374

Cochrane, Joan, Librn, Rideau Lakes Public Library, Delta Branch, 18 King St, Unit 2, Delta, ON, K0E 1G0, CANADA. Tel: 613-928-2991. Fax: 613-928-2991. p. 2803

Cochrane, Joan, Librn, Rideau Lakes Public Library, Portland Branch, Hwy 15, Portland, ON, K0G 1V0, CANADA. Tel: 613-272-2832. Fax: 613-272-2832. p. 2803

Cochrane, Joan, Librn, Rideau Lakes Public Library, South Elmsley, c/o Lombardy Public School RR 1, 596 Hwy 15, Lombardy, ON, K0G 1L0, CANADA. Tel: 613-284-9827. Fax: 613-284-1523. p. 2803

Cochrane, Joseph, Ref Supvr, Napa City-County Library, 580 Coombs St, Napa, CA, 94559-3396. Tel: 707-259-8240. Fax: 707-253-4615. p. 192

Cochrane, Kerry, Dir of Libr Serv, Adler School of Professional Psychology, 17 N Dearborn St, Chicago, IL, 60602. Tel: 312-261-4070. Fax: 312-201-8756. p. 605

Cochrane, Laurel, Bibliog Control Librn, University of Notre Dame, 2345 Biolchini Hall of Law, Notre Dame, IN, 46556-4640. Tel: 574-631-0983. Fax: 574-631-6371. p. 771

Cochrane, Linda, Coordr, Chemeketa Cooperative Regional Library Service, c/o Chemeketa Community College, 4000 Lancaster Dr NE, Salem, OR, 97305-1453. Tel: 503-399-5105. Fax: 503-399-7316. p. 2953

Cochrane, Lynn Scott, Dr, Head Librn, Prog Mgr, US Census Bureau Library, Suitland Federal Center, Rm 1L1001, 4600 Silver Hill Rd, Suitland, MD, 20746. Tel: 301-763-6325. Fax: 301-763-4407. p. 1043

Cochrum, Amanda, Coordr of Develop, Spartanburg County Public Libraries, 151 S Church St, Spartanburg, SC, 29306-3241. Tel: 864-596-3500. Fax: 864-596-3518. p. 2205

Cockburn, Brian, Librn, James Madison University Libraries & Educational Technologies, Music Library, MSC 7301, Harrisonburg, VA, 22807. Tel: 540-568-6978. Fax: 540-568-7819. p. 2470

Cockburn, Brian, Music Librn, James Madison University Libraries & Educational Technologies, 800 S Main St, Harrisonburg, VA, 22807-0001. Tel: 540-568-9678. Fax: 540-568-6339. p. 2470

Cockburn, Frances, Archives, West Nipissing Public Library, 225 rue Holditch, Ste 107, Sturgeon Falls, ON, P2B 1T1, CANADA. Tel: 705-753-2620. Fax: 705-753-2131. p. 2845

Cockburn, Jean, Online Serv, Douglas College Library, 700 Royal Ave, New Westminster, BC, V3M 5Z5, CANADA. Tel: 604-527-5184. Fax: 604-527-5193. p. 2734

Cockburn, Leslie, Young Adult & Adult Serv Coordr, York Library Region, Fredericton Public Library, 12 Carleton St, Fredericton, NB, E3B 5P4, CANADA. Tel: 506-460-2482. Fax: 506-460-2801. p. 2764

Cocker, Susanna, Libr Assoc/Tech Serv, John F Kennedy Memorial Library, 92 Hathaway St, Wallington, NJ, 07057. Tel: 973-471-1692. Fax: 973-471-1387. p. 1539

Cockerham, Robyn, Librn, Louisiana House of Representatives, PO Box 94012, Baton Rouge, LA, 70804-9012. Tel: 225-342-2430. Fax: 225-342-2431. p. 943

Cockram, Alison, Ref & Instruction Librn, New River Community College, 226 Martin Hall, Dublin, VA, 24084. Tel: 540-674-3600, Ext 4331. Fax: 540-676-3626. p. 2460

Cockrell, Barbara, Assoc Dean, Coll & Tech Serv, Western Michigan University, Arcadia at Vande Giessen St, Kalamazoo, MI, 49008-5353. Tel: 269-387-5143. Fax: 269-387-5077. p. 1198

Cockrell, Diane, Per, Ref, Montgomery College, Germantown Campus Library, 20200 Observation Dr, Germantown, MD, 20876. Tel: 301-353-7850. Fax: 301-353-7859. p. 1037

Cockrell, Lucinda Poole, Archivist, Coordr, Res Coll, Middle Tennessee State University, Center for Popular Music, John Bragg Mass Communication Bldg, Rm 140, 1301 E Main St, Murfreesboro, TN, 37132. Tel: 615-898-5884. Fax: 615-898-5829. p. 2254

Cockrell, Michael, Head, Info & Reader Serv, Kalamazoo Public Library, 315 S Rose St, Kalamazoo, MI, 49007-5264. Tel: 269-553-7841. Fax: 269-553-7999. p. 1197

Cockrum, Judi, Librn, Dahlgren Public Library, Third & Dale St, Dahlgren, IL, 62828. Tel: 618-736-2652. Fax: 618-736-2652. p. 632

Coco, Anne, Graphic Arts Librn, Academy of Motion Picture Arts & Sciences, 333 S La Cienega Blvd, Beverly Hills, CA, 90211. Tel: 310-247-3000, Ext 2274. Fax: 310-657-5193. p. 128

Coco, Mary Beth, Ch, Glen Cove Public Library, Four Glen Cove Ave, Glen Cove, NY, 11542-2885. Tel: 516-676-2130. Fax: 516-676-2788. p. 1628

Cocozzoli, Gary, Treas, Southeastern Michigan League of Libraries, Lawrence Technological University, 21000 W Ten Mile Rd, Southfield, MI, 48075. Tel: 248-204-3000. Fax: 248-204-3005. p. 2946

Cocozzoli, Gary R, Dir, Lawrence Technological University Library, 21000 W Ten Mile Rd, Southfield, MI, 48075-1058. Tel: 248-204-3000. Fax: 248-204-3005. p. 1228

Coda, Catherine, Head, Circ, Stratford Library Association, 2203 Main St, Stratford, CT, 06615. Tel: 203-385-4161. Fax: 203-381-2079. p. 371

Codding, Jennifer, Tech Serv Supvr, Eustis Memorial Library, 120 N Center St, Eustis, FL, 32726-3598. Tel: 352-357-5686. Fax: 352-357-5450. p. 439

Coddington, Heather, Actg Dir, Ch, Helen Lehmann Memorial Library, 17435 Fifth St, Montverde, FL, 34756. Tel: 407-469-3838. Fax: 407-469-2773. p. 470

Coder, Ann, Librn, Brookhaven College, 3939 Valley View, Farmers Branch, TX, 75244-4997. Tel: 972-860-4854. Fax: 972-860-4675. p. 2319

Codispoti, Margit, Coll Develop, Indiana University-Purdue University Fort Wayne, 2101 E Coliseum Blvd, Fort Wayne, IN, 46805-1499. Tel: 260-481-6507. Fax: 260-481-6509. p. 741

Coduri, Janice G, Dir, Wellesley Free Library, 530 Washington St, Wellesley, MA, 02482. Tel: 781-235-1610, Ext 1129. Fax: 781-235-0495. p. 1135

Coduri, Janice G, Dir, Wellesley Free Library, Fells Branch, 308 Weston Rd, Wellesley, MA, 02482. Tel: 781-235-1610, Ext 1129. Fax: 781-235-0495. p. 1135

Coduri, Janice G, Dir, Wellesley Free Library, Wellesley Hills Branch, 210 Washington St, Wellesley Hills, MA, 02481. Tel: 781-235-1610, Ext 1129. Fax: 781-235-0495. p. 1135

Cody, Chuck, AV, Managing Librn, Columbus Metropolitan Library, 96 S Grant Ave, Columbus, OH, 43215-4781. Tel: 614-645-2275. Fax: 614-849-1157. p. 1884

Cody, Chuck, Managing Librn, Columbus Metropolitan Library, Main Library, 96 S Grant Ave, Columbus, OH, 43215-4781. Tel: 614-645-2275. Fax: 614-849-1389. p. 1885

Cody, Jenon, Dir, Grand Junction Public Library, 106 E Main St, Grand Junction, IA, 50107. Tel: 515-738-2506. Fax: 515-738-2506. p. 818

Cody, Laura, Acq, United States Merchant Marine Academy, 300 Steamboat Rd, Kings Point, NY, 11024-1699. Tel: 516-726-5603. Fax: 516-726-5900. p. 1649

Cody, Shirley, Dir, Three Rivers Public Library, 920 W Michigan Ave, Three Rivers, MI, 49093-2137. Tel: 269-273-8666. Fax: 269-279-9654. p. 1230

Cody, Vicky, Asst Librn, Newfield Public Library, 198 Main St, Newfield, NY, 14867. Tel: 607-564-3594. Fax: 607-564-3594. p. 1705

Cody, Vivian, Librn, Hauptman-Woodward Medical Research Institute, 700 Ellicott St, Buffalo, NY, 14203. Tel: 716-898-8614. Fax: 716-898-8660. p. 1598

Coe, Bridgett, Asst Br Mgr, Kendallville Public Library, Limberlost Public, 164 Kelly St, Rome City, IN, 46784. Tel: 260-854-2775. Fax: 260-854-3382. p. 757

Coe, Cynthia K, Dir, East Moline Public Library, 740 16th Ave, East Moline, IL, 61244-2122. Tel: 309-755-9614. Fax: 309-755-3901. p. 638

Coe, Erica, Head, Instruction Serv, University of Washington Libraries, Tacoma Library, 1900 Commerce St, Box 358460, Tacoma, WA, 98402-3100. Tel: 253-692-4651. Fax: 253-692-4445. p. 2535

Coe, Erin, Chief Curator, Hyde Collection Library, 161 Warren St, Glens Falls, NY, 12801. Tel: 518-792-1761. Fax: 518-792-9197. p. 1629

Coe, Jan, Librn, Rio Hondo Community College Library, 3600 Workman Mill Rd, Whittier, CA, 90601. Tel: 562-908-3417. Fax: 562-463-4642. p. 283

Coe, Janiece, Circ, Bennington Public Library, 15505 Warehouse St, Bennington, NE, 68007. Tel: 402-238-2201. Fax: 402-238-2218. p. 1394

Coe, Jonathan, Head, Pub Serv, Niagara University Library, 5795 Lewiston Rd, Niagara University, NY, 14109. Tel: 716-286-8005. Fax: 716-286-8030. p. 1705

Coe, Judy, Dir, Osceola Public Library, 300 S Fillmore St, Osceola, IA, 50213-2237. Tel: 641-342-2237. Fax: 641-342-6057. p. 837

Coe, Linda, Librn, Florence-Darlington Technical College Libraries, Segars Library Health Sciences Campus, 320 W Cheves St, Florence, SC, 29501. Tel: 843-676-8575. p. 2194

Coe, Linda B, Librn, Florence-Darlington Technical College Libraries, 2715 W Lucas St, Florence, SC, 29501. Tel: 843-661-8032. Fax: 843-661-8266. p. 2193

Coelho, Gail, Tech Serv Supvr, Taunton Public Library, 12 Pleasant St, Taunton, MA, 02780. Tel: 508-821-1410. Fax: 508-821-1414. p. 1130

Coen, Jim, Ref Librn, Columbia University, Thomas J Watson Library of Business & Economics, 130 Uris Hall, 3022 Broadway, MC 9163, New York, NY, 10027. Tel: 212-854-7804. p. 1675

Coen, Julia C, Asst Dir, Westmont Public Library, 428 N Cass, Westmont, IL, 60559-1502. Tel: 630-969-5625. Fax: 630-969-6490. p. 717

Coffee, Marygail, Commun Serv, Winter Park Public Library, 460 E New England Ave, Winter Park, FL, 32789-4493. Tel: 407-623-3486. Fax: 407-623-3489. p. 505

Coffer, Stephanie A, District Dean, LRC Serv, Wayne County Community College District, 801 W Fort St, Detroit, MI, 48226-3010. Tel: 313-496-2358. p. 1172

Coffer, Stephanie A, District Dean, LRC Serv, Wayne County Community College District, Arthur Cartwright LRC Library (Downtown Campus), 1001 W Fort St, Detroit, MI, 48226-3096. Tel: 313-496-2358, Ext 2063. Fax: 313-962-4506. p. 1172

Coffey, Carol, Assoc Dir, Central Arkansas Library System, 100 Rock St, Little Rock, AR, 72201-4698. Tel: 501-918-3008. p. 106

Coffey, Erin, Adult Serv, Sr Ref Librn, Teen Serv, Clark Public Library, 303 Westfield Ave, Clark, NJ, 07066. Tel: 732-388-5999. Fax: 732-388-7866. p. 1479

Coffey, Georgette, Ref & Instruction Librn, Berkeley College Library, Three E 43rd St, New York, NY, 10017. Tel: 212-986-4343. Fax: 212-661-2940. p. 1670

Coffey, Irene D, Librn, Franklin Institute Library, 222 N 20th St, Philadelphia, PA, 19103-1194. Tel: 215-448-1239. Fax: 215-448-1364. p. 2106

Coffey, Jeanne, Librn, Sandstone Public Library, 119 N Fourth St, Sandstone, MN, 55072-0599. Tel: 320-245-2270. p. 1283

Coffey, Nancy, Tech Serv, Spokane Community College Library, Mailstop 2160, Learning Resources Ctr, Bldg 16, 1810 N Greene St, Spokane, WA, 99217-5399. Tel: 509-533-8822. Fax: 509-533-8818. p. 2536

Coffey, Patrick, Ref, Calumet City Public Library, 660 Manistee Ave, Calumet City, IL, 60409. Tel: 708-862-6220. Fax: 708-862-0872. p. 599

Coffin, Carl K, Dir, Colleton County Memorial Library, 600 Hampton St, Walterboro, SC, 29488-4098. Tel: 843-549-5621. Fax: 843-549-5122. p. 2207

Coffman, Hope, Dir, Rockport Public Library, 17 School St, Rockport, MA, 01966. Tel: 978-546-6934. Fax: 978-546-1011. p. 1121

Coffman, Mary, Asst Dir, The Museums of Oglebay Institute Library, Oglebay Institute, The Burton Center, Wheeling, WV, 26003. Tel: 304-242-7272. Fax: 304-242-7287. p. 2574

Coffman, Pat, Asst Dir, Clay County Public Library System, 1895 Town Center Blvd, Orange Park, FL, 32003. Tel: 904-278-3720. Fax: 904-278-6220. p. 475

Coffman, Steve, Dir, San Juan Public Library, 1010 S Standard St, San Juan, TX, 78589. Tel: 956-702-0926. Fax: 956-783-3444. p. 2384

Coffrin, Jill, Ch, Youth Serv, Dorothy Alling Memorial Library, 21 Library Lane, Williston, VT, 05495. Tel: 802-878-4918. Fax: 802-878-3964. p. 2440

Coffta, Michael J, Res Librn, Bloomsburg University of Pennsylvania, 400 E Second St, Bloomsburg, PA, 17815-1301. Tel: 570-389-4224. Fax: 570-389-3066. p. 2035

Cofield, Laura, Head, Acq, Folger Shakespeare Library, 201 E Capitol St SE, Washington, DC, 20003-1094. Tel: 202-544-4600. Fax: 202-544-4623. p. 400

Cofield, Veleda, Managing Librn, Clayton County Library System, 865 Battlecreek Rd, Jonesboro, GA, 30236. Tel: 770-473-3850. Fax: 770-473-3858. p. 536

Cogan, Jennifer, Youth Serv Librn, Bucks County Free Library, Samuel Pierce Branch, 491 Arthur Ave, Perkasie, PA, 18944-1033. Tel: 215-257-9718. Fax: 215-257-0759. p. 2050

Cogan, Lee, Curator, American Folk Art Museum, 45 W 53rd St, New York, NY, 10019. Tel: 212-265-1040. Fax: 212-265-2350. p. 1668

Cogan, Ruth, Dir, Union City Public Library, S Main & Stranahan, Union City, PA, 16438-1322. Tel: 814-438-3209. Fax: 814-438-8031. p. 2147

Cogar, Susanne Nirschl, Tech Serv Librn, Barberton Public Library, 602 W Park Ave, Barberton, OH, 44203-2458. Tel: 330-745-1194. Fax: 330-745-8261. p. 1857

Cogdill, Keith, Dr, Dir, National Institutes of Health Library, 10 Center Dr, Rm 1L25A, Bethesda, MD, 20892. Tel: 301-496-1080. Fax: 301-402-0254. p. 1021

Coger, Barbara, Dir, Hamilton Public Library, 13 Broad St, Hamilton, NY, 13346. Tel: 315-824-3060. Fax: 315-824-8420. p. 1633

Coggins, Timothy L, Assoc Dean, Info Tech, University of Richmond, William T Muse Law Library, 28 Westhampton Way, Richmond, VA, 23173. Tel: 804-289-8218. Fax: 804-289-8683. p. 2491

Coghill, Jeffrey G, Dir, Eastern AHEC Libr Serv/Head, Outreach Serv, East Carolina University, William E Laupus Health Sciences Library, 600 Moye Blvd, Health Sciences Bldg, Greenville, NC, 27834. Tel: 252-744-2066, Fax: 252-744-2672. p. 1798

Coghlan, Michael, Mgr Fac, Indianapolis-Marion County Public Library, 2450 N Meridian St, Indianapolis, IN, 46208. Tel: 317-275-4830. Fax: 317-269-5300. p. 753

Coghlan, Pamela, Librn Supvr, Lorain Public Library System, Domonkas Branch, 4125 E Lake Rd, Sheffield Lake, OH, 44054. Tel: 440-949-7410. Fax: 440-949-7741. p. 1911

Coghlan, Sam, Dir, Stratford Public Library, 19 Saint Andrew St, Stratford, ON, N5A 1A2, CANADA. Tel: 519-271-0220, Ext 15. Fax: 519-271-3843. p. 2845

Coglin, Sam, Chief Exec Officer, Perth County Information Network, c/o Stratford Public Library, 19 Saint Andrew St, Stratford, ON, N5A 1A2, CANADA. Tel: 519-271-0220, Ext 15. Fax: 519-271-3843. p. 2960

Cogswell, James A, Dir of Libr, University of Missouri-Columbia, Elmer Ellis Library, Ellis Library Bldg, Rm 104, Columbia, MO, 65201-5149. Tel: 573-882-4701. Fax: 573-882-8044. p. 1325

Cohan, L, Librn, Levy County Public Library System, AF Knotts Public, 11 56th St, Yankeetown, FL, 34498. Tel: 352-447-4212. Fax: 352-447-4212. p. 430

Cohan-Chase, Susan, Asst Librn, State Education Resource Center Library, 25 Industrial Park Rd, Middletown, CT, 06457-1516. Tel: 860-632-1485, Ext 218. Fax: 860-632-0438. p. 352

Cohee, Phillip, Asst Dir, Danville Public Library, 319 N Vermilion St, Danville, IL, 61832. Tel: 217-477-5223, Ext 118. Fax: 217-477-5230. p. 633

Cohen, Adele, Librn, Environment Canada, 201 - 401 Burrard St, Vancouver, BC, V6C 3S5, CANADA. Tel: 604-666-5914. Fax: 604-666-1788. p. 2741

Cohen, Amy L, Adminr, Harvard-Smithsonian Center for Astrophysics Library, 60 Garden St, MS-56, Cambridge, MA, 02138. Tel: 617-496-7808. Fax: 617-495-7199. p. 1077

Cohen, Andrea, Admin Coordr, Carnegie Mellon University, Hunt Library, 4909 Frew St, Pittsburgh, PA, 15213-3890. Tel: 412-268-2446. Fax: 412-268-2793. p. 2123

Cohen, Buzzard, Coll Develop, Alan Wofsy Fine Arts Reference Library, 1109 Geary Blvd, San Francisco, CA, 94109. Tel: 415-292-6500. Fax: 415-292-6594. p. 249

Cohen, Cheryl, Ref & Educ Serv Librn, Ossining Public Library, 53 Croton Ave, Ossining, NY, 10562-4903. Tel: 914-941-2416, Ext 315. Fax: 914-941-7464. p. 1712

Cohen, Corey, Circ, College of Southern Nevada, 6375 W Charleston Blvd, W10I, Las Vegas, NV, 89146. Tel: 702-651-5781. Fax: 702-651-5718. p. 1429

Cohen, David, Dean of Libr, College of Charleston, 205 Calhoun St, Charleston, SC, 29401-3519. Tel: 843-953-5530. Fax: 843-953-6319. p. 2184

Cohen, Deatra, YA Serv, Yolo County Library, Davis Branch, 315 E 14th St, Davis, CA, 95616. Tel: 530-757-5593. Fax: 530-757-5590. p. 284

Cohen, Debra, Ch, Cumberland Public Library, 1464 Diamond Hill Rd, Cumberland, RI, 02864-5510. Tel: 401-333-2552, Ext 125. Fax: 401-334-0578. p. 2165

Cohen, Eileen, Assoc Librn, University of New Mexico, Law Library, 1117 Stanford Dr NE, Albuquerque, NM, 87131-1441. Tel: 505-277-6236. Fax: 505-277-0068. p. 1551

Cohen, Jack, Curator, New Year Shooters & Mummers Museum Library, 1100 S Second St, Philadelphia, PA, 19147. Tel: 215-336-3050. Fax: 215-389-5630. p. 2113

Cohen, Joan G, Ser Librn, Bergen Community College, 400 Paramus Rd, Paramus, NJ, 07652-1595. Tel: 201-447-7984. Fax: 201-493-8167. p. 1517

Cohen, Jodi, Principal Librn, Tampa-Hillsborough County Public Library System, Upper Tampa Bay Regional Public Library, 1121 Countryway Blvd, Tampa, FL, 33626-2624. Fax: 813-964-2967. p. 498

Cohen, Joel, Librn, Beth Emet Synagogue, 1224 Dempster St, Evanston, IL, 60202. Tel: 847-869-4230. Fax: 847-869-7830. p. 643

Cohen, Joshua, Exec Dir, Mid-Hudson Library System, 103 Market St, Poughkeepsie, NY, 12601-4098. Tel: 845-471-6060. Fax: 845-454-5940. p. 1723

Cohen, Kathleen F, Assoc Dean of Libr, University of North Florida, Bldg 12-Library, One UNF Dr, Jacksonville, FL, 32224-2645. Tel: 904-620-2599. Fax: 904-620-2719. p. 455

Cohen, Kerry, Br Mgr, Suwannee River Regional Library, Greenville Public Library, 312 SW Church Ave, Greenville, FL, 32331. Tel: 850-948-2529. Fax: 850-948-5220. p. 461

Cohen, Lara, Ch, Riverdale Public Library, 93 Newark Pompton Tpk, Riverdale, NJ, 07457. Tel: 973-835-5044. Fax: 973-835-2175. p. 1527

Cohen, Linda K, Librn, Congregation Mishkan Israel Library, 785 Ridge Rd, Hamden, CT, 06517. Tel: 203-288-3877. Fax: 203-248-2148. p. 343

Cohen, Lucy R, Exec Dir, The Book Club of California, 312 Sutter St, Ste 510, San Francisco, CA, 94108-4320. Tel: 415-781-7532. Fax: 415-781-7537. p. 240

Cohen, Madeline, Dir, Newsweek, Inc, 395 Hudson St, New York, NY, 10014. Tel: 212-445-4680. Fax: 212-445-4107. p. 1696

Cohen, Madeline R, Dir, US Courts Library, Byron Rogers Courthouse, 1929 Stout St, Rm 430, Denver, CO, 80294. Tel: 303-844-3591. Fax: 303-844-5958. p. 303

Cohen, Marci, Ref Librn, Berklee College of Music Library, 150 Massachusetts Ave, Boston, MA, 02115. Tel: 617-747-8525. Fax: 617-747-2050. p. 1055

Cohen, Margaret, Head Librn, Boston College Libraries, Educational Resource Center, 140 Commonwealth Ave, Chestnut Hill, MA, 02467. Tel: 617-552-4919. Fax: 617-552-1769. p. 1081

Cohen, Marilyn, Librn, McGill University Libraries, Education & Curriculum Lab, 3700 McTavish St, 1st Flr, Montreal, QC, H3A 1Y2, CANADA. Tel: 514-398-8109. Fax: 514-398-2165. p. 2898

Cohen, Martin, Ref & Instruction Librn, Saint Mary's College Library, 1928 Saint Mary's Rd, Moraga, CA, 94575. Tel: 925-631-4229. Fax: 925-376-6097. p. 191

Cohen, Mary, Mgr, Tech Serv, Palos Verdes Library District, 701 Silver Spur Rd, Rolling Hills Estates, CA, 90274. Tel: 310-377-9584, Ext 242. Fax: 310-541-6807. p. 219

Cohen, Michael, Prof, University of Michigan, 304 West Hall, 1085 S University, Ann Arbor, MI, 48109-1107. Tel: 734-763-2285. Fax: 734-764-2475. p. 2967

Cohen, Naomi, Ref Serv, Saint Joseph's University, Francis A Drexel Library, 5600 City Ave, Philadelphia, PA, 19131-1395. Tel: 610-660-1057. Fax: 610-660-1916. p. 2116

Cohen, Randi, Music, Gratz College, Abner & Mary Schreiber Jewish Music Library, 7605 Old York Rd, Melrose Park, PA, 19027. Tel: 215-635-7300. Fax: 215-635-7320. p. 2088

Cohen, Rebecca, Supv Librn, Youth Serv Librn, Newport Public Library, 35 NW Nye St, Newport, OR, 97365-3714. Tel: 541-265-2153. Fax: 541-574-9496. p. 2007

Cohen, Sandy, Mgr, Nashville Public Library, Library Service for the Deaf & Hard of Hearing, 615 Church St, Nashville, TN, 37219-2314. Tel: 615-862-5750. Fax: 615-862-5494. p. 2257

Cohen, Sarah, Assoc Univ Librn, California Polytechnic State University, One Grand Ave, San Luis Obispo, CA, 93407. Tel: 805-756-2345. Fax: 805-756-2346. p. 253

Cohen, Sarah, Assoc Librn, Head, Cat, Florida State University Libraries, Warren D Allen Music Library, Housewright Music Bldg, 122 N Copeland St, Tallahassee, FL, 32306-1180. Tel: 850-644-4137. Fax: 850-644-3982. p. 494

Cohen, Sarah, Info Literacy Librn, Champlain College Library, 163 S Willard St, Burlington, VT, 05401. Tel: 802-860-2717. p. 2420

Cohen, Scott, Dir, Jackson State Community College Library, 2046 North Pkwy, Jackson, TN, 38301. Tel: 731-425-2615. Fax: 731-425-2625. p. 2238

Cohen, Sharon, Libr Serv Dir, Burbank Public Library, 110 N Glenoaks Blvd, Burbank, CA, 91502-1203. Tel: 818-238-5600. Fax: 818-238-5553. p. 130

Cohen, Sharon, Librn, Gloucester, Lyceum & Sawyer Free Library, Two Dale Ave, Gloucester, MA, 01930-5906. Tel: 978-281-9763. Fax: 978-281-9770. p. 1091

Cohen, Steve, Exec VPres, Student Learning, Laney College, 900 Fallon St, Oakland, CA, 94607. Tel: 510-464-3493. Fax: 510-464-3264. p. 197

Cohen, Steven M, Sr Librn, Mendes & Mount, LLP, 750 Seventh Ave, New York, NY, 10019-6829. Tel: 212-261-8000, 212-261-8338. Fax: 212-261-8750. p. 1686

Cohen-Spiegel, Nancy, Librn, Foundation for Blood Research Library, Eight Science Park Rd, Scarborough, ME, 04070. Tel: 207-883-4131. Fax: 207-885-0807. p. 1000

Cohlman, Jennifer, Librn, Smithsonian Libraries, Cooper-Hewitt, National Design Museum Library, Two E 91st St, 3rd Flr, New York City, DC, 10128. Tel: 212-848-8333. Fax: 212-849-8339. p. 414

Cohn, Clare, Online Serv, New York Institute of Technology, PO Box 8000, Old Westbury, NY, 11568-8000. Tel: 516-686-7657. Fax: 516-686-1320. p. 1710

Cohn, Deborah, Librn & Archivist, Jewish Historical Society of Central Jersey Library, 222 Livingston Ave, New Brunswick, NJ, 08901. Tel: 732-249-4894. Fax: 732-745-7448. p. 1507

Cohn, Erika, Ref, Saint Louis University, Omer Poos Law Library, Morrissey Hall, 3700 Lindell Blvd, Saint Louis, MO, 63108-3478. Tel: 314-977-2759. Fax: 314-977-3966. p. 1361

Cohn, Joan, Pres, Indian & Colonial Research Center, Inc, 39 Main St Rte 27, Old Mystic, CT, 06372. Tel: 860-536-9771. p. 363

Cohn, John M, Dir, County College of Morris, 214 Center Grove Rd, Randolph, NJ, 07869-2086. p. 1525

Cohn, Judith, Univ Librn, University of Medicine & Dentistry of New Jersey, 30 12th Ave, Newark, NJ, 07103-2706. Tel: 973-972-4580. p. 1513

Cohn, Lisa, Librn, Bloomfield Public Library, 90 Broad St, Bloomfield, NJ, 07003. Tel: 973-566-6200, Ext 217. Fax: 973-566-6217. p. 1473

Cohn, Mary, Libr Dir, Austin Memorial Library, 220 S Bonham Ave, Cleveland, TX, 77327-4591. Tel: 281-592-3920. Fax: 281-593-0361. p. 2298

Cohn, Patricia, Sr Librn, Ch Serv, Warner Library, 121 N Broadway, Tarrytown, NY, 10591, Tel: 914-631-7734. Fax: 914-631-2324. p. 1754

Cohn, Roger, Asst Librn, NorthEast-Millerton Library, 75 Main St, Millerton, NY, 12546-5172. Tel: 518-789-3340. Fax: 518-789-6802. p. 1661

Cohn, Suzette, Doc Delivery, ILL, National Renewable Energy Laboratory Library, 15013 Denver West Pkwy, Golden, CO, 80401-3305. Tel: 303-275-4034. Fax: 303-275-4222. p. 310

Cohrs, Mary, Dir, Bellaire City Library, 5111 Jessamine, Bellaire, TX, 77401-4498. Tel: 713-662-8160. Fax: 713-662-8169. p. 2288

Coiffe, Dorothea, Archivist, Head, ILL, Media Serv, Borough of Manhattan Community College Library, 199 Chambers St, New York, NY, 10007. Tel: 212-220-1442. Fax: 212-748-7466. p. 1671

Coil, Tami, Co-Dir, Sloan Public Library, 311 Fourth St, Sloan, IA, 51055. Tel: 712-428-4200. p. 844

Coke, Barbara, Circ Asst, Midland Lutheran College, 900 N Clarkson, Fremont, NE, 68025. Tel: 402-941-6250. Fax: 402-727-6223. p. 1399

Coker, Ann F, Librn, Northeast Regional Library, Corinth Public Library, 1023 Fillmore St, Corinth, MS, 38834-4199. Tel: 662-287-2441. Fax: 662-286-8010. p. 1297

Coker, Brian, Head, Tech Serv, Middle Georgia Regional Library System, 1180 Washington Ave, Macon, GA, 31201-1790. Tel: 478-744-0813. Fax: 478-742-3161. p. 541

Coker, Cait, Coordr of Res Serv, Curator, Texas A&M University Libraries, Cushing Memorial Library & Archives, 5000 TAMU, College Station, TX, 77843-5000. Tel: 979-845-1951. Fax: 979-845-1441. p. 2299

Coker, Janea Kay, Br Supvr, Youth Serv Coordr, Barry-Lawrence Regional Library, Marionville Branch, 303 W Washington St, Marionville, MO, 65705. Tel: 417-463-2675. Fax: 417-463-2116. p. 1346

Coker, Joanne, YA Serv, Mary L Cook Public Library, 381 Old Stage Rd, Waynesville, OH, 45068. Tel: 513-897-4826. Fax: 513-897-9215. p. 1945

Coker, Lisa S, Mgr, Mat Serv, Sterling Municipal Library, Mary Elizabeth Wilbanks Ave, Baytown, TX, 77520. Tel: 281-427-7331. Fax: 281-420-5347. p. 2286

Coker, Rebecca, Librn, Hardin Northern Public Library, 153 N Main St, Dunkirk, OH, 45836-1064. Tel: 419-759-3558. Fax: 419-759-3558. p. 1897

Coker, Sylvia, Br Mgr, Enoch Pratt Free Library, Northwood Branch, 4420 Loch Raven Blvd, Baltimore, MD, 21218-1553. Tel: 410-396-6076. Fax: 410-396-6547. p. 1013

Colander, Joyce, Br Mgr, Chicago Public Library, Beverly, 1962 W 95th St, Chicago, IL, 60643. Tel: 312-747-9673. Fax: 312-747-5062. p. 608

Colaneri, Grace, Head, Literacy, Englewood Public Library, 31 Engle St, Englewood, NJ, 07631. Tel: 201-568-2215. Fax: 201-568-6895. p. 1484

Colantuoni, Joseph, Asst Br Mgr, Worcester County Library, Ocean City Branch, 10003 Coastal Hwy, Ocean City, MD, 21842. Tel: 410-524-1818. Fax: 410-289-5577. p. 1042

Colarosa, Dolores, Ch, Brentwood Library, 3501 Brownsville Rd, Pittsburgh, PA, 15227-3115. Tel: 412-882-5694. p. 2121

Colbeck, Lynda, Libr Mgr, Vancouver Island Regional Library, Parksville Branch, 100 Jensen Ave E, Parksville, BC, V9P 2G6, CANADA. Tel: 250-248-3841. Fax: 250-248-0170. p. 2733

Colbert, Dudley, Br Mgr, Norfolk Public Library, Blyden, 879 E Princess Anne Rd, Norfolk, VA, 23504. Tel: 757-441-2852. Fax: 757-441-1452. p. 2481

Colbert, Gary, Tech Serv, Ada Public Library, 124 S Rennie, Ada, OK, 74820. Tel: 580-436-8121. Fax: 580-436-0534. p. 1955

Colbert, Jan, Children & Young Adult Supvr, Germantown Community Library, 1925 Exeter Rd, Germantown, TN, 38138-2815. Tel: 901-757-7323, Ext 7468. Fax: 901-756-9940. p. 2235

Colbert, Judy, Mgr, Richard T Liddicoat Gemological Library & Information Center, 5345 Armada Dr, Carlsbad, CA, 92008. Tel: 760-603-4075. Fax: 760-603-4256. p. 132

Colbert, Mary, Librn, Dutchess County Genealogical Society Library, 204 Spackenkill Rd, Poughkeepsie, NY, 12603-5135. Tel: 845-462-4168. p. 1722

Colbert, Susan, Programming, Sparta Public Library, 211 W Broadway, Sparta, IL, 62286. Tel: 618-443-5014. Fax: 618-443-2952. p. 704

Colbert-Mar, Louise A, Libr Dir, Alliant International University, 5130 E Clinton Way, Fresno, CA, 93727. Tel: 559-253-2265. Fax: 559-253-2223. p. 150

Colborn, Nancy, Head, Info Literacy, Indiana University South Bend, 1700 Mishawaka Ave, South Bend, IN, 46615. Tel: 574-520-4321. Fax: 574-520-4472. p. 778

Colborne, Allison, Libr Dir, Museum of New Mexico, Museum of Indian Arts & Culture-Laboratory of Anthropology Library, 708 Camino Lejo, Santa Fe, NM, 87505. Tel: 505-476-1264. Fax: 505-476-1330. p. 1562

Colborne, Michael, Coordr, Pub Serv, Nova Scotia Provincial Library, 2021 Brunswick St, 2nd Flr, Halifax, NS, B3K 2Y5, CANADA. Tel: 902-424-4852. Fax: 902-424-0633. p. 2782

Colborne, Terry, Info Analyst, Fraser Milner Casgrain LLP, Bankers Ct, 15th Flr, 850 Second St SW, Calgary, AB, T2P 0R8, CANADA. Tel: 403-268-7000. Fax: 403-268-3100. p. 2691

Colbourne, Shona, Librn, Victoria Public Library, PO Box 190, Victoria, NL, A0A 4G0, CANADA. Tel: 709-596-3682. p. 2773

Colbow, Carol, Librn, Southeast Regional Library, Pangman Branch, 120 Mergens St, Pangman, SK, S0C 2C0, CANADA. Tel: 306-442-2119. p. 2930

Colburn, Joan, Dir, Mountain Area Health Education Center, 121 Hendersonville Rd, Asheville, NC, 28803. Tel: 828-257-4438. Fax: 828-257-4712. p. 1775

Colby, Anita, Librn, University of California Los Angeles Library, Science & Engineering Libraries, 8270 Boelter Hall, Los Angeles, CA, 90095. Tel: 310-825-3982. Fax: 310-206-9872. p. 179

Colby, Candia, Librn, Norton Public Library, One Washington Sq, Norton, KS, 67654-1615. Tel: 785-877-2481. p. 885

Colby, Celia, Dir, Spring Township Library, 78C Commerce Dr, Wyomissing, PA, 19610. Tel: 610-373-9888. Fax: 610-373-0334. p. 2159

Colby, Celia, VPres, Berks County Library Association, Reading Public Library, 100 S Fifth St, Reading, PA, 19602. Tel: 610-373-9888. p. 2953

Colby, Cheryl, Librn, Silas L Griffith Memorial Library, 74 S Main St, Danby, VT, 05739. Tel: 802-293-5106. p. 2422

Colby, Julie, Dir, Colebrook Public Library, 126 Main St, Colebrook, NH, 03576. Tel: 603-237-4808. p. 1442

Colby, Linda, Youth Serv, Mount Horeb Public Library, 105 Perimeter Rd, Mount Horeb, WI, 53572. Tel: 608-437-5021. Fax: 608-437-6264. p. 2623

Coldren, Cathy, Acq, Bellingham Public Library, 210 Central Ave, CS-9710, Bellingham, WA, 98227-9710. Tel: 360-778-7323. p. 2508

Coldwell, Paula J, Libr Tech, Nova Scotia Community College, 236 Belcher St, Kentville, NS, B4N 0A6, CANADA. Tel: 902-679-7380. Fax: 902-679-5187. p. 2783

Cole, Adam, Pub Serv Librn, Upper Moreland Free Public Library, 109 Park Ave, Willow Grove, PA, 19090-3277. Tel: 215-659-0741. Fax: 215-830-1223. p. 2157

Cole, Amberly, Head, Ref, Edward Gauche Fisher Public Library, 1289 Ingleside Ave, Athens, TN, 37303. Tel: 423-745-7782. Fax: 423-745-1763. p. 2224

Cole, Anna B, Librn, Miles & Stockbridge PC Library, Ten Light St, Baltimore, MD, 21202. Tel: 410-385-3671. Fax: 410-385-3700. p. 1016

Cole, Brad, Assoc Dir, Spec Coll & Archives, Utah State University, 3000 Old Main Hill, Logan, UT, 84322-3000. Tel: 435-797-8268. Fax: 435-797-2880. p. 2407

Cole, Caralinn, Librn, Winston & Strawn Library, 1111 Louisiana St, 25th Fl, Houston, TX, 77002. Tel: 713-787-1400. Fax: 713-787-1440. p. 2345

Cole, Cheryl, Dir, Vernon District Public Library, 115 E Main St, Vernon, MI, 48476. Tel: 989-288-6486. Fax: 989-288-2422. p. 1233

Cole, Christopher H, Actg Dep Dir, United States Department of Agriculture, 10301 Baltimore Ave, Beltsville, MD, 20705-2351. Tel: 301-504-7296. Fax: 301-504-5472. p. 1020

Cole, Claudia, Asst Dir, West Custer County Library District, 209 Main St, Westcliffe, CO, 81252. Tel: 719-783-9138. Fax: 719-783-2155. p. 325

Cole, Connie, Head, Jr Librn, Tiffin-Seneca Public Library, 77 Jefferson St, Tiffin, OH, 44883. Tel: 419-447-3751. Fax: 419-447-3045. p. 1938

Cole, Cynthia, Dir, Nippersink District Library, 5418 Hill Rd, Richmond, IL, 60071. Tel: 815-678-4014. Fax: 815-678-4484. p. 694

Cole, Cynthia, Ref Serv, Ser, Spec Coll Librn, Rust College, 150 E Rust Ave, Holly Springs, MS, 38635. Tel: 662-252-8000, Ext 4100. Fax: 662-252-8873. p. 1302

Cole, Darlene M, Mgr, Colorado Department of Corrections, Fremont Correctional Facility Library, US Hwy 50, Evans Blvd, Canon City, CO, 81215. Tel: 719-269-5002, Ext 3566. Fax: 719-269-5048. p. 293

Cole, David, Youth Serv, The William K Sanford Town Library, 629 Albany Shaker Rd, Loudonville, NY, 12211-1196. Tel: 518-458-9274. Fax: 518-438-0988. p. 1655

Cole, Delores, Ch, Desoto Parish Library, Stonewall Branch, 808 Hwy 171, Stonewall, LA, 71078. Tel: 318-925-9191. Fax: 318-925-3392. p. 956

Cole, Donald W, Dr, Pres, Organization Development Institute Library, 11234 Walnut Ridge Rd, Chesterland, OH, 44026. Tel: 440-729-7419. Fax: 440-729-9319. p. 1867

Cole, Faye, Dir, Lineville Public Library, 60119 Hwy 49, Lineville, AL, 36266. Tel: 256-396-5162. Fax: 256-396-5162. p. 23

Cole, Glenn, Adminr, Transportation Association of Canada, 2323 St Laurent Blvd, Ottawa, ON, K1G 4J8, CANADA. Tel: 613-736-1350. Fax: 613-736-1395. p. 2834

Cole, Jean, Asst Librn, Pontiac Free Library, 101 Greenwich Ave, Warwick, RI, 02886. Tel: 401-737-3292. Fax: 401-737-3292. p. 2177

Cole, Jean Marie, Circ, Guilderland Public Library, 2228 Western Ave, Guilderland, NY, 12084-9701. Tel: 518-456-2400. Fax: 518-456-0923. p. 1632

Cole, Jeffrey, Libr Asst, University of California, Berkeley, Giannini Foundation Library, 248 Giannini Hall, Berkeley, CA, 94720-3310. Tel: 510-642-7121. Fax: 510-643-8911. p. 128

Cole, Joanne M, Libr Mgr, York Library Region, Harvey Community Library, 2055 Rte 3, Harvey Station, NB, E6K 3W9, CANADA. Tel: 506-366-2206. Fax: 506-366-2210. p. 2764

Cole, Judy, Youth Serv, Finney County Public Library, 605 E Walnut St, Garden City, KS, 67846. Tel: 620-272-3680. Fax: 620-272-3682. p. 868

Cole, Julie A, Librn, Queen Elizabeth Hospital, 60 Riverside Dr, Charlottetown, PE, C1A 8T5, CANADA. Tel: 902-894-2371. Fax: 902-894-0259, 902-894-2424. p. 2875

Cole, Karen, Dir, University of Kansas Medical Center, 2100 W 39th Ave, Kansas City, KS, 66160-7180. Tel: 913-588-7166. Fax: 913-588-7304. p. 876

Cole, Kellie, Cat, Greene County Public Library, 120 N 12th St, Paragould, AR, 72450. Tel: 870-236-8711. Fax: 870-236-1442. p. 111

Cole, Leone, Dir, Watertown Free Public Library, 123 Main St, Watertown, MA, 02472. Tel: 617-972-6434. Fax: 617-926-4375. p. 1134

Cole, Lesa, Pub Serv, Iola Public Library, 218 E Madison Ave, Iola, KS, 66749. Tel: 620-365-3262. Fax: 620-365-5137. p. 874

Cole, Leslie, Dir, Burrell Information Center, 233 N Michigan Ave, Ste 2900, Chicago, IL, 60601. Tel: 312-297-9723. Fax: 312-297-9841. p. 607

Cole, Marian, Cat, Amarillo Public Library, 413 E Fourth Ave, Amarillo, TX, 79101. Tel: 806-378-3054. Fax: 806-378-9327. p. 2274

Cole, Marietta, Ch, Millinocket Memorial Library, Five Maine Ave, Millinocket, ME, 04462. Tel: 207-723-7020. Fax: 207-723-7020. p. 992

Cole, Mark, Dir, Satilla Regional Library, 200 S Madison Ave, Ste D, Douglas, GA, 31533. Tel: 912-384-4667. Fax: 912-389-4365. p. 530

Cole, Martha J, Ch, Chesapeake Public Library, 298 Cedar Rd, Chesapeake, VA, 23322-5512. Tel: 757-410-7127. Fax: 757-410-7112. p. 2456

Cole, Maureen, Libr Dir, Oregon City Public Library, 362 Warner Milne Rd, Oregon City, OR, 97045. Tel: 503-657-8269. Fax: 503-657-3702. p. 2009

Cole, Mitzi, Electronic Res Mgt Librn, NASA, Library, Bldg 21, Code 272, Greenbelt, MD, 20771. Tel: 301-286-9348. Fax: 301-286-1755. p. 1030

Cole, Pam, Actg Mgr, Adult Programmer, Upper Arlington Public Library, Lane Road Branch, 1945 Lane Rd, Upper Arlington, OH, 43220. Tel: 614-459-0273. Fax: 614-459-3437. p. 1891

Cole, Patience, Ch, Edward Ward Carmack Sumner County Public Library, 658 Hartsville Pike, Gallatin, TN, 37066-2509. Tel: 615-452-1722. Fax: 615-451-3319. p. 2235

Cole, Rebecca, Dir, Rushford Free Library, 9012 Main St, Rushford, NY, 14777-9700. Tel: 585-437-2533. Fax: 585-437-9940. p. 1736

Cole, Rebecca C, Dir, Sullivan County Public Library, 100 S Crowder St, Sullivan, IN, 47882. Tel: 812-268-4957. Fax: 812-268-5370. p. 780

Cole, Roshella, Librn, Tallahatchie County Library System, Tutwiler Branch, PO Box 214, Tutwiler, MS, 38963. Tel: 662-345-8475. Fax: 662-345-8475. p. 1295

Cole, Sarah, Librn, North East Multi-Regional Training, 355 Smoke Tree Business Park, North Aurora, IL, 60542-1723. Tel: 630-896-8860, Ext 108. Fax: 630-896-4422. p. 681

Cole, Shane, Head, Pub Serv, Brigham Young University-Idaho, 525 S Center St, Rexburg, ID, 83460-0405. Tel: 208-496-9522. Fax: 208-496-9503. p. 582

Cole, Susan W, Sci Librn, Colby College Libraries, Science Library, 5791 Mayflower Hill, Waterville, ME, 04901-4799. Tel: 207-859-5790. Fax: 207-859-5105. p. 1005

Cole, Suzi, Asst Dir, Scholarly Res & Serv/Sci Librn, Colby College Libraries, 5100 Mayflower Hill, Waterville, ME, 04901. Tel: 207-859-5791. Fax: 207-859-5105. p. 1005

Cole, Teresa, Dir, Dougherty County Public Library, 300 Pine Ave, Albany, GA, 31701-2533. Tel: 229-420-3200. Fax: 229-420-3215. p. 507

Cole, Timothy, Librn, University of Illinois Library at Urbana-Champaign, Mathematics, 1409 W Green St, 216 Altgeld Hall, Urbana, IL, 61801. Tel: 217-244-7837. p. 712

Coleburn, Robert, Dir, Syst Adminr, Fletcher Free Library, 235 College St, Burlington, VT, 05401. Tel: 802-865-7218. Fax: 802-865-7227. p. 2420

Colee, Lucinda, Dir, Volusia County Public Library, 1290 Indian Lake Rd, Daytona Beach, FL, 32124. Tel: 386-248-1745. Fax: 386-248-1746. p. 436

Colegrove, Brenda, Dir, Libr Serv, Iowa Lakes Community College Library, 3200 College Dr, Emmetsburg, IA, 50536. Tel: 712-852-5317. Fax: 712-852-3094. p. 814

Colegrove, Brenda, Dir, Iowa Lakes Community Colleges Library, 300 S 18th St, Estherville, IA, 51334. Tel: 712-362-7936. Fax: 712-362-5970. p. 815

Colegrove, Tod, Head Librn, University of Nevada-Reno, DeLaMare Library, 1664 N Virginia St, MS 262, Reno, NV, 89557-0262. Tel: 775-682-5644. Fax: 775-784-6949. p. 1433

Coleman, A Jennifer, Dir, Summerville Public Library, 114 Second Ave, Summerville, PA, 15864. Tel: 814-856-3169. Fax: 814-856-3169. p. 2144

Coleman, Alice, Librn, Wingate Baptist Church Library, 109 E Elm St, Wingate, NC, 28174. Tel: 704-233-4256. Fax: 704-233-0598. p. 1832

Coleman, Alice, Dir, Texarkana Public Library, 600 W Third St, Texarkana, TX, 75501-5054. Tel: 903-794-2149. Fax: 903-794-2139. p. 2392

Coleman, Anne, Archivist, Art Librn, Govt Doc, University of Alabama in Huntsville, 301 Sparkman Dr NW, Huntsville, AL, 35899. Tel: 256-824-6418. Fax: 256-824-6083. p. 22

Coleman, Anne, Asst Dean for Res Serv, University of North Carolina at Pembroke, Faculty Row, Pembroke, NC, 28372. Tel: 910-521-6516. Fax: 910-521-6547. p. 1814

Coleman, Charles, Dr, Dir, American Standards Testing Bureau, Inc, 40 Wall St, 28th Flr, New York, NY, 10005-2672. Tel: 212-943-3160. Fax: 212-825-2250. p. 1669

Coleman, Claire, Br Mgr, Calcasieu Parish Public Library, Central Library, 301 W Claude St, Lake Charles, LA, 70605. Tel: 337-721-7116. Fax: 337-475-8797. p. 953

Coleman, Claudia A, Libr Tech, United States Army, Public Health Command Library, 5158 Blackhawk Rd, BLDG E-5158, Aberdeen Proving Ground, MD, 21010-5403. Tel: 410-436-4236. Fax: 410-436-4602. p. 1009

Coleman, Coni, Br Mgr, Live Oak Public Libraries, Oglethorpe Mall Branch, Seven Mall Annex, Savannah, GA, 31406. Tel: 912-925-5432. Fax: 912-925-2031. p. 550

Coleman, Coni, Br Mgr, Live Oak Public Libraries, Southwest Chatham Branch, 14097 Abercorn St, Savannah, GA, 31419. Tel: 912-925-8305. p. 550

Coleman, Courtney, Info Serv, Northampton Community College, 3835 Green Pond Rd, Bethlehem, PA, 18020-7599. Tel: 610-861-5360. Fax: 610-861-5373. p. 2034

Coleman, Cynthia, Asst Dean, Bowie State University, 14000 Jericho Park Rd, Bowie, MD, 20715. Tel: 301-860-3850. Fax: 301-860-3848. p. 1022

Coleman, Dan, Mgr, Info Serv, Library System of Lancaster County, 1866 Colonial Village Lane, Ste 107, Lancaster, PA, 17601. Tel: 717-207-0500. Fax: 717-207-0504. p. 2077

Coleman, Darlene, Ser, Lehigh Carbon Community College Library, 4525 Education Park Dr, Schnecksville, PA, 18078-9372. Tel: 610-799-1196. Fax: 610-779-1159. p. 2136

Coleman, Edna, Br Mgr, Webster Parish Library, Heflin Branch, 7041 Hwy 531, Heflin, LA, 71039. Tel: 318-371-1027. Fax: 318-382-9613. p. 957

Coleman, Erica D, Ref Librn, Norfolk State University Library, 700 Park Ave, Norfolk, VA, 23504-8010. Tel: 757-823-2224. Fax: 757-823-2431. p. 2482

Coleman, Frances N, Dean of Libr, Mississippi State University, 395 Hardy Rd, Mississippi State, MS, 39762. Tel: 662-325-7668. Fax: 662-325-9344. p. 1309

Coleman, Georgia, Commun Outreach Mgr, Richland County Public Library, 1431 Assembly St, Columbia, SC, 29201-3101. Tel: 803-799-9084. Fax: 803-929-3448. p. 2188

Coleman, Gloria, Br Mgr, Nashville Public Library, Hermitage Branch, 3700 James Kay Lane, Hermitage, TN, 37076-3429. Tel: 615-880-3951. Fax: 615-880-3955. p. 2257

Coleman, Jill, Learning Res Ctr Coordr, Librn, Central Arizona College, 80440 E Aravaipa Rd, Winkelman, AZ, 85292. Tel: 520-357-2841. Fax: 520-357-2832. p. 90

Coleman, Josephine, Tech Serv, Springfield Town Library, 43 Main St, Springfield, VT, 05156. Tel: 802-885-3108. Fax: 802-885-4906. p. 2436

Coleman, Kathleen, Librn, Harvard Library, Herbert Weir Smyth Classical Library, Widener, Rm E, Cambridge, MA, 02138. Tel: 617-495-4027. Fax: 617-496-6720. p. 1076

Coleman, Keith, Media Spec, Northwest Mississippi Community College, 4975 Hwy 51 N, Senatobia, MS, 38668-1701. Tel: 662-562-3279. Fax: 662-562-3280. p. 1315

Coleman, Kim, Div Mgr, Tech Serv, High Point Public Library, 901 N Main St, High Point, NC, 27262. Tel: 336-883-3645. Fax: 336-883-3636. p. 1802

Coleman, Laurie, Librn, Longyear Museum Library, 1125 Boylston St, Chestnut Hill, MA, 02467. Tel: 617-278-9000. Fax: 617-278-9003. p. 1081

Coleman, Lesia J, Coordr, Info Serv, Adult Prog, Fiction & Media, Cullman County Public Library System, 200 Clark St NE, Cullman, AL, 35055. Tel: 256-734-1068. Fax: 256-734-6902. p. 13

Coleman, Leticia, In Charge, Walton, Lantaff, Schroeder & Carson, 9350 S Dixie Hwy, 10th Flr, Miami, FL, 33156. Tel: 305-671-1300. Fax: 305-670-7065. p. 469

Coleman, Linda, Head, Youth Serv, Auburn Hills Public Library, 3400 E Seyburn Dr, Auburn Hills, MI, 48326-2759. Tel: 248-370-9466. Fax: 248-370-9364. p. 1154

Coleman, Lois, Res & Instruction Librn, Barnard College, 3009 Broadway, New York, NY, 10027-6598. Tel: 212-854-9095. p. 1670

Coleman, Lynne, Librn, Waseca-Le Sueur Regional Library, Waterville Public, 210 E Paquin St, Waterville, MN, 56096. Tel: 507-362-8462. p. 1287

Coleman, Martha, Ref, Ser, University of Arkansas Fort Smith, 5210 Grand Ave, Fort Smith, AR, 72903. Tel: 479-788-7206. Fax: 479-788-7209. p. 101

Coleman, Martha, Asst Dir, Kurth Memorial Library, 706 S Raguet, Lufkin, TX, 75904. Tel: 936-630-0560. Fax: 936-639-2487. p. 2358

Coleman, Marty, Asst Dir, Tech Serv, First Regional Library, 370 W Commerce St, Hernando, MS, 38632. Tel: 662-429-4439. Fax: 662-429-8853. p. 1301

Coleman, Mary, Ref & Instruction Librn, Central Carolina Community College Libraries, 1105 Kelly Dr, Sanford, NC, 27330. Tel: 919-718-7244. Fax: 919-718-7378. p. 1823

Coleman, Mike, Reader Serv, Alabama Public Library Service, 6030 Monticello Dr, Montgomery, AL, 36130-6000. Tel: 334-213-3906. Fax: 334-213-3993. p. 27

Coleman, Noreen, Info Spec, Conference Board, Inc, 845 Third Ave, New York, NY, 10022. Tel: 212-759-0900. Fax: 212-836-9750. p. 1676

Coleman, Patrick, Librn, Tarrant Public Library, 1143 Ford Ave, Tarrant, AL, 35217-2437, Tel: 205-849-2825. p. 37

Coleman, Regina, Acq, Samford University Library, 800 Lakeshore Dr, Birmingham, AL, 35229. Tel: 205-726-2520. Fax: 205-726-4009. p. 9

Coleman, Ron, Syst Librn, United States Holocaust Memorial Museum Library, 100 Raoul Wallenberg Pl SW, Washington, DC, 20024. Tel: 202-479-9717. Fax: 202-479-9726. p. 420

Coleman, Rosetta, Br Mgr, Chicago Public Library, Martin Luther King Jr Branch, 3436 S King Dr, Chicago, IL, 60616. Tel: 312-747-7543. Fax: 312-747-3160. p. 609

Coleman, Sheila, Outreach Serv, State Library of Louisiana, 701 N Fourth St, Baton Rouge, LA, 70802-5232. Tel: 225-342-4942. Fax: 225-342-6817. p. 945

Coleman, Shirley, Tech Serv, Watonwan County Library, 125 Fifth St S, Saint James, MN, 56081. Tel: 507-375-1278. Fax: 507-375-5415. p. 1276

Coleman, Trish, Coll Develop Mgr, Saint Joseph County Public Library, 304 S Main, South Bend, IN, 46601-2125. Tel: 574-282-4646. Fax: 574-280-2763. p. 779

Coleman, Valerie, Librn, Chaminade University of Honolulu, 3140 Waialae Ave, Honolulu, HI, 96816-1578. Tel: 808-735-4725. Fax: 808-735-4891. p. 560

Coleman, Yvonne K, Head, Ch, Winchester Public Library, 80 Washington St, Winchester, MA, 01890. Tel: 781-721-7171, Ext 22. Fax: 781-721-7170. p. 1142

Coleman-Davidson, Jennifer, Chief Exec Officer, Bonnechere Union Public Library, 74 A Maple St, Eganville, ON, K0J 1T0, CANADA. Tel: 613-628-2400. Fax: 613-628-5377. p. 2803

Coles, Andrea, Electronic Serv Librn, King College, 1350 King College Rd, Bristol, TN, 37620. Tel: 423-652-4897. Fax: 423-652-4871. p. 2225

Coles, Beth, Libr Asst, New Virginia Public Library, 504 Book Alley, New Virginia, IA, 50210. Tel: 641-449-3614. p. 835

Coles, Brenda, Br Mgr, Iberville Parish Library, Rosedale Branch, 15695 Rosedale Rd, Rosedale, LA, 70772. Tel: 225-648-2213. Fax: 225-648-2213. p. 966

Coles, Catherine, Br Serv Librn, Haliburton County Public Library, Administrative Centre, 78 Maple Ave, Haliburton, ON, K0M 1S0, CANADA. Tel: 705-457-2241. Fax: 705-457-9586. p. 2807

Coles, Denise, Librn, Houston Community College Northeast College, Codwell Campus Library, 555 Community College Dr, Houston, TX, 77013-6127. Tel: 713-718-8354. Fax: 713-718-8330. p. 2337

Coles, Lynne, Librn, Wayne County Regional Library for the Blind & Physically Handicapped, 30555 Michigan Ave, Westland, MI, 48186-5310. Tel: 734-727-7300. Fax: 734-727-7333. p. 1236

Coles, Mary, Assoc Librn, Ada Community Library, Hidden Springs Branch, 5849 W Hidden Springs Dr, Boise, ID, 83714. Tel: 208-229-2665. p. 570

Coletti, Margo, Dir, Beth Israel Deaconess Medical Center, One Deaconess Rd, Boston, MA, 02215. Tel: 617-632-8480. Fax: 617-632-8316. p. 1055

Coleville, Mary Ann, Libr Asst, ITT Technical Institute, 4000 W Metropolitan Dr, Ste 100, Orange, CA, 92868. Tel: 714-941-2400. Fax: 714-535-1802. p. 201

Colfer, Debby, Br Mgr 1, Sno-Isle Libraries, Clinton Community Library, 4781 Deer Lake Rd, Clinton, WA, 98236. Tel: 360-341-4280. Fax: 360-341-2989. p. 2542

Colford, Michael, Dir, Coll & Info Res, Boston Public Library, 700 Boylston St, Boston, MA, 02117-0286. Tel: 617-536-5400. Fax: 617-236-4306. p. 1056

Colford, Scot, Web Serv Mgr, Boston Public Library, 700 Boylston St, Boston, MA, 02117-0286. Tel: 617-536-5400. Fax: 617-236-4306. p. 1056

Colgan, Karen, Mgr, Br Serv, Camden County Library District, Osage Beach Branch, 1064 Gutridge Lane, Osage Beach, MO, 65065. Tel: 573-348-3282. Fax: 573-348-2883. p. 1321

Colgan-Bennetts, Mary, Circ, Siuslaw Public Library District, 1460 Ninth St, Florence, OR, 97439-0022. Tel: 541-997-3132. Fax: 541-997-6473. p. 1998

Colglazier, Gail, Dir, American Independence Museum Library, One Governors Lane, Exeter, NH, 03833. Tel: 603-772-2622. Fax: 603-772-0861. p. 1447

Colglazier, Merle L, Librn, Bon Secours-Saint Mary's Hospital, 5801 Bremo Rd, Richmond, VA, 23226. Tel: 804-281-8247. Fax: 804-285-2448. p. 2487

Colgrove, Kathleen, In Charge, Ashland County Law Library, Courthouse, Rm 304, 201 W Main St, Ashland, WI, 54806. Tel: 715-682-7016. Fax: 715-682-7919. p. 2579

Colibaba, Dee, Librn, Palliser Regional Library, Rouleau Branch, 204 Main St, Rouleau, SK, S0G 4H0, CANADA. Tel: 306-776-2322. p. 2919

Colin, Todd, Librn, TELUS, 3777 Kingsway, 5th Flr, Burnaby, BC, V5H 3Z7, CANADA. Tel: 604-432-2671. Fax: 604-435-0510. p. 2726

Coll, Rhonda, ILL, Canada Department of Fisheries & Oceans, One Challenger Dr, Dartmouth, NS, B2Y 4A2, CANADA. Tel: 902-426-3683. Fax: 902-496-1544. p. 2778

Collar, Margaret, Hist Coll Librn, Florence County Library System, 509 S Dargan St, Florence, SC, 29506. Tel: 843-662-8424. Fax: 843-661-7544. p. 2193

Collard, Iris, Br Mgr, Yuma County Library District, Foothills Branch, 13226 E South Frontage Rd, Yuma, AZ, 85367. Tel: 928-342-1640. Fax: 928-305-0497. p. 91

Collard, Jaki, Asst Librn, Emery County Library, 115 N 100 East, Castle Dale, UT, 84513. Tel: 435-381-2554. Fax: 435-381-2699. p. 2403

Collard, Linda, Dir, Payson City Library, 66 S Main St, Payson, UT, 84651-2223. Tel: 801-465-5220. Fax: 801-465-5208. p. 2410

Collard, Mickie, Dir, Groffe Memorial Library, 118 South Middle St, Grayville, IL, 62844. Tel: 618-375-7121. Fax: 618-375-7121. p. 652

Collazo, Yamill, Tech Serv, Western Hemisphere Institute for Security Cooperation, Bldg 35, 35 Ridgeway Loop, Rm 257, Fort Benning, GA, 31905-6245. Tel: 706-545-1247, 706-545-4631. Fax: 706-545-4027. p. 533

Collebrusco, Pamm, Access Serv, Pub Serv Librn, Benedictine University Library, Charles E Becker Library, 1500 N Fifth St, Springfield, IL, 62702. Tel: 217-525-1420, Ext 235. Fax: 217-525-2651. p. 666

Collen, Bob, Info Res Mgr, American Association of State Highway & Transportation Officials Library, 444 N Capitol St NW, Ste 249, Washington, DC, 20001. Tel: 202-624-8918. Fax: 202-624-5806. p. 391

Collett, Connie, Br Mgr, Greene County Public Library, Yellow Springs Community Library, 415 Xenia Ave, Yellow Springs, OH, 45387-1837. Tel: 937-352-4003. Fax: 937-767-2044. p. 1952

Collett, Glenna, Librn, Central Arkansas Veterans Healthcare System, 4300 W Seventh St, Little Rock, AR, 72205-5484. Tel: 501-257-5620. Fax: 501-257-5626. p. 106

Collett, Howard, AV, Western Nevada Community College, 2201 W College Pkwy, Carson City, NV, 89703. Tel: 775-445-3229. Fax: 775-445-3363. p. 1426

Collett, Katherine, Archivist, Hamilton College, 198 College Hill Rd, Clinton, NY, 13323-1299. Tel: 315-859-4471. Fax: 315-859-4578. p. 1607

Collett, Mason, Librn, Leslie County Public Library, 22065 Main St, Hyden, KY, 41749. Tel: 606-672-2460. Fax: 606-672-4213. p. 918

Colletta, Donna, Mgr, Arizona Republic Library, 200 E Van Buren, Phoenix, AZ, 85004. Tel: 602-444-4446. Fax: 602-444-4294. p. 71

Colletta, Lillian, Head Librn, Kittochtinny Historical Society Library, 175 E King St, Chambersburg, PA, 17201. Tel: 717-264-1667. p. 2043

Collette, Daniel, Dir, Racine Louise Documentation Center, 500 Sherbrooke W, Montreal, QC, H3A 3G6, CANADA. Tel: 514-499-5188. Fax: 514-873-4900. p. 2897

Collette, Jennifer, Dir, Ref, Rolling Meadows Library, 3110 Martin Lane, Rolling Meadows, IL, 60008. Tel: 847-259-6050. Fax: 847-259-5319. p. 698

Collette, Maria, Dir, St Luke's Hospital-Allentown Campus, 1736 Hamilton St, Allentown, PA, 18104. Tel: 610-954-4650. Fax: 610-954-4651. p. 2027

Collette, Maria D, Dir, Libr Serv, St Luke's Hospital & Health Network, 801 Ostrum St, Bethlehem, PA, 18015. Tel: 610-954-4650. Fax: 610-954-4651. p. 2035

Collette, Michele, Youth Serv Librn, St Charles Public Library District, One S Sixth Ave, Saint Charles, IL, 60174-2105. Tel: 630-584-0076, Ext 235. Fax: 630-584-3448. p. 699

Colletti, Cyndy, Literacy Coordr, Illinois State Library, Gwendolyn Brooks Bldg, 300 S Second St, Springfield, IL, 62701-9713. Tel: 217-524-3529. Fax: 217-785-4326. p. 705

Colley, Lora, Librn, Little Dixie Regional Libraries, Huntsville Branch, 102 E Library St, Huntsville, MO, 65259-1125. Tel: 660-277-4518. Fax: 660-277-4333. p. 1346

Collie, Aaron, Librn, Michigan State University Library, Digital Sources & Multimedia Center, W432 Library, East Lansing, MI, 48824. Tel: 517-884-0867. Fax: 517-432-4795. p. 1175

Collier, Brad, Ref Serv Coordr, Jefferson County Rural Library District, 620 Cedar Ave, Port Hadlock, WA, 98339-9514. Tel: 360-385-6544. Fax: 360-385-7921. p. 2524

Collier, Cindy, Asst Dir, Tech, Benzie Shores District Library, 630 Main St, Frankfort, MI, 49635. Tel: 231-352-4671. Fax: 231-352-4671. p. 1181

Collier, Constance, Tech Serv, Thayer Public Library, 798 Washington St, Braintree, MA, 02184. Tel: 781-848-0405, Ext 4418. Fax: 781-356-5447. p. 1069

Collier, Doug, Circ, Norfolk Public Library, 308 Prospect Ave, Norfolk, NE, 68701-4138. Tel: 402-844-2105. Fax: 402-844-2102. p. 1410

Collier, Gwen, Librn, Buffalo & Erie County Public Library System, East Delavan, 1187 E Delavan, Buffalo, NY, 14215-3801. Tel: 716-896-4433. Fax: 716-896-4433. p. 1596

Collier, Jenny, Mgr, Ch Serv, Wood Dale Public Library District, 520 N Wood Dale Rd, Wood Dale, IL, 60191. Tel: 630-766-6762. Fax: 630-766-5715. p. 721

Collier, Mark, Coordr, Ref & Coll, Converse College, 580 E Main St, Spartanburg, SC, 29302. Tel: 864-596-9020, 864-596-9071. Fax: 864-596-9075. p. 2204

Collier, Oliver, ILL, Orange County Public Library, 137 W Margaret Lane, Hillsborough, NC, 27278. Tel: 919-245-2525. Fax: 919-644-3003. p. 1802

Collier, Tressy, Actg Dir, Ch, Blackstone Public Library, 86 Main St, Blackstone, MA, 01504-2277. Tel: 508-883-1931. Fax: 508-883-1531. p. 1054

Colligan, Eva, Libr Tech, Jewish Hospital, 4777 E Galbraith Rd, Cincinnati, OH, 45236. Tel: 513-686-5173. Fax: 513-686-5418. p. 1870

Colligan, Patrick, Exec Dir, 1st Cerebral Palsy of New Jersey, Seven Sanford Ave, Belleville, NJ, 07109. Tel: 973-751-0200. Fax: 973-751-4635. p. 1471

Colligan, Suzanne, Librn, Buffalo & Erie County Public Library System, Dudley, 2010 S Park, Buffalo, NY, 14220-1894. Tel: 716-823-1854. Fax: 716-823-1854. p. 1596

Collings, Dawn, Acq, Cat, Circ, Saddleback College, 28000 Marguerite Pkwy, Mission Viejo, CA, 92692. Tel: 949-582-4526. Fax: 949-364-0284. p. 187

Collings, F A, Circ Supvr, Collingswood Public Library, 771 Haddon Ave, Collingswood, NJ, 08108-3714. Tel: 856-858-0649. Fax: 856-858-5016. p. 1480

Collingwood, Joanne, Librn, Ontario Power Generation Library, 700 University Ave, H17G10, Toronto, ON, M5G 1X6, CANADA. Tel: 416-592-2715. Fax: 416-592-7532. p. 2857

Collins, Aaron, Librn, Huttonsville Correctional Center Library, US Rte 250, S, Huttonsville, WV, 26273. Tel: 304-335-2291, Ext 244. Fax: 304-335-4256. p. 2562

Collins, Alicemarie, Ch, Gladwyne Free Library, 362 Righters Mill Rd, Gladwyne, PA, 19035-1587. Tel: 610-642-3957. Fax: 610-642-3985. p. 2060

Collins, Aline, Pub Serv, Midland College, 3600 N Garfield, Midland, TX, 79705. Tel: 432-685-4560. Fax: 432-685-6710. p. 2363

Collins, Amber, Chief Librn, United States Air Force, Air Force Research Lab, Tyndall Research Site Technical Information Center, 139 Barnes Dr, Ste 2, Tyndall AFB, FL, 32403-5323. Tel: 850-283-6285. Fax: 850-283-6500. p. 501

Collins, Amber, Dir, Fletcher Free Library, 235 College St, Burlington, VT, 05401. Tel: 802-865-7214. Fax: 802-865-7227. p. 2420

Collins, Anne, Dir, Purchase Free Library, 3093 Purchase St, Purchase, NY, 10577. Tel: 914-948-0550. Fax: 914-328-3405. p. 1724

Collins, Anne-Marie, Chef de Div, Bibliothèques de Montrèal, Mile End, 5434, avenue du Parc, Montreal, QC, H2V 4G7, CANADA. Tel: 514-872-9966. Fax: 514-872-0531. p. 2890

Collins, Anne-Marie, Chef de Div, Bibliothèques de Montrèal, Plateau-Mont-Royal, 465, avenue du Mont-Royal Est, Montreal, QC, H2J 1W3, CANADA. Tel: 514-872-9966. Fax: 514-872-0532. p. 2891

Collins, Antoinette, Ref Serv, Saint Joseph College, 1678 Asylum Ave, West Hartford, CT, 06117-2791. Tel: 860-232-4571. Fax: 860-523-4356. p. 376

Collins, Barbara, Libr Dir, Moweaqua Public Library, 600 N Putnam St, Moweaqua, IL, 62550. Tel: 217-768-4700. Fax: 217-768-9070. p. 678

Collins, Beaulah, Dir, Baca County Public Library, Two Buttes Branch, Main St, Two Buttes, CO, 81084. p. 322

Collins, Beulah, Dir, Baca County Public Library, 1260 Main, Ste 1, Springfield, CO, 81073-1542. Tel: 719-523-6962. Fax: 719-523-6962. p. 322

Collins, Beverly, Asst Dir, Cedarbrake Library, 5602 State Hwy 317 N, Belton, TX, 76513. Tel: 254-780-2436. Fax: 254-780-2436. p. 2289

Collins, Bonita, Dir of Tech Serv, Thomas H Leath Memorial Library, 412 E Franklin St, Rockingham, NC, 28379-4995. Tel: 910-895-6337. Fax: 910-895-5851. p. 1820

Collins, Brenda, Tech Serv, Cape Cod Community College, 2240 Iyannough Rd, West Barnstable, MA, 02668-1599. Tel: 508-362-2131, Ext 4617. Fax: 508-375-4020. p. 1136

Collins, Brian, Archivist, Dallas Public Library, 1515 Young St, Dallas, TX, 75201-5499. Tel: 214-670-1435. Fax: 214-670-7839. p. 2306

Collins, Candis, Mgr, Ser, DePaul University Libraries, Vincent G Rinn Law Library, 25 E Jackson Blvd, 5th Flr, Chicago, IL, 60604-2287. Tel: 312-362-6155. Fax: 312-362-6908. p. 612

Collins, Carol, Adult Serv, Head Librn, Madison Public Library, 12 Old Point Ave, Madison, ME, 04950. Tel: 207-696-5626. p. 991

Collins, Carol, Cat, University of Tennessee, Taylor Law Center, 1505 W Cumberland Ave, Knoxville, TN, 37996-1800. Tel: 865-974-6552. Fax: 865-974-6571, 865-974-6595. p. 2243

Collins, Catherine, Br Mgr, Shreve Memorial Library, David Raines Branch, 2855 Martin Luther King Jr Dr, Shreveport, LA, 71107. Tel: 318-222-0824. Fax: 318-222-9154. p. 970

Collins, Catherine D, Asst Teaching Prof, Drexel University, Rush Bldg, Rm 306, 30 N 33rd St, Philadelphia, PA, 19104-2875. Tel: 215-895-2474. Fax: 215-895-2494. p. 2973

Collins, Cathy, Librn, Northwest Regional Library, Sulligent Public Library, 514 Elm St, Sulligent, AL, 35586-9053. Tel: 205-698-8631. Fax: 205-698-0232. p. 40

Collins, Chantay, Dir, Maynardville Public Library, 296 Main St, Maynardville, TN, 37807-3400. Tel: 865-992-7106. Fax: 865-992-0202. p. 2247

Collins, Cheryl, Dir, Br, Los Angeles Public Library System, 630 W Fifth St, Los Angeles, CA, 90071-2097. Tel: 213-228-7000. Fax: 213-228-7519. p. 172

Collins, Cheryl S, Tech Serv Librn, Menlo College, 1000 El Camino Real, Atherton, CA, 94027-4300. Tel: 650-543-3826. Fax: 650-543-3833. p. 122

Collins, Chris, Dir, L'Anse Area School-Public Library, 201 N Fourth St, L'Anse, MI, 49946-1499. Tel: 906-524-6213. Fax: 906-524-5331. p. 1200

Collins, Christel, Br Mgr, Hawaii State Public Library System, Manoa Public Library, 2716 Woodlawn Dr, Honolulu, HI, 96822-1841. Tel: 808-988-0459. Fax: 808-988-0458. p. 563

Collins, Cynthia, Libr Assoc for Outreach & Pub Serv, Weekend Librn, Barton College, 400 Atlantic Christian College Dr NE, Wilson, NC, 27893. Tel: 252-399-6503. Fax: 252-399-6571. p. 1831

Collins, D Cheryl, Dir, Riley County Historical Museum, 2309 Claflin Rd, Manhattan, KS, 66502-3421. Tel: 785-565-6490. Fax: 785-565-6491. p. 882

Collins, Daniel, Dir, Mayer Public Library, 10004 Wicks Ave, Mayer, AZ, 86333. Tel: 928-632-7370. Fax: 928-632-7370. p. 68

Collins, Dave, Pub Serv, Macalester College, 1600 Grand Ave, Saint Paul, MN, 55105-1899. Tel: 651-696-6347. Fax: 651-696-6617. p. 1279

Collins, David, Librn, Collins Correctional Facility Library, PO Box 490, Collins, NY, 14034-0490. Tel: 716-532-4588. p. 1609

Collins, Debra, Dir, Dallas Baptist University, 3000 Mountain Creek Pkwy, Dallas, TX, 75211-9299. Tel: 214-333-5213. Fax: 214-333-5323. p. 2305

Collins, Donna, Pub Serv, Hazard Community & Technical College, 601 Jefferson Ave, Jackson, KY, 41339. Tel: 606-666-7521. Fax: 606-666-8910. p. 919

Collins, Grace, Acq, Yeshiva University Libraries, Dr Lillian & Dr Rebecca Chutick Law Library, Benjamin N Cardozo School of Law, 55 Fifth Ave, New York, NY, 10003-4301. Tel: 212-790-0223. Fax: 212-790-0236. p. 1703

Collins, Harriet, ILL, Parkersburg & Wood County Public Library, 3100 Emerson Ave, Parkersburg, WV, 26104-2414. Tel: 304-420-4587. Fax: 304-420-4589. p. 2568

Collins, Jane, Asst Dir, Mary Wood Weldon Memorial Library, 107 W College St, Glasgow, KY, 42141. Tel: 270-651-2824. Fax: 270-651-2824. p. 915

Collins, Jean, Asst Dir, Louis B Goodall Memorial Library, 952 Main St, Sanford, ME, 04073. Tel: 207-324-4714. Fax: 207-324-5982. p. 999

Collins, Jean, Dean of Libr, Becker College, 13 Washburn Sq, Leicester, MA, 01524. Tel: 508-373-9709. Fax: 508-892-7472. p. 1098

Collins, Jean, Dean of Libr, Becker College, 61 Sever St, Worcester, MA, 01609. Tel: 508-373-9710. Fax: 508-849-5131. p. 1143

Collins, Jim, Tech Serv, The Morristown & Morris Township Library, One Miller Rd, Morristown, NJ, 07960. Tel: 973-538-6161. Fax: 973-267-4064. p. 1505

Collins, Jo, Pub Serv, Pocono Mountain Public Library, 5540 Memorial Blvd, Tobyhanna, PA, 18466. Tel: 570-894-8860. Fax: 570-894-8852. p. 2146

Collins, Jo Anna, Circ, University of Arkansas Libraries, Robert A & Vivian Young Law Library, School of Law, Waterman Hall 107, Fayetteville, AR, 72701-1201. Tel: 479-575-5254. Fax: 479-575-2053. p. 100

Collins, Joesephine, Circ, Hollins University, 7950 E Campus Dr, Roanoke, VA, 24020-1000. Tel: 540-362-6591, 540-362-7465. Fax: 540-362-6756. p. 2493

Collins, John W, III, Librn, Harvard Library, Gutman Library-Research Center, Graduate School of Educ, Six Appian Way, Cambridge, MA, 02138. Tel: 617-495-4225. Fax: 617-495-0540. p. 1075

Collins, Joseph, Evening Supvr, Vanderbilt University, Walker Management Library, Owen Graduate School of Management, 401 21st Ave S, Nashville, TN, 37203. Tel: 615-343-5946. Fax: 615-343-0061. p. 2261

Collins, Julie, Govt Doc, Mount Prospect Public Library, Ten S Emerson St, Mount Prospect, IL, 60056. Tel: 847-253-5675. Fax: 847-253-0642. p. 677

Collins, Kathleen, Reserves Librn, John Jay College of Criminal Justice, 899 Tenth Ave, New York, NY, 10019. Tel: 212-237-8242. Fax: 212-237-8221. p. 1684

Collins, Kathleen, Ref Coordr, University of Washington Libraries, Odegaard Undergraduate Library, Box 353080, Seattle, WA, 98195-3080. Tel: 206-685-2771. Fax: 206-685-8485. p. 2534

Collins, Katrina, Youth Serv, Neenah Public Library, 240 E Wisconsin Ave, Neenah, WI, 54956-3010. Tel: 920-886-6330. Fax: 920-886-6324. p. 2624

Collins, Kelly, Dir, Bolton Public Library, 738 Main St, Bolton, MA, 01740-1202. Tel: 978-779-2839. Fax: 978-779-2293. p. 1054

Collins, Kenlyn, Librn, Winnipeg Art Gallery, 300 Memorial Blvd, Winnipeg, MB, R3C 1V1, CANADA. Tel: 204-786-6641. Fax: 204-788-4998. p. 2759

Collins, LaDonna, Asst Librn, Knott County Public Library, 238 Hwy 160 S, Hindman, KY, 41822. Tel: 606-785-5412. Fax: 606-785-4299. p. 918

Collins, Laurie, Ch, Ipswich Public Library, 25 N Main St, Ipswich, MA, 01938-2217. Tel: 978-412-8713. Fax: 978-356-6647. p. 1097

Collins, LaVerne P, Dir, La Roche College, 9000 Babcock Blvd, Pittsburgh, PA, 15237. Tel: 412-536-1063. Fax: 412-536-1062. p. 2126

Colter, Cheri, Coordr, Acq, Indiana Wesleyan University, 4201 S Washington St, Marion, IN, 46953. Tel: 765-677-2193. Fax: 765-677-2676. p. 762

Colton, Norma, Libr Mgr, York County Public Library, Yorktown Branch, 8500 George Washington Memorial Hwy, Yorktown, VA, 23692. Tel: 757-890-3378. Fax: 757-890-2956. p. 2505

Coltrin, Emily, Br Mgr, Lyon County Library System, Dayton Valley Branch, 321 (Old) Dayton Valley Rd, Dayton, NV, 89403-8902. Tel: 775-246-6212. Fax: 775-246-6213. p. 1435

Columbus, Ellen, Head, Ref Serv, South Orange Public Library, 65 Scotland Rd, South Orange, NJ, 07079. Tel: 973-762-0230. Fax: 973-762-1469. p. 1531

Colville, Hannah, Mgr, Halifax Public Libraries, Bedford Branch, Wardour Centre, 15 Dartmouth Rd, Bedford, NS, B4A 3X6, CANADA. Tel: 902-490-5740. Fax: 902-490-5752. p. 2779

Colvin, Ian, Librn, Fraser Milner Casgrain LLP, Barristers & Solicitors, 400 Toronto Dominion Ctr, 77 King St W, Toronto, ON, M5K 0A1, CANADA. Tel: 416-863-4581. Fax: 416-863-4592. p. 2853

Colvin, Jenny, Music, Furman University Libraries, 3300 Poinsett Hwy, Greenville, SC, 29613-4100. Tel: 864-294-3797. Fax: 864-294-3004. p. 2195

Colvin, Jenny, Music, Furman University Libraries, Robert J Maxwell Music Library, Daniel Music Bldg, 3300 Poinsett Hwy, Greenville, SC, 29613. Tel: 864-294-3795. Fax: 864-294-3004. p. 2196

Colvin, Joanne, Asst Dir, Pub Serv, University of Baltimore, Law Library, 1415 Maryland Ave, Baltimore, MD, 21201. Tel: 410-837-4554. Fax: 410-837-4570. p. 1018

Colvin, Kim, Tech Serv, Washington State University Tri-Cities, 2770 University Dr, Richland, WA, 99354. Tel: 509-372-7430. Fax: 509-372-7281. p. 2526

Colvson, Mark, Assoc Dir, Marist College, 3399 North Rd, Poughkeepsie, NY, 12601-1387. Tel: 845-575-3199. Fax: 845-575-3150. p. 1722

Colwell, David, Tech Serv, Inver Hills Community College Library, 2500 80th St E, Inver Grove Heights, MN, 55076-3209. Tel: 651-450-3625. Fax: 651-450-3679. p. 1254

Colwell, Kathy, Head Librn, Edwardsburgh/Cardinal Public Library, Spencerville Branch, Five Henderson St, Spencerville, ON, K0E 1X0, CANADA. Tel: 613-658-5575. Fax: 613-658-5575. p. 2799

Colwell, Miriam, Libr Spec, Columbia University, Lamont-Doherty Geoscience Library, Lamont-Doherty Earth Observatory, 61 Rte 9 W, PO Box 1000, Palisades, NY, 10964-8000. Tel: 845-365-8808. Fax: 845-365-8151. p. 1674

Colwell, Priscilla, Dir, Putnam Public Library, 225 Kennedy Dr, Putnam, CT, 06260-1691. Tel: 860-963-6826. Fax: 860-963-6828. p. 365

Coly, Lisette, Exec Dir, Parapsychology Foundation Inc, 308 Front St, Greenport, NY, 11944. Tel: 212-628-1550, 631-477-2560. Fax: 212-628-1559. p. 1631

Colyard, Valerie, Chairperson, University of Arkansas-Pine Bluff, Human Sciences, Mail Slot 4971, Pine Bluff, AR, 71601. Tel: 870-575-8817. p. 113

Colyer, Eileen, Supvr, Ad Serv, Ridgewood Public Library, 125 N Maple Ave, Ridgewood, NJ, 07450-3288. Tel: 201-670-5600. Fax: 201-670-0293. p. 1526

Colyer, Pamela, Head, Cat, Interim Head of Tech Serv, Morehead State University, 150 University Blvd, Morehead, KY, 40351. Tel: 606-783-5118. Fax: 606-783-5037. p. 929

Combs, Doris, Chmn of Libr Board, Dorcas Library, 28 Main St, Prospect Harbor, ME, 04669. Tel: 207-963-4027. p. 998

Combs, George, Br Mgr, Alexandria Library, Local History/Special Collections, 717 Queen St, Alexandria, VA, 22314-2420. Tel: 703-746-1719. Fax: 703-746-1720. p. 2444

Combs, Jody, Assoc Dean, Vanderbilt University, 419 21st Ave S, Nashville, TN, 37203-2427. Tel: 615-322-7100. Fax: 615-343-8279. p. 2260

Combs, Leah, Ad, Perry County Public Library, 289 Black Gold Blvd, Hazard, KY, 41701. Tel: 606-436-2475, 606-436-4747. Fax: 606-436-0191. p. 917

Combs, Peggy, Sr Librn, Denver Public Library, Ross-Broadway, 33 E Bayaud Ave, Denver, CO, 80209-1503. Tel: 303-777-4845. Fax: 303-733-8601. p. 301

Combs, Rachel, Day Circ Supvr, Georgetown College, 400 E College St, Georgetown, KY, 40324. Tel: 502-863-8404. Fax: 502-868-7740. p. 915

Combs, Robyn, Librn, Missouri Department of Corrections, Jefferson City Correctional Center, 8200 No More Victims Rd, Jefferson City, MO, 65101-4539. Tel: 573-751-3224, Ext 1142. Fax: 573-751-0355. p. 1334

Comeau, Erin, Dir, Western Counties Regional Library, 405 Main St, Yarmouth, NS, B5A 1G3, CANADA. Tel: 902-742-2486. Fax: 902-742-6920. p. 2786

Comeau, Glenda, In Charge, Western Counties Regional Library, Clare, No 8196 Hwy One, Meteghan, NS, B0W 2J0, CANADA. Tel: 902-645-3350. p. 2787

Comeau, Mary, Librn, New Brunswick Department of Post-Secondary Education, Training & Labour Library, 470 York St, Fredericton, NB, E3B 5H1, CANADA. Tel: 506-453-8247. Fax: 506-453-3618. p. 2763

Comeaux, Anne, Asst Dir, Digital & Spec Coll, University of Texas at San Antonio Libraries, 7703 Floyd Curl Dr, MSC 7940, San Antonio, TX, 78229-3900. Tel: 210-567-2400. Fax: 210-567-2490. p. 2383

Comeaux, David, Fac Mgr, Calcasieu Parish Public Library, 301 W Claude St, Lake Charles, LA, 70605-3457. Tel: 337-721-7151. Fax: 337-475-8806. p. 953

Comegys, Marianne L, Dir, Louisiana State University Health Sciences Center, 1501 Kings Hwy, Shreveport, LA, 71130. Tel: 318-675-5449. Fax: 318-675-5442. p. 968

Comello, Pamela, Youth Serv, Sedona Public Library, 3250 White Bear Rd, Sedona, AZ, 86336. Tel: 928-282-7714. Fax: 928-282-5789. p. 81

Comen, Diane, Head, Ref, Glenview Public Library, 1930 Glenview Rd, Glenview, IL, 60025-2899. Tel: 847-729-7500. Fax: 847-729-7558. p. 650

Comer, Alberta Davis, Dean, Indiana State University, 510 North 6 1/2 St, Terre Haute, IN, 47809. Tel: 812-237-3700. Fax: 812-237-3376. p. 781

Comer, Cynthia, Instrul Serv Librn, Ref Serv, Oberlin College Library, 148 W College St, Oberlin, OH, 44074. Tel: 440-775-8285. Fax: 440-775-6586. p. 1924

Comer, Victoria G, Admin Serv, Volunteer State Community College Library, 1480 Nashville Pike, Gallatin, TN, 37066-3188. Tel: 615-230-3400, Ext 3496. Fax: 615-230-3410. p. 2235

Comerford, Jana, Bibliog Instr, Amarillo College Library, 2201 S Washington, Amarillo, TX, 79109. Tel: 806-371-5400. Fax: 806-371-5470. p. 2274

Comerford, Jeanie, Operations Mgr, Eagle Public Library, 100 N Stierman Way, Eagle, ID, 83616-5162. Tel: 208-939-6814. Fax: 208-939-1359. p. 574

Comerford, Kim Faux, Acq, Glenview Public Library, 1930 Glenview Rd, Glenview, IL, 60025-2899. Tel: 847-729-7500. Fax: 847-729-7558. p. 651

Comes, James, Assoc Dir, Educ & Res Serv, University of Massachusetts Medical School, 55 Lake Ave N, Worcester, MA, 01655-2397. Tel: 508-856-6810. Fax: 508-856-5039. p. 1145

Comfort, Sarah, Commun Libr Mgr, County of Los Angeles Public Library, Angelo M Iacoboni Library, 4990 Clark Ave, Lakewood, CA, 90712-2676. Tel: 562-866-1777. Fax: 562-866-1217. p. 142

Comiskey, Lisa, Libr Dir, Highgate Public Library, 17 Mill Hill, Highgate Center, VT, 05459. Tel: 802-868-3970. Fax: 802-868-4389. p. 2425

Comizio, Betsy, Dir, Montgomery Free Library, 133 Clinton St, Montgomery, NY, 12549. Tel: 845-457-5616. Fax: 845-457-5616. p. 1662

Commander, Patricia, Health Sci Librn, Winston-Salem State University, 601 Martin Luther King Jr Dr, Winston-Salem, NC, 27110. Tel: 336-750-8937. Fax: 336-750-2459. p. 1834

Commers, Amy, Youth Serv Librn, South Saint Paul Public Library, 106 Third Ave N, South Saint Paul, MN, 55075-2098. Tel: 651-554-3240. Fax: 651-554-3241. p. 1285

Commons, Roland, Ref Librn, Grayson County College Library, 6101 Grayson Dr, Denison, TX, 75020-8299. Tel: 903-463-8637. Fax: 903-465-4123. p. 2312

Comora, Cassie, Ad, Gray Public Library, Five Hancock St, Gray, ME, 04039. Tel: 207-657-4110. Fax: 207-657-4138. p. 986

Comport, Eric, Librn, Pima Community College, 2202 W Anklam Rd, Tucson, AZ, 85709-0001. Tel: 520-206-6821. Fax: 520-206-3059. p. 86

Compton, Beverly, Head, Tech Serv, Shelby County Public Library, 57 W Broadway, Shelbyville, IN, 46176. Tel: 317-398-7121, 317-835-2653. Fax: 317-398-4430. p. 778

Compton, Bruce, Asst City Librn, Helen Hall Library, 100 W Walker, League City, TX, 77573-3899. Tel: 281-554-1111. Fax: 281-554-1118. p. 2354

Compton, Bruce C, Sr Mgr/Archivist, Pew Charitable Trusts Library, One Commerce Sq, 2005 Market St, Ste 1700, Philadelphia, PA, 19103-7017. Tel: 215-575-9050. Fax: 215-575-4939. p. 2114

Compton, Jennifer, Archivist, Head, Tech Serv, Oklahoma Christian University, 2501 E Memorial Rd, Edmond, OK, 73013. Tel: 405-425-5314. Fax: 405-425-5313. p. 1962

Compton, Kevin, Ref Serv, Trinity International University, 2065 Half Day Rd, Deerfield, IL, 60015-1241. Tel: 847-317-4010. Fax: 847-317-4012. p. 635

Compton, Lawrence, Info Spec, University of New Mexico, 1919 Las Lomas NE, Albuquerque, NM, 87106. Tel: 505-277-2142. Fax: 505-277-2773. p. 1550

Compton, Norm, Mgr, Digital Production Ctr, Allen County Public Library, 900 Library Plaza, Fort Wayne, IN, 46802. Tel: 260-421-1246. Fax: 260-421-1386. p. 740

Compton, Sue, Dir, Flower Mound Public Library, 3030 Broadmoor Lane, Flower Mound, TX, 75022. Tel: 972-874-6151. Fax: 972-874-6466. p. 2319

Compton, Trisha, Ref Serv, Trinity International University, 2065 Half Day Rd, Deerfield, IL, 60015-1241. Tel: 847-317-4009. Fax: 847-317-4012. p. 635

Compton-Dzak, Emily R, Head, Ref (Info Serv), Deerfield Public Library, 920 Waukegan Rd, Deerfield, IL, 60015. Tel: 847-945-3311. Fax: 847-945-3402. p. 634

Compton-Engle, Tron, Dir, Info Tech, Case Western Reserve University, School of Law Library, 11075 East Blvd, Cleveland, OH, 44106-7148. Tel: 216-368-4702. Fax: 216-368-1002. p. 1876

Compton-Smith, Carole, Dir, Douglas College Library, 700 Royal Ave, New Westminster, BC, V3M 5Z5, CANADA. Tel: 604-527-5182. Fax: 604-527-5193. p. 2733

Compton-Smith, Linda, Circ, Whatcom Community College Library, 237 W Kellogg Rd, Bellingham, WA, 98226. Tel: 360-383-3300. p. 2509

Comstock, Mary Ann, Br Mgr, South Kingstown Public Library, Kingston Free Branch, 2605 Kingstown Rd, Kingston, RI, 02881. Tel: 401-783-8254. Fax: 401-783-8254. p. 2171

Comstock, Mary Ann, Br Mgr, South Kingstown Public Library, Robert Beverley Hale Library, 2601 Commodore Perry Hwy, Wakefield, RI, 02879. Tel: 401-783-5386. Fax: 401-783-5386. p. 2171

Comte, Valérie, Chef de Section, Bibliothèques de Montrèal, Benny, 3465, avenue Benny, Montreal, QC, H4B 2R9, CANADA. Tel: 514-872-7367. Fax: 514-872-0515. p. 2889

Comte, Valérie, Chef de Section, Bibliothèques de Montrèal, Interculturelle, 6767, chemin de la Côte-des-Neiges, Montréal, QC, H3S 2T6, CANADA. Tel: 514-872-7367. p. 2890

Cona, Lorraine E, Librn, Ref Serv, Arizona Department of Environmental Quality Library, 1110 W Washington St, Phoenix, AZ, 85007. Fax: 602-771-2399. p. 71

Conant, Susan, Interim Dir, Stonehill College, 320 Washington St, Easton, MA, 02357-4015. Tel: 508-565-1289. Fax: 508-565-1424. p. 1086

Conard, Bonnie, Circ, Rogue Community College, Table Rock Campus Library, 7800 Pacific Ave, White City, OR, 97503. Tel: 541-245-7820. Fax: 541-245-7975. p. 1999

Conard, Michelle, Head Librn, Fairfield Public Library, 300 SE Second St, Fairfield, IL, 62837. Tel: 618-842-4516. Fax: 618-842-6708. p. 645

Conaway, Tara, Dir, Flat River Community Library, 200 W Judd St, Greenville, MI, 48838-2225. Tel: 616-754-6359. Fax: 616-754-1398. p. 1186

Conaway, Teresa, Head, Instruction & Res, University of La Verne, 320 E D St, Ontario, CA, 91764. Tel: 909-460-2067. Fax: 909-460-2083. p. 200

Conca, Niki, Chief Librn, US Veterans Affairs Medical Center, 4100 W Third St, Dayton, OH, 45428. Tel: 937-268-6511, Ext 2379. Fax: 937-262-2181. p. 1894

Concepcion, Agnes, Operations Mgr, University of California, Berkeley, Chemistry, 100 Hildebrand Hall, Berkeley, CA, 94720-6000. Tel: 510-643-4477. Fax: 510-643-9041. p. 127

Concepcion, Arlene, Ref Serv, Pontifical Catholic University of Puerto Rico, Ramon Emeterio Betances St 482, Mayaguez, PR, 00680. Tel: 787-834-5151, Ext 5008. Fax: 787-831-7155. p. 2673

Concepcion, Luis, Dir, University of Puerto Rico, 130 Ave Universidad, Arecibo, PR, 00612-3145. Tel: 787-815-0000, Ext 3151. Fax: 787-878-9363. p. 2671

Conde, Teresa, Br Coordr, North Castle Public Library, 19 Whippoorwill Rd E, Armonk, NY, 10504. Tel: 914-273-3887. Fax: 914-273-5572. p. 1575

Condit, Shirley, Ref Librn, Pinal County Library District, 92 W Butte Ave, Florence, AZ, 85132. Tel: 520-866-6457. Fax: 520-866-6533. p. 63

Conditt, Elva, Dir, Area Health Education Center-Northwest Library, 1125 N College Ave, Fayetteville, AR, 72703. Tel: 479-521-7615. Fax: 479-442-1707. p. 99

Condley, Ednita, Head of Libr, Pope County Library System, Hector Branch, PO Box 293, Hector, AR, 72843. Tel: 479-284-0907. Fax: 479-284-0907. p. 114

Condon, Charles J, Dir, Appalachian School of Law Library, 1221 Edgewater Dr, Grundy, VA, 24614-7062. Tel: 276-935-6688, Ext 1309. Fax: 276-935-7138. p. 2467

Condon, Cheryl, Head, Circ, Cleve J Fredricksen Library, 100 N 19th St, Camp Hill, PA, 17011-3900. Tel: 717-761-3900. Fax: 717-761-5493. p. 2040

Condon, Christina, Head, Access Serv, Merrimack College, 315 Turnpike St, North Andover, MA, 01845. Tel: 978-837-5215. Fax: 978-837-5434. p. 1111

Condon, Eileen, Head, Syst, Webster University, 101 Edgar Rd, Saint Louis, MO, 63119. Tel: 314-246-7954. Fax: 314-968-7113. p. 1363

Condon, Joanne, Coordr, Cat, Coordr, ILL, Derby Public Library, 1600 E Walnut Grove, Derby, KS, 67037. Tel: 316-788-0760. Fax: 316-788-7313. p. 863

Condon, Joyce, Ref Serv, Exempla-Saint Joseph Hospital, 1835 Franklin St, Denver, CO, 80218-1191. Tel: 303-837-7375. Fax: 303-837-7977. p. 301

Condon, Judy, Ref Librn, Abington Public Library, 600 Gliniewicz Way, Abington, MA, 02351. Tel: 781-982-2139. Fax: 781-878-7361. p. 1047

Condon, Lorna, Curator, Historic New England, Library & Archives, 141 Cambridge St, Boston, MA, 02114. Tel: 617-227-3957, Ext 225. Fax: 617-973-9050. p. 1062

Condra, Reginald, Circ, Pierson Library, 5376 Shelburne Rd, Shelburne, VT, 05482. Tel: 802-985-5124. Fax: 802-985-5129. p. 2435

Cone, Lufonda, Doc, Nevada Power Co Library, 6226 W Sahara Ave, Las Vegas, NV, 89151. Tel: 702-367-5055. Fax: 702-227-2023. p. 1430

Cone, Michele, Dir, Gateway Community College, North Haven Campus, 88 Bassett Rd, North Haven, CT, 06473. Tel: 203-285-2340. Fax: 203-285-2342. p. 355

Cone, Vicki, Cat, Distance Educ, ILL, Anne Arundel Community College, 101 College Pkwy, Arnold, MD, 21012-1895. Tel: 410-777-2211. Fax: 410-777-2652. p. 1011

Cone, Walter, Access Serv, ILL, University of South Florida, Louis de la Parte Florida Mental Health Institute Research Library, 13301 Bruce B Downs Blvd, Tampa, FL, 33612-3899. Tel: 813-974-4471. Fax: 813-974-7242. p. 498

Conely, Pat, ILL, Online Serv, Bemidji State University, 1500 Birchmont Dr NE, Box 4, Bemidji, MN, 56601-2600. Tel: 218-755-3342. Fax: 218-755-2051. p. 1241

Conetto, Stephen, Syst Coordr, Mississippi State University, 395 Hardy Rd, Mississippi State, MS, 39762. Tel: 662-325-7668. Fax: 662-325-9344. p. 1309

Coney, Jo Ellen, Pub Serv, Roosevelt University, Robert R McCormick Tribune Foundation Library, 1400 N Roosevelt Blvd, Schaumburg, IL, 60173. Tel: 847-619-7980. Fax: 847-619-7983. p. 623

Coney, Stephanie, Tech Serv Mgr, Abraham Baldwin Agricultural College, 2802 Moore Hwy, Tifton, GA, 31793. Tel: 229-391-4990. Fax: 229-391-4991. p. 554

Congelosi, Catherine, Circ, Berkshire Athenaeum, One Wendell Ave, Pittsfield, MA, 01201-6385. Tel: 413-499-9480. Fax: 413-499-9489. p. 1117

Conger, D John, Ref Librn, Brown McCarroll, LLP Library, 111 Congress Ave, Ste 1400, Austin, TX, 78701-4043. Tel: 512-370-3449. Fax: 512-479-1101. p. 2279

Conger, John, Librn, Texas Commission on Environment Quality Library, 12100 Park 35 Circle, MC-196, Austin, TX, 78753. Tel: 512-239-0020. Fax: 512-239-0022. p. 2281

Conger, Mary Jane, Head, Cat, University of North Carolina at Greensboro, 320 Spring Garden St, Greensboro, NC, 27402. Tel: 336-334-5880. Fax: 336-334-5399. p. 1798

Congiardo, Wendy, Dir, Thomas B Norton Public Library, 221 W 19th Ave, Gulf Shores, AL, 36542. Tel: 251-968-1176. Fax: 251-968-1184. p. 19

Congleton, Robert, Librn, Rider University, 2083 Lawrenceville Rd, Lawrenceville, NJ, 08648-3099. Tel: 609-896-5111. Fax: 609-896-8029. p. 1494

Coniglio, Jamie, Head, Ref, George Mason University Libraries, 4400 University Dr, MSN 2FL, Fairfax, VA, 22030-4444. Tel: 703-993-2207. Fax: 703-993-2200. p. 2462

Coniglio, Mary, Reserves Librn, Phillips Theological Seminary Library, 901 N Mingo Rd, Tulsa, OK, 74116. Tel: 918-270-6427. Fax: 918-270-6490. p. 1982

Conine, Dee, Dir, Info Tech Coordr, Syst Adminr, Kaubisch Memorial Public Library, 205 Perry St, Fostoria, OH, 44830-2265. Tel: 419-435-2813. Fax: 419-435-5350. p. 1900

Conkey, Carey, Teen Serv, Watertown Free Public Library, 123 Main St, Watertown, MA, 02472. Tel: 617-972-6437. Fax: 617-926-4375. p. 1134

Conkis, Dixie M, Dir, La Grange Park Public Library District, 555 N LaGrange Rd, La Grange Park, IL, 60526-5644. Tel: 708-352-0100. Fax: 708-352-1606. p. 662

Conklin, Claudia, Ref & Instruction, William Carey University Libraries, 498 Tuscan Ave, Box 5, Hattiesburg, MS, 39401. Tel: 601-318-6169. Fax: 601-318-6171. p. 1301

Conklin, Curt E, Cat, Brigham Young University, Howard W Hunter Law Library, 256 JRCB, Provo, UT, 84602-8000. Tel: 801-422-3593. Fax: 801-422-0404. p. 2411

Conklin, Dixie A, Librn, Grenola Public Library, 205 S Main St, Grenola, KS, 67346. Tel: 620-358-3707. Fax: 620-358-3820. p. 870

Conklin, Elizabeth, ILL Spec, Lyndon State College, 1001 College Rd, Lyndonville, VT, 05851. Tel: 802-626-6366. Fax: 802-626-6331. p. 2427

Conklin, Katie, Syst Tech, Stonehill College, 320 Washington St, Easton, MA, 02357-4015. Tel: 508-565-1213. Fax: 508-565-1424. p. 1087

Conklin, Kurt, In Charge, SIECUS - Sexuality Information & Education Council of the United States, 90 John St, Ste 402, New York, NY, 10038. Tel: 212-819-9770. Fax: 212-819-9776. p. 1700

Conklin, Marilyn, Circ Mgr, Fred & Harriett Taylor Memorial Library, 21 William St, Hammondsport, NY, 14840. Tel: 607-569-2045. Fax: 607-569-3340. p. 1633

Conklin, Marlee, Br Mgr, Whitman County Rural Library District, Farmington Branch, E 203 Main St, Farmington, WA, 99128. Tel: 509-287-2500. p. 2513

Conklin, Susan, Hist Coll Librn, Genesee County History Department, Three W Main St, Batavia, NY, 14020-2021. Tel: 585-344-2550, Ext 2613. Fax: 585-344-8558. p. 1578

Conkling, Brigitte, Archivist, Concordia College, 171 White Plains Rd, Bronxville, NY, 10708. Tel: 914-337-9300, Ext 2202. Fax: 914-395-4893. p. 1588

Conkling, Diedre, Dir, Lincoln County Library District, 1247 NW Grove St, Ste 2, Newport, OR, 97365. Tel: 541-265-3066. Fax: 541-265-3066. p. 2007

Conlan, Teressa, Asst Librn, Toledo Museum of Art, 2445 Monroe St, Toledo, OH, 43620. Tel: 419-255-8000. Fax: 419-255-5638. p. 1940

Conlee, Mary Beth, Adult Serv, ILL, Burlington Public Library, 820 E Washington, Burlington, WA, 98233. Tel: 360-755-0760. Fax: 360-755-0717. p. 2511

Conley, Angie, Supvr, Youth Serv, Boyd County Public Library, 1740 Central Ave, Ashland, KY, 41101. Tel: 606-329-0090. Fax: 606-329-0578. p. 905

Conley, Donna, Chair, Department of Community Services, Government of Yukon, Pelly Crossing Community, Eliza Van Bibber School, Pelly Crossing, YT, Y0B 1P0, CANADA. Tel: 867-537-3041. Fax: 867-537-3103. p. 2933

Conley, Jerome, Asst Dean, Spec Librn, Miami University Libraries, 225 King Library, Oxford, OH, 45056. Tel: 513-529-3934. Fax: 513-529-3110. p. 1926

Conley, Jerome, Asst Dean, Spec Librn, Miami University Libraries, Business, Engineering, Science, & Technology Library, Laws Hall, Oxford, OH, 45056. Tel: 513-529-3934. Fax: 513-529-1736. p. 1926

Conley, Judy, Mgr, Washoe County Library System, Gerlach Community Library, 555 E Sunset Blvd, Gerlach, NV, 89412. Tel: 775-557-2326. Fax: 775-557-2587. p. 1434

Conley, Karen, Commun Relations Librn, Chillicothe & Ross County Public Library, 140 S Paint St, Chillicothe, OH, 45601. Tel: 740-702-4145. Fax: 740-702-4153. p. 1867

Conley, Kathleen, Ref & Instruction Librn, Harrisburg Area Community College, One HACC Dr, Harrisburg, PA, 17110-2999. Tel: 717-780-1186. Fax: 717-780-2462. p. 2065

Conley, Lori, Libr Asst II, Missouri Supreme Court Library, Supreme Court Bldg, 207 W High St, Jefferson City, MO, 65101. Tel: 573-751-7322. Fax: 573-751-2573. p. 1335

Conley, Marlene, Tech Serv, Hazard Community & Technical College Library, One Community College Dr, Hazard, KY, 41701. Tel: 606-487-3145. Fax: 606-439-1657. p. 916

Conley, Megan, Sci Literacy Librn, Wartburg College Library, 100 Wartburg Blvd, Waverly, IA, 50677-0903. Tel: 319-352-8696. Fax: 319-352-8312. p. 850

Conley, Michael, Br Mgr, Cape May County Library, Woodbine Branch, 800 Monroe St, Woodbine, NJ, 08270. Tel: 609-861-2501. p. 1477

Conley, Patricia M, Dir, Washington County Library, 8595 Central Park Pl, Woodbury, MN, 55125-9453. Tel: 651-275-8500. Fax: 651-275-8509. p. 1290

Conley, Peggy, Asst City Librn, Golconda Public Library, 126 W Main St, Golconda, IL, 62938. Tel: 618-683-6531. Fax: 618-683-6531. p. 651

Conley, Sean, Media Serv, Siena College, 515 Loudon Rd, Loudonville, NY, 12211-1462. Tel: 518-783-2539. Fax: 518-783-2570. p. 1655

Conley, Tamara, Circ Librn, Cardinal Stafford Library, 1300 S Steele St, Denver, CO, 80210. Tel: 303-715-3146. Fax: 303-715-2037. p. 298

Conley, Theresa R, Dir, Lyme Public Library, 482 Hamburg Rd, Lyme, CT, 06371-3110. Tel: 860-434-2272. Fax: 860-434-9972. p. 349

Conlin, David, Ref Librn, United States Marine Corps, Bldg 298, Marine Corps Air Station, Cherry Point, NC, 28533-0009. Tel: 252-466-3552. Fax: 252-466-2476. p. 1784

Conlon, Kathryn, AV, Henderson County Public Library, 301 N Washington St, Hendersonville, NC, 28739. Tel: 828-697-4725. Fax: 828-692-8449, 828-697-4700. p. 1801

Conlon, Mary, Librn, Connecticut Valley Hospital, Hallock Medical Library, Page Hall, Silver St, Middletown, CT, 06457. Tel: 860-262-5059. Fax: 860-262-5049. p. 351

Conlon, Yvonne, Circ Mgr, Saint Ambrose University Library, 518 W Locust St, Davenport, IA, 52803. Tel: 563-333-6474. Fax: 563-333-6248. p. 807

Conly, Erica, Br Mgr, Mississauga Library System, Erin Meadows, 2800 Erin Centre Blvd, Mississauga, ON, L5M 6R5, CANADA. Tel: 905-615-4750. p. 2823

Conn, Debra, Head, Ch, Upper St Clair Township Library, 1820 McLaughlin Run Rd, Upper St Clair, PA, 15241-2397. Tel: 412-835-5540. Fax: 412-835-6763. p. 2149

Conn, Janet Witten, Dir, New Martinsville Public Library, 160 Washington Ave, New Martinsville, WV, 26155. Tel: 304-455-4545. Fax: 304-455-4545. p. 2567

Conn, Kathy, Libr Mgr, Keephills Public Library, 51515 Range Rd 32A, Duffield, AB, T0E 0N0, CANADA. Tel: 780-731-0000, 780-731-3965. Fax: 780-731-2433. p. 2697

Conn, Krissy, Ch, Lone Star College System, CyFair Library, 9191 Barker Cypress Rd, Cypress, TX, 77433. Tel: 281-290-3214, 281-290-3219. p. 2340

Conn, Larry A, Dir, Webb Shadle Memorial Library, 301 W Dallas, Pleasantville, IA, 50225. Tel: 515-848-5617. Fax: 515-848-3272. p. 839

Conn, Linda, Libr Dir, Fleming Community Library, 506 N Fremont Ave, Fleming, CO, 80728. Tel: 970-265-2022. p. 306

Connaghan, Steve, Univ Librn, Catholic University of America, 620 Michigan Ave NE, 315 Mullen Library, Washington, DC, 20064. Tel: 202-319-5169. Fax: 202-319-4735. p. 395

Connell Cannon, Carol, Dir, Lee Memorial Library, 500 W Crescent Ave, Allendale, NJ, 07401-1799. Tel: 201-327-4338. Fax: 201-327-5838. p. 1469

Connell, Joanne, Librn, Brevard Community College, Dr Frank Elbert Williams Learning Resource Ctr, 1311 N US 1, Titusville, FL, 32796-2192. Tel: 321-433-5066. Fax: 321-433-5114. p. 500

Connell, Mark, Instr, Info & Computer Literacy, SUNY Cortland, 81 Prospect Terrace, Cortland, NY, 13045. Tel: 607-753-2525. Fax: 607-753-5669. p. 1611

Connell, Ruth, Electronic Serv Librn, Valparaiso University, 1410 Chapel Dr, Valparaiso, IN, 46383-6493. Tel: 219-464-5360. p. 783

Connell, Ruth, Tech Serv, John Carroll University, 20700 N Park Blvd, University Heights, OH, 44118. Tel: 216-397-1635. Fax: 216-397-4256. p. 1942

Connell, Sarah, Asst Librn, Tech Serv, Prudential Financial, Prudential Insurance Law Library, Four Plaza, 751 Broad St, Newark, NJ, 07102-3714. Tel: 973-802-6804. Fax: 973-802-2298. p. 1512

Connell, Suzan, Libr Res Coordr, Lincoln City Libraries, 136 S 14th St, Lincoln, NE, 68508-1899. Tel: 402-441-8575. Fax: 402-441-8586. p. 1404

Connell, Virginia, Head of Instruction, Concordia College, 901 S Eighth St, Moorhead, MN, 56562. Tel: 218-299-3237. Fax: 218-299-4253. p. 1265

Connelly, Frank, Ref, Larchmont Public Library, 121 Larchmont Ave, Larchmont, NY, 10538. Tel: 914-834-2281. p. 1651

Connelly, Jessica, Br Librn, Plymouth Public Library, 132 South St, Plymouth, MA, 02360-3309. Tel: 508-830-4250. Fax: 508-830-4258. p. 1118

Connelly, Jessica, Librn, Plymouth Public Library, Manomet Branch, 12 Strand Ave, Manomet, MA, 02345. Tel: 508-830-4185. p. 1118

Connelly, Maureen, YA Serv, John C Hart Memorial Library, 1130 Main St, Shrub Oak, NY, 10588. Tel: 914-245-5262. Fax: 914-245-2216. p. 1743

Conner, Anne, Dir, Littleton Regional Hospital, 600 St Johnsbury Rd, Littleton, NH, 03561. Tel: 603-444-9564. Fax: 603-444-7491. p. 1454

Conner, Anne, Dir, Coquille Public Library, 105 N Birch St, Coquille, OR, 97423-1299. Tel: 541-396-2166. Fax: 541-396-2174. p. 1993

Conner, Christy, Ch, Mauney Memorial Library, 100 S Piedmont Ave, Kings Mountain, NC, 28086. Tel: 704-739-2371. Fax: 704-734-4499. p. 1804

Conner, Jane S, Acq, Adult Coll Develop Librn, Campbell County Public Library, 684 Village Hwy, Lower Level, Rustburg, VA, 24588. Tel: 434-332-9560. Fax: 434-332-9697. p. 2495

Conner, Jill, Dir, Pueblo of Pojoaque Public Library, 37 Camino del Rincon, Ste 2, Santa Fe, NM, 87506-9810. Tel: 505-455-7511. Fax: 505-455-0501. p. 1563

Conner, Julie, Ch, Plano Public Library System, Gladys Harrington Library, 1501 E 18th St, Plano, TX, 75074. Tel: 972-941-7175. Fax: 972-941-7292. p. 2370

Conner, Marisa, Coordr, Youth Serv, Baltimore County Public Library, 320 York Rd, Towson, MD, 21204-5179. Tel: 410-887-0517. Fax: 410-887-6103. p. 1044

Conner, Marsha, Circ, Emmanuel School of Religion Library, One Walker Dr, Johnson City, TN, 37601-9438. Tel: 423-926-1186. Fax: 423-926-6198. p. 2239

Conner, Phyllis, Ch, Sheppard Memorial Library, 530 S Evans St, Greenville, NC, 27858-2308. Tel: 252-329-4878. Fax: 252-329-4587. p. 1799

Conner, Rosalind, Libr Dir, Sidney Memorial Public Library, Masonville Branch, 15565 State Hwy 8, Sidney, NY, 13838-2721. Tel: 607-265-3330. Fax: 607-265-3330. p. 1744

Conner, Shemka, Computer Librn, Noxubee County Library System, 103 E King St, Macon, MS, 39341-2832. Tel: 662-726-5461. Fax: 662-726-4694. p. 1307

Conner, Susan, Asst Dir, Head, Tech, Swampscott Public Library, 61 Burrill St, Swampscott, MA, 01907. Tel: 781-596-8867. Fax: 781-596-8826. p. 1130

Conners, Jenna, Ch, Ottumwa Public Library, 102 W Fourth St, Ottumwa, IA, 52501. Tel: 641-682-7563. Fax: 641-682-4970. p. 837

Conners, Mary, Mgr, Libr Serv, Brockton Hospital Library, 680 Centre St, Brockton, MA, 02302. Tel: 508-941-7207. Fax: 508-941-6412. p. 1070

Conners, Maureen, Dir, Belmont Public Library, 336 Concord Ave, Belmont, MA, 02478-0904. Tel: 617-489-2000, Ext 2852. Fax: 617-993-2893. p. 1052

Conness, Erinn, Youth Serv, Paul Sawyier Public Library, 319 Wapping St, Frankfort, KY, 40601-2605. Tel: 502-352-2665. Fax: 502-227-2250. p. 914

Connick, Judith, Spec Coll Librn, Ohio University Libraries, Mahn Center for Archives & Special Collections, Vernon R Alden Library, 30 Park Pl, Fifth Flr, Athens, OH, 45701-2978. Tel: 740-597-1771. Fax: 740-593-2708. p. 1856

Connick, Kathy, Librn, Centers for Disease Control, Robert A Taft Laboratories, 4676 Columbia Pkwy, Cincinnati, OH, 45226. Tel: 513-533-8321. Fax: 513-533-8382. p. 1868

Conniff, William P, Exec Dir, Panhandle Library Access Network, Five Miracle Strip Loop, Ste 8, Panama City Beach, FL, 32407-3850. Tel: 850-233-9051. Fax: 850-235-2286. p. 2940

Conning, Carmela, ILL, Ref Librn, Park County Public Library, 1500 Heart Mountain St, Cody, WY, 82414. Tel: 307-527-1880. Fax: 307-527-1888. p. 2653

Connley, Claire, Operations Mgr, Nampa Public Library, 101 11th Ave S, Nampa, ID, 83651. Tel: 208-468-5806. Fax: 208-318-0530. p. 580

Connolly, Ann E, Asst Dir, Head, Ref, Abbot Public Library, 235 Pleasant St, Marblehead, MA, 01945. Tel: 781-631-1481. Fax: 781-639-0558. p. 1102

Connolly, Danielle, Ch, Rose Memorial Library, 79 E Main St, Stony Point, NY, 10980-1699. Tel: 845-786-2100. Fax: 845-786-6042. p. 1750

Connolly, Erin, Br Mgr, Toledo-Lucas County Public Library, Sanger, 3030 W Central Ave, Toledo, OH, 43606. Tel: 419-259-5370. Fax: 419-536-9573. p. 1940

Connolly, Hilary, Cataloger, Mountain View Public Library, 125 S Oak St, Mountain View, MO, 65548. Tel: 417-934-6154. Fax: 417-934-5100. p. 1347

Connolly, Sybill, Ref, Southern Nazarene University, 4115 N College, Bethany, OK, 73008. Tel: 405-491-6350. Fax: 405-491-6355. p. 1958

Connor, Christina, Pub Serv, Ramapo College of New Jersey, 505 Ramapo Valley Rd, Mahwah, NJ, 07430-1623. Tel: 201 684 7584. p. 1498

Connor, Elizabeth, Interim Dir, Libr Serv, The Citadel, 171 Moultrie St, Charleston, SC, 29409-6140. Tel: 843-953-5116. Fax: 843-953-5190. p. 2184

Connor, Ellen L, Dir, Sturm Memorial Library, 130 N Bridge St, Manawa, WI, 54949-9517. Tel: 920-596-2252. Fax: 920-596-2234. p. 2611

Connor, Elsie, Asst Librn, Evart Public Library, 104 N Main St, Evart, MI, 49631. Tel: 231-734-5542. Fax: 231-734-5542. p. 1177

Connor, Georgianna, Ch, Ingalls Memorial Library, 203 Main St, Rindge, NH, 03461. Tel: 603-899-3303. Fax: 603-899-5797. p. 1463

Connor, Martha, Creative Serv Supvr, Fresno County Public Library, 2420 Mariposa St, Fresno, CA, 93721-2285. Tel: 559-600-7323. p. 151

Connor, Mary, Adult Serv, Public Library of Anniston-Calhoun County, 108 E Tenth St, Anniston, AL, 36201. Tel: 256-237-8501, 256-237-8503. Fax: 256-238-0474. p. 4

Connor, Patricia, Sister, Asst Librn, Marian College, 3200 Cold Spring Rd, Indianapolis, IN, 46222. Tel: 317-955-6090. Fax: 317-955-6418. p. 755

Connors, Bethanie, Ch Serv Librn, Romeo District Library, 65821 Van Dyke, Washington, MI, 48095. Tel: 586-752-0603. Fax: 586-752-8416. p. 1235

Connors, Claire, Librn, Westwood Public Library, Islington, 280 Washington St, Westwood, MA, 02090. Tel: 781-326-5914. p. 1139

Connors, Grant, Interdisciplinary Res Support Librn, Georgetown University, Dahlgren Memorial Library, Preclinical Science Bldg GM-7, 3900 Reservoir Rd NW, Washington, DC, 20007. Tel: 202-687-2914. Fax: 202-687-1862. p. 402

Connors, Laura, Asst Regional Libr Mgr, Broward County Division of Libraries, Northwest Regional, 3151 University Dr, Coral Springs, FL, 33065. Tel: 954-341-3900, Ext 248. Fax: 954-341-3980. p. 442

Connors, Margaret, Dir, Libr Serv, Fielding Graduate University, 2020 De La Vina St, Santa Barbara, CA, 93105. Tel: 805-690-4373. p. 260

Connors, Susan, Librn, Berry Creek Community Library, RR 2, Brooks, AB, T1R 1E2, CANADA. Tel: 403-566-3743. Fax: 403-566-3736. p. 2686

Connors, Tess, Cat, Arkansas Tech University, 305 West Q St, Russellville, AR, 72801-2222. Tel: 479-964-0558. Fax: 479-964-0559. p. 113

Connorton, Judith, Librn, City College of the City University of New York, Architecture Library, Spitzer Bldg, Rm 101, 160 Convent Ave, New York, NY, 10031. Tel: 212-650-8767. Fax: 212-650-7214. p. 1673

Conolly, Julie, ILL, Northeast Iowa Community College, 10250 Sundown Rd, Peosta, IA, 52068. Tel: 563-556-5110, Ext 224. Fax: 563-557-0340. p. 838

Conor, Erin, Performing Arts Librn, Reed College, 3203 SE Woodstock Blvd, Portland, OR, 97202-8199. Tel: 503-777-7702. Fax: 503-777-7786. p. 2014

Conover, Bernadette, Cat, Millville Public Library, 210 Buck St, Millville, NJ, 08332. Tel: 856-825-7087. Fax: 856-327-8572. p. 1502

Conover, John, Assoc Librn, Louisiana Universities Marine Consortium, 8124 Hwy 56, Chauvin, LA, 70344-2124. Tel: 985-851-2875. Fax: 985-851-2874. p. 947

Conrad, Alexander, Dep Libr Dir, Pinal County Library District, 92 W Butte Ave, Florence, AZ, 85132. Tel: 520-866-6457. Fax: 520-866-6533. p. 63

Conrad, Connie, Circ, Marian University, 45 S National Ave, Fond du Lac, WI, 54935. Tel: 920-923-7641, 920-923-8725. Fax: 920-923-7154. p. 2592

Conrad, Deborah K, Exec Dir, SAILS, Inc, 547 W Groves St, Ste 4, Middleboro, MA, 02346. Tel: 508-946-8600. Fax: 508-946-8605. p. 2945

Conrad, Ellen, Cat Supvr, Denison University Libraries, 400 W Loop, Granville, OH, 43023. Tel: 740-587-6753. Fax: 740-587-6285. p. 1902

Conrad, Patti, Ch, Helen Hall Library, 100 W Walker, League City, TX, 77573-3899. Tel: 281-554-1115. Fax: 281-554-1118. p. 2354

Conrad, Robert, Br Mgr, Chicago Public Library, Mayfair, 4400 W Lawrence Ave, Chicago, IL, 60630. Tel: 312-744-1254. Fax: 312-744-0609. p. 609

Conrad, Susan, Dir, Oscar Foss Memorial Library, 111 S Barnstead Rd, Center Barnstead, NH, 03225. Tel: 603-269-3900. Fax: 603-269-3900. p. 1440

Conrads, Doug, Interim Librn, Indiana Academy of Science, Indiana State Library, 140 N Senate Ave, Indianapolis, IN, 46204-2296. Tel: 317-232-3686. Fax: 317-232-3728. p. 751

Conroy, Brad, ILL, Cincinnati State Technical & Community College, 3520 Central Pkwy, Cincinnati, OH, 45223-2612. Tel: 513-569-4690. Fax: 513-559-1527. p. 1869

Conroy, Christine, Assoc Univ Librn, Coll Serv, Boston College Libraries, Thomas P O'Neill Jr Library (Central Library), 140 Commonwealth Ave, Chestnut Hill, MA, 02467. Tel: 617-552-1942. Fax: 617-552-0599. p. 1081

Conroy, Darrin, Dir, NYS Small Business Development Center Research Network, 22 Corporate Woods Blvd, 3rd Flr, Albany, NY, 12211. Tel: 518-641-0650. Fax: 518-443-5275. p. 1570

Conroy, Joyce, Dr, Dir, Roscoe Free Library, 85 Highland Ave, Roscoe, NY, 12776. Tel: 607-498-5574. Fax: 607-498-5574. p. 1735

Conroy, Margaret M, State Librn, Missouri State Library, James C Kirkpatrick State Information Ctr, 600 W Main St, Jefferson City, MO, 65101-1532. Fax: 573-751-3612. p. 1335

Conroy, Michelle, Librn, Bethel Library Association, Five Broad St, Bethel, ME, 04217. Tel: 207-824-2520. p. 977

Conroy, Patricia, Head, Ref, Cicero Public Library, 5225 W Cermak Rd, Cicero, IL, 60804. Tel: 708-652-8084. Fax: 708-652-8095. p. 629

Conroy, Patricia, Head, Ref, Cicero Public Library, South, 5444 W 34th St, Cicero, IL, 60804. Tel: 708-863-8440. Fax: 708-863-8455. p. 629

Conroy, Patricia, Dir, Douglas County Library, 720 Fillmore St, Alexandria, MN, 56308-1763. Tel: 320-762-3014. Fax: 320-762-3036. p. 1239

Conroy, Richard, Dir, Essex Library Association, Inc, 33 West Ave, Essex, CT, 06426-1196. Tel: 860-767-1560. Fax: 860-767-2500. p. 338

Conroy, Terrye, Asst Dir, Legal Res Instruction, University of South Carolina, Coleman Karesh Law Library, USC Law Ctr, 701 Main St, Columbia, SC, 29208. Tel: 803-777-5942. Fax: 803-777-9405. p. 2190

Consales, Judy, Dir, University of California Los Angeles Library, Louise M Darling Biomedical Library, 10833 LeConte Ave, 12-077 Center for the Health Sciences, Los Angeles, CA, 90095-1798. Tel: 310-825-5781. Fax: 310-825-0465. p. 178

Consales, Judy, Head of Libr, University of California Los Angeles Library, Science & Engineering Libraries, 8270 Boelter Hall, Los Angeles, CA, 90095. Tel: 310-825-3398. Fax: 310-206-9872. p. 179

Consales, Judy, Dir, National Network of Libraries of Medicine Pacific Southwest Region, Louise M Darling Biomedical Library, 12-077 Ctr for Health Science, Box 951798, Los Angeles, CA, 90095-1798. Tel: 310-825-5781. Fax: 310-825-5389. p. 2938

Considine, Michael, Head, Info Tech, Fordham University Libraries, 441 E Fordham Rd, Bronx, NY, 10458-5151. Tel: 718-817-3570. Fax: 718-817-3582. p. 1586

Considine, Susan L, Exec Dir, Fayetteville Free Library, 300 Orchard St, Fayetteville, NY, 13066-1386. Tel: 315-637-6374. Fax: 315-637-2306. p. 1622

Consiglio, David, Head, Res Support & Educ Tech, Bryn Mawr College, 101 N Merion Ave, Bryn Mawr, PA, 19010-2899. Tel: 610-526-6534. Fax: 610-526-7480. p. 2039

Consing, Augusto, Info Tech, Newbury College Library, 150 Fisher Ave, Brookline, MA, 02445-5796. Tel: 617-730-7070. Fax: 617-730-7239. p. 1071

Consoli, Joseph, Librn, Rutgers University Libraries, Art Library, Voorhees Hall, 71 Hamilton St, New Brunswick, NJ, 08901-1248. Tel: 732-932-1696. Fax: 732-932-6743. p. 1508

Consorto, Carol, ILL, Chestnut Hill College, 9601 Germantown Ave, Philadelphia, PA, 19118-2695. Tel: 215-242-9982. Fax: 215-248-7056. p. 2104

Constance, Catherine, Librn, Ref Serv, Department of Veterans Affairs, 3200 Vine St, Cincinnati, OH, 45220-2213. Tel: 513-475-6315. Fax: 513-475-6454. p. 1870

Constance, Joseph W, Jr, Dir, Saint Anselm College, 100 Saint Anselm Dr, Manchester, NH, 03102-1310. Tel: 603-641-7300. Fax: 603-641-7345. p. 1456

Constant, Kyle, Br Mgr, Trails Regional Library, Lexington Branch, 1008 Main St, Lexington, MO, 64067. Tel: 660-259-3071. Fax: 660-259-3071. p. 1371

Constant, Marcelynn, Librn, Wapiti Regional Library, James Smith Public Library, Box 3848, Melfort, SK, S0E 1A0, CANADA. Tel: 306-864-2955. p. 2922

Constantine, Joyce, Asst Librn, Vancouver Island Health Authority Medical Libraries, Royal Jubilee Hospital, 1952 Bay St, Victoria, BC, V8R 1J8, CANADA. Tel: 250-370-8612, 250-370-8723. Fax: 250-370-8274. p. 2746

Constantine, Robert, Libr Assoc, University of New Hampshire Library, Chemistry, Parsons Hall, 23 College Rd, Durham, NH, 03824-3598. Tel: 603-862-1083. Fax: 603-862-4278. p. 1446

Constantinescu, Teodora, Librn, Sir Mortimer B Davis Jewish General Hospital, Dr Henry Kravitz Library-Institute of Community & Family Psychiatry, 4333 Cote Ste Catherine Rd, Montreal, QC, H3T 1E4, CANADA. Tel: 514-340-8210, Ext 5243. Fax: 514-340-8104. p. 2901

Constantinou, Alice, Cat Librn, Saint Paul University Library, 223 Main St, Ottawa, ON, K1S 1C4, CANADA. Tel: 613-236-1393, Ext 2334. Fax: 613-751-4031. p. 2833

Constantinou, Constantia, Chief Librn, State University of New York Maritime College, Six Pennyfield Ave, Fort Schuyler, Bronx, NY, 10465. Tel: 718-409-7236. Fax: 718-409-7256. p. 1588

Constantz, Mark Q, Librn, San Mateo County, 222 W 39th Ave, San Mateo, CA, 94403. Tel: 650-573-2520. Fax: 650-573-3510. p. 255

Contant, H, Exec Dir, Society of Christian Schools In British Columbia Library, 7600 Glover Rd, Langley, BC, V2Y 1Y1, CANADA. Tel: 604-888-6366. Fax: 604-888-2791. p. 2731

Conte, Jeanne, Librn, Peel District School Board, 5650 Hurontario St, Mississauga, ON, L5R 1C6, CANADA. Tel: 905-890-1099, Ext 2601. Fax: 905-890-4780. p. 2823

Conte, Nora, County Librn, San Benito County Free Library, 470 Fifth St, Hollister, CA, 95023-3885. Tel: 831-636-4097. Fax: 831-636-4099. p. 158

Conti, Carolyn G, Librn, Gladwyne Free Library, 362 Righters Mill Rd, Gladwyne, PA, 19035-1587. Tel: 610-642-3957. Fax: 610-642-3985. p. 2060

Conti, Jeanne, Librn, Flasher Public Library, 104 Fifth Ave E, Flasher, ND, 58535. Tel: 701-597-3127. Fax: 701-597-3127. p. 1841

Contin, Laura, Br Mgr, Los Angeles Public Library System, Pacoima Branch, 13605 Van Nuys Blvd, Pacoima, CA, 91331-3697. Tel: 818-899-5203. Fax: 818-899-5336. p. 174

Contois, Mark, Dir, Framingham Public Library, 49 Lexington St, Framingham, MA, 01702-8278. Tel: 508-879-5570, Ext 4358. Fax: 508-820-7210. p. 1090

Contois, Nancy, Dir, Chicopee Public Library, Chicopee Falls, 216 Broadway, Chicopee, MA, 01020. Tel: 413-594-1820. p. 1081

Contois, Nancy, Dir, Chicopee Public Library, Fairview, 402 Britton St, Chicopee, MA, 01020. Tel: 413-533-8218. p. 1081

Contois, Nancy M, Dir, Chicopee Public Library, 449 Front St, Chicopee, MA, 01013. Tel: 413-594-1800. Fax: 413-594-1819. p. 1081

Contrata, Eugenie, Dir, Greenburgh Public Library, 300 Tarrytown Rd, Elmsford, NY, 10523. Tel: 914-721-8200. Fax: 914-721-8201. p. 1620

Contreras, Chris, Dir, St Francis Library, 11414 W Hwy 33, Coyle, OK, 73027. Tel: 405-466-3774. Fax: 405-466-3722. p. 1961

Contreras, Jeanette, Dir, Placentia Library District, 411 E Chapman Ave, Placentia, CA, 92870. Tel: 714-528-1906. Fax: 714-528-8236. p. 208

Contreras, Paula, Br Mgr, Santa Cruz City-County Library System Headquarters, Live Oak, 2380 Portola Dr, Santa Cruz, CA, 95062. Tel: 831-427-7706, Ext 7677. Fax: 831-427-7718. p. 264

Contreras, Paula, Ref Librn, Pennsylvania State University Libraries, Social Sciences, 201 Paterno Library, University Park, PA, 16802-1809. Tel: 814-865-3621. Fax: 814-865-1403. p. 2148

Contreras, Raul, Sr Librn, California Department of Corrections Library System, North Kern State Prison, 2737 W Cecil Ave, Delano, CA, 93215. Tel: 661-721-2345. p. 221

Contreras, Sarah, Dir, Norwalk Public Library, 46 W Main St, Norwalk, OH, 44857. Tel: 419-668-6063. Fax: 419-663-2190. p. 1924

Contreras, Sherri, Librn, Ukiah Public Library, 201 Hill St, Ukiah, OR, 97880. Tel: 541-427-3435. Fax: 541-427-3730. p. 2022

Contreras, Sylvia, Dir, Edgewood College Library, 1000 Edgewood College Dr, Madison, WI, 53711-1997. Tel: 608-663-3300. Fax: 608-663-6778. p. 2606

Contreras, Sylvia T, Librn, Mounce & Green, Meyers, Safi & Galatzan, 100 N Stanton, Ste 1000, El Paso, TX, 79901. Tel: 915-532-2000. Fax: 915-541-1597. p. 2317

Contursi, Ellie, Br Librn, London Public Library, Cherryhill, 301 Oxford St W, London, ON, N6H 1S6, CANADA. Tel: 519-439-6456. p. 2818

Convery, Kami, Coll Develop, Dowling College Library, 150 Idle Hour Blvd, Oakdale, NY, 11769-1999. Tel: 631-244-3283. Fax: 631-244-3374. p. 1709

Conville, Bryon, Dir, Copiah-Lincoln Community College, 151 Colin Dr, Mendenhall, MS, 39111. Tel: 601-849-0116. Fax: 601-849-0160. p. 1308

Conway, Catherine, Br Librn, Eastern Monroe Public Library, Smithfields Branch, Rte 209 at Pocono Square, Marshalls Creek, PA, 18335. Tel: 570-223-1881. p. 2144

Conway, Cathy, Ad, Pocono Mountain Public Library, 5540 Memorial Blvd, Tobyhanna, PA, 18466. Tel: 570-894-8860. Fax: 570-894-8852. p. 2146

Conway, Cheryl, Head, Tech Serv, University of Arkansas Libraries, 365 N McIlroy Ave, Fayetteville, AR, 72701-4002. Tel: 479-575-4812. Fax: 479-575-6656. p. 99

Conway, Colleen, Tech Serv Librn, Hope College, Van Wylen Library, 53 Graves Pl, Holland, MI, 49422. Tel: 616-395-7792. Fax: 616-395-7965. p. 1190

Conway, Eileen, Circ Supvr, Rockwall County Library, 1215 E Yellowjacket Lane, Rockwall, TX, 75087. Tel: 972-204-7700. Fax: 972-204-7709. p. 2377

Conway, Jane, Exec Dir, Highland Park Public Library, 494 Laurel Ave, Highland Park, IL, 60035-2690. Tel: 847-432-0216. Fax: 847-432-9139. p. 655

Conway, Janet, Br Mgr, San Bernardino Public Library, Howard M Rowe Branch, 108 E Marshall Blvd, San Bernardino, CA, 92404. Tel: 909-883-3411. Fax: 909-882-4941. p. 229

Conway, Jo, Br Mgr, Brazoria County Library System, Brazoria Branch, 620 S Brooks, Brazoria, TX, 77422-9022. Tel: 979-798-2372. Fax: 979-798-4013. p. 2275

Conway, Katie, Dir, North Freedom Public Library, 105 N Maple St, North Freedom, WI, 53951. Tel: 608-522-4571. Fax: 608-522-4574. p. 2626

Conway, Marilyn, Librn, Lewis County Public Library, 52 Second St, Vanceburg, KY, 41179. Tel: 606-796-2532. Fax: 606-796-2532. p. 936

Conway, Mark, Computer Support Spec, Web Serv, University of North Dakota, 215 Centennial Dr, Grand Forks, ND, 58202. Tel: 701-777-2204. Fax: 701-777-2217. p. 1843

Conway, Mary, Ref Serv, Web Serv, National Library of Medicine, Bldg 38, Rm 2E-17B, 8600 Rockville Pike, Bethesda, MD, 20894. Tel: 301-496-6308. Fax: 301-496-4450. p. 1022

Conway, Melissa, Dr, Head, Spec Coll & Archives, University of California, Riverside Libraries, 900 University Ave, Riverside, CA, 92521. Tel: 951-827-3233. p. 218

Conway, Merry, Assoc Librn, Anoka County Law Library, 325 E Main St, Anoka, MN, 55303. Tel: 763-422-7487. Fax: 763-422-7453. p. 1239

Conway, Michael, In Charge, Arizona Geological Survey, 416 W Congress St, Ste 100, Tucson, AZ, 85701. Tel: 520-770-3500. Fax: 520-770-3505. p. 85

Conway, Pat, Librn, Garfield County Public Library System, Glenwood Springs Branch, 413 Ninth St, Glenwood Springs, CO, 81601-3607. Tel: 970-945-5958. Fax: 970-945-7723. p. 319

Conway, Paul, Assoc Prof, University of Michigan, 304 West Hall, 1085 S University, Ann Arbor, MI, 48109-1107. Tel: 734-763-2285. Fax: 734-764-2475. p. 2967

Conway, Robert, Circ Mgr, University of Massachusetts at Boston, 100 Morrissey Blvd, Boston, MA, 02125-3300. Tel: 617-287-5948. p. 1068

Conwell, George, Dir, Hamilton Township Public Library, One Justice Samuel A Alito, Jr Way, Hamilton, NJ, 08619. Tel: 609-581-4060. Fax: 609-581-4067. p. 1490

Conwell, Idella, Dir, Dodge County Historical Society Library, 615 N Main, Mantorville, MN, 55955. Tel: 507-635-5508. p. 1258

Conwell, Joy, Circ, Iowa Wesleyan College, 107 W Broad St, Mount Pleasant, IA, 52641. Tel: 319-385-6316. Fax: 319-385-6324. p. 833

Conyers, Howard, Interim Dir, Washoe County Law Library, 75 Courth St, Rm 101, Reno, NV, 89501. Tel: 775-328-3250. Fax: 775-328-3441. p. 1433

Cook, Alice, Supvr, Pub Serv, Sterling Heights Public Library, 40255 Dodge Park Rd, Sterling Heights, MI, 48313-4140. Tel: 586-446-2640. Fax: 586-276-4067. p. 1229

Cook, Anita, Librn, Grand Rapids Community College, 140 Ransom NE Ave, Grand Rapids, MI, 49503. Tel: 616-234-3870. Fax: 616-234-3878. p. 1185

Cook, Barbara, Br Mgr, Mesa County Public Library District, DeBeque Joint Branch, 730 Minter Ave, DeBeque, CO, 81630. Tel: 970-283-8625. p. 311

Cook, Becky K R, Boards Comn Asst, North Carolina Legislative Library, 500 Legislative Office Bldg, 300 N Salisbury St, Raleigh, NC, 27603-5925. Tel: 919-733-9390. Fax: 919-715-5460. p. 1815

Cook, Beth, Mgr, Youth & Outreach Serv, Laramie County Library System, 2200 Pioneer Ave, Cheyenne, WY, 82001-3610. Tel: 307-773-7227. Fax: 307-634-2082. p. 2652

Cook, Betty, Br Mgr, Oconee Regional Library, Glascock County Library, 738 Railroad Ave, Gibson, GA, 30810. Tel: 706-598-9837. Fax: 706-598-2670. p. 531

Cook, Beverly, Dir, Seton Health Systems, 1300 Massachusetts Ave, Troy, NY, 12180. Tel: 518-268-5210. Fax: 518-268-5806. p. 1757

Cook, Brenda, ILL, Dalhousie University, Sir James Dunn Law Library, Weldon Law Bldg, 6061 University Ave, Halifax, NS, B3H 4H9, CANADA. Tel: 902-494-8858. Fax: 902-494-6669. p. 2780

Cook, Caitlyn, Instr, Ref Librn, Ocean County College Library, College Dr, Toms River, NJ, 08754. Tel: 732-255-0400, Ext 2163. Fax: 732-255-0421. p. 1533

Cook, Candi, Dir, Cimarron City Library, 120 N Main, Cimarron, KS, 67835. Tel: 620-855-3808. Fax: 620-855-3884. p. 860

Cook, Catharine, Dir, Chickasha Public Library, 527 W Iowa Ave, Chickasha, OK, 73018. Tel: 405-222-6077. Fax: 405-222-6072. p. 1959

Cook, Catherine, Superintendent, National Park Service, 3370 Lafayette Rd, Fort Oglethorpe, GA, 30742. Tel: 706-866-9241. p. 533

Cook, Charee, Dir, Crosby Public Library, 59 Main St, Antwerp, NY, 13608-4157. Tel: 315-659-8564. Fax: 315-659-8564. p. 1574

Cook, Cheryl, Head, Acq, University of California, Berkeley, Technical Services, 250 Moffit Library, Berkeley, CA, 94720-6000. Tel: 510-643-8239. Fax: 510-642-8331. p. 128

Cook, Chris, Assoc Dir, Basalt Regional Library District, 14 Midland Ave, Basalt, CO, 81621-8305. Tel: 970-927-4311. Fax: 970-927-1351. p. 289

Cook, Christine, Asst Librn, Grant County Library, 18 Mountain View St, Petersburg, WV, 26847-1524. Tel: 304-257-4122. Fax: 304-257-4122. p. 2569

Cook, Claudia, Ref Serv, Bernard E Witkin Alameda County Law Library, 12th & Oak St Bldg, 125 Twelfth St, Oakland, CA, 94607-4912. Tel: 510-208-4830. Fax: 510-208-4823. p. 199

Cook, Connie, Cat, Judson College, 306 E Dekalb, Marion, AL, 36756. Tel: 334-683-5184. Fax: 334-683-5188. p. 24

Cook, Dana, Dir, Hollis Public Library, 201 W Broadway & Second St, Hollis, OK, 73550. Tel: 580-688-2744. Fax: 580-688-9736. p. 1965

Cook, Danita, Librn, Preble County District Library, Eldorado Branch, 150 N Main St, Eaton, OH, 45321. Tel: 937-273-4933. Fax: 937-273-5673. p. 1898

Cook, Dave, III, Coordr, Illinois School for the Deaf, 125 Webster, Jacksonville, IL, 62650. Tel: 217-479-4241. Fax: 217-479-4244. p. 618

Cook, Deborah, Head, Access Serv, Georgetown University, 37th & N St NW, Washington, DC, 20057-1174. Tel: 202-687-7461. Fax: 202-687-7501. p. 402

Cook, Deborah, Educ & Libr Dir, Rayburn Correctional Center Library, 27268 Hwy 21, Angie, LA, 70426. Tel: 985-986-5000, Ext 5070. Fax: 985-986-5071. p. 941

Cook, Diana, Librn, Southeast Regional Library, Milestone Branch, 112 Main St, Milestone, SK, S0G 3L0, CANADA. Tel: 306-436-2112. p. 2930

Cook, Dixie, Prog Dir, Ignacio Community Library District, 470 Goddard Ave, Ignacio, CO, 81137. Tel: 970-563-9287. Fax: 970-563-9296. p. 313

Cook, Douglas, Distance Educ, Shippensburg University, 1871 Old Main Dr, Shippensburg, PA, 17257-2299. Tel: 717-477-1123, Ext 3312. Fax: 717-477-1389. p. 2140

Cook, Drea, Br Librn, Lake Agassiz Regional Library, Barnesville Public Library, 104 N Front St, Barnesville, MN, 56514. Tel: 218-354-2301. Fax: 218-354-7064. p. 1266

Cook, Ed, Fac Mgr, Baltimore County Public Library, 320 York Rd, Towson, MD, 21204-5179. Tel: 410-887-6136. Fax: 410-887-6103. p. 1044

Cook, Eleanor, Copyright Librn, Web Serv, Appalachian State University, 218 College St, Boone, NC, 28608. Tel: 828-262-2786. Fax: 828-262-3001. p. 1776

Cook, Eleanor, Asst Dir, Coll & Tech Serv, East Carolina University, J Y Joyner Library, E Fifth St, Greenville, NC, 27858-4353. Tel: 252-328-2598. Fax: 252-328-6892. p. 1798

Cook, Elizabeth, Archivist, Regis University, 3333 Regis Blvd, Denver, CO, 80221-1099. Tel: 303-458-4030. Fax: 303-964-5497. p. 303

Cook, Faith E, Asst Librn, Runnemede Free Public Library, Broadway & Black Horse Pike, Runnemede, NJ, 08078. Tel: 856-939-4688. Fax: 856-939-6371. p. 1528

Cook, Hansel, Archivist, Saint Mary's University, 5429 Inglis St, Halifax, NS, B3H 3C3, CANADA. Tel: 902-420-5508. Fax: 902-420-5561. p. 2782

Cook, Holly, Circ Supvr, Texarkana College, 2500 N Robison Rd, Texarkana, TX, 75599. Tel: 903-832-5565, Ext 3215. Fax: 903-831-7429. p. 2391

Cook, Hope Marie, Curric Center Librn, Eastern Connecticut State University, 83 Windham St, Willimantic, CT, 06226-2295. Tel: 860-465-4456. Fax: 860-465-5517. p. 378

Cook, Jan, ILL, Tech Serv, Lake County Library, 1425 N High St, Lakeport, CA, 95453-3800. Tel: 707-263-8816. Fax: 707-263-6796. p. 163

Cook, Jan, Coll Develop, Ref, Kansas Supreme Court, Kansas Judicial Ctr, 301 SW Tenth St, Topeka, KS, 66612-1502. Tel: 785-368-7369. Fax: 785-296-1863. p. 896

Cook, Jean, Instrul Serv Librn, Irvine Sullivan Ingram Library, University of West Georgia, 1601 Maple St, Carrollton, GA, 30118. Tel: 678-839-6498. Fax: 678-839-6511. p. 523

Cook, Jennifer, Librn, Missouri Department of Corrections, Moberly Correctional Center, Bus Rte 63 S, 5201 S Morley, Moberly, MO, 65270. Tel: 660-263-3778. Fax: 660-263-1730. p. 1334

Cook, Jerilee, Adult Serv, Ref Serv, Howell Carnegie District Library, 314 W Grand River Ave, Howell, MI, 48843. Tel: 517-546-0720. Fax: 517-546-1494. p. 1192

Cook, Joanita, Mgr, Thomas County Public Library System, Meigs Public Library, 3058 NE Railroad St, Meigs, GA, 31765. Tel: 229-683-3853. Fax: 229-683-3853. p. 553

Cook, Joyce, Br Mgr, Webster Parish Library, Doyline Branch, 333 Main St, Doyline, LA, 71023. Tel: 318-745-3800. Fax: 318-745-2170. p. 957

Cook, Kelli, Ch, West Plains Public Library, 750 W Broadway, West Plains, MO, 65775-2369. Tel: 417-256-4775. Fax: 417-256-8316. p. 1372

Cook, Kelly, Supv Librn, Hess Corp, 500 Dallas St, Level 2, Houston, TX, 77002. Tel: 713-609-5000. Fax: 713-609-5549. p. 2337

Cook, Kerry, Tech Serv, Pueblo Community College Library, 900 W Orman Ave, Pueblo, CO, 81004-1430. Tel: 719-549-3308. Fax: 719-549-3309. p. 321

Cook, Kevin, Electronic Res, State Law Library of Montana, 215 N Sanders, Helena, MT, 59601-4522. Tel: 406-444-3660. Fax: 406-444-3603. p. 1383

Cook, Lacie, Librn, Clayton Public Library, 17 Chestnut St, Clayton, NM, 88415. Tel: 575-374-9423. Fax: 575-374-9423. p. 1553

Cook, Lee, Dir, Sinai Hospital of Baltimore, 2401 W Belvedere, Baltimore, MD, 21215-5271. Tel: 410-601-5015. Fax: 410-664-7432. p. 1017

Cook, Leslie, Ch, Cabarrus County Public Library, 27 Union St N, Concord, NC, 28025-4793. Tel: 704-920-2050. Fax: 704-784-3822. p. 1785

Cook, Linda, Chief Exec Officer, Edmonton Public Library, Seven Sir Winston Churchill Sq, Edmonton, AB, T5J 2V4, CANADA. Tel: 780-496-7050. Fax: 780-496-7097. p. 2700

Cook, Linda, Head of Libr, Minnedosa Regional Library, 45 First Ave, Minnedosa, MB, R0J 1E0, CANADA. Tel: 204-867-2585. Fax: 204-867-6140. p. 2750

Cook, Lisa, In Charge, Florida Department of Corrections, 20421 Sheridan St, Fort Lauderdale, FL, 33332-2300. Tel: 954-252-6362. Fax: 954-680-4168. p. 443

Cook, Lisa M, Dir, Warren County Law Library Association, 500 Justice Dr, Lebanon, OH, 45036. Tel: 513-695-1381. Fax: 513-695-2947. p. 1909

Cook, Lois, Co-Librn, First United Methodist Church Library, 400 S Main St, Mount Pleasant, MI, 48858. Tel: 989-773-6934. Fax: 989-773-1855. p. 1211

Cook, Michele, Regional Librn, Syst Librn, Northwest Community College Library, 5331 McConnell Ave, Terrace, BC, V8G 4X2, CANADA. Tel: 250-638-5407. Fax: 250-635-1594. p. 2739

Cook, Nancy, Ch, Jefferson-Madison Regional Library, 201 E Market St, Charlottesville, VA, 22902-5287. Tel: 434-979-7151, Ext 206, 434-979-7151, Ext 207. Fax: 434-971-7035. p. 2453

Cook, Nedra Johnson, Librn, Covenant Health, 1915 White Ave, 3rd Flr, Knoxville, TN, 37916. Tel: 865-541-1293. Fax: 865-541-1762. p. 2241

Cook, Pat, Librn, Virginia Beach Public Library Department, Municipal Reference Services, 4100 Virginia Beach Blvd, Virginia Beach, VA, 23452. Tel: 757-385-4644. p. 2500

Cook, Patricia J, Cent Librn, Virginia Beach Public Library Department, Meyera E Oberndorf Central Library, 4100 Virginia Beach Blvd, Virginia Beach, VA, 23452. Tel: 757-385-0101. Fax: 757-431-3134. p. 2500

Cook, Paula, Ref Serv, Manchester Community College Library, Great Path, Manchester, CT, 06040. Tel: 860-512-2877. Fax: 860-512-2871. p. 350

Cook, Peggy, County Coordr, Pioneer Library System, Purcell Public, 919 N Ninth, Purcell, OK, 73080. Tel: 405-527-5546. Fax: 405-527-7140. p. 1970

Cook, Peggy Miller, Librn, Hillcrest Medical Center Library, 1120 S Utica Ave, Tulsa, OK, 74104-4090. Tel: 918-579-8357. Fax: 918-579-8388. p. 1981

Cook, Peter, Syst Librn, Falmouth Public Library, 300 Main St, Falmouth, MA, 02540. Tel: 508-457-2555. Fax: 508-457-2559. p. 1088

Cook, Rebecca, Dir, Poultney Public Library, 205 Main St, Poultney, VT, 05764. Tel: 802-287-5556. p. 2432

Cook, Ron, Librn, Tulsa City-County Library, Glenpool Branch, 730 E 141st St, Glenpool, OK, 74033. Tel: 918-746-5190. Fax: 918-746-5191. p. 1983

Cook, Ruth, Ch, New Hartford Public Library, Two Library Lane, New Hartford, NY, 13413-2815. Tel: 315-733-1535. Fax: 315-733-0795. p. 1665

Cook, Schuyler, Govt Doc/Spec Projects Librn, Cleveland State University, Cleveland-Marshall Law Library, Cleveland-Marshall College of Law, 1801 Euclid Ave, Cleveland, OH, 44115-2223. Tel: 216-523-7388. Fax: 216-687-6881. p. 1878

Cook, Steven, Dir, Starr Library, 68 W Market St, Rhinebeck, NY, 12572. Tel: 845-876-4030. Fax: 845-876-4030. p. 1727

Cook, Susan, Sr Librn, Ref, Rancho Mirage Public Library, 71-100 Hwy 111, Rancho Mirage, CA, 92270. Tel: 760-341-7323. Fax: 760-341-5213. p. 213

Cook, Susan, Mgr, Washington County Library, Wausau Public Library, Town Hall, 1607 Second Ave, Wausau, FL, 32463. Tel: 850-638-2532. Fax: 850-638-2532. p. 431

Cook, Teresa, Br Mgr, Bedford Public Library System, Moneta/Smith Mountain Lake Library, 13641 Moneta Rd, Moneta, VA, 24121. Tel: 540-297-6474. Fax: 540-297-6450. p. 2451

Cook, Wayne, Prog Dir, Rayburn Correctional Center Library, 27268 Hwy 21, Angie, LA, 70426. Tel: 985-986-5000, 985-986-5054. Fax: 985-986-5071. p. 941

Cooke, Carol, Res Support Serv, University of Manitoba Libraries, Neil John Maclean Health Sciences Library, 223 Brodie Centre, 727 McDermot Ave, Winnipeg, MB, R3E 3P5, CANADA. Tel: 204-789-3342, 204-789-3464. Fax: 204-789-3922. p. 2759

Cooke, Cynthia, Coordr, Info Serv, Norfolk State University Library, 700 Park Ave, Norfolk, VA, 23504-8010. Tel: 757-823-8517. Fax: 757-823-2431. p. 2482

Cooke, Harry, Dr, Dir of Libr, Gaston College, 201 Hwy 321 S, Dallas, NC, 28034-1499. Tel: 704-922-6359. Fax: 704-922-2342. p. 1786

Cooke, Harry, Dr, Dir of Libr, Gaston College, Harvey A Jonas Library, 511 S Aspen St, Lincolnton, NC, 28092. Tel: 704-748-1050. Fax: 704-748-1068. p. 1786

Cooke, Jackie, Asst Librn, G Robert Cotton Regional Correctional Facility Library, 3500 N Elm Rd, Jackson, MI, 49201. Tel: 517-780-5172. Fax: 517-780-5100. p. 1195

Cooke, James, Planning & Projects Mgr, Baltimore County Public Library, 320 York Rd, Towson, MD, 21204-5179. Tel: 410-887-3285. Fax: 410-887-6103. p. 1044

Cooke, LaCrystal, Br Mgr, Brooklyn Public Library, Stone Avenue, 581 Mother Gaston Blvd, Brooklyn, NY, 11212. Tel: 718-485-8347. Fax: 718-342-0748. p. 1592

Cooke, Lisa, Libr Assoc/Bks-By-Mail Coordr, Lee County Library System, Outreach Services, 21100 Three Oaks Pkwy, Estero, FL, 33928. Tel: 239-390-3232. Fax: 239-498-6424. p. 446

Cooke, Marischa B, Dir, Caldwell Community College & Technical Institute, 2855 Hickory Blvd, Hudson, NC, 28638. Tel: 828-726-2309. Fax: 828-726-2603. p. 1803

Cooke, Nicole, Asst Prof, University of Illinois at Urbana-Champaign, Library & Information Science Bldg, 501 E Daniel St, Champaign, IL, 61820-6211. Tel: 217-333-3280. Fax: 217-244-3302. p. 2965

Cooke, Sandy, Librn, Catawba County Library, Sherrills Ford Branch, 8456 Sherrills Ford Rd, Sherrills Ford, NC, 28673. Tel: 828-478-2729. Fax: 828-478-5837. p. 1813

Cooker, Janis, Youth Serv Coordr, Saint Mary's County Memorial Library, Lexington Park Branch, 21677 FDR Blvd, Lexington Park, MD, 20653. Tel: 301-863-8188, Ext 1006. Fax: 301-863-2550. p. 1035

Cooksey, Melanie, Assoc Dir, Pasco-Hernando Community College-North Campus, 11415 Ponce de Leon Blvd, Brooksville, FL, 34601-8698. Tel: 352-797-5006. Fax: 352-797-5080. p. 430

Cookson, Melissa, Cat Librn, Tarleton State University Library, 201 Saint Felix, Stephenville, TX, 76401. Tel: 254-968-9339. Fax: 254-968-9467. p. 2389

Cool, Colleen, Assoc Prof, Queens College of the City University of New York, Benjamin Rosenthal Library, Rm 254, 65-30 Kissena Blvd, Flushing, NY, 11367. Tel: 718-997-3790. Fax: 718-997-3797. p. 2970

Cooley, Abby, Mgr, Baltimore County Public Library, Reisterstown Branch, 21 Cockeys Mill Rd, Reisterstown, MD, 21136-1285. Tel: 410-887-1165. Fax: 410-833-8756. p. 1044

Cooley, Carol, Chief Exec Officer, The Blue Mountains Public Library, 173 Bruce St S, Thornbury, ON, N0H 2P0, CANADA. Tel: 519-599-3681. Fax: 519-599-7951. p. 2847

Cooley, Carol A, Dir, Oakland Public Library, 18 Church St, Oakland, ME, 04963. Tel: 207-465-7533, 207-465-9554. Fax: 207-465-9554. p. 994

Cooley, Daniel R, Dir, Dover Public Library, 525 N Walnut St, Dover, OH, 44622. Tel: 330-343-6123. Fax: 330-343-2087. p. 1896

Cooley, Ken, Assoc Univ Librn, Info Tech, Assoc Univ Librn, Tech Serv, University of Victoria Libraries, McPherson Library, PO Box 1800, Victoria, BC, V8W 3H5, CANADA. Tel: 250-721-8211. Fax: 250-721-8215. p. 2746

Cooley, Laura, Circ, ILL, Pub Serv, Saint John's College, 1160 Camino Cruz Blanca, Santa Fe, NM, 87505. Tel: 505-984-6044. Fax: 505-984-6004. p. 1563

Coolidge, Bill, Mgr, Sonoma County Library, Windsor Regional, 9291 Old Redwood Hwy, No 100, Windsor, CA, 95492. Tel: 707-838-1020. Fax: 707-838-8329. p. 268

Coombs, James A, Assoc Prof, Missouri State University, Duane G Meyer Library, 901 S National Ave, Springfield, MO, 65897. Tel: 417-836-4525. Fax: 417-836-4764. p. 2968

Coombs, Joanne, Libr Tech, Nova Scotia Community College, 1240 Grand Lake Rd, Sydney, NS, B1P 6J7, CANADA. Tel: 902-563-2102. Fax: 902-563-0511. p. 2785

Coomes, Phylis A, Cat, ILL, Labette Community College Library, 200 S 14th St, Parsons, KS, 67357. Tel: 620-820-1167. Fax: 620-421-1469. p. 889

Coomes, Ruth Ann, Pub Serv Coordr, Spalding University Library, 853 Library Lane, Louisville, KY, 40203-9986. Tel: 502-585-7130. Fax: 502-585-7156. p. 925

Coon, Julie, Libr Assoc, Lima Public Library, Spencerville Branch, 2489 Wisher Dr, Spencerville, OH, 45887. Tel: 419-647-4307. Fax: 419-647-6393. p. 1910

Coon, Kathleen, Dir, Montgomery, Mccracken, Walker & Rhoads LLP Library, 123 S Broad St, Philadelphia, PA, 19109. Tel: 215-772-7611. Fax: 215-772-7620. p. 2112

Coon, Laura Gayle, Circ Librn, Riley City Library, 206 S Broadway, Riley, KS, 66531. Tel: 785-485-2978. p. 892

Cooney, Martha, Dept Head, Long Island University Post, Center for Business Research Library, 720 Northern Blvd, 25-A, Brookville, NY, 11548. Tel: 516-299-2832. Fax: 516-299-4170. p. 1596

Cooney, Michael R, Tech Serv, Bayard Taylor Memorial Library, 216 E State St, Kennett Square, PA, 19348-3112. Tel: 610-444-2702. Fax: 610-444-1752. p. 2074

Coonrod, Denise, Librn, Howard College - San Angelo Library, 3501 N US Hwy 67, San Angelo, TX, 76905. Tel: 325-481-8300, Ext 309. Fax: 325-481-8321. p. 2379

Coons, Martha, YA Serv, Springfield City Library, 220 State St, Springfield, MA, 01103. Tel: 413-263-6828, Ext 425. Fax: 413-263-6817. p. 1127

Coons, Mary Patricia, Tech Serv/Ref Librn, Rushville Public Library, 130 W Third St, Rushville, IN, 46173-1899. Tel: 765-932-3496. Fax: 765-932-4528. p. 776

Coons, Teresa, Cat, North Carolina Agricultural & Technical State University, 1601 E Market St, Greensboro, NC, 27411-0002. Tel: 336-334-7669, Ext 3234. Fax: 336-334-7783. p. 1797

Cooper, Allison, Br Head, East Baton Rouge Parish Library, River Center, 120 St Louis St, Baton Rouge, LA, 70802. Tel: 225-389-4967. Fax: 225-389-8910. p. 943

Cooper, Amanda Reynolds, Dir, Lane Memorial Library, Two Academy Ave, Hampton, NH, 03842. Tel: 603-926-3368. Fax: 603-926-1348. p. 1449

Cooper, Amy, Librn, Calhoun County Public Library, Mill St N, Grantsville, WV, 26147. Tel: 304-354-6300. Fax: 304-354-6300. p. 2560

Cooper, Becky, Per, Black Hills State University, 1200 University St, Unit 9676, Spearfish, SD, 57799-9676. Tel: 605-642-6362. Fax: 605-642-6298. p. 2220

Cooper, Bob, Dir, Statewide Libr Res, Montana State Library, 1515 E Sixth Ave, Helena, MT, 59620-1800. Tel: 406-444-5431. Fax: 406-444-0266. p. 1383

Cooper, Brent, Ref Librn, Brazosport College Library, 500 College Dr, Lake Jackson, TX, 77566. Tel: 979-230-3366. Fax: 979-230-3185. p. 2352

Cooper, Bryan, Dir, Libr Serv, St Thomas University Library, 16401 NW 37th Ave, Miami Gardens, FL, 33054. Tel: 305-474-6814. Fax: 305-628-6666. p. 469

Cooper, Bryan, Dr, Assoc Dean, Tech & Digital Serv, Florida International University, 11200 SW Eighth St, Miami, FL, 33199. Tel: 305-348-2982. Fax: 305-348-0122. p. 465

Cooper, Byron D, Dir, University of Detroit Mercy Library, Kresge Law Library, 651 E Jefferson, Detroit, MI, 48226. Tel: 313-596-0239. Fax: 313-596-0245. p. 1172

Cooper, Caitlin, Ref Librn, Nunez Community College Library, 3710 Paris Rd, Chalmette, LA, 70043. Tel: 504-278-6230, 504-278-7498. Fax: 504-680-2584. p. 947

Cooper, Carol, Circ, Union Township Public Library, 27 Main St, Ripley, OH, 45167-1231. Tel: 937-392-4871. Fax: 937-392-1631. p. 1932

Cooper, Carrie Lynn, Dean, College of William & Mary in Virginia, Earl Gregg Swem Library, One Landrum Dr, Williamsburg, VA, 23187. Tel: 757-221-3050. Fax: 757-221-2635. p. 2502

Cooper, Charlotte, Ref Librn, Finger Lakes Community College, 4355 Lakeshore Dr, Canandaigua, NY, 14424-8395. Tel: 585-394-3500, Ext 7371. Fax: 585-394-8708. p. 1601

Cooper, Chris, Br Mgr, Humboldt County Library, Fortuna Branch, 753 14th St, Fortuna, CA, 95540-2113. Tel: 707-725-3460. p. 147

Cooper, Christopher, Supv Librn, Humboldt County Library, 1313 Third St, Eureka, CA, 95501-0553. Tel: 707-269-1918. p. 147

Cooper, Christopher, Access Serv, Southern New Hampshire University, 2500 N River Rd, Manchester, NH, 03106-1045. Tel: 603-668-2211, Ext 2160. Fax: 603-645-9685. p. 1456

Cooper, Constance, Dr, Chief Curator, Delaware Historical Society Research Library, 505 N Market St, Wilmington, DE, 19801. Tel: 302-295-2385. Fax: 302-655-7844. p. 387

Cooper, Cynthia, Dir, Peotone Public Library District, 515 N First St, Peotone, IL, 60468. Tel: 708-258-3436. Fax: 708-258-9796. p. 690

Cooper, Dale, In Charge, Florida Department of Corrections, Lawtey Correctional Institution Library, 7819 NW 228th St, Raiford, FL, 32026-2000. Tel: 904-782-2000, Ext 378. Fax: 904-782-1388. p. 485

Cooper, Darla, Dir, United States Air Force, McConnell AFB, 53476 Wichita St, Bldg 412, Wichita, KS, 67221. Tel: 316-759-4207. Fax: 316-759-4254. p. 900

Cooper, Daveta, Head, Tech Serv, Benicia Public Library, 150 East L St, Benicia, CA, 94510-3281. Tel: 707-746-4347. Fax: 707-747-8122. p. 126

Cooper, David L, Dir, Hamilton East Public Library, Fishers Branch, Five Municipal Dr, Fishers, IN, 46038-1574. Tel: 317-579-0300. Fax: 317-579-0309. p. 769

Cooper, David L, Dir, Hamilton East Public Library, One Library Plaza, Cumberland Rd, Noblesville, IN, 46060-5639. Tel: 317-770-3203. Fax: 317-776-6936. p. 769

Cooper, Dennis, Ch, Chelsea Public Library, 569 Broadway, Chelsea, MA, 02150-2991. Tel: 617-466-4350. Fax: 617-466-4359. p. 1080

Cooper, Dianne, Asst Librn, Scribner Public Library, 504 Main St, Scribner, NE, 68057. Tel: 402-664-3540. Fax: 402-664-3540. p. 1419

Cooper, Donna, Librn, Houston Love Memorial Library, Rossie Purcell Branch, 200 S Main St, Columbia, AL, 36319. Tel: 334-696-4417. p. 15

Cooper, Donna-Lynne, Head, Ch, Englewood Public Library, 31 Engle St, Englewood, NJ, 07631. Tel: 201-568-2215, Ext 243. Fax: 201-568-6895. p. 1484

Cooper, Elizabeth, Br Mgr, Benton County Public Library, Big Sandy Branch, 12 Front St, Big Sandy, TN, 38221. Tel: 731-593-0225. Fax: 731-593-0226. p. 2226

Cooper, Gary, Dir, Thomas University Library, 1501 Millpond Rd, Thomasville, GA, 31792. Tel: 229-226-1621. Fax: 229-226-1679. p. 554

Cooper, Gary, Pub Relations, New Jersey State Library, 185 W State St, Trenton, NJ, 08618. Tel: 609-278-2640, Ext 108. Fax: 609-278-2650. p. 1536

Cooper, George, Dir of Finance, Portland Public Library, Five Monument Sq, Portland, ME, 04101. Tel: 207-871-1700, Ext 760. Fax: 207-871-1703. p. 997

Cooper, Ginnie, Chief Librn/CEO, District of Columbia Public Library, 901 G St NW, Washington, DC, 20001-4599. Tel: 202-727-1101. Fax: 202-727-1129. p. 398

Cooper, Hope, Librn, Birmingham Public Library, 2100 Park Pl, Birmingham, AL, 35203. Tel: 205-226-3744. Fax: 205-226-3743. p. 7

Cooper, Hope, Tech Serv, Wesley Theological Seminary Library, 4500 Massachusetts Ave NW, Washington, DC, 20016-5690. Tel: 202-885-8658. Fax: 202-885-8691. p. 422

Cooper, Jackie Nazeri, Ref, Lawson State Community College Library, 3060 Wilson Rd SW, Birmingham, AL, 35221. Tel: 205-925-2515, Ext 6333, 205-929-6333. Fax: 205-925-3716. p. 8

Cooper, Jacqueline, Librn, Lawson State Community College Library, 1100 Ninth Ave SW, Bessemer, AL, 35022. Tel: 205-929-3434, 205-929-6333. Fax: 205-925-3716. p. 6

Cooper, James D, Dir, Salt Lake County Library Services, 2197 E Fort Union Blvd, Salt Lake City, UT, 84121-3139. Tel: 801-944-7504. Fax: 801-942-6323. p. 2413

Cooper, Jason, Cat, Syst Adminr, University of Montevallo, Station 6100, Montevallo, AL, 35115-6100. Tel: 205-665-6100. Fax: 205-665-6112. p. 27

Cooper, K J, Ch Serv Spec, La Conner Regional Library, 614 Morris St, La Conner, WA, 98257. Tel: 360-466-3352. Fax: 360-466-9178. p. 2519

Cooper, Kathleen, Librn, Sonoco Products Co, Inc, One N Second St, Hartsville, SC, 29550. Tel: 843-383-7000. Fax: 843-339-6120. p. 2198

Cooper, Kristy, Tech Librn/Adult Literacy Prog Coordr, Westland Public Library, 6123 Central City Pkwy, Westland, MI, 48185. Tel: 734-326-6123. Fax: 734-595-4612. p. 1236

Cooper, Lachelle, Tech Support, University of the District of Columbia, David A Clarke School of Law, Charles N & Hilda H M Mason Law Library, Bldg 39, Rm B-16, 4200 Connecticut Ave NW, Washington, DC, 20008. Tel: 202-274-7310. Fax: 202-274-7311. p. 421

Cooper, Lee, Librn, Cottage Grove Library & Community Center, 700 E Gibbs Ave, Cottage Grove, OR, 97424. Tel: 541-942-3828. Fax: 541-942-1267. p. 1995

Cooper, Lenora, Ch, East Saint Louis Public Library, 5300 State St, East Saint Louis, IL, 62203. Tel: 618-397-0991. Fax: 618-397-1260. p. 639

Cooper, Linda, Main Libr Supvr, Woodbridge Public Library, George Frederick Plaza, Woodbridge, NJ, 07095. Tel: 732-634-4450. p. 1545

Cooper, Linda, Br Mgr, Wake County Public Library System, Duraleigh Road Community Library, 5800 Duraleigh Rd, Raleigh, NC, 27612. Tel: 919-881-1318. Fax: 919-881-1317. p. 1817

Cooper, Linda, Assoc Prof, Queens College of the City University of New York, Benjamin Rosenthal Library, Rm 254, 65-30 Kissena Blvd, Flushing, NY, 11367. Tel: 718-997-3790. Fax: 718-997-3797. p. 2970

Cooper, Liz, Head, Res & Instruction, Auraria Library, 1100 Lawrence St, Denver, CO, 80204-2095. Tel: 303-552-3953. Fax: 303-556-3528. p. 298

Cooper, Margaret, Youth Serv Librn, George F Johnson Memorial Library, 1001 Park St, Endicott, NY, 13760. Tel: 607-757-5350. Fax: 607-757-2491. p. 1620

Cooper, Mark G, Interim Dir, University of South Carolina, Moving Image Research Collections, 707 Catawba St, Columbia, SC, 29201-4305. Tel: 803-777-2271. p. 2190

Cooper, Mary, Ref Librn, North Riverside Public Library District, 2400 S DesPlaines Ave, North Riverside, IL, 60546. Tel: 708-447-0869. Fax: 708-447-0526. p. 682

Cooper, Mary, Dir, Charles Ralph Holland Memorial Library, 205 West Hull Ave, Gainesboro, TN, 38562. Tel: 931-268-9190. Fax: 931-268-5706. p. 2235

Cooper, Mary Frances, Dir, Pres, Carnegie Library of Pittsburgh, 4400 Forbes Ave, Pittsburgh, PA, 15213-4080. Tel: 412-622-8874. Fax: 412-622-6278. p. 2122

Cooper, Mary Gail, Dir, Halifax Community College Library, 100 College Dr, Weldon, NC, 27890. Tel: 252-536-7237. Fax: 252-536-0474. p. 1829

Cooper, Matthew, Ref Librn, Thomas More College Library, 333 Thomas More Pkwy, Crestview Hills, KY, 41017-2599. Tel: 859-344-3300. Fax: 859-344-3342. p. 910

Cooper, Mavet, ILL, Osage City Public Library, 515 Main St, Osage City, KS, 66523. Tel: 785-528-2620, 785-528-3727. Fax: 785-528-4502. p. 886

Cooper Moore, Anne, Dean, Libr Affairs, Southern Illinois University Carbondale, 605 Agriculture Dr, Mailcode 6632, Carbondale, IL, 62901. Tel: 618-453-2522. p. 600

Cooper, Myrtle, Librn, Grafton Free Public Library, Library Rd, Grafton, NH, 03240. Tel: 603-523-7865. p. 1448

Cooper, Pamela J, Archivist, Indian River County Library System, 1600 21st St, Vero Beach, FL, 32960. Tel: 772-770-5060. Fax: 772-770-5066. p. 501

Cooper, Peggy, Assoc Dean, Boise State University, 1865 Cesar Chavez Lane, Boise, ID, 83725-1430. Tel: 208-426-2311. Fax: 208-334-2111. p. 570

Cooper, Ray, Br Mgr, Mississippi County Library System, Luxora Public, 215 Washington, Luxora, AR, 72358. Tel: 870-658-2421. Fax: 870-658-2421. p. 95

Cooper, Regina, Exec Dir, Springfield-Greene County Library District, 4653 S Campbell, Springfield, MO, 65810-1723. Tel: 417-882-0714. Fax: 417-883-9348. p. 1367

Cooper, Robin, Asst Librn, Hale County Public Library, 1103 Main St, Greensboro, AL, 36744. Tel: 334-624-3409. Fax: 334-624-3409. p. 19

Cooper, Rosemary, Dir, Albert Wisner Public Library, Two Colonial Ave, Warwick, NY, 10990-1191. Tel: 845-986-1047. Fax: 845-987-1228. p. 1763

Cooper, Sandra M, Dir, Sonoma County Library, 211 E St, Santa Rosa, CA, 95404. Tel: 707-545-0831. Fax: 707-575-0437. p. 267

Cooper, Stephanie, Dir, Sussex County Community College Library, One College Hill Rd, Newton, NJ, 07860. Tel: 973-300-2162. Fax: 973-300-2276. p. 1513

Cooper, Tammy, Librn, Fayette County Public Libraries, Gauley Bridge Branch, 286 Railroad St, Gauley Bridge, WV, 25085. Tel: 304-632-2172. Fax: 304-632-2172. p. 2568

Cooper, Tara L, Dir of Libr Serv, Union College, 310 College St, Campus Box D-21, Barbourville, KY, 40906-1499. Tel: 606-546-1241. Fax: 606-546-1239. p. 906

Cooper, Teresa, Asst Librn, Horseshoe Bend District Library, 392 Hwy 55, Horseshoe Bend, ID, 83629-9701. Tel: 208-793-2460. Fax: 208-793-2871. p. 576

Cooper, Tom, Dir, Webster Groves Public Library, 301 E Lockwood Ave, Webster Groves, MO, 63119-3102. Tel: 314-961-3784. Fax: 314-961-4233. p. 1372

Cooper, Virginia, Asst Dir, Rake Public Library, 123 N Main St, Rake, IA, 50465. Tel: 641-566-3388. Fax: 641-566-3388. p. 840

Cooper, Will, Librn, Fresno County Public Library, Fig Garden Regional, 3071 W Bullard, Fresno, CA, 93711. Tel: 559-600-4071. p. 152

Cooper, Yolanda, Dep Univ Librn, University of Miami Libraries, 1300 Memorial Dr, Coral Gables, FL, 33146. Tel: 305-284-3233. Fax: 305-284-4027. p. 434

Cooper-Bikman, Sheila, Librn, Stirling Municipal Library, PO Box 100, Stirling, AB, T0K 2E0, CANADA. Tel: 403-756-3665. p. 2718

Cooper-Wilson, Debbie L, Actg Dir, Ferguson Baptist Church Library, 509 Murphy Ave, Ferguson, KY, 42533. Tel: 606-679-1690. p. 912

Cooperstein, Susan, Bibliog Instr, Loyola-Notre Dame Library, Inc, 200 Winston Ave, Baltimore, MD, 21212. Tel: 410-617-6800. Fax: 410-617-6895. p. 1015

Coopey, Barbara, Asst Head, Access Serv, Pennsylvania State University Libraries, 510 Paterno Library, University Park, PA, 16802. Tel: 814-865-0401. Fax: 814-865-3665. p. 2148

Coorsh, Kathy, Chief Librn, Canadian Federation of Independent Business, 401-4141 Yonge St, Toronto, ON, M2P 2A6, CANADA. Tel: 416-222-8022, Ext 227. Fax: 416-222-4337. p. 2851

Coote Pack, Andrea, Br Mgr, Hancock County Library System, Pearlington Public Library, 6096 First St, Pearlington, MS, 39572. Tel: 228-533-0755. Fax: 228-533-0125. p. 1294

Coover, Dee, Dir, DeKalb Public Library, 309 Oak St, DeKalb, IL, 60115-3369. Tel: 815-756-9568. Fax: 815-756-7837. p. 635

Copans, Ruth, Col Librn, Spec Coll Librn, Skidmore College, 815 N Broadway, Saratoga Springs, NY, 12866. Tel: 518-580-5506. Fax: 518-580-5541. p. 1738

Cope, Angie, Cat, University of Wisconsin-Milwaukee Libraries, American Geographical Society Library, Golda Meir Library, 2311 E Hartford Ave, Milwaukee, WI, 53211. Tel: 414-229-3984, 414-229-6282. Fax: 414-229-3624. p. 2622

Cope, Diana, Dir, Fairview Public Library, 43 Walnut St, Margaretville, NY, 12455. Tel: 845-586-3791. Fax: 845-586-3791. p. 1658

Cope, Rodney W, Circ, University of Nebraska Medical Center, 600 S 42nd St, Omaha, NE, 68198-6705. Tel: 402-559-4006. Fax: 402-559-5498. p. 1415

Cope, Sandra, Librn, First Baptist Church Library-Waukesha, 247 Wisconsin Ave, Waukesha, WI, 53186. Tel: 262-549-9711. Fax: 262-542-1367. p. 2645

Copelan, Betty Jo, In Charge, Glenn Memorial United Methodist Church Library, 1660 N Decatur Rd NE, Atlanta, GA, 30307-1010. Tel: 404-634-3936. Fax: 404-634-1994. p. 516

Copeland, Aleta, Head, Tech Serv, Ouachita Parish Public Library, 1800 Stubbs Ave, Monroe, LA, 71201. Tel: 318-327-1490. Fax: 318-327-1373. p. 957

Copeland, Anne, Asst Dir, Bassett Historical Center, 3964 Fairystone Park Hwy, Bassett, VA, 24055. Tel: 276-629-9191. Fax: 276-629-9840. p. 2450

Copeland, Carl, Mgr, Northwest Regional Library System, Gulf County Public Library, 110 Library Dr, Port Saint Joe, FL, 32456. Tel: 850-229-8879. Fax: 850-229-8313. p. 481

Copeland, Charlene, Dir, Rushville Public Library, 104 N Monroe St, Rushville, IL, 62681-1364. Tel: 217-322-3030. Fax: 217-322-3030. p. 699

Copeland, Evonda, Supvr, Scottsdale Healthcare, Dr Robert C Foreman Health Sciences Library, Scottsdale Healthcare Osborn, 7400 E Osborn Rd, Scottsdale, AZ, 85251. Tel: 480-882-4870. Fax: 480-882-4200. p. 81

Copeland, Evonda, Supvr, Scottsdale Healthcare, Health Sciences Library, 9003 E Shea Blvd, Scottsdale, AZ, 85260. Tel: 480-323-3870. Fax: 480-323-3864. p. 81

Copeland, Gloria, Librn, Carter County Library District, Ellsinore Branch, PO Box 312, Ellsinore, MO, 63937. Tel: 573-322-0015. p. 1370

Copeland, Linda, Human Res Dir, New Orleans Public Library, 219 Loyola Ave, New Orleans, LA, 70112-2044. Tel: 504-529-7323, 504-596-2570. Fax: 504-596-2609. p. 962

Copeland, Marlene, Librn, Vanceboro Public Library, 7931 Main St, Vanceboro, NC, 28586. Tel: 252-244-0571. Fax: 252-244-0571. p. 1827

Copeland, Mary Frances, Asst Librn, Frederick Public Library, 200 E Grand, Frederick, OK, 73542. Tel: 580-335-3601. Fax: 580-335-3601. p. 1964

Copeland, Sandrine, Asst Librn, Western Town Library, 9172 Main St, Westernville, NY, 13486. Tel: 315-827-4118. Fax: 315-827-4118. p. 1767

Copeman, Deborah, Electronic Serv Librn, Nova Scotia Barristers' Society, 1815 Upper Water St, 7th Flr, Halifax, NS, B3J 1S7, CANADA. Tel: 902-425-2665. Fax: 902-422-1697. p. 2781

Copenhaver, Rita B, Supvr, Outreach Serv, Smyth-Bland Regional Library, 118 S Sheffey St, Marion, VA, 24354. Tel: 276-783-2323, Ext 33. Fax: 276-783-5279. p. 2477

Copley, Happy, Librn, Saint Mary's Regional Medical Center, PO Box 291, Lewiston, ME, 04243-0291. Tel: 207-777-8775. Fax: 207-777-8773. p. 989

Copley, Ruth Ann, Dir, Davidson County Public Library System, 602 S Main St, Lexington, NC, 27292. Tel: 336-242-2064. Fax: 336-248-4122. p. 1806

Coppen, David Peter, Spec Coll & Archives Librn, University of Rochester, Sibley Music Library, 27 Gibbs St, Rochester, NY, 14604-2596. Tel: 585-274-1350. Fax: 585-274-1380. p. 1733

Coppersmith, Erin, Librn, Kohler Public Library, 333 Upper Rd, Kohler, WI, 53044. Tel: 920-459-2923. Fax: 920-459-2930. p. 2602

Coppersmith, MaryAnne, Br Mgr, Shreve Memorial Library, Cedar Grove-Line Avenue Branch, 8303 Line Ave, Shreveport, LA, 71106. Tel: 318-868-3890. Fax: 318-868-2071. p. 969

Coppin, Mark, Mgr, Anne Carlsen Learning Center, 701 Third St NW, Jamestown, ND, 58401-2971. Tel: 701-952-5125. Fax: 701-952-5154. p. 1844

Coppinger, Leslie, Dir, Tracy City Public Library, 217 Shook St, Tracy City, TN, 37387-0277. Tel: 931-592-9714. Fax: 931-592-9715. p. 2267

Coppola, Debra, Dir, Tuckahoe Public Library, 71 Columbus Ave, Tuckahoe, NY, 10707. Tel: 914-961-2121. Fax: 914-961-3832. p. 1757

Coppola, Donna, Circ Supvr, Mount Pleasant Public Library, Mount Pleasant Branch, 125 Lozza Dr, Valhalla, NY, 10595-1268. Tel: 914-741-0276. Fax: 914-741-0228. p. 1719

Coppola, Gene, Dir, Palm Harbor Library, 2330 Nebraska Ave, Palm Harbor, FL, 34683. Tel: 727-784-3332. Fax: 727-785-6534. p. 480

Coppola, Sharon, Youth Serv, Saint Petersburg Public Library, 3745 Ninth Ave N, Saint Petersburg, FL, 33713. Tel: 727-893-7724. Fax: 727-892-5432. p. 488

Coppola, Susan, Head, Circ, Tappan Library, 93 Main St, Tappan, NY, 10983. Tel: 845-359-3877. p. 1754

Copsey, Mark, Tech Serv & Syst Librn, Walla Walla University Libraries, 104 S College Ave, College Place, WA, 99324-1159. Tel: 509-527-2134. Fax: 509-527-2001. p. 2513

Corall, Dawn, Ref Librn, Penn Area Library, 2001 Municipal Court, Harrison City, PA, 15636. Tel: 724-744-4414. Fax: 724-744-0226. p. 2066

Corallo, Robert, Librn, Pryor, Cashman LLP, Seven Times Square, New York, NY, 10036-6569. Tel: 212-421-4100. Fax: 212-326-0806. p. 1698

Corbeil, Diane, Librn, Iqaluit Centennial Library, Bag 189A, Iqaluit, NU, X0A 0H0, CANADA. Tel: 867-979-5400. Fax: 867-979-1373. p. 2789

Corbeil, Donna, Dir of Libr Serv, Berkeley Public Library, 2090 Kittredge St, Berkeley, CA, 94704. Tel: 510-981-6100. Fax: 510-981-6111. p. 126

Corbeil-Rivet, Ginette, Tech Serv Team Leader, Bibliotheque H J Hemens, 339 Chemin Grande-Cote, Rosemere, QC, J7A 1K2, CANADA. Tel: 450-621-6132. Fax: 450-621-6131. p. 2907

Corbett, Bryan, Archivist, University of Alberta, Archives, Books & Records Depository, 100 8170 50th St, Edmonton, AB, T6B 1E6, CANADA. Tel: 780-466-6118, 780-466-6123. Fax: 780-466-5210. p. 2702

Corbett, Felecia, Ref Librn, Center for Creative Leadership Library, One Leadership Pl, Greensboro, NC, 27410. Tel: 336-286-4083. Fax: 336-286-4087. p. 1795

Corbett, Hillary, Scholarly Communications Librn, Northeastern University Libraries, Snell Library, 360 Huntington Ave, Boston, MA, 02115. Tel: 617-373-2352. p. 1065

Corbett, Kathy, Dir, North Gorham Public Library, Two Standish Neck Rd, Gorham, ME, 04038-2469. Tel: 207-892-2575. Fax: 207-892-2573. p. 986

Corbett, Kimberly, Dir, East Mississippi Regional Library System, 116 Water St, Quitman, MS, 39355-2336. Tel: 601-776-3881. Fax: 601-776-6599. p. 1313

Corbett, Kirsten, Ref Librn, Youth/Young Adult Librn, Lane Memorial Library, Two Academy Ave, Hampton, NH, 03842. Tel: 603-926-3368. Fax: 603-926-1348. p. 1449

Corbett, Lauren, Dir, Res Serv, Wake Forest University, PO Box 7777, Winston-Salem, NC, 27109-7777. Tel: 336-758-6136. Fax: 336-758-3694, 336-758-8831. p. 1834

Corbett, Pat, Acq, University of Toronto Libraries, Victoria University Library, 71 Queens Park Crescent E, Toronto, ON, M5S 1K7, CANADA. Tel: 416-585-4471. Fax: 416-585-4591. p. 2867

Corbett, Rachel, Head, Ref, Bethel Park Public Library, 5100 W Library Ave, Bethel Park, PA, 15102. Tel: 412-831-6800, Ext 262; 412-851-2465. Fax: 412-835-9360. p. 2033

Corbett, Susan, VPres, North Carolina Biotechnology Center Library, 15 Alexander Dr, Research Triangle Park, NC, 27709. Tel: 919-541-9366. Fax: 919-990-9521. p. 1820

Corbin, Cheryl, Fiscal Officer, Marion Public Library, 445 E Church St, Marion, OH, 43302-4290. Tel: 740-383-9706. Fax: 740-382-9954. p. 1914

Corbin, Dana, Librn, Cedar Valley College Library, 3030 N Dallas Ave, Lancaster, TX, 75134-3799. Tel: 972-860-2973. Fax: 972-860-8221. p. 2353

Corbin, Delta, In Charge, Florida Department of Corrections, Apalachee Correctional Institution-East Unit Library, 35 Apalachee Dr, Sneads, FL, 32460-4166. Tel: 850-718-0728. p. 491

Corbin, Rachel, Circ, Sampson-Clinton Public Library, Roseboro Branch, 300 W Roseboro St, Roseboro, NC, 28382. Tel: 910-525-5436. p. 1784

Corbin-Hutchinson, Terri, Dir, Saint Joseph's College, 25 Audubon Ave, Patchogue, NY, 11772-2399. Tel: 631-447-3232. Fax: 631-654-3255. p. 1715

Corbin-Lewis, Lorri, Coordr, Circ, North Tonawanda Public Library, 505 Meadow Dr, North Tonawanda, NY, 14120-2888. Tel: 716-693-4132. Fax: 716-693-0719. p. 1707

Corbitt, Janet, Librn, West Virginia Northern Community College Library, New Martinsville Campus, 141 Main St, New Martinsville, WV, 26155. Tel: 304-455-4684, Ext 4701. p. 2575

Corbitt, Patty, Circ & User Serv, Town of Vail Public Library, 292 W Meadow Dr, Vail, CO, 81657. Tel: 970-479-2331. Fax: 970-479-2192. p. 325

Corbus, Lesley, Librn, San Luis Obispo County Library, Nipomo Branch, 918 W Tefft, Nipomo, CA, 93444. Tel: 805-929-3994. Fax: 805-929-5476. p. 254

Corcoran, Dennis, Dir, Hingham Public Library, 66 Leavitt St, Hingham, MA, 02043. Tel: 781-741-1405. Fax: 781-749-0956. p. 1095

Corcoran, Kathryn L, Archives Dir, Libr Serv Dir, Mus Librn, Munson-Williams-Proctor Arts Institute Library, 310 Genesee St, Utica, NY, 13502. Tel: 315-797-0000, Ext 2228. Fax: 315-797-5608. p. 1759

Corcoran, Lois, ILL Librn, Silsby Free Public Library, 226 Main St, Charlestown, NH, 03603. Tel: 603-826-7793. Fax: 603-826-7793. p. 1441

Corcoran, Mary Beth, Media Ctr Mgr, Wilmington College, Pyle Ctr 1227, 1870 Quaker Way, Wilmington, OH, 45177-2473. Tel: 937-382-6661, Ext 350. Fax: 937-383-8571. p. 1949

Corcoran, Monica, Librn, Theological Education Association of Mid America, Southern Baptist Theological Seminary, 2825 Lexington Rd, Louisville, KY, 40280. Tel: 502-897-4807. Fax: 502-897-4600. p. 2944

Corcoran, Nancy, Sr Librn, Hennepin County Library, Pierre Bottineau, 55 Broadway St NE, Minneapolis, MN, 55413-1811. Tel: 612-543-6078. Fax: 612-543-6852. p. 1263

Corcoran, Nancy, Sr Librn, Hennepin County Library, Saint Anthony, 2941 Pentagon Dr NE, Saint Anthony, MN, 55418-3209. Tel: 612-543-6078. Fax: 612-543-6077. p. 1264

Cordell, Douglas, Ser/Electronic Res Librn, Los Angeles County Museum of Art, 5905 Wilshire Blvd, Los Angeles, CA, 90036-4597. Tel: 323-857-6531. Fax: 323-857-4790. p. 172

Corder, Bill, Youth Serv Librn, Robeson County Public Library, 101 N Chestnut St, Lumberton, NC, 28358-5639. Tel: 910-738-4859. Fax: 910-739-8321. p. 1808

Cordero, Ana Rosa, Asst Dir, Tech Serv, University of Puerto Rico Library System, University of Puerto Rico, Rio Piedras Campus, San Juan, PR, 00931. Tel: 787-764-0000, Ext 5222. Fax: 787-772-1479. p. 2677

Cordero, Damaris, Coll Develop, Dir, Amaury Veray Music Library, 350 Rafael Lamar, Hato Rey, PR, 00918. Tel: 787-751-0160, Ext 256. Fax: 787-754-5934. p. 2673

Cordes, Christopher Sean, Instrul Serv Librn, Western Illinois University Libraries, One University Circle, Macomb, IL, 61455. Tel: 309-298-2785, Ext 3. Fax: 309-298-2791. p. 669

Cordes, Ellen, Head, Tech Serv, Yale University Library, Lewis Walpole Library, 154 Main St, Farmington, CT, 06032. Tel: 860-677-2140. Fax: 860-677-6369. p. 359

Cordes, Mary, District Circ Mgr, Hayner Public Library District, 326 Belle St, Alton, IL, 62002. Tel: 618-462-0677. Fax: 618-462-0665. p. 588

Cording, Carl, Cat, Tech Serv, College of Saint Rose, 392-396 Western Ave, Albany, NY, 12203. Tel: 518-458-5382. Fax: 518-454-2897. p. 1568

Cordle, Al, Ref Librn-Sylvania Campus, Portland Community College Library, 12000 SW 49th AV, Portland, OR, 97219. Tel: 971-722-4592. Fax: 971-722-8397. p. 2013

Cordon, Matt, Assoc Dir, Baylor University Libraries, Sheridan & John Eddie Williams Legal Research & Technology Center, 1114 S University Parks Dr, One Bear Pl, No 97128, Waco, TX, 76798-7128. Tel: 254-710-2168. Fax: 254-710-2294. p. 2397

Cordova, Dan, Head Librn, Colorado Supreme Court Library, 101 W Colfax Ave, Ste A, Denver, CO, 80202. Tel: 303-837-3720. Fax: 303-864-4510. p. 300

Cordoza, Arlene, Access Serv, Massachusetts Maritime Academy, 101 Academy Dr, Buzzards Bay, MA, 02532. Tel: 508-830-5034. Fax: 508-830-5074. p. 1072

Corey, Brenda, Libr Tech, New Hampshire State Library, Gallen State Office Park, Dolloff Bldg, 117 Pleasant St, Concord, NH, 03301-3852. Tel: 603-271-2417, 603-271-3429. Fax: 603-271-8370. p. 1443

Corey, Denise, Dep Chief Librn, Cumberland Public Libraries, 21 Acadia St, 2nd Flr, Amherst, NS, B4H 4W3, CANADA. Tel: 902-667-2135. Fax: 902-667-1360. p. 2777

Corey, Gail, In Charge, Klamath County Library Services District, Loyd DeLap Law Library, 126 S Third St, Klamath Falls, OR, 97601-6388. Tel: 541-883-5128. Fax: 541-885-3624. p. 2002

Corey, James, Dir, Florida Center for Library Automation, 5830 NW 39th Ave, Gainesville, FL, 32606. Tel: 352-392-9020, Ext 322. Fax: 352-392-9185. p. 2940

Corey, Karen M, Asst Dir, Purdue University, 2200 169th St, Hammond, IN, 46323-2094. Tel: 219-989-2674. Fax: 219-989-2205. p. 747

Corey, Katherine D, Librn, Washburn Memorial Library, 1290 Main St, Washburn, ME, 04786. Tel: 207-455-4814. p. 1005

Coriaty, Nancy, Dep Town Librn-Br Serv, Fairfield Public Library, 1080 Old Post Rd, Fairfield, CT, 06824. Tel: 203-255-7307. p. 339

Coriaty, Nancy, Dep Town Librn, Fairfield Public Library, Fairfield Woods, 1147 Fairfield Woods Rd, Fairfield, CT, 06825. Tel: 203-255-7310. Fax: 203-255-7311. p. 339

Corioso, April, Librn, Los Medanos College Library, 2700 E Leland Rd, Pittsburg, CA, 94565. Tel: 925-439-2181, Ext 3385. p. 208

Coriston, Anne L, VPres, Pub Serv, The New York Public Library - Astor, Lenox & Tilden Foundations, 476 Fifth Ave, (@ 42nd St), New York, NY, 10018-2788. Tel: 212-930-0953. Fax: 212-930-9217. p. 1690

Cork, Florene, Access Serv, ILL, Supvr, ILL, Buena Vista University Library, 610 W Fourth St, Storm Lake, IA, 50588. Tel: 712-749-2127, 712-749-2203. Fax: 712-749-2059. p. 846

Cork, Robin, Circ Supvr, Marquette University, Sensenbrenner Hall, 1103 W Wisconsin Ave, Milwaukee, WI, 53233-2313. Tel: 414-288-7092. Fax: 414-288-5914. p. 2618

Cork, Sheila A, Librn, New Orleans Museum of Art, One Collins Diboll Circle City Park, New Orleans, LA, 70124. Tel: 504-658-4117. Fax: 504-658-4199. p. 962

Corkrum, Dalia, Col Librn, Whitman College, 345 Boyer Ave, Walla Walla, WA, 99362. Tel: 509-527-5193. Fax: 509-527-5900. p. 2547

Corl, Susan, Head, Ref, Holmes County District Public Library, 3102 Glen Dr, Millersburg, OH, 44654. Tel: 330-674-5972. Fax: 330-674-1938. p. 1918

Corless, Caitlin, Asst Librn II, Essex Free Library, Two Browns River Rd, Essex, VT, 05451. Tel: 802-879-0313. p. 2423

Corley, Betty, Libr Dir, Odenville Public Library, 200 Alabama St, Odenville, AL, 35120. Tel: 205-629-5901. Fax: 205-629-5324. p. 32

Corley, Eunice, Asst Librn, Copiah-Jefferson Regional Library System, 223 S Extension St, Hazlehurst, MS, 39083-3339. Tel: 601-894-1681. Fax: 601-894-1672. p. 1301

Corley, Maurina, Librn, Cameron Public Library, 304 E Third St, Cameron, TX, 76520. Tel: 254-697-2401. Fax: 254-697-2401. p. 2294

Corley, Pamela, Info Spec, University of Southern California Libraries, Norris Medical Library, 2003 Zonal Ave, Los Angeles, CA, 90089-9130. Tel: 323-442-1125. Fax: 323-221-1235. p. 179

Corlis, Timothy, Head, Presv, Rutgers University Libraries, Special Collections & University Archives, 169 College Ave, New Brunswick, NJ, 08901-1163. Tel: 848-932-6147. Fax: 732-932-7012. p. 1509

Corman, Brenda, Syst Librn, Lock Haven University of Pennsylvania, 401 N Fairview Ave, Lock Haven, PA, 17745-2390. Tel: 570-484-2309. Fax: 570-484-2506. p. 2082

Corman, Linda Wilson, Nicholls Librn & Dir Graham Libr, University of Toronto Libraries, John W Graham Library, University of Trinity College, Trinity College, Six Hoskin Ave, Toronto, ON, M5S 1H8, CANADA. Tel: 416-978-2653. Fax: 416-978-2797. p. 2866

Cormier, Catherine, Br Mgr, San Francisco Public Library, Mission Bay Branch Library, 960 Fourth St, San Francisco, CA, 94158-1628. Tel: 415-355-2838. Fax: 415-947-0723. p. 246

Cormier, Jacqueline A, Librn, Moncton Area Lawyers' Association, 145 Assomption Blvd, Moncton, NB, E1C 0R2, CANADA. Tel: 506-389-1649. Fax: 506-856-6031. p. 2766

Cormier, L J, Circ, Kingston Library, 55 Franklin St, Kingston, NY, 12401. Tel: 845-331-0507. Fax: 845-331-7981. p. 1650

Cormier, Lynn, Libr Dir, Albert-Westmorland-Kent Regional Library, Riverview Public, 34 Honour House Ct, Riverview, NB, E1B 3Y9, CANADA. Tel: 506-387-2108. Fax: 506-387-4970. p. 2765

Cormier, Susan Draper, Dir, Connecticut State Library, Willimantic Library Service Center, 1320 Main St, Ste 25, Willimantic, CT, 06226-1944. Tel: 860-456-1717. Fax: 860-423-5874. p. 345

Cornacchia, James, Librn, Raytheon Co, 1847 W Main Rd, Portsmouth, RI, 02871-1087. Tel: 401-842-4372. Fax: 401-842-5206. p. 2171

Cornelio, Alice, Tech Serv Librn, El Camino College, 16007 S Crenshaw Blvd, Torrance, CA, 90506. Tel: 310-660-3593, Ext 3522. Fax: 310-660-3513. p. 275

Cornelius, Barbara, Tech Coordr, Nebraska Wesleyan University, 50th & St Paul, Lincoln, NE, 68504. Tel: 402-465-2400. Fax: 402-465-2189. p. 1406

Cornelius, Blaine, Info Serv, ILL Mgr, Cherry Valley Public Library District, 755 E State St, Cherry Valley, IL, 61016-9699. Tel: 815-332-5161, Ext 26. Fax: 815-332-2441. p. 604

Cornelius, James, PhD, Lincoln Curator, Illinois Historic Preservation Agency, 112 N Sixth St, Springfield, IL, 62701. Tel: 217-785-7954. Fax: 217-785-6250. p. 705

Cornelius, Jason, Assoc Librn, Genealogy, Logan Library, 255 N Main, Logan, UT, 84321-3914. Tel: 435-716-9143. Fax: 435-716-9145. p. 2407

Cornelius, Lisa, Dir, Red River County Public Library, 307 N Walnut, Clarksville, TX, 75426-3038. Tel: 903-427-3991. Fax: 903-427-3991. p. 2297

Cornelius, Mary, Ref, Villanova University, Law Library, Garey Hall, 299 N Spring Mill Rd, Villanova, PA, 19085. Tel: 610-519-7189. Fax: 610-519-7033. p. 2150

Cornelius, Rex, Interim Digital Serv Mgr, Wichita Public Library, 223 S Main St, Wichita, KS, 67202. Tel: 316-261-8522. Fax: 316-262-4540. p. 901

Corneliuson, Bernadette, Acq, Carlos Albizu University Library, 2173 NW 99 Ave, Miami, FL, 33172. Tel: 305-593-1223, Ext 131. Fax: 305-593-8318. p. 464

Cornell, John, Librn, California Department of Corrections Library System, San Quentin State Prison Library, 100 Main St, San Quentin, CA, 94964. Tel: 415-454-1460, Ext 3384. Fax: 415-455-5049. p. 222

Cornell, John, Pres, Hillsboro Community Library, 316 Elenora St, Hillsboro, NM, 88042. Tel: 575-895-3349. Fax: 575-895-3349. p. 1556

Cornell, Karen, Acq, Coll Develop, Pellissippi State Technical Community College, 10915 Harding Valley Rd, Knoxville, TN, 37933. Tel: 865-694-6621. Fax: 865-694-6625. p. 2243

Cornell, Kim, Asst Univ Librn, Western University - Libraries, Allyn & Betty Taylor Library, 1151 Richmond St, Ste 2, London, ON, N6A 5B7, CANADA. Tel: 519-661-2111, Ext 86362. Fax: 519-661-3435. p. 2819

Cornell, Melanie, Syst Librn, University of New Hampshire School of Law, Two White St, Concord, NH, 03301. Tel: 603-228-1541, Ext 1130. Fax: 603-228-0388. p. 1443

Cornelson, Melanie, Ch & Youth Librn, Thomasville Public Library, 1401 Mosley Dr, Thomasville, AL, 36784. Tel: 334-636-5343. Fax: 334-636-5343. p. 37

Cornett, John, Librn, National Solar Observatory, One Loop Dr, Sunspot, NM, 88349. Tel: 575-434-7024. Fax: 575-434-7029. p. 1565

Cornette, Jackie, Outreach Serv Librn, Watauga County Public Library, Western Watauga, 1085 Old US Hwy 421, Sugar Grove, NC, 28692. Tel: 828-297-5515. Fax: 828-297-7805. p. 1777

Cornish, Alan, Head, Syst, Washington State University Libraries, 100 Dairy Rd, Pullman, WA, 99164. Tel: 509-335-1895. Fax: 509-335-6721. p. 2525

Cornish, Cliff, Mgr, Vancouver Island Health Authority Medical Libraries, Royal Jubilee Hospital, 1952 Bay St, Victoria, BC, V8R 1J8, CANADA. Tel: 250-370-8612, 250-370-8723. Fax: 250-370-8274. p. 2746

Cornish, Donald, Cat, Lewis & Clark Library, 120 S Last Chance Gulch, Helena, MT, 59601. Tel: 406-447-1690. Fax: 406-447-1687. p. 1382

Cornn, Jean, Outreach Librn, Atlanta-Fulton Public Library System, Sandy Springs Regional Library, 395 Mount Vernon Hwy, Sandy Springs, GA, 30328. Tel: 404-303-6130. Fax: 404-303-6133. p. 512

Cornwell, Doug, Ref, Palm Beach State College, 4200 Congress Ave, Mail Sta 17, Lake Worth, FL, 33461. Tel: 561-868-3800. Fax: 561-868-3708. p. 459

Cornwell, Robena, Head Music Libr, University of Florida Libraries, 535 Library W, Gainesville, FL, 32611-7000. Tel: 352-273-2815. Fax: 352-846-2748. p. 450

Corona, Linda, Dir, Edgewater Free Public Library, 49 Hudson Ave, Edgewater, NJ, 07020. Tel: 201-224-6144. Fax: 201-886-3395. p. 1483

Corona, Vicky, Asst Librn, El Paso County Law Library, 500 E San Antonio St, Rm 1202, El Paso, TX, 79901. Tel: 915-546-2245. Fax: 915-542-0440. p. 2316

Coronado, Deborah, Managing Librn, Austin Public Library, Oak Springs, 3101 Oak Springs Dr, Austin, TX, 78702. Tel: 512-974-9920. Fax: 512-974-9924. p. 2279

Coronella, Stephen, Dir, Putney Public Library, 55 Main St, Putney, VT, 05346. Tel: 802-387-4407. p. 2433

Corprew, Lamont, Chief Financial Officer, Prince George's County Memorial Library System, 6532 Adelphi Rd, Hyattsville, MD, 20782-2098. Tel: 301-699-3500. Fax: 301-699-0668. p. 1032

Corpus, Paula, Asst Librn, Ladd Public Library District, 125 N Main St, Ladd, IL, 61329. Tel: 815-894-3254. Fax: 815-894-3254. p. 662

Corpuz, Carleen, Br Mgr, Hawaii State Public Library System, Mountain View Public & School Library, 18-1235 Volcano Hwy, Mountain View, HI, 96771. Tel: 808-968-2322. Fax: 808-968-2323. p. 563

Corpuz, Laura, Circ & ILL Coordr, Bradley University, 1501 W Bradley Ave, Peoria, IL, 61625. Tel: 309-677-2850. Fax: 309-677-2558. p. 690

Corradini, Diane, Adult Serv, Circ, Herrick District Library, 300 S River Ave, Holland, MI, 49423-3290. Tel: 616-355-3100. p. 1190

Corradino, Veronica, Circ Mgr, Augusta State University, 2500 Walton Way, Augusta, GA, 30904-2200. Tel: 706-737-1745. Fax: 706-667-4415. p. 518

Corrado, Bonnie, Librn, Tivoli Free Library, 86 Broadway, Tivoli, NY, 12583. Tel: 845-757-3771. p. 1755

Correa, Elizabeth, Dir, Info Mgt, Texas Department of Health & Human Services, 1901 N Hwy 87, Big Spring, TX, 79720. Tel: 432-268-7400. Fax: 432-268-7401. p. 2290

Correa, Loida, Ser Librn, University of Puerto Rico, Minillas Park, 170, 174 Rd, Bayamon, PR, 00959-1919. Tel: 787-993-0000, Ext 3222, 787-993-8857. Fax: 787-993-8914. p. 2672

Correa, Madlyn, Head Librn, Massachusetts Trial Court Law Libraries, Superior Courthouse, 186 S Main St, Fall River, MA, 02721. Tel: 508-491-3475. Fax: 508-491-3482. p. 1088

Correia, Jacqueline, Ser, Wilmington University Library, 320 DuPont Hwy, New Castle, DE, 19720. Tel: 302-328-9401. Fax: 302-328-0914. p. 385

Correia, Jennie, Librn, Planned Parenthood Federation of America, Inc, 434 W 33rd St, New York, NY, 10001. Tel: 212-261-4716. p. 1697

Correia, Patricia, Dir, Admin Serv, Jefferson County Public Library, 10200 W 20th Ave, Lakewood, CO, 80215. Tel: 303-275-2206. Fax: 303-275-2202. p. 315

Corriell, Suzanne B, Ref Serv, University of Richmond, William T Muse Law Library, 28 Westhampton Way, Richmond, VA, 23173. Tel: 804-289-8217. Fax: 804-289-8683. p. 2491

Corrigal, Norma, Librn, Lakeland Library Region, Turtleford Branch, Box 146, Turtleford, SK, S0M 2Y0, CANADA. Tel: 306-845-2074. p. 2920

Corrigan, Andy, Assoc Dean, Tulane University, 7001 Freret St, New Orleans, LA, 70118-5682. Tel: 504-865-5679. Fax: 504-865-6773. p. 963

Corrigan, Christopher, Adaptive Tech Training Coordr, DC Regional Library for the Blind & Physically Handicapped, Adaptive Services Division, Rm 215, 901 G St NW, Washington, DC, 20001. Tel: 202-727-2143. Fax: 202-727-0322. p. 397

Corrigan, Ellen, Cat/Digitization Libr, Eastern Illinois University, 600 Lincoln Ave, Charleston, IL, 61920. Tel: 217-581-8456. p. 603

Corrington, Barbara, Cat, Sallie Logan Public Library, 1808 Walnut St, Murphysboro, IL, 62966. Tel: 618-684-3271. Fax: 618-684-2392. p. 678

Corrion, Mae, Asst Dir, Ch, Jesup Memorial Library, 34 Mount Desert St, Bar Harbor, ME, 04609-1727. Tel: 207-288-4245. p. 976

Corriveau, Josee, Dir, College de Rosemont (Cegep) Bibliotheque, 6400 16th Ave, Montreal, QC, H1X 2S9, CANADA. Tel: 514-376-1620, Ext 265. Fax: 514-376-1440. p. 2894

Corry, Donna, Dir, Flora Public Library, 216 N Main, Flora, IL, 62839-1510. Tel: 618-662-6553. Fax: 618-662-5007. p. 646

Corry, Frank, Dep Dir, Bus Operations, Mount Prospect Public Library, Ten S Emerson St, Mount Prospect, IL, 60056. Tel: 847-253-5675. Fax: 847-253-0642. p. 677

Corry, Kanzenberg, Curator of Archival Coll, Norman Rockwell Museum, Nine Glendale Rd, Stockbridge, MA, 01262. Tel: 413-298-4100. Fax: 413-298-4145. p. 1128

Corry, Terri, Asst Dir, Tech, Cora J Belden Library, 33 Church St, Rocky Hill, CT, 06067-1568. Tel: 860-258-7621. p. 365

Corso, Judy, Tech Serv, Mastics-Moriches-Shirley Community Library, 407 William Floyd Pkwy, Shirley, NY, 11967. Tel: 631-399-1511. Fax: 631-281-4442. p. 1743

Cortale, Joseph, Head, Ch, Floyd Memorial Library, 539 First St, Greenport, NY, 11944-1399. Tel: 631-477-0660. Fax: 631-477-2647. p. 1631

Corter, Chris, Head Librn, Chemung County Library District, Horseheads Free Library, 405 S Main St, Horseheads, NY, 14845. Tel: 607-739-4581. Fax: 607-739-4592. p. 1619

Cortes, Daisy, Pub Serv Librn, Riverside County Law Library, 3989 Lemon St, Riverside, CA, 92501-4203. Tel: 951-368-0368. Fax: 951-368-0185. p. 217

Cortez, Cassandra, Dir, Lytle Public Library, 19325 Farm Rd, No 2790, Lytle, TX, 78052. Tel: 830-709-4142. Fax: 830-772-3675. p. 2358

Cortez, Edwin M, Dir, University of Tennessee, Knoxville, 451 Communications Bldg, 1345 Circle Park Dr, Knoxville, TN, 37996-0341. Tel: 865-974-2148. Fax: 865-974-4967. p. 2974

Cortez, Elisa, Access Serv, Loma Linda University, 11072 Anderson St, Loma Linda, CA, 92350-0001. Tel: 909-558-4581. Fax: 909-558-4121. p. 165

Cortez, Luticia, Br Mgr, Lafourche Parish Public Library, Choctaw Branch, 1887 Choctaw Rd, Thibodaux, LA, 70301. Tel: 985-633-6453. p. 971

Cortinas, Mario, Dir, Webb County Library, Hwy 359, Mirando City, TX, 78369. Tel: 361-586-4626. Fax: 361-586-5060. p. 2363

Cortney, Ashley, Libr Dir, Edgemont Public Library, 412 Second Ave, Edgemont, SD, 57735. Tel: 605-662-7712. Fax: 605-662-7922. p. 2212

Corts, Paul R, Pres, Council for Christian Colleges & Universities, 321 Eighth St NE, Washington, DC, 20002. Tel: 202-546-8713. Fax: 202-546-8913. p. 2940

Corvey, S James, Dean, Mountain View College, 4849 W Illinois, Dallas, TX, 75211-6599. Tel: 214-860-8525. Fax: 214-860-8667. p. 2309

Corvin, Andrea, Asst Dir, Edgewood Community Library, 95 Hwy 344 N, Edgewood, NM, 87015-6764. Tel: 505-281-0138. Fax: 505-281-0138. p. 1554

Corvino, Ellen, Br Mgr, Brooklyn Public Library, McKinley Park, 6802 Fort Hamilton Pkwy, Brooklyn, NY, 11219. Tel: 718-748-8001. Fax: 718-748-7746. p. 1591

Corwin, Deirdre, Ref Serv, Fordham University Westchester Library, 400 Westchester Ave, West Harrison, NY, 10604. Tel: 914-367-3055. p. 1766

Corwin, Rhonda, Librn, Ruth Dole Memorial Library, 121 N Burrton Ave, Burrton, KS, 67020. Tel: 620-463-7902. p. 859

Cory, Eckart, Mgr, Youth Serv, Fellin Octavia Public Library, Children's Branch, 200 W Aztec Ave, Gallup, NM, 87301. Tel: 505-726-6120. Fax: 505-863-9350. p. 1556

Cory, Shelly, Dir, Roy R Estle Memorial Library, 1308 Walnut St, Dallas Center, IA, 50063. Tel: 515-992-3185. Fax: 515-992-4929. p. 806

Cosanici, Dragomir, Supv Librn, California State Legislative Counsel, 925 L St, Lower Level, Sacramento, CA, 95814-3772. Tel: 916-341-8036. p. 223

Cosby, Deborah, Br Mgr, Fauquier County Public Library, John Marshall Branch, 4133 Rectortown Rd, Marshall, VA, 20115. Tel: 540-364-4910. Fax: 540-364-4911. p. 2501

Cosby, Kathrine, Librn, Courtland Public Library, 215 College St, Courtland, AL, 35618. Tel: 256-637-9988. p. 13

Cosby, Sherri, Div Mgr, Support Serv, Oceanside Public Library, 330 N Coast Hwy, Oceanside, CA, 92054-2824. Tel: 760-435-5609. Fax: 760-435-9614. p. 199

Coscino, Lisa, Exec Dir, Monterey History & Art Association, 155 Van Buren St, Monterey, CA, 93940. Tel: 831-372-1838. p. 189

Cosgray, Judith, Ref Serv, Tech Serv, Pickerington Public Library, 201 Opportunity Way, Pickerington, OH, 43147-1296. Tel: 614-837-4104. Fax: 614-837-8425. p. 1930

Cosgriff, Christa, Dir, Forest City Public Library, 115 East L St, Forest City, IA, 50436. Tel: 641-585-4542. Fax: 641-585-2939. p. 816

Cosgrove, James B, Dir, Marlboro Free Library, 1251 Rte 9W, Marlboro, NY, 12542-5411. Tel: 845-236-7272. Fax: 845-236-7635. p. 1658

Cosgrove, Jo Ann, ILL, Taylor University, 236 W Reade Ave, Upland, IN, 46989-1001. Tel: 765-998-5530. Fax: 765-998-5569. p. 783

Cosgrove, Joan, ILL, Carbondale Public Library, Five N Main St, Carbondale, PA, 18407-2303. Tel: 570-282-4281. Fax: jcosgrove@albright.org. p. 2041

Cosgrove, Kathy E, Ref Serv, Federal Reserve Bank of Saint Louis, One Federal Reserve Bank Plaza, Saint Louis, MO, 63102-2005. Tel: 314-444-8552. Fax: 314-444-8694. p. 1354

Cosgrove, Nancy, Head, Ser Acq, Saint Thomas Aquinas College, 125 Rte 340, Sparkill, NY, 10976. Tel: 845-398-4214. Fax: 845-359-9537. p. 1746

Cosgrove, Patricia, Dir, White River Valley Museum Library, 918 H St SE, Auburn, WA, 98002. Tel: 253-288-7433. Fax: 253-931-3098. p. 2507

Cosgrove, Ruth, Adult Serv, Kirkland Town Library, 55 1/2 College St, Clinton, NY, 13323. Tel: 315-853-2038. Fax: 315-853-1785. p. 1608

Coski, John, Dir, Museum of the Confederacy, 1201 E Clay St, Richmond, VA, 23219. Tel: 804-649-1861. Fax: 804-644-7150. p. 2489

Coslick, Sue, Circ Serv, Somerset County Library System, One Vogt Dr, Bridgewater, NJ, 08807-2136. Tel: 908-526-4016, Ext 151. p. 1475

Coslor, Mindy McCormick, Dean of Libr, Learning Res & Basic Skills, Skagit Valley College, 2405 E College Way, Mount Vernon, WA, 98273-5899. Tel: 360-416-7761. Fax: 360-416-7698. p. 2521

Cosolotto, Andria, Ch, Gutekunst Public Library, 309 Second St SE, State Center, IA, 50247-0550. Tel: 641-483-2741. Fax: 641-483-2131. p. 846

Cosper, Debbie, Libr Dir, Boyd County Public Library, 1740 Central Ave, Ashland, KY, 41101. Tel: 606-329-0090. Fax: 606-329-0578. p. 905

Cosper, Debbie, Libr Dir, Boyd County Public Library, Kyova Branch, 10699 US Rte 60, Ste 920, Ashland, KY, 41102. Tel: 606-929-5346. Fax: 606-929-5471. p. 905

Coss, Terri, Teen Serv, Somerset County Library System, Watchung Public, 12 Stirling Rd, Watchung, NJ, 07069. Tel: 908-561-0117. Fax: 908-769-1145. p. 1475

Cossard, Patricia Kosco, Librn, University of Maryland Libraries, Architecture Library, College Park, MD, 20742-7011. Tel: 301-405-6317. Fax: 301-314-9583. p. 1025

Cossentine, Anne, Pub Serv, Okanagan College Library, 1000 KLO Rd, Kelowna, BC, V1Y 4X8, CANADA. p. 2730

Cossey, Cherl Broadway, Chairperson, Pope County Historical Society, 809 S Lake Shore Dr, Glenwood, MN, 56334. Tel: 320-634-3293. p. 1252

Costa, Anthony, Serv Mgr, Califa, 32 W 25th Ave, Ste 201, San Mateo, CA, 94403. Tel: 650-572-2746. Fax: 650-349-5089. p. 2938

Costa, David, Syst Adminr, Sparta Public Library, 22 Woodport Rd, Sparta, NJ, 07871. Tel: 973-729-3101. Fax: 973-729-1755. p. 1531

Costa, Lenny, In Charge, Merced County Library, Los Banos Branch, 1312 Seventh St, Los Banos, CA, 93635-4753. Tel: 209-826-5254. p. 186

Costa, Maria, In Charge, Radiation Safety Institute of Canada, 165 Avenue Rd, Ste 300, Toronto, ON, M5R 3S4, CANADA. Tel: 416-650-9090, Ext 21. Fax: 416-650-9920. p. 2857

Costa, Nicole, Librn, Rec Mgr, National Fire Protection Association, One Batterymarch Park, Quincy, MA, 02169-7471. Tel: 617 984 7475. Fax: 617-984-7060. p. 1119

Costa, Sarah, Libr Dir, Calef Memorial Library, 2964 VT Rte 110, Washington, VT, 05675. Tel: 802-883-2343. Fax: 802-883-9387. p. 2438

Costales, Cindy, Adult & Teen Serv Mgr, Sr Librn, Monterey Park Bruggemeyer Library, 318 S Ramona Ave, Monterey Park, CA, 91754-3399. Tel: 626-307-1398. Fax: 626-288-4251. p. 190

Costanza, Jane, Head, Discovery Serv, Trinity University, One Trinity Pl, San Antonio, TX, 78212-7200. Tel: 210-999-7612. Fax: 210-999-8182. p. 2383

Costanzo, Phyllis, Circ, Hewlett-Woodmere Public Library, 1125 Broadway, Hewlett, NY, 11557-0903. Tel: 516-374-1967. Fax: 516-569-1229. p. 1636

Costanzo-Lee, Liz, Coll Develop, Res Develop Coordr, Mesa Public Library, 64 E First St, Mesa, AZ, 85201-6768. Tel: 480-644-4709. Fax: 480-644-2991. p. 69

Costello, Barbara, Govt Doc & Res Librn, Stetson University, 421 N Woodland Blvd, Unit 8418, DeLand, FL, 32723. Tel: 386-822-7185. p. 437

Costello, Betty, Head, Circ, Bergenfield Public Library, 50 W Clinton Ave, Bergenfield, NJ, 07621-2799. Tel: 201-387-4040, Ext 826. Fax: 201-387-9004. p. 1472

Costello, Colleen, Ch, Vernon Area Public Library District, 300 Olde Half Day Rd, Lincolnshire, IL, 60069-2901. Tel: 847-634-3650. Fax: 847-634-8449. p. 666

Costello, Harriet, Head, Ch, Patchogue-Medford Library, 54-60 E Main St, Patchogue, NY, 11772. Tel: 631-654-4700, Ext 263. Fax: 631-289-3999. p. 1715

Costello, Joe, Info Serv Spec, Bronson Methodist Hospital, 601 John St, Box B, Kalamazoo, MI, 49007. Tel: 269-341-6318. Fax: 269-341-8828. p. 1196

Costello, Leanne, Head, Adult Serv, Windsor Public Library, 323 Broad St, Windsor, CT, 06095. Tel: 860-285-1920. Fax: 860-285-1889. p. 379

Costello, Leslianne, Youth Serv Librn, Norton Public Library, 68 E Main St, Norton, MA, 02766. Tel: 508-285-0265. Fax: 508-285-0266. p. 1114

Costello, Patricia, Chief, Neighborhood Libr Serv, Enoch Pratt Free Library, 400 Cathedral St, Baltimore, MD, 21201-4484. Tel: 410-396-5430. Fax: 410-396-1441. p. 1012

Coster, Kathy, Support Serv Sr Mgr, Youth Serv Sr Libr Mgr, Scottsdale Public Library, 3839 N Drinkwater Blvd, Scottsdale, AZ, 85251-4467. Tel: 480-312-7323. Fax: 480-312-7993. p. 81

Costes, Miguelita, Br Head, Toronto Public Library, Queen/Saulter, 765 Queen St E, Toronto, ON, M4M 1H3, CANADA. Tel: 416-393-7723. Fax: 416-393-7423. p. 2863

Costilla, Jani, Libr Dir, Northwest Indian College Library, 2520 Kwina Rd, Bellingham, WA, 98226. Tel: 360-392-4214. Fax: 360-733-3385. p. 2508

Costin, Katherine, Librn, Little Company of Mary Hospital, 2800 W 95th St, Evergreen Park, IL, 60805. Tel: 708-422-6200, Ext 5299. Fax: 708-229-5885. p. 645

Costner, Bernice, Circ, New Hartford Public Library, Two Library Lane, New Hartford, NY, 13413-2815. Tel: 315-733-1535. Fax: 315-733-0795. p. 1665

Coston, Patricia, Mgr, ILL, Xavier University of Louisiana, One Drexel Dr, New Orleans, LA, 70125-1098. Tel: 504-520-5056. Fax: 504-520-7940. p. 964

Coston, Robert, Librn, New River Community & Technical College, 101 Church St, Lewisburg, WV, 24901-0151. Tel: 304-647-6575. Fax: 304-647-6592. p. 2564

Côté, Andrée, Ch, Bibliotheque Municipale de Gatineau, 144, boul de l'Hôpital, local 317, Gatineau, QC, J8T 7S7, CANADA. Tel: 819-243-2345, Ext 7462. Fax: 819-243-2399. p. 2882

Cote, Andree, Ref, Bibliotheque Municipale de Sainte-Foy, 999 Place de Ville, CP 218, Sainte-Foy, QC, G1V 4E1, CANADA. Tel: 418-641-6301. Fax: 418-654-4172. p. 2910

Cote, Anne, Librn, Northeast Regional Correctional Facility Library, 1270 US Rte 5 S, Saint Johnsbury, VT, 05819. Tel: 802-751-1410. Fax: 802-748-1482. p. 2435

Cote, Cynthia, Chief Exec Officer, Penetanguishene Public Library, 24 Simcoe St, Penetanguishene, ON, L9M 1R6, CANADA. Tel: 705-549-7164. Fax: 705-549-3932. p. 2835

Cote, Denise, Electronic Res, Ref, College of DuPage Library, 425 Fawell Blvd, Glen Ellyn, IL, 60137-6599. Tel: 630-942-2092. Fax: 630-858-8757. p. 649

Cote, Donna, Dir, Central Rappahannock Regional Library, 1201 Caroline St, Fredericksburg, VA, 22401-3761. Tel: 540-372-1144. Fax: 540-373-9411. p. 2465

Côté, Jean-Charles, Librn, Archives Provinciales des Capucins, 3650 Blvd de la Rousseliere, Montreal, QC, H1A 2X9, CANADA. Tel: 514-642-5391, Ext 308. Fax: 514-642-5033. p. 2887

Côté, Jean-Charles, Librn, Bibliotheque franciscaine provinciale des Capucins, 3650 boul de la Rousseliere, Montreal, QC, H1A 2X9, CANADA. Tel: 514-642-5391, Ext 308. Fax: 514-642-5033. p. 2888

Cote, Jean-Yves, Librn, HEC Montreal, 3000, chemin de la Cote-Sainte-Catherine, Montreal, QC, H3T 2A7, CANADA. Tel: 514-340-3657. Fax: 514-340-5639. p. 2896

Côté, Lucie, Libr Tech, Hopital de L'Enfant Jesus, 1401 18th St, Quebec, QC, G1J 1Z4, CANADA. Tel: 418-649-5686. Fax: 418-649-5627. p. 2905

Cote, Regis, Libr Serv Supvr, Institut de Recherche d'Hydro-Quebec Bibliotheque, 1800 Lionel-Boulet Blvd, CP 1000, Varennes, QC, J3X 1S1, CANADA. Tel: 450-652-1343. Fax: 450-652-8040. p. 2914

Cote, Suzanne, Head, Tech Serv, Amesbury Public Library, 149 Main St, Amesbury, MA, 01913. Tel: 978-388-8148. p. 1048

Cote-Foster, Melanie, Libr Tech, Cegep de Baie-Comeau, 537 boul Blanche, Baie Comeau, QC, G5C 2B2, CANADA. Tel: 418-589-5707, Ext 325. Fax: 418-589-9842. p. 2879

Cote-Rumsey, Darcie, Actg Adminr, Northwest Hospital Center, 5401 Old Court Rd, Randallstown, MD, 21133. Tel: 410-521-2200, Ext 55682. Fax: 410-496-7549. p. 1037

Cotham, Steve, Hist Coll Librn, Knox County Public Library System, 500 W Church Ave, Knoxville, TN, 37902-2505. Tel: 865-215-8808. Fax: 865-215-8742. p. 2241

Cothern, Cynthia, Librn, Carnegie-Schuyler Library, 303 E Second St, Pana, IL, 62557. Tel: 217-562-2326. Fax: 217-562-2343. p. 688

Cothren, Constance Jean, Librn, Cleburne County Library, Greers Ferry Branch, Greers Ferry Lake Plaza, 8249 Edgemont Rd, Ste 9, Greers Ferry, AR, 72067. Tel: 501-825-8677. p. 103

Cothren, Janelle, Br Mgr, Public Library of Mount Vernon & Knox County, Fredericktown Community, One Burgett Dr, Fredericktown, OH, 43019. Tel: 740-694-2665. Fax: 740-694-3106. p. 1919

Cothren, Jeff, Tech Coordr, Hershey Public Library, 701 Cocoa Ave, Hershey, PA, 17033. Tel: 717-533-6555. Fax: 717-534-1666. p. 2069

Cothren, Zack, County Librn, Cleburne County Library, 1010 W Searcy St, Heber Springs, AR, 72543. Tel: 501-362-2477. Fax: 501-362-2606. p. 103

Cothren-Millsaps, Vickie L, Tech Serv, Wilkes Community College, 1328 Collegiate Dr, Wilkesboro, NC, 28697. Tel: 336-838-6513. Fax: 336-838-6515. p. 1830

Cothron, Jane, Cat, Lincoln County Library District, 1247 NW Grove St, Ste 2, Newport, OR, 97365. Tel: 541-265-3066. Fax: 541-265-3066. p. 2007

Cotner, Cindy, Ref Serv, University of Missouri-Columbia, Elmer Ellis Library, Ellis Library Bldg, Rm 104, Columbia, MO, 65201-5149. Tel: 573-882-4693. Fax: 573-882-8044. p. 1325

Cotney, Rebecca, Librn, Hawkes Library, 100 W Eighth St, West Point, GA, 31833. Tel: 706-645-1549. Fax: 706-645-1549. p. 557

Cotrufo, Margaret, Asst Librn, North Carolina State Museum of Natural Sciences, 11 W Jones St, Raleigh, NC, 27601-1029. Tel: 919-733-7450, Ext 208. Fax: 919-715-2356. p. 1816

Cotsonis, Joachim, Dir, Hellenic College-Holy Cross Greek Orthodox School of Theology, 50 Goddard Ave, Brookline, MA, 02445-7496. Tel: 617-850-1243. Fax: 617-850-1470. p. 1071

Cotsoridis, Paul, Circ, United States Navy, Academic Resources Information Center (ARIC), 440 Meyerkord Rd, Newport, RI, 02841. Tel: 401-841-4352, 401-841-6631. Fax: 401-841-2805. p. 2170

Cott, Catharine, Ref Librn, University of Denver, Westminster Law Library, 2255 E Evans Ave, Denver, CO, 80208. Tel: 303-871-6188. Fax: 303-871-6999. p. 304

Cott, Nancy F, Dir, Harvard Library, Arthur & Elizabeth Schlesinger Library on the History of Women in America, Three James St, Cambridge, MA, 02138-3766. Tel: 617-495-8263. Fax: 617-496-8340. p. 1076

Cotta, Donald, Br Mgr, Tulare County Library, Tipton Branch, 221 N Evans Rd, Tipton, CA, 93272. Tel: 559-752-4236. Fax: 559-752-7307. p. 281

Cotten, Barbara, Librn, Carnegie Public Library, Carnegie Memorial Bldg, 22 S Broadway, Carnegie, OK, 73015. Tel: 580-654-1980. p. 1959

Cotten, Charles, Dir, The Presidential Archives, 4919 E University Blvd, Odessa, TX, 79762. Tel: 432-363-7737. Fax: 432-552-2851. p. 2366

Cotter, Allan, Br Mgr, Dakota County Library System, Pleasant Hill, 1490 S Frontage Rd, Hastings, MN, 55033. Tel: 651-438-0204. Fax: 651-480-4944. p. 1249

Cotter, Bob, Assoc VPres, Info Res, Xavier University, 3800 Victory Pkwy, Cincinnati, OH, 45207-5211. Tel: 513 745-3183. Fax: 513-745-1932. p. 1875

Cotter, Catherine, Ref/Instruction Librn, University of New Brunswick Libraries, Gerard V La Forest Law Library, Ludlow Hall, 2nd Flr, 41 Dineen Dr, Fredericton, NB, E3B 5A3, CANADA. Tel: 506-453-4734. Fax: 506-451-6948, 506-453-5186. p. 2764

Cotter, Kathleen, Br Mgr, Great Neck Library, Station, 40-B Great Neck Rd, Great Neck, NY, 11021. Tel: 516-466-8055, Ext 233. Fax: 516-466-4917. p. 1630

Cotter, Kerry J, Librn, Libr Supvr, Northern Virginia Community College Libraries, Woodbridge Library, 15200 Neabsco Mills Rd, Seefeldt 427, Woodbridge, VA, 22191. Tel: 703-878-5785. Fax: 703-670-8433. p. 2447

Cotter, Michael, Media Spec, New York Medical College, Basic Science Bldg, 95 Grasslands Rd, Valhalla, NY, 10595. Tel: 914-594-3675. Fax: 914-594-3171. p. 1760

Cotter, Robert, Librn, Newfoundland Department of Municipal & Provincial Affairs, Confederation Bldg, W Block, St. John's, NL, A1B 4J6, CANADA. Tel: 709-729-3088, 709-729-3090. Fax: 709-729-0477. p. 2773

Cotter, Robert M, Dir, Xavier University, Instructional Technology Services, 3800 Victory Pkwy, Cincinnati, OH, 45207-5211. Tel: 513-745-3183. Fax: 513-745-1932. p. 1875

Cotter, Teresa, Ch, Port Chester-Rye Brook Public Library, One Haseco Ave, Port Chester, NY, 10573. Tel: 914-939-6710, Ext 108. Fax: 914-939-4735. p. 1720

Cotter, Virginia L, Br Mgr, Hampton Public Library, Northampton, 936 Big Bethel Rd, Hampton, VA, 23669. Tel: 757-825-4558. Fax: 757-825-4646. p. 2468

Cotterman, Billie, Tech Serv, Hastings College, 705 E Seventh St, Hastings, NE, 68901-7620. Tel: 402-461-7330. Fax: 402-461-7480. p. 1401

Cottier, Pearl, Dir, Oglala Lakota College, LaCreek College Center, PO Box 629, Martin, SD, 57551. Tel: 605-685-6407. Fax: 605-685-6887. p. 2214

Cottle, Bonnie, Tech Coordr, Tiverton Library Services, 238 Highland Rd, Tiverton, RI, 02878. Tel: 401-625-6796. Fax: 401-625-5499. p. 2176

Cottman, Darren, Head of Libr, Free Library of Philadelphia, Blanche A Nixon Library - Cobbs Creek Branch, 5800 Cobbs Creek Pkwy, Philadelphia, PA, 19143-3036. Tel: 215-685-1973. Fax: 215-685-1974. p. 2108

Cottman, Rose, Head, Circ, Somerset County Library System, 11767 Beechwood St, Princess Anne, MD, 21853. Tel: 410-651-0852, Ext 11. Fax: 410-651-1388. p. 1036

Cotto-Hilliman, Leticia, Asst Commun Librn, Hartford Public Library, Park, 744 Park St, Hartford, CT, 06106. Tel: 860-695-7500. Fax: 860-722-6878. p. 346

Cotton, Kathy, Circ Mgr, Cumberland County Public Library & Information Center, 300 Maiden Lane, Fayetteville, NC, 28301-5000. Tel: 910-483-7727. Fax: 910-486-5372. p. 1792

Cotton, Lyn, Cat Librn, Ser, Cardinal Stafford Library, 1300 S Steele St, Denver, CO, 80210. Tel: 303-715-3228. Fax: 303-715-2037. p. 298

Cotton, Ruth, Ref Librn, Atlanta-Fulton Public Library System, Sandy Springs Regional Library, 395 Mount Vernon Hwy, Sandy Springs, GA, 30328. Tel: 404-303-6130. Fax: 404-303-6133. p. 512

Cotton, Stephanie, Dir, Mendham Township Library, One Cherry Lane, Brookside, NJ, 07926. Tel: 973-543-4018. Fax: 973-543-5472. p. 1475

Cottone, Catherine, Genealogist, Lyon Township Public Library, 27005 S Milford Rd, South Lyon, MI, 48178. Tel: 248-437-8800. Fax: 248-437-4621. p. 1227

Cottone, Joan, Cat, State University of New York College at Geneseo, SUNY Geneseo, One College Circle, Geneseo, NY, 14454-1498. p. 1627

Cottoy, Fay, Head, Circ, Keiser University Library System, 1500 NW 49th St, Fort Lauderdale, FL, 33309. Tel: 954-351-4035. Fax: 954-351-4051. p. 443

Cottrell, Anne, Head, Youth Serv, Alexandrian Public Library, 115 W Fifth St, Mount Vernon, IN, 47620. Tel: 812-838-3286. Fax: 812-838-9639. p. 766

Cottrell, Genevieve, Dir of Libr, Southern Adventist University, 4851 Industrial Dr, Collegedale, TN, 37315. Tel: 423-236-2795. Fax: 423-236-1788. p. 2230

Cottrell, Janet, Dir, Champlain College Library, 163 S Willard St, Burlington, VT, 05401. Tel: 802-865-6492. p. 2420

Cottrell, Stanley, Tech Serv, Southern Adventist University, 4851 Industrial Dr, Collegedale, TN, 37315. Tel: 423-236-2798. Fax: 423-236-1788. p. 2230

Cottrell, Terry, Dir, University of St Francis, 500 Wilcox St, Joliet, IL, 60435. Tel: 815-740-4292. Fax: 815-740-3364. p. 660

Cottrill, Chris, Ref Librn, Smithsonian Libraries, National Museum of American History Library, NMAH Rm 5016, MRC 630, 14th & Constitution Ave NW, Washington, DC, 20560. Tel: 202-633-3859. Fax: 202-357-4256. p. 415

Couch, Elaine, Dir, Perry County Public Library, 289 Black Gold Blvd, Hazard, KY, 41701. Tel: 606-436-2475, 606-436-4747. Fax: 606-436-0191. p. 916

Couch, Jeanette, Dir, Sutton Free Library, Five Corporation Hill, Sutton Mills, NH, 03221. Tel: 603-927-4927. p. 1466

Couch, Nena, Curator, Ohio State University LIBRARIES, Jerome Lawrence & Robert E Lee Theatre Research Institute Library, 1430 Lincoln Tower, 1800 Cannon Dr, Columbus, OH, 43210-1230. Tel: 614-292-6614. Fax: 614-688-8417. p. 1888

Couch, Thomas, Dir, Owyhee County Historical Society, 17085 Basey St, Murphy, ID, 83650. Tel: 208-495-2319. Fax: 208-495-9824. p. 580

Couch-Thomas, Cheryl, Coll Mgt Librn, William Jewell College, 500 College Hill, Liberty, MO, 64068-1843. Tel: 816-415-7613. Fax: 816-415-5021. p. 1343

Couck, Lynn, Syst Mgr, Lenox Township Library, 58976 Main St, New Haven, MI, 48048-2685. Tel: 586-749-3430. Fax: 586-749-3245. p. 1214

Coughlan-Lambly, Judith, Head, Tech Serv, Dalhousie University, W K Kellogg Health Sciences Library, Tupper Medical Bldg, 5850 College St, Halifax, NS, B3H 1X5, CANADA. p. 2780

Coughlin, Carol, Dir, Virginia Institute of Marine Science, College of William & Mary, Rte 1208, Greate Rd, Gloucester Point, VA, 23062. Tel: 804-684-7114. Fax: 804-684-7113. p. 2467

Coughlin, Elizabeth, Head, Ch, Swampscott Public Library, 61 Burrill St, Swampscott, MA, 01907. Tel: 781-596-8867. Fax: 781-596-8826. p. 1130

Coughlin, Richard J, Dean, Libr & Mus, Truman State University, 100 E Normal, Kirksville, MO, 63501-4211. Tel: 660-785-4038. p. 1342

Coulas, Janet, Chief Exec Officer, Petawawa Public Library, 16 Civic Centre Rd, Petawawa, ON, K8H 3H5, CANADA. Tel: 613-687-2227. Fax: 613-687-2527. p. 2835

Coulombe, Solange, Acq, Cegep de Trois-Rivieres Bibliotheque, 3175 Laviolette, Trois-Rivieres, QC, G9A 5E6, CANADA. Tel: 819-376-1721, Ext 2609. Fax: 819-693-3844. p. 2914

Coultas, Simon, Adult Serv, Henderson County Public Library, 301 N Washington St, Hendersonville, NC, 28739. Tel: 828-697-4725. Fax: 828-692-8449, 828-697-4700. p. 1801

Coulter, Ann, Dir, Libr Serv, Southwestern Community College, 1501 W Townline, Creston, IA, 50801. Tel: 641-782-1340. Fax: 641-782-1301. p. 805

Coulter, Brenda, Pub Serv Coordr, Tye Preston Memorial Library, 16311 S Access Rd, Canyon Lake, TX, 78133-5301. Tel: 830-964-3744. Fax: 830-964-3126. p. 2295

Coulter, Carolyn, Tech & Virtual Serv Officer, Pikes Peak Library District, 20 N Cascade Ave, Colorado Springs, CO, 80903. Tel: 719-531-6333. p. 296

Coulter, Cynthia M, Head, Tech Serv, University of Northern Iowa Library, 1227 W 27th St, Cedar Falls, IA, 50613-3675. Tel: 319-273-2801. Fax: 319-273-2913. p. 799

Coulter, David, Libr Mgr, Grapevine Public Library, 1201 Municipal Way, Grapevine, TX, 76051. Tel: 817-410-3415. Fax: 817-410-3084. p. 2329

Coulter, Kelly, Virtual Serv Mgr, Richland County Public Library, 1431 Assembly St, Columbia, SC, 29201-3101. Tel: 803-799-9084. Fax: 803-929-3448. p. 2188

Coulter, Laura, Ref, Howard Payne University, 1000 Fisk Ave, Brownwood, TX, 76801. Tel: 325-649-8091. Fax: 325-649-8904. p. 2292

Coulter, Tara, Librn, Herb Society of America Library, 9019 Kirtland Chardon Rd, Kirtland, OH, 44094. Tel: 440-256-0514. Fax: 440-256-0541. p. 1907

Coumoyer, Suzette, In Charge, Rio Tinto Iron & Titanium Inc, 1625 Rte Marie-Victorin, Sorel-Tracy, QC, J3R 1M6, CANADA. Tel: 450-746-3000, Ext 2065. Fax: 450-746-3391. p. 2913

Council, Evelyn, Assoc Dir, Coll Develop, Fayetteville State University, 1200 Murchison Rd, Fayetteville, NC, 28301-4298. Tel: 910-672-1520. Fax: 910-672-1746. p. 1793

Council, Floyd, Regional Mgr, Saint Louis Public Library, Julia Davis Branch, 4415 Natural Bridge Rd, Saint Louis, MO, 63115. Tel: 314-383-3021. Fax: 314-383-0251. p. 1360

Council, Kimberly, Ref Librn, Sullivan & Cromwell LLP, 125 Broad St, New York, NY, 10004. Tel: 212-558-3780. Fax: 212-558-3346. p. 1700

Counihan, Martha, Archivist, The College of New Rochelle, 29 Castle Pl, New Rochelle, NY, 10805-2308. Tel: 914-654-5345. Fax: 914-654-5884. p. 1666

Courant, Paul N, Univ Librn, University of Michigan, 818 Hatcher Graduate Library, Ann Arbor, MI, 48109-1205. Tel: 734-764-9356. Fax: 734-763-5080. p. 1152

Courcelles, Michel, Librn, INRS - Institut Armand-Frappier - Bibliotheque, 531 blvd des Prairies, Laval, QC, H7V 1B7, CANADA. Tel: 450-687-5010, Ext 4340. Fax: 450-686-5501. p. 2886

Courchesne, Luce Anne, Prof, College de Maisonneuve, 3800, rue Sherbrooke Est, Montreal, QC, H1X 2A2, CANADA. Tel: 514-254-7131. Fax: 514-251-9741. p. 2978

Courie, Amanda M, Mgr, Youth Serv, Caroline County Public Library, 100 Market St, Denton, MD, 21629. Tel: 410-479-1343. Fax: 410-479-1443. p. 1027

Courie, John, Mgr, Libr Syst, Caroline County Public Library, 100 Market St, Denton, MD, 21629. Tel: 410-479-1343. Fax: 410-479-1443. p. 1027

Courier, William, Bus & Finance Mgr, Cambridge Public Library, 449 Broadway, Cambridge, MA, 02138. Tel: 617-349-4413. Fax: 617-349-3108. p. 1073

Cournoyer, Marsha, Libr Serv Supvr, The Villages Public Library, Saddlebrook Ctr, 325 Belvedere Blvd, The Villages, FL, 32162. Tel: 352-259-5739. Fax: 352-259-5748. p. 500

Cournyea, Judy, Acq, Circ, Unity Library & Archives, 1901 NW Blue Pkwy, Unity Village, MO, 64065-0001. Tel: 816-524-3550, Ext 2370. p. 1370

Courouleau, Jeffrey, Dir, Perry Carnegie Library, 302 N Seventh St, Perry, OK, 73077. Tel: 580-336-4721. Fax: 580-336-5497. p. 1976

Courson, Bruce, Dir, The Sandwich Glass Museum Library, 129 Main St, Sandwich, MA, 02563-2233. Tel: 508-888-0251. Fax: 508-888-4941. p. 1122

Court, David G, Libr Mgr, Desert Foothills Library, 38443 N Schoolhouse Rd, Cave Creek, AZ, 85331. Tel: 480-488-2286. Fax: 480-595-8353. p. 59

Courtade, Johanne, Tech Serv, West Deptford Public Library, 420 Crown Point Rd, West Deptford, NJ, 08086-9598. Tel: 856-845-5593. Fax: 856-848-3689. p. 1541

Courtemanche, Brian, Dir, Endicott College Library, 376 Hale St, Beverly, MA, 01915. Tel: 978-232-2279. Fax: 978-232-2700. p. 1054

Courtney, Aida, Br Coordr, Parsippany-Troy Hills Free Public Library, Lake Hiawatha Branch, 68 Nokomis Ave, Lake Hiawatha, NJ, 07034. Tel: 973-335-0952. Fax: 973-335-8610. p. 1518

Courtney, Henry, Librn, Lockheed Martin Corp, 700 N Frederick Ave, Gaithersburg, MD, 20879. Tel: 301-240-5500. Fax: 301-240-6855. p. 1030

Courtney, John, Assoc Dir, Support Serv & HR, Pikes Peak Library District, 20 N Cascade Ave, Colorado Springs, CO, 80903. Tel: 719-531-6333. p. 296

Courtney, Kathie, AV, Louisville Public Library, 700 Lincoln Ave, Louisville, OH, 44641-1474. Tel: 330-875-1696. Fax: 330-875-3530. p. 1912

Courtney, Mary E, Ref, College of Our Lady of the Elms, 291 Springfield St, Chicopee, MA, 01013-2839. Tel: 413-265-2280. Fax: 413-594-7418. p. 1082

Courtney, Michele, Asst Dir, Illinois CPA Society, 550 W Jackson, Ste 900, Chicago, IL, 60661. Tel: 312-601-4613. Fax: 312-906-8045. p. 614

Courtney, Ralph, Ref & Instruction, University of Alaska Anchorage, Consortium Library, 3211 Providence Dr, Anchorage, AK, 99508-8176. Tel: 907-786-1871. Fax: 907-786-1834. p. 45

Courtney, Rhonda, Access Serv Librn, St Lawrence University, 23 Romoda Dr, Canton, NY, 13617. Tel: 315-229-5479. Fax: 315-229-5729. p. 1602

Courtney, Sandra, Cataloger, Horsham Township Library, 435 Babylon Rd, Horsham, PA, 19044-1224. Tel: 215-443-2609, Ext 211. Fax: 215-443-2697. p. 2069

Courtney, Vince, Head, Tech Serv, State University of New York at Fredonia, 280 Central Ave, Fredonia, NY, 14063. Tel: 716-673-3182. Fax: 716-673-3185. p. 1624

Coury, Melissa, Librn, Middle Haddam Public Library, Two Knowles Landing, Middle Haddam, CT, 06456. Tel: 860-267-9093. p. 351

Cousar, Harnethia, Ref, United States Department of Health & Human Services, National Center for Health Statistics Staff Research Library, 3311 Toledo Rd, Rm 2403, Hyattsville, MD, 20782. Tel: 301-458-4775. Fax: 301-458-4019. p. 1039

Cousar, Judith, Campus Librn, ECPI University, 4800 Airport Center Pkwy, Charlotte, NC, 28208. Tel: 704-399-1010, Ext 244. Fax: 704-399-9144. p. 1783

Couser, Yvette, Head, Ch, Merrimack Public Library, 470 Daniel Webster Hwy, Merrimack, NH, 03054-3694. Tel: 603-424-5021. Fax: 603-424-7312. p. 1457

Cousineau, Laura, Dir, Dartmouth College Library, Biomedical Libraries (Dana Biomedical & Matthews-Fuller Health Sciences Library), Dana Biomedical Library/HB 6168, 64 College St, Hanover, NH, 03755-3563. Tel: 603-650-1662. Fax: 603-650-1789. p. 1450

Cousineau, Laura, Asst Dir, Prog & Serv Develop, Medical University of South Carolina Library, 171 Ashley Ave, Ste 300, Charleston, SC, 29425-0001. Tel: 843-792-9211. Fax: 843-792-7947. p. 2184

Cousineau, Sue, Librn, Douglas County Library System, Reedsport Branch, 395 Winchester St, Reedsport, OR, 97467. Tel: 541-271-3500. Fax: 541-271-1027. p. 2016

Cousino, Marsha, Ref, Johnson County Community College, 12345 College Blvd, Box 21, Overland Park, KS, 66210. Tel: 913-469-8500, Ext 3987. Fax: 913-469-3816. p. 888

Cousins, Dale, Regional Libr Supvr, Wake County Public Library System, Cameron Village Regional Library, 1930 Clark Ave, Raleigh, NC, 27605. Tel: 919-856-6726. Fax: 919-856-6722. p. 1817

Cousins, Richard, Librn, White & Case LLP, 701 13th St NW, Washington, DC, 20005-3807. Tel: 202-626-6475. Fax: 202-639-9355. p. 422

Couts, Mona C, Exec Dir, Triangle Research Libraries Network, Wilson Library, CB No 3940, Chapel Hill, NC, 27514-8890. Tel: 919-962-8022. Fax: 919-962-4452. p. 2951

Couts, Pat, Dr, Prof, University of Central Oklahoma, 100 N University Dr, Edmond, OK, 73034. Tel: 405-974-5888. Fax: 405-974-3857. p. 2972

Coutts, Brian, Dr, Pub Serv, Western Kentucky University Libraries, Helm-Cravens Library Complex, 1906 College Heights Blvd, No 11067, Bowling Green, KY, 42101-1067. Tel: 270-745-2905. Fax: 270-745-6422. p. 908

Coutu, Aaron, Asst Dir, Cumberland Public Library, 1464 Diamond Hill Rd, Cumberland, RI, 02864-5510. Tel: 401-333-2552. Fax: 401-334-0578. p. 2165

Coutu, Aaron, Youth/Young Adult Librn, Greenville Public Library, 573 Putnam Pike, Greenville, RI, 02828-2195. Tel: 401-949-3630. Fax: 401-949-0530. p. 2166

Coutu, Serge, Res, Societe de Genealogie de l'Outaouais Bibliotheque, 855, boul de la Gappe, Gatineau, QC, J8T 8H9, CANADA. Tel: 819-568-8798, 819-643-0888. Fax: 819-568-5933. p. 2884

Couture, Ann, Acq, Coos Bay Public Library, 525 Anderson St, Coos Bay, OR, 97420-1678. Tel: 541-269-1101. Fax: 541-269-7567. p. 1993

Couture, Denis, Dir, Reseau des bibliotheques de la Ville de Quebec, 3515 Clemenceau, Beauport, QC, G1C 7R5, CANADA. Tel: 418-641-6501, Ext 3545. Fax: 418-666-6173. p. 2880

Couture, Faye, Dir, United States Army, Fort Stewart Main Post Library, 316 Lindquist Rd, Fort Stewart, GA, 31314-5126. Tel: 912-767-2260, 912-767-2828. Fax: 912-767-3794. p. 533

Couture, Norma, Mgr, Springfield City Library, Indian Orchard Branch, 44 Oak St, Indian Orchard, MA, 01151. Tel: 413-263-6846. Fax: 413-263-6848. p. 1127

Couture, Norma, Mgr, Springfield City Library, Pine Point Branch, 204 Boston Rd, Springfield, MA, 01109. Tel: 413-263-6855. Fax: 413-263-6857. p. 1127

Couture, Norma, Mgr, Springfield City Library, Sixteen Acres Branch, 1187 Parker St, Springfield, MA, 01129. Tel: 413-263-6858. Fax: 413-263-6860. p. 1128

Couvillion, Carol, Br Mgr, Avoyelles Parish Library, Moreauville Branch, Community Ctr, Tassin St, Moreauville, LA, 71355. Tel: 318-985-2767. p. 956

Couvillion, Shirley L, Dir, Van Meter Public Library, 505 Grant St, Van Meter, IA, 50261. Tel: 515-996-2435. Fax: 515-996-2207. p. 848

Couvillon, Emily, Pub Serv Librn, University of Saint Thomas, 1100 W Main, Houston, TX, 77006. Tel: 713-525-3891. Fax: 713-525-3886. p. 2344

Cove, Cheryl, Librn, Raytheon Co, 528 Boston Post Rd, Sudbury, MA, 01776-3375. Tel: 978-440-2282. Fax: 978-440-4412. p. 1130

Cove, Jeanne, Br Mgr, Montgomery County-Norristown Public Library, Upper Perkiomen Valley, 350 Main St, Red Hill, PA, 18076. Tel: 215-679-2020. p. 2099

Covell, Judy, Coll Mgr, Timberland Regional Library, 415 Tumwater Blvd SW, Tumwater, WA, 98501-5799. Tel: 360-943-5001, Ext 2526. Fax: 360-586-6838. p. 2543

Covelli, Emma, Librn, Grand Canyon University, 3300 W Camelback Rd, Phoenix, AZ, 85017-3030. Tel: 602-639-6641. Fax: 602-639-7835. p. 73

Coventry, Jennifer, Ch, Newcomerstown Public Library, 123 E Main St, Newcomerstown, OH, 43832-1093. Tel: 740-498-8228. Fax: 740-498-8221. p. 1922

Covert, Carl, Dir of Libr Serv, Paris Junior College, 2400 Clarksville St, Paris, TX, 75460. Tel: 903-782-0215, 903-782-0415. Fax: 903-782-0356. p. 2368

Covert, Claudia, Reader Serv Librn, Rhode Island School of Design Library, 15 Westminster St, Providence, RI, 02903. Tel: 401-709-5908. Fax: 401-709-5932. p. 2174

Covert-Vail, Lucinda, Pub Serv, New York University, 70 Washington Sq S, New York, NY, 10012-1091. Tel: 212-998-2505. Fax: 212-995-4070. p. 1695

Covetta, Melvyn, Ref Librn, Vanguard University of Southern California, 55 Fair Dr, Costa Mesa, CA, 92626. Tel: 714-556-3610, Ext 2400. Fax: 714-966-5478. p. 137

Covi, Lisa, Asst Prof, Rutgers, The State University of New Jersey, Four Huntington St, New Brunswick, NJ, 08901-1071. Tel: 732-932-7500, Ext 8955. Fax: 732-932-2644. p. 2969

Covington, Christine, Head, Ser, Interim Head, Ref, North Carolina Central University, 1801 Fayetteville St, Durham, NC, 27707-3129. Tel: 919-530-7311. Fax: 919-530-7612. p. 1789

Covington, Dean, Dir, Lyon College, 2300 Highland Rd, Batesville, AR, 72501-3699. Tel: 870-307-7206. Fax: 870-307-7279. p. 93

Covington, Diane, Chem & Biol Librn, Carnegie Mellon University, Mellon Institute Library, 4400 Fifth Ave, 4th Flr, Pittsburgh, PA, 15213-3890. Tel: 412-268-3171. Fax: 412-268-6945. p. 2124

Covington, Julia B, Ref Librn, North Carolina Legislative Library, 500 Legislative Office Bldg, 300 N Salisbury St, Raleigh, NC, 27603-5925. Tel: 919-733-9390. Fax: 919-715-5460. p. 1815

Covington, Michele, Librn, Kellyville Public Library, 230 E Buffalo, Kellyville, OK, 74039. Tel: 918-247-3740. Fax: 918-247-3740. p. 1966

Covington, Paula, Bibliographer, Vanderbilt University, Central Library, 419 21st Ave S, Nashville, TN, 37203-2427. Tel: 615-322-6282. Fax: 615-343-7451. p. 2260

Covington, Tommy, Librn, Northeast Regional Library, Ripley Public Library, 308 N Commerce St, Ripley, MS, 38663-1721. Tel: 662-837-7773. Fax: 662-837-7773. p. 1297

Covino, Laura, Librn, Center for Modern Psychoanalytic Studies Library, 16 W Tenth St, New York, NY, 10011. Tel: 212-260-7050, Ext 15. Fax: 212-228-6410. p. 1672

Covinton, Candace, Dir, Packwaukee Public Library, N3511 State St, Packwaukee, WI, 53953. Tel: 608-589-5202. Fax: 608-589-5202. p. 2629

Covley-Walker, Mary Jane, Dir, Dunkirk Free Library, 536 Central Ave, Dunkirk, NY, 14048. Tel: 716-366-2511. Fax: 716-366-2525. p. 1616

Covone, Nicole, Dir, Libr Serv, Johnson & Wales University, 1701 NE 127th St, North Miami, FL, 33181. Tel: 305-892-5398. p. 472

Cowan, Barbara, Circ, Per, Purchasing, Conception Abbey & Seminary Library, 37174 State Hwy W, Conception, MO, 64433. Tel: 660-944-2803. Fax: 660-944-2833. p. 1326

Cowan, David G, Dir, Libr Serv, South Texas College of Law, 1303 San Jacinto St, Houston, TX, 77002-7000. Tel: 713-646-1711. Fax: 713-659-2217. p. 2342

Cowan, Deanna, Info Serv, McGill University Libraries, Life Sciences Library, McIntyre Medical Science Bldg, 3655 Promenade Sir William Osler, Montreal, QC, H3G 1Y6, CANADA. Tel: 514-398-4475, Ext 09669. Fax: 514-398-3890. p. 2898

Cowan, Friedgard, Cat/Metadata Librn, George Mason University Libraries, 4400 University Dr, MSN 2FL, Fairfax, VA, 22030-4444. Tel: 703-993-2250. Fax: 703-993-2200. p. 2462

Cowan, Helen, Ch, Vineland Public Library, 1058 E Landis Ave, Vineland, NJ, 08360. Tel: 856-794-4244. Fax: 856-691-0366. p. 1538

Cowan, Janet, Admin Coordr, Norfolk County Public Library, 46 Colborne St S, Simcoe, ON, N3Y 4H3, CANADA. Tel: 519-426-3506, Ext 1258. Fax: 519-426-0657. p. 2841

Cowan, Kathy, Sr Ref Librn, Maryland Institute College of Art, 1401 Mount Royal Ave, Baltimore, MD, 21217. Tel: 410-225-2304, 410-225-2311. Fax: 410-225-2316. p. 1015

Cowan, Leanna, Dir, Alvarado Public Library, 210 N Baugh St, Alvarado, TX, 76009. Tel: 817-783-7323. Fax: 817-783-7323. p. 2273

Cowan, Pamela, Asst Dir, Head, Ch, Manchester Public Library, 586 Main St, Manchester, CT, 06040. Tel: 860-643-2471. Fax: 860-643-9453. p. 350

Cowan, Penny, Dir, Tech & Info Serv, University of the South, 735 University Ave, Sewanee, TN, 37383-1000. Tel: 931-598-1573. Fax: 931-598-1702. p. 2265

Cowan, Scott T, Libr Asst, American Medical Association, 515 N State St, 9th Flr, Chicago, IL, 60654. Tel: 312-464-4855. Fax: 312-464-5226. p. 606

Coward, Barb, Dir, Cortland Community Library, 63 S Somonauk Rd, Cortland, IL, 60112. Tel: 815-756-7274. Fax: 815-748-4491. p. 631

Coward, David, Acq, Luther Seminary Library, Gullixson Hall, 2375 Como Ave, Saint Paul, MN, 55108. Tel: 651-641-3263. Fax: 651-641-3280. p. 1278

Cowart, Alice, Cat, Gardendale Martha Moore Public Library, 995 Mt Olive Rd, Gardendale, AL, 35071. Tel: 205-631-6639. Fax: 205-631-0146. p. 18

Cowden, Nancy A, Tech Serv, Oklahoma City University, Law Library, 2501 N Blackwelder, Oklahoma City, OK, 73106. Tel: 405-208-5271. Fax: 405-208-5172. p. 1974

Cowe, Carol, Libr Serv Supvr, Moore County Library, 101 Saunders St, Carthage, NC, 28327. Tel: 910-947-5335. Fax: 910-947-3660. p. 1779

Cowell, Ann, Librn, Massachusetts Department of Corrections, Institutional Library at Old Colony Correctional Center, One Administration Rd, Bridgewater, MA, 02324. Tel: 508-279-6006, Ext 6803. p. 1070

Cowell, Cynthia, Libr Serv Dir, Newport Beach Public Library, Central Library, 1000 Avocado Ave, Newport Beach, CA, 92660-6301. Tel: 949-717-3800. Fax: 949-640-5681. p. 194

Cowell, Elizabeth, Assoc Dir, Pub Serv, University of California, 1156 High St, Santa Cruz, CA, 95064. Tel: 831-459-2076. Fax: 831-459-8206. p. 264

Cowell, Fillamay, Ch, Russell County Public Library, 94 N Main, Jamestown, KY, 42629. Tel: 270-343-3545. Fax: 270-343-2019. p. 919

Cowell, Mike, Br Mgr, Chatham County Public Libraries, Wren Memorial Library, 500 N Second Ave, Siler City, NC, 27344. Tel: 919-742-2016. Fax: 919-66-3121. p. 1823

Cowen, Crystel, Libr Asst, University of Western Ontario, North Campus Bldg, Rm 280, London, ON, N6A 5B7, CANADA. Tel: 519-661-2111, Ext 88489. Fax: 519-661-3848. p. 2819

Cowen, Diane, Br Mgr, Santa Cruz City-County Library System Headquarters, Garfield Park, 705 Woodrow Ave, Santa Cruz, CA, 95060. Tel: 831-427-7706 x7763. Fax: 831-427-7729. p. 264

Cowen, James, ILL, Mgr, Circ Serv, Ocean County College Library, College Dr, Toms River, NJ, 08754. Tel: 732-255-0392. Fax: 732-255-0421. p. 1533

Cowen, Janet L, Dir, Maine Medical Center Library, 22 Bramhall St, Portland, ME, 04102. Tel: 207-662-4079. Fax: 207-761-3027. p. 997

Cowen, Vangie, Dir, M-C Community Library, 200 W Grace St, Cleghorn, IA, 51014. Tel: 712-436-2521. Fax: 712-436-2695. p. 802

Cowfer, Elizabeth, Br Mgr, Ross Annie Halenbake Library, Renovo Area Library, 317 Seventh St, Renovo, PA, 17764. Tel: 570-923-0390. p. 2083

Cowgill, Allison, Head, Ref, California State University, Fresno, Henry Madden Library, 5200 N Barton Ave, Mail Stop ML-34, Fresno, CA, 93740-8014. Tel: 559-278-1022. Fax: 559-278-6952. p. 150

Cowie, Darlene, Br Mgr, Thompson-Nicola Regional District Library System, Clearwater Branch, 422 Murtle Crescent, Clearwater, BC, V0E 1N1, CANADA. Tel: 250-674-2543. p. 2729

Cowie, Jamie, Early Childhood Educator, Teck Centennial Library, Ten Kirkland St E, Kirkland Lake, ON, P2N 1P1, CANADA. Tel: 705-567-7966. Fax: 705-568-6303. p. 2815

Cowie, Laura, Mgr, Winnipeg School Division, 1075 Wellington Ave, Winnipeg, MB, R3E 0J7, CANADA. Tel: 204-788-0203. Fax: 204-783-9628. p. 2760

Cowling, Charles, Ref Serv, State University of New York College at Brockport, 350 New Campus Dr, Brockport, NY, 14420-2997. Tel: 585-395-2140. Fax: 585-395-5651. p. 1585

Cowling, Lola, Ref Librn, Austin Community College, Riverside Campus Library, 1020 Grove Blvd, Austin, TX, 78741. Tel: 512-223-6134. Fax: 512-223-6703. p. 2278

Cowperthwaite, Carol A, Librn, United States Army, Bldg 530, 301 C St, Yuma, AZ, 85365-9848. Tel: 928-328-2558. Fax: 928-328-3055. p. 91

Cox, Agnes, Librn, Sullivan County Public Library, Carlisle Public, 201 N Ledgerwood St, Carlisle, IN, 47838. Tel: 812-398-4480. p. 780

Cox, Alma, Librn, Southwest Arkansas Regional Library, Fulton Branch, Little River St, Fulton, AR, 71838. Tel: 870-896-2756. p. 103

Cox, Amanda, Network Adminr, Henry County Public Library System, 1001 Florence McGarity Blvd, McDonough, GA, 30252. Tel: 678-432-5212. Fax: 678-432-6153. p. 544

Cox, April L, Br Mgr, Surrey Public Library, City Centre, 10350 University Dr, Surrey, BC, V3T 4B8, CANADA. Tel: 604-598-7430. Fax: 604-598-7421. p. 2739

Cox, Carl, Coordr, Librn, College of Marin Library, 835 College Ave, Kentfield, CA, 94904. Tel: 415-457-8811, 415-485-9656. Fax: 415-457-5395. p. 161

Cox, Cathy, Coll Develop, Mission College Library, 3000 Mission College Blvd, Santa Clara, CA, 95054-1897. Tel: 408-855-5165. Fax: 408-855-5462. p. 262

Cox, Charles, Dir, Pine Forest Regional Library, 210 Front St, Richton, MS, 39476-1510. Tel: 601-788-6539. Fax: 601-788-9743. p. 1314

Cox, Cheryl, Ch, Springfield Town Library, 43 Main St, Springfield, VT, 05156. Tel: 802-885-3108. Fax: 802-885-4906. p. 2436

Cox, Chlista, Interim Mgr, First Baptist Church Library, 1200 Beech Ave, McAllen, TX, 78501. Tel: 956-686-7418. Fax: 956-630-4940. p. 2360

Cox, Christian, Ch, Marion County Public Library, 321 Monroe St, Fairmont, WV, 26554-2952. Tel: 304-366-1210. Fax: 304-366-4831. p. 2559

Cox, Christine, Dir, Church of Jesus Christ of Latter-Day Saints, Church History Library & Archives, 50 E North Temple, Salt Lake City, UT, 84150. Tel: 801-240-3603. Fax: 801-240-1845. p. 2412

Cox, Christopher, Dean of Libr Serv, University of Northern Iowa Library, 1227 W 27th St, Cedar Falls, IA, 50613-3675. Tel: 319-273-2737. Fax: 319-273-2913. p. 799

Cox, Deborah, Ref Serv, Lone Star College System, Montgomery College Library, 3200 College Park Dr, Conroe, TX, 77384. Tel: 936-273-7490. Fax: 936-273-7395. p. 2340

Cox, Denise, Head Librn, J T & E J Crumbaugh Memorial Public Church Library, 405 E Center St, Le Roy, IL, 61752-1723. Tel: 309-962-3911. p. 664

Cox, Dwayne, Head Archivist, Head, Spec Coll, Auburn University, Ralph Brown Draughon Library, 231 Mell St, Auburn, AL, 36849. Tel: 334-844-1707. Fax: 334-844-4424. p. 5

Cox, Fran, Chairperson, Castor Municipal Library, 5103 51 St, Castor, AB, T0C 0X0, CANADA. Tel: 403-882-3999. Fax: 403-882-3915. p. 2694

Cox, Gary S, Pres, Association of Independent Kentucky Colleges & Universities, 484 Chenault Rd, Frankfort, KY, 40601. Tel: 502-695-5007. Fax: 502-695-5057. p. 2944

Cox, Gerald, ILL, Harding University, 915 E Market St, Searcy, AR, 72149-2267. Tel: 501-279-4354. p. 114

Cox, Gwin L, Circ, Mount Olive College, 634 Henderson St, Mount Olive, NC, 28365-1699. Tel: 919-658-7869, Ext 1413. Fax: 919-658-8934. p. 1811

Cox, Heidi, Dir, Town Hall Library, N 76 W 31429 Hwy VV, North Lake, WI, 53064. Tel: 262-966-2933. Fax: 262-966-3365. p. 2626

Cox, Jaclyn, Dir, Rocky J Adkins Public Library, Main St, Sandy Hook, KY, 41171. Tel: 606-738-5796. Fax: 606-738-4980. p. 934

Cox, Jan, Head Librn, Indiana University, School of Dentistry Library, 1121 W Michigan St, Rm 128, Indianapolis, IN, 46202-5186. Tel: 317-274-5207. Fax: 317-278-1256. p. 753

Cox, Janet, Libr Mgr, Pikes Peak Library District, Ruth Holley Library, 685 N Murray Blvd, Colorado Springs, CO, 80915. Tel: 719-597-5377. p. 296

Cox, Janet, Mgr, Pikes Peak Library District, High Prairie Library, 7035 Old Meridian Rd, Falcon, CO, 80831. Tel: 719-260-3650. p. 296

Cox, Janet, Regional Supvr, Wythe-Grayson Regional Library, 147 S Independence Ave, Independence, VA, 24348-2800. Tel: 276-773-2761. Fax: 276-773-3289. p. 2472

Cox, Jason, Pub Relations, Bluffton Public Library, 145 S Main St, Bluffton, OH, 45817. Tel: 419-358-5016. Fax: 419-358-9653. p. 1860

Cox, Jeanette B, Govt Doc, Florida Agricultural & Mechanical University Libraries, 1500 S Martin Luther King Blvd, Tallahassee, FL, 32307-4700. Tel: 850-599-3370. Fax: 850-561-2293. p. 492

Cox, Jennifer, Dir, Art Institute of Portland Library, 1122 NW Davis St, Portland, OR, 97209-2911. Tel: 503-228-6528. Fax: 503-228-2895. p. 2009

Cox, Jennifer A, Asst Librn, Illinois Institute of Art - Chicago Library, 350 N Orleans St, Chicago, IL, 60654-1593. Tel: 312-777-8728, 312-777-8730. Fax: 312-777-8782. p. 615

Cox, Joan, Librn, Sunshine Township Library, Main St, Mason City, NE, 68855. p. 1408

Cox, Joe, Dir, University of Toronto Libraries, Faculty of Information Inforum, 140 Saint George St, 4th Flr, Toronto, ON, M5S 3G6, CANADA. Tel: 416-978-5766. Fax: 416-978-5769. p. 2865

Cox, Joe, Dir, Info Serv, University of Toronto, 140 St George St, Toronto, ON, M5S 3G6, CANADA. Tel: 416-978-3234. Fax: 416-978-5762. p. 2978

Cox, Joseph, Fr, Per, Saint Meinrad Archabbey & School of Theology, 200 Hill Dr, Saint Meinrad, IN, 47577. Tel: 812-357-6401. Fax: 812-357-6398. p. 777

Cox, Judy, Dir, Mercer County Library, 601 Grant, Princeton, MO, 64673. Tel: 660-748-3725. Fax: 660-748-3723. p. 1350

Cox, Julia, Ch, Penticton Public Library, 785 Main St, Penticton, BC, V2A 5E3, CANADA. Tel: 250-770-7783. Fax: 250-770-7787. p. 2735

Cox, Katherine, Asst Dir, Southgate Veterans Memorial Library, 14680 Dix-Toledo Rd, Southgate, MI, 48195. Tel: 734-258-3002. Fax: 734-284-9477. p. 1229

Cox, Kathryn, Ref Librn, Liberty University Library, 1971 University Blvd, Lynchburg, VA, 24502. Tel: 434-592-4934. Fax: 434-582-2728. p. 2476

Cox, Kathy, Head, Tech Serv, Trails Regional Library, 432 N Holden St, Warrensburg, MO, 64093. Tel: 660-747-1699. Fax: 660-747-5774. p. 1371

Cox, Kiersten, Instr, University of South Florida, 4202 Fowler Ave, CIS 1040, Tampa, FL, 33620-7800. Tel: 813-974-3520. Fax: 813-974-6840. p. 2964

Cox, Kyle, Exec Dir, Mid-Columbia Libraries, 405 S Dayton, Kennewick, WA, 99336. Tel: 509-582-4745. Fax: 509-737-6349. p. 2518

Cox, Laura, Mgr, Access Serv, Arizona State University Libraries, Library at the Polytechnic Campus, Academic Ctr, Bldg 20, 5988 S Backus Mall, Mesa, AZ, 85212. Tel: 480-727-1911. Fax: 480-727-1077. p. 84

Cox, Leana J, Acq Mgr, Interim Librn, Colorado Northwestern Community College Library, 500 Kennedy Dr, CNCC-Box 29, Rangely, CO, 81648. Tel: 970-675-3334, 970-675-3576. Fax: 970-675-3267. p. 321

Cox, Lucy, Intl Law Librn, Ref Librn, Rutgers University Libraries, Camden Law Library, 217 N Fifth St, Camden, NJ, 08102-1203. Tel: 856-225-6464. p. 1477

Cox, Lynn M, Asst Librn, Southeast Kentucky Community & Technical College, 207 Chrisman Hall, 700 College Rd, Cumberland, KY, 40823. Tel: 606-589-3074. Fax: 606-589-4941. p. 911

Cox, Michael, Youth Serv, Pueblo City-County Library District, 100 E Abriendo Ave, Pueblo, CO, 81004-4290. Tel: 719-562-5618. Fax: 719-562-5619. p. 320

Cox, Michelle, Asst Dir, Newcomerstown Public Library, 123 E Main St, Newcomerstown, OH, 43832-1093. Tel: 740-498-8228. Fax: 740-498-8221. p. 1922

Cox, Pam, Asst Librn, Albemarle Regional Library, Northampton Memorial Library, 207 W Jefferson St, Jackson, NC, 27845. Tel: 252-534-3571. Fax: 252-534-1017. p. 1835

Cox, Patrick, Access Serv, Acq Mgr, Concordia University Library, 2811 NE Holman St, Portland, OR, 97211-6067. Tel: 503-493-6461. Fax: 503-280-8697. p. 2010

Cox, Patrick, Asst Dir, University of Texas Libraries, Center for American History, SRH 2-101, D1100, University of Texas at Austin, Austin, TX, 78712. Tel: 512-495-4515. Fax: 512-495-4542. p. 2284

Cox, Patti, Commun Br Supvr, Pierce County Library System, Steilacoom Branch, 2950 Steilacoom Blvd SW, Steilacoom, WA, 98388-5107. Tel: 253-548-3313. Fax: 253-589-7095. p. 2540

Cox, Rebecca, Ref Librn, Park University Library, 8700 NW River Park Dr, Parkville, MO, 64152. Tel: 816-584-6840. Fax: 816-741-4911. p. 1349

Cox, Richard, Prof, University of Pittsburgh, 135 N Bellefield Ave, Pittsburgh, PA, 15260. Tel: 412-624-5230. Fax: 412-624-5231. p. 2973

Cox, Robert, Head, Spec Coll & Archives, University of Massachusetts Amherst, 154 Hicks Way, Amherst, MA, 01003-9275. Tel: 413-545-2780. Fax: 413-545-6873. p. 1049

Cox, Roxanne, Ref Serv, YA, University of Nebraska Medical Center, 600 S 42nd St, Omaha, NE, 68198-6705. Tel: 402-559-7228. Fax: 402-559-5498. p. 1415

Cox, Sandra, Br Head, Toronto Public Library, Bendale, 1515 Danforth Rd, Toronto, ON, M1J 1H5, CANADA. Tel: 416-396-8910. Fax: 416-396-3608. p. 2860

Cox, Sharon, Commun Libr Mgr, Queens Borough Public Library, Laurelton Community Library, 134-26 225th St, Laurelton, NY, 11413. Tel: 718-528-2822. Fax: 718-723-6837. p. 1645

Cox, Sharon, Dep Librn, Huron County Library, Administration Office, 77722B London Rd, Clinton, ON, N0M 1L0, CANADA. Tel: 519-482-5457. Fax: 519-482-7820. p. 2799

Cox, Steven, Spec Coll & Archives Librn, University of Tennessee at Chattanooga Library, 615 McCallie Ave, Dept 6456, Chattanooga, TN, 37403-2598. Tel: 423-425-4501. Fax: 423-425-4775. p. 2228

Cox, Suellen, Ref, Paulina June & George Pollak Library, 800 N State College Blvd, Fullerton, CA, 92834. Tel: 714-278-2714. Fax: 714-278-2439. p. 154

Cox, Summer, Ref, Rockingham County Public Library, 527 Boone Rd, Eden, NC, 27288. Tel: 336-627-1106. Fax: 336-623-1258. p. 1790

Cox, Sylvia, Librn, National Park Service, Federal Bldg, Rm 474, 100 Centennial Mall North, Lincoln, NE, 68508. Tel: 402-437-5392, Ext 110. Fax: 402-437-5098. p. 1405

Cox, Tami, Mgr, East Moline Public Library, 740 16th Ave, East Moline, IL, 61244-2122. Tel: 309-755-9614. Fax: 309-755-3901. p. 638

Cox, Thomas, Info Tech, Tufts University, 35 Professors Row, Medford, MA, 02155-5816. Tel: 617-627-4318. Fax: 617-627-3002. p. 1104

Cox, Toni, Dir, Radford Public Library, 30 W Main St, Radford, VA, 24141. Tel: 540-731-3621. Fax: 540-731-4857. p. 2487

Cox, Tresa, Libr Mgr, Apache County Library District, Sanders Public, I-40, Exit 339, 191 N Frontage Rd E, Sanders, AZ, 86512. Tel: 928-688-2677. Fax: 928-688-2677. p. 80

Cox-Bailey, Wanda, Br Mgr, Wake County Public Library System, Richard B Harrison Community Library, 1313 New Bern Ave, Raleigh, NC, 27610. Tel: 919-856-5724. Fax: 919-856-6943. p. 1818

Cox-Johnson, Deb, Br Mgr, Great River Regional Library, Howard Lake Library, 617 Sixth Ave, Howard Lake, MN, 55349-5644. Tel: 320-543-2020. Fax: 320-543-2020. p. 1275

Cox-Paul, Lori, Archival Operations, National Archives & Records Administration, 400 W Pershing Rd, Kansas City, MO, 64108. Tel: 816-268-8000. Fax: 816-268-8038. p. 1339

Coxe, Bobbie, Tech Serv, Marlboro County Library, 200 John Corry Rd, Bennettsville, SC, 29512. Tel: 843-479-5630. Fax: 843-479-5645. p. 2182

Coy, Carolene, Librn, Bradford Public Library, 138 E Main St, Bradford, OH, 45308-1108. Tel: 937-448-2612. Fax: 937-448-2615. p. 1861

Coy, Diana, Asst Dir, Head, Ref, Paulding County Carnegie Library, 205 S Main St, Paulding, OH, 45879-1492. Tel: 419-399-2032. Fax: 419-399-2114. p. 1928

Coy, Howard L, Jr, Dir, Vernon Parish Library, 1401 Nolan Trace, Leesville, LA, 71446. Tel: 337-239-2027. Fax: 337-238-0666. p. 955

Coy, Julie, Visual Res Librn, Haverford College, 370 Lancaster Ave, Haverford, PA, 19041-1392. Tel: 610-896-1128. Fax: 610-896-1102. p. 2067

Coy, Kathy, Libr Tech, Shippensburg University, 1871 Old Main Dr, Shippensburg, PA, 17257-2299. Tel: 717-477-1466. Fax: 717-477-1389. p. 2140

Coy, Silvia, Circ Supvr, University of Saint Thomas, 1100 W Main, Houston, TX, 77006. Tel: 713-525-2192. Fax: 713-525-3886. p. 2344

Coyan, Wanda, Dir, Historical Society of Alpine County, One School St, Markleeville, CA, 96120. Tel: 530-694-2317. Fax: 530-694-1087. p. 184

Coyle, Kathryn, Tech Serv Librn, University of the Arts University Libraries, Anderson Hall, 1st Flr, 333 S Broad St, Philadelphia, PA, 19102. Tel: 215-717-6285. Fax: 215-717-6287. p. 2119

Coyle, Pamela, Dir, Martinsburg-Berkeley County Public Library, 101 W King St, Martinsburg, WV, 25401. Tel: 304-267-8933. Fax: 304-267-9720. p. 2565

Coyler, Joni, Ref & Instruction Librn, Ivy Technical Community College, 50 W Fall Creek Pkwy N Dr, Indianapolis, IN, 46208-5752. Tel: 317-917-7149. Fax: 317-921-4355. p. 755

Coyne, Catherine, Asst Dir, Head, Youth Serv, Ames Free Library, 53 Main St, North Easton, MA, 02356. Tel: 508-238-2000. Fax: 508-238-2980. p. 1112

Coyne, Michael, Syst Librn, Thompson Rivers University, 900 McGill Rd, Kamloops, BC, V2C 5N3, CANADA. Tel: 250-828-5300. Fax: 250-828-5313. p. 2730

Cozzens, Susan E, Mgr, Popular Mats, Westlake Porter Public Library, 27333 Center Ridge Rd, Westlake, OH, 44145-3925. Tel: 440-871-2600. Fax: 440-871-6969. p. 1947

Crabb, John, Tech Serv, Reformed Theological Seminary Library, 5422 Clinton Blvd, Jackson, MS, 39209-3099. Tel: 601-923-1623. Fax: 601-923-1621. p. 1305

Crabill, Jane, Sr Librn, United States Army, Marquat Memorial Library, Bank Hall, Bldg D-3915, 3004 Ardennes St, Fort Bragg, NC, 28310-9610. Tel: 910-432-8184. Fax: 910-432-7788. p. 1794

Crabtree, Carol, In Charge, Red Clay State Historic Area Library, 1140 Red Clay Park Rd SW, Cleveland, TN, 37311. Tel: 423-478-0339. Fax: 423-614-7251. p. 2230

Crabtree, Frances, Librn, Aldersgate United Methodist Church Library, 4115 Dewey Ave, Rochester, NY, 14616. Tel: 585-663-3665. Fax: 585-865-8442. p. 1728

Crabtree, Katherine, Librn, Springtown Public Library, 626 N Main St, Springtown, TX, 76082-2541. Tel: 817-523-5862. Fax: 817-523-5922. p. 2388

Crabtree, Martin, Ref Librn, Mercer County Community College Library, 1200 Old Trenton Rd, West Windsor, NJ, 08550. Tel: 609-570-3545. Fax: 609-570-3845. p. 1542

Crabtree, Tara, Librn, California Court of Appeal Fifth Appellate District Library, 2424 Ventura St, Fresno, CA, 93721. Tel: 559-445-5686. Fax: 559-445-6684. p. 150

Craddock, Lynn, Br Mgr, Dallas Public Library, Kleberg-Rylie, 1301 Edd Rd, Dallas, TX, 75253-4010. Tel: 214-670-8471. Fax: 214-670-8474. p. 2307

Craff, Nancy, Dir, Birmingham Public Library, 310 Main St, Birmingham, IA, 52535. Tel: 319-498-4423. p. 796

Craft, Anna, Metada Cataloger, University of North Carolina at Greensboro, 320 Spring Garden St, Greensboro, NC, 27402. Tel: 336-334-5880. Fax: 336-334-5399. p. 1798

Craft, Carol A, Head, Ser, Delgado Community College, Bldg 10, Rm 116, 615 City Park Ave, New Orleans, LA, 70119. Tel: 504-671-5321. p. 959

Craft, Deborah, Dir, Citronelle Memorial Library, 7855 State St, Citronelle, AL, 36522. Tel: 251-866-7319. Fax: 251-866-5210. p. 12

Craft, Garnet, Ch, Magee Public Library, 120 First St NW, Magee, MS, 39111. Tel: 601-849-3747. Fax: 601-849-6609. p. 1307

Craft, Jamie, Asst Librn, Alden-Ewell Free Library, 13280 Broadway, Alden, NY, 14004. Tel: 716-937-7082. Fax: 716-937-7082. p. 1571

Craft, Jennifer, Circ, United States Navy, 1002 Balch Blvd, Bldg 1003, Stennis Space Center, MS, 39522-5001. Tel: 228-688-4597. Fax: 228-688-4191. p. 1315

Craft, Judith, Libr Spec, Leestown Learning Commons, Bluegrass Community & Technical College, Oswald Bldg, 470 Cooper Dr, Lexington, KY, 40506-0235. Tel: 859-246-6712. Fax: 859-246-4675. p. 920

Craft, Lori, Dir, Clarendon Hills Public Library, Seven N Prospect Ave, Clarendon Hills, IL, 60514. Tel: 630-323-8188. Fax: 630-323-8189. p. 629

Craft, Lori Anne, Dir, Hillside Public Library, 405 N Hillside Ave, Hillside, IL, 60162-1295. Tel: 708-449-7510. Fax: 708-449-6119. p. 656

Craft, Rebekah, Adult Serv, Rochester Hills Public Library, 500 Olde Towne Rd, Rochester, MI, 48307-2043. Tel: 248-650-7132. Fax: 248-650-7131. p. 1222

Crafts, Amanda, Librn, Bass Harbor Memorial Library, 89 Bernard Rd, Bernard, ME, 04612. Tel: 207-244-3798. p. 977

Cragg, Dana, Librn, Petersburg Public Library, Rodof Sholom Branch, 1865 S Sycamore St, Petersburg, VA, 23805. Tel: 804-733-2393. Fax: 804-733-2422. p. 2484

Crago, Rebecca, Archivist, Dept Head, Ref, Frederick County Archives & Research Center Library, 24 E Church St, Frederick, MD, 21701. Tel: 301-663-1188. Fax: 301-663-0526. p. 1028

Craig, Adam, Supvr, Essex County Library, Ruthven Branch, 1695 Elgin St, Ruthven, ON, N0P 2G0, CANADA. Tel: 226-946-1529, Ext 221. p. 2804

Craig, Amber, Librn, Wyoming State Penitentiary Library, 2900 S Higley Blvd, Rawlins, WY, 82301. Tel: 307-328-1441. Fax: 307-328-7471. p. 2659

Craig, Angela, Teen Serv, Charlotte Mecklenburg Library, ImaginOn: The Joe & Joan Martin Center, 300 E Seventh St, Charlotte, NC, 28202. Tel: 704-416-4600. Fax: 704-416-4700. p. 1782

Craig, Anne, Dir, Illinois State Library, Gwendolyn Brooks Bldg, 300 S Second St, Springfield, IL, 62701-9713. Tel: 217-782-2994. Fax: 217-785-4326. p. 705

Craig, Anne, Dir, Illinois Library & Information Network, c/o Illinois State Library, Gwendolyn Brooks Bldg, 300 S Second St, Springfield, IL, 62701-1796. Tel: 217-782-2994. Fax: 217-785-4326. p. 2942

Craig, Brenda, Circ, Public Library of Brookline, 361 Washington St, Brookline, MA, 02445. Tel: 617-730-2370. Fax: 617-730-2160. p. 1071

Craig, Calvin, Ref Serv, Gaston College, 201 Hwy 321 S, Dallas, NC, 28034-1499. Tel: 704-922-6359. Fax: 704-922-2342. p. 1786

Craig, Carol, Asst Librn, Ch, Hartington Public Library, 106 S Broadway, Hartington, NE, 68739. Tel: 402-254-6245. Fax: 402-254-6245. p. 1401

Craig, Cathy, Cat/Ref Librn, Laredo Community College, West End Washington St, Laredo, TX, 78040. Tel: 956-721-5813. Fax: 956-721-5447. p. 2353

Craig, Christine, ILL, Dutchess Community College Library, 53 Pendell Rd, Poughkeepsie, NY, 12601-1595. Tel: 845-431-8630. Fax: 845-431-8995. p. 1722

Craig, Dale, Res Mgr, Lake County Historical Society, 415 Riverside Dr, Painesville, OH, 44077. Tel: 440-639-2945. Fax: 440-255-8980. p. 1926

Craig, Edward L, Jr, Ref, Samford University Library, Lucille Stewart Beeson Law Library, 800 Lakeshore Dr, Birmingham, AL, 35229. Tel: 205-726-2714. Fax: 205-726-2644. p. 9

Craig, Gena, Syst Librn, Central Piedmont Community College Library, 1201 Elizabeth Ave, Charlotte, NC, 28235. Tel: 704-330-6755. Fax: 704-330-6887. p. 1781

Craig, Gladys, Librn, Ashland Community Library, 57 Exchange St, Ashland, ME, 04732. Tel: 207-435-6532. p. 973

Craig, James, Biological Sci Librn/Instrul Serv Librn, University of Massachusetts Amherst, Science & Engineering Library, A273 Lederle Graduate Research Ctr Lowrise, Amherst, MA, 01003. Tel: 413-545-1370. Fax: 413-577-1534. p. 1049

Craig, Jane, Br Mgr, Main Libr, Palm Beach County Library System, 3650 Summit Blvd, West Palm Beach, FL, 33406-4198. Tel: 561-233-2600. Fax: 561-233-2627. p. 503

Craig, Julie, Libr Mgr, Haut-Saint-Jean Regional Library, Andrew & Laura McCain Public Library, 8 McCain St, Florenceville-Bristol, NB, E7L 3H6, CANADA. Tel: 506-392-5294. Fax: 506-392-8108. p. 2762

Craig, Lora L, Dir, Anchor Point Public Library, 72251 Milo Fritz Ave, Anchor Point, AK, 99556. Tel: 907-235-5692. Fax: 907-235-5692. p. 43

Craig, Margie, Asst Librn, Waynesville Township Library, 303 E Second St, Waynesville, IL, 61778. Tel: 217-949-5111. Fax: 217-949-5111. p. 716

Craig, Margie, Computer Serv, Washington University Libraries, Kopolow Business Library, One Brookings Dr, Campus Box 1133, Saint Louis, MO, 63130-4899. Tel: 314-935-6332. Fax: 314-935-4970. p. 1363

Craig, Mary Pat, Curric Librn, Framingham State College, 100 State St, Framingham, MA, 01701. Tel: 508-626-4657. Fax: 508-626-4649. p. 1090

Craig, Missie, Dir, Carnegie Public Library, 114 Delta Ave, Clarksdale, MS, 38614-4212. Tel: 662-624-4461. Fax: 662-627-4344. p. 1295

Craig, Paula, Head Librn, Northwestern State University Libraries, 1800 Line Ave, Shreveport, LA, 71101. Tel: 318-677-3007. Fax: 318-676-7087. p. 968

Craig, Roberta, Coordr, Munson Healthcare, Community Health Library, 550 Munson Ave, Ste 100, Traverse City, MI, 49686. Tel: 231-935-9265. Fax: 231-935-9267. p. 1231

Craig, Sandra, Dir, Wabash Valley College, 2200 College Dr, Mount Carmel, IL, 62863. Tel: 618-262-8641, Ext 3400. Fax: 618-262-8962. p. 676

Craig, Sonja, Librn, Paige Memorial Library, 87 Petersham Rd, Hardwick, MA, 01037. Tel: 413-477-6704. p. 1094

Craig, Sunny, Ch, Lincoln County Library, LaBarge Branch, 262 Main St, LaBarge, WY, 83123. Tel: 307-386-2571. Fax: 307-386-2569. p. 2656

Craig, Susan, Dir, Valencia Community College, 850 W Morse Blvd, Winter Park, FL, 32789. Tel: 407-582-6815. Fax: 407-582-6014. p. 505

Craig, Susan, Dir, Iowa City Public Library, 123 S Linn St, Iowa City, IA, 52240. Tel: 319-356-5241. Fax: 319-356-5494. p. 822

Craig, Susan, Librn, University of Kansas Libraries, Murphy Art & Architecture Library, 1301 Mississippi St, Lawrence, KS, 66045-7500. Tel: 785-864-3020. Fax: 785-864-4608. p. 878

Craig, Tara, Ref Serv Supvr, Columbia University, Archives, Butler Library, 6th Flr, 114th St, MC 1127, New York, NY, 10027. Tel: 212-854-3786. Fax: 212-854-1365. p. 1674

Craig, Tara, Ref Supvr, Columbia University, Rare Book & Manuscript, Butler Library, 6th Flr E, 535 W 114th St, New York, NY, 10027. Tel: 212-854-2231, 212-854-5590. Fax: 212-854-1365. p. 1675

Craig, Thomas B, Dir of Libr Serv, University of Texas Health Science Center at Tyler, 11937 US Hwy 271, Tyler, TX, 75708. Tel: 903-877-2865. Fax: 903-877-5412. p. 2394

Craig, Tina, Circ, Ch, Hudson Public Library, Three Washington St at The Rotary, Hudson, MA, 01749-2499. Tel: 978-568-9644. Fax: 978-568-9646. p. 1096

Craigle, Mary, Bur Chief, Montana Department of Commerce, 301 S Park, Helena, MT, 59620. Tel: 406-841-2740. Fax: 406-841-2731. p. 1382

Craigle, Valeri, Access Technologies Librn, University of Utah, S J Quinney Law Library, 332 S 1400 East, Salt Lake City, UT, 84112-0731. Tel: 801-585-5475. Fax: 801-585-3033. p. 2415

Craiglow, Hilary A, Dir, Vanderbilt University, Walker Management Library, Owen Graduate School of Management, 401 21st Ave S, Nashville, TN, 37203. Tel: 615-323-4182. Fax: 615-343-0061. p. 2261

Craigwell, Jean, Cat, Organization of American States, 19th & Constitution Ave NW, Washington, DC, 20006-4499. Tel: 202-458-6172. Fax: 202-458-3914. p. 412

Crain, Colleen, Exec Dir, Community Library Association, 415 Spruce Ave N, Ketchum, ID, 83340. Tel: 208-726-3493. p. 577

Crain, Ellen, Ref Librn, Jackson County Library, 213 Walnut St, Newport, AR, 72112-3325. Tel: 870-523-2952. Fax: 870-523-5218. p. 111

Crain, Joyce, Librn, Henderson County Public Library, Etowah Branch, 101 Brickyard Rd, Etowah, NC, 28729. Tel: 828-891-6577. Fax: 828-890-7798. p. 1801

Crain, Laura, Assoc Dir, Coll Serv, Saint Michael's College, One Winooski Park, Box L, Colchester, VT, 05439-2525. Tel: 802-654-2388. Fax: 802-654-2630. p. 2422

Crain, Martha, Bibliog Instr, ILL, Gordon College, 255 Grapevine Rd, Wenham, MA, 01984-1899. Tel: 978-867-4339. Fax: 978-867-4660. p. 1136

Crain, Mary, Media Prod, New Jersey State Library, Talking Book & Braille Center, 2300 Stuyvesant Ave, Trenton, NJ, 08618. Tel: 609-406-7179, Ext 809. Fax: 609-406-7181. p. 1536

Craine, Susan, Circ Coordr, Milanof-Schock Library, 1184 Anderson Ferry Rd, Mount Joy, PA, 17552. Tel: 717-653-1510. Fax: 717-653-6590. p. 2093

Cramblet, Laura, Libr Dir, Bellaire Public Library, 330 32nd St, Bellaire, OH, 43906. Tel: 740-676-9421. Fax: 740-676-7940. p. 1858

Cramer, Carol, Youth Serv Coordr, Zion-Benton Public Library District, 2400 Gabriel Ave, Zion, IL, 60099. Tel: 847-872-4680, Ext 116. Fax: 847-872-4942. p. 722

Cramer, Jane, Govt Doc, Per, Brooklyn College Library, 2900 Bedford Ave, Brooklyn, NY, 11210-2889. Tel: 718-951-5332. Fax: 718-951-4540. p. 1589

Cramer, Janice, Ref, Southern Nazarene University, 4115 N College, Bethany, OK, 73008. Tel: 405-491-6350. Fax: 405-491-6355. p. 1958

Cramer, Steve, Bus Librn, University of North Carolina at Greensboro, 320 Spring Garden St, Greensboro, NC, 27402. Tel: 336-256-0346. Fax: 336-334-5399. p. 1798

Cramer, Susan, Dr, Assoc Prof, University of Wisconsin Oshkosh, 800 Algoma Blvd, Oshkosh, WI, 54901. Tel: 920-424-0338. Fax: 920-424-0858. p. 2977

Cramer, William, Govt Doc, Spec Coll Librn, Oakland University Library, 2200 N Squirrel Rd, Rochester, MI, 48309-4402. Tel: 248-370-2480. Fax: 248-370-2474. p. 1221

Cramner, Cathy, Br Librn, Community District Library, Corunna/Caledonia Township Branch, 210 E Corunna Ave, Corunna, MI, 48817. Tel: 989-743-4800. Fax: 989-743-5502. p. 1166

Cramp, Isabelle, Libr Mgr, Morinville Public Library, 10119 100th Ave, Morinville, AB, T8R 1P8, CANADA. Tel: 780-939-3292. Fax: 780-939-2757. p. 2711

Crandall, Diane, Dir, Myers Memorial Library, 26 Ivory St, Frewsburg, NY, 14738-9517. Tel: 716-569-5515. Fax: 716-569-2605. p. 1625

Crandall, Ginette, Asst Librn, Wainwright Public Library, 921 Third Ave, Wainwright, AB, T9W 1C5, CANADA. Tel: 780-842-2673. Fax: 780-842-2340. p. 2721

Crandall, Linda Evelyn, Ch, John Mosser Public Library District, 106 W Meek St, Abingdon, IL, 61410-1451. Tel: 309-462-3129. Fax: 309-462-3129. p. 587

Crandall, Michael, Sr Lecturer, University of Washington, Mary Gates Hall, Ste 370, Campus Box 352840, Seattle, WA, 98195-2840. Tel: 206-685-9937. Fax: 206-616-3152. p. 2976

Crandall, Paul, Head Librn, Capital Area District Libraries, Stockbridge Library, 200 Wood St, Stockbridge, MI, 49285. Tel: 517-851-7810. Fax: 517-851-8612. p. 1200

Crandall, Steve, Dir, Alfred University, Herrick Memorial Library, One Saxon Dr, Alfred, NY, 14802. Tel: 607-871-2987. Fax: 607-871-2299. p. 1572

Crandell, Adam, Librn, Haverford College, Music, Union Bldg, 370 W Lancaster Ave, Haverford, PA, 19041. Tel: 610-896-1169. Fax: 610-896-1102. p. 2067

Crandell, Adam, Music Librn, Haverford College, 370 Lancaster Ave, Haverford, PA, 19041-1392. Tel: 610-896-1169. Fax: 610-896-1102. p. 2067

Crane, Anne, Cat, Syst Adminr, Friends University, 2100 W University St, Wichita, KS, 67213-3397. Tel: 316-295-5610. Fax: 316-295-5080. p. 900

Crane, Conrad C, Dr, Dir, United States Army Heritage & Education Center, 950 Soldiers Dr, Carlisle, PA, 17013-5021. Tel: 717-245-4483. Fax: 717-245-3067. p. 2042

Crane, Doug, Br Mgr, Palm Beach County Library System, Wellington Branch, 1951 Royal Fern Dr, Wellington, FL, 33414. Tel: 561-790-6070. Fax: 561-790-6078. p. 503

Crane, Elaine, Ch, Wilbraham Public Library, 25 Crane Park Dr, Wilbraham, MA, 01095-1799. Tel: 413-596-6141. Fax: 413-596-5090. p. 1140

Crane, Janet, Asst Librn, Access Serv, University of New Orleans, 2000 Lakeshore Dr, New Orleans, LA, 70148. Tel: 504-280-6556. Fax: 504-280-7277. p. 964

Crane, Jill, Cat, Saint Mary's University, Louis J Blume Library, One Camino Santa Maria, San Antonio, TX, 78228-8608. Tel: 210-436-3441. Fax: 210-436-3782. p. 2381

Crane, John G, Dep Librn, Dartmouth College Library, 6025 Baker Berry Library, Rm 115, Hanover, NH, 03755-3525. Tel: 603-646-2236. Fax: 603-646-3702. p. 1450

Crane, Joyce, Dir, Goodland & Grant Township Public Library, 111 S Newton St, Goodland, IN, 47948. Tel: 219-297-4431. Fax: 219-297-4431. p. 745

Crane, Michele, Asst Dir, Porter Memorial Library, 87 Main St, Blandford, MA, 01008-9518. Tel: 413-848-2853. Fax: 413-848-2853. p. 1054

Crane, Pamela, Librn, Onondaga County Public Library, Beauchamp, 2111 S Salina St, Syracuse, NY, 13205. Tel: 315-435-3395. Fax: 315-435-2729. p. 1752

Crane, Patty, Ref Librn, Joplin Public Library, 300 S Main, Joplin, MO, 64801. Tel: 417-623-7953. Fax: 417-625-4728. p. 1335

Crane, Peter, Dir, Mount Washington Observatory, 2779 Main St, North Conway, NH, 03860. Tel: 603-356-2137. Fax: 603-356-0307. p. 1460

Crane, Priscilla, Ref Serv, Thayer Public Library, 798 Washington St, Braintree, MA, 02184. Tel: 781-848-0405, Ext 4407. Fax: 781-356-5447. p. 1069

Crane, Rachel, Info & Res Serv, Wichita State University Libraries, 1845 Fairmount, Wichita, KS, 67260-0068. Tel: 316-978-5078. Tel: 316-978-3048. p. 902

Crane, Rachel, Librn, Wichita State University Libraries, Music Library, C 116 DFAC, Wichita, KS, 67260-0053. Tel: 316-978-3029. Fax: 316-978-3584. p. 902

Crane, Ruth, Tech Serv Mgr, Emma S Clark Memorial Library, 120 Main St, Setauket, NY, 11733-2868. Tel: 631-941-4080. Fax: 631-941-4541. p. 1742

Crane, Stephanie, Librn, Central Georgia Technical College Library, Milledgeville Campus, 54 Hwy 22 W, Milledgeville, GA, 31061. Tel: 478-445-2333. Fax: 478-445-2346. p. 540

Cranford, Amy, AV Coll, Martinsburg-Berkeley County Public Library, 101 W King St, Martinsburg, WV, 25401. Tel: 304-267-8933. Fax: 304-267-9720. p. 2565

Cranmer, Donna, Tech Serv Librn, Siouxland Libraries, 200 N Dakota Ave, Sioux Falls, SD, 57104. Tel: 605-367-8712. Fax: 605-367-4312. p. 2218

Cranshaw, Dianne, Librn, County of Prince Edward Libraries, 211 County Rd 29, Consecon, ON, K0K 1T0, CANADA. Tel: 613-392-1106. Fax: 613-392-4461. p. 2800

Cranshaw, Dianne, ILL, County of Prince Edward Libraries, 208 Main St, Picton, ON, K0K 2T0, CANADA. Tel: 613-476-5962. Fax: 613-476-3325. p. 2836

Cranshaw, Dianne, Librn, County of Prince Edward Libraries, 261 Main St, Wellington, ON, K0K 3L0, CANADA. Tel: 613-399-2023. p. 2870

Cranshaw, Moira, YA Librn, Sunderland Public Library, 20 School St, Sunderland, MA, 01375. Tel: 413-665-2642. Fax: 413-665-1435. p. 1130

Cranston, Laurie, Syst Coordr, Woodbury Public Library, 33 Delaware St, Woodbury, NJ, 08096. Tel: 856-845-2611. p. 1545

Cranston, Linda A, Tech Serv, United States Department of Justice, MCB No 4, Quantico, VA, 22135. Tel: 703-632-3203. Fax: 703-632-3214. p. 2487

Cranston, Sally, Dir, William B Ogden Free Library, 42 Gardiner Pl, Walton, NY, 13856. Tel: 607-865-5929. Fax: 607-865-6821. p. 1762

Cranstoun, Sarah, Dir, Summersville Public Library, 6201 Webster Rd, Summersville, WV, 26651. Tel: 304-872-0844. Fax: 304-872-0845. p. 2572

Crapo, Eric, Dir, Chester College of New England, 40 Chester St, Chester, NH, 03036-4301. Tel: 603-887-7454. Fax: 603-887-1777. p. 1441

Crary, Kitty, Sr Librn, Adult & YA Serv, Orange Public Library & History Center, 407 E Chapman Ave, Orange, CA, 92866-1509. Tel: 714-288-2416. Fax: 714-771-6126. p. 201

Crary, Terese, Br Operations Supvr, Mesa Public Library, Red Mountain Branch, 635 N Power Rd, Mesa, AZ, 85205. Tel: 480-644-3862. Fax: 480-644-3559. p. 69

Crash, Sally, Dir, Thomas Baker Slick Memorial Library, 6220 Culebra Rd, MS 84, San Antonio, TX, 78238-5166. Tel: 210-522-2125. Fax: 210-522-5479. p. 2382

Crater, Joann, Asst Librn, Hudson Public Library, 205 S Market, Hudson, MI, 49247. Tel: 517-448-3801. Fax: 517-448-5095. p. 1192

Crautmann, Marian, Dir, Ellendale Public Library, 75 First St S, Ellendale, ND, 58436. Tel: 701-349-3852. p. 1840

Cravedi, Eileen, Access Serv Librn, College of the Holy Cross, One College St, Worcester, MA, 01610. Tel: 508-793-2672. Fax: 508-793-2372. p. 1143

Craven, Michael, Web Content Coordr, Maryland State Law Library, Courts of Appeal Bldg, 361 Rowe Blvd, Annapolis, MD, 21401-1697. Tel: 410-260-1430. Fax: 410-260-1572, 410-974-2063. p. 1010

Crawfis, Justin, Head, Circ, Bluffton Public Library, 145 S Main St, Bluffton, OH, 45817. Tel: 419-358-5016. Fax: 419-358-9653. p. 1860

Crawford, Anne, Ch, Saint Johns County Public Library System, Ponte Vedra Beach Branch, 101 Library Blvd, Ponte Vedra Beach, FL, 32082. Tel: 904-827-6952. Fax: 904-827-6955. p. 487

Crawford, Betsy, Area Res Mgr, E Region, Indianapolis-Marion County Public Library, 2450 N Meridian St, Indianapolis, IN, 46208. Tel: 317-275-4465. Fax: 317-269-5300. p. 753

Crawford, Betsy, Br Mgr, Indianapolis-Marion County Public Library, Lawrence, 7898 N Hague Rd, Indianapolis, IN, 46256-1754. Tel: 317-275-4460. p. 754

Crawford, Canon, Electronic Res, Marylhurst University, 17600 Pacific Hwy (Hwy 43), Marylhurst, OR, 97036-7036. Tel: 503-699-6261, Ext 3379. Fax: 503-636-1957. p. 2004

Crawford, Cathy, Dir, Columbus Junction Public Library, 232 Second St, Columbus Junction, IA, 52738-1028. Tel: 319-728-7972. Fax: 319-728-2303. p. 804

Crawford, Celeste, Librn, Niagara County Genealogical Society Library, 215 Niagara St, Lockport, NY, 14094-2605. Tel: 716-433-1033. p. 1653

Crawford, Charlie, Dean, Tacoma Community College Library, 6501 S 19th St, Tacoma, WA, 98466-6100. Tel: 253-566-6005. Fax: 253-566-5398. p. 2540

Crawford, Claire, Dir, Geneseo Public Library District, 805 North Chicago St, Geneseo, IL, 61254. Tel: 309-944-6452. Fax: 309-944-6721. p. 648

Crawford, Claretta, Libr Dir, United States Army, Bruce C Clarke Library Academic Services Division, Bldg 3202, 597 Manscen Loop, Ste 200, Fort Leonard Wood, MO, 65473-8928. Tel: 573-563-4109. Fax: 573-563-4118. p. 1328

Crawford, David, Archivist, Creighton University, 2500 California Plaza, Omaha, NE, 68178-0209. Tel: 402-280-2746. Fax: 402-280-2435. p. 1412

Crawford, Donna, Mgr, Rapides Parish Library, Hineston Branch, 1810 Hwy 121, Hineston, LA, 71438. Tel: 318-793-8461. Fax: 318-793-0691. p. 940

Crawford, Eileen, Assoc Dir, Coll Develop Officer, Vanderbilt University, Divinity Library, 419 21st Ave S, Nashville, TN, 37203-2427. Tel: 615-322-2865. Fax: 615-343-8279. p. 2260

Crawford, Elizabeth, Libr Coordr, New Brunswick Community College, 1234 Mountain Rd, Moncton, NB, E1C 8H9, CANADA. Tel: 506-856-2226. Fax: 506-856-3180. p. 2766

Crawford, Ellen, Tech Serv, West Bridgewater Public Library, 80 Howard St, West Bridgewater, MA, 02379-1710. Tel: 508-894-1255. Fax: 508-894-1258. p. 1137

Crawford, Esther, Head, Kelley Ctr for Govt Pub & Micro, Rice University, 6100 Main, MS-44, Houston, TX, 77005. Tel: 713-348-6212. Fax: 713-348-5258. p. 2341

Crawford, Gregory A, Dr, Dir, Pennsylvania State University-Harrisburg Library, 351 Olmsted Dr, Middletown, PA, 17057-4850. Tel: 717-948-6070. Fax: 717-948-6757. p. 2089

Crawford, Hilda, Circ, Coalinga-Huron USD Library District, 305 N Fourth St, Coalinga, CA, 93210. Tel: 559-935-1676. Fax: 559-935-1058. p. 135

Crawford, Jane, Librn, Jones Day, 1420 Peachtree St NE, Atlanta, GA, 30309. Tel: 404-581-8118. Fax: 404-581-8330. p. 516

Crawford, Jane, Managing Librn I, Sno-Isle Libraries, Mukilteo Community Library, 4675 Harbour Pointe Blvd, Mukilteo, WA, 98275. Tel: 425-493-8202. Fax: 425-493-1601. p. 2542

Crawford, Janice, Tech Serv Librn, Lakeland Public Library, 100 Lake Morton Dr, Lakeland, FL, 33801-5375. Tel: 863-834-4280. Fax: 863-834-4293. p. 459

Crawford, John, Adult Serv, Woodford County Library, 115 N Main St, Versailles, KY, 40383-1289. Tel: 859-873-5191. Fax: 859-873-1542. p. 936

Crawford, John, Asst Dir, Cataloger, United States Army Dugway Proving Ground, 5124 Kister Ave, IMWE-DUG-MWL MS1, Dugway, UT, 84022-1097. Tel: 435-831-2178. Fax: 435-831-3543. p. 2404

Crawford, Karyl, Circ Mgr, Bluffton University, One University Dr, Bluffton, OH, 45817-2104. Tel: 419-358-3271. Fax: 419-358-3384. p. 1860

Crawford, Kathy, Ch, Larue County Public Library, 201 S Lincoln Blvd, Hodgenville, KY, 42748. Tel: 270-358-3851. Fax: 270-358-8647. p. 918

Crawford, Kayarcenes, Libr Asst I, Montgomery City-County Public Library System, Juliette Hampton Morgan Memorial Library (Main Library), 245 High St, Montgomery, AL, 36104. Tel: 334-240-4999. Fax: 334-240-4980. p. 30

Crawford, Kimberly, Tech Serv, Iredell County Public Library, 201 N Tradd St, Statesville, NC, 28677. Tel: 704-878-3147. Fax: 704-878-5449. p. 1825

Crawford, Lee, Tech Serv, Canon City Public Library, 516 Macon Ave, Canon City, CO, 81212-3380. Tel: 719-269-9020. Fax: 719-269-9031. p. 293

Crawford, Lynn, ILL Tech, Indiana Wesleyan University, 4201 S Washington St, Marion, IN, 46953. Tel: 765-677-2184. Fax: 765-677-2676. p. 762

Crawford, Marjorie E, Head, Tech Serv, Rutgers University Library for the Center for Law & Justice, 123 Washington St, Newark, NJ, 07102-3094. Tel: 973-353-3144. Fax: 973-353-1356. p. 1513

Crawford, Mary, Dir, New Lisbon Memorial Library, 115 W Park St, New Lisbon, WI, 53950-1250. Tel: 608-562-3213. Fax: 608-562-3213. p. 2625

Crawford, Myrna, Br Head, Regina Public Library, George Bothwell Branch, 2787 Gordon Rd, Regina, SK, S4S 6H7, CANADA. Tel: 306-777-6091. Fax: 306-949-7267. p. 2923

Crawford, Noreen, Circ Librn, Ashland Town Library, 42 Main St, Ashland, NH, 03217. Tel: 603-968-7928. Fax: 603-968-7928. p. 1438

Crawford, Patricia, Access Serv Librn, Bryant University, 1150 Douglas Pike, Smithfield, RI, 02917-1284. Tel: 401-232-6125. Fax: 401-232-6126. p. 2176

Crawford, Rebecca, Youth Serv, Somerset County Library System, One Vogt Dr, Bridgewater, NJ, 08807-2136. p. 1475

Crawford, Rick, Librn IV, San Diego Public Library, 820 E St, San Diego, CA, 92101-6478. Tel: 619-236-5852. Fax: 619-238-6639. p. 235

Crawford, Sandra, Librn, Floyd County Library, 111 S Wall St, Floydada, TX, 79235. Tel: 806-983-4922. Fax: 806-983-4922. p. 2319

Crawford, Scott, Br Librn, Chambers County Library System, Juanita Hargraves Memorial Branch, 924 Hwy 124, Winnie, TX, 77665. Tel: 409-296-8245. Fax: 409-296-8243. p. 2275

Crawford, Shirley, Tech Coordr, Lake County Public Library, 1115 Harrison Ave, Leadville, CO, 80461-3398. Tel: 719-486-0569. Fax: 719-486-3544. p. 316

Crawford, Sonia, Br Mgr, Gadsden County Public Library, Chattahoochee Public Library, 300 Maple St, Chattahoochee, FL, 32324. Tel: 850-663-2707. Fax: 850-663-4598. p. 485

Crawford, Terri, Dep Dir, Lee County Library System, 2345 Union St, Fort Myers, FL, 33901-3917. Tel: 239-533-4832. Fax: 239-485-1100. p. 445

Crawford, Terri, Dir, Watonga Public Library, 301 N Prouty, Watonga, OK, 73772. Tel: 580-623-7748. Fax: 580-623-7747. p. 1985

Crawford, Theresa Ann, Libr Dir, Bremond Public Library & Visitors Center, 115 S Main St, Bremond, TX, 76629. Tel: 254-746-7752. Fax: 254-746-7065. p. 2291

Crawford, Timothy, Librn, California Department of Corrections Library System, Correctional Training Facility, Hwy 101 N, Soledad, CA, 93960. Tel: 831-678-3951. Fax: 831-678-5910. p. 221

Crawford, William, Librn, Grand Lodge of Iowa, AF & AM, 813 First Ave SE, Cedar Rapids, IA, 52406. Tel: 319-365-1438. Fax: 319-365-1439. p. 800

Crawford, William, Media Spec, Cape Fear Community College, 415 N Second St, Wilmington, NC, 28401-3993. Tel: 910-362-7038. Fax: 910-362-7005. p. 1830

Crawford-Oppenheimer, Christine, Info Serv, Culinary Institute of America, 1946 Campus Dr, Hyde Park, NY, 12538-1499. Tel: 845-451-1747. Fax: 845-451-1092. p. 1639

Crawley, Gwen, In Charge, Sexuality Education Resource Centre, 200-226 Osborne St N, Winnipeg, MB, R3C 1V4, CANADA. Tel: 204-982-7800. Fax: 204-982-7819. p. 2757

Crawley, Martha, Cat, Cumberland County Public Library & Information Center, 300 Maiden Lane, Fayetteville, NC, 28301-5000. Tel: 910-483-7727. Fax: 910-486-5372. p. 1792

Crawley, Mildred, Circ, Decatur County Library, Court Sq, 20 W Market St, Decaturville, TN, 38329. Tel: 731-852-3325. Fax: 731-852-2351. p. 2232

Crawley, Sandra, Br Coordr, Birmingham Public Library, 2100 Park Pl, Birmingham, AL, 35203. Tel: 205-226-4005. Fax: 205-226-3750. p. 7

Crawley, Sandra, Librn, Birmingham Public Library, Avondale, 509 40th St S, Birmingham, AL, 35222. Tel: 205-226-4005. Fax: 205-595-5824. p. 7

Crawley-Low, Jill, Asst Dean, University of Saskatchewan Libraries, Murray Library, Three Campus Dr, Saskatoon, SK, S7N 5A4, CANADA. Tel: 306-966-7425. Fax: 306-966-6040. p. 2927

Crawshaw, Mamie, Asst Librn, McCracken Public Library, 303 Main St, McCracken, KS, 67556. Tel: 785-394-2444. Fax: 785-394-2444. p. 882

Crawshaw, Ruth, Dir, McCracken Public Library, 303 Main St, McCracken, KS, 67556. Tel: 785-394-2444. Fax: 785-394-2444. p. 882

Cray, Katherine, Dir, UBS Warburg Library, 299 Park Ave, New York, NY, 10171-0099. Tel: 212-821-3000. p. 1701

Crayne, Tiffany, Tech Serv Supvr, Greenwood County Library, 600 S Main St, Greenwood, SC, 29646. Tel: 864-941-4650. Fax: 864-941-4651. p. 2197

Creaden, Joyce, Head, Tech Serv, Westwood Free Public Library, 49 Park Ave, Westwood, NJ, 07675. Tel: 201-664-0583. Fax: 201-664-6088. p. 1543

Creager, Carol, Dir, Mary Baldwin College, 109 E Frederick St, Staunton, VA, 24401. Tel: 540-887-7310. Fax: 540-887-7137. p. 2496

Creager, Shirley, Ch, McIntosh Memorial Library, 118 E Jefferson St, Viroqua, WI, 54665. Tel: 608-637-7151, Ext 4. Fax: 608-637-8608. p. 2643

Creamer, Angela, Dir, Estancia Public Library, Tenth & Highland, Estancia, NM, 87016. Tel: 505-384-9655. Fax: 505-384-9655. p. 1555

Creamer, Debbie, Dr, Dir, Iliff School of Theology, 2201 S University Blvd, Denver, CO, 80210. Tel: 303-765-3173. Fax: 303-777-0164. p. 302

Creamer, John, Info & Referral, Penn Yan Public Library, 214 Main St, Penn Yan, NY, 14527. Tel: 315-536-6114. Fax: 315-536-0131. p. 1716

Creamer, Tim, Librn, Thaddeus Stevens College of Technology, 750 E King St, Lancaster, PA, 17602-3198. Tel: 717-391-3503. Fax: 717-396-7186. p. 2078

Crean, Mary, Chief Develop Officer, Hartford Public Library, 500 Main St, Hartford, CT, 06103-3075. Tel: 860-695-6360. Fax: 860-722-6900. p. 345

Creazzo, Jeannine, Mgr, Saint Peter's University Hospital Library, 254 Easton Ave, New Brunswick, NJ, 08903. Tel: 732-745-8545. Fax: 732-937-6091. p. 1509

Crebaum, Linda, Acq Librn, Arkansas State University, 322 University Loop West Circle, State University, AR, 72401. Tel: 870-972-3077. Fax: 870-972-3199. p. 115

Credicott, Judy, Dir, Breckenridge Library, 209 N Breckenridge Ave, Breckenridge, TX, 76424. Tel: 254-559-5505. Fax: 254-559-5505. p. 2291

Credle, Ellen, Interim Co-Dir, Youth Serv, West Linn Public Library, 1595 Burns St, West Linn, OR, 97068-3231. Tel: 503-656-7853, Ext 3031. Fax: 503-656-2746. p. 2022

Creech, John, Syst Coordr, Central Washington University, 400 E University Way, Ellensburg, WA, 98926-7548. Tel: 509-963-1901. Fax: 509-963-3684. p. 2514

Creech, Robin, Br Mgr, Columbus County Public Library, East Columbus Library, 103 Church Rd, Riegelwood, NC, 28456. Tel: 910-655-4157. Fax: 910-655-9414. p. 1829

Creed, Carissa, Circ, San Francisco Conservatory of Music, 1201 Ortega St, San Francisco, CA, 94122. Tel: 415-564-8086, 415-759-3413. Fax: 415-759-3499. p. 245

Creed-Dikeogu, Gloria, Dir, Libr Serv, Ottawa University, 1001 S Cedar, Ottawa, KS, 66067-3399. Tel: 785-242-5200, Ext 5445. Fax: 785-229-1012. p. 887

Creedon, Catherine, Dir, John Jermain Memorial Library, 201 Main St, Sag Harbor, NY, 11963. Tel: 631-725-0049, Ext 23. Fax: 631-725-0597. p. 1737

Creef, Tama, Archivist, North Carolina Office of Archives & History, One Festival Park Blvd, Manteo, NC, 27954. Tel: 252-473-2655. Fax: 252-473-1483. p. 1808

Creek, Ashley, Access Serv, ILL, University of Saint Mary, 4100 S Fourth St Trafficway, Leavenworth, KS, 66048-5082. Tel: 913-758-6306. Fax: 913-758-6200. p. 879

Creek, David, Asst Dir, Commun Libr Serv, Rochester Public Library, 115 South Ave, Rochester, NY, 14604-1896. Tel: 585-428-8345. Fax: 585-428-8353. p. 1732

Creek, Joanne, Asst Librn, Piper City Public Library District, 39 W Main, Piper City, IL, 60959. Tel: 815-686-9234. Fax: 815-686-9234. p. 691

Creel, Sandra, Asst Librn, Marengo County Public Library, 507 N Main St, Linden, AL, 36748. Tel: 334-295-2246. Fax: 334-295-2265. p. 23

Creel-Erb, Angie, Dir, Libr Serv, Arizona Western College & NAU Yuma Branch Campus, 2020 S Ave 8E, Yuma, AZ, 85366. Tel: 928-344-7777. Fax: 928-344-7751. p. 90

Creelman, Kathryn, Pub Serv Coordr, Orangeville Public Library, One Mill St, Orangeville, ON, L9W 2M2, CANADA. Tel: 519-941-0610, Ext 5232. Fax: 519-941-4698. p. 2826

Creenan, Karen E, Exec Dir, Finger Lakes Library System, 119 E Green St, Ithaca, NY, 14850. Tel: 607-273-4074. Fax: 607-273-3618. p. 1642

Creevy, Jennifer, Acq/Ser Librn, Law Library of Louisiana, Louisiana Supreme Court, 2nd Flr, 400 Royal St, New Orleans, LA, 70130-2104. Tel: 504-310-2400. Fax: 504-310-2419. p. 960

Cregar, Jodie, Cataloger, Franklin County Public Library District, Laurel Public Library, 200 N Clay St, Laurel, IN, 47024. Tel: 765-698-2582. Fax: 765-698-2626. p. 730

Creger, Amber, Kid's World Mgr, Arlington Heights Memorial Library, 500 N Dunton Ave, Arlington Heights, IL, 60004-5966. Tel: 847-506-2619. Fax: 847-506-2650. p. 589

Crego, Linda, Br Coordr, Flagler County Public Library, 2500 Palm Coast Pkwy NW, Palm Coast, FL, 32137. Tel: 386-446-6763. Fax: 386-446-6773. p. 479

Crego, Linda, Br Mgr, Flagler County Public Library, Bunnell Branch, 103 E Moody Blvd, Bunnell, FL, 32110. Tel: 386-437-7390. Fax: 386-437-7390. p. 480

Crehore, Mary, Dir, Avon Lake Public Library, 32649 Electric Blvd, Avon Lake, OH, 44012-1669. Tel: 440-933-3851. Fax: 440-933-5659. p. 1856

Creider, Laurence, Dr, Head, Archives & Spec Coll, New Mexico State University Library, 2911 McFie Circle, Las Cruces, NM, 88003. Tel: 575-646-4756. Fax: 575-646-6940. p. 1558

Creighton, Sean, Exec Dir, Southwestern Ohio Council for Higher Education, Miami Valley Research Park, 3155 Research Blvd, Ste 204, Dayton, OH, 45420-4015. Tel: 937-258-8890, Ext 11. Fax: 937-258-8899. p. 2952

Creitz, Abigail, Tech Serv & Syst Librn, Vincennes University, Shake Learning Resources Center, 1002 N First St, Vincennes, IN, 47591. Tel: 812-888-5807. Fax: 812-888-5471. p. 784

Crelia, Barbara, Asst Librn, Wewoka Public Library, 118 W Fifth, Wewoka, OK, 74884. Tel: 405-257-3225. Fax: 405-257-5049. p. 1986

Crelinsten, Michael, Exec Dir, Bibliotheque Publique Juive, One carré Cummings, 5151 ch de la Cote Ste Catherine, Montreal, QC, H3W 1M6, CANADA. Tel: 514-345-2627, Ext 3222. Fax: 514-342-6477. p. 2888

Crema, Leonora, Assoc Univ Librn, Client Serv & Prog, University of British Columbia Library, 1961 East Mall, Vancouver, BC, V6T 1Z1, CANADA. Tel: 604-282-8473. p. 2742

Cremer, Judith, Dir, Pottawatomie Wabaunsee Regional Library, 306 N Fifth St, Saint Marys, KS, 66536-1404. Tel: 785-437-2778. Fax: 785-437-2778. p. 892

Crenner, Christopher, Dr, Dir, Kansas University Medical Center, 1020-1030 Robinson Bldg, 3901 Rainbow Blvd, Kansas City, KS, 66160-7311. Tel: 913-588-7040. Fax: 913-588-7060. p. 875

Crenshaw, Carol, Librn, Centralia Regional Library District, Irvington Branch, 208 S Fifth St, Irvington, IL, 62848-0130. Tel: 618-249-8143. Fax: 618-249-8143. p. 602

Crenshaw, Clayton, Web Librn, University of North Texas Health Science Center at Fort Worth, 3500 Camp Bowie Blvd, Fort Worth, TX, 76107-2699. Tel: 817-735-2070. Fax: 817-763-0325. p. 2324

Crenshaw, Elizabeth, Ref Librn, Long Island University, One University Plaza, Brooklyn, NY, 11201-9926. Tel: 718-488-1081. Fax: 718-780-4057. p. 1593

Crenshaw, Gwendolyn, Br Mgr, Denver Public Library, Bear Valley, 5171 W Dartmouth, Denver, CO, 80236-2006. Tel: 303-935-0616. Fax: 303-934-9403. p. 301

Crenshaw, Gwendolyn, Br Mgr, Denver Public Library, Ross-Broadway, 33 E Bayaud Ave, Denver, CO, 80209-1503. Tel: 303-777-4845. Fax: 303-733-8601. p. 301

Crenshaw, Gwendolyn, Br Mgr, Denver Public Library, Ross-Cherry Creek, 305 Milwaukee St, Denver, CO, 80206-4329. Tel: 303-331-4016. Fax: 303-331-3860. p. 301

Crenshaw, Gwendolyn, Br Mgr, Denver Public Library, Ross-University Hills, 4310 E Amherst Ave, Denver, CO, 80222-6703. Tel: 303-757-2714. Fax: 303-692-5606. p. 301

Crenshaw, Gwendolyn, Br Mgr, Denver Public Library, Schlessman, 100 Poplar St, Denver, CO, 80220-4522. Tel: 720-865-0000. Fax: 720-865-0047. p. 301

Crenshaw, Gwendolyn, Br Mgr, Denver Public Library, Smiley, 4501 W 46th Ave, Denver, CO, 80212-2582. Tel: 303-477-3622. Fax: 303-455-5613. p. 301

Crenshaw, Jan C, Dir, San Jacinto College North, 5800 Uvalde Rd, Houston, TX, 77049-4599. Tel: 281-459-7116. Fax: 281-459-7166. p. 2342

Crenshaw, Jennifer, Pub Serv Mgr, Pickens County Library System, 304 Biltmore Rd, Easley, SC, 29640. Tel: 864-850-7077. Fax: 864-850-7088. p. 2193

Crenshaw, Marie, Head Ref Librn, Clarence Dillon Public Library, 2336 Lamington Rd, Bedminster, NJ, 07921. Tel: 908-234-2325. Fax: 908-781-9402. p. 1471

Crenshaw, Melissa, Br Mgr, Greenwood County Library, Ware Shoals Community Library, 54 S Greenwood Ave, Ware Shoals, SC, 29692. Tel: 864-456-2813. Fax: 864-456-2813. p. 2197

Crenshaw, Pam, Archives Librn, Vanguard University of Southern California, 55 Fair Dr, Costa Mesa, CA, 92626. Tel: 714-556-3610, Ext 2400. Fax: 714-966-5478. p. 137

Crenshaw, Shirley, Librn, Pine Forest Regional Library, Conner-Graham Memorial, 101 Willow St, Seminary, MS, 39479. Tel: 601-722-9041. Fax: 601-722-9041. p. 1314

Crepeau, Elaine, Tech Serv, Belvedere-Tiburon Library, 1501 Tiburon Blvd, Tiburon, CA, 94920. Tel: 415-789-2665. Fax: 415-789-2650. p. 275

Crescimanno, Terry, Adult Serv, Cromwell Belden Public Library, 39 West St, Cromwell, CT, 06416. Tel: 860-632-3460. Fax: 860-632-3484. p. 334

Crespin, Cynthia, Librn, Santo Domingo Public Library, PO Box 160, Santo Domingo Pueblo, NM, 87052-0160. Tel: 505-465-2214, Ext 226. Fax: 505-465-2688. p. 1565

Crespo, Edna, Librn, Bayview Correctional Facility Library, 550 W 20th St, New York, NY, 10011. Tel: 212-255-7590. Fax: 212-255-7590, Ext 2099. p. 1670

Crespo, Hilda, VPres, Aspira Association Library, 1444 I St NW 8th Flr, Ste 800, Washington, DC, 20005. Tel: 202-835-3600. Fax: 202-835-3613. p. 393

Crespo, Javier, Assoc Dir, University of Massachusetts Medical School, 55 Lake Ave N, Worcester, MA, 01655-2397. Tel: 508-856-2223. Fax: 508-856-5039. p. 1145

Crespo, Javier, Assoc Dir, National Network of Libraries of Medicine New England Region, University of Massachusetts Medical School, 222 Maple Ave, Shrewsbury, MA, 01545-2732. Tel: 508-856-5979. Fax: 508-856-5977. p. 2945

Cress, Anne, Dep Exec Dir, Jefferson County Public Library, 10200 W 20th Ave, Lakewood, CO, 80215. Tel: 303-275-6170. Fax: 303-275-2202. p. 315

Cress, Betty, Asst Dir, Poplar Creek Public Library District, 1405 S Park Ave, Streamwood, IL, 60107-2997. Tel: 630-837-6800. Fax: 630-837-6823. p. 708

Cress, Jacqueline, Librn, Hillsborough Community College, Dale Mabry Campus Library, 4001 Tampa Bay Blvd, Tampa, FL, 33614-7820. Tel: 813-253-7381. Fax: 813-253-7400. p. 496

Cressler, Bruce, Dir, Helvetia Library, Main St, Helvetia, WV, 26224. Tel: 304-924-5063. Fax: 304-924-5063. p. 2560

Cressler, Walter, Dr, Sci, West Chester University, 25 W Rosedale Ave, West Chester, PA, 19383. Tel: 610-436-1072. p. 2153

Cressman, Denise, Ch, Delphos Public Library, 309 W Second St, Delphos, OH, 45833-1695. Tel: 419-695-4015. Fax: 419-695-4025. p. 1896

Cressman, Laurie, Librn, Muncy Public Library, 108 S Main St, Muncy, PA, 17756-0119. Tel: 570-546-5014. Fax: 570-546-5014. p. 2093

Cresswell, Frances, Actg Dir, Dorchester County Public Library, 303 Gay St, Cambridge, MD, 21613. Tel: 410-228-7331. Fax: 410-228-6313. p. 1022

Cresswell, Samantha, Head, Circ, Elmhurst Public Library, 125 S Prospect, Elmhurst, IL, 60126-3298. Tel: 630-279-8696. Fax: 630-279-0636. p. 642

Cretano, Bobbie, Dir, Elmwood Park Public Library, 210 Lee St, Elmwood Park, NJ, 07407. Tel: 201-796-2449. Fax: 201-703-1425. p. 1484

Crews, C Daniel, Dr, Archivist, Moravian Church in America, Southern Province, 457 S Church St, Winston-Salem, NC, 27101-5314. Tel: 336-722-1742, Ext 1501. Fax: 336-725-4514. p. 1833

Crews, Gloria, Youth Serv, Shalimar Public Library, Six Tenth Ave, Shalimar, FL, 32579. Tel: 850-609-1515. p. 491

Crews, Julie, Access Serv Coordr, Louisiana College, 1140 College Blvd, Pineville, LA, 71359. Tel: 318-487-7109. Fax: 318-487-7143. p. 965

Crews, Lucy, Cat, Ser, Mary Baldwin College, 109 E Frederick St, Staunton, VA, 24401. Tel: 540-887-7088. Fax: 540-887-7137. p. 2496

Crews, Marissa, Librn, Wright County Library, Laura Ingalls Wilder Library, PO Box 586, Mansfield, MO, 65704-3245. Tel: 417-924-8068. Fax: 417-924-3045. p. 1330

Crews, Richelle, Br Mgr, Riverside County Library System, Eastvale Library, 7447 Cleveland Ave, Corona, CA, 92880. Tel: 951-273-1520. Fax: 951-273-9442. p. 217

Cribbs, Terra, Ch, Atlanta-Fulton Public Library System, Northeast-Spruill Oaks Regional Library, 9560 Spruill Rd, Alpharetta, GA, 30022. Tel: 770-360-8820. Fax: 770-360-8823. p. 512

Crichton, Deirdre, Dir, Parkland Regional Library, Hwy 52 W, Yorkton, SK, S3N 3Z4, CANADA. Tel: 306-783-7022. Fax: 306-782-2844. p. 2931

Crider, Bonita, Cat, Houston Baptist University, 7502 Fondren Rd, Houston, TX, 77074-3298. Tel: 281-649-3179. Fax: 281-649-3489. p. 2337

Crider, Jeanne, Dir, Lamar County Library System, 122 Shelby Speights Dr, Purvis, MS, 39475. Tel: 601-794-8651. Fax: 601-794-5068. p. 1312

Crider, Jeanne, Librn, Lamar County Library System, Lumberton Public, 106 W Main Ave, Lumberton, MS, 39455. Tel: 601-796-4227. Fax: 601-796-4227. p. 1312

Crider, Jo, Br Mgr, Aiken-Bamberg-Barnwell-Edgefield Regional Library System, Williston Branch, 5121 Springfield Rd, Williston, SC, 29853-9762. Tel: 803-266-3027. Fax: 803-266-3027. p. 2179

Crider, Pam, Sr Librn, San Jose Public Library, Almaden, 6445 Camden Ave, San Jose, CA, 95120. Tel: 408-808-3040. Fax: 408-997-1212. p. 251

Crider, Pam, Sr Librn, San Jose Public Library, Edenvale, 101 Branham Lane E, San Jose, CA, 95111. Tel: 408-808-3036. Fax: 408-224-9836. p. 251

Cridland-Hughes, Jed, Acq/ILL Librn, Ref Librn, Fresno County Public Law Library, Fresno County Courthouse, Rm 600, 1100 Van Ness Ave, Fresno, CA, 93721-2017. Tel: 559-237-2227. Fax: 559-442-4960. p. 151

Crill, Kathryn, Dir, West Bonner Library District, 219 Main St, Priest River, ID, 83856. Tel: 208-448-2207. p. 582

Crilly, Jody, Mgr, Calgary Public Library, Village Square, 2623 56th St NE, Calgary, AB, T1Y 6E7, CANADA. p. 2691

Crim-Weithman, Jessi, Assoc Dir, Support Serv, Westerville Public Library, 126 S State St, Westerville, OH, 43081-2095. Tel: 614-882-7277, Ext 134. Fax: 614-882-4160. p. 1946

Crimi, Kyle, Lending Serv Coordr, Cedar Crest College, 100 College Dr, Allentown, PA, 18104-6196. Tel: 610-606-4666, Ext 3387. Fax: 610-740-3769. p. 2026

Crimmins, John, Head of Libr, Free Library of Philadelphia, Queen Memorial Branch, 1201 S 23rd St, Philadelphia, PA, 19146-4316. Tel: 215-685-1869, 215-685-1899. Fax: 215-685-1654. p. 2109

Criner, Ashlee, Br Head, Lowell Public Library, Shelby Branch, 23323 Shelby Rd, Shelby, IN, 46377. Tel: 219-552-0809. p. 762

Cring, Janice, ILL, Lafayette Public Library, 301 W Congress, Lafayette, LA, 70501-6866. Tel: 337-261-5775. Fax: 337-261-5782. p. 952

Crippen, Donna, Curator, El Monte Museum of History Library, 3150 N Tyler Ave, El Monte, CA, 91731-6307. Tel: 626-444-3813, 626-580-2232. Fax: 626-444-8142. p. 146

Crisostimo, Theresa, ILL, Haddon Heights Public Library, 608 Station Ave, Haddon Heights, NJ, 08035-1907. Tel: 856-547-7132. Fax: 856-547-2867. p. 1489

Crisostomo, Jenny, Circ Mgr, Morris Area Public Library District, 604 Liberty St, Morris, IL, 60450. Tel: 815-942-6880. Fax: 815-942-6415. p. 675

Crispino, Lyn, Coordr, Gaylord Hospital, PO Box 400, Wallingford, CT, 06492. Tel: 203-741-3328. Fax: 203-284-2892. p. 373

Crispino, Marie, Pub Serv, Scranton Public Library, Albright Memorial Bldg, 500 Vine St, Scranton, PA, 18509-3298. Tel: 570-348-3000. Fax: 570-348-3020. p. 2138

Crissinger, John, Archivist, Ref, Ohio State University LIBRARIES, Newark Campus Library, Warner Library & Student Center, 1179 University Dr, Newark, OH, 43055-1797. Tel: 740-366-9307. Fax: 740-366-9264. p. 1889

Crissman, Crystal Sue, Libr Serv Mgr, Hollidaysburg Area Public Library, 405 Clark St, Hollidaysburg, PA, 16648-2100. Tel: 814-695-5961. Fax: 814-695-6824. p. 2069

Crist, Angela, Cat, William Penn University, 201 Trueblood Ave, Oskaloosa, IA, 52577. Tel: 641-673-1096. Fax: 641-673-1098. p. 837

Crist, Chris, Bus Mgr, Yolo County Library, Admin Off, 226 Buckeye St, Woodland, CA, 95695-2600. Tel: 530-757-5597. Fax: 530-666-8006. p. 284

Crist, Sue, Librn, Milford District Library, Two S Grant Ave, Milford, IL, 60953-1399. Tel: 815-889-4722. Fax: 815-889-4722. p. 674

Cristiano, Nancy, Supvr, Spec Serv, New Hampshire State Library, 20 Park St, Concord, NH, 03301-6314. Tel: 603-271-1188. Fax: 603-271-2205, 603-271-6826. p. 1443

Cristina, Suzanne, Mgr, United Technologies Corp, Hamilton Sundstrand, One Hamilton Rd, MS 1-3-BC38, Windsor Locks, CT, 06096-1010. Tel: 860-654-4352. Fax: 860-660-2118. p. 379

Criswell, Jay, Tech Serv, Stillwater Public Library, 1107 S Duck St, Stillwater, OK, 74074. Tel: 405-372-3633, Ext 121. Fax: 405-624-0552. p. 1978

Critchell, Susan, Librn, Livingston Free Library, Old Post Rd, Livingston, NY, 12541. Tel: 518-851-2270. Fax: 518-851-2270. p. 1653

Critchfield, Ron, Dr, Dir, Jessamine County Public Library, 600 S Main St, Nicholasville, KY, 40356-1839. Tel: 859-885-3523, Ext 223. Fax: 859-885-5164. p. 931

Critchley, Valerie, Assoc Univ Librn, Carleton University Library, 1125 Colonel By Dr, Ottawa, ON, K1S 5B6, CANADA. Tel: 613-520-2600, Ext 1808. Fax: 613-520-2750. p. 2830

Crites, Billie, Br Mgr, Orange County Library, Gordonsville Branch, 200 S Main St, Gordonsville, VA, 22942. Tel: 540-832-0712. Fax: 540-832-0849. p. 2483

Crites, Emma, Pres, Wilson County Historical Society, 420 N Seventh St, Fredonia, KS, 66736-1315. Tel: 620-378-3965. p. 868

Crittenden, Linda, Principal Librn, New Brunswick Free Public Library, 60 Livingston Ave, New Brunswick, NJ, 08901-2597. Tel: 732-745-5108. Fax: 732-846-0226. p. 1508

Critz, Lori, Head, Fac Engagement, Georgia Institute of Technology Library, 704 Cherry St, Atlanta, GA, 30332-0900. Tel: 404-894-4501. Fax: 404-894-6084. p. 515

Croad-Teeple, Patricia, Asst Dir, Libr Serv, Bay Mills Community College, 12214 W Lakeshore Dr, Brimley, MI, 49715-9320. Tel: 906-248-3354, Ext 4202. Fax: 906-248-2432. p. 1160

Croatt-Moore, Carrie, Instruction Coordr, Ref Librn, Wayne State University Libraries, Science & Engineering, 5048 Gullen Mall, Detroit, MI, 48202-3918. Tel: 313-577-0277. Fax: 313-577-3613. p. 1173

Crocco, Stephen D, Dir, Princeton Theological Seminary, Mercer St & Library Pl, Princeton, NJ, 08542. Tel: 609-497-7930. Fax: 609-497-1826. p. 1522

Crock, Mary Ellen, Acq, Cat, Tech Serv, Altoona Area Public Library, 1600 Fifth Ave, Altoona, PA, 16602-3693. Tel: 814-946-0417, Ext 128. Fax: 814-946-3230. p. 2028

Crocker, Daniel, Coordr, Electronic Res, Ref Librn, Emerson College Library, 120 Boylston St, Boston, MA, 02116-4624. Tel: 617-824-8332. Fax: 617-824-7817. p. 1060

Crocker, Jan, Dir, Ulysses Township Library, 410 C St, Ulysses, NE, 68669. Tel: 402-549-2451. Fax: 402-549-2450. p. 1421

Crocker, Jeff, Coordr, Support Serv, West Bloomfield Township Public Library, 4600 Walnut Lake Rd, West Bloomfield, MI, 48323. Tel: 248-232-2207. Fax: 248-232-2291. p. 1236

Crocker, Jill, ILL, Richmond Memorial Library, 19 Ross St, Batavia, NY, 14020. Tel: 585-343-9550. Fax: 585-344-4651. p. 1578

Crocker, Karen, Libr Tech, Sutter County Free Library, Sutter Branch, 2147 California St, Sutter, CA, 95982. Tel: 530-755-0485. p. 286

Crocker, Wayne M, Dir, Petersburg Public Library, 137 S Sycamore St, Petersburg, VA, 23803. Tel: 804-733-2387. Fax: 804-733-7972. p. 2484

Crocker, Wilbalene, Asst Librn, Beene-Pearson Public Library, 208 Elm Ave, South Pittsburg, TN, 37380-1312. Tel: 423-837-6513. Fax: 423-837-6612. p. 2266

Crockett, April, Website Mgr, Tennessee Technological University, 1100 N Peachtree Ave, Cookeville, TN, 38505. Tel: 931-372-3326. Fax: 931-372-6112. p. 2231

Crockett, Gail, Head, Tech Serv, University of Houston, 2602 N Ben Jordan St, Victoria, TX, 77901-5699. Tel: 361-570-4177. Fax: 361-570-4155. p. 2395

Crockett, John, Curator, Santa Ynez Valley Historical Society, 3596 Sagunto St, Santa Ynez, CA, 93460. Tel: 805-688-7889. Fax: 805-688-1109. p. 268

Crockwell, Eric, Ref, Payette Associates, 285 Summer St, Boston, MA, 02210. Tel: 617-895-1000. Fax: 617-895-1002. p. 1066

Croft, Betty, Tech Serv, United States Navy, Naval Health Research Center, Wilkins Biomedical Library, Gate 4, Barracks Bldg 333, McClelland & Patterson Rds, San Diego, CA, 92152. Tel: 619-553-8426. Fax: 619-553-0213. p. 238

Croft, Cheri, Libr Tech, Wisconsin Indianhead Technical College, 1019 S Knowles Ave, New Richmond, WI, 54017. Tel: 715-246-6561, Ext 4222. Fax: 715-246-2777. p. 2625

Croft, Janet, Head, Access Serv, University of Oklahoma, 401 W Brooks, Norman, OK, 73019. Tel: 405-325-2611. Fax: 405-325-7550. p. 1971

Croft, Kathy, Circ, State University of New York, College at Oneonta, 108 Ravine Pkwy, Oneonta, NY, 13820. Tel: 607-436-2725. Fax: 607-436-3081. p. 1711

Croft, Renee, Fac Projects Mgr, Maryland State Department of Education, 200 W Baltimore St, Baltimore, MD, 21201-2595. Tel: 410-767-0445. Fax: 410-333-2507. p. 1015

Croft, Vicki F, Head of Libr, Washington State University Libraries, Animal Health Library, 170 Wegner Hall, Pullman, WA, 99164. Tel: 509-335-9556. Fax: 509-335-5158. p. 2525

Crogh, Audrey, Dir, Meadows Valley Public Library District, 400 Virginia St, New Meadows, ID, 83654. Tel: 208-347-3147. Fax: 208-347-4121. p. 581

Crohan, Catherine, Coordr, Instruction, Siena College, 515 Loudon Rd, Loudonville, NY, 12211-1462. Tel: 518-782-6731. Fax: 518-783-2570. p. 1655

Cromer, Angelina, Br Mgr, Granville County Library System, Stovall Branch, 101 Hwy 15, Stovall, NC, 27582. Tel: 919-693-5722. Fax: 919-693-5722. p. 1814

Cromer, Dan, Dir, Libr Serv, Ai Miami International University of Art & Design Library, 1501 Biscayne Blvd, Ste 100, Miami, FL, 33132-1418. Tel: 305-428-5909. Fax: 305-374-7946. p. 464

Cromer, Jennifer, Librn, Pub Serv, Lewis-Clark State College Library, 500 Eighth Ave, Lewiston, ID, 83501. Tel: 208-792-2829. Fax: 208-792-2831. p. 578

Cromi, Patricia, Managing Librn, Timken Co, 4500 Mount Pleasant Rd, TEC-06, North Canton, OH, 44720. Tel: 330-471-2049. Fax: 330-471-2282. p. 1923

Cromley, Jami, Dir, Community District Library, 231 N Shiawassee St, Corunna, MI, 48817. Tel: 989-743-3287. Fax: 989-743-5496. p. 1166

Cromley, Leticia, Circ Supvr, Nicholson Memorial Library System, 625 Austin St, Garland, TX, 75040-6365. Tel: 972-205-2500. Fax: 972-205-2523. p. 2327

Crompton, Mary, Mgr, Northrop Grumman Corp, 600 Hicks Rd, MS M3300, Rolling Meadows, IL, 60008. Tel: 224-625-4592. Fax: 224-625-5756. p. 698

Cromwell, Emily, Librn, George H Stowell Free Library, 24 School St, Cornish Flat, NH, 03746. Tel: 603-543-3644. p. 1444

Cromwell, Kara, Assoc Dir, Abilene Public Library, 209 NW Fourth, Abilene, KS, 67410-2690. Tel: 785-263-3082. Fax: 785-263-2274. p. 855

Cromwell, Patricia, Tech Serv, Weatherford Public Library, 1014 Charles St, Weatherford, TX, 76086-5098. Tel: 817-598-4158. Fax: 817-598-4161. p. 2399

Cron, Sarah L, Dr, Dir, Colorado Mesa University, 1200 College Pl, Grand Junction, CO, 81501. Tel: 970-248-1846. Fax: 970-248-1930. p. 310

Cronce, Sandra, Head, Youth Serv, Willingboro Public Library, Willingboro Town Ctr, 220 Willingboro Pkwy, Willingboro, NJ, 08046. Tel: 609-877-0476, 609-877-6668. Fax: 609-835-1699. p. 1544

Croneis, Karen, Assoc Dean, University of Alabama, University Libraries, University of Alabama Campus, Capstone Dr, Tuscaloosa, AL, 35487. Tel: 205-348-5569. Fax: 205-348-8833. p. 38

Cronim, John, Dir, Revere Public Library, 179 Beach St, Revere, MA, 02151. Tel: 781-286-8380. Fax: 781-286-8382. p. 1120

Cronin, Catherine, Head, Circ, Bentley College, 175 Forest St, Waltham, MA, 02452-4705. Tel: 781-891-2168. Fax: 781-891-2830. p. 1132

Cronin, Jailynn, ILL, Warren-Trumbull County Public Library, 444 Mahoning Ave NW, Warren, OH, 44483. Tel: 330-399-8807. Fax: 330-395-3988. p. 1944

Cronin, Kathleen, Ch, New Rochelle Public Library, One Library Plaza, New Rochelle, NY, 10801. Tel: 914-632-7878, Ext 1000. Fax: 914-632-0262. p. 1666

Cronin, Kathleen, Head, Ch, New Rochelle Public Library, Huguenot Children's Library, 794 North Ave, New Rochelle, NY, 10801. Tel: 914-632-7878. Fax: 914-632-0262. p. 1667

Cronin, Kerry, Dir, Concord Free Public Library, 129 Main St, Concord, MA, 01742-2494. Tel: 978-318-3377. Fax: 978-318-3344. p. 1082

Cronin, Kevin-Andrew, Evening & Weekend Access Serv Mgr, East Carolina University, Music Library, A J Fletcher Music Ctr, Rm A110, Greenville, NC, 27858. Tel: 252-328-6250. Fax: 252-328-1243. p. 1799

Cronin, Mary, Dir, Madison Library, 1895 Village Rd, Madison, NH, 03849. Tel: 603-367-8545. Fax: 603-367-4479. p. 1455

Cronin, Nick, Dir, Rocky River Public Library, 1600 Hampton Rd, Rocky River, OH, 44116-2699. Tel: 440-895-3711. Fax: 440-333-4184. p. 1932

Cronin, Ray, Chief Exec Officer, Dir, Art Gallery of Nova Scotia Library, 1723 Hollis St, Halifax, NS, B3J 3C8, CANADA. Tel: 902-424-7542. Fax: 902-424-7359. p. 2780

Cronk, Beth, Head Librn, Litchfield Public Library, 216 N Marshall Ave, Litchfield, MN, 55355. Tel: 320-693-2483. Fax: 320-693-2484. p. 1256

Cronk, Jennifer, Curator, Aurora History Museum Library, 15051 E Alameda Pkwy, Aurora, CO, 80012. Tel: 303-739-6660. Fax: 303-739-6657. p. 288

Cronk, Judy, Dir, Keya Paha County Library, 118 Main St, Springview, NE, 68778. Tel: 402-497-2626. Fax: 402-497-2627. p. 1420

Cronk, Linda, Br Mgr, Porter County Public Library System, South Haven, 403 West, 700 North, Valparaiso, IN, 46385-8407. Tel: 219-759-4474. Fax: 219-759-4454. p. 783

Cronkhite, Jan, Dir, Weller Public Library, 212 Main St, Waitsburg, WA, 99361. Tel: 509-337-8149. p. 2546

Cronon, Dianne, Mgr, Northwest Georgia Regional Library System, Calhoun-Gordon County Library, 100 N Park Ave, Calhoun, GA, 30701. Tel: 706-624-1456. Fax: 706-624-1458. p. 528

Crook, Don, Cataloger, Iberia Parish Library, 445 E Main St, New Iberia, LA, 70560-3710. Tel: 337-364-7024, 337-364-7074. Fax: 337-364-7042. p. 959

Crook, Kay, Ser, University of Arkansas-Monticello Library, 514 University Dr, Monticello, AR, 71656. Tel: 870-460-1080. Fax: 870-460-1980. p. 110

Crook, Thea, Exec Dir, Congregation Rodfei Zedek, 5200 Hyde Park Blvd, Chicago, IL, 60615. Tel: 773-752-2770, Ext 106. Fax: 773-752-0330. p. 611

Crooker, Cynthia, Assoc Head, Coll Develop & Mgt, Yale University Library, Harvey Cushing/John Hay Whitney Medical Library, Sterling Hall of Medicine, 333 Cedar St, L110 SHM, New Haven, CT, 06520. Tel: 203-785-5352. Fax: 203-785-5636. p. 358

Crooks, Doreen, Cat, University of Miami, Louis Calder Memorial Library, Miller School of Medicine, 1601 NW Tenth Ave, Miami, FL, 33136. Tel: 305-243-6931. Fax: 305-325-8853. p. 469

Crooks, Laura, Dir, Alexander County Library, 77 First Ave SW, Taylorsville, NC, 28681. Tel: 828-632-4058. Fax: 828-632-1094. p. 1827

Crooks, Melissa, Circ Mgr, Coeur d'Alene Public Library, 702 E Front Ave, Coeur d'Alene, ID, 83814-2373. Tel: 208-769-2315. Fax: 208-769-2381. p. 573

Cropper, Dale V, Coll Develop Mgr, Brown County Library, 515 Pine St, Green Bay, WI, 54301. Tel: 920-448-5801. Fax: 920-448-4376. p. 2595

Cropper, Indira, Evening Librn, Eastern Correctional Institution, West Library, 30420 Revells Neck Rd, Westover, MD, 21890-3358. Tel: 410-845-4000, Ext 6423. Fax: 410-845-4206. p. 1046

Cropper, Maureen, Electronic Res Librn, Bluegrass Community & Technical College, Oswald Bldg, 470 Cooper Dr, Lexington, KY, 40506-0235. Tel: 859-246-6394. Fax: 859-246-4675. p. 920

Crosby, Jacqueline, In Charge, Dawson Technical Institute, 3901 S State St, Chicago, IL, 60609. Tel: 773-451-2087. Fax: 773-451-2090. p. 612

Crosby, Jeanne, Cataloger, Granby Public Library, One Library Lane, Granby, MA, 01033-9416. Tel: 413-467-3320. Fax: 413-467-3320. p. 1091

Crosby, Jeffrey E, Admin Librn, San Joaquin Valley Library System, 2420 Mariposa St, Fresno, CA, 93721. Tel: 559-600-6283. Fax: 559-600-6295. p. 153

Crosby, Jennifer, Dir, Granby Public Library, One Library Lane, Granby, MA, 01033-9416. Tel: 413-467-3320. Fax: 413-467-3320. p. 1091

Crosby, Karen, Librn, Calgary Herald Library, 215 16th St SE, Calgary, AB, T2P 0W8, CANADA. Tel: 403-235-7361. Fax: 403-235-7379. p. 2688

Crosby, Kathy, Head Librn, Brooklyn Botanic Garden Library, 1000 Washington Ave, Brooklyn, NY, 11225. Tel: 718-623-7303. Fax: 718-857-2430. p. 1589

Crosby, Linda, Syst Coordr, Fanshawe College, 1001 Fanshawe College Blvd, London, ON, N5Y 5R6, CANADA. Tel: 519-452-4240. Fax: 519-452-4473. p. 2817

Crosby, Nan, Br Mgr, Madison County Library System, Ridgeland Public Library, 397 Hwy 51 N, Ridgeland, MS, 39157. Tel: 601-856-4536. Fax: 601-856-3748. p. 1295

Crosby, Patricia, Br Mgr, Toledo-Lucas County Public Library, Reynolds Corners, 4833 Dorr St, Toledo, OH, 43615. Tel: 419-259-5320. Fax: 419-531-4076. p. 1940

Crosby, Sheila, Br Mgr, Pioneer Library System, Moore Public, 225 S Howard, Moore, OK, 73160. Tel: 405-793-5100. Fax: 405-793-8755. p. 1970

Crose, Mike, Admin Serv Mgr, Timberland Regional Library, 415 Tumwater Blvd SW, Tumwater, WA, 98501-5799. Tel: 360-943-5001, Ext 2517. Fax: 360-586-6838. p. 2543

Crosetto, Alice, Coordr, Coll Develop, University of Toledo, 2801 W Bancroft St, Mail Stop 509, Toledo, OH, 43606-3390. Tel: 419-530-2760. Fax: 419-530-2726. p. 1941

Crosland, Linda, Libr Dir, Garden Ridge Library, 9400 Municipal Pkwy, Garden Ridge, TX, 78266. Tel: 210-651-6570. p. 2327

Cross, Andrew, Law Bk Coordr, Dallas County Law Library, George Allen Courts Bldg, 600 Commerce St, Ste 292, Dallas, TX, 75202-4606. Tel: 214-653-6947. Fax: 214-653-6103. p. 2305

Cross, Anne, Dir, Center Line Public Library, 7345 Weingartz St, Center Line, MI, 48015-1462. Tel: 586-758-8274. Fax: 586-755-9234. p. 1162

Cross, Bobbi, Dir, Schnader, Harrison, Segal & Lewis Library, 1600 Market St, Ste 3600, Philadelphia, PA, 19103. Tel: 215-751-2399. Fax: 215-751-2205. p. 2116

Cross, Denise, Tech Serv & Syst Librn, Quinsigamond Community College, 670 W Boylston St, Worcester, MA, 01606-2092. Tel: 508-854-4480. Fax: 508-854-4204. p. 1144

Cross, Douglas, Dean of Libr, Walters State Community College, 500 S Davy Crockett Pkwy, Morristown, TN, 37813-6899. Tel: 423-585-6901. Fax: 423-585-6959. p. 2253

Cross, Ella, Ref/Govt Doc Librn, University of Wisconsin-Superior, PO Box 2000, Belknap & Catlin, Superior, WI, 54880-2000. Tel: 715-394-8512. Fax: 715-394-8462. p. 2641

Cross, Ella, Asst Prof, University of Wisconsin-Superior, Belknap & Catlin, PO Box 2000, Superior, WI, 54880. Tel: 715-394-8512. Fax: 715-394-8462. p. 2977

Cross, Esther, Head, Ch, Reed Memorial Library, 167 E Main St, Ravenna, OH, 44266-3197. Tel: 330-296-2827. Fax: 330-296-3780. p. 1931

Cross, Jane, Chief Librn, United States Marine Band, Marine Barracks Annex & Band Support Facility, Seventh & L Sts SE, Washington, DC, 20003. Tel: 202-433-4298. Fax: 202-433-2221. p. 420

Cross, Jennifer, AV, Info Tech, Pembroke Public Library, 237 Victoria St, Pembroke, ON, K8A 4K5, CANADA. Tel: 613-732-8844. Fax: 613-732-1116. p. 2835

Cross, Jennifer D, Cat, West Liberty University, CSC No 135, West Liberty, WV, 26074. Tel: 304-336-8035. Fax: 304-336-8186. p. 2574

Cross, Jim, Dir, Riceville Public Library, 307 Woodland Ave, Riceville, IA, 50466. Tel: 641-985-2273. Fax: 641-985-4002. p. 840

Cross, Kerrie, Archivist, University of Dayton Libraries, 300 College Park Dr, Dayton, OH, 45469-1360. Tel: 937-229-4267. Fax: 937-229-4215. p. 1894

Cross, Lois, Extn Spec, Metropolitan Library System in Oklahoma County, Nicoma Park Extension Library, 2240 Overholser, Nicoma Park, OK, 73066-0250. Tel: 405-769-9452. Fax: 405-769-4020. p. 1973

Cross, Mary, Librn, Meadowlark Public Library, 208 Main St, Lewis, KS, 67552. Tel: 620-324-5743. p. 879

Cross, Mary R, Syst Coordr, Columbia College, 1301 Columbia College Dr, Columbia, SC, 29203-9987. Tel: 803-786-3691. Fax: 803-786-3700. p. 2187

Cross, Michael, Dir, Wisconsin Department of Public Instruction, Public Library Development Team, 125 S Webster St, Madison, WI, 53702. Tel: 608-267-9225. Fax: 608-266-2529. p. 2610

Cross, Paula, Ref Serv, Middlesex Community College, Federal Bldg, E Merrimack St, Lowell, MA, 01852. Tel: 978-937-5454. Fax: 978-656-3031. p. 1100

Cross, Scott, Archivist, Oshkosh Public Museum Library, 1331 Algoma Blvd, Oshkosh, WI, 54901-2799. Tel: 920-236-5773. Fax: 920-424-4738. p. 2628

Cross, Susan, Govt Doc, ILL, Alma College Library, 614 W Superior St, Alma, MI, 48801. Tel: 989-463-7229. Fax: 989-463-8694. p. 1149

Cross-Maser, Cecile M, Librn, East Central Regional Library, Hinckley Public Library, 106 First St SE, Hinckley, MN, 55037. Tel: 320-384-6351. Fax: 320-384-6351. p. 1244

Cross-Roen, Carol Ann, Head, Ch, Medicine Hat Public Library, 414 First St SE, Medicine Hat, AB, T1A 0A8, CANADA. Tel: 403-502-8527. Fax: 403-502-8529. p. 2711

Crossen, Patrick, Head, Tech Serv, Southwest Public Libraries, SPL Admin, 3359 Park St, Grove City, OH, 43123. Tel: 614-875-6716. Fax: 614-875-2219. p. 1903

Crosser, Karen, Dir, Libr Serv, Regional Medical Library, 223 E Jackson, Jonesboro, AR, 72401. Tel: 870-972-1290. Fax: 870-931-0839. p. 105

Crosser, Karen, Dir, Northeast Arkansas Hospital Library Consortium, 223 E Jackson, Jonesboro, AR, 72401. Tel: 870-972-1290. Fax: 870-931-0839. p. 2937

Crossett, Laura, Br Mgr, Park County Public Library, Meeteetse Branch, 2107 Idaho, Meeteetse, WY, 82433. Tel: 307-868-2248. Fax: 307-868-2248. p. 2654

Crossfield, Nancy, Mgr, William O Owen Medical Library, Saint Agnes Medical Ctr, 1303 E Herndon Ave, No 70, Fresno, CA, 93720-1234. Tel: 559-450-3322. Fax: 559-450-3315. p. 153

Crossland, Linda, Librn, Calmar Public Library, 101 S Washington St, Calmar, IA, 52132. Tel: 563-562-3010. Fax: 563-562-3010. p. 798

Crosslin, Kathy, Ref, Kilpatrick Stockton, 1100 Peachtree St, Ste 2800, Atlanta, GA, 30309. Tel: 404-815-6261. Fax: 404-815-6555. p. 516

Crossman, Barbara, Dir, Jacksonville Public Library, 502 S Jackson St, Jacksonville, TX, 75766. Tel: 903-586-7664. Fax: 903-586-3397. p. 2347

Crosson, Helen M, Dir, Cold Spring Harbor Library, 95 Harbor Rd, Cold Spring Harbor, NY, 11724. Tel: 631-692-6820. Fax: 631-692-6827. p. 1609

Crosson, Kathy, Br Mgr, East Central Georgia Regional Library, Appleby Branch, 2260 Walton Way, Augusta, GA, 30904. Tel: 706-736-6244. Fax: 706-481-0616. p. 519

Crosthwaite, Margaret, Libr Mgr, Albert-Westmorland-Kent Regional Library, Salisbury Public, 3215 Main St, Salisbury, NB, E4J 2K7, CANADA. Tel: 506-372-3240. Fax: 506-372-3261. p. 2765

Croston, Kendel, Dir, Stark County Law Library, 110 Central Plaza S, Ste 401, Canton, OH, 44702. Tel: 330-451-7380. Fax: 330-451-7381. p. 1865

Croteau, Bill, Info Tech Dir, South Carolina State Library, 1430-1500 Senate St, Columbia, SC, 29201. Tel: 803-734-8651. Fax: 803-734-8676. p. 2189

Croteau, Jeff, Mgr, Libr & Archives, Scottish Rite Masonic Museum & Library, Inc, 33 Marrett Rd, Lexington, MA, 02421. Tel: 781-457-4109, 781-457-4125. Fax: 781-861-9846 (call first). p. 1099

Crothers, Karen R, Asst Dir, Packer Engineering Inc, 1950 N Washington St, Naperville, IL, 60563-1366. Tel: 630-577-1964. Fax: 630-577-1989. p. 679

Crotts, Brenda, Br Librn, Butte County Library, Paradise Branch, 5922 Clark Rd, Paradise, CA, 95969-4896. Tel: 530-872-6320. Fax: 530-872-6322. p. 202

Crotts, Brenda, Br Mgr, Butte County Library, 1820 Mitchell Ave, Oroville, CA, 95966-5387. Tel: 530-538-7196. Fax: 530-538-7235. p. 202

Crotts, Joe, Head, Circ & Reserve, California State University, Chico, 400 W First St, Chico, CA, 95929-0295. Tel: 530-898-6675. Fax: 530-898-4443. p. 133

Crotwell, Gracie, Circ Supvr, Mississippi College, 151 E Griffith St, Jackson, MS, 39201-1391. Tel: 601-925-7120. Fax: 601-925-7112. p. 1304

Crouch, Kathy, Br Librn, Madison County Public Library, 507 W Main St, Richmond, KY, 40475. Tel: 859-623-6704. Fax: 859-623-2023. p. 934

Crouch, Sharon, Librn, Asbury First United Methodist Church Library, 1050 East Ave, Rochester, NY, 14607. Tel: 585-271-1050. Fax: 585-271-3743. p. 1728

Crouch, Tinker, Pres, Deer Isle-Stonington Historical Society Library, Archives & Museum, Rte 15A/416 Sunset Rd, Deer Isle, ME, 04627. Tel: 207-348-6400. p. 983

Crough, Carol, Librn, Smith-Ennismore-Lakefield Public Library, 551 Ennis Rd, Ennismore, ON, K0L 1T0, CANADA. Tel: 705-292-8022. Fax: 705-292-8022. p. 2804

Crouse, Bernice, Dir, Franklin County Library System, 101 Ragged Edge Rd S, Chambersburg, PA, 17202. Tel: 717-709-0282. Fax: 717-263-2248. p. 2043

Crouse, Heather L, Librn, Hunterdon Developmental Center Library, 40 Pittstown Rd, Clinton, NJ, 08809. Tel: 908-735-4031, Ext 1411. Fax: 908-730-1311. p. 1479

Crouse, Lyn, Dir, Elyria Public Library System, 320 Washington Ave, Elyria, OH, 44035-5199. Tel: 440-323-5747. Fax: 440-323-5788. p. 1898

Crouthamel, Paul, Adult Serv, Escondido Public Library, 239 S Kalmia St, Escondido, CA, 92025. Tel: 760-839-4814. Fax: 760-741-4255. p. 146

Crovisier, Ron, Bibliog Instr, Ref, Dutchess Community College Library, 53 Pendell Rd, Poughkeepsie, NY, 12601-1595. Tel: 845-431-8642. Fax: 845-431-8995. p. 1722

Crow, Alysa, Ch, Abilene Public Library, South Branch Library, 1401 S Danville, Abilene, TX, 79605. Tel: 325-698-7565. Fax: 325-698-7621. p. 2272

Crow, Becky, Br Mgr, Nicholson Memorial Library System, Walnut Creek Branch Library, 3319 Edgewood, Garland, TX, 75042-7118. Tel: 972-205-2587. p. 2327

Crow, Beth, Dir, Blairstown Public Library, 305 Locust St, Ste 2, Blairstown, IA, 52209. Tel: 319-454-6497. Fax: 319-454-6495. p. 797

Crow, Jan, Br Mgr, Missouri River Regional Library, 214 Adams St, Jefferson City, MO, 65101-3244. Tel: 573-897-2951. p. 1335

Crow, Jan, Br Mgr, Missouri River Regional Library, Osage County, 1014 E Main St, Hwy 50, Linn, MO, 65051-9782. Tel: 573-897-2951. Fax: 573-897-3815. p. 1335

Crow, Nancy, Assoc Librn, Head, Pub Serv, Quincy University, 1800 College Ave, Quincy, IL, 62301-2699. Tel: 217-228-5432, Ext 3801. Fax: 217-228-5354. p. 693

Crow, Virginia, Libr Tech, Treasure Valley Community College Library, 650 College Blvd, Ontario, OR, 97914-3423. Tel: 541-881-5927. Fax: 541-881-2724. p. 2009

Crowder, Amy Witt, Dep Law Librn, Wisconsin State Law Library, 120 Martin Luther King Jr Blvd, 2nd Flr, Madison, WI, 53703. Tel: 608-267-2253. Fax: 608-267-2319. p. 2611

Crowder, Jane, Outreach Librn, Avery-Mitchell-Yancey Regional Library System, 289 Burnsville School Rd, Burnsville, NC, 28714. Tel: 828-682-4476. Fax: 828-682-6277. p. 1779

Crowder, Judy, Asst Librn, Hawkes Library, 100 W Eighth St, West Point, GA, 31833. Tel: 706-645-1549. Fax: 706-645-1549. p. 557

Crowder-Bell, Loretta, Dir, Bobby Martindale Memorial Library, 103 Washington Ave, Grand Junction, TN, 38039. Tel: 731-764-2716. p. 2235

Crowe, Chris, Pub Serv, Douglas County Library System, 1409 NE Diamond Lake Blvd, Roseburg, OR, 97470. Tel: 541-957-4635. Fax: 541-957-7798. p. 2016

Crowe, Cody, Pub Serv Librn, Monroe County Public Library, 500 W Fourth St, Tompkinsville, KY, 42167. Tel: 270-487-5301. Fax: 270-487-5309. p. 936

Crowe, Ione, Librn, Moccasin Bend Mental Health Institute, Health Sciences Library, 100 Moccasin Bend Rd, Chattanooga, TN, 37405. Tel: 423-785-3365. Fax: 423-785-3364. p. 2227

Crowe, Ione, Librn, Moccasin Bend Mental Health Institute, Patient Library, 100 Moccasin Bend Rd, Chattanooga, TN, 37405. Tel: 423-785-3365. Fax: 423-785-3364. p. 2228

Crowe, Kathryn, Assoc Dean, Pub Serv, University of North Carolina at Greensboro, 320 Spring Garden St, Greensboro, NC, 27402. Tel: 336-334-5880. Fax: 336-334-5399. p. 1797

Crowe, Lilah, Exec Dir, Itasca County Historical Society, Central School Bldg, Ten Fifth St NW, Grand Rapids, MN, 55744-2660. Tel: 218-326-6431. Fax: 218-326-7083. p. 1253

Crowe, Lillie, Dir, Bartram Trail Regional Library, 204 E Liberty St, Washington, GA, 30673. Tel: 706-678-7736. Fax: 706-678-1615. p. 556

Crowe, Linda, Librn, Augustana Lutheran Church Library, 5000 E Alameda Ave, Denver, CO, 80246. Tel: 303-388-4678. Fax: 303-388-1338. p. 298

Crowe, Linda, Exec Dir, Califa, 32 W 25th Ave, Ste 201, San Mateo, CA, 94403. Tel: 650-572-2746. Fax: 650-349-5089. p. 2938

Crowe, Lori, Pub Relations, Norfolk Public Library, 235 E Plume St, Norfolk, VA, 23510-1706. Tel: 757-664-7323. Fax: 757-441-5863. p. 2481

Crowe, Max, Dir, New Durham Public Library, Two Old Bay Rd, New Durham, NH, 03855-2214. Tel: 603-859-2201. Fax: 603-859-2201. p. 1459

Crowe, Sarah, Libr Asst, Wiregrass Georgia Technical College, 667 Perry House Rd, Fitzgerald, GA, 31750. Tel: 229-468-2012. Fax: 229-468-2110. p. 532

Crowe, Suzanne, Librn, Myers, Weinberg LLP, 724-240 Graham Ave, Winnipeg, MB, R3C 0J7, CANADA. Tel: 204-942-0501. Fax: 204-956-0625. p. 2757

Crowell, Beverly J, Pub Serv Librn, Alfred University, Scholes Library of Ceramics, New York State College of Ceramics at Alfred University, Two Pine St, Alfred, NY, 14802-1297. Tel: 607-871-2950. p. 1572

Crowell, Cindy, Librn, Schizophrenia Society of Nova Scotia Library, E C Purdy Bldg, Rm B23, 300 Pleasant St, Dartmouth, NS, B2Y 3Z9, CANADA. Tel: 902-465-2601. Fax: 902-465-5479. p. 2780

Crowell, Karen, Youth Serv Librn, Oakmont Carnegie Library, 700 Allegheny River Blvd, Oakmont, PA, 15139. Tel: 412-828-9532. Fax: 412-828-5979. p. 2100

Crowell, Lina, Ch, Warren County Library, 189 Route 519, Belvidere, NJ, 07823. Tel: 908-475-6322. Fax: 908-475-6359. p. 1472

Crowell, Nancy E, Dir, Scarborough Public Library, 48 Gorham Rd, Scarborough, ME, 04074. Tel: 207-883-4723. Fax: 207-883-9728. p. 1000

Crowell, Nelda, Archivist, Thunderbird School of Global Management, 15249 N 59th Ave, Glendale, AZ, 85306-6001. Tel: 602 978-7115. Fax: 602-978-7762. p. 64

Crowfoot, Susan, Librn I, Illinois Department of Corrections, 2268 E Morton Ave, Jacksonville, IL, 62650-9347. Tel: 217-245-1481, Ext 334. Fax: 217-245-1481, Ext 324. p. 658

Crowley, Beth, Dir, E C Scranton Memorial Library, 801 Boston Post Rd, Madison, CT, 06443. Tel: 203-245-7365. Fax: 203-245-7821. p. 349

Crowley, Carol, Librn, Sussex County Library System, Franklin Branch, 103 Main St, Franklin, NJ, 07416-1517. Tel: 973-827-6555. Fax: 973-827-9422. p. 1514

Crowley, Christine, Dean, Learning Res, Northwest Vista College, Redbud Hall, 3535 N Ellison Dr, San Antonio, TX, 78251. Tel: 210-486-4572. Fax: 210-486-9105. p. 2380

Crowley, Colleen, Ch, Chippewa Falls Public Library, 105 W Central, Chippewa Falls, WI, 54729-2397. Tel: 715-723-1146. Fax: 715-720-6922. p. 2585

Crowley, Donald, Computer Tech, Seymour Public Library District, 176-178 Genesee St, Auburn, NY, 13021. Tel: 315-252-2571. Fax: 315-252-7985. p. 1576

Crowley, Janice, Circ, Dedham Public Library, Endicott, 257 Mount Vernon St, Dedham, MA, 02026. Tel: 781-326-5339. p. 1084

Crowley, Kim, Dir, Flathead County Library, 247 First Ave E, Kalispell, MT, 59901. Tel: 406-758-5826. Fax: 406-758-5868. p. 1384

Crowley, Mary, Mgr, Sequoyah Regional Library System, Cherokee County Law Library, Cherokee County Justice Ctr, 90 North St, Ste 250, Canton, GA, 30114. Tel: 770-720-6358. p. 523

Crowley, Rachel, Dir, Rose-Hulman Institute of Technology, 5500 Wabash Ave, Terre Haute, IN, 47803. Tel: 812-877-8200. Fax: 812-877-8579. p. 781

Crowley, Sally, Librn, Greensfelder, Hemker & Gale, PC Library, Ten S Broadway, Ste 2000, Saint Louis, MO, 63102. Tel: 314-241-9090. Fax: 314-241-8624. p. 1355

Crowley, Stephen J, Dir, Putnam County Library System, 601 College Rd, Palatka, FL, 32177-3873. Tel: 386-329-0126. Fax: 386-329-1240. p. 478

Crowley, Susan, Ref Serv, Dickstein Shapiro LLP, Research Services, 1825 Eye St NW, Washington, DC, 20006. Tel: 202-420-4999. Fax: 202-420-2201. p. 398

Crowner, Dee, Dir, North Liberty Community Library, 520 W Cherry St, North Liberty, IA, 52317-9797. Tel: 319-626-5701. Fax: 319-626-5722. p. 835

Crowson, Joan, Librn, Campbell Foundation Library, 1211 Union Ave, Ste 510, Memphis, TN, 38104. Tel: 901-759-3271. Fax: 901-759-3278. p. 2248

Crowson, Sue, Librn, Brookhaven College, 3939 Valley View, Farmers Branch, TX, 75244-4997. Tel: 972-860-4854. Fax: 972-860-4675. p. 2319

Crowther, Janet, Outreach Serv Dir, Williamsburg Regional Library, 7770 Croaker Rd, Williamsburg, VA, 23188-7064. Tel: 757-259-4066. Fax: 757-259-4079, 757-259-7798. p. 2503

Crowther, Mary, Librn, Westmoreland Public Library, 33 S Village Rd, Westmoreland, NH, 03467. Tel: 603-399-7750. p. 1468

Crowther, Sherry, Chief Librn, Lester B Pearson College of the Pacific, 650 Pearson College Dr, Victoria, BC, V9C 4H7, CANADA. Tel: 250-391-2423. Fax: 250-391-2412. p. 2745

Croy-Vanwely, Marcia Heather, Head, Libr Serv, Fisheries & Oceans Canada, 401 Burrard St, Ste 200, Vancouver, BC, V6C 3S4, CANADA. Tel: 604-666-6371. Fax: 604-666-3145. p. 2741

Cruce, Sarah, Automation Spec, Rainsville Public Library, 941 E Main St, Rainsville, AL, 35986. Tel: 256-638-3311. Fax: 256-638-3314. p. 34

Crudup, Mary, Acq, Tom Green County Library System, 113 W Beauregard, San Angelo, TX, 76903. Tel: 915-655-7321. Fax: 915-659-4027. p. 2378

Crugnola, David, ILL, Ref, Nassau Community College, One Education Dr, Garden City, NY, 11530-6793. Tel: 516-572-7400. Fax: 516-572-7846. p. 1626

Cruickshank, Barbara, Dir, Beaver Island District Library, 26400 Donegal Bay Rd, Beaver Island, MI, 49782. Tel: 231-448-2701. Fax: 231-448-2801. p. 1156

Cruickshank, Fern, ILL, SIAST-Saskatchewan Institute of Applied Science & Technology, ldylwyld Dr & 33rd St W, Saskatoon, SK, S7K 3R5, CANADA. Tel: 306-659-4040. Fax: 306-964-1222. p. 2927

Cruickshank, John, Librn, Skidaway Institute of Oceanography Library, Ten Ocean Science Circle, Savannah, GA, 31411-1011. Tel: 912-598-2474. Fax: 912-598-2391. p. 551

Crum, Cathy, Cat Supvr, Kentucky Department for Libraries & Archives, 300 Coffee Tree Rd, Frankfort, KY, 40601. Tel: 502-564-8300. Fax: 502-564-5773. p. 913

Crum, Janet, Dir, City of Hope, 1500 East Duarte Rd, Duarte, CA, 91010. Tel: 626-301-8497. Fax: 909-357-1929. p. 144

Crum, Janet, Head, Admin Serv, Head, Syst, Oregon Health & Science University Library, 3181 SW Sam Jackson Park Rd, Portland, OR, 97239-3098. Tel: 503-494-0691. Fax: 503-494-3227. p. 2013

Crumb, Sandra, Asst Dir, Hamilton Public Library, 13 Broad St, Hamilton, NY, 13346. Tel: 315-824-3060. Fax: 315-824-8420. p. 1633

Crumby, Brad, Br Mgr, Saline County Public Library, Mabel Boswell Memorial Library - Bryant, 201 Pricket Rd, Bryant, AR, 72022. Tel: 501-847-2166. Fax: 501-847-4524. p. 95

Crume, Sarah, Ref Librn, Indiana Wesleyan University, 4201 S Washington St, Marion, IN, 46953. Tel: 765-677-2334. Fax: 765-677-2676. p. 762

Crume, Tabin, Ref Librn, Sacramento Public Library, North Natomas Library, 2500 New Market Dr, Sacramento, CA, 95835. p. 225

Crumley, Sean, Syst & Cat Librn, United States Agency for International Development, 1300 Pennsylvania Ave NW, Rm M01-010, Washington, DC, 20523-1000. Tel: 202-712-0579. Fax: 202-216-3515. p. 417

Crumlish, Sandra, Mgr, St Jude Medical, Inc - Cardiac Rhythm Management Div, 15900 Valley View Ct, Sylmar, CA, 91342. Tel: 818-493-3101. Fax: 818-362-8142. p. 274

Crummey, Karon J, Client Serv Librn, Government of Canada, Federal Courts & Tax Court of Canada, Courts Administration Service-Library Services, 90 Sparks St, Ottawa, ON, K1A 0H9, CANADA. Tel: 613-943-0839. Fax: 613-943-5303. p. 2831

Crump, Amy, Libr Dir, Marshall Public Library, 214 N Lafayette, Marshall, MO, 65340. Tel: 660-886-3391. Fax: 660-886-2492. p. 1344

Crump, Carol, Libr Assoc, Desoto Parish Library, Pelican Branch, 145 Jackson Ave, Pelican, LA, 71063-2803. Tel: 318-755-2353. Fax: 318-755-2031. p. 956

Crump, Cynthia, Mgr, Libr Serv, St Clair College of Applied Arts & Technology Library, 2000 Talbot Rd W, Windsor, ON, N9A 6S4, CANADA. Tel: 519-972-2739. Fax: 519-972-2757. p. 2871

Crump, Dan, Ref Serv, American River College Library, 4700 College Oak Dr, Sacramento, CA, 95841. Tel: 916-484-8455. Fax: 916-484-8018, 916-484-8657. p. 220

Crump, Julie, Br Mgr, Main Libr, Ouachita Parish Public Library, 1800 Stubbs Ave, Monroe, LA, 71201. Tel: 318-327-1490. Fax: 318-327-1373. p. 957

Crump, Laurel, Dir, Pub Serv, University of North Florida, Bldg 12-Library, One UNF Dr, Jacksonville, FL, 32224-2645. Tel: 904-620-2247. Fax: 904-620-2719. p. 455

Crump, Lois, Cataloger, Librn, Bath County Memorial Library, 24 W Main St, Owingsville, KY, 40360. Tel: 606-674-2531. Fax: 606-674-2531. p. 931

Crump, Michele, Head, Access Support, University of Florida Libraries, 535 Library W, Gainesville, FL, 32611-7000. Tel: 352-273-2717. Fax: 352-392-6540. p. 449

Crump, Sarah, Mgr, Desoto Parish Library, Pelican Branch, 145 Jackson Ave, Pelican, LA, 71063-2803. Tel: 318-755-2353. Fax: 318-755-2031. p. 956

Crumpacker, Kathy, Librn, Saint Bernardine Medical Center, 2101 N Waterman Ave, San Bernardino, CA, 92404. Tel: 909-883-8711. Fax: 909-881-7171. p. 228

Crumpler, Dawn L, Cat Librn, United States Military Academy Library, Jefferson Hall Library & Learning Center, 758 Cullum Rd, West Point, NY, 10996. Tel: 845-938-3833. Fax: 845-938-4000. p. 1767

Crumpton, Michael, Asst Dean, Admin Serv, University of North Carolina at Greensboro, 320 Spring Garden St, Greensboro, NC, 27402. Tel: 336-334-5880. Fax: 336-334-5399. p. 1797

Crumrin, Robin, Assoc Dean, Coll & Info Access, Indiana University-Purdue University Indianapolis, 755 W Michigan St, Indianapolis, IN, 46202-5195. Tel: 317-278-2327. Fax: 317-278-0368. p. 753

Crumrin, Timothy, Assoc Dir, Conner Prairie, 13400 Allisonville Rd, Fishers, IN, 46038-4499. Tel: 317-776-6000. Fax: 317-776-6014. p. 740

Cruse, Cheryl, Syst/Tech Proc Librn, Shasta College Library, 11555 Old Oregon Trail, Redding, CA, 96003-7692. Tel: 530-242-2348. p. 214

Cruse, David, Electronic Serv, Adrian College, 110 S Madison St, Adrian, MI, 49221. Tel: 517-265-5161, Ext 4241. Fax: 517-264-3748. p. 1147

Crusenberry, Joyce P, Ser, Virginia Highlands Community College Library, 100 VHCC Dr, Abingdon, VA, 24210. Tel: 276-739-2470. Fax: 276-739-2593. p. 2443

Cruz, Brandii, Archivist, Asst Curator, Fayette Public Library, 855 S Jefferson, La Grange, TX, 78945. Tel: 979-968-3765. Fax: 979-968-5357. p. 2351

Cruz, Carlos, Instrul Designer, Brooklyn College Library, 2900 Bedford Ave, Brooklyn, NY, 11210-2889. Tel: 718-951-4667. Fax: 718-951-4540. p. 1589

Cruz, Craig, Libr Mgr, Krames Health Sciences Library, Krames Health & Safety, 1100 Grundy Lane, San Bruno, CA, 94066. Tel: 650-244-4333. Fax: 650-244-4345. p. 230

Cruz, Jane, Ref Serv, Ad, Delphi Public Library, 222 E Main St, Delphi, IN, 46923. Tel: 765-564-2929. Fax: 765-564-4746. p. 735

Cruz, Jane, Br Mgr, Delphi Public Library, Northwest Carroll Branch, 164 W Forest St, Yeoman, IN, 47997. Tel: 765-564-2929. p. 736

Cruz, John, Circ, Stevens Institute of Technology, Castle Point on Hudson, Hoboken, NJ, 07030. Tel: 201-216-5334. Fax: 201-216-8319. p. 1491

Cruz, Lorna, Libr Supvr, Joeten-Kiyu Public Library, Tinian Public, PO Box 520704, Tinian, MP, 96952. Tel: 670-433-0504. p. 2669

Cruz, Noemi, Dir, Calhoun County Library, 200 W Mahan, Port Lavaca, TX, 77979. Tel: 361-552-7323. Fax: 361-552-4926. p. 2371

Cruz, Nydia, Asst Admin, Stevens Institute of Technology, Castle Point on Hudson, Hoboken, NJ, 07030. Tel: 201-216-5200. Fax: 201-216-8319. p. 1491

Cruz, Rebecca, Libr Mgr, Pikes Peak Library District, Fountain Library, 230 S Main St, Fountain, CO, 80817. Tel: 719-382-5347. p. 296

Cruz, Rebecca, Libr Mgr, Pikes Peak Library District, Sand Creek Library, 1821 S Academy Blvd, Colorado Springs, CO, 80916. Tel: 719-597-7070. p. 296

Cruz, Rosario, ILL/Doc Delivery Serv, Saint Thomas University Library, Law Library, 16401 NW 37th Ave, Miami Gardens, FL, 33054. Tel: 305-623-2368. Fax: 305-623-2337. p. 469

Cruz, Rosario M, Ser, St Thomas University Library, 16401 NW 37th Ave, Miami Gardens, FL, 33054. Tel: 305-474-6862. Fax: 305-628-6666. p. 469

Cryan-Hicks, Kathy, Commun Relations Librn, Chelmsford Public Library, 25 Boston Rd, Chelmsford, MA, 01824-3088. Tel: 978-256-5521. Fax: 978-256-8511. p. 1080

Cryans, Linda, Asst Librn, Canada Department of Justice Montreal Headquarters Library, East Tower, 9th flr, No 200 Quest boul Rene-Levesque W, Montreal, QC, H2Z 1X4, CANADA. Tel: 514-283-6674, 514-283-8739. Fax: 514-283-6425. p. 2892

Cryderman, Deborah, Librn, Camrose Public Library, 4710 50th Ave, Camrose, AB, T4V 0R8, CANADA. Tel: 780-672-4214. Fax: 780-672-9165. p. 2694

Crymes, Martha, Br Mgr, Morehouse Parish Library, Collinston Branch, 4620 Main St, Collinston, LA, 71229. Tel: 318-874-3531. p. 941

Crysel, Laverne, Dir, Kountze Public Library, 800 S Redwood Ave, Kountze, TX, 77625. Tel: 409-246-2826. Fax: 409-246-4659. p. 2351

Cubbins, Elaine, Col Librn, Tohono O'odham Community College Library, Hwy 86 Milepost 115.5 N, Sells, AZ, 85634. Tel: 520-383-0032. Fax: 520-383-8403. p. 81

Cubit, James, Dir, Lake Forest College, 555 N Sheridan, Lake Forest, IL, 60045. Tel: 847-735-5054. Fax: 847-735-6297. p. 663

Cubitt, Sally V, Head, Tech Serv, Todd Wehr Library, St Norbert College, 301 Third St, De Pere, WI, 54115. Tel: 920-403-3280. Fax: 920-403-4067. p. 2587

Cuccia, Kevin, Ref, Louisiana Tech University, Everett St at The Columns, Ruston, LA, 71272. Tel: 318-257-3555. Fax: 318-257-2579. p. 966

Cucco, Jane, Dir, Monroeville Public Library, 34 Monroe St, Monroeville, OH, 44847. Tel: 419-465-2035. Fax: 419-465-2812. p. 1918

Cuddy, Colleen, Dir, Cornell University Library, The Samuel J Wood Library & The C V Starr Biomedical Information Center, 1300 York Ave, C115, Box 67, New York, NY, 10065-4896. Tel: 212-746-6050. Fax: 212-746-6494. p. 1642

Cuddy, Colleen, Interim Dir, New York University School of Medicine, John & Bertha E Waldmann Memorial Dental Library, 423 East 23rd St, 2nd Flr S, New York, NY, 10010. Tel: 212-998-9794. Fax: 212-995-3529. p. 1696

Cuddy, Ed, Br Head, Winnipeg Public Library, Henderson, 1-1050 Henderson Hwy, Winnipeg, MB, R2K 2M5, CANADA. Tel: 204-986-4314. Fax: 204-986-3065. p. 2760

Cudiner, Shelley, Ref, University of Connecticut at Stamford, One University Pl, Stamford, CT, 06901-2315. Tel: 203-251-8521. Fax: 203-251-8501. p. 370

Cuenco, Marlene, Pub Serv, Supreme Court Law Library, 417 S King St, Rm 115, Honolulu, HI, 96813. Tel: 808-539-4964. Fax: 808-539-4974. p. 565

Cuesta, Emerita, Syst Librn, University of Miami, 1311 Miller Dr, Coral Gables, FL, 33146. Tel: 305-284-2251. Fax: 305-284-3554. p. 434

Cuestas, Carolyn, Circ, Laramie County Community College Library, 1400 E College Dr, Cheyenne, WY, 82007-3204. Tel: 307-778-1205. Fax: 307-778-1399. p. 2652

Cuff, Lynn, Librn, College of the North Atlantic, Bay St George, 432 Massachusetts Dr, Stephenville, NL, A2N 2Z6, CANADA. Tel: 709-643-7752. Fax: 709-643-7786. p. 2771

Cuff, Lynn, Prov Coordr, College of the North Atlantic, One Prince Philip Dr, St. John's, NL, A1C 5P7, CANADA. Tel: 709-643-7762. Fax: 709-758-7231. p. 2771

Cui, Wei-Jie, Br Mgr, Burlington County Library, Pinelands, 39 Allen Ave, Medford, NJ, 08055. Tel: 609-654-6113. Fax: 609-953-2142. p. 1543

Culbert, Shaleen, Dir, Glenwood City Public Library, 127 Pine St, Glenwood City, WI, 54013-8554. Tel: 715-265-7443. Fax: 715-265-7307. p. 2594

Culhane, Bronwen, Head, Tech Proc, Helen M Plum Memorial Public Library District, 110 W Maple St, Lombard, IL, 60148-2594. Tel: 630-627-0316. Fax: 630-627-0336. p. 667

Culhane, Kay, Mgr, Access Serv, Aurora University, 315 S Gladstone, Aurora, IL, 60506-4877. Tel: 630-844-5437, 630-892-6431. Fax: 630-844-3848. p. 591

Culhane, Mary, Librn, Johnson & Wales University, 1701 NE 127th St, North Miami, FL, 33181. Tel: 305-892-7043. p. 472

Culhane, Mary, Tech Serv, North Miami Public Library, 835 NE 132nd St, North Miami, FL, 33161. Tel: 305-891-5535. Fax: 305-892-0843. p. 473

Culjat, Karen, Librn, Atchison County Library, 200 S Main St, Rock Port, MO, 64482-1532. Tel: 660-744-5404. Fax: 660-744-2861. p. 1351

Cullen, Betsy, Br Mgr, Union County Public Library, Union West Regional, 123 Unionville-Indian Trail Rd, Indian Trail, NC, 28079. Tel: 704-821-7475. Fax: 704-821-4279. p. 1810

Cullen, Carol, Tech Serv, Mount Horeb Public Library, 105 Perimeter Rd, Mount Horeb, WI, 53572. Tel: 608-437-5021. Fax: 608-437-6264. p. 2623

Cullen, Colleen, Ref & Instrul Serv, Instr Coordr, Waukesha County Technical College Library, 800 Main St, Pewaukee, WI, 53072. Tel: 262-691-7877. Fax: 262-695-3402. p. 2629

Cullen, Gina, Mgr, Ontario Ministry of the Attorney General, 720 Bay St, Main Flr, Toronto, ON, M7A 2S9, CANADA. Tel: 416-326-4563. Fax: 416-326-4562. p. 2856

Cullen, Linda, Libr Dir, US Customs & Border Protection Library, 90 K St NE, 9th Flr, Washington, DC, 20004. Tel: 202-325-0130. Fax: 202-325-0170. p. 418

Cullen, Paula Costa, Adminr, Fall River Public Library, 104 N Main St, Fall River, MA, 02720. Tel: 508-324-2700. Fax: 508-324-2707. p. 1088

Culler, Lois H, Dir, Inova Fairfax Hospital, 3300 Gallows Rd, Falls Church, VA, 22042-3300. Tel: 703-776-3234. Fax: 703-776-3353. p. 2463

Culley, Jenifer, Mgr, Ser, Longwood University, Redford & Race St, Farmville, VA, 23909. Tel: 434-395-2447. Fax: 434-395-2453. p. 2463

Culley, Sharon, Asst Librn, Lyndon Carnegie Library, 127 E Sixth, Lyndon, KS, 66451. Tel: 785-828-4520. Fax: 785-828-4565. p. 880

Culley, Tammy, Head, Outreach Serv, Lebanon Public Library, 104 E Washington St, Lebanon, IN, 46052. Tel: 765-482-3460. Fax: 317-873-5059. p. 761

Cullinan, Eileen, Cat, Chicopee Public Library, 449 Front St, Chicopee, MA, 01013. Tel: 413-594-1800. Fax: 413-594-1819. p. 1081

Cullinan, Twylia, Librn, Arthur County Public Library, 205 Fir St, Arthur, NE, 69121. Tel: 308-764-2219. Fax: 308-764-2216. p. 1392

Cullinane, Jane, Presv Librn, Connecticut State Library, 231 Capitol Ave, Hartford, CT, 06106. Tel: 860-757-6525. Fax: 860-757-6503. p. 345

Culling, Pat, Talking Bks, Macomb County Library, Macomb Library for the Blind & Physically Handicapped, 16480 Hall Rd, Clinton Township, MI, 48038-1132. Tel: 586-286-1580. Fax: 586-286-0634. p. 1164

Cullings, Karen, Dir, Commun Relations, Dauphin County Library System, 101 Walnut St, Harrisburg, PA, 17101. Tel: 717-234-4961, Ext 104. Fax: 717-234-7479. p. 2064

Cullnane, Chris W, ILL, Belhaven University, 1500 Peachtree St, Jackson, MS, 39202. Tel: 601-968-8810. Fax: 601-968-5968. p. 1303

Cullum, Carolyn, Ch, Edison Township Free Public Library, 340 Plainfield Ave, Edison, NJ, 08817. Tel: 732-287-2298. Fax: 732-819-9134. p. 1483

Cullum, Carolyn N, Coordr, Ch Serv, Edison Township Free Public Library, North Edison Branch, 777 Grove Ave, Edison, NJ, 08820. Tel: 732-548-3045. Fax: 732-549-5171. p. 1483

Cullum, Marguerite, Librn, Crazy Horse Memorial Library, 12151 Avenue of the Chiefs, Crazy Horse, SD, 57730-9506. Tel: 605-673-4681, Ext 285. Fax: 605-673-2185. p. 2211

Culp, Christine, Div Dir, Pub Serv, Alachua County Library District, 401 E University Ave, Gainesville, FL, 32601-5453. Tel: 352-334-3922. Fax: 352-334-3918. p. 448

Culp, Gwen, Computer Serv Mgr, Timberland Regional Library, 415 Tumwater Blvd SW, Tumwater, WA, 98501-5799. Tel: 360-943-5001, Ext 2518. Fax: 360-586-6838. p. 2543

Culp, Julie, Dir, Jonathan Trumbull Library, 580 Exeter Rd, Lebanon, CT, 06249. Tel: 860-642-2020, 860-642-7763. Fax: 860-642-4880. p. 349

Culpepper, Bryan, In Charge, National Park Service, 404 Watercress Dr, Van Buren, MO, 63965. Tel: 573-323-4236, Ext 4806. Fax: 573-323-4140. p. 1370

Culpepper, Jackie, Mgr, South Georgia Regional Library System, Statenville Branch, US Hwy 129 & Jackson St, Statenville, GA, 31648. Tel: 229-559-8182. p. 555

Culpepper, John, Chief Financial Officer, San Luis Obispo County Library, 995 Palm St, San Luis Obispo, CA, 93401. Tel: 805-781-5776. Fax: 805-781-1320. p. 253

Culpepper, Linda, Dir, The Detroit News, Inc, 615 W Lafayette Blvd, Detroit, MI, 48226. Tel: 313-222-2091. Fax: 313-222-2059. p. 1170

Culshaw, John, Prof, Sr Assoc Dean, University of Colorado Boulder, 1720 Pleasant St, 184 UCB, Boulder, CO, 80309-0184. Tel: 303-492-6252. Fax: 303-492-3340. p. 291

Culver, Bonnie, Br Mgr, Carbon County Library System, Medicine Bow Branch, 314 Sage St, Medicine Bow, WY, 82329. Tel: 307-379-2888. Fax: 307-379-2888. p. 2659

Culver, Chris, Youth Serv, Ventura County Library, Simi Valley Library, 2969 Tapo Canyon Rd, Simi Valley, CA, 93063. Tel: 805-526-1735. Fax: 805-526-1738. p. 280

Culver, Peg, Libr Dir, Bancroft Public Library, 181 Main St, Salem, NY, 12865. Tel: 518-854-7463. Fax: 518-854-7463. p. 1737

Culver, Scott, Librn, Lenawee County Library, Addison Branch, 102 S Talbot St, Addison, MI, 49220. Tel: 517-547-3414. Fax: 517-547-3414. p. 1147

Cumbey, Susan, Dir, Fort Ward Museum, 4301 W Braddock Rd, Alexandria, VA, 22304-1008. Tel: 703-838-4848. Fax: 703-671-7350. p. 2445

Cumbo, Cathy, Librn, Washington Adventist Hospital, 7600 Carroll Ave, Takoma Park, MD, 20912. Tel: 301-891-5260. Fax: 301-891-6087. p. 1043

Cumlet, Harolyn, Coll Develop, Head, Acq, Delgado Community College, Bldg 10, Rm 116, 615 City Park Ave, New Orleans, LA, 70119. Tel: 504-671-5327. p. 959

Cumming, Barbara, Law Librn, Watt, Tieder, Hoffar & Fitzgerald, 8405 Greensboro Dr, Ste 100, McLean, VA, 22102. Tel: 703-749-1019. Fax: 703-893-8029. p. 2478

Cumming, Greg, Archivist, Richard Nixon Library & Birthplace, 18001 Yorba Linda Blvd, Yorba Linda, CA, 92886. Tel: 714-993-5075. p. 285

Cumming, Leigh Ann, Librn, Nunavut Arctic College, PO Box 54, Cambridge Bay, NU, X0B 0C0, CANADA. Tel: 2789

Cumming, Linda, Mgr, Boulder Public Library, George F Reynolds Branch, 3595 Table Mesa Dr, Boulder, CO, 80305. Tel: 303-441-3120. Fax: 303-441-4094. p. 290

Cumming, Linda, Br Librn, Grand County Library District, Granby Branch, 55 Zero St, Granby, CO, 80446. Tel: 970-887-2149. Fax: 970-887-3851. p. 310

Cumming-Young, Elaine, Ref Librn, Massapequa Public Library, Central Avenue, 523 Central Ave, Massapequa, NY, 11758. Tel: 516-798-4607. Fax: 516-798-2804. p. 1658

Cummings, Alice R, Cat Mgr, Stone County Library, 322 West State Hwy 248, Galena, MO, 65656. Tel: 417-357-6410. Fax: 417-357-6695. p. 1329

Cummings, Carmen M, Dean of Libr Serv, Saint Johns River State College, 5001 St Johns Ave, Palatka, FL, 32177-3897. Tel: 386-312-4200. Fax: 386-325-4292. p. 478

Cummings, Dana, Coordr, Electronic Res, Bard College at Simon's Rock, 84 Alford Rd, Great Barrington, MA, 01230. Tel: 413-528-7284. Fax: 413-528-7380. p. 1092

Cummings, Edith B, Dir, Griffin Free Public Library, 22 Hooksett Rd, Auburn, NH, 03032. Tel: 603-483-5374. Fax: 603-483-0483. p. 1438

Cummings, Gail, Br Mgr, Willard Memorial Library, Wakeman Community Library, 33 Pleasant St, Wakeman, OH, 44889-9424. Tel: 440-839-2976. Fax: 440-839-2560. p. 1948

Cummings, Jennifer, Ch, Sherman Public Library, 421 N Travis, Sherman, TX, 75090-5975. Tel: 903-892-7240. Fax: 903-892-7101. p. 2387

Cummings, Joel, Head, Coll, Washington State University Libraries, 100 Dairy Rd, Pullman, WA, 99164. Tel: 509-335-6493. Fax: 509-335-6721. p. 2525

Cummings, Kathy, Br Librn, Hamlin-Lincoln County Public Library, Alum Creek Public, PO Box 530, Alum Creek, WV, 25003-0530. Tel: 304-756-9211. Fax: 304-756-9211. p. 2560

Cummings, Marge, Dir, Libr Serv, Clear Creek Baptist Bible College, 300 Clear Creek Rd, Pineville, KY, 40977. Tel: 606-337-3196. Fax: 606-337-2372. p. 933

Cummings, Mary, Ref Serv, Shawnee State University, 940 Second St, Portsmouth, OH, 45662-4344. Tel: 740-351-3461. Fax: 740-351-3432. p. 1931

Cummings, Mary, Librn, Rhode Island School for the Deaf Library, One Corliss Park, Providence, RI, 02908. Tel: 401-222-7441. Fax: 401-222-6998. p. 2174

Cummings, Mary, Dir, G E Bleskacek Memorial Library, 1519 17th Ave, Bloomer, WI, 54724. Tel: 715-568-2384. Fax: 715-568-2387. p. 2582

Cummings, Patricia K, Dir, Res Serv, Leonard, Street & Deinard, 150 S Fifth St, Ste 2300, Minneapolis, MN, 55402. Tel: 612-335-1616. Fax: 612-335-1657. p. 1260

Cummings, Rod, Automation Syst Coordr, Lincoln City Libraries, 136 S 14th St, Lincoln, NE, 68508-1899. Tel: 402-441-8522. Fax: 402-441-8586. p. 1404

Cummings, Roxanne, Circ, Mineral Area College, 5270 Flat River Rd, Park Hills, MO, 63601. Tel: 573-518-2141. Fax: 573-518-2162. p. 1349

Cummings, Theresa, Info Tech Mgr, Wake County Public Library System, 4020 Carya Dr, Raleigh, NC, 27610-2900. Tel: 919-250-1220. p. 1817

Cummins, Brenda, Librn, Dunklin County Library, Campbell Branch, 404 W Grand, Campbell, MO, 63933. Tel: 573-246-2112. p. 1342

Cummins, Grace, Asst Librn, Arnolds Park Public Library, Hwy 71, Arnolds Park, IA, 51331. Tel: 712-332-2033. p. 794

Cummins, Jean, Librn, Rhododendron Species Foundation & Botanical Garden, 2525 S 336th St, Federal Way, WA, 98003. Tel: 253-838-4646, 253-927-6960. Fax: 253-838-4686. p. 2516

Cummins, Milla, Dir, Livingston-Park County Public Library, 228 W Callender St, Livingston, MT, 59047-2618. Tel: 406-222-0862. Fax: 406-222-6522. p. 1385

Cummins, Patti, ILL, Southwest Kansas Library System, 100 Military Ave, Ste 210, Dodge City, KS, 67801-4484. Tel: 620-225-1231. Fax: 620-225-0252. p. 864

Cummins, Thom, Librn, Smithsonian Libraries, National Museum of Natural History Library, Nat Museum of Natural Hist, Rm 51, MRC 154, Tenth St & Constitution Ave NW, Washington, DC, 20013-0712. Tel: 202-633-1680. Fax: 202-357-1896. p. 415

Cunard, Gail, Dir, Harness Racing Museum & Hall of Fame, 240 Main St, Goshen, NY, 10924-2157. Tel: 845-294-6330. Fax: 845-294-3463. p. 1629

Cundiff, Patty, Human Res, Pulaski County Public Library, 304 S Main St, Somerset, KY, 42501-1402. Tel: 606-679-8401. Fax: 606-679-1779. p. 935

Cuneo, Lynn, Tech Serv, Calaveras County Library, 891 Mountain Ranch Rd, San Andreas, CA, 95249. Tel: 209-754-6510. Fax: 209-754-6512. p. 226

Cunha, Linda R, Asst Dir, Westport Free Public Library, 408 Old County Rd, Westport, MA, 02790. Tel: 508-636-1100. Fax: 508-636-1102. p. 1139

Cunio, Bridget, Ref Librn, Endicott College Library, 376 Hale St, Beverly, MA, 01915. Tel: 978-232-2285. Fax: 978-232-2700. p. 1054

Cunneen, Judy, Cat, Tech Serv, Olympic College, 1600 Chester Ave, Bremerton, WA, 98337. Tel: 360-475-7250. Fax: 360-475-7261. p. 2510

Cunniff, Nina, Dep Chief Exec Officer, Bradford-West Gwillimbury Public Library, 425 Holland St W, Bradford, ON, L3Z 0J2, CANADA. Tel: 905-775-3328. Fax: 905-775-1236. p. 2796

Cunningham, Billie, Info Serv, Catawba College, 2300 W Innes St, Salisbury, NC, 28144-2488. Tel: 704-637-4448. Fax: 704-637-4304. p. 1822

Cunningham, Carolyn, Br Mgr, St Joseph Public Library, 927 Felix St, Saint Joseph, MO, 64501-2799. Tel: 816-232-7729. Fax: 816-279-3372. p. 1352

Cunningham, Carolyn, Ref Serv, Shaler North Hills Library, 1822 Mount Royal Blvd, Glenshaw, PA, 15116. Tel: 412-486-0211. Fax: 412-486-8286. p. 2061

Cunningham, Ceil, Librn, Macsherry Library, 112 Walton St, Alexandria Bay, NY, 13607. Tel: 315-482-2241. Fax: 315-482-2241. p. 1572

Cunningham, Charlotte, Mgr, Youth Serv, Willard Memorial Library, Six W Emerald St, Willard, OH, 44890-1498. Tel: 419-933-8564. Fax: 419-933-4783. p. 1948

Cunningham, D, Head Ref Librn, Reed Smith LLP, 1999 Harrison St, Oakland, CA, 94612. Tel: 510-466-6195. Fax: 510-273-8832. p. 198

Cunningham, Deana, Adult Serv, Granville County Library System, 210 Main St, Oxford, NC, 27565-3321. Tel: 919-693-1121. Fax: 919-693-2244. p. 1813

Cunningham, Deborah, Circ Supvr, Stoneham Public Library, 431 Main St, Stoneham, MA, 02180. Tel: 781-438-1324. Fax: 781-279-3836. p. 1129

Cunningham, Deborah, Head, Ref, Harborfields Public Library, 31 Broadway, Greenlawn, NY, 11740-1382. Tel: 631-757-4200. Fax: 631-757-7216. p. 1631

Cunningham, Denyse, Curator, Broward County Historical Commission Library, 301 SW 13th Ave, Fort Lauderdale, FL, 33312. Tel: 954-357-5553. Fax: 954-357-5522. p. 442

Cunningham, Diana, Tech Serv Supvr, Brighton District Library, 100 Library Dr, Brighton, MI, 48116. Tel: 810-229-6571, Ext 220. Fax: 810-229-3161. p. 1159

Cunningham, Diana, Assoc Dean, Dir, New York Medical College, Basic Science Bldg, 95 Grasslands Rd, Valhalla, NY, 10595. Tel: 914-594-4200. Fax: 914-594-3171. p. 1760

Cunningham, Donna, Dir, Athens Municipal Library, 410 E Hargrave St, Athens, IL, 62613-9702. Tel: 217-636-8047. Fax: 217-636-8763. p. 590

Cunningham, Elora, Librn, Web Coordr, Community College of Allegheny County, 808 Ridge Ave, Pittsburgh, PA, 15212-6003. Tel: 412-237-2585. Fax: 412-237-6563. p. 2124

Cunningham, Janelle, Libr Coordr, Ball Memorial Hospital, 2401 W University Ave, Muncie, IN, 47303-3499. Tel: 765-747-3204. Fax: 765-747-0137. p. 766

Cunningham, Jill, Librn, Douglas County Library System, Yoncalla Branch, 194 Birch, Yoncalla, OR, 97499. Tel: 541-849-2128. Fax: 541-849-2128. p. 2016

Cunningham, Kathleen, Ref Serv, Henry Ford Community College, 5101 Evergreen Rd, Dearborn, MI, 48128-1495. Tel: 313-845-9763. Fax: 313-845-9795. p. 1167

Cunningham, Kay, Mus Dir, SullivanMunce Cultural Center, 225 W Hawthorne St, Zionsville, IN, 46077. Tel: 317-873-4900. p. 789

Cunningham, Kay, Dir, Christian Brothers University, 650 E Pkwy South, Memphis, TN, 38104. Tel: 901-321-3432. Fax: 901-321-3219. p. 2248

Cunningham, Keith, Librn, Alabama Department of Corrections, 1000 Saint Clair Rd, Springville, AL, 35146-9790. Tel: 205-467-6111, Ext 610. p. 36

Cunningham, Kristin, Dir, Okmulgee Public Library, 218 S Okmulgee Ave, Okmulgee, OK, 74447. Tel: 918-756-1448. Fax: 918-758-1148. p. 1975

Cunningham, Leigh, Coll & Instruction Librn, Medicine Hat College Library, 299 College Dr SE, Medicine Hat, AB, T1A 3Y6, CANADA. Tel: 403-529-3867. Fax: 403-504-3634. p. 2711

Cunningham, Leslie, Doc, Albany Law School, 80 New Scotland Ave, Albany, NY, 12208. Tel: 518-445-2340. Fax: 518-472-5842. p. 1568

Cunningham, Lois, Cat, Sparta Public Library, 211 W Broadway, Sparta, IL, 62286. Tel: 618-443-5014. Fax: 618-443-2952. p. 704

Cunningham, Maureen, Tech Serv, Tappan Library, 93 Main St, Tappan, NY, 10983. Tel: 845-359-3877. p. 1754

Cunningham, Michelle, Cataloger, Miles City Public Library, One S Tenth St, Miles City, MT, 59301-3398. Tel: 406-234-1496. Fax: 406-234-2095. p. 1386

Cunningham, Nancy A, Dir, Acad Serv, University of South Florida, Tampa Campus Library, 4101 USF Apple Dr, LIB122, Tampa, FL, 33620. Tel: 813-974-0450. Fax: 813-974-5153. p. 499

Cunningham, Nancy A, Dr, Dir, Roswell Park Cancer Institute, Elm & Carlton Sts, Buffalo, NY, 14263. Tel: 716-845-5966. Fax: 716-845-8699. p. 1598

Cunningham Putt, Twyla, Mgr, SEARCH Group, Inc Library, 7311 Greenhaven Dr, Ste 145, Sacramento, CA, 95831. Tel: 916-392-2550. Fax: 916-392-8440. p. 225

Cunningham, Robert, Librn, New York State Judicial Department, M Dolores Denman Courthouse, 50 East Ave, Ste 100, Rochester, NY, 14604-2214. Tel: 585-530-3250. Fax: 585-530-3270. p. 1731

Cunningham, Sojourna, Chief Librn, ECPI University, 4101 Doie Cope Rd, Raleigh, NC, 27613. Tel: 919-571-0057, Ext 210. Fax: 919-571-0780. p. 1815

Cunningham, Susan, Supvr, Circ/Registration/AV, Inglewood Public Library, 101 W Manchester Blvd, Inglewood, CA, 90301-1771. Tel: 310-412-5397. Fax: 310-412-8848. p. 159

Cunningham, Susan, Info Analyst, Albemarle Corp Library, Information Services, 451 Florida St, 15th Flr, Baton Rouge, LA, 70801-1700. Tel: 225-388-7402 (customer serv). Fax: 225-388-7686. p. 942

Cunningham, Vicki, ILL, Pontiac Public Library, 211 E Madison St, Pontiac, IL, 61764. Tel: 815-844-7229. Fax: 815-844-3475. p. 692

Cunningham, Wendy, Sr Libr Asst, Burlington Public Library, 34 Library Lane, Burlington, CT, 06013. Tel: 860-673-3331. Fax: 860-673-0897. p. 333

Cunningham-Kruppa, Ellen, Dir, University of Texas at Austin, One University Sta, D7000, Austin, TX, 78712-0390. Tel: 512-471-3821. Fax: 512-471-3971. p. 2975

Cunnion, Katherine, Ref, Umpqua Community College Library, 1140 Umpqua College Rd, Roseburg, OR, 97470. Tel: 541-440-7681. Fax: 541-440-4637. p. 2017

Cunnyngham, Beau, Asst Dir, Tipton County Public Library, 127 E Madison St, Tipton, IN, 46072-1993. Tel: 765-675-8761. Fax: 765-675-4475. p. 782

Cuperus, Beth, Dir, Fulda Memorial Library, 101 Third St NE, Fulda, MN, 56131-1106. Tel: 507-425-3277. p. 1252

Cupryk, Robert, Ref, University of Medicine & Dentistry of New Jersey, PO Box 19, New Brunswick, NJ, 08903. Tel: 732-235-7604. Fax: 732-235-7826. p. 1509

Curbow, Joan, Cat, Ser, Buena Vista University Library, 610 W Fourth St, Storm Lake, IA, 50588. Tel: 712-749-2094. Fax: 712-749-2059. p. 846

Curci-Gonzalez, Lucy, Dir, Libr & Info Serv, Kenyon & Kenyon LLP, One Broadway, 10th Flr, New York, NY, 10004-1007. Tel: 212-425-7200. Fax: 212-908-6113. p. 1684

Curell, Ed, Librn, Terrace Public Library, 4610 Park Ave, Terrace, BC, V8G 1V6, CANADA. Tel: 250-638-8177. Fax: 250-635-6207. p. 2739

Cureton, Janice, Librn, Dunklin County Library, Arbyrd Branch, 100A N Douglas Ave, Arbyrd, MO, 63821. Tel: 573-654-2385. p. 1342

Cureton, Janice, Librn, Dunklin County Library, Cardwell Branch, Main St, Cardwell, MO, 63829. Tel: 573-654-3366. p. 1342

Curin, Brenda, ILL, Thunderbird School of Global Management, 15249 N 59th Ave, Glendale, AZ, 85306-6001. Tel: 602-978-7235. Fax: 602-978-7762. p. 64

Curlee, Mimi, Govt Doc, Ser, Charlotte Mecklenburg Library, 310 N Tryon St, Charlotte, NC, 28202-2176. Tel: 704-416-0101. Fax: 704-416-0130. p. 1781

Curley, Kathleen, Dir, Pima Community College, District Library Services, 4905B E Broadway Blvd, Tucson, AZ, 85709-1140. Tel: 520-206-7267. Fax: 520-206-6201. p. 86

Curley, Patricia, Dir, Stockton Springs Community Library, Six Station St, Stockton Springs, ME, 04981. Tel: 207-567-4147. Fax: 207-567-4147. p. 1003

Curlin, Nelda, Adult Serv, Nicholas P Sims Library, 515 W Main, Waxahachie, TX, 75165-3235. Tel: 972-937-2671. Fax: 972-937-4409. p. 2398

Curnes, Janice, Librn, Department of Veterans Affairs, VA Medical Ctr, 5000 W National Ave, Milwaukee, WI, 53295. Tel: 414-384-2000, Ext 42342. Fax: 414-382-5334. p. 2618

Curnes, Janice, Coordr, Southeastern Wisconsin Health Science Library Consortium, Veteran's Admin Ctr Medical Library, 5000 W National Ave, Milwaukee, WI, 53295. Tel: 414-384-2000, Ext 42342. Fax: 414-382-5334. p. 2958

Curnutt, Nan, Br Mgr, Louisville Free Public Library, Okolona, 7709 Preston Hwy, Louisville, KY, 40219. Tel: 502-964-3515. Fax: 502-964-7025. p. 924

Curotto, Nick, Access Serv, Asst Librn, Virginia Museum of Fine Arts Library, 200 N Boulevard, Richmond, VA, 23220-4007. Tel: 804-340-5523. Fax: 804-340-1431. p. 2492

Curran, Annabelle, Archivist, Moore College of Art & Design, 20th St & The Parkway, Philadelphia, PA, 19103-1179. Tel: 215-965-4057. Fax: 215-965-8544. p. 2112

Curran, Beth, Head, Ref, Providence Public Library, 150 Empire St, Providence, RI, 02903-3283. Tel: 401-455-8010. Fax: 401-455-8065, 401-455-8080. p. 2173

Curran, Candace, Coordr, ILL, Wheeler Memorial Library, 49 E Main St, Orange, MA, 01364-1267. Tel: 978-544-2495. Fax: 978-544-1116. p. 1116

Curran, George, Chair, Southwestern Virginia Health Information Librarians, Carilion Health Sciences Library, Belleview at Jefferson St, Roanoke, VA, 24033. Tel: 540-689-1771. Fax: 540-689-1770. p. 2957

Curran, George L, III, Dir, Health Sci Libr, RMH Healthcare, 2010 Health Campus Dr, Harrisonburg, VA, 22801-3293. Tel: 540-689-1777. Fax: 540-689-1770. p. 2471

Curran, Hugh, Br Librn, Bronson Silas Library, Bunker Hill, 192 Bunker Hill Ave, Waterbury, CT, 06708. Tel: 203-574-8240. p. 374

Currano, Judith, Librn, University of Pennsylvania Libraries, Chemistry, 3301 Spruce St, 5th Flr, Philadelphia, PA, 19104-6323. Tel: 215-898-2177. Fax: 215-898-0741. p. 2119

Curras, Nuria, Librn, Valencia Community College, 850 W Morse Blvd, Winter Park, FL, 32789. Tel: 407-582-6814. Fax: 407-582-6014. p. 505

Curras, Nurria, Dir, ITT Technical Institute, 1400 International Pkwy S, Lake Mary, FL, 32746. Tel: 407-936-0572. Fax: 407-936-0512. p. 458

Current, Evelyn, Circ Serv Supvr, Muncie Center Township Public Library, 2005 S High St, Muncie, IN, 47302. Tel: 765-741-7330. Fax: 765-747-8211. p. 767

Current, Martha, Ch, Roseland Free Public Library, 20 Roseland Ave, Roseland, NJ, 07068-1235. Tel: 973-226-8636. Fax: 973-226-6429. p. 1527

Current, Michael, Govt Doc, University of Wisconsin-La Crosse, 1631 Pine St, La Crosse, WI, 54601-3748. Tel: 608-785-8739. Fax: 608-785-8639. p. 2603

Current, R Diane, Br Coordr, Middletown Public Library, Trenton Branch, 21 E State St, Trenton, OH, 45067. Tel: 513-988-9930. Fax: 513-988-5059. p. 1917

Currie, Betty, Br Coordr, Central Mississippi Regional Library System, 104 Office Park Dr, Brandon, MS, 39042-2404. Tel: 601-825-0100. Fax: 601-825-0199. p. 1294

Currie, Cindy, Librn, Talladega County Law Library, Talladega County Judicial Bldg, Northeast St, Talladega, AL, 35161. Tel: 256-761-2116. Fax: 256-480-5293. p. 37

Currie, Colette, Supvr, Essex County Library, Woodslee Branch, 100 S Middle Rd, Woodslee, ON, N0R 1V0, CANADA. Tel: 226-946-1529, Ext 231. p. 2804

Currie, Gregg, Col Librn, Selkirk College Library, 301 Frank Beinder Way, Castlegar, BC, V1N 3J1, CANADA. Tel: 250-365-1263. Fax: 250-365-7259. p. 2726

Currie, Jan, Pub Serv, Northwest Community College Library, 5331 McConnell Ave, Terrace, BC, V8G 4X2, CANADA. Tel: 250-638-5407. Fax: 250-635-1594. p. 2739

Currie, Jean, Dir, The History Center in Tompkins County, 401 E State St, Ste 100, Ithaca, NY, 14850. Tel: 607-273-8284. Fax: 607-273-6107. p. 1642

Currie, Kelly D, Dir, Delphi Public Library, 222 E Main St, Delphi, IN, 46923. Tel: 765-564-2929, Ext 21. Fax: 765-564-4746. p. 735

Currie, L, Head Librn, University of Saskatchewan Libraries, Education, Education Bldg, Rm 2003, 28 Campus Dr, Saskatoon, SK, S7N 0X1, CANADA. Tel: 306-966-5973. Fax: 306-966-2444. p. 2927

Currie, Lyn, Head Librn, University of Saskatchewan Libraries, Natural Sciences Library, 180 Geology Bldg, 114 Science Pl, Saskatoon, SK, S7N 5E2, CANADA. Tel: 306-966-6049. Fax: 306-966-6040. p. 2927

Currie, Lyn, Librn, University of Saskatchewan Libraries, Engineering, 1B08 Engineering Bldg, 57 Campus Dr, Saskatoon, SK, S7N 5A9, CANADA. Tel: 306-966-5978. Fax: 306-966-1352. p. 2927

Currie, Nancy, Dir, Republic-Michigamme Public Library, Rte 1, Box 201-A, 227 Maple St, Republic, MI, 49879-9998. Tel: 906-376-2239, 906-376-2277. Fax: 906-376-8299. p. 1221

Currie, Nancy, Dir/Fiscal Officer, Madison Public Library, 6111 Middle Ridge Rd, Madison, OH, 44057-2818. Tel: 440-428-2189. Fax: 440-428-7402. p. 1912

Currie, William W, Librn, Bowling Green State University, One University Dr, 2nd Flr, Huron, OH, 44839-9791. Tel: 419-433-5560, Ext 20739. Fax: 419-433-9696. p. 1905

Currier, Michelle, Dir of Libr Serv, State University of New York College of Technology, 34 Cornell Dr, Canton, NY, 13617-1098. Tel: 315-386-7055. Fax: 315-386-7931. p. 1602

Currier, Patricia, Asst Librn, Dudley-Tucker Library, Six Epping St, Raymond, NH, 03077. Tel: 603-895-2633. Fax: 603-895-0904. p. 1463

Currin, Alex, Head, ILL, Head, Per, Anderson County Library, 300 N McDuffie St, Anderson, SC, 29621-5643. Tel: 864-260-4500. Fax: 864-260-4510. p. 2180

Curris, Cheryl, Asst Dir, Rangeley Public Library, Seven Lake St, Rangeley, ME, 04970. Tel: 207-864-5529. Fax: 207-864-2523. p. 998

Curry, Alexis, Head Librn, Los Angeles County Museum of Art, 5905 Wilshire Blvd, Los Angeles, CA, 90036-4597. Tel: 323-857-6122. Fax: 323-857-4790. p. 172

Curry, Barbara, Ch, Autauga-Prattville Public Library, 254 Doster St, Prattville, AL, 36067-3933. Tel: 334-365-3396. Fax: 334-365-3397. p. 34

Curry, Brian, Librn, Cherry Hospital, U-4 Bldg, 1st Flr, 201 Stevens Mill Rd, Goldsboro, NC, 27530. Tel: 919-731-3447, Ext 232. Fax: 919-731-3429. p. 1795

Curry, Deborah, Head, Acq, State University of New York at Oswego, SUNY Oswego, 7060 State Rte 104, Oswego, NY, 13126-3514. Tel: 315-312-3545. Fax: 315-312-3194. p. 1713

Curry, Diana, Info Spec, Fort Smith Public Library, 3201 Rogers Ave, Fort Smith, AR, 72903. Tel: 479-783-0229. Fax: 479-782-8571. p. 100

Curry, Diane, Curator, Hayward Area Historical Society Museum Library, 22380 Foothill Blvd, Hayward, CA, 94541. Tel: 510-581-0223. Fax: 510-581-0217. p. 157

Curry, Elaine M, Librn, Hazleton General Hospital, 700 E Broad St, Hazleton, PA, 18201. Tel: 570-501-4800. Fax: 570-501-4840. p. 2068

Curry, Elizabeth, Tech Serv Coordr, Hilbert College, 5200 S Park Ave, Hamburg, NY, 14075. Tel: 716-649-7900, Ext 246. Fax: 716-648-6530. p. 1632

Curry, Esther, Asst Dir, C E Brehm Memorial Public Library District, 101 S Seventh St, Mount Vernon, IL, 62864. Tel: 618-242-6322. Fax: 618-242-0810. p. 677

Curry, Jane, Br Head, Vancouver Public Library, Marpole Branch, 8386 Granville St, Vancouver, BC, V6P 4Z7, CANADA. Tel: 604-665-3978. Fax: 604-665-3552. p. 2744

Curry, Janet, Br Mgr, Mobile Public Library, West Regional, 5555 Grelot Rd, Mobile, AL, 36609. Tel: 251-340-8555. Fax: 251-304-2160. p. 26

Curry, Janice, Librn, Southwest Arkansas Regional Library, Howard County Library, 426 N Main St, Ste 5, Nashville, AR, 71852. Tel: 870-845-2566. Fax: 870-845-7532. p. 103

Curry, Judy, Br Head, Toronto Public Library, Urban Affairs, Metro Hall, 55 John St, Toronto, ON, M5V 3C6, CANADA. Tel: 416-397-7241. Fax: 416-397-7245. p. 2863

Curry, Kathleen, Librn, Good Samaritan Hospital, 5601 Loch Raven Blvd, Baltimore, MD, 21239-2905. Tel: 410-532-3891. Fax: 410-532-4381. p. 1013

Curry, Kris, Dir, New Albin Public Library, 176 Elm St, New Albin, IA, 52160. Tel: 563-544-4747. Fax: 563-544-4757. p. 834

Curry, Larrie Spier, Dir, VPres, Shaker Village of Pleasant Hill Museum Library, 3501 Lexington Rd, Harrodsburg, KY, 40330. Tel: 859-734-5411. Fax: 859-734-7278. p. 916

Curry, Marcella M, Dir, South Dennis Free Public Library, 389 Main St, South Dennis, MA, 02660. Tel: 508-394-8954. Fax: 508-394-4392. p. 1125

Curry, Mary, ILL, Trinity College Library, 300 Summit St, Hartford, CT, 06106. Tel: 860-297-2255. Fax: 860-297-2251. p. 347

Curry, Maureen, Br Head Librn, Okanagan Regional Library, 1430 KLO Rd, Kelowna, BC, V1W 3P6, CANADA. Tel: 250-860-4033. Fax: 250-861-8696. p. 2730

Curry, Pat, Dir, Nancy Nail Memorial Library, 124 S Pearl St, Mart, TX, 76664-1425. Tel: 254-876-2465. Fax: 254-876-2465. p. 2360

Curry, Stephanie, Librn, Reedley College Library, 995 N Reed Ave, Reedley, CA, 93654. Tel: 559-638-0362. Fax: 559-638-0384. p. 216

Curry, Vera, Automation Librn, Finkelstein Memorial Library, 24 Chestnut St, Spring Valley, NY, 10977-5594. Tel: 845-352-5700. Fax: 845-352-2319. p. 1746

Curry, Yvonne, Sr Librn, Praxair, Inc Library, 175 E Park Dr, Tonawanda, NY, 14151. Tel: 716-879-2031. Fax: 716-879-3101. p. 1755

Curry-Wimberly, Brenda, Librn, Northside Hospital, 1000 Johnson Ferry Rd NE, Atlanta, GA, 30342-1611. Tel: 404-851-6431. Fax: 404-851-6167. p. 517

Curtin, Nancy, Dir, Port Washington Public Library, One Library Dr, Port Washington, NY, 11050. Tel: 516-883-4400. Fax: 516-883-7927. p. 1721

Curtin, Raymond W, Dir, Interlakes Oncology Medical Library, 1555 Long Pond Rd, Rochester, NY, 14626. Tel: 585-723-7755. Fax: 585-723-7078. p. 1729

Curtis, Amy, Dir, DeRuyter Free Library, 735 Utica St, DeRuyter, NY, 13052-9613. Tel: 315-852-6262. Fax: 315-852-6262. p. 1614

Curtis, Andrea, Ch, Guelph Public Library, 100 Norfolk St, Guelph, ON, N1H 4J6, CANADA. Tel: 519-824-6220. Fax: 519-824-8342. p. 2807

Curtis, Betty, Tech Serv, King College, 1350 King College Rd, Bristol, TN, 37620. Tel: 423-652-4792. Fax: 423-652-4871. p. 2225

Curtis, Brenda, Dir, Librn, Linn County Library District No 3, 316 Main St, Blue Mound, KS, 66010. Tel: 913-756-2628. Fax: 913-756-2628. p. 858

Curtis, Dave, Dep Libr Dir, Carlsbad City Library, 1775 Dove Lane, Carlsbad, CA, 92011-4048. Tel: 760-602-2010. Fax: 760-602-7942. p. 132

Curtis, Debbie, Actg Librn, Southern Regional Education Board Library, 592 Tenth St NW, Atlanta, GA, 30318-5776. Tel: 404-875-9211, Ext 236. Fax: 404-872-1477. p. 518

Curtis, Donnelyn, Res Serv, University of Nevada-Reno, 1664 N Virginia St, Mailstop 0322, Reno, NV, 89557-0322. Tel: 775-682-5668. Fax: 775-784-4529. p. 1433

Curtis, Drucilla, Dept Supvr, Klamath County Library Services District, 126 S Third St, Klamath Falls, OR, 97601-6394. Tel: 541-882-8894. Fax: 541-882-6166. p. 2001

Curtis, Greg, Head Govt Publ, University of Maine, 5729 Fogler Library, Orono, ME, 04469-5729. Fax: 207-581-1653. p. 994

Curtis, Gregory, Dir, University of Maine at Presque Isle Library, 181 Main St, Presque Isle, ME, 04769-2888. Tel: 207-768-9599. Fax: 207-768-9644. p. 998

Curtis, Gwen, Cat & Ref, Maps Selector, University of Kentucky Libraries, Science Library, 211 King Bldg, Lexington, KY, 40506-0039. Tel: 859-257-1853. Fax: 859-323-3225. p. 922

Curtis, Janet, Libr Tech, SSG Paul D Savanuck Memorial Library, Defense Information School, 6500 Mapes Rd, Rm 1161, Fort George G Meade, MD, 20755. Tel: 301-677-4692. Fax: 301-677-4697. p. 1028

Curtis, Janet, Ch, Lapeer District Library, 201 Village West Dr S, Lapeer, MI, 48446-1699. Tel: 810-664-9521. Fax: 810-664-8527. p. 1202

Curtis, Jim, Dir, Portage Lake District Library, 58 Huron St, Houghton, MI, 49931-2194. Tel: 906-482-4570. Fax: 906-482-2129. p. 1192

Curtis, John, Cat Librn, Hampton University, 130 E Tyler St, Hampton, VA, 23668. Tel: 757-727-5183. Fax: 757-727-5952. p. 2468

Curtis, John C, Exec Dir, Allaire Village Inc, 4265 Atlantic Ave, Farmingdale, NJ, 07727. Tel: 732-919-3500. Fax: 732-938-3302. p. 1485

Curtis, Judy, Circ Supvr, Carpenter-Carse Library, 69 Ballards Corner Rd, Hinesburg, VT, 05461. Tel: 802-482-2878. p. 2426

Curtis, Lori, Spec Coll & Archives Librn, Loma Linda University, 11072 Anderson St, Loma Linda, CA, 92350-0001. Tel: 909-558-4581. Fax: 909-558-4121. p. 165

Curtis, Margaret, Librn, Chattanooga-Hamilton County Bicentennial Library, Eastgate, 5900 Bldg, 5705 Marlin Rd, Ste 1500, Chattanooga, TN, 37411. Tel: 423-855-2686. Fax: 423-855-2696. p. 2227

Curtis, Matthew, Head, Circ & Reserve, City University of New York, 365 Fifth Ave, New York, NY, 10016-4309. Tel: 212-817-7040. Fax: 212-817-2982. p. 1673

Curtis, Merilee, Pub Info Officer, St Charles Public Library District, One S Sixth Ave, Saint Charles, IL, 60174-2105. Tel: 630-584-0076, Ext 240. Fax: 630-584-3448. p. 699

Curtis, Michael, Ref Serv, Syst Librn, Broome Community College, 907 Front St, Binghamton, NY, 13905-1328. Tel: 607-778-5609. Fax: 607-778-5108. p. 1581

Curtis, Rita, Ch Librn Supvr, Durango Public Library, 1900 E Third Ave, Durango, CO, 81301. Tel: 970-375-3385. Fax: 970-375-3398. p. 304

Curtis, Roberta, Librn, Palliser Regional Library, Bethune Branch, Community Hall, 524 East St, Bethune, SK, S0G 0H0, CANADA. Tel: 306-638-3046. p. 2918

Curtis, Sue, Libr Mgr, Blue Ridge Community Library, PO Box 264, Blue Ridge, AB, T0E 0B0, CANADA. Tel: 780-648-7323. p. 2685

Curtis, Susan, Head, Ref, University of Georgia Libraries, Athens, GA, 30602-1641. Tel: 706-542-0654. Fax: 706-542-4144. p. 510

Curtis, Tracie, Head Librn, Apache Junction Public Library, 1177 N Idaho Rd, Apache Junction, AZ, 85219. Tel: 480-474-8555. Fax: 480-983-4540. p. 57

Curtis, Whitney, Asst Dir, Pub Serv, The University of Memphis, One N Front St, Memphis, TN, 38103. Tel: 901-678-4937. Fax: 901-678-5293. p. 2252

Curtis-Bonardi, Joyce, ILL, Bon Accord Public Library, PO Box 749, Bon Accord, AB, T0A 0K0, CANADA. Tel: 780-921-2540. Fax: 780-921-2580. p. 2685

Curuso, Yuusuf, Librn, Columbia University, Area Studies, 307 International Affairs Bldg, 420 W 118th St, New York, NY, 10027. Tel: 212-854-3630. Fax: 212-854-3834. p. 1674

Curzon, Betty Ann, Br Mgr, Door County Library, Sister Bay-Liberty Grove Branch, 301 Mill Rd, Sister Bay, WI, 54234. Tel: 920-854-2721. p. 2641

Cushing, Chris, Br Coordr, Caroline Library Inc, 17202 Richmond Tpk, Milford, VA, 22514. Tel: 804-633-5455. Fax: 804-633-9069. p. 2479

Cushing, Lee, Info Tech, Joplin Public Library, 300 S Main, Joplin, MO, 64801. Tel: 417-623-7953. Fax: 417-625-4728. p. 1335

Cushman, Aaron, Ref Serv, Taunton Public Library, 12 Pleasant St, Taunton, MA, 02780. Tel: 508-821-1410. Fax: 508-821-1414. p. 1131

Cushman, Melanie Meyers, Librn, Jewish Board of Family & Children Services, 120 W 57th St, New York, NY, 10019. Tel: 212-582-9100, Ext 1504. Fax: 212-956-0526. p. 1683

Cushman, Mellisa, Librn, CGH Medical Center, 100 E LeFevre Rd, Sterling, IL, 61081-1278. Tel: 815-625-0400, Ext 5794. p. 707

Cushman, Robert, Head, Libr Tech, State University of New York College at Brockport, 350 New Campus Dr, Brockport, NY, 14420-2997. Tel: 585-395-2032. Fax: 585-395-5651. p. 1585

Cushman, Ruth, Circ, West Lafayette Public Library, 208 W Columbia St, West Lafayette, IN, 47906. Tel: 765-743-2261. Fax: 765-743-0540. p. 787

Cushmeer, Traci E, Libr Dir, The Art Institute of Phoenix, 2233 W Dunlap Ave, Phoenix, AZ, 85021-2859. Tel: 602-331-7535. Fax: 602-216-3150. p. 72

Cusick, Cari, Dir, Hesston Public Library, 300 N Main St, Hesston, KS, 67062. Tel: 620-327-4666. Fax: 620-327-4459. p. 871

Cusker, Jeremy, Earth Sci & Eng Outreach Librn, Cornell University Library, Engineering, Virtual Library, Carpenter Hall, Ithaca, NY, 14853-2201. Tel: 607-254-6261. p. 1641

Cusker, Kit, Sr Librn, Denver Public Library, Park Hill, 4705 Montview Blvd, Denver, CO, 80207-3760. Tel: 303-331-4063. Fax: 303-388-2335. p. 301

Cusson, Gilles, Coordr, Cegep de Chicoutimi, 534 Jacques-Cartier, Est, Chicoutimi, QC, G7H 1Z6, CANADA. Tel: 418-549-9520, Ext 337. Fax: 418-549-1315. p. 2881

Cusson, Jean-François, Chef de Section, Bibliothèques de Montrèal, Belleville, 10400, avenue de Belleville, Montreal, QC, H1H 4Z7, CANADA. Tel: 514-328-4000, Ext 5620. Fax: 514-328-4298. p. 2889

Cusson, Jean-François, Chef de Section, Bibliothèques de Montrèal, Charleroi, 4740, rue de Charleroi, Montreal, QC, H1H 1V2, CANADA. Tel: 514-328-4000, Ext 5620. Fax: 514-328-4298. p. 2889

Cusson, Jean-François, Chef de Section, Bibliothèques de Montrèal, Henri-Bourassa, 5400, boulevard Henri-Bourassa Est, Montreal, QC, H1G 2S9, CANADA. Tel: 514-328-4000, Ext 5620. Fax: 514-328-4298. p. 2889

Cusson, Jean-François, Chef de Section, Bibliothèques de Montrèal, Maison culturelle et communautaire, 12002, boulevard Rolland, Montreal, QC, H1G 3W1, CANADA. Tel: 514-328-4000, Ext 5620. p. 2890

Custeau, Marc-Yvan, Tech Spec, Hopital Louis-H Lafontaine, 7401 Hochelaga, Montreal, QC, H1N 3M5, CANADA. Tel: 514-251-4000, Ext 2963. Fax: 514-251-0270. p. 2896

Custen, Barbara, Dir, Pub Serv, County of Los Angeles Public Library, 7400 E Imperial Hwy, Downey, CA, 90242-3375. Tel: 562-940-8409. Fax: 562-803-3032. p. 140

Custer, Angie, Dir, Carrollton Public Library, 509 S Main St, Carrollton, IL, 62016. Tel: 217-942-6715. Fax: 217-942-6005. p. 601

Custer, Carrie, Dir, Lindale Library, 200 E Hubbard St, Lindale, TX, 75771. Tel: 903-882-1900. Fax: 903-882-1236. p. 2356

Custer, Cheryl, Dir, Fendrick Library, 20 N Main St, Mercersburg, PA, 17236-1612. Tel: 717-328-9233. p. 2088

Custer, Joe, Dir, Saint Louis University, Omer Poos Law Library, Morrissey Hall, 3700 Lindell Blvd, Saint Louis, MO, 63108-3478. Tel: 314-977-4531. Fax: 314-977-3966. p. 1361

Custer, Joseph A, Assoc Dir, Head, Tech Serv, University of Kansas Libraries, Wheat Law Library, Green Hall, Rm 200, 1535 W 15th St, Lawrence, KS, 66045-7608. Tel: 785-864-3025. Fax: 785-864-3680. p. 878

Custer, Sharon, Ref, Eccles-Lesher Memorial Library, 673 Main St, Rimersburg, PA, 16248-4817. Tel: 814-473-3800. Fax: 814-473-8200. p. 2134

Custodio, Danny, In Charge, Rodman Hall Arts Centre Library, 109 Saint Paul Crescent, St. Catharines, ON, L2S 1M3, CANADA. Tel: 905-684-2925. Fax: 905-682-4733. p. 2843

Cutforth-Anderson, Lisa, Learning Res Ctr Coordr, Alberta Bible College Learning Resource Centre, 635 Northmount Dr NW, Calgary, AB, T2K 3J6, CANADA. Tel: 403-282-2994, Ext 242. Fax: 403-282-3084. p. 2687

Cuthbert, John, Curator, West Virginia University Libraries, WVU Libraries, 1549 University Ave, Morgantown, WV, 26506. Tel: 304-293-4040. Fax: 304-293-6638. p. 2566

Cuthbert, John, Curator, West Virginia University Libraries, West Virginia & Regional History Collection, 1549 University Ave, Morgantown, WV, 26506-6069. Tel: 304-293-3536. Fax: 304-293-3981. p. 2567

Cutinella, Stacy, Ref & 1st Year Learning Experience Librn, Augsburg College, 2211 Riverside Ave, Minneapolis, MN, 55454. Tel: 612-330-1604. Fax: 612-330-1436. p. 1259

Cutko, Kate, Librn, Bowdoinham Public Library, 13A School St, Bowdoinham, ME, 04008. Tel: 207-666-8405. p. 978

Cutler, Diane, Br Mgr, Kent District Library, Cascade Township Branch, 2870 Jack Smith Ave SE, Grand Rapids, MI, 49546. Tel: 616-784-2007. Fax: 616-647-3854. p. 1165

Cutler, Paul, Head, Circ, Plainville Public Library, 198 South St, Plainville, MA, 02762-1512. Tel: 508-695-1784. Fax: 508-695-6359. p. 1118

Cutler, Torie, Ch, Garland Public Library, 86 W Factory St, Garland, UT, 84312. Tel: 435-257-3117. Fax: 435-257-1217. p. 2406

Cutrer, Mary Ann, Br Mgr, Tangipahoa Parish Library, Loranger Branch, 19451 Hwy 40, Loranger, LA, 70446. Tel: 985-878-6224. Fax: 985-878-3571. p. 941

Cutright, Desiree, Human Res, Wayne County Public Library, 220 W Liberty St, Wooster, OH, 44691-3593. Tel: 330-804-4683. Fax: 330-262-1352. p. 1950

Cutright, Judith, Dir, Clay County Public Library, 116 Guffey St, Celina, TN, 38551-9802. Tel: 931-243-3442. Fax: 931-243-4876. p. 2226

Cutright, Patricia, Dean, Central Washington University, 400 E University Way, Ellensburg, WA, 98926-7548. Tel: 509-963-1901. Fax: 509-963-3684. p. 2514

Cutul, Anne-Marie, Info Tech, Scarsdale Public Library, 54 Olmsted Rd, Scarsdale, NY, 10583. Tel: 914-722-1300. Fax: 914-722-1305. p. 1739

Cvejanovich, Sue, Circ & Main Libr Adminr, Miami-Dade Public Library System, 101 W Flagler St, Miami, FL, 33130-1523. Tel: 305-375-3555. Fax: 305-375-3048. p. 466

Cwik, Marta, Head, Cat, Marist College, 3399 North Rd, Poughkeepsie, NY, 12601-1387. Tel: 845-575-3199. Fax: 845-575-3150. p. 1722

Cyfers, Sharon, Asst Librn, Chapmanville Public Library, 299 Vance St, Chapmanville, WV, 25508. Tel: 304-855-3405. Fax: 304-855-8590. p. 2555

Cynthia, MacNaught, Ch, East Longmeadow Public Library, 60 Center Sq, East Longmeadow, MA, 01028-2459. Tel: 413-525-5400. Fax: 413-525-0344. p. 1086

Cynthia, Stosse, Dir, Pembroke Town Library, 313 Pembroke St, Pembroke, NH, 03275. Tel: 603-485-7851. Fax: 603-485-3351. p. 1461

Cyr, Joan L, Librn, Stonehenge Study Group, 800 Palermo Dr, Santa Barbara, CA, 93105. Tel: 805-687-6029. p. 261

Cyr, Joanne, Adult Serv, Southington Public Library & Museum, 255 Main St, Southington, CT, 06489. Tel: 860-628-0947. Fax: 860-628-0488. p. 368

Cyr, Lyn, Dir, Port Leyden Community Library, 3145 Canal St, Port Leyden, NY, 13433. Tel: 315-348-6077. Fax: 315-348-4234. p. 1721

Cyr, Margery, Dir, Dover Public Library, 45 S State St, Dover, DE, 19901. Tel: 302-736-7030. Fax: 302-736-5087. p. 382

Cyr, Margery Kirby, Dir, Central Delaware Library Consortium, Dover Public Library, 45 S State St, Dover, DE, 19901. Tel: 302-736-7032. Fax: 302-736-5087. p. 2940

Cyr, Paul, Ref, New Bedford Free Public Library, 613 Pleasant St, New Bedford, MA, 02740-6203. Tel: 508-991-6275. Fax: 508-991-6368. p. 1108

Cyr, Vicki, Libr Mgr, San Luis Obispo County Library, Oceano Branch, 1551 17th St, Oceano, CA, 93445. Tel: 805-474-7478. Fax: 805-474-7479. p. 254

Cywinski, Luisa, Access Serv, Villanova University, 800 Lancaster Ave, Villanova, PA, 19085. Tel: 610-519-5215. Fax: 610-519-5018. p. 2150

Czaja, Pamela, Distance Educ, Monroe Community College, LeRoy V Good Library, 1000 E Henrietta Rd, Rochester, NY, 14692. Tel: 585-292-2308. p. 1730

Czajkowski, Sandra, Media Spec, Ad, Juilliard School, 60 Lincoln Center Plaza, New York, NY, 10023-6588. Tel: 212-799-5000, Ext 265. Fax: 212-769-6421. p. 1684

Czanyo, Elizabeth, Ref Librn, Canadian Medical Association, 1867 Alta Vista Dr, Ottawa, ON, K1G 0G8, CANADA. Tel: 800-663-7336, Ext 2245. Fax: 613-731-2076. p. 2829

Czarnik, Deb, Tech Serv Mgr, Lee County Library System, 2345 Union St, Fort Myers, FL, 33901-3917. Tel: 239-533-4180. Fax: 239-485-1100. p. 445

Czarnik, Deb, Mgr, Tech Serv & Coll Mgt, Lee County Library System, Processing Center, 881 Gunnery Rd N, Ste 2, Lehigh Acres, FL, 33971-1246. Tel: 239-461-7381. Fax: 239-461-7373. p. 446

Czarski, Rosemary, Mgr, Metropolitan Library System in Oklahoma County, Choctaw Library, 2525 Muzzy, Choctaw, OK, 73020. Tel: 405-390-8418. Fax: 405-606-3269. p. 1972

Czedik, Denice M, ILL, United States Army, AMSRD-NSC-OC-T, 20 Kansas St, Natick, MA, 01760-5056. Tel: 508-233-4306. Fax: 508-233-4248. p. 1108

Czekala, Barbara Campbell, Per, Ref Serv, Bryant Library, Two Paper Mill Rd, Roslyn, NY, 11576-2193. Tel: 516-621-2240. Fax: 516-621-7211. p. 1735

Czerny, Susan, Access Serv, Distance Educ, Univ Archivist, Kutztown University, 15200 Kutztown Rd, Bldg 5, Kutztown, PA, 19530-0735. Tel: 610-683-4484. Fax: 610-683-4747. p. 2075

Czesak, Cynthia, Dir, Paterson Free Public Library, 250 Broadway, Paterson, NJ, 07501. Tel: 973-321-1223. Fax: 973-321-1205. p. 1518

Czopek, Vanessa, County Librn, Stanislaus County Free Library, 1500 I St, Modesto, CA, 95354-1166. Tel: 209-558-7800. Fax: 209-529-4779. p. 188

D'Adamo, Charles, Exec Coordr, Alternative Press Center Library, 2040 N Milwaukee Ave, 2nd Flr, Chicago, IL, 60647. Tel: 312-451-8133. Fax: 773-772-4180. p. 605

D'Agostino, Cindy, Dir, Dormont Public Library, 2950 W Liberty Ave, Pittsburgh, PA, 15216-2594. Tel: 412-531-8754. Fax: 412-531-1601. p. 2125

D'Agostino, Lucia, Ref Librn, Columbia College, 1001 Rogers St, Columbia, MO, 65216. Tel: 573-875-7395. Fax: 573-875-7379. p. 1324

D'Agostino, Marcelo, Dir, Libr Serv, Pan American Health Organization Headquarters Library, 525 23rd St NW, Washington, DC, 20037. Tel: 202-974-3301. p. 412

D'Agostino, Pat, Tech Serv, Wood Library Association of Canandaigua, 134 N Main St, Canandaigua, NY, 14424-1295. Tel: 585-394-1381. Fax: 585-394-2954. p. 1601

D'Agosto, Marisa, Ref Librn, Merrick Library, 2279 Merrick Ave, Merrick, NY, 11566-4398. Tel: 516-377-6112. Fax: 516-377-1108. p. 1659

D'Aguanno, Brenda, Youth Serv, North Scituate Public Library, 606 W Greenville Rd, North Scituate, RI, 02857. Tel: 401-647-5133. Fax: 401-647-2206. p. 2170

D'Almeida, Diane, Coordr, Boston University Libraries, George H Beebe Communications Library, College of Communication, 640 Commonwealth Ave, Rm B31, Boston, MA, 02215. Tel: 617-353-9240. p. 1058

D'Amario, Patti, Asst Mgr, Springfield City Library, Indian Orchard Branch, 44 Oak St, Indian Orchard, MA, 01151. Tel: 413-263-6846. Fax: 413-263-6848. p. 1127

D'Amario, Patti, Asst Mgr, Springfield City Library, Pine Point Branch, 204 Boston Rd, Springfield, MA, 01109. Tel: 413-263-6855. Fax: 413-263-6857. p. 1127

D'Amario, Patti, Mgr, Borrower Serv, Springfield City Library, 220 State St, Springfield, MA, 01103. Tel: 413-263-6828, Ext 220. Fax: 413-263-6817. p. 1127

D'Amario, Patti, Asst Mgr, Springfield City Library, Sixteen Acres Branch, 1187 Parker St, Springfield, MA, 01129. Tel: 413-263-6858. Fax: 413-263-6860. p. 1128

D'Amato, Tara, Libr Dir, Port Jefferson Free Library, 100 Thompson St, Port Jefferson, NY, 11777-1897. Tel: 631-473-0022. Fax: 631-473-4765. p. 1721

D'Amato, Tara, Asst Dir, Mastics-Moriches-Shirley Community Library, 407 William Floyd Pkwy, Shirley, NY, 11967. Tel: 631-399-1511. Fax: 631-281-4442. p. 1743

D'Ambra, Linda, Librn, Providence Community Library, South Providence Library, 441 Prairie Ave, Providence, RI, 02905. Tel: 401-467-2619. p. 2173

D'Ambrosio, David, Asst Dir, Manlius Library, One Arkie Albanese Ave, Manlius, NY, 13104. Tel: 315-682-6400. Fax: 315-682-4490. p. 1657

D'Amore, Pamela S, Fiscal Officer, Girard Free Library, 105 E Prospect St, Girard, OH, 44420-1899. Tel: 330-545-2508. Fax: 330-545-8213. p. 1902

D'Amour, Heather, Metadata Librn, University of Calgary Library, 2500 University Dr NW, Calgary, AB, T2N 1N4, CANADA. Tel: 403-220-3591. Fax: 403-282-1218. p. 2693

D'Andraia, Frank, Serv Prof, University at Albany, State University of New York, Draper 116, 135 Western Ave, Albany, NY, 12222. Tel: 518-442-5118. Fax: 518-442-5367. p. 2970

D'Andrea, Joan, Bibliog Instr, Saint John's University Library, 8000 Utopia Pkwy, Queens, NY, 11439. Tel: 718-990-6735. Fax: 718-380-0353. p. 1725

D'Angelo, Edward, Mgr, Brooklyn Public Library, New Utrecht, 1743 86th St, Brooklyn, NY, 11214. Tel: 718-236-4086. Fax: 718-234-7702. p. 1592

D'Angelo, John, Head, Circ, Fordham University Libraries, 441 E Fordham Rd, Bronx, NY, 10458-5151. Tel: 718-817-3570. Fax: 718-817-3582. p. 1586

D'Angelo, Kathy, Head, Tech Serv, Gettysburg College, 300 N Washington St, Gettysburg, PA, 17325. Tel: 717-337-7007. Fax: 717-337-7001. p. 2059

D'Angelo, Tonie Ann, Ref Serv, Blauvelt Free Library, 541 Western Hwy, Blauvelt, NY, 10913. Tel: 845-359-2811. Fax: 845-398-0017. p. 1583

D'Antonio, Linda, Med Librn, UPMC Passavant, 9100 Babcock Blvd, Pittsburgh, PA, 15237-5842. Tel: 412-367-6320. Fax: 412-367-6889. p. 2129

D'Aoust, Maja, Librn, Philosophical Research Society Library, 3910 Los Feliz Blvd, Los Angeles, CA, 90027. Tel: 323-663-2167. Fax: 323-663-9443. p. 176

D'Arcy, Montalvo, Pub Relations, American Fire Sprinkler Association Library, 12750 Merit Dr, No 350, Dallas, TX, 75251. Tel: 214-349-5965. Fax: 214-343-8898. p. 2304

D'Avanza, Mia, Exhibitions Coordr, Ref, The LuEsther T Mertz Library, The New York Botanical Garden, 2900 Southern Blvd, Bronx, NY, 10458-5126. Tel: 718-817-8729. Fax: 718-817-8956. p. 1587

D'Elia, Joseph, Dir, A Holmes Johnson Memorial Library, 319 Lower Mill Bay Rd, Kodiak, AK, 99615. Tel: 907-486-8688. Fax: 907-486-8681. p. 51

D'Emal, Jacques, Res Serv Librn, Utah Valley University Library, 800 W University Pkwy, Orem, UT, 84058-5999. Tel: 801-863-8058. Fax: 801-863-7065. p. 2409

D'Entremont, Susan, Archivist, Capital District Library Council, 28 Essex St, Albany, NY, 12206. Tel: 518-438-2500. Fax: 518-438-2872. p. 2949

D'Errico, Megan, Ref, Proskauer Rose LLP Library, 1585 Broadway, Concourse Level, New York, NY, 10036. Tel: 212-969-5001. Fax: 212-969-2931. p. 1698

D'Haem, Dee, Br Mgr, Kitsap Regional Library, Manchester Branch, 8067 E Main St, Manchester, WA, 98353. Tel: 360-871-3921, Ext 9201. Fax: 360-871-6152. p. 2510

D'onofrio, Emil, Ref & Info Serv, Port Chester-Rye Brook Public Library, One Haseco Ave, Port Chester, NY, 10573. Tel: 914-939-6710. Fax: 914-939-4735. p. 1720

D'Onofrio-Jones, Mellissa, Dir of Libr Serv, Drumheller Public Library, 224 Centre St, Drumheller, AB, T0J 0Y2, CANADA. Tel: 403-823-1371. Fax: 403-823-3651. p. 2697

D'Ottavio, Susan, Syst Coordr, Cumberland County Library, 800 E Commerce St, Bridgeton, NJ, 08302-2295. Tel: 856-453-2210. Fax: 856-451-1940. p. 1474

D'Souza, Adrienne, Br Mgr, Chillicothe & Ross County Public Library, 140 S Paint St, Chillicothe, OH, 45601. Tel: 740-702-4145. Fax: 740-702-4153. p. 1867

D'Souza, Sandra, Tech Serv, Thomas Jefferson National Accelerator Facility Library, 12050 Jefferson Ave, ARC 126 (MS-1B), Newport News, VA, 23606. Tel: 757-269-6229. Fax: 757-269-7848. p. 2480

D'Urso, Lawrence, Head, Fiction/AV/Teen Serv, Mount Prospect Public Library, Ten S Emerson St, Mount Prospect, IL, 60056. Tel: 847-253-5675. Fax: 847-253-0642. p. 677

D'Yan, Alex, Ref Librn, Web Coordr, Little Falls Public Library, Eight Warren St, Little Falls, NJ, 07424. Tel: 973-256-2784. Fax: 973-256-6312. p. 1495

Da Rold, Joseph Hugh, Dir, Plainfield Public Library, 800 Park Ave, Plainfield, NJ, 07060-2594. Tel: 908-757-1111. Fax: 908-754-0063. p. 1521

Da Silva, Joann, Libr Tech, City of Winnipeg Water & Waste Department, 1199 Pacific Ave, Winnipeg, MB, R3E 3S8, CANADA. Tel: 204-986-3250. Fax: 204-224-0032. p. 2755

da Silva, Laura, Circ Serv Coordr, Assemblies of God Theological Seminary, 1435 N Glenstone Ave, Springfield, MO, 65802-2131. Tel: 417-268-1063. Fax: 417-268-1001. p. 1365

Da Sylva, Lyne, Assoc Prof, Universite de Montreal, 3150, rue Jean-Brillant, bur C-2004, Montreal, QC, H3T 1N8, CANADA. Tel: 514-343-6044. Fax: 514-343-5753. p. 2979

Dabbs, Mary Lou, Electronic Res, La Grange College, 601 Broad St, La Grange, GA, 30240-2999. Tel: 706-880-8027. Fax: 706-880-8040. p. 537

Dabkowski, Charles, Head, Acq, Niagara University Library, 5795 Lewiston Rd, Niagara University, NY, 14109. Tel: 716-286-8007. Fax: 716-286-8030. p. 1705

Dabler, Donna, Dir, Selby Township Library District, 101 Depot St, De Pue, IL, 61322. Tel: 815-447-2660. Fax: 815-447-2598. p. 633

Dabrishus, Mara, Archivist, Ref & Instruction Librn, Ursuline College, 2550 Lander Rd, Pepper Pike, OH, 44124-4398. Tel: 440-449-4202. Fax: 440-449-3180. p. 1929

Dacey, Edward, Ref Librn, United States Military Academy Library, Jefferson Hall Library & Learning Center, 758 Cullum Rd, West Point, NY, 10996. Tel: 845-938-3833. Fax: 845-938-4000. p. 1767

Dacey, Garett, Assoc Librn, North Las Vegas Library District, 2300 Civic Center Dr, North Las Vegas, NV, 89030-5839. Tel: 702-633-1070. Fax: 702-649-2576. p. 1432

DaCorte, Phyllis, Asst Dir, Ch, Acton Public Library, 60 Old Boston Post Rd, Old Saybrook, CT, 06475-2200. Tel: 860-395-3184. Fax: 860-395-2462. p. 363

Dade, Lucile, Dir, DeSoto Public Library, 211 E Pleasant Run Rd, Ste C, DeSoto, TX, 75115-3939. Tel: 972-230-9656. Fax: 972-230-5797. p. 2313

Dadson, Theresa, Acq, Coll Develop, University of Maryland-Eastern Shore, 11868 Academic Oval, Princess Anne, MD, 21853. Tel: 410-651-2200, 410-651-6621. Fax: 410-651-6269. p. 1036

Daebler, Cora, Tech Serv, United States Army, Morris J Swett Technical Library, Snow Hall 16, Bldg 730, Fort Sill, OK, 73503-5100. Tel: 580-442-4525. Fax: 580-442-7300. p. 1964

Daentl, Joy, Librn, Christ Church Library, 527 Pomfret St, Pomfret, CT, 06258. Tel: 860-928-7026. Fax: 860-963-2684. p. 364

Daeuber, Benjamin, Tech Librn, Fargo Public Library, 102 N Third St, Fargo, ND, 58102. Tel: 701-241-1472. Fax: 701-241-8581. p. 1841

Daffin, John, Librn, Georgia Department of Corrections, Office of Library Services, 153 Pinewood Rd, Leesburg, GA, 31763. Tel: 229-759-3113. Fax: 229-759-3065. p. 539

Dafilou, Lori, Exec Dir, Temple Adath Israel, 250 N Highland Ave, Merion Station, PA, 19066. Tel: 610-934-1903. Fax: 610-664-0959. p. 2088

Dagan, Scott, Dir, Mount Olive Public Library, 202 Flanders-Drakestown Rd, Flanders, NJ, 07836. Tel: 973-691-8686. Fax: 973-691-8542. p. 1485

Daganaar, Mark, Dir, Johnson County Community College, 12345 College Blvd, Box 21, Overland Park, KS, 66210. Tel: 913-469-3882. Fax: 913-469-3816. p. 888

Dagate, Jennifer, Libr Spec III, Louisiana State University, Medical Center Hospitals, Health Care Services Division, 1978 Industrial Blvd, Houma, LA, 70363. Tel: 985-873-1257. Fax: 985-873-1219. p. 951

Dagenbach, Kathy, Tech Serv, Notre Dame College, 4545 College Rd, South Euclid, OH, 44121. Tel: 216-373-5269. Fax: 216-381-3227. p. 1935

Dager, Jacqueline, Asst Libr Dir, Centerville Public Library Association, Inc, 585 Main St, Centerville, MA, 02632. Tel: 508-790-6220. Fax: 508-790-6218. p. 1079

Daggita, David, Asst Librn, Hannibal Free Library, 162 Oswego St, Hannibal, NY, 13074. Tel: 315-564-5471. Fax: 315-564-5471. p. 1634

Dagher, Fadi, Ref & Coll Develop Librn, Columbia University, Lehman Library, 420 W 118th St, New York, NY, 10027. Tel: 212-854-3794. Fax: 212-854-2495. p. 1675

Dagley, Helen, Librn, State Library of Iowa, 1112 E Grand Ave, Des Moines, IA, 50319. Tel: 515-281-4105. Fax: 515-281-6191. p. 810

Dagley, Lon E, Computer Librn, Mid-America Nazarene University, 2030 E College Way, Olathe, KS, 66062-1899. Tel: 913-971-3566. Fax: 913-971-3285. p. 886

Dague, Susan, Head, Tech Serv, East Greenbush Community Library, Ten Community Way, East Greenbush, NY, 12061. Tel: 518-477-7476. Fax: 518-477-6692. p. 1616

Dague, Wilma, Ser, Benedictine College Library, 1020 N Second St, Atchison, KS, 66002-1499. Tel: 913-360-7610. Fax: 913-360-7622. p. 856

Dagwah, Deborah, Dir, Alice M Ward Memorial Library, 27 Park St, Canaan, VT, 05903. Tel: 802-266-7135. Fax: 802-266-8159. p. 2421

Dahl, Jeanne, Librn, Raymond A Whitwer Tilden Public Library, 202 S Center St, Tilden, NE, 68781. Tel: 402-368-5306. Fax: 402-368-5515. p. 1421

Dahl, Jill, Br Mgr, Carnegie Library of McKeesport, Elizabeth Forward Branch, Central Elementary School, 401 Rock Run Rd, Elizabeth, PA, 15037. Tel: 412-896-2371. p. 2085

Dahl, Linda, Pub Info Mgr, Stark County District Library, 715 Market Ave N, Canton, OH, 44702-1018. Tel: 330-458-2699. Fax: 330-455-9596. p. 1864

Dahl, Mark, Interim Dir, Lewis & Clark College, Aubrey R Watzek Library, 0615 SW Palatine Hill Rd, Portland, OR, 97219-7899. Tel: 503-768-7339. Fax: 503-768-7282. p. 2011

Dahl, Paul Elliott, Dir, Kendall Young Library, 1201 Willson Ave, Webster City, IA, 50595-2294. Tel: 515-832-9100. Fax: 515-832-9102. p. 851

Dahl, Shirley A, Dr, Libr Dir, Nellie Pederson Civic Library, 403 W Third St, Clifton, TX, 76634. Tel: 254-675-6495. Fax: 254-675-3175. p. 2298

Dahle, Cloteele, Librn, Franklin County Library District, 109 S First E, Preston, ID, 83263. Tel: 208-852-0175. Fax: 208-852-0175. p. 582

Dahlem, Diane, Mgr, Circ Serv, Ann Arbor District Library, 343 S Fifth Ave, Ann Arbor, MI, 48104. Tel: 734-327-4281. Fax: 734-327-8305. p. 1150

Dahlen, Julie, Libr Mgr, Paso Robles Public Library, 1000 Spring St, Paso Robles, CA, 93446-2207. Tel: 805-237-3870. Fax: 805-238-3665. p. 207

Dahlen, Sarah, Ref & Instruction Librn, California State University-Monterey Bay, 100 Campus Ctr, Seaside, CA, 93955-8001. Tel: 831-582-4432. Fax: 831-582-3875. p. 268

Dahlen, Sue, ILL Librn, Wadleigh Memorial Library, 49 Nashua St, Milford, NH, 03055-3753. Tel: 603-673-2408. Fax: 603-672-6064. p. 1457

Dahlgreen, MaryKay, State Librn, Oregon State Library, 250 Winter St NE, Salem, OR, 97301-3950. Tel: 503-378-4243. Fax: 503-585-8059. p. 2018

Dahlgren, Dorothy, Dir, Museum of North Idaho Inc Archives, 115 Northwest Blvd, Coeur d'Alene, ID, 83816. Tel: 208-664-3448. p. 573

Dahlgren, Jodi, Libr Mgr, Wainwright Public Library, 921 Third Ave, Wainwright, AB, T9W 1C5, CANADA. Tel: 780-842-2673. Fax: 780-842-2340. p. 2721

Dahlgren, Lauren, Br Mgr, North Olympic Library System, Sequim Branch, 630 N Sequim Ave, Sequim, WA, 98382. Tel: 360-683-1161. Fax: 360-681-7811. p. 2524

Dahlin, Terry, Asst Univ Librn, Pub Serv, Brigham Young University, Harold B Lee Library, 2060 HBLL, Provo, UT, 84602. Tel: 801-422-2927. Fax: 801-422-0466. p. 2411

Dahlke, Lezlea, Youth Serv Librn, Winona Public Library, 151 W Fifth St, Winona, MN, 55987-3170. Tel: 507-452-4582. Fax: 507-452-5842. p. 1290

Dahlke, Melissa, Librn, Copeland Public Library, 109 Santa Fe St, Copeland, KS, 67837. Tel: 620-668-5559. p. 862

Dahlke, Nancy, Br Coordr, Marathon County Public Library, Joseph Dessert Branch, 123 Main St, Mosinee, WI, 54455-1441. Tel: 715-693-2144. Fax: 715-693-2144. p. 2646

Dahlman, Gavena, Coordr, Access Serv, Richland Community College, One College Park, Decatur, IL, 62521. Tel: 217-875-7200, Ext 301. Fax: 217-875-6961. p. 634

Dahlmeyer, Sharon, Librn, Godfrey Memorial Library, 134 Newfield St, Middletown, CT, 06457-2534. Tel: 860-346-4375. Fax: 860-347-9874. p. 351

Dahlstrom, Joe, Dr, Chairperson, Texas Council of Academic Libraries, VC/UHV Library, 2602 N Ben Jordan, Victoria, TX, 77901. Tel: 361-570-4150. Fax: 361-570-4155. p. 2956

Dahlstrom, Joe F, Dr, Dir, University of Houston, 2602 N Ben Jordan St, Victoria, TX, 77901-5699. Tel: 361-570-4150. Fax: 361-570-4155. p. 2395

Dahm, Mary C, Librn, Saint Louis County Law Library, Courts Bldg, Ste 536, 7900 Carondelet Ave, Clayton, MO, 63105. Tel: 314-615-4726. p. 1323

Dahma, Jameely, Mgr, District of Columbia Public Library, Juanita E Thornton/Shepherd Park Neighborhood Library, 7420 Georgia Ave NW, Washington, DC, 20012. Tel: 202-541-6100. p. 399

Dahms, Sharon, Librn, West Concord Public Library, 180 E Main St, West Concord, MN, 55985. Tel: 507-527-2031. Fax: 507-527-2031. p. 1288

Dahms-Stinson, Nancee, Youth Serv Coordr, Springfield-Greene County Library District, 4653 S Campbell, Springfield, MO, 65810-1723. Tel: 417-882-0714. Fax: 417-883-9348. p. 1367

Dahmus, Jeni, Archivist, Juilliard School, 60 Lincoln Center Plaza, New York, NY, 10023-6588. Tel: 212-799-5000, Ext 367. Fax: 212-769-6421. p. 1684

Dai, Weiqing, Commun Libr Mgr, Queens Borough Public Library, Lefferts Community Library, 103-34 Lefferts Blvd, Richmond Hill, NY, 11419. Tel: 718-843-5950. p. 1645

Daigle, Francine, Chief Librn, Hearst Public Library, 801 George St, Hearst, ON, P0L 1N0, CANADA. Tel: 705-372-2843. Fax: 705-372-2833. p. 2811

Dail, Nancy, Coll Mgt Librn, Richland County Public Library, 1431 Assembly St, Columbia, SC, 29201-3101. Tel: 803-799-9084. Fax: 803-929-3448. p. 2188

Dailey, Elizabeth J, Exec Dir, Onondaga County Public Library, The Galleries of Syracuse, 447 S Salina St, Syracuse, NY, 13202-2494. Fax: 315-435-8533. p. 1752

Dailey, Jackie, AV, Wells County Public Library, 200 W Washington St, Bluffton, IN, 46714-1999. Tel: 260-824-1612. Fax: 260-824-3129. p. 728

Dailey, Karen, Circ Mgr, Hartwick College, One Hartwick Dr, Oneonta, NY, 13820. Tel: 607-431-4440. Fax: 607-431-4457. p. 1710

Dailey, Kim, Cat, Arkansas State University, Palm & Iowa Sts, Beebe, AR, 72012. Tel: 501-882-8978. Fax: 501-882-8833. p. 94

Dailey, Laura, Dir, Goessel Public Library, 101 S Cedar, Goessel, KS, 67053. Tel: 620-367-8440. Fax: 620-367-2774. p. 869

Dailey, Lucinda, Ch, Christian County Library, 1005 N Fourth Ave, Ozark, MO, 65721. Tel: 417-581-2432. Fax: 417-581-8855. p. 1348

Dailey, Marcie, Asst Librn, Dorothy Hull Windsor Township Library, 405 W Jefferson St, Dimondale, MI, 48821. Tel: 517-646-0633. Fax: 517-646-7061. p. 1174

Dailey, Shannon, Youth Serv, Santa Fe Springs City Library, 11700 E Telegraph Rd, Santa Fe Springs, CA, 90670-3600. Tel: 562-868-7738. Fax: 562-929-3680. p. 265

Dailey, Susan, Br Librn, Wells County Public Library, Ossian Branch, 207 N Jefferson, Ossian, IN, 46777. Tel: 260-622-4691. Fax: 260-622-7030. p. 729

Dailey, Susan M, Br Coordr, Wells County Public Library, 200 W Washington St, Bluffton, IN, 46714-1999. Tel: 260-622-4691. Fax: 260-622-7030. p. 728

Dailey, Veronica, Circ, Maitland Public Library, 501 S Maitland Ave, Maitland, FL, 32751-5672. Tel: 407-647-7700. p. 462

Daily, Christine, Teen Serv Coordr, Seymour Library, 161 East Ave, Brockport, NY, 14420-1987. Tel: 585-637-1050. Fax: 585-637-1051. p. 1585

Daily, Dan, Archives & Spec Coll Librn, University of South Dakota, 414 E Clark St, Vermillion, SD, 57069. Tel: 605-677-8867. Fax: 605-677-6834. p. 2220

Daily, Daniel, Dir, Northwestern College, 101 Seventh St SW, Orange City, IA, 51041-1996. Tel: 712-707-7238. Fax: 712-707-7247. p. 836

Daily, Steven, Curator, Milwaukee County Historical Society, 910 N Old World Third St, Milwaukee, WI, 53203. Tel: 414-273-8288. Fax: 414-273-3268. p. 2619

Daizadeh, Kian, Actg Br Mgr, Los Angeles Public Library System, Will & Ariel Durant Branch, 7140 W Sunset Blvd, Los Angeles, CA, 90046. Tel: 323-876-2741. Fax: 323-876-0485. p. 173

Dajani, Virginia, Exec Dir, American Academy of Arts & Letters Library, 633 W 155th St, New York, NY, 10032. Tel: 212-368-6361. Fax: 212-491-4615. p. 1667

Daka, Paul, Head of Librl, Free Library of Philadelphia, Fox Chase Branch, 501 Rhawn St, Philadelphia, PA, 19111-2504. Tel: 215-685-0547. Fax: 215-685-0546. p. 2107

Daks, Evelyn, Prog Coordr, Finkelstein Memorial Library, 24 Chestnut St, Spring Valley, NY, 10977-5594. Tel: 845-352-5700. Fax: 845-352-2319. p. 1746

Dakshinamurti, Ganga, Ref Serv, University of Manitoba Libraries, Albert D Cohen Management Library, 208 Drake Centre, 181 Freedman Crescent, Winnipeg, MB, R3T 5V4, CANADA. Tel: 204-474-8441. Fax: 204-474-7542. p. 2758

Daku, Shauna, Librn, Southeast Regional Library, Arcola Branch, 127 Main St, Arcola, SK, S0C 0G0, CANADA. Tel: 306-455-2321. p. 2929

Dalbello, Marija, Asst Prof, Rutgers, The State University of New Jersey, Four Huntington St, New Brunswick, NJ, 08901-1071. Tel: 732-932-7500, Ext 8955. Fax: 732-932-2644. p. 2969

Dale, Christopher, Librn, Bryant & Stratton Business College, 465 Main St, Ste 400, Buffalo, NY, 14203. Tel: 716-884-9120, Ext 261. Fax: 716-884-0091. p. 1596

Dale, Denise, Ref Serv Coordr, Kwantlen Polytechnic University Library, 12666 72 Ave., Surrey, BC, V3W 2M8, CANADA. Tel: 604-599-2999. Fax: 604-599-2106. p. 2738

Dale, Howard, Chief, Info Mgt Spec, United Nations Childrens Fund Library, Three UN Plaza, H-12C UNICEF House, New York, NY, 10017. Tel: 212-326-7064. Fax: 212-303-7989. p. 1702

Dale, Jenny, First Year Instruction Coordr, Ref Librn, University of North Carolina at Greensboro, 320 Spring Garden St, Greensboro, NC, 27402. Tel: 336-256-0240. Fax: 336-334-5399. p. 1798

Dale, John, Pub Serv, Orange Coast College Library, 2701 Fairview Rd, Costa Mesa, CA, 92628. Tel: 714-432-5885. Fax: 714-432-6850. p. 137

Dale, John, Dir, Darlington Public Library, 203 W Main St, Darlington, IN, 47940. Tel: 765-794-4813. Fax: 765-794-4813. p. 735

Dale, Lisa, Libr Mgr, Folsom Public Library, 411 Stafford St, Folsom, CA, 95630. Tel: 916-355-7374. Fax: 916-355-7332. p. 148

Dale, Lisa, Tech Serv, Roseville Public Library, 225 Taylor St, Roseville, CA, 95678-2681. Tel: 916-774-5221. Fax: 916-773-5594. p. 220

Dale, Michele, Archives Mgr, City of Toronto Archives, 255 Spadina Rd, Toronto, ON, M5R 2V3, CANADA. Tel: 416-397-0778. Fax: 416-392-9685. p. 2852

Dale, Nancy E, Coordr, Swedish American Health System, 1401 E State St, Rockford, IL, 61104. Tel: 815-489-4556. Fax: 815-968-3713. p. 698

Dale, Paula, Mgr, Dayton Metro Library, Huber Heights, 6160 Chambersburg Rd, Dayton, OH, 45424. Tel: 937-496-8934. Fax: 937-496-4334. p. 1893

Dale, Ray, Pub Serv, Big Horn County Public Library, 419 N Custer Ave, Hardin, MT, 59034. Fax: 406-665-1804. p. 1381

Dale, Rella, Tech Serv Mgr, Avery-Mitchell-Yancey Regional Library System, 289 Burnsville School Rd, Burnsville, NC, 28714. Tel: 828-682-4476. Fax: 828-682-6277. p. 1779

Dale, Robert, Cat, Bibliotheque du College Dominicain de Philosophie et de Theologie, 96 Empress Ave, Ottawa, ON, K1R 7G3, CANADA. Tel: 613-233-5696, Ext 216. Fax: 613-233-6064. p. 2828

Dales, Carol, Coordr, Distance Learning, California State University Dominguez Hills, 1000 E Victoria St, Carson, CA, 90747. Tel: 310-243-2088. Fax: 310-516-4219. p. 132

Dalesandro, Anne, Dir, Law Libr & Assoc Prof of Law, Rutgers University Libraries, Camden Law Library, 217 N Fifth St, Camden, NJ, 08102-1203. Tel: 856-225-8182. p. 1476

Daley, Jan, Br Mgr, Saint Louis Public Library, Baden, 8448 Church Rd, Saint Louis, MO, 63147-1898. Tel: 314-388-2400. Fax: 314-388-0529. p. 1360

Daley, Laurie, Librn, Bullivant, Houser & Bailey, 300 Pioneer Tower, 888 SW Fifth Ave, Portland, OR, 97204-2089. Tel: 503-228-6351. Fax: 503-295-0915. p. 2010

Daley, Melissa, Assoc Dir, UBS Warburg Library, 299 Park Ave, New York, NY, 10171-0099. Tel: 212-821-3000. p. 1701

Daley, Sean, Dir, Bridgewater Public Library, 15 South St, Bridgewater, MA, 02324-2593. Tel: 508-697-3331. Fax: 508-279-1467. p. 1070

Daley, Sheila, Archivist, Noah Webster House & West Hartford Historical Society, 227 S Main St, West Hartford, CT, 06107-3430. Tel: 860-521-5362. Fax: 860-521-4036. p. 376

Dalgas, Esther, Librn, North Central Regional Library, Entiat Community, 14138 Kinzel St, Entiat, WA, 98822. Tel: 509-784-1517. Fax: 509-784-1517. p. 2548

Dalgetty, Christine, Br Mgr, Burlington Public Library, Tansley Woods, 1996 Itabashi Way, Burlington, ON, L7M 4J8, CANADA. Tel: 905-336-5583. Fax: 905-336-4266. p. 2798

Dalgleish, Jone, Br Head, Chatham-Kent Public Library, Tilbury Branch, Two Queen St, Tilbury, ON, N0P 2L0, CANADA. Tel: 519-682-0100. p. 2799

Dalimonte, David, Br Mgr, Onslow County Public Library, Law Library, 109 Old Bridge St, Jacksonville, NC, 28540. Tel: 910-455-4458, Ext 307. Fax: 910-989-2079. p. 1803

Dalina, Stephen, Rec Mgr, Rutgers University Libraries, Special Collections & University Archives, 169 College Ave, New Brunswick, NJ, 08901-1163. Tel: 848-932-6145. Fax: 732-932-7012. p. 1509

Daling, LaiLee, Circ, Wenatchee Valley College, 1300 Fifth St, Wenatchee, WA, 98801. Tel: 509-682-6710. Fax: 509-682-6711. p. 2549

Dalius, Kathryn, Libr Asst, Bucknell University, Serials, Library & Information Technology, Lewisburg, PA, 17837. Tel: 570-577-1663. p. 2080

Daliva, Sana, Br Mgr, Hawaii State Public Library System, Kahului Public Library, 90 School St, Kahului, HI, 96732-1627. Tel: 808-873-3097. Fax: 808-873-3094. p. 562

Dalkir, Kimiz, Assoc Prof, McGill University, 3661 Peel St, Montreal, QC, H3A 1X1, CANADA. Tel: 514-398-3364. Fax: 514-398-7193. p. 2979

Dallaire, Odette, Borrower Serv Librn, Institut de Formation Théologique de Montreal Bibliotheque, 2065, rue Sherbrooke Ouest, Montreal, QC, H3H 1G6, CANADA. Tel: 514-935-1169. Fax: 514-935-5497. p. 2896

Dallam, Linda, Dir, Librn, Mills & Petrie Memorial Library, 704 N First St, Ashton, IL, 61006. Tel: 815-453-2213. Fax: 815-453-2723. p. 590

Dallas, Larayne, Asst Librn, University of Texas Libraries, McKinney Engineering Library, One University Sta S5435, ECJ 1.300, Austin, TX, 78712. Tel: 512-495-4511. Fax: 512-495-4507. p. 2284

Dallas, Sara, Dir, Southern Adirondack Library System, 22 Whitney Pl, Saratoga Springs, NY, 12866-4596. Tel: 518-584-7300. Fax: 518-587-5589. p. 1739

Dallavalle, Ann, City Librn, Crowell Public Library, 1890 Huntington Dr, San Marino, CA, 91108-2595. Tel: 626-300-0775. Fax: 626-284-0766. p. 254

Dallman, Darlene, Head Librn, South Interlake Regional Library, 419 Main St, Stonewall, MB, R0C 2Z0, CANADA. Tel: 204-467-8415. Fax: 204-467-9809. p. 2752

Dalmoro, Annaliese, Librn, Hatch Energy Library, 840 Seventh Ave SW, Ste 700, Calgary, AB, T2P 3G2, CANADA. Tel: 403-920-3101. Fax: 403-266-5730. p. 2691

Dalrymple, Jennifer, Head, Circ, Bedford Free Public Library, Seven Mudge Way, Bedford, MA, 01730-2168. Tel: 781-275-9440. Fax: 781-275-3590. p. 1052

Dalrymple, Joan, Head, Access Serv, Bergen Community College, 400 Paramus Rd, Paramus, NJ, 07652-1595. Tel: 201-612-5236. Fax: 201-493-8167. p. 1517

Dalrymple, Prudence W, PhD, Dir, Inst for Healthcare Informatics, Res & Teaching Prof, Drexel University, Rush Bldg, Rm 306, 30 N 33rd St, Philadelphia, PA, 19104-2875. Tel: 215-895-2474. Fax: 215-895-2494. p. 2972

Dalrymple, Tam, Sr Info Serv Spec, OCLC Library, 6565 Kilgour Pl, Dublin, OH, 43017. Tel: 614-764-6000. Fax: 614-793-8707. p. 1896

Dalton, Ann, ILL, Ref, Hingham Public Library, 66 Leavitt St, Hingham, MA, 02043. Tel: 781-741-1405. Fax: 781-749-0956. p. 1095

Dalton, Belinda, Br Mgr, Simpson Kate Love Morgan County Library, Chesterhill Branch, 7520 Marion St, Chesterhill, OH, 43728. Tel: 740-554-7104. Fax: 740-554-7253. p. 1916

Dalton, Caryn, Circ Coordr, United Theological Seminary Library, 4501 Denlinger Rd, Trotwood, OH, 45426. Tel: 937-529-2201, Ext 3400. Fax: 937-529-2292. p. 1941

Dalton, Cherie, ILL Librn, Woodbury Public Library, 269 Main St S, Woodbury, CT, 06798. Tel: 203-263-3502. Fax: 203-263-0571. p. 380

Dalton Crone, Mannie, Br Mgr, Haywood County Public Library, Canton Branch, 11 Pennsylvania Ave, Canton, NC, 28716. Tel: 828-648-2924. Fax: 828-648-0377. p. 1829

Dalton, Greg, In Charge, Commonwealth Club of California, 595 Market St, San Francisco, CA, 94105. Tel: 415-597-6700. Fax: 415-597-6729. p. 241

Dalton, Jennifer, Dir, Coffeyville Public Library, 311 W Tenth, Coffeyville, KS, 67337-5816. Tel: 620-251-1370. Fax: 620-251-1512. p. 861

Dalton, Joan, Assoc Dean of Libr, University of Windsor, 401 Sunset Ave, Windsor, ON, N9B 3P4, CANADA. Tel: 519-253-3000, Ext 3165. p. 2871

Dalton, Jolene, Asst Librn, Emery County Library, Green River Branch, 85 S Long St, Green River, UT, 84525. Tel: 435-564-3349. Fax: 435-564-3399. p. 2404

Dalton, Kathleen, Ref Serv, YA, Susquehanna University, 514 University Ave, Selinsgrove, PA, 17870-1050. Tel: 570-372-4319. Fax: 570-372-4310. p. 2138

Dalton, Kelly, Cataloger, Orange County Library, 146A Madison Rd, Orange, VA, 22960. Tel: 540-661-5447. Fax: 540-672-5040. p. 2483

Dalton, Lisa, Asst Librn, Watertown Library Association, Oakville Branch, 55 Davis St, Oakville, CT, 06779. Tel: 860-945-5368. Fax: 860-945-7199. p. 375

Dalton, Malynda, Access Serv Librn, Ref Librn, Texas A&M International University, 5201 University Blvd, Laredo, TX, 78041-1900. Tel: 956-326-2400. Fax: 956-326-2399. p. 2354

Dalton, Melinda C, Dir, Minersville Public Library, 40 W Main St, Minersville, UT, 84752. Tel: 435-386-2267. Fax: 435-386-1813. p. 2407

Dalton, Patricia J, Ch, Art Circle Public Library, Cumberland County, 154 E First St, Crossville, TN, 38555-4696. Tel: 931-484-6790. Fax: 931-484-2350. p. 2232

Dalton, Rachel, Mgr, Ad Serv, Frisco Public Library, 6101 Frisco Square Blvd, Ste 3000, Frisco, TX, 75034-3000. Tel: 972-292-5669. Fax: 972-292-5699. p. 2325

Dalton, Rebecca, Acq, Supvr, Converse College, 580 E Main St, Spartanburg, SC, 29302. Tel: 864-596-9020, 864-596-9071. Fax: 864-596-9075. p. 2204

Dalton, Susan, Chief Exec Officer, Brock Township Public Library, 401 Simcoe St, Beaverton, ON, L0K 1A0, CANADA. Tel: 705-426-9283. Fax: 705-426-9353. p. 2794

Dalton, Susan, Chief Exec Officer, Brock Township Public Library, Timothy Findley Memorial Library - Cannington, 38 Laidlaw St, Cannington, ON, L0E 1E0, CANADA. Tel: 705-426-9283. Fax: 705-432-3282. p. 2794

Dalton, Susan, Chief Exec Officer, Brock Township Public Library, Sunderland Public Library, 41 Albert St, Sunderland, ON, L0C 1H0, CANADA. Tel: 613-426-9283. Fax: 705-357-3109. p. 2795

Daltonhurst, Kriska, Teen Serv Coordr, Librn I, Louisville Public Library, 951 Spruce St, Louisville, CO, 80027. Tel: 303-335-4849. Fax: 303-335-4833. p. 317

Dalusung, Joan, Libr Mgr, Henderson District Public Libraries, 280 S Green Valley Pkwy, Henderson, NV, 89012. Tel: 702-492-6580. Fax: 702-492-1711. p. 1428

Daly, Brooke, Librn, Alaska State Legislature, State Capitol, Juneau, AK, 99801-1182. Tel: 907-465-3808. Fax: 907-465-4844. p. 49

Daly, Coralina, Dir, Central Wyoming College Library, 2660 Peck Ave, Riverton, WY, 82501. Tel: 307-855-2141. Fax: 307-855-2094. p. 2659

Daly, Daphne, Managing Librn, Pima County Public Library, Murphy-Wilmot, 530 N Wilmot Rd, Tucson, AZ, 85711. Tel: 520-594-5620. Fax: 520-594-5421. p. 87

Daly, Edward, Cat, Per, Baldwin Public Library, 2385 Grand Ave, Baldwin, NY, 11510-3289. Tel: 516-223-6228. Fax: 516-623-7991. p. 1577

Daly, Jean, Coll Develop, Red Mill Museum Library, 56 Main St, Clinton, NJ, 08809. Tel: 908-735-4101. Fax: 908-735-0914. p. 1479

Daly, Jeanne, Librn, Sidney Community Library, 221 S David, Sidney, IL, 61877. Tel: 217-688-2332. p. 702

Daly, Lesley, Adminr, Wichita Falls Public Library, 600 11th St, Wichita Falls, TX, 76301-4604. Tel: 940-767-0868, Ext 229. Fax: 940-720-6672. p. 2401

Daly, Marie, Dir, Libr Serv, New England Historic Genealogical Society, 99-101 Newbury St, Boston, MA, 02116-3007. Tel: 617-226-1231. Fax: 617-536-7307. p. 1065

Daly, Michael, Asst Dir, Franklin University Library, Phillips Hall, 1st Flr, 303 S Grant Ave, Columbus, OH, 43215. Tel: 614-341-6252. Fax: 614-461-0957. p. 1886

Daly, Michael V, Pub Serv/Instruction Librn, Fulton-Montgomery Community College, 2805 State Hwy 67, Johnstown, NY, 12095-3790. Tel: 518-762-4651, Ext 5602. Fax: 518-762-3834. p. 1648

Daly, Rebecca, Libr Asst, Finlandia University, 601 Quincy St, Hancock, MI, 49930-1882. Tel: 906-487-7252. Fax: 906-487-7297. p. 1187

Daly, Tracy, Ch, Kokomo-Howard County Public Library, 220 N Union St, Kokomo, IN, 46901-4614. Tel: 765-457-3242. Fax: 765-457-3683. p. 758

Daly, Tracy, Br Mgr, Onslow County Public Library, Richlands Branch, 299 S Wilmington St, Richlands, NC, 28574. Tel: 910-324-5321. Fax: 910-324-4682. p. 1803

Daly, William, Archivist, Medgar Evers College, 1650 Bedford Ave, Brooklyn, NY, 11225-2010. Tel: 718-270-4881. Fax: 718-270-5182. p. 1593

Daly-Brosman, Sara, Adult Serv, Delphi Public Library, 222 E Main St, Delphi, IN, 46923. Tel: 765-564-2929. Fax: 765-564-4746. p. 735

Dalzell, Lee Ann, Cat, Georgia Southwestern State University, 800 Georgia Southwestern State University Dr, Americus, GA, 31709. Tel: 229-931-2258. Fax: 229-931-2265. p. 508

DaMaren, Linda, Acq, University of Guelph, 50 Stone Rd E, Guelph, ON, N1G 2W1, CANADA. Tel: 519-824-4120, Ext 53623. Fax: 519-824-6931. p. 2807

Damaso, Carol, Dir, Scottsdale Public Library, 3839 N Drinkwater Blvd, Scottsdale, AZ, 85251-4467. Tel: 480-312-7323. Fax: 480-312-7993. p. 81

Dambrosio, Ellen, Syst Librn, Modesto Junior College Library, 435 College Ave, Modesto, CA, 95350. Tel: 209-575-6235. Fax: 209-575-6669. p. 188

Dame, Cathy, Dir, Lebanon-Laclede County Library, 915 S Jefferson Ave, Lebanon, MO, 65536-3667. Tel: 417-532-2148. Fax: 417-532-7424. p. 1343

Dameron, Harriet, Libr Tech, Gaston College, 201 Hwy 321 S, Dallas, NC, 28034-1499. Tel: 704-922-6356. Fax: 704-922-2342. p. 1786

Dameron, Wilma, Head, Circ, Dulany Memorial Library, 501 S Broadway, Salisbury, MO, 65281. Tel: 660-388-5712. Fax: 660-388-5712. p. 1364

Dames, Christopher, Dean of Libr, University of Missouri-Saint Louis Libraries, One University Blvd, Saint Louis, MO, 63121. Tel: 314-516-5060. Fax: 314-516-5853. p. 1362

Dames, Kevin Matthew, Copyright & Info Adv, Syracuse University Library, 222 Waverly Ave, Syracuse, NY, 13244-2010. Tel: 315-443-2573. p. 1754

Dames, Rebecca, Br Mgr, Knox County Public Library System, West Knoxville Branch, 100 Golf Club Rd, Knoxville, TN, 37919-4801. Tel: 865-588-8813. Fax: 865-588-7580. p. 2242

Damewood, Jim, Dir, Walters State Community College, 500 S Davy Crockett Pkwy, Morristown, TN, 37813-6899. Tel: 423-585-2600. Fax: 423-585-6959. p. 2253

Damewood, Mindy, Tech Proc Mgr, Monmouth College, 700 E Broadway, Monmouth, IL, 61462-1963. Tel: 309-457-2334. Fax: 309-457-2226. p. 675

Damiano, Maureen, Circ Supvr, Ursinus College Library, 601 E Main St, Collegeville, PA, 19426. Tel: 610-409-3000, Ext 2290. Fax: 610-489-0634. p. 2046

Damico, Andrew, Head, Presv Serv, Rice University, 6100 Main, MS-44, Houston, TX, 77005. Tel: 713-348-2602. Fax: 713-348-5258. p. 2341

Damien, Brian, Br Adminr, Outreach Serv Librn, Portland Public Library, Five Monument Sq, Portland, ME, 04101. Tel: 207-871-1700, Ext 716. Fax: 207-871-1703. p. 997

Damm, Anne, Dir, Darcy Library of Beulah, 7238 Commercial St, Beulah, MI, 49617. Tel: 231-882-4037. p. 1157

Damon, Cora M, Librn, Maine General Medical Center, 149 North St, Waterville, ME, 04901-1000. Tel: 207-872-1224. Fax: 207-872-1460. p. 1005

Damore, Penelope, Ref, Miller, Canfield, Paddock & Stone Library, 150 W Jefferson, Ste 2500, Detroit, MI, 48226. Tel: 313-963-6420. Fax: 313-496-8452. p. 1171

Damos, Maryann, Exec Dir, Children's Museum of Oak Ridge, 461 W Outer Dr, Oak Ridge, TN, 37830-3714. Tel: 865-482-1074. Fax: 865-481-4889. p. 2262

Damphouse, P, Head, Adult Serv, Aurora Public Library, 15145 Young St, Aurora, ON, L4G 1M1, CANADA. Tel: 905-727-9493. Fax: 905-727-9374. p. 2793

Damptz, Rebecca, Archivist, Local Hist Librn, Decatur Public Library, 130 N Franklin St, Decatur, IL, 62523-1327. Tel: 217-421-9711. Fax: 217-233-4071. p. 634

Damschroder, Russ, Supvr, University of Toledo, 2801 W Bancroft St, Mail Stop 509, Toledo, OH, 43606-3390. Tel: 419-530-2443. Fax: 419-530-2726. p. 1941

Danaher, Ross W, Dir, Libr & Res Serv, The Parrott Centre, 376 Wallbridge-Loyalist Rd, Belleville, ON, K8N 5B9, CANADA. Tel: 613-969-1913, Ext 2339. Fax: 613-969-5183. p. 2795

Dance, Jane, Librn II, Round Rock Public Library, 216 E Main St, Round Rock, TX, 78664. Tel: 512-218-7000, 512-218-7003. Fax: 512-218-7061. p. 2377

Dance, Patricia, Res, Historic Saint Mary's City, 18401 Rosecroft Rd, Saint Mary's City, MD, 20686. Tel: 240-895-4974. Fax: 240-895-4968. p. 1040

Dance, Susan, Tech Serv, Orillia Public Library, 36 Mississaga St W, Orillia, ON, L3V 3A6, CANADA. Tel: 705-325-2338. Fax: 705-327-1744. p. 2826

Dancel, Redgie, Librn, Heald College, 341 Great Mall Pkwy, Milpitas, CA, 95035-8027. Tel: 408-934-4900, Ext 5127. Fax: 408-876-5202. p. 187

Dancer, Rusty, Mrs, Asst Dir, Info Serv Supvr, Craighead County Jonesboro Public Library, 315 W Oak Ave, Jonesboro, AR, 72401-3513. Tel: 870-935-5133, Ext 16. Fax: 870-935-7987. p. 104

Danchik, Margaret J, Head, Acq, United States Naval Academy, 589 McNair Rd, Annapolis, MD, 21402-5029. Tel: 410-293-6900. Fax: 410-293-6909. p. 1011

Dancik, Deborah B, Univ Librn, Willamette University, 900 State St, Salem, OR, 97301. Tel: 503-370-6561. Fax: 503-370-6141. p. 2018

Danciu, Tammie, Sr Info Spec, Hamilton Spectator Library, 44 Frid St, Hamilton, ON, L8N 3G3, CANADA. Tel: 905-526-3315. p. 2810

Dandle, Mary E, Tech Serv, Putnam County Library System, 601 College Rd, Palatka, FL, 32177-3873. Tel: 386-329-0126. Fax: 386-329-1240. p. 478

Daneault, Frances, Libr Asst, Bacon Free Library, 58 Eliot St, Natick, MA, 01760. Tel: 508-653-6730. p. 1107

Daneri, Mary Louise, Chief, Coll & Tech Mgt, Montgomery County Public Libraries, 21 Maryland Ave, Ste 310, Rockville, MD, 20850. Tel: 240-777-0031. p. 1038

Daneri, Mary Louise, Mgr, Montgomery County Public Libraries, Long Branch, 8800 Garland Ave, Silver Spring, MD, 20901. Tel: 240-777-0911. Fax: 301-565-7661. p. 1038

Daneshwar, Rimattee, Actg Librn, United States Army, 404 Pershing Loop, Fort Hamilton, Brooklyn, NY, 11252-5100. Tel: 718-630-4875. Fax: 718-630-4038. p. 1595

Danford, Patricia L, Dir, Caldwell Public Library, 517 Spruce St, Caldwell, OH, 43724-1135. Tel: 740-732-4506. Fax: 740-732-4795. p. 1863

Danford, Robert, Dir, Widener University, One University Pl, Chester, PA, 19013-5792. Tel: 610-499-4087. Fax: 610-499-4588. p. 2044

Danforth, Eleanore, Librn, Oneida Community Library, Green Earth Branch Library, W1273 Redtail Dr, De Pere, WI, 54155-9423. Tel: 920-833-7226. p. 2627

Danforth, Susan L, Asst Librn, John Carter Brown Library, Brown University, George & Brown Sts, Providence, RI, 02912. Tel: 401-863-2725. Fax: 401-863-3477. p. 2171

Dang, Shannen, Libr Spec, Alhambra Public Library, 101 S First St, Alhambra, CA, 91801-3432. Tel: 626-570-5008. Fax: 626-457-1104. p. 120

Danhart, Valerie, Circ, Paramus Public Library, E 116 Century Rd, Paramus, NJ, 07652-4398. Tel: 201-599-1300. Fax: 201-599-0059. p. 1517

Danie, Catherine, Asst Librn, Ashaway Free Library, 15 Knight St, Ashaway, RI, 02804-1410. Tel: 401-377-2770. Fax: 401-377-2770. p. 2163

Daniel, Bridget, Youth Serv Mgr, Wake County Public Library System, West Regional Library, 4000 Louis Stephens Dr, Cary, NC, 27519. Tel: 919-463-8524. p. 1818

Daniel, Christina, Circ, Mary Baldwin College, 109 E Frederick St, Staunton, VA, 24401. Tel: 540-887-7311. Fax: 540-887-7137. p. 2496

Daniel, Dominique, Info Literacy & Ref Librn, Oakland University Library, 2200 N Squirrel Rd, Rochester, MI, 48309-4402. Tel: 248-370-2478. Fax: 248-370-2474. p. 1221

Daniel, Donna, Tech Serv Librn, Dallas Baptist University, 3000 Mountain Creek Pkwy, Dallas, TX, 75211-9299. Tel: 214-333-5299. Fax: 214-333-5323. p. 2305

Daniel, Karen, Dir, Johnson County Public Library, 444 Main St, Paintsville, KY, 41240. Tel: 606-789-4355. Fax: 606-789-6758. p. 932

Daniel, Karen, Spec Coll & Archives Librn, Shippensburg University, 1871 Old Main Dr, Shippensburg, PA, 17257-2299. Tel: 717-477-1516. Fax: 717-477-1389. p. 2140

Daniel, Kay, Dir, Hockley County Memorial Library, 811 Austin St, Levelland, TX, 79336. Tel: 806-894-6750. Fax: 806-894-6917. p. 2355

Daniel, Kay, Librn, Raleigh County Public Library, Marsh Fork, 9802 Coal River Rd, Montcoal, WV, 25140. Tel: 304-854-2677. Fax: 304-854-2666. p. 2554

Daniel, Meredith, Dean, Learning Res, Piedmont Technical College Library, 620 N Emerald Rd, Bldg K, Greenwood, SC, 29646. Tel: 864-941-8441. Fax: 864-941-8558. p. 2197

Daniel, Nancy L, Archivist, Ref & Instrul Serv Librn, Res Librn, Western Piedmont Community College, 1001 Burkemont Ave, Morganton, NC, 28655-4504. Tel: 828-448-3160. Fax: 828-448-6173. p. 1811

Daniel, Robin, Libr Mgr, Northwest Area Health Education Center Library at Boone, Watauga Medical Ctr, 336 Deerfield Rd, Boone, NC, 28607-5008. Tel: 828-262-4300. Fax: 828-265-5048. p. 1777

Daniel, Sample, Mgr, Fort Bend County Libraries, 1001 Golfview Dr, Richmond, TX, 77469-5199. Tel: 281-341-2646. Fax: 281-341-2688. p. 2374

Daniel Walkuski, Julia, Assoc Librn, Syst Coordr, University of Michigan-Dearborn, 4901 Evergreen Rd, Dearborn, MI, 48128-2406. Tel: 313-593-5445. Fax: 313-593-5478. p. 1168

Daniel, Wanda, Mgr, Oconee Regional Library, Talking Book Center, 801 Bellevue Ave, Dublin, GA, 31021. Tel: 478-275-5382. Fax: 478-275-3821. p. 531

Daniele, Debbie, Circ Supvr, Fairleigh Dickinson University, 1000 River Rd, Teaneck, NJ, 07666-1914. Tel: 201-692-2279, Ext 2276. Fax: 201-692-9815. p. 1532

Danieli, Christine, Head, Reader Serv Div, United States Naval War College Library, 686 Cushing Rd, Newport, RI, 02841-1207. Tel: 401-841-2642. Fax: 401-841-6491. p. 2169

Daniels, Alicia, Actg Dir, Florida Free Library, 56 N County Rd, Florida, MA, 01247-9614. Tel: 413-664-0153. Fax: 413-663-3593. p. 1089

Daniels, Billie, Circ Coordr, Union College, 310 College St, Campus Box D-21, Barbourville, KY, 40906-1499. Tel: 606-546-1630. Fax: 606-546-1239. p. 906

Daniels, Caroline, Univ Archivist, University of Louisville Libraries, University Archives & Records Center, Ekstrom Library, 2215 S Third St, Louisville, KY, 40208. Tel: 502-852-6676. Fax: 502-852-7394. p. 927

Daniels, Caroline, Syst, Web & ILL Librn, Kwantlen Polytechnic University Library, 12666 72 Ave., Surrey, BC, V3W 2M8, CANADA. Tel: 604-599-2701. Fax: 604-599-2106. p. 2738

Daniels, Debbie, Mgr, Northwest Regional Library System, Parker Public Library, 4710 Second St, Parker, FL, 32404. Tel: 850-871-3092. Fax: 850-874-8978. p. 481

Daniels, Diane, Coord, Ad Serv, Coordr, AV, Mansfield-Richland County Public Library, 43 W Third St, Mansfield, OH, 44902-1295. Tel: 419-521-3121. Fax: 419-525-4750. p. 1912

Daniels, Donna, Head, Ref, University of Arkansas Libraries, 365 N McIlroy Ave, Fayetteville, AR, 72701-4002. Tel: 479-575-8417. Fax: 479-575-6656. p. 99

Daniels, Evelyn, Libr Tech, Saskatchewan Indian Cultural Centre, 305 - 2555 Grasswood Rd E, Saskatoon, SK, S7T 0K1, CANADA. Tel: 306-244-1146. Fax: 306-665-6520. p. 2926

Daniels, John, Cat, Libr Tech, Minneapolis Community & Technical College Library, Wheelock Whitney Hall, 1501 Hennepin Ave, Minneapolis, MN, 55403. Tel: 612-659-6290. Fax: 612-659-6295. p. 1261

Daniels, John W, Jr, Dr, Ref & Instruction Librn, Flagler College, 44 Sevilla St, Saint Augustine, FL, 32084-4302. Tel: 904-819-6206. Fax: 904-823-8511. p. 486

Daniels, Kate, Pres, Atlanta Health Science Libraries Consortium, Fran Golding Medical Library at Scottish Rite, 1001 Johnson Ferry Rd NE, Atlanta, GA, 30342-1600. Tel: 404-785-2157. Fax: 404-785-2155. p. 2941

Daniels, Kathleen, Ref Serv, Tech Serv, Minneapolis Community & Technical College Library, Wheelock Whitney Hall, 1501 Hennepin Ave, Minneapolis, MN, 55403. Tel: 612-659-6285. Fax: 612-659-6295. p. 1261

Daniels, Kenton, Head, Adult Serv, Licking County Library, 101 W Main St, Newark, OH, 43055-5054. Tel: 740-344-2177. Fax: 740-349-5535. p. 1922

Daniels, Kyle E, Dir, Everest Institute, 1630 Portland Ave, Rochester, NY, 14621. Tel: 585-266-0430, Ext 108. Fax: 585-266-8243. p. 1729

Daniels, Lewis B, III, Librn, Westbrook Public Library, 61 Goodspeed Dr, Westbrook, CT, 06498. Tel: 860-399-6422. Fax: 860-399-6344. p. 377

Daniels, Linda, Circ, Elkins-Randolph County Public Library, 416 Davis Ave, Elkins, WV, 26241. Tel: 304-637-0287. Fax: 304-637-0288. p. 2558

Daniels, Marian, Circ, Amarillo College Library, 2201 S Washington, Amarillo, TX, 79109. Tel: 806-371-5400. Fax: 806-371-5470. p. 2274

Daniels, Marilyn, Mgr, Latrobe Area Hospital, 121 W Second Ave, Latrobe, PA, 15650-1096. Tel: 724-537-1275. Fax: 724-537-1890. p. 2079

Daniels, Mark, Dr, Dir, American Indian Research Project, University of South Dakota, 414 E Clark St, 12 Dakota Hall, Vermillion, SD, 57069. Tel: 605-677-5209. Fax: 605-677-6525. p. 2220

Daniels, Nancy, Circ, Fiske Public Library, 110 Randall Rd, Wrentham, MA, 02093. Tel: 508-384-5440. Fax: 508-384-5443. p. 1146

Daniels, Paul, Archivist, Evangelical Lutheran Church In America, 2481 Como Ave, Saint Paul, MN, 55108. Tel: 651-641-3205. Fax: 651-641-3354. p. 1278

Daniels, Pete, Dir, Independence Public Library, 220 E Maple, Independence, KS, 67301-3899. Tel: 620-331-3030. Fax: 620-331-4093. p. 873

Daniels, Phyllis, Libr Asst, North Valley Public Library, 208 Main St, Stevensville, MT, 59870. Tel: 406-777-5061. Fax: 406-777-5061. p. 1388

Daniels, Samuel, Br Mgr, Monterey County Free Libraries, Marina Branch, 190 Seaside Circle, Marina, CA, 93933. Tel: 831-883-7506. Fax: 831-883-9473. p. 183

Daniels, Sharon, Librn, Wapiti Regional Library, Sturgeon Lake Public Library, RR 1, Site 12, Shellbrook, SK, S0J 0E0, CANADA. Tel: 306-764-5506. p. 2922

Daniels, Stephanie, Dir, Hartford Public Library, 15 Franklin St, Hartford, MI, 49057. Tel: 616-621-3408. Fax: 616-621-3073. p. 1188

Daniels, Sue, Youth Serv Librn, Elm Grove Public Library, 13600 W Juneau Blvd, Elm Grove, WI, 53122-1679. Tel: 262-782-6717. Fax: 262-780-4827. p. 2591

Daniels, Tracey, Commun Relations Spec, Polk County Public Library, 1289 W Mills St, Columbus, NC, 28722. Tel: 828-894-8721. Fax: 828-894-2761. p. 1785

Daniels-Howell, Todd, Assoc Dean, Admin & Spec Coll, Indiana University-Purdue University Indianapolis, 755 W Michigan St, Indianapolis, IN, 46202-5195. Tel: 317-274-0466. Fax: 317-278-0368. p. 753

Daniels-Richardson, Belinda S, Ref Serv, Guilford Technical Community College, 601 High Point Rd, Jamestown, NC, 27282. Tel: 336-334-4822, Ext 2636. Fax: 336-841-4350. p. 1803

Danielson, Carol, Br Mgr, Irving Public Library, East, 440 S Nursery Rd, Irving, TX, 75060. Tel: 972-721-3722. Fax: 972-721-3724. p. 2347

Danielson, Diane M, Dir, Palmerton Area Library Association, 402 Delaware Ave, Palmerton, PA, 18071-1995. Tel: 610-826-3424. Fax: 610-826-6248. p. 2101

Danis, Carl, Coll Develop Librn, University of North Carolina at Pembroke, Faculty Row, Pembroke, NC, 28372. Tel: 910-521-6516. Fax: 910-521-6547. p. 1814

Danish, Judy, Librn, Wayne County Regional Library for the Blind & Physically Handicapped, 30555 Michigan Ave, Westland, MI, 48186-5310. Tel: 734-727-7300. Fax: 734-727-7333. p. 1236

Danisher, Geoff, Ref Librn, Concordia College, 171 White Plains Rd, Bronxville, NY, 10708. Tel: 914-337-9300, Ext 2202. Fax: 914-395-4893. p. 1588

Danisher, Geoffrey, ILL, Sarah Lawrence College, One Mead Way, Bronxville, NY, 10708. Tel: 914-395-2474. Fax: 914-395-2473. p. 1588

Dankert, Holly Stec, Access & Res Serv Librn, School of the Art Institute of Chicago, 37 S Wabash Ave, Chicago, IL, 60603-3103. Tel: 312-899-5097. Fax: 312-899-1851. p. 624

Danko, Mary, Dir, Hartland Public Libraries, 153 Rte 5, Hartland, VT, 05048. Tel: 802-436-2473. Fax: 802-436-2473. p. 2425

Danko, Phyllis, Head, Ch, Wiggin Memorial Library, Ten Bunker Hill Ave, Stratham, NH, 03885. Tel: 603-772-4346. p. 1465

Danku, Pat, Librn, Wapiti Regional Library, Prairie River Public Library, General Delivery, Two Arras St, Prairie River, SK, S0E 1J0, CANADA. Tel: 306-889-4521. p. 2921

Danley, Pamela, Ch, The Frances Banta Waggoner Community Library, 505 Tenth St, DeWitt, IA, 52742-1335. Tel: 563-659-5523. Fax: 563-659-2901. p. 810

Dann, Beverly Ruth, Dir, Waverly Free Library, Elizabeth Sq, 18 Elizabeth St, Waverly, NY, 14892. Tel: 607-565-9341. Fax: 607-565-3960. p. 1764

Dann, Laura, Acq, Clearwater Public Library System, 100 N Osceola Ave, Clearwater, FL, 33755. Tel: 727-562-4970. Fax: 727-562-4977. p. 432

Dann, Lucinda, Ch, Melbourne Public Library, 540 E Fee Ave, Melbourne, FL, 32901. Tel: 321-952-4514. Fax: 321-952-4518. p. 463

Dann, Rich, Dir, Norfolk Library, Nine Greenwoods Rd E, Norfolk, CT, 06058-1320. Tel: 860-542-5075. Fax: 860-542-1795. p. 361

Danna, Maria, Head, Adult Serv, Auburn Hills Public Library, 3400 E Seyburn Dr, Auburn Hills, MI, 48326-2759. Tel: 248-370-9466. Fax: 248-370-9364. p. 1154

Dannecker, Joyce, Dir, Northwest Regional Library System, 898 W 11 St, Panama City, FL, 32401. Tel: 850-522-2100. Fax: 850-522-2138. p. 480

Dannehl, Karen, Ref Librn, Great Basin College Library, 1500 College Pkwy, Elko, NV, 89801. Tel: 775-753-2300. Fax: 775-753-2296. p. 1427

Danneker, John, Dir, George Washington University, Eckles Library, 2100 Foxhall Rd NW, Washington, DC, 20007-1199. Tel: 202-242-6621. Fax: 202-242-6632. p. 402

Dannelley, Leta J, Librn, CHRISTUS Spohn Health System, 2606 Hospital Blvd, Corpus Christi, TX, 78405. Tel: 361-902-4197, 361-902-4990. Fax: 361-902-4198. p. 2301

Dannenberg, Anne, Dir, Huntington Public Library, 2156 Main Rd, Huntington, VT, 05462. Tel: 802-434-4583. p. 2426

Danner, Brandy, YA Serv, Wilmington Memorial Library, 175 Middlesex Ave, Wilmington, MA, 01887-2779. Tel: 978-658-2967. Fax: 978-658-9699. p. 1141

Danner, Charles A, Ref/Tech Support Librn, Portage County Public Library, Charles M White Library Bldg, 1001 Main St, Stevens Point, WI, 54481-2860. Tel: 715-345-5360. Fax: 715-346-1239. p. 2640

Danner, Linda M, Coordr, Franklin & Marshall College, 450 College Ave, Lancaster, PA, 17603-3318. Tel: 717-291-4216. Fax: 717-291-4160. p. 2076

Danner, Pat, ILL, Conception Abbey & Seminary Library, 37174 State Hwy W, Conception, MO, 64433. Tel: 660-944-2803. Fax: 660-944-2833. p. 1326

Danner, Richard A, Sr Assoc Dean for Info Serv, Duke University Libraries, School of Law Library, 210 Science Dr, Durham, NC, 27708. Tel: 919-613-7115. Fax: 919-613-7237. p. 1788

Danner, Sarah, In Charge, Oglala Lakota College, Nursing College Center, PO Box 861, Pine Ridge, SD, 57770. Tel: 605-867-5856. Fax: 605-867-5724. p. 2214

Dano, Reece, Cat, Boston University Libraries, Music Library, 771 Commonwealth Ave, Boston, MA, 02215. Tel: 617-353-3705. Fax: 617-353-2084. p. 1058

Danowski, Dennis, Dir, Macomb Public Library District, 235 S Lafayette St, Macomb, IL, 61455-2231. Tel: 309-833-2714. Fax: 309-833-2714. p. 668

Danowski, Fred, Info Syst Librn, Milford Public Library, 57 New Haven Ave, Milford, CT, 06460. Tel: 203-783-3290. Fax: 203-877-1072. p. 352

Dansak, Carol, Circ, Garden Valley District Library, 342 Village Circle, Garden Valley, ID, 83622-8040. Tel: 208-462-3317. Fax: 208-462-3758. p. 574

Dansby, Claudia, Acq, University of Toledo, LaValley Law Library, Mail Stop 508, 2801 W Bancroft St, Toledo, OH, 43606-3390. Tel: 419-530-2733. Fax: 419-530-5121. p. 1941

Dansby, David, Asst Dir, Hickman County Public Library, 120 W Swan St, Centerville, TN, 37033. Tel: 931-729-5130. Fax: 931-729-6950. p. 2226

Danser, Sarah, Asst Librn, Maine Maritime Academy, Pleasant St, Box C-1, Castine, ME, 04420. Tel: 207-326-2262. Fax: 207-326-2261. p. 981

Dansker, George, Dir, Notre Dame Seminary Library, 2901 S Carrollton Ave, New Orleans, LA, 70118-4391. Tel: 504-866-7426, Ext 3700. Fax: 504-866-6260. p. 962

Dantzler, Barbara, GIL Express & Circ Asst, Clayton State University, 2000 Clayton State Blvd, Morrow, GA, 30260. Tel: 678-466-4325. Fax: 678-466-4349. p. 545

Danyliuk, Janet, Dir, Ukrainian Museum of Canada Library, 910 Spadina Crescent E, Saskatoon, SK, S7K 3H5, CANADA. Tel: 306-244-3800. Fax: 306-652-7620. p. 2927

Danyluk, Nadia, Children & Youth Serv Librn, Owen Sound & North Grey Union Public Library, 824 First Ave W, Owen Sound, ON, N4K 4K4, CANADA. Tel: 519-376-6623. Fax: 519-376-7170. p. 2834

Danziger, Margaret, Dep Dir, Toledo-Lucas County Public Library, 325 N Michigan St, Toledo, OH, 43604-6614. Tel: 419-259-5207. Fax: 419-255-1334. p. 1939

Daoust, Daniele, Prof, College Lionel-Groulx, 100, rue Duquet, Sainte-Therese, QC, J7E 3G6, CANADA. Tel: 450-430-3120, Ext 407. Fax: 450-971-7883. p. 2979

Darabaner, Ellen, Circuit Librn, Claxton-Hepburn Medical Center Library, 214 King St, Ogdensburg, NY, 13669. Tel: 315-393-3600, Ext 5632. Fax: 315-393-8506. p. 1709

Darabaner, Ellen, Librn, Samaritan Medical Center, 830 Washington St, Watertown, NY, 13601. Tel: 315-785-4191. Fax: 315-779-5173. p. 1764

Darais, Suzanne, Head, Info Tech, University of Utah, S J Quinney Law Library, 332 S 1400 East, Salt Lake City, UT, 84112-0731. Tel: 801-585-3074. Fax: 801-585-3033. p. 2415

Darby, David, Curator, Firefighters' Museum of Nova Scotia Library, 451 Main St, Yarmouth, NS, B5A 1G9, CANADA. Tel: 902-742-5525. Fax: 902-742-5525. p. 2786

Darby, Della, Chair, Cat, Tech Serv, Samford University Library, 800 Lakeshore Dr, Birmingham, AL, 35229. Tel: 205-726-2078. Fax: 205-726-4009. p. 9

Darby, Jonathan, Ref Librn, Ref/ILL/Instruction, South University Library, 5355 Vaughn Rd, Montgomery, AL, 36116-1120. Tel: 334-395-8800. Fax: 334-395-8859. p. 31

Darby, Julia, Asst Librn, Jesup Public Library, 721 Sixth St, Jesup, IA, 50648-0585. Tel: 319-827-1533. Fax: 319-827-1580. p. 824

Darby, Rhonda, Br Mgr, Pine Forest Regional Library, McHenry Public, 25 McHenry School Dr, McHenry, MS, 39561. Tel: 601-528-9465. Fax: 601-528-9465. p. 1314

Darby, Sharla, Managing Librn, Pima County Public Library, Himmel Park, 1035 N Treat, Tucson, AZ, 85716. Tel: 520-594-5305. Fax: 520-594-5306. p. 87

Darby, William, Librn, Birmingham Public Library, Eastwood, 4500 Montevallo Rd, Ste 107, Birmingham, AL, 35210. Tel: 205-591-4944. Fax: 205-956-2503. p. 7

Darbyshire, Denise, Librn, Lima Public Library, Spencerville Branch, 2489 Wisher Dr, Spencerville, OH, 45887. Tel: 419-647-4307. Fax: 419-647-6393. p. 1910

Darcangelo, Rosanne, Cat, Corning Community College, One Academic Dr, Corning, NY, 14830. Tel: 607-962-9251. Fax: 607-962-9466. p. 1610

Darcey, Pat, Tech Serv, Summit County Library, 6505 N Landmark Dr, Ste 100, Park City, UT, 84098-6009. Tel: 435-615-3901. Fax: 435-615-3905. p. 2410

Darch, Heather, Curator, Missisquoi Historical Society, Two River St, Stanbridge East, QC, J0J 2H0, CANADA. Tel: 450-248-3153. Fax: 450-248-0420. p. 2913

Darden, Barbara, Dr, Dean, Libr Serv, Kutztown University, 15200 Kutztown Rd, Bldg 5, Kutztown, PA, 19530-0735. Tel: 610-683-4484. Fax: 610-683-4747. p. 2075

Darden, Gwen, Cat Asst, Texas A&M University-Texarkana, 7101 University Ave, Texarkana, TX, 75503. Tel: 903-223-3093. Fax: 903-334-6695. p. 2392

Darden, LaKeshia, Curric/Media Librn, Campbell University, 113 Main St, Buies Creek, NC, 27506. Tel: 910-893-1460. Fax: 910-893-1470. p. 1778

Dardenne, Debra, Mgr, Southeast Arkansas Regional Library, Dumas Branch, 120 E Choctow, Dumas, AR, 71639. Tel: 870-382-5763. Fax: 870-382-5763. p. 110

Darding, Sara, Head, Youth Serv, Kewanee Public Library District, 102 S Tremont St, Kewanee, IL, 61443. Tel: 309-852-4505. Fax: 309-852-4466. p. 661

Dare, Sandra, Libr Asst, Columbia County Rural Library District, 111 S Third St, Dayton, WA, 99328-1342. Tel: 509-382-4131. Fax: 509-382-1059. p. 2514

Darenberg, Lisa, Ch, Saint Johns County Public Library System, Bartram Trail, 60 Davis Pond Blvd, Fruit Cove, FL, 32259-4390. Tel: 904-827-6962. Fax: 904-827-6965. p. 487

Darga, Carol M, Tech Serv, Dickinson Wright PLLC Library, 500 Woodward Ave, Ste 4000, Detroit, MI, 48226-3425. Tel: 313-223-3500. Fax: 313-223-3598. p. 1170

Darga, Richard, Dr, Assoc Dean, Tech & Learning Res, Chicago State University, 9501 S Martin Luther King Jr Dr, LIB 440, Chicago, IL, 60628-1598. Tel: 773-995-2378. Fax: 773-995-3772. p. 610

Dargan, Cindy, Commun Br Supvr, Pierce County Library System, Eatonville Branch, 205 Center St W, Eatonville, WA, 98328-9488. Tel: 253-548-3311. Fax: 360-832-7201. p. 2539

Dargan, Denise, Br Mgr, Anchorage Public Library, Scott & Wesley Gerrish Library, 680 Hightower Rd, Girdwood, AK, 99587. Tel: 907-343-4024, 907-783-2106. Fax: 907-783-3118. p. 44

Dargan, Michael, Ref, Waterloo Public Library, 415 Commercial St, Waterloo, IA, 50701-1385. Tel: 319-291-4521. Fax: 319-291-6736. p. 850

Dargelis, Christine, Asst Dir, Tech Serv, Middleborough Public Library, 102 N Main St, Middleborough, MA, 02346. Tel: 508-946-2470. Fax: 508-946-2473. p. 1105

Darimont, Carolyne, Mgr, ArcelorMittal Dofasco, 1390 Burlington St E, Hamilton, ON, L8N 3J5, CANADA. Tel: 905-548-7200, Ext 6223. Fax: 905-548-4653. p. 2808

Darin, Deborah, Ref Librn, Loyola University Chicago Libraries, Law School Library, 25 E Pearson St, 3rd Flr, Chicago, IL, 60611. Tel: 312-915-7131, 312-915-7200, 312-915-7202. Fax: 312-915-6797. p. 617

Dark, Cynthia, Pub Serv, Thomas Beaver Free Library, 205 Ferry St, Danville, PA, 17821-1939. Tel: 570-275-4180. Fax: 570-275-8480. p. 2049

Darkhosh, Susan, Mgr, Lending Serv, Princeton Public Library, 65 Witherspoon St, Princeton, NJ, 08542. Tel: 609-924-9529, Ext 272. Fax: 609-924-6109. p. 1522

Darlack, James, Ref, Gordon-Conwell Theological Seminary, 130 Essex St, South Hamilton, MA, 01982-2317. Tel: 978-646-4074. Fax: 978-646-4567. p. 1125

Darling, Freda, Asst Librn, Junction City Public Library, 726 Greenwood St, Junction City, OR, 97448-1628. Tel: 541-998-8942. p. 2001

Darling, Jane, Asst Dir, Coppell Public Library, 177 N Hertz Rd, Coppell, TX, 75019. Tel: 972-304-3660. Fax: 972-304-3622. p. 2301

Darling, Jason, Br Mgr, Albany Public Library, Downtown Carnegie, 302 Ferry St SW, Albany, OR, 97321-2216. Tel: 541-917-7585. p. 1989

Darling, Karen, Head, Acq, University of Missouri-Columbia, Elmer Ellis Library, Ellis Library Bldg, Rm 104, Columbia, MO, 65201-5149. Tel: 573-882-2835. Fax: 573-882-8044. p. 1325

Darling, Rebecca, Ch, Town of Ballston Community Library, Two Lawmar Lane, Burnt Hills, NY, 12027. Tel: 518-399-8174. Fax: 518-399-1687. p. 1600

Darling, Ruth E, Co-Dir, Bernville Area Community Library, 6721 Bernville Rd, Bernville, PA, 19506. Tel: 610-488-1302. Fax: 270-479-1302. p. 2032

Darlington, Janice, Librn, North Central Regional Library, Pateros Community, 174 Pateros Mall, Pateros, WA, 98846. Tel: 509-923-2298. Fax: 509-923-2298. p. 2549

Darlington, Kate, ILL Librn, Conway Public Library, 15 Main St, Conway, NH, 03818. Tel: 603-447-5552. Fax: 603-447-6921. p. 1444

Darlington, Pam, Asst Dir, Exeter Public Library, Four Chestnut St, Exeter, NH, 03833. Tel: 603-772-3101, 603-772-6036. Fax: 603-772-7548. p. 1447

Darnall, Jackie, Circ, Campbell County Public Library System, 2101 S 4-J Rd, Gillette, WY, 82718-5205. Tel: 307-687-0009. Fax: 307-686-4009. p. 2655

Darnall, Kimberly, Br Librn, Marshall County Public Library System, Hardin, 104 Second St, Hardin, KY, 42048. Tel: 270-437-4275. Fax: 270-437-4609. p. 907

Darne, Bruce, Librn, Marinette County Library System, Goodman Library Station, One Falcon Crest, Goodman, WI, 54125. Tel: 715-336-2575. Fax: 715-336-2576. p. 2612

Darne, Bruce, Librn, Marinette County Library System, Niagara Public Library, 1029 Roosevelt Rd, Niagara, WI, 54151-1205. Tel: 715-251-3236. Fax: 715-251-3236. p. 2612

Darnell, Barbara, Treas, Thorntown Public Library, 124 N Market St, Thorntown, IN, 46071-1144. Tel: 765-436-7348. Fax: 765-436-7011. p. 782

Darnell, Polly, Archivist, Librn, Shelburne Museum Library, 5555 Shelburne Rd, Shelburne, VT, 05482-7491. Tel: 802-985-3346, Ext 3379. Fax: 802-985-2331. p. 2435

Darnell, Winnie, Br Mgr, Washington County Library System, Glen Allan Library, 970 E Lake Washington Rd, Glen Allan, MS, 38744. Tel: 662-839-4066. Fax: 662-839-4066. p. 1298

Darnobid, Marybeth, Ch, YA Serv, Blauvelt Free Library, 541 Western Hwy, Blauvelt, NY, 10913. Tel: 845-359-2811. Fax: 845-398-0017. p. 1583

Darnton, Robert, Dir, Harvard Library, 1341 Massachusetts Ave, Wadsworth House, Cambridge, MA, 02138. Tel: 617-495-3650. Fax: 617-495-0370. p. 1073

Darowski, Shannon, Young Readers & Teen Serv Coordr, North Kingstown Free Library, 100 Boone St, North Kingstown, RI, 02852-5176. Tel: 401-294-3306. Fax: 401-294-1690. p. 2170

Darr, Jonelle Prether, Exec Dir, Cumberland County Library System, 19 S West St, Carlisle, PA, 17013-2839. Tel: 717-240-6175. p. 2041

Darr, Karleen, Head, Coll Serv, University of California, Davis, 100 NW Quad, Davis, CA, 95616-5292. Tel: 530-752-6561. Fax: 530-752-3148. p. 139

Darragh, Martina, Ref, National Reference Center for Bioethics Literature, Georgetown University, 37th & O St NW, Washington, DC, 20057. Tel: 202-687-3885. Fax: 202-687-6770. p. 411

Darrah, Joseph, Pres, Park County Bar Association, Court House, 1002 Sheridan Ave, Cody, WY, 82414. Tel: 307-754-2254. Fax: 307-527-8687. p. 2653

Darrington, Amy, Libr Dir, Singletary Memorial Library, 207 E Sixth St, Rusk, TX, 75785. Tel: 903-683-5916. Fax: 903-683-5964. p. 2378

Darrington, Jeremy, Politics Librn, Princeton University, Politics & Law Collections, Firestone Library, A-17-J-1, One Washington Rd, Princeton, NJ, 08544. Tel: 609-258-3209, 609-258-3701. p. 1524

Darrough, Melony, Br Mgr, Pine Bluff & Jefferson County Library System, Altheimer Public Library, 222 S Edline, Altheimer, AR, 72004-8589. Tel: 870-766-8499. Fax: 870-766-8499. p. 112

Darrow, Kathy, Librn, Fulbright & Jaworski Library, 300 Convent St, Ste 2200, San Antonio, TX, 78205-3792. Tel: 210-224-5575. p. 2380

Darrow, Pamela, Librn, Porter Memorial Library, 87 Main St, Blandford, MA, 01008-9518. Tel: 413-848-2853. Fax: 413-848-2853. p. 1054

Darrow, Sheila, Archivist, Central State University, 1400 Brush Row Rd, Wilberforce, OH, 45384. Tel: 937-376-6521. Fax: 937-376-6132. p. 1948

Darsidan, Charlotte, Libr Spec, Clinton Community College Library, 1000 Lincoln Blvd, Clinton, IA, 52732. Tel: 563-244-7046. Fax: 563-244-7107. p. 803

Darst, Valerie J, Dir of Libr Serv, Moberly Area Community College, Main Bldg, 2nd Flr, 101 College Ave, Moberly, MO, 65270-1304. Tel: 660-263-4110, Ext 244. Fax: 660-263-6448. p. 1346

Dart, Diana, Commun Relations Coordr, Brighton District Library, 100 Library Dr, Brighton, MI, 48116. Tel: 810-229-6571, Ext 211. Fax: 810-229-3161. p. 1159

Dart, Olivia, Libr Operations, Todd Wehr Library, St Norbert College, 301 Third St, De Pere, WI, 54115. Tel: 920-403-3061. Fax: 920-403-4064. p. 2587

Darter, Lorie, Cat, Pope County Library System, 116 E Third St, Russellville, AR, 72801. Tel: 479-968-4368. Fax: 479-968-3222. p. 114

Darvil, Kathleen, Ref, Brooklyn Law School Library, 250 Joralemon St, Brooklyn, NY, 11201. Tel: 718-780-7544. Fax: 718-780-0369. p. 1590

Darwine, Debbie, Head, Ref, La Grange Public Library, Ten W Cossitt Ave, La Grange, IL, 60525. Tel: 708-352-0576, Ext 24. p. 662

Das, Pradeep, Dir, Beulah Heights University, 892 Berne St SE, Atlanta, GA, 30316. Tel: 404-627-2681. Fax: 404-627-0702. p. 513

Das, Ranjna, Actg Dir, Burlington County Library, Five Pioneer Blvd, Westampton, NJ, 08060. Tel: 609-267-9660, Ext 3021. Fax: 609-267-4091. p. 1542

Das, Sulekha, Dir, Whippanong Library, 1000 Rte 10, Whippany, NJ, 07981. Tel: 973-428-2460. Fax: 973-515-3771. p. 1544

Dasgupta, Anamika, Coordr, Electronic Res, Head, ILL, Webmaster, York College Library, 94-20 Guy R Brewer Blvd, Jamaica, NY, 11451. Tel: 718-262-2034. Fax: 718-262-2027, 718-262-2997. p. 1646

DasGupta, Krishna, Sr Librn, Tech Serv, Worcester State College, 486 Chandler St, Worcester, MA, 01602-2597. Tel: 508-929-8802. Fax: 508-929-8198. p. 1145

Dasher, Leah, Coll Develop, Learning Res Spec, Southeastern Technical College, 211 S Tillman St, Glennville, GA, 30427. Tel: 912-654-5276, Ext 4125. Fax: 912-654-5223. p. 535

Dasher, Leah, Librn, Southeastern Technical College Library, 346 Kite Rd, Swainsboro, GA, 30401. Tel: 478-289-2322. Fax: 478-289-2322. p. 553

Dasher, Leah, Coll Develop, Learning Res Spec, Southeastern Technical College, 3001 E First St, Vidalia, GA, 30474. Tel: 912-538-3132. Fax: 912-538-3156. p. 556

Dasher, Paula, ILL, Coeur d'Alene Public Library, 702 E Front Ave, Coeur d'Alene, ID, 83814-2373. Tel: 208-769-2315. Fax: 208-769-2381. p. 573

DaSilva, Allison, ILL, Reading Public Library, 64 Middlesex Ave, Reading, MA, 01867-2550. Tel: 781-942-6721. Fax: 781-942-9106. p. 1120

DaSilva, Patricia, Mgr, Circ, ILL & Copy Ctr, University of Montana, Maureen & Mike Mansfield Library, 32 Campus Dr, No 9936, Missoula, MT, 59812-9936. Tel: 406-243-6866. Fax: 406-243-4067. p. 1386

Dassler, Julie, Ch, Shawano City-County Library, 128 S Sawyer St, Shawano, WI, 54166-2496. Tel: 715-526-3829. Fax: 715-526-6772. p. 2636

Date, Sandra, Dir, Star Tribune, 425 Portland Ave, Minneapolis, MN, 55488. Tel: 613-673-7176. Fax: 612-673-4459. p. 1261

Datig, Ilka, Ref & Instruction Librn, Mary Baldwin College, 109 E Frederick St, Staunton, VA, 24401. Tel: 540-887-7299. Fax: 540-887-7137. p. 2496

Datko, Curtis, Access Serv Librn, Alvernia University, 400 St Bernardine St, Reading, PA, 19607-1737. Tel: 610-568-1534. Fax: 610-796-8347. p. 2132

Dator, Jim, Dir, Hawaii Research Center for Futures Studies, Social Sciences Bldg, 2424 Maile Way, Rm 704 F, Honolulu, HI, 96822. Tel: 808-956-6601. Fax: 808-956-2889. p. 561

Datres, Lorraine, Tech Serv, Saint Clair County Library System, 210 McMorran Blvd, Port Huron, MI, 48060-4098. Tel: 810-987-7323, Ext 150. Fax: 810-987-7874. p. 1219

Datta, Anutosh, Circ Supvr, Ohio State University LIBRARIES, Food, Agricultural & Environmental Sciences, 045 Agriculture Administration Bldg, 2120 Fyffe Rd, Columbus, OH, 43210-1066. Tel: 614-292-6125. Fax: 614-292-0590. p. 1887

Dattilo, Mary, Dir, Levi E Coe Library, 414 Main St, Middlefield, CT, 06455-1207. Tel: 860-349-3857. Fax: 860-349-2131. p. 351

Daub, Lloyd G, Dir, Bryant & Stratton College Library-Milwaukee, 310 W Wisconsin Ave, Ste 500, Milwaukee, WI, 53203-2200. Tel: 414-276-5200. Fax: 414-276-3930. p. 2617

Daub, Marilyn, Librn, Wabasso Public Library, 1248 Oak St, Wabasso, MN, 56293. Tel: 507-342-5279. Fax: 507-342-2329. p. 1287

Daubenspeck, Pam, Br Coordr, Warren-Trumbull County Public Library, 444 Mahoning Ave NW, Warren, OH, 44483. Tel: 330-399-8807. Fax: 330-395-3988. p. 1944

Dauble, Darcy, Dir, Libr & Media, Walla Walla Community College Library, 500 Tausick Way, Walla Walla, WA, 99362-9267. Tel: 509-527-4292. Fax: 509-527-4480. p. 2547

Daubs, Judy, Dir, Norris City Memorial Public Library District, 603 S Division St, Norris City, IL, 62869. Tel: 618-378-3713. Fax: 618-378-3713. p. 681

Daudon, Lisa, Librn, Starksboro Public Library, 2827 Rte 116, Starksboro, VT, 05487. Tel: 802-453-3732. p. 2436

Daugert, Katie, Broadcast & Ref Librn, NPR Library, 635 Massachusetts Ave NW, Washington, DC, 20001. Fax: 202-513-3056. p. 412

Daugherty, Brien, Librn, Alaska State Legislature, State Capitol, Juneau, AK, 99801-1182. Tel: 907-465-3808. Fax: 907-465-4844. p. 49

Daugherty, Connie, Head, Tech Serv, Montana Tech Library, 1300 W Park St, Butte, MT, 59701-8997. Tel: 406-496-4668. Fax: 406-496-4133. p. 1376

Daugherty, Debbie, Dir, Wynnewood Public Library, 108 N Dean A McGee Ave, Wynnewood, OK, 73098. Tel: 405-665-2512. Fax: 405-665-4619. p. 1986

Daugherty, Jane C, Ref Librn, Thomas B Norton Public Library, 221 W 19th Ave, Gulf Shores, AL, 36542. Tel: 251-968-1176. Fax: 251-968-1184. p. 19

Daugherty, Jennifer, Dir, Ref, Laurel County Public Library District, 120 College Park Dr, London, KY, 40741. Tel: 606-864-5759. Fax: 606-862-8057. p. 922

Daugherty, Kassie, Librn, Bessemer Trust Co, 630 Fifth Ave, 37th Flr, New York, NY, 10111. Tel: 212-651-1037. p. 1670

Daugherty, Mary, Br Mgr, Hardin County Public Library, Radcliff Branch, 800 S Logston, Radcliff, KY, 40160. Tel: 270-351-9999. p. 912

Daugherty, Seth, Ref, El Camino College, 16007 S Crenshaw Blvd, Torrance, CA, 90506. Tel: 310-660-3525. Fax: 310-660-3513. p. 275

Daugherty, Tom, Librn, First Presbyterian Church of Charleston Library, 16 Leon Sullivan Way, Charleston, WV, 25301. Tel: 304-343-8961. Fax: 304-343-8970. p. 2556

Daughety, Leard, Dir, Oconee Regional Library, 801 Bellevue Ave, Dublin, GA, 31021. Tel: 478-272-5710. Fax: 478-275-5381. p. 531

Daught, Gary F, Coll Develop, Dir, Milligan College, 200 Blowers Blvd, Milligan College, TN, 37682. Tel: 423-461-8703. Fax: 423-461-8984. p. 2253

Daughtridge, Dee, Br Mgr, McDowell County Public Library, Marion Davis Memorial Branch, 65 Mitchell St, Old Fort, NC, 28762. Tel: 828-668-7111. Fax: 828-668-4013. p. 1809

Daughtridge, Vicki, Head, Access Serv & Doc Delivery, East Carolina University, William E Laupus Health Sciences Library, 600 Moye Blvd, Health Sciences Bldg, Greenville, NC, 27834. Tel: 252-744-2219. Fax: 252-744-3311. p. 1799

Dauler, Carol, Ref, Sonnenschein, Nath & Rosenthal, 8000 Sears Tower, 233 S Wacker Dr, Ste 7800, Chicago, IL, 60606-6404. Tel: 312-876-8000. Fax: 312-876-7934. p. 625

Daumer-Gutjahr, Carol, Mgr, Lake County Public Library, Hobart Branch, 100 Main St, Hobart, IN, 46342-4391. Tel: 219-942-2243. Fax: 219-947-1823. p. 764

Daumer-Gutjahr, Carol, Mgr, Lake County Public Library, Lake Station-New Chicago Branch, 2007 Central Ave, Lake Station, IN, 46405-2061. Tel: 219-962-2409. Fax: 219-962-8460. p. 764

Daun-Bedford, Sheri, Ch, Woodridge Public Library, Three Plaza Dr, Woodridge, IL, 60517-5014. Tel: 630-964-7899. Fax: 630-964-0175. p. 721

Dauray, Charles, Pres, College of Life Foundation, 8661 Corkscrew Rd, Estero, FL, 33928-3203. Tel: 239-992-2184. Fax: 239-495-0201. p. 439

Davainis, Dava, Fac Librn, Quincy College, Newport Hall, Rm 103, 150 Newport Ave, Quincy, MA, 02171. Tel: 617-984-1680. Fax: 617-984-1782. p. 1119

Dave, Greeta, Cat Librn, Saint Augustine's College, 1315 Oakwood Ave, Raleigh, NC, 27610-2298. Tel: 919-516-4145. Fax: 919-516-4758. p. 1817

Dave, Hansen, Mgr, Electronic Res, Saint Mary's College Library, 1928 Saint Mary's Rd, Moraga, CA, 94575. Tel: 925-631-4229. Fax: 925-376-6097. p. 191

Davenport, Blair, Curator, National Park Service, Hwy 190, Park Headquarters, Death Valley, CA, 92328. Tel: 760-786-3200, Ext 287. Fax: 760-786-2169. p. 140

Davenport, Debbe, Br Librn, Crittenden County Library, 100 N Currie St, Marion, AR, 72364. Tel: 870-739-3238. Fax: 870-739-4624. p. 109

Davenport, Heather, Ch, Fort Sumner Public Library, 235 W Sumner Ave, Fort Sumner, NM, 88119. Tel: 505-355-2832. Fax: 505-355-7732. p. 1555

Davenport, Janet, Dir, Keene Memorial Library, 1030 N Broad St, Fremont, NE, 68025-4199. Tel: 402-727-2694. Fax: 402-727-2693. p. 1399

Davenport, Leslie, Circ Mgr, Wayne County Public Library, 220 W Liberty St, Wooster, OH, 44691-3593. Tel: 330-804-4660. Fax: 330-262-1352. p. 1950

Davenport, Lisa, Ch, Carlinville Public Library, 510 N Broad St, Carlinville, IL, 62626-1019. Tel: 217-854-3505. Fax: 217-854-5349. p. 600

Davenport, Mary, Head, Circ, Upper Merion Township Library, 175 W Valley Forge Rd, King of Prussia, PA, 19406-2399. Tel: 610-265-1196. Fax: 610-265-3398. p. 2074

Davenport, Mina, Librn, Children's Hospital & Research Center Oakland, 747 52nd St, 4th Flr, Oakland, CA, 94609. Tel: 510-428-3448. Fax: 510-601-3963. p. 196

Davenport, Montell, Ref, Cook County Law Library, 2900 Richard J Daley Ctr, 50 W Washington, Chicago, IL, 60602. Tel: 312-603-5423. Fax: 312-603-4716. p. 611

Davenport, Nan, Dir, Wetmore Community Library, 95 County Rd 393, Wetmore, CO, 81253. Tel: 719-784-6669. Fax: 719-784-2301. p. 326

Davenport, Nancy, Univ Librn, American University Library, 4400 Massachusetts Ave NW, Washington, DC, 20016-8046. Tel: 202-885-3237. Fax: 202-885-3226. p. 393

Davenport, Rae, Asst Librn, Northumberland Public Library, 31 State St, Groveton, NH, 03582. Tel: 603-636-2066. Fax: 603-636-2066. p. 1449

Davenport, Sara E, Tech Serv, Cayuga County Community College, 197 Franklin St, Auburn, NY, 13021. Tel: 315-294-8596. Fax: 315-255-2050. p. 1576

Davenport, Willie, Librn, Florida Department of Corrections, 33123 Oil Well Rd, Punta Gorda, FL, 33955-9701. Tel: 941-833-2522. Fax: 941-575-5751. p. 485

Davey, Jane, Br Coordr, Schaumburg Township District Library, Hoffman Estates Branch, 1550 Hassell Rd, Hoffman Estates, IL, 60169. Tel: 847-923-3456. Fax: 847-923-3466. p. 701

Davey, Jane, Coll Librn, Northwest Museum of Art & Culture-Eastern Washington State Historical Society, 2316 W First Ave, Spokane, WA, 99201-1099. Tel: 509-363-5342. Fax: 509-363-5303. p. 2536

Davey, Janice, Circ Librn, West Perth Public Library, 105 Saint Andrew St, Mitchell, ON, N0K 1N0, CANADA. Tel: 519-348-9234. Fax: 519-348-4540. p. 2823

Davey, John H, Libr Mgr, Alston & Bird, LLP Library, 90 Park Ave, 12th Flr, New York, NY, 10016. Tel: 212-210-9526. Fax: 212-210-9444. p. 1667

Davey, Kendra, Managing Librn, Pima County Public Library, Geasa-Marana, 13370 Lon Adams Rd, Marana, AZ, 85653. Tel: 520-594-5255. Fax: 520-594-5256. p. 87

Davey, Linda, Circ, Ref, Holdrege Area Public Library, 604 East Ave, Holdrege, NE, 68949. Tel: 308-995-6556. Fax: 308-995-5732. p. 1402

Davi, Susan, Head, Coll Develop, University of Delaware Library, 181 S College Ave, Newark, DE, 19717-5267. Tel: 302-831-2231. Fax: 302-831-1046. p. 386

Daviau, Sarah, Br Mgr, Arlington County Department of Libraries, Aurora Hills, 735 18th St S, Arlington, VA, 22202. Tel: 703-228-5716. Fax: 703-892-9378. p. 2448

David, Cynthia, Librn, Catholic Medical Center, 100 McGregor St, Manchester, NH, 03102-3770. Tel: 603-663-6520. Fax: 603-668-5348. p. 1455

David, James, In Charge, National Park Service, 1207 Emery Hwy, Macon, GA, 31217-4399. Tel: 478-752-8257. Fax: 478-752-8259. p. 541

David, Kenneth, In Charge, Eastern Counties Regional Library, Petit de Grat Branch, 3435 Hwy, No 206, Petit de Grat, NS, B0E 2L0, CANADA. Tel: 902-226-3534. Fax: 902-226-3534. p. 2783

David, Magolis, Dr, Interim Dir, Libr Serv, Bloomsburg University of Pennsylvania, 400 E Second St, Bloomsburg, PA, 17815-1301. Tel: 570-389-4921. Fax: 570-389-3066. p. 2035

David, Sophie, Bibliothecaire Responsable, Bibliothèques de Montrèal, L'Île-Bizard, 500, montée de l'Église, Montreal, QC, H9C 1G9, CANADA. Tel: 514-620-7400. Fax: 514-620-4153. p. 2890

Davidson, Annette, Librn, First Presbyterian Church Library, 869 N Euclid Ave, Upland, CA, 91786. Tel: 909-982-8811. Fax: 909-985-8014. p. 278

Davidson, Becky, Outreach Serv Librn, Lasalle Parish Library, 3108 N First St, Jena, LA, 71342. Tel: 318-992-5675. Fax: 318-992-7374, 318-992-7394. p. 951

Davidson Brewer, Carolyn, Exec Dir, North Texas Library Partners, 6320 Southwest Blvd, Ste 101, Fort Worth, TX, 76109-3961. Tel: 817-377-4440. Fax: 817-377-8020. p. 2323

Davidson, Carmen, Librn, Western Baptist Hospital Library, 2501 Kentucky Ave, Paducah, KY, 42003-3200. Tel: 270-575-2108. Fax: 270-575-2164. p. 932

Davidson, Catherine A, Librn, United States Courts Library, 222 W Seventh Ave, Rm 181, Anchorage, AK, 99513-7586. Tel: 907-271-5655. Fax: 907-271-5640. p. 45

Davidson, Chris, Asst Librn, Missouri School for the Blind Library, 3815 Magnolia Ave, Saint Louis, MO, 63110. Tel: 314-776-4320, Ext 3257. Fax: 314-773-3762. p. 1356

Davidson, Connie, Dir, Newton Public Library & Museum, 100 S Van Buren St, Newton, IL, 62448. Tel: 618-783-8141. Fax: 618-783-8149. p. 680

Davidson, Crystal L, Access Serv, King College, 1350 King College Rd, Bristol, TN, 37620. Tel: 423-652-4716. Fax: 423-652-4871. p. 2225

Davidson, Dona, Coordr, Pub Serv, Ser Librn, Oklahoma State University - Tulsa Library, 700 N Greenwood Ave, Tulsa, OK, 74106-0700. Tel: 918-594-1839. Fax: 918-594-8145. p. 1981

Davidson, Jane, In Charge, City of Kawartha Lakes Public Library, Woodville Branch, 78 King St, Woodville, ON, K0M 2T0, CANADA. Tel: 705-439-2160. Fax: 705-439-1726. p. 2816

Davidson, Joan, Asst Librn, Fort Nelson Public Library, 5315-50th Ave S, Box 330, Fort Nelson, BC, V0C 1R0, CANADA. Tel: 250-774-6777. Fax: 250-774-6777. p. 2728

Davidson, Judy, Pub Info Officer, Calcasieu Parish Public Library, 301 W Claude St, Lake Charles, LA, 70605-3457. Tel: 337-721-7148. Fax: 337-475-8806. p. 953

Davidson, Karen, Coordr, Northeast Iowa Community College, 1625 Hwy 150, Calmar, IA, 52132. Tel: 563-562-3263, Ext 257. Fax: 563-562-4361. p. 798

Davidson, LaToya, Human Res Mgr, Twin Lakes Library System, 151 S Jefferson St SE, Milledgeville, GA, 31061-3419. Tel: 478-452-0677. Fax: 478-452-0680. p. 545

Davidson, Laura, Dean of Libr, Meredith College, 3800 Hillsborough St, Raleigh, NC, 27607-5298. Tel: 919-760-8531. Fax: 919-760-2830. p. 1815

Davidson, Laurie, Assoc Dir, Info Serv, Georgetown University, Dahlgren Memorial Library, Preclinical Science Bldg GM-7, 3900 Reservoir Rd NW, Washington, DC, 20007. Tel: 202-687-7708. Fax: 202-687-1862. p. 402

Davidson, Linda, Librn, Kingston Community Library, 120 Madison 2605, Kingston, AR, 72742. Tel: 479-665-2745. Fax: 479-665-2745. p. 105

Davidson, Linda, Librn, Georgetown Public Library, 102 W West St, Georgetown, IL, 61846. Tel: 217-662-2164. Fax: 217-662-6790. p. 649

Davidson, M, Librn, Oregon State Penitentiary Library, 2605 State St, Salem, OR, 97310. Tel: 503-378-2081. p. 2018

Davidson, M, Librn, Oregon State Penitentiary Library, OSP Minimum, 2809 State St, Salem, OR, 97310. Tel: 503-378-2081. p. 2018

Davidson, Mary, Youth Serv Librn, Calais Free Library, Nine Union St, Calais, ME, 04619. Tel: 207-454-2758. Fax: 207-454-2765. p. 980

Davidson, Mary, Tech Serv Supvr, Oregon Public Library, 256 Brook St, Oregon, WI, 53575. Tel: 608-835-3656. Fax: 608-835-2856. p. 2627

Davidson, Melissa, Ad, Staunton Public Library, One Churchville Ave, Staunton, VA, 24401. Tel: 540-332-3902. Fax: 540-332-3906. p. 2496

Davidson, Merrie, Ref Librn, University of Saint Thomas, Charles J Keffer Library, 1000 LaSalle Ave, MOH 206, Minneapolis, MN, 55403. Tel: 651-962-4661. Fax: 651-962-4648. p. 1282

Davidson, Moira, Head, Tech Serv, Lakehead University Library, 955 Oliver Rd, Thunder Bay, ON, P7B 5E1, CANADA. Tel: 807-343-8315. Fax: 807-343-8007. p. 2848

Davidson, Russell, III, Dir & Sr Instrul Designer, Instrul Design Studio, University of Detroit Mercy Library, 4001 W McNichols Rd, Detroit, MI, 48221-3038. Tel: 313-578-0579. Fax: 313-993-1780. p. 1172

Davidson, Saleena, YA Serv, South Brunswick Public Library, 110 Kingston Lane, Monmouth Junction, NJ, 08852. Tel: 732-329-4000, Ext 7280. Fax: 732-329-0573. p. 1502

Davidson, Sara, Head, User Communication & Instruction, University of California, Merced Library, 5200 N Lake Rd, Merced, CA, 95343-5001. Tel: 209-205-8237. Fax: 209-228-4271. p. 186

Davidson, Sheryl, Ch, Abilene Public Library, 209 NW Fourth, Abilene, KS, 67410-2690. Tel: 785-263-1303. Fax: 785-263-2274. p. 855

Davidson, Shirley, In Charge, Elko-Lander-Eureka County Library System, Beowawe Branch, Hwy 306, Main St, HC 66, Unit 1, Box 3, Beowawe, NV, 89821. Tel: 775-468-2103. p. 1427

Davidson, Shirley, In Charge, Elko-Lander-Eureka County Library System, Cresent Valley Branch, Cresent Valley Town Ctr, 5045 Tenabo Ave, Cresent Valley, NV, 89821. Tel: 775-468-0249. p. 1427

Davidson, Stephen A, Asst Dir, National Society of the Daughters of the American Revolution, DAR Library, 1776 D St NW, Washington, DC, 20006-5303. Tel: 202-879-3229. Fax: 202-879-3227. p. 411

Davies, Anne, Librn, Waseca-Le Sueur Regional Library, Elysian Branch, 196 W Main St, Elysian, MN, 56028. Tel: 507-267-4411. p. 1287

Davies, April, Acq & Cat, State University of New York College of Agriculture & Technology, 142 Schenectady Ave, Cobleskill, NY, 12043. Tel: 518-255-5887. Fax: 518-255-5843. p. 1608

Davies, Beth, Br Head, Vancouver Public Library, Carnegie Reading Room, 401 Main St, Vancouver, BC, V6A 2T7, CANADA. Tel: 604-665-3010. Fax: 604-665-3016. p. 2744

Davies, Camille, Librn, Alexandria Public Library, 421 Main St, Alexandria, SD, 57311. Tel: 605-239-4549. p. 2210

Davies, Charlotte Walch, Youth Serv, Kilbourn Public Library, 620 Elm St, Wisconsin Dells, WI, 53965. Tel: 608-254-2146. p. 2650

Davies, Cheryl, Chief Librn, Thompson Public Library, 81 Thompson Dr N, Thompson, MB, R8N 0C3, CANADA. Tel: 204-677-3717. Fax: 204-778-5844. p. 2753

Davies, Cindy L, Assoc Librn, Coll Mgr, Syst Librn, South Dakota School of Mines & Technology, 501 E Saint Joseph St, Rapid City, SD, 57701-3995. Tel: 605-394-2418. Fax: 605-394-1256. p. 2217

Davies, Donna, Adult Serv, Coll Develop, Weston Public Library, 87 School St, Weston, MA, 02493. Tel: 781-893-3312. Fax: 781-529-0174. p. 1139

Davies, Elaine, Dir, Jefferson County District Library, Heart of the Valley Branch, 1252 E 1500 N, Terreton, ID, 83450. Tel: 208-663-4834. Fax: 208-663-4834. p. 579

Davies, Elizabeth, Br Mgr, Burnaby Public Library, Cameron Branch, 9523 Cameron St, Burnaby, BC, V3J 1L6, CANADA. Tel: 604-421-5454. p. 2725

Davies, Evan, Dr, Dir, Institute of Historical Survey Foundation Library, 3035 S Main, Las Cruces, NM, 88005-3756. Tel: 575-525-3035. Fax: 575-525-0106. p. 1558

Davies, John R, Dir, Libr Serv, Argosy University, 4401 N Himes Ave, Ste 150, Tampa, FL, 33614. Tel: jdavies@edmc.edu. Fax: 813-874-1989. p. 496

Davies, Julian, Archivist, Siena College, 515 Loudon Rd, Loudonville, NY, 12211-1462. Tel: 518-782-6703. Fax: 518-783-2570. p. 1655

Davies, Kathy, Chair, Res & Educ Serv, Georgia Health Sciences University, 1459 Laney-Walker Blvd, Augusta, GA, 30912-4400. Tel: 706-721-9911. Fax: 706-721-2018. p. 520

Davies, Kathy, Libr Mgr, Claresholm Public Library, 211 49th Ave W, Claresholm, AB, T0L 0T0, CANADA. Tel: 403-625-4168. Fax: 403-625-2939. p. 2695

Davies, Nicolle Ingui, Exec Dir, Arapahoe Library District, 12855 E Adam Aircraft Circle, Englewood, CO, 80112. Tel: 303-542-7279. Fax: 303-798-2485. p. 305

Davies, Videe, Asst Librn, Houston Public Library, 3150 14th St, Houston, BC, V0J 1Z0, CANADA. Tel: 250-845-2256. Fax: 250-845-2088. p. 2729

Davies-Wilson, Dennis, Dir, University of New Mexico, 4000 University Dr, Los Alamos, NM, 87544. Tel: 505-662-0343. Fax: 505-662-0344. p. 1559

Davignon, Jeff, Dir, Walworth-Seely Public Library, 3600 Lorraine Dr, Walworth, NY, 14568. Tel: 315-986-1511. Fax: 315-986-5917. p. 1762

Davila, Sonia de la Cruz, Dir, University of Puerto Rico Library, Cayey Campus, 205 Ave Antonio R Barcelo, Cayey, PR, 00736. Tel: 787-738-2161, Ext 2021, 787-738-5651. Fax: 787-263-2108. p. 2672

Davis, Abby, Acq, Cat, Southern New England School of Law Library, 333 Faunce Corner Rd, North Dartmouth, MA, 02747. Tel: 508-998-9888. p. 1112

Davis, Agnes, Dir, Tinicum Memorial Public Library, 620 Seneca St, Essington, PA, 19029-1199. Tel: 610-521-9344. Fax: 610-521-3463. p. 2056

Davis, Al, Dir, Barrie Public Library, 60 Worsley St, Barrie, ON, L4M 1L6, CANADA. Tel: 705-728-1010, Ext 7500. Fax: 705-728-4322. p. 2793

Davis, Alexandra, Librn, Ottawa Hospital, Civic Campus Library, 1053 Carling Ave, D-1, Ottawa, ON, K1Y 4E9, CANADA. Tel: 613-798-5555, Ext 14450. Fax: 613-761-5292. p. 2832

Davis, Allan, Automation Syst Coordr, University of Wisconsin-Whitewater Library, 800 W Main St, Whitewater, WI, 53190. Tel: 262-472-5011. Fax: 262-472-5727. p. 2649

Davis, Allyson, Dir, Aiken Technical College Library, 2276 Jefferson Davis Hwy, Graniteville, SC, 29829. Tel: 803-593-9954, Ext 1755. Fax: 803-593-2169. p. 2195

Davis, Amanda, Br Head, Harnett County Public Library, Angier Public, 28 N Raleigh St, Angier, NC, 27501-6073. Tel: 919-639-4413. Fax: 919-639-2412. p. 1807

Davis, Amy, Dir, Richland Community Library, 111 E Main St, Richland, PA, 17087. Tel: 717-866-4939. Fax: 717-866-2661. p. 2134

Davis, Andrew Carl, Dir, Grand Valley Public Library, One N School St, Orwell, OH, 44076. Tel: 440-437-6545, 440-536-9159. Fax: 440-437-1017. p. 1925

Davis, Ann, Supvr, Ch Serv, Napa City-County Library, 580 Coombs St, Napa, CA, 94559-3396. Tel: 707-253-4079. Fax: 707-253-4615. p. 192

Davis, Ann, Dir, Stafford Library, Ten Levinthal Run, Stafford, CT, 06075. Tel: 860-684-2852. Fax: 860-684-2128. p. 369

Davis, Anne, Dir, Gardiner Public Library, 152 Water St, Gardiner, ME, 04345. Tel: 207-582-3312. Fax: 207-582-6104. p. 986

Davis, Annette, Youth Serv Librn, Rantoul Public Library, 106 W Flessner, Rantoul, IL, 61866. Tel: 217-893-3955. Fax: 217-893-3961. p. 693

Davis, Annette, ILL, Carteret Community College Library, 201 College Circle, Morehead City, NC, 28557. Tel: 252-222-6213. Fax: 252-222-6219. p. 1810

Davis, Barb, Ref Librn, William Woods University, One University Ave, Fulton, MO, 65251. Tel: 573-592-4291. Fax: 573-592-1159. p. 1329

Davis, Barbara, Youth Ref Librn, Fruitville Public Library, 100 Coburn Rd, Sarasota, FL, 34240. Tel: 941-861-2500. Fax: 941-861-2528. p. 489

Davis, Barbara, Commun Relations Librn, New Rochelle Public Library, One Library Plaza, New Rochelle, NY, 10801. Tel: 914-632-7878, Ext 1000. Fax: 914-632-0262. p. 1666

Davis, Barbara, Br Mgr, Albemarle Regional Library, Northampton Memorial Library, 207 W Jefferson St, Jackson, NC, 27845. Tel: 252-534-3571. Fax: 252-534-1017. p. 1835

Davis, Barbara, Librn, Newport Hospital, 11 Friendship St, Newport, RI, 02840. Tel: 401-845-1311. Fax: 401-845-1073. p. 2169

Davis, Barbara J, Dir, Libr Serv, Taft, Stettinius & Hollister Library, 425 Walnut St, Ste 1800, Cincinnati, OH, 45202-3957. Tel: 513-381-2838. Fax: 513-381-0205. p. 1873

Davis, Ben, Acq Librn, Georgia College & State University, 320 N Wayne St, Milledgeville, GA, 31061-3397. Tel: 478-445-4047. Fax: 478-445-6847. p. 544

Davis, Betsy, Circ Librn, New England College, 28 Bridge St, Henniker, NH, 03242-3298. Tel: 603-428-2344. Fax: 603-428-4273. p. 1451

Davis, Bonita, Br Mgr, Starke County Public Library System, Koontz Lake Branch, 7954 N State Rd 23, Walkerton, IN, 46574. Tel: 574-586-3353. p. 758

Davis, Bonnie, Circ, Roseville Public Library, 225 Taylor St, Roseville, CA, 95678-2681. Tel: 916-774-5221. Fax: 916-773-5594. p. 220

Davis, Brenda, Librn II, Ref Librn, Montgomery City-County Public Library System, Juliette Hampton Morgan Memorial Library (Main Library), 245 High St, Montgomery, AL, 36104. Tel: 334-240-4999. Fax: 334-240-4980. p. 30

Davis, Brenda, Dir, Caruthersville Public Library, 707 W 13th St, Caruthersville, MO, 63830. Tel: 573-333-2480. Fax: 573-333-0552. p. 1322

Davis, Carenado V, Interim Dir, Libr Serv Coordr, Lenoir Community College, 231 Hwy 58 S, Kinston, NC, 28504-6836. Tel: 252-527-6223, Ext 504. Fax: 252-527-0192. p. 1805

Davis, Carla, Dir, Mkt, Akron-Summit County Public Library, 60 S High St, Akron, OH, 44326. Tel: 330-643-9090. Fax: 330-643-9160. p. 1852

Davis, Carol, Ref Serv, Woodland Public Library, 250 First St, Woodland, CA, 95695-3411. Tel: 530-661-5980. Fax: 530-666-5408. p. 284

Davis, Caroline, Head, Coll & e-Res Mgt, Eastern Connecticut State University, 83 Windham St, Willimantic, CT, 06226-2295. Tel: 860-465-5562. Fax: 860-465-5521. p. 378

Davis, Celia, Tech Serv, Ottawa University, 1001 S Cedar, Ottawa, KS, 66067-3399. Tel: 785-242-5200, Ext 5448. Fax: 785-229-1012. p. 887

Davis, Charlene, Dir of Libr Serv, Kentucky Department for Libraries & Archives, 300 Coffee Tree Rd, Frankfort, KY, 40601. Tel: 502-564-8300. Fax: 502-564-5773. p. 913

Davis, Charles, Ref, Statesboro Regional Public Libraries, 124 S Main St, Statesboro, GA, 30458. Tel: 912-764-1339. Fax: 912-764-1348. p. 552

Davis, Charles N, Dr, Exec Dir, University of Missouri-Columbia, Freedom of Information Center, 101 Reynolds Journalism Institute, Columbia, MO, 65211-0012. Tel: 573-882-5736. Fax: 573-884-6204. p. 1326

Davis, Cherie, Dir, Ronceverte Public Library, 712 W Main St, Ronceverte, WV, 24970. Tel: 304-647-7400. Fax: 304-647-7651. p. 2571

Davis, Christy, Supv Librn, Klamath County Library Services District, 126 S Third St, Klamath Falls, OR, 97601-6394. Tel: 541-882-8894. Fax: 541-882-6166. p. 2001

Davis, Claudia, Libr Tech, Elizabeth City State University, 1704 Weeksville Rd, Elizabeth City, NC, 27909. Tel: 252-335-8512. Fax: 252-335-3552. p. 1790

Davis, Craig, Dir, Adult Serv, Chicago Public Library, 400 S State St, Chicago, IL, 60605. Tel: 312-747-4252. Fax: 312-747-4968. p. 608

Davis, Cynthia, Dir, Lake Region Community College, 379 Belmont Rd, Laconia, NH, 03246. Tel: 603-524-3207. Fax: 603-524-8084. p. 1453

Davis, Danette, Ch, Seymour Public Library District, 176-178 Genesee St, Auburn, NY, 13021. Tel: 315-252-2571. Fax: 315-252-7985. p. 1576

Davis, Danita, Visual Res Spec, Indiana University-Purdue University, Herron Art Library, Herron School of Art & Design, 735 W New York St, Indianapolis, IN, 46202. Tel: 317-278-9439. Fax: 317-278-9497. p. 753

Davis, Daphne, Mgr, Tech Serv, San Miguel County Public Library District 1, 100 W Pacific Ave, Telluride, CO, 81435-2189. Tel: 970-728-4519. Fax: 970-728-3340. p. 323

Davis, Darlene, Coordr, Youth Serv, Ludington Public Library, Five S Bryn Mawr Ave, Bryn Mawr, PA, 19010-3471. Tel: 610-525-1776. Fax: 610-525-1783. p. 2039

Davis, Dell, Dir, Pub Serv, University of the Incarnate Word, 4301 Broadway, UPO Box 297, San Antonio, TX, 78209-6397. Tel: 210-829-6054. Fax: 210-829-6041. p. 2384

Davis, Deniece, Acq/Cat Tech, Govt Doc, Oregon Institute of Technology Library, 3201 Campus Dr, Klamath Falls, OR, 97601-8801. Tel: 541-885-1772. Fax: 541-885-1777. p. 2002

Davis, Denise, Dep Dir, Sacramento Public Library, 828 I St, Sacramento, CA, 95814. Tel: 916-264-2770. Fax: 916-264-2755. p. 224

Davis, Denise, Dir, Cecil County Public Library, 301 Newark Ave, Elkton, MD, 21921-5441. Tel: 410-996-5600. Fax: 410-996-5604. p. 1027

Davis, Diane A, Asst Dir, Bethlehem Area Public Library, 11 W Church St, Bethlehem, PA, 18018. Tel: 610-867-3761, Ext 212. Fax: 610-867-2767. p. 2033

Davis, Dick, Res Mgr, Sharon Regional Health System, 740 E State St, Sharon, PA, 16146. Tel: 724-983-3911, Ext 3873. Fax: 724-983-5621. p. 2139

Davis, Dolores, Asst Librn, Yoakum County Library, 901 Ave E, Plains, TX, 79355. Tel: 806-456-8725. Fax: 806-456-7056. p. 2370

Davis, Donald G, Jr, Prof, University of Texas at Austin, One University Sta, D7000, Austin, TX, 78712-0390. Tel: 512-471-3821. Fax: 512-471-3971. p. 2975

Davis, Donald O, Admin Dir, Lowndes County Historical Society & Museum, 305 W Central Ave, Valdosta, GA, 31601-5404. Tel: 229-247-4780. Fax: 229-247-2840. p. 555

Davis, Donna, Asst Dir, Pub Serv, The Library of Hattiesburg, Petal, Forrest County, 329 Hardy St, Hattiesburg, MS, 39401-3496. Tel: 601-582-4461. Fax: 601-582-5338. p. 1300

Davis, Donna, Br Mgr, Summit County Library, Kamas Branch, 110 N Main, Kamas, UT, 84036. Tel: 435-615-3080. Fax: 435-783-6693. p. 2410

Davis, Dorothy, Br Mgr, Concordia Parish Library, Clayton Branch, 8723 Hwy 566, Clayton, LA, 71326. Tel: 318-757-6460. p. 949

Davis, Ed, Asst Dir, Libr Serv, Marion County Library, 308 Old Main, Yellville, AR, 72687. Tel: 870-449-6015. Fax: 870-449-6015. p. 117

Davis, Elaine, Mgr, LaPalme Health Sciences Library, 320 Pomfret St, Putnam, CT, 06260. Tel: 860-928-6541, Ext 2596. Fax: 860-928-1398. p. 365

Davis, Elizabeth, Coordr, Info/Student Serv, California State University Dominguez Hills, 1000 E Victoria St, Carson, CA, 90747. Tel: 310-243-3679. Fax: 310-516-4219. p. 132

Davis, Elizabeth, Librn, Columbia University, The Gabe M Wiener Music & Arts Library, 701 Dodge Hall, 2960 Broadway, New York, NY, 10027. Tel: 212-854-7604. Fax: 212-854-4748. p. 1675

Davis, Ellie, Mgr, Youth Serv, Sweetwater County Library System, 300 N First East, Green River, WY, 82935. Tel: 307-875-3615, Ext 1300. Fax: 307-872-3203. p. 2655

Davis, Esther O, In Charge, Yuba County Law Library, 915 Eighth St, Marysville, CA, 95901. Tel: 530-749-7565. Fax: 530-749-7513. p. 184

Davis, Eva, Dir, Canton Public Library, 1200 S Canton Center Rd, Canton, MI, 48188-1600. Tel: 734-397-0999, Ext 1065. Fax: 734-397-1130. p. 1160

Davis, Evan T, Asst Dir, Br Mgr, Edison Township Free Public Library, North Edison Branch, 777 Grove Ave, Edison, NJ, 08820. Tel: 732-548-3045. Fax: 732-549-5171. p. 1483

Davis, Evan T, Asst Dir, Edison Township Free Public Library, 340 Plainfield Ave, Edison, NJ, 08817. Tel: 732-548-3045. Fax: 732-549-5171. p. 1483

Davis, Frank, Head, Ref Commons, University of Kentucky Libraries, Medical Center Library, 800 Rose St, Lexington, KY, 40536-0298. Tel: 859-323-3983. Fax: 859-323-1040. p. 922

Davis, G H, Asst Librn, Frost, Brown & Todd LLC, 400 W Market St, 32nd Flr, Louisville, KY, 40202-3363. Tel: 513-651-6800. Fax: 513-651-6981. p. 923

Davis, G Kevin, Dir, Messenger Public Library of North Aurora, 113 Oak St, North Aurora, IL, 60542. Tel: 630-896-0240, Ext 2345. Fax: 630-896-4654. p. 681

Davis, G Megan, Weber State University, 2901 University Circle, Ogden, UT, 84408-2901. Tel: 801-626-6069. Fax: 801-626-7045. p. 2409

Davis, Gainor B, Pres & Chief Exec Officer, Western Reserve Historical Society Research Library, 10825 East Blvd, Cleveland, OH, 44106-1777. Tel: 216-721-5722. Fax: 216-721-0891. p. 1881

Davis, Geralyn, Br Mgr, East Baton Rouge Parish Library, Greenwell Springs Road Regional, 11300 Greenwell Springs Rd, Baton Rouge, LA, 70814. Tel: 225-274-4440. Fax: 225-274-4454. p. 943

Davis, Glenda, Asst Librn, Wallace Community College, 3000 Earl Goodwin Pkwy, Selma, AL, 36701. Tel: 334-876-9344, 334-876-9345. Fax: 334-876-9314. p. 36

Davis, Gloria, Br Mgr, Public Library Association of Annapolis & Anne Arundel County, Inc, Annapolis Area, 1410 West St, Annapolis, MD, 21401. Tel: 410-222-1750. Fax: 410-222-1116. p. 1010

Davis, Gregory, Asst Dir, Info Tech, Iowa State University Library, 302 Parks Library, Ames, IA, 50011-2140. Tel: 515-294-1442, 515-294-1443. Fax: 515-294-5525. p. 793

Davis, Gwen, Ref, Florence Public Library, 104 W Main St, Florence, MS, 39073. Tel: 601-845-6032. Fax: 601-845-4625. p. 1298

Davis, Hazel, Libr Dir, Rio Salado College, 2323 W 14th St, Tempe, AZ, 85281. Tel: 480-517-8273. Fax: 480-517-8449. p. 84

Davis, Heather, Librn, Kentucky School for the Blind Library, 1867 Frankfort Ave, Louisville, KY, 40206. Tel: 502-897-1583, Ext 254. Fax: 502-897-2850. p. 924

Davis, Heather, Libr Tech, Eagle Mountain Public Library, 1650 E Stagecoach Run, Eagle Mountain, UT, 84005. Tel: 801-789-6623. Fax: 801-789-6653. p. 2405

Davis, Heidi, Librn, Temple Sinai Library, 363 Penfield Rd, Rochester, NY, 14625. Tel: 585-381-6890. Fax: 585-381-4921. p. 1733

Davis, Jackie, Mgr, Coll Serv, Anderson City, Anderson, Stony Creek & Union Townships Public Library, 111 E 12th St, Anderson, IN, 46016-2701. Tel: 765-641-2455. Fax: 765-641-2197. p. 723

Davis, Jacqueline Z, Dir, New York Public Library - Astor, Lenox & Tilden Foundations, New York Public Library for the Performing Arts, Library for the Performing Arts, 40 Lincoln Center Plaza, New York, NY, 10023-7498. Tel: 212-870-1643. Fax: 212-870-1860. p. 1692

Davis, Jacqueline Z, Dir, New York Public Library - Astor, Lenox & Tilden Foundations, The New York Library for the Performing Arts, Dorothy & Lewis B Cullman Center, 40 Lincoln Center Plaza, New York, NY, 10023-7498. Tel: 212-870-1630. p. 1692

Davis, Jan, Tech Serv, Grayslake Area Public Library District, 100 Library Lane, Grayslake, IL, 60030-1684. Tel: 847-223-5313. Fax: 847-223-6482. p. 652

Davis, Jan, Adminr, Oklahoma Department of Libraries, 200 NE 18th St, Oklahoma City, OK, 73105. Tel: 405-521-2502. Fax: 405-525-7804. p. 1974

Davis, Jana, Cat, Abilene Christian University, 221 Brown Library, ACU Box 29208, Abilene, TX, 79699-9208. Tel: 325-674-2344. Fax: 325-674-2202. p. 2271

Davis, Jane, Cat Librn, Middle Tennessee State University, MTSU, PO Box 13, Murfreesboro, TN, 37132. Tel: 615-898-2529. p. 2254

Davis, Jane, Libr Tech, West Burke Public Library, 135 Main St, West Burke, VT, 05871. Tel: 802-467-3328. p. 2439

Davis, Janet, Acq, Bay City Public Library, 1100 Seventh St, Bay City, TX, 77414. Tel: 979-245-6931. Fax: 979-245-2614. p. 2286

Davis, Janet L, Librn, Opp Public Library, 1604 N Main St, Opp, AL, 36467. Tel: 334-493-6423. Fax: 334-493-6423. p. 32

Davis, Janice, Librn, Thompson-Sawyer Public Library, 403 W Third St, Quanah, TX, 79252. Tel: 940-663-2654. p. 2372

Davis, Jean, Dir, Marshall County Historical Society Library, 314 Fifth St, Lacon, IL, 61540. Tel: 309-246-2349, p. 662

Davis, Jean, Interim Dir, Brooklyn Law School Library, 250 Joralemon St, Brooklyn, NY, 11201. Tel: 718-780-7975. Fax: 718-780-0369. p. 1590

Davis, Jean, Intl Law Librn, Ref, Brooklyn Law School Library, 250 Joralemon St, Brooklyn, NY, 11201. Tel: 718-780-7534. Fax: 718-780-0369. p. 1590

Davis, Jeannine, Youth Serv Librn, Lakeland Public Library, 100 Lake Morton Dr, Lakeland, FL, 33801-5375. Tel: 863-834-4280. Fax: 863-834-4293. p. 459

Davis, Jeff, Circ, Spokane Falls Community College, 3410 Ft George Wright Dr, MS 3020, Spokane, WA, 99224-5288. Tel: 509-533-3217. Fax: 509-533-3144. p. 2537

Davis, Jennie, Ref Librn, Vance-Granville Community College, South Campus, 1547 S Campus Dr, Creedmoor, NC, 27522-7381. Tel: 919-528-1752. Fax: 919-528-1752. p. 1800

Davis, Jennifer, Med Librn, Lakes Region General Hospital, 80 Highland St, Laconia, NH, 03246-3298. Tel: 603-527-2837. Fax: 603-527-7197. p. 1453

Davis, Jim, Dir, Louisiana Ctr for the Bk, State Library of Louisiana, 701 N Fourth St, Baton Rouge, LA, 70802-5232. Tel: 225-342-9714. Fax: 225-219-4804. p. 945

Davis, Jim, Dept Head, Ref, State Historical Society of North Dakota, North Dakota Heritage Ctr, 612 E Boulevard Ave, Bismarck, ND, 58505-0830. Tel: 701-328-2539. Fax: 701-328-2650. p. 1838

Davis, Jimi, Asst Dir, Lancaster Veterans Memorial Library, 1600 Veterans Memorial Pkwy, Lancaster, TX, 75134. Tel: 972-227-1080. Fax: 972-227-5560. p. 2353

Davis, Jo, Libr Dir, United States Air Force, 99 FSS/FSDL, 4311 N Washington Blvd, Bldg 312, Ste 101, Nellis AFB, NV, 89191-7064. Tel: 702-652-4484. p. 1431

Davis, Jo Ellen, Admin Serv Mgr, California State University Dominguez Hills, 1000 E Victoria St, Carson, CA, 90747. Tel: 310-243-2207. Fax: 310-516-4219. p. 132

Davis, Joan, Br Mgr, Washington County Library System, Avon Library, 874 Riverside Rd, Avon, MS, 38723. Tel: 662-332-9346. Fax: 662-332-9346. p. 1298

Davis, Johnnie, Media Ctr Coordr, Mississippi Delta Community College, 414 Hwy 3 South, Moorhead, MS, 38761. Tel: 662-246-6384. Fax: 662-246-8627. p. 1309

Davis, Joseph, Ref & Instruction Librn, Roosevelt University, Robert R McCormick Tribune Foundation Library, 1400 N Roosevelt Blvd, Schaumburg, IL, 60173. Tel: 847-619-7980. Fax: 847-619-7983. p. 623

Davis, Joy, Librn, Scotland County Memorial Library, Wagram Branch, PO Box 118, Wagram, NC, 28396-0118. Tel: 910-369-2966. p. 1806

Davis, Joyce, Dean, Emporia State University, 1200 Commercial St, Box 4051, Emporia, KS, 66801. Tel: 620-341-5207. Fax: 620-341-5997. p. 866

Davis, Joyce, Tech Serv Librn, Wolfeboro Public Library, 259 S Main St, Wolfeboro, NH, 03894. Tel: 603-569-2428. Fax: 603-569-8180. p. 1468

Davis, Juanita, Librn, Tabernacle Baptist Church Library, 150 Tabernacle Dr, Carrollton, GA, 30117. Tel: 770-832-7063, Ext 38. Fax: 770-834-2777. p. 523

Davis, Judy, Asst Librn, Richwood Public Library, Eight White Ave, Richwood, WV, 26261. Tel: 304-846-6099. Fax: 304-846-9290. p. 2570

Davis, Judy Ann, Res Sharing Librn, University of Washington Libraries, Marian Gould Gallagher Law Library, William H Gates Hall, Box 353025, Seattle, WA, 98195-3025. Tel: 206-543-4262. Fax: 206-685-2165. p. 2534

Davis, Julia, Dir, Kiel Public Library, 511 Third St, Kiel, WI, 53042. Tel: 920-894-7122. Fax: 920-894-4023. p. 2602

Davis, Julianna S, Tech Serv, University of Mississippi, Three Grove Loop, University, MS, 38677. Tel: 662-915-6832. Fax: 662-915-7731. p. 1316

Davis, Julie, Govt Doc, Boise Public Library, 715 S Capitol Blvd, Boise, ID, 83702. Tel: 208-384-4441. p. 570

Davis, Julie A, Acq, Cat, Golden West College, 15744 Golden West St, Huntington Beach, CA, 92647. Tel: 714-895-8741, Ext 55207. Fax: 714-895-8926. p. 158

Davis, Karen, Mgr, Ivy Tech Community College of Indiana, One Ivy Way, Logansport, IN, 46947. Tel: 574-753-5101. Fax: 574-753-5103. p. 761

Davis, Karen, Br Mgr, Lexington Public Library, Northside, 1737 Russell Cave Rd, Lexington, KY, 40505. Tel: 859-231-5500. Fax: 859-422-6898. p. 921

Davis, Karen, Supvr, Lowry Nature Center Library, PO Box 270, Victoria, MN, 55386-0270. Tel: 763-694-7650. Fax: 952-472-5420. p. 1286

Davis, Karen, Br Mgr, Martins Ferry Public Library, Bethesda Branch, 112 N Main St, Bethesda, OH, 43719. Tel: 740-484-4532. Fax: 740-484-4732. p. 1914

Davis, Karen A, Librn, VA Northern Indiana Healthcare Systems, 1700 E 38th St, Marion, IN, 46953. Tel: 765-677-3110. Fax: 765-677-3111. p. 763

Davis, Karen A, Librn, Glenstone Baptist Church, 413 S Glenstone, Springfield, MO, 65802. Tel: 417-869-6361. Fax: 417-869-2306. p. 1366

Davis, Karla, Dir, Kennedy Library of Konawa, 700 W South, Konawa, OK, 74849. Tel: 580-925-3662. Fax: 580-925-3882. p. 1967

Davis, Kat, Dir, Pendleton Public Library, 502 SW Dorion Ave, Pendleton, OR, 97801-1698. Tel: 541-966-0210. Fax: 541-966-0382. p. 2009

Davis, Kathy, Asst Librn, University of Arkansas-Monticello Library, 514 University Dr, Monticello, AR, 71656. Tel: 870-460-1080. Fax: 870-460-1980. p. 110

Davis, Kathy, Dr, Dir, University of Wisconsin-Stevens Point, 900 Reserve St, Stevens Point, WI, 54481-1985. Tel: 715-346-4193. Fax: 715-346-2367. p. 2640

Davis, Kay, Dir, Washington County Library, 201 E Third St, Plymouth, NC, 27962. Tel: 252-793-2113. Fax: 252-793-2818. p. 1814

Davis, Kay, ILL, Ser, Lincoln Memorial University, Cumberland Gap Pkwy, Box 2012, Harrogate, TN, 37752. Tel: 423-869-6220. Fax: 423-869-6426. p. 2236

Davis, Kay E, Dir, Pettigrew Regional Library, 201 E Third St, Plymouth, NC, 27962. Tel: 252-793-2875. Fax: 252-793-2818. p. 1814

Davis, Kevin, Dir, South Portland Public Library, 482 Broadway, South Portland, ME, 04106. Tel: 207-767-7660. Fax: 207-767-7626. p. 1002

Davis, Kevin, Dir, South Portland Public Library, Memorial Branch, 155 Wescott Rd, South Portland, ME, 04106. Tel: 207-775-1835. Fax: 207-773-1036. p. 1002

Davis, Kim, Circ, Rend Lake College, 468 N Ken Gray Pkwy, Ina, IL, 62846. Tel: 618-437-5321. Fax: 618-437-5677. p. 658

Davis, Kim, Libr Dir, Castroville Public Library, 802 London St, Castroville, TX, 78009. Tel: 830-931-4095. Fax: 830-931-9050. p. 2295

Davis, Kirk, Chief Librn, Department of Veterans Affairs Medical Center, 500 Foothill Dr, Salt Lake City, UT, 84148. Tel: 801-584-1209. Fax: 801-584-1251. p. 2412

Davis, Laquita, In Charge, Neuse Regional Library, La Grange Public Library, 119 E Washington St, La Grange, NC, 28551. Tel: 252-566-3722. Fax: 252-566-9768. p. 1805

Davis, Laquita, Librn, Neuse Regional Library, Greene County Public Library, 229 Kingold Blvd, Snow Hill, NC, 28580. Tel: 252-747-3437. Fax: 252-747-7489. p. 1805

Davis, Laurel, Ref Spec, Commonwealth of Massachusetts, One Ashburton Pl, Boston, MA, 02108. Tel: 617-693-2060, 617-693-2098. Fax: 617-727-6016. p. 1059

Davis, Laurel, Curator, Spec Coll, Legal Info Librn, Boston College, 885 Centre St, Newton Centre, MA, 02459. Tel: 617-552-4410. Fax: 617-552-2889. p. 1110

Davis, Laverne, Asst Librn, Newark Beth Israel Medical Center, 201 Lyons Ave, Newark, NJ, 07112. Tel: 973-926-7441. Fax: 973-923-4280. p. 1511

Davis, Lee, Cat, Northern Virginia Community College Libraries, Media Processing Services, 8333 Little River Tpk, Annandale, VA, 22003-3796. Tel: 703-323-3348. Fax: 703-323-3831. p. 2447

Davis, Lesia, Dir, Campbell River Museum & Archives, 470 Island Hwy, Campbell River, BC, V9W 4Z9, CANADA. Tel: 250-287-3103. Fax: 250-286-0109. p. 2726

Davis, Linda, Dir, Librn, Moundville Public Library, 411 Market St, Moundville, AL, 35474. Tel: 205-371-2283. Fax: 205-371-2283. p. 31

Davis, Linda, Acq Librn, Georgetown University, Georgetown Law Library (John Wolff & Edward Bennett Williams Libraries), 111 G St NW, Washington, DC, 20001. Fax: 202-662-9168. p. 403

Davis, Linda, Mgr, Ad Serv, Wayne County Public Library, 220 W Liberty St, Wooster, OH, 44691-3593. Tel: 330-804-4667. Fax: 330-262-1352. p. 1950

Davis, Linda, Asst Librn, Madison County Library, Inc, 402 N Main St, Madison, VA, 22727. Tel: 540-948-4720. Fax: 540-948-4919. p. 2477

Davis, Linda Morgan, Asst Dir, Albuquerque-Bernalillo County Library System, 501 Copper Ave NW, Albuquerque, NM, 87102. Tel: 505-768-5152. Fax: 505-768-5191. p. 1548

Davis, Lisa, Librn, Elwood Township Carnegie Library, 104 N State St, Ridge Farm, IL, 61870. Tel: 217-247-2820. Fax: 217-247-2835. p. 694

Davis, Lori, Dir, Melcher-Dallas Public Library, 101 E Center St, Melcher-Dallas, IA, 50163. Tel: 641-947-6700. Fax: 641-947-6700. p. 831

Davis, Lorraine, Coordr, Acq, Pine Manor College, 400 Heath St, Chestnut Hill, MA, 02467. Tel: 617-731-7084. Fax: 617-731-7045. p. 1081

Davis, Luise, Support Serv Librn, Douglas County Public Library, 1625 Library Lane, Minden, NV, 89423-4420. Tel: 775-782-9841. Fax: 775-782-5754. p. 1431

Davis, M Jill, Dir, Hendrick Hudson Free Library, 185 Kings Ferry Rd, Montrose, NY, 10548. Tel: 914-739-5654. Fax: 914-739-5659. p. 1663

Davis, Madeline, Librn, Temple Beth Zion Library, 805 Delaware Ave, Buffalo, NY, 14209. Tel: 716-836-6565. p. 1599

Davis, Maile, Br Mgr, Hawaii State Public Library System, Kaimuki Public Library, 1041 Koko Head Ave, Honolulu, HI, 96816-3707. Tel: 808-733-8422. Fax: 808-733-8426. p. 562

Davis, Marc, Syst Coordr, Drake University, 2725 University Ave, Des Moines, IA, 50311. Tel: 515-271-1934. Fax: 515-271-3933. p. 809

Davis, Margaret, Librn, Bingham Memorial Hospital, 98 Poplar St, Blackfoot, ID, 83221. Tel: 208-785-4100, Ext 3332. Fax: 208-785-7606. p. 569

Davis, Margaret, Ch, East Greenwich Free Library, 82 Peirce St, East Greenwich, RI, 02818. Tel: 401-884-9510. Fax: 401-884-3790. p. 2165

Davis, Marie, Asst Librn, Abraham Baldwin Agricultural College, 2802 Moore Hwy, Tifton, GA, 31793. Tel: 229-391-4990. Fax: 229-391-4991. p. 554

Davis, Marie, ILL, Ellsworth Public Library, 20 State St, Ellsworth, ME, 04605. Tel: 207-667-6363. Fax: 207-667-4901. p. 984

Davis, Mary Ann, Librn, Arizona Department of Economic Security, Ann C Dew Library, 2800 N Hwy 87, Coolidge, AZ, 85228. Tel: 520-723-4151, Ext 1306. p. 60

Davis, Mary Jo, Interim Dir, Central Michigan University, Kromer Instructional Materials Center, 134 EHS Bldg, Mount Pleasant, MI, 48859. Tel: 989-774-3549. p. 1211

Davis, Mary Katie, Ref Librn, Philander Smith College, 900 Daisy Bates Dr, Little Rock, AR, 72202. Tel: 501-370-5262. Fax: 501-370-5307. p. 107

Davis, Mary Kay, Cat, Tech Serv, Panola College, 1109 W Panola St, Carthage, TX, 75633. Tel: 903-693-1162. Fax: 903-693-1115. p. 2295

Davis, Mary M, Res Librn, Unilever HPC NA, Trumbull Corporate Park, 40 Merritt Blvd, Trumbull, CT, 06611. Tel: 203-377-8300, Ext 4312. p. 373

Davis, Maureen, Adult Serv, John C Hart Memorial Library, 1130 Main St, Shrub Oak, NY, 10588. Tel: 914-245-5262. Fax: 914-245-2216. p. 1743

Davis, Melanie, ILL Coordr, University of Florida Libraries, 535 Library W, Gainesville, FL, 32611-7000. Tel: 352-273-2522. Fax: 352-392-7251. p. 450

Davis, Melissa, Br Mgr, Springfield-Greene County Library District, Library Station, 2535 N Kansas Expressway, Springfield, MO, 65803-1114. Tel: 417-865-1340. Fax: 417-862-6514. p. 1368

Davis, Melvin, Dr, Dir, Libr Serv, University of North Alabama, One Harrison Plaza, Box 5028, Florence, AL, 35632-0001. Tel: 256-765-4241. Fax: 256-765-4438. p. 17

Davis, Melvina, Ch, LeClaire Community Library, 323 Wisconsin St, LeClaire, IA, 52753. Tel: 563-289-4242, Ext 4. p. 827

Davis, Michael, Admin Librn, Chicago Heights Public Library, 25 W 15th St, Chicago Heights, IL, 60411-3488. Tel: 708-754-0323. Fax: 708-754-0325. p. 628

Davis, Miyo, Tech Serv, St Francis College Library, 180 Remsen St, Brooklyn, NY, 11201. Tel: 718-489-5206. Fax: 718-489-3402. p. 1594

Davis, Monica, Librn, Stevenson Public Library, 102 W Main St, Stevenson, AL, 35772. Tel: 256-437-3008. Fax: 256-437-0031. p. 36

Davis, Nancy, Br Mgr, Marin County Free Library, Marin City Branch, 164 Donahue, Marin City, CA, 94965. Tel: 415-332-6159. p. 257

Davis, Nancy, Sr Librn, Marin County Free Library, Corte Madera Branch, 707 Meadowsweet, Corte Madera, CA, 94925-1717. Tel: 415-924-4844. p. 257

Davis, Nancy, ILL, McAllen Memorial Library, 601 N Main, McAllen, TX, 78501-4666. Tel: 956-688-3300. Fax: 956-688-3301. p. 2360

Davis, Natalie, Circ Supvr, Little Priest Tribal College Library, 601 E College Dr, Winnebago, NE, 68071. Tel: 402-878-3334. Fax: 402-878-2319. p. 1423

Davis, Pam, Tech Serv, Elizabeth Jones Library, 1050 Fairfield Ave, Grenada, MS, 38901-3605. Tel: 662-226-2072. Fax: 662-226-8747. p. 1299

Davis, Phyllis, Ch, Matteson Public Library, 801 S School St, Matteson, IL, 60443-1897. Tel: 708-748-4431. Fax: 708-748-0510. p. 671

Davis, Phyllis, Dir, Wisconsin Public Library Consortium, c/o South Central Library System, 5250 E Terrace Dr, Madison, WI, 53718. Tel: 608-246-7975. Fax: 608-246-7958. p. 2958

Davis, Rachel Q, Ch, Thomas Memorial Library, Six Scott Dyer Rd, Cape Elizabeth, ME, 04107. Tel: 207-799-1720. p. 980

Davis, Rebecca, Asst Head, Health Sci Libr, University of California, Davis, 4610 X St, Sacramento, CA, 95817. Tel: 916-734-3529. Fax: 916-734-7418. p. 225

Davis, Renee, Coll Develop, University of Mary Washington, 1801 College Ave, Fredericksburg, VA, 22401-4665. Tel: 540-654-1758. Fax: 540-654-1067. p. 2466

Davis, Rhonda, Exec Dir, Historic Mobile Preservation Society, 300 Oakleigh Pl, Mobile, AL, 36604. Tel: 251-432-6161. p. 25

Davis, Richelle, Tech Serv, University of Maine at Farmington, 116 South St, Farmington, ME, 04938-1990. Tel: 207-778-7210. Fax: 207-778-7223. p. 985

Davis, Robert H, Librn, Columbia University, Area Studies, 307 International Affairs Bldg, 420 W 118th St, New York, NY, 10027. Tel: 212-854-3630. Fax: 212-854-3834. p. 1674

Davis, Robert H, Jr, Librn, Columbia University, Russian, Eurasian & East European Studies, 306 International Affairs Bldg, 420 W 118th St, New York, NY, 10027. Tel: 212-854-4701. Fax: 212-854-3834. p. 1675

Davis, Robert J, Dir, Seward & Kissel LLP, One Battery Park Plaza, New York, NY, 10004. Tel: 212-574-1478. Fax: 212-480-8421. p. 1699

Davis, Robert L, III, Librn, Prince William County Circuit Court, Judicial Ctr, Rm 039, JU-170, 9311 Lee Ave, Manassas, VA, 20110-5555. Tel: 703-792-6262. Fax: 703-792-5390. p. 2477

Davis, Robin, Ch, Richfield Public Library, 83 E Center St, Richfield, UT, 84701. Tel: 435-896-5169. Fax: 435-896-6512. p. 2411

Davis, Roger, Ser, Kent State University, 6000 Frank Ave NW, North Canton, OH, 44720-7548. Tel: 330-244-3328. Fax: 330-494-6212. p. 1923

Davis, Roger, AV Coordr, Nicolet Area Technical College, 5364 College Dr, Rhinelander, WI, 54501. Tel: 715-365-4428. Fax: 715-365-4404. p. 2633

Davis, Ron, IT & Security Mgr, New Castle Public Library, 207 E North St, New Castle, PA, 16101-3691. Tel: 724-658-6659. Fax: 724-658-7209. p. 2096

Davis, Ronald W, Pub Serv, Ref Serv, Delaware State University, 1200 N Dupont Hwy, Dover, DE, 19901-2277. Tel: 302-857-6187. Fax: 302-857-6177. p. 382

Davis, Ronnie, Br Mgr, Alameda County Library, Albany Branch, 1247 Marin Ave, Albany, CA, 94706-1796. Tel: 510-526-3720. Fax: 510-526-8754. p. 149

Davis, Rose, Br Mgr, Shreve Memorial Library, Mooretown, 4360 Hollywood Ave, Shreveport, LA, 71109. Tel: 318-636-5524. Fax: 318-636-6438. p. 969

Davis, Ruth, Librn, Frenchboro Library, Schoolhouse Hill, Frenchboro, ME, 04635. Tel: 207-334-2948. p. 986

Davis, Ruth, Youth Serv Supvr, Jackson/Hinds Library System, Eudora Welty Library (Main Library), 300 North State St, Jackson, MS, 39201-1705. Tel: 601-968-5820, Ext 5800. Fax: 601-968-5806. p. 1303

Davis, Sallie, Circ, Bellingham Technical College Library, 3028 Lindbergh Ave, Bellingham, WA, 98225-1599. Tel: 360-752-8383. Fax: 360-752-8384. p. 2508

Davis, Sally, Br Mgr, Williams County Public Library, Stryker Branch, 304 S Defiance St, Stryker, OH, 43557. Tel: 419-682-5081. Fax: 419-682-5081. p. 1862

Davis, Sandra, Libr Dir, Fannie Brown Booth Memorial Library, 619 Tenaha St, Center, TX, 75935. Tel: 936-598-5522. Fax: 936-598-7854. p. 2296

Davis, Sara, Librn, Jacobs Engineering Library, 5995 Rogerdale Rd, Houston, TX, 77072. Tel: 832-351-7025. Fax: 832-351-7700. p. 2340

Davis, Sara, Ser, Fremont County Library System, Riverton Branch, 1330 W Park, Riverton, WY, 82501. Tel: 307-856-3556. Fax: 307-857-3722. p. 2657

Davis, Sarah, ILL, National Oceanic & Atmospheric Administration, 1315 East West Hwy, 2nd Flr, Silver Spring, MD, 20910. Tel: 301-713-2600, Ext 157. Fax: 301-713-4598. p. 1042

Davis, Sarah, Br Mgr, Albemarle Regional Library, Sallie Harrell Jenkins Memorial Library, 302 Broad St, Aulander, NC, 27805. Tel: 252-345-4461. Fax: 252-345-8000. p. 1835

Davis, Sarah, Br Supvr, Harris County Public Library, Stratford Branch, 509 Stratford, Highlands, TX, 77562. Tel: 281-426-3521. Fax: 281-426-4354. p. 2336

Davis, Scott, Dir, Fremont Public Library District, 1170 N Midlothian Rd, Mundelein, IL, 60060. Tel: 847-566-8702. Fax: 847-566-0204. p. 678

Davis, Scott, Dr, Prof, Indiana State University, Curric, Instruction & Media Tech Dept, Terre Haute, IN, 47809. Tel: 812-237-2954. Fax: 812-237-4556. p. 2965

Davis, Sharon, Br Mgr, Harrison County Library System, Margaret Sherry Branch Library, 2141 Popps Ferry Rd, Biloxi, MS, 39532-4251. Tel: 228-388-1633. Fax: 228-388-0920. p. 1300

Davis, Shelley, Librn, S E D Systems, Inc Library, 18 Innovation Blvd, Saskatoon, SK, S7K 3P7, CANADA. Tel: 306-931-3425. Fax: 306-933-1486. p. 2926

Davis, Shelly, Dir of Libr Serv, Saint Joseph's College, 278 Whites Bridge Rd, Standish, ME, 04084-5263. Tel: 207-893-7726. Fax: 207-893-7883. p. 1002

Davis, Sheri, Br Mgr, San Diego County Library, Jacumba Branch, 44605 Old Hwy 80, Jacumba, CA, 91934. Tel: 619-766-4608. Fax: 619-766-9206. p. 233

Davis, Sherry, Res Librn, Cryovac Sealed Air Corporate Library, 100 Rogers Bridge Rd, Duncan, SC, 29334. Tel: 864-433-2313. Fax: 864-433-3636. p. 2193

Davis, Shirley, Librn, Dolores County Public Library, Cahone Reading Center, Cahone Recreation Ctr, Cahone, CO, 81320. Tel: 970-562-4626. p. 304

Davis, Stephanie, Dir, Wells County Public Library, 200 W Washington St, Bluffton, IN, 46714-1999. Tel: 260-824-1612. Fax: 260-824-3129. p. 728

Davis, Stephanie, Educ Librn, Spring Arbor University, 106 E Main St, Spring Arbor, MI, 49283. Tel: 800-968-9103, Ext 1435. Fax: 517-750-2108. p. 1229

Davis, Stephanie DeLano, Libr Dir, Jackson Community College, 2111 Emmons Rd, Jackson, MI, 49201-8399. Tel: 517-796-8482. Fax: 517-796-8623. p. 1195

Davis, Steven, Mgr, Kirkwood Library, 6000 Kirkwood Hwy, Wilmington, DE, 19808-4817. Tel: 302-995-7663. Fax: 302-995-7687. p. 388

Davis, Susan, Librn, Burnley Memorial Library, 401 Oak, Cottonwood Falls, KS, 66845. Tel: 620-273-8588. Fax: 620-273-8588. p. 862

Davis, Susan E, Exec Dir, Pottstown Regional Public Library, 500 E High St, Pottstown, PA, 19464-5656. Tel: 610-970-6551. Fax: 610-970-6553. p. 2131

Davis, Susan E, PhD, Assoc Teaching Prof, Drexel University, Rush Bldg, Rm 306, 30 N 33rd St, Philadelphia, PA, 19104-2875. Tel: 215-895-2474. Fax: 215-895-2494. p. 2972

Davis, Susan G, Prof, University of Illinois at Urbana-Champaign, Library & Information Science Bldg, 501 E Daniel St, Champaign, IL, 61820-6211. Tel: 217-333-3280. Fax: 217-244-3302. p. 2965

Davis, Suzanne, Youth Serv, East Bonner County Free Library District, 1407 Cedar St, Sandpoint, ID, 83864-2052. Tel: 208-263-6930, Ext 211. Fax: 208-263-8320. p. 583

Davis, Suzanne, Dir, Sterling County Public Library, 301 Main, Sterling City, TX, 76951. Tel: 325-378-2212. Fax: 325-378-3303. p. 2389

Davis, Tanya, Law Librn, Law Society of New Brunswick Library, Justice Bldg, Fredericton, NB, E3B 5H1, CANADA. Tel: 506-453-2500. Fax: 506-453-9438. p. 2763

Davis, Ted, Asst Librn, Monroe County Public Library, 103 South St, Union, WV, 24983. Tel: 304-772-3038. Fax: 304-772-4052. p. 2573

Davis, Terri, Asst Dir, Rapid City Public Library, 610 Quincy St, Rapid City, SD, 57701-3630. Tel: 605-394-6139, Ext 223. Fax: 605-394-4064. p. 2217

Davis, Thomas, Librn, North Carolina Supreme Court Library, 500 Justice Bldg, Two E Morgan St, Raleigh, NC, 27601-1428. Tel: 919-831-5709. Fax: 919-831-5732. p. 1816

Davis, Traycee, Law Librn, Richland County Law Library Resources Board, 50 Park Ave E, Mansfield, OH, 44902. Tel: 419-774-5595. p. 1913

Davis, Trisha, In Charge, Tuolumne County Free Library, Tuolumne City Branch, 18636 Main St, Tuolumne, CA, 95379. Tel: 209-928-3612. p. 269

Davis, Troy, Dir, Media Serv, College of William & Mary in Virginia, Earl Gregg Swem Library, One Landrum Dr, Williamsburg, VA, 23187. Tel: 757-221-2643. Fax: 757-221-2635. p. 2502

Davis, Virginia, Librn, Chicago Sun-Times, 350 N Orleans St, Chicago, IL, 60654. Tel: 312-321-2594. Fax: 312-321-3084. p. 610

Davis, Vivian, Br Mgr, Haywood County Public Library, Maggie Valley, Town Hall, 3987 Soco Rd, Maggie Valley, NC, 28751. Tel: 828-926-0461, Ext 6. p. 1829

Davis, Wanda, Dir, Hinton Public Library, 115 E Main, Hinton, OK, 73047. Tel: 405-542-6167. Fax: 405-542-6167. p. 1965

Davis, Wanda, Librn, Mackenzie Public Library, 400 Skeena Dr, Mackenzie, BC, V0J 2C0, CANADA. Tel: 250-997-6343. Fax: 250-997-5792. p. 2731

Davis, Wendy, Asst Dir, Pulaski Technical College Library, 3000 W Scenic Dr, North Little Rock, AR, 72118-3347. Tel: 501-812-2272. Fax: 501-812-2315. p. 111

Davis, Wendy, Librn, Adult Serv, Lake Forest Library, 360 E Deerpath Ave, Lake Forest, IL, 60045-2252. Tel: 847-810-4615. Fax: 847-234-1453. p. 663

Davis, Yolanda, Asst Librn, American Medical Association, 515 N State St, 9th Flr, Chicago, IL, 60654. Tel: 312-464-4855. Fax: 312-464-5226. p. 606

Davis, Zoe, Sr Ref Librn, United States Senate Library, SRB-15 Senate Russell Bldg, Washington, DC, 20510-7112. Tel: 202-224-7106. Fax: 202-224-0879. p. 421

Davis-Kahl, Stephanie, Scholarly Communications Librn, Illinois Wesleyan University, One Ames Plaza, Bloomington, IL, 61701-7188. Tel: 309-556-3010. Fax: 309-556-3706. p. 595

Davis-Little, Carla, Librn, Monroe Public Library, 3B School St, Monroe Bridge, MA, 01350. Tel: 413-424-5272. p. 1106

Davis-Northrup, Matilda, Head, Tech Serv, Ohio Dominican University Library, 1216 Sunbury Rd, Columbus, OH, 43219. Tel: 614-251-4757. Fax: 614-252-2650. p. 1886

Davis-Witherow, Leah, Archivist, Colorado Springs Pioneers Museum, 215 S Tejon St, Colorado Springs, CO, 80903. Tel: 719-385-5650. Fax: 719-385-5645. p. 295

Davison, Barbara, Br Mgr, Central Rappahannock Regional Library, Salem Church, 2607 Salem Church Rd, Fredericksburg, VA, 22407-6451. Tel: 540-785-9267. Fax: 540-785-9443. p. 2466

Davison, Dorothy, Dean of Libr, Wagner College, One Campus Rd, Staten Island, NY, 10301-4495. Tel: 718-420-4221. Fax: 718-420-4218. p. 1748

Davison, Frieda, Dean of Libr, University of South Carolina Upstate Library, 800 University Way, Spartanburg, SC, 29303. Tel: 864-503-5610. Fax: 864-503-5601. p. 2205

Davison, Jennifer, Librn, Adams Public Library, 190 Main St, Adams, OR, 97810. Tel: 541-566-3038. Fax: 541-566-2077. p. 1989

Davison, Laura, Asst Dir, Access, Delivery & Outreach Serv, University of Kentucky Libraries, Medical Center Library, 800 Rose St, Lexington, KY, 40536-0298. Tel: 859-323-6138. Fax: 859-323-1040. p. 922

Davison, Lisa M, Head, Circ, Rock Island Public Library, 401 19th St, Rock Island, IL, 61201. Tel: 309-732-7350. Fax: 309-732-7342. p. 696

Davison, Louise, Librn, Fort Assiniboine Public Library, 35 State Ave, Fort Assiniboine, AB, T0G 1A0, CANADA. Tel: 780-584-2227. Fax: 780-674-8575. p. 2704

Davison, Patrick, Ref Librn, Hazard Community & Technical College Library, One Community College Dr, Hazard, KY, 41701. Tel: 606-487-3145. Fax: 606-439-1657. p. 916

Davison, Susan, Circ, ILL, Louisiana State University, One University Pl, Shreveport, LA, 71115-2399. Tel: 318-797-5225. Fax: 318-797-5156. p. 968

Davison, Wayne, Cataloger, Saint Patrick's Seminary, 320 Middlefield Rd, Menlo Park, CA, 94025. Tel: 650-321-5655. Fax: 650-323-5447. p. 185

Davison-Turley, Whitney, Info & Reader Serv Mgr, Johnson County Library, 9875 W 87th St, Overland Park, KS, 66212. Tel: 913-495-2473. Fax: 913-495-2460. p. 888

Davitt, Jennifer, Head, Res Serv, Georgetown University, Georgetown Law Library (John Wolff & Edward Bennett Williams Libraries), 111 G St NW, Washington, DC, 20001. Fax: 202-662-9168. p. 403

Daw, Lynn K, Tech Serv Librn, Monmouth College, 700 E Broadway, Monmouth, IL, 61462-1963. Tel: 309-457-2187. Fax: 309-457-2226. p. 675

Daw, Michael, Dir, Golden Gate University, School of Law Library, 536 Mission St, San Francisco, CA, 94105. Tel: 415-442-6680. Fax: 415-512-9395. p. 242

Dawber, Michael, Chief Exec Officer, Rainy River Public Library, 334 Fourth St, Rainy River, ON, P0W 1L0, CANADA. Tel: 807-852-3375. Fax: 807-852-3375. p. 2838

Dawdy, Chris, Libr Dir, Brighton Memorial Library, 110 N Main, Brighton, IL, 62012. Tel: 618-372-8450. Fax: 618-372-7450. p. 597

Dawe, Sean, Dir, Department of Justice, East Block, Confederation Bldg, 5th Flr, 100 Prince Philip Dr, St. John's, NL, A1B 4J6, CANADA. Tel: 709-729-2861. Fax: 709-729-1370. p. 2772

Dawes, Trevor, Circ, Princeton University, One Washington Rd, Princeton, NJ, 08544-2098. Tel: 609-258-3231. Fax: 609-258-0441. p. 1523

Dawkins, Maxine, Br Librn, Kemper-Newton Regional Library System, J Elliott McMullan Library, 300 W Church St, Newton, MS, 39345-2208. Tel: 601-683-3367. Fax: 601-683-3367. p. 1316

Dawkins, Sandra, Librn, Buffalo Public Library, Hwy 79, Buffalo, TX, 75831. Tel: 903-322-4146. Fax: 903-322-3253. p. 2293

Dawkins, Shirley, Br Mgr, East Central Georgia Regional Library, Lincoln County Library, 181 N Peachtree, Lincolnton, GA, 30817. Tel: 706-359-4014. Fax: 706-359-1105. p. 520

Dawson, Warren, Info Tech, Syst Adminr, Ela Area Public Library District, 275 Mohawk Trail, Lake Zurich, IL, 60047. Tel: 847-438-3433. Fax: 847-438-9290. p. 663

Dawood, Masef, In Charge, Ahmadiyya Muslim Association Library, 525 Kylemore Ave, Winnipeg, MB, R3L 1B5, CANADA. Tel: 204-475-2642. Fax: 204-452-2455. p. 2754

Dawsari, Elizabeth, Dir, Frank Lloyd Wright School of Architecture, Taliesin West, Scottsdale, AZ, 85261-4430. Tel: 480-860-2700. Fax: 480-860-8472. p. 80

Dawsey, Joseph, Acq, Cat, Piedmont College, 165 Central Ave, Demorest, GA, 30535. Tel: 706-776-0111. Fax: 706-776-3338. p. 530

Dawson, Alma, Dr, Prof, Louisiana State University, 267 Coates Hall, Baton Rouge, LA, 70803. Tel: 225-578-3158. Fax: 225-578-4581. p. 2966

Dawson, Amy, YA Serv, Catawba County Library, 115 West C St, Newton, NC, 28658. Tel: 828-465-8664. Fax: 828-465-8983. p. 1813

Dawson, Barbara, Br Head, Napoleon Public Library, McClure Community, 110 Cross St, McClure, OH, 43534-0035. Tel: 419-748-8922. Fax: 419-748-8917. p. 1920

Dawson, Barbara J, Curator, Printed Works, Cincinnati Museum Center At Union Terminal, 1301 Western Ave, Cincinnati, OH, 45203. Tel: 513-287-7098. Fax: 513-287-7095. p. 1869

Dawson, Charlotte, ILL, Clearwater Public Library, 109 E Ross St, Clearwater, KS, 67026-7824. Tel: 620-584-6474. Fax: 620-584-2995. p. 861

Dawson, Chrystal, Access Serv, Bellevue University, 1000 Galvin Rd S, Bellevue, NE, 68005. Tel: 402-557-7305. Fax: 402-557-5427. p. 1393

Dawson, Elaine B, Dir, Newark Public Library, 121 High St, Newark, NY, 14513-1492. Tel: 315-331-4370. Fax: 315-331-0552. p. 1704

Dawson, Georgie, Asst Admin, Ruth Enlow Library of Garrett County, Six N Second St, Oakland, MD, 21550-1393. Tel: 301-334-3996. Fax: 301-334-4152. p. 1035

Dawson, Gillian, YA Librn, Orange County Library, 146A Madison Rd, Orange, VA, 22960. Tel: 540-661-5445. Fax: 540-672-5040. p. 2483

Dawson, Jeff, Dir, Lester Public Library, 1001 Adams St, Two Rivers, WI, 54241. Tel: 920-793-7104. Fax: 920-793-7150. p. 2643

Dawson, Jeffery, Mgr, Youth Serv, Topeka & Shawnee County Public Library, 1515 SW Tenth Ave, Topeka, KS, 66604-1374. Tel: 785-580-4400. Fax: 785-580-4496. p. 897

Dawson, Jeffrey, Archives Supvr, State Historical Society of Iowa-Des Moines Library, 600 E Locust, Des Moines, IA, 50319-0290. Tel: 515-281-6200. Fax: 515-282-0502. p. 810

Dawson, Jennifer, Librn, Citrus Research & Education Center, 700 Experiment Station Rd, Lake Alfred, FL, 33850-2299. Tel: 863-956-1151. Fax: 863-956-4631. p. 457

Dawson, Joanne, Ref Serv, Arizona Republic Library, 200 E Van Buren, Phoenix, AZ, 85004. Tel: 602-444-4446. Fax: 602-444-4294. p. 71

Dawson, Judy, Info Serv, Ref, Jefferson State Community College, 2601 Carson Rd, Birmingham, AL, 35215-3098. Tel: 205-856-7786. Fax: 205-856-8512. p. 8

Dawson, Julie Eng, Assoc Librn, Princeton Theological Seminary, Mercer St & Library Pl, Princeton, NJ, 08542. Tel: 609-497-7940. Fax: 609-497-1826. p. 1522

Dawson, Keith, Librn, Life Pacific College Alumni Library, 1100 W Covina Blvd, San Dimas, CA, 91773-3203. Tel: 909-706-3008. Fax: 909-599-6690. p. 239

Dawson, Linda, Br Mgr, Mississippi County Library System, Wilson Public, One Park St, Wilson, AR, 72395. Tel: 870-655-8414. Fax: 870-655-8414. p. 96

Dawson, Margaret, Circ, Lone Star College System, Tomball College Library, 30555 Tomball Pkwy, Tomball, TX, 77375-4036. Tel: 832-559-4206. Fax: 832-559-4248. p. 2340

Dawson, Marie, Ch, County of Prince Edward Libraries, 208 Main St, Picton, ON, K0K 2T0, CANADA. Tel: 613-476-5962. Fax: 613-476-3325. p. 2836

Dawson, Mary Jo, Dir, Aiken-Bamberg-Barnwell-Edgefield Regional Library System, 314 Chesterfield St SW, Aiken, SC, 29801-7171. Tel: 803-642-7575. Fax: 803-642-7597. p. 2179

Dawson, Pat, Libr Mgr, Fraser Valley Regional Library, City of Langley Library, 20399 Douglas Crescent, Langley, BC, V3A 4B3, CANADA. Tel: 604-514-2850. Fax: 604-534-2985. p. 2723

Dawson, Pat, Libr Mgr, Fraser Valley Regional Library, Terry Fox Library, 2470 Mary Hill Rd, Port Coquitlam, BC, V3C 3B1, CANADA. Tel: 604-927-7999. Fax: 604-941-8365. p. 2723

Dawson, Patricia, Head, ILL, Albertus Magnus College Library, 700 Prospect St, New Haven, CT, 06511. Tel: 203-773-8594. Fax: 203-773-8588. p. 355

Dawson, Patrick J, Dean, Northern Illinois University Libraries, DeKalb, IL, 60115-2868. Tel: 815-753-9801. p. 635

Dawson, Rose T, Dir, Alexandria Library, 5005 Duke St, Alexandria, VA, 22304. Tel: 703-746-1777. p. 2444

Dawson, Terry P, Dir, Appleton Public Library, 225 N Oneida St, Appleton, WI, 54911-4780. Tel: 920-832-6170. Fax: 920-832-6182. p. 2578

Dawson, Vicki, Cat, Berkley Public Library, Three N Main St, Berkley, MA, 02779. Tel: 508-822-3329. Fax: 508-824-2471. p. 1053

Dawson, Vicki L, Dir, James White Memorial Library, Five Washburn Rd, East Freetown, MA, 02717-1220. Tel: 508-763-5344. p. 1086

Dawson-Valentine, Allyson F, Adjunct Fac Librn, Harrisburg Area Community College, 1641 Old Philadelphia Pike, Lancaster, PA, 17602. Tel: 717-358-2986. Fax: 717-358-2952. p. 2076

Day, Adam, Computer Support Spec, Twin Falls Public Library, 201 Fourth Ave E, Twin Falls, ID, 83301-6397. Tel: 208-733-2964. Fax: 208-733-2965. p. 584

Day, Ann, Chief Librn, Creston Public Library Association, 531-16th Ave S, Creston, BC, V0B 1G5, CANADA. Tel: 250-428-4141. Fax: 250-428-4703. p. 2727

Day, Annette, Head, Coll Mgt, North Carolina State University Libraries, Two Broughton Dr, Raleigh, NC, 27695. Tel: 919-515-3833. Fax: 919-515-3628. p. 1816

Day, Bonnie, Librn, Emery County Library, Elmo Branch, 15 S 100 East, Elmo, UT, 84521. Tel: 435-653-2558. Fax: 435-653-2553. p. 2403

Day, Brenda, Archivist, Baker University, 518 Eighth St, Baldwin City, KS, 66006-0065. Tel: 785-594-8380. Fax: 785-594-6721. p. 857

Day, Cassaundra, Br Supvr, Anderson City, Anderson, Stony Creek & Union Townships Public Library, Lapel Public, 610 Main St, Lapel, IN, 46051. Tel: 765-534-4654. Fax: 765-534-4654. p. 724

Day, Cathy, Librn, Bethel Public Library, 106 Main St, Bethel, VT, 05032. Tel: 802-234-9107. p. 2419

Day, Christopher, Digital Serv Librn, School of the Art Institute of Chicago, 37 S Wabash Ave, Chicago, IL, 60603-3103. Tel: 312-899-5097. Fax: 312-899-1851. p. 624

Day, D, Bibliog Instr, Ref, Ohio University-Zanesville/ Zane State College, 1425 Newark Rd, Zanesville, OH, 43701. Tel: 740-588-1408. Fax: 740-453-0706. p. 1954

Day, Danielle, Youth Serv Librn, Carnegie-Stout Public Library, 360 W 11th St, Dubuque, IA, 52001. Tel: 563-589-4138. Fax: 563-589-4217. p. 811

Day, David, Music, Brigham Young University, Harold B Lee Library, 2060 HBLL, Provo, UT, 84602. Tel: 801-422-2927. Fax: 801-422-0466. p. 2411

Day, Dee, Circ Supvr, William Jewell College, 500 College Hill, Liberty, MO, 64068-1843. Tel: 816-415-7609. Fax: 816-415-5021. p. 1343

Day, Denise, Librn, Mattawamkeag Public Library, 327 Main St, Mattawamkeag, ME, 04459. Tel: 207-736-7013. Fax: 207-736-2545. p. 991

Day, Elaine L, Dir, Syst Librn, Web Serv, Averett University Library, 344 W Main St, Danville, VA, 24541-2849. Tel: 434-791-5696. Fax: 434-791-5637. p. 2459

Day, Essy, Dir, Clinton Public Library, 118 S Hicks St, Clinton, TN, 37716-2826. Tel: 865-457-0519. Fax: 865-457-4233. p. 2230

Day, Evan, YA Serv, Rogers Public Library, 711 S Dixieland Rd, Rogers, AR, 72758. Tel: 479-621-1152, Ext 32. Fax: 479-621-1165. p. 113

Day Gibson, Peggy, Dir, Orleans County Historical Society, Inc, 109 Old Stone House Rd, Brownington, VT, 05860. Tel: 802-754-2022. Fax: 802-754-9336. p. 2420

Day, Jane, Pub Serv, Duke University Libraries, Ford Library, One Towerview Rd, Durham, NC, 27708. Tel: 919-660-7874. Fax: 919-660-7950. p. 1787

Day, Janet Vaill, Dir, Woodbridge Town Library, Ten Newton Rd, Woodbridge, CT, 06525. Tel: 203-389-3435. Fax: 203-389-3457. p. 380

Day, Janice, Actg Chief Librn, Pincher Creek Municipal Library, 899 Main St, Pincher Creek, AB, T0K 1W0, CANADA. Tel: 403-627-3813. Fax: 403-627-2847. p. 2713

Day, Jean, Ch, Oak Lawn Public Library, 9427 S Raymond Ave, Oak Lawn, IL, 60453-2434. Tel: 708-422-4990. Fax: 708-422-5061. p. 683

Day, Jill, Acq & Cat Mgr, Grant MacEwan University Library, 10700 104th Ave, Edmonton, AB, T5J 4S2, CANADA. Tel: 780-497-5850. Fax: 780-497-5895. p. 2701

Day, Joanne, Head of Libr, Albertus Magnus College Library, 700 Prospect St, New Haven, CT, 06511. Tel: 203-773-8594. Fax: 203-773-8588. p. 355

Day, John, Instrul Serv Librn, Nassau Community College, One Education Dr, Garden City, NY, 11530-6793. Tel: 516-572-7400. Fax: 516-572-7846. p. 1626

Day, Joy, ILL, Pub Serv, Young Harris College, One College St, Young Harris, GA, 30582. Tel: 706-379-4313. Fax: 706-379-4314. p. 558

Day, Luke, Br Mgr, Harlan County Public Library, Rebecca Caudill Public, 310 W Main St, Cumberland, KY, 40823. Tel: 606-589-2409. Fax: 606-589-2409. p. 916

Day, Marlin, Libr Mgr, Alachua County Library District, Newberry Branch, 110 S Seaboard Dr, Newberry, FL, 32669. Tel: 352-472-1135. Fax: 352-472-1136. p. 448

Day, Matthew, Head, Support Serv, Royal Oak Public Library, 222 E Eleven Mile Rd, Royal Oak, MI, 48067-2633. Tel: 248-246-3732. Fax: 248-246-3701. p. 1223

Day, Nancy, Head, Tech Serv, Hamilton-Wenham Public Library, 14 Union St, South Hamilton, MA, 01982. Tel: 978-468-5577, Ext 16. Fax: 978-468-5535. p. 1125

Day, Norma, Librn, Lake City Public Library, 226 N Main St, Lake City, TN, 37769. Tel: 865-426-6762. Fax: 865-426-9235. p. 2244

Day, Patti, Mgr, Washoe County Library System, North Valleys Library, 1075 N Hills Blvd, No 340, Reno, NV, 89506. Tel: 775-972-0271. Fax: 775-972-6810. p. 1434

Day, Ron, Asst Dir, Br Mgr, Pineville-Bell County Public Library, 214 Walnut St, Pineville, KY, 40977. Tel: 606-337-3422. Fax: 606-337-9862. p. 933

Day, Ross, Acq, Metropolitan Museum of Art, Thomas J Watson Library, 1000 Fifth Ave, New York, NY, 10028-0198. Tel: 212-650-2949. Fax: 212-570-3847. p. 1686

Day, Ross, Head of Libr, Metropolitan Museum of Art, Robert Goldwater Library, 1000 Fifth Ave, New York, NY, 10028-0198. Tel: 212-570-3707. Fax: 212-570-3879. p. 1686

Day, Sandy, Archivist, Public Library of Steubenville & Jefferson County, 407 S Fourth St, Steubenville, OH, 43952-2942. Tel: 740-264-6166. Fax: 740-282-2919. p. 1936

Day, Sarah, Ch, Dr Grace O Doane Alden Public Library, 1012 Water St, Alden, IA, 50006. Tel: 515-859-3820. Fax: 515-859-3919. p. 792

Day, Sherry, ILL, Mohawk Valley Community College Library, 1101 Sherman Dr, Utica, NY, 13501-5394. Tel: 315-792-5669. Fax: 315-792-5666. p. 1759

Day, Tricia F, Adminr, American Association of Textile Chemists & Colorists Library, One Davis Dr, Research Triangle Park, NC, 27709. Tel: 919-549-3534. Fax: 919-549-8933. p. 1819

Day-Lowe, Sharon, Tech Serv, Gaston College, 201 Hwy 321 S, Dallas, NC, 28034-1499. Tel: 704-922-6361. Fax: 704-922-2342. p. 1786

Day-Myron, Maggie, ILL, Tech Serv, WeirFoulds Library, The Exchange Tower, Ste1600, 130 King St W, Toronto, ON, M5X 1J5, CANADA. Tel: 416-365-1110, Ext 2327. Fax: 416-365-1876. p. 2867

Dayall, Susan, Actg Libr Dir, Archivist, Hampshire College Library, 893 West St, Amherst, MA, 01002-5001. Tel: 413-559-5761. Fax: 413-559-5419. p. 1048

Dayday, Eulogio, Web Adminr, Art Center College of Design, 1700 Lida St, Pasadena, CA, 91103. Tel: 626-396-2236. Fax: 626-568-0428. p. 205

Dayday, Juliet, Cinema Libr Mgr, Art Center College of Design, 1700 Lida St, Pasadena, CA, 91103. Tel: 626-396-2235. Fax: 626-568-0428. p. 205

Dayer, Ken, Asst Dir/Pub Serv Mgr, Silver City Public Library, 408 Main St, Silver City, IA, 51571. Tel: 712-525-9053. Fax: 712-525-9053. p. 843

Dayton, April, Chief Librn, Koyukuk Community Library, 300 Vista Rd, Koyukuk, AK, 99754. Tel: 907-927-2245, Ext 2301. p. 51

Dayton, Barbara, Dir, Mohawk Community Library, 200 S Sycamore Ave, Sycamore, OH, 44882. Tel: 419-927-2407. Fax: 419-927-2958. p. 1937

Dayton, Douglas, Librn, Koyukuk Community Library, 300 Vista Rd, Koyukuk, AK, 99754. Tel: 907-927-2224. p. 51

Dayton, Jennifer D, Head, Readers Advisory, Darien Library, 1441 Post Rd, Darien, CT, 06820-5419. Tel: 203-669-5226. Fax: 203-655-1547. p. 336

Dayton, Sandy, Head, Ch, Great Bend Public Library, 1409 Williams St, Great Bend, KS, 67530-4090. Tel: 620-792-2409. Fax: 620-792-5495, 620-793-7270. p. 869

Dayton, Stuart K, Media Spec, Ad, University of Nebraska Medical Center, 600 S 42nd St, Omaha, NE, 68198-6705. Tel: 402-559-6334. Fax: 402-559-5498. p. 1415

Daze, Colleen, Dir, SLIC, New Jersey State Library, 185 W State St, Trenton, NJ, 08618. Tel: 609-278-2640, Ext 118. Fax: 609-278-2645. p. 1536

Dazet, Neil, Info Serv, Brooklyn College Library, 2900 Bedford Ave, Brooklyn, NY, 11210-2889. Tel: 718-758-8241. Fax: 718-951-4540. p. 1589

Dazey, Megan, Head, Cat/Database Section of Bibliog Mgt Serv, University of Montana, Maureen & Mike Mansfield Library, 32 Campus Dr, No 9936, Missoula, MT, 59812-9936. Tel: 406-243-4728. Fax: 406-243-4067. p. 1386

De Abreu, Belinha, PhD, Asst Teaching Prof, Drexel University, Rush Bldg, Rm 306, 30 N 33rd St, Philadelphia, PA, 19104-2875. Tel: 215-895-2474. Fax: 215-895-2494. p. 2973

De Araujo, Georgia, Asst Dir, Boyle County Public Library, 1857 S Danville Bypass, Danville, KY, 40422. Tel: 859-236-8466. Fax: 859-236-7692. p. 911

De Barros, Rosa, Br Head, Toronto Public Library, Victoria Village, 184 Sloane Ave, Toronto, ON, M4A 2C4, CANADA. Tel: 416-395-5950. Fax: 416-395-5418. p. 2863

De Boeck, Carol, Br Mgr, Surrey Public Library, Cloverdale, 5642 176A St, Surrey, BC, V3S 4G9, CANADA. Tel: 604-598-7330. Fax: 604-598-7321. p. 2739

De Boeck, Carol, Br Mgr, Surrey Public Library, Fleetwood, 15996 84th Ave, Surrey, BC, V3S 2N7, CANADA. Tel: 604-598-7340. Fax: 604-598-7321. p. 2739

De Castro, Carmelita, Cat, United States Senate Library, SRB-15 Senate Russell Bldg, Washington, DC, 20510-7112. Tel: 202-224-7106. Fax: 202-224-0879. p. 421

De Cecco, Susanna, Cat, Widener University, School of Law Library, 4601 Concord Pike, Wilmington, DE, 19803. Tel: 302-477-2069. Fax: 302-477-2240. p. 389

De Dominicis, Florence, Br Mgr, Oakville Public Library, Central, 120 Navy St, Oakville, ON, L6J 2Z4, CANADA. Tel: 905-815-2042, Ext 5041. Fax: 905-815-2024. p. 2825

de Farber, Bess, Grants Mgr, University of Florida Libraries, 535 Library W, Gainesville, FL, 32611-7000. Tel: 352-273-2505. Fax: 352-392-7251. p. 450

De Graaff, Ann, Circ, Millbrook Free Library, Three Friendly Lane, Millbrook, NY, 12545. Tel: 845-677-3611. Fax: 845-677-5127. p. 1661

De Hernandez, Diana, Access Serv Mgr, Miami-Dade Public Library System, 101 W Flagler St, Miami, FL, 33130-1523. Tel: 305-375-8321. Fax: 305-375-3048. p. 466

De Herrera, Maria, Dir, Conejos County Library, PO Box 63, La Jara, CO, 81140-0063. Tel: 719-274-5858. Fax: 719-274-5858. p. 314

de Jagar, Eileen, Supvr, Elgin County Public Library, Fred Bodsworth Public Library of Port Burwell, 21 Pitt St, Port Burwell, ON, N0J 1T0, CANADA. Tel: 519-874-4754. Fax: 519-874-4436. p. 2844

de Jager, Eileen, Supvr, Elgin County Public Library, Bayham Township, 9366 Plank Rd, Straffordville, ON, N0J 1Y0, CANADA. Tel: 519-866-3584. Fax: 519-866-3219. p. 2844

De Jager, Elberta, Dir, Edgerton Public Library, 811 First Ave, Edgerton, MN, 56128. Tel: 507-442-7071. Fax: 507-442-7071. p. 1249

De Jardin, Carole, Ch, Appleton Public Library, 225 N Oneida St, Appleton, WI, 54911-4780. Tel: 920-832-6187. Fax: 920-832-6182. p. 2578

De Jesus, Alma, Head, Ref, Proskauer Rose LLP Library, 1585 Broadway, Concourse Level, New York, NY, 10036. Tel: 212-969-5001. Fax: 212-969-2931. p. 1698

De Jesus, Anthony, Legis Spec, United States Nuclear Regulatory Commission, Law Library, 11555 Rockville Pike, Rockville, MD, 20852. Tel: 301-415-2814. Fax: 301-415-3725. p. 1040

de Jesus Ayala-Schueneman, Maria, Dr, Prof & Assoc Dir of Pub Serv, Texas A&M University-Kingsville, 700 University Blvd, MSC 197, Kingsville, TX, 78363-8202. Tel: 361-593-3097. Fax: 361-593-4093. p. 2351

De Jong, Maryellen, Commun Serv, Danbury Public Library, 170 Main St, Danbury, CT, 06810. Tel: 203-796-8061. Fax: 203-797-4501. p. 335

De Krey, Gary, Archivist, Norwegian-American Historical Association Archives, 1510 St Olaf Ave, Northfield, MN, 55057. Tel: 507-786-3221. Fax: 507-786-3734. p. 1269

de la Chapelle, Anne, Electronic Serv & Emerging Tech Librn, Clinton Community College, 136 Clinton Point Dr, Plattsburgh, NY, 12901-5690. Tel: 518-562-4244. Fax: 518-562-4116. p. 1718

de la Chevrotière, François, Dir, Cegep de L'Abitibi - Temiscamingue Bibliotheque, 425 Boul du College, Rouyn-Noranda, QC, J9X 5M5, CANADA. Tel: 819-762-0931, Ext 1216. Fax: 819-762-2071. p. 2908

De la Cour, Marian A, Librn, Jordan Hospital, 275 Sandwich St, Plymouth, MA, 02360. Tel: 508-830-2157. Fax: 508-830-2887. p. 1118

De La Fontaine, John, Syst Librn, Occidental College Library, 1600 Campus Rd, Los Angeles, CA, 90041. Tel: 323-259-2914. Fax: 323-341-4991. p. 176

De La Garza, Mary, Mrg, Admin Serv, University of Texas Libraries, Population Research Center Library, Main Bldg 1800, G1800, Austin, TX, 78712. Tel: 512-471-8332. Fax: 512-471-4886. p. 2284

de la Herran, Isidro, Librn, Hallmark Cards, Inc, Business Research Library, 2501 McGee, No 203, Kansas City, MO, 64108. Tel: 816-274-4648. Fax: 816-274-7394. p. 1337

De la Vega, Amalia, Acq, Ser, University of Miami, Louis Calder Memorial Library, Miller School of Medicine, 1601 NW Tenth Ave, Miami, FL, 33136. Tel: 305-243-6901. Fax: 305-325-8853. p. 469

De Leon, Jorge, Librn, Yale University Library, The William Robertson Coe Ornithology Library, Environmental Science Ctr, Rm 151, 21 Sachem St, New Haven, CT, 06520-8118. Tel: 203-436-4892. p. 357

De Leur, Michael, Libr Mgr, Vancouver Island Regional Library, Port Alberni Branch, 4245 Wallace St, Port Alberni, BC, V9Y 3Y6, CANADA. Tel: 250-723-9511. Fax: 250-723-5366. p. 2733

De Locke, Claudia, In Charge, Huntington Beach Public Library System, Oak View, 17251 Oak Lane, Huntington Beach, CA, 92648. Tel: 714-375-5068. Fax: 714-375-5073. p. 159

De los Santos, Lynda, Pub Serv, Tarrant County College, Jenkins Garrett Library-South Campus, 5301 Campus Dr, Fort Worth, TX, 76119. Tel: 817-515-4524. Fax: 817-515-4436. p. 2323

De Luise, Alexandra, Instrul Serv Librn, Queens College, Benjamin S Rosenthal Library, 65-30 Kissena Blvd, Flushing, NY, 11367-0904. Tel: 718-997-3700. Fax: 718-997-3753. p. 1623

De Luna, Carolyn, Ref/Electronic Serv Librn, Edgewood College Library, 1000 Edgewood College Dr, Madison, WI, 53711-1997. Tel: 608-663-3300. Fax: 608-663-6778. p. 2606

De Montigny, Marie-Hélène, Acq of Monographs, Institut de Formation Théologique de Montreal Bibliotheque, 2065, rue Sherbrooke Ouest, Montreal, QC, H3H 1G6, CANADA. Tel: 514-935-1169. Fax: 514-935-5497. p. 2896

de Perio Wittman, Jessica, Dir, Info Tech Serv, University of Connecticut, 39 Elizabeth St, Hartford, CT, 06105-2287. Tel: 860-570-5059. Fax: 860-570-5104. p. 348

De Ramus, Yolanda, Actg Chief Dep, Asst Dir, Adm Serv, County of Los Angeles Public Library, 7400 E Imperial Hwy, Downey, CA, 90242-3375. Tel: 562-940-8406. Fax: 562-803-3032. p. 140

de Repentigny, Sylvie, In Charge, Bibliotheque Municipale de Pincourt, 225 boul Pincourt, Pincourt, QC, J7V 9T2, CANADA. Tel: 514-425-1104. Fax: 514-425-6668. p. 2902

De Rochefort-Reynolds, Denise, Librn, Frank Carlson Library, 702 Broadway, Concordia, KS, 66901. Tel: 785-243-2250. p. 862

De Rooy, Geraldine, Dir, Kelso Public Library, 314 Academy St, Kelso, WA, 98626-4196. Tel: 360-423-8110. Fax: 360-425-5195. p. 2518

De Santis, Melissa, Dep Dir, University of Colorado Denver, 12950 E Montview Blvd, Aurora, CO, 80045. Tel: 303-724-2152. Fax: 303-724-2166. p. 289

De Sha, Shirley, Dir, Sullivan County Public Library, 109 E Second St, Milan, MO, 63556. Tel: 660-265-3911. Fax: 660-265-3911. p. 1345

De Soto, Randy A, Dir, Saint John the Baptist Parish Library, 2920 New Hwy 51, LaPlace, LA, 70068. Tel: 985-652-2225, 985-652-6857. Fax: 985-652-8005. p. 954

De Souza, Rose, Instruction & Ref Librn, Vanier College Library, 821 Ave Sainte-Croix, Saint Laurent, QC, H4X 3L9, CANADA. Tel: 514-744-7500, Ext 7540. Fax: 514-744-7545. p. 2909

De Souza, Yvonne, Head Librn, Columbia College Library, 500-555 Seymour St, Vancouver, BC, V6B 6J9, CANADA. Tel: 604-683-8360, Ext 325. Fax: 604-682-7191. p. 2740

De Verges, Jolene, Image Librn, Massachusetts Institute of Technology Libraries, Rotch Visual Collections, Bldg 7-304, 77 Massachusetts Ave, Cambridge, MA, 02139-4307. Tel: 617-253-5593. p. 1078

De Vidas, Mireille, Sr Librn, Parade Publications, Inc, 711 Third Avenue, 7th Flr, New York, NY, 10017-4014. Tel: 212-450-7000. Fax: 212-450-7283. p. 1697

De Villers, Gisele, Coll Mgt, University of Ottawa Libraries, 65 University, Ottawa, ON, K1N 6N5, CANADA. Tel: 613-562-5800, Ext 3591. Fax: 613-562-5195. p. 2834

De Vries, Christine, Presv Mgr, University of Colorado Boulder, 1720 Pleasant St, 184 UCB, Boulder, CO, 80309-0184. Tel: 303-492-8122. Fax: 303-492-3340. p. 291

De Vries, Eileen, Dir, Culinary Institute of America, 1946 Campus Dr, Hyde Park, NY, 12538-1499. Tel: 845-451-1747. Fax: 845-451-1092. p. 1639

De Vries, Janet, Archivist, Boynton Beach City Library, 208 S Seacrest Blvd, Boynton Beach, FL, 33435. Tel: 561-742-6390. Fax: 561-742-6381. p. 429

De Vries, Jeffrey, Ref Librn, La Sierra University Library, 4500 Riverwalk Pkwy, Riverside, CA, 92505-3344. Tel: 951-785-2397. Fax: 951-785-2445. p. 217

De Wind, Lynell, Dir, Planning & Organizational Res, Grand Valley State University Libraries, One Campus Dr, Allendale, MI, 49401-9403. Tel: 616-331-3005. p. 1149

De Wit, Wim, Head, Dept of Archit, Getty Research Institute, 1200 Getty Center Dr, Ste 1100, Los Angeles, CA, 90049-1688. Tel: 310-440-7390. Fax: 310-440-7780. p. 170

De Yampert, Vicki J, Dir, University of Arkansas for Medical Sciences South Arkansas Library, 460 W Oak, El Dorado, AR, 71730. Tel: 870-881-4403, 870-881-4404. Fax: 870-862-0570. p. 98

Dea, May, In Charge, Multnomah County Library, Gregory Heights, 7921 NE Sandy Blvd, Portland, OR, 97213-7150. Tel: 503-988-5386. Fax: 503-988-5278. p. 2012

Deacy, Linda L, Dir, Douglas County Public Library, 1625 Library Lane, Minden, NV, 89423-4420. Tel: 775-782-9841. Fax: 775-782-5754. p. 1431

Deacy, Linda L, Dir, Douglas County Public Library, Lake Tahoe, 233 Warrior Way, Zephyr Cove, NV, 89448. Tel: 775-588-6411. Fax: 775-588-6464. p. 1431

Deady, Donna, YA Serv, Norwood Public Library, 198 Summit St, Norwood, NJ, 07648-1835. Tel: 201-768-9555. Fax: 201-767-2176. p. 1515

Deady, S Eleanor, Ref, Regis College Library, 235 Wellesley St, Weston, MA, 02493. Tel: 781-768-7300. Fax: 781-768-7323. p. 1139

Deakins, Bonnie, Circ, Thorntown Public Library, 124 N Market St, Thorntown, IN, 46071-1144. Tel: 765-436-7348. Fax: 765-436-7011. p. 782

Deakyne, William, Exec Dir, East Lyme Public Library, Inc, 39 Society Rd, Niantic, CT, 06357-1100. Tel: 860-739-6926. Fax: 860-691-0020. p. 361

Deal, Kathy, Br Mgr, Lake County Public Library, Highland Branch, 2841 Jewett St, Highland, IN, 46322-1617. Tel: 219-838-2394. p. 764

Deal, Kay, Dir, Davis Memorial Library, 928 Cape Rd, Limington, ME, 04049-3907. Tel: 207-637-2422. Fax: 207-637-2422. p. 990

DeAlmeida, Claudia, Circ Coordr, Roger Williams University Library, Architecture, One Old Ferry Rd, Bristol, RI, 02809-2921. Tel: 401-254-3679. p. 2164

Dealy, Michael T, Mgr, University of Kansas, 4150 W Monroe St, Wichita, KS, 67209. Tel: 316-943-2343, Ext 203. Fax: 316-943-1261. p. 900

Dean, April, Librn, Priceville Public Library, 103 Faye Dr, Priceville, AL, 35603. Tel: 256-584-0230. Fax: 256-584-0230. p. 34

Dean, Barbara, Digital Projects Librn, Federal Reserve Bank of Saint Louis, One Federal Reserve Bank Plaza, Saint Louis, MO, 63102-2005. Tel: 314-444-8961. Fax: 314-444-8694. p. 1354

Dean, Barbara, Ref, Midland Lutheran College, 900 N Clarkson, Fremont, NE, 68025. Tel: 402-941-6250. Fax: 402-727-6223. p. 1399

Dean, Becky, Acq, Louisiana State University, One University Pl, Shreveport, LA, 71115-2399. Tel: 318-798-4157. Fax: 318-797-5156. p. 968

Dean, Beth, Dir, Guntersville Public Library, 1240 O'Brig Ave, Guntersville, AL, 35976. Tel: 256-571-7595. Fax: 256-571-7596. p. 19

Dean, Betsy, Coll Develop, Stonehill College, 320 Washington St, Easton, MA, 02357-4015. Tel: 508-565-1329. Fax: 508-565-1424. p. 1086

Dean, Clyde, Chief Librn, National Geodetic Survey Library, 1315 East West Hwy, N/NGS43, SSMC III, No 8200, Silver Spring, MD, 20910. Tel: 301-713-3249, Ext 130. Fax: 301-713-4327. p. 1041

Dean, Darlene, Librn, Lansing Community Library, 108 S Second St, Lansing, KS, 66043. Tel: 913-727-2929. Fax: 913-727-1538. p. 877

Dean, Deborah, Br Head, Shasta Public Libraries, Burney Library, 37038 Siskiyou St, Burney, CA, 96013. Tel: 530-335-4317. Fax: 530-335-4317. p. 214

Dean, Dianne, Librn, Southgate Public Library, 80 Proton St, Dundalk, ON, N0C 1B0, CANADA. Tel: 519-923-3248. Fax: 519-923-3248. p. 2802

Dean, Elaine, Ref & Instruction, Pennsylvania State University, College of Medicine, Penn State Hershey, Harrell Health Sciences Library, 500 University Dr, Hershey, PA, 17033. Tel: 717-531-8581. Fax: 717-531-8635. p. 2069

Dean, Frances, Libr Dir, Bolivar Free Library, 390 Main St, Bolivar, NY, 14715-0512. Tel: 585-928-2015. Fax: 585-928-2015. p. 1583

Dean, Jennifer, Head, Acq & Coll Develop, Saginaw Valley State University, 7400 Bay Rd, University Center, MI, 48710. Tel: 989-964-7092. Fax: 989-964-4383. p. 1232

Dean, Jill, Librn, Wardsboro Free Public Library, 170 Main St, Wardsboro, VT, 05355. Tel: 802-896-6988. p. 2438

Dean, Kara, Ch, Walpole Public Library, 65 Common St, Walpole, MA, 02081. Tel: 508-660-7340. Fax: 508-660-2714. p. 1132

Dean, Kent, Mgr, Salt Lake County Library Services, Whitmore Branch, 2197 E Fort Union Blvd, Salt Lake City, UT, 84121-3139. Tel: 801-944-7535. Fax: 801-944-7534. p. 2414

Dean, Latoya, Librn, Florida Department of Corrections, South Florida Reception Center Library (Main Unit), 14000 NW 41 St, Miami, FL, 33178-3003. Tel: 305-592-9567, Ext 4104. Fax: 305-470-5765. p. 465

Dean, LeAnn Lindquist, Dir, University of Minnesota-Morris, 600 E Fourth St, Morris, MN, 56267. Tel: 320-589-6226. Fax: 320-589-6168. p. 1267

Dean, Linda T, Br Supvr, Smyth-Bland Regional Library, Chilhowie Public, 807 Chilhowie St, Chilhowie, VA, 24319. Tel: 276-646-3404. Fax: 276-646-3406. p. 2477

Dean, Marianne Quarre, Dir, Libr Develop, San Jose State University, One Washington Sq, San Jose, CA, 95192-0028. Tel: 408-924-1474. Fax: 408-808-2141. p. 251

Dean, Marlene, Ref Serv, Monroeville Public Library, 4000 Gateway Campus Blvd, Monroeville, PA, 15146-3381. Tel: 412-372-0500. Fax: 412-372-1168. p. 2091

Dean, Neera, Circ, Western Connecticut State University, 181 White St, Danbury, CT, 06810. Tel: 203-837-9100. Fax: 203-837-9108. p. 335

Dean, Patricia, Info Coordr, Infrastructure Health & Safety Association Library, 21 Voyager Ct S, Etobicoke, ON, M9W 5M7, CANADA. Tel: 416-679-4065. Fax: 416-674-8866. p. 2804

Dean, Phyllis, Librn, North Central Regional Library, Warden Community, 305 S Main St, Warden, WA, 98857-9680. Tel: 509-349-2226. Fax: 509-349-2226. p. 2549

Dean, Rebecca, Br Mgr, Shreve Memorial Library, Hosston Branch, 15487 US Hwy 71, Hosston, LA, 71043. Tel: 318-287-3265. Fax: 318-287-3265. p. 969

Dean, Sharon, Dr, Dir, Mus & Libr Serv, Ohio Historical Society, 800 E 17th Ave, Columbus, OH, 43211. Tel: 614-297-2510. Fax: 614-297-2546. p. 1887

Dean, Sydne, Assoc Dir, Pub Serv, Pikes Peak Library District, 20 N Cascade Ave, Colorado Springs, CO, 80903. Tel: 719-531-6333. p. 296

Dean, Sydne, Assoc Dir, Pikes Peak Library District, East Library, 5550 N Union Blvd, Colorado Springs, CO, 80918. Tel: 719-531-6333. Fax: 719-528-5289. p. 296

Dean, Sydne, Assoc Dir, Pikes Peak Library District, Penrose Library, 20 N Cascade Ave, Colorado Springs, CO, 80903. Tel: 719-531-6333. p. 296

Dean, Tamara, Dir, Fairhope Public Library, 501 Fairhope Ave, Fairhope, AL, 36532. Tel: 251-928-7483. Fax: 251-928-9717. p. 16

Dean, Tarrah, Ch, Adams Memorial Library, 1112 Ligonier St, Latrobe, PA, 15650. Tel: 724-539-1972. Fax: 724-537-0338. p. 2078

Dean, Theresa, Dir, Eagle Public Library, Second & Amundsen, Eagle, AK, 99738. Tel: 907-547-2334. p. 47

Dean, Toni, Ch, Congregational Church of Patchogue, 95 E Main St, Patchogue, NY, 11772. Tel: 631-475-1235. Fax: 631-207-9470. p. 1715

Dean, Valerie, Br Mgr, Calaveras County Library, Copperopolis Branch, 90 Copper Cove Dr, Unit C, Copperopolis, CA, 95228. Tel: 209-785-0920. p. 227

Deane, Catherine, Dep Dir, Pub Serv, Mount Prospect Public Library, Ten S Emerson St, Mount Prospect, IL, 60056. Tel: 847-253-5675. Fax: 847-253-0642. p. 677

Deane Cummings, Delilah, Librn, London Public Library, W O Carson Branch, 465 Quebec St, London, ON, N5W 3Y4, CANADA. Tel: 519-438-4287. p. 2818

Deane, Debbie, Dir, Mount Jewett Memorial Library, Seven Main St, Mount Jewett, PA, 16740. Tel: 814-778-5588. Fax: 814-778-5588. p. 2093

Deane, Paul, Med Librn, Alexian Brothers Medical Library, 800 Biesterfield Rd, Elk Grove Village, IL, 60007-3397. Tel: 847-437-5500, Ext 4750. Fax: 847-981-5336. p. 641

Deane, Roxanna, Dir, Tye Preston Memorial Library, 16311 S Access Rd, Canyon Lake, TX, 78133-5301. Tel: 830-964-3744. Fax: 830-964-3126. p. 2295

DeAngelo, Elizabeth, Tech Librn, Northern Virginia Community College Libraries, Medical Education Campus, 6699 Springfield Center Dr, Rm 341, Springfield, VA, 22150. Tel: 703-822-6684. Fax: 703-822-6612. p. 2447

DeAngelo, Karen, Dir, Town of Ballston Community Library, Two Lawmar Lane, Burnt Hills, NY, 12027. Tel: 518-399-8174. Fax: 518-399-1687. p. 1600

Deans, Janet, Head, Circ, Canal Fulton Public Library, 154 Market St NE, Canal Fulton, OH, 44614-1196. Tel: 330-854-4148. Fax: 330-854-9520. p. 1863

Dear, Beverly, Dir, Sanilac District Library, 7130 Main St, Port Sanilac, MI, 48469. Tel: 810-622-8623. p. 1220

Dear, Laura, Sr Mgr, Spencer Stuart Library, 401 N Michigan Ave, Ste 2600, Chicago, IL, 60611. Tel: 312-822-0088. Fax: 312-822-0117. p. 625

Dearborn, David Curtis, Ref Librn, New England Historic Genealogical Society Library, 99-101 Newbury St, Boston, MA, 02116-3007. Tel: 617-536-5740. Fax: 617-536-7307. p. 1065

Deardorff, Claudia, Sr Librn, Division of Juvenile Justice of Department of Corrections, 3100 Wright Rd, Camarillo, CA, 93010-8307. Tel: 805-485-7951. Fax: 805-485-2801. p. 131

Deardorff, Julie, Dir, Coll Serv, Cedarville University, 251 N Main St, Cedarville, OH, 45314-0601. Tel: 937-766-7840. Fax: 937-766-2337. p. 1865

Deare, Carolyn, Ref, Wheaton Public Library, 225 N Cross St, Wheaton, IL, 60187-5376. Tel: 630-868-7592. Fax: 630-668-8950. p. 719

Dearie, Tammy, Assoc Univ Librn, Admin Serv, University of California, San Diego, 9500 Gilman Dr, Mail Code 0175G, La Jolla, CA, 92093-0175. Tel: 858-534-3336. Fax: 858-534-4970. p. 162

Dearing, Daniel, Dir, James Boyd Holmes Public Library, 230 Tucker Rd, Helena, AL, 35080-7036. Tel: 205-664-8308. Fax: 205-664-4593. p. 20

Dearing, Diana, Adult Coll Develop Officer, Lee County Library System, 2345 Union St, Fort Myers, FL, 33901-3917. Tel: 239-533-4179. Fax: 239-485-1100. p. 445

Dearing, Diana, Adult Coll Develop Librn, Lee County Library System, Processing Center, 881 Gunnery Rd N, Ste 2, Lehigh Acres, FL, 33971-1246. Tel: 239-461-7382. Fax: 239-461-7373. p. 446

Dearing, Teresa A, Dir, Dansville Public Library, 200 Main St, Dansville, NY, 14437. Tel: 585-335-6720. Fax: 585-335-6133. p. 1613

DeArmey, Jim, Coordr, Info Serv, Baltimore County Public Library, 320 York Rd, Towson, MD, 21204-5179. Tel: 410-887-6124. Fax: 410-887-6103. p. 1044

Dearmond, Nancy, Librn, Bullitt County Public Library, Mount Washington Branch, 311 Snapp St, Mount Washington, KY, 40047-7627. Tel: 502-538-7560. Fax: 502-538-2696. p. 935

Dearth, Betty, Librn, Industrial Technology Centre, 200-78 Innovation Dr, Winnipeg, MB, R3T 6C2, CANADA. Tel: 204-480-0336. Fax: 204-480-0345. p. 2755

Dearth, Kim, Dir, Wonewoc Public Library, 305 Center St, Wonewoc, WI, 53968-9398. Tel: 608-464-7625. p. 2650

Deary, Demetria, Access Serv, Folsom Lake College Library, Ten College Pkwy, Folsom, CA, 95630. Tel: 916-608-6704. Fax: 916-608-6533. p. 148

Dease, Melissa, Adult Serv, Arlington Public Library System, Northeast, 1905 Brown Blvd, Arlington, TX, 76006-4605. Tel: 817-277-5573. Fax: 817-276-8649. p. 2276

Deaton, Becky, Children's Librn, Circ Serv, Haltom City Public Library, 4809 Haltom Rd, Haltom City, TX, 76117-3622. Tel: 817-222-7815. Fax: 817-834-1446. p. 2330

Deaton, Teresa, Ch, Preble County District Library, 450 S Barron St, Eaton, OH, 45320-2402. Tel: 937-456-4331. Fax: 937-456-6092. p. 1897

Deats, John, Dir, Midland College, 3600 N Garfield, Midland, TX, 79705. Tel: 432-685-4726. Fax: 432-685-6710. p. 2363

Deaven, Paul, Admin Serv, Dakota County Library System, 1340 Wescott Rd, Eagan, MN, 55123-1099. Tel: 651-450-2927. Fax: 651-450-2915. p. 1249

Deaver, Brian, Librn, Dechert Law Library, 1095 Ave of the Americas, 30th Fl, New York, NY, 10036. Tel: 212-698-3515. Fax: 212-698-3599. p. 1677

Deaver, Rebecca, Asst Dir, Woburn Public Library, 45 Pleasant St, Woburn, MA, 01801. Tel: 781-933-0148. Fax: 781-938-7860. p. 1142

Deavy, Judy, Mgr, Libr Serv, Canada Department of Justice, 900-840 Howe St, Vancouver, BC, V6Z 2S9, CANADA. Tel: 604-666-0549. Fax: 604-666-3038. p. 2740

DeBalzo Green, Helen, Ref Librn, Lorain County Community College, 1005 Abbe Rd N, North Elyria, OH, 44035-1691. Tel: 440-366-7289. Fax: 440-366-4127. p. 1924

DeBarathy, Nancy, Ch, Butte-Silver Bow Public Library, 226 W Broadway St, Butte, MT, 59701-9297. Tel: 406-723-3361, Ext 12. Fax: 406-782-1825. p. 1376

DeBaun, Laura A, Bus Mgr/Consult, Northeast Kansas Library System, 4317 W Sixth St, Lawrence, KS, 66049. Tel: 785-838-4090. Fax: 785-838-3989. p. 878

DeBeau-Melting, Linda, Assoc Univ Librn, Organizational Develop, University of Minnesota Libraries-Twin Cities, 499 O Meredith Wilson Library, 309 19th Ave S, Minneapolis, MN, 55455-0414. Tel: 612-625-9148. Fax: 612-626-9353. p. 1262

Debeljak, Elizabeth, Doc Delivery, Res Serv, International Development Research Centre Library, 150 Kent St, Ottawa, ON, K1G 3H9, CANADA. Tel: 613-236-6163. Fax: 613-563-3858. p. 2831

DeBell, Carole, Sr Librn, Lincoln Memorial Library, 240 California Dr, Yountville, CA, 94599-1445. Tel: 707-944-4792. p. 285

DeBell, Carole, Sr Librn, Veterans Home of California, 250 California Dr, Yountville, CA, 94599-1446. Tel: 707-944-4600. p. 285

DeBenedet, Dayna, Actg Libr Dir, Chaleur Library Region, 150 St George St, Ste 1, Bathurst, NB, E2Q 1B5, CANADA. Tel: 506-548-0706. Fax: 506-548-0708. p. 2761

DeBenedictis, Kim, Br Mgr, Akron-Summit County Public Library, Firestone Park, 1486 Aster Ave, Akron, OH, 44301-2104. Tel: 330-724-2126. Fax: 330-724-4391. p. 1852

DeBerry, Amber, Commun Relations Mgr, Douglas County Libraries, 100 S Wilcox, Castle Rock, CO, 80104. Tel: 303-688-7641. Fax: 303-688-7655. p. 294

DeBiase, Andrea, Dir, Carrabassett Valley Library, 3209 Carrabassett Dr, Carrabassett, ME, 04947-9724. Tel: 207-235-3535. Fax: 207-237-3536. p. 981

Debicki, Ruth, Librn, Sudbury Rock & Lapidary Society Library, 456 Kaireen St, Sudbury, ON, P3E 5R9, CANADA. Tel: 705-522-5140. Fax: 705-522-5140. p. 2847

Deblois, Marc, Asst Dir of Br, Bibliothèques de Laval, 1535 boul Chomedey, Laval, QC, H7V 3Z4, CANADA. Tel: 450-978-6888, Ext 5649. Fax: 450-978-5833. p. 2886

Deblois, Robert, Circ, Conservatoire de Musique de Quebec Bibliotheque, 270 rue Saint-Amable, Quebec, QC, G1R 5G1, CANADA. Tel: 418-643-2190, Ext 234. Fax: 418-644-9658. p. 2904

Debner, Stephanie, Fac Librn-Cascade Campus, Portland Community College Library, 12000 SW 49th AV, Portland, OR, 97219. Tel: 971-722-5697. Fax: 971-722-8397. p. 2013

Deboard, Larry, In Charge, Spring Creek Correctional Center Library, PO Box 2109, Seward, AK, 99664. Tel: 907-224-8200. Fax: 907-224-8062. p. 53

DeBoer, Kathleen, Pub Serv, Organization for Economic Cooperation & Development, 2001 L St NW, Ste 650, Washington, DC, 20036-4922. Tel: 202-822-3866. Fax: 202-785-0350. p. 412

DeBole, Stacy, YA Serv, Everett Public Libraries, 410 Broadway, Everett, MA, 02149. Tel: 617-394-2300. Fax: 617-389-1230. p. 1087

DeBolt, Dean, Spec Coll & Archives Librn, University of West Florida, 11000 University Pkwy, Pensacola, FL, 32514-5750. Tel: 850-474-2213. Fax: 850-474-3338. p. 482

DeBolt, Judy, Br Mgr, Phoenix Public Library, Juniper Library, 1825 W Union Hills Dr, Phoenix, AZ, 85027. Tel: 602-262- 4636. p. 76

DeBolt, Vicki, Assoc Dir, Mercer County District Library, 303 N Main St, Celina, OH, 45822. Tel: 419-586-4442. Fax: 419-586-3222. p. 1866

DeBona, Anita L, Librn, Northampton County Law Library, 669 Washington St, Easton, PA, 18042-7468. Tel: 610-559-6751. Fax: 610-559-6750. p. 2052

Deboo, Shireen, Website Mgr, South Seattle Community College, 6000 16th Ave SW, Seattle, WA, 98106-1499. Tel: 206-768-6847. Fax: 206-763-5155. p. 2532

Deborah, Musser, Coordr, Tech Serv, Cabell County Public Library, 455 Ninth Street Plaza, Huntington, WV, 25701. Tel: 304-528-5700. Fax: 304-528-5701. p. 2561

Debord, Jon, Doc Delivery, United States Geological Survey Library, 345 Middlefield Rd, Bldg 15 (MS-955), Menlo Park, CA, 94025-3591. Tel: 650-329-5144. Fax: 650-329-5132. p. 185

DeBorde, Damon, Electronic Res, Ref Librn, Jacksonville University, 2800 University Blvd N, Jacksonville, FL, 32211-3394. Tel: 904-256-7269. Fax: 904-256-7259. p. 454

DeBore, Bob, Dir, A Chance to Grow, 1800 Second St NE, Minneapolis, MN, 55418. Tel: 612-789-1236. Fax: 612-706-5555. p. 1259

DeBore, Kathy, Dir, A Chance to Grow, 1800 Second St NE, Minneapolis, MN, 55418. Tel: 612-789-1236. Fax: 612-706-5555. p. 1259

Debose, Janice, Librn, Singing River Hospital System, 2809 Denny Ave, Pascagoula, MS, 39581. Tel: 228-809-5040. Fax: 228-809-5439. p. 1311

DeBoy, Kathleen, Cataloger, Dona Ana Community College Library, 3400 S Espina, Rm 260, Las Cruces, NM, 88003. Tel: 575-527-7555. Fax: 575-527-7636. p. 1558

Debraggio, Anne, Dir, Kirkland Town Library, 55 1/2 College St, Clinton, NY, 13323. Tel: 315-853-2038. Fax: 315-853-1785. p. 1608

Debris, Rosemary, Dir, Florence Community Library, 1000 S Willow St, Florence, AZ, 85232. Tel: 520-868-9471. Fax: 520-868-4651. p. 63

DeBrower, Amy, Asst Dir, Tech Serv, Rivier College, 420 S Main St, Nashua, NH, 03060-5086. Tel: 603-897-8671. Fax: 603-897-8889. p. 1459

deBruijn, Deb, Exec Dir, Canadian Research Knowledge Network, Preston Sq, Tower 2, 200 343 Preston St, Ottawa, ON, K1S IN4, CANADA. Tel: 613-907-7029. Fax: 866-903-9094. p. 2959

DeBruin, Nathaniel, Univ Archivist & Ms Librn, Marshall University Libraries, One John Marshall Dr, Huntington, WV, 25755-2060. Tel: 304-696-3525. Fax: 304-696-5858. p. 2562

DeBruyne, Jennifer, Supvr, Middlesex County Library, Wardsville Branch, 21935 Hagerty Rd, Wardsville, ON, N0L 2N0, CANADA. Tel: 519-693-4208. p. 2845

DeBuhan, Melanie, Prof, College Francois-Xavier-Garneau, 1660 blvd de l'Entente, Quebec, QC, G1S 4S3, CANADA. Tel: 418-688-8310, Ext 3504. Fax: 418-681-9384. p. 2978

Debus, Dave, Educ Dir, Department of Human Services-Youth Corrections, 2844 Downing St, Denver, CO, 80205. Tel: 303-291-8950. Fax: 303-291-8990. p. 301

DeBuse-Potter, Gail, Dir, Museum of the Fur Trade Library, 6321 Hwy 20, Chadron, NE, 69337. Tel: 308-432-3843. Fax: 308-432-5963. p. 1395

Debusk, Lisa, Librn, Charter College Library, 2221 E Northern Lights Blvd, Anchorage, AK, 99508. Tel: 907-277-1000, 907-777-1328. Fax: 907-274-3342. p. 45

Dec, Myra, Head, Info Serv, National Park Service, 415 Washington Ave, Rte 1, Bayfield, WI, 54814. Tel: 715-779-3397, Ext 301. Fax: 715-779-3049. p. 2581

DeCaen, Vincent, Br Head, Toronto Public Library, Burrows Hall, 1081 Progress Ave, Toronto, ON, M1B 5Z6, CANADA. Tel: 416-396-8740. Fax: 416-396-3559. p. 2860

DeCapua, Gene, Librn, State of Ohio Department of Corrections, 5701 Burnette Rd, Leavittsburg, OH, 44430. Tel: 330-898-0820, Ext 5140. Fax: 330-898-2011. p. 1909

DeCardenas, Jorge, Head, Syst Admin, Stow-Munroe Falls Public Library, 3512 Darrow Rd, Stow, OH, 44224. Tel: 330-688-3295. p. 1937

DeCarlo, Mary, Librn, Syracuse University Library, Carnegie Library, Carnegie Bldg, Syracuse, NY, 13244-2010. Tel: 315-443-2092. Fax: 315-443-5549. p. 1754

DeCarolis, Lisa, Circ Coordr, Smith College Libraries, Hillyer Art Library, Brown Fine Arts Ctr, Smith College, Northampton, MA, 01063. Tel: 413-585-2942. Fax: 413-585-6975. p. 1114

DeCesare, Julie, Media Coordr, Boston College Libraries, Thomas P O'Neill Jr Library (Central Library), 140 Commonwealth Ave, Chestnut Hill, MA, 02467. Tel: 617-552-8995. Fax: 617-552-0599. p. 1081

DeCesare, Julie, Res & Ref Serv, Providence College, One Cunningham Sq, Providence, RI, 02918-0001. Tel: 401 865-1252. Fax: 401-865-2823. p. 2173

Dechert, Caroline, Dir, Free Library of New Hope & Solebury, 93 W Ferry St, New Hope, PA, 18938-1332. Tel: 215-862-2330. Fax: 215-862-1071. p. 2096

Dechert, Otnie L, Tech Serv & Circ Supvr, Brown County Library, 515 Pine St, Green Bay, WI, 54301. Tel: 920-448-5831. Fax: 920-448-6254. p. 2595

Dechert-Sage, Rebecca, Chief Librn/CEO, Northperth Public Library, 260 Main St W, Listowel, ON, N4W 1A1, CANADA. Tel: 519-291-4621. Fax: 519-291-2235. p. 2816

Dechow, Doug, Sci Librn, Chapman University, One University Dr, Orange, CA, 92866-1099. Tel: 714-532-7756. Fax: 714-532-7743. p. 200

DeCicco, Darby, Ch, New Brunswick Free Public Library, 60 Livingston Ave, New Brunswick, NJ, 08901-2597. Tel: 732-745-5108, Ext 15. Fax: 732-846-0226. p. 1508

Decker, Amanda, Br Mgr, Franklin Township Free Public Library, Franklin Park Branch, 3391 Rte 27 S, Ste 101, Franklin Park, NJ, 08823. Tel: 732-873-8700, option 5. Fax: 732-297-3391. p. 1529

Decker, Greg, Cat Librn, Georgetown College, 400 E College St, Georgetown, KY, 40324. Tel: 502-863-8409. Fax: 502-868-7740. p. 915

Decker, Hope, Dir, Cohocton Public Library, 15 S Main St, Cohocton, NY, 14826. Tel: 585-384-5170. Fax: 585-384-9044. p. 1608

Decker, Jennifer, Circ/Cat Librn, Thomas-Wilhite Memorial Library, 101 E Thomas, Perkins, OK, 74059. Tel: 405-547-5185. Fax: 405-547-1040. p. 1976

Decker, John W, Archivist, Ref, Stearns History Museum, 235 33rd Ave S, Saint Cloud, MN, 56301-3752. Tel: 320-253-8424. Fax: 320-253-2172. p. 1276

Decker, Judy J, Ch Serv Librn, Quincy Public Library, 526 Jersey St, Quincy, IL, 62301-3996. Tel: 217-223-1309, Ext 219. Fax: 217-222-5672. p. 693

Decker, Lauren, Ch, Kershaw County Library, 1304 Broad St, Camden, SC, 29020-3595. Tel: 803-425-1508. Fax: 803-425-7180. p. 2182

Decker, Marianna, Br Mgr, Cass County Public Library, Pleasant Hill Branch, 1108 N Hwy No 7, Pleasant Hill, MO, 64080. Tel: 816-987-2231. p. 1330

Decker, Mark, Teen Serv, Edwin A Bemis Public Library, 6014 S Datura St, Littleton, CO, 80120-2636. Tel: 303-795-3961. Fax: 303-795-3996. p. 316

Decker, Mary Lou, Tech Serv, Kingston Library, 55 Franklin St, Kingston, NY, 12401. Tel: 845-331-0507. Fax: 845-331-7981. p. 1650

Decker, Melissa, Asst Dir, Grayson County Public Library, 130 E Market St, Leitchfield, KY, 42754-1439. Tel: 270-259-5455. Fax: 270-259-4552. p. 920

Decker, Nelia, Asst Librn, West Tisbury Free Public Library, 1042 State Rd, West Tisbury, MA, 02575. Tel: 508-693-3366. Fax: 508-696-0130. p. 1138

Decker, Sandra, Libr Serv Mgr, Missouri Baptist Medical Center, 3015 N Ballas Rd, Saint Louis, MO, 63131. Tel: 314-996-5531. Fax: 314-996-5031. p. 1356

Decker, Steven D, Dir, Cedar City Public Library in the Park, 303 N 100 East, Cedar City, UT, 84720. Tel: 435-586-6661. Fax: 435-865-7280. p. 2404

Decker, Terri, Cat, Midwestern State University, 3410 Taft Ave, Wichita Falls, TX, 76308-2099. Tel: 940-397-4175. Fax: 940-397-4689. p. 2400

Decker, Vicki, Librn, Collingsworth Public Library, 711 15th St, Wellington, TX, 79095. Tel: 806-447-2116. Fax: 806-447-5240. p. 2399

Deckert, Carol, Head, Adult Serv, Redford Township District Library, 25320 W Six Mile, Redford, MI, 48240. Tel: 313-531-5960. Fax: 313-531-1721. p. 1220

Deckert, Eileen, Tech Serv, Huron Public Library, 521 Dakota Ave S, Huron, SD, 57350. Tel: 605-353-8530. Fax: 605-353-8531. p. 2213

Declay, Reva, Dir, Cibecue Community Library, One Main St, Cibecue, AZ, 85911. Tel: 928-332-2621. Fax: 928-332-2442. p. 60

Declerck, Luc, Assoc Univ Librn, Tech Serv, University of California, San Diego, 9500 Gilman Dr, Mail Code 0175G, La Jolla, CA, 92093-0175. Tel: 858-534-3336. Fax: 858-534-4970. p. 162

DeClerck, Ruth, Asst Librn, Massey & Township Public Library, 185 Grove, Massey, ON, P0P 1P0, CANADA. Tel: 705-865-2641. Fax: 705-865-1781. p. 2820

DeClet, Jaime, Br Mgr, Cleveland Public Library, Jefferson, 850 Jefferson Ave, Cleveland, OH, 44113. Tel: 216-623-7004. Fax: 216-623-7007. p. 1878

Declet, Jaime, Br Mgr, Cleveland Public Library, South, 3096 Scranton Rd, Cleveland, OH, 44113. Tel: 216-623-7060. Fax: 216-623-7063. p. 1878

DeCloux, Becky, Dir, Lena Public Library, 200 E Main St, Lena, WI, 54139. Tel: 920-829-5335. Fax: 920-829-5335. p. 2605

DeClue, Stephanie, Dir, William Jewell College, 500 College Hill, Liberty, MO, 64068-1843. Tel: 816-415-7606. Fax: 816-415-5021. p. 1343

DeClue, Stephanie, Dir, State Fair Community College, 3201 W 16th St, Sedalia, MO, 65301-2199. Tel: 660-530-5842. Fax: 660-530-5820. p. 1365

Decock, Collette, Dir, Mount Angel Public Library, 290 E Charles St, Mount Angel, OR, 97362. Tel: 503-845-6401. Fax: 503-845-6261. p. 2007

DeConinck, Christina, Circ Supvr, Tecumseh District Library, 215 N Ottawa St, Tecumseh, MI, 49286-1564. Tel: 517-423-2238. Fax: 517-423-5519. p. 1230

Decore, Michael, Info, Res & Access Mgr, Alberta Law Libraries, , Law Courts North, 5th Flr, 1A Sir Winston Churchill Sq, Edmonton, AB, T5J 0R2, CANADA. Tel: 780-427-3327. Fax: 780-427-0481. p. 2698

DeCoster, Elizabeth, User Serv Librn, Goucher College Library, 1021 Dulaney Valley Rd, Baltimore, MD, 21204. Tel: 410-337-6361. Fax: 410-337-6419. p. 1014

DeCoster, Ryan, Asst Dir, Learning Support Serv/Ref Librn, Baker College of Muskegon Library, 1903 Marquette Ave, Muskegon, MI, 49442-3404. Tel: 231-777-5330. Fax: 231-777-5334. p. 1212

DeCota, Evelyn F, Dir, Philbrick-James Library, Four Church St, Deerfield, NH, 03037-1426. Tel: 603-463-7187. p. 1444

DeCovich, Cheryl, Tech Coordr, Auburn Hills Public Library, 3400 E Seyburn Dr, Auburn Hills, MI, 48326-2759. Tel: 248-370-9466. Fax: 248-370-9364. p. 1154

DeCramer, Linda, Ch, Ripon Public Library, 120 Jefferson St, Ripon, WI, 54971-1395. Tel: 920-748-6160. Fax: 920-748-6298. p. 2634

DeCristofaro, Kimberly, Dir, Connetquot Public Library, 760 Ocean Ave, Bohemia, NY, 11716. Tel: 631-567-5079. Fax: 631-567-5137. p. 1583

DeCrosby, Joan, In Charge, Alternative Energy Resources Organization Library, 432 N Last Chance Gulch St, Helena, MT, 59601-5014. Tel: 406-443-7272. Fax: 406-442-9120. p. 1381

DeDecker, Sherry, Info Serv, University of California, Santa Barbara, Santa Barbara, CA, 93106-9010. Tel: 805-893-3713. Fax: 805-893-7010. p. 261

Dedon, Diane, Librn, Taylors Falls Public Library, 473 Bench St, Taylors Falls, MN, 55084. Tel: 651-465-6905. p. 1285

Dedrick, Katherine, Librn, Southlake Regional Health Center, 596 Davis Dr, Newmarket, ON, L3Y 2P9, CANADA. Tel: 905-895-4521, Ext 2327. Fax: 905-830-5989. p. 2824

Dedwyler, Jackie, Librn, Northwest Mississippi Community College, 5197 WE Ross Pkwy, Southaven, MS, 38671. Tel: 662-280-6164. Fax: 662-280-6161. p. 1315

Deeb, Mary Jane, Chief, Library of Congress, African & Middle Eastern Division, Jefferson Bldg, Rm 220, 101 Independence Ave SE, Washington, DC, 20540-4820. Tel: 202-707-7937. Fax: 202-252-3180. p. 406

Deeds, Amy, Circ Mgr, Granville Public Library, 217 E Broadway, Granville, OH, 43023-1398. Tel: 740-587-0196. Fax: 740-587-0197. p. 1903

Deeds, Darla, Librn, Bird City Public Library, 110 E Fourth St, Bird City, KS, 67731. Tel: 785-734-2203. p. 858

Deeds, Leland, Librn, Acad Computing Support, Syst Librn, Union Theological Seminary & Presbyterian School of Christian Education, 3401 Brook Rd, Richmond, VA, 23227. Tel: 804-278-4310. Fax: 804-278-4375. p. 2490

Deegan, Denise, Coll Mgr, The Clay Center for the Arts & Sciences of West Virginia, 300 Leon Sullivan Way, Charleston, WV, 25301. Tel: 304-561-3526. p. 2556

Deegan, Nancy, Librn, Central Arizona College, 8470 N Overfield Rd, Coolidge, AZ, 85128. Tel: 520-494-5286. Fax: 520-494-5284. p. 60

Deegan, Rosemary L, Dir, Albright College, 13th & Exeter Sts, Reading, PA, 19604. Tel: 610-921-7202. Fax: 610-921-7509. p. 2132

Deekle, Peter, Dr, Dean, Univ Libr Serv, Roger Williams University Library, One Old Ferry Rd, Bristol, RI, 02809. Tel: 401-254-3063. Fax: 401-254-3631. p. 2164

Deeley, Nina, Tech Serv, Jefferson Community & Technical College, 109 E Broadway, Louisville, KY, 40202. Tel: 502-213-2373. p. 924

Deem, Mary, Asst Dir, Fiscal Officer, Carnegie Public Library, 219 E Fourth St, East Liverpool, OH, 43920-3143. Tel: 330-385-2048, Ext 103. Fax: 330-385-7600. p. 1897

Deemer, Kevin, Dir, Kent State University, 3431 W 13th St, Ashtabula, OH, 44004-2298. Tel: 440-964-4239. Fax: 440-964-4271. p. 1856

Deemer, Pamela, Head, Cat, Emory University School of Law, 1301 Clifton Rd, Atlanta, GA, 30322. Tel: 404-727-0850. Fax: 404-727-2202. p. 514

Deeming, Kathleen, Head, Access Serv, Rosemont College Library, 1400 Montgomery Ave, Rosemont, PA, 19010-1631. Tel: 610-527-0200, Ext 2271. Fax: 610-525-2930. p. 2135

Deen, Rosa, Circ, Satilla Regional Library, 200 S Madison Ave, Ste D, Douglas, GA, 31533. Tel: 912-384-4667. Fax: 912-389-4365. p. 530

Deen, Subiatu, Librn, Montefiore Hospital-North Division, 600 E 233rd St, Rm B-11, Bronx, NY, 10466. Tel: 718-920-9869. Fax: 718-920-9407. p. 1588

Deeney, Susan, Br Mgr, Harford County Public Library, Edgewood Branch, 629 Edgewood Rd, Edgewood, MD, 21040-2607. Tel: 410-612-1600. Fax: 410-612-1602. p. 1020

Deer, Susan E B, Assoc Dir, Tech Serv, New York State Historical Association, 5798 State Hwy 80, Cooperstown, NY, 13326. Tel: 607-547-1470. Fax: 607-547-1405. p. 1610

Deering, Carol, Librn, United States Geological Survey, Mundt Federal Bldg, 47914 252nd St, Sioux Falls, SD, 57198-0001. Tel: 605-594-2611. Fax: 605-594-6589. p. 2219

Deering-Barrett, Debra, Access Serv, ILL, Jacksonville State University Library, 700 Pelham Rd N, Jacksonville, AL, 36265. Tel: 256-782-5255. Fax: 256-782-5872. p. 22

Deerr, Kathleen, Asst Dir, Natl Family Pl Libr, Middle Country Public Library, 101 Eastwood Blvd, Centereach, NY, 11720. Tel: 631-585-9393, Ext 204. Fax: 631-585-5035. p. 1604

Deery, Diane, Head Librn, Fordham University Westchester Library, 400 Westchester Ave, West Harrison, NY, 10604. Tel: 914-367-3058. p. 1766

Dees, Marsha, Br Coordr, Pender County Public Library, 103 S Cowan St, Burgaw, NC, 28425. Tel: 910-259-1234. Fax: 910-259-0656. p. 1778

Dees, Marsha, Br Mgr, Pender County Public Library, Hampstead Branch, 75 Library Dr, Hampstead, NC, 28443. Tel: 910-270-4603. Fax: 910-270-5015. p. 1778

Dees, Sue, Librn, Gallop, Johnson & Neuman LC, 101 S Hanley Rd, Ste 1700, Saint Louis, MO, 63105. Tel: 314-615-6000. Fax: 314-615-6001. p. 1355

Dees, Suzanne, Dir, Upper Peninsula Library for the Blind & Physically Handicapped, 1615 Presque Isle Ave, Marquette, MI, 49855. Tel: 906-228-7697. Fax: 906-228-5627. p. 1207

Dees, Suzanne, Treas, Upper Peninsula Region of Library Cooperation, Inc, 1615 Presque Isle Ave, Marquette, MI, 49855. Tel: 906-228-7697. Fax: 906-228-5627. p. 2946

Deever, Brenda, Adult Serv, Fairport Public Library, One Fairport Village Landing, Fairport, NY, 14450. Tel: 585-223-9091. Fax: 585-223-3998. p. 1621

DeFabrizio, Robert, Mgr, Libr Serv, Goulston & Storrs, PC, 400 Atlantic Ave, Boston, MA, 02110. Tel: 617-482-1776. p. 1061

DeFalco, Michael, Webmaster, Brimfield Public Library, 25 Main St, Brimfield, MA, 01010-9701. Tel: 413-245-3518. Fax: 413-245-3468. p. 1070

Defanti, Diana, Adult Serv, ILL, Allentown Public Library, 1210 Hamilton St, Allentown, PA, 18102. Tel: 610-820-2400. Fax: 610-820-0640. p. 2026

DeFazio, Veronica, Youth Serv Dept Head, Des Plaines Public Library, 1501 Ellinwood St, Des Plaines, IL, 60016-4553. Tel: 847-376-2791. Fax: 847-827-7974. p. 636

DeFeo, Marie, Librn, United Health Services, 33-57 Harrison St, Johnson City, NY, 13790. Tel: 607-763-6030. Fax: 607-763-5992. p. 1647

Deffenbaugh, James T, Br Librn, College of William & Mary in Virginia, Earl Gregg Swem Library, One Landrum Dr, Williamsburg, VA, 23187. Tel: 757-221-3057. Fax: 757-221-2635. p. 2502

Deffendall, Robin, Br Mgr, Cumberland County Public Library & Information Center, Bordeaux, 3711 Village Dr, Fayetteville, NC, 28304-1530. Tel: 910-424-4008. Fax: 910-423-1456. p. 1792

DeFillo, Carlotta, In Charge, Staten Island Historical Society Library, 441 Clarke Ave, Staten Island, NY, 10306. Tel: 718-351-1611, Ext 299. Fax: 718-979-6102. p. 1748

DeFino, Melissa, Spec Coll & Digital Projects Metadata Librn, Rutgers University Libraries, Special Collections & University Archives, 169 College Ave, New Brunswick, NJ, 08901-1163. Tel: 848-445-5881. Fax: 732-445-5888. p. 1509

DeFino, Pamela, Br Mgr, Cuyahoga County Public Library, Berea Branch, Seven Berea Commons, Berea, OH, 44017-2524. Tel: 440-234-5475. Fax: 440-234-2932. p. 1927

DeFoe, Richard, Dir of Libr Serv, Nunez Community College Library, 3710 Paris Rd, Chalmette, LA, 70043. Tel: 504-278-6230, 504-278-7498. Fax: 504-680-2584. p. 947

DeForest, Tim, Circ, Ringling College of Art & Design, 2700 N Tamiami Trail, Sarasota, FL, 34234. Tel: 941-359-7587. Fax: 941-359-7632. p. 490

DeForest, Wendy, Asst Dir, Huntington Public Library, 2156 Main Rd, Huntington, VT, 05462. Tel: 802-434-4583. p. 2426

DeFors, Douglas, Coll Mgr, Marin History Museum Library, 1125 B St, San Rafael, CA, 94901. Tel: 415-454-8538. Fax: 415-454-6137. p. 257

DeFosse, Molly, Fiscal Officer, Public Library of Cincinnati & Hamilton County, 800 Vine St, Cincinnati, OH, 45202-2009. Tel: 513-369-6967. Fax: 513-369-6993. p. 1871

DeFosse, Shirley, Dir, Central Village Public Library, 51 Black Hill Rd, Central Village, CT, 06332. Tel: 860-564-7753. Fax: 860-564-2738. p. 333

DeFranco, Francine, Dir, Coll Serv, University of Connecticut Library, 369 Fairfield Rd, Storrs, CT, 06269-1005. Tel: 860-486-2219. Fax: 860-486-0584. p. 370

DeFrank, Audrey, Actg Dean, Libr Serv, University of Nebraska at Omaha, 6001 Dodge St, Omaha, NE, 68182-0237. Tel: 402-554-3200. Fax: 402-554-3215. p. 1414

DeFranza, Regan, Health Sci Librn, Clarkson University Library, Health Sciences Library, Clarkson Hall - 2nd Flr, CU Box 5880, Eight Clarkson Ave, Potsdam, NY, 13699-5880. Tel: 315-268-3760. Fax: 315-268-7655. p. 1722

DeFriese, Greg, Head of Libr, Chattanooga-Hamilton County Bicentennial Library, South Chattanooga, 925 W 39th St, Chattanooga, TN, 37410. Tel: 423-757-5310. Fax: 423-825-7239. p. 2227

deFuria, Anne, Head, Ref, Berkeley Heights Public Library, 290 Plainfield Ave, Berkeley Heights, NJ, 07922. Tel: 908-464-9333. Fax: 908-464-7098. p. 1472

DeGarmo, Todd, Spec Coll & Archives Librn, Crandall Public Library, 251 Glen St, Glens Falls, NY, 12801-3593. Tel: 518-792-6508. Fax: 518-792-5251. p. 1629

DeGeer, Beth, Asst Dir, Bartlesville Public Library, 600 S Johnstone, Bartlesville, OK, 74003. Tel: 918-338-4164. Fax: 918-337-5338. p. 1957

Degenhardt, Christina, Dean, Everest University, 1199 E Bay Dr, Largo, FL, 33770. Tel: 727-725-2688. Fax: 727-796-3722. p. 460

Degenhardt, Sarah, Librn, Lakeland Library Region, Goodsoil Branch, 301 Main St N, Goodsoil, SK, S0M 1A0, CANADA. Tel: 306-238-2155. Fax: 306-238-2155. p. 2920

DeGennaro, June, Coll Mgt, Quinnipiac University, 275 Mount Carmel Ave, Hamden, CT, 06518. Tel: 203-582-8944. Fax: 203-582-3451. p. 343

DeGeorge, Beth, Librn, Union League of Philadelphia Library, 140 S Broad St, Philadelphia, PA, 19102. Tel: 215-587-5594. Fax: 215-587-5598. p. 2118

Deger, Beth, Dir of Libr Serv, Clark State Community College Library, 570 E Leffel Lane, Springfield, OH, 45505. Tel: 937-328-6023. Fax: 937-328-6133. p. 1935

DeGeus, Marilyn J, Dir, Kansas City University of Medicine & Biosciences D'Angelo Library, 1750 Independence Ave, Kansas City, MO, 64106-1453. Tel: 816-654-7260. Fax: 816-654-7261. p. 1338

DeGhelder, Tim, Br Mgr, Saint Charles City County Library District, Deer Run Branch, 1300 N Main, O'Fallon, MO, 63366-2013. Tel: 636-978-3251, 636-980-1332. Fax: 636-978-3209. p. 1364

DeGiacomo, Lynne, Exec Adminir, Cohasset Historical Society Library, 106 S Main St, Cohasset, MA, 02025. Tel: 781-383-1434. Fax: 781-383-1190. p. 1082

DeGlopper-Banks, Kristine, Dir, Newfane Free Library, 2761 Maple Ave, Newfane, NY, 14108. Tel: 716-778-9344. Fax: 716-778-9344. p. 1705

Degnan, Kathleen, Ref Librn, Chicago State University, 9501 S Martin Luther King Jr Dr, LIB 440, Chicago, IL, 60628-1598. Tel: 773-995-2980. Fax: 773-995-3772. p. 610

DeGraff, Laura, Dir, DDB Chicago, 200 E Randolph, Chicago, IL, 60601. Tel: 312-552-6000, Ext 6934. Fax: 312-552-2379. p. 612

Degrasse, Suzanne, Br Mgr, Athens Regional Library System, Madison County, 1315 Hwy 98 W, Danielsville, GA, 30633. Tel: 706-795-5597. Fax: 706-795-0830. p. 509

DeGrassi, D, Ch, Bellmore Memorial Library, 2288 Bedford Ave, Bellmore, NY, 11710. Tel: 516-785-2990. Fax: 516-783-8550. p. 1580

Degrees, Jackelyn, Dir, Burnet, Duckworth & Palmer, LLP, 2400, 525-Eighth Ave SW, Calgary, AB, T2P 1G1, CANADA. Tel: 403-260-0100. Fax: 403-260-0332. p. 2688

DeGreve, Luann, Assoc Univ Librn, Benedictine University Library, 5700 College Rd, Lisle, IL, 60532-0900. Tel: 630-829-6197. Fax: 630-960-9451. p. 666

DeGroat, Jennifer, Head Librn, Capital Area District Libraries, Aurelius Library, 1939 S Aurelius Rd, Mason, MI, 48854-9763. Tel: 517-628-3743. Fax: 517-628-2141. p. 1200

Degroat, Karen, ILL, United States Army, Brooke Army Medical Center Library, Medical Library MCHE-EDL, 3551 Roger Brooke Dr, Bldg 3600, Rm 371-17, Fort Sam Houston, TX, 78234-6200. Tel: 210-916-1119. Fax: 210-916-5709. p. 2320

DeGroff, Erin, Ser, University of Rochester, River Campus Libraries, 755 Library Rd, Rochester, NY, 14627-0055. Tel: 585-275-4461. Fax: 585-273-5309. p. 1733

DeGroot, Joanne, Librn, Carmangay Municipal Library, 416 Grand Ave, Carmangay, AB, T0L 0N0, CANADA. Tel: 403-643-3777. Fax: 403-643-3777. p. 2694

DeGuzman, Thomas, Ref, Santa Clara University, Heafey Law Library, School of Law, 500 El Camino Real, Santa Clara, CA, 95053-0430. Tel: 408-554-5327. Fax: 408-554-5318. p. 263

Degyansky, Kathleen, Asst Dir, White Plains Public Library, 100 Martine Ave, White Plains, NY, 10601-2599. Tel: 914-422-1400. Fax: 914-422-1462. p. 1769

DeHaai, Peter, Webmaster, Cedar Grove Public Library, 131 Van Altena Ave, Cedar Grove, WI, 53013. Tel: 920-668-6834. Fax: 920-668-8744. p. 2585

DeHaan, Eric, Br Mgr, Kent District Library, Tyrone Township Branch, 43 S Main St, Kent City, MI, 49330. Tel: 616-784-2007. Fax: 616-647-3904. p. 1166

DeHaan, Lori, Librn, Oakfield Public Library, 130 N Main St, Oakfield, WI, 53065-9563. Tel: 920-583-4552. Fax: 920-583-2544. p. 2626

DeHart, Brian, Instrul Serv Librn, Ref Serv, DePaul University Libraries, Loop, One E Jackson Blvd, 10th Flr, Chicago, IL, 60604. Tel: 312-362-5403. Fax: 312-362-6186. p. 612

DeHart, Liz, Head Librn, University of Texas Libraries, Marine Science, Marine Science Institute, 750 Channelview Dr, Port Aransas, TX, 78373-5015. Tel: 361-749-6723, 361-749-6778. Fax: 361-749-6725. p. 2284

Dehler, Frank, Circ, York Public Library, 15 Long Sands Rd, York, ME, 03909. Tel: 207-363-2818. Fax: 207-363-7250. p. 1008

Dehnel, Sharon, Cat Librn, Syst, Dallas Baptist University, 3000 Mountain Creek Pkwy, Dallas, TX, 75211-9299. Tel: 214-333-5392. Fax: 214-333-5323. p. 2305

Dehoff, Christine, Chair, Erie Community College-City Campus, 121 Ellicott St, Buffalo, NY, 14203. Tel: 716-851-1076. Fax: 716-270-5987. p. 1598

DeHoll, Cheryl, Tech Serv, Anderson University Library, 316 Boulevard, Anderson, SC, 29621. Tel: 864-231-2050. Fax: 864-231-2191. p. 2181

DeHudy, Darlene, Ref Librn, Muskegon Community College, 221 S Quarterline Rd, Muskegon, MI, 49442. Tel: 231-777-0268. Fax: 231-777-0279. p. 1213

Deibel, Marcia, Librn, Torbay Public Library, 1288A Torbay Rd, Torbay, NL, A1K 1B2, CANADA. Tel: 709-437-6571. Fax: 709-437-6571. p. 2773

Deich, Ione, Dir, Hutchinson Memorial Library, 228 N High St, Randolph, WI, 53956. Tel: 920-326-4640. Fax: 920-326-4642. p. 2632

Deichert, Diana D, Librn, Westchester County Historical Society Library, 2199 Saw Mill River Rd, Elmsford, NY, 10523. Tel: 914-592-4323. Fax: 914-592-4338. p. 1620

Deighan, Jane, Assoc Dir, Budget & Planning, Embry-Riddle Aeronautical University, 600 S Clyde Morris Blvd, Daytona Beach, FL, 32114-3900. Tel: 386-226-6589. Fax: 386-226-6368. p. 436

Deighton, Anne, Univ Librn, Lakehead University Library, 955 Oliver Rd, Thunder Bay, ON, P7B 5E1, CANADA. Tel: 807-343-8205. Fax: 807-343-8007. p. 2848

Deighton, Anne, Univ Librn, Lakehead University Library, Education Library, Lakehead University, Bora Laskin Bldg, Thunder Bay, ON, P7B 5E1, CANADA. Tel: 807-343-8205. Fax: 807-346-7996. p. 2848

Deike, Hilary, Head, Libr Human Res, Iowa State University Library, 302 Parks Library, Ames, IA, 50011-2140. Tel: 515-294-1442, 515-294-1443. Fax: 515-294-5525. p. 793

Deinken, Jill, Ch, Redwood Falls Public Library, 509 S Lincoln St, Redwood Falls, MN, 56283. Tel: 507-627-8650. Fax: 507-627-5004. p. 1272

Deis, Louise, Sci & Tech Ref Librn, Princeton University, Biology, Fine Hall Library, McDonnell Hall, One Washington Ave, Princeton, NJ, 08544. Tel: 609-258-3235. Fax: 609-258-2627. p. 1523

Deis, Louise Frey, Sci & Tech Ref Librn, Princeton University, Geosciences & Maps, Fine Hall Wing, B-Level, Peter B Lewis Library, Princeton, NJ, 08544. Tel: 609-258-3235. Fax: 609-258-4607. p. 1523

Deissler, Christa Harrelson, PhD, Sch Libr Emphasis Area Coordr, University of Georgia, College of Education, 224 River's Crossing, Athens, GA, 30602-7144. Tel: 706-542-4110. Fax: 706-542-4032. p. 2964

Deister, Robin, Ch, Lake County Public Library, 1115 Harrison Ave, Leadville, CO, 80461-3398. Tel: 719-486-0569. Fax: 719-486-3544. p. 316

Deitch, Linda, Archive & Coll Mgr, Columbus Dispatch Editorial Library, 34 S Third St, Columbus, OH, 43215. Tel: 614-461-5177. Fax: 614-469-6165. p. 1884

Deiters, Jim, Dir, Blue Island Public Library, 2433 York St, Blue Island, IL, 60406-2011. Tel: 708-388-1078, Ext 14. Fax: 708-388-1143. p. 596

Deiters, Jim, Dir, Oak Lawn Public Library, 9427 S Raymond Ave, Oak Lawn, IL, 60453-2434. Tel: 708-422-4990. Fax: 708-422-5061. p. 683

Deitrick, Bernard E, Librn, Neshaminy-Warwick Presbyterian Church Library, 1401 Meetinghouse Rd, Warminster, PA, 18974. Tel: 215-343-6060. p. 2150

Deitrick, Pam, Br Mgr, Des Moines Public Library, Franklin Avenue, 5000 Franklin Ave, Des Moines, IA, 50310. Tel: 515-283-4152. Fax: 515-271-8734. p. 808

Deitzer, Margaret, Adult Serv, Ref, Peters Township Public Library, 616 E McMurray Rd, McMurray, PA, 15317-3495. Tel: 724-941-9430. Fax: 724-941-9438. p. 2086

DeJarnette, Franklin, Libr Tech, Department of Veterans Affairs, 1100 Tunnel Rd, Asheville, NC, 28805. Tel: 828-299-2525. Fax: 828-299-2500. p. 1774

DeJarnette, Steve, Br Mgr, Dougherty County Public Library, Tallulah Massey Branch, 2004 Stratford Dr, Albany, GA, 31705. Tel: 229-420-3250. p. 507

DeJeagher, Emily, Circ, Howell Carnegie District Library, 314 W Grand River Ave, Howell, MI, 48843. Tel: 517-546-0720. Fax: 517-546-1494. p. 1192

DeJoice, Mary Jo, Head, Liaison & Outreach Serv, Georgia State University Library, 100 Decatur St SE, Atlanta, GA, 30303-3202. Tel: 404-413-2853. Fax: 404-413-2701. p. 516

Dejoie, Kathy, Dir, Florida Department of Education, 325 W Gaines St, Tallahassee, FL, 32399-0400. Tel: 850-245-0983. Fax: 850-245-0987. p. 493

DeJong, Kelly, Br Support, Stormont, Dundas & Glengarry County Library, Chesterville Branch, One Mill St, Chesterville, ON, K0C 1H0, CANADA. Tel: 613-448-2616. p. 2801

DeJonker-Berry, Debra, Dir, Provincetown Public Library, 356 Commercial St, Provincetown, MA, 02657-2209. Tel: 508-487-7094. p. 1119

Deken, Jean Marie, Mgr, Stanford University Libraries, Stanford Linear Accelerator Center Research Library, 2575 Sand Hill Rd, MS82, Menlo Park, CA, 94025. Tel: 650-926-2411. Fax: 650-926-4905. p. 271

DeKezel, Dianne, Librn, Valley Regional Library, 141 Main St S, South Morris, MB, R0G 1K0, CANADA. Tel: 204-746-2136. Fax: 204-746-6953. p. 2752

Dekker, Lisa, Br Mgr, Louisville Free Public Library, Fern Creek, 6768 Bardstown Rd, Louisville, KY, 40291. Tel: 502-231-4605. Fax: 502-239-3336. p. 924

Dekle, DeAnne, Ch, Roswell Public Library, 301 N Pennsylvania Ave, Roswell, NM, 88201. Tel: 575-622-7101. Fax: 575-622-7107. p. 1561

DeKock, Alisun, Mgr, Libr Serv, John G Shedd Aquarium Library, 1200 S Lake Shore Dr, Chicago, IL, 60605. Tel: 312-692-3217. Fax: 312-939-3430. p. 624

DeKorver, Michelle, Asst Librn, Highland City Library, 5400 W Civic Center Dr, Ste 2, Highland, UT, 84003. Tel: 801-772-4528. Fax: 801-756-6903. p. 2406

DeKoven, Michael, Support Serv Mgr, North Vancouver District Public Library, 1277 Lynn Valley Rd, North Vancouver, BC, V7J 2A1, CANADA. Tel: 604-990-5800. Fax: 604-984-7600. p. 2734

Dekovich, Margaret, Br Mgr, Clinton-Macomb Public Library, South, 35891 S Gratiot Ave, Clinton Township, MI, 48035. Tel: 586-226-5071. Fax: 586-226-5078. p. 1164

Del Biondo, Sherri, Librn, Pennsylvania Public Utility Commission Library, Commonwealth Keystone Bldg, 400 North St, Harrisburg, PA, 17120-0079. Tel: 717-783-1740. Fax: 717-783-3458. p. 2066

Del Conte, Tamara, Br Mgr, Monterey County Free Libraries, Prunedale, 17822 Moro Rd, Salinas, CA, 93907. Tel: 831-663-2292. Fax: 831-663-0203. p. 183

Del Duca, Tracey, Librn, Interchurch Center, 475 Riverside Dr, Rm 900, New York, NY, 10115. Tel: 212-870-3804. Fax: 212-870-2440. p. 1682

Del Rosso, Maria, Dir, Fauquier County Public Library, 11 Winchester St, Warrenton, VA, 20186-2825. Tel: 540-347-8750, Ext 5327. Fax: 540-349-3278. p. 2500

del Val, Jackie, Learning Res Coordr, Hillsborough Community College, Collaboration Studio, Rm 139, 1602 N 15th St, Tampa, FL, 33605. Tel: 813-259-6059. Fax: 813-253-7510. p. 496

Del Valle, Pilar Ortiz, ILL, Inter-American University of Puerto Rico, Information Access Center, Carr PR 1, Esq Calle Francisco Sein, Hato Rey, PR, 00919. Tel: 787-250-1912, Ext 2160, 787-250-1912, Ext 2514. Fax: 787-751-3915. p. 2673

Del Vecchio, Kelly, Librn, Sandusky Bay Law Library Association, Inc, 247 Columbus Ave, Sandusky, OH, 44870. Tel: 419-626-4823. Fax: 419-626-4826. p. 1934

Del Vecchio, Nancy, Coll Develop, Sacred Heart University, 5151 Park Ave, Fairfield, CT, 06825-1000. Tel: 203-371-7701. Fax: 203-374-9968. p. 339

Del Vecchio, Rosemary A, Librn, New York State Office of the State Comptroller Library, 110 State St, 14th Flr, 14EB02, Albany, NY, 12236. Tel: 518-473-5960. Fax: 518-473-1900. p. 1570

Delachevrotiere, Francois, Dir, Bibliotheque Cegep et Universite du Quebec en Abitibi-Temiscamingue, 425 Blvd du College, BP 8000, Rouyn-Noranda, QC, J9X 5M5, CANADA. Tel: 819-762-0931, Ext 1112. Fax: 819-762-2071. p. 2908

Delalis, George, Admin Librn, Chandler Public Library, Basha, 5990 S Val Vista Dr, Chandler, AZ, 85249. Tel: 480-782-2856. Fax: 480-782-2855. p. 59

DeLamatre, Jodie, Ref Serv, Ad, Hudson Library & Historical Society, 96 Library St, Hudson, OH, 44236-5122. Tel: 330-653-6658. Fax: 330-650-3373. p. 1905

Delancey, Materne, In Charge, Washington Art Association Library, Four Bryan Plaza, Washington Depot, CT, 06794. Tel: 860-868-2878. p. 374

DeLand, Rob, Dir, Vandercook College of Music, 3140 S Federal St, Chicago, IL, 60616-3731. Tel: 312-225-6288, Ext 301. Fax: 312-225-5211. p. 627

Delaney, Jody, Dir, Dolores Tillinghast Memorial Library, 234 N Fourth St, Harpers Ferry, IA, 52146. Tel: 563-586-2524. Fax: 563-586-2524. p. 820

Delaney, Kevin, Outreach Serv Librn, Orange County Public Library, 137 W Margaret Lane, Hillsborough, NC, 27278. Tel: 919-245-2525. Fax: 919-644-3003. p. 1802

Delaney, Kristine, Libr Mgr, Crouse Hospital Library, 736 Irving Ave, Syracuse, NY, 13210. Tel: 315-470-7380. Fax: 315-470-7443. p. 1751

Delaney, Lori, Head Librn, Carolina Population Center Library, University of North Carolina at Chapel Hill, 302 University Sq E, 123 W Franklin St, Chapel Hill, NC, 27516-2524. Tel: 919-962-3081. Fax: 919-962-7217. p. 1780

Delaney, Margaret, Asst Dir, Ref & Adult Serv, Burlington County Library, Five Pioneer Blvd, Westampton, NJ, 08060. Tel: 609-267-9660, Ext 3074. Fax: 609-267-4091. p. 1542

Delaney, Meg, Humanities Mgr, Toledo-Lucas County Public Library, 325 N Michigan St, Toledo, OH, 43604-6614. Tel: 419-259-5218. Fax: 419-259-5243. p. 1939

Delaney, Paige, Dir, Alpine Public Library, 203 N Seventh St, Alpine, TX, 79830. Tel: 432-837-2621. Fax: 432-837-2501. p. 2273

Delaney, Terry, Asst Librn, Syst, White River Public Library, 123 Superior St, White River, ON, P0M 3G0, CANADA. Tel: 807-822-1113. Fax: 807-822-1113. p. 2871

Delaney-Lehman, Maureen, Cat Librn, Lake Superior State University, 906 Ryan Ave, Sault Sainte Marie, MI, 49783. Tel: 906-635-2815. Fax: 906-635-2193. p. 1226

DeLang, Val, Educ Dir, Monterey Museum of Art Library, 559 Pacific St, Monterey, CA, 93940. Tel: 831-372-5477, Ext 24. Fax: 831-372-5680. p. 190

Delano, Daisy, Ch, Taunton Public Library, 12 Pleasant St, Taunton, MA, 02780. Tel: 508-821-1410. Fax: 508-821-1414. p. 1131

DeLano, Fred, Pres, Riley County Kansas Genealogical Society Library, 2005 Claflin, Manhattan, KS, 66502-3415. Tel: 785-565-6495. p. 882

Delapass, Pat, Supvr, Ser, Laredo Community College, West End Washington St, Laredo, TX, 78040. Tel: 956-721-5276. Fax: 956-721-5447. p. 2353

Delaski, Sandra, Libr Tech, Sierra Nevada College, 999 Tahoe Blvd, Incline Village, NV, 89450-9500. Tel: 775-831-1314, Ext 7501, 775-881-7501. Fax: 775-832-6134. p. 1428

DeLaughter, Maureen, YA Serv, The William K Sanford Town Library, 629 Albany Shaker Rd, Loudonville, NY, 12211-1196. Tel: 518-458-9274. Fax: 518-438-0988. p. 1655

Delaunay, Charlene, Librn, Wyoming Department of Corrections, 40 Honor Farm Rd, Riverton, WY, 82501-8400. Tel: 307-856-9578. Fax: 307-856-2505. p. 2659

Delauw, Diane, Librn, Crowsnest Pass Municipal Library, PO Box 1177, Blairmore, AB, T0K 0E0, CANADA. Tel: 403-562-8393. Fax: 403-562-8397. p. 2685

Delbango, Richard, Media Spec, Nassau Community College, One Education Dr, Garden City, NY, 11530-6793. Tel: 516-572-7400. Fax: 516-572-7846. p. 1626

Delcurla, Shay, Chair, Brookdale Community College, 765 Newman Springs Rd, Lincroft, NJ, 07738-1597. Tel: 732-224-2438. Fax: 732-224-2982. p. 1495

Delcuze, Elaine K, Ref Serv, Mountain Regional Library System, 698 Miller St, Young Harris, GA, 30582. Tel: 706-379-3732. Fax: 706-379-2047. p. 558

DelDuca, Barbara, Adult Serv, ILL, Medford Public Library, 111 High St, Medford, MA, 02155. Tel: 781-395-7950. Fax: 781-391-2261. p. 1104

Deleget, Patrice, Sr Librn, Torrance Public Library, Southeast, 23115 S Arlington Ave, Torrance, CA, 90501-5816. Tel: 310-530-5044. Fax: 310-530-5181. p. 276

Delene, Elizabeth, Archivist, Bishop Baraga Association Archives, 347 Rock St, Marquette, MI, 49855. Tel: 906-227-9117. Fax: 906-228-2469. p. 1206

DeLeon, Daphne, Adminr, Nevada State Library & Archives, 100 N Stewart St, Carson City, NV, 89701-4285. Tel: 775-684-3315. Fax: 775-684-3330. p. 1426

Deleon, Daphne, Adminr, Nevada State Library & Archives, Archives & Records, 100 N Stewart St, Carson City, NV, 89701-4285. Tel: 775-684-3313. Fax: 775-684-3311. p. 1426

DeLeon, Elizabeth, AV, Librn, Team Leader, Texas Department of State Health Services, 1100 W 49th St, Austin, TX, 78756-3199. Tel: 512-776-2787. Fax: 512-776-7474 (AV Library), 512-776-7683. p. 2282

DeLeon, Maricela, Asst Dir, Wauseon Public Library, 117 E Elm St, Wauseon, OH, 43567. Tel: 419-335-6626. Fax: 419-335-0642. p. 1945

DeLeon, Mary, Circ, Hurst Public Library, 901 Precinct Line Rd, Hurst, TX, 76053. Tel: 817-788-7300. Fax: 817-590-9515. p. 2345

Delevan, Kelly, Instrul Serv/CORE Librn, Le Moyne College, 1419 Salt Springs Rd, Syracuse, NY, 13214-1301. Tel: 315-445-4154. Fax: 315-445-4642. p. 1751

DeLeve, Scott, Pub Serv, University of Mississippi, Three Grove Loop, University, MS, 38677. Tel: 662-915-6834. Fax: 662-915-7731. p. 1316

Delfield, Jeffrey, County Librn, Marianna Black Library, 33 Fryemont St, Bryson City, NC, 28713. Tel: 828-488-3030. Fax: 828-488-9857. p. 1778

Delfon, Cheryl, Co-Chair, Irvine Valley College Library, 5500 Irvine Center Dr, Irvine, CA, 92618-4399. Tel: 949-451-5261. Fax: 949-451-5796. p. 160

Delfs, Shirley, Librn, Garwin Public Library, 208 Main St, Garwin, IA, 50632. Tel: 641-499-2024. Fax: 641-499-2024. p. 817

Delgadillo, Rachel, Sr Libr Supvr, Roseville Public Library, 225 Taylor St, Roseville, CA, 95678-2681. Tel: 916-774-5221. Fax: 916-773-5594. p. 220

Delgadillo-Romo, Isabel, Br Mgr, San Francisco Public Library, Mission Branch Library, 300 Bartlett St, San Francisco, CA, 94110. Tel: 415-355-2800. Fax: 415-648-6566. p. 246

Delgado, Anna L, Ser, St Philip's College, 1801 Martin Luther King Dr, San Antonio, TX, 78203-2098. Tel: 210-486-2330. Fax: 210-486-2335. p. 2381

Delgado, Beatriz, Librn, Clint ISD Public Library, 12625 Alameda Ave, Clint, TX, 79836. Tel: 915-926-8017. Fax: 915-851-3895. p. 2298

Delgado, Betty, Asst Librn, Buffalo Center Public Library, 221 N Main St, Buffalo Center, IA, 50424. Tel: 641-562-2546. Fax: 641-562-2546. p. 797

Delgado, Diana, Assoc Dir, User Support Res & Edu, Cornell University Library, The Samuel J Wood Library & The C V Starr Biomedical Information Center, 1300 York Ave, C115, Box 67, New York, NY, 10065-4896. Tel: 212-746-6050. Fax: 212-746-6494. p. 1642

Delgado, Jessica M, Syst Librn, Ochsner Clinic Foundation, 1st Flr Hospital, 1514 Jefferson Hwy, New Orleans, LA, 70121-2429. Tel: 504-842-3760. Fax: 504-842-5339. p. 962

Delgado, Martin, Commun Libr Mgr, County of Los Angeles Public Library, Huntington Park Library, 6518 Miles Ave, Huntington Park, CA, 90255-4388. Tel: 323-583-1461. Fax: 323-587-2061. p. 142

Delgado, Michelle, Ch, Brazoria County Library System, Lake Jackson Branch, 250 Circle Way, Lake Jackson, TX, 77566. Tel: 979-415-2590. Fax: 979-415-2993. p. 2275

Delgado, Rita, Ch, David M Hunt Library, 63 Main St, Falls Village, CT, 06031. Tel: 860-824-7424. p. 339

Delgado, Ronnie, Mgr, San Antonio Public Library, Carver, 3350 E Commerce, San Antonio, TX, 78220. Tel: 210-225-7801. Fax: 210-472-3480. p. 2382

Delgado, William, Asst Librn, Hispanic Society of America Library, 613 W 155th St, New York, NY, 10032. Tel: 212-926-2234, Ext 260. Fax: 212-690-0743. p. 1681

Delgatty, Janet, Libr Mgr, Vancouver Island Regional Library, Woss Branch, PO Box 5280, Woss, BC, V0N 3P0, CANADA. Tel: 250-281-2263. Fax: 250-281-2273. p. 2733

Delia, Ann, In Charge, PKF Library, 29 Broadway, 4th Flr, New York, NY, 10006. Tel: 212-867-8000, Ext 437. Fax: 212-687-4346. p. 1697

Delimont, Barbara, Ser, Battelle Energy Alliance, LLC, 1776 Science Center Dr, MS 2300, Idaho Falls, ID, 83415-2300. Tel: 208-526-1185. Fax: 208-526-0211. p. 576

Delimont, Esther, Librn, Lebanon-Community Library, 404 N Main St, Lebanon, KS, 66952-9721. Tel: 785-389-5711. Fax: 785-389-5711. p. 879

DeLisa, Karen, Ch, Riverhead Free Library, 330 Court St, Riverhead, NY, 11901-2885. Tel: 631-727-3228. Fax: 631-727-4762. p. 1728

Deliso, Katherine, ILL Librn, Ref Serv, American International College, 1000 State St, Springfield, MA, 01109. Tel: 413-205-3225. Fax: 413-205-3904. p. 1126

Delivuk, John, Syst Librn, Geneva College, 3200 College Ave, Beaver Falls, PA, 15010-3599. Tel: 724-847-6563. Fax: 724-847-6687. p. 2031

DeLizio, Carissa, Col Librn, Franklin Pierce University Library, 40 University Dr, Rindge, NH, 03461-3114. Tel: 603-899-4140. Fax: 603-899-4375. p. 1463

Delker, Kathy, Asst Libr Dir, Instruction Coordr, Ref Librn, Friends University, 2100 W University St, Wichita, KS, 67213-3397. Tel: 316-295-5808. Fax: 316-295-5080. p. 900

Dell, Esther, ILL, Ref Serv, Pennsylvania State University, College of Medicine, Penn State Hershey, Harrell Health Sciences Library, 500 University Dr, Hershey, PA, 17033. Tel: 717-531-8626. Fax: 717-531-8635. p. 2069

Dell, Marin, Ref, Florida State University Libraries, College of Law Library, 425 W Jefferson St, Tallahassee, FL, 32306. Tel: 850-644-4578. Fax: 850-644-5216. p. 494

Dell'Olio, Vesna, Bibliothecaire Responsable, Bibliothèques de Montrèal, Plateau-Mont-Royal, 465, avenue du Mont-Royal Est, Montreal, QC, H2J 1W3, CANADA. Tel: 514-872-0725. Fax: 514-872-0532. p. 2891

Della Barba, Maureen, Libr Tech, Maryland State Law Library, Courts of Appeal Bldg, 361 Rowe Blvd, Annapolis, MD, 21401-1697. Tel: 410-260-1430. Fax: 410-260-1572, 410-974-2063. p. 1010

Della Marna, Jodi, Archives, Cat, Per, Orange Coast College Library, 2701 Fairview Rd, Costa Mesa, CA, 92628. Tel: 714-432-5885. Fax: 714-432-6850. p. 137

Della Sala, Carolyn, Supvr, Somerset County Library System, Branchburg Reading Station, The Station House, Olive St, Neshanic Station, NJ, 08853. Tel: 908-369-5355. p. 1475

Della Valle, Madelyn, Asst Curator, Windsor Community Museum, 254 Pitt St W, Windsor, ON, N9A 5L5, CANADA. Tel: 519-253-1812. Fax: 519-253-0919. p. 2871

DellaCava, Brenda, Libr Asst, Cummings & Lockwood, Six Landmark Sq, Stamford, CT, 06901. Tel: 203-351-4375. Fax: 203-708-3847. p. 369

Dellapenna, Nancy, Asst Dir, West Springfield Public Library, 200 Park St, West Springfield, MA, 01089. Tel: 413-736-4561. Fax: 413-736-6469. p. 1137

Dellate, Cara, Asst Archivist, Res, Staten Island Institute of Arts & Sciences, Snug Harbor Cultural Center, 1000 Richmond Terrace, Bldg H, Staten Island, NY, 10301. Tel: 718-727-1135. Fax: 718-273-5683. p. 1748

Dellatori, Randie, Dir, Putnam County Public Library District, 214 N Fourth St, Hennepin, IL, 61327. Tel: 815-925-7020. Fax: 815-925-7020. p. 654

DelleCave, Joan, Adult Serv, Piscataway Township Free Public Library, 500 Hoes Lane, Piscataway, NJ, 08854. Tel: 732-463-1633. Fax: 732-463-9022. p. 1520

Dellenbaugh, Mark, User Experience Librn, Arlington Public Library System, 101 E Abram St, MS 10-0100, Arlington, TX, 76010-1183. Tel: 817-459-6900. Fax: 817-459-6936. p. 2276

Delli-Gatti, Barbara, Syst Coordr, Life Chiropractic College-West Library, 25001 Industrial Blvd, Hayward, CA, 94545. Tel: 510-780-4507. Fax: 510-780-4590. p. 158

Dellihoue, Melissa, Cat Asst, Dillard University, 2601 Gentilly Blvd, New Orleans, LA, 70122-3097. Tel: 504-816-4784. Fax: 504-816-4787. p. 960

Dellinger, Don, Dir, Kaltreider-Benfer Library, 147 S Charles St, Red Lion, PA, 17356. Tel: 717-244-2032. Fax: 717-246-2394. p. 2134

Dellinger, Zoe, Circ Supvr, Shenandoah County Library, 514 Stoney Creek Blvd, Edinburg, VA, 22824. Tel: 540-984-8200. Fax: 540-984-8207. p. 2460

Delly, Brandi, Circ, Enoch Pratt Free Library, 400 Cathedral St, Baltimore, MD, 21201-4484. Tel: 410-396-5430. Fax: 410-396-1441. p. 1012

Delmas, Susan, Dir, Lewis Cooper Junior Memorial Library, 200 S Sixth St, Opelika, AL, 36801. Tel: 334-705-5380. Fax: 334-705-5381. p. 32

DelMastro, Melinda, Dir, Goose Creek Township Carnegie Library, 220 N Highway Ave, De Land, IL, 61839. Tel: 217-664-3572. Fax: 217-664-3624. p. 633

Delmhorst, Wynne, Mgr, Info Serv, Greenwich Library, 101 W Putnam Ave, Greenwich, CT, 06830-5387. Tel: 203-622-7921. Fax: 203-622-7959. p. 341

Delmonico, Marita F, Tech Serv, Kessler Foundation Medical Library, 1199 Pleasant Valley Way, West Orange, NJ, 07052-1499. Tel: 973-324-3523. Fax: 973-243-6835. p. 1541

Delneky, Akos, Libr Serv Mgr, Valencia Community College, 1800 Denn John Lane, Kissimmee, FL, 34744. Tel: 407-582-4155. Fax: 407-582-4280. p. 456

Delneky, Akos, Librn, International College Library, 2655 Northbrooke Dr, Naples, FL, 34119. Tel: 239-513-1122, Ext 6177. Fax: 239-598-6250, 239-938-7886. p. 471

Delneo, Catherine, Br Mgr, San Francisco Public Library, Park Branch Library, 1833 Page St, San Francisco, CA, 94117-1909. Tel: 415-355-5656. Fax: 415-752-2290. p. 246

DeLoach, Charlotte, Mgr, Evans County Public Library, 701 W Main, Claxton, GA, 30417. Tel: 912-739-1801. Fax: 912-739-0522. p. 525

DeLoach, Marva, Cat, Coll Develop, Diablo Valley College Library, 321 Golf Club Rd, Pleasant Hill, CA, 94523-1576. Tel: 925-685-1230, Ext 2780. Fax: 925-798-3588. p. 210

DeLong, Edward, Asst Prof, Missouri State University, Duane G Meyer Library, 901 S National Ave, Springfield, MO, 65897. Tel: 417-836-4525. Fax: 417-836-4764. p. 2968

Delong, Heather, Br Librn, Tay Township Public Library, 715 Fourth Ave, Port McNicoll, ON, L0K 1R0, CANADA. Tel: 705-534-3511. Fax: 705-534-3511. p. 2838

DeLong, Jackie, Ser Librn, Anderson University, Robert A Nicholson Library, 1100 E Fifth St, Anderson, IN, 46012-3495. Tel: 765-641-4277. Fax: 765-641-3850. p. 724

DeLong, Kathleen, Assoc Univ Librn, University of Alberta, University Library, 5-02 Cameron Libr, Edmonton, AB, T6G 2J8, CANADA. Tel: 780-492-3790. Fax: 780-492-8302. p. 2702

deLong, Suzanne, Assoc Dir, Embry-Riddle Aeronautical University, 3700 Willow Creek Rd, Prescott, AZ, 86301-3720. Tel: 928-777-6658. p. 78

DeLooze, Leslie, Adult Serv, Commun Librn, Richmond Memorial Library, 19 Ross St, Batavia, NY, 14020. Tel: 585-343-9550. Fax: 585-344-4651. p. 1578

Delorey, Karen, Ref, MassBay Community College, Learning Resource Center, 19 Flagg Dr, Framingham, MA, 01702-5928. Tel: 508-270-4215. Fax: 508-270-4216. p. 1134

deLorimier, Lucinda, Br Mgr, Nevada County Library, Truckee Library, 10031 Levon Ave, Truckee, CA, 96161-4800. Tel: 530-582-7846. p. 194

Delovio, Maureen, Ref, West Warwick Public Library, 1043 Main St, West Warwick, RI, 02893. Tel: 401-828-3750. Fax: 401-828-8493. p. 2178

Delozier, Eric, Coord, Coll Develop, Sci, Eng & Tech Ref Librn, Pennsylvania State University-Harrisburg Library, 351 Olmsted Dr, Middletown, PA, 17057-4850. Tel: 717-948-6373. Fax: 717-948-6757. p. 2089

Delperdang, Jennifer, Br Supvr, Sioux City Public Library, Schroeder-Morningside Branch Library, 4005 Morningside Ave, Sioux City, IA, 51106-2448. Tel: 712-255-2924. p. 844

Delphin, Ann, Circ Sr Mgr/ILL, Memphis Public Library & Information Center, 3030 Poplar Ave, Memphis, TN, 38111-3527. Tel: 901-415-2705. Fax: 901-323-7108. p. 2249

DeLuca, Cindy, Libr Dir, Barrett Paradise Friendly Library, 6500 Rte 191, Corner Rte 191/390 & Sand Spring Dr, Cresco, PA, 18326. Tel: 570-595-7171. Fax: 570-595-7879. p. 2048

DeLuca, Karen, Chief Librn, Arnprior Public Library, 21 Madawaska St, Arnprior, ON, K7S 1R6, CANADA. Tel: 613-623-2279. Fax: 613-623-0281. p. 2792

DeLucia, Peter, Librn, Morris County Law Library, Court House, Eight Ann St, Morristown, NJ, 07963-0900. Tel: 973-656-3917. Fax: 973-656-3949. p. 1505

DeLuna, Rachael, Dir, Whiting Public Library, 1735 Oliver St, Whiting, IN, 46394-1794. Tel: 219-473-4700, 219-659-0269. Fax: 219-659-5833. p. 788

Deluney, Joanne, Librn, College of the North Atlantic, Clarenville Campus, 69 Pleasant St, Clarenville, NL, A5A 1V9, CANADA. Tel: 709-466-6940. Fax: 709-466-2771. p. 2771

Delury, Michael, Managing Librn III, Sno-Isle Libraries, Lynnwood Community Library, 19200 44th Ave W, Lynnwood, WA, 98036. Tel: 425-778-2148. Fax: 425-774-7764. p. 2542

DelVecchio, Camille, Librn, Penfield Public Library, 1985 Baird Rd, Penfield, NY, 14526. Tel: 585-340-8720. Fax: 585-340-8748. p. 1716

DelVecchio, Nancy, Circ Mgr, ILL, Hudson Public Library, Three Washington St at The Rotary, Hudson, MA, 01749-2499. Tel: 978-568-9644. Fax: 978-568-9646. p. 1096

Delvin, Robert, Fine Arts Librn, Illinois Wesleyan University, One Ames Plaza, Bloomington, IL, 61701-7188. Tel: 309-556-3003. Fax: 309-556-3706. p. 595

Demanett, Paula, Tech Serv Librn, Fresno City College Library, 1101 E University Ave, Fresno, CA, 93741. Tel: 559-442-8204. Fax: 559-265-5758. p. 151

Demarais, Christine, Ch, Fletcher Free Library, 235 College St, Burlington, VT, 05401. Tel: 802-865-7216. Fax: 802-865-7227. p. 2421

DeMaranville, Mark, Dir, Bryant Free Library, 455 Berkshire Trail, Rte 9, Cummington, MA, 01026-9610. Tel: 413-634-0109. p. 1083

DeMarco, Patti, Librn, Media Spec, Georgia Department of Corrections, Office of Library Services, 3620 Harris Rd, Waycross, GA, 31503. Tel: 912-285-6400. Fax: 912-287-6520. p. 557

Demarest, Dorothy, Local Hist Librn, East Central Georgia Regional Library, 902 Greene St, Augusta, GA, 30901. Tel: 706-821-2600. Fax: 706-724-6762. p. 519

Demarest, Geralynn, Chairperson, Librn, Columbia-Greene Community College Library, 4400 Rte 23, Hudson, NY, 12534. Tel: 518-828-4181, Ext 3290. Fax: 518-828-4396. p. 1638

Demaris, F Scott, Electronic Serv, Blank Rome LLP, One Logan Sq, 18th & Cherry Sts, Philadelphia, PA, 19103-6998. Tel: 215-569-5485. Fax: 215-569-5546. p. 2103

Demaris, Scott, Mgr, Reed Smith LLP, 2500 One Liberty Pl, 1650 Market St, Philadelphia, PA, 19103. Tel: 215-851-1413. Fax: 215-851-1420. p. 2115

DeMaro, Jennifer A, Chief, Reader Serv, United States Air Force, Air Force Institute of Technology Academic Library FL3319, AFIT/ENWL, 2950 Hobson Way, Bldg 642, Wright-Patterson AFB, OH, 45433-7765. Tel: 937-255-6565, Ext 4206. Fax: 937-656-7746. p. 1951

DeMars, Jeanne, Automation Coordr, Traverse Des Sioux Library System, 1400 Madison Ave, Ste 622, Mankato, MN, 56001-5488. Tel: 507-625-6169. Fax: 507-625-4049. p. 1257

Demars, Paula, Librn, Hill City Public Library, 488 Main, Hill City, SD, 57745. Tel: 605-574-4529. Fax: 605-574-4529. p. 2213

DeMars, Tina, In Charge, Lanxess, Inc, 1265 S Vidal St, Sarnia, ON, N7T 7M2, CANADA. Tel: 519-337-8251, Ext 5106. p. 2839

DeMarse, William, Pres, Odell Public Library District, 301 E Richard St, Odell, IL, 60460. Tel: 815-998-2012. Fax: 815-998-2339. p. 684

DeMartini, Becky, Tech Librn, Brigham Young University-Hawaii, 55-220 Kulanui St, BYU-Hawaii, No 1966, Laie, HI, 96762-1294. Tel: 808-675-3946. Fax: 808-675-3877. p. 567

DeMartino, Sherrie, Mgr, Fairfield Area Library, 31 Wortz Dr, Fairfield, PA, 17340. Tel: 717-642-6009. Fax: 717-642-6430. p. 2057

Demas, Christopher, Pub Serv Librn, Tech Serv, Northeast State Community College, 2425 Hwy 75, Blountville, TN, 37617-6350. Tel: 423-354-2429. Fax: 423-323-0254. p. 2224

Demas, Jean, Literacy Coordr, Lisle Library District, 777 Front St, Lisle, IL, 60532-3599. Tel: 630-971-1675. Fax: 630-971-1701. p. 666

Demas, Robin, Head, Circ, Concord Free Public Library, 129 Main St, Concord, MA, 01742-2494. Tel: 978-318-3300. Fax: 978-318-3344. p. 1082

Demas, Samuel, Librn, Carleton College, One N College St, Northfield, MN, 55057-4097. Tel: 507-222-4267. Fax: 507-222-4087. p. 1269

DeMasi, Susan, Media Spec, Suffolk County Community College, 533 College Rd, Selden, NY, 11784-2899. Tel: 631-451-4800. Fax: 631-451-4697. p. 1742

DeMatteo, Nicole, Br Mgr, Ocean County Library, Point Pleasant Branch, 834 Beaver Dam Rd, Point Pleasant, NJ, 08742-3853. Tel: 732-295-1555. Fax: 732-714-1578. p. 1534

DeMay, Norma, Libr Dir, Douglas Library, 108 Main St, Canaan, CT, 06018. Tel: 860-824-7863. Fax: 860-824-7863. p. 333

Dembowski, Walter, Head, Ref, Trumbull Library, 33 Quality St, Trumbull, CT, 06611. Tel: 203-452-5197. Fax: 203-452-5125. p. 373

Demby-Miller, Zandra, AV, Warren County-Vicksburg Public Library, 700 Veto St, Vicksburg, MS, 39180-3595. Tel: 601-636-6411. Fax: 601-634-4809. p. 1317

Demczuk, Lisa, Librn, University of Manitoba Libraries, Victoria General Hospital Library, 2340 Pembina Hwy, Winnipeg, MB, R3T 2E8, CANADA. Tel: 204-477-3284. Fax: 204-269-7936. p. 2759

DeMeglio, Ramona, Adult Serv, Hurst Public Library, 901 Precinct Line Rd, Hurst, TX, 76053. Tel: 817-788-7300. Fax: 817-590-9515. p. 2345

DeMeis, Pamela, Br Mgr, Pike County Public Library, Dingman Township, 100 Bond Ct, Milford, PA, 18337-7793. Tel: 570-686-7045. Fax: 570-686-1798. p. 2090

Dement, David, Asst Dir, Clinical & Br Serv, Bellevue Medical Library, 462 First Ave & 27th St, 14N12, New York, NY, 10016. Tel: 212-562-6535. Fax: 212-562-3506. p. 1670

Dement, Mary, Br Librn, Reynolds County Library District, 2306 Pine St, Centerville, MO, 63633. Tel: 573-648-2471. Fax: 573-648-2471. p. 1323

Dement, Mary, Br Librn, Reynolds County Library District, Lesterville Branch, 33285 Hwy 21, Lesterville, MO, 63654. Tel: 573-637-2532. Fax: 573-637-2532. p. 1323

Demeo, Jan, Head, Circ, Wayland Free Public Library, Five Concord Rd, Wayland, MA, 01778. Tel: 508-358-2311. Fax: 508-358-5249. p. 1134

DeMeo, Mary Ann, Tech Serv, Safety Harbor Public Library, 101 Second St N, Safety Harbor, FL, 34695. Tel: 727-724-1525. Fax: 727-724-1533. p. 486

Demer, Margaret M, Dir, Br Serv, Martinsburg-Berkeley County Public Library, Musselman-South Berkeley Community Library, 126 Excellence Way, Rte 11 S, Inwood, WV, 25428. Tel: 304-229-2220. Fax: 304-229-7163. p. 2565

Demeroukas, Marie, Archivist, Librn, Shiloh Museum of Ozark History Library, 118 W Johnson Ave, Springdale, AR, 72764. Tel: 479-750-8165. Fax: 479-750-8693. p. 115

Demers, Annette, Actg Law Librn & Lectr in Law, University of Windsor, Paul Martin Law Library, Ron W Ianni Law Bldg, 401 Sunset Ave, Windsor, ON, N9B 3P4, CANADA. Tel: 519-253-3000, Ext 2977. Fax: 519-973-7064. p. 2871

Demers, Karen, Adult Serv, Wilbraham Public Library, 25 Crane Park Dr, Wilbraham, MA, 01095-1799. Tel: 413-596-6141. Fax: 413-596-5090. p. 1140

Demers, Michel, Chef de Div, Bibliothèques de Montréal, Frontenac, 2550, rue Ontario Est, Montreal, QC, H2K 1W7, CANADA. Tel: 514-872-5594. Fax: 514-872-7893. p. 2889

Demers, Michel, Div Head, Bibliothèques de Montrèal, Père-Ambroise, 2093, rue de la Visitation, Montreal, QC, H2L 3C9, CANADA. Tel: 514-872-5594. Fax: 514-872-1626. p. 2891

Demes, April, Chairperson, Glenwood Municipal Library, 59 Main Ave, Glenwood, AB, T0K 2R0, CANADA. Tel: 403-393-7260. p. 2705

DeMey, Kathy, Ref, Calvin College & Calvin Theological Seminary, 1855 Knollcrest Circle SE, Grand Rapids, MI, 49546-4402. Tel: 616-526-6310. Fax: 616-526-6470. p. 1184

DeMilia, Carl, Dir, New Milford Public Library, 24 Main St, New Milford, CT, 06776. Tel: 860-355-1191, Ext 210. Fax: 860-350-9579. p. 360

DeMings, Lisa, Dir, Info Syst, Brandeis University Libraries, 415 South St, Mailstop 045, Waltham, MA, 02454-9110. Tel: 781-736-7777. Fax: 781-736-4719. p. 1132

Demko, Diane, Actg Br Mgr, Scranton Public Library, Nancy Kay Holmes Branch, 1032 Green Ridge St at Wyoming Ave, Scranton, PA, 18509. Tel: 570-207-0764. p. 2138

Demlow, Ada M, Head Librn, Kinchafoonee Regional Library System, Randolph County Library, 200 E Pearl St, Cuthbert, GA, 39840-1474. Tel: 229-732-2566. Fax: 229-732-6824. p. 528

DeMoor, Margo, Asst Mgr, Edmonton Public Library, Woodcroft, 13420 114th Ave, Edmonton, AB, T5M 2Y5, CANADA. Tel: 780-496-6891. Fax: 780-496-7089. p. 2700

Demopoulos, Marta, Dir, United States Air Force, Patrick Air Force Base Library, Bldg 722B, 842 Falcon Ave, Patrick AFB, FL, 32925-3439. Tel: 321-494-6881. Fax: 321-494-4190. p. 481

DeMorest, Joanne Hauck, Dir, Ottawa Office of the Auditor General, West Tower, 240 Sparks St, 11th Flr, Ottawa, ON, K1A 0G6, CANADA. Tel: 613-995-3708. Fax: 613-952-5131. p. 2832

Demorest, Seri, Librn, Madeline Island Public Library, One Library St, La Pointe, WI, 54850. Tel: 715-747-3662. Fax: 715-747-3661. p. 2604

Demoruelle, Hope, Asst Dir, Evangeline Parish Library, 242 W Main St, Ville Platte, LA, 70586. Tel: 337-363-1369. Fax: 337-363-2353. p. 971

DeMoss, Jim, Distance Educ, Info Serv Librn, North Idaho College Library, 1000 W Garden Ave, Coeur d'Alene, ID, 83814-2199. Tel: 208-769-3355. Fax: 208-769-3428. p. 573

Dempf, Linda, Dr, Music & Media Librn, The College of New Jersey Library, 2000 Pennington Rd, Ewing, NJ, 08628-0718. Tel: 609-771-2311, 609-771-2332. Fax: 609-637-5177. p. 1484

Dempsey, Anne, Librn, Hartford Library, 1587 Maple, Hartford, VT, 05047. Tel: 802-296-2568. Fax: 802-296-7452. p. 2425

Dempsey, Bob, In Charge, Congoleum Corp, 861 Sloan Ave, Trenton, NJ, 08619. Tel: 609-584-3264. Fax: 609-584-3305. p. 1535

Dempsey, Cindy, Asst Librn, Coleman Public Library, 402 Commercial Ave, Coleman, TX, 76834-4202. Tel: 325-625-3043. Fax: 325-625-3629. p. 2298

Dempsey, Gina, Circ, ILL, Columbia College, 1301 Columbia College Dr, Columbia, SC, 29203-9987. Tel: 803-786-3878. Fax: 803-786-3700. p. 2187

Dempsey, Jan, Dir, Hamilton-Wenham Public Library, 14 Union St, South Hamilton, MA, 01982. Tel: 978-468-5577, Ext 21. Fax: 978-468-5535. p. 1125

Dempsey, John, Coll Develop, Ref, Finkelstein Memorial Library, 24 Chestnut St, Spring Valley, NY, 10977-5594. Tel: 845-352-5700. Fax: 845-352-2319. p. 1746

Dempsey, Megan, Instrul Serv Librn, Raritan Valley Community College, 118 Lamington Rd, Branchburg, Somerville, NJ, 08876. Tel: 908-526-1200, Ext 8412. Fax: 908-526-2985. p. 1530

Dempsey, Paula, Doc Delivery, DePaul University Libraries, Loop, One E Jackson Blvd, 10th Flr, Chicago, IL, 60604. Tel: 312-362-5403. Fax: 312-362-6186. p. 612

Dempsey, Sharon K, Syst Adminr, Smyth-Bland Regional Library, 118 S Sheffey St, Marion, VA, 24354. Tel: 276-783-2323. Fax: 276-783-5279. p. 2477

Demsky, Kathleen M, Assoc Prof, Dir, Andrews University, Architectural Resource Center, 8435 E Campus Circle Dr, Berrien Springs, MI, 49104-0450. Tel: 269-471-2418. Fax: 269-471-6261. p. 1157

Demson, Venetia V, Regional Librn, DC Regional Library for the Blind & Physically Handicapped, Adaptive Services Division, Rm 215, 901 G St NW, Washington, DC, 20001. Tel: 202-559-5368 (videophone), 202-727-2142. Fax: 202-727-0322. p. 397

DeMuro, Linda, Dir, Ohio State University LIBRARIES, Grant Morrow III MD Library at Nationwide Children's Hospital, 700 Children's Dr, Rm ED-244, Columbus, OH, 43205. Tel: 614-722-3203. Fax: 614-722-3205. p. 1889

DeNardis, Donna, Coordr, Ser, Coordr, Tech Serv, Nichols College, 124 Center Rd, Dudley, MA, 01571. Tel: 508-213-2229. Fax: 508-213-2323. p. 1085

Denault, Carole, Libr Tech, Bibliotheques Publiques de Longueuil, Claude-Henri Grignon Branch, 1660 rue Bourassa, Longueuil, QC, J4J 3A4, CANADA. Tel: 450-463-7180. Fax: 450-646-6710. p. 2886

Denault, Lori J, Automation & Financial Serv Mgr, Brown County Library, 515 Pine St, Green Bay, WI, 54301. Tel: 920-448-4400. Fax: 920-448-5802. p. 2595

Denault, Susan, Ref Librn, Massachusetts College of Liberal Arts, 375 Church St, Ste 9250, North Adams, MA, 01247. Tel: 413-662-5321. Fax: 413-662-5286. p. 1111

DenBleyker, Karin, Tech Serv Dir, Mississippi College, 151 E Griffith St, Jackson, MS, 39201-1391. Tel: 601-925-7120. Fax: 601-925-7112. p. 1304

Denby, Greg, Managing Librn, Columbus Metropolitan Library, Northside, 1423 N High St, Columbus, OH, 43201. Tel: 614-645-2275. Fax: 614-479-4119. p. 1885

Denby, Greg, Managing Librn, Columbus Metropolitan Library, Whetstone Branch, 3909 N High St, Columbus, OH, 43214. Tel: 614-645-2275. Fax: 614-479-4159. p. 1885

Dendy, James, Head, Res & Instruction, Northeastern University Libraries, Snell Library, 360 Huntington Ave, Boston, MA, 02115. Tel: 617-373-3344. p. 1065

Dene, Jezmynne, Dir, Portneuf District Library, 5210 Stuart Ave, Chubbuck, ID, 83202-2214. Tel: 208-237-2192. Fax: 208-237-2194. p. 573

Deneka, Kelly, Librn, Evergreen Regional Library, Riverton Branch, 56 Laura Ave, Riverton, MB, R0C 2R0, CANADA. Tel: 204-378-2988. p. 2749

DeNell, Linda, Dir, Caestecker Public Library, 518 Hill St, Green Lake, WI, 54941-8828. Tel: 920-294-3572. Fax: 920-294-6055. p. 2596

DeNero-Ackroyd, Kim, Br Mgr, Willoughby-Eastlake Public Library, Willoughby Branch, 30 Public Sq, Willoughby, OH, 44094. Tel: 440-942-3200. Fax: 440-942-4312. p. 1949

Denesevich, Cynthia, Ref & Instrul Serv Librn, Iona College, 715 North Ave, New Rochelle, NY, 10801-1890. Tel: 914-633-2525. Fax: 914-633-2136. p. 1666

Deng, Connie, Cat, Southwestern Law School, 3050 Wilshire Blvd, Los Angeles, CA, 90010. Tel: 213-738-5771. Fax: 213-738-5792. p. 177

Deng, Margaret, Librn, Union County College Libraries, Kellogg Library, 40 W Jersey St, Elizabeth, NJ, 07202-2314. Tel: 908-965-6075. p. 1480

Dengel, Bette Sue, Dir, Beaver County Law Library, Court House, 810 Third St, Beaver, PA, 15009. Tel: 724-770-4659. Fax: 724-728-4133. p. 2031

Denham, Rudi, Chief Librn, St Thomas Public Library, 153 Curtis St, St. Thomas, ON, N5P 3Z7, CANADA. Tel: 519-631-6050. Fax: 519-631-1987. p. 2844

Denholm, Patricia, Dean, Libr Serv, Bergen Community College, 400 Paramus Rd, Paramus, NJ, 07652-1595. Tel: 201-447-7131. Fax: 201-493-8167. p. 1517

Deni-Owen, Sue Ellen, Commun Relations Librn, Chippewa River District Library, 301 S University Ave, Mount Pleasant, MI, 48858-2597. Tel: 989-772-3488, Ext 27. Fax: 989-772-3280. p. 1211

DeNigris, Cathleen, Dep Dir, New Haven Free Public Library, 133 Elm St, New Haven, CT, 06510. Tel: 203-946-8130. Fax: 203-946-8140. p. 355

Dening, Karen R, Librn, William H Bush Memorial Library, 5605 Whitaker Rd, Martinsburg, NY, 13404. Tel: 315-376-7490. Fax: 315-376-3096. p. 1658

Denis, Chris, Mrs, Br Support, Stormont, Dundas & Glengarry County Library, Long Sault Branch, 50 Milles Roches Rd (Fire Hall), Long Sault, ON, K0C 1P0, CANADA. Tel: 613-534-2605. Fax: 613-534-4641. p. 2801

Denis, Joan, Dir, Oconto Falls Community Library, 251 N Main St, Oconto Falls, WI, 54154-1048. Tel: 920-846-2673. Fax: 920-846-9946. p. 2626

Denis, Micheline, Librn, Bibliotheque Sport et Loisir, Ministere de l'Education, du Loisir et du Sport, 100 Laviolette, Bur 306, Trois-Rivieres, QC, G9A 5S9, CANADA. Tel: 819-371-6033, Ext 4429. Fax: 819-371-6992. p. 2913

Denison, Denise, Ref Serv, Oklahoma Wesleyan University Library, 2201 Silver Lake Rd, Bartlesville, OK, 74006-6299. Tel: 918-335-6285. Fax: 918-335-6220. p. 1958

Denison, Gerrie, ILL Librn, Ref, State of Vermont Department of Libraries, 109 State St, Montpelier, VT, 05609-0601. Tel: 802-828-2735. Fax: 802-828-2199. p. 2429

Denison, Gerrie, Ref Librn, Vermont Resource Sharing Network, Vermont Dept of Libraries, 109 State St, Montpelier, VT, 05609-0601. Tel: 802-828-3261. Fax: 802-828-1481. p. 2956

Denison, Lynn, Head, Tech Serv, Rowan Public Library, 201 W Fisher St, Salisbury, NC, 28144-4935. Tel: 704-216-8242. Fax: 704-216-8237. p. 1822

Denman, Joan E, Sr Archivist, Florida State University, Department of History, Bellamy Bldg, Tallahassee, FL, 32306-2200. Tel: 850-644-9033. Fax: 850-644-6402. p. 494

Denman, Nancy, Ch, Duxbury Free Library, 77 Alden St, Duxbury, MA, 02332. Tel: 781-934-2721, Ext 116. Fax: 781-934-0663. p. 1085

Denman, Ron, Dir, Chilliwack Museum & Historical Society, 45820 Spadina Ave, Chilliwack, BC, V2P 1T3, CANADA. Tel: 604-795-5210, 604-795-9255. Fax: 604-795-5291. p. 2726

Dennahower, Beth, Mgr, Fernie Chamber of Commerce, 102 Commerce Rd, Fernie, BC, V0B 1M5, CANADA. Tel: 250-423-6868. Fax: 250-423-3811. p. 2728

Dennard, Harold, AV Tech, Lawson State Community College Library, 1100 Ninth Ave SW, Bessemer, AL, 35022. Tel: 205-929-3434, 205-929-6333. Fax: 205-925-3716. p. 6

Denne, Doug, Archivist & Curator of Rare Bks, Hanover College, 121 Scenic Dr, Hanover, IN, 47243. Tel: 812-866-7182. Fax: 812-866-7172. p. 748

Denner, Catherine, Ref Serv, Edison Township Free Public Library, 340 Plainfield Ave, Edison, NJ, 08817. Tel: 732-287-2298. Fax: 732-819-9134. p. 1483

Denner, Cathy, Ref Serv, Ad, Edison Township Free Public Library, North Edison Branch, 777 Grove Ave, Edison, NJ, 08820. Tel: 732-548-3045. Fax: 732-549-5171. p. 1483

Dennett, John, Circ, NHTI, Concord's Community College, 31 College Dr, Concord, NH, 03301-7425. Tel: 603-271-7186. Fax: 603-271-7189. p. 1443

Dennett, Marie, Cat Librn, United States Military Academy Library, Jefferson Hall Library & Learning Center, 758 Cullum Rd, West Point, NY, 10996. Tel: 845-938-3833. Fax: 845-938-4000. p. 1767

Denney, Lauren, Dir, Calumet City Public Library, 660 Manistee Ave, Calumet City, IL, 60409. Tel: 708-862-6220, Ext 244. Fax: 708-862-0872. p. 599

Dennie, David, Br Mgr, Norfolk Public Library, Jordan-Newby, 961 Park Ave, Norfolk, VA, 23504. Tel: 757-441-2843. Fax: 757-441-1453. p. 2482

Dennigan, Kerry, Coordr, Griffin Hospital, 130 Division St, Derby, CT, 06418. Tel: 203-732-7399. Fax: 203-732-1390. p. 336

Denning, Kylee D, Curator, Haggin Museum, 1201 N Pershing Ave, Stockton, CA, 95203-1699. Tel: 209-940-6324. Fax: 209-940-6304. p. 272

Denning, Nedina, Librn, Gackle Public Library, 302 Main St, Gackle, ND, 58442. Tel: 701-485-3374. p. 1842

Denning, Ruth, Cat, Saint Meinrad Archabbey & School of Theology, 200 Hill Dr, Saint Meinrad, IN, 47577. Tel: 812-357-6401. Fax: 812-357-6398. p. 777

Dennis, Ashley, Circ Supvr, Autauga-Prattville Public Library, 254 Doster St, Prattville, AL, 36067-3933. Tel: 334-365-3396. Fax: 334-365-3397. p. 34

Dennis, Candace, Librn, Theresa Public Library, 290 Mayville St, Theresa, WI, 53091-0307. Tel: 920-488-2342. Fax: 920-488-2342. p. 2642

Dennis, Carole, Youth Serv, Haywood County Public Library, 678 S Haywood St, Waynesville, NC, 28786-4398. Tel: 828-452-5169, Ext 2511. Fax: 828-452-6746. p. 1829

Dennis, Christopher, Head, Coll Develop, Memorial University of Newfoundland, Queen Elizabeth II Library, 234 Elizabeth Ave, St. John's, NL, A1B 3Y1, CANADA. Tel: 709-737-3214. Tel: 709-737-2153. p. 2773

Dennis, Deborah, Assoc Dir, Camden County Library System, 203 Laurel Rd, Voorhees, NJ, 08043. Tel: 856-772-1636, Ext 3344. Fax: 856-772-6105. p. 1538

Dennis, Farber, Mgr, Libr Syst & Support Serv, United States Navy, Seven Grace Hopper Ave, Monterey, CA, 93943-5501. Tel: 831-656-4403. Fax: 831-656-4769. p. 190

Dennis, Gloria, Br Mgr, Atlanta-Fulton Public Library System, Cleveland Avenue, 47 Cleveland Ave, Atlanta, GA, 30315. Tel: 404-762-4116. Fax: 404-762-4118. p. 511

Dennis, James, Librn, Northpoint Training Center, 710 Walter Reed Rd, Burgin, KY, 40310. Tel: 859-239-7012, Ext 2070. Fax: 859-239-7173. p. 908

Dennis, Jill, Dir, Farmington Public Library, 205 Elm St, Farmington, IA, 52626. Tel: 319-878-3702. Fax: 319-878-3727. p. 816

Dennis, Lawrence W, Dr, Dean, Col of Communication & Info, Florida State University, College of Communication & Information, 142 Collegiate Loop, Tallahassee, FL, 32306-2100. Tel: 850-644-8741. Fax: 850-644-9763. p. 2963

Dennis, Lorene, Ch, Orangeburg County Library, 510 Louis St, Orangeburg, SC, 29115-5030. Tel: 803-531-4636. Fax: 803-533-5860. p. 2201

Dennis, Lynn, Automation Coordr, Head, Tech Serv, Roselle Public Library District, 40 S Park St, Roselle, IL, 60172-2020. Tel: 630-529-1641, Ext 241. Fax: 630-529-7579. p. 699

Dennis, Lynn, Outreach Serv Librn, Newport Public Library, 35 NW Nye St, Newport, OR, 97365-3714. Tel: 541-265-2153. Fax: 541-574-9496. p. 2007

Dennis, Melissa, Instrul Serv Librn, Ref, Delta State University, Laflore Circle at Fifth Ave, Cleveland, MS, 38733-2599. Tel: 662-846-4440. Fax: 662-846-4443. p. 1296

Dennis, Michelle, Br Mgr, Colusa County Free Library, Arbuckle Branch, 610 King St, Arbuckle, CA, 95912. Tel: 530-476-2526. Fax: 530-476-2526. p. 135

Dennis, Michelle, Dir, Clinton Public Library, 214 Mill St, Clinton, WI, 53525-9459. Tel: 608-676-5569. p. 2585

Dennis, Michelle, Head, Circ, Hedberg Public Library, 316 S Main St, Janesville, WI, 53545. Tel: 608-758-6610. Fax: 608-758-6583. p. 2599

Dennis, Nancy, Sci & Tech Librn, Salem State University Library, 352 Lafayette St, Salem, MA, 01970-5353. Tel: 978-542-6218. Fax: 978-542-6596. p. 1122

Dennis, Nancy, Asst Dean, University of New Mexico-University Libraries, 1900 Roma NE, Albuquerque, NM, 87131-0001. Tel: 505-277-2585. p. 1550

Dennis, Nancy, Assoc Dean, Fac & Access Serv, University of New Mexico, Centennial Science & Engineering Library, 211 Terrace St NE, Albuquerque, NM, 87131-0001. Tel: 505-277-2585. Fax: 505-277-0702. p. 1551

Dennis, Pamela, Dr, Dir, Lambuth University, 705 Lambuth Blvd, Jackson, TN, 38301. Tel: 731-425-3479. Fax: 731-425-3200. p. 2238

Dennis, Peggy, In Charge, Pictou - Antigonish Regional Library, Stellarton Library, Ford St, Stellarton, NS, B0K 1S0, CANADA. Tel: 902-755-1638. p. 2784

Dennis, Robert, Rec Librn, Harvard Library, Eda Kuhn Loeb Music Library, Music Bldg, Harvard University, Cambridge, MA, 02138. Tel: 617-495-2794. Fax: 617-496-4636. p. 1076

Dennison, Dave, Managing Librn, Columbus Metropolitan Library, Reynoldsburg Branch, 1402 Brice Rd, Reynoldsburg, OH, 43068. Tel: 614-645-2275. Fax: 614-479-4349. p. 1885

Dennison, Deborah, Head, Cat, Case Western Reserve University, School of Law Library, 11075 East Blvd, Cleveland, OH, 44106-7148. Tel: 216-368-6040. Fax: 216-368-1002. p. 1876

Dennison, Mary, Librn, University Center Rochester, 851 30 Ave SE, Rochester, MN, 55904. Tel: 507-285-7233. Fax: 507-281-7772. p. 1273

Dennison, Russ, Instruction & Archives Librn, Winona State University, 175 W Mark St, Winona, MN, 55987-5838. Tel: 507-457-5143. p. 1290

Denniston, Amy, Ref Serv, Reed Smith LLP, 1301 K St NW, Ste 1100, E Tower, Washington, DC, 20005-3317. Tel: 202-414-9200. Fax: 202-414-9299. p. 413

Denniston, Donald, Pub Serv, Boston University Libraries, Music Library, 771 Commonwealth Ave, Boston, MA, 02215. Tel: 617-353-3705. Fax: 617-353-2084. p. 1058

Denniston, Susan, Head, Pub Serv, Sunnyvale Public Library, 665 W Olive Ave, Sunnyvale, CA, 94086-7622. Tel: 408-730-7300. Fax: 408-735-8767. p. 273

Denny, Emmett, Asst Dir, Tech Serv, Florida Agricultural & Mechanical University Libraries, 1500 S Martin Luther King Blvd, Tallahassee, FL, 32307-4700. Tel: 850-599-3926. Fax: 850-561-2293. p. 492

Denny, Joyce, Cat, Grant County Public Library District, 201 Barnes Rd, Williamstown, KY, 41097-9482. Tel: 859-824-2080. Fax: 859-824-2083. p. 937

Denny, William, Govt Doc/Distance Learning Librn, California University of Pennsylvania, 250 University Ave, California, PA, 15419-1394. Tel: 724-938-4451. Fax: 724-938-5901. p. 2040

DeNoms, Essie, Asst Regional Libr Mgr, Broward County Division of Libraries, African-American Research Library & Cultural Center, 2650 Sistrunk Blvd, Fort Lauderdale, FL, 33311. Tel: 954-357-5979. Fax: 954-357-6257. p. 441

Denslaw, Debra, Ref Librn, Indiana University, Ruth Lilly Law Library, 530 W New York St, Indianapolis, IN, 46202-3225. Tel: 317-274-3884, 317-274-4028. Fax: 317-274-8825. p. 752

Densmore, Amanda, Mgr, Ch Serv, Mentor Public Library, 8215 Mentor Ave, Mentor, OH, 44060. Tel: 440-255-8811. Fax: 440-255-0520. p. 1917

Densmore, Christopher, Curator, Friends Historical Library of Swarthmore College, 500 College Ave, Swarthmore, PA, 19081-1399. Tel: 610-328-8499. Fax: 610-690-5728. p. 2144

Densmore, Mari, Librn, Skagit County Historical Museum, 501 S Fourth St, La Conner, WA, 98257. Tel: 360-466-3365. Fax: 360-466-1611. p. 2519

Densmore, Richard, Pub Serv, Baldwin Wallace University, 57 E Bagley Rd, Berea, OH, 44017. Tel: 440-826-2204. Fax: 440-826-8558. p. 1859

Densow, Sherylann, Librn, Oklahoma Department of Wildlife Conservation, 500 E Constellation, Norman, OK, 73072. Tel: 405-325-7288. p. 1970

Dent, Beverly, Librn, R Iris Brammer Public Library, 109 Mary St, Narrows, VA, 24124. Tel: 540-726-2884. Fax: 540-726-3050. p. 2479

Dent, Christina, Instruction Librn, Emerson College Library, 120 Boylston St, Boston, MA, 02116-4624. Tel: 617-824-8364. Fax: 617-824-7817. p. 1060

Dent, Crystal, Cat, Jefferson College of Health Sciences, 920 S Jefferson St, Roanoke, VA, 24016. Tel: 540-985-8273. Fax: 540-224-4404. p. 2494

Dent, Johnnie O, Commun Libr Mgr, Queens Borough Public Library, East Elmhurst Community Library, 95-06 Astoria Blvd, East Elmhurst, NY, 11369. Tel: 718-424-2619. Fax: 718-651-7045. p. 1644

Dent, Lavetta, Mgr, Metropolitan Library System in Oklahoma County, The Village Library, 10307 N Pennsylvania Ave, The Village, OK, 73120. Tel: 405-755-0710. Fax: 405-606-3502. p. 1973

Dent, Valeda Frances, Dean, Univ Libr, Long Island University Post, 720 Northern Blvd, Brookville, NY, 11548. Tel: 516-299-2307. Fax: 516-299-4169. p. 1595

Denton, Carla, Bus Mgr, Ramsey Public Library, 401 S Superior St, Ramsey, IL, 62080. Tel: 618-423-2019. Fax: 618-423-2120. p. 693

Denton, Francesca, Dir, Daniel Webster College, 20 University Dr, Nashua, NH, 03063-1300. Tel: 603-577-6559. Fax: 603-577-6199. p. 1458

Denton, Nancy K, Dir, Hamilton Public Library, 861 Broadway St, Hamilton, IL, 62341. Tel: 217-847-2219. Fax: 217-847-3014. p. 653

Denton, William, Librn, Arts & Letters Club Library, 14 Elm St, Toronto, ON, M5G 1G7, CANADA. Tel: 416-597-0223. Fax: 416-597-9544. p. 2850

Denue, Gary, AV, Southern Illinois University Edwardsville, Campus Box 1063, 30 Hairpin Circle, Edwardsville, IL, 62026-1063. Tel: 618-650-2632. Fax: 618-650-2717. p. 639

Deon, Judy, Ref Librn, Selkirk College Library, 301 Frank Beinder Way, Castlegar, BC, V1N 3J1, CANADA. Tel: 250-365-1382. Fax: 250-365-7259. p. 2726

DeOrsay, Paul B, Exec Dir, Cold Spring Harbor Whaling Museum Library, Main St, Cold Spring Harbor, NY, 11724. Tel: 631-367-3418. Fax: 631-692-7037. p. 1609

DePaola, Debbie, Asst Dir, Head Librn, South Bannock Library District, Lava Hot Springs Branch, 33 E Main St, Lava Hot Springs, ID, 83246-9999. Tel: 208-776-5301. Fax: 208-776-5301. p. 573

Depaoli, Lynn, Dir, Clarksburg Town Library, 711 W Cross Rd, Clarksburg, MA, 01247. Tel: 413-664-6050. Fax: 413-664-6384. p. 1082

DeParma, Mary Jane, Br Coordr, Carnegie Library of McKeesport, White Oak Branch, McAllister Lodge, 169 Victoria Dr, White Oak, PA, 15131. Tel: 412-678-2002. p. 2085

DePatis, Jodie, Dir, Bradley Public Library District, 296 N Fulton Ave, Bradley, IL, 60915. Tel: 815-932-6245. Fax: 815-932-6278. p. 597

DePietro, Mary, Dir, East Syracuse Free Library, 4990 James St, East Syracuse, NY, 13057. Tel: 315-437-4841. Fax: 315-437-5982. p. 1617

Depkin, Claudia, Dir, Haverstraw Kings Daughters Public Library, Ten W Ramapo Rd, Garnerville, NY, 10923. Tel: 845-786-3800. Fax: 845-786-3791. p. 1626

Depkin, Claudia, Dir, Tuxedo Park Library, 227 Rte 17, Tuxedo Park, NY, 10987-4405. Tel: 845-351-2207. Fax: 845-351-2213. p. 1757

DePollo, Alison, ILL, East Tennessee State University, Sherrod Library, Seehorn Dr & Lake St, Johnson City, TN, 37614-0204. Tel: 423-439-4337. Fax: 423-439-5222. p. 2239

DePonceau, Barbara A, Dir, Wilcox Public Library, 536 Marvin St, Wilcox, PA, 15870. Tel: 814-929-5639. Fax: 814-929-9934. p. 2155

DePope, Leigh Ann, Ser Librn, Salisbury University, 1101 Camden Ave, Salisbury, MD, 21801-6863. Tel: 410-543-6130. Fax: 410-543-6203. p. 1040

Depperschmidt, Diane, Asst Librn, Smith Center Public Library, 117 W Court St, Smith Center, KS, 66967-2601. Tel: 785-282-3361. Fax: 785-282-6740. p. 894

Deprey, Nate, Dir, Osceola Public Library, 102 Chieftain St, Osceola, WI, 54020. Tel: 715-294-2310. Fax: 715-755-3510. p. 2627

DePriest, Heather, Web Developer, Blaine County Library, 94 Fourth St, Chinook, MT, 59523. Tel: 406-357-2932. Fax: 406-357-2552. p. 1376

DePriest, Tonya, Coordr Librn, Patron/Commun Serv & Libr Mgt, Hennepin County Library, Brookdale, 6125 Shingle Creek Pkwy, Brooklyn Center, MN, 55430-2110. Tel: 612-543-8126. Fax: 612-543-5602. p. 1263

DePriest, Tonya, Coordr Librn, Patron/Commun Serv & Libr Mgt, Hennepin County Library, Edina, 5280 Grandview Sq, Edina, MN, 55436. Tel: 612-543-8126. Fax: 612-543-6327. p. 1263

DePriest, Tonya, Coordr Librn, Patron/Commun Serv & Libr Mgt, Hennepin County Library, Pierre Bottineau, 55 Broadway St NE, Minneapolis, MN, 55413-1811. Tel: 612-543-8126. Fax: 612-543-6852. p. 1263

DePriest, Tonya, Coordr Librn, Patron/Commun Serv & Libr Mgt, Hennepin County Library, Linden Hills, 2900 W 43rd St, Minneapolis, MN, 55410-1515. Tel: 612-543-8126. Fax: 612-543-6827. p. 1264

DePriest, Tonya, Coordr Librn, Patron/Commun Serv & Libr Mgt, Hennepin County Library, Northeast, 2200 Central Ave NE, Minneapolis, MN, 55418-3708. Tel: 612-543-8126. Fax: 612-543-6777. p. 1264

DePriest, Tonya, Coordr Librn, Patron/Commun Serv & Libr Mgt, Hennepin County Library, Plymouth, 15700 36th Ave N, Plymouth, MN, 55446. Tel: 612-543-8126. Fax: 612-543-5827. p. 1264

DePriest, Tonya, Coordr Librn, Patron/Commun Serv & Libr Mgt, Hennepin County Library, Rockford Road, 6401 42nd Ave N, Crystal, MN, 55427-1499. Tel: 612-543-8126. Fax: 612-543-5877. p. 1264

DePriest, Tonya, Coordr Librn, Patron/Commun Serv & Libr Mgt, Hennepin County Library, Saint Anthony, 2941 Pentagon Dr NE, Saint Anthony, MN, 55418-3209. Tel: 612-543-8126. Fax: 612-543-6077. p. 1264

DePriest, Tonya, Coordr Librn, Patron/Commun Serv & Libr Mgt, Hennepin County Library, Webber Park, 4310 Webber Pkwy, Minneapolis, MN, 55412. Tel: 612-543-8126. Fax: 612-543-6752. p. 1265

DePriester, Margaret, Archivist, Moraga Historical Society Archives, 1500 Saint Mary's Rd, Moraga, CA, 94556-2037. Tel: 925-377-8734. p. 191

DeProspo, Leigh, Dir, Greenbaum, Rowe, Smith & Davis LLP, 99 Wood Ave S, Woodbridge, NJ, 07095. Tel: 732-549-5600. Fax: 732-549-1881. p. 1545

Deptula, Maria, Dir, Berkeley College, Paramus Campus, 64 E Midland Ave, Paramus, NJ, 07652-3367. Tel: 201-967-9667, Ext 1764. Fax: 201-265-6446. p. 1545

DePuydt, Peter J, Archivist/Ref Librn, Elizabethtown College, One Alpha Dr, Elizabethtown, PA, 17022-2227. Tel: 717-361-1453. Fax: 717-361-1167. p. 2053

Der, Lorraine, Ch, Hamilton-Wenham Public Library, 14 Union St, South Hamilton, MA, 01982. Tel: 978-468-5577, Ext 13, 12. Fax: 978-468-5535. p. 1125

Der Mugrdechian, Barlow, Dr, Dir, California State University, Fresno, Sahatdjian Library, Armenian Studies Program, 5245 N Backer Ave PB4, Fresno, CA, 93740-8001. Tel: 559-278-2669. Fax: 559-278-2129. p. 151

Der, Pearl, Head, Circ, Wellesley Free Library, 530 Washington St, Wellesley, MA, 02482. Tel: 781-235-1610, Ext 1131. Fax: 781-235-0495. p. 1135

Deragon, Normand T, Pres, American-French Genealogical Society Library, 78 Earle St, Woonsocket, RI, 02895. Tel: 401-765-6141. Fax: 401-597-6290. p. 2178

DeRamus, Joe, Br Mgr, Kern County Library, Shafter Branch, 236 James St, Shafter, CA, 93263-2031. Tel: 661-746-2156. p. 125

Derascavage, Margaret, Dir, Otto Bruyns Public Library of Northfield, 241 W Mill Rd, Northfield, NJ, 08225. Tel: 609-646-4476. Fax: 609-484-9006. p. 1515

Derbecker, Henny, Br Mgr, Wellington County Library, Clifford Branch, Seven Brown St N, Box 14, Clifford, ON, N0G 1M0, CANADA. Tel: 519-327-8328. p. 2805

Dereberry, Christine, Instrul Designer, Cardinal Stritch University Library, 6801 N Yates Rd, Milwaukee, WI, 53207-3985. Tel: 414-410-4455. Fax: 414-410-4268. p. 2617

DeRemer, Jennifer, Adult Serv, Public Library of Arlington, 700 Massachusetts Ave, Arlington, MA, 02476. Tel: 781-316-3200, 781-316-3233. Fax: 781-316-3209. p. 1050

DeRenzis, Ann, Dir, Phillipsburg Free Public Library, 200 Frost Ave, Phillipsburg, NJ, 08865. Tel: 908-454-3712. Fax: 908-859-4667. p. 1520

Derenzy, Maureen, Dir, Otsego County Library, 700 S Otsego Ave, Gaylord, MI, 49735-1723. Tel: 989-732-5841, Ext 15. Fax: 989-732-9401. p. 1182

DeRespino, Doris, Librn, Veterans Memorial Library, 30 Main St, Patten, ME, 04765. Tel: 207-528-2164. p. 995

Derfler, Lisa, Tech Serv, Camden County Library System, 203 Laurel Rd, Voorhees, NJ, 08043. Tel: 856-772-1636, Ext 3333. Fax: 856-772-6105. p. 1538

Dergousoff, Gina, Librn, Parkland Regional Library, Canora Branch, 223 Eighth Ave, Canora, SK, S0A 0L0, CANADA. Tel: 306-563-6877. p. 2931

Derkits, Jill E, Pub Relations/Adult Prog, Elk Grove Village Public Library, 1001 Wellington Ave, Elk Grove Village, IL, 60007-3391. Tel: 847-439-0447. Fax: 847-439-0475. p. 641

Derks, Kristine, Ref Serv, Ser, Aquinas College, 1607 Robinson Rd SE, Grand Rapids, MI, 49506-1799. Tel: 616-632-2133. Fax: 616-732-4534. p. 1183

Derksen, James, Librn, Newman Theological College Library, 10012 84 St NW, Edmonton, AB, T6A 0B2, CANADA. Tel: 780-392-2450. Fax: 780-462-4013. p. 2701

Derla, Alaine, Librn, Wapiti Regional Library, St Brieux Public Library, 50 Third Ave, St. Brieux, SK, S0K 3V0, CANADA. Tel: 306-275-2133. p. 2922

Dermody, Diane, Mgr, Medina County District Library, Highland Library, 4160 Ridge Rd, Medina, OH, 44256-8618. Tel: 330-278-4271. Fax: 330-239-1378. p. 1916

Dermody, Rita, Head, Tech Serv, King County Law Library, W 621 King County Courthouse, 516 Third Ave, Seattle, WA, 98104. Tel: 206-296-0940. Fax: 206-205-0513. p. 2528

Dermott, Lynn N, Librn, New Hampshire Youth Services Center, 1056 N River Rd, Manchester, NH, 03104. Tel: 603-625-5471. Fax: 603-665-9381. p. 1456

Dermott, Maureen, Asst Dir, Access Serv, Dickinson College, 333 W High St, Carlisle, PA, 17013-2896. Tel: 717-245-1397. Fax: 717-245-1439. p. 2042

Derogatis, Joan, Dir, St Clare's Health Services, 25 Pocono Rd, Denville, NJ, 07834. Tel: 973-625-6547. Fax: 973-625-6678. p. 1481

DeRooy, Carola, Archivist, US National Park Service, One Bear Valley Rd, Point Reyes Station, CA, 94956. Tel: 415-464-5125. Fax: 415-464-5229. p. 211

DeRosa, Rich, Librn, Department of Veterans Affairs, 215 N Main St, White River Junction, VT, 05009. Tel: 802-295-9363, Ext 5236. p. 2439

DeRose Bell, Gina M, Dir, Siskiyou County Public Law Library, Courthouse, 311 Fourth St, Yreka, CA, 96097. Tel: 530-842-8390. Fax: 530-842-8339. p. 285

Derr, Janice, Circ, Night Supvr Librn, Eastern Illinois University, 600 Lincoln Ave, Charleston, IL, 61920. Tel: 217-549-1936. p. 603

Derr, Jenna, Cat, Warren Library Association, 205 Market St, Warren, PA, 16365. Tel: 814-723-4650. Fax: 814-723-4521. p. 2151

Derrick, April, Circ/Per, Arkansas State University, Palm & Iowa Sts, Beebe, AR, 72012. Tel: 501-882-8979. Fax: 501-882-8833. p. 94

Derrick, Marlene, Dir, Mercy Medical Center, 1320 Mercy Dr NW, Canton, OH, 44708. Tel: 330-489-1462. Fax: 330-489-1127. p. 1864

Derrick, Ted, AV Coll, Mid-Continent Public Library, 15616 E US Hwy 24, Independence, MO, 64050-2098. Tel: 816-836-5200. Fax: 816-521-7253. p. 1332

Derrough, Emily, Head, Ref, Head, Youth Serv, South Mainland Library, 7921 Ron Beatty Blvd, Micco, FL, 32976. Tel: 772-664-4066. Fax: 772-664-0534. p. 470

Derry, Bill, Asst Dir, Innovation & User Experience, Westport Library Association, 20 Jesup Rd, Westport, CT, 06880. Tel: 203-291-4820. Fax: 203-227-3829. p. 377

Derry, Sebastian, Dir, College of Mount Saint Vincent, 6301 Riverdale Ave, Bronx, NY, 10471-1093. Tel: 718-405-3395. Fax: 718-601-2091. p. 1586

Derryberry, Susan, ILL, Stetson University, 421 N Woodland Blvd, Unit 8418, DeLand, FL, 32723. Tel: 386-822-4034. p. 437

Derstine, Stephanie, Supvr, Pennsylvania State Lehigh Valley Library, 8380 Mohr Lane, Fogelsville, PA, 18051-9999. Tel: 610-285-5031. Fax: 610-285-5158. p. 2057

DeRue, Cheryll, Dir, H F Brigham Free Public Library, 104 Main St, Bakersfield, VT, 05441. Tel: 802-827-4414. p. 2417

DeRuiter, Brandi, Ch, Three Rivers Public Library, 920 W Michigan Ave, Three Rivers, MI, 49093-2137. Tel: 269-273-8666. Fax: 269-279-9654. p. 1230

Derum, Claudia, Ref Serv, College of the Desert Library, 43-500 Monterey, Palm Desert, CA, 92260. Tel: 760-773-2563. Fax: 760-568-5955. p. 203

Dery, Alain, Mgr, Centre de Sante et de Services Sociaux Richelieu-Yamaska, 2750 boul Laframboise, Saint-Hyacinthe, QC, J2S 4Y8, CANADA. Tel: 450-771-3333, Ext 3242. Fax: 450-771-3552. p. 2910

Dery, Joanne, Head Librn, Montreal Museum of Fine Arts, 3430 Ave du Musee, Montreal, QC, H3G 2C7, CANADA. Tel: 514-285-1600, Ext 159. Fax: 514-285-5655. p. 2900

Dery-Allard, Armande, Ref, Cegep de Jonquiere, 2505 rue St Hubert, Jonquiere, QC, G7X 7W2, CANADA. Tel: 418-547-2191. Fax: 418-547-0917. p. 2884

Des Champs, Carolyn, Libr Mgr, Apache County Library District, Saint Johns Public, 35 S Third W, Saint Johns, AZ, 85936. Tel: 928-337-4405. Fax: 928-337-2224. p. 80

Des Rosiers, Barbara, Head, Access Serv, University of Connecticut Library, 369 Fairfield Rd, Storrs, CT, 06269-1005. Tel: 860-486-2219. Fax: 860-486-0584. p. 370

Desai, Anuj, Asst Prof, University of Wisconsin-Madison, 4217 H C White Hall, 600 N Park St, Madison, WI, 53706. Tel: 608-263-7605. Fax: 608-263-4849. p. 2976

Desai, Kalpana, Dir, Saint John's Episcopal Hospital-South Shore Division, 327 Beach 19th St, Far Rockaway, NY, 11691. Tel: 718-869-7699. Fax: 718-869-8528. p. 1621

Desai, Lata, Librn, SM Stoller Corp, 4021 National Parks Hwy, Carlsbad, NM, 88220. Tel: 575-234-7618. Fax: 575-234-7076. p. 1553

Desai, Yogini, ILL, Cobb County Public Library System, 266 Roswell St, Marietta, GA, 30060-2004. Tel: 770-528-2320. Fax: 770-528-2349. p. 542

DeSalvo, Michelle, Librn, Casper College, 125 College Dr, Casper, WY, 82601. Tel: 307-268-2269. Fax: 307-268-2682. p. 2651

DeSalvo, Patricia, Dean, Seminole Community College Library, 100 Weldon Blvd, Sanford, FL, 32773-6199. Tel: 407-328-2136. Fax: 407-328-2233. p. 489

Desannoy, Jeffrey, Ref Librn, Alverno College Library, 3401 S 39th St, Milwaukee, WI, 53215. Tel: 414-382-6355. Fax: 414-382-6354. p. 2617

DeSantis, Kathleen, Dir, Mayville Library, 92 S Erie St, Mayville, NY, 14757. Tel: 716-753-7362. Fax: 716-753-7360. p. 1659

DeSart, Mel, Head Librn, University of Washington Libraries, Engineering Library, Engineering Library Bldg, Box 352170, Seattle, WA, 98195-2170. Tel: 206-685-8369. Fax: 206-543-3305. p. 2533

Desaulniers, Maryse, Res, College de Rosemont (Cegep) Bibliotheque, 6400 16th Ave, Montreal, QC, H1X 2S9, CANADA. Tel: 514-376-1620, Ext 265. Fax: 514-376-1440. p. 2894

Desautels, Jeanne, Head, Ch, Bibliotheque Municipale Eva-Senecal, 450 Marquette St, Sherbrooke, QC, J1H 1M4, CANADA. Tel: 819-821-5861. Fax: 819-822-6110. p. 2912

desBordes, Mary, Libr Dir, Saint Charles Parish Library, 160 W Campus Dr, Destrehan, LA, 70047. Tel: 985-764-2366. Fax: 985-764-0447. p. 948

Deschamps, Andre, Admin Dir, Cegep de Valleyfield Bibliotheque, 80 St Thomas St, Valleyfield, QC, J6T 4J7, CANADA. Tel: 450-370-4860. Fax: 450-377-6011. p. 2914

Deschamps, Christiane, Coll Develop, White Plains Public Library, 100 Martine Ave, White Plains, NY, 10601-2599. Tel: 914-422-1400. Fax: 914-422-1462. p. 1769

Deschamps, Joanne, Tech Serv, Cegep de Granby Haute-Yamaska, 235 Saint Jacques St, Granby, QC, J2G 3N1, CANADA. Tel: 450-372-6614, Ext 1205. Fax: 450-372-6565. p. 2884

Deschatelets, Mary, Chief Exec Officer, Terrace Bay Public Library, 1010B Hwy 17 & Selkirk Ave, Terrace Bay, ON, P0T 2W0, CANADA. Tel: 807-825-3315, Ext 234. Fax: 807-825-1249. p. 2847

Descheneaux, Jose, Librn, College O'Sullivan Library, 1191 de la Montagne, Montreal, QC, H3G 1Z2, CANADA. Tel: 514-866-4622. Fax: 514-866-0668. p. 2894

DeSciora, Susan O, Dir, Hewlett-Woodmere Public Library, 1125 Broadway, Hewlett, NY, 11557-0903. Tel: 516-374-1967. Fax: 516-569-1229. p. 1636

Desenfants, Adam, Tech Master & Adv, Libr Tech, Clear Lake City Library, 125 Third Ave S, Clear Lake, SD, 57226. Tel: 605-874-2013. p. 2211

Desharnais, Vicki, Ch, Hooksett Public Library, 1701B Hooksett Rd, Hooksett, NH, 03106-1852. Tel: 603-485-6092. Fax: 603-485-6193. p. 1451

Deshautelles, Angelle, Dir, Ascension Parish Library, 500 Mississippi St, Donaldsonville, LA, 70346-2535. Tel: 225-473-8052. Fax: 225-644-0063. p. 949

DeShazo, Kristina, Acq Librn, Electronic Res Librn, Oregon Health & Science University Library, 3181 SW Sam Jackson Park Rd, Portland, OR, 97239-3098. Tel: 503-494-1637. Fax: 503-494-3227. p. 2013

DeShazo, Tracey, Youth Serv Librn, Silver Lake Library, 203 Railroad St, Silver Lake, KS, 66539. Tel: 785-582-5141. Fax: 785-582-4282. p. 894

DeShazor, Brian, Dir, Pacifica Foundation, 3729 Cahuenga Blvd W, North Hollywood, CA, 91604. Tel: 818-506-1077, Ext 263. Fax: 818-506-1084. p. 194

Deshotel, Floretta, Br Mgr, Evangeline Parish Library, Mamou Branch, 317 Second St, Ste A, Mamou, LA, 70554. Tel: 337-468-5750. Fax: 337-468-5750. p. 971

Desierto, Mark R, Computer Serv, Venable LLP Library, 750 E Pratt St, 9th Flr, Baltimore, MD, 21202. Tel: 410-244-7840. Fax: 410-244-7742. p. 1019

Désilets, Marie, Coll Develop, Prog Coordr, Bibliothèques de Montrèal, 801, rue Brennan, 5e Etage, Bureau 5206, Montreal, QC, H3C 0G4, CANADA. Tel: 514-872-2449. Fax: 514-872-0530. p. 2889

Désilets, Marie, Librn Spec, Hopital Louis-H Lafontaine, 7401 Hochelaga, Montreal, QC, H1N 3M5, CANADA. Tel: 514-251-4000, Ext 2332. Fax: 514-251-0270. p. 2896

Desimon, Diane, Adult Serv, Greece Public Library, Two Vince Tofany Blvd, Greece, NY, 14612. Tel: 585-225-8951. Fax: 585-225-2777. p. 1630

DeSimone, David, Mgr, New York University School of Medicine, Herman Robbins Medical Library, Hospital for Joint Diseases, 301 E 17th St, No 206, New York, NY, 10003. Tel: 212-598-6275. Fax: 212-598-6634. p. 1696

DeSimone, Eileen M, Librn, Touro College Libraries, 43 W 23rd St, Fifth Fl, New York, NY, 10010. Tel: 631-665-1600, Ext 6224. Fax: 631-665-6263. p. 1701

Desjardins, Ghislaine, Dir, College Bourget Bibliotheque, 65 rue Saint Pierre, Rigaud, QC, J0P 1P0, CANADA. Tel: 450-451-0815. Fax: 450-451-4171. p. 2907

Desjardins, Guy, Librn, Bibliotheque Municipale de Sorel-Tracy, 145 rue George, Sorel-Tracy, QC, J3P 1C7, CANADA. Tel: 450-780-5750. Fax: 450-780-5758. p. 2913

Desjardins, Johanne, Acq, Cegep de Saint-Laurent Bibliotheque, 625 Boul Ste-Croix, Saint Laurent, QC, H4L 3X7, CANADA. Tel: 514-747-6521. Fax: 514-748-1249, 514-855-1942. p. 2909

Desjardins, Ken, Res, Kirkland & Ellis LLP Library, 300 N LaSalle St, 11th Flr, Chicago, IL, 60654. Tel: 312-862-2358. Fax: 312-862-2200. p. 616

Desjardins, Lucienne, Head of Libr, West Nipissing Public Library, Field Branch, 59 rue Ecole, Field, ON, P0H 1M0, CANADA. Tel: 705-758-6610. Fax: 705-758-6610. p. 2846

Desjardins, Lucienne, Librn, West Nipissing Public Library, Cache Bay Branch, 55 Cache St, Cache Bay, ON, P0H 1G0, CANADA. Tel: 705-753-9393. Fax: 705-753-9393. p. 2846

Desjardins, Michel, Librn, Centre Hospitalier de Gaspe, 215 York Blvd W, Gaspe, QC, G4X 2W2, CANADA. Tel: 418-368-3301. Fax: 418-368-6850. p. 2882

Desjarlais, Bette, Dir, Support Serv, Saskatchewan Legislative Library, 234-2405 Legislative Dr, Regina, SK, S4S 0B3, CANADA. Tel: 306-787-2278. Fax: 306-787-7400. p. 2924

Desmarais, Cindy, Supvr, Info Entrepreneurs, 380 Saint Antoine Ouest, Bureau W 204, Montreal, QC, H2Y 3X7, CANADA. Tel: 514-496-4636. Fax: 514-496-5934. p. 2896

Desmarais, Elisabeth, Dir, Tewksbury Public Library, 300 Chandler St, Tewksbury, MA, 01876. Tel: 978-640-4490. p. 1131

DesMarais, Janis, Visual Arts Res Librn, College of the Holy Cross, One College St, Worcester, MA, 01610. Tel: 508-793-2453. Fax: 508-793-2372. p. 1143

Desmarais, Maryanne, Dir, Chase Library, Seven Main St, West Harwich, MA, 02671-1041. Tel: 508-432-2610. p. 1137

Desmarais, Norman, Acq, Providence College, One Cunningham Sq, Providence, RI, 02918-0001. Tel: 401 865-2241. Fax: 401-865-2823. p. 2173

Desmarchait, Joelle, Pub Serv, Chateauguay Municipal Library, 25 Maple Blvd, Chateauguay, QC, J6J 3P7, CANADA. Tel: 450-698-3085. Fax: 450-698-3109. p. 2880

Desmareis, Maryanne, Dir, Harwich Port Library Association, 49 Lower Bank St, Harwich Port, MA, 02646. Tel: 508-432-3320. p. 1094

Desmond, Kelly B, Dir, United States Air Force, Base Library, 16SVS/SVMG, Hurlburt Field, FL, 32544. Tel: 850-884-6947. Fax: 850-884-6050. p. 452

Desmond, Patricia, Dir, Hudson Public Library, Three Washington St at The Rotary, Hudson, MA, 01749-2499. Tel: 978-568-9644. Fax: 978-568-9646. p. 1096

Desnoyers, Nicole, Acq, College de Rosemont (Cegep) Bibliotheque, 6400 16th Ave, Montreal, QC, H1X 2S9, CANADA. Tel: 514-376-1620, Ext 265. Fax: 514-376-1440. p. 2894

DeSoer, Debby, Dir, Ellensburg Public Library, 209 N Ruby St, Ellensburg, WA, 98926-3397. Tel: 509-962-7250. Fax: 509-962-7295. p. 2514

Desormeau, Monique, Educ Curator, Flint Institute of Arts, 1120 E Kearsley St, Flint, MI, 48503-1915. Tel: 810-237-7386. Fax: 810-234-1692. p. 1179

Desouza, Kevin, Asst Prof, University of Washington, Mary Gates Hall, Ste 370, Campus Box 352840, Seattle, WA, 98195-2840. Tel: 206-685-9937. Fax: 206-616-3152. p. 2976

DeSouza, Lorraine, Librn, Reed Smith LLP, 1301 K St NW, Ste 1100, E Tower, Washington, DC, 20005-3317. Tel: 202-414-9200. Fax: 202-414-9299. p. 413

Despain, Anne-Marie, Dir of Libr Serv, San Mateo County Library, Library Administration, 125 Lessingia Ct, San Mateo, CA, 94402-4000. Tel: 650-312-5245. Fax: 650-312-5382. p. 255

Desper, Susan, In Charge, Prickett, Jones, Elliott, 1310 King St, Wilmington, DE, 19801. Tel: 302-888-6500, Ext 4105. Fax: 302-658-8111. p. 388

Desrocher, Alice, Asst Librn, ArcelorMittal Dofasco, 1390 Burlington St E, Hamilton, ON, L8N 3J5, CANADA. Tel: 905-548-7200, Ext 6223. Fax: 905-548-4653. p. 2808

Desrochers, Cyndi, Dir, North Kingstown Free Library, 100 Boone St, North Kingstown, RI, 02852-5176. Tel: 401-294-3306. Fax: 401-294-1690. p. 2170

Desrochers, Cyndi, Asst Dir, West Warwick Public Library, 1043 Main St, West Warwick, RI, 02893. Tel: 401-828-3750. Fax: 401-828-4730. p. 2178

Desrochers, Deborah, Dir, Town of Lake Pleasant Public Library, 2864 State Hwy 8, Speculator, NY, 12164. Tel: 518-548-4411. Fax: 518-548-8395. p. 1746

Desrosiers, Roland, Librn, Centre d'Animation, de Developpement et de Recherche en Education-Bibliotheque, 1940 Est Blvd Henri Bourassa, Montreal, QC, H2B 1S2, CANADA. Tel: 514-381-8891, Ext 246. Fax: 514-381-4086. p. 2892

Desselles, Arlene, Archivist, Mercer University Atlanta, 3001 Mercer University Dr, Atlanta, GA, 30341. Tel: 678-547-6283. Fax: 678-547-6270. p. 517

Dessouky, Ibtesam, Acq, Instrul Serv Librn, Ref Serv, Los Angeles Harbor College, 1111 Figueroa Pl, Wilmington, CA, 90744-2397. Tel: 310-233-4473. Fax: 310-233-4689. p. 284

Dessy, Blane K, Dir, United States Department of Justice, 950 Pennsylvania Ave, Ste 5313, Washington, DC, 20530. Tel: 202-514-2133. Fax: 202-514-3546. p. 419

deStefano, Daniel A, Dir, Nahant Public Library, 15 Pleasant St, Nahant, MA, 01908. Tel: 781-581-0306. p. 1107

DeStefano, Elaine, Asst Librn, Elkins Public Library, Nine Center Rd, Canterbury, NH, 03224. Tel: 603-783-4386. Fax: 603-783-4817. p. 1440

Detamore, Gail, Br Mgr, Middle Georgia Regional Library System, Oglethorpe Public Library, 115 Chatham St, Oglethorpe, GA, 31068-9103. Tel: 478-472-7116. Fax: 478-472-7116. p. 541

Detering, Sharon, Dept Head, Ref, Perry Public Library, 3753 Main St, Perry, OH, 44081-9501. Tel: 440-259-3300. Fax: 440-259-3977. p. 1929

Deters, Mandy, Libr Dir, Corning City Library, 6221 Fifth St, Corning, KS, 66417-8485. Tel: 785-868-2755. Fax: 785-868-2755. p. 862

Dethloff, Nora, ILL Coordr, University of Houston, M D Anderson Library, 114 University Libraries, Houston, TX, 77204-2000. Tel: 713-743-9800. Fax: 713-743-9811. p. 2343

Dethman, John, Access Serv, University of Missouri-Columbia, Law Library, 203 Hulston Hall, Columbia, MO, 65211-4190. Tel: 573-884-1760. Fax: 573-882-9676. p. 1326

Detlefsen, Ellen, Assoc Prof, University of Pittsburgh, 135 N Bellefield Ave, Pittsburgh, PA, 15260. Tel: 412-624-5230. Fax: 412-624-5231. p. 2973

Detterbeck, Kimberly, Art Librn, State University of New York, 735 Anderson Hill Rd, Purchase, NY, 10577-1400. Tel: 914-251-6406. Fax: 914-251-6437. p. 1724

Dettlaff, Christine, Dir, Redlands Community College, 1300 S Country Club Rd, El Reno, OK, 73036. Tel: 405-422-1255. Fax: 405-422-1200. p. 1963

Dettmer, Amy, Asst Dir, Grand Rapids Area Library, 140 NE Second St, Grand Rapids, MN, 55744-2601. Tel: 218-326-7640. Fax: 218-326-7644. p. 1253

Deubert, Linda, Dir, Heermance Memorial Library, One Ely St, Coxsackie, NY, 12051. Tel: 518-731-8084. Fax: 518-731-8264. p. 1612

Deuble, Amy, Tech Serv Mgr, Marion Public Library, 445 E Church St, Marion, OH, 43302-4290. Tel: 740-387-0992. Fax: 740-382-9954. p. 1914

Deuink, Amy, Asst Librn, Pennsylvania State University, Altoona College, 3000 Ivyside Park, Altoona, PA, 16601-3760. Tel: 814-949-5252. Fax: 814-949-5246, 814-949-5520. p. 2028

Deursen, Kathy Van, Dir, Bartlett Public Library, Main St, Bartlett, NH, 03812. Tel: 603-374-2755. Fax: 603-374-2755. p. 1438

Deuschle, Rick, Dir, Info & Fac, Hussey-Mayfield Memorial Public Library, 250 N Fifth St, Zionsville, IN, 46077-1324. Tel: 317-873-3149. Fax: 317-873-8339. p. 789

Deutch, Miriam, Assoc Librn, Access Serv & Res, Brooklyn College Library, 2900 Bedford Ave, Brooklyn, NY, 11210-2889. Tel: 718-951-5221. Fax: 718-951-4540. p. 1589

Deutsch, Ellen, Librn, Penn Commercial Business/Technical School, 242 Oak Spring Rd, Washington, PA, 15301-2871. Tel: 724-222-5330. Fax: 724-222-4722. p. 2151

Deutsch, Karen, Dir, Wayland Free Library, 101 W Naples St, Wayland, NY, 14572. Tel: 585-728-5380. Fax: 585-728-5002. p. 1765

Devadason, Francis J, Librn, Kansas Department of Corrections, 1607 State St, Ellsworth, KS, 67439. Tel: 785-472-5501, Ext 250; 785-472-6250. Fax: 785-472-4032. p. 865

Devaney, Paula, Adminr, Dukes Law Library, PO Box 1267, Edgartown, MA, 02539. Tel: 508-627-4668. p. 1087

DeVaney, Sandra, ILL, Carson City Library, 900 N Roop St, Carson City, NV, 89701. Tel: 775-887-2244. Fax: 775-887-2273. p. 1425

DeVarennes, Mary, Tech Serv, Lee Library Association, 100 Main St, Lee, MA, 01238-1688. Tel: 413-243-0385. Fax: 413-243-0381. p. 1098

DeVargas, Rochelle Kelly, Dir, Mkt & Communications, Saint Mary Corwin Medical Center, Dorcy Cancer Center Resource Library, 1008 Minnequa Ave, Pueblo, CO, 81004. Tel: 719-557-4000. p. 321

DeVargas, Rochelle Kelly, Dir, Pub Relations, Saint Mary Corwin Medical Center, 1008 Minnequa Ave, Pueblo, CO, 81004-9988. Tel: 719-560-5598. Fax: 719-560-4018. p. 321

Devaughn, Jay S, Dir of Libr Serv, Community College of Aurora, 16000 E Centretech Pkwy, Aurora, CO, 80011-9036. Tel: 303-360-4740. Fax: 303-360-4824. p. 288

Deveau, Alyce, Dir, Swampscott Public Library, 61 Burrill St, Swampscott, MA, 01907. Tel: 781-596-8867. Fax: 781-596-8826. p. 1130

Deveau, Jay, Law Librn, Charles B Swartwood Supreme Court Library, 203-205 Lake St, Elmira, NY, 14901. Tel: 607-737-2983. Fax: 607-733-9863. p. 1620

Deveau, Leo, Br Mgr, Regina Public Library, Prince of Wales, 445-14th Ave, Regina, SK, S4N 6T5, CANADA. Tel: 306-777-6085. Fax: 306-949-7272. p. 2923

Devenney, Cheryl, Libr Serv Coordr, Mount San Jacinto College, Menifee Valley, 28237 La Piedra, Menifee Valley, CA, 92584. Tel: 951-639-5455. Fax: 951-672-0874. p. 249

Devereaux, Karen M, Circ Supvr, Virginia Wesleyan College, 1584 Wesleyan Dr, Norfolk, VA, 23502-5599. Tel: 757-455-3219. Fax: 757-455-2129. p. 2483

Devereaux, Margaret, Instruction Librn, Cayuga County Community College, 197 Franklin St, Auburn, NY, 13021. Tel: 315-294-8596. Fax: 315-255-2050. p. 1576

Devereaux, Mary Jo, Med Librn, Community Medical Center, 1800 Mulberry St, 1st Flr, Scranton, PA, 18510. Tel: 570-969-8197. Fax: 570-969-8902. p. 2137

Devereaux, Sarah, ILL Librn, Bismarck Veterans Memorial Public Library, 515 N Fifth St, Bismarck, ND, 58503-4081. Tel: 701-355-1480. Fax: 701-221-3729. p. 1837

DeVille, Sarah, Ref Librn, Canizaro Library at Ave Maria University, 5251 Avila Ave, Ave Maria, FL, 34142. Tel: 239-280-2422. p. 426

DeVillers, Gloria, Chair, Department of Community Services, Government of Yukon, Tagish Community, Tagish Community Association Bldg, Tagish, YT, Y0B 1T0, CANADA. Tel: 867-399-3418. p. 2933

Devillier, Audrey, Cat, Tech Serv Adminr, Iberville Parish Library, 24605 J Gerald Berret Blvd, Plaquemine, LA, 70764. Tel: 225-687-2520, 225-687-4397. Fax: 225-687-9719. p. 965

DeVillier, Maureen, Libr Asst I, Saint Martin Parish Library, Arnaudville Branch, 1021 Overton St, Arnaudville, LA, 70512-3226. Tel: 337-754-5037. Fax: 337-754-5037. p. 967

DeVillier, Maureen, Libr Asst I, Saint Martin Parish Library, Parks Branch, 1012 Martin St, Parks, LA, 70582. Tel: 337-845-4693. Fax: 337-845-4693. p. 967

Devillo, Paul, Web Coordr, Charlotte Mecklenburg Library, 310 N Tryon St, Charlotte, NC, 28202-2176. Tel: 704-416-0101. Fax: 704-416-0130. p. 1782

Devin, Robin, Pub Serv, Robert L Carothers Library & Learning Commons, 15 Lippitt Rd, Kingston, RI, 02881. Tel: 401-874-2640. Fax: 401-874-4608. p. 2168

Devin, Tim, Cat, Presv, New England School of Law Library, 154 Stuart St, Boston, MA, 02116-5687. Tel: 617-422-7282. Fax: 617-422-7303. p. 1065

Devin, Yves, Librn, Centre de Recherche Lionel-Groulx, 261 Bloomfield Ave, Outremont, QC, H2V 3R6, CANADA. Tel: 514-271-4759, Ext 226. Fax: 514-271-6369. p. 2902

Devine, Christopher, Pub Serv, Robert Morris University Library, 6001 University Blvd, Moon Township, PA, 15108-1189. Tel: 412-397-6872. Fax: 412-397-4288. p. 2092

Devine, Jane, Chairperson, Fiorello H LaGuardia Community College Library, 31-10 Thomson Ave, Long Island City, NY, 11101. Tel: 718-482-5421. Fax: 718-482-5444, 718-609-2011. p. 1654

Devine, Michael, Dir, National Archives & Records Administration, 500 W US Hwy 24, Independence, MO, 64050-1798. Tel: 816-268-8200. Fax: 816-268-8295. p. 1333

Devine, Miriam, Dir, Amenia Free Library, 3309 Rte 343, Amenia, NY, 12501-5543. Tel: 845-373-8273. Fax: 845-373-8273. p. 1573

Devine, Timothy, Asst Dir, Hennepin County Law Library, C-2451 Government Ctr, 300 S Sixth St, Minneapolis, MN, 55487. Tel: 612-348-7982. Fax: 612-348-4230. p. 1260

Devino, Paula, Mgr, Appoquinimink Community Library, 651 N Broad St, Ste 101, Middletown, DE, 19709-6401. Tel: 302-378-5588. Fax: 302-378-5594. p. 384

Devino, Robert S, Dir, Finkelstein Memorial Library, 24 Chestnut St, Spring Valley, NY, 10977-5594. Tel: 845-352-5700. Fax: 845-352-2319. p. 1746

Devisfruto, June, In Charge, US National Park Service, PO Box 30757, Savannah, GA, 31410-0757. Tel: 912-786-5787. Fax: 912-786-6023. p. 551

Devito, Jennifer, Dir, Libr Serv, Briarcliffe College Library, 1055 Stewart Ave, Bethpage, NY, 11714. Tel: 516-918-3628. Fax: 516-470-6020. p. 1581

DeVito, Jennifer, Libr Dir, Briarcliffe College Library, Patchogue Campus, 225 W Main St, Patchogue, NY, 11772. Tel: 631-654-5300, 631-730-2006. Fax: 631-654-5082. p. 1581

DeVito, Paula, YA Serv, East Meadow Public Library, 1886 Front St, East Meadow, NY, 11554-1705. Tel: 516-794-2570. Fax: 516-794-1272. p. 1617

Devitt, Glenn E, Dir, Summit Free Public Library, 75 Maple St, Summit, NJ, 07901-9984. Tel: 908-273-0350. Fax: 908-273-0031. p. 1532

Devlin, Elizabeth, Commun Serv, Wallingford Public Library, 200 N Main St, Wallingford, CT, 06492-3791. Tel: 203-265-6754. Fax: 203-269-5698. p. 373

Devlin, Fran, Br Mgr, Calaveras County Library, Arnold Branch, 1065 Blagen Rd, Arnold, CA, 95223. Tel: 209-795-1009. p. 227

Devlin, John, Managing Dir, American Irish Historical Society Library, 991 Fifth Ave, New York, NY, 10028. Tel: 212-288-2263. Fax: 212-628-7927. p. 1668

Devlin, Krista, Ch, Clarendon Hills Public Library, Seven N Prospect Ave, Clarendon Hills, IL, 60514. Tel: 630-323-8188. Fax: 630-323-8189. p. 629

Devlin, Linda, Dir, Camden County Library System, 203 Laurel Rd, Voorhees, NJ, 08043. Tel: 856-772-1636. Fax: 856-772-6105. p. 1538

Devlin, Nancy, Head, Ch, Eisenhower Public Library District, 4613 N Oketo Ave, Harwood Heights, IL, 60706. Tel: 708-867-7828. Fax: 708-867-1535. p. 654

Devos, Dorrene, Cat Librn, University of North Dakota, 215 Centennial Dr, Grand Forks, ND, 58202. Tel: 701-777-2204. Fax: 701-777-2217. p. 1843

Devoss, Elaine, Br Mgr, Chesterfield County Public Library, Chester Branch, 11800 Centre St, Chester, VA, 23831. Tel: 804-748-6314. p. 2457

DeVoss, Nancy, Mgr, Pike-Amite-Walthall Library System, Osyka Branch, 568 W Railroad Ave, Osyka, MS, 39657. Tel: 601-542-5147. p. 1308

Devou, Darcel, Circ Mgr, Gray Public Library, Five Hancock St, Gray, ME, 04039. Tel: 207-657-4110. Fax: 207-657-4138. p. 986

Devoy, Diane H, Adult Serv, Waynesboro Public Library, 600 S Wayne Ave, Waynesboro, VA, 22980. Tel: 540-942-6746. Fax: 540-942-6753. p. 2501

Devries, Anne, Librn, St Joseph Healthcare Centre for Mountain Health Services, 100 W Fifth St, Hamilton, ON, L8N 3K7, CANADA. Tel: 905-388-2511, Ext 36322. Fax: 905-388-7141. p. 2811

DeVries, Janet, Dir, Lime Springs Public Library, 112 W Main St, Lime Springs, IA, 52155. Tel: 563-566-2207. Fax: 563-566-2207. p. 828

DeVries, Julie, County Librn, Middlesex County Library, 34B Frank St, Strathroy, ON, N7G 2R4, CANADA. Tel: 519-245-8237. Fax: 519-245-8238. p. 2845

DeVries, Michael, Br Mgr, Lamar County Library System, Oak Grove Public, 4958 Old Hwy 11, Hattiesburg, MS, 39402. Tel: 601-296-1620. Fax: 601-296-1620. p. 1312

DeVries, Norma, Dir, Lake City Public Library, 110 E Washington St, Lake City, IA, 51449-1718. Tel: 712-464-3413. Fax: 712-464-3413. p. 826

Dew, Stephen, Dr, Coordr, Coll Develop, University of North Carolina at Greensboro, 320 Spring Garden St, Greensboro, NC, 27402. Tel: 336-334-5880. Fax: 336-334-5399. p. 1798

Dewald, Judy, Dir of Libr Serv, Redwater Public Library, 4915 48th St, Redwater, AB, T0A 2W0, CANADA. Tel: 780-942-3464. p. 2715

Dewald, Nancy H, Ref Librn, Pennsylvania State University, Berks Campus, Tulpehocken Rd, Reading, PA, 19610. Tel: 610-396-6243. Fax: 610-396-6249. p. 2133

DeWall, Lola, Dir, Pocahontas Public Library, 14 Second Ave NW, Pocahontas, IA, 50574. Tel: 712-335-4471. Fax: 712-335-4471. p. 839

DeWalt, Jim, Head Librn, Free Library of Philadelphia, Social Science & History, 1901 Vine St, Philadelphia, PA, 19103-1189. Tel: 215-686-5396. p. 2109

Dewberry, Angela, Ch, Millbrook Public Library, 3650 Grandview Rd, Millbrook, AL, 36054. Tel: 334-285-6688, Ext 21. Fax: 334-285-0152. p. 25

Dewberry, Melody, Assoc Dir, Tech Serv, Guthrie Memorial Library - Hanover's Public Library, Two Library Pl, Hanover, PA, 17331-2283. Tel: 717-632-5183. Fax: 717-632-7565. p. 2064

Dewberry, Suzanne, Archivist, National Archives & Records Administration, 5780 Jonesboro Rd, Morrow, GA, 30260. Tel: 770-968-2100. Fax: 770-968-2457. p. 545

DeWeese, Devin, Dir, Indiana University, Research Institute for Inner Asian Studies, Indiana University, Goodbody Hall 344, 1011 E Third St, Bloomington, IN, 47405-7005. Tel: 812-855-1605, 812-855-9510. Fax: 812-855-7500. p. 727

DeWeese, June, Librn, Enterprise Public Library, 202 S Factory, Enterprise, KS, 67441. Tel: 785-263-8351. p. 866

DeWeese, June L, Head, Access Serv, University of Missouri-Columbia, Elmer Ellis Library, Ellis Library Bldg, Rm 104, Columbia, MO, 65201-5149. Tel: 573-882-7315. Fax: 573-882-8044. p. 1325

Dewell, Dora D, Pub Serv Mgr, Smyth-Bland Regional Library, 118 S Sheffey St, Marion, VA, 24354. Tel: 276-783-2323. Fax: 276-783-5279. p. 2477

Dewey, Barbara I, Dean of Univ Libr & Scholarly Communications, Pennsylvania State University Libraries, 510 Paterno Library, University Park, PA, 16802. Tel: 814-865-0401. Fax: 814-865-3665. p. 2147

Dewey, Barbara I, Dean of Libr, University of Tennessee, Knoxville, 1015 Volunteer Blvd, Knoxville, TN, 37996-1000. Tel: 865-974-4127. Fax: 865-974-4259. p. 2243

Dewey, Dawne, Head, Spec Coll & Archives, Wright State University Libraries, 126 Dunbar Library, 3640 Colonel Glenn Hwy, Dayton, OH, 45435-0001. Tel: 937-775-2011. Fax: 937-775-4109. p. 1895

Dewey, Elizabeth, Ch, Hendrick Hudson Free Library, 185 Kings Ferry Rd, Montrose, NY, 10548. Tel: 914-739-5654. Fax: 914-739-5659. p. 1663

Dewey, Judy, Dir, Madison Library District, 73 N Center, Rexburg, ID, 83440-1539. Tel: 208-356-3461. p. 582

Dewey, Nadine, Librn, Trenton Public Library, 406 Main St, Trenton, NE, 69044. Tel: 308-334-5413. p. 1421

Dewey, Tom, Librn, Jefferson National Expansion Memorial Library, 11 N Fourth St, Saint Louis, MO, 63102. Tel: 314-655-1632. Fax: 314-655-1652. p. 1355

Dewing, Barbara, Tech Serv, North Hampton Public Library, 237A Atlantic Ave, North Hampton, NH, 03862-2341. Tel: 603-964-6326. Fax: 603-964-1107. p. 1461

Dewing, Roberta, Dir, Kentland-Jefferson Township Public Library, 201 E Graham St, Kentland, IN, 47951-1233. Tel: 219-474-5044. Fax: 219-474-5351. p. 757

DeWinter, Marietta, Asst Dir, Tech Serv, Barry University, 11300 NE Second Ave, Miami, FL, 33161. Tel: 305-899-4813. Fax: 305-899-4792. p. 464

DeWitt, Carolyn, Ch, Gooding Public Library, 306 Fifth Ave W, Gooding, ID, 83330-1205. Tel: 208-934-4089. Fax: 208-934-4089. p. 574

DeWitt, Catherine, Ch, Georgetown Peabody Library, Lincoln Park, Georgetown, MA, 01833. Tel: 978-352-5728. Fax: 978-352-7415. p. 1091

DeWitt, Dixie D, Financial & Bus Serv Mgr, Ball State University Libraries, 2000 W University Ave, Muncie, IN, 47306-1099. Tel: 765-285-5277. Fax: 765-285-2008. p. 766

DeWitt, Gloria, Librn, Sunshine City Library, 207 Kansas St, Prairie View, KS, 67664. Tel: 785-973-2265. p. 891

DeWitt, Harvey, Bldg Mgr/Supvr, Redford Township District Library, 25320 W Six Mile, Redford, MI, 48240. Tel: 313-531-5960. Fax: 313-531-1721. p. 1220

DeWitt, Karen, Head of Libr, North Carolina State University Libraries, Harrye B Lyons Design Library, 209 Brooks Hall, Campus Box 7701, Raleigh, NC, 27695-7701. Tel: 919-513-3860. Fax: 919-515-7330. p. 1816

Dewitt, Linda, Librn, Copiah-Jefferson Regional Library System, Georgetown Library, 1164 Railroad Ave, Georgetown, MS, 39078. Tel: 601-858-2202. Fax: 601-858-2202. p. 1301

DeWitt, Matt, Libr Mgr, Saint Louis Christian College Library, 1360 Grandview Dr, Florissant, MO, 63033. Tel: 314-837-6777, Ext 1512. Fax: 314-837-8291. p. 1328

DeWitt, Melinda, Operations Librn, Alliant International University, 10455 Pomerado Rd, San Diego, CA, 92131-1799. Tel: 858-635-4692. Fax: 858-635-4599. p. 230

Dewitt, Viv, ILL, Lord Fairfax Community College, 173 Skirmisher Lane, Middletown, VA, 22645-1745. Tel: 540-868-7172. Fax: 540-868-7171. p. 2479

DeWitz, Susan, Financial Dir, North Central Regional Library, 16 N Columbia St, Wenatchee, WA, 98801-8103. Tel: 509-663-1117, Ext 120. Fax: 509-662-8060. p. 2548

Dewolf, Pierre, Librn, Institut Teccart Inc Library, 3030 Hochelaga, Montreal, QC, H1W 1G2, CANADA. Tel: 514-526-2501. Fax: 514-526-9192. p. 2897

DeWolfe, Barbara, Curator, University of Michigan, William L Clements Library, 909 S University Ave, Ann Arbor, MI, 48109-1190. Tel: 734-764-2347. Fax: 734-647-0716. p. 1152

Dewsnap-Shipley, Jennifer, First Flr Ref Mgr, Miami-Dade Public Library System, 101 W Flagler St, Miami, FL, 33130-1523. Tel: 305-375-5231. Fax: 305-375-3048. p. 466

Dexter, Anne, Youth Serv Dir, Neligh Public Library, 710 Main St, Neligh, NE, 68756-1246. Tel: 402-887-5140. Fax: 402-887-4530. p. 1409

Dexter, Susan, Librn, Northminster Presbyterian Church, 2434 Wilmington Rd, New Castle, PA, 16105. Tel: 724-658-9051. Fax: 724-658-9613. p. 2096

Dey, Anita, Head, Ref Serv, Saginaw Valley State University, 7400 Bay Rd, University Center, MI, 48710. Tel: 989-964-7094. Fax: 989-964-4383. p. 1232

Dey, William L, Dir, Danville Community College, 1008 S Main St, Danville, VA, 24541-4004. Tel: 434-797-8454. Fax: 434-797-8415. p. 2459

Deyoe, Nancy, Asst Dean, Tech Serv, Wichita State University Libraries, 1845 Fairmount, Wichita, KS, 67260-0068. Tel: 316-978-5140. Fax: 316-978-3048. p. 902

DeYoung, Joanna, Ser, Covenant Theological Seminary, 12330 Conway Rd, Saint Louis, MO, 63141. Tel: 314-392-4108. Fax: 314-392-4116, 314-434-4819. p. 1354

DeYoung, Marie, Univ Librn, Saint Mary's University, 5429 Inglis St, Halifax, NS, B3H 3C3, CANADA. Tel: 902-420-5532. Fax: 902-420-5561. p. 2782

Deyrup, Marta J, Coordr, Cat, Seton Hall University Libraries, Walsh Library Bldg, 400 S Orange Ave, South Orange, NJ, 07079. Tel: 973-275-2223. Fax: 973-761-9432. p. 1530

Dezarn, Olivia, Acq & Cat, Clay County Public Library, 211 Bridge St, Manchester, KY, 40962. Tel: 606-598-2617. Fax: 606-598-4671. p. 928

DeZwaan, Delys, Coll Develop, Head, Ref, Suffern Free Library, 210 Lafayette Ave, Suffern, NY, 10901. Tel: 845-357-1237. Fax: 845-357-3156. p. 1750

Dhakar, Vandana, Librn, Manchester Community College, 1066 Front St, Manchester, NH, 03102. Tel: 603-668-6706, Ext 212. Fax: 603-668-5354. p. 1456

Dhanyamraju, Radha, Ref, North Brunswick Free Public Library, 880 Hermann Rd, North Brunswick, NJ, 08902. Tel: 732-246-3545. Fax: 732-246-1341. p. 1514

Dhargay, Sonam, Circ & Ref, Sheridan College Library, 1430 Trafalgar Rd, Oakville, ON, L6H 2L1, CANADA. Tel: 905-845-9430. Fax: 905-815-4123. p. 2826

Dhawan, Amrita, Head, Info Serv, City College of the City University of New York, North Academic Ctr, 160 Convent Ave, New York, NY, 10031. Tel: 212-650-5763. Fax: 212-650-7604. p. 1672

Di Bella, Christine, Archivist, Institute for Advanced Study Libraries, Einstein Dr, Princeton, NJ, 08540. Tel: 609-734-8375. Fax: 609-924-8399, 609-951-4515. p. 1522

Di Campo, Pierre, Head, Libr & Info Serv, Canada Agriculture & Agri-Food Canada, 3600 Blvd Casavant W, Saint-Hyacinthe, QC, J2S 8E3, CANADA. Tel: 450-768-3247, 450-773-1105. Fax: 450-773-8461. p. 2910

Di Memmo, Frank, Media Spec, Reserves, Southern Adventist University, 4851 Industrial Dr, Collegedale, TN, 37315. Tel: 423-236-2727. Fax: 423-236-1788. p. 2230

Di Napoli, Yolanda, Head, Circ, New Milford Public Library, 200 Dahlia Ave, New Milford, NJ, 07646-1812. Tel: 201-262-1221. Fax: 201-262-5639. p. 1510

Dial, Carolyn, Br Mgr, Harris County Public Library, North Channel, 15741 Wallisville Rd, Houston, TX, 77049. Tel: 281-457-1631. p. 2336

Dial, David, Ref Librn, Indiana Wesleyan University, 4201 S Washington St, Marion, IN, 46953. Tel: 216-525-6171. Fax: 765-677-2676. p. 762

Dial, Frances, Dir, Ridgely Public Library, 134 N Main St, Ridgely, TN, 38080-1316. Tel: 731-264-5809. Fax: 731-264-5809. p. 2264

Dial, Melissa, Daily Operations & Tech Serv Supvr, Florence-Lauderdale Public Library, 350 N Wood Ave, Florence, AL, 35630. Tel: 256-764-6564. Fax: 256-764-6629. p. 17

Dial, Ron, Head, Ref, United States Air Force, Air University - Muir S Fairchild Research Information Center, 600 Chennault Circle, Maxwell AFB, AL, 36112-6010. Tel: 334-953-2347. p. 24

Dial, Wanda, Br Mgr, Shreve Memorial Library, Means/Ida Branch, 7016 E Magnolia Lane, Ida, LA, 71044. Tel: 318-284-3416. p. 969

Dialy, Louise, Ch, Phillipsburg Free Public Library, 200 Frost Ave, Phillipsburg, NJ, 08865. Tel: 908-454-3712. Fax: 908-859-4667. p. 1520

Diamanti, Jane, Dir, Halton Hills Public Library, Nine Church St, Georgetown, ON, L7G 2A3, CANADA. Tel: 905-873-2681. Fax: 905-873-6118. p. 2806

Diamond, Cheryl, Br Mgr, Cleveland Public Library, Fulton, 3545 Fulton Rd, Cleveland, OH, 44109. Tel: 216-623-6969. Fax: 216-623-6972. p. 1878

Diamond, Danielle, Head, Teen Serv, Coal City Public Library District, 85 N Garfield St, Coal City, IL, 60416. Tel: 815-634-4552. Fax: 815-634-2950. p. 630

Diamond, Hélène, Chef de Section, Serv de Techniques, Bibliothèques de Montréal, Saint-Laurent, 1380, rue de l'Église, Montreal, QC, H4L 2H2, CANADA. Tel: 514-855-6000, Ext 4728. Fax: 514-855-6129. p. 2891

Diamond, Helene, Chief of Br Serv, Bibliotheque Municipale, 51 rue Jeannotte, Vaudreuil-Dorion, QC, J7V 6E6, CANADA. Tel: 450-455-5588. Fax: 450-455-5653. p. 2914

Diamond, Lucia, Sr Ref Librn, University of California, Berkeley, Law, 225 Boalt Hall, Berkeley, CA, 94720. Tel: 510-642-4044. Fax: 510-643-5039. p. 128

Diamond, Randy, Dir, University of Missouri-Columbia, Law Library, 203 Hulston Hall, Columbia, MO, 65211-4190. Tel: 573-882-2935. Fax: 573-882-9676. p. 1326

Diamond, Timothy R, Chief Knowledge Officer, Cleveland Public Library, 325 Superior Ave, Cleveland, OH, 44114-1271. Tel: 216-623-2832. p. 1877

Diamond, Tom, Head, Ref & Coll Develop, Louisiana State University Libraries, 295 Middleton Library, Baton Rouge, LA, 70803. Tel: 225-578-6572. Fax: 225-578-9432. p. 943

Diamond, Trevor, Integrated Syst Librn, Bergen County Cooperative Library System, 810 Main St, Hackensack, NJ, 07601. Tel: 201-489-1904. Fax: 201-489-4215. p. 2948

Diamond, Wendy, Head, Ref & Instruction, California State University, Chico, 400 W First St, Chico, CA, 95929-0295. Tel: 530-898-6139. Fax: 530-898-4443. p. 133

Diana, Falk, Dir, Norwin Public Library Association Inc, 100 Caruthers Ln, Irwin, PA, 15642. Tel: 724-863-4700. Fax: 724-863-6195. p. 2072

Diaz, Bob, Librn, University of Arizona, Music Collection, 1510 E University Blvd, Tucson, AZ, 85721-0055. Tel: 520-621-7010. Fax: 520-626-1630. p. 89

Diaz, Carlos, Head, Doc Serv, Evergreen State College, Library Bldg, Rm 2300, 2700 Evergreen Pkwy NW, Olympia, WA, 98505-0002. Tel: 360-867-6251; 360-867-6165. Fax: 360-867-6790. p. 2522

Diaz, Claudia C, Co-Dir, Albion College, 602 E Cass St, Albion, MI, 49224-1879. Tel: 517-629-0386. Fax: 517-629-0504. p. 1148

Diaz, Diane, Dir, Hialeah-John F Kennedy Library, 190 W 49th St, Hialeah, FL, 33012-3798. Tel: 305-818-9140. Fax: 305-818-9144. p. 450

Diaz, Elizabeth, Circ, Waterford Township Public Library, 2204 Atco Ave, Atco, NJ, 08004. Tel: 856-767-7727. Fax: 856-753-8998. p. 1469

Diaz, Holly, Librn, Greenville News-Piedmont Library, 305 S Main St, Greenville, SC, 29601-2640. Tel: 864-298-4158. Fax: 864-298-4395. p. 2197

Diaz, Jose, Head, Ref, Hostos Community College Library, 475 Grand Concourse, A-207, Bronx, NY, 10451. Tel: 718-518-4212. Fax: 718-518-4206. p. 1587

Diaz, Josie, Head, Cat, Fort Morgan Public Library, 414 Main St, Fort Morgan, CO, 80701. Tel: 970-542-4000. Fax: 970-542-4013. p. 308

Diaz Lopez, Aura, Head Librn, Rare Bks, University of Puerto Rico Library System, Josefina Del Toro Fulladosa Collection, Rare Books & Manuscripts, Rio Piedras Campus, San Juan, PR, 00931. Tel: 787-764-0000, Ext 7920. Fax: 787-763-5685. p. 2677

Diaz, Mary, Librn, Armona Community Library, 11115 C St, Armona, CA, 93202. Tel: 559-583-5005. Fax: 559-583-5004. p. 122

Diaz, Mayra, Mgr, Youth Serv, Frisco Public Library, 6101 Frisco Square Blvd, Ste 3000, Frisco, TX, 75034-3000. Tel: 972-292-5669. Fax: 972-292-5699. p. 2325

Diaz, Michelle, Acq of New Ser, Coll Develop, Missouri Western State University, 4525 Downs Dr, Saint Joseph, MO, 64507-2294. Tel: 816-271-4368. Fax: 816-271-4574. p. 1352

Diaz, Nancy, Dir, Hamilton Public Library, 201 N Pecan St, Hamilton, TX, 76531. Tel: 254-386-3474. Fax: 254-386-4447. p. 2330

Diaz, Raymond, Tech Coordr, Lehman College, City University of New York, 250 Bedford Park Blvd W, Bronx, NY, 10468-1589. Tel: 718-960-7772. Fax: 718-960-8952. p. 1587

Diaz, Rodrigo, Sr Librn, Tampa-Hillsborough County Public Library System, Egypt Lake Partnership Library, 3403 W Lambright St, Tampa, FL, 33614-4618. Fax: 813-554-5109. p. 497

Diaz, Roland, Tech Spec, Joe Barnhart Bee County Public Library, 110 W Corpus Christi St, Beeville, TX, 78102-5604. Tel: 361-362-4901. Fax: 361-358-8694. p. 2288

Diaz, Sebastian, Head, Admin Serv, University of Texas at El Paso Library, 500 W University Ave, El Paso, TX, 79968-0582. Tel: 915-747-6721. Fax: 915-747-5345. p. 2317

Diaz, Sharon, Exec Dir, Congregation Solel Library, 1301 Clavey Rd, Highland Park, IL, 60035. Tel: 847-433-3555. Fax: 847-433-3573. p. 655

Diaz-Latorre, Sonia, Dir, University of the Sacred Heart, Rosales St, PO Box 12383, Santurce, PR, 00914-0383. Tel: 787-728-1515, Ext 4356. Fax: 787-268-8868. p. 2678

Dibarbora, Lisa, Electronic Res, Humber College, 205 Humber College Blvd, Toronto, ON, M9W 5L7, CANADA. Tel: 416-675-6622, Ext 5593. Fax: 416-675-7439. p. 2854

DiBartolo, Tammy, Coordr, Outreach Serv, Rapides Parish Library, 411 Washington St, Alexandria, LA, 71301-8338. Tel: 318-442-2483, Ext 1906. Fax: 318-445-6478. p. 940

DiBattista, Susan, Mgr, Niagara Falls Public Library, 4848 Victoria Ave, Niagara Falls, ON, L2E 4C5, CANADA. Tel: 905-356-8080. Fax: 905-356-7004. p. 2824

Dibble, Amy, Access Serv & Syst, Corning Community College, One Academic Dr, Corning, NY, 14830. Tel: 607-962-9251. Fax: 607-962-9466. p. 1610

Dibble, Janice, Ref Serv, Ad, Oshkosh Public Library, 106 Washington Ave, Oshkosh, WI, 54901-4985. Tel: 920-236-5201, 920-236-5205. Fax: 920-236-5227. p. 2628

Dibble, Mark, Instruction & Outreach, Pub Serv, Texas Lutheran University, 1000 W Court St, Seguin, TX, 78155-5978. Tel: 830-372-8100. Fax: 830-372-8156. p. 2386

DiBella, Matthew J, Mgr, Libr Serv, Salem Community College Library, 460 Hollywood Ave, Carneys Point, NJ, 08069. Tel: 856-351-2681. p. 1477

DiBerardino, Donna, Youth Serv, Sayville Library, 11 Collins Ave, Sayville, NY, 11782-3199. Tel: 631-589-4440. Fax: 631-589-6128. p. 1739

DiBiase, Paula, Dir, Hope Library, 374 North Rd, Hope, RI, 02831-1245. Tel: 401-821-7910. Fax: 401-822-4068. p. 2167

DiBlasio, Ann M, Supvr, Circ, Moorestown Public Library, 111 W Second St, Moorestown, NJ, 08057-2481. Tel: 856-234-0333. Fax: 856-778-9536. p. 1504

DiCampo, Pierre, Librn, Agriculture Canada, 430 Gouin Blvd, Saint-Jean-Sur-Richelieu, QC, J3B 3E6, CANADA. Tel: 450-346-4494. Fax: 450-346-7740. p. 2911

DiCarlo, Michael A, Dean of Libr Serv, Louisiana Tech University, Everett St at The Columns, Ruston, LA, 71272. Tel: 318-257-3555. Fax: 318-257-2579. p. 966

DiCesare, Ann, Head Librn, Reader's Digest Association Inc Library, Reader's Digest Rd, 750 Third Ave, New York, NY, 10017. Tel: 646-293-6070. p. 1698

Dich, Nour, ILL, Baker & McKenzie LLP Library, 815 Connecticut Ave NW, Ste 900, Washington, DC, 20006-4078. Tel: 202-452-7052. Fax: 202-452-7074. p. 394

Dichtenberg, Carol, Dir, Chandler-Gilbert Community College Library, 2626 E Pecos Rd, Chandler, AZ, 85225-2499. Tel: 480-857-5133. p. 59

Dicioccio, Karen, Circ, Pasquotank-Camden Library, 100 E Colonial Ave, Elizabeth City, NC, 27909. Tel: 252-335-2473, 252-335-7536. Fax: 252-331-7449. p. 1791

Dick, Alphie, Asst Dir, Silver Lake Library, 203 Railroad St, Silver Lake, KS, 66539. Tel: 785-582-5141. Fax: 785-582-4282. p. 894

Dick, Barb, Librn, Wapiti Regional Library, Gronlid Public Library, One Railway Ave, Gronlid, SK, S0E 0W0, CANADA. Tel: 306-277-4633. Fax: 306-277-4633. p. 2921

Dick, Janis, Doc Delivery, NASA, 21000 Brookpark Rd, MS 60-3, Cleveland, OH, 44135. Fax: 216-433-5777. p. 1880

Dick, Judy, Librn, Bethany Presbyterian Church Library, 3000 Dewey Ave, Rochester, NY, 14616. Tel: 585-663-3000. Fax: 585-663-5325. p. 1728

Dick, Lena, Dir, Mary Sommerville Free Library, 509 Main St, Mound City, KS, 66056. Tel: 913-795-2788. Fax: 913-795-2801. p. 884

Dick, Lianna, Tech Serv, Texas State Technical College, 3801 Campus Dr, Waco, TX, 76705. Tel: 254-867-4846. Fax: 254-867-2339. p. 2397

Dick, Michael, Circ Mgr, University of Maryland, Baltimore County, 1000 Hilltop Circle, Baltimore, MD, 21250. Tel: 410-455-2356. p. 1018

Dick, Randall, Ref Serv, Lancaster Bible College Library, 901 Eden Rd, Lancaster, PA, 17601-5036. Tel: 717-560-8250. Fax: 717-560-8265. p. 2076

Dick, Victoria, Librn, York County Library System, Collinsville Community, 2632 Delta Rd, Brogue, PA, 17309. Tel: 717-927-9014. Fax: 717-927-9664. p. 2160

Dickason, John, Dir, Claremont School of Theology Library, 1325 N College Ave, Claremont, CA, 91711. Tel: 909-447-2512. p. 134

Dickens, Jeffrey, Info Literacy, Mitchell College Library, 437 Pequot Ave, New London, CT, 06320-4498. Tel: 860-701-5156. Fax: 860-701-5099. p. 360

Dickens, Kacy, In Charge, Beauregard Parish Library, Singer Branch, 9130 Hwy 27, Singer, LA, 70660. Tel: 337-463-6217. p. 948

Dickens, Kristie, Outreach Serv Librn, Centerville-Center Township Public Library, 126 E Main St, Centerville, IN, 47330-1206. Tel: 765-855-5223. Fax: 765-855-2009. p. 731

Dickens, Linda, Circ, Butler Public Library, 100 W Atkinson, Butler, MO, 64730. Tel: 660-679-4321. Fax: 660-679-4321. p. 1321

Dickens, Meredith, Br Mgr, Jefferson-Madison Regional Library, Gordon Ave, 1500 Gordon Ave, Charlottesville, VA, 22903-1997. Tel: 434-296-5544. Fax: 434-295-8737. p. 2454

Dickens, Rosa, Interim Librn, Crawford Long Hospital - Emory Healthcare, 550 Peachtree St, Atlanta, GA, 30308-2225. Tel: 404-686-2637. p. 514

Dickensheet, Barbi, Asst Circ Mgr, Drury University, 900 N Benton Ave, Springfield, MO, 65802. Tel: 417-873-7486. Fax: 417-873-7432. p. 1366

Dickenson, Nancy, Chief Librn, Stanford Health Library, 2-B Stanford Shopping Ctr, Palo Alto, CA, 94304. Tel: 650-725-8400. Fax: 650-725-1444. p. 205

Dickerman, Jeanne, Dir, Littleton Public Library, 92 Main St, Littleton, NH, 03561-1238. Tel: 603-444-5741. Fax: 603-444-1706. p. 1454

Dickers, Beatrice, In Charge, Memorial University of Newfoundland, Labrador Institute of Northern Studies Information Centre Library, Sta B, PO Box 490, Labrador, NL, A0P 1E0, CANADA. Tel: 709-896-6210. Fax: 709-896-2970. p. 2773

Dickerson, Amy, Ch, Gallatin County Public Library, 209 W Market St, Warsaw, KY, 41095. Tel: 859-567-2786. Fax: 859-567-4750. p. 936

Dickerson, Carol, Dir, Colorado College, 1021 N Cascade Ave, Colorado Springs, CO, 80903-3252. Tel: 719-389-6658. Fax: 719-389-6082. p. 294

Dickerson, Carol, Dir, Freeport Public Library, 100 E Douglas St, Freeport, IL, 61032. Tel: 815-233-3000. Fax: 815-233-1099. p. 647

Dickerson, Constance, Br Mgr, Cleveland Heights-University Heights Public Library, Noble Neighborhood, 2800 Noble Rd, Cleveland Heights, OH, 44121-2208. Tel: 216-932-3600, Ext 257. Fax: 216-291-1798. p. 1882

Dickerson, Donna, Acq, United States Department of the Army, CEHEC-ZL Casey Bldg, 7701 Telegraph Rd, Alexandria, VA, 22315-3860. Tel: 703-428-6388. Fax: 703-428-6310. p. 2446

Dickerson, Jeannae, Br Mgr, Trails Regional Library, Holden Branch, 207 S Main St, Holden, MO, 64040. Tel: 816-732-4545. p. 1371

Dickerson, Linda, Commun Libr Mgr, County of Los Angeles Public Library, View Park Library, 3854 W 54th St, Los Angeles, CA, 90043-2297. Tel: 323-293-5371. Fax: 323-292-4330. p. 143

Dickerson, Lon R, Dir, Jefferson Parish Library, 4747 W Napoleon Ave, Metairie, LA, 70001. Tel: 504-838-1133. Fax: 504-849-8834. p. 956

Dickerson, Maridelle, Librn, Tombigbee Regional Library System, Dorothy J Lowe Memorial Public Library, 182 Main St, Nettleton, MS, 38858-6075. Tel: 662-963-2011. Fax: 662-963-2014. p. 1318

Dickerson, Richard, Archivist, University of Houston, M D Anderson Library, 114 University Libraries, Houston, TX, 77204-2000. Tel: 713-743-9800. Fax: 713-743-9811. p. 2343

Dickerson, Shirley, Dir, Stephen F Austin State University, 1936 North St, Nacogdoches, TX, 75962. Tel: 936-468-4636. Fax: 936-468-7610. p. 2364

Dickes, Janis, Cat, Tech Serv, Mount Mercy University, 1330 Elmhurst Dr NE, Cedar Rapids, IA, 52402-4797. Tel: 319-368-6465. Fax: 319-363-9060. p. 801

Dickey, Alison, Librn, Currier Museum of Art, 201 Myrtle Way, Manchester, NH, 03104. Tel: 603-669-6144. Fax: 603-669-4166. p. 1455

Dickey, Dorothy, Outreach Coordr, Upper Peninsula Library for the Blind & Physically Handicapped, 1615 Presque Isle Ave, Marquette, MI, 49855. Tel: 906-228-7697. Fax: 906-228-5627. p. 1207

Dickey, Rita, ILL, Tallahassee Community College Library, 444 Appleyard Dr, Tallahassee, FL, 32304-2895. Tel: 850-201-8396. Fax: 850-201-8380. p. 495

Dickey, Robert, Librn, Arent Fox PLLC Library, 1050 Connecticut Ave NW, Washington, DC, 20036-5339. Tel: 202-857-6000. Fax: 202-857-6395. p. 393

Dickey, Tammy, Asst Dir, Kearny County Library, 101 E Prairie, Lakin, KS, 67860. Tel: 620-355-6674. Fax: 620-355-6801. p. 877

Dickey, Wanda D, Dir of Libr, Florida College, 119 N Glen Arven Ave, Temple Terrace, FL, 33617-5578. Tel: 813-988-5131, Ext 211. p. 500

Dickey-Whitish, Cheryl, Libr Dir, Brown Memorial Library, 53 Railroad St, Clinton, ME, 04927-3200. Tel: 207-426-8686. Fax: 207-426-8686. p. 982

Dickie, Edwin, Librn, Haley & Aldrich Inc, Library, 465 Medford St, Ste 2200, Boston, MA, 02129. Tel: 617-886-7426. Fax: 617-886-7726. p. 1061

Dickie, Elaine, Dir, Barrhead Public Library, 5103 53rd Ave, Barrhead, AB, T7N 1N9, CANADA. Tel: 780-674-8519. Fax: 780-674-8520. p. 2684

Dickinson, Charles, Dir, Coloma Public Library, 151 W Center St, Coloma, MI, 49038. Tel: 269-468-3431. Fax: 269-468-8077. p. 1165

Dickinson, Don, Librn, Saint Mark's Presbyterian Church Library, 3809 E Third St, Tucson, AZ, 85716. Tel: 520-325-1001. Fax: 520-327-4599. p. 88

Dickinson, Elaine, Asst Dir, Libr Serv, Capital University, One College & Main, Columbus, OH, 43209. Tel: 614-236-6668. Fax: 614-236-6490. p. 1883

Dickinson, Jack, Bibliographer, Marshall University Libraries, One John Marshall Dr, Huntington, WV, 25755-2060. Tel: 304-696-3097. Fax: 304-696-5858. p. 2562

Dickinson, Julia B, Asst Libr Dir, Saint Ambrose University Library, 518 W Locust St, Davenport, IA, 52803. Tel: 563-333-6244. Fax: 563-333-6248. p. 807

Dickinson, Linda, Acq/Coll Develop Librn, Hunter College Libraries, 695 Park Ave, New York, NY, 10065. Tel: 212-772-4168. Fax: 212-772-5113. p. 1682

Dickinson, Luren E, Dir, Shaker Heights Public Library, 16500 Van Aken Blvd, Shaker Heights, OH, 44120-5318. Tel: 216-991-2030. Fax: 216-991-5951. p. 1934

Dickinson, Lynda, Coordr, Jefferson State Community College, 2601 Carson Rd, Birmingham, AL, 35215-3098. Tel: 205-520-5530. Fax: 205-530-5931. p. 8

Dickinson, Ray, Dir, Cocoa Beach Public Library, 550 N Brevard Ave, Cocoa Beach, FL, 32931. Tel: 321-868-1104. Fax: 321-868-1107. p. 433

Dickinson, Sarah, Instrul Serv & Res Librn, Harvard Library, Frances Loeb Library, Harvard Graduate School of Design, 48 Quincy St, Gund Hall, Cambridge, MA, 02138. Tel: 617-495-9163. p. 1076

Dickison, Julie, In Charge, The Ombudsman Library, 548 York St, Fredericton, NB, E3B 3R2, CANADA. Tel: 506-453-2789. Fax: 506-453-5599. p. 2763

Dickler, Jan, Br Librn, Bucks County Free Library, Pennwood, 301 S Pine St, Langhorne, PA, 19047-2887. Tel: 215-757-2510. Fax: 215-757-9579. p. 2050

Dickman, Anneliese, Dir, Res, Public Policy Forum, 633 W Wisconsin Ave, Ste 406, Milwaukee, WI, 53203. Tel: 414-276-8240. Fax: 414-276-9962. p. 2621

Dickman, Corinne, Libr Mgr, Washoe County Library System, Sparks Library, 1125 12th St, Sparks, NV, 89431. Tel: 775-352-3204. Fax: 775-352-3207. p. 1434

Dickson, Andrea, Support Serv Librn, Wixom Public Library, 49015 Pontiac Trail, Wixom, MI, 48393-2567. Tel: 248-624-2512. Fax: 248-624-0862. p. 1237

Dickson, Dawntwo, In Charge, Florida Department of Corrections, Lowell Correctional Annex Branch, 11120 NW Gainesville Rd, Ocala, FL, 34482. Tel: 352-401-5323. p. 473

Dickson, Kelly, Libr Tech, Natural Resources Canada Library, Hugh John Flemming Forestry Centre, 1350 Regent St S, Fredericton, NB, E3B 5P7, CANADA. Tel: 506-452-3541, 506-452-3614. Fax: 506-452-3525. p. 2763

Dickson, Kirsty, Tech Serv, Vancouver School of Theology, 6000 Iona Dr, Vancouver, BC, V6T 1L4, CANADA. Tel: 604-822-9430. Fax: 604-822-9212. p. 2744

Dickson, Robert T, Dir, Mason County District Library, 217 E Ludington Ave, Ludington, MI, 49431-2118. Tel: 231-843-8465. Fax: 231-843-1491. p. 1204

Dickson, Theresa, Asst Dir, Planning & Operations, Pioneer Library System, 225 N Webster Ave, Norman, OK, 73069-7133. Tel: 405-701-2643. Fax: 405-701-2649. p. 1970

Didham, Reginald A, Acq, Cat, The Boston Conservatory, Eight The Fenway, Boston, MA, 02215-4099. Tel: 617-912-9130. Fax: 617-912-9101. p. 1056

Didiano, Jo, Circ, University of Alaska Anchorage, Matanuska-Susitna College, 8295 E College Dr, Palmer, AK, 99645. Tel: 907-745-9740. Fax: 907-745-9777. p. 52

Didier, Elaine, Dr, Dir, National Archives & Records Administration, 1000 Beal Ave, Ann Arbor, MI, 48109-2114. Tel: 734-205-0566. Fax: 734-205-0571. p. 1151

DiDonato, James A, Exec Dir, Round Lake Area Public Library District, 906 Hart Rd, Round Lake, IL, 60073. Tel: 847-546-7060, Ext 127. Fax: 847-546-7104. p. 699

Didonna, Tom, Educ Dir, Mason General Hospital Library, 901 Mountain View Dr, Shelton, WA, 98584-4401. Tel: 360-427-3609. Fax: 360-427-1921. p. 2535

Didrickson, Betsy, Librn, International Crane Foundation, E-11376 Shady Lane Rd, Baraboo, WI, 53913-9778. Tel: 608-356-9462, Ext 124. Fax: 608-356-9465. p. 2580

Didriksson, Sonia, Sr Ref Librn, Suffolk University, 73 Tremont St, Boston, MA, 02108. Tel: 617-573-8535. Fax: 617-573-8756. p. 1067

Diede, Charles, Dir, Northwest University, 5520 108th Ave NE, Kirkland, WA, 98083-0579. Tel: 425-889-5263. Fax: 425-889-7801. p. 2519

Diedrichs, Carol, Dir, Ohio State University LIBRARIES, William Oxley Thompson Library, 1858 Neil Ave Mall, Columbus, OH, 43210-1286. Tel: 614-292-2365. Fax: 614-292-2443. p. 1889

Diegelman, Amy, YA Librn, Vineyard Haven Public Library, 200 Main St, Vineyard Haven, MA, 02568-9710. Tel: 508-696-4211, Ext 14. Fax: 508-696-7495. p. 1132

Diehl, Barb, Tech Serv, Riverdale Public Library District, 208 W 144th St, Riverdale, IL, 60827-2788. Tel: 708-841-3311. Fax: 708-841-1805. p. 695

Diehl, Duane, Tech Serv, United Methodist Publishing House Library, 201 Eighth Ave S, Nashville, TN, 37203. Tel: 615-749-6335. Fax: 615-749-6128. p. 2260

Diehl, Marisa, Bibliog Instr, Ref Serv, Los Angeles Pierce College Library, 6201 Winnetka Ave, Woodland Hills, CA, 91371. Tel: 818-710-4267. Fax: 818-719-9058. p. 285

Diehl, Melody, Asst Librn, Regent University Library, 1000 Regent University Dr, Virginia Beach, VA, 23464. Tel: 757-352-4542. Fax: 757-352-4167. p. 2499

Diehl, Sue, Ref & Libr Instruction, Montreat College, 310 Gaither Circle, Montreat, NC, 28757. Tel: 828-669-8012, Ext 3504. Fax: 828-350-2083. p. 1810

Diehm, Kim, Youth Serv Librn, Boulder City Library, 701 Adams Blvd, Boulder City, NV, 89005-2697. Tel: 702-293-1281. Fax: 702-293-0239. p. 1425

Diekmann, Florian, PhD, Librn, Ohio State University LIBRARIES, Food, Agricultural & Environmental Sciences, 045 Agriculture Administration Bldg, 2120 Fyffe Rd, Columbus, OH, 43210-1066. Tel: 614-292-6125. Fax: 614-292-0590. p. 1887

DiEleuterio, Rachael, Head Librn, Delaware Art Museum, 2301 Kentmere Pkwy, Wilmington, DE, 19806. Tel: 302-571-9590, Ext 540. Fax: 302-571-0220. p. 387

Diem, Laveta, Librn, VA-Northern Indiana Health Care System, 2121 Lake Ave, 142D, Fort Wayne, IN, 46805. Tel: 260-426-5431, Ext 71330. Fax: 260-460-1490. p. 743

Diemert, Susan, Cat, Fairhope Public Library, 501 Fairhope Ave, Fairhope, AL, 36532. Tel: 251-928-7483. Fax: 251-928-9717. p. 16

Diener, Julia A, Asst Librn, Chino Valley Public Library, 1020 W Palomino Rd, Chino Valley, AZ, 86323-5500. Tel: 928-636-2687. Fax: 928-636-9129. p. 60

Dieno, Lesley, Exec Dir, Okanagan Regional Library, 1430 KLO Rd, Kelowna, BC, V1W 3P6, CANADA. Tel: 250-860-4033, Ext 1111. Fax: 250-861-8696. p. 2730

Dierauer, Joyce, Dir, Summit County Library, 0037 Peak One Dr, Frisco, CO, 80443. Tel: 970-668-4130. Fax: 970-668-5556. p. 308

Dierker, Vicky, Dir, Mackinaw District Public Library, 117 S Main, Mackinaw, IL, 61755. Tel: 309-359-8022. Fax: 309-359-6502. p. 668

Dierks, Blaise, Adult Serv, River Forest Public Library, 735 Lathrop Ave, River Forest, IL, 60305-1883. Tel: 708-366-5205, Ext 318. Fax: 708-366-8699. p. 694

Dies, Roseann, Online Serv, Ref, Meadville Public Library, 848 N Main St, Meadville, PA, 16335-2689. Tel: 814-336-1773. Fax: 814-333-8173. p. 2086

Diesing, Jane, Br Mgr, Manistee County Library, Onekama Branch, 5283 Main St, Onekama, MI, 49675-9701. Tel: 616-889-4041. p. 1206

Diesner, Jana, Asst Prof, University of Illinois at Urbana-Champaign, Library & Information Science Bldg, 501 E Daniel St, Champaign, IL, 61820-6211. Tel: 217-333-3280. Fax: 217-244-3302. p. 2965

Dieterich, Gretchen, Dir, Blanchardville Public Library, 208 Mason St, Blanchardville, WI, 53506. Tel: 608-523-2055. Fax: 608-523-4321. p. 2582

Dieterle, Karen, Librn, Chinook Regional Library, Burstall Branch, Martin St & Hamilton Ave, Burstall, SK, S0N 0H0, CANADA. Tel: 306-679-2177. p. 2928

Dietrich, Dianne, Physics & Astronomy Librn, Cornell University Library, Physical Sciences Library, Virtual Library, 283 Clark Hall, Ithaca, NY, 14853. Tel: 607-255-4016. Fax: 607-255-5288. p. 1642

Dietrich, Ginny, Librn, National Weather Center Library, 120 David L Boren Blvd, Ste 4300, Norman, OK, 73072-7303. Tel: 405-325-1171. Fax: 405-325-1130. p. 1970

Dietrich, Jan, Coordr, Zoological Society of Cincinnati Library, 3400 Vine St, Cincinnati, OH, 45220-1399. Tel: 513-559-7760. Fax: 513-475-6101, 513-559-7776. p. 1875

Dietrich, Julie, Pub Serv, Blessing Health Professions Library, Broadway at 11th St, Quincy, IL, 62305. Tel: 217-228-5520, Ext 6970. Fax: 217-223-6400. p. 693

Dietrich, Marsha, ILL, Bill Memorial Library, 240 Monument St, Groton, CT, 06340. Tel: 860-445-0392. Fax: 860-449-8971. p. 342

Dietrich, Suzanne, Dir, Madison County Historical Museum & Archival Library, 715 N Main St, Edwardsville, IL, 62025-1111. Tel: 618-656-7562, 618-656-7569. Fax: 618-659-3457. p. 639

Dietrich, Theresa, Circ, A Holmes Johnson Memorial Library, 319 Lower Mill Bay Rd, Kodiak, AK, 99615. Tel: 907-486-8682. Fax: 907-486-8681. p. 51

Dietsche, Courtney, Dir, Evelyn Goldberg Briggs Memorial Library, 68235 S Main St, Iron River, WI, 54847. Tel: 715-372-5451. Fax: 715-372-5451. p. 2599

Diette, Paul, Acq Mgr, Dep Chief Exec Officer, Haldimand County Public Library, 111 Broad St E, Dunnville, ON, N1A 2X5, CANADA. Tel: 905-318-3272. Fax: 905-774-4294. p. 2802

Diette, Paul, Br Coordr, Haldimand County Public Library, Cayuga Branch, 28 Cayuga St N, Cayuga, ON, N0A 1E0, CANADA. Tel: 905-772-5726. Fax: 905-772-5726. p. 2803

Diette, Paul, Br Coordr, Haldimand County Public Library, Dunnville Branch, 317 Chestnut St, Dunnville, ON, N1A 2H4, CANADA. Tel: 905-772-5726. Fax: 905-774-2530. p. 2803

Diette, Paul, Br Coordr, Haldimand County Public Library, Selkirk Branch, 34 Main St W, Selkirk, ON, N0A 1P0, CANADA. Tel: 905-776-2127. Fax: 905-776-3116. p. 2803

Dietz, Kearney E, Pres, Arkansas Independent Colleges & Universities, Firstar Bldg, One Riverfront Pl, Ste 610, North Little Rock, AR, 72114. Tel: 501-378-0843. Fax: 501-374-1523. p. 2937

Dietz, Rick, Syst Supvr, California State University, Stanislaus, One University Circle, Turlock, CA, 95382. p. 277

Dietz, Rosalie, Dir, Malvern Public Library, One E First Ave, Malvern, PA, 19355-2743. Tel: 610-644-7259. Fax: 610-644-5204. p. 2083

Dievendorf, Marcia, Dir, Caro Area District Library, 840 W Frank St, Caro, MI, 48723. Tel: 989-673-4329, Ext 102. Fax: 989-673-4777. p. 1161

Difazio, Robert, Librn, Austen Riggs Center, Inc, 25 Main St, PO Box 962, Stockbridge, MA, 01262. Tel: 413-298-5511, Ext 5259. Fax: 413-298-4020. p. 1129

DiFelice, Beth, Assoc Dir, Head, Pub Serv, Arizona State University, College of Law, 110 S McAllister Ave, Tempe, AZ, 85287-7806. Tel: 480-965-4871. Fax: 480-965-4283. p. 83

DiFelice, Clara, Dir, Beaumont Library District, 125 E Eighth St, Beaumont, CA, 92223-2194. Tel: 951-845-1357. Fax: 951-845-6217. p. 125

Difeterici, Amanda, Head, Libr & Info Serv, South University, Nine Science Ct, Columbia, SC, 29203. Tel: 803-935-4301, 803-935-4331. Fax: 803-935-4382. p. 2189

Diffenderfer, Bridget, Asst Librn, CAE USA, Inc Library, 4908 Tampa West Blvd, Tampa, FL, 33634. Tel: 813-887-1540. Fax: 813-901-6417. p. 496

Diffenderfer, Judy, Head, Acq, Marist College, 3399 North Rd, Poughkeepsie, NY, 12601-1387. Tel: 845-575-3199. Fax: 845-575-3150. p. 1722

DiFiore, Patricia, Adult Serv, Cranberry Public Library, 2525 Rochester Rd, Ste 300, Cranberry Township, PA, 16066-6423. Tel: 724-776-9100, Ext 1126. Fax: 724-776-2490. p. 2048

Digan, Stacey, Librn, Saul Ewing LLP, 500 E Pratt St, 9th Flr, Baltimore, MD, 21202. Tel: 410-332-8832. Fax: 410-332-8862. p. 1017

Digan, Stacey, Libr Dir, Saul Ewing LLP, Centre Sq W, 1500 Market St, 38th Flr, Philadelphia, PA, 19102. Tel: 215-972-7873. Fax: 215-972-1945. p. 2116

Digby, Julie, Br Coordr, Flint River Regional Library, Tyrone Public Library, 143 Commerce Dr, Tyrone, GA, 30290. Tel: 770-487-1565. p. 535

DiGennaro, Debbie, Br Mgr, Toledo-Lucas County Public Library, Heatherdowns, 3265 Glanzman, Toledo, OH, 43614. Tel: 419-259-5270. Fax: 419-382-3231. p. 1939

Diggs, Jackie, Dir, Foard County Library, 110 E California St, Crowell, TX, 79227. Tel: 940-684-1250. Fax: 940-684-1250. p. 2303

DiGiacoma, Cheryl, Ch, Northampton Area Public Library, 1615 Laubach Ave, Northampton, PA, 18067-1597. Tel: 610-262-7537. Fax: 610-262-4356. p. 2100

DiGiacomo, Allsion, In Charge, Center for the Advancement of Jewish Education, 4200 Biscayne Blvd, Miami, FL, 33137-3279. Tel: 305-576-4030, Ext 154. Fax: 305-576-0307. p. 465

DiGiacomo, Sandra J, Info Spec, Hoffmann-La Roche, Inc, 340 Kingsland St, Bldg 76/3, Nutley, NJ, 07110-1199. Tel: 973-935-3092. Fax: 973-235-4632. p. 1515

DiGiallonardo, Bonnie, Ref Librn, Nova Southeastern University, 3200 S University Dr, Fort Lauderdale, FL, 33328. Tel: 954-262-3106. Fax: 954-262-1821. p. 443

Digianantonio, Barbara, Asst Dir, Louisville Public Library, 700 Lincoln Ave, Louisville, OH, 44641-1474. Tel: 330-875-1696. Fax: 330-875-3530. p. 1912

DiGiovanni, Kathleen, Acq, Oakland Public Library, 125 14th St, Oakland, CA, 94612. Tel: 510-238-4704. Fax: 510-238-2232. p. 197

DiGiustino, Elizabeth, Cataloger, Head, Tech Serv, Saint Vincent College & Seminary Library, 300 Fraser Purchase Rd, Latrobe, PA, 15650-2690. Tel: 724-805-2966. Fax: 724-805-2905. p. 2079

Digmann, Nancy, Dir, Ross & Elizabeth Baty Monticello Public Library, 205 E Grand St, Monticello, IA, 52310-1617. Tel: 319-465-3354. Fax: 319-465-4587. p. 833

Dignan, Annette, Librn, Greater Vancouver Regional District Library, 4330 Kingsway, Burnaby, BC, V5H 4G8, CANADA. Tel: 604-432-6335. Fax: 604-432-6445. p. 2725

Dignan, Michael F, Dir, Paris Public Library, 37 Market Sq, South Paris, ME, 04281. Tel: 207-743-6994. p. 1001

DiGregorio, Antonia, Sr Asst Librn, Access Serv, State University of New York, 223 Store Hill Rd, Old Westbury, NY, 11568. Tel: 516-876-3226. Fax: 516-876-3325. p. 1710

Dikcis, Catherine, Mgr, Methodist Healthcare, 7700 Floyd Curl Dr, San Antonio, TX, 78229. Tel: 210-575-4583. p. 2380

Dikun, Joan, Adult Serv, Tech Serv, Millis Public Library, 25 Auburn Rd, Millis, MA, 02054-1203. Tel: 508-376-8282. Fax: 508-376-1278. p. 1106

DiLandro, Daniel, Archives & Spec Coll Librn, State University of New York College at Buffalo, 1300 Elmwood Ave, Buffalo, NY, 14222-1095. Tel: 716-878-6304. Fax: 716-878-3134. p. 1599

Dilcher, Meryl, In Charge, Peachtree Presbyterian Church, 3434 Roswell Rd NW, Atlanta, GA, 30305. Tel: 404-842-5813. Fax: 404-842-5858. p. 517

DiLeonardo, John, District Librn, New Castle Public Library, 207 E North St, New Castle, PA, 16101-3691. Tel: 724-658-6659. Fax: 724-658-7209. p. 2096

DiLeonardo, Olivia, Br Mgr, Suffolk Public Library System, North Suffolk Library, 2000 Bennett's Creek Park Rd, Suffolk, VA, 23435. Tel: 757-514-7150. p. 2497

Dilger-Hill, Jeannie, Dir, La Grange Public Library, Ten W Cossitt Ave, La Grange, IL, 60525. Tel: 708-352-0576, Ext 11. p. 662

Dilks, Jeff, Dir, Salem Free Public Library, 112 W Broadway, Salem, NJ, 08079-1302. Tel: 856-935-0526. Fax: 856-935-5110. p. 1528

Dill, Emily A, Interim Exec Dir, University Library of Columbus, 4555 Central Ave, LC 1600, Columbus, IN, 47203. Tel: 812-314-8703. Fax: 812-314-8722. p. 733

Dill, Mike, Coordr, Lakeland Specialty Hospital, 6418 Deans Hill Rd, Berrien Center, MI, 49102-9750. Tel: 269-982-4904. Fax: 269-982-4993. p. 1157

Dill, Nita, Coordr, Sunflower County Library System, Henry M Seymour Library, 201 Cypress Dr, Indianola, MS, 38751. Tel: 662-887-1672. Fax: 662-887-2641. p. 1302

Dill, Sally, Br Mgr, Knox County Public Library System, Halls Branch, 4518 E Emory Rd, Knoxville, TN, 37938. Tel: 865-922-2552. Fax: 865-922-6543. p. 2242

Dillard, George, Adult Prog Coordr, Missouri River Regional Library, 214 Adams St, Jefferson City, MO, 65101-3244. Tel: 573-634-6064, Ext 250. p. 1335

Dillard, Janice, Librn, Museum of Contemporary Art Library, 220 E Chicago Ave, Chicago, IL, 60611-2604. Tel: 312-397-3894. Fax: 312-397-4099. p. 619

Dillard, Peggy, Dir, Libr & Archives, Woodrow Wilson Presidential Library Foundation, 20 N Coalter St, Staunton, VA, 24401-4332. Tel: 540-885-0897. Fax: 540-886-9874. p. 2497

Dillard, Sara, Cat, Texas Christian University, 2913 Lowden St, TCU Box 298400, Fort Worth, TX, 76129. Tel: 817-257-7106. Fax: 817-257-7282. p. 2323

Dillard, Thomas W, Jr, Dir of Libr, Cabarrus County Public Library, 27 Union St N, Concord, NC, 28025-4793. Tel: 704-920-2050. Fax: 704-784-3822. p. 1785

Dillashaw Price, Deborah, Head, Circ, Greenwood County Library, 600 S Main St, Greenwood, SC, 29646. Tel: 864-941-4653. Fax: 864-941-4651. p. 2197

Dillehay, Bette, Dir, Mathews Memorial Library, Main St, Mathews, VA, 23109. Tel: 804-725-5747. Fax: 804-725-7668. p. 2478

Dillen, Judith, Dir, New Cumberland Public Library, One Benjamin Plaza, New Cumberland, PA, 17070-1597. Tel: 717-774-7820. Fax: 717-774-7824. p. 2096

Diller, David F, Dir, Glen Lake Community Library, 10115 W Front St, Empire, MI, 49630-9418. Tel: 231-326-5361. Fax: 231-326-5361. p. 1177

Diller, Karen, Assoc Libr Dir, Washington State University Libraries, 14204 NE Salmon Creek Ave, Vancouver, WA, 98686. Tel: 360-546-9246. Fax: 360-546-9039. p. 2546

Dilley, Denise, Commun Libr Mgr, County of Los Angeles Public Library, Charter Oak Library, 20540 E Arrow Hwy, Ste K, Covina, CA, 91724-1238. Tel: 626-339-2151. Fax: 626-339-2799. p. 141

Dilley, Sarah, Sr Libr Assoc, Ohio University Chillicothe Campus, 101 University Dr, Chillicothe, OH, 45601-0629. Tel: 740-774-7201. Fax: 740-774-7268. p. 1867

Dillie, Tom, Exec Dir, Minerva Public Library, 677 Lynnwood Dr, Minerva, OH, 44657-1200. Tel: 330-868-4101. Fax: 330-868-4267. p. 1918

Dilline, Jim, Prog Officer for Digital Coll, Greater Western Library Alliance, 5109 Cherry St, Kansas City, MO, 64110. Tel: 816-926-8765. Fax: 816-926-8790. p. 2947

Dillinger, Diana, Dir, Bourbonnais Public Library District, 250 W John Casey Rd, Bourbonnais, IL, 60914. Tel: 815-933-1727. Fax: 815-933-1961. p. 596

Dillinger, Mary Ada, Cat Librn, Olivet Nazarene University, One University Ave, Bourbonnais, IL, 60914-2271. Tel: 815-939-5144. Fax: 815-939-5170. p. 596

Dillinger, Susan D, Dir, New Port Richey Public Library, 5939 Main St, New Port Richey, FL, 34652. Tel: 727-853-1263. Fax: 727-853-1280. p. 472

Dillingham, Missy, Libr Serv Mgr, The Brentwood Library, 8109 Concord Rd, Brentwood, TN, 37027. Tel: 615-371-0090, Ext 8380. Fax: 615-371-2238. p. 2225

Dillman, Jenelle, Librn, Perkins & Will Architects, Inc, 330 N Wabash Ave, Ste 3600, Chicago, IL, 60611-3608. Tel: 312-755-0770. Fax: 312-755-0775. p. 622

Dillmann, Alison, Librn, Southeast Louisiana Hospital, 23515 Hwy 190, Mandeville, LA, 70470. Tel: 985-626-6596. Fax: 985-626-6424. p. 955

Dillmann, Alison, Dir, New Orleans Adolescent Hospital, 210 State St, New Orleans, LA, 70118. Tel: 504-897-4639. Fax: 504-896-2652. p. 961

Dillmann, George J, Libr Coordr, Cornell University Library, Adelson Library, Laboratory of Ornithology, 159 Sapsucker Woods Rd, Ithaca, NY, 14850-1999. Tel: 607-254-2165. Fax: 607-254-2111. p. 1641

Dillon, Aimee, Br Mgr, Central Rappahannock Regional Library, Newton Branch, 22 Coles Point Rd, Hague, VA, 22469. Tel: 804-472-3820. Fax: 804-472-5104. p. 2466

Dillon, Andrew, Dean, Prof, University of Texas at Austin, One University Sta, D7000, Austin, TX, 78712-0390. Tel: 512-471-3821. Fax: 512-471-3971. p. 2975

Dillon, April, Dir, Hemphill County Library, 500 Main St, Canadian, TX, 79014. Tel: 806-323-5282. Fax: 806-323-6102. p. 2294

Dillon, Bernadette, Dir, Libr & Info Serv, Hastings Public Library, 312 Beaver St, Hastings, PA, 16646. Tel: 814-247-8231. Fax: 814-247-8871. p. 2067

Dillon, Catherine M, Dir, Info Serv, Jackson Lewis LLP, 666 Third Ave, 29th Flr, New York, NY, 10017-4030. Tel: 212-545-4033. p. 1683

Dillon, Cy, Dir, Ferrum College, 150 Wiley Dr, Ferrum, VA, 24088. Tel: 540-365-4426. Fax: 540-365-4423. p. 2463

Dillon, Cy, Dir, Hampden Sydney College, 257 Via Sacra, HSC Box 7, Hampden Sydney, VA, 23943. Tel: 434-223-6197. Fax: 434-223-6351. p. 2468

Dillon, Diana, Cat, Sinte Gleska University Library, E Hwy 18, Mission, SD, 57555. Tel: 605-856-8100, 605-856-8112. Fax: 605-856-2011. p. 2215

Dillon, Jack, Dir, Bartlett Arboretum Association, Inc Library, 151 Brookdale Rd, Stamford, CT, 06903-4199. Tel: 203-322-6971. Fax: 203-595-9168. p. 369

Dillon, John, Asst Dir, Saint Anselm College, 100 Saint Anselm Dr, Manchester, NH, 03102-1310. Tel: 603-641-7300. Fax: 603-641-7345. p. 1456

Dillon, Karen, Librn, Carilion Clinic, Belleview at Jefferson St, Roanoke, VA, 24033. Tel: 540-981-8039. Fax: 540-981-8666. p. 2493

Dillon, Kathleen, Librn, Houston Community College - Southwest College, West Loop Center Library, 5601 West Loop S, Houston, TX, 77081-2221. Tel: 713-718-7880. Fax: 713-718-7881. p. 2338

Dillon, Mary P, Coll Develop, University of Miami, Louis Calder Memorial Library, Miller School of Medicine, 1601 NW Tenth Ave, Miami, FL, 33136. Tel: 305-243-5767. Fax: 305-325-8853. p. 469

Dillon, Michelle, Mgr, Portage County District Library, Pierce Streetsboro, 8990 Kirby Lane, Streetsboro, OH, 44241-1723. Tel: 330-626-4458. Fax: 330-626-1737. p. 1901

Dillon, Patrick, Fac Librn, Quincy College, Newport Hall, Rm 103, 150 Newport Ave, Quincy, MA, 02171. Tel: 617-984-1680. Fax: 617-984-1782. p. 1119

Dills, Carla, Asst Dir, Woodford County Library, 115 N Main St, Versailles, KY, 40383-1289. Tel: 859-873-5191. Fax: 859-873-1542. p. 936

Dills, Joyce, In Charge, Point Marion Public Library, 399 Ontario St, Point Marion, PA, 15474. Tel: 724-725-9553. Fax: 724-725-9553. p. 2131

Dilmore, Donald, Dr, Assoc VPres, Edinboro University of Pennsylvania, 200 Tartan Ave, Edinboro, PA, 16444. Tel: 814-732-2779. Fax: 814-732-2883. p. 2053

Dilworth, Matthew, Ref Serv Coordr, Indiana University East Campus Library, 2325 Chester Blvd, Richmond, IN, 47374. Tel: 765-973-8311. Fax: 765-973-8315. p. 775

DiMarco, Scott R, Dir, Mansfield University, Mansfield, PA, 16933. Tel: 570-662-4670. Fax: 570-662-4993. p. 2084

DiMaria, Grace, Adult Serv, Hempstead Public Library, 115 Nichols Ct, Hempstead, NY, 11550-3199. Tel: 516-481-6990. Fax: 516-481-6719. p. 1634

DiMassa, Michael, Mgr, Yale University Library, Library Shelving Facility, 147 Leeder Hill Rd, Hamden, CT, 06518. Tel: 203-432-9140. Fax: 203-432-9139. p. 358

Dimassis, Nick, Asst Dir, East Central Regional Library, 244 S Birch, Cambridge, MN, 55008-1588. Tel: 763-689-7390. Fax: 763-689-7389. p. 1243

DiMattia, Ernest A, Jr, Pres, The Ferguson Library, One Public Library Plaza, 96 Broad St, Stamford, CT, 06904. Tel: 203-964-1000, Ext 8200. Fax: 203-357-9098. p. 369

Dimbleby, Allison, Ch, Harmony Library, 195 Putnam Pike, Harmony, RI, 02829. Tel: 401-949-2850. Fax: 401-949-2868. p. 2167

Dimenstein, Catherine, Librn, Carondelet Saint Mary's Hospital, 1601 W St Mary's Rd, Tucson, AZ, 85745. Tel: 520-872-4974. Fax: 520-872-4936. p. 86

DiMento, C J, Ref Serv, Oceanside Public Library, 330 N Coast Hwy, Oceanside, CA, 92054-2824. Tel: 760-435-5600. Fax: 760-435-9614. p. 199

DiMeo, Michelle, PhD, The S Gordon Castigliano Dir of Libr Digital Initiatives, College of Physicians of Philadelphia, 19 S 22nd St, Philadelphia, PA, 19103-3097. Tel: 215-399-2306. Fax: 215-561-6477. p. 2104

DiMichele, Donna, Libr Prog Mgr, State of Rhode Island Office of Library & Information Services, One Capitol Hill, 4th Flr, Providence, RI, 02908. Tel: 401-574-9303. Fax: 401-574-9320. p. 2175

Diminture, Cynthia, Head Librn, Newburyport Public Library, 94 State St, Newburyport, MA, 01950-6619. Tel: 978-465-4428, Ext 222. Fax: 978-463-0394. p. 1109

Dimitriadis, Deborah, Tech Serv Librn, Griffin Free Public Library, 22 Hooksett Rd, Auburn, NH, 03032. Tel: 603-483-5374. Fax: 603-483-0483. p. 1438

Dimmock, Nora, Head, Multimedia, University of Rochester, Multimedia Center, Rush Rhees Library, Rochester, NY, 14627. Tel: 585-273-5010. Fax: 585-273-1032. p. 1733

Dimoff, Mary, Info Spec, USW International Union Library, 3340 Perimeter Hill Dr, Nashville, TN, 37211. Tel: 615-834-8590, Ext 720. Fax: 615-831-6792. p. 2260

Dimond, Trish, Asst Dir, Urbandale Public Library, 3520 86th St, Urbandale, IA, 50322-4056. Tel: 515-278-3945. Fax: 515-278-3918. p. 848

Dimunation, Mark G, Div Chief, Library of Congress, Rare Book & Special Collections Division, Thomas Jefferson Bldg, Deck A, Washington, DC, 20540. Tel: 202-707-5434. Fax: 202-707-4142. p. 407

Dimyan, Roxanne, Ref Librn (Info Serv), Clark College, Mail Stop LIB 112, 1933 Fort Vancouver Way, Vancouver, WA, 98663-3598. Tel: 360-992-2427. Fax: 360-992-2869. p. 2545

Din, Judy, Tech Serv Mgr, United States Department of the Interior Library, 1849 C St NW, Rm 1151, Washington, DC, 20240. Tel: 202-208-3402. Fax: 202-208-6773. p. 419

Dina, Yemisi, Head, Pub Serv, York University Libraries, Osgoode Hall Law School Library, One Scholar's Walk, York University, Toronto, ON, M3J 1P3, CANADA. Tel: 416-650-8404. Fax: 416-736-5298. p. 2868

Dinallo, Antonello, Fac Coordr, Human Res, Drexel University Health Sciences Libraries, 245 N 15th St MS 449, Philadelphia, PA, 19102-1192. Tel: 215-762-7186. Fax: 215-762-8180. p. 2105

DiNardo, Carl, Ref Librn, Lock Haven University of Pennsylvania, 401 N Fairview Ave, Lock Haven, PA, 17745-2390. Tel: 570-484-2854. Fax: 570-484-2506. p. 2082

DiNatale, Jim, Mgr, Res, Dickstein Shapiro LLP, Research Services, 1825 Eye St NW, Washington, DC, 20006. Tel: 202-420-4999. Fax: 202-420-2201. p. 398

Dindo, John, Coordr, Marine Environmental Sciences Consortium, Dauphin Island Sea Lab, 101 Bienville Blvd, Dauphin Island, AL, 36528. Tel: 251-861-2141. Fax: 251-861-4646. p. 2937

Dineen, Darlene, Mgr, Salt Lake County Library Services, Columbus Branch, 2530 S 500 East, South Salt Lake City, UT, 84106-1316. Tel: 801-944-7606. Fax: 801-412-0944. p. 2414

Dineen, Dorothy, Dir, Mexico Public Library, 3269 Main St, Mexico, NY, 13114. Tel: 315-963-3012. Fax: 315-963-7317. p. 1660

Dinehart, Terrill, Acq, Keuka College, 141 Central Ave, Keuka Park, NY, 14478-0038. Tel: 315-279-5224, 315-279-5632. Fax: 315-279-5334. p. 1649

Ding, Lina, Br Mgr, Brooklyn Public Library, Bedford, 496 Franklin Ave, Brooklyn, NY, 11238. Tel: 718-623-0012. Fax: 718-622-9919. p. 1590

Dinges, Carol, Libr Serv Mgr, Lebanon Public Library, 55 Academy St, Lebanon, OR, 97355-3320. Tel: 541-258-4232. Fax: 541-258-4958. p. 2004

Dingle, Erin, Br Mgr, Frederick County Public Libraries, Emmitsburg Branch, 300-A S Seton Ave, Unit 2 J, Emmitsburg, MD, 21727. Tel: 301-600-6329. Fax: 301-600-6330. p. 1029

Dingle, Erin, Librn, Frederick County Public Libraries, Thurmont Branch, 76 E Moser Rd, Thurmont, MD, 21788. Tel: 301-600-7200. p. 1029

Dingledy, Frederick, Ref Serv, College of William & Mary in Virginia, The Wolf Law Library, 613 S Henry St, Williamsburg, VA, 23187. Tel: 757-221-3255. Fax: 757-221-3051. p. 2502

Dingley, Brenda, Dir, Scholarly Communications, University of Missouri-Kansas City Libraries, 800 E 51st St, Kansas City, MO, 64110. Tel: 816-235-2226. Fax: 816-333-5584. p. 1341

Dingley, Dennis, Circ, Chino Valley Public Library, 1020 W Palomino Rd, Chino Valley, AZ, 86323-5500. Tel: 928-636-2687. Fax: 928-636-9129. p. 60

Dingman, Elizabeth, Ref Librn/Trainer, Gowling Lafleur Henderson LLP, One First Canadian Pl, 100 King St W, Ste 1600, Toronto, ON, M5X 1G5, CANADA. Tel: 416-862-7287. Fax: 416-862-7661. p. 2854

Dingus, Mary, Librn, Missouri School for the Blind Library, 3815 Magnolia Ave, Saint Louis, MO, 63110. Tel: 314-776-4320, Ext 3257. Fax: 314-773-3762. p. 1356

Dini, Karen, Reader Serv, Addison Public Library, Four Friendship Plaza, Addison, IL, 60101. Tel: 630-458-3313. Fax: 630-543-6645. p. 587

Dinkelman, Andrea, Librn, Iowa State University Library, Veterinary Medical Library, 2280 College of Veterinary Med, Ames, IA, 50011. Tel: 515-294-2225. Fax: 515-294-1954. p. 793

Dinkins, Debora, Head, Tech Serv, Stetson University, 421 N Woodland Blvd, Unit 8418, DeLand, FL, 32723. Tel: 386-822-7179. p. 437

Dinkins, Julie, Circ Mgr, Sonoma State University Library, 1801 E Cotati Ave, Rohnert Park, CA, 94928-3609. Tel: 707-664-4077. Fax: 707-664-2090. p. 219

Dinneen, Beverly, Ch, Gale Free Library, 23 Highland St, Holden, MA, 01520-2599. Tel: 508-210-4191. Fax: 508-829-0232. p. 1095

Dinniman, Margo P, Dir, Brandywine Hospital & Trauma Center, 201 Reeceville Rd, Coatesville, PA, 19320. Tel: 610-383-8147. Fax: 610-383-8243. p. 2046

DiNoble, Lisa, Head, Coll & Database Mgt, National Gallery of Canada Library, 380 Sussex Dr, Ottawa, ON, K1N 9N4, CANADA. Tel: 613-990-0594. Fax: 613-990-9818. p. 2832

Dintaman, Sonya, Dir, Carnegie Public Library of Steuben County, 322 S Wayne St, Angola, IN, 46703. Tel: 260-665-3362. Fax: 260-665-8958. p. 724

Dinu, Simona, Br Mgr, Hamilton Public Library, Saltfleet, 131 Gray Rd, Stoney Creek, ON, L8G 3V3, CANADA. Tel: 905-546-3200, Ext 3417. p. 2809

Dinu, Simona, Br Mgr, Hamilton Public Library, Stoney Creek Branch, 777 Hwy 8, Stoney Creek, ON, L8E 5J4, CANADA. Tel: 905-546-3200, Ext 1046. p. 2809

Dinville, Julia, Adult Serv, Bellevue Public Library, 1003 Lincoln Rd, Bellevue, NE, 68005-3199. Tel: 402-293-3157. Fax: 402-293-3163. p. 1393

Dinwiddie, Mollie, Dean, Libr Serv, University of Central Missouri, 601 S Missouri, Warrensburg, MO, 64093. Tel: 660-543-4140. Fax: 660-543-4144. p. 1371

Dinwoodie, Inez E, Assoc Dept Head, The MITRE Corporation, 202 Burlington Rd, MS C222, Bedford, MA, 01730. Tel: 703-983-5342. Fax: 703-983-3350. p. 1052

Dinwoody, Bryan E, Dir, Alma Public Library, 351 N Court, Alma, MI, 48801-1999. Tel: 989-463-3966, Ext 110. Fax: 989-466-5901. p. 1149

Diodato, Louise, Electronic Res Librn, Cardinal Stritch University Library, 6801 N Yates Rd, Milwaukee, WI, 53207-3985. Tel: 414-410-4265. Fax: lwdiodato@stritch.edu. p. 2617

Dion, E Ann, Br Mgr, Horry County Memorial Library, Bucksport, 7657 Hwy 701 S, Conway, SC, 29527. Tel: 843-397-1950. Fax: 843-397-1951. p. 2191

Dion, Gilles, AV, College LaSalle, Bureau 4100, 2000 Saint Catherine St W, Montreal, QC, H3H 2T2, CANADA. Tel: 514-939-2006, Ext 4439. Fax: 514-939-7292. p. 2894

Dion, Joanne, Bibliothecaire Responsable, Bibliothèques de Montrèal, Riviere-des-Prairies, 9001, boulevard Perras, Montreal, QC, H1E 3J7, CANADA. Tel: 514-872-9386. Fax: 514-872-9650. p. 2891

Dion, Pascale, Circ, Institut National de la Recherche Scientifique, Universite du Quebec, 490 de la Couronne, local 1401, Quebec, QC, G1K 9A9, CANADA. Tel: 418-654-2577. Fax: 418-654-2660. p. 2905

Dionne, Claire, Chief Exec Officer, Township of Russell Public Library, Embrun Branch, 1215 St Augustin St, Embrun, ON, K0A 1W1, CANADA. Tel: 613-443-3636. Fax: 613-445-8014. p. 2839

Dionne, Claire, Head of Libr, Township of Russell Public Library, 1053 Concession St, Box 280, Russell, ON, K4R 1E1, CANADA. Tel: 613-445-5331. Fax: 613-445-8014. p. 2839

Dionne, Joseph R, Dir, Nashua Public Library, Two Court St, Nashua, NH, 03060. Tel: 603-589-4620. Fax: 603-594-3457. p. 1458

Dionne, Karen, Librn, Bibliotheque Municipale Anne-Marie-D'Amours, 145, rue de l'Arena, Trois-Pistoles, QC, G0L 4K0, CANADA. Tel: 418-851-2374. Fax: 418-851-3567. p. 2913

Diorio, Geri, Ch, Ridgefield Library Association Inc, 472 Main St, Ridgefield, CT, 06877-4585. Tel: 203-438-2282. Fax: 203-438-4558. p. 365

DiPaolo, Denise, Libr Dir, Shelter Island Public Library, 37 N Ferry Rd, Shelter Island, NY, 11964. Tel: 631-749-0042. Fax: 631-749-1575. p. 1742

DiPaolo, Janet, Instrul Serv Librn, University of Massachusetts at Boston, 100 Morrissey Blvd, Boston, MA, 02125-3300. Tel: 617-287-5939. p. 1068

DiPardo, Claire, Librn, Hay Group, Wanamaker Bldg, 100 Penn Square E, Philadelphia, PA, 19107-3388. Tel: 215-861-2434. Fax: 215-861-2102. p. 2110

Dipilato, Renee, Br Mgr, Alexandria Library, Charles E Beatley Jr Central (Hqtrs), 5005 Duke St, Alexandria, VA, 22304-2903. Tel: 703-746-1728. p. 2444

DiPonzio-Heise, Laura, Head, Circ, Rochester Institute of Technology, 90 Lomb Memorial Dr, Rochester, NY, 14623-5604. Tel: 585-475-5819. Fax: 585-475-7007. p. 1731

Dipple, Beth, Dir, Sheboygan County Historical Research Center Library, 518 Water St, Sheboygan Falls, WI, 53085. Tel: 920-467-4667. Fax: 920-467-1395. p. 2638

Dippold, Colleen, Pub Serv & Libr Instruction Coordr, Hilbert College, 5200 S Park Ave, Hamburg, NY, 14075. Tel: 716-649-7900, Ext 315. Fax: 716-648-6530. p. 1632

Diptee, Jennifer, Asst Dir, Miami Dade College, Kendall Campus Library, 11011 SW 104th St, Miami, FL, 33176-3393. Tel: 305-237-0996, 305-237-2015, 305-237-2291. Fax: 305-237-2923. p. 466

Diputado, Courtney, Libr Asst, Contra Costa County Library, Prewett Library, 4703 Lone Tree Way, Antioch, CA, 94531. Tel: 925-776-3060. p. 209

Dirig, Robert, Archivist, Art Center College of Design, 1700 Lida St, Pasadena, CA, 91103. Tel: 626-396-2231. Fax: 626-568-0428. p. 205

Dirk, Ruth, Asst Librn, Bleyhl Community Library, 311 Division St, Grandview, WA, 98930-1398. Tel: 509-882-9217. p. 2516

Dirks, Kay, Supvr, North Central Regional Library, Ephrata Public Library, 45 Alder NW, Ephrata, WA, 98823-1663. Tel: 509-754-3971. Fax: 509-754-3971. p. 2548

Dirks, Timothy, Dir, Fargo Public Library, 102 N Third St, Fargo, ND, 58102. Tel: 701-241-1493. Fax: 701-241-8581. p. 1841

Dirkse, Judy, Ch, Prog Coordr, Sioux Center Public Library, 102 S Main Ave, Sioux Center, IA, 51250-1801. Tel: 712-722-2138. Fax: 712-722-1235. p. 843

Dirlam, Dona Mary, Dir, Richard T Liddicoat Gemological Library & Information Center, 5345 Armada Dr, Carlsbad, CA, 92008. Tel: 760-603-4154. Fax: 760-603-4256. p. 132

DiRusso, Richard, Coll Develop Mgr, Pima County Public Library, 101 N Stone Ave, Tucson, AZ, 85701. Tel: 520-564-5600. Fax: 520-594-5621. p. 86

DiSalvo, Deborah, Assoc Dir, Access Serv, United States Military Academy Library, Jefferson Hall Library & Learning Center, 758 Cullum Rd, West Point, NY, 10996. Tel: 845-938-3833. Fax: 845-938-4000. p. 1767

DiSalvo, Evanna, Circ Supvr, Saint John Fisher College, 3690 East Ave, Rochester, NY, 14618-3599. Tel: 585-385-8165. Fax: 585-385-8445. p. 1732

DiSanto, Vicki, Ch, Somers Library, 80 Primrose St, Rte 139 & Reis Park, Somers, NY, 10589. Tel: 914-232-5717. Fax: 914-232-1035. p. 1745

Disanza, Mary, Dir, William E Dermody Free Public Library, 420 Hackensack St, Carlstadt, NJ, 07072. Tel: 201-438-8866. Fax: 201-438-2733. p. 1477

Disbro, Megan, Software Training & Web Spec Librn, Chautauqua-Cattaraugus Library System, 106 W Fifth St, Jamestown, NY, 14701. Tel: 716-484-7136. p. 1646

Disbro, Nancy, Dir, Andrews Dallas Township Public Library, 30 E Madison St, Andrews, IN, 46702. Tel: 260-786-3574. Fax: 260-786-3574. p. 724

Disbrow, Nancy, Assoc Prof, Southern Connecticut State University, 501 Crescent St, New Haven, CT, 06515. Tel: 203-392-5702. Fax: 203-392-5780. p. 2963

Disch, Amy, Libr Dir, Columbus Dispatch Editorial Library, 34 S Third St, Columbus, OH, 43215. Tel: 614-461-5177. Fax: 614-469-6165. p. 1884

Discher, Edie M, Syst Librn, Fargo Public Library, 102 N Third St, Fargo, ND, 58102. Tel: 701-241-1472. Fax: 701-241-8581. p. 1841

Dischner, Sue, Br Mgr, Elbert County Library District, Elbert Branch, 24489 Main St, Elbert, CO, 80106. Tel: 303-648-3533. Fax: 303-648-3853. p. 305

Dischner, Sue, Br Mgr, Elbert County Library District, Kiowa Branch, 331 Comanche, Kiowa, CO, 80117. Tel: 303-621-2111. Fax: 303-621-2754. p. 305

Dishan, Brad, Mgr, Libr Serv, Saint Joseph's Hospital, 268 Grosvenor St, London, ON, N6A 4V2, CANADA. Tel: 519-646-6000, Ext 65727. Fax: 519-646-6228. p. 2818

Dishman, Nadine, Curator, Wilson County Historical Society, 420 N Seventh St, Fredonia, KS, 66736-1315. Tel: 620-378-3965. p. 868

Dishon, Clay, Libr Commun Serv Mgr, Richmond Public Library, Westover Hills, 1408 Westover Hills Blvd, Richmond, VA, 23225. Tel: 804-646-0652. Fax: 804-646-8714. p. 2490

Disney, Doreen, Mgr, Waterloo Public Library, McCormick Branch, 500 Parkside Dr, Waterloo, ON, N2L 5J4, CANADA. Tel: 519-885-1920. Fax: 519-885-0076. p. 2870

Dissly, Lois, Head, Automation, Head, Tech Serv, Bozeman Public Library, 626 E Main St, Bozeman, MT, 59715. Tel: 406-582-2400. Fax: 406-582-2424. p. 1375

Distad, Merrill, Assoc Univ Librn, University of Alberta, University Library, 5-02 Cameron Libr, Edmonton, AB, T6G 2J8, CANADA. Tel: 780-492-3790. Fax: 780-492-8302. p. 2702

Distance, Doris Lynn, Br Mgr, Enoch Pratt Free Library, Herring Run, 3801 Erdman Ave, Baltimore, MD, 21213-2099. Tel: 410-396-0996. Fax: 410-396-0997. p. 1013

Distante, Deb, Bibliog Instr, Mt San Antonio College Library, 1100 N Grand Ave, Walnut, CA, 91789. Tel: 909-274-4260. Fax: 909-468-4011. p. 282

Distefano, Lynne, Librn, Alexandria Daily Town Talk Library, 1201 Third St, Alexandria, LA, 71301. Tel: 318-487-6330. Fax: 318-487-6488. p. 939

DiStefano, Marcia, Cat & Adult Serv, Okeechobee County Public Library, 206 SW 16th St, Okeechobee, FL, 34974. Tel: 863-763-3536. Fax: 863-763-5368. p. 474

Disterhaft, Diane, Co-Dir, Ref Serv, Berlin Public Library, 121 W Park Ave, Berlin, WI, 54923. Tel: 920-361-5420. Fax: 920-361-5424. p. 2582

Ditch, Stephanie, Mgr, Greenville County Library System, Greer (Jean M Smith) Branch, 505 Pennsylvania Ave, Greer, SC, 29650. Tel: 864-877-8722. Fax: 864-877-1422. p. 2196

Ditkoff, Jennifer, Coll Develop Librn, Head, Access Serv, Keene State College, 229 Main St, Keene, NH, 03435-3201. Tel: 603-358-2725. Fax: 603-358-2745. p. 1453

Ditmer, Brian, Distance Learning Spec, Central New Mexico Community College Libraries, 525 Buena Vista SE, Albuquerque, NM, 87106-4023. Tel: 505-224-3292. Fax: 505-224-3321. p. 1548

DiTomasso, Matt, Head, Circ & Tech Serv, Mount Pleasant Public Library, 350 Bedford Rd, Pleasantville, NY, 10570-3099. Tel: 914-769-0548. Fax: 914-769-6149. p. 1719

DiTommaso, Anthony, Librn, ECPI University, Newport News Campus Library, 1001 Omni Blvd, Ste 100, Newport News, VA, 23606. Tel: 757-838-9191, Ext 74234. Fax: 757-827-5351. p. 2499

Ditta, Joseph, Ref Librn, New York Historical Society Library, 170 Central Park W, New York, NY, 10024. Tel: 212-873-3400. Fax: 212-875-1591. p. 1689

Dittemore, Margaret R, Librn, Smithsonian Libraries, John Wesley Powell Library of Anthropology, Nat Museum of Natural Hist, Rm 331, MRC 112, Tenth St & Constitution Ave NW, Washington, DC, 20560-0112. Tel: 202-633-1638. Fax: 202-357-1896. p. 415

Dittman, Sherri, Coordr, Paul Oliver Memorial Hospital, 224 Park Ave, Frankfort, MI, 49635. Tel: 231-352-2312. p. 1181

Dittmar, Dawn, Teen Serv, Highland Township Public Library, 444 Beach Farm Circle, Highland, MI, 48357. Tel: 248-887-2218. Fax: 248-887-5179. p. 1189

Dittmar, Laurie, Br Mgr, La Porte County Public Library, Fish Lake, 7981 E State Rd 4, Walkerton, IN, 46574. Tel: 219-369-1337. Fax: 219-369-1337. p. 759

Dittmar, Marni, Librn, TMC HealthCare, 5301 E Grant Rd, Tucson, AZ, 85712. Tel: 520-324-5140. Fax: 520-324-5363. p. 88

Dittmer, Arlis D, Dir, Blessing Health Professions Library, Broadway at 11th St, Quincy, IL, 62305. Tel: 217-228-5520, Ext 6971. Fax: 217-223-6400. p. 693

Dittmer, Mary, Asst Dir, The Frances Banta Waggoner Community Library, 505 Tenth St, DeWitt, IA, 52742-1335. Tel: 563-659-5523. Fax: 563-659-2901. p. 810

Ditto, Waynette, Dir, Hewitt Public Library, 100 Zuni Dr, Hewitt, TX, 76643. Tel: 254-666-2442. Fax: 254-666-6025. p. 2332

Dittoe, Patti, Libr Mgr, Ohio State University LIBRARIES, Orton Memorial Library of Geology, 180 Orton Hall, 155 S Oval Mall, Columbus, OH, 43210. Tel: 614-292-6549. p. 1889

Dittrich, Patricia, Br Mgr, Fort Bend County Libraries, Albert George Branch, 9230 Gene St, Needville, TX, 77461-8313. Tel: 979-793-4270. Fax: 281-342-5992. p. 2375

DiTullio, Patty, Dir, Amesbury Public Library, 149 Main St, Amesbury, MA, 01913. Tel: 978-388-8148. p. 1048

Ditz, Anita, Ch, Schlow Centre Region Library, 211 S Allen St, State College, PA, 16801-4806. Tel: 814-235-7817. Fax: 814-238-8508. p. 2143

Ditzel, Sallie, Librn, Sanborn-Pekin Free Library, 5884 West St, Sanborn, NY, 14132. Tel: 716-731-9933. Fax: 716-731-9933. p. 1738

Ditzler, Cindy, Dir, Northern Illinois University Libraries, Regional History Center, Founders Library, DeKalb, IL, 60115. Tel: 815-753-9392. p. 635

Ditzler, Cindy, Univ Archivist, Northern Illinois University Libraries, DeKalb, IL, 60115-2868. Tel: 815-753-9392. p. 635

Ditzler, Wyatt, Computer Serv Mgr, Beloit Public Library, 605 Eclipse Blvd, Beloit, WI, 53511. Tel: 608-364-5755. Fax: 608-364-2907. p. 2581

Divan, Susan, Libr Dir, Media Spec, Youth Rehabilitation & Treatment Center Library, 2802 30th Ave, Kearney, NE, 68845-9599. Tel: 308-338-2011, Ext 287. Fax: 308-865-5323. p. 1403

Divelbiss, Mary Lou, Librn, Tulsa City-County Library, Charles Page Branch, 551 E Fourth St, Sand Springs, OK, 74063. Tel: 918-591-4585. Fax: 918-591-4586. p. 1983

Divine, Christy, Develop Dir, Mkt Dir, Live Oak Public Libraries, 2002 Bull St, Savannah, GA, 31401. Tel: 912-652-3600. Fax: 912-652-3638. p. 550

Dix, Amy, Ch, Wardsboro Free Public Library, 170 Main St, Wardsboro, VT, 05355. Tel: 802-896-6988. p. 2438

Dix, Brook J, Librn, Stockton Public Library, 124 N Cedar, Stockton, KS, 67669-1636. Tel: 785-425-6372. Fax: 785-425-6372. p. 895

Dix, Lucy, Reader Serv, New Mexico State Library, Library for the Blind & Physically Handicapped, 1209 Camino Carlos Rey, Santa Fe, NM, 87507-5166. Tel: 505-476-9770. Fax: 505-476-9776. p. 1563

Dix, Rene, Librn, Birchard Public Library of Sandusky County, Woodville Branch, 101 E Main, Woodville, OH, 43469. Tel: 419-849-2744. p. 1900

Dix, Stephen, Dir, Muskegon Area District Library, 4845 Airline Rd, Unit 5, Muskegon, MI, 49444-4503. Tel: 231-737-6248. Fax: 231-737-6307. p. 1212

Dixen, Rebecca, Dir, Baldwin Public Library, 400 Cedar St, Baldwin, WI, 54002-0475. Tel: 715-684-3813. Fax: 715-684-5115. p. 2580

Dixey, Mary, Dir, Rensselaer at Hartford, 275 Windsor St, Hartford, CT, 06120-2991. Tel: 860-548-2490. Fax: 860-548-7904. p. 347

Dixon, Ann, Dir, Homer Public Library, 500 Hazel Ave, Homer, AK, 99603. Tel: 907-235-3180, Ext 21. Fax: 907-235-3136. p. 49

Dixon, Ann, Dir, Harding University, 915 E Market St, Searcy, AR, 72149-2267. Tel: 501-279-4354. p. 114

Dixon, Barbara, Dir, Barton Rees Pogue Memorial Library, 29 W Washington St, Upland, IN, 46989. Tel: 765-998-2971. Fax: 765-998-2961. p. 782

Dixon, Bonnie, Tech Serv, California State University, 9001 Stockdale Hwy, Bakersfield, CA, 93311-1022. Tel: 661-664-3263. Fax: 661-654-3238. p. 123

Dixon, Bruce, Dr, Dir, Allegheny County Health Department Library, 301 39th St, Pittsburgh, PA, 15201. Tel: 412-578-8028. Fax: 412-578-8144. p. 2121

Dixon, Catherine, Libr Dir, St John's College Library, 60 College Ave, Annapolis, MD, 21401. Tel: 410-626-2550. Fax: 410-295-6936. p. 1011

Dixon, Celeste, Librn, US National Park Service, 1767 Hwy 156, Larned, KS, 67550-9803. Tel: 620-285-6911. Fax: 620-285-3571. p. 877

Dixon, Christopher, Archives & Ref, Saint Joseph's University, Francis A Drexel Library, 5600 City Ave, Philadelphia, PA, 19131-1395. Tel: 610-660-1905. Fax: 610-660-1916. p. 2116

Dixon, Daniela, Br Mgr, Fairfax County Public Library, Great Falls Branch, 9830 Georgetown Pike, Great Falls, VA, 22066-2634. Tel: 703-757-8560. p. 2461

Dixon, Donna, Circ, Cuyahoga Falls Library, 2015 Third St, Cuyahoga Falls, OH, 44221-3294. Tel: 330-928-2117, Ext 108. Fax: 330-928-2535. p. 1892

Dixon, Janet, Dir, Edward U Demmer Memorial Library, 6961 W School St, Three Lakes, WI, 54562. Tel: 715-546-3391. Fax: 715-546-2930. p. 2642

Dixon, Jill, Dir, Pub Serv, State University of New York at Binghamton, Science Library, Vestal Pkwy E, Binghamton, NY, 13902. Tel: 607-777-3510. Fax: 607-777-4848. p. 1582

Dixon, Karen, Ref Librn, Hopkinton Town Library, 61 Houston Dr, Contoocook, NH, 03229. Tel: 603-746-3663. Fax: 603-746-6799. p. 1444

Dixon, Lizette, Ch, Columbus County Public Library, 407 N Powell Blvd, Whiteville, NC, 28472. Tel: 910-642-3116. Fax: 910-642-3839. p. 1829

Dixon, Marcia, ILL, Barry University, 11300 NE Second Ave, Miami, FL, 33161. Tel: 305-899-3760. Fax: 305-899-4792. p. 464

Dixon, Minneola, Archivist, Oakwood College, 7000 Adventist Blvd, Huntsville, AL, 35896. Tel: 256-726-7246. Fax: 256-726-7538. p. 22

Dixon, Missy, Ch, Bellaire City Library, 5111 Jessamine, Bellaire, TX, 77401-4498. Tel: 713-662-8164. Fax: 713-662-8169. p. 2288

Dixon, Pat, Syst Coordr, California State University, East Bay Library, 25800 Carlos Bee Blvd, Hayward, CA, 94542-3052. Tel: 510-885-2554. Fax: 510-885-2049. p. 157

Dixon, Pat, Dir, East Berlin Community Library, 105 Locust St, East Berlin, PA, 17316. Tel: 717-259-9000. Fax: 717-259-7651. p. 2051

Dixon, Patricia, Librn, Arizona Department of Corrections - Adult Institutions, 4374 Butte Ave, Florence, AZ, 85232. Tel: 520-868-0201, Ext 6850. Fax: 520-868-8556. p. 63

Dixon, Rebecca, Chief Financial Officer, Indianapolis-Marion County Public Library, 2450 N Meridian St, Indianapolis, IN, 46208. Tel: 317-275-4850. Fax: 317-269-5300. p. 753

Dixon, Richard, Librn, Lucas Signatone Corp Library, 393 Tomkins Ct Ste J, Gilroy, CA, 95020. Tel: 408-848-2851. Fax: 408-848-5763. p. 154

Dixon, Robin Miller, Br Head, NASA, Library, Bldg 21, Code 272, Greenbelt, MD, 20771. Tel: 301-286-9230. Fax: 301-286-1755. p. 1030

Dixon, Rose, Asst Librn, Jefferson County District Library, Hamer Branch, 2450 E 2100 North, Hamer, ID, 83425. Tel: 208-662-5275. Fax: 208-662-5213. p. 578

Dixon, Rosie, Mgr, Arkansas Democrat Gazette News Library, 121 E Capitol, Little Rock, AR, 72201. Tel: 501-378-3498. Fax: 501-378-3489. p. 105

Dixon, Sandra, In Charge, Eastern Counties Regional Library, Canso Branch, 130 School St, Canso, NS, B0H 1H0, CANADA. Tel: 902-366-2955. Fax: 902-366-2955. p. 2783

Dixon, Steve G, Librn, State University of New York College of Technology, Bush Hall, Two Main St, Delhi, NY, 13753. Tel: 607-746-4642. Fax: 607-746-4327. p. 1613

Dixon, Terry, Librn, North Central Regional Library, Twisp Community, 201 N Methow Valley Hwy, Twisp, WA, 98856. Tel: 509-997-4681. Fax: 509-997-4681. p. 2549

Dixon, Vicki, Librn, Rochester College, 800 W Avon Rd, Rochester Hills, MI, 48307. Tel: 248-218-2260. Fax: 248-218-2265. p. 1222

Dixon, Victor, Ref Librn, Webmaster, Maywood Public Library District, 121 S Fifth Ave, Maywood, IL, 60153. Tel: 708-343-1847, Ext 20. Fax: 708-343-2115. p. 672

Dixon-Fyle, Joyce, Coll Develop, DePauw University, 11 E Larrabee St, Greencastle, IN, 46135. Tel: 765-658-4420. Fax: 765-658-4017. p. 746

Dizard, Robert, Dep Librn, Library of Congress, 101 Independence Ave at First St SE, Washington, DC, 20540. Tel: 202-707-5000. Fax: 202-707-1925. p. 406

Djevalikian, Sonia, Head Librn, Bibliotheque de Kirkland, 17100 Hymus Blvd, Kirkland, QC, H9J 2W2, CANADA. Tel: 514-630-2726. Fax: 514-630-2716. p. 2884

Djirdjirian, Anna, Dep Dir, United States Court of International Trade, One Federal Plaza, New York, NY, 10278. Tel: 212-264-2816. Fax: 212-264-3242. p. 1702

Djokic, Mirela, Pub Serv Librn, Kwantlen Polytechnic University Library, 12666 72 Ave., Surrey, BC, V3W 2M8, CANADA. Tel: 604-599-3389. Fax: 604-599-2106. p. 2738

Djordjevic, Zorica, Libr Tech, Team Leader, Hopital de L'Enfant Jesus, 1401 18th St, Quebec, QC, G1J 1Z4, CANADA. Tel: 418-649-5686. Fax: 418-649-5627. p. 2905

Djordjevic, Zorica, Libr Tech, Team Leader, Hospital du Saint-Sacrement, 1050, Chemin Sainte-Foy, Quebec, QC, G1S 4L8, CANADA. Tel: 418-682-7511, Ext 2128. Fax: 418-682-7730. p. 2905

Djurdjevic, Danijela, Head, Tech Serv, Community Library, 24615 89th St, Salem, WI, 53168. Tel: 262-843-3348. Fax: 262-843-3144. p. 2636

Djurdjevic, Danijela, Ref Serv, Community Library, Twin Lakes Branch, 110 S Lake Ave, Twin Lakes, WI, 53181. Tel: 262-877-4281. Fax: 262-877-2682. p. 2636

Djurovic, Nada, Librn, Deloitte & Touche, 2800-1055 Dunsmuir St, Ste 2200, Vancouver, BC, V7X 1P4, CANADA. Tel: 604-669-4466. Fax: 604-685-0458. p. 2741

Dmohowski, Joe, Ser Librn, Whittier College, Bonnie Bell Wardman Library, 7031 Founders Hill Rd, Whittier, CA, 90608-9984. Tel: 562-907-4246. Fax: 562-698-7168. p. 283

Dmytryshyn, Linda, Coordr, Central 1 Credit Union Corporate Information Centre, 1441 Creekside Dr, Vancouver, BC, V6J 4S7, CANADA. Tel: 604-737-5971. p. 2740

Doades, Bernice, Tech Serv, Knox County Public Library, 502 N Seventh St, Vincennes, IN, 47591-2119. Tel: 812-886-4380. Fax: 812-886-0342. p. 784

Doak, Gordon A, Pres, National Association of Animal Breeders Library, 401 Bernadette Dr, Columbia, MO, 65203. Tel: 573-445-4406. Fax: 573-446-2279. p. 1324

Doan, Tomalee, Head of Libr, Purdue University Libraries, Humanities, Social Science & Education Library, Stewart Ctr 135, 504 W State St, West Lafayette, IN, 47907-2058. Tel: 765-494-2831. Fax: 765-494-9007. p. 786

Doan, Tomalee, Head, Mgt & Econ Libr, Purdue University Libraries, Management & Economics, Krannert Bldg, 2nd Flr, 403 W State St, West Lafayette, IN, 47907-2058. Tel: 765-494-2928. Fax: 765-494-2923. p. 787

Doane, Bernetta, Bibliog Instr, La Salle University, 1900 W Olney Ave, Philadelphia, PA, 19141-1199. Tel: 215-951-1962. Fax: 215-951-1595. p. 2111

Doane, Jeff, Circ, Maryland Institute College of Art, 1401 Mount Royal Ave, Baltimore, MD, 21217. Tel: 410-225-2304, 410-225-2311. Fax: 410-225-2316. p. 1015

Dobb, Linda S, Univ Librn, California State University, East Bay Library, 25800 Carlos Bee Blvd, Hayward, CA, 94542-3052. Tel: 510-885-3664. Fax: 510-885-2049. p. 157

Dobbins, Elizabeth, Circ Mgr, Campbell University, 113 Main St, Buies Creek, NC, 27506. Tel: 910-893-1460. Fax: 910-893-1470. p. 1778

Dobbins, John, Discovery Serv Librn, Occidental College Library, 1600 Campus Rd, Los Angeles, CA, 90041. Tel: 323-259-2833. Fax: 323-341-4991. p. 176

Dobbins, Julie, Dir, Libr Serv, Melville Library, 4010 S Mulberry St, Pine Bluff, AR, 71603. Tel: 870-541-7629. Fax: 870-541-7628. p. 112

Dobbins, Nancy, Admin Serv, Craighead County Jonesboro Public Library, 315 W Oak Ave, Jonesboro, AR, 72401-3513. Tel: 870-935-5133, Ext 30. Fax: 870-935-7987. p. 104

Dobbs, Aaron, Web Developer, Shippensburg University, 1871 Old Main Dr, Shippensburg, PA, 17257-2299. Tel: 717-477-1018. Fax: 717-477-1389. p. 2140

Dobbs, Brenda, Circ Librn, Tombigbee Regional Library System, Evans Memorial Library, 105 N Long St, Aberdeen, MS, 39730. Tel: 662-369-4601. Fax: 662-369-2971. p. 1318

Dobbs, Cheryl, Asst Dir, Greenwood Public Library, 310 S Meridian St, Greenwood, IN, 46143-3135. Tel: 317-881-1953. Fax: 317-881-1963. p. 747

Dobbs, Denise, Librn, Crowell Public Library, 1890 Huntington Dr, San Marino, CA, 91108-2595. Tel: 626-300-0777, Ext 541. Fax: 626-284-0766. p. 254

Dobbs, Gwen, Dir, Northwest Arkansas Community College Library, One College Dr, Bentonville, AR, 72712-5091. Tel: 479-619-4244. Fax: 479-619-4115. p. 95

Dobbs, Kevin, Dean, Yuba Community College, 2088 N Beale Rd, Marysville, CA, 95901. Tel: 530-741-6762. Fax: 530-741-6824. p. 184

Dobbs, Paul, Dir, Massachusetts College of Art & Design, 621 Huntington Ave, Boston, MA, 02115-5882. Tel: 617-879-7150. Fax: 617-879-7110. p. 1063

Dobbs, Susan, Dir, Human Res, Anythink Libraries, 5877 E 120th Ave, Thornton, CO, 80602. Tel: 303-288-2001. Fax: 303-451-0190. p. 323

Dobda, Kathyanne, Asst Dir, Pub Serv, Cleveland State University, University Library, Rhodes Tower, 2121 Euclid Ave, Cleveland, OH, 44115-2214. Tel: 216-875-9738. Fax: 216-687-9380. p. 1879

Dobi, Hanko H, Dir, University of New Haven, 300 Boston Post Rd, West Haven, CT, 06516. Tel: 203-932-7191. Fax: 203-932-1469. p. 377

Dobias, Dale, Asst Dir, United Theological Seminary of the Twin Cities, 3000 Fifth St NW, New Brighton, MN, 55112-2598. Tel: 651-255-6142. Fax: 651-633-4315. p. 1267

Dobie, Dawn, Ref, Bakersfield College, 1801 Panorama Dr, Bakersfield, CA, 93305-1298. Tel: 661-395-4461. Fax: 661-395-4397. p. 123

Dobiesz, Robert, Archivist, Asst Dir, Gannon University, 109 University Sq, Erie, PA, 16541. Tel: 814-871-7557. Fax: 814-871-5666. p. 2055

Dobinson, Susan, Librn, Escambia County Law Library, 190 Governmental Ctr, Pensacola, FL, 32502. Tel: 850-595-4468. Fax: 850-595-4470. p. 481

Doble, Frank, Reader Serv, Ref Serv, Onondaga Community College, 4585 W Seneca Tpk, Syracuse, NY, 13215-4585. Tel: 315-498-2334. Fax: 315-498-7213. p. 1752

Doblos, Vince, Ref, College of Southern Maryland Library, 8730 Mitchell Rd, La Plata, MD, 20646. Tel: 301-934-7626. Fax: 301-934-7699. p. 1034

Dobos, Lou, Ref Serv, Ad, Hudson Library & Historical Society, 96 Library St, Hudson, OH, 44236-5122. Tel: 330-653-6658. Fax: 330-650-3373. p. 1905

Dobransky, Janice R, Br Mgr, Coastal Plain Regional Library, Cook County, 213 E Second St, Adel, GA, 31620. Tel: 229-896-3652. Fax: 229-896-3652. p. 554

Dobrea, George, Dir, Romanian Ethnic Arts Museum Library, 3256 Warren Rd, Cleveland, OH, 44111. Tel: 216-941-5550. Fax: 216-941-3068. p. 1881

Dobrogosz, Karen, Ch, Avery-Mitchell-Yancey Regional Library System, 289 Burnsville School Rd, Burnsville, NC, 28714. Tel: 828-682-4476. Fax: 828-682-6277. p. 1779

Dobroski, Charles, Librn, Trinity Valley Community College Library, Anderson County, 2970 Hwy 19 N, Palestine, TX, 75802. Tel: 903-729-0256. Fax: 903-729-2325. p. 2277

Dobrovolny, Linda, Tech Serv, Yankton Community Library, 515 Walnut, Yankton, SD, 57078-4042. Tel: 605-668-5275. Fax: 605-668-5277. p. 2222

Dobson, Christine, Libr Serv Mgr-Cent, Irving Public Library, 801 W Irving Blvd, Irving, TX, 75015. Tel: 972-721-2748. Fax: 972-721-2463. p. 2346

Dobson, Dawn, ILL, Corning Community College, One Academic Dr, Corning, NY, 14830. Tel: 607-962-9251. Fax: 607-962-9466. p. 1610

Dobson, Elizabeth, Librn, Centennial College of Applied Arts & Technology, Ashtonbee Campus Library, 75 Ashtonbee Rd, Scarborough, ON, M1L 4N4, CANADA. Tel: 416-289-5000, Ext 7000. Fax: 416-289-5017. p. 2840

Dobson, Guy, Syst Librn, Drew University Library, 36 Madison Ave, Madison, NJ, 07940. Tel: 973-408-3207. Fax: 973-408-3770. p. 1497

Dobson, Linda, Dir, Huntsville Public Library, 1216 14th St, Huntsville, TX, 77340. Tel: 936-291-5470. Fax: 936-291-5418. p. 2345

Dobson, Mary, Librn, Cape Breton University Library, 1250 Grand Lake Rd, Sydney, NS, B1P 6L2, CANADA. Tel: 902-563-1421. Fax: 902-563-1826. p. 2785

Dobson, Wes, Dir, Nipawin Bible College Library, Hwy 35 S, Nipawin, SK, S0E 1E0, CANADA. Tel: 306-862-5095. Fax: 306-862-3651. p. 2919

Dobyns, Kevin, Dir, Everest University, 8226 Phillips Hwy, Jacksonville, FL, 32256. Tel: 904-731-4949. Fax: 904-731-0599. p. 452

Docker, Jean, Dir, Oxford Public Library, 42 Washington Ave, Oxford, NJ, 07863-3037. Tel: 908-453-2625. p. 1517

Dockery, Cindy, Librn, Amarillo Public Library, East Branch, 2232 E 27th St, Amarillo, TX, 79103. Tel: 806-342-1589. Fax: 806-342-1591. p. 2274

Dockery, Dana, Automation Syst Coordr, Palm Harbor Library, 2330 Nebraska Ave, Palm Harbor, FL, 34683. Tel: 727-784-3332. Fax: 727-785-6534. p. 480

Dockery, Emory S, Jr, Pres, Darby Foundation, 311 General Darby St, Fort Smith, AR, 72902. Tel: 479-782-3388. Fax: 479-783-7590. p. 100

Dockray, Sarah, Area Dir, Learning Res, North Platte Community College, 601 W State Farm Rd, North Platte, NE, 69101. Tel: 308-535-3727. Fax: 308-535-3794. p. 1410

Dockter, Sally, Head, Ref, University of North Dakota, 3051 University Ave, Stop 9000, Grand Forks, ND, 58202-9000. Tel: 701-777-4640. Fax: 701-777-3319. p. 1843

Doctor, David, Ref Serv, Lane Community College Library, 4000 E 30th Ave, Eugene, OR, 97405-0640. Tel: 541-463-5278. Fax: 541-463-4150. p. 1996

Dodd, Anita, Access Serv, Librn, Douglas County Public Library, 301 SW Third Ave, Ava, MO, 65608. Tel: 417-683-5633. Fax: 417-683-5633. p. 1319

Dodd, Barb, Asst Librn, Southeast Regional Library, Estevan Branch, Leisure Ctr, 701 Souris Ave N, Estevan, SK, S4A 2T1, CANADA. Tel: 306-636-1620, 306-636-1626. Fax: 306-634-5830. p. 2929

Dodd, Becky, Librn, Wellsville City Library, 115 W Sixth St, Wellsville, KS, 66092. Tel: 785-883-2870. Fax: 785-883-2870. p. 899

Dodd, Beth, Head Librn, University of Texas Libraries, Architecture & Planning, Mail Code S5430, BTL 200, Austin, TX, 78713-8916. Tel: 512-495-4623. p. 2283

Dodd, David, Dir, San Rafael Public Library, 1100 E St, San Rafael, CA, 94901-1900. Tel: 415-485-3323. Fax: 415-485-3112. p. 257

Dodd, Jim, Media Serv, Whatcom Community College Library, 237 W Kellogg Rd, Bellingham, WA, 98226. Tel: 360-383-3300. p. 2509

Dodd, Samantha, Archivist, Res, Dallas Historical Society, PO Box 150038, Hall of State in Fair Park, Dallas, TX, 75315-0038. Tel: 214-239-8141. Fax: 214-239-8146. p. 2305

Dodds, Kathrin, Info Spec, Mississippi State University, Architecture, 121 Giles Hall, 889 Collegeview St, Mississippi State, MS, 39762. Tel: 662-325-2204. Fax: 662-325-8872. p. 1309

Dodds, Kevin, Dir, Yellowhead Regional Library, 433 King St, Spruce Grove, AB, T7X 2Y1, CANADA. Tel: 780-962-2003, Ext 226. Fax: 780-962-2770. p. 2717

Dodds, Lori Bull, Law Librn, Collin County Law Library, Courthouse, Ste 10216, 2100 Bloomdale Rd, McKinney, TX, 75071. Tel: 972-548-4260. Fax: 972-547-5734. p. 2361

Dodds, Ruth, Libr Tech, Sutter County Free Library, Browns, 1248 Pacific Ave, Rio Oso, CA, 95674. Tel: 530-633-2170. p. 286

Dodge, Betty, Co-Dir, Newport Free Library, 7390 Main St, Newport, NY, 13416-3500. Tel: 315-845-8533. p. 1705

Dodge, Bill, Med Librn, PPH Medical Library, Palomar Medical Ctr, 555 E Valley Pkwy, Escondido, CA, 92025. Tel: 760-739-3146. Fax: 760-739-3229. p. 147

Dodge, Heather, Info Serv, Manhattan College, 4513 Manhattan College Pkwy, Riverdale, NY, 10471. Tel: 718-862-7166. Fax: 718-862-8028. p. 1728

Dodge, Hillary, Ch, Windsor-Severance Library, 720 Third St, Windsor, CO, 80550-5109. Tel: 970-686-5603. Fax: 970-686-2502. p. 326

Dodge, Lynn L, Dir, Lynchburg Public Library, 2315 Memorial Ave, Lynchburg, VA, 24501. Tel: 434-455-6300. p. 2476

Dodge, Martha, Youth Serv, Ellsworth Public Library, 20 State St, Ellsworth, ME, 04605. Tel: 207-667-6363. Fax: 207-667-4901. p. 984

Dodge, Robin, Librn, Fashion Institute of Design & Merchandising, 919 S Grand Ave, Los Angeles, CA, 90015-1421. Tel: 213-624-1200, Ext 3376. Fax: 213-624-9365. p. 170

Dodge, Sara, Ref, Toccoa Falls College, PO Box 800749, Toccoa Falls, GA, 30598. Tel: 706-886-6831, Ext 5300. Fax: 706-282-6010. p. 554

Dodge, Sarah, Coordr, Info Serv, Ajax Public Library, 55 Harwood Ave S, Ajax, ON, L1S 2H8, CANADA. Tel: 905-683-4000, Ext 8802. Fax: 905-683-6960. p. 2791

Dodington, Anne, Br Mgr, Huron County Library, Brussels Branch, 402 Turnberry St, Brussels, ON, N0G 1H0, CANADA. Tel: 519-887-6448. p. 2799

Dodington, Anne, Br Mgr, Huron County Library, Hensall Branch, 108 King St, Hensall, ON, N0M 1X0, CANADA. Tel: 519-262-2445. p. 2800

Dodington, Anne, Br Mgr, Huron County Library, Seaforth Branch, 108 Main St S, Seaforth, ON, N0K 1W0, CANADA. Tel: 519-527-1430. p. 2800

Dodson, Adrienne, Assoc Librn, Inglewood Public Library, 101 W Manchester Blvd, Inglewood, CA, 90301-1771. Tel: 310-412-5397. Fax: 310-412-8848. p. 159

Dodson, Amy, Br Mgr, Riverside County Library System, Cathedral City Library, 33520 Date Palm Dr, Cathedral City, CA, 92234-4725. Tel: 760-770-9050. Fax: 760-770-9828. p. 217

Dodson, Debi, Libr Dir, Shenandoah Area Free Public Library, 15 W Washington St, Shenandoah, PA, 17976-1708. Tel: 570-462-9829. Fax: 570-462-2772. p. 2139

Dodson, Donna, Asst Librn, Tech Serv, Mount Ida College, Wadsworth Library, 777 Dedham St, Newton, MA, 02459. Tel: 617-928-4552. Fax: 617-928-4038. p. 1110

Dodson, Frank L, Dir, Roanoke Bible College, 715 N Poindexter St, Elizabeth City, NC, 27909-4054. Tel: 252-334-2057. Fax: 252-334-2071. p. 1791

Dodson, Howard, Dir, Howard University Libraries, 500 Howard Pl NW, Washington, DC, 20059. Tel: 202-806-7234. Fax: 202-806-5903. p. 403

Dodson, Jackie, Assoc Dir, Waco-McLennan County Library System, 1717 Austin Ave, Waco, TX, 76701-1794. Tel: 254-750-5941. Fax: 254-750-5940. p. 2397

Dodson, Jill, Circ Librn, Hope Welty Public Library District, 100 S Madison St, Cerro Gordo, IL, 61818. Tel: 217-763-5001. Fax: 217-763-5391. p. 602

Dodson, Laura, ILL, Norfolk Public Library, 235 E Plume St, Norfolk, VA, 23510-1706. Tel: 757-664-7323. Fax: 757-441-5863. p. 2481

Dodson, Linda, Dir, United States Air Force, 37 Harris St, Columbus AFB, MS, 39710-5102. Tel: 662-434-2934. Fax: 662-434-6291. p. 1297

Dodson, Mary, Ad, Oro Valley Public Library, 1305 W Naranja Dr, Oro Valley, AZ, 85737-9762. Tel: 520-229-5300. Fax: 520-229-5319. p. 70

Dodson, Susan, Head, Circ Serv, Pikes Peak Community College Library, 5675 S Academy Blvd, C7, Colorado Springs, CO, 80906-5498. p. 296

Dodson, Tresia, Dir, Granville County Library System, 210 Main St, Oxford, NC, 27565-3321. Tel: 919-693-1121. Fax: 919-693-2244. p. 1813

Dodwell, Catherine, Ref Librn, Garfield Public Library, 500 Midland Ave, Garfield, NJ, 07026. Tel: 973-478-3800. Fax: 973-478-7162. p. 1487

Doe, Douglas, Assoc Archivist, Rhode Island School of Design Library, 15 Westminster St, Providence, RI, 02903. Tel: 401-709-5922. Fax: 401-709-5932. p. 2174

Doebele, Elena, Mgr, Calgary Public Library, Southwood, 924 Southland Dr SW, Calgary, AB, T2W 0J9, CANADA. p. 2690

Doeden, Constance, Dir, Eureka Public Library, 606 N Main St, Eureka, KS, 67045. Tel: 620-583-6222. Fax: 620-583-6222. p. 866

Doege, Marsha C, Dir, Utica Public Library, 7530 Auburn Rd, Utica, MI, 48317-5216. Tel: 586-731-4141. Fax: 586-731-0769. p. 1233

Doehla, Mary, Ms Spec, Van Rensselaer - Rankin Family Historic Cherry Hill Museum & Library, 523 1/2 S Pearl St, Albany, NY, 12202. Tel: 518-434-4791. Fax: 518-434-4806. p. 1571

Doell, Linda, In Charge, Meyer, Suozzi, English & Klein, 990 Stewart Ave, Ste 300, Garden City, NY, 11530. Tel: 516-741-6565. Fax: 516-741-6706. p. 1626

Doellgast, Brigitte, Dir, Goethe-Institut New York, 72 Spring St, 11th Flr, New York, NY, 10012. Tel: 212-439-8700. Fax: 212-439-8705. p. 1680

Doennig, David R, Dir, Stone County Library, 322 West State Hwy 248, Galena, MO, 65656. Tel: 417-357-6410. Fax: 417-357-6695. p. 1329

Doepker, Rachel, Circ Supvr, Ref Librn, Ohio State University LIBRARIES, Agricultural Technical Institute Library, Halterman Hall, 1328 Dover Rd, Wooster, OH, 44691-4000. Tel: 330-287-1326. Fax: 330-287-1333. p. 1887

Doepker, Sharon, Librn, Prairie Agricultural Machinery Institute Library, 2215 Eighth Ave, Humboldt, SK, S0K 2A0, CANADA. Tel: 306-682-5033. Fax: 306-682-5080. p. 2917

Doerge, Janet, Asst Dir, Randolph Township Free Public Library, 28 Calais Rd, Randolph, NJ, 07869. Tel: 973-895-3556. Fax: 973-895-4946. p. 1525

Doerhoff, Nancy, Br Mgr, Saint Louis Public Library, Machacek, 6424 Scanlan Ave, Saint Louis, MO, 63139. Tel: 314-781-2948. Fax: 314-781-8441. p. 1360

Doering, Anita T, Archivist, La Crosse Public Library, 800 Main St, La Crosse, WI, 54601. Tel: 608-789-7156. Fax: 608-789-7106. p. 2603

Doering, David, Dir, La Valle Public Library, 101 W Main, La Valle, WI, 53941-9564. Tel: 608-985-8383. Fax: 608-985-8382. p. 2604

Doering, Peter, Coordr, Santa Clara County Office of Education, 1290 Ridder Park Dr, Mail Code 232, San Jose, CA, 95131. Tel: 408-453-6800. Fax: 408-453-6815. p. 252

Doering, Thomas R, Res Coordr, Nebraska Department of Economic Development Library, 301 Centennial Mall S, Lincoln, NE, 68509. Tel: 402-471-3111. Fax: 402-471-3778. p. 1405

Doering, William, Automation Librn, Cat, University of Wisconsin-La Crosse, 1631 Pine St, La Crosse, WI, 54601-3748. Tel: 608-785-8399. Fax: 608-785-8639. p. 2603

Doerksen, Brad, Dir, Briercrest College & Seminary, 510 College Dr, Caronport, SK, S0H 0S0, CANADA. Tel: 306-756-3252. Fax: 306-756-5521. p. 2917

Doerkson, Maria, Librn, Wapiti Regional Library, Carrot River Public Library, Town Office/Library Complex, Main St, Carrot River, SK, S0E 0L0, CANADA. Tel: 306-768-2501. p. 2921

Doesburgh, John P, Dir, Atlantic Care Regional Medical Center, 1925 Pacific Ave, Atlantic City, NJ, 08401. Tel: 609-441-8966. Fax: 609-441-2137. p. 1469

Doescher, Starla, Head, Acq, University of Oklahoma, 401 W Brooks, Norman, OK, 73019. Tel: 405-325-2141. Fax: 405-325-7550. p. 1971

Doffek, Pam, Dir, Florida State University Libraries, Goldstein Library, 142 Collegiate Loop, Tallahassee, FL, 32306. Tel: 850-644-0461. Fax: 850-644-0460. p. 495

Doherty, Ann, Librn, Connecticut Judicial Branch Law Libraries, New Haven Law Library, New Haven Courthouse, 235 Church St, New Haven, CT, 06510. Tel: 203-503-6828. Fax: 203-789-6499. p. 344

Doherty, Ben, Res Librn, University of Virginia, Arthur J Morris Law Library, 580 Massie Rd, Charlottesville, VA, 22903-1789. Tel: 434-924-7726. Fax: 434-982-2232. p. 2455

Doherty, Heather, Cat, Reserves, University of New Brunswick Libraries, Gerard V La Forest Law Library, Ludlow Hall, 2nd Flr, 41 Dineen

Dr, Fredericton, NB, E3B 5A3, CANADA. Tel: 506-453-4734. Fax: 506-451-6948, 506-453-5186. p. 2764

Doherty, Jean, Admin Coordr, Glenn H Curtiss Museum of Local History, 8419 State Rte 54, Hammondsport, NY, 14840-0326. Tel: 607-569-2160. Fax: 607-569-2040. p. 1633

Doherty, Juliette, Ad, Rye Public Library, 581 Washington Rd, Rye, NH, 03870. Tel: 603-964-8401. Fax: 603-964-7065. p. 1464

Doherty, Katherine M, Libr Dir, White Mountains Community College, 2020 Riverside Dr, Berlin, NH, 03570-3799. Tel: 603-752-1113, Ext 3086. Fax: 603-752-6335. p. 1439

Doherty, Katie, Librn, Dummer Public Library, 63 Hill Rd, Milan, NH, 03588-9711. Tel: 603-449-0995. p. 1457

Doherty, Lisa, Libr Tech, University of Toronto Libraries, John H Daniels Faculty of Architecture, Landscape & Design, Shore + Moffat Library, 230 College St, 2nd Flr, Toronto, ON, M5T 1R2, CANADA. Tel: 416-978-2649. Fax: 416-971-2094. p. 2865

Doherty, Marilyn, Circ Serv Mgr, Alexandria Library, James M Duncan Jr Branch, 2501 Commonwealth Ave, Alexandria, VA, 22301. Tel: 703-746-1705. Fax: 703-746-1785. p. 2444

Doherty, Mary, Dir, Winn Parish Library, 205 W Main St, Winnfield, LA, 71483-2718. Tel: 318-628-4478. Fax: 318-628-9820. p. 972

Doherty, Mary, Bibliog Instr, Online Serv, Ref, State University of New York Downstate Medical Center, 395 Lenox Rd, Brooklyn, NY, 11203. Tel: 718-270-7400. Fax: 718-270-7413, 718-270-7468. p. 1595

Doherty, Paul, Youth Serv, Larchmont Public Library, 121 Larchmont Ave, Larchmont, NY, 10538. Tel: 914-834-2281. p. 1651

Doherty, Paula B, Dir, Libr Serv, Peninsula College Library, 1502 E Lauridsen Blvd, Port Angeles, WA, 98362-6698. Tel: 360-417-6280. Fax: 360-417-6295. p. 2524

Doherty, R Austin, In Charge, Hogan & Hartson LLP, 555 13th St NW, Ste 10W-100, Washington, DC, 20004-1109. Tel: 202-637-8700. Fax: 202-637-5910. p. 403

Doherty, Ryan, Curator, Southern Alberta Art Gallery Library, 601 Third Ave S, Lethbridge, AB, T1J 0H4, CANADA. Tel: 403-327-8770. Fax: 403-328-3913. p. 2710

Doherty, Sally, Br Mgr, Jacksonville Public Library, Regency Square, 9900 Regency Square Blvd, Jacksonville, FL, 32225-6539. Tel: 904-726-5142. Fax: 904-726-5153. p. 454

Doherty, Teresa, Head, Circ, Virginia Commonwealth University Libraries, James Cabell Branch Library, Monroe Park Campus, 901 Park Ave, Richmond, VA, 23284-2033. Tel: 804-828-1111. Fax: 804-828-0151. p. 2492

Doherty, Trafford, Dir, Glenn H Curtiss Museum of Local History, 8419 State Rte 54, Hammondsport, NY, 14840-0326. Tel: 607-569-2160. Fax: 607-569-2040. p. 1633

Dohlin, Jon, Dir, New York Aquarium, W Eighth St & Surf Ave, Brooklyn, NY, 11224. Tel: 718-265-3406, 718-265-3437. Fax: 718-265-3420. p. 1593

Dohnalek, Eileen, Br Mgr, Chicago Public Library, Brighton Park, 4314 S Archer Ave, Chicago, IL, 60632. Tel: 312-747-0666. Fax: 312-747-0665. p. 608

Dohnalek, Richard, Br Mgr, Chicago Public Library, Lincoln Belmont, 1659 W Melrose St, Chicago, IL, 60657. Tel: 312-744-0166. Fax: 312-742-1633. p. 609

Dohner, Jeanette, Pub Relations Tech, Milton-Union Public Library, 560 S Main St, West Milton, OH, 45383. Tel: 937-698-5515. Fax: 937-698-3774. p. 1946

Doi, Olga, Libr Dir, Galway Public Library, 5264 Sacandaga Rd, Galway, NY, 12074. Tel: 518-882-6385. Fax: 518-882-6385. p. 1625

Doig, Kathy, Asst Dir, Davis & Elkins College, 100 Campus Dr, Elkins, WV, 26241. Tel: 304-637-1359. Fax: 304-637-1415. p. 2558

Doig, Nancy, Asst Librn, Museum of Western Art Library, 1550 Bandera Hwy, Kerrville, TX, 78028-9547. Tel: 830-896-2553. Fax: 830-257-5206. p. 2349

Doil, James, Ref, Tech Coordr, O'Fallon Public Library, 120 Civic Plaza, O'Fallon, IL, 62269-2692. Tel: 618-632-3783. Fax: 618-632-3759. p. 684

Doiron, Allen, AV, Provincial Archives of New Brunswick, 23 Dineen Dr, Fredericton, NB, E3B 5A3, CANADA. Tel: 506-453-2122. Fax: 506-453-3288. p. 2763

Dojka, John, Head, Coll Mgt, Inst Archivist, Rensselaer Libraries, Rensselaer Polytechnic Inst, 110 Eighth St, Troy, NY, 12180-3590. Tel: 518-276-8300. Fax: 518-276-2044. p. 1756

Doksansky, Iris, Archivist, Midland Lutheran College, 900 N Clarkson, Fremont, NE, 68025. Tel: 402-941-6250. Fax: 402-727-6223. p. 1399

Dolak, Fritz, Dr, Mgr, Univ Copyright Ctr, Ball State University Libraries, 2000 W University Ave, Muncie, IN, 47306-1099. Tel: 765-285-5330. Fax: 765-285-2008. p. 766

Dolamore, Heidi, Sr Commun Libr Mgr, Contra Costa County Library, Pleasant Hill Library, 1750 Oak Park Blvd, Pleasant Hill, CA, 94523-4497. Tel: 925-646-6434. Fax: 925-646-6040. p. 209

Dolan, Anne Marie, Dir, West Babylon Public Library, 211 Rte 109, West Babylon, NY, 11704. Tel: 631-669-5445. Fax: 631-669-6539. p. 1765

Dolan, Charles, Tech Serv, Middlesex County College Library, 2600 Woodbridge Ave, Edison, NJ, 08818. Tel: 732-906-4254. Fax: 732-906-4159. p. 1483

Dolan, Eileen, Asst Librn, Kramer, Levin, Naftalis & Frankel LLP, 1177 Avenue of the Americas, New York, NY, 10036. Tel: 212-715-9321. Fax: 212-715-8000. p. 1684

Dolan, Ellen M, Dir, Shrewsbury Public Library, 609 Main St, Shrewsbury, MA, 01545. Tel: 508-841-8537. Fax: 508-841-8540. p. 1124

Dolan, Jane, Cat, West Lafayette Public Library, 208 W Columbia St, West Lafayette, IN, 47906. Tel: 765-743-2261. Fax: 765-743-0540. p. 787

Dolan, Mary, Per, Sonoma State University Library, 1801 E Cotati Ave, Rohnert Park, CA, 94928-3609. Tel: 707-664-2073. Fax: 707-664-2090. p. 219

Dolan, Meghan, Head, Numeric Data Serv, Harvard Library, Social Sciences Program, Lamont Library, Level B, Harvard University, Cambridge, MA, 02138. Tel: 617-495-2106. Fax: 617-496-5570. p. 1076

Dolan, Nancy, Exec Dir, Quincy Public Library, 526 Jersey St, Quincy, IL, 62301-3996. Tel: 217-223-1309, Ext 204. Fax: 217-222-5672. p. 693

Dolan, Pat, Librn, Washington County Library, Washington County Law Library, Washington County Courthouse, 14949 62nd St N, Rm 1005, Stillwater, MN, 55082. Tel: 651-430-6330. Fax: 651-430-6331. p. 1290

Dolan, Sarah, Asst Librn, Mount Ida College, Wadsworth Library, 777 Dedham St, Newton, MA, 02459. Tel: 617-928-4552. Fax: 617-928-4038. p. 1110

Dolan, Tom, Dir, De Anza College, 21250 Stevens Creek Blvd, Cupertino, CA, 95014-5793. Tel: 408-864-8764. Fax: 408-864-8603. p. 138

Dolbashian, Diane, Librn, Corning Museum of Glass, Five Museum Way, Corning, NY, 14830. Tel: 607-974-8119. Fax: 607-974-8677. p. 1611

Dolce, Jonathan, Youth Serv, Maitland Public Library, 501 S Maitland Ave, Maitland, FL, 32751-5672. Tel: 407-647-7700. p. 462

Dole, Elizabeth, Acq Librn, Salem State University Library, 352 Lafayette St, Salem, MA, 01970-5353. Tel: 978-542-6477. Fax: 978-542-6596. p. 1122

Dole, Karen F, Dir, North Iowa Area Community College Library, 500 College Dr, Mason City, IA, 50401. Tel: 641-422-4232. Fax: 641-422-4131. p. 831

Dole, Rana, Med Librn, Boca Raton Community Hospital, 800 Meadows Rd, Boca Raton, FL, 33486. Tel: 561-955-4088. Fax: 561-955-4825. p. 428

Dole, Wanda, Dean, University of Arkansas at Little Rock, 2801 S University Ave, Little Rock, AR, 72204. Tel: 501-569-3123. Fax: 501-569-3017. p. 107

Dolen, Roxanne, Doc Delivery, University of Texas, M D Anderson Cancer Center Research Medical Library, 1400 Pressler St, Houston, TX, 77030-3722. Tel: 713-745-7432. Fax: 713-563-3650. p. 2344

Dolence, Travis, Distance Learning & Web Librn, Minnesota State University Moorhead, 1104 Seventh Ave S, Moorhead, MN, 56563. Tel: 218-477-2922. Fax: 218-477-5924. p. 1266

Dolgos, Joe, Br Librn, Ascension Parish Library, Galvez, 40300 Hwy 42, Prairieville, LA, 70769. Tel: 225-622-3339. Fax: 225-622-2550. p. 949

Dolhanczyk, Rachel, Dir, Ocean City Historical Museum, 1735 Simpson Ave, Ocean City, NJ, 08226. Tel: 609-399-1801. Fax: 609-399-0544. p. 1516

Dolim, David, Adult & Teen Serv Supvr, Arcadia Public Library, 20 W Duarte Rd, Arcadia, CA, 91006. Tel: 626-821-4327. Fax: 626-447-8050. p. 121

Dolin, Carol, Dir, Sugar Grove Public Library District, 125 S Municipal Dr, Sugar Grove, IL, 60554. Tel: 630-466-4686, Ext 309. Fax: 630-466-4189. p. 708

Doline, Patricia, Ref Serv, Henry Ford Community College, 5101 Evergreen Rd, Dearborn, MI, 48128-1495. Tel: 313-845-9762. Fax: 313-845-9795. p. 1167

Dolinger, Elizabeth, Info Literacy Librn, Keene State College, 229 Main St, Keene, NH, 03435-3201. Tel: 603-358-2749. Fax: 603-358-2745. p. 1453

Dolinger, Elizabeth, Circ Librn, South University, Nine Science Ct, Columbia, SC, 29203. Tel: 803-935-4301, 803-935-4331. Fax: 803-935-4382. p. 2189

Dolinger, Lesley, Dir, Patten Free Library, 33 Summer St, Bath, ME, 04530. Tel: 207-443-5141. Fax: 207-443-3514. p. 976

Dolive, Mark, Dir, Libr Serv, Tarrant County College, 2100 Southeast Pkwy, Arlington, TX, 76018. Tel: 817-515-3083. Fax: 817-515-3183. p. 2277

Doll, Carrol, Dr, Coordr, Old Dominion University Learning Resources Center, College of Education, Rm 244, 5215 Hampton Blvd, Norfolk, VA, 23529-0161. Tel: 757-683-3222. Fax: 757-683-5862. p. 2975

Doll, DeAnn, Mgr, Human Res, Ann Arbor District Library, 343 S Fifth Ave, Ann Arbor, MI, 48104. Tel: 734-327-4273. p. 1150

Doll, Dee, Acq Asst, William Jewell College, 500 College Hill, Liberty, MO, 64068-1843. Tel: 816-415-7609. Fax: 816-415-5021. p. 1343

Dollar, Daniel, Head, Coll Develop & Mgt, Yale University Library, Harvey Cushing/John Hay Whitney Medical Library, Sterling Hall of Medicine, 333 Cedar St, L110 SHM, New Haven, CT, 06520. Tel: 203-785-5352. Fax: 203-785-5636. p. 358

Dollar, Estelle, ILL Librn, Robert L Williams Public Library, 323 W Beech, Durant, OK, 74701. Tel: 580-924-3486. Fax: 580-924-8843. p. 1962

Dolle, Donna, Bus Mgr, New Canaan Library, 151 Main St, New Canaan, CT, 06840. Tel: 203-594-5000. Fax: 203-594-5026. p. 354

Dollinger, Janie A, Dir, Lanark Public Library, 110 W Carroll St, Lanark, IL, 61046. Tel: 815-493-2166. Fax: 815-493-8045. p. 664

Dollisch, Patricia, Tech Serv, DeKalb County Public Library, Administrative Office, 215 Sycamore St, 4th Flr, Decatur, GA, 30030. Tel: 404-370-8450. Fax: 404-370-8469. p. 529

Dolma, Kunchog, Ser, Marymount Manhattan College, 221 E 71st St, New York, NY, 10021. Tel: 212-774-4807. Fax: 212-458-8207. p. 1685

Dolman, Ann, Outreach/Pub Serv Librn, Barton College, 400 Atlantic Christian College Dr NE, Wilson, NC, 27893. Tel: 252-399-6507. Fax: 252-399-6571. p. 1831

Dolman, Heather, Pub Serv Mgr, St Albert Public Library, Five Saint Anne St, St. Albert, AB, T8N 3Z9, CANADA. Tel: 780-459-1530. Fax: 780-458-5772. p. 2717

Dolph, Julie, Br Mgr, Trails Regional Library, Knob Noster Branch, 202 N Adams, Knob Noster, MO, 65336. Tel: 660-563-2997. Fax: 660-747-5774. p. 1371

Dolson, Anita, Head Librn, West Union District Library, 209 W Union St, West Union, IL, 62477-0138. Tel: 217-279-3556. Fax: 217-279-3556. p. 717

Dolyniuk, Maureen, Archivist, Archives of Manitoba, 130-200 Vaughan St, Winnipeg, MB, R3C 1T5, CANADA. Tel: 204-945-3971. Fax: 204-948-2008. p. 2754

Doman, Monica, Cat, Syst, Cypress College Library, 9200 Valley View St, Cypress, CA, 90630-5897. Tel: 714-484-7067. Fax: 714-826-6723. p. 138

Doman, Shelly, In Charge, University College of the North Libraries, Thompson Campus, 504 Princeton Dr, Thompson, MB, R8N 0A5, CANADA. Tel: 204-677-6408. Fax: 204-677-6416. p. 2753

Domann, Mary, Circ Supvr, Atchison Public Library, 401 Kansas Ave, Atchison, KS, 66002-2495. Tel: 913-367-1902, Ext 203. Fax: 913-367-2717. p. 856

Dombourian, Sona J, Dir, Lafayette Public Library, 301 W Congress, Lafayette, LA, 70501-6866. Tel: 337-261-5775. Fax: 337-261-5782. p. 952

Dombraski, Jerry, Adult Ref, New Berlin Public Library, 15105 Library Lane, New Berlin, WI, 53151. Tel: 262-785-4980. Fax: 262-785-4984. p. 2625

Dombroski, Segrid, Dir, Dundee Library, 32 Water St, Dundee, NY, 14837. Tel: 607-243-5938. Fax: 607-243-7733. p. 1616

Dombrosky, Marge, Br Mgr, Gloucester County Library System, Swedesboro Branch, 1442 Kings Hwy, Swedesboro, NJ, 08085. Tel: 856-467-0111. Fax: 856-241-0594. p. 1507

Dombrowski, Agnes J, Asst Librn, Remington-Carpenter Township Public Library, 105 N Ohio St, Remington, IN, 47977. Tel: 219-261-2543. Fax: 219-261-3800. p. 774

Dombrowski, Andrea, ILL, Northwestern Connecticut Community College Library, Park Pl E, Winsted, CT, 06098. Tel: 860-738-6478. Fax: 860-379-4995. p. 379

Dombrowski, Clare, Ch, Amesbury Public Library, 149 Main St, Amesbury, MA, 01913. Tel: 978-388-8148. p. 1048

Dombrowski, Janet, Info Serv, New Mexico State Library, 1209 Camino Carlos Rey, Santa Fe, NM, 87507. Tel: 505-476-9710. Fax: 505-476-9701. p. 1563

Domecq, Marie-Cecile, Librn, Bibliotheque de l'Hopital Montfort, 713 Chemin Montreal, Ottawa, ON, K1K 4A9, CANADA. Tel: 613-746-4621, Ext 6045. Fax: 613-748-4922. p. 2828

Domeij, Vi, Librn, Palliser Regional Library, Mortlach Branch, 112 Rose St, Mortlach, SK, S0H 3E0, CANADA. Tel: 306-355-2202. p. 2919

Domes, Robert A, Circ, Ref Serv, Gateway Technical College, 1001 S Main St, Racine, WI, 53403-1582. Tel: 262-619-6370. Fax: 262-619-6221. p. 2632

Domick, Timothy, Dir, Rockland Community College Library, 145 College Rd, Suffern, NY, 10901. Tel: 845-574-4122. Fax: 845-574-4424. p. 1750

Domier, Sharon, Bibliographer, University of Massachusetts Amherst, 154 Hicks Way, Amherst, MA, 01003-9275. Tel: 413-577-2633. Fax: 413-545-6873. p. 1049

Domine, Kay, Spec Projects, College of William & Mary in Virginia, Earl Gregg Swem Library, One Landrum Dr, Williamsburg, VA, 23187. Tel: 757-221-3091. Fax: 757-221-2635. p. 2502

Domingo, Lea, Br Mgr, Hawaii State Public Library System, Kahuku Public & School Library, 56-490 Kamehameha Hwy, Kahuku, HI, 96731. Tel: 808-293-8935. Fax: 808-293-8937. p. 562

Domingos, Deb, Ch, Brookhaven Free Library, 273 Beaver Dam Rd, Brookhaven, NY, 11719. Tel: 631-286-1923. Fax: 631-286-0120. p. 1589

Domingues, Larry, Libr Mgr, Jefferson County Public Library, Arvada Library, 7525 W 57th Ave, Arvada, CO, 80002. Tel: 303-235-5275. p. 315

Dominguez, Jennifer, Libr Asst, Elvis Maxine Gilliam Memorial Public Library, 205 E Beltline Rd, Wilmer, TX, 75172. Tel: 972-441-3713. Fax: 972-525-3914. p. 2401

Dominguez, Maria, Br Mgr, Phoenix Public Library, Ocotillo Library & Workforce Literacy Center, 102 W Southern Ave, Phoenix, AZ, 85041-4806. p. 76

Dominguez, Rosa, Head Librn, Balmorhea Public Library, 102 SW Main St, Balmorhea, TX, 79718. Tel: 432-375-2522. Fax: 432-375-0225. p. 2286

Dominguez, Terry, Circ Supvr, Laredo Community College, West End Washington St, Laredo, TX, 78040. Tel: 956-721-5275. Fax: 956-721-5447. p. 2353

Dominianni, Beth, Dir, Mark Twain Library, Rte 53 & Diamond Hill Rd, Redding, CT, 06896. Tel: 203-938-2545. Fax: 203-938-4026. p. 365

Dominici, Judy, ILL Librn, Nashua Public Library, Two Court St, Nashua, NH, 03060. Tel: 603-589-4600. Fax: 603-594-3457. p. 1458

Dominicis, Eric, Dir, Miami Dade College, Kendall Campus Library, 11011 SW 104th St, Miami, FL, 33176-3393. Tel: 305-237-0996, 305-237-2015, 305-237-2291. Fax: 305-237-2923. p. 466

Dominick, Emily Hughes, Assoc Archivist, Providence Archives, 4800 37th Ave SW, Seattle, WA, 98126. Tel: 206-923-4011. Fax: 206-923-4001. p. 2530

Dominick, Johnice, Dir, Green Forest Public Library, 206 E Main St, Green Forest, AR, 72638-2627. Tel: 870-438-6700. Fax: 870-438-4586. p. 101

Dominique, Jane, Dir, Evergreen Community Library, 253 Maple St, Metamora, OH, 43540. Tel: 419-644-2771. Fax: 419-644-5778. p. 1917

Dominy, Peggy, Ref Librn, Drexel University Libraries, Hagerty Library, 33rd & Market Sts, Philadelphia, PA, 19104-2875. Tel: 215-895-2754. Fax: 215-895-6950. p. 2105

Dompierre, Louise, Pres, Muriel Isabel Bostwick Library, 123 King St W, Hamilton, ON, L8P 4S8, CANADA. Tel: 905-527-6610. Fax: 905-577-6940. p. 2808

Domschot, Betsy S, Librn, Consumers Energy, Legal Library, One Energy Plaza, Jackson, MI, 49201. Tel: 517-788-1088. Fax: 517-788-1682. p. 1195

Donabedian, David, Head, Access Serv, Hunter College Libraries, 695 Park Ave, New York, NY, 10065. Tel: 212-772-4176. Fax: 212-772-4142. p. 1682

Donadio, Lisa, ILS Adminr, Vermont Law School, 68 North Windsor, South Royalton, VT, 05068. Tel: 802-831-1442. Fax: 802-763-7159. p. 2436

Donaghy, Katrina, Tech Serv Librn, Eureka College, 301 E College Ave, Eureka, IL, 61530-1563. Tel: 309-467-6380. Fax: 309-467-6386. p. 643

Donahoe, Jessica, Head, Cat, Webmaster, University of Wisconsin - Platteville, One University Plaza, Platteville, WI, 53818. Tel: 608-342-1348. Fax: 608-342-1645. p. 2630

Donahoo, Diana, Pub Relations, Centralia Regional Library District, 515 E Broadway, Centralia, IL, 62801. Tel: 618-532-5222. Fax: 618-532-8578. p. 602

Donahue, Ann E, Dir, University of New Hampshire at Manchester Library, 400 Commercial St, Manchester, NH, 03101. Tel: 603-641-4123. Fax: 603-641-4124. p. 1456

Donahue, Cheryl, Ch, Canton Public Library, 40 Dyer Ave, Canton, CT, 06019. Tel: 860-693-5800. Fax: 860-693-5804. p. 333

Donahue, Frank, Librn, Philadelphia Newspapers, Inc, 400 N Broad St, Philadelphia, PA, 19130-4099. Tel: 215-854-4660. Fax: 215-854-5697. p. 2114

Donahue, Janice E, Asst Dean, Tech Serv, Florida Atlantic University, 777 Glades Rd, Boca Raton, FL, 33431. Tel: 561-297-2767. Fax: 561-297-0253. p. 428

Donahue, Kathryn, Head, Tech Serv, University of Maine at Fort Kent, 23 University Dr, Fort Kent, ME, 04743. Tel: 207-834-7525. Fax: 207-834-7518. p. 986

Donahue, Katie, Asst Libr Dir & Info Literacy Coordr, Hilbert College, 5200 S Park Ave, Hamburg, NY, 14075. Tel: 716-649-7900, Ext 245. Fax: 716-648-6530. p. 1632

Donahue, Roberta, Ch, Mystic & Noank Library, Inc, 40 Library St, Mystic, CT, 06355. Tel: 860-536-7721. Fax: 860-536-2350. p. 353

Donald, Nagolski, User Serv Librn, Loyola University Chicago Libraries, Health Sciences Library, Bldg 101, Rm 1717, 2160 S First Ave, Maywood, IL, 60153-5585. Tel: 708-216-9192. Fax: 708-216-8115. p. 617

Donaldson, Beverly, Librn, Detroit Garden Center, Inc Library, 1900 E Jefferson Ave, Ste 227, Detroit, MI, 48207-1456. Tel: 313-259-6363. Fax: 313-259-0107. p. 1169

Donaldson, Camille, Librn, Contra Costa Times News Research Department, 2640 Shadelands Dr, Walnut Creek, CA, 94598. Tel: 925-943-8353. Fax: 925-943-8362. p. 282

Donaldson, Cindy, ILL, Kelso Public Library, 314 Academy St, Kelso, WA, 98626-4196. Tel: 360-423-8110. Fax: 360-425-5195. p. 2518

Donaldson, Deb, Head, Tech Serv, Chappaqua Public Library, 195 S Greeley Ave, Chappaqua, NY, 10514. Tel: 917-238-4779, Ext 107. Fax: 914-238-3597. p. 1605

Donaldson, Jan, Head Librn, Wayne County Historical Society, Hwy 2, 515 E Jefferson St, Corydon, IA, 50060. Tel: 641-872-2211 (Museum). p. 804

Donaldson, Jennifer, Librn, Woodstock Historical Society, Inc, 26 Elm St, Woodstock, VT, 05091. Tel: 802-457-1822. Fax: 802-457-2811. p. 2441

Donaldson, Jerilynn, Ref Librn, Saul Ewing LLP, Centre Sq W, 1500 Market St, 38th Flr, Philadelphia, PA, 19102. Tel: 215-972-7873. Fax: 215-972-1945. p. 2116

Donaldson, Jo, Res, Lucasfilm Research Library, PO Box 2009, San Rafael, CA, 94912. Tel: 415-662-1912. p. 257

Donaldson, Joann, Libr Coordr, Des Moines Register, 715 Locust St, Des Moines, IA, 50309-3703. Tel: 515-284-8077. Fax: 515-286-2511. p. 808

Donaldson, Kelly, Coll Develop, Info Serv, Librn, Seneca College of Applied Arts & Technology, Newnham Campus (Main), 1750 Finch Ave E, North York, ON, M2J 2X5, CANADA. Tel: 416-491-5050, Ext 26139. Fax: 416-492-7184. p. 2813

Donaldson, Martin, Assoc Teaching Prof, Drexel University, Rush Bldg, Rm 306, 30 N 33rd St, Philadelphia, PA, 19104-2875. Tel: 215-895-2474. Fax: 215-895-2494. p. 2973

Donaldson, Nell, Acq, ILL, Chipola College Library, 3094 Indian Circle, Marianna, FL, 32446. Tel: 850-718-2273. Fax: 850-718-2349. p. 462

Donaldson, Penny, Dir, Libr Serv, Highland Community College Library, 606 W Main, Highland, KS, 66035. Tel: 785-442-6054. Fax: 785-442-6101. p. 871

Donaldson, Rhonda, Access Serv Librn, Oklahoma Panhandle State University, 409 W Sewell, Goodwell, OK, 73939. Tel: 580-349-1547. Fax: 580-349-1541. p. 1964

Donaldson, Rhonda, Electronic Res/Coll Develop Coordr, Shepherd University, 301 N King St, Shepherdstown, WV, 25443. Fax: 304-876-0731. p. 2571

Donaldson, Thomas, Cataloger, United States Marine Corps, Bldg 298, Marine Corps Air Station, Cherry Point, NC, 28533-0009. Tel: 252-466-3552. Fax: 252-466-5402. p. 1784

Donaldson, Tim, Mgr, Tech Serv & Automation, Westlake Porter Public Library, 27333 Center Ridge Rd, Westlake, OH, 44145-3925. Tel: 440-871-2600. Fax: 440-871-6969. p. 1947

Donat, Nafi, Librn, Carl Robinson Correctional Institution Library, 285 Shaker Rd, Enfield, CT, 06083. Tel: 860-763-6230. Fax: 860-763-6345. p. 338

Donath, Carolyn, Dir, Conrad Public Library, 15 Fourth Ave SW, Conrad, MT, 59425. Tel: 406-271-5751. Fax: 406-271-5751. p. 1377

Donatiello, Joann, Population Res Librn, Princeton University, Donald E Stokes Library - Public & International Affairs & Population Research, Wallace Hall, Princeton, NJ, 08544. Tel: 609-258-1377. Fax: 609-258-6844. p. 1524

Doncevic, John, Dir, Geneva College, 3200 College Ave, Beaver Falls, PA, 15010-3599. Tel: 724-847-6563. Fax: 724-847-6687. p. 2031

Donches, Lynn, Chief Librn, Rodale Inc, 400 S Tenth St, Emmaus, PA, 18098. Tel: 610-967-8729, 610-967-8880. Fax: 610-967-8100. p. 2054

Dondero, Ann, Ch, Forest Grove City Library, 2114 Pacific Ave, Forest Grove, OR, 97116-9019. Tel: 503-992-3281. Fax: 503-992-3333. p. 1998

Dondertman, Anne, Head of Libr, University of Toronto Libraries, Thomas Fisher Rare Books Library, 120 St George St, Toronto, ON, M5S 1A5, CANADA. Tel: 416-978-5332. Fax: 416-978-1667. p. 2866

Donegan, Pam, Cat Librn, Institute of American Indian & Alaska Native Culture & Arts Development Library, 83 Avan Nu Po Rd, Santa Fe, NM, 87508. Tel: 505-424-5715. Fax: 505-424-3131. p. 1562

Donellan, Kathy, Asst Dir, Support Serv, San Antonio Public Library, 600 Soledad, San Antonio, TX, 78205-2786. Tel: 210-207-2572. Fax: 210-207-2603. p. 2382

Donelson, Frances, Dir, Bacone College Library, 2299 Old Bacone Rd, Muskogee, OK, 74403. Tel: 918-781-7263. Fax: 918-687-5913, 918-781-7376. p. 1969

Donelson, Gretchen, Libr Mgr, Ohio State University LIBRARIES, Fine Arts, Wexner Center for the Arts, 1871 N High St, Columbus, OH, 43210. Tel: 614-292-6184. Fax: 614-292-4573. p. 1887

Dong, Pamela, Assoc Prof, Tech Serv Librn, Ocean County College Library, College Dr, Toms River, NJ, 08754. Tel: 732-255-0392. Fax: 732-255-0421. p. 1533

Donick, Caroline H, Dir, Alice Curtis Desmond & Hamilton Fish Library, 472 Rte 403, Garrison, NY, 10524. Tel: 845-424-3020. Fax: 845-424-4061. p. 1627

Donigan, Linda, Ch, YA Librn, Bennington Free Library, 101 Silver St, Bennington, VT, 05201. Tel: 802-442-9051. p. 2418

Donlan, Jeff, Dir, Salida Regional Library, 405 E St, Salida, CO, 81201. Tel: 719-539-4826. p. 322

Donlan, Rebecca, Asst Dir, Coll Mgt & Tech Serv, Florida Gulf Coast University Library, 10501 FGCU Blvd S, Fort Myers, FL, 33965-6501. Tel: 239-590-7641. p. 444

Donley, Leah, Tech Serv, Brookhaven National Laboratory, Research Library, Bldg 477, Upton, NY, 11973-5000. Tel: 631-344-5069. Fax: 631-344-2090. p. 1758

Donn, Judy, Mgr, Libr Serv, Southcoast Medical Libraries, 101 Page St, New Bedford, MA, 02740. Tel: 508-961-5267. Fax: 508-961-5263. p. 1109

Donnald, Edward, Dir, Moses Cone Health System, Moses H Cone Memorial Hospital Library, 1200 N Elm St, Greensboro, NC, 27401. Tel: 336-832-7484. Fax: 336-832-7328. p. 1797

Donne, Mary, Ref, South Brunswick Public Library, 110 Kingston Lane, Monmouth Junction, NJ, 08852. Tel: 732-329-4000, Ext 7638. Fax: 732-329-0573. p. 1502

Donnell, Barb, Adult Ref Librn, Pendleton Community Library, 595 E Water St, Pendleton, IN, 46064-1070. Tel: 765-778-7527, Ext 109. Fax: 765-778-7529. p. 772

Donnell, Leslie, Dir & Mgr, Coll & Digital Content, Harvard Library, John F Kennedy School of Government Library, 79 John F Kennedy St, Cambridge, MA, 02138. Tel: 617-495-1300. Fax: 617-495-1972. p. 1075

Donnell, Ramsey, Head, Access Serv, The John Marshall Law School, 315 S Plymouth Ct, Chicago, IL, 60604. Tel: 312-427-2737. Fax: 312-427-8307. p. 618

Donnell, Val, Supvr, Outreach Serv, Ames Public Library, 515 Douglas Ave, Ames, IA, 50010. Tel: 515-239-5668. Fax: 515-233-9001. p. 792

Donnellan, Anne, Head, Tech Serv, Oshawa Public Library, 65 Bagot St, Oshawa, ON, L1H 1N2, CANADA. Tel: 905-579-6111. Fax: 905-433-8107. p. 2827

Donnelly, Alison, Youth Serv, Collinsville Memorial Public Library District, 408 W Main St, Collinsville, IL, 62234. Tel: 618-344-1112. Fax: 618-345-6401. p. 630

Donnelly, Anna Alston, Coll Coordr, Washington National Cathedral, Massachusetts & Wisconsin Aves NW, Washington, DC, 20016-5098. Tel: 202-537-6200. p. 422

Donnelly, Barbara R, Chief, Coll Develop Br, United States Naval War College Library, 686 Cushing Rd, Newport, RI, 02841-1207. Tel: 401-841-4345. Fax: 401-841-6491. p. 2169

Donnelly, Caitlin, Archivist, Daughters of the Republic of Texas Library at the Alamo, 300 Alamo Plaza, San Antonio, TX, 78205. Tel: 210-225-1071. Fax: 210-212-8514. p. 2379

Donnelly, Celia, Mgr, News Res & Chief Librn, The Globe & Mail Library, 444 Front St W, Toronto, ON, M5V 2S9, CANADA. Tel: 416-585-5229. p. 2853

Donnelly, Christine, Br Mgr, Sacramento Public Library, Colonial Heights Community Library, 4799 Stockton Blvd, Sacramento, CA, 95820. p. 224

Donnelly, Christine, Br Mgr, Sacramento Public Library, Valley Hi-North Laguna Library, 7400 Imagination Pkwy, Sacramento, CA, 95823. Tel: 916-264-2700. p. 225

Donnelly, Christopher, Asst Libr Dir, Boston Herald, One Herald Sq, Boston, MA, 02118. Tel: 617-619-6680. Fax: 617-619-6450. p. 1056

Donnelly, Jaimie, Tech & Access Serv Librn, Georgian Court University, 900 Lakewood Ave, Lakewood, NJ, 08701-2697. Tel: 732-987-2435. Fax: 732-987-2017. p. 1493

Donnelly, Jeff, Syst, Georgian Court University, 900 Lakewood Ave, Lakewood, NJ, 08701-2697. Tel: 732-987-2419. Fax: 732-987-2017. p. 1493

Donnelly, Lynne, In Charge, Healthcare Association of New York State, One Empire Dr, Rensselaer, NY, 12144. Tel: 518-431-7834. Fax: 518-431-7812. p. 1726

Donnelly, Mary, Head, Access Serv, ILL, Fairleigh Dickinson University, 285 Madison Ave, M-LAO-03, Madison, NJ, 07940. Tel: 973-443-8515. Fax: 973-443-8525. p. 1497

Donnelly, Nancy, Tech Serv Dir, Central Bible College, 3000 N Grant Ave, Springfield, MO, 65803. Tel: 417-833-2551, Ext 1164. Fax: 417-833-5478. p. 1366

Donnelly, Patricia, Acq, University of New Haven, 300 Boston Post Rd, West Haven, CT, 06516. Tel: 203-932-7190. Fax: 203-932-1469. p. 377

Donnelly, Robert, Chairperson, Lomond Municipal Library, Two Railway Ave N, Lomond, AB, T0L 1G0, CANADA. Tel: 403-792-3934. Fax: 403-792-3934. p. 2710

Donnelly, Terrence, Dir, Maplewood Public Library, 7550 Lohmeyer Ave, Maplewood, MO, 63143. Tel: 314-781-7323. Fax: 314-781-2191. p. 1344

Donnely, Terri, Ch Serv Librn, Tekamah Public Library, 204 S 13th St, Tekamah, NE, 68061-1304. Tel: 402-374-2453. Fax: 402-374-2453. p. 1421

Donnery, Mary C, Dir, Croton Free Library, 171 Cleveland Dr, Croton-on-Hudson, NY, 10520. Tel: 914-271-6612. Fax: 914-271-0931. p. 1612

Donohoe, Heather, Asst Br Mgr, Pine Forest Regional Library, McHenry Public, 25 McHenry School Dr, McHenry, MS, 39561. Tel: 601-528-9465. Fax: 601-528-9465. p. 1314

Donohoe, Kate-Lee, Librn, Southeast Regional Library, Estevan Branch, Leisure Ctr, 701 Souris Ave N, Estevan, SK, S4A 2T1, CANADA. Tel: 306-636-1620, 306-636-1626. Fax: 306-634-5830. p. 2929

Donohue, Deirdre, Chief Librn, International Center of Photography Library, Concourse, 1114 Avenue of the Americas, New York, NY, 10036-7703. Tel: 212-857-0004. Fax: 212-857-0091. p. 1683

Donohue, Diana, Dir, Gallitzin Public Library, 411 Convent St, Ste 30, Gallitzin, PA, 16641-1234. Tel: 814-886-4041. Fax: 814-886-2125. p. 2059

Donohue, John J, Head, Circ, McAllen Memorial Library, 601 N Main, McAllen, TX, 78501-4666. Tel: 956-688-3300. Fax: 956-688-3301. p. 2360

Donohue, Kathleen, Ref, Franciscan University of Steubenville, 1235 University Blvd, Steubenville, OH, 43952-1763. Tel: 740-283-6208. Fax: 740-284-7239. p. 1936

Donohue, Kenneth, Head, Info Serv, Saint Thomas Aquinas College, 125 Rte 340, Sparkill, NY, 10976. Tel: 845-398-4219. Fax: 845-359-9537. p. 1746

Donohue, Lee, Ch, Acton Memorial Library, 486 Main St, Acton, MA, 01720. Tel: 978-264-9641. Fax: 978-635-0073. p. 1047

Donohue, Lorena, Curator, Dep Dir, Littleton Historical Museum Research Center, 6028 S Gallup, Littleton, CO, 80120. Tel: 303-795-3950. Fax: 303-730-9818. p. 317

Donohue, Mary, Dir, Fulton-Montgomery Community College, 2805 State Hwy 67, Johnstown, NY, 12095-3790. Tel: 518-762-4651, Ext 5610. Fax: 518-762-3834. p. 1648

Donohue, Nanette, Tech Serv, Champaign Public Library, 200 W Green St, Champaign, IL, 61820-5193. Tel: 217-403-2050. Fax: 217-403-2053. p. 602

Donovan, Beryl, Dir, Gafney Library, Inc, 14 High St, Sanbornville, NH, 03872. Tel: 603-522-3401. Fax: 603-522-7123. p. 1464

Donovan, Dana, ILL, Kensington Social & Public Library, 126 Amesbury Rd, Kensington, NH, 03833-5621. Tel: 603-772-5022. Fax: 603-778-2953. p. 1453

Donovan, Elizabeth, Commun Outreach Coordr, North Kingstown Free Library, 100 Boone St, North Kingstown, RI, 02852-5176. Tel: 401-294-3306. Fax: 401-294-1690. p. 2172

Donovan, James, Dir, University of Kentucky Libraries, Law Library, 620 S Limestone St, Lexington, KY, 40506-0048. Tel: 859-257-8351. Fax: 859-323-4906. p. 922

Donovan, James M, Librn, Saint John Medical Center, 1923 S Utica, Tulsa, OK, 74104. Tel: 918-744-2970. Fax: 918-744-3209. p. 1982

Donovan, Joanne, Librn, Quincy Medical Center Library, 114 Whitwell St, Quincy, MA, 02169. Tel: 617-773-6100, Ext 4094. Fax: 617-376-1650. p. 1120

Donovan, John, In Charge, Henry County Law Library, 609 N Perry St, Napoleon, OH, 43545. Tel: 419-599-1936. Fax: 419-592-4451. p. 1919

Donovan, Kathy, Librn, Pontiac Correctional Center Library, 700 W Lincoln St, Pontiac, IL, 61764-2323. Tel: 815-842-2816, Ext 672. Fax: 815-842-3051. p. 692

Donovan, Margaret, Tech Coordr, Cary Memorial Library, 1874 Massachusetts Ave, Lexington, MA, 02420. Tel: 781-862-6288, Ext 152. Fax: 781-862-7355. p. 1099

Donovan, Paul, Law Librn, State of Vermont Department of Libraries, 109 State St, Montpelier, VT, 05609-0601. Tel: 802-828-2734. Fax: 802-828-2199. p. 2429

Donovan, Priscilla, Dir, Leander Public Library, 1011 S Bagdad Rd, Leander, TX, 78641. Tel: 512-259-5259. p. 2354

Donovan, Sherri, Ch, Richard A Mautino Memorial Library, 215 E Cleveland St, Spring Valley, IL, 61362. Tel: 815-663-4741. Fax: 815-663-1040. p. 704

Donovan, Susan, Dir, Willoughby Wallace Memorial Library, 146 Thimble Islands Rd, Stony Creek, CT, 06405. Tel: 203-488-8702. Fax: 203-315-3347. p. 370

Donovan, Terry, Pub Serv Librn, Portage College Library, 9531 94th Ave, Lac La Biche, AB, T0A 2C0, CANADA. Tel: 780-623-5650. Fax: 780-623-5656. p. 2708

Donton, T, Computer Serv, North Shore Public Library, 250 Rte 25A, Shoreham, NY, 11786-9677. Tel: 631-929-4488. Fax: 631-929-4551. p. 1743

Dood, Terri, Head, Ref & Adult Serv, Bozeman Public Library, 626 E Main St, Bozeman, MT, 59715. Tel: 406-582-2406. Fax: 406-582-2424. p. 1375

Doody, Tina Marie, Ref Serv, Plainfield Public Library, 800 Park Ave, Plainfield, NJ, 07060-2594. Tel: 908-757-1111. Fax: 908-754-0063. p. 1521

Dooe, Frederick C, Tech Serv, Belmont Public Library, 336 Concord Ave, Belmont, MA, 02478-0904. Tel: 617-489-2000, 617-993-2850. Fax: 617-993-2893. p. 1052

Dooley, Catherine, Librn, Public Library of Brookline, Coolidge Corner, 31 Pleasant St, Brookline, MA, 02446. Tel: 617-730-2380. Fax: 617-734-4565. p. 1072

Dooley, Jim, Head, Coll Serv, University of California, Merced Library, 5200 N Lake Rd, Merced, CA, 95343-5001. Tel: 209-658-7161. Fax: 209-228-4271. p. 186

Dooley, Marietta, Distance Educ Librn, Alvernia University, 400 St Bernardine St, Reading, PA, 19607-1737. Tel: 215-635-4734. Fax: 610-796-8347. p. 2132

Dooley, Sheila, Dir, Libr Serv, The Dalles-Wasco County Library, 722 Court St, The Dalles, OR, 97058-2270. Tel: 541-296-2815. Fax: 541-296-4179. p. 2020

Dooley, Stephanie, Ref Librn, K&L Gates Law Library, Hearst Tower, 214 N Tryon St, 47th Flr, Charlotte, NC, 28202. Tel: 704-331-7553. Fax: 704-353-3253. p. 1783

Dooley, Susan K, Dir, Idlewild Public Library, 4713 E Baldwin Rd, Idlewild, MI, 49642-9737. Tel: 231-745-7652. Fax: 231-745-7652. p. 1193

Dooling, Michael C, Librn, Waterbury Republican & American Library, 389 Meadow St, Waterbury, CT, 06702. Tel: 203-574-3636, Ext 1497. Fax: 203-596-9277. p. 375

Doolittle, Elizabeth, Pub Serv, University of Southern Mississippi, 730 E Beach Blvd, Long Beach, MS, 39560-2698. Tel: 228-214-3455. Fax: 228-865-4544. p. 1307

Doone, Margaret, Bus Mgr/Fiscal Officer, Worthington Libraries, 820 High St, Worthington, OH, 43085. Tel: 614-807-2609. Fax: 614-807-2642. p. 1950

Doore, Martha M, Librn, Albion Public Library, 18 Main St, Albion, ME, 04910. Tel: 207-437-2220. p. 973

Dopman, Arthur, Treas, Somers Historical Society Library, Elephant Hotel, 335 Rte 202, Somers, NY, 10589-3204. Tel: 914-277-4977. p. 1745

Dopp, Bethany, Libr Assoc, Rocky Mountain College, 1511 Poly Dr, Billings, MT, 59102-1796. Tel: 406-657-1087. Fax: 406-657-1085. p. 1374

Dorais-Beauregard, Genevieve, Dir Gen, Centre de documentation sur l'education des adultes et la condition feminine, 110 rue Ste-Therese, Ste 101, Montreal, QC, H2Y 1E6, CANADA. Tel: 514-876-1180. Fax: 514-876-1325. p. 2892

Doran, Deirdre, Librn, Sasaki Associates, Inc Library, 64 Pleasant St, Watertown, MA, 02472. Tel: 617-923-7131. Fax: 617-924-2748. p. 1134

Doran, Kirk, Tech Serv Librn, Dickinson College, 333 W High St, Carlisle, PA, 17013-2896. Tel: 717-245-1397. Fax: 717-245-1439. p. 2042

Doran, Pat, ILL Coordr, Loyola University New Orleans, 6363 Saint Charles Ave, New Orleans, LA, 70118-6195. Tel: 504-864-7111. Fax: 504-864-7247. p. 961

Doran, Pat, Curator, Interim Dir, Skagit County Historical Museum, 501 S Fourth St, La Conner, WA, 98257. Tel: 360-466-3365. Fax: 360-466-1611. p. 2519

Dorantes, Denise, ILL, Cranbrook Academy of Art Library, 39221 Woodward Ave, Bloomfield Hills, MI, 48304. Tel: 248-645-3363. Fax: 248-645-3464. p. 1158

Dorbin, Betty, Br Mgr, Talbot County Free Library, Tilghman Branch, 21374 Foster Ave, Tilghman, MD, 21671. Tel: 410-886-9816. p. 1027

Dorchak, Andy, Head, Ref, Case Western Reserve University, School of Law Library, 11075 East Blvd, Cleveland, OH, 44106-7148. Tel: 216-368-2842. Fax: 216-368-1002. p. 1876

Dore, George, Br Mgr, Lake County Library System, East Lake County Library, 31340 County Rd 437 South, Sorrento, FL, 32776. Tel: 352-383-9980. Fax: 352-383-9982. p. 500

Dorfman, Andrew, Media Librn, Regis University, 3333 Regis Blvd, Denver, CO, 80221-1099. Tel: 303-458-4030. Fax: 303-964-5497. p. 303

Dorfman, Joan, Spec Coll Librn, Bloomfield Public Library, 90 Broad St, Bloomfield, NJ, 07003. Tel: 973-566-6200. Fax: 973-566-6217. p. 1473

Dorgan, Marlene, Head of Libr, University of Alberta, John W Scott Health Sciences Library, Walter C Mackenzie Health Sciences Ctr 2K3 28, Edmonton, AB, T6G 2R7, CANADA. Tel: 780-492-7945. Fax: 780-492-6960. p. 2702

Doria, Joann, Ref, Proskauer Rose LLP Library, 1585 Broadway, Concourse Level, New York, NY, 10036. Tel: 212-969-5001. Fax: 212-969-2931. p. 1698

Dorio, Terrie, Br Mgr, Santa Monica Public Library, Montana Avenue, 1704 Montana Ave, Santa Monica, CA, 90403-1908. Tel: 310-829-7081. Fax: 310-829-3691. p. 266

Dorko, Kathryn, Dir, Libr & Info Serv, Editorial Projects in Education Library, 6935 Arlington Rd, Bethesda, MD, 20814. Tel: 301-280-3100. Fax: 301-280-3200. p. 1021

Dorlac, Michael, Ref Librn, Lindenwood University, 209 S Kingshighway, Saint Charles, MO, 63301. Tel: 636-949-4347. Fax: 636-949-4822. p. 1351

Dorland, Denise, Librn, Andrew Public Library, PO Box 180, Andrew, AB, T0B 0C0, CANADA. Tel: 780-365-3501, Ext 225. Fax: 780-365-3734. p. 2683

Dorman, Bill, Br Mgr, Tangipahoa Parish Library, Hammond Branch, 314 E Thomas, Hammond, LA, 70401. Tel: 985-345-0937, 985-345-3909. Fax: 985-345-2188. p. 941

Dorman, Geraldine Anne, Br Mgr, San Francisco Public Library, Parkside Branch Library, 1200 Taraval St, San Francisco, CA, 94116-2452. Tel: 415-355-5770. Fax: 415-566-8014. p. 246

Dorman, Linda, In Charge, National Economic Research Associates, Inc Library, 777 S Figueroa St, Ste 4200, Los Angeles, CA, 90017. Tel: 213-346-3000. Fax: 213-346-3030. p. 176

Dorman, Mary Ellen, Librn, Belcher Memorial Library, 4452 VT Rte 107, Gaysville, VT, 05746-0144. Tel: 802-234-6608. Fax: 802-234-6608. p. 2424

Dorman, Robert, PhD, Monographs Librn, Oklahoma City University, Dulaney-Browne Library, 2501 N Blackwelder, Oklahoma City, OK, 73106. Tel: 405-208-5068. Fax: 405-208-5291. p. 1974

Dormody, Katherine, Dir, Gilford Public Library, 31 Potter Hill Rd, Gilford, NH, 03249-6803. Tel: 603-524-6042. Fax: 603-524-1218. p. 1448

Dornbaum, Robin L, Dir, Flushing Hospital Medical Center, 45th Ave at Parsons Blvd, Flushing, NY, 11355. Tel: 718-670-5653. Fax: 718-670-3089. p. 1623

Dorner, Jennifer, Head, Instruction & User Serv, University of California, Berkeley, The Teaching Library, 302 Moffitt Library, Berkeley, CA, 94720-6000. Tel: 510-643-9959. Fax: 510-642-9454. p. 128

Dorner, John, Librn, Illinois Lodge of Research, 614 E Lincoln Ave, Normal, IL, 61761. Tel: 309-452-3109. p. 681

Doro, Karen, Children's & YA Librn, Oak Creek Public Library, 8620 S Howell Ave, Oak Creek, WI, 53154. Tel: 414-764-4400. Fax: 414-768-6583. p. 2626

Dorobish, Gerry, Ref Serv, Pennsylvania State University, One University Dr, Uniontown, PA, 15401. Tel: 724-430-4154. Fax: 724-430-4152. p. 2147

Dorogi, Ruth, Dir, Ahira Hall Memorial Library, 37 W Main, Brocton, NY, 14716-9747. Tel: 716-792-9418. Fax: 716-792-7334. p. 1585

Dorothey, Ginny, Librn, Greater West Central Public Library District, Bowen Branch, 116 Fifth St, Bowen, IL, 62316. Tel: 217-842-5573. Fax: 217-842-5573. p. 591

Dorpalen, Peter, Exec Dir, Council of Governments of the Central Naugatuck Valley Library, 60 N Main St, 3rd Flr, Waterbury, CT, 06702-1403. Tel: 203-757-0535. Fax: 203-756-7688. p. 374

Dorr, Kathryn, Librn, Western Town Library, 9172 Main St, Westernville, NY, 13486. Tel: 315-827-4118. Fax: 315-827-4118. p. 1767

Dorrel, Ruth Ellen, Archivist, Franklin College, 101 Branigin Blvd, Franklin, IN, 46131-2623. Tel: 317-738-8164. Fax: 317-738-8787. p. 743

Dorrel, Sara, ILL, Franklin County Public Library District, 919 Main St, Brookville, IN, 47012-1498. Tel: 765-647-4031. Fax: 765-647-0278. p. 730

Dorrell, Cara, ILL, Southeastern Public Library System of Oklahoma, 401 N Second St, McAlester, OK, 74501. Tel: 918-426-0456. Fax: 918-426-0543. p. 1968

Dorriety, Mary S, Librn, Florence County Library System, Timmonsville Public Library, 111 S Warren St, Timmonsville, SC, 29161-1743. Tel: 843-346-2941. Fax: 843-346-2931. p. 2193

Dorris, C Scott, Digital Info Serv Mgr, Georgetown University, Dahlgren Memorial Library, Preclinical Science Bldg GM-7, 3900 Reservoir Rd NW, Washington, DC, 20007. Tel: 202-687-2942. Fax: 202-687-1862. p. 402

Dorrity, Raija, Librn, Boeing Huntsville, 499 Boeing Blvd, M/S JC-73, Huntsville, AL, 35824-3001. Tel: 256-461-2549. Fax: 256-461-5290. p. 21

Dorsch, Josephine, Prof, University of Illinois at Chicago, Library of the Health Sciences, Peoria, One Illinois Dr, Peoria, IL, 61605. Tel: 309-671-8489. Fax: 309-671-8495. p. 627

Dorscht, Melanie, Librn, Hilton Union Public Library, 3085 Marks St, Hilton Beach, ON, P0R 1G0, CANADA. Tel: 705-255-3520. p. 2811

Dorsey, Britta, Literacy Coordr, YA Librn, Thorntown Public Library, 124 N Market St, Thorntown, IN, 46071-1144. Tel: 765-436-7348. Fax: 765-436-7011. p. 782

Dorsey, Dewana, Br Mgr, Chicago Public Library, West Pullman, 830 W 119th St, Chicago, IL, 60628. Tel: 312-747-1425. Fax: 312-747-1082. p. 610

Dorsey, Leigh, Doc Delivery, ILL, University of Wisconsin-Milwaukee Libraries, 2311 E Hartford Ave, Milwaukee, WI, 53211. Tel: 414-229-4785, 414-229-6202. Fax: 414-229-6766. p. 2622

Dorsey, Nellie E, Librn, Vista Health Systems, East Site, 1324 N Sheridan Rd, Waukegan, IL, 60085. Tel: 847-360-3000, Ext 5144. Fax: 847-360-2402. p. 716

Dorsey, Sarah, Music Librn, University of North Carolina at Greensboro, 320 Spring Garden St, Greensboro, NC, 27402. Tel: 336-334-5880. Fax: 336-334-5399. p. 1798

Dorskind, Shauna, Media Librn, University of Toronto Libraries, Media Commons, 130 St George St, Toronto, ON, M5S 1A5, CANADA. Tel: 416-978-6785. Fax: 416-978-8707. p. 2866

Dorst, Tom, Dir, Admin & Planning, Consortium of Academic & Research Libraries in Illinois, 100 Trade Ctr Dr, Ste 303, Champaign, IL, 61820. Tel: 217-206-7856. Fax: 217-244-7596. p. 2942

Dortenzio, Patricia A, Asst Dir, North Haven Memorial Library, 17 Elm St, North Haven, CT, 06473. Tel: 203-239-5803. Fax: 203-234-2130. p. 362

Dorwaldt, Lynn, Librn, Wagner Free Institute of Science Library, 1700 W Montgomery Ave, Philadelphia, PA, 19121. Tel: 215-763-6529, Ext 12. Fax: 215-763-1299. p. 2120

Dory, Joyce, Dir of Admin Serv Div, Nuclear Waste Technical Review Board Library, 2300 Clarendon Blvd, Ste 1300, Arlington, VA, 22201. Tel: 703-235-4473. Fax: 703-235-4495. p. 2450

Dos Santos, Anthony, Br Mgr, Alameda County Library, San Lorenzo Branch, 395 Paseo Grande, San Lorenzo, CA, 94580-2491. Tel: 510-670-6283, Ext 11. Fax: 510-317-8497. p. 149

Dosalua, Geraldine, Youth Serv, Artesia Public Library, 306 W Richardson Ave, Artesia, NM, 88210-2499. Tel: 575-746-4252. Fax: 575-746-3075. p. 1551

Dosch, Constance, Br Mgr, Los Angeles Public Library System, Lake View Terrace, 12002 Osborne St, Los Angeles, CA, 91342. Tel: 818-890-7404. Fax: 818-897-2738. p. 173

Dose, Carrie, Ch, Jackson County Library, 311 Third St, Jackson, MN, 56143-1600. Tel: 507-847-4748. Fax: 507-847-5470. p. 1255

Doshi, Ameet, Head, User Experience, Georgia Institute of Technology Library, 704 Cherry St, Atlanta, GA, 30332-0900. Tel: 404-894-4501. Fax: 404-894-6084. p. 515

Doss, Georgina, Mgr, Cabell County Public Library, Milton Branch, 1140 Smith St, Milton, WV, 25541. Tel: 304-743-6711. Fax: 304-743-6747. p. 2561

Doss, Kathy, Librn, Tulsa City-County Library, Brookside, 1207 E 45th Pl, Tulsa, OK, 74105. Tel: 918-746-5012. Fax: 918-746-5014. p. 1982

Doss, Priscilla, Mgr, Metropolitan Library System in Oklahoma County, Belle Isle Library, 5501 N Villa, Oklahoma City, OK, 73112-7164. Tel: 405-843-9601. Fax: 405-843-4560. p. 1972

Doss, Sharon, Librn, First United Methodist Church Library, 1201 Lavaca, Austin, TX, 78701-1831. Tel: 512-478-5684. Fax: 512-478-6169. p. 2280

Dossey, Sue, Librn, Coleman Public Library, 402 Commercial Ave, Coleman, TX, 76834-4202. Tel: 325-625-3043. Fax: 325-625-3629. p. 2298

Dosu, Tabzeera, Dean of Libr, California State University, Sacramento Library, 2000 State University Dr E, Sacramento, CA, 95819-6039. Tel: 916-278-4179. Fax: 916-278-5917. p. 223

Doten, Sonya M, Libr Tech, United States Environmental Protection Agency, One Sabine Island Dr, Gulf Breeze, FL, 32561-5299. Tel: 850-934-9218. Fax: 850-934-2409. p. 450

Doto, Christina, Dir, Park Ridge Public Library, 51 Park Ave, Park Ridge, NJ, 07656. Tel: 201-391-5151. Fax: 201-391-2739. p. 1517

Dotolo, Lawrence G, Dr, Pres, Virginia Tidewater Consortium for Higher Education, 4900 Powhatan Ave, Norfolk, VA, 23529. Tel: 757-683-3183. Fax: 757-683-4515. p. 2957

Dotson, Beverly, Librn, Independent Baptist College Library, 5101 Western Center Blvd, Fort Worth, TX, 76137. Tel: 817-514-6364. Fax: 817-281-8257. p. 2322

Dotson, Elisha, Librn, Cook County Law Library, Domestic Violence, 555 W Harrison St, Chicago, IL, 60607. Tel: 312-325-9390. Fax: 312-325-9391. p. 612

Dotson, Eloise, Librn, Lafayette Public Library, Scott Branch, 5808 W Cameron St, Scott, LA, 70583. Tel: 337-232-9321. p. 953

Dotson, Lane Kaye, Dr, Asst Prof, East Carolina University, 101 Umstead Residence Hall, Greenville, NC, 27858-4353. Tel: 252-328-2787. Fax: 252-328-4368. p. 2971

Dotson, Maureen, Fac Coordr, San Diego State University Library & Information Access, 5500 Campanile Dr, San Diego, CA, 92182-8050. Tel: 619-594-4472. Fax: 619-594-3270. p. 237

Dotson, Michelle, Dir, Northumberland Public Library, Inc, 7204 Northumberland Hwy, Heathsville, VA, 22473. Tel: 804-580-5051. Fax: 804-580-5202. p. 2471

Dotten, Rose, Chief Exec Officer, Shelburne Public Library, 201 Owen Sound St, Shelburne, ON, L0N 1S0, CANADA. Tel: 519-925-2168. Fax: 519-925-6555. p. 2841

Dotterer, Douglas H, Dir, Stow-Munroe Falls Public Library, 3512 Darrow Rd, Stow, OH, 44224. Tel: 330-688-3295. p. 1937

Doty, Genie, Ch, Warren County Public Library District, 62 Public Sq, Monmouth, IL, 61462. Tel: 309-734-3166. Fax: 309-734-5955. p. 675

Doty, Marlene, Dir of Libr Serv, Berkeley College, 44 Rifle Camp Rd, Woodland Park, NJ, 07424. Tel: 973-278-5400. Fax: 973-278-9141. p. 1545

Doty, Marlene, Dir, Berkeley College Library, Three E 43rd St, New York, NY, 10017. Tel: 212-986-4343. Fax: 212-661-2940. p. 1670

Doty, Paul A, Electronic Res, St Lawrence University, 23 Romoda Dr, Canton, NY, 13617. Tel: 315-229-5483. Fax: 315-229-5729. p. 1602

Doty, Paula, Doc, Ref Serv, Nevada Supreme Court Library, Supreme Court Bldg, 201 S Carson St, Ste 100, Carson City, NV, 89701-4702. Tel: 775-684-1640. Fax: 775-684-1662. p. 1426

Doty, Philip, Prof, University of Texas at Austin, One University Sta, D7000, Austin, TX, 78712-0390. Tel: 512-471-3821. Fax: 512-471-3971. p. 2975

Dotzheimer, Linda, Tech Serv, Decatur Public Library, 504 Cherry St NE, Decatur, AL, 35601. Tel: 256-353-2993. Fax: 256-350-6736. p. 14

Douberly, Laura, Br Mgr, Edgecombe County Memorial Library, Pinetops Branch, 201 S First St, Pinetops, NC, 27864. Tel: 252-827-4621. Fax: 252-827-4621. p. 1827

Doubledee, Gale, Librn, Springfield News-Leader Library, 651 Boonville, Springfield, MO, 65806. Tel: 417-836-1215. Fax: 417-837-1381. p. 1368

Doucet, Suzanne, Librn, Chaleur Regional Hospital, 1750 Sunset Dr, Bathurst, NB, E2A 4L7, CANADA. Tel: 506-544-2446. Fax: 506-544-2017. p. 2761

Doucett, Elisabeth, Dir, Brunswick Public Library Association, 23 Pleasant St, Brunswick, ME, 04011-2295. Tel: 207-725-5242, Ext 211. Fax: 207-725-6313. p. 979

Doucette, Daniel, Librn, Peabody Historical Society & Museum, 35 Washington St, Peabody, MA, 01960-5520. Tel: 978-531-0805. Fax: 978-531-7292. p. 1116

Doucette, Joanne, Access Serv, Head, Tech Serv, Massachusetts College of Pharmacy & Health Sciences, 179 Longwood Ave, Boston, MA, 02115-5896. Tel: 617-732-2805. Fax: 617-278-1566. p. 1063

Doucette, Patricia, Mgr, Libr Serv, Holland College Library Services, 140 Weymouth St, Charlottetown, PE, C1A 4Z1, CANADA. Tel: 902-566-9558. Fax: 902-566-9522. p. 2875

Doud, Laurel, Librn, Fresno City College Library, 1101 E University Ave, Fresno, CA, 93741. Tel: 559-442-8204. Fax: 559-265-5758. p. 151

Doud, Mary, Dep Dir, Kalamazoo Public Library, 315 S Rose St, Kalamazoo, MI, 49007-5264. Tel: 269-553-7829. Fax: 269-553-7999. p. 1197

Dougall, Jane, Coll Develop, Ref Serv, Bard College, One Library Rd, Annandale-on-Hudson, NY, 12504. Tel: 845-758-7620. Fax: 845-758-5801. p. 1574

Dougay, John, Automation Tech, Tyler Junior College, 1327 S Baxter St, Tyler, TX, 75701. Tel: 903-510-2577. Fax: 903-510-2639. p. 2393

Dougher, Doris, Circ, ILL, Richton Park Public Library District, 4045 Sauk Trail, Richton Park, IL, 60471. Tel: 708-481-5333. Fax: 708-481-4343. p. 694

Dougherty, Chanda, In Charge, Ivinson Memorial Hospital Library, 255 N 30th St, Laramie, WY, 82072. Tel: 307-742-2141, Ext 5288. Fax: 307-721-9804. p. 2657

Dougherty, Jane, ILL, Ref, Hazleton Area Public Library, 55 N Church St, Hazleton, PA, 18201-5893. Tel: 570-454-2961. Fax: 570-454-0630. p. 2068

Dougherty, Kate, Geosciences & Maps Librn, University of Arkansas Libraries, 365 N McIlroy Ave, Fayetteville, AR, 72701-4002. Tel: 479-575-2241. Fax: 479-575-6656. p. 99

Dougherty, Michaeleen, Coordr, Circ, Gwynedd-Mercy College, 1325 Sumneytown Pike, Gwynedd Valley, PA, 19437. Tel: 215-646-7300, Ext 493. Fax: 215-641-5596. p. 2063

Dougherty, Michele, AV, Cataloger, Harcum College Library, 750 Montgomery Ave, Bryn Mawr, PA, 19010-3476. Tel: 610-526-6022. Fax: 610-526-6086. p. 2039

Dougherty, Roberta L, Librn, University of Texas Libraries, Middle Eastern Library Program, 21st & Speedway, Austin, TX, 78713. Tel: 512-495-4322. Fax: 512-495-4296. p. 2284

Dougherty-Johnson, Lily, YA Librn, Floyd Memorial Library, 539 First St, Greenport, NY, 11944-1399. Tel: 631-477-0660. Fax: 631-477-2647. p. 1631

Doughtie, Sarah, Asst Librn, Albemarle Regional Library, Gates County Public Library, 115 Court St, Gatesville, NC, 27938-9507. Tel: 252-357-0110. Fax: 252-357-1285. p. 1835

Doughty, Elaine D, Res Asst, Harvard Library, Harvard Forest Library, 324 N Main St, Petersham, MA, 01366. Tel: 978-724-3302. Fax: 978-724-3595. p. 1075

Doughty, Helen M, Librn, John Muir Medical Center Library, 1601 Ygnacio Valley Rd, Walnut Creek, CA, 94598-3237. Tel: 925-947-5231. Fax: 925-947-3237. p. 282

Doughty, Wendy, ILL, Grant Parish Library, 300 Main St, Colfax, LA, 71417-1830. Tel: 318-627-9920. Fax: 318-627-9900. p. 947

Douglas, Andrea, Dir, Dunbarton Public Library, 1004 School St, Dunbarton, NH, 03046-4816. Tel: 603-774-3546. Fax: 603-774-5563. p. 1445

Douglas, Christyne, Archivist, Meharry Medical College Library, 1005 Dr D B Todd Jr Blvd, Nashville, TN, 37208. Tel: 615-327-6470. Fax: 615-327-6448. p. 2257

Douglas, Emily, Librn, Tallahassee Campus, Keiser University Library System, 1500 NW 49th St, Fort Lauderdale, FL, 33309. Tel: 954-351-4035. Fax: 954-351-4051. p. 443

Douglas, Gayle, Assoc Dean, University of South Carolina, 1501 Greene St, Columbia, SC, 29208. Tel: 803-777-3858. Fax: 803-777-7938. p. 2973

Douglas, Gretchen, Instr, Info & Computer Literacy, SUNY Cortland, 81 Prospect Terrace, Cortland, NY, 13045. Tel: 607-753-2525. Fax: 607-753-5669. p. 1611

Douglas, Jacqueline, Circ Serv, West Hartford Public Library, 20 S Main St, West Hartford, CT, 06107-2432. Tel: 860-561-6950. Fax: 860-561-6976. p. 376

Douglas, Janice, Head, Acq, Madison County Library, Inc, 402 N Main St, Madison, VA, 22727. Tel: 540-948-4720. Fax: 540-948-4919. p. 2477

Douglas, Jeffrey A, Dir, Knox College, Two E South St, Galesburg, IL, 61401. Tel: 309-341-7491. Fax: 309-341-7799. p. 648

Douglas, Jennifer, Head, Tech Serv, Grand Prairie Public Library System, 901 Conover Dr, Grand Prairie, TX, 75051. Tel: 972-237-5700. Fax: 972-237-5750. p. 2329

Douglas, Jim, Dir, Nichols College, 124 Center Rd, Dudley, MA, 01571. Tel: 508-213-2333. Fax: 508-213-2323. p. 1085

Douglas, Jonetta, Sr Librn, Legislative Services Agency Library, State Capitol Bldg, Ground Flr, Des Moines, IA, 50319. Tel: 515-281-3312. Fax: 515-281-8027. p. 810

Douglas, Judy, Dir, Saint Clair County Public Library, 139 Fifth Ave, Ashville, AL, 35953. Tel: 205-594-3694. Fax: 205-594-3695. p. 5

Douglas, Karen, Librn, Passavant Area Hospital, 1600 W Walnut, Jacksonville, IL, 62650. Tel: 217-245-9541, Ext 3424. Fax: 217-245-0230. p. 659

Douglas, Karen B, Head, Coll Serv, Duke University Libraries, School of Law Library, 210 Science Dr, Durham, NC, 27708. Tel: 919-613-7116. Fax: 919-613-7237. p. 1788

Douglas, Katherine Meredith, Actg Chief Librn, Knox County Governmental Law Library, M-99 City County Bldg, 400 Main St, Knoxville, TN, 37902. Tel: 865-215-2368. Fax: 865-215-2920, 865-215-4283. p. 2241

Douglas, Kay, Lead Libr Tech, University of Washington Libraries, Natural Sciences, Allen Library S, Ground & First Flrs, Box 352900, Seattle, WA, 98195-2900. Tel: 206-543-1243. Fax: 206-685-1665. p. 2534

Douglas, Kimberly, Librn, California Institute of Technology, Astrophysics, 1201 E California Blvd, M/C 105-24, Pasadena, CA, 91125. Tel: 626-395-4008. p. 205

Douglas, Kimberly, Univ Librn, California Institute of Technology, 1200 E California Blvd, M/C 1-32, Pasadena, CA, 91125-3200. Tel: 626-395-6416. Fax: 626-792-7540. p. 205

Douglas, Mary, Youth Serv Coordr, LeRoy Collins Leon County Public Library System, 200 W Park Ave, Tallahassee, FL, 32301-7720. Tel: 850-606-2665. Fax: 850-606-2601. p. 492

Douglas, Michael, Librn, Bethesda North Hospital, 10500 Montgomery Rd, Cincinnati, OH, 45242. Tel: 513-872-2443. Fax: 513-745-1220. p. 1868

Douglas, Michael, Dir, TriHealth, Inc, 375 Dixmyth Ave, Cincinnati, OH, 45220-2489. Tel: 513-862-2433. Fax: 513-862-4984. p. 1873

Douglas, Scott, In Charge, Centre for Christian Studies Library, Woodsworth House, 60 Maryland St, Winnipeg, MB, R3G 1K7, CANADA. Tel: 204-783-4490, Ext 26. Fax: 204-786-3012. p. 2755

Douglas, Sherri, Youth Serv, Anchorage Public Library, 3600 Denali St, Anchorage, AK, 99503. Tel: 907-343-2840. Fax: 907-343-2930. p. 44

Douglas, Shirley, Librn, Mound City Public Library, 224 High St, Mound City, IL, 62963. Tel: 618-748-9427. p. 676

Douglas-Williams, Tara, Div Head, Morehouse School of Medicine Library, 720 Westview Dr SW, Atlanta, GA, 30310-1495. Tel: 404-752-1542. Fax: 404-752-1049. p. 517

Douglass, Joan, Circ Librn, Bennington Free Library, 101 Silver St, Bennington, VT, 05201. Tel: 802-442-9051. p. 2418

Douglass, Lauren, Head, Tech Serv, East Lansing Public Library, 950 Abbott Rd, East Lansing, MI, 48823-3105. Tel: 517-351-2420, Ext 104. Fax: 517-351-9536. p. 1175

Douglass, Marilee, Circ, Plymouth Public Library, 201 N Center St, Plymouth, IN, 46563. Tel: 574-936-2324. Fax: 574-936-7423. p. 773

Doumato, Lamia, Head, Reader Serv, National Gallery of Art Library, Fourth St & Constitution Ave NW, Washington, DC, 20565. Tel: 202-842-6510. Fax: 202-789-3068. p. 409

Douros, Deborah, Br Mgr, Sacramento Public Library, North Highlands/Antelope Library, 4235 Antelope Rd, Antelope, CA, 95843. p. 225

Doute, Christian, Syst Mgr, Virgin Islands Division of Libraries, Archives & Museums, 23 Dronningens Gade, Saint Thomas, VI, 00802. Tel: 340-774-3407. Fax: 340-775-1887. p. 2679

Douthit, Joyce, Mgr, Southeast Arkansas Regional Library, Arkansas City Branch, PO Box 447, Arkansas City, AR, 71630. p. 109

Douthit, Joyce, Mgr, Southeast Arkansas Regional Library, Gould Branch, PO Box 683, Gould, AR, 71643-0683. Tel: 870-263-1001. Fax: 870-263-1001. p. 110

Douthit, Joyce, Mgr, Southeast Arkansas Regional Library, Tillar Branch, PO Box 136, Tillar, AR, 71670-0136. Tel: 870-367-8584. p. 110

Douthit, Joyce, Mgr, Southeast Arkansas Regional Library, Watson Branch, PO Box 205, Watson, AR, 71674. Tel: 870-644-3655. Fax: 870-644-3655. p. 110

Douthitt, Rita, Dir, Jasper-Dubois County Contractual Public Library, 1116 Main St, Jasper, IN, 47546-2899. Tel: 812-482-2712. Fax: 812-482-7123. p. 756

Douthwright, Ivan W, Librn, Atlantic Baptist University, 333 Gorge Rd, Moncton, NB, E1C 3H9, CANADA. Tel: 506-863-6443. Fax: 506-858-9694. p. 2765

Doutre, Robin, Circ Mgr, Michigan State University, 115 Law College Bldg, East Lansing, MI, 48824-1300. Tel: 517-432-6869. Fax: 517-432-6861. p. 1175

Dover, Michelle, Head, Circ, Bud Werner Memorial Library, 1289 Lincoln Ave, Steamboat Springs, CO, 80487. Tel: 970-879-0240. Fax: 970-879-3476. p. 323

Dover, Wendy, Access Serv Librn, Gulf Coast State College Library, 5230 W Hwy 98, Panama City, FL, 32401. Tel: 850-872-3893. Fax: 850-872-3861. p. 480

Dovico, Judy, Librn, Batavia Public Library, 902 Third St, Batavia, IA, 52533. Tel: 641-662-2317. p. 795

Dow, Elizabeth, Dr, Prof, Louisiana State University, 267 Coates Hall, Baton Rouge, LA, 70803. Tel: 225-578-3158. Fax: 225-578-4581. p. 2966

Dow, Marilyn, Dir, University of Detroit Mercy Library, School of Dentistry, Corktown Campus, 2700 Martin Luther King Jr Blvd, Detroit, MI, 48208-2576. Tel: 313-494-6900. Fax: 313-494-6838. p. 1172

Dow, Mary, Ser, Morris College, 100 W College St, Sumter, SC, 29150-3599. Tel: 803-934-3230. Fax: 803-778-2923. p. 2206

Dow, Tracey, Cat, Annie Halenbake Ross Library, 232 W Main St, Lock Haven, PA, 17745-1241. Tel: 570-748-3321. Fax: 570-748-1050. p. 2082

Dow, Victoria E, Dir, West Chester Public Library, 415 N Church St, West Chester, PA, 19380-2401. Tel: 610-696-1721. Fax: 610-429-1077. p. 2153

Dowal, Linda, Ch, Dir, Gordon-Nash Library, 69 Main St, New Hampton, NH, 03256. Tel: 603-744-8061. Fax: 603-744-6555. p. 1459

Dowd, Catherine, Librn, Mgr, Ontario Provincial Police, 777 Memorial Ave, Orillia, ON, L3V 7V3, CANADA. Tel: 705-329-6886. Fax: 705-329-6887. p. 2826

Dowd, Chris, Reserves, University of Puget Sound, 1500 N Warner St, Campus Mail Box 1021, Tacoma, WA, 98416-1021. Tel: 253-879-3618. Fax: 253-879-3670. p. 2541

Dowd, Frank, Ref, Edison State College, 8099 College Pkwy SW, Bldg J, Fort Myers, FL, 33919. Tel: 239-489-9449. Fax: 239-489-9095. p. 444

Dowd, Nathan, Tech Coordr, Madison Area Technical College, 3550 Anderson St, Rm 230, Madison, WI, 53704. Tel: 608-246-6637. Fax: 608-246-6644. p. 2606

Dowdey, Don, Dean, Sul Ross State University, PO Box C-109, Alpine, TX, 79832-0001. Tel: 432-837-8123. Fax: 432-837-8400. p. 2273

Dowdle, Mark, Circ, California State University, 9001 Stockdale Hwy, Bakersfield, CA, 93311-1022. Tel: 661-654-3233. Fax: 661-654-3238. p. 123

Dowdy, Beverly, Head, Electronic Res & Ser Mgt, Duke University Libraries, 411 Chapel Dr, Durham, NC, 27708. Tel: 919-613-5185. Fax: 919-660-5923. p. 1787

Dowdy, Elayne, Per, Ser, North Georgia College & State University, 238 Georgia Circle, Dahlonega, GA, 30597-3001. Tel: 706-864-1519. p. 528

Dowdy, Jeff, Asst Librn, Bainbridge College Library, 2500 E Shotwell St, Bainbridge, GA, 39818. Tel: 229-248-2590. Fax: 229-248-2589. p. 521

Dowdy, Vivian, Adult Serv, Auburndale Public Library, 100 W Bridgers Ave, Auburndale, FL, 33823. Tel: 863-965-5548. Fax: 863-965-5554. p. 425

Dowdy, Wayne, Sr Mgr, Hist/Genealogy Dept, Memphis Public Library & Information Center, 3030 Poplar Ave, Memphis, TN, 38111-3527. Tel: 901-415-2744. Fax: 901-323-7108. p. 2249

Dowell, Connie Vinita, Dean of Libr, Vanderbilt University, 419 21st Ave S, Nashville, TN, 37203-2427. Tel: 615-322-7100. Fax: 615-343-8279. p. 2260

Dowell, Gail, Head, Tech Serv, Hudson Library & Historical Society, 96 Library St, Hudson, OH, 44236-5122. Tel: 330-653-6658. Fax: 330-650-3373. p. 1905

Dowell, Nancy E, Dir, Vigo County Public Library, One Library Sq, Terre Haute, IN, 47807. Tel: 812-232-1113. Fax: 812-232-3208. p. 782

Dowell, Trisha, Librn, Charles J Rike Memorial Library, 203 Orange St, Farmersville, TX, 75442. Tel: 972-782-6681. Fax: 972-782-7608. p. 2319

Dowell, Virgie, Asst Dir, Madison-Jefferson County Public Library, 420 W Main St, Madison, IN, 47250-3796. Tel: 812-265-2744. Fax: 812-265-2217. p. 762

Dower, Karen, ILL, Delaware Technical & Community College, 400 Stanton-Christiana Rd, Newark, DE, 19713-2197. Tel: 302-454-3939. Fax: 302-453-3079. p. 385

Dowgiert, Rebecca, Health Sci Librn, Info Spec, University of Bridgeport, 126 Park Ave, Bridgeport, CT, 06604-5620. Tel: 203-576-4528. Fax: 203-576-4791. p. 332

Dowland, Sandra, Dir, Dr Nathan Porter Public Library, 228 N Front St, Greenfield, TN, 38230-9998. Tel: 731-235-9932. Fax: 731-235-9932. p. 2236

Dowling, Elizabeth, Ref Librn, Washington Carnegie Public Library, 300 W Main St, Washington, IN, 47501-2698. Tel: 812-254-4586. Fax: 812-254-4585. p. 786

Dowling, Heidi, Tech Serv Mgr, Columbus Metropolitan Library, 96 S Grant Ave, Columbus, OH, 43215-4781. Tel: 614-645-2275. Fax: 614-849-1157. p. 1884

Dowling, Shelley, Ref Serv, College of William & Mary in Virginia, The Wolf Law Library, 613 S Henry St, Williamsburg, VA, 23187. Tel: 757-221-3255. Fax: 757-221-3051. p. 2502

Dowling, Teri, Fine Arts Librn, California College of the Arts Libraries, Simpson Library, 1111 Eighth St, San Francisco, CA, 94107. p. 196

Down, Nancy, Chair, Archival Coll & Br, Bowling Green State University Libraries, 204 Wm T Jerome Library, Bowling Green, OH, 43403-0170. p. 1861

Down, Nancy, Head Librn, Bowling Green State University Libraries, Ray & Pat Browne Popular Culture Library, Jerome Library, 4th Flr, Bowling Green, OH, 43403. Tel: 419-372-6054. Fax: 419-372-7996. p. 1861

Down, Nancy, Head Librn, Consortium of Popular Culture Collections in the Midwest, c/o Popular Culture Library, Bowling Green State University, Bowling Green, OH, 43403-0600. Tel: 419-372-6054. Fax: 419-372-7996. p. 2952

Downen, Virgil, Librn, Centralia Regional Library District, Odin Community, 219 E Main St, Odin, IL, 62870. Tel: 618-775-8309. Fax: 618-775-8309. p. 602

Downer, Diane, Dir, Gering Public Library, 1055 P St, Gering, NE, 69341. Tel: 308-436-6868. Fax: 308-436-6869. p. 1399

Downer, Sherida, Assoc Prof, Auburn University, 4036 Haley Ctr, Auburn, AL, 36849-5221. Tel: 334-844-4460. Fax: 334-844-3072. p. 2961

Downes, Kathy, Sr Assoc Dean, Univ Libr, Wichita State University Libraries, 1845 Fairmount, Wichita, KS, 67260-0068. Tel: 316-978-3582. Fax: 316-978-3048. p. 902

Downes, Marie, Dir, West Deptford Public Library, 420 Crown Point Rd, West Deptford, NJ, 08086-9598. Tel: 856-845-5593. Fax: 856-848-3689. p. 1541

Downey, Anne, Head, Conserv, American Philosophical Society Library, 105 S Fifth St, Philadelphia, PA, 19106-3386. Tel: 215-440-3412. Fax: 215-440-3423. p. 2102

Downey, Dawn, Tech Asst II - Access Serv, Potomac State College of West Virginia University, 101 Fort Ave, Keyser, WV, 26726. Tel: 304-788-6901. Fax: 304-788-6946. p. 2563

Downey, Doug, Librn, Saint Giles' Episcopal Church, 3025 Walters Ave, Northbrook, IL, 60062. Tel: 847-272-6622. Fax: 847-272-7664. p. 682

Downey, Greg, Asst Prof, University of Wisconsin-Madison, 4217 H C White Hall, 600 N Park St, Madison, WI, 53706. Tel: 608-263-2916. Fax: 608-263-4849. p. 2976

Downey, Joyce, Coordr, University of Rhode Island, 15 Pier Rd, Narragansett, RI, 02882-1197. Tel: 401-874-6161. Fax: 401-874-6101. p. 2168

Downey, Judith, Librn, New Bedford Free Public Library, Casa da Saudade, 58 Crapo St, New Bedford, MA, 02740. Tel: 508-991-6218. Fax: 508-979-1705. p. 1108

Downey, Maria, Coll Mgt, Kent State University Libraries, 1125 Risman Dr, Kent, OH, 44242. Tel: 330-672-5000. Fax: 330-672-4811. p. 1907

Downey, Nancy, Media Spec, Ad, Massapequa Public Library, Central Avenue, 523 Central Ave, Massapequa, NY, 11758. Tel: 516-798-4607, Ext 306. Fax: 516-798-2804. p. 1658

Downey, Roberta, Circ, Kellogg-Hubbard Library, 135 Main St, Montpelier, VT, 05602. Tel: 802-223-3338. Fax: 802-223-3338. p. 2429

Downie Banks, Margaret, Interim Exec Dir, University of South Dakota, National Music Museum Library, 414 E Clark St, Vermillion, SD, 57069-2390. Tel: 605-677-5306. Fax: 605-677-6995. p. 2221

Downie, J Stephen, Assoc Dean, Prof, University of Illinois at Urbana-Champaign, Library & Information Science Bldg, 501 E Daniel St, Champaign, IL, 61820-6211. Tel: 217-333-3280. Fax: 217-244-3302. p. 2965

Downie, Judith A, Humanities & Govt Doc Librn, California State University, 333 S Twin Oaks Valley Rd, San Marcos, CA, 92096-0001. Tel: 760-750-4340. Fax: 760-750-3287. p. 254

Downing, Arthur, Dr, Chief Librn, Baruch College-CUNY, 151 E 25 St, Box H-0520, New York, NY, 10010-2313. Tel: 646-312-1026. p. 1670

Downing, Carol, Head, Tech Serv, Peace Library System, 8301 110 St, Grande Prairie, AB, T8W 6T2, CANADA. Tel: 780-538-4656. Fax: 780-539-5285. p. 2705

Downing, Eileen, ILL, Lee County Library System, 2345 Union St, Fort Myers, FL, 33901-3917. Tel: 239-533-4185. Fax: 239-485-1100. p. 445

Downing, Eileen, ILL/Doc Delivery Serv, Lee County Library System, Processing Center, 881 Gunnery Rd N, Ste 2, Lehigh Acres, FL, 33971-1246. Tel: 239-461-7322. Fax: 239-461-7373. p. 446

Downing, Joanne, Asst Dir, Fort Bend County Libraries, 1001 Golfview Dr, Richmond, TX, 77469-5199. Tel: 281-341-2617. Fax: 281-341-2688. p. 2374

Downing, Karen, ILL, Institute for Advanced Study Libraries, Einstein Dr, Princeton, NJ, 08540. Tel: 609-734-8181, 609-734-8276. Fax: 609-924-8399, 609-951-4515. p. 1522

Downing, Laura, Head, Ref, Arkansas State University, 322 University Loop West Circle, State University, AR, 72401. Tel: 870-972-3077. Fax: 870-972-3199. p. 115

Downing, Lisa, Adult Serv, Asst Dir, Forbes Library, 20 West St, Northampton, MA, 01060-3798. Tel: 413-587-1011. Fax: 413-587-1015. p. 1113

Downing, Sarah, Asst Curator, Cataloger, Librn, North Carolina Office of Archives & History, One Festival Park Blvd, Manteo, NC, 27954. Tel: 252-473-2655. Fax: 252-473-1483. p. 1808

Downs, Bill, Adult Serv, Ref, Matteson Public Library, 801 S School St, Matteson, IL, 60443-1897. Tel: 708-748-4431. Fax: 708-748-0510. p. 671

Downs, Charlotte, Librn, East Burke Community Library, 368 Rt 114, East Burke, VT, 05832. Tel: 802-626-9823. p. 2423

Downs, Ina, ILL, Roosevelt County Library, 220 Second Ave S, Wolf Point, MT, 59201-1599. Tel: 406-653-2411. Fax: 406-653-1365. p. 1390

Downs, Kathy, Asst Librn, Smithfield Public Library, 25 N Main St, Smithfield, UT, 84335-1957. Tel: 435-563-3555. p. 2416

Downs, Pat, Principal Librn, Prog Serv, San Diego County Library, 5560 Overland Ave, Ste 110, San Diego, CA, 92123. Tel: 858-694-2370. Fax: 858-495-5981. p. 233

Downs, Robert, Circ Serv Coordr, California State University Dominguez Hills, 1000 E Victoria St, Carson, CA, 90747. Tel: 310-243-2404. Fax: 310-516-4219. p. 132

Downs, Rondi, Librn, First Presbyterian Church Library, Nine S Eighth Ave, Yakima, WA, 98902. Tel: 509-248-7940. Fax: 509-248-0937. p. 2550

Dowsing Toliver, Virginia, Assoc Univ Librn, Admin, Washington University Libraries, One Brookings Dr, Campus Box 1061, Saint Louis, MO, 63130-4862. Tel: 314-935-5400. Fax: 314-935-4045. p. 1362

Doyel, Wendy, Youth Serv Librn, Woodbine Public Library, 58 Fifth St, Woodbine, IA, 51579. Tel: 712-647-2750. Fax: 712-647-2750. p. 853

Doyle, Ann, Br Head, University of British Columbia Library, Xwi7xwa Library-First Nations House of Learning, 1985 West Mall, Vancouver, BC, V6T 1Z2, CANADA. Tel: 604-822-2385. p. 2743

Doyle, Brandie, Ref, Russell Library, 123 Broad St, Middletown, CT, 06457. Tel: 860-347-2528, Ext 121. p. 352

Doyle, Bridget, Regional Coordr, Northern New York Library Network, 6721 US Hwy 11, Potsdam, NY, 13676. Tel: 315-265-1119. Fax: 315-265-1881. p. 2950

Doyle, Caren, Head Librn, Carroll, Burdick & McDonough, 44 Montgomery St, Ste 400, San Francisco, CA, 94104. Tel: 415-989-5900. Fax: 415-989-0932. p. 241

Doyle, Carol, Maps & Govt Info Librn, California State University, Fresno, Henry Madden Library, 5200 N Barton Ave, Mail Stop ML-34, Fresno, CA, 93740-8014. Tel: 559-278-2335. Fax: 559-278-6952. p. 150

Doyle, Carolyn, Br Librn, London Public Library, Fred Landon Branch, 167 Wortley Rd, London, ON, N6C 3P6, CANADA. Tel: 519-439-6240. p. 2818

Doyle, Catherine, Libr Dir, Nazareth College of Rochester Library, 4245 East Ave, Rochester, NY, 14618-3790. Tel: 585-389-2123. Fax: 585-389-2145. p. 1730

Doyle, Cathy, ILL, Bradford Area Public Library, 67 W Washington St, Bradford, PA, 16701-1234. Tel: 814-362-6527. Fax: 814-362-4168. p. 2037

Doyle, Darly, Bus & Finance Mgr, Poplar Creek Public Library District, 1405 S Park Ave, Streamwood, IL, 60107-2997. Tel: 630-837-6800. Fax: 630-837-6823. p. 708

Doyle, Dennis, Dir, Ulster County Planning Board Library, County Office Bldg, 244 Fair St, Kingston, NY, 12402. Tel: 845-340-3340. Fax: 845-340-3429. p. 1650

Doyle, Jacqueline, Head Librn, AHSL-Phoenix, University of Arizona, Arizona Health Sciences Library, 1501 N Campbell Ave, Tucson, AZ, 85724. Tel: 602-827-2031. Fax: 602-827-2048. p. 88

Doyle, Jeannine, Asst Dep Dir-Human Res/Labor Relations Officer, Buffalo & Erie County Public Library System, One Lafayette Sq, Buffalo, NY, 14203-1887. Tel: 716-858-8900. Fax: 716-858-6211. p. 1596

Doyle, John, Circ Serv Mgr, Park Ridge Public Library, 20 S Prospect, Park Ridge, IL, 60068-4188. Tel: 847-825-3123. Fax: 847-825-0001. p. 688

Doyle, John, Assoc Librn, Washington & Lee University, Wilbur C Hall Law Library, Lewis Hall, E Denny Circle, Lexington, VA, 24450. Tel: 540-458-8554. Fax: 540-458-8967. p. 2474

Doyle, Judith A, Librn, New York State Department of Correctional Services, 50 E Court St, Hudson, NY, 12534-2429. Tel: 518-828-4311, Ext 4600. Fax: 518-828-4311, Ext 2099. p. 1638

Doyle, June, Tech Serv, Southeastern Public Library System of Oklahoma, 401 N Second St, McAlester, OK, 74501. Tel: 918-426-0456. Fax: 918-426-0543. p. 1968

Doyle, Karen, Librn, Will County Law Library, 14 W Jefferson St, Ste 453, Joliet, IL, 60432-4300. Tel: 815-727-8536. Fax: 815-727-8785. p. 660

Doyle, Kathleen, Dir, Pennington Public Library, 30 N Main St, Pennington, NJ, 08534. Tel: 609-737-0404. Fax: 609-737-2948. p. 1519

Doyle, Lee, Tech Serv, Moses Greeley Parker Memorial Library, 28 Arlington St, Dracut, MA, 01826. Tel: 978-454-5474. Fax: 978-454-9120. p. 1085

Doyle, Liz, Supvry Librn, United States Environmental Protection Agency, 1200 Sixth Ave, Mail-Stop OMP-104, Seattle, WA, 98101. Tel: 206-553-2134. Fax: 206-553-6346. p. 2533

Doyle, Marie, Ref Librn, Missoula Public Library, 301 E Main, Missoula, MT, 59802-4799. Tel: 406-721-2665. Fax: 406-728-5900. p. 1386

Doyle, Martha, Librn, United States Courts Library, 600 E Monroe St, Rm 305, Springfield, IL, 62701. Tel: 217-492-4191. Fax: 217-492-4192. p. 707

Doyle, Megan, Adult Serv, East Brunswick Public Library, Two Jean Walling Civic Center, East Brunswick, NJ, 08816-3599. Tel: 732-390-6950. Fax: 732-390-6796. p. 1481

Doyle, Mickey, Head, Circ, Ref & Instruction Librn, University of Michigan-Flint, 303 E Kearsley St, Flint, MI, 48502-1950. Tel: 810-762-3401. Fax: 810-762-3133. p. 1181

Doyle, Nancy, Adult Serv, Circ & Stacks Coordr, Vols Serv Coordr, Millis Public Library, 25 Auburn Rd, Millis, MA, 02054-1203. Tel: 508-376-8282. Fax: 508-376-1278. p. 1106

Doyle, Pat, Br Mgr, Jacksonville Public Library, Beaches Regional, 600 Third St, Neptune Beach, FL, 32266-5014. Tel: 904-241-1141. Fax: 904-241-4965. p. 453

Doyle, Richard, Dir, Coe College, 1220 First Ave NE, Cedar Rapids, IA, 52402-5092. Tel: 319-399-8023. Fax: 319-399-8019. p. 800

Doyle, Sara A, Coll Develop, Ref Serv, Ad, Sioux City Public Library, 529 Pierce St, Sioux City, IA, 51101-1203. Tel: 712-255-2933. p. 844

Doyle, Suzanne, Ch, St Francis Public Library, 4230 S Nicholson Ave, Saint Francis, WI, 53235. Tel: 414-481-7323. Fax: 414-481-8949. p. 2635

Doyle, Theresa, Ch, Margaret E Heggan Free Public Library of the Township of Washington, 606 Delsea Dr, Sewell, NJ, 08080. Tel: 856-589-3334. Fax: 856-582-2042. p. 1529

Doyle, Thomas, Archivist, Woburn Public Library, 45 Pleasant St, Woburn, MA, 01801. Tel: 781-933-0148. Fax: 781-938-7860. p. 1142

Doyle-Maher, Barbara, Govt Doc, Tech Serv, University of Tennessee, Knoxville, Agriculture-Veterinary Medicine, A-113 Veterinary Teaching Hospital, 2407 Joe Johnson Dr, Knoxville, TN, 37996-4541. Tel: 865-974-4735. Fax: 865-974-4732. p. 2244

Doylen, Michael, Interim Asst Dir, User Serv Div, University of Wisconsin-Milwaukee Libraries, 2311 E Hartford Ave, Milwaukee, WI, 53211. Tel: 414-229-4785, 414-229-6202. Fax: 414-229-6766. p. 2622

Doyon, Jennifer, Tech Serv, Teen Serv, The Brookfield Library, 182 Whisconier Rd, Brookfield, CT, 06804. Tel: 203-775-6241. Fax: 203-740-7723. p. 332

Dozier, Wanda, Asst Librn, Santa Clara Pueblo Community Library, PO Box 580, Espanola, NM, 87532-0580. Tel: 505-753-7326. p. 1555

Draayer, Ingrid, Head, Access Serv, Carleton University Library, 1125 Colonel By Dr, Ottawa, ON, K1S 5B6, CANADA. Tel: 613-520-2600, Ext 2729. Fax: 613-520-2750. p. 2830

Drabinski, Emily, Ref/Instruction Librn, Long Island University, One University Plaza, Brooklyn, NY, 11201-9926. Tel: 718-488-1081. Fax: 718-780-4057. p. 1593

Drabkin, Denise, Br Head, Toronto Public Library, Brookbanks, 210 Brookbanks Dr, Toronto, ON, M3A 2T8, CANADA. Tel: 416-395-5480. Fax: 416-395-5436. p. 2860

Drach, Allan, Circ Asst, Holy Family University Library, 9801 Frankford Ave, Philadelphia, PA, 19114. Tel: 267-341-3315, 267-341-3316. Fax: 215-632-8067. p. 2111

Drachman, Ruth, Librn, Tinmouth Public Library, MountainView Rd, Tinmouth, VT, 05773. Tel: 802-446-2498. Fax: 802-446-2498. p. 2437

Draeger, Barbara, Head, Adult Serv, New Berlin Public Library, 15105 Library Lane, New Berlin, WI, 53151. Tel: 262-785-4980. Fax: 262-785-4984. p. 2625

Dragann, Kathleen, Adjunct Fac Librn, Harrisburg Area Community College, 1641 Old Philadelphia Pike, Lancaster, PA, 17602. Tel: 717-358-2986. Fax: 717-358-2952. p. 2076

Drager, Beverly, Dir, Casselton Public Library, 701 First St N, Casselton, ND, 58012. Tel: 701-347-4861, Ext 13. Fax: 701-347-4505. p. 1839

Drago, Antoinette, Dir, Metropolitan Hospital Center, 1901 First Ave & 97th St, New York, NY, 10029. Tel: 212-423-6055. Fax: 212-423-7961. p. 1686

Dragos, Devra, Tech & Access Serv Dir, Nebraska Library Commission, The Atrium, 1200 N St, Ste 120, Lincoln, NE, 68508-2023. Fax: 402-471-2083. p. 1406

Dragotta, Nancy A, Mgr, North Carolina Museum of Life & Science Library, 433 W Murray Ave, Durham, NC, 27704-3101. Tel: 919-220-5429. Fax: 919-220-5575. p. 1789

Draine, Kathleen, Ref, Sandy Public Library, 38980 Proctor Blvd, Sandy, OR, 97055-8040. Tel: 503-668-5537. Fax: 503-668-3153. p. 2019

Drake, Alyson, Ref Librn, University of South Carolina, Coleman Karesh Law Library, USC Law Ctr, 701 Main St, Columbia, SC, 29208. Tel: 803-777-5942. Fax: 803-777-9405. p. 2190

Drake, Carlene, Dir, Loma Linda University, 11072 Anderson St, Loma Linda, CA, 92350-0001. Tel: 909-558-4581. Fax: 909-558-4121. p. 165

Drake, Cindy S, Curator, Tech Serv, Nebraska State Historical Society Library, 1500 R St, Lincoln, NE, 68508. Tel: 402-471-4786. Fax: 402-471-8922. p. 1406

Drake, Frank, Dir, Libr Serv, Arnstein & Lehr LLP Library, 120 S Riverside Plaza, Ste 1200, Chicago, IL, 60606-3910. Tel: 312-876-7170. Fax: 312-876-0288. p. 606

Drake, Katie, Librn, Graham & Dunn, Pier 70, 2801 Alaskan Way, Ste 300, Seattle, WA, 98121-1128. Tel: 206-624-8300. Fax: 206-340-9599. p. 2527

Drake, Kelly, Digital Serv, Mystic Seaport Museum, 75 Greenmanville Ave, Mystic, CT, 06355. Tel: 860-572-5367. Fax: 860-572-5394. p. 353

Drake, Kristen, Media Spec, Shaker Heights Public Library, 16500 Van Aken Blvd, Shaker Heights, OH, 44120-5318. Tel: 216-991-2030. Fax: 216-991-5951. p. 1934

Drake, Marla, Ch, Ozark-Dale County Public Library, Inc, 416 James St, Ozark, AL, 36360. Tel: 334-774-2399, 334-774-5480. p. 33

Drake, Melinda Anne, Info Literacy Librn, The California Maritime Academy Library, 200 Maritime Academy Dr, Vallejo, CA, 94590. Tel: 707-654-1097. Fax: 707-654-1094. p. 278

Drake, Mike, Br Mgr, Tulare County Library, Visalia Headquarters Branch, 200 W Oak Ave, Visalia, CA, 93291. Tel: 559-713-2704. Fax: 559-737-4586. p. 281

Drake, Myra, Circ, Mineral County Public Library, 110 First St, Hawthorne, NV, 89415. Tel: 775-945-2778. Fax: 775-945-0703. p. 1428

Drake, Paul B, Circ/ILL Librn, University of Guam, UOG Sta, Mangilao, GU, 96923. Tel: 671-735-2345. Fax: 671-734-6882. p. 2667

Drake, Robert, Mgr, Main Libr, Chattanooga-Hamilton County Bicentennial Library, 1001 Broad St, Chattanooga, TN, 37402-2652. Tel: 423-757-5426. Fax: 423-757-4994. p. 2226

Drake, Shirley, Librn, CH2M Hill, 2300 NW Walnut Blvd, Corvallis, OR, 97330-3596. Tel: 541-752-4271, Ext 3652. Fax: 541-752-0276. p. 1994

Drake, Shirley, Librn, CH2M Hill Inc Library, 2020 SW Fourth Ave, 3rd Flr, Portland, OR, 97201. Tel: 503-235-5000. Fax: 503-736-2000. p. 2010

Drake, Sylvia, Tech Serv, Brazoria County Library System, 451 N Velasco, Ste 250, Angleton, TX, 77515. Tel: 979-864-1544. Fax: 979-864-1273. p. 2275

Drakes, Olivia, ILL, Wenatchee Valley College, 1300 Fifth St, Wenatchee, WA, 98801. Tel: 509-682-6712. Fax: 509-682-6711. p. 2550

Dramstad, Desiree, Libr Dir, Montana State Prison Library, 600 Conley Lake Rd, Deer Lodge, MT, 59722. Tel: 406-846-1320, Ext 2410. Fax: 406-846-2951. p. 1377

Drane, Marcia, Dir, Fluvanna County Library, 8880 James Madison Hwy, Fork Union, VA, 23055. Tel: 434-842-2230. Fax: 434-842-2230. p. 2464

Draney, Rachelle, Ch, Lincoln County Library, Alpine Branch, 243 River Circle, Alpine, WY, 83126. Tel: 307-654-7323. Fax: 307-654-2158. p. 2656

Drapeau, Glenda, Librn, Freeland Holmes Library, 109 Pleasant St, Oxford, ME, 04270-4206. Tel: 207-539-4016. p. 995

Draper, Eleanore, Asst Librn, Roann Paw Paw Township Public Library, 240 S Chippewa Rd, Roann, IN, 46974. Tel: 765-833-5231. Fax: 765-833-5231. p. 775

Draper, Jenny, Dir, Kendallville Public Library, 221 S Park Ave, Kendallville, IN, 46755-2248. Tel: 260-343-2010. Fax: 260-343-2011. p. 756

Draper, Kate, Pub Serv, Sierra Vista Public Library, 2600 E Tacoma, Sierra Vista, AZ, 85635-1399. Tel: 520-458-4225. Fax: 520-458-5377. p. 82

Draper, Mary, Dir, General N B Baker Public Library, 315 Ash St, Sutherland, IA, 51058. Tel: 712-446-3839. Fax: 712-446-3839. p. 847

Draper, Nancy, III, Dir, Libr Serv, Hillsdale Free Will Baptist College Library, 3701 S I-35, Moore, OK, 73160. Tel: 405-912-9025. Fax: 405-912-9050. p. 1969

Draper, Norma J, Mgr, Northrop Grumman Mission Systems, 12011 Sunset Hills Rd, Reston, VA, 20190. Tel: 703-345-7738. Fax: 703-345-7735. p. 2487

Draper, Stacy P, Curator, Rensselaer County Historical Society, 57 Second St, Troy, NY, 12180. Tel: 518-244-6846. Fax: 518-273-1264. p. 1756

Draper, Wayne, Librn II, Broward County Division of Libraries, Talking Book Library, 100 S Andrews Ave, Fort Lauderdale, FL, 33301. Tel: 954-357-7555. Fax: 954-357-7413. p. 442

Draskovich, Margaret, Cataloger, Flagler College, 44 Sevilla St, Saint Augustine, FL, 32084-4302. Tel: 904-819-6206. Fax: 904-823-8511. p. 486

Draves, Ken, Dep Dir, Poudre River Public Library District, 201 Peterson St, Fort Collins, CO, 80524-2990. Tel: 970-221-6740. Fax: 970-221-6398. p. 307

Draves, Ken, Br Mgr, Poudre River Public Library District, Harmony Library, 4616 S Shields St, Fort Collins, CO, 80526-3812. Tel: 970-204-8206. Fax: 970-204-8444. p. 308

Drawe, Kay, Librn, Rob & Bessie Welder Wildlife Foundation Library, 10620 Hwy 77 N, Sinton, TX, 78387. Tel: 361-364-2643. Fax: 361-364-2650. p. 2387

Drawe, Scott, Br Mgr, Chicago Public Library, Near North, 310 W Division, Chicago, IL, 60610. Tel: 312-744-0991. Fax: 312-744-6221. p. 609

Drayson, Pamela, Dr, Chief Librn, University of Ontario Institute of Technology Library, 2000 Simcoe St N, Oshawa, ON, L1H 7K4, CANADA. Tel: 905-721-8668, Ext 2214. Fax: 905-721-8668, Ext 3029. p. 2827

Drazek, Michael, Dir, Pompton Lakes Public Library, 333 Wanaque Ave, Pompton Lakes, NJ, 07442. Tel: 973-835-0482. Fax: 973-835-4767. p. 1521

Dreaden, Sandra, Ref Librn, Robert L F Sikes Public Library, 1445 Commerce Dr, Crestview, FL, 32539. Tel: 850-682-4432. Fax: 850-689-4788. p. 434

Dreblow, Deanna, Dir, Wolcott Community Public Library, 101 E North St, Wolcott, IN, 47995. Tel: 219-279-2695. Fax: 219-279-2692. p. 789

Dreesman, Lisa, Librn, Des Moines Area Community College Library, 906 N Grant Rd, Carroll, IA, 51401. Tel: 712-792-1755, 712-792-8316. Fax: 712-792-8500. p. 798

Dreher, Barbara, Coll Develop, Ref, West Hempstead Public Library, 500 Hempstead Ave, West Hempstead, NY, 11552. Tel: 516-481-6591. Fax: 516-481-2608. p. 1766

Dreher, Derick, Dir, Rosenbach Museum & Library, 2010 DeLancey Pl, Philadelphia, PA, 19103. Tel: 215-732-1600, Ext 121. Fax: 215-545-7529. p. 2116

Drennan, Elizabeth, Ch, Poplar Creek Public Library District, 1405 S Park Ave, Streamwood, IL, 60107-2997. Tel: 630-837-6800. Fax: 630-837-6823. p. 708

Drennan, Gail, Libr Tech, New Mexico Junior College, One Thunderbird Circle, Hobbs, NM, 88240. Tel: 575-492-2870. Fax: 575-492-2883. p. 1556

Drepaul, Norma, Ref & Tech Librn, Lone Star College System, North Harris College Library, 2700 W W Thorne Dr, Houston, TX, 77073. Tel: 281-618-5491. Fax: 281-618-5695. p. 2340

Dresang, Eliza, Cleary Prof of Ch & Youth Serv, University of Washington, Mary Gates Hall, Ste 370, Campus Box 352840, Seattle, WA, 98195-2840. Tel: 206-685-9937. Fax: 206-616-3152. p. 2976

Dreschel, Karen, Youth Serv, Titusville Public Library, 2121 S Hopkins Ave, Titusville, FL, 32780. Tel: 321-264-5026. Fax: 321-264-5030. p. 500

Dresley, Susan C, Dir, John A Volpe National Transportation Systems Center, 55 Broadway, Bldg 1, 2nd Flr, Cambridge, MA, 02142-1093. Tel: 617-494-2306. Fax: 617-494-3125. p. 1078

Dressler, Emma, Libr Dir, Fernie Heritage Library, 492 Third Ave, Fernie, BC, V0B 1M0, CANADA. Tel: 250-423-4458. Fax: 250-423-7906. p. 2728

Dressler, Ginger, Cat Supvr, Mississippi College, 151 E Griffith St, Jackson, MS, 39201-1391. Tel: 601-925-7120. Fax: 601-925-7112. p. 1304

Dressler, Lo Rae, Br Supvr, Blue Earth County Library System, Lake Crystal Branch, 100 Robinson St, Lake Crystal, MN, 56055. Tel: 507-726-2726. Fax: 507-726-2265. p. 1257

Dressler, Marci, Head, Ch, Ossining Public Library, 53 Croton Ave, Ossining, NY, 10562-4903. Tel: 914-941-2416. Fax: 914-941-7464. p. 1712

Dressler, Mina, Br Mgr, Hickman County Public Library, East Hickman Public Library, 5009 Hwy 100, Lyles, TN, 37098. Tel: 931-670-5767. Fax: 931-670-1933. p. 2226

Dressler, Rona, Head, Ref, Tech Coordr, Patchogue-Medford Library, 54-60 E Main St, Patchogue, NY, 11772. Tel: 631-654-4700, Ext 230. Fax: 631-289-3999. p. 1715

Dressler, Ronald, Mgr, Hershey Foods Corp, 1025 Reese Ave, Hershey, PA, 17033-2272. Tel: 717-534-5106. Fax: 717-534-5069. p. 2069

Drevo, Karen, Head, Youth Serv, Norfolk Public Library, 308 Prospect Ave, Norfolk, NE, 68701-4138. Tel: 402-844-2108. Fax: 402-844-2102. p. 1410

Drew, Ann, Dir, Butte-Silver Bow Public Library, 226 W Broadway St, Butte, MT, 59701-9297. Tel: 406-723-3361. Fax: 406-782-1825. p. 1376

Drew, Anthony E, Dir, Info Tech & Syst, Queens Borough Public Library, 89-11 Merrick Blvd, Jamaica, NY, 11432. Tel: 718-990-0840. p. 1643

Drew, Christine, Mgr, Instruction & Outreach, Worcester Polytechnic Institute, 100 Institute Rd, Worcester, MA, 01609-2280. Tel: 508-831-5410. Fax: 508-831-5829. p. 1145

Drew, Elliot A, Dir, Suffolk Public Library System, 443 W Washington St, Suffolk, VA, 23434. Tel: 757-514-7323. Fax: 757-539-7155. p. 2497

Drew, Hadiya, Dir, Summit Public Library District, 6233 S Archer Rd, Summit, IL, 60501. Tel: 708-458-1545. Fax: 708-458-1842. p. 709

Drew, Marlene, Dir, Ramsdell Public Library, 1087 Main St, Housatonic, MA, 01236-9730. Tel: 413-274-3738. p. 1096

Drew, Rebecca J, Librn, Katahdin Public Library, 20 Library St, Island Falls, ME, 04747. Tel: 207-463-2372. p. 988

Drew, Sally, Dir, Wisconsin Department of Public Instruction, Reference & Loan Library, 2109 S Stoughton Rd, Madison, WI, 53716-2899. Tel: 608-224-6161. Fax: 608-224-6178. p. 2610

Drew, Sara, Electronic Res Librn, Cabrini College Library, 610 King of Prussia Rd, Radnor, PA, 19087-3698. Tel: 610-902-8249. Fax: 610-902-8539. p. 2132

Drewello, Daphne, Dir, Alfred Dickey Public Library, 105 SE Third St, Jamestown, ND, 58401. Tel: 701-252-2990. Fax: 701-252-6030. p. 1844

Drewello, Daphne, Dir, Stutsman County Library, 910 Fifth St SE, Jamestown, ND, 58401. Tel: 701-252-1531. Fax: 701-252-2217. p. 1844

Drewes, Mary Hegle, Asst Libr Dir, Head, Coll Develop, University of North Dakota, 3051 University Ave, Stop 9000, Grand Forks, ND, 58202-9000. Tel: 701-777-4630. Fax: 701-777-3319. p. 1843

Drewitz, Jessica, Pub Serv, Pepperdine University Libraries, School of Law-Jerene Appleby Harnish Law Library, 24255 Pacific Coast Hwy, Malibu, CA, 90263. Tel: 310-506-4643. Fax: 310-506-4836. p. 182

Drewry, Elizabeth, Librn, The Library at Birmingham Botanical Garden, 2612 Lane Park Rd, Birmingham, AL, 35223. Tel: 205-414-3932. Fax: 205-414-3922. p. 8

Drews, James, Acq of New Ser, Anaheim Public Library, 500 W Broadway, Anaheim, CA, 92805-3699. Tel: 714-765-1840. p. 120

Drexler, Julie, Br Head, York University Libraries, Leslie Frost Library, Glendon Campus, 2275 Bayview Ave, Toronto, ON, M4N 3M6, CANADA. Tel: 416-736-2100, Ext 88262. Fax: 416-487-6705. p. 2868

Drexter, Britani, Asst Librn, Kirkland Public Library, 513 W Main St, Kirkland, IL, 60146. Tel: 815-522-6260. Fax: 815-522-6260. p. 661

Drey, Christine, Librn, Early Public Library, 107 Main St, Early, IA, 50535-5010. Tel: 712-273-5334. Fax: 712-273-5251. p. 813

Drey, Marian, Librn, United States Courts Library, 300 Fannin St, Rm 5012, Shreveport, LA, 71101-6305. Tel: 318-676-3230. Fax: 318-934-4866. p. 970

Dreyer, Kathleen M, Head of Libr, Columbia University, Thomas J Watson Library of Business & Economics, 130 Uris Hall, 3022 Broadway, MC 9163, New York, NY, 10027. Tel: 212-854-7803. Fax: 212-854-5723. p. 1675

Dreyer, Katie, Youth Serv Librn, Pella Public Library, 603 Main St, Pella, IA, 50219-1592. Tel: 641-628-4268. Fax: 641-628-1735. p. 838

Dreyer, Kelly, Coordr, Mohave County Library District, Valle Vista Community Library, 7264 Concho Dr, Ste B, Kingman, AZ, 86401-9105. Tel: 928-692-7662. Fax: 928-692-7662. p. 67

Dreyer, Marilyn, Cat, Santa Clara University, Heafey Law Library, School of Law, 500 El Camino Real, Santa Clara, CA, 95053-0430. Tel: 408-554-5307. Fax: 408-554-5318. p. 263

Dreyfus, Janine, Librn, Anshe Hesed Temple Library, 930 Liberty St, Erie, PA, 16502. Tel: 814-454-2426. Fax: 814-454-2427. p. 2055

Drickamer, Karen, Archivist, Head, Spec Coll, Gettysburg College, 300 N Washington St, Gettysburg, PA, 17325. Tel: 717-337-7015. Fax: 717-337-7001. p. 2059

Driemeyer, Sheila, Assoc Dir, Libr Serv, East Central College Library, 1964 Prairie Dell Rd, Union, MO, 63084-4344. Tel: 636-584-6560. Fax: 636-583-1897. p. 1369

Driesner, Barbara, Youth Serv Librn, Edwardsville Public Library, 112 S Kansas St, Edwardsville, IL, 62025. Tel: 618-692-7556. Fax: 618-692-9566. p. 639

Driessen, Lynn, Librn, Outagamie County Law Library, 320 S Walnut St, Appleton, WI, 54911. Tel: 920-832-5149. Fax: 920-832-5115. p. 2578

Driggers, Patti, Asst Mgr, Dixie County Public Library, 16328 SE Hwy 19, Cross City, FL, 32628. Tel: 352-498-1219. Fax: 352-498-1408. p. 435

Drinka, Kevin, Libr Mgr, Maricopa Community Library, 44240 W Maricopa, Casa Grande Hwy, Maricopa, AZ, 85239. Tel: 520-568-2926. Fax: 520-568-2680. p. 68

Drinkwine, Linda, Asst Librn, Black Watch Memorial Library, 99 Montcalm St, Ticonderoga, NY, 12883. Tel: 518-585-7380. Fax: 518-585-3209. p. 1755

Driscoll, Alaina, Media Serv, Willoughby Wallace Memorial Library, 146 Thimble Islands Rd, Stony Creek, CT, 06405. Tel: 203-488-8702. Fax: 203-315-3347. p. 370

Driscoll, Heather Dawn, Circ Mgr, Maine College of Art, 522 Congress St, Portland, ME, 04101. Tel: 207-775-5153, Ext 5091. Fax: 207-772-5069. p. 996

Driscoll, Lori, Dir, Gulf Coast State College Library, 5230 W Hwy 98, Panama City, FL, 32401. Tel: 850-872-3893. Fax: 850-872-3861. p. 480

Driscoll, Martha J, Syst Coordr, North of Boston Library Exchange, Inc, 26 Cherry Hill Dr, Danvers, MA, 01923. Tel: 978-777-8844. Fax: 978-750-8472. p. 2945

Driskell, Mike, Info Tech Mgr, Arlington Heights Memorial Library, 500 N Dunton Ave, Arlington Heights, IL, 60004-5966. Tel: 847-870-3695. Fax: 847-506-2650. p. 589

Drissi, Susan K, Libr Dir, Chillicothe Public Library District, 430 N Bradley Ave, Chillicothe, IL, 61523-1920. Tel: 309-274-2719. Fax: 309-274-3000. p. 628

Driver, Anita, Dir, Jerseyville Public Library, 105 N Liberty St, Jerseyville, IL, 62052-1512. Tel: 618-498-9514. Fax: 618-498-3036. p. 659

Driver, Berry, Dr, Dean of Libr, Southwestern Baptist Theological Seminary Libraries, 2001 W Seminary Dr, Fort Worth, TX, 76115-2157. Tel: 817-923-1921, Ext 4000. Fax: 817-921-8765. p. 2323

Driver, Carol, User Serv Librn, West Kentucky Community & Technical College, 4810 Alben Barkley Dr, Paducah, KY, 42001. Tel: 270-534-3197. Fax: 270-554-6218. p. 932

Driver, Claudia, Ref Serv, Ad, Springdale Public Library, 405 S Pleasant St, Springdale, AR, 72764. Tel: 479-750-8180. Fax: 479-750-8182. p. 115

Driver, Lisa C, Dean, Pitt Community College, Hwy 11 S, Greenville, NC, 27835. Tel: 252-321-4357. Fax: 252-321-4404. p. 1799

Driver, Tina, Librn, Walla Walla County Law Library, County Courthouse, 315 W Main St, Walla Walla, WA, 99362. Tel: 509-527-3229. Fax: 509-527-3214. p. 2547

Drkula, Mark, Coordr, ILL, Rice Lake Public Library, Two E Marshall St, Rice Lake, WI, 54868. Tel: 715-234-4861. Fax: 715-234-5026. p. 2633

Drmacich, Jessika, Archivist, Norman Rockwell Museum, Nine Glendale Rd, Stockbridge, MA, 01262. Tel: 413-298-4100. Fax: 413-298-4145. p. 1128

Drobney, Joe, Ser, Slippery Rock University of Pennsylvania, Slippery Rock, PA, 16057-9989. Tel: 724-738-2058. Fax: 724-738-2661. p. 2140

Drobnicki, John A, Head, Tech Serv, York College Library, 94-20 Guy R Brewer Blvd, Jamaica, NY, 11451. Tel: 718-262-2025. Fax: 718-262-2027, 718-262-2997. p. 1646

Drobny, Daria, Dir, Rehabilitation Institute of Michigan, 261 Mack Blvd, Detroit, MI, 48201-2417. Tel: 313-745-9860. Fax: 313-745-9863. p. 1171

Drodt, Barb, Br Librn, Monroe County Library System, Ida Branch, 3016 Lewis Ave, Ida, MI, 48140. Tel: 734-269-2191. Fax: 734-269-3315. p. 1210

Droegmiller, Elaine, Dir, Cushing Community Library, 202 Main St, Cushing, IA, 51018. Tel: 712-384-2501. p. 805

Drolshagen, Joanne, Youth Serv, New Milford Public Library, 200 Dahlia Ave, New Milford, NJ, 07646-1812. Tel: 201-262-1221. Fax: 201-262-5639. p. 1510

Drolsum, Chris, Ref, Maryland Institute College of Art, 1401 Mount Royal Ave, Baltimore, MD, 21217. Tel: 410-225-2304, 410-225-2311. Fax: 410-225-2316. p. 1015

Drone-Silvers, Scott, Dir, Libr Serv, Lake Land College Library, 5001 Lake Land Blvd, Mattoon, IL, 61938. Tel: 217-234-5367. Fax: 217-234-5533. p. 671

Drost, Carol A, Assoc Univ Librn, Tech Serv, Willamette University, 900 State St, Salem, OR, 97301. Tel: 503-370-6715. Fax: 503-370-6141. p. 2018

Drost, Jack, Syst Librn, University of Alabama in Huntsville, 301 Sparkman Dr NW, Huntsville, AL, 35899. Tel: 256-824-7407. Fax: 256-824-6083. p. 22

Drotleff, June E, AV, YA Serv, Salem Public Library, 821 E State St, Salem, OH, 44460-2298. Tel: 330-332-0042. Fax: 330-332-4488. p. 1934

Drott, M Carl, PhD, Assoc Prof, Drexel University, Rush Bldg, Rm 306, 30 N 33rd St, Philadelphia, PA, 19104-2875. Tel: 215-895-2474. Fax: 215-895-2494. p. 2972

Druash, Jacque, Bibliog Instr, Tallahassee Community College Library, 444 Appleyard Dr, Tallahassee, FL, 32304-2895. Tel: 850-201-8396. Fax: 850-201-8380. p. 495

Druckman, Rosanne, Exec Dir, Hartford Consortium For Higher Education, 950 Main St, Ste 314, Hartford, CT, 06103. Tel: 860-906-5016. Fax: 860-906-5118. p. 2939

Druckrey, Melissa, Actg Dir, Jackson State University, Information Services Library, 3825 Ridgewood Rd, Jackson, MS, 39211. Tel: 601-432-6313. Fax: 601-432-6144. p. 1303

Druffel, Ann, Acq, Coordr, SKYNET UFO Research Library, 257 Sycamore Glen, Pasadena, CA, 91105-1350. Tel: 323-256-8655. p. 207

Drugash, Mary Sue, Ref, Delaware Technical & Community College, PO Box 630, Sea Shore Hwy, Georgetown, DE, 19947-0630. Tel: 302-856-9033. Fax: 302-858-5462. p. 383

Druhan, Chris, YA Serv, Altamonte Springs City Library, 281 N Maitland Ave, Altamonte Springs, FL, 32701. Tel: 407-571-8830. Fax: 407-571-8834. p. 425

Drulia, Megen R, Acad Serv Officer II, Wayne State University, 106 Kresge Library, Detroit, MI, 48202. Tel: 313-577-8543. Fax: 313-577-7563. p. 2967

Drum, Denette, Assoc Dir, Central Community College, 4500 63rd St, Columbus, NE, 68601. Tel: 402-562-1445. Fax: 402-562-1227. p. 1396

Drumheller, Janet, Mgr, Ref Serv, Knox County Public Library System, 500 W Church Ave, Knoxville, TN, 37902-2505. Tel: 865-215-8723. Fax: 865-215-8742. p. 2241

Drummey, Peter, Librn, Massachusetts Historical Society Library, 1154 Boylston St, Boston, MA, 02215-3695. Tel: 617-646-0501. Fax: 617-859-0074. p. 1063

Drummond, Gaynell, Spec Coll Librn, Hampton Public Library, 4207 Victoria Blvd, Hampton, VA, 23669-4243. Tel: 757-727-1154. Fax: 757-727-1152. p. 2468

Drummond, Linda, Librn, Valley Medical Center Library, 400 S 43rd St, Renton, WA, 98055. Tel: 425-228-3440, Ext 3904. Fax: 425-656-5095. p. 2526

Drummond, Paula, Coordr, Youth Serv, St Marys Community Public Library, 140 S Chestnut St, Saint Marys, OH, 45885-2307. Tel: 419-394-7471. Fax: 419-394-7291. p. 1933

Drummond, Sheila, Head, Ref Serv, Medicine Hat Public Library, 414 First St SE, Medicine Hat, AB, T1A 0A8, CANADA. Tel: 403-502-8527. Fax: 403-502-8529. p. 2711

Drummond, Vicky, Coordr, Nellie Langford Rowell Women's Study Library, 204 Founders College, 4700 Keele St, Toronto, ON, M3J 1P3, CANADA. Tel: 416-736-2100, Ext 33219. Fax: 416-736-5732. p. 2855

Drury, Claire, Br Supvr, Bruce County Public Library, Tobermory Branch, 22 Bay St S, Tobermory, ON, N0H 2R0, CANADA. Tel: 519-596-2446. p. 2837

Drury, Clare, Br Supvr, Bruce County Public Library, Lion's Head Branch, Main St, Lion's Head, ON, N0H 1W0, CANADA. Tel: 519-793-3844. Fax: 519-793-3844. p. 2837

Drury, Clare, Br Supvr, Bruce County Public Library, Wiarton Branch, 578 Brown St, Wiarton, ON, N0H 2T0, CANADA. Tel: 519-534-2602. Fax: 519-534-2602. p. 2837

Drury, Deborah, Exec Dir, Elizabethtown Public Library, Ten S Market St, Elizabethtown, PA, 17022-2307. Tel: 717-367-7467. Fax: 717-367-5019. p. 2053

Drury, Denise, Librn, Banff Public Library, 101 Bear St, Banff, AB, T1L 1H3, CANADA. Tel: 403-762-2661. Fax: 403-762-3805. p. 2684

Drury, Kathryn, Mgr, Info & Partnership Serv, Brantford Public Library, 173 Colborne St, Brantford, ON, N3T 2G8, CANADA. Tel: 519-756-2220, Ext 309. Fax: 519-756-4979. p. 2796

Drury, Sandra, Circ, Nassau County Public Library System, Hilliard Branch, 15821 CR 108, Hilliard, FL, 32046. Tel: 904-845-2495. Fax: 904-845-2449. p. 440

Druzdel, Marek, Asst Prof, University of Pittsburgh, 135 N Bellefield Ave, Pittsburgh, PA, 15260. Tel: 412-624-5230. Fax: 412-624-5231. p. 2973

Dryden, Donald, Coordr, Coll Develop, Coordr, Electronic Res, Coordr, Tech Serv, Meharry Medical College Library, 1005 Dr D B Todd Jr Blvd, Nashville, TN, 37208. Tel: 615-327-6465. Fax: 615-327-6448. p. 2257

Dryden, Joyce, Librn, Lucile L Morgan Public Library, 541 Ross St, Heflin, AL, 36264. Tel: 256-463-2259. Fax: 256-463-2259. p. 20

Dryden, Nancy, Ref, Regional Campus Libr Dir, University of Connecticut at Stamford, One University Pl, Stamford, CT, 06901-2315. Tel: 203-251-8439. Fax: 203-251-8501. p. 370

Dryer, Barbara A, Info Serv Spec, Council of Michigan Foundations, One S Harbor Dr, Ste 3, Grand Haven, MI, 49417. Tel: 616-842-7080. Fax: 616-842-1760. p. 1183

Drysdale, Andrew, Curator, Warren County Cultural & Heritage Commission Library, Shippen Manor, Eight Belvidere Ave, Oxford, NJ, 07863. Tel: 908-453-4381. Fax: 908-453-4981. p. 1517

Du Ruisseau, Manon, Info Serv, Ecole Polytechnique de Montreal Bibliotheque, 2500, chemin de Polytechnique, Montreal, QC, H3T 1J4, CANADA. Tel: 514-340-4666. Fax: 514-340-4026. p. 2895

Du, Yunfei, Dr, Assoc Prof, University of North Texas, 1155 Union Circle, Denton, TX, 76203-5017. Tel: 940-565-3565. Fax: 940-565-3101. p. 2975

Duan, Carol, Br Mgr, Los Angeles Public Library System, Robertson, 1719 S Robertson Blvd, Los Angeles, CA, 90035-4316. Tel: 310-840-2147. Fax: 310-840-2156. p. 174

Duane, Erin, Access Serv, Solano Community College Library, 4000 Suisun Valley Rd, Fairfield, CA, 94534. Tel: 707-864-7132. Fax: 707-864-7231. p. 148

Duangudom, Savanida, Campus Librn, Wake Technical Community College, Northern Wake Library, 6600 Louisburg Rd, Bldg B, Rm 239, Raleigh, NC, 27616. Tel: 919-532-5553. p. 1818

Duangudom, Suvanida, Instrul Serv/Ref Librn, Wake Technical Community College, 9101 Fayetteville Rd, Raleigh, NC, 27603-5696. Tel: 919-866-5644. Fax: 919-662-3575. p. 1818

Duarte, Sharon A, Cataloger, Oil City Library, Two Central Ave, Oil City, PA, 16301-2795. Tel: 814-678-3071. Fax: 814-676-8028. p. 2100

Duball, Cheri L, Acq, Tech Serv, Washington & Jefferson College Library, 60 S Lincoln St, Washington, PA, 15301. Tel: 724-223-6104. Fax: 724-223-5272. p. 2151

Dubansky, Mindell, Conserv Librn, Metropolitan Museum of Art, Thomas J Watson Library, 1000 Fifth Ave, New York, NY, 10028-0198. Tel: 212-570-3220. Fax: 212-570-3847. p. 1686

Dubard, Ann, Librn, Central Mississippi Medical Center, 1850 Chadwick Dr, Jackson, MS, 39204. Tel: 601-376-1000, 601-376-1148. Fax: 601-376-2761. p. 1303

DuBard, Melanie, Sr Res Spec, Nelson, Mullins, Riley & Scarborough, 1320 Main St, Ste 1700, Columbia, SC, 29201. Tel: 803-255-9367. Fax: 803-255-7500. p. 2188

Dubaz, Paul, Br Mgr, Main Libr, Harrison County Library System, Biloxi Central Library, 580 Howard Ave, Biloxi, MS, 39530-2303. Tel: 228-436-3095. Fax: 228-436-3097. p. 1299

Dubb, Kayla, Dir of Educ, Brooklyn Children's Museum, 145 Brooklyn Ave, Brooklyn, NY, 11213. Tel: 718-735-4400, Ext 144. Fax: 718-773-4975. p. 1589

Dubbe, Della, Dir, Glacier County Library, 21 First Ave SE, Cut Bank, MT, 59427. Tel: 406-873-4572. Fax: 406-873-4845. p. 1377

Dubbe, Della, Dir, Glacier County Library, East Glacier Park Branch, PO Box 234, East Glacier Park, MT, 59434. Tel: 406-873-4572. p. 1377

Dubbelde, Nan, Mgr, Chevron Global Library Houston, 3901 Briarpark Dr, Houston, TX, 77042. Tel: 713-954-6007. Fax: 713-954-6907. p. 2334

Dubbelde, Nan M, Libr Mgr, Chevron Information Technology Company, Division of Chevron USA, Inc, 100 Chevron Way, Bldg 50 Rm 1212, Richmond, CA, 94802. Tel: 510-242-4755. Fax: 510-242-5621. p. 216

Dube, Colin, Programming, Atlanta-Fulton Public Library System, Auburn Avenue Research Library on African-American Culture & History, 101 Auburn Ave NE, Atlanta, GA, 30303. Tel: 404-730-4001, Ext 199. Fax: 404-730-5879. p. 511

Dube, Dominique, Interim Head Librn, Conservatoire de Musique de Quebec Bibliotheque, 270 rue Saint-Amable, Quebec, QC, G1R 5G1, CANADA. Tel: 418-643-2190, Ext 224. Fax: 418-644-9658. p. 2904

Dubé, Jocelyne, Cat, Cegep de La Pocatiere, 140 Fourth Ave, La Pocatiere, QC, G0R 1Z0, CANADA. Tel: 418-856-1525. Fax: 418-856-4589. p. 2885

Dube, Liane, Chief Librn, Centre Hospitalier Regional trois-Rivieres Pavillon Ste-Marie, 1991 boul du Carmel, Trois-Rivieres, QC, G8Z 3R9, CANADA. Tel: 819-697-3333, Ext 69878. Fax: 819-378-9850. p. 2914

Dube, Lorraine, Librn, St Charles Public Library, 22 St Anne, Rm 216-217, Saint Charles, ON, P0M 2W0, CANADA. Tel: 705-867-5332. Fax: 705-867-2511. p. 2839

Dube, Marguerite, Libr Dir, Chester County Library System, 450 Exton Square Pkwy, Exton, PA, 19341-2496. Tel: 610-280-2600. Fax: 610-280-2688. p. 2056

Dube, Miguelle, Database Mgt, Planning & Develop Librn, Bibliothèques de Montréal, 801, rue Brennan, 5e Etage, Bureau 5206, Montreal, QC, H3C 0G4, CANADA. Tel: 514-872-8771. Fax: 514-872-0530. p. 2889

Dube, Sheila, Ch, Springvale Public Library, 443 Main St, Springvale, ME, 04083. Tel: 207-324-4624. p. 1002

Dubin, Alan, Res Spec, Orrick, Herrington & Sutcliffe, 666 Fifth Ave, New York, NY, 10103. Tel: 212-506-5340. Fax: 212-506-5151. p. 1696

Dubin, David, Assoc Prof, University of Illinois at Urbana-Champaign, Library & Information Science Bldg, 501 E Daniel St, Champaign, IL, 61820-6211. Tel: 217-333-3280. Fax: 217-244-3302. p. 2965

Dubinski, Cindy, Ad, East Fishkill Public Library District, 348 Rte 376, Hopewell Junction, NY, 12533-6075. Tel: 845-221-9943, Ext 225. Fax: 845-226-1404. p. 1637

Dubis, Jane, Librn, Uxbridge Township Public Library, Nine Toronto St S, Uxbridge, ON, L9P 1P7, CANADA. Tel: 905-852-9747. Fax: 905-852-9749. p. 2868

Dubnjakovic, Ana, Head Librn, University of South Carolina, Music, 813 Assembly St, Columbia, SC, 29208. Tel: 803-777-5425. Fax: 803-777-1426. p. 2190

DuBois, Carolyn, Ch, Abington Township Public Library, 1030 Old York Rd, Abington, PA, 19001-4594. Tel: 215-885-5180. Fax: 215-885-9242. p. 2025

Dubois, Cynthia, Head, Doc, Nicholls State University, 906 E First St, Thibodaux, LA, 70310. Tel: 985-448-4646, 985-448-4660. Fax: 985-448-4925. p. 971

Dubois, Diane C, Dir, Caribou Public Library, 30 High St, Caribou, ME, 04736. Tel: 207-493-4214. Fax: 207-493-4654. p. 981

Dubois, Guy, Adult Serv, Bibliotheque Municipale de Gatineau, 144, boul de l'Hôpital, local 317, Gatineau, QC, J8T 7S7, CANADA. Tel: 819-243-2345, Ext 7461. Fax: 819-595-7487. p. 2882

Dubois, Guy, Ad, Bibliotheque Municipale de Gatineau, Édifice Pierre Papin, CP 1970 Succ. Hull, Gatineau, QC, J8X 3Y9, CANADA. p. 2882

Dubois, Jessica, Libr Tech, St Lawrence College Library, Two Saint Lawrence Dr, Cornwall, ON, K6H 4Z1, CANADA. Tel: 613-933-6080, Ext 2701. p. 2801

DuBois, Linda, Mgr, New Jersey State Police Training Bureau Library, Training Bureau, Sea Girt, NJ, 08750. Tel: 732-449-5200, Ext 5215. Fax: 732-449-8763. p. 1529

DuBois, Lori, Ref & Instrul Serv Librn, Williams College, 55 Sawyer Library Dr, Williamstown, MA, 01267. Tel: 413-597-4614. Fax: 413-597-4106. p. 1141

Dubois, Pat, Br Mgr, Grant Parish Library, Montgomery Branch, 940 Caddo St, Montgomery, LA, 71454. Tel: 318-646-3660. Fax: 318-646-3660. p. 947

Dubois, Roger, Admin Serv Mgr, Idaho Commission for Libraries, 325 W State St, Boise, ID, 83702-6072. Tel: 208-334-2150. Fax: 208-334-4016. p. 571

DuBois, Rosemary, ILL, San Bernardino Public Library, 555 W Sixth St, San Bernardino, CA, 92410-3001. Tel: 909-381-8215. Fax: 909-381-8229. p. 229

DuBois, Sharon, Mgr, Bartram Trail Regional Library, Taliaferro County, 117 Askin St, Crawfordville, GA, 30631. Tel: 706-456-2531. Fax: 706-456-2531. p. 556

Dubre, Vandy, Instruction/Distance Educ Librn, University of Texas at Tyler Library, 3900 University Blvd, Tyler, TX, 75799. Tel: 903-566-7167. Fax: 903-566-2513. p. 2394

Dubsky, S, Digital Serv & Coll Mgt Librn, Prairie State College Library, 202 S Halsted St, Chicago Heights, IL, 60411-8200. Tel: 708-709-3550. Fax: 708-709-3940. p. 628

Dubuc, Julie, Ref, Cinematheque Quebecoise, 335 boul de Maisonneuve est, Montreal, QC, H2X 1K1, CANADA. Tel: 514-842-9768, Ext 262. Fax: 514-842-1816. p. 2893

Dubuque, Christine, Librn, Dechert Law Library, 200 Clarendon St, 27th Flr, Boston, MA, 02116. Tel: 617-728-7100, Ext 7198. Fax: 617-426-6567. p. 1060

Dubyk, Patricia, Librn, County of Prince Edward Libraries, 300 Main St, Bloomfield, ON, K0K 1G0, CANADA. Tel: 613-393-3400. Fax: 613-393-1887. p. 2795

Ducar, Lynn, Ref Librn, Elgin Community College, 1700 Spartan Dr, Elgin, IL, 60123. Tel: 847-214-7337. p. 641

Ducas, Ada, Head, Health Sci Libr, University of Manitoba Libraries, Neil John Maclean Health Sciences Library, 223 Brodie Centre, 727 McDermot Ave, Winnipeg, MB, R3E 3P5, CANADA. Tel: 204-789-3342, 204-789-3464. Fax: 204-789-3922. p. 2759

Duce, Debra, Chief Librn, Huntsville Public Library, Seven Minerva St E, Huntsville, ON, P1H 1W4, CANADA. Tel: 705-789-5232. p. 2811

Ducey, Mary Ellen, Archivist, University of Nebraska-Lincoln, 1248 R St, Lincoln, NE, 68588-4100. Tel: 402-472-2526. p. 1407

Ducey, Richard E, Dir, University of Tulsa Libraries, Mabee Legal Information Center, 3120 E Fourth Pl, Tulsa, OK, 74104-3189. Tel: 918-631-2404. Fax: 918-631-3556. p. 1984

Ducharme, Natalie, Adult Serv, Kelley Library, 234 Main St, Salem, NH, 03079-3190. Tel: 603-898-7064. Fax: 603-898-8583. p. 1464

Ducharme, Terri, Asst Dir, Tyngsborough Public Library, 25 Bryant Lane, Tyngsboro, MA, 01879-1003. Tel: 978-649-7361. Fax: 978-649-2578. p. 1131

DuChemin, Jill, Dir, Salem Public Library, 212 N Main St, Salem, IN, 47167. Tel: 812-883-5600. Fax: 812-883-1609. p. 777

Duchesne, André-Yves, Mgr, User Serv, Bibliotheque Municipale de Gatineau, Édifice Pierre Papin, CP 1970 Succ. Hull, Gatineau, QC, J8X 3Y9, CANADA. p. 2882

Duchesne, André-Yves, Pub Relations Librn, Bibliotheque Municipale de Gatineau, 144, boul de l'Hôpital, local 317, Gatineau, QC, J8T 7S7, CANADA. Tel: 819-595-7464. Fax: 819-595-7479. p. 2882

Duchesneau, Nancy, In Charge, Bibliotheque Municipale de Loretteville-Chrystine-Brouillet, 264 Rue Racine, Loretteville, QC, G2B 1E7, CANADA. Tel: 418-641-6120. Fax: 418-842-3866. p. 2887

Duchesneau, Nancy, In Charge, Bibliotheque Gabrielle-Roy, Neufchâtel, 4060 rue Blain, Quebec, QC, G2B 4P3, CANADA. Tel: 418-641-6794. p. 2903

Duchon, Maire I, Dir, Manhattan College, 4513 Manhattan College Pkwy, Riverdale, NY, 10471. Tel: 718-862-7166. Fax: 718-862-8028. p. 1728

Duck, Janie, Br Mgr, Mississippi County Library System, Keiser Public, 112 E Main, Keiser, AR, 72351. Tel: 870-526-2300. p. 95

Duck, Patricia, Dir, University of Pittsburgh at Greensburg, 150 Finoli Dr, Greensburg, PA, 15601-5898. Tel: 724-836-9687. Fax: 724-836-7043. p. 2062

Ducklin, Michelle H, Acq Librn, Girard Free Library, 105 E Prospect St, Girard, OH, 44420-1899. Tel: 330-545-2508. Fax: 330-545-8213. p. 1902

Duckworth, Margaret, Ch, Granville County Library System, 210 Main St, Oxford, NC, 27565-3321. Tel: 919-693-1121. Fax: 919-693-2244. p. 1813

Duckworth, Samantha, Ad, Ref Librn, Whitman Public Library, 100 Webster St, Whitman, MA, 02382. Tel: 781-447-7613. Fax: 781-447-7678. p. 1140

Duclo, Rhonda, Asst Dir, Delta County Libraries, 149 E Main St, Hotchkiss, CO, 81419. p. 313

Duclo, Rhonda, Mgr, Delta County Libraries, 49 E Main, Hotchkiss, CO, 81419. Tel: 970-872-4153. Fax: 970-872-3834. p. 313

Ducote, Dominique, In Charge, Lafayette Public Library, Duson Branch, 708 First St, Duson, LA, 70529. Tel: 337-873-3521. p. 952

Ducote, Patsy, Br Mgr, Huntsville-Madison Public Library, Bailey Cove Library, 1409 Weatherly Plaza, Huntsville, AL, 35803. Tel: 256-881-0257. p. 21

Ducotey, Janie, Libr Dir, Catoosa Public Library, 105 E Oak, Catoosa, OK, 74015. Tel: 918-266-1684. Fax: 918-266-1685. p. 1959

Duczek, Michele, Ref Serv, Lloydminster Public Library, 5010 49th St, Lloydminster, AB, T9V 0K2, CANADA. Tel: 780-875-0850. Fax: 780-875-6523. p. 2710

Duda, Andrea L, Sci, University of California, Santa Barbara, Santa Barbara, CA, 93106-9010. Tel: 805-893-2647. Fax: 805-893-7010. p. 261

Dudash, Andrew, Ref, Juniata College, 1815 Moore St, Huntingdon, PA, 16652-2120. Tel: 814-641-3450. Fax: 814-641-3435. p. 2070

Dudding, David, Dir, Info Tech, Ohio University Libraries, 30 Park Pl, Athens, OH, 45701-2978. Tel: 740-593-0981. Fax: 740-593-2708. p. 1856

Dudding, Janet, Coll Develop, Volusia County Public Library, 1290 Indian Lake Rd, Daytona Beach, FL, 32124. Tel: 386-248-1745. Fax: 386-248-1746. p. 436

Duddleson, Dawn, Librn, King County Department of Natural Resources & Parks, 201 S Jackson St, Ste 190, Seattle, WA, 98104. Tel: 206-684-1129. Fax: 206-296-0192. p. 2528

Dude, Rosanna, Dir, Wilmot Public Library, 11 N Wilmot Rd, Wilmot, NH, 03287-4302. Tel: 603-526-6804. Fax: 603-526-6804. p. 1468

Dudeck, Sharon, Ch, Tinley Park Public Library, 7851 Timber Dr, Tinley Park, IL, 60477-3398. Tel: 708-532-0160, Ext 2. Fax: 708-532-2981. p. 709

Dudek, David, Electronic Serv, Ref & Instrul Serv, Instr Coordr, Washington College, 300 Washington Ave, Chestertown, MD, 21620-1197. Tel: 410-778-7292. Fax: 410-778-7288. p. 1023

Dudenhoffer, Cynthia, Dir, Info Serv, Central Methodist College, 411 Central Methodist Sq, Fayette, MO, 65248. Tel: 660-248-6271. Fax: 660-248-6226. p. 1327

Dudgeon, Stephanie, Librn, Golder Associates Ltd Library, 2390 Argentina Rd, Mississauga, ON, L5N 5Z7, CANADA. Tel: 905-567-4444, Ext 205. Fax: 905-567-6561. p. 2822

Dudley, Benjamin, Syst Adminr, East Central Georgia Regional Library, 902 Greene St, Augusta, GA, 30901. Tel: 706-821-2600. Fax: 706-724-6762. p. 519

Dudley, Brandon, Dir, Tech & Info Serv, Sonoma State University Library, 1801 E Cotati Ave, Rohnert Park, CA, 94928-3609. Tel: 707-664-2986. Fax: 707-664-2090. p. 219

Dudley, Deborah, Br Mgr, Sampson-Clinton Public Library, Roseboro Branch, 300 W Roseboro St, Roseboro, NC, 28382. Tel: 910-525-5436. p. 1784

Dudley, Erlene A, Dir, William Woods University, One University Ave, Fulton, MO, 65251. Tel: 573-592-4291. Fax: 573-592-1159. p. 1328

Dudley, Hadi, Dir, Bentonville Public Library, 405 S Main St, Bentonville, AR, 72712. Tel: 479-271-3192. Fax: 479-271-6775. p. 95

Dudley, John, Pres, Schuylkill Haven Free Public Library, 104 Saint John St, Schuylkill Haven, PA, 17972-1614. Tel: 570-385-0542. Fax: 570-385-2523. p. 2136

Dudley, Linnea, Head of Ref & Instrul Serv, Head, Access Serv, Marygrove College Library, 8425 W McNichols Rd, Detroit, MI, 48221-2599. Tel: 313-927-1349. Fax: 313-927-1366. p. 1171

Dudley, Susan, Br Librn, Caldwell County Public Library, Granite Falls Public, 24 S Main St, Granite Falls, NC, 28630. Tel: 828-396-7703. Fax: 828-396-2723. p. 1806

Dudley, Susan, Br Librn, Caldwell County Public Library, Hudson Public, 530 Central St, Hudson, NC, 28638-1230. Tel: 828-728-4207. Fax: 828-726-1325. p. 1806

Dudley, Travis, Res Asst, Florida Attorney General's Law Library, Collins Bldg, 107 W Gaines St, Rm 437, Tallahassee, FL, 32399-1050. Tel: 850-414-3300. Fax: 850-921-5784. p. 493

Dudley, Travis, Dean of Libr, Our Lady of the Lake College Library, 5329 Didesse St, Baton Rouge, LA, 70808. Tel: 225-768-1731. Fax: 225-761-7303. p. 944

Dudley, William, Br Mgr, Maricopa County Library District, Aguila Branch, 51300 W US Hwy 60, Aguila, AZ, 85320. Tel: 602-652-3481. Fax: 602-652-3484. p. 74

Dueker, Arlene, Dir, Kaskaskia College Library, 27210 College Rd, Centralia, IL, 62801. Tel: 618-545-3131. Fax: 618-532-9241. p. 602

Duell, Rhonda, Asst County Librn, Potter-Tioga Library System, 502 Park Ave, Coudersport, PA, 16915-1672. Tel: 814-274-7422. Fax: 814-274-9137. p. 2047

Duer, Judy, Dir, Temple Public Library, 100 W Adams Ave, Temple, TX, 76501-7641. Tel: 254-298-5707. Fax: 254-298-5328. p. 2391

Duernberger, Amy, Database Mgr, South Carolina State Library, 1430-1500 Senate St, Columbia, SC, 29201. Tel: 803-737-7736. Fax: 803-734-8676. p. 2189

Duerr, Larry, Asst Dir, Alverno College Library, 3401 S 39th St, Milwaukee, WI, 53215. Tel: 414-382-6173. Fax: 414-382-6354. p. 2617

Duesenberg, Judy, Librn, Temple Judea Mizpah Library, 8610 Niles Center Rd, Skokie, IL, 60077. Tel: 847-676-1566. Fax: 847-676-1579. p. 703

Duesing, Ann, Outreach Serv Librn, University of Virginia's College at Wise, One College Ave, Wise, VA, 24293. Tel: 276-328-0168. Fax: 276-328-0105. p. 2504

Duesterhoeft, Diane, Bibliog Instr, Ref, Saint Mary's University, Louis J Blume Library, One Camino Santa Maria, San Antonio, TX, 78228-8608. Tel: 210-436-3441. Fax: 210-436-3782. p. 2381

Duevel, Casey, Electronic Res, Sci Librn, Minnesota State University, Mankato, ML3097, Mankato, MN, 56001. Tel: 507-389-5952. Fax: 507-389-5155. p. 1257

Dufault, Andrea, Automation Coordr, Hillsborough Community College, Collaboration Studio, Rm 139, 1602 N 15th St, Tampa, FL, 33605. Tel: 813-259-6059. Fax: 813-253-7510. p. 496

Dufault, Thelma, Asst Librn, Sangerville Public Library, One Town Hall Ave, Sangerville, ME, 04479. Tel: 207-876-3491. p. 1000

Duff, Barb, Coordr, Libr Serv, Robert McLaughlin Gallery Library, 72 Queen St, Civic Centre, Oshawa, ON, L1H 3Z3, CANADA. Tel: 905-576-3000, Ext 102. p. 2827

Duff, Brenda, Asst Dir, Ela Area Public Library District, 275 Mohawk Trail, Lake Zurich, IL, 60047. Tel: 847-438-3433. Fax: 847-438-9290. p. 663

Duff, Cameron, Dir, Sheridan County Public Library System, 335 W Alger St, Sheridan, WY, 82801-3899. Tel: 307-674-8585, Ext 12. p. 2660

Duff, Heather, Libr Tech, Klohn Crippen Berger Ltd, 2955 Virtual Way, Ste 500, Vancouver, BC, V5M 4X6, CANADA. Tel: 604-251-8435. Fax: 604-669-3835. p. 2741

Duff, Rhonda, Cataloger, Coll Develop, Barry-Lawrence Regional Library, 213 Sixth St, Monett, MO, 65708-2147. Tel: 417-235-6646. Fax: 417-235-6799. p. 1346

Duff, Sara, Coll Librn, Gulf Coast State College Library, 5230 W Hwy 98, Panama City, FL, 32401. Tel: 850-872-3893. Fax: 850-872-3861. p. 480

Duff, Sara, Coordr, Tech Serv, Northwest Missouri State University, 800 University Dr, Maryville, MO, 64468-6001. Tel: 660-562-1192. Fax: 660-562-1049. p. 1344

Duffey, Suzanne, Librn, Montgomery County Law Library, 251 S Lawrence St, Montgomery, AL, 36104. Tel: 334-832-1394. Fax: 334-265-9536. p. 31

Duffin, Barbara, Curator, United Methodist Church, Peninsula-Delaware, 6362 Bay Rd, Frederica, DE, 19946. Tel: 302-335-5544. p. 383

Duffin, Glenda, Extn Serv, Guelph Public Library, 100 Norfolk St, Guelph, ON, N1H 4J6, CANADA. Tel: 519-824-6220. Fax: 519-824-8342. p. 2807

Duffin, Terri, Br Coordr, Indiana University Bloomington, Fine Arts Library, Fine Arts Museum, 1133 E Seventh St, Bloomington, IN, 47405. Tel: 812-855-3314. Fax: 812-855-3443. p. 727

Dufft, Carolynn, Librn, Raquette Lake Free Library, One Dillon Rd, Raquette Lake, NY, 13436. Tel: 315-354-4005. Fax: 315-354-4005. p. 1726

Duffy, Austin, ILL Librn, John Jay College of Criminal Justice, 899 Tenth Ave, New York, NY, 10019. Tel: 212-237-8246, 212-237-8265. Fax: 212-237-8221. p. 1684

Duffy, Bill, Head, Ref, William Paterson University of New Jersey, 300 Pompton Rd, Wayne, NJ, 07470. Tel: 973-720-3191. Fax: 973-720-3171. p. 1540

Duffy, Brian, Head Librn, Pennsylvania Academy of Fine Arts Library, 128 N Broad St, Philadelphia, PA, 19102. Tel: 215-972-7600, Ext 2030. Fax: 215-569-0153. p. 2113

Duffy, Deanna, Adult Serv, Electronic Res, Ref, Boulder City Library, 701 Adams Blvd, Boulder City, NV, 89005-2697. Tel: 702-293-1281. Fax: 702-293-0239. p. 1425

Duffy, Ellen, Youth Serv Coordr, Timberland Regional Library, 415 Tumwater Blvd SW, Tumwater, WA, 98501-5799. Tel: 360-943-5001, Ext 2576. Fax: 360-586-6838. p. 2543

Duffy, James, Acq, Collectors Club of Chicago Library, 1029 N Dearborn St, Chicago, IL, 60610. Tel: 312-642-7981. p. 611

Duffy, Jane, Dean, Univ Libr, University of Winnipeg Library, 515 Portage Ave, Winnipeg, MB, R3B 2E9, CANADA. Tel: 204-786-9801. Fax: 204-783-8910. p. 2759

Duffy, Judy, Doc Delivery, Saint John's Mercy Medical Center, Tower B, 621 S New Ballas Rd, Ste 1000, Saint Louis, MO, 63141. Tel: 314-251-6340. Fax: 314-251-4299. p. 1357

Duffy, Karen, Actg Librn, Nebraska Center for the Education of Children Who Are Blind or Visually Impaired, 824 Tenth Ave, Nebraska City, NE, 68410. Tel: 402-873-5513. Fax: 402-873-3463. p. 1409

Duffy, Mark J, Dir, The Archives of the Episcopal Church, 606 Rathervue Pl, Austin, TX, 78705. Tel: 512-472-6816. Fax: 512-480-0437. p. 2278

Duffy, Mary, Asst Dean, University of South Alabama, 5901 USA Drive N, Rm 145, Mobile, AL, 36688. Tel: 251-460-7021. Fax: 251-460-7181. p. 26

Duffy, Mary, Head, Libr Info Res Serv, University of Texas at El Paso Library, 500 W University Ave, El Paso, TX, 79968-0582. Tel: 915-747-6739. Fax: 915-747-5345. p. 2317

Duffy, Michael, IV, Music Librn, Northern Illinois University Libraries, Music, School of Music, Rm 175, DeKalb, IL, 60115. Tel: 815-753-9839. Fax: 815-753-9836. p. 635

Duffy, Shannon, Ch, Atlanta-Fulton Public Library System, Dr Robert E Fulton Regional at Ocee, 5090 Abbotts Bridge Rd, Alpharetta, GA, 30005-4601. Tel: 770-360-8897. Fax: 770-360-8892. p. 512

Duffy, Sharon, In Charge, Genesis Healthcare System, 2951 Maple Ave, Zanesville, OH, 43701-1465. Tel: 740-454-4624. Fax: 740-454-4799. p. 1953

Duffy, Shawn, Asst Dir, Wauwatosa Public Library, 7635 W North Ave, Wauwatosa, WI, 53213-1718. Tel: 414-471-8484. Fax: 414-479-8984. p. 2647

Duffy, Steve, Cat, Simpson College, 508 North C St, Indianola, IA, 50125-1216. Tel: 515-961-1663. Fax: 515-961-1363. p. 822

Duffy, Vandy, Ch, Kensington Social & Public Library, 126 Amesbury Rd, Kensington, NH, 03833-5621. Tel: 603-772-5022. Fax: 603-778-2953. p. 1453

Dufort, Anne-Marie, Libr Tech, Bibliotheque de Montreal-Est, 11370 rue Notre-Dame Est, 3e etage, Montreal-Est, QC, H1B 2W6, CANADA. Tel: 514-868-4222, 514-868-4223. Fax: 514-868-4225, 514-868-5277. p. 2902

Dufort, Michelle, Dir, Grafton Public Library, 204 Main St, Grafton, VT, 05146. Tel: 802-843-2404. p. 2424

Dufort, Robert, Admin Librn, Cegep St Jean Sur Richelieu Bibliotheque, 30 boul du Seminaire, CP 1018, Saint-Jean-Sur-Richelieu, QC, J3B 7B1, CANADA. Tel: 450-347-5301, Ext 2333. Fax: 450-347-3329, 450-358-9350. p. 2911

Dufour, Christine, Asst Prof, Universite de Montreal, 3150, rue Jean-Brillant, bur C-2004, Montreal, QC, H3T 1N8, CANADA. Tel: 514-343-6044. Fax: 514-343-5753. p. 2979

Dufour, J P, Dir, Cegep de Jonquiere, 2505 rue St Hubert, Jonquiere, QC, G7X 7W2, CANADA. Tel: 418-547-2191. Fax: 418-547-0917. p. 2884

Dufresne, Nicole, Circ, Warwick Public Library, 600 Sandy Lane, Warwick, RI, 02889-8298. Tel: 401-739-5440, Ext 113. Fax: 401-732-2055. p. 2177

Dugal, Diane L, Tech Serv Librn, Bridgewater Public Library, 15 South St, Bridgewater, MA, 02324-2593. Tel: 508-697-3331. Fax: 508-279-1467. p. 1070

Dugan, Carol Lee, Dir, Carnegie Public Library, 120 Jefferson St, Monte Vista, CO, 81144-1797. Tel: 719-852-3931. Fax: 719-852-0821. p. 318

Dugan, Carol Lee, Dir, Carnegie Public Library, South Fork Branch, 0031 Mall St, South Fork, CO, 81154. Tel: 719-873-5079. Fax: 719-852-0821. p. 318

Dugan, Frank, Mgr, Public Library of Cincinnati & Hamilton County, Corryville, 2802 Vine St, Cincinnati, OH, 45219. Tel: 513-369-6034. Fax: 513-369-4471. p. 1871

Dugan, Kathleen, Mgr Fac, Lehigh University, Linderman Library, 30 Library Dr, Bethlehem, PA, 18015. Tel: 610-758-4925. Fax: 610-758-6091. p. 2034

Dugan, Kathleen M, Chief Admin Officer, Librn, Cleveland Law Library Association, One W Lakeside Ave, 4th Flr, Cleveland, OH, 44113-1023. Tel: 216-861-5070. Fax: 216-861-1606. p. 1877

Dugan, Kathy, Dir, Willoughby-Eastlake Public Library, 263 E 305th St, Willowick, OH, 44095. Tel: 440-943-2203. Fax: 440-943-2383. p. 1948

Dugan, Kristine, Reader Serv, Merrick Library, 2279 Merrick Ave, Merrick, NY, 11566-4398. Tel: 516-377-6112. Fax: 516-377-1108. p. 1659

Dugan, Paula, Head, Ch, Newport Public Library, 300 Spring St, Newport, RI, 02840. Tel: 401-847-8720. Fax: 401-842-0841. p. 2169

Dugas, Beverly, Bus Mgr, State Library of Louisiana, 701 N Fourth St, Baton Rouge, LA, 70802-5232. Tel: 225-342-4923. Fax: 225-219-4804. p. 945

Dugas, Cheryl, Librn, Lafayette Public Library, Broussard Branch, 100 W Main St, Broussard, LA, 70518. Tel: 337-837-3936. p. 952

Dugas, Ginette, Info Res, Librn, Montreal City Planning Department, 303 Notre-Dame est Bureau 5A-37, Montreal, QC, H2Y 3Y8, CANADA. Tel: 514-872-4119. Fax: 514-872-7726. p. 2899

Dugas, Rebecca, Br Mgr, Washington Parish Library System, Enon, 14073 Hwy 16, Franklinton, LA, 70438. Tel: 985-839-9385. p. 950

Dugdale, Tracey, Head, Ch, Norman Williams Public Library, Ten S Park St, Woodstock, VT, 05091. Tel: 802-457-2295. Fax: 802-457-5181. p. 2440

Duggan, James E, Assoc Dir, Southern Illinois University Carbondale, Law Library, Lesar Law Bldg, 1150 Douglas Dr, Carbondale, IL, 62901. Tel: 618-453-8791. Fax: 618-453-8728. p. 600

Duggan, James E, Dir, Law Libr & Assoc Prof of Law, Tulane University, Law Library, 6329 Freret St, New Orleans, LA, 70118-6231. Tel: 504-865-5952. Fax: 504-865-5917. p. 963

Duggan, Lynchie, Circ, Woodford County Library, 115 N Main St, Versailles, KY, 40383-1289. Tel: 859-873-5191. Fax: 859-873-1542. p. 936

Duggan, Mary Kathleen, Sister, Archivist, D'Youville College, 320 Porter Ave, Buffalo, NY, 14201-1084. Tel: 716-829-7618. Fax: 716-829-7770. p. 1597

Duggan, Michael, Supvry Archivist, National Archives & Records Administration, 40 Presidential Dr, Simi Valley, CA, 93065. Tel: 805-577-4000. Fax: 805-577-4074. p. 269

Duhon, Alice, Br Mgr, Cameron Parish Library, Lowry, 460 Lowry Hwy, Lake Arthur, LA, 70549. Tel: 337-774-3030. Fax: 337-774-3032. p. 946

Duhon, Lucy, Coordr, Ser & Electronic Res, University of Toledo, 2801 W Bancroft St, Mail Stop 509, Toledo, OH, 43606-3390. Tel: 419-530-2838. Fax: 419-530-2726. p. 1941

Duhoun, Rhonda, Cataloger, Cameron Parish Library, 501 Marshall St, Cameron, LA, 70631. Tel: 337-775-5421. Fax: 337-775-5346. p. 946

Duhr, Vicki, Dir, Princeton Public Library, 424 W Water St, Princeton, WI, 54968-9147. Tel: 920-295-6777. Fax: 920-295-3303. p. 2632

Duilefano, Debbie, Librn, American Samoa Office of Library Services, Leone School - Community, Vailoa Village, AS, 96799. Tel: 684-688-7458. Fax: 684-633-4240. p. 2665

Duimstra, Scott, Assoc Dir, Pub Serv, Capital Area District Libraries, 401 S Capitol Ave, Lansing, MI, 48933. Tel: 517-367-0813. Fax: 517-374-1068. p. 1200

DuJardin, Tamara, Librn, Everest University, 5421 Diplomat Circle, Orlando, FL, 32810. Tel: 407-628-5870, Ext 144. Fax: 407-628-1344. p. 475

Dujas, Jacqueline, Archivist, Federation des Caisses Populaires Acadiennes, Place de l'Arcadie 295 boul Saint Pierre ouest, Caraquet, NB, E1W 1B7, CANADA. Tel: 506-726-4510. Fax: 506-726-4001. p. 2762

Dujin, Veljko, Curator of Coll, Morikami Museum, 4000 Morikami Park Rd, Delray Beach, FL, 33446. Tel: 561-495-0233, Ext 217. Fax: 561-499-2557. p. 437

Dujmic, Linda, Cataloger, Carnegie Mellon University, Hunt Library, 4909 Frew St, Pittsburgh, PA, 15213-3890. Tel: 412-268-2446. Fax: 412-268-2793. p. 2123

Dujmovich, Christine-Louise, Electronic Res & Ref Librn, Justice Institute of British Columbia Library, 715 McBride Blvd, New Westminster, BC, V3L 5T4, CANADA. Tel: 604-528-5597. Fax: 604-528-5593. p. 2734

Dukart, David, Br Mgr, Public Library of Cincinnati & Hamilton County, Pleasant Ridge, 6233 Montgomery Rd, Cincinnati, OH, 45213. Tel: 513-369-4488. Fax: 513-369-4489. p. 1872

Duke, Darcy, Tech Serv, Massachusetts Institute of Technology Libraries, Barker Engineering, Bldg 10-500, 77 Massachusetts Ave, Cambridge, MA, 02139-4307. Tel: 617-253-9370. Fax: 617-258-5623. p. 1077

Duke, Deborah, Coordr, Western Counties Regional Library, 405 Main St, Yarmouth, NS, B5A 1G3, CANADA. Tel: 902-742-2486. Fax: 902-742-6920. p. 2786

Duke, Del, Circ & User Serv, Electronic Res Librn/Libr Webmaster, Southern Arkansas University, 100 E University, Magnolia, AR, 71753-5000. Tel: 870-235-4175. Fax: 870-235-5018. p. 108

Duke, Fiona, Br Mgr, Indianapolis-Marion County Public Library, East Washington, 2822 E Washington St, Indianapolis, IN, 46201-4215. Tel: 317-275-4360. p. 754

Duke, Gary, Instrul Serv Librn, Richland College Library, 12800 Abrams Rd, Dallas, TX, 75243-2199. Tel: 972-238-6081. p. 2309

Duke, Joan, Main Libr Coordr, Erie County Public Library, 160 E Front St, Erie, PA, 16507. Tel: 814-451-6911. Fax: 814-451-6907. p. 2055

Duke, John K, Sr Assoc Univ Librn, Virginia Commonwealth University Libraries, 901 Park Ave, Richmond, VA, 23284-2033. Tel: 804-827-3624. Fax: 804-828-0151. p. 2492

Duke, Julie, Asst Dir, Williamson County Public Library, 1314 Columbia Ave, Franklin, TN, 37064-3626. Tel: 615-595-1281. Fax: 615-595-1245. p. 2234

Duke, Kris, Br Mgr, Kern County Library, California City Branch, 9507 California City Blvd, California City, CA, 93505-2291. Tel: 760-373-4757. Fax: 760-373-4757. p. 124

Duke, Lynda, Academic Outreach Librn, Illinois Wesleyan University, One Ames Plaza, Bloomington, IL, 61701-7188. Tel: 309-556-3220. Fax: 309-556-3706. p. 595

Duke, Patrick, Dir, Wilsonville Public Library, 8200 SW Wilsonville Rd, Wilsonville, OR, 97070. Tel: 503-570-1590. Fax: 503-682-8685. p. 2023

Dukelow, Ruth, Exec Dir, Cooperating Libraries in Consortium, 1619 Dayton Ave, Ste 204, Saint Paul, MN, 55104. Tel: 651-644-3878. Fax: 651-644-6258. p. 2946

Dukes, Torrey, Ref Serv, North Shore Community College Library, One Ferncroft Rd, Danvers, MA, 01923-4093. Tel: 978-739-6244. Fax: 978-739-5500. p. 1083

Duket, Tim, Dir, Marinette County Law Library, 1926 Hall Ave, Marinette, WI, 54143-1717. Tel: 715-732-7449, 715-732-7450. p. 2612

Dulac, Kathy, Asst Dir, Ch, Milton Public Library, 39 Bombadier Rd, Milton, VT, 05468. Tel: 802-893-4644. Fax: 802-893-1005. p. 2429

Dulaney, Richard, Librn, Cissna Park Community Library District, 511 N Second St, Cissna Park, IL, 60924. Tel: 815-457-2452. Fax: 815-457-3033. p. 629

Dulaney, Sandi, Librn, University of Virginia, Biology-Psychology, 290-A Gilmer Hall, 485 McCormick Rd, Charlottesville, VA, 22903. Tel: 434-982-5260. Fax: 434-982-5626. p. 2454

Dulavitch, Lois, In Charge, Clarion University of Pennsylvania, 840 Wood St, Clarion, PA, 16214. Tel: 814-393-2271. Fax: 814-393-2150. p. 2972

Dulay, Sarah, Dir of Libr Serv, Northwestern College, Bridgeview Campus, 7725 S Harlem Ave, Bridgeview, IL, 60455. Tel: 708-237-5000. Fax: 708-237-5005. p. 621

Dulay, Sarah, Dir, Libr Serv, Northwestern College, 4811 N Milwaukee Ave, Chicago, IL, 60630. Tel: 708-237-5000. Fax: 773-205-2126. p. 621

Dulay, Sarah, Dir, Northwestern College, Naperville Campus, 1809 N Mill St, Naperville, IL, 60563. Tel: 630-753-9091. Fax: 630-753-9823. p. 621

Dulay, Vivian, Ch, Glendale Public Library, Casa Verdugo, 1151 N Brand Blvd, Glendale, CA, 91202-2503. Tel: 818-548-2047. Fax: 818-548-8052. p. 155

Dulepski, Deborah, Assoc Univ Librn, University of Bridgeport, 126 Park Ave, Bridgeport, CT, 06604-5620. Tel: 203-576-2388. Fax: 203-576-4791. p. 332

Dulepski, Deborah, Asst Dir, Access Serv, Montgomery County Community College, 340 DeKalb Pike, Blue Bell, PA, 19422-0796. Tel: 215-641-6300, 215-641-6596. Fax: 215-619-7182. p. 2036

Dulin, Kim, Assoc Dir, Coll Develop & Digitization, Harvard Library, Harvard Law School Library, Langdell Hall, 1545 Massachusetts Ave, Cambridge, MA, 02138. Tel: 617-495-3170. Fax: 617-495-4449. p. 1075

Duling, Sandy, Dir, Castleton State College, 178 Alumni Dr, Castleton, VT, 05735. Tel: 802-468-1256. Fax: 802-468-1475. p. 2421

Dull, Jeff, Distance Learning Librn, Liberty University Library, 1971 University Blvd, Lynchburg, VA, 24502. Tel: 434-582-2821. Fax: 434-582-2728. p. 2476

Dull, Margaret, Cat/Metadata Librn, Goucher College Library, 1021 Dulaney Valley Rd, Baltimore, MD, 21204. Tel: 410-337-6371. Fax: 410-337-6419. p. 1014

Dull, Pamela, Circ Mgr, William Jeanes Memorial Library, 4051 Joshua Rd, Lafayette Hill, PA, 19444-1400. Tel: 610-828-0441. Fax: 610-828-4049. p. 2075

Dulude, Carolyn, Librn, San Diego County Public Law Library, East County, 250 E Main, El Cajon, CA, 92020-3941. Tel: 619-441-4451. Fax: 619-441-0235. p. 234

Dumaine, Paul R, Mgr, Libr & Info Res, Adler Pollock & Sheehan PC Library, One Citizens Plaza, 8th Flr, Providence, RI, 02903. Tel: 401-274-7200. Fax: 401-751-0604. p. 2171

Dumais, Claude, Admin Dir, Chief Librn, Bibliotheque Publique de Chicoutimi, 155, rue Racine Est, Chicoutimi, QC, G7H 1R5, CANADA. Tel: 418-698-3000, Ext 4179. Fax: 418-698-5359. p. 2880

Dumapay, Joanne, Librn, Gordon & Rees LLP, 275 Battery St, 20th Flr, San Francisco, CA, 94111. Tel: 415-986-5900. Fax: 415-986-8054. p. 242

Dumar, Mary, Med Librn, OSF Saint Anthony Medical Center, 5666 E State St, Rockford, IL, 61108-2472. Tel: 815-227-2558. Fax: 815-227-2904. p. 697

Dumas, Janet, Ch, Wheaton Public Library, 225 N Cross St, Wheaton, IL, 60187-5376. Tel: 630-868-7543. Fax: 630-668-8950. p. 719

Dumas, Jessie, Asst Dir, Adams Memorial Library, 205 Central St, Central Falls, RI, 02863. Tel: 401-727-7440. Fax: 401-727-7442. p. 2164

Dumas, Maryse, Chief Librn, Ordre des Infirmieres et Infirmiers du Quebec, 4200 Boul Dorchester Ouest, Montreal, QC, H3Z 1V4, CANADA. Tel: 514-935-2501, Ext 277. Fax: 514-935-5273. p. 2900

Dumas, Nona, Mgr, Southeast Arkansas Regional Library, Monticello Branch, 107 E Jackson, Monticello, AR, 71655. Tel: 870-367-8583. Fax: 870-367-5166. p. 110

Dumas, Sarah, Librn, Orleans County Historical Society, Inc, 109 Old Stone House Rd, Brownington, VT, 05860. Tel: 802-754-2022. Fax: 802-754-9336. p. 2420

Dumas, Sheila, Tech Serv, Palmdale City Library, 700 E Palmdale Blvd, Palmdale, CA, 93550. Tel: 661-267-5600. Fax: 661-267-5606. p. 203

Dumas, Willie Mae, Per Coordr, University of South Carolina Aiken, 471 University Pkwy, Aiken, SC, 29801. Tel: 803-648-6851, Ext 3465. Fax: 803-641-3302. p. 2180

Dumbleton, Mary, Librn, Florida State College at Jacksonville, North Campus, 4501 Capper Rd, Jacksonville, FL, 32218-4499. Tel: 904-766-6717. Fax: 904-766-6640. p. 453

DuMee, Cheri L, Ref Serv, Palm Beach Atlantic University, 300 Pembroke Pl, West Palm Beach, FL, 33401-6503. Tel: 561-803-2230. Fax: 561-803-2235. p. 503

Dumeis, Madaline, In Charge, Bibliotheque Charles H Blais, 1445 ave Maguire, Sillery, QC, G1T 2W9, CANADA. Tel: 418-641-6276. Fax: 418-684-2169. p. 2912

Dumigan, Elizabeth, Br Mgr, Akron-Summit County Public Library, Fairlawn-Bath, 3101 Smith Rd, Akron, OH, 44333. Tel: 330-666-4888. Fax: 330-666-8741. p. 1852

Dumont, Carole, Circ, Per, Racine Louise Documentation Center, 500 Sherbrooke W, Montreal, QC, H3A 3G6, CANADA. Tel: 514-499-5188. Fax: 514-873-4900. p. 2897

Dumont, Lori, Circ, Manchester-by-the-Sea Public Library, 15 Union St, Manchester-by-the-Sea, MA, 01944. Tel: 978-526-7711. Fax: 978-526-2018. p. 1102

Dumont, Paul E, Dir, Dallas County Community College District, 4343 Interstate 30, Mesquite, TX, 75150. Tel: 972-860-7700. Fax: 972-860-4062. p. 2362

Dumont, Richard, Dir, Ecole Polytechnique de Montreal Bibliotheque, 2500, chemin de Polytechnique, Montreal, QC, H3T 1J4, CANADA. Tel: 514-340-4666. Fax: 514-340-4026. p. 2895

Dumouchel, Amy, Electronic Res Librn, Suffolk University, 73 Tremont St, Boston, MA, 02108. Tel: 617-573-8535. Fax: 617-573-8756. p. 1067

DuMouchel, Margaret, Head, Circ, Macomb County Library, 16480 Hall Rd, Clinton Township, MI, 48038-1132. Tel: 586-412-5965. Fax: 586-412-5958. p. 1164

Dumoulin, Nicole, Librn, Emploi Quebec, 276 rue St-Jacques, 6e etage, Montreal, QC, H2Y 1N3, CANADA. Tel: 514-864-3086. Fax: 514-864-3239. p. 2895

Dunagan, Dyan, Librn, Muleshoe Area Public Library, 322 W Second, Muleshoe, TX, 79347. Tel: 806-272-4707. Fax: 806-272-5031. p. 2364

Dunaway, Cleta, Assoc Dir, Tech Serv, Newberry College, 2100 College St, Newberry, SC, 29108-2197. Tel: 803-321-5229. Fax: 803-321-5232. p. 2201

Dunaway, Randy, Libr Dir, Alvord Public Library, 117 N Wickham St, Alvord, TX, 76225-5325. Tel: 940-427-2842. Fax: 940-427-2948. p. 2273

Dunay, Carin, Head, Access & Coll Serv, Southern Maine Community College Library, Two Fort Rd, South Portland, ME, 04106. Tel: 207-741-5521. Fax: 207-741-5522. p. 1002

Dunbar, Cindy, Actg Chief Exec Officer, Perth East Public Library, 19 Mill St E, Milverton, ON, N0K 1M0, CANADA. Tel: 519-595-8395. p. 2822

Dunbar, Doreen, Librn, Elmworth Community Library, Box 23, Elmworth, AB, T0H 1J0, CANADA. Tel: 780-354-2930. Fax: 780-354-3639. p. 2703

Dunbar, Ian, Ref & Ad Serv Librn, Ames Free Library, 53 Main St, North Easton, MA, 02356. Tel: 508-238-2000. Fax: 508-238-2980. p. 1112

Dunbar, Jeanne, Ch, Bonner Springs City Library, 200 E Third St, Bonner Springs, KS, 66012-1047. Tel: 913-441-2665. Fax: 913-441-2660. p. 858

Dunbar, June, Coordr, Youth Serv, Vigo County Public Library, One Library Sq, Terre Haute, IN, 47807. Tel: 812-232-1113, Ext 2222. Fax: 812-232-3208. p. 782

Dunbar, Ortus, Dir, South Beloit Public Library, 630 Blackhawk Blvd, South Beloit, IL, 61080-1919. Tel: 815-389-2495. Fax: 815-389-0871. p. 703

Dunbar, Robert, Librn, Indiana University, Research Institute for Inner Asian Studies, Indiana University, Goodbody Hall 344, 1011 E Third St, Bloomington, IN, 47405-7005. Tel: 812-855-1605, 812-855-9510. Fax: 812-855-7500. p. 727

Duncan, Alexandra, Librn, Buncombe County Public Libraries, East Asheville, 902 Tunnel Rd, Asheville, NC, 28805. Tel: 828-250-4738. p. 1774

Duncan, Barbara, Librn, Stanfield Public Library, 180 W Coe Ave, Stanfield, OR, 97875. Tel: 541-449-1254. Fax: 541-449-3264. p. 2020

Duncan, Bonnie, Libr Dir, Abington Social Library, 536 Hampton Rd, Abington, CT, 06230. Tel: 860-974-0415. Fax: 860-974-3950. p. 329

Duncan, Carol, Dir, Wisner Public Library, PO Box 547, Wisner, NE, 68791-9999. Tel: 402-529-6018. Fax: 402-529-6018. p. 1423

Duncan, Cheri, Head, Acq, James Madison University Libraries & Educational Technologies, 800 S Main St, Harrisonburg, VA, 22807-0001. Tel: 540-568-3543. Fax: 540-568-6339. p. 2470

Duncan, Claire, Dir, Texas Medical Association, 401 W 15th, Austin, TX, 78701-1680. Tel: 512-370-1300. p. 2282

Duncan, Deborah, Ch, Coquitlam Public Library, 575 Poirier St, Coquitlam, BC, V3J 6A9, CANADA. Tel: 604-937-4142. Fax: 604-931-6739. p. 2727

Duncan, Diana, Tech Serv Librn, Field Museum of Natural History Library, 1400 S Lake Shore Dr, Chicago, IL, 60605-2498. Tel: 312-665-7894. Fax: 312-665-7893. p. 613

Duncan, Diane, Dir, Putnam County Library System, 50 E Broad St, Cookeville, TN, 38501. Tel: 931-526-2416. Fax: 931-372-8517. p. 2231

Duncan, Emma, Br Mgr, Brampton Library, Four Corners Branch, 65 Queen St E, Brampton, ON, L6W 3L6, CANADA. Tel: 905-793-4636, Ext 4318. Fax: 905-453-4602. p. 2796

Duncan, Jennifer, Head, Coll Develop, Utah State University, 3000 Old Main Hill, Logan, UT, 84322-3000. Tel: 435-797-8148. Fax: 435-797-2880. p. 2407

Duncan, Jenny, Dir, Oklahoma State University, 1801 E Fourth, Okmulgee, OK, 74447-0088. Tel: 918-293-5488. Fax: 918-293-4628. p. 1975

Duncan, Jim, Exec Dir, Colorado Library Consortium, 770 W Hampden Ave, Ste 75, Centennial, CO, 80112. Tel: 303-422-1150. Fax: 303-431-9752. p. 2939

Duncan, Kaethryn, Dir, Northwood University Library, 1114 W FM 1382, Cedar Hill, TX, 75104. Tel: 972-293-5436. Fax: 972-293-7026. p. 2296

Duncan, Lenora, Br Mgr, Stone County Library, 326 W Washington St, Mountain View, AR, 72560. Tel: 870-269-3100. p. 110

Duncan, Liz, Per, East Bonner County Free Library District, 1407 Cedar St, Sandpoint, ID, 83864-2052. Tel: 208-263-6930. Fax: 208-263-8320. p. 583

Duncan, Lucy E, Tech Serv, St Philip's College, 1801 Martin Luther King Dr, San Antonio, TX, 78203-2098. Tel: 210-486-2330. Fax: 210-486-2335. p. 2381

Duncan, Margaret, Circ Serv Mgr, Union University, 1050 Union University Dr, Jackson, TN, 38305-3697. Tel: 731-661-5070. Fax: 731-661-5175. p. 2238

Duncan, Melanie, Librn, Middle Georgia Regional Library System, Shurling Branch, Shurlington Plaza, 1769 Shurling Dr, Macon, GA, 31211-2152. Tel: 478-744-0875. Fax: 478-744-0876. p. 541

Duncan, Michael, ILL, Waco-McLennan County Library System, 1717 Austin Ave, Waco, TX, 76701-1794. Tel: 254-750-5941. Fax: 254-750-5940. p. 2397

Duncan, Nita, Br Mgr, Uinta County Library, Mountain View Branch, Second & Cedar St, Mountain View, WY, 82939. Tel: 307-782-3161. Fax: 307-782-6640. p. 2655

Duncan, Peggy, Br Assoc, Modoc County Library, Cedarville Branch, 460 Main St, Cedarville, CA, 96104. Tel: 530-279-2614. p. 120

Duncan, Pierre, Librn, Institut de Technologie Agro-Alimentaire, Campus Lapocatiere, 401 rue Poire, La Pocatiere, QC, G0R 1Z0, CANADA. Tel: 418-856-1110, Ext 258. Fax: 418-856-1719. p. 2885

Duncan, Robert, Syst Librn, Lafayette College, 710 Sullivan Rd, Easton, PA, 18042-1797. Tel: 610-330-5156. Fax: 610-252-0370. p. 2052

Duncan, Samantha, Librn, University College of the North, Box 880, Norway House, MB, R0B 1B0, CANADA. Tel: 204-359-6296. Fax: 204-359-6262. p. 2750

Duncan, Samuel, Libr Dir, Amon Carter Museum of American Art, 3501 Camp Bowie Blvd, Fort Worth, TX, 76107-2695. Tel: 817-738-1933. Fax: 817-989-5079. p. 2321

Duncan, Suzanne, Librn, Sentara Norfolk General Hospital, 600 Gresham Dr, Norfolk, VA, 23507. Tel: 757-388-3000, 757-388-3693. Fax: 757-388-2514. p. 2483

Duncan, Thomasina, In Charge, Paterson Free Public Library, First Ward, 56 N Main St, Paterson, NJ, 07522. Tel: 973-357-3021. p. 1518

Duncan, Wesley, Librn, Huttonsville Correctional Center Library, US Rte 250, S, Huttonsville, WV, 26273. Tel: 304-335-2291, Ext 244. Fax: 304-335-4256. p. 2562

Duncan-Kinard, Nicole, Ref, Community College of Philadelphia Library, 1700 Spring Garden St, Philadelphia, PA, 19130. Tel: 215-751-8407. Fax: 215-751-8762. p. 2104

Dundas, Bonnie, Ch, John G McCullough Free Library Inc, Two Main St, North Bennington, VT, 05257. Tel: 802-447-7121. Fax: 802-445-1080. p. 2430

Dunehoo, Andrew, Dir, Fort Morgan Public Library, 414 Main St, Fort Morgan, CO, 80701. Tel: 970-542-4000. Fax: 970-542-4013. p. 308

Dunford, Karen, Mgr, Naperville Public Library, Naper Boulevard, 2035 S Naper Blvd, Naperville, IL, 60565-3353. Tel: 630-961-4100, Ext 2210. Fax: 630-961-4119. p. 679

Dungan, Barbara, Librn, Preble County District Library, New Paris Branch, 115 N Washington St, New Paris, OH, 45347. Tel: 937-437-7242. Fax: 937-437-0772. p. 1898

Dungan, Doris, Cat, Puget Sound Regional Council, 1011 Western Ave, Ste 500, Seattle, WA, 98104-1035. Tel: 206-464-7532. Fax: 206-587-4825. p. 2530

Dungan, Helen, Cat, Lafayette College, 710 Sullivan Rd, Easton, PA, 18042-1797. Tel: 610-330-5160. Fax: 610-252-0370. p. 2052

Dungey, Earl, Asst Librn, Washington State Library, McNeil Island Correction Center, PO Box 88900, MS-WT-01, Steilacoom, WA, 98388-0900. Tel: 253-512-6586. Fax: 253-512-6587. p. 2545

Dunham, David, Ref Librn, Gardner-Webb University, 110 S Main St, Boiling Springs, NC, 28017. Tel: 704-406-3051. Fax: 704-406-4623. p. 1776

Dunham, Elizabeth, Res Serv Spec, University of Tennessee, Knoxville, Special Collections, 121 Hodges Library, 1015 Volunteer Blvd, Knoxville, TN, 37996-1000. Tel: 865-974-4480. p. 2244

Dunham, Janice, Assoc Librn, Pub Serv, John Jay College of Criminal Justice, 899 Tenth Ave, New York, NY, 10019. Tel: 212-237-8256. Fax: 212-237-8221. p. 1683

Dunham, Karen, Ch, Groton Public Library, 99 Main St, Groton, MA, 01450. Tel: 978-448-1168. Fax: 978-448-1169. p. 1093

Dunham, Kassie, Mgr, Libr Serv, Kellogg Community College, 450 North Ave, Battle Creek, MI, 49017-3397. Tel: 269-965-4122, Ext 2613. Fax: 269-965-4133. p. 1155

Dunham, Lin, Librn, Holly Community Library, 1620 FM 2869, Teaching Library, Hawkins, TX, 75765. Tel: 903-769-5142. p. 2331

Dunham, Linda, Librn, Bleyhl Community Library, 311 Division St, Grandview, WA, 98930-1398. Tel: 509-882-9217. p. 2516

Dunham, Mary, Tech Serv, Howard Payne University, 1000 Fisk Ave, Brownwood, TX, 76801. Tel: 325-649-8093. Fax: 325-649-8904. p. 2292

Dunham-LaGree, Carrie, Librn, Digital Literacy & Gen Educ, Drake University, 2725 University Ave, Des Moines, IA, 50311. Tel: 515-271-2175. Fax: 515-271-3933. p. 809

Dunikowski, Lynn, Dir, Libr Serv, Library Service of the College of Family Physicians of Canada, Rm 106K, Natural Sciences Centre, University of Western Ontario, London, ON, N6A 5B7, CANADA. Tel: 519-661-3170. Fax: 519-661-3880. p. 2817

Dunkan, Sally, Ch, Jackson County Library, 213 Walnut St, Newport, AR, 72112-3325. Tel: 870-523-2952. Fax: 870-523-5218. p. 111

Dunkelberg, Todd, Br Mgr, Deschutes Public Library District, Redmond Branch, 827 SW Deschutes Ave, Redmond, OR, 97756. Tel: 541-312-1051. Fax: 541-548-6358. p. 1992

Dunkelberg, Todd, Dir, Deschutes Public Library District, 507 NW Wall St, Bend, OR, 97701-2698. Tel: 541-312-1021. Fax: 541-389-2982. p. 1992

Dunkelberger, Frances, Librn, Immanuel Church Library, 2414 Pennsylvania Ave, Wilmington, DE, 19806. Tel: 302-652-3121. Fax: 302-652-1078. p. 388

Dunkelberger, John, Dir, Adult Serv, The Urbana Free Library, 210 W Green St, Urbana, IL, 61801-5326. Tel: 217-367-4057. Fax: 217-367-4061. p. 713

Dunkelberger, Robert A, Archivist & Spec Coll Librn, Historian, Res Librn, Bloomsburg University of Pennsylvania, 400 E Second St, Bloomsburg, PA, 17815-1301. Tel: 570-389-4224. Fax: 570-389-3066. p. 2035

Dunker, Diane, Librn, Rising City Community Library, 675 Main St, Rising City, NE, 68658-3868. p. 1418

Dunker-Bendigo, Susan, Librn, Jackson Public Library, 125 Main St, Jackson, NH, 03846. Tel: 603-383-9731. Fax: 603-383-9731. p. 1452

Dunkle, Barbara, Ch, Sanibel Public Library District, 770 Dunlop Rd, Sanibel, FL, 33957. Tel: 239-472-2483. Fax: 239-472-9524. p. 489

Dunkle, Rebecca, Assoc Univ Librn, Libr Operations, University of Michigan, 818 Hatcher Graduate Library, Ann Arbor, MI, 48109-1205. Tel: 734-764-9356. Fax: 734-763-5080. p. 1152

Dunklee, Joanna, Cat Librn, California State University Dominguez Hills, 1000 E Victoria St, Carson, CA, 90747. Tel: 310-243-3062. Fax: 310-516-4219. p. 132

Dunkley, Cora, Dr, Assoc Prof, University of South Florida, 4202 Fowler Ave, CIS 1040, Tampa, FL, 33620-7800. Tel: 813-974-3520. Fax: 813-974-6840. p. 2964

Dunkley, Diane, Dir, National Society of the Daughters of the American Revolution, Museum Reference Library, 1776 D St NW, Washington, DC, 20006. Tel: 202-879-3241. Fax: 202-628-0820. p. 411

Dunkley, Joy, Head, Access Serv, Borough of Manhattan Community College Library, 199 Chambers St, New York, NY, 10007. Tel: 212-220-8000, Ext 5259. Fax: 212-748-7466. p. 1671

Dunkly, Jim, Assoc Univ Librn, University of the South, 735 University Ave, Sewanee, TN, 37383-1000. Tel: 931-598-1267. Fax: 931-598-1702. p. 2265

Dunlany, Dan, Librn, Forum Health-Western Reserve Healthcare, 500 Gypsy Lane, Youngstown, OH, 44501. Tel: 330-884-3476, 330-884-3494. p. 1952

Dunlap, Dorothy, Libr Tech, Tech Serv, Polk State College, 999 Ave H NE, Winter Haven, FL, 33881-4299. Tel: 863-297-1040. Fax: 863-297-1065. p. 504

Dunlap, Ellen S, Pres, American Antiquarian Society Library, 185 Salisbury St, Worcester, MA, 01609-1634. Tel: 508-755-5221. Fax: 508-753-3311. p. 1143

Dunlap, Isaac Hunter, Info Syst, Western Illinois University Libraries, One University Circle, Macomb, IL, 61455. Tel: 309-298-2745. Fax: 309-298-2791. p. 669

Dunlap, Lanee, Asst Librn, Head, Doc Delivery/ILL, Ref Serv, University of Arkansas-Monticello Library, 514 University Dr, Monticello, AR, 71656. Tel: 870-460-1080. Fax: 870-460-1980. p. 110

Dunlap, Sam, Head, Coll Develop, University of California, San Diego, Social Science & Humanities Library, 9500 Gilman Dr, Mail Code 0175R, La Jolla, CA, 92093-0175. Tel: 858-822-3943. Fax: 858-534-7548. p. 162

Dunlap, Sue, Presv Mgr, Rare Bks, The College of Wooster Libraries, 1140 Beall Ave, Wooster, OH, 44691-2364. Tel: 330-263-2107. Fax: 330-263-2253. p. 1949

Dunlap, Walter J, Dir, Fergus Falls Public Library, 205 E Hampden, Fergus Falls, MN, 56537-2930. Tel: 218-739-9387. Fax: 218-736-5131. p. 1251

Dunlop, Donna, Dir, Hopkinton Town Library, 61 Houston Dr, Contoocook, NH, 03229. Tel: 603-746-3663. Fax: 603-746-6799. p. 1444

Dunlop, Jennifer, YA Librn, Lakeview Public Library, 1120 Woodfield Rd, Rockville Centre, NY, 11570. Tel: 516-536-3071. Fax: 516-536-6260. p. 1734

Dunlop, Lee, Media Spec, Mount Vernon Nazarene University, 800 Martinsburg Rd, Mount Vernon, OH, 43050-9500. Tel: 740-397-9000, Ext 4240. Fax: 740-397-8847. p. 1919

Dunlow, Dianne, Acq, Blackwater Regional Library, 22511 Main St, Courtland, VA, 23837. Tel: 757-653-2821. Fax: 757-653-9374. p. 2458

Dunmire, Cary, Librn, West Georgia Regional Library, 710 Rome St, Carrollton, GA, 30117. Tel: 770-836-6711. Fax: 770-836-4787. p. 523

Dunn, Adina, Asst Librn, Dublin Public Library, 206 W Blackjack St, Dublin, TX, 76446. Tel: 254-445-4141. Fax: 254-445-2176. p. 2314

Dunn, Andrea Mary, Librn, Williams Public Library, 113 S First St, Williams, AZ, 86046. Tel: 928-635-2263. Fax: 928-635-4495. p. 90

Dunn, Barbara, Br Mgr, Ouachita Parish Public Library, West Monroe Branch, 315 Cypress, West Monroe, LA, 71291. Tel: 318-327-1365. Fax: 318-329-4062. p. 958

Dunn, Barbara, Coordr, Libr Serv, Res, United Daughters of the Confederacy, 328 North Blvd, Richmond, VA, 23220-4009. Tel: 804-355-1636. Fax: 804-353-1396. p. 2491

Dunn, Barbara E, Dir, Hawaiian Historical Society Library, 560 Kawaiahao St, Honolulu, HI, 96813. Tel: 808-537-6271. Fax: 808-537-6271. p. 564

Dunn, Carolyn, Librn, Real Estate Board of New York, 570 Lexington Ave, 2nd Flr, New York, NY, 10022. Tel: 212-532-3100. Fax: 212-481-0420. p. 1698

Dunn, Catherine, Ad, Ref Librn, Dixon Public Library, 230 N First St, Dixon, CA, 95620-3028. Tel: 707-678-5447. Fax: 707-678-3515. p. 140

Dunn, Catherine, Head, Ref Serv, University of Connecticut, 39 Elizabeth St, Hartford, CT, 06105-2287. Tel: 860-570-5071. Fax: 860-570-5104. p. 348

Dunn, Catherine Carver, Sr VPres, External Affairs, The New York Public Library - Astor, Lenox & Tilden Foundations, 476 Fifth Ave, (@ 42nd St), New York, NY, 10018-2788. Tel: 212-930-0611. Fax: 212-592-7440. p. 1690

Dunn, Christine, HQ Adminr, Monroe County Public Library, 700 Fleming St, Key West, FL, 33040. Tel: 305-292-3595. Fax: 305-295-3626. p. 456

Dunn, Cliff, Br Mgr, Jackson County Library Services, Shady Cove Branch, 22477 Hwy 62, Shady Cove, OR, 97539-9718. Tel: 541-878-2270. Fax: 541-878-2270. p. 2005

Dunn, Dianne, Asst Librn, Altoona Public Library, 1303 Lynn Ave, Altoona, WI, 54720-0278. Tel: 715-839-5029. Fax: 715-830-5119. p. 2577

Dunn, Eva M, Dir, Bollinger County Library, 302 Conrad St, Marble Hill, MO, 63764. Tel: 573-238-2713. Fax: 573-238-2879. p. 1344

Dunn, Glenda, Ch, Lake County Public Library, 1115 Harrison Ave, Leadville, CO, 80461-3398. Tel: 719-486-0569. Fax: 719-486-3544. p. 316

Dunn, Harold, Dir, Lambertville Free Public Library, Six Lilly St, Lambertville, NJ, 08530. Tel: 609-397-0275. Fax: 609-397-1784. p. 1494

Dunn, Hedy, Dir, Los Alamos Historical Society, 1921 Juniper St, Los Alamos, NM, 87544. Tel: 505-662-6272. Fax: 505-662-6312. p. 1559

Dunn, Jackie, Acq, University of Arkansas Libraries, Robert A & Vivian Young Law Library, School of Law, Waterman Hall 107, Fayetteville, AR, 72701-1201. Tel: 479-575-7916. Fax: 479-575-2053. p. 100

Dunn, Janet, Ch, Westwood Free Public Library, 49 Park Ave, Westwood, NJ, 07675. Tel: 201-664-0583. Fax: 201-664-6088. p. 1543

Dunn, Jeff, Ref Librn, Weatherford College Library, 225 College Park Dr, Weatherford, TX, 76086. Tel: 817-594-5471, 817-598-6252. Fax: 817-598-6369, 817-599-9305. p. 2399

Dunn, John, Mgr, Tech Serv, St Catharines Public Library, 54 Church St, St. Catharines, ON, L2R 7K2, CANADA. Tel: 905-688-6103, Ext 202. Fax: 905-688-6292. p. 2843

Dunn, Kathryn, Tech & Metadata Librn, Rensselaer Libraries, Rensselaer Polytechnic Inst, 110 Eighth St, Troy, NY, 12180-3590. Tel: 518-276-8300. Fax: 518-276-2044. p. 1756

Dunn, Kristina, Archivist, South Carolina Confederate Relic Room & Military Museum Library, 301 Gervais St, Columbia, SC, 29201-3027. Tel: 803-737-8095. Fax: 803-737-8099. p. 2189

Dunn, Leah, Univ Librn, University of North Carolina at Asheville, One University Heights, CPO 1500, Asheville, NC, 28804-8504. Tel: 828-251-6545. p. 1775

Dunn, Leah McGinnis, Dir, Guilford College, 5800 W Friendly Ave, Greensboro, NC, 27410-4175. Tel: 336-316-2450. Fax: 336-316-2950. p. 1796

Dunn, Leoma, Asst Dir, Thomas More College Library, 333 Thomas More Pkwy, Crestview Hills, KY, 41017-2599. Tel: 859-344-3300. Fax: 859-344-3342. p. 910

Dunn, Lesle, Tech Serv, Shaler North Hills Library, 1822 Mount Royal Blvd, Glenshaw, PA, 15116. Tel: 412-486-0211. Fax: 412-486-8286. p. 2061

Dunn, Linda, Br Mgr, Lake County Public Library, Munster Branch, 8701 Calumet Ave, Munster, IN, 46321-2526. Tel: 219-836-8450. Fax: 219-836-5694. p. 764

Dunn, Linda, Dir, Waterloo-Grant Township Public Library, 300 S Wayne St, Waterloo, IN, 46793-0707. Tel: 260-837-4491. Fax: 260-837-9148. p. 786

Dunn, Lisa, Head, Ref, Colorado School of Mines, 1400 Illinois St, Golden, CO, 80401-1887. Tel: 303-273-3687. Fax: 303-273-3199. p. 309

Dunn, Lynda, Dir, South Central Area Library, 530 Main St, Edgeley, ND, 58433. Tel: 701-493-2769. Fax: 701-493-2959. p. 1840

Dunn, Marilyn, Dir, Gilmore City Public Library, 308 S Gilmore St, Gilmore City, IA, 50541-0283. Tel: 515-373-6562. p. 818

Dunn, Marilyn, Exec Dir, Harvard Library, Arthur & Elizabeth Schlesinger Library on the History of Women in America, Three James St, Cambridge, MA, 02138-3766. Tel: 617-495-8647. Fax: 617-496-8340. p. 1076

Dunn, Marilyn, Sister, Librn, Presentation College Library, Lakota Campus, PO Box 1070, Eagle Butte, SD, 57625. Tel: 605-964-4071. Fax: 605-964-1111. p. 2210

Dunn, Mary E, Dir, Tomahawk Public Library, 300 W Lincoln Ave, Tomahawk, WI, 54487. Tel: 715-453-2455. Fax: 715-453-1630. p. 2642

Dunn, Megan, Ref, United States Senate Library, SRB-15 Senate Russell Bldg, Washington, DC, 20510-7112. Tel: 202-224-7106. Fax: 202-224-0879. p. 421

Dunn, Melanie, ILL Librn, University of Tennessee at Chattanooga Library, 615 McCallie Ave, Dept 6456, Chattanooga, TN, 37403-2598. Tel: 423-425-4501. Fax: 423-425-4775. p. 2228

Dunn, Nancy, Mgr, Artesia Historical Museum & Art Center, 505 W Richardson Ave, Artesia, NM, 88210. Tel: 575-748-2390. Fax: 575-746-3886 (Attn: Museum). p. 1551

Dunn, Patrick, Ref Librn, Elko-Lander-Eureka County Library System, 720 Court St, Elko, NV, 89801. Tel: 775-738-3066. Fax: 775-738-8262. p. 1426

Dunn, Stephanie, Communications Mgr, Nickel Institute Library, 2700-161 Bay St, Toronto, ON, M5J 2S1, CANADA. Tel: 416-591-7999. p. 2856

Dunn, Therese, Sr Librn, Tech Serv, San Leandro Public Library, 300 Estudillo Ave, San Leandro, CA, 94577. Tel: 510-577-3958. Fax: 510-577-3967. p. 252

Dunn, Valerie, Librn, Southeast Regional Library, Ogema Branch, 117 Main St, Ogema, SK, S0C 1Y0, CANADA. Tel: 306-459-2985. p. 2930

Dunne, Cliff, Br Mgr, Jackson County Library Services, Butte Falls Branch, 626 Fir St, Butte Falls, OR, 97522. Tel: 541-865-3511. Fax: 541-865-3511. p. 2005

Dunne, Cliff, Br Mgr, Jackson County Library Services, Prospect Branch, 150 Mill Creek Dr, Prospect, OR, 97536. Tel: 541-560-3668. Fax: 541-560-3668. p. 2005

Dunne, Jennifer, Ch, Moorestown Public Library, 111 W Second St, Moorestown, NJ, 08057-2481. Tel: 856-234-0333. Fax: 856-778-9536. p. 1504

Dunne, Maureen, Circ, Prospect Heights Public Library District, 12 N Elm St, Prospect Heights, IL, 60070-1450. Tel: 847-259-3500. Fax: 847-259-4602. p. 692

Dunne, Virginia, Per, Dominican College Library, 480 Western Hwy, Blauvelt, NY, 10913-2000. Tel: 845-848-7505. Fax: 845-359-2525. p. 1583

Dunne-Thayer, Elaine, Dir, Massena Public Library, 41 Glenn St, Massena, NY, 13662. Tel: 315-769-9914. Fax: 315-769-5978. p, 1658

Dunneback, Mary, Ref, Oak Lawn Public Library, 9427 S Raymond Ave, Oak Lawn, IL, 60453-2434. Tel: 708-422-4990. Fax: 708-422-5061. p. 683

Dunnigan, Brian Leigh, Curator, Head, Reader Serv, University of Michigan, William L Clements Library, 909 S University Ave, Ann Arbor, MI, 48109-1190. Tel: 734-764-2347. Fax: 734-647-0716. p. 1152

Dunnigan, Virginia, Govt Doc, Saint Thomas Aquinas College, 125 Rte 340, Sparkill, NY, 10976. Tel: 845-398-4216. Fax: 845-359-9537. p. 1746

Dunning, Beth, Librn, McGill University Libraries, Howard Ross Library of Management, Samuel Bronfman Bldg, 1001 Sherbrooke St W, 2nd Flr, Montreal, QC, H3A 1G5, CANADA. Tel: 514-398-4690. Fax: 514-398-5046. p. 2899

Dunning, Dianna, Dir, Chelsea Public Library, 600 Station St, Chelsea, IA, 52215. Tel: 641-489-2525. Fax: 641-489-2525. p. 801

Dunning, Laurie, Librn Spec, Ventura County Library, Oak Park Library, 899 N Kanan Rd, Oak Park, CA, 91377. Tel: 818-889-2239. Fax: 818-706-9746. p. 280

Dunning, Linda, Dir, Rockwell Public Library, 307 Main St, Rockwell, IA, 50469. Tel: 641-822-3268. Fax: 641-822-3168. p. 841

Dunning, Pamela, Dir, Wiscasset Public Library, 21 High St, Wiscasset, ME, 04578-4119. Tel: 207-882-7161. Fax: 207-882-6698. p. 1008

Dunning, Sue, Dir, Webber International University, 1201 State Rd 17, Babson Park, FL, 33827. Tel: 863-638-2937. Fax: 863-638-2778. p. 426

Dunning-Torbett, Kathleen, Libr Dir, United States Navy, Crew's Library, Naval Hospital, Box 555191, Camp Pendleton, CA, 92055-5191. Tel: 760-725-1229. Fax: 760-725-4156. p. 131

Dunning-Torbett, Kathleen, Libr Dir, United States Navy, Medical Library, Naval Hospital, Box 555191, Camp Pendleton, CA, 92055-5191. Tel: 760-725-1229. Fax: 760-725-4156. p. 131

Dunphy, Christina, Archives Coordr, Champlain College Library, 163 S Willard St, Burlington, VT, 05401. Tel: 802-860-2717. p. 2420

Dunphy, Sally, Tech Info Spec, National Forest Service Library, 240 W Prospect Rd, Fort Collins, CO, 80526. Tel: 970-498-1268. Fax: 970-498-1059. p. 307

Dunphy, Sandra, Res & Instruction Librn, Northeastern University Libraries, Snell Library, 360 Huntington Ave, Boston, MA, 02115. Tel: 617-373-5322. p. 1065

Dunscombe, Edward Andrew, Dir, George F Johnson Memorial Library, 1001 Park St, Endicott, NY, 13760. Tel: 607-757-2415. Fax: 607-757-2491. p. 1620

Dunscombe, Sharon, Adult Serv, ILL, Your Home Public Library, 107 Main St, Johnson City, NY, 13790. Tel: 607-797-4816. Fax: 607-798-8895. p. 1647

Dunseth, Brenda, Youth Serv Dept Head, Highland Township Public Library, 444 Beach Farm Circle, Highland, MI, 48357. Tel: 248-887-2218. Fax: 248-887-5179. p. 1189

Dunshee, Melanie, Asst Dean, Libr Serv, Duke University Libraries, School of Law Library, 210 Science Dr, Durham, NC, 27708. Tel: 919-613-7119. Fax: 919-613-7237. p. 1788

Dunsmore, Renate, Br Mgr, Onondaga County Public Library, Charles E White Branch, 763 Butternut St, Syracuse, NY, 13208. Tel: 315-435-3519. Fax: 315-435-3367. p. 1753

Dunsmore-Porter, Linda, Exec Dir, Saskatchewan Genealogical Society Library, 110 - 1514 11th Ave, Regina, SK, S4P 0H2, CANADA. Tel: 306-780-9207. Fax: 306-780-3615. p. 2924

Dunson, Kathy, Br Mgr, Mid-Continent Public Library, Lone Jack Branch, 211 N Bynum Rd, Lone Jack, MO, 64070-9604. Tel: 816-697-2528. Fax: 816-697-2917. p. 1333

Dunton, Kathryn, Ch, Pearle L Crawford Memorial Library, 40 Schofield Ave, Dudley, MA, 01571. Tel: 508-949-8021. Fax: 508-949-8026. p. 1085

Dunton, Sabra, Dir, Middlesex Reading Center, 1216 Rte 245, Middlesex, NY, 14507. Tel: 585-554-6945. p. 1660

Dupelle, Lisa, Dir, Human Res, Hamilton Public Library, 55 York Blvd, Hamilton, ON, L8R 3K1, CANADA. Tel: 905-546-3200. Fax: 905-546-3204. p. 2808

DuPerow, Paula, Librn, Cuyahoga Community College, Western Campus Library, 11000 Pleasant Valley Rd, Parma, OH, 44130-5199. Tel: 216-987-5412. Fax: 216-987-5050. p. 1879

Duperron, Karen, Librn, Ashmont Community Library, PO Box 330, Ashmont, AB, T0A 0C0, CANADA. Tel: 780-726-3793, 780-726-3877. Fax: 780-726-3777. p. 2684

Duplaga, Jennifer, Spec Coll Adminr, Kentucky Historical Society, 100 W Broadway, Frankfort, KY, 40601. Tel: 502-564-1792. Fax: 502-564-4701. p. 913

Duplessis, Linda, Dir, Peace Library System, 8301 110 St, Grande Prairie, AB, T8W 6T2, CANADA. Tel: 780-538-4656. Fax: 780-539-5285. p. 2705

Dupont, Dianne, Br Mgr, Nicholson Memorial Library System, North Garland Branch, 3845 N Garland Ave, Garland, TX, 75040. Tel: 972-205-2803. p. 2327

Dupont, Inge, Head, Reader Serv, The Morgan Library, 225 Madison Ave, New York, NY, 10016. Tel: 212-685-0008. p. 1687

Dupont, Patricia, Asst Dir, Lunenburg Public Library, 1023 Massachusetts Ave, Lunenburg, MA, 01462. Tel: 978-582-4140. Fax: 978-582-4141. p. 1101

Dupras, Rheba, Head, Info Serv, University of Alaska Fairbanks, 310 Tanana Dr, Fairbanks, AK, 99775. Tel: 907-474-6692. Fax: 907-474-6841. p. 48

DuPraw, Katie, Div Mgr, San Jose Public Library, 150 E San Fernando St, San Jose, CA, 95112-3580. Tel: 408-808-2192. p. 250

Dupree, Jason, Pub Serv Librn, Southwestern Oklahoma State University, 100 Campus Dr, Weatherford, OK, 73096-3002. Tel: 580-774-7023. Fax: 580-774-3112. p. 1985

Dupree, Nancy, Librn, University Presbyterian Church, 1127 Eighth St, Tuscaloosa, AL, 35401. Tel: 205-758-5422. Fax: 205-758-5422. p. 39

Dupree, Robert Scott, Dr, Dir, Libr Serv & Univ Res, University of Dallas, 1845 E Northgate Dr, Irving, TX, 75062-4736. Tel: 972-721-5328. Fax: 972-721-4010. p. 2347

Dupree, Sandra, Head, Ref, Coventry Public Library, 1672 Flat River Rd, Coventry, RI, 02816. Tel: 401-822-9100. Fax: 401-822-9133. p. 2164

Dupuis, Elizabeth, Assoc Univ Librn, University of California, Berkeley, 255 Doe Library, Berkeley, CA, 94720-6000. Tel: 510-642-3773. Fax: 510-643-8179. p. 127

Dupuis, Francine, Chef de Section, Bibliothèques de Montréal, Saint-Pierre, 183, rue des Érables, Montreal, QC, H8R 1B1, CANADA. Tel: 514-634-3471, Ext 336. Fax: 514-634-8194. p. 2891

Dupuis, Francine, Chef de Section, Bibliothèques de Montréal, Saul-Bellow, 3100, rue Saint-Antoine, Montreal, QC, H8S 4B8, CANADA. Tel: 514-634-3471, Ext 336. Fax: 514-634-8194. p. 2892

Dupuis, Gisele, Librn, Waterloo Public Library, CP 700, 650 Rue de la Cour, Waterloo, QC, J0E 2N0, CANADA. Tel: 450-539-2268. Fax: 450-539-2528. p. 2915

Dupuis, Marie-Helene, Head, Ref, Ecole Polytechnique de Montreal Bibliotheque, 2500, chemin de Polytechnique, Montreal, QC, H3T 1J4, CANADA. Tel: 514-340-4666. Fax: 514-340-4026. p. 2895

Dupuis, Peggy, Bus Mgr, Calcasieu Parish Public Library, 301 W Claude St, Lake Charles, LA, 70605-3457. Tel: 337-721-7154. Fax: 337-475-8806. p. 953

Dupuy, Ashley, Undergrad Libr Instruction, Kennesaw State University, 1000 Chastain Rd, Kennesaw, GA, 30144. Tel: 770-499-3590. Fax: 770-423-6185. p. 537

Dupuy, Michelle, Dir, Bibliotheque Municipale, 51 rue Jeannotte, Vaudreuil-Dorion, QC, J7V 6E6, CANADA. Tel: 450-455-5588. Fax: 450-455-5653. p. 2914

Duquesne, Charles, AV, Media Spec, Moore College of Art & Design, 20th St & The Parkway, Philadelphia, PA, 19103-1179. Tel: 215-965-4060. Fax: 215-965-8544. p. 2112

Duquette, Lynn, Librn, Nova Scotia Department of Education Library, 2021 Brunswick St, Halifax, NS, B3J 2S9, CANADA. Tel: 902-424-4920. Fax: 902-424-0519. p. 2782

Duquette, Susanne Costa, Dir, Taunton Public Library, 12 Pleasant St, Taunton, MA, 02780. Tel: 508-821-1410. Fax: 508-821-1414. p. 1130

Duran, Arthur S, Bus Off Mgr, Yuma County Library District, 2951 S 21st Dr, Yuma, AZ, 85364. Tel: 928-373-6463. Fax: 928-782-9420. p. 91

Duran, Carrie, Coll Mgr, Schiele Museum of Natural History Library, 1500 E Garrison Blvd, Gastonia, NC, 28054-5199. Tel: 704-869-1009. Fax: 704-866-6041. p. 1795

Duran, Jason, Circ, Belvedere-Tiburon Library, 1501 Tiburon Blvd, Tiburon, CA, 94920. Tel: 415-789-2665. Fax: 415-789-2650. p. 275

Duran, Jennifer, Mgr, Sonoma County Library, Santa Rosa Rincon Valley Regional, 6959 Montecito Blvd, Santa Rosa, CA, 95409. Tel: 707-537-0162. Fax: 707-537-0174. p. 268

Duran, Mark, Res, Playboy Enterprises, Inc, 680 N Lake Shore Dr, Chicago, IL, 60611. Tel: 312-751-8000, Ext 2529. Fax: 312-751-2818. p. 622

Durand, Kathleen A, Dir, Lake City Public Library, 201 S High St, Lake City, MN, 55041. Tel: 651-345-4013. Fax: 651-345-5923. p. 1255

Durand, Rolande, Librn, Bibliotheque Saint-Joachim Library, 29 Normandeau Bay, La Broquerie, MB, R0A 0W0, CANADA. Tel: 204-424-9533. Fax: 204-424-5610. p. 2749

Durand, Sheila, Chief Librn/CEO, Muskoka Lakes Library Board, 69 Joseph St, Port Carling, ON, P0B 1J0, CANADA. Tel: 705-765-5650. Fax: 705-765-0422. p. 2837

Durand, Susan, Asst Librn, Abington Public Library, 600 Gliniewicz Way, Abington, MA, 02351. Tel: 781-982-2139. Fax: 781-878-7361. p. 1047

Durans, Meledie, Ref Supvr, Davis County Library, Central Branch, 155 N Wasatch Dr, Layton, UT, 84041. Tel: 801-547-0729. p. 2405

Durant, Ben, Media Serv, Asnuntuck Community College, 170 Elm St, Enfield, CT, 06082-0068. Tel: 860-253-3074. Fax: 860-253-9310. p. 338

Durant, Galina, Librn, Stewart Public Library, 824 A Main St, Stewart, BC, V0T 1W0, CANADA. Tel: 250-636-2380. Fax: 250-636-2380. p. 2738

Durant, Joyce M, Dean, Francis Marion University, 4822 East Palmetto St, Florence, SC, 29506. Tel: 843-661-1300. Fax: 843-661-1309. p. 2194

Durant, Olivia, Teen Serv, YA Serv, Webster Public Library, Webster Plaza, 980 Ridge Rd, Webster, NY, 14580. Tel: 585-872-7075. p. 1765

Durante, David, Br Mgr, Pierce County Library System, Lakewood Branch, 6300 Wildaire Rd SW, Lakewood, WA, 98499. Tel: 253-548-3302. Fax: 253-589-7377. p. 2539

Duranti, Luciana, Prof, University of British Columbia, The Irving K Barber Centre, 1961 E Mall, Ste 470, Vancouver, BC, V6T 1Z1, CANADA. Tel: 604-822-2404. Fax: 604-822-6006. p. 2977

Durbin, Mark, Acq, John Marshall Law School, 1422 W Peachtree St NW, Atlanta, GA, 30309. Tel: 404-872-3593, Ext 119. Fax: 404-873-3802. p. 516

Duree, Karen, Asst Dir, Libr Operations, Jefferson County Library, 5678 State Rd PP, High Ridge, MO, 63049-2216. Tel: 636-461-1914. Fax: 636-461-1915. p. 1331

Duree, Karen, Br Mgr, Jefferson County Library, Windsor, 7479 Metropolitian Blvd, Barnhart, MO, 63012. Tel: 636-461-1914. Fax: 636-461-1915. p. 1331

Duren, Vickie, Bus Mgr, Public Library of Johnston County & Smithfield, 305 E Market St, Smithfield, NC, 27577-3919. Tel: 919-934-8146. Fax: 919-934-8084. p. 1824

DuRepos Theriault, Helene, Mgr, Haut-Saint-Jean Regional Library, La Moisson Public, 206 Canada St, Saint Quentin, NB, E8A 1H1, CANADA. Tel: 506-235-1955. Fax: 506-235-1957. p. 2762

Durette, Diane, Head, Ref Serv, Lucy Robbins Welles Library, 95 Cedar St, Newington, CT, 06111-2645. Tel: 860-665-8705. Fax: 860-667-1255. p. 361

Durfee, Edmund, Prof, University of Michigan, 304 West Hall, 1085 S University, Ann Arbor, MI, 48109-1107. Tel: 734-763-2285. Fax: 734-764-2475. p. 2967

Durfee, Shirley, Asst Librn, Bridgton Hospital, Ten Hospital Dr, Bridgton, ME, 04009. Tel: 207-647-6084. p. 978

Durgan, Tracey, Dir, Town Librn, Montgomery Town Library, 86 Mountain Rd, Montgomery Center, VT, 05471. Tel: 802-326-3113. p. 2429

Durgin, Margaret, County Librn, Tech Serv, Tuolumne County Free Library, 480 Greenley Rd, Sonora, CA, 95370-5956. Tel: 209-533-5507. Fax: 209-533-0936. p. 269

Durham, Billie, Pub Serv, Montgomery Community College Library, 1011 Page St, Troy, NC, 27371. Tel: 910-576-6222, Ext 520. Fax: 910-576-2176. p. 1827

Durham, David, Curator of Archival Coll, University of Alabama, School of Law Library, 101 Paul Bryant Dr, Tuscaloosa, AL, 35487. Tel: 205-348-5925. Fax: 205-348-1112. p. 38

Durham, Debbie, Librn, Tennessee State Law Library, Supreme Court Bldg, 6 Hwy 45 By-Pass, Jackson, TN, 38301. Tel: 731-423-5849. p. 2238

Durham, Jennifer, Asst Dir, Coordr, Statesboro Regional Public Libraries, 124 S Main St, Statesboro, GA, 30458. Tel: 912-764-1343. Fax: 912-764-1348. p. 552

Durham, Judy A, Supvr, Circ, Southeastern Baptist Theological Seminary Library, 114 N Wingate St, Wake Forest, NC, 27587. Tel: 919-556-3104. Fax: 919-863-8150. p. 1827

Durham, Mardi J, Ref, Iredell County Public Library, 201 N Tradd St, Statesville, NC, 28677. Tel: 704-878-3109. Fax: 704-878-5449. p. 1825

Durham, Mark, Dir, Effie & Wilton Hebert Public Library, 2025 Merriman St, Port Neches, TX, 77651. Tel: 409-722-4554. Fax: 409-719-4296. p. 2372

Durham, Robbye, Libr Mgr, United States Army, Keith A Campbell Memorial Library, 2601 Harney Rd, Ste 29, Fort Sam Houston, TX, 78234-5029. Tel: 210-221-4387, 210-221-4702. Fax: 210-227-5921. p. 2320

Durham, Suzanne, Head, Spec Coll, Irvine Sullivan Ingram Library, University of West Georgia, 1601 Maple St, Carrollton, GA, 30118. Tel: 678-839-6361. Fax: 678-839-6511. p. 523

Durham, William, Br Mgr, Forsyth County Public Library, Walkertown Branch, 2969 Main St, Walkertown, NC, 27051. Tel: 336-703-2990. Fax: 336-595-9080. p. 1833

Durio, Mary, Head, Ctr for Digital Coll, University of Delaware Library, 181 S College Ave, Newark, DE, 19717-5267. Tel: 302-831-2231. Fax: 302-831-1046. p. 386

Durivage, Catherine A, Dir, Minnesota Braille & Talking Book Library, 388 SE Sixth Ave, Faribault, MN, 55021-6340. Tel: 507-384-6860. Fax: 507-333-4832. p. 1251

Durivage, Mary Jo, Librn, Department of Veterans Affairs Library Service, 4646 John R St, Detroit, MI, 48201. Tel: 313-576-1000, Ext 3380. Fax: 313-576-1048. p. 1169

Durk, Mary Rose, Pub Serv, Ref Serv, Delaware State University, 1200 N Dupont Hwy, Dover, DE, 19901-2277. Tel: 302-857-7886. Fax: 302-857-6177. p. 382

Durkin, Brigid, Exec Dir, Danbury Scott-Fanton Museum & Historical Society, 43 Main St, Danbury, CT, 06810. Tel: 203-743-5200. Fax: 203-743-1131. p. 335

Durkin, Claire Toomey, Assoc Dir, Res & Instruction, The John Marshall Law School, 315 S Plymouth Ct, Chicago, IL, 60604. Tel: 312-427-2737. Fax: 312-427-8307. p. 618

Durkin, Debra, Circ & ILL, University of Maine at Fort Kent, 23 University Dr, Fort Kent, ME, 04743. Tel: 207-834-7525. Fax: 207-834-7518. p. 986

Durkin, Lynn, Dir, Town of Inlet Public Library, 168 State Rte 28, Inlet, NY, 13360. Tel: 315-357-6494. Fax: 315-357-6494. p. 1640

Durkin, Tom, Head of Libr, University of Wisconsin-Madison, Social Science Reference Library, 1180 Observatory Drl, Rm 8432, Madison, WI, 53706. Tel: 608-263-4072. p. 2609

Durler, Jolene, Govt Doc, Dodge City Community College, 2501 N 14th, Dodge City, KS, 67801. Tel: 620-225-1321, Ext 287, 620-227-9287. Fax: 620-225-0918. p. 863

Durley, Marsha, Head Librn, Beacon Falls Public Library, Ten Maple Ave, Beacon Falls, CT, 06403. Tel: 203-729-1441. Fax: 203-729-4927. p. 330

Durman, Chris, Librn, University of Tennessee, Knoxville, George F DeVine Music Library, 301 Music Bldg, 1741 Volunteer Blvd, Knoxville, TN, 37996-2600. Tel: 865-974-7542. Fax: 865-974-0564. p. 2244

Durman, George, Art & Music Librn, Free Public Library of Bayonne, 697 Avenue C, Bayonne, NJ, 07002. Tel: 201-858-6970. Fax: 201-437-6928. p. 1470

Durniak, Barbara, Head, Reader Serv, Vassar College Library, 124 Raymond Ave, Maildrop 20, Poughkeepsie, NY, 12604-0020. Tel: 845-437-5760. Fax: 845-437-5864. p. 1723

Durnin, Carolyn, Dir, Grafton Community Library, 2455 NY2, Grafton, NY, 12082. Tel: 518-279-0580. Fax: 518-279-0580. p. 1630

Durocher, Connie, Br Mgr, Saint Mary Parish Library, West End, 100 Charenton Rd, Baldwin, LA, 70514. Tel: 337-923-6205. Fax: 337-923-4507. p. 950

Durocher, Ève, Chef de Section, Bibliothèques de Montrèal, Pierrefonds, 13555, boulevard Pierrefonds, Montreal, QC, H9A 1A6, CANADA. Tel: 514-620-4181, Ext 2219. Fax: 514-620-5503. p. 2891

Durr, Chris, Teen & Tech Coordr, Kirkwood Public Library, 140 E Jefferson Ave, Kirkwood, MO, 63122. Tel: 314-821-5770, Ext 1020. Fax: 314-822-3755. p. 1342

Durrance, Joan C, Prof, University of Michigan, 304 West Hall, 1085 S University, Ann Arbor, MI, 48109-1107. Tel: 734-763-2285. Fax: 734-764-2475. p. 2967

Durrance, Jocelyn, Asst Dir, Pitkin County Library, 120 N Mill St, Aspen, CO, 81611. Tel: 970-925-4025. Fax: 970-925-3935. p. 288

Durre, Inge, Dir, Foundation for Blind Children Library & Media Center, 1235 E Harmont Dr, Phoenix, AZ, 85020-3864. Tel: 602-678-5810, 602-678-5816. Fax: 602-678-5811. p. 73

Durrence, Carol, ILL, Tech Serv, Marion County Public Library System, 2720 E Silver Springs Blvd, Ocala, FL, 34470. Tel: 352-671-8551. Fax: 352-368-4545. p. 474

Durrett, Brenda, Pub Serv, Columbus-Lowndes Public Library, 314 N Seventh St, Columbus, MS, 39701. Tel: 662-329-5300. Fax: 662-329-5156. p. 1297

Durusau, Carol, Ch, Newton County Library System, 7116 Floyd St NE, Covington, GA, 30014. Tel: 770-787-3231. Fax: 770-784-2092. p. 527

Duryea, Paul, Br Mgr, Kenton County Public Library, William E Durr Branch, 1992 Walton-Nicholson Rd, Independence, KY, 41051. Tel: 859-962-4036. Fax: 859-962-4037. p. 910

Dusek, Tari L, Dir, Thomas Township Library, 8207 Shields Dr, Saginaw, MI, 48609-4814. Tel: 989-781-3770. Fax: 989-781-3881. p. 1224

Dusenbury, Renee, Media Librn, Central Carolina Community College Libraries, 1105 Kelly Dr, Sanford, NC, 27330. Tel: 919-718-7435. Fax: 919-718-7378. p. 1823

Dusing, Betty, Cat, Park University Library, 8700 NW River Park Dr, Parkville, MO, 64152. Tel: 816-584-6281. Fax: 816-741-4911. p. 1349

Dusman, Elizabeth, Librn, Cape May County Library, Upper Cape Branch, 2050 Rte 631, Petersburg, NJ, 08270. Tel: 609-628-2607. p. 1477

Duso, Gail, Librn, Russell Public Library, 162 Main St, Russell, MA, 01071. Tel: 413-862-3102. Fax: 413-862-3106. p. 1121

Dussault, Chantal, Head, Archives & Rec Libr, Canadian Museum of Nature Library & Archives, PO Box 3443, Sta D, Ottawa, ON, K1P 6P4, CANADA. Tel: 613-364-4047. Fax: 613-364-4026. p. 2829

Dussault, Louis-Marie, Dir of Libr, College Edouard-Montpetit Bibliotheque, 945 Chemin de Chambly, Longueuil, QC, J4H 3M6, CANADA. Tel: 450-678-3561, Ext 4236. Fax: 450-677-2945. p. 2887

Dustman, Teresa, Circ, Wells County Public Library, 200 W Washington St, Bluffton, IN, 46714-1999. Tel: 260-824-1612. Fax: 260-824-3129. p. 728

Duszkiewicz, Irene A, Dir, Hempstead Public Library, 115 Nichols Ct, Hempstead, NY, 11550-3199. Tel: 516-481-6990. Fax: 516-481-6719. p. 1634

Dutch, Lois, Librn, Waldo County General Hospital, 118 Northport Ave, Belfast, ME, 04915. Tel: 207-338-2500, Ext 4154. Fax: 207-338-6029. p. 977

Dutcher, Henry, Dir, Enfield Public Library, 104 Middle Rd, Enfield, CT, 06082. Tel: 860-763-7510. Fax: 860-763-7514. p. 338

Dutcher, Roger, Head, Tech Serv, Beloit Public Library, 605 Eclipse Blvd, Beloit, WI, 53511. Tel: 608-364-2897. Fax: 608-364-2907. p. 2581

Dutcher-Walls, Patricia, Dir, Vancouver School of Theology, 6000 Iona Dr, Vancouver, BC, V6T 1L4, CANADA. Tel: 604-822-9430. Fax: 604-822-9212. p. 2744

DuTell, Debbie, Tech Serv Supvr, Northwest Christian University, 1188 Kincade, Eugene, OR, 97401. Tel: 541-684-7246. Fax: 541-684-7307. p. 1997

Dutka, Andrew, Archives, Broward College, 3501 SW Davie Rd, Davie, FL, 33314. Tel: 954-201-6648. Fax: 954-201-6490. p. 435

Dutka, Jeanne, Librn, Hunterdon Medical Center Library, 2100 Wescott Dr, 6th Flr, Flemington, NJ, 08822. Tel: 908-788-6100, Ext 3220. Fax: 908-788-2537. p. 1486

Dutler, Sue, Libr Dir, Robert Morris University, 401 S State St, Chicago, IL, 60605. Tel: 312-935-2202, 312-935-2203. Fax: 312-935-2207. p. 623

Dutra, Deborah, Commun Relations Librn, Taunton Public Library, 12 Pleasant St, Taunton, MA, 02780. Tel: 508-821-1410. Fax: 508-821-1414. p. 1130

Dutschke, Consuelo, Curator, Medieval & Renaissance Ms, Columbia University, Rare Book & Manuscript, Butler Library, 6th Flr E, 535 W 114th St, New York, NY, 10027. Tel: 212-854-4139. Fax: 212-854-1365. p. 1675

Dutta, Deepti, Ref Librn, Free Public Library of Hasbrouck Heights, 320 Boulevard, Hasbrouck Heights, NJ, 07604. Tel: 201-288-6653. Fax: 201-288-5467. p. 1490

Dutta, Gouri, Head, Cat, Head, Tech Serv, North Carolina Central University, 1801 Fayetteville St, Durham, NC, 27707-3129. Tel: 919-560-6430. Fax: 919-530-7612. p. 1789

Dutta, Sukamoy, Pub Serv Librn, Syst Librn, Saint Augustine's College, 1315 Oakwood Ave, Raleigh, NC, 27610-2298. Tel: 919-516-4145. Fax: 919-516-4758. p. 1817

Duttlinger, Beth, Dir, Lillie M Evans Library District, 207 N Walnut Ave, Princeville, IL, 61559. Tel: 309-385-4540. Fax: 309-385-2661. p. 692

Dutton, Cynthia, Dir, Cuba Circulating Library, 39 E Main St, Cuba, NY, 14727. Tel: 585-968-1668. Fax: 585-968-3004. p. 1613

Dutton, Pauline, Circ, Tech Serv, Altadena Library District, 600 E Mariposa St, Altadena, CA, 91001. Tel: 626-798-0833. Fax: 626-798-5351. p. 120

Duval, Andree, Actg Dir, Dep Dir, Port Moody Public Library, 100 Newport Dr, Port Moody, BC, V3H 3E1, CANADA. Tel: 604-469-4575, 604-469-4577. Fax: 604-469-4576. p. 2735

Duval, Cynthia, Chief Curator, Museum of Arts & Sciences, 352 S Nova Rd, Daytona Beach, FL, 32114. Tel: 386-255-0285. Fax: 386-255-5040. p. 436

Duvall, Gayla Elizabeth, Dir, Clinton County Public Library, 302 King Dr, Albany, KY, 42602-1603. Tel: 606-387-5989. Fax: 606-387-5989. p. 905

DuVall, Mickey, Dir, Bastrop Public Library, 1100 Church St, Bastrop, TX, 78602. Tel: 512-321-5441. Fax: 512-321-3163. p. 2286

Duvall, Robbie, Br Mgr, Pope County Library System, Atkins Centennial Branch, 216 NE First St, Atkins, AR, 72823. Tel: 479-641-7904. Fax: 479-641-1169. p. 114

Duvall, Scott, Asst Univ Librn, Spec Coll Librn, Brigham Young University, Harold B Lee Library, 2060 HBLL, Provo, UT, 84602. Tel: 801-422-2927. Fax: 801-422-0466. p. 2411

DuVernay, Lisa, Tech Serv, Library at the Mariners' Museum, 100 Museum Dr, Newport News, VA, 23606-3759. Tel: 757-591-7788. Fax: 757-591-7310. p. 2480

Duvernoy, Bernadette, Asst Dir, Mkt & Pub Relations, Hayner Public Library District, 326 Belle St, Alton, IL, 62002. Tel: 618-462-0677. Fax: 618-462-0665. p. 588

Duwel, Lucretia, Head, Youth Serv, Stratford Library Association, 2203 Main St, Stratford, CT, 06615. Tel: 203-385-4167. Fax: 203-381-2079. p. 371

Dux-Ideus, Sherrie, Managing Librn, Central Community College, Hastings Campus, 550 S Technical Blvd, Hastings, NE, 68902-1024. Tel: 402-461-2538. Fax: 402-460-2135. p. 1401

Dvorak, Diane, Cat, Circ, Mount Marty College Library, 1105 W Eighth St, Yankton, SD, 57078-3724. Tel: 605-668-1555. Fax: 605-668-1357. p. 2222

Dvorak, Karrie L, Dir/Curator, Nebraska United Methodist Historical Center Archives, Nebraska Wesleyan University, Cochrane-Woods Library, Lower Level, 52nd & Huntington, Lincoln, NE, 68504. Tel: 402-465-2175. Fax: 402-464-6203. p. 1406

Dvorzak, Marie, Librn, University of Wisconsin-Madison, C K Leith Library of Geology & Geophysics, 1215 W Dayton St, Madison, WI, 53706-1692. Tel: 608-262-8956. Fax: 608-262-0693. p. 2609

Dworkin, Rachel, Archivist, Chemung County Historical Society, Inc, 415 E Water St, Elmira, NY, 14901. Tel: 607-734-4167. Fax: 607-734-1565. p. 1619

Dwyer, Dianna, Librn, Glendale Community College, 6000 W Olive Ave, Glendale, AZ, 85302. Tel: 623-845-3108. Fax: 623-845-3102. p. 64

Dwyer, Hayley, Br Mgr, Porter County Public Library System, Kouts Public, 101 E Daumer Rd, Kouts, IN, 46347. Tel: 219-766-2271. Fax: 219-766-2273. p. 783

Dwyer, Kathryn Elizabeth, Curator, Northwestern Ontario Sports Hall of Fame Library, 219 May St S, Thunder Bay, ON, P7E 1B5, CANADA. Tel: 807-622-2852. Fax: 807-622-2736. p. 2848

Dwyer, Liz, Br Head, North Grenville Public Library, Burritts Rapids Branch, One Grenville St, Burritts Rapids, ON, K0G 1B0, CANADA. Tel: 613-269-3636. p. 2812

Dwyer, Tara, Ch, William B Ogden Free Library, 42 Gardiner Pl, Walton, NY, 13856. Tel: 607-865-5929. Fax: 607-865-6821. p. 1762

Dwyer, William, Instrul Serv Librn, University of Montana Western, 710 S Atlantic St, Dillon, MT, 59725. Tel: 406-683-7164. Fax: 406-683-7493. p. 1378

Dyal, Donald, Dr, Dean, Texas Tech University Libraries, 18th & Boston Ave, Lubbock, TX, 79409-0002. Tel: 806-742-2261. Fax: 806-742-0737. p. 2358

Dybwad, G L, Librn, Telephone Museum of New Mexico Library, 110 Fourth St NW, Albuquerque, NM, 87102. Tel: 505-296-9047. Fax: 505-332-4088. p. 1550

Dyck, Elaine, Br Librn, South Central Regional Library, Winkler Branch, 160 Main St, Winkler, MB, R6W 4B4, CANADA. Tel: 204-325-7174. p. 2753

Dyck, Helen, Libr Asst, Barnwell Public Library, 500 Second St W, Barnwell, AB, T0K 0B0, CANADA. Tel: 403-223-3626. p. 2684

Dyck, Margaret, Libr Tech, Department of Fisheries & Oceans Canada, Central & Arctic Region, 501 University Crescent, Winnipeg, MB, R3T 2N6, CANADA. Tel: 204-983-5170. Fax: 204-984-4668. p. 2755

Dyck, Neva, Librn, Peabody Township Library, 214 Walnut St, Peabody, KS, 66866. Tel: 620-983-2502. p. 889

Dyck, Ron, Dir, Info Tech & Fac Div, Toronto Public Library, 789 Yonge St, Toronto, ON, M4W 2G8, CANADA. Tel: 416-393-7131. Fax: 416-393-7229. p. 2860

Dyckman, Lise M, Dir, California Institute of Integral Studies, 1453 Mission St, 2nd Flr, San Francisco, CA, 94103. Tel: 415-755-6181. Fax: 415-575-1264. p. 240

Dye, Carol, Br Mgr, Middle Georgia Regional Library System, Jones County Public Library, Railroad Ave, Gray, GA, 31032. Tel: 478-986-6626. Fax: 478-986-6626. p. 541

Dye, Emily, Br Mgr, Nashville Public Library, Edmondson Pike, 5501 Edmondson Pike, Nashville, TN, 37211-5808. Tel: 615-880-3957. Fax: 615-880-3961. p. 2257

Dye, Jane, ILL, Hiram College Library, 11694 Hayden St, Hiram, OH, 44234. Tel: 330-569-5354, 330-569-5489. Fax: 330-569-5491. p. 1905

Dye, Judy, Access Serv Coordr, Southern Oregon University, 1250 Siskiyou Blvd, Ashland, OR, 97520-5076. Tel: 541-552-6825. Fax: 541-552-6429. p. 1990

Dye, Willanne, Libr Tech, Colorado Department of Corrections, Colorado Women's Correctional Facility Library, 3800 Grandview Ave, Canon City, CO, 81212. Tel: 719-269-4707, Ext 3818. Fax: 719-269-4716. p. 293

Dyer, Celeste M, Libr Dir, Cumberland Public Library, 1464 Diamond Hill Rd, Cumberland, RI, 02864-5510. Tel: 401-333-2552, Ext 5. Fax: 401-334-0578. p. 2165

Dyer, Charles R, Dir, San Diego County Public Law Library, 1105 Front St, San Diego, CA, 92101-3904. Tel: 619-531-3904. Fax: 619-238-7716. p. 234

Dyer, Cynthia M, Col Librn/Archivist, Simpson College, 508 North C St, Indianola, IA, 50125-1216. Tel: 515-961-1663. Fax: 515-961-1363. p. 822

Dyer, Eileen, Coordr, Youth Serv, Cranston Public Library, 140 Sockanosset Cross Rd, Cranston, RI, 02920-5539. Tel: 401-943-9080. Fax: 401-946-5079. p. 2164

Dyer, Eileen, Br Librn, Cranston Public Library, Arlington Reading Room, 1064 Cranston St, Cranston, RI, 02920-7344. Tel: 401-943-9080. p. 2165

Dyer, Elizabeth, Pub Serv Librn, University of New England Libraries, Josephine S Abplanalp Library, Portland Campus, 716 Stevens Ave, Portland, ME, 04103. Tel: 207-221-4333. Fax: 207-221-4893. p. 978

Dyer, Fiona, Mgr, Lethbridge College, 3000 College Dr S, Lethbridge, AB, T1K 1L6, CANADA. Tel: 403-320-3352. p. 2709

Dyer, Maxine, Libr Asst, Brook-Iroquois-Washington Public Library, 100 W Main St, Brook, IN, 47922. Tel: 219-275-2471. Fax: 219-275-8471. p. 730

Dyer, Michael, Maritime Curator, Old Dartmouth Historical Society, 791 Purchase St, New Bedford, MA, 02740-6398. Tel: 508-997-0046, Ext 137. Fax: 508-207-1064. p. 1109

Dyer, Nancy, Archivist, Librn, National Watch & Clock Museum, 514 Poplar St, Columbia, PA, 17512-2124. Tel: 717-684-8261, Ext 214. Fax: 717-684-0142. p. 2046

Dyer, Victor, Dir, Ipswich Public Library, 25 N Main St, Ipswich, MA, 01938-2217. Tel: 978-356-6649. Fax: 978-356-6647. p. 1097

Dyer-Hurdon, Michelle, Librn, Phoenix College, 1202 W Thomas Rd, Phoenix, AZ, 85013. Tel: 602-285-7457. Fax: 602-285-7368. p. 76

Dyess, Anissa, Librn, East Mississippi Regional Library System, Quitman Public Library, 116 Water St, Quitman, MS, 39355. Tel: 601-776-2492. Fax: 601-776-6599. p. 1313

Dyess, Peggy, ILL, Flagler College, 44 Sevilla St, Saint Augustine, FL, 32084-4302. Tel: 904-819-6206. Fax: 904-823-8511. p. 486

Dykens, Margaret, Dir, San Diego Natural History Museum, Balboa Park, 1788 El Prado, San Diego, CA, 92101. Tel: 619-255-0225. Fax: 619-232-0248. p. 235

Dykes, Andy, Mgr, Greenville County Library System, Berea (Sarah Dobey Jones) Branch, 111 N Hwy 25 Bypass, Greenville, SC, 29617. Tel: 864-246-1695. Fax: 864-246-1765. p. 2196

Dykes, Barbara, Head, Circ, University of the South, 735 University Ave, Sewanee, TN, 37383-1000. Tel: 931-598-1486. Fax: 931-598-1702. p. 2265

Dykes, Christopher, Instrul Serv Librn, University of Houston, The O'Quinn Law Library, 12 Law Library, Houston, TX, 77204-6054. Tel: 713-743-2300. Fax: 713-743-2296. p. 2343

Dyki, Janet, Dir, Elk Township Library, 29 E Lapeer St, Peck, MI, 48466. Tel: 810-378-5409. Fax: 810-378-5016. p. 1217

Dyki, Judy, Dir, Libr Serv, Cranbrook Academy of Art Library, 39221 Woodward Ave, Bloomfield Hills, MI, 48304. Tel: 248-645-3364. Fax: 248-645-3464. p. 1158

Dykshoorn, Sharon Kay, Libr Serv Dir, Western Iowa Technical Community College, 4647 Stone Ave, Sioux City, IA, 51106. Tel: 712-274-8733, Ext 1239. Fax: 712-274-6423. p. 844

Dykstra, Fran, Asst Dir, Sheldon Public Library, 925 Fourth Ave, Sheldon, IA, 51201-1517. Tel: 712-324-2442. Fax: 712-324-2442. p. 842

Dykstra, Kathy, Ch, Sturgis Public Library, 1040 Second St, Sturgis, SD, 57785-1595. Tel: 605-347-2624. Fax: 605-720-7211. p. 2220

Dykstra, Nadine, Dir, George Public Library, 119 S Main St, George, IA, 51237. Tel: 712-475-3897. p. 818

Dykstra, Russell J, Dir, Theological School of Protestant Reformed Churches Library, 4949 Ivanrest Ave SW, Grandville, MI, 49418-9709. Tel: 616-531-1490. Fax: 616-531-3033. p. 1186

Dykstra, Sharon, Supvr, Ventura County Library, Oak View Library, 555 Mahoney Ave, Oak View, CA, 93022. Tel: 805-649-1523. Fax: 805-649-5591. p. 280

Dylag, Marie, Ch, Plymouth Public Library, 201 N Center St, Plymouth, IN, 46563. Tel: 574-936-2324. Fax: 574-936-7423. p. 773

Dylla, Daniel, Librn, Houston Community College - Northwest College, Katy Campus Library, 1550 Foxlake Dr, Houston, TX, 77084-6029. Tel: 713-718-5747. Fax: 281-492-6075. p. 2338

Dyment, Jeni, Ch, Brighton Public Library, 35 Alice St, Brighton, ON, K0K 1H0, CANADA. Tel: 613-475-2511. p. 2797

Dymond, Janet, Sr Librn, Eastern Correctional Facility Library, PO Box 338, Napanoch, NY, 12458-0338. Tel: 845-647-7400, Ext 4600. Fax: 845-647-7400, Ext 5099. p. 1664

Dynia, Judith, Librn, Cuyahoga Community College, Western Campus Library, 11000 Pleasant Valley Rd, Parma, OH, 44130-5199. Tel: 216-987-5414. Fax: 216-987-5050. p. 1879

Dynneson, Leanne, Circ & Ref, Unicoi County Public Library, 201 Nolichucky Ave, Erwin, TN, 37650-1237. Tel: 423-743-6533. Fax: 423-743-0275. p. 2234

Dysart, Janice, Sci Librn, University of Missouri-Columbia, Elmer Ellis Library, Ellis Library Bldg, Rm 104, Columbia, MO, 65201-5149. Tel: 573-882-1828. Fax: 573-882-8044. p. 1325

Dysart, Jennifer, Libr Dir, Green River Community College, 12401 SE 320th St, Auburn, WA, 98092-3699. Tel: 253-833-9111, 253-924-0180. Fax: 253-288-3436, 253-288-3491. p. 2507

Dyson, Candy, Outreach Serv Librn, Tyler Junior College, 1327 S Baxter St, Tyler, TX, 75701. Tel: 903-510-2308. Fax: 903-510-2639. p. 2393

Dyson, Rick, Ref, Missouri Western State University, 4525 Downs Dr, Saint Joseph, MO, 64507-2294. Tel: 816-271-4368. Fax: 816-271-4574. p. 1352

Dyszlewski, Nicole, Sr Law Librn, Maine State Law & Legislative Reference Library, 43 State House Sta, Augusta, ME, 04333-0043. Tel: 207-287-1600. Fax: 207-287-6467. p. 974

Dziedzina, Christine A, Chief Librn, Metrohealth Medical Center, 2500 MetroHealth Dr, Cleveland, OH, 44101-1998. Tel: 216-778-5623. Fax: 216-778-8242. p. 1880

Dzierba, Judith, Cat/Archives Mgr, Library of Rush University Medical Center, Armour Academic Ctr, 600 S Paulina St, 5th Flr, Chicago, IL, 60612-3874. Tel: 312-942-2731. Fax: 312-942-3143. p. 617

Dzierzak, Edward, Dir, Health Sci Libr, Marshall University Libraries, One John Marshall Dr, Huntington, WV, 25755-2060. Tel: 304-691-1753. Fax: 304-691-1766. p. 2561

Dzierzak, Edward, Dir, Marshall University Libraries, Joan C Edwards School of Medicine Health Science Libraries, 1600 Medical Center Dr, Ste 2400, Huntington, WV, 25701-3655. Tel: 304-691-1750. Fax: 304-691-1766. p. 2562

Dzierzbicki, Monica, Youth Serv, Indian Prairie Public Library District, 401 Plainfield Rd, Darien, IL, 60561-4207. Tel: 630-887-8760. Fax: 630-887-8801. p. 633

Dzuba, Tyler, Physics-Optics-Astronomy Librn, University of Rochester, Physics-Optics-Astronomy Library - River Campus, 374 Bausch & Lomb Hall, Rochester, NY, 14627-0171. Tel: 585-275-7659. Fax: 585-273-5321. p. 1733

Dzurko, Ann, Librn, Samuel A Weiss Community Library, 440 Monongahela Ave, Glassport, PA, 15045-1474. Tel: 412-672-7400. p. 2061

Eade, Linda S, Librn, Yosemite National Park Service, Museum Bldg, PO Box 577, Yosemite, CA, 95389-0577. Tel: 209-372-0280. Fax: 209-372-0255. p. 285

Eadens, Ruth Ann, ILL, Warren County Public Library, 1225 State St, Bowling Green, KY, 42101. Tel: 270-781-4882. Fax: 270-781-7323. p. 907

Eades, Ming-Pei, Doc Delivery, Lockheed Martin Missiles & Fire Control, 1701 W Marshall Dr, Grand Prairie, TX, 75051. Tel: 972-603-7155. Fax: 972-603-0182. p. 2329

Eadie, Jeanne, Dir, Arthur Hufnagel Public Library of Glen Rock, 32 Main St, Glen Rock, PA, 17327. Tel: 717-235-1127. Fax: 717-235-0330. p. 2061

Eads, Sonja R, Dir of Libr Serv, Maysville Community & Technical College, 1755 US Hwy 68, Maysville, KY, 41056. Tel: 606-759-7141, Ext 66126. Fax: 606-759-7176. p. 928

Eagan, Linda, Ch, Lynbrook Public Library, 56 Eldert St, Lynbrook, NY, 11563. Tel: 516-599-8630. Fax: 516-596-1312. p. 1655

Eagans, Allison, Supv Librn, Ch, Murrieta Public Library, Eight Town Sq, Murrieta, CA, 92562. Tel: 951-304-2665. Fax: 951-696-0165. p. 192

Eager, Bob, Circ, Madison County Public Library, 507 W Main St, Richmond, KY, 40475. Tel: 859-623-6704. Fax: 859-623-2023. p. 934

Eager, Margaret, Libr Tech, Nova Scotia Community College, 226 Reeves St, Port Hawkesbury, NS, B9A 2W2, CANADA. Tel: 902-625-2380, 902-625-4364. Fax: 902-625-0193. p. 2784

Eagles, Shannon, Tech Serv Librn, Western State College, 600 N Adams St, Gunnison, CO, 81231. Tel: 970-943-2399. Fax: 970-943-2042. p. 312

Eaglesham, Carolyn, ILL, Edward U Demmer Memorial Library, 6961 W School St, Three Lakes, WI, 54562. Tel: 715-546-3391. Fax: 715-546-2930. p. 2642

Eahr, Joan, Coordr, Ser, Ref, California Institute of Integral Studies, 1453 Mission St, 2nd Flr, San Francisco, CA, 94103. Tel: 415-575-6182. Fax: 415-575-1264. p. 241

Eakes, Sara G, Dir, Libr & Res Serv, Nixon Peabody LLP, 401 Ninth St NW, Ste 900, Washington, DC, 20004. Tel: 202-585-8000, Ext 8320. Fax: 202-585-8080. p. 411

Eales, Barbara, Webmaster, Ventura County Library, 5600 Everglades St, Ste A, Ventura, CA, 93003. Tel: 805-218-5360. Fax: 805-677-7173. p. 279

Ealey, Brenda, Adminr, Southeast Nebraska Library System, 5730 R St, Ste C-1, Lincoln, NE, 68505. Tel: 402-467-6188. Fax: 402-467-6196. p. 2948

Eames, Barbara, Info Spec, National Economic Research Associates, Inc Library, 1255 23rd St NW, Ste 600, Washington, DC, 20037. Tel: 202-466-3510. Fax: 202-466-9285. p. 409

Eames, Barbara, Sr Assoc, Info Res N Am, National Economic Research Associates, Inc, 360 Hamilton Ave, 10th Flr, White Plains, NY, 10601. Tel: 202-466-9271. Fax: 914-448-4040. p. 1768

Eames, Brenda, Librn, TIRR Memorial Hermann, 1333 Moursund Ave, Houston, TX, 77030. Tel: 713-797-5947. Fax: 713-797-7549. p. 2343

Eames, Cathy, Head Librn, Children's Hospital of Michigan, Medical Library, 3901 Beaubien Blvd, 1st Flr, Detroit, MI, 48201. Tel: 313-745-0252, 313-745-5322. p. 1169

Eames, Dave, Br Mgr, Montgomery County Memorial Library System, R B Tullis Branch, 21569 US Hwy 59, New Caney, TX, 77357. Tel: 281-577-8968. Fax: 281-577-8992. p. 2301

Eames, Nancy, Youth Serv Coordr, Toledo-Lucas County Public Library, 325 N Michigan St, Toledo, OH, 43604-6614. Tel: 419-259-5207. Fax: 419-255-1334. p. 1939

Eandi, Eileen, Assoc Dir, Educ & Res Serv, University of Southern California Libraries, Norris Medical Library, 2003 Zonal Ave, Los Angeles, CA, 90089-9130. Tel: 323-442-1133. Fax: 323-221-1235. p. 179

Eannace, Paula J, Sr Librn, New York Supreme Court, 235 Elizabeth St, Utica, NY, 13501. Tel: 315-798-5703. Fax: 315-798-6470. p. 1759

Eannel, Lois, Asst Dir, Youth Serv, Palm Harbor Library, 2330 Nebraska Ave, Palm Harbor, FL, 34683. Tel: 727-784-3332. Fax: 727-785-6534. p. 480

Eannel, Lois, Ch, Palm Harbor Library, 2330 Nebraska Ave, Palm Harbor, FL, 34683. Tel: 727-784-3332. Fax: 727-785-6534. p. 480

Eareckson, Christine, Head, ILL, Talbot County Free Library, 100 W Dover St, Easton, MD, 21601-2620. Tel: 410-822-1626. Fax: 410-820-8217. p. 1027

Earel, Anne, Ref, Augustana College Library, 3435 9 1/2 Ave, Rock Island, IL, 61201-2296. Tel: 309-794-7266. Fax: 309-794-7640. p. 696

Earhart, Joyce, Regional Librn, Lord Fairfax Community College, 173 Skirmisher Lane, Middletown, VA, 22645-1745. Tel: 540-868-7157. Fax: 540-868-7171. p. 2479

Earl, Gary, Circ Supvr, Lake County Library System, Cooper Memorial Library, 2525 Oakley Seaver Dr, Clermont, FL, 34711. Tel: 352-536-2262. Fax: 352-536-2259. p. 500

Earl, Larry, Exec Dir, Mayme A Clayton Library & Museum, 4130 Overland Ave, Culver City, CA, 90230-3734. Tel: 310-202-1647. Fax: 310-202-1617. p. 138

Earl, Lisa, Curator, Johnson County Historical Society, 302 N Main St, Warrensburg, MO, 64093. Tel: 660-747-6480. p. 1371

Earl, Martha, Bibliog Instr, Coll Develop, Ref, University of Tennessee Graduate School of Medicine, 1924 Alcoa Hwy, Box U-111, Knoxville, TN, 37920. Tel: 865-305-6616. Fax: 865-305-9527. p. 2243

Earl, Susan, Dir, The Brentwood Library, 8109 Concord Rd, Brentwood, TN, 37027. Tel: 615-371-0090, Ext 8010. Fax: 615-371-2238. p. 2225

Earle, Letti, Librn, United States Navy, MWR Library, 2003 D St, Bldg 318, El Centro, CA, 92243. Tel: 760-339-2470. Fax: 760-339-2470. p. 146

Earles, Jennie, Librn, Trapper Creek Public Library, Mile 115 Parks Hwy, Trapper Creek, AK, 99683. Tel: 907-733-1546. Fax: 907-733-1546. p. 54

Earles, Laura, Head of Libr, University of Arizona, Center for Creative Photography, 1030 N Olive Rd, Tucson, AZ, 85721-0001. Tel: 520-621-7968. Fax: 520-621-9444. p. 89

Earles, Phyllis, Univ Archivist, Prairie View A&M University, PO Box 519, MS 1040, Prairie View, TX, 77446-0519. Tel: 936-261-1516. Fax: 936-261-1539. p. 2372

Earley, Melanie, Ad, Tecumseh District Library, 215 N Ottawa St, Tecumseh, MI, 49286-1564. Tel: 517-423-2238. Fax: 517-423-5519. p. 1230

Earley, Susan, Librn, Chamberlain, Hrdlicka, White, Williams & Martin, 1200 Smith St, Ste 1400, Houston, TX, 77002. Tel: 713-658-2547. Fax: 713-658-2553. p. 2334

Earll, Mary Beth, ILL, Gannon University, 109 University Sq, Erie, PA, 16541. Tel: 814-871-7557. Fax: 814-871-5666. p. 2055

Earls, Stephanie, Librn, Utah Department of Natural Resources Library, 1594 W North Temple, Salt Lake City, UT, 84114. Tel: 801-537-3333. Fax: 801-537-3400. p. 2415

Early, Charles, Ref Librn, NASA, Library, Bldg 21, Code 272, Greenbelt, MD, 20771. Tel: 301-286-0887. Fax: 301-286-1755. p. 1030

Early, Nancy, Br Mgr, Caledon Public Library, Alton Branch, 35 Station Rd, Alton, ON, L7K 0E2, CANADA. Tel: 519-941-5480. p. 2795

Early, Wendy, Librn, Research Planning Inc Library, 1121 Park St, Columbia, SC, 29201-3137. Tel: 803-256-7322. Fax: 803-254-6445. p. 2188

Earlywine, Shantelle, Ch, Malvern Public Library, 502 Main St, Malvern, IA, 51551. Tel: 712-624-8554. Fax: 712-624-8245. p. 829

Earman, Cynthia D, Tech Serv, United States Army, Bldg 417, Rm 120, 239 Sheridan Ave, Fort Myer, VA, 22211. Tel: 703-696-3555. Fax: 703-696-8587. p. 2465

Earnest, Greta K, Acq, Asst Dir, Coll Develop Officer, Fashion Institute of Technology-SUNY, Seventh Ave at 27th St, New York, NY, 10001-5992. Tel: 212-217-4366. Fax: 212-217-4371. p. 1678

Earnest, Janice Yates, Dir, Autauga-Prattville Public Library, 254 Doster St, Prattville, AL, 36067-3933. Tel: 334-365-3396. Fax: 334-365-3397. p. 34

Earnest, Kim, Dir, Mediapolis Public Library, 128 N Orchard St, Mediapolis, IA, 52637. Tel: 319-394-3895. Fax: 319-394-3916. p. 831

Earnest, Ola May, Pres, Linn County Museum & Genealogy Library, Dunlap Park, 307 E Park St, Pleasanton, KS, 66075. Tel: 913-352-8739. Fax: 913-352-8739. p. 890

Earp, Christy, Librn, Wilkes Community College, 1328 Collegiate Dr, Wilkesboro, NC, 28697. Tel: 336-838-6117. Fax: 336-838-6515. p. 1830

Earwood, Mary, Librn, River Oaks Public Library, 4900 River Oaks Blvd, River Oaks, TX, 76114. Tel: 817-624-7344. Fax: 817-624-6214. p. 2376

Eash, Lynnell, Br Mgr, Branch District Library, Bronson Branch, 207 N Matteson St, Bronson, MI, 49028-1308. Tel: 517-369-3785. Fax: 517-369-3785. p. 1164

Easley, Margaret, Circ, Polk County Public Library, Saluda Branch, 44 W Main St, Saluda, NC, 28773-0398. Tel: 828-749-2117. Fax: 828-749-2118. p. 1785

Eason, Catherine, Assoc Librn, US Courts Library, Byron Rogers Courthouse, 1929 Stout St, Rm 430, Denver, CO, 80294. Tel: 303-844-3591. Fax: 303-844-5958. p. 303

Eason, Jenny, Ref Librn, Flagler College, 44 Sevilla St, Saint Augustine, FL, 32084-4302. Tel: 904-819-6206. Fax: 904-823-8511. p. 486

Eason, Susan, Dir, Catholic Archives of Texas, 1600 N Congress, Austin, TX, 78711. Tel: 512-476-6296. Fax: 512-476-3715. p. 2280

East, Karen, Dir, Michigan Legislative Service Bureau, Boji Tower, 4th Flr, Lansing, MI, 48909. Tel: 517-373-5200. Fax: 517-373-0171. p. 1202

East, Karen, Libr Dir, Beldon Noble Memorial Library, 2759 Essex Rd, Essex, NY, 12936. Tel: 518-963-8079. Fax: 518-963-8079. p. 1621

Easter, Mandy, Librn, State Library of Iowa, State Capitol Bldg, 1007 E Grand Ave, Des Moines, IA, 50319. Tel: 515-281-5124. Fax: 515-281-6515. p. 810

Easterbrook, David, Curator, Africana, Northwestern University Library, 1970 Campus Dr, Evanston, IL, 60208-2300. Tel: 847-491-7658. p. 644

Easterby-Gannett, Sharon, Assoc Dir, Christiana Hospital Library, Christiana Hospital, 4755 Ogletown Stanton Rd, Newark, DE, 19718-0002. Tel: 302-733-1164. Fax: 302-733-1365. p. 385

Easterday, Barb, Coordr, Acq, Bluffton University, One University Dr, Bluffton, OH, 45817-2104. Tel: 419-358-3271. Fax: 419-358-3384. p. 1860

Easterday, Victoria, Librn, Humboldt County Library, McDermitt Branch, Hwy 95, McDermitt, NV, 89421. Tel: 775-532-8014. Fax: 775-532-8018. p. 1435

Easterling, Michelle, Br Mgr, Polkville Public Library, 6670 Hwy 13, Morton, MS, 39117. Tel: 601-537-3115. Fax: 601-537-3115. p. 1309

Easterly, Jane, Asst Dir, Galesburg Public Library, 40 E Simmons St, Galesburg, IL, 61401-4591. Tel: 309-343-6118. Fax: 309-343-4877. p. 648

Easterwood, Deanne, Asst Librn, Southeastern Bible College Library, 2545 Valleydale Rd, Birmingham, AL, 35244. Tel: 205-970-9233. Fax: 205-970-9207. p. 9

Eastham, Rosanne, Dir, Tyler County Public Library, Main & Broad Sts, Middlebourne, WV, 26149. Tel: 304-758-4304. Fax: 304-758-4304. p. 2565

Eastin, Susan, Librn, Department of Human Services-Youth Corrections, 2200 O St, Greeley, CO, 80631-9503. Tel: 970-304-6277. Fax: 970-304-6274. p. 311

Eastland, Judy, Dir, Libr & Info Serv, Michigan Molecular Institute, 1910 W St Andrews Rd, Midland, MI, 48640. Tel: 989-832-5555, Ext 552. Fax: 989-832-5560. p. 1208

Eastman, Brittany, Youth Serv Librn, Media-Upper Providence Free Library, One E Front St, Media, PA, 19063. Tel: 610-566-1918. Fax: 610-566-9056. p. 2087

Eastman, Cynthia, Librn, Kennedy-Jenks Consultants, Inc Library, 303 Second St, Ste 300 South, San Francisco, CA, 94107. Tel: 415-243-2150. Fax: 415-896-0999. p. 243

Eastman, Donna, Admin Serv, Roseland Free Public Library, 20 Roseland Ave, Roseland, NJ, 07068-1235. Tel: 973-226-8636. Fax: 973-226-6429. p. 1527

Easton, Bill, Instruction & Ref Librn, Monterey Peninsula College Library, 980 Fremont Blvd, Monterey, CA, 93940-4704. Tel: 831-645-1382. Fax: 831-645-1308. p. 190

Easton, Dale, Mgr, New Bedford Free Public Library, Wilks, 1911 Acushnet Ave, New Bedford, MA, 02746. Tel: 508-991-6214. Fax: 508-998-6039. p. 1108

Eastridge, Todd, Circ, Washington County Public Library, 205 Oak Hill St, Abingdon, VA, 24210. Tel: 276-676-6222. Fax: 276-676-6235. p. 2443

Eastwood, Cynthia, ILL, East Baton Rouge Parish Library, 7711 Goodwood Blvd, Baton Rouge, LA, 70806-7625. Tel: 225-231-3700. Fax: 225-231-3736. p. 942

Eastwood, Justin, Acq Asst, University of Tennessee, Knoxville, Special Collections, 121 Hodges Library, 1015 Volunteer Blvd, Knoxville, TN, 37996-1000. Tel: 865-974-4480. p. 2244

Eastwood, Marylin, Br Head, Somerville Public Library, East, 115 Broadway, Somerville, MA, 02145. Tel: 617-623-5000, Ext 2970. Fax: 617-623-9403. p. 1124

Eatherton, Linda, Librn, Montgomery City Public Library, 224 N Allen St, Montgomery City, MO, 63361. Tel: 573-564-8022. Fax: 573-564-6159. p. 1347

Eaton, Amy J, Libr Mgr, Perkins Coie Library, 1201 Third Ave, Ste 4900, Seattle, WA, 98101. Tel: 206-359-8444. Fax: 206-359-9444. p. 2529

Eaton, Betsy, Librn, Converse Free Library, 38 Union St, Lyme, NH, 03768-9702. Tel: 603-795-4622. Fax: 603-795-9346. p. 1454

Eaton, Brenda, Librn, Wyandotte County Law Library, Court House, 710 N Seventh St, Ste 500, Kansas City, KS, 66101-3999. Tel: 913-573-2899. Fax: 913-573-2892. p. 876

Eaton, Denny, Per, Johnson Bible College, 7900 Johnson Dr, Knoxville, TN, 37998. Tel: 865-251-2277. Fax: 865-251-2278. p. 2241

Eaton, Diane, Ch, Townsend Public Library, 276 Main St, Townsend, MA, 01469-1513. Tel: 978-597-1714. Fax: 978-597-2779. p. 1131

Eaton, E Gale, Dr, Dir, Prof, University of Rhode Island, Rodman Hall, 94 W Alumni Ave, Ste 2, Kingston, RI, 02881-0815. Tel: 401-874-4651. Fax: 401-874-4964. p. 2973

Eaton, J, Law Librn, University of Manitoba Libraries, E K Williams Law Library, 401 Robson Hall, 224 Dysart Rd, Winnipeg, MB, R3T 2N2, CANADA. Tel: 204-474-9996. Fax: 204-474-7582. p. 2759

Eaton, Joan, Libr Asst, Burnet County Library System, Oakalla Public Library, 29011 FM 963, Oakalla, TX, 78608. Tel: 512-556-9085. Fax: 512-556-9085. p. 2294

Eaton, Kathleen, Chief Librn, Confederation Centre Public Library, Queen & Richmond St, Charlottetown, PE, C1A 8G8, CANADA. Tel: 902-368-4654. Fax: 902-368-4652. p. 2875

Eaton, Kathleen, Prov Librn, Prince Edward Island Public Library Service, 89 Red Head Rd, Morell, PE, C0A 1S0, CANADA. Tel: 902-961-7316. Fax: 902-961-7322. p. 2876

Eaton, Linda, Dir, Kirchner-French Memorial Library, 101 Main St, Peterson, IA, 51047. Tel: 712-295-6705. Fax: 712-295-6705. p. 838

Eaton, Linda, Librn, Mankato City Library, 210 N Commercial St, Mankato, KS, 66956-2006. Tel: 785-378-3885. p. 882

Eaton, Mary Candace, Dir, Little Traverse History Museum Library, 100 Depot Ct, Petoskey, MI, 49770. Tel: 231-347-2620. Fax: 231-347-2875. p. 1217

Eaton, Nancy, Commun Serv, Webmaster, Duluth Public Library, 520 W Superior St, Duluth, MN, 55802. Tel: 218-730-4236. Fax: 218-723-3815, 218-723-3822. p. 1247

Eaton, Patricia, Ch, Kellogg Free Library, 5681 Telephone Rd Exten, Cincinnatus, NY, 13040. Tel: 607-863-4300. Fax: 607-863-3430. p. 1606

Eaton, Robert, AV, Albany Law School, 80 New Scotland Ave, Albany, NY, 12208. Tel: 518-445-2340. Fax: 518-472-5842. p. 1568

Eaton, Shirley, Circ, Freed-Hardeman University, 158 E Main St, Henderson, TN, 38340-2399. Tel: 731-989-6067. Fax: 731-989-6065. p. 2237

Ebbers, Laurie, Ref, Nobles County Library, 407 12th St, Worthington, MN, 56187. Tel: 507-372-2981. Fax: 507-372-2982. p. 1291

Ebbers, Susan K, Dir, United Theological Seminary of the Twin Cities, 3000 Fifth St NW, New Brighton, MN, 55112-2598. Tel: 651-255-6142. Fax: 651-633-4315. p. 1267

Ebbett, Gwendolyn, Dean of Libr, University of Windsor, 401 Sunset Ave, Windsor, ON, N9B 3P4, CANADA. Tel: 519-253-3000, Ext 3161. p. 2871

Ebbinghouse, Carol David, Head Librn, California Second District Court of Appeals, 300 S Spring St, Rm 3547, Los Angeles, CA, 90013. Tel: 213-830-7241. Fax: 213-897-2429. p. 169

Ebbs, Corinne, Head, Res, Westfield State University, 577 Western Ave, Westfield, MA, 01085-2580. Tel: 413-572-5251. Fax: 413-572-5520. p. 1138

Ebel, John, Genealogy Serv, Ref Serv, Jamestown Public Library, 200 W Main St, Jamestown, NC, 27282. Tel: 336-454-4815. Fax: 336-454-0630. p. 1803

Ebel-Northup, Cheryl, Dir, Wyoming Free Circulating Library, 114 S Academy St, Wyoming, NY, 14591. Tel: 585-495-6840. Fax: 585-495-6840. p. 1771

Eberhardt, Emily, Asst Dir, Oakland City University, 605 W Columbia St, Oakland City, IN, 47660. Tel: 812-749-1268. Fax: 812-749-1414. p. 771

Eberhardt, Herman, Curator, National Archives & Records Administration, 4079 Albany Post Rd, Hyde Park, NY, 12538. Tel: 845-486-7770. Fax: 845-486-1147. p. 1640

Eberhardt, Lewis, Librn, OSHA-US Department of Labor, 2020 S Arlington Heights Rd, Arlington Heights, IL, 60005. Tel: 847-759-7797. Fax: 847-759-7748. p. 590

Eberhart, George M, Librn, J Allen Hynek Center for UFO Studies, PO Box 31335, Chicago, IL, 60631. Tel: 773-271-3611. p. 614

Eberhart, Kristin, YA Librn, East Central Georgia Regional Library, 902 Greene St, Augusta, GA, 30901. Tel: 706-821-2600. Fax: 706-724-6762. p. 519

Eberle, Lucille, Librn, Parkland Regional Library, Lake Lenore Branch, PO Box 34, Lake Lenore, SK, S0K 2J0, CANADA. Tel: 306-368-2500. p. 2932

Eberle, Richard, Mgr, Santa Cruz City-County Library System Headquarters, Central, 224 Church St, Santa Cruz, CA, 95060-3873. Tel: 831-427-7706, Ext 7717. Fax: 831-427-7701. p. 264

Eberle, Rita, Cat Librn, Springfield Public Library, 225 Fifth St, Springfield, OR, 97477-4697. Tel: 541-726-3766. Fax: 541-726-3747. p. 2020

Eberline, Katherine, Ch, Brookings Public Library, 515 Third St, Brookings, SD, 57006. Tel: 605-692-9407. Fax: 605-692-9386. p. 2210

Eberly, Cheryl, Principal Librn, YA, Santa Ana Public Library, 26 Civic Center Plaza, Santa Ana, CA, 92701-4010. Tel: 714-647-5288. Fax: 714-647-5296. p. 259

Eberly, Terri, Asst Librn, Auld Public Library, 537 N Webster St, Red Cloud, NE, 68970. Tel: 402-746-3352. p. 1417

Ebersole, Margie, Libr Tech, Claysburg Area Public Library, 957 Bedford St, Claysburg, PA, 16625. Tel: 814-239-8647. Fax: 814-239-2782. p. 2045

Ebersole, Noriko, Visual Res, Nelson-Atkins Museum of Art, 4525 Oak St, Kansas City, MO, 64111-1873. Tel: 816-751-1214. Fax: 816-751-0498. p. 1340

Eberst, Brenda, Tech Serv, Hamilton Township Public Library, One Justice Samuel A Alito, Jr Way, Hamilton, NJ, 08619. Tel: 609-581-4060. Fax: 609-581-4067. p. 1490

Ebert, Heather, Mgr, Marion County Law Library, 258 W Center St, Marion, OH, 43302. Tel: 740-223-4170. p. 1914

Ebert, Kathy, Br Mgr, Monroe County Public Library, Helen Wadley Branch, PO Box 1129, Islamorada, FL, 33036-1129. Tel: 305-664-4645. Fax: 305-853-7312. p. 456

Ebert, Lisa, Ad, Cardington-Lincoln Public Library, 128 E Main St, Cardington, OH, 43315. Tel: 419-864-8181. Fax: 419-864-8184. p. 1865

Ebert, Loretta, Res Libr Dir, New York State Library, Cultural Education Center, 222 Madison Ave, Empire State Plaza, Albany, NY, 12230. Tel: 518-473-1189. Fax: 518-474-5786. p. 1570

Ebert, Luce, In Charge, Bibliotheque de la Polyvalente de Thetford Mines, 561 rue St Patrick, Thetford Mines, QC, G6G 5W1, CANADA. Tel: 418-338-7832. Fax: 418-338-7851. p. 2913

Ebert, Nicolle, Coordr, Access Serv, Eureka College, 301 E College Ave, Eureka, IL, 61530-1563. Tel: 309-467-6380. Fax: 309-467-6386. p. 643

Ebertz, Susan J, Dir, Wartburg Theological Seminary, 333 Wartburg Pl, Dubuque, IA, 52003. Tel: 563-589-0267. Fax: 563-589-0333. p. 812

Ebetsch, Sue, Coordr, Illinois State Data Center Cooperative, 607 E Adams St, IL-3, Springfield, IL, 62701. Tel: 217-524-0187, 217-782-1381. Fax: 217-558-5146. p. 705

Eblin, Kristi, Dir, Meigs County District Public Library, 216 W Main, Pomeroy, OH, 45769-1032. Tel: 740-992-5813. Fax: 740-992-6140. p. 1930

Eblin, Kristi, Dir, Meigs County District Public Library, Eastern, 38850 State Rte 7, Reedsville, OH, 45572. Tel: 740-985-3747. Fax: 740-985-3746. p. 1930

Eblin, Kristi, Dir, Meigs County District Public Library, Middleport Branch, 178 S Third St, Middleport, OH, 45760. Tel: 740-992-5713. Fax: 740-992-4207. p. 1930

Eby, Annette, Asst Librn, Southeast Regional Library, Bienfait Branch, 414 Main St, Bienfait, SK, S0C 0M0, CANADA. Tel: 306-388-2995. Fax: 306-388-2883. p. 2929

Eby, Carole, Librn, Bob Jones University, Music, 1700 Wade Hampton Blvd, Greenville, SC, 29614. Tel: 864-242-5100, Ext 2705. Fax: 864-467-9302. p. 2195

Eby, Kathy, Asst Librn, Brescia University, 717 Frederica St, Owensboro, KY, 42301. Tel: 270-686-4213. Fax: 270-686-4266. p. 931

Eccles, Kim, Assoc Dir, Mercer University Atlanta, 3001 Mercer University Dr, Atlanta, GA, 30341. Tel: 678-547-6271. Fax: 678-547-6270. p. 517

Echavarria, Kathy, Youth Serv Librn, Douglas County Public Library, 1625 Library Lane, Minden, NV, 89423-4420. Tel: 775-782-9841. Fax: 775-782-5754. p. 1431

Echeverria, Chelsa, Ref Supvr, Davis County Library, South Branch, 725 S Main St, Bountiful, UT, 84010. Tel: 801-295-8732. p. 2405

Echols, Becky, Librn, Northwest Technical Institute, 709 S Old Missouri Rd, Springdale, AR, 72764. Tel: 479-751-8824, Ext 140. Fax: 479-756-8744. p. 115

Echols, Jeanelle, Libr Tech, NAS Meridian Library, 220 Fuller Rd, Meridian, MS, 39309. Tel: 601-679-2623. Fax: 601-679-5106. p. 1308

Echord, Jess G, Libr Dir, United States Air Force, 23 FSS/FSDL, 3010 Robinson Rd, Bldg 328, Moody AFB, GA, 31699-1594. Tel: 229-257-3018, 229-257-3539. Fax: 229-257-4119. p. 545

Echtenkamp, Kristin, Librn, Northern State University, 1200 S Jay St, Aberdeen, SD, 57401-7198. Tel: 605-626-2645. Fax: 605-626-2473. p. 2209

Eck, Michael, Dir, Mount Holly Public Library, 307 High St, Mount Holly, NJ, 08060. Tel: 609-267-7111. p. 1506

Eck, Roberta, Asst Librn, Olney Public Library, 400 W Main St, Olney, IL, 62450. Tel: 618-392-3711. Fax: 618-392-3139. p. 685

Eck, Shannon, Br Mgr, Public Library of Cincinnati & Hamilton County, Monfort Heights, 3825 W Fork Rd, Cincinnati, OH, 45247. Tel: 513-369-4472. Fax: 513-369-4473. p. 1872

Eckard, April, Librn, Rudd Public Library, 308 Chickasaw St, Rudd, IA, 50471. Tel: 641-395-2385. Fax: 641-395-2385. p. 841

Eckart, Cory, Mgr, Youth Serv, Octavia Fellin Public Library, 115 W Hill Ave, Gallup, NM, 87301. Tel: 505-726-6120. Fax: 505-863-9350. p. 1556

Eckart, Rita, Librn, Arkansas River Valley Regional Library System, Boyd T & Mollie Gattis-Logan County Library, 100 E Academy, Paris, AR, 72855-4432. Tel: 479-963-2371. Fax: 479-963-9243. p. 97

Eckart, Vi, Libr Dir, Harrison County Public Library, 105 N Capitol Ave, Corydon, IN, 47112. Tel: 812-738-5407. Fax: 812-738-5408. p. 734

Eckelbarger, Krys, Asst Librn, Roann Paw Paw Township Public Library, 240 S Chippewa Rd, Roann, IN, 46974. Tel: 765-833-5231. Fax: 765-833-5231. p. 775

Eckenrod, J Victoria, Dir, Galion Public Library Association, 123 N Market St, Galion, OH, 44833. Tel: 419-468-3203. Fax: 419-468-7298. p. 1901

Eckerle, Mary Theresa, Dir, Marion Public Library, 600 S Washington St, Marion, IN, 46953-1992. Tel: 765-668-2900. Fax: 765-668-2911. p. 763

Eckerman, Nancy L, Spec Coll Librn, Indiana University, Ruth Lilly Medical Library, 975 W Walnut St, IB 100, Indianapolis, IN, 46202-5121. Tel: 317-274-2076. Fax: 317-278-2349. p. 752

Eckert, Brent, Tech Serv Librn, Rock Valley College Library, Educational Resources Center, 3301 N Mulford Rd, Rockford, IL, 61114. Tel: 815-921-4604. Fax: 815-921-4629. p. 697

Eckert, Dan, Librn, Holy Family Memorial, 2300 Western Ave, Manitowoc, WI, 54220-3712. Tel: 920-684-2260. Fax: 920-684-2009. p. 2612

Eckert, Daniel, Head, Electronic Res & ILL, Western New England University, 1215 Wilbraham Rd, Springfield, MA, 01119. Tel: 413-782-1535. Fax: 413-796-2011. p. 1128

Eckert, David, Ch, Camden County Library System, 203 Laurel Rd, Voorhees, NJ, 08043. Tel: 856-772-1636, Ext 3360. Fax: 856-772-6105. p. 1538

Eckert, Mary, Dir, Millstadt Library, 115 W Laurel St, Millstadt, IL, 62260. Tel: 618-476-1887. Fax: 618-476-1887. p. 674

Eckert, Nancy, Ch, Alexander Mitchell Public Library, 519 S Kline St, Aberdeen, SD, 57401-4495. Tel: 605-626-7097. Fax: 605-626-3506. p. 2209

Eckert, Sharon, Dir of Tech Serv, University of New England Libraries, 11 Hills Beach Rd, Biddeford, ME, 04005. Tel: 207-602-2364. Fax: 207-602-5922. p. 978

Eckert, Tim, Archivist, Washington State Office of Secretary of State, 1129 Washington St SE, Olympia, WA, 98504-2283. Tel: 509-963-2136. Fax: 509-963-1753. p. 2523

Eckert, Vikki, Br Mgr, Mansfield-Richland County Public Library, Butler Branch, 21 Elm St, Butler, OH, 44822. Tel: 419-883-2220. Fax: 419-883-2220. p. 1912

Eckhardt, Allison, Mgr, Outreach Serv, Springfield-Greene County Library District, Outreach Services, 4653 S Campbell, Springfield, MO, 65810-8113. Tel: 417-883-5366. Fax: 417-889-2547. p. 1368

Eckhardt, Jeanne, Librn, Worden Public Library District, 111 E Wall St, Worden, IL, 62097. Tel: 618-459-7171. p. 721

Eckhardt, Vicki, Asst Librn, Texas Lutheran University, 1000 W Court St, Seguin, TX, 78155-5978. Tel: 830-372-8100. Fax: 830-372-8156. p. 2386

Eckhoff, Cherie, Asst Librn, Reinbeck Public Library, 501 Clark St, Reinbeck, IA, 50669. Tel: 319-788-2652. Fax: 319-788-2826. p. 840

Eckl, Cristina, Dir, Ref Serv, Wildman, Harrold, Allen & Dixon LLP, 225 W Wacker Dr, Ste 3000, Chicago, IL, 60606. Tel: 312-201-2383. Fax: 312-201-2555. p. 628

Eckley, Laura, Libr Dir, Larchmont Public Library, 121 Larchmont Ave, Larchmont, NY, 10538. Tel: 914-834-2281. p. 1651

Ecklund, Betty, Librn, Margaret Shontz Memorial Library, 145 Second St, Conneaut Lake, PA, 16316-5117. Tel: 814-382-6666. Fax: 814-382-6666. p. 2047

Eckman, Catherine, Pub Serv, Midlands Technical College Library, 1260 Lexington Dr, West Columbia, SC, 29170-2176. Tel: 803-822-3537. Fax: 803-822-3670. p. 2207

Eckman, Chuck, Univ Librn, Simon Fraser University Library, 8888 University Dr, Burnaby, BC, V5A 1S6, CANADA. Tel: 778-782-3265. Fax: 778-782-3023. p. 2725

Eckman, Lisa, Cent Libr & Ext Serv Mgr, Fresno County Public Library, 2420 Mariposa St, Fresno, CA, 93721-2285. Tel: 559-488-3205. p. 151

Eckman, Mary Ellen, Circ, Rider University, 2083 Lawrenceville Rd, Lawrenceville, NJ, 08648-3099. Tel: 609-896-5111. Fax: 609-896-8029. p. 1494

Eckman, Terrance, Librn, Fresno County Public Library, Leo Politi Branch, 5771 N First St, Fresno, CA, 93710-6269. Tel: 559-431-6450. p. 152

Economos, Lucia, Circ, Glenside Public Library District, 25 E Fullerton Ave, Glendale Heights, IL, 60139-2697. Tel: 630-260-1550. Fax: 630-260-1433. p. 650

Ecret, Deborah, Coll Develop, Pennsville Public Library, 190 S Broadway, Pennsville, NJ, 08070. Tel: 856-678-5473. Fax: 856-678-8121. p. 1519

Ecsedy, Brenda, Dir, Acad Res, Wheelock College Library, 132 The Riverway, Boston, MA, 02215-4815. Tel: 617-879-2225. Fax: 617-879-2408. p. 1068

Eddington, Wanda, Librn, Greater West Central Public Library District, 202 Center St, Augusta, IL, 62311. Tel: 217-392-2211. Fax: 217-392-2211. p. 591

Edds, Carolyn, Res, Times Publishing Co, 490 First Ave S, Saint Petersburg, FL, 33701-4223. Tel: 727-893-8111. Fax: 727-893-8107. p. 488

Eddy, Daniel, Jr, Chairperson, Colorado River Indian Tribes Public Library-Archives, Second Ave & Mohave Rd, Rte 1, Box 23-B, Parker, AZ, 85344. Tel: 928-669-9211. Fax: 928-669-8262. p. 70

Eddy, Diane, Managing Librn, Hawaii State Public Library System, Hawaii State Library, 478 S King St, Honolulu, HI, 96813. Tel: 808-586-3500. Fax: 808-586-3943. p. 562

Eddy, Heather, Br Mgr, Kern County Library, Northeast Branch, 3725 Columbus St, Bakersfield, CA, 93306-2719. Tel: 661-871-9017. p. 124

Eddy, Heather, Br Mgr, Kern County Library, Eleanor N Wilson Branch, 1901 Wilson Rd, Bakersfield, CA, 93304-5612. Tel: 661-834-4044. p. 125

Eddy, Paul, Libr Adminr, Beaumont Public Library System, 801 Pearl St, Beaumont, TX, 77701. Tel: 409-981-5912. Fax: 409-838-6838. p. 2287

Eddy, Roberta, Librn, NASA, Tech Lib E-105, Wallops Island, VA, 23337. Tel: 757-824-1065. Fax: 757-824-1716. p. 2500

Edel, Deborah, Coordr, Lesbian Herstory Archives, 484 14th St, Brooklyn, NY, 11215-5702. Tel: 718-768-3953. Fax: 718-768-4663. p. 1593

Edelen, Edna, Libr Tech, Colorado Department of Corrections, Sterling Correctional Facility Library-East Side, 12101 Hwy 61, Sterling, CO, 80751. Tel: 970-521-3827. Fax: 970-521-8905. p. 323

Edelen, Joe, Librn, License/Contract Negotiator, University of South Dakota, 414 E Clark St, Vermillion, SD, 57069. Tel: 605-677-5371. Fax: 605-677-6834. p. 2220

Edelman, Lisa, Ch, Community Library Association, 415 Spruce Ave N, Ketchum, ID, 83340. Tel: 208-726-3493, Ext 116. p. 577

Eden, Brad, Assoc Univ Librn, Tech Serv, University of California, Santa Barbara, Santa Barbara, CA, 93106-9010. Tel: 805-893-4261. Fax: 805-893-7010. p. 261

Eden, Bradford Lee, PhD, Dean of Libr Serv, Valparaiso University, 1410 Chapel Dr, Valparaiso, IN, 46383-6493. Tel: 219-464-5500. p. 783

Eden, Veronica, Libr Mgr, Washington County Cooperative Library Services, West Slope Community Library, 3678 SW 78th Ave, Portland, OR, 97225-9019. Tel: 503-292-6416. Fax: 503-292-6932. p. 2001

Edens, John, Univ Archivist, University at Buffalo Libraries-State University of New York, 420 Capen Hall, Buffalo, NY, 14260-1670. Tel: 716-645-2916. Fax: 716-645-3714. p. 1599

Edens, Wes, Electronic Res, Thunderbird School of Global Management, 15249 N 59th Ave, Glendale, AZ, 85306-6001. Tel: 602-978-7897. Fax: 602-978-7762. p. 64

Eder, Jonathon, Lending & Ref Serv Adminr, The Mary Baker Eddy Library, Lending & Reference Services, 200 Massachusetts Ave, P02-10, Boston, MA, 02115-3017. Tel: 617-450-7131. p. 1060

Eder, Sonya, Librn, Fraser Milner Casgrain Library, One Place Ville Marie, 39th Flr, Montreal, QC, H3B 4M7, CANADA. Tel: 514-878-8890. Fax: 514-866-2241. p. 2895

Eder, Suzanne Kahn, Educ Dir, Dorothy Fish Coastal Resource Library at Wells Reserve, 342 Laudholm Farm Rd, Wells, ME, 04090. Tel: 207-646-1555, Ext 116. Fax: 207-646-2930. p. 1006

Edevold, Karen, Br Librn, Lake Agassiz Regional Library, Bagley Public Library, 21 Main Ave N, Bagley, MN, 56621. Tel: 218-694-6201. Fax: 218-694-6201. p. 1266

Edgar, Bill, Coordr, Libr Sci, Missouri State University, Duane G Meyer Library, 901 S National Ave, Springfield, MO, 65897. Tel: 417-836-4529. Fax: 417-836-4764. p. 2968

Edgar, Christine, Head, Access Serv, University of New Haven, 300 Boston Post Rd, West Haven, CT, 06516. Tel: 203-932-7190. Fax: 203-932-1469. p. 377

Edgar, Connie, Tech Serv, Corban University Library, 5000 Deer Park Dr SE, Salem, OR, 97317-9392. Tel: 503-375-7016. Fax: 503-375-7196. p. 2017

Edgar, Gerald, Bus Mgr, Central Michigan University, Park 407, Mount Pleasant, MI, 48859. Tel: 989-774-6415. Fax: 989-774-2179. p. 1211

Edgar, Jennifer, Librn, New Brunswick Community College, 950 Grandview Ave, Saint John, NB, E2L 3V1, CANADA. Tel: 506-658-6727. Fax: 506-643-2853. p. 2767

Edgar, Karen, Head, Ch, Sumter County Library, 111 N Harvin St, Sumter, SC, 29150. Tel: 803-773-7273. Fax: 803-773-4875. p. 2206

Edgar, Lynne, Ref & Circ Librn, Crowder College, 601 Laclede Ave, Neosho, MO, 64850. Tel: 417-455-5610. Fax: 417-451-4280. p. 1347

Edgar, Nancy, Ch, York Library Region, Fredericton Public Library, 12 Carleton St, Fredericton, NB, E3B 5P4, CANADA. Tel: 506-460-2900. Fax: 506-460-2801. p. 2764

Edgar, Richard, Libr Spec, Humboldt County Law Library, Courthouse, 825 Fourth St, RM 812, Eureka, CA, 95501. Tel: 707-476-2356. Fax: 707-445-6297. p. 147

Edgar, Sonia, Asst Librn, Livingstone College, Hood Theological Seminary Library, 1810 Lutheran Synod Dr, Salisbury, NC, 28144. Tel: 704-636-6779, 704-636-6840. Fax: 704-636-7699. p. 1822

Edgcombe, Frank, Ref Librn, Hampton University, 130 E Tyler St, Hampton, VA, 23668. Tel: 757-727-5371. Fax: 757-727-5952. p. 2468

Edgcombe, Frank, Ref Serv, Hampton University, Nursing, 130 E Tyler St, Hampton, VA, 23668. Tel: 757-727-5371. Fax: 757-727-5952. p. 2468

Edge, Dana, Ref Librn/Bus Liaison, Western Carolina University, 176 Central Dr, Cullowhee, NC, 28723. Tel: 828-227-3413. Fax: 828-227-7015. p. 1786

Edge, Kippy, Ch, San Patricio County Library System, 313 N Rachal St, Rm 226, Sinton, TX, 78387-2663. Tel: 361-364-6199. Fax: 361-364-6117. p. 2387

Edgecomb, Catherine, Br Supvr, Kern County Library, Buttonwillow Branch, 116 Buttonwillow Dr, Buttonwillow, CA, 93206. Tel: 661-764-5337. Fax: 661-764-5337. p. 124

Edgecomb, Catherine, Br Mgr, Kern County Library, Taft Branch, 27 Emmons Park Dr, Taft, CA, 93268-2310. Tel: 661-763-3294. Fax: 661-763-1237. p. 125

Edgerton, Alison, Automation Librn, Tech Serv Dir, Kitchigami Regional Library, 310 Second St N, Pine River, MN, 56474. Tel: 218-587-2171. Fax: 218-587-4855. p. 1270

Edgerton, Curtis, Cat, ILL, Louisburg College, 501 N Main St, Louisburg, NC, 27549-7704. Tel: 919-497-3269. Fax: 919-496-5444. p. 1807

Edgerton, Janet G, Chief Librn, North Carolina State Museum of Natural Sciences, 11 W Jones St, Raleigh, NC, 27601-1029. Tel: 919-733-7450, Ext 208. Fax: 919-715-2356. p. 1816

Edgington, Linda, Dir, Arizona Department of Education Library, 1535 W Jefferson St, Bin 6, Phoenix, AZ, 85007. Tel: 602-542-5416. p. 71

Edick, Mary, Asst Librn, Dublin Public Library, 1114 Main St, Dublin, NH, 03444. Tel: 603-563-8658. Fax: 603-563-8751. p. 1445

Edinger, Elizabeth, Assoc Dir, Catholic University of America, Judge Kathryn J DuFour Law Library, 3600 John McCormack Rd NE, Washington, DC, 20064-8206. Tel: 202-319-5228. Fax: 202-319-5581. p. 396

Edington, Lynne, Grad Col Librn, Marshall University Libraries, One John Marshall Dr, Huntington, WV, 25755-2060. Tel: 304-746-8902. Fax: 304-746-8905. p. 2561

Edington, Lynne, Librn, Marshall University Libraries, Graduate College Library, 100 Angus E Peyton Dr, South Charleston, WV, 25303-1600. Tel: 304-746-8900. Fax: 304-746-8905. p. 2562

Edington, Natalie, Mgr, Public Library Association of Annapolis & Anne Arundel County, Inc, Brooklyn Park, One E 11th Ave, Baltimore, MD, 21225. Tel: 410-222-6260. Fax: 410-222-6263. p. 1010

Edleman, Alexis, Coordr, Circ, Oberlin College Library, Mary M Vial Music Library, Oberlin Conservatory of Music, 77 W College St, Oberlin, OH, 44074-1588. Tel: 440-775-8280. Fax: 440-775-8203. p. 1925

Edlira, Agalliu, Chief Librn, Touro College Libraries, 43 W 23rd St, Fifth Fl, New York, NY, 10010. Tel: 718-252-7800, Ext 217. Fax: 212-627-3696. p. 1701

Edminster, R William, Asst Dir, McHenry Public Library District, 809 N Front St, McHenry, IL, 60050. Tel: 815-385-0036. Fax: 815-385-7085. p. 672

Edminston, Sara, Adult Serv, Outreach/Commun Relations Librn, Adams County Library System, 140 Baltimore St, Gettysburg, PA, 17325-2311. Tel: 717-334-5716. Fax: 717-334-7992. p. 2059

Edmiston, Rebecca, Asst Librn, Castle Rock Public Library, 137 Cowlitz St W, Castle Rock, WA, 98611-8998. Tel: 360-274-6961. Fax: 360-274-4876. p. 2511

Edmond, Marlon, Circ, New York University School of Medicine, Medical Science Bldg 195, 550 First Ave, New York, NY, 10016-6450. Tel: 212-263-5397. Fax: 212-263-6534. p. 1696

Edmond, Veyshon, Br Mgr, Chicago Public Library, Bessie Coleman Branch, 731 E 63rd St, Chicago, IL, 60637. Tel: 312-747-7760. Fax: 312-747-7768. p. 608

Edmonds, Amy L, Music Librn, Ball State University Libraries, Music Collections, Bracken Library BL-106, Muncie, IN, 47306. Tel: 765-285-5065. Fax: 765-285-2644. p. 767

Edmonds, Beth, Dir, Freeport Community Library, Ten Library Dr, Freeport, ME, 04032. Tel: 207-865-3307. Fax: 207-865-1395. p. 986

Edmonds, Ed, Assoc Dean, Dir, University of Notre Dame, 2345 Biolchini Hall of Law, Notre Dame, IN, 46556-4640. Tel: 574-631-5916. Fax: 574-631-6371. p. 771

Edmonds, Keith, Tech Serv, Atlanta VA Medical Center Library, 1670 Clairmont Rd, Decatur, GA, 30033-4004. Tel: 404-321-6111, Ext 7672. Fax: 404-728-7781. p. 529

Edmonds, Michael, Dep Dir, Wisconsin Historical Society Library, 816 State St, Madison, WI, 53706. Tel: 608-264-6534. Fax: 608-264-6520. p. 2610

Edmonds, Randi, Librn, Palliser Regional Library, Avonlea Branch, 201 Main St W, Avonlea, SK, S0H 0C0, CANADA. Tel: 306-868-2076. Fax: 306-868-2221. p. 2918

Edmonds, Susan, Tech Serv, The State Library of Massachusetts, State House, Rm 341, 24 Beacon St, Boston, MA, 02133. Tel: 617-727-7456. Fax: 617-727-5819. p. 1067

Edmonds, Susan, Dir, Milford Town Library, 80 Spruce St, Milford, MA, 01757. Tel: 508-473-0651, 508-473-2145. Fax: 508-473-8651. p. 1105

Edmonds, Susan, Pub Serv Asst, Columbus-Lowndes Public Library, Artesia Public, PO Box 186, Artesia, MS, 39736. Tel: 662-272-5255. Fax: 662-272-5255. p. 1297

Edmondson, Brenda, Br Mgr, Wilson County Public Library, East Wilson Branch, 6000-C Ward Blvd, Wilson, NC, 27893-6488. Tel: 252-237-2627. Fax: 252-237-2627. p. 1831

Edmondson, Debra E, Librn, ADI Ltd Library, 1133 Regent St, Ste 300, Fredericton, NB, E3B 3Z2, CANADA. Tel: 506-454-8000. Fax: 506-459-3954. p. 2762

Edmondson, Kay, ILL, Texas Christian University, 2913 Lowden St, TCU Box 298400, Fort Worth, TX, 76129. Tel: 817-257-7106. Fax: 817-257-7282. p. 2323

Edmonson, Macey, Pub Serv, University of Mississippi, Three Grove Loop, University, MS, 38677. Tel: 662-915-6819. Fax: 662-915-7731. p. 1316

Edmonson, Teffany, Ch, Atlanta-Fulton Public Library System, Southwest Regional Library, 3665 Cascade Rd SW, Atlanta, GA, 30331. Tel: 404-699-6363. Fax: 404-699-6381. p. 512

Edmonson, Christine, Ref Librn, Cleveland Museum of Art, 11150 East Blvd, Cleveland, OH, 44106-1797. Tel: 216-707-2530. Fax: 216-421-0921. p. 1877

Edmonson, James, Curator, Cleveland Health Sciences Library, School of Medicine, Robbins Bldg, 2109 Adelbert Rd, Cleveland, OH, 44106-4914. Tel: 216-368-6391. Fax: 216-368-3008, 216-368-6421. p. 1876

Edmonson, James, Chief Curator, Cleveland Health Sciences Library, Dittrick Medical History Center, 11000 Euclid Ave, Cleveland, OH, 44106-7130. Tel: 216-368-3648. Fax: 216-368-0165. p. 1877

Edmunds, Brock, Access Serv, Asst Librn, Boston University Libraries, Frederic S Pardee Management Library, Boston University School of Management, 595 Commonwealth Ave, Boston, MA, 02215. Tel: 617-353-4311. Fax: 617-353-4307. p. 1058

Edmunds, Eileen, Regional Librn, Malaspina University-College Library, 900 Fifth St, Nanaimo, BC, V9R 5S5, CANADA. Tel: 250-753-3245, Ext 2272. Fax: 250-740-6473. p. 2732

Edmunson-Morton, Tiah K, Archivist, Oregon State University Libraries, University Archives & Special Collections, 121 Valley Library, Corvallis, OR, 97331-4501. Tel: 541-737-7387. Fax: 541-737-3453. p. 1995

Edner, Margaret, Res, Nevada Power Co Library, 6226 W Sahara Ave, Las Vegas, NV, 89151. Tel: 702-367-5055. Fax: 702-227-2023. p. 1430

Edscorn, Steven R, Dir, Memphis Theological Seminary Library, 168 E Parkway S, Memphis, TN, 38104. Tel: 901-458-8232. Fax: 901-452-4051. p. 2250

Edson, Barbara, AV, Midland County Public Library, 301 W Missouri, Midland, TX, 79701. Tel: 432-688-4320. Fax: 432-688-4939. p. 2363

Edson, Cynthia, Assoc Dir, Ref, Richards Memorial Library, 118 N Washington St, North Attleboro, MA, 02760. Tel: 508-699-0122. Fax: 508-699-8075. p. 1112

Edson, John, Dir, Hamburg Public Library, 102 Buffalo St, Hamburg, NY, 14075-5097. Tel: 716-649-4415. Fax: 716-649-4160. p. 1632

Edson, Kimberly, Head, Reader Serv, Rochester Public Library, 101 Second St SE, Rochester, MN, 55904-3776. Tel: 507-328-2325. Fax: 507-328-2384. p. 1273

Edstrom, Jim, Tech Serv Coordr, William Rainey Harper College Library, 1200 W Algonquin Rd, Palatine, IL, 60067. Tel: 847-925-6763. Fax: 847-925-6164. p. 687

Edwards, Alfred, Ref Librn, United States Army, Aviation Center Library, Bldg 212,Fifth Ave & Novosal, Fort Rucker, AL, 36362-5000. Tel: 334-255-3695. Fax: 334-255-1567. p. 18

Edwards, Amy, Coordr, Libr Serv, Meridian Health, Riverview Medical Center, One Riverview Plaza, Red Bank, NJ, 07701. Tel: 732-530-2275. Fax: 732-530-2394. p. 1525

Edwards, Andrea, Dir, Unadilla Public Library, 193 Main, Unadilla, NY, 13849. Tel: 607-369-3131. Fax: 607-369-4500. p. 1757

Edwards, Angela, Dir, Beaver Public Library, 55 W Center St, Beaver, UT, 84713. Tel: 435-438-5274. Fax: 435-438-5826. p. 2403

Edwards, Belinda C, ILL, Troy University Library, 309 Wallace Hall, 501 University Ave, Troy, AL, 36082. Tel: 334-670-3266. Fax: 334-670-3694. p. 37

Edwards, Beth, Librn, Mid-Mississippi Regional Library System, Winston County, 301 W Park St, Louisville, MS, 39339-3018. Tel: 662-773-3212. Fax: 662-773-8434. p. 1306

Edwards, Brenda, Libr Dir, Blue Ridge Township Public Library, 116 E Oliver St, Mansfield, IL, 61854. Tel: 217-489-9033. Fax: 217-489-9320. p. 670

Edwards, Brian, Actg Mgr, Alameda County Library, Newark Branch, 6300 Civic Terrace Ave, Newark, CA, 94560-3795. Tel: 510-795-2627. Fax: 510-797-3019. p. 149

Edwards, Carly, Libr Dir, Mound City Public Library, 207 E Sixth St, Mound City, MO, 64470. Tel: 660-442-5700. Fax: 660-442-3149. p. 1347

Edwards, Carol, Mgr, Ch Serv, Denver Public Library, Pauline Robinson Branch, 5575 E 33rd Ave, Denver, CO, 80207-2027. Tel: 720-865-1307. Fax: 720-865-1470. p. 301

Edwards, Connie, Ch, Brigham City Library, 26 E Forest, Brigham City, UT, 84302-2198. Tel: 435-723-5850. Fax: 435-723-2813. p. 2403

Edwards, Courtney, Pub Serv, Alabama Supreme Court & State Law Library, Heflin-Torbert Judicial Bldg, 300 Dexter Ave, Montgomery, AL, 36104. Tel: 334-229-0578. Fax: 334-229-0543. p. 28

Edwards, Eric, Pub Serv Librn, Ref, Benedictine University Library, Charles E Becker Library, 1500 N Fifth St, Springfield, IL, 62702. Tel: 217-525-1420, Ext 235. Fax: 217-525-2651. p. 666

Edwards, Estella, Dir, Dr Martin Luther King Jr Library, 955 E University Blvd, Melbourne, FL, 32901. Tel: 321-952-4511. Fax: 321-952-4512. p. 463

Edwards, Freda, Dir, Altamont Public Library, 407 Houston St, Altamont, KS, 67330. Tel: 620-784-5530. p. 855

Edwards, Garris, Libr Tech II, Farmville Public Library, 4276 W Church St, Farmville, NC, 27828. Tel: 252-753-3355. Fax: 252-753-2855. p. 1792

Edwards, Gene, Circ Mgr, Chesapeake Public Library, Russell Memorial, 2808 Taylor Rd, Chesapeake, VA, 23321-2210. Tel: 757-410-7023. Fax: 757-410-7029. p. 2456

Edwards, Greg, Dep Dir, Public Library of Cincinnati & Hamilton County, 800 Vine St, Cincinnati, OH, 45202-2009. Tel: 513-369-4418. Fax: 513-369-6993. p. 1871

Edwards, Guy P, Dir, East Islip Public Library, 381 E Main St, East Islip, NY, 11730-2896. Tel: 631-581-9200, Ext 7. Fax: 631-581-2245. p. 1617

Edwards, Inez, Circ, Tech Serv, Texas A&M University Central Texas, 1901 S Clear Creek Rd, Killeen, TX, 76549. Tel: 254-526-1676. Fax: 254-526-1589, 254-526-1993. p. 2350

Edwards, Jackie, Librn, United Steelworkers of America Library, 234 Eglinton Ave E, 8th Flr, Toronto, ON, M4P 1K7, CANADA. Tel: 416-487-1571. Fax: 416-482-5548. p. 2864

Edwards, Jan, Sr Librn, International College Library, 2655 Northbrooke Dr, Naples, FL, 34119. Tel: 239-482-0019, Ext 7811. Fax: 239-598-6250, 239-938-7886. p. 471

Edwards, Jane, Head, Ref, Michigan State University, 115 Law College Bldg, East Lansing, MI, 48824-1300. Tel: 517-432-6867. Fax: 517-432-6861. p. 1175

Edwards, Jean, Actg Dir, Cumberland County Library, 800 E Commerce St, Bridgeton, NJ, 08302-2295. Tel: 856-453-2210. Fax: 856-451-1940. p. 1474

Edwards, Jean-Marc, Assoc Univ Librn, Info Tech & Syst, Concordia University Libraries, 1400 de Maisonneuve Blvd W, LB 209, Montreal, QC, H3G 1M8, CANADA. Tel: 514-848-2424, Ext 7732. Fax: 514-848-2882. p. 2894

Edwards, Jerry, Coordr, Santa Fe Springs City Library, 11700 E Telegraph Rd, Santa Fe Springs, CA, 90670-3600. Tel: 562-868-7738. Fax: 562-929-3680. p. 265

Edwards, Joanne, Access Serv Librn, Johnson State College Library, 337 College Hill, Johnson, VT, 05656. Tel: 802-635-1266. Fax: 802-635-1294. p. 2426

Edwards, John, Dir, Willett Free Library, 45 Ferry Rd, Saunderstown, RI, 02874. Tel: 401-294-2081. Fax: 401-294-2081. p. 2175

Edwards, John D, Assoc Dean, Drake University, Drake Law Library, Opperman Hall, 2615 Carpenter Ave, Des Moines, IA, 50311-4505. Tel: 515-271-2141. Fax: 515-271-2530. p. 809

Edwards, Joyce, Librn, Missouri Department of Corrections, Northeast Correctional Center, 13698 Airport Rd, Bowling Green, MO, 63334. Tel: 573-324-9975. Fax: 573-324-5028. p. 1335

Edwards, Judith, Acq Librn, Cataloger, SS Cyril & Methodius Seminary, 3535 Indian Trail, Orchard Lake, MI, 48324. Tel: 248-706-4211. Fax: 248-683-0526. p. 1215

Edwards, Judy, Libr Asst, Youth Serv, Barry-Lawrence Regional Library, Miller Branch, 112 E Main St, Miller, MO, 65707. Tel: 417-452-3466. Fax: 417-452-3466. p. 1346

Edwards, Kathy, Circ Mgr, Friends University, 2100 W University St, Wichita, KS, 67213-3397. Tel: 316-295-5607. Fax: 316-295-5080. p. 900

Edwards, Kathy, Asst Librn, Clemson University Libraries, Gunnin Architecture Library, 112 Lee Hall, Clemson University, Clemson, SC, 29634-0501. Tel: 864-656-3933. Fax: 864-656-3932. p. 2186

Edwards, Kelli, Circ, Brookhaven Free Library, 273 Beaver Dam Rd, Brookhaven, NY, 11719. Tel: 631-286-1923. Fax: 631-286-0120. p. 1589

Edwards, Kelly, Librn, Baker College of Cass City Library, 6667 Main St, Cass City, MI, 48726-1558. Tel: 989-872-6019. Fax: 989-872-6001. p. 1161

Edwards, Kirsten, Br Mgr, Chattahoochee Valley Libraries, North Columbus Branch, 5689 Armour Rd, Columbus, GA, 31909-4513. Tel: 706-748-2855. Fax: 706-748-2859. p. 526

Edwards, Kitty, Circ, Polk County Public Library, 1289 W Mills St, Columbus, NC, 28722. Tel: 828-894-8721. Fax: 828-894-2761. p. 1785

Edwards, Kristina, Tech Serv, University of Hartford Libraries, 200 Bloomfield Ave, West Hartford, CT, 06117. Tel: 860-768-4264. p. 376

Edwards, Lane, Br Mgr, Cuyahoga County Public Library, Solon Branch, 34125 Portz Pkwy, Solon, OH, 44139-6803. Tel: 440-248-8777. Fax: 440-248-5369. p. 1928

Edwards, Linda, Libr Tech, Naval History & Heritage, 805 Kidder-Breese St SE, Washington, DC, 20374-5060. Tel: 202-433-4132. Fax: 202-433-9553. p. 411

Edwards, Lucious, Archivist, Virginia State University, One Hayden Dr, Petersburg, VA, 23806-0001. Tel: 804-524-5749. Fax: 805-524-5815. p. 2484

Edwards, Marybeth, ILL, Caritas St Elizabeth's Medical Center, 736 Cambridge St, Boston, MA, 02135. Tel: 617-789-2177. Fax: 617-789-5081. p. 1059

Edwards, Marybeth, Mgr, Roger Williams Medical Center, 825 Chalkstone Ave, Providence, RI, 02908. Tel: 401-456-2036. Fax: 401-456-2191. p. 2175

Edwards, Michael, Online Serv, Ser, Hampshire College Library, 893 West St, Amherst, MA, 01002-5001. Tel: 413-559-5440. Fax: 413-559-5419. p. 1048

Edwards, Michelle, Bibliog Instr, Red Deer College Library, 100 College Blvd, Red Deer, AB, T4N 5H5, CANADA. Tel: 403-342-3344. Fax: 403-346-8500. p. 2714

Edwards, Michelle, Info Tech, Red Deer College Library, 100 College Blvd, Red Deer, AB, T4N 5H5, CANADA. Tel: 403-342-3344. Fax: 403-346-8500. p. 2714

Edwards, Mike, Librn, Sandia Baptist Church, 9429 Constitution NE, Albuquerque, NM, 87112. Tel: 505-292-2713, 505-292-2717. Fax: 505-296-3009. p. 1550

Edwards, Monica, Youth Serv, Logan County Public Library, 201 W Sixth St, Russellville, KY, 42276. Tel: 270-726-6129. Fax: 270-726-6127. p. 934

Edwards, Monte D, Mgr, Council on Foundations, 2121 Crystal Dr, Ste 700, Arlington, VA, 22202. Tel: 703-879-0600. Fax: 703-879-0800. p. 2449

Edwards, Natalie, Instruction Librn, Gardner-Webb University, 110 S Main St, Boiling Springs, NC, 28017. Tel: 704-406-3274. Fax: 704-406-4623. p. 1776

Edwards, Nicole, Librn, Rodman Public Library, Branch in the Mall, 2500 W State St, Alliance, OH, 44601. Tel: 330-821-1313. p. 1854

Edwards, Nitisue, Archivist, Southern University at Shreveport, 3050 Martin Luther King Jr Dr, Shreveport, LA, 71107. Tel: 318-670-6392. Fax: 318-674-3403. p. 970

Edwards, Pamela, Assoc Librn, Pub Serv, Calcasieu Parish Public Library, 301 W Claude St, Lake Charles, LA, 70605-3457. Tel: 337-721-7149. Fax: 337-475-8806. p. 953

Edwards, Pat, Ch, Pryor Public Library, 505 E Graham, Pryor, OK, 74361. Tel: 918-825-0777. Fax: 918-825-0856. p. 1976

Edwards, Patricia, Dir, Jefferson County Library System, 306 E Broad St, Louisville, GA, 30434. Tel: 478-625-3751. Fax: 478-625-7683. p. 539

Edwards, Paul, Assoc Prof, University of Michigan, 304 West Hall, 1085 S University, Ann Arbor, MI, 48109-1107. Tel: 734-763-2285. Fax: 734-764-2475. p. 2967

Edwards, Peggy, Librn, Houston Community College - Northwest College, Spring Branch Campus Library, 1010 W Sam Houston Pkwy N, Houston, TX, 77043-5008. Tel: 713-718-5655. Fax: 713-718-5745. p. 2338

Edwards, Robert, Asst City Librn, Decatur Public Library, 130 N Franklin St, Decatur, IL, 62523-1327. Tel: 217-421-9702. Fax: 217-233-4071. p. 633

Edwards, Ronald G, Dir, Western Technical College Library, 400 Seventh St N, R201, La Crosse, WI, 54601. Tel: 608-785-9142. p. 2604

Edwards, Rosa, Coordr, Wilson Medical Center Library, 1705 Tarboro St SW, Wilson, NC, 27893-3428. Tel: 252-399-8253. Fax: 252-399-8119. p. 1831

Edwards, Sandra, Head, Ref, Rice University, 6100 Main, MS-44, Houston, TX, 77005. Tel: 713-348-2504. Fax: 713-348-5258. p. 2341

Edwards, Sandy, Br Mgr, Maricopa County Library District, Ed Robson Branch, 9330 East Riggs Rd, Sun Lakes, AZ, 85248. Tel: 602-652-3276. Fax: 602-652-3280. p. 75

Edwards, Shawn, Electronic Serv Coordr, Bradley University, 1501 W Bradley Ave, Peoria, IL, 61625. Tel: 309-677-2850. Fax: 309-677-2558. p. 690

Edwards, Stephanie, Ch, Champaign Public Library, 200 W Green St, Champaign, IL, 61820-5193. Tel: 217-403-2050. Fax: 217-403-2053. p. 602

Edwards, Stephanie, Coll Develop, Roger Williams University, Ten Metacom Ave, Bristol, RI, 02809-5171. Tel: 401-254-4539. Fax: 401-254-4543. p. 2163

Edwards, Susan, Head of Libr, University of California, Berkeley, Social Welfare, 227 Haviland Hall, Berkeley, CA, 94720-6000. Tel: 510-642-4432. Fax: 510-643-1476. p. 128

Edwards, Susan, Archivist, Salem State University Library, 352 Lafayette St, Salem, MA, 01970-5353. Tel: 978-542-6781. Fax: 978-542-6596. p. 1122

Edwards, Susan M, Dir, Little Silver Public Library, 484 Prospect.Ave, Little Silver, NJ, 07739. Tel: 732-747-9649. p. 1496

Edwards, Susane, Head, Educ & Psychol Libr, University of California, Berkeley, Education Psychology, 2600 Tolman Hall, Berkeley, CA, 94720-6000. Tel: 510-642-4209. Fax: 510-642-8224. p. 127

Edwards, Tammie, Ch, Harriman Public Library, 601 Walden St, Harriman, TN, 37748-2506. Tel: 865-882-3195. Fax: 865-882-3188. p. 2236

Edwards, Taryn, Mkt & Membership Spec/Ref Librn, Mechanics' Institute Library, 57 Post St, San Francisco, CA, 94104-5003. Tel: 415-393-0103. Fax: 415-421-4192. p. 243

Edwards, Teresa, Syst Coordr, Saint John's University Library, 8000 Utopia Pkwy, Queens, NY, 11439. Tel: 718-990-6735. Fax: 718-380-0353. p. 1725

Edwards, William, Ref Librn, University of Toronto Libraries, Pontifical Institute for Mediaeval Studies, 113 Saint Joseph St, Toronto, ON, M5S 1J4, CANADA. Tel: 416-926-1300, Ext 3423. Fax: 416-926-7262. p. 2867

Eells, Linda, Head, Ref, University of Minnesota Libraries-Twin Cities, Entomology, Fisheries & Wildlife, 375 Hodson Hall, 1980 Folwell Ave, Saint Paul, MN, 55108. Tel: 612-624-9288. Fax: 612-624-0719. p. 1262

Eels, Sharon, Br Librn, Horry County Memorial Library, Socastee, 141 707-Connector Rd, Myrtle Beach, SC, 29588. Tel: 843-215-4700. Fax: 843-215-2801. p. 2191

Eertmoed, Tom, Ref, Illinois Central College, One College Dr, East Peoria, IL, 61635-0001. Tel: 309-694-5461. Fax: 309-694-5473. p. 638

Effraim, Cynthia, Br Mgr, Long Beach Public Library, North, 5571 Orange Ave, Long Beach, CA, 90805. Tel: 562-570-1047. p. 167

Efron, Miles, Asst Prof, University of Illinois at Urbana-Champaign, Library & Information Science Bldg, 501 E Daniel St, Champaign, IL, 61820-6211. Tel: 217-333-3280. Fax: 217-244-3302. p. 2965

Efta, Janina, ILL, Ref Serv, Kenai Community Library, 163 Main St Loop, Kenai, AK, 99611-7723. Tel: 907-283-4378. Fax: 907-283-2266. p. 50

Efteland, Susan, Chief Librn, VA Greater Los Angeles Health Care System, 11301 Wilshire Blvd, W142D, Los Angeles, CA, 90073. Tel: 310-268-3003. Fax: 310-268-4919. p. 180

Efthimiadis, Efthimis, Assoc Prof, University of Washington, Mary Gates Hall, Ste 370, Campus Box 352840, Seattle, WA, 98195-2840. Tel: 206-685-9937. Fax: 206-616-3152. p. 2976

Egan, Andrew, Talking Bks, State of Rhode Island Office of Library & Information Services, One Capitol Hill, 4th Flr, Providence, RI, 02908. Tel: 401-574-9312. Fax: 401-574-9320. p. 2175

Egan, Andrew I, Regional Librn, State of Rhode Island Office of Library & Information Services, One Capitol Hill, Providence, RI, 02908. Tel: 401-222-5767. Fax: 401-222-4195. p. 2175

Egan, Elizabeth J, Dir, Gloucester City Library, 50 N Railroad Ave, Gloucester City, NJ, 08030. Tel: 856-456-4181. Fax: 856-456-6724. p. 1488

Egan, Gwen, Librn, Bare Hill Correctional Facility Library, 181 Brand Rd, Malone, NY, 12953. Tel: 518-483-8411. Fax: 518-483-8411, Ext 2099. p. 1656

Egan, Karen, LSTA Coordr, Illinois State Library, Gwendolyn Brooks Bldg, 300 S Second St, Springfield, IL, 62701-9713. Tel: 217-782-7749. Fax: 217-785-4326. p. 705

Egan, Laurel, Librn, St James Healthcare, 400 S Clark St, Butte, MT, 59701. Tel: 406-723-2523. Fax: 406-723-2813. p. 1376

Egan, Nancy, Electronic Res Librn, Media Librn, John Jay College of Criminal Justice, 899 Tenth Ave, New York, NY, 10019. Tel: 212-237-8269. Fax: 212-237-8221. p. 1684

Egan, Noelle, Electronic Res Librn, Drexel University Libraries, Hagerty Library, 33rd & Market Sts, Philadelphia, PA, 19104-2875. Tel: 215-895-2752. Fax: 215-895-2070. p. 2105

Egan, Robert, Acq, Cat, Raritan Valley Community College, 118 Lamington Rd, Branchburg, Somerville, NJ, 08876. Tel: 908-526-1200, Ext 8300. Fax: 908-526-2985. p. 1530

Egebrecht, Linda, Asst Dir, Park Ridge Public Library, 20 S Prospect, Park Ridge, IL, 60068-4188. Tel: 847-720-3221. Fax: 847-825-0001. p. 688

Egeland, Mindwell S, Dir, University of Iowa Hospitals & Clinics, 8016 JCP, 200 Hawkins Dr, Iowa City, IA, 52242-1046. Tel: 319-384-8908. Fax: 319-353-8793. p. 823

Egeland, Sherry, Librn, Chinook Regional Library, Sceptre Branch, 128 Kingsway, Sceptre, SK, S0N 2H0, CANADA. Tel: 306-623-4244. p. 2928

Eger, Karen McCarthy, Dir, Springvale Public Library, 443 Main St, Springvale, ME, 04083. Tel: 207-324-4624. p. 1002

Eger, Tina, Ref/User Instruction Librn, Carthage College, 2001 Alford Park Dr, Kenosha, WI, 53140-1900. Tel: 262-551-5900. Fax: 262-551-5904. p. 2601

Egger-Sider, Francine, Tech Serv, Fiorello H LaGuardia Community College Library, 31-10 Thomson Ave, Long Island City, NY, 11101. Tel: 718-482-5421. Fax: 718-482-5444, 718-609-2011. p. 1654

Eggerman, Cora, Br Mgr, Hawaii State Public Library System, Waimanalo Public & School Library, 41-1320 Kalanianaole Hwy, Waimanalo, HI, 96795. Tel: 808-259-2610. Fax: 808-259-2612. p. 563

Eggers, Betsy K, Dir, Napoleon Public Library, 310 W Clinton St, Napoleon, OH, 43545-1472. Tel: 419-592-2531. Fax: 419-599-1472. p. 1919

Eggers, Dawn, Coll Develop, Louisburg Public Library, 206 S Broadway, Louisburg, KS, 66053. Tel: 913-837-2217. Fax: 913-837-2218. p. 880

Eggers, Denise, Librn, Saint Paul's College Library, 3015 Fourth St NE, Washington, DC, 20017. Tel: 202-269-2545. Fax: 202-269-2507. p. 413

Eggers, Glee, Coordr, Libr Serv, Riley County Kansas Genealogical Society Library, 2005 Claflin, Manhattan, KS, 66502-3415. Tel: 785-565-6495. p. 882

Eggers, Lee Ann M, Pub Relations, User Serv, Labette Community College Library, 200 S 14th St, Parsons, KS, 67357. Tel: 620-820-1167. Fax: 620-421-1469. p. 889

Eggers, Thomas D, Dir, Eagle Pass Public Library, 589 Main St, Eagle Pass, TX, 78852. Tel: 830-773-2516. Fax: 830-773-4204. p. 2315

Eggert, Mary, Res, Kirkland & Ellis LLP Library, 300 N LaSalle St, 11th Flr, Chicago, IL, 60654. Tel: 312-862-3851. Fax: 312-862-2200. p. 616

Eggert, Maureen, Assoc Dir, Wake Forest University, Professional Center Library, Worrell Professional Ctr for Law & Management, 1834 Wake Forest Rd, Winston-Salem, NC, 27106. Tel: 336-758-5072. Fax: 336-758-6077. p. 1834

Eggert, Rose, Adminr, Minnesota State Horticultural Society Library, 2705 Lincoln Dr, Roseville, MN, 55113-1334. Tel: 651-643-3601. Fax: 651-643-3638. p. 1273

Eggleston, Anne-Marie, Dir, Libr Serv, Kishwaukee College Library, 21193 Malta Rd, Malta, IL, 60150-9699. Tel: 815-825-2086, Ext 3660. Fax: 815-825-2072. p. 669

Eggleston, Bette, Ad, Jennings County Public Library, 2375 N State Hwy 3, North Vernon, IN, 47265-1596. Tel: 812-346-2091. Fax: 812-346-2127. p. 769

Egle, Shelly, Acq, A Holmes Johnson Memorial Library, 319 Lower Mill Bay Rd, Kodiak, AK, 99615. Tel: 907-486-8685. Fax: 907-486-8681. p. 51

Egle-Gaber, Karen, Outreach Librn, Nashua Public Library, Two Court St, Nashua, NH, 03060. Tel: 603-589-4600. Fax: 603-594-3457. p. 1458

Egleston, Charles Lee, Librn & Archivist, George Mercer Jr School of Theology, 65 Fourth St, Garden City, NY, 11530. Tel: 516-248-4800, Ext 39. Fax: 516-248-4883. p. 1626

Egleston, Dythe-Mary, Asst Librn, Tuolumne County Genealogical Society Library, 158 W Bradford St, Sonora, CA, 95370-4920. Tel: 209-532-1317. p. 269

Egleston, Elizabeth, Br Librn, London Public Library, Stoney Creek, 920 Sunningdale Rd E, London, ON, N5X 0H5, CANADA. Tel: 519-930-2065. p. 2818

Egli, Bruce, Dir, Carnegie Free Library of Swissvale, 1800 Monongahela Ave, Swissvale, PA, 15218-2312. Tel: 412-731-2300. Fax: 412-731-6716. p. 2145

Egloff, Fred, Librn, Museum of Western Art Library, 1550 Bandera Hwy, Kerrville, TX, 78028-9547. Tel: 830-896-2553. Fax: 830-257-5206. p. 2349

Egoavil, Juanita, Br Mgr, Newark Public Library, Branch Brook, 235 Clifton Ave, Newark, NJ, 07104. Tel: 973-733-7760. p. 1512

Egros, Bonnie, Dir, Belle Vernon Public Library, 505 Speer St, Belle Vernon, PA, 15012-1540. Tel: 724-929-6642. Fax: 724-929-4197. p. 2032

Ehas, Nancy, Dir, Wilmington Public Library of Clinton County, 268 N South St, Wilmington, OH, 45177-1696. Tel: 937-382-2417. Fax: 937-382-1692. p. 1949

Ehde, Ava, Mgr, Libr Serv, Manatee County Public Library System, 1301 Barcarrota Blvd W, Bradenton, FL, 34205. Tel: 941-748-5555. Fax: 941-749-7191. p. 429

Ehinger, Kelly A, Dir, Adams Public Library System, 128 S Third St, Decatur, IN, 46733-1691. Tel: 260-724-2605. Fax: 260-724-2877. p. 735

Ehlers, Marla, Asst Libr Dir, Grand Rapids Public Library, 111 Library St NE, Grand Rapids, MI, 49503-3268. Tel: 616-988-5400. Fax: 616-988-5419. p. 1185

Ehlers, Nikki, Dir, Humboldt Public Library, 30 Sixth St N, Humboldt, IA, 50548. Tel: 515-332-1925. Fax: 515-332-1926. p. 821

Ehlert, Laird, Exec Dir, New York Legislative Service, Inc Library, 15 Maiden Lane, Ste 1000, New York, NY, 10038. Tel: 212-962-2826. Fax: 212-962-1420. p. 1689

Ehmen, Patti, Br Mgr, Huntsville-Madison Public Library, Bessie K Russell Branch Library, 3011 C Sparkman Dr, Huntsville, AL, 35810. Tel: 256-859-9050. p. 21

Ehmke, Sue, Libr Assoc, Blackwater Regional Library, Claremont Public, 91 Mancha Ave, Claremont, VA, 23899. Tel: 757-866-8627. Fax: 757-866-8628. p. 2458

Ehnis, Shirley A, Asst Dir, Adrian Public Library, 143 E Maumee St, Adrian, MI, 49221-2773. Tel: 517-265-2265. Fax: 517-265-8847. p. 1147

Ehnow, Marian, Circ, Chestnut Hill College, 9601 Germantown Ave, Philadelphia, PA, 19118-2695. Tel: 215-248-7052. Fax: 215-248-7056. p. 2104

Ehr, Elizabeth, Tech Serv Librn, Viterbo University, 900 Viterbo Dr, La Crosse, WI, 54601. Tel: 608-796-3265. Fax: 608-796-3275. p. 2603

Ehrenberg, Adam, Circ, Reserves, Flagler College, 44 Sevilla St, Saint Augustine, FL, 32084-4302. Tel: 904-819-6206. Fax: 904-823-8511. p. 486

Ehrenberg, Ann Marie, Br Mgr, Mercer County Library System, Robbinsville Branch, 42 Allentown-Robbinsville Rd, Robbinsville, NJ, 08691. Tel: 609-259-2150. Fax: 609-259-1411. p. 1494

Ehrenhart, Jane, Head, Ref, Illinois Historic Preservation Agency, 112 N Sixth St, Springfield, IL, 62701. Tel: 217-785-7945. Fax: 217-785-6250. p. 705

Ehrensperger, David, Electronic Res Librn, Luzerne County Community College Library, 1333 S Prospect St, Nanticoke, PA, 18634-3899. Tel: 800-377-5222, Ext 7439. Fax: 570-735-6130. p. 2094

Ehrich, Peaches, Supv Librn-City Br, Stockton-San Joaquin County Public Library, 605 N El Dorado St, Stockton, CA, 95202. Tel: 209-937-8261. Fax: 209-937-8547. p. 272

Ehrig-Burgess, Kristi, Libr Mgr, Mingei International Museum, 1439 El Prado, San Diego, CA, 92101-1617. Tel: 619-239-0003, Ext 132. Fax: 619-239-0605. p. 232

Ehrman, Deborah, Assoc Dir, Libr Experiences, Salt Lake City Public Library, 210 E 400 S, Salt Lake City, UT, 84111-3280. Tel: 801-524-8204. Fax: 801-322-8194. p. 2413

Ehrnst, Elizabeth, Archives & Digital Coll Librn, Georgia O'Keeffe Museum, 217 Johnson St, Santa Fe, NM, 87501. Tel: 505-946-1011. Fax: 505-946-1093. p. 1563

Ehrsam, Harriet, Librn, Union Library Company of Hatborough, 243 S York Rd, Hatboro, PA, 19040-3429. Tel: 215-672-1420. Fax: 215-672-1546. p. 2067

Ei, Susan, Ch, Pequot Library, 720 Pequot Ave, Southport, CT, 06890-1496. Tel: 203-259-0346, Ext 18. Fax: 203-259-5602. p. 368

Eich, Janet, Board Pres, Port Carbon Public Library, 111 Pike St, Port Carbon, PA, 17965-1814. Tel: 570-622-6115. Fax: 570-622-6115. p. 2131

Eichelberger, Marianne, Libr Dir, Newton Public Library, 720 N Oak, Newton, KS, 67114. Tel: 316-283-2890. Fax: 316-283-2916. p. 884

Eichelberger, Michelle, Instr, Syst/Electronic Serv Librn, Genesee Community College, One College Rd, Batavia, NY, 14020-9704. Tel: 585-343-0055, Ext 6458. Fax: 585-345-6933. p. 1578

Eichenberg, Paul, Mgr, Human Res, Spokane County Library District, 4322 N Argonne Rd, Spokane, WA, 99212-1868. Tel: 509-893-8200. Fax: 509-893-8472. p. 2536

Eichenberg, Sandra, Music, Baldwin Wallace University, Riemenschneider Bach Institute, Boesel Musical Arts Bldg., 49 Seminary St, Berea, OH, 44017-2088. Tel: 440-826-2044. Fax: 440-826-8138. p. 1859

Eichenlaub, Joann, Circ Serv Mgr, Roger & Peggy Madigan Library, 999 Hagan Way, Williamsport, PA, 17701. Tel: 570-327-4523. Fax: 570-327-4503. p. 2156

Eichholtz, Lisa, Pub Serv, Jefferson Community & Technical College, 109 E Broadway, Louisville, KY, 40202. Tel: 502-213-2281. p. 924

Eichmann, David, Dr, Assoc Prof, University of Iowa, 3087 Main Library, Iowa City, IA, 52242-1420. Tel: 319-335-5707. Fax: 319-335-5374. p. 2965

Eichner, Holly A, Adminr, Northcoast Behavioral Healthcare Library, 930 S Detroit Ave, Toledo, OH, 43614-2701. Tel: 419-381-1881, Ext 4780. Fax: 419-389-1967. p. 1939

Eichner, Kurt, Librn, Massachusetts Department of Corrections, State Hospital Library, 20 Administration Rd, Bridgewater, MA, 02324. Tel: 508-279-4500, Ext 4600. Fax: 508-279-4502. p. 1070

Eick, Patricia, Head, Circ, Roseville Public Library, 29777 Gratiot Ave, Roseville, MI, 48066. Tel: 586-445-5407. Fax: 586-445-5499. p. 1223

Eickhoff, Dennis, Librn, Colton Hepburn Library, 84 Main St, Colton, NY, 13625. Tel: 315-262-2310. Fax: 315-262-2182. p. 1609

Eickholt, Jann, Br Mgr, Putnam County District Library, Ottoville-Monterey Branch, 349 Wayne St, Ottoville, OH, 45876. Tel: 419-453-2111. p. 1926

Eickmeyer, Alice, Librn, Southwestern College, 2625 E Cactus Rd, Phoenix, AZ, 85032-7097. Tel: 602-992-6101, Ext 117. Fax: 602-404-2159. p. 77

Eidell, Linda, ILL, Meadville Public Library, 848 N Main St, Meadville, PA, 16335-2689. Tel: 814-336-1773. Fax: 814-333-8173. p. 2086

Eidelman, Diane, Mem Serv Coordr, Suffolk Cooperative Library System, 627 N Sunrise Service Rd, Bellport, NY, 11713. Tel: 631-286-1600. Fax: 631-286-1647. p. 1580

Eidem, Matt, Archivist, New Albany-Floyd County Public Library, 180 W Spring St, New Albany, IN, 47150-3692. Tel: 812-944-8464. Fax: 812-949-3532. p. 768

Eidsvik, Jean-Paul, Dir, Finance & Fac, University of British Columbia Library, 1961 East Mall, Vancouver, BC, V6T 1Z1, CANADA. Tel: 604-822-5903. p. 2742

Eidt, Christine, Sr Libr Tech, Stewart McKelvey, 1959 Upper Water St, Ste 900, Halifax, NS, B3J 3N2, CANADA. Tel: 902-420-3200. Fax: 902-420-1417. p. 2781

Eifert, Darrell, Ad, Lane Memorial Library, Two Academy Ave, Hampton, NH, 03842. Tel: 603-926-3368. Fax: 603-926-1348. p. 1449

Eifert, Ron, Asst Dir, Sikeston Public Library, 121 E North St, Sikeston, MO, 63801. Tel: 573-471-4140. Fax: 573-471-6048. p. 1365

Eifert, Ruth, Dir, Libr Serv, Georgetown Peabody Library, Lincoln Park, Georgetown, MA, 01833. Tel: 978-352-5728. Fax: 978-352-7415. p. 1091

Eifler, David, Librn, University of California, Berkeley, Environmental Design, 210 Wurster Hall, Berkeley, CA, 94720-6000. Tel: 510-643-7422. Fax: 510-642-8266. p. 127

Eifling, Janice K, Librn, United States Department of Agriculture, 1920 Dayton Ave, Ames, IA, 50010. Tel: 515-337-7271. p. 793

Eigelsbach, Bill, Res Serv Spec, University of Tennessee, Knoxville, Special Collections, 121 Hodges Library, 1015 Volunteer Blvd, Knoxville, TN, 37996-1000. Tel: 865-974-4480. p. 2244

Eigsti, Jennifer, Asst Dir, Adm Serv, University of Missouri-Kansas City Libraries, 800 E 51st St, Kansas City, MO, 64110. Tel: 816-235-1533. Fax: 816-333-5584. p. 1341

Eike, Betty, Cat, Longwood University, Redford & Race St, Farmville, VA, 23909. Tel: 434-395-2449. Fax: 434-395-2453. p. 2463

Eike, Claire, Dir, School of the Art Institute of Chicago, 37 S Wabash Ave, Chicago, IL, 60603-3103. Tel: 312-899-5097. Fax: 312-899-1851. p. 624

Eikelboom, Janny, Assoc VPres, Libr Info Tech, Redeemer College Library, 777 Garner Rd E, Ancaster, ON, L9K 1J4, CANADA. Tel: 905-648-2131. Fax: 905-648-2134. p. 2792

Eilberg, Joshua, Libr Asst, Newbury College Library, 150 Fisher Ave, Brookline, MA, 02445-5796. Tel: 617-738-2425. Fax: 617-730-7239. p. 1071

Eileen, Chen, Librn, Foundation for Student Communication, Princeton University, 48 University Pl, Rm 305, Princeton, NJ, 08540. Tel: 609-258-1111. Fax: 609-258-1222. p. 1522

Eilering, Susan, Dir, MacMurray College, 447 E College Ave, Jacksonville, IL, 62650-2510. Tel: 217-479-7106. Fax: 217-245-5214. p. 659

Eimer, Marianne, Head, Instrul Serv, Head, Ref, State University of New York at Fredonia, 280 Central Ave, Fredonia, NY, 14063. Tel: 716-673-3181. Fax: 716-673-3185. p. 1624

Einblau, Linda, Doc Delivery, College of Physicians & Surgeons of British Columbia, 100-1383 W Eighth Ave, Vancouver, BC, V6H 4C4, CANADA. Tel: 604-733-6671. Fax: 604-737-8582. p. 2740

Einhaus, Karen, Circ Serv, Seneca Public Library District, 210 N Main St, Seneca, IL, 61360. Tel: 815-357-6566. Fax: 815-357-6568. p. 701

Einstadler, Laura, County Librn, Amador County Law Library, 530 Sutter St, Jackson, CA, 95642. p. 160

Einstadter, Laura, County Librn, Amador County Library, 530 Sutter St, Jackson, CA, 95642. Tel: 209-223-6400. Fax: 209-223-6303. p. 160

Einwalter, Jennifer, Dir, Slinger Community Library, 220 Slinger Rd, Slinger, WI, 53086-9586. Tel: 262-644-6171. Fax: 262-644-8061. p. 2638

Eirish, Donna, Librn, Tehama County Law Library, Courthouse, Rm 38, 633 Washington St, Red Bluff, CA, 96080. Tel: 530-529-5033. Fax: 530-527-9255. p. 213

Eisch, Lisa, Dir, Hancock Public Library, 114 S Main St, Hancock, WI, 54943. Tel: 715-249-5817. Fax: 715-249-5815. p. 2597

Eiseman, Jason, Ref Librn, Yale University Library, Lillian Goldman Library Yale Law School, 127 Wall St, New Haven, CT, 06511. Tel: 203-432-1600. Fax: 203-432-2112. p. 358

Eisen, David J, Dir, Mishawaka-Penn-Harris Public Library, 209 Lincoln Way E, Mishawaka, IN, 46544-2084. Tel: 574-259-5277, Ext 300. Fax: 574-254-5585, 574-255-8489. p. 765

Eisen, Ellen, Librn, Atlantic County Library System, Ventnor Branch, 6500 Atlantic Ave, Ventnor, NJ, 08406. Tel: 609-823-4614. Fax: 609-823-2639. p. 1500

Eisenberg, Debra, Dir, North Shore University Hospital, 300 Community Dr, Manhasset, NY, 11030. Tel: 516-562-4324. Fax: 516-562-2865. p. 1657

Eisenberg, Judy, Ref, West Hartford Public Library, 20 S Main St, West Hartford, CT, 06107-2432. Tel: 860-561-6950. Fax: 860-561-6976. p. 376

Eisenberg, Michael, Prof, University of Washington, Mary Gates Hall, Ste 370, Campus Box 352840, Seattle, WA, 98195-2840. Tel: 206-685-9937. Fax: 206-616-3152. p. 2976

Eisenberg, Wendy, Br Supvr, Fresno County Public Library, 2420 Mariposa St, Fresno, CA, 93721-2285. Tel: 559-600-7323. p. 151

Eisenga, Diane, Libr Coordr, McBain Community Library, 107 E Maple St, McBain, MI, 49657-9672. Tel: 231-825-2197. Fax: 231-825-2477. p. 1207

Eisenhauer, Janet, Librn, Rick Warren Memorial Public Library District, 114 S Fourth St, Elkville, IL, 62932-1097. Tel: 618-568-1843. Fax: 618-568-1843. p. 642

Eisenman, Bonnie, Adminr, Congregation Beth Ahabah Museum & Archives Trust, 1109 W Franklin St, Richmond, VA, 23220. Tel: 804-353-2668. Fax: 804-358-3451. p. 2488

Eisenstein, Caroline, Librn, New Hanover County Public Library, 201 Chestnut St, Wilmington, NC, 28401. Tel: 910-798-6331. Fax: 910-798-6312. p. 1830

Eisentrager, Deb, Dir, Dumont Community Library, 602 Second St, Dumont, IA, 50625. Tel: 641-857-3304. Fax: 641-857-3304. p. 812

Eisler, M A, ILL, Kenora Public Library, 24 Main St S, Kenora, ON, P9N 1S7, CANADA. Tel: 807-467-2081. Fax: 807-467-2085. p. 2812

Eisler, Melody Sky, Br Mgr, Kitsap Regional Library, Silverdale Branch, 3450 NW Carlton St, Silverdale, WA, 98383-8325. Tel: 360-692-2779. Fax: 360-698-7702. p. 2510

Eisley, Kathy, Circ, Milton Public Library, 23 S Front St, Milton, PA, 17847. Tel: 570-742-7111. Fax: 570-742-7137. p. 2090

Eisman, Harriet, Dir, Watkins Glen Public Library, 610 S Decatur St, Watkins Glen, NY, 14891. Tel: 607-535-2346. Fax: 607-535-7338. p. 1764

Eissinger, Richard, New Technologies Librn, Southern Utah University, 351 W University Blvd, Cedar City, UT, 84720. Tel: 435-586-5435. Fax: 435-865-8152. p. 2404

Eiszner, Margaret, Librn, Saint Luke's Episcopal Church Library, 247 W Lovell St, Kalamazoo, MI, 49007. Tel: 269-345-8553. Fax: 269-345-5559. p. 1198

Eiten, Keith, Media Spec, Wheaton College, 510 Irving Ave, Wheaton, IL, 60187-5593. Tel: 630-752-5092. Fax: 630-752-5855. p. 718

Ekeroth, Shelley, Coll Develop Coordr, County of Los Angeles Public Library, 7400 E Imperial Hwy, Downey, CA, 90242-3375. Tel: 562-940-8503. Fax: 562-803-3032. p. 140

Ekkebus, Susan, Librn, First United Methodist Church, 1350 Oak Ridge Tpk, Oak Ridge, TN, 37830. Tel: 865-483-4357. p. 2262

Ekleberry, John, Librn, Genesee District Library, Vera B Rison-Beecher Library, 1386 W Coldwater Rd, Flint, MI, 48505. Tel: 810-789-2800. Fax: 810-789-2882. p. 1180

Eklund, Janet, Adminr, Libr Operations, New Hampshire State Library, 20 Park St, Concord, NH, 03301-6314. Tel: 603-271-2392. Fax: 603-271-2205, 603-271-6826. p. 1443

Ekman, Sheila, Head, Ref, Bentley College, 175 Forest St, Waltham, MA, 02452-4705. Tel: 781-891-2168. Fax: 781-891-2830. p. 1132

El Shabazz, Yusuf, Libr Asst I, Montgomery City-County Public Library System, Rufus A Lewis Regional Branch Library, 3095 Mobile Hwy, Montgomery, AL, 36108. Tel: 334-240-4848. Fax: 334-240-4847. p. 30

El-Khayat, Yamila, Outreach Serv Librn, University of Arizona, Arizona Health Sciences Library, 1501 N Campbell Ave, Tucson, AZ, 85724. Tel: 520-626-6121. Fax: 520-626-2922. p. 88

El-Talmas, Alaa, Mgr, Access & Mat Mgt, Brantford Public Library, 173 Colborne St, Brantford, ON, N3T 2G8, CANADA. Tel: 519-756-2220, Ext 314. Fax: 519-756-4979. p. 2796

Elacate, Jose, Circ, ILL, Jefferson College of Health Sciences, 920 S Jefferson St, Roanoke, VA, 24016. Tel: 540-985-9767. Fax: 540-224-4404. p. 2494

Elam, Gary, Circ, Iredell County Public Library, 201 N Tradd St, Statesville, NC, 28677. Tel: 704-928-2405. Fax: 704-878-5449. p. 1825

Elam, Lynn, Dir, Algonquin Area Public Library District, 2600 Harnish Dr, Algonquin, IL, 60102-5900. Tel: 847-458-6060, 847-658-4343. Fax: 847-458-9370. p. 588

Elam, Lynn, Exec Dir, Hinsdale Public Library, 20 E Maple St, Hinsdale, IL, 60521. Tel: 630-986-1976. Fax: 630-986-9654. p. 656

Elam, Pamela, Librn, Hockley County Memorial Library, Sundown Branch, 207 E Richardson, Sundown, TX, 79372. Tel: 806-229-3133. p. 2355

Eland, Susan, Librn, Brownfield Public Library, 216 Main St, Brownfield, ME, 04010. Tel: 207-935-3003. p. 979

Eland, Thomas, Chair, Minneapolis Community & Technical College Library, Wheelock Whitney Hall, 1501 Hennepin Ave, Minneapolis, MN, 55403. Tel: 612-659-6286. Fax: 612-659-6295. p. 1261

Elberbrook, Ruth V, Dir, University of Wisconsin, 2000 W Fifth St, Marshfield, WI, 54449-3310. Tel: 715-389-6512, 715-389-6531. Fax: 715-389-6539. p. 2613

Elbers, Martha, Librn, United States Navy, 1002 Balch Blvd, Bldg 1003, Stennis Space Center, MS, 39522-5001. Tel: 228-688-4597. Fax: 228-688-4191. p. 1315

Elberson, Teresa, Adminr, Lafayette Public Library, 301 W Congress, Lafayette, LA, 70501-6866. Tel: 337-261-5764. Fax: 337-261-5782. p. 952

Elder, Abigail, Mgr, Tualatin Public Library, 18878 SW Martinazzi, Tualatin, OR, 97062. Tel: 503-691-3066. Fax: 503-692-3512. p. 2022

Elder, Carol, Mgr, Toronto Star Newspapers Ltd Library, One Yonge St, 5th Flr, Toronto, ON, M5E 1E6, CANADA. Tel: 416-869-4491. Fax: 416-865-3994. p. 2864

Elder, Carol, Chair, Langara College, 100 W 49th Ave, Vancouver, BC, V5Y 2Z6, CANADA. Tel: 604-323-5364, 604-323-5862. Fax: 604-323-5010. p. 2977

Elder, Jane, Ref Librn, Southern Methodist University, Bridwell Library-Perkins School of Theology, 6005 Bishop Blvd, Dallas, TX, 75205. Tel: 214-768-3483. Fax: 214-768-4295. p. 2310

Elder, Janet, Tech Serv, Grove City College, 300 Campus Dr, Grove City, PA, 16127-2198. Tel: 724-458-3823. Fax: 724-458-2181. p. 2063

Elder, Joyce, Librn, Piedmont Medical Center Library, 222 S Herlong Ave, Rock Hill, SC, 29732-1158. Tel: 803-329-1234. Fax: 803-980-1353. p. 2202

Elder, Kate, Dir, Libr Serv, Colorado Mental Health Institute at Fort Logan, 3520 W Oxford Ave, Denver, CO, 80236. Tel: 303-866-7844. Fax: 303-866-7090. p. 299

Elder, Nancy, Head Librn, University of Texas Libraries, Life Science (Biology, Pharmacy), Main Bldg 220, Austin, TX, 78713. Tel: 512-495-4635. Fax: 512-495-4638. p. 2284

Elder, Rick, Dir, Libr Serv, Bay Mills Community College, 12214 W Lakeshore Dr, Brimley, MI, 49715-9320. Tel: 906-248-3354, Ext 4202. Fax: 906-248-2432. p. 1160

Elder, Ruth E, Cataloger, Troy University Library, 309 Wallace Hall, 501 University Ave, Troy, AL, 36082. Tel: 334-670-3874. Fax: 334-670-3694. p. 37

Elder, Sarah, Curator of Coll, St Joseph Museums Inc, 3406 Frederick Ave, Saint Joseph, MO, 64506. Tel: 816-232-8471. Fax: 816-232-8482. p. 1352

Elder, Susan, Mgr, US Courts Library, Byron Rogers Courthouse, 1929 Stout St, Rm 430, Denver, CO, 80294. Tel: 303-844-3591. Fax: 303-844-5958. p. 303

Elderwind, Jean, Adminr, Carroll & Madison Library System, 106 Spring St, Berryville, AR, 72616-3846. Tel: 870-423-5300. Fax: 870-423-7117. p. 95

Elderwind, Jean, Dir, Eureka Springs Carnegie Public Library, 194 Spring St, Eureka Springs, AR, 72632. Tel: 479-253-8754. Fax: 479-253-7807. p. 98

Eldevik, Bruce, Chair, Minnesota Theological Library Association, Luther Seminary Library, 2375 Como Ave, Saint Paul, MN, 55108. Tel: 651-641-3447. p. 2947

Eldevik, Bruce E, Ref, Luther Seminary Library, Gullixson Hall, 2375 Como Ave, Saint Paul, MN, 55108. Tel: 651-641-3226. Fax: 651-641-3280. p. 1278

Eldon, Kay, Asst Dir, Newport Public Library, 35 NW Nye St, Newport, OR, 97365-3714. Tel: 541-265-2153. Fax: 541-574-9496. p. 2007

Eldred, Janet Marie, Dir, Holidaysburg Area Public Library, 405 Clark St, Hollidaysburg, PA, 16648-2100. Tel: 814-695-5961. Fax: 814-695-6824. p. 2069

Eldred, Kim, Librn, Vermontville Township Library, 120 E First St, Vermontville, MI, 49096. Tel: 517-726-1362. Fax: 517-726-1362. p. 1233

Eldridge, Joanne, Dir, Lorain Public Library System, 351 Sixth St, Lorain, OH, 44052. Tel: 440-244-1192, Ext 227. Fax: 440-244-1733. p. 1911

Eldridge, Marlene, Librn, Noroton Presbyterian Church Library, PO Box 3401, Darien, CT, 06820. Tel: 203-655-1451. p. 336

Eldridge, Sheryl, Ref Librn, Supv Librn, Newport Public Library, 35 NW Nye St, Newport, OR, 97365-3714. Tel: 541-265-2153. Fax: 541-574-9496. p. 2007

Elgee, Charlene, Mgr, Citizen & Immigration Canada Library Services, 300 Slater St, Journal Towers N, 3rd Flr, Ottawa, ON, K1A 1L1, CANADA. Tel: 613-954-1474. Fax: 613-954-7892. p. 2830

Elgin, Fran, Librn, Victor Valley Community College Library, 18422 Bear Valley Rd, Victorville, CA, 92395-5850. Tel: 760-245-4271, Ext 2262. Fax: 760-245-4373. p. 280

Elgin-Smith, Teri, Law Librn, A Max Brewer Memorial Law Library, Harry T & Harriette V Moore Justice Ctr, 2825 Judge Fran Jamieson Way, Viera, FL, 32940. Tel: 321-617-7295. Fax: 321-617-7303. p. 502

Elguezabal, Carmen, Dir, City of Presidio Library, 1200 E O'Reilly St, Presidio, TX, 79845. Tel: 432-229-3317. Fax: 432-229-4640. p. 2372

Elguindi, Anne, Acq Librn, American University Library, 4400 Massachusetts Ave NW, Washington, DC, 20016-8046. Tel: 202-885-3840. Fax: 202-885-3226. p. 393

Elhadad, Francine, Chef de Div, Bibliothèques de Montrèal, Ahuntsic, 10300, rue Lajeunesse, Montreal, QC, H3L 2E5, CANADA. Tel: 514-872-8421. Fax: 514-872-4601. p. 2889

Elhadad, Francine, Chef de Div, Bibliothèques de Montrèal, Cartierville, 5900, rue De Salaberry, Montreal, QC, H4J 1J1, CANADA. Tel: 514-872-8421. Fax: 514-872-4601. p. 2889

Elhadad, Francine, Chef de Div, Bibliothèques de Montrèal, Salaberry, 4170, rue De Salaberry, Montreal, QC, H4J 1H1, CANADA. Tel: 514-872-8421. Fax: 514-872-4601. p. 2891

Elias, Evelyn, In Charge, CRC Press Inc Library, 6000 Broken Sound Pkwy NW, Ste 300, Boca Raton, FL, 33487. Tel: 561-994-0555. Fax: 561-998-9784. p. 428

Elias, Marie Irma, Assoc Dir, Montefiore Medical Center, 111 E 210th St, Bronx, NY, 10467. Tel: 718-920-4666. Fax: 718-920-4658. p. 1588

Eliason, Jim, Dir, Necedah Memorial Library, 216 S Main St, Necedah, WI, 54646. Tel: 608-565-7979. p. 2624

Eliason, Kari, Dir, Manhattan Community Library, 200 W Fulton Ave, Manhattan, MT, 59741. Tel: 406-284-3341, Ext 222. p. 1386

Eliason, Tember, Tech Serv Coordr, Seward Community Library Museum, 239 Six Ave, Seward, AK, 99664. Tel: 907-224-4082. Fax: 907-224-3521. p. 53

Eliceiri, Ellen, Head, Coll Develop, Head, Ref, Webster University, 101 Edgar Rd, Saint Louis, MO, 63119. Tel: 314-968-6951. Fax: 314-968-7113. p. 1363

Elie, Anthony, Pub Serv Librn, Columbia University, The Burke Library at Union Theological Seminary, 3041 Broadway, New York, NY, 10027. Tel: 212-851-5607. Fax: 212-851-5613. p. 1674

Elieson, Victoria, Dir, Sanger Public Library, 501 Bolivar St, Sanger, TX, 76266. Tel: 940-458-3257. p. 2385

Eling, Jeff, Head, Ref (Info Serv), Licking County Library, 101 W Main St, Newark, OH, 43055-5054. Tel: 740-349-5521. Fax: 740-349-5535. p. 1922

Elish, Barbara, Dir, Winthrop University Hospital, 259 First St, Mineola, NY, 11501. Tel: 516-663-2783. Fax: 516-663-8171. p. 1661

Elizabeth, Gray, Dir, Rutledge Public Library, 8030 Rutledge Pk, Rutledge, TN, 37861. Tel: 865-828-4784. Fax: 865-828-4784. p. 2264

Elizabeth, Luann, Asst Librn, Macsherry Library, 112 Walton St, Alexandria Bay, NY, 13607. Tel: 315-482-2241. Fax: 315-482-2241. p. 1572

Elizabeth, MacDonald, Dean of Libr Serv, Lindenwood University, 209 S Kingshighway, Saint Charles, MO, 63301. Tel: 636-949-4396. Fax: 636-949-4822. p. 1351

Elizabeth, Nikki, Circ Mgr, Snow College, 141 E Center St, Ephraim, UT, 84627. Tel: 435-283-7363. Fax: 435-283-7369. p. 2405

Elk, Jilda, Circ Supvr, Oral Roberts University Library, 7777 South Lewis Ave, Tulsa, OK, 74171. Tel: 918-495-6392. Fax: 918-495-6893. p. 1981

Elkington, Rene, Asst Dir, Adams County Library, 569 N Cedar St, Ste 1, Adams, WI, 53910-9800. Tel: 608-339-4250. Fax: 608-339-4575. p. 2577

Elkins, Carolyn, Asst Univ Librn, Florida Agricultural & Mechanical University Libraries, Frederic S Humphries Science Research Center, 307 Pershint St, Tallahassee, FL, 32309. Tel: 850-599-3393. Fax: 850-599-3422. p. 493

Elkins, Helen, Dir of Libr Serv, Rotan Public Library, 404 E Sammy Baugh, Rotan, TX, 79546-3820. Tel: 325-735-3362. p. 2377

Elkins, Jan, Mgr, Salt Lake County Library Services, Hunter Branch, 4740 W 4100 South, Salt Lake City, UT, 84120-4948. Tel: 801-944-7593. Fax: 801-968-8350. p. 2414

Elkins, Katy, Govt Doc, Texarkana College, 2500 N Robison Rd, Texarkana, TX, 75599. Tel: 903-832-5565, Ext 3028. Fax: 903-831-7429. p. 2391

Elkins, Rose, Acq, Supvr, National University Library, 9393 Lightwave Ave, San Diego, CA, 92123-1447. Tel: 858-541-7918. Fax: 858-541-7997. p. 232

Elkins, Steve, Asst Dir, Tech Serv, Villanova University, Law Library, Garey Hall, 299 N Spring Mill Rd, Villanova, PA, 19085. Tel: 610-519-7780. Fax: 610-519-7033. p. 2150

Elkins, Susan G, Electronic Ser Librn, Angelo State University Library, 2025 S Johnson, San Angelo, TX, 76904-5079. Tel: 325-486-6548. Fax: 325-942-2198. p. 2378

Elkins, Vicki S, Dir, Zephyrhills Public Library, 5347 Eighth St, Zephyrhills, FL, 33542. Tel: 813-780-0064. Fax: 813-780-0066. p. 505

Ellair, Jeffrey A, Dir, University of Wisconsin Sheboygan, One University Dr, Sheboygan, WI, 53081-4789. Tel: 920-459-6625. Fax: 920-459-6602. p. 2637

Elledge, Debra, Spec Coll, Portland Public Library, 301 Portland Blvd, Portland, TN, 37148-1229. Tel: 615-325-2279. Fax: 615-325-7061. p. 2263

Ellefsen, David, Dir, Great Basin College Library, 1500 College Pkwy, Elko, NV, 89801. Tel: 775-753-2222. Fax: 775-753-2296. p. 1427

Ellen, Dawn, Dir, Lee County Public Library, 200 N Main St, Bishopville, SC, 29010. Tel: 803-484-5921. Fax: 803-484-4177. p. 2182

Ellenberg, Lena, Head, Circ, Cheltenham Township Library System, Glenside Free Library, 215 S Keswick Ave, Glenside, PA, 19038-4420. Tel: 215-885-0455. Fax: 215-885-1019. p. 2061

Ellenberger, Sheila, Dr, Libr Dir, Muskingum University Library, 163 Stormont St, New Concord, OH, 43762-1199. Tel: 740-826-8260. Fax: 740-826-8404. p. 1920

Ellenberger, Valerie J, Ch, Shenango Valley Community Library, 11 N Sharpsville Ave, Sharon, PA, 16146. Tel: 724-981-4360. Fax: 724-981-5208. p. 2139

Ellenbogen, Kirsten, Dir, Science Museum of Minnesota, 120 W Kellogg Blvd, Saint Paul, MN, 55102. Tel: 651-221-9424. Fax: 651-221-4750. p. 1282

Ellenson, Melinda, Ref, Huron Public Library, 521 Dakota Ave S, Huron, SD, 57350. Tel: 605-353-8530. Fax: 605-353-8531. p. 2213

Eller, Chad, Automation Serv, Gaston-Lincoln Regional Library, 1555 E Garrison Blvd, Gastonia, NC, 28054. Tel: 704-868-2164. Fax: 704-853-6012. p. 1794

Eller, Cindy, Dir, Sheridan County Library, 801 Royal Ave, Hoxie, KS, 67740. Tel: 785-675-3102. p. 872

Eller, Jeff, Head, Tech Serv, Tulane University, Law Library, 6329 Freret St, New Orleans, LA, 70118-6231. Tel: 504-862-8866. Fax: 504-865-5917. p. 963

Eller, Linda M, Dir, National Theatre Conservatory, 1101 13th St, Denver, CO, 80204. Tel: 303-446-4869. Fax: 303-825-2117. p. 302

Eller, Stephanie Julianna, Libr Serv Mgr, Philadelphia Zoo Library, 3400 W Girard Ave, Philadelphia, PA, 19104. Tel: 215-243-5216. Fax: 215-243-0219. p. 2115

Eller Teglas, Rebecca, Ch, Larchmont Public Library, 121 Larchmont Ave, Larchmont, NY, 10538. Tel: 914-834-2281. p. 1651

Ellermann, Kay, Librn, Mohave County Historical Society, 400 W Beale St, Kingman, AZ, 86401. Tel: 928-753-3195. Fax: 928-718-1562. p. 66

Ellermann, Marissa, Pub Serv Librn, Vincennes University, Shake Learning Resources Center, 1002 N First St, Vincennes, IN, 47591. Tel: 812-888-4427. Fax: 812-888-5471. p. 784

Ellermeier, Karrie, Cat, Bennington Public Library, 15505 Warehouse St, Bennington, NE, 68007. Tel: 402-238-2201. Fax: 402-238-2218. p. 1394

Ellermeyer, Robert, Ref Serv Librn, Holy Family University Library, 9801 Frankford Ave, Philadelphia, PA, 19114. Tel: 267-341-3315, 267-341-3316. Fax: 215-632-8067. p. 2111

Ellern, Gillian, Head, Syst, Western Carolina University, 176 Central Dr, Cullowhee, NC, 28723. Tel: 828-227-3746. Fax: 828-227-7015. p. 1786

Ellett, Robert, Cat, Joint Forces Staff College Library, 7800 Hampton Blvd, Norfolk, VA, 23511-1702. Tel: 757-443-6405. Fax: 757-443-6047. p. 2481

Ellicott, Laurie, Per, Estacada Public Library, 825 NW Wade St, Estacada, OR, 97023. Tel: 503-630-8273. Fax: 503-630-8282. p. 1996

Ellifrett, Bill, Commun Relations Librn, Clarksburg-Harrison Public Library, 404 W Pike St, Clarksburg, WV, 26301. Tel: 304-627-2236. Fax: 304-627-2239. p. 2557

Elligott, Michelle, Archivist, Museum of Modern Art Library, 11 W 53rd St, New York, NY, 10019-5498. Tel: 212-708-9436. Fax: 212-333-1122. p. 1687

Ellinger, Antonette Joan, Mgr, Hay Memorial Library, 105 S Broad, Sackets Harbor, NY, 13685. Tel: 315-646-2228. Fax: 315-646-2228. p. 1737

Ellingford, Tam, Acq of Monographs, Tech Support, Battelle Energy Alliance, LLC, 1776 Science Center Dr, MS 2300, Idaho Falls, ID, 83415-2300. Tel: 208-526-1185. Fax: 208-526-0211. p. 576

Ellingham, Dawn, Head, Circ, Mokena Community Public Library District, 11327 W 195th St, Mokena, IL, 60448. Tel: 708-479-9663. Fax: 708-479-9684. p. 674

Ellinghausen, Judy, Adminr, Cascade County Historical Society Archives, High Plains Heritage Ctr, 422 Second St S, Great Falls, MT, 59405. Tel: 406-727-7474. Fax: 406-761-3805. p. 1379

Ellinghausen, Judy, Tech Serv Supvr, Great Falls Public Library, 301 Second Ave N, Great Falls, MT, 59401-2593. Tel: 406-453-0349, Ext 216. Fax: 406-453-0181. p. 1380

Ellingson, Daniel, Info Serv, Platteville Public Library, 65 S Elm, Platteville, WI, 53818. Tel: 608-348-7441. Fax: 608-348-9923. p. 2630

Ellingson, Elaine, Librn, Rolette Public Library, 1015 First Ave, Rolette, ND, 58366. Tel: 701-246-3849. p. 1848

Ellingson, Nancy, Librn, Iowa Correctional Institution for Women, 300 Elm Ave SW, Mitchellville, IA, 50169. Tel: 515-967-4236, Ext 1221. Fax: 515-967-5347. p. 832

Ellingson, Pamela F, Dir, Lakes Country Public Library, 15235 Hwy 32, Lakewood, WI, 54138. Tel: 715-276-9020. Fax: 715-276-7151. p. 2604

Ellingsworth, Ruth, Librn, Russell & District Regional Library, Binscarth Branch, 106 Russell St, Binscarth, MB, R0J 0G0, CANADA. Tel: 204-532-2447. p. 2751

Ellingsworth, Ruth, Librn, Russell & District Regional Library, PO Box 340, Russell, MB, R0J 1W0, CANADA. Tel: 204-773-3127. Fax: 204-773-3127. p. 2751

Ellington, Christy E, Asst Librn, Yadkin County Public Library, 233 E Main St, Yadkinville, NC, 27055. Tel: 336-679-8792. Fax: 336-679-4625. p. 1835

Ellington, Howard W, Exec Dir, Wichita Center for the Arts, 9112 E Central, Wichita, KS, 67206. Tel: 316-634-2787. Fax: 316-634-0593. p. 901

Elliot, Amanda, Libr Tech, County of Carleton Law Library, Ottawa Court House, 2004-161 Elgin St, Ottawa, ON, K2P 2K1, CANADA. Tel: 613-233-7386. Fax: 613-238-3788. p. 2830

Elliot, Carole, Asst Librn, Joseph Patch Library, 320 New Hampshire, Rte 25, Warren, NH, 03279-9716. Tel: 603-764-9072. p. 1467

Elliot, Paula, Tech Serv, Forbes Library, 20 West St, Northampton, MA, 01060-3798. Tel: 413-587-1011. Fax: 413-587-1015. p. 1113

Elliott, Archie, Cat, Boston University Libraries, Music Library, 771 Commonwealth Ave, Boston, MA, 02215. Tel: 617-353-3705. Fax: 617-353-2084. p. 1058

Elliott, Becky, Br Mgr, Putnam County Library, Hurricane Branch, 410 Midland Trail, Hurricane, WV, 25526. Tel: 304-562-6711. Fax: 304-562-6711. p. 2562

Elliott, Bonnie, Interim Dir, Dartmouth Heritage Museum Library, Evergreen house, 26 Newcastle St, Dartmouth, NS, B2Y 3M5, CANADA. Tel: 902-464-2300. Fax: 902-464-8210. p. 2779

Elliott, Brenda, Librn, Sebastian County Law Library, 623 Garrison Ave, Ste 418, Fort Smith, AR, 72901. Tel: 479-783-4730. Fax: 479-783-4730. p. 101

Elliott, C Danial, Arcadia Dir, Libr & Archives, Philadelphia Museum of Art Library, Ruth & Raymond G Perelman Bldg, 2525 Pennsylvania Ave, Philadelphia, PA, 19130. Tel: 215-684-7651. Fax: 215-236-0534. p. 2114

Elliott, Carol, Asst Dir, Nelson County Public Library, 201 Cathedral Manor, Bardstown, KY, 40004-1515. Tel: 502-348-3714. Fax: 502-348-5578. p. 906

Elliott, Cindy, Budget Off Mgr, Longwood University, Redford & Race St, Farmville, VA, 23909. Tel: 434-395-2440. Fax: 434-395-2453. p. 2463

Elliott, Curleen, Acq, Norwalk Community College, 188 Richards Ave, Norwalk, CT, 06854-1655. Tel: 203-857-7200. Fax: 203-857-7380. p. 362

Elliott, Dan, Adminr, First Christian Church Library, 2323 Broadway, Lubbock, TX, 79401. Tel: 806-763-1995. Fax: 806-763-5904. p. 2357

Elliott, Davis, Tech Info Spec/Libr Syst, Naval History & Heritage, 805 Kidder-Breese St SE, Washington, DC, 20374-5060. Tel: 202-433-4132. Fax: 202-433-9553. p. 411

Elliott, Donna, Ref Librn, North Merrick Public Library, 1691 Meadowbrook Rd, North Merrick, NY, 11566. Tel: 516-378-7474. Fax: 516-378-0876. p. 1706

Elliott, Dorothy, Mgr, Kansas City Public Library, Plaza, 4801 Main St, Kansas City, MO, 64112-2765. Tel: 816-701-3581. Fax: 816-701-3491. p. 1338

Elliott, Jane, Acq Asst, ILL Asst, West Virginia University Institute of Technology, 405 Fayette Pike, Montgomery, WV, 25136-2436. Tel: 304-442-3816; 304-442-3324. Fax: 304-442-3091. p. 2565

Elliott, Jennifer, Librn, Philadelphia Newspapers, Inc, 400 N Broad St, Philadelphia, PA, 19130-4099. Tel: 215-854-4660. Fax: 215-854-5697. p. 2114

Elliott, Jim, Ref, Gadsden County Public Library, 7325 Pat Thomas Pkwy, Quincy, FL, 32351. Tel: 850-627-7106. Fax: 850-627-7775. p. 485

Elliott, Jo, Mgr, Sheridan County Public Library System, Story Branch, 20 N Piney, Story, WY, 82842. Tel: 307-683-2922. Fax: 307-683-2922. p. 2660

Elliott, Joan, Librn, Saskatchewan Teachers' Federation, 2317 Arlington Ave, Saskatoon, SK, S7J 2H8, CANADA. Tel: 306-373-1660. Fax: 306-374-1122. p. 2926

Elliott, John, Coll Develop, Wayland Baptist University, 1900 W Seventh, Plainview, TX, 79072-6957. Tel: 806-291-3704. Fax: 806-291-1964. p. 2370

Elliott, John, Head, Tech Serv, Edgewood College Library, 1000 Edgewood College Dr, Madison, WI, 53711-1997. Tel: 608-663-3300. Fax: 608-663-6778. p. 2606

Elliott, Julie, Coordr, Pub Relations & Outreach, Indiana University South Bend, 1700 Mishawaka Ave, South Bend, IN, 46615. Tel: 574-520-4410. Fax: 574-520-4472. p. 778

Elliott, Karen, Coll Develop, Havana Public Library District, 201 W Adams St, Havana, IL, 62644-1321. Tel: 309-543-4701. Fax: 309-543-2715. p. 654

Elliott, Kathleen, In Charge, Cobb Institute of Archaelogy Library, Mississippi State University, Rm 206, PO Box AR, Mississippi State, MS, 39762. Tel: 662-325-3826. Fax: 662-325-8690. p. 1308

Elliott, Kelly, Librn, Lincoln County Law Association Library, 59 Church St, St. Catharines, ON, L2R 3C3, CANADA. Tel: 905-685-9094. Fax: 905-685-0981. p. 2843

Elliott, Kenneth R, Dir, Reformed Theological Seminary Library, 5422 Clinton Blvd, Jackson, MS, 39209-3099. Tel: 601-923-1623. Fax: 601-923-1621. p. 1305

Elliott, Lois, Circ Supvr, Lawrence Public Library, 51 Lawrence St, Lawrence, MA, 01841. Tel: 978-620-3600. Fax: 978-688-3142. p. 1098

Elliott, Marna, Supvr, Somerset County Library System, Washington Valley, Washington Valley Rd, Martinsville, NJ, 08836. Tel: 732-356-2363. p. 1475

Elliott, Mildred, Librn, Sheppard Memorial Library, George Washington Carver Library, 618 W 14th Ave, Greenville, NC, 27834-3016. Tel: 252-329-4583. Fax: 252-329-4126. p. 1799

Elliott, Pinkey, Coordr, Mohave County Library District, Meadview Community Library, 149 Meadview Blvd, Meadview, AZ, 86444. Tel: 928-564-2535. Fax: 928-564-2535. p. 67

Elliott, Riette Susie, Chief Librn, Bevill State Community College, 1411 Indiana Ave, Jasper, AL, 35501-4967. Tel: 205-387-0511, Ext 5718. Fax: 205-387-5190. p. 23

Elliott, Stuart, Pres, Clay County Archives & Historical Library, 210 E Franklin St, Liberty, MO, 64068-1790. Tel: 816-781-3611. p. 1343

Elliott, Susan, Tech Serv Dir, Odessa College, 201 W University Blvd, Odessa, TX, 79764. Tel: 432-335-6640. Fax: 432-335-6610. p. 2366

Elliott, Susan N, Asst Dir, Pub Serv, University of Dayton School of Law, 300 College Park, Dayton, OH, 45469-2780. Tel: 937-229-2314. Fax: 937-229-2555. p. 1894

Elliott, Tamara, Ref, United States Senate Library, SRB-15 Senate Russell Bldg, Washington, DC, 20510-7112. Tel: 202-224-7106. Fax: 202-224-0879. p. 421

Elliott, Todd, Dir, Portsmouth Public Library, 601 Court St, Portsmouth, VA, 23704-3604. Tel: 757-393-8501. p. 2485

Elliott, Todd, Ref Librn, Tidewater Community College, 1700 College Crescent, Virginia Beach, VA, 23453. Fax: 757-427-0327. p. 2500

Elliott, Tracy, Dir, Manatee Community College Library, 5840 26th St W, Bradenton, FL, 34207. Tel: 941-752-5399. Fax: 941-752-5308. p. 429

Elliott, Tracy, Head Librn/Prog Dir II, Saint Petersburg College, Saint Petersburg-Gibbs Campus Library, 6605 Fifth Ave N, Saint Petersburg, FL, 33710. Tel: 727-341-7197. Fax: 727-341-7188. p. 483

Elliott, Valerie E, Libr Mgr, Lane Public Libraries, Smith Library of Regional History, 15 S College Ave, Oxford, OH, 45056. Tel: 513-523-3035. Fax: 513-523-6661. p. 1904

Elliott-Coutts, Nora, Head, Ch, North Bay Public Library, 271 Worthington St E, North Bay, ON, P1B 1H1, CANADA. Tel: 705-474-4830. Fax: 705-495-4010. p. 2825

Ellis, Aimee, Head of Libr, Department of Indian Affairs & Northern Development, 335-300 Main St, Whitehorse, YT, Y1A 2B5, CANADA. Tel: 867-667-3111. Fax: 867-667-3888. p. 2934

Ellis, Anne, Br Mgr, Abilene Public Library, Mockingbird Branch, 1214 N Mockingbird, Abilene, TX, 79603. Tel: 325-437-7323. p. 2272

Ellis, Annie, Asst Librn, Boonville Community Public Library, 121 W Main St, Boonville, NC, 27011-9125. Tel: 336-367-7737. Fax: 336-367-7767. p. 1777

Ellis, Barbara Gail, Info Serv Librn, Lutheran Brethren Seminary, 815 W Vernon Ave, Fergus Falls, MN, 56537. Tel: 218-739-1248. p. 1251

Ellis, Barbara S, Dir, Hershey Public Library, 701 Cocoa Ave, Hershey, PA, 17033. Tel: 717-533-6555, Ext 3715. Fax: 717-534-1666. p. 2069

Ellis, Billy, Head, Res Serv, Troutman Sanders LLP, 600 Peachtree St NE, Ste 5200, Atlanta, GA, 30308-2216. Tel: 404-885-3196. Fax: 404-962-6783. p. 518

Ellis, Bonni, Circ Serv Mgr, St Charles Public Library District, One S Sixth Ave, Saint Charles, IL, 60174-2105. Tel: 630-584-0076, Ext 257. Fax: 630-584-3448. p. 699

Ellis, Bonnie, Librn, Edmondson Public Library, 61 Waterford St, Edmondson, AR, 72332. Tel: 870-735-6946. Fax: 870-735-6988. p. 98

Ellis, Danelle, Pub Serv, Tarrant County College, Northwest Campus Walsh Library, 4801 Marine Creek Pkwy, Fort Worth, TX, 76179. Tel: 817-515-7725. Fax: 817-515-7720. p. 2323

Ellis, David, Br Mgr, Los Angeles Public Library System, San Pedro Regional, 931 S Gaffey St, San Pedro, CA, 90731-1349. Tel: 310-548-7779. Fax: 310-548-7453. p. 174

Ellis, Devon, Br Mgr, Enoch Pratt Free Library, Hampden, 3641 Falls Rd, Baltimore, MD, 21211-1815. Tel: 410-396-6043. Fax: 410-396-7152. p. 1013

Ellis, Donna, Br Mgr, Tulare County Library, Springville Branch, 35800 Hwy 190, Springville, CA, 93265. Tel: 559-539-2624. Fax: 559-539-6307. p. 281

Ellis, Donna, Br Mgr, Tulare County Library, Strathmore Branch, 19646 Rd 230, Strathmore, CA, 93267-9608. Tel: 559-568-1087. Fax: 559-568-0633. p. 281

Ellis, Elizabeth, Youth Serv Coordr, Louisburg Public Library, 206 S Broadway, Louisburg, KS, 66053. Tel: 913-837-2217. Fax: 913-837-2218. p. 880

Ellis, Glen, Libr Tech, City of Winnipeg Water & Waste Department, 1199 Pacific Ave, Winnipeg, MB, R3E 3S8, CANADA. Tel: 204-986-3250. Fax: 204-224-0032. p. 2755

Ellis, Jean, Sr Librn, Ref, Passaic Public Library, 195 Gregory Ave, Passaic, NJ, 07055. Tel: 973-779-0474. Fax: 973-779-0889. p. 1518

Ellis, Jill, Tech Serv, Western Nebraska Community College Library, 1601 E 27th NE, Scottsbluff, NE, 69361-1899. Tel: 308-635-6040. Fax: 308-635-6086. p. 1418

Ellis, Joyce M, Dir, Minnie Stevens Piper Foundation, 1250 NE Loop 410, Ste 810, San Antonio, TX, 78209-1539. Tel: 210-525-8494. Fax: 210-341-6627. p. 2381

Ellis, Judith, In Charge, Zeeland Community Hospital, 8333 Felch St, Zeeland, MI, 49464. Tel: 616-772-5775. Fax: 616-748-8748. p. 1238

Ellis, Julie, Head, Access Serv, Biola University Library, 13800 Biola Ave, La Mirada, CA, 90639. Tel: 562-944-0351, Ext 5604. Fax: 562-903-4840. p. 162

Ellis, Karen, Dir, Taylor Public Library, 801 Vance St, Taylor, TX, 76574. Tel: 512-352-3434. Fax: 512-352-8080. p. 2390

Ellis, Kathy, Librn, Moody Community Library, 108 Fifth St, Moody, TX, 76557. Tel: 254-853-2004. Fax: 254-853-9704. p. 2363

Ellis, Lawrence E, Dir, Libr Serv, Newberry College, 2100 College St, Newberry, SC, 29108-2197. Tel: 803-321-5229. Fax: 803-321-5232. p. 2201

Ellis, Mark, Head, Govt Doc, East Tennessee State University, Sherrod Library, Seehorn Dr & Lake St, Johnson City, TN, 37614-0204. Tel: 423-439-4715. Fax: 423-439-5222. p. 2239

Ellis, Mark, Mgr, Ref & Info Serv, Richmond Public Library, 100-7700 Minoru Gate, Richmond, BC, V6Y 1R9, CANADA. Tel: 604-231-6410. Fax: 604-273-0459. p. 2736

Ellis, Mary, Br Supvr, Pine Bluff & Jefferson County Library System, White Hall Public Library, 300 Anderson St, White Hall, AR, 71602. Tel: 870-267-1564. Fax: 870-247-2613. p. 112

Ellis, Mary, Dir, Hyndman Londonderry Public Library, 161 Clarence St, Hyndman, PA, 15545. Tel: 814-842-3782. Fax: 814-842-3737. p. 2070

Ellis, Mary Ellen, Librn, Mid-Mississippi Regional Library System, Carthage-Leake County, 114 E Franklin St, Carthage, MS, 39051-3716. Tel: 601-267-7821. Fax: 601-267-5530. p. 1306

Ellis, Melinda, Dir, Hazel M Lewis Library, 511 Third Ave, Powers, OR, 97466. Tel: 541-439-5311. Fax: 541-439-5311. p. 2015

Ellis, Natalie P, Chief Librn, Attorney General's Office, 200 Saint Paul Pl, 18th Flr, Baltimore, MD, 21202. Tel: 410-576-6400. Fax: 410-576-7002. p. 1011

Ellis, Patricia, Librn, Southborough Public Library, 25 Main St, Southborough, MA, 01772. Tel: 508-485-5031. Fax: 508-229-4451. p. 1126

Ellis, Patrick, Head of Libr, Dalhousie University, W K Kellogg Health Sciences Library, Tupper Medical Bldg, 5850 College St, Halifax, NS, B3H 1X5, CANADA. p. 2780

Ellis, Patsy S, Librn, James H Quillen VA Medical Center, Lamont & Sidney Sts, Mountain Home, TN, 37684. Tel: 423-926-1171, Ext 7452, 423-926-1171, Ext 7453. Fax: 423-979-3440. p. 2254

Ellis, Roseann, Br Mgr, Colusa County Free Library, Grimes Branch, 240 Main St, Grimes, CA, 95950. Tel: 530-437-2428. Fax: 530-437-2428. p. 136

Ellis, Rosemary, Cat, Roane State Community College Library, 276 Patton Lane, Harriman, TN, 37748. Tel: 865-354-4464. Fax: 865-882-4562. p. 2236

Ellis, Sarita, Head Librn, Meridian Public Library, 118 N Main St, Meridian, TX, 76665. Tel: 254-435-9100. Fax: 254-435-9800. p. 2362

Ellis, Shannon, Asst Librn, Pemberton & District Public Library, 7390 Cottonwood St, Pemberton, BC, V0N 2L0, CANADA. Tel: 604-894-6916. Fax: 604-894-6916. p. 2735

Ellis, Tamara R, Dir, Dally Memorial Library, 37252 Mound St, Sardis, OH, 43946. Tel: 740-483-1288. Fax: 740-483-2311. p. 1934

Ellis, Teresa, Theological Librn, Hardin-Simmons University, 2341 Hickory St, Abilene, TX, 79698. Tel: 325-670-1236. Fax: 325-677-8351. p. 2272

Ellis, Ursula, Mgr, Deaconess Hospital, 5501 N Portland, Oklahoma City, OK, 73112-2097. Tel: 405-604-4523. p. 1971

Ellis-Danquah, La Ventra, Librn III, Wayne State University Libraries, Vera P Shiffman Medical Library & Learning Resources Centers,

Rackham Bldg Rm 044, 60 Farnsworth, Detroit, MI, 48202. Tel: 313-577-9083. Fax: 313-577-6668. p. 1173

Ellison, Alicia, Librn, Hillsborough Community College, Ybor City Campus Learning Resources Center, 1502 E Ninth Ave, Tampa, FL, 33605. Tel: 813-253-7731. Fax: 813-259-6070. p. 496

Ellison, Anne, Coll Develop, Madison County Library System, 102 Priestley St, Canton, MS, 39046-4599. p. 1295

Ellison, Beecher, Law Librn, Josephine County Law Library, County Courthouse, 500 NW Sixth St, Grants Pass, OR, 97526. Tel: 541-474-5488. Fax: 541-474-5223. p. 1999

Ellison, David J, Coll Develop Coordr, Manitowoc Public Library, 707 Quay St, Manitowoc, WI, 54220. Tel: 920-686-3000. p. 2612

Ellison, Kurt, Br Mgr, Monterey County Free Libraries, Castroville Branch, 11160 Speegle St, Castroville, CA, 95012. Tel: 831-769-8724. Fax: 831-633-6315. p. 183

Ellison, Mary, Ch, Western District Library, 1111 Fourth St, Orion, IL, 61273. Tel: 309-526-8375. Fax: 309-526-8375. p. 686

Ellison, Shari, Br Mgr, Mid-Continent Public Library, Smithville Branch, 120 Richardson St, Smithville, MO, 64089-9038. Tel: 816-532-0116. Fax: 816-532-0145. p. 1333

Ellison, Tammy, Asst Librn, Culver-Stockton College, One College Hill, Canton, MO, 63435. Tel: 573-288-6641. Fax: 573-288-6615. p. 1321

Elliston, Margaret, Archivist, St Thomas University Library, 16401 NW 37th Ave, Miami Gardens, FL, 33054. Tel: 305-648-6669. Fax: 305-628-6666. p. 469

Ells, Jean, Reader Serv Mgr, Wake County Public Library System, Cameron Village Regional Library, 1930 Clark Ave, Raleigh, NC, 27605. Tel: 919-856-6727. Fax: 919-856-6722. p. 1817

Ellshoff, Coral, Libr Dir, Punxsutawney Memorial Library, 301 E Mahoning St, Punxsutawney, PA, 15767-2198. Tel: 814-938-5020. Fax: 814-938-3180. p. 2132

Ellsworth, Leslie K, Head, Circ, Olathe Public Library, 201 E Park St, Olathe, KS, 66061. Tel: 913-971-6856. Fax: 913-971-6809. p. 886

Ellsworth, Marie, Dir, Librn, Caldwell-Lake George Library, 336 Canada St, Lake George, NY, 12845-1118. Tel: 518-668-2528. Fax: 518-668-2528. p. 1650

Ellwanger, Kerry, Librn, National College, Charlottesville Campus Library, 1819 Emmet St, Charlottesville, VA, 22901. Tel: 434-295-0136. Fax: 434-979-8061. p. 2495

Ellwanger, Richard, Dir, Seminole Nation Museum Library, 524 S Wewoka, Wewoka, OK, 74884. Tel: 405-257-5580. p. 1986

Ellzey, John, Ref, Ricks Memorial Library (Yazoo Library Association), 310 N Main St, Yazoo City, MS, 39194-4253. Tel: 662-746-5557. Fax: 662-746-7309. p. 1318

Elman, Caroline, Ref Librn, Providence Holy Cross Medical Center, 15031 Rinaldi St, Mission Hills, CA, 91346-9600. Tel: 818-496-4545. Fax: 818-496-4481. p. 187

Elman, Sarah S, Head, Tech Serv, Columbia University, C V Starr East Asian Library, 300 Kent Hall, MC 3901, 1140 Amsterdam Ave, New York, NY, 10027. Tel: 212-854-4318. Fax: 212-662-6286. p. 1675

Elmborg, James K, Dr, Assoc Prof, University of Iowa, 3087 Main Library, Iowa City, IA, 52242-1420. Tel: 319-335-5707. Fax: 319-335-5374. p. 2965

Elmer, David, Asst Curator, Harvard Library, Milman Parry Collection of Oral Literature, Widener, Rm MC, Cambridge, MA, 02138. Tel: 617-496-2499. p. 1076

Elmore, Janice, Adult Serv, Steger-South Chicago Heights Public Library District, 54 E 31st St, Steger, IL, 60475. Tel: 708-755-5040. Fax: 708-755-2504. p. 707

Elmore, Julie, Dir, Oakland City-Columbia Township Public Library, 210 S Main, Oakland City, IN, 47660. Tel: 812-749-3559. Fax: 812-749-3558. p. 771

Elmore, Leslie, Cat, Ref Serv, Notre Dame de Namur University Library, 1500 Ralston Ave, Belmont, CA, 94002-1908. Tel: 650-508-3435. Fax: 650-508-3697. p. 126

Elmore, Linda, Librn, United States Department of the Interior, W 904 Riverside Ave, Rm 202, Spokane, WA, 99201. Tel: 509-368-3101. Fax: 509-368-3199. p. 2538

Elmore, Michael, Tech Serv, Barnard College, 3009 Broadway, New York, NY, 10027-6598. Tel: 212-854-3953. p. 1670

Elmore, Rheena, Dir, Faulkner State Community College, 1900 Hwy 31 S, Bay Minette, AL, 36507. Tel: 251-580-2145. Fax: 251-937-5140. p. 6

Elo, Jennifer A, Adminr, Crafton United Presbyterian Church Library, 80 Bradford Ave, Pittsburgh, PA, 15205. Tel: 412-921-2293. Fax: 412-921-0348. p. 2124

Eloe, Richard, Br Mgr, San Bernardino County Library, Lake Arrowhead, 27235 Hwy 189, Blue Jay, CA, 92317. Tel: 909-337-3118. Fax: 909-337-2287. p. 228

Eloise, Stemmle, Librn, Jewish Community Center, 3600 Dutchman's Lane, Louisville, KY, 40205. Tel: 502-459-0660, Ext 107. Fax: 502-459-6885. p. 924

Eloyan, Arpine, Ch, Glendale Public Library, Pacific Park, 501 S Pacific Ave, Glendale, CA, 91204. Tel: 818-548-3760. Fax: 818-409-7154. p. 155

Elpern, Joanne, Doc Delivery, ILL, Western Connecticut State University, 181 White St, Danbury, CT, 06810. Tel: 203-837-9114. Fax: 203-837-9108. p. 335

Elphick, Sue, Head, Circ, Boyertown Community Library, 29 E Philadelphia Ave, Boyertown, PA, 19512-1124. Tel: 610-369-0496. Fax: 610-369-0542. p. 2036

Elridge, Eartha, Asst Librn, Myers University, 3921 Chester Ave, Cleveland, OH, 44114. Tel: 216-432-8990. Fax: 216-426-9296. p. 1880

Elrod, Dianne, Acq, Haltom City Public Library, 4809 Haltom Rd, Haltom City, TX, 76117-3622. Tel: 817-222-7793. Fax: 817-834-1446. p. 2330

Elrod, Melisa, Cat, R W Norton Art Gallery, 4747 Creswell Ave, Shreveport, LA, 71106-1899. Tel: 318-865-4201. Fax: 318-869-0435. p. 968

Elrod, Velvet Lace, Br Mgr, Aiken-Bamberg-Barnwell-Edgefield Regional Library System, Denmark Branch, 19 Maple Ave, Denmark, SC, 29042. Tel: 803-793-4511. Fax: 803-793-4511. p. 2179

Elsa, Sue, ILL, East Bonner County Free Library District, 1407 Cedar St, Sandpoint, ID, 83864-2052. Tel: 208-263-6930. Fax: 208-263-8320. p. 583

Elsea, Amanda, Librn, Silverpeak Library, Goldfield Public Library, 233 Crook St, Goldfield, NV, 89013. Tel: 775-485-3236. Fax: 775-485-3236. p. 1434

Elsea, Margaret, Br Mgr, Sullivan County Public Library, 1655 Blountville Blvd, Blountville, TN, 37617. Tel: 423-279-2714. Fax: 423-279-2836. p. 2224

Elsen, Carol, Coll Develop Mgr, Instrul Serv Librn, Ref Serv, University of Wisconsin-Whitewater Library, 800 W Main St, Whitewater, WI, 53190. Tel: 262-472-5751. Fax: 262-472-5727. p. 2649

Elser, Carl, Br Mgr, San Bernardino County Library, Rialto Branch, 251 W First St, Rialto, CA, 92376. Tel: 909-875-0144. Fax: 909-875-2801. p. 229

Elsmlie, Kirsty, Br Head, Vancouver Public Library, Hastings, 2674 E Hastings St, Vancouver, BC, V5K 1Z6, CANADA. Tel: 604-665-3959. Fax: 604-665-3930. p. 2744

Elsner, Ann, Dir, Admin Serv, Duke University Libraries, 411 Chapel Dr, Durham, NC, 27708. Tel: 919-660-5947. Fax: 919-660-5923. p. 1787

Elsner, Betsy L, Circ Mgr, Erskine College & Theological Seminary, One Depot St, Due West, SC, 29639. Tel: 864-379-8898. Fax: 864-379-2900. p. 2193

Elsner, Jackie, Br Mgr, Athens Regional Library System, Oconee County - Watkinsville Branch, 1080 Experiment Station Rd, Watkinsville, GA, 30677. Tel: 706-769-3951. Fax: 706-769-3952. p. 509

Elson, Kathy, Acq & ILL Tech, Alberta Government Library, 10025 Jasper Ave, 15th Flr, Edmonton, AB, T5J 2N3, CANADA. Tel: 780-415-0223. Fax: 780-422-9694. p. 2698

Elston, Carol, Librn, Hope City Library, PO Box 115, Hope, ND, 58046-0115. Tel: 701-945-2796. p. 1844

Elsweiler, John, Assoc Dean, Pub Serv, Utah State University, 3000 Old Main Hill, Logan, UT, 84322-3000. Tel: 435-797-2636. Fax: 435-797-2880. p. 2407

Elthinstone, Cara, Librn, Parkland Regional Library, Wadena Branch, 86 First St NE, Wadena, SK, S0A 4J0, CANADA. Tel: 306-338-2293. p. 2932

Elton, Sandra, Librn, Lincoln Correctional Center Library, 3216 W Van Dorn St, Lincoln, NE, 68522. Tel: 402-471-2861, Ext 6137. Fax: 402-479-6100. p. 1405

Elturk, Mary Byrne, Adult Serv, Ref Serv, Pacific Grove Public Library, 550 Central Ave, Pacific Grove, CA, 93950-2789. Tel: 831-648-5760, Ext 17. Fax: 831-373-3268. p. 203

Eltus, Maria Ileana, Circ, North Miami Beach Public Library, 1601 NE 164th St, North Miami Beach, FL, 33162-4099. Tel: 305-948-2970. Fax: 305-787-6007. p. 473

Elum, Hatatu, Librn, G Robert Cotton Regional Correctional Facility Library, 3500 N Elm Rd, Jackson, MI, 49201. Tel: 517-780-5172. Fax: 517-780-5100. p. 1195

Elusta, Grushenska, ILL, Broward College, 3501 SW Davie Rd, Davie, FL, 33314. Tel: 954-201-6648. Fax: 954-201-6490. p. 435

Elve, Renay, Syst Mgr, Cromaine District Library, 3688 N Hartland Rd, Hartland, MI, 48353. Tel: 810-632-5200, Ext 100. p. 1189

Elvey, Luann, Librn, Iosco-Arenac District Library, East Tawas Branch, 204 Sawyer St, East Tawas, MI, 48730. Tel: 989-362-6162. Fax: 989-362-1449. p. 1176

Elvidge, Marlaine, Head of Libr, West Grey Public Library, 240 Garafraxa St N, Durham, ON, N0G 1R0, CANADA. Tel: 519-369-2107. Fax: 519-369-9966. p. 2803

Elvin, Donna, Librn, Marquette Community Library, 121 N Washington, Marquette, KS, 67464-0389. Tel: 785-546-2561. p. 882

Elwell, Brent, Actg Librn, Maine Department of Corrections, Bolduc Correctional Facility Library, 516 Cushing Rd, Warren, ME, 04864. Tel: 207-273-2036. Fax: 207-273-5124. p. 1004

Elwell, Kathy, Asst Dir, Ramsey Free Public Library, 30 Wyckoff Ave, Ramsey, NJ, 07446. Tel: 201-327-1445. Fax: 201-327-3687. p. 1525

Elwess, Carolyn, Archivist, Park University Library, 8700 NW River Park Dr, Parkville, MO, 64152. Tel: 816-584-6891. Fax: 816-741-4911. p. 1349

Elwood, Marjorie, Mgr, Jefferson County Public Library, Belmar, 555 S Alison Pkwy, Lakewood, CO, 80226. p. 315

Ely, Chris, Librn, Whitewright Public Library, 200 Grand St, Whitewright, TX, 75491. Tel: 903-364-2955. Fax: 903-364-5680. p. 2400

Ely, Laura, Asst Librn, Wyalusing Public Library, 202 Church St, Wyalusing, PA, 18853. Tel: 570-746-1711. Fax: 570-746-1671. p. 2158

Ely, Steve, Ref Librn, West Texas A&M University, University Dr & 26th St, Canyon, TX, 79016. Tel: 806-651-2229. Fax: 806-651-2213. p. 2294

Ely, Yasuko, Tech Serv, Susquehanna County Historical Society & Free Library Association, Two Monument Sq, Montrose, PA, 18801-1115. Tel: 570-278-1881. Fax: 570-278-9336. p. 2092

Emadi, Lori, Head, Metadata & Taxonomy, RAND Corporation Library, 1776 Main St, M1LIB, Santa Monica, CA, 90407. Tel: 310-393-0411, Ext 7788. Fax: 310-451-7029. p. 266

Emart, Melanie, Librn, Competition Tribunal Library, 90 Sparks St, Ste 600, Ottawa, ON, K1P 5B4, CANADA. Tel: 613-957-7850. Fax: 613-957-3170. p. 2830

Embree, Anna, Assoc Prof, University of Alabama, 514 Main Library, Tuscaloosa, AL, 35487. Tel: 205-348-4610. Fax: 205-348-3746. p. 2961

Embree, Julia, Dir, Nora Sparks Warren Library, 210 N Willow St, Pauls Valley, OK, 73075. Tel: 405-238-5188. Fax: 405-238-5188. p. 1976

Embrey, Barbara, Coordr, APA - The Engineered Wood Association, 7011 S 19th St, Tacoma, WA, 98466-5333. Tel: 253-565-6600, Ext 461. Fax: 253-565-7265. p. 2538

Embry, Connie, Asst Librn, Butler County Public Library, 116 W Ohio St, Morgantown, KY, 42261. Tel: 270-526-4722. Fax: 270-526-4722. p. 930

Emde, Sue, Govt Doc, University of Iowa Libraries, Law Library, 200 Boyd Law Bldg, Iowa City, IA, 52242-1166. Tel: 319-335-9040. Fax: 319-335-9039. p. 823

Emdy, Aaron, Cat, Van Alstyne Public Library, 151 W Cooper St, Van Alstyne, TX, 75495. Tel: 903-482-5991. Fax: 903-482-1316. p. 2395

Emel, Astrid, Circ Librn, Saint John's University Library, Rittenberg Law Library, 8000 Utopia Pkwy, Queens, NY, 11439. Tel: 718-990-6651, 718-990-6659. Fax: 718-990-6649. p. 1725

Emeley, Linda, Curator, Ray County Historical Society & Museum Library, 901 W Royle St, Richmond, MO, 64085-1545. Tel: 816-776-2305. p. 1350

Emerick, Dan, Librn, State Library of Florida, The Capitol, Rm 701, Tallahassee, FL, 32399. Tel: 850-245-6799. p. 495

Emerson, Claudine, Dir, Berry Memorial Library, 93 Main St, Bar Mills, ME, 04004. Tel: 207-929-5484. p. 976

Emerson, Jill, YA Librn, Maryville Public Library, 509 N Main, Maryville, MO, 64468. Tel: 660-582-5281. Fax: 660-582-2411. p. 1344

Emerson, Laurie, Ch, Otis Library, Two Cliff St, Norwich, CT, 06360. Tel: 860-889-2365. Fax: 860-886-4744. p. 362

Emerson, Linda, Asst Librn, Mullan Public Library, 117 Hunter Ave, Mullan, ID, 83846. Tel: 208-744-1220. Fax: 208-744-1220. p. 580

Emerson, Linda, Br Mgr, Nashville Public Library, Hadley Park, 1039 28th Ave N, Nashville, TN, 37208-2809. Tel: 615-862-5865. Fax: 615-862-5887. p. 2257

Emerson, Melanie E, Reader Serv Librn, Art Institute of Chicago, 111 S Michigan Ave, Chicago, IL, 60603. Tel: 312-443-3671. Fax: 312-443-0849. p. 606

Emerson, Nancy G, Asst Mgr, San Diego Museum of Art Library, 1450 El Prado, San Diego, CA, 92101. Tel: 619-696-1958. Fax: 619-232-9367. p. 235

Emerson, Sally, Acq, Southern California Genealogical Society, 417 Irving Dr, Burbank, CA, 91504-2408. Tel: 818-843-7247. Fax: 818-843-7262. p. 130

Emerson, Steve, Dr, Dir, California Baptist University, 8432 Magnolia Ave, Riverside, CA, 92504. Tel: 951-343-4228. p. 216

Emery, Amber, Ch, Fargo Public Library, 102 N Third St, Fargo, ND, 58102. Tel: 701-241-1495. Fax: 701-241-8581. p. 1841

Emery, Amy, Coordr, Acq, Tigard Public Library, 13500 SW Hall Blvd, Tigard, OR, 97223-8111. Tel: 503-684-6537, Ext 2513. Fax: 503-598-7515, 503-718-2797. p. 2021

Emery, Jill, Coll Develop Librn, Portland State University Library, 1875 SW Park Ave, Portland, OR, 97201-3220. Tel: 503-725-4506. Fax: 503-725-4524. p. 2014

Emery, Pauline, Dir, Southeast Steuben County Library, 300 Civic Center Plaza, Ste 101, Corning, NY, 14830. Tel: 607-936-3713. Fax: 607-936-1714. p. 1611

Emery, Rayeanna, Circ Supvr, Perry County Public Library, 289 Black Gold Blvd, Hazard, KY, 41701. Tel: 606-436-2475, 606-436-4747. Fax: 606-436-0191. p. 917

Emery, Robert, Asst Dir, Albany Law School, 80 New Scotland Ave, Albany, NY, 12208. Tel: 518-445-2340. Fax: 518-472-5842. p. 1568

Emery, Sharla, Dir, Carteret Free Public Library, 100 Cooke Ave, Carteret, NJ, 07008. Tel: 732-541-3830. Fax: 732-541-6948. p. 1478

Emesih, Stephanie, Librn, Houston Community College Central College, Central Campus Library, 1300 Holman, Houston, TX, 77004. Tel: 713-718-6133. Fax: 713-718-6154. p. 2337

Emin, Sonel, Automation Syst Coordr, Nassau Community College, One Education Dr, Garden City, NY, 11530-6793. Tel: 516-572-7400. Fax: 516-572-7846. p. 1626

Emlen, Candy, Librn, Southwest Harbor Public Library, 338 Main St, Southwest Harbor, ME, 04679. Tel: 207-244-7065. Fax: 207-244-7065. p. 1002

Emmert, Joan, Br Mgr, Indianapolis-Marion County Public Library, Infozone, The Children's Museum, 3000 N Meridian St, Indianapolis, IN, 46208. Tel: 317-275-4430. p. 754

Emmett, Gail, Ser Spec, Gainesville State College, 3820 Mundy Mill Rd, Oakwood, GA, 30566. Tel: 678-717-3840. Fax: 770-718-3657. p. 547

Emmons, Myra, Dir, Brookline Public Library, 16 Main St, Brookline, NH, 03033. Tel: 603-673-3330. Fax: 603-673-0735. p. 1440

Emmons, Paul, Music, West Chester University, 25 W Rosedale Ave, West Chester, PA, 19383. Tel: 610-436-2379. p. 2153

Emmons, Paul, Music Librn, West Chester University, Presser Music Library, School of Music & Performing Arts Center, West Chester, PA, 19383. Tel: 610-436-2379, 610-436-2430. Fax: 610-436-2873. p. 2154

Emmons, Paula, Dir, Coweta Public Library, 120 E Sycamore, Coweta, OK, 74429. Tel: 918-486-6532. Fax: 918-486-3497. p. 1961

Emmons, Tim, Reader Serv, Alabama Public Library Service, 6030 Monticello Dr, Montgomery, AL, 36130-6000. Tel: 334-213-3906. Fax: 334-213-3993. p. 27

Emmons-Andarawis, Deborah, Curator, Van Rensselear - Rankin Family Historic Cherry Hill Museum & Library, 523 1/2 S Pearl St, Albany, NY, 12202. Tel: 518-434-4791. Fax: 518-434-4806. p. 1571

Emmrich, Mary K, Dir, Newton County Public Library, 9444 N 315 W, Lake Village, IN, 46349. Tel: 219-992-3490. Fax: 219-992-9198. p. 760

Emon, Danielle, Cat, Libr Tech, Tech Serv, The Parrott Centre, 376 Wallbridge-Loyalist Rd, Belleville, ON, K8N 5B9, CANADA. Tel: 613-969-1913, Ext 2183. Fax: 613-969-5183. p. 2795

Emond, James, Librn, Bristol Community College, 777 Elsbree St, Fall River, MA, 02720. Tel: 508-678-2811, Ext 2316. Fax: 508-730-3270. p. 1088

Emond, Julie, Libr Tech, Institut Universitaire de Cardiologie et de Pneumologie de Québec Bibliotheque, 2725 Chemin Ste-Foy, Quebec, QC, G1V 4G5, CANADA. Tel: 418-656-4563. Fax: 418-656-4720. p. 2905

Emons, Margaret, Head, Tech Serv, Nebraska Wesleyan University, 50th & St Paul, Lincoln, NE, 68504. Tel: 402-465-2400. Fax: 402-465-2189. p. 1406

Emory, Gina, Tech Coordr, East Bonner County Free Library District, 1407 Cedar St, Sandpoint, ID, 83864-2052. Tel: 208-263-6930. Fax: 208-263-8320. p. 583

Emperado, Mercedes Lopez, Head of Libr, FEMA/DHS Library, 500 C St SW, Rm 123, Washington, DC, 20472. Tel: 202-646-3771. Fax: 202-646-4295. p. 400

Empey, Jacque, Dir, Jordanville Public Library, 189 Main St, Jordanville, NY, 13361-2729. Tel: 315-858-2874. Fax: 315-858-2874. p. 1648

Emprimo, David, Tech Serv, Jacksonville Public Library, 502 S Jackson St, Jacksonville, TX, 75766. Tel: 903-586-7664. Fax: 903-586-3397. p. 2347

Emrich, Priscilla E, Librn, Murphy Memorial Library, 601 W Church St, Livingston, TX, 77351. Tel: 936-327-4252. Fax: 936-327-4162. p. 2356

Emrick, Matt, Librn, Parkersburg & Wood County Public Library, Williamstown Branch, 201 W Fifth St, Williamstown, WV, 26187. Tel: 304-375-6052. Fax: 304-375-6052. p. 2568

Emrick, Sue, Ch, Upper Arlington Public Library, Lane Road Branch, 1945 Lane Rd, Upper Arlington, OH, 43220. Tel: 614-459-0273. Fax: 614-459-3437. p. 1891

Emsig, Maryann, Librn, Good Samaritan Hospital, 1000 Montauk Hwy, West Islip, NY, 11795. Tel: 631-376-3380. Fax: 631-376-4166. p. 1766

Emter, Adam, Pub Relations Coordr, North Dakota State Library, Library Memorial Bldg, 604 East Blvd Ave, Dept 250, Bismarck, ND, 58505-0800. Tel: 701-328-4656. Fax: 701-328-2040. p. 1838

Emuke, Fiona, Librn, Parkland Regional Library, Foam Lake Branch, 402 Cameron St, Foam Lake, SK, S0A 1A0, CANADA. Tel: 306-272-3660. p. 2932

Encarnacion-Torres, Jorge, Prof, University of Puerto Rico, Rio Piedras Campus, PO Box 21906, San Juan, PR, 00931-1906. Tel: 787-764-0000, Ext 1286, 787-764-0000, Ext 5028. Fax: 787-764-2311. p. 2977

Encarnado, Marillyn, Asst Librn, Mercy Hospital & Medical Center, 2525 S Michigan Ave, Chicago, IL, 60616-2477. Tel: 312-567-2363. Fax: 312-567-7086. p. 618

Encinas, Angela, Br Mgr, San Bernardino Public Library, Paul Villasenor Branch, 525 N Mount Vernon Ave, San Bernardino, CA, 90411. Tel: 909-383-5156. Fax: 909-381-1766. p. 229

Encinas, Veronica, Ref Serv, Los Alamos County Library System, 2400 Central Ave, Los Alamos, NM, 87544. Tel: 505-662-8240. Fax: 505-662-8245. p. 1559

Endelman, Judith E, Dir, The Henry Ford, 20900 Oakwood Blvd, Dearborn, MI, 48124-5029. Tel: 313-982-6020, 313-982-6070. Fax: 313-982-6244. p. 1167

Ender, Deniz, Mrs, Managing Librn, Rex Healthcare Library, 4420 Lake Boone Trail, Raleigh, NC, 27607. Tel: 919-784-3032. Fax: 919-784-1670. p. 1816

Enderle, Karen H, Dir, Louis Bennett Public Library, 148 Court Ave, Weston, WV, 26452. Tel: 304-269-5151. Fax: 304-269-7332. p. 2574

Enders, Naulayne, Asst Librn, Kentucky Christian University, 100 Academic Pkwy, Grayson, KY, 41143-2205. Tel: 606-474-3240. Fax: 606-474-3123. p. 915

Endicott, Elizabeth Stroup, Law Librn, Administrative Office of the United States Courts Library, One Columbus Circle NE, Ste 4-400, Washington, DC, 20544. Tel: 202-502-1237. Fax: 202-502-2833. p. 391

Endicott, Jay, Computer Serv, Asbury Theological Seminary, 204 N Lexington Ave, Wilmore, KY, 40390-1199. Tel: 859-858-2233. Fax: 859-858-2330. p. 938

Endicott, Philip Edward, Brother, Dir, Taneyhills Community Library, 200 S Fourth St, Branson, MO, 65616-2738. Tel: 417-334-1418. Fax: 417-334-1629. p. 1320

Endicott-Popovsky, Barbara, Sr Lecturer, University of Washington, Mary Gates Hall, Ste 370, Campus Box 352840, Seattle, WA, 98195-2840. Tel: 206-685-9937. Fax: 206-616-3152. p. 2976

Endres, Jennifer E, Dir, Prairie du Sac Public Library, 560 Park Ave, Prairie du Sac, WI, 53578-1199. Tel: 608-643-8318. Fax: 608-643-4897. p. 2631

Endrizzi, Jane, Pub Serv, Warren County Library, 189 Route 519, Belvidere, NJ, 07823. Tel: 908-475-6322. Fax: 908-475-6359. p. 1472

Endrizzi, Jane, Asst Dir, Centenary College, 400 Jefferson St, Hackettstown, NJ, 07840. Tel: 908-852-1400, Ext 2345. Fax: 908-850-9528. p. 1489

Eng, Catherine, Supvr, Paramus Public Library, Charles E Reid Branch, W 239 Midland Ave, Paramus, NJ, 07652. Tel: 201-444-4911. p. 1517

Eng, Cathy, Br Coordr, Paramus Public Library, E 116 Century Rd, Paramus, NJ, 07652-4398. Tel: 201-599-1300. Fax: 201-599-0059. p. 1517

Eng, Lan, Librn, Chicago Sinai Congregation, 15 W Delaware Pl, Chicago, IL, 60610. Tel: 312-867-7000. Fax: 312-867-7006. p. 610

Eng, Mamie, Dir, Henry Waldinger Memorial Library, 60 Verona Pl, Valley Stream, NY, 11582-3011. Tel: 516-825-6422. Fax: 516-825-6551. p. 1761

Eng, Pauline, Res Serv Librn, Tyler Public Library, 201 S College Ave, Tyler, TX, 75702-7381. Tel: 903-593-7323. Fax: 903-531-1329. p. 2394

Eng, Sidney, Chief Librn, Borough of Manhattan Community College Library, 199 Chambers St, New York, NY, 10007. Tel: 212-220-1499. Fax: 212-748-7466. p. 1671

Engberg, Bonnie, Asst Librn, Women's Christian Association Healthcare System, 207 Foote Ave, Jamestown, NY, 14701-9975. Tel: 716-664-8124. Fax: 716-484-1089. p. 1647

Enge, Kate, ILL, Juneau Public Libraries, 292 Marine Way, Juneau, AK, 99801. Tel: 907-586-5324. Fax: 907-586-3419. p. 50

Engebretson, Carolyn, Board Pres, Becker County Historical Society, 714 Summit Ave, Detroit Lakes, MN, 56501. Tel: 218-847-2938. p. 1247

Engebretson, Mary, Head, Ref, University of South Alabama, 5901 USA Drive N, Rm 145, Mobile, AL, 36688. Tel: 251-460-2825. Fax: 251-460-7181. p. 26

Engebretson, Pat, Librn, Belle Fourche Public Library, 905 Fifth Ave, Belle Fourche, SD, 57717-1795. Tel: 605-892-4407. p. 2210

Engebretson, Terri, Circ, Cleveland State Community College Library, 3535 Adkisson Dr, Cleveland, TN, 37312-2813. Tel: 423-478-6209. Fax: 423-478-6255. p. 2229

Engel, Carl, Ref Serv, Ad, Morley Library, 184 Phelps St, Painesville, OH, 44077-3926. Tel: 440-352-3383. Fax: 440-352-9097. p. 1927

Engel, Claire, Dir, Libr Serv, Troutman Sanders LLP, 600 Peachtree St NE, Ste 5200, Atlanta, GA, 30308-2216. Tel: 404-885-3196. Fax: 404-962-6783. p. 518

Engel, Denise, Dir, Wakefield Public Library, 401 Hancock St, Wakefield, MI, 49968. Tel: 906-229-5236. Fax: 906-229-5974. p. 1233

Engel, Elisabeth, Curator, Waukesha County Historical Society & Museum, 101 W Main St, Waukesha, WI, 53186. Tel: 262-521-2859. Fax: 262-521-2865. p. 2645

Engel, Jeanne, Librn, Johnson Public Library, Seven Library Dr, Johnson, VT, 05656. Tel: 802-635-7141. p. 2426

Engel, June, Br Mgr, San Diego County Library, Imperial Beach Branch, 810 Imperial Beach Blvd, Imperial Beach, CA, 91932-2798. Tel: 619-424-6981. Fax: 619-424-8749. p. 233

Engel, Kathy, Dir, Henderson Public Library, 111 S Sixth St, Henderson, MN, 56044-7734. Tel: 507-248-3880. p. 1254

Engel, Kevin, Sci Librn, Grinnell College Libraries, 1111 Sixth Ave, Grinnell, IA, 50112-1770. Tel: 641-269-4234. Fax: 641-269-4283. p. 819

Engel, Martha, Librn, Southeast Regional Library, Lampman Branch, 302 Main St, Lampman, SK, S0C 1N0, CANADA. Tel: 306-487-2202. p. 2930

Engel, Peg, Br Tech, Monroe County Library System, Blue Bush, 2210 Blue Bush, Monroe, MI, 48162-9643. Tel: 734-242-4085. Fax: 734-242-0023. p. 1210

Engel, Peggy, Circ, Columbus Public Library, 2504 14th St, Columbus, NE, 68601-4988. Tel: 402-564-7116. Fax: 402-563-3378. p. 1396

Engel, Ryan, Spec Coll & AV, University of Wisconsin-Madison, Primate Center - Lawrence Jacobsen Library, 1220 Capitol Ct, Madison, WI, 53715. Tel: 608-263-3512. Fax: 608-263-4031. p. 2609

Engelbert, Alan, Dir, Kanawha County Public Library, 123 Capitol St, Charleston, WV, 25301. Tel: 304-343-4646. Fax: 304-348-6530. p. 2556

Engelbrecht, Betsy, Dir, Burnet County Library System, 100 E Washington St, Burnet, TX, 78611. Tel: 512-715-5228. Fax: 512-715-5249. p. 2293

Engelbrecht, Mark, Br Mgr, Charlotte Mecklenburg Library, Mint Hill Branch, 6840 Matthews-Mint Hill Rd, Mint Hill, NC, 28227. Tel: 704-416-5200. Fax: 704-416-5300. p. 1782

Engeldinger, Eugene A, Dir, VPres for Acad Info Serv, Carthage College, 2001 Alford Park Dr, Kenosha, WI, 53140-1900. Tel: 262-551-5900. Fax: 262-551-5904. p. 2601

Engeldinger, Gene, Dir, Libr & Acad Info Serv, Sacred Heart School of Theology, 7335 S Hwy 100, Franklin, WI, 53132. Tel: 414-425-8300, Ext 7278. Fax: 414-529-6992. p. 2593

Engelfried, Stephen, Youth Serv Librn, Wilsonville Public Library, 8200 SW Wilsonville Rd, Wilsonville, OR, 97070. Tel: 503-570-1592. Fax: 503-682-8685. p. 2023

Engelhardt, Carolyn Hardin, Dir, Ministry Res Ctr, Yale University Library, Divinity School Library, 409 Prospect St, New Haven, CT, 06511-2108. Tel: 203-432-5319. Fax: 203-432-3906. p. 357

Engelmann, Susan, Br Mgr, Q B Boydstun Library, 201 E South Ave, Fort Gibson, OK, 74434. Tel: 918-478-3587. Fax: 918-478-4599. p. 1963

Engelmann, Susan, Head Librn, Rieger Memorial Library, 116 N Broadway, Haskell, OK, 74436. Tel: 918-482-3614. Fax: 918-482-3266. p. 1965

Engelmann, Susan, Mgr, Kansas Public Library, Hwy 412 & Oak St, Kansas, OK, 74347. Tel: 918-868-5257. Fax: 918-868-2350. p. 1966

Engels, Christine, Archives Mgr, Cincinnati Museum Center At Union Terminal, 1301 Western Ave, Cincinnati, OH, 45203. Tel: 513-287-7066. Fax: 513-287-7095. p. 1869

Engels, Mary, Dir, Connecticut State Library, Middletown Library Service Center, 786 S Main St, Middletown, CT, 06457. Tel: 860-704-2207. Fax: 860-704-2228. p. 345

Engelsman, Sharon, Dir, Salem Township Library, 3007 142nd Ave, Burnips, MI, 49314. Tel: 616-896-8170. Fax: 616-896-8035. p. 1160

Engelson, Leslie, Tech Serv Librn, Murray State University, 205 Waterfield Library, Dean's Office, Murray, KY, 42071-3307. Tel: 270-809-4818. Fax: 270-809-3736. p. 930

Engelson, Leslie, Tech Serv Librn, Northwest University, 5520 108th Ave NE, Kirkland, WA, 98083-0579. Tel: 425-889-5339. Fax: 425-889-7801. p. 2519

Engelter, Patricia, Coordr, Acq, Albion College, 602 E Cass St, Albion, MI, 49224-1879. Tel: 517-629-0285. Fax: 517-629-0504. p. 1148

Engemann, Patricia, Ch, Harlan Community Library, 718 Court St, Harlan, IA, 51537. Tel: 712-755-5934. Fax: 712-755-3952. p. 820

Enger, Kathy B, Exec Dir, Northern Lights Library Network, 103 Graystone Plaza, Detroit Lakes, MN, 56501-3041. Tel: 218-847-2825. Fax: 218-847-1461. p. 2947

Engeszer, Robert, Assoc Dir, Translational Res Support, Washington University Libraries, Bernard Becker Medical Library, 660 S Euclid Ave, Campus Box 8132, Saint Louis, MO, 63110. Tel: 314-362-4735. Fax: 314-454-6606. p. 1362

England, Jason, Computer Instrul Serv Librn, Robertson County Public Library, 207 N Main St, Mount Olivet, KY, 41064. Tel: 606-724-5746. Fax: 606-724-5746. p. 930

England, Louise, Govt Doc Librn, Alberta Legislature Library, 216 Legislature Bldg, 10800-97 Ave, Edmonton, AB, T5K 2B6, CANADA. Tel: 780-415-4502. Fax: 780-427-6016. p. 2699

England-Biggs, Laura, Youth Serv Librn, Keene Memorial Library, 1030 N Broad St, Fremont, NE, 68025-4199. Tel: 402-727-2694. Fax: 402-727-2693. p. 1399

Engle, Charles, Br Mgr, Lonesome Pine Regional Library, J Fred Matthews Memorial, 16552 Wise St, Saint Paul, VA, 24283-3522. Tel: 276-762-9702. Fax: 276-762-0528. p. 2504

Engle, Jonathan, Tech Serv, Rowayton Library, 33 Highland Ave, Rowayton, CT, 06853. Tel: 203-838-5038. Fax: 203-523-0438, 928-437-5038. p. 366

Engle, Karen, Br Head, Daly City Public Library, Bayshore, 460 Martin St, Daly City, CA, 94014. Tel: 650-991-8074. Fax: 415-508-0860. p. 138

Engle, Paul, Dir, Libr Serv, Berklee College of Music Library, 150 Massachusetts Ave, Boston, MA, 02115. Tel: 617-747-8683. Fax: 617-747-2050. p. 1055

Englehardt, Debra, Dir, Huntington Public Library, 338 Main St, Huntington, NY, 11743. Tel: 631-427-5165. Fax: 631-421-7131. p. 1639

Engleman, Melissa, Instruction Coordr, University of Minnesota-Morris, 600 E Fourth St, Morris, MN, 56267. Tel: 320-589-6227. Fax: 320-589-6168. p. 1267

Engler, Romona, Dir, Lyon County Public Library, 261 Commerce St, Eddyville, KY, 42038. Tel: 270-388-7720. Fax: 270-388-7735. p. 911

Engler, Shanna, Br Mgr, Elbert County Library District, Simla Branch, 504 Washington, Simla, CO, 80835. Tel: 719-541-2573. Fax: 719-541-2152. p. 305

Engler, Shanna, Br Mgr, Mesa County Public Library District, Orchard Mesa, 2736 Unaweep Ave, Grand Junction, CO, 81503. Tel: 970-243-0181. Fax: 970-241-9762. p. 311

Englerth, Edward, Network Adminr, Hastings Public Library, 227 E State St, Hastings, MI, 49058-1817. Tel: 269-945-4263. Fax: 269-948-3874. p. 1189

English, Alison, Head of Libr, Vanguard University of Southern California, 55 Fair Dr, Costa Mesa, CA, 92626. Tel: 714-556-3610, Ext 2400. Fax: 714-966-5478. p. 137

English, Anna Marie, Dir, Cameron County Public Library, 27 W Fourth St, Emporium, PA, 15834. Tel: 814-486-8011. Fax: 814-486-3725. p. 2054

English, Bernie, Librn, Indiana Hand to Shoulder Center Library, 8501 Harcourt Rd, Indianapolis, IN, 46260. Tel: 317-471-4340. Fax: 317-876-0462. p. 751

English, Denise K, Dir, Libr Serv, Lake-Sumter Community College Library, 9501 US Hwy 441, Leesburg, FL, 34788-8751. Tel: 352-365-3563. Fax: 352-365-3590. p. 461

English, Eva, Dir, Fort Belknap College Library & Tribal Archives, Hwy 2 & 66, Harlem, MT, 59526. Tel: 406-353-2607. Fax: 406-353-2898. p. 1381

English, Janine, Asst Librn, New Woodstock Free Library, 2106 Main St, New Woodstock, NY, 13122-8718. Tel: 315-662-3134. p. 1667

English, Madelyn, Adult Prog & Publicity Mgr, Bernardsville Public Library, One Anderson Hill Rd, Bernardsville, NJ, 07924. Tel: 908-766-0118. Fax: 908-766-2464. p. 1472

English, Margaret, Chief Librn, University of Toronto Libraries, Department of Fine Art, Sidney Smith Hall, Rm 6032B, 100 Saint George St, Toronto, ON, M5S 3G3, CANADA. Tel: 416-978-5006. Fax: 416-978-1491. p. 2865

English, Michael, Access Serv Librn, Salisbury University, 1101 Camden Ave, Salisbury, MD, 21801-6863. Tel: 410-543-6130. Fax: 410-543-6203. p. 1040

English, Ray, Dir, Oberlin College Library, 148 W College St, Oberlin, OH, 44074. Tel: 440-775-8285. Fax: 440-775-6586. p. 1924

English, Zach, Campus Librn, Everglades University, 5002 T-REX Ave, Ste 100, Boca Raton, FL, 33431. Tel: 561-912-1211. Fax: 561-912-1191. p. 428

Englot, Shannon, In Charge, Lakeland Library Region, Medstead Branch, Box 13, Medstead, SK, S0M 1W0, CANADA. Tel: 306-342-4988. p. 2920

Engman, Eva, Cat & Acq, Okanagan College Library, 1000 KLO Rd, Kelowna, BC, V1Y 4X8, CANADA. p. 2730

Engram, Sandra, Pub Serv Librn, Illinois College of Optometry Library, 3241 S Michigan Ave, Chicago, IL, 60616-3878. Tel: 312-949-7160. Fax: 312-949-7337. p. 614

Engsberg, Rebecca, Pub Serv, Mercer University Atlanta, 3001 Mercer University Dr, Atlanta, GA, 30341. Tel: 678-547-6402. Fax: 678-547-6270. p. 517

Engskov, Carol Ann, Librn, Berryville Public Library, 104 Spring St, Berryville, AR, 72616. Tel: 870-423-2323. Fax: 870-423-2432. p. 95

Engst, Elaine, Dir, Cornell University Library, Division of Rare & Manuscript Collections, 2B Carl A Kroch Library, Ithaca, NY, 14853. Tel: 607-255-3530. Fax: 607-255-9524. p. 1641

Engstrom, Barbara Swatt, Ref, Seattle University, School of Law Library, Sullivan Hall, 901 12th Ave, Seattle, WA, 98122-4411. Tel: 206-398-4221. Fax: 206-398-4194. p. 2532

Engstrom, Greg, Dr, Librn, Eastern Kentucky University Libraries, The Elizabeth K Baker Music Library, Foster Bldg, 521 Lancaster Ave, Richmond, KY, 40475. Tel: 859-622-1795. Fax: 859-622-1174. p. 934

Engvall, Lisa, Libr Mgr, Washington State Library, Department of Labor & Industries, 7273 Linderson Way SW, Tumwater, WA, 98501. Tel: 360-902-5498. Fax: 360-902-6335. p. 2544

Engwall, Keith, Head, Syst, Catawba College, 2300 W Innes St, Salisbury, NC, 28144-2488. Tel: 704-637-4212. Fax: 704-637-4304. p. 1822

Engwall, Lee, Youth Serv, Millicent Library, 45 Centre St, Fairhaven, MA, 02719. Tel: 508-992-5342. Fax: 508-993-7288. p. 1087

Enlow, Billie, Librn, Saint Elmo Public Library District, 311 W Cumberland Rd, Saint Elmo, IL, 62458. Tel: 618-829-5544. Fax: 618-829-9104. p. 700

Enlow, Cathy, Tech Serv, Brookings Public Library, 515 Third St, Brookings, SD, 57006. Tel: 605-692-9407. Fax: 605-692-9386. p. 2210

Enman, Donna R, Circ Supvr, Co-Dir, Tech Serv Supvr, Rockville Public Library, Inc, 52 Union St, Vernon, CT, 06066-3155. Tel: 860-875-5892. Fax: 860-875-9795. p. 373

Ennen, Rita, Dir, Libr Serv, Dickinson State University, 291 Campus Dr, Dickinson, ND, 58601. Tel: 701-483-2883. Fax: 701-483-2006. p. 1840

Ennis, Cindy, Ser, New Orleans Baptist Theological Seminary, 4110 Seminary Pl, New Orleans, LA, 70126. Tel: 504-282-4455, Ext 3288. Fax: 504-816-8429. p. 961

Ennis, Joan, Reader Serv Librn, Northfield Public Library, 210 Washington St, Northfield, MN, 55057. Tel: 507-645-1818. Fax: 507-645-1820. p. 1269

Ennis, Kathleen, Instruction Librn, Modesto Junior College Library, 435 College Ave, Modesto, CA, 95350. Tel: 209-575-6409. Fax: 209-575-7796. p. 188

Ennis, Lisa, Automation Syst Coordr, University of Alabama at Birmingham, Lister Hill Library of the Health Sciences, 1700 University Blvd, Birmingham, AL, 35294-0013. Tel: 205-934-5460. Fax: 205-934-3545. p. 10

Ennis, Patricia, Circ, Free Library of Springfield Township, 1600 Paper Mill Rd, Wyndmoor, PA, 19038. Tel: 215-836-5300. Fax: 215-836-2404. p. 2158

Ennis, Reed, Asst Librn, State Law Library, 700 Capital Ave, Ste 200, Frankfort, KY, 40601-3489. Tel: 502-564-4848. Fax: 502-564-5041. p. 914

Enniss, Stephen, Dr, Librn, Folger Shakespeare Library, 201 E Capitol St SE, Washington, DC, 20003-1094. Tel: 202-544-4600. Fax: 202-544-4623. p. 400

Enns, Carol, Librn, Canada Agriculture & Agri-Food Canada, RR 3, Box 1000A, Brandon, MB, R7A 5Y3, CANADA. Tel: 204-578-3595. Fax: 204-728-3858. p. 2748

Enns, Carolyn, Librn, Buset & Partners, 1121 Barton St, Thunder Bay, ON, P7B 5N3, CANADA. Tel: 807-623-2500. Fax: 807-622-7808. p. 2848

Enns-Rempel, Kevin, Archivist, Dir, Fresno Pacific University, 1717 S Chestnut Ave, Fresno, CA, 93702. Tel: 559-453-2225. Fax: 559-453-2124. p. 153

Enoch, Larry, Dr, Instr, University of North Texas, 1155 Union Circle, Denton, TX, 76203-5017. Tel: 940-565-2445. Fax: 940-565-3101. p. 2975

Enos, Elizabeth, Ref, Eastchester Public Library, 11 Oak Ridge Pl, Eastchester, NY, 10709. Tel: 914-793-5055. Fax: 914-793-7862. p. 1618

Enos, Karen, Asst Librn, Sugar Grove Free Library, Harmon & School Sts, Sugar Grove, PA, 16350. Tel: 814-489-7872. Fax: 814-489-7826. p. 2144

Enos, Randall, Youth Serv Consult, Ramapo Catskill Library System, 619 Rte 17M, Middletown, NY, 10940-4395. Tel: 845-343-1131, Ext 240. Fax: 845-343-1205. p. 1660

Enos, Yvette, In Charge, Merced County Library, Livingston Branch, 1212 Main St, Livingston, CA, 95334-1297. Tel: 209-394-7330. p. 186

Enrich, Rachel, Ch, Portsmouth Public Library, 601 Court St, Portsmouth, VA, 23704-3604. Tel: 757-393-8501. p. 2485

Enrietta, Mary Kay, Librn, Grand Prairie of the West Public Library District, 142 W Jackson St, Virden, IL, 62690-1257. Tel: 217-965-3015. Fax: 217-965-3801. p. 714

Enright, Adele, Librn, Rio Hondo Community College Library, 3600 Workman Mill Rd, Whittier, CA, 90601. Tel: 562-908-3417. Fax: 562-463-4642. p. 283

Enright, Beth, Br Mgr, Placer County Library, Loomis Branch, 6050 Library Dr, Loomis, CA, 95650. Tel: 916-652-7061. Fax: 916-652-5156. p. 123

Enright, Jan Brue, Circ, ILL, Augustana College, 2001 S Summit Ave, Sioux Falls, SD, 57197-0001. Tel: 605-274-4493. Fax: 605-274-5447. p. 2218

Enright, Jane E, Dir, Prescott Public Library, 800 Borner St N, Prescott, WI, 54021-1703. Tel: 715-262-5555. Fax: 715-262-4229. p. 2631

Enright, Patricia, Chief Librn, Kingston Frontenac Public Library, 130 Johnson St, Kingston, ON, K7L 1X8, CANADA. Tel: 613-549-8888, Ext 1230. Fax: 613-549-8476. p. 2813

Enright, Zachary, Archivist, New England Osteopathic Heritage Ctr, University of New England Libraries, 11 Hills Beach Rd, Biddeford, ME, 04005. Tel: 207-602-2131. Fax: 207-602-5922. p. 978

Enriquez, Igri S, Dir, Puerto Rico Regional Library for the Blind & Physically Handicapped, 520 Ponce De Leon Ave, Ste 2, San Juan, PR, 00901. Tel: 787-723-2519. Fax: 787-721-8177. p. 2676

Ensanian, Elisabeth Anahid, Chief Librn, Ensanian Physicochemical Institute, Barden Brook Rd, Eldred, PA, 16731. Tel: 814-225-3296. p. 2053

Ensel, Ellen H, Knowledge Mgr, United States Institute of Peace, 2301 Constitution Ave NW, Washington, DC, 20037. Tel: 202-429-3895. p. 420

Ensign, David, Dir, University of Louisville Libraries, Brandeis School of Law Library, 2301 S Third St, Louisville, KY, 40208. Tel: 502-852-6392. Fax: 502-852-8906. p. 926

Ensley, Cathy, Ch, Latah County Library District, 110 S Jefferson, Moscow, ID, 83843-2833. Tel: 208-882-3925. Fax: 208-882-5098. p. 579

Ensley, Rosanna, Res Sharing Librn, Adams State University, 208 Edgemont Ave, Alamosa, CO, 81101-2373. Tel: 719-587-7187. Fax: 719-587-7590. p. 287

Ensminger, Bob, Librn, Iowa State Penitentiary, Library, Three John Bennett Dr, Fort Madison, IA, 52627. Tel: 319-372-5432, Ext 215, 319-372-5432, Ext 255. Fax: 319-372-6967. p. 817

Ensor, Lorraine, Head, Tech Serv, South Hadley Public Library, 27 Bardwell St, South Hadley, MA, 01075. Tel: 413-538-5045. Fax: 413-539-9250. p. 1125

Ensor, Pat, Exec Dir, Libr Serv, University of Houston-Downtown, One Main St, Houston, TX, 77002. Tel: 713-221-8181, 713-221-8182. Fax: 713-221-8037. p. 2343

Enstrom, Bona-Carol, Br Supvr, Cass Lake Community Library, 223 Cedar, Cass Lake, MN, 56633. Tel: 218-335-8865. Fax: 218-335-8865. p. 1244

Enterline, Keri, Librn, Everest University, Tampa Campus Library-West Hillsborough, 3319 W Hillsborough Ave, Tampa, FL, 33614. Tel: 813-879-6000, Ext 117. Fax: 813-875-7764. p. 496

Entwisle, Chris, Circ, Camden County Library System, 203 Laurel Rd, Voorhees, NJ, 08043. Tel: 856-772-1636, Ext 3309. Fax: 856-772-6105. p. 1538

Enyart, Michael G, Head Librn, University of Wisconsin-Madison, Business Library, Grainger Hall, Rm 2200, 975 University Ave, Madison, WI, 53706. Tel: 608-263-3902. Fax: 608-262-9001. p. 2608

Ephraim, Jesse, Dir, Roanoke Public Library, 308 S Walnut St, Roanoke, TX, 76262. Tel: 817-491-2691. Fax: 817-491-2729. p. 2376

Epley, Susan L, Dir, West End Library, 1724 State Rte 235, Laurelton, PA, 17835. Tel: 570-922-4773. Fax: 570-922-1162. p. 2079

Epling, Jimmie, Dir, Wayne County Public Library, 220 W Liberty St, Wooster, OH, 44691-3593. Tel: 330-262-0986. Fax: 330-262-1352. p. 1950

Eplite, Maureen, Asst Librn, Waters Corp, 34 Maple St, Milford, MA, 01757. Tel: 508-478-2000. Fax: 508-482-2417. p. 1106

Epp, Adam, Syst Librn, Northwest University, 5520 108th Ave NE, Kirkland, WA, 98083-0579. Tel: 424-889-5201. Fax: 425-889-7801. p. 2519

Epp, Mary Anne, Dir, British Columbia College & Institute Library Services, Langara College Library, 100 W 49th Ave, Vancouver, BC, V5Y 2Z6, CANADA. Tel: 604-323-5627. Fax: 604-323-5577. p. 2959

Epp, Ruth, Ref Librn, Manitoba Hydro Library, 360 Portage Ave, Winnipeg, MB, R3C 30G8, CANADA. Tel: 204-360-3212. Fax: 204-360-6104. p. 2756

Eppard, Philip B, Dr, Chair, University at Albany, State University of New York, Draper 116, 135 Western Ave, Albany, NY, 12222. Tel: 518-442-5119. Fax: peppard@albany.edu. p. 2970

Epperly, Eula, Librn, George Gamble Library, 29 Rte 104, Danbury, NH, 03230-0209. Tel: 603-768-3765. p. 1444

Epperly, Judy, Dir, Wright County Library, 125 Court Sq, Hartville, MO, 65667-9998. Tel: 417-741-7595. Fax: 417-741-7927. p. 1330

Epperson, Annie, Ref, University of Northern Colorado Libraries, 501 20th St, Greeley, CO, 80639. Tel: 970-351-1535. Fax: 970-351-2963. p. 312

Epperson, Kathleen, Asst Librn, University of Cincinnati, 4200 Clermont College Dr, Batavia, OH, 45103-1785. Tel: 513-558-7010. Fax: 513-732-5237. p. 1858

Epperson, Peggy, Dir, Central Virginia Regional Library, 217 W Third St, Farmville, VA, 23901. Tel: 434-392-6924. Fax: 434-392-9784. p. 2463

Epperson, Terrence, Dr, Librn, The College of New Jersey Library, 2000 Pennington Rd, Ewing, NJ, 08628-0718. Tel: 609-771-2311, 609-771-2332. Fax: 609-637-5177. p. 1484

Eppinger, Monica, Asst Dir, Elizabeth Public Library, 11 S Broad St, Elizabeth, NJ, 07202. Tel: 908-354-6060. Fax: 908-354-5845. p. 1483

Epps, Jean, Media Serv, Shelton State Community College, 9500 Old Greensboro Rd, Tuscaloosa, AL, 35405. Tel: 205-391-2970. Fax: 205-391-3926. p. 38

Epps, Linda, In Charge, Crabtree Correctional Center, Rte 1, Box 8, Helena, OK, 73741-9606. Tel: 580-852-3221. p. 1965

Epps, Linda, ILL, Sul Ross State University, PO Box C-109, Alpine, TX, 79832-0001. Tel: 432-837-8123. Fax: 432-837-8400. p. 2273

Epps, W Ron, Ref & Print Res Librn, Campbell University, 113 Main St, Buies Creek, NC, 27506. Tel: 910-893-1460. Fax: 910-893-1470. p. 1778

Epstein, Barbara A, Dir, University of Pittsburgh, 200 Scaife Hall, 3550 Terrace St, Pittsburgh, PA, 15261. Fax: 412-648-9020. p. 2129

Epstein, Carmen, Youth Serv Librn, Urbandale Public Library, 3520 86th St, Urbandale, IA, 50322-4056. Tel: 515-278-3945. Fax: 515-278-3918. p. 848

Epstein, Edward, Head, Mat Mgt, Public Library Association of Annapolis & Anne Arundel County, Inc, Five Harry S Truman Pkwy, Annapolis, MD, 21401. Tel: 410-222-7371. Fax: 410-222-7188. p. 1010

Epstein, Emily, Cat Librn, University of Colorado Denver, 12950 E Montview Blvd, Aurora, CO, 80045. Tel: 303-724-2152. Fax: 303-724-2166. p. 289

Epstein, Michael, Electronic Res, University of San Diego, Helen K & James S Copley Library, 5998 Alcala Park, San Diego, CA, 92110. Tel: 619-260-4617. p. 239

Epstein, Michelle, Adult Serv, Northport-East Northport Public Library, 151 Laurel Ave, Northport, NY, 11768. Tel: 631-261-6930. Fax: 631-261-6718. p. 1707

Epstein, Rheda, Res & Tech Serv Mgr, Durham County Library, 300 N Roxboro St, Durham, NC, 27701. Tel: 919-560-0187. Fax: 919-560-0137. p. 1788

Epstein, Robert A, Librn, Mount Zion Temple, 1300 Summit Ave, Saint Paul, MN, 55105. Tel: 651-698-3881. Fax: 651-698-1263. p. 1280

Epstein, Su, Dir, Saxton B Little Free Library, Inc, 319 Rte 87, Columbia, CT, 06237-1143. Tel: 860-228-0350. Fax: 860-228-1569. p. 334

Epstein, Susan, Head, Pub Serv, Florida State University Libraries, Charlotte Edwards Maguire Medical Library, 1115 W Call St, Tallahassee, FL, 32304-3556. Tel: 850-644-3883. Fax: 850-644-9942. p. 495

Erb, Debbie, Librn, Ransom Public Library, 411 S Vermont, Ransom, KS, 67572. Tel: 785-731-2855. Fax: 785-731-2518. p. 891

Erb, Deborah, Mgr, Massillon Public Library, Pam S Belloni Branch, 12000 Navarre Rd SW, Brewster, OH, 44662-9486. Tel: 330-767-9939. Fax: 330-767-0192. p. 1915

Erbe, Ellen, Head of Libr, University of Delaware Library, Marine Studies, 700 Pilotown Rd, Lewes, DE, 19958. Tel: 302-645-4290. p. 386

Erbe, Evalina, Dir, Jamesburg Public Library, 229 Gatzmer Ave, Jamesburg, NJ, 08831. Tel: 732-521-0440. Fax: 732-521-6136. p. 1492

Erben, Richard, Circ, Nassau Community College, One Education Dr, Garden City, NY, 11530-6793. Tel: 516-572-7400. Fax: 516-572-7846. p. 1626

Erbes, Bill, Asst Dir, Bensenville Community Public Library, 200 S Church Rd, Bensenville, IL, 60106. Tel: 630-766-4642, Ext 427. Fax: 630-766-0788. p. 594

Erbrecht, Annette, Librn, Akin, Gump, Strauss, Hauer & Feld LLP, 1333 New Hampshire Ave NW, Washington, DC, 20036-1564. Tel: 202-887-4000. Fax: 202-887-4288. p. 391

Erceg, Lynn, ILL, Columbia-Greene Community College Library, 4400 Rte 23, Hudson, NY, 12534. Tel: 518-828-4181, Ext 3289. Fax: 518-828-4396. p. 1638

Erdall-Van De Riet, Joanne C, Dir, Thompson-Hickman Free County Library, 217 Idaho St, Virginia City, MT, 59755. Tel: 406-843-5346. Fax: 406-843-5347. p. 1389

Erdel, Tim, Archivist, Bethel College, 1001 W McKinley Ave, Mishawaka, IN, 46545. Tel: 574-257-2570. Fax: 574-257-3499. p. 765

Erdelez, Sanda, Prof, University of Missouri-Columbia, 303 Townsend Hall, Columbia, MO, 65211. Tel: 573-882-4546. Fax: 573-884-2917. p. 2968

Erdman, Barbara, Dr, Asst Prof, University of Wisconsin-Eau Claire, 105 Garfield Ave, Eau Claire, WI, 54702. Tel: 715-836-2635. Fax: 715-836-5099. p. 2976

Erdman, Janet, Librn, Fairview-Ridges Hospital, 201 E Nicollet Blvd, Burnsville, MN, 55337. Tel: 952-892-2414. Fax: 952-892-2277. p. 1243

Erdman, Sue, Dir, Joseph T Simpson Public Library, 16 N Walnut St, Mechanicsburg, PA, 17055-3362. Tel: 717-766-0171. Fax: 717-766-0152. p. 2087

Erdmann, Christopher, Head Librn, Harvard-Smithsonian Center for Astrophysics Library, 60 Garden St, MS-56, Cambridge, MA, 02138. Tel: 617-495-7289. Fax: 617-495-7199. p. 1077

Erdmann, Sandra, Asst Dir, Dover Public Library, 73 Locust St, Dover, NH, 03820-3785. Tel: 603-516-6050. Fax: 603-516-6053. p. 1445

Erdmann, Sandra, Syst Librn, Dover Public Library, 73 Locust St, Dover, NH, 03820-3785. Tel: 603-516-6050. Fax: 603-516-6053. p. 1445

Erenyi, Zvi, Coll Develop, Yeshiva University Libraries, Mendel Gottesman Library of Hebraica-Judaica, 2520 Amsterdam Ave, New York, NY, 10033. Tel: 212-960-5382. Fax: 212-960-0066. p. 1704

Eresuma, Emily, Sr Med Librn, Primary Children's Medical Center Library, 100 N Mario Capecchi Dr, Salt Lake City, UT, 84113. Tel: 801-662-1390. Fax: 801-662-1393. p. 2413

Eresuma, Emily, Chair, Utah Health Sciences Library Consortium, c/o Univ Utah, Spencer S Eccles Health Sci Library, Ten N 1900 East, Salt Lake City, UT, 84112-5890. Tel: 801-662-1391. Fax: 801-581-3632. p. 2956

Erganian, Richard, Librn, The Vineyard, 100 W Shaw Ave, Fresno, CA, 93704. Tel: 559-222-0182. p. 153

Erhardt, Melissa, Dir, Chateaugay Memorial Library, Four John St, Chateaugay, NY, 12920. Tel: 518-497-0400. Fax: 518-497-3126. p. 1605

Erhart, Melanie, Br Mgr, Prince William Public Library System, Independent Hill Neighborhood, 14418 Bristow Rd, Manassas, VA, 20112-3932. Tel: 703-792-5668. Fax: 703-791-2721. p. 2486

Erick, Marcie, Asst Librn, Southeast Regional Library, Arcola Branch, 127 Main St, Arcola, SK, S0C 0G0, CANADA. Tel: 306-455-2321. p. 2929

Erick, Marla, Dir, Archer Public Library, 203 Sanford St, Archer, IA, 51231. Tel: 712-723-5629. p. 794

Erickson, Charles, Librn, Northwest Regional Library, Roseau Public Library, 121 Center St E, Roseau, MN, 56751. Tel: 218-463-2825. Fax: 218-463-2825. p. 1286

Erickson, Christine, Head, Children's Dept, Teen Librn, Bangor Public Library, 145 Harlow St, Bangor, ME, 04401-1802. Tel: 207-947-8336. Fax: 207-945-6694. p. 975

Erickson, Cindy, Dir, Soda Springs Public Library, 149 S Main, Soda Springs, ID, 83276-1496. Tel: 208-547-2606. Fax: 208-547-2606. p. 584

Erickson, Dolores, Dir, Courtland Community Library, 403 Main St, Courtland, KS, 66939. Tel: 785-374-4260. p. 862

Erickson, Emily H, Librn, Mary Greeley Medical Center Library, 1111 Duff Ave, Ames, IA, 50010. Tel: 515-239-2154. Fax: 515-239-2020. p. 793

Erickson, Gwen Gosney, Col Archivist, Guilford College, 5800 W Friendly Ave, Greensboro, NC, 27410-4175. Tel: 336-316-2450. Fax: 336-316-2950. p. 1796

Erickson, Janice, Dir, Shasta Public Libraries, 1100 Parkview Ave, Redding, CA, 96001. Tel: 530-245-7250. p. 214

Erickson, Jean, Asst Dir, Franklin Park Public Library District, 10311 Grand Ave, Franklin Park, IL, 60131. Tel: 847-455-6016. Fax: 847-455-6416. p. 647

Erickson, Jill, Ad, Ref Supvr, Falmouth Public Library, 300 Main St, Falmouth, MA, 02540. Tel: 508-457-2555. Fax: 508-457-2559. p. 1088

Erickson, Jon, Ref Librn, Vanderbilt University, Science & Engineering, 3200 Stevenson Ctr, 419 21st Ave S, Nashville, TN, 37240-0007. Tel: 615-343-7105. Fax: 615-343-7249. p. 2261

Erickson, Julie, Electronic Res Coordr, South Dakota State Library, 800 Governors Dr, Pierre, SD, 57501-2294. Tel: 605-773-3131. p. 2216

Erickson, Laurie, Dir, Ontario Public Library, 313 Main St, Ontario, WI, 54651. Tel: 608-337-4651. Fax: 608-337-4814. p. 2627

Erickson, Lisa, Exec Dir, Centre County Library & Historical Museum, 200 N Allegheny St, Bellefonte, PA, 16823-1601. Tel: 814-355-1516. Fax: 814-355-2700. p. 2032

Erickson, Marie, Head, Pub Serv, Law Library of Louisiana, Louisiana Supreme Court, 2nd Flr, 400 Royal St, New Orleans, LA, 70130-2104. Tel: 504-310-2400. Fax: 504-310-2419. p. 960

Erickson, Marsha, Dir, Coatesville Area Public Library, 501 E Lincoln Hwy, Coatesville, PA, 19320-3413. Tel: 610-384-4115. Fax: 610-384-7551. p. 2046

Erickson, Monica Jean, Dir, Chatfield Public Library, 314 S Main St, Chatfield, MN, 55923. Tel: 507-867-3480. Fax: 507-867-3480. p. 1245

Erickson, Muriel, Br Mgr, Pine River Public Library, 212 Park Ave, Pine River, MN, 56474. Tel: 218-587-4639. Fax: 218-587-3107. p. 1271

Erickson, Paula, Asst Librn, Blackduck Community Library, 72 First St SE, Blackduck, MN, 56630. Tel: 218-835-6600. Fax: 218-835-6600. p. 1241

Erickson, Rita, Librn, Mohall Public Library, 115 W Main, Mohall, ND, 58761. Tel: 701-756-7242. p. 1847

Erickson, Su, Br Librn, Robert Morris University, 905 Meridian Lake Dr, Aurora, IL, 60504. Tel: 630-375-8209. Fax: 630-375-8193. p. 592

Erickson, Sue, Dir, Virginia Wesleyan College, 1584 Wesleyan Dr, Norfolk, VA, 23502-5599. Tel: 757-455-3224. Fax: 757-455-2129. p. 2483

Erickson, Tamera Marie, Dir, Jackson County Library, 311 Third St, Jackson, MN, 56143-1600. Tel: 507-847-4748. Fax: 507-847-5470. p. 1255

Erickson, Trina, Dir, McIntosh Memorial Library, 118 E Jefferson St, Viroqua, WI, 54665. Tel: 608-637-7151. Fax: 608-637-8608. p. 2643

Erickson, Wanda, Br Mgr, Great River Regional Library, Upsala Library, 117 Main St, Upsala, MN, 56384. Tel: 320-573-4282. Fax: 320-573-4282. p. 1276

Ericson, Christie, E-Res Mgt, University of Alaska Anchorage, Consortium Library, 3211 Providence Dr, Anchorage, AK, 99508-8176. Tel: 907-786-1990. Fax: 907-786-1834. p. 45

Ericson, Karl, Ref Serv Librn, Lansing Community College Library, 200 Technology & Learning Ctr, 419 N Capitol Ave, Lansing, MI, 48933. Tel: 517-483-1650. Fax: 517-483-5300. p. 1201

Ericson, Margaret, Scholarly Res & Serv/Arts Librn, Colby College Libraries, 5100 Mayflower Hill, Waterville, ME, 04901. Tel: 207-859-5662. Fax: 207-859-5105. p. 1005

Ericson, Margaret D, Scholarly Res & Serv/Arts Librn, Colby College Libraries, Bixler Art & Music Library, 5660 Mayflower Hill, Waterville, ME, 04901. Tel: 207-859-5602. Fax: 207-859-5105. p. 1005

Ericsson, Jennifer, Ch, Baker Free Library, 509 South St, Bow, NH, 03304-3413. Tel: 603-224-7113. Fax: 603-224-2063. p. 1439

Ericsson, Paul, Br Mgr, Bemidji Public Library, 509 America Ave NW, Bemidji, MN, 56601. Tel: 218-751-3963. Fax: 218-333-0523. p. 1240

Eriksen, Mark J, Access Serv Librn, Winona State University, 175 W Mark St, Winona, MN, 55987-5838. Tel: 507-457-5486. p. 1290

Erikson, Joyce, Dir, Rowan Public Library, 101 Main St, Rowan, IA, 50470-5005. Tel: 641-853-2327. Fax: 641-853-2327. p. 841

Erikson, Rich, Head, Adult Serv, Round Lake Area Public Library District, 906 Hart Rd, Round Lake, IL, 60073. Tel: 847-546-7060, Ext 114. Fax: 847-546-7104. p. 699

Erikstrup, Tammy, Br Mgr, Orange County Library District, North Orange, 1211 E Semoran Blvd, Apopka, FL, 32703. p. 476

Erin, Joyce, Dir, Redbank Valley Public Library, 720 Broad St, New Bethlehem, PA, 16242-1107. Tel: 814-275-2870. Fax: 814-275-2875. p. 2095

Erisson, Julie, Librn, Wright & Greenhill PC, 221 W Sixth St, Ste 1800, Austin, TX, 78701-3495. Tel: 512-476-4600, Ext 327. Fax: 512-476-5382. p. 2285

Eritano, Mary, Circ & Outreach, Barberton Public Library, 602 W Park Ave, Barberton, OH, 44203-2458. Tel: 330-745-1194. Fax: 330-745-8261. p. 1857

Erlandson, Lynne, Adult Serv, Cedar Mill Community Library, 12505 NW Cornell Rd, Portland, OR, 97229. Tel: 503-644-0043. Fax: 503-644-3964. p. 2010

Erlandson, Rene, Dir, Virtual Serv, University of Nebraska at Omaha, 6001 Dodge St, Omaha, NE, 68182-0237. Tel: 402-554-2144. Fax: 402-554-3215. p. 1414

Erm, Mary, Ch, Eastern Monroe Public Library, 1002 N Ninth St, Stroudsburg, PA, 18360. Tel: 570-421-0800. Fax: 570-421-0212. p. 2143

Erman, Lucy, Ref Librn, Sofia University Library, 1069 E Meadow Circle, Palo Alto, CA, 94303. Tel: 650-493-4430, Ext 251. Fax: 650-852-9780. p. 205

Ermenc, Christine, Dir, Windsor Historical Society Library, 96 Palisado Ave, Windsor, CT, 06095. Tel: 860-688-3813. Fax: 860-687-1633. p. 379

Ernat, Marlene, Dir, Utica Public Library District, Mill & Grove Sts, Utica, IL, 61373. Tel: 815-667-4509. Fax: 815-667-4140. p. 713

Ernest, Laster, Info Tech, American InterContinental University, Dunwoody Campus-Media Center, 6600 Peachtree-Dunwoody Rd, 500 Embassy Row, Atlanta, GA, 30328. Tel: 404-965-6443. p. 510

Erney, Diana, Ref Librn, Rodale Inc, 400 S Tenth St, Emmaus, PA, 18098. Tel: 610-967-8729, 610-967-8880. Fax: 610-967-8100. p. 2054

Ernsbarger, Edell, Dir, Glasco City Library, 206 E Main St, Glasco, KS, 67445. Tel: 785-568-2313. p. 868

Ernst, Ann, ILL, Rogers Memorial Library, 91 Coopers Farm Rd, Southampton, NY, 11968. Tel: 631-283-0774. Fax: 631-287-6539. p. 1746

Ernst, Barry, Commun Libr Mgr, Queens Borough Public Library, Briarwood Community Library, 85-12 Main St, Briarwood, NY, 11435. Tel: 718-658-1680. p. 1644

Ernst, Beth, Libr Coordr, Alberta Law Libraries - Red Deer, Courthouse, 4909 - 48 Ave, Red Deer, AB, T4N 3T5, CANADA. Tel: 403-340-5499. Fax: 403-340-7194. p. 2714

Ernst, Laurie, Dir, Dolores County Public Library, 425N Main St, Dove Creek, CO, 81324. Tel: 970-677-2389. Fax: 970-677-2389. p. 304

Ernst, Linda, Dir, Mahanoy City Public Library, 17-19 W Mahanoy Ave, Mahanoy City, PA, 17948-2615. Tel: 570-773-1610. p. 2083

Ernst, Linda, ILL, Allegheny College Library, 555 N Main St, Meadville, PA, 16335. Tel: 814-332-3768. Fax: 814-337-5673. p. 2086

Ernst, Melissa, Br Mgr, Ocean County Library, Plumsted Branch, 119 Evergreen Rd, New Egypt, NJ, 08533. Tel: 609-758-7888. Fax: 609-758-6997. p. 1534

Ernst, Sonia, Ch, Sibley Public Library, 406 Ninth St, Sibley, IA, 51249. Tel: 712-754-2888. Fax: 712-754-2590. p. 843

Ernst, Vicki, Head, Circ, Tech Serv Supvr, West Nyack Free Library, 65 Strawtown Rd, West Nyack, NY, 10994. Tel: 845-358-6081. Fax: 845-358-4071. p. 1766

Errico, Lisa A, Cat, Nassau Community College, One Education Dr, Garden City, NY, 11530-6793. Tel: 516-572-7400. Fax: 516-572-7846. p. 1626

Erskine, Pam, Asst Librn, Mason County Public Library, 218 E Third St, Maysville, KY, 41056. Tel: 606-564-3286. Fax: 606-564-5408. p. 928

Ertelt, Celeste, Libr Dir, Lake Region State College, 1801 College Dr N, Devils Lake, ND, 58301. Tel: 701-662-1533. Fax: 701-662-1570. p. 1839

Ertelt, Victoria, Adminr, Mount Angel Abbey Library, One Abbey Dr, Saint Benedict, OR, 97373. Tel: 503-845-3303, 503-845-3317. Fax: 503-845-3500. p. 2017

Ertin, Donna, Mgr, Access Serv, Case Western Reserve University, School of Law Library, 11075 East Blvd, Cleveland, OH, 44106-7148. Tel: 216-368-8510. Fax: 216-368-1002. p. 1876

Ertle, Andrea, Ref, Fort Morgan Public Library, 414 Main St, Fort Morgan, CO, 80701. Tel: 970-542-4000. Fax: 970-542-4013. p. 308

Ertle, Sharon F, Circ, Madison County Library System, Flora Public Library, 168 Carter St No C, Flora, MS, 39071. Tel: 601-879-8835. Fax: 601-879-8835. p. 1295

Ertz, Jason, Ref, College of DuPage Library, 425 Fawell Blvd, Glen Ellyn, IL, 60137-6599. Tel: 630-942-3317. Fax: 630-858-8757. p. 649

Ervin, Catherine, Circ, Stetson University, 421 N Woodland Blvd, Unit 8418, DeLand, FL, 32723. Tel: 386-822-7187. p. 437

Ervin, Deborah, Asst Libr Dir, Concord Free Public Library, 129 Main St, Concord, MA, 01742-2494. Tel: 978-318-3300. Fax: 978-318-3344. p. 1082

Ervin, Karen, Librn, Warren State Hospital, 33 Main Dr, North Warren, PA, 16365. Tel: 814-726-4223. Fax: 814-726-4562. p. 2099

Ervin, Seth, Tech Serv Coordr, Union County Public Library, 316 E Windsor St, Monroe, NC, 28112. Tel: 704-283-8184. Fax: 704-282-0657. p. 1810

Erviti, Manuel, Librn, University of California, Berkeley, Jean Gray Hargrove Music Library, Hargrove Music Library, Berkeley, CA, 94720-6000. Tel: 510-642-2428. Fax: 510-642-8237. p. 128

Erwin, Clarissa, Dir, College of Southern Nevada, 6375 W Charleston Blvd, W10I, Las Vegas, NV, 89146. Tel: 702-651-5863. Fax: 702-651-5718. p. 1429

Erwin, Joanna, Librn, Memorial Hospital, 600 Northern Blvd, Albany, NY, 12204. Tel: 518-471-3264. Fax: 518-447-3559. p. 1569

Erwin, Joanna, Dir, Samaritan Hospital, 2215 Burdett Ave, Troy, NY, 12180. Tel: 518-271-3300. Fax: 518-271-3303. p. 1756

Erwin, Lauren, Asst Dir, Acq, Cat & Proc, Hayner Public Library District, 326 Belle St, Alton, IL, 62002. Tel: 618-462-0677. Fax: 618-462-0665. p. 588

Erwin, Sarah, Dir, Kirkwood Public Library, 140 E Jefferson Ave, Kirkwood, MO, 63122. Tel: 314-821-5770, Ext 1016. Fax: 314-822-3755. p. 1342

Erwin, Shelley, Head, Archives & Spec Coll, California Institute of Technology, 1200 E California Blvd, M/C 1-32, Pasadena, CA, 91125-3200. Tel: 626-395-3149, Ext 2702. Fax: 626-792-7540. p. 205

Erwin, Sherri, Ch, Coquille Public Library, 105 N Birch St, Coquille, OR, 97423-1299. Tel: 541-396-2166. Fax: 541-396-2174. p. 1993

Esarey, Mark, Mgr, Illinois Historic Preservation Agency, 30 Ramey St, Collinsville, IL, 62234. Tel: 618-346-5160. Fax: 618-346-5162. p. 630

Esau, Belle, Librn, Petersburg Public Library, 103 S Second St, Petersburg, NE, 68652. Tel: 402-386-5755. p. 1416

Esau, Erika, Librn, Los Angeles County Museum of Art, Robert Gore Rifkind Center for German Expressionist Studies, 5905 Wilshire Blvd, Los Angeles, CA, 90036. Tel: 323-857-6257. Fax: 323-857-4790. p. 172

Esau, Lyle, Librn, International Bible College Library, 401 Trinity Lane, Moose Jaw, SK, S6H 0E3, CANADA. Tel: 306-692-4041. Fax: 306-692-7968. p. 2918

Escalada, Kathleen, Pres, Pimeria Alta Historical Society Library & Museum, 136 N Grand Ave, Nogales, AZ, 85621. Tel: 520-287-4621. p. 70

Escalante, Eric, Head, Access Serv, Western State College, 600 N Adams St, Gunnison, CO, 81231. Tel: 970-943-2053. Fax: 970-943-2042. p. 312

Escalante, Maria, Dir, College of Menominee Nation Library, N 172 Hwy 47/55, Keshena, WI, 54135. Tel: 715-799-5600, Ext 3003. Fax: 715-799-5605. p. 2602

Escalera, Milagros, Ref & Instrul Serv Librn, Amaury Veray Music Library, 350 Rafael Lamar, Hato Rey, PR, 00918. Tel: 787-751-0160, Ext 256. Fax: 787-754-5934. p. 2673

Escamilla, Mary Ann, Ref, Robert J Kleberg Public Library, 220 N Fourth St, Kingsville, TX, 78363. Tel: 361-592-6381. p. 2350

Escamilla, Nancy, YA Serv, Lied Scottsbluff Public Library, 1809 Third Ave, Scottsbluff, NE, 69361-2493. Tel: 308-630-6250. Fax: 308-630-6293. p. 1418

Escandon, Marlene, Tech Serv, Universidad Adventista de las Antillas, Carr 106 Km 2 Interior, Bo La Quinta, Mayaguez, PR, 00680. Tel: 787-834-9595, Ext 2216. Fax: 787-834-6015. p. 2674

Esche, Maria, Ref Serv, Ad, Moorestown Public Library, 111 W Second St, Moorestown, NJ, 08057-2481. Tel: 856-234-0333. Fax: 856-778-9536. p. 1504

Eschenbauch, Pam, Dir, Presque Isle Community Library, 8306 School Loop Rd, Presque Isle, WI, 54557. Tel: 715-686-7613. Fax: 715-686-2588. p. 2631

Eschenfelder, Kristin, Asst Prof, University of Wisconsin-Madison, 4217 H C White Hall, 600 N Park St, Madison, WI, 53706. Tel: 608-263-2105. Fax: 608-263-4849. p. 2976

Eschete, Darryl, Dir, West Des Moines Public Library, 4000 Mills Civic Pkwy, West Des Moines, IA, 50265-2049. Tel: 515-222-3400. Fax: 515-222-3401. p. 852

Eschli, Lisa, Info Spec, GlaxoSmithKline, 7333 Mississauga Rd N, Mississauga, ON, L5N 6L4, CANADA. Tel: 905-819-3000, Ext 6023. Fax: 905-819-3096. p. 2822

Escobar, Hector, Dir, Educ & Info Delivery, University of Dayton Libraries, 300 College Park Dr, Dayton, OH, 45469-1360. Tel: 937-229-5141. Fax: 937-229-4950. p. 1894

Escobar, Imelda, Br Mgr, Starr County Public Library, 4192 W Hwy 83, Larosita, TX, 78582. Tel: 956-849-4453. p. 2354

Escobar, Nelson, Head, Mat Mgt, Teachers College, Columbia University, 525 W 120th St, New York, NY, 10027-6696. Tel: 212-678-3035. p. 1701

Escobar, Victoria, Acq, Altadena Library District, 600 E Mariposa St, Altadena, CA, 91001. Tel: 626-798-0833. Fax: 626-798-5351. p. 120

Escobar-Matute, Louix, Librn, Tulsa City-County Library, Hardesty Regional Library, 8316 E 93rd St, Tulsa, OK, 74133. Tel: 918-250-7307. Fax: 918-250-7843. p. 1983

Escobedo, Franklin L, YA Serv, Oceanside Public Library, 330 N Coast Hwy, Oceanside, CA, 92054-2824. Tel: 760-435-5577. Fax: 760-435-9614. p. 199

Escoffier, Deirdre, Ch, Uniondale Public Library, 400 Uniondale Ave, Uniondale, NY, 11553-1995. Tel: 516-489-2220, Ext 215. Fax: 516-489-4005. p. 1758

Escoto, Allison, Acq, Touro College, 225 Eastview Dr, Central Islip, NY, 11722-4539. Tel: 631-761-7163. Fax: 631-761-7159. p. 1605

Escoto, Cindy, Supvr, Ventura County Library, Piru Library, 3811 Center St, Piru, CA, 93040. Tel: 805-521-1753. Fax: 805-521-0729. p. 280

Escudero, Estella B, Librn, Mount Sinai Hospital Medical Center, California Ave at 15th St, Chicago, IL, 60608. Tel: 773-257-6558. Fax: 773-257-6135. p. 619

Esham, Aleta L, Tech Serv, Delaware Technical & Community College, PO Box 630, Sea Shore Hwy, Georgetown, DE, 19947-0630. Tel: 302-856-9033. Fax: 302-858-5462. p. 383

Eshbach, Barbara, Actg Head Librn, Penn State University York, 1031 Edgecomb Ave, York, PA, 17403-3398. Tel: 717-771-4023. Fax: 717-771-4022. p. 2159

Eshbach, Sue, Librn, Sharon Hill Public Library, 246 Sharon Ave, Sharon Hill, PA, 19079-2098. Tel: 610-586-3993. Fax: 610-586-8233. p. 2139

Eshleman, Carol, YA Serv, North Platte Public Library, 120 W Fourth St, North Platte, NE, 69101-3993. Tel: 308-535-8036. Fax: 308-535-8296. p. 1410

Eshleman, Joe, Ref & Instruction Librn, Johnson & Wales University, 801 W Trade St, Charlotte, NC, 28202. Tel: 980-598-1605. p. 1783

Eshleman, Ronald L, Dir, Vibration Institute Library, 6262 S Kingery Hwy, Ste 212, Willowbrook, IL, 60527. Tel: 630-654-2254. Fax: 630-654-2271. p. 719

Eshun, Elizabeth Patricia, Commun Libr Mgr, Queens Borough Public Library, Rosedale Community Library, 144-20 243rd St, Rosedale, NY, 11422. Tel: 718-528-8490. p. 1645

Esidore, Gayle, Libr Asst, Middlesex Community College, 100 Training Hill Rd, Middletown, CT, 06457-4889. Tel: 860-343-5829. Fax: 860-343-5874. p. 351

Eskin, Erik, Head Librn, Free Library of Philadelphia, Ramonita G De Rodriguez Branch, 600 W Girard Ave, Philadelphia, PA, 19123-1311. Tel: 215-686-1767, 215-686-1768. Fax: 215-686-1769. p. 2107

Eskin, Marcie, Librn, Beth Hillel Congregation Library, 3220 Big Tree Lane, Wilmette, IL, 60091. Tel: 847-256-1213, Ext 29. Fax: 847-256-3225. p. 719

Eskridge, Beverly, Circ/AV, Gordon College Library, 419 College Dr, Barnesville, GA, 30204. Tel: 770-358-5078. Fax: 770-358-5240. p. 521

Eskridge, Honora, Head of Libr, North Carolina State University Libraries, Burlington Textiles Library, 4411 College of Textiles, Campus Box 8301, Raleigh, NC, 27695-8301. Tel: 919-515-6120. Fax: 919-515-3926. p. 1816

Eskridge, Lori, Hispanic Outreach, New Albany-Floyd County Public Library, 180 W Spring St, New Albany, IN, 47150-3692. Tel: 812-944-8464. Fax: 812-949-3532. p. 768

Eskridge, Randi, Head, Ch, Saline County Public Library, 1800 Smithers Dr, Benton, AR, 72015. Tel: 501-778-4766. Fax: 501-778-0536. p. 94

Eskridge, Sherry L, Access Serv Librn, Head, Circ, Arkansas State University, 322 University Loop West Circle, State University, AR, 72401. Tel: 870-972-3077. Fax: 870-972-3199. p. 115

Eskritt, Julie, Coop Libr Mgr, Donaldson Co, Inc, PO Box 1299, MS 301, Minneapolis, MN, 55440-1299. Tel: 952-887-3019. Fax: 952-887-3555. p. 1259

Esler, Anne, Ref Librn, Dartmouth College Library, Feldberg Business Administration & Engineering Library, 6193 Murdough Ctr, Hanover, NH, 03755-3560. Tel: 603-646-2191. Fax: 603-646-2384. p. 1450

Esler, Linda, Principal Librn, Bloomfield Public Library, 90 Broad St, Bloomfield, NJ, 07003. Tel: 973-566-6200, Ext 228. Fax: 973-566-6217. p. 1473

Esmailka, Alyson, Librn, Charles Evans Community Library, 299 Antoski Dr, Galena, AK, 99741. Tel: 907-656-1883, Ext 127. Fax: 907-656-1769. p. 48

Esmonde, Gary, Head Librn, Cleveland Botanical Garden, 11030 East Blvd, Cleveland, OH, 44106. Tel: 216-707-2812. Fax: 216-721-1694, 216-721-2056. p. 1876

Esparo, Daniela, Br Head, Vancouver Public Library, Kitsilano, 2425 Macdonald St, Vancouver, BC, V6K 3Y9, CANADA. Tel: 604-665-3976. Fax: 604-665-3931. p. 2744

Esparza, Julia, Mgr, Libr Serv, Deaconess Hospital, 600 Mary St, Evansville, IN, 47747. Tel: 812-450-3384, 812-450-3385. Fax: 812-450-7255. p. 738

Espenschied, Barbara, Acq, Edison Township Free Public Library, 340 Plainfield Ave, Edison, NJ, 08817. Tel: 732-287-2298. Fax: 732-819-9134. p. 1483

Esper, Elizabeth, Dir, Brockway Memorial Library, 10021 NE Second Ave, Miami Shores, FL, 33138. Tel: 305-758-8107. p. 470

Espinosa, Carlos, Adjunct Ref Librn, University of Miami, 1311 Miller Dr, Coral Gables, FL, 33146. Tel: 305-284-2251. Fax: 305-284-3554. p. 434

Espinosa, Connie, Librn, Department of Human Services-Youth Corrections, 1406 W 17th St, Pueblo, CO, 81003-1929. Tel: 719-546-4934. Fax: 719-546-4917. p. 320

Espinosa, Nance, Spec Coll, Fresno County Public Library, 2420 Mariposa St, Fresno, CA, 93721-2285. Tel: 559-600-7323. p. 151

Espinoza, Ester, Dir, Idalou Community Library, 210 Main St, Idalou, TX, 79329. Tel: 806-892-2114. p. 2346

Espinoza, Margaret, Adult Serv, Lead Librn, Prescott Public Library, 215 E Goodwin St, Prescott, AZ, 86303. Tel: 928-777-1509. Fax: 928-771-5829. p. 78

Espinoza, Martha, Mgr, Heald College, 255 W Bullard Ave, Fresno, CA, 93704. Tel: 559-438-4222. Fax: 559-438-0948. p. 153

Espiritu, Florence, Ref Serv, Diablo Valley College Library, 321 Golf Club Rd, Pleasant Hill, CA, 94523-1576. Tel: 925-685-1230, Ext 2239. Fax: 925-798-3588. p. 210

Espitia, Sadys, Asst Librn, Curtis, Mallet-Prevost, Colt & Mosle Library, 101 Park Ave, New York, NY, 10178-0061. Tel: 212-696-6138. Fax: 212-697-1559. p. 1676

Espitia, Sadys, Res, Weil, Gotshal & Manges Library, 767 Fifth Ave, New York, NY, 10153. Tel: 212-310-8626. Fax: 212-310-8007. p. 1702

Esposito, Fred W, Dir, Alaska Vocational Technical Center, 519 Fourth Ave, Seward, AK, 99664. Tel: 907-224-6105. Fax: 907-224-6020. p. 53

Esposito, Jackie, Univ Archivist, Pennsylvania State University Libraries, 510 Paterno Library, University Park, PA, 16802. Tel: 814-865-0401. Fax: 814-865-3665. p. 2148

Esposito, Jackie, Univ Archivist, Pennsylvania State University Libraries, Eberly Family Special Collections Library, 104 Paterno Library, University Park, PA, 16802-1808. Tel: 814-863-3791. Fax: 814-863-5318. p. 2148

Esposito, Joseph, Librn, Mayo Clinic Scottsdale Libraries, 13400 E Shea Blvd, Scottsdale, AZ, 85259. Tel: 480-301-8443. Fax: 480-301-7005. p. 80

Esposito, Shaun, Head, Pub Serv, University of Arizona, James E Rogers College of Law Library, PO Box 210176, Tucson, AZ, 85721-0176. Tel: 520-621-1413. Fax: 520-621-3138. p. 89

Esquevin, Christian R, Dir of Libr Serv, Coronado Public Library, 640 Orange Ave, Coronado, CA, 92118-1526. Tel: 619-522-7395. Fax: 619-435-4205. p. 136

Esquibel, Oresta, Head Librn, Trinity County Library, 211 N Main St, Weaverville, CA, 96093. Tel: 530-623-1373. Fax: 530-623-4427. p. 282

Essency, Janet, Cat, Bridgewater State College, Ten Shaw Rd, Bridgewater, MA, 02325. Tel: 508-531-1757. Fax: 508-531-1349, 508-531-6103. p. 1070

Essenmacher, Cecila, Tech Serv, Langston University, PO Box 1600, Langston, OK, 73050-1600. Tel: 405-466-3293. Fax: 405-466-3459. p. 1967

Essenmacher, Jillian, Head, Adult Serv, Salem-South Lyon District Library, 9800 Pontiac Trail, South Lyon, MI, 48178-1307. Tel: 248-437-6431. Fax: 248-437-6593. p. 1227

Esser, Linda, Teaching Prof, University of Missouri-Columbia, 303 Townsend Hall, Columbia, MO, 65211. Tel: 573-882-4546. Fax: 573-884-2917. p. 2969

Esser, Patrick, Tech Mgr, Omaha Public Library, 215 S 15th St, Omaha, NE, 68102-1629. Tel: 402-444-4800. Fax: 402-444-4504. p. 1414

Essex-Webster, Julie, Head, Coll Serv, Karr Tuttle Campbell, 1201 Third Ave, Ste 2900, Seattle, WA, 98101-3028. Tel: 206-224-8187. Fax: 206-682-7100. p. 2528

Essien, Victor, Foreign Law, Intl Law Librn, Fordham University School of Law, 140 W 62nd St, New York, NY, 10023-7485. Tel: 212-636-6913. Fax: 212-930-8818. p. 1678

Essig, Mary, Mgr, Libr Serv, West Virginia School of Osteopathic Medicine Library, 400 N Lee St, Lewisburg, WV, 24901. Tel: 304-647-6261. Fax: 304-645-4443. p. 2564

Essinger, Catherine, Coordr, University of Houston, William R Jenkins Architecture & Art Library, 122 Architecture Bldg, Houston, TX, 77204-4000. Tel: 713-743-2340. Fax: 713-743-9917. p. 2343

Esslami, Mohammed, Br Mgr, Fairfax County Public Library, Woodrow Wilson Branch, 6101 Knollwood Dr, Falls Church, VA, 22041-1798. Tel: 703-820-8774. p. 2461

Esslinger, Mark, Dir, Wayne County Public Library, 1200 Oak St, Kenova, WV, 25530-1335. Tel: 304-453-2462. Fax: 304-453-2462. p. 2563

Estabrook, Alex, Head, Circ, Teen Librn, Merrimack Public Library, 470 Daniel Webster Hwy, Merrimack, NH, 03054-3694. Tel: 603-424-5021. Fax: 603-424-7312. p. 1457

Estabrook, Alexia, Dir, Helen L DeRoy Medical Library, 16001 W Nine Mile Rd, Southfield, MI, 48075. Tel: 248-849-3294. Fax: 248-849-3201. p. 1228

Estel, Terri, Asst Dir, Sandusky Library, 114 W Adams St, Sandusky, OH, 44870. Tel: 419-625-3834. Fax: 419-625-4574. p. 1934

Estelle, Lorraine, Adult Serv, A K Smiley Public Library, 125 W Vine St, Redlands, CA, 92373. Tel: 909-798-7565. Fax: 909-798-7566. p. 215

Estelle, Myron, IT & Security Mgr, Cumberland County Library, 800 E Commerce St, Bridgeton, NJ, 08302-2295. Tel: 856-453-2210. Fax: 856-451-1940. p. 1474

Estelle-Holmer, Suzanne, Ref & Instrul Serv Librn, Yale University Library, Divinity School Library, 409 Prospect St, New Haven, CT, 06511-2108. Tel: 203-432-5290. Fax: 203-432-5356. p. 357

Ester, Katie, Actg Adult Coordr, Southfield Public Library, 26300 Evergreen Rd, Southfield, MI, 48076. Tel: 248-796-4389. Fax: 248-796-4305. p. 1228

Estes, Alicia, Bus Librn, New York University, 70 Washington Sq S, New York, NY, 10012-1091. Tel: 212-998-2505. Fax: 212-995-4070. p. 1695

Estes, Alicia, Librn, New York University, United Nations Collection, Elmer Holmes Bobst Libr, 70 Washington Sq S, New York, NY, 10012. Tel: 212-998-2610. Fax: 212-995-4442. p. 1695

Estes, April, Libr Assoc, Morrison & Mary Wiley Library District, 206 W Main St, Elmwood, IL, 61529-9641. Tel: 309-742-2431. Fax: 309-742-8298. p. 642

Estes, Dawn, Librn, Falkville Public Library, Seven N First Ave, Falkville, AL, 35622. Tel: 256-784-5822. Fax: 256-784-5525. p. 16

Estes, Elizabeth W, Dir, Libr Serv, Stanly Community College, Snyder Bldg, Albemarle, NC, 28001. Tel: 704-991-0337. Fax: 704-991-0112. p. 1773

Estes, Helena, Ch, Case Memorial Library, 176 Tyler City Rd, Orange, CT, 06477-2498. Tel: 203-891-2170. Fax: 203-891-2190. p. 364

Estes, James, Info Serv Librn, Wesley Theological Seminary Library, 4500 Massachusetts Ave NW, Washington, DC, 20016-5690. Tel: 202-885-8695. Fax: 202-885-8691. p. 422

Estes, Marilyn, Acq Librn, American University, 4801 Massachusetts Ave NW, Washington, DC, 20016-8182. Tel: 202-274-4346. Fax: 202-274-4365. p. 393

Estes, Mark E, Dir, Bernard E Witkin Alameda County Law Library, 12th & Oak St Bldg, 125 Twelfth St, Oakland, CA, 94607-4912. Tel: 510-272-6481. Fax: 510-208-4823. p. 199

Estes, Mark E, Dir, Witkin Bernard E Alameda County Law Library, South County Branch, 224 W Winton Ave, Rm 162, Hayward, CA, 94544. Tel: 510-670-5230. Fax: 510-670-5292. p. 199

Estes, Patricia, Libr Tech, California Department of Corrections Library System, Centinela State Prison, 2302 Brown Rd, Imperial, CA, 92251. Tel: 760-337-7900, Ext 6356. Fax: 760-337-7631. p. 221

Estes, Susan, Outreach Serv Librn, Liverpool Public Library, 310 Tulip St, Liverpool, NY, 13088-4997. Tel: 315-457-0310. Fax: 315-453-7867. p. 1653

Esteves, Lucilia, In Charge, Luso-American Life Insurance Society, Seven Hartwell Ave, Lexington, MA, 02421. Tel: 781-676-2002. Fax: 781-541-6191. p. 1099

Esteves, Roberto, Serv Consult, Califa, 32 W 25th Ave, Ste 201, San Mateo, CA, 94403. Tel: 650-572-2746. Fax: 650-349-5089. p. 2938

Estey, Lori, Asst Librn, Meriden Library, 22 Bean Rd, Meriden, NH, 03770. Tel: 603-469-3252. p. 1457

Estey, Samantha, Ref, Nicholas P Sims Library, 515 W Main, Waxahachie, TX, 75165-3235. Tel: 972-937-2671. Fax: 972-937-4409. p. 2398

Estis, Donna, Ch, ILL & Distance Libr Serv Spec, Lasalle Parish Library, 3108 N First St, Jena, LA, 71342. Tel: 318-992-5675. Fax: 318-992-7374, 318-992-7394. p. 951

Estrada, Anna, Librn, Charlotte Public Library, 77 Yule St, Charlotte, TX, 78011. Tel: 830-277-1212. Fax: 830-277-1212. p. 2297

Estrada, Bonnie, Dir, Talcott Free Public Library, 101 E Main St, Rockton, IL, 61072. Tel: 815-624-7511. Fax: 815-624-1176. p. 698

Estrada, Eugene, Br Mgr, Los Angeles Public Library System, El Sereno, 5226 Huntington Dr S, Los Angeles, CA, 90032. Tel: 323-225-9201. Fax: 323-441-0112. p. 173

Estrada, Heather, Cat, Electronic Res, Blue Mountain Community College Library, 2411 NW Carden Ave, Pendleton, OR, 97801. Tel: 541-278-5913. Fax: 541-276-6119. p. 2009

Estrada, Raquel, Librn, University of Texas at Brownsville & Texas Southmost College Library, 80 Fort Brown St, Brownsville, TX, 78521. Tel: 956-882-7267. Fax: 956-882-5495. p. 2292

Estrada-Lopez, Janine, Librn, Missouri Court of Appeals Library, 1300 Oak St, Kansas City, MO, 64106-2970. Tel: 816-889-3639. Fax: 816-889-3668. p. 1339

Esty, Anna, Per Asst, Berklee College of Music Library, 150 Massachusetts Ave, Boston, MA, 02115. Tel: 617-747-2599. Fax: 617-747-2050. p. 1055

Esty, Donna, Librn, Hebron Library, Eight Church Lane, Hebron, NH, 03241. Tel: 603-744-7998. p. 1451

Esty, Lynn, Asst Librn, Weathersfield Proctor Library, 5181 Rte 5, Ascutney, VT, 05030. Tel: 802-674-2863. p. 2417

Esvang, Karen, Ref Serv, Ad, Menomonee Falls Public Library, W156 N8436 Pilgrim Rd, Menomonee Falls, WI, 53051. Tel: 262-532-8900. Fax: 262-532-8939. p. 2614

Etemad, Behnam, Dir, Northeastern State University, Muskogee Campus Library, 2400 W Shawnee St, Muskogee, OK, 74401. Tel: 918-456-5511, Ext 5021. Fax: 918-458-2101. p. 1980

Ethen, Anne, Adult Serv, Newton Public Library, 720 N Oak, Newton, KS, 67114. Tel: 316-283-2890. Fax: 316-283-2916. p. 884

Etheridge, Robbie, Circ Mgr, Chesapeake Public Library, Major Hillard Library, 824 Old George Washington Hwy N, Chesapeake, VA, 23323-2214. Tel: 757-410-7087. Fax: 757-410-7088, 757-410-7089. p. 2456

Ethier-Danis, Mireille, Mgr, Libr Serv, Bruyere Continuing Care Library, 43 Bruyere St, Ottawa, ON, K1N 5C8, CANADA. Tel: 613-562-6262, Ext 4054. Fax: 613-562-4237. p. 2828

Ethington, Christie, In Charge, San Antonio First Baptist Church, 515 McCullough St, San Antonio, TX, 78215. Tel: 210-226-0363, Ext 219. Fax: 210-299-2633. p. 2382

Ethington, Jenny, Teen Librn, Arlington Public Library System, 101 E Abram St, MS 10-0100, Arlington, TX, 76010-1183. Tel: 817-459-6900. Fax: 817-459-6936. p. 2276

Etling, Jean, Asst Dir, Pub Serv, Fox River Valley Public Library District, 555 Barrington Ave, Dundee, IL, 60118-1496. Tel: 847-428-3661. Fax: 847-428-0521. p. 637

Etschmaier, Gale S, Dr, Dean of Libr, San Diego State University Library & Information Access, 5500 Campanile Dr, San Diego, CA, 92182-8050. Tel: 619-594-6728. Fax: 619-594-3270. p. 237

Etter, Mary J, Dir, South Windsor Public Library, 1550 Sullivan Ave, South Windsor, CT, 06074. Tel: 860-644-1541. Fax: 860-644-7645. p. 368

Ettinger, Renee, Ref Coordr, University of Wisconsin-Green Bay, 2420 Nicolet Dr, Green Bay, WI, 54311-7001. Tel: 920-465-2542. Fax: 920-465-2136. p. 2596

Etzel, Allison, Mgr, Libr Operations, University of South Florida Saint Petersburg, 140 Seventh Ave S, POY118, Saint Petersburg, FL, 33701. Tel: 727-873-4401. Fax: 727-873-4196. p. 489

Etzel, Brent, Dir, Pub Serv, Cedarville University, 251 N Main St, Cedarville, OH, 45314-0601. Tel: 937-766-7840. Fax: 937-766-2337. p. 1865

Etzweiler, Holly, Libr Mgr, Dauphin County Library System, Johnson Memorial, 799 E Center St, Millersburg, PA, 17061. Tel: 717-692-2658. Fax: 717-692-5003. p. 2064

Etzweiller, Holly, Libr Mgr, Dauphin County Library System, Elizabethville Area Library, 80 N Market St, Elizabethville, PA, 17023. Tel: 717-362-9825. Fax: 717-362-8119. p. 2064

Etzwiler, Holly, Libr Mgr, Dauphin County Library System, Northern Dauphin Library, 683 Main St, Lykens, PA, 17048. Tel: 717-453-9315. Fax: 717-453-9524. p. 2064

Eubank, Misty, Tech Serv, Cleveland Bradley County Public Library, 795 Church St NE, Cleveland, TN, 37311-5295. Tel: 423-472-2163. Fax: 423-339-9791. p. 2229

Eubank, Susan, Dir, Oldham County Public Library, 308 Yager Ave, La Grange, KY, 40031. Tel: 502-222-9713, Ext 304. Fax: 502-222-1141. p. 919

Eubank, Susan C, Plant Sci Librn, Los Angeles County Arboretum & Botanic Garden, 301 N Baldwin Ave, Arcadia, CA, 91007-2697. Tel: 626-821-3213. Fax: 626-445-1217. p. 121

Eubanks, Carolyn T, Cat, Petersburg Public Library, 137 S Sycamore St, Petersburg, VA, 23803. Tel: 804-733-2387. Fax: 804-733-7972. p. 2484

Eubanks, Debbie, Circ Supvr, Killeen City Library System, 205 E Church Ave, Killeen, TX, 76541. Tel: 254-501-8990. Fax: 254-501-7704. p. 2350

Eubanks, Jake, Ref/Instruction Librn, Indiana State University, 510 North 6 1/2 St, Terre Haute, IN, 47809. Tel: 812-237-7978. Fax: 812-237-3376. p. 781

Eubanks, Laurie, Coordr, West Georgia Regional Library, 710 Rome St, Carrollton, GA, 30117. Tel: 770-836-6711. Fax: 770-836-4787. p. 523

Eubanks, Lecia, Asst Dir, Cherokee Regional Library System, 305 S Duke St, LaFayette, GA, 30728-2936. Tel: 706-638-7557. Fax: 706-638-3979. p. 538

Eubanks, Toni, Librn, Barton Public Library, 100 Church St, Barton, VT, 05822. Tel: 802-525-6524. Fax: 802-525-6524. p. 2418

Eubanks, Toni, Librn, Glover Public Library, 51 Beanhill Rd, Glover, VT, 05839. Tel: 802-525-4365. p. 2424

Eudy, Nancy, Libr Supvr, Southwest Baptist University Libraries, Wisdom Library, SBU Salem Ctr, 501 S Grand St, Salem, MO, 65560. Tel: 573-729-7071. Fax: 573-729-6949. p. 1320

Euemduan, Osmera, Tech Serv, Largo Public Library, 120 Central Park Dr, Largo, FL, 33771. Tel: 727-587-6715. Fax: 727-586-7353. p. 460

Eugene, Patrick, ILL, Manatt, Phelps & Phillips LLP, 700 12th St NW, Ste 1100, Washington, DC, 20005-4075. Tel: 202-585-6500, 202-585-6680. Fax: 202-585-6600. p. 408

Eula, Oliphant, Coordr, Texas Woman's University, 5500 Southwestern Medical Ave, Dallas, TX, 75235-7200. Tel: 214-689-6580. Fax: 214-689-6583. p. 2311

Euler, Helen, Librn, Wright County Library, Laura Ingalls Wilder Library, PO Box 586, Mansfield, MO, 65704-3245. Tel: 417-924-8068. Fax: 417-924-3045. p. 1330

Eure, Mylinda, Asst Librn, Albemarle Regional Library, Gates County Public Library, 115 Court St, Gatesville, NC, 27938-9507. Tel: 252-357-0110. Fax: 252-357-1285. p. 1835

Eusea, Geraldine, Head, Circ & Reserve, Nicholls State University, 906 E First St, Thibodaux, LA, 70310. Tel: 985-448-4646, 985-448-4660. Fax: 985-448-4925. p. 971

Eusfice, B, Asst Librn, Nissen Public Library, 217 W Fifth, Saint Ansgar, IA, 50472-0040. Tel: 641-713-2218. Fax: 641-713-4716. p. 842

Eustace, Jamie, Pub Serv Adminr, Sterling Municipal Library, Mary Elizabeth Wilbanks Ave, Baytown, TX, 77520. Tel: 281-427-7331. Fax: 281-420-5347. p. 2287

Eustis, Joanne, Dr, Univ Librn, Case Western Reserve University, 11055 Euclid Ave, Cleveland, OH, 44106. Tel: 216-368-3506. Fax: 216-368-6950. p. 1876

Eustis, Tammy, Head Librn, Killingworth Library Association, 301 Rte 81, Killingworth, CT, 06419-1218. Tel: 860-663-2000. Fax: 860-663-2783. p. 348

Eutsler, Betty, Librn, Kinmundy Public Library, 111 S Monroe St, Kinmundy, IL, 62854. Tel: 618-547-3250. Fax: 618-547-3258. p. 661

Evangelista, Ernie, Mgr, Federal Reserve Bank of Atlanta, 1000 Peachtree St NE, Atlanta, GA, 30309-4470. Tel: 404-498-8867. Fax: 404-498-7931. p. 515

Evanoff, Joanne, Libr Serv & Tech Mgr, Embry-Riddle Aeronautical University, 3700 Willow Creek Rd, Prescott, AZ, 86301-3720. Tel: 928-777-3802. p. 78

Evans, Alice, Bus Mgr, Northwest Kansas Library System, Two Washington Sq, Norton, KS, 67654-1615. Tel: 785-877-5148. Fax: 785-877-5697. p. 885

Evans, Andrew, Head Ref/Govt Doc Librn, Washburn University, School of Law Library, 1700 SW College Ave, Topeka, KS, 66621. Tel: 785-670-1787. Fax: 785-670-3194. p. 897

Evans, Anita, Dir, University of Wisconsin-La Crosse, 1631 Pine St, La Crosse, WI, 54601-3748. Tel: 608-785-8805. Fax: 608-785-8639. p. 2603

Evans, Ann Sasser, Mgr, Libr Serv, Danville Regional Medical Center, 142 S Main St, Danville, VA, 24541. Tel: 434-799-4418. Fax: 434-799-2255. p. 2460

Evans, Annis, Pub Serv Librn, Acq, Northeast State Community College, 2425 Hwy 75, Blountville, TN, 37617-6350. Tel: 423-354-2429. Fax: 423-323-0254. p. 2224

Evans, Audrey, Br Mgr, Lonesome Pine Regional Library, Lee County Public, 406 Joslyn Ave, Pennington Gap, VA, 24277. Tel: 276-546-1141. Fax: 276-546-5136. p. 2504

Evans, Barbara, Librn, National Louis University Library & Learning Support, Lisle, 850 Warrenville Rd, Lisle, IL, 60532. Tel: 630-874-4531. Fax: 630-874-4531. p. 619

Evans, Barbara, Asst Dir, Pub Serv, First Regional Library, 370 W Commerce St, Hernando, MS, 38632. Tel: 662-429-4439. Fax: 662-429-8853. p. 1301

Evans, Barbara, Br Librn, Mohawk Valley Community College Library, 1101 Sherman Dr, Utica, NY, 13501-5394. Tel: 315-334-7714. Fax: 315-792-5666. p. 1759

Evans, Beth, Electronic Res, Brooklyn College Library, 2900 Bedford Ave, Brooklyn, NY, 11210-2889. Tel: 718-951-5336. Fax: 718-951-4540. p. 1589

Evans, Betty, Head, Cat, Sweet Briar College, 134 Chapel Rd, Sweet Briar, VA, 24595-1200. Tel: 434-381-6138. Fax: 434-381-6173. p. 2497

Evans, Betty, Asst Prof, Missouri State University, Duane G Meyer Library, 901 S National Ave, Springfield, MO, 65897. Tel: 417-836-4525. Fax: 417-836-4764. p. 2968

Evans, Bruce, Cat & Metadata Serv Unit Leader, Baylor University Libraries, Moody Memorial Library, 1312 S Third, Waco, TX, 76798. p. 2396

Evans, Carla, Librn, Proskauer Rose LLP Library, 1001 Pennsylvania Ave NW, Ste 400 S, Washington, DC, 20004-2533. Tel: 202-416-6823. Fax: 202-416-6899. p. 413

Evans, Celeste, Ref Librn, United States Military Academy Library, Jefferson Hall Library & Learning Center, 758 Cullum Rd, West Point, NY, 10996. Tel: 845-938-3833. Fax: 845-938-4000. p. 1767

Evans, Christina, Assoc Librn, Devereux Foundation, 444 Devereux Dr, Villanova, PA, 19085. Tel: 610-542-3056. Fax: 610-542-3092. p. 2149

Evans, Christine, Head, Circ Serv, California State University, Fresno, Henry Madden Library, 5200 N Barton Ave, Mail Stop ML-34, Fresno, CA, 93740-8014. Tel: 559-278-2403. Fax: 559-278-6952. p. 150

Evans, Christine, Tech Serv, Abbot Public Library, 235 Pleasant St, Marblehead, MA, 01945. Tel: 781-631-1481. Fax: 781-639-0558. p. 1102

Evans, Dale, Acq Tech, Southwestern Oklahoma State University, 100 Campus Dr, Weatherford, OK, 73096-3002. Tel: 580-774-3737. Fax: 580-774-3112. p. 1985

Evans, Dan, Dir, Caterpillar Inc, 14009 Old Galena Rd, Mossville, IL, 61552. Tel: 309-578-4473. Fax: 309-578-6733. p. 676

Evans, Darla, Circ, Louisville Public Library, 700 Lincoln Ave, Louisville, OH, 44641-1474. Tel: 330-875-1696. Fax: 330-875-3530. p. 1912

Evans, Dave, Tech Serv Coordr, Biblical Theological Seminary Library, 200 N Main St, Hatfield, PA, 19440-2499. Tel: 215-368-5000, Ext 123. Fax: 215-368-6906. p. 2067

Evans, David, Dir of Libr Serv, Calvary Baptist Theological Seminary Library, 1380 S Valley Forge Rd, Lansdale, PA, 19446-4797. Tel: 215-368-7538, Ext 137. Fax: 215-368-1003. p. 2078

Evans, David, Dr, Asst VPres, Libr Serv, Kennesaw State University, 1000 Chastain Rd, Kennesaw, GA, 30144. Tel: 770-423-6194. Fax: 770-423-6185. p. 537

Evans, Doris, Librn, Canton Township Library, 203 N Main St, Canton, KS, 67428. Tel: 620-628-4349. p. 859

Evans, Edward, Dr, Librn, Museum of Northern Arizona-Harold S Colton Memorial Library, 3101 N Fort Valley Rd, Flagstaff, AZ, 86001. Tel: 928-774-5211, Ext 256. Fax: 928-779-1527. p. 62

Evans, Elizabeth, Dir, Point Park University Library, 414 Wood St, Pittsburgh, PA, 15222. Tel: 412-392-3161. Fax: 412-392-3168. p. 2127

Evans, Elizabeth, Ref, ILL & Gov Doc, Hampton University, 130 E Tyler St, Hampton, VA, 23668. Tel: 757-727-5371. Fax: 757-727-5952. p. 2468

Evans, Evelyn, Librn, Harrie P Woodson Memorial Library, 704 W Hwy 21, Caldwell, TX, 77836-1129. Tel: 979-567-4111. Fax: 979-567-4962. p. 2294

Evans, Gayles E, Dr, Asst Prof, Chicago State University, 9501 S King Dr, Chicago, IL, 60628-1598. Tel: 773-995-2503. p. 2964

Evans, Gwen, Exec Dir, Ohio Library & Information Network, 35 E Chestnut St, 8th Flr, Columbus, OH, 43215-2541. Tel: 614-485-6726. Fax: 614-228-1807. p. 2952

Evans, James, Cat, Head, Tech Serv, Louisiana State University, One University Pl, Shreveport, LA, 71115-2399. Tel: 318-797-5070. Fax: 318-797-5156. p. 968

Evans, Jane, Librn, East Mississippi Regional Library System, Enterprise Public, Ritchey St, Enterprise, MS, 39330. Tel: 601-659-3564. p. 1313

Evans, Janet, Mgr, Pennsylvania Horticultural Society, 100 N 20th St, Philadelphia, PA, 19103-1495. Tel: 215-988-8772. Fax: 215-988-8783. p. 2113

Evans, Janice, Circ, ILL, Christiana Hospital Library, Christiana Hospital, 4755 Ogletown Stanton Rd, Newark, DE, 19718-0002. Tel: 302-733-1138. Fax: 302-733-1365. p. 385

Evans, Jean, Exec Dir, American Lung Association in Hawaii, 680 Iwilei Rd, Ste 575, Honolulu, HI, 96817. Tel: 808-537-5966, Ext 209. Fax: 808-537-5971. p. 559

Evans, Jean, Archives Librn, Coll Develop Librn, Ref & Instruction Librn, Illinois Mathematics & Science Academy, 1500 W Sullivan Rd, Aurora, IL, 60506-1000. Tel: 630-907-5920. Fax: 630-907-5004. p. 591

Evans, Jennifer, Prov Librn, Nova Scotia Provincial Library, 2021 Brunswick St, 2nd Flr, Halifax, NS, B3K 2Y5, CANADA. Tel: 902-424-2455. Fax: 902-424-0633. p. 2782

Evans, Jo An M, Librn, Saint Elmo Public Library District, Beecher City Branch, 108 N James St, Beecher City, IL, 62414. Tel: 618-487-9400. p. 700

Evans, Joan, Mgr, Br Serv, Camden County Library District, Macks Creek Branch, 90 State Rd N, Macks Creek, MO, 65786. Tel: 573-363-5530. p. 1321

Evans, Jody, Tech Serv, Fort Richardson Post Library, IMPA-FRA-HRE PL, Bldg 7, Chilkoot Ave, Fort Richardson, AK, 99505-0055. Tel: 907-384-1648. Fax: 907-384-7534. p. 48

Evans, John E, Dr, Head, Libr Info Syst Dept, University Libraries, University of Memphis, 126 Ned R McWherter Library, Memphis, TN, 38152-3250. Tel: 901-678-4485. p. 2252

Evans, Jon, Dir, Hirsch Library, Museum of Fine Arts, Houston, 1001 Bissonnet St, Houston, TX, 77005-1803. Tel: 713-639-7393. Fax: 713-639-7707. p. 2337

Evans, Karen, Ref/Instruction Librn, Indiana State University, 510 North 6 1/2 St, Terre Haute, IN, 47809. Tel: 812-237-8824. Fax: 812-237-3376. p. 781

Evans, Kathy, Br Mgr, Hall County Library System, East Hall & Special Needs Library, 2435 Old Cornelia Hwy, Gainesville, GA, 30507. Tel: 770-532-3311, Ext 161. Fax: 770-531-2502. p. 534

Evans, Kathy, Health Res Ctr Coordr, Prince County Hospital, 65 Roy Boates Ave, Summerside, PE, C1N 6M8, CANADA. Tel: 902-438-4225. Fax: 902-438-4221. p. 2877

Evans, Katrina, Asst Dir, Columbia County Public Library, 308 NW Columbia Ave, Lake City, FL, 32055. Tel: 386-758-2101. Fax: 386-758-2135. p. 457

Evans, Kenneth, Librn, Tarrant County College, 2100 Southeast Pkwy, Arlington, TX, 76018. Tel: 817-515-3085. Fax: 817-515-3183. p. 2277

Evans, Larry, Dir, Trenton Public Library, 406 Main St, Trenton, NE, 69044. Tel: 308-334-5413. p. 1421

Evans, Larry Ann, Dir, Wayne County Historical Society Museum Library, 21 Butternut St, Lyons, NY, 14489. Tel: 315-946-4943. Fax: 315-946-0069. p. 1656

Evans, Laura, Dir, Sherrard Public Library District, 200 Fifth Ave, Sherrard, IL, 61281-8608. Tel: 309-593-2178. Fax: 309-593-2179. p. 702

Evans, Liz, Tech Serv Librn, Medaille College Library, 18 Agassiz Circle, Buffalo, NY, 14214. Tel: 716-880-2283. Fax: 716-884-9638. p. 1598

Evans, Lois, Librn, J T & E J Crumbaugh Memorial Public Church Library, 405 E Center St, Le Roy, IL, 61752-1723. Tel: 309-962-3911. p. 664

Evans, Lori, Adult Serv, Libr Asst, Barry-Lawrence Regional Library, Mount Vernon Branch, 206 W Water, Mount Vernon, MO, 65712. Tel: 417-466-2921. Fax: 417-466-2936. p. 1346

Evans, Lorrie, Res & Instruction Librn, Auraria Library, 1100 Lawrence St, Denver, CO, 80204-2095. Tel: 303-556-6776. Fax: 303-556-3528. p. 298

Evans, Lynn, ILL, Lyon County Library System, 20 Nevin Way, Yerington, NV, 89447. Tel: 775-463-6645. Fax: 775-463-6646. p. 1435

Evans, Mahala, Develop Officer, Anythink Libraries, 5877 E 120th Ave, Thornton, CO, 80602. Tel: 303-288-2001. Fax: 303-451-0190. p. 323

Evans, Mark, AV, Florida State University Libraries, College of Law Library, 425 W Jefferson St, Tallahassee, FL, 32306. Tel: 850-644-4578. Fax: 850-644-5216. p. 494

Evans, Mary Anne, Dir, Info Serv, Lennox & Addington County Public Library, 97 Thomas St E, Napanee, ON, K7R 3S9, CANADA. Tel: 613-354-4883. Fax: 613-354-3112. p. 2824

Evans, Meredith, Circ Mgr, Florida Coastal School of Law, 8787 Baypine Rd, Jacksonville, FL, 32256. Tel: 904-680-7608. Fax: 904-680-7677. p. 452

Evans, Michael, Adult Prog Coordr, Hastings Public Library, 227 E State St, Hastings, MI, 49058-1817. Tel: 269-945-4263. Fax: 269-948-3874. p. 1189

Evans, Michael, Mgr, Greenville County Library System, Mauldin (W Jack Greer) Branch, 800 W Butler Rd, Greenville, SC, 29607. Tel: 864-277-7397. Fax: 864-277-7389. p. 2196

Evans, Nancy, Dir, Res Serv, Winthrop & Weinstine, 225 S Sixth St, Ste 3500, Minneapolis, MN, 55402. Tel: 612-604-6450. Fax: 612-604-6850. p. 1263

Evans, Nell, Br Head, Chatham-Kent Public Library, Bothwell Branch, 320 Main St, Bothwell, ON, N0P 1C0, CANADA. Tel: 519-695-2844. Fax: 519-695-5079. p. 2799

Evans, Patricia, Dir, Victor Free Library, 15 W Main, Victor, NY, 14564. Tel: 585-924-2637. Fax: 585-924-1893. p. 1761

Evans, Patricia, Ch, Haverford Township Free Library, 1601 Darby Rd, Havertown, PA, 19083-3798. Tel: 610-446-3082, Ext 205. Fax: 610-853-3090. p. 2067

Evans, Patricia, Tech Serv Librn, North Grenville Public Library, Norenberg Bldg, One Water St, Kemptville, ON, K0G 1J0, CANADA. Tel: 613-258-4711, Ext 5. Fax: 613-258-4134. p. 2812

Evans, Peggy, Acq Mgr, Shreve Memorial Library, 424 Texas St, Shreveport, LA, 71101. Tel: 318-226-5876. Fax: 318-429-4387. p. 969

Evans, Rita, Dir, Institute of Transportation Studies Library, 412 McLaughlin Hall, MC 1720, Berkeley, CA, 94720-1720. Tel: 510-643-3564. Fax: 510-642-9180. p. 127

Evans, Robin, Head, Ref Serv, Foley & Lardner LLP, 3000 K St NW, 4th Flr, Washington, DC, 20007. Tel: 202-672-5536. Fax: 202-672-5399. p. 400

Evans, Robin, In Charge, Elko-Lander-Eureka County Library System, Eureka Branch, 10190 Monroe St, Eureka, NV, 89316. Tel: 775-237-5307. p. 1427

Evans, Ruth, Div Head, Alabama Public Library Service, 6030 Monticello Dr, Montgomery, AL, 36130-6000. Tel: 334-213-3906. Fax: 334-213-3993. p. 27

Evans, Sheila, Dir, Hoke County Public Library, 334 N Main St, Raeford, NC, 28376. Tel: 910-875-2502. Fax: 910-875-2207. p. 1815

Evans, Sherry, Pub Serv Librn, Portsmouth Public Library, 175 Parrott Ave, Portsmouth, NH, 03801-4452. Tel: 603-766-1703. Fax: 603-433-0981. p. 1463

Evans, Sue, Librn, Greenup County Public Libraries, McKell Public, 22 McKell Lane, South Shore, KY, 41175. Tel: 606-932-4478. Fax: 606-932-4478. p. 915

Evans, Susan, Dir, Yuma Public Library, 114 W Third Ave, Yuma, CO, 80759-2402. Tel: 970-848-2368. Fax: 970-848-0423. p. 326

Evans, Susan, Head, Res & Info Serv, King's University College at the University of Western Ontario, 266 Epworth Ave, London, ON, N6A 2M3, CANADA. Tel: 519-433-3491, Ext 4327. Fax: 519-963-0307. p. 2817

Evans, Susan M, Dir of Libr, Yuma County Library District, 2951 S 21st Dr, Yuma, AZ, 85364. Tel: 928-373-6462. Fax: 928-782-9420. p. 91

Evans, Thomas R, State Librn, Rhode Island State Library, State House, Rm 208, 82 Smith St, Providence, RI, 02903. Tel: 401-222-2473. Fax: 401-222-3034. p. 2175

Evans, Tiffany, PhD, Dean, Learning Res, Salt Lake Community College Libraries, 4600 S Redwood Rd, Salt Lake City, UT, 84123-3197. Tel: 801-957-4905. Fax: 801-957-4414. p. 2413

Evans, Tina, Ref Librn, Fort Lewis College Library, 1000 Rim Dr, Durango, CO, 81301-3999. Tel: 970-247-7250. Fax: 970-247-7149. p. 305

Evans, Tyler S, Automation Librn, United States Air Force, Air University - Muir S Fairchild Research Information Center, 600 Chennault Circle, Maxwell AFB, AL, 36112-6010. Tel: 334-953-2474. p. 24

Evans, Veronica, Br Mgr, Riverside County Library System, Lake Tamarisk Library, 43880 Lake Tamarisk Dr, Desert Center, CA, 92239. Tel: 760-227-3273. Fax: 760-227-3273. p. 217

Evans, Vicki, Br Mgr, Knox County Public Library System, Howard Pinkston Branch, 7732 Martin Mill Pike, Knoxville, TN, 37920. Tel: 865-573-0436. Fax: 865-573-1351. p. 2242

Evans-Cantrell, Deborah, Cat/Ref Librn, Indianapolis Museum of Art, 4000 Michigan Rd, Indianapolis, IN, 46208-3326. Tel: 317-920-2647. Fax: 317-926-8931. p. 754

Evans-Conrad, Barb, Librn, Bear Point Community Library, PO Box 43, Bear Canyon, AB, T0H 0B0, CANADA. Tel: 780-595-3771. Fax: 780-595-3762. p. 2685

Evans-Cullen, Heather, Ch, Gibsons & District Public Library, 470 S Fletcher Rd, Gibsons, BC, V0N 1V0, CANADA. Tel: 604-886-2130. Fax: 604-886-2689. p. 2728

Evans-Perez, Kimberly, Ch, Lilly Library, 19 Meadow St, Florence, MA, 01062. Tel: 413-587-1500. Fax: 413-587-1504. p. 1089

Evans-Perry, Ginny, Automation Librn, San Bernardino Public Library, 555 W Sixth St, San Bernardino, CA, 92410-3001. Tel: 909-381-8215. Fax: 909-381-8229. p. 229

Evans-Perry, Virginia, Librn, San Bernardino Valley College Library, 701 S Mount Vernon Ave, San Bernardino, CA, 92410. Tel: 909-384-8699. p. 229

Evanson, Karen, Asst Dir, Finance/Admin, Delray Beach Public Library, 100 W Atlantic Ave, Delray Beach, FL, 33444. Tel: 561-266-9489. Fax: 561-266-9757. p. 437

Evavold, Kathy, Archivist, Curator, Otter Tail County Historical Society, 1110 Lincoln Ave W, Fergus Falls, MN, 56537. Tel: 218-736-6038. Fax: 218-739-3075. p. 1251

Eveland, Ruth, Dir, Jesup Memorial Library, 34 Mount Desert St, Bar Harbor, ME, 04609-1727. Tel: 207-288-4245. p. 976

Evelsizer, Elsie, Dir, Forrest Public Library District, 301 W James, Forrest, IL, 61741. Tel: 815-657-8805. Fax: 815-657-8837. p. 646

Evenhaugen, Anne, Ref Librn, Smithsonian Libraries, Smithsonian American Art Museum/National Portrait Gallery Library, Victor Bldg, Rm 2100, MRC 975, 750 Ninth St NW, Washington, DC, 20560. Tel: 202-633-8230. Fax: 202-633-8232. p. 415

Evensen, Sharon, Dir, Vermilion Community College Library, 1900 E Camp St, Ely, MN, 55731. Tel: 218-365-7226. Fax: 218-365-7218. p. 1250

Evenson, Carolyn, In Charge, Tillamook County Library, South County, 6200 Camp St, Pacific City, OR, 97135. Tel: 503-965-6163. Fax: 503-965-6163. p. 2021

Evenson, L, Librn, Freeborn County Historical Museum Library, 1031 N Bridge Ave, Albert Lea, MN, 56007. Tel: 507-373-8003. Fax: 507-552-1269. p. 1239

Evensvold, Marty, Dir, Coffeyville Community College, 400 W 11th, Coffeyville, KS, 67337-5064. Tel: 620-252-7220. Fax: 620-252-7366. p. 861

Everaere, Genevieve, Ref Serv Coordr, College Jean-de-Brebeuf, 5625 rue Decelles, Montreal, QC, H3T 1W4, CANADA. Tel: 514-342-9342, Ext 5261. Fax: 514-342-1558. p. 2894

Everett, Audra, Asst Dir, Western Sullivan Public Library, 19 Center St, Jeffersonville, NY, 12748. Tel: 845-482-4350. Fax: 845-482-3092. p. 1647

Everett, Bonnie, Librn, Allen County Law Library, Court of Appeals, Rm 102, 204 N Main St, Lima, OH, 45801-4456. Tel: 419-999-4272. p. 1909

Everett, David, Dir, Hiram College Library, 11694 Hayden St, Hiram, OH, 44234. Tel: 330-569-5354, 330-569-5489. Fax: 330-569-5491. p. 1905

Everett, Julia B, Dir, Libr Serv, Northeast Alabama Community College, 138 Alabama Hwy 35, Rainsville, AL, 35986. Tel: 256-228-6001, Ext 226. Fax: 256-228-4350. p. 34

Everett, Leslie, Circ, Computer Serv, Massachusetts College of Art & Design, 621 Huntington Ave, Boston, MA, 02115-5882. Tel: 617-879-7150. Fax: 617-879-7110. p. 1063

Everett, Peter, Pub Serv Librn, Housatonic Community College Library, 900 Lafayette Blvd, Bridgeport, CT, 06604. Tel: 203-332-5074. Fax: 203-332-5252. p. 331

Everett, Richard, Head, Ref & Instruction, United States Coast Guard Academy Library, 35 Mohegan Ave, New London, CT, 06320-4195. Tel: 860-444-8510. Fax: 860-444-8516. p. 360

Everett, Robert, Dir, Springfield Public Library, 225 Fifth St, Springfield, OR, 97477-4697. Tel: 541-726-3766. Fax: 541-726-3747. p. 2020

Everhart, Kim, Librn, Greeley Village Public Library, 102 S Kildare St, Greeley, NE, 68842. Tel: 308-428-4010. Fax: 308-428-2675. p. 1400

Everhart, Nancy, Dr, Assoc Prof, Dir, PALM Ctr, Florida State University, College of Communication & Information, 142 Collegiate Loop, Tallahassee, FL, 32306-2100. Tel: 850-644-8122. Fax: 850-644-9763. p. 2963

Everingham, Jessica, Dir, Altamaha Technical College Library, 1777 W Cherry St, Jesup, GA, 31545. Tel: 912-427-1929. Fax: 912-427-1929. p. 536

Everlove, Nora J, Librn, Rupert J Smith Law Library of Saint Lucie County, 218 S Second St, Courthouse Addition, Rm 102, Fort Pierce, FL, 34950. Tel: 772-462-2370. Fax: 772-462-2145. p. 447

Everly, Robin, Librn, Smithsonian Libraries, Botany & Horticulture Library, Nat Museum of Natural Hist, Rm W422, MRC 154, Tenth St & Constitution Ave NW, Washington, DC, 20560. Tel: 202-633-2146. Fax: 202-357-1896. p. 414

Everman, Diane M, Archivist, Saul Brodsky Jewish Community Library, 12 Millstone Campus Dr, Saint Louis, MO, 63146-5776. Tel: 314-442-3720. Fax: 314-432-1277. p. 1353

Evermon, Vandy, Tech Serv Librn, Columbia College, 1001 Rogers St, Columbia, MO, 65216. Tel: 573-875-7370. Fax: 573-875-7379. p. 1324

Evernham, Debbie, ILL, Mercer County Library System, 2751 Brunswick Pike, Lawrenceville, NJ, 08648-4132. Tel: 609-882-9246. Fax: 609-538-9238. p. 1494

Everrett, Karen, City Librn, San Bernardino County Library, Victorville City Branch, 15011 Circle Dr, Victorville, CA, 92395. Tel: 760-245-4222. Fax: 760-245-2273. p. 229

Evers, Carol, Dir, Coldwater Public Library, 305 W Main St, Coldwater, OH, 45828-1604. Tel: 419-678-2431. Fax: 419-678-8516. p. 1882

Evers, Renate, Head Librn, Center for Jewish History, 15 W 16 St, New York, NY, 10011-6301. Tel: 212-744-6400. Fax: 212-988-1305. p. 1672

Evers, Sofianne, Br Assoc, Watonwan County Library, Darfur Branch, PO Box 191, Darfur, MN, 56022-0190. Tel: 507-877-5010. p. 1277

Everson, Jill, Mgr, Department of Veterans Affairs, 2500 Overlook Terrace, Madison, WI, 53705-2286. Tel: 608-256-1901, 608-280-7173. Fax: 608-280-7108. p. 2606

Everstine, Carrie, Mgr, Libr Serv, Howard Anderson Power Memorial Library, Magee-Womens Hospital, 300 Halket St, Pittsburgh, PA, 15213. Tel: 412-641-4985. Fax: 412-641-4854. p. 2127

Eves, Jamie, Dir, Windham Textile & History Museum, 411 Main St, Willimantic, CT, 06226. Tel: 860-456-2178. p. 378

Evetts, Rosemary, Archivist, Spec Coll Librn, Auraria Library, 1100 Lawrence St, Denver, CO, 80204-2095. Tel: 303-556-3530. Fax: 303-556-3528. p. 298

Evitts, Beth A, Dir, HACC Central Pennsylvania's Community College, 731 Old Harrisburg Rd, Gettysburg, PA, 17325. Tel: 717-337-3855, Ext 3027. Fax: 717-337-2329. p. 2060

Evonne, Edgington, Br Mgr, Omaha Public Library, Willa Cather Branch, 1905 S 44th St, Omaha, NE, 68105-2807. Tel: 402-444-4851. Fax: 402-444-6662. p. 1414

Evrard, Carol, Ch, Spencer County Public Library, 210 Walnut St, Rockport, IN, 47635-1398. Tel: 812-649-4866. Fax: 812-649-4018. p. 776

Ewald, Valerie, Assoc Librn, Twentieth Century Club Library, Main St, Almond, NY, 14804. Tel: 607-276-6311. Fax: 607-276-6311. p. 1572

Ewell, Lana, Dir, Watauga Public Library, 7109 Whitley Rd, Watauga, TX, 76148-2024. Tel: 817-514-5855. Fax: 817-581-3910. p. 2398

Ewen, Eric, Head, Cat, University of San Francisco, 2130 Fulton St, San Francisco, CA, 94117-1080. Tel: 415-422-5361. Fax: 415-422-5949. p. 248

Ewers, Ryan, Supvr, Aurora Public Library, Central, 14949 E Alameda Pkwy, Aurora, CO, 80012. Tel: 303-739-6625. p. 288

Ewert, George, Dir, Museum of Mobile, 111 S Royal St, Mobile, AL, 36602-3101. Tel: 251-208-7569. Fax: 251-208-7686. p. 26

Ewick, Dave, Dir, Southfield Public Library, 26300 Evergreen Rd, Southfield, MI, 48076. Tel: 248-796-4300. Fax: 248-796-4305. p. 1228

Ewing, Barbara, Librn, Meadville Medical Center, 751 Liberty St, Meadville, PA, 16335. Tel: 814-333-5740. Fax: 814-333-5714. p. 2086

Ewing, Carol, Librn, Massachusetts Trial Court, 57 Providence Hwy, Norwood, MA, 02062. Tel: 781-769-7483. Fax: 781-769-7836. p. 1115

Ewing, Connie, Info Spec, Louisville Metro Planning Commission, 444 S Fifth St, Ste 300, Louisville, KY, 40202. Tel: 502-574-6230. Fax: 502-574-8129. p. 925

Ewing, Gina, Instrul Tech Consult, Mitchell College Library, 437 Pequot Ave, New London, CT, 06320-4498. Tel: 860-701-5156. Fax: 860-701-5099. p. 360

Ewing, Jennifer, Cat, Ref Serv, San Diego Christian College, 2100 Greenfield Dr, El Cajon, CA, 92019-1161. Tel: 619-201-8682. Fax: 619-201-8799. p. 145

Ewing, LaVoyce, Librn, Boone County Library, 221 W Stephenson, Harrison, AR, 72601-4225. Tel: 870-741-5913. Fax: 870-741-5946. p. 102

Ewing, Mark, Librn, Delta College Library, 1961 Delta Rd, University Center, MI, 48710. Tel: 989-686-9822. Fax: 989-686-4131. p. 1232

Ewing, Mark, Adminr, Saint Paul's United Methodist Church, 225 W Griggs Ave, Las Cruces, NM, 88005-2608. Tel: 575-526-6689, Ext 1002. Fax: 575-524-7660. p. 1558

Ewing, Molly, Humanities Librn, Saint John's University, 2835 Abbey Plaza, Collegeville, MN, 56321. Tel: 320-363-5513. Fax: 320-363-2126. p. 1246

Ewing, Molly, Humanities Librn, College of Saint Benedict, 37 S College Ave, Saint Joseph, MN, 56374. Tel: 320-363-5513. Fax: 320-363-5197. p. 1277

Ewy, Barb, Asst City Librn, Hanston City Library, 105 N Logan, Hanston, KS, 67849-9409. Tel: 620-623-4987. p. 870

Exendine, David, Libr Asst, Rushville Public Library, 207 Sprague St, Rushville, NE, 69360. Tel: 308-327-2740. Fax: 308-327-2740. p. 1418

Exner, Nina, Ref Librn, North Carolina Agricultural & Technical State University, 1601 E Market St, Greensboro, NC, 27411-0002. Tel: 336-334-7159, Ext 3257. Fax: 336-334-7783. p. 1797

Extavour, Doris, ILL, Toronto Rehab, 550 University Ave, Toronto, ON, M5G 2A2, CANADA. Tel: 416-597-3422, Ext 3050. Fax: 416-591-6515. p. 2864

Exterkamp, Cynthia, Pub Serv, Richard C Sullivan Public Library of Wilton Manors, 500 NE 26th St, Wilton Manors, FL, 33305. Tel: 954-390-2195. Fax: 954-390-2183. p. 504

Exton, Benet, Brother, Archivist, Cat Librn, Saint Gregory's University, 1900 W MacArthur St, Shawnee, OK, 74804. Tel: 405-878-5109. Fax: 405-878-5198. p. 1977

Exum, Jessie, Head, Youth Serv, Crystal Lake Public Library, 126 Paddock St, Crystal Lake, IL, 60014. Tel: 815-459-1687. Fax: 815-459-9581. p. 632

Eyberg, Ellen, Regional Br Mgr, El Paso Public Library, Esperanza Acosta Moreno Regional, 12480 Pebble Hills Blvd, El Paso, TX, 79938. Tel: 915-921-7001. Fax: 915-856-2977. p. 2316

Eye, John, Dr, Dean of Libr Serv, Southern Utah University, 351 W University Blvd, Cedar City, UT, 84720. Tel: 435-865-8392. Fax: 435-865-8152. p. 2404

Eye, Judy, Asst Librn, Washington County Library, 235 E High St, Potosi, MO, 63664. Tel: 573-438-4691. Fax: 573-438-6423. p. 1350

Eye, Lisa, Libr Asst III, Staunton Public Library, Talking Book Center, One Churchville Ave, Staunton, VA, 24401-3229. Tel: 540-885-6215. Fax: 540-332-3906. p. 2497

Eyeberg, Cindy, ILL, North Iowa Area Community College Library, 500 College Dr, Mason City, IA, 50401. Tel: 641-422-4232. Fax: 641-422-4131. p. 831

Eyler, Carol, Tech Serv, Carleton College, One N College St, Northfield, MN, 55057-4097. Tel: 507-222-4268. Fax: 507-222-4087. p. 1269

Eyman, Carol, Commun Serv, Nashua Public Library, Two Court St, Nashua, NH, 03060. Tel: 603-589-4610. Fax: 603-594-3457. p. 1458

Eymann, Marcia, Mgr, Sacramento Archives & Museum Collection Center, 551 Sequoia Pacific Blvd, Sacramento, CA, 95814-0229. Tel: 916-264-7072. Fax: 916-264-7582. p. 224

Eyolfson, Valerie, Librn, Evergreen Regional Library, 65 First Ave, Gimli, MB, R0C 1B0, CANADA. Tel: 204-642-7912. Fax: 204-642-8319. p. 2749

Eysie, Loretta, Ch, Westwood Public Library, 668 High St, Westwood, MA, 02090. Tel: 781-320-1043. Fax: 781-326-5383. p. 1139

Ezell, Mike, Br Mgr, Fort Smith Public Library, 3201 Rogers Ave, Fort Smith, AR, 72903. Tel: 479-484-5650. Fax: 479-484-5658. p. 100

Ezell, Mike, Br Mgr, Fort Smith Public Library, Dallas Street, 8100 Dallas St, Forth Smith, AR, 72903. Tel: 479-484-5650. Fax: 479-484-5658. p. 100

Ezio, Darlene, Chairperson, Willingdon Public Library, 4911-52 Ave, Willingdon, AB, T0B 4R0, CANADA. Tel: 780-367-2146, 780-367-2642. p. 2722

Ezquerro, Dorothy, Per, Burlingame Public Library, 480 Primrose Rd, Burlingame, CA, 94010-4083. Tel: 650-558-7431. Fax: 650-342-1948. p. 130

Ezzeal, Linda, Librn, Northwest Regional Library, Weatherford Public Library, 307 Fourth Ave, Red Bay, AL, 35582. Tel: 256-356-9255. p. 40

Faaborg, Sherri, Syst Coordr, Maryland Institute College of Art, 1401 Mount Royal Ave, Baltimore, MD, 21217. Tel: 410-225-2304, 410-225-2311. Fax: 410-225-2316. p. 1015

Fabbi, Jennifer, Head of Libr, University of Nevada, Las Vegas Libraries, Curriculum Materials, Carlson Education Bldg, Rm 101, Las Vegas, NV, 89154. Tel: 702-895-3593. Fax: 702-895-3528. p. 1431

Fabbro, Elaine, Head, Info Literacy & Pub Serv, Athabasca University Library, One University Dr, Athabasca, AB, T9S 3A3, CANADA. Tel: 780-675-6254. Fax: 780-675-6478. p. 2684

Fabbro, Robert, Ref & Access Serv Librn, Ontario College of Art & Design, 100 McCaul St, Toronto, ON, M5T 1W1, CANADA. Tel: 416-977-6000, Ext 343. Fax: 416-977-6006. p. 2856

Faber, Carissa, Librn, Neponset Public Library, 201 W Commercial St, Neponset, IL, 61345. Tel: 309-594-2204. Fax: 309-594-2204. p. 679

Faber, Carolyn, Media Coll Mgr, School of the Art Institute of Chicago, 37 S Wabash Ave, Chicago, IL, 60603-3103. Tel: 312-899-5097. Fax: 312-899-1851. p. 624

Faber, Rose M, Head, Adult Serv, Barrington Public Library District, 505 N Northwest Hwy, Barrington, IL, 60010. Tel: 847-382-1300. Fax: 847-382-1261. p. 592

Fabian, Adam, Res, Parade Publications, Inc, 711 Third Avenue, 7th Flr, New York, NY, 10017-4014. Tel: 212-450-7000. Fax: 212-450-7283. p. 1697

Fabian, Carole Ann, Dir, Columbia University, Avery Architectural & Fine Arts Library, 1172 Amsterdam Ave, MC 0301, New York, NY, 10027. Tel: 212-854-3068. Fax: 212-854-8904. p. 1674

Fabian, Christine, Conservator, Art Institute of Chicago, 111 S Michigan Ave, Chicago, IL, 60603. Tel: 312-443-3671. Fax: 312-443-0849. p. 606

Fabian, George, Pres, Collectors Club of Chicago Library, 1029 N Dearborn St, Chicago, IL, 60610. Tel: 847-364-6868. p. 611

Fabian, Jamie, Ref, Parkersburg & Wood County Public Library, 3100 Emerson Ave, Parkersburg, WV, 26104-2414. Tel: 304-420-4587. Fax: 304-420-4589. p. 2568

Fabian, Robert, Librn, Butler, Rubin, Saltarelli & Boyd LLP, Three First National Plaza, 70 W Madison St, Ste 1800, Chicago, IL, 60602. Tel: 312-444-9660. Fax: 312-444-9287. p. 607

Fabiano, James, Librn, Linden Free Public Library, 31 E Henry St, Linden, NJ, 07036. Tel: 908-298-3830. Fax: 908-486-2636. p. 1495

Fabiano, Lisa, Circ Supvr, Ulster County Community College, Stone Ridge, NY, 12484. Tel: 845-687-5213. Fax: 845-687-5220. p. 1749

Fabiszak, Dennis, Dir, East Hampton Library, 159 Main St, East Hampton, NY, 11937. Tel: 631-324-0222, Ext 7. Fax: 631-329-5947. p. 1616

Fabiszewski, Mary, Cat, Massachusetts Historical Society Library, 1154 Boylston St, Boston, MA, 02215-3695. Tel: 617-646-0504. Fax: 617-859-0074. p. 1063

Fabro, Andrew, Head Librn, Environment Canada, 201 - 401 Burrard St, Vancouver, BC, V6C 3S5, CANADA. Tel: 604-666-5914. Fax: 604-666-1788. p. 2741

Facchiano, Paul, Dir, Central Islip Public Library, 33 Hawthorne Ave, Central Islip, NY, 11722. Tel: 631-234-9333. Fax: 631-234-9386. p. 1604

Facer, Kathleen, Ref & Tech Librn, Richmond Memorial Library, 19 Ross St, Batavia, NY, 14020. Tel: 585-343-9550. Fax: 585-344-4651. p. 1578

Facincani, Greg, Govt Doc, Tech Serv, Rhode Island State Library, State House, Rm 208, 82 Smith St, Providence, RI, 02903. Tel: 401-222-2473. Fax: 401-222-3034. p. 2175

Fackler, Donna, Ch, Meade County Public Library, 400 Library Pl, Brandenburg, KY, 40108-1045. Tel: 270-422-2094. Fax: 270-422-3133. p. 908

Fader, Pat, Tech & Support Mgr, St Albert Public Library, Five Saint Anne St, St. Albert, AB, T8N 3Z9, CANADA. Tel: 780-459-1530. Fax: 780-458-5772. p. 2717

Fadum, Hans, Tech Serv, Malaspina University-College Library, 900 Fifth St, Nanaimo, BC, V9R 5S5, CANADA. Tel: 250-753-3245, Ext 2270. Fax: 250-740-6473. p. 2732

Fafard, Donna, Librn, Chinook Regional Library, Morse Branch, Village Recreational Complex, Main St, Morse, SK, S0H 3C0, CANADA. Tel: 306-629-3335. p. 2928

Fagan, Bertha, Dir, Adair Public Library, 310 Audubon, Adair, IA, 50002. Tel: 641-742-3323. Fax: 641-742-3323. p. 791

Fagan, Cathy, Circ Supvr, South Kingstown Public Library, 1057 Kingstown Rd, Peace Dale, RI, 02879-2434. Tel: 401-783-4085, 401-789-1555. Fax: 401-782-6370. p. 2171

Fagan, Charling Chang, Dir, Libr Serv, Sarah Lawrence College, One Mead Way, Bronxville, NY, 10708. Tel: 914-395-2471. Fax: 914-395-2473. p. 1588

Fagan, Christine, Coll Develop & Acq Librn, Roger Williams University Library, One Old Ferry Rd, Bristol, RI, 02809. Tel: 401-254-3029. Fax: 401-254-3631. p. 2164

Fagan, Kathy, Libr Asst, Neuse Regional Library, Pollocksville Public Library, 415 Green Hill St, Pollocksville, NC, 28573. Tel: 252-224-5011. Fax: 252-224-5011. p. 1805

Fagan, Robert, Prog Coordr, Hubbard Free Library, 115 Second St, Hallowell, ME, 04347. Tel: 207-622-6582. p. 987

Fagen, Diane A, Librn, American Veterinary Medical Association Library, 1931 N Meacham Rd, Ste 100, Schaumburg, IL, 30173-4360. Tel: 847-925-8070, Ext 6770. Fax: 847-925-9329. p. 700

Fagerholm, Judy, Br Mgr, Menlo Park Public Library, Belle Haven, 413 Ivy Dr, Menlo Park, CA, 94025. Tel: 650-330-2540. p. 185

Fagerstone, Michelle, Dir, Hamilton Public Library, 312 N Davis St, Hamilton, MO, 64644. Tel: 816-583-4832. Fax: 816-583-7501. p. 1329

Fagnan, Vivianne, Bibliog Serv Librn, Alberta Legislature Library, 216 Legislature Bldg, 10800-97 Ave, Edmonton, AB, T5K 2B6, CANADA. Tel: 780-427-5893. Fax: 780-427-6016. p. 2699

Faherty, Brendan, Circ Supvr, Mount Horeb Public Library, 105 Perimeter Rd, Mount Horeb, WI, 53572. Tel: 608-437-5021. Fax: 608-437-6264. p. 2623

Fahey, Cathy, Humanities Librn, Salem State University Library, 352 Lafayette St, Salem, MA, 01970-5353. Tel: 978-542-7203. Fax: 978-542-6596. p. 1122

Fahey, Filis, Head, Acq, Mount Allison University Libraries & Archives, 49 York St, Sackville, NB, E4L 1C6, CANADA. Tel: 506-364-2566. Fax: 506-364-2617. p. 2766

Fahey, Jim, Archivist, Dir, Braintree Historical Society, Inc Library, 85 Quincey Ave, Braintree, MA, 02184-4416. Tel: 781-843-1518. Fax: 781-380-0731. p. 1069

Fahr, Susan Hilt, In Charge, Beauregard Parish Library, Merryville Branch, 1007 Hwy 110, Merryville, LA, 70653. Tel: 337-463-6217. Fax: 337-462-5434. p. 948

Fahrmann, Melissa, Dir, Baton Rouge General Medical Center, 3600 Florida Blvd, Baton Rouge, LA, 70806. Tel: 225-387-7012. Fax: 225-381-6116. p. 942

Faiivae, Loring, Syst Adminr, Feleti Barstow Public Library, PO Box 997687, Pago Pago, AS, 96799. Tel: 684-633-5816. Fax: 684-633-5823. p. 2666

Faiks, Angi, Coll Develop, Macalester College, 1600 Grand Ave, Saint Paul, MN, 55105-1899. Tel: 651-696-6208. Fax: 651-696-6617. p. 1279

Faile, Timothy, Tech Serv Librn, Concordia Theological Seminary, 6600 N Clinton St, Fort Wayne, IN, 46825. Tel: 260-452-3147. Fax: 260-452-2126. p. 741

Fain, Carolyn, Mgr, Youth Serv, Westlake Porter Public Library, 27333 Center Ridge Rd, Westlake, OH, 44145-3925. Tel: 440-871-2600. Fax: 440-871-6969. p. 1947

Fain, Margaret, Head, Pub Serv, Coastal Carolina University, 755 Hwy 544, Conway, SC, 29526. Tel: 843-349-2410. Fax: 843-349-2412. p. 2191

Fain, Marilyn, Br Librn, McDowell Public Library, Iaeger Branch, West Virginia Ave, Iaeger, WV, 24844. Tel: 304-938-3825. Fax: 304-938-3825. p. 2574

Fair, Darcy, Youth Serv Mgr, Bucks County Free Library, Yardley-Makefield Branch, 1080 Edgewood Rd, Yardley, PA, 19067-1648. Tel: 215-493-9020. Fax: 215-493-0279. p. 2050

Fair, Demi, Dir, Paul Smith Library of Southern York County, 80 Constitution Ave, Shrewsbury, PA, 17361-1710. Tel: 717-235-4313. Fax: 717-235-8553. p. 2140

Fair, Kathy, Dir, Kilgore College, 1100 Broadway, Kilgore, TX, 75662. Tel: 903-983-8639. Fax: 903-983-8638. p. 2350

Fairbairn, Mary, Instrul Serv Librn, Furman University Libraries, 3300 Poinsett Hwy, Greenville, SC, 29613-4100. Tel: 864-294-3226. Fax: 864-294-3004. p. 2195

Fairbanks, Daphne, TechLab Coordr, Hope College, Van Wylen Library, 53 Graves Pl, Holland, MI, 49422. Tel: 616-395-7283. Fax: 616-395-7965. p. 1191

Fairbanks, Julene, Librn, Skagway Public Library, 769 State St, Skagway, AK, 99840. Tel: 907-983-2665. Fax: 907-983-2666. p. 53

Fairbanks, Kathryn, Librn, Massachusetts Archaeological Society Research Library, 17 Jackson St, Middleborough, MA, 02346-2413. Tel: 508-947-9005. Fax: 508-947-9005. p. 1105

Fairbanks, Linda, Head, Tech Serv, Oak Brook Public Library, 600 Oak Brook Rd, Oak Brook, IL, 60523. Tel: 630-368-7716. Fax: 630-368-7704, 630-990-4509. p. 683

Fairchild, Frances F, Dir, Chazy Public Library, 9633 Rte 9, Chazy, NY, 12921. Tel: 518-846-7676. Fax: 518-846-7676. p. 1606

Fairchild, Gay, Adult Serv, Miami Public Library, 200 N Main, Miami, OK, 74354. Tel: 918-541-2292. Fax: 918-542-9363. p. 1968

Fairchild, Lynda, Br Mgr, Waller County Library, Brookshire Pattison Branch, 3815 Sixth St, Brookshire, TX, 77423. Tel: 281-375-5550. Fax: 281-934-3516. p. 2332

Faircloth, Gail, Libr Res Coordr, Jackson Parish Library, 614 S Polk Ave, Jonesboro, LA, 71251-3442. Tel: 318-259-5697, 318-259-5698. Fax: 318-259-8984. p. 952

Fairclough, Ian, Cat/Metadata Librn, George Mason University Libraries, 4400 University Dr, MSN 2FL, Fairfax, VA, 22030-4444. Tel: 703-993-2250. Fax: 703-993-2200. p. 2462

Fairey, Elaine, Assoc Univ Librn, Learning & Res Serv, Simon Fraser University Library, 8888 University Dr, Burnaby, BC, V5A 1S6, CANADA. Tel: 778-782-3252. Fax: 778-782-3023. p. 2725

Fairfield, Miriam Stauffer, Ref & Instrul Serv, Instr Coordr, Geneva College, 3200 College Ave, Beaver Falls, PA, 15010-3599. Tel: 724-847-6563. Fax: 724-847-6687. p. 2031

Fairley, Gerald, Curator, Alaska Masonic Library & Museum, 518 E 14th St, Anchorage, AK, 99501-2213. Tel: 907-276-2665. p. 43

Fairley, Mike, Supvr, Computer Serv, Kansas City, Kansas Public Library, 625 Minnesota Ave, Kansas City, KS, 66101. Tel: 913-279-2361. Fax: 913-279-2033. p. 875

Fairley, Valerie, Librn, Mississippi Gulf Coast Community College, PO Box 548, Perkinston, MS, 39573-0011. Tel: 601-528-8905. Fax: 601-928-6359. p. 1311

Fairlie, David, Librn, Clarence Public Library, Three Town Pl, Clarence, NY, 14031. Tel: 716-741-2650. Fax: 716-741-1243. p. 1607

Fairman, Christina, Circ Supvr, Wesley Theological Seminary Library, 4500 Massachusetts Ave NW, Washington, DC, 20016-5690. Tel: 202-885-8695. Fax: 202-885-8691. p. 422

Fairman, Elisabeth, Sr Curator, Rare Bks & Ms, Yale University Library, Center for British Art, 1080 Chapel St, New Haven, CT, 06520. Tel: 203-432-2814. Fax: 203-432-9613. p. 357

Fairman, Liz, Automation Syst Coordr, Tech Serv, Superior Court Law Library, 101 W Jefferson, Phoenix, AZ, 85003. Tel: 602-506-3462. Fax: 602-506-2940. p. 77

Fairtile, Linda, Music Librn, University of Richmond, 28 Westhampton Way, Richmond, VA, 23173. Tel: 804-287-6849. Fax: 804-287-6899. p. 2491

Fairtile, Linda B, Dr, Librn, University of Richmond, Parsons Music Library, Modlin Center for the Arts, Webb Tower, University of Richmond, VA, 23173. Tel: 804-287-6849. Fax: 804-287-6899. p. 2491

Fairtolth, Gail, Libr Serv Mgr, Gadsden County Public Library, 7325 Pat Thomas Pkwy, Quincy, FL, 32351. Tel: 850-627-7106. Fax: 850-627-7775. p. 485

Faison, Colanda, Tech Serv, Sampson-Clinton Public Library, 217 Graham St, Clinton, NC, 28328. Tel: 910-592-4153. Fax: 910-590-3504. p. 1784

Faison, Vernice, Librn, North Carolina Central University, Music, 1801 Fayetteville St, Durham, NC, 27707. Tel: 919-530-6220. Fax: 919-530-7979. p. 1789

Faist, Jennifer, Digital Coll Curator, Libr Syst Adminr, Art Center College of Design, 1700 Lida St, Pasadena, CA, 91103. Tel: 626-396-2236. Fax: 626-568-0428. p. 205

Fait, Jennifer, Youth Serv, Richton Park Public Library District, 4045 Sauk Trail, Richton Park, IL, 60471. Tel: 708-481-5333. Fax: 708-481-4343. p. 694

Faith, Kathy, In Charge, Siouxland Libraries, Baltic Branch, 213 St Olaf, Baltic, SD, 57003. Tel: 605-529-5415. Fax: 605-529-5415. p. 2219

Faix, Allison, ILL, Ref Serv, Coastal Carolina University, 755 Hwy 544, Conway, SC, 29526. Tel: 843-349-2511. Fax: 843-349-2412. p. 2191

Faklis, Ruth E, Dir, Prairie Trails Public Library District, 8449 S Moody, Burbank, IL, 60459-2525. Tel: 708-430-3688. Fax: 708-430-5596. p. 598

Fal, Andrew J, Head, Cat, Ref Serv, Berlin-Peck Memorial Library, 234 Kensington Rd, Berlin, CT, 06037. Tel: 860-828-7125. Fax: 860-829-1848. p. 330

Falanga, Rose, Libr Mgr, Exploratorium Learning Commons, 3601 Lyon St, San Francisco, CA, 94123. Tel: 415-561-0343. Fax: 415-561-0370. p. 242

Falanga, Rose, Adminr, Bay Area Library & Information Network, 1462 Cedar St, Berkeley, CA, 94702. Tel: 510-525-4726. p. 398

Falardeau, Patrick, Dir, Bibliotheque de Coaticook, Inc, 34 rue Main Est, Coaticook, QC, J1A 1N2, CANADA. Tel: 819-849-4013. Fax: 819-849-0479. p. 2881

Falardeau, Patrick, Dir, Bibliotheque de Farnham, Inc, 479 rue Hotel de Ville, Farnham, QC, J2N 2H3, CANADA. Tel: 450-293-3375. Fax: 450-293-2989. p. 2882

Falasco, Jennifer, Libr Assoc, Housatonic Community College Library, 900 Lafayette Blvd, Bridgeport, CT, 06604. Tel: 203-332-5070. Fax: 203-332-5252. p. 332

Falbo, Anna, Sister, Dir, Villa Maria College Library, 240 Pine Ridge Rd, Buffalo, NY, 14225-3999. Tel: 716-961-1862. Fax: 716-896-0705. p. 1599

Falcinelli, Ellen, Mgr, Redwood Empire Association, Pier 39, Ste Q5, 2nd Level, San Francisco, CA, 94133. Tel: 415-956-3491. Fax: 415-956-0209. p. 244

Falck, Kara, Teen Serv Librn, Shaler North Hills Library, 1822 Mount Royal Blvd, Glenshaw, PA, 15116. Tel: 412-486-0211. Fax: 412-486-8286. p. 2061

Falcone, Edward, Dep Dir, Yonkers Public Library, One Larkin Ctr, Yonkers, NY, 10701. Tel: 914-337-1500. Fax: 914-376-3004. p. 1771

Falconer, Elena, Outreach Serv Librn, Westchester Library System, 540 White Plains Rd, Ste 200, Tarrytown, NY, 10591-5110. Tel: 914-231-3240. Fax: 914-674-4185. p. 1755

Falcone, Elena, Dir, Consumer Reports, 101 Truman Ave, Yonkers, NY, 10703-1057. Tel: 914-378-2265. Fax: 914-378-2913. p. 1771

Falconer, Patty, Youth Serv Librn, Hampstead Public Library, Nine Mary E Clark Dr, Hampstead, NH, 03841. Tel: 603-329-6411. Fax: 603-329-6036. p. 1449

Fales, Judy, Libr Asst, Olivet College Library, 333 S Main St, Olivet, MI, 49076-9730. Tel: 269-749-7595. Fax: 269-749-7121. p. 1215

Falgner, Susan, Head, Pub Serv, College of Mount Saint Joseph, 5701 Delhi Rd, Cincinnati, OH, 45233-1671. Tel: 513-244-4352. Fax: 513-244-4355. p. 1869

Faling, Andrea, Archivist, Assoc Dir, Nebraska State Historical Society Library, 1500 R St, Lincoln, NE, 68508. Tel: 402-471-4785. Fax: 402-471-8922. p. 1406

Falk, Carrie, Tech Coordr, Shenandoah Public Library, 201 S Elm St, Shenandoah, IA, 51601. Tel: 712-246-2315. Fax: 712-246-5847. p. 843

Falk, Diane M, Mgr, The Washington Times Corp, The Library/Research Dept, 3600 New York Ave NE, Washington, DC, 20002-1947. Tel: 202-636-3334. Fax: 202-636-3323. p. 422

Falk, Gayle A, Dir, Burlington Public Library, 166 E Jefferson St, Burlington, WI, 53105. Tel: 262-763-7623. Fax: 262-763-1938. p. 2584

Falk, Lynn, Acq, Mercyhurst College, 501 E 38th St, Erie, PA, 16546. Tel: 814-824-2236. Fax: 814-824-2219. p. 2056

Falk, Patty, Spec Coll Cataloger, Bowling Green State University Libraries, Music Library & Sound Recordings Archives, Jerome Library, 3rd Flr, Bowling Green, OH, 43403. Tel: 419-372-0266. Fax: 419-372-2499. p. 1861

Falk, Rosie, Librn, Effingham Community Library, 414 Main St, Effingham, KS, 66023. Tel: 913-833-5881. Fax: 913-833-5881. p. 864

Falk, Susan, State Law Librn, Alaska State Court Law Library, 303 K St, Anchorage, AK, 99501. Tel: 907-264-0585. Fax: 907-264-0733. p. 44

Falken, Gretchen, Circ, Boyertown Community Library, 29 E Philadelphia Ave, Boyertown, PA, 19512-1124. Tel: 610-369-0496. Fax: 610-369-0542. p. 2036

Falkenstein-Doyle, Cheri, Curator, Wheelwright Museum of the American Indian, 704 Camino Lejo, Santa Fe, NM, 87505. Tel: 505-982-4636. Fax: 505-989-7386. p. 1565

Falkinburg, Helene, Librn/Cat, Kennesaw State University, 1000 Chastain Rd, Kennesaw, GA, 30144. Tel: 770-423-6660. Fax: 770-423-6185. p. 537

Falkner, Andrea, Head, Ch, Wilton Library Association, 137 Old Ridgefield Rd, Wilton, CT, 06897-3019. Tel: 203-762-3950. Fax: 203-834-1166. p. 378

Falkowitz, Staci, Br Mgr, Charlotte Mecklenburg Library, Scaleybark Branch, 101 Scaleybark Rd, Charlotte, NC, 28209. Tel: 704-416-6400. Fax: 704-416-6500. p. 1782

Falkowski, David, Govt Doc, Eastern New Mexico University, 1300 S Ave K, Sta 32, Portales, NM, 88130-7402. Tel: 575-562-2788. Fax: 575-562-2647. p. 1560

Falkowski, Jennifer, Training Coordr, Southern Maryland Regional Library Association, Inc, 37600 New Market Rd, Charlotte Hall, MD, 20622-3041. Tel: 301-843-3634, 301-884-0436, 301-934-9442. Fax: 301-884-0438. p. 1023

Fall, Lena, Librn, Whiteriver Public Library, Chief Ave N, Whiteriver, AZ, 85941. Tel: 928-338-4884. Fax: 928-338-4470. p. 89

Falla, Beth, Dir, Lied Imperial Public Library, 703 Broadway, Imperial, NE, 69033. Tel: 308-882-4754. p. 1402

Falla, Bonnie, Pub Serv, Ref, Moravian College & Moravian Theological Seminary, 1200 Main St, Bethlehem, PA, 18018-6650. Tel: 610-861-1676. Fax: 610-861-1577. p. 2034

Fallen, Robert, Tech Librn, Atlanta University Center, 111 James P Brawley Dr SW, Atlanta, GA, 30314. Tel: 404-978-2058. Fax: 404-577-5158. p. 513

Fallin, Glenna Clark, Libr Dir, West Feliciana Parish Public Library, 11865 Ferdinand St, Saint Francisville, LA, 70775-4341. Tel: 225-635-3364. Fax: 225-635-4986. p. 967

Falling-Rain, Sunny, Br Mgr, Humboldt County Library, McKinleyville Branch, 1606 Pickett Rd, McKinleyville, CA, 95519. Tel: 707-839-4459. p. 147

Fallmaier, John, Tech Serv, Oswego Public Library District, 32 W Jefferson St, Oswego, IL, 60543. Tel: 630-554-3150. Fax: 630-978-1307. p. 686

Fallon, Gregory, Asst Dean, Passaic County Community College, One College Blvd, Paterson, NJ, 07505. Tel: 973-684-5896. Fax: 973-684-6675. p. 1518

Fallon, Linda, Adult Serv Mgr, Beaverton City Library, 12375 SW Fifth St, Beaverton, OR, 97005-2883. Tel: 503-526-2676. Fax: 503-526-2636. p. 1991

Fallon, Margaret S, Librn, Klehr, Harrison, Harvey, Branzburg & Ellers, 260 S Broad St, Philadelphia, PA, 19102-5003. Tel: 215-569-3091. Fax: 215-568-6603. p. 2111

Falls, Jo, Pub Prog Dir, Tohono Chul Park Library, 7366 N Paseo del Norte, Tucson, AZ, 85704. Tel: 520-742-6455, Ext 228. Fax: 520-797-1213. p. 88

Falls, Karen, Asst Dir, Delta County Public Library, 300 W Dallas Ave, Cooper, TX, 75432-1632. Tel: 903-395-4575. Fax: 903-395-4556. p. 2301

Falo, Jamie, Dir, Murrysville Community Library, 4130 Sardis Rd, Murrysville, PA, 15668-1120. Tel: 724-327-1102, Ext 153. Fax: 724-327-7142. p. 2094

Falo, Jamie K, Dir, Libr Serv, Mount Pleasant Free Public Library, 120 S Church St, Mount Pleasant, PA, 15666-1879. Tel: 724-547-3850. Fax: 724-547-0324. p. 2093

Faloon, Ronda, Dir, Cape Ann Museum Library/Archives, 27 Pleasant St, Gloucester, MA, 01930. Tel: 978-283-0455. Fax: 978-283-4141. p. 1091

Falzon, Judith, Br Mgr, Saint Joseph County Public Library, Virginia M Tutt Branch, 2223 S Miami St, South Bend, IN, 46613. Tel: 574-282-4637. p. 779

Fama, Jane, Assoc Dir, User Serv, University of Massachusetts Medical School, 55 Lake Ave N, Worcester, MA, 01655-2397. Tel: 508-856-2099. Fax: 508-856-5039. p. 1145

Familar, Patricia B, Br Mgr, Albemarle Regional Library, Gates County Public Library, 115 Court St, Gatesville, NC, 27938-9507. Tel: 252-357-0110. Fax: 252-357-1285. p. 1835

Famolare, Lee-Anne, Head, Tech Serv, Museum of Fine Arts, Boston, 300 Massachusetts Ave, Boston, MA, 02115. Tel: 617-369-3385. Fax: 617-369-4257. p. 1064

Fan, Fengzhi, Syst Coordr, University of Medicine & Dentistry of New Jersey, PO Box 19, New Brunswick, NJ, 08903. Tel: 732-235-7605. Fax: 732-235-7826. p. 1509

Fance, Kristin, ILL, Ref, Houston Baptist University, 7502 Fondren Rd, Houston, TX, 77074-3298. Tel: 281-649-3435. Fax: 281-649-3489. p. 2337

Fancher, Brooks, Info Tech Mgr, Homewood Public Library, 1721 Oxmoor Rd, Homewood, AL, 35209-4085. Tel: 205-332-6600. Fax: 205-802-6424. p. 20

Fancher, Catherine, Ch, Dudley-Tucker Library, Six Epping St, Raymond, NH, 03077. Tel: 603-895-2633. Fax: 603-895-0904. p. 1463

Fancy, Margaret, Coll Develop, Mount Allison University Libraries & Archives, 49 York St, Sackville, NB, E4L 1C6, CANADA. Tel: 506-364-2585. Fax: 506-364-2617. p. 2766

Fandrich, Jan, Ref & Coll Develop Librn, Montana State University, 1500 University Dr, Billings, MT, 59101-0298. Tel: 406-657-1665. Fax: 406-657-2037. p. 1374

Fandrich, Jill, In Charge, New York Supreme Court, Cayuga County Court House, 152 Genesee St, Auburn, NY, 13021. Tel: 315-255-4310. Fax: 315-255-4322. p. 1576

Fanelli, Lee, Br Supvr, Marion County Public Library System, Reddick Public Library, 15150 NW Gainsville Rd, Reddick, FL, 32686-3221. Tel: 352-438-2566. Fax: 352-438-2567. p. 474

Fanelly, Laurie, Financial & Admin Serv Dir, University of Pennsylvania Libraries, 3420 Walnut St, Philadelphia, PA, 19104-6206. Tel: 215-898-0892. Fax: 215-898-0559. p. 2118

Fang, Qian (Jan), Circ Mgr, Librn, Mgr, Per, Athens Technical College Library, 800 US Hwy 29 N, Athens, GA, 30601-1500. Tel: 706-355-5020. Fax: 706-355-5162. p. 509

Fang, Wei, Digital Serv, Rutgers University Library for the Center for Law & Justice, 123 Washington St, Newark, NJ, 07102-3094. Tel: 973-353-3061. Fax: 973-353-1356. p. 1513

Fangmeyer, Kerry, Asst Librn, Mascoutah Public Library, Three W Church St, Mascoutah, IL, 62258. Tel: 618-566-2562. Fax: 618-566-2563. p. 671

Faniel, Ixchel, Asst Prof, University of Michigan, 304 West Hall, 1085 S University, Ann Arbor, MI, 48109-1107. Tel: 734-763-2285. Fax: 734-764-2475. p. 2967

Fann, Kelly, Dir, Tonganoxie Public Library, 303 S Bury St, Tonganoxie, KS, 66086-9608. Tel: 913-845-3281. Fax: 913-845-2962. p. 896

Fann, Linda, Librn, Saint Clair County Public Library, Steele Branch, 78 Hill Top, Steele, AL, 35987. Tel: 256-538-0811. Fax: 256 538-0811. p. 5

Fann, Sharon, Librn, Ozark Regional Library, Bourbon Branch, 575 Elm, Bourbon, MO, 65441. Tel: 573-732-5313. p. 1333

Fannin, Amy, Dir, Darby Community Public Library, 101 1/2 Marshall St, Darby, MT, 59829. Tel: 406-821-4771. Fax: 406-821-3964. p. 1377

Fannin, JoEllen, Br Mgr, Greene County Public Library, Winters-Bellbrook Community Library, 57 W Franklin St, Bellbrook, OH, 45305-1904. Tel: 937-352-4004. Fax: 937-848-3074. p. 1951

Fanning, Karen, Coordr, Libr Assoc, Verde Valley Medical Center, 269 S Candy Lane, Cottonwood, AZ, 86326. Tel: 928-639-6444. Fax: 928-639-6457. p. 61

Fannon, Ellen, Head, Ref, Merrick Library, 2279 Merrick Ave, Merrick, NY, 11566-4398. Tel: 516-377-6112, Ext 102. Fax: 516-377-1108. p. 1659

Fannon, Kathy, Ad, Romeo District Library, 65821 Van Dyke, Washington, MI, 48095. Tel: 586-752-0603. Fax: 586-752-8416. p. 1235

Fanslow, Mary, Supvr, Eastman Chemical Co, Bldg 150B, PO Box 1972, Kingsport, TN, 37662-5150. Tel: 423-229-1845. Fax: 423-229-6114. p. 2240

Fant, Laurel, Coll Mgr, Rock County Historical Society, 933 Mineral Point Ave, Janesville, WI, 53545. Tel: 608-756-4509. Fax: 608-741-9596. p. 2600

Fanta, David P, Asst Librn, Chapman & Cutler, 111 W Monroe, Chicago, IL, 60603-4096. Tel: 312-845-3450. Fax: 312-701-6620. p. 607

Fantroy, Lagena, Librn, National Marine Fisheries Service, 3209 Frederick St, Pascagoula, MS, 39568. Tel: 228-762-4591. Fax: 228-769-9200. p. 1311

Faour, Bill, Dir, Electronic Computer Programming College Inc Library, 3805 Brainerd Rd, Chattanooga, TN, 37411. Tel: 423-624-0077. Fax: 423-624-1575. p. 2227

Farabee, Cheryl, Ref Serv, Washington State University Tri-Cities, 2770 University Dr, Richland, WA, 99354. Tel: 509-372-7387. Fax: 509-372-7281. p. 2526

Faraday, Joanna, Dir, Northern Westchester Hospital, 400 E Main St, Mount Kisco, NY, 10549-0802. Tel: 914-666-1259. Fax: 914-666-1940. p. 1664

Farara, Joseph, Dir, Johnson State College Library, 337 College Hill, Johnson, VT, 05656. Tel: 802-635-1274. Fax: 802-635-1294. p. 2426

Farber, Meryl P, Dir, Case Memorial Library, 176 Tyler City Rd, Orange, CT, 06477-2498. Tel: 203-891-2170. Fax: 203-891-2190. p. 364

Farber, Saskia, Clinical Libr Coordr, Drusch Professional Library, 11830 Westline Industrial Dr, Ste 106, Saint Louis, MO, 63146. Tel: 314-991-6213. Fax: 314-991-6284. p. 1354

Fardy, Mary, Ref Serv, Middlesex Community College, Federal Bldg, E Merrimack St, Lowell, MA, 01852. Tel: 978-937-5454. Fax: 978-656-3031. p. 1100

Farge, James, Curator, Rare Bks, University of Toronto Libraries, Pontifical Institute for Mediaeval Studies, 113 Saint Joseph St, Toronto, ON, M5S 1J4, CANADA. Tel: 416-926-7146. Fax: 416-926-7262. p. 2867

Fargo, Jean, Br Mgr, Wake County Public Library System, Leesville Community Library, 5105 Country Trail, Raleigh, NC, 27613. Tel: 919-571-6665. Fax: 919-571-6666. p. 1818

Fargo, Katie, YA Serv, E C Scranton Memorial Library, 801 Boston Post Rd, Madison, CT, 06443. Tel: 203-245-7365. Fax: 203-245-7821. p. 349

Farhood, Rosey, Dir, Leonard Public Library, 102 S Main St, Leonard, TX, 75452. Tel: 903-587-2391. Fax: 903-587-0311. p. 2355

Farid, Susan, Head, Circ, Des Plaines Public Library, 1501 Ellinwood St, Des Plaines, IL, 60016-4553. Tel: 847-376-2790. Fax: 847-827-7974. p. 636

Farides, Cliff, Dir, Mill Memorial Library, 495 E Main St, Nanticoke, PA, 18634-1897. Tel: 570-735-3030. Fax: 570-735-0340. p. 2094

Faries, Cindy, Mgr, Texas Department of State Health Services, 1100 W 49th St, Austin, TX, 78756-3199. Tel: 512-776-6492. Fax: 512-776-7474 (AV Library), 512-776-7683. p. 2282

Farina, Robert A, Dir, United States Trademark Office Law Library, 600 Dulany St, MDE 4B5, Alexandria, VA, 22314-5791. Tel: 571-272-9690. Fax: 571-273-9690. p. 2446

Faris, Christine, Head, Tech Serv, Haverford Township Free Library, 1601 Darby Rd, Havertown, PA, 19083-3798. Tel: 610-446-3082, Ext 210. Fax: 610-853-3090. p. 2067

Faris, Crystal, Dir, Teen Serv, The Kansas City Public Library, 14 W Tenth St, Kansas City, MO, 64105. Tel: 816-701-3513. Fax: 816-701-3401. p. 1338

Faris, Lucy, Librn, McElroy, Deutsch, Mulvaney & Carpenter, LLP, Law Library, Three Gateway Ctr, 100 Mulberry St, Newark, NJ, 07102. Tel: 973-622-7711, Ext 2065. Fax: 973-622-5314. p. 1505

Faris, Theresa, Librn II, Round Rock Public Library, 216 E Main St, Round Rock, TX, 78664. Tel: 512-218-7000, 512-218-7003. Fax: 512-218-7061. p. 2377

Fariss, Linda, Assoc Dir, Indiana University, School of Law Library, Maurer School of Law, 211 S Indiana Ave, Bloomington, IN, 47405. Tel: 812-855-9666. Fax: 812-855-7099. p. 727

Farkas, Jacklyn, Dir, Teen Serv, Liberty Center Public Library, 124 East St, Liberty Center, OH, 43532. Tel: 419-533-5721. Fax: 419-533-4849. p. 1909

Farkas, Joyce, Dir, Southgate Veterans Memorial Library, 14680 Dix-Toledo Rd, Southgate, MI, 48195. Tel: 734-258-3002. Fax: 734-284-9477. p. 1229

Farkas, Julie, Dir, Novi Public Library, 45245 W Ten Mile Rd, Novi, MI, 48375. Tel: 248-349-0720. Fax: 248-349-6520. p. 1214

Farkas, Meredith, Head, Instrul Serv, Portland State University Library, 1875 SW Park Ave, Portland, OR, 97201-3220. Tel: 503-725-4577. Fax: 503-725-4524. p. 2014

Farkas, Robert, Coll Develop, United States Book Exchange Library, 2969 W 25th St, Cleveland, OH, 44113-5393. Tel: 216-241-6960. Fax: 216-241-6966. p. 1881

Farkas, Susan, Mgr, Edison Electric Institute, 701 Pennsylvania Ave NW, 3rd Flr, Washington, DC, 20004-2696. Tel: 202-508-5623. p. 399

Farley, Becky, Tech Info Spec, United States Department of Labor, 1301 Airport Rd, Beaver, WV, 25813-9426. Tel: 304-256-3267. Fax: 304-256-3372. p. 2553

Farley, Beth, Ref & Coll Develop Librn, Bellingham Public Library, 210 Central Ave, CS-9710, Bellingham, WA, 98227-9710. Tel: 360-778-7323. p. 2508

Farley, Billie, Mgr, Waco-McLennan County Library System, East Waco, 901 Elm, Waco, TX, 76704-2659. Tel: 254-750-8620. Fax: 254-750-8413. p. 2397

Farley, Cathy M, Dir, White County Public Library, 11 N Church St, Sparta, TN, 38583-2299. Tel: 931-836-3613. Fax: 931-836-2570. p. 2266

Farley, Cindy, Acctg & Finance Mgr, Lancaster Public Library, 125 N Duke St, Lancaster, PA, 17602-2883. Tel: 717-394-2651, Ext 130. Fax: 717-394-3083. p. 2077

Farley, Doylenne, Br Mgr, Putnam County Library System, Monterey Branch, 401 E Commercial Ave, Monterey, TN, 38574. Tel: 931-839-2103. Fax: 931-839-2103. p. 2231

Farley, Elaine, Dir, Haines Falls Free Library, 52 N Lake Rd, Haines Falls, NY, 12436. Tel: 518-589-5707. Fax: 518-589-0311. p. 1632

Farley, Jane, Tech Serv, Blue Ridge Regional Library, 310 E Church St, Martinsville, VA, 24112-2999. Tel: 276-403-5434. Fax: 276-632-1660. p. 2477

Farley, Kim, Instrul Serv Librn, Lansing Community College Library, 200 Technology & Learning Ctr, 419 N Capitol Ave, Lansing, MI, 48933. Tel: 517-483-1662. Fax: 517-483-5300. p. 1201

Farley, Nathan, Electronic Serv Librn, Northwestern College, 3003 Snelling Ave N, Saint Paul, MN, 55113. Tel: 651-631-5241. Fax: 651-631-5598. p. 1280

Farley, Shirley, Acq, Iowa Wesleyan College, 107 W Broad St, Mount Pleasant, IA, 52641. Tel: 319-385-6316. Fax: 319-385-6324. p. 833

Farley, Teresa, Asst Librn, Ref Serv, Florida Supreme Court Library, 500 S Duval St, Tallahassee, FL, 32399-1926. Tel: 850-488-8919. Fax: 850-922-5219. p. 495

Farley, Yvonne S, Dir, United States Department of Labor, 1301 Airport Rd, Beaver, WV, 25813-9426. Tel: 304-256-3531. Fax: 304-256-3372. p. 2553

Farlow, Steve, Dir, Braswell Memorial Public Library, 727 N Grace St, Rocky Mount, NC, 27804-4842. Tel: 252-442-1951. Fax: 252-442-7366. p. 1820

Farmer, Angela, Mgr, Public Library of Cincinnati & Hamilton County, Information & Reference, South Bldg, 2nd Flr, 800 Vine St, Cincinnati, OH, 45202-2009. Tel: 513-369-6934. Fax: 513-665-3388. p. 1872

Farmer, Casey, Circ Librn, Crittenden County Public Library, 204 W Carlisle St, Marion, KY, 42064-1727. Tel: 270-965-3354. Fax: 270-965-3354. p. 928

Farmer, Dana, Librn, East Mississippi Regional Library System, Bay Springs Municipal, 815 S Court St, Bay Springs, MS, 39422. Tel: 601-764-2291. Fax: 601-764-2291. p. 1313

Farmer, Deborah, Br Mgr, Whatcom County Library System, Blaine Branch, 610 Third St, Blaine, WA, 98230. Tel: 360-332-8146. Fax: 360-332-8146. p. 2509

Farmer, Elizabeth, Youth Serv, Coventry Public Library, 1672 Flat River Rd, Coventry, RI, 02816. Tel: 401-822-9100. Fax: 401-822-9133. p. 2164

Farmer, Jaketha, IT Spec, Bossier Parish Central Library, 2206 Beckett St, Bossier City, LA, 71111. Tel: 318-746-1693. Fax: 318-746-7768. p. 945

Farmer, Katherine, Res & Instruction Librn, Murray State University, 205 Waterfield Library, Dean's Office, Murray, KY, 42071-3307. Tel: 270-809-6180. Fax: 270-809-3736. p. 930

Farmer, Lesley S J, Dr, Coordr, California State University, Long Beach, Dept of Advanced Studies in Education & Counseling, 1250 Bellflower Blvd, Long Beach, CA, 90840-2201. Tel: 562-985-4509. Fax: 562-985-4534. p. 2962

Farmer, Maggie, Br Mgr, Memphis Public Library, Randolph Branch, 3752 Given, Memphis, TN, 38122. Tel: 901-452-1068. Fax: 901-454-9594. p. 2250

Farmer, Susan, Br Head, Toronto Public Library, Todmorden Room, 1081 1/2 Pape Ave (at Torrens), Toronto, ON, M4K 3W6, CANADA. Tel: 416-396-3875. Fax: 416-396-3864. p. 2863

Farmer, Tracy, Head, Syst, Arkansas State University, 322 University Loop West Circle, State University, AR, 72401. Tel: 870-972-3077. Fax: 870-972-3199. p. 115

Farmer-Morrison, Geraldine, Ch, Levittown Public Library, One Bluegrass Lane, Levittown, NY, 11756-1292. Tel: 516-731-5728. Fax: 516-735-3168. p. 1652

Farnan, David, Assoc Dir, Commun Serv, Douglas County Libraries, 100 S Wilcox, Castle Rock, CO, 80104. Tel: 303-791-7323. Fax: 303-688-7655. p. 294

Farnell, Pat, Bibliog Instr, Librn, Online Serv, Fugro, Inc, 6100 Hillcroft, Houston, TX, 77081. Tel: 713-369-5500. Fax: 713-369-5570. p. 2335

Farner, Marical, Assoc Dir, Admin Serv, Auraria Library, 1100 Lawrence St, Denver, CO, 80204-2095. Tel: 303-556-3525. Fax: 303-556-3528. p. 298

Farneth, David, Asst Dir, Getty Research Institute, 1200 Getty Center Dr, Ste 1100, Los Angeles, CA, 90049-1688. Tel: 310-440-7390. Fax: 310-440-7780. p. 170

Farnham, Frank C, Pres, Frank C Farnham Company Inc Library, 210 W Front St, Ste 5, Media, PA, 19063-3101. Tel: 610-892-8008. Fax: 610-892-8050. p. 2087

Farnham, John, Presv Officer, Philadelphia Historical Commission Library, City Hall, Rm 576, Philadelphia, PA, 19107. Tel: 215-686-7660. Fax: 215-686-7674. p. 2114

Farnham, Maryanne, Asst Dir, Peru Public Library, 102 N Main St, Peru, IN, 46970-2338. Tel: 765-473-3069. Fax: 765-473-3060. p. 772

Farnsworth, Julie, Dir, Pleasanton Public Library, 400 Old Bernal Ave, Pleasanton, CA, 94566-7012. Tel: 925-931-3406. Fax: 925-846-8517. p. 210

Farquahar, Jennifer, Head, Bibliog Serv, Head of Instruction, Suffolk County Community College, 533 College Rd, Selden, NY, 11784-2899. Tel: 631-451-4800. Fax: 631-451-4697. p. 1742

Farr, Ann, Dir, Greenbrier County Public Library, 152 Robert W McCormick Dr, Lewisburg, WV, 24901. Tel: 304-647-7568. Fax: 304-647-7569. p. 2563

Farr, Carole, Librn, Georgia Department of Corrections, Office of Library Services, 777 Underwood Rd, Trion, GA, 30753. Tel: 706-857-0484. Fax: 706-857-0551. p. 554

Farr, Connie, Ref, Richland Public Library, 955 Northgate Dr, Richland, WA, 99352-3539. Tel: 509-942-7446. Fax: 509-942-7442. p. 2526

Farr, Emily, Dir, Long Lake Library, 1195 Main St, Long Lake, NY, 12847. Tel: 518-624-3825. Fax: 518-624-2172. p. 1654

Farr, Gail E, Archivist, Holy Family University Library, 9801 Frankford Ave, Philadelphia, PA, 19114. Tel: 267-341-3414. Fax: 215-632-8067. p. 2111

Farr, Melissa, Libr Tech, Harrisburg Area Community College, 1641 Old Philadelphia Pike, Lancaster, PA, 17602. Tel: 717-358-2986. Fax: 717-358-2952. p. 2076

Farr-Kindler, Laurie, Patron/Ref Serv, Islip Public Library, 71 Monell Ave, Islip, NY, 11751-3999. Tel: 631-581-5933. Fax: 631-277-8429. p. 1641

Farral, Shari, Dir, Hanover Township Library, 204 Jefferson St, Hanover, IL, 61041. Tel: 815-591-3517. Fax: 815-591-3517. p. 653

Farrar, Christi Showman, Ref Serv, YA, Woburn Public Library, 45 Pleasant St, Woburn, MA, 01801. Tel: 781-933-0148. Fax: 781-938-7860. p. 1142

Farrar, Judith, Assoc Librn, Archives & Spec Coll, University of Massachusetts Dartmouth Library, 285 Old Westport Rd, North Dartmouth, MA, 02747-2300. Tel: 508-999-8686. Fax: 508-999-8424. p. 1112

Farrar, Paula, Actg Head, University of British Columbia Library, Art, Architecture & Planning, Irving K Barber Learning Ctr, 1961 East Mall, Vancouver, BC, V6T 1Z1, CANADA. Tel: 604-822-3943. Fax: 604-822-3779. p. 2743

Farrar, Sarah M, Dir, Richards Library, 36 Elm St, Warrensburg, NY, 12885. Tel: 518-623-3011. Fax: 518-623-3011. p. 1762

Farrar, Susan, Bus Mgr, Blue Hill Public Library, Five Parker Point Rd, Blue Hill, ME, 04614-0821. Tel: 207-374-5515. Fax: 207-374-5254. p. 978

Farrar, Valerie, Br Supvr, Davenport Public Library, Fairmount Street, 3000 N Fairmount St, Davenport, IA, 52804-1160. Tel: 563-328-6830. Fax: 563-326-7806. p. 806

Farrar, Viola, Librn, West Fairlee Free Public Library, 894 Vt Rte 113, Unit 3, West Fairlee, VT, 05083-4405. Tel: 802-333-3502. p. 2439

Farrell, Ben, Evening Coordr, University of Oregon Libraries, John E Jaqua Law Library, William W Knight Law Ctr, 2nd Flr, 1515 Agate St, Eugene, OR, 97403-1221. Tel: 541-346-1658. Fax: 541-346-1669. p. 1997

Farrell, Bernie, Sr Librn, Hennepin County Library, Minneapolis Central, 300 Nicollet Mall, Minneapolis, MN, 55401. Tel: 612-543-8030. Fax: 612-543-8173. p. 1264

Farrell, Charlene, Librn, Institute of Noetic Sciences Library, 625 Second St, Ste 200, Petaluma, CA, 94952-9524. Tel: 707-775-3500. Fax: 707-781-7420. p. 207

Farrell, Fred, Mgr, Provincial Archives of New Brunswick, 23 Dineen Dr, Fredericton, NB, E3B 5A3, CANADA. Tel: 506-453-2122. Fax: 506-453-3288. p. 2763

Farrell, James L, Jr, Dir, Ossining Public Library, 53 Croton Ave, Ossining, NY, 10562-4903. Tel: 914-941-2416. Fax: 914-941-7464. p. 1712

Farrell, Joan, Dir, Frackville Free Public Library, 56 N Lehigh Ave, Frackville, PA, 17931-1424. Tel: 570-874-3382. Fax: 570-874-3382. p. 2058

Farrell, Krista, Asst Libr Dir, Jefferson-Madison Regional Library, 201 E Market St, Charlottesville, VA, 22902-5287. Tel: 434-979-7151, Ext 206, 434-979-7151, Ext 207. Fax: 434-979-0278. p. 2453

Farrell, Leslie, Continuing Education & Consulting Librn, Outagamie Waupaca Library System, 225 N Oneida, Appleton, WI, 54911-4780. Tel: 920-832-6190. Fax: 920-832-6422. p. 2578

Farrell, Lisa, Dir, Libr Serv, East Central College Library, 1964 Prairie Dell Rd, Union, MO, 63084-4344. Tel: 636-584-6560. Fax: 636-583-1897. p. 1369

Farrell, Maggie, Dean, University of Wyoming Libraries, 13th & Ivinson, Laramie, WY, 82071. Tel: 307-766-3279. Fax: 307-766-2510. p. 2658

Farrell, Maria, Head, Circ, Ocean City Free Public Library, 1735 Simpson Ave, Ste 4, Ocean City, NJ, 08226. Tel: 609-399-2434. Fax: 609-398-0751. p. 1515

Farrell, Mark, Curator, Princeton University, Department of Rare Books, One Washington Rd, Princeton, NJ, 08544. Tel: 609-258-3184. p. 1523

Farrell, Mary, Br Mgr, Oakland Public Library, Lakeview, 550 El Embarcadero, Oakland, CA, 94610. Tel: 510-238-7344. Fax: 510-238-6760. p. 198

Farrell, Mary, Ref Serv, YA, Abbot Public Library, 235 Pleasant St, Marblehead, MA, 01945. Tel: 781-631-1481. Fax: 781-639-0558. p. 1102

Farrell, Mary, Ch, George Holmes Bixby Memorial Library, 52 Main St, Francestown, NH, 03043-3025. Tel: 603-547-2730. Fax: 603-547-2730. p. 1447

Farrell, Mary, Dir, Walpole Town Library, Bridge Memorial Library, 48 Main St, Walpole, NH, 03608. Tel: 603-756-9806. Fax: 603-756-3140. p. 1466

Farrell, Mary Anne, Cat, Delaware Technical & Community College, 333 Shipley St, Wilmington, DE, 19801. Tel: 302-573-5431. Fax: 302-577-2038. p. 387

Farrell, Pat, Ref & Instruction Librn, Roosevelt University, Robert R McCormick Tribune Foundation Library, 1400 N Roosevelt Blvd, Schaumburg, IL, 60173. Tel: 847-619-7980. Fax: 847-619-7983. p. 623

Farrell, Robert, Bibliog Instr, Lehman College, City University of New York, 250 Bedford Park Blvd W, Bronx, NY, 10468-1589. Tel: 718-960-7761. Fax: 718-960-8952. p. 1587

Farrell, Sandy, Libr Dir, Hobbs Public Library, 509 N Shipp, Hobbs, NM, 88240. Tel: 575-397-9328. Fax: 575-397-1508. p. 1556

Farrell, Sean, Asst Dir, Ref/Automated Syst, The Library of Hattiesburg, Petal, Forrest County, 329 Hardy St, Hattiesburg, MS, 39401-3496. Tel: 601-582-4461. Fax: 601-582-5338. p. 1300

Farrell, Sherry, Head, Acq, University of Missouri-Kansas City Libraries, 800 E 51st St, Kansas City, MO, 64110. Tel: 816-235-6461. Fax: 816-333-5584. p. 1341

Farrier, Maureen, Br Librn, Crook County Library, Moorcroft Branch, 105 E Converse, Moorcroft, WY, 82721. Tel: 307-756-3232. Fax: 307-756-3232. p. 2661

Farrington, James, Head, Pub Serv, University of Rochester, Sibley Music Library, 27 Gibbs St, Rochester, NY, 14604-2596. Tel: 585-274-1350. Fax: 585-274-1380. p. 1733

Farrington, Janet, Dir, Andover Public Library, 46 Church St, Andover, ME, 04216. Tel: 207-392-4841. p. 973

Farrington, Kim, Access Serv, ILL, Central Connecticut State University, 1615 Stanley St, New Britain, CT, 06050. Tel: 860-832-3403. Fax: 860-832-3409. p. 353

Farrington, Lynne, Curator of Printed Bks, University of Pennsylvania Libraries, Rare Book & Manuscript Library, 3420 Walnut St, Philadelphia, PA, 19104. Tel: 215-746-5828. p. 2119

Farrington, Sandy, Dir, East Hounsfield Free Library, 19438 NYS Rte 3, Watertown, NY, 13601. Tel: 315-788-0637. p. 1763

Farris, Annie, Borrower Serv Librn, Siskiyou County Public Library, Mount Shasta Branch, 515 E Alma St, Mount Shasta, CA, 96067. Tel: 530-926-2031. Fax: 530-926-2031. p. 286

Farris, David, Exec Dir, Congregation Beth Ahabah Museum & Archives Trust, 1109 W Franklin St, Richmond, VA, 23220. Tel: 804-353-2668. Fax: 804-358-3451. p. 2488

Farris, Janell, Head, Cat, Port Arthur Public Library, 4615 Ninth Ave, Port Arthur, TX, 77642. Tel: 409-985-8838, Ext 2229. Fax: 409-985-5969. p. 2371

Farris, Judy, Asst Librn, Cutler Public Library, Civic Ctr, 409 S Main, Cutler, IL, 62238. Tel: 618-497-2961. Fax: 618-497-8818. p. 632

Farris, Ruth Ann, Dir, First Baptist Church, First & A St SW, Miami, OK, 74355. Tel: 918-542-1691. Fax: 918-542-1753. p. 1968

Farrow, Lucy I, Dean of Libr, Head, Pub Serv, Auburn University, 7440 East Dr, Montgomery, AL, 36117. Tel: 334-244-3200. Fax: 334-244-3720. p. 28

Farrugia, A Denise, Youth Serv Mgr, St Charles Public Library District, One S Sixth Ave, Saint Charles, IL, 60174-2105. Tel: 630-584-0076, Ext 236. Fax: 630-584-3448. p. 699

Farry, Diane, Libr Asst, Cotuit Library, 871 Main St, Cotuit, MA, 02635. Tel: 508-428-8141. Fax: 508-428-4636. p. 1083

Farshidpour, Kian, Circ, Saddleback College, 28000 Marguerite Pkwy, Mission Viejo, CA, 92692. Tel: 949-582-4876. Fax: 949-364-0284. p. 187

Farstad, Sam, Admin Serv Mgr, Albany County Public Library, 310 S Eighth St, Laramie, WY, 82070-3969. Tel: 307-721-2580. Fax: 307-721-2584. p. 2657

Farstad, Sheila, Librn, Southeast Regional Library, Bienfait Branch, 414 Main St, Bienfait, SK, S0C 0M0, CANADA. Tel: 306-388-2995. Fax: 306-388-2883. p. 2929

Farthing, Matthew, Ser Librn, Owens Community College Library, 30335 Oregon Rd, Perrysburg, OH, 43551. Tel: 567-661-7023. Fax: 567-661-7021. p. 1929

Farthing, Pat, Instrul Mat Coordr, Appalachian State University, 218 College St, Boone, NC, 28608. Tel: 828-262-2778. Fax: 828-262-3001. p. 1777

Farver, Bonnie Lou, Exec Dir, Columbia County Historical & Genealogical Society Library, 225 Market St, Bloomsburg, PA, 17815-0360. Tel: 570-784-1600. p. 2036

Farwell, Beth, Assoc Dir, Cent Libr, Baylor University Libraries, Moody Memorial Library, 1312 S Third, Waco, TX, 76798. Tel: 254-710-3679. p. 2396

Farwell, Bob, Dir, Otis Library, Two Cliff St, Norwich, CT, 06360. Tel: 860-889-2365. Fax: 860-886-4744. p. 362

Farynk, Linda, Dir, Saginaw Valley State University, 7400 Bay Rd, University Center, MI, 48710. Tel: 989-964-4236. Fax: 989-964-4383. p. 1232

Farzan, Pam, Asst Librn, Douglas Library, 108 Main St, Canaan, CT, 06018. Tel: 860-824-7863. Fax: 860-824-7863. p. 333

Fasching, Tom, Librn, US Courts Library, 402 E State St, Rm 301, Trenton, NJ, 08608. Tel: 609-989-2345. Fax: 609-989-0485. p. 1536

Fascinato, Lynne, ILL, Web Coordr, Meaford Public Library, 15 Trowbridge St W, Meaford, ON, N4L 1V4, CANADA. Tel: 519-538-1060, Ext 1123. Fax: 519-538-1808. p. 2821

Fashion, Mashell, Asst Dir, East Central Georgia Regional Library, 902 Greene St, Augusta, GA, 30901. Tel: 706-821-2602. Fax: 706-724-6762. p. 519

Fashion, Sharon M, Coordr, Youth Serv, Dep Dir, Berkeley County Library System, 1003 Hwy 52, Moncks Corner, SC, 29461. Tel: 843-719-4227. p. 2200

Fashion, Valerie, Librn, United States Army, Groninger Library, Bldg 1313, Army Transportation Ctr, Washington Blvd, Fort Eustis, VA, 23604-5107. Tel: 757-878-5017, 757-878-5583. Fax: 757-878-1024. p. 2465

Fashun, Dianne, Librn, Beaver Dam Community Hospitals, Inc Library, 707 S University Ave, Beaver Dam, WI, 53916. Tel: 920-887-4124. Fax: 920-887-4187. p. 2581

Fast, Bonnie, Acq & Cat, Cypress College Library, 9200 Valley View St, Cypress, CA, 90630-5897. Tel: 714-484-7072. Fax: 714-826-6723. p. 138

Fast, Karl, Asst Prof, Kent State University, 314 Library, Kent, OH, 44242-0001. Tel: 330-672-2782. Fax: 330-672-7965. p. 2972

Fast, Margaret, Ref Librn, Western Washington University, 516 High St, MS 9103, Bellingham, WA, 98225. Tel: 360-650-3174. Fax: 360-650-3044. p. 2509

Fast, Pam, Dir, Buhler Public Library, 121 N Main St, Buhler, KS, 67522-0664. Tel: 620-543-2241. Fax: 620-543-2241. p. 859

Fasulo, Deb, Asst Dir, AV, Waltham Public Library, 735 Main St, Waltham, MA, 02451. Tel: 781-314-3432. Fax: 781-314-3426. p. 1133

Fasulo, Rebecca, Librn, Corinth Free Library, 89 Main St, Corinth, NY, 12822. Tel: 518-654-6913. Fax: 518-654-6913. p. 1610

Fate, Emily, Mgr, Los Angeles Public Library System, West Valley Area, 19036 Vanowen, Reseda, CA, 91335. Tel: 818-895-3661. Fax: 818-895-3656. p. 174

Fatherly, Jo Anne, Asst Librn, Grinnell Library Association, 2642 E Main St, Wappingers Falls, NY, 12590. Tel: 845-297-3428. Fax: 845-297-1506. p. 1762

Fatkin, Kathy, Dir, Eastern Idaho Regional Medical Center, PO Box 2077, Idaho Falls, ID, 83403-2077. Tel: 208-529-6077. Fax: 208-529-7014. p. 576

Fatkin, Kathy, Dir, Idaho Health Information Association, c/o Eastern Idaho Regional Medical Center, PO Box 2077, Idaho Falls, ID, 83403. Tel: 208-529-6077. Fax: 208-529-7014. p. 2941

Fattig, Teri, Libr Dir, College of Southern Idaho Library, 315 Falls Ave, Twin Falls, ID, 83301-3367. Tel: 208-732-6500. Fax: 208-736-3087. p. 584

Fattig, Teri, Dir, College of Southern Idaho, Gerald R Meyerhoeffer Bldg, Main Flr, Twin Falls, ID, 83303. Tel: 208-732-6501. Fax: 208-736-3087. p. 2964

Fatzer, Jill B, Prof, University of New Orleans, College of Education, Rm 342, New Orleans, LA, 70148. Tel: 504-280-6251, 504-280-6528. Fax: 504-280-1120. p. 2967

Faucett, Lauren, Libr Spec, Technical College of the Lowcountry, 921 Ribaut Rd, Beaufort, SC, 29902-5441. Tel: 843-525-8304. Fax: 843-525-8346. p. 2181

Faucheaux, Sherrill A, Head, Cat, Nicholls State University, 906 E First St, Thibodaux, LA, 70310. Tel: 985-448-4635. Fax: 985-448-4925. p. 971

Faucher, Linda, Dir, Cary Library, 107 Main St, Houlton, ME, 04730. Tel: 207-532-1302. Fax: 207-532-4350. p. 988

Faulconer, Tina, Acq, University of Mary Washington, 1801 College Ave, Fredericksburg, VA, 22401-4665. Tel: 540-654-1761. Fax: 540-654-1067. p. 2466

Faulhaber, Lee D, Librn, Federal Reserve Bank of Cleveland, 1455 E Sixth St, Cleveland, OH, 44114. Tel: 216-579-2052, 216-579-2961. Fax: 216-579-3172. p. 1880

Faulhaber, Terri, Tech Serv Librn, Cleveland Law Library Association, One W Lakeside Ave, 4th Flr, Cleveland, OH, 44113-1023. Tel: 216-861-5070. Fax: 216-861-1606. p. 1877

Faulk, Emmet, Info Tech, Saint Mark's Episcopal Church, 315 E Pecan St, San Antonio, TX, 78205. Tel: 210-226-2426. Fax: 210-226-2468. p. 2381

Faulk, Joyce, Br Mgr, Middle Georgia Regional Library System, Twiggs County Public Library, 101 Ash St, Jeffersonville, GA, 31044. Tel: 478-945-3814. Fax: 478-945-3814. p. 541

Faulk, Sara, Tech Serv, LMI Library, 2000 Corporate Ridge, McLean, VA, 22102-7805. Tel: 703-917-7214. Fax: 703-917-7474. p. 2478

Faulkner, Carole, Commun Relations Librn, Logan County Public Library, 201 W Sixth St, Russellville, KY, 42276. Tel: 270-726-6129. Fax: 270-726-6127. p. 934

Faulkner, Deborah, Adult Serv, Indian Valley Public Library, 100 E Church Ave, Telford, PA, 18969. Tel: 215-723-9109. Fax: 215-723-0583. p. 2145

Faulkner, Kristen, ILL, Ser, Polk State College, 999 Ave H NE, Winter Haven, FL, 33881-4299. Tel: 863-297-1040. Fax: 863-297-1065. p. 504

Faulkner, Mary B, District Dir, Edison State College, 8099 College Pkwy SW, Bldg J, Fort Myers, FL, 33919. Tel: 239-489-9032. Fax: 239-489-9095. p. 444

Faulkner, Ronnie W, Dr, Libr Develop & Head, Tech Serv, Winthrop University, 824 Oakland Ave, Rock Hill, SC, 29733. Tel: 803-323-2262. Fax: 803-323-2215. p. 2203

Faulkner, Sharon, Dir, Learning Res, Montgomery Community College Library, 1011 Page St, Troy, NC, 27371. Tel: 910-576-6222, Ext 201. Fax: 910-576-2176. p. 1827

Faulkner, Stephanie, Circ Supvr, Knox County Public Library System, 500 W Church Ave, Knoxville, TN, 37902-2505. Tel: 865-215-8750. Fax: 865-215-8742. p. 2241

Faunt, Sandy, Librn, Drayton Valley Municipal Library, 5120 - 52 St, Drayton Valley, AB, T7A 1A1, CANADA. Tel: 780-514-2228. Fax: 780-514-2532. p. 2696

Faupel, William D, Dir, Wesley Theological Seminary Library, 4500 Massachusetts Ave NW, Washington, DC, 20016-5690. Tel: 202-885-8960. Fax: 202-885-8691. p. 422

Faust, Bradley D, Asst Dean, Libr Info Tech, Ball State University Libraries, 2000 W University Ave, Muncie, IN, 47306-1099. Tel: 765-285-5277. Fax: 765-285-2008. p. 766

Faust, David, Librn, University of Minnesota Libraries-Twin Cities, Ames Library of South Asia, S-10 Wilson Library, 309 19th Ave S, Minneapolis, MN, 55455. Tel: 612-624-4857. Fax: 612-626-9353. p. 1262

Faust, Diane, Ser, Pittsburgh Theological Seminary, 616 N Highland Ave, Pittsburgh, PA, 15206-2596. Tel: 412-924-1360. Fax: 412-362-2329. p. 2127

Faust, Jeffrey, Dir, Libr Serv, Jefferson Davis Community College, 220 Alco Dr, Brewton, AL, 36426. Tel: 251-809-1581. Fax: 251-809-1548. p. 11

Faust, Kathy, Head, Tech Serv, Lewis & Clark College, Paul L Boley Law Library, Lewis & Clark Law School, 10015 SW Terwilliger Blvd, Portland, OR, 97219. Tel: 503-768-6776. Fax: 503-768-6760. p. 2011

Faust, Leona, Librn, United States Senate Library, SRB-15 Senate Russell Bldg, Washington, DC, 20510-7112. Tel: 202-224-7106. Fax: 202-224-0879. p. 421

Faust, Lindsay, Teen Librn, Helen Hall Library, 100 W Walker, League City, TX, 77573-3899. Tel: 281-554-1102. Fax: 281-554-1118. p. 2354

Faust, Lori, Youth Serv, Warren-Trumbull County Public Library, 444 Mahoning Ave NW, Warren, OH, 44483. Tel: 330-399-8807. Fax: 330-395-3988. p. 1944

Faust, Nancy, Ref, Seyfarth Shaw, 131 S Dearborn St, Ste 2400, Chicago, IL, 60603-5577. Tel: 312-460-5000. Fax: 312-460-7000. p. 624

Faust, Teresa, Librn, Vermont Regional Library for the Blind & Physically Handicapped, Vermont Dept of Libraries Special Services Unit, 578 Paine Turnpike N, Berlin, VT, 05602. Tel: 802-828-3273. Fax: 802-828-2199. p. 2419

Favat, Jodee, Dir, Gibbsboro Public Library, Borough Hall, 49 Kirkwood Rd, Gibbsboro, NJ, 08026. Tel: 856-435-3656. p. 1487

Favata, Pat, Librn, Library of Historical Society of Newburgh Bay & the Highlands, 189 Montgomery St, Newburgh, NY, 12550. Tel: 845-561-2585. p. 1704

Favata, Shay, Dir, Nichols Memorial Library, 169 Main St, Kingston, NH, 03848-0128. Tel: 603-642-3521. Fax: 603-642-3135. p. 1453

Favreau, Marilyn, Ref Librn, Scotch Plains Public Library, 1927 Bartle Ave, Scotch Plains, NJ, 07076-1212. Tel: 908-322-5007. Fax: 908-322-0190. p. 1528

Fawcett, Brad, Libr Dir, Vanguard College Library, 12140 103 St, Edmonton, AB, T5G 2J9, CANADA. Tel: 780-452-0808. Fax: 780-452-5803. p. 2703

Fawcett, Debra, Dir, Colorado State Literacy Resource Center, 201 E Colfax Ave, Denver, CO, 80203. Tel: 303-866-6914. Fax: 303-866-6947. p. 299

Fawcett, Linda, Librn, Butterfield Library, 3534 US Rte 5, Westminster, VT, 05158. Tel: 802-722-4891. p. 2439

Fawcett, Patrick, Librn, Taylor McCaffrey, 400 St Mary Ave, 9th Flr, Winnipeg, MB, R3C 4K5, CANADA. Tel: 204-988-0463. Fax: 204-957-0945. p. 2757

Fawcett, Tonya, Dir of Libr Serv, Grace College & Grace Theological Seminary, 200 Seminary Dr, Winona Lake, IN, 46590. Tel: 574-372-5100, Ext 6291. Fax: 574-372-5176. p. 789

Fawver, Darlene, Coordr, Music & Tech Serv, Converse College, 580 E Main St, Spartanburg, SC, 29302. Tel: 864-596-9025. Fax: 864-596-9075. p. 2204

Fay, Janet, Head, Circ, Cresskill Public Library, 53 Union Ave, Cresskill, NJ, 07626. Tel: 201-567-3521. Fax: 201-567-5067. p. 1480

Fay, Jocelyn, Dir, Libr Serv, Review & Herald Publishing Association, 55 W Oak Ridge Dr, Hagerstown, MD, 21740. Tel: 301-393-4141. Fax: 301-393-4055. p. 1031

Fay, Marge, Circ Supvr, Naperville Public Library, Naper Boulevard, 2035 S Naper Blvd, Naperville, IL, 60565-3353. Tel: 630-961-4100, Ext 2216. Fax: 630-961-4119. p. 679

Faye, Hadley, Ref Serv, University of Tulsa Libraries, Mabee Legal Information Center, 3120 E Fourth Pl, Tulsa, OK, 74104-3189. Tel: 918-631-2404. Fax: 918-631-3556. p. 1984

Fayoyin, Mary Jo, Dir, Savannah State University, 2200 Tompkins Rd, Savannah, GA, 31404. Tel: 912-356-2183. Fax: 912-356-2874. p. 551

Fazal, S, Reader Serv, State University of New York Maritime College, Six Pennyfield Ave, Fort Schuyler, Bronx, NY, 10465. Tel: 718-409-7231. Fax: 718-409-7256. p. 1588

Fazekas, Monica, Dir, Western University - Libraries, Music, Talbot College, Rm 234, London, ON, N6A 3K7, CANADA. Tel: 519-661-2111, Ext 85334. Fax: 519-661-3927. p. 2819

Fazenbaker Race, Stephanie, Asst Dir, Northeast Florida Library Information Network, 2233 Park Ave, Ste 402, Orange Park, FL, 32073. Tel: 904-278-5620. Fax: 904-278-5625. p. 2940

Fazio, Laura, Tech Serv, Dolton Public Library District, 14037 Lincoln, Dolton, IL, 60419-1091. Tel: 708-849-2385. Fax: 708-841-2725. p. 637

Fazio, Patricia, Coll Develop, Camden County College Library, College Dr, Blackwood, NJ, 08012. Tel: 856-227-7200, Ext 4402. Fax: 856-374-4897. p. 1473

Fazio, Wende, Adult Serv, Mary Meuser Memorial Library, 1803 Northampton St, Easton, PA, 18042-3183. Tel: 610-258-3040. p. 2052

Feagin, James, Dir, Hagerstown Community College Library, 11400 Robinwood Dr, Hagerstown, MD, 21742-6590. Tel: 301-790-2800, Ext 237. Fax: 301-393-3681. p. 1030

Feagle, Julie, Interim Dir, Dundee Public Library, 202 E Main St, Dundee, FL, 33838. Tel: 863-439-9424. Fax: 863-439-9426. p. 438

Fearer, Katie, Pub Serv Librn, Alaska State Library, 333 Willoughby Ave, State Office Bldg, 8th Flr, Juneau, AK, 99801. Tel: 907-465-2910. Fax: 907-465-2151. p. 49

Fearn, Andrew, Br Librn, Brazoria County Library System, Pearland Branch, 3522 Liberty Dr, Pearland, TX, 77581. Tel: 281-485-4876. Fax: 281-485-5576. p. 2276

Fearn, Bryan, Head, Ref, Henderson District Public Libraries, 280 S Green Valley Pkwy, Henderson, NV, 89012. Tel: 702-492-7252. Fax: 702-492-1711. p. 1428

Fearn, Bryan, In Charge, Multnomah County Library, Troutdale, 2451 SW Cherry Park Rd, Troutdale, OR, 97060. Tel: 503-988-5355. Fax: 503-988-5145. p. 2012

Fearn, Shelley, Reader Serv, Union County Public Library, 316 E Windsor St, Monroe, NC, 28112. Tel: 704-283-8184. Fax: 704-282-0657. p. 1810

Fearnley, Meg, Librn, Brown Memorial Library, 78 W Main St, Bradford, NH, 03221-3308. Tel: 603-938-5562. p. 1439

Fearon, John, Dir, Mount Pleasant Public Library, 350 Bedford Rd, Pleasantville, NY, 10570-3099. Tel: 914-769-0548. Fax: 914-769-6149. p. 1719

Fears, Cynthia F, Circ Serv Coordr, Columbus State University Libraries, 4225 University Ave, Columbus, GA, 31907. Tel: 706-568-2042. Fax: 706-568-2084. p. 526

Feaster, Linda, Br Mgr, Ocean County Library, Long Beach Island Branch, 217 S Central Ave, Surf City, NJ, 08008-4800. Tel: 609-494-2480. Fax: 609-494-7850. p. 1534

Feathers, June, Asst Br Mgr, Sullivan County Public Library, 1655 Blountville Blvd, Blountville, TN, 37617. Tel: 423-279-2714. Fax: 423-279-2836. p. 2224

Fecho, Rachel, Br Mgr, Montgomery County-Norristown Public Library, Conshohocken Free Library, 301 Fayette St, Conshohocken, PA, 19428. Tel: 610-825-1656. Fax: 610-825-1685. p. 2098

Fechter, Dawn, Librn, Inglewood Public Library, 101 W Manchester Blvd, Inglewood, CA, 90301-1771. Tel: 310-412-5397. Fax: 310-412-8848. p. 159

Fecteau, Brenda, Tech Serv, Coventry Public Library, 1672 Flat River Rd, Coventry, RI, 02816. Tel: 401-822-6206. Fax: 401-822-9133. p. 2164

Fecteau, Lucie, Tech Serv, Commission des Normes du Travail, 400 blvd Jean-Lesage, 6th Flr, Quebec, QC, G1K 8W1, CANADA. Tel: 418-525-1661. Fax: 418-528-2219. p. 2904

Fedder, Mark, Dir, Manistee County Historical Museum, 425 River St, Manistee, MI, 49660. Tel: 231-723-5531. p. 1205

Feddern, Donna, Dir of Tech Serv, Escondido Public Library, 239 S Kalmia St, Escondido, CA, 92025. Tel: 760-839-4624. Fax: 760-741-4255. p. 146

Fedders, Shari, Dir, Boyden Public Library, 609 Webb St, Boyden, IA, 51234. Tel: 712-725-2281. Fax: 712-725-2224. p. 797

Fedeczko, Joyce, Info Res Dir, Group Technology Library & Information Services, 150 W Warrenville Rd, MC F1, Naperville, IL, 60563. Tel: 630-420-4850. Fax: 630-420-3697. p. 678

Federick, Neisha, Ref Asst, Texas A&M University-Texarkana, 7101 University Ave, Texarkana, TX, 75503. Tel: 903-223-3088. Fax: 903-334-6695. p. 2392

Federman, Barbara, Circ, Bryant Library, Two Paper Mill Rd, Roslyn, NY, 11576-2193. Tel: 516-621-2240. Fax: 516-621-7211. p. 1735

Federspiel, Beverly, Dir, City of Tonawanda Public Library, 333 Main St, Tonawanda, NY, 14150. Tel: 716-693-5043. Fax: 716-693-0825. p. 1755

Federspiel, Pamela W, Dir, Shelby County Public Library, 309 Eighth St, Shelbyville, KY, 40065. Tel: 502-633-3803. Fax: 502-633-4025. p. 935

Fedorijczuk, Jaroslaw, Regional Librn, Community College of Philadelphia Library, 1700 Spring Garden St, Philadelphia, PA, 19130. Tel: 215-751-8000. Fax: 215-751-8762. p. 2104

Fedorka, Katherine, Dir, Mansfield Public Library, Five Main St, Temple, NH, 03084. Tel: 603-878-3100. Fax: 603-878-0654. p. 1466

Fedors, Maurica, Mgr, Engelhard Corp, 25 Middlesex-Essex Tpk, Iselin, NJ, 08830. Tel: 732-205-5271. Fax: 732-205-6900. p. 1491

Fedynsky, Andrew, Dir, Ukrainian Museum-Archives Inc, 1202 Kenilworth Ave, Cleveland, OH, 44113. Tel: 216-781-4329. p. 1881

Fee, Kenny, In Charge, Wacker Silicones Corp, 3301 Sutton Rd, Adrian, MI, 49221. Tel: 517-264-8500. Fax: 517-264-8246. p. 1148

Fee, Victoria, Br Mgr, Albuquerque-Bernalillo County Library System, Los Griegos, 1000 Griegos Rd NW, Albuquerque, NM, 87107. Tel: 505-761-4020. Fax: 505-761-4014. p. 1548

Feehan, Corinne, Ch, D A Hurd Library, 41 High St, North Berwick, ME, 03906. Tel: 207-676-2215. Fax: 207-676-7976. p. 993

Feehan, Patricia E, Assoc Prof, University of South Carolina, 1501 Greene St, Columbia, SC, 29208. Tel: 803-777-3858. Fax: 803-777-7938. p. 2973

Feeley, Kathryn, Br Mgr, Cleveland Public Library, Garden Valley, 7201 Kinsman Rd, Ste 101, Cleveland, OH, 44104. Tel: 216-623-6976. Fax: 216-623-7186. p. 1878

Feeley, Kathryn, Br Mgr, Cleveland Public Library, Woodland, 5806 Woodland Ave, Cleveland, OH, 44104. Tel: 216-623-7109. Fax: 216-623-7113. p. 1878

Feeney, James, Jr, Circ, Boston Athenaeum, 10 1/2 Beacon St, Boston, MA, 02108-3777. Tel: 617-227-0270. Fax: 617-227-5266. p. 1056

Feeney, Rosemary S, Dir, Northport Historical Society, 215 Main St, Northport, NY, 11768. Tel: 631-757-9859. Fax: 631-757-9398. p. 1707

Feenker, Cherie, Acq, Samford University Library, Lucille Stewart Beeson Law Library, 800 Lakeshore Dr, Birmingham, AL, 35229. Tel: 205-726-2714. Fax: 205-726-2644. p. 9

Feeser, Sally, Libr Tech, HACC Central Pennsylvania's Community College, 731 Old Harrisburg Rd, Gettysburg, PA, 17325. Tel: 717-337-1644. Fax: 717-337-2329. p. 2060

Fegan, Maryanne, Tech Serv, Centenary College, 400 Jefferson St, Hackettstown, NJ, 07840. Tel: 908-852-1400, Ext 2345. Fax: 908-850-9528. p. 1489

Feher, Jennifer Lynn, Librn, Ashtabula County Law Library, County Courthouse, 25 W Jefferson St, Jefferson, OH, 44047. Tel: 440-576-3690. Fax: 440-576-1506. p. 1906

Fehr, Jacob, Head, Tech Serv, Tumbler Ridge Public Library, 340 Front St, Tumbler Ridge, BC, V0C 2W0, CANADA. Tel: 250-242-4778. Fax: 250-242-4707. p. 2739

Fehr, Sarah, Librn, Vauxhall Public Library, PO Box 265, Vauxhall, AB, T0K 2K0, CANADA. Tel: 403-654-2370. Fax: 403-654-2370. p. 2720

Fehr, Shelli R, Dir, River Valley District Library, 214 S Main St, Port Byron, IL, 61275-9501. Tel: 309-523-3440. Fax: 309-523-3516. p. 692

Fehr, Tanya, Asst Librn, Chinook Regional Library, Glentworth Branch, Glentworth School, Glentworth, SK, S0H 1V0, CANADA. Tel: 306-266-4804. p. 2928

Feht, Karen, Ch, Eldora Public Library, 1202 Tenth St, Eldora, IA, 50627. Tel: 641-939-2173. Fax: 641-939-7563. p. 813

Feicht, Therese, Asst Dir, Geauga County Public Library, 12701 Ravenwood Dr, Chardon, OH, 44024-1336. Tel: 440-286-6811, 440-564-7131, 440-834-1856. Fax: 440-286-7419. p. 1866

Feider, Lynn A, Dr, Dir, Lutheran Theological Southern Seminary, 4201 N Main St, Columbia, SC, 29203. Tel: 803-461-3220, 803-786-5150. Fax: 803-461-3278. p. 2188

Feigal, Carla, Dir, Jewell Public Library, 216 Delaware, Jewell, KS, 66949. Tel: 785-428-3630. Fax: 785-428-3630. p. 874

Feigenbaum, Phyllis, Tech Serv, Bethpage Public Library, 47 Powell Ave, Bethpage, NY, 11714-3197. Tel: 516-931-3907. Fax: 516-931-3926. p. 1581

Feild, Peggy, ILL & Distance Libr Serv Spec, Loyola-Notre Dame Library, Inc, 200 Winston Ave, Baltimore, MD, 21212. Tel: 410-617-6800. Fax: 410-617-6895. p. 1015

Feilmeyer, Kimberly, Ref, Hamline University, Bush Memorial Library, 1536 Hewitt, Saint Paul, MN, 55104. Tel: 651-523-2375. Fax: 651-523-2199. p. 1278

Fein, James, Dir, Libr Serv, Washington County Community College Library, One College Dr, Calais, ME, 04619. Tel: 207-454-1050. Fax: 207-454-1053. p. 980

Fein, Michael T, Coordr, Libr Serv, Central Virginia Community College Library, Amherst Hall, Rm 2506, 3506 Wards Rd, Lynchburg, VA, 24502-2498. Tel: 434-832-7751. Fax: 434-386-4677. p. 2475

Fein, Mollie, Mgr, Baltimore County Public Library, Randallstown Branch, 8604 Liberty Rd, Randallstown, MD, 21133-4797. Tel: 410-887-0770. Fax: 410-521-3614. p. 1044

Feinberg, Beth, Br Mgr, Los Angeles Public Library System, John C Fremont Branch, 6121 Melrose Ave, Los Angeles, CA, 90038-3339. Tel: 323-962-3521. Fax: 323-962-4553. p. 173

Feinberg, Elizabeth, Sr Librn, Hennepin County Library, Southdale, 7001 York Ave S, Edina, MN, 55435-4287. Tel: 612-543-5990. Fax: 612-543-5976. p. 1264

Feinberg, Richard, Ref Serv, Stony Brook University, W-1502 Melville Library, John S Toll Rd, Stony Brook, NY, 11794-3300. Tel: 631-632-7100. Fax: 631-632-7116. p. 1749

Feinberg, Sandra, Dir, Middle Country Public Library, 101 Eastwood Blvd, Centereach, NY, 11720. Tel: 631-585-9393, Ext 200. Fax: 631-585-5035. p. 1604

Feingold, Carol, Asst Librn, Anna Jaques Hospital, 25 Highland Ave, Newburyport, MA, 01950. Tel: 978-463-1000, Ext 2480. Fax: 978-463-1286. p. 1109

Feinman, Jessica, Libr Assoc, French Institute-Alliance Francaise Library, 22 E 60th St, New York, NY, 10022-1077. Tel: 646-388-6638. Fax: 212-935-4119. p. 1679

Feinman, Rachel, Cat, Coll Develop, Rhodes College, 2000 North Pkwy, Memphis, TN, 38112-1694. Tel: 901-843-3893. Fax: 901-843-3404. p. 2251

Feir, Susan, Dir, Hastings-on-Hudson Public Library, Seven Maple Ave, Hastings-on-Hudson, NY, 10706. Tel: 914-478-3307. Fax: 914-478-4813. p. 1634

Feis, Nathaniel, Cat & Acq, School of the Art Institute of Chicago, 37 S Wabash Ave, Chicago, IL, 60603-3103. Tel: 312-899-5097. Fax: 312-899-1851. p. 624

Feitzinger, Alicja, Dir, Copiague Memorial Public Library, 50 Deauville Blvd, Copiague, NY, 11726-4100. Tel: 631-691-1111. Fax: 631-691-5098. p. 1610

Feitzinger, Alicja, Asst Dir, Half Hollow Hills Community Library, 55 Vanderbilt Pkwy, Dix Hills, NY, 11746. Tel: 631-421-4530. Fax: 631-421-0730. p. 1615

Fekety, Peter, Librn, Fort Worth Library, Seminary South, 501 E Bolt St, Fort Worth, TX, 76110. Tel: 817-926-0215. Fax: 817-926-1703. p. 2322

Feland, Heather, Asst Curator, Higgins Armory Museum, 100 Barber Ave, Worcester, MA, 01606-2444. Tel: 508-853-6015, Ext 23. Fax: 508-852-7697. p. 1144

Felardo, Peter, Archivist, New York University, Tamiment Library/Robert F Wagner Labor Archives, Elmer Holmes Bobst Library, 70 Washington Sq S, 10th Flr, New York, NY, 10012. Tel: 212-998-2630. p. 1695

Felbel, Dennis, Librn, University of Manitoba Libraries, Albert D Cohen Management Library, 208 Drake Centre, 181 Freedman Crescent, Winnipeg, MB, R3T 5V4, CANADA. Tel: 202-474-9064. Fax: 204-474-7542. p. 2758

Felber, Sue, Coordr, H Lee Moffitt Cancer Center & Research Institute, 12902 Magnolia Dr, Tampa, FL, 33612. Tel: 813-745-7295. Fax: 813-745-3084. p. 497

Felchlin, Marva, Dir, Autry National Center, Autry Library, 4700 Western Heritage Way, Los Angeles, CA, 90027-1462. Tel: 323-667-2000, Ext 349. Fax: 323-660-5721. p. 168

Felchuk, Jane Ellen, Dir, North Judson-Wayne Township Public Library, 208 Keller Ave, North Judson, IN, 46366. Tel: 574-896-2841. Fax: 574-896-2892. p. 769

Feld, Norma, Asst Librn, Yeshiva University Libraries, Dr Lillian & Dr Rebecca Chutick Law Library, Benjamin N Cardozo School of Law, 55 Fifth Ave, New York, NY, 10003-4301. Tel: 212-790-0023. Fax: 212-790-0236. p. 1703

Feldbauer, Doris, Librn, Angelica Free Library, 55 W Main St, Angelica, NY, 14709. Tel: 585-466-7860. p. 1574

Felder, Jimmie, Dir, Hayneville-Lowndes County
Public Library, 215B Tuskeena St, Hayneville,
AL, 36040. Tel: 334-548-2686. Fax:
334-548-5427. p. 20

Felder, Timothy, Media Spec, Orangeburg-Calhoun
Technical College, 3250 Saint Matthews Rd NE,
Orangeburg, SC, 29118. Tel: 803-535-1262. Fax:
803-535-1240. p. 2201

Feldman, Adam, Ref Serv, AIDS Library, 1233
Locust St, 2nd Flr, Philadelphia, PA, 19107. Tel:
215-985-4851. Fax: 215-985-4492. p. 2102

Feldman, Irwin, Librn, Lake County Library,
Redbud, 14785 Burns Valley Rd, Clearlake,
CA, 95422-0600. Tel: 707-994-5115. Fax:
707-995-6012. p. 163

Feldman, Jonquil, Dir of Briscoe Libr & Outreach
Serv, University of Texas Health Science Center
at San Antonio Libraries, 7703 Floyd Curl Dr,
MSC 7940, San Antonio, TX, 78229-3900. Tel:
210-567-2400. Fax: 210-567-2490. p. 2383

Feldman, Lois, Tech Serv Mgr, Morris Area Public
Library District, 604 Liberty St, Morris, IL,
60450. Tel: 815-942-6880. Fax: 815-942-6415.
p. 675

Feldman, Sari, Exec Dir, Cuyahoga County
Public Library, 2111 Snow Rd, Parma,
OH, 44134-2728. Tel: 216-398-1800. Fax:
216-398-1748. p. 1927

Feldman-Joy, Barbara, Librn, Miami Dade
College, Kendall Campus Library, 11011
SW 104th St, Miami, FL, 33176-3393. Tel:
305-237-0996, 305-237-2015, 305-237-2291.
Fax: 305-237-2923. p. 466

Feldt, Candice, Tech Serv, Harvard Library, Eda
Kuhn Loeb Music Library, Music Bldg, Harvard
University, Cambridge, MA, 02138. Tel:
617-495-2794. Fax: 617-496-4636. p. 1076

Feldt, Pat, Br Mgr, Belleville Public Library, West
Branch, 3414 W Main St, Belleville, IL, 62226.
Tel: 618-233-4366. Fax: 618-233-1482. p. 593

Felice, Kayleigh, Outreach Librn, Bibliotheque
Municipale de Gatineau, Édifice Pierre Papin,
CP 1970 Succ. Hull, Gatineau, QC, J8X 3Y9,
CANADA. p. 2882

Feliciano, Ana M, ILL, Bayard Taylor Memorial
Library, 216 E State St, Kennett Square,
PA, 19348-3112. Tel: 610-444-2702. Fax:
610-444-1752. p. 2074

Feliu, Vinenc, Dir, University of the District of
Columbia, David A Clarke School of Law,
Charles N & Hilda H M Mason Law Library,
Bldg 39, Rm B-16, 4200 Connecticut Ave NW,
Washington, DC, 20008. Tel: 202-274-7354.
Fax: 202-274-7311. p. 421

Felix, Anne, Ref Serv, Grand Prairie Public Library
System, 901 Conover Dr, Grand Prairie, TX,
75051. Tel: 972-237-5700. Fax: 972-237-5750.
p. 2329

Felix, Deb, Assoc Dir, David & Joyce Milne
Public Library, 1095 Main St, Williamstown,
MA, 01267-2627. Tel: 413-458-5369. Fax:
413-458-3085. p. 1140

Felix, Lisa, Br Mgr, Mishawaka-Penn-Harris Public
Library, Bittersweet, 602 Bittersweet Rd,
Mishawaka, IN, 46544-4155. Tel: 574-259-0392,
Ext 223. Fax: 574-259-0399. p. 765

Felix, Loralyn O, Tech Serv Librn, Southern Utah
University, 351 W University Blvd, Cedar
City, UT, 84720. Tel: 435-586-7946. Fax:
435-865-8152. p. 2404

Felkner, Rebecca, Asst Dir, Grandview Heights
Public Library, 1685 W First Ave, Columbus,
OH, 43212. Tel: 614-486-2951. Fax:
614-481-7021. p. 1886

Fell, Gail, Ch, Greenburgh Public Library, 300
Tarrytown Rd, Elmsford, NY, 10523. Tel:
914-721-8200. Fax: 914-721-8201. p. 1620

Fell, Tony, Coordr, Grant Macewan College,
10700-104 Ave, 5-107B, Edmonton, AB, T5J
4S2, CANADA. Tel: 780-497-5274. Fax:
780-497-5385. p. 2977

Fell-Johnson, Barbara, Head Law Librn,
Massachusetts Trial Court, Courthouse, 99
Main St, Ste 1, Northampton, MA, 01060. Tel:
413-586-2297. Fax: 413-584-0870. p. 1113

Fellows, Mary, Youth & Family Serv, Upper
Hudson Library System, 28 Essex St, Albany,
NY, 12206. Tel: 518-437-9880, Ext 228. Fax:
518-437-9884. p. 1571

Fellows, Sharon, Historian, Cattaraugus County
Museum & Research Library, 9824 Rte 16,
Machias, NY, 14101. Tel: 716-353-8200. p. 1656

Fells, Bobbie, Acq Librn, Alcorn State University,
1000 ASU Dr, Alcorn State, MS, 39096-7500.
Tel: 601-877-6354. Fax: 601-877-3885. p. 1293

Fells, Matthew, Tech Serv, Simcoe County Archives,
1149 Hwy 26, RR 2, Minesing, ON, L0L 1Y2,
CANADA. Tel: 705-726-9300, Ext 1285. Fax:
705-725-5341. p. 2822

Felsten, Judith, Dir, RCS Community Library,
15 Mountain Rd, Ravena, NY, 12143. Tel:
518-756-2053. Fax: 518-756-8595. p. 1726

Felt, John, Head, Libr Tech, Head, Syst, Coastal
Carolina University, 755 Hwy 544, Conway, SC,
29526. Tel: 843-349-2402. Fax: 843-349-2412.
p. 2191

Felt, Linda, Asst Librn, Kirkland Public Library,
513 W Main St, Kirkland, IL, 60146. Tel:
815-522-6260. Fax: 815-522-6260. p. 661

Feltenberger, Rachel, Ch, Euless Public Library,
201 N Ector Dr, Euless, TX, 76039-3595. Tel:
617-685-1486. Fax: 817-267-1979. p. 2318

Feltes, Carol, Univ Librn, The Rockefeller
University, 1222 York Ave, Welch Hall, New
York, NY, 10065. Tel: 212-327-8909. Fax:
212-327-7349. p. 1698

Feltes, Mary Kay, Dir, Owatonna Public Library,
105 N Elm Ave, Owatonna, MN, 55060-2405.
Tel: 507-444-2460. Fax: 507-444-2465. p. 1270

Feltham, Kim, Info & Libr Mgr, Klohn Crippen
Berger Ltd, 2955 Virtual Way, Ste 500,
Vancouver, BC, V5M 4X6, CANADA. Tel:
604-251-8435. Fax: 604-669-3835. p. 2741

Felthousen, Robert, Ref Librn, Rogue Community
College, Wiseman Ctr, 3345 Redwood Hwy,
Grants Pass, OR, 97527. Tel: 541-956-7149.
Fax: 541-471-3588. p. 1999

Feltmann, Howard, Info Tech, Ref, Monmouth
Public Library, 168 S Ecols St, Monmouth, OR,
97361. Tel: 503-838-1932. Fax: 503-838-3899.
p. 2006

Felton, Alexandra, Emerging Tech Librn, Cochise
College Library, Andrea Cracchiolo Library, 901
N Colombo Ave, Sierra Vista, AZ, 85635. Tel:
520-515-5421. Fax: 520-515-5464. p. 61

Felton, Daniel, Chef de Div, Bibliothèques de
Montréal, Île-des-Soeurs, 260, rue Elgar,
Montreal, QC, H3E 1C9, CANADA. Tel:
514-732-7337. Fax: 514-765-7264. p. 2890

Felton, Daniel, Chef de Div, Bibliothèques de
Montréal, Verdun, 5955, rue Bannantyne,
Montreal, QC, H4H 1H6, CANADA. Tel:
514-765-7281. Fax: 514-765-7167. p. 2892

Felton, Marilyn, Librn, Copiah-Jefferson Regional
Library System, Jefferson County Library,
218 S Main St, Fayette, MS, 39069. Tel:
601-786-3982. Fax: 601-786-9646. p. 1301

Felty, Jayson L, Dir, Texas Biomedical Research
Institute, 7620 NW Loop 410, San Antonio, TX,
78227-5301. p. 2383

Felver, Richard, Ref Librn, Dartmouth College
Library, Feldberg Business Administration &
Engineering Library, 6193 Murdough Ctr,
Hanover, NH, 03755-3560. Tel: 603-646-2191.
Fax: 603-646-2384. p. 1450

Felver, Richard W, Distance & Off-Campus Serv,
Electronic Res, Southeastern University, 1000
Longfellow Blvd, Lakeland, FL, 33801. Tel:
863-667-5949. Fax: 863-669-4160. p. 460

Felx, Yolande, Tech Serv, Cegep de Saint-Laurent
Bibliotheque, 625 Boul Ste-Croix, Saint Laurent,
QC, H4L 3X7, CANADA. Tel: 514-747-6521.
Fax: 514-748-1249, 514-855-1942. p. 2909

Fen Pao, Yin, Assoc Dir, Info Serv, Gateway
Community & Technical College, Covington
Campus Library, 1025 Amsterdam Rd, Rm C
106, Covington, KY, 41011. Tel: 859-442-4148.
p. 911

Fender, Kimber L, Eva Jane Romaine Coombe
Dir, Public Library of Cincinnati & Hamilton
County, 800 Vine St, Cincinnati, OH,
45202-2009. Tel: 513-369-6972. Fax:
513-369-6993. p. 1871

Fendler, Robert, In Charge, Washington State
Library, Washington State Penitentiary Branch
Library-Medium, 1313 N 13th Ave, Walla Walla,
WA, 99362-1065. Tel: 509-525-3610, Ext 2088.
Fax: 509-526-6453. p. 2545

Fenelon, Pauline, Curator, Waseca County Historical
Society Library, 315 Second Ave NE, Waseca,
MN, 56093. Tel: 507-835-7700. p. 1287

Feng, Xia, Pub Serv Adminr, Youth Serv, New
Haven Free Public Library, 133 Elm St, New
Haven, CT, 06510. Tel: 203-946-2279. Fax:
203-946-8140. p. 355

Fenger, Michelle, Dir, Ronan City Library, 203 Main
St SW, Ronan, MT, 59864. Tel: 406-676-3682.
Fax: 406-676-3683. p. 1388

Fenger, Teresa, Dir, Liberty County Library, 100 E
First St, Chester, MT, 59522. Tel: 406-759-5445.
Fax: 406-759-5445. p. 1376

Fenimore, Jason, Ref Librn, Louis B Goodall
Memorial Library, 952 Main St, Sanford, ME,
04073. Tel: 207-324-4714. Fax: 207-324-5982.
p. 999

Fenn, Joann, Ch, Montrose Public Library, 202
Main St, Montrose, IA, 52639-0100. Tel:
319-463-5532. Fax: 319-463-5532. p. 833

Fennel, Troy, Supvr, California Department of
Corrections Library System, c/o The Office of
Correctional Education, 1515 S St, Sacramento,
CA, 95814-7243. Tel: 916-324-7504. Fax:
916-324-1416. p. 220

Fennell, Catherine, Exec Dir, Libr Serv, Rosemont
College Library, 1400 Montgomery Ave,
Rosemont, PA, 19010-1631. Tel: 610-527-0200,
Ext 2271. Fax: 610-525-2930. p. 2135

Fennell, Rose Ann, Coordr, Ch Serv, George H &
Laura E Brown Library, 122 Van Norden St,
Washington, NC, 27889. Tel: 252-946-4300.
Fax: 252-975-2015. p. 1828

Fennema, Audrey, Chief Librn, Fraser Lake Public
Library, 228 Endako Ave, Fraser Lake, BC,
V0J 1S0, CANADA. Tel: 250-699-8888. Fax:
250-699-8899. p. 2728

Fenner, Charlene, Libr Spec, Federal Reserve Bank
of Richmond, 701 E Byrd St, Richmond, VA,
23219. Tel: 804-697-8125. Fax: 804-697-8134.
p. 2488

Fennewald, Joseph A, Head Librn, Pennsylvania
State University, 76 University Dr, Hazleton,
PA, 18202-8025. Tel: 570-450-3172. Fax:
570-450-3128. p. 2068

Fenrick, Brad, Mgr, Info Tech, Fraser Valley
Regional Library, 34589 Delair Rd, Abbotsford,
BC, V2S 5Y1, CANADA. Tel: 604-859-7141.
Fax: 604-859-5701. p. 2723

Fenselau, Nanci Jeanne, Adult Serv, Allentown
Public Library, 1210 Hamilton St, Allentown,
PA, 18102. Tel: 610-820-2400. Fax:
610-820-0640. p. 2026

Fenske, David E, PhD, Dean, Drexel University,
Rush Bldg, Rm 306, 30 N 33rd St, Philadelphia,
PA, 19104-2875. Tel: 215-895-2474. Fax:
215-895-2494. p. 2972

Fenske, Fay, ILL, Bellingham Public Library, 210
Central Ave, CS-9710, Bellingham, WA,
98227-9710. Tel: 360-778-7323. p. 2508

Fensterstock, Laurie, Ch, Merrick Library, 2279
Merrick Ave, Merrick, NY, 11566-4398. Tel:
516-377-6112. Fax: 516-377-1108. p. 1659

Fenton, Diane, Librn, Garden Grove Public Library,
103 Main St, Garden Grove, IA, 50103. Tel:
641-443-2172. p. 817

Fenton, Elaine, Librn, Court of Appeals Eleventh
Circuit Library, 56 Forsyth St NW, Atlanta, GA,
30303. Tel: 404-335-6500. Fax: 404-335-6510.
p. 514

Fenton, Kim, Librn, Keuka College, 141 Central
Ave, Keuka Park, NY, 14478-0038. Tel:
315-279-5411. Fax: 315-279-5334. p. 1649

Fenton, Lori, Tech Librn, Washburn University, 1700 SW College Ave, Topeka, KS, 66621. Tel: 785-670-1984. Fax: 785-670-3223. p. 897

Fenton, Nicole L, Adminr, Dir, Garibaldi & Meucci Museum, 420 Tompkins Ave, Staten Island, NY, 10305. Tel: 718-442-1608. Fax: 718-442-8635. p. 1747

Fenwick, Brad, Hist Instr/Pub Serv Librn, Hutchinson Community College, 1300 N Plum St, Hutchinson, KS, 67501. Tel: 620-665-3338. Fax: 620-665-3392. p. 873

Fenwick, Elizabeth, Chief Exec Officer, Bradford-West Gwillimbury Public Library, 425 Holland St W, Bradford, ON, L3Z 0J2, CANADA. Tel: 905-775-3328. Fax: 905-775-1236. p. 2796

Fenwick, Melissa, Librn, Patoka Public Library, 210 W Bond St, Patoka, IL, 62875-1032. Tel: 618-432-5019. Fax: 618-432-5019. p. 689

Ferate-Soto, Paola, Managing Librn, Austin Public Library, Southeast Austin Community Branch, 5803 Nuckols Crossing Rd, Austin, TX, 78744. Tel: 512-462-1452. Fax: 512-447-7639. p. 2279

Ferber, Pamela Gibbs, Br Mgr, Porter County Public Library System, Hebron Public, 201 W Sigler St, Hebron, IN, 46341. Tel: 219-996-3684. Fax: 219-996-3680. p. 783

Ferber, Susan, Prog Coordr, West Nyack Free Library, 65 Strawtown Rd, West Nyack, NY, 10994. Tel: 845-358-6081. Fax: 845-358-4071. p. 1766

Ferchalk, Sheila, Dir, South Fork Public Library, 320 Main St, South Fork, PA, 15956-9998. Tel: 814-495-4812. Fax: 814-495-7369. p. 2142

Ferchedau, Stefania, Librn, Romanian Cultural Institute, 200 E 38th St, New York, NY, 10016. Tel: 212-687-0180. Fax: 212-687-0181. p. 1698

Ferdinand-Grant, Ita, Librn, George Brown College of Applied Arts & Technology, 160 Kendal Ave, Toronto, ON, M5R 1M3, CANADA. Tel: 416-415-5000, Ext 4635. Fax: 416-415-4765. p. 2853

Ferdula, Tammy-Jo, Dir, United States Navy, Base Library, Naval Submarine Base New London, Bldg 164, Groton, CT, 06349. Tel: 860-694-2578, 860-694-3723. Fax: 860-694-2578. p. 342

Ferencz, Sarah, Archivist, Whitby Public Library, Whitby Archives, 405 Dundas St W, Whitby, ON, L1N 6A1, CANADA. Tel: 905-668-6531, Ext 2023. p. 2871

Fereres-Moskowitz, Raquel, Project Coordr, Long Island Jewish Medical Center, 270-05 76th Ave, New Hyde Park, NY, 11040. Tel: 718-470-7070. Fax: 718-470-6150. p. 1665

Fergison, Drue, Dir, Lanesboro Public Library, 202 Parkway Ave S, Lanesboro, MN, 55949. Tel: 507-467-2649. Fax: 507-467-2346. p. 1256

Fergus, Judi, Dir, United Methodist Church - South Georgia Conference, Epworth-by-the-Sea, 100 Arthur Moore Dr, Saint Simons Island, GA, 31522. Tel: 912-638-4050. Fax: 912-638-9050. p. 549

Fergusen, Colleen, Asst Dir, Hearst Free Library, 401 Main St, Anaconda, MT, 59711. Tel: 406-563-6932. Fax: 406-563-5393. p. 1373

Ferguson, Amy, Instrul Serv Librn, Richland College Library, 12800 Abrams Rd, Dallas, TX, 75243-2199. Tel: 972-238-6081. p. 2309

Ferguson, Ann, Curator, Bonner County Historical Society, 611 S Ella Ave, Sandpoint, ID, 83864. Tel: 208-263-2344. p. 583

Ferguson, Barb, ILL, Franklin Public Library, 421 12th St, Franklin, PA, 16323-0421. Tel: 814-432-5062. Fax: 814-432-8998. p. 2058

Ferguson, Barb, Br Head, Toronto Public Library, Davenport, 1246 Shaw St, Toronto, ON, M6G 3P1, CANADA. Tel: 416-393-7732. Fax: 416-393-7588. p. 2861

Ferguson, Barbara, Admin Dir, Eva K Bowlby Public Library, 311 N West St, Waynesburg, PA, 15370-1238. Tel: 724-627-9776. Fax: 724-852-1900. p. 2152

Ferguson, Benjamin, Syst Spec, Valley City State University Library, 101 College St SW, Valley City, ND, 58072-4098. Tel: 701-845-7276. Fax: 701-845-7437. p. 1848

Ferguson, Bernice, Librn, Carnegie Regional Library, Michigan Public, PO Box 331, Michigan, ND, 58259. Tel: 701-259-2122. p. 1842

Ferguson Cavanaugh, Joanne, Br Mgr, Omaha Public Library, Charles B Washington Branch, 2868 Ames Ave, Omaha, NE, 68111–2426. Tel: 402-444-4849. Fax: 402-444-6658. p. 1414

Ferguson, Chris, Assoc Provost, Info & Tech Serv, Pacific Lutheran University, 12180 Park Ave S, Tacoma, WA, 98447-0001. Tel: 253-535-7500. Fax: 253-535-7315. p. 2539

Ferguson, Cris, Electronic Res, Furman University Libraries, 3300 Poinsett Hwy, Greenville, SC, 29613-4100. Tel: 864-294-2713. Fax: 864-294-3004. p. 2195

Ferguson, Cristie, Distance Educ, Panola College, 1109 W Panola St, Carthage, TX, 75633. Tel: 903-693-2091. Fax: 903-693-1115. p. 2295

Ferguson, Donna, Tech Coordr, Sequoyah Regional Library System, 116 Brown Industrial Pkwy, Canton, GA, 30114-2899. Tel: 770-479-3090, Ext 221. Fax: 770-479-3069. p. 523

Ferguson, Frank, Mgr, Network Serv, Plymouth District Library, 223 S Main St, Plymouth, MI, 48170-1687. Tel: 734-453-0750, Ext 239. Fax: 734-453-0733. p. 1218

Ferguson, Irene, Asst Librn, Atlantic Baptist University, 333 Gorge Rd, Moncton, NB, E1C 3H9, CANADA. Tel: 506-863-6443. Fax: 506-858-9694. p. 2765

Ferguson, Jean, Head, Res & Ref Serv, Duke University Libraries, 411 Chapel Dr, Durham, NC, 27708. Tel: 919-660-5928. Fax: 919-660-5923. p. 1787

Ferguson, Jen, Asst Head, Res & Instruction, Sci & Data Serv, Northeastern University Libraries, Snell Library, 360 Huntington Ave, Boston, MA, 02115. Tel: 617-373-3853. p. 1065

Ferguson, Jennifer, Librn, Simmons College, Miller/Knopf Career Resource Library, One Palace Rd, Rm P304E, Boston, MA, 02115. Tel: 617-521-2742. Fax: 617-521-3093. p. 1067

Ferguson, Jennifer, Ref Librn, Rivier College, 420 S Main St, Nashua, NH, 03060-5086. Tel: 603-897-8673. Fax: 603-897-8889. p. 1459

Ferguson, Jessame, Dir, McDaniel College, Two College Hill, Westminster, MD, 21157-4390. Tel: 410-857-2281. Fax: 410-857-2748. p. 1046

Ferguson, Kathleen, Pub Serv, Ridley Township Public Library, 100 E MacDade Blvd, Folsom, PA, 19033-2592. Tel: 610-583-0593. Fax: 610-583-9505. p. 2057

Ferguson, Kim, Librn II, Northern Maine Community College Library, 33 Edgemont Dr, Presque Isle, ME, 04769-2016. Tel: 207-768-2735. Fax: 207-768-2823. p. 998

Ferguson, Kimberly, Head, Ref, United States Senate Library, SRB-15 Senate Russell Bldg, Washington, DC, 20510-7112. Tel: 202-224-7106. Fax: 202-224-0879. p. 421

Ferguson, Marion, Circ Librn, Texas Southern University, 3100 Cleburne Ave, Houston, TX, 77004. Tel: 713-313-4417. Fax: 713-313-1080. p. 2342

Ferguson, Mark, Dir, Rec Mgt, National Archives & Records Administration, Denver Federal Ctr, Bldg 48, W Sixth Ave & Kipling St, Denver, CO, 80225-0307. Tel: 303-407-5740. Fax: 303-407-5707. p. 302

Ferguson, Mark, Head, Ser Acq, Per, College of Saint Elizabeth, Two Convent Rd, Morristown, NJ, 07960-6989. Tel: 973-290-4237. Fax: 973-290-4226. p. 1504

Ferguson, Mary, Info Serv, Canada Institute for Scientific & Technical Information, National Research Council of Canada, 717 White Lake Rd, Penticton, BC, V2A 6J9, CANADA. Tel: 250-497-2311. Fax: 250-493-7767. p. 2735

Ferguson, Neal, Dir, Libr Serv, Borden Ladner Gervais LLP, World Exchange Plaza, 100 Queen St, Ste 1100, Ottawa, ON, K1P 1J9, CANADA. Tel: 613-787-3553. Fax: 613-230-8842. p. 2828

Ferguson, Pat, Spec Coll Librn, Shreve Memorial Library, 424 Texas St, Shreveport, LA, 71101. Tel: 318-226-5888. Fax: 318-226-4780. p. 969

Ferguson, Paul, Curator, Chilliwack Museum & Historical Society, 45820 Spadina Ave, Chilliwack, BC, V2P 1T3, CANADA. Tel: 604-795-5210, 604-795-9255. Fax: 604-795-5291. p. 2726

Ferguson, Robert, Data Officer, Washington State University Libraries, 100 Dairy Rd, Pullman, WA, 99164. Tel: 509-335-2520. Fax: 509-335-6721. p. 2525

Ferguson, Sarah, Dean, Brookhaven College, 3939 Valley View, Farmers Branch, TX, 75244-4997. Tel: 972-860-4854. Fax: 972-860-4675. p. 2319

Ferguson, Sharon, Acq, Catawba College, 2300 W Innes St, Salisbury, NC, 28144-2488. Tel: 704-637-4224. Fax: 704-637-4304. p. 1822

Ferguson, Stephen, Asst Univ Librn, Rare Bks & Spec Coll, Curator, Rare Bks, Princeton University, One Washington Rd, Princeton, NJ, 08544-2098. Tel: 609-258-3165. Fax: 609-258-0441. p. 1523

Ferguson, Teresa, Tech Serv Mgr, Tigard Public Library, 13500 SW Hall Blvd, Tigard, OR, 97223-8111. Tel: 503-684-6537, Ext 2505. Fax: 503-598-7515, 503-718-2797. p. 2021

Ferguson, Terry, Librn, Montana State Hospital Library, 151 Blizzard Way, Warm Springs, MT, 59756. Tel: 406-693-7133. Fax: 406-693-7127. p. 1390

Ferguson, Victoria, Br Adminr, Noble County Public Library, East, 104 Ley St, Avilla, IN, 46710. Tel: 260-897-3900. Fax: 260-897-3900. p. 723

Fergusson, David G, Dep Dir, Forsyth County Public Library, 660 W Fifth St, Winston-Salem, NC, 27101. Tel: 336-703-3015. Fax: 336-727-2549. p. 1832

Fergusson, Eden, Dir, Raynham Public Library, 760 S Main St, Raynham, MA, 02767. Tel: 508-823-1344. Fax: 508-824-0494. p. 1120

Ferier, Lawana, Ch, Humboldt County Library, 85 E Fifth St, Winnemucca, NV, 89445. Tel: 775-623-6388. Fax: 775-623-6438. p. 1435

Ferimer, Suzanne, Librn, University of Houston, Optometry Library, 505 J Davis Armistead Bldg, Houston, TX, 77204-2020. Tel: 713-743-1912. Fax: 713-743-2001. p. 2343

Ferington, Karen, Cat, Niagara County Community College, 3111 Saunders Settlement Rd, Sanborn, NY, 14132. Tel: 716-614-6787. Fax: 716-614-6816, 716-614-6828. p. 1737

Ferkol, Holly, Br Mgr, Willoughby-Eastlake Public Library, Willoughby Hills Branch, 35400 Chardon Rd, Willoughby Hills, OH, 44094. Tel: 440-942-3362. Fax: 440-942-3780. p. 1949

Ferkovich, Kelly, Tech Serv, Legacy Good Samaritan Hospital & Medical Center, 1015 NW 22nd Ave, Portland, OR, 97210. Tel: 503-413-7335. Fax: 503-413-8016. p. 2011

Ferland, Benoit, Dir, Bibliotheque et Archives nationales du Quebec, 475 de Maisonneuve E, Montreal, QC, H2L 5C4, CANADA. Tel: 514-873-1101, Ext 3752. Fax: 514-873-9312. p. 2888

Ferland, Denise, Librn, Bibliotheque Municipale, 530 Delage St, Office 102, Lac Saint-Charles, QC, G3G 1J2, CANADA. Tel: 418-641-6121. Fax: 419-849-2849. p. 2885

Ferland, Denise, In Charge, Bibliotheque Gabrielle-Roy, Bibliothèque Le Tournesol, 530, rue Delage, Quebec, QC, G3G 1J2, CANADA. Tel: 418-641-6121. p. 2903

Ferland, Line, Chef de Div, Bibliothèques de Montrèal, La Petite-Patrie, 6707, avenue De Lorimier, Montreal, QC, H2G 2P8, CANADA. Tel: 514-872-6557. Fax: 514-872-0526. p. 2890

Ferland, Line, Chef de Div, Bibliothèques de Montrèal, Rosemont, 3131, boulevard Rosemont, Montreal, QC, H1Y 1M4, CANADA. Tel: 514-872-6557. Fax: 514-872-0527. p. 2891

Ferlito, Carol, Dir, Oswego School District Public Library, 120 E Second St, Oswego, NY, 13126. Tel: 315-341-5867. Fax: 315-216-6492. p. 1713

Fermanich, Becky, Youth Serv Librn, Delta Township District Library, 5130 Davenport Dr, Lansing, MI, 48917-2040. Tel: 517-321-4014. Fax: 517-321-2080. p. 1200

Fermano, Lorraine, Sr Libr Asst, Millis Public Library, 25 Auburn Rd, Millis, MA, 02054-1203. Tel: 508-376-8282. Fax: 508-376-1278. p. 1106

Fernald, Jonathan, Coordr, Libr Serv, College of the Desert Library, 43-500 Monterey, Palm Desert, CA, 92260. Tel: 760-679-3775. Fax: 760-568-5955. p. 203

Fernandez, Angela, Libr Supvr-Popular Libr, Seneca Nation Library, 830 Broad St, Salamanca, NY, 14779. Tel: 716-945-3157. Fax: 716-945-9770. p. 1737

Fernandez, Belen, Dir, Franklin University Library, Phillips Hall, 1st Flr, 303 S Grant Ave, Columbus, OH, 43215. Tel: 614-341-6252. Fax: 614-461-0957. p. 1886

Fernandez, Belen C, Dir, Libr Serv, Capital University, One College & Main, Columbus, OH, 43209. Tel: 614-236-6241. Fax: 614-236-6490. p. 1883

Fernandez, Carmen, Librn, Neuse Regional Library, Pink Hill Public Library, 114 W Broadway, Pink Hill, NC, 28572. Tel: 252-568-3631. Fax: 252-568-3631. p. 1805

Fernandez, Dorthy, Libr Assoc, Northwestern State University Libraries, 1800 Line Ave, Shreveport, LA, 71101. Tel: 318-677-3007. Fax: 318-676-7087. p. 968

Fernandez, Jacqueline Lauren, Asst Dir, Albuquerque-Bernalillo County Library System, 501 Copper Ave NW, Albuquerque, NM, 87102. Tel: 505-768-5113. Fax: 505-768-5191. p. 1548

Fernandez, Joyce, Tech Serv, Sierra Vista Public Library, 2600 E Tacoma, Sierra Vista, AZ, 85635-1399. Tel: 520-458-4225. Fax: 520-458-5377. p. 82

Fernandez, Karen, Ref Librn, Highline Community College Library, 2400 S 240th St, MS 25-4, Des Moines, WA, 98198. Tel: 206-878-3710, Ext 3809. Fax: 206-870-3776. p. 2514

Fernandez, Leila, Head Librn, York University Libraries, Steacie Science & Engineering Library, 4700 Keele St, Toronto, ON, M3J 1P3, CANADA. Tel: 416-736-5639. Fax: 416-736-5452. p. 2868

Fernandez, Linda, Pub Serv, Pocono Mountain Public Library, 5540 Memorial Blvd, Tobyhanna, PA, 18466. Tel: 570-894-8860. Fax: 570-894-8852. p. 2146

Fernandez, Natalia, Multicultural Librn, Oregon State University Libraries, University Archives & Special Collections, 121 Valley Library, Corvallis, OR, 97331-4501. Tel: 541-737-2195. Fax: 541-737-3453. p. 1994

Fernandez, Peter, Ref Serv Librn, University of Tennessee, Knoxville, Agriculture-Veterinary Medicine, A-113 Veterinary Teaching Hospital, 2407 Joe Johnson Dr, Knoxville, TN, 37996-4541. Tel: 865-974-2886. Fax: 865-974-4732. p. 2244

Fernandez, R, Info Tech Spec, United States Air Force, 36 FSS/FSDL (FL 5240), Unit 14004, Box 28, APO AP, GU, 96543-4004. Tel: 671-366-4291. Fax: 671-366-2728. p. 2667

Fernandez, Susana, Dir, Chetco Community Public Library, 405 Alder St, Brookings, OR, 97415. Tel: 541-469-7738. Fax: 541-469-6746. p. 1992

Fernandez, Valerie, In Charge, Southern California University of Health Sciences, 16200 E Amber Valley Dr, Whittier, CA, 90604-4098. Tel: 562-947-8755, Ext 367. Fax: 562-902-3323. p. 283

Fernandez, Zenaida, Dir, Libr Serv, Miami Dade College, Wolfson Campus Library, 300 NE Second Ave, Miami, FL, 33132. Tel: 305-237-3452. Fax: 305-237-3707. p. 466

Fernandez-Baybay, Carmen, Admin Serv, University of San Francisco, 2130 Fulton St, San Francisco, CA, 94117-1080. Tel: 415-422-2035. Fax: 415-422-5949. p. 248

Fernandez-Keys, Alba, Head, Libr & Archives, Indianapolis Museum of Art, 4000 Michigan Rd, Indianapolis, IN, 46208-3326. Tel: 317-920-2647. Fax: 317-926-8931. p. 754

Fernando, Lane, Libr Tech, La Conner Regional Library, 614 Morris St, La Conner, WA, 98257. Tel: 360-466-3352. Fax: 360-466-9178. p. 2519

Fernitz, Kristin, Dir, Strasburg-Heisler Library, 143 Precision Ave, Strasburg, PA, 17579. Tel: 717-687-8969. Fax: 717-687-9795. p. 2143

Ferraccioli, Diane, ILL, Broome Community College, 907 Front St, Binghamton, NY, 13905-1328. Tel: 607-778-5376. Fax: 607-778-5108. p. 1581

Ferrance, Christal, Ref Librn, Central New Mexico Community College Libraries, 525 Buena Vista SE, Albuquerque, NM, 87106-4023. Tel: 505-224-3292. Fax: 505-224-3321. p. 1548

Ferrante, Michael, Head, Tech Serv, Johnson Free Public Library, 274 Main St, Hackensack, NJ, 07601-5797. Tel: 201-343-4169. Fax: 201-343-1395. p. 1489

Ferrante, Michael, Syst Librn, Franklin Township Free Public Library, 485 DeMott Lane, Somerset, NJ, 08873. Tel: 732-873-8700. Fax: 732-873-0746. p. 1529

Ferrara, Connie, Ref Serv, American River College Library, 4700 College Oak Dr, Sacramento, CA, 95841. Tel: 916-484-8455. Fax: 916-484-8018, 916-484-8657. p. 220

Ferrara, Marie, Spec Coll Librn, College of Charleston, 205 Calhoun St, Charleston, SC, 29401-3519. Tel: 843-953-5530. Fax: 843-953-6319. p. 2184

Ferrare, Carolina, Circ Mgr, Craft Memorial Library, 600 Commerce St, Bluefield, WV, 24701. Tel: 304-325-3943. Fax: 304-325-3702. p. 2555

Ferrari, Ann, Librn, Jefferson Regional Medical Center, Coal Valley Rd, Pittsburgh, PA, 15236. Tel: 412-469-5786. Fax: 412-469-5468. p. 2125

Ferrari, Michele, Ch, Islip Public Library, 71 Monell Ave, Islip, NY, 11751-3999. Tel: 631-581-5933. Fax: 631-277-8429. p. 1641

Ferrari, Sheila, Head, Youth Serv, Maywood Public Library District, 121 S Fifth Ave, Maywood, IL, 60153. Tel: 708-343-1847, Ext 24. Fax: 708-343-2115. p. 672

Ferraro, Deborah, Ch, Orange Public Library, 348 Main St, Orange, NJ, 07050-2794. Tel: 973-673-0153, Ext 15. Fax: 973-673-1847. p. 1516

Ferraro, Gail, ILL Librn, Exeter Public Library, Four Chestnut St, Exeter, NH, 03833. Tel: 603-772-3101, 603-772-6036. Fax: 603-772-7548. p. 1447

Ferraro, Linda, YA Serv, Amityville Public Library, Oak & John Sts, Amityville, NY, 11701. Tel: 631-264-0567. Fax: 631-264-2006. p. 1573

Ferrazza, Pamela, Circ Mgr, Shaker Heights Public Library, 16500 Van Aken Blvd, Shaker Heights, OH, 44120-5318. Tel: 216-991-2030. Fax: 216-991-5951. p. 1934

Ferreira, Ana Lidia, Br Supvr, Truckee Meadows Community College, Hi-Tech Center at Redfield, 18600 Wedge Pkwy, Bldg B, Reno, NV, 89511. Tel: 775-850-4049. Fax: 775-850-4030. p. 1433

Ferreira, Ana Lidia, Br Supvr, Truckee Meadows Community College, Meadowood Library, 5270 Neil Rd, Reno, NV, 89502. Tel: 775-850-4049. Fax: 775-850-4030. p. 1433

Ferrell, Betty, Librn, Beaufort County Community College Library, Hwy 264 E, Washington, NC, 27889. Tel: 252-940-6253. Fax: 252-946-9575. p. 1828

Ferrell, Janet, In Charge, United States Navy, General Library, Naval Support Facility-S Potomac, Strauss Ave, Bldg 620, Indian Head, MD, 20640. Tel: 301-744-4747. Fax: 301-744-4386. p. 1033

Ferrell, Lynne, Coordr, Libr Serv, Memorial Medical Center, 701 N First St, Springfield, IL, 62781-0001. Tel: 217-788-3331. Fax: 217-788-5540. p. 706

Ferrell, Lynne, Librn & Archivist, Schnepp Professional Library, Memorial Medical Ctr, 701 N First St, Springfield, IL, 62781. Tel: 217-788-3331. p. 706

Ferrell, Susan, Adult Serv, Shelby Township Library, 51680 Van Dyke, Shelby Township, MI, 48316-4448. Tel: 586-739-7414. Fax: 586-726-0535. p. 1227

Ferrell, Susan, Info Syst Tech, Southern West Virginia Community & Technical College, 3505 Daniel Boone Pkwy, Danville, WV, 25053. Tel: 304-369-2952, Ext 18. Fax: 304-369-2954. p. 2558

Ferrell, Travis, Supvry Librn, United States Army, Bruce C Clarke Library Academic Services Division, Bldg 3202, 597 Manscen Loop, Ste 200, Fort Leonard Wood, MO, 65473-8928. Tel: 573-563-4109. Fax: 573-563-4118. p. 1328

Ferren, Eileen, Asst Librn, Red Rock Public Library Board, 42 Salls St, Red Rock, ON, P0T 2P0, CANADA. Tel: 807-886-2558. Fax: 807-886-2558. p. 2838

Ferren, Emily, Dir, Charles County Public Library, Two Garrett Ave, La Plata, MD, 20646-5959. Tel: 301-934-9001. Fax: 301-934-2297. p. 1033

Ferrer, Daniel, Head, Syst, Central Michigan University, Park 407, Mount Pleasant, MI, 48859. Tel: 989-774-3500. Fax: 989-774-2179. p. 1211

Ferrer-Vincent, Ignacio, Sci Res & Instruction Librn, Auraria Library, 1100 Lawrence St, Denver, CO, 80204-2095. Tel: 303-556-4919. Fax: 303-556-3528. p. 298

Ferrer-Vinent, Susan, Cat Librn, Mgr, Denver Art Museum Library, 414 14th St, Denver, CO, 80204-2788. Tel: 720-913-0100. Fax: 720-913-0001. p. 300

Ferretti, Stephanie, Assoc Dir, Philadelphia College of Osteopathic Medicine, 4170 City Ave, Philadelphia, PA, 19131-1694. Tel: 215-871-6475. Fax: 215-871-6478. p. 2114

Ferriby, Martha, Dir, Hackley Public Library, 316 W Webster Ave, Muskegon, MI, 49440. Tel: 231-722-7276. Fax: 231-726-5567. p. 1212

Ferriby, P Gavin, PhD, Univ Librn, Sacred Heart University, 5151 Park Ave, Fairfield, CT, 06825-1000. Tel: 203-396-8283. Fax: 203-374-9968. p. 339

Ferrier, Douglass, Dir, Texas A&M International University, 5201 University Blvd, Laredo, TX, 78041-1900. Tel: 956-326-2400. Fax: 956-326-2399. p. 2354

Ferrier, Judy, Librn, Sedgewick Municipal Library, 5301 51st Ave, Sedgewick, AB, T0B 4C0, CANADA. Tel: 780-384-3003. Fax: 780-384-3003. p. 2716

Ferrier, Kayne, Librn, Grand Rapids Public Library, Yankee Clipper, 2025 Leonard NE, Grand Rapids, MI, 49505. Tel: 616-988-5415. Fax: 616-235-8349. p. 1185

Ferrill, Win, Curator, Lakewood's Heritage Center Library, 801 S Yarrow St, Lakewood, CO, 80226. Tel: 303-987-7850. Fax: 303-987-7851. p. 315

Ferris, Janice, Pub Serv, Rogers State University Library, 1701 W Will Rogers Blvd, Claremore, OK, 74017-3252. Tel: 918-343-7716. Fax: 918-343-7720. p. 1960

Ferris, Mary, Ch, Wood Library Association of Canandaigua, 134 N Main St, Canandaigua, NY, 14424-1295. Tel: 585-394-1381. Fax: 585-394-2954. p. 1601

Ferris, Pam, ILL, La Grange Public Library, Ten W Cossitt Ave, La Grange, IL, 60525. Tel: 708-352-0576, Ext 13. p. 662

Ferris, Valerie, Libr Asst, Calef Memorial Library, 2964 VT Rte 110, Washington, VT, 05675. Tel: 802-883-2343. Fax: 802-883-9387. p. 2438

Ferriss, Jeannie, Librn, Yellowstone Baptist College, 1515 S Shiloh Rd, Billings, MT, 59106. Tel: 406-656-9950. p. 1375

Ferriss, Jennifer, Tech Serv, Southern Adirondack Library System, 22 Whitney Pl, Saratoga Springs, NY, 12866-4596. Tel: 518-584-7300. Fax: 518-587-5589. p. 1739

Ferritti, Elisabete, Dir, New York Institute of Technology, 1855 Broadway, New York, NY, 10023. Tel: 212-261-1526. Fax: 212-261-1681. p. 1689

Ferro, Jen, Ref Serv, Lane Community College Library, 4000 E 30th Ave, Eugene, OR, 97405-0640. Tel: 541-463-5825. Fax: 541-463-4150. p. 1996

Ferro, Pat John, Br Mgr, Clifton Public Library, Allwood Branch, 44 Lyall Rd, Clifton, NJ, 07012. Tel: 973-471-0555. Fax: 973-471-9284. p. 1479

Ferro, Williams, Mat Mgt & Automated Serv, Hewlett-Woodmere Public Library, 1125 Broadway, Hewlett, NY, 11557-0903. Tel: 516-374-1967. Fax: 516-569-1229. p. 1636

Ferry, Barbara, Dir, Libr & Info Serv, National Geographic Society Library, 1146 16th St NW, Washington, DC, 20036. Tel: 202-857-7783. Fax: 202-429-5731. p. 410

Ferry, Betsy, Dir, Franklin Public Library, 118 Main St, Franklin, MA, 02038. Tel: 508-520-4940. p. 1090

Ferry, Janet, ILL, State University of New York at Fredonia, 280 Central Ave, Fredonia, NY, 14063. Tel: 716-673-3194. Fax: 716-673-3185. p. 1624

Ferstman, Leonard, Librn, University of Toronto Libraries, Innis College Library, Two Sussex Ave, Toronto, ON, M5S 1J5, CANADA. Tel: 416-978-4497. Fax: 416-946-0168. p. 2866

Fertig, Hinde, Asst Dir, Baker College of Clinton Township Library, 34950 Little Mack Ave, Clinton Township, MI, 48035-4701. Tel: 586-790-9584. Fax: 586-791-0967. p. 1163

Fertik, Emily S, Exec Dir, Wenham Museum, 132 Main St, Wenham, MA, 01984. Tel: 978-468-2377. Fax: 978-468-1763. p. 1136

Fertitta, Lee, Adult Serv, Port Washington Public Library, One Library Dr, Port Washington, NY, 11050. Tel: 516-883-4400. Fax: 516-883-7927. p. 1721

Ferverda, Cheryl, Mgr, Communications & Develop, Allen County Public Library, 900 Library Plaza, Fort Wayne, IN, 46802. Tel: 260-421-1265. Fax: 260-421-1386. p. 740

Feryok, Catherine, Tech Serv, Moundsville-Marshall County Public Library, 700 Fifth St, Moundsville, WV, 26041-1993. Tel: 304-845-6911. Fax: 304-845-6912. p. 2567

Feryok, J Allen, Doc, ILL, Tech Serv, Monessen Public Library & District Center, 326 Donner Ave, Monessen, PA, 15062-1182. Tel: 724-684-4750. Fax: 724-684-7077. p. 2091

Fescemyer, Kathy, Librn, Pennsylvania State University Libraries, Life Sciences, 401 Paterno Library, University Park, PA, 16802-1811. Tel: 814-865-3703. p. 2148

Fesemyer, Cindy, Dir, Columbus Public Library, 223 W James St, Columbus, WI, 53925-1572. Tel: 920-623-5910. Fax: 920-623-5928. p. 2586

Fesmire, Tom, Head, Info Mgt, Liberty University Library, 1971 University Blvd, Lynchburg, VA, 24502. Tel: 434-592-3356. Fax: 434-582-2728. p. 2476

Fesnak, Vera, Head, Circ, Wilfrid Laurier University Library, 75 University Ave W, Waterloo, ON, N2L 3C5, CANADA. Tel: 519-884-0710, Ext 3413. Fax: 519-884-3209. p. 2869

Fessenden, Ann T, Dir, United States Court of Appeals Library, Thomas F Eagleton US Courthouse, 111 S Tenth St, Rm 22-300, Saint Louis, MO, 63102. Tel: 314-244-2665. Fax: 314-244-2675. p. 1361

Fessler, Jessica, Ref Librn, Chesapeake Public Library, Greenbrier, 1214 Volvo Pkwy, Chesapeake, VA, 23320-7600. Tel: 757-410-7068. Fax: 757-410-7071. p. 2456

Fetch, Deborah, Database/Network Serv Librn, Austin Peay State University, 601 E College St, Clarksville, TN, 37044. Tel: 931-221-7617. Fax: 931-221-7296. p. 2228

Fetscher, Virginia, Actg Dir, Head, Tech Serv, Katonah Village Library, 26 Bedford Rd, Katonah, NY, 10536-2121. Tel: 914-232-3508. Fax: 914-232-0415. p. 1648

Fetter, Wayne, Dean, McNeese State University, 4205 Ryan St, Lake Charles, LA, 70605. Tel: 337-475-5432. Fax: 337-475-5467. p. 2966

Fetterlund, Susan, Librn, Palm Beach State College, 3160 PGA Blvd, Palm Beach Gardens, FL, 33410-2893. Tel: 561-207-5800. Fax: 561-207-5805. p. 479

Fetters, Val, Ch, Edwin A Bemis Public Library, 6014 S Datura St, Littleton, CO, 80120-2636. Tel: 303-795-3961. Fax: 303-795-3996. p. 316

Fetty, Stephanie, Asst Librn, Cat, Ch, Quitman Public Library, 202 East Goode St, Quitman, TX, 75783-2533. Tel: 903-763-4191. Fax: 903-763-2532. p. 2373

Fetty, William, Dir, University of South Carolina at Union Library, 309 E Academy St, Union, SC, 29379-1932. Tel: 864-429-8728. Fax: 864-427-3682. p. 2207

Fetzer, Mary, Actg Assoc Univ Librn, Res & Instrul Serv, Rutgers University Libraries, 169 College Ave, New Brunswick, NJ, 08901-1163. Tel: 732-932-7129, Ext 121. Fax: 732-932-7637. p. 1508

Fetzer, Mary, Actg Assoc Univ Librn, Rutgers University Libraries, Chemistry Library, Wright-Rieman Laboratories, 610 Taylor Rd, Piscataway, NJ, 08854-8066. Tel: 732-932-7129, Ext 121. Fax: 732-445-3255. p. 1508

Feucht, Geri, Dir, Horicon Public Library, 404 E Lake St, Horicon, WI, 53032-1297. Tel: 920-485-3535. Fax: 920-485-3536. p. 2598

Feuerhelm, Heidi, Ch, Murphy Memorial Library, 111 N Page, Monona, IA, 52159-0430. Tel: 563-539-2356. Fax: 563-539-2306. p. 832

Feustle, Maristella, Supvr, AV Serv & Coll, Southern Methodist University, Hamon Arts Library, 6101 N Bishop Blvd, Dallas, TX, 75275. Tel: 214-768-1855. Fax: 214-768-1800. p. 2310

Fewell, Rachel, Mgr, Coll Serv, Denver Public Library, Ten W 14th Ave Pkwy, Denver, CO, 80204-2731. Tel: 720-865-1111. Fax: 720-865-2087. p. 300

Fewell, Rachel, Sr Librn, Denver Public Library, Montbello, 12955 Albrook Dr, Denver, CO, 80239-4704. Tel: 303-373-0767. Fax: 303-371-3542. p. 301

Fey, Helen, Pres, San Antonio Art League & Museum, 130 King William St, San Antonio, TX, 78204. Tel: 210-223-1140. p. 2381

Feyl, Steven, Assoc Univ Librn, Pace University, 861 Bedford Rd, Pleasantville, NY, 10570-2799. Tel: 914-773-3233. Fax: 914-773-3508. p. 1719

Feynman, Eileen, Cat, Coll Develop, Ref, Lindenhurst Memorial Library, One Lee Ave, Lindenhurst, NY, 11757-5399. Tel: 631-957-7755. Fax: 631-957-7114. p. 1652

Fezell, Nancy, Tech Serv, Maurice M Pine Free Public Library, 10-01 Fair Lawn Ave, Fair Lawn, NJ, 07410. Tel: 201-796-3400. Fax: 201-794-6344. p. 1485

Fiala, Sarah, Librn, Genesee District Library, Genesee Valley Demonstration Location, 3293 S Linden Rd, Flint, MI, 48507. Tel: 810-732-1822. Fax: 810-732-1726. p. 1180

Fialkovich, Jason, Youth Serv Librn, Middletown Free Library, 21 N Pennell Rd, Lima, PA, 19037. Tel: 610-566-7828. Fax: 610-892-0880. p. 2082

Fiander, Anna, Libr Mgr, Canada Department of Fisheries & Oceans, One Challenger Dr, Dartmouth, NS, B2Y 4A2, CANADA. Tel: 902-426-3683. Fax: 902-496-1544. p. 2778

Fiander, Janice, Mgr, Halifax Public Libraries, Cole Harbour Branch, 51 Forest Hills Pkwy, Cole Harbour, NS, B2W 6C6, CANADA. Tel: 902-434-7228. Fax: 902-434-7448. p. 2779

Fiandt, Briana, Circ Librn, Santa Fe Community College Library, 6401 Richards Ave, Santa Fe, NM, 87508-4887. Tel: 505-428-1830. Fax: 505-428-1288. p. 1563

Fichera, Melissa, Br Mgr, Brazoria County Library System, West Columbia Branch, 518 E Brazos, West Columbia, TX, 77486. Tel: 979-345-3394. Fax: 979-345-3652. p. 2276

Fick, Gary, Info Spec, Seattle Pacific University Library, 3307 Third Ave W, Seattle, WA, 98119. Tel: 206-281-2423. Fax: 206-281-2930. p. 2530

Fick, Jodi, Asst Dir, Tech Serv, Siouxland Libraries, 200 N Dakota Ave, Sioux Falls, SD, 57104. Tel: 605-367-8713. Fax: 605-367-4312. p. 2218

Fick, John S, Assoc Dir, University of Missouri-Columbia, Academic Support Center Media Rental Library, 505 E Stewart Rd, Columbia, MO, 65211-2040. Tel: 573-882-3601. Fax: 573-882-6110. p. 1325

Fickett, Pat, Asst Dir, Whipple Free Library, Two Central Sq, New Boston, NH, 03070. Tel: 603-487-3391. Fax: 603-487-2886. p. 1459

Fidel, Raya, Prof, University of Washington, Mary Gates Hall, Ste 370, Campus Box 352840, Seattle, WA, 98195-2840. Tel: 206-685-9937. Fax: 206-616-3152. p. 2976

Fidishun, Dolores, Dr, Head Librn, Pennsylvania State University, 30 E Swedesford Rd, Malvern, PA, 19355. Tel: 610-648-3227. Fax: 610-725-5223. p. 2083

Fie, Nora B, Ch, Superior Public Library, 1530 Tower Ave, Superior, WI, 54880-2532. Tel: 715-394-8860. Fax: 715-394-8870. p. 2641

Fiedler, Ben, Coll Develop, Head, Ref, Seminole Community Library, 9200 113th St N, Seminole, FL, 33772. Tel: 727-394-6905. Fax: 727-398-3113. p. 491

Fiedler, Bobby, Ref, Musser Public Library, 304 Iowa Ave, Muscatine, IA, 52761-3875. Tel: 563-263-3065. Fax: 563-264-1033. p. 834

Fiedor, Connie, Mgr, Sheridan County Public Library System, Tongue River Branch, 145 Coffeen, Ranchester, WY, 82839. Tel: 307-655-9726. Fax: 307-655-9384. p. 2660

Fieg, Eugene, Cat, Claremont School of Theology Library, 1325 N College Ave, Claremont, CA, 91711. Tel: 909-447-2513. p. 134

Fiegen, Ann M, Bus Librn, California State University, 333 S Twin Oaks Valley Rd, San Marcos, CA, 92096-0001. Tel: 760-750-4340. Fax: 760-750-3287. p. 254

Fiegen, Dawne, Librn, Leeds & the Thousand Islands Public Library, Escott Branch, 1365 County Rd 2, Mallorytown, ON, K0E 1R0, CANADA. Tel: 613-659-3800. Fax: 613-659-3800. p. 2815

Fiegl, Allison, Dir, Clayville Library Association, 2265 Oneida St, Clayville, NY, 13322. Tel: 315-839-5893. Fax: 315-839-5070. p. 1607

Fiehn, Barbara, Dr, Asst Prof, Western Kentucky University, School of Teacher Education, 1092 Gary A Ransdell Hall, Normal St, WKU No 61030, Bowling Green, KY, 42101-1030. Tel: 270-745-6123. Fax: 270-745-6322. p. 2966

Field, Addison, Curator, Dir, Sheldon Museum & Cultural Center Library, 11 Main St, Haines, AK, 99827. Tel: 907-766-2366. Fax: 907-766-2368. p. 49

Field, Alida, Ref & Instrul Serv Librn, Notre Dame de Namur University Library, 1500 Ralston Ave, Belmont, CA, 94002-1908. Tel: 650-508-3748. Fax: 650-508-3697. p. 126

Field, Connie N, Mgr, Portland Cement Association, 5420 Old Orchard Rd, Skokie, IL, 60077-1083. Tel: 847-966-6200. Fax: 847-966-6221. p. 703

Field, Corinne, In Charge, Mid-Columbia Libraries, Othello Branch, 101 E Main St, Othello, WA, 99344. Tel: 509-488-9683. Fax: 509-488-5321. p. 2518

Field, Curtis, Dir, Canadian Consulate General Library, 1251 Avenue of the Americas, New York, NY, 10020-1175. Tel: 212-596-1623. Fax: 212-596-1646. p. 1671

Field, Heather, Head Librn, Ashaway Free Library, 15 Knight St, Ashaway, RI, 02804-1410. Tel: 401-377-2770. Fax: 401-377-2770. p. 2163

Field, Jay, VPres, Tech & Learning Res, Solano Community College Library, 4000 Suisun Valley Rd, Fairfield, CA, 94534. Tel: 707-864-7132. Fax: 707-864-7231. p. 148

Field, JoAnn V, Librn, Lied Winside Public Library, 417 Main St, Winside, NE, 68790. Tel: 402-286-1122. p. 1423

Field, Judith J, Prof in Residence, Wayne State University, 106 Kresge Library, Detroit, MI, 48202. Tel: 313-577-1825. Fax: 313-577-7563. p. 2968

Field, Kate, Dir, Kansas Department of Corrections, 500 S Reformatory Rd, Hutchinson, KS, 67501. Tel: 620-662-2321, Ext 4365. Fax: 620-662-5986. p. 873

Field, Ken, Campus Librn, Trent University, Oshawa Campus Library, 55 Thornton Rd S, Oshawa, ON, L1J 5Y1, CANADA. Tel: 905-435-5102, Ext 5065. p. 2836

Field, Ken, Circ Librn, Trent University, 1600 West Bank Dr, Peterborough, ON, K9J 7B8, CANADA. Tel: 705-748-1011, Ext 1324. Fax: 705-748-1126. p. 2836

Field, Ken, Librn, Trent University, Access Services Department, Thomas J Bata Library, 1600 W Bank Dr, Peterborough, ON, K9J 7B8, CANADA. Tel: 705-748-1011, Ext 1565. p. 2836

Field, Lucille, Librn, Lampf, Lipkind, Prupis & Petigrow, 80 Main St, West Orange, NJ, 07052-5482. Tel: 973-325-2100, Ext 240. Fax: 973-325-2839. p. 1541

Field, Tina, Librn, Walter T A Hansen Memorial Library, Ten Hansen St, Mars Hill, ME, 04758. Tel: 207-429-9625. p. 991

Fielder, Rosalind, Ref Librn, Chicago State University, 9501 S Martin Luther King Jr Dr, LIB 440, Chicago, IL, 60628-1598. Tel: 773-821-2431. Fax: 773-995-3772. p. 610

Fielding, Gail, ILL, Whitworth University, 300 W Hawthorne Rd, Spokane, WA, 99251-0001. Tel: 509-777-3260. Fax: 509-777-3221. p. 2538

Fielding, Jennifer, Ref Librn, Fitchburg State College, 160 Pearl St, Fitchburg, MA, 01420. Tel: 978 665-3197. Fax: 978-665-3069. p. 1089

Fielding, Robin, Librn, Temple Beth El, 385 High St, Fall River, MA, 02720. Tel: 508-674-3529. Fax: 508-674-3058. p. 1088

Fields, Angie, Asst Librn, Broken Bow Public Library, 404 Broadway, Broken Bow, OK, 74728. Tel: 580-584-2815. Fax: 580-584-9449. p. 1959

Fields, Ann, Dir, Bancroft Memorial Library, 50 Hopedale St, Hopedale, MA, 01747-1799. Tel: 508-634-2209. Fax: 508-634-8095. p. 1096

Fields, Ann M, Dir, H B Stamps Memorial Library, 407 E Main St, Rogersville, TN, 37857. Tel: 423-272-8710. Fax: 423-272-9261. p. 2264

Fields, Beatrice, Tech Serv Mgr, Kershaw County Library, 1304 Broad St, Camden, SC, 29020-3595. Tel: 803-425-1508. Fax: 803-425-7180. p. 2182

Fields, Betty, Br Mgr, Sabine Parish Library, Toledo Branch, 12350 Texas Hwy, Many, LA, 71449. Tel: 318-256-4152. p. 956

Fields, Catherine, Dir, Litchfield Historical Society, Seven South St, Litchfield, CT, 06759-0385. Tel: 860-567-4501. Fax: 860-567-3565. p. 349

Fields, Darlene, Per, Battelle Memorial Institute, 505 King Ave, Columbus, OH, 43201. Tel: 614-424-6305. Fax: 614-458-6302. p. 1883

Fields, Debbie, Br Mgr, Fairfield County District Library, Baltimore Branch, 205 E Market St, Baltimore, OH, 43105. Tel: 740-862-8505. p. 1908

Fields, Georgianna, Dir, Factoryville Public Library, 163 College Ave, Factoryville, PA, 18419. Tel: 570-945-3788. p. 2057

Fields, Gregory, Pub Serv, Miles College, 5500 Myron Massey Blvd, Fairfield, AL, 35064. Tel: 205-929-1000. Fax: 205-929-1635. p. 16

Fields, Julie, Ch, Alexandria Library, Charles E Beatley Jr Central (Hqtrs), 5005 Duke St, Alexandria, VA, 22304-2903. Tel: 703-746-1735. p. 2444

Fields, Karen, Mgr, Cabell County Public Library, Guyandotte, 203 Richmond St, Huntington, WV, 25702. Tel: 304-528-5698. Fax: 304-528-5698. p. 2561

Fields, Linda, Librn, Richfield Public Library, 83 E Center St, Richfield, UT, 84701. Tel: 435-896-5169. Fax: 435-896-6512. p. 2411

Fields, Lucy, Cat/Metadata Librn, University of Indianapolis, 1400 E Hanna Ave, Indianapolis, IN, 46227-3697. Tel: 317-788-3268. Fax: 317-788-3275. p. 755

Fields, Maria, Adult Serv, Atlanta-Fulton Public Library System, Alpharetta Library, 238 Canton St, Alpharetta, GA, 30004. Tel: 770-740-2425. Fax: 770-740-2427. p. 511

Fields, Mitzi, Br Mgr, Cecil County Public Library, Rising Sun Branch, 111 Colonial Way, Rising Sun, MD, 21911. Tel: 410-658-4025. Fax: 410-658-4024. p. 1027

Fields, Nancy, Librn, Roanoke Public Libraries, Jackson Park, 1101 Morningside St SE, Roanoke, VA, 24013-2515. Tel: 540-853-2640. Fax: 540-853-1156. p. 2494

Fields, Natalie, Br Mgr, Public Library of Cincinnati & Hamilton County, Deer Park, 3970 E Galbraith Rd, Cincinnati, OH, 45236. Tel: 513-369-4450. Fax: 513-369-4451. p. 1871

Fields, Rose, Librn, Merkel Public Library, 100 Kent St, Merkel, TX, 79536. Tel: 325-928-5054. Fax: 325-928-3171. p. 2362

Fields, Ruth, Cat, Thomaston Public Library, 248 Main St, Thomaston, CT, 06787. Tel: 860-283-4339. Fax: 860-283-4330. p. 372

Fields, Sharleen A, Libr Dir, West Buxton Public Library, 34 River Rd, S R 112, Buxton, ME, 04093-0348. Tel: 207-727-5898. p. 980

Fields, Sharon, Med Librn, Memorial Hospital at Gulfport, 4500 13th St, Gulfport, MS, 39501. Tel: 228-867-5366. Fax: 228-865-3214. p. 1300

Fields, Stacey, Dir, Human Res, Howard County Library System, 6600 Cradlerock Way, Columbia, MD, 21045-4912. Tel: 410-313-7750. Fax: 410-313-7742. p. 1026

Fields, Wilma, Web Coordr, Northwest Arkansas Genealogy Society, 405 S Main St, Bentonville Public Library, Bentonville, AR, 72712. Tel: 479-271-6820. p. 95

Fienberg, Jenny, Br Mgr, East Central Georgia Regional Library, Friedman Branch, 1447 Jackson Rd, Augusta, GA, 30909. Tel: 706-736-6758. Fax: 706-737-2034. p. 520

Fiencke, Jonathan, Ref Serv, United States Trademark Office Law Library, 600 Dulany St, MDE 4B65, Alexandria, VA, 22314-5791. Tel: 571-272-2759. Fax: 571-273-2759. p. 2446

Fiero, Angela, Sr Librn, Hennepin County Library, Franklin, 1314 E Franklin Ave, Minneapolis, MN, 55404-2924. Tel: 612-543-6928. Fax: 612-543-6927. p. 1263

Fierro, Robert, Br Supvr, Harris County Public Library, Galena Park Branch, 1500 Keene St, Galena Park, TX, 77547. Tel: 713-450-0982. Fax: 713-451-1131. p. 2336

Fierst, John, Ref Librn, Central Michigan University, Clarke Historical Library, 250 E Preston, Mount Pleasant, MI, 48859. Tel: 989-774-2601. Fax: 989-774-2160. p. 1211

Fieser, Cherie, Spec Projects Adminr, Curator of Bk Arts, Messiah College, One College Ave, Ste 3002, Mechanicsburg, PA, 17055. Tel: 717-691-6006, Ext 7181. Fax: 717-691-2356. p. 2087

Fiesinger, Janet, Sr Librn, Tech Serv, Logan Library, 255 N Main, Logan, UT, 84321-3914. Tel: 435-716-9123. Fax: 435-716-9145. p. 2407

Fieth, Ken, Archivist, Nashville Public Library, 615 Church St, Nashville, TN, 37219-2314. Tel: 615-862-5760. Fax: 615-862-5771. p. 2257

Fieth, Kenneth, Archivist, Nashville Public Library, Metropolitan Government Archives, 3801 Green Hills Village Dr, Nashville, TN, 37215-2610. Tel: 615-862-5880. Fax: 615-862-5883. p. 2257

Fifarek, Aimee, Tech & Content Sr Mgr, Scottsdale Public Library, 3839 N Drinkwater Blvd, Scottsdale, AZ, 85251-4467. Tel: 480-312-7323. Fax: 480-312-7993. p. 81

Fife, Eva, Br Mgr, Saint Charles Parish Library, Saint Rose Branch, 90 E Club Dr, Saint Rose, LA, 70087. Tel: 504-465-0646. Fax: 504-465-0629. p. 949

Fifer, Kathie, Ref Coordr, Warren-Newport Public Library District, 224 N O'Plaine Rd, Gurnee, IL, 60031. Tel: 847-244-5150, Ext 3002. Fax: 847-244-3499. p. 653

Figa, Elizabeth, Dr, Assoc Prof, University of North Texas, 1155 Union Circle, Denton, TX, 76203-5017. Tel: 940-565-2445. Fax: 940-565-3101. p. 2975

Figa, Jan, Libr Dir, Rockford College, 5050 E State St, Rockford, IL, 61108-2393. Tel: 815-226-4000, 815-226-4035. Fax: 815-226-4084. p. 697

Figgatt, Bonnie, Dept Head, Tech Serv, Sacred Heart University, 5151 Park Ave, Fairfield, CT, 06825-1000. Tel: 203-371-7749. Fax: 203-374-9968. p. 339

Figgins, Sherry, Dir, Pendleton County Public Library, 228 Main St, Falmouth, KY, 41040-1223. Tel: 859-654-8535. Fax: 859-654-8538. p. 912

Figgs, Tamika, Mgr, American Hotel & Lodging Association, 229 C N Hilton Hotel & College, University of Houston, Houston, TX, 77204-3028. Tel: 713-743-2515. p. 2334

Figiel-Krueger, Maria, Ref Librn, Rock Valley College Library, Educational Resources Center, 3301 N Mulford Rd, Rockford, IL, 61114. Tel: 815-921-4606. Fax: 815-921-4629. p. 697

Figlia, Ginny, Ch, Howland Public Library, 313 Main St, Beacon, NY, 12508. Tel: 845-831-1134. Fax: 845-831-1165. p. 1579

Figlioli, Catherine, Ref & Instruction Librn, Clinton Community College, 136 Clinton Point Dr, Plattsburgh, NY, 12901-5690. Tel: 518-562-4249. Fax: 518-562-4116. p. 1718

Figueras, Consuelo, Dir, Prof, University of Puerto Rico, Rio Piedras Campus, PO Box 21906, San Juan, PR, 00931-1906. Tel: 787-764-0000, Ext 1286, 787-764-0000, Ext 5028. Fax: 787-764-2311. p. 2977

Figueredo, Carrie Ann, Librn, Beckman Coulter, Inc, 11800 SW 147th Ave, M/C 21-BO1, Miami, FL, 33196-2500. Tel: 305-380-4230. Fax: 305-380-4344. p. 464

Figueredo, Danilo H, Dir, Bloomfield College Library, Liberty St & Oakland Ave, Bloomfield, NJ, 07003. Tel: 973-748-9000, Ext 337. Fax: 973-743-3998. p. 1473

Figueredo, Pedro, Tech Serv, St Thomas University Library, 16401 NW 37th Ave, Miami Gardens, FL, 33054. Tel: 305-474-6861. Fax: 305-628-6666. p. 469

Figueria, Ela, In Charge, City of Calgary Law Department Library, 800 Mecleod Trail SE, 12th Flr, No 8053, Calgary, AB, T2P 2M5, CANADA. Tel: 403-268-2429. Fax: 403-268-4634. p. 2691

Figueroa, Mark, Interim Dir, Libr Info Tech & Digital Initiatives, San Diego State University Library & Information Access, 5500 Campanile Dr, San Diego, CA, 92182-8050. Tel: 619-594-2945. Fax: 619-594-3270. p. 237

Figueroa-Marrero, Brunilda, Info Access Ctr Dir, Inter-American University of Puerto Rico, 104 Parque Industrial Turpeaux, Rd 1, Mercedita, PR, 00715-1602. Tel: 787-284-2127. Fax: 787-841-0103. p. 2674

Figueroa-Ortiz, Almaluces, Librn, University of Puerto Rico Library System, Caribbean & Latin American Studies Collection, Rio Piedras Campus, San Juan, PR, 00931. Tel: 787-764-0000, Ext 3339. Fax: 787-772-1479. p. 2677

Figura, Jackie, Librn, Wales Public Library, 77 Main St, Wales, MA, 01081. Tel: 413-245-9072. Fax: 413-245-9098. p. 1132

Fike, Elaine, Dir, Georgetown Public Library, 123 W Pine St, Georgetown, DE, 19947. Tel: 302-856-7958. p. 383

Fike, Gail, Tech Serv Librn, Conway Public Library, 15 Main St, Conway, NH, 03818. Tel: 603-447-5552. Fax: 603-447-6921. p. 1444

Fikes, Collette, Asst Librn, Wallace Community College, 3000 Earl Goodwin Pkwy, Selma, AL, 36701. Tel: 334-876-9344, 334-876-9345. Fax: 334-876-9314. p. 36

Fikes, Julie, Librn, Webmaster, Brandon Township Public Library, 304 South St, Ortonville, MI, 48462. Tel: 248-627-1460. Fax: 248-627-9880. p. 1215

Filander, E J, Dir, Monongahela Area Library, 813 W Main St, Monongahela, PA, 15063-2815. Tel: 724-258-5409. Fax: 724-258-5440. p. 2091

Filapek, Joe, Adult & Teen Serv Supvr, Naperville Public Library, 95th Street, 3015 Cedar Glade Dr, Naperville, IL, 60564. Tel: 630-961-4100, Ext 4940. Fax: 630-637-4870. p. 679

Filar-Williams, Beth, Distance Educ Librn, University of North Carolina at Greensboro, 320 Spring Garden St, Greensboro, NC, 27402. Tel: 336-256-1232. Fax: 336-334-5399. p. 1798

Filatreau, Kathy, Instructional Technologist, Whittier College, Bonnie Bell Wardman Library, 7031 Founders Hill Rd, Whittier, CA, 90608-9984. Tel: 562-907-4247. Fax: 562-698-7168. p. 283

Filberman, Joan, Head, Ref, Wantagh Public Library, 3285 Park Ave, Wantagh, NY, 11793. Tel: 516-221-1200. Fax: 516-826-9357. p. 1762

Filchagina, Elena, Pub Serv Coordr, Marist College, 3399 North Rd, Poughkeepsie, NY, 12601-1387. Tel: 845-575-3199. Fax: 845-575-3150. p. 1722

Filer, Phillis, Pub Serv Adminr, Alachua County Library District, 401 E University Ave, Gainesville, FL, 32601-5453. Tel: 352-334-3957. Fax: 352-334-3918. p. 448

Files, Carolyn, Br Mgr, Morehouse Parish Library, Oak Ridge Branch, 106 N Oak St, Oak Ridge, LA, 71264. Tel: 318-244-5329. p. 942

Filian, Levon, Dir, Armenian Missionary Association of America Library, 31 W Century Rd, Paramus, NJ, 07652. Tel: 201-265-2607. Fax: 201-265-6015. p. 1517

Filiatrault, Sylvie, Librn Coordr, Bibliotheque Charles-Edouard-Mailhot, 2, rue de L'Ermitage, Victoriaville, QC, G6P 6T2, CANADA. Tel: 819-758-8441. Fax: 819-758-9432. p. 2914

Filion, Ivan, Chief, Librn Serv/Commun Serv, Outreach Serv Librn, Bibliothèques de Montrèal, 801, rue Brennan, 5e Etage, Bureau 5206, Montreal, QC, H3C 0G4, CANADA. Tel: 514-872-9075. Fax: 514-872-0530. p. 2889

Filipkowski, Karen, Chief Librn, Houston Public Library, 3150 14th St, Houston, BC, V0J 1Z0, CANADA. Tel: 250-845-2256. Fax: 250-845-2088. p. 2729

Filipkowski, Karen, Chief Exec Officer, Barry's Bay & Area Public Library, Opeongo Line, No 19474, Barry's Bay, ON, K0J 1B0, CANADA. Tel: 613-756-2000. Fax: 613-756-2000. p. 2794

Filippelli, Carolyn, Digital Coll Librn, Ref, University of Arkansas Fort Smith, 5210 Grand Ave, Fort Smith, AR, 72903. Tel: 479-788-7206. Fax: 479-788-7209. p. 101

Filippo, Inga A, Instruction Librn, Austin Peay State University, 601 E College St, Clarksville, TN, 37044. Tel: 931-221-7381. Fax: 931-221-7296. p. 2228

Filippone, Ella F, Acq, Adminr, Passaic River Coalition, 330 Speedwell Ave, Morristown, NJ, 07960. Tel: 973-532-9830. Fax: 973-889-9172. p. 1505

Filippone, Joanna, Ref, Glen Cove Public Library, Four Glen Cove Ave, Glen Cove, NY, 11542-2885. Tel: 516-676-2130. Fax: 516-676-2788. p. 1628

Filippone, Robyn Swan, Head Librn, Pequot Library, 720 Pequot Ave, Southport, CT, 06890-1496. Tel: 203-259-0346, Ext 16. Fax: 203-259-5602. p. 368

Filkel, C Wesley, Dir, Graves Memorial Public Library, 717 Central Ave, Saint Paul, KS, 66771. Tel: 620-449-2001. Fax: 620-449-2001. p. 893

Filkin, Marsha, Dir, Elm Creek Township Library, 213 N Fifth St, Wilsey, KS, 66873-9768. Tel: 785-497-2289. p. 902

Filkins, Michelle, Head, Ref & Res Serv, Metropolitan State University, 645 E Seventh St, Saint Paul, MN, 55106. Tel: 651-793-1621. Fax: 651-793-1615. p. 1279

Filleul, Michelle, Head, Circ, Reading Public Library, 64 Middlesex Ave, Reading, MA, 01867-2550. Tel: 781-942-6702. Fax: 781-942-9106. p. 1120

Fillman, Ramona, Coordr, Shriners' Hospital Library, 1310 Punahou St, Honolulu, HI, 96826-1099. Tel: 808-951-3693. Fax: 808-942-8573. p. 565

Filstrup, Christian, Admin Dir, Stony Brook University, W-1502 Melville Library, John S Toll Rd, Stony Brook, NY, 11794-3300. Tel: 631-632-7100. Fax: 631-632-7116. p. 1749

Filupeit, Susan M, Cat, Mystic Seaport Museum, 75 Greenmanville Ave, Mystic, CT, 06355. Tel: 860-572-5367. Fax: 860-572-5394. p. 353

Finan, Patricia A, Dir, Huron City Museums Library, 7995 Pioneer Dr, Port Austin, MI, 48467-9400. Tel: 989-738-6007. Fax: 989-428-4123. p. 1219

Finan, Patrick E, Dir, McKinley Memorial Library, 40 N Main St, Niles, OH, 44446-5082. Tel: 330-652-1704. Fax: 330-652-5788. p. 1922

Finch, Ann, ILL, Media Spec, Leominster Public Library, 30 West St, Leominster, MA, 01453. Tel: 978-534-7522. Fax: 978-840-3357. p. 1098

Finch, Emily, Supvr, Elgin County Public Library, Port Stanley Branch, 302 Bridge St, Port Stanley, ON, N5L 1C3, CANADA. Tel: 519-782-4241. Fax: 519-782-4861. p. 2844

Finch, Emily, Supvr, Elgin County Public Library, Shedden Branch, 9557 Union Rd, Shedden, ON, N0L 2E0, CANADA. Tel: 519-764-2081. Fax: 519-764-2789. p. 2844

Finch, Hollister, Ch, Chesapeake Public Library, Major Hillard Library, 824 Old George Washington Hwy N, Chesapeake, VA, 23323-2214. Tel: 757-410-7082. Fax: 757-410-7088, 757-410-7089. p. 2456

Finch, Jennifer M, Dir, McLane, Graf, Raulerson & Middleton PA, 900 Elm St, Manchester, NH, 03101. Tel: 603-628-1428. Fax: 603-625-5650. p. 1456

Finch, Karol, Chair, First Congregational Church-United Church of Christ, 20 E Saint Vrain St, Colorado Springs, CO, 80903. Tel: 719-635-3549. Fax: 719-633-4715. p. 295

Finch, Kathy, Librn, Morrow Memorial United Methodist Church, 600 Ridgewood Rd, Maplewood, NJ, 07040-2161. Tel: 973-763-7676. Fax: 973-763-6798. p. 1499

Finch, Lynette, Dir, Nash Community College Library, 522 N Old Carriage Rd, Rocky Mount, NC, 27804-9441. Tel: 252-451-8244. Fax: 252-451-8401. p. 1821

Finch, Mary Jo, Br Mgr, Westbank Community Library District, 1309 Westbank Dr, Austin, TX, 78746. Tel: 512-381-1404. Fax: 512-327-3074. p. 2285

Finch, Mary Jo, Dir, Westbank Community Library District, 1309 Westbank Dr, Austin, TX, 78746. Tel: 512-327-3045. Fax: 512-327-3074. p. 2285

Finch, Mildred, Dir of Tech Serv, Spartanburg County Public Libraries, 151 S Church St, Spartanburg, SC, 29306-3241. Tel: 864-596-3500. Fax: 864-596-3518. p. 2205

Finch, Robert, Head, Ref, Rogers Public Library, 711 S Dixieland Rd, Rogers, AR, 72758. Tel: 479-621-1152, Ext 19. Fax: 479-621-1165. p. 113

Finch, Sara, Instrul Librn, Dona Ana Community College Library, East Mesa Campus, 2800 N Sonoma Ranch Blvd, Las Cruces, NM, 88011. Tel: 575-528-7260. Fax: 575-528-7422. p. 1558

Finch, Shelia, Pub Relations, White Smith Memorial Library, 213 College Ave, Jackson, AL, 36545. Tel: 251-246-4962. Fax: 251-246-9791. p. 22

Findeisen, Robin, Syst Librn, Stevenson University Library, 1525 Greenspring Valley Rd, Stevenson, MD, 21153. Tel: 410-486-7000, 443-334-2233. Fax: 410-486-7329. p. 1043

Finder, Lisa, Ser Librn, Hunter College Libraries, 695 Park Ave, New York, NY, 10065. Tel: 212-772-4186. Fax: 212-772-4142. p. 1682

Findlay, Karen, Asst Mgr, Dayton Metro Library, Huber Heights, 6160 Chambersburg Rd, Dayton, OH, 45424. Tel: 937-496-8934. Fax: 937-496-4334. p. 1893

Findlay, Lisa, Head Librn, Fredonia Public Library, 130 N Main, Fredonia, AZ, 86022. Tel: 928-643-7137. Fax: 928-643-7137. p. 64

Findlay, Rachel, Asst Librn, Dexter Public Library, 724 Marshall St, Dexter, IA, 50070. Tel: 515-789-4490. Fax: 515-789-4490. p. 810

Findlay, Sandra, Librn, Houser, Henry & Syron Law Library, 145 King St W, Ste 2000, Toronto, ON, M5H 2B6, CANADA. Tel: 416-362-3411. Fax: 416-362-3757. p. 2854

Findley, Erica, Digital Res/Metadata Librn, Pacific University Library, 2043 College Way, Forest Grove, OR, 97116. Tel: 503-352-1411. Fax: 503-352-1416. p. 1998

Findley, Sandy, ILL, Metropolitan Community College, Longview Campus Library, 500 SW Longview Rd, Lee's Summit, MO, 64081-2105. Tel: 816-604-2080. Fax: 816-604-2087. p. 1339

Findra, Pat, Ch Serv Librn, Monmouth County Library, 125 Symmes Dr, Manalapan, NJ, 07726. Tel: 732-431-7220. Fax: 732-308-2955. p. 1498

Fine, Gary, Asst Dir, Durland Alternatives Library, Cornell University, 127 Anabel Taylor Hall, Rm 127, Ithaca, NY, 14853-1001. Tel: 607-255-6486. Fax: 607-255-9985. p. 1642

Fine, Jana, Asst Dir, Outreach Serv, Tuscaloosa Public Library, 1801 Jack Warner Pkwy, Tuscaloosa, AL, 35401-1027. Tel: 205-345-5820, Ext 250. Fax: 205-752-8300. p. 38

Fine, Janet, Head, Circ, Great Neck Library, 159 Bayview Ave, Great Neck, NY, 11023-1938. Tel: 516-466-8055. Fax: 516-829-8297. p. 1630

Fine, Lorraine, Br Coordr, Siskiyou County Public Library, Tulelake Branch, 451 Main St, Tulelake, CA, 96134-9527. Tel: 530-667-2291. p. 286

Finegan, Kathleen, Dir, Avila University, 11901 Wornall Rd, Kansas City, MO, 64145. Tel: 816-501-3711. Fax: 816-501-2456. p. 1336

Finet, Scott, Dir, Board of Governors of The Federal Reserve System, Law Library, 20th & C St NW, MS 7, Washington, DC, 20551. Tel: 202-452-3040. Fax: 202-452-3101. p. 394

Finfrock, Carol, Br Supvr, Yuma County Library District, Wellton Branch, 28790 San Jose Ave, Wellton, AZ, 85356. Tel: 928-373-6552. Fax: 928-785-4410. p. 92

Finfrock, Ellen E, Dir, Polo Public Library District, 302 W Mason St, Polo, IL, 61064. Tel: 815-946-2713. Fax: 815-946-4127. p. 691

Finger, J, Curator, Nantucket Maria Mitchell Association, Two Vestal St, Nantucket, MA, 02554-2699. Tel: 508-228-9219. Fax: 508-228-1031. p. 1107

Fingerote, Barbara, Sr Researcher, McCarthy Tétrault LLP, T-D Centre, Ste 5300, Toronto Dominion Bank Tower, Toronto, ON, M5K 1E6, CANADA. Tel: 416-601-8200, Ext 542737. Fax: 416-868-0673. p. 2855

Finholt, Thomas, Assoc Dean, Prof, University of Michigan, 304 West Hall, 1085 S University, Ann Arbor, MI, 48109-1107. Tel: 734-763-2285. Fax: 734-764-2475. p. 2967

Finigan, Michael, Head, Access Serv & Doc Delivery, Duke University Libraries, 411 Chapel Dr, Durham, NC, 27708. Tel: 919-660-5872. Fax: 919-660-5923. p. 1787

Fink, Carol, Rare Bks, Library of Michigan, 702 W Kalamazoo St, Lansing, MI, 48915. Tel: 517-373-3765. Fax: 517-373-5700. p. 1201

Fink, Catherine, Dir, North Carolina Synod of the ELCA, 1988 Lutheran Synod Dr, Salisbury, NC, 28144. Tel: 704-633-4861, Ext 121. Fax: 704-638-0508. p. 1822

Fink, Cindy, Dir, Mosheim Public Library, 730 Main St, Mosheim, TN, 37818. Tel: 423-422-7937. Fax: 423-422-6492. p. 2253

Fink, Deborah, Prog & Communications Librn, University of Colorado Boulder, 1720 Pleasant St, 184 UCB, Boulder, CO, 80309-0184. Tel: 303-492-8302. Fax: 303-492-3340. p. 291

Fink, Diane, Head, Fiscal & Bus Serv, State Library of Ohio, 274 E First Ave, Ste 100, Columbus, OH, 43201. Tel: 614-644-6879. Fax: 614-466-3584. p. 1890

Fink, Dixie, Dir, Libr Serv, Keokuk Area Hospital, 1600 Morgan St, Keokuk, IA, 52632. Tel: 319-524-7150. Fax: 319-524-5317. p. 825

Fink, Ken, Ref, Pepperdine University Libraries, 24255 Pacific Coast Hwy, Malibu, CA, 90263. Tel: 310-506-4252. Fax: 310-506-7225. p. 182

Fink, Madonna, Sister, Ref, University of Saint Mary, 4100 S Fourth St Trafficway, Leavenworth, KS, 66048-5082. Tel: 913-758-6306. Fax: 913-758-6200. p. 879

Fink, Mark, Commun Librn, Santa Clara County Library District, Cupertino Library, 10800 Torre Ave, Cupertino, CA, 95014-3254. Tel: 408-446-1677, Ext 3300. Fax: 408-252-8749. p. 181

Fink, Marlene, Librn, Parkland Regional Library, Lipton Branch, 1103 Shamrock Ave, Lipton, SK, S0G 3B0, CANADA. Tel: 306-336-2288. p. 2932

Fink, Norma, Dir, Attica Public Library, 305 S Perry St, Attica, IN, 47918. Tel: 765-764-4194. Fax: 765-764-0906. p. 725

Fink, Norman, Dir, Centre Regionale de Services aux Bibliotheques Publiques de l'Abitibi-Temiscamingue-Nord-du-Quebec, 20 Quebec Ave, Rouyn-Noranda, QC, J9X 2E6, CANADA. Tel: 819-762-4305. Fax: 819-762-5309. p. 2908

Fink, Peggy Kim Hong, Br Mgr, Hawaii State Public Library System, Lanai Public & School Library, 555 Fraser Ave, Lanai City, HI, 96763. Tel: 808-565-7920. Fax: 808-565-7922. p. 562

Fink, Susan M, Info Spec, Rhodia Inc, 350 George Patterson Blvd, Bristol, PA, 19007. Tel: 215-781-6232. Fax: 215-781-6002. p. 2037

Fink, Tanis, Dir, Seneca College of Applied Arts & Technology, 13990 Dufferin St N, King City, ON, L7B 1B3, CANADA. Tel: 416-491-5050. Fax: 905-833-1106. p. 2813

Fink, Tanis, Dir, Seneca College of Applied Arts & Technology, Newnham Campus (Main), 1750 Finch Ave E, North York, ON, M2J 2X5, CANADA. Tel: 416-491-5050, Ext 77526. Fax: 416-491-3349. p. 2813

Finkbeiner, Mel, Libr Tech, OSF Saint Anthony Medical Center, 5666 E State St, Rockford, IL, 61108-2472. Tel: 815-227-2558. Fax: 815-227-2904. p. 697

Finkbeiner, Tedd, Ser, Calvary Baptist Theological Seminary Library, 1380 S Valley Forge Rd, Lansdale, PA, 19446-4797. Tel: 215-368-4444, Ext 137. Fax: 215-368-1003. p. 2078

Finkel, Laura, Spec Coll Librn, Vassar College Library, 124 Raymond Ave, Maildrop 20, Poughkeepsie, NY, 12604-0020. Tel: 845-437-5760. Fax: 845-437-5864. p. 1723

Finkey, Marisa, Coordr, Info Literacy, University of Wisconsin Oshkosh, 801 Elmwood Ave, Oshkosh, WI, 54901. Tel: 920-424-3436. Fax: 920-424-7338. p. 2628

Finklang, Julie, eBr Mgr, San Mateo County Library, Library Administration, 125 Lessingia Ct, San Mateo, CA, 94402-4000. Tel: 650-312-5296. Fax: 650-312-5382. p. 255

Finkle, Debbie, In Charge, Knesseth Israel Synagogue Library, 34 E Fulton St, Gloversville, NY, 12078. Tel: 518-725-0649. Fax: 518-725-0640. p. 1629

Finkle, Elizabeth, Vols Serv Coordr, Fresno County Public Library, 2420 Mariposa St, Fresno, CA, 93721-2285. Tel: 559-252-8657. p. 151

Finkral, Susan, Dir, Leigh Public Library, 156 Main St, Leigh, NE, 68643. Tel: 402-487-2507. Fax: 402-487-2507. p. 1403

Finlan, Cathy, Librn, Howe Memorial Library, 128 E Saginaw St, Breckenridge, MI, 48615. Tel: 989-842-3202. Fax: 989-842-3202. p. 1159

Finlay, Jane A, Asst Dir, Morse Institute Library, 14 E Central St, Natick, MA, 01760. Tel: 508-647-6526. Fax: 508-647-6526. p. 1107

Finlay, Lenore, Libr Asst, University of Manitoba Libraries, Bill Larson Library (Grace Hospital), 300 Booth Dr, Winnipeg, MB, R3J 3M7, CANADA. Tel: 204-837-0518. Fax: 204-897-9486. p. 2758

Finlay, Tom, Librn, University of Toronto Libraries, Centre of Criminology, 14 Queens Park Crescent W, Toronto, ON, M5S 3K9, CANADA. Tel: 416-978-7068, Ext 236. Fax: 416-978-4195. p. 2865

Finlayson, Irene, Pub Serv Coordr, North Country Community College Library, 23 Santanoni Ave, Saranac Lake, NY, 12983-2046. Tel: 518-891-2915, Ext 218. p. 1738

Finlayson, Kathy, Libr Tech, University of Manitoba, Misericordia Health Centre LIbrary, 99 Cornish Ave, Winnipeg, MB, R3C 1A2, CANADA. Tel: 204-788-8109. Fax: 204-889-4174. p. 2758

Finlayson, Sandy, Dir, Westminster Theological Seminary, 2960 W Church Rd, Glenside, PA, 19038. Tel: 215-572-3823. Fax: 215-887-3412. p. 2062

Finley, Barbara, Circ Librn, Caribou Public Library, 30 High St, Caribou, ME, 04736. Tel: 207-493-4214. Fax: 207-493-4654. p. 981

Finley, Deb, Dir/Librn, Hemingford Public Library, 812 Box Butte, Hemingford, NE, 69348. Tel: 308-487-3454. Fax: 308-487-3835. p. 1402

Finley, Gerry, Dir, Collingdale Public Library, 823 MacDade Blvd, Collingdale, PA, 19023-1422. Tel: 610-583-2214. Fax: 610-583-0172. p. 2046

Finley, Heath, Librn, Ontario Ministry of Natural Resources, 300 Water St, Peterborough, ON, K9J 8M5, CANADA. Tel: 705-755-1888. Fax: 705-755-1882. p. 2835

Finley, John, Archivist, Ref Serv, Central Methodist College, 411 Central Methodist Sq, Fayette, MO, 65248. Tel: 660-248-6271, Fax: 660-248-6226. p. 1327

Finley, Marie, Youth Serv, Rock Springs Public Library, 101 First St, Rock Springs, WI, 53961-8011. Tel: 608-522-5050. Fax: 608-522-5050. p. 2635

Finley, Tami, Ch, Youth Serv Mgr, Bettendorf Public Library Information Center, 2950 Learning Campus Dr, Bettendorf, IA, 52722. Tel: 563-344-4194. Fax: 563-344-4185. p. 796

Finley, Thomas, Asst Br Mgr, Dallas Public Library, North Oak Cliff, 302 W Tenth St, Dallas, TX, 75208-4617. Tel: 214-670-7555. Fax: 214-670-7548. p. 2307

Finley, Tom, Br Librn, Western Illinois University Libraries, One University Circle, Macomb, IL, 61455. Tel: 309-762-1598. Fax: 309-298-2791. p. 668

Finley, William, Dr, Head, Spec Coll, University of North Carolina at Greensboro, 320 Spring Garden St, Greensboro, NC, 27402. Tel: 336-334-5880. Fax: 336-334-5399. p. 1798

Finn, Carly, Ch, William B Ogden Free Library, 42 Gardiner Pl, Walton, NY, 13856. Tel: 607-865-5929. Fax: 607-865-6821. p. 1762

Finn, Irja, Ref Serv, Ad, Stevens Memorial Library, 345 Main St, North Andover, MA, 01845. Tel: 978-688-9505. Fax: 978-688-9507. p. 1112

Finn, John, Br Mgr, Beaverton City Library, 12375 SW Fifth St, Beaverton, OR, 97005-2883. Tel: 503-526-2381. Fax: 503-350-3645. p. 1991

Finn, John Michael, Dir, Hearst Free Library, 401 Main St, Anaconda, MT, 59711. Tel: 406-563-6932. Fax: 406-563-5393. p. 1373

Finn, Maureen, Br Mgr, Marysville Public Library, Raymond Branch, 21698 Main St, Raymond, OH, 43067. Tel: 937-246-4795. Fax: 937-246-2347. p. 1915

Finn, Nathan, Archivist, Southeastern Baptist Theological Seminary Library, 114 N Wingate St, Wake Forest, NC, 27587. Tel: 919-556-3104. Fax: 919-863-8150. p. 1827

Finn, Rea, Media Spec, Third Baptist Church Library, 620 N Grand Blvd, Saint Louis, MO, 63103. Tel: 314-533-7340, Ext 21. Fax: 314-533-7310. p. 1361

Finnegan, Brian, Ref Librn, Marshfield Clinic, 1000 N Oak Ave, Marshfield, WI, 54449-5777. Tel: 715-389-5272. Fax: 715-389-5366. p. 2613

Finnegan, Gregory A, Assoc Librn, Pub Serv, Head, Ref, Harvard Library, Tozzer Library, 21 Divinity Ave, Cambridge, MA, 02138. Tel: 617-495-1481, 617-495-2253. Fax: 617-496-2741. p. 1076

Finnegan, Katherine, Head Librn, Faith Theological Seminary Library, 529-531 Walker Ave, Baltimore, MD, 21212-2624. Tel: 410-323-6211. Fax: 410-323-6331. p. 1013

Finnegan, Kimberly, Dir, Panora Public Library, 102 N First St, Panora, IA, 50216. Tel: 641-755-2529. Fax: 641-755-3009. p. 838

Finnegan, Kris, Ch, Harrisville Public Library, Seven Canal St, Harrisville, NH, 03450. Tel: 603-827-2918. Fax: 603-827-2917. p. 1451

Finnegan, Kristine, Dir, Olivia Rodham Memorial Library, One Nelson Common Rd, Nelson, NH, 03457-9703. Tel: 603-847-3214. p. 1459

Finnegan, Mary, Head, Adult Serv, Corvallis-Benton County Public Library, 645 NW Monroe Ave, Corvallis, OR, 97330. Tel: 541-766-6993. p. 1994

Finnell, Joshua, Humanities Liaison Librn, Denison University Libraries, 400 W Loop, Granville, OH, 43023. Tel: 740-587-8651. Fax: 740-587-6285. p. 1902

Finnell, Tammy, Librn, Burr Oak City Library, 221 A Main St, Burr Oak, KS, 66936. Tel: 785-647-5597. Fax: 785-647-5597. p. 859

Finnerty, Jack, Dir, Scranton Public Library, Albright Memorial Bldg, 500 Vine St, Scranton, PA, 18509-3298. Tel: 570-348-3013. Fax: 570-348-3020. p. 2137

Finnerty, Sharon, Media Res Coordr, University of Scranton, Monroe & Linden, Scranton, PA, 18510-4634. Tel: 570-941-6330. Fax: 570-941-7817. p. 2138

Finnesand, Tana, Librn, The Frances Kibble Kenny Lake Public Library, Mile 5 Edgerton Hwy, Copper Center, AK, 99573-9703. Tel: 907-822-3015. Fax: 907-822-3015. p. 46

Finney, Andy, Tech Support Mgr, Mgt Team, North Idaho College Library, 1000 W Garden Ave, Coeur d'Alene, ID, 83814-2199. Tel: 208-769-3266. Fax: 208-769-3428. p. 573

Finney, Catherine, Acq, Assoc Col Librn, Coll, Central Oregon Community College Barber Library, 2600 NW College Way, Bend, OR, 97701-5998. Tel: 541-383-7559. Fax: 541-383-7406. p. 1991

Finney, Marc, Dir, Saint Paul's College, 115 College Dr, Lawrenceville, VA, 23868-1299. Tel: 434-848-1840. Fax: 434-848-1861. p. 2473

Finney, Maria, Res, Nevada Power Co Library, 6226 W Sahara Ave, Las Vegas, NV, 89151. Tel: 702-367-5055. Fax: 702-227-2023. p. 1430

Finney, Patrick, Circ Mgr, Daniel Boone Regional Library, 100 W Broadway, Columbia, MO, 65203. Tel: 573-443-3161. Fax: 573-443-3281. p. 1324

Finnicum, Ellen, Dir, Carroll County District Library, 70 Second St NE, Carrollton, OH, 44615. Tel: 330-627-2613. Fax: 330-627-2523. p. 1865

Finnicum, Ellen, Dir, Carroll County District Library, Malvern Branch, 710 E Porter St, Malvern, OH, 44644. Tel: 330-863-0636. Fax: 330-863-0419. p. 1865

Finnie, Jessica, Dir, Scituate Town Library, 85 Branch St, Scituate, MA, 02066. Tel: 781-545-8727. Fax: 781-545-8728. p. 1123

Finnie, Lisa, Cat Librn, University of Texas Health Science Center at San Antonio Libraries, 7703 Floyd Curl Dr, MSC 7940, San Antonio, TX, 78229-3900. Tel: 210-567-2400. Fax: 210-567-2490. p. 2383

Finnigan, Bev, Dir, Sidney Public Library, 1002 Illinois St, Sidney, IA, 51652. Tel: 712-374-6203. Fax: 712-374-6303. p. 843

Finnigan, William, Automation Librn, Nanuet Public Library, 149 Church St, Nanuet, NY, 10954. Tel: 845-623-4281. Fax: 845-623-2415. p. 1664

Fino, Ellen, Tech Serv, Midland College, 3600 N Garfield, Midland, TX, 79705. Tel: 432-685-4560. Fax: 432-685-6710. p. 2363

Fintel, Mimi, Br Mgr, Harris-Elmore Public Library, Genoa Branch, 602 West St, Genoa, OH, 43430. Tel: 419-855-3380. Fax: 419-855-7012. p. 1898

Fiola, Kathleen, Dir, Helen Hayes Hospital, Rte 9 W, West Haverstraw, NY, 10993. Tel: 845-786-4185. Fax: 845-786-4978. p. 1766

Fiore, Josephine, Br Mgr, Prince George's County Memorial, Upper Marlboro, 14730 Main St, Upper Marlboro, MD, 20772-3053. Tel: 301-627-9330. p. 1033

Fiorelli, Mary, Dir, Old Lyme, Two Library Lane, Old Lyme, CT, 06371. Tel: 860-434-1684. Fax: 860-434-9547. p. 363

Fiorillo, Andrea, Ad, Medfield Memorial Public Library, 468 Main St, Medfield, MA, 02052-2008. Tel: 508-359-4544. Fax: 508-359-8124. p. 1104

Fiorillo, Anthony, Curator, Museum of Nature & Science, 1318 S Second Ave, Dallas, TX, 75315. Tel: 214-428-5555. Fax: 214-428-4356. p. 2309

Fiorillo, Camille F, Chair, Libr & Info Studies, Palo Alto College, 1400 W Villaret St, San Antonio, TX, 78224-2499. Tel: 210-486-3560. Fax: 210-486-9184. p. 2380

Fiory, Cherilyn, Dir, Upper Dublin Public Library, 805 Loch Alsh Ave, Fort Washington, PA, 19034. Tel: 215-628-8744. p. 2058

Fiqueroa, Isabel, Br Mgr, Stanislaus County Free Library, Hughson Branch, 2412 Third St, Ste A, Hughson, CA, 95326. Tel: 209-883-2293. Fax: 209-883-2293. p. 188

Firchow, Heather, Sr Librn, Youth Serv Supvr, Torrance Public Library, 3301 Torrance Blvd, Torrance, CA, 90503. Tel: 310-618-5964. Fax: 310-618-5952. p. 276

Firchow, Nancy, Librn, Regional Medical Center of San Jose, 225 N Jackson Ave, San Jose, CA, 95116-1603. Tel: 408-259-5000, Ext 2230. Fax: 408-272-6458. p. 250

Firer, Ellen, Dir, Merrick Library, 2279 Merrick Ave, Merrick, NY, 11566-4398. Tel: 516-377-6112. Fax: 516-377-5197. p. 1659

Firestine, Scott, Asst Dir, Appomattox Regional Library, 209 E Cawson St, Hopewell, VA, 23860. Tel: 804-458-6329, 804-861-0322. Fax: 804-458-4349. p. 2472

Firestone, Kathy, Dir, Community Library of Allegheny Valley, 1522 Broadview Blvd, Natrona Heights, PA, 15065. Tel: 724-226-3491. Fax: 724-226-3821. p. 2094

Firestone, Kathy, Dir, Community Library of Allegheny Valley, Tarentum Branch, 400 Lock St, Tarentum, PA, 15084. Tel: 724-226-0770. Fax: 724-226-3526. p. 2095

Firestone, Marie, ILL, Palisades Free Library, 19 Closter Rd, Palisades, NY, 10964. Tel: 845-359-0136. Fax: 845-359-6124. p. 1714

Firestone, MaryEllen, Dir, East Brunswick Public Library, Two Jean Walling Civic Center, East Brunswick, NJ, 08816-3599. Tel: 732-390-6950. Fax: 732-390-6796. p. 1481

Firman, Carol, Libr Assoc, New Hampshire Division of Public Health Services, 29 Hazen Dr, Concord, NH, 03301. Tel: 603-271-0562, 603-271-7060. Fax: 603-271-0542. p. 1442

Firman, Peggy, Assoc Dir, Coll & Tech Serv, University of Puget Sound, 1500 N Warner St, Campus Mail Box 1021, Tacoma, WA, 98416-1021. Tel: 253-879-3615. Fax: 253-879-3670. p. 2541

Firsowicz, Anna, Pres, Polish Library, 1503 21st St NW, Washington, DC, 20036. Tel: 202-466-2665. p. 413

Firth, Jennifer, Head, Youth Serv, Long Beach Public Library, 111 W Park Ave, Long Beach, NY, 11561-3326. Tel: 516-432-7201. Fax: 516-889-4641. p. 1654

Firth, Jillian, Mgr, El Dorado County Library, Georgetown Branch, 6680 Orleans St, Georgetown, CA, 95634. Tel: 530-333-4724. Fax: 530-333-4724. p. 208

Fisch, Ronda W, Dir, Reed Smith LLP, 225 Fifth Ave, Pittsburgh, PA, 15222. Tel: 412-288-3377. Fax: 412-288-3063. p. 2128

Fischbach, Kelly, Dir, Carroll Public Library, 118 E Fifth St, Carroll, IA, 51401. Tel: 712-792-3432. Fax: 712-792-0141. p. 798

Fischbuch, Trish, Libr Mgr, Oyen Municipal Library, 105 Third Ave W, Oyen, AB, T0J 2J0, CANADA. Tel: 403-664-3580. Fax: 403-664-2520. p. 2713

Fischer, Barbara, Librn, Northrop Grumman IT-TASC, 4801 Stonecroft Blvd, Chantilly, VA, 20151-3822. Tel: 703-633-8300, Ext 4654. Fax: 703-449-7648. p. 2453

Fischer, Becky, Head, Circ, Saline County Public Library, 1800 Smithers Dr, Benton, AR, 72015. Tel: 501-778-4766. Fax: 501-778-0536. p. 94

Fischer, Brenda, Mgr, University of Michigan, Sumner & Laura Foster Library, 265 Lorch Hall, Ann Arbor, MI, 48109-1220. Tel: 734-763-6609. Fax: 734-764-2769. p. 1152

Fischer, Brenda, Circ, Jamestown College, 6070 College Lane, Jamestown, ND, 58405-0001. Tel: 701-252-3467. Fax: 701-253-4446. p. 1844

Fischer, Charles, Asst Dir, Access Serv, Loyola University Chicago Libraries, Law School Library, 25 E Pearson St, 3rd Flr, Chicago, IL, 60611. Tel: 312-915-7131, 312-915-7200, 312-915-7202. Fax: 312-915-6797. p. 617

Fischer, Christine, Head, Acq, University of North Carolina at Greensboro, 320 Spring Garden St, Greensboro, NC, 27402. Tel: 336-334-5880. Fax: 336-334-5399. p. 1798

Fischer, Dave, Tech Consult, Northwest Kansas Library System, Two Washington Sq, Norton, KS, 67654-1615. Tel: 785-877-5148. Fax: 785-877-5697. p. 885

Fischer, Debbie, Br Mgr, Latah County Library District, Deary Branch, 304 Second Ave, Deary, ID, 83823. Tel: 208-877-1664. Fax: 208-877-1664. p. 579

Fischer, Diane, Info Res, Mgr, Libr Serv, X L Global Services Corporate Library, 70 Seaview Ave, Stamford, CT, 06902-6036. Tel: 203-964-5216. Fax: 203-964-0763. p. 370

Fischer, Fayleen, Librn, Killdeer Public Library, PO Box 579, Killdeer, ND, 58640-0579. Tel: 701-764-5877. Fax: 701-764-5648. p. 1845

Fischer, Janice, Asst Librn, Chinook Regional Library, Shaunavon Branch, Grand Coteau Heritage & Cultural Ctr, 440 Centre St, Shaunavon, SK, S0N 2M0, CANADA. Tel: 306-297-3844. p. 2928

Fischer, Jayne, Tech Leader-Eng Standards, Cummins Filtration, 1801 Hwy 51-138, Stoughton, WI, 53589. Tel: 608-873-4370. Fax: 608-873-1550. p. 2640

Fischer, Joanne, Principal Librn, Lee County Library System, Lakes Regional, 15290 Bass Rd, Fort Myers, FL, 33919. Tel: 239-533-4000. Fax: 239-533-4040. p. 445

Fischer, Jody, Dir, Wall Lake Public Library, 116 Main St, Wall Lake, IA, 51466. Tel: 712-664-2983. Fax: 712-664-2577. p. 849

Fischer, Karen, Libr Mgr, Salem Public Library, West Salem, 395 Glen Creek Rd NW, Salem, OR, 97304. Tel: 503-588-6039. Fax: 503-588-6397. p. 2018

Fischer, Lynn, Tech Serv, Cocoa Beach Public Library, 550 N Brevard Ave, Cocoa Beach, FL, 32931. Tel: 321-868-1104. Fax: 321-868-1107. p. 433

Fischer, Mary Louise, Libr Supvr-Popular Libr, Frances T Bourne Jacaranda Public Library, 4143 Woodmere Park Blvd, Venice, FL, 34293. Tel: 941-861-1272. Fax: 941-486-2725. p. 501

Fischer, Paulette, Librn, Kidder County Library, 115 W Broadway, Steele, ND, 58482. Tel: 701-475-2855. p. 1848

Fischer, Phyllis A, Head Librn, Covidien, 3600 N Second St, Saint Louis, MO, 63147-3457. Tel: 314-654-1511. Fax: 314-654-1513. p. 1354

Fischer, Rosemary, Univ Archivist, Clayton State University, 2000 Clayton State Blvd, Morrow, GA, 30260. Tel: 678-466-4333. Fax: 678-466-4349. p. 545

Fischer, Sherry, Dir, Costilla County Library, 418 Gasper St, San Luis, CO, 81152. Tel: 719-672-3309. Fax: 719-672-3309. p. 322

Fischer, Susan, City Librn, Kathryn Schulkoski Library, 613 Seventh St, Eureka, SD, 57437. Tel: 605-284-2863. p. 2212

Fischer, Virginia, Doc, Reader Serv, University of Maine at Presque Isle Library, 181 Main St, Presque Isle, ME, 04769-2888. Tel: 207-768-9599. Fax: 207-768-9644. p. 998

Fischer, William T, Ref Serv, Res Serv, Montclair Free Public Library, 50 S Fullerton Ave, Montclair, NJ, 07042. Tel: 973-744-0500, Ext 2226. Fax: 973-744-5268. p. 1503

Fischier, Adrienne G, Librn, Harvard Library in New York, 35 W 44th St, New York, NY, 10036. Tel: 212-827-1246. Fax: 212-827-1251, Ext 1246. p. 1680

Fish, Barrett, Asst Librn, Ref, North Carolina Supreme Court Library, 500 Justice Bldg, Two E Morgan St, Raleigh, NC, 27601-1428. Tel: 919-831-5709. Fax: 919-831-5732. p. 1816

Fish, Cathleen J, Dir, Hillsboro Public Library, 120 E Grand, Hillsboro, KS, 67063-1598. Tel: 620-947-3827. Fax: 620-947-3810. p. 872

Fish, Elizabeth, Dir, University of Miami, 4600 Rickenbacker Causeway, Miami, FL, 33149-1098. Tel: 305-421-4021. Fax: 305-361-9306. p. 468

Fish, James H, Dir, Baltimore County Public Library, 320 York Rd, Towson, MD, 21204-5179. Tel: 410-887-6160. Fax: 410-887-6103. p. 1044

Fish, Maureen, In Charge, Osceola Library, Two W Branch Rd, Waterville Valley, NH, 03215. Tel: 603-236-4369. p. 1467

Fish, Nancy, Mgr, Ontario Power Generation Library, 700 University Ave, H17G10, Toronto, ON, M5G 1X6, CANADA. Tel: 416-592-2715. Fax: 416-592-7532. p. 2857

Fish, Shelly, Bus Mgr, Bedford Public Library, 1323 K St, Bedford, IN, 47421. Tel: 812-275-4471. Fax: 812-278-5244. p. 726

Fishe, Elizabeth, Librn, Hartford Hospital, Institute of Living Medical Library, Research Bldg 3, 200 Retreat Ave, Hartford, CT, 06106-5037. Tel: 860-545-7147. Fax: 860-545-7275. p. 345

Fishel, Martha, Pub Serv, National Library of Medicine, Bldg 38, Rm 2E-17B, 8600 Rockville Pike, Bethesda, MD, 20894. Tel: 301-496-6308. Fax: 301-496-4450. p. 1022

Fishel, Martha, Coordr, US National Library of Medicine, 8600 Rockville Pike, Bethesda, MD, 20894. Tel: 301-496-5501. Fax: 301-402-9334. p. 2945

Fishel, Teresa A, Dir, Macalester College, 1600 Grand Ave, Saint Paul, MN, 55105-1899. Tel: 651-696-6343. Fax: 651-696-6617. p. 1279

Fishelman, Trisha, Ch, Glen Rock Public Library, 315 Rock Rd, Glen Rock, NJ, 07452-1795. Tel: 201-670-3970. Fax: 201-445-0872. p. 1488

Fisher, Alana, Br Mgr, Cumberland County Public Library & Information Center, Hope Mills Branch, 3411 Golfview Rd, Hope Mills, NC, 28348-2266. Tel: 910-425-8455. Fax: 910-423-0997. p. 1792

Fisher, Alana, Dir, Nashville Public Library, 114 W Church St, Nashville, NC, 27856. Tel: 252-459-2106. Fax: 252-459-8819. p. 1812

Fisher, Amy, Mgr, Ref Serv, Mid-Continent Public Library, 15616 E US Hwy 24, Independence, MO, 64050-2098. Tel: 816-836-5200. Fax: 816-521-7253. p. 1332

Fisher, Annette, Info Literacy Librn, Marywood University Library, 2300 Adams Ave, Scranton, PA, 18509-1598. Tel: 570-961-4707. Fax: 570-961-4769. p. 2137

Fisher, Ashley, ILL Supvr, Judson University, 1151 N State St, Elgin, IL, 60123. Tel: 847-628-2032. Fax: 847-625-2045. p. 641

Fisher, Barbara, Librn, Mayer, Brown, Rowe & Maw Library, 1909 K St NW, Ste 1200, Washington, DC, 20006-1101. Tel: 202-263-3000, 202-263-3100, 202-263-3314. Fax: 202-263-3300. p. 408

Fisher, Becky, Acq Mgr, Longwood University, Redford & Race St, Farmville, VA, 23909. Tel: 434-395-2448. Fax: 434-395-2453. p. 2463

Fisher, Betty, Archives Coordr, University of Saint Thomas, 1100 W Main, Houston, TX, 77006. Tel: 713-525-3895. Fax: 713-525-2117. p. 2344

Fisher, Beverly, AV Coll, Cat, Circ, Helen Lehmann Memorial Library, 17435 Fifth St, Montverde, FL, 34756. Tel: 407-469-3838. Fax: 407-469-2773. p. 470

Fisher, Brett, Tech Coordr, Flathead County Library, 247 First Ave E, Kalispell, MT, 59901. Tel: 406-758-5820. Fax: 406-758-5868. p. 1384

Fisher, Carol, Librn, Talmage Public Library, 405 Main, Talmage, NE, 68448. Tel: 402-264-3875. p. 1421

Fisher, Carol, Librn, Southeast Regional Library, Lumsden Branch, 20 Third Ave, Lumsden, SK, S0G 3C0, CANADA. Tel: 306-731-1431. p. 2930

Fisher, Carola, Librn, Wayne Public Library, 3737 S Wayne Rd, Wayne, MI, 48184. Tel: 734-721-7832. Fax: 734-721-0341. p. 1235

Fisher, Carole, Asst Dir, Prog, Cora J Belden Library, 33 Church St, Rocky Hill, CT, 06067-1568. Tel: 860-258-7621. p. 365

Fisher, Carolyn, Head, Cat, Nodaway County Historical Society/Mary H Jackson Research Center, 110 N Walnut St, Maryville, MO, 64468-2251. Tel: 660-582-8176. Fax: 660-562-3377. p. 1344

Fisher, Cherl, Mgr, Carbon County Library System, Little Snake River Valley Branch, 105 Second St, Baggs, WY, 82321. Tel: 307-383-7323. Fax: 307-383-7323. p. 2659

Fisher, Cindy, Circ Mgr, Clinton-Macomb Public Library, North, 16800 24 Mile Rd, Macomb Township, MI, 48042. Tel: 586-226-5084. Fax: 586-226-5088. p. 1164

Fisher, Corinne, Head, Ch, Reading Public Library, 64 Middlesex Ave, Reading, MA, 01867-2550. Tel: 781-942-6705. Fax: 781-942-9106. p. 1120

Fisher, Darlene, Librn, Eastern Irrigation District, 550 Industrial Rd W, Brooks, AB, T1R 1B2, CANADA. Tel: 403-362-1400. Fax: 403-362-6206. p. 2686

Fisher, Debra, Mgr, O'Melveny & Myers LLP, 1625 Eye St NW, Washington, DC, 20006. Tel: 202-383-5300. Fax: 202-383-5414. p. 412

Fisher, Delores, ILL, University of Missouri-Columbia, Elmer Ellis Library, Ellis Library Bldg, Rm 104, Columbia, MO, 65201-5149. Tel: 573-882-1101. Fax: 573-882-8044. p. 1325

Fisher, Don, Librn, Allen County Public Library, Waynedale, 2200 Lower Huntington Rd, Fort Wayne, IN, 46819. Tel: 260-421-1365. Fax: 260-747-4123. p. 741

Fisher, Elise, Assoc Dir, Educ Tech, William Jewell College, 500 College Hill, Liberty, MO, 64068-1843. Tel: 816-415-7611. Fax: 816-415-5021. p. 1343

Fisher Hall, Angela, Assoc Dir, Birmingham Public Library, 2100 Park Pl, Birmingham, AL, 35203. Tel: 205-226-3600. Fax: 205-226-3743. p. 7

Fisher, Hannah, Info Serv Librn, University of Arizona, Arizona Health Sciences Library, 1501 N Campbell Ave, Tucson, AZ, 85724. Tel: 520-626-2933. Fax: 520-626-2922. p. 88

Fisher, Helen, Dir, Ontario City Library, 215 East C St, Ontario, CA, 91764. Tel: 909-395-2004. Fax: 909-395-2043. p. 200

Fisher Isaacs, Melissa, In Charge, University of Kansas, Department of Religious Studies, Smith Hall, Rm 109, 1300 Oread Ave, Lawrence, KS, 66045-7615. Tel: 785-864-4663. Fax: 785-864-5205. p. 878

Fisher, Janet, Dir, Law & Res Libr, Arizona State Library, Archives & Public Records, 1700 W Washington, Rm 200, Phoenix, AZ, 85007. Tel: 602-926-3870. Fax: 602-256-7984. p. 72

Fisher, Janice, Dir, Riverside Public Library, One Burling Rd, Riverside, IL, 60546. Tel: 708-442-6366. Fax: 708-442-9462. p. 695

Fisher, Jean, Cat/Bibliog Instruction Librn, West Virginia State University, Campus Box L17, Institute, WV, 25112. Tel: 304-766-3158. Fax: 304-766-4103. p. 2562

Fisher, Jeff, Canton Campus Librn, Chattahoochee Technical College Library, 980 S Cobb Dr SE, Marietta, GA, 30060-3300. Tel: 770-345-1392. Fax: 770-528-4454. p. 542

Fisher, Jennifer, In Charge, Video Outt, 1965 Main St, Vancouver, BC, V5T 3C1, CANADA. Tel: 604-872-8449. Fax: 604-876-1185. p. 2744

Fisher, Jo Ann, Libr Res Serv Mgr, Jones Day, 901 Lakeside Ave, Cleveland, OH, 44114. Tel: 216-586-3939. Fax: 216-579-0212. p. 1880

Fisher, Karen, Youth Serv Mgr, Salem Public Library, 585 Liberty St SE, Salem, OR, 97301. Tel: 503-588-6039. Fax: 503-588-6055. p. 2018

Fisher, Karen, Prof, University of Washington, Mary Gates Hall, Ste 370, Campus Box 352840, Seattle, WA, 98195-2840. Tel: 206-685-9937. Fax: 206-616-3152. p. 2976

Fisher, Karolyn, Librn, Newtown Library Co, 114 Centre Ave, Newtown, PA, 18940. Tel: 215-968-7659. p. 2098

Fisher, Katherine, Access Serv Librn, Evening Supvr, Drexel University Health Sciences Libraries, 245 N 15th St MS 449, Philadelphia, PA, 19102-1192. Tel: 215-762-1069. Fax: 215-762-8180. p. 2105

Fisher, Kathy, Ref & Instruction Librn, Ursuline College, 2550 Lander Rd, Pepper Pike, OH, 44124-4398. Tel: 440-449-4202. Fax: 440-449-3180. p. 1929

Fisher, Kathy, Asst Librn, Roy City Library, 122 Third St E, Roy, WA, 98580. Tel: 253-843-2331. Fax: 253-843-0279. p. 2527

Fisher, Katie, Circ, Iliff School of Theology, 2201 S University Blvd, Denver, CO, 80210. Tel: 303-765-3173. Fax: 303-777-0164. p. 302

Fisher, Kelly A, Pub Serv Librn, Eureka College, 301 E College Ave, Eureka, IL, 61530-1563. Tel: 309-467-6380. Fax: 309-467-6386. p. 643

Fisher, Kris, Librn, Mercy Hospital of Tiffin, 45 St Lawrence Dr, Tiffin, OH, 44883. Tel: 419-455-7000. p. 1938

Fisher, Laura, Dir, Mechanicville District Public Library, 190 N Main St, Mechanicville, NY, 12118. Tel: 518-664-4646. Fax: 518-664-8641. p. 1659

Fisher, Lee Ann, City Librn, Decatur Public Library, 130 N Franklin St, Decatur, IL, 62523-1327. Tel: 217-421-9713. Fax: 217-233-4071. p. 633

Fisher, Linda, Head Govt Publ, Indiana University South Bend, 1700 Mishawaka Ave, South Bend, IN, 46615. Tel: 574-520-4442. Fax: 574-520-4472. p. 778

Fisher, Lori, Dir, Baker Free Library, 509 South St, Bow, NH, 03304-3413. Tel: 603-224-7113. Fax: 603-224-2063. p. 1439

Fisher, Lori Ann, Curator, National Museum of Racing & Hall of Fame, 191 Union Ave, Saratoga Springs, NY, 12866. Tel: 518-584-0400, Ext 109. Fax: 518-584-4574. p. 1738

Fisher, LuAnn, Bibliog Instr, Hagerstown Community College Library, 11400 Robinwood Dr, Hagerstown, MD, 21742-6590. Tel: 301-790-2800, Ext 237. Fax: 301-393-3681. p. 1031

Fisher, Mary Jane, Dir, Coos County Library Service District, Tioga Hall, 1988 Newmark Ave, Coos Bay, OR, 97420. Tel: 541-888-7393. Fax: 541-888-1529. p. 2953

Fisher, Nancy D, Dir, Wickliffe Public Library, 1713 Lincoln Rd, Wickliffe, OH, 44092. Tel: 440-944-6010. Fax: 440-944-7264. p. 1947

Fisher, Naomi, Commun Librn, Fort Vancouver Regional Library District, Goldendale Community Library, 131 W Burgen, Goldendale, WA, 98620. Tel: 509-773-4487. p. 2546

Fisher, Patrice, Librn, University of Arkansas-Pine Bluff, Nursing Lab, 1200 University Dr, Mail Slot 4973, Pine Bluff, AR, 71611. Tel: 870-575-8220. Fax: 870-575-8229. p. 113

Fisher, Patricia, Dir, Toccoa Falls College, PO Box 800749, Toccoa Falls, GA, 30598. Tel: 706-886-6831, Ext 5300. Fax: 706-282-6010. p. 554

Fisher, Patricia, Ref, Cape Cod Community College, 2240 Iyannough Rd, West Barnstable, MA, 02668-1599. Tel: 508-362-2131, Ext 4636. Fax: 508-375-4020. p. 1136

Fisher, Patricia, Acq Librn, Ser Librn, Valley City State University Library, 101 College St SW, Valley City, ND, 58072-4098. Tel: 701-845-7276. Fax: 701-845-7437. p. 1848

Fisher, Patricia Ann, Dir, West Salem Public Library, 112 W South St, West Salem, IL, 62476-1206. Tel: 618-456-8970. Fax: 618-456-8970. p. 717

Fisher, Rayma, Asst Librn, Edgewood Public Library, 203 W Union St, Edgewood, IA, 52042. Tel: 563-928-6242. Fax: 563-928-6242. p. 813

Fisher, Sarah, Head Librn, Montgomery College, School of Art & Design, 7600 Takoma Ave, Takoma Park, MD, 20912. Tel: 240-567-1544. Fax: 301-649-2940. p. 1037

Fisher, Sarah, Head Librn, Montgomery College, Takoma Park Campus Library, 7600 Takoma Ave, Takoma Park, MD, 20912. Tel: 301-650-1544. Fax: 240-567-5820. p. 1037

Fisher, Shari, Bus & Finance Mgr, Arrowhead Library System, 5528 Emerald Ave, Mountain Iron, MN, 55768-2069. Tel: 218-741-3840. Fax: 218-748-2171. p. 1267

Fisher, Sheila, ILL, Susquehanna University, 514 University Ave, Selinsgrove, PA, 17870-1050. Tel: 570-372-4326. Fax: 570-372-4310. p. 2138

Fisher, Sondra K, Asst Dir, Syst Adminr, Girard Free Library, 105 E Prospect St, Girard, OH, 44420-1899. Tel: 330-545-2508. Fax: 330-545-8213. p. 1902

Fisher, Steven, Rare Bks, Spec Coll Librn, University of Denver, 2150 E Evans Ave, Denver, CO, 80208-2007. Tel: 303-871-3441. Fax: 303-871-2290. p. 303

Fisher, Susan, Br Head, Williamson County Public Library, Bethesda, 4905 Bethesda Rd, Thompson Station, TN, 37179-9231. Tel: 615-790-1887. Fax: 615-790-8426. p. 2234

Fisher, Suzanne, Adult Serv, Ref, Voorheesville Public Library, 51 School Rd, Voorheesville, NY, 12186. Tel: 518-765-2791. Fax: 518-765-3007. p. 1761

Fisher, Terry, Librn, Gable & Gotwals, Inc, 1100 Oneok Plaza, 100 W Fifth St, Tulsa, OK, 74103-4217. Tel: 918-595-4955. Fax: 918-595-4990. p. 1980

Fisher, Toi, Librn, Jeff Davis County Library, 100 Memorial Sq, Fort Davis, TX, 79734. Tel: 432-426-3802. Fax: 432-426-2225. p. 2320

Fisher, W Martin, Mgr, Recorded Media Coll, Middle Tennessee State University, Center for Popular Music, John Bragg Mass

Communication Bldg, Rm 140, 1301 E Main St, Murfreesboro, TN, 37132. Tel: 615-898-5509. Fax: 615-898-5829. p. 2254

Fisher-Giles, Janice, Chief Librn, Fort Lupton Public & School Library, 425 S Denver Ave, Fort Lupton, CO, 80621-1303. Tel: 303-857-7180. Fax: 303-857-7190. p. 308

Fisher-Herreman, Scarlett, Supvr, Tech Serv, Topeka & Shawnee County Public Library, 1515 SW Tenth Ave, Topeka, KS, 66604-1374. Tel: 785-580-4400. Fax: 785-580-4496. p. 897

Fisher-Miller, Mary, Dir, Chatsworth Township Library, 432 E Locust St, Chatsworth, IL, 60921. Tel: 815-635-3004. Fax: 815-635-3004. p. 604

Fishler, Claudia, Asst City Librn, Santa Monica Public Library, 601 Santa Monica Blvd, Santa Monica, CA, 90401. Tel: 310-458-8607. Fax: 310-394-8951. p. 266

Fishman, Cheryl, Youth Serv Librn, Boynton Beach City Library, 208 S Seacrest Blvd, Boynton Beach, FL, 33435. Tel: 561-742-6390. Fax: 561-742-6381. p. 429

Fishman, Karen, Archivist, Asst Curator, University of Maryland Libraries, Broadcast Pioneers Library of American Broadcasting, Hornbake Library, College Park, MD, 20742. Tel: 301-405-9160. Fax: 301-314-2634. p. 1025

Fishman, Natalya, Head, Ref, Morton Grove Public Library, 6140 Lincoln Ave, Morton Grove, IL, 60053-2989. Tel: 847-929-5117. Fax: 847-965-7903. p. 676

Fishman, Tammy, Head Librn, California Youth Authority, N A Chaderjian Youth Correctional Facility Library, 7650 S Newcastle Rd, Stockton, CA, 95213. Tel: 209-944-6444, Ext 6755. Fax: 209-944-6167. p. 272

Fisk, Francine, Dir, University of Tulsa Libraries, 2933 E Sixth St, Tulsa, OK, 74104-3123. Tel: 918-631-2495. Fax: 918-631-2150. p. 1984

Fisk, James, Ref/Bibliog Instruction Librn, Morningside College, 1601 Morningside Ave, Sioux City, IA, 51106. Tel: 712-274-5246. Fax: 712-274-5224. p. 844

Fiske, Marti, Dir, Dorothy Alling Memorial Library, 21 Library Lane, Williston, VT, 05495. Tel: 802-878-4918. Fax: 802-878-3964. p. 2440

Fisken, Patricia B, Head of Librn, Dartmouth College Library, Paddock Music Library, 6245 Hopkins Ctr, Hanover, NH, 03755. Tel: 603-646-3120. Fax: 603-646-1219. p. 1450

Fister, Barbara, Chair, Gustavus Adolphus College, 800 W College Ave, Saint Peter, MN, 56082. Tel: 507-933-7553. Fax: 507-933-6292. p. 1283

Fistrovic, Olivija, Dir, Libr Serv, Saints Mary & Elizabeth Medical Center, 2233 W Division St, Chicago, IL, 60622. Tel: 312-770-2219. Fax: 312-770-2221. p. 624

Fitch, Brooks, Dir of Develop, University of Massachusetts Amherst, 154 Hicks Way, Amherst, MA, 01003-9275. Tel: 413-545-6483. Fax: 413-545-6873. p. 1049

Fitch, Elizabeth, Br Mgr, Presque Isle District Library, Grand Lake Branch, 18132 Lake Esau Hwy, Presque Isle, MI, 49777. Tel: 989-595-5051. Fax: 989-595-3146. p. 1222

Fitch, Jacquie, Actg Librn, Napa State Hospital, John Stewart Richie Patients' Library, 2100 Napa-Vallejo Hwy, Napa, CA, 94558-6293. Tel: 707-253-5351. Fax: 707-253-5682. p. 193

Fitch, Leslie, Chief Exec Officer, Milton Public Library, 1010 Main St E, Milton, ON, L9T 6H7, CANADA. Tel: 905-875-2665, Ext 3252. Fax: 905-875-4324. p. 2822

Fitch, Linda, Librn, Education Northwest, 101 SW Main St, Ste 500, Portland, OR, 97204. Tel: 503-275-9554. Fax: 503-275-0458. p. 2010

Fitch, Meg, Librn, Castleton Free Library, Main St, Castleton, VT, 05735. Tel: 802-468-5574. p. 2421

Fitch, Sandra, Dir, Ritzville Library District No 2, 302 W Main Ave, Ritzville, WA, 99169. Tel: 509-659-1222. Fax: 509-659-1232. p. 2526

Fitch, Teresa, Admin Senior Librn, Breckenridge Library, 209 N Breckenridge Ave, Breckenridge, TX, 76424. Tel: 254-559-5505. Fax: 254-559-5505. p. 2291

Fitch, Wendy, Exec Dir, Museums Association of Saskatchewan, 424 McDonald St, Regina, SK, S4N 6E1, CANADA. Tel: 306-780-9280. Fax: 306-780-9463. p. 2923

Fitchett, Christine, Govt Doc, Tech Serv Librn, Vassar College Library, 124 Raymond Ave, Maildrop 20, Poughkeepsie, NY, 12604-0020. Tel: 845-437-5760. Fax: 845-437-5864. p. 1723

Fitchett, Taylor, Dir, University of Virginia, Arthur J Morris Law Library, 580 Massie Rd, Charlottesville, VA, 22903-1789. Tel: 434-924-7725. Fax: 434-924-7239. p. 2455

Fite, Diane, Asst Dir, Gilbreath Memorial Library, 916 N Main St, Winnsboro, TX, 75494. Tel: 903-342-6866. p. 2401

Fite, Donna, Mgr, Lamar County Library System, Purvis Public, 122 Shelby Speights Dr, Purvis, MS, 39475-4151. Tel: 601-794-6291. Fax: 601-794-6291. p. 1313

Fithen, Patricia, Ch, Union Township Public Library, 27 Main St, Ripley, OH, 45167-1231. Tel: 937-392-4871. Fax: 937-392-1631. p. 1932

Fithian, Cathy, Managing Librn, Columbus Metropolitan Library, Driving Park, 1566 E Livingston Ave, Columbus, OH, 43205. Tel: 614-645-2275. Fax: 614-479-4379. p. 1884

Fithian, Gail, Govt Doc, Boston Public Library, 700 Boylston St, Boston, MA, 02117-0286. Tel: 617-536-5400. Fax: 617-236-4306. p. 1056

Fitol, Janet, Ch, Ansonia Library, 53 S Cliff St, Ansonia, CT, 06401-1909. Tel: 203-734-6275. Fax: 203-732-4551. p. 329

Fittante, Patricia J, Ch, Escanaba Public Library, 400 Ludington St, Escanaba, MI, 49829. Tel: 906-789-7323. Fax: 906-786-0942. p. 1177

Fitterling, Lori A, Digital Serv, Ref Librn, Kansas City University of Medicine & Biosciences D'Angelo Library, 1750 Independence Ave, Kansas City, MO, 64106-1453. Tel: 816-654-7260. Fax: 816-654-7261. p. 1338

Fitts, Dorothy, Librn, First Regional Library, Lafayette County-Oxford Public Library, 401 Bramlett Blvd, Oxford, MS, 38655. Tel: 662-234-5751. Fax: 662-234-3155. p. 1301

Fitts, Michael, Access Serv, University of Alabama at Birmingham, Lister Hill Library of the Health Sciences, 1700 University Blvd, Birmingham, AL, 35294-0013. Tel: 205-934-5460. Fax: 205-934-3545. p. 10

Fitz-Gerald, Kerry, Ref, Seattle University, School of Law Library, Sullivan Hall, 901 12th Ave, Seattle, WA, 98122-4411. Tel: 206-398-4221. Fax: 206-398-4194. p. 2532

Fitzanko, Joe, Govt Doc, Peoria Public Library, 107 NE Monroe St, Peoria, IL, 61602-1070. Tel: 309-497-2145. Fax: 309-497-2007. p. 690

Fitzer, Maureen, Mgr, Libr Serv, Buckman Laboratories International, Inc, 1256 N McLean Blvd, Memphis, TN, 38108. Tel: 901-272-8585. Fax: 901-272-8583. p. 2248

Fitzgerald, Adele, Br Mgr, Cabarrus County Public Library, Harrisburg Branch, 201 Sims Pkwy, Harrisburg, NC, 28075. Tel: 704-920-2080. Fax: 704-455-2017. p. 1785

Fitzgerald, Angie, Educ Dir, Obion County Public Library, 1221 E Reelfoot Ave, Union City, TN, 38261-5097. Tel: 731-885-7000, 731-885-9411. Fax: 731-885-9638. p. 2268

Fitzgerald, Barbara, Teen Librn, Mount Prospect Public Library, Ten S Emerson St, Mount Prospect, IL, 60056. Tel: 847-253-5675. Fax: 847-253-0642. p. 677

Fitzgerald, Barbara, Adult Serv, Richard Salter Storrs Library, 693 Longmeadow St, Longmeadow, MA, 01106. Tel: 413-565-4181. Fax: 413-565-4183. p. 1100

Fitzgerald, Catherine, Chief Librn, New York City Law Department, 100 Church St, Rm 6-310, New York, NY, 10007. Tel: 212-788-1669. Fax: 212-788-1239. p. 1688

Fitzgerald, Constance, Archivist, Carmelite Monastery, 1318 Dulaney Valley Rd, Baltimore, MD, 21286-1399. Tel: 410-823-7415. Fax: 410-823-7418. p. 1012

Fitzgerald, Deborah R, Adult Serv, Joint Free Public Library of the Chathams, 214 Main St, Chatham, NJ, 07928. Tel: 973-635-0603. Fax: 973-635-7827. p. 1478

Fitzgerald, Desiree, Dir, Pomeroy Public Library, 114 S Ontario St, Pomeroy, IA, 50575-7702. Tel: 712-468-2311. Fax: 712-468-2311. p. 839

Fitzgerald, Diana, Librn, Sibley Memorial Hospital, 5255 Loughboro Rd NW, Washington, DC, 20016. Tel: 202-537-4110. p. 414

Fitzgerald, Edward, Dr, Dir, Quincy Historical Society Library, Adams Academy Bldg, Eight Adams St, Quincy, MA, 02169. Tel: 617-773-1144. Fax: 617-472-4990. p. 1120

Fitzgerald, Eileen, Adult Serv, Rowley Public Library, 141 Main St, Rowley, MA, 01969. Tel: 978-948-2850. Fax: 978-948-2266. p. 1121

Fitzgerald, Elizabeth, Head of Librn, Free Library of Philadelphia, Haverford Avenue Branch, 5543 Haverford Ave, Philadelphia, PA, 19139-1432. Tel: 215-685-1964, 215-685-1965. Fax: 215-685-1966. p. 2108

Fitzgerald, Gail, Prof, University of Missouri-Columbia, 303 Townsend Hall, Columbia, MO, 65211. Tel: 573-882-4546. Fax: 573-884-2917. p. 2968

Fitzgerald, Gregory, Head of Librn, Western Michigan University, Music & Dance, 3006 Dalton Ctr, 3rd Flr, Kalamazoo, MI, 49008. Tel: 269-387-5236. Fax: 269-387-5809. p. 1198

Fitzgerald, John, Head, Cat, Head, Circ, Tiverton Library Services, 238 Highland Rd, Tiverton, RI, 02878. Tel: 401-625-6796. Fax: 401-625-5499. p. 2176

Fitzgerald, Karen, Tech Serv Coordr, Douglas County Public Library, 1625 Library Lane, Minden, NV, 89423-4420. Tel: 775-782-9841. Fax: 775-782-5754. p. 1431

Fitzgerald, Kate, Circ, West Hartford Public Library, Julia Faxon Branch, 1073 New Britain Ave, West Hartford, CT, 06110. Tel: 860-561-8200. p. 376

Fitzgerald, Kerry, Asst Dir, Loutit District Library, 407 Columbus Ave, Grand Haven, MI, 49417. Tel: 616-842-5560, Ext 233. Fax: 616-847-0570. p. 1183

Fitzgerald, Linda, Tech Serv Mgr, Bloomington Public Library, 205 E Olive St, Bloomington, IL, 61701. Tel: 309-828-6091. Fax: 309-828-7312. p. 595

Fitzgerald, Linda, Circ Supvr, Plymouth Public Library, 132 South St, Plymouth, MA, 02360-3309. Tel: 508-830-4250. Fax: 508-830-4258. p. 1118

Fitzgerald, Liz, Dir, Glenside Public Library District, 25 E Fullerton Ave, Glendale Heights, IL, 60139-2697. Tel: 630-260-1550. Fax: 630-260-1433. p. 650

Fitzgerald, Michael, Electronic Serv Librn, University of the District of Columbia, Learning Resources Division, 4200 Connecticut Ave NW, Washington, DC, 20008. Tel: 202-274-6370. Fax: 202-274-6012. p. 421

Fitzgerald, Patrick, Librn/Mgr, Rockingham County Public Library, Madison Branch, 140 E Murphy St, Madison, NC, 27025. Tel: 336-548-6553. Fax: 336-548-2010. p. 1790

Fitzgerald, Patrick, Librn/Mgr, Rockingham County Public Library, Mayodan Branch, 101 N Tenth Ave, Mayodan, NC, 27027. Tel: 336-548-6951. Fax: 336-548-2015. p. 1790

Fitzgerald, Patrick, Librn/Mgr, Rockingham County Public Library, Stoneville Branch, 201 E Main St, Stoneville, NC, 27048-8714. Tel: 336-573-2094. Fax: 336-573-2774. p. 1790

Fitzgerald, Rebecca, Acq, Concordia College, 171 White Plains Rd, Bronxville, NY, 10708. Tel: 914-337-9300, Ext 2202. Fax: 914-395-4893. p. 1588

Fitzgerald, Sharon, Tech Serv, University of Maine, 5729 Fogler Library, Orono, ME, 04469-5729. Fax: 207-581-1653. p. 995

Fitzgerald-Bell, Susan, Br Mgr, Burlington Public Library, Aldershot, 550 Plains Rd E, Burlington, ON, L7T 2E3, CANADA. Tel: 905-333-9995. p. 2798

Fitzgibbon, Sheila, Sr Dir, Christopher & Dana Reeve Foundation, 636 Morris Tpk, Ste 3A, Short Hills, NJ, 07078. Tel: 973-467-8270. Fax: 973-467-9845. p. 1529

Fitzgibbon, Willow, Actg Head of Ref, Fayetteville Public Library, 401 W Mountain St, Fayetteville, AR, 72701. Tel: 479-856-7000. Fax: 479-571-0222. p. 99

Fitzgibbons, Eileen, Ch, Norfolk Library, Nine Greenwoods Rd E, Norfolk, CT, 06058-1320. Tel: 860-542-5075. Fax: 860-542-1795. p. 361

Fitzherbert, Casandra, Head, Access Serv, University of Southern Maine, 314 Forest Ave, Portland, ME, 04104. Tel: 207-780-4279. Fax: 207-780-4042. p. 998

Fitzhugh, Gerald, Asst Dir, Human Res, Security & Phys Plant, Newark Public Library, Five Washington St, Newark, NJ, 07101. Tel: 973-733-7748. Fax: 973-733-5648. p. 1511

Fitzhugh, Kathryn, Ref Serv, Spec Coll Librn, University of Arkansas at Little Rock, Pulaski County Law Library, 1203 McMath Ave, Little Rock, AR, 72202-5142. Tel: 501-324-9444. Fax: 501-324-9447. p. 107

Fitzmaurice, Judy, In Charge, Schenectady County Public Library, Rotterdam, 1100 N Westcott Rd, Rotterdam, NY, 12306. Tel: 518-356-3440. Fax: 518-356-3467. p. 1741

Fitzmorris, Margie, Br Supvr, Latah County Library District, Troy Branch, 402 S Main St, Troy, ID, 83871. Tel: 208-835-4311. Fax: 208-835-4311. p. 579

Fitzpatrick, Aidan, Digital Imaging Tech, School of the Art Institute of Chicago, 37 S Wabash Ave, Chicago, IL, 60603-3103. Tel: 312-899-5097. Fax: 312-899-1851. p. 624

Fitzpatrick, Frank, Dir, Orange County Sheriff-Coroner, 320 N Flower St, Santa Ana, CA, 92703-5002. Tel: 714-834-4510. Fax: 714-834-4519. p. 259

Fitzpatrick, Geoff, IT Serv Mgr, Whatcom County Library System, 5205 Northwest Dr, Bellingham, WA, 98226-9050. Tel: 360-384-3150. Fax: 360-384-4947. p. 2509

Fitzpatrick, Jane, Acq, City University of New York, 365 Fifth Ave, New York, NY, 10016-4309. Tel: 212-817-7056. Fax: 212-817-2982. p. 1673

Fitzpatrick, Katie, Head, Tech Serv, Upper Moreland Free Public Library, 109 Park Ave, Willow Grove, PA, 19090-3277. Tel: 215-659-0741. Fax: 215-830-1223. p. 2157

Fitzpatrick, Mary, Asst Librn, McLaren Regional Medical Center, 401 S Ballenger Hwy, Flint, MI, 48532-3685. Tel: 810-342-2141. Fax: 810-342-2269. p. 1180

Fitzpatrick, Robert, Emerging Tech Librn, Plymouth State University, Highland St, Plymouth, NH, 03264-1595. Tel: 603-535-2258. Fax: 603-535-2445. p. 1462

Fitzpatrick, Roberta Bronson, Assoc Dir, University of Medicine & Dentistry of New Jersey, 30 12th Ave, Newark, NJ, 07103-2706. Tel: 973-972-4580. p. 1513

Fitzpatrick, Sara, ILL, Webster University, 101 Edgar Rd, Saint Louis, MO, 63119. Tel: 314-246-7807. Fax: 314-968-7113. p. 1363

Fitzpatrick, Sarah L, Chief Librn, Department of Veterans Affairs, VA Domiciliary, 142-D, 8495 Crater Lake Hwy, White City, OR, 97503. Tel: 541-826-2111, Ext 3297. Fax: 541-830-3503. p. 2023

Fitzpatrick, Tara, Soc Sci Librn, Salem State University Library, 352 Lafayette St, Salem, MA, 01970-5353. Tel: 978-542-6765. Fax: 978-542-6596. p. 1122

Fitzsimmons, John, Libr Syst Spec, Ref Librn, Truckee Meadows Community College, 7000 Dandini Blvd, Reno, NV, 89512-3999. Tel: 775-674-7609. Fax: 775-673-8231. p. 1432

Fitzsimmons, Phillip, Ref & Digitization Librn, Southwestern Oklahoma State University, 100 Campus Dr, Weatherford, OK, 73096-3002. Tel: 580-774-3030. Fax: 580-774-3112. p. 1985

Fitzsimons, Pamela, Head, Circ, East Islip Public Library, 381 E Main St, East Islip, NY, 11730-2896. Tel: 631-581-9200. Fax: 631-581-2245. p. 1617

Fitzwater, Diana, Ref & Instrul Serv, Instr Coordr, College of DuPage Library, 425 Fawell Blvd, Glen Ellyn, IL, 60137-6599. Tel: 630-942-2078. Fax: 630-858-8757. p. 649

Fix, Trudy, Br Mgr, Fulton County Library, Hustontown Branch, 313 Pitt St, Ste B, Hustontown, PA, 17229. Tel: 717-987-3606. Fax: 717-987-3606. p. 2085

Fjeldsted, Steven Warren, Libr Dir, South Pasadena Public Library, 1100 Oxley St, South Pasadena, CA, 91030-3198. Tel: 626-403-7333. Fax: 626-403-7331. p. 270

Fjelstad, Paul, Librn, Kitsap County Law Library, 614 Division St, Port Orchard, WA, 98366. Tel: 360-613-5071. Fax: 360-337-5789. p. 2524

Flach, Barbara, Dir, Greenville Public Library, North St, Rte 32, Greenville, NY, 12083. Tel: 518-966-8205. Fax: 518-966-4822. p. 1631

Flageolle, Barbara, Librn, Wright County Library, Mountain Grove Branch, 206 Green St, Mountain Grove, MO, 65711. Tel: 417-926-4453. Fax: 417-926-6240. p. 1330

Flagg, Mary, Ch, New Berlin Public Library, 15105 Library Lane, New Berlin, WI, 53151. Tel: 262-785-4980. Fax: 262-785-4984. p. 2625

Flaherty, James C, Dir, Public Library of Brookline, 361 Washington St, Brookline, MA, 02445. Tel: 617-730-2360. Fax: 617-730-2160. p. 1071

Flaherty, Jane, Br Mgr, Thompson-Nicola Regional District Library System, Ashcroft Branch, 201 Brink St, Ashcroft, BC, V0K 1A0, CANADA. Tel: 250-453-9042. p. 2729

Flaherty, Jane, Br Mgr, Thompson-Nicola Regional District Library System, Cache Creek Branch, 1390 Quartz Rd, Cache Creek, BC, V0K 1H0, CANADA. Tel: 250-457-9953. p. 2729

Flaherty, Kathleen, Adult Serv, Providence Community Library, Mt Pleasant Library, 315 Academy Ave, Providence, RI, 02908. Tel: 401-272-0106. p. 2173

Flaherty, Marcella, Head, Access Serv, Harvard Library, Gutman Library-Research Center, Graduate School of Educ, Six Appian Way, Cambridge, MA, 02138. Tel: 617-495-4225. Fax: 617-495-0540. p. 1075

Flaherty, Margaret, Mgr, Oregon Trail Library District, Heppner Branch, 444 North Main St, Heppner, OR, 97836. Tel: 541-676-9964. Fax: 541-676-5900. p. 1992

Flaherty, Marie, Mgr, McCowan Memorial Library, 15 Pitman Ave, Pitman, NJ, 08071. Tel: 856-589-1656. Fax: 856-582-4982. p. 1520

Flaherty, Mary, Human Res Mgr, Boston Public Library, 700 Boylston St, Boston, MA, 02117-0286. Tel: 617-536-5400. Fax: 617-236-4306. p. 1056

Flaherty, Rose, Dir, Millville Free Public Library, 169 Main St, Millville, MA, 01529. Tel: 508-883-1887. Fax: 508-883-1887. p. 1106

Flahiff, Janice, Ref Librn, University of Toledo, Health Science Campus, Mail Stop 1061, 3000 Arlington Ave, Toledo, OH, 43614-5805. Tel: 419-383-4223. Fax: 419-383-6146. p. 1940

Flahive, Ryan, Archivist, Institute of American Indian & Alaska Native Culture & Arts Development Library, 83 Avan Nu Po Rd, Santa Fe, NM, 87508. Tel: 505-424-5715. Fax: 505-424-3131. p. 1562

Flake, Donna Bunting, Dir, SEAHEC Medical Library, 2131 S 17th St, Box 9025, Wilmington, NC, 28402-9025. Tel: 910-667-9227. Fax: 910-762-7600. p. 1831

Flaming, Vaughn, Libr Asst, Santa Clara Valley Medical Center, 751 S Bascom Ave, Rm 2E063, San Jose, CA, 95128. Tel: 408-885-5652. Fax: 408-885-5655. p. 252

Flammond, Bonnye, Asst Librn, Sisseton Wahpeton College Library, Agency Village, PO Box 689, Sisseton, SD, 57262-0698. Tel: 605-698-3966, Ext 1320. Fax: 605-698-3132. p. 2219

Flanagan, Christine, In Charge, United States Botanic Garden Library, 245 First St SW, Washington, DC, 20024. Tel: 202-226-8333. Fax: 202-225-1561. p. 417

Flanagan, John, Ref, Broadview Public Library District, 2226 S 16th Ave, Broadview, IL, 60155-4000. Tel: 708-345-1325. Fax: 708-345-5024. p. 597

Flanagan, Karen, Librn, Five Towns College Library, 305 N Service Rd, Dix Hills, NY, 11746. Tel: 631-656-2138. Fax: 631-656-2171. p. 1614

Flanagan, Laura, Dir, Ellicottville Memorial Library, 6499 Maples Rd, Ellicottville, NY, 14731. Tel: 716-699-2842. Fax: 716-699-5597. p. 1619

Flanagan, Laura, Ref Serv, Garden City Public Library, 60 Seventh St, Garden City, NY, 11530-2891. Tel: 516-742-8405. Fax: 516-742-2675. p. 1626

Flanagan, Nissa, Syst/Tech Serv, Merrill Memorial Library, 215 Main St, Yarmouth, ME, 04096. Tel: 207-846-4763. Fax: 207-846-2422. p. 1008

Flanagan, Pamela, Dir, Milo Free Public Library, Four Pleasant St, Milo, ME, 04463-1327. Tel: 207-943-2612. Fax: 207-943-2785. p. 992

Flanagan, Patricia, Assoc Univ Librn, Pub Serv, Virginia Commonwealth University Libraries, James Cabell Branch Library, Monroe Park Campus, 901 Park Ave, Richmond, VA, 23284-2033. Tel: 804-828-9136. Fax: 804-828-0151. p. 2492

Flanagan, Patrick, Ref Librn, Columbia University, Arthur W Diamond Law Library, 435 W 116th St, New York, NY, 10027. Tel: 212-854-3922. Fax: 212-854-3295. p. 1674

Flanary, Allie, Fac Librn-Sylvania Campus, Portland Community College Library, 12000 SW 49th AV, Portland, OR, 97219. Tel: 971-722-4686. Fax: 971-722-8397. p. 2013

Flance, Lynn, Librn, Department of Veterans Affairs, Patient Education Resource Center, 3601 S Sixth Ave, 7-14A, Tucson, AZ, 85723. Tel: 520-792-1450, Ext 6516. Fax: 520-629-4638. p. 86

Flance, Lynn, Librn, Department of Veterans Affairs, Southern Arizona VA Healthcare System, 3601 S Sixth Ave, Tucson, AZ, 85723. Tel: 520-629-1836. Fax: 520-629-4638. p. 86

Flanders, E Lorene, Dir, Univ Libr, Irvine Sullivan Ingram Library, University of West Georgia, 1601 Maple St, Carrollton, GA, 30118. Tel: 678-839-6498. Fax: 678-839-6511. p. 523

Flanders, Jane, Ch, Lincoln Public Library, Three Bedford Rd, Lincoln, MA, 01773. Tel: 781-259-8465. Fax: 781-259-1056. p. 1099

Flanders, Julie, Head, Tech Serv, College of Mount Saint Joseph, 5701 Delhi Rd, Cincinnati, OH, 45233-1671. Tel: 513-244-4798. Fax: 513-244-4355. p. 1869

Flanders, Kristin, Head, Tech Serv, Maywood Public Library District, 121 S Fifth Ave, Maywood, IL, 60153. Tel: 708-343-1847, Ext 15. Fax: 708-343-2115. p. 672

Flanders, Tammy, Ref Serv, University of Calgary Library, Doucette Library of Teaching Resources, 370 Education Block, 2500 University Dr NW, Calgary, AB, T2N 1N4, CANADA. Tel: 403-220-3984. Fax: 403-220-8211. p. 2693

Flandreau, Lee-Anne, Ref Serv, Ad, Forest Grove City Library, 2114 Pacific Ave, Forest Grove, OR, 97116-9019. Tel: 503-992-3248. Fax: 503-992-3333. p. 1998

Flannery, Malta, Asst Dir, Jackson County Public Library, 118 US Hwy, 421 N, McKee, KY, 40447. Tel: 606-287-8113. Fax: 606-287-7774. p. 928

Flannery, Melinda Reagor, Asst Univ Librn, Tech Serv, Rice University, 6100 Main, MS-44, Houston, TX, 77005. Tel: 713-348-3773. Fax: 713-348-5258. p. 2341

Flannery, Mike, Spec Coll Librn, University of Alabama at Birmingham, Lister Hill Library of the Health Sciences, 1700 University Blvd, Birmingham, AL, 35294-0013. Tel: 205-934-5460. Fax: 205-934-3545. p. 10

Flannery, Susan, Dir, Cambridge Public Library, 449 Broadway, Cambridge, MA, 02138. Tel: 617-349-4040. Fax: 617-349-4028. p. 1073

Flannery, Tatanya, Ref Serv, Weston Public Library, 87 School St, Weston, MA, 02493. Tel: 781-893-3312. Fax: 781-529-0174. p. 1139

Flannery-Climes, Mary Susan, Coll Develop, Middletown Thrall Library, 11-19 Depot St, Middletown, NY, 10940. Tel: 845-341-5454. Fax: 845-341-5480. p. 1660

Flanzraich, Gerri, Librn, New York Institute of Technology, PO Box 8000, Old Westbury, NY, 11568-8000. Tel: 516-686-7657. Fax: 516-686-1320. p. 1710

Flaspohler, Molly, Spec Projects Librn, Concordia College, 901 S Eighth St, Moorhead, MN, 56562. Tel: 218-299-4643. Fax: 218-299-4253. p. 1265

Flass, Kirsten, Dir, Rush Public Library, 5977 E Henrietta Rd, Rush, NY, 14543. Tel: 585-533-1370. Fax: 585-533-1546. p. 1736

Flater, Elizabeth, Coll Develop Librn, California Baptist University, 8432 Magnolia Ave, Riverside, CA, 92504. Tel: 951-552-8624. Fax: eflater@calbaptist.edu. p. 216

Flater, Melinda, Libr Dir, Salisbury Free Library, 641 Old Turnpike Rd, Salisbury, NH, 03268. Tel: 603-648-2278. Fax: 603-648-2278. p. 1464

Flath, Bruce, Cat, Mount Angel Abbey Library, One Abbey Dr, Saint Benedict, OR, 97373. Tel: 503-845-3303, 503-845-3317. Fax: 503-845-3500. p. 2017

Flath, Clara, ILL, E C Scranton Memorial Library, 801 Boston Post Rd, Madison, CT, 06443. Tel: 203-245-7365. Fax: 203-245-7821. p. 349

Flatley, Bob, Electronic Res, ILL, Per, Kutztown University, 15200 Kutztown Rd, Bldg 5, Kutztown, PA, 19530-0735. Tel: 610-683-4484. Fax: 610-683-4747. p. 2075

Flavell, Betty, Librn, Cottage Health System, 401 W Pueblo St, Santa Barbara, CA, 93105. Tel: 805-569-7240. Fax: 805-569-7588. p. 260

Flavell, Linda, Br Head, Toronto Public Library, Highland Creek, 3550 Ellesmere Rd, Toronto, ON, M1C 3Z2, CANADA. Tel: 416-396-8876. Fax: 416-396-3562. p. 2861

Flaxbart, David, Librn, University of Texas Libraries, Mallet Chemistry Library, Welch Hall 2.132, Austin, TX, 78712. Tel: 512-495-4600. p. 2284

Flaxbart, Jenifer, Ref, University of Texas Libraries, Perry-Castaneda Library (Main Library), 101 E 21st St, Austin, TX, 78712-1266. Tel: 512-495-4350. p. 2284

Flaxbeard, Lisa M, Dir, Bennington Public Library, 15505 Warehouse St, Bennington, NE, 68007. Tel: 402-238-2201. Fax: 402-238-2218. p. 1394

Flayer, Steven, Dir, Shiawassee District Library, 502 W Main St, Owosso, MI, 48867-2607. Tel: 989-725-5134. Fax: 989-723-5444. p. 1216

Fleagle, Ted, Dir, Human Res, Arapahoe Library District, 12855 E Adam Aircraft Circle, Englewood, CO, 80112. Tel: 303-542-7279. Fax: 303-798-2485. p. 305

Fleck, Janet, Adult Serv, Closter Public Library, 280 High St, Closter, NJ, 07624-1898. Tel: 201-768-4197. Fax: 201-768-4220. p. 1479

Fleck, Nancy, Assoc Dir, Tech Serv & Syst, Michigan State University Library, 100 Library, East Lansing, MI, 48824-1048. Tel: 517-884-6455. Fax: 517-353-8969. p. 1175

Fleckenstein, Jan, Assoc Dir, Head, Info Serv, Syracuse University College of Law Library, E I White Hall, Syracuse, NY, 13244-1030. Tel: 315-443-9531. Fax: 315-443-9567. p. 1753

Flecker, Dale P, Assoc Dir, Harvard Library, 1341 Massachusetts Ave, Wadsworth House, Cambridge, MA, 02138. Tel: 617-495-3650. Fax: 617-495-0370. p. 1073

Fleckner Ducey, Maxine, Librn, University of Wisconsin-Madison, Wisconsin Center for Film & Theater Research, 816 State St, Madison, WI, 53706. Tel: 608-264-6467. Fax: 608-264-6472. p. 2610

Fleeger, Dale, Dir, Weatherford Public Library, 1014 Charles St, Weatherford, TX, 76086-5098. Tel: 817-598-4269. Fax: 817-598-4161. p. 2399

Fleek, Laura, Librn, Fresno County Public Library, Woodward Park Regional, 944 E Perrin Ave, Fresno, CA, 93720. Tel: 559-600-3135. Fax: 559-600-1348. p. 153

Fleenor, Jennifer, Youth Serv Librn, Estacada Public Library, 825 NW Wade St, Estacada, OR, 97023. Tel: 503-630-8273. Fax: 503-630-8282. p. 1996

Fleet, Deborah D, Dir, Voluntown Public Library, 107 Main St, Voluntown, CT, 06384-1820. Tel: 860-376-0485. Fax: 860-376-4324. p. 373

Fleet, Frances A, Dir, Tiffin University, 139 Miami St, Tiffin, OH, 44883-2162. Tel: 419-448-3435. Fax: 419-443-5013. p. 1938

Fleetwood, Mark, Head Librn, Department of Veterans Affairs, 800 Hospital Dr, Columbia, MO, 65201. Tel: 573-814-6515. Fax: 573-814-6516. p. 1324

Fleiger, David, Asst Librn, Augusta Memorial Public Library, 113 N Stone St, Augusta, WI, 54722-6000. Tel: 715-286-2070. Fax: 715-286-5367. p. 2579

Fleischer, Alicia, Cat, Nogales-Santa Cruz County Public Library, 518 N Grand Ave, Nogales, AZ, 85621. Tel: 520-287-3343. Fax: 520-287-4823. p. 69

Fleischer, Anne, Br Mgr, Williams County Public Library, Edgerton Branch, 319 N Michigan Ave, Edgerton, OH, 43517. Tel: 419-298-3230. Fax: 419-298-3230. p. 1862

Fleischer, Constance, Ref Serv, University of Chicago Library, D'Angelo Law Library, 1121 E 60th St, Chicago, IL, 60637-2786. Tel: 773-702-0211. Fax: 773-702-2889. p. 627

Fleischer, Leona, Asst Librn, Jewish Federation Libraries, Archives of the Jewish Federation of Nashville & Middle Tennessee, 801 Percy Warner Blvd, Nashville, TN, 37205. Tel: 615-356-3242, Ext 255. Fax: 615-352-0056. p. 2256

Fleischer, Victor S, Head, Archival Serv, University of Akron Libraries, 315 Buchtel Mall, Akron, OH, 44325-1701. Tel: 330-972-6253. Fax: 330-972-6170. p. 1853

Fleishauer, Carol, Assoc Dir, Coll Serv, Massachusetts Institute of Technology Libraries, Office of the Director, 160 Memorial Dr, Cambridge, MA, 02142. Tel: 617-253-5651, 617-253-5655. Fax: 617-253-8894. p. 1077

Fleishman, Dorothy, Media Serv, Per, Ref, Paramus Public Library, E 116 Century Rd, Paramus, NJ, 07652-4398. Tel: 201-599-1300. Fax: 201-599-0059. p. 1517

Flem-Ath, Rand, Libr Mgr, Vancouver Island Regional Library, Masset Branch, 2123 Collison, Masset, BC, V0T 1M0, CANADA. Tel: 250-626-3663. Fax: 250-626-3663. p. 2733

Flem-Ath, Rand, Libr Mgr, Vancouver Island Regional Library, Port Clements Branch, 35 Cedar Ave W, Port Clements, BC, V0T 1R0, CANADA. Tel: 250-557-4402. Fax: 250-557-4402. p. 2733

Flem-Ath, Rand, Libr Mgr, Vancouver Island Regional Library, Port Renfrew Branch, General Delivery, Elementary School, Port Renfrew, BC, V0S 1K0, CANADA. Tel: 250-647-5423. Fax: 250-647-5400. p. 2733

Flem-Ath, Rand, Libr Mgr, Vancouver Island Regional Library, Queen Charlotte City Branch, Community Hall, 138 Bay, Queen Charlotte City, BC, V0T 1S0, CANADA. Tel: 250-559-4518. Fax: 250-559-4518. p. 2733

Flem-Ath, Rand, Libr Mgr, Vancouver Island Regional Library, Sandspit Branch, Seabreeze Plaza, Sandspit, BC, V0T 1T0, CANADA. Tel: 250-637-2247. Fax: 250-637-2247. p. 2733

Flem-Ath, Rand, Libr Mgr, Vancouver Island Regional Library, Tofino Branch, 331 Main St, Tofino, BC, V0R 2Z0, CANADA. Tel: 250-725-3713. Fax: 250-725-3743. p. 2733

Flem-Ath, Rand, Libr Mgr, Vancouver Island Regional Library, Ucluelet Branch, 1768 Peninsula, Ucluelet, BC, V0R 3A0, CANADA. Tel: 250-726-4642. Fax: 250-726-4622. p. 2733

Fleming, Adonna, In Charge, University of Nebraska-Lincoln, Geology Library, Bessey Hall, Rm 10, City Campus 0344, Lincoln, NE, 68588-0344. Tel: 402-472-3628. p. 1407

Fleming, Adonna, In Charge, University of Nebraska-Lincoln, Mathematics Library, 14 Avery Hall, Lincoln, NE, 68588-0129. Tel: 402-472-6900. p. 1407

Fleming, Ann, Head, Tech Serv, Palm Beach County Library System, Palm Beach County Library Annex, 4639 Lake Worth Rd, Greenacres, FL, 33463-3451. Tel: 561-649-5500. Fax: 561-649-5402. p. 503

Fleming, Ann, Tech Serv, Palm Beach County Library System, 3650 Summit Blvd, West Palm Beach, FL, 33406-4198. Tel: 561-649-5500. Fax: 561-233-2692. p. 503

Fleming, Bill, Asst Dir, Libr Tech, Library of Rush University Medical Center, Armour Academic Ctr, 600 S Paulina St, 5th Flr, Chicago, IL, 60612-3874. Tel: 312-942-6832. Fax: 312-942-2234. p. 617

Fleming, Bonnie Elizabeth, PhD, Music Librn, Oklahoma City University, Dulaney-Browne Library, 2501 N Blackwelder, Oklahoma City, OK, 73106. Tel: 405-208-5068. Fax: 405-208-5291. p. 1974

Fleming, Carol, Dir, Asheville-Buncombe Technical Community College, 340 Victoria Rd, Asheville, NC, 28801. Tel: 828-254-1921, Ext 301. Fax: 828-251-6074. p. 1774

Fleming, Cate, YA Serv, Harper Woods Public Library, 19601 Harper, Harper Woods, MI, 48225-2001. Tel: 313-343-2575. Fax: 313-343-2127. p. 1188

Fleming, Cindy, Educ Dir, Logan Regional Medical Center, 20 Hospital Dr, Logan, WV, 25601. Tel: 304-831-1556. Fax: 304-831-1669. p. 2564

Fleming, Darlene, Chief Librn, Veterans Affairs Medical Center, 77 Wainwright Dr, Walla Walla, WA, 99362-3994. Tel: 509-525-5200, Ext 22833. Fax: 509-527-6106. p. 2547

Fleming, Deborah, Ref & Assessment Librn, Alliant International University, 10455 Pomerado Rd, San Diego, CA, 92131-1799. Tel: 858-635-4474. Fax: 858-635-4599. p. 230

Fleming, Declan, Head, Tech Serv, University of California, San Diego, 9500 Gilman Dr, Mail Code 0175G, La Jolla, CA, 92093-0175. Tel: 858-534-7476. Fax: 858-534-6206. p. 162

Fleming, Geoffrey K, Dir, Southold Historical Society Museum Library, 54325 Main Rd, Southold, NY, 11971. Tel: 631-765-5500. Fax: 631-765-8510. p. 1746

Fleming, Janice, In Charge, Merrimack Valley Hospital, 140 Lincoln Ave, Haverhill, MA, 01830. Tel: 978-374-2000, 978-521-8542. p. 1094

Fleming, Jason, Interim Dir, Barton College, 400 Atlantic Christian College Dr NE, Wilson, NC, 27893. Tel: 252-399-6505. Fax: 252-399-6571. p. 1831

Fleming, John, Virtual Serv Mgr, Stanislaus County Free Library, 1500 I St, Modesto, CA, 95354-1166. Tel: 209-558-7800. Fax: 209-529-4779. p. 188

Fleming, Judy, Supvr, Access Serv, Glendale Community College, 6000 W Olive Ave, Glendale, AZ, 85302. Tel: 623-845-3117. Fax: 623-845-3102. p. 64

Fleming, Katherine L, Archivist, Barry University, 11300 NE Second Ave, Miami, FL, 33161. Tel: 305-899-3760. Fax: 305-899-4792. p. 464

Fleming, Nell, Librn, Wisconsin School for the Deaf, 309 W Walworth Ave, Delavan, WI, 53115. Tel: 262-728-7127, Ext 7133. Fax: 262-728-7129. p. 2588

Fleming, Nikki, Dep Dir, Baltimore City Department of Legislative Reference Library, City Hall, Rm 626, 100 N Holliday St, Baltimore, MD, 21202-3468. Tel: 410-396-4730. Fax: 410-396-8483. p. 1011

Fleming, Rachel, Coll Develop, Central College, Campus Box 6500, 812 University St, Pella, IA, 50219-1999. Tel: 641-628-5221. Fax: 641-628-5327. p. 838

Fleming, Renee J, Librn, Santa Cruz County Law Library, 701 Ocean St, Rm 070, Santa Cruz, CA, 95060. Tel: 831-420-2205. Fax: 831-457-2255. p. 264

Fleming, Robert, Exec Dir, Emerson College Library, 120 Boylston St, Boston, MA, 02116-4624. Tel: 617-824-8668. Fax: 617-824-7817. p. 1060

Fleming, Robyn, ILL, Metropolitan Museum of Art, Thomas J Watson Library, 1000 Fifth Ave, New York, NY, 10028-0198. Tel: 212-650-2225. Fax: 212-570-3847. p. 1686

Fleming, Sean, Asst Dir, Lebanon Public Library, Nine E Park St, Lebanon, NH, 03766. Tel: 603-448-2459. p. 1454

Fleming, Shelley, Supvr, Elgin County Public Library, Rodney Branch, 207 Furnival Rd, Rodney, ON, N0L 2C0, CANADA. Tel: 519-785-2100. Fax: 519-785-1734. p. 2844

Fleming, Shelley, Supvr, Elgin County Public Library, West Lorne Branch, 160A Main St, West Lorne, ON, N0L 2P0, CANADA. Tel: 519-768-1150. Fax: 519-768-0773. p. 2844

Fleming, Stephen, Dir, Global Intelligence Group, 285 Madison Ave, 10th Flr, New York, NY, 10017. Tel: 212-210-3983. Fax: 212-210-3918. p. 1680

Fleming, Sue, Med Librn, Via Christi Libraries, North Saint Francis Street, 929 N Saint Francis St, Wichita, KS, 67214-1315. Tel: 316-268-5982. Fax: 316-268-8694. p. 901

Fleming, Thomas, Pres, Rockford Institute Library, 928 N Main St, Rockford, IL, 61103. Tel: 815-964-5053. Fax: 815-964-9403. p. 697

Fleming, William, Admin Dir, Free Library of Philadelphia, 1901 Vine St, Philadelphia, PA, 19103-1189. Tel: 215-686-5303. Fax: 215-563-3628. p. 2106

Flemming, Carolyn, Ch, Glendale Public Library, 222 E Harvard St, Glendale, CA, 91205-1075. Tel: 818-548-3999. Fax: 818-409-7030. p. 155

Flemming, Clare, Libr Dir, Academy of Natural Sciences of Philadelphia, 1900 Benjamin Franklin Pkwy, Philadelphia, PA, 19103-1195. Tel: 215-299-1175. Fax: 215-299-1144. p. 2102

Flemming, Curt, Actg Libr Mgr, Battelle Memorial Institute, 505 King Ave, Columbus, OH, 43201. Tel: 614-424-6302. Fax: 614-458-6302. p. 1883

Flemming, Julie, Dir, Fox Lake Public Library, 117 W State St, Fox Lake, WI, 53933-9505. Tel: 920-928-3223. Fax: 920-928-3810. p. 2593

Flemming, Kathleen, Ref Coordr, Wayne State University Libraries, Science & Engineering, 5048 Gullen Mall, Detroit, MI, 48202-3918. Tel: 313-577-6310. Fax: 313-577-3613. p. 1173

Flengeris, Carla L, Libr Coordr, University of Regina, Luther College Library, University of Regina, 3737 Wascana Pkwy, Regina, SK, S4S 0A2, CANADA. Tel: 306-585-5030. Fax: 306-585-5267. p. 2925

Fleshman, Sandra, Prog Coordr, Rowan County Public Library, 175 Beacon Hill Dr, Morehead, KY, 40351. Tel: 606-784-7137. Fax: 606-784-2130. p. 929

Fletcher, A, Librn, Health One Presbyterian-Saint Luke's Medical Center, 1719 E 19th Ave, Denver, CO, 80218-1281. Tel: 303-839-6670. Fax: 303-869-1643. p. 302

Fletcher, Amy, Head, Tech Serv, Louis Bay 2nd Library, 345 Lafayette Ave, Hawthorne, NJ, 07506-2599. Tel: 973-427-5745, Ext 18. Fax: 973-427-5269. p. 1490

Fletcher, Barbara, Librn, Royal Public Library, 302 Main St, Royal, IA, 51357. Tel: 712-933-5500. p. 841

Fletcher, Carolyn, Dir, Gruver City Library, 504 King St, Gruver, TX, 79040. Tel: 806-733-2191. Fax: 806-733-2419. p. 2330

Fletcher, Daryl, Asst Dir, Tech Serv, Conyers-Rockdale Library System, 864 Green St, Conyers, GA, 30012. Tel: 770-388-5040. Fax: 770-388-5043. p. 527

Fletcher, Deborah, Supvr, Ventura County Library, Meiners Oaks Library, 114 N Padre Juan Ave, Meiners Oaks, CA, 93023. Tel: 805-646-4804. Fax: 805-646-8007. p. 280

Fletcher, Deborah, Ch, Ossining Public Library, 53 Croton Ave, Ossining, NY, 10562-4903. Tel: 914-941-2416. Fax: 914-941-7464. p. 1712

Fletcher, Elizabeth, Libr Asst, Justice Institute of British Columbia Library, 715 McBride Blvd, New Westminster, BC, V3L 5T4, CANADA. Tel: 604-528-5596. Fax: 604-528-5593. p. 2734

Fletcher, Emily, Dir, Fryeburg Public Library, 515 Main St, Fryeburg, ME, 04037. Tel: 207-935-2731. Fax: 207-935-7217. p. 986

Fletcher, Galen L, Govt Doc, Brigham Young University, Howard W Hunter Law Library, 256 JRCB, Provo, UT, 84602-8000. Tel: 801-422-3593. Fax: 801-422-0404. p. 2411

Fletcher, Heidi, Dir, Mount Sterling Public Library, 60 W Columbus St, Mount Sterling, OH, 43143. Tel: 740-869-2430. Fax: 740-869-3617. p. 1919

Fletcher, Kathy, Ref Librn, Pub Serv, University of New Hampshire School of Law, Two White St, Concord, NH, 03301. Tel: 603-228-1541, Ext 1130. Fax: 603-228-0388. p. 1443

Fletcher, Kim, Librn, Southwest Arkansas Regional Library, Pike County Library, 210 Second Ave, Murfreesboro, AR, 71958. Tel: 870-285-2575. Fax: 870-285-2660. p. 103

Fletcher, Kim, Youth Serv Coordr, Lawrence Public Library, 707 Vermont St, Lawrence, KS, 66044-2371. Tel: 785-843-3833. Fax: 785-843-3368. p. 878

Fletcher, Lezlie, Dir, Lake Charles Memorial Hospital, 1701 Oak Park Blvd, Lake Charles, LA, 70601-3713. Tel: 337-494-3127. Fax: 337-430-6966, 337-494-3231. p. 954

Fletcher, Nancy, Cat, Circ, ILL, University of Maine at Presque Isle Library, 181 Main St, Presque Isle, ME, 04769-2888. Tel: 207-768-9599. Fax: 207-768-9644. p. 998

Fletcher, Peg, Librn, Boulder Community Hospital, N Broadway & 1100 Balsam Ave, Boulder, CO, 80301. Tel: 303-440-2091. Fax: 303-938-3483. p. 290

Fletcher, Tracy, Cat & Proc Mgr, Saint Louis County Library, 1640 S Lindbergh Blvd, Saint Louis, MO, 63131-3598. Tel: 314-994-3300, Ext 2350. Fax: 314-997-7602. p. 1358

Fletcher, Vicki, Dir, Pendleton District Historical, Recreational & Tourism Commission, 125 E Queen St, Pendleton, SC, 29670. Tel: 864-646-3782. Fax: 864-646-2506. p. 2202

Fletcher, Yolanda, Ch Serv Librn, Mill Valley Public Library, 375 Throckmorton Ave, Mill Valley, CA, 94941-2698. Tel: 415-389-4292, Ext 119. Fax: 415-388-8929. p. 186

Flett, Theresa, Ref Librn, St Charles Community College, 4601 Mid Rivers Mall Dr, Cottleville, MO, 63376. Tel: 636-922-8587. Fax: 636-922-8433. p. 1326

Fleure, Lynn, Circ Supvr, Way Public Library, 101 E Indiana Ave, Perrysburg, OH, 43551. Tel: 419-874-3135, Ext 111. Fax: 419-874-6129. p. 1929

Fleuried, Christine, Pres, Boston Biomedical Library Consortium, c/o Dana Farber Cancer Trust, 44 Binney St, Boston, MA, 02115. Tel: 617-632-2489. Fax: 617-632-2488. p. 2945

Fleuriel, Christine W, Librn, Dana-Farber Cancer Institute, 44 Binney St, Boston, MA, 02115-6084. Tel: 617-632-3508. Fax: 617-632-2488. p. 1060

Fleury, Carol, Ref Serv, Morris College, 100 W College St, Sumter, SC, 29150-3599. Tel: 803-934-3230. Fax: 803-778-2923. p. 2206

Fleury, Odile, Librn, FPInnovations-Forintek, 319 rue Franquet, Quebec, QC, G1P 4R4, CANADA. Tel: 418-659-2647. Fax: 418-659-2922. p. 2905

Flewelling, Debra, Tech Coordr, Douglas College Library, 700 Royal Ave, New Westminster, BC, V3M 5Z5, CANADA. Tel: 604-527-5190. Fax: 604-527-5193. p. 2734

Flewelling, Janet, Ref & Tech Librn, Wallingford Public Library, 200 N Main St, Wallingford, CT, 06492-3791. Tel: 203-265-6754. Fax: 203-269-5698. p. 373

Flick, Amy, Bibliog Instr, Emory University School of Law, 1301 Clifton Rd, Atlanta, GA, 30322. Tel: 404-727-6797. Fax: 404-727-2202. p. 514

Flick, George Buddy, Adult Ref Librn, Adult Serv, Blanchard-Santa Paula Public Library District, 119 N Eighth St, Santa Paula, CA, 93060-2709. Tel: 805-525-3615. Fax: 805-933-2324. p. 266

Flick, Roger, Cat, Brigham Young University, Harold B Lee Library, 2060 HBLL, Provo, UT, 84602. Tel: 801-422-2927. Fax: 801-422-0466. p. 2411

Flickner, Kevin, Ref Asst, Columbia International University, 7435 Monticello Rd, Columbia, SC, 29203-1599. Tel: 803-807-5112. Fax: 803-744-1391. p. 2187

Fliegel, Deborah, Tech Serv, Carnegie-Stout Public Library, 360 W 11th St, Dubuque, IA, 52001. Tel: 563-589-4243. Fax: 563-589-4217. p. 811

Fliers, Mia, Head, Circ, Sedona Public Library, 3250 White Bear Rd, Sedona, AZ, 86336. Tel: 928-282-7714. Fax: 928-282-5789. p. 81

Flinchbaugh, Michelle, Acq Librn, University of Maryland, Baltimore County, 1000 Hilltop Circle, Baltimore, MD, 21250. Tel: 410-455-2356. Fax: 410-455-1598. p. 1018

Flinchbaugh, Stephanie, Br Mgr, Chicago Public Library, Garfield Ridge, 6348 S Archer Ave, Chicago, IL, 60638. Tel: 312-747-6094. Fax: 312-747-9465. p. 608

Fling, Jacqueline, Head, Ref, Lee County Library System, East County Regional, 881 Gunnery Rd N, Lehigh Acres, FL, 33971. Tel: 239-461-7316. Fax: 239-461-7321. p. 445

Flint, Angie, Librn, Spokesman-Review, 999 W Riverside Ave, Spokane, WA, 99201. Tel: 509-459-5524. Fax: 509-227-5865. p. 2538

Flint, Carolyn, Dir, Franklin Parish Library, 705 Prairie St, Winnsboro, LA, 71295-2629. Tel: 318-435-4336. Fax: 318-435-1990. p. 972

Flint, Foster, Asst Dean, Mississippi Gulf Coast Community College, 2226 Switzer Rd, Gulfport, MS, 39507. Tel: 228-895-2525. Fax: 228-896-2521. p. 1300

Flint, Helen, Br Head, Toronto Public Library, Danforth/Coxwell, 1675 Danforth Ave, Toronto, ON, M4C 5P2, CANADA. Tel: 416-393-7783. Fax: 416-393-7578. p. 2861

Flint, Judith, Youth Serv Librn, Kimball Public Library, 67 N Main St, Randolph, VT, 05060. Tel: 802-728-5073. Fax: 802-728-6735. p. 2433

Flint, Nancy, Ref Serv, Ad, Eustis Memorial Library, 120 N Center St, Eustis, FL, 32726-3598. Tel: 352-357-5686. Fax: 352-357-5450. p. 439

Flint, Ruth Ellen, Ref Serv, Ad, Louisville Free Public Library, Highlands-Shelby Park, Mid-City Mall, 1250 Bardstown Rd, Louisville, KY, 40204. Tel: 502-574-1672. Fax: 502-451-0548. p. 924

Flint, Winifred, Head, Circ, Boxford Town Library, Ten Elm St, Boxford, MA, 01921. Tel: 978-887-7323. Fax: 978-887-6352. p. 1069

Flinton, Pamela, Head, Access Serv, State University of New York, College at Oneonta, 108 Ravine Pkwy, Oneonta, NY, 13820. Tel: 607-436-2998. Fax: 607-436-3081. p. 1711

Fliss, Susan M, Assoc Librn, Res, Teaching & Learning, Interim Librn, Harvard Library, Harvard College Library (Headquarters in Harry Elkins Widener Memorial Library), Widener Library, Rm 110, Cambridge, MA, 02138. Tel: 617-495-2401. Fax: 617-496-4750. p. 1075

Flitcroft, Patricia, Ch, Coos Bay Public Library, 525 Anderson St, Coos Bay, OR, 97420-1678. Tel: 541-269-1101. Fax: 541-269-7567. p. 1993

Flohr, Karen, Asst Librn, Ch, Eloy Public Library, 100 E Seventh St, Eloy, AZ, 85231. Tel: 520-466-3814. Fax: 520-466-4433. p. 62

Flood, Nina, Librn, Chittenden Public Library, 223 Chittenden Rd, Chittenden, VT, 05737. Tel: 802-773-3531. Fax: 802-747-4814. p. 2421

Floodeen, Kyrstin, Children's & YA Librn, Kenai Community Library, 163 Main St Loop, Kenai, AK, 99611-7723. Tel: 907-283-4378. Fax: 907-283-2266. p. 50

Flook, Pamela, Tech Serv, Cambria County Library System & District Center, 248 Main St, Johnstown, PA, 15901. Tel: 814-536-5131. Fax: 814-536-6905. p. 2073

Floor, Frank, Asst Dir, East Smithfield Public Library, 50 Esmond St, Smithfield, RI, 02917-3016. Tel: 401-231-5150. Fax: 401-231-2940. p. 2176

Floor, Mark, Librn, Glendale Community College, 6000 W Olive Ave, Glendale, AZ, 85302. Tel: 623-845-3165. Fax: 623-845-3102. p. 64

Flora, Brenda, AV Archivist, Amistad Research Center, Tulane University, Tilton Hall, 6823 St Charles Ave, New Orleans, LA, 70118. Tel: 504-862-3222. Fax: 504-862-8961. p. 959

Flora, Vicki, Ref, Pinellas Park Public Library, 7770 52nd St, Pinellas Park, FL, 33781-3498. Tel: 727-541-0718. Fax: 727-541-0818. p. 483

Florek, Laura, Ch, Cedar Grove Free Public Library, One Municipal Plaza, Cedar Grove, NJ, 07009. Tel: 973-239-1447. Fax: 973-239-1275. p. 1478

Florence, Julie S, Dir, Lebanon Public Library, 101 S Broadway, Lebanon, OH, 45036. Tel: 513-932-2665. Fax: 513-932-7323. p. 1909

Florence-Walker, Patrice, Br Mgr, Orange County Library District, Eatonville Branch, 200 E Kennedy Blvd, Eatonville, FL, 32751. p. 476

Florenzen, Heidi, Internet Serv, Ref Librn, Hermiston Public Library, 235 E Gladys Ave, Hermiston, OR, 97838-1827. Tel: 541-567-2882. Fax: 541-667-5055. p. 2000

Flores, Amelia, Dir, Colorado River Indian Tribes Public Library-Archives, Second Ave & Mohave Rd, Rte 1, Box 23-B, Parker, AZ, 85344. Tel: 928-669-9211. Fax: 928-669-8262. p. 70

Flores, Gerardo, II, IT Mgr, Castroville Public Library, 802 London St, Castroville, TX, 78009. Tel: 830-931-4095. Fax: 830-931-9050. p. 2295

Flores, Holly, Acq, Corban University Library, 5000 Deer Park Dr SE, Salem, OR, 97317-9392. Tel: 503-375-7016. Fax: 503-375-7196. p. 2017

Flores, Islena, In Charge, Hialeah-John F Kennedy Library, Lua A Curtiss Branch, 501 E Fourth Ave, Hialeah, FL, 33010. Tel: 305-883-6950. Fax: 305-883-6951. p. 451

Flores, John, Librn, Brookhaven College, 3939 Valley View, Farmers Branch, TX, 75244-4997. Tel: 972-860-4854. Fax: 972-860-4675. p. 2319

Flores, John G, Librn, Dover Free Library, 22 Hollands Rd, East Dover, VT, 05341-9617. Tel: 802-348-7488. p. 2423

Flores, Kim, Br Mgr, Springfield-Greene County Library District, Brentwood, 2214 Brentwood Blvd, Springfield, MO, 65804. Tel: 417-883-1974. Fax: 417-883-6412. p. 1368

Flores, Luis, Asst Dir, Fac & Planning, Jacksonville Public Library, 303 N Laura St, Jacksonville, FL, 32202-3505. Tel: 904-630-7561. Fax: 904-630-2431. p. 453

Flores, Monica, Librn, Mount San Jacinto College, Menifee Valley, 28237 La Piedra, Menifee Valley, CA, 92584. Tel: 951-639-5455. Fax: 951-672-0874. p. 249

Flores, Patty, Ch, Elsa Public Library, 711 N Hidalgo St, Elsa, TX, 78543. Tel: 956-262-3061. Fax: 956-262-3066. p. 2318

Flores, Raymond, Assoc Dean, Info Tech, University of Southern California Libraries, Asa V Call Law Library, 699 Exposition Blvd, LAW 202, MC 0072, Los Angeles, CA, 90089-0072. Tel: 213-740-6482. Fax: 213-740-7179. p. 179

Flores-Caraballo, Eliut, Prof, University of Puerto Rico, Rio Piedras Campus, PO Box 21906, San Juan, PR, 00931-1906. Tel: 787-764-0000, Ext 1286, 787-764-0000, Ext 5028. Fax: 787-764-2311. p. 2977

Flores-Manges, Irma, Managing Librn, Austin Public Library, Will Hampton Branch at Oak Hill, 5125 Convict Hill Rd, Austin, TX, 78749. Tel: 512-974-9900. Fax: 512-974-9902. p. 2279

Florimonte, Jackie, Sr Tech Librn, Raytheon, Inc, 13510 N Central Expressway, MS 211, Dallas, TX, 75243-1108. Tel: 972-344-5034. Fax: 972-344-5042. p. 2309

Florio, Joseph, Online Serv, Davis Polk & Wardwell Library, 450 Lexington Ave, New York, NY, 10017. Tel: 212-450-4266. Fax: 212-450-5522. p. 1677

Florio, Lisa, Head, Ref, New Providence Memorial Library, 377 Elkwood Ave, New Providence, NJ, 07974-1837. Tel: 908-665-0311. Fax: 908-665-2319. p. 1510

Flory, Robin, Dir, Ottawa Library, 105 S Hickory St, Ottawa, KS, 66067-2306. Tel: 785-242-3080. Fax: 785-242-8789. p. 887

Floss, LeeAnn, Br Mgr, Charleston County Public Library, Saint Paul's Branch, 5153 Hwy 165, Hollywood, SC, 29449. Tel: 843-889-3300. Fax: 843-889-3605. p. 2183

Floss, LeeAnn, Asst Librn, Charleston Library Society, 164 King St, Charleston, SC, 29401. Tel: 843-723-9912. Fax: 843-723-3500. p. 2183

Flotten, Martha, In Charge, Multnomah County Library, Gresham Branch, 385 NW Miller Ave, Gresham, OR, 97030-7291. Tel: 503-988-5387. Fax: 503-988-5198. p. 2012

Flower, Amanda, Head, Bibliog Serv, Ursuline College, 2550 Lander Rd, Pepper Pike, OH, 44124-4398. Tel: 440-449-4202. Fax: 440-449-3180. p. 1929

Flower, Ann, Ref, Monterey Institute of International Studies, 425 Van Buren St, Monterey, CA, 93940. Tel: 831-647-4133. Fax: 831-647-3518. p. 190

Flower, Kenneth, Assoc Dir, Johns Hopkins University Libraries, The Sheridan Libraries, 3400 N Charles St, Baltimore, MD, 21218. Tel: 410-516-8325. Fax: 410-516-5080. p. 1014

Flowers, Anne, ILL, Marion & Ed Hughes Public Library, 2712 Nederland Ave, Nederland, TX, 77627-7015. Tel: 409-722-1255. Fax: 409-721-5469. p. 2365

Flowers, Deb, Dir, Jennie Trent Dew Library, 1101 Hutchings St, Goldthwaite, TX, 76844. Tel: 325-648-2447. Fax: 325-648-2447. p. 2328

Flowers, Deloris, Circ, Mary Wood Weldon Memorial Library, 107 W College St, Glasgow, KY, 42141. Tel: 270-651-2824. Fax: 270-651-2824. p. 915

Flowers, Geni, Asst Dir, Br Serv, University of South Carolina at Beaufort Library, One University Blvd, Bluffton, SC, 29909-6085. Tel: 843-521-4122. Fax: 843-208-8296. p. 2182

Flowers, Jamie, Mgr, San Antonio Public Library, Semmes, 15060 Judson Rd, San Antonio, TX, 78247. Tel: 210-650-9540. Fax: 210-650-4079. p. 2382

Flowers, Jamie, Mgr, San Antonio Public Library, Thousand Oaks, 4618 Thousand Oaks, San Antonio, TX, 78233. Tel: 210-657-5205. Fax: 210-657-6874. p. 2382

Flowers, Kelley F, Br Mgr, Atlanta-Fulton Public Library System, Bowen Homes, 2880 Yates Dr NW, Atlanta, GA, 30318. Tel: 404-792-4950. Fax: 404-792-4952. p. 511

Flowers, Laura, Coll Develop, Warren County Public Library, 1225 State St, Bowling Green, KY, 42101. Tel: 270-781-4882. Fax: 270-781-7323. p. 907

Flowers, Linda A, Syst Coordr, Ashland Public Library, 224 Claremont Ave, Ashland, OH, 44805. Tel: 419-289-8188, Ext 10. Fax: 419-281-8552. p. 1855

Flowers, Nathan, Ref, Francis Marion University, 4822 East Palmetto St, Florence, SC, 29506. Tel: 843-661-1302. Fax: 843-661-1309. p. 2194

Flowers, Robbie, Mgr, Detroit Public Library, Bowen, 3648 W Vernor, Detroit, MI, 48216-1441. Tel: 313-481-1540. p. 1170

Flowers, Zelma, Acq, Iredell County Public Library, 201 N Tradd St, Statesville, NC, 28677. Tel: 704-878-5448. Fax: 704-878-5449. p. 1825

Floyd, Debra, Br Mgr, Broward County Division of Libraries, Jan Moran Collier City Learning Library, 2800 NW Ninth Ct, Pompano Beach, FL, 33069-2149. Tel: 954-968-3820. Fax: 954-968-3822. p. 442

Floyd, James, Dr, Music, Hardin-Simmons University, 2341 Hickory St, Abilene, TX, 79698. Tel: 325-670-1236. Fax: 325-677-8351. p. 2272

Floyd, Kathryn, Cat, Geneva College, 3200 College Ave, Beaver Falls, PA, 15010-3599. Tel: 724-847-6688. Fax: 724-847-6687. p. 2031

Floyd, Kristi, Prog & Pub Relations Supvr, Westbank Community Library District, 1309 Westbank Dr, Austin, TX, 78746. Tel: 512-314-3583. Fax: 512-327-3074. p. 2285

Floyd, Linda, Librn, Abbeville Memorial Library, 301 Kirkland St, Abbeville, AL, 36310. Tel: 334-585-2818. Fax: 334-585-2818. p. 3

Floyd, Linda, Dir, Libr Serv, Georgia Northwestern Technical College, Bldg H, Rm 156, One Maurice Culberson Dr, Rome, GA, 30161. Tel: 706-295-6845. Fax: 706-295-6843. p. 548

Floyd, Linda, Evening Librn, Georgia Northwestern Technical College, Polk County Campus Library, 466 Brock Rd, Rockmart, GA, 30153. Tel: 678-757-2043. Fax: 678-757-1673. p. 548

Floyd, Lynn, Circ, Antioch Public Library District, 757 Main St, Antioch, IL, 60002. Tel: 847-395-0874, Ext 228. Fax: 847-395-5399. p. 589

Fluet, Aura A, Sr Asst Dir, Libr Serv, Episcopal Divinity School - Sherrill Library, 99 Brattle St, Cambridge, MA, 02138. Tel: 617-868-3450. Fax: 617-349-8849. p. 1073

Flugstad, Myron, Asst Dir, Head, Cat, Head, Tech Serv, Arkansas State University, 322 University Loop West Circle, State University, AR, 72401. Tel: 870-972-3077. Fax: 870-972-3199. p. 115

Fluharty, Delberta, AV Supvr, Ozark Christian College, 1111 N Main, Joplin, MO, 64801-4804. Tel: 417-626-1234, Ext 2712. Fax: 417-624-0090. p. 1336

Fluk, Louise, Instrul Serv Librn, Fiorello H LaGuardia Community College Library, 31-10 Thomson Ave, Long Island City, NY, 11101. Tel: 718-482-5421. Fax: 718-482-5444, 718-609-2011. p. 1654

Flum, Judith, Bibliog Instr, Contra Costa College Library, 2600 Mission Bell Dr, San Pablo, CA, 94806-3195. Tel: 510-235-7800, Ext 4445. Fax: 510-234-8161. p. 256

Flurschutz, Cindy, Librn, State University of New York, School of Applied Technology, 2530 River Rd, Wellsville, NY, 14895. Tel: 585-593-6270, Ext 3115. Fax: 607-587-3120. p. 1765

Flury, James, Mgr, Tech Serv, The Library Network, 41365 Vincenti Ct, Novi, MI, 48375. Tel: 248-536-3100. Fax: 248-536-3099. p. 2946

Flusche, Denise, Tech Serv, Lawton Public Library, 110 SW Fourth St, Lawton, OK, 73501-4034. Tel: 580-581-3450. Fax: 580-248-0243. p. 1967

Fly, Marjorie, Br Mgr, Tulare County Library, Exeter Branch, 230 E Chestnut, Exeter, CA, 93221. Tel: 559-592-5361. Fax: 559-592-4452. p. 281

Flynn, Ann, Ad, Marstons Mills Public Library, 2160 Main St, Marstons Mills, MA, 02648. Tel: 508-428-5175. Fax: 508-420-5194. p. 1103

Flynn, Anne, Head, Circ, North Merrick Public Library, 1691 Meadowbrook Rd, North Merrick, NY, 11566. Tel: 516-378-7474. Fax: 516-378-0876. p. 1706

Flynn, Ashley N, Libr Dir, Cresson Public Library, 231 Laurel Ave, Cresson, PA, 16630-1118. Tel: 814-886-2619. Fax: 814-886-9564. p. 2048

Flynn, Barbara, County Librn, Contra Costa County Library, 1750 Oak Park Blvd, Pleasant Hill, CA, 94523-4497. Tel: 925-646-6434. Fax: 925-646-6461. p. 208

Flynn, Barbara, Ch, Norwin Public Library Association Inc, 100 Caruthers Ln, Irwin, PA, 15642. Tel: 724-863-4700. Fax: 724-863-6195. p. 2072

Flynn, Barbara J, Assoc Dir, University of Louisiana at Lafayette, PO Box 40199, Lafayette, LA, 70504-0199. Tel: 337-482-6041. Fax: 337-482-5841. p. 953

Flynn, Christie J, Dir of Libr Operations, Pierce College Library, Puyallup Campus, 1601 39th Ave SE, Puyallup, WA, 98374. Tel: 253-840-8304. Fax: 253-840-8316. p. 2520

Flynn, Gary, Mgr, Libr Serv, Gateway Technical College, 3520 30th Ave, Kenosha, WI, 53144-1690. Tel: 262-564-2786. Fax: 262-564-2787. p. 2601

Flynn, Helen, Dir, Mifflin Community Library, Six Philadelphia Ave, Shillington, PA, 19607. Tel: 610-777-3911. Fax: 610-777-5516. p. 2139

Flynn, Holly, Librn, Michigan State University Library, Mathematics, D-101 Wells Hall, East Lansing, MI, 48824. Tel: 517-353-8852. Fax: 517-353-7215. p. 1175

Flynn, Jane, Children & Teen Librn, Bridgeport Public Library, 925 Broad St, Bridgeport, CT, 06604. Tel: 203-576-7403. Fax: 203-576-8255. p. 331

Flynn, Jeffrey, Tech Serv, Suffolk University, John Joseph Moakley Law Library, 120 Tremont St, Boston, MA, 02108-4977. Tel: 617-573-8177. p. 1067

Flynn, Jo Ann, Dir, Craigsville Library, 63 Library Lane, Craigsville, WV, 26205. Tel: 304-742-3532. Fax: 304-742-6904. p. 2558

Flynn, Kathleen M, Head Librn, Massachusetts Trial Court, 50 State St, Springfield, MA, 01103-2021. Tel: 413-748-7923. Fax: 413-734-2973. p. 1127

Flynn, Kathy, Head, Ref, Peabody Essex Museum, East India Sq, 161 Essex St, Salem, MA, 01970-3783. Tel: 978-745-9500. Fax: 978-741-9012. p. 1121

Flynn, Laura, Dir, Fort Plain Free Library, 19 Willett St, Fort Plain, NY, 13339-1130. Tel: 518-993-4646. Fax: 518-993-2455. p. 1624

Flynn, Lesia, Br Mgr, Huntsville-Madison Public Library, Tillman Hill Public Library of Hazel Green, 131 Knowledge Dr, Hazel Green, AL, 35750. Tel: 256-828-9529. p. 21

Flynn, Linda C, Dir, Blinn College Library, 800 Blinn Blvd, Brenham, TX, 77833. Tel: 979-830-4250. Fax: 979-830-4222. p. 2291

Flynn, Mari, Dir, Keystone College, One College Green, La Plume, PA, 18440-0200. Tel: 570-945-8332. Fax: 570-945-8969. p. 2075

Flynn, Marilyn, Pub Relations, North Merrick Public Library, 1691 Meadowbrook Rd, North Merrick, NY, 11566. Tel: 516-378-7474. Fax: 516-378-0876. p. 1706

Flynn, Mark C, Interim Dean, Libr Serv, Columbus State University Libraries, 4225 University Ave, Columbus, GA, 31907. Tel: 706-568-2080. Fax: 706-568-2084. p. 526

Flynn, Matthew, Res Spec, Global Intelligence Group, 285 Madison Ave, 10th Flr, New York, NY, 10017. Tel: 212-210-3983. Fax: 212-210-3918. p. 1680

Flynn, Patti, Br Coordr, Burlingame Public Library, 480 Primrose Rd, Burlingame, CA, 94010-4083. Tel: 650-340-6180. Fax: 650-342-1948. p. 130

Flynn, Roger, Assoc Prof, University of Pittsburgh, 135 N Bellefield Ave, Pittsburgh, PA, 15260. Tel: 412-624-5230. Fax: 412-624-5231. p. 2973

Flynn, Rosemary Pleva, Librn, University of North Dakota, Energy & Environmental Research Center Library, 15 North 23rd St, Stop 9018, Grand Forks, ND, 58202-9018. Tel: 701-777-5132. Fax: 701-777-5181. p. 1843

Flynn, Sean, Head, Info Serv, Greenfield Public Library, 402 Main St, Greenfield, MA, 01301. Tel: 413-772-1544. Fax: 413-772-1589. p. 1092

Flynn, Thomas, Dir, New York State Department of Health, Empire State Plaza, Albany, NY, 12201. Tel: 518-474-6172. Fax: 518-474-3933. p. 1569

Flynn, Thomas, Archivist, Winston-Salem State University, 601 Martin Luther King Jr Dr, Winston-Salem, NC, 27110. Tel: 336-750-2426. Fax: 336-750-2459. p. 1834

Flynt, Andy, Dir, Ref, Spartanburg County Public Libraries, 151 S Church St, Spartanburg, SC, 29306-3241. Tel: 864-596-3500. Fax: 864-596-3518. p. 2205

Foale, Tenna, Ch, Holliston Public Library, 752 Washington St, Holliston, MA, 01746. Tel: 508-429-0617. Fax: 508-429-0625. p. 1095

Fobert, John, Ser/Govt Doc Librn, Roger Williams University Library, One Old Ferry Rd, Bristol, RI, 02809. Tel: 401-254-3374. Fax: 401-254-3631. p. 2164

Focht, Debra, Asst Circ Mgr, Boyertown Community Library, 29 E Philadelphia Ave, Boyertown, PA, 19512-1124. Tel: 610-369-0496. Fax: 610-369-0542. p. 2036

Foege, William C, Dir, Info Tech Pub Serv, Polk State College, 999 Ave H NE, Winter Haven, FL, 33881-4299. Tel: 863-297-1040. Fax: 863-297-1064. p. 504

Foege, William C, Jr, Dir, Learning Res, Lakeland, Polk State College, Lakeland Campus Library, 3425 Winter Lake Rd, Sta 62, Lakeland, FL, 33803. Tel: 863-297-1042. Fax: 863-297-1064. p. 505

Foegelle, Joyce, Dir, ConocoPhillips Library Network, 600 N Dairy Ashford, OF 2047, Houston, TX, 77079. Tel: 281-293-4972. Fax: 281-293-4574. p. 2334

Foehringer, Ruth Ann, Circ, Seneca Public Library District, 210 N Main St, Seneca, IL, 61360. Tel: 815-357-6566. Fax: 815-357-6568. p. 701

Foertch, Cathy, Dir, West Seneca Public Library, 1300 Union Rd, West Seneca, NY, 14224. Tel: 716-674-2928. Fax: 716-674-9206. p. 1767

Fogarty, Donna, Dir, Jamestown Philomenian Library, 26 North Rd, Jamestown, RI, 02835. Tel: 401-423-7280. Fax: 401-423-7281. p. 2167

Fogarty, Molly, Dir, Springfield City Library, 220 State St, Springfield, MA, 01103. Tel: 413-263-6828, Ext 290. Fax: 413-263-6825. p. 1127

Fogarty, Nick, Dep Dir, Northwest Georgia Regional Library System, 310 Cappes St, Dalton, GA, 30720. Tel: 706-876-1360. Fax: 706-272-2977. p. 528

Fogarty, Shirley, Br Mgr, Pine Mountain Regional Library, Hightower Memorial, 800 W Gordon St, Thomaston, GA, 30286-3417. Tel: 706-647-8649. Fax: 706-647-3977. p. 542

Fogelbach, Karen, Br Supvr, Scenic Regional Library of Franklin, Gasconade & Warren Counties, Saint Clair Branch, 570 S Main St, Saint Clair, MO, 63077. Tel: 636-629-2546. p. 1369

Fogelman, Rita T, Dir, West Nyack Free Library, 65 Strawtown Rd, West Nyack, NY, 10994. Tel: 845-358-6081. Fax: 845-358-4071. p. 1766

Fogg, Ann Marie, Asst Librn, Circ Supvr, Avon Public Library, 280 W Main St, Avon, MA, 02322. Tel: 508-583-0378. Fax: 508-580-2757. p. 1051

Fogg, Charlotte, Br Mgr, Mifflin County Library, Allensville Branch, 39 Water St, Allensville, PA, 17002. Tel: 717-483-6968. Fax: 717-483-6968. p. 2081

Foghino, Kim, Dir, Mendon Township Library, 314 W Main St, Mendon, MI, 49072. Tel: 269-496-4865. Fax: 269-496-4635. p. 1208

Fogle, Don, Electronic Res, Show Low Public Library, 180 N Ninth St, Show Low, AZ, 85901. Tel: 928-532-4065. Fax: 928-532-4079. p. 82

Fogle, Lynn, Librn, Greenebaum, Doll & McDonald, 300 W Vine St, Ste 1100, Lexington, KY, 40507-1622. Tel: 859-288-4717. Fax: 859-255-2742. p. 920

Fogler, Helen, Librn, Thompson Free Library, 186 E Main St, Dover-Foxcroft, ME, 04426. Tel: 207-564-3350. Fax: 207-564-3531. p. 983

Foight, Michael, Digital Serv, Villanova University, 800 Lancaster Ave, Villanova, PA, 19085. Tel: 610-519-5185. Fax: 610-519-5018. p. 2150

Folaron, Nancy, Asst Dir, Shiawassee District Library, Durand Memorial Branch, 700 N Saginaw St, Durand, MI, 48429-1245. Tel: 989-288-3743. Fax: 989-288-3743. p. 1216

Folden, Kim, Dir, Jocko Valley Library, 212 Culloyah St, Arlee, MT, 59821. Tel: 406-726-3572. p. 1373

Folds, Dusty, Dir, Libr Serv, Gadsden State Community College, 1001 George Wallace Dr, Gadsden, AL, 35902. Tel: 256-549-8421. Fax: 256-549-8410. p. 18

Folensbee-Moore, Barbara, Dir, Libr Serv, Morgan Lewis & Bochius LLP, 1111 Pennsylvania Ave NW, Washington, DC, 20004-2541. Tel: 202-739-5131. Fax: 202-739-3001. p. 408

Foley, Beth, Br Mgr, Riverside County Library System, La Quinta Library, 78-080 Calle Estado, La Quinta, CA, 92253. Tel: 760-564-4767. Fax: 760-771-0237. p. 217

Foley, Bob, Dir, Malaspina University-College Library, 900 Fifth St, Nanaimo, BC, V9R 5S5, CANADA. Tel: 250-753-3245. Fax: 250-740-6473. p. 2732

Foley, Erin Elizabeth, Archivist, Circus World Museum, 415 Lynn St, Baraboo, WI, 53913. Tel: 608-356-8342, Ext 3283. Fax: 608-355-7959. p. 2580

Foley, Erin Elizabeth, Dir, Rio Community Library, 324 W Lyons St, Rio, WI, 53960. Tel: 920-992-3206. Fax: 920-992-3983. p. 2634

Foley, Gayle, Ch, Goodnight Memorial Library, 203 S Main St, Franklin, KY, 42134. Tel: 270-586-8397. Fax: 270-586-8397. p. 914

Foley, Jodie, State Archivist, Montana Historical Society, 225 N Roberts St, Helena, MT, 59601-4514. Tel: 406-444-7482. Fax: 406-444-5297. p. 1382

Foley, Joe, Circ, Salve Regina University, 100 Ochre Point Ave, Newport, RI, 02840-4192. Tel: 401-341-2330. Fax: 401-341-2951. p. 2169

Foley, Kathryn, Youth Serv, Meridian District Library, 1326 W Cherry Lane, Meridian, ID, 83646. Tel: 208-888-4451. Fax: 208-884-0745. p. 579

Foley, Lisa, Dir, Lake Tahoe Community College, One College Dr, South Lake Tahoe, CA, 96150. Tel: 530-541-4660, Ext 232. Fax: 530-541-7852. p. 270

Foley, Maureen, Head, Ch, Chelmsford Public Library, 25 Boston Rd, Chelmsford, MA, 01824-3088. Tel: 978-256-5521. Fax: 978-256-8511. p. 1079

Foley, Meredith, Asst Dir, Leominster Public Library, 30 West St, Leominster, MA, 01453. Tel: 978-534-7522. Fax: 978-840-3357. p. 1098

Foley, Patricia Colford, Chief Librn, Cape Breton District Health Authority, 1482 George St, Sydney, NS, B1P 1P3, CANADA. Tel: 902-567-8000, Ext 2738. Fax: 902-567-7878. p. 2784

Foley, Peter, Ms Spec, University of Missouri, 302 Newcomb Hall, 5100 Rockhill Rd, Kansas City, MO, 64110-2499. Tel: 816-235-1549. Fax: 816-235-5500. p. 1341

Foley, Robert, Dir, Fitchburg State College, 160 Pearl St, Fitchburg, MA, 01420. Tel: 978-665-3194, 978-665-3196. Fax: 978-665-3069. p. 1089

Foley, Wendy, Librn, Hillsborough Community College, Brandon Campus Learning Resources Center, 10414 E Columbus Dr, Tampa, FL, 33619-9640. Tel: 813-253-7803. p. 496

Folgate, Cathy Lynn, Asst Archivist, Art Center College of Design, 1700 Lida St, Pasadena, CA, 91103. Tel: 626-396-2208. Fax: 626-568-0428. p. 205

Folger, Jane, Ch, Maplewood Memorial Library, 51 Baker St, Maplewood, NJ, 07040-2618. Tel: 973-762-1622. Fax: 973-762-0762. p. 1499

Folino, Madelyn, Dir, Florida Public Library, Four Cohen Circle, Florida, NY, 10921-1514. Tel: 845-651-7659. Fax: 845-651-7689. p. 1623

Folino, Mary Beth, Circ, Coquitlam Public Library, 575 Poirier St, Coquitlam, BC, V3J 6A9, CANADA. Tel: 604-937-4141. Fax: 604-927-3570. p. 2727

Folk, Amanda, Pub Serv Librn, Ref, University of Pittsburgh at Greensburg, 150 Finoli Dr, Greensburg, PA, 15601-5898. Tel: 724-836-9687. Fax: 724-836-7043. p. 2062

Folk, Amy, Archivist, Coll Mgr, Oysterponds Historical Society, Village Lane, Orient, NY, 11957. Tel: 631-323-2480. p. 1712

Folk, Amy, Coll Mgr, Southold Historical Society Museum Library, 54325 Main Rd, Southold, NY, 11971. Tel: 631-765-5500. Fax: 631-765-8510. p. 1746

Folk, Carol, Coordr, Acq, Coordr, Ser, Pennsylvania State University, 30 E Swedesford Rd, Malvern, PA, 19355. Tel: 610-648-3228. Fax: 610-725-5223. p. 2083

Folkama, Deborah, Acq & Cat, Norfolk Public Library, 235 E Plume St, Norfolk, VA, 23510-1706. Tel: 757-664-7323. Fax: 757-441-5863. p. 2481

Folkama, Deborah, Tech Serv, Norfolk Public Library, 235 E Plume St, Norfolk, VA, 23510-1706. Tel: 757-664-7328, Ext 319. Fax: 757-441-5863. p. 2481

Folkerts, Dana, Youth Serv Librn, Thomas Ford Memorial Library, 800 Chestnut Ave, Western Springs, IL, 60558. Tel: 708-246-0520. Fax: 708-246-0403. p. 717

Folkerts, Marg, Dir, Anamosa Public Library & Learning Center, 600 E First St, Anamosa, IA, 52205. Tel: 319-462-2183. Fax: 319-462-5349. p. 793

Folkes, Denise, Br Mgr, Brooklyn Public Library, Ulmer Park, 2602 Bath Ave, Brooklyn, NY, 11214. Tel: 718-265-3443. Fax: 718-265-5115. p. 1592

Folkins, Betsy, ILL, Per, Graceland University, One University Pl, Lamoni, IA, 50140. Tel: 641-784-5483. Fax: 641-784-5497. p. 826

Follet, Joyce, Coll Develop Spec, Smith College Libraries, Sophia Smith Collection, Seven Neilson Dr, Northampton, MA, 01063. Tel: 413-585-2979. Fax: 413-585-2886. p. 1114

Follett, Paul, Genealogist, Lawton Public Library, 110 SW Fourth St, Lawton, OK, 73501-4034. Tel: 580-581-3450. Fax: 580-248-0243. p. 1967

Follette, Adrian, Info Spec, University of Southern California Libraries, Norris Medical Library, 2003 Zonal Ave, Los Angeles, CA, 90089-9130. Tel: 323-442-1972. Fax: 323-221-1235. p. 179

Follick, Edwin Duane, Dr, Dir, Libr & Info Serv, South Baylo University Library, 1126 N Brookhurst St, Anaheim, CA, 92801-1704. Tel: 714-533-1495. Fax: 714-533-6040. p. 121

Folmar, Heather, Libr Operations Mgr, Santa Ana Public Library, 26 Civic Center Plaza, Santa Ana, CA, 92701-4010. Tel: 714-647-5250. Fax: 714-647-5291. p. 259

Folse, Linda, Circ, Phillips Graduate Institute Library, 19900 Plummer St, Chatsworth, CA, 91311. Tel: 818-386-5640. Fax: 818-386-5696. p. 133

Folse, Stephanie, Info Tech, Texas Christian University, 2913 Lowden St, TCU Box 298400, Fort Worth, TX, 76129. Tel: 817-257-7106. Fax: 817-257-7282. p. 2323

Folsom, Betty, Head, Circ, Bedford Public Library, Three Meetinghouse Rd, Bedford, NH, 03110-5406. Tel: 603-472-2300, 603-472-3023. Fax: 603-472-2978. p. 1438

Folsom, Kristy, Dir, Manchester Public Library, 304 N Franklin St, Manchester, IA, 52057. Tel: 563-927-3719. Fax: 563-927-3058. p. 829

Folsom, Lee, Circ Supvr, Waterville Public Library, 73 Elm St, Waterville, ME, 04901-6078. Tel: 207-872-5433. Fax: 207-873-4779. p. 1006

Folsom, Patti, Asst Dir, Harmony Library, 195 Putnam Pike, Harmony, RI, 02829. Tel: 401-949-2850. Fax: 401-949-2868. p. 2167

Foltz, Kay, Cat, ILL, Mgr, Libr Serv, Ohio State University LIBRARIES, Louis Bromfield Library - Mansfield Campus, 1660 University Dr, Mansfield, OH, 44906-1599. Tel: 419-755-4013. Fax: 419-755-4327. p. 1887

Foltz, Melissa, Librn, Washington County Free Library, Boonsboro Free Library, 401 Potomac St, Boonsboro, MD, 21713. Tel: 301-432-5723. p. 1031

Foltz, Meredith, Head, Tech Serv, Sheppard Memorial Library, 530 S Evans St, Greenville, NC, 27858-2308. Tel: 252-329-4588. Fax: 252-329-4587. p. 1799

Folvik, Clare, Asst Librn, Greenwood Public Library, 346 S Copper St, Greenwood, BC, V0H 1J0, CANADA. Tel: 250-445-6111. Fax: 250-445-6111. p. 2729

Fomalont, Jessica, Librn, National Academies, Transportation Research Board Library, 500 Fifth St NW, Washington, DC, 20001. Tel: 202-334-2989. Fax: 202-334-2527. p. 409

Fonda, Mary, Br Librn, Moss Memorial Library, 26 Anderson St, Hayesville, NC, 28904-7371. Tel: 828-389-8401. Fax: 828-389-3734. p. 1800

Fondrie, Jeanne, Training & Develop Coordr, Whatcom County Library System, 5205 Northwest Dr, Bellingham, WA, 98226-9050. Tel: 360-384-3150. Fax: 360-384-4947. p. 2509

Fong, Florence, Librn, Kaiser-Permanente Medical Center, 1150 Veterans Blvd, Redwood City, CA, 94063. Tel: 650-299-2437. Fax: 650-299-2488. p. 215

Fong, Nancy, Libr Serv Mgr, San Leandro Public Library, 300 Estudillo Ave, San Leandro, CA, 94577. Tel: 510-577-3947. Fax: 510-577-3967. p. 252

Fong, Tina, ILL, Canmore Public Library, 950 Eighth Ave, Canmore, AB, T1W 2T1, CANADA. Tel: 403-678-2468. Fax: 403-678-2165. p. 2694

Fong, Yem, Dir, Scholarly Res Develop, University of Colorado Boulder, 1720 Pleasant St, 184 UCB, Boulder, CO, 80309-0184. Tel: 303-492-4414. Fax: 303-492-8775. p. 291

Fonken, Carol, Head, Circ, Southwestern University, 1100 E University Ave, Georgetown, TX, 78626. Tel: 512-863-1550. Fax: 512-863-8198. p. 2327

Fonseca, Anthony, Head, Ser, Nicholls State University, 906 E First St, Thibodaux, LA, 70310. Tel: 985-448-4646, 985-448-4660. Fax: 985-448-4925. p. 971

Fonseca, Josee, Res, NYS Small Business Development Center Research Network, 22 Corporate Woods Blvd, 3rd Flr, Albany, NY, 12211. Tel: 518-641-0650. Fax: 518-443-5275. p. 1570

Fonseca, Santiago, Computer Lab Asst, Laredo Community College, Senator Judith Zaffirini Library (South Library), 5500 S Zapata Hwy, Laredo, TX, 78046. Tel: 956-794-4267. Fax: 956-794-4375. p. 2353

Fontaine, Julie, Dir, Bibliotheque Municipale d'Asbestos, 351 Saint Luc Blvd, Asbestos, QC, J1T 2W4, CANADA. Tel: 819-879-4363. Fax: 819-879-0608. p. 2879

Fontaine, Nancy, Tech Serv Librn, Norwich Public Library, 368 Main St, Norwich, VT, 05055-9453. Tel: 802-649-1184. Fax: 802-649-3470. p. 2431

Fontaine, Ron, Info Serv Librn, Bridgeport Public Library, 925 Broad St, Bridgeport, CT, 06604. Tel: 203-576-7403. Fax: 203-576-8255. p. 331

Fontane, Walt, Asst Prof, Ref Librn, McNeese State University, 4205 Ryan St, Lake Charles, LA, 70609. Tel: 337-475-5729. Fax: 337-475-5719, 337-475-5727. p. 954

Fontanilla, Jennifer, Librn, Stockton-San Joaquin County Public Library, Linden Branch, 19059 E Main St, Linden, CA, 95236. Fax: 209-887-2075. p. 273

Fontem, Nic, Tech Serv Coordr, Takoma Park Maryland Library, 101 Philadelphia Ave, Takoma Park, MD, 20912. Tel: 301-891-7259. Fax: 301-270-0814. p. 1043

Fonteneau-McCann, Lynne, Dir, Bennington Free Library, 101 Silver St, Bennington, VT, 05201. Tel: 802-442-9051. p. 2418

Fontenette, Edward J, Dir, University of Arkansas-Pine Bluff, 1200 N University Dr, Pine Bluff, AR, 71601. Tel: 870-575-8000, Ext 8410. Fax: 870-575-4651. p. 112

Fontenot, Helen, Sister, Dir, Our Lady of Holy Cross College Library, 4123 Woodland Dr, New Orleans, LA, 70131. Tel: 504-394-7744. Fax: 504-391-2421. p. 962

Fontenot, Kirk, Tech Serv, United States Air Force, 744 Douhet Dr, Bldg 4244, Barksdale AFB, LA, 71110. Tel: 318-456-4182. Fax: 318-752-0509. p. 941

Fontenot, Tracy, In Charge, El Paso Museum of Art, One Art Festival Plaza, El Paso, TX, 79901. Tel: 915-532-1707. Fax: 915-532-1010. p. 2316

Fontenova, Amanda, Archivist, Librn, Luzerne County Historical Society, 49 S Franklin St, Wilkes-Barre, PA, 18701. Tel: 570-823-6244. Fax: 570-823-9011. p. 2155

Fontoura, Ana E, Dean, The College of New Rochelle, 29 Castle Pl, New Rochelle, NY, 10805-2308. Tel: 914-654-5345. Fax: 914-654-5884. p. 1666

Foo, Jane, Mgr, Libr Syst & Support Serv, Seneca College of Applied Arts & Technology, Newnham Campus (Main), 1750 Finch Ave E, North York, ON, M2J 2X5, CANADA. Tel: 416-491-5050, Ext 22011. Fax: 416-491-3349. p. 2813

Foor, Jamie, Educ Librn, Lock Haven University of Pennsylvania, 401 N Fairview Ave, Lock Haven, PA, 17745-2390. Tel: 570-484-2856. Fax: 570-484-2506. p. 2082

Foor, Mary, Ch, Dunkirk Public Library, 127 W Washington St, Dunkirk, IN, 47336-1218. Tel: 765-768-6872. Fax: 765-768-6894. p. 736

Foose, Patricia, Adult Serv, Circ, Altoona Area Public Library, 1600 Fifth Ave, Altoona, PA, 16602-3693. Tel: 814-946-0417, Ext 135. Fax: 814-946-3230. p. 2028

Foote, Cheryl S, Dir, Wellsville Carnegie Public Library, 115 E Ninth St, Wellsville, OH, 43968-1431. Tel: 330-532-1526. Fax: 330-532-3127. p. 1946

Foote, David M, E-Learning Instrul Support Lectr, Wayne State University, 106 Kresge Library, Detroit, MI, 48202. Tel: 313-577-5328. Fax: 313-577-7563. p. 2968

Foote, Jody, Geology Librn, University of Oklahoma, Geology, Youngblood Energy Library, R220, 100 E Boyd, Norman, OK, 73019. Tel: 405-325-6451. Fax: 405-325-6451. p. 1971

Foote, Margaret, Coordr, Coll Serv, Eastern Kentucky University Libraries, 521 Lancaster Ave, Richmond, KY, 40475-3102. Tel: 859-622-1778. Fax: 859-622-1174. p. 933

Foote, Martha, Mgr, Sun Life Assurance Company of Canada, 150 King St W, 4th Flr, Toronto, ON, M5H 1J9, CANADA. Tel: 416-204-3835. Fax: 416-595-0346. p. 2858

Foote, Michael, Dir, Mid-America Christian University, 3500 SW 119th St, Oklahoma City, OK, 73170-9797. Tel: 405-691-3800. Fax: 405-692-3165. p. 1973

Footlik, Janice B, Librn, North Shore Congregation Israel, 1185 Sheridan Rd, Glencoe, IL, 60022. Tel: 847-835-0724. Fax: 847-835-5613. p. 650

Footlik, Janice B, Librn, Ezra-Habonim, The Niles Township Jewish Congregation, 4500 Dempster, Skokie, IL, 60076. Tel: 847-675-4141. Fax: 847-675-0327. p. 702

Footz, Valerie, Legis Librn, Alberta Legislature Library, 216 Legislature Bldg, 10800-97 Ave, Edmonton, AB, T5K 2B6, CANADA. Tel: 780-427-0202. Fax: 780-427-6016. p. 2699

Footz, Yvonne, Assoc Mgr, Edmonton Public Library, Lois Hole Library, 17650-69 Ave NW, Edmonton, AB, T5T 3X9, CANADA. Tel: 780-442-0885. Fax: 780-442-0887. p. 2700

Foran, Melissa, Librn, Mitel Corporate Library, 350 Legget Dr, Ottawa, ON, K2K 2W7, CANADA. Tel: 613-592-2122, Ext 74407. Fax: 613-592-7803. p. 2832

Forand, Jeanne, Asst Dir, Petersham Memorial Library, 23 Common St, Petersham, MA, 01366. Tel: 978-724-3405. Fax: 978-724-0089. p. 1117

Forbes, Carrie, Ref, University of Denver, 2150 E Evans Ave, Denver, CO, 80208-2007. Tel: 303-871-3441. Fax: 303-871-2290. p. 304

Forbes, Donald, Dir, Libr Serv, Guilford Technical Community College, 601 High Point Rd, Jamestown, NC, 27282. Tel: 336-334-4822, Ext 2502. Fax: 336-841-4350. p. 1803

Forbes, John, Curator, Quayle Rare Bible Coll, Baker University, 518 Eighth St, Baldwin City, KS, 66006-0065. Tel: 785-594-8393. Fax: 785-594-6721. p. 857

Forbes, Lyndsay, Br Mgr, Cambridge Public Library, O'Neill Branch, 70 Rindge Ave, Cambridge, MA, 02140. Tel: 617-349-4023. Fax: 617-349-4422. p. 1073

Forbes, Maggie, Exec Dir, Andrew Carnegie Free Library & Music Hall, 300 Beechwood Ave, Carnegie, PA, 15106-2699. Tel: 412-276-3456. Fax: 412-276-9472. p. 2042

Forbes, Nancy, Librn, C G Jung Institute of Los Angeles, 10349 W Pico Blvd, Los Angeles, CA, 90064. Tel: 310-556-1193, Ext 229. Fax: 310-556-2290. p. 171

Forbes, Robert, Librn, Northeast Regional Library, Burnsville Public Library, Norman Ave, Burnsville, MS, 38833. Tel: 662-427-9258. Fax: 662-427-9258. p. 1297

Forbes, Sean, Mgr, University of Toronto Libraries, Business Information Centre Library, Joseph L Rotman School of Management, 105 Saint George St, Toronto, ON, M5S 1A5, CANADA. Tel: 416-978-1924. Fax: 416-978-1920. p. 2865

Forbes, Sheldon, Circ Mgr, Otis College of Art & Design Library, 9045 Lincoln Blvd, Westchester, CA, 90045. Tel: 310-665-6800, Ext 6930. Fax: 310-665-6998. p. 283

Forbes, Shirley, Librn, Southwest Arkansas Regional Library, Delight Branch, 420 Antioch St, Delight, AR, 71940. Tel: 870-379-2456. p. 103

Forbes, Susan, Librn, Kansas State Historical Society, 6425 SW Sixth Ave, Topeka, KS, 66615-1099. Tel: 785-272-8681. Fax: 785-272-8682. p. 896

Forbes, Susan, Asst Dir, Environmental Protection Agency Library - RTP, MD C267-01, 109 Alexander Dr, Research Triangle Park, NC, 27711. Tel: 919-541-2777. Fax: 919-541-1405. p. 1819

Forbes, Tammy, Libr Dir, Newton Public Library, 209 Oates Dr, Newton, AL, 36352. Tel: 334-299-3316. p. 32

Forbus, Bettye, Dir, Houston Love Memorial Library, 212 W Burdeshaw St, Dothan, AL, 36303. Tel: 334-793-9767. Fax: 334-793-6645. p. 15

Forbus, Julie, Asst Librn, Ch, Madison Public Library, 12 Old Point Ave, Madison, ME, 04950. Tel: 207-696-5626. p. 991

Force, Marilyn, Ad, Wyckoff Public Library, 200 Woodland Ave, Wyckoff, NJ, 07481. Tel: 201-891-4866. Fax: 201-891-3892. p. 1546

Force, Stephen E, Dir, Yonkers Public Library, One Larkin Ctr, Yonkers, NY, 10701. Tel: 914-337-1500. Fax: 914-376-3004. p. 1771

Forcum, Karen, Dir, San Benito County Law Library, Courthouse, 440 Fifth St, Hollister, CA, 95023. Tel: 831-636-4016, 831-636-4040. Fax: 831-636-4044. p. 158

Ford, Alice, Head Librn, White Hall Township Library, 119 E Sherman St, White Hall, IL, 62092. Tel: 217-374-6014. Fax: 217-374-6554. p. 719

Ford, April, Acq Mgr, Oklahoma Christian University, 2501 E Memorial Rd, Edmond, OK, 73013. Tel: 405-425-5319. Fax: 405-425-5313. p. 1962

Ford, Candace, Dir, PlaneTree Health Library, 10800 Torre Ave, 2nd Flr, Cupertino, CA, 95014. Tel: 408-358-5668, 408-446-1677, Ext 3350. Fax: 408-356-7312. p. 138

Ford, Candy, Asst Dir, Guthrie Public Library, 201 N Division, Guthrie, OK, 73044-3201. Tel: 405-282-0050. Fax: 405-282-2804. p. 1964

Ford, Caroline, Ref, Field Library of Peekskill, Four Nelson Ave, Peekskill, NY, 10566-2138. Tel: 914-737-1212. Fax: 914-862-9710. p. 1716

Ford, Charlotte, Dir, Birmingham-Southern College, 900 Arkadelphia Rd, Birmingham, AL, 35254. Tel: 205-226-4740. Fax: 205-226-4743. p. 8

Ford, Christine, Librn, National Park Service, 266 Warren Lane, Deer Lodge, MT, 59722. Tel: 406-846-2070, Ext 242. Fax: 406-846-3962. p. 1377

Ford, Darlene, Asst Dir, Customer Serv, SUNY Upstate Medical University, 766 Irving Ave, Syracuse, NY, 13210-1602. Tel: 315-464-7114. Fax: 315-464-4584. p. 1753

Ford, Dianne, Coordr, Ser/Govt Doc, Elon University, 308 N O'Kelly Ave, Elon, NC, 27244-0187. Tel: 336-278-6584. Fax: 336-278-6637. p. 1791

Ford, Don, Intl Law Librn, University of Iowa Libraries, Law Library, 200 Boyd Law Bldg, Iowa City, IA, 52242-1166. Tel: 319-335-9002. Fax: 319-335-9039. p. 823

Ford, Dylan, Asst Librn, Barnet Public Library, 147 Church St, Barnet, VT, 05821. Tel: 802-633-4436. Fax: 802-633-4436. p. 2417

Ford, Emily, Ref Librn, Oregon Health & Science University Library, 3181 SW Sam Jackson Park Rd, Portland, OR, 97239-3098. Tel: 503-494-3460. Fax: 503-494-3227. p. 2013

Ford, Gale, Asst Dir, Head, Youth Serv, Milford Public Library, 330 Family Dr, Milford, MI, 48381-2000. Tel: 248-684-0845. Fax: 248-684-2923. p. 1209

Ford, Glenna, Dir, Jacquelin E Opperman Memorial Library, 5790 State St, Kingston, MI, 48741. Tel: 989-683-2500. Fax: 989-683-2081. p. 1199

Ford, Griff, Asst Librn, Buncombe County Public Libraries, Swannanoa Branch, 101 W Charleston St, Swannanoa, NC, 28778. Tel: 828-250-6486. Fax: 828-686-5516. p. 1774

Ford, Jacque, Br Librn, Southwest Arkansas Regional Library, Gillham Branch, 102 N Second St, Gillham, AR, 71841-9511. Tel: 870-386-5665. Fax: 870-386-5665. p. 103

Ford, Janet L, Dir, Ritter Public Library, 5680 Liberty Ave, Vermilion, OH, 44089-1198. Tel: 440-967-3798, Ext 16. Fax: 440-967-7103. p. 1943

Ford, Janice, Govt Doc, Ouachita Baptist University, 410 Ouachita, OBU Box 3742, Arkadelphia, AR, 71998-0001. Tel: 870-245-5122. Fax: 870-245-5245. p. 93

Ford, Jennifer, Mgr, Info Serv, Gail Borden Public Library District, 270 N Grove Ave, Elgin, IL, 60120-5596. Tel: 847-695-4668. Fax: 847-742-0485. p. 640

Ford, Jody, Dir, Stone Ridge Public Library, Rte 209, Stone Ridge, NY, 12484. Tel: 845-687-7023. Fax: 845-687-0094. p. 1749

Ford, John, Jr, Res Info Spec, Desert Research Institute, 2215 Raggio Pkwy, Reno, NV, 89512-1095. Tel: 775-674-7042. Fax: 775-674-7183. p. 1432

Ford, Karin, Commun Librn, Fort Vancouver Regional Library District, Vancouver Community Library (Main Library), 901 C St, Vancouver, WA, 98660. Tel: 360-695-1566. p. 2546

Ford, Karin, Vancouver Commun Librn, Fort Vancouver Regional Library District, 1007 E Mill Plain Blvd, Vancouver, WA, 98663. Tel: 360-695-1561. Fax: 360-693-2681. p. 2546

Ford, Kathleen, Mgr, University of California, Los Angeles, Instructional Media Library, Powell Library, Rm 46, Los Angeles, CA, 90095-1517. Tel: 310-825-0755. Fax: 310-206-5392. p. 179

Ford, Katia, Dir, Miner Memorial Library, Three 2nd NH Tpk, East Lempster, NH, 03605. Tel: 603-865-5550. Fax: 603-863-8105. p. 1446

Ford, Kristin M, Librn, Idaho Legislative Reference Library, Capitol Annex, 514 W Jefferson St, Boise, ID, 83702. Tel: 208-334-4822. Fax: 208-334-2125. p. 571

Ford, Laura, Ch, Falmouth Public Library, 300 Main St, Falmouth, MA, 02540. Tel: 508-457-2555. Fax: 508-457-2559. p. 1088

Ford, Lena, Access Serv, Circ Serv, Case Western Reserve University, Lillian F & Milford J Harris Library, Mandel School of Applied Social Sciences, 11235 Bellflower Rd, Cleveland, OH, 44106-7164. Tel: 216-368-2302. Fax: 216-368-2106. p. 1876

Ford, Lorrita E, Dir, Libr & Learning Serv, College of San Mateo Library, Bldg 9, 1700 W Hillsdale Blvd, San Mateo, CA, 94402-3795. Tel: 650-574-6569. Fax: 650-574-6497. p. 255

Ford, Madeline, Interim Chief Librn, Hostos Community College Library, 475 Grand Concourse, A-207, Bronx, NY, 10451. Tel: 718-518-4221. Fax: 718-518-4206. p. 1587

Ford, Marcia, Archivist, Kokomo-Howard County Public Library, 220 N Union St, Kokomo, IN, 46901-4614. Tel: 765-457-3242. Fax: 765-457-3683. p. 758

Ford, Margaret, Librn, CAE, Inc, 8585 Cote de Liesse Rd, Saint Laurent, QC, H4L 4X4, CANADA. Tel: 514-341-6780, Ext 2113. Fax: 514-734-5616. p. 2909

Ford, Maria, Coordr, Catholic Health Initiatives, 555 S 70th St, Lincoln, NE, 68510. Tel: 402-219-7306. Fax: 402-219-7335. p. 1404

Ford, Mark, Access Serv & Syst, Pub Serv, Cosumnes River College Library, 8401 Center Pkwy, Sacramento, CA, 95823. Tel: 916-691-7628. Fax: 916-691-7349. p. 223

Ford, Mary Jane, Dr, Dir, University of Louisiana at LaFayette, USL Sta, Box 42051, Lafayette, LA, 70504. Tel: 337-482-6405. Fax: 337-482-5904. p. 2967

Ford, Melanie, Ref Serv, Indian Valley Public Library, 100 E Church Ave, Telford, PA, 18969. Tel: 215-723-9109. Fax: 215-723-0583. p. 2145

Ford, Miriam, Circ, Jefferson State Community College, 2601 Carson Rd, Birmingham, AL, 35215-3098. Tel: 205-856-7788. Fax: 205-856-8512. p. 8

Ford, Pamela, Dir, Stewart County Public Library, 102 Natcor Dr, Dover, TN, 37058. Tel: 931-232-3127. Fax: 931-232-3159. p. 2233

Ford, Patricia, Adult Serv, Eastham Public Library, 190 Samoset Rd, Eastham, MA, 02642. Tel: 508-240-5950. Fax: 508-240-0786. p. 1086

Ford, Peggy A, Res Coordr, City of Greeley, 714 Eighth St, Greeley, CO, 80631. Tel: 970-350-9219. Fax: 970-350-9570. p. 311

Ford, Peter, Mgr, Human Res, Allen County Public Library, 900 Library Plaza, Fort Wayne, IN, 46802. Tel: 260-421-1231. Fax: 260-421-1389. p. 740

Ford, Roberta C, Librn, Columbus State University Libraries, Music Library, 900 Broadway, Columbus, GA, 31901-2735. Tel: 706-641-5045. Fax: 706-649-7261. p. 526

Ford, Roberta C, Music Librn, Columbus State University Libraries, 4225 University Ave, Columbus, GA, 31907. Tel: 706-641-5047. Fax: 706-649-7261. p. 526

Ford, Rose, Dir, East Cleveland Public Library, 14101 Euclid Ave, East Cleveland, OH, 44112-3891. Tel: 216-541-4128. Fax: 216-541-1790. p. 1897

Ford, Ruth, ILL, Washington County Library System, 341 Main St, Greenville, MS, 38701-4097. Tel: 662-335-2331. Fax: 662-390-4758. p. 1298

Ford, Sharon, Dir, Swarthmore Public Library, Borough Hall, 121 Park Ave, Swarthmore, PA, 19081-1536. Tel: 610-543-0436, 610-543-3171. Fax: 610-328-6699. p. 2145

Ford, Stephen, Info Literacy Librn, Ref, Salisbury University, 1101 Camden Ave, Salisbury, MD, 21801-6863. Tel: 410-543-6130. Fax: 410-543-6203. p. 1040

Ford, Sue, Ch, New Milford Public Library, 24 Main St, New Milford, CT, 06776. Tel: 860-355-1191, Ext 204. Fax: 860-350-9579. p. 360

Ford, Sylverna V, Dr, Dean, Univ Libr, University Libraries, University of Memphis, 126 Ned R McWherter Library, Memphis, TN, 38152-3250. p. 2252

Ford, Venessa, Librn, Lonoke Prairie County Regional Library Headquarters, Ward Public, 405 Hickory St, Ste 100, Ward, AR, 72176. Tel: 501-941-3220. Fax: 501-941-3220. p. 108

Ford, Willie, Media Coordr, Palm Beach State College, 3000 St Lucie Ave, Boca Raton, FL, 33431-6415. Tel: 561-862-4800. Fax: 561-862-4805. p. 428

Forde, Barbara, Librn, Long Island Maritime Museum Library, 86 West Ave, West Sayville, NY, 11796-1908. Tel: 631-447-8679, 631-854-4974. Fax: 631-854-4979. p. 1767

Forde, Carolyn, Librn, Rusk County Community Library, 418 Corbett Ave, Ladysmith, WI, 54848-1396. Tel: 715-532-2604. Fax: 715-532-2658. p. 2604

Forde, Michelle, Youth Serv Librn, Nassau County Public Library System, 25 N Fourth St, Fernandina Beach, FL, 32034-4123. Tel: 904-548-4858. Fax: 904-277-7366. p. 439

Fordham, Cyndi, ILL, Wood Library Association of Canandaigua, 134 N Main St, Canandaigua, NY, 14424-1295. Tel: 585-394-1381. Fax: 585-394-2954. p. 1601

Fordham, Cynthia, Ch, Woburn Public Library, 45 Pleasant St, Woburn, MA, 01801. Tel: 781-933-0148. Fax: 781-938-7860. p. 1142

Fordham, Irma, Ref Serv, Melbourne Beach Public Library, 324 Ocean Ave, Melbourne Beach, FL, 32951. Tel: 321-956-5642. Fax: 321-953-6942. p. 464

Fordon, Elizabeth, Dr, Instr, Northampton Community College, 3835 Green Pond Rd, Bethlehem, PA, 18020. Tel: 610-861-5358. Fax: 610-861-5373. p. 2973

Fordon, Michael, Dir, Cornell University Library, Frank A Lee Library, New York State Agricultural Experiment Station, Jordan Hall, 630 W North St, Geneva, NY, 14456. Tel: 315-787-2214. Fax: 315-787-2276. p. 1642

Fore, Janet, Dir, Saint Mary's College, Notre Dame, IN, 46556-5001. Tel: 219-284-5281. Fax: 574-284-4791. p. 771

Fore, Joshua, Evening/Weekend Supvr, Drexel University Libraries, Hagerty Library, 33rd & Market Sts, Philadelphia, PA, 19104-2875. Tel: 215-895-2750. Fax: 215-895-2070. p. 2105

Fore, Tina M, Libr Tech, Department of Veterans Affairs, 17273 State Rte 104, Chillicothe, OH, 45601. Tel: 740-773-1141, Ext 7627. Fax: 740-772-7041. p. 1867

Fore, Trish, Asst Dir, Galax-Carroll Regional Library, Carroll County Public, 101 Beaver Dam Rd, Hillsville, VA, 24343. Tel: 276-236-2042. Fax: 276-236-5153. p. 2466

Fore, Virginia, Br Mgr, Enoch Pratt Free Library, Orleans Street, 1303 Orleans St, Baltimore, MD, 21231. Tel: 410-396-0970. Fax: 410-396-0979. p. 1013

Foreback, Margaret, Libr Asst II, State Correctional Institution, Laurel Highlands Library, 5706 Glades Pike, Somerset, PA, 15501. Tel: 814-445-6501. Fax: 814-443-0208. p. 2141

Foreman, Carol, Mgr, Delta County Libraries, Cedaredge Public, 180 SW Sixth Ave, Cedaredge, CO, 81413. Tel: 970-856-3518. Fax: 970-856-3577. p. 313

Foreman, Carrie, Youth Serv Librn, Transylvania County Library, 212 S Gaston, Brevard, NC, 28712. Tel: 828-884-3151, Ext 233. Fax: 828-877-4230. p. 1777

Foreman, James, Pub Serv Librn, Tarrant County College, 2100 Southeast Pkwy, Arlington, TX, 76018. Tel: 817-515-3089. Fax: 817-515-3183. p. 2277

Foreman, Larry, Head, Genealogy/Spec Coll, Ouachita Parish Public Library, 1800 Stubbs Ave, Monroe, LA, 71201. Tel: 318-327-1490. Fax: 318-327-1373. p. 957

Foreman, Linda, Br Mgr, Desoto Parish Library, Logansport Branch, 203 Hwy 5, Logansport, LA, 71049. Tel: 318-697-2311. Fax: 318-697-4081. p. 955

Foreman, Micah, Head, Outreach Serv, Lincoln Parish Library, 910 N Trenton St, Ruston, LA, 71270-3328. Tel: 318-513-6428. Fax: 318-251-5045. p. 966

Foreman, Pamela, Computer Serv, Pub Serv Librn, Webmaster/Ref Librn, Virginia Union University, 1500 N Lombardy St, Richmond, VA, 23220. Tel: 804-278-4119. Fax: 804-257-5818. p. 2493

Foreman, Randy, Ref Librn, Thomas M Cooley Law School Libraries, 300 S Capitol Ave, Lansing, MI, 48901. Tel: 517-371-5140, Ext 3305. Fax: 517-334-5715, 517-334-5717. p. 1202

Foreman, Robert, Coll Develop, Thunderbird School of Global Management, 15249 N 59th Ave, Glendale, AZ, 85306-6001. Tel: 602-978-7300. Fax: 602-978-7762. p. 64

Forer, Mary, Librn, Marathon County Historical Society Library, 410 McIndoe St, Wausau, WI, 54403. Tel: 715-848-0378. Fax: 715-848-0576. p. 2646

Forest, Dominic, Asst Prof, Universite de Montreal, 3150, rue Jean-Brillant, bur C-2004, Montreal, QC, H3T 1N8, CANADA. Tel: 514-343-6044. Fax: 514-343-5753. p. 2979

Forest, Monique, Asst Librn, National Theatre School of Canada Library, 5030 Rue Saint Denis, Montreal, QC, H2J 2L8, CANADA. Tel: 514-842-7954, Ext 125. Fax: 514-842-5661. p. 2900

Foresta, Allen, Sr Librn, Teachers College, Columbia University, 525 W 120th St, New York, NY, 10027-6696. Tel: 212-678-3026. p. 1701

Forester, Patricia, Ref Librn, Washington University Libraries, Kopolow Business Library, One Brookings Dr, Campus Box 1133, Saint Louis, MO, 63130-4899. Tel: 314-935-6963. Fax: 314-935-4970. p. 1363

Foret, Denise, Govt Doc, Louisiana State University, 2048 Johnson Hwy, Eunice, LA, 70535. Tel: 337-550-1380. Fax: 337-550-1455. p. 949

Forgeng, Jeffrey L, Dr, Curator, Higgins Armory Museum, 100 Barber Ave, Worcester, MA, 01606-2444. Tel: 508-853-6015, Ext 17. Fax: 508-852-7697. p. 1144

Forgette, Bill, Asst Admin, Glenside Public Library District, 25 E Fullerton Ave, Glendale Heights, IL, 60139-2697. Tel: 630-260-1550. Fax: 630-260-1433. p. 650

Forgit, Jen, Teen Serv Librn, Medfield Memorial Public Library, 468 Main St, Medfield, MA, 02052-2008. Tel: 508-359-4544. Fax: 508-359-8124. p. 1104

Forkin, Mary, Asst Dir, Stoneham Public Library, 431 Main St, Stoneham, MA, 02180. Tel: 781-438-1324. Fax: 781-279-3836. p. 1129

Forkner, Julie, Dir, Edward Gauche Fisher Public Library, 1289 Ingleside Ave, Athens, TN, 37303. Tel: 423-745-7782. Fax: 423-745-1763. p. 2224

Forkosh, Bonnie, Commun Serv, Wilmette Public Library District, 1242 Wilmette Ave, Wilmette, IL, 60091-2558. Tel: 847-256-6925. Fax: 847-256-6933. p. 720

Forman, Elaine, Ch, Public Library of Johnston County & Smithfield, 305 E Market St, Smithfield, NC, 27577-3919. Tel: 919-934-8146. Fax: 919-934-8084. p. 1824

Forman, Jack, Chairperson, San Diego Mesa College Library, 7250 Mesa College Dr, San Diego, CA, 92111-4998. Tel: 619-388-2546. Fax: 619-388-2922. p. 235

Forman, Lisa B, Asst Dir, Easton Public Library, 691 Morehouse Rd, Easton, CT, 06612. Tel: 203-261-0134. Fax: 203-261-0708. p. 338

Formichella, Laurie, Tech Serv, Beverly Public Library, 32 Essex St, Beverly, MA, 01915-4561. Tel: 978-921-6062. Fax: 978-922-8329. p. 1053

Forner, Denise, Sr Assoc, Data Coll, ipIQ/The Patent Board Research Library, 222 Haddon Ave, 3rd Flr, Westmont, NJ, 08108. Tel: 856-671-6800. Fax: 856-671-6801. p. 1543

Forness, Jean, Dir, Williamsville Public Library, 102 S Elm St, Williamsville, IL, 62693. Tel: 217-566-3520. Fax: 217-566-3481. p. 719

Forney, Marlene, Electronic Res Librn, Mesa Community College Library, 1833 W Southern Ave, Mesa, AZ, 85202. Tel: 480-461-7631. Fax: 480-461-7681. p. 68

Forney, Sally, Sr Bus Mgr, Arizona State University Libraries, Library at the Polytechnic Campus, Academic Ctr, Bldg 20, 5988 S Backus Mall, Mesa, AZ, 85212. Tel: 480-727-1059. Fax: 480-727-1077. p. 84

Fornof, Dorothy, Librn, Art Institute of Pittsburgh Library, 420 Boulevard of the Allies, Pittsburgh, PA, 15219-1328. Tel: 412-291-6357. Fax: 412-263-3715, 412-291-6300. p. 2121

Foroughi, Fahimeh, ILL, San Juan College Library, 4601 College Blvd, Farmington, NM, 87402. Tel: 505-566-3692. Fax: 505-566-3381. p. 1555

Forrest, Dan, Circ, ILL, Western Kentucky University Libraries, Helm-Cravens Library Complex, 1906 College Heights Blvd, No 11067, Bowling Green, KY, 42101-1067. Tel: 270-745-2905. Fax: 270-745-6422. p. 908

Forrest, Janet, Librn, Zama Community Library, PO Box 14, Zama City, AB, T0H 4E0, CANADA. Tel: 780-683-2888. p. 2722

Forrest, Kathleen, Libr Coordr, Otis College of Art & Design Library, 9045 Lincoln Blvd, Westchester, CA, 90045. Tel: 310-665-6800, Ext 6930. Fax: 310-665-6998. p. 283

Forrest, Lee, Tech Serv Librn, Concordia University, 7400 Augusta St, River Forest, IL, 60305-1499. Tel: 708-209-3254. Fax: 708-209-3175. p. 694

Forrest, Linda, ILL, Libr Tech, University of Arkansas-Monticello Library, 514 University Dr, Monticello, AR, 71656. Tel: 870-460-1080. Fax: 870-460-1980. p. 110

Forrest, Stuart, Syst Spec, Beaufort County Library, 311 Scott St, Beaufort, SC, 29902. Tel: 843-255-6450. p. 2181

Forrest, Tera, Youth Serv Librn, Crowell Public Library, 1890 Huntington Dr, San Marino, CA, 91108-2595. Tel: 626-300-0777, Ext 524. Fax: 626-284-0766. p. 254

Forrestal, Valerie, Info Serv Librn, Stevens Institute of Technology, Castle Point on Hudson, Hoboken, NJ, 07030. Tel: 201-216-5361. Fax: 201-216-8319. p. 1491

Forrester, Bernard, Archivist, Coordr, Spec Coll, Texas Southern University, 3100 Cleburne Ave, Houston, TX, 77004. Tel: 713-313-4416. Fax: 713-313-1080. p. 2342

Forrester, James, Head, Libr Syst, Ontario College of Art & Design, 100 McCaul St, Toronto, ON, M5T 1W1, CANADA. Tel: 416-977-6000, Ext 255. Fax: 416-977-6006. p. 2856

Forrester, Leslie Ann, Librn, Murphy, Sheneman, Julian & Rogers, 101 California St, 39th Flr, San Francisco, CA, 94111. Tel: 415-398-4700. Fax: 415-421-7879. p. 244

Forrester, Liz, Br Librn, South Central Regional Library, Altona Branch, PO Box 650, Altona, MB, R0G 0B0, CANADA. Tel: 204-324-1503. p. 2753

Forrester, Rick, Dir, Warren Public Library, 123 E Third St, Warren, IN, 46792. Tel: 260-375-3450. Fax: 260-375-3450. p. 785

Forry, Sonia, Libr Coordr, Cape May County Historical & Genealogical Society Library, 504 Rte 9 N, Cape May Court House, NJ, 08210-3090. Tel: 609-465-3535. Fax: 609-465-4274. p. 1477

Forsch, Elaine, Acq, Ser & Syst, Northeastern Ohio Universities College of Medicine, 4209 State Rd 44, Rootstown, OH, 44272. Tel: 330-325-6600. Fax: 330-325-0522. p. 1932

Forsee, Joe B, Dir, Northwest Georgia Regional Library System, 310 Cappes St, Dalton, GA, 30720. Tel: 706-876-1360. Fax: 706-272-2977. p. 528

Forsell, Polly, Acq, Cat Tech, Info Serv Supvr, Viterbo University, 900 Viterbo Dr, La Crosse, WI, 54601. Tel: 608-796-3271. Fax: 608-796-3275. p. 2603

Forshaw, Natalie, Bibliog Serv, Head, Acq, University of Alaska Fairbanks, 310 Tanana Dr, Fairbanks, AK, 99775. Tel: 907-474-7401. Fax: 907-474-6841. p. 48

Forslund, Lisa, Librn, North Hennepin Community College Library, 7411 85th Ave N, Brooklyn Park, MN, 55445-2298. Tel: 763-424-0732. Fax: 763-493-3569. p. 1243

Forsman, Dana, Ref Librn, Franklin Pierce University Library, 40 University Dr, Rindge, NH, 03461-3114. Tel: 603-899-4140. Fax: 603-899-4375. p. 1463

Forsman, Rick, Planning & Projects Dir, University of Colorado Denver, 12950 E Montview Blvd, Aurora, CO, 80045. Tel: 303-724-2152. Fax: 303-724-2166. p. 289

Forst, Catherine Phillips, Dir, Springfield Township Library, 12000 Davisburg Rd, Davisburg, MI, 48350. Tel: 248-846-6550. Fax: 248-846-6555. p. 1167

Forster, Charlotte, In Charge, Tillamook County Library, Manzanita Branch, 571 Laneda, Manzanita, OR, 97130. Tel: 503-368-6665. Fax: 503-368-6665. p. 2021

Forster, Liz, Asst Dir, Pub Serv, Forsyth County Public Library, 585 Dahlonega Rd, Cumming, GA, 30040-2109. Tel: 770-781-9840. Fax: 770-781-8089. p. 527

Forster, Liz, Dep Dir, Gwinnett County Public Library, 1001 Lawrenceville Hwy NW, Lawrenceville, GA, 30046-4707. Tel: 770-822-5340. p. 538

Forster, Margaret, Acq, Cat, ILL, University of New Brunswick Libraries, Gerard V La Forest Law Library, Ludlow Hall, 2nd Flr, 41 Dineen Dr, Fredericton, NB, E3B 5A3, CANADA. Tel: 506-453-4734. Fax: 506-451-6948, 506-453-5186. p. 2764

Forsthoefel, Carol, Librn, Mercer County Law Library, Court House, Rm 206, 101 N Main St, Celina, OH, 45822. Tel: 419-584-2572. Fax: 419-586-4000. p. 1866

Forsthoffer, Kathy, Br Mgr, Akron-Summit County Public Library, Kenmore, 969 Kenmore Blvd, Akron, OH, 44314-2302. Tel: 330-745-6126. Fax: 330-745-9947. p. 1852

Forsyth, Gloria, Assoc Dir, Pub Serv, Braswell Memorial Public Library, 727 N Grace St, Rocky Mount, NC, 27804-4842. Tel: 252-442-1951. Fax: 252-442-7366. p. 1820

Forsyth, Jaime, Exec Dir, Found, Kitsap Regional Library, 1301 Sylvan Way, Bremerton, WA, 98310-3498. Tel: 360-475-9039. Fax: 360-405-9128. p. 2510

Forsyth, Kate, Br Mgr, Bedford Public Library System, Forest Library, 15583 Forest Rd, Forest, VA, 24551. Tel: 434-525-1817. p. 2451

Forsyth Manchester, Penny, Br Mgr, Main Libr, North Vancouver District Public Library, Lynn Valley Main, 1277 Lynn Valley Rd, North Vancouver, BC, V7J 2A1, CANADA. Tel: 604-984-0286. Fax: 604-984-7600. p. 2734

Forsyth, Melissa M, Dir, Big Sandy Community & Technical College, One Bert T Combs Dr, Prestonsburg, KY, 41653. Tel: 606-889-4749. Fax: 606-886-8683. p. 933

Forsythe, Jill, Acq, Grove City College, 300 Campus Dr, Grove City, PA, 16127-2198. Tel: 724-458-2047. Fax: 724-458-2181. p. 2063

Forsythe, Paulette, Asst Librn, Dorion Public Library, 170 Dorion Loop Rd, Dorion, ON, P0T 1K0, CANADA. Tel: 807-857-2289. Fax: 807-857-2203. p. 2802

Forsythe, Scott M, Archivist, National Archives & Records Administration, 7358 S Pulaski Rd, Chicago, IL, 60629-5898. Tel: 773-948-9001. Fax: 773-948-9050. p. 619

Fort, Cindy, Libr Tech, The Parrott Centre, 376 Wallbridge-Loyalist Rd, Belleville, ON, K8N 5B9, CANADA. Tel: 613-969-1913, Ext 2595. Fax: 613-969-5183. p. 2795

Fort, James, Coordr, National Institute of Justice, 810 Seventh St NW, Rm 6304, Washington, DC, 20531. Tel: 202-307-6742. Fax: 202-307-6742. p. 410

Fort, Rebecca L, Circ Librn, Malone University, 2600 Cleveland Ave NW, Canton, OH, 44709-3897. Tel: 330-471-8313. Fax: 330-454-6977. p. 1863

Forte, Jane, Dir, Ridgefield Public Library, 527 Morse Ave, Ridgefield, NJ, 07657. Tel: 201-941-0192. Fax: 201-941-9354. p. 1526

Forte, Joseph E, Dir, Newman University, 3100 McCormick Ave, Wichita, KS, 67213-2097. Tel: 316-942-4291, Ext 2104. Fax: 316-942-1747. p. 900

Forte, Maria, Br Librn, London Public Library, E S Beacock Branch, 1280 Huron St, London, ON, N5Y 1A8, CANADA. Tel: 519-451-8140. p. 2817

Forte, Patti, Ch, McCowan Memorial Library, 15 Pitman Ave, Pitman, NJ, 08071. Tel: 856-589-1656. Fax: 856-582-4982. p. 1520

Forte-Parnell, Charlotte, Dean, Instrul Res/Extended Serv, Antelope Valley College Library, 3041 W Ave K, Lancaster, CA, 93536-5426. Tel: 661-722-6533. Fax: 661-722-6456. p. 163

Fortescue, Ann, Exec Dir, Springfield Museum of Art Library, 107 Cliff Park Rd, Springfield, OH, 45504-2501. Tel: 937-325-4673. Fax: 937-325-4674. p. 1936

Fortier, Dan, Libr Tech, Michigan Department of Corrections, 9625 Pierce Rd, Freeland, MI, 48623. Tel: 989-695-9880. Fax: 989-695-6345. p. 1182

Fortier, Jan Marie, Dean, Info Res, Mount Hood Community College Library, 26000 SE Stark St, Gresham, OR, 97030. Tel: 503-491-7161. Fax: 503-491-7389. p. 1999

Fortier, Lisa, Supvr, Saskatoon Public Library, Mayfair Branch, 602 33rd St W, Saskatoon, SK, S7L 0W1, CANADA. Tel: 306-975-7749. p. 2926

Fortier, Marie-Andrée, Archivist, Soeurs Ursulines de Quebec Archives, 18 Rue Donnacona, Quebec, QC, G1R 3Y7, CANADA. Tel: 418-692-2523. Fax: 418-692-1356. p. 2906

Fortier, Paula, Br Mgr, Phoenix Public Library, Mesquite Library, 4525 E Paradise Village Pkwy N, Phoenix, AZ, 85032-6853. p. 76

Fortier, Solange, Librn, Ministere de la Justice, 1200 route de l'Eglise, 4th Flr, Quebec, QC, G1V 4M1, CANADA. Tel: 418-643-8409. Fax: 418-643-9749. p. 2905

Fortier-Barnes, Catherine A, Head, Access Serv, University of Massachusetts Dartmouth Library, 285 Old Westport Rd, North Dartmouth, MA, 02747-2300. Tel: 508-999-8665. Fax: 508-999-8987. p. 1112

Fortin, Angelica, Br Mgr, San Diego County Library, San Marcos Branch, Two Civic Center Dr, San Marcos, CA, 92069-2949. Tel: 760-891-3008. Fax: 760-891-3015. p. 234

Fortin, Genevieve, Prof, College Lionel-Groulx, 100, rue Duquet, Sainte-Therese, QC, J7E 3G6, CANADA. Tel: 450-430-3120, Ext 407. Fax: 450-971-7883. p. 2979

Fortin, Jean-Luc, Reader Serv, Assemblee Nationale du Quebec Bibliotheque, 1035 Rue des Parlementaires, Edifice Pamphile-Lemay, Quebec, QC, G1A 1A3, CANADA. Tel: 418-643-2708. Fax: 418-646-3207. p. 2903

Fortin, Karen, Dir, Pinellas Park Public Library, 7770 52nd St, Pinellas Park, FL, 33781-3498. Tel: 727-541-0718. Fax: 727-541-0818. p. 483

Fortin, Lisa, ILL Librn, Gale Library, 16 S Main St, Newton, NH, 03858-3310. Tel: 603-382-4691. Fax: 603-382-2528. p. 1460

Fortin, Marcel, Head of Libr, University of Toronto Libraries, Data, Map & Government Information Services, John P Robarts Library, 130 Saint George St, 5th Flr, Toronto, ON, M5S 1A5, CANADA. Tel: 416-978-7628. Fax: 416-946-0522. p. 2865

Fortin, Marie-Claire, Dir, Bibliotheque Publique de La Malbaie, 363 rue Saint-Etienne (Chapel Community Center), La Malbaie, QC, G5A 1S8, CANADA. Tel: 418-665-6027. Fax: 418-665-6481. p. 2885

Fortin, Maurice G, Dr, Exec Dir, Libr Serv, Angelo State University Library, 2025 S Johnson, San Angelo, TX, 76904-5079. Tel: 325-942-2222. Fax: 325-942-2198. p. 2378

Fortin, Mitzi, Br Head, Okanagan Regional Library, Lumby Branch, 2250 Shields Ave, Lumby, BC, V0E 2G0, CANADA. Tel: 250-547-9528. p. 2730

Fortin, Richard, Dir, Charles M Bailey Public Library, 39 Bowdoin St, Winthrop, ME, 04364. Tel: 207-377-8673. p. 1007

Fortin, Tom, Dep Dir, Libr Serv, San Mateo County Library, Library Administration, 125 Lessingia Ct, San Mateo, CA, 94402-4000. Tel: 650-312-5256. Fax: 650-312-5382. p. 255

Fortin, Valerie, Coll Develop, McGill University Libraries, Life Sciences Library, McIntyre Medical Science Bldg, 3655 Promenade Sir William Osler, Montreal, QC, H3G 1Y6, CANADA. Tel: 514-398-4475, Ext 09671. Fax: 514-398-3890. p. 2898

Fortinberry, Peggy, Br Mgr, Tangipahoa Parish Library, Kentwood Branch, 101 Ave F, Kentwood, LA, 70444. Tel: 985-229-3596. Fax: 985-229-4566. p. 941

Fortner, Cathy, Dir, Free Methodist Church of North America, 770 N High School Rd, Indianapolis, IN, 46214. Tel: 317-244-3660. Fax: 317-244-1247. p. 751

Fortner, Marolyn, Mgr, Oconee Regional Library, Harlie Fulford Memorial, 301 Elm St, Wrightsville, GA, 31096. Tel: 478-864-3940. Fax: 478-864-0626. p. 531

Fortney, Helen Jane, Dir, Readstown Public Library, 129 W Wisconsin, Readstown, WI, 54652. Tel: 608-629-5465. Fax: 608-629-5465. p. 2633

Fortney, Katie, Asst Librn, University of California, 1156 High St, Santa Cruz, CA, 95064. Tel: 831-502-7505. Fax: 831-459-8206. p. 264

Fortney, Teresa, ILL, Oak Ridge Public Library, 1401 Oak Ridge Tpk, Oak Ridge, TN, 37830-6224. Tel: 865-425-3455. Fax: 865-425-3429. p. 2262

Forton, Janet B, Interim Dir, Scott Township Public Library, 301 Lindsay Rd, Scott Township, PA, 15106. Tel: 412-429-5380. Fax: 412-429-5370. p. 2136

Fortson, Thomas, Librn, El Rito Public Library, 182 Placitas Rd, El Rito, NM, 87530. Tel: 575-581-4608. Fax: 575-581-9591. p. 1554

Fortunato, Henry, Dir, Pub Affairs & Communication, The Kansas City Public Library, 14 W Tenth St, Kansas City, MO, 64105. Tel: 816-701-3514. Fax: 816-701-3401. p. 1338

Fortune, Nancy, Br Mgr, Wayne County Public Library, Shreve Branch, 189 W McConkey St, Shreve, OH, 44676-9301. Tel: 330-567-2219. Fax: 330-567-2791. p. 1950

Fortushniak, Jane, Br Mgr, Saint Clair County Library System, Burtchville Township, 7097 Second St, Lakeport, MI, 48059. Tel: 810-385-8550. p. 1219

Forward, Michelle, Mgr, Morrisville Public Library, 87 E Main St, Morrisville, NY, 13408. Tel: 315-684-9130. Fax: 315-684-9132. p. 1663

Forys, John W, Jr, Librn, University of Iowa Libraries, Engineering, 2001 Seamans Center, Iowa City, IA, 52242-1420. Tel: 319-335-6047. Fax: 319-335-5900. p. 823

Fosher, Mary, Asst Librn, Reed Free Library, Eight Village Rd, Surry, NH, 03431-8314. Tel: 603-352-1761. p. 1466

Fosmire, Michael, Librn, Purdue University Libraries, Earth & Atmospheric Sciences, Civil Engineering Bldg, Rm 2215, 550 Stadium Mall Dr, West Lafayette, IN, 47907-2058. Tel: 765-494-2858. Fax: 765-496-1210. p. 786

Fosmire, Michael, Head of Libr, Purdue University Libraries, Siegesmund Engineering Library, Potter Ctr 160, 500 Central Dr, West Lafayette, IN, 47907-2058. Tel: 765-494-2859. Fax: 765-496-3572. p. 787

Fosmire, Michael, Librn, Purdue University Libraries, Physics, Physics Bldg, Rm 290, West Lafayette, IN, 47907-1321. Tel: 765-494-2859. Fax: 765-494-0706. p. 787

Fosno, Sandra, Dir, Lenora Blackmore Public Library, 105 W Benton St, Windsor, MO, 65360. Tel: 660-647-2298. p. 1372

Fosnot, Marcia, Mgr, Res Mgt, Greenwich Library, 101 W Putnam Ave, Greenwich, CT, 06830-5387. Tel: 203-622-7926. Fax: 203-622-7959. p. 341

Foss, Ernest Francis, Jr, Learning Res Ctr Coordr, Heald College, 25500 Industrial Blvd, Hayward, CA, 94545. Tel: 510-783-2100. Fax: 510-783-3287. p. 157

Foss, Karen, Dir, Catawba County Library, 115 West C St, Newton, NC, 28658. Tel: 828-465-8664. Fax: 828-465-8983. p. 1813

Foss, Loretta, Mat Mgr, Vernon Area Public Library District, 300 Olde Half Day Rd, Lincolnshire, IL, 60069-2901. Tel: 847-634-3650. Fax: 847-634-8449. p. 666

Fosselman, Steve, Dir, Grand Island Public Library, 211 N Washington St, Grand Island, NE, 68801-5855. Tel: 308-385-5333. Fax: 308-385-5339. p. 1400

Fossett, John, Coll Mgr, Kitsap Regional Library, 1301 Sylvan Way, Bremerton, WA, 98310-3498. Tel: 360-405-9101. Fax: 360-405-9128. p. 2510

Fossum, Anne, Dir, Webster Public Library, 800 Main St, Webster, SD, 57274-1494. Tel: 605-345-3263. p. 2222

Foster, Amity, Archives, Coordr, AV, Concordia University, 1282 Concordia Ave, Saint Paul, MN, 55104. Tel: 651-641-8240. Fax: 651-641-8782. p. 1278

Foster, Ann, Librn, Saskatoon Public Library, Alice Turner Branch, 110 Nelson Rd, Saskatoon, SK, S7S 1K7, CANADA. Tel: 306-975-8127. Fax: 306-975-8130. p. 2926

Foster, Anne, Univ Archivist, University of Alaska Fairbanks, 310 Tanana Dr, Fairbanks, AK, 99775. Tel: 907-474-5590. Fax: 907-474-6841. p. 48

Foster, Anne, Outreach Librn, Marion County Public Library, 201 E Main St, Lebanon, KY, 40033-1133. Tel: 270-692-4698. Fax: 270-692-9555. p. 920

Foster, Anne, Librn, Northern Michigan Regional Hospital, 416 Connable Ave, Petoskey, MI, 49770. Tel: 231-487-4500. Fax: 231-487-7892. p. 1217

Foster, Benjamin R, Curator, Yale University Library, Babylonian Collection, 130 Wall St, New Haven, CT, 06520. Tel: 203-432-1837. Fax: 203-432-7231. p. 356

Foster, Bernadette, Dir, Greece Public Library, Two Vince Tofany Blvd, Greece, NY, 14612. Tel: 585-225-8951. Fax: 585-225-2777. p. 1630

Foster, Cira, Info Tech Spec, Utica Public Library, 303 Genesee St, Utica, NY, 13501. Tel: 315-735-2279. Fax: 315-734-1034. p. 1760

Foster, Connie, Interim Dean of Libr, Western Kentucky University Libraries, Helm-Cravens Library Complex, 1906 College Heights Blvd, No 11067, Bowling Green, KY, 42101-1067. Tel: 270-745-2905. Fax: 270-745-6422. p. 907

Foster, Deborah, Access Serv, Pub Serv, Fayetteville Technical Community College, 2201 Hull Rd, Fayetteville, NC, 28303. Tel: 910-678-8257. Fax: 910-678-8401. p. 1793

Foster, Dixie, Asst Dir, Denison Public Library, 300 W Gandy St, Denison, TX, 75020-3153. Tel: 903-465-1797. Fax: 903-465-1130. p. 2312

Foster, Donald, Librn, Calvary Episcopal Church Library, 123 S Ninth St, Columbia, MO, 65201. Tel: 573-449-3194. Fax: 573-442-9392. p. 1324

Foster, Elaine, Librn, Carmi Public Library, 103 Slocumb St, Carmi, IL, 62821. Tel: 618-382-5277. Fax: 618-384-3118. p. 601

Foster, Elinor, Dean, Libr Serv, University of North Carolina at Pembroke, Faculty Row, Pembroke, NC, 28372. Tel: 910-521-6516. Fax: 910-521-6547. p. 1814

Foster, Forrest, Access Serv, Winston-Salem State University, 601 Martin Luther King Jr Dr, Winston-Salem, NC, 27110. Tel: 336-750-2843. Fax: 336-750-2459. p. 1834

Foster, Jack, Bus Mgr, St Catharines Public Library, 54 Church St, St. Catharines, ON, L2R 7K2, CANADA. Tel: 905-688-6103, Ext 213. Fax: 905-688-6292. p. 2843

Foster, Janice M, Librn, Saint Joseph Health Center, 1000 Carondelet Dr, Kansas City, MO, 64114-4673. Tel: 816-942-4400, Ext 2160. Fax: 816-943-2592. p. 1340

Foster, Jean, Br Librn, Spartanburg County Public Libraries, Boiling Springs Library, 871 Double Bridge Rd, Boiling Springs, SC, 29316. Tel: 864-578-3665. p. 2205

Foster, Jennifer, Asst Prof, Bus Ref, Texas A&M University Libraries, West Campus Library, Olsen Blvd, Bldg 1511, College Station, TX, 77843-5001. Tel: 979-862-1982. Fax: 979-862-2977. p. 2299

Foster, Jennifer, Media Spec, University of Houston, 2602 N Ben Jordan St, Victoria, TX, 77901-5699. Tel: 361-570-4177. Fax: 361-570-4155. p. 2395

Foster, Jenny, Dir of Libr Serv, Argosy University, 1001 Bishop St, Ste 400, Honolulu, HI, 96813. Tel: 808-536-5555. Fax: 808-536-5505. p. 559

Foster, Jill, Librn, W B Lewis Public Library, 55 Ridge Rd, Deep River, ON, K0J 1P0, CANADA. Tel: 613-584-4244. Fax: 613-584-1405. p. 2802

Foster, Jill Katherine, Regional Dir, York Library Region, Four Carleton St, Fredericton, NB, E3B 5P4, CANADA. Tel: 506-453-5380. Fax: 506-457-4878. p. 2764

Foster, Juanita, Sr Librn, Hennepin County Library, Rockford Road, 6401 42nd Ave N, Crystal, MN, 55427-1499. Tel: 612-543-5878. Fax: 612-543-5877. p. 1264

Foster, Juanita, Sr Librn, Hennepin County Library, Webber Park, 4310 Webber Pkwy, Minneapolis, MN, 55412. Tel: 612-543-5878. Fax: 612-543-6752. p. 1265

Foster, Judy, Ref, Catawba County Library, 115 West C St, Newton, NC, 28658. Tel: 828-465-8664. Fax: 828-465-8983. p. 1813

Foster, Julianne, Chairperson, Holden Municipal Library, 4912-50 St, Holden, AB, T0B 2C0, CANADA. Tel: 780-688-3838. Fax: 780-688-3838. p. 2707

Foster, Kelli, Tech Serv Mgr, Kaubisch Memorial Public Library, 205 Perry St, Fostoria, OH, 44830-2265. Tel: 419-435-2813. Fax: 419-435-5350. p. 1900

Foster, LaDonna, Br Mgr, Boone-Madison Public Library, Whitesville Branch, 38175 Coal River Rd, Whitesville, WV, 25209. Tel: 304-854-0196. Fax: 304-854-0196. p. 2564

Foster, Lorna, Librn, Lakeland Library Region, Maidstone Branch, Box 429, Maidstone, SK, S0M 1M0, CANADA. Tel: 306-893-4153. Fax: 306-893-4158. p. 2920

Foster, Lynn, Br Mgr, Aiken-Bamberg-Barnwell-Edgefield Regional Library System, Trenton Branch, 117 Watson Rd, Trenton, SC, 29847. Tel: 803-275-2538. p. 2179

Foster, Mary, Circ Supvr, Pennsylvania State University - Dickinson School of Law (University Libraries), 1170 Harrisburg Pike, Carlisle, PA, 17013-1617. Tel: 717-240-5009. Fax: 717-240-5127. p. 2042

Foster, Mary, Dir, Susquehanna County Law Library, Court House, Montrose, PA, 18801. Tel: 570-278-4600. p. 2092

Foster, Mary Gail, Librn, Oklahoma Department of Human Services, 114 NE 31st St, Oklahoma City, OK, 73105. Tel: 405-962-1717. Fax: 405-962-1740. p. 1974

Foster, Mary Louise Irene, Dir, Libr Serv, Northeast Community College, 801 E Benjamin Ave, Norfolk, NE, 68702. Tel: 402-844-7131. Fax: 402-844-7293. p. 1410

Foster, Melissa, Asst Librn, Monterey County Law Library, 100 W Alisal, Ste 144, Salinas, CA, 93901. Tel: 831-755-5046. Fax: 831-422-9593. p. 226

Foster, Melissa, Asst Librn, Monterey County Law Library, Monterey Branch, Monterey County Court House, 1200 Aguajito Rd, Rm 202, Monterey, CA, 93940. Tel: 831-647-7746. Fax: 831-372-6036. p. 226

Foster, Mimi, Ad, Ascension Parish Library, 500 Mississippi St, Donaldsonville, LA, 70346-2535. Tel: 225-473-8052. Fax: 225-473-9522. p. 949

Foster, Neale, Acq, Circ, J Sargeant Reynolds Community College Library, Downtown Campus-Library & Information Services, 700 E Jackson St, 2nd Flr, Richmond, VA, 23219-1543. Tel: 804-523-5211. Fax: 804-786-6200. p. 2488

Foster, Rebecca W, Fiscal Officer, Lewis & Clark Library, 120 S Last Chance Gulch, Helena, MT, 59601. Tel: 406-447-1690, Ext 112. Fax: 406-447-1687. p. 1382

Foster, Robert, Dir, New England Air Museum, Bradley Int Airport, Windsor Locks, CT, 06096. Tel: 860-623-3305. Fax: 860-627-2820. p. 379

Foster, Ron, Assoc Librn, State University of New York Institute of Technology, Rte 12 N & Horatio St, Utica, NY, 13502. Tel: 315-792-7245. Fax: 315-792-7517. p. 1759

Foster, Rosanne, Dir, Traer Public Library, 531 Second St, Traer, IA, 50675. Tel: 319-478-2180. Fax: 319-478-2180. p. 848

Foster, Sally, Librn, Coolidge Library, 17 S Main St, Solon, ME, 04979. Tel: 207-643-2562. p. 1001

Foster, Sandra, Dir, Cosby Community Library, 3292 Cosby Hwy, Cosby, TN, 37722-0052. Tel: 423-487-5885. Fax: 423-487-5885. p. 2232

Foster, Sarah, Br Mgr, Whatcom County Library System, Lynden Branch, 216 Fourth St, Lynden, WA, 98264. Tel: 360-354-4883. Fax: 360-354-3149. p. 2509

Foster, Sarah, Ref Serv Coordr, Res Br Mgr, Whatcom County Library System, 5205 Northwest Dr, Bellingham, WA, 98226-9050. Tel: 360-384-3150. Fax: 360-384-4947. p. 2509

Foster, Shirley, Dir, United States Air Force, Bolling Air Force Base Library, FL 7054 HQ 11 MSG/SVMG, 410 Tinker St Bolling AFB, Washington, DC, 20032-0703. Tel: 202-767-5578. Fax: 202-404-8526. p. 417

Foster, Stephen, Univ Librn, Wright State University Libraries, 126 Dunbar Library, 3640 Colonel Glenn Hwy, Dayton, OH, 45435-0001. Tel: 937-775-4125. Fax: 937-775-4109. p. 1894

Foster, Susan, Ref Librn, Dewey & LeBoeuf LLP Library, 1301 Avenue of the Americas, 22nd Flr, New York, NY, 10019. Tel: 212-259-8000. Fax: 212-259-6679. p. 1677

Foster, Susan A, Ch, Rock Island Public Library, 401 19th St, Rock Island, IL, 61201. Tel: 309-732-7362. Fax: 309-732-7342. p. 696

Foster, Tahirih, Br Mgr, Hawaii State Public Library System, Honokaa Public Library, 45-3380 Mamane St, Bldg 3, Honokaa, HI, 96727. Tel: 808-775-8881. Fax: 808-775-8882. p. 562

Foster, Valerie, Tech Serv, Camp Verde Community Library, 130 Black Bridge Loop Rd, Camp Verde, AZ, 86322. Tel: 928-567-3414. Fax: 928-567-9583. p. 59

Foster, Valerie, Librn, Maple Springs Baptist Bible College & Seminary Library, 4130 Belt Rd, Capitol Heights, MD, 20743. Tel: 301-736-3631. Fax: 301-735-6507. p. 1023

Foster-Galasso, Mary, Dir, Evangeline Parish Library, 242 W Main St, Ville Platte, LA, 70586. Tel: 337-363-1369. Fax: 337-363-2353. p. 971

Foth, Agnes, ILL, Jake Epp Library, 255 Elmdale Dr, Steinbach, MB, R5G 1N6, CANADA. Tel: 204-326-6841. Fax: 204-326-6859. p. 2752

Foth, Nancy, Extn Serv Mgr, Toledo-Lucas County Public Library, 325 N Michigan St, Toledo, OH, 43604-6614. Tel: 419-259-5238. Fax: 419-259-5119. p. 1939

Foti, Robert, Bus Mgr, Portage District Library, 300 Library Lane, Portage, MI, 49002. Tel: 269-329-4542, Ext 702. Fax: 269-324-9222. p. 1220

Fotovat, Zahra, Sr Librn, Glendale Adventist Medical Center Library, 1509 Wilson Terrace, Glendale, CA, 91206. Tel: 818-409-8034. Fax: 818-546-5633. p. 155

Fotovat, Zahra, Med Librn, White Memorial Medical Center, 1720 Cesar E Chavez Ave, Los Angeles, CA, 90033-2462. Tel: 323-260-5715. Fax: 323-260-5748. p. 180

Fouberg, Vera, Librn, Letcher Public Library, 105 W Main St, Letcher, SD, 57359. Tel: 605-248-2689. p. 2214

Foucault, Luc, Tech Serv, Ecole Polytechnique de Montreal Bibliotheque, 2500, chemin de Polytechnique, Montreal, QC, H3T 1J4, CANADA. Tel: 514-340-4666. Fax: 514-340-4026. p. 2895

Foucher, Judy M, Head Librn, Greenwood Public Library, 346 S Copper St, Greenwood, BC, V0H 1J0, CANADA. Tel: 250-445-6111. Fax: 250-445-6111. p. 2729

Fougstedt, Susan, Asst Dir, Head, Ref, Pollard Memorial Library, 401 Merrimack St, Lowell, MA, 01852. Tel: 978-970-4120. Fax: 978-970-4117. p. 1100

Foulger, Neil, Coll Develop, Alabama State University, 915 S Jackson St, Montgomery, AL, 36104. Tel: 334-229-4106, 334-229-6890. Fax: 334-229-4911, 334-229-4940. p. 28

Foulks, Beth, Librn, Ponca Public Library, 203 Second St, Ponca, NE, 68770. Tel: 402-755-2739. p. 1417

Fountain, Jackee, Librn, Glencoe Public Library, 719 13th St E, Glencoe, MN, 55336-1597. Tel: 320-864-3919. Fax: 320-864-1919. p. 1252

Fountain, Jackie, Librn, Brownton Public Library, 528 Second St N, Brownton, MN, 55312. Tel: 320-328-5900. Fax: 320-328-5318. p. 1243

Fountain, Jessica, Circ Coordr, Hoyt Library, 284 Wyoming Ave, Kingston, PA, 18704-3597. Tel: 570-287-2013. Fax: 570-283-2081. p. 2074

Fountain, Joanna, Dr, Assoc Prof, Sam Houston State University, 1921 Ave J, Huntsville, TX, 77340. Tel: 936-294-4133. Fax: 936-294-1153. p. 2974

Fountain, Kathleen C, Head, Coll Develop, Washington State University Libraries, 14204 NE Salmon Creek Ave, Vancouver, WA, 98686. Tel: 360-546-9694. Fax: 360-546-9039. p. 2546

Fourhman-Shaull, Lila, Librn, York County Heritage Trust, 250 E Market St, York, PA, 17403. Tel: 717-848-1587. Fax: 717-812-1204. p. 2160

Fourie, Robert, Youth Serv Librn, DeForest Area Public Library, 203 Library St, DeForest, WI, 53532. Tel: 608-846-5482. Fax: 608-846-6875. p. 2588

Fourman, Deborah, Asst Dir, Arcanum Public Library, 101 W North St, Arcanum, OH, 45304-1126. Tel: 937-692-8484. Fax: 937-692-8916. p. 1854

Fournier, Danielle, ILL, Ecole de Technologie Superieure (Service de la bibliotheque), 1100 rue Notre-Dame Ouest, Montreal, QC, H3C 1K3, CANADA. Tel: 514-396-8946. Fax: 514-396-8633. p. 2895

Fournier, Donna, Librn, Swarthmore College, Daniel Underhill Music & Dance, 500 College Ave, Swarthmore, PA, 19081-1399. Tel: 610-328-8231. p. 2145

Fournier, Donna, Performing Arts Librn, Swarthmore College, 500 College Ave, Swarthmore, PA, 19081-1081. Tel: 610-328-8231. Fax: 610-328-7329. p. 2145

Fournier, Gaston, Cat, Ecole de Technologie Superieure (Service de la bibliotheque), 1100 rue Notre-Dame Ouest, Montreal, QC, H3C 1K3, CANADA. Tel: 514-396-8946. Fax: 514-396-8633. p. 2895

Fournier, Karen, Dir, Canaan Public Library, 288 Main St, Canaan, ME, 04924. Tel: 207-474-6397. p. 980

Fournier, Kimberly, Coordr, Coll Develop, William Rainey Harper College Library, 1200 W Algonquin Rd, Palatine, IL, 60067. Tel: 847-925-6882. Fax: 847-925-6164. p. 687

Fournier, Randolph, Dr, Dean, Learning & Tech Res, Northern Virginia Community College Libraries, Loudoun Campus, 1000 Harry Flood Byrd Hwy, Sterling, VA, 20164-8699. Tel: 703-948-7798. Fax: 703-404-7374. p. 2447

Fournier, Randy, Dir, Libr Serv, Manchester Community College Library, Great Path, Manchester, CT, 06040. Tel: 860-512-2872. Fax: 860-512-2871. p. 350

Fournier-Viger, David, Ref, Cegep de L'Abitibi - Temiscamingue Bibliotheque, 425 Boul du College, Rouyn-Noranda, QC, J9X 5M5, CANADA. Tel: 819-762-0931, Ext 1216. Fax: 819-762-2071. p. 2908

Foust, Dorothy, Curator, Madera County Historical Society, 210 W Yosemite Ave, Madera, CA, 93637-3533. Tel: 559-673-0291. p. 181

Foust, Molly, Dir, Ulysses Philomathic Library, 74 E Main St, Trumansburg, NY, 14886. Tel: 607-387-5623. Fax: 607-387-3823. p. 1757

Fout, Deborah, Dir, Homewood Public Library, 1721 Oxmoor Rd, Homewood, AL, 35209-4085. Tel: 205-332-6600. Fax: 205-802-6424. p. 20

Foutch, Leslie J, Librn, Vanderbilt University, The Peabody Library, 230 Appleton Pl, PBM 135, Nashville, TN, 37203. Tel: 615-343-7541. Fax: 615-343-7923. p. 2261

Fouts, Mary, District Librn, Operations Mgr, Pend Oreille County Library District, 109 S Union St, Newport, WA, 99156. Tel: 509-447-2111. Fax: 509-447-2806. p. 2521

Fouts, Mary, District Librn, Operations Mgr, Pend Oreille County Library District, Newport Public Library, 116 S Washington Ave, Newport, WA, 99156. Tel: 509-447-2111. Fax: 509-447-2806. p. 2522

Fouts, Terry, Asst Librn, Ashland Town Library, 42 Main St, Ashland, NH, 03217. Tel: 603-968-7928. Fax: 603-968-7928. p. 1438

Foutts, Carol, Dir, R H Johnson Library, 13801 W Meeker Blvd, Sun City West, AZ, 85375-4406. Tel: 623-544-6130. Fax: 623-544-6131. p. 82

Fowler, Carol, Reader Serv, Alabama Institute for the Deaf & Blind, 705 South St, Talladega, AL, 35160. Tel: 256-761-3237. Fax: 256-761-3561. p. 37

Fowler, Cathy, Ch, Merrimac Public Library, 34 W Main St, Merrimac, MA, 01860. Tel: 978-346-9441. Fax: 978-346-8272. p. 1105

Fowler, Christina, Br Mgr, Dillon County Library, 600 E Main St, Dillon, SC, 29536. Tel: 843-774-0330. Fax: 843-774-0733. p. 2192

Fowler, Clara, Mgr, Info Serv, University of Texas, M D Anderson Cancer Center Research Medical Library, 1400 Pressler St, Houston, TX, 77030-3722. Tel: 713-792-2282. Fax: 713-563-3650. p. 2344

Fowler, Debbie, Mgr, Southeast Arkansas Regional Library, McGehee Branch, 211 N Fourth St, McGehee, AR, 71654. Tel: 870-222-4097. Fax: 870-222-4097. p. 110

Fowler, Deborah, Ref Serv, University of Hartford Libraries, 200 Bloomfield Ave, West Hartford, CT, 06117. Tel: 860-768-4264. p. 376

Fowler, Deborah, Librn, Toronto Urban Development Services, Metro Hall, 22nd Flr, Toronto, ON, M5V 3C6, CANADA. Tel: 416-392-1526. Fax: 416-392-3821. p. 2864

Fowler, Dolores, Found & Develop Officer, Pikes Peak Library District, 20 N Cascade Ave, Colorado Springs, CO, 80903. Tel: 719-531-6333. p. 296

Fowler, Elizabeth, Dir, Chesapeake Public Library, 298 Cedar Rd, Chesapeake, VA, 23322-5512. Tel: 757-410-7102. Fax: 757-410-7112. p. 2456

Fowler, George, Assoc Univ Librn, Old Dominion University Libraries, 4427 Hampton Blvd, Norfolk, VA, 23529-0256. Tel: 757-683-4159. Fax: 757-683-5767. p. 2482

Fowler, Heidi, Ref Librn, Grafton Public Library, 35 Grafton Common, Grafton, MA, 01519. Tel: 508-839-4649. Fax: 508-839-7726. p. 1091

Fowler, Heidi E, Dir, Townsend Public Library, 276 Main St, Townsend, MA, 01469-1513. Tel: 978-597-1714. Fax: 978-597-2779. p. 1131

Fowler, Jason, Assoc Librn, Res Serv & Archivist, Southern Baptist Theological Seminary, 2825 Lexington Rd, Louisville, KY, 40280-0294. p. 925

Fowler, Jennifer L, Mrs, Librn, Loup City Public Library, 800 N Eighth St, Loup City, NE, 68853. Tel: 308-745-1589. p. 1407

Fowler, Kristine, Librn, University of Minnesota Libraries-Twin Cities, Mathematics, 310 Vincent Hall, 206 Church St SE, Minneapolis, MN, 55455. Tel: 612-624-6075. Fax: 612-624-4302. p. 1262

Fowler, Landra, Cat/Ref Librn, Southwest Texas Junior College, 2401 Garner Field Rd, Uvalde, TX, 78801. Tel: 830-591-7251. Fax: 830-591-4186. p. 2394

Fowler, Larry, In Charge, Pendleton Correctional Facility, 4490 W Reformatory Rd, Pendleton, IN, 46064. Tel: 765-778-2107, Ext 1221. Fax: 765-778-1431. p. 772

Fowler, Larry, In Charge, Pendleton Correctional Facility, Law, 4490 W Reformatory Rd, Pendleton, IN, 46064. Tel: 765-778-2107. Fax: 765-778-3395. p. 772

Fowler, Linda, Asst Dir, Watkins Glen Public Library, 610 S Decatur St, Watkins Glen, NY, 14891. Tel: 607-535-2346. Fax: 607-535-7338. p. 1764

Fowler, Luci, Br Mgr, Jackson County Public Library System, Graceville Branch, 5314 Brown St, Graceville, FL, 32440. Tel: 850-263-3659. Fax: 850-263-3652. p. 462

Fowler, Marilyn, Librn, Mental Health Center Library, 1333 Iris Ave, Boulder, CO, 80304-2296. Tel: 303-443-8500, Ext 273. Fax: 303-449-6029. p. 290

Fowler, Maura, Circ Supvr, University of Utah, S J Quinney Law Library, 332 S 1400 East, Salt Lake City, UT, 84112-0731. Tel: 801-581-6296. Fax: 801-585-3033. p. 2415

Fowler, Melinda, Dir, Sand Lake Town Library, 8428 Miller Hill Rd, Averill Park, NY, 12018. Tel: 518-674-5050. Fax: 518-674-5050. p. 1576

Fowler, Nancy, Asst Dir, Lebanon-Wilson County Library, 108 S Hatton Ave, Lebanon, TN, 37087-3590. Tel: 615-444-0632. Fax: 615-444-0535. p. 2245

Fowler, Norma, Head Librn, Tech Serv, Sedona Public Library, 3250 White Bear Rd, Sedona, AZ, 86336. Tel: 928-282-7714. Fax: 928-282-5789. p. 81

Fowler, Patti, Regional Br Operations Mgr, Austin Public Library, Manchaca Road, 5500 Manchaca Rd, Austin, TX, 78745. Tel: 512-974-8700. Fax: 512-974-8701. p. 2279

Fowler, Paula, Dir, Keewatin Public Library, 125 W Third Ave, Keewatin, MN, 55753. Tel: 218-778-6377. Fax: 218-778-6193. p. 1255

Fowler, Ronald A, Ch, Petoskey Public Library, 500 E Mitchell St, Petoskey, MI, 49770. Tel: 231-758-3100. Fax: 231-758-3106. p. 1217

Fowler, Rose, Asst Librn, Madison County Public Library, Hwy 412 & Gaskill, Huntsville, AR, 72740. Tel: 479-738-2754. Fax: 479-738-2754. p. 104

Fowler, Theresa, Librn, Tulsa City-County Library, Martin Regional Library, 2601 S Garnett, Tulsa, OK, 74129. Tel: 918-669-6340. Fax: 918-669-6344. p. 1983

Fowler, Victoria, Curator, Carroll County Farm Museum, 500 S Center St, Westminster, MD, 21157. Tel: 410-386-3880. Fax: 410-876-8544. p. 1045

Fowley, Linda, Librn, Akerman Senterfitt LLP Law Library, 750 9th St NW, Ste 750, Washington, DC, 20001. Tel: 202-393-6222. Fax: 202-393-5959. p. 391

Fowlie, Linda, Dir, Akerman, Senterfitt & Eidson PA, 420 S Orange Ave, Ste 1200, Orlando, FL, 32801. Tel: 407-423-4000. Fax: 407-843-6610. p. 475

Fowlkes, Ashley, Ch, Outreach Mgr, Pub Relations, Warren County Public Library, 1225 State St, Bowling Green, KY, 42101. Tel: 270-782-0252. Fax: 270-781-7323. p. 907

Fox, Annie, Librn, Front Range Community College-Larimer Campus, 4616 S Shields, Fort Collins, CO, 80526. Tel: 970-204-8207. Fax: 970-204-8444. p. 307

Fox, Betty, Spec Serv, Argie Cooper Public Library, 100 S Main St, Shelbyville, TN, 37160-3984. Tel: 931-684-7323. Fax: 931-685-4848. p. 2265

Fox, Beverly, Dir, Bainbridge Free Library, 13 N Main, Bainbridge, NY, 13733. Tel: 607-967-5305. Fax: 607-967-5305. p. 1577

Fox, Brandy, Librn, Evansville Psychiatric Children's Center Library, 3300 E Morgan Ave, Evansville, IN, 47715. Tel: 812-477-6436, Ext 225. Fax: 812-474-4248. p. 738

Fox, Brooke, Univ Archivist, Medical University of South Carolina Library, 171 Ashley Ave, Ste 300, Charleston, SC, 29425-0001. Tel: 843-792-9211. Fax: 843-792-7947. p. 2184

Fox, Bruce, Br Mgr, Chicago Public Library, Roden, 6083 N Northwest Hwy, Chicago, IL, 60631. Tel: 312-744-1478. Fax: 312-744-4245. p. 609

Fox, Cassandra, Supvr, Access Serv, Massachusetts Institute of Technology Libraries, Barker Engineering, Bldg 10-500, 77 Massachusetts Ave, Cambridge, MA, 02139-4307. Tel: 617-324-6212. Fax: 617-258-5623. p. 1077

Fox, Christopher D, Curator, Fort Ticonderoga Museum, Fort Rd, Ticonderoga, NY, 12883. Tel: 518-585-2821, Ext 229. Fax: 518-585-2210. p. 1755

Fox, Darin K, Dir, University of Oklahoma, Donald E Pray Law Library, 300 Timberdell Rd, Norman, OK, 73019. Tel: 405-325-4311. Fax: 405-325-6282. p. 1971

Fox, Doug, Syst Librn, University of Toronto Libraries, Victoria University Library, 71 Queens Park Crescent E, Toronto, ON, M5S 1K7, CANADA. Tel: 416-585-4471. Fax: 416-585-4591. p. 2867

Fox, E Brooke, Archivist, Medical University of South Carolina Library, Waring Historical Library, 175 Ashley Ave, Charleston, SC, 29425-0001. Tel: 843-792-2288. Fax: 843-792-8619. p. 2185

Fox, Eddie P, Br Librn, Noxubee County Library System, Vista J Daniel Memorial, 402 Residence St, Shuqualak, MS, 39361-9740. Tel: 662-793-9576. p. 1307

Fox, Elizabeth, Info Serv, South Dakota State University, 1300 N Campus Dr, Box 2115, Brookings, SD, 57007-1098. Tel: 605-688-5569. Fax: 605-688-6133. p. 2210

Fox, Fran, Asst Librn, Oswayo Valley Memorial Library, 103 N Pleasant St, Shinglehouse, PA, 16748. Tel: 814-697-6691. Fax: 814-697-6691. p. 2140

Fox, Gene, Dir, New Castle Library, 301 Wentworth Rd, New Castle, NH, 03854. Tel: 603-431-6773. Fax: 603-431-6773. p. 1459

Fox, Gloria, Dir, Luttrell Public Library, 115 Park Rd, Luttrell, TN, 37779. Tel: 865-992-0208. Fax: 865-992-4354. p. 2245

Fox, James, Head, Spec Coll & Archives, University of Oregon Libraries, 1501 Kincaid St, Eugene, OR, 97403-1299. Tel: 541-346-3056. Fax: 541-346-3485. p. 1997

Fox, Jane, YA Serv, Plainfield-Guilford Township Public Library, 1120 Stafford Rd, Plainfield, IN, 46168-2230. Tel: 317-839-6602. Fax: 317-838-3805. p. 773

Fox, Jane, Librn, Grand Bank Public Library, Church St, Grand Bank, NL, A0E 1W0, CANADA. Tel: 709-832-0310. Fax: 709-832-0310. p. 2770

Fox, Jeff, Librn, Illinois Lodge of Research, 614 E Lincoln Ave, Normal, IL, 61761. Tel: 309-219-1427. p. 681

Fox, Jill, Dir, Mayville District Public Library, 6090 Fulton St, Mayville, MI, 48744. Tel: 989-843-6522. Fax: 989-843-0078. p. 1207

Fox, Joe, Instrul Serv Librn, Cedarville University, 251 N Main St, Cedarville, OH, 45314-0601. Tel: 937-766-7840. Fax: 937-766-2337. p. 1865

Fox, Judy, Assoc Dean, Access, Bibliog & Info Serv, Washington University Libraries, One Brookings Dr, Campus Box 1061, Saint Louis, MO, 63130-4862. Tel: 314-935-5421. Fax: 314-935-4045. p. 1362

Fox, Karen, Libr Dir, Fairbury Public Library, 601 Seventh St, Fairbury, NE, 68352. Tel: 402-729-2843. Fax: 402-729-2880. p. 1398

Fox, Katherine, Head, Ref, University of Texas Libraries, Center for American History, SRH 2-101, D1100, University of Texas at Austin, Austin, TX, 78712. Tel: 512-495-4515. Fax: 512-495-4542. p. 2284

Fox, Ken, Librn, Law Society of Saskatchewan Libraries, Court House, 2425 Victoria Ave, Regina, SK, S4P 3M3, CANADA. Tel: 306-569-8020. Fax: 306-569-0155. p. 2922

Fox, Linda, Dir, Chester Public Library, 21 W Main St, Chester, CT, 06412. Tel: 860-526-0018. p. 334

Fox, Linda, Dir, New Fairfield Free Public Library, Two Brush Hill Rd, New Fairfield, CT, 06812. Tel: 203-312-5679. Fax: 203-312-5685. p. 354

Fox, Linda, Ch, Oskaloosa Public Library, 301 S Market St, Oskaloosa, IA, 52577. Tel: 641-673-0441. Fax: 641-673-6237. p. 837

Fox, Lisa, Cat, Bolivar-Harpers Ferry Public Library, 151 Polk St, Harpers Ferry, WV, 25425. Tel: 304-535-2301. Fax: 304-535-2301. p. 2560

Fox, Lynne, Educ Librn, University of Colorado Denver, 12950 E Montview Blvd, Aurora, CO, 80045. Tel: 303-724-2152. Fax: 303-724-2166. p. 289

Fox, Lysanne, Br Head, Vancouver Public Library, South Hill, 6076 Fraser St, Vancouver, BC, V5W 2Z7, CANADA. Tel: 604-665-3965. Fax: 604-665-3440. p. 2744

Fox, Mary, Archivist, Dallas Baptist University, 3000 Mountain Creek Pkwy, Dallas, TX, 75211-9299. Tel: 214-333-5210. Fax: 214-333-5323. p. 2305

Fox, Monica, Syst Librn, Chippewa River District Library, 301 S University Ave, Mount Pleasant, MI, 48858-2597. Tel: 989-772-3488, Ext 32. Fax: 989-772-3280. p. 1211

Fox, Nancy, Cat, Mount Union College Library, 1972 Clark Ave, Alliance, OH, 44601-3993. Tel: 330-823-3844. Fax: 330-823-3963. p. 1854

Fox, Pamela Jean, Asst Librn, Bahai Reference Library of Peoria, 5209 N University, Peoria, IL, 61614. Tel: 309-691-9311. Fax: 309-691-4407. p. 690

Fox, Patricia, Assoc Dir, Widener University, Harrisburg Campus Law Library, 3800 Vartan Way, Harrisburg, DE, 17110. Tel: 717-541-3935. Fax: 717-541-3998. p. 389

Fox, Rachel, Ch, Port Washington Public Library, One Library Dr, Port Washington, NY, 11050. Tel: 516-883-4400. Fax: 516-883-7927. p. 1721

Fox, Robert E, Jr, Dean, University of Louisville Libraries, 2215 S Third St, Louisville, KY, 40292. Tel: 502-852-6745. Fax: 502-852-7394. p. 926

Fox, Robin, Bus Mgr, Escondido History Center, 321 N Broadway, Escondido, CA, 92025. Tel: 760-743-8207. Fax: 760-743-8267. p. 146

Fox, Rosalie, Dir, Libr & Info Mgt, Supreme Court of Canada Library, 301 Wellington St, Ottawa, ON, K1A 0J1, CANADA. Tel: 613-996-9971. Fax: 613-952-2832. p. 2833

Fox, Shannon, Coordr, Electronic Res, Austin College, 900 N Grand Ave, Ste 6L, Sherman, TX, 75090-4402. Tel: 903-813-2559. Fax: 903-813-2297. p. 2387

Fox, Tina, Br Mgr, Grant Parish Library, Dry Prong Branch, 605 Russell Hataway St, Dry Prong, LA, 71423. Tel: 318-899-7588. Fax: 318-899-7588. p. 947

Fox, Willa Lyn, Librn, Olive-Harvey College, City Colleges of Chicago, 10001 S Woodlawn Ave, Rm 2423, Chicago, IL, 60628. Tel: 773-291-6360. Fax: 773-291-6463. p. 622

Foxhoven, Sheila, Asst Dir, Algona Public Library, 210 N Phillips St, Algona, IA, 50511. Tel: 515-295-5476. Fax: 515-295-3307. p. 792

Foxworth, Laura, Ch, Starkville-Oktibbeha County Public Library System, 326 University Dr, Starkville, MS, 39759. Tel: 662-323-2766, 662-323-2783. Fax: 662-323-9140. p. 1315

Foy, Anne, Circ, ILL, Lower Providence Community Library, 50 Parklane Dr, Eagleville, PA, 19403-1171. Tel: 610-666-6640. Fax: 610-666-5109. p. 2051

Foy, Jennifer, Syst, Westminster College, 1840 S 1300 East, Salt Lake City, UT, 84105-3697. Tel: 801-832-2250. Fax: 801-832-3109. p. 2415

Foy, Patricia L, Head, Circ Serv, Mercer County Library System, 2751 Brunswick Pike, Lawrenceville, NJ, 08648-4132. Tel: 609-882-9246. Fax: 609-538-9238. p. 1494

Foy, Valerie, Librn, Guildhall Public Library, Rt 102 N, Guildhall, VT, 05905. Tel: 802-676-3054. p. 2425

Foyle, Helen, Tech Serv, Haston Free Public Library, 161 N Main St, North Brookfield, MA, 01535. Tel: 508-867-0208. Fax: 508-867-0216. p. 1112

Fraas, Julia, Instrul Serv Librn & Coordr of Ref & Assessment, Oakton Community College Library, 1600 E Golf Rd, Rm 1410, Des Plaines, IL, 60016. Tel: 847-635-1642, 847-635-1644. Fax: 847-635-1987. p. 636

Fracchia, Charles, Dept Head, City College of San Francisco, 50 Phelan Ave, San Francisco, CA, 94112. Tel: 415-452-5454. Fax: 415-452-5588. p. 241

Frackowski, Marlena, Asst Dean, The College of New Jersey Library, 2000 Pennington Rd, Ewing, NJ, 08628-0718. Tel: 609-771-2311, 609-771-2332. Fax: 609-637-5177. p. 1484

Fradette, André, Actg Librn, Hydro Quebec Bibliotheque, 800, De Maisonneuve E, blvd, 2nd Flr, Montreal, QC, H2L 4M8, CANADA. Tel: 514-840-3000, Ext 5939. Fax: 514-840-5044. p. 2896

Fradette, Erin, Librn, Regina Public Library, Regent Place, 331 Albert St, Regina, SK, S4R 2N6, CANADA. Tel: 306-777-6086. Fax: 306-949-7269. p. 2923

Fragola, Patricia, Head, Circ, University of Wisconsin-Whitewater Library, 800 W Main St, Whitewater, WI, 53190. Tel: 262-472-5673. Fax: 262-472-5727. p. 2649

Frake, Diane F, Pub Serv, University of Hawaii, 2525 Dole St, Honolulu, HI, 96822-2328. Tel: 808-956-5581, 808-956-7583. Fax: 808-956-4615. p. 565

Frakes, Laura, Commun Libr Mgr, County of Los Angeles Public Library, Culver City Julian Dixon Library, 4975 Overland Ave, Culver City, CA, 90230-4299. Tel: 310-559-1676. Fax: 310-559-2994. p. 141

Frakes, Linda, ILL, Phoenix College, 1202 W Thomas Rd, Phoenix, AZ, 85013. Tel: 602-285-7457. Fax: 602-285-7368. p. 76

Fralick, Caitlin, Br Mgr, Hamilton Public Library, Locke, 285 Locke St S, Hamilton, ON, L8P 4C2, CANADA. Tel: 905-546-3200, Ext 3400. p. 2809

Fralick, Caitlin, Br Mgr, Hamilton Public Library, Westdale, 955 King St W, Hamilton, ON, L8S 1K9, CANADA. Tel: 905-546-3200, Ext 3400. p. 2810

Frame, Rebecca, Br Serv Mgr, Yolo County Library, Clarksburg Branch, 52915 Netherlands Ave, Clarksburg, CA, 95612-5007. Tel: 916-744-1755. Fax: 916-744-1755. p. 284

Frame, Stefanie, Dir of Southern California Libr Serv, Foley & Lardner LLP, 555 S Flower St, Ste 3500, Los Angeles, CA, 90071-2411. Tel: 213-972-4500. Fax: 213-486-0065. p. 170

Frame, Steve, Sr Librn, Torrance Public Library, North Torrance, 3604 Artesia Blvd, Torrance, CA, 90504-3315. Tel: 310-323-7200. Fax: 310-323-9687. p. 276

Frampton, Jann, Circ, Huachuca City Public Library, 506 N Gonzales Blvd, Huachuca City, AZ, 85616-9610. Tel: 520-456-1063. Fax: 520-456-1063. p. 65

Frampton, Kathy, Outreach Coordr, Syst, Slippery Rock University of Pennsylvania, Slippery Rock, PA, 16057-9989. Tel: 724-738-2058. Fax: 724-738-2661. p. 2140

France, Erik, Asst Dir, Tarrant County College, Jenkins Garrett Library-South Campus, 5301 Campus Dr, Fort Worth, TX, 76119. Tel: 817-515-4524. Fax: 817-515-4436. p. 2323

France, Jane, Ch, Bala-Cynwyd Library, 131 Old Lancaster Rd, Bala Cynwyd, PA, 19004-3037. Tel: 610-664-1196. Fax: 610-664-5534. p. 2030

France, Jim, Dir, South Haven Memorial Library, 314 Broadway St, South Haven, MI, 49090. Tel: 269-637-2403. Fax: 269-639-1685. p. 1227

France, Suzanne, Lifelong Learning Mgr, Wake County Public Library System, West Regional Library, 4000 Louis Stephens Dr, Cary, NC, 27519. Tel: 919-463-8507. p. 1818

Franchetto, Barbara, Dir, Consortium of Ontario Libraries, 111 Peter St, Ste 902, Toronto, ON, M5V 2H1, CANADA. Tel: 416-961-1669, Ext 5104. Fax: 416-961-5122. p. 2959

Franchois, George, Libr Dir, United States Department of the Interior Library, 1849 C St NW, Rm 1151, Washington, DC, 20240. Tel: 202-208-3796. Fax: 202-208-6773. p. 419

Franchuk, Ingrid, Chairperson, Gibbons Municipal Library, 4807 50th Ave, Gibbons, AB, T0A 1N0, CANADA. Tel: 780-923-2004. Fax: 780-923-2015. p. 2705

Franchuk, Lenore, Librn, Carrington City Library, 55 Ninth Ave S, Carrington, ND, 58421-1198. Tel: 701-652-3921. Fax: 701-652-3922. p. 1839

Francini, Jeanette, Head, Coll Mgt, Lucy Robbins Welles Library, 95 Cedar St, Newington, CT, 06111-2645. Tel: 860-665-8714. Fax: 860-667-1255. p. 361

Francini, Linda, ILL, Old Bridge Public Library, One Old Bridge Plaza, Old Bridge, NJ, 08857-2498. Tel: 732-721-5600, Ext 5034. Fax: 732-679-0556. p. 1516

Francis, Brenda, Ch, Youth Serv Coordr, Spring Green Community Library, 230 E Monroe St, Spring Green, WI, 53588-8035. Tel: 608-588-2276. p. 2639

Francis, Catherine, Br Support, Stormont, Dundas & Glengarry County Library, Iroquois Branch, One Dundas St & Elizabeth St, Iroquois, ON, K0E 1K0, CANADA. Tel: 613-652-4377. p. 2801

Francis, Catherine, Br Support, Stormont, Dundas & Glengarry County Library, Morrisburg Branch, 28 Ottawa St (Arena SE), Morrisburg, ON, K0C 1X0, CANADA. Tel: 613-543-3384. Fax: 613-543-2427. p. 2802

Francis, Cindy A, Assoc Prof/Librn/Coll Develop & LMS Adminr, Genesee Community College, One College Rd, Batavia, NY, 14020-9704. Tel: 585-343-0055, Ext 6126. Fax: 585-345-6933. p. 1578

Francis, Claire, Adult Serv, Uinta County Library, 701 Main St, Evanston, WY, 82930. Tel: 307-789-2770. Fax: 307-789-0148. p. 2655

Francis, Deirdre, Dir, Personnel & Staff Develop, Georgetown University, 37th & N St NW, Washington, DC, 20057-1174. Tel: 202-687-3980. Fax: 202-687-7501. p. 402

Francis, Frances, Librn, Boston Public Library, South Boston, 646 E Broadway, Boston, MA, 02127-1589. Tel: 617-268-0180. Fax: 617-464-2568. p. 1057

Francis, Frank, Libr Supvr, Inglewood Public Library, 101 W Manchester Blvd, Inglewood, CA, 90301-1771. Tel: 310-412-5397. Fax: 310-412-8848. p. 159

Francis, Georgianna J, Admin Librn, Buncombe County Public Libraries, 67 Haywood St, Asheville, NC, 28801. Tel: 828-250-4700. Fax: 828-250-4746. p. 1774

Francis, Kiffany, Metadata Librn, Cleveland State University, University Library, Rhodes Tower, 2121 Euclid Ave, Cleveland, OH, 44115-2214. Tel: 216-687-3869. Fax: 216-687-9380. p. 1879

Francis, Laura, Info Serv, National Business & Disability Council, 201 I U Willetts Rd, Albertson, NY, 11507-1599. Tel: 516-465-1519. Fax: 516-465-3730. p. 1571

Francis, Lola, Ref/IT Librn, McKendree University, 701 College Rd, Lebanon, IL, 62254-1299. Tel: 618-537-6950. Fax: 618-537-8411. p. 664

Francis, Marcia, Dir, Health Sci Libr, Idaho State University, Idaho State University, 850 S Ninth Ave, Pocatello, ID, 83209-8089. Tel: 208-282-4182. Fax: 208-282-4295. p. 581

Francis, Marcia, Dir, Idaho State University, Idaho Health Sciences Library, 850 S Ninth Ave, Pocatello, ID, 83201-5314. Tel: 208-282-4182. Fax: 202-282-4295. p. 582

Francis, Marion W, Adminr, Public Library Association of Annapolis & Anne Arundel County, Inc, Five Harry S Truman Pkwy, Annapolis, MD, 21401. Tel: 410-222-7234. Fax: 410-222-7188. p. 1010

Francis, Mary, Ref & Instruction Librn, Dakota State University, 820 N Washington Ave, Madison, SD, 57042-1799. Tel: 605-256-5845. Fax: 605-256-5208. p. 2214

Francis, Michiko, Head, ILL, Evergreen State College, Library Bldg, Rm 2300, 2700 Evergreen Pkwy NW, Olympia, WA, 98505-0002. Tel: 360-867-6250. Fax: 360-867-6790. p. 2522

Francis, Mona, Coordr, Meryman Library of Aquatic Research, 10408 Bloomingdale Ave, Riverview, FL, 33569. Tel: 813-626-9551. Fax: 813-623-6613. p. 485

Francis, Sara, Outreach Librn, Wyoming State Library, 2800 Central Ave, Cheyenne, WY, 82002. Tel: 307-777-6333. Fax: 307-777-6289. p. 2653

Francis, Tysha, Librn, Fairfield Public Library, 412 North D St, Fairfield, NE, 68938. Tel: 402-726-2220. Fax: 402-726-2220. p. 1398

Francisco, Grace, Mgr, Youth Serv, Oceanside Public Library, 330 N Coast Hwy, Oceanside, CA, 92054-2824. Tel: 760-435-5638. Fax: 760-435-9614. p. 199

Francisco, MaryLynn, Dir, United States Department of Defense, 7500 GEOINT Dr, Mail Stop S14-SR, Springfield, VA, 22150-7500. Tel: 571-557-1594. p. 2496

Francisco-Revilla, Luis, Asst Prof, University of Texas at Austin, One University Sta, D7000, Austin, TX, 78712-0390. Tel: 512-471-3821. Fax: 512-471-3971. p. 2975

Franciskovich, Jolene, Dir, Coal City Public Library District, 85 N Garfield St, Coal City, IL, 60416. Tel: 815-634-4552. Fax: 815-634-2950. p. 630

Franck, Carol, Info Literacy, State University of New York College at Potsdam, 44 Pierrepont Ave, Potsdam, NY, 13676-2294. Tel: 315-267-3310. Fax: 315-267-2744. p. 1722

Franco, Adrienne, Sr Ref & Instrul Serv Librn, Iona College, 715 North Ave, New Rochelle, NY, 10801-1890. Tel: 914-633-2348. Fax: 914-633-2136. p. 1666

Franco, Cynthia, Cataloger/Ref Librn, Southern Methodist University, DeGolyer Library of Special Collections, 6404 Robert S Hyer Lane, Dallas, TX, 75275. Tel: 214-768-3605. Fax: 214-768-1565. p. 2310

Franco, Janis, Local Hist & Genealogy Librn, Meriden Public Library, 105 Miller St, Meriden, CT, 06450. Tel: 203-238-2344, 203-238-2346. Fax: 203-238-3647. p. 350

Franco, Marcela, Head of Libr, Free Library of Philadelphia, Kensington Branch, 104 W Dauphin St, Philadelphia, PA, 19133-3701. Tel: 215-685-9996. Fax: 215-685-9997. p. 2108

Franco, Mary Anne, Head, Network Serv, Wilton Library Association, 137 Old Ridgefield Rd, Wilton, CT, 06897-3019. Tel: 203-762-3950. Fax: 203-834-1166. p. 378

Francoeur, Erin, Dir, Finney County Public Library, 605 E Walnut St, Garden City, KS, 67846. Tel: 620-272-3680. Fax: 620-272-3682. p. 868

Francoeur, Marthe, Chief Librn, College de Bois-de-Boulogne Bibliotheque, 10555, ave de Bois-de-Boulogne, Montreal, QC, H4N 1L4, CANADA. Tel: 514-332-3000, Ext 6467. Fax: 514-332-0083. p. 2893

Francois, Kristin, Acq, Cat, Porter, Wright, Morris & Arthur, LLP, Huntington Ctr, 41 S High St, Columbus, OH, 43215-6194. Tel: 216-443-2511. Fax: 614-227-2100. p. 1890

Francoline, Ellen, Med Librn, Eastern Connecticut Health Network, 71 Haynes St, Manchester, CT, 06040-4188. Tel: 860-647-6853. Fax: 860-647-6443. p. 349

Frandrup, Dominic, Asst Libr Dir, Waupaca Area Public Library, 107 S Main St, Waupaca, WI, 54981-1521. Tel: 715-258-4414. p. 2645

Franek, Claire R, Libr Dir, Muhlenberg County Libraries, 117 S Main St, Greenville, KY, 42345. Tel: 270-338-4760. Fax: 270-338-4000. p. 915

Franek, Melissa, Mgr, Public Library of Cincinnati & Hamilton County, Children's Learning Center, North Bldg, 1st Flr, 800 Vine St, Cincinnati, OH, 45202-2009. Tel: 513-369-6922. Fax: 513-369-3123. p. 1871

Frank, Anne, Pres, Montgomery County Library & Information Network Consortium, 301 Fayette St, 2nd Flr, Conshohocken, PA, 19428. Tel: 610-238-0580. Fax: 610-238-0581. p. 2954

Frank, Anne M, Dir, Lansdale Public Library, 301 Vine St, Lansdale, PA, 19446-3690. Tel: 215-855-3228. Fax: 215-855-6440. p. 2078

Frank, Barbara, Ref Serv, Waco-McLennan County Library System, 1717 Austin Ave, Waco, TX, 76701-1794. Tel: 254-750-5941. Fax: 254-750-5940. p. 2397

Frank, Christine D, Dir, Library of Rush University Medical Center, Armour Academic Ctr, 600 S Paulina St, 5th Flr, Chicago, IL, 60612-3874. Tel: 312-942-8735. Fax: 312-942-3143. p. 617

Frank, Dennis, Archivist, Saint Bonaventure University, 3261 W State Rd, Saint Bonaventure, NY, 14778. Tel: 716-375-2322. Fax: 716-375-2389. p. 1737

Frank, Diane, Librn, Cumberland County Law Library, Cumberland County Courthouse, 1st Flr, Broad & Fayette Sts, Bridgeton, NJ, 08302. Tel: 856-451-8000, 856-453-4530, 856-853-3539. p. 1474

Frank, Diane, Librn, Gloucester County Law Library, 70 Hunter St, Woodbury, NJ, 08096. Tel: 856-686-7449. p. 1545

Frank, Dick, Mgr, Cannon Beach Library, 131 N Hemlock, Cannon Beach, OR, 97110. Tel: 503-436-1391. p. 1993

Frank, Edwin G, Curator, Head, Presv & Spec Coll, University Libraries, University of Memphis, 126 Ned R McWherter Library, Memphis, TN, 38152-3250. Tel: 901-678-2210. p. 2252

Frank, Ellen, Chairperson - Pub Libr Board, Kitscoty Public Library, 4910 51 St, Kitscoty, AB, T0B 2P0, CANADA. Tel: 780-846-2822. Fax: 780-846-2215. p. 2708

Frank, Harry, Head, Access Serv, East Carolina University, Music Library, A J Fletcher Music Ctr, Rm A110, Greenville, NC, 27858. Tel: 252-328-1242. Fax: 252-328-1243. p. 1799

Frank, Jean, Librn, North Central Regional Library, Cashmere Community, 300 Woodring, Cashmere, WA, 98815-1061. Tel: 509-782-3314. p. 2548

Frank, John, Br Mgr, Los Angeles Public Library System, Vassie D Wright Memorial-Jefferson Branch, 2211 W Jefferson Blvd, Los Angeles, CA, 90018-3798. Tel: 323-734-8573. Fax: 323-737-2885. p. 174

Frank, Karen, Dir, Greenwood Public Library, 619 Main St, Greenwood, NE, 68366. Tel: 402-789-2301. Fax: 402-789-2323. p. 1400

Frank, Larry, Dir, Knox County Public Library System, 500 W Church Ave, Knoxville, TN, 37902-2505. Tel: 865-215-8750. Fax: 865-215-8742. p. 2241

Frank, Lynn M, Dir, Crown Point Community Library, 214 S Court St, Crown Point, IN, 46307. Tel: 219-663-0270, 219-663-0271. Fax: 219-663-0403. p. 734

Frank, Marietta, Instrul & Ref Librn, University of Pittsburgh at Bradford, 300 Campus Dr, Bradford, PA, 16701. Tel: 814-362-7610. Fax: 814-362-7688. p. 2037

Frank, Marietta A, Interim Dir, University of Pittsburgh at Bradford, 300 Campus Dr, Bradford, PA, 16701. Tel: 814-362-7614. Fax: 814-362-7688. p. 2037

Frank, Marilyn, Librn, Christ United Methodist Church Library, 380 Mineola Ave, Akron, OH, 44320-1935. Tel: 330-836-5563. Fax: 330-836-7209. p. 1853

Frank, Mary, Dir, Peck Memorial Library, 24 Main St, Marathon, NY, 13803. Tel: 607-849-6135. Fax: 607-849-3799. p. 1657

Frank, Maureen Sherr, Dir, Atlantic City Free Public Library, One N Tennessee Ave, Atlantic City, NJ, 08401. Tel: 609-345-2269, Ext 3001. Fax: 609-345-5570. p. 1470

Frank, Megan, Librn, US Geological Survey, 2150 Centre Ave, Bldg C, Fort Collins, CO, 80526-8118. Tel: 970-226-9403. Fax: 970-226-9230. p. 308

Frank, Owen, Ref Librn, Chemung County Library District, 101 E Church St, Elmira, NY, 14901-2799. Tel: 607-733-9173. Fax: 607-733-9176. p. 1619

Frank, Polly, Ref Librn, Supvr, ILL, Minnesota State University, Mankato, ML3097, Mankato, MN, 56001. Tel: 507-389-5952. Fax: 507-389-5155. p. 1257

Frank, Rebecca, Head Librn/Prod Dir I, Saint Petersburg College, Processing Center, 6021 142nd Ave N, Clearwater, FL, 33760. Tel: 727-341-3759. Fax: 727-341-3399. p. 483

Frank, Robin, Ch, Framingham Public Library, Christa Corrigan McAuliffe Branch, Ten Nicholas Rd, Framingham, MA, 01701-3469. Tel: 508-532-5636. Fax: 508-788-1930. p. 1090

Frank, Sandy, Head, Circ, Head, ILL, Thomas Ford Memorial Library, 800 Chestnut Ave, Western Springs, IL, 60558. Tel: 708-246-0520. Fax: 708-246-0403. p. 717

Frank, Stuart M, PhD, Sr Curator, Old Dartmouth Historical Society, 791 Purchase St, New Bedford, MA, 02740-6398. Tel: 508-997-0046. Fax: 508-207-1064. p. 1109

Frank, Sylvia, Dir, Toronto International Film Festival Group, Two Carlton St, E Mezzanine, Toronto, ON, M5B 1J3, CANADA. Tel: 416-967-1517. Fax: 416-967-0628. p. 2859

Frank, Tim, Chairperson, Hussar Municipal Library, Hussar School, Hussar, AB, T0J 1S0, CANADA. Tel: 403-787-3781, Ext 4813. Fax: 403-787-3922. p. 2707

Frank, Valerie, Dir, Blaine County Library, 94 Fourth St, Chinook, MT, 59523. Tel: 406-357-2932. Fax: 406-357-2552. p. 1376

Frank, William, Curator, Huntington Library, 1151 Oxford Rd, San Marino, CA, 91108. Tel: 626-405-2122. Fax: 626-449-5720. p. 255

Frank-de Ois, Jan, Dir, Shenandoah Public Library, 201 S Elm St, Shenandoah, IA, 51601. Tel: 712-246-2315. Fax: 712-246-5847. p. 843

Franke, Charlotte, Libr Assoc, Brown County Library, Denmark Branch, 450 N Wall St, Denmark, WI, 54208. Tel: 920-863-6613. Fax: 920-863-3001. p. 2595

Frankel, Elka, Br Supvr, Mercer County Library System, Hollowbrook Community Center, 320 Hollowbrook Dr, Trenton, NJ, 08638. Tel: 609-883-5914. Fax: 609-883-3511. p. 1494

Frankel, Frederick, Asst Librn, United States Court of International Trade, One Federal Plaza, New York, NY, 10278. Tel: 212-264-2816. Fax: 212-264-3242. p. 1702

Frankel, Joe, Tech Serv Librn, Inyo County Free Library, 168 N Edwards St, Independence, CA, 93526. Tel: 760-878-0260. Fax: 760-878-0360. p. 159

Frankel, Kenneth, Head of Ref & Instrul Serv, Florida Atlantic University, 777 Glades Rd, Boca Raton, FL, 33431. Tel: 561-297-0079. Fax: 561-297-2189. p. 428

Franken, Kathy, Br Mgr, Flathead County Library, Marion Branch, PO Box 1048, Marion, MT, 59925-1048. Tel: 406-854-2333. p. 1384

Frankena, Joann, Sr Librn, Hennepin County Library, Minneapolis Central, 300 Nicollet Mall, Minneapolis, MN, 55401. Tel: 612-543-8080. Fax: 612-543-8173. p. 1264

Frankford, Celia, Librn, Abington Township Public Library, Roslyn Branch, 2412 Avondale Ave, Roslyn, PA, 19001-4203. Tel: 215-886-9818. Fax: 215-886-9818. p. 2025

Frankiewicz, Jane, Dir, Spooner Memorial Library, 421 High St, Spooner, WI, 54801-1431. Tel: 715-635-2792. Fax: 715-635-2147. p. 2639

Frankland, Marilyn, Mgr, Access Serv, Daniel Webster College, 20 University Dr, Nashua, NH, 03063-1300. Tel: 603-577-6559. Fax: 603-577-6199. p. 1458

Frankland, Trisha, Co-Dir, Lodi Woman's Club Public Library, 130 Lodi St, Lodi, WI, 53555-1217. Tel: 608-592-4130. Fax: 608-592-2327. p. 2605

Franklin, Ailesia, Dir, Dunkirk Public Library, 127 W Washington St, Dunkirk, IN, 47336-1218. Tel: 765-768-6872. Fax: 765-768-6894. p. 736

Franklin, Beatrice, ILL, University of Alaska Southeast, 11120 Glacier Hwy, Juneau, AK, 99801-8676. Tel: 907-796-6483. Fax: 907-796-6249. p. 50

Franklin, Brinley, Vice Provost for Libr, University of Connecticut Library, 369 Fairfield Rd, Storrs, CT, 06269-1005. Tel: 860-486-2219. Fax: 860-486-0584. p. 370

Franklin, Cheryl, Dir, Navasota Public Library, 1411 E Washington Ave, Navasota, TX, 77868-3240. Tel: 936-825-6744. Fax: 936-825-4106. p. 2365

Franklin, Cheryl, Dir, Navasota Public Library, Horlock House History Center, 1215 E Washington Ave, Navasota, TX, 77868. Tel: 936-825-7055. p. 2365

Franklin, Donna, Tech Serv, Southern Union State Community College, 750 Robert St, Wadley, AL, 36276. Tel: 256-395-2211, Ext 5130. Fax: 256-395-2215. p. 40

Franklin, Donna, Mgr, Lake Blackshear Regional Library System, Schley County, 54 S Broad St, Ellaville, GA, 31806-3457. Tel: 229-937-2004. Fax: 229-937-2004. p. 508

Franklin, Gerald, Head of Libr, Free Library of Philadelphia, Richmond Branch, 2987 Almond St, Philadelphia, PA, 19134-4955. Tel: 215-685-9992, 215-685-9993. Fax: 215-291-5312. p. 2109

Franklin, Howard, III, Data Mgr, North Carolina Biotechnology Center Library, 15 Alexander Dr, Research Triangle Park, NC, 27709. Tel: 919-541-9366. Fax: 919-990-9521. p. 1820

Franklin, Janice R, Dr, Dean, Alabama State University, 915 S Jackson St, Montgomery, AL, 36104. Tel: 334-229-4106, 334-229-6890. Fax: 334-229-4911, 334-229-4940. p. 28

Franklin, Janis, Chairperson, Grande Cache Municipal Library, 10601 Shand Ave, Grande Cache, AB, T0E 0Y0, CANADA. Tel: 780-827-2081. Fax: 780-827-3112. p. 2705

Franklin, Jill, Librn, Knowledge Systems Institute, 3420 Main St, Skokie, IL, 60076. Tel: 847-679-3135. Fax: 847-679-3166. p. 703

Franklin, Jonathan, Assoc Law Librn, University of Washington Libraries, Marian Gould Gallagher Law Library, William H Gates Hall, Box 353025, Seattle, WA, 98195-3025. Fax: 206-685-2165. p. 2534

Franklin, Jonathan, Chief, Libr, Archives & Res Fel Prog, National Gallery of Canada Library, 380 Sussex Dr, Ottawa, ON, K1N 9N4, CANADA. Tel: 613-990-0590. Fax: 613-990-9818. p. 2832

Franklin, Karen, Serv Delivery Librn, Stormont, Dundas & Glengarry County Library, 26 Pitt St, Cornwall, ON, K6J 3P2, CANADA. Tel: 613-936-8777, Ext 211. Fax: 613-936-2532. p. 2801

Franklin, Kathleen, Librn, Mount Calm Public Library, 222 Allyn Ave, Mount Calm, TX, 76673. Tel: 254-993-2761. p. 2364

Franklin, Kay, Librn, United States Environmental Protection Agency, One Sabine Island Dr, Gulf Breeze, FL, 32561-5299. Tel: 850-934-9218. Fax: 850-934-2409. p. 450

Franklin, Lavon, AV, Black Hawk College-East Campus, 26230 Black Hawk Rd, Galva, IL, 61434. Tel: 309-852-5671, Ext 1731. Fax: 309-852-0038. p. 648

Franklin, Mary, Tech Serv, Women's Christian Association Healthcare System, 207 Foote Ave, Jamestown, NY, 14701-9975. Tel: 716-664-8124. Fax: 716-484-1089. p. 1647

Franklin, Phyllis, Ch, Linton Public Library, 95 SE First St, Linton, IN, 47441. Tel: 812-847-7802. Fax: 812-847-4695. p. 761

Franklin, Ryan A, Dir, Mattoon Public Library, 1600 Charleston Ave, Mattoon, IL, 61938-3635. Tel: 217-234-2621. Fax: 217-234-2660. p. 672

Franklin, Sandra G, Dir, Emory University Libraries, Woodruff Health Sciences Center Library, 1462 Clifton Rd NE, Atlanta, GA, 30322. Tel: 404-727-8727. Fax: 404-727-9821. p. 514

Franklin, Sharon, Br Mgr, Boone County Public Library, Walton Branch, 21 S Main St, Walton, KY, 41094-1135. Fax: 859-485-7049. p. 909

Franklin, Susan, Media Spec, Ref, Hastings College, 705 E Seventh St, Hastings, NE, 68901-7620. Tel: 402-461-7330. Fax: 402-461-7480. p. 1401

Franklin-McInnis, Jennifer, Dep Chief Librn, Mgr, Br, Essex County Library, 360 Fairview Ave W, Ste 101, Essex, ON, N8M 1Y3, CANADA. Tel: 519-776-5241. Fax: 519-776-6851. p. 2804

Franks, Brenda, Dir, Lied Public Library, 508 Iowa St, Essex, IA, 51638. Tel: 712-379-3355. Fax: 712-379-3355. p. 815

Franks, Dana, Ref Librn, Highline Community College Library, 2400 S 240th St, MS 25-4, Des Moines, WA, 98198. Tel: 206-878-3710, Ext 3240. Fax: 206-870-3776. p. 2514

Franks, James, Assoc Archivist, University of Alberta, Archives, Books & Records Depository, 100 8170 50th St, Edmonton, AB, T6B 1E6, CANADA. Tel: 780-466-6118, 780-466-6123. Fax: 780-466-5210. p. 2702

Franks, Jeffrey, Head, Ref, University of Akron Libraries, 315 Buchtel Mall, Akron, OH, 44325-1701. Tel: 330-972-6052. Fax: 330-972-2317. p. 1853

Franks, Maria, Dir, Legal Information Society of Nova Scotia Library, 5523 B Young St, Halifax, NS, B3K 1Z7, CANADA. Tel: 902-454-2198. Fax: 902-455-3105. p. 2781

Franks, Mercedes, Asst Dir, Nacogdoches Public Library, 1112 North St, Nacogdoches, TX, 75961-4482. Tel: 936-559-2970. Fax: 936-569-8282. p. 2364

Franks, Rita, Govt Pub Librn, Louisiana Tech University, Everett St at The Columns, Ruston, LA, 71272. Tel: 318-257-3555. Fax: 318-257-2579. p. 966

Franks, Sara, Instruction & Outreach, Saint Joseph's University, Francis A Drexel Library, 5600 City Ave, Philadelphia, PA, 19131-1395. Tel: 610-660-1913. Fax: 610-660-1916. p. 2116

Frankunas, Lori, Br Mgr, Rochester Public Library, Phillis Wheatley Community, 33 Dr Samuel McCree Way, Rochester, NY, 14608. Tel: 585-428-8212. p. 1732

Fransblow, Penny, Head, Norman Berman Children's Libr, Bibliotheque Publique Juive, One carré Cummings, 5151 ch de la Cote Ste Catherine, Montreal, QC, H3W 1M6, CANADA. Tel: 514-345-2627, Ext 3028. Fax: 514-342-6477. p. 2888

Fransen, Linda, Dir, Cottonwood County Historical Society Library, 812 Fourth Ave, Windom, MN, 56101. Tel: 507-831-1134. Fax: 507-831-2665. p. 1289

Fransen, Pattie, Br Mgr, Peoria Public Library, Sunrise Mountain, 21109 N 98th Ave, Peoria, AZ, 85382. Tel: 623-773-8655. Fax: 623-773-8670. p. 71

Fransioli, Sherry, Cat, Brevard College, One Brevard College Dr, Brevard, NC, 28712-4283. Tel: 828-884-8368. p. 1777

Franssen, Brian, Bus Librn, Yuma County Library District, 2951 S 21st Dr, Yuma, AZ, 85364. Tel: 928-314-2446. Fax: 928-782-9420. p. 91

Frantes, Naomi, Head, Access & Br Serv, University of North Dakota, 3051 University Ave, Stop 9000, Grand Forks, ND, 58202-9000. Tel: 701-777-4648. Fax: 701-777-3319. p. 1843

Frantz, Diana, Treas, Cooperating Hospital Libraries of the Lehigh Valley Area, Saint Luke's Hospital, Estes Library, 801 Ostrum St, Bethlehem, PA, 18015. Tel: 610-954-3407. Fax: 610-954-4651. p. 2954

Frantz, Diane, Asst Dir, St Luke's Hospital & Health Network, 801 Ostrum St, Bethlehem, PA, 18015. Tel: 610-954-3407. Fax: 610-954-4651. p. 2035

Frantz, Paul, Head, Ref & Res Serv, University of Oregon Libraries, 1501 Kincaid St, Eugene, OR, 97403-1299. Tel: 541-346-3056. Fax: 541-346-3485. p. 1997

Franz, David J, Dir, Hillsdale Free Public Library, 509 Hillsdale Ave, Hillsdale, NJ, 07642. Tel: 201-358-5072. Fax: 201-358-5074. p. 1491

Franz, Eilleen, Ch, New Cumberland Public Library, One Benjamin Plaza, New Cumberland, PA, 17070-1597. Tel: 717-774-7820. Fax: 717-774-7824. p. 2096

Franz, Jacqueline, Librn, Boonville-Warrick County Public Library, Tennyson Branch, 318 N Main St, Tennyson, IN, 47637. Tel: 812-567-8933. p. 729

Franz, Janet L, Dir, Kanabec County Historical Society, 805 W Forest Ave, Mora, MN, 55051-1466. Tel: 320-679-1665. Fax: 320-679-1673. p. 1267

Franz, Patty, Supv Librn, Pamunkey Regional Library, 7527 Library Dr, Hanover, VA, 23069. Tel: 804-537-6211. Fax: 804-537-6389. p. 2469

Franzello, Joseph J, Head of Libr, United States Air Force, 2511 Kennedy Circle, No 155, Brooks AFB, TX, 78235-5116. Tel: 210-536-3321. Fax: 210-536-3239. p. 2292

Franzen, June, Dir, Phelps Public Library, 4495 Town Hall Rd, Phelps, WI, 54554. Tel: 715-545-2887. Fax: 715-545-2887. p. 2629

Franzen, Leslie, Br Mgr 1, Sno-Isle Libraries, Coupeville Community Library, 788 NW Alexander St, Coupeville, WA, 98239. Tel: 360-678-4911. Fax: 360-678-5261. p. 2542

Franzen, Renae, Dir, Spillville Public Library, 201 Oak St, Spillville, IA, 52168. Tel: 563-562-4373. Fax: 563-562-4373. p. 845

Franzese, Carol, ILL, Peninsula Public Library, 280 Central Ave, Lawrence, NY, 11559. Tel: 516-239-3262. Fax: 516-239-8425. p. 1651

Franzetti, Tara, Ch, Lee Memorial Library, 500 W Crescent Ave, Allendale, NJ, 07401-1799. Tel: 201-327-4338. Fax: 201-327-5838. p. 1469

Fraone, Kimberly, Assoc Dir, Kean University, 1000 Morris Ave, Union, NJ, 07083. Tel: 908-737-4600. Fax: 908-737-4620. p. 1537

Frappier, Steve, Syst Adminr, Williams County Public Library, 107 E High St, Bryan, OH, 43506-1702. Tel: 419-636-6734. Fax: 419-636-3970. p. 1862

Fraquelli, Mary, Librn, Traverse Area District Library, Kingsley Branch, 104 S Brownson Ave, Kingsley, MI, 49649. Tel: 231-263-5484. Fax: 231-263-5526. p. 1231

Frary, Steve, Acq, Southeastern Baptist Theological Seminary Library, 114 N Wingate St, Wake Forest, NC, 27587. Tel: 919-556-3104. Fax: 919-863-8150. p. 1827

Fraser, Alex, Br Mgr, Chicago Public Library, North Pulaski, 4300 W North Ave, Chicago, IL, 60639. Tel: 312-744-9573. Fax: 312-744-7365. p. 609

Fraser, Allie, Head, Coll Serv, AIDS Library, 1233 Locust St, 2nd Flr, Philadelphia, PA, 19107. Tel: 215-985-4851. Fax: 215-985-4492. p. 2102

Fraser, Anne, Mgr, Libr Serv, Kaiser-Permanente Medical Center, 4733 Sunset Blvd, 1st Flr, Los Angeles, CA, 90027. Tel: 323-783-8568. Fax: 323-783-4192. p. 171

Fraser, Darla, Chief Librn, Orangeville Public Library, One Mill St, Orangeville, ON, L9W 2M2, CANADA. Tel: 519-941-0610, Ext 5222. Fax: 519-941-4698. p. 2826

Fraser, Elizabeth, Ref Supvr, Kanawha County Public Library, 123 Capitol St, Charleston, WV, 25301. Tel: 304-343-4646. Fax: 304-348-6530. p. 2556

Fraser, Elizabeth, Librn, Brigham Memorial Library, 131 Plain St, Sharon, WI, 53585. Tel: 262-736-4249. Fax: 262-736-3239. p. 2636

Fraser, Frances, Archives, Pub Serv, The California Maritime Academy Library, 200 Maritime Academy Dr, Vallejo, CA, 94590. Tel: 707-654-1089. Fax: 707-654-1094. p. 278

Fraser, G, Info Spec, Canadian Pacific Railway, 401 Ninth Ave SW, 7th Flr, Calgary, AB, T2P 4Z4, CANADA. Tel: 403-319-6193. Fax: 403-319-6257. p. 2691

Fraser, Gary, Dir, Lima Public Library, 650 W Market St, Lima, OH, 45801. Tel: 419-228-5113. Fax: 419-224-2669. p. 1910

Fraser, Janet, Head, Bibliog & Coll Serv, University of New Brunswick, Saint John Campus, 100 Tucker Park Rd, Saint John, NB, E2L 4L5, CANADA. Tel: 506-648-5710. p. 2767

Fraser, Jeanie, Med Librn, Seton Medical Center, 1900 Sullivan Ave, Ground Flr Hospital, Daly City, CA, 94015. Tel: 650-991-6315, 650-991-6700. Fax: 650-991-6638. p. 139

Fraser, Jeanmarie, Assoc Dean, Learning Res, Pub Serv, Cape Cod Community College, 2240 Iyannough Rd, West Barnstable, MA, 02668-1599. Tel: 508-362-2131, Ext 4618. Fax: 508-375-4020. p. 1136

Fraser, John, Dir, Seminole Tribe of Florida, Rte 6, Box 668, Okeechobee, FL, 34974-8912. Tel: 863-763-4236, 863-763-5520. Fax: 863-763-0679. p. 474

Fraser, Lucette, Librn, Centre de Veille Sur l'efficacite Energetique, 5700, 4e Ave Ouest, 4e Etage, Bureau B405, Charlesbourg, QC, G1H 6R1, CANADA. Tel: 418-627-6379, Ext 8030. Fax: 418-643-5828. p. 2880

Fraser, M Robert, Dr, Assoc Dir, Scholarly Res, University of Michigan-Dearborn, 4901 Evergreen Rd, Dearborn, MI, 48128-2406. Tel: 313-593-3740. Fax: 313-593-5478. p. 1168

Fraser, Mary Jane, Librn, Whitefish Lake First Nation Public Library, PO Box 39, Naughton, ON, P0M 2M0, CANADA. Tel: 705-692-0807. Fax: 705-692-5010. p. 2824

Fraser, Matthew, Ref Librn, University of Mobile, 5735 College Pkwy, Mobile, AL, 36613-2842. Tel: 251-442-2244. Fax: 251-442-2515. p. 26

Fraser, Meredith, Librn, East Rochester Public Library, 111 W Elm St, East Rochester, NY, 14445. Tel: 585-586-8302. p. 1617

Fraser, Philip, Librn, Bibliotheque du College Dominicain de Philosophie et de Theologie, 96 Empress Ave, Ottawa, ON, K1R 7G3, CANADA. Tel: 613-233-5696, Ext 216. Fax: 613-233-6064. p. 2828

Fraser, Richard, Librn, South Ryegate Public Library, Inc, 140 Church St, South Ryegate, VT, 05069. Tel: 802-584-3238. p. 2436

Fraser, Sonja, Staff Coordr, Saint Leo University, 33701 State Rd 52, Saint Leo, FL, 33574. Tel: 352-588-8258. Fax: 352-588-8484. p. 487

Fraser, Susan, Dir, The LuEsther T Mertz Library, The New York Botanical Garden, 2900 Southern Blvd, Bronx, NY, 10458-5126. Tel: 718-817-8879. Fax: 718-817-8956. p. 1587

Fraser, Victoria, Supvr, Haliburton County Public Library, Dysart Branch, 78 Maple Ave, Haliburton, ON, K0M 1S0, CANADA. Tel: 705-457-1791. p. 2807

Frasier, Robert, Syst Librn, Mercer University, Jack Tarver Library, 1300 Edgewood Ave, Macon, GA, 31207. Tel: 478 301 2027. Fax: 478-301-2111. p. 540

Frasure, Carol, Dir, Chapman Public Library, 402 N Marshall, Chapman, KS, 67431. Tel: 785-922-6548. Fax: 785-922-6548. p. 860

Fratena, Monicah, Ad, AV, La Porte County Public Library, 904 Indiana Ave, La Porte, IN, 46350-3435. Tel: 219-362-6156. Fax: 219-362-6158. p. 758

Frater, Jonathan, Head, Tech Serv, Metropolitan College of New York Library, 431 Canal St, 12th Flr, New York, NY, 10013. Tel: 212-343-1234, Ext 2017. Fax: 212-343-7398. p. 1686

Frater, Laura A, Librn, Metrohealth Medical Center, 2500 MetroHealth Dr, Cleveland, OH, 44101-1998. Tel: 216-778-5623. Fax: 216-778-8242. p. 1880

Fratt, Linda, Head, Pub Serv, Trinity International University, 2065 Half Day Rd, Deerfield, IL, 60015-1241. Tel: 847-317-4003. Fax: 847-317-4012. p. 635

Fraumeni, Mike, Librn, Hamilton Health Sciences, 699 Concession St, Hamilton, ON, L8V 5C2, CANADA. Tel: 905-387-9711, Ext 65100. Fax: 905-575-6317. p. 2808

Frawley, Ellen, Circ Supvr, Pearl River Public Library, 80 Franklin Ave, Pearl River, NY, 10965. Tel: 845-735-4084. Fax: 845-735-4041. p. 1716

Frawley, Joseph, Tech Serv & Syst Librn, Connecticut College, 270 Mohegan Ave, New London, CT, 06320-4196. Tel: 860-439-2670. Fax: 860-439-2871. p. 359

Frawley, Thomas, Br Librn, Providence Community Library, Olneyville Library, One Olneyville Sq, Providence, RI, 02909. Tel: 401-421-4084. p. 2173

Fray, George, Head, Syst, Florida International University, 11200 SW Eighth St, Miami, FL, 33199. Tel: 305-348-2488. Fax: 305-348-6450. p. 465

Frazee, Deanna A, Dir, Killeen City Library System, 205 E Church Ave, Killeen, TX, 76541. Tel: 254-501-8995. Fax: 254-501-7704. p. 2350

Frazer, Claudia, Coordr, Digital Initiatives, Drake University, 2725 University Ave, Des Moines, IA, 50311. Tel: 515-271-3776. Fax: 515-271-3933. p. 809

Frazer, Frances, Cat, Saint Lucie County Library System, 101 Melody Lane, Fort Pierce, FL, 34950-4402. Tel: 772-462-2193. Fax: 772-462-2750. p. 447

Frazer, Helen, Assoc Dir, Pub Serv, University of the District of Columbia, David A Clarke School of Law, Charles N & Hilda H M Mason Law Library, Bldg 39, Rm B-16, 4200 Connecticut Ave NW, Washington, DC, 20008. Tel: 202-274-7356. Fax: 202-274-7311. p. 421

Frazer, Stuart, Head, Access Serv, Old Dominion University Libraries, 4427 Hampton Blvd, Norfolk, VA, 23529-0256. Tel: 757-683-4174. Fax: 757-683-5767. p. 2482

Frazier, Charlotte, Dir, Support Serv, Tulsa City-County Library, 400 Civic Ctr, Tulsa, OK, 74103. Tel: 918-596-7977. Fax: 918-596-7964. p. 1982

Frazier, Cindy, Br Supvr, Barry-Lawrence Regional Library, Monett Branch, 213 Sixth St, Monett, MO, 65708. Tel: 417-235-6646. Fax: 417-235-6799. p. 1346

Frazier, Deena, Coll Serv Librn, Boston College, 885 Centre St, Newton Centre, MA, 02459. Tel: 617-552-4409. Fax: 617-552-2889. p. 1110

Frazier, Doug, Univ Librn, Armstrong Atlantic State University, 11935 Abercorn St, Savannah, GA, 31419. Tel: 912-344-2818. Fax: 912-344-3457. p. 549

Frazier, India, Mkt & Communications Spec, Upper Dublin Public Library, 805 Loch Alsh Ave, Fort Washington, PA, 19034. Tel: 215-628-8744. p. 2058

Frazier, Jean, Dir, Beach Haven Free Public Library, 247 N Beach Ave, Beach Haven, NJ, 08008-1865. Tel: 609-492-7081. Fax: 609-492-1048. p. 1471

Frazier, Jennifer, Librn, State Law Library, 700 Capital Ave, Ste 200, Frankfort, KY, 40601-3489. Tel: 502-564-4848. Fax: 502-564-5041. p. 914

Frazier, Joan, Librn, Haskell County Library, 300 N Ave E, Haskell, TX, 79521-5706. Tel: 940-864-2747. Fax: 940-864-6164. p. 2331

Frazier, Joyce, Cataloger, Barry-Lawrence Regional Library, 213 Sixth St, Monett, MO, 65708-2147. Tel: 417-235-6646. Fax: 417-235-6799. p. 1346

Frazier, Katrina, Cat, Nassau Community College, One Education Dr, Garden City, NY, 11530-6793. Tel: 516-572-7400. Fax: 516-572-7846. p. 1626

Frazier, Kenneth, Dir, University of Wisconsin-Madison, 728 State St, Madison, WI, 53706. Tel: 608-262-2600. Fax: 608-265-2754. p. 2608

Frazier, Lucile, Dir, Stamford Carnegie Library, 600 E McHarg St, Stamford, TX, 79553. Tel: 325-773-2532. Fax: 325-773-2654. p. 2389

Frazier, Meg, Info Literacy/Electronic Serv Librn, Bradley University, 1501 W Bradley Ave, Peoria, IL, 61625. Tel: 309-677-2850. Fax: 309-677-2558. p. 690

Frazier, Pamela, Dir, Ch Serv, Crandall Public Library, 251 Glen St, Glens Falls, NY, 12801-3593. Tel: 518-792-6508. Fax: 518-792-5251. p. 1629

Frazier, Rose, Media/Ser/ILL Librn, Tuskegee University, Hollis Burke Frissell Bldg, 1200 W Old Montgomery Rd, Tuskegee, AL, 36088. Tel: 334-727-8892, 334-727-8894. Fax: 334-727-9282. p. 39

Frazza, Christian, Dir, Carroll College, 1601 N Benton Ave, Helena, MT, 59625. Tel: 406-447-4340. Fax: 406-447-4525. p. 1381

Frear, Jack, Mgr, Loudoun County Public Library, Outreach Services, 380 Old Waterford Rd NW, Leesburg, VA, 20176. Tel: 703-771-3107. Fax: 703-771-5680. p. 2474

Frear, Marian, Librn, Sandia Medical Library, 601 Martin Luther King Ave NE, Albuquerque, NM, 87102-3670. Tel: 505-727-8291. Fax: 505-727-8121. p. 1550

Freas, Lynda, Family Libr Serv Dir, Anythink Libraries, 5877 E 120th Ave, Thornton, CO, 80602. Tel: 303-288-2001. Fax: 303-451-0190. p. 323

Freburg, Nancy, Dir, Petroleum County Community Library, 205 S Broadway, Winnett, MT, 59087. Tel: 406-429-2451. Fax: 406-429-7631. p. 1390

Frechette, Casey, Online Res & Develop Dir, University of South Florida Saint Petersburg, 140 Seventh Ave S, POY118, Saint Petersburg, FL, 33701. Tel: 727-873-4401. Fax: 727-873-4196. p. 489

Frechette, Liz, Instrul Serv Librn, Ref, Naugatuck Valley Community College, 750 Chase Pkwy, Waterbury, CT, 06708. Tel: 203-575-8024. Fax: 203-575-8062. p. 375

Frechette, Shannon, Libr Tech, Copper Mountain College, 6162 Rotary Way, Joshua Tree, CA, 92252. Tel: 760-366-3791, Ext 5901. Fax: 760-366-5256. p. 161

Frechette, Valerie O, Assoc Librn, ILL, Central Maine Community College Library, 1250 Turner St, Auburn, ME, 04210-6498. Tel: 207-755-5218. Fax: 207-755-5494. p. 974

Fred, Kent, In Charge, Project for Public Spaces, Inc, 700 Broadway, 4th Flr, New York, NY, 10003. Tel: 212-620-5660. Fax: 212-620-3821. p. 1698

Freda, Kristin, Dir of Libr Serv, ILL Librn, Bank Street College of Education Library, 610 W 112th St, 5th Flr, New York, NY, 10025. Tel: 212-875-4455. Fax: 212-875-4558. p. 1669

Fredenburg, Lila Daum, Dir, Admin Serv, Rutgers University Libraries, 169 College Ave, New Brunswick, NJ, 08901-1163. Tel: 732-932-7505. Fax: 732-932-7637. p. 1508

Frederick, Betty, Extn Serv Mgr, Saint Johns County Public Library System, 6670 US 1 South, Saint Augustine, FL, 32086. Tel: 904-827-6928. p. 486

Frederick, Donna, Head, Ch, Gladwin County District Library, 402 James Robertson Dr, Gladwin, MI, 48624. Tel: 989-426-8221. Fax: 989-426-6958. p. 1183

Frederick, Karen, ILL, Bala-Cynwyd Library, 131 Old Lancaster Rd, Bala Cynwyd, PA, 19004-3037. Tel: 610-664-1196. Fax: 610-664-5534. p. 2030

Frederick, Kathleen O, Libr Spec, Harrisburg Area Community College, 2010 Pennsylvania Ave, York, PA, 17404. Tel: 717-718-0328, Ext 3520. Fax: 717-718-8967. p. 2159

Frederick, Lydia, In Charge, United States Environmental Protection Agency, 1595 Wynkoop St, 8OC-L, Denver, CO, 80202-2466. Tel: 303-312-6312. Fax: 303-312-7061. p. 303

Frederick, Marcille, Dir, Trinity Christian College, 6601 W College Dr, Palos Heights, IL, 60463. Tel: 708-597-3000, Ext 4797. Fax: 708-385-5665. p. 687

Frederick, Mary, Mgr, Info Serv, Springfield City Library, 220 State St, Springfield, MA, 01103. Tel: 413-263-6828, Ext 202. Fax: 413-263-6817. p. 1127

Frederick, Sabrina, Dir, Fort Branch-Johnson Township Public Library, 107 E Locust St, Fort Branch, IN, 47648. Tel: 812-753-4212. p. 740

Frederick, Sabrina, Dir, Pike County Public Library, 1104 Main St, Petersburg, IN, 47567. Tel: 812-354-6257. Fax: 812-354-6259. p. 773

Frederick, Sabrina, Dir, Pike County Public Library, Otwell Branch, 2301 N Spring St, Otwell, IN, 47564. Tel: 812-380-0066. Fax: 812-380-0037. p. 773

Frederick, Sabrina, Dir, Pike County Public Library, Winslow Branch, 105 E Center St, Winslow, IN, 47598. Tel: 812-789-5423. Fax: 812-789-9496. p. 773

Frederick, Stephanie, ILL Mgr, Valparaiso University, 1410 Chapel Dr, Valparaiso, IN, 46383-6493. Tel: 219-464-5500. p. 783

Frederick, Susan, Ref, Chester County Library System, 450 Exton Square Pkwy, Exton, PA, 19341-2496. Tel: 610-280-2600. Fax: 610-280-2688. p. 2056

Fredericks, Linda, Govt Doc, King County Library System, 960 Newport Way NW, Issaquah, WA, 98027. Tel: 425-450-1782. Fax: 425-369-3255. p. 2516

Fredericks, Matthew D, Acad Serv Officer I, Wayne State University, 106 Kresge Library, Detroit, MI, 48202. Tel: 313-577-2446. Fax: 313-577-7563. p. 2967

Fredericks, Nancy, Libr Adminr, Pasco County Library System, 8012 Library Rd, Hudson, FL, 34667. Tel: 727-861-3020. Fax: 727-861-3025. p. 451

Fredericks, Regina, Info Serv Coordr, Liverpool Public Library, 310 Tulip St, Liverpool, NY, 13088-4997. Tel: 315-457-0310. Fax: 315-453-7867. p. 1653

Fredericks, Valerie, Ref Serv Librn, Fairfield Public Library, 1080 Old Post Rd, Fairfield, CT, 06824. Tel: 203-256-3155. p. 339

Fredericksen, Grant A, Dir, Illinois Prairie District Public Library, 208 E Partridge, Metamora, IL, 61548. Tel: 309-367-4594. Fax: 309-367-2687. p. 673

Fredericksen, Julie, Dir, Corona Public Library, 650 S Main St, Corona, CA, 92882. Tel: 951-736-2381. Fax: 951-736-2499. p. 136

Frederiksen, Linda, Head, Access Serv, Washington State University Libraries, 14204 NE Salmon Creek Ave, Vancouver, WA, 98686. Tel: 360-546-9683. Fax: 360-546-9039. p. 2546

Frederiksen, Patience, Grants Adminr & Mkt, Alaska State Library, Library Development, 344 W Third Ave, Ste 125, Anchorage, AK, 99501. Tel: 907-269-6570. Fax: 907-269-6580. p. 44

Frederiksen, Patience, Regional Librn, Alaska State Library, Talking Book Center, 344 W Third Ave, Ste 125, Anchorage, AK, 99501. Tel: 907-269-6566. Fax: 907-269-6580. p. 44

Frederking, Brenda, Asst Librn, Plainville Memorial Library, 200 SW First St, Plainville, KS, 67663. Tel: 785-434-2786. Fax: 785-434-2786. p. 890

Fredette, Hillary, Head, Access & Media Serv, West Virginia University Libraries, WVU Libraries, 1549 University Ave, Morgantown, WV, 26506. Tel: 304-293-4040. Fax: 304-293-6638. p. 2566

Fredette, Kathy, Dir, Lake Agassiz Regional Library, 118 S Fifth St, Moorhead, MN, 56560-2756. Tel: 218-233-3757. Fax: 218-233-7556. p. 1265

Fredette, Kevin, Pub Serv, West Virginia University Libraries, George R Farmer, Jr College of Law Library, One Law Center Dr, Morgantown, WV, 26506. Tel: 304-293-7640. Fax: 304-293-6020. p. 2566

Fredette, Sharon, Mgr, Pub Serv, Warwick Public Library, 600 Sandy Lane, Warwick, RI, 02889-8298. Tel: 401-739-5440, Ext 230. Fax: 401-732-2055. p. 2177

Fredine, Anne, Asst Regional Dir, Lake Agassiz Regional Library, 118 S Fifth St, Moorhead, MN, 56560-2756. Tel: 218-233-3757 Ext 111. Fax: 218-233-7556. p. 1265

Fredricksen, Lin, Head, Ref, Kansas State Historical Society, 6425 SW Sixth Ave, Topeka, KS, 66615-1099. Tel: 785-272-8681. Fax: 785-272-8682. p. 896

Fredrickson, Dennis, Neighborhood Serv Mgr, Spokane Public Library, 906 W Main Ave, Spokane, WA, 99201-0976. Tel: 509-444-5334. Fax: 509-444-5365. p. 2537

Fredrickson, Jill, Tech Serv, Spooner Memorial Library, 421 High St, Spooner, WI, 54801-1431. Tel: 715-635-2792. Fax: 715-635-2147. p. 2639

Fredrickson, Karen, Ref Serv, YA, Bellwood Public Library, 600 Bohland Ave, Bellwood, IL, 60104-1896. Tel: 708-547-7393. Fax: 708-547-9352. p. 593

Fredsti, Lisa, Dir, Twentieth Century Fox Film Corp, 10201 W Pico Blvd, No 89/105, Los Angeles, CA, 90035. Tel: 310-369-2782. Fax: 310-369-3645. p. 178

Free, Martha, Br Supvr, Marion County Public Library System, Marion Oaks Public Library, 294 Marion Oaks Lane, Ocala, FL, 34473. Tel: 352-438-2570. Fax: 352-438-2572. p. 474

Free, Ruth Ann, Librn, Itawamba Community College, 2176 S Eason Blvd, Tupelo, MS, 38804. Tel: 662-620-5092. Fax: 662-620-5095. p. 1316

Free, Shelly, Acq, Logan County Public Library, 201 W Sixth St, Russellville, KY, 42276. Tel: 270-726-6129. Fax: 270-726-6127. p. 934

Freeburg, Colleen, Circ & ILL Coordr, Lewis University Library, One University Pkwy, Unit 300, Romeoville, IL, 60446-2200. Tel: 815-836-5300. Fax: 815-838-9456. p. 698

Freeburg, Paulina, Dir, Plummer Public Library, 800 D St, Plummer, ID, 83851. Tel: 208-686-1812. Fax: 208-686-1084. p. 581

Freed, Mark, Ref, Cambridge Public Library, 449 Broadway, Cambridge, MA, 02138. Tel: 617-349-4040. Fax: 617-349-4028. p. 1073

Freed, Mindy, Br Mgr, Markham Public Library, Thornhill Community Branch, 7755 Bayview Ave, Thornhill, ON, L3T 4P1, CANADA. Tel: 905-513-7977, Ext 3524. Fax: 905-881-2935. p. 2820

Freed, Mindy, Br Mgr, Markham Public Library, Thornhill Village Branch, 10 Colborne St, Thornhill, ON, L3T 1Z6, CANADA. Tel: 905-513-7977, Ext 3524. Fax: 905-881-0149. p. 2820

Freed, Sharon, Br Mgr, Monterey County Free Libraries, Seaside Branch, 550 Harcourt Ave, Seaside, CA, 93955. Tel: 831-899-2055. Fax: 831-899-2735. p. 183

Freedman, Howard, Dir, Jewish Community Library, 1835 Ellis St, San Francisco, CA, 94115. Tel: 415-567-3327, Ext 705. p. 243

Freedman, Jenna, Res & Instruction Librn, Barnard College, 3009 Broadway, New York, NY, 10027-6598. Tel: 212-854-4615. p. 1670

Freedman, Joyce, Dr, Librn, Beth El Ner Tamid Library, 715 Paxon Hollow Rd, Broomall, PA, 19008-9998. Tel: 610-356-8700, 610-544-1111. Fax: 610-544-7364. p. 2038

Freedman, L, Librn, Congregation B'Nai Israel, 4401 Indian School Rd NE, Albuquerque, NM, 87110-3914. Tel: 505-266-0155. Fax: 505-268-6136. p. 1549

Freedman, Myron, Exec Dir, Hayward Area Historical Society Museum Library, 22380 Foothill Blvd, Hayward, CA, 94541. Tel: 510-581-0223. Fax: 510-581-0217. p. 157

Freedman, Phyllis D, Dr, Dean, Learning Res, Salem International University Benedum Library, KD Hurley Blvd, Salem, WV, 26426. Tel: 304-326-1238. Fax: 304-326-1240. p. 2571

Freedman, Shin, Acq, Ser, Framingham State College, 100 State St, Framingham, MA, 01701. Tel: 508-626-4666. Fax: 508-626-4649. p. 1090

Freedman, Sue, Asst Dir, Rosemary Garfoot Public Library, 2107 Julius St, Cross Plains, WI, 53528-9499. Tel: 608-798-3881. Fax: 608-798-0196. p. 2587

Freedman, Suzi, Br Mgr, Burlington County Library, Bordentown Branch, 18 E Union St, Bordentown, NJ, 08505. Tel: 609-298-0622. Fax: 609-298-4297. p. 1542

Freedman, Terri, Head of Libr, Bryn Mawr College, Lois & Reginald Collier Science Library, 101 N Merion Ave, Bryn Mawr, PA, 19104-2899. Tel: 610-526-5118. Fax: 610-526-7464. p. 2039

Freedman, Thomas, Project Librn, Columbia University, Avery Architectural & Fine Arts Library, 1172 Amsterdam Ave, MC 0301, New York, NY, 10027. Tel: 212-854-6199. Fax: 212-854-8904. p. 1674

Freeh, MaryBeth, Dir, Cedar Crest College, 100 College Dr, Allentown, PA, 18104-6196. Tel: 610-606-4666, Ext 3387. Fax: 610-740-3769. p. 2026

Freeland, Patricia, Ch, Marshall County Public Library System, 1003 Poplar St, Benton, KY, 42025. Tel: 270-527-9969. Fax: 270-527-0506. p. 907

Freeland, Sarah B, Ref Librn, Ser, Groton Public Library, 52 Newtown Rd, Groton, CT, 06340. Tel: 860-441-6750. Fax: 860-448-0363. p. 342

Freeland, Vickey, Dir, Owen County Public Library, Ten S Montgomery St, Spencer, IN, 47460-1713. Tel: 812-829-3392. Fax: 812-829-6165. p. 780

Freels, Jeanette, Commun Libr Mgr, County of Los Angeles Public Library, La Puente Library, 15920 E Central Ave, La Puente, CA, 91744-5499. Tel: 626-968-4613. Fax: 626-369-0294. p. 142

Freeman, Anita S, Dir, Randolph Township Free Public Library, 28 Calais Rd, Randolph, NJ, 07869. Tel: 973-895-3556. Fax: 973-895-4946. p. 1525

Freeman Benanti, Jeanine, Dir, West Sangamon Public Library District, 103 E Illinois St, New Berlin, IL, 62670. Tel: 217-488-7733. p. 680

Freeman, Beth Anne, Dir, Oklahoma State University - Center for Health Sciences, 1111 W 17th St, Tulsa, OK, 74107-1898. Tel: 918-561-8449. Fax: 918-561-8412. p. 1981

Freeman, Beth Anne, Dir, Oklahoma State University - Tulsa Library, 700 N Greenwood Ave, Tulsa, OK, 74106-0700. Tel: 918-594-8130. Fax: 918-594-8145. p. 1981

Freeman, Brook, Head of Libr, Free Library of Philadelphia, Welsh Road Branch, 9233 Roosevelt Blvd, Philadelphia, PA, 19114-2205. Tel: 215-685-0497, 215-685-0498. Fax: 215-685-0496. p. 2109

Freeman, Carol, Coll Develop Librn, Forsyth Technical Community College Library, 2100 Silas Creek Pkwy, Winston-Salem, NC, 27103. Tel: 336-734-7176. Fax: 336-761-2465. p. 1833

Freeman, Cheryl, Librn, Atchison County Library, Tarkio Branch, 405 S 11th St, Tarkio, MO, 64491. Tel: 660-736-5832. p. 1351

Freeman, Chris, City Librn/Dep Dir, Commun Serv, Stockton-San Joaquin County Public Library, 605 N El Dorado St, Stockton, CA, 95202. Tel: 209-937-8364. Fax: 209-937-8683. p. 272

Freeman, Deryl, Cataloger, Wheaton College Library, 26 E Main St, Norton, MA, 02766-2322. p. 1115

Freeman, Dottie, Adminr, Carroll County Farm Museum, 500 S Center St, Westminster, MD, 21157. Tel: 410-386-3880. Fax: 410-876-8544. p. 1045

Freeman, Douglas, Assoc Librn, Head of Libr, Indiana University Bloomington, Optometry Library, Optometry 301, 800 E Atwater Ave, Bloomington, IN, 47405. Tel: 812-855-8629. Fax: 812-855-6616. p. 728

Freeman, Ellyn, Electronic Res, Schulte Roth & Zabel LLP, 919 Third Ave, New York, NY, 10022. Tel: 212-756-2321. Fax: 212-593-5955. p. 1699

Freeman, Gretchen, Assoc Dir, Tech, Salt Lake County Library Services, 2197 E Fort Union Blvd, Salt Lake City, UT, 84121-3139. Tel: 801-943-4636. Fax: 801-942-6323. p. 2413

Freeman, Helen, Cat, Gloucester, Lyceum & Sawyer Free Library, Two Dale Ave, Gloucester, MA, 01930-5906. Tel: 978-281-9763. Fax: 978-281-9770. p. 1091

Freeman, Iva M, Dir, Kendall College Library, 900 N North Branch St, 6th Flr, Rm 620, Chicago, IL, 60642. Tel: 312-752-2530. Fax: 312-752-2541. p. 616

Freeman, James, Librn, Pine Forest Regional Library, Richton Public, 210 Front St, Richton, MS, 39476. Tel: 601-788-6539. Fax: 601-788-9743. p. 1314

Freeman, Joyce, Cat, Taylor County Public Library, 200 Beech St, Grafton, WV, 26354. Tel: 304-265-6121. Fax: 304-265-6122. p. 2559

Freeman, Katie, Librn, Dallas County Library, Sparkman Branch, 186 Dallas 208, Sparkman, AR, 71763. p. 100

Freeman, Kyri A, Librn, Barstow College, 2700 Barstow Rd, Barstow, CA, 92311. Tel: 760-252-2411, Ext 7270. Fax: 760-252-6725. p. 125

Freeman, Marilyn, Dir, Pilgrim United Church of Christ Memorial Library, 130 Broad Blvd, Cuyahoga Falls, OH, 44221. Tel: 330-928-4847. Fax: 330-928-1017. p. 1892

Freeman, Michael J, Dir of Libr, Utah Valley University Library, 800 W University Pkwy, Orem, UT, 84058-5999. Tel: 801-863-8751. Fax: 801-863-7065. p. 2409

Freeman, Morgan, Librn, Palliser Regional Library, Tugaske Branch, 106 Ogema St, Tugaske, SK, S0H 4B0, CANADA. Tel: 306-759-2215. p. 2919

Freeman, Nancy, Outreach Serv Librn, Huntington Public Library, 338 Main St, Huntington, NY, 11743. Tel: 631-427-5165. Fax: 631-421-7131. p. 1639

Freeman, Rebecca T, Asst Librn, University of South Carolina, Medford Library, 476 Hubbard Dr, Lancaster, SC, 29720. Tel: 803-313-7062. Fax: 803-313-7107. p. 2190

Freeman, Rodney, Br Mgr, Indianapolis-Marion County Public Library, Spades Park, 1801 Nowland Ave, Indianapolis, IN, 46201-1158. Tel: 317-275-4520. p. 754

Freeman, Rodney, Br Mgr, Saint Louis Public Library, Walnut Park, 5760 W Florissant Ave, Saint Louis, MO, 63120. Tel: 314-383-1210. Fax: 314-383-2079. p. 1360

Freeman, Scott, Adult Serv, Stillwater Public Library, 1107 S Duck St, Stillwater, OK, 74074. Tel: 405-372-3633, Ext 102. Fax: 405-624-0552. p. 1978

Freeman, Shirley, Managing Librn, Columbus Metropolitan Library, Whitehall Branch, 4371 E Broad St, Columbus, OH, 43213. Tel: 614-645-2275. Fax: 614-479-4329. p. 1885

Freeman, Tina, Br Mgr, Terrebonne Parish Library, Chauvin Branch, 5500 Hwy 56, Chauvin, LA, 70344. Tel: 985-594-9771. Fax: 985-594-7506. p. 951

Freeman, Valerie, Ref Librn, Johnson & Wales University, 801 W Trade St, Charlotte, NC, 28202. Tel: 980-598-1609. p. 1783

Freemon, Richard, Br Head, Tuscaloosa Public Library, Brown Library, 300 Bobby Miller Pkwy, Tuscaloosa, AL, 35405. Tel: 205-391-9989. Fax: 205-391-9355. p. 38

Freemyer, Vickie, Dir, Haxtun Public Library, 141 S Colorado Ave, Haxtun, CO, 80731-2711. Tel: 970-774-6106. Fax: 970-774-6288. p. 312

Freeny, Micki, Coordr, Ch & Youth Serv, District of Columbia Public Library, 901 G St NW, Washington, DC, 20001-4599. Tel: 202-727-1101. Fax: 202-727-1129. p. 398

Freer, Rebecca, Dir, Norwell Public Library, 64 South St, Norwell, MA, 02061-2433. Tel: 781-659-2015. Fax: 781-659-6755. p. 1115

Freer, Verna, Admin Serv, Eastern Kentucky University Libraries, 521 Lancaster Ave, Richmond, KY, 40475-3102. Tel: 859-622-1778. Fax: 859-622-1174. p. 933

Freese, Melanie, Cat Librn, Hofstra University, 123 Hofstra University, Hempstead, NY, 11549. p. 1635

Freese, Rosie, Circ, Sampson-Clinton Public Library, Miriam B Lamb Memorial, 144 S Church Ave, Garland, NC, 28441. Tel: 910-529-2441. p. 1784

Freeston, Lois, Asst Dir, ILL, Ref Serv, Nesmith Library, Eight Fellows Rd, Windham, NH, 03087. Tel: 603-432-7154. Fax: 603-537-0097. p. 1468

Freeze, Chad, Dir, Corsicana Public Library, 100 N 12th St, Corsicana, TX, 75110. Tel: 903-654-4810, 903-654-4813. Fax: 903-654-4814. p. 2302

Freeze, Debbi, Libr Asst, Siskiyou County Public Library, McCloud Branch, 300 E Colombero Dr, McCloud, CA, 96057. Tel: 530-964-2169. p. 286

Freeze, Nancy, Exec Dir, Kelley House Museum, Inc, 45007 Albion St, Mendocino, CA, 95460. Tel: 707-937-5791. Fax: 707-937-2156. p. 184

Fregia, Martha, Adult Serv, Asst Librn, Cat, Quitman Public Library, 202 East Goode St, Quitman, TX, 75783-2533. Tel: 903-763-4191. Fax: 903-763-2532. p. 2373

Freiband, Susan, Prof, University of Puerto Rico, Rio Piedras Campus, PO Box 21906, San Juan, PR, 00931-1906. Tel: 787-764-0000, Ext 1286, 787-764-0000, Ext 5028. Fax: 787-764-2311. p. 2977

Freiburger, Gary A, Dir, University of Arizona, Arizona Health Sciences Library, 1501 N Campbell Ave, Tucson, AZ, 85724. Tel: 520-626-6121. Fax: 520-626-2922. p. 88

Freidline, Sandra, Dir, Caney City Library, 100 N Ridgeway, Caney, KS, 67333. Tel: 316-879-5341. Fax: 620-879-5829. p. 859

Freier, Mary P, Head, Pub Serv, Northern Michigan University, 1401 Presque Isle, Marquette, MI, 49855. Tel: 906-227-1061. Fax: 906-227-1333. p. 1206

Freiermuth, Diane, Dep Dir, Saint Louis Public Library, 1415 Olive St, Saint Louis, MO, 63103-2315. Tel: 314-539-0300. Fax: 314-241-3840. p. 1359

Freiheit, Kathy, Dir, Pflugerville Community Library, 102 Tenth St, Pflugerville, TX, 78660. Tel: 512-251-9185. Fax: 512-990-8791. p. 2369

Freilich, Jeffrey, Librn, Ivins, Philips & Barker Library, 1700 Pennsylvania Ave NW, Ste 600, Washington, DC, 20006. Tel: 202-393-7600. Fax: 202-347-4256. p. 405

Freilich, Mary, Head Govt Publ, University Libraries, University of Memphis, 126 Ned R McWherter Library, Memphis, TN, 38152-3250. Tel: 901-678-8203. p. 2252

Freimarck, Fran, Libr Dir, Pamunkey Regional Library, 7527 Library Dr, Hanover, VA, 23069. Tel: 804-537-6211. Fax: 804-537-6389. p. 2469

Freise, Sharon, Dir, Head Librn, Bond Public Library, 208 S Chestnut St, Wenona, IL, 61377. Tel: 815-853-4665. Fax: 815-853-4665. p. 717

Freitag, Anne, Librn, Special Education Service Agency Library, 3501 Denali St, Ste 101, Anchorage, AK, 99503. Tel: 907-334-1301. Fax: 907-562-0545. p. 45

Freitag, Bethany, Ad, Goodwin Library, 422 Main St, Farmington, NH, 03835-1519. Tel: 603-755-2944. Fax: 603-755-2944. p. 1447

Freitag, Susan, Ad, ILL Librn, Elm Grove Public Library, 13600 W Juneau Blvd, Elm Grove, WI, 53122-1679. Tel: 262-782-6717. Fax: 262-780-4827. p. 2591

Frembling, Jonathan, Archivist, Ref Serv Mgr, Amon Carter Museum of American Art, 3501 Camp Bowie Blvd, Fort Worth, TX, 76107-2695. Tel: 817-738-1933. Fax: 817-989-5079. p. 2321

French, Alice, Tech Serv, Willamette University, 900 State St, Salem, OR, 97301. Tel: 503-370-6476. Fax: 503-370-6141. p. 2019

French, Christiana, Ref, Greenebaum, Doll & McDonald, 3500 National City Tower, Louisville, KY, 40202-3140. Tel: 502-589-4200. Fax: 502-587-3695. p. 923

French, Dawn S, Sr Analyst - Knowledge Serv, R&D, Cristal USA, Inc, 6752 Baymeadow Dr, Glen Burnie, MD, 21060. Tel: 410-762-1117. Fax: 410-762-1030. p. 1030

French, Deborah, Dir, T O H P Burnham Public Library, 30 Martin St, Essex, MA, 01929. Tel: 978-768-7410. Fax: 978-768-3370. p. 1087

French, Eric, Libr Tech, Smithsonian Libraries, Museum Studies & Reference Library, Nat Museum of Natural Hist, Tenth St & Constitution Ave NW, Rm 27, MRC 154, Washington, DC, 20560. Tel: 202-633-1703. Fax: 202-786-2443. p. 415

French, Julie, Tech Serv Librn, Sturgis Library, 3090 Main St, Barnstable, MA, 02630. Tel: 508-362-6636. Fax: 508-362-5467. p. 1051

French, Katherine, Dir, Danforth Museum of Art, 123 Union Ave, Framingham, MA, 01702. Tel: 508-620-0050. Fax: 508-872-5542. p. 1089

French, Kathryn, Librn, S M Dunlap Memorial Library, 300 W Main St, Italy, TX, 76651. Tel: 972-483-6481. p. 2347

French, Kay, Librn, Houston County Public Library, 21 Spring St, Erin, TN, 37061-4073. Tel: 931-289-3858. Fax: 931-289-4967. p. 2234

French, Kenneth, Dir, East Rutherford Memorial Library, 143 Boiling Springs Ave, East Rutherford, NJ, 07073. Tel: 201-939-3930. Fax: 201-939-1231. p. 1482

French, Lona, Librn, Wright Institute Library, 2728 Durant Ave, Berkeley, CA, 94704. Tel: 510-841-9230, Ext 121. Fax: 510-841-0167. p. 128

French, Lynn, Chief Librn, Ch, Sally Stretch Keen Memorial Library, 94 Main St, Vincentown, NJ, 08088. Tel: 609-859-3598. Fax: 609-859-4029. p. 1537

French, Mary-Catherine, Dir, Lodi Whittier Library, 2155 E Seneca St, Lodi, NY, 14860. Tel: 607-582-6218. Fax: 607-582-6218. p. 1654

French, Monette, Circ, Holmes County Public Library, 303 N J Harvey Etheridge, Bonifay, FL, 32425. Tel: 850-547-3573. Fax: 850-547-2801. p. 429

French, Robert B, Dir, Louisville Academy of Music Library, 2740 Frankfort Ave, Louisville, KY, 40206-2669. Tel: 502-893-7885. p. 924

French, Sandra, Ch, Middle Georgia Regional Library System, 1180 Washington Ave, Macon, GA, 31201-1790. Tel: 478-744-0859. Fax: 478-742-3161. p. 541

French, Shelley, Ad, Goodall City Library, 203 West A St, Ogallala, NE, 69153-2544. Tel: 308-284-4354. Fax: 308-284-6390. p. 1411

French, Sherry, Prog Chair, Northland Pioneer College, PO Box 610, Holbrook, AZ, 86025-0610. Tel: 928-532-6123. Fax: 928-532-6121. p. 2962

French, Thomas R, Assoc Dean, Syracuse University College of Law Library, E I White Hall, Syracuse, NY, 13244-1030. Tel: 315-443-9571. Fax: 315-443-9567. p. 1753

French-Baril, Janet, Librn, Carleton Place Public Library, 101 Beckwith St, Carleton Place, ON, K7C 2T3, CANADA. Tel: 613-257-2702. p. 2799

Frenchak, David J, Pres, Seminary Consortium for Urban Pastoral Education, 200 N Michigan Ave, Ste 502, Chicago, IL, 60601. Tel: 312-726-1200. Fax: 312-726-0425. p. 624

Frenette, Amelie, Prof, College Francois-Xavier-Garneau, 1660 blvd de l'Entente, Quebec, QC, G1S 4S3, CANADA. Tel: 418-688-8310, Ext 3504. Fax: 418-681-9384. p. 2978

Frenette, Guy, Asst Librn, Libr Tech, Jardin Botanique de Montreal Bibliotheque, 4101 Sherbrooke St E, Montreal, QC, H1X 2B2, CANADA. Tel: 514-872-1440, 514-872-1824. Fax: 514-872-5167. p. 2897

Frenette, Martine, Libr Mgr, Centre de Services Partagés du Québec, 700 rue St-Amable, RC, Quebec, QC, G1R 5E5, CANADA. Tel: 418-643-1515. Fax: 418-646-8132. p. 2904

Freng, Sarah, Acq, Black Hills State University, 1200 University St, Unit 9676, Spearfish, SD, 57799-9676. Tel: 605-642-6250. Fax: 605-642-6298. p. 2220

Frengel, Elizabeth, Reader Serv Mgr, Society of the Cincinnati Library, 2118 Massachusetts Ave NW, Washington, DC, 20008. Tel: 202-785-2040, Ext 411. Fax: 202-785-0729. p. 416

Frenkel, Ann, Asst Univ Librn, Res & Instrul Serv, University of California, Riverside Libraries, 900 University Ave, Riverside, CA, 92521. Tel: 951-827-4824. p. 218

Frenkel, Ann, Contact, Multimedia Libr, University of California, Riverside Libraries, Multimedia Library, Interdisciplinary Bldg South, Rm 2117, Riverside, CA, 92521. Tel: 951-827-5606. Fax: 951-827-5753. p. 219

Frenzel, Linda, Dir, Camden Public Library, 57 Second St, Camden, NY, 13316. Tel: 315-245-1980. Fax: 315-245-1980. p. 1600

Frenzel, Phyllis, Dir, United States Air Force, 15 SVS/SVMG, 990 Mills Blvd, Bldg 595, Hickam AFB, HI, 96853-5316. Tel: 808-449-8299. Fax: 808-449-8298. p. 559

Frerichs, Deena, Circ Librn, Martin County Library, 110 N Park St, Fairmont, MN, 56031-2822. Tel: 507-238-4207. Fax: 507-238-4208. p. 1250

Frerichs, Jeannie, Dir, Akron Public Library, 350 Reed St, Akron, IA, 51001. Tel: 712-568-2601. Fax: 712-568-2601. p. 791

Frerichs, Mary Ann, Br Mgr, Martin County Library, Welcome Branch, 304 First St, Welcome, MN, 56181. Tel: 507-728-8376. p. 1250

Fretz, Lynne, Adult Serv, Brighton Memorial Library, 2300 Elmwood Ave, Rochester, NY, 14618. Tel: 585-784-5300. Fax: 585-784-5333. p. 1728

Freudenberg, Kit, Develop Dir, Westminster College, National Churchill Museum, 501 Westminster Ave, Fulton, MO, 65251-1299. Tel: 573-592-5022. Fax: 573-592-5222. p. 1328

Freudenberger, Erica, Libr Dir, Red Hook Public Library, 7444 S Broadway, Red Hook, NY, 12571. Tel: 845-758-3241. p. 1726

Freund, Laurie, ILL, Ref, Waukesha County Federated Library System, 831 N Grand Ave, Ste 220, Waukesha, WI, 53186-4822. Tel: 262-896-8080. Fax: 262-896-8086. p. 2645

Freund, LeiLani, Interim Chair, Libr West/Humanities & Soc Sci Libr, University of Florida Libraries, 535 Library W, Gainesville, FL, 32611-7000. Tel: 352-273-2615. Fax: 352-392-8118. p. 449

Freund, Luanne, Asst Prof, University of British Columbia, The Irving K Barber Centre, 1961 E Mall, Ste 470, Vancouver, BC, V6T 1Z1, CANADA. Tel: 604-822-2404. Fax: 604-822-6006. p. 2977

Freund, Sandy, Br Mgr, Fairfax County Public Library, Richard Byrd Branch, 7250 Commerce St, Springfield, VA, 22150-3499. Tel: 703-451-8055. p. 2461

Frevert, Rhonda J, Dir, Burlington Public Library, 210 Court St, Burlington, IA, 52601. Tel: 319-753-1647. Fax: 319-753-0789. p. 797

Frew, Gail, Head, Automation, Head, Tech Serv, Osterhout Free Library, 71 S Franklin St, Wilkes-Barre, PA, 18701-1287. Tel: 570-823-0156. Fax: 570-823-5477. p. 2155

Frew, Julia, Dir, Milford Public Library, 101 N Main St, Milford, IN, 46542. Tel: 574-658-4312. Fax: 574-658-9454. p. 765

Frey, Cathy, Asst Librn, Danvers Township Library, 117 E Exchange St, Danvers, IL, 61732-9347. Tel: 309-963-4269. Fax: 309-963-4269. p. 632

Frey, Charles, Mgr, Ref Serv, Neal, Gerber & Eisenberg LLP, Two N La Salle St, Ste 1700, Chicago, IL, 60602. Tel: 312-269-5267. Fax: 312-578-1793. p. 620

Frey, Charles, Res Librn, Nelson, Mullins, Riley & Scarborough, 1320 Main St, Ste 1700, Columbia, SC, 29201. Tel: 843-534-4320. Fax: 803-255-7500. p. 2188

Frey, Charles J, Spec Coll Librn, Bradley University, Virginius H Chase Special Collections Center, 1501 W Bradley Ave, Peoria, IL, 61625. Tel: 309-677-2822. p. 690

Frey, Dean, Librn, Red Deer Public Library, 4818 49th St, Red Deer, AB, T4N 1T9, CANADA. Tel: 403-346-4576. Fax: 403-341-3110. p. 2714

Frey, Elizabeth, Circ Supvr, West Milford Township Library, 1490 Union Valley Rd, West Milford, NJ, 07480. Tel: 973-728-2891. Fax: 973-728-2106. p. 1541

Frey, Jeffrey L, Librn, Stoll Keenon Ogden PLLC, 300 W Vine St, Ste 2100, Lexington, KY, 40507-1801. Tel: 859-231-3000. Fax: 859-253-1093. p. 921

Frey, Laura, Interim Br Mgr, West Georgia Regional Library, Villa Rica Public Library, 70 Horace Luther Dr, Villa Rica, GA, 30180. Tel: 770-459-7012. Fax: 770-459-7960. p. 524

Frey, Maris, Ch, Stonington Free Library, 20 High St, Stonington, CT, 06378. Tel: 860-535-0658. Fax: 860-535-3945. p. 370

Frey, Martha, Outreach Serv Librn, Ref, Bibliotheque de Brossard, 7855 San Francisco Ave, Brossard, QC, J4X 2A4, CANADA. Tel: 450-923-6350, Ext 6285. Fax: 450-923-7042. p. 2880

Frey, Scott, Ref Librn, Western State Law Library, 1111 N State College Blvd, Fullerton, CA, 92831-3014. Tel: 714-459-1113. Fax: 714-871-4806. p. 154

Frey, Sharon, Libr Assoc/Acq Section, Howard Community College Library, 10901 Little Patuxent Pkwy, Columbia, MD, 21044. Tel: 443-518-4813. Fax: 443-518-4993. p. 1025

Frey, Susan, Interim Dept Chair, Circ, Indiana State University, 510 North 6 1/2 St, Terre Haute, IN, 47809. Tel: 812-237-2545. Fax: 812-237-3376. p. 781

Frey, Tracy, Asst Librn, Trenton Public Library, 118 E Indiana, Trenton, IL, 62293. Tel: 618-224-7662. Fax: 618-224-7671. p. 710

Freyermuth, Allison, Head of Libr, Free Library of Philadelphia, Fishtown Community Branch, 1217 E Montgomery Ave, Philadelphia, PA, 19125-3445. Tel: 215-685-9990, 215-685-9991. Fax: 215-685-9989. p. 2107

Freyman, Marcia, Info Serv Librn, Bluegrass Community & Technical College, Oswald Bldg, 470 Cooper Dr, Lexington, KY, 40506-0235. Tel: 859-246-6396. Fax: 859-246-4675. p. 920

Freymann, Lynn, Ref Serv, Normal Public Library, 206 W College Ave, Normal, IL, 61761. Tel: 309-452-1757. Fax: 309-452-5312. p. 681

Freymiller, Peggy S, Circ, ILL, Southwest Wisconsin Library System, 1775 Fourth St, Fennimore, WI, 53809-1137. Tel: 608-822-2052. Fax: 608-822-6251. p. 2591

Freymiller, Trudi, Dir, Dwight T Parker Public Library, 925 Lincoln Ave, Fennimore, WI, 53809-1743. Tel: 608-822-6294. p. 2591

Freytag, Lindsay, Librn, Licking Memorial Hospital, 1320 W Main St, Newark, OH, 43055-3699. Tel: 740-348-4130. Fax: 740-348-4012. p. 1922

Freytag, Riana, Circ Serv Librn, Chester C Corbin Public Library, Two Lake St, Webster, MA, 01570. Tel: 508-949-3880. Fax: 508-949-0537. p. 1134

Friars, Crystal, Asst Librn, Stettler Public Library, 6202 44th Ave, 2nd Flr, Stettler, AB, T0C 2L1, CANADA. Tel: 403-742-2292. Fax: 403-742-5481. p. 2718

Fribley, John, Libr Dir, Ivy Tech Community College, 220 Dean Johnson Blvd, South Bend, IN, 46601. Tel: 574-289-7001, Ext 5341. Fax: 574-236-7165. p. 778

Fribley, Karla, Coordr, Instruction, Ref Librn, Emerson College Library, 120 Boylston St, Boston, MA, 02116-4624. Tel: 617-824-8330. Fax: 617-824-7817. p. 1060

Frick, Carol D, Dept Chair, University of New Mexico, 200 College Rd, Gallup, NM, 87301. Tel: 505-863-7531. Fax: 505-863-7624. p. 1556

Frick, Marty, Dir, West Custer County Library District, 209 Main St, Westcliffe, CO, 81252. Tel: 719-783-9138. Fax: 719-783-2155. p. 325

Frick, Teresa, Tech Serv-Section Head, Orange County Library, 146A Madison Rd, Orange, VA, 22960. Tel: 540-661-5448. Fax: 540-672-5040. p. 2483

Frick, William, Mgr, Warren County Historical Society, 102 W Walton St, Warrenton, MO, 63383-1918. Tel: 636-456-3820. p. 1371

Fricke, Julie, Ref Librn, Web Librn, Lawrence University, 113 S Lawe St, Appleton, WI, 54911-5683. Tel: 920-832-6967. p. 2578

Fricke, Martin, Dr, Assoc Dir, Info Serv, Assoc Prof, University of Arizona, 1515 E First St, Tucson, AZ, 85719. Tel: 520-621-3491. Fax: 520-621-3279. p. 2962

Fricker, Janet S, Exec Dir, Bethlehem Area Public Library, 11 W Church St, Bethlehem, PA, 18018. Tel: 610-867-3761, Ext 215. Fax: 610-867-2767. p. 2033

Fridie, Stephanie, Ref, Salisbury University, 1101 Camden Ave, Salisbury, MD, 21801-6863. Tel: 410-543-6130. Fax: 410-543-6203. p. 1040

Fridmann, Geraldine, Br Mgr, Cape May County Library, Stone Harbor Branch, 9508 Second Ave, Stone Harbor, NJ, 08247. Tel: 609-368-6809. p. 1477

Fried, Alison, Health Sci Librn, Wayne State University Libraries, Vera P Shiffman Medical Library & Learning Resources Centers, Rackham Bldg Rm 044, 60 Farnsworth, Detroit, MI, 48202. Tel: 313-577-1088. Fax: 313-577-6668. p. 1173

Fried, Helen, County Librn, OC Public Libraries, 1501 E St Andrew Pl, Santa Ana, CA, 92705-4048. Tel: 714-566-3000. Fax: 714-566-3042. p. 258

Fried, Michelle C, Libr Spec, Carnegie Mellon University, Software Engineering Institute Library, 4500 Fifth Ave, Pittsburgh, PA, 15213-2612. Tel: 412-268-7607. Fax: 412-268-1340. p. 2124

Friedberg, Zoe, Librn, Psychoanalytic Center of Philadelphia Library, Rockland-East Fairmount Park, 3810 Mount Pleasant Dr, Philadelphia, PA, 19121-1002. Tel: 215-235-2345. Fax: 215-235-2388. p. 2115

Friede, Eric, Asst Divinity Librn, Tech Serv, Yale University Library, Divinity School Library, 409 Prospect St, New Haven, CT, 06511-2108. Tel: 203-432-6372. Fax: 203-432-3906. p. 357

Friedel, Megan, Archives, University of Alaska Anchorage, Consortium Library, 3211 Providence Dr, Anchorage, AK, 99508-8176. Tel: 907-786-1871. Fax: 907-786-1834. p. 45

Friedell, Jeanne, Librn, Oak Park Public Library, Dole Branch, 255 Augusta St, Oak Park, IL, 60302. Tel: 708-386-9032. Fax: 708-445-2385. p. 684

Frieder, Richard, Assoc Librn, Commun Develop & Civic Serv, Hartford Public Library, 500 Main St, Hartford, CT, 06103-3075. Tel: 860-695-6365. Fax: 860-722-6900. p. 346

Friedgen-Veitch, Lori L, Ch, Helen Kate Furness Free Library, 100 N Providence Rd, Wallingford, PA, 19086. Tel: 610-566-9331. Fax: 610-566-9337. p. 2150

Friedkline, Nancy, Librn, North Powder Library, 290 E St, North Powder, OR, 97867. Tel: 541-898-2175. Fax: 541-898-2175. p. 2008

Friedl, Eleanor, Coll Develop, Ref, Fairleigh Dickinson University, 285 Madison Ave, M-LAO-03, Madison, NJ, 07940. Tel: 973-443-8515. Fax: 973-443-8525. p. 1497

Friedland, Nancy, Media Librn, Performing Arts Librn, Columbia University, Philip L Milstein Family College Library, 208 Butler Library, 535 W 114th St, New York, NY, 10027. Tel: 212-854-5327. Fax: 212-854-0089. p. 1675

Friedlander, Zoe, Syst Librn, Academy of Motion Picture Arts & Sciences, 333 S La Cienega Blvd, Beverly Hills, CA, 90211. Tel: 310-247-3000, Ext 2239. Fax: 310-657-5193. p. 129

Friedli, Lori, Ref, Mamaroneck Public Library District, 136 Prospect Ave, Mamaroneck, NY, 10543. Tel: 914-698-1250. Fax: 914-381-3088. p. 1657

Friedline, Bruce, Circ Serv, Mishawaka-Penn-Harris Public Library, 209 Lincoln Way E, Mishawaka, IN, 46544-2084. Tel: 574-259-5277, Ext 209. Fax: 574-254-5585, 574-255-8489. p. 765

Friedlund, Carolyn, Head, Info Serv, Fox River Valley Public Library District, 555 Barrington Ave, Dundee, IL, 60118-1496. Tel: 847-428-3661. Fax: 847-428-0521. p. 637

Friedman, Amy, Adult Serv, YA Serv, George H & Ella M Rodgers Memorial Library, 194 Derry Rd, Hudson, NH, 03051. Tel: 603-886-6030. Fax: 603-816-4501. p. 1452

Friedman, Batya, Prof, University of Washington, Mary Gates Hall, Ste 370, Campus Box 352840, Seattle, WA, 98195-2840. Tel: 206-685-9937. Fax: 206-616-3152. p. 2976

Friedman, Catherine R, Assoc Univ Librn, User Serv, University of California, San Diego, 9500 Gilman Dr, Mail Code 0175G, La Jolla, CA, 92093-0175. Tel: 858-534-1278. Fax: 858-534-4970. p. 162

Friedman, Dale, Ref/YA, River Vale Free Public Library, 412 Rivervale Rd, River Vale, NJ, 07675. Tel: 201-391-2323. Fax: 201-391-6599. p. 1526

Friedman, Deborah, Coordr, Access Serv, University of Massachusetts Lowell Libraries, 61 Wilder St, Lowell, MA, 01854-3098. Tel: 978-934-4572. Fax: 978-934-3015. p. 1100

Friedman, Elaine, Librn, Congregation Shalom, 7630 N Santa Monica Blvd, Milwaukee, WI, 53217. Tel: 414-352-9288. Fax: 414-352-9280. p. 2618

Friedman, Helen, Ch, North Merrick Public Library, 1691 Meadowbrook Rd, North Merrick, NY, 11566. Tel: 516-378-7474. Fax: 516-378-0876. p. 1706

Friedman, Jane, ILL, Central College, Campus Box 6500, 812 University St, Pella, IA, 50219-1999. Tel: 641-628-5219. Fax: 641-628-5327. p. 838

Friedman, Jennifer, Coll Mgr, Pub Serv, Massachusetts Institute of Technology Libraries, Rotch Library-Architecture & Planning, Bldg 7-238, 77 Massachusetts Ave, Cambridge, MA, 02139-4307. Tel: 617-258-5595. Fax: 617-253-9331. p. 1078

Friedman, Jennifer, Dir, West Acton Citizen's Library, 21 Windsor Ave, West Acton, MA, 01720-2809. Tel: 978-264-9652. p. 1136

Friedman, Jennifer, Head, Ref, Scarsdale Public Library, 54 Olmsted Rd, Scarsdale, NY, 10583. Tel: 914-722-1300. Fax: 914-722-1305. p. 1739

Friedman, Jennifer, Librn, Mendota Mental Health Institute, 301 Troy Dr, Madison, WI, 53704-1599. Tel: 608-301-1196. Fax: 608-301-1169. p. 2607

Friedman, Joanne, Sr Ch, Kearny Public Library, 318 Kearny Ave, Kearny, NJ, 07032. Tel: 201-998-2666. Fax: 201-998-1141. p. 1493

Friedman, Lydia, Dir, Maimonides Medical Center, Administration, 4802 Tenth Ave, Fifth Fl, Brooklyn, NY, 11219. Tel: 718-283-7406. Fax: 718-283-7063. p. 1593

Friedman, Rebecca, Asst Librn, Princeton University, Marquand Library of Art & Archaeology, McCormick Hall, Princeton, NJ, 08544. Tel: 609-258-3783. Fax: 609-258-7650. p. 1524

Friedman, Stanford, Librn, Conde Nast Publications Library, Four Times Sq, New York, NY, 10036. Tel: 212-286-8245. Fax: 212-286-6763. p. 1675

Friedman, Yelena, Dir, Staten Island University Hospital, 475 Seaview Ave, Staten Island, NY, 10305. Tel: 718-226-9545. Fax: 718-226-8582. p. 1748

Friedow, Linda, Dir, Britt Public Library, 132 Main Ave S, Britt, IA, 50423-1628. Tel: 641-843-4245. Fax: 641-843-4245. p. 797

Friedrich, Gustav W, Dean, Prof, Rutgers, The State University of New Jersey, Four Huntington St, New Brunswick, NJ, 08901-1071. Tel: 732-932-7500, Ext 8955. Fax: 732-932-2644. p. 2969

Friedrich, Steve, Exec Dir, Temple Sinai, 1401 N Limekiln Pike, Dresher, PA, 19025. Tel: 215-643-6510, Ext 110. Fax: 215-643-9441. p. 2050

Friehs, Curt, Sr Asst Librn, Ref, State University of New York, 223 Store Hill Rd, Old Westbury, NY, 11568. Tel: 516-876-2895. Fax: 516-876-3325. p. 1710

Frieling, Tom, Head, Access Serv, University of Georgia Libraries, Athens, GA, 30602-1641. Tel: 706-542-3256. Fax: 706-542-4144. p. 510

Friend, Danielle, Ch, Robert J Kleberg Public Library, 220 N Fourth St, Kingsville, TX, 78363. Tel: 361-592-6381. p. 2350

Friend, Diana, Pub Relations Mgr, Topeka & Shawnee County Public Library, 1515 SW Tenth Ave, Topeka, KS, 66604-1374. Tel: 785-580-4400. Fax: 785-580-4496. p. 897

Friend, Linda, Head of Scholarly Communications Serv, Pennsylvania State University Libraries, 510 Paterno Library, University Park, PA, 16802. Tel: 814-865-0401. Fax: 814-865-3665. p. 2148

Frierson, Amy, Dir, Houston Museum of Decorative Arts, 201 High St, Chattanooga, TN, 37403. Tel: 423-267-7176. Fax: 423-267-7177. p. 2227

Fries, Elizabeth, Br Librn, Southeast Regional Library, Qu'Appelle Branch, Town Hall, 25-9th Ave, Qu'Appelle, SK, S0G 4A0, CANADA. Tel: 306-699-2902. Fax: 306-699-2306. p. 2930

Fries, James R, Head of Libr, Dartmouth College Library, Feldberg Business Administration & Engineering Library, 6193 Murdough Ctr, Hanover, NH, 03755-3560. Tel: 603-646-2191. Fax: 603-646-2384. p. 1450

Friese, Christine, Asst State Librn, State of Vermont Department of Libraries, 109 State St, Montpelier, VT, 05609-0601. Tel: 802-828-2714. Fax: 802-828-2199. p. 2429

Friese, Sonja, In Charge, First Baptist Church of Lakewood Library, 5336 Arbor Rd, Long Beach, CA, 90808. Tel: 562-420-1471. Fax: 562-420-9140. p. 166

Friesen, Mary, Dir, Wyocena Public Library, 165 E Dodge St, Wyocena, WI, 53969. Tel: 608-429-4899. Fax: 608-429-4902. p. 2650

Friesen, Paul, Assoc Librn, Canadian Mennonite University Library, 500 Shaftesbury Blvd, Winnipeg, MB, R3P 2N2, CANADA. Tel: 204-487-3300, Ext 319. Fax: 204-837-7415. p. 2754

Friesen, Susanne, Sr Cataloger, Goshen Public Library, 601 S Fifth St, Goshen, IN, 46526-3994. Tel: 574-533-9531. Fax: 574-533-5211. p. 746

Friesner, Lynn, Ref Mgr, Council Bluffs Public Library, 400 Willow Ave, Council Bluffs, IA, 51503-4269. Tel: 712-323-7553, Ext 135. Fax: 712-323-1269. p. 805

Friesz, Teena, Asst Librn, Miles Community College Library, 2715 Dickinson, Miles City, MT, 59301. Tel: 406-874-6105. Fax: 406-874-6282. p. 1386

Frigon, Marcelle, In Charge, Complexe Hospitalier de la Sagamie, 305 Ave Saint Vallier, CP 5006, Chicoutimi, QC, G7H 5H6, CANADA. Tel: 418-541-1000, 418-541-1234, Ext 2496. Fax: 418-541-1145. p. 2881

Frisbee, Holly, Librn, New York Academy of Art Library, 111 Franklin St, New York, NY, 10013-2911. Tel: 212.966.0300, Ext 964. Fax: 212-966-3217. p. 1688

Frisbee, Stephen, Dir of Libr, Mohawk Valley Community College Library, 1101 Sherman Dr, Utica, NY, 13501-5394. Tel: 315-792-5408. Fax: 315-792-5666. p. 1759

Frisby, Laura, Dir, Toulon Public Library District, 306 W Jefferson, Toulon, IL, 61483. Tel: 309-286-5791. Fax: 309-286-4481. p. 710

Frisch, Paul, Dr, Dean of Libr, Dir, Our Lady of the Lake University, 411 SW 24th St, San Antonio, TX, 78207-4689. Tel: 210-434-6711, Ext 2324, Fax: 210-436-1616. p. 2380

Frisch, Sheila, Sr Libr Asst, Englewood Public Library, 31 Engle St, Englewood, NJ, 07631. Tel: 201-568-2215. Fax: 201-568-6895. p. 1484

Frischkorn, Mary-Ann, Circ Tech Support, Malone University, 2600 Cleveland Ave NW, Canton, OH, 44709-3897. Tel: 330-471-8317. Fax: 330-454-6977. p. 1863

Frisina, Brian, Libr & Archives Paraprofessional 4, Washington State Library, Department of Labor & Industries, 7273 Linderson Way SW, Tumwater, WA, 98501. Tel: 360-902-5498. Fax: 360-902-6335. p. 2544

Frison, Renato, Mgr, User Serv, Fordham University Libraries, 441 E Fordham Rd, Bronx, NY, 10458-5151. Tel: 718-817-3570. Fax: 718-817-3582. p. 1586

Frisse, Carol, Archivist, Madison County Historical Museum & Archival Library, 715 N Main St, Edwardsville, IL, 62025-1111. Tel: 618-656-7562, 618-656-7569. Fax: 618-659-3457. p. 639

Fritch, Steve, AV, Redondo Beach Public Library, 303 N Pacific Coast Hwy, Redondo Beach, CA, 90277. Tel: 310-318-0675. Fax: 310-318-3809. p. 215

Frith, Greg, Automation Syst Coordr, Shreve Memorial Library, 424 Texas St, Shreveport, LA, 71101. Tel: 318-226-5897. Fax: 318-226-4780. p. 969

Fritsch, Barbara, Ch, Plumb Memorial Library, 65 Wooster St, Shelton, CT, 06484. Tel: 203-924-9461. Fax: 203-924-8422. p. 367

Fritsch, Lynn H, Librn, Stites & Harbison, 400 W Market St, Ste 1800, Louisville, KY, 40202. Tel: 502-587-3400. Fax: 502-587-6391. p. 926

Fritts, Ari, Youth Serv Librn, Madison County Public Library, 507 W Main St, Richmond, KY, 40475. Tel: 859-623-6704. Fax: 859-623-2023. p. 934

Fritts, Jack, Univ Librn, Benedictine University Library, 5700 College Rd, Lisle, IL, 60532-0900. Tel: 630-829-6050. Fax: 630-960-9451. p. 666

Fritts, Karen Orr, Govt Doc/Develop Librn, University of North Carolina at Pembroke, Faculty Row, Pembroke, NC, 28372. Tel: 910-521-6516. Fax: 910-521-6547. p. 1814

Fritts, Mary, Dir, Lyons Public Library, 305 Main, Lyons, NE, 68038. Tel: 402-687-2895. Fax: 402-687-2895. p. 1407

Fritz, Connie, Sci Librn, Rensselaer Libraries, Rensselaer Polytechnic Inst, 110 Eighth St, Troy, NY, 12180-3590. Tel: 518-276-8300. Fax: 518-276-2044. p. 1756

Fritz, Darla, Librn, Wyotech Library (Wyoming Technical Institute), 500 Innovation Dr, Blairsville, PA, 15717. Tel: 724-459-9500. Fax: 724-459-6499. p. 2035

Fritz, Linda, Librn, Elmer Library, 120 S Main St, Elmer, NJ, 08318. Tel: 856-358-2014. Fax: 856-358-2014. p. 1484

Fritz, Melanie, Libr Supvr-Popular Libr, Rio Salado College, 2323 W 14th St, Tempe, AZ, 85281. Tel: 480-517-8424. Fax: 480-517-8449. p. 84

Fritz, Natalie, Curatorial Asst, Clark County Historical Society, 117 S Fountain Ave, Springfield, OH, 45502-1207. Tel: 937-324-0657. Fax: 937-324-1992. p. 1935

Fritz, Pam, Dir, Baxter International, 25212 W Illinois Rte 120, RLT 22, Round Lake, IL, 60073. Tel: 847-270-5360. Fax: 847-270-5381. p. 699

Fritz, Rebecca, ILL, Walnut Public Library District, 101 Heaton, Walnut, IL, 61376. Tel: 815-379-2159. Fax: 815-379-2159. p. 715

Fritz, Ruth T, Librn, Woodstown-Pilesgrove Public Library, 14 School Lane, Woodstown, NJ, 08098-1331. Tel: 856-769-0098. p. 1546

Fritz, Sandra, Digital Imaging Prog Coordr, Illinois State Library, Gwendolyn Brooks Bldg, 300 S Second St, Springfield, IL, 62701-9713. Tel: 217-558-2064. Fax: 217-785-4326. p. 705

Fritz, William, Br Mgr, Broward County Division of Libraries, Lauderdale Lakes Branch, 3580 W Oakland Park Blvd, Lauderdale Lakes, FL, 33311. Tel: 954-357-8650. Fax: 954-357-8653. p. 441

Frizol, Laura, Dir, LaSalle Public Library, 305 Marquette St, LaSalle, IL, 61301. Tel: 815-223-2341. Fax: 815-223-2353. p. 664

Frizzell, Dixie, Dir, Camp Wood Public Library, 117 S Nueces, Camp Wood, TX, 78833-0828. Tel: 830-597-3208. Fax: 830-597-3208. p. 2294

Frizzell, George, Head, Spec Coll, Western Carolina University, 176 Central Dr, Cullowhee, NC, 28723. Tel: 828-227-7474. Fax: 828-227-7015. p. 1786

Frizzell, Robert, Dir, University of Arkansas Fort Smith, 5210 Grand Ave, Fort Smith, AR, 72903. Tel: 479-788-7205. Fax: 479-788-7209. p. 101

Froebel, Shonna, Mgr, Ad Serv, Barrie Public Library, 60 Worsley St, Barrie, ON, L4M 1L6, CANADA. Tel: 705-728-1010, Ext 7014. Fax: 705-728-4322. p. 2793

Froehlich, Conrad G, Dir, Martin & Osa Johnson Safari Museum, 111 N Lincoln Ave, Chanute, KS, 66720. Tel: 620-431-2730. Fax: 620-431-2730. p. 860

Froehlich, Thomas, Dr, Prof, Kent State University, 314 Library, Kent, OH, 44242-0001. Tel: 330-672-2782. Fax: 330-672-7965. p. 2971

Froelich, Lennet, Dir, Dudley Township Public Library, 105 N Sequoyah St, Satanta, KS, 67870. Tel: 620-649-2213. Fax: 620-649-2213. p. 893

Froese, Vic, PhD, Libr Dir, Canadian Mennonite University Library, 500 Shaftesbury Blvd, Winnipeg, MB, R3P 2N2, CANADA. Tel: 204-487-3300, Ext 393. Fax: 204-837-7415. p. 2754

Frogner, Raymond, Assoc Archivist, University of Alberta, Archives, Books & Records Depository, 100 8170 50th St, Edmonton, AB, T6B 1E6, CANADA. Tel: 780-466-6118, 780-466-6123. Fax: 780-466-5210. p. 2702

Froman, Darla, Mgr, Weston Public Library, Grand Rapids Branch, 17620 Bridge St, Grand Rapids, OH, 43522. Tel: 419-832-5231. Fax: 419-832-8104. p. 1947

Fromm, Jim, Dir of Tech Serv, University of Arizona, 1510 E University Blvd, Tucson, AZ, 85721. Tel: 520-621-6441. p. 88

Fromm, Jim, Asst Dean, Tech Serv, University of Arizona, Technical Services, 1510 E University Blvd, Tucson, AZ, 85721. Tel: 520-548-9447. Fax: 520-621-8276. p. 89

Fromm, Nancy, Asst Librn, Franklin Ferguson Memorial Library, 410 N B St, Cripple Creek, CO, 80813. Tel: 719-689-2800. Fax: 719-689-3187. p. 297

Frommelt, Gene, Media Spec, Vernon College, 4400 College Dr, Vernon, TX, 76384. Tel: 940-552-6291, Ext 2220. Fax: 940-552-0288. p. 2395

Fromwiller, Laura, Head, Ref, Lapeer District Library, 201 Village West Dr S, Lapeer, MI, 48446-1699. Tel: 810-664-9521. Fax: 810-664-8527. p. 1202

Fronmueller, Julie, Outreach & Instruction Librn, Colorado State University Pueblo Library, 2200 Bonforte Blvd, Pueblo, CO, 81001-4901. Tel: 719-549-2361. Fax: 719-549-2738. p. 320

Frontino, Anne, Tech Serv, Haddonfield Public Library, 60 Haddon Ave, Haddonfield, NJ, 08033-2422. Tel: 856-429-1304. Fax: 856-429-3760. p. 1489

Frontz, Kim, Archivist, Arizona Historical Society, 949 E Second St, Tucson, AZ, 85719. Tel: 520-617-1148. Fax: 520-629-8966. p. 85

Frontz, Stephanie, Librn, University of Rochester, Art-Music, Rush Rhees Library, Rochester, NY, 14627. Tel: 585-275-4476. Fax: 585-273-1032. p. 1733

Frosch, June, Dep Libr Dir, New Mexico Military Institute, Toles Learning Center, 101 W College Blvd, Roswell, NM, 88201-5173. Tel: 575-624-8384. Fax: 575-624-8390. p. 1561

Frosch, Melissa, AV Coll, Cat, Circ Media, Quitman Public Library, 202 East Goode St, Quitman, TX, 75783-2533. Tel: 903-763-4191. Fax: 903-763-2532. p. 2373

Frosina, Len, Network Serv, Comsewogue Public Library, 170 Terryville Rd, Port Jefferson Station, NY, 11776. Tel: 631-928-1212. Fax: 631-928-6307. p. 1721

Frost, Bob, Librn, United Medical Technologies Corp, 3804 Arrow Lakes Dr S, Jacksonville, FL, 32257. Tel: 904-288-8832. p. 455

Frost, C Olivia, Prof, University of Michigan, 304 West Hall, 1085 S University, Ann Arbor, MI, 48109-1107. Tel: 734-763-2285. Fax: 734-764-2475. p. 2967

Frost, Carol, Div Mgr, San Jose Public Library, 150 E San Fernando St, San Jose, CA, 95112-3580. Tel: 408-808-2048. p. 250

Frost, Jean, Librn, Colorado Department of Corrections, Centennial Correctional Facility Library, PO Box 600, Canon City, CO, 81215-0600. Tel: 719-269-5546. Fax: 719-269-5545. p. 293

Frost, Judith G, Dir, Libr Serv, Central Maine Community College Library, 1250 Turner St, Auburn, ME, 04210-6498. Tel: 207-755-5266. Fax: 207-755-5494. p. 974

Frost, Lynn, Libr Dir, Junction City Public Library, 726 Greenwood St, Junction City, OR, 97448-1628. Tel: 541-998-8942. p. 2001

Frost, Martha, Libr Asst, Millinocket Memorial Library, Five Maine Ave, Millinocket, ME, 04462. Tel: 207-723-7020. Fax: 207-723-7020. p. 992

Frost, Meggan, Pub Serv Librn, Paul Smiths College of Arts & Sciences, Rte's 30 & 86, Paul Smiths, NY, 12970. Tel: 518-327-6462. Fax: 518-327-6350. p. 1715

Frost, Nancy, Acq, Orange County Library, 146A Madison Rd, Orange, VA, 22960. Tel: 540-661-5446. Fax: 540-672-5040. p. 2483

Frost, Rachelle, Ch, Norma Anders Public Library, 320 Main St, Dysart, IA, 52224. Tel: 319-476-5210. Fax: 319-476-2671. p. 812

Frost, Robert, Assoc Prof, University of Michigan, 304 West Hall, 1085 S University, Ann Arbor, MI, 48109-1107. Tel: 734-763-2285. Fax: 734-764-2475. p. 2967

Frost, Rose, Dir, New Albany-Floyd County Public Library, 180 W Spring St, New Albany, IN, 47150-3692. Tel: 812-944-8464. Fax: 812-949-3532. p. 768

Frost, Rose, Dir, Platteville Public Library, 65 S Elm, Platteville, WI, 53818. Tel: 608-348-7441, Ext 5. Fax: 608-348-9923. p. 2630

Frostman, Dan, Head, Circ, Middlebury College Library, 110 Storrs Ave, Middlebury, VT, 05753-6007. Tel: 802-443-5798. Fax: 802-443-2074, 802-443-5698. p. 2428

Frowein, Marcia, Ref, Joliet Public Library, 150 N Ottawa St, Joliet, IL, 60432-4192. Tel: 815-740-2660. Fax: 815-740-6161. p. 660

Fruehling, Douglas, Bibliog Instr, Online Serv, Ref, Point Loma Nazarene University, 3900 Lomaland Dr, San Diego, CA, 92106-2899. Tel: 619-849-2355. Fax: 619-222-0711. p. 232

Frumento, Katherine Stemmer, Dir, Libr Serv, Greenwich Hospital, Five Perryridge Rd, Greenwich, CT, 06830. Tel: 203-863-3285. Fax: 203-863-4664. p. 341

Frumkin, Jeremy, Chief Tech Strategist, University of Arizona, 1510 E University Blvd, Tucson, AZ, 85721. Tel: 520-621-6441. p. 88

Frusciano, Thomas, Univ Archivist, Rutgers University Libraries, Special Collections & University Archives, 169 College Ave, New Brunswick, NJ, 08901-1163. Tel: 848-932-6149. Fax: 732-932-7012. p. 1509

Frutchey, Jim, Coll Develop Librn, Interim Dir, Marywood University Library, 2300 Adams Ave, Scranton, PA, 18509-1598. Tel: 570-961-4707. Fax: 570-961-4769. p. 2137

Fry, Arla Marie, Ch, Liberty Center Public Library, 124 East St, Liberty Center, OH, 43532. Tel: 419-533-5721. Fax: 419-533-4849. p. 1909

Fry, Carolyn, Librn, Henderson County Public Library District, 110 Hillcrest Dr, Biggsville, IL, 61418-9736. Tel: 309-627-2450. Fax: 309-627-2830. p. 595

Fry, Carri, Youth Serv Coordr, Derby Public Library, 1600 E Walnut Grove, Derby, KS, 67037. Tel: 316-788-0760. Fax: 316-788-7313. p. 863

Fry, Carrie, Electronic Res, Info Spec, Syst Librn, Seattle Pacific University Library, 3307 Third Ave W, Seattle, WA, 98119. Tel: 206-281-2124. Fax: 206-281-2936. p. 2530

Fry, David, Electronic Res, Darton College, 2400 Gillionville Rd, Albany, GA, 31707. Tel: 229-317-6933. Fax: 229-317-6652. p. 507

Fry, Deb, Prog Coordr, Whitworth University, 300 W Hawthorne Rd, Spokane, WA, 99251-0001. Tel: 509-777-3207. Fax: 509-777-3221. p. 2538

Fry, Eric, Br Mgr, Allen County Public Library, Grabill Branch, 13521 State St, Grabill, IN, 46741. Tel: 260-421-1325. Fax: 260-627-7578. p. 740

Fry, Ian, Libr Spec, Gateway Community & Technical College, Covington Campus Library, 1025 Amsterdam Rd, Rm C 106, Covington, KY, 41011. Tel: 859-442-1697. p. 911

Fry, Jhanna, Dir, Agness Community Library, 3905 Cougar Lane, Agness, OR, 97406. Tel: 541-247-6323. Fax: 541-247-6323. p. 1989

Fry, Kaia, Dir, Deerfield Public Library, 12 W Nelson St, Deerfield, WI, 53531-9669. Tel: 608-764-8102. p. 2588

Fry, Kathleen, Librn, Arizona Department of Corrections - Adult Institutions, 6911 N BDI Blvd, Douglas, AZ, 85608. Tel: 520-364-7521, Ext 34522. Fax: 520-805-5971. p. 61

Fry, Marcus X, Tech Serv Librn, Concordia University Texas Library, 11400 Concordia University Dr, Austin, TX, 78726. Tel: 512-313-5050. p. 2280

Fry, MaryAnne C, Dir, Info Resources & Res, King & Spalding, 1180 Peachtree St NE, Flr 17, Atlanta, GA, 30309. Tel: 404-572-4600, Ext 3300. Fax: 404-572-5123. p. 516

Fry, Morel, Admin Serv, Old Dominion University Libraries, 4427 Hampton Blvd, Norfolk, VA, 23529-0256. Tel: 757-683-4143. Fax: 757-683-5767. p. 2482

Fry, Shana, Br Mgr, Pub Serv Coordr, Arlington Public Library System, Lake Arlington, 4000 W Green Oaks Blvd, Arlington, TX, 76016-4442. Tel: 817-478-3762. Fax: 817-561-9823. p. 2276

Fry, Verna, Libr Asst, Youth Serv, Barry-Lawrence Regional Library, Cassville Branch, 301 W 17th St, Cassville, MO, 65625-1044. Tel: 417-847-2121. Fax: 417-847-4679. p. 1346

Fryar, Linda, Librn, United States Air Force, 882nd Training Group Academic Library, 882 TRG/TSOL, 939 Missile Rd Bldg 1900, Sheppard AFB, TX, 76311-2245. Tel: 940-676-3802. Fax: 940-676-4025. p. 2386

Fryback, Jo Ann, Bus Mgr, Pendleton Community Library, 595 E Water St, Pendleton, IN, 46064-1070. Tel: 765-778-7527, Ext 108. Fax: 765-778-7529. p. 772

Frybort, Carla, Libr Dir, Leduc Public Library, Two Alexandra Park, Leduc, AB, T9E 4C4, CANADA. Tel: 780-986-2637. Fax: 780-986-3462. p. 2709

Fryd, Rachel, Head of Libr, Free Library of Philadelphia, Wynnefield Branch, 5325 Overbrook Ave, Philadelphia, PA, 19131-1498. Tel: 215-685-0298, 215-685-0299. Fax: 215-685-0294. p. 2109

Frye, Betti George, Tech Serv, Ashland Community & Technical College, 1400 College Dr, Ashland, KY, 41101. Tel: 606-326-2141. Fax: 606-326-2186. p. 905

Frye, Cindy, Ch, Fort Morgan Public Library, 414 Main St, Fort Morgan, CO, 80701. Tel: 970-542-4000. Fax: 970-542-4013. p. 308

Frye, Ingeborg, Br Head, Beaufort, Hyde & Martin County Regional Library, Ocracoke Branch, 225 Back Rd, Ocracoke, NC, 27960. Tel: 252-928-4436. Fax: 252-928-2633. p. 1828

Frye, Jacqueline, Network Serv, Harnett County Public Library, 601 S Main St, Lillington, NC, 27546-6107. Tel: 910-893-3446. Fax: 910-893-3001. p. 1806

Frye, Jonathan, Sr Librn, California Youth Authority, O H Close Youth Correctional Facility Library, 7650 S Newcastle Rd, Stockton, CA, 95213-9001. Tel: 209-944-6346. Fax: 209-944-6136. p. 272

Frye, Michael, Life Sci Librn, Winston-Salem State University, 601 Martin Luther King Jr Dr, Winston-Salem, NC, 27110. Tel: 336-750-2532. Fax: 336-750-2459. p. 1834

Frye, Sarah, Instrul Serv Librn, Ref, Pierce College Library, 9401 Farwest Dr SW, Lakewood, WA, 98498. Tel: 253-964-6303. Fax: 253-964-6713. p. 2519

Fryer, Jane, Circ/Customer Serv Mgr, White Lake Community Library, 3900 White Lake Dr, Whitehall, MI, 49461-9257. Tel: 231-894-9531. Fax: 231-893-8821. p. 1237

Fryer, Kim, Br Mgr, Richland Parish Library, Delhi Branch, 520 Main St, Delhi, LA, 71232. Tel: 318-878-5121. Fax: 318-878-0674. p. 966

Fryer, Philip, Media Spec, Loyola-Notre Dame Library, Inc, 200 Winston Ave, Baltimore, MD, 21212. Tel: 410-617-6800. Fax: 410-617-6895. p. 1015

Fryer, Richard, Librn, Illinois Youth Center, 3825 Campton Hills Rd, Saint Charles, IL, 60175. Tel: 630-584-0506, Ext 284. Fax: 630-584-1126. p. 699

Fryer, Will, Dir, De Soto Public Library, 111 S Houghton St, De Soto, WI, 54624. Tel: 608-648-3593. p. 2588

Frykberg, Dru, Librn, Minnesota Department of Employment & Economic Development Library, 1st National Bank Bldg, 332 Minnesota St, Ste E200, Saint Paul, MN, 55101-1351. Tel: 651-259-7188. Fax: 651-215-3841. p. 1279

Fryman, Bill, Head, Libr Syst, Washington University Libraries, One Brookings Dr, Campus Box 1061, Saint Louis, MO, 63130-4862. Tel: 314-935-5400. Fax: 314-935-4045. p. 1362

Frymark, Kathy, Dir, Saint Francis Seminary, 3257 S Lake Dr, Saint Francis, WI, 53235-0905. Tel: 414-747-6479. Fax: 414-747-6483. p. 2635

Frymire, Chris, Mgr, Heald College, 1605 E March Lane, Stockton, CA, 95210. Tel: 209-473-5200. Fax: 209-473-5287. p. 272

Frymire, Paula C, Dir, Crane County Library, 701 S Alford St, Crane, TX, 79731-2521. Tel: 432-558-1142. Fax: 432-558-1144. p. 2303

Fu, Jennifer, Head of GIS Ctr, Florida International University, 11200 SW Eighth St, Miami, FL, 33199. Tel: 305-348-3138. Fax: 305-348-6445. p. 465

Fu, Johanna, Commun Libr Mgr, Queens Borough Public Library, Auburndale Community Library, 25-55 Francis Lewis Blvd, Flushing, NY, 11358. Tel: 718-352-2027. p. 1644

Fu, Li, Coordr, Access Serv, Chicago State University, 9501 S Martin Luther King Jr Dr, LIB 440, Chicago, IL, 60628-1598. Tel: 773-821-2804. Fax: 773-995-3772. p. 610

Fucci, Lynnette, Ch, Monroe Township Public Library, Four Municipal Plaza, Monroe Township, NJ, 08831-1900. Tel: 732-521-5000, Ext 125. Fax: 732-521-4766. p. 1503

Fuccillo, Vincent, Actg Librn, In Charge, Istituto Italiano di Cultura, Biblioteca, 686 Park Ave, New York, NY, 10065. Tel: 212-879-4242. Fax: 212-861-4018. p. 1683

Fuchs, Beth, Ref Serv, Moravian College & Moravian Theological Seminary, 1200 Main St, Bethlehem, PA, 18018-6650. Tel: 610-625-7965. Fax: 610-861-1577. p. 2034

Fuchs, John, Dir, Kent Memorial Library, 50 N Main St (Junction of Rtes 75 & 168), Suffield, CT, 06078-2117. Tel: 860-668-3896. Fax: 860-668-3895. p. 371

Fuchs, Patti, Ch, Indian River County Library System, 1600 21st St, Vero Beach, FL, 32960. Tel: 772-770-5060. Fax: 772-770-5066. p. 501

Fudell, Anita, Managing Librn, Austin Public Library, Twin Oaks, 1800 S Fifth St, Austin, TX, 78704. Tel: 512-974-9980. Fax: 512-974-9988. p. 2279

Fuehring, Debbie, Ref, Massena Public Library, 41 Glenn St, Massena, NY, 13662. Tel: 315-769-9914. Fax: 315-769-5978. p. 1658

Fuemmeler, Judy, Dir, Library District Number One, Doniphan County, 105 N Main, Troy, KS, 66087. Tel: 785-985-2597. Fax: 785-985-2602. p. 898

Fuemmeler, Rosetta, Dir, Lewis Library of Glasgow, 315 Market St, Glasgow, MO, 65254-1537. Tel: 660-338-2395. p. 1329

Fuentes, Claudia, Circ Supvr, University of Texas Libraries, McKinney Engineering Library, One University Sta S5435, ECJ 1.300, Austin, TX, 78712. Tel: 512-495-4511. Fax: 512-495-4507. p. 2284

Fuentes, Marinilda, Media Spec, University of Puerto Rico, 130 Ave Universidad, Arecibo, PR, 00612-3145. Tel: 787-815-0000, Ext 3151. Fax: 787-878-9363. p. 2671

Fuerst, Julia, Res Serv Mgr, DLA Piper US LLP, 2000 University Ave, East Palo Alto, CA, 94303. Tel: 650-833-2000. Fax: 650-833-2001. p. 144

Fuerstenau, Jane E, Dir, Kenai Peninsula College Library, 156 College Rd, Soldotna, AK, 99669. Tel: 907-262-0385. Fax: 907-262-0386. p. 53

Fuertges, Daniel, Coordr, Access Serv, Bradley University, 1501 W Bradley Ave, Peoria, IL, 61625. Tel: 309-677-2850. Fax: 309-677-2558. p. 690

Fugate, David, IT Spec, Mechanicsburg Public Library, 60 S Main St, Mechanicsburg, OH, 43044. Tel: 937-834-2004. Fax: 937-834-3396. p. 1916

Fugleberg, Marjorie, Ser, Mayville State University, 330 Third St NE, Mayville, ND, 58257. Tel: 701-788-4817. Fax: 701-788-4846. p. 1846

Fuhrman, Tim, Dean, Info Serv, Big Bend Community College Library, 7662 Chanute St, Moses Lake, WA, 98837. Tel: 509-793-2350. Fax: 509-762-2402. p. 2521

Fuhrmann, Dorothy, Acq, Circ, Ref, Los Angeles City College Library, 855 N Vermont Ave, Los Angeles, CA, 90029. Tel: 323-953-4000. Fax: 323-953-4013. p. 171

Fuhro, Laura, Head, Ch, Berkeley Heights Public Library, 290 Plainfield Ave, Berkeley Heights, NJ, 07922. Tel: 908-464-9333. Fax: 908-464-7098. p. 1472

Fujioka, Ann, Head, Tech Serv, Hawaii State Public Library System, Office of the State Librarian, 44 Merchant St, Honolulu, HI, 96813. Tel: 808-831-6871. Fax: 808-831-7899. p. 561

Fujita, Sachiyo, Spec Coll Librn, Kapiolani Community College Library, 4303 Diamond Head Rd, Honolulu, HI, 96816. Tel: 808-734-9757. Fax: 808-734-9453. p. 564

Fukumoto, Elaine, Commun Libr Mgr, County of Los Angeles Public Library, Masao W Satow Library, 14433 S Crenshaw Blvd, Gardena, CA, 90249-3142. Tel: 310-679-0638. Fax: 310-970-0275. p. 143

Fulbright, Alice, Instrul Serv Librn, Richland College Library, 12800 Abrams Rd, Dallas, TX, 75243-2199. Tel: 972-238-6081. p. 2309

Fulcher, Betty, Circ, Blue Ridge Regional Library, 310 E Church St, Martinsville, VA, 24112-2999. Tel: 276-403-5430. Fax: 276-632-1660. p. 2477

Fulcher, Tammy, Adult Serv, Sheppard Memorial Library, 530 S Evans St, Greenville, NC, 27858-2308. Tel: 252-329-4254. Fax: 252-329-4587. p. 1799

Fulcher-Anderson, Josephine, Supvr, Ferguson Library, South End, 34 Woodland Ave, Stamford, CT, 06902. Tel: 203-964-1000, Ext 8281. Fax: 203-969-0797. p. 369

Fulchino, Stephen, Dir, New Bedford Free Public Library, 613 Pleasant St, New Bedford, MA, 02740-6203. Tel: 508-961-3044. Fax: 508-991-6368. p. 1108

Fulchino, Stephen, Dir, New Bedford Free Public Library, Casa da Saudade, 58 Crapo St, New Bedford, MA, 02740. Tel: 508-961-3044. Fax: 508-979-1705. p. 1108

Fulchino, Stephen, Dir, New Bedford Free Public Library, Francis J Lawler Branch, 745 Rockdale Ave, New Bedford, MA, 02740. Tel: 508-961-3044. Fax: 508-961-3077. p. 1108

Fulchino, Stephen, Dir, New Bedford Free Public Library, Howland Green, Three Rodney French Blvd, New Bedford, MA, 02744. Tel: 508-961-3044. Fax: 508-979-1774. p. 1108

Fulchino, Stephen, Dir, New Bedford Free Public Library, Wilks, 1911 Acushnet Ave, New Bedford, MA, 02746. Tel: 508-961-3044. Fax: 508-998-6039. p. 1108

Fulda, Thomas, Ref Serv, Visual Res, Wentworth Institute of Technology, 550 Huntington Ave, Boston, MA, 02115-5998. Tel: 617-989-4040. Fax: 617-989-4091. p. 1068

Fulford, Laurel, Dir, Orford Free Library, 2539 Rte 25A, Orfordville, NH, 03777. Tel: 603-353-9166. Fax: 603-353-9166. p. 1461

Fulford, Margaret, Librn, Laidlaw Library at University College, University of Toronto, Laidlaw Wing, 2nd Flr, 15 King's College Circle, Toronto, ON, M5S 3H7, CANADA. Tel: 416-978-4634. p. 2855

Fulkerson, Danna, Dir, Conway Springs City Library, 210 W Spring St, Conway Springs, KS, 67031. Tel: 620-456-2859. Fax: 620-456-3294. p. 862

Fulkerson, Diane, Instrul Serv Librn, Irvine Sullivan Ingram Library, University of West Georgia, 1601 Maple St, Carrollton, GA, 30118. Tel: 678-839-6498. Fax: 678-839-6511. p. 523

Fulkerson, Marilyn, Circ Mgr, Manhattan Public Library, 629 Poyntz Ave, Manhattan, KS, 66502-6086. Tel: 785-776-4741. Fax: 785-776-1545. p. 881

Fulkerson, Nancy, ILL, Ref Serv, Boyne District Library, 201 E Main St, Boyne City, MI, 49712. Tel: 231-582-7861. Fax: 231-582-2998. p. 1159

Fulks, Randall, Ref Librn, Gallia County District Library, Seven Spruce St, Gallipolis, OH, 45631. Tel: 740-446-7323. Fax: 740-446-1701. p. 1901

Fuller, Andrea, Dir, Worthington-Jefferson Township Public Library, 26 N Commercial St, Worthington, IN, 47471-1415. Tel: 812-875-3815. Fax: 812-875-3815. p. 789

Fuller, Ann, Head, Circ/ILL, Armstrong Atlantic State University, 11935 Abercorn St, Savannah, GA, 31419. Tel: 912-344-3027. Fax: 912-344-3457. p. 549

Fuller, Ann, Asst Librn, Rusk County Library, Morrow, 111 W Rusk, Mount Enterprise, TX, 75681. Tel: 903-822-3532. p. 2332

Fuller, Annie, Ref Librn, University City Public Library, 6701 Delmar Blvd, University City, MO, 63130. Tel: 314-727-3150. Fax: 314-727-6005. p. 1370

Fuller, Candace L, Librn, United States Army, Patton Museum of Cavalry & Armor Emert L Davis Memorial Library, 4554 Fayette Ave, Fort Knox, KY, 40121. Tel: 502-624-6968. Fax: 502-624-2364. p. 913

Fuller, Carolyn T, Dir, Henry County Public Library System, 1001 Florence McGarity Blvd, McDonough, GA, 30252. Tel: 678-432-5116. Fax: 678-432-6153. p. 544

Fuller, Cindy, Libr Dir, Millikin University, 1184 W Main, Decatur, IL, 62522. Tel: 217-424-6214. Fax: 217-424-3992. p. 634

Fuller, David, Outreach Serv Mgr, Alachua County Library District, 401 E University Ave, Gainesville, FL, 32601-5453. Tel: 352-334-3991. Fax: 352-334-3994. p. 448

Fuller, David, Outreach Serv Mgr, Alachua County Library District, Sheriff's Department of the Jail, 3333 NE 39th Ave, Gainesville, FL, 32609-2699. Tel: 352-334-3991. Fax: 352-334-3904. p. 449

Fuller, Elizabeth E, Librn, Rosenbach Museum & Library, 2010 DeLancey Pl, Philadelphia, PA, 19103. Tel: 215-732-1600, Ext 115. Fax: 215-545-7529. p. 2116

Fuller, Karen, Head Librn, Pennsylvania State University, College Pl, Hiller Bldg, Rm 113, 301 E DuBois Ave, Du Bois, PA, 15801. Tel: 814-375-4756. Fax: 814-375-4784. p. 2051

Fuller, Kathy, Circ Mgr, Oklahoma Christian University, 2501 E Memorial Rd, Edmond, OK, 73013. Tel: 405-425-5312. Fax: 405-425-5313. p. 1962

Fuller, LeVerne, Children's Serv Coordr, Greenwood County Library, 600 S Main St, Greenwood, SC, 29646. Tel: 864-941-4650. Fax: 864-941-4651. p. 2197

Fuller, Lisa, Dir, Commun Engagement, Worthington Libraries, 820 High St, Worthington, OH, 43085. Tel: 614-807-2604. Fax: 614-807-2642. p. 1950

Fuller, Liz, Sr Commun Libr Mgr, Contra Costa County Library, Brentwood Library, 104 Oak St, Brentwood, CA, 94513-1359. Tel: 925-516-5290. p. 209

Fuller, Mary, Supv Law Librn, Connecticut Judicial Branch Law Libraries, Waterbury Law Library, Waterbury Courthouse, 300 Grand St, Waterbury, CT, 06702. Tel: 203-591-3338. Fax: 203-596-4137. p. 344

Fuller, Nancy, Librn, Currie Library, Shelter Bldg, Rm 100, Elm St & Fisher Ave, Greensboro, NC, 27401. Tel: 336-478-4712. Fax: 336-275-9398. p. 1796

Fuller, Peter, Dir, Seekonk Public Library, 410 Newman Ave, Seekonk, MA, 02771. Tel: 508-336-8230, Ext 101. Fax: 508-336-6437. p. 1123

Fuller, Rebecca, Dir, Brownfield Public Library, 216 Main St, Brownfield, ME, 04010. Tel: 207-935-3003. p. 979

Fuller, Rosemary, In Charge, Elko-Lander-Eureka County Library System, Battle Mountain Branch, 625 S Broad St, Battle Mountain, NV, 89820. Tel: 775-635-2534. p. 1427

Fuller, Ruth, Br Mgr, West Georgia Regional Library, Whitesburg Public Library, 800 Main St, Whitesburg, GA, 30185. Tel: 770-834-0713. p. 524

Fuller, Sandra, Libr Tech, Northeastern State University, Muskogee Campus Library, 2400 W Shawnee St, Muskogee, OK, 74401. Tel: 918-456-5511, Ext 5021. Fax: 918-458-2101. p. 1980

Fuller, Sandy, Librn, Ruden, McClosky, Smith, Schuster & Russell, 200 E Broward Blvd, PO Box 1900, Fort Lauderdale, FL, 33302. Tel: 954-764-6660. Fax: 954-333-4053. p. 444

Fuller, Sherrilynne, Prof, University of Washington, Mary Gates Hall, Ste 370, Campus Box 352840, Seattle, WA, 98195-2840. Tel: 206-685-9937. Fax: 206-616-3152. p. 2976

Fuller, Susan, ILL Librn, Wolfeboro Public Library, 259 S Main St, Wolfeboro, NH, 03894. Tel: 603-569-2428. Fax: 603-569-8180. p. 1468

Fullerton, Christina, ILL, Pub Serv, Ref Serv, Polk State College, 999 Ave H NE, Winter Haven, FL, 33881-4299. Tel: 863-297-1040. Fax: 863-297-1065. p. 504

Fullerton, Christine, Pub Serv, Chadron State College, 300 E 12th St, Chadron, NE, 69337. Tel: 308-432-6271. p. 1395

Fullerton, Mary, Supvr, Renton Public Library, Highlands, 2902 NE 12th St, Renton, WA, 98056. Tel: 425-430-6790. p. 2526

Fullerton, Rebecca, Archivist, Librn, Appalachian Mountain Club, Five Joy St, Boston, MA, 02108. Tel: 617-391-6629. Fax: 617-523-0722. p. 1055

Fulling, Richard, Coll & Access Serv Librn, Barton College, 400 Atlantic Christian College Dr NE, Wilson, NC, 27893. Tel: 252-399-6504. Fax: 252-399-6571. p. 1831

Fulmer, June, Ch, Oxford Public Library, 213 Choccolocco St, Oxford, AL, 36203. Tel: 256-831-1750. Fax: 256-835-6798. p. 33

Fulmer, LaWanda, Br Mgr, Aiken-Bamberg-Barnwell-Edgefield Regional Library System, Nancy Bonnette - Wagener Branch Library, 204 Park St, Wagener, SC, 29164. Tel: 803-564-5396. Fax: 803-564-5396. p. 2179

Fulmer, Mary Anne, Dir, Penn Area Library, 2001 Municipal Court, Harrison City, PA, 15636. Tel: 724-744-4414. Fax: 724-744-0226. p. 2066

Fulmer, Russell, Pub Serv, Georgia Highlands College Libraries, 3175 Cedartown Hwy SE, Rome, GA, 30161. Tel: 706-295-6318. Fax: 706-295-6365. p. 548

Fulsom, Margaret, Librn, Department of Veterans Affairs, 109 Bee St, Charleston, SC, 29401-5799. Tel: 843-789-7274, 843-789-7494. Fax: 843-805-5975. p. 2184

Fulton, Barbara, Librn, Long Ridge Library, 191 Long Ridge Rd, Danbury, CT, 06810-8463. Tel: 203-748-7520. p. 335

Fulton, Brian, Mgr, Scranton Times-Tribune, 149 Penn Ave, Scranton, PA, 18503. Tel: 570-348-9140. Fax: 570-348-9135. p. 2138

Fulton, Delores G, Librn, Piedmont Baptist College & Graduate School, 420 S Broad St, Winston-Salem, NC, 27101. Tel: 336-725-8344, Ext 7009. Fax: 336-725-5522. p. 1833

Fulton, Kathy, Dir, Temple College, 2600 S First St, Temple, TX, 76504. Tel: 254-298-8426. Fax: 254-298-8430. p. 2391

Fulton, Marianne, Head of Libr, Free Library of Philadelphia, Andorra Branch, 705 E Cathedral Rd, Philadelphia, PA, 19128-2106. Tel: 215-482-4350, 215-685-2552. Fax: 215-478-7635. p. 2106

Fulton, Melissa, Ch, Mason County Public Library, 218 E Third St, Maysville, KY, 41056. Tel: 606-564-3286. Fax: 606-564-5408. p. 928

Fulton, Robert, Mgr, California State University, PO Box 490, Baker, CA, 92309. Tel: 714-936-0461. p. 123

Fulton, Sandy, Circ, Winslow Public Library, 420 W Gilmore St, Winslow, AZ, 86047. Tel: 928-289-4982. Fax: 928-289-4182. p. 90

Fulton, Stephanie, Exec Dir, University of Texas, M D Anderson Cancer Center Research Medical Library, 1400 Pressler St, Houston, TX, 77030-3722. Tel: 713-792-2293. Fax: 713-563-3650. p. 2344

Fulton, Tara Lynn, Dean of Libr & Info Serv, Lock Haven University of Pennsylvania, 401 N Fairview Ave, Lock Haven, PA, 17745-2390. Tel: 570-484-2309. Fax: 570-484-2506. p. 2082

Fulton-Lyne, Liz, Coordr, Libr Instruction, NorQuest College, 10215-108th St, 5th Flr, Edmonton, AB, T5J 1L6, CANADA. Tel: 708-644-6070. Fax: 780-644-6082. p. 2701

Fultz, D Elizabeth, Libr Mgr, Washington-Centerville Public Library, 111 W Spring Valley Rd, Centerville, OH, 45458. Tel: 937-610-4480. Fax: 937-610-4481. p. 1866

Fultz, Karla, Br Mgr, Faulkner-Van Buren Regional Library System, Van Buren County, 119 Shake Rag Rd, Clinton, AR, 72031. Tel: 501-745-2100. Fax: 501-745-5860. p. 96

Fultz, Norma Gomez, Dir, Rio Grande City Public Library, 591 E Canales St, Rio Grande City, TX, 78582-3588. Tel: 956-487-4389. Fax: 956-487-7390. p. 2375

Fulweiler, Rebecca, Dir, Suffolk University, 73 Tremont St, Boston, MA, 02108. Tel: 617-573-8535. Fax: 617-573-8756. p. 1067

Funabiki, Ruth, Head, Tech Serv, University of Idaho Library, College of Law, 711 Rayburn St, Moscow, ID, 83844. Tel: 208-885-6521. Fax: 208-885-2743. p. 580

Fund, Claire, Admin Dir, College of Charleston, 205 Calhoun St, Charleston, SC, 29401-3519. Tel: 843-953-5530. Fax: 843-953-6319. p. 2184

Fundis, Lois Aleta, Ref, Mary H Weir Public Library, 3442 Main St, Weirton, WV, 26062. Tel: 304-797-8510. Fax: 304-797-8526. p. 2573

Fung, Hing Choi, Librn I, New Jersey Department of Labor Library, John Fitch Plaza, 5th Flr, Trenton, NJ, 08611. Tel: 609-292-2035. Fax: 609-984-5456. p. 1535

Fung, Melissa, Law Ref Librn/Foreign & Intl Spec, University of San Diego, Katherine M & George M Pardee Jr Legal Research Center, 5998 Alcala Park, San Diego, CA, 92110-2492. Tel: 619-260-4734. Fax: 619-260-4616. p. 239

Funk, Donna, Circ/ILL Librn, Ivy Technical Community College, 50 W Fall Creek Pkwy N Dr, Indianapolis, IN, 46208-5752. Tel: 317-917-7143. Fax: 317-921-4355. p. 755

Funk, Elaine, Acq, Muskingum University Library, 163 Stormont St, New Concord, OH, 43762-1199. Tel: 740-826-8153. Fax: 740-826-8404. p. 1920

Funk, Jennifer, Asst Librn, Priest Lake Public Library, 28769 N Hwy 57, Priest Lake, ID, 83856. Tel: 208-443-2454. Fax: 208-443-2454. p. 582

Funk, Jennifer, Pub Serv Librn, McKendree University, 701 College Rd, Lebanon, IL, 62254-1299. Tel: 618-537-6950. Fax: 618-537-8411. p. 664

Funk, Karen, Dir, Washakie County Library System, 1019 Coburn Ave, Worland, WY, 82401. Tel: 307-347-2231. Fax: 307-347-2248. p. 2661

Funk, Karen, Libr Dir, Washakie County Library System, Ten Sleep Branch, 200 N Fir St, Ten Sleep, WY, 82442. Tel: 307-366-2348. p. 2661

Funk, Mark E, Assoc Dir, Res Mgt, Cornell University Library, The Samuel J Wood Library & The C V Starr Biomedical Information Center, 1300 York Ave, C115, Box 67, New York, NY, 10065-4896. Tel: 212-746-6050. Fax: 212-746-6494. p. 1642

Funk, Noelle, Head of Libr, Jefferson-Madison Regional Library, Scottsville Branch, 330 Bird St, Scottsville, VA, 24590. Tel: 434-286-3541. Fax: 434-286-4744. p. 2454

Funk, Rachael, Youth Serv, Morristown Centennial Library, Seven Richmond St, Morrisville, VT, 05661. Tel: 802-888-3853. p. 2430

Funk, Sandy, Librn, Embudo Valley Public Library, 217 Hwy 75, Dixon, NM, 87527. Tel: 505-579-9181. Fax: 505-579-9128. p. 1554

Funke, Rebecca, Dir, Des Moines Area Community College Library, 2006 S Ankeny Blvd, Ankeny, IA, 50023. Tel: 515-964-6328. Fax: 515-965-7126. p. 793

Funke, Rebecca, Dir, Des Moines Area Community College, 1125 Hancock Dr, Boone, IA, 50036-5326. Tel: 515-433-5040. Fax: 515-433-5044. p. 797

Funkhouser, Brenda, Librn, Eldorado Memorial Public Library District, 1001 Grant St, Eldorado, IL, 62930-1714. Tel: 618-273-7922. Fax: 618-273-4402. p. 640

Funkhouser, Erin, Ch, Beaver Area Memorial Library, 100 College Ave, Beaver, PA, 15009-2794. Tel: 724-775-1132. Fax: 724-775-6982. p. 2031

Funmaker, Mary, ILL Spec, United States Forest Service, One Gifford Pinchot Dr, Madison, WI, 53726-2398. Tel: 608-231-9313. Fax: 608-231-9311. p. 2608

Funtik, Lynne, Sr Ref Librn, Cedarville University, 251 N Main St, Cedarville, OH, 45314-0601. Tel: 937-766-7840. Fax: 937-766-2337. p. 1865

Fuqua, Vicki, Ref Librn, Chappaqua Public Library, 195 S Greeley Ave, Chappaqua, NY, 10514. Tel: 914-238-4779. Fax: 914-238-3597. p. 1605

Furber, Louise, Dir, Phelps Community Memorial Library, Eight Banta St, Ste 200, Phelps, NY, 14532. Tel: 315-548-3120. Fax: 315-548-5314. p. 1717

Furey, Darren, Tech Serv Librn, University of New Brunswick Libraries, Gerard V La Forest Law Library, Ludlow Hall, 2nd Flr, 41 Dineen Dr, Fredericton, NB, E3B 5A3, CANADA. Tel: 506-453-4734. Fax: 506-451-6948, 506-453-5186. p. 2764

Furey, Donna, Ch, Garden City Public Library, 60 Seventh St, Garden City, NY, 11530-2891. Tel: 516-742-8405. Fax: 516-742-2675. p. 1626

Furgason, Sharon, Dir, McCowan Memorial Library, 15 Pitman Ave, Pitman, NJ, 08071. Tel: 856-589-1656. Fax: 856-582-4982. p. 1520

Furgeson, Michelle, Librn, Newton Town Library, 51 South Center St, Newton, UT, 84327. Tel: 435-563-9283. p. 2408

Furi, Gerald M, Asst Dir, Farmington Community Library, 32737 W 12 Mile Rd, Farmington Hills, MI, 48334-3302. Tel: 248-848-4302. Fax: 248-553-3228. p. 1178

Furlong, Katherine, Access Serv, Lafayette College, 710 Sullivan Rd, Easton, PA, 18042-1797. Tel: 610-330-5669. Fax: 610-252-0370. p. 2052

Furlong-Head, Georgina, Br Mgr, Whatcom County Library System, North Fork Community Library, 7506 Kendall Rd, Maple Falls, WA, 98266. Tel: 360-599-2020. Fax: 360-599-2020. p. 2509

Furlough, Michael, Assoc Dean, Res & Scholarly Communication & Co-Dir of Digital Publ, Copyright Librn, Pennsylvania State University Libraries, 510 Paterno Library, University Park, PA, 16802. Tel: 814-865-0401. Fax: 814-865-3665. p. 2148

Furman, Anya, Ref Librn, South College Library, 3904 Lonas Dr, Knoxville, TN, 37909. Tel: 865-251-1750, 865-251-1832. p. 2243

Furnas, George, Prof, University of Michigan, 304 West Hall, 1085 S University, Ann Arbor, MI, 48109-1107. Tel: 734-763-2285. Fax: 734-764-2475. p. 2967

Furness, Adrienne, Ch, Webster Public Library, Webster Plaza, 980 Ridge Rd, Webster, NY, 14580. Tel: 585-872-7075. p. 1765

Furness, Amy, Spec Coll Archivist, Art Gallery of Ontario, 317 Dundas St W, Toronto, ON, M5T 1G4, CANADA. Tel: 416-979-6642. Fax: 416-979-6602. p. 2850

Furnish, Carol, Instrul Serv Librn, Outreach Serv Librn, Northern Kentucky University, Nunn Dr, Highland Heights, KY, 41099. Tel: 859-572-5396. Fax: 859-572-6529, 859-572-6664. p. 917

Furnish, Rebecca, Acq Mgr, Admin Serv, Christian Theological Seminary Library, 1000 W 42nd St, Indianapolis, IN, 46208. Tel: 317-931-2370. Fax: 317-931-2363. p. 750

Furo-Bonnstetter, Karen, Dir, Woodville Community Library, 124 Main St, Woodville, WI, 54028. Tel: 715-698-2430. Fax: 715-698-2441. p. 2650

Furr, Patty, Exec Dir, Hancock County Library System, 312 Hwy 90, Bay Saint Louis, MS, 39520-3595. Tel: 228-467-5282. Fax: 228-467-5503. p. 1293

Furr, Sandra, Dir, Benton County Public Library, 102 N Van Buren Ave, Fowler, IN, 47944-1299. Tel: 765-884-1720. Fax: 765-884-1720. p. 743

Furrer, Dave, Mgr, Ladish Co, 5481 S Packard Ave, Cudahy, WI, 53110. Tel: 414-747-3063. Fax: 414-747-3036. p. 2587

Furrh, Jamie, Outreach Serv Librn, Per, Ref, Texas Health Harris Methodist Fort Worth Hospital, 1301 Pennsylvania Ave, Fort Worth, TX, 76104. Tel: 817-250-3191. Fax: 817-250-5119. p. 2324

Furrow, Stephanie, Head, Ref Serv, York Library Region, Four Carleton St, Fredericton, NB, E3B 5P4, CANADA. Tel: 506-460-2807. Fax: 506-460-2801. p. 2764

Furrow, Stephanie, Head, Ref Serv, York Library Region, Fredericton Public Library, 12 Carleton St, Fredericton, NB, E3B 5P4, CANADA. Tel: 506-460-2807. Fax: 506-460-2801. p. 2764

Furrows, Marie, Head, Adult Serv, Cerritos Library, 18025 Bloomfield Ave, Cerritos, CA, 90703. Tel: 562-916-1350. Fax: 562-916-1375. p. 133

Furtado, Debra, Supv Librn-County Br, Stockton-San Joaquin County Public Library, 605 N El Dorado St, Stockton, CA, 95202. Tel: 209-456-8677. Fax: 209-937-8683. p. 272

Furtak, Luba, Sr Librn, Ref, Passaic Public Library, 195 Gregory Ave, Passaic, NJ, 07055. Tel: 973-779-0474. Fax: 973-779-0889. p. 1518

Furtak, Yaro, Ref Serv, Passaic County Community College, One College Blvd, Paterson, NJ, 07505. Tel: 973-684-5696. Fax: 973-684-6675. p. 1518

Furtney, Gloria, Tech Librn, Genaire Ltd Library, 468 Niagara Stone Rd, Rural Route 4, Niagara-on-the-Lake, ON, L0S 1J0, CANADA. Tel: 905-684-1165. Fax: 905-684-2412. p. 2824

Furukawa, Mark, Mgr, Lake County Public Library, Forty-First Avenue, 3491 W 41st Ave, Gary, IN, 46408-3007. Tel: 219-980-5180. Fax: 219-985-8057. p. 764

Fusco, Christy, Dir, Monroeville Public Library, 4000 Gateway Campus Blvd, Monroeville, PA, 15146-3381. Tel: 412-372-0500. Fax: 412-372-1168. p. 2091

Fusco, Lisa, Lecturer, University of Washington, Mary Gates Hall, Ste 370, Campus Box 352840, Seattle, WA, 98195-2840. Tel: 206-685-9937. Fax: 206-616-3152. p. 2976

Fusco, Marjorie, Res, Outcomes & Assessment, Dowling College Library, 150 Idle Hour Blvd, Oakdale, NY, 11769-1999. Tel: 631-244-3284. Fax: 631-244-3374. p. 1709

Fusich, Monica, Head, Info & Outreach Serv, California State University, Fresno, Henry Madden Library, 5200 N Barton Ave, Mail Stop ML-34, Fresno, CA, 93740-8014. Tel: 559-278-7673. Fax: 559-278-6952. p. 150

Fusik, Dolores, Librn, Satterlee, Stephens, Burke & Burke, 230 Park Ave, New York, NY, 10169. Tel: 212-818-9200. Fax: 212-818-9606. p. 1699

Fuson, Courtney, Educ Res Librn, Electronic Res Librn, Belmont University, 1900 Belmont Blvd, Nashville, TN, 37212-3757. Tel: 615-460-6782. Fax: 615-460-5641. p. 2255

Fussell, Jamie, Dir, David Wade Correctional Center, 670 Bell Hill Rd, Homer, LA, 71040. Tel: 318-927-0424, Ext 427. Fax: 318-927-0423, 318-927-0459. p. 951

Fuston, Fredia, Librn, Turkey Public Library, Sixth & Lyles St, Turkey, TX, 79261. Tel: 806-423-1092. Fax: 806-423-1221. p. 2393

Futa, Debra, Asst Dir, Saint Joseph County Public Library, 304 S Main, South Bend, IN, 46601-2125. Tel: 574-282-4646. Fax: 574-280-2763. p. 779

Futch, Lynn, Dr, Dean, Libr Serv, Ogeechee Technical College Library, One Joe Kennedy Blvd, Statesboro, GA, 30458. Tel: 912-871-1886. Fax: 912-486-7003. p. 552

Futoransky, Donna J, Dir, Marine Museum at Fall River, Inc Library, 70 Water St, Fall River, MA, 02721. Tel: 508-674-3533. Fax: 508-674-3534. p. 1088

Futrell, Iva, Head, Res Serv, George Mason University Libraries, School of Law, 3301 N Fairfax Dr, Arlington, VA, 22201-4426. Tel: 703-993-8120. Fax: 703-993-8113. p. 2462

Futrelle, Diane P, Dir, Libr Instrul Tech & Communications, North Carolina School of Science & Mathematics Library, Library, Instructional Technologies & Communications, 1219 Broad St, Durham, NC, 27705. Tel: 919-416-2929. Fax: 919-416-2890. p. 1789

Fyffe, Richard, Col Librn, Grinnell College Libraries, 1111 Sixth Ave, Grinnell, IA, 50112-1770. Tel: 641-269-3350. Fax: 641-269-4283. p. 819

Fyler, Marsha, Dir, Bennett County Library, 101 Main St, Martin, SD, 57551. Tel: 605-685-6556. p. 2214

Gabaldon Winningham, Camila, Coll Develop, Tech Serv, Western Oregon University, Wayne & Lynn Hamersly Library, 345 N Monmouth Ave, Monmouth, OR, 97361-1396. Tel: 503-838-8653. Fax: 503-838-8399. p. 2006

Gabbard, Paula, Bibliographer, Indexer, Columbia University, Avery Architectural & Fine Arts Library, 1172 Amsterdam Ave, MC 0301, New York, NY, 10027. Tel: 212-854-6199. Fax: 212-854-8904. p. 1674

Gabehart, Alan D, Dr, Dean, Louisiana State University, One University Pl, Shreveport, LA, 71115-2399. Tel: 318-798-5069. Fax: 318-797-5156. p. 968

Gabehart, Jan, Br Mgr, Elbert County Library District, Elizabeth Branch, Tel: 303-646-3416. Fax: 303-646-9217. p. 305

Gabel, Beryl, Archivist, Lakeshore Museum Center Archives, 471 W Western Ave, Muskegon, MI, 49440-1040. Tel: 231-722-0278. Fax: 231-728-4119. p. 1212

Gabel, Jeff, Cat Librn, Brooklyn Law School Library, 250 Joralemon St, Brooklyn, NY, 11201. Tel: 718-780-7978. Fax: 718-780-0369. p. 1590

Gaber, Elaine R, Dir, Sadie Pope Dowdell Library of South Amboy, 100 Harold G Hoffman Plaza, South Amboy, NJ, 08879. Tel: 732-721-6060. Fax: 732-721-1054. p. 1530

Gabianelli, Linda, Ch, Prosser Public Library, One Tunxis Ave, Bloomfield, CT, 06002-2476. Tel: 860-243-9721. Fax: 860-242-1629. p. 330

Gable, Anne, Div Chief, Mat & Tech Mgt, Arlington County Department of Libraries, 1015 N Quincy St, Arlington, VA, 22201. Tel: 703-228-5981. Fax: 703-228-3354. p. 2448

Gable, Patricia, Ref, Fiction & Teen Serv Mgr, Saint Joseph County Public Library, 304 S Main, South Bend, IN, 46601-2125. Tel: 574-282-4646. Fax: 574-280-2763. p. 779

Gabobe, Jamal, Media Tech, University of Washington Libraries, Tacoma Library, 1900 Commerce St, Box 358460, Tacoma, WA, 98402-3100. Tel: 253-692-4643. Fax: 253-692-4445. p. 2535

Gaboury, John, Dean, Univ Libr, University of Toledo, 2801 W Bancroft St, Mail Stop 509, Toledo, OH, 43606-3390. Tel: 419-530-4488. Fax: 419-530-2403. p. 1941

Gabridge, Tracy, Head Librn, Massachusetts Institute of Technology Libraries, Barker Engineering, Bldg 10-500, 77 Massachusetts Ave, Cambridge, MA, 02139-4307. Tel: 617-253-8971. Fax: 617-258-5623. p. 1077

Gabridge, Tracy, Head Librn, Massachusetts Institute of Technology Libraries, Science, Bldg 14S-134, 77 Massachusetts Ave, Cambridge, MA, 02139-4307. Tel: 617-253-8971. Fax: 617-253-6365. p. 1078

Gabriel, Claire, Dir, Info Serv, Russell Sage Foundation Library, 112 E 64th St, New York, NY, 10065. Tel: 212-752-8641. Fax: 212-688-2684. p. 1698

Gabriel, Joseph, Head, Libr Syst, Head, Tech Serv, Harvard Library, Gutman Library-Research Center, Graduate School of Educ, Six Appian Way, Cambridge, MA, 02138. Tel: 617-495-4225. Fax: 617-495-0540. p. 1075

Gabriel, Kristina, ILL, Wayne County Public Library, 1001 E Ash St, Goldsboro, NC, 27530. Tel: 919-735-1824. Fax: 919-731-2889. p. 1795

Gabriel, Lindsay, Dir, Greenwich Free Library, 148 Main St, Greenwich, NY, 12834. Tel: 518-692-7157. Fax: 518-692-7157. p. 1632

Gabriel, Madeline, Librn III/Ref, Beverly Hills Public Library, 444 N Rexford Dr, Beverly Hills, CA, 90210-4877. Tel: 310-288-2220. Fax: 310-278-3387. p. 129

Gabriel, Michael, Asst Archivist, Ref/Instruction Librn, Roosevelt University, 430 S Michigan Ave, Chicago, IL, 60605. Tel: 312-341-3645. Fax: 312-341-2425. p. 623

Gabriel-Smith, Mary Jane, Br Mgr, Oconee Regional Library, Treutlen County, 585 Second St, Soperton, GA, 30457. Tel: 912-529-6683. Fax: 912-529-6050. p. 531

Gabriele, Joyce, Circ, ILL, Reader Serv, Suffolk County Community College, 1001 Crooked Hill Rd, Brentwood, NY, 11717. Tel: 631-851-6740. Fax: 631-851-6509. p. 1584

Gabriele, Joyce, Electronic Res Librn, Suffolk County Community College, 533 College Rd, Selden, NY, 11784-2899. Tel: 631-451-4800. Fax: 631-451-4697. p. 1742

Gadbois, Carrie, Asst Dir, Tech Librn, Newmarket Public Library, One Elm St, Newmarket, NH, 03857-1201. Tel: 603-659-5311. Fax: 603-659-8849. p. 1460

Gadbois, Mary J, Per, New England School of Law Library, 154 Stuart St, Boston, MA, 02116-5687. Tel: 617-422-7202. Fax: 617-422-7303. p. 1065

Gadd, Pamela, Libr Asst, Nashville State Technical Community College, 120 White Bridge Rd, Nashville, TN, 37209-4515. Tel: 615-353-3552. Fax: 615-353-3558. p. 2258

Gaddie, Sheila, Ref Librn, Lawrence Technological University Library, 21000 W Ten Mile Rd, Southfield, MI, 48075-1058. Tel: 248-204-3000. Fax: 248-204-3005. p. 1228

Gaddis, Carolyn M, Dir, Wyoming County Public Library, Castle Rock Ave, Pineville, WV, 24874. Tel: 304-732-6228. p. 2569

Gaddis, Jwiana, Outreach Serv Librn, Jessamine County Public Library, 600 S Main St, Nicholasville, KY, 40356-1839. Tel: 859-885-3523. Fax: 859-885-5164. p. 931

Gaddy, Angie, Librn, Allin Township Library, 116 W Main St, Stanford, IL, 61774. Tel: 309-379-4631. Fax: 309-379-4122. p. 707

Gadikian, Randy, Dir, Libr Serv, State University of New York at Fredonia, 280 Central Ave, Fredonia, NY, 14063. Tel: 716-673-3181. Fax: 716-673-3185. p. 1624

Gadoury, Nancy, Librn, Centre de Santé et de Services Sociaux du Nord de Lanaudière Bibliothèque, 1000 Blvd Ste-Anne, Saint Charles Borromee, QC, J6E 6J2, CANADA. Tel: 450-759-8222. Fax: 450-759-7343. p. 2908

Gadrix, Vincent, Dir, Laughlin Memorial Library, 99 Eleventh St, Ambridge, PA, 15003-2305. Tel: 724-266-3857. Fax: 724-266-5670. p. 2028

Gadsby, Joanna, Ref & Instruction Librn, University of Maryland, Baltimore County, 1000 Hilltop Circle, Baltimore, MD, 21250. Tel: 410-455-2356. p. 1018

Gaebe, Ann, Librn, Tulsa City-County Library, Broken Arrow Branch, 300 W Broadway, Broken Arrow, OK, 74012. Tel: 918-251-5359. Fax: 918-258-0324. p. 1982

Gaedecke, Gabrielle, Tech Serv, Public Health Ontario, 81 Resources Rd, Toronto, ON, M9P 3T1, CANADA. Tel: 416-235-5935. Fax: 416-235-6196. p. 2857

Gaedeke, Andrea, Dir, Licia & Mason Beekley Community Library, Ten Central Ave, New Hartford, CT, 06057. Tel: 860-379-7235. Fax: 860-379-5806. p. 355

Gaetano, Darlene, Head, Coll Mgt, University of La Verne, 320 E D St, Ontario, CA, 91764. Tel: 909-460-2064. Fax: 909-460-2083. p. 200

Gaetjens, Allen Stuart, Dir of Libr, Motlow State Community College Libraries, Ledford Mill Rd, Tullahoma, TN, 37388. Fax: 931-393-1516. p. 2267

Gaetz, Ivan, Dean, Regis University, 3333 Regis Blvd, Denver, CO, 80221-1099. Tel: 303-458-4030. Fax: 303-964-5497. p. 303

Gaffey, Ruth, Head, Ch, Wallingford Public Library, 200 N Main St, Wallingford, CT, 06492-3791. Tel: 203-265-6754. Fax: 203-269-5698. p. 373

Gaffney, Donna, Coordr, The Diocese of Colorado Springs, 228 N Cascade Ave, Colorado Springs, CO, 80903. Tel: 719-636-2345, Ext 6446. Fax: 719-866-6453. p. 295

Gafford, Carol, Youth Serv Librn, Swansea Free Public Library, 69 Main St, Swansea, MA, 02777. Tel: 508-674-9609. Fax: 508-675-5444. p. 1130

Gage, Anna Marie, ILL, Parkland Regional Library, Hwy 52 W, Yorkton, SK, S3N 3Z4, CANADA. Tel: 306-783-7022. Fax: 306-782-2844. p. 2931

Gage, Jacque, Dir, Joplin Public Library, 300 S Main, Joplin, MO, 64801. Tel: 417-623-7953. Fax: 417-625-4728. p. 1335

Gage, James, Govt Doc, New England School of Law Library, 154 Stuart St, Boston, MA, 02116-5687. Tel: 617-422-7310. Fax: 617-422-7303. p. 1065

Gage, Jeannette, Fiscal Officer, Grand Valley Public Library, One N School St, Orwell, OH, 44076. Tel: 440-437-6545, 440-536-9159. Fax: 440-437-1017. p. 1925

Gage, Karen, Librn, Emerson Public Library, 701 Morton Ave, Emerson, IA, 51533. Tel: 712-824-7867. Fax: 712-824-7867. p. 814

Gage, Mary-Alice, Br Mgr, Broward County Division of Libraries, Lauderhill Mall Branch, 4257 NW 12th St, Lauderhill, FL, 33313. Tel: 954-791-1000. Fax: 954-791-1002. p. 441

Gage, Matthew, Head, Access Serv, Linfield College, Portland Campus, 2255 NW Northrup, Portland, OR, 97210. Tel: 503-413-7696. Fax: 503-413-8016. p. 2005

Gage, Phyllis, Head, Tech Serv, Tech Coordr, Pearl River County Library System, 900 Goodyear Blvd, Picayune, MS, 39466. Tel: 601-798-5081. Fax: 601-798-5082. p. 1311

Gage, Sharon, Adult Serv, Warren Library Association, 205 Market St, Warren, PA, 16365. Tel: 814-723-4650. Fax: 814-723-4521. p. 2150

Gaghan, Daniel, Access Serv Librn, North Dakota State College of Science, 800 Sixth St N, Wahpeton, ND, 58076-0001. Tel: 701-671-2611. Fax: 701-671-2674. p. 1849

Gagliardi, Maria, Dir, Palisades Free Library, 19 Closter Rd, Palisades, NY, 10964. Tel: 845-359-0136. Fax: 845-359-6124. p. 1714

Gagliolo, Marilyn, Librn, Millstadt Library, 115 W Laurel St, Millstadt, IL, 62260. Tel: 618-476-1887. Fax: 618-476-1887. p. 674

Gagne, Andree, Asst Librn, Bonfield Public Library, 365 Hwy 531, Bonfield, ON, P0H 1E0, CANADA. Tel: 705-776-2396. Fax: 705-776-1154. p. 2795

Gagné Lalonde, Lyne, Libr Assoc, Université de Guelph-Campus d'Alfred, Bibliothèque, 31 Saint Paul St, Alfred, ON, K0B 1A0, CANADA. Tel: 613-679-2218. Fax: 613-679-2423. p. 2791

Gagne, Mary, Asst Circ Librn, Aldrich Public Library, Six Washington St, Barre, VT, 05641-4227. Tel: 802-476-7550. Fax: 802-479-0450 (Call before sending fax). p. 2418

Gagne, Mireille, Librn, Conseil de la Langue Francaise, 800 Place Youville, 13e Etage, Quebec, QC, G1R 3P4, CANADA. Tel: 418-646-1127. Fax: 418-644-7654. p. 2904

Gagnier, Richard, Ref, Chili Public Library, 3333 Chili Ave, Rochester, NY, 14624-5494. Tel: 585-889-2200. Fax: 585-889-5819. p. 1729

Gagnon, Aimee, YA Librn, Dover Town Library, 56 Dedham St, Dover, MA, 02030-2214. Tel: 508-785-8113. Fax: 508-785-0138. p. 1085

Gagnon, Alain, Dir, Ecole Nationale d'Administration Publique Libraries, 555 Blvd Charest E, Quebec, QC, G1K 9E5, CANADA. Tel: 418-641-3000. Fax: 418-641-3060. p. 2904

Gagnon, Brigitte, Pub Serv, Bibliotheque de Brossard, 7855 San Francisco Ave, Brossard, QC, J4X 2A4, CANADA. Tel: 450-923-6350, Ext 6288. Fax: 450-923-7042. p. 2880

Gagnon, Claude, Res, KPMG Research, 2000 McGill College Ave Ste 1900, Montreal, QC, H3A 3H8, CANADA. Tel: 514-840-2254. Fax: 514-840-2162. p. 2897

Gagnon, Francois, Tech Serv Librn, Bibliotheque Municipale de Gatineau, 144, boul de l'Hôpital, local 317, Gatineau, QC, J8T 7S7, CANADA. Tel: 819-243-2345, Ext 2510. Fax: 819-243-2301. p. 2882

Gagnon, François, Mgr, Tech Serv, Bibliotheque Municipale de Gatineau, Édifice Pierre Papin, CP 1970 Succ. Hull, Gatineau, QC, J8X 3Y9, CANADA. p. 2882

Gagnon, Jean, Tech Coordr, Bibliotheque Municipale, 51 rue Jeannotte, Vaudreuil-Dorion, QC, J7V 6E6, CANADA. Tel: 450-455-5588. Fax: 450-455-5653. p. 2914

Gagnon, Jean-Roch, Dir, Centre Regional Services aux Bibliotheques Publiques de la Cote-Nord, Inc, 59 Napoleon, Sept Iles, QC, G4R 5C5, CANADA. Tel: 418-962-1020. Fax: 418-962-5124. p. 2912

Gagnon, Karen, Librn, Providence Care Mental Health Services, 752 King St W, Kingston, ON, K7L 4X3, CANADA. Tel: 613-546-1101, Ext 5745. p. 2814

Gagnon, Karen, Dir, Libr Serv, Providence Care, St Marys of the Lake Hospital, 340 Union St, Kingston, ON, K7L 5A2, CANADA. Tel: 613-548-7222, Ext 2218. Fax: 613-544-1184. p. 2814

Gagnon, Lise, Librn, Smooth Rock Falls Public Library, 120 Ross Rd, Smooth Rock Falls, ON, P0L 2B0, CANADA. Tel: 705-338-2318. Fax: 705-338-2330. p. 2842

Gagnon, Mark, Chief Exec Officer, New Tecumseth Public Library, 17 Victoria St E, Alliston, ON, L9R 1V6, CANADA. Tel: 705-435-0250. Fax: 705-435-0750. p. 2791

Gagnon, Nicole, Librn, Bibliothèque Lisette-Morin (Municipale de Rimouski), 110 de l'Eveche est, CP 710, Rimouski, QC, G5L 7C7, CANADA. Tel: 418-724-3164. Fax: 418-724-3139. p. 2907

Gagnon, Penny, Dir, Ocean Park Memorial Library, 11 Temple Ave, Ocean Park, ME, 04063. Tel: 207-934-9068. Fax: 207-934-2823. p. 994

Gagnon, Ronald A, Exec Dir, North of Boston Library Exchange, Inc, 26 Cherry Hill Dr, Danvers, MA, 01923. Tel: 978-777-8844. Fax: 978-750-8472. p. 2945

Gagnon, Susan, ILL, Saint Anselm College, 100 Saint Anselm Dr, Manchester, NH, 03102-1310. Tel: 603-641-7300. Fax: 603-641-7345. p. 1456

Gagnon, Yolande, Circ, Ser, University of New Brunswick Libraries, Gerard V La Forest Law Library, Ludlow Hall, 2nd Flr, 41 Dineen Dr, Fredericton, NB, E3B 5A3, CANADA. Tel: 506-453-4734. Fax: 506-451-6948, 506-453-5186. p. 2764

Gagnor, Martin, Head, Ref & Adult Serv, Auburn Public Library, 49 Spring St, Auburn, ME, 04210. Tel: 207-333-6640. Fax: 207-333-6644. p. 974

Gaherty, Sherry, Asst Dir, Lenox Library Association, 18 Main St, Lenox, MA, 01240. Tel: 413-637-0197. Fax: 413-637-2115. p. 1098

Gahl, Norma, Info Serv, Newbury College Library, 150 Fisher Ave, Brookline, MA, 02445-5796. Tel: 617-730-7070. Fax: 617-730-7239. p. 1071

Gaieck, Frederick, Librn, Ohio Reformatory for Women, 1479 Collins Ave, Marysville, OH, 43040-1581. Tel: 937-642-1065, Ext 2064. Fax: 937-645-3835. p. 1915

Gail, Ellis, Br Mgr, Maricopa County Library District, El Mirage Branch, 14011 N First Ave, El Mirage, AZ, 85335. Tel: 602-652-3381. Fax: 602-652-3390. p. 74

Gailey, Janice, Br Mgr, Pelahatchie Public Library, 603 Hwy 80 East, Pelahatchie, MS, 39145. Tel: 601-854-8764. Fax: 601-854-8764. p. 1311

Gaillard, Carol, Dir, Cheney Library, 77 Classic St, Hoosick Falls, NY, 12090-1326. Tel: 518-686-9401. Fax: 518-686-9401. p. 1637

Gailloux, Jonathan, Librn, Bibliotheque ministerielle/Ministere de la Culture et des Communications du Quebec, Bldg Guy Frégault, 225 Grande Allee Est, Block C, Quebec, QC, G1R 5G5, CANADA. Tel: 418 380-2325, Ext 7006. Fax: 418-380-2326. p. 2903

Gailunas, Paul, Head, Circ, Paul Pratt Memorial Library, 35 Ripley Rd, Cohasset, MA, 02025-2097. Tel: 781-383-1348. Fax: 781-383-1698. p. 1082

Gainer, Laurel, Dir, Umatilla Public Library, 412 Hatfield Dr, Umatilla, FL, 32784-8913. Tel: 352-669-3284. Fax: 352-669-2927. p. 501

Gaines, Angela S, Computer Serv, Southern University, Oliver B Spellman Law Library, 56 Roosevelt Steptoe, Baton Rouge, LA, 70813. Tel: 225-771-4922. Fax: 225-771-6254. p. 944

Gaines, Ayanna, Ref Serv, Elmhurst College, 190 Prospect St, Elmhurst, IL, 60126. Tel: 630-617-3160. Fax: 630-617-3332. p. 642

Gaines, Carol L, Dep Dir, Laurens County Library, 1017 W Main St, Laurens, SC, 29360. Tel: 864-833-1853. Fax: 864-681-0598. p. 2199

Gaines, Elizabeth, Br Librn, Crook County Library, Hulett Branch, 115 N Hwy 24, Hulett, WY, 82720. Tel: 307-467-5676. Fax: 307-467-5250. p. 2661

Gaines, Erin, Ch, Temple Public Library, 100 W Adams Ave, Temple, TX, 76501-7641. Tel: 254-298-5289. Fax: 254-298-5328. p. 2391

Gaines, Mary, Dir, Saint Petersburg Public Library, 3745 Ninth Ave N, Saint Petersburg, FL, 33713. Tel: 727-893-7268. Fax: 727-892-5432. p. 488

Gaines, Nora, Acq Librn, Bank Street College of Education Library, 610 W 112th St, 5th Flr, New York, NY, 10025. Tel: 212-875-4457. Fax: 212-875-4558. p. 1669

Gaines, Shelia, Access Serv, Carson-Newman College, 1634 Russell Ave, Jefferson City, TN, 37760. Tel: 865-471-3534. Fax: 865-471-3450. p. 2239

Gaines-Ra, Karma, Info Spec, Norfolk State University Library, Virginia Beach Higher Education Resource Center, 1881 University Dr, Virginia Beach, VA, 23453-8080. Tel: 757-368-4162. Fax: 757-368-4151. p. 2482

Gainey, Kimyatta, ILL, DePaul University Libraries, Vincent G Rinn Law Library, 25 E Jackson Blvd, 5th Flr, Chicago, IL, 60604-2287. Tel: 312-362-5123. Fax: 312-362-6908. p. 612

Gainey, Lilah, Syst Coordr, Eastern New Mexico University, 1300 S Ave K, Sta 32, Portales, NM, 88130-7402. Tel: 575-562-2640. Fax: 575-562-2647. p. 1560

Gainor, Larry, Ref, San Jacinto College South, 13735 Beamer Rd, Houston, TX, 77089-6099. Tel: 281-922-3416. Fax: 281-922-3470. p. 2342

Gainous, Tamara, Outreach Serv, Shelton State Community College, 9500 Old Greensboro Rd, Tuscaloosa, AL, 35405. Tel: 205-391-2248. Fax: 205-391-3926. p. 38

Gaither, Edmund B, Chief Curator, Exec Dir, Museum of National Center of Afro-American Artists, 300 Walnut Ave, Boston, MA, 02119. Tel: 617-442-8614. Fax: 617-445-5525. p. 1064

Gaither, Ingrid, Dir, Great Cranberry Library, 251 Cranberry Rd, Cranberry Isles, ME, 04625. Tel: 207-244-7358. Fax: 207-244-7358. p. 982

Gajan, Toni, Dir, John K Tener Library, 638 Fallowfield Ave, Charleroi, PA, 15022-1996. Tel: 724-483-8282. Fax: 724-483-3478. p. 2044

Gal, Jennifer, Br Mgr, Hamilton Public Library, Red Hill, 695 Queenston Rd, Hamilton, ON, L8G 1A1, CANADA. Tel: 905-546-3200, Ext 2976. p. 2809

Gala, Lauren, Sci Librn, University of Pennsylvania Libraries, Math-Physics-Astronomy Library, David Rittenhouse Lab, 209 S 33rd St, Philadelphia, PA, 19104-6317. Tel: 215-898-8173. Fax: 215-573-2009. p. 2119

Galaida, Megan, Dir, Council for Advancement & Support of Education, 1307 New York Ave, Ste 1000, Washington, DC, 20005-4701. Tel: 202-328-2273. p. 397

Galan-Garcia, Sylva, Mgr, Los Angeles Public Library System, Northeast Area, 6145 N Figueroa St, Los Angeles, CA, 90042. Tel: 323-255-1875. Fax: 323-256-8459. p. 174

Galante, Joan, YA Serv, Levittown Public Library, One Bluegrass Lane, Levittown, NY, 11756-1292. Tel: 516-731-5728. Fax: 516-735-3168. p. 1652

Galante, Thomas W, Pres & Chief Exec Officer, Queens Borough Public Library, 89-11 Merrick Blvd, Jamaica, NY, 11432. Tel: 718-990-0794. p. 1643

Galarraga, Denise, Libr Dir, Osceola Library System, Buenaventura Lakes Branch, 405 Buenaventura Blvd, Kissimmee, FL, 34743. Tel: 407-742-8888. p. 456

Galarraga, Denise, Dir, Jackson County Library Services, 205 S Central Ave, Medford, OR, 97501-2730. Tel: 541-774-8679. Fax: 541-774-6748. p. 2005

Galassini, Gigi, Dir, Telephone Museum of New Mexico Library, 110 Fourth St NW, Albuquerque, NM, 87102. Tel: 505-842-2937. Fax: 505-332-4088. p. 1550

Galbraith, James, Assoc Dir, Coll & Scholarly Res, DePaul University Libraries, 2350 N Kenmore, Chicago, IL, 60614. Tel: 773-325-3725, 773-325-7862. Fax: 773-325-7870. p. 612

Galbraith, Joseph E, Dir, Moorestown Public Library, 111 W Second St, Moorestown, NJ, 08057-2481. Tel: 856-234-0333. Fax: 856-778-9536. p. 1504

Galbraith, Marie, Dir, Mattatuck Historical Society Library, 144 W Main St, Waterbury, CT, 06702. Tel: 203-753-0381, Ext 15. Fax: 203-756-6283. p. 374

Galbraith, Nora E, Res Sharing Librn, Florida Southern College, 111 Lake Hollingsworth Dr, Lakeland, FL, 33801-5698. Tel: 863-616-6454. Fax: 863-680-4126. p. 459

Galbraith, Patricia, Managing Librn, Bell Memorial Library, 16 East St, Nunda, NY, 14517. Tel: 585-468-2266. Fax: 585-468-2266. p. 1708

Galbreath, Ella, Dir, Everest University, 225 N Federal Hwy, Pompano, FL, 33062. Tel: 954-783-7339, Ext 223. Fax: 954-783-9023. p. 484

Galbreath, Leslie, Dr, Dir of Libr, Northwest Missouri State University, 800 University Dr, Maryville, MO, 64468-6001. Tel: 660-562-1192. Fax: 660-562-1049. p. 1344

Gale, Crystal, Asst Prof, Missouri State University, Duane G Meyer Library, 901 S National Ave, Springfield, MO, 65897. Tel: 417-836-4525. Fax: 417-836-4764. p. 2968

Gale, Rita, Pub Serv Adminr, Strategic Mgt, Fac & Cap Projects, Montgomery County Public Library, 21 Maryland Ave, Ste 310, Rockville, MD, 20850. Tel: 240-777-0002. Fax: 240-777-0008. p. 1038

Gale, Virginia, Librn, Provena Saint Joseph Medical Center, 333 N Madison St, Joliet, IL, 60435. Tel: 815-725-7133, Ext 3530. Fax: 815-773-7755. p. 660

Galeel, Yousuf, Librn, District of Columbia Superior Court Judges Library, 500 Indiana Ave NW, Rm 5400, Washington, DC, 20001-2131. Tel: 202-879-1435. p. 399

Galembeske, Beth, Librn, Brownell Library, 44 Commons, Little Compton, RI, 02837. Tel: 401-635-8562. Fax: 401-635-8562. p. 2168

Galentine-Steis, Midge, Dir, Abraham Baldwin Agricultural College, 2802 Moore Hwy, Tifton, GA, 31793. Tel: 229-391-4993. Fax: 229-391-4991. p. 554

Galentine-Steis, Midge, Dir, Okefenokee Regional Library, 401 Lee Ave, Waycross, GA, 31501. Tel: 912-287-4978. Fax: 912-284-2533. p. 557

Gales, Andrea, Archivist, Spec Coll Librn, Trevecca Nazarene University, 73 Lester Ave, Nashville, TN, 37210-4227. Tel: 615-248-1798. Fax: 615-248-1452. p. 2259

Gales, Joyce, Librn, Henry Laird Library, PO Box 128, Belpre, KS, 67519-0128. Tel: 620-995-3322. p. 858

Galeski, Patricia, Archivist, Keene Valley Library Association, 1796 Rte 73, Keene Valley, NY, 12943. Tel: 518-576-4335. Fax: 518-576-4693. p. 1648

Galetti-Bosi, Amy, Dir, Ladd Public Library District, 125 N Main St, Ladd, IL, 61329. Tel: 815-894-3254. Fax: 815-894-3254. p. 662

Galfano, Paul, Assoc Dir, Berkeley College Library, Three E 43rd St, New York, NY, 10017. Tel: 212-986-4343. Fax: 212-661-2940. p. 1670

Galganski, Carol, Libr Mgr, Legacy Emanuel Hospital & Health Center Library, 2801 N Gantenbein Ave, Portland, OR, 97227. Tel: 503-413-2558. Fax: 503-413-2544. p. 2011

Galganski, Carol, Mgr, Ref Serv, Legacy Good Samaritan Hospital & Medical Center, 1015 NW 22nd Ave, Portland, OR, 97210. Tel: 503-413-7335. Fax: 503-413-8016. p. 2011

Galik, Barbara A, Exec Dir, Bradley University, 1501 W Bradley Ave, Peoria, IL, 61625. Tel: 309-677-2830. Fax: 309-677-2558. p. 690

Galilova, Irina, Mrg, Admin Serv, SEFLIN - Southeast Florida Library Information Network, Inc, Wimberly Library, Office 452, Florida Atlantic University, 777 Glades Rd, Boca Raton, FL, 33431. Tel: 561-208-0984. Fax: 561-208-0995. p. 2940

Galindo, Becky, Head, Tech Serv, Pittsburg Public Library, 308 N Walnut, Pittsburg, KS, 66762-4732. Tel: 620-231-8110. Fax: 620-232-2258. p. 890

Galindo, Greta, Libr Serv Dir, Woodland Public Library, 250 First St, Woodland, CA, 95695-3411. Tel: 530-661-5980. Fax: 530-666-5408. p. 284

Gall, Carole, Develop Officer, Indiana University, Ruth Lilly Medical Library, 975 W Walnut St, IB 100, Indianapolis, IN, 46202-5121. Tel: 317-274-1411. Fax: 317-278-2349. p. 752

Gall, Lorraine, Librn, Howells Public Library, 130 N Third St, Howells, NE, 68641. Tel: 402-986-1210. Fax: 402-986-1210. p. 1402

Gall, Rocksie, Asst Librn, Valley Public Library, 210 N Locust St, Valley, NE, 68064. Tel: 402-359-9924. Fax: 402-359-9924. p. 1422

Gall, Stacy, Mgr, Libr Serv, Grant Medical Center, 285 E State St, Ste 210, Columbus, OH, 43215. Tel: 614-566-9468. Fax: 614-566-8451. p. 1886

Gall, Stacy, Dir, Ohio Health-Riverside Methodist Hospital, 3535 Olentangy River Rd, Columbus, OH, 43214-3998. Tel: 614-566-5230. Fax: 614-544-6967. p. 1887

Gallagher, Dan, Ad, Chester C Corbin Public Library, Two Lake St, Webster, MA, 01570. Tel: 508-949-3880. Fax: 508-949-0537. p. 1134

Gallagher, Diane, Per, College of the Holy Cross, One College St, Worcester, MA, 01610. Tel: 508-793-3543. Fax: 508-793-2372. p. 1143

Gallagher, Ed, Dir, Albany Public Library, 1390 Waverly Dr SE, Albany, OR, 97322. Tel: 541-917-7589. Fax: 541-917-7586. p. 1989

Gallagher, Heather, Dir, Poseyville Carnegie Public Library, 55 S Cale St, Poseyville, IN, 47633. Tel: 812-874-3418. Fax: 812-874-2026. p. 773

Gallagher, Holly, Curator, Marin History Museum Library, 1125 B St, San Rafael, CA, 94901. Tel: 415-454-8538. Fax: 415-454-6137. p. 257

Gallagher, Jane O, Dir, Middlebury Public Library, 30 Crest Rd, Middlebury, CT, 06762. Tel: 203-758-2634. Fax: 203-577-4164. p. 351

Gallagher, Jeanne, Circ, Notre Dame de Namur University Library, 1500 Ralston Ave, Belmont, CA, 94002-1908. Tel: 650-508-3748. Fax: 650-508-3697. p. 126

Gallagher, Joann, Dir, Daniel Pierce Library, 328 Main St, Grahamsville, NY, 12740-5412. Tel: 845-985-7233. Fax: 845-985-0135. p. 1630

Gallagher, John, Dep Dir, Pub Serv, Yale University Library, Harvey Cushing/John Hay Whitney Medical Library, Sterling Hall of Medicine, 333 Cedar St, L110 SHM, New Haven, CT, 06520. Tel: 202-785-5356. Fax: 203-785-5636. p. 358

Gallagher, Kathleen, Librn, University of California, Berkeley, Anthropology, 230 Kroeber Hall, Berkeley, CA, 94720-6000. Tel: 510-642-5339. Fax: 510-643-9293. p. 127

Gallagher, Kevin, Dir, Middletown Thrall Library, 11-19 Depot St, Middletown, NY, 10940. Tel: 845-341-5454. Fax: 845-341-5480. p. 1660

Gallagher, Kristin, Tech Serv, Fairport Public Library, One Fairport Village Landing, Fairport, NY, 14450. Tel: 585-223-9091. Fax: 585-223-3998. p. 1621

Gallagher, Linda, Mgr, Libr Recs, Wentworth Institute of Technology, 550 Huntington Ave, Boston, MA, 02115-5998. Tel: 617-989-4040. Fax: 617-989-4091. p. 1068

Gallagher, Mary Anne, Ref Librn, Saint Leo University, 33701 State Rd 52, Saint Leo, FL, 33574. Tel: 352-588-7867. Fax: 352-588-8484. p. 487

Gallagher, Mary E, Sister, Archivist, Spec Coll Librn, College of Our Lady of the Elms, 291 Springfield St, Chicopee, MA, 01013-2839. Tel: 413-265-2280, Ext 2354. Fax: 413-594-7418. p. 1082

Gallagher, Maureen, Br Mgr, Martin County Library System, Hoke Library, 1150 NW Jack Williams Way, Jensen Beach, FL, 34957. Tel: 772-463-2870. Fax: 772-463-2874. p. 492

Gallagher, Nancy, Br Mgr, Morgantown Public Library System, 373 Spruce St, Morgantown, WV, 26505. Tel: 304-291-7425. Fax: 304-291-7427. p. 2566

Gallagher, Nancy, Librn, Morgantown Public Library, Cheat Area, 121 Crosby Rd, Morgantown, WV, 26508. Tel: 304-594-1020. Fax: 304-594-1020. p. 2566

Gallagher, Nancy, Librn, Morgantown Public Library, Clinton District Library, 2005 Grafton Rd, Morgantown, WV, 26508. Tel: 304-291-0703. Fax: 304-291-0703. p. 2566

Gallagher, Terence, Actg Dir, Libr Serv, Canizaro Library at Ave Maria University, 5251 Avila Ave, Ave Maria, FL, 34142. Tel: 239-280-2557. p. 426

Gallagher, Terri, Dir, Rochester Public Library, 252 Adams St, Rochester, PA, 15074-2137. Tel: 724-774-7783. Fax: 724-774-6518. p. 2135

Gallagher, Terry, Circ, North Castle Public Library, 19 Whippoorwill Rd E, Armonk, NY, 10504. Tel: 914-273-3887. Fax: 914-273-5572. p. 1575

Gallagher, W Gregory, Librn, The Century Association Library, Seven W 43rd St, New York, NY, 10036. Tel: 212-944-0090. Fax: 212-840-3609. p. 1672

Gallagher, William, Res, National Soaring Museum, Harris Hill, 51 Soaring Hill Dr, Elmira, NY, 14903-9204. Tel: 607-734-3128. Fax: 607-732-6745. p. 1620

Gallagher-Starr, Scott, Ref & Instruction Librn, Northwest Christian University, 1188 Kincade, Eugene, OR, 97401. Tel: 541-684-7235. Fax: 541-684-7307. p. 1997

Gallaher, Allison, Circ, ILL, Oberlin College Library, 148 W College St, Oberlin, OH, 44074. Tel: 440-775-8285. Fax: 440-775-6586. p. 1924

Gallaher, Sharon, Librn, Nanty Glo Public Library, 942 Roberts St, Nanty Glo, PA, 15943-0296. Tel: 814-749-0111. Fax: 814-749-0111. p. 2094

Gallaher, Sheri, Head, Fac Serv, University of Arkansas Libraries, 365 N McIlroy Ave, Fayetteville, AR, 72701-4002. Tel: 479-575-3808. Fax: 479-575-6656. p. 99

Gallant, Angela, Circ Serv, Fort McMurray Public Library, 151 MacDonald Dr, Fort McMurray, AB, T9H 5C5, CANADA. Tel: 780-743-7800. Fax: 780-743-7938. p. 2704

Gallant, Carol, Dir, Langworthy Public Library, 24 Spring St, Hope Valley, RI, 02832-1620. Tel: 401-539-2851. Fax: 401-539-2851. p. 2167

Gallant, Jean, Adult Serv, Holmes Public Library, 470 Plymouth St, Halifax, MA, 02338. Tel: 781-293-2271. Fax: 781-294-8518. p. 1093

Gallant, Jeffrey, Instr, Libr Sci & Ref Librn, Valdosta State University, 1500 N Patterson St, Valdosta, GA, 31698-0150. Tel: 229-333-5860. Fax: 229-259-5055. p. 555

Gallant, Jennifer Jung, Assoc Dir, Elyria Public Library System, 320 Washington Ave, Elyria, OH, 44035-5199. Tel: 440-323-5747. Fax: 440-323-5788. p. 1898

Gallant, Jennifer Jung, Assoc Dir, Elyria Public Library System, West River, 1194 West River Rd N, Elyria, OH, 44035. Tel: 440-324-2270. Fax: 440-324-4766. p. 1898

Gallant, Jimmy, Res, KPMG Research, 2000 McGill College Ave Ste 1900, Montreal, QC, H3A 3H8, CANADA. Tel: 514-840-2362. Fax: 514-840-2162. p. 2897

Gallant, Mary, Commun Serv, Medford Public Library, 111 High St, Medford, MA, 02155. Tel: 781-395-7950. Fax: 781-391-2261. p. 1104

Gallant, Patricia, Acad Librn, Acadia University, 50 Acadia St, Wolfville, NS, B4P 2R6, CANADA. Tel: 902-585-1249. Fax: 902-585-1748. p. 2786

Gallas, Martin H, Dir, Illinois College, 245 Park St, Jacksonville, IL, 62650. Tel: 217-245-3020. Fax: 217-245-3082. p. 658

Gallaway, Barbara, Circ Mgr, North Central Regional Library, Moses Lake Community, 418 E Fifth Ave, Moses Lake, WA, 98837-1797. Tel: 509-765-3489. Fax: 509-766-0286. p. 2549

Gallaway, Beth, Dir, Grafton Public Library, 35 Grafton Common, Grafton, MA, 01519. Tel: 508-839-4649. Fax: 508-839-7726. p. 1091

Gallaway, Sue, Dean of Library & eLearning, Centralia College, 600 Centralia College Blvd, Centralia, WA, 98531. Tel: 360-736-9391, Ext 304. Fax: 360-330-7502. p. 2511

Gallaway, Teri Oaks, Libr Syst & Web Coordr, Loyola University New Orleans, 6363 Saint Charles Ave, New Orleans, LA, 70118-6195. Tel: 504-864-7111. Fax: 504-864-7247. p. 961

Gallego, Amanda, Librn, South Carolina Attorney General's Office Library, 1000 Assembly St, Ste 743, Columbia, SC, 29201-3117. Tel: 803-734-3769. Fax: 803-253-6283. p. 2188

Gallegos, Bee, Librn, Arizona State University Libraries, Fletcher Library, 4701 W Thunderbird Rd, Glendale, AZ, 85306. Tel: 602-543-5718. Fax: 602-543-8540. p. 83

Gallegos, Diana, Librn, Vaughn Public Library, Yucca St, Vaughn, NM, 88353. Tel: 575-584-2580. p. 1566

Gallegos, Nidia, Spec Coll Librn, Grant County Library, 215 E Grant Ave, Ulysses, KS, 67880-2958. Tel: 620-356-1433. Fax: 620-356-1344. p. 898

Gallen, Michael A, Dir, Libr Serv, Flagler College, 44 Sevilla St, Saint Augustine, FL, 32084-4302. Tel: 904-819-6206. Fax: 904-823-8511. p. 486

Galley, Jenna, Ch, Somerset County Library System, Peapack & Gladstone Public, School St, Peapack, NJ, 07977. Tel: 908-234-0598. Fax: 908-719-2236. p. 1475

Galli, Matthew, Circ Mgr, Web Coordr, Great Basin College Library, 1500 College Pkwy, Elko, NV, 89801. Tel: 775-753-2222. Fax: 775-753-2296. p. 1427

Galligan, Sara, Librn, Ramsey County Law Library, 1815 Court House, Saint Paul, MN, 55102. Tel: 651-266-8391. Fax: 651-266-8399. p. 1280

Gallilee, Patty, Head, Acq, Head, Ser, Simon Fraser University Library, 8888 University Dr, Burnaby, BC, V5A 1S6, CANADA. Tel: 778-782-3916. Fax: 778-782-3023. p. 2726

Gallinger, Susan R, Dir, Livermore Public Library, 1188 S Livermore Ave, Livermore, CA, 94550. Tel: 925-373-5500. Fax: 925-373-5503. p. 164

Gallion, Sandra, Dir, Balch Springs Public Library, 12450 Elam Rd, Balch Springs, TX, 75180. Tel: 972-913-3000. Fax: 972-286-8856. p. 2285

Gallis, Caroline C, Dir, Warminster Township Free Library, 1076 Emma Lane, Warminster, PA, 18974. Tel: 215-672-4362. Fax: 215-672-3604. p. 2150

Gallman, Erik, Exec Dir, Whitfield-Murray Historical Society, 715 Chattanooga Ave, Dalton, GA, 30720. Tel: 706-278-0217. p. 528

Gallman, Gwen, Librn, Copiah-Jefferson Regional Library System, J T Biggs Jr Memorial Library, 200 S Jackson St, Crystal Springs, MS, 39059. Tel: 601-892-3205. Fax: 601-892-2138. p. 1301

Gallo, Adrienne, Br Librn, Cranston Public Library, Oak Lawn Branch, 230 Wilbur Ave, Cranston, RI, 02921-1046. Tel: 401-942-1787. p. 2165

Gallo, Barbara, Dir, Centre County Law Library, Court House, 3rd Flr, Bellefonte, PA, 16823. Tel: 814-355-6727. Fax: 814-355-6707. p. 2032

Gallo, Kathy, Tech Serv, Georgia Perimeter College, 555 N Indian Creek Dr, Clarkston, GA, 30021-2396. Tel: 678-891-3663. Fax: 404-298-4919. p. 525

Gallo, Molly, Librn, Ridgemont Public Library, Ridgeway Branch, 109 Main St, Ridgeway, OH, 43345. Tel: 937-363-3066. Fax: 937-363-3066. p. 1919

Gallo, Phyllis, Librn, Saint Paul's Episcopal Church Library, 310 Elizabeth St, Maumee, OH, 43537. Tel: 419-893-3381. p. 1915

Gallos, Phil, Tech Serv Coordr, North Country Community College Library, 23 Santanoni Ave, Saranac Lake, NY, 12983-2046. Tel: 518-891-2915, Ext 218. p. 1738

Galloway, Beverly, Circ Supvr, University of Nevada, Las Vegas Libraries, Wiener-Rogers Law Library, William S Boyd School of Law, 4505 Maryland Pkwy, Las Vegas, NV, 89154-1080. Tel: 702-895-2400. Fax: 702-895-2410. p. 1431

Galloway, Denise, Libr Tech, Copyright, The Parrott Centre, 376 Wallbridge-Loyalist Rd, Belleville, ON, K8N 5B9, CANADA. Tel: 613-969-1913, Ext 2595. Fax: 613-969-5183. p. 2795

Galloway, Elizabeth, Dir, VPres, Art Center College of Design, 1700 Lida St, Pasadena, CA, 91103. Tel: 626-396-2231. Fax: 626-568-0428. p. 205

Galloway, Jeannie G, Pub Serv, Alice Lloyd College, 100 Purpose Rd, Pippa Passes, KY, 41844. Tel: 606-368-6117. Fax: 606-368-6212. p. 933

Galloway, John, Mgr, Kellogg, Brown & Root Library, 601 Jefferson Ave, Houston, TX, 77002. Tel: 713-753-8466. Fax: 713-753-6226. p. 2340

Galloway, Linda, Librn, Syracuse University Library, Carnegie Library, Carnegie Bldg, Syracuse, NY, 13244-2010. Tel: 315-443-2160. Fax: 315-443-5549. p. 1754

Galloway, Patricia, Prof, University of Texas at Austin, One University Sta, D7000, Austin, TX, 78712-0390. Tel: 512-471-3821. Fax: 512-471-3971. p. 2975

Galloway, Sue, Librn, Oklahoma School for the Deaf Library, 1100 E Oklahoma St, Sulphur, OK, 73086. Tel: 580-622-4900. Fax: 580-622-4959. p. 1979

Gallucci, Kaija, Circ, Swansea Free Public Library, 69 Main St, Swansea, MA, 02777. Tel: 508-674-9609. Fax: 508-675-5444. p. 1130

Gallups, Shelia, Asst Librn, Columbiana Public Library, 50 Lester St, Columbiana, AL, 35051. Tel: 205-669-5812. Fax: 205-669-5803. p. 13

Galm, Molly, Dir, Northwest Iowa Community College Library, 603 W Park St, Sheldon, IA, 51201. Tel: 712-324-5061. Fax: 712-324-4157. p. 842

Galmiche, Leigh, Br Librn, Plaquemines Parish Library, Port Sulphur Branch, 139 Delta St, Port Sulphur, LA, 70083. Tel: 504-564-3681, 985-564-3682. Fax: 504-564-3274. p. 945

Galonek, Donna, Asst Dir, Auburn Public Library, 369 Southbridge St, Auburn, MA, 01501. Tel: 508-832-7790. Fax: 508-832-7792. p. 1051

Galonska, Ann, Dir, Mansfield Historical Society, 954 Storrs Rd, Storrs, CT, 06268. Tel: 860-429-6575. p. 370

Galstad, Alison Ames, Dir, Coralville Public Library, 1401 Fifth St, Coralville, IA, 52241. Tel: 319-248-1850. Fax: 319-248-1890. p. 804

Galuschak, George R, Librn, Montvale Free Public Library, 12 Mercedes Dr, Ste 100, Montvale, NJ, 07645. Tel: 201-391-5090. Fax: 201-307-5647. p. 1503

Galusha, Donna, Asst Librn, Platteville Public Library, 504 Marion Ave, Platteville, CO, 80651. Tel: 970-785-2231. Fax: 970-785-0708. p. 320

Galvan, Ade, Mgr, Heald College, Seven Sierra Gate Plaza, Roseville, CA, 95678. Tel: 916-789-8600. Fax: 916-789-8616. p. 220

Galvan, Ethan, Head, Ref, West Caldwell Public Library, 30 Clinton Rd, West Caldwell, NJ, 07006. Tel: 973-226-5441. Fax: 973-228-7572. p. 1540

Galvan, Maureen, Sr Mgr, Human Res, Palatine Public Library District, 700 N North Ct, Palatine, IL, 60067-8159. Tel: 847-358-5881. p. 686

Galvin, Brian, Dir, Educational Research Service, 1001 N Fairfax St, Ste 500, Alexandria, VA, 22314. Tel: 703-243-2100. Fax: 703-243-1985. p. 2445

Galvin, Colleen, Commun Librn, Deschutes Public Library District, Sisters Branch, 110 N Cedar St, Sisters, OR, 97759. Tel: 541-312-1070. Fax: 541-549-9620. p. 1992

Galvin, Jeanne, Chief Librn, Queensborough Community College, City University of New York, 222-05 56th Ave, Bayside, NY, 11364-1497. Tel: 718-631-6220. Fax: 718-281-5012. p. 1579

Galvin, Kathryn, Librn, Buffalo & Erie County Public Library System, Niagara, 280 Porter, Buffalo, NY, 14201-1030. Tel: 716-882-1537. Fax: 716-882-1537. p. 1597

Galway, Mary E, Librn, Chrisman Public Library, 108 N Illinois St, Chrisman, IL, 61924. Tel: 217-269-3011. Fax: 217-269-3011. p. 629

Gamache, Kathleen A, Librn, Clark Hill PLC, 500 Woodward Ave, Ste 3500, Detroit, MI, 48226-3435. Tel: 313-965-8300, Ext 8277. Fax: 313-965-8252. p. 1169

Gamache-Vaillancourt, Genevieve, Info Serv, Ecole Polytechnique de Montreal Bibliotheque, 2500, chemin de Polytechnique, Montreal, QC, H3T 1J4, CANADA. Tel: 514-340-4666. Fax: 514-340-4026. p. 2895

Gamaluddin, Constance F, Pub Serv Coordr, Ref Librn, Clarion University of Pennsylvania, 840 Wood St, Clarion, PA, 16214. Tel: 814-393-2329. Fax: 814-393-2344. p. 2045

Gambell, Jennifer, Dir, Operations, West Bend Public Library, 316 S Broadway, West Bend, IA, 50597. Tel: 515-887-6411. Fax: 515-887-6412. p. 851

Gambill, Henry, Br Mgr, Los Angeles Public Library System, Donald Bruce Kaufman-Brentwood Branch, 11820 San Vincente Blvd, Los Angeles, CA, 90049-5055. Tel: 310-575-8273. Fax: 310-575-8276. p. 173

Gamble, Elizabeth, Librn, Massey & Township Public Library, 185 Grove, Massey, ON, P0P 1P0, CANADA. Tel: 705-865-2641. Fax: 705-865-1781. p. 2820

Gamble, Jeanne, Libr & Archives Asst, Historic New England, Library & Archives, 141 Cambridge St, Boston, MA, 02114. Tel: 617-227-3957, Ext 271. Fax: 617-973-9050. p. 1062

Gamble, Lydia, Head, Ch, Stow-Munroe Falls Public Library, 3512 Darrow Rd, Stow, OH, 44224. Tel: 330-688-3295. p. 1937

Gamble, Lynn, Acq, Cat, College of Our Lady of the Elms, 291 Springfield St, Chicopee, MA, 01013-2839. Tel: 413-265-2280. Fax: 413-594-7418. p. 1082

Gambling, Jessica, Archivist, Los Angeles County Museum of Art, 5905 Wilshire Blvd, Los Angeles, CA, 90036-4597. Tel: 323-857-6118. Fax: 323-857-4790. p. 172

Gambon, Lynn, Dir, South Piedmont Community College, Cyber Center, 680 Hwy 74 W, Polkton, NC, 28135. Tel: 704-290-5855. Fax: 704-290-5880. p. 1814

Gambrell, Carol, Br Coordr, Pemberville Public Library, Luckey Branch, PO Box 190, Luckey, OH, 43443. Tel: 419-833-6040. Fax: 419-833-6040. p. 1928

Gambrill, Linda, Tech Serv Mgr, Montgomery County Memorial Library System, 104 I-45 N, Conroe, TX, 77301-2720. Tel: 936-788-8377, Ext 229. Fax: 936-788-8398. p. 2300

Gamby, Glenda, Pub Serv, Chadron State College, 300 E 12th St, Chadron, NE, 69337. Tel: 308-432-6271. p. 1395

Gamez, Jose A, Libr Dir, McAllen Memorial Library, 601 N Main, McAllen, TX, 78501-4666. Tel: 956-688-3300, Ext 112. Fax: 956-688-3301. p. 2360

Gamma, Lynn, Archivist, United States Air Force, Historical Research Agency, AFHRA, 600 Chennault Circle, Bldg 1405, Maxwell AFB, AL, 36112-6424. Tel: 334-953-2395. Fax: 334-953-4096. p. 25

Gammon, Julia A, Head, Acq, University of Akron Libraries, 315 Buchtel Mall, Akron, OH, 44325-1701. Tel: 330-972-6254. Fax: 330-972-5106. p. 1853

Gammon, Susan, Mgr, Libr Serv, General Dynamics Advanced Information Systems, 2305 Mission College Blvd, Ste 101, Santa Clara, CA, 95054. Tel: 650-966-2003, 650-966-3860. Fax: 650-966-2449. p. 262

Gamp, Jane, Dean, San Francisco Law School Library at Alliant International University, 20 Haight St, San Francisco, CA, 94102. Tel: 415-626-5550. Fax: 415-626-5584. p. 245

Gampfer, Scott, Dir, Cincinnati Museum Center At Union Terminal, 1301 Western Ave, Cincinnati, OH, 45203. Tel: 513-287-7084. p. 1869

Gancarz, Anne, Commun Serv, Chicopee Public Library, 449 Front St, Chicopee, MA, 01013. Tel: 413-594-1800. Fax: 413-594-1819. p. 1081

Gancos, Keli, Youth Serv Librn, Ellsworth Public Library, 20 State St, Ellsworth, ME, 04605. Tel: 207-667-6363. Fax: 207-667-4901. p. 984

Gandhi, Subash, Instrul Serv Librn, Ref Serv, Queens College, Benjamin S Rosenthal Library, 65-30 Kissena Blvd, Flushing, NY, 11367-0904. Tel: 718-997-3700. Fax: 718-997-3753. p. 1623

Gandron, Marie L, Dir, Hudson Falls Free Library, 220 Main St, Hudson Falls, NY, 12839. Tel: 518-747-6406. Fax: 518-747-6406. p. 1639

Gandt, Eunice, Ref/Instruction Librn, University of Wisconsin-Madison, Business Library, Grainger Hall, Rm 2200, 975 University Ave, Madison, WI, 53706. Tel: 608-262-5935. Fax: 608-262-9001. p. 2608

Gandy, April, Circ, Gateway Technical College, 1001 S Main St, Racine, WI, 53403-1582. Tel: 262-619-6414. Fax: 262-619-6221. p. 2632

Gandy, Doris G, Dir, Darlington County Historical Commission, 204 Hewitt St, Darlington, SC, 29532. Tel: 843-398-4710. Fax: 843-398-4742. p. 2192

Gandy, Patricia, Dir, Perth Amboy Free Public Library, 196 Jefferson St, Perth Amboy, NJ, 08861. Tel: 732-826-2600. Fax: 732-324-8079. p. 1519

Gane, Gayla, Librn, Chinook Regional Library, Chaplin Branch, Second Ave Hall Complex, Chaplin, SK, S0H 0V0, CANADA. Tel: 306-395-2524. p. 2928

Ganger, Gail, Dir, Luther Area Public Library, 115 State St, Luther, MI, 49656. Tel: 231-797-8006. Fax: 231-797-8010. p. 1204

Gangestad, Kristie, Libr Serv Supvr, Western Nevada Community College, 2201 W College Pkwy, Carson City, NV, 89703. Tel: 775-445-3229. Fax: 775-445-3363. p. 1426

Gangone, Lucy, Librn, Lake Panasoffkee Library, 1500 County Rd 459, Lake Panasoffkee, FL, 33538. Tel: 352-793-8608. Fax: 352-793-4665. p. 458

Gangone, Lucy, Dir, Leesburg Public Library, 100 E Main St, Leesburg, FL, 34748. Tel: 352-728-9790. Fax: 352-728-9794. p. 461

Ganguli, Momota, Librn, Institute for Advanced Study Libraries, Einstein Dr, Princeton, NJ, 08540. Tel: 609-734-8181, 609-734-8276. Fax: 609-924-8399, 609-951-4515. p. 1522

Gangwer, Valerie, Media Serv, Mary Baldwin College, 109 E Frederick St, Staunton, VA, 24401. Tel: 540-887-7267. Fax: 540-887-7137. p. 2496

Ganitch, Olga, Dir, TCI College of Technology, 320 W 31st St, New York, NY, 10001. Tel: 212-594-4000, Ext 5279. Fax: 212-330-0894. p. 1700

Gann, Linda, Instr, University of North Carolina at Greensboro, School of Education, 349 Curry Bldg, Greensboro, NC, 27402. Tel: 336-334-3479. Fax: 336-334-5060. p. 2971

Gann, Sheila, Syst Librn, British Columbia Legislative Library, Parliament Bldgs, Victoria, BC, V8V 1X4, CANADA. Tel: 250-387-1051. Fax: 250-356-1373. p. 2744

Gann, Vicky, Libr Tech, New Mexico Junior College, One Thunderbird Circle, Hobbs, NM, 88240. Tel: 575-492-2870. Fax: 575-492-2883. p. 1556

Gannaway, Paula, Assoc Librn, Coll Develop, Per, Lubbock Christian University Library, 5601 19th St, Lubbock, TX, 79407-2009. Tel: 806-720-7326. p. 2357

Gannon, Barbara, Sunday Ref Librn, Southern New Hampshire University, 2500 N River Rd, Manchester, NH, 03106-1045. Tel: 603-645-9605. Fax: 603-645-9685. p. 1456

Gannon, Michael, Assoc Dir, Admin Serv, Prince George's County Memorial Library System, 6532 Adelphi Rd, Hyattsville, MD, 20782-2098. Tel: 301-699-3500. Fax: 301-699-1368. p. 1032

Gannon, Vicky, Head, Circ, Pace University, 78 N Broadway, White Plains, NY, 10603. Tel: 914-422-4369. Fax: 914-422-4139. p. 1769

Gano, Judy A, Librn, Clinton County Law Library, 46 S South St, Wilmington, OH, 45177. Tel: 937-382-2428. Fax: 937-382-7632. p. 1949

Ganong, Peggy, Tech Serv, New Milford Public Library, 24 Main St, New Milford, CT, 06776. Tel: 860-355-1191. Fax: 860-350-9579. p. 360

Gansen, Georgine, Librn, Scott County Library System, Belle Plaine Public Library, 125 W Main St, Belle Plaine, MN, 56011-1245. Tel: 952-873-6767. Fax: 952-873-6767. p. 1284

Ganske, Maxine, Libr Asst III, Kansas State University Libraries, Paul Weigel Library of Architecture, Planning & Design, 323 Seaton Hall, Manhattan, KS, 66506. Tel: 785-532-5978. Fax: 785-532-6722. p. 881

Ganski, Kate, Tech Serv, Saint Francis Seminary, 3257 S Lake Dr, Saint Francis, WI, 53235-0905. Tel: 414-747-6479. Fax: 414-747-6483. p. 2635

Ganson, Judy, Dir, Coll Mgt & Syst, University of Arkansas Libraries, 365 N McIlroy Ave, Fayetteville, AR, 72701-4002. Tel: 479-575-2130. Fax: 479-575-6656. p. 99

Gansz, David, VPres, Info Tech, Edison Community College Library, 1973 Edison Dr, Piqua, OH, 45356. Tel: 937-778-7951. Fax: 937-778-7958. p. 1930

Gant, Brandon, Assoc Dir, Syst Serv, Consortium of Academic & Research Libraries in Illinois, 100 Trade Ctr Dr, Ste 303, Champaign, IL, 61820. Tel: 217-333-4802. Fax: 217-244-7596. p. 2942

Gant, Elizabeth, Librn, Seagoville Public Library, 702 N Hwy 175, Seagoville, TX, 75159-1774. Tel: 972-287-7720. Fax: 972-287-3891. p. 2385

Gant, Jon, Assoc Prof, University of Illinois at Urbana-Champaign, Library & Information Science Bldg, 501 E Daniel St, Champaign, IL, 61820-6211. Tel: 217-333-3280. Fax: 217-244-3302. p. 2965

Gant, Rebecca, Ch, Pankhurst Memorial Library, Three S Jefferson Ave, Amboy, IL, 61310-1400. Tel: 815-857-3925. Fax: 815-857-3065. p. 588

Gants, Bob, Br Mgr, Horry County Memorial Library, Green Sea-Floyds Branch, 5331 Hwy 9, Green Sea, SC, 29545. Tel: 843-392-0994. Fax: 843-392-0996. p. 2191

Gantt, Amy, Head, Teen Serv, Licking County Library, 101 W Main St, Newark, OH, 43055-5054. Tel: 740-349-5552. Fax: 740-349-5535. p. 1922

Gantt, John, Head, Tech Serv, Auburn University, 7440 East Dr, Montgomery, AL, 36117. Tel: 334-244-3200. Fax: 334-244-3720. p. 28

Ganyard, Paula M, Dir, University of Wisconsin-Green Bay, 2420 Nicolet Dr, Green Bay, WI, 54311-7001. Tel: 920-465-2333. Fax: 920-465-2136. p. 2596

Ganzevoort, Thomas, Instruction Librn, Columbus State University Libraries, 4225 University Ave, Columbus, GA, 31907. Tel: 706-565-3683. Fax: 706-568-2084. p. 526

Gao, Frank, Cat, Rider University, 2083 Lawrenceville Rd, Lawrenceville, NJ, 08648-3099. Tel: 609-896-5111. Fax: 609-896-8029. p. 1494

Gao, Joy, Pub Serv Librn, Govt Doc, Ohio Wesleyan University, 43 Rowland, Delaware, OH, 43015-2370. Tel: 740-368-3238. Fax: 740-368-3222. p. 1896

Gao, Vera, E-Res Cat Librn, Auraria Library, 1100 Lawrence St, Denver, CO, 80204-2095. Tel: 303-556-5269. Fax: 303-556-3528. p. 298

Gao, Wenli, Instrul Serv Librn, State University of New York, PO Box 902, Morrisville, NY, 13408-0902. Tel: 315-684-6055. Fax: 315-684-6115. p. 1663

Gaona, Antonia, Libr Supvr, Westminster Public Library, 3705 W 112th Ave, Westminster, CO, 80031. Tel: 303-658-2610. Fax: 303-404-5135. p. 326

Garabedian, Mike, Cat Librn, Whittier College, Bonnie Bell Wardman Library, 7031 Founders Hill Rd, Whittier, CA, 90608-9984. Tel: 562-907-4247. Fax: 562-698-7168. p. 283

Garafalo, Karen A, Interim Dir, Philmont Public Library, 101 Main St, Philmont, NY, 12565-1001. Tel: 518-672-5010. Fax: 518-672-5010. p. 1717

Garant, Eric, Instrul Serv Librn, Saddleback College, 28000 Marguerite Pkwy, Mission Viejo, CA, 92692. Tel: 949-582-4627. Fax: 949-364-0284. p. 187

Garavaglia, Barbara, Asst Dir, University of Michigan, Law Library, 801 Monroe St, Ann Arbor, MI, 48109-1210. Tel: 734-764-9338. Fax: 734-615-0178. p. 1152

Garbarino, Susan, Ref & Instruction Librn, Saint Mary's College Library, 1928 Saint Mary's Rd, Moraga, CA, 94575. Tel: 925-631-4229. Fax: 925-376-6097. p. 191

Garber, Gina, Digital Serv Librn, Austin Peay State University, 601 E College St, Clarksville, TN, 37044. Tel: 931-221-7028. Fax: 931-221-7296. p. 2228

Garber, Judith, Circ, Tech Serv, Northern Wyoming Community College District, 3059 Coffeen Ave, Sheridan, WY, 82801-1500. Tel: 307-674-6446. Fax: 307-674-3350. p. 2660

Garber, Lauren, Head, Pub Serv, The Master's Seminary Library, 13248 Roscoe Blvd, Sun Valley, CA, 91352. Tel: 818-909-5634. Fax: 818-909-5680. p. 273

Garber, Linda, Acq, Supvr, McDaniel College, Two College Hill, Westminster, MD, 21157-4390. Tel: 410-857-2285. Fax: 410-857-2748. p. 1046

Garber, Tracy, Br Mgr, Kern County Library, Olive Drive Fire Research Center, 5642 Victor St, Bakersfield, CA, 93308-4056. Tel: 661-391-7106. Fax: 661-399-5763. p. 124

Garbison, Deborah, Librn, Minnesota Correctional Facility, 970 Pickett St N, Education/Library, Bayport, MN, 55003-1490. Tel: 651-779-2700, Ext 2575. Fax: 651-351-3602. p. 1240

Garbison, Martha, Sr Librn, Denver Public Library, Virginia Village, 1500 S Dahlia St, Denver, CO, 80222. Tel: 303-757-6662. Fax: 303-692-0721. p. 301

Garboden, Mary, Head, Outreach Serv, Ypsilanti District Library, Superior Township, 8975 MacArthur Blvd, Ypsilanti, MI, 48198. Tel: 734-482-3747. Fax: 734-482-3757. p. 1238

Garcia, Adolfo, Pres, Hidalgo County Library System, c/o Pharr Memorial LIbrary, 121 E Cherokee St, Pharr, TX, 78577-4826. Tel: 956-787-3966. Fax: 956-787-3345. p. 2369

Garcia, Adolfo, Dir, Pharr Memorial Library, 121 E Cherokee St, Pharr, TX, 78577-4826. Tel: 956-787-3966. Fax: 956-787-3345. p. 2369

Garcia, Aida R, Dir, Zapata County Public Library, 901 Kennedy St, Zapata, TX, 78076. Tel: 956-765-5351. Fax: 956-765-1578. p. 2402

Garcia, Alex, LAII Teen/Spanish Outreach Coordr, Yuma County Library District, 2951 S 21st Dr, Yuma, AZ, 85364. Tel: 928-782-1871. Fax: 928-782-9420. p. 91

Garcia, Alfa J, Asst Librn, New York State Psychiatric Institute, 1051 Riverside Dr, Box 114, New York, NY, 10032. Tel: 212-543-5675. Fax: 212-543-5092. p. 1694

Garcia, Angelica, Supvry Librn, United States Army, Sergeants Major Academy Learning Resources Center, Commandant USASMA, Biggs Field, 11291 Sgt E Churchill St, Fort Bliss, TX, 79918-8002. Tel: 915-744-8176, 915-744-8451. Fax: 915-744-8484. p. 2320

Garcia, Angelica Maria, Librn, South Texas College Library, 3201 W Pecan Blvd, McAllen, TX, 78501-6661. Tel: 956-872-8330. Fax: 956-872-7202. p. 2361

Garcia, Angie, Librn, Washington County Free Library, Leonard P Snyder Memorial, 12624 Broadfording Rd, Clear Spring, MD, 21722. Tel: 301-842-2730. Fax: 301-842-2829. p. 1031

Garcia, Avelina, Commun Libr Supvr, Yakima Valley Libraries, Harrah Library, 21 E Pioneer, Harrah, WA, 98933. Tel: 509-848-3458. Fax: 509-848-3458. p. 2550

Garcia, Cecilia, Librn, International Specialty Products, 1361 Alps Rd, Wayne, NJ, 07470. Tel: 973-628-4000, Ext 3899. Fax: 973-628-3404. p. 1539

Garcia, Clemente, Librn, Dustin Michael Sekula Memorial Library, 1906 S Closner Blvd, Edinburg, TX, 78539. Tel: 956-383-6246. Fax: 956-318-3123. p. 2315

Garcia, Cyndy, Asst Dir, The Albuquerque Museum of Art & History, 2000 Mountain Rd NW, Albuquerque, NM, 87104. Tel: 505-243-7255. Fax: 505-764-6546. p. 1548

Garcia, Edward, Libr Dir, Cranston Public Library, 140 Sockanosset Cross Rd, Cranston, RI, 02920-5539. Tel: 401-943-9080. Fax: 401-946-5079. p. 2164

Garcia, Elizabeth, Br Mgr, Chicago Public Library, West Lawn, 4020 W 63rd St, Chicago, IL, 60629. Tel: 312-747-7381. Fax: 312-747-9281. p. 610

Garcia, Eric, In Charge, Imperial County Free Library, Salton City Branch, 2098 Frontage Rd, Salton City, CA, 92275. Tel: 760-604-6956. p. 146

Garcia, Ermulinda, Asst Librn, Dilley Public Library, 231 W FM 117, Dilley, TX, 78017. Tel: 830-965-1951. Fax: 830-965-4131. p. 2314

Garcia, Ernestina, Br Mgr, Kern County Library, Wasco Branch, 1102 Seventh St, Wasco, CA, 93280-1801. Tel: 661-758-2114. p. 125

Garcia, Florinda, Ref Spec, Central New Mexico Community College Libraries, South Valley Campus Library, 5816 Isleta SW, Rm SV 106, Albuquerque, NM, 87105. Tel: 505-224-5016. Fax: 505-224-5074. p. 1549

Garcia, Gonzalo, Online Serv, Ref, Syst, Golden West College, 15744 Golden West St, Huntington Beach, CA, 92647. Tel: 714-895-8741, Ext 55250. Fax: 714-895-8926. p. 158

Garcia, Hayley, Network Serv, Riverside Community College District, 4800 Magnolia Ave, Riverside, CA, 92506-1299. Tel: 951-222-8651. Fax: 951-328-3679. p. 217

Garcia, Janette, Archivist, Spec Coll, The University of Texas-Pan American Library, 1201 W University Dr, Edinburg, TX, 78541-2999. Tel: 956-665-2990. Fax: 956-665-5396. p. 2315

Garcia, Jose, Tech Serv, United States Court of Appeals, Federal Bldg, Rm 121, 150 Chardon Ave, Hato Rey, PR, 00918. Tel: 787-772-3096. Fax: 787-766-5747. p. 2673

Garcia, Kathy, Commun Libr Supvr, Yakima Valley Libraries, Buena Library, 801 Buena Rd, Buena, WA, 98921. Tel: 509-865-3390. Fax: 509-865-3390. p. 2550

Garcia, Lisa, Br Mgr, San Bernardino County Library, Phelan Memorial Library, 9800 Clovis Rd, Phelan, CA, 92371. Tel: 760-868-3053. Fax: 760-868-1386. p. 228

Garcia, Lourdes, Ref Librn, El Paso Community College Library, Northwest Campus-Jenna Welch & Laura Busch Community Library, 6701 S Desert Blvd, El Paso, TX, 79932. Tel: 915-831-8840. Fax: 915-831-8816. p. 2316

Garcia, Maria Isabel, Librn, All Saints Catholic Church, 5231 Meadowcreek at Arapaho, Dallas, TX, 75248-4046. Tel: 972-778-0327. Fax: 972-233-5401. p. 2304

Garcia, Maria Yanira, Ch, Zapata County Public Library, 901 Kennedy St, Zapata, TX, 78076. Tel: 956-765-5351. Fax: 956-765-1578. p. 2402

Garcia, Marie, Cat Librn, Robert L F Sikes Public Library, 1445 Commerce Dr, Crestview, FL, 32539. Tel: 850-682-4432. Fax: 850-689-4788. p. 434

Garcia, Mary, Soc Sci Dept Mgr, Miami-Dade Public Library System, 101 W Flagler St, Miami, FL, 33130-1523. Tel: 305-375-5575. Fax: 305-375-3048. p. 466

Garcia, Michael, Librn, Saint Elizabeth Medical Center, 2215 Genesee St, Utica, NY, 13501. Tel: 315-798-8209. p. 1759

Garcia, Moriana, Natural Sci Liaison Librn, Denison University Libraries, 400 W Loop, Granville, OH, 43023. Tel: 740-587-5714. Fax: 740-587-6285. p. 1902

Garcia, Nora, Librn, Pontificia Catholic University of Puerto Rico, Arecibo, PO Box 144045, Arecibo, PR, 00614-4045. Tel: 787-881-1212, Ext 6028. Fax: 787-881-0777. p. 2671

Garcia, Orly, Circ, St Thomas University Library, 16401 NW 37th Ave, Miami Gardens, FL, 33054. Tel: 305-628-6667. Fax: 305-628-6666. p. 469

Garcia, Pam, Asst Dir, Waupun Public Library, 123 S Forest St, Waupun, WI, 53963. Tel: 920-324-7925. p. 2646

Garcia, Penny, Dr, Assoc Prof, University of Wisconsin Oshkosh, 800 Algoma Blvd, Oshkosh, WI, 54901. Tel: 920-424-0881. Fax: 920-424-0858. p. 2977

Garcia, Rebecca, Commun Libr Mgr, County of Los Angeles Public Library, El Camino Real Library, 4264 E Whittier Blvd, Los Angeles, CA, 90023-2036. Tel: 323-269-8102. Fax: 323-268-5186. p. 141

Garcia, Rosa, Ch, Georgetown Public Library, 402 W Eighth St, Georgetown, TX, 78626-5503. Fax: 512-930-3764. p. 2327

Garcia, RuthAnn, Br Mgr, Palo Alto City Library, Mitchell Park, 3700 Middlefield Rd, Palo Alto, CA, 94303. Fax: 650-856-7925. p. 204

Garcia, Sarah, Ref, Suffolk Public Library System, 443 W Washington St, Suffolk, VA, 23434. Tel: 757-514-7323. Fax: 757-539-7155. p. 2497

Garcia, Sherry, Coordr, Nicola Valley Institute of Technology Library, 4155 Belshaw St, Merritt, BC, V1K 1R1, CANADA. Tel: 250-378-3303. Fax: 250-378-3332. p. 2731

Garcia, Sonia, Libr Tech, Camarena Memorial Library, 850 Encinas Ave, Calexico, CA, 92231. Tel: 760-768-2170. Fax: 760-357-0404. p. 131

Garcia, Susie, Site Supvr, Riverside Public Library, Casa Blanca Library & Family Learning Center, 2985 Madison St, Riverside, CA, 92504-4480. Tel: 951-826-2120. Fax: 951-826-2120. p. 218

Garcia, Tanya, Librn, Eden Public Library, 117 Market St, Eden, TX, 76837. Tel: 325-869-7761. Fax: 325-869-8212. p. 2315

Garcia, Veronica, Circ, Wharton County Junior College, 911 Boling Hwy, Wharton, TX, 77488-3298. Tel: 979-532-6953. Fax: 979-532-6527. p. 2399

Garcia-Barcena, Jenny, Librn, University of Miami Hospital Library, 1400 NW 12th Ave, Miami, FL, 33136. Tel: 305-325-5737. Fax: 305-325-5736. p. 469

Garcia-Colon, Miguel, Br Mgr, Greenwich Library, Byram Shubert Branch, 21 Mead Ave, Greenwich, CT, 06830-6812. Tel: 203-531-0426. Fax: 203-531-0789. p. 342

Garcia-Duer, Ovejovicta, Dir, University of California, 300 Frank H Ogawa Plaza, Ste 410, Oakland, CA, 94612. Tel: 510-302-2000. Fax: 510-302-2001. p. 199

Garcia-Hernandez, Carlos, Asst Libr Dir, Inter-American University of Puerto Rico, San German Campus, Ave Inter-American University, Rd 102, K 30 6, San German, PR, 00683-9801. Tel: 787-264-1912, Ext 7523. Fax: 787-264-2544. p. 2675

Garcia-Ortiz, Francisco, Commun Libr Supvr, Yakima Valley Libraries, Granger Library, 508 Sunnyside Ave, Granger, WA, 98932. Tel: 509-854-1446. Fax: 509-854-1446. p. 2550

Garcia-Ortiz, Francisco, Librn, Yakima Valley Libraries, Sunnyside Library, 621 Grant, Sunnyside, WA, 98944. Tel: 509-837-3234. Fax: 509-837-3234. p. 2551

Garcia-Ortiz, Francisco, Dr, Managing Librn, Yakima Valley Libraries, 102 N Third St, Yakima, WA, 98901-2759. Tel: 509-452-8541. Fax: 509-575-2093. p. 2550

Garcia-Pena, Idilio, Archivist, City College of the City University of New York, Dominican Studies Institute Research Library & Archives, NAC 2/204, 160 Convent Ave, New York, NY, 10031-0198. Tel: 212-650-7170, 212-650-7496. Fax: 212-650-7489. p. 1673

Garcia-Pendleton, Rosemary, Dir, Miami Dade College, Bldg D, 500 College Terrace, Homestead, FL, 33030. Tel: 305-237-5139. Fax: 305-237-5084. p. 451

Gardella, Robin, Coordr, Tech Serv, Southfield Public Library, 26300 Evergreen Rd, Southfield, MI, 48076. Tel: 248-796-4340. Fax: 248-796-4305. p. 1228

Gardener, Carol, Librn, Argosy University, 1515 Central Pkwy, Eagan, MN, 55121. Tel: 651-846-3351. Fax: 651-994-0105. p. 1249

Gardenour, Diane, Dir, Ingalls Memorial Library, 203 Main St, Rindge, NH, 03461. Tel: 603-899-3303. Fax: 603-899-5797. p. 1463

Gardepe, Cindy, Dir, Delaware Valley Hospital, One Titus Pl, Walton, NY, 13856. Tel: 607-865-2100, Ext 2171. Fax: 607-865-2114. p. 1762

Gardham, Bruce, Sr Librn, Toronto Public Health Library, 277 Victoria St, 6th Flr, Toronto, ON, M5B 1W2, CANADA. Tel: 416-338-7865. Fax: 416-338-0489. p. 2859

Gardin, T Hershel, Dean, Michigan Jewish Institute Library, 25401 Coolidge Hwy, Oak Park, MI, 48237. Tel: 248-414-6900, Ext 101. Fax: 248-414-6907. p. 1215

Gardiner, Carol, Br Serv Mgr, Lambton County Library, 787 Broadway St, Wyoming, ON, N0N 1T0, CANADA. Tel: 519-845-3324, Ext 5238. Fax: 519-845-0700. p. 2872

Gardiner, Catherine, Tech Serv Supvr, Florida Gulf Coast University Library, 10501 FGCU Blvd S, Fort Myers, FL, 33965-6501. Tel: 239-590-7640. p. 445

Gardiner, Deb, Dir, High River Centennial Library, 909 First St SW, High River, AB, T1V 1A5, CANADA. Tel: 403-652-2917. Fax: 403-652-7203. p. 2707

Gardiner, Karyn, Head, YA, Durham Public Library, Seven Maple Ave, Durham, CT, 06422. Tel: 860-349-9544. Fax: 860-349-1897. p. 337

Gardiner, Lori, Circ Supvr, Davis County Library, Northwest Branch, 1875 S 2000 West, Syracuse, UT, 84075-9359. Tel: 801-825-7080. Fax: 801-825-7083. p. 2405

Gardiner, Reid L, Librn, Montana Masonic Library, 425 N Park Ave, Helena, MT, 59624. Tel: 406-442-7774. Fax: 406-442-1321. p. 1382

Gardiner, Sascha, Ch, Hagaman Memorial Library, 227 Main St, East Haven, CT, 06512-3003. Tel: 203-468-3890. Fax: 203-468-3892. p. 337

Gardiner, Susan, Br Mgr, Ocean County Library, Brick Branch, 301 Chambers Bridge Rd, Brick, NJ, 08723-2803. Tel: 732-477-4513. Fax: 732-920-9314. p. 1534

Gardner, Adrienne, Youth Serv, Hunterdon County Library, 314 State Rte 12, Flemington, NJ, 08822. Tel: 908-788-1444. Fax: 908-806-4862. p. 1486

Gardner, Allison, Librn, United States Navy, Naval Undersea Warfare Center Division, Newport Technical Library, 1176 Howell St, Bldg 101, Newport, RI, 02841. Tel: 401-832-4338. Fax: 401-832-3699. p. 2170

Gardner, Amanda, Asst Mgr, Adult Serv, Rockford Public Library, 215 N Wyman St, Rockford, IL, 61101-1023. Tel: 815-965-7606. Fax: 815-965-0866. p. 697

Gardner, Andrew, Assoc Dir, Libraries Online, Inc, 100 Riverview Ctr, Ste 252, Middletown, CT, 06457. Tel: 860-347-1704. Fax: 860-346-3707. p. 2939

Gardner, Annie, Adult Serv, Cabarrus County Public Library, Kannapolis Branch, 850 Mountain St, Kannapolis, NC, 28081. Tel: 704-920-1180. Fax: 704-938-3512. p. 1785

Gardner, Barb, Librn, Coulter Public Library, 111 Main St, Coulter, IA, 50431. Tel: 641-866-6798. Fax: 641-866-6798. p. 804

Gardner, Betina, Interim Dean, Eastern Kentucky University Libraries, 521 Lancaster Ave, Richmond, KY, 40475-3102. Tel: 859-622-1778. Fax: 859-622-1174. p. 933

Gardner, Betina L, Coordr, Pub Serv, Eastern Kentucky University Libraries, 521 Lancaster Ave, Richmond, KY, 40475-3102. Tel: 859-622-1778. Fax: 859-622-1174. p. 933

Gardner, Diane, Mgr, McLaren Regional Medical Center, 401 S Ballenger Hwy, Flint, MI, 48532-3685. Tel: 810-342-2141. Fax: 810-342-2269. p. 1180

Gardner, Diane, Tech Serv, McLaren Regional Medical Center, 401 S Ballenger Hwy, Flint, MI, 48532-3685. Tel: 810-342-2141. Fax: 810-342-2269. p. 1180

Gardner, Fay, Mgr, Outreach Serv, Jackson County Public Library, 303 W Second St, Seymour, IN, 47274-2147. Tel: 812-522-3412, Ext 234. Fax: 812-522-5456. p. 777

Gardner, Gene, Pres, Colorado Council of Medical Librarians, PO Box 101058, Denver, CO, 80210-1058. Tel: 303-724-2124. Fax: 303-724-2154. p. 2939

Gardner, Jeanette, Head, Circ, Middle Georgia Regional Library System, 1180 Washington Ave, Macon, GA, 31201-1790. Tel: 478-744-0800, 478-744-0841. Fax: 478-742-3161. p. 541

Gardner, Jill, Dir, Potomac State College of West Virginia University, 101 Fort Ave, Keyser, WV, 26726. Tel: 304-788-6901. Fax: 304-788-6946. p. 2563

Gardner, Jim, Dir, Franciscan Friars of the Atonement Library, Graymoor Rte 9, Garrison, NY, 10524-0300. Tel: 845-424-3671. Fax: 845-424-2162. p. 1627

Gardner, Judith, Info & Tech Serv Librn, Ochsner Clinic Foundation, 1st Flr Hospital, 1514 Jefferson Hwy, New Orleans, LA, 70121-2429. Tel: 504-842-3760. Fax: 504-842-5339. p. 962

Gardner, Justin, Librn, American Printing House for the Blind, Inc, 1839 Frankfort Ave, Louisville, KY, 40206. p. 923

Gardner, Kerry Ann, Pub Serv Librn, El Paso Community College Library, Valle Verde Campus Library, 919 Hunter St, El Paso, TX, 79915. Tel: 915-831-2255. p. 2316

Gardner, Lana, Dir, Cherokee County Public Library, 300 E Rutledge Ave, Gaffney, SC, 29340-2227. Tel: 864-487-2711. Fax: 864-487-2752. p. 2194

Gardner, Laura, Coll Develop, Peterborough Public Library, 345 Aylmer St N, Peterborough, ON, K9H 3V7, CANADA. Tel: 705-745-5382. Fax: 705-745-8958. p. 2836

Gardner, Lindsy, Dir of Libr Serv, Lancaster Community Library, 235 School St, Kilmarnock, VA, 22482-3830. Tel: 804-435-1729. Fax: 804-435-0255. p. 2472

Gardner, Lucy, Dir, Universite du Quebec a Montreal Bibliotheque, CP 8889 Succ Centre-Ville, Montreal, QC, H3C 3P3, CANADA. Tel: 514-987-3824. Fax: 514-987-3542. p. 2902

Gardner, Lynn L, Supvr, Per, Mount Hood Community College Library, 26000 SE Stark St, Gresham, OR, 97030. Tel: 503-352-1408. Fax: 503-491-7389. p. 1999

Gardner, Mark, Librn, Schroeter, Goldmark & Bender Law Library, 810 Third Ave, Ste 500, Seattle, WA, 98104. Tel: 206-622-8000. Fax: 206-682-2305. p. 2530

Gardner, Marybeth, Admin Librn, Chandler Public Library, 22 S Delaware, Chandler, AZ, 85225. Tel: 480-782-2816. Fax: 480-782-2823. p. 59

Gardner, Meggan, Curator, Dir, Librn, Royal Canadian Golf Association Library & Archives, 1333 Dorval Dr, Oakville, ON, L6J 4Z3, CANADA. Tel: 905-849-9700. Fax: 905-845-7040. p. 2826

Gardner, Melanie, Actg Assoc Dir, Info Products, United States Department of Agriculture, 10301 Baltimore Ave, Beltsville, MD, 20705-2351. Tel: 301-504-6207. Fax: 301-504-5472. p. 1020

Gardner, Melissa, Dir, Village of Berkeley Public Library, 1637 Taft Ave, Berkeley, IL, 60163-1499. Tel: 708-544-6017. Fax: 708-544-7551. p. 594

Gardner, Morris, YA Serv, Atlanta-Fulton Public Library System, Roswell Regional Library, 115 Norcross St, Roswell, GA, 30075. Tel: 770-640-3075. Fax: 770-640-3077. p. 512

Gardner, Nancy, Head, Circ, Avon Grove Library, 117 Rosehill Ave, West Grove, PA, 19390-1214. Tel: 610-869-2004. Fax: 610-869-2957. p. 2154

Gardner, Nora, Asst Librn, Carter, Ledyard & Milburn Library, Two Wall St, New York, NY, 10005. Tel: 212-238-8691. Fax: 212-732-3232. p. 1671

Gardner, Priscilla, Dir, Jersey City Free Public Library, 472 Jersey Ave, Jersey City, NJ, 07302-3499. Tel: 201-547-4788. Fax: 201-547-4584. p. 1492

Gardner, Rachel M, Ref Librn, Monmouth University, 400 Cedar Ave, West Long Branch, NJ, 07764. Tel: 732-571-3450, Ext 7560. Fax: 732-263-5124. p. 1541

Gardner, Rebecca, Librn, Rutgers University Libraries, Stephen & Lucy Chang Science Library, Walter E Foran Hall, 59 Dudley Rd, New Brunswick, NJ, 08901-8520. Tel: 732-932-0305, Ext 114. Fax: 732-932-0311. p. 1508

Gardner, Sally, Librn, Glee Merritt Kelley Community Library, 320 School Hill Dr, Wolcott, VT, 05680. Tel: 802-472-6551. Fax: 802-472-6295. p. 2440

Gardner, Susan, Head, Ref & Instruction, Loyola Marymount University, One LMU Dr, MS 8200, Los Angeles, CA, 90045-2659. Tel: 310-338-7680. Fax: 310-338-4366. p. 175

Gardner, Susan, Acq, Extn Serv, Easton Area Public Library & District Center, 515 Church St, Easton, PA, 18042-3587. Tel: 610-258-2917. Fax: 610-253-2231. p. 2052

Gardner, Tom, Br Mgr, Public Library of Cincinnati & Hamilton County, Cheviot, 3711 Robb Ave, Cincinnati, OH, 45211. Tel: 513-369-6015. Fax: 513-369-6048. p. 1871

Gardner, W, Dir, Oskaloosa Public Library, 301 S Market St, Oskaloosa, IA, 52577. Tel: 641-673-0441. Fax: 641-673-6237. p. 837

Gardner, W Jeanne, Dir, Libr Serv, Pueblo Community College Library, 900 W Orman Ave, Pueblo, CO, 81004-1430. Tel: 719-549-3308. Fax: 719-549-3309. p. 321

Garduno, Katherine, Circ Supvr, Los Alamos County Library System, 2400 Central Ave, Los Alamos, NM, 87544. Tel: 505-662-8240. Fax: 505-662-8245. p. 1559

Garetz, Sara, Mkt & Communications Spec, National Forest Service Library, 240 W Prospect Rd, Fort Collins, CO, 80526. Tel: 510-758-7685. Fax: 970-498-1059. p. 307

Garewal, Kevin, Acq & Coll Develop Librn, Cleveland State University, Cleveland-Marshall Law Library, Cleveland-Marshall College of Law, 1801 Euclid Ave, Cleveland, OH, 44115-2223. Tel: 216-523-7393. Fax: 216-687-6881. p. 1878

Garey, Mary Evelyn, Br Librn, Moundsville-Marshall County Public Library, Cameron Public, Benedum Bldg, 44 Main St, Cameron, WV, 26033. Tel: 304-686-2140. Fax: 304-686-2140. p. 2567

Garg, Yash, Curric Mat Librn, North Carolina Central University, 1801 Fayetteville St, Durham, NC, 27707-3129. Tel: 919-530-6383. Fax: 919-530-7612. p. 1789

Gargan, Karen, Assoc Dir, Finance, Douglas County Libraries, 100 S Wilcox, Castle Rock, CO, 80104. Tel: 303-688-7623. Fax: 303-688-7655. p. 294

Gargan, William, Info Serv, Brooklyn College Library, 2900 Bedford Ave, Brooklyn, NY, 11210-2889. Tel: 718-951-5341. Fax: 718-951-4540. p. 1589

Garibay, Amy, Dir, Eatontown Library, 33 Broad St, Eatontown, NJ, 07724-1594. Tel: 732-389-2665. Fax: 732-389-7665. p. 1482

Garin, Lalaine, In Charge, Kern Medical Center, 1700 Mt Vernon Ave, Bakersfield, CA, 93306. Tel: 661-326-2227. Fax: 661-862-7654. p. 125

Gario, Michelle, Adult Serv, Seekonk Public Library, 410 Newman Ave, Seekonk, MA, 02771. Tel: 508-336-8230, Ext 130. Fax: 508-336-6437. p. 1123

Garity, Betty, Head, Acq, Fordham University Libraries, 441 E Fordham Rd, Bronx, NY, 10458-5151. Tel: 718-817-3570. Fax: 718-817-3582. p. 1586

Garity, Carrie, Coordr, Fort Atkinson Memorial Hospital, 611 E Sherman Ave, Fort Atkinson, WI, 53538. Tel: 920-568-5194. Fax: 920-568-5195. p. 2592

Garity, Carrie, Coordr, South Central Wisconsin Health Science Library Consortium, c/o Fort Healthcare Medical Library, 611 Sherman Ave E, Fort Atkinson, WI, 53538. Tel: 920-568-5194. Fax: 920-568-5195. p. 2958

Garity, Joe, Ref & Instrul Serv, Instr Coordr, University of San Francisco, 2130 Fulton St, San Francisco, CA, 94117-1080. Tel: 415-422-5386. Fax: 415-422-5949. p. 248

Garland, Bobi, Dir, Western Costume Co, 11041 Vanowen St, North Hollywood, CA, 91605. Tel: 818-760-0902, Ext 148. Fax: 818-508-2182. p. 195

Garland, Carol, Mgr, Sodus Community Library, 17 Maple Ave, Sodus, NY, 14551. Tel: 315-483-9292. Fax: 315-483-9616. p. 1744

Garland, James H, Exec Dir, Bishop Baraga Association Archives, 347 Rock St, Marquette, MI, 49855. Tel: 906-227-9117. Fax: 906-228-2469. p. 1206

Garland, Mercy, Ch, Chappaqua Public Library, 195 S Greeley Ave, Chappaqua, NY, 10514. Tel: 914-238-4779. Fax: 914-238-3597. p. 1605

Garland, Robert, Dir, Mount Union College Library, 1972 Clark Ave, Alliance, OH, 44601-3993. Tel: 330-823-3844. Fax: 330-823-3963. p. 1854

Garlets, Diane, Dir, Athens Community Library, 106 E Burr Oak St, Athens, MI, 49011-9793. Tel: 269-729-4479. p. 1154

Garlinska, Ala, Librn, South Central College Library, 1225 SW Third St, Faribault, MN, 55021. Tel: 507-332-5883. Fax: 507-332-5888. p. 1251

Garloch, Betsy, Syst Librn, Gannon University, 109 University Sq, Erie, PA, 16541. Tel: 814-871-7557. Fax: 814-871-5666. p. 2055

Garm, Mary, Adminr, Lackawanna County Library System, 520 Vine St, Scranton, PA, 18509-3298. Tel: 570-348-3003. Fax: 570-348-3028. p. 2137

Garm, Mary, Instr, Northampton Community College, 3835 Green Pond Rd, Bethlehem, PA, 18020. Tel: 610-861-5358. Fax: 610-861-5373. p. 2973

Garman, Kari J, Dir, Libr Serv, Hudson Area Public Library District, 104 Pearl St, Hudson, IL, 61748. Tel: 309-726-1103. Fax: 309-726-1646. p. 657

Garman, Marsha, Interim Head, Acq, Yale University Library, Sterling Memorial Library, 120 High St, New Haven, CT, 06520. Tel: 203-432-8373. Fax: 203-432-1294. p. 359

Garmon, Kim, Br Mgr, Haywood County Public Library, Fines Creek, Fines Creek Community Bldg, 190 Fines Creek Rd, Clyde, NC, 28721. Tel: 828-627-0146. p. 1829

Garmon, Kim, Tech Serv, Haywood County Public Library, 678 S Haywood St, Waynesville, NC, 28786-4398. Tel: 828-452-5169, Ext 2513. Fax: 828-452-6746. p. 1829

Garmon, Maureen, Access Serv, University of Arizona, James E Rogers College of Law Library, PO Box 210176, Tucson, AZ, 85721-0176. Tel: 520-621-1413. Fax: 520-621-3138. p. 89

Garms, Hila, Asst Librn, Elkader Public Library, 130 N Main St, Elkader, IA, 52043. Tel: 563-245-1446. Fax: 563-245-1446. p. 814

Garneau, Hal, ILL, Vineyard Haven Public Library, 200 Main St, Vineyard Haven, MA, 02568-9710. Tel: 508-696-4211, Ext 12. Fax: 508-696-7495. p. 1132

Garneau, Michele, Asst Dir, Kelley Library, 234 Main St, Salem, NH, 03079-3190. Tel: 603-898-7064. Fax: 603-898-8583. p. 1464

Garner, Anne, Libr Dir, Wayne County Public Library, 150 S Main St, Monticello, KY, 42633. Tel: 606-348-8565. Fax: 606-348-3829. p. 929

Garner, Carolyn, Ref Librn, Pamunkey Regional Library, 7527 Library Dr, Hanover, VA, 23069. Tel: 804-537-6211. Fax: 804-537-6389. p. 2469

Garner, Donna, Head, Circ, Meredith College, 3800 Hillsborough St, Raleigh, NC, 27607-5298. Tel: 919-760-8531. Fax: 919-760-2830. p. 1815

Garner, Gloria, Circ, Fayetteville State University, 1200 Murchison Rd, Fayetteville, NC, 28301-4298. Tel: 910-672-1236. Fax: 910-672-1746. p. 1793

Garner, Ivy, Librn, Johns Hopkins University Libraries, Adolf Meyer Library, 600 N Wolfe St, Baltimore, MD, 21205. Tel: 410-955-5819. Fax: 410-955-0860. p. 1014

Garner, Jennifer, Asst Dir, North Liberty Community Library, 520 W Cherry St, North Liberty, IA, 52317-9797. Tel: 319-626-5701. Fax: 319-626-5722. p. 835

Garner, Judith, Archivist, American Jewish Historical Society, New England Branch, Hebrew College, 160 Herrick Rd, Newton Centre, MA, 02459. Tel: 617-559-8884. Fax: 617-559-8881. p. 1110

Garner, Madelyn C, Ref, San Jacinto College North, 5800 Uvalde Rd, Houston, TX, 77049-4599, Tel: 281-459-7116. Fax: 281-459-7166. p. 2342

Garner, Margaret, Ser, University of Oklahoma Health Sciences Center, 1000 Stanton L Young Blvd, Oklahoma City, OK, 73117-1213. Tel: 405-271-2285, Ext 48756. Fax: 405-271-3297. p. 1975

Garner, Mary, Librn, Tyringham Free Public Library, 118 Main Rd, Tyringham, MA, 01264-9700. Tel: 413-243-1373. p. 1131

Garner, Nancy, Asst Dir, Knowledge Serv, Jenkins Law Library, 833 Chestnut St, Ste 1220, Philadelphia, PA, 19107-4429. Tel: 215-574-7944. Fax: 215-574-7920. p. 2111

Garner, Ruth, Circ Mgr, Marion County Sub-District Library, 212 S Main St, Palmyra, MO, 63461. Tel: 573-769-2830. Fax: 573-769-0405. p. 1348

Garner, Sharon, Asst Dir, Peotone Public Library District, 515 N First St, Peotone, IL, 60468. Tel: 708-258-3436. Fax: 708-258-9796. p. 690

Garner, Susan, Archivist, Diocese of Amarillo, 1800 N Spring St, Amarillo, TX, 79107. Tel: 806-383-2243, Ext 120. Fax: 806-383-8452. p. 2274

Garner, Teresa, Librn, Rogersville Public Library, 74 Bank St, Rogersville, AL, 35652. Tel: 256-247-0151. Fax: 256-247-0144. p. 35

Garnett, Ann, Ref Serv, Garden City Public Library, 60 Seventh St, Garden City, NY, 11530-2891. Tel: 516-742-8405. Fax: 516-742-2675. p. 1626

Garnett, Joyce, Univ Librn, Western University - Libraries, 1151 Richmond St, Ste 200, London, ON, N6A 3K7, CANADA. Tel: 519-661-3165. Fax: 519-661-3493. p. 2819

Garnsey, Beth, Dept Chair, Ref, Oakland Community College, Woodland Hall, 7350 Cooley Lake Rd, Waterford, MI, 48327-4187. Tel: 248-942-3128. Fax: 248-942-3132. p. 1235

Garnsey, Jeannie, Asst Librn, Kellogg Public Library, 16 W Market Ave, Kellogg, ID, 83837-2499. Tel: 208-786-7231. Fax: 208-784-1100. p. 577

Garofalo, Charlotte, Dir, Reading Room Association of Gouverneur, 60 Church St, Gouverneur, NY, 13642. Tel: 315-287-0191. Fax: 315-287-0191. p. 1629

Garofalo, Denise A, Syst & Cat Serv Librn, Mount Saint Mary College, 330 Powell Ave, Newburgh, NY, 12550-3494. Tel: 845-569-3519. Fax: 845-561-0999. p. 1704

Garoutte, Janice, Coordr, Mohave County Library District, Chloride Community Library, 4901 Payroll Ave, Chloride, AZ, 86413. Tel: 928-565-2200. Fax: 928-565-2200. p. 67

Garr, David, Exec Dir, South Carolina AHEC, c/o Medical University of SC, 19 Hagood Ave, Ste 802, Charleston, SC, 29425. Tel: 843-792-4431. Fax: 843-792-4430. p. 2955

Garred, Lisa, Circ, ILL, Libr Asst, University of Texas Health Science Center at Tyler, 11937 US Hwy 271, Tyler, TX, 75708. Tel: 903-877-2865. Fax: 903-877-5412. p. 2394

Garrera, Joseph, Exec Dir, Lehigh County Historical Society, Lehigh Valley Heritage Museum, 432 W Walnut St, Allentown, PA, 18102-5428. Tel: 610-435-1074, Ext 19. Fax: 610-435-9812. p. 2026

Garretson, Camille, Dir, Morris Plains Library, 77 Glenbrook Rd, Morris Plains, NJ, 07950. Tel: 973-538-2599. Fax: 973-538-8974. p. 1504

Garrett, Amy, Head, Adult Serv, Stow-Munroe Falls Public Library, 3512 Darrow Rd, Stow, OH, 44224. Tel: 330-688-3295. p. 1937

Garrett, Cynthia D, Libr Mgr, Josey Health Sciences Library, Palmetto Health Richland, Five Richland Medical Park, Columbia, SC, 29203. Tel: 803-434-6312. Fax: 803-434-2651. p. 2187

Garrett, Gisele A, Dir, Ariton-Dot Laney Memorial Library, 30 W Main St, Ariton, AL, 36311. Tel: 334-762-2463. Fax: 334-762-3354. p. 4

Garrett, Jeffrey, Assoc Univ Librn, Spec Librn, Northwestern University Library, 1970 Campus Dr, Evanston, IL, 60208-2300. Tel: 847-491-7658. p. 644

Garrett, Joan, Adult Serv, Belvedere-Tiburon Library, 1501 Tiburon Blvd, Tiburon, CA, 94920. Tel: 415-789-2665. Fax: 415-789-2650. p. 275

Garrett, Judy, Dir, Gentry County Library, 304 N Park, Stanberry, MO, 64489. Tel: 660-783-2335. Fax: 660-783-2335. p. 1368

Garrett, LeAnn, Automation Syst Coordr, Mt San Antonio College Library, 1100 N Grand Ave, Walnut, CA, 91789. Tel: 909-274-4260. Fax: 909-468-4011. p. 282

Garrett, Lynda, Librn, USGS Patuxent Wildlife Research Center Library, 12100 Beech Forest Rd, Laurel, MD, 20708-4030. Tel: 301-497-5550. Fax: 301-497-5545. p. 1035

Garrett, Margaret, Asst Dir, Guilderland Public Library, 2228 Western Ave, Guilderland, NY, 12084-9701. Tel: 518-456-2400. Fax: 518-456-0923. p. 1632

Garrett, Marietta J, Librn, Newark United Methodist Church, 69 E Main St, Newark, DE, 19711-4645. Tel: 302-738-6741. p. 385

Garrett, Mary Beth, Ch Serv Librn, Alpine Public Library, 203 N Seventh St, Alpine, TX, 79830. Tel: 432-837-2621. Fax: 432-837-2501. p. 2273

Garrett, Mary Jane, Tech Serv, Northlake Public Library District, 231 N Wolf Rd, Northlake, IL, 60164. Tel: 708-562-2301. Fax: 708-562-8120. p. 683

Garrett, Melinda, Coll Develop, Mansfield-Richland County Public Library, 43 W Third St, Mansfield, OH, 44902-1295. Tel: 419-521-3133. Fax: 419-525-4750. p. 1912

Garrett, Melissa, Asst Librn, Union College, 310 College St, Campus Box D-21, Barbourville, KY, 40906-1499. Tel: 606-546-1242. Fax: 606-546-1239. p. 906

Garrett, Nicole, Archivist, Albion College, 602 E Cass St, Albion, MI, 49224-1879. Tel: 517-629-0487. Fax: 517-629-0504. p. 1148

Garrett, Pat, Dir, Capitan Public Library, 101 E Second St, Capitan, NM, 88316. Tel: 575-354-3035. Fax: 575-354-3223. p. 1552

Garrett, Paula, Dir, Illinois Mathematics & Science Academy, 1500 W Sullivan Rd, Aurora, IL, 60506-1000. Tel: 630-907-5953. Fax: 630-907-5004. p. 591

Garrett, Susan, In Charge, Schenectady County Public Library, Niskayuna, 2400 Nott St E, Niskayuna, NY, 12309. Tel: 518-386-2249. Fax: 518-386-2249. p. 1741

Garrett, Thad, Libr Asst, Catholic University of America, Music, 101 Ward Hall, 620 Michigan St, Washington, DC, 20064. Tel: 202-319-5424. Fax: 202-319-6280. p. 396

Garrett, William, Dr, Head, Ref & Pub Serv, Troy University Library, 309 Wallace Hall, 501 University Ave, Troy, AL, 36082. Tel: 334-670-3257. Fax: 334-670-3694. p. 37

Garrido, Ailene, Br Mgr, Calaveras County Library, Valley Springs Branch, 240 Pine St, Valley Springs, CA, 95252. Tel: 209-772-1318. p. 227

Garriott, C J, Librn, Calhoun County Library, Seadrift Branch, 103 W Dallas, Seadrift, TX, 77983. Tel: 361-785-4241. Fax: 361-785-2346. p. 2372

Garriott, Mary Beth, Ref Librn, Centre College of Kentucky, 600 W Walnut St, Danville, KY, 40422. Tel: 859-238-5272. Fax: 859-236-7925. p. 911

Garrison, Anne, Humanities Librn, Swarthmore College, 500 College Ave, Swarthmore, PA, 19081-1081. Tel: 610-328-8492. Fax: 610-328-7329. p. 2145

Garrison, Avery, Asst Librn, Ranger College, 1100 College Circle, Ranger, TX, 76470-3298. Tel: 254-647-1414. Fax: 254-647-1656. p. 2373

Garrison, Betty L, Ref/Bus Librn, Elon University, 308 N O'Kelly Ave, Elon, NC, 27244-0187. Tel: 336-278-6581. Fax: 336-278-6637. p. 1791

Garrison, Cheryl, Br Mgr, Kent District Library, Byron Township Branch, 8191 Byron Center Ave SW, Byron Center, MI, 49315. Tel: 616-784-2007. p. 1165

Garrison, Cyndi, Cat, University of the Southwest, 6610 Lovington Hwy, T-30, Hobbs, NM, 88240. Tel: 575-392-6565, Ext 2141. Fax: 575-392-6006. p. 1557

Garrison, Frances S, Ref, Mansfield University, Mansfield, PA, 16933. Tel: 570-662-4688. Fax: 570-662-4993. p. 2084

Garrison, Jan Marlene, Adult/Young Adult Serv Librn, Rushville Public Library, 130 W Third St, Rushville, IN, 46173-1899. Tel: 765-932-3496. Fax: 765-932-4528. p. 776

Garrison, Jean, Librn, Mercy Hospital Library Services, 3663 S Miami Ave, Miami, FL, 33133. Tel: 305-285-2160. Fax: 305-285-2128. p. 466

Garrison, Judith, Head, Ref & Libr Instruction, Armstrong Atlantic State University, 11935 Abercorn St, Savannah, GA, 31419. Tel: 912-344-3027. Fax: 912-344-3457. p. 549

Garrison, Judith, Ref Serv, Indiana University-Purdue University Fort Wayne, 2101 E Coliseum Blvd, Fort Wayne, IN, 46805-1499. Tel: 260-481-6499. Fax: 260-481-6509. p. 741

Garrison, Judy, Head, Acq, University of Texas at San Antonio Libraries, One UTSA Circle, San Antonio, TX, 78249-0671. Tel: 210-458-5507. p. 2383

Garrison, Julie, Assoc Dean, Res & Instruction, Grand Valley State University Libraries, One Campus Dr, Allendale, MI, 49401-9403. Tel: 616-331-3636. p. 1149

Garrison, Margie, Librn, Havelock-Craven County Public Library, 301 Cunningham Blvd, Havelock, NC, 28532. Tel: 252-447-7509. Fax: 252-447-7422. p. 1800

Garrison, Margie Marie, Head Librn, Havelock-Craven County Public Library, 301 Cunningham Blvd, Havelock, NC, 28532. Tel: 252-447-7509. Fax: 252-447-7422. p. 1800

Garrison, Scott, Dean, Ferris State University Library, 1010 Campus Dr, Big Rapids, MI, 49307-2279. Tel: 231-591-3500. Fax: 231-591-3724. p. 1158

Garrison, Scott, Assoc Dean, Pub Serv & Tech, Western Michigan University, Arcadia at Vande Giessen St, Kalamazoo, MI, 49008-5353. Tel: 269-387-5239. Fax: 269-387-5077. p. 1198

Garrison, Susan, In Charge, Womble, Carlyle, Sandridge & Rice, One W Fourth St, Winston-Salem, NC, 27101. Tel: 336-747-4757. Fax: 336-721-3660. p. 1835

Garrison, William A, Dean, University of South Florida, Tampa Campus Library, 4101 USF Apple Dr, LIB122, Tampa, FL, 33620. Tel: 813-974-1642. Fax: 813-974-5153. p. 499

Garrison, Yvonne, Br Librn, Park County Public Library, 350 Bulldogger Rd, Bailey, CO, 80421-2379. Tel: 303-838-5539. Fax: 303-838-2351. p. 289

Garrison-Whitmore, Sandra L, Dir, Intercultural Communication Institute & Summer Institute for Intercultural Communication, 8835 SW Canyon Lane, Ste 238, Portland, OR, 97225. Tel: 503-297-4622. Fax: 503-297-4695. p. 2011

Garritano, Jeremy, Librn, Purdue University Libraries, M G Mellon Library of Chemistry, Wetherill Lab of Chemistry Bldg, Rm 301, West Lafayette, IN, 47907-1333. Tel: 765-494-2862. p. 787

Garrod, Bruce, Librn, University of Toronto Libraries, Mathematical Sciences, Sidney Smith Hall, 100 Saint George St, Rm 622, Toronto, ON, M5S 1A1, CANADA. Tel: 416-978-8624. Fax: 416-978-4107. p. 2866

Garrow, Valerie, Librn, Akwesasne Cultural Center Library, 321 State Rte 37, Hogansburg, NY, 13655. Tel: 518-358-2240. Fax: 518-358-2649. p. 1637

Garside, Barbara, Librn, Hoag Memorial Hospital Presbyterian, One Hoag Dr, Newport Beach, CA, 92658. Tel: 949-764-8308. Fax: 949-764-5729. p. 194

Garside, Cynthia, Acq, Rivier College, 420 S Main St, Nashua, NH, 03060-5086. Tel: 603-897-8535. Fax: 603-897-8889. p. 1459

Garson, Deborah, Head, Res & Instruction, Harvard Library, Gutman Library-Research Center, Graduate School of Educ, Six Appian Way, Cambridge, MA, 02138. Tel: 617-495-4225. Fax: 617-495-0540. p. 1075

Garstad, Roxy, Tech Librn, Grant MacEwan University Library, 10700 104th Ave, Edmonton, AB, T5J 4S2, CANADA. Tel: 780-497-5850. Fax: 780-497-5895. p. 2701

Garstecki, Maria, Br Mgr, Mount Prospect Public Library, South Branch, 1711 W Algonquin Rd, Mount Prospect, IL, 60056. Tel: 847-590-4090. p. 677

Garthwait, Clayton, Access Serv, ILL, West Chester University, 25 W Rosedale Ave, West Chester, PA, 19383. Tel: 610-436-3409. p. 2153

Gartler, Marc, Dir, Harrington College of Design Library, 200 W Madison St, Chicago, IL, 60606. Tel: 312-697-3318. Fax: 312-697-8115. p. 614

Gartler, Marc, Br Supvr, Madison Public Library, Hawthorne Branch, 2707 E Washington Ave, Madison, WI, 53704. Tel: 608-246-4548. Fax: 608-246-4549. p. 2607

Gartler, Marc, Br Supvr, Madison Public Library, Lakeview, 2845 N Sherman Ave, Madison, WI, 53704. Tel: 608-246-4547. Fax: 608-246-4699. p. 2607

Garton, Kathy, Dir, Chilton Public Library, 221 Park St, Chilton, WI, 53014. Tel: 920-849-4414. Fax: 920-849-2370. p. 2585

Garton, Margo A, Dir, Partridge Public Library, 23 S Main St, Partridge, KS, 67566. Tel: 620-567-2467. Fax: 620-567-2467. p. 889

Garton, Megan, Instruction Coordr, Ref Librn, Tulane University, Law Library, 6329 Freret St, New Orleans, LA, 70118-6231. Tel: 504-865-5941. Fax: 504-865-5917. p. 963

Garton, Scott, Head of Libr, Northwestern University, Chicago, Joseph Schaffner Library, Wieboldt Hall, 2nd Flr, 339 E Chicago Ave, Chicago, IL, 60611. Tel: 312-503-0720. Fax: 312-503-8930. p. 621

Garton, Scott, Actg Head of Ref, Northwestern University Library, 1970 Campus Dr, Evanston, IL, 60208-2300. Tel: 847-491-7658. p. 644

Gartung, Christine, Librn, Worcester Free Library, 168 Main St, Ste 2, Worcester, NY, 12197. Tel: 607-397-7309. p. 1771

Garven, Beverly, Head Librn, Inuvik Centennial Library, 100 Mackenzie Rd, Inuvik, NT, X0E 0T0, CANADA. Tel: 867-777-8620. Fax: 867-777-8621. p. 2775

Garverick, Jeffrey, Libr Mgr, Department of Veterans Affairs, 1601 Kirkwood Hwy, Rm 7002, Wilmington, DE, 19805-4988. Tel: 302-994-2511, Ext 4255, 302-994-2511, Ext 4381. Fax: 302-633-5285. p. 387

Garvey, Jeffrey M, Dir, Libr Serv, Samaritan Medical Center, 830 Washington St, Watertown, NY, 13601. Tel: 315-785-4191. Fax: 315-779-5173. p. 1764

Garvey, Maureen, Dir, Bellmore Memorial Library, 2288 Bedford Ave, Bellmore, NY, 11710. Tel: 516-785-2990. Fax: 516-783-8550. p. 1580

Garvey, Maureen, Asst Dir, Merrick Library, 2279 Merrick Ave, Merrick, NY, 11566-4398. Tel: 516-377-6112, Ext 124. Fax: 516-377-1108. p. 1659

Garvey, Patricia A, Head Librn, SNR Denton, 1221 Avenue of the Americas, 24th Flr, New York, NY, 10020. Tel: 212-768-6700. Fax: 212-768-6800. p. 1700

Garvin, Denise, Circ, Duxbury Free Library, 77 Alden St, Duxbury, MA, 02332. Tel: 781-934-2721, Ext 107. Fax: 781-934-0663. p. 1085

Garvin, Pam, Circ, Vernon College, 4400 College Dr, Vernon, TX, 76384. Tel: 940-552-6291, Ext 2220. Fax: 940-552-0288. p. 2395

Garvin, Rebecca, Mgr, Environmental Protection Agency, 290 Broadway, 16th Flr, New York, NY, 10007. Tel: 212-637-3185. Fax: 212-637-3086. p. 1677

Garvin, Thomas, Head Bldg Serv, Mount Prospect Public Library, Ten S Emerson St, Mount Prospect, IL, 60056. Tel: 847-253-5675. Fax: 847-253-0642. p. 677

Garvin, Virginia, Dir, Whitesboro Public Library, 308 W Main, Whitesboro, TX, 76273. Tel: 903-564-5432. Fax: 903-564-6105. p. 2400

Garwood, Rosemary, Dir, Pequannock Township Public Library, 477 Newark Pompton Tpk, Pompton Plains, NJ, 07444. Tel: 973-835-7460. Fax: 973-835-1928. p. 1521

Garwood, Susan, Dir, Rice County Historical Society, 1814 Second Ave NW, Faribault, MN, 55021. Tel: 507-332-2121. Fax: 507-332-2121. p. 1251

Gary, Andy, Ref Librn, Clark County Public Library, 370 S Burns Ave, Winchester, KY, 40391-1876. Tel: 859-744-5661. Fax: 859-744-5993. p. 938

Gary, Rushbrooke, Librn, Roanoke Public Libraries, Melrose, 2607 Salem Tpk, Roanoke, VA, 24017. Tel: 540-853-2648. Fax: 540-853-1030. p. 2494

Garza, Antoinette, Archivist, Our Lady of the Lake University, 411 SW 24th St, San Antonio, TX, 78207-4689. Tel: 210-434-6711, Ext 2324. Fax: 210-436-1616. p. 2380

Garza, Blanca, Head, Ref, Elsa Public Library, 711 N Hidalgo St, Elsa, TX, 78543. Tel: 956-262-3061. Fax: 956-262-3066. p. 2318

Garza, David, Pub Serv, Ref, Los Angeles Mission College Library, 13356 Eldridge Ave, Sylmar, CA, 91342-3200. Tel: 818-364-7750. Fax: 818-364-7749. p. 274

Garza, Debbie, Dir, Dawson County Library, 511 N Third St, Lamesa, TX, 79331. Tel: 806-872-6502. Fax: 806-872-2435. p. 2353

Garza, Elva, Regional Br Operations Mgr, Austin Public Library, Daniel E Ruiz Branch, 1600 Grove Blvd, Austin, TX, 78741. Tel: 512-974-7500. Fax: 512-386-9146. p. 2279

Garza, Enola, Librn, Ed Rachal Memorial Library, 203 S Calixto Mora Ave, Falfurrias, TX, 78355. Tel: 361-325-2144. Fax: 361-325-3743. p. 2318

Garza, Javier F, Archivist, University of Texas, M D Anderson Cancer Center Research Medical Library, 1400 Pressler St, Houston, TX, 77030-3722. Tel: 713-792-2285. Fax: 713-563-3650. p. 2344

Garza, Kimberlee, Mgr, Support Serv, Tempe Public Library, 3500 S Rural Rd, Tempe, AZ, 85282. Tel: 480-350-5557. Fax: 480-350-5544. p. 84

Garza, M'Liss, Ref, Santa Barbara City College, 721 Cliff Dr, Santa Barbara, CA, 93109-2394. Tel: 805-965-0581, Ext 2634. Fax: 805-965-0771. p. 260

Garza, Mary, Circ, Temple Public Library, 100 W Adams Ave, Temple, TX, 76501-7641. Tel: 254-298-5706. Fax: 254-298-5328. p. 2391

Garza, Noemi, Cat, Alicia Salinas City of Alice Public Library, 401 E Third St, Alice, TX, 78332. Tel: 361-664-9506. Fax: 361-668-3248. p. 2273

Garza, Noemi, Dir, Pub Serv, South Texas College Library, 3201 W Pecan Blvd, McAllen, TX, 78501-6661. Tel: 956-872-8330. Fax: 956-872-7202. p. 2361

Garza, Ronda, Dir, Kismet Public Library, 503 Main St, Kismet, KS, 67859-9615. Tel: 620-563-7357. Fax: 620-563-7143. p. 876

Garza, Rosario, Dir, 49-99 Cooperative Library System, c/o Southern California Library Cooperative, 248 E Foothill Blvd, Ste 101, Monrovia, CA, 91016. Tel: 626-359-6111. Fax: 626-359-0001. p. 2938

Garza, Rosario, Dir, Southern California Library Cooperative, 248 E Foothill Blvd, Ste 101, Monrovia, CA, 91016-5522. Tel: 626-359-6111. Fax: 626-359-0001. p. 2939

Garza, Roxanne, Ref Coordr, Laredo Community College, West End Washington St, Laredo, TX, 78040. Tel: 956-721-5280. Fax: 956-721-5447. p. 2353

Garzillo, Robert, Tech Serv Librn, Rhode Island School of Design Library, 15 Westminster St, Providence, RI, 02903. Tel: 401-709-5944. Fax: 401-709-5932. p. 2174

Garzini, Elva, Librn, Scott-Sebastian Regional Library, Scott County Library, 141 Second St, Waldron, AR, 72958. Tel: 479-637-3516. Fax: 479-637-3516. p. 102

Garzon, Gerard G, Dep Dir, Interim Dir, Oakland Public Library, 125 14th St, Oakland, CA, 94612. Tel: 510-238-6720. Fax: 510-238-2232. p. 197

Garzon, Gerry, Assoc Dir, Oakland Public Library, Main Library, 125 14th St, Oakland, CA, 94612. Tel: 510-238-3134. Fax: 510-238-2232. p. 198

Gascon, Guy, Supvr, Libr & Training, International Development Research Centre Library, 150 Kent St, Ottawa, ON, K1G 3H9, CANADA. Tel: 613-236-6163. Fax: 613-563-3858. p. 2831

Gasiewski, Ellen, Coordr, Tri-State College Library Cooperative, c/o Rosemont College Library, 1400 Montgomery Ave, Rosemont, PA, 19010-1699. Tel: 610-525-0796. Fax: 610-525-1939. p. 2955

Gaskell, Carolyn, Dir of Libr, Walla Walla University Libraries, 104 S College Ave, College Place, WA, 99324-1159. Tel: 509-527-2134. Fax: 509-527-2001. p. 2513

Gaskell, Judith A, Librn, Supreme Court of the United States Library, One First St NE, Washington, DC, 20543. Tel: 202-479-3037. Fax: 202-479-3477. p. 416

Gaskell, Millicent, Head Librn, Massachusetts Institute of Technology Libraries, Dewey Library for Management & Social Sciences, MIT Bldg, Rm E53-100, 30 Wadsworth St, Cambridge, MA, 02139. Tel: 617-253-5619. Fax: 617-253-0642. p. 1078

Gaskill, Geraldine, Dep Dir, Horry County Memorial Library, 1008 Fifth Ave, Conway, SC, 29526. Tel: 843-248-1544. Fax: 843-248-1548. p. 2191

Gaskill, Jean, Dir, Surrey Township Public Library, 105 E Michigan, Farwell, MI, 48622. Tel: 989-588-9782. Fax: 989-588-4488. p. 1178

Gaskill, Norine, Libr Serv Coordr, Murrell Memorial Library, Missouri Valley College, Tech Center Bldg, 500 E College St, Marshall, MO, 65340. Tel: 660-831-4180, 660-831-4181. Fax: 660-831-4068. p. 1344

Gaskin, Annette, Librn, Northern Inyo Hospital, 150 Pioneer Lane, Bishop, CA, 93514. Tel: 760-873-5811, Ext 2279. Fax: 760-872-5879. p. 129

Gaskin, Christine, Dir, Southern Methodist College, 541 Broughton St, Orangeburg, SC, 29115. Tel: 803-534-7826, Ext 106. Fax: 803-534-7827. p. 2202

Gaskin, Laura, Ref, Buncombe County Public Libraries, 67 Haywood St, Asheville, NC, 28801. Tel: 828-250-4700. Fax: 828-250-4746. p. 1774

Gaskin-Noel, Susan, Bibliog Instr, Webmaster, Mercy College Libraries, 555 Broadway, Dobbs Ferry, NY, 10522. Tel: 914-674-7672. Fax: 914-674-7581. p. 1615

Gaskins, Paul, Circ, Canada College Library, Bldg 9, 3rd Flr, 4200 Farm Hill Blvd, Redwood City, CA, 94061-1099. Tel: 650-306-3267. Fax: 650-306-3434. p. 215

Gaskins, Rose Ann, Librn, Sullivan County Public Library, Farmersburg Public, 116 W Main St, Farmersburg, IN, 47850. Tel: 812-696-2194. p. 780

Gaspar, Janice, Head, Tech Serv, Providence Public Library, 150 Empire St, Providence, RI, 02903-3283. Tel: 401-455-8021. Fax: 401-455-8075. p. 2173

Gaspard, Chris, Head, Access Serv, University of Texas Health Science Center at San Antonio Libraries, 7703 Floyd Curl Dr, MSC 7940, San Antonio, TX, 78229-3900. Tel: 210-567-2400. Fax: 210-567-2490. p. 2383

Gaspard, Rusty, Ref & Instruction Librn, Louisiana State University at Alexandria, 8100 Hwy 71 S, Alexandria, LA, 71302. Tel: 318-473-6438. Fax: 318-473-6556. p. 940

Gasparro, Joseph, Local Hist & Ref Librn, Boonton Holmes Public Library, 621 Main St, Boonton, NJ, 07005. Tel: 973-334-2980. Fax: 973-334-3917. p. 1473

Gaspen, Kaye, Dir, Trinity University, 125 Michigan Ave NE, Washington, DC, 20017. Tel: 202-884-9350. Fax: 202-884-9241. p. 417

Gasper, Ariel, Asst Librn, United States Marine Corps, Library Services, Bldg 1146, Camp Pendleton, CA, 92055. Tel: 760-725-5104, 760-725-5669. Fax: 760-725-6569. p. 131

Gasperecz, Mamie, Exec Dir, Hermann-Grima House Library, 820 Saint Louis St, New Orleans, LA, 70112. Tel: 504-525-5661. Fax: 504-568-9735. p. 960

Gasperecz, Mamie, Exec Dir, Gallier House Library, 1132 Royal St, New Orleans, LA, 70116. Tel: 504-525-5661. Fax: 504-568-9735. p. 960

Gass, A Beverly, Dean, Learning Res, Guilford Technical Community College, 601 High Point Rd, Jamestown, NC, 27282. Tel: 336-334-4822, Ext 2434. Fax: 336-841-4350. p. 1803

Gass, Adrienne, Ch, Louisville Public Library, 951 Spruce St, Louisville, CO, 80027. Tel: 303-335-4849. Fax: 303-335-4833. p. 317

Gass, John, Info Spec, Jefferson Community & Technical College, Southwest Campus Library, 1000 Community College Dr, Louisville, KY, 40272. Tel: 502-213-7388. Fax: 502-935-8653. p. 924

Gass, Steven, Assoc Dir, Pub Serv, Massachusetts Institute of Technology Libraries, Office of the Director, 160 Memorial Dr, Cambridge, MA, 02142. Tel: 617-253-7058. Fax: 617-253-8894. p. 1077

Gasser, Les, Prof, University of Illinois at Urbana-Champaign, Library & Information Science Bldg, 501 E Daniel St, Champaign, IL, 61820-6211. Tel: 217-333-3280. Fax: 217-244-3302. p. 2965

Gasser, Maxine, Youth Serv, Amherst County Public Library, 382 S Main St, Amherst, VA, 24521. Tel: 434-946-9488. Fax: 434-946-9348. p. 2447

Gasser, Sharon, Assoc Dean of Libr & Educ Tech, James Madison University Libraries & Educational Technologies, 800 S Main St, Harrisonburg, VA, 22807-0001. Tel: 540-568-6160. Fax: 540-568-6339. p. 2470

Gassett, Stephen R, Assoc Librn, Kimbell Art Museum Library, 3333 Camp Bowie Blvd, Fort Worth, TX, 76107. Tel: 817-332-8451. Fax: 817-877-1264. p. 2322

Gassewitz, Debra, Pres, Sport Information Resource Centre (SIRC), 116 Rue Albert St, Ste 400, Ottawa, ON, K1P 5G3, CANADA. Tel: 613-231-7472. Fax: 613-231-3739. p. 2833

Gassler, Claudette, YA Serv, Scarsdale Public Library, 54 Olmsted Rd, Scarsdale, NY, 10583. Tel: 914-722-1300. Fax: 914-722-1305. p. 1739

Gasson, Susan, PhD, Assoc Prof, Drexel University, Rush Bldg, Rm 306, 30 N 33rd St, Philadelphia, PA, 19104-2875. Tel: 215-895-2474. Fax: 215-895-2494. p. 2972

Gast, Cari A, Head, Children's & Teen Curric, Howard County Library System, 6600 Cradlerock Way, Columbia, MD, 21045-4912. Tel: 410-313-7750. Fax: 410-313-7742. p. 1026

Gast, Dena, Libr Spec, Copper Mountain College, 6162 Rotary Way, Joshua Tree, CA, 92252. Tel: 760-366-3791, Ext 5902. Fax: 760-366-5256. p. 161

Gast, Janet, Br Mgr, Los Angeles Public Library System, Platt, 23600 Victory Blvd, Woodland Hills, CA, 91367. Tel: 818-340-9386. Fax: 818-340-9645. p. 174

Gast, Julie, Bus Mgr, L E Phillips Memorial Public Library, 400 Eau Claire St, Eau Claire, WI, 54701. Tel: 715-839-5063. Fax: 715-839-5310. p. 2590

Gastineau, Audrey S, ILL, Ardmore Higher Education Center Library, 611 Veterans Blvd, Ardmore, OK, 73401. Tel: 580-220-2855. Fax: 580-223-5611. p. 1956

Gaston, Betty Jo, Librn, Saint Petersburg College, Saint Petersburg-Gibbs Campus Library, 6605 Fifth Ave N, Saint Petersburg, FL, 33710. Tel: 727-341-7179. Fax: 727-341-7188. p. 483

Gatchell, Linda, Dir, Dorcas Carey Public Library, 236 E Findlay St, Carey, OH, 43316-1250. Tel: 419-396-7921. Fax: 419-396-3046. p. 1865

Gateley, Stephen, Librn/Mgr, E C Dargan Library, One Lifeway Plaza, Nashville, TN, 37234-0142. Tel: 615-251-2000. Fax: 615-277-8433. p. 2255

Gateley, Stephen, Res Librn, Virginia Davis Laskey Research Library, 1008 19th Ave S, Nashville, TN, 37212-2126. Tel: 615-340-7477. Fax: 615-340-7551. p. 2256

Gately, Lynne, Ad, Kimball Public Library, 67 N Main St, Randolph, VT, 05060. Tel: 802-728-5073. Fax: 802-728-6735. p. 2433

Gatenby, Ruth, Br Support, Stormont, Dundas & Glengarry County Library, Winchester Branch, 547 St Lawrence St, Winchester, ON, K0C 2K0, CANADA. Tel: 613-774-2612. Fax: 613-774-5866. p. 2802

Gates, Anitra, Mgr, Tech Serv, Erie County Public Library, 160 E Front St, Erie, PA, 16507. Tel: 814-451-6919. Fax: 814-451-6907. p. 2055

Gates, Anitra, Dir, Mercyhurst College, Ridge Library - North East Campus, 16 W Division St, North East, PA, 16428. Tel: 814-725-6116. Fax: 814-725-6112. p. 2056

Gates, Crystal, Dir, Jackson Parish Library, 614 S Polk Ave, Jonesboro, LA, 71251-3442. Tel: 318-259-5697, 318-259-5698. Fax: 318-259-9984. p. 952

Gates, Diana, Deaf Coll Librn, Gallaudet University Library, 800 Florida Ave NE, Washington, DC, 20002-3095. Tel: 202-651-5063. p. 401

Gates, Donald, Br Mgr, Norfolk Public Library, Larchmont, 6525 Hampton Blvd, Norfolk, VA, 23508. Tel: 757-441-5335. Fax: 757-441-1451. p. 2482

Gates, Eileen, Dir, Porter Memorial Library, 87 Main St, Blandford, MA, 01008-9518. Tel: 413-848-2853. Fax: 413-848-2853. p. 1054

Gates, Elizabeth, Archivist, Spec Coll, Rhodes College, 2000 North Pkwy, Memphis, TN, 38112-1694. Tel: 901-843-3902. Fax: 901-843-3404. p. 2251

Gates, Jane, Head Librn, Albion Public Library, Six N Fourth St, Albion, IL, 62806. Tel: 618-445-3314. p. 587

Gates, Jeanette, Librn, Donnelly College, 608 N 18th St, Kansas City, KS, 66102. Tel: 913-621-8735. Fax: 913-621-8719. p. 875

Gates, Jeffery, Info Serv Librn, Cedarville University, 251 N Main St, Cedarville, OH, 45314-0601. Tel: 937-766-7840. Fax: 937-766-2337. p. 1865

Gates, Jill, Br Mgr, Tazewell County Public Library, Bluefield Branch, 108 Huffard Dr, Bluefield, VA, 24605. Tel: 276-326-1577. Fax: 276-322-5705. p. 2498

Gates, Jim, Dir, National Baseball Hall of Fame & Museum, Inc, 25 Main St, Cooperstown, NY, 13326-0590. Tel: 607-547-0330. Fax: 607-547-4094. p. 1610

Gates, Martha, Interim Exec Dir, Pequot Library, 720 Pequot Ave, Southport, CT, 06890-1496. Tel: 203-259-0346, Ext 17. Fax: 203-259-5602. p. 368

Gates, Sue, Dir, Dacotah Prairie Museum, 21 S Main St, Aberdeen, SD, 57402. Tel: 605-626-7117. Fax: 605-626-4026. p. 2209

Gates, Tom, Head, Archit Libr, Kent State University Libraries, Joseph F Morbito Architecture Library, 309 Taylor Hall, Kent, OH, 44242-0001. Tel: 330-672-0931. p. 1907

Gates, Tom, Librn, Kent State University Libraries, Fashion, 131 Rockwell Hall, Kent, OH, 44242-0001. Tel: 330-672-9500. Fax: 330-672-9578. p. 1907

Gatesman, Mark, Pub Serv, Georgia Highlands College Libraries, 3175 Cedartown Hwy SE, Rome, GA, 30161. Tel: 706-295-6318. Fax: 706-295-6365. p. 548

Gathegi, John, Dr, Prof, University of South Florida, 4202 Fowler Ave, CIS 1040, Tampa, FL, 33620-7800. Tel: 813-974-5322. Fax: 813-974-6840. p. 2964

Gatheright, Sherry, Asst Librn, Antlers Public Library, 104 SE Second St, Antlers, OK, 74523-4000. Tel: 580-298-5649. Fax: 580-298-3567. p. 1956

Gathers, Dawn, Librn, Pocahontas Public Library, 14 Second Ave NW, Pocahontas, IA, 50574. Tel: 712-335-4471. Fax: 712-335-4471. p. 839

Gatin, Susan, Mgr, Libr Serv, Assiniboine Community College Library, 1430 Victoria Ave E, Brandon, MB, R7A 2A9, CANADA. Tel: 204-725-8727, Ext 6637. Fax: 204-725-8740. p. 2747

Gatlabayan, Mariecris, Archivist, University of Alaska Anchorage, Consortium Library, 3211 Providence Dr, Anchorage, AK, 99508-8176. Tel: 907-786-1871. Fax: 907-786-1834. p. 45

Gatlin, Elisabeth, Instr, Pub Serv Librn, Felician College Library, 262 S Main St, Lodi, NJ, 07644-2198. Tel: 201-559-6125. Fax: 201-559-6148. p. 1496

Gatson, Gwendolyn, Tech Serv, The Edward Waters College Library, 1658 Kings Rd, Jacksonville, FL, 32209. Tel: 904-470-8083. Fax: 904-470-8032. p. 452

Gatten, Jeff, Dean, California Institute of the Arts, 24700 McBean Pkwy, Valencia, CA, 91355. Tel: 661-253-7885. Fax: 661-254-4561. p. 278

Gatten, Raida, Access Serv Librn, Woodbury University Library, 7500 Glenoaks Blvd, Burbank, CA, 91510-1099. Tel: 818-252-5200. Fax: 818-767-4534. p. 130

Gatti, Eileen, Asst Dir, Vermont Technical College, Main St, Randolph Center, VT, 05061. Tel: 802-728-1237. Fax: 802-728-1506. p. 2433

Gatti, Olivia, Youth Serv Librn, Newbury Town Library, 0 Lunt St, Byfield, MA, 01922-1232. Tel: 978-465-0539. Fax: 978-465-1071. p. 1072

Gattin, Leroy, Dir, Lonoke Prairie County Regional Library Headquarters, 204 E Second St, Lonoke, AR, 72086-2858. Tel: 501-676-6635. Fax: 501-676-7687. p. 108

Gatto, J, Ser, Tech Serv, North Shore Public Library, 250 Rte 25A, Shoreham, NY, 11786-9677. Tel: 631-929-4488. Fax: 631-929-4551. p. 1743

Gatzke, Jeanine, Assoc Syst Adminr, Tech Serv, Concordia University, 1282 Concordia Ave, Saint Paul, MN, 55104. Tel: 651-641-8242. Fax: 651-641-8782. p. 1278

Gau, Jean, Libr Asst I, Marshall-Lyon County Library, 301 W Lyon St, Marshall, MN, 56258. Tel: 507-537-7003. p. 1258

Gau, Linda, Libr Serv Tech, Northcentral Technical College Library, 1000 W Campus Dr, Wausau, WI, 54401. Tel: 715-803-1056. Fax: 715-675-9776. p. 2646

Gaub, Stephanie, Photo Archivist, Orange County Regional History Center, 65 E Central Blvd, Orlando, FL, 32801. Tel: 407-836-8559. Fax: 407-836-8550. p. 477

Gaud, Connie, Circ Mgr, Rogers Memorial Library, 91 Coopers Farm Rd, Southampton, NY, 11968. Tel: 631-283-0774. Fax: 631-287-6539. p. 1746

Gauder, Heidi, Coordr, Instruction & Ref, University of Dayton Libraries, 300 College Park Dr, Dayton, OH, 45469-1360. Tel: 937-229-4259. Fax: 937-229-4215. p. 1894

Gaudet, Katina, Ref Librn, Lafourche Parish Public Library, South Lafourche Public Library, 16241 East Main St, CutOff, LA, 70345. Tel: 985-632-7140. Fax: 985-632-4963. p. 971

Gaudet, Lauri, Asst Librn, Gale Library, 16 S Main St, Newton, NH, 03858-3310. Tel: 603-382-4691. Fax: 603-382-2528. p. 1460

Gaudet, Mark, Br Head, Toronto Public Library, Humber Bay, 200 Park Lawn Rd, Toronto, ON, M8Y 3J1, CANADA. Tel: 416-394-5300. Fax: 416-394-5072. p. 2862

Gaudin, Charles, Per, Belhaven University, 1500 Peachtree St, Jackson, MS, 39202. Tel: 601-968-5951. Fax: 601-968-5968. p. 1303

Gaudin, Kytara, Head, Access Serv, State Library of Louisiana, 701 N Fourth St, Baton Rouge, LA, 70802-5232. Tel: 225-342-4920. Fax: 225-219-4804. p. 945

Gaudin, Kytara A, Head, Access Serv, Loan SHARK, State Library of Louisiana, 701 N Fourth St, Baton Rouge, LA, 70802. Tel: 225-342-4920, 342-4918. Fax: 225-219-4725. p. 2944

Gaudreau, Frédéric, Tech Serv, Canadian Police College Library, Canadian Police College, One Sandridge Rd, Bldg C, Ottawa, ON, K1G 3J2, CANADA. Tel: 613-993-3225. Fax: 613-993-2220. p. 2829

Gaudreau, Josée, Tech Serv, College Francois-Xavier-Garneau, 1660 blvd de l'Entente, Quebec, QC, G1S 4S3, CANADA. Tel: 418-688-8310, Ext 3504. Fax: 418-681-9384. p. 2978

Gaudreau, Louis, Ref, Cegep de Chicoutimi, 534 Jacques-Cartier, Est, Chicoutimi, QC, G7H 1Z6, CANADA. Tel: 418-549-9520, Ext 337. Fax: 418-549-1315. p. 2881

Gaudreau, Luke, Res & Instruction Librn, Harvard Library, John F Kennedy School of Government Library, 79 John F Kennedy St, Cambridge, MA, 02138. Tel: 617-495-1300. Fax: 617-495-1972. p. 1075

Gaudreau, Pierre, Actg Librn, Hydro Quebec Bibliotheque, 800, De Maisonneuve E, blvd, 2nd Flr, Montreal, QC, H2L 4M8, CANADA. Tel: 514-840-3000, Ext 5939. Fax: 514-840-5044. p. 2896

Gauerke, Debbie, Br Coordr, Marathon County Public Library, Edgar Branch, 224 S Third Ave, Edgar, WI, 54426. Tel: 715-352-3155. Fax: 715-352-3155. p. 2646

Gauger, Barbara, Coll Develop, Librn, Sci, University of South Dakota, 414 E Clark St, Vermillion, SD, 57069. Tel: 605-677-5371. Fax: 605-677-6834. p. 2220

Gauger, Cynthia, Asst Librn, Western Plains Library System, Weatherford Public Library, 219 E Frankin, Weatherford, OK, 73096-5134. Tel: 580-772-3591. Fax: 580-772-3591. p. 1961

Gaughan, Marion, Cat, Oskaloosa Public Library, 301 S Market St, Oskaloosa, IA, 52577. Tel: 641-673-0441. Fax: 641-673-6237. p. 837

Gaul, Ben, Librn, Baker & Hostetler Library, 65 E State St, Ste 2100, Columbus, OH, 43215-4260. Tel: 614-228-1541, Ext 2608. Fax: 614-462-2616. p. 1883

Gault, Carrie, Librn, UPMC Horizon, 2200 Memorial Dr, Farrell, PA, 16121. Tel: 724-589-6322, 724-983-7558. Fax: 724-589-6587. p. 2057

Gault, Elizabeth, Ref Librn, Lone Star College System, Tomball College Library, 30555 Tomball Pkwy, Tomball, TX, 77375-4036. Tel: 832-559-4206. Fax: 832-559-4248. p. 2340

Gault, Erin, Pub Serv Librn, Lamar County Library System, Purvis Public, 122 Shelby Speights Dr, Purvis, MS, 39475-4151. Tel: 601-794-6291. Fax: 601-794-6291. p. 1313

Gault, Linda, Br Mgr, Santa Cruz City-County Library System Headquarters, Scotts Valley Branch, 251 Kings Valley Rd, Scotts Valley, CA, 95066. Tel: 831-427-7712. Fax: 831-427-7719. p. 264

Gault, Mary Kaye, Coordr, Access Serv, University of South Carolina Upstate Library, 800 University Way, Spartanburg, SC, 29303. Tel: 864-503-5679. Fax: 864-503-5601. p. 2205

Gault, Melody, Dir, Franklin County Public Library District, 919 Main St, Brookville, IN, 47012-1498. Tel: 765-647-4031. Fax: 765-647-0278. p. 730

Gault, Melody, Dir, Franklin County Public Library District, Laurel Public Library, 200 N Clay St, Laurel, IN, 47024. Tel: 765-698-2582. Fax: 765-698-2626. p. 730

Gault, Robin, Assoc Dir, Florida State University Libraries, College of Law Library, 425 W Jefferson St, Tallahassee, FL, 32306. Tel: 850-644-7487. Fax: 850-644-5216. p. 494

Gault, Stephanie, Cat Librn, Belhaven University, 1500 Peachtree St, Jackson, MS, 39202. Tel: 601-968-5949. Fax: 601-968-5968. p. 1303

Gaumer, Alice, Asst Dir, Indianola Public Library, 207 North B St, Indianola, IA, 50125. Tel: 515-961-9418. Fax: 515-961-9419. p. 822

Gaumond, George R, Dr, Univ Librn, Valdosta State University, Odum Library - MLIS, 1500 N Patterson St, Valdosta, GA, 31698-0144. Tel: 229-333-5860. Fax: 229-259-5055. p. 2964

Gauna, Audrey, Asst Librn, Proskauer Rose LLP, 2049 Century Park E, Ste 3200, Los Angeles, CA, 90067. Tel: 310-284-5683, 310-557-2900. Fax: 310-557-2193. p. 177

Gaunt, Marianne, Univ Librn, VPres for Info Serv, Rutgers University Libraries, 169 College Ave, New Brunswick, NJ, 08901-1163. Tel: 732-932-7505. Fax: 732-932-7637. p. 1508

Gaus, Timothy, Mgr, Libr Serv, H J Heinz Co, 1000 Ericsson Dr, Warrendale, PA, 15086. Tel: 724-778-5683. Fax: 724-778-5625. p. 2151

Gauss, Nancy, Dir, Western State College, 600 N Adams St, Gunnison, CO, 81231. Tel: 970-943-2898. Fax: 970-943-2042. p. 312

Gaut, Nancy, Br Mgr, Warren-Trumbull County Public Library, Brookfield Branch, 7032 Grove St, Brookfield, OH, 44403. Tel: 330-448-8134. p. 1944

Gauthier, Bernice, Cat/Acq Tech, Stormont, Dundas & Glengarry County Library, 26 Pitt St, Cornwall, ON, K6J 3P2, CANADA. Tel: 613-936-8777, Ext 213. Fax: 613-936-2532. p. 2801

Gauthier, Johanne, Per, Cegep de Chicoutimi, 534 Jacques-Cartier, Est, Chicoutimi, QC, G7H 1Z6, CANADA. Tel: 418-549-9520, Ext 337. Fax: 418-549-1315. p. 2881

Gauthier, Mona, Librn, Bibliotheque Ste Anne, 16 Rue de l'Eglise, Sainte Anne, MB, R5H 1H8, CANADA. Tel: 204-422-9958. Fax: 204-422-9958. p. 2751

Gauthier, Paula J, Dir, Brandon Township Public Library, 304 South St, Ortonville, MI, 48462. Tel: 248-627-1470. Fax: 248-627-9880. p. 1215

Gavalis, Amy, Ch, Lincoln Public Library, Three Bedford Rd, Lincoln, MA, 01773. Tel: 781-259-8465. Fax: 781-259-1056. p. 1099

Gavelin, Marla, Librn, Chinook Regional Library, Glentworth Branch, Glentworth School, Glentworth, SK, S0H 1V0, CANADA. Tel: 306-266-4804. p. 2928

Gavenman, Ilene, Ch, YA Serv, Blanchard-Santa Paula Public Library District, 119 N Eighth St, Santa Paula, CA, 93060-2709. Tel: 805-525-3615. Fax: 805-933-2324. p. 266

Gavett, Franklin, Head, Borrower Serv, Colgate University, 13 Oak Dr, Hamilton, NY, 13346-1398. Tel: 315-228-7300. Fax: 315-228-7934. p. 1633

Gavin, Christy, Librn, California State University, 9001 Stockdale Hwy, Bakersfield, CA, 93311-1022. Tel: 661-654-3237. Fax: 661-654-3238. p. 123

Gavin, Diane, Commun Libr Mgr, County of Los Angeles Public Library, Antelope Valley Bookmobile, 601 W Lancaster Blvd, Lancaster, CA, 93534. Tel: 661-948-8270. Fax: 661-949-7386. p. 140

Gavin, Sonia, Libr Dir, Montana Legislative Reference Center, State Capitol, Rm 10, Helena, MT, 59620. Tel: 406-444-3588. Fax: 406-444-2588. p. 1382

Gavino, Edith, Support Serv Mgr, Braille Institute Library Services, 741 N Vermont Ave, Los Angeles, CA, 90029-3514. Tel: 323-663-1111, Ext 1284. Fax: 323-662-2440. p. 168

Gaw, Galena, Dir, South Carolina School for the Deaf & the Blind, 355 Cedar Springs Rd, Spartanburg, SC, 29302-4699. Tel: 864-577-7642, 864-585-7711. Fax: 864-577-7649. p. 2204

Gawdyna, Lori, Librn, Saint Elizabeth Health Center, 1044 Belmont Ave, Youngstown, OH, 44501-1790. Tel: 330-480-3039. Fax: 330-480-3044. p. 1953

Gawel, Diane, Br Supvr, Western Manitoba Regional Library, Carberry-North Cypress Branch, 115 Main St, Carberry, MB, R0K 0H0, CANADA. Tel: 204-834-3043. p. 2748

Gawlik, Gail, Head, Tech Serv, University of St Francis, 500 Wilcox St, Joliet, IL, 60435. Tel: 815-740-3449. Fax: 815-740-3364. p. 660

Gawne, Shirley, Acq, Workers' Compensation Board of British Columbia Library, 6951 Westminster Hwy, Richmond, BC, V7C 1C6, CANADA. Tel: 604-231-8450. Fax: 604-279-7608. p. 2737

Gawron, Chris, Coordr, Circ, Hershey Public Library, 701 Cocoa Ave, Hershey, PA, 17033. Tel: 717-533-6555. Fax: 717-534-1666. p. 2069

Gawronski, Christopher, Br Mgr, Milwaukee Public Library, Bay View, 2566 S Kinnickinnic Ave, Milwaukee, WI, 53207. Tel: 414-286-3019. Fax: 414-286-8459. p. 2620

Gawronski, Pam, Librn, Gannett Co Inc, 120 E Lenawee, Lansing, MI, 48919. Tel: 517-377-1008. Fax: 517-377-1298. p. 1201

Gay, Agnes, Asst Archivist, Oglala Lakota College, Three Mile Creek Rd, Kyle, SD, 57752. Tel: 605-455-6069. Fax: 605-455-6070. p. 2213

Gay, Bruce, Head, Tech Serv, Milwaukee Public Library, 814 W Wisconsin Ave, Milwaukee, WI, 53233-2385. Tel: 414-286-3000. Fax: 414-286-2794. p. 2620

Gay, Craig, Interim Dir, Regent College, 5800 University Blvd, Vancouver, BC, V6T 2E4, CANADA. Tel: 604-224-3245, Ext 322. Fax: 604-224-3097. p. 2742

Gay, David, Intl Law Librn, University of Tulsa Libraries, Mabee Legal Information Center, 3120 E Fourth Pl, Tulsa, OK, 74104-3189. Tel: 918-631-2404. Fax: 918-631-3556. p. 1984

Gay, Pamela, Librn, San Diego Aero-Space Museum, Inc, 2001 Pan American Plaza, Balboa Park, San Diego, CA, 92101-1636. Tel: 619-234-8291, Ext 25. Fax: 619-233-4526. p. 232

Gay, Patricia, Ch, Troup-Harris Regional Library System, 115 Alford St, La Grange, GA, 30240-3041. Tel: 706-882-7784, Ext 21. Fax: 706-883-7342. p. 537

Gay, Sherry, Ch, Payson City Library, 66 S Main St, Payson, UT, 84651-2223. Tel: 801-465-5220. Fax: 801-465-5208. p. 2410

Gay, William David, Ref, Arizona State University, College of Law, 110 S McAllister Ave, Tempe, AZ, 85287-7806. Tel: 480-965-4860. Fax: 480-965-4283. p. 83

Gaydet, Dinah, Ref Librn, Atlanta-Fulton Public Library System, South Fulton Regional Library, 4055 Flatshoals Rd SW, Union City, GA, 30291. Tel: 770-306-3092. Fax: 770-306-3127. p. 512

Gaydon, Eva, Dir, Blue Earth Community Library, 124 W Seventh St, Blue Earth, MN, 56013-1308. Tel: 507-526-5012. Fax: 507-526-4683. p. 1242

Gaydos, Judith E, Librn, University of Pittsburgh at Titusville, 520 E Main St, Titusville, PA, 16354. Tel: 814-827-4512. Fax: 814-827-4449. p. 2146

Gayhart, Mickie, Librn, Preble County District Library, West Elkton Branch, PO Box 100, West Elkton, OH, 45070. Tel: 937-787-4873. Fax: 937-787-3153. p. 1898

Gaylard, Valerie, ILL, Virginia Military Institute, Letcher Ave, Lexington, VA, 24450. Tel: 540-464-7228. Fax: 540-464-7279. p. 2474

Gaylor, Lisa, Sr Serv, James Kennedy Public Library, 320 First Ave E, Dyersville, IA, 52040. Tel: 563-875-8912. Fax: 563-875-6162. p. 812

Gaylor, Mary Lee, Ref Librn, Riverhead Free Library, 330 Court St, Riverhead, NY, 11901-2885. Tel: 631-727-3228. Fax: 631-727-4762. p. 1728

Gaylor, Philleatra, Adminr, Smith, Currie & Hancock, 2700 Marquis One Tower, 245 Peachtree Center Ave, NE, Atlanta, GA, 30303-1227. Tel: 404-582-8098. Fax: 404-688-0671. p. 518

Gaylord, Margaret Ann, Head Librn, Edwardsburgh/Cardinal Public Library, 618 County Rd 2, Cardinal, ON, K0E 1E0, CANADA. Tel: 613-657-3822. p. 2798

Gaylord, Philleatra, Chattanooga Satellite Librn, US Court of Appeals for the Sixth Circuit Library, 312 Potter Stewart US Courthouse, Cincinnati, OH, 45202. Tel: 423-752-5331. Fax: 513-564-7329. p. 1873

Gaylord, Thomas, Res/Fac Serv Librn, Illinois Institute of Technology, Chicago-Kent College of Law Library, 565 W Adams St, Chicago, IL, 60661. Tel: 312-906-5643. Fax: 312-906-5679. p. 615

Gaynor, Cynthia, Head, Ref, Reed Memorial Library, 167 E Main St, Ravenna, OH, 44266-3197. Tel: 330-296-2827. Fax: 330-296-3780. p. 1931

Gaynor, Kathy, Info Serv Librn, Thompson Rivers University, 900 McGill Rd, Kamloops, BC, V2C 5N3, CANADA. Tel: 250-828-5300. Fax: 250-828-5313. p. 2730

Gayton, Joel, Br Mgr, Walla Walla County Rural Library District, Plaza Library, 1640 Plaza Way, Walla Walla, WA, 99362. Tel: 509-525-5161. Fax: 509-525-5161. p. 2547

Gaza, Joyce, Librn, Butte County Public Law Library, 1675 Montgomery St, Oroville, CA, 95965. Tel: 530-538-7122. Fax: 530-534-1499. p. 202

Gazan, Rich, Asst Prof, University of Hawaii, 2550 The Mall, Honolulu, HI, 96822. Tel: 808-956-7321. Fax: 808-956-5835. p. 2964

Gazaway, Vicki, Human Res, Sequoyah Regional Library System, 116 Brown Industrial Pkwy, Canton, GA, 30114-2899. Tel: 770-479-3090, Ext 221. Fax: 770-479-3069. p. 523

Gazo, Dominique, Chef de Section, Serv Publics, Bibliothèques de Montrèal, Saint-Laurent, 1380, rue de l'Église, Montreal, QC, H4L 2H2, CANADA. Tel: 514-855-6000, Ext 4726. Fax: 514-855-6129. p. 2891

Gazsi, Anne-Marie, Coordr, AMEC Americas, 801 Sixth Ave SW, Ste 900, Calgary, AB, T2P 3W3, CANADA. Tel: 403-298-4518. Fax: 403-298-4125. p. 2688

Gazzarari, Michael, Circ Supvr, Redford Township District Library, 25320 W Six Mile, Redford, MI, 48240. Tel: 313-531-5960. Fax: 313-531-1721. p. 1220

Gazzo, Bridget, Res Serv, Harvard Library, Dumbarton Oaks Research Library, 1703 32nd St NW, Washington, MA, 20007. Tel: 202-339-6400. Fax: 202-625-0279. p. 1074

Ge, Sherry, Syst Librn, Tennessee State University, 3500 John A Merritt Blvd, Nashville, TN, 37209. Tel: 615-963-5237. Fax: 615-963-5216. p. 2259

Gearhart, Amanda, Dir, Kittanning Public Library, 280 N Jefferson, Kittanning, PA, 16201. Tel: 724-543-1383. Fax: 724-543-1621. p. 2074

Gearhart, Marianne, Assoc Dir, Fairfax County Public Library, 12000 Government Center Pkwy, Ste 324, Fairfax, VA, 22035-0012. Tel: 703-324-3100. Fax: 703-324-8365. p. 2461

Gearhart, Melissa, Acq, West Georgia Regional Library, 710 Rome St, Carrollton, GA, 30117. Tel: 770-836-6711. Fax: 770-836-4787. p. 523

Geary, Brian, Librn, The American Society for Nondestructive Testing Library, 1711 Arlingate Lane, Columbus, OH, 43228. Tel: 614-274-6003, Ext 245. Fax: 614-274-6899. p. 1883

Geary, Carol, Ch, Sutton Free Public Library, Four Uxbridge Rd, Sutton, MA, 01590. Tel: 508-865-8752. Fax: 508-865-8751. p. 1130

Geary, Gini, ILL, University of Alaska Anchorage, Matanuska-Susitna College, 8295 E College Dr, Palmer, AK, 99645. Tel: 907-745-9740. Fax: 907-745-9777. p. 52

Geary, Gregg, Head Librn, University of Hawaii at Manoa Library, Gregg M Sinclair Library, 2425 Campus Rd, Honolulu, HI, 96822. Tel: 808-956-5425. Fax: 808-956-5952. p. 566

Geary, Mary K, Pub Serv Librn, Northwestern University Library, Transportation Library, 1970 Campus Dr, Evanston, IL, 60208. Tel: 847-467-5325. Fax: 847-491-8601. p. 644

Gebb, Billie Anne, Librn, Frontier Nursing Service Library, 195 School St, Hyden, KY, 41749. Tel: 606-672-2312. Fax: 606-672-3779. p. 918

Gebel, Doris, Youth Serv, Northport-East Northport Public Library, 151 Laurel Ave, Northport, NY, 11768. Tel: 631-261-6930. Fax: 631-261-6718. p. 1707

Gebelein, Maureen, Dir, Fullerton Public Library, 353 W Commonwealth Ave, Fullerton, CA, 92832-1796. Tel: 714-738-6380. Fax: 714-447-3280. p. 154

Gebhard, Darla, Res, Brown County Historical Society, Two N Broadway, New Ulm, MN, 56073. Tel: 507-233-2616, 507-233-2619. Fax: 507-354-1068. p. 1268

Gebhard, Lyn, Ch, Sparta Public Library, 22 Woodport Rd, Sparta, NJ, 07871. Tel: 973-729-3101. Fax: 973-729-1755. p. 1531

Gebhardt, Denise, Asst Librn, Chinook Regional Library, Eastend Branch, Eastend Memorial Hall, Eastend, SK, S0N 0T0, CANADA. Tel: 306-295-3788. p. 2928

Gebhardt, Maria, Mgr, Bus Serv, Broward County Division of Libraries, 100 S Andrews Ave, Fort Lauderdale, FL, 33301. Tel: 954-357-7750. Fax: 954-357-5733. p. 440

Gebhardt, Patricia V, Dir, Pub Serv, Gail Borden Public Library District, 270 N Grove Ave, Elgin, IL, 60120-5596. Tel: 847-429-5982. Fax: 847-742-0485. p. 640

Gebhardt, Roberta, Tech Serv Librn, Montana Historical Society, 225 N Roberts St, Helena, MT, 59601-4514. Tel: 406-444-4702. Fax: 406-444-5297. p. 1382

Gebhert, Sarah, Librn, Lenawee County Library, Clayton Branch, 3457 State St, Clayton, MI, 49235-9205. Tel: 517-445-2619. Fax: 517-445-2619. p. 1147

Geddes, Faye, Head Librn, Raymond Public Library, 15 Broadway S, Raymond, AB, T0K 2S0, CANADA. Tel: 403-752-4785. Fax: 587-271-4710. p. 2714

Gedell, Karla, Res Librn, Minnesota Attorney General Library, Bremer Tower, Ste 1050, 445 Minnesota St, Saint Paul, MN, 55101-2109. Tel: 651-757-1050, 651-757-1055. Fax: 651-296-7000. p. 1279

Gedeon, Randle J, Monographic Acq Librn, Western Michigan University, Arcadia at Vande Giessen St, Kalamazoo, MI, 49008-5353. Tel: 269-387-5227. Fax: 269-387-5193. p. 1198

Gedevanishvili, Elene, Dir, Art Institute of Houston Library, 14400 Northwest Freeway, Houston, TX, 77040. Tel: 713-353-4142. Fax: 713-966-2701. p. 2334

Geditz, Pat, Librn, South Dakota School for the Blind & Visually Impaired, 423 17th Ave SE, Aberdeen, SD, 57401-7699. Tel: 605-626-2580. p. 2210

Gee, Brad, Coordr, Ref & Instrul Serv, University of Wisconsin-River Falls, 410 S Third St, River Falls, WI, 54022. Tel: 715-425-3552. Fax: 715-425-0609. p. 2635

Gee, Charles B, Dir, Pine Mountain Regional Library, 218 Perry St NW, Manchester, GA, 31816-1317. Tel: 706-846-3851. Fax: 706-846-8455, 706-846-9632. p. 542

Gee, Joanna, Commun Libr Mgr, County of Los Angeles Public Library, Duarte Library, 1301 Buena Vista St, Duarte, CA, 91010-2410. Tel: 626-358-1865. Fax: 626-303-4917. p. 141

Gee, Ka-Chuen, Cat, Head, Tech Serv, Lehman College, City University of New York, 250 Bedford Park Blvd W, Bronx, NY, 10468-1589. Tel: 718-960-8428. Fax: 718-960-8952. p. 1587

Geenwood, Honora, Ad, South Saint Paul Public Library, 106 Third Ave N, South Saint Paul, MN, 55075-2098. Tel: 651-554-3240. Fax: 651-554-3241. p. 1285

Geer, Gary, Coll Develop, University of South Carolina, 1322 Greene St, Columbia, SC, 29208-0103. Tel: 803-777-3142. p. 2189

Geer, Linda, Asst Dir, H J Nugen Public Library, 103 E Main St, New London, IA, 52645. Tel: 319-367-7704. Fax: 319-367-7710. p. 835

Geer, Sharon, Asst Librn, Voluntown Public Library, 107 Main St, Voluntown, CT, 06384-1820. Tel: 860-376-0485. Fax: 860-376-4324. p. 373

Geernaert, Pamela, Ch & Youth Librn, Vista Grande Public Library, 14 Avenida Torreon, Santa Fe, NM, 87508-9199. Tel: 505-466-7323. Fax: 505-466-3889. p. 1564

Geffert, Bryn, Librn of the Col, Amherst College, Amherst, MA, 01002. Fax: 413-542-2662. p. 1048

Geffner, Linda, Dir, Saint Joseph College, 1678 Asylum Ave, West Hartford, CT, 06117-2791. Tel: 860-232-4571. Fax: 860-523-4356. p. 376

Geffner, Meryl, Ref & Instruction Librn, Edmonds Community College Library, 20000 68th Ave W, Lynnwood, WA, 98036. Tel: 425-640-1529. p. 2520

Gegenhuber, Susan, Principal Librn, Pasadena Public Library, 285 E Walnut St, Pasadena, CA, 91101. Tel: 626-744-4066. Fax: 626-585-8396. p. 207

Gehn, Diane, Circ, Andalusia Township Library, 503 W Second St, Andalusia, IL, 61232. Tel: 309-798-2542. Fax: 309-798-2310. p. 588

Gehrig, Debbie, Head, Circ, Dunlap Public Library District, 302 S First St, Dunlap, IL, 61525. Tel: 309-243-5716. Fax: 309-243-5874. p. 638

Gehrig, J Scott, Dir, Sheboygan Falls Memorial Library, 330 Buffalo St, Sheboygan Falls, WI, 53085-1399. Tel: 920-467-7908. p. 2638

Gehring, Dan, Dir, Eldora Public Library, 1202 Tenth St, Eldora, IA, 50627. Tel: 641-939-2173. Fax: 641-939-7563. p. 813

Gehring, Kathleen, Res Support & Instruction Librn, Connecticut College, 270 Mohegan Ave, New London, CT, 06320-4196. Tel: 860-439-5225. Fax: 860-439-2871. p. 359

Gehring, Michelle, Librn, McLean-Mercer Regional Library, Garrison Branch, 32 S Main, Garrison, ND, 58540-7287. Tel: 701-463-7336. p. 1848

Gehring, Suzanne, Head, Archives & Instrul Serv, Asbury University, One Macklem Dr, Wilmore, KY, 40390-1198. Tel: 859-858-3511, Ext 2270. Fax: 859-858-3921. p. 938

Gehrke, Amanda, Youth Serv Librn, Madison Heights Public Library, 240 W 13 Mile Rd, Madison Heights, MI, 48071-1894. Tel: 248-588-7763. Fax: 248-588-2470. p. 1205

Gehrke, Lynne, Br Librn, Wisconsin State Law Library, Milwaukee Legal Resource Center, Courthouse, Rm 307A, 901 N Ninth St, Milwaukee, WI, 53233. Tel: 414-278-4900. Fax: 414-223-1818. p. 2611

Gehrking, Mary Jo, Tech Serv, The Alliance for Children & Families, 11700 W Lake Park Dr, Milwaukee, WI, 53224. Tel: 414-359-1040, Ext 3615. Fax: 414-359-1074. p. 2616

Geibel, Jeanne, Mgr, Kent County Public Library, North County, 111-B1 N Main St, Galena, MD, 21635. Tel: 410-648-5380. p. 1023

Geibel, Jeanne, Mgr, Kent County Public Library, Rock Hall, 5585 Main St Municipal Bldg, Chestertown, MD, 21661. Tel: 410-639-7162. p. 1023

Geiger, Brent, Br Mgr, Saint Tammany Parish Library, Covington Branch, 310 W 21st Ave, Covington, LA, 70433. Tel: 985-893-6280. Fax: 985-893-6283. p. 948

Geiger, Chet, Dir, Homer Public Library, 385 South St NW, Homer, OH, 43027. Tel: 740-892-2020. Fax: 740-892-2036. p. 1905

Geiger, Debbie, Circ Supvr, Bradford County Public Library, 456 W Pratt St, Starke, FL, 32091-3396. Tel: 904-368-3911. Fax: 904-964-2164. p. 491

Geiger, Joseph N, Jr, Dir, West Virginia Archives & History Library, Cultural Ctr, 1900 Kanawha Blvd E, Charleston, WV, 25305-0300. Tel: 304-558-0230. Fax: 304-558-4193. p. 2556

Geiger, Kate, Dir, Indiana Free Library, Inc, 845 Philadelphia St, Indiana, PA, 15701-3908. Tel: 724-465-8841. Fax: 724-465-9902. p. 2071

Geiger, Richard, Dir, San Francisco Chronicle Library, 901 Mission St, San Francisco, CA, 94103. Tel: 415-777-6001. Fax: 415-896-0668. p. 245

Geiger, Susan, Ref Serv Librn, Elizabeth City State University, 1704 Weeksville Rd, Elizabeth City, NC, 27909. Tel: 252-335-3586. Fax: 252-335-3446. p. 1790

Geisel, Mary, Ch, Starke County Public Library System, 152 W Culver Rd, Knox, IN, 46534-2220. Tel: 574-772-7323. p. 757

Geiser, Julie, Librn, Wyoming Pioneer Home Library, 141 Pioneer Home Dr, Thermopolis, WY, 82443-2451. Tel: 307-864-3151. Fax: 307-864-2934. p. 2661

Geisinger, Christi, Circ, ILL, Manchester Community College Library, Great Path, Manchester, CT, 06040. Tel: 860-512-2880. Fax: 860-512-2871. p. 350

Geisler, Gary, Asst Prof, University of Texas at Austin, One University Sta, D7000, Austin, TX, 78712-0390. Tel: 512-471-3821. Fax: 512-471-3971. p. 2975

Geisser, Gail, Circ Mgr, Rhode Island School of Design Library, 15 Westminster St, Providence, RI, 02903. Tel: 401-709-5900. Fax: 401-709-5932. p. 2174

Geist, Mary, Regional Librn, Brunswick Correctional Center, 1147 Planters Rd, PO Box 207C, Lawrenceville, VA, 23868-3499. Tel: 434-848-4131, Ext 1146. Fax: 434-848-0971. p. 2473

Geitner, Lorin, Ref Librn, Chapman University School of Law, 370 N Glassell St, Rm 325, Orange, CA, 92866. Tel: 714-628-2537. p. 201

Gejdos, Lorie, Librn, Southeast Regional Library, Regina Beach Branch, 133 Donovel Crescent, Regina Beach, SK, S0G 4C0, CANADA. Tel: 306-729-2062. p. 2930

Gekosky, Sandra, Librn, Appalachian Behavioral Healthcare, Patients' Library, 100 Hospital Dr, Athens, OH, 45701. Tel: 740-594-5000. Fax: 740-594-3006. p. 1856

Gekosky, Sandra, Librn, Appalachian Behavioral Healthcare, Staff Library, 100 Hospital Dr, Athens, OH, 45701. Tel: 740-594-5000. Fax: 740-594-3006. p. 1856

Gelber, Irwin, Exec Dir, Saint Johnsbury Athenaeum, 1171 Main St, Saint Johnsbury, VT, 05819-2289. Tel: 802-748-8291. Fax: 802-748-8086. p. 2435

Gelbwasser, Sherry, Librn, Asnuntuck Community College, 170 Elm St, Enfield, CT, 06082-0068. Tel: 860-253-3161. Fax: 860-253-9310. p. 338

Gelderman, Cynthia Ann, Dir, Hartley Public Library, 91 First St SE, Hartley, IA, 51346. Tel: 712-928-2080. Fax: 712-928-2823. p. 820

Geldermann, Anne, Ref Serv, United States Trademark Office Law Library, 600 Dulany St, MDE 4B5, Alexandria, VA, 22314-5791. Tel: 571-270-1504. Fax: 571-273-1504. p. 2446

Geldmacher, Bonnie, Acq, Brigham Young University, Howard W Hunter Law Library, 256 JRCB, Provo, UT, 84602-8000. Tel: 801-422-3593. Fax: 801-422-0404. p. 2411

Gele, Susan, Pub Relations, Central Arkansas Library System, 100 Rock St, Little Rock, AR, 72201-4698. Tel: 501-918-3086. p. 106

Geleske, Jo, Dir, Wakarusa Public Library, 124 N Elkhart St, Wakarusa, IN, 46573. Tel: 574-862-2465. Fax: 574-862-4156. p. 785

Gelhausen, Michael J, Dir, Hartford Public Library, 115 N Main St, Hartford, WI, 53027-1596. Tel: 262-673-8241. Fax: 262-673-8300. p. 2597

Gelineau, Pamela, Govt Doc, Per, Johnson State College Library, 337 College Hill, Johnson, VT, 05656. Tel: 802-635-1271. Fax: 802-635-1294. p. 2427

Gelineau, Renate, Asst Circ Librn, Aldrich Public Library, Six Washington St, Barre, VT, 05641-4227. Tel: 802-476-7550. Fax: 802-479-0450 (Call before sending fax). p. 2418

Gelinski, Patricia, Ch, Garfield Public Library, 500 Midland Ave, Garfield, NJ, 07026. Tel: 973-478-3800. Fax: 973-478-7162. p. 1487

Gelis, Doug Andre, Librn, Washington State Library, Washington Corrections Center for Women, 9601 Bujacich Rd NW, MS WP-04, Gig Harbor, WA, 98332-8300. Tel: 253-858-4230. Fax: 253-858-4271. p. 2545

Geller, Linda, Ref, Governors State University Library, One University Pkwy, University Park, IL, 60466-0975. Tel: 708-534-4136. Fax: 708-534-4564. p. 711

Geller, Marie, Coordr, Ch Serv, Briggs Public Library, 108 E Railroad St, Saint Johns, MI, 48879-1526. Tel: 989-224-4702. Fax: 989-224-1205. p. 1225

Geller, Marilyn, Coll Mgt Librn, Lesley University, 89 Brattle St, Cambridge, MA, 02138-2790. Tel: 617-349-8840. Fax: 617-349-8849. p. 1077

Geller, Miriam, Librn, Children's Hospital Boston Library, William B Stem Radiology Library, Dept Radiology, Main 2, 300 Longwood Ave, Boston, MA, 02115. Tel: 617-355-5840, 617-735-6481. Fax: 617-730-0573. p. 1059

Gelles, Karen, Acq, Farmingdale State College of New York, 2350 Broadhollow Rd, Farmingdale, NY, 11735-1021. Tel: 631-420-2040. Fax: 631-420-2473. p. 1622

Gelles, Karen, Ref, Farmingdale State College of New York, 2350 Broadhollow Rd, Farmingdale, NY, 11735-1021. Tel: 631-420-2040. Fax: 631-420-2473. p. 1622

Gellner, Brenda, Ch, Parkersburg & Wood County Public Library, 3100 Emerson Ave, Parkersburg, WV, 26104-2414. Tel: 304-420-4587, Ext 20. Fax: 304-420-4589. p. 2568

Gelover, Karen, Ref Librn, Palm Beach State College, 1977 College Dr, Belle Glade, FL, 33430. Tel: 561-993-1192. Fax: 561-993-1157. p. 427

Gelskey, LeAnn, Dir, Hailey Public Library, Seven W Croy St, Hailey, ID, 83333. Tel: 208-788-2036. Fax: 208-788-7646. p. 575

Gelsomino, Julia, Ch, Aurora Town Public Library, 550 Main St, East Aurora, NY, 14052. Tel: 716-652-4440. Fax: 716-655-5875. p. 1616

Gemberling, Thomas, Br Mgr, Phoenix Public Library, Acacia Library, 750 E Townley Ave, Phoenix, AZ, 85020. p. 76

Gemmill, Sally, Prog & Rental Mgr, Wilton Library Association, 137 Old Ridgefield Rd, Wilton, CT, 06897-3019. Tel: 203-762-3950. Fax: 203-834-1166. p. 378

Genardo, Patricia, Circ Mgr, National University of Health Sciences Learning Resource Center, 200 E Roosevelt Rd, Bldg C, Lombard, IL, 60148-4583. Tel: 630-889-6597. Fax: 630-495-6658. p. 667

Gendelman, Shelia, Libr Dir, Temple Sinai, 1401 N Limekiln Pike, Dresher, PA, 19025. Tel: 215-643-6510, Ext 110. Fax: 215-643-9441. p. 2050

Gendron, France P, Dir, Bibliotheque Municipale de Warwick, 181 rue Saint-Louis, Warwick, QC, J0A 1M0, CANADA. Tel: 819-358-4325. Fax: 819-358-4326. p. 2915

Gendron, Francine, Librn, HEC Montreal, 3000, chemin de la Cote-Sainte-Catherine, Montreal, QC, H3T 2A7, CANADA. Tel: 514-340-6215. Fax: 514-340-5639. p. 2896

Gendron, Heather, Librn, Virginia Polytechnic Institute & State University Libraries, Art & Architecture, Cowgill Hall, 3rd Flr, Blacksburg, VA, 24062. Tel: 540-231-9272. p. 2451

Genest, France, Chef de Section, Bibliothèques de Montrèal, Belleville, 10400, avenue de Belleville, Montreal, QC, H1H 4Z7, CANADA. Tel: 514-328-4000, Ext 4130. Fax: 514-328-4298. p. 2889

Genest, France, Chef de Section, Bibliothèques de Montrèal, Charleroi, 4740, rue de Charleroi, Montreal, QC, H1H 1V2, CANADA. Tel: 514-328-4000, Ext 4130. Fax: 514-328-4298. p. 2889

Genest, France, Chef de Section, Bibliothèques de Montrèal, Henri-Bourassa, 5400, boulevard Henri-Bourassa Est, Montreal, QC, H1G 2S9, CANADA. Tel: 514-328-4000, Ext 4130. Fax: 514-328-4298. p. 2889

Genest, France, Chef de Section, Bibliothèques de Montrèal, Maison culturelle et communautaire, 12002, boulevard Rolland, Montreal, QC, H1G 3W1, CANADA. Tel: 514-328-4000, Ext 4130. p. 2890

Genest, Marie-France, Coll Develop, Youth Serv, Bibliothèques de Montrèal, 801, rue Brennan, 5e Etage, Bureau 5206, Montreal, QC, H3C 0G4, CANADA. Tel: 514-872-2910. Fax: 514-872-0530. p. 2889

Genesy, Dave, Dir, Redwood City Public Library, 1044 Middlefield Rd, Redwood City, CA, 94063-1868. Tel: 650-780-7018. Fax: 650-780-7069. p. 215

Geng, Zhong, Head, Tech Proc, Syst/Electronic Res Librn, Marywood University Library, 2300 Adams Ave, Scranton, PA, 18509-1598. Tel: 570-961-4707. Fax: 570-961-4769. p. 2137

Gengele, Glen, Dir, Oklahoma City Museum of Art, 415 Couch Dr, Oklahoma City, OK, 73102. Tel: 405-236-3100. Fax: 405-236-3122. p. 1974

Gengler, Matthew, Access Serv Librn, Cleveland Museum of Art, 11150 East Blvd, Cleveland, OH, 44106-1797. Tel: 216-707-2530. Fax: 216-421-0921. p. 1877

Genisio, Nancy, Circ, Phillips Public Library, 286 Cherry St, Phillips, WI, 54555-1240. Tel: 715-339-2868. p. 2629

Gennett, Sherry, Head, Ch, Gloversville Public Library, 58 E Fulton St, Gloversville, NY, 12078. Tel: 518-725-2819. Fax: 518-773-0292. p. 1629

Genovese, Liza, Librn, Northeastern University Libraries, 430 Nahant Rd, Nahant, MA, 01908. Tel: 781-581-7370. Fax: 781-581-6076. p. 1107

Genovese, Robert, Head, Tech Serv, University of Arizona, James E Rogers College of Law Library, PO Box 210176, Tucson, AZ, 85721-0176. Tel: 520-621-1413. Fax: 520-621-3138. p. 89

Genovese-Shulman, Cindy, Regional Mgr, Broward County Division of Libraries, 100 S Andrews Ave, Fort Lauderdale, FL, 33301. Tel: 954-357-7417. Fax: 954-357-6122. p. 441

Gensichen, Thomas F, Syst Coordr, University of Nebraska Medical Center, 600 S 42nd St, Omaha, NE, 68198-6705. Tel: 402-559-8119. Fax: 402-559-5498. p. 1415

Gensler, Elana, Computer Coordr, West Hempstead Public Library, 500 Hempstead Ave, West Hempstead, NY, 11552. Tel: 516-481-6591. Fax: 516-481-2608. p. 1766

Gensler, Janice, Acq, Wharton County Junior College, 911 Boling Hwy, Wharton, TX, 77488-3298. Tel: 979-532-6953. Fax: 979-532-6527. p. 2399

Genson, Thomas J, Dir, Herrick District Library, 300 S River Ave, Holland, MI, 49423-3290. Tel: 616-355-3100. p. 1190

Genter, Justin, Syst Coordr, Nioga Library System, 6575 Wheeler Rd, Lockport, NY, 14094. Tel: 716-434-6167, Ext 11. Fax: 716-434-8231. p. 1653

Genther, Marilyn, Exec Dir, Mount Prospect Public Library, Ten S Emerson St, Mount Prospect, IL, 60056. Tel: 847-253-5675. Fax: 847-253-5977. p. 677

Gentile, Dee M, Info Officer, Printing Industries of America, 200 Deer Run Rd, Sewickley, PA, 15143-2600. Tel: 412-741-6860. Fax: 412-741-2311. p. 2139

Gentis, Mary Lou, Supvr, Ad Serv, Muncie Center Township Public Library, 2005 S High St, Muncie, IN, 47302. Tel: 765-741-5153. Fax: 765-747-8211. p. 767

Gentry, Cam, Med Librn, Via Christi Libraries, East Harry Street, 3600 E Harry St, Wichita, KS, 67218. Tel: 316-689-5376. Fax: 316-691-6721. p. 901

Gentry, Deborah, Outreach Serv Librn, Saint Joseph Public Library, East Hills Library, 502 N Woodbine Rd, Saint Joseph, MO, 64506. Tel: 816-236-2107. Fax: 816-236-1429. p. 1353

Gentry, Jana, Br Mgr, West Georgia Regional Library, Buchanan-Haralson Public Library, 145 Courthouse Sq, Buchanan, GA, 30113. Tel: 770-646-3369. Fax: 770-646-1103. p. 524

Gentry, John C, Controller, Henrico County Public Library, 1001 N Laburnum Ave, Henrico, VA, 23223-2705. Tel: 804-290-9000. Fax: 804-222-5566. p. 2471

Gentry, Linda, Exec Dir, Camden County Historical Society, Park Blvd & Euclid Ave, Camden, NJ, 08103. Tel: 856-964-3333. p. 1476

Gentry, Reynelda, Librn, Vonore Public Library, 611 Church St, Vonore, TN, 37885-0308. Tel: 423-884-6729. Fax: 423-884-6729. p. 2268

Gentz, April, Asst Dir, Thorp Public Library, 401 S Conway Dr, Thorp, WI, 54771. Tel: 715-669-5953. Fax: 715-669-7319. p. 2642

Gentzler, Lynn Wolf, Assoc Dir, State Historical Society of Missouri Library, 1020 Lowry St, Columbia, MO, 65201-7298. Tel: 573-882-7083. Fax: 573-884-4950. p. 1324

Genuardi, Carmen, Librn, Sunnybrook Health Sciences Centre, Library Services, Holland Orthopaedic & Arthritic Centre, 43 Wellesley St E, Toronto, ON, M4Y 1H1, CANADA. Tel: 416-967-8545. Fax: 416-967-8605. p. 2858

Genzel, Jane, Asst Dir, Muskego Public Library, S73 W16663 Janesville Rd, Muskego, WI, 53150. Tel: 262-971-2100. Fax: 262-971-2115. p. 2623

Genzen, David, Dir of Tech, Cleveland State University, Cleveland-Marshall Law Library, Cleveland-Marshall College of Law, 1801 Euclid Ave, Cleveland, OH, 44115-2223. Tel: 216-523-7372. Fax: 216-687-6881. p. 1878

Geoffino, Tina, Librn, Bridgeport Public Library, Black Rock, Tel: 203-576-7427. p. 331

Geoffino, Tom, Dir, New Rochelle Public Library, One Library Plaza, New Rochelle, NY, 10801. Tel: 914-632-7878, Ext 1200. Fax: 914-632-0262. p. 1666

Geoffrey, Maureen, Acq, Chicopee Public Library, 449 Front St, Chicopee, MA, 01013. Tel: 413-594-1800. Fax: 413-594-1819. p. 1081

Georgas, Helen, Librn, Brooklyn Public Library, 2900 Bedford Ave, Brooklyn, NY, 11210-2889. Tel: 718-951-5336. Fax: 718-951-4540. p. 1589

George, Amber, Br Librn, Sweetwater County Library System, Superior Branch Library, Three N Main, Superior, WY, 82945. Tel: 307-352-6671. Fax: 307-352-6671. p. 2656

George, Becky, Archivist, Craft Memorial Library, 600 Commerce St, Bluefield, WV, 24701. Tel: 304-325-3943. Fax: 304-325-3702. p. 2555

George, Bette, Circ Mgr, Mount Union College Library, 1972 Clark Ave, Alliance, OH, 44601-3993. Tel: 330-823-3844. Fax: 330-823-3963. p. 1854

George, Bruce, Dir, Oil City Library, Two Central Ave, Oil City, PA, 16301-2795. Tel: 814-678-3072. Fax: 814-676-8028. p. 2100

George, Cathy, Librn, Huffman Memorial United Methodist Church Library, 2802 Renick St, Saint Joseph, MO, 64507-1897. Tel: 816-232-7809. Fax: 816-233-0683. p. 1352

George, Chrissy, Ch, Middlesex Public Library, 1300 Mountain Ave, Middlesex, NJ, 08846. Tel: 732-356-6602. Fax: 732-356-8420. p. 1501

George, Christa, Supvr, NASA, 2101 NASA Pkwy, Houston, TX, 77058-3696. Tel: 281-483-2491. Fax: 281-244-6624. p. 2341

George, Deborah, Div Dir, Mats Mgt, Gwinnett County Public Library, 1001 Lawrenceville Hwy NW, Lawrenceville, GA, 30046-4707. Tel: 770-822-5330. p. 538

George, Elizabeth, Young People's Librn, Walla Walla Public Library, 238 E Alder, Walla Walla, WA, 99362. Tel: 509-524-4431. Fax: 509-524-7950. p. 2547

George, Harold, Br Mgr, Saint Johns County Public Library System, Anastasia Island Branch, 124 Seagrove Main St, Saint Augustine Beach, FL, 32080. Tel: 904-209-3731. Fax: 904-209-3735. p. 487

George, Jennifer, Adult Serv, Atchison Public Library, 401 Kansas Ave, Atchison, KS, 66002-2495. Tel: 913-367-1902. Fax: 913-367-2717. p. 856

George, Jon, Tech Serv, River Falls Public Library, 140 Union St, River Falls, WI, 54022. Tel: 715-425-0905, Ext 120. Fax: 715-425-0914. p. 2634

George, Karen A, Br Mgr, Stilwell Public Library, Five N Sixth St, Stilwell, OK, 74960. Tel: 918-696-7512. Fax: 918-696-4007. p. 1979

George, Karen L, Dir, Atlantic County Library System, 40 Farragut Ave, Mays Landing, NJ, 08330-1750. Tel: 609-625-2776. Fax: 609-625-8143. p. 1500

George, Kathy, Ch, Gray Public Library, Five Hancock St, Gray, ME, 04039. Tel: 207-657-4110. Fax: 207-657-4138. p. 986

George, Mary, Asst Dir, Libr Serv, Placer County Library, 350 Nevada St, Auburn, CA, 95603-3789. Tel: 530-886-4500, 530-886-4550. Fax: 530-886-4555. p. 122

George, Mary, Asst Dir, Placer County Library, Rocklin Branch, 4890 Granite Dr, Rocklin, CA, 95677-2547. Tel: 916-624-3133. Fax: 916-632-9152. p. 123

George, Mary, Head, Tech Serv, Xavier University of Louisiana, One Drexel Dr, New Orleans, LA, 70125-1098. Tel: 504-520-5294. Fax: 504-520-7940. p. 964

George, Mary, Sr Ref Librn, Princeton University, One Washington Rd, Princeton, NJ, 08544-2098. Tel: 609-258-3254. Fax: 609-258-0441. p. 1523

George, Melinda, Ch, Garland Smith Public Library, 407 W Seminole, Marlow, OK, 73055. Tel: 580-658-5354. Fax: 580-658-9110. p. 1967

George, Nancy, Electronic Res Librn, Salem State University Library, 352 Lafayette St, Salem, MA, 01970-5353. Tel: 978-542-7182. Fax: 978-542-6596. p. 1122

George, Nancy K, Circ, Scott Township Public Library, 301 Lindsay Rd, Scott Township, PA, 15106. Tel: 412-429-5380. Fax: 412-429-5370. p. 2136

George, Paul M, Assoc Dean & Dir, University of Pennsylvania Libraries, Biddle Law Library, Tanenbaum Hall, Flrs 3-5, 3443 Sansom St, Philadelphia, PA, 19104. Tel: 215-898-7488. Fax: 215-898-6619. p. 2119

George, Regina, Libr Dir, Covington-Veedersburg Public Library, 622 Fifth St, Covington, IN, 47932. Tel: 765-793-2572. Fax: 765-793-2621. p. 734

George, Regina, Libr Dir, Covington-Veedersburg Public Library, Veedersburg Public, 408 N Main St, Veedersburg, IN, 47987. Tel: 765-294-2808. Fax: 765-294-4648. p. 734

George, Steven, Br Mgr, Jackson District Library, Eastern, 3125 E Michigan Ave, Jackson, MI, 49201. Tel: 517-788-4074. Fax: 517-788-4645. p. 1196

George, Tanya, Tech Serv, Folsom Lake College Library, Ten College Pkwy, Folsom, CA, 95630. Tel: 916-608-6587. Fax: 916-608-6533. p. 148

Georgeff, Angie, Dir, Unicoi County Public Library, 201 Nolichucky Ave, Erwin, TN, 37650-1237. Tel: 423-743-6533. Fax: 423-743-0275. p. 2234

Georgeson, Thelma, Dir, Rosalind Keshin Kittay Public Library, 2827 Hwy 153, West Rupert, VT, 05768. Tel: 802-394-2444. Fax: 802-394-2444. p. 2439

Georget, Henry, Miami Campus Libr Dir, Keiser University Library System, 1500 NW 49th St, Fort Lauderdale, FL, 33309. Tel: 954-351-4035. Fax: 954-351-4051. p. 443

Georghiou, John, Dir, Plattekill Public Library, 2047 State Rte 32, Modena, NY, 12548. Tel: 845-883-7286. Fax: 845-883-7295. p. 1662

Georgieva, Rennie, Assoc Archivist, Head Librn, American Psychological Association, 750 First St NE, Rm 3012, Washington, DC, 20002-4242. Tel: 202-336-5664. Fax: 202-336-5643. p. 392

Gepner, Mary Kathryn, Librn, Mount Ayr Public Library, 121 W Monroe St, Mount Ayr, IA, 50854. Tel: 641-464-2159. Fax: 641-464-2159. p. 833

Geraci, Diane, Head Librn, Harvard Library, Social Sciences Program, Lamont Library, Level B, Harvard University, Cambridge, MA, 02138. Tel: 617-496-2532. Fax: 617-496-5570. p. 1076

Geraci, Diane, Assoc Dir, Info Res, Massachusetts Institute of Technology Libraries, Office of the Director, 160 Memorial Dr, Cambridge, MA, 02142. Tel: 617-253-5962. Fax: 617-253-8894. p. 1077

Geraci, Gail, Circ, Safety Harbor Public Library, 101 Second St N, Safety Harbor, FL, 34695. Tel: 727-724-1525. Fax: 727-724-1533. p. 486

Geraets, Jayne, Head Librn, Elmwood Public Library, 111 N Main St, Elmwood, WI, 54740. Tel: 715-639-2615. Fax: 715-639-2615. p. 2591

Geraghty, Ellen, Ref Serv, Midwestern University Library, 555 31st St, Downers Grove, IL, 60515. Tel: 630-515-6200. Fax: 630-515-6195. p. 637

Geragotelis, Mary, Dir, Scotland Public Library, 21 Brook Rd, Scotland, CT, 06264. Tel: 860-423-1492. Fax: 860-423-1526. p. 366

Gerakopoulos, Carolyn, Dir, Oneida Public Library, 220 Broad St, Oneida, NY, 13421. Tel: 315-363-3050. p. 1710

Gerald, Ann, Circ Librn, Bridgewater Public Library, 15 South St, Bridgewater, MA, 02324-2593. Tel: 508-697-3331. Fax: 508-279-1467. p. 1070

Geran, Jennifer, Librn IV, San Diego Public Library, 820 E St, San Diego, CA, 92101-6478. Tel: 619-236-5820. Fax: 619-238-6639. p. 235

Gerard, Gerald B, Librn, Canadian Institute of Chartered Accountants, 277 Wellington St W, Toronto, ON, M5V 3H2, CANADA. Tel: 416-204-3307. Fax: 416-977-8585. p. 2851

Gerard, Mary, Librn, West Yellowstone Public Library, 23 N Dunraven St, West Yellowstone, MT, 59758. Tel: 406-646-9017. Fax: 406-646-7311. p. 1390

Gerardo, Norma, Ref Librn, Camarena Memorial Library, 850 Encinas Ave, Calexico, CA, 92231. Tel: 760-768-2170. Fax: 760-357-0404. p. 131

Gerbasi-Askeland, Tracy, Asst Librn, Shilo Community Library, PO Box 177, Shilo, MB, R0K 2A0, CANADA. p. 2752

Gerber, Demita, Dir, Monona Public Library, 1000 Nichols Rd, Monona, WI, 53716-2531. Tel: 608-222-6127. Fax: 608-222-8590. p. 2623

Gerber, Kathryn, Libr Dir, Berne Public Library, 166 N Sprunger St, Berne, IN, 46711-1595. Tel: 260-589-2809. Fax: 260-589-2940. p. 726

Gerber, Michael, Pres, Atlanta Regional Council for Higher Education, 50 Hurt Plaza, Ste 735, Atlanta, GA, 30303-2923. Tel: 404-651-2668. Fax: 404-880-9816. p. 2941

Gerdes, Catherine, Assoc Univ Librn, Planning & Admin Serv, University of North Carolina at Chapel Hill, Davis Library, 208 Raleigh St, Campus Box 3900, Chapel Hill, NC, 27514-8890. p. 1780

Gerdes, Neil, Dr, Librn, Chicago Theological Seminary, 5757 S University Ave, Chicago, IL, 60637-1507. Tel: 773-322-0247. Fax: 773-752-7194. p. 611

Gerdes, Neil W, Dean of Libr, Meadville-Lombard Theological School Library, 5701 S Woodlawn Ave, Chicago, IL, 60637. Tel: 773-256-3000, Ext 225. Fax: 773-256-3007. p. 618

Gerding, Jolie, Libr Dir, Longton Library, 512A Kansas Ave, Longton, KS, 67352. Tel: 620-642-6012. Fax: 620-642-6012. p. 880

Gere, Gus, Librn, Palliser Regional Library, Wood Mountain Branch, Second Ave W, Wood Mountain, SK, S0H 4L0, CANADA. Tel: 306-266-2110. p. 2919

Gere, Heather, Info Serv Supvr, Dartmouth College Library, Baker-Berry Library, 6025 Baker-Berry Library, Hanover, NH, 03755-3525. Tel: 603-646-2560. Fax: 603-646-2167. p. 1450

Geremia, Cynthia, Asst Dir, Libr Tech, Purdue Pharma LP & Associated Companies, One Stamford Forum, 201 Tresser Blvd, Stamford, CT, 06901. Tel: 203-588-7267. Fax: 203-588-6212. p. 369

Gerencser, James, Col Archivist, Dickinson College, 333 W High St, Carlisle, PA, 17013-2896. Tel: 717-245-1397. Fax: 717-245-1439. p. 2042

Gerety, Lorraine, Visual Res Curator, School of Visual Arts, 380 Second Ave, 2nd Flr, New York, NY, 10010-3994. Tel: 212-592-2667. Fax: 212-592-2655. p. 1699

Gerharter, Nicholle, Ref Librn, Natrona County Public Library, 307 E Second St, Casper, WY, 82601. Tel: 307-237-4935. Fax: 307-266-3734. p. 2652

Gerheim, Brian, Head, Per, Evergreen State College, Library Bldg, Rm 2300, 2700 Evergreen Pkwy NW, Olympia, WA, 98505-0002. Tel: 360-867-6255. Fax: 360-867-6790. p. 2522

Gerhold, Albert, Computer Ctr Mgr, Drexel University Health Sciences Libraries, 245 N 15th St MS 449, Philadelphia, PA, 19102-1192. Fax: 215-762-8180. p. 2105

Gerica, Angela, Acq, Eastern Nazarene College, 23 E Elm Ave, Quincy, MA, 02170. Tel: 617-745-3850. Fax: 617-745-3913. p. 1119

Gerig, Reginald, Tech Coordr, Supreme Court of the United States Library, One First St NE, Washington, DC, 20543. Tel: 202-479-3037. Fax: 202-479-3477. p. 416

Geringer, Ellen, Coordr, Contra Costa College Library, 2600 Mission Bell Dr, San Pablo, CA, 94806-3195. Tel: 510-235-7800, Ext 4457. Fax: 510-234-8161. p. 256

Gerke, Jennifer, Head, Bus Libr, University of Colorado Boulder, 1720 Pleasant St, 184 UCB, Boulder, CO, 80309-0184. Tel: 303-735-6804. Fax: 303-492-3340. p. 291

Gerke, Jennifer, Head of Libr, University of Colorado Boulder, William M White Business Library, Koelbel Bldg, Leeds College of Business, Boulder, CO, 80309. Tel: 303-735-6804. Fax: 303-735-0333. p. 292

Gerken, LeAnn, Dir, Little Rock Public Library, 402 Main St, Little Rock, IA, 51243. Tel: 712-479-2298. Fax: 712-479-2298. p. 828

Gerken, Louis, Mgr, American Scientific Corp Library, 3250 Holly Way, Chula Vista, CA, 91910-3217. Tel: 619-422-1754. Fax: 619-426-1280. p. 134

Gerlach, Pat, Area Librn, Saint Paul Public Library, West Seventh, 265 Oneida St, Saint Paul, MN, 55102. Tel: 651-298-5516. p. 1282

Gerlach, Sharrel, Ref, Southwestern Law School, 3050 Wilshire Blvd, Los Angeles, CA, 90010. Tel: 213-738-5771. Fax: 213-738-5792. p. 177

Gerlich, Bella Karr, PhD, Univ Librn, Dominican University, 7900 W Division St, River Forest, IL, 60305-1066. Tel: 708-524-6873. Fax: 708-366-5360. p. 694

Gerling, Angela, Dir of Libr Serv, Westminster College, Reeves Memorial Library, 501 Westminster Ave, Fulton, MO, 65251-1299. Tel: 573-592-5245. Fax: 573-642-6356. p. 1328

Gerlinger, Judy, Br Mgr, Campbell County Public Library, Timbrook Branch, 21039 Timberlake Rd, Ste F, Lynchburg, VA, 24502. Tel: 434-239-1190. Fax: 434-237-6784. p. 2495

Gerlott, Eleanor, Librn, Lancaster County Law Library, 50 N Duke St, Lancaster, PA, 17602. Tel: 717-299-8090. Fax: 717-295-2509. p. 2076

Germain, Barbara L, Dir, Johnstown Public Library, 38 S Market St, Johnstown, NY, 12095. Tel: 518-762-8317. Fax: 518-762-9776. p. 1648

Germain, Cassie, Circ Librn, Caribou Public Library, 30 High St, Caribou, ME, 04736. Tel: 207-493-4214. Fax: 207-493-4654. p. 981

Germain, Nicole Termini, Br Mgr, San Francisco Public Library, Portola Branch Library, 380 Bacon St (at Goettingen), San Francisco, CA, 94134-1526. Tel: 415-355-5660. Fax: 415-468-1644. p. 246

German, Jennifer, Br Mgr, Kent District Library, Krause Memorial Branch, 140 E Bridge St, Rockford, MI, 49341. Tel: 616-784-2007. Fax: 616-647-3944. p. 1166

German, Lisa, Assoc Dean, Coll, Info & Access Serv, Pennsylvania State University Libraries, 510 Paterno Library, University Park, PA, 16802. Tel: 814-865-0401. Fax: 814-865-3665. p. 2147

German, Sarah, Ch, Conrad Public Library, 114 N Main Ave, Conrad, IA, 50621. Tel: 641-366-2583. Fax: 641-366-3105. p. 804

Germann, Angee, Librn, Carrollton Public Library, One N Folger, Carrollton, MO, 64633. Tel: 660-542-0183. Fax: 660-542-0654. p. 1322

Germann, Ruth, Br Mgr, Cambridge Libraries & Galleries, Preston, 435 King St E, Cambridge, ON, N3H 3N1, CANADA. Tel: 519-653-3632. Fax: 519-621-2080. p. 2798

Germek, George, Ref Serv, Monmouth University, 400 Cedar Ave, West Long Branch, NJ, 07764. Tel: 732-571-3450, Ext 4403. Fax: 732-263-5124. p. 1541

Germer, Mark, Dr, Music Librn, University of the Arts University Libraries, Anderson Hall, 1st Flr, 333 S Broad St, Philadelphia, PA, 19102. Tel: 215-717-6293. Fax: 215-717-6287. p. 2119

Germer, Mark, Dr, Librn, University of the Arts University Libraries, Music Library, Merriam Theater, 3rd Flr, 250 S Broad St, Philadelphia, PA, 19102. Tel: 215-717-6293. Fax: 215-717-6287. p. 2120

Germon, Leah, Ch, Atlanta-Fulton Public Library System, Dr Robert E Fulton Regional at Ocee, 5090 Abbotts Bridge Rd, Alpharetta, GA, 30005-4601. Tel: 770-360-8897. Fax: 770-360-8892. p. 512

Germroth, Michael, Ref Librn, Central New Mexico Community College Libraries, Rio Rancho Campus Library, 2601 Campus Blvd NE, Rm 112, Rio Rancho, NM, 87144. Tel: 505-224-4953. p. 1548

Germscheid, Patti, Librn, Waseca-Le Sueur Regional Library, Le Center Public, Ten W Tyrone St, Le Center, MN, 56057. Tel: 507-357-6792. p. 1287

Gernand, Bradley E, Mgr, Institute for Defense Analyses Library, 4850 Mark Center Dr, Alexandria, VA, 22311. Tel: 703-845-2405. Fax: 703-820-7194. p. 2445

Gernatt, Annette, Librn, Hulbert Public Library of the Town of Concord, 18 Chapel St, Springville, NY, 14141. Tel: 716-592-7742. p. 1747

Gerolami, Natasha, Head Librn, Huntington University, Laurentian Campus, 935 Ramsey Lake Rd, Sudbury, ON, P3E 2C6, CANADA. Tel: 705-673-4126, Ext 248. Fax: 705-673-6917. p. 2846

Gerolami, Tim, Ref Librn, Mount Ida College, Wadsworth Library, 777 Dedham St, Newton, MA, 02459. Tel: 617-928-4552. Fax: 617-928-4038. p. 1110

Gerolami, Tim, Ref & Instruction Librn, Cape Cod Community College, 2240 Iyannough Rd, West Barnstable, MA, 02668-1599. Tel: 508-362-2131, Ext 4351. Fax: 508-375-4020. p. 1136

Geronzin, Kathy, Librn, Maquoketa Public Library, 126 S Second St, Maquoketa, IA, 52060. Tel: 563-652-3874. p. 829

Geroy, Mira, Br Mgr, Alameda County Library, Union City Branch, 34007 Alvarado-Niles Rd, Union City, CA, 94587-4498. Tel: 510-745-1464. Fax: 510-487-7241. p. 149

Gerrity, Kate, Cat Librn, Amherst College, Amherst, MA, 01002. Fax: 413-542-2662. p. 1048

Gerrity, Robert, Assoc Univ Librn, Syst & Info Tech, Boston College Libraries, Thomas P O'Neill Jr Library (Central Library), 140 Commonwealth Ave, Chestnut Hill, MA, 02467. Tel: 617-552-3155. Fax: 617-552-0599. p. 1081

Gerry, Emily E, Ch, Eustis Memorial Library, 120 N Center St, Eustis, FL, 32726-3598. Tel: 352-357-0896. Fax: 352-357-5450. p. 439

Gerschel, Dana, Librn, Yale Club Library, 50 Vanderbilt Ave, New York, NY, 10017. Tel: 212-716-2129. Fax: 212-716-2158. p. 1703

Gerscher, Anna, Libr Tech, College of Emmanuel & St Chad Library, 114 Seminary Crescent, Saskatoon, SK, S7N 0X3, CANADA. Tel: 306-975-1554. Fax: 306-934-2683. p. 2925

Gershenfeld, Nancy, Sr Lecturer, University of Washington, Mary Gates Hall, Ste 370, Campus Box 352840, Seattle, WA, 98195-2840. Tel: 206-685-9937. Fax: 206-616-3152. p. 2976

Gershman, Joann, Dir, Stratford Free Public Library, 303 Union Ave, Stratford, NJ, 08084. Tel: 856-783-0602. Fax: 856-435-8757. p. 1532

Gershuny, Alan, Circ, University of Winnipeg Library, 515 Portage Ave, Winnipeg, MB, R3B 2E9, CANADA. Tel: 204-786-9801. Fax: 204-783-8910. p. 2759

Gersitz, Lorraine, Librn, Ref Coordr, Cerritos College Library, 11110 Alondra Blvd, Norwalk, CA, 90650. Tel: 562-860-2451, Ext 2414. Fax: 562-467-5002. p. 195

Gerson, Kevin, Dir, Law Libr, University of California Los Angeles Library, Hugh & Hazel Darling Law Library, 112 Law Bldg, Box 951458, 385 Charles E Young Dr E, Los Angeles, CA, 90095-1458. Tel: 310-825-7826. Fax: 310-825-1372. p. 178

Gerson, Pat, Acq, University of Saint Thomas, 1100 W Main, Houston, TX, 77006. Tel: 713-525-2191. Fax: 713-525-3886. p. 2344

Gerst, Jan, Librn, Nauvoo Public Library, 1270 Mulholland St, Nauvoo, IL, 62354. Tel: 217-453-2707. Fax: 217-453-2707. p. 679

Gerstbacher, Emily, Br Mgr, Riverside County Library System, Grace Mellman Community Library (Temecula County Center Library), 41000 County Center Dr, Temecula, CA, 92591. Tel: 909-600-6266. Fax: 951-600-6265. p. 218

Gerstein, Charlotte, Instruction/Ref Serv, Castleton State College, 178 Alumni Dr, Castleton, VT, 05735. Tel: 802-468-1256. Fax: 802-468-1475. p. 2421

Gerstle, Steven, Ref & Instruction Librn, College of Alameda, 555 Ralph Appezzato Memorial Pkwy, Alameda, CA, 94501. Tel: 510-748-5217. Fax: 510-748-2380. p. 119

Gerstung, Cheri, Ref Serv, Ulster County Community College, Stone Ridge, NY, 12484. Tel: 845-687-5213. Fax: 845-687-5220. p. 1749

Gerton, Ginger, Librn, Ober, Kaler, Grimes & Shriver Law Library, 120 E Baltimore St, Ste 800, Baltimore, MD, 21202-1643. Tel: 410-230-7181, 410-685-1120. Fax: 410-547-0699. p. 1017

Gertsch, Karen, Asst Librn, Ned R McWherter Weakley County Library, 341 Linden St, Dresden, TN, 38225-1400. Tel: 731-364-2678. Fax: 731-364-2599. p. 2233

Gertz, Janet, Dir, Presv Serv, Columbia University, Butler Library, Rm 517, 535 W 114th St, New York, NY, 10027. Tel: 212-854-7309. Fax: 212-854-9099. p. 1674

Gervais, Sylvie, Syst Librn, Universite du Quebec en Outaouais, 283, Blvd Alexandre-Tache, Case postale 1250, succ Hull, Gatineau, QC, J8X 3X7, CANADA. Tel: 819-595-3900, Ext 1789. Fax: 819-773-1669. p. 2884

Gervasio, Darcy, Ref & Instruction Librn, State University of New York, 735 Anderson Hill Rd, Purchase, NY, 10577-1400. Tel: 914-251-6423. Fax: 914-251-6437. p. 1724

Gervits, Maya, Dir, New Jersey Institute of Technology, Barbara & Leonard Littman Architecture Library, 456 Weston Hall, 323 King Blvd, Newark, NJ, 07102-1982. Tel: 973-596-3083. Fax: 973-643-5601. p. 1511

Gerwatowski, Kathleen, Co-Dir, Brown, Rudnick, Berlack, Israels LLP, One Financial Ctr, Boston, MA, 02111. Tel: 617-856-8213. Fax: 617-856-8201. p. 1059

Gesch, E'Lonna, Librn, Milligan Public Library, 424 Main St, Milligan, NE, 68406. Tel: 402-629-4405. p. 1408

Geselman, Brenda, Br Librn, Carson City Public Library, Crystal Community, 221 W Lake St, Crystal, MI, 48818. Tel: 989-235-6111. Fax: 989-235-6111. p. 1161

Geser, Mary, Dir, Gilliam County Library, 310 S Main, Condon, OR, 97823. Tel: 541-384-6052. Fax: 541-384-6052. p. 1993

Gessner, Robert, Syst Librn, Susquehanna University, 514 University Ave, Selinsgrove, PA, 17870-1050. Tel: 570-372-4322. Fax: 570-372-4310. p. 2138

Getchell, Charles M, Jr, Dir, Quinnipiac University, 275 Mount Carmel Ave, Hamden, CT, 06518. Tel: 203-582-8631. Fax: 203-582-3451. p. 343

Getchell, Mary, Communications Dir, Pierce County Library System, 3005 112th St E, Tacoma, WA, 98446-2215. Tel: 253-548-3428. Fax: 253-537-4600. p. 2539

Getchell, Sylvia Fitts, Curator, Librn, Newmarket Historical Society, Granite St, Newmarket, NH, 03857. Tel: 603-659-3652. p. 1460

Getman, Risa, Head, Ref & Adult Serv, Hendrick Hudson Free Library, 185 Kings Ferry Rd, Montrose, NY, 10548. Tel: 914-739-5654. Fax: 914-739-5659. p. 1663

Gettel, Betty, Asst Dir, Ch, Caro Area District Library, 840 W Frank St, Caro, MI, 48723. Tel: 989-673-4329, Ext 103. Fax: 989-673-4777. p. 1161

Getter, Susan, Supvr, Circ, South Mainland Library, 7921 Ron Beatty Blvd, Micco, FL, 32976. Tel: 772-664-4066. Fax: 772-664-0534. p. 470

Getting, Becky, Mgr, Ad Serv, Flower Mound Public Library, 3030 Broadmoor Lane, Flower Mound, TX, 75022. Tel: 972-874-6152. Fax: 972-874-6466. p. 2319

Gettle, Amy, Circ, Burlingame Public Library, 480 Primrose Rd, Burlingame, CA, 94010-4083. Tel: 650-558-7450. Fax: 650-342-1948. p. 130

Getts, Marilyn, Br Librn, Davis County Library, Central Branch, 155 N Wasatch Dr, Layton, UT, 84041. Tel: 801-547-0729. p. 2405

Getty, Jane, Librn, Amsterdam Free Library, 28 Church St, Amsterdam, NY, 12010. Tel: 518-842-1080. Fax: 518-842-1169. p. 1573

Getty, Kevin, Head, Info Serv, Warren-Newport Public Library District, 224 N O'Plaine Rd, Gurnee, IL, 60031. Tel: 847-244-5150, Ext 3015. Fax: 847-244-3499. p. 653

Getty, Liz, Librn, Stanstead College, 450 Dufferin St, Stanstead, QC, J0B 3E0, CANADA. Tel: 819-876-7891, Ext 226. Fax: 819-876-5891. p. 2913

Getty, Nancy, Instrul Serv Librn, Glendale Community College Library, 1500 N Verdugo Rd, Glendale, CA, 91208-2894. Tel: 818-240-1000, Ext 5574. Fax: 818-246-5107. p. 155

Getz, Roger, Dir, Wesley College Library, 120 N State St, Dover, DE, 19901. Tel: 302-736-2455. Fax: 302-736-2533. p. 382

Getze, Frederick B, Assoc Librn, University of Delaware Library, Agricultural, Townsend Hall, Rm 025, Newark, DE, 19717. Tel: 302-831-2530. p. 386

Getzschman, Emily, Mkt Mgr, Omaha Public Library, 215 S 15th St, Omaha, NE, 68102-1629. Tel: 402-444-4800. Fax: 402-444-4504. p. 1414

Geuther, Christina, Electronic Res Librn, University of Saint Mary of the Lake - Mundelein Seminary, 1000 E Maple Ave, Mundelein, IL, 60060. Tel: 847-970-8945. Fax: 847-566-5229. p. 678

Gewenian, W, Librn, Armenian Numismatic Society Research Library, 8511 Beverly Park Pl, Pico Rivera, CA, 90660-1920. Tel: 562-695-0380. p. 208

Gewirtz, David, Head, Info Tech, Georgetown University, 37th & N St NW, Washington, DC, 20057-1174. Tel: 202-687-7385. Fax: 202-687-7501. p. 402

Gewirtz, Sarah, Info Literacy Librn, Saint John's University, 2835 Abbey Plaza, Collegeville, MN, 56321. Tel: 320-363-5802. Fax: 320-363-2126. p. 1246

Gewirtz, Sarah, Info Literacy Librn, College of Saint Benedict, 37 S College Ave, Saint Joseph, MN, 56374. Tel: 320-363-5802. Fax: 320-363-5197. p. 1277

Gewissler, Laura, Dir, Georgian Court University, 900 Lakewood Ave, Lakewood, NJ, 08701-2697. Tel: 732-987-2425. Fax: 732-987-2017. p. 1493

Geyer, Barb, Asst City Librn, Beresford Public Library, 115 S Third St, Beresford, SD, 57004-1798. Tel: 605-763-2782. Fax: 605-763-2403. p. 2210

Geyer, Enid, Assoc Dean, Dir, Info Tech, Albany Medical College, 47 New Scotland Ave, MC 63, Albany, NY, 12208. Tel: 518-262-5530. Fax: 518-262-5820. p. 1568

Geyer, Richard, Ref Serv, Adrian College, 110 S Madison St, Adrian, MI, 49221. Tel: 517-265-5161, Ext 4220. Fax: 517-264-3748. p. 1147

Ghajar, Mina, Head, Info Serv, College of Saint Elizabeth, Two Convent Rd, Morristown, NJ, 07960-6989. Tel: 973-290-4237. Fax: 973-290-4226. p. 1504

Ghaly, Samy, Librn Spec, Florida Department of Corrections, 3950 Tiger Bay Rd, Daytona Beach, FL, 32124-1098. Tel: 386-323-1195. Fax: 386-323-1006. p. 436

Ghaouti, Loubna, Dir, Universite Laval Bibliotheque, Bibliotheque des Sciences Humaines et Sociales, Pavillon Jean-Charles-Bonenfant, 2345, allée des Bibliothèques, Quebec, QC, G1V 0A6, CANADA. Fax: 418-656-3048. p. 2906

Gharst, Loretta, Assoc Librn, Coll & Computing Serv, Calcasieu Parish Public Library, 301 W Claude St, Lake Charles, LA, 70605-3457. Tel: 337-721-7150. Fax: 337-475-8806. p. 953

Ghazar, Krista, Adult Ref Librn, Madison Heights Public Library, 240 W 13 Mile Rd, Madison Heights, MI, 48071-1894. Tel: 248-837-2850. Fax: 248-588-2470. p. 1205

Ghazarian, Ara, Curator, Armenian Cultural Foundation Library, 441 Mystic St, Arlington, MA, 02474-1108. Tel: 781-646-3090. Fax: 781-646-3090. p. 1050

Ghee, Elizabeth, Ch, South Huntington Public Library, 145 Pidgeon Hill Rd, Huntington Station, NY, 11746. Tel: 631-549-4411. Fax: 631-549-1266. p. 1639

Gherman, Paul, Interim Dean, New College of Florida University of South Florida Sarasota Manatee, 5800 Bay Shore Rd, Sarasota, FL, 34243-2109. Tel: 941-487-4401. Fax: 941-487-4307. p. 490

Ghezzi, Ridie S, Head, Instruction Serv, Head, Res Serv, Dartmouth College Library, Baker-Berry Library, 6025 Baker-Berry Library, Hanover, NH, 03755-3525. Tel: 603-646-2560. Fax: 603-646-2167. p. 1450

Ghinazzi, Connie, Ref, Augustana College Library, 3435 9 1/2 Ave, Rock Island, IL, 61201-2296. Tel: 309-794-7266. Fax: 309-794-7640. p. 696

Ghormley, Sue Ann, Librn, John F Henderson Public Library, 116 N Williams, Westville, OK, 74965. Tel: 918-723-5002. Fax: 918-723-3400. p. 1986

Ghosh, Cheryl, Head of Libr, University of Cincinnati Libraries, College of Education, Criminal Justice & Human Services Library, 400 Teachers College, Cincinnati, OH, 45221. Tel: 513-556-1758. Fax: 513-556-2122. p. 1874

Ghosh, Suchandra, Tech Serv Coordr, City of Calabasas Library, 200 Civic Center Way, Calabasas, CA, 91302. Tel: 818-225-7616. Fax: 818-225-7728. p. 131

Ghoshal, Shyamalika, ILL, Ref Librn, United States Department of the Interior Library, 1849 C St NW, Rm 1151, Washington, DC, 20240. Tel: 202-208-3309. Fax: 202-208-6773. p. 419

Ghougassian, Houri, Librn, Armenian Apostolic Church of America, 138 E 39th St, New York, NY, 10016. Tel: 212-689-7810. Fax: 212-689-7168. p. 1669

Giacobbi, Sharon, Head, Access Serv, Rhode Island College, 600 Mt Pleasant Ave, Providence, RI, 02908-1924. Tel: 401-456-8126. Fax: 401-456-9646. p. 2174

Giaimo, Catherine L, Asst Librn, The Masonic Library & Museum of Pennsylvania, Masonic Temple, One N Broad St, Philadelphia, PA, 19107-2520. Tel: 215-988-1933. Fax: 215-988-1953. p. 2112

Giambi, M Dina, Assoc Univ Librn, Tech Serv & Res Mgt, University of Delaware Library, 181 S College Ave, Newark, DE, 19717-5267. Tel: 302-831-2231. Fax: 302-831-1046. p. 386

Giameo, Fran, Ch, Roselle Park, 404 Chestnut St, Roselle Park, NJ, 07204-1506. Tel: 908-245-2456. Fax: 908-245-9204. p. 1528

Giancaterino, Dan, Educ Serv Mgr, Jenkins Law Library, 833 Chestnut St, Ste 1220, Philadelphia, PA, 19107-4429. Tel: 215-574-7945. Fax: 215-574-7920. p. 2111

Gianettino, Lisa, Assoc Librn, West Virginia University, 300 Campus Dr, Parkersburg, WV, 26104. Tel: 304-424-8260. Fax: 304-424-8349. p. 2568

Giangreco, Tom, Govt Doc, Fordham University Libraries, 441 E Fordham Rd, Bronx, NY, 10458-5151. Tel: 718-817-3570. Fax: 718-817-3582. p. 1586

Gianlorenzo, Nancy, Br Librn, Cranston Public Library, Knightsville Branch, 1847 Cranston St, Cranston, RI, 02920-4112. Tel: 401-942-2504. p. 2165

Giannelli, Gary, IT Dir, The Ferguson Library, One Public Library Plaza, 96 Broad St, Stamford, CT, 06904. Tel: 203-964-1000, Ext 8270. Fax: 203-357-9098. p. 369

Gianni, Steve, Multimedia, Northbrook Public Library, 1201 Cedar Lane, Northbrook, IL, 60062-4581. Tel: 847-272-6224. Fax: 847-272-5362. p. 682

Giannini, Tula, Dean, Pratt Institute, 144 W 14th St, 6th Flr, New York, NY, 10011-7301. Tel: 212-647-7682. Fax: 212-367-2492. p. 2970

Gianniny, Susan, Asst Librn, James L Hamner Public Library, 16351 Dunn St, Amelia, VA, 23002. Tel: 804-561-4559. Fax: 804-561-3174. p. 2447

Giannoni, Christine, Mus Librn, Field Museum of Natural History Library, 1400 S Lake Shore Dr, Chicago, IL, 60605-2498. Tel: 312-665-7894. Fax: 312-665-7893. p. 613

Giannoni, Christine, Mus Librn, Chicago Area Museum Libraries, c/o Library, The Field Museum, 1400 S Lake Shore Dr, Chicago, IL, 60605-2496. Tel: 312-665-7970. Fax: 312-665-7893. p. 2942

Gianoulis, Helen, Br Mgr, Huron County Library, Bayfield Branch, 20 Main St, Bayfield, ON, N0M 1G0, CANADA. Tel: 519-524-9261. p. 2799

Gianoulis, Helen, Br Mgr, Huron County Library, Goderich Branch, 52 Montreal St, Goderich, ON, N7A 2G4, CANADA. Tel: 519-524-9261. p. 2800

Giard, Elizabeth, Coll Mgr, Harriet Beecher Stowe Center Library, 77 Forest St, Hartford, CT, 06105-3296. Tel: 860-522-9258, Ext 313. Fax: 860-522-9259. p. 347

Giardina, Cecily A H, Assoc Law Librn, Govt Doc/Acq, Pennsylvania State University - Dickinson School of Law (University Libraries), 1170 Harrisburg Pike, Carlisle, PA, 17013-1617. Tel: 717-240-5226. Fax: 717-240-5127. p. 2042

Giarrizzo, Ellen, Head, Circ, Sunnyvale Public Library, 665 W Olive Ave, Sunnyvale, CA, 94086-7622. Tel: 408-730-7300. Fax: 408-735-8767. p. 273

Gibb, Kalen, Syst Coordr, Mount Royal University Library, 4825 Mount Royal Gate SW, Calgary, AB, T3E 6K6, CANADA. Tel: 403-440-8516. Fax: 403-440-6758. p. 2692

Gibb, Karen, Librn, Entwistle Public Library, 5232 - 50 St, Entwistle, AB, T0E 0S0, CANADA. Tel: 780-727-3811. Fax: 780-727-2440. p. 2703

Gibbens, Leslie, Librn, Marie Ellison Memorial Library, 480 S Hwy 107, Del Rio, TN, 37727-9625. Tel: 423-487-5929. Fax: 423-487-5929. p. 2233

Gibbon, Connie, Librn, Louis A Weiss Memorial Hospital, 4646 N Marine Dr, Chicago, IL, 60640. Tel: 773-564-5820. Fax: 773-564-5829. p. 627

Gibbon, Cynthia, Mrs, Assoc Dean, Libr Serv, Shippensburg University, 1871 Old Main Dr, Shippensburg, PA, 17257-2299. Tel: 717-477-1475. Fax: 717-477-1389. p. 2140

Gibbons, Amy, Librn, Armoral Tuttle Public Library, 301 N Plymouth Ave, New Plymouth, ID, 83655. Tel: 208-278-5338. Fax: 208-278-5330. p. 581

Gibbons, Barb, Librn, Palliser Regional Library, Willow Bunch Branch, Two Ave F S, Willow Bunch, SK, S0H 4K0, CANADA. Tel: 306-473-2393. p. 2919

Gibbons, Brenda, Ch, YA Serv, Pahrump Community Library, 701 E St, Pahrump, NV, 89048-2164. Tel: 775-727-5930. Fax: 775-727-6209. p. 1432

Gibbons, Dennis, Head, Coll Develop, Texas Christian University, 2913 Lowden St, TCU Box 298400, Fort Worth, TX, 76129. Tel: 817-257-7106. Fax: 817-257-7282. p. 2323

Gibbons, Donna M, Acq of Monographs, Cat, Web Coordr, Sir Mortimer B Davis Jewish General Hospital, 3755 Cote Ste Catherine Rd, A-200, Montreal, QC, H3T 1E2, CANADA. Tel: 514-340-8222, Ext 2391. Fax: 514-340-7552. p. 2901

Gibbons, Gina, Adult Serv, Brentwood Public Library, 8765 Eulalie Ave, Brentwood, MO, 63144. Tel: 314-963-8636. Fax: 314-962-8675. p. 1320

Gibbons, Judith, Tech Serv, Roselle Park, 404 Chestnut St, Roselle Park, NJ, 07204-1506. Tel: 908-245-2456. Fax: 908-245-9204. p. 1528

Gibbons, Milo H, ILL, Wilmington University Library, 320 DuPont Hwy, New Castle, DE, 19720. Tel: 302-328-9401. Fax: 302-328-0914. p. 385

Gibbons, Susan, Univ Librn, Yale University Library, 120 High St, New Haven, CT, 06520. p. 356

Gibbons, Susan, Dean, University of Rochester, Art-Music, Rush Rhees Library, Rochester, NY, 14627. Tel: 585-275-4476. Fax: 585-273-1032. p. 1733

Gibbons, Susan, Dean, University of Rochester, Business & Government Information Library, Rush Rhees Library, Rochester, NY, 14627. Tel: 585-275-4482. Fax: 585-273-5316. p. 1733

Gibbons, Susan, Dean, University of Rochester, Carlson Science & Engineering Library, 160 Trustee Rd, Rochester, NY, 14627-0236. Tel: 585-275-4488. Fax: 585-273-4656. p. 1733

Gibbons, Susan, Dean, University of Rochester, Laboratory for Laser Energetics Library, 250 E River Rd, Rochester, NY, 14623. Tel: 585-275-4479. Fax: 585-273-3663. p. 1733

Gibbons, Susan, Dean, University of Rochester, Multimedia Center, Rush Rhees Library, Rochester, NY, 14627. Tel: 585-273-5009. Fax: 585-273-1032. p. 1733

Gibbons, Susan, Dean, University of Rochester, Rossell Hope Robbins Library, Rush Rhees Library, Rm 416, Rochester, NY, 14627. Tel: 585-275-0110. p. 1733

Gibbons, Valerie, Head, Ref & Info Serv, Lakehead University Library, 955 Oliver Rd, Thunder Bay, ON, P7B 5E1, CANADA. Tel: 807-343-8165. Fax: 807-343-8007. p. 2848

Gibbons, William, Head, Ref, City College of the City University of New York, North Academic Ctr, 160 Convent Ave, New York, NY, 10031. Tel: 212-650-7602. Fax: 212-650-7604. p. 1672

Gibbs, Athelia, Librn, Eva Public Library, 4549 Hwy 55 E, Eva, AL, 35621. Tel: 256-796-8638. Fax: 256-796-8638. p. 16

Gibbs, Carol, ILL, Ivy Tech Community College of Indiana, Northeast, 3800 N Anthony Blvd, Fort Wayne, IN, 46805-1430. Tel: 260-480-4172, 260-482-9171. Fax: 260-480-4121. p. 742

Gibbs, Daniel, Dir, Ardmore Public Library, 320 E St NW, Ardmore, OK, 73401. Tel: 580-223-8290. Fax: 580-221-3240. p. 1956

Gibbs, Donald, Bibliographer, University of Texas Libraries, Nettie Lee Benson Latin American Collection, Sid Richardson Hall 1-108, Austin, TX, 78713-8916. Tel: 512-495-4520. Fax: 512-495-4568. p. 2283

Gibbs, George, Head of Libr, University of Kansas Libraries, Gorton Music & Dance Library, 1530 Naismith Dr, Lawrence, KS, 66045-3102. Tel: 785-864-3282. Fax: 785-864-5310. p. 878

Gibbs, Hope, Circ Supvr, Trinity International University, 2065 Half Day Rd, Deerfield, IL, 60015-1241. Tel: 847-317-4000. Fax: 847-317-4012. p. 635

Gibbs, Keisha, Managing Librn, Columbus Metropolitan Library, Martin Luther King Branch, 1600 E Long St, Columbus, OH, 43203. Tel: 614-645-2275. Fax: 614-479-4219. p. 1884

Gibbs, Lavonna, Acq, Nottoway County Public Libraries, 414 Tyler St, Crewe, VA, 23930. Tel: 434-645-9310. Fax: 434-645-8513. p. 2458

Gibbs, Linda, Acq, Ref Serv, Lambton College, 1457 London Rd, Sarnia, ON, N7S 6K4, CANADA. Tel: 519-541-2441. Fax: 519-541-2426. p. 2839

Gibbs, Margaret, Dir, Historian, Essex County Historical Society, 7590 Court St, Elizabethtown, NY, 12932. Tel: 518-873-6466. Fax: 518-873-6466. p. 1618

Gibbs, Marilyn Y, Dir, Claflin University, 400 Magnolia St, Orangeburg, SC, 29115. Tel: 803-535-5307, 803-535-5309. Fax: 803-535-5091. p. 2201

Gibbs, Nancy, Dept Head, Acq, Duke University Libraries, 411 Chapel Dr, Durham, NC, 27708. Tel: 919-660-5894. Fax: 919-660-5923. p. 1787

Gibbs, Nancy A, Tech Serv, St Pete Beach Public Library, 365 73rd Ave, Saint Pete Beach, FL, 33706-1996. Tel: 727-363-9238. Fax: 727-552-1760. p. 487

Gibbs, Paulette, Ref, New Albany-Floyd County Public Library, 180 W Spring St, New Albany, IN, 47150-3692. Tel: 812-944-8464. Fax: 812-949-3532. p. 768

Gibbs, Sherril, Assoc Librn, Iowa Wesleyan College, 107 W Broad St, Mount Pleasant, IA, 52641. Tel: 319-385-6316. Fax: 319-385-6324. p. 833

Gibbs, Stephanie, In Charge, Beauregard Parish Library, South Beauregard, 6713 Hwy 12, Ragley, LA, 70657. Tel: 337-463-6217. Fax: 337-462-5434. p. 948

Gibbs, Terri, Br Mgr, Denton Public Library, 502 Oakland St, Denton, TX, 76201. Tel: 940-349-8776. Fax: 940-349-8101. p. 2312

Gibbs-Brady, Irene, Ch, Provincetown Public Library, 356 Commercial St, Provincetown, MA, 02657-2209. Tel: 508-487-7094. p. 1119

Gibert, Ken, Br Mgr, Orange County Library District, Hiawassee, 7391 W Colonial Dr, Orlando, FL, 32818. Fax: 407-521-2461. p. 476

Gibian, Germain, Librn, Dunham Tavern Museum Library, 6709 Euclid Ave, Cleveland, OH, 44103-3913. Tel: 216-431-1060. Fax: 216-431-1060. p. 1879

Gibler, Debra, Dir, Kellogg Public Library, 16 W Market Ave, Kellogg, ID, 83837-2499. Tel: 208-786-7231. Fax: 208-784-1100. p. 577

Giblin, Paul, Ref, Kelley Library, 234 Main St, Salem, NH, 03079-3190. Tel: 603-898-7064. Fax: 603-898-8583. p. 1464

Gibney, Jessica, Tech Serv, Neumann College Library, One Neumann Dr, Aston, PA, 19014-1298. Tel: 610-361-5416. Fax: 610-459-1370. p. 2030

Gibney, Joy, Circ Librn, Wythe-Grayson Regional Library, Whitetop Public, 16309 Highlands Pkwy, Whitetop, VA, 24292. Tel: 276-388-2873. Fax: 276-388-2873. p. 2472

Gibradze, Leila, Assoc Dir, Florida State University Libraries, Goldstein Library, 142 Collegiate Loop, Tallahassee, FL, 32306. Tel: 850-645-8418. Fax: 850-644-0460. p. 495

Gibrich, Christie, Br Librn, Grand Prairie Public Library System, Bowles Life Center Branch, 2750 Graham St, Grand Prairie, TX, 75050. Tel: 972-237-5740. p. 2329

Gibson, Alison, Dir, Union Township Public Library, Aberdeen Branch Library, 1730 US Rte 52, Aberdeen, OH, 45101-9302. Tel: 937-392-4871. Fax: 937-795-2681. p. 1932

Gibson, Alison J, Dir, Union Township Public Library, 27 Main St, Ripley, OH, 45167-1231. Tel: 937-392-4871. Fax: 937-392-1631. p. 1932

Gibson, Amy, Ch, Killeen City Library System, 205 E Church Ave, Killeen, TX, 76541. Tel: 254-501-7874. Fax: 254-501-7704. p. 2350

Gibson, Andrew, Assoc Librn, Five Towns College Library, 305 N Service Rd, Dix Hills, NY, 11746. Tel: 631-656-2133. Fax: 631-656-2171. p. 1614

Gibson, Argent, Ref Librn, Atlanta Metropolitan State College Library, 1630 Metropolitan Pkwy SW, Atlanta, GA, 30310. Tel: 404-756-4010. Fax: 404-756-5613. p. 513

Gibson, Barbara, Ref Serv, Ad, Thomas Nelson Community College Library, Wythe Hall 228, 99 Thomas Nelson Dr, Hampton, VA, 23666. Tel: 757-825-2878. Fax: 757-825-2870. p. 2469

Gibson, Becky, Circ, Monroe Public Library, 19 Plains Rd, Monroe, NH, 03771. Tel: 603-638-4736. p. 1458

Gibson, Celeste, Br Mgr, Atlanta-Fulton Public Library System, Adams Park Library, 2231 Campbellton Rd SW, Atlanta, GA, 30311. Tel: 404-752-8763. Fax: 404-752-8765. p. 511

Gibson, Chris, Mobile Serv Mgr, Indian Trails Public Library District, 355 S Schoenbeck Rd, Wheeling, IL, 60090. Tel: 847-459-4100. Fax: 847-459-4760. p. 719

Gibson, Chuck, Dir, Worthington Libraries, 820 High St, Worthington, OH, 43085. Tel: 614-807-2601. Fax: 614-807-2642. p. 1950

Gibson, Claudia, Dir, Chestatee Regional Library System, 342 Allen St, Dawsonville, GA, 30534. Tel: 706-344-3690. Fax: 706-344-3692. p. 529

Gibson, Dana, Dir, Combined Community Library, 1007 Main St, Ordway, CO, 81063-1316. Tel: 719-267-3296. Fax: 719-267-3823. p. 319

Gibson, Debra Rhodes, Dir, Saint Johns County Public Library System, 6670 US 1 South, Saint Augustine, FL, 32086. Tel: 904-827-6926. p. 486

Gibson, Denise M, Asst Librn, Mercer University, Walter F George School of Law, Furman Smith Law Library, 1021 Georgia Ave, Macon, GA, 31201-1001. Tel: 478-301-5905. Fax: 478-301-2284. p. 540

Gibson, Diane, Head Librn, The Columbian Newspaper Information Resource Center, 415 W Sixth St, Vancouver, WA, 98660. Tel: 360-759-8036. Fax: 360-737-6211. p. 2546

Gibson, Donna, Mgr, Memorial Sloan-Kettering Cancer Center Medical Library, 430 East 67th St, New York, NY, 10065. Tel: 212-639-2109. Fax: 212-717-3048. p. 1686

Gibson, Donna Riis, Libr Dir, Paul Sawyier Public Library, 319 Wapping St, Frankfort, KY, 40601-2605. Tel: 502-352-2665. Fax: 502-227-2250. p. 914

Gibson, Elizabeth, Pres, Everett C Benton Library, 75 Oakley Rd, Belmont, MA, 02478-0125. Tel: 617-489-0988. p. 1053

Gibson, George, ILL, North Miami Beach Public Library, 1601 NE 164th St, North Miami Beach, FL, 33162-4099. Tel: 305-948-2970. Fax: 305-787-6007. p. 473

Gibson, Ingrid, ILL Librn, Harvard Library, Dumbarton Oaks Research Library, 1703 32nd St NW, Washington, MA, 20007. Tel: 202-339-6400. Fax: 202-625-0279. p. 1074

Gibson, Jacque, Evening Supvr, ILL Asst, Northwest Nazarene University, 623 University Blvd, Nampa, ID, 83686. Fax: 208-467-8610. p. 580

Gibson, Jesse, Dir, Thomas H Leath Memorial Library, 412 E Franklin St, Rockingham, NC, 28379-4995. Tel: 910-895-6337. Fax: 910-895-5851. p. 1820

Gibson, Joyce, Librn, Southwest Arkansas Regional Library, Nevada County Library, 121 W Main, Prescott, AR, 71857. Tel: 870-887-5846. Fax: 870-887-8226. p. 103

Gibson, Judy Maxine, Dir, Libr Serv, Amberton University, 1700 Eastgate Dr, Garland, TX, 75041. Tel: 972-279-6511, Ext 136. Fax: 972-686-5567. p. 2327

Gibson, June, Librn, Coleman Public Library, 712 Central Ave, Coleman, FL, 33521-0456. Tel: 352-748-4598. Fax: 352-748-5384. p. 434

Gibson, Ken, Coll Develop, Dir, Hanover College, 121 Scenic Dr, Hanover, IN, 47243. Tel: 812-866-7160. Fax: 812-866-7172. p. 748

Gibson, Kerry, Govt Doc, Per, Tech Serv Librn, Ursinus College Library, 601 E Main St, Collegeville, PA, 19426. Tel: 610-409-3000, Ext 2460. Fax: 610-489-0634. p. 2046

Gibson, Kimberly, Dr, Instrul Serv Librn, Our Lady of the Lake University, 411 SW 24th St, San Antonio, TX, 78207-4689. Tel: 210-434-6711, Ext 2324. Fax: 210-436-1616. p. 2380

Gibson, Kristen, Ref Librn, Wittenberg University, 807 Woodlawn Ave, Springfield, OH, 45504. Tel: 937-327-7533. Fax: 937-327-6139. p. 1936

Gibson, Marci, Tech Serv, Workers' Compensation Board of British Columbia Library, 6951 Westminster Hwy, Richmond, BC, V7C 1C6, CANADA. Tel: 604-231-8450. Fax: 604-279-7608. p. 2737

Gibson, Marilyn, Librn, James C Poole Jr Memorial Library, 420 Prairie Ave, Eutaw, AL, 35462-1165. Tel: 205-372-9026. Fax: 205-372-9026. p. 16

Gibson, Meghan, ILL, Jefferson County Rural Library District, 620 Cedar Ave, Port Hadlock, WA, 98339-9514. Tel: 360-385-6544. Fax: 360-385-7921. p. 2524

Gibson, Melissa, Ref Librn, Scott County Public Library, 104 S Bradford Lane, Georgetown, KY, 40324-2335. Tel: 502-863-3566. Fax: 502-863-9621. p. 915

Gibson, Nancy, Instrul Tech Librn, Austin Peay State University, 601 E College St, Clarksville, TN, 37044. Tel: 931-221-6166. Fax: 931-221-7296. p. 2228

Gibson, Natalie, Ref Mgr, East Central Georgia Regional Library, Columbia County Public Library, 7022 Evans Town Center Blvd, Evans, GA, 30809. Tel: 706-447-7671. Fax: 706-868-3351. p. 519

Gibson, Penny, Ref, University of Alabama, School of Law Library, 101 Paul Bryant Dr, Tuscaloosa, AL, 35487. Tel: 205-348-5925. Fax: 205-348-1112. p. 38

Gibson, Quiana, Br Librn, Plaquemines Parish Library, Port Sulphur Branch, 139 Delta St, Port Sulphur, LA, 70083. Tel: 504-564-3681, 985-564-3682. Fax: 504-564-3274. p. 945

Gibson, Rita, Access Serv Coordr, State Law Library of Montana, 215 N Sanders, Helena, MT, 59601-4522. Tel: 406-444-3660. Fax: 406-444-3603. p. 1383

Gibson, Robin, Ch & Youth Librn, Northern Tier Library Association, 4015 Dickey Rd, Gibsonia, PA, 15044-9713. Tel: 724-449-2665. Fax: 724-443-6755. p. 2060

Gibson, Ruth Ann, Head, Tech Serv, Mississippi College, 101 W College St, Clinton, MS, 39058. Tel: 601-925-3433. Fax: 601-925-3435. p. 1296

Gibson, Sally, Tech Serv Adminr, Creighton University, 2500 California Plaza, Omaha, NE, 68178-0209. Tel: 402-280-2228. Fax: 402-280-2435. p. 1412

Gibson, Sandy, Asst Librn, Babbitt Public Library, 71 South Dr, Babbitt, MN, 55706-1232. Tel: 218-827-3345. Fax: 218-827-3345. p. 1240

Gibson, Sherrie R, Dir, Library of Graham, 910 Cherry St, Graham, TX, 76450-3547. Tel: 940-549-0600. Fax: 940-549-8624. p. 2329

Gibson, Stephani, Ref Librn, Hackley Public Library, 316 W Webster Ave, Muskegon, MI, 49440. Tel: 231-722-7276. Fax: 231-726-5567. p. 1212

Gibson, Susan M, Asst Br Mgr, Ross Annie Halenbake Library, Friendship Community Library, Eagle Valley Rd, Beech Creek, PA, 16822. Tel: 570-962-2048. p. 2083

Gibson, Suzanne, Sr Mgr, Sci Info Analysis, Aventis Pharmaceuticals Library, Scientific Information & Library Services, 1041 Rt 202-206, Mail Stop: BRW K-303A, Bridgewater, NJ, 08807-6800. Tel: 908-231-4952. Fax: 908-231-2802. p. 1474

Gibson, Teresa, Asst Librn, Aliceville Public Library, 416 Third Ave NE, Aliceville, AL, 35442. Tel: 205-373-6691. Fax: 205-373-3731. p. 4

Gibson, Tess, Asst Head, Access Serv, Head, ILL, University of Arkansas Libraries, 365 N McIlroy Ave, Fayetteville, AR, 72701-4002. Tel: 479-575-2925. Fax: 479-575-6656. p. 99

Gibson, Toby, Circ Serv Mgr, Library of Rush University Medical Center, Armour Academic Ctr, 600 S Paulina St, 5th Flr, Chicago, IL, 60612-3874. Tel: 312-942-2279. Fax: 312-942-3143. p. 617

Gibson, Twyla, Asst Prof, University of Missouri-Columbia, 303 Townsend Hall, Columbia, MO, 65211. Tel: 573-882-4546. Fax: 573-884-2917. p. 2969

Gibson, William, Exec Dir, Hastings Regional Center, 4200 W Second St, Hastings, NE, 68901-9700. Tel: 402-462-1971, Ext 3391. Fax: 402-460-3100. p. 1401

Gick, Carolina, Sr Commun Libr Mgr, Contra Costa County Library, Walnut Creek Library, 1644 N Broadway, Walnut Creek, CA, 94596-4297. Tel: 925-977-3340. Fax: 925-646-6048. p. 210

Gick, Carolina, Sr Commun Libr Mgr, Contra Costa County Library, Ygnacio Valley (Thurman G Casey Memorial), 2661 Oak Grove Rd, Walnut Creek, CA, 94598-3627. Tel: 925-938-1481. Fax: 925-646-6026. p. 210

Gick, Julie, Librn, New York State Supreme Court, First Judicial District Civil Law Library, 60 Centre St, New York, NY, 10007. Tel: 646-386-3670. Fax: 212-374-8159. p. 1695

Gideon, Angelita, Circ Supvr, San Bernardino Valley College Library, 701 S Mount Vernon Ave, San Bernardino, CA, 92410. Tel: 909-384-8567. p. 229

Gidley, Shirley, Librn, Tulsa City-County Library, Schusterman-Benson Library, 3333 E 32nd Pl, Tulsa, OK, 74135. Tel: 918-746-5024. Fax: 918-746-5026. p. 1983

Giduz, Ellen, Libr Mgr, Charlotte Mecklenburg Library, Cornelius Branch, 21105 Catawba Ave, Cornelius, NC, 28031. Tel: 704-416-3800. Fax: 704-416-3900. p. 1782

Giduz, Ellen, Mgr, Charlotte Mecklenburg Library, Davidson Branch, 119 Main St, Davidson, NC, 28036. Tel: 704-416-4000. p. 1782

Gielec, L, Br Mgr, New Orleans Public Library, Martin Luther King Jr Branch, 1611 Caffin Ave, New Orleans, LA, 70117. Tel: 504-942-0834. Fax: 504-234-2699. p. 962

Gier, Cindy, Head, Circ, Pittsburg Public Library, 308 N Walnut, Pittsburg, KS, 66762-4732. Tel: 620-231-8110. Fax: 620-232-2258. p. 890

Gierlach, Marian Baker, Br Coordr, Cochise County Library District, Alice Woods Sunizona Library at Ash Creek School, 6460 E Hwy 181, Pearce, AZ, 85625. Tel: 520-824-3145. Fax: 520-824-3145. p. 58

Gierloff, Tami, Assoc Dir, Lewis & Clark College, Paul L Boley Law Library, Lewis & Clark Law School, 10015 SW Terwilliger Blvd, Portland, OR, 97219. Tel: 503-768-6776. Fax: 503-768-6760. p. 2011

Giesbrecht, Don, Pres & Chief Exec Officer, Canadian Child Care Federation, 700 Industrial Ave, Ste 600, Ottawa, ON, K1G 0Y9, CANADA. Tel: 613-729-5289, Ext 220. Fax: 613-729-3159. p. 2829

Giesbrecht, JoAnne, Librn, Skagit County Law Library, County Courthouse, 205 W Kincaid, Rm 104, Mount Vernon, WA, 98273. Tel: 360-336-9324. Fax: 360-336-9336. p. 2521

Gieschen, Anna, Head, Ref, Wegner Health Science Information Center, 1400 W 22nd St, Ste 100, Sioux Falls, SD, 57105. Tel: 605-357-1400. Fax: 605-357-1490. p. 2219

Giese, Cindy, Circ, Mayville Public Library, 111 N Main St, Mayville, WI, 53050. Tel: 920-387-7910. Fax: 920-387-7917. p. 2613

Giese, Liz, Librn, Swedish Covenant Hospital, 5145 N California Ave, Chicago, IL, 60625. Tel: 773-878-8200, Ext 5312. Fax: 773-878-1624. p. 625

Giesecke, Joan, Librn, University of Nebraska-Lincoln, Extension Center, 4502 Ave I, Scottsbluff, NE, 69361. Tel: 308-632-1230. Fax: 308-632-1365. p. 1407

Giesecke, Joan R, Dr, Dean, University of Nebraska-Lincoln, 1248 R St, Lincoln, NE, 68588-4100. Tel: 402-472-2526. p. 1407

Gieseke, Shari, Libr Asst, Saint Cloud Hospital, 1406 Sixth Ave N, Saint Cloud, MN, 56303. Tel: 320-251-2700, Ext 54686. Fax: 320-656-7039. p. 1276

Giesking, Tammy, Br Mgr, Las Vegas-Clark County Library District, Centennial Hills Library, 6711 N Buffalo Dr, Las Vegas, NV, 89131. Tel: 702-507-6100. Fax: 702-507-6147. p. 1429

Giffey, Anne, Asst Librn, Pub Serv, Knox College, Two E South St, Galesburg, IL, 61401. Tel: 309-341-7483. Fax: 309-341-7799. p. 648

Giffin, Meredith, Mgr, Wyeth Canada, Scientific Information, 1025 Boul Marcel-Laurin, Saint Laurent, QC, H4R 1J6, CANADA. Tel: 514-748-3734. Fax: 514-744-0550. p. 2909

Gifford, D, Youth Serv Mgr, Teton County Library, 125 Virginian Lane, Jackson, WY, 83001. Tel: 307-733-2164, Ext 221. Fax: 307-733-4568. p. 2656

Gifford, Jeffrey, Circ, Clearwater Public Library System, 100 N Osceola Ave, Clearwater, FL, 33755. Tel: 727-562-4970. Fax: 727-562-4974. p. 432

Gifford, Marcie, Computer Serv, Sidney Memorial Public Library, Eight River St, Sidney, NY, 13838. Tel: 607-563-1200, 607-563-8021. Fax: 607-563-7675. p. 1743

Gifford, Nancy, Librn, Schenectady County Public Library, Scotia Branch, 14 Mohawk Ave, Scotia, NY, 12302. Tel: 518-386-2247. Fax: 518-366-2247. p. 1741

Gifford, Paul, Archivist, University of Michigan-Flint, 303 E Kearsley St, Flint, MI, 48502-1950. Tel: 810-762-3402. Fax: 810-762-3133. p. 1181

Gifford, Sanford, Dr, Dir, Archives, Boston Psychoanalytic Society & Institute, Inc, 169 Herrick Rd, Newton, MA, 02459. Tel: 617-266-0953, Ext 104. Fax: 857-255-3253. p. 1109

Gigee, Janet S, Dir, Spalding Memorial Library, 724 S Main St, Athens, PA, 18810-1010. Tel: 570-888-7117. Fax: 570-882-9202. p. 2030

Giglio, David, Head, Tech Serv, Dover Public Library, 45 S State St, Dover, DE, 19901. Tel: 302-736-7030. Fax: 302-736-5087. p. 382

Gigliotti, Mary Jo, Archivist, State University of New York College at Brockport, 350 New Campus Dr, Brockport, NY, 14420-2997. Tel: 585-395-5834. Fax: 585-395-5651. p. 1585

Gigliotti-Guridi, Chandra, Dir, Chesapeake College, PO Box 8, Wye Mills, MD, 21679. Tel: 410-827-5860. Fax: 410-827-5257. p. 1046

Gignac, Donie, Managing Librn, Pima County Public Library, Joyner-Green Valley, 601 N La Canada Dr, Green Valley, AZ, 85614. Tel: 520-594-5295. Fax: 520-770-4113. p. 87

Giguere, Marlene, Dir, Brenau University, 625 Academy St NE, Gainesville, GA, 30501-3343. Tel: 770-538-4722. Fax: 770-534-6254. p. 534

Gil, Aimee, ILL, Hood College, 401 Rosemont Ave, Frederick, MD, 21701. Tel: 301-696-3695. Fax: 301-696-3796. p. 1029

Gil, Eduardo, Head, Per, Montclair State University, One Normal Ave, Montclair, NJ, 07043-1699. Tel: 973-655-5286. Fax: 973-655-7780. p. 1503

Gil, Esther, Online Serv, University of Denver, 2150 E Evans Ave, Denver, CO, 80208-2007. Tel: 303-871-3441. Fax: 303-871-2290. p. 303

Gil, Isabel, In Charge, Hialeah-John F Kennedy Library, West Hialeah e-Library, 7400 W 24th Ave, Hialeah, FL, 33016. Tel: 305-698-3615. Fax: 305-698-3616. p. 451

Gil-Gomez, Marilouise, Asst Dir, Los Angeles County Harbor UCLA Medical Center, 1000 W Carson St, Torrance, CA, 90509-2910. Tel: 310-222-2372. Fax: 310-533-5146. p. 275

Gilbert, Abella, Ref, Pacific Union College, One Angwin Ave, Angwin, CA, 94508-9705. Tel: 707-965-6244. Fax: 707-965-6504. p. 121

Gilbert, Amy, Assoc Dir, Dominican University of California, 50 Acacia Ave, San Rafael, CA, 94901-2298. Tel: 415-485-3251. Fax: 415-459-2309. p. 256

Gilbert, Barbara, Librn, Temple Israel Library, 4737 Deerfield Pl, Vestal, NY, 13850-3762. Tel: 607-723-7461. p. 1761

Gilbert, Beth, Dir, Mountain View Public Library, 125 S Oak St, Mountain View, MO, 65548. Tel: 417-934-6154. Fax: 417-934-5100. p. 1347

Gilbert, Betsy, Dir, Fairport Public Library, One Fairport Village Landing, Fairport, NY, 14450. Tel: 585-223-9091. Fax: 585-223-3998. p. 1621

Gilbert, Bonnie B, Dir, Vance Township Library, 107 S Main St, Fairmount, IL, 61841. Tel: 217-733-2164. Fax: 217-733-2164. p. 645

Gilbert, Bruce, Dir, Digital Libr & Instruction, Drake University, 2725 University Ave, Des Moines, IA, 50311. Tel: 515-271-4821. Fax: 515-271-3933. p. 809

Gilbert, Danielle, Asst Librn, Fasken Martineau DuMoulin LLP, 800 Victoria Sq, Montreal, QC, H4Z 1E9, CANADA. Tel: 514-397-7400, 514-397-7439. Fax: 514-397-7600. p. 2895

Gilbert, Deborah, Dir, Children's National Medical Center, 111 Michigan Ave NW, Washington, DC, 20010-2970. Tel: 202-476-3195. Fax: 202-476-5318. p. 396

Gilbert, Debra, Br Supvr, Jackson/Hinds Library System, Richard Wright Library, 515 W McDowell Rd, Jackson, MS, 39204-5547. Tel: 601-372-1621. Fax: 601-372-7083. p. 1303

Gilbert, Edi, Libr Assoc, Lafayette Natural History Museum & Planetarium, 433 Jefferson St, Lafayette, LA, 70501-7013. Tel: 337-291-5420. Fax: 337-291-5464. p. 952

Gilbert, Eileen, Dir, Boscawen Public Library, 116 N Main St, Boscawen, NH, 03303-1123. Tel: 603-753-8576. p. 1439

Gilbert, Gail, Dir, University of Louisville Libraries, Margaret Bridwell Art Library, Schneider Hall, Belknap Campus, Louisville, KY, 40292. Tel: 502-852-6741. p. 926

Gilbert, James, Ref, Cedar Crest College, 100 College Dr, Allentown, PA, 18104-6196. Tel: 610-606-4666, Ext 3387. Fax: 610-740-3769. p. 2026

Gilbert, James, Tech Coordr, Whitehall Township Public Library, 3700 Mechanicsville Rd, Whitehall, PA, 18052-3399. Tel: 610-432-4339. Fax: 610-432-9387. p. 2155

Gilbert, Jean, Asst Dir, Northern Oklahoma College, 1220 E Grand Ave, Tonkawa, OK, 74653-4022. Tel: 580-628-6250. Fax: 580-628-6209. p. 1980

Gilbert, Judie, Circ, Louisiana State University Libraries, LSU School of Veterinary Medicine Library, Skip Bertman Dr, Baton Rouge, LA, 70803-8414. Tel: 225-578-9800. Fax: 225-578-9798. p. 944

Gilbert, Julie, Coll Access/Ref, Gustavus Adolphus College, 800 W College Ave, Saint Peter, MN, 56082. Tel: 507-933-7552. Fax: 507-933-6292. p. 1283

Gilbert, Kathy, Ser Tech, Pierce College Library, 9401 Farwest Dr SW, Lakewood, WA, 98498. Tel: 253-964-6740. Fax: 253-964-6713. p. 2519

Gilbert, Kristine, Librn, New York Supreme Court, Three E Pulteney Sq, Bath, NY, 14810. Tel: 607-664-2099. Fax: 607-776-7715. p. 1578

Gilbert, Lauren, Head, Commun Serv, Sachem Public Library, 150 Holbrook Rd, Holbrook, NY, 11741. Tel: 631-588-5024. Fax: 631-588-5064. p. 1637

Gilbert, Lauren B, Info Serv, Cold Spring Harbor Library, 95 Harbor Rd, Cold Spring Harbor, NY, 11724. Tel: 631-692-6820. Fax: 631-692-6827. p. 1609

Gilbert, Lois, Br Coordr, La Crosse Public Library, North Community, 1552 Kane St, La Crosse, WI, 54603. Tel: 608-789-7189. Fax: 608-789-7104. p. 2603

Gilbert, Lois, Br Coordr, La Crosse Public Library, South Community, 1307 S 16th St, La Crosse, WI, 54601. Tel: 608-789-7189. Fax: 608-789-7105. p. 2603

Gilbert, Mary, Asst Univ Librn, Coll Mgt, Towson University, 8000 York Rd, Towson, MD, 21252-0001. Tel: 410-704-4926. Fax: 410-704-3760. p. 1045

Gilbert, Nicole, Br Mgr, Jackson District Library, Napoleon Branch, 6755 S Brooklyn Rd, Napoleon, MI, 49261. Tel: 517-536-4266. Fax: 517-536-0531. p. 1196

Gilbert, Olga, Librn, Mono County Free Library, Coleville, 111591 Hwy 395, Coleville, CA, 96107. Tel: 530-495-2788. Fax: 530-495-2295. p. 182

Gilbert, Paula, Head, Youth Serv, Martin Memorial Library, 159 E Market St, York, PA, 17401-1269. Tel: 717-846-5300. Fax: 717-848-2330. p. 2159

Gilbert, Paula, Pres, Pennsylvania Library Association, 220 Cumberland Pkwy, Ste 10, Mechanicsburg, PA, 17055. Tel: 717-766-7663. Fax: 717-766-5440. p. 2954

Gilbert, Peter J, Dir, Lawrence University, 113 S Lawe St, Appleton, WI, 54911-5683. Tel: 920-832-7353. Fax: 920-832-6967. p. 2578

Gilbert, Sandra, Circ, Iberville Parish Library, 24605 J Gerald Berret Blvd, Plaquemine, LA, 70764. Tel: 225-687-2520, 225-687-4397. Fax: 225-687-9719. p. 965

Gilbert, Scott, Ref Librn, Lone Star College System, The University Center Library, 3232 College Park Dr, The Woodlands, TX, 77384. Tel: 281-618-7140, 936-273-7562. Fax: 936-273-7616. p. 2340

Gilbert, Sylvie, Dir, Artexte Information Centre, 460 Saint-Catherine W, Ste 508, Montreal, QC, H3B 1A7, CANADA. Tel: 514-874-0049. p. 2888

Gilbert, Timothy, Electronic Res, Mount Olive Public Library, 202 Flanders-Drakestown Rd, Flanders, NJ, 07836. Tel: 973-691-8686. Fax: 973-691-8542. p. 1485

Gilbert-Stadigh, Debbie, Head, Circ Serv, University of Texas at Dallas, 800 W Campbell Rd, Richardson, TX, 75080. Tel: 972-883-2950. Fax: 972-883-2473. p. 2374

Gilberto, James, Librn, New York State Legislative Library, State Capitol, Rm 337, Albany, NY, 12224-0345. Tel: 518-455-2468. Fax: 518-426-6901. p. 1569

Gilbertson, Beverley, Dir, Bibliotheque de Beaconsfield, 303 Boulevard, Beaconsfield, QC, H9W 4A7, CANADA. Tel: 514-428-4466. Fax: 514-428-4477. p. 2880

Gilbertson, Crystal, Libr Coordr, Alberta Law Libraries - Vermilion, Provincial Bldg, 4701-42nd St, Vermilion, AB, T9X 1J9, CANADA. Tel: 780-853-8249. Fax: 780-853-8200. p. 2720

Gilbertson, Darvy, Libr Mgr, Brownfield Public Library, Box 63, Brownfield, AB, T0C 0R0, CANADA. Tel: 403-578-2247. Fax: 403-578-4208. p. 2686

Gilbertson, Mary, Head, Monographs, University of Arkansas Libraries, 365 N McIlroy Ave, Fayetteville, AR, 72701-4002. Tel: 479-575-5417. Fax: 479-575-6656. p. 99

Gilbraith, Rhonda, Ref, Bethel University Library, 3900 Bethel Dr, Saint Paul, MN, 55112. Tel: 651-638-6222. Fax: 651-638-6001. p. 1277

Gilbreth, Donna, Ref/Info Serv Supvr, New Hampshire State Library, 20 Park St, Concord, NH, 03301-6314. Tel: 603-271-2060. Fax: 603-271-2205, 603-271-6826. p. 1443

Gilchrist, Debra, Dean, Libr & Institutional Effectiveness, Pierce College Library, 9401 Farwest Dr SW, Lakewood, WA, 98498. Tel: 253-964-6553. Fax: 253-964-6713. p. 2519

Gilchrist, Debra, Dr, Dean, Libr & Institutional Effectiveness, Pierce College Library, Puyallup Campus, 1601 39th Ave SE, Puyallup, WA, 98374. Tel: 253-964-6553. Fax: 252-964-6713. p. 2520

Gilchrist, Martin C, Pres, Urban Research & Development Corp Library, 28 W Broad St, Bethlehem, PA, 18018. Tel: 610-865-0701. Fax: 610-868-7613. p. 2035

Gilchrist, Nancy, Librn, J B Nickells Memorial Library, 215 S Pecan St, Luling, TX, 78648. Tel: 830-875-2813. p. 2358

Gildea, Ruthann, Dir, Butler Hospital, 345 Blackstone Blvd, Providence, RI, 02906. Tel: 401-455-6248. Fax: 401-455-6293. p. 2172

Gilder, Betsy, Mgr, Medina County District Library, Lodi Community, 635 Wooster St, Lodi, OH, 44254-1311. Tel: 330-948-1885. Fax: 330-948-2410. p. 1916

Gilderson-Duwe, Jeff, Dir, Oshkosh Public Library, 106 Washington Ave, Oshkosh, WI, 54901-4985. Tel: 920-236-5201, 920-236-5205. Fax: 920-236-5228. p. 2628

Gilderson-Duwe, Jeff, Dir, Winnefox Library System, 106 Washington Ave, Oshkosh, WI, 54901-4985. Tel: 920-236-5220. Fax: 920-236-5228. p. 2628

Gildone, Stephanie, Youth Serv, Conneaut Public Library, 304 Buffalo St, Conneaut, OH, 44030-2658. Tel: 440-593-1608. Fax: 440-593-4470. p. 1891

Gile, Kathryn, Librn, Scandia City Library, 409 Fourth St, Scandia, KS, 66966. Tel: 785-335-2271. Fax: 785-335-2271. p. 893

Gilera, Cheryl, Commun Libr Mgr, County of Los Angeles Public Library, Bell Gardens Library, 7110 S Garfield Ave, Bell Gardens, CA, 90201-3244. Tel: 562-927-1309. Fax: 562-928-4512. p. 141

Giles, Bob, Curator, Harvard Library, Nieman Foundation-Bill Kovach Collection of Contemporary Journalism Library, One Francis Ave, Cambridge, MA, 02138. Tel: 617-495-2237. Fax: 617-495-8976. p. 1076

Giles, Crystal, Cat, Tech Serv Librn, Northwest Mississippi Community College, 4975 Hwy 51 N, Senatobia, MS, 38668-1701. Tel: 662-562-3904. Fax: 662-562-3280. p. 1315

Giles, Jeffrey, Res, Schulte Roth & Zabel LLP, 919 Third Ave, New York, NY, 10022. Tel: 212-756-2304. Fax: 212-593-5955. p. 1699

Giles, Judy, Asst Librn, Paden City Public Library, 114 S Fourth Ave, Paden City, WV, 26159. Tel: 304-337-9333. Fax: 304-337-9333. p. 2568

Giles, Karen, Pres, Cincinnati College of Mortuary Science Library, 645 W North Bend Rd, Cincinnati, OH, 45224-1428. Tel: 513-761-2020. Fax: 513-761-3333. p. 1869

Giles, Wadad, Cataloger, North Carolina Central University, School of Law Library, 1512 S Alston Ave, Durham, NC, 27707. Tel: 919-530-7177. Fax: 919-530-7926. p. 1789

Giles-Smith, Lori, Librn, University of Manitoba Libraries, Bill Larson Library (Grace Hospital), 300 Booth Dr, Winnipeg, MB, R3J 3M7, CANADA. Tel: 204-837-0127. Fax: 204-897-9486. p. 2758

Gilgenbach, Cara, Curator, Spec Coll & Univ Archives, Kent State University Libraries, 1125 Risman Dr, Kent, OH, 44242. Tel: 330-672-1677. Fax: 330-672-4811. p. 1907

Gilgenbach, Lisa, Ch & Home Schooling, Barberton Public Library, 602 W Park Ave, Barberton, OH, 44203-2458. Tel: 330-745-1194. Fax: 330-745-8261. p. 1857

Gilgore, Jan, Dir, Youngstown Free Library, 240 Lockport St, Youngstown, NY, 14174. Tel: 716-745-3555. Fax: 716-745-7122. p. 1772

Gilham, Erin, Tech Serv, Blackfeet Community College, US Hwy Two & 89, Browning, MT, 59417. Tel: 406-338-5441. Fax: 406-338-5454. p. 1376

Gilham, Laura, Librn, Northeast Mississippi Community College, 101 Cunningham Blvd, Booneville, MS, 38829. Tel: 662-720-7584. Fax: 662-728-2428. p. 1294

Gilhula, Terry, Info & Res Mgr, Knoxville-Knox County Metropolitan Planning Commission Library, City & County Bldg, Ste 403, 400 Main St, Knoxville, TN, 37902-2476. Tel: 865-215-2500. Fax: 865-215-2068. p. 2242

Gilkey, Peggy, Librn, Dunklin County Library, Clarkton Branch, 113 S Main St, Clarkton, MO, 63837. Tel: 573-448-3803. p. 1342

Gill, Carole, Ch, Buckley Public Library, 408 Dewey Ave, Poteau, OK, 74953. Tel: 918-647-3833, 918-647-4444. Fax: 918-647-8910. p. 1976

Gill, Carolyn F, Cat, Overdues/Circ, Reserves, York Technical College Library, 452 S Anderson Rd, Rock Hill, SC, 29730. Tel: 803-327-8025. Fax: 803-327-4535. p. 2203

Gill, Dennis, Dept Chair, Treasure Valley Community College Library, 650 College Blvd, Ontario, OR, 97914-3423. Tel: 541-881-5915. Fax: 541-881-2724. p. 2009

Gill, Don, Librn/Cat, Santa Barbara County Genealogical Society, 316 Castillo St, Santa Barbara, CA, 93101-3814. Tel: 805 967-7236. p. 260

Gill, Donald, Reader Serv, United States Merchant Marine Academy, 300 Steamboat Rd, Kings Point, NY, 11024-1699. Tel: 516-726-5747. Fax: 516-726-5900. p. 1649

Gill, Heather, Human Res Mgr, Genesee District Library, G-4195 W Pasadena Ave, Flint, MI, 48504. Tel: 810-230-3340. Fax: 810-732-1161. p. 1179

Gill, James, Mgr, Extn & Tech Serv, Tuscarawas County Public Library, 121 Fair Ave NW, New Philadelphia, OH, 44663-2600. Tel: 330-364-4474. Fax: 330-364-8217. p. 1921

Gill, Jamie, Ser Librn, Tech Serv Supvr, Eckerd College, 4200 54th Ave S, Saint Petersburg, FL, 33711. Tel: 727-864-8337. Fax: 727-864-8997. p. 488

Gill, Jessica, Archivist, Newburyport Public Library, 94 State St, Newburyport, MA, 01950-6619. Tel: 978-465-4428, Ext 229. Fax: 978-463-0394. p. 1109

Gill, Joan, Circ, ILL, Neosho County Community College, 800 W 14th St, Chanute, KS, 66720-2699. Tel: 620-431-2820, Ext 244. Fax: 620-432-9841. p. 860

Gill, Johnny, Librn, Cook County Law Library, Skokie Branch, 5600 W Old Orchard Rd, Skokie, IL, 60077. Tel: 847-470-7298. Fax: 847-470-7526. p. 612

Gill, Judith, Librn, Wood County Law Library, One Courthouse Sq, Bowling Green, OH, 43402. Tel: 419-353-3921. Fax: 419-352-9269. p. 1861

Gill, Kathy, Librn, New Straitsville Public Library, 102 E Main St, New Straitsville, OH, 43766. Tel: 740-394-2717. Fax: 740-394-2817. p. 1921

Gill, Kayce D, Electronic Res/Ser Librn, Lipscomb University, One University Park Dr, Nashville, TN, 37204-3951. Tel: 615-966-5763. Fax: 615-966-5874. p. 2257

Gill, Linda, Br Mgr, Calcasieu Parish Public Library, Southwest Louisiana Genealogical & Historical Library, 411 Pujo St, Lake Charles, LA, 70601-4254. Tel: 337-721-7110. Fax: 337-437-3490. p. 954

Gill, Matthew, Commun Libr Mgr, County of Los Angeles Public Library, Castaic Library, 27971 Sloan Canyon Rd, Castaic, CA, 91384. Tel: 661-257-7410. Fax: 661-257-5959. p. 141

Gill, Nita, Adult Serv, Brookings Public Library, 515 Third St, Brookings, SD, 57006. Tel: 605-692-9407. Fax: 605-692-9386. p. 2210

Gill, Sharon, Prof, Murray State University, 3201 Alexander Hall, Murray, KY, 42071-3309. Tel: 270-809-2500. Fax: 270-809-3799. p. 2966

Gill, Tom, Instrul Media Coordr, North Central College, 320 E School St, Naperville, IL, 60540. Tel: 630-637-5723. Fax: 630-637-5716. p. 679

Gillahan, Donna, Asst Dir, Ch, Dir of Outreach, Clay County Public Library, 211 Bridge St, Manchester, KEY, 40962. Tel: 606-598-2617. Fax: 606-598-4671. p. 928

Gillam, Michelle, Asst Br Librn, Crook County Library, Hulett Branch, 115 N Hwy 24, Hulett, WY, 82720. Tel: 307-467-5676. Fax: 307-467-5250. p. 2661

Gillane, Daniel, Librn IV, Lafayette Public Library, 301 W Congress, Lafayette, LA, 70501-6866. Tel: 337-261-5799. Fax: 337-261-5782. p. 952

Gillard, Y, Libr Tech, Ross King Memorial Public Library, 65 Olympic Dr, Mount Pearl, NL, A1N 5H6, CANADA. Tel: 709-368-3603, 709-368-7338. Fax: 709-368-0758. p. 2770

Gillcrist, Christopher, Exec Dir, Great Lakes Historical Society, Inland Seas Maritime Museum, 480 Main St, Vermilion, OH, 44089. Tel: 440-967-3467. Fax: 440-967-1519. p. 1943

Gille, Dorothy Nelsen, Ref, Bank of America Merrill Lynch & Co, 250 Vesey St, 24th Flr, New York, NY, 10080. Tel: 212-449-3814. Fax: 212-449-1379. p. 1669

Gillen, Katherine, Dir, United States Air Force, Bldg 219, 7424 N Homer Dr, 56 SVS/SVMG FL 4887, Luke AFB, AZ, 85309-1220. Tel: 623-856-7191. Fax: 623-935-2023. p. 68

Gilles, Frances, Evening/Weekend Ref Librn, Benedictine University Library, 5700 College Rd, Lisle, IL, 60532-0900. Tel: 630-829-6050. Fax: 630-960-9451. p. 666

Gilles, Lesley, Mgr, Kootenai-Shoshone Area Libraries, Pinehurst-Kingston Branch, 107 Main St, Pinehurst, ID, 83850. Tel: 208-682-3483. Fax: 208-682-3483. p. 575

Gillespie, Amy, Dir, Lansdowne Public Library, 55 S Lansdowne Ave, Lansdowne, PA, 19050-2804. Tel: 610-623-0239. Fax: 610-623-6825. p. 2078

Gillespie, Carol, Librn, Dearborn County Hospital, 600 Wilson Creek, Lawrenceburg, IN, 47025. Tel: 812-537-1010. Fax: 812-537-2833. p. 760

Gillespie, David M, Dr, Dir, Frostburg State University, One Stadium Dr, Frostburg, MD, 21532. Tel: 301-687-4396. Fax: 301-687-7069. p. 1029

Gillespie, Donna, Dir, Crandall-Combine Community Library, 13385 FM 3039, Crandall, TX, 75114. Tel: 972-427-8170. Fax: 972-427-8171. p. 2303

Gillespie, Eric, Dir, Colonel Robert R McCormick Research Center, One S 151 Winfield Rd, Wheaton, IL, 60189-6097. Tel: 630-260-8186. Fax: 630-260-9298. p. 718

Gillespie, Esther, Delivery Serv Mgr, Hayner Public Library District, 326 Belle St, Alton, IL, 62002. Tel: 618-462-0677. Fax: 618-462-0665. p. 588

Gillespie, Fawn, Head, Ref, Hagaman Memorial Library, 227 Main St, East Haven, CT, 06512-3003. Tel: 203-468-3890. Fax: 203-468-3892. p. 337

Gillespie, Gail, Librn, Northern State Prison Library, 168 Frontage Rd, Newark, NJ, 07114-3794. Tel: 973-465-0068, Ext 4521. Fax: 973-578-4393. p. 1512

Gillespie, Gerry, Head, Adult Serv, Stratford Library Association, 2203 Main St, Stratford, CT, 06615. Tel: 203-385-4161. Fax: 203-381-2079. p. 371

Gillespie, Jane, Coordr, Coll Mgt, Saint Louis University, 3650 Lindell Blvd, Saint Louis, MO, 63108-3302. Tel: 314-977-3592. Fax: 314-977-3108. p. 1360

Gillespie, Joan, Exec Dir, Ocean State Libraries, 300 Centerville Rd, Ste 103 S, Warwick, RI, 02886-0226. Tel: 401-738-2200. Fax: 401-736-8949. p. 2955

Gillespie, Kellie, Br Coordr, Mesa Public Library, Red Mountain Branch, 635 N Power Rd, Mesa, AZ, 85205. Tel: 480-644-3569. Fax: 480-644-3559. p. 69

Gillespie, Linda, Librn, Rhome Public Library, 265 BC Rhome Ave, Rhome, TX, 76078. Tel: 817-636-2767. p. 2374

Gillespie, Lisa, Chief Librn, Aiken-Bamberg-Barnwell-Edgefield Regional Library System, Barnwell County, 40 Burr St, Barnwell, SC, 29812-1917. Tel: 803-259-3612. Fax: 803-259-7497. p. 2179

Gillespie, Pamela, Dean, Libr Serv, City College of the City University of New York, North Academic Ctr, 160 Convent Ave, New York, NY, 10031. Tel: 212-650-7155. Fax: 212-650-7604. p. 1672

Gillespie, Terri, Dir, Saint Elmo Public Library District, 311 W Cumberland Rd, Saint Elmo, IL, 62458. Tel: 618-829-5544. Fax: 618-829-9104. p. 700

Gillespie, Terri, Dir, Saint Elmo Public Library District, Beecher City Branch, 108 N James St, Beecher City, IL, 62414. Tel: 618-487-9400. p. 700

Gillett, Aileen, Librn, West Hartford Library, 5133 Rte 14, West Hartford, VT, 05084. Tel: 802-295-7992. Fax: 802-295-7992. p. 2439

Gillett, Michele, Librn, Albuquerque-Bernalillo County Library System, East Mountain, One Old Tijeras Rd, Tijeras, NM, 87059. Tel: 505-281-8509. Fax: 505-281-8510. p. 1548

Gillette, Angela, Br Mgr, Mid-Continent Public Library, Kearney Branch, 100 S Platte-Clay Way, Kearney, MO, 64060-7640. Tel: 816-628-5055. Fax: 816-628-5645. p. 1332

Gillette, Bronwen, Librn, Reading Public Library, Northeast, 1348 N 11th St, Reading, PA, 19604-1509. Tel: 610-655-6361. Fax: 610-655-6668. p. 2133

Gillette, John, YA Librn, Bettendorf Public Library Information Center, 2950 Learning Campus Dr, Bettendorf, IA, 52722. Tel: 563-344-4175. Fax: 563-344-4185. p. 796

Gillette, Mary Ann, Ref, Delaware County Community College Library, 901 S Media Line Rd, Media, PA, 19063-1094. Tel: 610-359-5149, 610-359-5326. Fax: 610-359-5272. p. 2087

Gillette, Susan, Librn, Deerfield Correctional Center, 21360 Deerfield Dr, Capron, VA, 23829. Tel: 434-658-4368. Fax: 434-658-4371. p. 2453

Gilley, Jennifer R, Head Librn, Pennsylvania State University, New Kensington, 3550 Seventh St Rd, Rte 780, Upper Burrell, PA, 15068-1798. Tel: 724-334-6076. Fax: 724-334-6113. p. 2149

Gilley, Sharon A, Dir, Lucius Beebe Memorial Library, 345 Main St, Wakefield, MA, 01880-5093. Tel: 781-246-6335. Fax: 781-246-6385. p. 1132

Gilley, Susan, Mgr, Libr Serv, Oklahoma Department of Libraries, 200 NE 18th St, Oklahoma City, OK, 73105. Tel: 405-521-2502. Fax: 405-525-7804. p. 1974

Gilley, Terence Michael, Dir of Libr Serv, Mountain Empire Community College, 3441 Mountain Empire Rd, Big Stone Gap, VA, 24219. Tel: 276-523-2400, Ext 304. Fax: 276-523-8220. p. 2451

Gilliam, Anita, Librn, Springfield News-Sun Library, 202 N Limestone St, Springfield, OH, 45503. Tel: 937-328-0348. Fax: 937-328-0328. p. 1936

Gilliam, Ellen, Mgr, Portland Public Library, Burbank, 377 Stevens Ave, Portland, ME, 04103. Tel: 207-774-4229. Fax: 207-871-1721. p. 997

Gilliam, Karen, Librn, Broughton Hospital, John S McKee Jr Memorial Library, 1000 S Sterling St, Morganton, NC, 28655. Tel: 828-433-2303. Fax: 828-433-2097. p. 1811

Gilliam, Kathy, Dir, Del Norte Public Library, 790 Grand Ave, Del Norte, CO, 81132. Tel: 719-657-2633. Fax: 719-657-2633. p. 297

Gilliam, Teresa, Asst Dir, Waynesboro Public Library, 600 S Wayne Ave, Waynesboro, VA, 22980. Tel: 540-942-6746. Fax: 540-942-6753. p. 2501

Gilliard, Bruce, Ref Librn, West Milford Township Library, 1490 Union Valley Rd, West Milford, NJ, 07480. Tel: 973-728-2820. Fax: 973-728-2106. p. 1541

Gilliard, Sylvia, Librn & TOC/Instr, United States Navy, Naval Consolidated Brig Library, Bldg 3107, 1050 Remount Rd, Charleston, SC, 29406-3515. Tel: 843-743-0306, Ext 3059. Fax: 843-743-0339, 843-743-0364. p. 2185

Gillie, Esther, Coordr, Pub Serv, Ref Librn, Roberts Wesleyan College & Northeastern Seminary, 2301 Westside Dr, Rochester, NY, 14624-1997. Tel: 585-594-6141. Fax: 585-594-6543. p. 1731

Gillie, Michelle, Acq, Coll Develop, St Lawrence University, 23 Romoda Dr, Canton, NY, 13617. Tel: 315-229-5834. Fax: 315-229-7447. p. 1602

Gillies, Irene B, Dir, Eldredge Public Library, 564 Main St, Chatham, MA, 02633-2296. Tel: 508-945-5170. Fax: 508-945-5173. p. 1079

Gillies, Ronald J, Dir, Lloydminster Public Library, 5010 49th St, Lloydminster, AB, T9V 0K2, CANADA. Tel: 780-875-0850. Fax: 780-875-6523. p. 2710

Gilligan, Ann T, Chief Opearting Officer, Pub Serv, Howard County Library System, 6600 Cradlerock Way, Columbia, MD, 21045-4912. Tel: 410-313-7750. Fax: 410-313-7742. p. 1026

Gillihan, Karen, Dir, Goodland Public Library, 812 Broadway, Goodland, KS, 67735. Tel: 785-899-5461. Fax: 785-899-5461. p. 869

Gililan, Julia, Dir, White Sulphur Springs Public Library, 203 W Main St, White Sulphur Springs, WV, 24986-2411. Tel: 304-536-1171. Fax: 304-536-3801. p. 2575

Gilliland, Jerry S, Dir, Stanton Community Library, 310 Broad Ave, Stanton, IA, 51573. Tel: 712-829-2290. Fax: 712-829-2607. p. 845

Gilliland, Kris, Dir, University of Mississippi, Three Grove Loop, University, MS, 38677. Tel: 662-915-6836. Fax: 662-915-7731. p. 1316

Gilliland, Lise, Dir, Cochise County Library District, Old High School, 2nd Flr, 100 Clawson, Bisbee, AZ, 85603. Tel: 520-432-8930. Fax: 520-432-7339. p. 58

Gillis, Arlene, Libr Asst, Bastyr University Library, 14500 Juanita Dr NE, Kenmore, WA, 98028. Tel: 425-602-3393. Fax: 425-602-3188. p. 2518

Gillis, Bill, Ref & Instruction Librn, George Washington University, Eckles Library, 2100 Foxhall Rd NW, Washington, DC, 20007-1199. Tel: 202-242-8290. Fax: 202-242-6632. p. 402

Gillis, Heather, Res Access Cordr, University of California, Merced Library, 5200 N Lake Rd, Merced, CA, 95343-5001. Tel: 209-228-2945. Fax: 209-228-4271. p. 186

Gillis, Heidi, Mgr, Mkt & Develop, Baltimore County Public Library, 320 York Rd, Towson, MD, 21204-5179. Tel: 410-887-2457. Fax: 410-887-6103. p. 1044

Gillis, June, Asst Librn, ILL, Fort Meade Public Library, 75 E Broadway, Fort Meade, FL, 33841-2998. Tel: 863-285-8287. Fax: 863-285-9159. p. 444

Gillis, Kelly, Br Tech, Prince Edward Island Public Library Service, Alberton Public, 460 Main St, Alberton, PE, C0B 1B0, CANADA. Tel: 902-853-3049. p. 2876

Gillis, Nancy, Dir, Nebraska State Historical Society, John G Neihardt State Historic Site, 306 W Elm, Bancroft, NE, 68004. Tel: 402-648-3388. Fax: 402-648-3388. p. 1392

Gillis, Roger, Archivist, Mount Saint Vincent University Library, 166 Bedford Hwy, Halifax, NS, B3M 2J6, CANADA. Tel: 902-457-6401. Fax: 902-457-6445. p. 2781

Gillis, Theresa, Ref, Eastern Oregon University, One University Blvd, La Grande, OR, 97850. Tel: 541-962-3540. Fax: 541-962-3335. p. 2003

Gillispie, Jan, Ch & Youth Librn, New Castle-Henry County Public Library, 376 S 15th St, New Castle, IN, 47362-3205. Tel: 765-529-0362, Ext 366. Fax: 765-521-3581. p. 768

Gilliss, Apryl, Head, Ref, Butler Area Public Library, 218 N McKean St, Butler, PA, 16001-4971. Tel: 724-287-1715, Ext 113. Fax: 724-285-5090. p. 2039

Gillogly, Holly, Adult Serv Coordr, Louisburg Public Library, 206 S Broadway, Louisburg, KS, 66053. Tel: 913-837-2217. Fax: 913-837-2218. p. 880

Gillon, Robyn, Dir, Lynbrook Public Library, 56 Eldert St, Lynbrook, NY, 11563. Tel: 516-599-8630. Fax: 516-596-1312. p. 1655

Gills, Tina, Develop Mgr, Richland County Public Library, 1431 Assembly St, Columbia, SC, 29201-3101. Tel: 803-799-9084. Fax: 803-929-3448. p. 2188

Gillum, Gary, Humanities & Soc Sci Librn, Brigham Young University, Harold B Lee Library, 2060 HBLL, Provo, UT, 84602. Tel: 801-422-2927. Fax: 801-422-0466. p. 2411

Gillum, Karen, Scholarly Res & Serv/Humanities Librn, Colby College Libraries, 5100 Mayflower Hill, Waterville, ME, 04901. Tel: 207-859-5123. Fax: 207-859-5105. p. 1005

Gilly, Nancy, Librn, William W Backus Hospital, 326 Washington St, Norwich, CT, 06360-2733. Tel: 860-823-6327. Fax: 860-892-2704. p. 362

Gilman, Chad, Tech Serv, Inver Hills Community College Library, 2500 80th St E, Inver Grove Heights, MN, 55076-3209. Tel: 651-450-3876. Fax: 651-450-3679. p. 1254

Gilman, Connie, Br Mgr, Prince William Public Library System, Chinn Park Regional, 13065 Chinn Park Dr, Prince William, VA, 22192-5073. Tel: 703-792-4800. Fax: 703-792-4612. p. 2486

Gilman, Gail, Librn, Huntington Woods Public Library, 26415 Scotia, Huntington Woods, MI, 48070-1198. Tel: 248-543-9720. Fax: 248-543-2559. p. 1193

Gilman, Isaac, Scholarly Communications & Res Serv Librn, Pacific University Library, 2043 College Way, Forest Grove, OR, 97116. Tel: 503-352-7209. Fax: 503-352-1416. p. 1998

Gilman, Lynn, Assoc Librn, University of Wisconsin-Rock County Library, 2909 Kellogg Ave, Janesville, WI, 53546-5606. Tel: 608-758-6531. Fax: 608-758-6560. p. 2600

Gilman, Mark, Asst Mgr, Dallas Public Library, 1515 Young St, Dallas, TX, 75201-5499. Tel: 214-670-1400. Fax: 214-670-7839. p. 2306

Gilman, Patty, Librn, Bellevue Public Library, 115 E Pine, Bellevue, ID, 83313. Tel: 208-788-2128. Fax: 208-788-2128. p. 569

Gilmore, Carolyn, Coordr, Pub Serv, Dawson College Library, 3040 Sherbrooke St W, Westmount, QC, H3Z 1A4, CANADA. Tel: 514-931-8731, Ext 1736. Fax: 514-931-3567. p. 2915

Gilmore, Cathy, Asst Dir, Upper Moreland Free Public Library, 109 Park Ave, Willow Grove, PA, 19090-3277. Tel: 215-659-0741. Fax: 215-830-1223. p. 2157

Gilmore, Joanne R, Dir, Fiscal Officer, Upper Sandusky Community Library, 301 N Sandusky Ave, Upper Sandusky, OH, 43351-1139. Tel: 419-294-1345. Fax: 419-294-4499. p. 1942

Gilmore, Jodi, Res, Manitoba Labour Board Library, 175 Hargrave St, 5th Flr, Winnipeg, MB, R3C 3R8, CANADA. Tel: 204-945-5046. Fax: 204-945-1296. p. 2757

Gilmore, Julie, Tech Serv, Kentucky Wesleyan College, 3000 Frederica St, Owensboro, KY, 42301. Tel: 270-852-3259. Fax: 270-926-3196. p. 931

Gilmore, Julie, Tech Serv Librn, Christian Brothers University, 650 E Pkwy South, Memphis, TN, 38104. Tel: 901-321-3432. Fax: 901-321-3219. p. 2248

Gilmore, Kathy, Dir, Olney Community Library & Arts Center, 807 W Hamilton St, Olney, TX, 76374. Tel: 940-564-5513. Fax: 940-564-3453. p. 2367

Gilmore, Lil, Librn, The Frances Kibble Kenny Lake Public Library, Mile 5 Edgerton Hwy, Copper Center, AK, 99573-9703. Tel: 907-822-3015. Fax: 907-822-3015. p. 46

Gilmore, Virginia, Dir, Appleton City Public Library, 105 W Fourth St, Appleton City, MO, 64724-1401. Tel: 660-476-5513. Fax: 660-476-5513. p. 1319

Gilmour, Ron, Web Serv Librn, Ithaca College Library, 953 Danby Rd, Ithaca, NY, 14850-7060. Tel: 607-274-3206. Fax: 607-274-1539. p. 1643

Gilner, David J, Dr, Dir of Libr, Hebrew Union College-Jewish Institute of Religion, HUC-JIR, 3101 Clifton Ave, Cincinnati, OH, 45220-2488. Tel: 513-487-3273. Fax: 513-221-0519. p. 1870

Gilpatrick, Brenda, Dir, Red Bud Public Library, 925 S Main St, Red Bud, IL, 62278. Tel: 618-282-2255. Fax: 618-282-4055. p. 694

Gilpin, Barbara, Asst Librn, Ch, Jonesville Public Library, 150 W Main St, Jonesville, NC, 28642. Tel: 336-835-7604. Fax: 336-526-4226. p. 1804

Gilpin, Sarah H, YA Librn, Girard Free Library, 105 E Prospect St, Girard, OH, 44420-1899. Tel: 330-545-2508. Fax: 330-545-8213. p. 1902

Gilreath, Charles, Dean, Texas A&M University Libraries, 5000 TAMU, College Station, TX, 77843-5000. Tel: 979-845-8111. Fax: 979-845-6238. p. 2298

Gilroy, Corinne, Libr Tech, Atlantic Provinces Special Education Authority Library, 5940 South St, Halifax, NS, B3H 1S6, CANADA. Tel: 902-424-5639, 902-424-8524. Fax: 902-424-3808. p. 2780

Gilroy, Michael, Dir, East Haddam Free Public Library, 18 Plains Rd, Moodus, CT, 06469. Tel: 860-873-8248. Fax: 860-873-1269, 860-873-8248. p. 353

Gilson, Caroline, Sci Librn, DePauw University, Prevo Library, Julian Science & Math Ctr, Greencastle, IN, 46135. Tel: 765-658-4515. p. 746

Gilson, Diane, Asst Dir, ILL Librn, Gordon-Nash Library, 69 Main St, New Hampton, NH, 03256. Tel: 603-744-8061. Fax: 603-744-6555. p. 1459

Gilson, Eric, Head, ILL, Ref & Instrul Serv Librn, Rutgers University Libraries, Camden Law Library, 217 N Fifth St, Camden, NJ, 08102-1203. Tel: 856-225-6462. p. 1477

Gilson, Kathy, Dir, Aubrey Area Library, 226 Countryside Dr, Aubrey, TX, 76227. Tel: 940-365-9162. Fax: 940-365-9411. p. 2277

Gilson, Tom, Ref, College of Charleston, 205 Calhoun St, Charleston, SC, 29401-3519. Tel: 843-953-5530. Fax: 843-953-6319. p. 2184

Gilstrap, Donald L, Dr, Dean, Univ Libr, Wichita State University Libraries, 1845 Fairmount, Wichita, KS, 67260-0068. Tel: 316-978-3582. Fax: 316-978-3048. p. 902

Gilton, Donna L, Dr, Prof, University of Rhode Island, Rodman Hall, 94 W Alumni Ave, Ste 2, Kingston, RI, 02881-0815. Tel: 401-874-4630. Fax: 401-874-4964. p. 2973

Giltrop, Jennifer, Dir, Pub Serv, District of Columbia Public Library, 901 G St NW, Washington, DC, 20001-4599. Tel: 202-727-1101. Fax: 202-727-1129. p. 398

Gilwood, Ruth, Br Support, Stormont, Dundas & Glengarry County Library, Morewood Branch, 21 Russel St, Morewood, ON, K0A 2R0, CANADA. Tel: 613-448-3822. p. 2802

Gimble, Stephanie, Sr Librn, Irving Public Library, Valley Ranch, 401 Cimmaron Trail, Irving, TX, 75063-4680. Tel: 972-721-4669. Fax: 972-831-0672. p. 2347

Gimblin, Mimi, Librn, Shasta County Public Law Library, 1500 Court St, Rm B-7, Redding, CA, 96001. Tel: 530-245-6243. Fax: 530-245-6966. p. 214

Ginardi, Emily, Librn, Department of Veterans Affairs Dorn Medical Center, 6439 Garners Ferry Rd, Columbia, SC, 29209-1639. Tel: 803-776-4000, Ext 7315. Fax: 803-695-6874. p. 2187

Gincley, Leslie, Mgr, Ch & Youth Serv, Frederick County Public Libraries, 110 E Patrick St, Frederick, MD, 21701. Tel: 301-600-1613. Fax: 301-600-3789. p. 1028

Gindin, Kathy, Librn, Atlantic County Library System, Longport Branch, 2305 Atlantic Ave, Longport, NJ, 08403. Tel: 609-487-0272. Fax: 609-487-9521. p. 1500

Gingery, James, Dir, Milwaukee County Federated Library System, 709 N Eighth St, Milwaukee, WI, 53233-2414. Tel: 414-286-8149. Fax: 414-286-3209. p. 2619

Ginkel, Nadine, Libr Syst & Operations Dir, Denver Seminary, 6399 S Santa Fe Dr, Littleton, CO, 80120-2912. Tel: 303-762-6955. Fax: 303-762-6950. p. 317

Ginn, David S, PhD, Dir, Boston University Libraries, Alumni Medical Library, 715 Albany St L-12, Boston, MA, 02118-2394. Tel: 617-638-4232. Fax: 617-638-4233. p. 1058

Ginsberg, Deborah, Educ Tech Librn, Head, Fac Serv, Head, Res Serv, Illinois Institute of Technology, Chicago-Kent College of Law Library, 565 W Adams St, Chicago, IL, 60661. Tel: 312-906-5673. Fax: 312-906-5679. p. 615

Ginsberg, Laraine, Res, Schulte Roth & Zabel LLP, 919 Third Ave, New York, NY, 10022. Tel: 212-756-2309. Fax: 212-593-5955. p. 1699

Ginsberg, Rachel, Librn, Stantec Architecture Inc Library, 901 Market St, Ste 600, San Francisco, CA, 94103. Tel: 415-882-9500. Fax: 415-882-9523. p. 247

Ginsky, Andrea, Ref Serv, Selby Public Library, 1331 First St, Sarasota, FL, 34236-4899. Tel: 941-861-1100. Fax: 941-316-1188. p. 490

Ginsparg, Elie, Head Librn, Hebrew Theological College, 7135 N Carpenter Rd, Skokie, IL, 60077-3263. Tel: 847-982-2500. Fax: 847-674-6381. p. 702

Ginther, James, Dr, Archivist, Library of the Marine Corps, Gray Research Ctr, 2040 Broadway St, Quantico, VA, 22134-5107. Tel: 703-784-4409. Fax: 703-784-4665. p. 2486

Ginther, Vicky, Ad, Fauquier County Public Library, 11 Winchester St, Warrenton, VA, 20186-2825. Tel: 540-349-1793. Fax: 540-349-3278. p. 2500

Ginzburg, Barbara, Electronic Serv, Washburn University, School of Law Library, 1700 SW College Ave, Topeka, KS, 66621. Tel: 785-670-1087. Fax: 785-670-3194. p. 897

Gioiosa, Dan, Mgr, Access Serv, Ajax Public Library, 55 Harwood Ave S, Ajax, ON, L1S 2H8, CANADA. Tel: 905-683-4000, Ext 8824. Fax: 905-683-6960. p. 2791

Gionet, André, Head Librn, Canadian Agriculture Library-Fredericton, 850 Lincoln Rd, Fredericton, NB, E3B 4Z7, CANADA. Tel: 506-452-4810. Fax: 506-452-3316. p. 2762

Gionet, Mylene May, Libr Mgr, Chaleur Library Region, Bas-Caraquet Public Library, 8185-2 rue Saint Paul, Bas-Caraquet, NB, E1W 6C4, CANADA. Tel: 506-726-2775. Fax: 506-726-2770. p. 2761

Gionfriddo, Lana, Libr Assoc II, Lorain Public Library System, Domonkas Branch, 4125 E Lake Rd, Sheffield Lake, OH, 44054. Tel: 440-949-7410. Fax: 440-949-7741. p. 1911

Giono, Angela, Librn, Broadwater School & Community Library, 201 N Spruce, Townsend, MT, 59644. Tel: 406-266-5060. Fax: 406-266-4962. p. 1389

Giop, Diane, Head, Tech Serv, Butte-Silver Bow Public Library, 226 W Broadway St, Butte, MT, 59701-9297. Tel: 406-723-3361. Fax: 406-782-1825. p. 1376

Giordano, Barbara, Libr Dir, Melrose Park Public Library, 801 N Broadway, Melrose Park, IL, 60160. Tel: 708-343-3391. Fax: 708-531-5327. p. 673

Giordano, Kate, ILL Librn, Portsmouth Public Library, 175 Parrott Ave, Portsmouth, NH, 03801-4452. Tel: 603-427-1540. Fax: 603-433-0981. p. 1463

Giordano, Kelly, Libr Mgr, Children's Book Council Library, 12 W 37th St, 2nd Flr, New York, NY, 10018-7480. Tel: 212-966-1990. Fax: 212-966-2073. p. 1672

Giorgi, Betty, Head, Adult Serv, Wilmette Public Library District, 1242 Wilmette Ave, Wilmette, IL, 60091-2558. Tel: 847-256-6936. Fax: 847-256-6933. p. 719

Giotsas, Kathy, Dir, West Haven Public Library, 300 Elm St, West Haven, CT, 06516-4692. Tel: 203-937-4233. p. 377

Giotsas, Kathy, Dir, Wolcott Public Library, 469 Bound Line Rd, Wolcott, CT, 06716. Tel: 203-879-8110. Fax: 203-879-8109. p. 380

Giovanneillo, Brenda, Automation Syst Coordr, Nassau Library System, 900 Jerusalem Ave, Uniondale, NY, 11553-3039. Tel: 516-292-8920, Ext 241. Fax: 516-565-0950. p. 1758

Giovannone, Gina, Librn, University of Texas Libraries, Classics, Waggener Hall 1, Austin, TX, 78713. Tel: 512-495-4690. p. 2284

Giovenale, Sharon, Librn, University of Connecticut Library, Pharmacy, Pharmacy/Biology Bldg, 69 North Eagleville Rd, Rm 228, Storrs, CT, 06269-3092. Tel: 860-486-2218. Fax: 860-486-4998. p. 371

Gipp, Gerald, Exec Dir, American Indian Higher Education Consortium, 121 Oronoco St, Alexandria, VA, 22314. Tel: 703-838-0400. Fax: 703-838-0388. p. 2957

Gipson, Debra, Circ, Lewis & Clark Community College, 5800 Godfrey Rd, Godfrey, IL, 62035. Tel: 618-466-3411, Ext 4301. Fax: 618-468-4301. p. 651

Gipson, Karen, Mgr, Rapides Parish Library, Westside Regional, 5416 Provine Pl, Alexandria, LA, 71303. Tel: 318-442-2483, Ext 1903. Fax: 318-442-7678. p. 940

Gipson, Terasa, Info Spec, Villa Maria College Library, 240 Pine Ridge Rd, Buffalo, NY, 14225-3999. Tel: 716-961-1863. Fax: 716-896-0705. p. 1599

Gipson-Perry, Denise, Head, Circ, California State University, San Bernardino, 5500 University Pkwy, San Bernardino, CA, 92407-2318. Tel: 909-537-5084, 909-537-5092. Fax: 909-537-7048. p. 227

Giradina, Barbara, Librn, Onondaga County Public Library, Betts, 4862 S Salina St, Syracuse, NY, 13205. Tel: 315-435-1940. Fax: 315-435-1944. p. 1752

Giraldez, Karla, Supvr, Brown County Library, Southwest Branch, 974 Ninth St, Green Bay, WI, 54304. Tel: 920-492-4910. Fax: 920-492-4911. p. 2595

Giralico, John A, Dir, Elting Memorial Library, 93 Main St, New Paltz, NY, 12561-1593. Tel: 845-255-5030. Fax: 845-255-5818. p. 1665

Girard, Athena, Cataloger, Elko-Lander-Eureka County Library System, 720 Court St, Elko, NV, 89801. Tel: 775-738-3066. Fax: 775-738-8262. p. 1426

Girard, Suzanne, Archivist, Dir, Le Seminaire Saint-Joseph de Trois-Rivieres, 858 rue Laviolette, local 221, Trois-Rivieres, QC, G9A 5S3, CANADA. Tel: 819-376-4459, Ext 135. Fax: 819-378-0607. p. 2914

Gire, Judith A, Dir, Law Libr, University of New Hampshire School of Law, Two White St, Concord, NH, 03301. Tel: 603-228-1541, Ext 1130. Fax: 603-228-0388. p. 1443

Girgo, Tina, Librn, Broughton Hospital, 1000 S Sterling St, Morganton, NC, 28655. Tel: 828-433-2435. Fax: 828-433-2097. p. 1811

Giroir, Thomas, Br Mgr, Librn II, Jefferson Parish Library, Belle Terre, 5550 Belle Terre Rd, Marrero, LA, 70072. Tel: 504-349-5910. Fax: 504-349-5914. p. 956

Girouard, Terry, Curator, Dir, Libr Serv, Western Museum of Mining & Industry Library, 225 N Gate Blvd, I-25 Exit 156-A, Colorado Springs, CO, 80921. Tel: 719-495-2182. Fax: 719-488-9261. p. 297

Giroux, Ghislaine, Libr Asst, International Civil Aviation Organization, 999 University St, Montreal, QC, H3C 5H7, CANADA. Tel: 514-954-8207. Fax: 514-954-6077. p. 2897

Giroux, Jeanette, Tech Serv, St Clair College, 1001 Grand Ave W, Chatham, ON, N7M 5W4, CANADA. Tel: 519-354-9100, Ext 3232, 519-354-9100, Ext 3273. Fax: 519-354-5496. p. 2799

Girsberger, Russ, Chief Librn, United States Armed Forces School of Music, JEB Little Creek, 1420 Gator Blvd, Virginia Beach, VA, 23459-2617. Tel: 757-462-5734. Fax: 757-462-7294. p. 2500

Girton, Poppy, Dir, Carnegie Public Library, 127 S North St, Washington Court House, OH, 43160. Tel: 740-335-2540. Fax: 740-335-8409. p. 1945

Girven, Wendy, Pub Serv, University of Alaska Southeast, 11120 Glacier Hwy, Juneau, AK, 99801-8676. Tel: 907-796-6515. Fax: 907-796-6249. p. 50

Gisclair, Karen, Br Mgr, Avoyelles Parish Library, Cottonport Branch, 209 Cottonport Ave, Cottonport, LA, 71327. Tel: 318-876-3411. Fax: 318-876-2404. p. 956

Gish, Ann, Librn, Grande Prairie Regional College, 10726 106th Ave, Grande Prairie, AB, T8V 4C4, CANADA. Tel: 780-539-2940. Fax: 780-539-2730. p. 2705

Gisi, Stephina, Asst Librn, Harvey Public Library, 119 E Tenth St, Harvey, ND, 58341. Tel: 701-324-2156. Fax: 701-324-2156. p. 1844

Gist, Vicki, Dir, Montana State University-Northern, 300 11th St W, Havre, MT, 59501. Tel: 406-265-3706. Fax: 406-265-3799. p. 1381

Giszczak, Dennis, Cat Librn, Thomas M Cooley Law School Libraries, 300 S Capitol Ave, Lansing, MI, 48901. Tel: 517-371-5140, Ext 3412. Fax: 517-334-5715, 517-334-5717. p. 1202

Gitau, Nicole, Ref/Instruction/Info Commons Librn, Saint Joseph's College, 222 Clinton Ave, Brooklyn, NY, 11205-3697. Tel: 718-940-5879. Fax: 718-636-7250. p. 1594

Gits, Carrie, Head Librn, Austin Community College, Rio Grande Campus Library, 1212 Rio Grande, Austin, TX, 78701. Tel: 512-223-3066. Fax: 512-223-3430. p. 2278

Gits, Francie, Pres, Leelanau Historical Society, 203 E Cedar St, Leland, MI, 49654. Tel: 231-256-7475. Fax: 231-256-7650. p. 1203

Gitsch, Ann, Pres, Buchanan County Genealogical Society Library, 103 Fourth Ave SE, Independence, IA, 50644. Tel: 319-334-9333. p. 822

Gitt, Cynthia, Ch, Holdrege Area Public Library, 604 East Ave, Holdrege, NE, 68949. Tel: 308-995-6556. Fax: 308-995-5732. p. 1402

Gittens, Letitia, Librn, The Florence A S Williams Public Library, 1122 King St Christiansted, Saint Croix, VI, 00820-4951. Tel: 340-773-5715. Fax: 340-773-5327. p. 2679

Gittens, Letitia G, Head Librn, Virgin Islands Division of Libraries, Archives & Museums, Regional Library for the Blind & Physically Handicapped, 3012 Golden Rock, Christiansted, Saint Croix, VI, 00820. Tel: 340-773-5715. Fax: 340-772-3545. p. 2680

Gittlein, Deandra, Dir, Wichita County Library, 208 S Fourth St, Leoti, KS, 67861. Tel: 620-375-4322. p. 879

Gitto, Marisa, Dir, Curric Libr, College of Saint Rose, 392-396 Western Ave, Albany, NY, 12203. Tel: 518-337-4986. Fax: 518-454-2897. p. 1568

Giudice, Mary Jo, Dir of Libr, Dallas Public Library, 1515 Young St, Dallas, TX, 75201-5499. Tel: 214-670-1400. Fax: 214-670-7839. p. 2306

Giuliani, Laura, Tech Serv, Huntington Public Library, 338 Main St, Huntington, NY, 11743. Tel: 631-427-5165. Fax: 631-421-7131. p. 1639

Giuliani, M, Access Serv, Peterborough Public Library, 345 Aylmer St N, Peterborough, ON, K9H 3V7, CANADA. Tel: 705-745-5382. Fax: 705-745-8958. p. 2836

Giuliano, Marie, Bus Off Mgr, The Ferguson Library, One Public Library Plaza, 96 Broad St, Stamford, CT, 06904. Tel: 203-964-1000, Ext 8210. Fax: 203-357-9098. p. 369

Giullian, Karen, Children's Serv Coordr, Goodwin Library, 422 Main St, Farmington, NH, 03835-1519. Tel: 603-755-2944. Fax: 603-755-2944. p. 1447

Giunta, Laura, Ch, Garden City Public Library, 60 Seventh St, Garden City, NY, 11530-2891. Tel: 516-742-8405. Fax: 516-742-2675. p. 1626

Giunta, Mary, Dir, Columbia University, Lehman Library, 420 W 118th St, New York, NY, 10027. Tel: 212-854-3794. Fax: 212-854-2495. p. 1675

Giuse, Nunzia B, Dir, Vanderbilt University, Annette & Irwin Eskind Biomedical Library, 2209 Garland Ave, Nashville, TN, 37232-8340. Tel: 615-936-1402. Fax: 615-936-1384. p. 2260

Giustini, Dean, Librn, University of British Columbia Library, Biomedical, Gordon & Leslie Diamond Health Care Ctr, 2775 Laurel St, 2nd Flr, Vancouver, BC, V5Z 1M9, CANADA. Tel: 604-875-4111, Ext 6-2392. Fax: 604-875-4689. p. 2743

Giyer, Jessie, Cat, Palmer Public Library, 655 S Valley Way, Palmer, AK, 99645. Tel: 907-745-4690. Fax: 907-746-3570. p. 52

Gjelten, Daniel Ross, Dir of Libr, University of Saint Thomas, 2115 Summit Ave, Mail Box 5004, Saint Paul, MN, 55105. Tel: 651-962-5005. Fax: 651-962-5406. p. 1282

Gjerde, Ryan, Digital Initiatives Librn, Head, Libr Operations, Luther College, 700 College Dr, Decorah, IA, 52101. Tel: 563-387-1288. Fax: 563-387-1657. p. 807

Gjestson, Chris, In Charge, Dane County Regional Planning Commission Library, 30 W Mifflin St, Ste 402, Madison, WI, 53703. Tel: 608-266-4137. Fax: 608-266-9117. p. 2606

Glaab, Christine L, Librn, Surface Transportation Board Library, 395 E St SW, Washington, DC, 20024. Tel: 202-245-0406. Fax: 202-245-0462. p. 416

Glab, Suzanne, Librn, Shearman & Sterling LLP, 4 Embarcadero Ctr, Ste 3800, San Francisco, CA, 94111-5974. Tel: 415-616-1100. Fax: 415-616-1199. p. 247

Glackin, Barbara, Assoc Dean, Boise State University, 1865 Cesar Chavez Lane, Boise, ID, 83725-1430. Tel: 208-426-5902. Fax: 208-334-2111. p. 570

Gladding, Denise, Mgr, Knolls Atomic Power Laboratory Inc, Library, 35 Front St, Schenectady, NY, 12305. Tel: 518-395-4918. Fax: 518-395-7761. p. 1740

Gladfelter, Linda, ILL, Guthrie Memorial Library - Hanover's Public Library, Two Library Pl, Hanover, PA, 17331-2283. Tel: 717-632-5183. Fax: 717-632-7565. p. 2064

Gladfelter, M Ellen V, Asst Law Librn, Dauphin County Law Library, Dauphin County Courthouse, Front & Market Sts, 4th Flr, Harrisburg, PA, 17101. Tel: 717-780-6605. Fax: 717-780-6481. p. 2064

Gladstone, Russell, Access Serv Librn, Western Connecticut State University, 181 White St, Danbury, CT, 06810. Tel: 203-837-9102. Fax: 203-837-9108. p. 335

Gladstone, Susan, Dir of Develop, Concord Free Public Library, 129 Main St, Concord, MA, 01742-2494. Tel: 978-318-3300. Fax: 978-318-3344. p. 1082

Gladwell, Marilyn, Circ, Doc Delivery, Mid-Columbia Medical Center, 200 E Fourth St, The Dalles, OR, 97058. Tel: 541-296-8444. Fax: 541-296-6054. p. 2021

Glaesemann, Jodene, Br Supvr, Lincoln City Libraries, Bess Dodson Walt Branch, 6701 S 14th St, Lincoln, NE, 68512. Tel: 402-441-4460. Fax: 402-441-4463. p. 1405

Glancy, Christie, Ref, University of Mary Washington, 1801 College Ave, Fredericksburg, VA, 22401-4665. Tel: 540-654-1740. Fax: 540-654-1067. p. 2466

Glanders, Jeanne, Assoc Dir, AV, Elkhart Public Library, 300 S Second St, Elkhart, IN, 46516-3184. Tel: 574-522-3333. Fax: 574-293-9213, 574-522-2174. p. 737

Glannon, Ann, Assoc Dir, Coll Mgt Librn, Wheelock College Library, 132 The Riverway, Boston, MA, 02215-4815. Tel: 617-879-2251. Fax: 617-879-2408. p. 1068

Glanzer, Mary Anne, Coordr, Tidewater Community College, 120 Campus Dr, Portsmouth, VA, 23701. Fax: 757-822-2149. p. 2485

Glasbrenner, Gloria Jean, Dir, Libr & Info Serv, Frost, Brown & Todd LLC, 400 W Market St, 32nd Flr, Louisville, KY, 40202-3363. Tel: 502-779-8440. Fax: 502-581-1087. p. 923

Glasby, Jane, Assoc Librn, San Francisco Botanical Garden Society at Strybing Arboretum, 1199 Ninth Ave, (Ninth Ave at Lincoln Way), San Francisco, CA, 94122-2384. Tel: 415-661-1316, Ext 303. Fax: 415-661-3539. p. 244

Glaser, Earleen, Archivist, Ref Librn, Mercyhurst College, 501 E 38th St, Erie, PA, 16546. Tel: 814-824-2190. Fax: 814-824-2219. p. 2056

Glaser, Earleen, Archivist, Northwest Interlibrary Cooperative of Pennsylvania, Mercyhurst University Library, 501 E 38th St, Erie, PA, 16546. Tel: 814-824-2190. Fax: 814-824-2219. p. 2954

Glaser, Heather, Curator, University of Pennsylvania Libraries, 3420 Walnut St, Philadelphia, PA, 19104-6206. Tel: 215-898-7086. Fax: 215-898-0559. p. 2118

Glaser, Stacy, Dir, University of Alaska Fairbanks, 604 Third St, Kotzebue, AK, 99752. Tel: 907-442-2410. Fax: 907-442-2322. p. 51

Glasgow, Amanda, Libr Dir, Northwest Regional Library, Mary Wallace Cobb Memorial Library, 110 First Ave, Vernon, AL, 35592. Tel: 205-695-6123. Fax: 205-695-1006. p. 40

Glasgow, Linda, Archivist, Librn, Riley County Historical Museum, 2309 Claflin Rd, Manhattan, KS, 66502-3421. Tel: 785-565-6490. Fax: 785-565-6491. p. 882

Glasgow, Linda, Libr Asst, Angie Williams Cox Public Library, 119 N Main St, Pardeeville, WI, 53954-0370. Tel: 608-429-2354. Fax: 608-429-4308. p. 2629

Glasgow, Sharon, Asst Librn, Eldon Public Library, 608 W Elm St, Eldon, IA, 52554. Tel: 641-652-7517. Fax: 641-652-7517. p. 813

Glashagel, Kristy, Librn, ECPI University, 1001 Keys Dr, No 100, Greenville, SC, 29615-4232. Tel: 864-288-2828. Fax: 864-288-2930. p. 2195

Glass, Amy, Bibliog Instr, Illinois Central College, One College Dr, East Peoria, IL, 61635-0001. Tel: 309-694-5461. Fax: 309-694-5473. p. 638

Glass, Anthony R, Libr Dir, Eureka College, 301 E College Ave, Eureka, IL, 61530-1563. Tel: 309-467-6380. Fax: 309-467-6386. p. 643

Glass, Bob, Libr Dir, Piedmont College, 165 Central Ave, Demorest, GA, 30535. Tel: 706-776-0111. Fax: 706-776-3338. p. 530

Glass, Eric, Metadata Librn, Columbia University, Lehman Library, 420 W 118th St, New York, NY, 10027. Tel: 212-854-3794. Fax: 212-854-2495. p. 1675

Glass, Ian, Librn, Institute for Wetland & Waterfowl Research Library, One Mallard Bay at Hwy 220, Stonewall, MB, R0C 2Z0, CANADA. Tel: 204-467-3276. Fax: 204-467-9028. p. 2752

Glass, Joe, Tech Serv/Circ Librn, Notre Dame College, 4545 College Rd, South Euclid, OH, 44121. Tel: 216-373-5360. Fax: 216-381-3227. p. 1935

Glass, Karen, Dir, Keene Valley Library Association, 1796 Rte 73, Keene Valley, NY, 12943. Tel: 518-576-4335. Fax: 518-576-4693. p. 1648

Glass, Lora, ILL, Ref, Niceville Public Library, 206 N Partin Dr, Niceville, FL, 32578. Tel: 850-729-4070. Fax: 850-729-4053. p. 472

Glass, Mary Hay, Acq/Syst Librn, American College of Obstetricians & Gynecologists, 409 12th St SW, Washington, DC, 20024-2188. Tel: 202-863-2518. Fax: 202-484-1595. p. 392

Glass, Rhonda, Dir, Metcalfe County Public Library, 200 S Main St, Edmonton, KY, 42129. Tel: 270-432-4981. Fax: 270-432-4981. p. 912

Glass, Robert, Spec Coll, Tech Serv, Centre College of Kentucky, 600 W Walnut St, Danville, KY, 40422. Tel: 859-238-5272. Fax: 859-236-7925. p. 911

Glassco, Pam, Br Supvr, Barry-Lawrence Regional Library, Miller Branch, 112 E Main St, Miller, MO, 65707. Tel: 417-452-3466. Fax: 417-452-3466. p. 1346

Glasser, Larissa, Librn, Harvard Library, Arnold Arboretum Horticultural Library, 125 Arborway, Jamaica Plain, MA, 02130. Tel: 617-522-1086. Fax: 617-524-1418. p. 1074

Glasser, Robin, Dir, Norfolk Public Library, 139 Main St, Norfolk, MA, 02056. Tel: 508-528-3380. Fax: 508-528-6417. p. 1111

Glasser, Robin, Pres, SAILS, Inc, 547 W Groves St, Ste 4, Middleboro, MA, 02346. Tel: 508-946-8600. Fax: 508-946-8605. p. 2945

Glassman, Nancy, Info Tech, Albert Einstein College of Medicine, 1300 Morris Park Ave, Bronx, NY, 10461. Tel: 718-430-3108. Fax: 718-430-8795. p.1586

Glassman, Paul, Assoc Prof, Dir of Libr Serv, Felician College Library, 262 S Main St, Lodi, NJ, 07644-2198. Tel: 201-559-6071. Fax: 201-559-6148. p. 1496

Glassman, Zina, Librn, Beth Tzedec Congregation, 1700 Bathurst St, Toronto, ON, M5P 3K3, CANADA. Tel: 416-781-3514, Ext 225. Fax: 416-781-0150. p. 2850

Glatz, Kristin, Dir, Prairie Creek Public Library District, 501 Carriage House Lane, Dwight, IL, 60420-1399. Tel: 815-584-3061. Fax: 815-584-3120. p. 638

Glauber, Daniel, Ref Serv, Scarsdale Public Library, 54 Olmsted Rd, Scarsdale, NY, 10583. Tel: 914-722-1300. Fax: 914-722-1305. p. 1739

Glauber, Leni, Asst Dir, Scarsdale Public Library, 54 Olmsted Rd, Scarsdale, NY, 10583. Tel: 914-722-1300. Fax: 914-722-1305. p. 1739

Glavash, Keith, Assoc Dir, Admin Serv, Massachusetts Institute of Technology Libraries, Office of the Director, 160 Memorial Dr, Cambridge, MA, 02142. Tel: 617-253-7059. Fax: 617-253-0583. p. 1077

Glaze, Gail, Tech Serv, University of Wisconsin-Madison, Business Library, Grainger Hall, Rm 2200, 975 University Ave, Madison, WI, 53706. Tel: 608-262-4007. Fax: 608-262-9001. p. 2608

Glaze, Shelley, Librn, Siletz Public Library, 243 W Buford, Siletz, OR, 97380. Tel: 541-444-2855. p. 2019

Glazener, Patricia, Ch, Buncombe County Public Libraries, 67 Haywood St, Asheville, NC, 28801. Tel: 828-250-4700. Fax: 828-250-4746. p. 1774

Glazer, Liz, Head, Commun Serv, Lake Villa District Library, 1001 E Grand Ave, Lake Villa, IL, 60046. Tel: 847-356-7711, Ext 213. Fax: 847-265-9595. p. 663

Glazer, Marylou, Chief Librn, Department of Veterans Affairs, 79 Middleville Rd, Northport, NY, 11768-2290. Tel: 631-261-4400, Ext 2966. Fax: 631-754-7992. p. 1707

Gleason, Diana, Head, Pub Serv, University of Idaho Library, College of Law, 711 Rayburn St, Moscow, ID, 83844. Tel: 208-885-2161. Fax: 208-885-2743. p. 580

Gleason, James S, Dir, The Republican Library, 1860 Main St, Springfield, MA, 01101. Tel: 413-788-1151. Fax: 413-788-1301. p. 1127

Gleason, Jessica, Br Mgr, Hawaii State Public Library System, Kihei Public Library, 35 Waimahaihai St, Kihei, HI, 96753-8015. Tel: 808-875-6833. Fax: 808-875-6834. p. 562

Gleason, Joan, Head, Circ/ILL, Jericho Public Library, One Merry Lane, Jericho, NY, 11753. Tel: 516-935-6790. Fax: 516-433-9581. p. 1647

Gleason, Kristine, Mgr, Alexander Findley Community Library, 2883 North Rd, Findley Lake, NY, 14736. Tel: 716-769-6568. Fax: 716-769-7207. p. 1622

Gleason, Linda, ILL, Jaffrey Public Library, 38 Main St, Jaffrey, NH, 03452-1196. Tel: 603-532-7301. Fax: 603-532-7301. p. 1452

Gleason, Susan P, Dir, Rowe Town Library, 318 Zoar Rd, Rowe, MA, 01367-9998. Tel: 413-339-4761. Fax: 413-339-4761. p. 1121

Gleason, Suzanne, Ref Librn, Lindenwood University, 209 S Kingshighway, Saint Charles, MO, 63301. Tel: 636-949-4881. Fax: 636-949-4822. p. 1351

Gleason, Virginia, Librn, St Paul United Methodist Church Library, 413 E Walnut, Springfield, MO, 65806. Tel: 417-866-4326. p. 1367

Gleaton, Terri, Ref Serv Librn, Clovis-Carver Public Library, 701 N Main, Clovis, NM, 88101. Tel: 505-769-7840. Fax: 505-769-7842. p. 1553

Gleave, Teresa, Dir, Libr & Info Serv, Fasken Martineau DuMoulin LLP Library, 2900-550 Burrard St, Vancouver, BC, V6C 0A3, CANADA. Tel: 604-631-4804. Fax: 604-631-3232. p. 2741

Gleaves, Chuck, Dir, Kingwood Center Library, 900 Park Ave W, Mansfield, OH, 44906-2999. Tel: 419-522-0211. Fax: 419-522-0211, Ext 132. p. 1912

Gleeson, Margaret, Tech Librn, Nashua Public Library, Two Court St, Nashua, NH, 03060. Tel: 603-589-4600. Fax: 603-594-3457. p. 1458

Gleeson, Phyllis, Tech Serv, Enfield Public Library, 104 Middle Rd, Enfield, CT, 06082. Tel: 860-763-7510. Fax: 860-763-7514. p. 338

Gleiberman, P, YA Serv, Bellmore Memorial Library, 2288 Bedford Ave, Bellmore, NY, 11710. Tel: 516-785-2990. Fax: 516-783-8550. p. 1580

Gleichauf, Carol, Ch, Dodgeville Public Library, 139 S Iowa St, Dodgeville, WI, 53533. Tel: 608-935-3728. Fax: 608-935-9405. p. 2588

Gleisner, Anjie, Librn, Grand Rapids Public Library, Madison Square, 1201 Madison SE, Grand Rapids, MI, 49507. Tel: 616-988-5411. Fax: 616-245-1403. p. 1185

Glendening, Mary, Dir, Middletown Free Library, 21 N Pennell Rd, Lima, PA, 19037. Tel: 610-566-7828. Fax: 610-892-0880. p. 2082

Glendening, Mary, Dir, Narberth Community Library, 80 Windsor Ave, Narberth, PA, 19072-2296. Tel: 610-664-2878. Fax: 610-667-3245. p. 2094

Glendenning, Bonnie, Info Serv, ILL, Jefferson County Rural Library District, 620 Cedar Ave, Port Hadlock, WA, 98339-9514. Tel: 360-385-6544. Fax: 360-385-7921. p. 2524

Glendenning, Karin, Dir, Signal Mountain Public Library, 1114 James Blvd, Signal Mountain, TN, 37377-2509. Tel: 423-886-7323. Fax: 423-886-3735. p. 2265

Glendinning, Jo-Ann, Dir, Fruitland Park Library, 205 W Berckman St, Fruitland Park, FL, 34731. Tel: 352-360-6561. Fax: 352-360-6691. p. 447

Glendinning, Mary, Ref Librn, NPR Library, 635 Massachusetts Ave NW, Washington, DC, 20001. Fax: 202-513-3056. p. 412

Glendon, Julia, ILL, Acton Memorial Library, 486 Main St, Acton, MA, 01720. Tel: 978-264-9641. Fax: 978-635-0073. p. 1047

Glenicki, Linda, Bus & Finance Mgr, King County Library System, 960 Newport Way NW, Issaquah, WA, 98027. Tel: 425-369-3260. Fax: 425-369-3255. p. 2516

Glenn, David, Head, Tech Serv, Naval Surface Warfare Center, 9500 MacArthur Blvd, West Bethesda, MD, 20817-5700. Tel: 301-227-1433. Fax: 301-227-5307. p. 1045

Glenn, Lucy, Ref Librn/Pub Serv Coordr, Pulaski County Public Library System, 60 W Third St, Pulaski, VA, 24301. Tel: 540-980-7770. Fax: 540-980-7775. p. 2486

Glenn, Mary, Dir, Upton County Public Library, 212 W Seventh St, McCamey, TX, 79752. Tel: 432-652-8718. Fax: 432-652-3858. p. 2361

Glenn, Nancy, Librn, Chinook Regional Library, Climax Branch, PO Box 323, Climax, SK, S0N 0N0, CANADA. Tel: 306-293-2229. p. 2928

Glenn, Sara, Ch, Coralville Public Library, 1401 Fifth St, Coralville, IA, 52241. Tel: 319-248-1850. Fax: 319-248-1890. p. 804

Glenn, Susan, Sr Librn, Hennepin County Library, Brookdale, 6125 Shingle Creek Pkwy, Brooklyn Center, MN, 55430-2110. Tel: 612-543-5631. Fax: 612-543-5602. p. 1263

Glennan, Barbara, Asst Dir, Pub Serv, California Western School of Law Library, 290 Cedar St, San Diego, CA, 92101. Tel: 619-525-1499. Fax: 619-685-2918. p. 231

Glentworth, Nicole, Libr Mgr, Fraser Valley Regional Library, Agassiz Library, 7140 Cheam Ave, Agassiz, BC, V0M 1A0, CANADA. Tel: 604-796-9510. Fax: 604-796-9517. p. 2723

Glentworth, Nicole, Libr Mgr, Fraser Valley Regional Library, Boston Bar Library, Box 400, Boston Bar Elementary School, 47643 Old Boston Bar Rd, Boston Bar, BC, V0K 1C0, CANADA. Tel: 604-867-8847. Fax: 604-867-9549. p. 2723

Glentworth, Nicole, Libr Mgr, Fraser Valley Regional Library, Chilliwack Library, 45860 First Ave, Chilliwack, BC, V2P 7K1, CANADA. Tel: 604-792-1941. Fax: 604-532-7483. p. 2723

Glentworth, Nicole, Libr Mgr, Fraser Valley Regional Library, Hope Library, 1005A - Sixth Ave, Hope, BC, V0X 1L0, CANADA. Tel: 604-869-2313. Fax: nicole.glenwor@fvrl.bc.ca. p. 2723

Glentworth, Nicole, Libr Mgr, Fraser Valley Regional Library, Yale Library, Box 17, Yale Elementary School, 65050 Albert St, Yale, BC, V0K 2S0, CANADA. Tel: 604-863-2279. Fax: 604-863-0138. p. 2724

Glentworth, Nicole, Libr Mgr, Fraser Valley Regional Library, Yarrow Library, 4670 Community St, Yarrow, BC, V2R 5E1, CANADA. Tel: 604-823-4664. Fax: 604-823-4686. p. 2724

Glerum, Heather, Media Librn, University of Toronto Libraries, Scarborough Library, Scarborough College, 1265 Military Trail, Scarborough, ON, M1C 1A4, CANADA. Tel: 416-287-7481. Fax: 416-287-7507. p. 2867

Glerzaif, Jocelyne, Librn, Bibliotheque Dentinger, Central Ave SE, No 027, Falher, AB, T0H 1M0, CANADA. Tel: 780-837-2776. Fax: 780-837-8755. p. 2704

Glessner, Debra, Dir, Libr Serv, Willkie Farr & Gallagher LLP, 787 Seventh Ave, New York, NY, 10019. Tel: 212-728-8700. Fax: 212-728-3303. p. 1703

Glew, Don, Coordr, Smith-Kettlewell Eye Research Institute Library, 2318 Fillmore St, San Francisco, CA, 94115. Tel: 415-345-2000. Fax: 415-345-8455. p. 247

Glew, Dorothy, Info Literacy, Moravian College & Moravian Theological Seminary, 1200 Main St, Bethlehem, PA, 18018-6650. Tel: 610-861-1579. Fax: 610-861-1577. p. 2034

Glick, Nancy I, Dir, Havana Public Library District, 201 W Adams St, Havana, IL, 62644-1321. Tel: 309-543-4701. Fax: 309-543-2715. p. 654

Glick, Shelley, Ref Librn, Briarcliff Manor Public Library, One Library Rd, Briarcliff Manor, NY, 10510. Tel: 914-941-7072. Fax: 914-941-7091. p. 1585

Glickman, Irene, Ch, Irvington Public Library, 12 S Astor St, Irvington, NY, 10533. Tel: 914-591-7840. Fax: 914-591-0347. p. 1640

Glidewell, Sherry, Asst Dir, Elma Ross Public Library, 1011 E Main St, Brownsville, TN, 38012-2652. Tel: 731-772-9534. Fax: 731-772-5416. p. 2225

Gliebe, Jennifer, Youth Serv Librn, Cardington-Lincoln Public Library, 128 E Main St, Cardington, OH, 43315. Tel: 419-864-8181. Fax: 419-864-8184. p. 1865

Glinka, Charlee, Coll Develop Coordr, Lawrence Public Library, 707 Vermont St, Lawrence, KS, 66044-2371. Tel: 785-843-3833, Ext 104. Fax: 785-843-3368. p. 877

Glise, Tamara, Asst Libr Dir, Cedar Rapids Public Library West, 2600 Edgewood Rd SW, Ste 330, Cedar Rapids, IA, 52404. Tel: 319-398-5123. Fax: 319-398-0476. p. 800

Glispy, Ian, Mgr, Blank Rome LLP Library, 600 New Hampshire Ave NW, Ste 1200, Washington, DC, 20037. Tel: 202-944-3527. Fax: 202-772-5858. p. 394

Glisson, Lane, Evening Ref Librn, Borough of Manhattan Community College Library, 199 Chambers St, New York, NY, 10007. Tel: 212-220-8000, Ext 7112. Fax: 212-748-7466. p. 1671

Glisson, Mark, Tech Librn, Hooksett Public Library, 1701B Hooksett Rd, Hooksett, NH, 03106-1852. Tel: 603-485-6092. Fax: 603-485-6193. p. 1451

Glod, Barbara, Librn, Crane Thomas Public Library, Wollaston Branch, 41 Beale St, Quincy, MA, 02170. Tel: 617-376-1330. Fax: 617-376-1430. p. 1119

Glod, Carol, Dr, Dean, Salem State University, Graduate School, 352 Lafayette St, Salem, MA, 01970. Tel: 978-542-6000, 978-542-7044. Fax: 978-542-7215. p. 2967

Gloede, Yvonne, Dir, Jackson Memorial Library, 38 Main St, Tenants Harbor, ME, 04860. Tel: 207-372-8961. p. 1003

Glogowski, Maryruth F, Assoc VPres, Libr & Instrul Tech, State University of New York College at Buffalo, 1300 Elmwood Ave, Buffalo, NY, 14222-1095. Tel: 716-878-6314. Fax: 716-878-3134. p. 1599

Gloo, Linda, Circ, Eastham Public Library, 190 Samoset Rd, Eastham, MA, 02642. Tel: 508-240-5950. Fax: 508-240-0786. p. 1086

Gloor, Laura, Dir, Peace River Museum, Archives & Mackenzie Centre, 10302 99th St, Peace River, AB, T8S 1K1, CANADA. Tel: 780-624-4261. Fax: 780-624-4270. p. 2713

Gloria, Trevett, Dir, Thornton Public Library, 412 Main St, Thornton, IA, 50479. Tel: 641-998-2416. Fax: 641-998-2470. p. 847

Glorioso, Ann, Spec Coll & Archives Librn, Tech Serv, Levittown Public Library, One Bluegrass Lane, Levittown, NY, 11756-1292. Tel: 516-731-5728. Fax: 516-735-3168. p. 1652

Glorioso, Anne, Circ & Info Serv Librn, University of Wisconsin-Madison, Kurt Wendt Engineering Library, 215 N Randall Ave, Madison, WI, 53706. Tel: 608-262-3493. Fax: 608-262-4739, 608-265-8751. p. 2610

Glorioso, Kimberly Koko, Sr Ref Librn, Tulane University, Law Library, 6329 Freret St, New Orleans, LA, 70118-6231. Tel: 504-865-5902. Fax: 504-865-5917. p. 963

Glosh, Carol, Circ, Salem Public Library, 28 E Main St, Salem, VA, 24153. Tel: 540-375-3089. Fax: 540-389-7054. p. 2496

Glossinger, Don, Dir, Michigan City Public Library, 100 E Fourth St, Michigan City, IN, 46360-3393. Tel: 219-873-3050. Fax: 219-873-3068. p. 764

Glossner, Andrea, ILL, Ref Librn, Annie Halenbake Ross Library, 232 W Main St, Lock Haven, PA, 17745-1241. Tel: 570-748-3321. Fax: 570-748-1050. p. 2082

Glotfelty, Corene, Archivist, Ref Librn, Clarion University of Pennsylvania, 840 Wood St, Clarion, PA, 16214. Tel: 814-393-1805. Fax: 814-393-2344. p. 2045

Gloutnay, Diane, Cat, College de Rosemont (Cegep) Bibliotheque, 6400 16th Ave, Montreal, QC, H1X 2S9, CANADA. Tel: 514-376-1620, Ext 265. Fax: 514-376-1440. p. 2894

Glover, Art, Assoc Dir, Human Res, Douglas County Libraries, 100 S Wilcox, Castle Rock, CO, 80104. Tel: 303-688-7631. Fax: 303-688-7655. p. 294

Glover, Barbara, Govt Doc, Per, Eastern Michigan University, 955 W Circle Dr Library, Rm 200, Ypsilanti, MI, 48197. Tel: 734-487-0020, Ext 2233. p. 1238

Glover, Beverly, Circ, J Sargeant Reynolds Community College Library, Parham Campus-Library & Information Services, 1651 E Parham Rd, Richmond, VA, 23228. Tel: 804-523-5326. Fax: 804-371-3086. p. 2489

Glover, Carol, Librn, Tatum Community Library, 323 E Broadway, Tatum, NM, 88267. Tel: 505-398-4822. Fax: 505-398-4823. p. 1566

Glover, Charlotte, Ch, Ketchikan Public Library, 629 Dock St, Ketchikan, AK, 99901. Tel: 907-225-3331. Fax: 907-225-0153. p. 50

Glover, Elizabeth, Libr Tech, University of Toronto Libraries, Department of Physics, McLennan Physical Laboratories, 60 St George St, Rm 211C, Toronto, ON, M5S 1A1, CANADA. Tel: 416-978-5188. Fax: 416-978-5919. p. 2865

Glover, Jan, Educ Serv Librn, Yale University Library, Harvey Cushing/John Hay Whitney Medical Library, Sterling Hall of Medicine, 333 Cedar St, L110 SHM, New Haven, CT, 06520. Tel: 203-737-2962. Fax: 203-785-5636. p. 358

Glover, Jesse, Educ Supvr, New Jersey Department of Corrections, Eight Production Way, Avenel, NJ, 07001. Tel: 732-574-2250, Ext 8017. Fax: 732-382-8912. p. 1470

Glover, Kristin, Res Librn, University of Virginia, Arthur J Morris Law Library, 580 Massie Rd, Charlottesville, VA, 22903-1789. Tel: 434-243-2494. Fax: 434-982-2232. p. 2455

Glover, Sandy, Asst Dir, Camas Public Library, 625 NE Fourth Ave, Camas, WA, 98607. Tel: 360-834-4692. Fax: 360-834-0199. p. 2511

Glover, Sharon, Circ, Geneva College, 3200 College Ave, Beaver Falls, PA, 15010-3599. Tel: 724-847-6563. Fax: 724-847-6687. p. 2031

Glover, Susan, Prints & Rare Bks, Boston Public Library, 700 Boylston St, Boston, MA, 02117-0286. Tel: 617-536-5400. Fax: 617-236-4306. p. 1056

Glover, Thelma, Assoc Dir, Cobb County Public Library System, 266 Roswell St, Marietta, GA, 30060-2004. Tel: 770-528-2335. Fax: 770-528-2349. p. 542

Glover, Tina, Demographer, Sacramento Area Council of Governments Library, 1415 L St, Ste 300, Sacramento, CA, 95814. Tel: 916-321-9000. Fax: 916-321-9551. p. 224

Glowacki, Blanka, ILL, Sir Mortimer B Davis Jewish General Hospital, 3755 Cote Ste Catherine Rd, A-200, Montreal, QC, H3T 1E2, CANADA. Tel: 514-340-8222, Ext 5928. Fax: 514-340-7552. p. 2901

Glowczewski, Joanne, Br Supvr, Boonslick Regional Library, Warsaw Branch, 102 E Jackson, Warsaw, MO, 65355. Tel: 660-438-5211. Fax: 660-438-9567. p. 1365

Gloyn, Bernie, Asst Dir, Statistics Canada Library, 100 Tunney's Pasture Driveway, Ottawa, ON, K1A 0T6, CANADA. Tel: 613-951-8218. Fax: 613-951-0939. p. 2833

Gluck, Jeannine Cyr, Dir, Eastern Connecticut Health Network, 71 Haynes St, Manchester, CT, 06040-4188. Tel: 860-647-6853. Fax: 860-647-6443. p. 349

Gluck, Marc, Br Mgr, Public Library Association of Annapolis & Anne Arundel County, Inc, Edgewater, 25 Stepneys Lane, Edgewater, MD, 21037. Tel: 410-222-1538. Fax: 410-222-1543. p. 1010

Gluckman, Lauren, Asst Law Librn, Ref, Pennsylvania State University - Dickinson School of Law (University Libraries), 1170 Harrisburg Pike, Carlisle, PA, 17013-1617. Tel: 814-865-8875. Fax: 717-240-5127. p. 2042

Gluckman, Norman, Libr Dir, Avalon Free Public Library, 235-32nd St, Avalon, NJ, 08202-1766. Tel: 609-967-7155. Fax: 609-967-4723. p. 1470

Glueckert, John P, Dir, University of Southern California Libraries, Jennifer Ann Wilson Dental Library & Learning Center, 925 W 34th St, DEN 21, University Park - MC 0641, Los Angeles, CA, 90089-0641. Tel: 213-740-6476. Fax: 213-748-8565. p. 179

Gluibizzi, Amanda, Ref, Ohio State University LIBRARIES, Fine Arts, Wexner Center for the Arts, 1871 N High St, Columbus, OH, 43210. Tel: 614-292-6184. Fax: 614-292-4573. p. 1887

Glynn, Denise, Head, Cat, DePaul University Libraries, Vincent G Rinn Law Library, 25 E Jackson Blvd, 5th Flr, Chicago, IL, 60604-2287. Tel: 312-362-8121, 312-362-8701. Fax: 312-362-6908. p. 612

Glynn, John, Br Mgr, Chicago Public Library, Albany Park, 5150 N Kimball Ave, Chicago, IL, 60625. Tel: 312-744-1933. Fax: 312-744-6266. p. 608

Glynn, Mary Lou, Librn, Library District Number One, Doniphan County, Highland Branch, 306 W Main, Highland, KS, 66035. Tel: 785-442-3078. p. 898

Glynn, Nancy, ILL, Sharon Public Library, 11 N Main St, Sharon, MA, 02067-1299. Tel: 781-784-1578. Fax: 781-784-4728. p. 1123

Gmeiner, Timothy, Music Librn, Belmont University, 1900 Belmont Blvd, Nashville, TN, 37212-3757. Tel: 615-460-5495. Fax: 615-460-5641. p. 2255

Gmelin, Michael, Ref, Kauai Community College, 3-1901 Kaumualii Hwy, Lihue, HI, 96766. Tel: 808-245-8233. Fax: 808-245-8294. p. 567

Gmiter, Chris, Mgr, Carnegie Library of Pittsburgh, East Liberty, 130 S Whitfield St, Pittsburgh, PA, 15206-3408. Tel: 412-363-8232. p. 2123

Gnagey, Sandra, Librn, Columbia Township Library, 6456 Center St, Unionville, MI, 48767. Tel: 989-674-2651. Fax: 989-674-2138. p. 1232

Gnassi, Bruno, Univ Librn, Mount Allison University Libraries & Archives, 49 York St, Sackville, NB, E4L 1C6, CANADA. Tel: 506-364-2567. Fax: 506-364-2617. p. 2766

Gnassi, Bruno, Univ Librn, John Bassett Memorial Library, 2600 College St, Sherbrooke, QC, J1M 0C8, CANADA. Tel: 819-822-9600, Ext 2483. Fax: 819-822-9644. p. 2912

Gnat, Colleen, Head, Youth Serv, Cicero Public Library, 5225 W Cermak Rd, Cicero, IL, 60804. Tel: 708-652-8084. Fax: 708-652-8095. p. 629

Gnerre, Elizabeth, Cat, Ref, Los Angeles City College Library, 855 N Vermont Ave, Los Angeles, CA, 90029. Tel: 323-953-4000, Ext 2409. Fax: 323-953-4013. p. 171

Gnissios, Todd, Dir, Lethbridge Public Library, 810 Fifth Ave S, Lethbridge, AB, T1J 4C4, CANADA. Tel: 403-380-7340. Fax: 403-329-1478. p. 2709

Gnitzcavich, Nancy, Librn, Gilbert Library, Inc, 38 Main St, Northfield, CT, 06778. Tel: 860-283-8176. p. 362

Gnuschke, Rodema, ILL, Missouri Western State University, 4525 Downs Dr, Saint Joseph, MO, 64507-2294. Tel: 816-271-4368. Fax: 816-271-4574. p. 1352

Goans, Doag, Head, Info Tech & Develop, Georgia Institute of Technology Library, 704 Cherry St, Atlanta, GA, 30332-0900. Tel: 404-894-4501. Fax: 404-894-6084. p. 515

Goans, Douglas, Webmaster, Georgia State University Library, 100 Decatur St SE, Atlanta, GA, 30303-3202. Tel: 404-413-2772. Fax: 404-413-2701. p. 516

Goard, Susan, Head, E-Access & Assessment, Supreme Court of Canada Library, 301 Wellington St, Ottawa, ON, K1A 0J1, CANADA. Tel: 613-996-8129. Fax: 613-952-2832. p. 2833

Gobart, Michelle, Dir, Crandon Public Library, 110 W Polk St, Crandon, WI, 54520-1458. Tel: 715-478-3784. Fax: 715-478-3784. p. 2587

Gobeil, Beth, Circ/Acq, Lady Lake Public Library, 225 W Guava St, Lady Lake, FL, 32159. Tel: 352-753-2957. Fax: 352-753-3361. p. 457

Gobeil, Lucie, Dir, Centre Regional de Services aux Bibliotheques Publiques de la Capitale-Nationale et de la Chaudiere-Appalaches Inc, 3189 rue Albert-Demers, Charny, QC, G6X 3A1, CANADA. Tel: 418-832-6166. Fax: 418-832-6168. p. 2880

Goben, Anna, Head, Ref Serv, Webmaster, Lebanon Public Library, 104 E Washington St, Lebanon, IN, 46052. Tel: 765-482-3460. Fax: 317-873-5059. p. 761

Gobert, Tammy, Automation Archivist, Rensselaer Libraries, Rensselaer Polytechnic Inst, 110 Eighth St, Troy, NY, 12180-3590. Tel: 518-276-8300. Fax: 518-276-2044. p. 1756

Gobin, Kip, Ser Librn, University of Virginia, Arthur J Morris Law Library, 580 Massie Rd, Charlottesville, VA, 22903-1789. Tel: 434-924-3745. Fax: 434-982-2232. p. 2455

Gobin, Lynn, Librn, Bibliotheque Saint Claude Library, 50 First St, Saint Claude, MB, R0G 1Z0, CANADA. Tel: 204-379-2524. p. 2751

Goble, Beth, Dir, Govt Info Serv, Nebraska Library Commission, The Atrium, 1200 N St, Ste 120, Lincoln, NE, 68508-2023. Fax: 402-471-2083. p. 1406

Goble, Bonnie, Dir, Cleve J Fredricksen Library, 100 N 19th St, Camp Hill, PA, 17011-3900. Tel: 717-761-3900. Fax: 717-761-5493. p. 2040

Goble, Bonnie, Libr Dir, Fredricksen Cleve J Library, East Pennsboro, 98 S Enola Dr, Enola, PA, 17025. Tel: 717-732-4274. Fax: 717-732-6478. p. 2040

Goble, Linda, Librn, Kentucky State Reformatory Library, 3001 W Hwy 146, La Grange, KY, 40032. Tel: 502-222-9441. Fax: 502-222-9022. p. 919

Gobrecht, Edward, Pres of Board, Tower-Porter Community Library, 230 E Grand Ave, Tower City, PA, 17980-1124. Tel: 717-647-4900. p. 2146

Gochnaur, Holly, Ch, Fourth Presbyterian Church, 5500 River Rd, Bethesda, MD, 20816-3399. Tel: 301-320-3434. Fax: 301-320-6315. p. 1021

Gockley, Jeana, Ch, Joplin Public Library, 300 S Main, Joplin, MO, 64801. Tel: 417-623-7953. Fax: 417-625-4728. p. 1335

Godavari, N, Librn, University of Manitoba Libraries, Donald W Craik Engineering Library, 351 Engineering Bldg, Winnipeg, MB, R3T 2N2, CANADA. Tel: 204-474-6360. Fax: 204-474-7520. p. 2758

Godbout, Gaetan, Pres, Societe Historique de la Cote-du-Sud Bibliotheque, 100 Fourth Ave, La Pocatiere, QC, G0R 1Z0, CANADA. Tel: 418-856-2104. Fax: 418-856-2104. p. 2885

Godbout, Muriel K, Libr Dir, Wells College, 170 Main St, Aurora, NY, 13026-0500. Tel: 315 364-3356. Fax: 315-364-3412. p. 1576

Goddard, Debra, Dir, Rainelle Municipal Public Library, 312 Seventh St, Rainelle, WV, 25962-1649. Tel: 304-438-3008. Fax: 304-438-3008. p. 2570

Goddard, Lisa, Div Head, Syst Coordr, Memorial University of Newfoundland, Queen Elizabeth II Library, 234 Elizabeth Ave, St. John's, NL, A1B 3Y1, CANADA. Tel: 709-737-2124. Fax: 709-737-2153. p. 2773

Goddard, Matthew, Digital Serv, California Baptist University, 8432 Magnolia Ave, Riverside, CA, 92504. Tel: 951-343-4365. p. 216

Goddard, Rosalind, Bibliog Instruction/Ref, Los Angeles City College Library, 855 N Vermont Ave, Los Angeles, CA, 90029. Tel: 323-953-4000, Ext 2399. Fax: 323-953-4013. p. 171

Goddard, Stacey, Adult Serv, Spokane County Library District, Spokane Valley Library, 12004 E Main Ave, Spokane Valley, WA, 99206-5114. Tel: 509-893-8400. Fax: 509-893-8483. p. 2537

Godec, Kathy, Circ, ILL, Northern Michigan University, 1401 Presque Isle, Marquette, MI, 49855. Tel: 906-227-2261. Fax: 906-227-1333. p. 1207

Godell, Joan, Libr Mgr, Children's Hospital Los Angeles, 4650 Sunset Blvd, MS41, Los Angeles, CA, 90027-0700. Tel: 323-361-2254. Fax: 323-361-4844. p. 169

Godell, Joan, Outreach Med Librn, University of Southern California Libraries, Norris Medical Library, 2003 Zonal Ave, Los Angeles, CA, 90089-9130. Tel: 323-442-1112. Fax: 323-221-1235. p. 179

Godfrey, Brenna, Asst Libr Dir, John C Fremont Library District, 130 Church Ave, Florence, CO, 81226. Tel: 719-784-4649. Fax: 719-784-4937. p. 307

Godfrey, Edna, Ch, Atlanta-Fulton Public Library System, Georgia-Hill Library, 250 Georgia Ave SE, Atlanta, GA, 30312. Tel: 404-730-5427. Fax: 404-730-5429. p. 512

Godfrey, I, Acq, University of Victoria Libraries, Diana M Priestly Law Library, PO Box 2300, STN CSC, Victoria, BC, V8W 3B1, CANADA. Tel: 250-721-8565. Fax: 250-472-4174. p. 2746

Godfrey, Joel, Mrs, Acq, Admin Serv, Huntingdon College, 1500 E Fairview Ave, Montgomery, AL, 36106. Tel: 334-833-4421. Fax: 334-263-4465. p. 29

Godfrey, Jon R, Librn, Smyth Public Library, 55 High St, Candia, NH, 03034. Tel: 603-483-8245. Fax: 603-483-5217. p. 1440

Godfrey, Laura, Librn, LearningLinks Resource Centre, 3930 20th St SW, Calgary, AB, T2T 4Z9, CANADA. Tel: 403-249-4606, 403-686-9300. Fax: 403-686-0627. p. 2692

Godfrey, Ruth, Ch, Morgantown Public Library System, 373 Spruce St, Morgantown, WV, 26505. Tel: 304-291-7425. Fax: 304-291-7427. p. 2566

Godfrey, Sue, Internet Serv, Ironworld Discovery Center, 801 SW Hwy 169, Ste 1, Chisholm, MN, 55719. Tel: 218-254-1222, 218-254-7959. Fax: 218-254-7971. p. 1245

Godiana, Ariana, Ch, Parker Public Library, 1001 S Navajo Ave, Parker, AZ, 85344. Tel: 928-669-2622. Fax: 928-669-8668. p. 70

Godin, Alice, ILL Supvr, Johnson State College Library, 337 College Hill, Johnson, VT, 05656. Tel: 802-635-1274. Fax: 802-635-1294. p. 2427

Godin, Francine, Documentalist, Quebec Commission Des Services Juridiques Library, Two Complexe Desjardins, Ste 1404, Montreal, QC, H5B 1B3, CANADA. Tel: 514-873-3562. Fax: 514-873-9263. p. 2900

Godin, Kathy, Ch, Berlin Public Library, 270 Main St, Berlin, NH, 03570. Tel: 603-752-5210. Fax: 603-752-8568. p. 1439

Godin, Maud, Coordr, Librn, Bibliotheque du Cegep Limoilou, 1300 Eighth Ave, Quebec, QC, G1G 5L5, CANADA. Tel: 418-647-6600. Fax: 418-647-6793. p. 2903

Godin, Pauline, Libr Mgr, Chaleur Library Region, Laval-Goupil Public Library, 128 Mgr Chiasson St, Shippagan, NB, E8S 1X7, CANADA. Tel: 506-336-3920. Fax: 506-336-3921. p. 2761

Godina, Ally, Outreach Serv, Windsor-Severance Library, 720 Third St, Windsor, CO, 80550-5109. Tel: 970-686-5603. Fax: 970-686-2502. p. 326

Godino, Hope, Dir, Exeter Public Library, Four Chestnut St, Exeter, NH, 03833. Tel: 603-772-3101, 603-772-6036. Fax: 603-772-7548. p. 1447

Godleski, Nancy, Asst Dean, Coll, Vanderbilt University, 419 21st Ave S, Nashville, TN, 37203-2427. Tel: 615-322-7100. Fax: 615-343-8279. p. 2260

Godon, Daniel, Assoc Dir, Universite du Quebec en Outaouais, 283, Blvd Alexandre-Tache, Case postale 1250, succ Hull, Gatineau, QC, J8X 3X7, CANADA. Tel: 819-595-3900, Ext 1945. Fax: 819-773-1669. p. 2884

Godsey, James M, Dir, Crossroads College, 920 Mayowood Rd SW, Rochester, MN, 55902. Tel: 507-535-3330, 507-535-3331. Fax: 507-288-9046. p. 1272

Godwin, Debbie, Dir, Sammy Brown Library, 522 W College St, Carthage, TX, 75633. Tel: 903-693-6741. Fax: 903-693-4503. p. 2295

Godwin, Joyce, Dir, Indianola Public Library, 207 North B St, Indianola, IA, 50125. Tel: 515-961-9418. Fax: 515-961-9419. p. 822

Godwin, Kathryn, Ch, Hanson Public Library, 132 Maquan St, Hanson, MA, 02341. Tel: 781-293-2151. Fax: 781-293-6801. p. 1093

Godwin, Rebecca, Circ, Samuel Roberts Noble Foundation, Inc, 2510 Sam Noble Pkwy, Ardmore, OK, 73401. Tel: 580-224-6268. Fax: 580-224-6265. p. 1957

Godziela, Mary Jo, Dir, Chicago Public Library, Conrad Sulzer Regional, 4455 N Lincoln Ave, Chicago, IL, 60625. Tel: 312-744-7616. Fax: 312-744-2899. p. 609

Godzik, Susan M, Cat, ILL, Mackinaw Area Public Library, 528 W Central Ave, Mackinaw City, MI, 49701-9681. Tel: 231-436-5451. Fax: 231-436-7344. p. 1205

Godzuik, Ann, Libr Mgr, Myrnam Community Library, New Myrnam School, 5105-50 St, Myrnam, AB, T0B 3K0, CANADA. Tel: 780-366-3801. Fax: 780-366-2332. p. 2712

Goebel, Heather, Br Mgr, Maricopa County Library District, Gila Bend Branch, 202 N Euclid, Gila Bend, AZ, 85337. Tel: 602-652-3396. Fax: 602-652-3398. p. 74

Goebel, Nancy, Head Librn, University of Alberta, 4901 46th Ave, Camrose, AB, T4V 2R3, CANADA. Tel: 780-679-1189. Fax: 780-679-1594. p. 2694

Goedde, Gayle, Librn, Alaska State Library, 333 Willoughby Ave, State Office Bldg, 8th Flr, Juneau, AK, 99801. Tel: 907-465-2910. Fax: 907-465-2151. p. 49

Goeden, Kerrie, Support Serv Mgr, South Central Library System, 4610 S Biltmore Lane, Ste 101, Madison, WI, 53718-2153. Tel: 608-246-7972. Fax: 608-246-7958. p. 2607

Goedert, Dee, Head, Access Serv, University of Nebraska at Kearney, 2508 11th Ave, Kearney, NE, 68849-2240. Tel: 308-865-8597. Fax: 308-865-8722. p. 1403

Goeken, Brian, In Charge, Commission on Chicago Landmarks Library, 33 N La Salle St, Ste 1600, Chicago, IL, 60602. Tel: 312-744-3200. Fax: 312-744-9140. p. 611

Goeman, Ann, Coordr, Charlotte Community Library, 226 S Bostwick St, Charlotte, MI, 48813-1801. Tel: 517-543-8859. Fax: 517-543-8868. p. 1162

Goergen, Liza, Asst Librn, Elbow Lake Public Library, 117 Central Ave N, Elbow Lake, MN, 56531. Tel: 218-685-6850. Fax: 218-685-6852. p. 1249

Goergen, Thomas, Asst Dir, Genesee County Metropolitan Planning Commission Library, 1101 Beach St, Rm 223, Flint, MI, 48502-1470. Tel: 810-257-3010. Fax: 810-257-3185. p. 1179

Goerner, Doris, Libr Asst, Tech Serv, Paul Memorial Library, 76 Main St, Newfields, NH, 03856-8312. Tel: 603-778-8169. Fax: 603-772-9004. p. 1460

Goerner, R, Archives, Fairleigh Dickinson University, 1000 River Rd, Teaneck, NJ, 07666-1914. Tel: 201-692-2450. Fax: 201-692-9815. p. 1532

Goers, Willona, Dir, Johnston Public Library, 6700 Merle Hay Rd, Johnston, IA, 50131-0327. Tel: 515-278-5233. Fax: 515-278-4975. p. 824

Goertz, Gretchen, Circ, Syst, Tech Serv, Douglas College Library, 700 Royal Ave, New Westminster, BC, V3M 5Z5, CANADA. Tel: 604-527-5259. Fax: 604-527-5193. p. 2733

Goertz, Mark, Coll Mgt, Libr Instruction, Vancouver Community College, 250 W Pender St, Vancouver, BC, V6B 1S9, CANADA. Tel: 604-443-8566. Fax: 604-443-8588. p. 2743

Goertzen, Glenda, Libr Tech, First Nations University of Canada, Northern Campus Library, 1301 Central Ave, Prince Albert, SK, S6V 4W1, CANADA. Tel: 306-765-3333, Ext 7425. Fax: 306-765-3330. p. 2922

Goerz, Chris, Librn, Tomahawk Public Library, PO Box 69, Tomahawk, AB, T0E 2H0, CANADA. Tel: 780-339-3935. Fax: 780-339-2121. p. 2719

Goeser, Bonnie C, Librn, Greeley & Hansen Engineering Library, 100 S Wacker Dr, Ste 1400, Chicago, IL, 60606-4004. Tel: 312-578-2380. Fax: 312-558-1986. p. 614

Goethert, Gay D, Mgr, United States Air Force, FL 2804, 100 Kindel Dr, Ste C212, Arnold AFB, TN, 37389-3212. Tel: 931-454-4429. Fax: 931-454-5421. p. 2223

Goetsch, Jim, Ref, Friends of the Third World, Inc, 611 W Wayne St, Fort Wayne, IN, 46802-2167. Tel: 260-422-6821. Fax: 260-422-1650. p. 741

Goetsch, Lori A, Dean of Libr, Kansas State University Libraries, 137 Hale Library, 1100 Mid-Campus Dr, Manhattan, KS, 66506. Tel: 785-532-7402. Fax: 785-532-7415. p. 881

Goetschius, Barbara, Coll Develop, RCS Community Library, 15 Mountain Rd, Ravena, NY, 12143. Tel: 518-756-2053. Fax: 518-756-8595. p. 1726

Goetting, Denise, Cat, University of Louisiana at Lafayette, PO Box 40199, Lafayette, LA, 70504-0199. Tel: 337-482-6197. Fax: 337-482-5841. p. 953

Goetz, Joseph, Info Literacy Librn, University of Saint Thomas, 1100 W Main, Houston, TX, 77006. Tel: 713-942-5972. Fax: 713-525-3886. p. 2344

Goetz, Tom, Ref Serv Coordr, William Rainey Harper College Library, 1200 W Algonquin Rd, Palatine, IL, 60067. Tel: 847-925-6252. Fax: 847-925-6164. p. 687

Goetzfridt, Nick J, Dr, Acq/Coll Develop Librn, University of Guam, UOG Sta, Mangilao, GU, 96923. Tel: 671-735-2300. Fax: 671-734-6882. p. 2667

Goetzman, David, Dir, Adams State University, 208 Edgemont Ave, Alamosa, CO, 81101-2373. Tel: 719-587-7781. Fax: 719-587-7590. p. 287

Goff, Christina, Dir, Los Medanos College Library, 2700 E Leland Rd, Pittsburg, CA, 94565. Tel: 925-439-2181. p. 208

Goff, David, Cat, Lake-Sumter Community College Library, 9501 US Hwy 441, Leesburg, FL, 34788-8751. Tel: 352-365-3527. Fax: 352-365-3590. p. 461

Goff, Emily, Adult Serv, Pankhurst Memorial Library, Three S Jefferson Ave, Amboy, IL, 61310-1400. Tel: 815-857-3925. Fax: 815-857-3065. p. 588

Goff, Florence D, Assoc Chief Info Officer, Bryn Mawr College, 101 N Merion Ave, Bryn Mawr, PA, 19010-2899. Tel: 610-526-5275. Fax: 610-526-7480. p. 2039

Goff, James, Syst Librn, Rochester General Hospital, 1425 Portland Ave, Rochester, NY, 14621. Tel: 585-922-4702. Fax: 585-544-1504. p. 1731

Goff, Joan, Libr Supvr-Popular Libr, Roseville Public Library, 225 Taylor St, Roseville, CA, 95678-2681. Tel: 916-774-5221. Fax: 916-773-5594. p. 220

Goff, Karen E, State Librn, West Virginia Library Commission, State Capitol Complex, 1900 Kanawha Blvd E, Charleston, WV, 25305-0620. Tel: 304-558-2041. Fax: 304-558-2044. p. 2557

Goff, Linda, Head, Libr Instruction, California State University, Sacramento Library, 2000 State University Dr E, Sacramento, CA, 95819-6039. Tel: 916-278-5981. Fax: 916-278-5917. p. 223

Goff, Linda, Youth Serv Coordr, Lake County Library System, 2401 Woodlea Rd, Tavares, FL, 32778. Tel: 352-253-6169. Fax: 352-253-6184. p. 499

Goff, Mary Anne, Dir, Keeseville Free Library, 1721 Front St, Keeseville, NY, 12944. Tel: 518-834-9054. Fax: 518-834-9054. p. 1648

Goff, Matt, Br Librn, Davis County Library, Northwest Branch, 1875 S 2000 West, Syracuse, UT, 84075-9359. Tel: 801-825-7080. Fax: 801-825-7083. p. 2405

Goff, Renate, Dir, Caledonia Library, 3108 Main St, Caledonia, NY, 14423. Tel: 585-538-4512. Fax: 585-538-4978. p. 1600

Goff, Sarah, Coordr, Quad City Area Biomedical Consortium, Great River Medical Ctr Library, 1221 S Gear Ave, West Burlington, IA, 52655. Tel: 319-768-4075. Fax: 319-768-4080. p. 2943

Goff, Susan, Teen Serv, Dover Public Library, 45 S State St, Dover, DE, 19901. Tel: 302-736-7030. Fax: 302-736-5087. p. 382

Goffin, Jordan, Spec Coll Librn, Providence Public Library, 150 Empire St, Providence, RI, 02903-3283. Tel: 401-455-8000. Fax: 401-455-8065, 401-455-8080. p. 2173

Goggins, Sean P, PhD, Asst Prof, Drexel University, Rush Bldg, Rm 306, 30 N 33rd St, Philadelphia, PA, 19104-2875. Tel: 215-895-2474. Fax: 215-895-2494. p. 2972

Goguen, Annick, Actg Libr Mgr, Albert-Westmorland-Kent Regional Library, Bibliotheque Publique de Rogersville, 65, rue de l'Ecole, Unit 1, Rogersville, NB, E4Y 1V4, CANADA. Tel: 506-775-2102. Fax: 506-775-2087. p. 2765

Goguen, Krista F, Fac Outreach Librn, Pasadena City College Library, 1570 E Colorado Blvd, Pasadena, CA, 91106-2003. Tel: 626-585-7360. Fax: 626-585-7913. p. 206

Goguen, Pierre, Ref Librn, Universite de Moncton, 415 Ave de l'Universite, Moncton, NB, E1A 3E9, CANADA. Tel: 506-858-4012. Fax: 506-858-4086. p. 2766

Goheen, Rick, Asst Dean, Assoc Prof, University of Toledo, LaValley Law Library, Mail Stop 508, 2801 W Bancroft St, Toledo, OH, 43606-3390. Tel: 419-530-2733. Fax: 419-530-5121. p. 1941

Gohn, Trudy, Br Mgr, Wellington County Library, Marden Branch, 7368 Wellington Rd 30, RR 5, Guelph, ON, N1H 6J2, CANADA. Tel: 519-763-7445. Fax: 519-763-0706. p. 2805

Going, Linda, Asst Librn, Wallkill Public Library, Seven Bona Ventura Ave, Wallkill, NY, 12589-4422. Tel: 845-895-3707. Fax: 845-895-8659. p. 1762

Goings, Kirsten, Asst Librn, Crystal City Public Library, 736 Mississippi Ave, Crystal City, MO, 63019-1646. Tel: 636-937-7166. Fax: 636-937-3193. p. 1327

Golanty, Deb, Sr Librn, Denver Botanic Gardens, 909 York St, Denver, CO, 80206-3799. Tel: 720-865-3570. Fax: 720-865-3685. p. 300

Golban, Zoya, Law Librn, Marion County Law Library, City-County Bldg, 200 E Washington St, Ste T-360, Indianapolis, IN, 46204. Tel: 317-327-5499. Fax: 317-327-3844. p. 755

Golban, Zoya, Dir, NYS Supreme Court Library, Ninth Judicial District, 9th Flr, 111 Dr Martin Luther King Blvd, White Plains, NY, 10601. Tel: 914-824-5660. p. 1768

Gold, Anna K, Univ Librn, California Polytechnic State University, One Grand Ave, San Luis Obispo, CA, 93407. Tel: 805-756-5786. Fax: 805-756-2346. p. 253

Gold, Anne, Ref, United States Environmental Protection Agency Region 3, 1650 Arch St, 3PM52, Philadelphia, PA, 19103. Tel: 215-814-5362. Fax: 215-814-5253. p. 2118

Gold, Clair, In Charge, Prosperos Servers' Center Library, PO Box 4969, Culver City, CA, 90231-4969. Tel: 310-287-1663. Fax: 310-287-0157. p. 138

Gold, Debra, Electronic Serv Librn, Lakehead University Library, 955 Oliver Rd, Thunder Bay, ON, P7B 5E1, CANADA. Tel: 807-343-8129. Fax: 807-343-8007. p. 2848

Gold, Helene, Electronic Serv, Ref Serv, Web Developer, Eckerd College, 4200 54th Ave S, Saint Petersburg, FL, 33711. Tel: 727-864-8337. Fax: 727-864-8997. p. 488

Gold, Peggy, Dir, Moore County Public Library, PO Box 602, Lynchburg, TN, 37352-0602. Tel: 931-759-7285. Fax: 931-759-6393. p. 2245

Gold, Sandra, Dir, Locke Lord Bissell & Liddell LLP, 111 S Wacker Dr, Chicago, IL, 60606. Tel: 312-443-0646. Fax: 312-443-0336. p. 617

Goldade, Stacey, Head, Statewide Cat Develop, North Dakota State Library, Library Memorial Bldg, 604 East Blvd Ave, Dept 250, Bismarck, ND, 58505-0800. Tel: 701-328-1860. Fax: 701-328-2040. p. 1838

Goldbach, Karen M, Coordr, Tech Serv, Carlow University, 3333 Fifth Ave, Pittsburgh, PA, 15213. Tel: 412-578-6145. Fax: 412-578-6242. p. 2122

Goldberg, Betsy, Librn, New Haven Free Public Library, Fair Haven, 182 Grand Ave, New Haven, CT, 06513. Tel: 203-946-8115. p. 355

Goldberg, Debby, Coordr, Literary Prog, Jewish Community Center of Greater Washington, 6125 Montrose Rd, Rockville, MD, 20852. Tel: 301-348-3816. Fax: 301-881-5512. p. 1037

Goldberg, Gail, Mgr, Rapides Parish Library, J W McDonald Branch, 1075 Hwy 497, Glenmora, LA, 71433. Tel: 318-748-4848. Fax: 318-748-4851. p. 940

Goldberg, Harriet, Pub Serv Librn, Jeffersonville Township Public Library, 211 E Court Ave, Jeffersonville, IN, 47130. Tel: 812-285-5630. Fax: 812-285-5639. p. 756

Goldberg, Irene, Dir, Monroe Township Public Library, Four Municipal Plaza, Monroe Township, NJ, 08831-1900. Tel: 732-521-5000, Ext 107. Fax: 732-521-4766. p. 1503

Goldberg, Joe, Dir, Humphreys County Library System, 105 S Hayden, Belzoni, MS, 39038. Tel: 662-247-3606. Fax: 662-247-3443. p. 1294

Goldberg, Kenneth P, Librn, Northeast Ohio Areawide Coordinating Agency, 1299 Superior Ave, Cleveland, OH, 44114-3204. Tel: 216-241-2414, Ext 240. Fax: 216-621-3024. p. 1880

Goldberg, Martin, Head Librn, Pennsylvania State University, 100 University Dr, Monaca, PA, 15061. Tel: 724-773-3791. Fax: 724-773-3793. p. 2091

Goldberg, Rebecca, Ch, Fletcher Free Library, 235 College St, Burlington, VT, 05401. Tel: 802-863-3403. Fax: 802-865-7227. p. 2421

Goldberg, Rhoda L, Libr Dir, Harris County Public Library, 8080 El Rio, Houston, TX, 77054. Tel: 713-749-9011. Fax: 713-749-9090. p. 2335

Goldberg, Ronnie, Asst Dir, Access Serv, State University of New York at Binghamton, Library Annex at Conklin, 400 Corporate Pkwy, Conklin, NY, 13748. Tel: 607-777-2325. Fax: 607-775-8339. p. 1582

Goldberg, Tyler, Head, Tech Serv, University of Louisville Libraries, William F Ekstrom Library, Belknap Campus, 2215 S Third St, Louisville, KY, 40292. Tel: 502-852-8723. Fax: 502-852-7394. p. 927

Golden, Beatrice, Circ, Morris College, 100 W College St, Sumter, SC, 29150-3599. Tel: 803-934-3230. Fax: 803-778-2923. p. 2206

Golden, Brooke, Mgr, Lake Spokane Library, 6176 Hwy 291, Nine Mile Falls, WA, 99026-9026. Tel: 509-276-3329. Fax: 509-276-1339. p. 2522

Golden, Gale, Supvr, University of Arkansas Libraries, Fine Arts, 104 Fine Arts Bldg, Fayetteville, AR, 72701. Tel: 479-575-3499. p. 100

Golden, Gary A, Dir, Rutgers University Libraries, Paul Robeson Library, Camden, 300 N Fourth St, Camden, NJ, 08102-1404. Tel: 856-225-2828. Fax: 856-225-6428. p. 1477

Golden, Judy, Dir, Clark County Library, 609 Caddo St, Arkadelphia, AR, 71923. Tel: 870-246-2271. Fax: 870-246-4189. p. 93

Golden, Judy, Dir, Clark County Library, Gurdon Public, 204 E Walnut, Gurdon, AR, 71743. Tel: 870-353-2911. p. 93

Golden, LaDon, Mgr, Henry County Public Library System, Locust Grove Public Library, 115 Locust Grove Griffin Rd, Locust Grove, GA, 30248. Tel: 770-954-2810. Fax: 770-954-2811. p. 544

Golden, Patrick, Prog Serv Dir, Williamsburg Regional Library, 7770 Croaker Rd, Williamsburg, VA, 23188-7064. Tel: 757-259-4071. Fax: 757-259-4079, 757-259-7798. p. 2503

Golden, Sue, ILL Coordr, Pacific Lutheran University, 12180 Park Ave S, Tacoma, WA, 98447-0001. Tel: 253-535-7500. Fax: 253-535-7315. p. 2539

Golden, Timothy, Cat, Boyden Library, Ten Bird St, Foxborough, MA, 02035. Tel: 508-543-1245. Fax: 508-543-1193. p. 1089

Golder, Cathy, Dir, Green Free Library, 14 N Center St, Canton, PA, 17724-1304. Tel: 570-673-5744. Fax: 570-673-5005. p. 2041

Goldfarb, Gail, Ch, East Meadow Public Library, 1886 Front St, East Meadow, NY, 11554-1705. Tel: 516-794-2570. Fax: 516-794-1272. p. 1617

Goldfarb, Kathleen, Tech Serv Librn, College of the Mainland Library, 1200 Amburn Rd, Texas City, TX, 77591-2499. Tel: 409-938-1211, Ext 202. Fax: 409-938-8918. p. 2392

Goldfein, David, Automation Syst Coordr, La Crosse Public Library, 800 Main St, La Crosse, WI, 54601. Tel: 608-789-7142. Fax: 608-789-7106. p. 2603

Goldfrank, Elizabeth, Asst Dir, Hicksville Public Library, 169 Jerusalem Ave, Hicksville, NY, 11801. Tel: 516-931-1417. Fax: 516-822-5672. p. 1636

Goldin, Barbara, Dir, Emily Williston Memorial Library, Nine Park St, Easthampton, MA, 01027. Tel: 413-527-1031. Fax: 413-527-3765. p. 1086

Goldin, Jill, Ch, Stephen Wise Free Synagogue, 30 W 68th St, New York, NY, 10023. Tel: 212-877-4050, Ext 238. Fax: 212-787-7108. p. 1703

Goldin, Sally, Librn, Pelham Library, Two S Valley Rd, Pelham, MA, 01002. Tel: 413-253-0657. Fax: 413-253-0594. p. 1117

Goldman, Bernadine, Asst Libr Mgr, Los Alamos County Library System, 2400 Central Ave, Los Alamos, NM, 87544. Tel: 505-662-8254. Fax: 505-662-8245. p. 1559

Goldman, Beth, Adult Serv, Morrill Memorial Library, 33 Walpole St, Norwood, MA, 02062-1206. Tel: 781-769-0200. Fax: 781-769-6083. p. 1115

Goldman, Crystal, Bibliog Instr, Lincoln Memorial University, Cumberland Gap Pkwy, Box 2012, Harrogate, TN, 37752. Tel: 423-869-7079. Fax: 423-869-6426. p. 2236

Goldman, Elizabeth, Chief Exec Officer, Perth & District Union Public Library, 30 Herriott St, Perth, ON, K7H 1T2, CANADA. Tel: 613-267-1224. Fax: 613-267-7899. p. 2835

Goldman, Helen, Cat, Auburn University, Ralph Brown Draughon Library, 231 Mell St, Auburn, AL, 36849. Tel: 334-844-0241. Fax: 334-844-4424. p. 5

Goldman, Jaime, Ref Librn II, Nova Southeastern University Libraries, William S Richardson Library, Oceanographic Center, 8000 N Ocean Dr, Dania Beach, FL, 33004. Tel: 954-262-3643, 954-262-3681. Fax: 954-262-4021. p. 444

Goldman, Jennifer, Curator, Huntington Library, 1151 Oxford Rd, San Marino, CA, 91108. Tel: 626-405-2208. Fax: 626-449-5720. p. 255

Goldman, Linda, Br Head, Toronto Public Library, St Lawrence, 171 Front St E, Toronto, ON, M5A 4H3, CANADA. Tel: 416-393-7655. Fax: 416-393-7419. p. 2863

Goldner, Susan D, Cat, Ref Serv, University of Arkansas at Little Rock, Pulaski County Law Library, 1203 McMath Ave, Little Rock, AR, 72202-5142. Tel: 501-324-9444. Fax: 501-324-9447. p. 107

Goldsberry, Suellen, Dir, Pickerington Public Library, 201 Opportunity Way, Pickerington, OH, 43147-1296. Tel: 614-837-4104. Fax: 614-837-8425. p. 1930

Goldsberry, Susan, Br Mgr, Pioneer Library System, Tecumseh Public, 114 N Broadway, Tecumseh, OK, 74873. Tel: 405-598-5955. Fax: 405-598-5416. p. 1971

Goldsmith, David, Assoc Dir, Mat Mgt, North Carolina State University Libraries, Two Broughton Dr, Raleigh, NC, 27695. Tel: 919-515-7188. Fax: 919-515-3628. p. 1816

Goldsmith, Kristine, Ch Serv Spec, Pub Relations Coordr, Rossford Public Library, 720 Dixie Hwy, Rossford, OH, 43460-1289. Tel: 419-666-0924. Fax: 419-666-1989. p. 1932

Goldsmith, Lynn, Circ, Lawrence Memorial Library, 40 North St, Bristol, VT, 05443. Tel: 802-453-2366. p. 2420

Goldsmith, Melissa, Ref Librn, Nicholls State University, 906 E First St, Thibodaux, LA, 70310. Tel: 985-448-4646, 985-448-4660. Fax: 985-448-4925. p. 971

Goldsmith, Nora, Access Serv, Glendale Public Library, 222 E Harvard St, Glendale, CA, 91205-1075. Tel: 818-548-4020. Fax: 818-548-7225. p. 155

Goldstein, Doris, Dir, National Reference Center for Bioethics Literature, Georgetown University, 37th & O St NW, Washington, DC, 20057. Tel: 202-687-3885. Fax: 202-687-6770. p. 411

Goldstein, Jeremy, Tech Serv Supvr, Berkshire Athenaeum, One Wendell Ave, Pittsfield, MA, 01201-6385. Tel: 413-499-9480. Fax: 413-499-9489. p. 1117

Goldstein, Karin J, Curator of Coll & Libr, Plimoth
Plantation, 137 Warren Ave, Plymouth, MA,
02360-2436. Tel: 508-746-1622, Ext 8379. Fax:
508-746-4978. p. 1118

Goldstein, Louise, Circ, Waltham Public Library,
735 Main St, Waltham, MA, 02451. Tel:
781-314-3425. Fax: 781-314-3426. p. 1133

Goldstein, Marcy, Dr, Dir, The National Archives
at San Francisco, 1000 Commodore Dr, San
Bruno, CA, 94066-2350. Tel: 650-238-3501.
Fax: 650-238-3510. p. 230

Goldstein, Robert, Music Librn, NPR Library, 635
Massachusetts Ave NW, Washington, DC,
20001. Fax: 202-513-3056. p. 412

Goldstein, Robert, Pres, Fast Pulse Technology, Inc
Library, 220 Midland Ave, Saddle Brook, NJ,
07663. Tel: 973-478-5757. Fax: 973-478-6115.
p. 1528

Goldstein, Robert, Chief Financial Officer, Kitsap
Regional Library, 1301 Sylvan Way, Bremerton,
WA, 98310-3498. Tel: 360-405-9137. Fax:
360-405-9128. p. 2510

Goldstein, Rosalyn, Cat, Widener University, One
University Pl, Chester, PA, 19013-5792. Tel:
610-499-4079. Fax: 610-499-4588. p. 2044

Goldstein, Sarah, Visual Res Librn, Vassar
College Library, 124 Raymond Ave, Maildrop
20, Poughkeepsie, NY, 12604-0020. Tel:
845-437-5760. Fax: 845-437-5864. p. 1723

Goldthwaite, Cathy, Circ, ILL Librn, Derry
Public Library, 64 E Broadway, Derry,
NH, 03038-2412. Tel: 603-432-6140. Fax:
603-432-6128. p. 1444

Goldthwaite, Donna, Regional Ref Librn, Springfield
City Library, 220 State St, Springfield, MA,
01103. Tel: 413-263-6828, Ext 437. Fax:
413-263-6817. p. 1127

Goldtooth, Pearl, Mgr, Flagstaff City-Coconino
County Public Library System, Tuba City Public
Library, 78 Main St, Tuba City, AZ, 86045. Tel:
928-283-5856. Fax: 928-283-6188. p. 62

Goldy, Scott, Instrul Librn, Rock Valley College
Library, Educational Resources Center, 3301
N Mulford Rd, Rockford, IL, 61114. Tel:
815-921-4605. Fax: 815-921-4629. p. 697

Goldyn, Amy, Finance Mgr, Genesee District
Library, G-4195 W Pasadena Ave, Flint, MI,
48504. Tel: 810-230-3334. Fax: 810-732-1161.
p. 1179

Goleman, Kathy, Librn, Divernon Township Library,
221 S Second St, Divernon, IL, 62530. Tel:
217-628-3813. Fax: 217-628-3813. p. 636

Golemon, Larry, Exec Dir, Washington Theological
Consortium, 487 Michigan Ave NE, Washington,
DC, 20017-1585. Tel: 202-832-2675. Fax:
202-526-0818. p. 2940

Golia, Laura, Youth Serv - Prog, Sadie Pope
Dowdell Library of South Amboy, 100 Harold G
Hoffman Plaza, South Amboy, NJ, 08879. Tel:
732-721-6060. Fax: 732-721-1054. p. 1530

Goliak, Ann, Electronic Serv Coordr, Library of
Rush University Medical Center, Armour
Academic Ctr, 600 S Paulina St, 5th Flr,
Chicago, IL, 60612-3874. Tel: 312-942-8558.
Fax: 312-942-3143. p. 617

Golian-Lui, Linda Marie, Dr, Univ Librn, University
of Hawaii at Hilo Library, 200 W Kawili St,
Hilo, HI, 96720-4091. Tel: 808-974-7759. Fax:
808-974-7329. p. 559

Golinski-Foisy, Antonia, Dir, West Springfield
Public Library, 200 Park St, West Springfield,
MA, 01089. Tel: 413-736-4561, Ext 102. Fax:
413-736-6469. p. 1137

Gollata, James A, Dir, University of
Wisconsin-Richland, 1200 US Hwy 14 W,
Richland Center, WI, 53581-1399. Tel:
608-647-6186, Ext 220. Fax: 608-647-6225.
p. 2634

Goller, Robert, Dir, Aurora Historical Society, 363
Oakwood Ave, East Aurora, NY, 14052-2319.
Tel: 716-652-4735. p. 1616

Golliher, Dawn, Circ, Rio Community Library,
324 W Lyons St, Rio, WI, 53960. Tel:
920-992-3206. Fax: 920-992-3983. p. 2634

Gollon, David V, Music, Pitkin County Library,
120 N Mill St, Aspen, CO, 81611. Tel:
970-925-4025. Fax: 970-925-3935. p. 288

Golodnitsky, Anna, Acq, Cataloger, University
of Toronto Libraries, Caven Library, Knox
College, 59 Saint George St, Toronto, ON,
M5S 2E6, CANADA. Tel: 416-978-6719. Fax:
416-971-2133. p. 2865

Golovko, Linda, Libr Operations, Southern
California Genealogical Society, 417 Irving Dr,
Burbank, CA, 91504-2408. Tel: 818-843-7247.
Fax: 818-843-7262. p. 130

Golrick, Jill, Dir, Norwalk Hospital, Maple St,
Norwalk, CT, 06856. Tel: 203-852-2793. Fax:
203-855-3575. p. 362

Golrick, Michael, Head, Ref, State Library of
Louisiana, 701 N Fourth St, Baton Rouge,
LA, 70802-5232. Tel: 225-219-4726. Fax:
225-219-4804. p. 945

Golston, Jenifer, Youth Serv Coordr, Bedford Public
Library System, 321 N Bridge St, Bedford, VA,
24523-1924. Tel: 540-586-8911, Ext 2108. Fax:
540-586-8875. p. 2450

Goltz, Cheryl A, Dir, Rolla Free Public Library, 900
Pine St, Rolla, MO, 65401. Tel: 573-364-2604.
Fax: 573-341-5768. p. 1351

Golub, Andrew J, Dean of Libr Serv, University of
New England Libraries, 11 Hills Beach Rd,
Biddeford, ME, 04005. Tel: 207-602-2361. Fax:
207-602-5922. p. 978

Golub, Andrew J, Dean of Libr Serv, University of
New England Libraries, Josephine S Abplanalp
Library, Portland Campus, 716 Stevens Ave,
Portland, ME, 04103. Tel: 207-602-2319. Fax:
207-221-4893. p. 978

Golubosky, Sally, Dir, Tabor Public Library, 805
Main St, Tabor, IA, 51653. Tel: 712-629-2735.
Fax: 712-629-2735. p. 847

Golubski, Tamara, Supvr, Youth Serv, Richardson
Public Library, 900 Civic Center Dr, Richardson,
TX, 75080. Tel: 972-744-4383. Fax:
972-744-5806. p. 2374

Golv, Naomi, Br Mgr, Dakota County Library
System, Burnhaven Community, 1101 W
County Rd 42, Burnsville, MN, 55306. Tel:
952-891-0306. Fax: 952-435-3476. p. 1249

Gomarlo, Jennifer, Asst Librn, Stratton Free Library,
Nine Main St, West Swanzey, NH, 03446. Tel:
603-352-9391. p. 1467

Gomes, Alexandra, Assoc Dir, Pub Serv/Instruction,
George Washington University, Paul Himmelfarb
Health Sciences Library, 2300 I St NW,
Washington, DC, 20037. Tel: 202-994-1825.
Fax: 202-994-4343. p. 402

Gomes, Debra, Ser, Syst Coordr, College of Our
Lady of the Elms, 291 Springfield St, Chicopee,
MA, 01013-2839. Tel: 413-265-2280, Ext 2316.
Fax: 413-594-7418. p. 1082

Gomes, Dulce, Br Head, Toronto Public Library,
Mount Pleasant, 599 Mount Pleasant Rd,
Toronto, ON, M4S 2M5, CANADA. Tel:
416-393-7737. Fax: 416-393-7414. p. 2862

Gometz, Anne E, Ref, Gaston-Lincoln Regional
Library, 1555 E Garrison Blvd, Gastonia, NC,
28054. Tel: 704-868-2164. Fax: 704-853-6012.
p. 1794

Gomez, Angie, Circ, Benedictine College Library,
1020 N Second St, Atchison, KS, 66002-1499.
Tel: 913-360-7608. Fax: 913-360-7622. p. 856

Gomez, Ann, Govt Doc, Rhode Island State
Library, State House, Rm 208, 82 Smith St,
Providence, RI, 02903. Tel: 401-222-2473. Fax:
401-222-3034. p. 2175

Gomez, Evelyn, Ref, Kramer, Levin, Naftalis &
Frankel LLP, 1177 Avenue of the Americas,
New York, NY, 10036. Tel: 212-715-9321. Fax:
212-715-8000. p. 1684

Gomez, Guillermo, Music Libr Supvr, West Chester
University, Presser Music Library, School of
Music & Performing Arts Center, West Chester,
PA, 19383. Tel: 610-436-2379, 610-436-2430.
Fax: 610-436-2873. p. 2154

Gomez, Isela, Doc Delivery, California State
Polytechnic University Library, 3801 W Temple
Ave, Bldg 15, Pomona, CA, 91768. Tel:
909-869-5250. Fax: 909-869-6922. p. 211

Gomez, Maria, Info Literacy Librn, Universidad
del Turabo, PO Box 3030, Gurabo, PR,
00778-3030. Tel: 787-743-7979, Ext 4501. Fax:
787-743-7924. p. 2673

Gomez, Mary, Tech Serv Librn, Rockingham
Community College, 315 Wrenn Memorial Rd,
Wentworth, NC, 27375. Tel: 336-342-4261, Ext
2320. Fax: 336-342-1203. p. 1829

Gomez, Ricardo, Asst Prof, University of
Washington, Mary Gates Hall, Ste 370, Campus
Box 352840, Seattle, WA, 98195-2840. Tel:
206-685-9937. Fax: 206-616-3152. p. 2976

Gomez, Sherry, Interim Dir, Kern County Library,
701 Truxtun Ave, Bakersfield, CA, 93301-4816.
Tel: 661-868-0700. Fax: 661-868-0799. p. 124

Gomez, Sol, Managing Librn, Pima County
Public Library, Valencia, 202 W Valencia Rd,
Tucson, AZ, 85706. Tel: 520-594-5390. Fax:
520-594-5391. p. 87

Gomez-Beloz, Selina, Sr Libr Mgr, Timberland
Regional Library, Lacey Branch, 500 College St
SE, Lacey, WA, 98503-1240. Tel: 360-491-3860.
Fax: 360-459-6714. p. 2543

Gomien, Jenny, Br Mgr, Public Library of Cincinnati
& Hamilton County, Clifton, 351 Ludlow Ave,
Cincinnati, OH, 45220. Tel: 513-369-4447. Fax:
513-369-4448. p. 1871

Gomm, Matthew, Dir, Goshen Free Public Library,
42 Main St, Goshen, MA, 01032-9608. Tel:
413-268-7033. p. 1091

Gomm, Matthew, Actg Dir, Goshen Public Library
& Historical Society, 203 Main St, Goshen, NY,
10924. Tel: 845-294-6606. Fax: 845-294-7158.
p. 1629

Gomoll, Brian, Circ Desk Mgr, Clarke University,
1550 Clarke Dr, Dubuque, IA, 52001. Tel:
563-588-6320. Fax: 563-588-8160. p. 811

Gomoll, Kim, Mgr, Steinman Enterprises, Eight
W King St, Lancaster, PA, 17603-3824. Tel:
717-291-8773. p. 2078

Goncalves, Aline, Info Literacy, Ref Librn, Yukon
College Library, 500 College Dr, Whitehorse,
YT, Y1A 5K4, CANADA. Tel: 867-668-8870.
Fax: 867-668-8808. p. 2934

Gondek, Angel, Supvr, Multimedia Support Ctr/Circ,
Columbus State Community College Library,
550 E Spring St, Columbus, OH, 43215. Tel:
614-287-2267. Fax: 614-287-2457. p. 1885

Gonen, Lynn T, Div Mgr, Queens Borough Public
Library, Youth Services Division, 89-11 Merrick
Blvd, Jamaica, NY, 11432. Tel: 718-990-0767,
718-990-0768. p. 1646

Gong, Regan, Br Mgr, San Francisco Public Library,
Anza Branch Library, 550 37th Ave, San
Francisco, CA, 94121-2691. Tel: 415-355-5717.
p. 246

Gong, Xiao Mei, Bus Librn, Western Connecticut
State University, Robert S Young Business
Library, 181 White St, Danbury, CT,
06810-6885. Tel: 203-837-9139. Fax:
203-837-9135. p. 335

Gongaware, Cindy, Dir, Aguilar Public Library,
146 W Main St, Aguilar, CO, 81020. Tel:
719-941-4426. p. 287

Gongloff, Ann, Asst Librn, Nanty Glo Public
Library, 942 Roberts St, Nanty Glo, PA,
15943-0296. Tel: 814-749-0111. Fax:
814-749-0111. p. 2094

Goniwiecha, Mark C, Ref & Info Literacy
Instruction, University of Guam, UOG Sta,
Mangilao, GU, 96923. Tel: 671-735-2340. Fax:
671-734-6882. p. 2667

Gonnella, Debbie, Br Mgr, Josephine Community
Libraries, Inc, Williams Branch, 20695 Williams
Hwy, Williams, OR, 97544. Tel: 541-846-7020.
p. 1999

Gonnerman, Kasia, Ref & Instrul Serv Librn, Saint
Olaf College, Rolvaag Memorial Library, Glasoe
Science Library, Halvorson Music Library, 1510
Saint Olaf Ave, Northfield, MN, 55057-1097.
Tel: 507-786-3501. Fax: 507-786-3734. p. 1269

Gontarek, Mary, AV, Per, Owatonna Public Library, 105 N Elm Ave, Owatonna, MN, 55060-2405. Tel: 507-444-2460. Fax: 507-444-2465. p. 1270

Gontrum, Barbara, Asst Dean, University of Maryland, Baltimore, Thurgood Marshall Law Library, 501 W Fayette St, Baltimore, MD, 21201-1768. Tel: 410-706-7270. Fax: 410-706-8354. p. 1019

Gonzale, Angela, Dir, Warsaw Public Library, 130 N Main St, Warsaw, NY, 14569. Tel: 585-786-5650. Fax: 585-786-8706. p. 1762

Gonzales, Andrea, Pub Serv, Western Nebraska Community College Library, 1601 E 27th NE, Scottsbluff, NE, 69361-1899. Tel: 308-635-6040. Fax: 308-635-6086. p. 1418

Gonzales, Chris, ILL, Sheridan County Public Library System, 335 W Alger St, Sheridan, WY, 82801-3899. Tel: 307-674-8585, Ext 5. p. 2660

Gonzales, Dara, Dir, McIver's Grant Public Library, 204 N Mill, Dyersburg, TN, 38024-4631. Tel: 731-285-5032. Fax: 731-285-9332. p. 2233

Gonzales, Florie, Librn, Sutton County Library, 306 E Mulberry St, Sonora, TX, 76950. Tel: 325-387-2111. Fax: 325-387-9044. p. 2388

Gonzales, Garin, Br Mgr, Madera County Library, Ranchos Branch, 37167 Avenue 12, Ste 4C, Madera, CA, 93638-8725. Tel: 559-645-1214. Fax: 559-645-1216. p. 182

Gonzales, Janet, ILL, California State University, 9001 Stockdale Hwy, Bakersfield, CA, 93311-1022. Tel: 661-654-2129. Fax: 661-654-3238. p. 123

Gonzales, Jessie, Librn, Wharton County Library, Louise Branch, 803 Third St, Louise, TX, 77455. Tel: 979-648-2018. p. 2400

Gonzales, Joe, Dean, Libr Serv, San Joaquin Delta College, 5151 Pacific Ave, Stockton, CA, 95207-6370. Tel: 209-954-5139. Fax: 209-954-5691. p. 272

Gonzales, John O DLR, Exec Dir, State Libr Info Ctr, Joeten-Kiyu Public Library, Beach Rd, Susupe, Saipan, MP, 96950. Tel: 670-235-7315. Fax: 670-235-7550. p. 2669

Gonzales, Laura, Mgr, District of Columbia Public Library, Washington Highlands, 115 Atlantic St SW, Washington, DC, 20032. Tel: 202-645-5880. p. 399

Gonzales, Laura, Libr Tech, New Mexico State Library, 356-D E Ninth St, Cimarron, NM, 87714. Tel: 575-376-2474. Fax: 575-376-2433. p. 1553

Gonzales, Lynn, Ch, Youth Serv, W T Bland Public Library, 1995 N Donnelly St, Mount Dora, FL, 32757. Tel: 352-735-7180. Fax: 352-735-0074. p. 470

Gonzales, Margie, Librn, Ward County Library, Barstow Branch, PO Box 74, Barstow, TX, 79719-0074. Tel: 432-445-5205. p. 2363

Gonzales, Mark, Dean, Evergreen Valley College Library, 3095 Yerba Buena Rd, San Jose, CA, 95135. Tel: 408-223-6792. Fax: 408-532-1925. p. 249

Gonzales, Matthia, Sr Libr Asst, Englewood Public Library, 31 Engle St, Englewood, NJ, 07631. Tel: 201-568-2215. Fax: 201-568-6895. p. 1484

Gonzales, Patty, Bus Librn, Fort Bend County Libraries, 1001 Golfview Dr, Richmond, TX, 77469-5199. Tel: 281-341-2644. Fax: 281-341-2688. p. 2374

Gonzales, Reyes, Librn, New Mexico State Library, 423 W Nobles, Tucumcari, NM, 88401. Tel: 575-461-1206. Fax: 575-461-1824. p. 1566

Gonzales, Rhonda, Dean of Libr, Colorado State University Pueblo Library, 2200 Bonforte Blvd, Pueblo, CO, 81001-4901. Tel: 719-549-2361. Fax: 719-549-2738. p. 320

Gonzales, Sonia, Libr Supvr, Howard County Junior College, Southwest Collegiate Institute for the Deaf - Library, 3200 Ave C, Big Spring, TX, 79720. Tel: 432-218-4056. Fax: 432-264-3726. p. 2289

Gonzalez, Adrian, Coll Librn, Tech Serv, Val Verde County Library, 300 Spring St, Del Rio, TX, 78840. Tel: 830-774-7595. Fax: 830-774-7607. p. 2312

Gonzalez, Allegra, Digital Initiatives Librn, Claremont Colleges Library, 800 Dartmouth Ave, Claremont, CA, 91711. Tel: 909-621-8014. p. 134

Gonzalez, Andre, Head, Circ, Arcadia Public Library, 20 W Duarte Rd, Arcadia, CA, 91006. Tel: 626-294-4804. Fax: 626-447-8050. p. 121

Gonzalez, Armando, Managing Librn, Paul, Weiss, Rifkind, Wharton & Garrison Library, 1285 Avenue of the Americas, New York, NY, 10019-6064. Tel: 212-373-2401. Fax: 212-373-2268. p. 1697

Gonzalez, Autumn, Regional Librn, Indiana State Library, 140 N Senate Ave, Indianapolis, IN, 46204-2296. Tel: 317-232-3738. Fax: 317-232-3728. p. 752

Gonzalez, Carlos M, Spec Coll Librn, University of the Sacred Heart, Rosales St, PO Box 12383, Santurce, PR, 00914-0383. Tel: 787-728-1515, Ext 4353. Fax: 787-268-8868. p. 2678

Gonzalez, Carolyn Ellis, Head, Tech Serv, Our Lady of the Lake University, 411 SW 24th St, San Antonio, TX, 78207-4689. Tel: 210-434-6711, Ext 2324. Fax: 210-436-1616. p. 2380

Gonzalez, David, Dir, Morenci Community Library, Morenci Plaza, Morenci, AZ, 85540. Tel: 928-865-2775. Fax: 928-865-3130. p. 69

Gonzalez, David, Computer Serv Librn, Lakeland Public Library, 100 Lake Morton Dr, Lakeland, FL, 33801-5375. Tel: 863-834-4280. Fax: 863-834-4293. p. 459

Gonzalez, Eleanor, Res, Shearman & Sterling Library, 801 Pennsylvania Ave NW, Ste 900, Washington, DC, 20004-2634. Tel: 202-508-8055. Fax: 202-508-8100. p. 414

Gonzalez, Eleanor, In Charge, Shearman & Sterling LLP Library, 599 Lexington Ave, New York, NY, 10022-6069. Tel: 212-848-4627. Fax: 646-848-4627. p. 1699

Gonzalez, Elisa I, Cat, Pontifical Catholic University of Puerto Rico, Ramon Emeterio Betances St 482, Mayaguez, PR, 00680. Tel: 787-834-5151, Ext 5008. Fax: 787-831-7155. p. 2673

Gonzalez, Eva, Head Librn, Plano Public Library System, Gladys Harrington Library, 1501 E 18th St, Plano, TX, 75074. Tel: 972-941-7175. Fax: 972-941-7292. p. 2370

Gonzalez, Frank, Media Librn, Glendale Community College, 6000 W Olive Ave, Glendale, AZ, 85302. Tel: 623-845-3120. Fax: 623-845-3102. p. 64

Gonzalez, Gilbert, Res, Rutherford B Hayes Presidential Center Library, Spiegel Grove, Fremont, OH, 43420-2796. Tel: 419-332-2081, Ext 222. Fax: 419-332-4952. p. 1900

Gonzalez, Gilda, ILL, Mercy College Libraries, 555 Broadway, Dobbs Ferry, NY, 10522. Tel: 914-674-7580. Fax: 914-674-7581. p. 1615

Gonzalez, Irma, Br Mgr, San Bernardino County Library, Mentone Senior Center & Library, 1331 Opal Ave, Mentone, CA, 92359. Tel: 909-794-0327. Fax: 909-794-2657. p. 228

Gonzalez, Janette, Librn, Kean University, 1000 Morris Ave, Union, NJ, 07083. Tel: 908-737-4600. Fax: 908-737-4620. p. 1537

Gonzalez, Jesse, Asst Dir, Circ, Houston Academy of Medicine, 1133 John Freeman Blvd, Houston, TX, 77030. Tel: 713-799-7148. Fax: 713-790-7052. p. 2337

Gonzalez, Jorge, Lang Dept Mgr, Miami-Dade Public Library System, 101 W Flagler St, Miami, FL, 33130-1523. Tel: 305-375-5579. Fax: 305-375-3048. p. 466

Gonzalez, Jose, Ref Serv, Brownsville Public Library System, 2600 Central Blvd, Brownsville, TX, 78520-8824. Tel: 956-548-1055. Fax: 956-548-0684. p. 2292

Gonzalez, Joseantonio, Br Mgr, Monterey County Free Libraries, Pajaro Branch, 29 Bishop St, Pajaro, CA, 95076. Tel: 831-761-2545. Fax: 831-768-7782. p. 183

Gonzalez, Judy, Librn, Converse Consultants East Library, Rte 10 W, Ste 10, Whippany, NJ, 07981. Tel: 973-428-0934. Fax: 973-428-0713. p. 1544

Gonzalez, Julio C, Archivist, The Music Center of Los Angeles County Archives, 135 N Grand Ave, Los Angeles, CA, 90012-3013. Tel: 213-972-7499. Fax: 213-972-3132. p. 176

Gonzalez, Kelly, Dep Dir, University of Texas Southwestern Medical Center Library, 5323 Harry Hines Blvd, Dallas, TX, 75390-9049. Tel: 214-648-2001. Fax: 214-648-2826. p. 2311

Gonzalez, Laura, Mgr, District of Columbia Public Library, Georgetown, 3260 R St NW, Washington, DC, 20007. Tel: 202-724-8783, 202-727-0232. p. 398

Gonzalez, Lazara, Circ, College of Southern Nevada, Cheyenne Campus, 3200 E Cheyenne Ave, C2A, North Las Vegas, NV, 89030. Tel: 702-651-4014. Fax: 702-643-4812. p. 1429

Gonzalez, Margarita, Head, Ref, University of Puerto Rico, Conrado F Asenjo Library (Medical Sciences Campus), Medical Sciences Campus, Main Bldg, Unit C, San Juan, PR, 00935. Tel: 787-751-8199, 758-2525, Ext 1200. Fax: 787-759-6713, 282-6438. p. 2676

Gonzalez, Maria, Ref Librn, Barry University, 11300 NE Second Ave, Miami, FL, 33161. Tel: 305-899-3761. Fax: 305-899-4792. p. 464

Gonzalez, Maria del C, Acq, Pontifical Catholic University Of Puerto Rico, Monseignor Fremiot Torres Oliver Legal Information & Research Center, 2250 Avenida Las Americas, Ste 544, Ponce, PR, 00717-9997. Tel: 787-841-2000 Ext.1857. Fax: 787-841-5354. p. 2675

Gonzalez, Mario, Dir, Passaic Public Library, 195 Gregory Ave, Passaic, NJ, 07055. Tel: 973-779-0474. Fax: 973-779-0889. p. 1518

Gonzalez, Millie, Ref Serv, Framingham State College, 100 State St, Framingham, MA, 01701. Tel: 508-626-4655. Fax: 508-626-4649. p. 1090

Gonzalez, Nancy, Cat Librn, Chapman University, One University Dr, Orange, CA, 92866-1099. Tel: 714-532-7756. Fax: 714-532-7743. p. 200

Gonzalez, Pamela M, Per/Acq Tech, Minnesota Department of Transportation Library, 395 John Ireland Blvd, MS 155, Saint Paul, MN, 55155. Tel: 651-366-3749. Fax: 651-366-3789. p. 1279

Gonzalez, Rafael, Commun Libr Mgr, County of Los Angeles Public Library, Baldwin Park Library, 4181 Baldwin Park Blvd, Baldwin Park, CA, 91706-3203. Tel: 626-962-6947. Fax: 626-337-6631. p. 140

Gonzalez, Rebecca, Circ, Fort Stockton Public Library, 500 N Water St, Fort Stockton, TX, 79735. Tel: 432-336-3374. Fax: 432-336-6648. p. 2321

Gonzalez, Rosie, Asst Librn, Reeves County Library, 505 S Park St, Pecos, TX, 79772-3735. Tel: 432-445-5340. Fax: 432-445-1028. p. 2369

Gonzalez, Victoria, Dir, Sargeant Fernando de la Rosa Memorial Library, 416 N Tower Rd, Alamo, TX, 78516-2317. Tel: 956-787-6160. Fax: 956-787-5154. p. 2272

Gonzalez, Virginia, Circ Supvr, Fort Worth Library, 500 W Third St, Fort Worth, TX, 76102. Tel: 817-871-7795. Fax: 817-871-7734. p. 2321

Gonzalez, Yamilka, Asst Librn, Carlos Albizu University Library, 2173 NW 99 Ave, Miami, FL, 33172. Tel: 305-593-1223, Ext 131. Fax: 305-593-8318. p. 464

Gonzalez-Garza, Ida, Dir, Nueces County Keach Family Library, 100 Terry Shamsie Blvd, Robstown, TX, 78380. Tel: 361-387-4817. Fax: 361-387-7964. p. 2376

Gonzalez-Rahming, Judith, Mgr, Bellevue Medical Library, Patients Library, First Ave & 27th St, New York, NY, 10016. Tel: 212-562-3833. p. 1670

Goobaad, Tonny, Archivist Tech, Northern Marianas College, Pacific Collection, PO Box 501250, Saipan, MP, 96950. Tel: 670-234-5498, Ext 1111. Fax: 670-234-0759. p. 2669

Gooch, B J, Spec Coll Librn, Transylvania University Library, 300 N Broadway, Lexington, KY, 40508. Tel: 859-246-5002. Fax: 859-233-8779. p. 921

Gooch, Mark, Tech Librn, The College of Wooster Libraries, 1140 Beall Ave, Wooster, OH, 44691-2364. Tel: 330-263-2522. Fax: 330-263-2253. p. 1949

Gooch, Melissa, Br Mgr, San Francisco Public Library, Bernal Heights Branch Library, 500 Cortland Ave, San Francisco, CA, 94110-5612. Tel: 415-355-2810. Fax: 415-642-9951. p. 246

Good, Ellen, Youth Serv, Camas Public Library, 625 NE Fourth Ave, Camas, WA, 98607. Tel: 360-834-4692. Fax: 360-834-0199. p. 2511

Good, Janet, Br Mgr, Summit County Library, North Branch, PO Box 1248, Silverthorne, CO, 80498-1248. Tel: 970-468-5887. Fax: 970-513-0854. p. 309

Good, Larisa, Libr Dir, Warren County Public Library District, 62 Public Sq, Monmouth, IL, 61462. Tel: 309-734-3166. Fax: 309-734-5955. p. 675

Good, Leslie, Br Mgr, Douglas County Libraries, Philip S Miller Library, 100 S Wilcox St, Castle Rock, CO, 80104-2726. Tel: 303-791-7323. Fax: 303-688-7615. p. 294

Good, Leslie, Circ, Douglas County Libraries, Roxborough, 8357 N Rampart Range Rd, Ste 200, Littleton, CO, 80125. Tel: 303-791-7323. p. 294

Good, Leslie, Mgr, Douglas County Libraries, Louviers Library, 7885 Louviers Blvd, Louviers, CO, 80131. Tel: 303-791-7323. Fax: 303-791-7323. p. 294

Good, Megan, Dir, Libr & Archives, Independence Seaport Museum Library, 211 S Columbus Blvd, Philadelphia, PA, 19106. Tel: 215-413-8640. p. 2111

Good, Patty, Circ Supvr, Interim Dir, Seymour Library, 161 East Ave, Brockport, NY, 14420-1987. Tel: 585-637-1050. Fax: 585-637-1051. p. 1585

Good, Sara, Coll Mgr, Bucks County Historical Society, 84 S Pine St, Doylestown, PA, 18901-4999. Tel: 215-345-0210, Ext 141. Fax: 215-230-0823. p. 2050

Goodale, Heidi, Mgr, Coll Develop, Norfolk County Public Library, 46 Colborne St S, Simcoe, ON, N3Y 4H3, CANADA. Tel: 519-426-3506. Fax: 519-426-0657. p. 2841

Goodale, Martha, Librn, Monroe Community Library, Eight Swan Lake Ave, Monroe, ME, 04951. Tel: 207-525-3515. Fax: 207-525-6602. p. 992

Goodart, Jennine, Head, ILL, Trinity International University, 2065 Half Day Rd, Deerfield, IL, 60015-1241. Tel: 847-317-4000. Fax: 847-317-4012. p. 635

Goodchild, Christine, Ref Librn, North Shore Community College Library, One Ferncroft Rd, Danvers, MA, 01923-4093. Tel: 978-739-5532. Fax: 978-739-5500. p. 1083

Goode, Beth R B, Ch, Stewart Free Library, Eight Levi Stewart Dr, Corinna, ME, 04928. Tel: 207-278-2454. Fax: 207-278-5200. p. 982

Goode, Deidre, Head, Ch, Great Neck Library, 159 Bayview Ave, Great Neck, NY, 11023-1938. Tel: 516-466-8055. Fax: 516-829-8297. p. 1630

Goode, Kathy, Asst Dir, Casey County Public Library, 238 Middleburg St, Liberty, KY, 42539. Tel: 606-787-9381. Fax: 606-787-7720. p. 922

Goodell, Barbara J, Dir, Wharton County Library, 1920 N Fulton, Wharton, TX, 77488. Tel: 979-532-8080. p. 2400

Goodell, Evelyn, Librn, Nakusp Public Library Association, 92 W Sixth Ave, Nakusp, BC, V0G 1R0, CANADA. Tel: 250-265-3363. Fax: 250-265-3363. p. 2732

Goodell, Karen, Info & Instruction Librn, Palmer College of Chiropractic-Davenport Campus, 1000 Brady St, Davenport, IA, 52803-5287. Tel: 563-884-5725. Fax: 563-884-5897. p. 806

Goodemote, Jenny, Ref Librn, YA Librn, Wood Library Association of Canandaigua, 134 N Main St, Canandaigua, NY, 14424-1295. Tel: 585-394-1381. Fax: 585-394-2954. p. 1601

Gooden, Sandy, Libr Dir, Garrett Memorial Library, 123 S Main, Moulton, IA, 52572-1327. Tel: 641-642-3664. Fax: 641-642-3664. p. 833

Gooder, Carole, Librn, Christ Church Library, 527 Pomfret St, Pomfret, CT, 06258. Tel: 860-928-7026. Fax: 860-963-2684. p. 364

Gooder, Linda, Librn, Franklin Public Library, 1502 P St, Franklin, NE, 68939-1200. Tel: 308-425-3162. Fax: 308-425-3500. p. 1399

Goodfellow, Rebekah, Circ, Coll Mgt, ILL, J Sargeant Reynolds Community College Library, Downtown Campus-Library & Information Services, 700 E Jackson St, 2nd Flr, Richmond, VA, 23219-1543. Tel: 804-523-5211. Fax: 804-786-6200. p. 2488

Goodgion, Laurel, Dir, Wethersfield Public Library, 515 Silas Deane Hwy, Wethersfield, CT, 06109. Tel: 860-529-2665. Fax: 860-257-2822. p. 378

Goodhart, Ann, Chief Librn, West Vancouver Memorial Library, 1950 Marine Dr, West Vancouver, BC, V7V 1J8, CANADA. Tel: 604-925-7400. Fax: 604-925-5933. p. 2746

Goodhope, Jeanie, Media Spec, Everett Community College, 2000 Tower St, Everett, WA, 98201-1352. Tel: 425-388-9348. Fax: 425-388-9144. p. 2515

Goodhue, Kathryn, Dir of Libr, Chatham-Kent Public Library, 120 Queen St, Chatham, ON, N7M 2G6, CANADA. Tel: 519-354-2940. Fax: 519-354-7366. p. 2799

Goodier, Marin, Librn, Providence Medical Center Library, 8929 Parallel Pkwy, Kansas City, KS, 66112-0430. Tel: 913-596-3990. Fax: 913-596-4906. p. 875

Goodin, Cindy, Tech Serv, Pender County Public Library, 103 S Cowan St, Burgaw, NC, 28425. Tel: 910-259-1234. Fax: 910-259-0656. p. 1778

Goodin, Helen, Coll Develop Librn, Lake Agassiz Regional Library, 118 S Fifth St, Moorhead, MN, 56560-2756. Tel: 218-233-3757. Fax: 218-233-7556. p. 1265

Goodin, John, Tech Serv Librn, Luther College, 700 College Dr, Decorah, IA, 52101. Tel: 563-387-2124. Fax: 563-387-1657. p. 807

Goodine, Scott, Archivist, Archives of Manitoba, 130-200 Vaughan St, Winnipeg, MB, R3C 1T5, CANADA. Tel: 204-945-3971. Fax: 204-948-2008. p. 2754

Goodman, Brittney, Assoc VPres & Dean, Minnesota State University Moorhead, 1104 Seventh Ave S, Moorhead, MN, 56563. Tel: 218-477-2923. Fax: 218-477-5924. p. 1266

Goodman, Carol, Regional Mgr, Troutman Sanders LLP, 1001 Haxall Point, Richmond, VA, 23219. Tel: 804-697-1200. Fax: 804-697-1339. p. 2490

Goodman, Christopher Todd, Access Serv Librn, Covenant Theological Seminary, 12330 Conway Rd, Saint Louis, MO, 63141. Tel: 314-392-4103. Fax: 314-392-4116, 314-434-4819. p. 1354

Goodman, Cindy, Circ, Sullivan County Public Library, 100 S Crowder St, Sullivan, IN, 47882. Tel: 812-268-4957. Fax: 812-268-5370. p. 780

Goodman, Dexter, Head Librn, Plano Public Library System, Maribelle M Davis Library, 7501-B Independence Pkwy, Plano, TX, 75025. Tel: 972-208-8000. Fax: 972-208-8037. p. 2370

Goodman, Diane L, Librn, Blessed Edmund Rice School of Pastoral Ministry, 10299 SW Peace River St, Arcadia, FL, 34269. Tel: 941-766-7334, Ext 37. Fax: 941-629-8555. p. 425

Goodman, Eric B, Sr Mgr, Appraisal Institute, 200 W Madison, Ste 1500, Chicago, IL, 60606. Tel: 312-335-4467. Fax: 312-335-4486. p. 606

Goodman, Gloria, Br Mgr, Monroe County Public Library, George Dolezal - Marathon Branch, 3251 Overseas Hwy, Marathon, FL, 33050. Tel: 305-743-5156. Fax: 305-289-6093. p. 456

Goodman, Gwynn, Librn, Collier County Public Library, Marco Island Branch, 210 S Heathwood Dr, Marco Island, FL, 34145. Tel: 239-394-3272. Fax: 239-394-2383. p. 471

Goodman, Jane, Head, Ref, The University of Texas-Pan American Library, 1201 W University Dr, Edinburg, TX, 78541-2999. Tel: 956-665-3306. Fax: 956-665-5396. p. 2315

Goodman, Karen, Pres, Capital Area Health Consortium, 270 Farmington Ave, Ste 352, Farmington, CT, 06032-1994. Tel: 860-676-1110. Fax: 860-676-1303. p. 2939

Goodman, Maggie, Dir, Johnson City Library District, 209 Nugent St, Johnson City, TX, 78636. Tel: 830-868-4469. Fax: 830-868-4469. p. 2348

Goodman, Marla, Adult Serv, YA Serv, Indian River County Library System, 1600 21st St, Vero Beach, FL, 32960. Tel: 772-770-5060. Fax: 772-770-5066. p. 501

Goodman, Mary, Br Mgr, Portsmouth Public Library, Manor, 1401 Elmhurst Lane, Portsmouth, VA, 23701. Tel: 757-465-2916. p. 2485

Goodman, Roy, Asst Librn, Curator, American Philosophical Society Library, 105 S Fifth St, Philadelphia, PA, 19106-3386. Tel: 215-440-3408. Fax: 215-440-3423. p. 2102

Goodrich, Allan, Chief Archivist, National Archives & Records Administration, Columbia Point, Boston, MA, 02125. Tel: 617-514-1600. Fax: 617-514-1593. p. 1064

Goodrich, Jeanne, Exec Dir, Las Vegas-Clark County Library District, 7060 W Windmill Lane, Las Vegas, NV, 89113. Tel: 702-734-7323. p. 1429

Goodrich, Judith A, Dir, Logan County Libraries, 220 N Main St, Bellefontaine, OH, 43311-2228. Tel: 937-599-4189. Fax: 937-599-5503. p. 1859

Goodrich, Lana, Circ, Central College, Campus Box 6500, 812 University St, Pella, IA, 50219-1999. Tel: 641-628-5219. Fax: 641-628-5327. p. 838

Goodrich, Mona, ILL, Buckley Public Library, 408 Dewey Ave, Poteau, OK, 74953. Tel: 918-647-3833, 918-647-4444. Fax: 918-647-8910. p. 1976

Goodrich, Nadine O, Librn, Lakeside Public Library, 915 N Lake Rd, Lakeside, OR, 97449. Tel: 541-759-4432. Fax: 541-759-4752. p. 2003

Goodrich, Sean, Mgr, Buffalo & Erie County Public Library System, North Park, 975 Hertel Ave, Buffalo, NY, 14216. Tel: 716-875-3748. Fax: 716-875-3748. p. 1597

Goodridge, Kathleen Powers, Cat Librn, William J Campbell Library of the US Courts, 219 S Dearborn St, Rm 1637, Chicago, IL, 60604-1769. Tel: 312-435-5660. Fax: 312-408-5031. p. 607

Goodro, Brenda, Asst Librn, Lyman Public Library, 313 Jeffers St, Lyman, NE, 69352. Tel: 308-787-1366. Fax: 308-787-1366. p. 1407

Goodsell, Leo J, Dir, Historic Westville, Inc Library, 1850 Martin Luther King Jr Dr, Lumpkin, GA, 31815. Tel: 229-838-6310. Fax: 229-838-4000. p. 540

Goodson, Carol, Head, Access Serv, Irvine Sullivan Ingram Library, University of West Georgia, 1601 Maple St, Carrollton, GA, 30118. Tel: 678-839-6498. Fax: 678-839-6511. p. 523

Goodson, Jennifer, Dir, Fort Smith Public Library, 3201 Rogers Ave, Fort Smith, AR, 72903. Tel: 479-783-0229. Fax: 479-782-8571. p. 100

Goodson, Martha G, Spec Projects Librn, West Georgia Regional Library, 710 Rome St, Carrollton, GA, 30117. Tel: 770-836-6711. Fax: 770-836-4787. p. 523

Goodson, Pam, Br Mgr, Lake County Library System, Astor County Library, 54905 Alco Rd, Astor, FL, 32102. Tel: 352-759-9913. Fax: 352-759-9923. p. 500

Goodstein, Alex, Pub Serv, Tech Serv, Pocono Mountain Public Library, 5540 Memorial Blvd, Tobyhanna, PA, 18466. Tel: 570-894-8860. Fax: 570-894-8852. p. 2146

Goodvin, Renee, Bibliog Instr, Sul Ross State University, PO Box C-109, Alpine, TX, 79832-0001. Tel: 432-837-8123. Fax: 432-837-8400. p. 2273

Goodwater, Leanna, Librn, Santa Clara University, 500 El Camino Real, Santa Clara, CA, 95053-0500. Tel: 408-554-6830. Fax: 408-554-6827. p. 263

Goodwin, Barbara, Librn, Windsor Historical Society Library, 96 Palisado Ave, Windsor, CT, 06095. Tel: 860-688-3813. Fax: 860-687-1633. p. 379

Goodwin, Carol, Head, Tech Serv, Newport News Public Library System, 700 Town Center Dr, Ste 300, Newport News, VA, 23606. Tel: 757-926-1350. Fax: 757-926-1365. p. 2480

Goodwin, David, Circ Librn, Fordham University School of Law, 140 W 62nd St, New York, NY, 10023-7485. Tel: 212-636-6901. Fax: 212-930-8818. p. 1678

Goodwin, Debbie, Circ, Muskogee Public Library, 801 W Okmulgee, Muskogee, OK, 74401. Tel: 918-682-6657. Fax: 918-682-9466. p. 1969

Goodwin, Desiree, Librn, Carol R Johnson & Associates, Inc Library, 115 Broad St, Boston, MA, 02110-3032. Tel: 617-896-2653. Fax: 617-896-2340. p. 1062

Goodwin, Iris, Tech Serv Librn, Oregon Institute of Technology Library, 3201 Campus Dr, Klamath Falls, OR, 97601-8801. Tel: 541-885-1965. Fax: 541-885-1777. p. 2002

Goodwin, Jane, Dep Dir, Fairfax County Public Library, 12000 Government Center Pkwy, Ste 324, Fairfax, VA, 22035-0012. Tel: 703-324-3100. Fax: 703-324-8365. p. 2461

Goodwin, Joan, Head, Circ & Course Reserves, San Diego State University Library & Information Access, 5500 Campanile Dr, San Diego, CA, 92182-8050. Tel: 619-594-6759. Fax: 619-594-3270. p. 237

Goodwin, John, AV, North Central Missouri College Library, Geyer Hall, Rm 103, 1301 Main St, Trenton, MO, 64683. Tel: 660-359-3948, Ext 1322, 660-359-3948, Ext 1325, 660-359-3948, Ext 1335, 660-359-3948, Ext 322. Fax: 660-359-2211. p. 1369

Goodwin, Kathie, Acq, Supvr, University of New Hampshire School of Law, Two White St, Concord, NH, 03301. Tel: 603-228-1541, Ext 1130. Fax: 603-228-0388. p. 1443

Goodwin, Kathy, Coll Mgt Serv, Coastal Carolina University, 755 Hwy 544, Conway, SC, 29526. Tel: 843-349-2402. Fax: 843-349-2412. p. 2191

Goodwin, Lynne, Circ Supvr, John Curtis Free Library, 534 Hanover St, Hanover, MA, 02339-2228. Tel: 781-826-2972. Fax: 781-826-3130. p. 1093

Goodwin, Maida, Outreach Coordr, Smith College Libraries, Sophia Smith Collection, Seven Neilson Dr, Northampton, MA, 01063. Tel: 413-585-2996. Fax: 413-585-2886. p. 1114

Goodwin, Mary Ann, Dean of Instruction, Libr & Distance Learning Serv, Spokane Falls Community College, 3410 Ft George Wright Dr, MS 3020, Spokane, WA, 99224-5288. Tel: 509-537-3820. Fax: 509-533-3820. p. 2537

Goodwin, Maureen, Info Spec, Pfizer Canada, Inc, 17300 Trans-Canada Hwy, Pointe-Claire, QC, H9J 2M5, CANADA. Tel: 514-426-7060. Fax: 514-426-7558. p. 2903

Goodwin, Nancy, Dir, Middlesex Hospital, 28 Crescent St, Middletown, CT, 06457-7005. Tel: 860-358-6286. Fax: 860-358-6115. p. 352

Goodwin, Richard E, Dir, Guernsey County District Public Library, 800 Steubenville Ave, Cambridge, OH, 43725-2385. Tel: 740-432-5946. Fax: 740-432-7142. p. 1863

Goodwin, Robert, Dir, Guernsey County District Public Library, Byesville Branch, 100 Glass Ave, Byesville, OH, 43723. Tel: 740-685-2236. Fax: 740-685-6105. p. 1863

Goodwin, Sandi, Dir, Valley Falls Free Library, 42 State St, Valley Falls, NY, 12185. Tel: 518-753-4230. Fax: 518-753-4230. p. 1760

Goodwin, Susan, Ch, Merrick Library, 2279 Merrick Ave, Merrick, NY, 11566-4398. Tel: 516-377-6112. Fax: 516-377-1108. p. 1659

Goodwin, Susan, User Serv & Learning & Outreach, Texas A&M University Libraries, 5000 TAMU, College Station, TX, 77843-5000. Tel: 979-458-0114. Fax: 979-845-6238. p. 2299

Goodwyn, Donna, Head, Ref, Elmhurst College, 190 Prospect St, Elmhurst, IL, 60126. Tel: 630-617-3171. Fax: 630-617-3332. p. 642

Goody, Kevin, YA Serv, Thomas Memorial Library, Six Scott Dyer Rd, Cape Elizabeth, ME, 04107. Tel: 207-799-1720. p. 980

Goodyear, Dennis, Tech Serv, Avila University, 11901 Wornall Rd, Kansas City, MO, 64145. Tel: 816-501-3710. Fax: 816-501-2456. p. 1336

Goolsby, Mary, Project & Events Coordr, Baylor University Libraries, W R Poage Legislative Library, Baylor Collections of Political Materials, 201 Baylor Ave, Waco, TX, 76706. Tel: 254-710-6735. Fax: 254-710-3059. p. 2396

Goolsby, Teresa, Libr Dir, Chickasaw Public Library, 224 Grant St, Chickasaw, AL, 36611. Tel: 251-452-6465. Fax: 251-452-6465. p. 12

Goon, Rachel, Librn, Tacoma Community College Library, 6501 S 19th St, Tacoma, WA, 98466-6100. Tel: 253-566-5204. Fax: 253-566-5398. p. 2540

Goonis, Kimberly, Supvr, User Serv, Seminole Community Library, 9200 113th St N, Seminole, FL, 33772. Tel: 727-394-6905. Fax: 727-398-3113. p. 491

Goonis, Patty, YA Serv, Livonia Public Library, Carl Sandburg Branch, 30100 W Seven Mile Rd, Livonia, MI, 48152-1918. Tel: 248-893-4010. Fax: 248-476-6230. p. 1204

Goontz, Donna, Co-Dir, Pine Grove Public Library, Main St, Pine Grove, WV, 26419. Tel: 304-889-3288. Fax: 304-889-3288. p. 2569

Goorahoo, Susan, Cent Info Serv & Ext Serv Supvr, Fresno County Public Library, 2420 Mariposa St, Fresno, CA, 93721-2285. Tel: 559-600-7323. p. 151

Gora, Jean C, Mgr, Res, LOMA, 2300 Windy Ridge Pkwy, Ste 600, Atlanta, GA, 30339. Tel: 770-984-3722. Fax: 770-984-6422. p. 516

Goral, Miki, Ref, University of California Los Angeles Library, College Library, Powell Library Bldg, Los Angeles, CA, 90095. Tel: 310-825-5756. Fax: 310-206-9312. p. 178

Goran, Joyce, Librn, Bibliotheque Dentinger, Central Ave SE, No 027, Falher, AB, T0H 1M0, CANADA. Tel: 780-837-2776. Fax: 780-837-8755. p. 2704

Gorda, Ronald, Librn, Cranford Free Public Library, 224 Walnut Ave, Cranford, NJ, 07016-2931. Tel: 908-709-7272. Fax: 908-709-1658. p. 1480

Gorden, Bette, Curator, Saint Louis Mercantile Library at the University of Missouri-St Louis, Thomas Jefferson Library Bldg, One University Blvd, Saint Louis, MO, 63121-4400. Tel: 314-516-7244. Fax: 314-516-7241. p. 1359

Gorder, Erika, Assoc Univ Archivist, Rutgers University Libraries, Special Collections & University Archives, 169 College Ave, New Brunswick, NJ, 08901-1163. Tel: 848-932-6150. Fax: 732-932-7012. p. 1509

Gordinier, Patricia, Ref, Butt-Holdsworth Memorial Library, 505 Water St, Kerrville, TX, 78028. Tel: 830-257-8422. Fax: 830-792-5552. p. 2349

Gordon, Andrea, Dir, Serv Develop, Burlington Public Library, 2331 New St, Burlington, ON, L7R 1J4, CANADA. Tel: 905-639-3611. Fax: 905-681-7277. p. 2797

Gordon, Beth, Doc, Yeshiva University Libraries, Dr Lillian & Dr Rebecca Chutick Law Library, Benjamin N Cardozo School of Law, 55 Fifth Ave, New York, NY, 10003-4301. Tel: 212-790-0223. Fax: 212-790-0236. p. 1703

Gordon, Carol, Ref & Instrul Serv Librn, Southern Illinois University School of Medicine Library, 801 N Rutledge, Springfield, IL, 62702. Tel: 217-545-2658. Fax: 217-545-0988. p. 706

Gordon, Carol, Assoc Prof, Rutgers, The State University of New Jersey, Four Huntington St, New Brunswick, NJ, 08901-1071. Tel: 732-932-7500, Ext 8955. Fax: 732-932-2644. p. 2969

Gordon, Cynthia, Br Mgr, Allendale-Hampton-Jasper Regional Library, Estill Branch, 276 Third Ave, Estill, SC, 29918-4827. Tel: 803-625-4560. Fax: 803-625-3341. p. 2180

Gordon, Denise, Br Head, Toronto Public Library, Don Mills, 888 Lawrence Ave E, Toronto, ON, M3C 1P6, CANADA. Tel: 416-395-5710. Fax: 416-395-5715. p. 2861

Gordon, Dwain, Dep Dir, Libr Develop & Serv, Arkansas State Library, 900 W Capitol, Ste 100, Little Rock, AR, 72201-3108. Tel: 501-682-2863. Fax: 501-682-1529. p. 105

Gordon, Erin, Info Tech, Hollins University, 7950 E Campus Dr, Roanoke, VA, 24020-1000. Tel: 540-362-6653. Fax: 540-362-6756. p. 2493

Gordon, Frances, Dir, Larkspur Public Library, 400 Magnolia Ave, Larkspur, CA, 94939. Tel: 415-927-5005. Fax: 415-927-5136. p. 163

Gordon, Gayle, Dir, Commerce Public Library, 1210 Park St, Commerce, TX, 75428. Tel: 903-886-6858. Fax: 903-886-7239. p. 2300

Gordon, Gerald, Coll Develop Librn, Radford University, 801 E Main St, Radford, VA, 24142-0001. Tel: 540-831-6140. Fax: 540-831-6138. p. 2487

Gordon, Helen, Librn, Central Presbyterian Church Library, 3501 Campbell St, Kansas City, MO, 64109. Tel: 816-931-2515. Fax: 816-931-0882. p. 1337

Gordon, Ian, Head, Circ Serv, Brock University, 500 Glenridge Ave, St. Catharines, ON, L2S 3A1, CANADA. Tel: 905-688-5550, Ext 3727. Fax: 905-988-5490. p. 2842

Gordon, Jeff, Librn, National Security Technologies, 755 C East Flamingo, Las Vegas, NV, 89119. Tel: 702-794-5117, 702-794-5121. Fax: 702-794-5198. p. 1430

Gordon, Jill, Librn, Saint Louis Zoo Library, One Government Dr, Saint Louis, MO, 63110. Tel: 314-781-0900, Ext 4554. Fax: 314-646-5535. p. 1361

Gordon, Joan, Asst Admin, Andrew Jergens Co, 2535 Spring Grove Ave, Cincinnati, OH, 45214. Tel: 513-421-1400, 513-455-5362. Fax: 513-455-5363. p. 1870

Gordon, Karen, Dir, The Whitehall Free Library, 12 William St, Whitehall, NY, 12887. Tel: 518-499-1366. Fax: 518-499-1366. p. 1769

Gordon, Kate, Head, Admin Budget, University of Alaska Anchorage, Consortium Library, 3211 Providence Dr, Anchorage, AK, 99508-8176. Tel: 907-786-1903. Fax: 907-786-1834. p. 45

Gordon, Kathleen, Youth Serv Librn, Derby Neck Library, 307 Hawthorne Ave, Derby, CT, 06418-1199. Tel: 203-734-1492. Fax: 203-732-2913. p. 336

Gordon, Kathy, Libr Tech, Berkshire Medical Center, 725 North St, Pittsfield, MA, 01201. Tel: 413-447-2734. p. 1117

Gordon, Keisha, Libr Assoc, Anadarko Community Library, 215 W Broadway, Anadarko, OK, 73005-2841. Tel: 405-247-7351. Fax: 405-247-2024. p. 1956

Gordon, Larissa, Br Librn, Ref & Instrul Serv Librn, Wilmington University Library, 320 DuPont Hwy, New Castle, DE, 19720. Tel: 302-328-9401. Fax: 302-328-0914. p. 385

Gordon, Larissa, Ref Librn, Arcadia University, 450 S Easton Rd, Glenside, PA, 19038-3295. Tel: 215-572-2136. Fax: 215-572-0240. p. 2061

Gordon, Linda, Circ, Athens-Limestone Public Library, 405 E South St, Athens, AL, 35611. Tel: 256-232-1233. Fax: 256-232-1250. p. 5

Gordon, Linda, Prof, Res & Instruction Librn, University of La Verne, 2040 Third St, La Verne, CA, 91750. Tel: 909-593-3511, Ext 4305. Fax: 909-392-2733. p. 162

Gordon, Lois, Outreach Serv Librn, Mohawk Valley Library System, 858 Duanesburg Rd, Schenectady, NY, 12306-1057. Tel: 518-355-2010. Fax: 518-355-0674. p. 1740

Gordon, Lorelee, Chief Librn/CEO, Bruce Mines
& Plummer Additional Union Public Library,
33 Desbarats St, Bruce Mines, ON, P0R
1C0, CANADA. Tel: 705-785-3370. Fax:
705-785-3370. p. 2797

Gordon, Madelaine A, Principal Librn, Ohio
Attorney General, 30 E Broad St, 15th Flr,
Columbus, OH, 43215. Tel: 614-466-2465,
614-466-4534. Fax: 614-752-9867. p. 1886

Gordon, Martin, Acq, Franklin & Marshall College,
450 College Ave, Lancaster, PA, 17603-3318.
Tel: 717-291-3842. Fax: 717-291-4160. p. 2076

Gordon, Mary Pat, Librn, FHN Memorial Hospital,
1045 W Stephenson St, Freeport, IL, 61032. Tel:
815-599-6132. Fax: 815-599-6858. p. 647

Gordon, Maurice, Librn, Boston Public Library,
Mattapan, Ten Hazelton St, Dorchester,
MA, 02126-3198. Tel: 617-298-9218. Fax:
617-298-7590. p. 1057

Gordon, Nancie Anne, Circ, Buckley Public
Library, 408 Dewey Ave, Poteau, OK, 74953.
Tel: 918-647-3833, 918-647-4444. Fax:
918-647-8910. p. 1976

Gordon, Nilufar, Mrs, Librn, Association for Baha'i
Studies, 34 Copernicus St, Ottawa, ON, K1N
7K4, CANADA. Tel: 613-233-1903, Ext 106.
Fax: 613-233-3644. p. 2828

Gordon, Peg, Cat, Allentown Public Library, 1210
Hamilton St, Allentown, PA, 18102. Tel:
610-820-2400. Fax: 610-820-0640. p. 2026

Gordon, Rabbi Israel, Adminr, Rabbinical College
of America, 226 Sussex Ave, Morristown,
NJ, 07960-3600. Tel: 973-267-9404. Fax:
973-267-5208. p. 1505

Gordon, Robert W, Dr, Dir, Libr & Res Serv,
Siena Heights University Library, 1247 E Siena
Heights Dr, Adrian, MI, 49221-1796. Tel:
517-264-7152. Fax: 517-264-7711. p. 1147

Gordon, Rosemary, Asst Dir, Libr Serv, Southern
College of Optometry Library, 1245 Madison
Ave, Memphis, TN, 38104. Tel: 901-722-3239.
Fax: 901-722-3292. p. 2251

Gordon, Sandra, Youth Serv, North Miami Beach
Public Library, 1601 NE 164th St, North Miami
Beach, FL, 33162-4099. Tel: 305-948-2970. Fax:
305-787-6007. p. 473

Gordon, Sarah, In Charge, Wright & Talisman,
1200 G St NW, Ste 600, Washington,
DC, 20005-3802. Tel: 202-393-1200. Fax:
202-393-1240. p. 423

Gordon, Sharon, Dir, National Watch & Clock
Museum, 514 Poplar St, Columbia, PA,
17512-2124. Tel: 717-684-8261, Ext 224. Fax:
717-684-0142. p. 2046

Gordon, Shirley, Librn, Calhoun County Library,
Port O'Connor Branch, Hwy 185 & Sixth St,
Port O'Connor, TX, 77982. Tel: 361-983-4365.
Fax: 316-983-4365. p. 2372

Gordon, Terry, Assoc Dir, Emory University School
of Law, 1301 Clifton Rd, Atlanta, GA, 30322.
Tel: 404-727-6950. Fax: 404-727-2202. p. 514

Gordon, Theresa, Info Spec, United States
Department of Transportation, National Highway
Traffic Safety Administration-Technical
Information Services, NPO-400, 1200 New
Jersey Ave SE, Washington, DC, 20590. Fax:
202-493-2833. p. 420

Gordon, Tom, Pub Serv, Forsyth Technical
Community College Library, 2100 Silas
Creek Pkwy, Winston-Salem, NC, 27103. Tel:
336-734-7219. Fax: 336-761-2465. p. 1833

Gordon, Valerie, Cat, University of Alabama at
Birmingham, Lister Hill Library of the Health
Sciences, 1700 University Blvd, Birmingham,
AL, 35294-0013. Tel: 205-934-5460. Fax:
205-934-3545. p. 10

Gordon, Virginia, ILL, United States Army, US
Army Logistics University, Bldg 12420, 562
Quarters Rd, Fort Lee, VA, 23801-1705. Tel:
804-765-4722. Fax: 804-765-4660. p. 2465

Gordon, Wendy, Ref Serv, Saddleback College,
28000 Marguerite Pkwy, Mission Viejo, CA,
92692. Tel: 949-582-4932. Fax: 949-364-0284.
p. 187

Gordon, Willie H, Head, Pub Serv, North Georgia
College & State University, 238 Georgia Circle,
Dahlonega, GA, 30597-3001. p. 527

Gore, Emily, Assoc Dean, Digital Scholarship &
Tech Serv, Florida State University Libraries,
Strozier Library Bldg, 116 Honors Way,
Tallahassee, FL, 32306-0001. Tel: 850-644-2706.
p. 494

Gore, Pamela, Acq, Gordon-Conwell Theological
Seminary, 130 Essex St, South Hamilton,
MA, 01982-2317. Tel: 978-646-4078. Fax:
978-646-4567. p. 1125

Gore, Robert, Visual Arts Librn, University
of California Los Angeles Library, The
Arts Library, 1400 Public Policy Bldg, Los
Angeles, CA, 90095. Tel: 310-206-5426. Fax:
310-825-1303. p. 178

Gore, Sally A, Pres, Massachusetts Health Sciences
Libraries Network, Lamar soutter Library,
UMass Medical School, 55 Lake Ave, n,
worcester, MA, 01655. Tel: 508-856-1966.
p. 2945

Gore, Sonny, Librn, Centralia Community Library,
520 Fourth St, Centralia, KS, 66415. Tel:
785-857-3331. p. 860

Gore, Thomas, Tech Serv Librn, Greenville
Technical College Library, 620 S Pleasantburg
Dr, Greenville, SC, 29607. Tel: 864-250-8320.
Fax: 864-250-8506. p. 2197

Gores, Julie, Dir, Madison Area Technical College,
3550 Anderson St, Rm 230, Madison, WI,
53704. Tel: 608-246-6633. Fax: 608-246-6644.
p. 2606

Gores, Valerie, Br Mgr, Newark Public Library, Van
Buren, 140 Van Buren St, Newark, NJ, 07105.
Tel: 973-733-7750. Fax: 973-733-3897. p. 1512

Gorgas, Alice, Librn, Riverview Public Library,
14300 Sibley Rd, Riverview, MI, 48193. Tel:
734-283-1250. Fax: 734-283-6843. p. 1221

Gorham, Lucas, Ref Librn, Galesburg Public Library,
40 E Simmons St, Galesburg, IL, 61401-4591.
Tel: 309-343-6118. Fax: 309-343-4877. p. 648

Gorjevsky, Jane, Curator, Carnegie Archives,
Columbia University, Rare Book & Manuscript,
Butler Library, 6th Flr E, 535 W 114th St,
New York, NY, 10027. Tel: 212-854-8937. Fax:
212-854-1365. p. 1675

Gorka, Gary, Dir, Dominican University of
California, 50 Acacia Ave, San Rafael,
CA, 94901-2298. Tel: 415-485-3251. Fax:
415-459-2309. p. 256

Gorman, Art, Librn, Blackburn Correctional
Complex Library, 3111 Spurn Rd, Lexington,
KY, 40511. Tel: 859-246-2366. Fax:
859-246-2376. p. 920

Gorman, Bruce, Dep Exec Dir, Halifax Public
Libraries, 60 Alderney Dr, Dartmouth, NS,
B2Y 4P8, CANADA. Tel: 902-490-5744. Fax:
902-490-5762. p. 2779

Gorman, Daria, Cat, University of Medicine &
Dentistry of New Jersey, 30 12th Ave, Newark,
NJ, 07103-2706. Tel: 973-972-4580. p. 1513

Gorman, Jacque, YA Librn, Milford Town
Library, 80 Spruce St, Milford, MA, 01757.
Tel: 508-473-0651, 508-473-2145. Fax:
508-473-8651. p. 1105

Gorman, Joanne, Head, Ref, Middletown Public
Library, 700 W Main Rd, Middletown,
RI, 02842-6391. Tel: 401-846-1573. Fax:
401-846-3031. p. 2168

Gorman, Keith, Dr, Interim Head, Spec Coll
& Archives, University of North Carolina
at Greensboro, 320 Spring Garden St,
Greensboro, NC, 27402. Tel: 336-334-5880. Fax:
336-334-5399. p. 1798

Gorman, Linda, Ref Serv, Nassau Community
College, One Education Dr, Garden City,
NY, 11530-6793. Tel: 516-572-7400. Fax:
516-572-7846. p. 1626

Gorman, Maeleah, Asst Mgr, Springfield City
Library, East Forest Park Branch, 122-124
Island Pond Rd, Springfield, MA, 01118. Tel:
413-263-6836. Fax: 413-263-6838. p. 1127

Gorman, Maeleah, Asst Mgr, Springfield City
Library, Forest Park Branch, 380 Belmont Ave,
Springfield, MA, 01108. Tel: 413-263-6843.
Fax: 413-263-6845. p. 1127

Gorman, Maeleah, Asst Mgr, Springfield City
Library, Mason Square Branch, 765 State St,
Springfield, MA, 01109. Tel: 413-263-6853.
Fax: 413-263-6854. p. 1127

Gorman, Maureen, Asst Dir, Pub Serv, The College
of New Jersey Library, 2000 Pennington Rd,
Ewing, NJ, 08628-0718. Tel: 609-771-2311,
609-771-2332. Fax: 609-637-5177. p. 1484

Gorman, Peggy, Ch, Plainedge Public Library, 1060
Hicksville Rd, Massapequa, NY, 11758. Tel:
516-735-4133. Fax: 516-735-4192. p. 1658

Gorman, Robert M, Head, Ref, Winthrop University,
824 Oakland Ave, Rock Hill, SC, 29733. Tel:
803-323-2259. Fax: 803-323-2215. p. 2203

Gorman, Ruth, Coordr, Outreach Serv, London
Public Library, 20 E First St, London, OH,
43140. Tel: 740-852-9543. Fax: 740-852-3691.
p. 1911

Gormican, Mary Ellen, Dir, Marian University,
45 S National Ave, Fond du Lac, WI, 54935.
Tel: 920-923-7641, 920-923-8725. Fax:
920-923-7154. p. 2592

Gormley, Alice, Head, Ser, Marquette University
Libraries, 1355 W Wisconsin Ave, Milwaukee,
WI, 53233. Tel: 414-288-7252. Fax:
414-288-8740. p. 2618

Gormley, John, ILL, Manhattan College, 4513
Manhattan College Pkwy, Riverdale, NY, 10471.
Tel: 718-862-7166. Fax: 718-862-8028. p. 1728

Gormley, Maureen, Head, Ref, Dakota County
Library System, 1340 Wescott Rd, Eagan,
MN, 55123-1099. Tel: 651-450-2938. Fax:
651-450-2915. p. 1249

Gormley, Pam, Dir, Skidompha Public Library, 184
Main St, Damariscotta, ME, 04543-4670. Tel:
207-563-5513. Fax: 207-563-1941. p. 983

Gorney, Robert, Librn, Genesee District Library,
Baker Park, G-3410 S Grand Traverse,
Burton, MI, 48529. Tel: 810-742-7860. Fax:
810-742-2927. p. 1179

Gorrell, L Renee, Dir, Libr & Info Serv, Goldfarb
School of Nursing at Barnes-Jewish College,
MS:90-30-697, 4483 Duncan Ave, Saint
Louis, MO, 63110. Tel: 314-454-8171. Fax:
314-454-1690. p. 1355

Gorshe, Phyllis, Dir, Dunedin Public Library,
223 Douglas Ave, Dunedin, FL, 34698. Tel:
727-298-3080, Ext 226. Fax: 727-298-3088.
p. 438

Gorski, Holly, Human Res Dir, Pierce County
Library System, 3005 112th St E, Tacoma,
WA, 98446-2215. Tel: 253-548-3354. Fax:
253-537-4600. p. 2539

Gorski, Stanley, Coll Develop Coordr, Spec Coll
Librn, Philadelphia University, 4201 Henry
Ave, Philadelphia, PA, 19144-5497. Tel:
215-951-2581. Fax: 215-951-2574. p. 2115

Gorsline, Dayle, Mrs, Acq, Electronic Res,
Libr Tech, The Parrott Centre, 376
Wallbridge-Loyalist Rd, Belleville, ON, K8N
5B9, CANADA. Tel: 613-969-1913, Ext 2339.
Fax: 613-969-5183. p. 2795

Gorst, Semra, Circ, ILL, Page Public Library, 479
S Lake Powell Blvd, Page, AZ, 86040. Tel:
928-645-4131. Fax: 928-645-5804. p. 70

Gorsuch, Christopher, Coll Mgt Mgr, LeRoy Collins
Leon County Public Library System, 200 W
Park Ave, Tallahassee, FL, 32301-7720. Tel:
850-606-2665. Fax: 850-606-2607. p. 492

Gort, Dale D, Info Tech Spec, Mead Public
Library, 710 N Eighth St, Sheboygan, WI,
53081-4563. Tel: 920-459-3400, Ext 3415. Fax:
920-459-0204. p. 2637

Gortze, Nora, Librn, Yolo County Library, Knights
Landing Branch, 42351 Third St, Knights
Landing, CA, 95645. Tel: 530-735-6593. Fax:
530-735-6593. p. 285

Gortze, Nora, Librn, Yolo County Library, Yolo
Branch, 37750 Sacramento St, Yolo, CA, 95697.
Tel: 530-662-2363. Fax: 530-662-2363. p. 285

Gorup, J, Circ, South Seattle Community College, 6000 16th Ave SW, Seattle, WA, 98106-1499. Tel: 206-768-6404. Fax: 206-763-5155. p. 2532

Gorvine, Natalie, Asst Librn, Children's Hospital of Philadelphia, 34th & Civic Center Blvd, Philadelphia, PA, 19104. Tel: 215-590-2317. Fax: 215-590-1470. p. 2104

Gorzalski, Pam, Ref, Cat & Med Librn, Milwaukee School of Engineering, 500 E Kilbourn Ave, Milwaukee, WI, 53202. Tel: 414-277-7141. Fax: 414-277-7186. p. 2620

Gorzelsky, Stefanie, Syst & Emerging Tech Librn, Centre County Library & Historical Museum, 200 N Allegheny St, Bellefonte, PA, 16823-1601. Tel: 814-355-1516. Fax: 814-355-2700. p. 2032

Gosbee, Robin B, Librn, Denmark Public Library, 121 E Main St, Denmark, ME, 04022. Tel: 207-452-2200. p. 983

Gosdeck, David M, Dir, Martin Luther College Library, 1995 Luther Ct, New Ulm, MN, 56073-3965. Tel: 507-354-8221, Ext 296. Fax: 507-233-9107. p. 1268

Gosh, Kim, Librn, Baker College of Flint, 1050 W Bristol Rd, Flint, MI, 48507-5508. Tel: 810-766-2016. Fax: 810-766-2013. p. 1179

Goshulak, Ted, Univ Librn, Trinity Western University, 7600 Glover Rd, Langley, BC, V2Y 1Y1, CANADA. Tel: 604-513-2121, Ext 3905. Fax: 604-513-2063. p. 2731

Goslen, Alan, Ref & Instruction Librn, Cleveland State Community College Library, 3535 Adkisson Dr, Cleveland, TN, 37312-2813. Tel: 423-478-6209. Fax: 423-478-6255. p. 2229

Gosnell, Joan, Archivist, Southern Methodist University, DeGolyer Library of Special Collections, 6404 Robert S Hyer Lane, Dallas, TX, 75275. Tel: 214-768-2261. Fax: 214-768-1565. p. 2310

Gosnell, Linda, Supv Librn, Pamunkey Regional Library, 7527 Library Dr, Hanover, VA, 23069. Tel: 804-537-6211. Fax: 804-537-6389. p. 2469

Goss, Barbara, Youth Spec, Greenwood-Leflore Public Library System, 405 W Washington St, Greenwood, MS, 38930-4297. Tel: 662-453-3634. Fax: 662-453-0683. p. 1299

Goss, Fred, Dir, Greensboro Historical Museum Archives Library, 130 Summit Ave, Greensboro, NC, 27401-3004. Tel: 336-373-2306. Fax: 336-373-2204. p. 1796

Goss, Irena, Ch, John C Hart Memorial Library, 1130 Main St, Shrub Oak, NY, 10588. Tel: 914-245-5262. Fax: 914-245-2216. p. 1743

Goss, Laura, Asst Dir, Adams County Library System, 140 Baltimore St, Gettysburg, PA, 17325-2311. Tel: 717-334-5716. Fax: 717-334-7992. p. 2059

Goss, Renee, Librn, Northeast Alabama Community College, 138 Alabama Hwy 35, Rainsville, AL, 35986. Tel: 256-228-6001, Ext 329. Fax: 256-228-4350. p. 34

Goss, Renee, Dir, Sidney Public Library, 121 Third Ave NW, Sidney, MT, 59270-4025. Tel: 406-433-1917. Fax: 406-433-4642. p. 1388

Goss, Tina, Dir, Westside Public Library, 5151 Walnut Grove Rd, Walnut Grove, AL, 35990. Tel: 205-589-6699. Fax: 205-589-6699. p. 40

Gossage, Peggy, Ch, George Hail Free Library, 530 Main St, Warren, RI, 02885. Tel: 401-245-7686. Fax: 401-245-7470. p. 2177

Gossage, Peggy H, Regional Librn, William Carey University Libraries, Tradition Library, 19640 Hwy 67, Biloxi, MS, 39532-8666. Tel: 228-702-1890. p. 1301

Gossard, Becky, Asst Dir, Carnegie Public Library, 120 Jefferson St, Monte Vista, CO, 81144-1797. Tel: 719-852-3931. Fax: 719-852-0821. p. 318

Gosse, Mike, In Charge, National Park Service, RR 3, Box 200, American Fork, UT, 84003-9803. Tel: 801-756-5239. Fax: 801-756-5661. p. 2403

Gossett, J Gabriel, Extended Educ Librn, Western Washington University, 516 High St, MS 9103, Bellingham, WA, 98225. Tel: 360-650-7555. Fax: 360-650-3044. p. 2509

Gossett, Reginald, Head, Libr Syst, Stephen F Austin State University, 1936 North St, Nacogdoches, TX, 75962. Tel: 936-468-1488. Fax: 936-468-7610. p. 2364

Gossin, Anna, Librn, Jewish Community Center of Greater Rochester, 1200 Edgewood Ave, Rochester, NY, 14618-5408. Tel: 585-461-2000, Ext 607. Fax: 585-461-0805. p. 1730

Gossin, Anna, Librn, Jewish Community Center of Greater Rochester, Israel Emiot Memorial Yiddish Library, 1200 Edgewood Ave, Rochester, NY, 14618-5408. Tel: 585-461-2000, Ext 607. Fax: 585-461-0805. p. 1730

Gost, Karyn, Teen Serv, Belleville Public Library & Information Center, 221 Washington Ave, Belleville, NJ, 07109-3189. Tel: 973-450-3434. Fax: 973-450-9518, 973-759-6731. p. 1471

Goswami, Sukrit, Dir, Saugerties Public Library, 91 Washington Ave, Saugerties, NY, 12477. Tel: 845-246-4317. Fax: 845-246-0858. p. 1739

Gotch, Julie, Dir, Libr Syst & Tech Serv, Davenport University, 6191 Kraft Ave SE, Grand Rapids, MI, 49512. Tel: 616-554-5612. Fax: 616-554-5226. p. 1184

Gotchall, Sarah, Electronic Res, University of Arizona, James E Rogers College of Law Library, PO Box 210176, Tucson, AZ, 85721-0176. Tel: 520-621-1413. Fax: 520-621-3138. p. 89

Goto, David, Ref Librn, Chapman University, One University Dr, Orange, CA, 92866-1099. Tel: 714-532-7756. Fax: 714-532-7743. p. 200

Gotsch, Joyce, Outreach & Promotion, Dowling College Library, 150 Idle Hour Blvd, Oakdale, NY, 11769-1999. Tel: 631-244-3150. Fax: 631-244-3374. p. 1709

Gotsch, Melissa, Mgr, Baltimore County Public Library, Catonsville, 1100 Frederick Rd, Baltimore, MD, 21228-5092. Tel: 410-887-0951. Fax: 410-788-8166. p. 1044

Gotte, Thomas, Asst Commun Relations Coordr, Iberia Parish Library, 445 E Main St, New Iberia, LA, 70560-3710. Tel: 337-364-7024, 337-364-7074. Fax: 337-364-7042. p. 959

Gottfried, Erika, Curator, New York University, Tamiment Library/Robert F Wagner Labor Archives, Elmer Holmes Bobst Library, 70 Washington Sq S, 10th Flr, New York, NY, 10012. Tel: 212-998-2630. p. 1695

Gottfried, John, Bus Librn, Western Kentucky University Libraries, Helm-Cravens Library Complex, 1906 College Heights Blvd, No 11067, Bowling Green, KY, 42101-1067. Tel: 270-745-6176. Fax: 270-745-6422. p. 907

Gottfried, Patricia, Head, Teen Serv, Haverstraw Kings Daughters Public Library, Village Library, 85 Main St, Haverstraw, NY, 10927. Tel: 845-429-3445. Fax: 845-429-7313. p. 1627

Gottlieb, Dan, Assoc Dean, Coll & Tech Serv, University of Cincinnati Libraries, PO Box 210033, Cincinnati, OH, 45221-0033. Tel: 513-556-1464. Fax: 513-556-0325. p. 1874

Gottlieb, Jane, VPres, Libr & Info Serv, Juilliard School, 60 Lincoln Center Plaza, New York, NY, 10023-6588. Tel: 212-799-5000, Ext 265. Fax: 212-769-6421. p. 1684

Gottlieb, Peter, Dir, Wisconsin Historical Society Library, 816 State St, Madison, WI, 53706. Tel: 608-264-6534. Fax: 608-264-6520. p. 2610

Gotto, Anthea, VPres, Cambridge Scientific Abstracts Library, 7200 Wisconsin Ave, Bethesda, MD, 20814. Tel: 301-961-6795. Fax: 301-961-6720. p. 1021

Gottsch, Cindy, Head, Ref, Northwestern Oklahoma State University, 709 Oklahoma Blvd, Alva, OK, 73717. Tel: 580-327-8572. Fax: 580-327-8501. p. 1956

Gottschalk, Alice R, Circ/Vols Serv, Camp Verde Community Library, 130 Black Bridge Loop Rd, Camp Verde, AZ, 86322. Tel: 928-567-3414. Fax: 928-567-9583. p. 59

Gottschalk, Paul, Bus Mgr, Evanston Public Library, 1703 Orrington, Evanston, IL, 60201. Tel: 847-448-8600, 847-866-0300. Fax: 847-866-0313. p. 643

Gottschall, Bruce, Syst Coordr, Kutztown University, 15200 Kutztown Rd, Bldg 5, Kutztown, PA, 19530-0735. Tel: 610-683-4484. Fax: 610-683-4747. p. 2075

Gottshall, Judith L, Librn, Veterans Affairs Central Iowa Health Care Systems-Knoxville Division, 1515 W Pleasant St, Knoxville, IA, 50138-3399. Tel: 641-828-5127. Fax: 641-828-5084. p. 826

Gotz, Jackie, Dir, East Troy Lions Public Library, 3094 Graydon Ave, East Troy, WI, 53120. Tel: 262-642-6262. p. 2589

Gouba, Marie, Libr Spec, Dartmouth College Library, Paddock Music Library, 6245 Hopkins Ctr, Hanover, NH, 03755. Tel: 603-646-3234. Fax: 603-646-1219. p. 1450

Goudeaux, Alice, Cent Ref Mgr, Timberland Regional Library, 415 Tumwater Blvd SW, Tumwater, WA, 98501-5799. Tel: 360-943-5001, Ext 2620. Fax: 360-586-6838. p. 2543

Goudie, Allen R, Chief Librn, United States Army, 4300 Camp Hale Rd, Fort Drum, NY, 13602-5284. Tel: 315-772-4502. Fax: 315-772-8529. p. 1623

Gouge, Linda B, Head Librn, Mitchell County Public Library, 18 N Mitchell Ave, Bakersville, NC, 28705. Tel: 828-688-2511. p. 1775

Gough, Barbara, Dir, Kemper-Newton Regional Library System, 101 Peachtree St, Union, MS, 39365-2617. Tel: 601-774-9297. Fax: 601-774-5096. p. 1316

Gough, Maggie, Dir, Elmont Public Library, 700 Hempstead Tpk, Elmont, NY, 11003-1896. Tel: 516-354-5280. Fax: 516-354-3276. p. 1620

Gough, Margaret Mary, Sister, Archivist, St Walburg Monastery Archives, 2500 Amsterdam Rd, Villa Hills, KY, 41017. Tel: 859-331-6324. Fax: 859-331-2136. p. 936

Gough, Sue, Librn, Tyndall Public Library, PO Box 26, Tyndall, SD, 57066-0026. Tel: 605-589-3266. p. 2220

Goughnour, Mary, ILL Tech, Citizens Library, 55 S College St, Washington, PA, 15301. Tel: 724-222-2400. Fax: 724-222-2606. p. 2151

Goulart, Juanita, Asst Dir, Millicent Library, 45 Centre St, Fairhaven, MA, 02719. Tel: 508-992-5342. Fax: 508-993-7288. p. 1087

Gould, Amy, Head, Tech Serv, Kewanee Public Library District, 102 S Tremont St, Kewanee, IL, 61443. Tel: 309-852-4505. Fax: 309-852-4466. p. 661

Gould, Beth, Librn, Enterprise Library, 60 Main St, Brockton, MA, 02303. Tel: 508-586-6200. Fax: 508-586-6506. p. 1071

Gould, Don, Commun Libr Mgr, County of Los Angeles Public Library, Manhattan Beach Library, 1320 Highland Ave, Manhattan Beach, CA, 90266-4789. Tel: 310-545-8595. Fax: 310-545-5394. p. 142

Gould, Gretchen, Bibliographer, Maps Librn, Ref Librn, University of Northern Iowa Library, 1227 W 27th St, Cedar Falls, IA, 50613-3675. Tel: 319-273-6327. Fax: 319-273-2913. p. 799

Gould, Katherine R, Dir, Palos Verdes Library District, 701 Silver Spur Rd, Rolling Hills Estates, CA, 90274. Tel: 310-377-9584, Ext 200. Fax: 310-541-6807. p. 219

Gould, Kim, Circ Coordr, Burlington County Library, Five Pioneer Blvd, Westampton, NJ, 08060. Tel: 609-267-9660, Ext 3037. Fax: 609-267-4091. p. 1542

Gould, Kristeen, Br Mgr, Indianapolis-Marion County Public Library, East Thirty-Eighth Street, 5420 E 38th St, Indianapolis, IN, 46218-1873. Tel: 317-275-4350. p. 754

Gould, Laura, Circ Supvr, Hastings Public Library, 227 E State St, Hastings, MI, 49058-1817. Tel: 269-945-4263. Fax: 269-948-3874. p. 1189

Gould, Laurel, Cat, Berkeley Heights Public Library, 290 Plainfield Ave, Berkeley Heights, NJ, 07922. Tel: 908-464-9333. Fax: 908-464-7098. p. 1472

Gould, Margot, Adult Prog Serv Dir, Cocoa Beach Public Library, 550 N Brevard Ave, Cocoa Beach, FL, 32931. Tel: 321-868-1104. Fax: 321-868-1107. p. 433

Gould, Mary Cheyney, Music Dir, Bagaduce Music Lending Library, Five Music Library Lane, Blue Hill, ME, 04614. Tel: 207-374-5454. Fax: 207-374-2733. p. 978

Gould, Patricia, Dir, Fort Walton Beach Library, 185 Miracle Strip Pkwy SE, Fort Walton Beach, FL, 32548. Tel: 850-833-9590. Fax: 850-833-9659. p. 447

Gould, Tammy, Circ, ILL, Springfield Town Library, 43 Main St, Springfield, VT, 05156. Tel: 802-885-3108. Fax: 802-885-4906. p. 2436

Goupil, Mario, Coordr, College Francois-Xavier-Garneau, 1660 blvd de l'Entente, Quebec, QC, G1S 4S3, CANADA. Tel: 418-688-8310, Ext 3504. Fax: 418-681-9384. p. 2978

Gourley, Don, Assoc Dir, Info Serv, United States Department of Agriculture, 10301 Baltimore Ave, Beltsville, MD, 20705-2351. Tel: 301-504-5755. Fax: 301-504-5472. p. 1020

Gouse, Valerie, Librn, Cumberland County College Library, 3322 College Dr, Vineland, NJ, 08360. Tel: 856-691-8600, Ext 261. Fax: 856-691-1969. p. 1538

Gouveia, Grace, Head, Genealogical Serv, Frankfort Community Public Library, 208 W Clinton St, Frankfort, IN, 46041. Tel: 765-654-8746. Fax: 765-654-8747. p. 743

Gouwens, Elizabeth, Librn, Salt River Project Library, 1600 N Priest Dr, Tempe, AZ, 85281-1213. Tel: 602-236-5676. Fax: 602-629-8585. p. 84

Govan, Jennifer L, Asst Dir, Res Info Serv, Teachers College, Columbia University, 525 W 120th St, New York, NY, 10027-6696. Tel: 212-678-3022. p. 1701

Govan, Merle, Mgr, Calhoun County Library, 900 FR Huff Dr, Saint Matthews, SC, 29135-1261. Tel: 803-874-3389. Fax: 803-874-4154. p. 2204

Gove, Katharine M, Dir, G A R Memorial Library, 490 Main St, West Newbury, MA, 01985-1115. Tel: 978-363-1105. Fax: 978-363-1116. p. 1137

Govea, Shelly, Dir, Siloam Springs Public Library, 401 W University St, Siloam Springs, AR, 72761. Tel: 479-524-4236. Fax: 479-524-3908. p. 115

Gover, Harvey, Asst Librn, Washington State University Tri-Cities, 2770 University Dr, Richland, WA, 99354. Tel: 509-372-7204. Fax: 509-372-7281. p. 2526

Gover, Jill, Dir, Luck Public Library, 21 Second Ave W, Luck, WI, 54853. Tel: 715-472-2770. Fax: 715-472-4312. p. 2606

Goverman, Gloria, Dir, East Fishkill Public Library District, 348 Rte 376, Hopewell Junction, NY, 12533-6075. Tel: 845-221-9943. Fax: 845-226-1404. p. 1637

Govern, Jim, Fac Coordr, Maricopa County Library District, 2700 N Central Ave, Ste 700, Phoenix, AZ, 85004. Tel: 602-652-3046. Fax: 602-652-3071. p. 74

Gow, Athel, Mgr, University of Guelph, Library Centre for Students with Disabilities, 50 Stone Rd E, Guelph, ON, N1G 2W1, CANADA. Tel: 519-824-4120, Ext 52312. p. 2807

Gow, Martha Parks, Librn, Nuclear Energy Institute Library, 1776 I St NW, Ste 400, Washington, DC, 20006-3708. Tel: 202-739-8135. Fax: 202-533-0152. p. 412

Gowan, Cameron, Librn, Jones Day, 51 Louisiana Ave NW, Washington, DC, 20001-2113. Tel: 202-879-3939, 202-879-3953. Fax: 202-626-1700. p. 406

Gower, Wanda, Bus Mgr, Logan County Public Library, 201 W Sixth St, Russellville, KY, 42276. Tel: 270-726-6129. Fax: 270-726-6127. p. 934

Gowin, Ruth, Ref Asst, Longwood University, Redford & Race St, Farmville, VA, 23909. Tel: 434-395-2741. Fax: 434-395-2453. p. 2463

Gowing, Cheryl, Dir, Info Mgt & Syst, University of Miami Libraries, 1300 Memorial Dr, Coral Gables, FL, 33146. Tel: 305-284-3233. Fax: 305-284-4027. p. 434

Gowman, Randall, Asst Dir, Pub Serv, Gordon College, 255 Grapevine Rd, Wenham, MA, 01984-1899. Tel: 978-867-4339. Fax: 978-867-4660. p. 1136

Goyda, Ed, Dir, Lewes Public Library, 111 Adams Ave, Lewes, DE, 19958. Tel: 302-645-2733. Fax: 302-645-6235. p. 384

Goyda, Ed, Libr Dir, Boyertown Community Library, 29 E Philadelphia Ave, Boyertown, PA, 19512-1124. Tel: 610-369-0496. Fax: 610-369-0542. p. 2036

Goyette, Anne, Per, Ecole de Technologie Superieure (Service de la bibliotheque), 1100 rue Notre-Dame Ouest, Montreal, QC, H3C 1K3, CANADA. Tel: 514-396-8946. Fax: 514-396-8633. p. 2895

Goyette, Heather, Cat Librn, United States Military Academy Library, Jefferson Hall Library & Learning Center, 758 Cullum Rd, West Point, NY, 10996. Tel: 845-938-3833. Fax: 845-938-4000. p. 1767

Goyette, Marie, Dir, Bibliotheque Gabrielle-Roy, 350 est Saint-Joseph, Quebec, QC, G1K 3B2, CANADA. Tel: 418-641-6789. Fax: 418-641-6787. p. 2903

Goykin, Robert, Asst Dir, Smithtown Library, Nesconset Branch, 127-20 Smithtown Blvd, Nesconset, NY, 11767. Tel: 631-265-3994. Fax: 631-265-8158. p. 1744

Goykin, Robert, Asst Dir, Smithtown Library, One N Country Rd, Smithtown, NY, 11787. Tel: 631-265-2072. Fax: 631-265-2044. p. 1744

Goymerac, Tony, Info Mgr, Teton County Library, 125 Virginian Lane, Jackson, WY, 83001. Tel: 307-733-2164, Ext 131. Fax: 307-733-4568. p. 2656

Gozdz, Henry, Librn, Bergen County Law Library, Bergen County Justice Center, Ten Main St, 1st Flr, Hackensack, NJ, 07601. Tel: 201-527-2274. Fax: 201-371-1121. p. 1488

Graba, Kim, Librn, Racine Correctional Institution Library, 2019 Wisconsin St, Sturtevant, WI, 53177. Tel: 262-886-3214, Ext 3800. Fax: 262-886-3514. p. 2641

Grabarcyzk, Marge, Tech Serv, Rossford Public Library, 720 Dixie Hwy, Rossford, OH, 43460-1289. Tel: 419-666-0924. Fax: 419-666-1989. p. 1932

Grabbe, Kaye, Dir, Lake Forest Library, 360 E Deerpath Ave, Lake Forest, IL, 60045-2252. Tel: 847-810-4602. Fax: 847-234-1453. p. 663

Grabeal, Janet, Purchasing Coordr, Southwestern Oklahoma State University, 100 Campus Dr, Weatherford, OK, 73096-3002. Tel: 580-774-7023. Fax: 580-774-3112. p. 1985

Graber, BreAnn Marie, Librn, Duluth News Tribune Library, 424 W First St, Duluth, MN, 55802. Tel: 218-723-5374. Fax: 218-720-4120. p. 1247

Graber, David, Dir, Wayne State College, 1111 Main St, Wayne, NE, 68787. Tel: 402-375-7272. Fax: 402-375-7538. p. 1423

Graber, Janelle, Dir, Eckhart Public Library, 603 S Jackson St, Auburn, IN, 46706-2298. Tel: 260-925-2414. Fax: 260-925-9376. p. 725

Graboski, Jill, Ch, Newton Free Library, 330 Homer St, Newton Centre, MA, 02459-1429. Tel: 617-796-1360. Fax: 617-965-8457. p. 1110

Grabowska, Flora, Ref Librn, Sci Librn, Vassar College Library, 124 Raymond Ave, Maildrop 20, Poughkeepsie, NY, 12604-0020. Tel: 845-437-5760. Fax: 845-437-5864. p. 1723

Grabowski, Lisa, Pub Serv Librn, Arapahoe Community College, 5900 S Santa Fe Dr, Littleton, CO, 80160. Tel: 303-797-5746. Fax: 303-798-4173. p. 316

Grabowski, Mark, Head, Libr Data & Server Mgt, University of Delaware Library, 181 S College Ave, Newark, DE, 19717-5267. Tel: 302-831-2231. Fax: 302-831-1046. p. 386

Grabowski, Ray, Librn, Lake Shore Railway Historical Society Museum & Library, 31 Wall St (at Robinson St), North East, PA, 16428-1223. Tel: 814-725-1911. Fax: 814-725-1911. p. 2099

Grace, Anna H, Dir, Wadsworth Library, 24 Center St, Geneseo, NY, 14454. Tel: 585-243-0440. Fax: 585-243-0429. p. 1627

Grace, Anne L, Asst Dir, Ch, Elbert County Public Library, 345 Heard St, Elberton, GA, 30635. Tel: 706-283-5375. Fax: 706-283-5456. p. 532

Grace, Barbara, Ch, Garden City Public Library, 60 Seventh St, Garden City, NY, 11530-2891. Tel: 516-742-8405. Fax: 516-742-2675. p. 1626

Grace, Darcia M, Dir, Nenana Public Library, 202 E Second & Market, Nenana, AK, 99760. Tel: 907-832-5812. Fax: 907-832-5899. p. 51

Grace, Debbie, Libr Tech, San Francisco Maritime Library, Fort Mason Ctr, Bldg E, 3rd Flr, San Francisco, CA, 94123. Tel: 415-561-7030. Fax: 415-556-1624. p. 245

Grace, Kathleen, Acq, Oshkosh Public Library, 106 Washington Ave, Oshkosh, WI, 54901-4985. Tel: 920-236-5232. Fax: 920-236-5228. p. 2628

Grace, Kevin, Head of Libr, University of Cincinnati Libraries, Archives & Rare Books, 808 Blegen Library, Cincinnati, OH, 45221. Tel: 513-556-1959. Fax: 513-556-2113. p. 1874

Grace, Michael, City Librn, Fiske Free Library, 108 Broad St, Claremont, NH, 03743-2673. Tel: 603-542-7017. Fax: 603-542-7029. p. 1441

Grace, Peter, In Charge, St Paul of the Cross Province, 86-45 Edgerton Blvd, Jamaica, NY, 11432-0024. Tel: 718-739-6502. Fax: 718-657-0543. p. 1646

Grace, Sylvia, Coordr, Tech Serv, North Tonawanda Public Library, 505 Meadow Dr, North Tonawanda, NY, 14120-2888. Tel: 716-693-4132. Fax: 716-693-0719. p. 1707

Grace, Trudie, Curator, Putnam County Historical Society & Foundry School Museum Library, 63 Chestnut St, Cold Spring, NY, 10516. Tel: 845-265-4010. Fax: 845-265-2884. p. 1608

Grace, William, Br Mgr, Beaumont Public Library System, Tyrrell Historical, 695 Pearl St, Beaumont, TX, 77701. Tel: 409-833-2759. Fax: 409-833-5828. p. 2287

Graceffo, Mark, Librn, Saint Peter's College, Hudson Terrace, Englewood Cliffs, NJ, 07632. Tel: 201-985-2962. Fax: 201-568-6614. p. 1484

Grach, Maya, Acq Librn, Webster University, 101 Edgar Rd, Saint Louis, MO, 63119. Tel: 314-968-6971. Fax: 314-968-7113. p. 1363

Gracia, Socorro, Asst Librn, Dr Hector P Garcia Memorial Library, 434 S Ohio St, Mercedes, TX, 78570. Tel: 956-565-2371. Fax: 956-565-9458. p. 2362

Gracy, David B, Prof, University of Texas at Austin, One University Sta, D7000, Austin, TX, 78712-0390. Tel: 512-471-3821. Fax: 512-471-3971. p. 2975

Gracy, Karen, Asst Prof, Kent State University, 314 Library, Kent, OH, 44242-0001. Tel: 330-672-2782. Fax: 330-672-7965. p. 2972

Gracy, Karen, Asst Prof, University of Pittsburgh, 135 N Bellefield Ave, Pittsburgh, PA, 15260. Tel: 412-624-5230. Fax: 412-624-5231. p. 2973

Gradone, Claire, Asst Dir, Youth Serv Librn, Brewster Ladies' Library Association, 1822 Main St, Brewster, MA, 02631. Tel: 508-896-3913. Fax: 508-896-9372. p. 1069

Gradowski, Gail, Librn, Santa Clara University, 500 El Camino Real, Santa Clara, CA, 95053-0500. Tel: 408-554-6830. Fax: 408-554-6827. p. 263

Grady, Carole, Asst Librn, Sutton Memorial Library, 201 S Saunders, Sutton, NE, 68979. Tel: 402-773-5259. Fax: 402-773-5259. p. 1420

Grady, Eileen, Dir, Operations, Samuels Public Library, 538 Villa Ave, Front Royal, VA, 22630. Tel: 540-635-3153. Fax: 540-635-7229. p. 2466

Grady, Ife B, Ref Librn, North Carolina Central University, 1801 Fayetteville St, Durham, NC, 27707-3129. Tel: 919-530-7314. Fax: 919-530-7612. p. 1789

Grady, Joanne, Head, Ref, West Milford Township Library, 1490 Union Valley Rd, West Milford, NJ, 07480. Tel: 973-728-2885. Fax: 973-728-2106. p. 1541

Grady, Patricia M, Interim Dir, Leicester Public Library, 1136 Main St, Leicester, MA, 01524-0389. Tel: 508-892-7020. Fax: 508-892-7045. p. 1098

Grady, Peggy, Librn, William D Block Memorial Law Library, 18 N County St, Waukegan, IL, 60085-4339. Tel: 847-377-2800. p. 716

Graefe, Cynthia, Librn, Athabasca Municipal Library, 4716 48th St, Athabasca, AB, T9S 2B6, CANADA. Tel: 780-675-2735. Fax: 780-675-2735. p. 2684

Graesser, Christine L, Dir, Connecticut Legislative Library, Legislative Office Bldg, Rm 5400, 300 Capitol Ave, Hartford, CT, 06106-1591. Tel: 860-240-8887. Fax: 860-240-8881. p. 344

Graessli, Kathleen, Librn, Parkland Regional Library, Punnichy Branch, PO Box 550, Punnichy, SK, S0A 3C0, CANADA. Tel: 306-835-2265. p. 2932

Graf, Betty, Mgr, Cat Dept, University of Waterloo Library, 200 University Ave W, Waterloo, ON, N2L 3G1, CANADA. Tel: 519-888-4567, Ext 36584. Fax: 519-888-4320. p. 2869

Graf, Linda, Librn, Alice L Pendleton Library, 309 Main Rd, Islesboro, ME, 04848-4505. Tel: 207-734-2218. p. 988

Graf, Mary L, Youth Serv Librn, Brownell Library, Six Lincoln St, Essex Junction, VT, 05452-3154. Tel: 802-878-6956. Fax: 802-878-6946. p. 2423

Graf, Patrick, Dir, Info Tech, Rolling Meadows Library, 3110 Martin Lane, Rolling Meadows, IL, 60008. Tel: 847-259-6050. Fax: 847-259-5319. p. 698

Grafenstein, Marna, ILL, Baldwin Public Library, 400 Cedar St, Baldwin, WI, 54002-0475. Tel: 715-684-3813. Fax: 715-684-5115. p. 2580

Graff, Kimberly, Dir, Rensselaerville Library, 1459 County Rte 351, Rensselaerville, NY, 12147. Tel: 518-797-3949. Fax: 518-797-5211. p. 1727

Graff, Matthew, Dir, Cohoes Public Library, 169 Mohawk St, Cohoes, NY, 12047. Tel: 518-235-2570. Fax: 518-237-4195. p. 1608

Graff, Rosetta, Librn, Kinsley Public Library, 208 E Eighth St, Kinsley, KS, 67547-1422. Tel: 620-659-3341. p. 876

Graff, Terry, Curator, Dep Dir, Beaverbrook Art Gallery Library, 703 Queen St, Fredericton, NB, E3B 5A6, CANADA. Tel: 506-458-2028. Fax: 506-459-7450. p. 2762

Graffagnino, J Kevin, Dir, University of Michigan, William L Clements Library, 909 S University Ave, Ann Arbor, MI, 48109-1190. Tel: 734-764-2347. Fax: 734-647-0716. p. 1152

Grafsgaard, Audrey, Asst Librn, North Dakota Legislative Council Library, 600 E Boulevard Ave, Bismarck, ND, 58505-0660. Tel: 701-328-4900. Fax: 701-328-3615. p. 1838

Grafton, Cathy, Libr Dir, Odell Public Library District, 301 E Richard St, Odell, IL, 60460. Tel: 815-998-2012. Fax: 815-998-2339. p. 684

Grafton, Jennifer, Libr Dir, Coulterville Public Library, 103 S Fourth St, Coulterville, IL, 62237. Tel: 618-758-3013. Fax: 618-758-3013. p. 631

Grafton, Karla, Circ, ILL, Westminster Theological Seminary, 2960 W Church Rd, Glenside, PA, 19038. Tel: 215-572-3821. Fax: 215-887-3412. p. 2062

Grafton, Suzanne, Tech Serv, Meridian Community College, 910 Hwy 19 N, Meridian, MS, 39307. Tel: 601-484-8766. Fax: 601-482-3936. p. 1308

Gragert, Steven K, Assoc Dir/Librn, Will Rogers Memorial Museum Library, 1720 W Will Rogers Blvd, Claremore, OK, 74017. Tel: 918-343-8118. Fax: 918-343-8119. p. 1960

Gragg, Douglas, Librn, Theological Education Association of Mid America, Southern Baptist Theological Seminary, 2825 Lexington Rd, Louisville, KY, 40280. Tel: 502-897-4807. Fax: 502-897-4600. p. 2944

Gragg, Douglas L, Dr, Dir, Louisville Presbyterian Theological Seminary, 1044 Alta Vista Rd, Louisville, KY, 40205-1798. Tel: 502-895-3411, Ext 343. Fax: 502-895-1096. p. 925

Gragg, Phillip, Ref Librn, Louisiana State University Libraries, Paul M Hebert Law Center, One E Campus Dr, Baton Rouge, LA, 70803-1000. Tel: 225-578-4952. Fax: 225-578-5773. p. 944

Gragg, Wendell, Automation Coordr, Bryan College Station Public Library System, 201 E 26th St, Bryan, TX, 77803-5356. Tel: 979-209-5600. Fax: 979-209-5610. p. 2292

Grah, Tammy, Admin Librn, Chester Public Library, 733 State St, Chester, IL, 62233. Tel: 618-826-3711. Fax: 618-826-2733. p. 604

Graham, Amy, Chair, Ohev Shalom Synagogue, Two Chester Rd, Wallingford, PA, 19086. Tel: 610-874-1465. Fax: 610-874-1466. p. 2150

Graham, Andrea, YA Serv, South Country Library, 22 Station Rd, Bellport, NY, 11713. Tel: 631-286-0818. Fax: 631-286-4873. p. 1580

Graham, Ann, Br Mgr, Brandon Public Library, 1475 W Government St, Brandon, MS, 39042. Tel: 601-825-2672. Fax: 601-825-4186. p. 1294

Graham, Anne, Librn, Massachusetts Institute of Technology Libraries, Barker Engineering, Bldg 10-500, 77 Massachusetts Ave, Cambridge, MA, 02139-4307. Tel: 617-253-7744. Fax: 617-258-5623. p. 1077

Graham, Anne M, Librn, Highland Presbyterian Church, 708 Highland Ave, New Castle, PA, 16101. Tel: 724-654-7391. p. 2096

Graham, Barbara, Assoc Dir, Harvard Library, 1341 Massachusetts Ave, Wadsworth House, Cambridge, MA, 02138. Tel: 617-495-3650. Fax: 617-495-0370. p. 1073

Graham, Becky, Dir, Central Lake District Library, 7900 Maple St, Central Lake, MI, 49622. Tel: 231-544-2517. Fax: 231-544-5016. p. 1162

Graham, Beth, Pub Relations Mgr, San Antonio Public Library, 600 Soledad, San Antonio, TX, 78205-2786. Tel: 210-207-2638. Fax: 210-207-2603. p. 2382

Graham, Beverly, Asst Dir, Client Relations, Bank of Canada, 234 Wellington St, Ottawa, ON, K1A 0G9, CANADA. Tel: 613-782-8987. Fax: 613-782-7387. p. 2828

Graham, Bill, In Charge, Garrett County Circuit Court Library, Courthouse, Rm 107B, 203 S Fourth St, Oakland, MD, 21550. Tel: 301-334-1934. Fax: 301-334-5042. p. 1036

Graham, Bonnie, Computer Lab Coordr, Piedmont Technical College Library, 620 N Emerald Rd, Bldg K, Greenwood, SC, 29646. Tel: 864-941-8348. Fax: 864-941-8558. p. 2197

Graham, Carolyn, Asst Librn, Jake Epp Library, 255 Elmdale Dr, Steinbach, MB, R5G 1N6, CANADA. Tel: 204-326-6841. Fax: 204-326-6859. p. 2752

Graham, Cynthia, Br Mgr, Saint Catherine University, 2004 Randolph Ave, Mail F-10, Saint Paul, MN, 55105-1794. Tel: 651-690-7780. Fax: 651-690-8636. p. 1281

Graham, Cynthia, Librn, Saint Catherine University, Minneapolis Campus, 601 25th Ave S, Minneapolis, MN, 55454. Tel: 651-690-7780. p. 1281

Graham, David, Coll Mgr, Supreme Court of the United States Library, One First St NE, Washington, DC, 20543. Tel: 202-479-3037. Fax: 202-479-3477. p. 416

Graham, Deborah, Dir, Belen Public Library, 333 Becker Ave, Belen, NM, 87002. Tel: 505-864-7522. p. 1552

Graham, Denise, Mgr, Carnegie Library of Pittsburgh, Homewood, 7101 Hamilton Ave, Pittsburgh, PA, 15208-1052. Tel: 412-731-3080. p. 2123

Graham, Evelyn, Per, Keyano College Library, 8115 Franklin Ave, Fort McMurray, AB, T9H 2H7, CANADA. Tel: 780-791-4916. Fax: 780-791-1555. p. 2704

Graham, Helen, Circ, Voorhees College, 5480 Voorhees Rd, Denmark, SC, 29042. Tel: 803-793-3351, Ext 7095. Fax: 803-793-0471. p. 2192

Graham, Jamie, Librn, Seattle Children's Hospital, 4800 Sand Point Way NE, W-6850, Seattle, WA, 98105. Tel: 206-987-2098. Fax: 206-987-3838. p. 2530

Graham, Jeanette, Mgr, District of Columbia Public Library, Woodridge, 1801 Hamlin St NE, Washington, DC, 20018. Tel: 202-541-6226. p. 399

Graham, Joanne, Librn, United States Department of Energy, Energy Library, MA-90, Rm GE 180/FORS, 1000 Independence Ave SW, Washington, DC, 20585. Tel: 202-586-3112, 202-586-9534. Fax: 202-586-0573. p. 418

Graham, John-Bauer, Dean of Libr Serv, Jacksonville State University Library, 700 Pelham Rd N, Jacksonville, AL, 36265. Tel: 256-782-5255. Fax: 256-782-5872. p. 22

Graham, Joy, Dir, San Francisco General Hospital, 1001 Potrero Ave, Bldg 30, San Francisco, CA, 94110. Tel: 415-206-3114. Fax: 415-206-6102. p. 245

Graham, Julia, Adult Serv, Willimantic Public Library, 905 Main St, Willimantic, CT, 06226. Tel: 860-465-2176. Fax: 860-465-3083. p. 378

Graham, Kurt, Curator, Buffalo Bill Historical Center, 720 Sheridan Ave, Cody, WY, 82414. Tel: 307-578-4059. Fax: 307-527-6042. p. 2653

Graham, Lori A, Librn, Jameson Health System Library, 1211 Wilmington Ave, New Castle, PA, 16105-2595. Tel: 724-656-4050. Fax: 724-656-4267. p. 2096

Graham, Marilyn, Pub Serv Mgr, Lee County Library System, 2345 Union St, Fort Myers, FL, 33901-3917. Tel: 239-533-4807. Fax: 239-485-1100. p. 445

Graham, Marilynn, Dir, Ref, United States Department of Agriculture, Economic Research Service Resource Center, 1800 M St, Rm N-3050, Washington, DC, 20036. Tel: 202-694-5065. Fax: 202-694-5689. p. 418

Graham, Mary, Librn, Arizona State Museum Library, University of Arizona, 1013 E University Blvd, Tucson, AZ, 85721-0026. Tel: 520-621-4695. Fax: 520-621-2976. p. 85

Graham, Mary, Dep Dir, Neighborhood Serv, Brooklyn Public Library, Grand Army Plaza, Brooklyn, NY, 11238-5698. Tel: 718-230-2442. Fax: 718-398-3947. p. 1590

Graham, Mary, Cat, Coquille Public Library, 105 N Birch St, Coquille, OR, 97423-1299. Tel: 541-396-2166. Fax: 541-396-2174. p. 1993

Graham, Matt Patrick, Dr, Dir, Emory University Libraries, Pitts Theology Library, Candler School of Theology, 505 S Kilgo Circle NE, Atlanta, GA, 30322-2810. Tel: 404-727-4166. Fax: 404-727-1219. p. 514

Graham, Melissa, Librn, ECPI University, 7802 Airport Center Dr, Greensboro, NC, 27409. Tel: 336-665-1400. Fax: 336-664-0801. p. 1796

Graham, Michael, Med Librn/CME Coordr, Saint John Medical Center, 1615 Delaware St, Longview, WA, 98632-2310. Tel: 360-414-7462. Fax: 360-414-7463. p. 2520

Graham, Pamela, Dir, Columbia University, Area Studies, 307 International Affairs Bldg, 420 W 118th St, New York, NY, 10027. Tel: 212-854-8401. Fax: 212-854-3834. p. 1674

Graham, Paul M, Cat & Syst Librn, East Stroudsburg University, 216 Normal St, East Stroudsburg, PA, 18301-2999. Tel: 570-422-3797. Fax: 570-422-3151. p. 2051

Graham, Penny, Libr Mgr, West Feliciana Parish Public Library, 11865 Ferdinand St, Saint Francisville, LA, 70775-4341. Tel: 225-635-3364. Fax: 225-635-4986. p. 967

Graham, Ralph, Circ, ILL, Madison Public Library, 39 Keep St, Madison, NJ, 07940. Tel: 973-377-0722. Fax: 973-377-3142. p. 1498

Graham, Rebecca, Libr Operations, Harvard Library, Francis A Countway Library of Medicine, Boston Med Libr-Harvard Med Libr, Ten Shattuck St, Boston, MA, 02115. Tel: 617-432-4807. p. 1074

Graham, Regina, Asst Dir, Dixie Regional
Library System, 111 N Main St, Pontotoc,
MS, 38863-2103. Tel: 662-489-3960. Fax:
662-489-7777. p. 1311

Graham, Sandy, Br Mgr, Kent District Library, Alto
Branch, 6071 Linfield Ave, Alto, MI, 49302.
Tel: 616-784-2007. Fax: 616-647-3824. p. 1165

Graham, Sheila D, Admin Dir, Cherokee Public
Library, 118 Church St, Cherokee, AL, 35616.
Tel: 256-359-4384. Fax: 256-359-4016. p. 12

Graham, Sheneta, Librn, Illinois Youth Center, 30
W 200 Ferry Rd, Warrenville, IL, 60555. Tel:
630-983-6231, Ext 262. Fax: 630-983-6213.
p. 715

Graham, Stephanie, Br Head, Winnipeg Public
Library, St Vital, 6 Fermor Ave, Winnipeg, MB,
R2M 0Y2, CANADA. Tel: 204-986-5625. Fax:
204-986-3173. p. 2760

Graham, Susan, Spec Coll Librn, University
of Maryland, Baltimore County, 1000
Hilltop Circle, Baltimore, MD, 21250. Tel:
410-455-2356. Fax: 410-455-1567. p. 1018

Graham, Suzanne, Dir, Ray Township Library, 64255
Wolcott Rd, Ray, MI, 48096. Tel: 586-749-7130.
Fax: 586-749-6190. p. 1220

Graham, Suzanne R, Cat Serv Librn, University
of Georgia, 225 Herty Dr, Athens, GA,
30602-6018. Tel: 706-542-5082. Fax:
706-542-5130. p. 510

Graham, Tauni, Circ, ILL, Reserves, Ohio State
University LIBRARIES, Newark Campus
Library, Warner Library & Student Center, 1179
University Dr, Newark, OH, 43055-1797. Tel:
740-366-9307. Fax: 740-366-9264. p. 1889

Graham, Vicki L, Br Mgr, Massanutten Regional
Library, North River, 118 Mount Crawford Ave,
Bridgewater, VA, 22812. Tel: 540-828-4492.
Fax: 540-828-2987. p. 2470

Graham, William, Coordr, Digitalization & Web
Serv, Chicago State University, 9501 S
Martin Luther King Jr Dr, LIB 440, Chicago,
IL, 60628-1598. Tel: 773-995-2257. Fax:
773-995-3772. p. 610

Grahame, Gita, Libr Tech, Sheep River Library,
129 Main St NE, Turner Valley, AB, T0L
2A0, CANADA. Tel: 403-933-3278. Fax:
403-933-3298. p. 2719

Grahame, Vicki, Actg Asst Univ Librn, Tech Serv,
University of California Library, PO Box 19557,
Irvine, CA, 92623-9557. Tel: 949-824-7643.
p. 160

Grahek, David, Assoc Dir, University of Maryland,
Baltimore, Thurgood Marshall Law Library, 501
W Fayette St, Baltimore, MD, 21201-1768. Tel:
410-706-2025. Fax: 410-706-8354. p. 1019

Grailer, Joseph, Dir, University of
Missouri-Columbia, 5400 Arsenal St, Saint
Louis, MO, 63139-1403. Tel: 314-877-6522.
Fax: 314-877-6521. p. 1362

Grainger, Carol, Asst Librn, Josiah Carpenter
Library, 41 Main St, Pittsfield, NH, 03263. Tel:
603-435-8406. p. 1462

Grajczyk, Estelle, ILL, Colchester - East Hants
Regional Library, 754 Prince St, Truro, NS,
B2N 1G9, CANADA. Tel: 902-895-0235,
902-895-1625, 902-895-4183. Fax:
902-895-7149. p. 2786

Grajek, Sara, Ch, Suffolk Public Library System,
North Suffolk Library, 2000 Bennett's
Creek Park Rd, Suffolk, VA, 23435. Tel:
757-514-7150. p. 2497

Gralenski, Fred, Librn, Pembroke Library
Association, 221 Old County Rd, Pembroke,
ME, 04666. Tel: 207-726-4745. Fax:
207-726-4745. p. 995

Grallo, Jacqui, Ref & Instrul Tech Librn, California
State University-Monterey Bay, 100 Campus Ctr,
Seaside, CA, 93955-8001. Tel: 831-582-3142.
Fax: 831-582-3875. p. 268

Gram, Carmel, Dir, Lawrence General Hospital, One
General St, Lawrence, MA, 01841-2997. Tel:
978-683-4000, Ext 2221. p. 1097

Gram, Diane M, Br Supvr, Hesburgh Libraries,
Chemistry-Physics, 231 Nieuwland Science Hall,
Notre Dame, IN, 46556. Tel: 574-631-7203. Fax:
574-631-9661. p. 770

Gramazio, Gabrielle, Libr Asst, City College Library
- Fort Lauderdale, 2000 W Commercial Blvd,
Ste 200, Fort Lauderdale, FL, 33309-3001. Tel:
954-492-5353, Ext 2239. Fax: 954-491-1965.
p. 443

Gramer, Kristen, Asst Dir, Lewes Public Library,
111 Adams Ave, Lewes, DE, 19958. Tel:
302-645-2733. Fax: 302-645-6235. p. 384

Gramlich, Charles, Librn, Sullivan Correctional
Facility Library, 325 Riverside Dr, Fallsburg,
NY, 12733. Tel: 845-434-2080. Fax:
845-434-2080. p. 1621

Gramlich, Laura, Ref Librn, Bacon Memorial
District Library, 45 Vinewood, Wyandotte,
MI, 48192-5221. Tel: 734-246-8357. Fax:
734-282-1540. p. 1237

Gramling, Deborah C, Instr, Ref & Info Serv,
South Carolina State University, 300 College
St NE, Orangeburg, SC, 29115-4427. Tel:
803-536-8647. Fax: 803-536-8902. p. 2202

Gramm, Christine, Br Mgr, Medina County
District Library, 210 S Broadway, Medina,
OH, 44256. Tel: 330-722-6235, Ext 2007. Fax:
330-725-2053. p. 1916

Gramowski, Kari, Youth Serv Dir, Emmetsburg
Public Library, 707 N Superior St, Emmetsburg,
IA, 50536. Tel: 712-852-4009. Fax:
712-852-3785. p. 814

Grams, Sandra, Librn, Greendale Public Library,
5647 Broad St, Greendale, WI, 53129-1887. Tel:
414-423-2136. Fax: 414-423-2139. p. 2596

Granade, Ray, Dr, Dir, Ouachita Baptist University,
410 Ouachita, OBU Box 3742, Arkadelphia,
AR, 71998-0001. Tel: 870-245-5121. Fax:
870-245-5245. p. 93

Granado, Sharon, Youth Serv Mgr, Arlington Public
Library System, 101 E Abram St, MS 10-0100,
Arlington, TX, 76010-1183. Tel: 817-459-6900.
Fax: 817-459-6936. p. 2276

Granados, Daniel, Commun Libr Mgr, County
of Los Angeles Public Library, Hawthorne
Library, 12700 S Grevillea Ave, Hawthorne,
CA, 90250-4396. Tel: 310-679-8193. Fax:
310-679-4846. p. 141

Granados, Daniel, Commun Libr Mgr, County
of Los Angeles Public Library, Woodcrest
Library, 1340 W 106th St, Los Angeles,
CA, 90044-1626. Tel: 323-757-9373. Fax:
323-756-4907. p. 144

Granados, Osvaldo, ILL, The Amargosa Valley
Library, 829 E Farm Rd, HCR 69, Box
401T, Amargosa Valley, NV, 89020. Tel:
775-372-5340. Fax: 775-372-1188. p. 1425

Granath, Jack, Br Mgr, Kansas City, Kansas Public
Library, South Branch, 3401 Strong Ave, Kansas
City, KS, 66106. Tel: 913-722-7400. Fax:
913-722-7402. p. 875

Granath, Kim, Head, Info & Res Serv, University
of Montana, Maureen & Mike Mansfield
Library, 32 Campus Dr, No 9936, Missoula,
MT, 59812-9936. Tel: 406-243-6017. Fax:
406-243-4067. p. 1386

Granatino, Jane, Libr Dir, Uxbridge Free
Public Library, 15 N Main St, Uxbridge,
MA, 01569-1822. Tel: 508-278-8624. Fax:
508-278-8618. p. 1132

Granda, Candy, Second Flr Ref Mgr, Miami-Dade
Public Library System, 101 W Flagler St,
Miami, FL, 33130-1523. Tel: 305-375-1031.
Fax: 305-375-3048. p. 466

Granda, Julio, Urban Affairs Dept Mgr, Miami-Dade
Public Library System, 101 W Flagler St,
Miami, FL, 33130-1523. Tel: 305-375-5231.
Fax: 305-375-3048. p. 466

Grande, Dolores, Ser Librn, John Jay College of
Criminal Justice, 899 Tenth Ave, New York, NY,
10019. Tel: 212-237-8235. Fax: 212-237-8221.
p. 1684

Grande, M.J., Youth Serv, Juneau Public Libraries,
292 Marine Way, Juneau, AK, 99801. Tel:
907-586-5324. Fax: 907-586-3419. p. 50

Grandfield, Ana, Dir, Lake County Public Library,
1919 W 81st Ave, Merrillville, IN, 46410-5488.
Tel: 219-769-3541. Fax: 219-756-9358. p. 763

Grandgeorge, Jan, Dir, Eagle Grove Memorial
Library, 101 S Cadwell, Eagle Grove, IA,
50533. Tel: 515-448-4115. Fax: 515-448-5279.
p. 813

Grandin, Marilyn, Br Mgr, Warren County Library,
Catherine Dickson Hofman Branch, Four
Lambert Rd, Blairstown, NJ, 07825. Tel:
908-362-8335. Fax: 908-362-7775. p. 1472

Grandison, Faye, Librn, Blackwater Regional
Library, Surry Public, 11640 Rolfe Hwy, Surry,
VA, 23883-2736. Tel: 757-294-3949. Fax:
757-294-0803. p. 2458

Grandmaison, Ann, Coordr, Electronic Res, Northern
Essex Community College, 100 Elliott St,
Haverhill, MA, 01830. Tel: 978-556-3426. Fax:
978-556-3738. p. 1094

Grandstaff, Judy, Dir, Blue Hill Public Library,
317 W Gage St, Blue Hill, NE, 68930. Tel:
402-756-2701. p. 1394

Graney, Carol H, Assoc Provost, Dir, Univ Libr,
University of the Arts University Libraries,
Anderson Hall, 1st Flr, 333 S Broad St,
Philadelphia, PA, 19102. Tel: 215-717-6281.
Fax: 215-717-6287. p. 2119

Granger, Karen, Head, Cat, Traverse Des Sioux
Library System, 1400 Madison Ave, Ste 622,
Mankato, MN, 56001-5488. Tel: 507-625-6169.
Fax: 507-625-4049. p. 1257

Granger, Lanette, Syst & Tech Serv Librn, Citrus
College, 1000 W Foothill Blvd, Glendora,
CA, 91741-1899. Tel: 626-914-8640. Fax:
626-963-2531. p. 156

Granger, Melissa, Acq Mgr, Tangipahoa Parish
Library, Administration Office, 200 E Mulberry
St, Amite, LA, 70422. Tel: 985-748-7559. Fax:
985-748-2812. p. 941

Granger, Nancy, Head Librn, Houston County
Public Library System, 1201 Washington Ave,
Perry, GA, 31069. Tel: 478-987-3050. Fax:
478-987-4572. p. 547

Granger, Nancy, Head Librn, Houston County Public
Library System, Perry Branch, 1201 Washington
Ave, Perry, GA, 31069. Tel: 478-987-3050. Fax:
478-987-4572. p. 547

Granicy, Linda, Adult Serv, ILL, Monrovia
Public Library, 321 S Myrtle Ave, Monrovia,
CA, 91016-2848. Tel: 626-256-8253. Fax:
626-256-8255. p. 189

Grannis, Chris, YA Librn, Marion Public Library,
1095 Sixth Ave, Marion, IA, 52302. Tel:
319-377-3412. Fax: 319-377-0113. p. 830

Granrud, Marilyn, Tech Serv, Stoughton Public
Library, 304 S Fourth St, Stoughton, WI,
53589-0191. Tel: 608-873-6281. Fax:
608-873-0108. p. 2640

Grant, Beverly, Br Mgr, Kinchafoonee Regional
Library System, Quitman County Library, 39
Old School Rd, Georgetown, GA, 39854. Tel:
229-334-8972. p. 528

Grant, Bonita Craft, NJ Bibliogr & Head, Pub Serv,
Rutgers University Libraries, Special Collections
& University Archives, 169 College Ave, New
Brunswick, NJ, 08901-1163. Tel: 848-932-6148.
Fax: 732-932-7012. p. 1509

Grant, Cathy, Chief Exec Officer, Pickering Public
Library, One The Esplanade, Pickering, ON,
L1V 6K7, CANADA. Tel: 905-831-6265, Ext
6236. Fax: 905-831-6927. p. 2836

Grant, Constance, Head, Tech Serv, Catawba
College, 2300 W Innes St, Salisbury, NC,
28144-2488. Tel: 704-637-4228. Fax:
704-637-4304. p. 1822

Grant, Desmond, Info Tech & Fac Mgr,
Pueblo City-County Library District, 100 E
Abriendo Ave, Pueblo, CO, 81004-4290. Tel:
719-562-5622. Fax: 719-562-5619. p. 320

Grant, Diana, Asst Dir, Weedsport Library, 2795 E
Brutus St, Weedsport, NY, 13166-8720. Tel:
315-834-6222. Fax: 315-834-8621. p. 1765

Grant, Elizabeth, Head, Acq, Head, Cat, University of the South, 735 University Ave, Sewanee, TN, 37383-1000. Tel: 931-598-1663. Fax: 931-598-1702. p. 2265

Grant, Jerry, Dir, Res Serv, Shaker Museum & Library, 88 Shaker Museum Rd, Old Chatham, NY, 12136. Tel: 518-794-9100, Ext 211. Fax: 518-794-8621. p. 1710

Grant, JoAnn, Br Mgr, Chicago Public Library, Austin, 5615 W Race Ave, Chicago, IL, 60644. Tel: 312-746-5038. Fax: 312-746-5192. p. 608

Grant, Joy, Libr Mgr, Wabasca Public Library, PO Box 638, Wabasca, AB, T0G 2K0, CANADA. Tel: 780-891-2203. Fax: 780-891-2402. p. 2721

Grant, Judy, Adminr, Dir, Shirley M Wright Memorial Library, 11455 Fremont St, Trempealeau, WI, 54661-9247. Tel: 608-534-6197. Fax: 608-534-6197. p. 2642

Grant, Julienne, Foreign & Intl Law Librn, Loyola University Chicago Libraries, Law School Library, 25 E Pearson St, 3rd Flr, Chicago, IL, 60611. Tel: 312-915-8520. Fax: 312-915-6797. p. 617

Grant, Katy, Ch, Louisville Free Public Library, Shawnee, 3912 W Broadway, Louisville, KY, 40211. Tel: 502-574-1722. Fax: 502-776-9983. p. 924

Grant, Laura, Children & Youth Serv Librn, Millis Public Library, 25 Auburn Rd, Millis, MA, 02054-1203. Tel: 508-376-8282. Fax: 508-376-1278. p. 1106

Grant, Marca, Ch, Croton Free Library, 171 Cleveland Dr, Croton-on-Hudson, NY, 10520. Tel: 914-862-1025. Fax: 914-271-0931. p. 1612

Grant, Mary, Operations Mgr, University of Calgary Library, Health Sciences Library, Health Sci Ctr, 3330 Hospital Dr NW, Calgary, AB, T2N 4N1, CANADA. Tel: 403-220-5035. Fax: 403-210-9847. p. 2693

Grant, Melody, Librn, Montana Department of Corrections, Two Riverside Rd, Boulder, MT, 59632. Tel: 406-225-4500. Fax: 406-225-4511. p. 1375

Grant, Natasha, Res Serv Librn, Lowenstein Sandler PC Library, 65 Livingston Ave, Roseland, NJ, 07068. Tel: 973-597-2500. Fax: 973-597-2400. p. 1527

Grant, Nathaniel, Head, Media Production, Chicago State University, 9501 S Martin Luther King Jr Dr, LIB 440, Chicago, IL, 60628-1598. Tel: 773-995-3851. Fax: 773-995-3772. p. 610

Grant, Robin, Info Serv, Ref & Instruction Librn, Macon State College Library, 100 College Station Dr, Macon, GA, 31206-5144. Tel: 478-471-2866. Fax: 478-471-2869. p. 540

Grant, Susan, Head, Tech Serv, Southern Maryland Regional Library Association, Inc, 37600 New Market Rd, Charlotte Hall, MD, 20622-3041. Tel: 301-843-3634, 301-884-0436, 301-934-9442. Fax: 301-884-0438. p. 1023

Grant, Susan, Dir, North Hampton Public Library, 237A Atlantic Ave, North Hampton, NH, 03862-2341. Tel: 603-964-6326. Fax: 603-964-1107. p. 1461

Grant, Sylvia, Tech Serv, Vanderbilt University, Walker Management Library, Owen Graduate School of Management, 401 21st Ave S, Nashville, TN, 37203. Tel: 615-343-8252. Fax: 615-343-0061. p. 2261

Grant, Wallace, Libr Mgr, United States Army, 404 Pershing Loop, Fort Hamilton, Brooklyn, NY, 11252-5100. Tel: 718-630-4040. Fax: 718-630-4038. p. 1595

Grant, Zachary, Ref Librn (Info Serv), Clark College, Mail Stop LIB 112, 1933 Fort Vancouver Way, Vancouver, WA, 98663-3598. Tel: 360-992-2971. Fax: 360-992-2869. p. 2545

Grant-Braybrook, Linda, Librn, Border Regional Library, 312 Seventh Ave, Virden, MB, R0M 2C0, CANADA. Tel: 204-748-3862. Fax: 204-748-3862. p. 2753

Grantano, Cheryl K, Asst Dir, South San Francisco Public Library, 840 W Orange Ave, South San Francisco, CA, 94080-3125. Tel: 650-829-3876. Fax: 650-829-3866. p. 270

Grantz, Diane, Dir, Mercy Medical Center Library, 1410 N Fourth St, Clinton, IA, 52732. Tel: 563-244-5555. Fax: 563-244-5592. p. 803

Granville, Sarah, Teen Serv & Prog, Barberton Public Library, 602 W Park Ave, Barberton, OH, 44203-2458. Tel: 330-745-1194. Fax: 330-745-8261. p. 1857

Grapes, Amy A, Adjunct Fac Librn, Harrisburg Area Community College, 2010 Pennsylvania Ave, York, PA, 17404. Tel: 717-718-0328, Ext 3520. Fax: 717-718-8967. p. 2159

Grapes, Shelley E, Asst Librn, Boone Area Library, 129 N Mill St, Birdsboro, PA, 19508-2340. Tel: 610-582-5666. Fax: 610-582-6826. p. 2035

Gras, Sara, Ref, Brooklyn Law School Library, 250 Joralemon St, Brooklyn, NY, 11201. Tel: 718-780-7538. Fax: 718-780-0369. p. 1590

Grasberger, Margy, Head, Info Serv, Thomas Jefferson University, 1020 Walnut St, Philadelphia, PA, 19107. Tel: 215-503-7815. Fax: 215-923-3203. p. 2118

Grasdock, Donna, In Charge, Bellingham Public Library, Fairhaven, 1117 12th St, Bellingham, WA, 98225. Tel: 360-778-7188. Fax: 360-778-7192. p. 2508

Grasela, Joseph, Jr, Pub Serv Librn, Kansas City Kansas Community College Library, 7250 State Ave, Kansas City, KS, 66112-3098. Tel: 913-288-7650. Fax: 913-288-7606. p. 875

Grasmick, Amy, Librn, Kimball Public Library, 67 N Main St, Randolph, VT, 05060. Tel: 802-728-5073. Fax: 802-728-6735. p. 2433

Grass, Gene, Info Serv, Southington Public Library & Museum, 255 Main St, Southington, CT, 06489. Tel: 860-628-0947. Fax: 860-628-0488. p. 368

Grass, Joyce, Dir, Tekamah Public Library, 204 S 13th St, Tekamah, NE, 68061-1304. Tel: 402-374-2453. Fax: 402-374-2453. p. 1421

Grassel, Denni, Dir, Delmont Public Library, 77 Greensburg St, Delmont, PA, 15626. Tel: 724-468-5329. Fax: 724-468-5329. p. 2049

Grasto, Jenny, Campus Librn, North Dakota State University Libraries, Architecture & Landscape Architecture, 711 Second Ave N, Fargo, ND, 58102. Tel: 701-231-8616. Fax: 701-231-6128. p. 1841

Grate, Valerie, Ref, Russell Library, 123 Broad St, Middletown, CT, 06457. Tel: 860-347-2528. p. 352

Gratop, Mary Beth, Br Mgr, Toledo-Lucas County Public Library, Oregon Branch, 3340 Dustin Rd, Oregon, OH, 43616. Tel: 419-259-5250. Fax: 419-691-3341. p. 1940

Gratten, Lindsay, Youth Serv Librn, Fletcher Memorial Library, 88 Main St, Ludlow, VT, 05149. Tel: 802-228-3517, 802-228-8921. p. 2427

Gratton, Elin, Acq, University of Puget Sound, 1500 N Warner St, Campus Mail Box 1021, Tacoma, WA, 98416-1021. Tel: 253-879-2668. Fax: 253-879-3670. p. 2541

Gratton-Tétreault, Noëlle, Res Mgr, Bibliotheque Municipale de Gatineau, Édifice Pierre Papin, CP 1970 Succ. Hull, Gatineau, QC, J8X 3Y9, CANADA. p. 2882

Gratz, Erin, Asst Prof, Instrul Tech Librn, Web Librn, University of La Verne, 2040 Third St, La Verne, CA, 91750. Tel: 909-593-3511, Ext 4305. Fax: 909-392-2733. p. 162

Gratz, Robin J, Dir, Manchester College, 604 E College Ave, North Manchester, IN, 46962. Tel: 260-982-5360. Fax: 260-982-5362. p. 769

Grauerholz, Henrietta, Librn, Byron Public Library, 119 Kansas Ave, Byron, NE, 68325. Tel: 402-236-8752. p. 1395

Graulich, Candace, Dir, Hustisford Community Library, 609 W Juneau St, Hustisford, WI, 53034. Tel: 920-349-3463. Fax: 920-349-4540. p. 2599

Graulich, Mary, Circ Supvr, Dexter District Library, 3255 Alpine St, Dexter, MI, 48130. Tel: 734-426-4477. Fax: 734-426-1217. p. 1174

Gravel, Ghislaine, Head Librn, Armstrong Township Public Library, 35 Tenth St, Earlton, ON, P0J 1E0, CANADA. Tel: 705-563-2717. Fax: 705-563-2093. p. 2803

Graveline, Jeff, Ref Librn, University of Alabama at Birmingham, Mervyn H Sterne Library, 917 13th St S, Birmingham, AL, 35205. Tel: 205-934-6364. p. 10

Graveline, Laura, Visual Arts Librn, Dartmouth College Library, Baker-Berry Library, 6025 Baker-Berry Library, Hanover, NH, 03755-3525. Tel: 603-646-2560. Fax: 603-646-2167. p. 1450

Graveline, Laura, Visual Arts Librn, Dartmouth College Library, Sherman Art Library, Carpentar Hall, Hinman Box 6025, Hanover, NH, 03755-3570. Tel: 603-646-3831. Fax: 603-646-1218. p. 1450

Graveline, Rachel, Dir, Institut Raymond-Dewar Rehabilitation Centre for the Deaf, Deafblind & Hard of Hearing, 3600, rue Berri, Montreal, QC, H2L 4G9, CANADA. Tel: 514-284-2214, Ext 3610. Fax: 514-284-5086. p. 2897

Gravelle, Cheryl, Dir, Williamson Free Public Library, 6380 Rte 21, Ste 1, Williamson, NY, 14589. Tel: 315-589-2048. Fax: 315-589-5077. p. 1769

Graves, Betty, Librn, Lafayette-Orinda Presbyterian Church Library, 49 Knox Dr, Lafayette, CA, 94549. Tel: 925-283-8722. Fax: 925-283-0138. p. 163

Graves, Brandy, Youth Serv Dir, Shelby County Public Library, 57 W Broadway, Shelbyville, IN, 46176. Tel: 317-398-7121, 317-835-2653. Fax: 317-398-4430. p. 778

Graves, Diane J, Univ Librn, Trinity University, One Trinity Pl, San Antonio, TX, 78212-7200. Tel: 210-999-8121. Fax: 210-999-8182. p. 2383

Graves, Ed, Asst Dir, Rutland Free Library, Ten Court St, Rutland, VT, 05701-4058. Tel: 802-773-1860. Fax: 802-773-1825. p. 2434

Graves, Elizabeth, Coordr of Tech Processes, Northwestern State University Libraries, 913 University Pkwy, Natchitoches, LA, 71497. Tel: 313-357-4585. Fax: 318-357-4470. p. 958

Graves, Ellen, Librn, Bluffs Public Library, 110 N Bluffs St, Bluffs, IL, 62621. Tel: 217-754-3804. Fax: 217-754-3804. p. 596

Graves, Franklin, Info Tech Operations Mgr, University of North Carolina at Greensboro, 320 Spring Garden St, Greensboro, NC, 27402. Tel: 336-256-1211. Fax: 336-334-5399. p. 1798

Graves, Howard, Chair, Tech Serv, Sr Asst Dean, Libr Syst, Hofstra University, 123 Hofstra University, Hempstead, NY, 11549. Tel: 516-463-6429. Fax: 516-463-6438. p. 1635

Graves, Jackie, Asst Librn, Sandusky District Library, 55 E Sanilac Ave, Sandusky, MI, 48471-1146. Tel: 810-648-2644. Fax: 810-648-1904. p. 1226

Graves, Margaret, Tech Serv Librn, Pease Public Library, One Russell St, Plymouth, NH, 03264-1414. Tel: 603-536-2616. Fax: 603-536-2369. p. 1462

Graves, Mellisa, Librn, Pike Library, 1585 Mount Moosilauke Hwy, Pike, NH, 03780-5677. Tel: 603-989-9847. p. 1462

Graves, Michele, City Librn, Eagle Mountain Public Library, 1650 E Stagecoach Run, Eagle Mountain, UT, 84005. Tel: 801-789-6623. Fax: 801-789-6653. p. 2405

Graves, Sheri, Librn, Ulysses Library Association, 401 N Main St, Ulysses, PA, 16948. Tel: 814-848-7226. Fax: 814-848-7226. p. 2147

Graves, Sherry, Dir, Workingmen's Institute Library, 407 W Tavern St, New Harmony, IN, 47631. Tel: 812-682-4806. Fax: 812-682-4806. p. 768

Graves, Tess, Tech Serv, Flesh Public Library, 124 W Greene St, Piqua, OH, 45356-2399. Tel: 937-773-6753. Fax: 937-773-5981. p. 1930

Graves, Virginia, Head, Cat, Northern Virginia Community College Libraries, Media Processing Services, 8333 Little River Tpk, Annandale, VA, 22003-3796. Tel: 703-323-3095. Fax: 703-323-3831. p. 2447

Graves, William, Tech Serv, Harvard-Smithsonian Center for Astrophysics Library, 60 Garden St, MS-56, Cambridge, MA, 02138. Tel: 617-496-7550. Fax: 617-495-7199. p. 1077

Graves, Zeke, Tech Serv, Polk County Public Library, 1289 W Mills St, Columbus, NC, 28722. Tel: 828-894-8721. Fax: 828-894-2761. p. 1785

Graves-Blevins, Brenda, Sci Librn, University of Missouri-Columbia, Elmer Ellis Library, Ellis Library Bldg, Rm 104, Columbia, MO, 65201-5149. Tel: 573-882-1827. Fax: 573-882-8044. p. 1325

Graves-Onken, Carmon, Librn, Good Samaritan Hospital Library, 520 S Seventh St, Vincennes, IN, 47591. Tel: 812-882-5220, 812-885-3228. Fax: 812-885-3089. p. 784

Gravette, Tony, AV, Jacksonville State University Library, 700 Pelham Rd N, Jacksonville, AL, 36265. Tel: 256-782-5255. Fax: 256-782-5872. p. 22

Gravier, Frank, Bibliographer, Librn, University of California, 1156 High St, Santa Cruz, CA, 95064. Tel: 831-459-3319. Fax: 831-459-8206. p. 264

Gray, Alan Kirk, Asst Dir, Operations, Darien Library, 1441 Post Rd, Darien, CT, 06820-5419. Tel: 203-669-5224. Fax: 203-655-1547. p. 336

Gray, Alice, Asst Librn, Heyworth Public Library District, 119 E Main St, Heyworth, IL, 61745. Tel: 309-473-2313. Fax: 309-473-9253. p. 655

Gray, Allan, Dir, Northwest Regional Library System, 181 1/2 S Main St, Bowling Green, OH, 43402. Tel: 419-352-2903. Fax: 419-353-8310. p. 2952

Gray, Allison, Librn, Santa Barbara Public Library, Goleta Branch, 500 N Fairview Ave, Goleta, CA, 93117. Tel: 805-964-7878. p. 261

Gray, Anita L, Dir of Libr Serv, Huntington College, 2303 College Ave, Huntington, IN, 46750. Tel: 260-359-4063. Fax: 260-358-3698. p. 748

Gray, Anne, In Charge, Historic Jefferson College Library, PO Box 700, Washington, MS, 39190. Tel: 601-442-2901. Fax: 601-442-2902. p. 1317

Gray, Barbara, Br Mgr, Columbia County Public Library, West Branch, 435 NW Hall of Fame Dr, Lake City, FL, 32055. Tel: 386-758-1321. p. 457

Gray, Barbara, Dir, Res, New York Times, Reference Library, 620 Eight Ave, 5th Flr, New York, NY, 10018. Tel: 212-556-7428. Fax: 212-556-4448. p. 1695

Gray, Barrie, Br Head, Toronto Public Library, Parliament Street, 269 Gerrard St E, Toronto, ON, M5A 2G6, CANADA. Tel: 416-393-7663. Fax: 416-393-7413. p. 2862

Gray, Barry, Cat, Tech Serv, Edinboro University of Pennsylvania, 200 Tartan Ave, Edinboro, PA, 16444. Tel: 814-732-2779. Fax: 814-732-2883. p. 2053

Gray, Becky, Ch, George Coon Public Library, 114 S Harrison St, Princeton, KY, 42445-1946. Tel: 270-365-2884. Fax: 270-365-2892. p. 933

Gray, Bethany, Asst Dir, Lowell Public Library, 1505 E Commercial Ave, Lowell, IN, 46356-1899. Tel: 219-696-7704. Fax: 219-696-5280. p. 762

Gray, Bob, ILL Librn, Ref Librn, East Central Regional Library, 244 S Birch, Cambridge, MN, 55008-1588. Tel: 763-689-7390. Fax: 763-689-7389. p. 1243

Gray, Carol, Asst Dir, Gloucester, Lyceum & Sawyer Free Library, Two Dale Ave, Gloucester, MA, 01930-5906. Tel: 978-281-9763. Fax: 978-281-9770. p. 1091

Gray, Carolyn, Librn, Manitoba Association of Playwrights Library, 100 Arthur St, Ste 503, Winnipeg, MB, R3B 1H3, CANADA. Tel: 204-942-8941. Fax: 204-942-1555. p. 2756

Gray, Catherine, Librn, Idaho State University, University Library Center, 1776 Science Center Dr, Rm 250, Idaho Falls, ID, 83402. Tel: 208-282-7906. Fax: 208-282-7910. p. 582

Gray, David, Asst Dir, Hancock County Public Library, 900 W McKenzie Rd, Greenfield, IN, 46140-1741. Tel: 317-462-5141. Fax: 317-462-5711. p. 746

Gray, David, Dir, Lord Fairfax Community College, 173 Skirmisher Lane, Middletown, VA, 22645-1745. Tel: 540-868-7154. Fax: 540-868-7171. p. 2479

Gray, David, Dir, Lord Fairfax Community College, Bob G Sowder Library, 6480 College St, Warrenton, VA, 20187-8820. Tel: 540-347-6259. p. 2479

Gray, Deanna, Human Res Mgr, Somerset County Library System, One Vogt Dr, Bridgewater, NJ, 08807-2136. Tel: 908-526-4016, Ext 133. p. 1475

Gray, Deanna, Librn, Cochranton Area Public Library, 107 W Pine St, Cochranton, PA, 16314-0296. Tel: 814-425-3996. Fax: 814-425-3996. p. 2046

Gray, Deborah, Dir, Lincoln Library, 222 W River Rd, Lincoln, VT, 05443. Tel: 802-453-2665. p. 2427

Gray, Dottie, Mgr, Libr Serv, National School Boards Association Library, 1680 Duke St, Alexandria, VA, 22314-3493. Tel: 703-838-6731. Fax: 703-548-5516. p. 2446

Gray, Elaine, Dir, Hinsdale County Library District, 221 Silver St, Lake City, CO, 81235. Tel: 970-944-2615. Fax: 970-944-4102. p. 314

Gray, Elizabeth, Asst County Librn, Yolo County Library, Admin Off, 226 Buckeye St, Woodland, CA, 95695-2600. Tel: 530-666-8084. Fax: 530-666-8006. p. 284

Gray, George, Pres, Medfield Historical Society Library, Six Pleasant St, Medfield, MA, 02052. Tel: 508-359-4773. p. 1103

Gray, Gwen, Soc Sci Librn, University of Missouri-Columbia, Elmer Ellis Library, Ellis Library Bldg, Rm 104, Columbia, MO, 65201-5149. Tel: 573-882-9162. Fax: 573-882-8044. p. 1325

Gray, Jane, Librn, Vanderhoof Public Library, 230 E Stuart St, Bag 6000, Vanderhoof, BC, V0J 3A0, CANADA. Tel: 250-567-4060. Fax: 250-567-4458. p. 2744

Gray, Jill, Dir, Charles City Public Library, 106 Milwaukee Mall, Charles City, IA, 50616-2281. Tel: 641-257-6319. Fax: 641-257-6325. p. 801

Gray, Jim, Tech Serv, Wake Technical Community College, 9101 Fayetteville Rd, Raleigh, NC, 27603-5696. Tel: 919-866-5644. Fax: 919-662-3575. p. 1818

Gray, Jody, Automation Syst Coordr, Horry County Memorial Library, 1008 Fifth Ave, Conway, SC, 29526. Tel: 843-248-1544. Fax: 843-248-1548. p. 2191

Gray, Johnnie, Media/ILL Librn, Christopher Newport University, One Avenue of the Arts, Newport News, VA, 23606. Tel: 757-594-7249. Fax: 757-594-7717. p. 2479

Gray, Judith, Head, Ref Serv, Concord Free Public Library, 129 Main St, Concord, MA, 01742-2494. Tel: 978-318-3300. Fax: 978-318-3344. p. 1082

Gray, Judy, Librn, Finley-Sharon Library, 302 Broadway, Finley, ND, 58230. Tel: 701-524-2420. p. 1841

Gray, Julie, Librn, Fife Lake Public Library, 77 Lakecrest Lane, Fife Lake, MI, 49633. Tel: 231-879-4101. Fax: 231-879-3360. p. 1178

Gray, Karen, Ch, Linden Free Public Library, 31 E Henry St, Linden, NJ, 07036. Tel: 908-298-3830. Fax: 908-486-2636. p. 1495

Gray, Kate, Br Serv Coordr, San Antonio Public Library, 600 Soledad, San Antonio, TX, 78205-2786. Tel: 210-207-2661. Fax: 210-207-2603. p. 2382

Gray, Kay, Circ, Dowagiac District Library, 211 Commercial St, Dowagiac, MI, 49047-1728. Tel: 269-782-3826. Fax: 269-782-9798. p. 1174

Gray, Kelly, Ref, Clovis Community College Library, 417 Schepps Blvd, Clovis, NM, 88101. Tel: 575-769-4080. Fax: 575-769-4190. p. 1553

Gray, Kevin, Asst Dir, Law Librn, Pennsylvania State University - Dickinson School of Law (University Libraries), 1170 Harrisburg Pike, Carlisle, PA, 17013-1617. Tel: 717-240-5267. Fax: 717-240-5127. p. 2042

Gray, Kristine, VPres, Res & Sr Coordr, Res, C D Howe Institute Library, 67 Yonge St, Ste 300, Toronto, ON, M5E 1J8, CANADA. Tel: 416-865-1904, Ext 2606. Fax: 416-865-1866. p. 2854

Gray, Lesli, Head, Acq & Ser, State Library of Louisiana, 701 N Fourth St, Baton Rouge, LA, 70802-5232. Tel: 225-342-4937. Fax: 225-219-4804. p. 945

Gray, Linda, Res Librn, Nelson, Mullins, Riley & Scarborough, 1320 Main St, Ste 1700, Columbia, SC, 29201. Tel: 404-817-6228. Fax: 803-255-7500. p. 2188

Gray, Linda, Librn, Nelson, Mullins, Riley & Scarborough, 104 S Main St, Ste 900, Greenville, SC, 29601. Tel: 864-250-2300. Fax: 864-232-2925. p. 2197

Gray, Linda, Dir, Lon Morris College, 800 College Ave, Jacksonville, TX, 75766. Tel: 903-589-4024. Fax: 903-586-8562. p. 2347

Gray, Lollie, Dir, Festus Public Library, 222 N Mill St, Festus, MO, 63028. Tel: 636-937-2017. Fax: 636-937-3439. p. 1327

Gray, Marge, Libr Tech, MacEwan Grant University Library, South Campus Library, 7319 29th Ave, Edmonton, AB, T6K 2P1, CANADA. Tel: 780-497-4052. Fax: 780-497-4184. p. 2701

Gray, Mark, Mgr, Libr & Tech Support Serv, Sir Sandford Fleming College of Applied Arts & Technology Library, 599 Brealey Dr, Peterborough, ON, K9J 7B1, CANADA. Tel: 705-749-5530. Fax: 705-749-5542. p. 2836

Gray, Mary, Asst Librn, Hamilton Public Library, 312 N Davis St, Hamilton, MO, 64644. Tel: 816-583-4832. Fax: 816-583-7501. p. 1329

Gray, Mattie, Br Librn, Memphis Public Library, Randolph Branch, 3752 Given, Memphis, TN, 38122. Tel: 901-452-1068. Fax: 901-454-9594. p. 2250

Gray, Micca, Ref Librn, Santa Rosa Junior College, 1501 Mendocino Ave, Santa Rosa, CA, 95401. Tel: 707-527-4261 (Media Servs), 707-527-4391. Fax: 707-527-4545. p. 267

Gray, Michelle, Managing Dir, Warren County Historical Society, 210 Fourth Ave, Warren, PA, 16365. Tel: 814-723-1795. Fax: 814-723-1795. p. 2150

Gray, Mike, Asst Dir, Public Library of Steubenville & Jefferson County, 407 S Fourth St, Steubenville, OH, 43952-2942. Tel: 740-282-9782. Fax: 740-282-2919. p. 1936

Gray, Misty, Dir, Storm Lake Public Library, 609 Cayuga St, Storm Lake, IA, 50588. Tel: 712-732-8026. Fax: 712-732-7609. p. 846

Gray, Nancy, Circ, Washburn University, School of Law Library, 1700 SW College Ave, Topeka, KS, 66621. Tel: 785-670-1783. Fax: 785-670-3194. p. 897

Gray, Patricia, Br Mgr, Cleveland Heights-University Heights Public Library, Coventry Village, 1925 Coventry Rd, Cleveland Heights, OH, 44118-2001. Tel: 216-932-3600, Ext 620. Fax: 216-321-0739. p. 1882

Gray, Paul, Mgr, Network Serv, Tarrant County College, 828 Harwood Rd, Hurst, TX, 76054-3219. Tel: 817-515-6623. p. 2346

Gray, Phyllis J, Dir, Royal Center-Boone Township Public Library, 203 N Chicago, Royal Center, IN, 46978. Tel: 574-643-3185. Fax: 574-643-5003. p. 776

Gray, Roberta, Pub Serv Librn, University of New England Libraries, Josephine S Abplanalp Library, Portland Campus, 716 Stevens Ave, Portland, ME, 04103. Tel: 207-221-4323. Fax: 207-221-4893. p. 978

Gray, Seneca, Head, Ref, Lewis & Clark College, Paul L Boley Law Library, Lewis & Clark Law School, 10015 SW Terwilliger Blvd, Portland, OR, 97219. Tel: 503-768-6776. Fax: 503-768-6760. p. 2011

Gray, Sheila, Libr Spec, Gateway Community & Technical College, 790 Thomas More Pkwy, Rm E 213, Edgewood, KY, 41017. Tel: 859-442-4157. Fax: 859-341-6859. p. 911

Gray, Sue, Circ, Saint Catherine University, Minneapolis Campus, 601 25th Ave S, Minneapolis, MN, 55454. Tel: 651-690-7898. p. 1281

Gray, Suzanne, Info Literacy Librn, Eastern Michigan University, 955 W Circle Dr Library, Rm 200, Ypsilanti, MI, 48197. Tel: 734-487-0020, Ext 2130. Fax: 734-487-8861. p. 1238

Gray, Sylvia, Asst Librn, James L Hamner Public Library, 16351 Dunn St, Amelia, VA, 23002. Tel: 804-561-4559. Fax: 804-561-3174. p. 2447

Gray, Teddy, Pub Serv Librn, Biological & Environ Sci Libr, Duke University Libraries, 411 Chapel Dr, Durham, NC, 27708. Tel: 919-660-5971. Fax: 919-681-7606. p. 1787

Gray, Warren F, Dir, Southeast Kentucky Community & Technical College, 207 Chrisman Hall, 700 College Rd, Cumberland, KY, 40823. Tel: 606-589-3074. Fax: 606-589-4941. p. 911

Gray-Williams, Donna, Tech Serv, Lake County Library System, 2401 Woodlea Rd, Tavares, FL, 32778. Tel: 352-253-6161. Fax: 352-253-6184. p. 499

Graybeal, Kathy, Dir, Sussex County Department of Libraries, 22215 DuPont Blvd, Georgetown, DE, 19947-2809. Tel: 302-855-7890. Fax: 302-855-7895. p. 383

Graybill, Jeremy, Dir, Mkt & Communications, Multnomah County Library, 205 NE Russell St, Portland, OR, 97212-3796. Tel: 503-988-5498. Fax: 503-988-5441. p. 2011

Graybill, Verna, Govt Doc, Northwestern Oklahoma State University, 709 Oklahoma Blvd, Alva, OK, 73717. Tel: 580-327-8576. Fax: 580-327-8501. p. 1956

Graykin, Melissa J, ILL Librn, Philbrick-James Library, Four Church St, Deerfield, NH, 03037-1426. Tel: 603-463-7187. p. 1444

Grayson, Charles, Chief Librn/CEO, Espanola Public Library, 245 Avery Dr, Espanola, ON, P5E 1S4, CANADA. Tel: 705-869-2940. Fax: 705-869-6463. p. 2804

Grayson, Debra, Coordr, White Smith Memorial Library, 213 College Ave, Jackson, AL, 36545. Tel: 251-246-4962. Fax: 251-246-9791. p. 22

Grayson, Dianne, Monographs Tech Serv Librn, University of Southern Indiana, 8600 University Blvd, Evansville, IN, 47712. Tel: 812-464-1905. Fax: 812-465-1693. p. 739

Grayson, Regina, Asst Dir, Luverne Public Library, 148 E Third St, Luverne, AL, 36049. Tel: 334-335-5326. Fax: 334-335-6402. p. 24

Grayson, Sue, Archivist, Circ, Rare Bks, Hudson Valley Community College, 80 Vandenburgh Ave, Troy, NY, 12180. Tel: 518-629-7555. Fax: 518-629-7509. p. 1756

Graziano, Patti A, Dir, Plain Dealer Publishing Co, 1801 Superior Ave, Cleveland, OH, 44114-2198. Tel: 216-999-4195. Fax: 216-999-6363. p. 1881

Graziano, Ron, Dir, Fac Develop, Carnegie Library of Pittsburgh, 4400 Forbes Ave, Pittsburgh, PA, 15213-4080. Tel: 412-622-1016. Fax: 412-688-8600. p. 2122

Graziano, Sue, Mgr, Santa Cruz City-County Library System Headquarters, Central, 224 Church St, Santa Cruz, CA, 95060-3873. Tel: 831-427-7706, Ext 7725. Fax: 831-427-7701. p. 264

Grazier, Goolcher, Asst Br Mgr, Worcester County Library, Ocean City Branch, 10003 Coastal Hwy, Ocean City, MD, 21842. Tel: 410-524-1818. Fax: 410-289-5577. p. 1042

Greaber, Karen, Managing Librn, Pima County Public Library, Dewhirst Catalina, 15631 N Oracle Rd, No 199, Catalina, AZ, 85739. Tel: 520-594-5240. Fax: 520-594-5241. p. 87

Grealish, William, Librn, Gibbs College of Boston, 126 Newbury St, Boston, MA, 02116. Tel: 617-578-7100, 617-578-7178. Fax: 617-578-7163. p. 1061

Grealish-Rust, Ann, Dir, Tiverton Library Services, 238 Highland Rd, Tiverton, RI, 02878. Tel: 401-625-6796. Fax: 401-625-5499. p. 2176

Grealy, Deborah, PhD, Assoc Dean, Prog Dir, Saint Catherine University, 2004 Randolph Ave, Mailstop No 4125, Saint Paul, MN, 55105. Tel: 651-690-6802. Fax: 651-690-8724. p. 2968

Greany, Patty, Pub Serv Librn, Emory & Henry College, 30480 Armbrister Dr, Emory, VA, 24327. Tel: 276-944-6208. Fax: 276-944-4592. p. 2460

Greathouse, Deb, Coll Develop, Librn, Delta City Library, 76 N 200 W, Delta, UT, 84624-9424. Tel: 435-864-4945. Fax: 435-864-4313. p. 2404

Greathouse, Debbie, Br Librn, Roane County Public Library, Walton Public Library, Two Cunningham Lane, Walton, WV, 25286. Tel: 304-577-6071. Fax: 304-577-6071. p. 2572

Greathouse, Janet, Librn, Calera Public Library, 9700 Hwy 25, Calera, AL, 35040. Tel: 205-668-3514. Fax: 205-668-3515. p. 11

Greaves, Lee, Teen/Adult Serv Dept Head, Hussey-Mayfield Memorial Public Library, 250 N Fifth St, Zionsville, IN, 46077-1324. Tel: 317-873-3149, Ext 12450. Fax: 317-873-8339. p. 789

Greaves, Winny, Librn, Northminster Presbyterian Church Library, 7720 Alaska Ave NW, Washington, DC, 20012. Tel: 202-829-5311. Fax: 202-726-6899. p. 412

Grebasch, Dave, Dir, Maxwell Public Library, 107 Main St, Maxwell, IA, 50161. Tel: 515-387-8780. Fax: 515-387-8780. p. 831

Grebl, James, Dr, Mgr, San Diego Museum of Art Library, 1450 El Prado, San Diego, CA, 92101. Tel: 619-696-1959. Fax: 619-232-9367. p. 235

Greco, Kathy, Librn, Rivkin Radler LLP, 926 RexCorp Plaza, Uniondale, NY, 11556-0926. Tel: 516-357-3453, 516-357-3454, 516-357-3455. Fax: 516-357-3333. p. 1758

Greco, Nancy, Instruction & Archives Librn, Saint John Fisher College, 3690 East Ave, Rochester, NY, 14618-3599. Tel: 585-385-8139. Fax: 585-385-8445. p. 1732

Greco, Phillip R, Dir, Weehawken Free Public Library, 49 Hauxhurst Ave, Ste 1, Weehawken, NJ, 07086. Tel: 201-863-7823. Fax: 201-863-7958. p. 1540

Greco, Sophie, AV Tech, Ontario Office of the Fire Marshal, 5775 Yonge St, 7th Flr, Toronto, ON, M2M 4J1, CANADA. Tel: 416-325-3121. Fax: 416-325-3213. p. 2856

Greco, Theresa, Librn, Osborn Maledon, 2929 N Central, 21st Flr, Phoenix, AZ, 85012-2794. Tel: 602-640-9210. Fax: 602-640-9050. p. 75

Greczek, Maryann, Ref Serv, Middlesex Public Library, 1300 Mountain Ave, Middlesex, NJ, 08846. Tel: 732-356-6602. Fax: 732-356-8420. p. 1501

Greear, Cori, Pub Serv Librn, Winter Haven Public Library, 325 Ave A NW, Winter Haven, FL, 33881. Tel: 863-291-5880. Fax: 863-298-7708. p. 505

Greeley, Marilyn, Asst Dir, East Bridgewater Public Library, 32 Union St, East Bridgewater, MA, 02333-1598. Tel: 508-378-1616. Fax: 508-378-1617. p. 1085

Greeley, Shawn P, Municipal Video Spec, Groton Public Library, 52 Newtown Rd, Groton, CT, 06340. Tel: 860-441-6750. Fax: 860-448-0363. p. 342

Green, Aaron, Tech Mgr, Clinton-Macomb Public Library, 40900 Romeo Plank Rd, Clinton Township, MI, 48038-2955. Tel: 586-226-5017. Fax: 586-226-5008. p. 1164

Green, Alan, Head of Libr, Ohio State University LIBRARIES, Music & Dance, 166 Sullivant Hall, 1813 N High St, Columbus, OH, 43210-1307. Tel: 614-292-2319. Fax: 614-247-6794. p. 1889

Green, Amanda, Youth Serv, Plain City Public Library, 305 W Main St, Plain City, OH, 43064-1148. Tel: 614-873-4912, Ext 30. Fax: 614-873-8364. p. 1930

Green, Amanda, Head of Libr, Royal Tyrrell Museum of Palaeontology Library, Midland Provincial Park, Hwy 838 N Dinosaur Trail, Box 7500, Drumheller, AB, T0J 0Y0, CANADA. Tel: 403-823-7707, Ext 6213. Fax: 403-823-7131. p. 2697

Green, Andrea, Librn, Northeast Regional Library, Belmont Public Library, 102 S Third St, Belmont, MS, 38827. Tel: 662-454-7841. Fax: 662-454-7841. p. 1297

Green, Ann, Sr Res Analyst, SNR Denton LLP Library, 1301 K St NW, Ste 600E, Washington, DC, 20005. Tel: 202-408-6452. Fax: 202-408-6399. p. 415

Green, Anne, Literacy Coordr, James Prendergast Library Association, 509 Cherry St, Jamestown, NY, 14701. Tel: 716-484-7135. Fax: 716-487-1148. p. 1647

Green, Barbara, Circ, Lake County Library, 1425 N High St, Lakeport, CA, 95453-3800. Tel: 707-263-8816. Fax: 707-263-6796. p. 163

Green, Betty, Dir, Truro Public Library, 114 E Center St, Truro, IA, 50257. Tel: 641-765-4220. Fax: 641-765-4220. p. 848

Green, Bradley, Dir, Harvey Mitchell Memorial Library, 151 Main St, Epping, NH, 03042. Tel: 603-679-5944. Fax: 603-679-5884. p. 1446

Green, Brenda, Instrul Serv Librn, University of Tennessee-Memphis, 877 Madison Ave, Memphis, TN, 38163. Tel: 901-448-4759. Fax: 901-448-7235. p. 2252

Green, Brenda Lee, In Charge, Planned Parenthood of Western Pennsylvania, Inc, 933 Liberty Ave, Pittsburgh, PA, 15222-3701. Tel: 412-434-8969. Fax: 412-434-8974. p. 2127

Green, Carol, Librn, Chattanooga-Hamilton County Bicentennial Library, Northgate, 520 Northgate Mall, Chattanooga, TN, 37415-6924. Tel: 423-870-0632. Fax: 423-870-0619. p. 2227

Green, Carole, ILL, Keystone College, One College Green, La Plume, PA, 18440-0200. Tel: 570-945-8332. Fax: 570-945-8969. p. 2075

Green, Cecelia, Dir, Distance Learning, Edison Community College Library, 1973 Edison Dr, Piqua, OH, 45356. Tel: 937-778-7883. Fax: 937-778-7958. p. 1930

Green, Charlotte, Tech Serv, NHTI, Concord's Community College, 31 College Dr, Concord, NH, 03301-7425. Tel: 603-271-7187. Fax: 603-271-7189. p. 1443

Green, Cheryl, Dir, Clay Center Public Library, 117 W Edgar St, Clay Center, NE, 68933. Tel: 402-762-3861. Fax: 402-762-3861. p. 1396

Green, Cindy, Commun Librn, Monroe County Library System, Dorsch Memorial, 18 E First St, Monroe, MI, 48161-2227. Tel: 734-241-7878. Fax: 734-241-7879. p. 1210

Green, Dale, YA Serv, Eagle Valley Library District, 600 Broadway, Eagle, CO, 81631. Tel: 970-328-8800. Fax: 970-328-6901. p. 305

Green, Dave, Assoc Univ Librn, Coll & Info, Northeastern Illinois University, 5500 N Saint Louis Ave, Chicago, IL, 60625-4699. Tel: 773-442-4414. Fax: 773-442-4531. p. 620

Green, Debb, Coordr, Ch Serv, Iowa City Public Library, 123 S Linn St, Iowa City, IA, 52240. Tel: 319-887-6019. Fax: 319-356-5494. p. 822

Green, Debra L, Dir, Fred C Fischer Library, 167 Fourth St, Belleville, MI, 48111. Tel: 734-699-3291. Fax: 734-699-6352. p. 1156

Green, Denise, Coordr, Tech Serv & Electronic Res, Millikin University, 1184 W Main, Decatur, IL, 62522. Tel: 217-424-6214. Fax: 217-424-3992. p. 634

Green, Denise, Media Librn, Cleveland Institute of Music, 11021 East Blvd, Cleveland, OH, 44106-1776. Tel: 216-707-4503. Fax: 216-791-3063. p. 1877

Green, Diane, Head Librn, Great Falls Genealogy Society Library, 422 Second St S, Great Falls, MT, 59405. Tel: 406-727-3922. p. 1380

Green, Donna, Archivist, Curator, Fayette Public Library, 855 S Jefferson, La Grange, TX, 78945. Tel: 979-968-3765. Fax: 979-968-5357. p. 2351

Green, Doris, ILL, Jackson County Public Library System, 2929 Green St, Marianna, FL, 32446. Tel: 850-482-9631. Fax: 850-482-9632. p. 462

Green, Edna, Dir, Selma University, 1501 Lapsley St, Selma, AL, 36701. Tel: 334-874-7673. Fax: 334-872-7746. p. 36

Green, Elsie, Tech Serv Librn, Bartlesville Public Library, 600 S Johnstone, Bartlesville, OK, 74003. Tel: 918-338-4161. Fax: 918-337-5338. p. 1957

Green, Esme, Dir, Goodnow Library, 21 Concord Rd, Sudbury, MA, 01776-2383. Tel: 978-443-1035, Ext 5. Fax: 978-443-1047. p. 1129

Green, Evelyn, Info Spec, Cigna Co Library, 900 Cottage Grove Rd, Bloomfield, CT, 06002. Tel: 860-226-3257. Fax: 860-226-5128. p. 330

Green, Gary, Info Tech, Kalamazoo Public Library, 315 S Rose St, Kalamazoo, MI, 49007-5264. Tel: 269-553-7861. Fax: 269-553-7999. p. 1197

Green, Harriett, English & Digital Humanities Librn, University of Illinois Library at Urbana-Champaign, Literatures & Languages, 225 Main Libr, 1408 W Gregory Dr, Urbana, IL, 61801. Tel: 217-333-4942. Fax: 217-333-2214. p. 712

Green, Heather, Br Mgr, Richland County Public Library, The Link, Ballentine, 1321 Dutch Fork Rd, Irmo, SC, 29063. Tel: 803-781-5026. p. 2188

Green, James N, Librn, Library Company of Philadelphia, 1314 Locust St, Philadelphia, PA, 19107-5698. Tel: 215-546-3181. Fax: 215-546-5167. p. 2112

Green, Janet B, Librn, Mgr, FM Global, 1151 Boston-Providence Tpk, Norwood, MA, 02062. Tel: 781-762-4300. Fax: 781-762-9375. p. 1115

Green, Jean E, Commun Serv Supvr, Bedford Public Library, 2424 Forest Ridge Dr, Bedford, TX, 76021. Tel: 817-952-2370. Fax: 817-952-2396. p. 2288

Green, Jennifer, Electronic Res & Cat Librn, Bethel University, 325 Cherry Ave, McKenzie, TN, 38201. Tel: 731-352-4083. Fax: 731-352-4070. p. 2247

Green, Jeremy, Pub Serv Librn, Carroll Community College, 1601 Washington Rd, Westminster, MD, 21157-6944. Tel: 410-386-8335. Fax: 410-386-8331. p. 1045

Green, Joseph, Head, Customer Serv, Boynton Beach City Library, 208 S Seacrest Blvd, Boynton Beach, FL, 33435. Tel: 561-742-6390. Fax: 561-742-6381. p. 429

Green, Judy, Ref & Instruction, University of Alaska Anchorage, Consortium Library, 3211 Providence Dr, Anchorage, AK, 99508-8176. Tel: 907-786-1871. Fax: 907-786-1834. p. 45

Green, K'Lani, Br Serv Librn, Oconee County Public Library, 501 W South Broad St, Walhalla, SC, 29691. Tel: 864-638-4133. Fax: 864-638-4132. p. 2207

Green, Karen, Adminr, KZF Design Library, 655 Eden Park Dr, Cincinnati, OH, 45202. Tel: 513-621-6211. Fax: 513-621-6530. p. 1870

Green, Keitha, Dir, Lyman Public Library, 313 Jeffers St, Lyman, NE, 69352. Tel: 308-787-1366. Fax: 308-787-1366. p. 1407

Green, Kenneth, Librn, Gary Public Library, Brunswick Branch, 4030 W Fifth Ave, Gary, IN, 46406. Tel: 219-944-9402. Fax: 219-944-9644. p. 744

Green, Kim, Cat Tech, Chesapeake College, PO Box 8, Wye Mills, MD, 21679. Tel: 410-827-5860 Ext. 292. Fax: 410-827-5257. p. 1046

Green, Laura, Mgr, Libr & Res Serv, Bryan Cave Law Library, 700 13th St NW, Ste 700, Washington, DC, 20005-3960. Tel: 202-508-6055. Fax: 202-508-6200. p. 395

Green, Laura Gayle, Head Librn, Florida State University Libraries, Warren D Allen Music Library, Housewright Music Bldg, 122 N Copeland St, Tallahassee, FL, 32306-1180. Tel: 850-644-3999. Fax: 850-644-3982. p. 494

Green, Laura Gayle, Dir, Music/Media Libr, University of Missouri-Kansas City Libraries, 800 E 51st St, Kansas City, MO, 64110. Tel: 816-235-1679. Fax: 816-333-5584. p. 1341

Green, Laurie, Librn, Leach Public Library, 130 Park Ave, Irasburg, VT, 05845. Tel: 802-754-2526. p. 2426

Green, Linda, Ref Mgr, Rapides Parish Library, 411 Washington St, Alexandria, LA, 71301-8338. Tel: 318-445-241, Ext 1030. Fax: 318-445-6478. p. 940

Green, Lindolyn, In Charge, Georgia Department of Corrections, Office of Library Services, 335 County Farm Rd, Zebulon, GA, 30295. Tel: 770-567-0531. Fax: 770-567-0257. p. 558

Green, Lisa, Br Mgr, Toledo-Lucas County Public Library, Lagrange Central, 3422 Lagrange St, Toledo, OH, 43608. Tel: 419-259-5280. Fax: 419-242-3052. p. 1940

Green, Marcus, Archivist, LandMark Communications, 200 E Market St, Greensboro, NC, 27401-2910. Tel: 336-373-7044. Fax: 336-373-4437. p. 1797

Green, Mary Beth, Dir, Learning Res, Lurleen B Wallace Community College Library, 1000 Danalley Blvd, Andalusia, AL, 36420. Tel: 334-881-2265. Fax: 334-881-2300. p. 4

Green, Monique, Cat, Moultrie-Colquitt County Library, 204 Fifth St SE, Moultrie, GA, 31768. Tel: 229-985-6540. Fax: 229-985-0936. p. 545

Green, Nancy, Br Mgr, Ouachita Parish Public Library, West Ouachita Branch, 188 Hwy 546, West Monroe, LA, 71291. Tel: 318-397-5414. Fax: 318-397-8659. p. 958

Green, Nancy J, Librn, La Follette Public Library, 201 S Tennesee Ave, La Follette, TN, 37766-3606. Tel: 423-562-5154. Fax: 423-562-0013. p. 2244

Green, Patricia W, Dir, Mgr, Archives & Rec Mgt, Aerospace Corp, 2360 E El Segundo Blvd, El Segundo, CA, 90245-4691. Tel: 310-336-6093. Fax: 310-336-0624. p. 146

Green, Paula, Dir, Fort Hills Hospital, 102-01 66 Rd, Forest Hills, NY, 11375. Tel: 718-830-4000. Fax: 718-830-4344. p. 1623

Green, Rachael, Govt Doc, Louisiana State University, One University Pl, Shreveport, LA, 71115-2399. Tel: 318-798-4158. Fax: 318-797-5156. p. 968

Green, Remlee, Librn, Massachusetts Institute of Technology Libraries, Barker Engineering, Bldg 10-500, 77 Massachusetts Ave, Cambridge, MA, 02139-4307. Tel: 617-253-4088. Fax: 617-258-5623. p. 1077

Green, Remlee, Librn, Massachusetts Institute of Technology Libraries, Science, Bldg 14S-134, 77 Massachusetts Ave, Cambridge, MA, 02139-4307. Tel: 617-253-4088. Fax: 617-253-6365. p. 1078

Green, Robert W, Vice Chancellor, Libr Serv, Info Res & Tech, University of Massachusetts Dartmouth Library, 285 Old Westport Rd, North Dartmouth, MA, 02747-2300. Tel: 508-999-8260. Fax: 508-999-8987. p. 1112

Green, Roger, Res, NYS Small Business Development Center Research Network, 22 Corporate Woods Blvd, 3rd Flr, Albany, NY, 12211. Tel: 518-641-0650. Fax: 518-443-5275. p. 1570

Green, Sandra, Head, Circ, Metropolitan College of New York Library, 431 Canal St, 12th Flr, New York, NY, 10013. Tel: 212-343-1234, Ext 2003. Fax: 212-343-7398. p. 1686

Green, Shay, Br Mgr, Pine Bluff & Jefferson County Library System, Watson Chapel Public Library, 4120 Camden Rd, Pine Bluff, AR, 71603. Tel: 870-879-3406. Fax: 870-879-6437. p. 112

Green, Sheila, Ref Librn, University of Denver, Westminster Law Library, 2255 E Evans Ave, Denver, CO, 80208. Tel: 303-871-6188. Fax: 303-871-6999. p. 304

Green, Shelley, Br Mgr, Siskiyou County Public Library, Weed Branch, 780 S Davis St, Weed, CA, 96094. Tel: 530-938-4769. p. 286

Green Stanhope, Kate, Regional Mgr, Libr Serv, McInnes Cooper Library, 1300-1969 Upper Water St, Halifax, NS, B3J 2V1, CANADA. Tel: 902-444-8468. Fax: 902-425-6350, 902-425-6386. p. 2781

Green, Susan, Cat, Saint Ambrose University Library, 518 W Locust St, Davenport, IA, 52803. Tel: 563-333-6469. Fax: 563-333-6248. p. 807

Green, Susan, Br Mgr, Charlotte Mecklenburg Library, Morrison Regional Library, 7015 Morrison Blvd, Charlotte, NC, 28211. Tel: 704-416-5400. p. 1782

Green, Tammy, ILL, University of Missouri-Columbia, Elmer Ellis Library, Ellis Library Bldg, Rm 104, Columbia, MO, 65201-5149. Tel: 573-882-3224. Fax: 573-882-8044. p. 1325

Green, Terri, Librn, Palomino Horse Breeders of America Library, 15253 E Skelly Dr, Tulsa, OK, 74116-2637. Tel: 918-438-1234. Fax: 918-438-1232. p. 1982

Green, Terry, Actg Librn, Georgia Department of Corrections, Office of Library Services, 210 Longbridge Rd, Helena, GA, 31037. Tel: 229-868-7721. Fax: 229-868-6509. p. 536

Green, Vickey, Dir, Lee Public Library, 312 W Pacific, Gladewater, TX, 75647-2135. Tel: 903-845-2640. Fax: 903-845-2648. p. 2328

Green, Vicki, Regional Mgr, Cobb County Public Library System, South Cobb, 805 Clay Rd, Mableton, GA, 30126. Tel: 678-398-5828. Fax: 678-398-5833. p. 543

Green, Virginia, Librn, Gadsden County Public Library, Havana Public, 203 E Fifth Ave, Havana, FL, 32333. Tel: 850-539-2844. p. 485

Green, Wanda, Adult Serv, Tom Green County Library System, 113 W Beauregard, San Angelo, TX, 76903. Tel: 915-655-7321. Fax: 915-659-4027. p. 2378

Green, Yolanda, Librn, Georgia Department of Corrections, Office of Library Services, Hwy 49 S, Oglethorpe, GA, 31068. Tel: 478-472-3486. Fax: 478-472-3524. p. 547

Greenaway, Cecily, Ref Librn, Vineyard Haven Public Library, 200 Main St, Vineyard Haven, MA, 02568-9710. Tel: 508-696-4211, Ext 15. Fax: 508-696-7495. p. 1132

Greenbaum, Dale, Tech Serv, Euclid Public Library, 631 E 222nd St, Euclid, OH, 44123-2091. Tel: 216-261-5300, Ext 120. Fax: 216-261-0575. p. 1899

Greenbaum, Diane, Pub Serv, Wickliffe Public Library, 1713 Lincoln Rd, Wickliffe, OH, 44092. Tel: 440-944-6010. Fax: 440-944-7264. p. 1947

Greenberg, Arlene, Chief Librn, Sir Mortimer B Davis Jewish General Hospital, 3755 Cote Ste Catherine Rd, A-200, Montreal, QC, H3T 1E2, CANADA. Tel: 514-340-8222, Ext 5930. Fax: 514-340-7552. p. 2901

Greenberg, Barbara, Dir, Freehold Public Library, 28 1/2 E Main St, Freehold, NJ, 07728-2202. Tel: 732-462-5135. Fax: 732-577-9598. p. 1487

Greenberg, Charles, Coordr, Curric & Res Support, Yale University Library, Harvey Cushing/John Hay Whitney Medical Library, Sterling Hall of Medicine, 333 Cedar St, L110 SHM, New Haven, CT, 06520. Tel: 203-737-2960. Fax: 203-785-5636. p. 358

Greenberg, Eva, Ref, Oberlin Public Library, 65 S Main St, Oberlin, OH, 44074-1626. Tel: 440-775-4790. Fax: 440-774-2880. p. 1925

Greenberg, Linda, Ref/YA, Ridgefield Park Free Public Library, 107 Cedar St, Ridgefield Park, NJ, 07660. Tel: 201-641-0689. Fax: 201-440-1058. p. 1526

Greenberg, Mark I, Dr, Dir, Spec & Digital Coll, Fla Studies Ctr & Holocaust & Genocide Prog, University of South Florida, Tampa Campus Library, 4101 USF Apple Dr, LIB122, Tampa, FL, 33620. Tel: 813-974-4141. Fax: 813-974-5153. p. 499

Greenberg, Michael, Info Res, CUH2A Inc Library, 1000 Lenox Dr, Lawrenceville, NJ, 08648-2312. Tel: 609-791-7247. Fax: 609-791-7719. p. 1494

Greenberg, Ruth, Coll Develop, Bergen County Cooperative Library System, 810 Main St, Hackensack, NJ, 07601. Tel: 201-489-1904. Fax: 201-489-4215. p. 2948

Greenblatt, Ellen, Scholarly Communications Librn, Auraria Library, 1100 Lawrence St, Denver, CO, 80204-2095. Tel: 303-556-6704. Fax: 303-556-3528. p. 298

Greenburg, Alice, Dir, Putnam County Public Library, 103 E Poplar St, Greencastle, IN, 46135-1655. Tel: 765-653-2755. Fax: 765-653-2756. p. 746

Greenburg, Geoff, Coll Develop Librn, Ref, Roosevelt University, 430 S Michigan Ave, Chicago, IL, 60605. Tel: 312-341-2318. Fax: 312-341-2425. p. 623

Greene, Amy, Chief Adminr/Curator of Coll & Exhibitions, Headley-Whitney Museum Library, 4435 Old Frankfort Pike, Lexington, KY, 40510. Tel: 859-255-6653. Fax: 859-255-8375. p. 920

Greene, Ann, Dir, Eau Claire District Library, 6528 E Main St, Eau Claire, MI, 49111. Tel: 269-461-6241. Fax: 269-461-3721. p. 1176

Greene, Anne, Coll Develop Mgr, Montgomery-Floyd Regional Library System, 125 Sheltman St, Christiansburg, VA, 24073. Tel: 540-382-6965. Fax: 540-382-6964. p. 2457

Greene, Beverly, Dir, Middlesborough-Bell County Public Library, 126 S 20th St, Middlesboro, KY, 40965-1212. Tel: 606-248-5304. Fax: 606-248-8766. p. 929

Greene, Beverly, Dir, Pineville-Bell County Public Library, 214 Walnut St, Pineville, KY, 40977. Tel: 606-337-3422. Fax: 606-337-9862. p. 933

Greene, Beverly, Circ, Memorial University of Newfoundland, Ferriss Hodgett Library, University Dr, Corner Brook, NL, A2H 6P9, CANADA. Tel: 709-637-6267. Fax: 709-637-6273, 709-639-8125. p. 2772

Greene, Brian, Head, Access Serv, Northeastern University Libraries, Snell Library, 360 Huntington Ave, Boston, MA, 02115. Tel: 617-373-2401. p. 1065

Greene, Brian A, Prog Mgr, WYLD Network, c/o Wyoming State Library, 516 S Greeley Hwy, Cheyenne, WY, 82002-0060. Tel: 307-777-6339. Fax: 307-777-6289. p. 2958

Greene, Casey, Head, Spec Coll, Rosenberg Library, 2310 Sealy Ave, Galveston, TX, 77550. Tel: 409-763-8854, Ext 117. Fax: 409-763-0275. p. 2326

Greene, Daniel, Interim Dir, Res & Acad Prog, Newberry Library, 60 W Walton St, Chicago, IL, 60610-3305. Tel: 312-255-3535. p. 620

Greene, Erika, Literacy Coordr, Lake County Library System, 2401 Woodlea Rd, Tavares, FL, 32778. Tel: 352-253-6183. Fax: 352-253-6184. p. 499

Greene, Fern, Commun Libr Supvr, Yakima Valley Libraries, Zillah Library, 109 Seventh St, Zillah, WA, 98953. Tel: 509-829-6707. Fax: 509-829-6707. p. 2551

Greene, Grace, Youth Serv Libr Consult, State of Vermont Department of Libraries, 109 State St, Montpelier, VT, 05609-0601. Tel: 802-828-6954. Fax: 802-828-2199. p. 2429

Greene, Jane, Actg Dir, Lynch Public Library, 423 W Hoffman, Lynch, NE, 68746. Tel: 402-569-3491. p. 1407

Greene, Jean, Admin Librn, Hinds Community College, Utica Campus Learning Resources/Library, Hwy 18 W, Utica, MS, 39175-9599. Tel: 601-885-7034. p. 1313

Greene, Jennifer, Ref/Archives Librn, University of Southern Indiana, 8600 University Blvd, Evansville, IN, 47712. Tel: 812-464-1832. Fax: 812-465-1693. p. 739

Greene, Jenny, Ref Serv, Ad, Hudson Library & Historical Society, 96 Library St, Hudson, OH, 44236-5122. Tel: 330-653-6658. Fax: 330-650-3373. p. 1905

Greene, Katherine, Automation Serv, University of Kansas Libraries, Wheat Law Library, Green Hall, Rm 200, 1535 W 15th St, Lawrence, KS, 66045-7608. Tel: 785-864-3025. Fax: 785-864-3680. p. 878

Greene, Kingsley W, Dir, The Sage Colleges, 140 New Scotland Ave, Albany, NY, 12208. Tel: 518-244-2346. Fax: 518-244-2400. p. 1570

Greene, Kingsley W, Dir, The Sage Colleges, 45 Ferry St, Troy, NY, 12180. Tel: 518-244-2346. Fax: 518-244-2400. p. 1756

Greene, Lindsey, Med Librn, John C Lincoln Health Network, 250 E Dunlap Ave, Phoenix, AZ, 85020. Tel: 602-870-6328. Fax: 602-997-9325. p. 74

Greene, Lindsey, Med Librn, Lincoln John C Health Network, Chapman Memorial Medical Library, 19829 N 27th Ave, Phoenix, AZ, 85027. Tel: 623-879-5288. Fax: 623-879-1563. p. 74

Greene, Linette, YA Librn, Missoula Public Library, 301 E Main, Missoula, MT, 59802-4799. Tel: 406-721-2665. Fax: 406-728-5900. p. 1386

Greene, Loretta Zwolak, Archives Dir, Providence Archives, 4800 37th Ave SW, Seattle, WA, 98126. Tel: 206-923-4010. Fax: 206-923-4001. p. 2530

Greene, Louise, Dir, Libr Serv, Richland Community College, One College Park, Decatur, IL, 62521. Tel: 217-875-7200, Ext 302. Fax: 217-875-6961. p. 634

Greene, Louise, Art Librn, Ref Librn, University of Maryland Libraries, Architecture Library, College Park, MD, 20742-7011. Tel: 301-405-6317. Fax: 301-314-9583. p. 1025

Greene, Louise, Ref, University of Maryland Libraries, Art Library, Art/Sociology Bldg, College Park, MD, 20742. Tel: 301-405-9061. Fax: 301-314-9725. p. 1025

Greene, Marilyn, Electronic Res Librn, Lamar State College-Orange Library, 410 Front St, Orange, TX, 77630-5796. Tel: 409-882-3084. Fax: 409-883-7552. p. 2367

Greene, Michael, Ser, Wake Forest University, Professional Center Library, Worrell Professional Ctr for Law & Management, 1834 Wake Forest Rd, Winston-Salem, NC, 27106. Tel: 336-758-5438. Fax: 336-758-6077. p. 1834

Greene, Mira, Head, Tech Serv, University of Tulsa Libraries, Mabee Legal Information Center, 3120 E Fourth Pl, Tulsa, OK, 74104-3189. Tel: 918-631-2404. Fax: 918-631-3556. p. 1984

Greene, Mira, Cat, University of Texas Medical Branch, 301 University Blvd, Galveston, TX, 77555-1035. Tel: 409-772-1971. Fax: 409-762-9782. p. 2327

Greene, Nancy K, Dir, Ridgewood Public Library, 125 N Maple Ave, Ridgewood, NJ, 07450-3288. Tel: 201-670-5600. Fax: 201-670-0293. p. 1526

Greene, Richard, Libr Tech, Smithsonian Libraries, National Museum of Natural History Library, Nat Museum of Natural Hist, Rm 51, MRC 154, Tenth St & Constitution Ave NW, Washington, DC, 20013-0712. Tel: 202-633-1672. Fax: 202-357-1896. p. 415

Greene, Richard O, Dir, Mid-Mississippi Regional Library System, 201 S Huntington St, Kosciusko, MS, 39090-9002. Tel: 662-289-5151. Fax: 662-289-5106. p. 1306

Greene, Sandra, Multimedia, Saint Joseph's College, Hwy 231 S, Rensselaer, IN, 47978. Tel: 219-866-6190. Fax: 219-866-6135. p. 774

Greene, Sandra L, Asst Librn, Waveland-Brown Township Public Library, 115 E Green, Waveland, IN, 47989. Tel: 765-435-2700. Fax: 765-435-2434. p. 786

Greene, Sarah, Ch, Tech Librn, Youth Serv, Caldwell County Public Library, 120 Hospital Ave, Lenoir, NC, 28645-4454. Tel: 828-757-1270. Fax: 828-757-1413. p. 1806

Greene, Victoria, Dep Dir, Wicomico Public Library, 122 S Division St, Salisbury, MD, 21801. Tel: 410-749-3612, Ext 112. Fax: 410-548-2968. p. 1040

Greenebaum, David, Prog Coordr, Georgia Interactive Network for Medical Information, c/o Mercer University School of Medicine, 1550 College St, Macon, GA, 31207. Tel: 478-301-2827. Fax: 478-301-2051. p. 2941

Greenfield, Charles K, In Charge, Legal Aid Society of Hawaii Library, 924 Bethel St, Honolulu, HI, 96813. Tel: 808-527-8010, 808-536-4302. Fax: 808-527-8088. p. 564

Greenfield, Christina, ILL, Big Horn County Library, 430 West C St, Basin, WY, 82410. Tel: 307-568-2388. Fax: 307-568-2011. p. 2651

Greenfield, Deana, Librn, National Louis University Library & Learning Support, 122 S Michigan Ave, Chicago, IL, 60603. Tel: 312-261-3565. Fax: 312-261-3565. p. 619

Greenholz, Carol, Cat, Tech Serv, Farmingdale State College of New York, 2350 Broadhollow Rd, Farmingdale, NY, 11735-1021. Tel: 631-420-2040. Fax: 631-420-2473. p. 1622

Greening, Carol, Librn, Southeast Regional Library, Rocanville Branch, 218 Ellice St, Rocanville, SK, S0A 3L0, CANADA. Tel: 306-645-2088. p. 2931

Greenland, Amy, Dir, Hastings Public Library, 517 W Fourth St, Hastings, NE, 68901-7560. Tel: 402-461-2346. Fax: 402-461-2359. p. 1401

Greenland, Nicole, VPres, Bay Area Library & Information Network, 1462 Cedar St, Berkeley, CA, 94702. Tel: 510-436-1462. p. 2938

Greenlaw, Evelyn, Dir, University of Southern Maine, 51 Westminster St, Lewiston, ME, 04240. Tel: 207-753-6541. Fax: 207-753-6543. p. 990

Greenlaw, Evelyn, Dir of Libr/Media Serv, University of Southern Maine, 314 Forest Ave, Portland, ME, 04104. Tel: 207-780-5660. Fax: 207-780-4042. p. 998

Greenleaf, Rene L, Dir, Hammond Public Library, 564 State St, Hammond, IN, 46320-1532. Tel: 219-931-5100. Fax: 219-931-3474. p. 747

Greenleaf, Sara, Head, Tech Serv, Hobart & William Smith Colleges, 334 Pulteney St, Geneva, NY, 14456. Tel: 315-781-3550. Fax: 315-781-3560. p. 1627

Greenlee, Carmen, Instrul Media Serv Librn, Bowdoin College Library, 3000 College Sta, Brunswick, ME, 04011-8421. Tel: 207-725-3286. p. 979

Greenlee, Carmen, Instrul Media Serv Librn, Bowdoin College Library, Language Media Center, Sills Hall, 1st Flr, 8200 College Sta, Brunswick, ME, 04011-8242. Tel: 207-725-3702. p. 979

Greenlee, Edwin, Assoc Dir, University of Pennsylvania Libraries, Biddle Law Library, Tanenbaum Hall, Flrs 3-5, 3443 Sansom St, Philadelphia, PA, 19104. Tel: 215-898-7488. Fax: 215-898-6619. p. 2119

Greenlee, Michael, Assoc Law Librn, Idaho State Law Library, 322 E Front St, Ste 560, Boise, ID, 83702. Tel: 208-364-4554. Fax: 208-334-2467. p. 571

Greenlee, Pamela, Grad Sch Res Librn, Olivet Nazarene University, One University Ave, Bourbonnais, IL, 60914-2271. Tel: 815-939-5439. Fax: 815-939-5170. p. 596

Greenly, Eric, Archivist, Lorain County Historical Society, 509 Washington Ave, Elyria, OH, 44035. Tel: 440-322-3341. Fax: 440-322-2817. p. 1898

Greenstein, K G, Librn, Ohlone College, 43600 Mission Blvd, Fremont, CA, 94539. Tel: 510-659-6000, Ext 5272. Fax: 510-659-6265. p. 149

Greenstein, Patricia, Asst Dir, Res Mgt, East Carolina University, William E Laupus Health Sciences Library, 600 Moye Blvd, Health Sciences Bldg, Greenville, NC, 27834. Tel: 252-744-2243. Fax: 252-744-2672. p. 1799

Greenstreet, Jennifer, Dir, Ada Public Library, 124 S Rennie, Ada, OK, 74820. Tel: 580-436-8121. Fax: 580-436-0534. p. 1955

Greenwald, Diane, Dir, Warwick Public Library, 600 Sandy Lane, Warwick, RI, 02889-8298. Tel: 401-739-5440, Ext 223. Fax: 401-732-2055. p. 2177

Greenwald, Dolores, Dir, Williamson County Public Library, 1314 Columbia Ave, Franklin, TN, 37064-3626. Tel: 615-595-1240. Fax: 615-595-1245. p. 2234

Greenwalt, Toby, Virtual Serv Coordr, Skokie Public Library, 5215 Oakton St, Skokie, IL, 60077-3680. Tel: 847-673-7774. Fax: 847-673-7797. p. 703

Greenward, Joseph, Dir, Lane Public Libraries, 300 N Third St, Hamilton, OH, 45011-1629. Tel: 513-894-7156. Fax: 513-894-2718. p. 1903

Greenway, Annette, Br Mgr, Abbeville County Library System, 201 S Main St, Abbeville, SC, 29620. Tel: 864-459-4009. Fax: 864-459-4009. p. 2179

Greenwell, Michael, Asst Dir, Nelson County Public Library, 201 Cathedral Manor, Bardstown, KY, 40004-1515. Tel: 502-348-3714. Fax: 502-348-5578. p. 906

Greenwell, Stacey, Assoc Dean, Acad Affairs/Res, University of Kentucky Libraries, I-85, 401 Hilltop Ave, Lexington, KY, 40506-0456. Tel: 859-257-0500, Ext 2002. p. 921

Greenwold, Amy, Libr Mgr, Oregon Research Institute Library, 1715 Franklin Blvd, Eugene, OR, 97403-1983. Tel: 541-484-2123. Fax: 541-484-1108. p. 1997

Greenwood, Aleteia, Head, Sci & Eng, University of British Columbia Library, Science & Engineering, Irving K Barber Learning Ctr, 1961 East Mall, Vancouver, BC, V6T 1Z1, CANADA. Tel: 604-822-0689. Fax: 604-822-5366. p. 2743

Greenwood, Anne, Librn, St Paul's Episcopal Church, Rock Creek Church Rd & Webster St NW, Washington, DC, 20011. Tel: 202-726-2080. Fax: 202-726-1084. p. 413

Greenwood, Christine, Br Mgr, Madison County Library System, Canton Public Library, 102 Priestley St, Canton, MS, 39046. Tel: 601-859-3202. Fax: 601-859-2728. p. 1295

Greenwood, JoAnn, Librn, Department of Veterans Affairs, 4800 Memorial Dr, Waco, TX, 76711. Tel: 254-297-3272. Fax: 254-297-5335. p. 2397

Greenwood, Joanne, Supv Librn, Department of Veterans Affairs, 1901 Veterans Memorial Dr, 14LIB-T, Temple, TX, 76504. Tel: 254-743-0607. Fax: 254-743-0183. p. 2390

Greenwood, Miriam, Librn, Modrall, Sperling, Roehl, Harris & Sisk, PO Box 2168, Albuquerque, NM, 87103. Tel: 505-848-1800. Fax: 505-848-9710. p. 1549

Greenwood, Pamela, Chief Exec Officer, Ignace Public Library, 36 Main St, Ignace, ON, P0T 1T0, CANADA. Tel: 807-934-2280. Fax: 807-934-6452. p. 2812

Greenwood, Wendy, Coll Develop, Ref Mgr, Tech Serv Mgr, Grandview Heights Public Library, 1685 W First Ave, Columbus, OH, 43212. Tel: 614-486-2951. Fax: 614-481-7021. p. 1886

Greer, Ann, Distance Educ, ILL, Southern Adventist University, 4851 Industrial Dr, Collegedale, TN, 37315. Tel: 423-236-2791. Fax: 423-236-1788. p. 2230

Greer, Elektra, Ch, Longmont Public Library, 409 Fourth Ave, Longmont, CO, 80501-6006. Tel: 303-651-8781. Fax: 303-651-8911. p. 317

Greer, James A, Br Mgr, Librn III, Montgomery City-County Public Library System, Ramer Branch Library, 5444 State Hwy 94, Ramer, AL, 36069-5008. Tel: 334-562-3364. Fax: 334-562-3889. p. 30

Greer, Johanne, Dir, Libr & Info Serv, Maryland Department of Legislative Services Library, 90 State Circle, Annapolis, MD, 21401. Tel: 410-946-5400. Fax: 410-946-5405. p. 1010

Greer, John, Head, Tech & Syst Serv, University of Montana, Maureen & Mike Mansfield Library, 32 Campus Dr, No 9936, Missoula, MT, 59812-9936. Tel: 406-243-2539. Fax: 406-243-4067. p. 1386

Greer, Karla, Dean, Educ Res, Eastfield College Library, 3737 Motley Dr, Mesquite, TX, 75150-2033. Tel: 972-860-7173. p. 2362

Greer, Kathy, Ch, Deer Park Public Library, 44 Lake Ave, Deer Park, NY, 11729-6047. Tel: 631-586-3000. Fax: 631-586-3006. p. 1613

Greer, Kecia, Reader Serv, South Carolina State Library, 1430 Senate St, Columbia, SC, 29201-3710. Tel: 803-734-4611. Fax: 803-734-4610. p. 2189

Greer, Nancy B, Librn, United States Environmental Protection Agency National Enforcement Investigations Center, Denver Federal Ctr, Bldg 25, Door W-2, Denver, CO, 80225. Fax: 303-462-9354. p. 303

Greer, Patricia L, Per, Ref Serv, University of Tennessee at Martin, Ten Wayne Fisher Dr, Martin, TN, 38238. Tel: 731-881-7064. Fax: 731-881-7074. p. 2246

Grefe, Richard, Sr Ref Librn (Info Serv), Washington & Lee University, University Library, 204 W Washington St, Lexington, VA, 24450-2116. Tel: 540-458-8648. Fax: 540-458-8964. p. 2475

Greges, Chrystie, Librn, Northern Virginia Community College Libraries, Manassas Campus, Colgan Hall, Rm 129, 6901 Sudley Rd, Manassas, VA, 20109-2399. Tel: 703-257-6639. Fax: 703-368-1069. p. 2447

Gregg, Cody, Interim Assoc Dean, South Texas College Library, 3201 W Pecan Blvd, McAllen, TX, 78501-6661. Tel: 956-872-8330. Fax: 956-872-7202. p. 2361

Gregg, Diane, Dr, Prof, Georgia College & State University, Campus Box 079, Milledgeville, GA, 31061. Tel: 478-445-5004, Ext 2515. Fax: 478-445-2513. p. 2964

Gregg, Frances, Br Mgr, Evon A Ford Public Library, 208 Spring St, Taylorsville, MS, 39168. Tel: 601-785-4361. Fax: 601-785-6611. p. 1315

Gregg, Judith, Sr Librn, King Pub Ref & Res Unit, San Jose Public Library, 150 E San Fernando St, San Jose, CA, 95112-3580. Tel: 408-808-2195. Fax: 408-808-2395. p. 250

Gregg, Liz, Asst County Librn, Jackson County Public Library, 310 Keener St, Sylva, NC, 28779-3241. Tel: 828-586-2016, Ext 313. Fax: 828-586-3423. p. 1826

Gregg, Martha, Tech/Pub Serv Librn, Butler Community College Libraries, 901 S Haverhill Rd, El Dorado, KS, 67042-3280. Tel: 316-323-6842. Fax: 316-322-3315. p. 864

Gregg, Michele, Distance Learning & Embedded Librn, Tri-County Technical College Library, 7900 Hwy 76, Pendleton, SC, 29670. Tel: 864-646-1750. Fax: 864-646-1543. p. 2202

Gregg, Susan, Ref Librn, College of Southern Nevada, Cheyenne Campus, 3200 E Cheyenne Ave, C2A, North Las Vegas, NV, 89030. Tel: 702-651-4622. Fax: 702-643-4812. p. 1429

Gregoire, Pierre, Dir, Frankfort Public Library District, 21119 S Pfeiffer Rd, Frankfort, IL, 60423-8699. Tel: 815-469-2423. Fax: 815-469-9307. p. 646

Gregoire-Voskamp, Percy, Librn, Portage la Prairie Regional Library, 40-B Royal Rd N, Portage la Prairie, MB, R1N 1V1, CANADA. Tel: 204-857-4271. Fax: 204-239-4387. p. 2750

Gregor, Paul, Br Mgr, Greene County Public Library, Jamestown Community Library, 86B Seaman Dr, Jamestown, OH, 45335. Tel: 937-352-4005. Fax: 937-675-6605. p. 1951

Gregory, Alison, Instrul Serv Librn & Coordr, Info Literacy & Outreach, Lycoming College, 700 College Pl, Williamsport, PA, 17701-5192. Tel: 570-321-4087. Fax: 570-321-4090. p. 2156

Gregory, Cadigan, Librn, Mount Caesar Union Library, 628 Old Homestead Hwy, Swanzey, NH, 03446-2312. Tel: 603-357-0456. p. 1466

Gregory, Curtis, In Charge, US National Park Service, 5646 Carver Rd, Diamond, MO, 64840-8314. Tel: 417-325-4151. Fax: 417-325-4231. p. 1327

Gregory, Cynthia, Head, Electronic Res, College of Mount Saint Joseph, 5701 Delhi Rd, Cincinnati, OH, 45233-1671. Tel: 513-244-4762. Fax: 513-244-4355. p. 1869

Gregory, David, Assoc Dean, Res & Access, Iowa State University Library, 302 Parks Library, Ames, IA, 50011-2140. Tel: 515-294-1442, 515-294-1443. Fax: 515-294-5525. p. 793

Gregory, David, Actg Dean, Libr Serv, Morehead State University, 150 University Blvd, Morehead, KY, 40351. Tel: 606-783-5100. Fax: 606-783-5037. p. 929

Gregory, Dennis, Dir, New Baden Public Library, 210 N First St, New Baden, IL, 62265. Tel: 618-588-4554. Fax: 618-588-4554. p. 679

Gregory, Diane, ILL, Ref, Franklin Square Public Library, 19 Lincoln Rd, Franklin Square, NY, 11010. Tel: 516-488-3444. Fax: 516-354-3368. p. 1624

Gregory, Dudley James, Actg Mgr, United States Navy, Bldg 63, Rm 208 NIOC, Sugar Grove, WV, 26815. Tel: 304-249-6321. Fax: 304-249-6385. p. 2572

Gregory, Ed, Librn, Brewers Association of Canada Library, 45 O'Connor St, Ste 650, Ottawa, ON, K1P 1A4, CANADA. Tel: 613-232-9601. Fax: 613-232-2283. p. 2828

Gregory, Gwen, Bibliog Serv, Colorado College, 1021 N Cascade Ave, Colorado Springs, CO, 80903-3252. Tel: 719-389-6658. Fax: 719-389-6082. p. 294

Gregory, Gwen, Assoc Dir, Access & Organization, The John Marshall Law School, 315 S Plymouth Ct, Chicago, IL, 60604. Tel: 312-427-2737. Fax: 312-427-8307. p. 618

Gregory, Holly, Dir, Breckinridge County Public Library, 112 S Main St, Hardinsburg, KY, 40143. Tel: 270-756-2323. Fax: 270-756-5634. p. 915

Gregory, Jackie, Librn, Jewish Federation Libraries, Akiva Library, 809 Percy Warner Blvd, Nashville, TN, 37205. Tel: 615-356-1880, Ext 19. Fax: 615-356-1850. p. 2256

Gregory, Johnny, Div Head, Arkansas Workers' Compensation Commission Library, 324 Spring St, Little Rock, AR, 72201. Tel: 501-682-2697. Fax: 501-682-6761. p. 106

Gregory, Laura, Asst Librn, Leanna Hicks Public Library, 2005 Inkster Rd, Inkster, MI, 48141. Tel: 313-563-2822. Fax: 313-274-5130. p. 1193

Gregory, Laurel, Dir, University of Hawaii Center, West Hawaii, 81-964 Halekii St, Kealakekua, HI, 96750. Tel: 808-322-4858, 808-322-4862. Fax: 808-322-4859. p. 566

Gregory, Mary, Ch, Nevada Public Library, 631 K Ave, Nevada, IA, 50201. Tel: 515-382-2628. Fax: 515-382-3552. p. 834

Gregory, Nancy, Librn, Scottsboro Public Library, 1002 S Broad St, Scottsboro, AL, 35768. Tel: 256-574-4335. Fax: 256-259-4457. p. 35

Gregory, Patricia, PhD, Asst Univ Librn, Res & Assessment, Saint Louis University, 3650 Lindell Blvd, Saint Louis, MO, 63108-3302. Tel: 314-977-3107. Fax: 314-977-3108. p. 1360

Gregory, Sophia, Cat Librn, Campbell University, Norman Adrian Wiggins School of Law Library, 225 Hillsborough St, Ste 203, Raleigh, NC, 27603. Tel: 919-865-5869. Fax: 919-865-5995. p. 1778

Gregory, Susan, Dir, Bozeman Public Library, 626 E Main St, Bozeman, MT, 59715. Tel: 406-582-2400. Fax: 406-582-2424. p. 1375

Gregory, Susan, Tech Serv, Union County Carnegie Library, 300 E South St, Union, SC, 29379-2392. Tel: 864-427-7140. Fax: 864-427-4687. p. 2207

Gregory, Tammy, Br Head, Mackinaw Area Public Library, Pellston Branch, 125 N Milton St, Pellston, MI, 49769-9301. Tel: 231-539-8858. p. 1205

Gregory, Theresa, Asst Dir, Hartland Public Libraries, 153 Rte 5, Hartland, VT, 05048. Tel: 802-436-2473. Fax: 802-436-2473. p. 2425

Gregory, Vicki L, Prof, University of South Florida, 4202 Fowler Ave, CIS 1040, Tampa, FL, 33620-7800. Tel: 813-974-3520. Fax: 813-974-6840. p. 2964

Gregoski, Mary, Dir, Palmer Library, 202 Commercial St, Palmer, NE, 68864. Tel: 308-894-5305. Fax: 308-894-8245. p. 1416

Gregus, Bridget, Acq of Monographs & Journals, AV Coll, ILL Spec, Charlotte Community Library, 226 S Bostwick St, Charlotte, MI, 48813-1801. Tel: 517-543-8859. Fax: 517-543-8868. p. 1162

Greibrok, Patty, Ch, Albert Lea Public Library, 211 E Clark St, Albert Lea, MN, 56007. Tel: 507-377-4350. Fax: 507-377-4339. p. 1239

Greifenkamp, Katie, Br Mgr, Public Library of Cincinnati & Hamilton County, Anderson, 7450 State Rd, Cincinnati, OH, 45230. Tel: 513-369-6030. Fax: 513-369-4444. p. 1871

Greifenstein, Charles B, Archives, Ms, American Philosophical Society Library, 105 S Fifth St, Philadelphia, PA, 19106-3386. Tel: 215-440-3404. Fax: 215-440-3423. p. 2103

Greil, Amy E, Ch, Pomfret Public Library, 449 Pomfret St, Pomfret, CT, 06258. Tel: 860-928-3475. p. 364

Greil, Barbara, Ref Librn, State University of New York, College of Technology, Upper Colleg Dr, Alfred, NY, 14802. Tel: 607-587-4313. Fax: 607-587-4351. p. 1572

Greiner, Amy G, Ch, Wells County Public Library, 200 W Washington St, Bluffton, IN, 46714-1999. Tel: 260-824-1612. Fax: 260-824-3129. p. 728

Greiner, Anthony (Tony), Fac Librn-Cascade Campus, Portland Community College Library, 12000 SW 49th AV, Portland, OR, 97219. Tel: 971-722-5333. Fax: 971-722-8397. p. 2013

Greiner, Marilyn, Asst Dir, Greenburgh Public Library, 300 Tarrytown Rd, Elmsford, NY, 10523. Tel: 914-721-8220. Fax: 914-721-8201. p. 1620

Greitzer, Darrin, Dean, Glendale University, 220 N Glendale Ave, Glendale, CA, 91206. Tel: 818-247-0770. Fax: 818-247-0872. p. 155

Grell, Krystyna, Librn, Polish Museum of America Library, 984 N Milwaukee Ave, Chicago, IL, 60642-4101. Tel: 773-384-3352, Ext 101. Fax: 773-384-3799. p. 622

Grellier, Julie, Ref Librn, Douglas College Library, 700 Royal Ave, New Westminster, BC, V3M 5Z5, CANADA. Tel: 604-527-5183. Fax: 604-527-5193. p. 2733

Gremard, April, Br Librn, Reynolds County Library District, Ellington Branch, 130 S Main, Ellington, MO, 63638. Tel: 573-663-7289. Fax: 573-663-7289. p. 1323

Gremmels, Jill, Libr Dir, Davidson College, 209 Ridge Rd, Davidson, NC, 28035-0001. Tel: 704-894-2331. Fax: 704-894-2625. p. 1786

Grenell, Paula, Ref Librn, College of Southern Nevada, Henderson Campus, 700 S College Dr, H1A, Henderson, NV, 89002. Tel: 702-651-3066. Fax: 702-651-3513. p. 1429

Grenier, Amanda, Libr Dir, Chester C Corbin Public Library, Two Lake St, Webster, MA, 01570. Tel: 508-949-3880. Fax: 508-949-0537. p. 1134

Grenier, Andre, Admin Dir, Cegep de Valleyfield Bibliotheque, 80 St Thomas St, Valleyfield, QC, J6T 4J7, CANADA. Tel: 450-370-4860. Fax: 450-377-6011. p. 2914

Grenier, Beth, Librn, Saint-Gobain Abrasives Library, One New Bond St, Worcester, MA, 01606-2614. Tel: 508-795-2001. Fax: 508-795-5755. p. 1144

Grenier, Jeffrey, Pres, Watertown Historical Society Library, 22 De Forest St, Watertown, CT, 06795. Tel: 860-274-1050. p. 375

Grenier, Stephanie, Dir, Fasken Martineau DuMoulin LLP, 800 Victoria Sq, Montreal, QC, H4Z 1E9, CANADA. Tel: 514-397-4320. Fax: 514-397-7600. p. 2895

Grenier, Therese, Librn, National Association for Hispanic Elderly Library, 234 E Colorado Blvd, Ste 300, Pasadena, CA, 91101. Tel: 626-564-1988. Fax: 626-564-2659. p. 206

Grenier, Tina M, Coll Mgt Librn, North Dakota State College of Science, 800 Sixth St N, Wahpeton, ND, 58076-0001. Tel: 701-671-2612. Fax: 701-671-2674. p. 1849

Grennan, Jon, Dir, Sullivan County Community College, 112 College Rd, Loch Sheldrake, NY, 12759-5108. Tel: 845-434-5750, Ext 4208. p. 1653

Grenot, Teresa, Dean of Libr, Humboldt State University Library, One Harpst St, Arcata, CA, 95521-8299. Tel: 707-826-3441. Fax: 707-826-3440. p. 122

Gres, Dusty, Dir, Ohoopee Regional Library System, 610 Jackson St, Vidalia, GA, 30474-2835. Tel: 912-537-9283. Fax: 912-537-3735. p. 555

Gresco, Deborah, Librn, Carrolltown Public Library, 140 E Carroll St, Carrolltown, PA, 15722. Tel: 814-344-6300. Fax: 814-344-6355. p. 2042

Gresehover, Beverly, Assoc Dir, Res, University of Maryland, Baltimore, Health Sciences & Human Services Library, 601 W Lombard St, Baltimore, MD, 21201. Tel: 410-706-1784. Fax: 410-706-3101. p. 1019

Gresham, JoAnn H, Br Mgr, Cabarrus County Public Library, 27 Union St N, Concord, NC, 28025-4793. Tel: 704-920-2050. Fax: 704-784-3822. p. 1785

Gresham, Joanne, Cat, Barber Scotia College, 145 Cabarrus Ave W, Concord, NC, 28025. Tel: 704-789-2953. Fax: 704-789-2955. p. 1785

Gresham, Keith, Assoc Univ Librn, Res & Instrul Serv, Princeton University, One Washington Rd, Princeton, NJ, 08544-2098. Tel: 609-258-1470. Fax: 609-258-0441. p. 1523

Gresham, Lisa, Pub Serv Coordr, Whatcom County Library System, 5205 Northwest Dr, Bellingham, WA, 98226-9050. Tel: 360-384-3150. Fax: 360-384-4947. p. 2509

Gresham, Marilyn, Tech Serv, Coastal Carolina Community College, 444 Western Blvd, Jacksonville, NC, 28546-6877. Tel: 910-455-1221, 910-938-6237. Fax: 910-455-7027. p. 1803

Gresko, Nancy, Dir, Westmoreland County Federated Library System, 226 Donohoe Rd, Greensburg, PA, 15601. Tel: 724-420-5638. p. 2062

Gresko, Tina, Ch, Flenniken Public Library, 102 E George St, Carmichaels, PA, 15320-1202. Tel: 724-966-5263. Fax: 724-966-9511. p. 2042

Gress, Andrew M, Dir, Libr Serv, Kaplan University, 4655 NW 121st St, Des Moines, IA, 50323. Tel: 515-727-2100, Ext 208. Fax: 515-727-2115. p. 810

Gress, Denise, Exec Dir, Saskatchewan Choral Federation Library, 201-1870 Lorne St, Regina, SK, S4P 2L7, CANADA. Tel: 306-780-9230. Fax: 306-781-6021. p. 2923

Gress, Stephanie, Curator, Suffolk County Vanderbilt Museum Library, 180 Little Neck Rd, Centerport, NY, 17721. Tel: 631-854-5508, 631-854-5551. Fax: 631-854-5594. p. 1604

Gresser, Marylyn, Chief Librn, United States Department of Veterans Affairs, 1601 SW Archer Rd, Gainesville, FL, 32608-1197. Tel: 352-376-1611, Ext 6313. Fax: 352-374-6148. p. 449

Gresser, Marylyn, Chief Librn, North Florida/South Georgia Veterans Health System, 619 S Marion Ave, Lake City, FL, 32025. Tel: 352-376-1611, Ext 6312. Fax: 352-374-6148. p. 458

Gretchen, Leslie, ILL, Portland Community College Library, 12000 SW 49th AV, Portland, OR, 97219. Tel: 971-722-7190. Fax: 971-722-8397. p. 2013

Gretchyn, Amy, Adult Serv, Glen Cove Public Library, Four Glen Cove Ave, Glen Cove, NY, 11542-2885. Tel: 516-676-2130. Fax: 516-676-2788. p. 1628

Grether, Barbara, Librn, Danville Community College, 1008 S Main St, Danville, VA, 24541-4004. Tel: 434-797-8453. Fax: 434-797-8415. p. 2459

Gretzinger, Tannis, Legis Librn, Legislative Library of Manitoba, 200 Vaughan St, Rm 100, Winnipeg, MB, R3C 1T5, CANADA. Tel: 204-945-4330. Fax: 204-948-1312. p. 2756

Greuber, Gayle, Dir, Dutton S Peterson Memorial Library, 106 First St, Odessa, NY, 14869. Tel: 607-594-2791. Fax: 607-594-2791. p. 1709

Greuber, Lori, Cat, Lake Erie College, 391 W Washington St, Painesville, OH, 44077-3309. Tel: 440-375-7402. p. 1926

Greufe, Carolyn, Br Mgr, Des Moines Public Library, East Side, 2559 Hubbell Ave, Des Moines, IA, 50317. Tel: 515-283-4152. Fax: 515-248-6256. p. 808

Greufe, Carolyn E, Br Mgr, Des Moines Public Library, North Side, 3516 Fifth Ave, Des Moines, IA, 50313. Tel: 515-283-4152. Fax: 515-242-2684. p. 808

Greule, Sharon, Dir, Peru Library, Six W Main Rd, Peru, MA, 01235-9254. Tel: 413-655-8650. p. 1117

Grev, Heather, YA Librn, Sherburne Memorial Library, PO Box 73, Killington, VT, 05751. Tel: 802-422-4251, 802-422-9765. Fax: 802-422-4323. p. 2427

Greville, Nicole, Ad, Fort McMurray Public Library, 151 MacDonald Dr, Fort McMurray, AB, T9H 5C5, CANADA. Tel: 780-743-7800. Fax: 780-743-7938. p. 2704

Grey, Diane, Archives Mgr, Tampa Tribune Co, 200 S Parker St, Tampa, FL, 33606. Tel: 813-259-7070. Fax: 813-259-8199. p. 498

Grey, Jackie, Dir, Support Serv, Seneca Falls Library, 47 Cayuga St, Seneca Falls, NY, 13148. Tel: 315-568-8265, Ext 4. Fax: 315-568-1606. p. 1742

Grey, Jessica, Dir, Larson Memorial Public Library, 1595 Johnson Dr, Lakeside, AZ, 85929. Tel: 928-368-6688. p. 68

Grey, Mariana, Librn, Florida Department of Corrections, 3142 Thomas Dr, Bonifay, FL, 32425. Tel: 850-547-8658. Fax: 850-547-0522. p. 428

Grey, Mariana, Ref Librn, United States Air Force, Air Force Research Lab, Tyndall Research Site Technical Information Center, 139 Barnes Dr, Ste 2, Tyndall AFB, FL, 32403-5323. Tel: 850-283-6285. Fax: 850-283-6500. p. 501

Grey, Rosemary, Ch, Elizabeth Taber Library, Eight Spring St, Marion, MA, 02738. Tel: 508-748-1252. Fax: 508-748-0939. p. 1102

Grey, Susan, Librn, Jaquith Public Library, Old Schoolhouse Common, 122 School St, Marshfield, VT, 05658. Tel: 802-426-3581. Fax: 802-426-3045. p. 2428

Grey, Wilma J, Dir, Newark Public Library, Five Washington St, Newark, NJ, 07101. Tel: 973-733-7784, 973-733-7800. Fax: 973-733-5648. p. 1511

Greybill, Lisa, Adminr, Columbia Public Library, 24 S Sixth St, Columbia, PA, 17512-1599. Tel: 717-684-2255. Fax: 717-684-5920. p. 2046

Grice, Ann, Supv Librn, Circ, Bernards Township Library, 32 S Maple Ave, Basking Ridge, NJ, 07920-1216. Tel: 908-204-3031. Fax: 908-766-1580. p. 1470

Grice, Janette, Dir, Interlochen Public Library, 9700 Riley Rd, Interlochen, MI, 49643. Tel: 231-276-6767. Fax: 231-276-5172. p. 1193

Grice, Julie, Head, Ch, Shreve Memorial Library, Hamilton/South Caddo Branch, 2111 Bert Kouns Industrial Loop, Shreveport, LA, 71118. Tel: 318-687-6824. Fax: 318-686-0971. p. 969

Grice, Rosie, Librn, Gila County Law Library, 1400 E Ash St, Globe, AZ, 85501. Tel: 928-425-3231. Fax: 928-425-0319. p. 64

Grieb, Sarah K, Bus Mgr, University of Nebraska at Omaha, 6001 Dodge St, Omaha, NE, 68182-0237. Tel: 402-554-2916. Fax: 402-554-3215. p. 1414

Grieco, Larry, Dir, Teikyo Loretto Heights University Library, 3001 S Federal Blvd, Denver, CO, 80236. Tel: 303-937-4042. Fax: 303-937-4224. p. 303

Grieco, Lawrence, Dir, Gilpin County Public Library District, 15131 Hwy 119, Black Hawk, CO, 80422. Tel: 303-582-5777. Fax: 303-582-3938. p. 289

Griener, Joanne, Exec Dir, Mgt Serv, Edmonton Public Library, Seven Sir Winston Churchill Sq, Edmonton, AB, T5J 2V4, CANADA. Tel: 780-496-6822. Fax: 780-496-1885. p. 2700

Grier, Amy, Dir of Educ, St Joseph Museums Inc, 3406 Frederick Ave, Saint Joseph, MO, 64506. Tel: 816-232-8471. Fax: 816-232-8482. p. 1352

Grier, P J, Dir, Delaware Library Consortium, Delaware Academy of Medicine, 4765 Ogletown Stanton Rd, Ste L10, Newark, DE, 19713. Tel: 302-376-0314. Fax: 302-733-3885. p. 2940

Grier, Sheila, Commun Librn, Deschutes Public Library District, Sunriver Area Branch, 56855 Venture Lane, Sunriver, OR, 97707. Tel: 541-312-1081. Fax: 541-593-9286. p. 1992

Griesbach, Kurt, In Charge, Hellmuth, Obata & Kassabaum, Inc Library, 2711 N Haskell, Ste 2250, Dallas, TX, 75204. Tel: 214-720-6000. Fax: 214-720-6005. p. 2308

Griese, Norma, Libr Asst, Melvin Public Library, 232 Main St, Melvin, IA, 51350. Tel: 712-736-2107. p. 831

Griesen, David, Librn, Illinois Institute of Technology, 6502 S Archer Rd, Summit Argo, IL, 60501. Tel: 708-563-8160, 708-563-8163. Fax: 708-563-1873. p. 709

Grieser, Ruth, Head, Tech Serv, Archbold Community Library, 205 Stryker St, Archbold, OH, 43502-1142. Tel: 419-446-2783. Fax: 419-446-2142. p. 1854

Grieshaber-Otto, Susan, Librn, Parkland Regional Library, 5404 56th Ave, Lacombe, AB, T4L 1G1, CANADA. Tel: 403-782-3850. Fax: 403-782-4650. p. 2709

Griest, Lisa, Dir, Yavapai College Library, 1100 E Sheldon St, Bldg 19, Prescott, AZ, 86301. Tel: 928-776-2132. Fax: 928-776-2275. p. 78

Griffen, Shon, Ref Librn, Poplar Bluff Public Library, 318 N Main St, Poplar Bluff, MO, 63901. Tel: 573-686-8639. Fax: 573-785-6876. p. 1349

Griffey, Jason, Head, Info Tech, University of Tennessee at Chattanooga Library, 615 McCallie Ave, Dept 6456, Chattanooga, TN, 37403-2598. Tel: 423-425-4501. Fax: 423-425-4775. p. 2228

Griffin, Alyssa, Asst Librn, Lanesborough Public Library, 83 N Main St, Lanesborough, MA, 01237. Tel: 413-442-0222. Fax: 413-443-5811. p. 1097

Griffin, Amy, Libr Asst, La Conner Regional Library, 614 Morris St, La Conner, WA, 98257. Tel: 360-466-3352. Fax: 360-466-9178. p. 2519

Griffin, Burnella, Ser, Elizabeth City State University, 1704 Weeksville Rd, Elizabeth City, NC, 27909. Tel: 252-335-3432. Fax: 252-335-3446. p. 1791

Griffin, Carolene, Ref Librn, North Carolina Central University, 1801 Fayetteville St, Durham, NC, 27707-3129. Tel: 919-530-5237. Fax: 919-530-7612. p. 1789

Griffin, Christine, Librn, Compass Lexecon, 332 S Michigan Ave, Ste 1300, Chicago, IL, 60604-4306. Tel: 312-322-0200. Fax: 312-322-0218. p. 611

Griffin, Diane, Asst Br Mgr, Ch, Librn I, Montgomery City-County Public Library System, Ramer Branch Library, 5444 State Hwy 94, Ramer, AL, 36069-5008. Tel: 334-562-3364. Fax: 334-562-3889. p. 30

Griffin, Dixie, Br Mgr, Baker County Public Library, Huntington Branch, 55 E Jefferson, Huntington, OR, 97907. Tel: 541-869-2440. Fax: 541-869-2440. p. 1991

Griffin, Eryn, Br Mgr, San Bernardino County Library, Janice Horst Branch, 33103 Old Woman Springs Rd, Lucerne Valley, CA, 92356. Tel: 760-248-7521. Fax: 760-248-1131. p. 228

Griffin, Felix, Tech Serv, Neshoba County Public Library, 230 Beacon St, Philadelphia, MS, 39350. Tel: 601-656-4911. Fax: 601-656-6894. p. 1311

Griffin, Glenda, Ser Cataloger, Sam Houston State University, 1830 Bobby K Marks Dr, Huntsville, TX, 77340. Tel: 936-294-1614. Fax: 936-294-3780. p. 2345

Griffin, Greta, Ch, Switzerland County Public Library, 205 Ferry St, Vevay, IN, 47043. Tel: 812-427-3363. Fax: 812-427-3654. p. 784

Griffin, Heather, Circ, Nassau County Public Library System, Callahan Branch, 450077 State Rd 200, Callahan, FL, 32011-3767. Tel: 904-879-3434. Fax: 904-879-0636. p. 440

Griffin, Howard, Head, Ch, Orland Park Public Library, 14921 Ravinia Ave, Orland Park, IL, 60462. Tel: 708-428-5100. Fax: 708-349-8322. p. 686

Griffin, Jackie, Dir, Ventura County Library, 5600 Everglades St, Ste A, Ventura, CA, 93003. Tel: 805-677-7153. Fax: 805-677-7173. p. 279

Griffin, Jacque, Dir, Gila County Library District, 1400 E Ash St, Globe, AZ, 85501-1414. Tel: 928-402-8768, 928-402-8770. Fax: 928-425-3462. p. 64

Griffin, Jeff, Dir of Libr, New Orleans Baptist Theological Seminary, 1000 Johnson Ferry Rd, Ste C115, Marietta, GA, 30068. Tel: 770-321-1606. Fax: 770-321-5363. p. 543

Griffin, Jeff, Dr, Dean of Libr, New Orleans Baptist Theological Seminary, 4110 Seminary Pl, New Orleans, LA, 70126. Tel: 504-282-4455, Ext 3288. Fax: 504-816-8429. p. 961

Griffin, Jenny A, Librn, Heritage College & Seminary Library, 175 Holiday Inn Dr, Cambridge, ON, N3C 3T2, CANADA. Tel: 519-651-2869. Fax: 519-651-2870. p. 2798

Griffin, JoAnne, Ser Librn, Tufts University, 145 Harrison Ave, Boston, MA, 02111-1843. Tel: 617-636-2452. Fax: 617-636-4039. p. 1068

Griffin, John F, Dir, United States Air Force, Air Force Research Laboratory Library, Five Wright St, Hanscom AFB, MA, 01731-3004. Tel: 781-377-4742. Fax: 781-377-4896. p. 1093

Griffin, John L, Media Spec, Ad, Pitt Community College, Hwy 11 S, Greenville, NC, 27835. Tel: 252-321-4345. Fax: 252-321-4404. p. 1799

Griffin, John P, Computer Tech, Libby Memorial Library, 27 Staples St, Old Orchard Beach, ME, 04064. Tel: 207-934-4351. p. 994

Griffin, Lolita, Br Mgr, Chicago Public Library, Jeffery Manor, 2401 E 100th St, Chicago, IL, 60617. Tel: 312-747-6479. Fax: 312-747-7679. p. 609

Griffin, Marian Hallett, Dir, West Melbourne Public Library, 2755 Wingate Blvd, West Melbourne, FL, 32904. Tel: 321-952-4508. Fax: 321-952-4510. p. 502

Griffin, Mark, Ref Librn, Logan County Public Library, 201 W Sixth St, Russellville, KY, 42276. Tel: 270-726-6129. Fax: 270-726-6127. p. 934

Griffin, Mary, Br Head, Cullman County Public Library System, Garden City Public, Municipal Bldg, Hwy 31, Garden City, AL, 35070. Tel: 256-352-4552. Fax: 256-734-6902. p. 13

Griffin, Mary, Fac Mgr, Omaha Public Library, 215 S 15th St, Omaha, NE, 68102-1629. Tel: 402-444-3470. Fax: 402-444-4504. p. 1413

Griffin, Mary, Librn, Taft Public Library, 501 Green Ave, Taft, TX, 78390-2711. Tel: 361-528-3512. Fax: 361-528-3515. p. 2390

Griffin, Patricia S, Ref Serv, Roanoke Bible College, 715 N Poindexter St, Elizabeth City, NC, 27909-4054. Tel: 252-334-2057. Fax: 252-334-2071. p. 1791

Griffin, Rhonda, Dir, Gunn Memorial Public Library, 161 Main St E, Yanceyville, NC, 27379. Tel: 336-694-6241. Fax: 336-694-9846. p. 1835

Griffin, Sasha, Project Cat Archivist, Luther College, 700 College Dr, Decorah, IA, 52101. Tel: 563-387-1725. Fax: 563-387-1657. p. 807

Griffin, Shelby Jean, Asst Librn, Starkville-Oktibbeha County Public, Sturgis Public Library, 2732 Hwy 12 W, Sturgis, MS, 39769. Tel: 662-465-7493. Fax: 662-465-7493. p. 1315

Griffin, Swalena, Ch, Atlanta-Fulton Public Library System, Northside Library, 3295 Northside Pkwy NW, Atlanta, GA, 30327. Tel: 404-814-3508. Fax: 404-814-3511. p. 512

Griffin, Terrance, Computer & Info Res Librn, Pine Bluff & Jefferson County Library System, Main Library, 200 E Eighth Ave, Pine Bluff, AR, 71601. Tel: 870-534-4802. Fax: 870-534-8707. p. 112

Griffing, Elizabeth, Ref Serv, Chesapeake Public Library, Major Hillard Library, 824 Old George Washington Hwy N, Chesapeake, VA, 23323-2214. Tel: 757-410-7075. Fax: 757-410-7088, 757-410-7089. p. 2456

Griffing, Janet, Mkt, Pub Relations, Ella M Everhard Public Library, 132 Broad St, Wadsworth, OH, 44281-1897. Tel: 330-335-2604. Fax: 330-334-6605. p. 1943

Griffing, Jean, Tech Serv, A K Smiley Public Library, 125 W Vine St, Redlands, CA, 92373. Tel: 909-798-7565. Fax: 909-798-7566. p. 215

Griffis, Jaime, Mgr, Pub & Br Serv, Barrie Public Library, 60 Worsley St, Barrie, ON, L4M 1L6, CANADA. Tel: 705-728-1010, Ext 7009. Fax: 705-728-4322. p. 2793

Griffis, Jaime, Mgr, Br & Pub Serv, Barrie Public Library, Painswick Branch, 48 Dean Ave, Barrie, ON, L4N 0C2, CANADA. Tel: 705-728-1010, Ext 7009. Fax: 705-728-4322. p. 2794

Griffis, Kathy, Assoc Dir, Coastal Plain Regional Library, 2014 Chestnut Ave, Tifton, GA, 31794. Tel: 229-386-3400. Fax: 229-386-7007. p. 554

Griffith, Cathy, Asst Head, Access Serv, University of North Carolina at Greensboro, 320 Spring Garden St, Greensboro, NC, 27402. Tel: 336-334-5492. Fax: 336-334-5399. p. 1798

Griffith, Cathy, Asst Dir, Adm Serv, Johnson City Public Library, 100 W Millard St, Johnson City, TN, 37604. Tel: 423-434-4463. Fax: 423-434-4469. p. 2240

Griffith, Charlotte, Ref Librn, Muskegon Community College, 221 S Quarterline Rd, Muskegon, MI, 49442. Tel: 231-777-0260. Fax: 231-777-0279. p. 1213

Griffith, Dorothy K, Dir, Greenup County Public Libraries, 614 Main St, Greenup, KY, 41144-1036. Tel: 606-473-6514. Fax: 606-473-6514. p. 915

Griffith, Earl, Asst Dir, Coll & Scholarly Res, Denison University Libraries, 400 W Loop, Granville, OH, 43023. Tel: 740-587-6619. Fax: 740-587-6285. p. 1902

Griffith, Gail, Head, Adult & Info Serv, Midland Public Library, 320 King St, Midland, ON, L4R 3M6, CANADA. Tel: 705-526-4216. Fax: 705-526-1474. p. 2821

Griffith, Gail L, Dep Dir, Ref, Carroll County Public Library, 115 Airport Dr, Westminster, MD, 21157. Tel: 410-386-4500, Ext 131. Fax: 410-386-4509. p. 1045

Griffith, Jan, Ser, Hamline University, Bush Memorial Library, 1536 Hewitt, Saint Paul, MN, 55104. Tel: 651-523-2375. Fax: 651-523-2199. p. 1278

Griffith, Jane, Actg Dir, University of Kansas School of Medicine-Wichita, 1010 N Kansas, Wichita, KS, 67214-3199. Tel: 316-293-2629. Fax: 316-293-2608. p. 900

Griffith, Jayne, Exec Dir, Head Librn, Wawa Public Library, 40 Broadway Ave, Wawa, ON, P0S 1K0, CANADA. Tel: 705-856-2062. Fax: 705-856-1488. p. 2870

Griffith, Jeanne, Youth Serv, Socorro Public Library, 401 Park St, Socorro, NM, 87801-4544. Tel: 505-835-1114. Fax: 505-835-1182. p. 1565

Griffith, Jill, Ch, Red Deer Public Library, 4818 49th St, Red Deer, AB, T4N 1T9, CANADA. Tel: 403-346-4576. Fax: 403-341-3110. p. 2714

Griffith, Julie, Pres, Northern California Consortium of Psychology Libraries, Argosy University, San Francisco Bay Area Campus, 1005 Atlantic Ave, Alameda, CA, 94133. Tel: 510-837-3715. p. 2938

Griffith, Leah, Dir, Newberg Public Library, 503 E Hancock St, Newberg, OR, 97132-2899. Tel: 503-537-1256. Fax: 503-538-9720. p. 2007

Griffith, Margaret, Coordr, Pasco County Library System, Regency Park, 9701 Little Rd, New Port Richey, FL, 34654. Tel: 727-861-3049. Fax: 727-861-3011. p. 452

Griffith, Marsha, Pub Serv Librn, Tusculum College, Hwy 107, 60 Shiloh Rd, Greeneville, TN, 37743. Tel: 423-636-7320, Ext 5122. Fax: 423-787-8498. p. 2236

Griffith, Natalie, Br Mgr, San Bernardino County Library, Newton T Bass Branch, 14901 Dale Evans Pkwy, Apple Valley, CA, 92307. Tel: 760-247-2022. Fax: 760-247-7099. p. 228

Griffith, Patricia, Adult Serv, Schlow Centre Region Library, 211 S Allen St, State College, PA, 16801-4806. Tel: 814-237-6236. Fax: 814-238-8508. p. 2143

Griffith, ReBecca, Mgr, Libr Serv, Southern State Community College, 100 Hobart Dr, Hillsboro, OH, 45133-9487. Tel: 937-393-3431, Ext 2684. Fax: 937-393-9370, 937-695-8093. p. 1904

Griffith, Rene, Ch, El Paso Public Library, 149 W First St, El Paso, IL, 61738. Tel: 309-527-4360. Fax: 309-527-7100. p. 640

Griffith, Robin, Librn, Palacios Library, Inc, Blessing Branch, 812 Tenth St, Blessing, TX, 77419. Tel: 361-588-7717. Fax: 361-588-7717. p. 2368

Griffith, Sarah, Asst Librn, United States Courts Library, 700 Stewart St, Rm 19105, Seattle, WA, 98101. Tel: 206-370-8975. Fax: 206-370-8976. p. 2533

Griffith, Valerie, Adult Serv, Greenburgh Public Library, 300 Tarrytown Rd, Elmsford, NY, 10523. Tel: 914-721-8209. Fax: 914-721-8201. p. 1620

Griffith-Kees, Julie, Cat, University of Alabama, School of Law Library, 101 Paul Bryant Dr, Tuscaloosa, AL, 35487. Tel: 205-348-5925. Fax: 205-348-1112. p. 38

Griffiths, Barbara, Circ, Flagstaff City-Coconino County Public Library System, 300 W Aspen, Flagstaff, AZ, 86001. Tel: 928-213-2331. Fax: 928-774-9573. p. 62

Griffiths, Barbara, Bus Mgr, Wilmette Public Library District, 1242 Wilmette Ave, Wilmette, IL, 60091-2558. Tel: 847-256-6910. Fax: 847-256-6911. p. 719

Griffiths, Jean, Adminr, Unitarian Universalist Church Library, 4831 E 22nd St, Tucson, AZ, 85711-4903. Tel: 520-748-1551. Fax: 520-748-0178. p. 88

Griffiths, Kim L, Dir, Tremonton City Library, 210 N Tremont St, Tremonton, UT, 84337-1329. Tel: 435-257-9525. Fax: 435-257-9526. p. 2416

Griffiths, Sue, Actg Br Mgr, Pasco County Library System, Hudson Regional, 8012 Library Rd, Hudson, FL, 34667. Tel: 727-861-3040. Fax: 727-861-3025. p. 451

Griffiths-Bender, Wendy, Librn, Columbia College Library, 11600 Columbia College Dr, Sonora, CA, 95370-8581. Tel: 209-588-5179. Fax: 209-588-5121. p. 269

Griffitts, Michael, Libr Dir, Morgan County Public Library, 151 University Dr, West Liberty, KY, 41472. Tel: 606-743-4151. Fax: 606-743-2170. p. 937

Grifo, Hattie, Dir, Cragsmoor Free Library, 355 Cragsmoor Rd, Cragsmoor, NY, 12420. Tel: 845-647-4611. Fax: 845-647-4611. p. 1612

Grift, Barb, Asst Librn, Victoria Municipal Library, 102 Stewart Ave, Holland, MB, R0G 0X0, CANADA. Tel: 204-526-2011. p. 2749

Grigalonis, Mary, Libr Dir, Minersville Public Library Association Inc, 220 S Fourth St, Minersville, PA, 17954. Tel: 570-544-5196. Fax: 570-544-5196. p. 2090

Grigg, Alex, Libr Mgr, University of Kentucky Libraries, Lexmark Library, Dept 990, Bldg 005-1, 740 New Circle Rd NW, Lexington, KY, 40551. Tel: 859-232-3783. Fax: 859-232-5728. p. 922

Grigg, Karen, Asst Dir, Coll Develop, Duke University Libraries, Medical Center Library, DUMC Box 3702, Ten Bryan-Searle Dr, Durham, NC, 27710-0001. Tel: 919-660-1122. Fax: 919-681-7599. p. 1788

Grigg, Pamela, Dir, Taylor County Public Library, 403 N Washington St, Perry, FL, 32347-2791. Tel: 850-838-3512. Fax: 850-838-3514. p. 483

Grigg, Pamela, Dir, Roddenbery Memorial Library, 320 N Broad St, Cairo, GA, 39828-2109. Tel: 229-377-3632. Fax: 229-377-7204. p. 522

Griggs, La Ferne D, Ref, Andalusia Public Library, 212 S Three Notch St, Andalusia, AL, 36420. Tel: 334-222-6612. Fax: 334-222-6612. p. 4

Griggs, Paula J, Librn, Milo Public Library, 123 Main St, Milo, IA, 50166. Tel: 641-942-6557. Fax: 641-942-6557. p. 832

Griggs, Robert, VPres, Bemidji State University, 1500 Birchmont Dr NE, Box 4, Bemidji, MN, 56601-2600. Tel: 218-755-3342. Fax: 218-755-2051. p. 1241

Griggs, Ronald, VPres, Libr & Info Serv, Kenyon College Library & Information Services, 103 College Dr, Gambier, OH, 43022-9624. Tel: 740-427-5186. Fax: 740-427-5272. p. 1901

Griggs, Sue, Asst Dir, Bolivar Free Library, 390 Main St, Bolivar, NY, 14715-0512. Tel: 585-928-2015. Fax: 585-928-2015. p. 1583

Griggs, Sue, Ch, Spanish Fork Public Library, 49 S Main St, Spanish Fork, UT, 84660-2030. Tel: 801-804-4480. Fax: 801-798-5014. p. 2416

Grigor, Catherine S, Mgr, Pub Relations & Mkt, Pennsylvania State University Libraries, 510 Paterno Library, University Park, PA, 16802. Tel: 814-863-4240. Fax: 814-865-2344. p. 2148

Grigsby, Alice B, Dir, Learning Res, El Camino College, 16007 S Crenshaw Blvd, Torrance, CA, 90506. Tel: 310-660-3525. Fax: 310-660-3513. p. 275

Grigsby, Barbara, Acq, Asst Dir, Athens State University Library, 407 E Pryor St, Athens, AL, 35611. Tel: 256-233-8218. Fax: 256-233-6547. p. 5

Grilli, Leanne, Res, Blake, Cassels & Graydon LLP, Commerce Ct W, 199 Bay St, Ste 4000, Toronto, ON, M5L 1A9, CANADA. Tel: 416-863-2650. Fax: 416-863-2653. p. 2850

Grillo, Paula, ILL, Ref, Ipswich Public Library, 25 N Main St, Ipswich, MA, 01938-2217. Tel: 978-356-6648. Fax: 978-356-6647. p. 1097

Grillo, Peter, PhD, Asst Teaching Prof, Drexel University, Rush Bldg, Rm 306, 30 N 33rd St, Philadelphia, PA, 19104-2875. Tel: 215-895-2474. Fax: 215-895-2494. p. 2973

Grillon, Marion, Ch, North Adams Public Library, 74 Church St, North Adams, MA, 01247. Tel: 413-662-3133. Fax: 413-662-3039. p. 1111

Grills, Lyla, YA Librn, Penfield Public Library, 1985 Baird Rd, Penfield, NY, 14526. Tel: 585-340-8720. Fax: 585-340-8748. p. 1716

Grim, Jessica, Coll Develop, Oberlin College Library, 148 W College St, Oberlin, OH, 44074. Tel: 440-775-8285. Fax: 440-775-6586. p. 1924

Grimard, Nicole, Coll Develop, Dir, Bibliotheque Municipale Guy-Belisle Saint Eustache, 80 blvd Arthur Sauve, Saint Eustache, QC, J7R 2H7, CANADA. Tel: 450-974-5035. Fax: 450-974-5054. p. 2908

Grime, Rachael, Adult Serv/Young Adult Librarian, Little Dixie Regional Libraries, 111 N Fourth St, Moberly, MO, 65270-1577. Tel: 660-263-4426. Fax: 660-263-4024. p. 1345

Grimenstein, Kathy, Br Head, Williamson County Public Library, Fairview Branch, 2240 Fairview Blvd, Fairview, TN, 37062-9011. Tel: 615-224-6087. Fax: 615-799-1399. p. 2234

Grimes, Ann D, Ref Serv, Ad, Salem Public Library, 821 E State St, Salem, OH, 44460-2298. Tel: 330-332-0042. Fax: 330-332-4488. p. 1934

Grimes, Barbara, Assoc Librn, State University of New York Institute of Technology, Rte 12 N & Horatio St, Utica, NY, 13502. Tel: 315-792-7245. Fax: 315-792-7517. p. 1759

Grimes, Betty, Librn, Boonville-Warrick County Public Library, Elberfeld Branch, 175 Sycamore, Elberfeld, IN, 47613. Tel: 812-983-4029. p. 729

Grimes, Deborah, Dr, Dir, Shelton State Community College, 9500 Old Greensboro Rd, Tuscaloosa, AL, 35405. Tel: 205-391-3925. Fax: 205-391-3926. p. 38

Grimes, Morgan, Dir, Marengo Library System, 211 E Washington, Demopolis, AL, 36732. Tel: 334-289-1595. Fax: 334-289-8260. p. 15

Grimes, Morgan, Electronic Res Librn, National Endowment for Democracy Library, 1025 F St NW, Ste 800, Washington, DC, 20004. Tel: 202-378-9700. Fax: 202-378-9407. p. 409

Grimes, Tim, Mgr, Commun Relations & Mkt, Ann Arbor District Library, 343 S Fifth Ave, Ann Arbor, MI, 48104. Tel: 734-327-4265. Fax: 734-327-8355. p. 1150

Grimes, Tony, Librn, Smoky Valley Library District, Manhattan Branch, Schoolhouse & Gold Sts, Manhattan, NV, 89022. Tel: 775-487-2326. Fax: 775-377-2699. p. 1434

Grimes, Vivian, Ref, Clovis-Carver Public Library, 701 N Main, Clovis, NM, 88101. Tel: 505-769-7840. Fax: 505-769-7842. p. 1553

Grimli, Vicki, Librn, Graceville Public Library, 415 Studdart Ave, Graceville, MN, 56240. Tel: 320-748-7332. Fax: 320-748-7338. p. 1252

Grimli, Vicki, Br Mgr, Ortonville Public Library, 412 Second St NW, Ortonville, MN, 56278-1415. Tel: 320-839-2494. Fax: 320-839-3784. p. 1270

Grimm, Candy, Libr Adminr, Colusa County Free Library, 738 Market St, Colusa, CA, 95932. Tel: 530-458-7671. Fax: 530-458-7358. p. 135

Grimm, Erica, Br Mgr, Jackson District Library, Brooklyn Branch, 207 N Main St, Brooklyn, MI, 49230. Tel: 517-592-3406. Fax: 517-592-3054. p. 1195

Grimm, Heidi, Dir, Merrill Memorial Library, 215 Main St, Yarmouth, ME, 04096. Tel: 207-846-4763. Fax: 207-846-2422. p. 1008

Grimm, Irene, Dept Head, Librn, Community College of Allegheny County, 1750 Clairton Rd, West Mifflin, PA, 15122-3097. Tel: 412-469-6295. Fax: 412-469-6370. p. 2154

Grimm, Teresa, Distance Educ Libm, Lakeland College, W3718 South Dr, Plymouth, WI, 53073. Tel: 920-565-1238. Fax: 920-565-1206. p. 2630

Grimmett, Deborah, Actg Dir, Abington Public Library, 600 Gliniewicz Way, Abington, MA, 02351. Tel: 781-982-2139. Fax: 781-878-7361. p. 1047

Grimsbo, Liz, Ser, Simpson College, 508 North C St, Indianola, IA, 50125-1216. Tel: 515-961-1485. Fax: 515-961-1363. p. 822

Grimse, Denise, Dir, Weeks Public Library, 36 Post Rd, Greenland, NH, 03840-2312. Tel: 603-436-8548. Fax: 603-427-0913. p. 1449

Grimshaw, Beverly, Librn, Scioto County Law Library, Scioto County Court House, 3rd Flr, 602 Seventh St, Portsmouth, OH, 45662. Tel: 740-355-8259. Fax: 740-353-9480. p. 1931

Grimshaw, Carrie, Dir, Merriam-Gilbert Public Library, Three W Main St, West Brookfield, MA, 01585. Tel: 508-867-1410. Fax: 508-867-1409. p. 1137

Grimshaw-Haven, Kathleen, Librn, Clifton Public Library, 292 Piaget Ave, Clifton, NJ, 07011. Tel: 973-772-5500. p. 1479

Grimsley, Ramona L, Spec Projects/Pub Relations Librn, Berkeley County Library System, 1003 Hwy 52, Moncks Corner, SC, 29461. Tel: 843-719-4240. p. 2200

Grimsley, Susan, Br Mgr, Southwest Georgia Regional Library, Miller County-James W Merritt Jr Memorial Library, 259 E Main St, Colquitt, GA, 39837. Tel: 229-758-3131. Fax: 229-758-3131. p. 521

Grinch, Stephen, Archivist, Otterbein University, 138 W Main St, Westerville, OH, 43081. Tel: 614-823-1761. Fax: 614-823-1921. p. 1946

Grindrod, Kim, Adult Serv, Ashe County Public Library, 148 Library Dr, West Jefferson, NC, 28694. Tel: 336-846-2041. Fax: 336-846-7503. p. 1829

Grindrod, Kim A, Br Supvr, Gaston County Public Library, Cherryville Branch, 605 E Main St, Cherryville, NC, 28021. Tel: 704-435-6767. Fax: 704-435-6767. p. 1794

Grindstaff, Pam, Librn, Flint-Groves Baptist Church Library, 2017 E Ozark Ave, Gastonia, NC, 28054. Tel: 704-865-4068. Fax: 704-865-8008. p. 1794

Griner, Carol, Libr Mgr, Eckville Municipal Library, 4855-51 Ave, Eckville, AB, T0M 0X0, CANADA. Tel: 403-746-3240. Fax: 403-746-5348. p. 2697

Grinnell, David, Archivist, Historical Society of Western Pennsylvania, 1212 Smallman St, Pittsburgh, PA, 15222. Tel: 412-454-6364. Fax: 412-454-6028. p. 2125

Grinnell, Gennett, Assoc Librn, Tech Serv, James Blackstone Memorial Library, 758 Main St, Branford, CT, 06405-3697. Tel: 203-488-1441. Fax: 203-481-6077. p. 331

Grinnell, Marilyn, Adult Prog Coordr, Hamburg Township Library, 10411 Merrill Rd, Hamburg, MI, 48139. Tel: 810-231-1771. Fax: 810-231-1520. p. 1187

Grinolds, Becky, ILL, Ser, Lewis-Clark State College Library, 500 Eighth Ave, Lewiston, ID, 83501. Tel: 208-792-2236. Fax: 208-792-2831. p. 578

Grise, Carol, Outreach Serv Librn, Fontana Regional Library, 33 Fryemont St, Bryson City, NC, 28713. Tel: 828-488-2382. Fax: 828-488-2638. p. 1778

Grise, Lucie, Acq, Hopital Maisonneuve-Rosemont, 5415 boul de l'Assomption, Montreal, QC, H1T 2M4, CANADA. Tel: 514-252-3462. Fax: 514-252-3574. p. 2896

Grisham, Brenda L, Librn, Drumright Public Library, 104 E Broadway, Drumright, OK, 74030. Tel: 918-352-2228. Fax: 918-352-9261. p. 1961

Grishman, Beth, Sr Commun Libr Mgr, Contra Costa County Library, Orinda Library, 26 Orinda Way, Orinda, CA, 94563-2555. Tel: 925-254-2184. Fax: 925-253-8629. p. 209

Grissom, Sandra, Librn, Columbia County Library, Library for the Blind & Physically Handicapped, 220 E Main St, Magnolia, AR, 71753. Tel: 870-234-0399. Fax: 870-234-5077. p. 108

Griswold, Mary, Circ Supvr, Kalamazoo College, 1200 Academy St, Kalamazoo, MI, 49006-3285. Tel: 269-337-5731. Fax: 269-337-7143. p. 1197

Griswold, Regine, Librn, Lowell Community Library, 2170 Vermont Rte 100, Lowell, VT, 05847. Tel: 802-744-2447. p. 2427

Griswold, Sarah, Dir, Seabury Society for the Preservation of the Glebe House, Inc, 49 Hollow Rd, Woodbury, CT, 06798. Tel: 203-263-2855. Fax: 203-263-6726. p. 380

Gritten, Tim, Dept Chair, Syst, Interim Assoc Dean, Indiana State University, 510 North 6 1/2 St, Terre Haute, IN, 47809. Tel: 812-237-3700. Fax: 812-237-3376. p. 781

Gritton, Thomas, In Charge, Winnebago County Court House, Court House, 415 Jackson St, Oshkosh, WI, 54903-4794. Tel: 920-236-4808. Fax: 920-303-4783. p. 2628

Grochowski, Paul, Librn, University of Michigan, Art, Architecture & Engineering Library, Duderstadt Ctr, 2281 Bonnisteel Blvd, Ann Arbor, MI, 48109-2094. Tel: 734-647-5747. Fax: 734-764-4487. p. 1152

Grochowsky, Steve, Electronic Res, Stanly County Public Library, 133 E Main St, Albemarle, NC, 28001. Tel: 704-986-3759. Fax: 704-983-6713. p. 1773

Grodin, Barbara, Ch, Oyster Bay-East Norwich Public Library, 89 E Main St, Oyster Bay, NY, 11771. Tel: 516-922-1212. Fax: 516-922-6453. p. 1714

Grodin, Erica, Head, Tech Serv, Finkelstein Memorial Library, 24 Chestnut St, Spring Valley, NY, 10977-5594. Tel: 845-352-5700. Fax: 845-352-2319. p. 1746

Grodinsky, Deborah, Adult Serv, Skokie Public Library, 5215 Oakton St, Skokie, IL, 60077-3680. Tel: 847-673-7774. Fax: 847-673-7797. p. 703

Grodofsky, Linda, Asst Mgr, Springfield City Library, East Springfield Branch, 21 Osborne Terrace, Springfield, MA, 01104. Tel: 413-263-6840. Fax: 413-263-6842. p. 1127

Grodofsky, Linda, Asst Mgr, Springfield City Library, Liberty Branch, 773 Liberty St, Springfield, MA, 01104. Tel: 413-263-6849. Fax: 413-263-6851. p. 1127

Groen, Allan J, Prov Librn, Confederation Centre Public Library, Queen & Richmond St, Charlottetown, PE, C1A 8G8, CANADA. Tel: 902-368-4649. Fax: 902-368-4652. p. 2875

Groenwald, Rosemary, Head, Tech Serv, Mount Prospect Public Library, Ten S Emerson St, Mount Prospect, IL, 60056. Tel: 847-253-5675. Fax: 847-253-0642. p. 677

Groesbeck, Margaret Adams, Head, Pub Serv, Amherst College, Amherst, MA, 01002. Fax: 413-542-2662. p. 1048

Groesch, Fayth, Head, Circ, Bethel Park Public Library, 5100 W Library Ave, Bethel Park, PA, 15102. Tel: 412-831-6800, Ext 262, 412-851-2465. Fax: 412-835-9360. p. 2033

Groet, Paulette, Libr Tech, Oskaloosa Public Library, 301 S Market St, Oskaloosa, IA, 52577. Tel: 641-673-0441. Fax: 641-673-6237. p. 837

Grof-Iannelli, Martie, Mgr, Fanshawe College, 1001 Fanshawe College Blvd, London, ON, N5Y 5R6, CANADA. Tel: 519-452-4240. Fax: 519-452-4473. p. 2817

Groft, Tammis, Chief Curator, Dep Dir, Coll, Albany Institute of History & Art, 125 Washington Ave, Albany, NY, 12210-2296. Tel: 518-463-4478. Fax: 518-463-5506. p. 1567

Grogan, Siobhan M, Dir, Cragin Memorial Library, Eight Linwood Ave, Colchester, CT, 06415. Tel: 860-537-5752. Fax: 860-537-4559. p. 334

Grogg, Christine, Operations Mgr, Eckhart Public Library, 603 S Jackson St, Auburn, IN, 46706-2298. Tel: 260-925-2414. Fax: 260-925-9376. p. 725

Groh, Kathleen, Librn, Waseca-Le Sueur Regional Library, Janesville Public, 102 W Second, Janesville, MN, 56048-3009. Tel: 507-234-6605. p. 1287

Grohs, Kim, Syst Coordr, Sussex County Library System, 125 Morris Tpk, Newton, NJ, 07860-0076. Tel: 973-948-3660. Fax: 973-948-2071. p. 1514

Grohs, Peggy, Libr Asst, Licia & Mason Beekley Community Library, Ten Central Ave, New Hartford, CT, 06057. Tel: 860-379-7235. Fax: 860-379-5806. p. 355

Grohs, Stephanie, Coll Develop, Ref Serv, Napa Valley College Library, 1700 Bldg, 2277 Napa-Vallejo Hwy, Napa, CA, 94558. Tel: 707-256-7400. Fax: 707-253-3015. p. 193

Grohse, Malik, Ref Librn, Atlanta-Fulton Public Library System, Southwest Regional Library, 3665 Cascade Rd SW, Atlanta, GA, 30331. Tel: 404-699-6363. Fax: 404-699-6381. p. 512

Grolbert, Doris, Dir, Clackamas County Library, 16201 SE McLoughlin Blvd, Oak Grove, OR, 97267-4653. Tel: 503-650-3112. p. 2008

Grolbert, Doris, Dir, Clackamas County Library, Clackamas Corner, 11750 SE 82nd Ave, Ste D, Portland, OR, 97086. Tel: 503-650-3112. p. 2008

Grolbert, Doris, Dir, Clackamas County Library, Hoodland, 68256 E Hwy 26, Welches, OR, 97067. Tel: 503-650-3112. p. 2008

Groleau, Sandra, Doc, Bates College, 48 Campus Ave, Lewiston, ME, 04240. Tel: 207-786-6268. Fax: 207-786-6055. p. 989

Groman, Robert, Spec Coll Librn, Amarillo Public Library, 413 E Fourth Ave, Amarillo, TX, 79101. Tel: 806-378-3054. Fax: 806-378-9327. p. 2274

Gromatzky, Steven, Dir, Libr Serv, Benedictine College Library, 1020 N Second St, Atchison, KS, 66002-1499. Tel: 913-360-7511. Fax: 913-360-7622. p. 856

Grombly, Amanda, Librn III, Tulare County Library, Visalia Headquarters Branch, 200 W Oak Ave, Visalia, CA, 93291. Tel: 559-713-2710. Fax: 559-737-4586. p. 281

Grona, Marian, Dir, Libr Serv, Vernon College, 4400 College Dr, Vernon, TX, 76384. Tel: 940-552-6291, Ext 2220. Fax: 940-552-0288. p. 2395

Grondin, Yvon, Dir, Bibliotheque Municipale Alice-Lane, Six Ave Radisson, Baie Comeau, QC, G4Z 1W4, CANADA. Tel: 418-296-8305. Fax: 418-296-8328. p. 2879

Grondin-Lyons, Sheila, Circ Supvr, York Library Region, Fredericton Public Library, 12 Carleton St, Fredericton, NB, E3B 5P4, CANADA. Tel: 506-460-2804. Fax: 506-460-2801. p. 2764

Gronemyer, Kate, Ref & Instruction Librn, Oregon State University, 2600 NW College Way, Bend, OR, 97701-5998. Tel: 541-322-3163. Fax: 541-383-7507. p. 1992

Gronholm, Shirley, Dir, Hartford Hospital, ERC Bldg-3, 80 Seymour St, Hartford, CT, 06102. Tel: 860-545-2420. Fax: 860-545-2572. p. 345

Gronlund, Gregg, Br Mgr, Orange County Library District, West Oaks, 1821 E Silver Star Rd, Ocoee, FL, 34761. p. 476

Gronwald, Daniel, Mgr, Northeast Sustainable Energy Association, 50 Miles St, Greenfield, MA, 01301. Tel: 413-774-6051, Ext 10. Fax: 413-774-6053. p. 1093

Groom, Barbara, Librn, Mercy Medical Center, 801 Fifth St, Sioux City, IA, 51101. Tel: 712-279-2310. p. 843

Groom, Judy, Dir, Freeburg Area Library, 407 S Belleville, Freeburg, IL, 62243. Tel: 618-539-5454. Fax: 618-539-5854. p. 647

Grooms, Russell, Ref Librn, Horry-Georgetown Technical College, Elizabeth Mattocks Chapin Memorial Library on the Grand Strand Campus, 3639 Pampas Dr, Myrtle Beach, SC, 29577. Tel: 843-477-2012. Fax: 843-477-2153. p. 2192

Grooms, Russell, Ref & Instruction Librn, Northern Virginia Community College Libraries, Woodbridge Library, 15200 Neabsco Mills Rd, Seefeldt 427, Woodbridge, VA, 22191. Tel: 703-878-5727. Fax: 703-670-8433. p. 2448

Grooms, Veronica, Librn, Madison County Library, 605 S May, Madisonville, TX, 77864. Tel: 936-348-6118. Fax: 936-348-6118. p. 2359

Groppa, Judith, Exec Dir, Darien Historical Society, Inc Library, 45 Old Kings Hwy N, Darien, CT, 06820. Tel: 203-655-9233. Fax: 203-656-3892. p. 336

Groppe, Jeanette, Dir, Scribner Public Library, 504 Main St, Scribner, NE, 68057. Tel: 402-664-3540. Fax: 402-664-3540. p. 1419

Grosberg, Judy, Librn, National Cancer Institute, 6116 Executive Blvd, Rm 3068, Bethesda, MD, 20892. Tel: 301-496-6756. Fax: 301-496-7096. p. 1021

Grosch, Mary, Head, Spec Coll, Unit Head, Govt Publ/Govt Doc, Northern Illinois University Libraries, DeKalb, IL, 60115-2868. Tel: 815-753-9841. p. 635

Groshong, Sue, Librn, Seattle Children's Hospital, 4800 Sand Point Way NE, W-6850, Seattle, WA, 98105. Tel: 206-987-2098. Fax: 206-987-3838. p. 2530

Groskopf, Amy, Assoc Dir, Res, Davenport Public Library, 321 Main St, Davenport, IA, 52801-1490. Tel: 563-328-6850. Fax: 563-326-7809. p. 806

Groskurth, Sheryl, Dir, Cedar Falls Public Library, 524 Main St, Cedar Falls, IA, 50613-2830. Tel: 319-268-5541. Fax: 319-273-8648. p. 799

Groskurth, Sheryl, Dir, Waterloo Public Library, 415 Commercial St, Waterloo, IA, 50701-1385. Tel: 319-291-4521. Fax: 319-291-6736. p. 850

Gross, April, Syst Coordr, Fulton County Public Library, 320 W Seventh St, Rochester, IN, 46975-1332. Tel: 574-223-2713. Fax: 574-223-5102. p. 776

Gross, Asia, Br Mgr, Saint Charles City County Library District, McClay, 2760 McClay Rd, Saint Charles, MO, 63303-5427. Tel: 636-441-7577. Fax: 636-441-5898. p. 1364

Gross, Calvin, Coordr, Tech Syst & Serv, Berea College, 100 Campus Dr, Berea, KY, 40404. Tel: 859-985-3364. Fax: 859-985-3912. p. 907

Gross, Catherine, Head, Ch, Decatur Public Library, 130 N Franklin St, Decatur, IL, 62523-1327. Tel: 217-421-9722. Fax: 217-233-4071. p. 634

Gross, Claudia, Actg Libr Dir, Orwigsburg Area Free Public Library, 214 E Independent St, Orwigsburg, PA, 17961-2304. Tel: 570-366-1638. Fax: 570-366-5414. p. 2101

Gross, Elaine, Ch, Hawkins Memorial Library, 308 Main St, La Porte City, IA, 50651. Tel: 319-342-3025. Fax: 319-342-3025. p. 826

Gross, Florence, Librn, Westchester Reform Temple Library, 255 Mamaroneck Rd, Scarsdale, NY, 10583. Tel: 914-723-7727. Fax: 914-723-5946. p. 1739

Gross, Jacki, Libr Dir, Seguin-Guadalupe County Public Library, 707 E College St, Seguin, TX, 78155-3217. Tel: 830-401-2466. Fax: 830-401-2477. p. 2386

Gross, Jennifer L, Ref Librn, University of Nevada, Las Vegas Libraries, Wiener-Rogers Law Library, William S Boyd School of Law, 4505 Maryland Pkwy, Las Vegas, NV, 89154-1080. Tel: 702-895-2400. Fax: 702-895-2410. p. 1431

Gross, Jill, Adult Serv, Tappan Library, 93 Main St, Tappan, NY, 10983. Tel: 845-359-3877. p. 1754

Gross, Ken, Prog Dir, Camden Public Library, 55 Main St, Camden, ME, 04843-1703. Tel: 207-236-3440. Fax: 207-236-6673. p. 980

Gross, Kirt, Curator, Dearborn Historical Museum Library, McFadden-Ross House, 915 Brady St, Dearborn, MI, 48126. Tel: 313-565-3000. Fax: 313-565-4848. p. 1167

Gross, Linda, Ref Librn, Hagley Museum & Library, 298 Buck Rd E, Wilmington, DE, 19807. Tel: 302-658-2400. Fax: 302-658-0568. p. 388

Gross, Lois, Ch, Hoboken Public Library, 500 Park Ave, Hoboken, NJ, 07030. Tel: 201-420-2346. Fax: 201-420-2299. p. 1491

Gross, Pat, In Charge, Charleston County Public Library, McClellanville Branch, 222 Baker St, McClellanville, SC, 29458. Tel: 843-887-3699. Fax: 843-887-3144. p. 2183

Gross, Patty, Dir, Council District Library, 104 California Ave, Council, ID, 83612. Tel: 208-253-6004. Fax: 208-253-6004. p. 573

Gross, Stephan, Head, Tech Serv, Jewish Education Service of North America, Inc, 318 W 39th St, 5th Flr, New York, NY, 10018. Tel: 212-284-6950. Fax: 212-284-6951. p. 1683

Gross, Stephanie, Electronic Reserves Librn, Yeshiva University Libraries, Pollack Library-Landowne Bloom Library, Wilf Campus, 2520 Amsterdam Ave, New York, NY, 10033. Tel: 212-960-5378, 212-960-5379, 212-960-5380. Fax: 212-960-0066. p. 1704

Gross, Stephen, Dir, West Central Minnesota Historical Research Center, University of Minnesota, 600 E Fourth St, Morris, MN, 56267. Tel: 320-589-6278. Fax: 320-589-3811. p. 1267

Gross, Valerie J, Pres & Chief Exec Officer, Howard County Library System, 6600 Cradlerock Way, Columbia, MD, 21045-4912. Tel: 410-313-7750. Fax: 410-313-7742. p. 1026

Gross, Velma, Coll Develop, Saint Mary's Public Library, 127 Center St, Saint Mary's, PA, 15857. Tel: 814-834-6141. Fax: 814-834-9814. p. 2135

Grossardt, Sharon, Dir, Saint Charles Public Library, 125 W 11th St, Saint Charles, MN, 55972-1141. Tel: 507-932-3227. p. 1274

Grossett, Charlene, Co-Dir, Newport Free Library, 7390 Main St, Newport, NY, 13416-3500. Tel: 315-845-8533. p. 1705

Grossett, Sharon, Librn, Michigan Department of Corrections, 17601 Mound Rd, Detroit, MI, 48212. Tel: 313-368-8300, Ext 52327. Fax: 313-368-8972. p. 1171

Grosshans, Maxine, Res, University of Maryland, Baltimore, Thurgood Marshall Law Library, 501 W Fayette St, Baltimore, MD, 21201-1768. Tel: 410-706-0791. Fax: 410-706-8354. p. 1019

Grossholz, Lori, Tech Serv, Gannon University, 109 University Sq, Erie, PA, 16541. Tel: 814-871-7557. Fax: 814-871-5666. p. 2055

Grosshuesch, Susan, Dir, Kewaunee Public Library, 822 Juneau St, Kewaunee, WI, 54216-1200. Tel: 920-388-5015. Fax: 920-388-5016. p. 2602

Grossi, Kristin, Children's Programmer, Swarthmore Public Library, Borough Hall, 121 Park Ave, Swarthmore, PA, 19081-1536. Tel: 610-543-0436, 610-543-3171. Fax: 610-328-6699. p. 2145

Grossklaus, Debbie, Media Spec, Musser Public Library, 304 Iowa Ave, Muscatine, IA, 52761-3875. Tel: 563-263-3065. Fax: 563-264-1033. p. 834

Grossman, David, Hist Rm Librn, Mill Valley Public Library, 375 Throckmorton Ave, Mill Valley, CA, 94941-2698. Tel: 415-389-4292, Ext 131. Fax: 415-388-8929. p. 186

Grossman, Holly, In Charge, Allstate Insurance Co, Allstate Specialty Operations Department, 51 W Higgins Rd, T1A, South Barrington, IL, 60010. Tel: 847-551-2079. Fax: 847-551-4737. p. 682

Grossman, Mike, ILL, Duluth Public Library, 520 W Superior St, Duluth, MN, 55802. Tel: 218-730-4200. Fax: 218-723-3815, 218-723-3822. p. 1247

Grossman, Nancy, Admin Serv, BCC-UCF Joint Use Library, 1519 Clearlake Rd, Cocoa, FL, 32922. Tel: 321-433-7804. Fax: 321-433-7678. p. 433

Grossman, Rachael, Outreach Coordr, Kellogg-Hubbard Library, 135 Main St, Montpelier, VT, 05602. Tel: 802-223-3338. Fax: 802-223-3338. p. 2429

Grossman, Robert, Head Librn, Philadelphia Orchestra Library, 300 S Broad St, Philadelphia, PA, 19102-4297. Tel: 215-670-2343. Fax: 215-985-0746. p. 2115

Grossman, Sue, Ch, Mount Pleasant Public Library, 350 Bedford Rd, Pleasantville, NY, 10570-3099. Tel: 914-769-0548. Fax: 914-769-6149. p. 1719

Grosso, Tara, Ref Librn, John Curtis Free Library, 534 Hanover St, Hanover, MA, 02339-2228. Tel: 781-826-2972. Fax: 781-826-3130. p. 1093

Grote, Patty, Dir, Mason County Library, 410 Post Hill, Mason, TX, 76856. Tel: 325-347-5446. Fax: 325-347-6562. p. 2360

Groth, Angela Z, Dir, Ardsley Public Library, Nine American Legion Dr, Ardsley, NY, 10502. Tel: 914-693-6636. Fax: 914-693-6837. p. 1574

Groth, Sandy, Librn, Aurora Free Library, 370 Main St, Aurora, NY, 13026. Tel: 315-364-8074. Fax: 315-364-8074. p. 1576

Grothe, Karen, Bus Mgr, Chippewa Falls Public Library, 105 W Central, Chippewa Falls, WI, 54729-2397. Tel: 715-723-1146. Fax: 715-720-6922. p. 2585

Grotluschen, Heather, Dir, Ashton Public Library, 3029 Third St, Ashton, IA, 51232. Tel: 712-724-6426. Fax: 712-724-6426. p. 794

Grotophorst, Wally, Assoc Univ Librn, George Mason University Libraries, 4400 University Dr, MSN 2FL, Fairfax, VA, 22030-4444. Tel: 703-993-9005. Fax: 703-993-2200. p. 2462

Grotyohann, Susan, Ref, Monroe Township Public Library, Four Municipal Plaza, Monroe Township, NJ, 08831-1900. Tel: 732-521-5000, Ext 153. Fax: 732-521-4766. p. 1503

Grout, Barbara, Dir, Memorial Hospital Library, 4500 Memorial Dr, Belleville, IL, 62226-5360. Tel: 618-257-5343. Fax: 618-257-6825. p. 593

Grout, Jean, Teen Librn, Exeter Public Library, Four Chestnut St, Exeter, NH, 03833. Tel: 603-772-3101, 603-772-6036. Fax: 603-772-7548. p. 1447

Grout, Nancy, Dir, Satellite Beach Public Library, 751 Jamaica Blvd, Satellite Beach, FL, 32937. Tel: 321-779-4004. Fax: 321-779-4036. p. 490

Grouwstra, Clara, Libr Mgr, Mannville Centenial Public Library, PO Box 186, Mannville, AB, T0B 2W0, CANADA. Tel: 780-763-3611. Fax: 780-763-3688. p. 2711

Grove, Cheryl, Circ Supvr, Coronado Public Library, 640 Orange Ave, Coronado, CA, 92118-1526. Tel: 619-522-2472. Fax: 619-435-4205. p. 137

Grove, Donna, Per, Juniata College, 1815 Moore St, Huntingdon, PA, 16652-2120. Tel: 814-641-3450. Fax: 814-641-3435. p. 2070

Grove, Judy, Commun Relations Coordr, Villa Park Public Library, 305 S Ardmore Ave, Villa Park, IL, 60181-2698. Tel: 630-834-1164. Fax: 630-834-0489. p. 714

Grove, Lynda, Br Mgr, San Bernardino County Library, Yucca Valley Branch, 57098 Twentynine Palms Hwy, Yucca Valley, CA, 92284. Tel: 760-228-5455. Fax: 760-228-5459. p. 229

Grove, Margaret, Univ Librn, Brock University, 500 Glenridge Ave, St. Catharines, ON, L2S 3A1, CANADA. Tel: 905-688-5550, Ext 3226. Fax: 905-988-5490. p. 2842

Grove, Marsha, Dir, Champaign Public Library, 200 W Green St, Champaign, IL, 61820-5193. Tel: 217-403-2050. Fax: 217-403-2053. p. 602

Grove, Monica, Librn, Sangudo Public Library, 5131 53rd Ave, Sangudo, AB, T0E 2A0, CANADA. Tel: 780-785-3431. Fax: 780-785-3179. p. 2716

Grove, Robyn, Dir, Iola Village Library, 180 S Main St, Iola, WI, 54945-9689. Tel: 715-445-4330. Fax: 715-445-2917. p. 2599

Grove, Steven J, Dir, Franzello AeroMedical Library, USAFSAM/EDL, 2949 Fifth St, Area B, Dayton, OH, 45433. p. 1893

Groveman, Burnette, Librn, Temple Sinai Library, 425 Roslyn Rd, Roslyn Heights, NY, 11577. Tel: 516-621-6800. Fax: 516-625-6020. p. 1736

Grover, Mark, Humanities & Soc Sci Librn, Brigham Young University, Harold B Lee Library, 2060 HBLL, Provo, UT, 84602. Tel: 801-422-2927. Fax: 801-422-0466. p. 2411

Grover, Patricia, Dir, Delta Public Library, 402 Main St, Delta, OH, 43515-1304. Tel: 419-822-3110. Fax: 419-822-5310. p. 1896

Grover, Sharon, Head, Youth Serv, Hedberg Public Library, 316 S Main St, Janesville, WI, 53545. Tel: 608-758-6584. Fax: 608-758-6583. p. 2599

Groves, Deana, Actg Head, Tech Serv, Cat, Western Kentucky University Libraries, Helm-Cravens Library Complex, 1906 College Heights Blvd, No 11067, Bowling Green, KY, 42101-1067. Tel: 270-745-4197. Fax: 270-745-6422. p. 907

Groves, Elwood, Librn, Pocahontas County Free Libraries, Hillsboro Public, Third St, Hillsboro, WV, 24946. Tel: 304-653-4936. Fax: 304-653-4936. p. 2565

Groves, Gloria, Librn, North Central Regional Library, Chelan Community, 417 S Bradley St, Chelan, WA, 98816. Tel: 509-682-5131. Fax: 509-682-5131. p. 2548

Groves, Nicholas T, Dr, Dir, Joe Buley Memorial Library, 35240 N Grant St, Third Lake, IL, 60030. Tel: 847-223-5971. p. 709

Groves, Polly, Asst Librn, Hyndman Londonderry Public Library, 161 Clarence St, Hyndman, PA, 15545. Tel: 814-842-3782. Fax: 814-842-3737. p. 2070

Groves, Tara, Principal Libr Asst, Salem County Library Commission, 900 Rte 45, Bldg 3, Pilesgrove, NJ, 08098. Tel: 856-769-1082. Fax: 856-769-2018. p. 1520

Groves, Teresa, Ch, Roddenbery Memorial Library, 320 N Broad St, Cairo, GA, 39828-2109. Tel: 229-377-3632. Fax: 229-377-7204. p. 522

Grow, Brenda, Br Mgr, Bethlehem Area Public Library, 11 W Church St, Bethlehem, PA, 18018. Tel: 610-867-7852. Fax: 610-867-2767. p. 2033

Grow, Brenda, Br Mgr, Bethlehem Area Public Library, South Side, 400 Webster St, Bethlehem, PA, 18015. Tel: 610-867-7852. Fax: 610-867-9821. p. 2034

Grow, John, Librn, Carter County Library District, Grandin Branch, PO Box 274, Grandin, MO, 63943-0274. Tel: 573-593-4084. p. 1370

Grow, Mary, Librn, Albert Church Brown Memorial Library, 37 Main St, China-Village, ME, 04358. Tel: 207-968-2926. p. 982

Growney, Kathy, Dean, Univ Libr, Southern New Hampshire University, 2500 N River Rd, Manchester, NH, 03106-1045. Tel: 603-668-2211, Ext 2166. Fax: 603-645-9685. p. 1456

Grubb, Debra, Archivist, Bedford Historical Society Library, 30 S Park St, Bedford, OH, 44146-3635. Tel: 440-232-0796. p. 1858

Grubb, Jason, Libr Mgr, Sweetwater County Library System, White Mountain Library, 2935 Sweetwater Dr, Rock Springs, WY, 82901-4331. Tel: 307-362-2665, Ext 3410. Fax: 307-352-6655. p. 2656

Grubb, Jeff, Adult & Teen Serv, Supv Librn, Santa Clara County Library District, Morgan Hill Branch, 660 W Main Ave, Morgan Hill, CA, 95037-4128. Tel: 408-779-3196. Fax: 408-779-0883. p. 181

Grubb, John, Pub Serv Librn, Tech Serv, Northeast State Community College, 2425 Hwy 75, Blountville, TN, 37617-6350. Tel: 423-354-2429. Fax: 423-323-0254. p. 2224

Grubb, Stephen, Mgr, E-Serv, Broward County Division of Libraries, 100 S Andrews Ave, Fort Lauderdale, FL, 33301. Tel: 954-357-7977. Fax: 954-357-5548. p. 440

Grubbs, Amy, Mgr, Greenville County Library System, Travelers Rest (Sargent) Branch, 17 Center St, Travelers Rest, SC, 29690. Tel: 864-834-3650. Fax: 864-834-4686. p. 2196

Grubbs, Beth, Librn, Regional Medical Center of Orangeburg & Calhoun Counties, 3000 St Matthews Rd, Orangeburg, SC, 29118. Tel: 803-395-2275. Fax: 803-395-2557. p. 2201

Grubbs, Kirsten, Br Mgr, Mid-Continent Public Library, Excelsior Springs Branch, 1460 Kearney Rd, Excelsior Springs, MO, 64024-1746. Tel: 816-630-6721. Fax: 816-630-5021. p. 1332

Grube, Glenn, Automated Serv, West Hartford Public Library, 20 S Main St, West Hartford, CT, 06107-2432. Tel: 860-561-6950. Fax: 860-561-6976. p. 376

Gruben, Karl, Assoc Dean, Libr & Info Serv, University of San Diego, Katherine M & George M Pardee Jr Legal Research Center, 5998 Alcala Park, San Diego, CA, 92110-2492. Tel: 619-260-4542. Fax: 619-260-4616. p. 239

Gruben, Karl T, Dir, Saint Thomas University Library, Law Library, 16401 NW 37th Ave, Miami Gardens, FL, 33054. Tel: 305-623-2341. Fax: 305-623-2337. p. 469

Gruber, Dana, Mgr, Fort Hamilton Hospital, 630 Eaton Ave, Hamilton, OH, 45013. Tel: 513-867-2248, 513-867-2870. Fax: 513-867-2558. p. 1903

Gruber, Ellen, Dir, The Wagnalls Memorial Library, 150 E Columbus St, Lithopolis, OH, 43136. Tel: 614-837-4765. Fax: 614-837-0781. p. 1910

Gruber, Inese, Dir, Windham Public Library, 217 Windham Center Rd, Windham, ME, 04062. Tel: 207-892-1908. Fax: 207-892-1915. p. 1007

Gruber, Karen A, Acq & Budget Mgr, Muhlenberg College, 2400 Chew St, Allentown, PA, 18104-5586. Tel: 484-664-3570. Fax: 484-664-3511. p. 2027

Gruber, Krista, Head, Per, Suffolk County Community College, 533 College Rd, Selden, NY, 11784-2899. Tel: 631-451-4800. Fax: 631-451-4697. p. 1742

Gruber, Marissa, Youth Serv Librn, Lied Public Library, 100 E Garfield St, Clarinda, IA, 51632. Tel: 712-542-2416. Fax: 712-542-3590. p. 802

Gruber, Mary, Lit Prog Mgr, Mercantile Library Association, 414 Walnut St, Cincinnati, OH, 45202. Tel: 513-621-0717. Fax: 513-621-2023. p. 1871

Grublin, Elaine, Reader Serv, Massachusetts Historical Society Library, 1154 Boylston St, Boston, MA, 02215-3695. Tel: 617-646-0509. Fax: 617-859-0074. p. 1063

Grudnoski, Jennifer, Commun Librn, Monroe County Library System, Dundee Branch, 144 E Main St, Dundee, MI, 48131-1202. Tel: 734-529-3310. Fax: 734-529-3310. p. 1210

Grudzien, Pamela, Head, Tech Serv, Central Michigan University, Park 407, Mount Pleasant, MI, 48859. Tel: 989-774-6488. Fax: 989-774-2179. p. 1211

Gruel, Harriet, Actg Asst Librn, Casselton Public Library, 701 First St N, Casselton, ND, 58012. Tel: 701-347-4861, Ext 13. Fax: 701-347-4505. p. 1839

Gruenberg, Terri, Librn, Mackall, Crounse & Moore, 1400 AT&T Tower, 901 Marquette Ave, Minneapolis, MN, 55402-2859. Tel: 612-305-1687. Fax: 612-305-1414. p. 1260

Gruenburg, Carol, Librn, Miller & Chevalier, 655 15th St NW, Ste 900, Washington, DC, 20005-5701. Tel: 202-626-6094. Fax: 202-626-5801. p. 408

Gruenebaum, Eva, Coll Develop, West Nyack Free Library, 65 Strawtown Rd, West Nyack, NY, 10994. Tel: 845-358-6081. Fax: 845-358-4071. p. 1766

Gruenwald, Amanda, Res Spec, Clausen Miller Research Services Dept, Ten S LaSalle St, 16th Flr, Chicago, IL, 60603-1098. Tel: 312-606-7887. Fax: 312-606-7777. p. 611

Grugel, Chris, Ref/Media Serv Librn, Carthage College, 2001 Alford Park Dr, Kenosha, WI, 53140-1900. Tel: 262-551-5900. Fax: 262-551-5904. p. 2601

Grula, John, Librn, Observatories of the Carnegie Institution of Washington, 813 Santa Barbara St, Pasadena, CA, 91101. Tel: 626-304-0228. Fax: 626-795-8136. p. 206

Grumet, Elinor, Per, Yeshiva University Libraries, Hedi Steinberg Library, 245 Lexington Ave, New York, NY, 10016. Tel: 212-340-7720. Fax: 212-340-7808. p. 1704

Grumman, Joanne, Ch, Bethel Public Library, 189 Greenwood Ave, Bethel, CT, 06801-2598. Tel: 203-794-8756. Fax: 203-794-8761. p. 330

Grundman, Patricia W, Ch, Hall Memorial Library, 93 Main St, Ellington, CT, 06029. Tel: 860-870-3160. Fax: 860-870-3163. p. 338

Grundset, Eric G, Coll Develop, Dir, National Society of the Daughters of the American Revolution, DAR Library, 1776 D St NW, Washington, DC, 20006-5303. Tel: 202-879-3229. Fax: 202-879-3227. p. 411

Grundstrom, Lynn, Dir, Farman Free Library, 760 Thornten Rd, Ellington, NY, 14732. Tel: 716-287-2945. Fax: 716-287-3694. p. 1619

Grundy, Diane, Dir, Ref, Grove City College, 300 Campus Dr, Grove City, PA, 16127-2198. Tel: 724-458-2047. Fax: 724-458-2181. p. 2063

Grunert, Merrilee, Librn, Parkland Regional Library, Kelliher Branch, 413 Second Ave, Kelliher, SK, S0A 1V0, CANADA. Tel: 306-675-2110. p. 2932

Grunes, Judith, Librn, B'Nai Zion Congregation, 245 Southfield Rd, Shreveport, LA, 71105. Tel: 318-861-2122. Fax: 318-861-7961. p. 967

Gruninger, Laura, Youth Serv, Mercer County Library System, 2751 Brunswick Pike, Lawrenceville, NJ, 08648-4132. Tel: 609-989-6921. Fax: 609-538-9238. p. 1494

Grunow, Gregg, Librn, Newport News Public Library System, Main Street, 110 Main St, Newport News, VA, 23601. Tel: 757-591-4858. Fax: 757-591-7425. p. 2480

Grunseth, Erica, Dir, Abbotsford Public Library, 203 Birch St, Abbotsford, WI, 54405. Tel: 715-223-3920. Fax: 715-223-4979. p. 2577

Grunst, Gail, Head, Circ, Round Lake Area Public Library District, 906 Hart Rd, Round Lake, IL, 60073. Tel: 847-546-7060, Ext 111. Fax: 847-546-7104. p. 699

Grunwell, John, Acq, Per, Brookings Institution Library, 1775 Massachusetts Ave NW, Washington, DC, 20036. Tel: 202-797-6240. Fax: 202-797-2970. p. 394

Grupe, Janice, Dir, Cockrell Hill Public Library, 4125 W Clarendon, Dallas, TX, 75211. Tel: 214-330-9935. Fax: 214-330-5483. p. 2305

Grussing, Jake, Coll Develop, Great River Regional Library, 1300 W St Germain St, Saint Cloud, MN, 56301-3667. Tel: 320-650-2531. Fax: 320-650-2501. p. 1274

Grussing, Pam, Asst Librn, Jackson County Library, 311 Third St, Jackson, MN, 56143-1600. Tel: 507-847-4748. Fax: 507-847-5470. p. 1255

Gruszka, Enid, Br Mgr, Milwaukee Public Library, Washington Park, 2121 N Sherman Blvd, Milwaukee, WI, 53208. Tel: 414-286-3066. Fax: 414-286-8471. p. 2620

Grutzeck, Laura, Visual Res Librn, University of the Arts University Libraries, Anderson Hall, 1st Flr, 333 S Broad St, Philadelphia, PA, 19102. Tel: 215-717-6294. Fax: 215-717-6287. p. 2119

Grutzeck, Laura, Visual Res Librn, University of the Arts University Libraries, Visual Resources Collection, Anderson Hall, Mezzanine, 333 S Broad St, Philadelphia, PA, 19102. Tel: 215-717-6294. Fax: 215-717-6287. p. 2120

Grymek-Nowinowski, Bozena, Actg Librn, Toronto Catholic District School Board, 80 Sheppard Ave E, Toronto, ON, M2N 6E8, CANADA. Tel: 416-222-8282, Ext 5324. Fax: 416-229-5392. p. 2859

Grynwich, Julie, Dir, New Buffalo Township Public Library, 33 N Thompson St, New Buffalo, MI, 49117. Tel: 269-469-2933. Fax: 269-469-3521. p. 1213

Grypp, Betty, Librn, Greendale Public Library, 5647 Broad St, Greendale, WI, 53129-1887. Tel: 414-423-2136. Fax: 414-423-2139. p. 2596

Gryszkiewicz, Janice, Info Serv, Westfield Athenaeum, Six Elm St, Westfield, MA, 01085-2997. Tel: 413-568-7833. Fax: 413-568-0988. p. 1138

Gualtieri, Robert, Dir, Hamden Public Library, 2901 Dixwell Ave, Hamden, CT, 06518-3135. Tel: 203-287-2686. Fax: 203-287-2685. p. 343

Guan, Amy, Ser, Tech Serv, Napa Valley College Library, 1700 Bldg, 2277 Napa-Vallejo Hwy, Napa, CA, 94558. Tel: 707-256-7400. Fax: 707-253-3015. p. 193

Guan, Wei, Computer Serv, Ref Serv, Free Public Library of the Borough of Fort Lee, 320 Main St, Fort Lee, NJ, 07024. Tel: 201-592-3614. Fax: 201-585-0375. p. 1486

Guarcello, Catherine, Librn, Caritas St Elizabeth's Medical Center, 736 Cambridge St, Boston, MA, 02135. Tel: 617-789-2177. Fax: 617-789-5081. p. 1059

Guarino, Kimberly A, ILL Coordr, Wheaton College Library, 26 E Main St, Norton, MA, 02766-2322. Tel: 508-286-5821. p. 1115

Guarino, Patricia, Adult Serv, Hoover Public Library, 200 Municipal Dr, Hoover, AL, 35216. Tel: 205-444-7810. Fax: 205-444-7878. p. 20

Guarino-Kozlowicz, Liz, Br Mgr, Kent District Library, Caledonia Township Branch, 6260 92nd St SE, Caledonia, MI, 49316. Tel: 616-784-2007. p. 1165

Guarria, Charles, Acq Librn, Long Island University, One University Plaza, Brooklyn, NY, 11201-9926. Tel: 718-488-1081. Fax: 718-780-4057. p. 1593

Guastavino, Catherine, Assoc Prof, McGill University, 3661 Peel St, Montreal, QC, H3A 1X1, CANADA. Tel: 514-398-1709. Fax: 514-398-7193. p. 2979

Guay, Gisèle, Librn, Universite du Quebec, CP 8889, Succ Centre-Ville, 1255 Rue St Denis, Locale-A-1200, Montreal, QC, H3C 3P3, CANADA. Tel: 514-987-6134. Fax: 514-987-0262. p. 2902

Gubbin, Barbara A B, Dir, Jacksonville Public Library, 303 N Laura St, Jacksonville, FL, 32202-3505. Tel: 904-630-2665. Fax: 904-630-2431. p. 453

Gudenas, Jean, Head, Coll Support Serv, Loyola University Chicago Libraries, Health Sciences Library, Bldg 101, Rm 1717, 2160 S First Ave, Maywood, IL, 60153-5585. Tel: 708-216-5311. Fax: 708-216-8115. p. 617

Guderjahn, Lindsey, Dir, United States Air Force, 5 FSS/FSDL, 210 Missile Ave, Bldg 156 Unit 1, Minot AFB, ND, 58705-5026. Tel: 701-723-3344. Fax: 701-727-9850. p. 1847

Guebert, Lois, Tech Serv, University of Saint Mary of the Lake - Mundelein Seminary, 1000 E Maple Ave, Mundelein, IL, 60060. Tel: 847-970-4820. Fax: 847-566-5229. p. 678

Guedea, Esther, Evening Circ Supvr, Goshen College, Harold & Wilma Good Library, 1700 S Main, Goshen, IN, 46526-4794. Tel: 574-535-7427. Fax: 574-535-7438. p. 745

Guedel, Robyn, Br Mgr, Stark County District Library, North Branch, 189 25th St NW, Canton, OH, 44709. Tel: 330-456-4356. Fax: 330-580-1806. p. 1864

Guedon, Mary, Ref & Instrul Serv Librn, Notre Dame de Namur University Library, 1500 Ralston Ave, Belmont, CA, 94002-1908. Tel: 650-508-3748. Fax: 650-508-3697. p. 126

Guelda, Sue, Outreach Serv Librn, Carroll County Public Library, 136 Court St, Carrollton, KY, 41008. Tel: 502-732-7020. Fax: 502-732-7122. p. 909

Guelzow, Deborah, Acq, NASA, Kennedy Space Center, FL, 32899. Tel: 321-867-3600. Fax: 321-867-4534. p. 455

Guem, Mia, Archives, Staff Librn, Northeastern University Libraries, Snell Library, 360 Huntington Ave, Boston, MA, 02115. Tel: 617-373-2351. p. 1065

Guengerich, Anna Marie, Librn, University of Iowa, Blommers Measurement Resources Library, 304 Lindquist Ctr, Iowa City, IA, 52242-1587. Tel: 319-335-5416. Fax: 319-335-6038. p. 823

Guenter, Helen, Assoc Librn, Head, Ref & Ser, University of Arkansas-Monticello Library, 514 University Dr, Monticello, AR, 71656. Tel: 870-460-1080. Fax: 870-460-1980. p. 110

Guenther, Anne, Assoc Libr Dir, Circ, Fresno Pacific University, 1717 S Chestnut Ave, Fresno, CA, 93702. Tel: 599-453-2121. Fax: 559-453-2124. p. 153

Guenther, Beverly A, Ch, Saint Paris Public Library, 127 E Main St, Saint Paris, OH, 43072. Tel: 937-663-4349. Fax: 937-663-0297. p. 1933

Guenther, Brian, Librn, Fresno County Public Library, Talking Book Library for the Blind, 770 N San Pablo, Fresno, CA, 93728-3640. Tel: 559-600-3217. p. 152

Guenther, Jenna, Info Serv, Juneau Public Libraries, 292 Marine Way, Juneau, AK, 99801. Tel: 907-586-5324. Fax: 907-586-3419. p. 50

Guenther, Jim, Dir, Pickaway County District Public Library, 1160 N Court St, Circleville, OH, 43113-1725. Tel: 740-477-1644, Ext 223. Fax: 740-474-2855. p. 1875

Guenther, Mary Anne, Coordr, Libr Serv, North Island College, 2300 Ryan Rd, Courtenay, BC, V9N 8N6, CANADA. Tel: 250-334-5001. Fax: 250-334-5291. p. 2727

Guenther, Robin, Teen Serv Librn, Moorestown Public Library, 111 W Second St, Moorestown, NJ, 08057-2481. Tel: 856-234-0333. Fax: 856-778-9536. p. 1504

Guerin, Katie, Dir of Libr Serv, North Shelby County Library, 5521 Cahaba Valley Rd, Birmingham, AL, 35242. Tel: 205-439-5540. Fax: 205-439-5503. p. 9

Guerin, Susan, Ref Serv, Ad, Comsewogue Public Library, 170 Terryville Rd, Port Jefferson Station, NY, 11776. Tel: 631-928-1212. Fax: 631-928-6307. p. 1721

Guernsey, Carolyn, Syst Coordr, Southwest Kansas Library System, 100 Military Ave, Ste 210, Dodge City, KS, 67801-4484. Tel: 620-225-1231. Fax: 620-225-0252. p. 864

Guerra, Jesenia, Librn, Corpus Christi Museum of Science & History, 1900 N Chaparral, Corpus Christi, TX, 78401. Tel: 361-826-4663. Fax: 361-884-7392. p. 2301

Guerra, Juan J, Dir of Libr Serv, Head Librn, Brownsville Public Library System, 2600 Central Blvd, Brownsville, TX, 78520-8824. Tel: 956-548-1055. Fax: 956-548-0684. p. 2292

Guerra, Kathleen, Asst City Librn, Pleasanton Public Library, 321 N Main, Pleasanton, TX, 78064. Tel: 830-569-3622. Fax: 830-569-6082. p. 2371

Guerra, Leticia, Asst Br Mgr, Rio Grande City Public Library, 591 E Canales St, Rio Grande City, TX, 78582-3588. Tel: 956-487-4389. Fax: 956-487-7390. p. 2375

Guerra, Lizette, Librn, University of California Los Angeles Library, Chicano Studies Research Center Library & Archive, 144 Haines Hall, Los Angeles, CA, 90095-1544. Tel: 310-206-6052. Fax: 310-206-1784. p. 178

Guerra, Michelle, Librn, Betsie Valley District Library, 14731 Thompson Ave, Thompsonville, MI, 49683. Tel: 231-378-2716. Fax: 231-378-2716. p. 1230

Guerrero, Anita Finkle, Info Spec, The LuEsther T Mertz Library, The New York Botanical Garden, 2900 Southern Blvd, Bronx, NY, 10458-5126. Tel: 718-817-8681. Fax: 718-817-8956. p. 1587

Guerrero, Dalia, In Charge, Maricopa County Library District, Hollyhock, 15844 N Hollyhock, Surprise, AZ, 85374. Tel: 602-652-3486. Fax: 602-652-3489. p. 74

Guerrero, Elma, Circ, Dustin Michael Sekula Memorial Library, 1906 S Closner Blvd, Edinburg, TX, 78539. Tel: 956-383-6246. Fax: 956-318-3123. p. 2315

Guerrero, Emma, Commun Libr Mgr, County of Los Angeles Public Library, Urban Outreach Bookmobile, 1601 W Covina Pkwy, West Covina, CA, 91790. Tel: 626-338-8373. Fax: 626-337-5166. p. 143

Guerrero, Robert, Law Librn, Libr Mgr, Richards, Layton & Finger Library, 920 King St, Wilmington, DE, 19801. Tel: 302-651-7775. Fax: 302-498-7700, 302-651-7701. p. 388

Guerrero, Robert, Librn, GlaxoSmithKline Pharmaceuticals, Research & Development Library, UW2322, 709 Swedeland Rd, King of Prussia, PA, 19406-2799. Tel: 610-270-6400. Fax: 610-270-4127. p. 2110

Guerrero, Tammy S, Soc Sci Librn, Purdue University, 2200 169th St, Hammond, IN, 46323-2094. Tel: 219-989-2675. Fax: 219-989-2070. p. 747

Guerrero, Teresita, Lead Libr Tech, University of Washington Libraries, Natural Sciences, Allen Library S, Ground & First Flrs, Box 352900, Seattle, WA, 98195-2900. Tel: 206-685-1554. Fax: 206-685-1665. p. 2534

Guerrero, Victor, Circ, William Penn University, 201 Trueblood Ave, Oskaloosa, IA, 52577. Tel: 641-673-1096. Fax: 641-673-1098. p. 837

Guerrieri, Rose, Dir, Kent State University, 4314 Mahoning Ave NW, Warren, OH, 44483-1998. Tel: 330-675-8866. Fax: 330-675-8825. p. 1944

Guess, Kathleen, Children/Youth Librn, Crittenden County Public Library, 204 W Carlisle St, Marion, KY, 42064-1727. Tel: 270-965-3354. Fax: 270-965-3354. p. 928

Guessferd, Mimi, Med Librn, Parkland Medical Center, One Parkland Dr, Derry, NH, 03038. Tel: 603-421-2318. Fax: 603-421-2060. p. 1445

Guest, Betty, Librn, Southeast Regional Library, Yellow Grass Branch, 213 Souris St, Yellow Grass, SK, S0G 5J0, CANADA. Tel: 306-465-2574. p. 2931

Guest, Charles, Dr, Chair, University of South Alabama, 3800 UCOM-University Commons, Mobile, AL, 36688. Tel: 251-380-2861. Fax: 251-380-2713. p. 2961

Guest, Graham, Archives Mgr, Pahkisimon Nuye?ah Library System, 118 Avro Pl, Air Ronge, CANADA. Tel: 306-425-4525. Fax: 306-425-4572. p. 2917

Guetierrez, Mariano, Coordr, Circ, University of Puerto Rico Library, Cayey Campus, 205 Ave Antonio R Barcelo, Cayey, PR, 00736. Tel: 787-738-2161, Ext 2021, 787-738-5651. Fax: 787-263-2108. p. 2672

Guevremont, Johanne, Librn, Bibliotheque de Beloeil, 620 rue Richelieu, Beloeil, QC, J3G 5E8, CANADA. Tel: 450-467-7872. Fax: 450-467-3257. p. 2880

Gufarotti, Vivian, Asst Dir, Mount Pleasant Public Library, 350 Bedford Rd, Pleasantville, NY, 10570-3099. Tel: 914-769-0548. Fax: 914-769-6149. p. 1719

Gufarotti, Vivian, Br Mgr, Mount Pleasant Public Library, Mount Pleasant Branch, 125 Lozza Dr, Valhalla, NY, 10595-1268. Tel: 914-741-0276. Fax: 914-741-0228. p. 1719

Guffey, Janice, Br Mgr, Central Arkansas Library System, Max Milam Branch, 609 Aplin Ave, Perryville, AR, 72126. Tel: 501-889-2554. p. 106

Guffey, Karen M, Br Mgr, Nelsonville Public Library, Glouster Public, 20 Toledo St, Glouster, OH, 45732. Tel: 740-767-3670. Fax: 740-767-3670. p. 1920

Guggemos, Eva, Archives/Spec Coll & Instrul Serv Librn, Pacific University Library, 2043 College Way, Forest Grove, OR, 97116. Tel: 503-352-1415. Fax: 503-352-1416. p. 1998

Guggenbiller, Brenda, Youth Serv, Ashland Public Library, 224 Claremont Ave, Ashland, OH, 44805. Tel: 419-289-8188, Ext 16. Fax: 419-281-8552. p. 1855

Guggisberg, Donna, Librn, Clever Public Library, 210 S Clarke, Clever, MO, 65631. Tel: 417-743-2277. Fax: 417-743-2277. p. 1323

Guglielmin, Susan, Br Head, Toronto Public Library, Thorncliffe, 48 Thorncliffe Park Dr, Toronto, ON, M4H 1J7, CANADA. Tel: 416-396-3865. Fax: 416-396-3866. p. 2863

Guglielmo, Angela, Head, Circ, Bridgeport Public Library, 925 Broad St, Bridgeport, CT, 06604. Tel: 203-576-7419. Fax: 203-576-8255. p. 331

Gugliotti, Lisa, Ref, Henry Carter Hull Library, Inc, Ten Killingworth Tpk, Clinton, CT, 06413. Tel: 860-669-2342. Fax: 860-669-8318. p. 334

Gugluizza, Barbara, Asst Dir, Elmhurst Hospital Center, 79-01 Broadway, D3-52A, Elmhurst, NY, 11373. Tel: 718-334-2040. Fax: 718-334-5690. p. 1619

Guida, Earlene, In Charge, Tennessee Department of Corrections, 3881 Stewarts Lane, Nashville, TN, 37218-5256. Tel: 615-741-1255. Fax: 615-253-6323, 615-741-1245. p. 2258

Guida, Pat, Br Mgr, Troup-Harris Regional Library System, Hogansville Public Library, 600 E Main St, Hogansville, GA, 30230. Tel: 706-637-6230. p. 538

Guida, Tina, Ref, Cedar Crest College, 100 College Dr, Allentown, PA, 18104-6196. Tel: 610-606-4666, Ext 3387. Fax: 610-740-3769. p. 2026

Guidal, Kathy, Ch, Elmont Public Library, 700 Hempstead Tpk, Elmont, NY, 11003-1896. Tel: 516-354-5280. Fax: 516-354-3276. p. 1620

Guidinger, Jayne, Syst Adminr, Gorge LINK Library Consortium, c/o Hood River County Library, 601 State St, Hood River, OR, 97031. Tel: 541-387-7064. p. 2953

Guido, Mary, Librn, California Highway Patrol, 601 N Seventh St, Sacramento, CA, 95811. Tel: 916-657-7220. p. 222

Guidry, Martha, Br Mgr, Terrebonne Parish Library, Bayou Dularge, 837 Bayou Dularge Rd, Houma, LA, 70363. Tel: 985-851-1752. Fax: 985-851-0287. p. 951

Guidry, Nancy, Ref, Bakersfield College, 1801 Panorama Dr, Bakersfield, CA, 93305-1298. Tel: 661-395-4461. Fax: 661-395-4397. p. 123

Guidry, Nancy, Br Mgr, Iberia Parish Library, St Peter Street Branch, 1111 W Saint Peter St, New Iberia, LA, 70560. Tel: 337-364-7670. Fax: 337-364-7261. p. 959

Guidry, Susan, Assoc Librn, Avoyelles Parish Library, 104 N Washington St, Marksville, LA, 71351-2496. Tel: 318-253-7559. Fax: 318-253-6361. p. 956

Guijarro, Nieves, Chief Librn, Burk's Falls, Armour & Ryerson Union Public Library, 39 Copeland St, Burk's Falls, ON, P0A 1C0, CANADA. Tel: 705-382-3327. Fax: 705-382-3327. p. 2797

Guilbert, France, Libr Tech, Archives Provinciales des Capucins, 3650 Blvd de la Rousseliere, Montreal, QC, H1A 2X9, CANADA. Tel: 514-642-5391, Ext 347. Fax: 514-642-5033. p. 2887

Guilbert, France, Libr Tech, Bibliotheque franciscaine provinciale des Capucins, 3650 boul de la Rousseliere, Montreal, QC, H1A 2X9, CANADA. Tel: 514-642-5391, Ext 347. Fax: 514-642-5033. p. 2888

Guildford, Mary, Acq, Actg Librn, Curator, Nova Scotia Museum of Industry Library, 147 N Foord St, Stellarton, NS, B0K 1S0, CANADA. Tel: 902-755-5425. Fax: 902-755-7045. p. 2784

Guildner, Kay, Support Serv, University of Wisconsin-Milwaukee Libraries, American Geographical Society Library, Golda Meir Library, 2311 E Hartford Ave, Milwaukee, WI, 53211. Tel: 414-229-3984, 414-229-6282. Fax: 414-229-3624. p. 2622

Guildroy, Jonathan, Media Spec, Port Washington Public Library, One Library Dr, Port Washington, NY, 11050. Tel: 516-883-4400. Fax: 516-883-7927. p. 1721

Guiliano, Maryanne, Youth Serv Librn, River Edge Free Public Library, 685 Elm Ave, River Edge, NJ, 07661. Tel: 201-261-1663. Fax: 201-986-0214. p. 1526

Guillas, Jean-Louis, Dir, Parkland Regional Library, 504 Main St N, Dauphin, MB, R7N 1C9, CANADA. Tel: 204-638-6410. Fax: 204-638-9483. p. 2748

Guillemette, Lori, Vice Chair, Parry Sound & Area Access Network, c/o Parry Sound Public Library, 29 Mary St, Parry Sound, ON, P2A 1E3, CANADA. Tel: 705-746-9601. Fax: 705-746-9601. p. 2960

Guillemette-Labory, Louise, Dir of Libr, Bibliothèques de Montrèal, 801, rue Brennan, 5e Etage, Bureau 5206, Montreal, QC, H3C 0G4, CANADA. Tel: 514-872-1608. Fax: 514-872-0530. p. 2889

Guillen, Timothy, Librn, Pembroke Pines Campus, Keiser University Library System, 1500 NW 49th St, Fort Lauderdale, FL, 33309. Tel: 954-351-4035, Fax: 954-351-4051. p. 443

Guillet, Jean-Pierre, Assoc Dir, Pub Serv, Cegep St Jean Sur Richelieu Bibliotheque, 30 boul du Seminaire, CP 1018, Saint-Jean-Sur-Richelieu, QC, J3B 7B1, CANADA. Tel: 450-347-5301, Ext 2333. Fax: 450-347-3329, 450-358-9350. p. 2911

Guillory, David, Cat Librn, ILL Librn, McNeese State University, 4205 Ryan St, Lake Charles, LA, 70609. Tel: 337-475-5716. Fax: 337-475-5719, 337-475-5727. p. 954

Guillory, Pamela, Br Mgr, Evangeline Parish Library, Reverend Leslie T H Prescott Branch, 111 Walnut St, Pine Prairie, LA, 70576. Tel: 337-599-3179. Fax: 337-599-3188. p. 971

Guillory, Stephanie, Br Mgr, Opelousas-Eunice Public Library, Eunice Public, 222 S Second St, Eunice, LA, 70535. Tel: 337-457-7120. Fax: 337-457-7114. p. 965

Guillou, Christian, Ser & Microcomputers, Douglas College Library, 700 Royal Ave, New Westminster, BC, V3M 5Z5, CANADA. Tel: 604-527-5184. Fax: 604-527-5193. p. 2734

Guin, Claudia, Dir, City County Library, 1717 Main St, Tahoka, TX, 79373. Tel: 806-561-4050. Fax: 806-561-4051. p. 2390

Guinan, Marcella, Br Mgr, Manistee County Library, Keddie Norconk Memorial, 12325 Virginia St, Bear Lake, MI, 49614. Tel: 231-864-2700. p. 1205

Guinn, Richard, Cat, Tech Serv, University of Texas, School of Public Health Library, 1200 Herman Pressler Blvd, Houston, TX, 77030-3900. Tel: 713-500-9121. Fax: 713-500-9125. p. 2344

Guinn-Chipman, Susan, Res & Teaching Assoc, University of Colorado Boulder, Archives & Special Collections, 1720 Pleasant St, Boulder, CO, 80309-0184. Tel: 303-492-5739. Fax: 303-492-1881. p. 291

Guinnee, Eli, Dir, Patterson Library, 40 S Portage St, Westfield, NY, 14787. Tel: 716-326-2154. Fax: 716-326-2554. p. 1768

Guinther, Angela, Br Mgr, Cleveland Public Library, Carnegie West, 1900 Fulton Rd, Cleveland, OH, 44113. Tel: 216-623-6927. Fax: 216-623-6929. p. 1878

Guise, Janneka, Head Librn, University of Manitoba Libraries, Eckhardt-Gramatté Music Library, 223-4 Music Bldg, 65 Dafoe Rd, Winnipeg, MB, R3T 2N2, CANADA. Tel: 204-474-9567. Fax: 204-474-7253. p. 2758

Guitron- Rodriguez, Miguel, Br Mgr, Riverside County Library System, Coachella Library, 1538 Seventh St, Coachella, CA, 92236. Tel: 760-398-5148. Fax: 760-398-1068. p. 217

Guitron-Rodriguez, Miguel, Br Mgr, Riverside County Library System, Mecca Library, 91-260 Ave 66, Mecca, CA, 92254. Tel: 760-396-2363. Fax: 760-396-1503. p. 218

Guittar, Michelle, Soc Sci Librn, Northeastern Illinois University, 5500 N Saint Louis Ave, Chicago, IL, 60625-4699. Tel: 773-442-4445. Fax: 773-442-4531. p. 621

Gulacsy, Elizabeth, Archivist, Alfred University, Scholes Library of Ceramics, New York State College of Ceramics at Alfred University, Two Pine St, Alfred, NY, 14802-1297. Tel: 607-871-2948. p. 1572

Gulati, Andrew, Electronic Serv, Franklin & Marshall College, 450 College Ave, Lancaster, PA, 17603-3318. Tel: 717-291-4261. Fax: 717-291-4160. p. 2076

Gulick, James, Bibliographer, Ref Librn, Haverford College, 370 Lancaster Ave, Haverford, PA, 19041-1392. Tel: 610-896-1170. Fax: 610-896-1102. p. 2067

Gullacher, Darcy, Head Librn, Rocky Mountain College Library, 4039 Brentwood Rd NW, Calgary, AB, T2L 1L1, CANADA. Tel: 403-284-5100. Fax: 403-220-9567. p. 2692

Gullatt, David, Dr, Dean, Louisiana Tech University, College of Education, PO Box 3163, Ruston, LA, 71272. Tel: 318-257-3712, 318-257-4606. Fax: 318-257-2960. p. 2966

Gullerid, Aaron, Librn, Church of the Lutheran Conference, 501 Grover Rd, Eau Claire, WI, 54701. Tel: 715-836-6636. Fax: 715-836-6634. p. 2589

Gulley, Faye, Librn, Genesee District Library, Flushing Area, 120 N Maple, Flushing, MI, 48433. Tel: 810-659-9755. Fax: 810-659-1781. p. 1180

Gulley, T Jane, Br Mgr, Newton County Public Library, Morocco Community Library, 205 S West St, Morocco, IN, 47963. Tel: 219-285-2664. Fax: 219-285-0009. p. 760

Gulley, Wendy S, Librn, United States Navy, Historic Ship Nautilus-Submarine Force Library & Archives, One Crystal Lake Rd, Groton, CT, 06340-2464. Tel: 860-694-3558. Fax: 860-694-4150. p. 342

Gullickson, Jennifer, Asst Librn, Tech Serv, Dominican Theological Library, 487 Michigan Ave NE, Washington, DC, 20017-1585. Tel: 202-495-3821. Fax: 202-495-3873. p. 399

Gullickson, Lynn Sue, Tech Serv, Wheaton College, 510 Irving Ave, Wheaton, IL, 60187-5593. Tel: 630-752-5964. Fax: 630-752-5855. p. 718

Gullion, Drucie, Chair, Charleston Academic Libraries Consortium, PO Box 118067, Charleston, SC, 29423-8067. Tel: 843-574-6088. Fax: 843-574-6484. p. 2955

Gullion, Robert, Libr Assoc, Desoto Parish Library, Stonewall Branch, 808 Hwy 171, Stonewall, LA, 71078. Tel: 318-925-9191. Fax: 318-925-3392. p. 956

Gulliver, Nancy, Librn, Atascadero State Hospital, Logan Patient's Library, 10333 El Camino Real, Atascadero, CA, 93422. Tel: 805-468-2520. Fax: 805-468-3027. p. 122

Gulliver, Nancy, Librn, Atascadero State Hospital, Logan Professional Library, 10333 El Camino Real, Atascadero, CA, 93422. Tel: 805-468-2491. Fax: 805-468-3027. p. 122

Gullon, Ismael, Assoc Librn, Mercer University, Walter F George School of Law, Furman Smith Law Library, 1021 Georgia Ave, Macon, GA, 31201-1001. Tel: 478-301-5904. Fax: 478-301-2284. p. 540

Gulnac, Donna, Dir, Access Serv, Dir, Info Serv, University of California Los Angeles Library, Hugh & Hazel Darling Law Library, 112 Law Bldg, Box 951458, 385 Charles E Young Dr E, Los Angeles, CA, 90095-1458. Tel: 310-825-7826. Fax: 310-825-1372. p. 178

Gumbarevic, Milan, AV, Hillsborough Community College, Dale Mabry Campus Library, 4001 Tampa Bay Blvd, Tampa, FL, 33614-7820. Tel: 813-253-7381. Fax: 813-253-7400. p. 496

Gumbel, Jim, Properties Mgr, Allen County Public Library, 900 Library Plaza, Fort Wayne, IN, 46802. Tel: 260-421-1275. Fax: 260-421-1386. p. 740

Gummere, Judy, Ref Librn, Lake Forest Library, 360 E Deerpath Ave, Lake Forest, IL, 60045-2252. Tel: 847-810-4621. Fax: 847-234-1453. p. 663

Gumowsky, Sharon, Librn, Elkford Public Library, 816 Michele Rd, Elkford, BC, V0B 1H0, CANADA. Tel: 250-865-2912. Fax: 250-865-2460. p. 2728

Gunckel, David L, Dir, Libr Serv, Sierra Vista Public Library, 2600 E Tacoma, Sierra Vista, AZ, 85635-1399. Tel: 520-458-4225. Fax: 520-458-5377. p. 82

Gunderson, Emrick, Computer Syst Mgr, Hedberg Public Library, 316 S Main St, Janesville, WI, 53545. Tel: 608-758-6599. Fax: 608-758-6583. p. 2600

Gunderson, Gayle, Dir, Colorado Christian University, 8787 W Alameda Ave, Lakewood, CO, 80226. Tel: 303-963-3250. Fax: 303-963-3251. p. 314

Gunderson, Jan, Circ, University of North Dakota, School of Medicine and Health Sciences, 501 N Columbia Rd, Stop 9002, Grand Forks, ND, 58202-9002. Tel: 701-777-3993. Fax: 701-777-4790. p. 1842

Gunderson, Jeff, Librn, San Francisco Art Institute, 800 Chestnut St, San Francisco, CA, 94133. Tel: 415-749-4559. p. 244

Gunderson, Muriel, Dir, Black River Falls Public Library, 222 Fillmore St, Black River Falls, WI, 54615. Tel: 715-284-4112. Fax: 715-284-5369. p. 2582

Gundlach, Kathryn, Readers' Serv Manager, Wake County Public Library System, West Regional Library, 4000 Louis Stephens Dr, Cary, NC, 27519. Tel: 919-463-8506. p. 1818

Gundred, Catherine, Circ, Whatcom Community College Library, 237 W Kellogg Rd, Bellingham, WA, 98226. Tel: 360-383-3300. p. 2509

Gundy, Larry, Network Adminr, Birchard Public Library of Sandusky County, 423 Croghan St, Fremont, OH, 43420. Tel: 419-334-7101. Fax: 419-334-4788. p. 1900

Gunn, Brenda, Asst Dir, University of Texas Libraries, Center for American History, SRH 2-101, D1100, University of Texas at Austin, Austin, TX, 78712. Tel: 512-495-4515. Fax: 512-495-4542. p. 2284

Gunn Bromley, Susan, Curator, Norwalk Museum, 41 N Main St, South Norwalk, CT, 06854-2702. Tel: 203-866-0202. p. 367

Gunn, Chris, AV, Hillsborough Community College, Brandon Campus Learning Resources Center, 10414 E Columbus Dr, Tampa, FL, 33619-9640. Tel: 813-253-7803. p. 496

Gunn, Cindie, Dir, B J Hill Library, 402 W Travis St, Holland, TX, 76534-3015. Tel: 254-657-2884. Fax: 254-657-2845. p. 2333

Gunn, Kevin, Coordr, Libr Serv, Catholic University of America, Religious Studies-Philosophy & Humanities Libraries, 620 Michigan Ave NE, 312 Mullen Library, Washington, DC, 20064. Tel: 202-319-5075. Fax: 202-319-4735. p. 396

Gunn, Mariela, Digital Serv Librn, Oakland University Library, 2200 N Squirrel Rd, Rochester, MI, 48309-4402. Tel: 248-370-2464. Fax: 248-370-2474. p. 1221

Gunn, Phil, Asst Librn, Church of Jesus Christ of Latter-Day Saints, 41 S Hobson, Mesa, AZ, 85204. Tel: 480-964-1200. Fax: 480-964-7137. p. 68

Gunn, Tonya, Librn, Hitchcock Memorial Museum & Library, 1252 Rte 100, Westfield, VT, 05874. Tel: 802-744-8258. p. 2439

Gunnarson, Martha, Asst Dir, Ser, Worcester Polytechnic Institute, 100 Institute Rd, Worcester, MA, 01609-2280. Tel: 508-831-5410. Fax: 508-831-5829. p. 1145

Gunning, Anita, Head, Tech Serv, Tipton County Public Library, 127 E Madison St, Tipton, IN, 46072-1993. Tel: 765-675-8761. Fax: 765-675-4475. p. 782

Gunning, Claire, ILL, Cooper Union for Advancement of Science & Art Library, Seven E Seventh St, New York, NY, 10003. Tel: 212-353-4186. Fax: 212-353-4017. p. 1676

Gunning, Kathleen, Dir, Susquehanna University, 514 University Ave, Selinsgrove, PA, 17870-1050. Tel: 570-372-4320. Fax: 570-372-4310. p. 2138

Gunning, Pamela, Youth Serv Dept Head, Pearl River Public Library, 80 Franklin Ave, Pearl River, NY, 10965. Tel: 845-735-4084. Fax: 845-735-4041. p. 1716

Gunningham, Regan, Head Librn, SIAST Libraries, 1100 15th St E, Prince Albert, SK, S6V 6G1, CANADA. Tel: 306-765-1550. Fax: 306-953-7064. p. 2921

Gunnoe, Betty, Acq, Martinsburg-Berkeley County Public Library, 101 W King St, Martinsburg, WV, 25401. Tel: 304-267-8933. Fax: 304-267-9720. p. 2565

Gunsaulis, Judy, Dir, Fayette County Public Libraries, 531 Summit St, Oak Hill, WV, 25901. Tel: 304-465-0121. Fax: 304-465-5306. p. 2567

Gunsch, Andrew, IT Mgr, Canal Fulton Public Library, 154 Market St NE, Canal Fulton, OH, 44614-1196. Tel: 330-854-4148. Fax: 330-854-9520. p. 1863

Gunstream, Lori, Asst Dir, Alexander Memorial Library, 201 S Center St, Cotulla, TX, 78014-2255. Tel: 830-879-2601. Fax: 830-879-2601. p. 2303

Gunter, Glenda, Assoc Prof, University of Central Florida, College of Education, PO Box 161250, Orlando, FL, 32816. Tel: 407-823-3502. Fax: 407-823-4880. p. 2963

Gunter, Judy, Librn, Chinook Regional Library, Val Marie Branch, Val Marie Village Complex, Val Marie, SK, S0N 2T0, CANADA. Tel: 306-298-2133. p. 2929

Gunter, Linda, Head, Access Serv, Claremont Colleges Library, 800 Dartmouth Ave, Claremont, CA, 91711. Tel: 909-621-8014. p. 134

Gunther, Alan, Librn, Providence Community Library, Smith Hill Library, 31 Candace St, Providence, RI, 02908. Tel: 401-272-4140. p. 2173

Gunther, Jason, Librn, Federal Correctional Institution Library, 9595 W Quincy Ave, Littleton, CO, 80123. Tel: 303-985-1566, Ext 1216. Fax: 303-763-2599. p. 317

Gunther, Lory, Dir, Town of Mendon Public Library, 15 Monroe St, Honeoye Falls, NY, 14472. Tel: 585-624-6067. Fax: 585-624-4255. p. 1637

Gunther, Paul, Librn, Minnesota Orchestra Music Library, 1111 Nicollet Mall, Minneapolis, MN, 55403. Tel: 612-371-5622. Fax: 612-371-0838. p. 1261

Gunto, David, Ref, Dykema Gossett PLLC, 400 Renaissance Ctr, 38th Flr, Detroit, MI, 48243. Tel: 313-568-6714. Fax: 313-568-6735. p. 1171

Gunzenhauser, Jackie, Libr Dir, Humeston Public Library, 302 Broad St, Humeston, IA, 50123. Tel: 641-877-4811. p. 821

Guo, May, Res Librn, DLA Piper US LLP, 500 Eighth St NW, Washington, DC, 20004. Tel: 202-799-4000. Fax: 202-799-5000. p. 399

Guo, Pipei, Ref, United States Air Force, 355 SVS/SVMG, 5427 E Madera St, Bldg 4339, Davis Monthan AFB, AZ, 85707-4930. Tel: 520-228-7148. Fax: 520-228-3998. p. 61

Gupton, Karen, Coordr, Media Spec, Tennessee State University, 3500 John A Merritt Blvd, Nashville, TN, 37209. Tel: 615-963-5743. Fax: 615-963-5745. p. 2259

Gurbanov, Katherine, Head, Circ, Head, Tech, Marlborough Public Library, 35 W Main St, Marlborough, MA, 01752-5510. Tel: 508-624-6998. Fax: 508-485-1494. p. 1103

Gurcke, Karl, Historian, United States National Park Service, Park Headquarters, Second Ave & Broadway, Skagway, AK, 99840. Tel: 907-983-2921. Fax: 907-983-9249. p. 53

Gurdak, Summer, Ch, Warren Township Public Library, 210 Burnett Ave, Warren, IL, 61087. Tel: 815-745-2076. Fax: 815-745-2076. p. 715

Gurley, Cally, Curator, University of New England Libraries, Josephine S Abplanalp Library, Portland Campus, 716 Stevens Ave, Portland, ME, 04103. Tel: 207-221-4324. Fax: 207-221-4893. p. 978

Gurner, Joseph, Dir, Blackmur Memorial Library, 608 Blackmur Dr, Water Valley, MS, 38965-6070. Tel: 662-473-2444. Fax: 662-473-2444. p. 1317

Gurney, Kathy, Govt Doc & Ser Tech, Montana State University, 1500 University Dr, Billings, MT, 59101-0298. Tel: 406-657-1659. Fax: 406-657-2037. p. 1374

Gurrola, Rosemary, Commun Libr Mgr, County of Los Angeles Public Library, Montebello Library, 1550 W Beverly Blvd, Montebello, CA, 90640-3993. Tel: 323-722-6551. Fax: 323-722-3018. p. 142

Gurrola, Rosemary, Commun Libr Mgr, County of Los Angeles Public Library, Pico Rivera Library, 9001 Mines Ave, Pico Rivera, CA, 90660-3098. Tel: 562-942-7394. Fax: 562-942-7779. p. 143

Gurtler, Karen, Librn, Ruby Community Library, Ten Kennedy Way, Ruby, AK, 99768. Fax: 907-468-4443. p. 52

Gurtner, Diane, Info Scientist, Kraft Foods/Oscar Mayer Foods, 910 Mayer Ave, Madison, WI, 53704. Tel: 608-285-4025. Fax: 608-285-6010. p. 2606

Gurung, Purna, Admin Serv Coordr, Rochester Public Library, 101 Second St SE, Rochester, MN, 55904-3776. Tel: 507-328-2300. Fax: 507-328-2384. p. 1273

Gurzenda, Mary-Jean, Head, Ref Serv, West Orange Free Public Library, 46 Mount Pleasant Ave, West Orange, NJ, 07052-4903. Tel: 973-736-0198. Fax: 973-736-1655. p. 1541

Gushue, Rhoda M, Dir, Bedford Hills Free Library, 26 Main St, Bedford Hills, NY, 10507-1832. Tel: 914-666-6472. Fax: 914-666-6473. p. 1579

Guss, Erin, Br Mgr, Saint Louis Public Library, Barr, 1701 S Jefferson Ave, Saint Louis, MO, 63104. Tel: 314-771-7040. Fax: 314-771-9054. p. 1360

Gustafson, Charles, AV, Lake Superior State University, 906 Ryan Ave, Sault Sainte Marie, MI, 49783. Tel: 906-635-2815. Fax: 906-635-2193. p. 1226

Gustafson, Diane, Librn, Southwestern College Library, 900 Otay Lakes Rd, Chula Vista, CA, 91910-7299. Tel: 619-482-6433. Fax: 619-482-6417. p. 134

Gustafson, Eric, Dir, Derby Public Library, 1600 E Walnut Grove, Derby, KS, 67037. Tel: 316-788-0760. Fax: 316-788-7313. p. 863

Gustafson, Glen, Access Serv/Reserves/Ref Librn, Sidley Austin LLP Library, 555 W Fifth St, Ste 4000, Los Angeles, CA, 90013. Tel: 213-896-6193. Fax: 213-896-6600. p. 177

Gustafson, Janet L, Librn, Sheffield Township Library, 20 Leather St, Sheffield, PA, 16347. Tel: 814-968-3439. Fax: 814-968-5761. p. 2139

Gustafson, Jennifer, Practicum Coordr, Wayne State University, 106 Kresge Library, Detroit, MI, 48202. Tel: 313-577-1825. Fax: 313-577-7563. p. 2968

Gustafson, Julia, Access Serv, The College of Wooster Libraries, 1140 Beall Ave, Wooster, OH, 44691-2364. Tel: 330-263-2315. Fax: 330-263-2253. p. 1949

Gustafson, Mattie, Coll Mgt Librn, Newport Public Library, 300 Spring St, Newport, RI, 02840. Tel: 401-847-8720. Fax: 401-842-0841. p. 2169

Gustafson, Melissa, Coordr, Battelle Seattle Research Center, 1100 Dexter Ave N, Ste 400, Seattle, WA, 98109-3598. Tel: 206-528-3370. Fax: 614-458-0182. p. 2527

Gustafson, Sarah, Librn, Klohn Crippen Berger Ltd, 500 2618 Hopewell Pl NE, Calgary, AB, T1Y 7J7, CANADA. Tel: 403-731-6880. p. 2692

Gustasson, Laurel, Mgr, Saint Petersburg Public Library, 3745 Ninth Ave N, Saint Petersburg, FL, 33713. Tel: 727-893-7724. Fax: 727-892-5432. p. 488

Gustavson, Carrie, Dir, Bisbee Mining & Historical Museum, Five Copper Queen Plaza, Bisbee, AZ, 85603. Tel: 520-432-7071. Fax: 520-432-7800. p. 58

Gustavson, Jo Ann, Dir, Neillsville Public Library, 409 Hewett St, Neillsville, WI, 54456-1923. Tel: 715-743-2558. Fax: 715-743-6213. p. 2624

Gustely, Margo M, Res Operations Mgr, Greenberg Traurig LLP, 1221 Brickell Ave, Miami, FL, 33131. Tel: 305-579-0667. Fax: 305-579-0717. p. 465

Guston, Judith M, Curator, Rosenbach Museum & Library, 2010 DeLancey Pl, Philadelphia, PA, 19103. Tel: 215-732-1600, Ext 112. Fax: 215-545-7529. p. 2116

Gusts, Lilita, Dr, Dir, Libr & Res Serv, Council on Foreign Relations Library, 58 E 68th St, New York, NY, 10065. Tel: 212-434-9400. Fax: 212-434-9824. p. 1676

Gut, Rachel, Mgr, Outreach Serv, Dayton Metro Library, Outreach Services, 2293 Arbor Blvd, Dayton, OH, 45439. Tel: 937-227-9520. Fax: 937-496-4356. p. 1893

Gutek, Marya, Librn, Genesee District Library, Forest Township, 123 W Main St, Otisville, MI, 48463. Tel: 810-631-6330. Fax: 810-631-6076. p. 1180

Gutekanst, Joe, ILL Coordr, Davidson College, 209 Ridge Rd, Davidson, NC, 28035-0001. Tel: 704-894-2331. Fax: 704-894-2625. p. 1786

Gutelius, Alexandra, Dir, Clifton Park-Halfmoon Public Library, 475 Moe Rd, Clifton Park, NY, 12065-3808. Tel: 518-371-8622. Fax: 518-371-3799. p. 1607

Guter, Bruce, Dir, Pomona Public Library, 625 S Garey Ave, Pomona, CA, 91766-3322. Tel: 909-620-2036. Fax: 909-620-3713. p. 211

Guth, Laura, Youth Serv Dir, Adel Public Library, 303 S Tenth St, Adel, IA, 50003-1797. Tel: 515-993-3512. Fax: 515-993-3191. p. 791

Guth, LuMarie, Govt Doc Librn, Columbus State University Libraries, 4225 University Ave, Columbus, GA, 31907. Tel: 706-565-3497. Fax: 706-568-2084. p. 526

Guthmiller, Barb, Actg Librn, Leola Public Library, 802 Main St, Leola, SD, 57456. Tel: 605-439-3383. p. 2214

Guthmiller, Christine, Dir, Kanawha Public Library, 120 N Main, Kanawha, IA, 50447. Tel: 641-762-3595. Fax: 641-762-3807. p. 825

Guthrie, Alyce N, VPres, PT Boats, Inc, 1384 Cordova Cove, Ste 2, Memphis, TN, 38138-2200. Tel: 901-755-8440. p. 2250

Guthrie, Cassie, Exec Dir, Pioneer Library System, 2557 State Rte 21, Canandaigua, NY, 14424. Tel: 585-394-8260. Fax: 585-394-1935. p. 1601

Guthrie, Diana, Dir, Pleasanton Public Library, 321 N Main, Pleasanton, TX, 78064. Tel: 830-569-3622. Fax: 830-569-6082. p. 2371

Guthrie, Robin, Br Mgr, Placer County Library, Foresthill Branch, 24580 Main St, Foresthill, CA, 95631. Tel: 530-367-2785. Fax: 530-367-4721. p. 123

Guthrie, Tara, Acq, Carteret Community College Library, 201 College Circle, Morehead City, NC, 28557. Tel: 252-222-6214. Fax: 252-222-6219. p. 1810

Guthrie, Tara, Dir of Libr Serv, Central Carolina Community College Libraries, 1105 Kelly Dr, Sanford, NC, 27330. Tel: 919-718-7245. Fax: 919-718-7378. p. 1823

Guthrie, Virginia, Br Coordr, Birmingham Public Library, 2100 Park Pl, Birmingham, AL, 35203. Tel: 205-226-4018. Fax: 205-226-3755. p. 7

Guthrie, Virginia, Librn, Birmingham Public Library, Five Points West, 4812 Avenue W, Ensley, Birmingham, AL, 35208. Tel: 205-226-4013. Fax: 205-780-8152. p. 7

Guthrie-McNaughton, Isabella, Librn, Institute for Christian Studies, 229 College St, Toronto, ON, M5T 1R4, CANADA. Tel: 416-979-2331, Ext 250. Fax: 416-979-2332. p. 2854

Guthro, Clem P, Dir, Colby College Libraries, 5100 Mayflower Hill, Waterville, ME, 04901. Tel: 207-859-5100, 207-859-5101. Fax: 207-859-5105. p. 1005

Gutierrez, Carolyn, Govt Doc, Info Serv, Rogers State University Library, 1701 W Will Rogers Blvd, Claremore, OK, 74017-3252. Tel: 918-343-7786. Fax: 918-343-7897. p. 1960

Gutierrez, Jolene, Librn, Denver Academy Library, 4400 E Iliff Ave, Denver, CO, 80222. Tel: 303-777-5870. Fax: 303-777-5893. p. 300

Gutierrez, Judy, Librn, University Club Library, 1135 16th St NW, Washington, DC, 20036. Tel: 202-862-8800. Fax: 202-296-2347. p. 421

Gutierrez, Laura, Access Serv Librn, University of North Texas Health Science Center at Fort Worth, 3500 Camp Bowie Blvd, Fort Worth, TX, 76107-2699. Tel: 817-735-2070. Fax: 817-763-0325. p. 2324

Gutierrez, Louise, Br Mgr, Riverside County Library System, Highgrove Library, 690 W Center St, Highgrove, CA, 92507. Tel: 951-682-1507. Fax: 951-321-4107. p. 217

Gutierrez, Louise, Br Mgr, Riverside County Library System, Nuview Library, 29990 Lake View Ave, Nuevo, CA, 92567. Tel: 951-928-0769. Fax: 951-928-3360. p. 218

Gutierrez, Margo, Asst Head Librn, University of Texas Libraries, Nettie Lee Benson Latin American Collection, Sid Richardson Hall 1-108, Austin, TX, 78713-8916. Tel: 512-495-4520. Fax: 512-495-4568. p. 2283

Gutierrez, Marta, Admin Serv, St Thomas University Library, 16401 NW 37th Ave, Miami Gardens, FL, 33054. Tel: 305-628-6672. Fax: 305-628-6666. p. 469

Gutierrez, Rene L, Doc, Organization of American States, 19th & Constitution Ave NW, Washington, DC, 20006-4499. Tel: 202-458-6233. Fax: 202-458-3914. p. 412

Gutierrez, Sarah, Libr Asst, Jackson Walker Law Library, 1401 McKinney, Ste 1900, Houston, TX, 77010. Tel: 713-752-4317. Fax: 713-752-4221. p. 2345

Gutierrez, Veronica, Law Librn, Atascadero State Hospital, Logan Patient's Library, 10333 El Camino Real, Atascadero, CA, 93422. Tel: 805-468-3343. Fax: 805-468-3027. p. 122

Gutmann, Ted, Dir, Emma S Clark Memorial Library, 120 Main St, Setauket, NY, 11733-2868. Tel: 631-941-4080. Fax: 631-941-4541. p. 1742

Gutow, Esther, Dir, University Hospitals Case Medical Center, 11100 Euclid Ave, Lakeside 3119, Cleveland, OH, 44106. Tel: 216-844-1208. Fax: 216-844-1207. p. 1881

Gutschenritter, Victoria, Asst Dir, Mishawaka-Penn-Harris Public Library, 209 Lincoln Way E, Mishawaka, IN, 46544-2084. Tel: 574-259-5277, Ext 228. Fax: 574-254-5585, 574-255-8489. p. 765

Gutstein, Margo, Tech Serv, Simon Wiesenthal Center & Museum of Tolerance, 1399 S Roxbury Dr, Los Angeles, CA, 90035-4709. Tel: 310-772-7605. Fax: 310-277-6568. p. 177

Gutting, Ann, Asst Dir, Ref Librn, Winthrop Public Library & Museum, Two Metcalf Sq, Winthrop, MA, 02152-3157. Tel: 617-846-1703. Fax: 617-846-7083. p. 1142

Guttman, Renata, Head, User Serv, Centre Canadien d'Architecture/Canadian Centre for Architecture, 1920 rue Baile, Montreal, QC, H3H 2S6, CANADA. Tel: 514-939-7000. Fax: 514-939-7020. p. 2892

Gutz, Linda, Dir, Osmond Public Library, 412 N State St, Osmond, NE, 68765. Tel: 402-748-3382. Fax: 402-748-3382. p. 1415

Guy, Bennett, Syst Dir of Libr, Bryant & Stratton Business College, 465 Main St, Ste 400, Buffalo, NY, 14203. Tel: 716-884-9120, Ext 261. Fax: 716-884-0091. p. 1596

Guy, Bruce, Dir, Gladwin County District Library, 402 James Robertson Dr, Gladwin, MI, 48624. Tel: 989-426-8221. Fax: 989-426-6958. p. 1183

Guy, Debbie, Supvr, Middlesex County Library, Thorndale Branch, 21790 Fairview Rd, Thorndale, ON, N0M 2P0, CANADA. Tel: 519-461-1150. Fax: 519-461-0561. p. 2845

Guy, Donald, Mgr, Tech Libr Operations, Sandia National Laboratories, PO Box 5800, MS 0899, Albuquerque, NM, 87185-0899. Tel: 505-845-8287. Fax: 505-844-3143. p. 1550

Guy, Emmett, Jr, Br Mgr, Washington Parish Library System, Bogalusa Branch, 304 Ave F, Bogalusa, LA, 70427. Tel: 985-735-1961. Fax: 985-735-1996. p. 950

Guy, Laura, Syst Librn, Colorado School of Mines, 1400 Illinois St, Golden, CO, 80401-1887. Tel: 303-384-2355. Fax: 303-273-3199. p. 309

Guy, Louise, Ref, Ministere de la Sante et des Services Sociaux, 1075, Chemin Ste-Foy, 5e etage, Quebec, QC, G1S 2M1, CANADA. Tel: 418-266-7017. Fax: 418-266-7024. p. 2905

Guy, Louise, In Charge, Regie de L'Assurance-Maladie du Quebec, 1125 Chemin Saint-Louis, 7E, Sillery, QC, G1S 1E7, CANADA. Tel: 418-682-5118. Fax: 418-528-6864. p. 2913

Guy, Misty, Dir, Lovett Memorial Library, 111 N Houston, Pampa, TX, 79065. Tel: 806-669-5780. Fax: 806-669-5782. p. 2368

Guyan, Tracy, Asst Dir, Tech, Terrebonne Parish Library, 151 Library Dr, Houma, LA, 70360. Tel: 985-876-5861. Fax: 985-917-0582. p. 951

Guyette, Frederick W, Govt Doc, Ref Serv, Erskine College & Theological Seminary, One Depot St, Due West, SC, 29639. Tel: 864-379-8898. Fax: 864-379-2900. p. 2193

Guyonneau, Christine, Archivist, University of Indianapolis, 1400 E Hanna Ave, Indianapolis, IN, 46227-3697. Tel: 317-788-3431. Fax: 317-788-3275. p. 755

Guyote, Gerri, Asst Dir, Peabody Institute Library, 82 Main St, Peabody, MA, 01960-5592. Tel: 978-531-0100. Fax: 978-532-1797. p. 1116

Guyton, Clara L, Mgr, Howard University Libraries, Founders & Undergraduate Library, 500 Howard Pl NW, Washington, DC, 20059. Tel: 202-806-7237. p. 404

Guyton, Connie, Br Mgr, Sampson-Clinton Public Library, Miriam B Lamb Memorial, 144 S Church Ave, Garland, NC, 28441. Tel: 910-529-2441. p. 1784

Guyton, Patricia, Br Mgr, Public Library Association of Annapolis & Anne Arundel County, Inc, South County, 5940 Deale-Churchton Rd, Deale, MD, 20751. Tel: 410-222-1925. Fax: 410-222-1910. p. 1011

Guzenski, Betsy, Pres, Washington Township Historical Society Library, Six Fairview Ave, Long Valley, NJ, 07853-3172. Tel: 908-876-9696. p. 1497

Guzewich, Marsha, Dir, Rogers Environmental Education Center, 2721 State Hwy 80, Sherburne, NY, 13460. Tel: 607-674-4017. Fax: 607-674-2655. p. 1743

Guzman, Alberto, Ref Serv, Inter-American University of Puerto Rico, School of Law Library, PO Box 70351, Hato Rey, PR, 00936. Tel: 787-751-1912. Fax: 787-753-6851. p. 2673

Guzman, George, Admin Serv Mgr, Riverside Public Library, 3581 Mission Inn Ave, Riverside, CA, 92501. Tel: 951-826-5201. Fax: 951-788-1528. p. 218

Guzzetti, Barbara, Dr, Prof, Arizona State University, Farmer Bldg 434, Tempe, AZ, 85287. Tel: 480-965-4602. Fax: 480-965-1863. p. 2961

Guzzo, Cynthia, Head of Acq/Cataloging, Smithtown Library, One N Country Rd, Smithtown, NY, 11787. Tel: 631-265-2072. Fax: 631-265-2044. p. 1744

Guzzo, Stacie, Br Librn, Romeo District Library, Kezar Branch, 107 Church St, Romeo, MI, 48065. Tel: 586-752-2583. Fax: 586-336-7300. p. 1235

Guzzy, Judith, Tech Serv Librn, Johnson County Community College, 12345 College Blvd, Box 21, Overland Park, KS, 66210. Tel: 913-469-8500, Ext 4151. Fax: 913-469-3816. p. 888

Gwiazda, Cynthia, Commun Serv Librn, Hagaman Memorial Library, 227 Main St, East Haven, CT, 06512-3003. Tel: 203-468-3890. Fax: 203-468-3892. p. 337

Gwilt, Roberta, Assoc Dean, Access & Res Mgt, Syracuse University Library, 222 Waverly Ave, Syracuse, NY, 13244-2010. Tel: 315-443-2573. p. 1754

Gwin, James, Coll Develop Librn, University of Richmond, 28 Westhampton Way, Richmond, VA, 23173. Tel: 804-289-8458. Fax: 804-289-8757. p. 2491

Gwinett, Lori, Govt Doc, Georgia Southern University, 1400 Southern Dr, Statesboro, GA, 30458. Tel: 912-478-5117. Fax: 912-478-0093. p. 552

Gwinn, Nancy E, Dir of Libr, Smithsonian Libraries, Nat Museum of Natural Hist, Rm 22, MRC154, Tenth St & Constitution Ave NW, Washington, DC, 20002. Tel: 202-633-2240. Fax: 202-633-4315. p. 414

Gwinn, Sherry, Asst Librn, Summers County Public Library, 201 Temple St, Hinton, WV, 25951. Tel: 304-466-4490. Fax: 304-466-5260. p. 2560

Gwizdalski, Candace, Mgr, Advocate Trinity Hospital, 2320 E 93rd St, Chicago, IL, 60617. Tel: 773-967-5564, Ext 5300. Fax: 773-967-5808. p. 605

Gwyn, Cathy, Ch, Atlanta-Fulton Public Library System, West End Library, 525 Peeples St SW, Atlanta, GA, 30310. Tel: 404-752-8740. Fax: 404-752-8742. p. 513

Gwyn, Lydia, Access Serv Mgr/Day, Fashion Institute of Technology-SUNY, Seventh Ave at 27th St, New York, NY, 10001-5992. Tel: 212-217-4363. Fax: 212-217-4371. p. 1678

Gwyn, Mary P, Ref, Lexington County Public Library System, Irmo Branch, 6251 St Andrews Rd, Columbia, SC, 29212-3152. Tel: 803-798-7880. Fax: 803-798-8570. p. 2199

Gwyn, Pat, Librn, Mount Airy Public Library, 145 Rockford St, Mount Airy, NC, 27030-4759. Tel: 336-789-5108. Fax: 336-786-5838. p. 1811

Gwynn, Barbara, Ref, Charlotte Mecklenburg Library, 310 N Tryon St, Charlotte, NC, 28202-2176. Tel: 704-416-0101. Fax: 704-416-0130. p. 1782

Gwynn, David, Digital Projects Coordr, University of North Carolina at Greensboro, 320 Spring Garden St, Greensboro, NC, 27402. Tel: 336-256-2606. Fax: 336-334-5399. p. 1798

Gwynne, Melissa, Supv Librn, Burbank Public Library, Northwest, 3323 W Victory Blvd, Burbank, CA, 91505-1543. Tel: 818-238-5640. Fax: 818-238-5642. p. 130

Gyger, Carol, IT Mgr, Poudre River Public Library District, 201 Peterson St, Fort Collins, CO, 80524-2990. Tel: 970-221-6740. Fax: 970-221-6398. p. 308

Gysel, Lisa D, Librn, Thompson Cariboo Shuswap Health Sciences Library, 311 Columbia St, Kamloops, BC, V2C 2T1, CANADA. Tel: 250-314-2234. Fax: 250-314-2189. p. 2729

Gyulveszi, Jane, Prog Coordr, Pub Relations Coordr, Youth Serv Coordr, Crawford County Library System, 201 Plum St, Grayling, MI, 49738. Tel: 989-348-9214. Fax: 989-348-9294. p. 1186

Ha-Tran, Patty, Admin Senior Librn, Multicultural Association of Nova Scotia Library, 1113 Marginal Rd, Halifax, NS, B3H 4P7, CANADA. Tel: 902-423-6534. Fax: 902-422-0881. p. 2781

Haack, Joyce, Web Coordr, Scott Community College Library, 500 Belmont Rd, Bettendorf, IA, 52722. Tel: 563-441-4156. Fax: 563-441-4154. p. 796

Haacker, Dan, Asst Dir, Milton Public Library, 476 Canton Ave, Milton, MA, 02186-3299. Tel: 617-698-5757. Fax: 617-698-0441. p. 1106

Haaften, Joel, Dir, Rock County Historical Society, 933 Mineral Point Ave, Janesville, WI, 53545. Tel: 608-756-4509. Fax: 608-741-9596. p. 2600

Haag, Angela, Res, Central Nevada Museum & Historical Society, 1900 Logan Field Rd, Tonopah, NV, 89049. Tel: 775-482-9676. Fax: 775-482-5423. p. 1434

Haag, Doris, Dir, Winkler Ctr for the Hist of Health Professions, University of Cincinnati Libraries, Donald C Harrison Health Sciences Library, PO Box 670574, Cincinnati, OH, 45267-0574. Tel: 513-558-0123. Fax: 513-558-2682. p. 1874

Haag, Doris, Dir, University of Cincinnati Libraries, Henry R Winkler Center for the History of the Health Professions, PO Box 670574, Cincinnati, OH, 45267-0574. Tel: 513-558-5123. Fax: 513-558-2199. p. 1874

Haag, Elli, ILL, Valemount Public Library, 1090A Main St, Valemount, BC, V0E 2Z0, CANADA. Tel: 250-566-4367. Fax: 250-566-4278. p. 2740

Haag, Jeannie, Tech Serv, Latah County Library District, 110 S Jefferson, Moscow, ID, 83843-2833. Tel: 208-882-3925. Fax: 208-882-5098. p. 579

Haag, Nancy, Ref, North Haven Memorial Library, 17 Elm St, North Haven, CT, 06473. Tel: 203-239-5803. Fax: 203-234-2130. p. 362

Haag, Nancy, Computer Serv Mgr, Kansas City, Kansas Public Library, 625 Minnesota Ave, Kansas City, KS, 66101. Tel: 913-279-2670. Fax: 913-279-2033. p. 875

Haakinson, Traci, Admin Serv Mgr, Carson City Library, 900 N Roop St, Carson City, NV, 89701. Tel: 775-887-2244. Fax: 775-887-2273. p. 1425

Haar, Annemarie Poniz, Digital Archivist, California College of the Arts Libraries, 5212 Broadway, Oakland, CA, 94618. p. 196

Haar, Patti, Dir, Patterson Library, 1167 Rte 311, Patterson, NY, 12563-2801. Tel: 845-878-6121. Fax: 845-878-3116. p. 1715

Haas, Anne, Art Librn, Bowdoin College Library, Pierce Art Library, Visual Arts Ctr, 9301 College Sta, Brunswick, ME, 04011-8493. Tel: 207-725-3690. p. 979

Haas, Diane, Metadata Serv Tech, University of Oregon Libraries, John E Jaqua Law Library, William W Knight Law Ctr, 2nd Flr, 1515 Agate St, Eugene, OR, 97403-1221. Tel: 541-346-1656. Fax: 541-346-1669. p. 1997

Haas, Jane, Ref Librn, Santa Barbara City College, 721 Cliff Dr, Santa Barbara, CA, 93109-2394. Tel: 805-730-4430. Fax: 805-965-0771. p. 260

Haas, Janel, Dir, Way Public Library, 101 E Indiana Ave, Perrysburg, OH, 43551. Tel: 419-874-3135, Ext 102. Fax: 419-874-6129. p. 1929

Haas, Jennifer, Head, Info Serv & Res, University of Waterloo Library, Davis Centre Library, 200 University Ave W, Waterloo, ON, N2L 3G1, CANADA. Tel: 519-888-4567, Ext. 37469. Fax: 519-888-4311. p. 2870

Haas, Marianna, Acq, Head, Tech Serv, Musser Public Library, 304 Iowa Ave, Muscatine, IA, 52761-3875. Tel: 563-263-3065. Fax: 563-264-1033. p. 834

Haas, Nicole, Ref Serv Librn, West Babylon Public Library, 211 Rte 109, West Babylon, NY, 11704. Tel: 631-669-5445. Fax: 631-669-6539. p. 1765

Haas, Paul, Fac Serv Librn, George Mason University Libraries, School of Law, 3301 N Fairfax Dr, Arlington, VA, 22201-4426. Tel: 703-993-8120. Fax: 703-993-8113. p. 2462

Haas, Steve, Ser, Case Western Reserve University, School of Law Library, 11075 East Blvd, Cleveland, OH, 44106-7148. Tel: 216-368-1001. Fax: 216-368-1002. p. 1876

Haas, Tony, Librn, Stoel Rives LLP, 900 SW Fifth Ave, Ste 2600, Portland, OR, 97204. Tel: 503-294-9576. Fax: 503-220-2480. p. 2014

Haase-Thomas, Amy, Cat, Electronic Res, Dominican College Library, 480 Western Hwy, Blauvelt, NY, 10913-2000. Tel: 845-848-7505. Fax: 845-359-2525. p. 1583

Habata, Michael, Cat, Tech Serv, Los Angeles Pierce College Library, 6201 Winnetka Ave, Woodland Hills, CA, 91371. Tel: 818-719-6409. Fax: 818-719-9058. p. 285

Habeck, Carolyn R, Dir, Hortonville Public Library, 102 W Main St, Hortonville, WI, 54944. Tel: 920-779-4279. Fax: 920-779-4279. p. 2598

Habeck, Penny, Digital Librn, Shawano City-County Library, 128 S Sawyer St, Shawano, WI, 54166-2496. Tel: 715-526-3829. Fax: 715-526-6772. p. 2636

Habegger, Lisa, Dir of Libr Serv, The Indiana Youth Institute, 603 E Washington St, Ste 800, Indianapolis, IN, 46204-2692. Tel: 317-396-2700. Fax: 317-396-2701. p. 753

Habener, Marie, Libr Dir, Dillon City Library, 121 S Idaho, Dillon, MT, 59725-2500. Tel: 406-683-4544. p. 1378

Haber, Dympna, Sr, Cat, Fordham University Westchester Library, 400 Westchester Ave, West Harrison, NY, 10604. Tel: 914-367-3056. p. 1766

Haber, Lauren, Librn, Mat, Skidmore, Owings & Merrill, 14 Wall St, New York, NY, 10005. Tel: 212-298-9300. Fax: 212-298-9500. p. 1700

Haber, Mark, Instrul Serv Librn, Ref Serv, The College of New Rochelle, 29 Castle Pl, New Rochelle, NY, 10805-2308. Tel: 914-654-5345. Fax: 914-654-5884. p. 1666

Haberkern, Michaela, Dept Head, Ref, Hinsdale Public Library, 20 E Maple St, Hinsdale, IL, 60521. Tel: 630-986-1976. Fax: 630-986-9654. p. 656

Haberl, Pam, Teen Librn, J J Hands Library, 609 Second St, Lohrville, IA, 51453. Tel: 712-465-4115. Fax: 712-465-4115. p. 828

Haberli, Joann, Dir, Louise Adelia Read Memorial Library, 104 Read St, Hancock, NY, 13783. Tel: 607-637-2519. Fax: 607-637-3377. p. 1634

Habermacher, Caroline, Dir, Sabinal Public Library, 412 N Center St, Sabinal, TX, 78881. Tel: 830-988-2911. Fax: 830-988-2633. p. 2378

Haberman, David, Head, Student Serv, University of North Dakota, 215 Centennial Dr, Grand Forks, ND, 58202. Tel: 701-777-2204. Fax: 701-777-2217. p. 1843

Haberman, Karen, Dir, Northern Plains Public Library, 216 Second St, Ault, CO, 80610. Tel: 970-834-1259. Fax: 970-834-1259. p. 288

Habermas, Mary E, Dir, John Brown University Library, 2000 W University, Siloam Springs, AR, 72761. Tel: 479-524-7202. Fax: 479-524-7335. p. 115

Habib, Faten, Mrs, Dept Chair, Moorpark College Library, 7075 Campus Rd, Moorpark, CA, 93021-1695. Tel: 805-378-1450. Fax: 805-378-1470. p. 191

Habich, Elizabeth C, Dir, Admin & Finance, Northeastern University Libraries, Snell Library, 360 Huntington Ave, Boston, MA, 02115. Tel: 617-373-4924. p. 1065

Habicht, Fran, Circ Supvr, Everett Public Library, 2702 Hoyt Ave, Everett, WA, 98201-3556. Tel: 425-257-8034. Fax: 425-257-8017. p. 2515

Habousha, Racheline, Pub Serv, Albert Einstein College of Medicine, 1300 Morris Park Ave, Bronx, NY, 10461. Tel: 718-430-3115. Fax: 718-430-8795. p. 1586

Hache, Nicole, Libr Coordr, Champlain Regional College, 900 Riverside Dr, Saint Lambert, QC, J4P 3P2, CANADA. Tel: 450-672-7360. Fax: 450-672-2152. p. 2908

Hachey, Babs, Circ, ILL, Spokane Falls Community College, 3410 Ft George Wright Dr, MS 3020, Spokane, WA, 99224-5288. Tel: 509-533-3818. Fax: 509-533-3144. p. 2537

Hack, Janet, Ref & Web Serv Librn, University of Maryland, Baltimore County, 1000 Hilltop Circle, Baltimore, MD, 21250. Tel: 410-455-2356. p. 1018

Hack, Janie, Librn, Thompson, Hine LLP, 2000 Courthouse Plaza NE, Ten W Second St, Dayton, OH, 45402. Tel: 937-331-6023. Fax: 937-443-6635. p. 1894

Hackbarth, Barbara, Circ, Nicolet Area Technical College, 5364 College Dr, Rhinelander, WI, 54501. Tel: 715-365-4691. Fax: 715-365-4404. p. 2633

Hacken, Richard, Humanities & Soc Sci Librn, Brigham Young University, Harold B Lee Library, 2060 HBLL, Provo, UT, 84602. Tel: 801-422-2927. Fax: 801-422-0466. p. 2411

Hacker, Alesia, Mgr, Cat Dept, Plano Community Library District, 15 W North St, Plano, IL, 60545. Tel: 630-552-2009. Fax: 630-552-1008. p. 691

Hacker, Bethany, Commun Relations Spec, Harford County Public Library, 1221-A Brass Mill Rd, Belcamp, MD, 21017-1209. Tel: 410-273-5600, Ext 2243. Fax: 410-273-5606. p. 1020

Hacker, Linda, MetroCenter Librn, State University of New York College at Brockport, 350 New Campus Dr, Brockport, NY, 14420-2997. Tel: 585-395-2770. Fax: 585-395-5651. p. 1585

Hacker, Susan, Dr, Head, Ref Serv, Willingboro Public Library, Willingboro Town Ctr, 220 Willingboro Pkwy, Willingboro, NJ, 08046. Tel: 609-877-0476, 609-877-6668. Fax: 609-835-1699. p. 1544

Hackert, Brian, ILL, Ref Librn, Peterborough Town Library, Two Concord St, Peterborough, NH, 03458. Tel: 603-924-8040. Fax: 603-924-8041. p. 1462

Hackett, Colleen, Ch, Plainsboro Free Public Library, 9 Van Doren St, Plainsboro, NJ, 08536. Tel: 609-275-2899. Fax: 609-799-5883. p. 1521

Hackett, Nancy, Head, Circ, Redwood Library & Athenaeum, 50 Bellevue Ave, Newport, RI, 02840-3292. Tel: 401-847-0292. Fax: 401-847-0192. p. 2169

Hackett, Rosemary, Librn, Elkland Area Community Library, 110 Parkway Ave, Elkland, PA, 16920-1311. Tel: 814-258-7576. Fax: 814-258-7414. p. 2054

Hackett, Ruth, Mgr, Carbon County Library System, Saratoga Branch, 503 W Elm St, Saratoga, WY, 82331. Tel: 307-326-8209. Fax: 307-326-8209. p. 2659

Hackett, Sharon, Coordr, Doc, Centre de documentation sur l'education des adultes et la condition feminine, 110 rue Ste-Therese, Ste 101, Montreal, QC, H2Y 1E6, CANADA. Tel: 514-876-1180. Fax: 514-876-1325. p. 2892

Hackett, Tim, Head Librn, Merritt College Library, 12500 Campus Dr, Oakland, CA, 94619. Tel: 510-436-2461. Fax: 510-531-4960. p. 197

Hackman, Donna, Br Mgr, Bedford Public Library System, Montvale Library, 11575 W Lynchburg-Salem Tpk, Montvale, VA, 24122. Tel: 540-947-2200. Fax: 540-947-0300. p. 2451

Hackman, Janice, Libr Spec, Harrisburg Area Community College, 1641 Old Philadelphia Pike, Lancaster, PA, 17602. Tel: 717-358-2986. Fax: 717-358-2952. p. 2076

Hackner, Mindy, Dir, Dalton Free Public Library, 462 Main St, Dalton, MA, 01226. Tel: 413-684-6112. Fax: 413-684-4750. p. 1083

Hackney, Alyce, Ref Librn, Pamunkey Regional Library, 7527 Library Dr, Hanover, VA, 23069. Tel: 804-537-6211. Fax: 804-537-6389. p. 2469

Hackney, Alyce, Ref Serv, Pamunkey Regional Library, Richard S Gillis Jr - Ashland Branch, 201 S Railroad Ave, Ashland, VA, 23005. Tel: 804-798-4072. Fax: 804-798-6276. p. 2469

Hackney, Carrie, Head Librn, Howard University Libraries, Divinity, 1400 Shepherd St NE, Washington, DC, 20017. Tel: 202-806-0768. Fax: 202-806-0711. p. 404

Hackney, Carrie, Head Librn, Howard University Libraries, Social Work, 601 Howard Pl NW, Washington, DC, 20059. Tel: 202-806-7316. p. 404

Hackney, Nancy, Br Head, Brazoria County Library System, Lake Jackson Branch, 250 Circle Way, Lake Jackson, TX, 77566. Tel: 979-415-2590. Fax: 979-415-2993. p. 2275

Hackney, Sharon, Media Spec, Truman State University, 100 E Normal, Kirksville, MO, 63501-4211. Tel: 660-785-7366. p. 1342

Hackworth, Linda, Circ, North Canton Public Library, 185 N Main St, North Canton, OH, 44720-2595. Tel: 330-499-4712. Fax: 330-499-7356. p. 1923

Hackworth, Mary, Ref Librn, Greenebaum, Doll & McDonald, 300 W Vine St, Ste 1100, Lexington, KY, 40507-1622. Tel: 859-288-4717. Fax: 859-255-2742. p. 920

Haddad, April, Inst Librn, Justice Institute of British Columbia Library, 715 McBride Blvd, New Westminster, BC, V3L 5T4, CANADA. Tel: 604-528-5594. Fax: 604-528-5593. p. 2734

Haddaway, Emily, Digital Librn, Ohio Wesleyan University, 43 Rowland, Delaware, OH, 43015-2370. Tel: 740-368-3233. Fax: 740-368-3222. p. 1896

Hadden, Helen, Librn, Muriel Isabel Bostwick Library, 123 King St W, Hamilton, ON, L8P 4S8, CANADA. Tel: 905-527-6610. Fax: 905-577-6940. p. 2808

Hadden, Juanita, Br Mgr, DeKalb County Public Library, Henagar Branch, 17163 Alabama Hwy 75, Henagar, AL, 35978. Tel: 256-657-1380. p. 17

Hadden, Linda, Dir, Duplin County Library, 107 Bowden Dr, Kenansville, NC, 28349-0930. Tel: 910-296-2117. Fax: 910-296-2172. p. 1804

Hadden, Melissa, Dir, Latt Maxcy Memorial Library, 15 N Magnolia Ave, Frostproof, FL, 33843. Tel: 863-635-7857. Fax: 863-635-8502. p. 447

Haddock, Kristin, Dir, Julia Crowder McClellan Memorial Library, 15 W 14th St, Mounds, OK, 74047. Tel: 918-827-3949. Fax: 918-827-6010. p. 1969

Haddock, Suzanne, Dir, Nogales-Santa Cruz County Public Library, 518 N Grand Ave, Nogales, AZ, 85621. Tel: 520-287-3343. Fax: 520-287-4823. p. 69

Haddox, Allen, Librn, American Insurance Association, 2101 L St NW, Ste 400, Washington, DC, 20037. Tel: 202-828-7183. Fax: 202-495-7879. p. 392

Hadeler, Kurt, Dir, Mahwah Public Library, 100 Ridge Rd, Mahwah, NJ, 07430. Tel: 201-529-7323. Fax: 201-529-9027. p. 1498

Haderlie, Brooks, Asst Univ Librn, Brigham Young University-Idaho, 525 S Center St, Rexburg, ID, 83460-0405. Tel: 208-496-9522. Fax: 208-496-9503. p. 582

Hadley, Becky, Readers' Advisor Librn, Marshall Public Library, 113 S Garfield, Pocatello, ID, 83204-5722. Tel: 208-232-1263. Fax: 208-232-9266. p. 582

Hadley, Beth, Libr Mgr, Sinclairville Free Library, 15 Main St, Sinclairville, NY, 14782. Tel: 716-962-5885. Fax: 716-962-5885. p. 1744

Hadley, Diana L, Librn, Douglas County Law Library, Justice Bldg, Rm 305, Roseburg, OR, 97470. Tel: 541-440-4341. p. 2016

Hadley, Ginger, Co-Mgr, Sonoma County Library, Occidental Branch, 73 Main St, Occidental, CA, 95465. Tel: 707-874-3080. p. 267

Hadley, Joseph, Exec Dir, Northeast Ohio Four County Regional Planning & Development Organization, 180 E South St, Akron, OH, 44311. Tel: 330-252-0337. Fax: 330-252-0664. p. 1853

Hadley, Kit, Dir, Saint Paul Public Library, 90 W Fourth St, Saint Paul, MN, 55102-1668. Tel: 651-266-7070. Fax: 651-266-7060. p. 1281

Hadley, Laurie, Libr Asst, Cotuit Library, 871 Main St, Cotuit, MA, 02635. Tel: 508-428-8141. Fax: 508-428-4636. p. 1083

Hadley, Sandy, Dir, Herbert F Tyler Memorial Library, 821 N Shawnee, Dewey, OK, 74029. Tel: 918-534-2106. p. 1961

Hadley, Theresa, Ch, Whatcom County Library System, 5205 Northwest Dr, Bellingham, WA, 98226-9050. Tel: 360-384-3150. Fax: 360-384-4947. p. 2509

Hady, Maureen, Coordr, Tech Serv, J Sargeant Reynolds Community College Library, Goochland Campus-Library & Information Services, 1851 Dickinson Rd, Goochland, VA, 23285. Tel: 804-523-5442. Fax: 804-556-5750. p. 2489

Hadziev, Rina, Br Head, Greater Victoria Public Library Board, Juan de Fuca Branch, 1759 Island Hwy, Victoria, BC, V9B 1J1, CANADA. Tel: 250-391-0653. Fax: 250-391-0879. p. 2745

Hadzor, Tom, Dir of Develop, Duke University Libraries, 411 Chapel Dr, Durham, NC, 27708. Tel: 919-660-5940. Fax: 919-660-5923. p. 1787

Haeckel, Kimberly, Supvr, Stack Maintenance, Inglewood Public Library, 101 W Manchester Blvd, Inglewood, CA, 90301-1771. Tel: 310-412-5397. Fax: 310-412-8848. p. 159

Haefliger, Kathleen, Music & Performing Arts Librn, Chicago State University, 9501 S Martin Luther King Jr Dr, LIB 440, Chicago, IL, 60628-1598. Tel: 773-995-2277. Fax: 773-995-3772. p. 610

Haemker, Charles, Dir, Manistee County Library, 95 Maple St, Manistee, MI, 49660. Tel: 231-723-2510, 231-723-2519. Fax: 231-723-8270. p. 1205

Haessner, Elaine C, Dir, International Society for Vehicle Preservation Library, 8987 E Tonque Verde, No 309-300, Tucson, AZ, 85749-9399. Tel: 520-749-2260. p. 86

Hafeman, Robert E, Libr Dir, Moline Public Library, 3210 41st St, Moline, IL, 61265. Tel: 309-736-5723. Fax: 309-797-3751. p. 674

Haferd, Julie, Head, Media Libr, Tiffin-Seneca Public Library, 77 Jefferson St, Tiffin, OH, 44883. Tel: 419-447-3751. Fax: 419-447-3045. p. 1938

Hafermann, Kelly, Instrul Serv Librn, Ref Serv, University of Wisconsin-Whitewater Library, 800 W Main St, Whitewater, WI, 53190. Tel: 262-472-5525. Fax: 262-472-5727. p. 2649

Hafezi, Kasra, Dir, Info Tech Serv Div, Saint John's University Library, Rittenberg Law Library, 8000 Utopia Pkwy, Queens, NY, 11439. Tel: 718-990-6651, 718-990-6659. Fax: 718-990-6649. p. 1725

Haff, Sally E, Librn, Memorial Healthcare System, 3501 Johnson St, Hollywood, FL, 33021. Tel: 954-985-5840. Fax: 954-967-2951. p. 451

Haffer, Michelle, Ch, Webster Groves Public Library, 301 E Lockwood Ave, Webster Groves, MO, 63119-3102. Tel: 314-961-7262. Fax: 314-961-4233. p. 1372

Hafner, Arthur W, PhD, Dr, Dean, Univ Libr, Ball State University Libraries, 2000 W University Ave, Muncie, IN, 47306-1099. Tel: 765-285-5277. Fax: 765-285-2008. p. 766

Hafner, Joseph, Assoc Dir, Coll Serv, McGill University Libraries, 3459 McTavish St, Montreal, QC, H3A 1Y1, CANADA. Tel: 514-398-4788. Fax: 514-398-8919. p. 2898

Hafner, Nadine, Archivist, Union of British Columbia Indian Chiefs, 342 Water St, 4th Flr, Vancouver, BC, V6B 1B6, CANADA. Tel: 604-684-0231. Fax: 604-684-5726. p. 2742

Hafs, Cindy, Adminr, Iowa Central Community College, Webster City Center, 1725 Beach St, Webster City, IA, 50595. Tel: 515-832-1632, Ext 2821. Fax: 515-576-0099, Ext 2820. p. 817

Hagadone, Jackie, Librn, Roosevelt County Library, Poplar City Public, 208 Third Ave W, Poplar, MT, 59255. Tel: 406-768-3749. p. 1390

Hagadorn, Alexis, Conservator, Presv, Columbia University, The Burke Library at Union Theological Seminary, 3041 Broadway, New York, NY, 10027. Tel: 212-851-5607. Fax: 212-851-5613. p. 1674

Hagan, Ashley, Ref Serv, Fort Smith Public Library, 3201 Rogers Ave, Fort Smith, AR, 72903. Tel: 479-783-0229. Fax: 479-782-8571. p. 100

Hagan, Brandon, Circ, Daviess County Public Library, 2020 Frederica St, Owensboro, KY, 42301. Tel: 270-684-0211. Fax: 270-684-0218. p. 931

Hagan, Judy, Dir, Atkinson Public Library, 113 W State St, Atkinson, NE, 68713. Tel: 402-925-2855. Fax: 402-925-2855. p. 1392

Hagan, Lee, Support Serv Div Mgr, Santa Clara City Library, 2635 Homestead Rd, Santa Clara, CA, 95051. Tel: 408-615-2961. Fax: 408-247-9657. p. 262

Hagan, Marylee, Exec Dir, Vigo County Historical Museum Library, 1411 S Sixth St, Terre Haute, IN, 47802. Tel: 812-235-9717. Fax: 812-235-4998. p. 781

Hagar, Angela, ILL, Saint Francis Xavier University, West St, Antigonish, NS, B2G 2W5, CANADA. Tel: 902-867-2267. Fax: 902-867-5153. p. 2777

Hagar, Julia, Librn, Sarasota Campus, Keiser University Library System, 1500 NW 49th St, Fort Lauderdale, FL, 33309. Tel: 954-351-4035. Fax: 954-351-4051. p. 443

Hage, Anne, Dir, Huntington Woods Public Library, 26415 Scotia, Huntington Woods, MI, 48070-1198. Tel: 248-543-9720. Fax: 248-543-2559. p. 1193

Hage, Christine Lind, Dir, Rochester Hills Public Library, 500 Olde Towne Rd, Rochester, MI, 48307-2043. Tel: 248-656-2900. Fax: 248-650-7121. p. 1222

Hage, Lisa, Br Mgr, Saint Paul Public Library, West Seventh, 265 Oneida St, Saint Paul, MN, 55102. Tel: 651-298-5516. p. 1282

Hagedorn, Daniel, Curator, Museum of Flight, 9404 E Marginal Way S, Seattle, WA, 98108-4097. Tel: 206-764-5700. Fax: 206-764-5707. p. 2529

Hagedorn, Jeff, Syst Mgr, Medical College of Wisconsin Libraries, Health Research Ctr, 3rd Flr, 8701 Watertown Plank Rd, Milwaukee, WI, 53226-0509. Tel: 414-955-8515. Fax: 414-955-6532. p. 2619

Hagedorn, Linda, Head, Adult Serv, Franklin Lakes Free Public Library, 470 DeKorte Dr, Franklin Lakes, NJ, 07417. Tel: 201-891-2224. Fax: 201-891-5102. p. 1486

Hagelaar, Dave -, Assoc Dir, Libr & Archives, University of Toronto Libraries, John M Kelly Library, University of Saint Michael's College, 113 Saint Joseph St, Toronto, ON, M5S 1J4, CANADA. Tel: 416-926-7250. Fax: 416-926-7262. p. 2866

Hagelberger, Cindy S, Instr, Ref Serv Librn, Genesee Community College, One College Rd, Batavia, NY, 14020-9704. Tel: 585-343-0055, Ext 6231. Fax: 585-345-6933. p. 1578

Hageman, Betsy, Dir, Knowledge Mgt & Communications, National Association of Chain Drug Stores, 1776 Wilson Blvd, Ste 200, Arlington, VA, 22209. Tel: 703-549-3001. p. 2450

Hageman, Bob, Br Mgr, Seattle Public Library, Queen Anne Branch, 400 W Garfield St, Seattle, WA, 98119. Tel: 206-386-4227. p. 2531

Hagemann, John F, Dir, University of South Dakota, McKusick Law Library, 414 E Clark St, Vermillion, SD, 57069-2390. Tel: 605-677-5041. Fax: 605-677-5417. p. 2220

Hagemeier, Deborah A, Asst Dir, Tech Serv, Augustana College, 2001 S Summit Ave, Sioux Falls, SD, 57197-0001. Tel: 605-274-5354. Fax: 605-274-5447. p. 2218

Hagemeister, Vicky, Librn, Currituck County Public Library, 4261 Caratoke Hwy, Barco, NC, 27917-9707. Tel: 252-453-8345. Fax: 252-453-8717. p. 1775

Hagen, Barb, In Charge, Northwest State Correctional Facility, 3649 Lower Newton Rd, Swanton, VT, 05488. Tel: 802-527-4342. Fax: 802-527-7534. p. 2437

Hagen, Geraldine, Tech Serv, United States Marine Corps, Seaside Square Library, San Onofre, Bldg 51093, Camp Pendleton, CA, 92055. Tel: 760-725-7325. Fax: 760-763-1360. p. 131

Hagen, Janet, Dr, Prof, University of Wisconsin Oshkosh, 800 Algoma Blvd, Oshkosh, WI, 54901. Tel: 920-424-0336. Fax: 920-424-0858. p. 2977

Hagen, Katie, Acq, Supvr, Northwestern College, 3003 Snelling Ave N, Saint Paul, MN, 55113. Tel: 651-631-5241. Fax: 651-631-5598. p. 1280

Hagen, Sharon, Librn, Enchant Community Library, 234 Center St, Enchant, AB, T0K 0V0, CANADA. Tel: 403-739-3835. p. 2703

Hagen, Tim, Head, Adult Serv, Interim Dir, Tiffin-Seneca Public Library, 77 Jefferson St, Tiffin, OH, 44883. Tel: 419-447-3751. Fax: 419-447-3045. p. 1938

Hagenhoff, Betty, Asst Dir, Missouri River Regional Library, 214 Adams St, Jefferson City, MO, 65101-3244. Tel: 573-634-6064, Ext 249. p. 1335

Hager, Frances, Acq, Arkansas Tech University, 305 West Q St, Russellville, AR, 72801-2222. Tel: 479-964-0561. Fax: 479-964-0559. p. 113

Hager, Gregory M, Dir, Willard Library of Evansville, 21 First Ave, Evansville, IN, 47710-1294. Tel: 812-425-4309. Fax: 812-421-9742. p. 739

Hager, Linda, Librn, Wisconsin Veterans' Home Library, Hwy QQ, King, WI, 54946. Tel: 715-258-5586, Ext 2366. Fax: 715-258-5736. p. 2602

Hager, Mary Ann, Mgr, Lunar & Planetary Institute, 3600 Bay Area Blvd, Houston, TX, 77058-1113. Tel: 281-486-2182. Fax: 281-486-2186. p. 2341

Hager, Tina Irene, Libr Dir, Little Elm Public Library, 100 W Eldorado Pkwy, Little Elm, TX, 75068. Tel: 214-975-0430. Fax: 972-377-5546. p. 2356

Hagerman, David, Librn, Elgin Mental Health Center Library, 750 S State St, Elgin, IL, 60123-7692. Tel: 847-742-1040, Ext 3437. Fax: 847-429-4923. p. 641

Hagfeldt, Sue, Br Mgr, Columbia County Rural Library District, 111 S Third St, Dayton, WA, 99328-1342. Tel: 509-382-4131. Fax: 509-382-1059. p. 2514

Haggan, Laurie, Tech Serv, University of Hartford Libraries, 200 Bloomfield Ave, West Hartford, CT, 06117. Tel: 860-768-4264. p. 376

Haggard, Lynn, Pub Serv, Fort Hays State University, 600 Park St, Hays, KS, 67601-4099. Tel: 785-628-5566. Fax: 785-628-4096. p. 871

Haggard, Matthew, Instrul Serv/Ref Librn, Nichols College, 124 Center Rd, Dudley, MA, 01571. Tel: 508-213-2437. Fax: 508-213-2323. p. 1085

Haggart, Linda, Asst Librn, Chinook Regional Library, Abbey Branch, 133 Main St, Abbey, SK, S0N 0A0, CANADA. Tel: 306-689-2202. p. 2928

Haggarty, Penny, Acq Librn, Thompson Rivers University, 900 McGill Rd, Kamloops, BC, V2C 5N3, CANADA. Tel: 250-828-5300. Fax: 250-828-5313. p. 2730

Haggerty, Gary, Dean, Learning Res, Berklee College of Music Library, 150 Massachusetts Ave, Boston, MA, 02115. Tel: 617-747-2603. Fax: 617-747-2050. p. 1055

Haggerty, Lynnette, Asst Dir, Ardmore Public Library, 320 E St NW, Ardmore, OK, 73401. Tel: 580-223-8290. Fax: 580-221-3240. p. 1956

Haggerty, Margaret, Ref, Waterford Township Public Library, 2204 Atco Ave, Atco, NJ, 08004. Tel: 856-767-7727. Fax: 856-753-8998. p. 1469

Haggerty, Sally, Assoc Dir/Librn, Sterling College, 125 W Cooper, Sterling, KS, 67579-1533. Tel: 620-278-4234. Fax: 620-278-4414. p. 895

Haggins, Angela, Librn, Smithsonian Libraries, Smithsonian Environmental Research Center Library, 647 Contees Wharf Rd, Edgewater, DC, 21037. Tel: 443-482-2273. Fax: 443-482-2286. p. 415

Haggstrom, David G, Dir, State University of New York, College of Technology, Upper Colleg Dr, Alfred, NY, 14802. Tel: 607-587-4313. Fax: 607-587-4351. p. 1572

Hagins, Nancy R, Librn, Freeport Area Library, 428 Market St, Freeport, PA, 16229-1122. Tel: 724-295-3616. Fax: 724-295-3616. p. 2059

Hagle, Robyn, Librn, Perkins Coie Library, 1201 Third Ave, Ste 4900, Seattle, WA, 98101. Tel: 206-359-8444. Fax: 206-359-9444. p. 2529

Haglund, Kristine A, Archivist, Head of Libr, Denver Museum of Nature & Science, 2001 Colorado Blvd, Denver, CO, 80205-5798. Tel: 303-370-6362, 303-370-8353. Fax: 303-331-6492. p. 300

Hagmaier, Laura, W Palm Beach Campus Libr Dir, Keiser University Library System, 1500 NW 49th St, Fort Lauderdale, FL, 33309. Tel: 954-351-4035. Fax: 954-351-4051. p. 443

Hagness, Carol, Ref Serv, University of Wisconsin-Stout Library, 315 Tenth Ave, Menomonie, WI, 54751-0790. Tel: 715-232-1892. Fax: 715-232-1783. p. 2615

Hagney, Elln, Exec Dir, Charles River Museum of Industry Library, 154 Moody St, Waltham, MA, 02453. Tel: 781-893-5410. Fax: 781-891-4536. p. 1133

Hagood, Barbara, Dir, Vista Grande Public Library, 14 Avenida Torreon, Santa Fe, NM, 87508-9199. Tel: 505-466-7323. Fax: 505-466-3889. p. 1564

Hagood, John, Ref, National Gallery of Art Library, Fourth St & Constitution Ave NW, Washington, DC, 20565. Tel: 202-842-6511. Fax: 202-789-3068. p. 409

Hagopian, David, Actg Br Mgr, Los Angeles Public Library System, Encino-Tarzana Branch, 18231 Ventura Blvd, Tarzana, CA, 91356-3620. Tel: 818-343-1983. Fax: 818-343-7867. p. 173

Hagstrom, Carla, Instrul Serv Librn, University of Toronto Libraries, Gerstein Science Information Centre, Seven & Nine Kings College Circle, Toronto, ON, M5S 1A5, CANADA. Tel: 416-978-7668. Fax: 416-971-2848. p. 2866

Hagstrom, Rebecca, Head, Bibliog Serv, Meriden Public Library, 105 Miller St, Meriden, CT, 06450. Tel: 203-630-6350. Fax: 203-238-3647. p. 350

Hagstrom, Steven W, Dr, Dir, Libr Serv, Tarrant County College, 828 Harwood Rd, Hurst, TX, 76054-3219. Tel: 817-515-6637. p. 2346

Hague, Amy, Curator, Smith College Libraries, Sophia Smith Collection, Seven Neilson Dr, Northampton, MA, 01063. Tel: 413-585-2977. Fax: 413-585-2886. p. 1114

Hague, Christine, Dir, Weare Public Library, Ten Paige Memorial Lane, Weare, NH, 03281. Tel: 603-529-2044. Fax: 603-529-7341. p. 1467

Hagyard, Alan, Exec Dir, Libraries Online, Inc, 100 Riverview Ctr, Ste 252, Middletown, CT, 06457. Tel: 860-347-1704. Fax: 860-346-3707. p. 2939

Hahn, Edward, Bus Librn, Weber State University, 2901 University Circle, Ogden, UT, 84408-2901. Tel: 801-626-8662. Fax: 801-626-7045. p. 2409

Hahn, Jerilyn, Ch, Boone Daniel Regional Library, Callaway County Public Library, 710 Court St, Fulton, MO, 65251. Tel: 573-642-7261. Fax: 573-642-4439. p. 1324

Hahn, Kim, Librn, Southern Wasco County Library, 410 Deschutes Ave, Maupin, OR, 97037. Tel: 541-395-2208. Fax: 541-395-2208. p. 2004

Hahn, Larry, Dir, Dodge Library, Nine Fisk Rd, West Chazy, NY, 12992. Tel: 518-493-6131. Fax: 518-493-3393. p. 1765

Hahn, Linda, Tech Serv, Flemington Free Public Library, 118 Main St, Flemington, NJ, 08822. Tel: 908-782-5733. Fax: 908-782-3875. p. 1486

Hahn, Mitch, Ref/Tech Proc, North Shore Library, 6800 N Port Washington Rd, Glendale, WI, 53217. Tel: 414-351-3461. Fax: 414-351-3528. p. 2594

Hahn, Nancy, Librn, Bushnell-Sage Library, 48 Main St, Sheffield, MA, 01257. Tel: 413-229-7004. Fax: 413-229-7003. p. 1123

Hahn, Penny, Libr Tech, Moorpark College Library, 7075 Campus Rd, Moorpark, CA, 93021-1695. Tel: 805-378-1450. Fax: 805-378-1470. p. 191

Hahn, Rita, Dir, Glendale Area Public Library Inc, Community Bldg, 961 Forest St, Coalport, PA, 16627. Tel: 814-672-4378. p. 2046

Hahn, Rosemary, Cat, Washington University Libraries, Law Library, Washington Univ Sch Law, Anheuser-Busch Hall, One Brookings Dr, Campus Box 1171, Saint Louis, MO, 63130. Tel: 314-935-6415. Fax: 314-935-7125. p. 1363

Hahn, Susan H, Mgr, Unisys Corp, One Unisys Way, Ste E3-112, Blue Bell, PA, 19424. Tel: 215-986-2324. p. 2036

Hahn, Suzan, Off-Campus Libr Serv, University of Alaska Fairbanks, 310 Tanana Dr, Fairbanks, AK, 99775. Tel: 907-474-5241. Fax: 907-474-6841. p. 48

Hahn, Suzanne, Dir, Ref & Libr Info Serv, Indiana Historical Society Library, 450 W Ohio St, Indianapolis, IN, 46202-3269. Tel: 317-234-0039. Fax: 317-234-0168. p. 752

Haichert, Colleen, Libr Tech, St Paul's Hospital of Saskatoon, 1702 20th St W, Saskatoon, SK, S7M 0Z9, CANADA. Tel: 306-655-5224. Fax: 306-655-5209. p. 2926

Haider, Nevine, Tech Serv, Concordia College, 171 White Plains Rd, Bronxville, NY, 10708. Tel: 914-337-9300, Ext 2202. Fax: 914-395-4893. p. 1588

Haigh, Adam E, Govt Doc, Web Serv, Lander University, 320 Stanley Ave, Greenwood, SC, 29649-2099. Tel: 864-388-8029. Fax: 864-388-8816. p. 2197

Haigh, Eileen, Tech Serv Librn, Staunton Public Library, One Churchville Ave, Staunton, VA, 24401. Tel: 540-332-3902. Fax: 540-332-3906. p. 2496

Haigh, Jane, Commun Serv Librn, Madison Heights Public Library, 240 W 13 Mile Rd, Madison Heights, MI, 48071-1894. Tel: 248-837-2856. Fax: 248-588-2470. p. 1205

Haigh, Marcia, Dir, Belgrade Public Library, One Center Dr, Belgrade, ME, 04917-4407. Tel: 207-495-3508. Fax: 207-495-3508. p. 977

Haight, Larry L, Dir, Libr Serv, Simpson University, 2211 College View Dr, Redding, CA, 96003-8606. Tel: 530-226-4110. Fax: 530-226-4858. p. 214

Haight, Tiffany, Dir, Shelby Area District Library, 189 Maple St, Shelby, MI, 49455-1134. Tel: 231-861-4565. Fax: 231-861-6868. p. 1227

Haigler, Sheila, Librn, Chilton Clanton Library, Maplesville Public Library, 9400 AL Hwy 22, Maplesville, AL, 36750. Tel: 334-366-4211. Fax: 334-366-4210. p. 12

Haile, Becky, Dir, Tellico Village Public Library, 304 Lakeside Plaza, Loudon, TN, 37774-4160. Tel: 865-458-8762. Fax: 865-458-8762. p. 2245

Haile, Bess, Dir, Essex Public Library, 117 N Church Lane, Tappahannock, VA, 22560. Tel: 804-443-4945. Fax: 804-443-6444. p. 2497

Haile, Deborah, Head, Cat & Tech Serv, Tuskegee University, Hollis Burke Frissell Bldg, 1200 W Old Montgomery Rd, Tuskegee, AL, 36088. Tel: 334-727-8898. Fax: 334-727-9282. p. 39

Haile, Geri, Br Mgr, Mid-Continent Public Library, Blue Ridge Branch, 9253 Blue Ridge Blvd, Kansas City, MO, 64138-4028. Tel: 816-761-3382. Fax: 816-761-7074. p. 1332

Hailey, Phillip, Circ Serv, Volunteer State Community College Library, 1480 Nashville Pike, Gallatin, TN, 37066-3188. Tel: 615-230-3400, Ext 3402. Fax: 615-230-3410. p. 2235

Hailston, Deborah, Dir, Libr Serv, Faxton Saint Luke's Health Care, 1656 Champlin Ave, Utica, NY, 13502. Tel: 315-624-6059. Fax: 315-624-6947. p. 1758

Haimes, Anne, Br Adminr, Interim Dir, Atlanta-Fulton Public Library System, One Margaret Mitchell Sq, Atlanta, GA, 30303-1089. Tel: 404-730-1881. Fax: 404-730-1990. p. 511

Haimes, Stephanie, Dir, W T Bland Public Library, 1995 N Donnelly St, Mount Dora, FL, 32757. Tel: 352-735-7180. Fax: 352-735-0074. p. 470

Haimovsky, Kira, Head, Ser & Electronic Res, Fordham University Libraries, 441 E Fordham Rd, Bronx, NY, 10458-5151. Tel: 718-817-3570. Fax: 718-817-3582. p. 1586

Hainer, Eugene, Exec Dir, Colorado State Library, 201 E Colfax Ave, Rm 309, Denver, CO, 80203-1799. Tel: 303-866-6900. Fax: 303-866-6940. p. 299

Haines, Ann H, Mgr, Kaiser Permanente Northwest Regional, Kaiser Sunnyside Medical Ctr, 10180 SE Sunnyside Road, Clackamas, OR, 97015. Tel: 503-571-4293. Fax: 503-571-4291. p. 1993

Haines, Annette, Librn, University of Michigan, Art, Architecture & Engineering Library, Duderstadt Ctr, 2281 Bonnisteel Blvd, Ann Arbor, MI, 48109-2094. Tel: 734-647-5747. Fax: 734-764-4487. p. 1152

Haines, Carol, Dir, Pub Relations, Concord Museum Library, 200 Lexington Rd, Concord, MA, 01742. Tel: 978-369-9763. Fax: 978-369-9660. p. 1082

Haines, Carolyn, Cataloger, Wichita Falls Public Library, 600 11th St, Wichita Falls, TX, 76301-4604. Tel: 940-767-0868, Ext 231. Fax: 940-720-6672. p. 2401

Haines, Cathy, Support Serv Mgr, Leesburg Public Library, 100 E Main St, Leesburg, FL, 34748. Tel: 352-728-9790. Fax: 352-728-9794. p. 461

Haines, Cathy, Librn, Capon Bridge Public Library, Rte 50, Capon Bridge, WV, 26711. Tel: 304-856-3777. Fax: 304-856-3777. p. 2555

Haines, Darla Vornberger, Subj Librn, Tech Serv, Manchester College, 604 E College Ave, North Manchester, IN, 46962. Tel: 260-982-5949. Fax: 260-982-5362. p. 769

Haines, Kim, Dir of Develop, Massanutten Regional Library, 174 S Main St, Harrisonburg, VA, 22801. Tel: 540-434-4475. Fax: 540-434-4382. p. 2470

Haines, Linda, Br Mgr, Cambridge Public Library, Boudreau (Observatory Hill) Branch, 245 Concord Ave, Cambridge, MA, 02138. Tel: 617-349-4017. Fax: 617-349-4424. p. 1073

Haines, Margaret, Univ Librn, Carleton University Library, 1125 Colonel By Dr, Ottawa, ON, K1S 5B6, CANADA. Tel: 613-520-2600, Ext 8260. Fax: 613-520-2750. p. 2830

Haines, Mary, Dir, South Country Library, 22 Station Rd, Bellport, NY, 11713. Tel: 631-286-0818. Fax: 631-286-4873. p. 1580

Haines, Norma, Librn, Brown Memorial Library, Two Norton Pl, East Baldwin, ME, 04024. Tel: 207-787-3155. p. 984

Haines, Randy, Ch, East Lyme Public Library, Inc, 39 Society Rd, Niantic, CT, 06357-1100. Tel: 860-739-6926. Fax: 860-691-0020. p. 361

Haines, Renee, Dir, Allentown Public Library, 1210 Hamilton St, Allentown, PA, 18102. Tel: 610-820-2400. Fax: 610-820-0640. p. 2026

Haines, Sharon, Librn, Greenup County Public Libraries, Flatwoods Public, 1705 Argillite Rd, Flatwoods, KY, 41139. Tel: 606-836-3771. Fax: 606-836-8674. p. 915

Haines, William, ILL, Emory University School of Law, 1301 Clifton Rd, Atlanta, GA, 30322. Tel: 404-727-4322. Fax: 404-727-2202. p. 514

Hainline, Ben K, Dir, Northern Oklahoma College, 1220 E Grand Ave, Tonkawa, OK, 74653-4022. Tel: 580-628-6253. Fax: 580-628-6209. p. 1980

Hainline, Pat, Asst Librn, Blandinsville-Hire District Library, 130 S Main St, Blandinsville, IL, 61420. Tel: 309-652-3166. Fax: 309-652-3166. p. 595

Hair, Miriam, Exec Dir, Municipal Association of South Carolina, 1411 Gervais St, Columbia, SC, 29201. Tel: 803-933-1204. Fax: 803-933-1299. p. 2188

Haire, Donna L, Dir, Newman Riga Library, One Village Park, Churchville, NY, 14428. Tel: 585-293-2009. Fax: 585-293-0932. p. 1606

Haire, Paul, Assoc Dir, Temple College, 2600 S First St, Temple, TX, 76504. Tel: 254-298-8426. Fax: 254-298-8430. p. 2391

Hairston, Faith, Br Mgr, Toledo-Lucas County Public Library, Kent, 3101 Collingwood Blvd, Toledo, OH, 43610. Tel: 419-259-5340. Fax: 419-243-6536. p. 1940

Hairston, Tiffany, Asst Librn, American University Library, 4400 Massachusetts Ave NW, Washington, DC, 20016-8046. Tel: 202-885-3233. Fax: 202-885-3226. p. 393

Haitz, M Cherie, Dir, Mount Auburn Hospital, 330 Mount Auburn St, Cambridge, MA, 02238. Tel: 617-499-5109. Fax: 617-499-5433. p. 1078

Hajas, Sandra, Learning Res Supvr, Ventura College, 4667 Telegraph Rd, Ventura, CA, 93003-3889. Tel: 805-654-6400, Ext 3124. Fax: 805-648-8900. p. 279

Hajder, Michelle, Info Literacy Librn, Walden University Library, 100 Washington Ave S, Ste 900, Minneapolis, MN, 55401. p. 1262

Hajdik, David, Distance Learning, Soc Sci Librn, Tennessee Technological University, 1100 N Peachtree Ave, Cookeville, TN, 38505. Tel: 931-372-3326. Fax: 931-372-6112. p. 2231

Hajjar, Tania, Ref, Montrose Regional Library District, 320 S Second St, Montrose, CO, 81401-3909. Tel: 970-249-9656. Fax: 970-240-1901. p. 318

Haka, Clifford H, Dir, Michigan State University Library, 100 Library, East Lansing, MI, 48824-1048. Tel: 517-355-2341. Fax: 517-432-3532. p. 1175

Hakala, Joan, Ref Serv, Saint Johns County Public Library System, Ponte Vedra Beach Branch, 101 Library Blvd, Ponte Vedra Beach, FL, 32082. Tel: 904-827-6953. Fax: 904-827-6955. p. 487

Hakala-Ausperk, Catherine, Dep Dir, Cleveland Heights-University Heights Public Library, 2345 Lee Rd, Cleveland Heights, OH, 44118-3493. Tel: 216-932-3600, Ext 276. Fax: 216-932-0932. p. 1882

Hakes, Jay, Dr, Dir, National Archives & Records Administration, 441 Freedom Pkwy, Atlanta, GA, 30307. Tel: 404-865-7113. Fax: 404-865-7102. p. 517

Hakim, Noureen, Circ, Cheshire Public Library, 104 Main St, Cheshire, CT, 06410-2499. Tel: 203-272-2245. Fax: 203-272-7714. p. 333

Halbedel, Susan, Br Mgr, Peach Public Libraries, Byron Public, 105 W Church St, Byron, GA, 31008. Tel: 478-956-2200. Fax: 478-956-5688. p. 534

Halbeisen, Johanna, Dir, New Song Library, PO Box 295, Northampton, MA, 01061-0295. Tel: 413-586-9485. p. 1113

Halbersma, Andrea L, Dir, Lester Public Library of Vesper, 6550 Virginia St, Vesper, WI, 54489-9999. Tel: 715-569-4669. p. 2643

Halbert, Carol, Ch, Tombigbee Regional Library System, Amory Municipal Library, 401 Second Ave N at Fourth St, Amory, MS, 38821. Tel: 662-256-5261. Fax: 662-256-6321. p. 1318

Halbert, Martin, Dean of Libr, University of North Texas Libraries, PO Box 305190, Denton, TX, 76203-5190. Tel: 940-565-2413. Fax: 940-369-8760. p. 2313

Halbert, Martin, Dr, Assoc Prof, University of North Texas, 1155 Union Circle, Denton, TX, 76203-5017. Tel: 940-565-2445. Fax: 940-565-3101. p. 2975

Halbleib, Victoria, Asst Dir, Oakley Public Library, 700 W Third St, Oakley, KS, 67748-1256. Tel: 785-671-4776. Fax: 785-671-3868. p. 885

Halcli, Rebecca, Tech Serv, Glencoe Public Library, 320 Park Ave, Glencoe, IL, 60022-1597. Tel: 847-835-5056. Fax: 847-835-5648. p. 650

Halcomb, Joy, Librn, Pulaski County Public Library, Burnside Branch, 85 E French Ave, Burnside, KY, 42519. Tel: 606-561-5287. Fax: 606-561-5287. p. 935

Halcums, Bob, Actg Dir, Newton County Library System, 7116 Floyd St NE, Covington, GA, 30014. Tel: 770-787-3231. Fax: 770-784-2092. p. 527

Haldaman, Jen, Digicenter, Furman University Libraries, 3300 Poinsett Hwy, Greenville, SC, 29613-4100. Tel: 864-294-3733. Fax: 864-294-3004. p. 2195

Haldane, Jackie, In Charge, Parmalat Canada, Ltd, 65 Bathurst St, London, ON, N6B IN8, CANADA. Tel: 519-667-7705. Fax: 519-667-7725. p. 2818

Halder, Gita, In Charge, St Joseph's Baptist Healthcare, PO Box 4227, Tampa, FL, 33677. Tel: 813-870-4659. Fax: 813-870-4479. p. 497

Hale, Alison, Mgr, Canadian Transportation Agency Library, 15 Eddy St, Gatineau, QC, K1A 0N9, CANADA. Tel: 819-953-0482. Fax: 819-953-9815. p. 2883

Hale, Brenda, Librn, Russell Public Library, 24 Pestle St, Russell, NY, 13684. Tel: 315-347-2115. Fax: 315-347-2115. p. 1736

Hale, Jon, Asst Librn, Johnson Bible College, 7900 Johnson Dr, Knoxville, TN, 37998. Tel: 865-251-2277. Fax: 865-251-2278. p. 2241

Hale, Katherine, Dir, Southern Prairie Library System, 421 N Hudson, Altus, OK, 73521. Tel: 580-477-2890. Fax: 580-477-3626. p. 1955

Hale, Kathleen, Librn, Valley Mills Public Library, 405 Fifth St, Valley Mills, TX, 76689. Tel: 254-932-6370. Fax: 254-932-5608. p. 2394

Hale, Kathy, Dir, Savonburg Public Library, 101A S Walnut, Savonburg, KS, 66772. Tel: 620-754-3835. p. 893

Hale, Kim, Head, Mkt & Outreach, Columbia College Chicago Library, 624 S Michigan Ave, Chicago, IL, 60605-1996. Tel: 312-369-7355. Fax: 312-344-8062. p. 611

Hale, Kristi, Libr Mgr, Washington-Centerville Public Library, Woodbourne, 6060 Far Hills Ave, Centerville, OH, 45459-1924. Tel: 937-610-4484. Fax: 937-435-6812. p. 1866

Hale, Lana, Dir, Knox County Public Library, 206 Knox St, Barbourville, KY, 40906. Tel: 606-546-5339, Ext 5. Fax: 606-546-3602. p. 906

Hale, Linda, Br Mgr, Plumas County Library, Portola Branch, 34 Third Ave, Portola, CA, 96122. Tel: 530-832-4241. Fax: 530-832-4241. p. 212

Hale, Pamela, Br Mgr, Montgomery-Floyd Regional Library System, 125 Sheltman St, Christiansburg, VA, 24073. Tel: 540-382-6965. Fax: 540-382-6964. p. 2457

Hale, Susan, Assoc Dir, Philo Public Library District, 115 E Washington St, Philo, IL, 61864. Tel: 217-684-2896. Fax: 217-684-2719. p. 691

Hale, Ted, Dep Dir, Arizona State Library, Archives & Public Records, 1700 W Washington, Rm 200, Phoenix, AZ, 85007. Tel: 602-926-3736. Fax: 602-256-7983. p. 72

Hale-Janeke, Amy, Head, Ref, United States Court of Appeals, 600 Camp St, Rm 106, New Orleans, LA, 70130. Tel: 504-310-7797. Fax: 504-310-7578. p. 964

Hales, Andrea, Librn, Museum of Contemporary Art San Diego, 700 Prospect St, La Jolla, CA, 92037. Tel: 858-454-3541, Ext 132. Fax: 858-454-6985. p. 161

Hales, David A, Coll, Westminster College, 1840 S 1300 East, Salt Lake City, UT, 84105-3697. Tel: 801-832-2250. Fax: 801-832-3109. p. 2415

Hales, John D, Jr, Dir, Suwannee River Regional Library, 1848 Ohio Ave S, Dr Martin Luther King Jr Ave S, Live Oak, FL, 32064-4517. Tel: 386-362-5779. Fax: 386-364-6071. p. 461

Hales, Karen, Dir, LDS Business College Library, 95 N 300 West, Salt Lake City, UT, 84101-3500. Tel: 801-524-8149. Fax: 801-524-1900. p. 2413

Haley, Alice, Res Librn, American Society for Quality, 600 N Plankinton Ave, Milwaukee, WI, 53203-2914. Tel: 414-298-8789. Fax: 414-765-8660. p. 2617

Haley, Ann, Adult Serv Coordr, Central Rappahannock Regional Library, 1201 Caroline St, Fredericksburg, VA, 22401-3761. Tel: 540-372-1144. Fax: 540-373-9411. p. 2465

Haley, Brian, Dean, Sierra Joint Community College District, 5000 Rocklin Rd, Rocklin, CA, 95677. Tel: 916-660-7230. Fax: 916-630-4539. p. 219

Haley, Brian, Ref Librn, New Hampshire Law Library, Supreme Court Bldg, One Charles Doe Dr, Concord, NH, 03301-6160. Tel: 603-271-3777. Fax: 603-513-5450. p. 1443

Haley, Carol, Dir, Stratton Free Library, Nine Main St, West Swanzey, NH, 03446. Tel: 603-352-9391. p. 1467

Haley, Daniel J, Ref, Pasadena City College Library, 1570 E Colorado Blvd, Pasadena, CA, 91106-2003. Tel: 626-585-7830. Fax: 626-585-7913. p. 206

Haley, Gwendolyn, Supvr, Youth Serv, Spokane County Library District, North Spokane Library, 44 E Hawthorne Rd, Spokane, WA, 99218-1597. Tel: 509-893-8350. Fax: 509-893-8481. p. 2537

Haley, Jan, Managing Librn, Saint Thomas Hospital, 4220 Harding Rd, Nashville, TN, 37202. Tel: 615-222-6658. Fax: 615-222-6765. p. 2258

Haley, Kathleen Randall, Info Serv Librn, University of Massachusetts Dartmouth Library, 285 Old Westport Rd, North Dartmouth, MA, 02747-2300. Tel: 508-999-8670. Fax: 508-999-8987. p. 1112

Haley, Lisa, Br Mgr, Saint Tammany Parish Library, Lee Road Branch, 79213 Hwy 40, Covington, LA, 70435. Tel: 985-893-6284. Fax: 985-893-6284. p. 948

Haley, Pamela, Mgr, Libr Serv, Stormont, Dundas & Glengarry County Library, 26 Pitt St, Cornwall, ON, K6J 3P2, CANADA. Tel: 613-936-8777. Fax: 613-936-2532. p. 2801

Haley, Quing, Instructional Technologist, Chicago State University, 9501 S Martin Luther King Jr Dr, LIB 440, Chicago, IL, 60628-1598. Tel: 773-995-2948. Fax: 773-995-3772. p. 610

Haley, Rob, ILL, Haverford College, 370 Lancaster Ave, Haverford, PA, 19041-1392. Tel: 610-896-1175. Fax: 610-896-1102. p. 2067

Haley, Susan, Br Mgr, Mid-Continent Public Library, Raytown Branch, 6131 Raytown Rd, Raytown, MO, 64133-4006. Tel: 816-353-2052. Fax: 816-353-5518. p. 1333

Haley, Susan Ewing, Supvry Curator, National Park Service, Park Archives & Records Ctr, Bldg 667, Presidio of San Francisco, San Francisco, CA, 94129. Tel: 415-561-2804. Fax: 415-441-1618. p. 244

Halfpenny, Amanda, Actg Libr Dir, Chaleur Library Region, Tracadie-Sheila Public Library, 3620 Main St, Tracadie-Sheila, NB, E1X 1C9, CANADA. Tel: 506-393-4005. Fax: 506-394-4009. p. 2761

Halgren, Kathy, Dir, South Saint Paul Public Library, 106 Third Ave N, South Saint Paul, MN, 55075-2098. Tel: 651-554-3240. Fax: 651-554-3241. p. 1285

Haliani, Brittney, Dir, Cottage Health System, 401 W Pueblo St, Santa Barbara, CA, 93105. Tel: 805-569-7240. Fax: 805-569-7588. p. 260

Halicki, Kenneth, Librn, Vedder, Price, 222 N LaSalle, Chicago, IL, 60601. Tel: 312-609-7500. Fax: 312-609-5005. p. 627

Halikias, Shannon, Br Coordr, Aurora Public Library, Eola, 555 S Eola Rd, Aurora, IL, 60504-8992. Tel: 630-264-3400. Fax: 630-898-5220. p. 591

Haliotis, John, Head, Tech, Round Lake Area Public Library District, 906 Hart Rd, Round Lake, IL, 60073. Tel: 847-546-7060. Fax: 847-546-7104. p. 699

Halkovich, Celia, Tech Serv Librn, Ursuline College, 2550 Lander Rd, Pepper Pike, OH, 44124-4398. Tel: 440-449-4202. Fax: 440-449-3180. p. 1929

Hall, Alan Craig, Dir, Public Library of Steubenville & Jefferson County, 407 S Fourth St, Steubenville, OH, 43952-2942. Tel: 740-282-9782. Fax: 740-282-2919. p. 1936

Hall, Ann, Libr Mgr, Venice Public Library, 300 S Nokomis Ave, Venice, FL, 34285-2416. Tel: 941-861-1350. Fax: 941-486-2345. p. 501

Hall, Anne, Ref/Archives Librn, Federal Reserve Bank of San Francisco, 101 Market St, San Francisco, CA, 94105-1579. Tel: 415-974-3216. Fax: 415-974-3429. p. 242

Hall, Anne, Librn, Fort Wayne Museum of Art, 311 E Main St, Fort Wayne, IN, 46802. Tel: 260-422-6467. Fax: 260-422-1374. p. 741

Hall, Anne, Commun Relations, Lebanon County Library System, 125 N Seventh St, Lebanon, PA, 17046. Tel: 717-273-7624. Fax: 717-273-2719. p. 2080

Hall, Barbara, Res Archivist, Academy of Motion Picture Arts & Sciences, 333 S La Cienega Blvd, Beverly Hills, CA, 90211. Tel: 310-247-3000, Ext 2218. Fax: 310-657-5193. p. 129

Hall, Benjamin, Dir, Williamsburg County Library, 215 N Jackson, Kingstree, SC, 29556-3319. Tel: 843-355-9486. Fax: 843-355-9991. p. 2198

Hall, Beth, Admin & Pub Serv Mgr, Owen Sound & North Grey Union Public Library, 824 First Ave W, Owen Sound, ON, N4K 4K4, CANADA. Tel: 519-376-6623. Fax: 519-376-7170. p. 2834

Hall, Betty, Br Mgr, Prichard Public Library, Mitchell, 4440 Highpoint Blvd, Eight Mile, AL, 36613. Tel: 251-452-7846. Fax: 251-452-6517. p. 34

Hall, Betty, Librn, Alaska Housing Finance Corp, 4300 Boniface Pkwy, Anchorage, AK, 99504. Tel: 907-330-8166. Fax: 907-338-1747. p. 43

Hall, Betty, Br Mgr, Shreve Memorial Library, Gilliam Branch, 12797 Main St, Gilliam, LA, 71029. Tel: 318-296-4227. Fax: 318-296-4227. p. 969

Hall, Betty J, Dir, Prichard Public Library, 300 W Love Joy Loop, Prichard, AL, 36610. Tel: 251-452-7847. Fax: 251-452-7935. p. 34

Hall, Bill, Head, Access Serv, University of San Diego, Helen K & James S Copley Library, 5998 Alcala Park, San Diego, CA, 92110. Fax: 619-260-4617. p. 239

Hall, Brenda, Bus Mgr, Muskegon Area District Library, 4845 Airline Rd, Unit 5, Muskegon, MI, 49444-4503. Tel: 231-737-6248. Fax: 231-737-6307. p. 1212

Hall, Brent, Dir, Maine Maritime Academy, Pleasant St, Box C-1, Castine, ME, 04420. Tel: 207-326-2260. Fax: 207-326-2261. p. 981

Hall, Candace, Librn, Chase Emerson Memorial Library, 17 Main St, Deer Isle, ME, 04627. Tel: 207-348-2899. p. 983

Hall, Carol, Admin Librn, Worth Public Library District, 6917 W 111th St, Worth, IL, 60482. Tel: 708-448-2855. Fax: 708-448-9174. p. 721

Hall, Cathy, Librn, Wilmington Public Library, North Wilmington, 3400 N Market St, Wilmington, DE, 19802. Tel: 302-761-4290. Fax: 302-761-4291. p. 389

Hall, Cherice, Librn, Columbia College Hollywood, 18618 Oxnard St, Tarzana, CA, 91356. Tel: 818-401-1027. Fax: 818-345-9053. p. 274

Hall, Cherlyn, Libr Asst I, Montgomery City-County Public Library System, Coliseum Boulevard Branch Library, 840 Coliseum Blvd, Montgomery, AL, 36109. Tel: 334-271-7005. Fax: 334-244-5754. p. 29

Hall, Colleen, Ch, Jessamine County Public Library, 600 S Main St, Nicholasville, KY, 40356-1839. Tel: 859-885-3523. Fax: 859-885-5164. p. 931

Hall, Colleen, Outreach Serv Librn, Saint Louis County Library, 1640 S Lindbergh Blvd, Saint Louis, MO, 63131-3598. Tel: 314-994-3300, Ext 2330. Fax: 314-997-7602. p. 1358

Hall, Danea, Distance Educ, Fort Bend County Libraries, 1001 Golfview Dr, Richmond, TX, 77469-5199. Tel: 281-341-2692. Fax: 281-341-2690. p. 2375

Hall, Darlene, Bus Mgr, Scott County Public Library, 108 S Main St, Scottsburg, IN, 47170. Tel: 812-752-2751. Fax: 812-752-2878. p. 777

Hall, Darren, Digital Serv Librn, Marymount College Library, 30800 Palos Verdes Dr E, Rancho Palos Verdes, CA, 90275-6299. Tel: 310-303-7304. Fax: 310-377-6223. p. 213

Hall, David, Tech Serv Supvr, Alameda Free Library, 1550 Oak St, Alameda, CA, 94501-2932. Tel: 510-747-7730. p. 119

Hall, Debbie, Librn, North Kawartha Public Library, 175 Burleigh St, Apsley, ON, K0L 1A0, CANADA. Tel: 705-656-4333. Fax: 705-656-2538. p. 2792

Hall, DeBora, Asst Librn, American Sports Medicine Institute, 2660 Tenth Ave S, Ste 505, Birmingham, AL, 35205. Tel: 205-918-2130. Fax: 205-918-2178. p. 6

Hall, Deborah, Coordr, Grants & Spec Projects, Arkansas State Library, 900 W Capitol, Ste 100, Little Rock, AR, 72201-3108. Tel: 501-682-2053. Fax: 501-682-1529. p. 105

Hall, Deborah, Ch, Nephi Public Library, 21 E First N, Nephi, UT, 84648-1501. Tel: 435-623-1312. Fax: 435-623-5443. p. 2408

Hall, DeRese, Acq, Jefferson County Library District, 241 SE Seventh St, Madras, OR, 97741-1611. Tel: 541-475-3351. Fax: 541-475-7434. p. 2004

Hall, Diane, Ch, Reveille United Methodist Church Library, 4200 Cary Street Rd, Richmond, VA, 23221. Tel: 804-359-6041. Fax: 804-359-6090. p. 2489

Hall, Dianne, Info Tech, East Brunswick Public Library, Two Jean Walling Civic Center, East Brunswick, NJ, 08816-3599. Tel: 732-390-6680. Fax: 732-390-6796. p. 1481

Hall, Dianne, Tech Serv, Comsewogue Public Library, 170 Terryville Rd, Port Jefferson Station, NY, 11776. Tel: 631-928-1212. Fax: 631-928-6307. p. 1721

Hall, Elizabeth, Asst Dir, Gibbsboro Public Library, Borough Hall, 49 Kirkwood Rd, Gibbsboro, NJ, 08026. Tel: 856-435-3656. p. 1487

Hall, Elizabeth, Dir, Allens Hill Free Library, 3818 County Rd 40, Bloomfield, NY, 14469. Tel: 585-229-5636. Fax: 585-229-2460. p. 1583

Hall, Elysabeth, Head, Tech Serv, Willamette University, J W Long Law Library, 245 Winter St SE, Salem, OR, 97301. Tel: 503-370-6386. Fax: 503-375-5426. p. 2019

Hall, H Palmer, Dr, Dir, Saint Mary's University, Louis J Blume Library, One Camino Santa Maria, San Antonio, TX, 78228-8608. Tel: 210-436-3441. Fax: 210-436-3782. p. 2381

Hall, Holly, Dir, Deborah Rawson Memorial Library, Eight River Rd, Jericho, VT, 05465. Tel: 802-899-4962. Fax: 802-899-5257. p. 2426

Hall, Homer L, Libr Dir, Floyd County Public Library, 18 N Arnold Ave, Prestonsburg, KY, 41653-1269. Tel: 606-886-2981. Fax: 606-886-2284. p. 933

Hall, James, Exec Dir, Up Front, Inc, 12360 SW 132nd St, Ste 215, Miami, FL, 33186. Tel: 786-242-8222. Fax: 786-242-8759. p. 469

Hall, Jane, Dir, Argos Public Library, 119 W Walnut St, Argos, IN, 46501-1025. Tel: 574-892-5818. Fax: 574-892-5818. p. 724

Hall, Jeff, Libr Serv Dir, Rowan Public Library, 201 W Fisher St, Salisbury, NC, 28144-4935. Tel: 704-216-8231. Fax: 704-216-8237. p. 1822

Hall, Jenay Ellen, Ch, Circ, Letcher County Public Libraries, 220 Main St, Whitesburg, KY, 41858. Tel: 606-633-7547. Fax: 606-633-3407. p. 937

Hall, Jeni, Circ Supvr, Davis County Library, 38 S 100 East, Farmington, UT, 84025. Tel: 801-451-2322. Fax: 801-451-9561. p. 2405

Hall, Jennie, Adult Serv, McPherson Public Library, 214 W Marlin, McPherson, KS, 67460-4299. Tel: 620-245-2570. Fax: 620-245-2567. p. 883

Hall, Jennifer, Librn, First Regional Library, Batesville Public Library, 206 Hwy 51 N, Batesville, MS, 38606. Tel: 662-563-1038. Fax: 662-563-6640. p. 1301

Hall, Jerrie, Assoc Dir, Coordr, Tech Serv, Oklahoma State University - Tulsa Library, 700 N Greenwood Ave, Tulsa, OK, 74106-0700. Tel: 918-594-8130. Fax: 918-594-8145. p. 1981

Hall, JoAnn T, Dir, Libr Serv, United States Navy, Naval Hospital, 100 Brewster Blvd, Camp Lejeune, NC, 28547. Tel: 910-450-4076. Fax: 910-450-3941. p. 1779

Hall, Jodi, Head, Youth Serv, Lucius E & Elsie C Burch Library, 501 Poplar View Pkwy, Collierville, TN, 38017. Tel: 901-457-2600. Fax: 901-854-5893. p. 2230

Hall, Joe, Librn, Snyder County Libraries, McClure Community Library, PO Box 370, McClure, PA, 17841-0370. Tel: 570-658-7700. Fax: 570-658-7700. p. 2138

Hall, John JD, Libr Mgr, Library for the Blind & Physically Handicapped, 900 W Capitol Ave, Ste 100, Little Rock, AR, 72201-3108. Tel: 501-682-1155. Fax: 501-682-1529. p. 106

Hall, Karen, ILL, Cambria County Library System & District Center, 248 Main St, Johnstown, PA, 15901. Tel: 814-536-5131. Fax: 814-536-6905. p. 2073

Hall, Karin, Coll Develop, Capilano College Library, 2055 Purcell Way, North Vancouver, BC, V7J 3H5, CANADA. Tel: 604-986-1911, Ext 2164. Fax: 604-984-1728. p. 2734

Hall, Kate, Dir, New Lenox Public Library District, 120 Veterans Pkwy, New Lenox, IL, 60451. Tel: 815-485-2605. Fax: 815-485-2548. p. 680

Hall, Katherine, Asst Dir, Pub Serv, Ohio State University LIBRARIES, Michael E Moritz Law Library, 55 W 12th Ave, Columbus, OH, 43210-1391. Tel: 614-688-5540. Fax: 614-292-3202. p. 1888

Hall, Kathy, Spec Coll Librn, Middlesborough-Bell County Public Library, 126 S 20th St, Middlesboro, KY, 40965-1212. Tel: 606-248-4812. Fax: 606-248-8766. p. 929

Hall, Kori, Info Serv Mgr, Waukesha Public Library, 321 Wisconsin Ave, Waukesha, WI, 53186-4786. Tel: 262-524-3904. Fax: 262-524-3677. p. 2645

Hall, Leigh, Syst Librn, Chattahoochee Technical College Library, 980 S Cobb Dr SE, Marietta, GA, 30060-3300. Tel: 770-528-6461. Fax: 770-528-4454. p. 542

Hall, Leslie, Bus Mgr, Cleveland Law Library Association, One W Lakeside Ave, 4th Flr, Cleveland, OH, 44113-1023. Tel: 216-861-5070. Fax: 216-861-1606. p. 1877

Hall, Lina, Dir, Oak Harbor Public Library, 147 W Main St, Oak Harbor, OH, 43449-1344. Tel: 419-898-7001. Fax: 419-898-0747. p. 1924

Hall, Linda, Librn, Sangerville Public Library, One Town Hall Ave, Sangerville, ME, 04479. Tel: 207-876-3491. p. 1000

Hall, Linda, Dir, Solomon Wright Library, 97 Main St, Pownal, VT, 05261. Tel: 802-823-5400. Fax: 802-823-5400. p. 2432

Hall, Loretta, Circ, Denison Public Library, 300 W Gandy St, Denison, TX, 75020-3153. Tel: 903-465-1797. Fax: 903-465-1130. p. 2312

Hall, Lucinda, Maps Librn, Dartmouth College Library, Baker-Berry Library, 6025 Baker-Berry Library, Hanover, NH, 03755-3525. Tel: 603-646-2560. Fax: 603-646-2167. p. 1450

Hall, Madelyn, Med Librn, Southwest Washington Medical Center Library, Health Education Ctr, 400 NE Mother Joseph Pl, Vancouver, WA, 98664. Tel: 360-514-3167. Fax: 360-514-6466. p. 2546

Hall, Maraine, Ref Librn, Grambling State University, 403 Main St, Grambling, LA, 71245. Tel: 318-274-2229. Fax: 318-274-3268. p. 950

Hall, Marcy, Outreach Serv Mgr, Erie County Public Library, 160 E Front St, Erie, PA, 16507. Tel: 814-451-6959. Fax: 814-451-6907. p. 2055

Hall, Margery, Head Librn, Ludington Public Library, Five S Bryn Mawr Ave, Bryn Mawr, PA, 19010-3471. Tel: 610-525-1776. Fax: 610-525-1783. p. 2039

Hall, Mary, Adult Serv Mgr, Bedford Public Library, 1323 K St, Bedford, IN, 47421. Tel: 812-275-4471. Fax: 812-278-5244. p. 726

Hall, Matthew, Assoc Libr Dir, Worcester Polytechnic Institute, 100 Institute Rd, Worcester, MA, 01609-2280. Tel: 508-831-5410. Fax: 508-831-5829. p. 1145

Hall, Milta, Assoc Dir, Pub Serv, DePaul University Libraries, Vincent G Rinn Law Library, 25 E Jackson Blvd, 5th Flr, Chicago, IL, 60604-2287. Tel: 312-362-5093. Fax: 312-362-6908. p. 612

Hall, Molly, Cat, Marion & Ed Hughes Public Library, 2712 Nederland Ave, Nederland, TX, 77627-7015. Tel: 409-722-1255. Fax: 409-721-5469. p. 2365

Hall, Nancy, Youth Serv Librn, Mercer County Library, 601 Grant, Princeton, MO, 64673. Tel: 660-748-3725. Fax: 660-748-3723. p. 1350

Hall, Pamela L, Librn, Legal Aid Foundation of Los Angeles, 1102 Crenshaw Blvd, Los Angeles, CA, 90019. Tel: 323-801-7940. Fax: 323-801-7921. p. 171

Hall, Pat, Libr Dir, Barclay College, 100 E Cherry St, Haviland, KS, 67059. Tel: 620-862-5274. Fax: 620-862-5403. p. 870

Hall, Patrice, Librn, Lois High Berstler Community Health Library, 35 Hope Dr, HS-07, Hershey, PA, 17033. Tel: 717-531-4032. Fax: 717-531-5942. p. 2068

Hall, Patricia, Dir, McCook Public Library, 802 Norris Ave, McCook, NE, 69001-3143. Tel: 308-345-1906. Fax: 308-345-1461. p. 1408

Hall, Patti, Br Mgr, Worcester County Library, Ocean Pines Branch, 11107 Cathell Rd, Berlin, MD, 21811. Tel: 410-208-4014. p. 1042

Hall, Ray, Dir, Mexico-Audrain County Library District, 305 W Jackson St, Mexico, MO, 65265. Tel: 573-581-4939. Fax: 573-581-7510. p. 1345

Hall, Rebekah, Acq, Trinity International University, 2065 Half Day Rd, Deerfield, IL, 60015-1241. Tel: 847-317-4007. Fax: 847-317-4012. p. 635

Hall, Retha, Sr Librn, Central Piedmont Community College Library, 1201 Elizabeth Ave, Charlotte, NC, 28235. Tel: 704-330-4816. Fax: 704-330-6887. p. 1781

Hall, Robin, Circ, Ventress Memorial Library, 15 Library Plaza, Marshfield, MA, 02050. Tel: 781-834-5535. Fax: 781-837-8362. p. 1103

Hall, Robin, Ref Librn, Rockland Memorial Library, 20 Belmont St, Rockland, MA, 02370-2232. Tel: 781-878-1236. Fax: 781-878-4013. p. 1120

Hall, Ruth, Cataloger, Coll Mgt Librn, Palmer College of Chiropractic-Davenport Campus, 1000 Brady St, Davenport, IA, 52803-5287. Tel: 563-884-5671. Fax: 563-884-5897. p. 806

Hall, Sandra, Asst Librn, Southeastern Technical College Library, 346 Kite Rd, Swainsboro, GA, 30401. Tel: 478-289-2322. Fax: 478-289-2322. p. 553

Hall, Sarah, Librn, Watchtower Bible School of Gilead Library, 100 Watchtower Dr, Patterson, NY, 12563-9204. Tel: 718-560-5000. p. 1715

Hall, Scott, Coordr, ILL, South Dakota School of Mines & Technology, 501 E Saint Joseph St, Rapid City, SD, 57701-3995. Tel: 605-394-2418. Fax: 605-394-1256. p. 2217

Hall, Sharon, Br Mgr, Anythink Libraries, Anythink Bennett, 495 Seventh St, Bennett, CO, 80102. Tel: 303-405-3231. Fax: 303-644-5419. p. 323

Hall, Stephanie, Libr Dir, Meinders Community Library, 1401 Seventh St SW, Pipestone, MN, 56164. Tel: 507-825-6714. Fax: 507-562-7374. p. 1271

Hall, Sue, Asst Dir, Bay City Public Library, 1100 Seventh St, Bay City, TX, 77414. Tel: 979-245-6931. Fax: 979-245-2614. p. 2286

Hall, Susan, Assoc Prof, Librn, Mississippi State University, Architecture, 121 Giles Hall, 889 Collegeview St, Mississippi State, MS, 39762. Tel: 662-325-2204. Fax: 662-325-8872. p. 1309

Hall, Susan, Tech Serv Librn, Saint Gregory's University, 1900 W MacArthur St, Shawnee, OK, 74804. Tel: 405-878-5409. Fax: 405-878-5198. p. 1977

Hall, Taffey, Archivist, Southern Baptist Historical Library & Archives, 901 Commerce St, Ste 400, Nashville, TN, 37203-3630. Tel: 615-244-0344. Fax: 615-782-4821. p. 2258

Hall, Terri, Tech Serv, Peru Public Library, 102 E Main St, Peru, IN, 46970-2338. Tel: 765-473-3069. Fax: 765-473-3060. p. 772

Hall, Todd M, Dir, Austin Graduate School of Theology, 7640 Guadalupe St, Austin, TX, 78752-1333. Tel: 512-476-2772. Fax: 512-476-3919. p. 2278

Hall, Tomi, Dir, Libr Serv, Tennessee General Assembly, Office of Legal Services, G-12 War Memorial Bldg, Nashville, TN, 37243-0059. Tel: 615-741-3057. Fax: 615-741-1146. p. 2258

Hall, Tonia, Asst Dir, Extn Serv, Southwest Public Libraries, SPL Admin, 3359 Park St, Grove City, OH, 43123. Tel: 614-875-6716. Fax: 614-875-2219. p. 1903

Hall, Tracie, Acq Librn, Chapman University School of Law, 370 N Glassell St, Rm 325, Orange, CA, 92866. Tel: 714-628-2539. p. 200

Hall, Wanda B, Assoc Dir, United Methodist Historical Society, 2200 St Paul St, Baltimore, MD, 21218-5897. Tel: 410-889-4458. Fax: 410-889-1501. p. 1018

Hall, Wendy, Br Mgr, Boulder Public Library, Carnegie Branch for Local History, 1125 Pine St, Boulder, CO, 80302-4024. Tel: 303-441-4096. Fax: 720-406-7452. p. 290

Hall, Wyolanda, Br Mgr, Shreve Memorial Library, Mavice Colley Wallette Branch, 363 Hearne Ave, Shreveport, LA, 71103. Tel: 318-425-3630. Fax: 318-226-8311. p. 970

Hall-Agent, Robyn, Cat, Morris College, 100 W College St, Sumter, SC, 29150-3599. Tel: 803-934-3230. Fax: 803-778-2923. p. 2206

Hall-Ellis, Sylvia, Interim Dir, University of Denver, Westminster Law Library, 2255 E Evans Ave, Denver, CO, 80208. Tel: 303-871-6188. Fax: 303-871-6999. p. 304

Halla-Sindelar, Jennifer, Br Mgr, Saint Louis Public Library, Carondelet, 6800 Michigan Ave, Saint Louis, MO, 63111. Tel: 314-752-9224. Fax: 314-752-7794. p. 1360

Hallack, Vikki, Mgr, Poplar Creek Public Library District, Sonya Crawshaw Branch, 4300 Audrey Lane, Hanover Park, IL, 60133. Tel: 630-372-0052. Fax: 630-372-0024. p. 708

Halladay, Sylvia, Syst Librn, Tech Serv, Clark State Community College Library, 570 E Leffel Lane, Springfield, OH, 45505. Tel: 937 328-6021. Fax: 937 328-6033. p. 1935

Hallam, Karen, Librn, Jonesboro Public Library, 412 S Main, Jonesboro, IL, 62952. Tel: 618-833-8121. Fax: 618-833-8121. p. 660

Hallam-Miller, Jill, Librn, Central Pennsylvania College Library, 600 Valley Rd, Summerdale, PA, 17093. Tel: 717-728-2227. Fax: 717-728-2300. p. 2144

Hallas, Barbara, Asst Libr Dir, Shelter Rock Public Library, 165 Searingtown Rd, Albertson, NY, 11507. Tel: 516-248-7343. p. 1571

Hallberg, Betty, Br Assoc, Modoc County Library, Lookout Branch, Lookout Park, Lookout, CA, 96054. Tel: 530-294-5776. p. 120

Hallblade, Shirley, Dr, Dean of Libr, University of North Florida, Bldg 12-Library, One UNF Dr, Jacksonville, FL, 32224-2645. Tel: 904-620-2587. Fax: 904-620-2719. p. 455

Halle, Penny, Head, Pub Serv, Muskego Public Library, S73 W16663 Janesville Rd, Muskego, WI, 53150. Tel: 262-971-2106. Fax: 262-971-2115. p. 2623

Hallen, Marilynn, Librn, Larkin, Hoffman, Daly & Lindgren, 7900 Xerxes Ave S, Ste 1500, Bloomington, MN, 55431. Tel: 952-835-3800. Fax: 952-896-3333. p. 1241

Haller, Andrea, Cat, Tech Serv, Toledo Public Library, 173 NW Seventh St, Toledo, OR, 97391. Tel: 541-336-3132. Fax: 541-336-3428. p. 2021

Haller, Dorcas, Librn, Community College of Rhode Island, One Hilton St, Providence, RI, 02905-2304. Tel: 401-455-6085. Fax: 401-455-6087. p. 2172

Haller, Gail, Librn, National Oceanic & Atmospheric Administration, Forrestal Campus, US Rte 1, 201 Forrestal Rd, Princeton, NJ, 08542. Tel: 609-452-6500. Fax: 609-987-5063. p. 1522

Haller, Hal, Dir, Luther Rice Seminary, 3038 Evans Mill Rd, Lithonia, GA, 30038. Tel: 770-484-1204, Ext 222. Fax: 770-484-1155. p. 539

Haller, James, Dir, Spartanburg Methodist College, 1000 Powell Mill Rd, Spartanburg, SC, 29301. Tel: 864-587-4208. Fax: 864-587-4352. p. 2205

Haller, Martinique, Head, Info Literacy & Instruction Serv, Roosevelt University, 430 S Michigan Ave, Chicago, IL, 60605. Tel: 312-341-2125. Fax: 312-341-2425. p. 623

Haller, Robert A, Dir, Anthology Film Archives, 32 Second Ave, New York, NY, 10003. Tel: 212-505-5181. Fax: 212-477-2714. p. 1669

Hallerberg, Gretchen, Dir, Cleveland Clinic Alumni Library, 9500 Euclid Ave, NA30, Cleveland, OH, 44195-5243. Tel: 216-445-7333. Fax: 216-444-0271. p. 1876

Hallerman, Anne R, Sr Libr Mgr, Federal Reserve Bank of Richmond, 701 E Byrd St, Richmond, VA, 23219. Tel: 804-697-8125. Fax: 804-697-8134. p. 2488

Hallett, Leigh, Dir, Newport Public Library, 154 Main St, Newport, ME, 04953-1139. Tel: 207-368-5074. p. 993

Halley, Geeta, Librn II, Round Rock Public Library, 216 E Main St, Round Rock, TX, 78664. Tel: 512-218-7014. Fax: 512-218-7061. p. 2377

Halliburton, Mary Hartman, Br Operations Adminr, Tusculum College, Knoxville Campus, 1305 Centerpoint Blvd, Knoxville, TN, 37932. Tel: 865-693-1177, Ext 5016. Fax: 865-531-0524. p. 2236

Halliburton, Meredith, Circ, Western Connecticut State University, 181 White St, Danbury, CT, 06810. Tel: 203-837-9100. Fax: 203-837-9108. p. 335

Halliday, Blane, AV, Collier County Public Library, 2385 Orange Blossom Dr, Naples, FL, 34109. Tel: 239-593-0334. Fax: 239-254-8167. p. 471

Halliday, Blane, Librn, Collier County Public Library, Vanderbilt Beach, 788 Vanderbilt Beach Rd, Naples, FL, 34108. Tel: 239-597-8444. Fax: 239-597-3653. p. 471

Halliday, Heather, Head, Adult Serv, Newmarket Public Library, 438 Park Ave, Newmarket, ON, L3Y 1W1, CANADA. Tel: 905-953-5110. Fax: 905-953-5104. p. 2824

Halliday, John, Dir, Jefferson-Madison Regional Library, 201 E Market St, Charlottesville, VA, 22902-5287. Tel: 434-979-7151, Ext 206, 434-979-7151, Ext 207. Fax: 434-971-7035. p. 2453

Halliday, Karen, Librn, Clackamas Community College, 19600 S Molalla Ave, Oregon City, OR, 97045. Tel: 503-657-6958, Ext 2289. Fax: 503-655-8925. p. 2009

Halliday, Wayne, Info Tech, Lehman College, City University of New York, 250 Bedford Park Blvd W, Bronx, NY, 10468-1589. Tel: 718-960-7768. Fax: 718-960-7127. p. 1587

Halligan, Amy, Libr Supvr-Popular Libr, University of Washington Libraries, Media Center, Odegaard Undergraduate Library, Mezzanine Level, Box 353080, Seattle, WA, 98195-3080. Tel: 206-543-6051. Fax: 206-685-8485. p. 2534

Halligan, Ann, Tech Serv Librn, Weatherford College Library, 225 College Park Dr, Weatherford, TX, 76086. Tel: 817-598-6250. Fax: 817-598-6369, 817-599-9305. p. 2399

Halligan, Jane, Mgr, Attorney General's Office, 1101 Washington St SE, Ste 260, Olympia, WA, 98504. Tel: 360-753-2681. Fax: 360-753-3490. p. 2522

Hallinan, Patricia, Ref, John C Hart Memorial Library, 1130 Main St, Shrub Oak, NY, 10588. Tel: 914-245-5262. Fax: 914-245-2216. p. 1743

Halling, Nancee, Br Librn, United States Court of Appeals, 1102 US Courthouse, 300 S Fourth St, Rm 1102, Minneapolis, MN, 55415. Tel: 612-664-5830. Fax: 612-664-5835. p. 1262

Hallmark, Julie, Prof, University of Texas at Austin, One University Sta, D7000, Austin, TX, 78712-0390. Tel: 512-471-3821. Fax: 512-471-3971. p. 2975

Halloran, Jack, In Charge, Manomet Center for Conservation Sciences Library, PO Box 1770, Manomet, MA, 02345. Tel: 508-224-6521. Fax: 508-224-9220. p. 1102

Halloran, Jude, Dir, Highland Township Public Library, 444 Beach Farm Circle, Highland, MI, 48357. Tel: 248-887-2218, Ext 110. Fax: 248-887-5179. p. 1189

Halloran, Katherine G, Asst Dir, Millington Arbela District Library, 8530 Depot St, Millington, MI, 48746. Tel: 989-871-2003. Fax: 989-871-5594. p. 1209

Halloway, Patty, Tech Serv, Seminole Community Library, 9200 113th St N, Seminole, FL, 33772. Tel: 727-394-6905. Fax: 727-398-3113. p. 491

Hallowell, Nancy L, Dir, Libr Serv, Upper Darby Township & Sellers Memorial Free Public Library, 76 S State Rd, Upper Darby, PA, 19082. Tel: 610-789-4440. p. 2149

Hallowell, Susie, Sci Ref Spec, St John's River Water Management District, 4049 Reid St, Palatka, FL, 32177. Tel: 386-329-4190. Fax: 386-329-4890. p. 479

Hallquist, Judy, Librn, Katherine Shaw Bethea Hospital, 403 E First St, Dixon, IL, 61021. Tel: 815-285-5532. Fax: 815-285-5938. p. 636

Hallquist, Lynn, Asst Librn, Anchorage Daily News Library, 1001 Northway Dr, Anchorage, AK, 99508. Tel: 907-257-4593. Fax: 907-258-2157. p. 44

Hallyburton, Ann, Ref Librn/Health Sci Liaison, Western Carolina University, 176 Central Dr, Cullowhee, NC, 28723. Tel: 828-227-3418. Fax: 828-227-7015. p. 1786

Halperin, Michael, Dir, University of Pennsylvania Libraries, Lippincott-Wharton School, 3420 Walnut St, Philadelphia, PA, 19104-6207. Tel: 215-898-9434. Fax: 215-898-2261. p. 2119

Halsall, Jane, Ch, McHenry Public Library District, 809 N Front St, McHenry, IL, 60050. Tel: 815-385-0036. Fax: 815-385-7085. p. 672

Halsey, Cindy, Head Librn, Technical College of the Lowcountry, 921 Ribaut Rd, Beaufort, SC, 29902-5441. Tel: 843-525-8304. Fax: 843-525-8346. p. 2181

Halstead, Bruce, Dir, World Life Research Institute Library, 23000 Grand Terrace Rd, Colton, CA, 92324. Tel: 909-825-4773. Fax: 909-783-3477. p. 135

Halstead, Charity, Ch, Grundy County-Jewett Norris Library, 1331 Main St, Trenton, MO, 64683. Tel: 660-359-3577. Fax: 660-359-6220. p. 1368

Halstead, Deanna, Head, Ch, Boone-Madison Public Library, 375 Main St, Madison, WV, 25130-1295. Tel: 304-369-7842. Fax: 304-369-2950. p. 2564

Halstead, Sarah, Circ, Pasquotank-Camden Library, 100 E Colonial Ave, Elizabeth City, NC, 27909. Tel: 252-335-2473, 252-335-7536. Fax: 252-331-7449. p. 1791

Halsted, Deborah, Sr Assoc Dir, Operations, Houston Academy of Medicine, 1133 John Freeman Blvd, Houston, TX, 77030. Tel: 713-795-4200. Fax: 713-799-7163. p. 2337

Halsted, Pat, Librn, Searcy County Library, 202 E Main St, Marshall, AR, 72650. Tel: 870-448-2420. Fax: 870-448-5453. p. 109

Halteman, Ellen Louise, Dir of Coll, California State Railroad Museum Library, 113 I St, Sacramento, CA, 95814. Tel: 916-323-2158. Fax: 916-327-5655. p. 223

Halter, Kerry K, Tech Serv Coordr, Batavia Public Library District, Ten S Batavia Ave, Batavia, IL, 60510-2793. Tel: 630-879-1393. Fax: 630-879-9118. p. 593

Halter, Linda, Tech Serv, Western Wyoming Community College, 2500 College Dr, Rock Springs, WY, 82902. Tel: 307-382-1703. Fax: 307-382-7665. p. 2659

Haluszka, Carly, Asst Librn, Harlem Public Library, 37 First Ave S, Harlem, MT, 59526. Tel: 406-353-2712. Fax: 406-353-2616. p. 1381

Halvarsson-Stapen, Elisabeth, Librn, Consulate General of Sweden, One Dag Hammarskjold Plaza, 45th Flr, Second Ave at 48th St, New York, NY, 10017-2201. Tel: 212-583-2550. p. 1676

Halverson, Elisabeth, Children's & YA Librn, Woodward Memorial Library, Seven Wolcott St, LeRoy, NY, 14482. Tel: 585-768-8300. Fax: 585-768-4768. p. 1651

Halverson, Eric, Dir, Big Horn County Public Library, 419 N Custer Ave, Hardin, MT, 59034. Fax: 406-665-1804. p. 1381

Halverson, Kathleen, Asst Dean, Head, Pub Serv, Keene State College, 229 Main St, Keene, NH, 03435-3201. Tel: 603-358-2712. Fax: 603-358-2745. p. 1453

Halverson, Larry, Commun Relations Coordr, Loutit District Library, 407 Columbus Ave, Grand Haven, MI, 49417. Tel: 616-842-5560, Ext 222. Fax: 616-847-0570. p. 1183

Halverson, Pat, Librn, Kennebec Public Library, 203 S Main St, Kennebec, SD, 57544. Tel: 605-869-2207. p. 2213

Halvorsen, Charles, E-Br Mgr, Alachua County Library District, 401 E University Ave, Gainesville, FL, 32601-5453. Tel: 352-334-3923. Fax: 352-334-3918. p. 448

Halvorsen, Cheryl P, Law Librn, Blank Rome LLP, One Logan Sq, 18th & Cherry Sts, Philadelphia, PA, 19103-6998. Tel: 215-988-6978. Fax: 215-569-5546. p. 2103

Halvorson, Hjordis, VPres, Libr Serv, Newberry Library, 60 W Walton St, Chicago, IL, 60610-3305. Tel: 312-255-3590. p. 620

Halzack, Maria, Head, Ch, Township of Washington Public Library, 144 Woodfield Rd, Washington Township, NJ, 07676. Tel: 201-664-4586. Fax: 201-664-7331. p. 1539

Ham, Melanie, Dir, Libr Serv, Catawba Hospital, 5525 Catawba Hospital Dr, Catawba, VA, 24070. Tel: 540-375-4300. Fax: 540-375-4348. p. 2453

Ham, Susan, Br Mgr, San Bernardino County Library, Hesperia Branch, 9650 Seventh Ave, Hesperia, CA, 92345. Tel: 760-244-4898. Fax: 760-244-1530. p. 228

Ham, Virginia, Head, Ch, Lincoln Parish Library, 910 N Trenton St, Ruston, LA, 71270-3328. Tel: 318-513-6413. Fax: 318-251-5045. p. 966

Hamada, Susan, Assoc Dir, Prog, Outreach & Ref, Salt Lake County Library Services, 2197 E Fort Union Blvd, Salt Lake City, UT, 84121-3139. Tel: 801-944-7513. Fax: 801-942-6323. p. 2413

Hamaker, Chuck, Coll Mgt, Tech Serv, University of North Carolina at Charlotte, 9201 University City Blvd, Charlotte, NC, 28223-0001. Tel: 704-687-2825. Fax: 704-687-3050. p. 1784

Hamand, Lisa, Tech Serv, Starke County Public Library System, 152 W Culver Rd, Knox, IN, 46534-2220. Tel: 574-772-7323. p. 757

Hamar, Patty, Librn, Jackson County Library, Long Valley Branch, PO Box 21, Long Valley, SD, 57547. Tel: 605-462-6259. p. 2213

Hamasu, Claire, Assoc Dir, National Network of Libraries of Medicine Midcontinental Region, Univ Utah, Spencer S Eccles Health Sci Libr, Bldg 589, Ten N 1900 E, Salt Lake City, UT, 84112-5890. Tel: 801-587-3412. Fax: 801-581-3632. p. 2956

Hamberg, Cheryl, Asst Librn, Tech Serv, Fisk University, Fisk University, 1000 17th Ave N, Nashville, TN, 37208-3051. Tel: 615-329-8733. Fax: 615-329-8761. p. 2256

Hamberry, Roxanne Griffin, Res Librn, Bryan Cave LLP, 1290 Avenue of the Americas, New York, NY, 10104. Tel: 212-541-2165. Fax: 212-541-1465. p. 1671

Hambleton, John, Libr Syst Support, Northern Michigan University, 1401 Presque Isle, Marquette, MI, 49855. Tel: 906-227-2741. Fax: 906-227-1333. p. 1207

Hambley, Douglas, Librn, Samaritan Albany General Hospital, 1046 Sixth Ave SW, Albany, OR, 97321. Tel: 541-812-4446. Fax: 541-812-4482. p. 1989

Hamblin, Daryle, Mrs, Br Mgr, Lafourche Parish Public Library, Larose Branch, 305 E Fifth St, Larose, LA, 70373. Tel: 985-693-3336. Fax: 985-693-3336. p. 971

Hamblin, Kathy, Circ, Madison County Public Library, Berea Branch, 319 Chestnut St, Berea, KY, 40403. Tel: 859-986-7112. Fax: 859-986-7208. p. 934

Hamblin, Melissa, Acq, Memphis Theological Seminary Library, 168 E Parkway S, Memphis, TN, 38104. Tel: 901-334-5824. Fax: 901-452-4051. p. 2250

Hambright, Tom, Historian, Monroe County Public Library, 700 Fleming St, Key West, FL, 33040. Tel: 305-292-3595. Fax: 305-295-3626. p. 456

Hamburger, Mary, Asst Dir, Tech Serv, Ohio State University LIBRARIES, Michael E Moritz Law Library, 55 W 12th Ave, Columbus, OH, 43210-1391. Tel: 614-292-9466. Fax: 614-292-3202. p. 1888

Hamby, Joan, Ref Librn, Point Park University Library, 414 Wood St, Pittsburgh, PA, 15222. Tel: 412-392-3162. Fax: 412-392-3168. p. 2127

Hamby, Tracy, Tech Serv, Central Arkansas Library System, 100 Rock St, Little Rock, AR, 72201-4698. Tel: 501-918-3071. p. 106

Hamdan, Kareemah, Asst Br Mgr, Chesterfield County Public Library, Enon, 1801 Enon Church Rd, Chester, VA, 23836. Tel: 804-530-3403. p. 2457

Hamdan, Karemmah, Asst Br Mgr, Chesterfield County Public Library, Ettrick-Matoaca, 4501 River Rd, Petersburg, VA, 23803. Tel: 804-526-8087. p. 2457

Hamel, Kathy, Admin Serv Mgr, Glendale Public Library, 5959 W Brown St, Glendale, AZ, 85302-1248. Tel: 623-930-3556. Fax: 623-842-2161. p. 64

Hamel, Louise, Mgr, Ontario Ministry of the Attorney General - Court of Appeal Justice Judges Library, Osgoode Hall, 130 Queen St W, Toronto, ON, M5H 2N5, CANADA. Tel: 416-327-5750. Fax: 416-327-6797. p. 2856

Hamel, Ray, Dir, University of Wisconsin-Madison, Primate Center - Lawrence Jacobsen Library, 1220 Capitol Ct, Madison, WI, 53715. Tel: 608-263-3512. Fax: 608-263-4031. p. 2609

Hamelers, Rachel, Ref Serv Librn, Muhlenberg College, 2400 Chew St, Allentown, PA, 18104-5586. Tel: 484-664-3500. Fax: 484-664-3511. p. 2027

Hamelin, Marcil, Exec Dir, Inter-American Organization for Higher Education Library, 333, Grande Allee Est, Bureau 230, Quebec, QC, G1R 2H8, CANADA. Tel: 418-650-1515. Fax: 418-650-1519. p. 2905

Hamelink, Nelva, Pub Serv, Cincinnati Christian University, 2700 Glenway Ave, Cincinnati, OH, 45204-3200. Tel: 513-244-8680. Fax: 513-244-8434. p. 1869

Hamer, Judah, Dir, Rutherford Public Library, 150 Park Ave, Rutherford, NJ, 07070. Tel: 201-939-8600. Fax: 201-939-4108. p. 1528

Hamerly, Don W, Asst Prof, Dir, Sch Libr Media Prog, Dominican University, 7900 W Division St, River Forest, IL, 60305. Tel: 708-524-6845. Fax: 708-524-6657. p. 2965

Hamerly, Michael, Cat, John Carter Brown Library, Brown University, George & Brown Sts, Providence, RI, 02912. Tel: 401-863-2725. Fax: 401-863-3477. p. 2171

Hamersky, Steve, ILL, Tech Serv, Newman University, 3100 McCormick Ave, Wichita, KS, 67213-2097. Tel: 316-942-4291, Ext 2108. Fax: 316-942-1747. p. 900

Hamiel, Michelle, Mgr, Baltimore County Public Library, Woodlawn Branch, 1811 Woodlawn Dr, Baltimore, MD, 21207-4074. Tel: 410-887-1336. Fax: 410-281-9584. p. 1045

Hamil, Margaret M, Exec Dir, Glencoe Public Library, 320 Park Ave, Glencoe, IL, 60022-1597. Tel: 847-835-5056. Fax: 847-835-5648. p. 650

Hamill, Lois, Univ Archivist, Northern Kentucky University, University Dr, Highland Heights, KY, 41099. Tel: 859-572-5863. Fax: 859-572-5390. p. 917

Hamill-Hill, Cathy, In Charge, City of Kawartha Lakes Public Library, Oakwood Branch, 932 Hwy 7, Oakwood, ON, K0M 2M0, CANADA. Tel: 705-953-9060. Fax: 705-953-9355. p. 2816

Hamilos, Sue, Head, Ref, Wellesley Free Library, 530 Washington St, Wellesley, MA, 02482. Tel: 781-235-1610, Ext 1110. Fax: 781-235-0495. p. 1135

Hamilton, Amber, Circ Librn, Silver Lake Library, 203 Railroad St, Silver Lake, KS, 66539. Tel: 785-582-5141. Fax: 785-582-4282. p. 894

Hamilton, Andrew, Ref Librn, Oregon Health & Science University Library, 3181 SW Sam Jackson Park Rd, Portland, OR, 97239-3098. Tel: 503-494-3460. Fax: 503-494-3227. p. 2013

Hamilton, Ann, Assoc Dean, Georgia Southern University, 1400 Southern Dr, Statesboro, GA, 30458. Tel: 912-478-5115. Fax: 912-478-0093. p. 552

Hamilton, Ann, Govt Doc, Ref Serv, Coastal Carolina University, 755 Hwy 544, Conway, SC, 29526. Tel: 843-349-2409. Fax: 843-349-2412. p. 2191

Hamilton, Ashley, In Charge, Reading Public Museum Library, 500 Museum Rd, Reading, PA, 19611-1425. Tel: 610-371-5850. Fax: 610-371-5632. p. 2134

Hamilton, B Parker, Dir of Libr, Montgomery County Public Libraries, 21 Maryland Ave, Ste 310, Rockville, MD, 20850. Tel: 240-777-0002. p. 1038

Hamilton, Barbara, Mgr, Institute for Defense Analysis Library, 805 Bunn Dr, Princeton, NJ, 08540. Tel: 609-924-4600. Fax: 609-924-3061. p. 1522

Hamilton, Barry, Dr, Librn, Roberts Wesleyan College & Northeastern Seminary, 2301 Westside Dr, Rochester, NY, 14624-1997. Tel: 585-594-6893. Fax: 585-594-6543. p. 1731

Hamilton, Billie, Librn, Blue Mound Community Library, 1600 Bell Avenue, Fort Worth, TX, 76131-1002. Tel: 817-847-4095. Fax: 817-232-8050. p. 2321

Hamilton, Brandy, Readers' Serv Manager, Wake County Public Library System, Southeast Regional Library, 908 Seventh Ave, Garner, NC, 27529. Tel: 919-662-2269. Fax: 919-662-2270. p. 1818

Hamilton, Carole, Youth/Young Adult Librn, Moses Greeley Parker Memorial Library, 28 Arlington St, Dracut, MA, 01826. Tel: 978-454-5474. Fax: 978-454-9120. p. 1085

Hamilton, Cassandra, Youth Serv, Hackley Public Library, 316 W Webster Ave, Muskegon, MI, 49440. Tel: 231-722-7276, Ext 229. Fax: 231-726-5567. p. 1212

Hamilton, Cindy, Head, Circ, Baker College of Flint, 1050 W Bristol Rd, Flint, MI, 48507-5508. Tel: 810-766-4228. Fax: 810-766-2013. p. 1179

Hamilton, Clifford, Dir, Leslie County Public Library, 22065 Main St, Hyden, KY, 41749. Tel: 606-672-2460. Fax: 606-672-4213. p. 918

Hamilton, D'Ann, Mgr, Fabricators & Manufacturers Association International, 833 Featherstone Rd, Rockford, IL, 61107-6302. Tel: 815-399-8700. Fax: 815-484-7700. p. 696

Hamilton, Darren, Librn, William Osler Health Centre - Etobicoke Hospital Campus, 101 Humber College Blvd, Etobicoke, ON, M9V 1R8, CANADA. Tel: 416-747-3400, Ext 33334. Fax: 416-747-3484. p. 2804

Hamilton, Deb, Dir, Verdigre Public Library, 101 E Third St, Verdigre, NE, 68783. Tel: 402-668-2677. Fax: 402-668-2677. p. 1422

Hamilton, Elizabeth, Dir, Frankford Public Library, Eight Main St, Frankford, DE, 19945. Tel: 302-732-9351. Fax: 302-732-3353. p. 383

Hamilton, Elna, Librn, Crook Community Library, Fourth St, Crook, CO, 80726. Tel: 970-886-2833. p. 297

Hamilton, Evelyn, Ref, Natchitoches Parish Library, 450 Second St, Natchitoches, LA, 71457-4649. Tel: 318-357-3280. Fax: 318-357-7073. p. 958

Hamilton, Harriette, Asst Librn, Pettee Memorial Library, 16 S Main St, Wilmington, VT, 05363. Tel: 802-464-8557. p. 2440

Hamilton, Helen, Hist Coll Librn, Kingsport Public Library & Archives, 400 Broad St, Kingsport, TN, 37660-4292. Tel: 423-224-2539. Fax: 423-224-2558. p. 2240

Hamilton, Jan, Youth Serv Librn, Prince Memorial Library, 266 Main St, Cumberland, ME, 04021-9754. Tel: 207-829-2215. Fax: 207-829-2221. p. 982

Hamilton, Jane, Librn, Florida Department of Corrections, 5563 Tenth St, Malone, FL, 32445. Tel: 850-569-5260, Ext 246. Fax: 850-569-5996. p. 462

Hamilton, Jeanne, Libr Dir, Carnegie Public Library, 712 Sixth St, Charleston, IL, 61920. Tel: 217-345-4913. Fax: 217-348-5616. p. 603

Hamilton, Jennifer, Dir, Appaloosa Museum & Heritage Center, 2720 W Pullman Rd, Moscow, ID, 83843. Tel: 208-882-5578. Fax: 208-882-8150. p. 579

Hamilton, Jennifer, Librn, Wendell Public Library, 375 First Ave E, Wendell, ID, 83355. Tel: 208-536-6195. p. 585

Hamilton, Jennifer, Ref Librn, Terrebonne Parish Library, 151 Library Dr, Houma, LA, 70360. Tel: 985-876-5861. Fax: 985-917-0582. p. 951

Hamilton, Katherine, Asst Dir, Leslie County Public Library, 22065 Main St, Hyden, KY, 41749. Tel: 606-672-2460. Fax: 606-672-4213. p. 918

Hamilton, Kelly, Br Mgr, Coordr, Outreach Serv, Sevier County Public Library System, Seymour Branch, 137 W Macon Lane, Seymour, TN, 37865. Tel: 865-573-0728. Fax: 865-573-0662. p. 2265

Hamilton, Kelly, Br Mgr, Sevier County Public Library System, Kodak Branch, 319 W Dumplin Valley Rd, Kodak, TN, 37764. Tel: 865-933-0078. Fax: 865-933-5888. p. 2265

Hamilton, Laura, Head Librn, Siletz Public Library, 243 W Buford, Siletz, OR, 97380. Tel: 541-444-2855. p. 2019

Hamilton, Leslie, Genealogy Librn, ILL Librn, Collinsville Memorial Public Library District, 408 W Main St, Collinsville, IL, 62234. Tel: 618-344-1112. Fax: 618-345-6401. p. 630

Hamilton, Margaret L, Dir, Greenwood Public Library, 310 S Meridian St, Greenwood, IN, 46143-3135. Tel: 317-881-1953. Fax: 317-881-1963. p. 747

Hamilton, Mary, Dir, Bradshaw H Grady Chambers County Library, Lafayette Pilot Public Library, 198 First St SE, Lafayette, AL, 36862. Tel: 334-864-0012. p. 39

Hamilton, Mary, Curator, Oscar Getz Museum of Whiskey History Library, 114 N Fifth St, Bardstown, KY, 40004. Tel: 502-348-2999. p. 906

Hamilton, Mary A, Tech Serv, Dixie Regional Library System, 111 N Main St, Pontotoc, MS, 38863-2103. Tel: 662-489-3960. Fax: 662-489-7777. p. 1311

Hamilton, Mary H, Dir, H Grady Bradshaw Chambers County Library, 3419 20th Ave, Valley, AL, 36854. Tel: 334-768-2161. Fax: 334-768-7272. p. 39

Hamilton, Matt, IT Mgr, Anythink Libraries, 5877 E 120th Ave, Thornton, CO, 80602. Tel: 303-288-2001. Fax: 303-451-0190. p. 323

Hamilton, Melodie, Ser & Electronic Res Librn, Connecticut College, 270 Mohegan Ave, New London, CT, 06320-4196. Tel: 860-439-2669. Fax: 860-439-2871. p. 359

Hamilton, Meredith L, Dir, Brownsville Free Public Library, 100 Seneca St, Brownsville, PA, 15417-1974. Tel: 724-785-7272. Fax: 724-785-6087. p. 2038

Hamilton, Nanette, Tech Serv Librn, Berkeley County Library System, 1003 Hwy 52, Moncks Corner, SC, 29461. Tel: 843-719-4273. p. 2200

Hamilton, Pat, Dir, Shoshone Public Library, 211 S Rail St, Shoshone, ID, 83352-0236. Tel: 208-886-2843. Fax: 208-886-2426. p. 584

Hamilton, Pat, Dir, Weiser Public Library, 628 E First St, Weiser, ID, 83672-2241. Tel: 208-549-1243. p. 585

Hamilton, Pat A, Dir, Gooding Public Library, 306 Fifth Ave W, Gooding, ID, 83330-1205. Tel: 208-934-4089. Fax: 208-934-4089. p. 574

Hamilton, Patricia, Librn, Logansport-Cass County Public Library, Galveston Branch, 304 E Jackson, Galveston, IN, 46932. Tel: 574-699-6170. Fax: 574-699-6171. p. 761

Hamilton, Patricia, Dir, Rapid City Regional Hospital, 353 Fairmont Blvd, Rapid City, SD, 57701. Tel: 605-719-7101. Fax: 605-719-1578. p. 2217

Hamilton, Rebecca, State Librn, State Library of Louisiana, 701 N Fourth St, Baton Rouge, LA, 70802-5232. Tel: 225-342-4923. Fax: 225-219-4804. p. 945

Hamilton, Rhonda, Tech Librn, Mercer County Library, 601 Grant, Princeton, MO, 64673. Tel: 660-748-3725. Fax: 660-748-3723. p. 1350

Hamilton, Rita, City Librn, Phoenix Public Library, 1221 N Central Ave, Phoenix, AZ, 85004-1820. Tel: 602-262-4636. Fax: 602-261-8836. p. 76

Hamilton, Robert, Coll Develop, Ref Librn, Hobbs Public Library, 509 N Shipp, Hobbs, NM, 88240. Tel: 575-397-9328. Fax: 575-397-1508. p. 1556

Hamilton, Rosalee, Asst Librn, Thomas County Library, 503 Main St, Thedford, NE, 69166. Tel: 308-645-2237. p. 1421

Hamilton, Shelley, Mgr, Triodyne Inc, 3054 N Lake Terrace, Glenview, IL, 60026. Tel: 847-677-4730. Fax: 847-647-2047. p. 651

Hamilton, Sue, Br Supvr, Caledon Public Library, Belfountain Branch, 17247 Shaw's Creek Rd, Caledon, ON, L7K 0E8, CANADA. Tel: 519-927-5701. p. 2795

Hamilton, Susan, Libr Tech, College of the North Atlantic, Grand Falls-Windsor Campus, Five Cromer Ave, Grand Falls-Windsor, NL, A2A 1X3, CANADA. Tel: 709-292-5637. Fax: 709-489-5765. p. 2771

Hamilton, Wendy, Mgr of Content, Abbott, 100 Abbott Park Rd, AP 6B, Abbott Park, IL, 60064-6107. Tel: 847 935-3529. Fax: 847-937-6333. p. 587

Hamilton, Yvonne, Librn, College of New Rochelle, Co-op City Campus, 755 Co-op City Blvd, Bronx, NY, 10475. Tel: 718-320-0300, Ext 232. Fax: 718-379-1680. p. 1666

Hamilton-Smith, Katherine, Dir, Lake County Discovery Museum, 27277 Forest Preserve Dr, Wauconda, IL, 60084. Tel: 847-968-3380. Fax: 847-526-1545. p. 716

Hamiton, Susan, Head, Circ, Lewisboro Library, 15 Main St, South Salem, NY, 10590-1413. Tel: 914-763-3857. Fax: 914-763-2193. p. 1745

Hamlett, Ellen, Librn, Rube Sessions Memorial Library, 298 Rusk Ave, Wells, TX, 75976. Tel: 936-867-4757. Fax: 936-867-4760. p. 2399

Hamlett, Rebecca, Ref/Archives Librn, William Jewell College, 500 College Hill, Liberty, MO, 64068-1843. Tel: 816-415-7609. Fax: 816-415-5021. p. 1343

Hamlett, Toni H, Cat, Hampden Sydney College, 257 Via Sacra, HSC Box 7, Hampden Sydney, VA, 23943. Tel: 434-223-6267. Fax: 434-223-6351. p. 2468

Hamlin, Linda G, Librn, Dobson Community Library, 205 S Main St, Dobson, NC, 27017. Tel: 336-386-8208. Fax: 336-386-4086. p. 1786

Hamlin, Nancy, Dir, Buckley Public Library, 408 Dewey Ave, Poteau, OK, 74953. Tel: 918-647-3833, 918-647-4444. Fax: 918-647-8910. p. 1976

Hamlin, Tina, Librn, Hyde County Library, 107 Commercial SE, Highmore, SD, 57345. Tel: 605-852-2514. p. 2212

Hamlin, Tom, Librn, Bell County Forestry Library, 560 Correctional Dr, Pineville, KY, 40977. Tel: 606-337-7065. Fax: 606-337-1312. p. 933

Hamm, Andrew, Dir, West Islip Public Library, Three Higbie Lane, West Islip, NY, 11795-3999. Tel: 631-661-7080. Fax: 631-661-7137. p. 1766

Hamm, Cathy, Dir, Edinburgh Wright-Hageman Public Library, 119 W Main Cross, Edinburgh, IN, 46124-1499. Tel: 812-526-5487. Fax: 812-526-7057. p. 736

Hamm, Greg, Librn, Beatrice State Developmental Center, 3000 Lincoln Blvd, Beatrice, NE, 68310. Tel: 402-223-6175. Fax: 402-223-7546. p. 1393

Hamm, Linda, Br Librn, Kemper-Newton Regional Library System, Union Public, 101 Peachtree, Union, MS, 39365-2617. Tel: 601-774-5096. Fax: 601-774-5096. p. 1316

Hamm, Margo, Librn, Maysville Community & Technical College, 1755 US Hwy 68, Maysville, KY, 41056. Tel: 606-759-7141, Ext 66125. Fax: 606-759-7176. p. 928

Hamm, Marie Summerlin, Asst Dir, Coll Develop, Regent University, 1000 Regent University Dr, Virginia Beach, VA, 23464-9800. Tel: 757-352-4233. Fax: 757-352-4451. p. 2499

Hamm, Sandra, ILL, Saint Mary's University, 5429 Inglis St, Halifax, NS, B3H 3C3, CANADA. Tel: 902-420-5547. Fax: 902-420-5561. p. 2782

Hamm, Tamara, Ch, Dover Free Library, 22 Hollands Rd, East Dover, VT, 05341-9617. Tel: 802-348-7488. p. 2423

Hamm, Thomas D, Dr, Curator, Friends Coll, Dir, Spec Coll, Prof of Hist, Earlham College, 801 National Rd W, Richmond, IN, 47374-4095. Tel: 765-983-1511. Fax: 765-983-1304. p. 774

Hamm, Yvonne, Br Librn, Kemper-Newton Regional Library System, Decatur Public, 306 Broad St, Decatur, MS, 39327. Tel: 601-635-2777. p. 1316

Hammack, Lisa, Dir, Children & YA, Tell City-Perry County Public Library, 2328 Tell St, Tell City, IN, 47586. Tel: 812-547-2661. Fax: 812-547-3038. p. 780

Hamman, Ruth, Ref Serv, Passaic County Community College, One College Blvd, Paterson, NJ, 07505. Tel: 973-684-5880. Fax: 973-684-6675. p. 1518

Hamman, Sharon, Sr Librn, Lee County Library System, Riverdale Branch, 2421 Buckingham Rd, Fort Myers, FL, 33905. Tel: 239-461-3130. Fax: 239-694-6146. p. 446

Hammang, Carol, Ref, Loveland Public Library, 300 N Adams Ave, Loveland, CO, 80537-5754. Tel: 970-962-2589. Fax: 970-962-2905. p. 317

Hammann, Leslie, Coordr, Bachelor of Libr Info Prog, Northern Kentucky University, University Dr, Highland Heights, KY, 41099. Tel: 859-572-6157. Fax: 859-572-5390. p. 917

Hammat, Angela, Librn, Marietta Memorial Hospital, 401 Matthew St, Marietta, OH, 45750-1699. Tel: 740-374-1400. Fax: 740-374-4959. p. 1913

Hammel, Steven, Br Mgr, Librn II, Jefferson Parish Library, Lafitte Branch, 4917 City Park Dr, Ste B, Lafitte, LA, 70067. Tel: 504-689-5097. Fax: 504-689-3354. p. 956

Hammell, Peter, Dir, National Museum of Racing & Hall of Fame, 191 Union Ave, Saratoga Springs, NY, 12866. Tel: 518-584-0400. Fax: 518-584-4574. p. 1738

Hammer, Claudine, Sister, Asst Librn, Queen of the Holy Rosary College Library, 43326 Mission Blvd, Fremont, CA, 94539. Tel: 510-657-2468. p. 150

Hammer, Daniel, Head, Reader Serv, Historic New Orleans Collection, 410 Chartres St, New Orleans, LA, 70130-2102. Tel: 504-598-7112. Fax: 504-598-7168. p. 960

Hammer, Eve, Commun Libr Mgr, Queens Borough Public Library, Bay Terrace Community Library, 18-36 Bell Blvd, Bayside, NY, 11360. Tel: 718-423-7004, 718-746-1794. p. 1644

Hammer-Schneider, Susan, Head, Serv for Blind & Handicapped, North Dakota State Library, Library Memorial Bldg, 604 East Blvd Ave, Dept 250, Bismarck, ND, 58505-0800. Tel: 701-328-2185. Fax: 701-328-2040. p. 1838

Hammerlund, Lynn, Tech Serv, Judson University, 1151 N State St, Elgin, IL, 60123. Tel: 847-628-2035. Fax: 847-625-2045. p. 641

Hammerly, Kathy, Librn, Osram Sylvania Library, Hawes St, Towanda, PA, 18848. Tel: 570-268-5322. Fax: 570-268-5350. p. 2146

Hammerschmidt, Claire, Librn, Camden County Library District, Sunrise Beach Branch, 14156 N State Hwy 5, Sunrise Beach, MO, 65079. Tel: 573-374-6982. Fax: 573-374-6982. p. 1321

Hammersla, Keith, Head, Ref (Info Serv), Martinsburg-Berkeley County Public Library, 101 W King St, Martinsburg, WV, 25401. Tel: 304-267-8933. Fax: 304-267-9720. p. 2565

Hammersley, Laura, Dir, Hawkins Memorial Library, 308 Main St, La Porte City, IA, 50651. Tel: 319-342-3025. Fax: 319-342-3025. p. 826

Hammerstrand, Kristine, Dir, User Serv, Consortium of Academic & Research Libraries in Illinois, 100 Trade Ctr Dr, Ste 303, Champaign, IL, 61820. Tel: 217-244-7593. Fax: 217-244-7596. p. 2942

Hammerstrom, Kirsten, Dep Dir, Coll, Rhode Island Historical Society Library, 121 Hope St, Providence, RI, 02906. Tel: 401-273-8107, Ext 13. Fax: 401-751-7930. p. 2174

Hammes, Laura, Coordr, Right to Life of Michigan, 233 N Walnut St, Lansing, MI, 48933-1121. Tel: 517-487-3376. Fax: 517-487-6453. p. 1202

Hammett, Beverly, Dir, Webster Parish Library, 521 East & West St, Minden, LA, 71055. Tel: 318-371-3080. Fax: 318-371-3081. p. 957

Hammett, Marcia, Br Mgr, Calvert County Public Library, 850 Costley Way, Prince Frederick, MD, 20678. Tel: 410-535-0291. Fax: 410-535-3022. p. 1036

Hammett, Paula, Head, Coll Develop, Web Serv, Sonoma State University Library, 1801 E Cotati Ave, Rohnert Park, CA, 94928-3609. Tel: 707-664-3912. Fax: 707-664-2090. p. 219

Hammill, Sarah, Distance Learning Librn, Florida International University, 3000 NE 151st St, North Miami, FL, 33181-3600. Tel: 305-919-5604. Fax: 305-919-5914. p. 472

Hammock, Dianne, Electronic Serv, Auburn Public Library, 749 E Thach Ave, Auburn, AL, 36830. Tel: 334-501-3190. p. 5

Hammon, Carma, Br Mgr, Prairie-River Library District, Winchester Community, 314 Nezperce St, Winchester, ID, 83555. Tel: 208-924-5164. Fax: 208-924-5164. p. 577

Hammon, Pat, Med Librn, Potomac Hospital, 2300 Opitz Blvd, Woodbridge, VA, 22191. Tel: 703-670-1331. Fax: 703-878-1619. p. 2505

Hammon, Ruth, Dir, Rainsville Public Library, 941 E Main St, Rainsville, AL, 35986. Tel: 256-638-3311. Fax: 256-638-3314. p. 34

Hammond, Andrew, Librn, Muskegon Area District Library, Egelston Branch, 5428 E Apple Ave, Muskegon, MI, 49442-3008. Tel: 231-788-6477. Fax: 231-724-6675. p. 1213

Hammond, Ann, Exec Dir, Lexington Public Library, 140 E Main St, Lexington, KY, 40507-1376. Tel: 859-231-5599. Fax: 859-231-5598. p. 920

Hammond, Carol, Dir, Thunderbird School of Global Management, 15249 N 59th Ave, Glendale, AZ, 85306-6001. Tel: 602-978-7234. Fax: 602-978-7762. p. 64

Hammond, Claire, Mgr, Parsons Corp, 100 W Walnut, Pasadena, CA, 91124. Tel: 626-440-3998. Fax: 626-440-2630. p. 206

Hammond, Elizabeth D, Dean of Libr, Mercer University, Jack Tarver Library, 1300 Edgewood Ave, Macon, GA, 31207. Tel: 478-301-2960. Fax: 478-301-2111. p. 540

Hammond, Ellen H, Curator, Yale University Library, Sterling Memorial Library, 120 High St, New Haven, CT, 06520. Tel: 203-432-1791. Fax: 203-432-1294. p. 359

Hammond, Gary, In Charge, Nassau County Museum Research Library, Sands Point Preserve, 127 Middleneck Rd, Port Washington, NY, 11050. Tel: 516-571-7901. Fax: 516-571-7909. p. 1721

Hammond, Grace, Ref, Sturgis Public Library, 1040 Second St, Sturgis, SD, 57785-1595. Tel: 605-347-2624. Fax: 605-720-7211. p. 2220

Hammond, Heidi, PhD, Asst Prof, Saint Catherine University, 2004 Randolph Ave, Mailstop No 4125, Saint Paul, MN, 55105. Tel: 651-690-6802. Fax: 651-690-8724. p. 2968

Hammond, Jaime, Ref Serv, Ser, Naugatuck Valley Community College, 750 Chase Pkwy, Waterbury, CT, 06708. Tel: 203-575-8024. Fax: 203-575-8062. p. 375

Hammond, John J, Exec Dir, Northern New York Library Network, 6721 US Hwy 11, Potsdam, NY, 13676. Tel: 315-265-1119. Fax: 315-265-1881. p. 2950

Hammond, Ken, Librn, Orr & Reno Law Library, One Eagle Sq, Concord, NH, 03301-4905. Tel: 603-223-9105. Fax: 603-223-9005. p. 1443

Hammond, Lee, Coll, National Library of Medicine, Bldg 38, Rm 2E-17B, 8600 Rockville Pike, Bethesda, MD, 20894. Tel: 301-496-6308. Fax: 301-496-4450. p. 1022

Hammond, Mark, Librn, Southwestern College Library, 900 Otay Lakes Rd, Chula Vista, CA, 91910-7299. Tel: 619-421-6700, Ext 5781. Fax: 619-482-6417. p. 134

Hammond, Mary Jo, Ch, Lincoln Memorial Library, 21 W Broadway, Lincoln, ME, 04457. Tel: 207-794-2765. Fax: 207-794-2606. p. 990

Hammond, Michele, Assoc Dir, Morgan State University, 1700 E Cold Spring Lane, Baltimore, MD, 21251. Tel: 443-885-3477. p. 1016

Hammond, Miriam, Mgr, White County Public Library, 10 Colonial Dr, Cleveland, GA, 30528. Tel: 706-865-5572. Fax: 706-219-3621. p. 525

Hammond, Pat, ILL, Northwest Kansas Library System, Two Washington Sq, Norton, KS, 67654-1615. Tel: 785-877-5148. Fax: 785-877-5697. p. 885

Hammond, Shana, Actg Mgr, The Resource Center at Mercy Memorial, 1011 14th Ave NW, Ardmore, OK, 73401. Tel: 580-220-6654. Fax: 580-220-6599. p. 1957

Hammond, Wayne G, Asst Librn, Williams College, Chapin Library, 96 School St, Apt 3, Williamstown, MA, 01267. Tel: 413-597-2462. Fax: 413-597-2929. p. 1141

Hammonds, Robert, Cat Librn, Fairmont State University, 1201 Locust Ave, Fairmont, WV, 26554. Tel: 304-367-4697. Fax: 304-367-4677. p. 2559

Hammonds, Robert, Asst Prof, Fairmont State College, School of Education, 1201 Locust Ave, Fairmont, WV, 26554. Tel: 304-367-4697. Fax: 304-367-4677. p. 2976

Hammons, Jane E, Ref & Instruction Librn, Pikeville College, 147 Sycamore St, Pikeville, KY, 41501-9118. Tel: 606-218-5609. Fax: 606-218-5613. p. 933

Hammons, Jeanette M, Dir, Elko-Lander-Eureka County Library System, 720 Court St, Elko, NV, 89801. Tel: 775-738-3066. Fax: 775-738-8262. p. 1426

Hammons, Meredith B, Dr, Ref/Syst Librn, Emory University Libraries, Pitts Theology Library, Candler School of Theology, 505 S Kilgo Circle NE, Atlanta, GA, 30322-2810. Tel: 404-727-5094. Fax: 404-727-1219. p. 514

Hammontree, Clara Sue, Dir, Greenback Public Library, 6889 Morganton Rd, Greenback, TN, 37742-4143. Tel: 865-856-2841. Fax: 865-856-2841. p. 2236

Hammontree, Jennifer, Librn, Basin Judith County Free Library, Hobson Community Library, 210 Central Ave, Hobson, MT, 59452. Tel: 406-423-5453. p. 1388

Hamner, Judith B, Law Librn, Jackson Walker, LLP, 100 Congress Ave, Ste 1100, Austin, TX, 78701-4099. Tel: 512-236-2306. Fax: 512-236-2002. p. 2280

Hamontree, LaDonna, Circ & Ref, Graves County Public Library, 601 N 17th St, Mayfield, KY, 42066. Tel: 270-247-2911. Fax: 270-247-2991. p. 928

Hampe, Ellen L, Asst Dir, Coralville Public Library, 1401 Fifth St, Coralville, IA, 52241. Tel: 319-248-1850. Fax: 319-248-1890. p. 804

Hampson, Jean, Ch, Marion Public Library, 1095 Sixth Ave, Marion, IA, 52302. Tel: 319-377-3412. Fax: 319-377-0113. p. 830

Hampton, Blossom, Cat, United States Army, Bldg 35, One C Tree Rd, McAlester, OK, 74501. Tel: 918-420-8707. Fax: 918-420-8473. p. 1968

Hampton, Brian, Spec Events Coordr, Murrell Memorial Library, Missouri Valley College, Tech Center Bldg, 500 E College St, Marshall, MO, 65340. Tel: 660-831-4180, 660-831-4181. Fax: 660-831-4068. p. 1344

Hampton, Dantrea, Per/Ref Librn, Kentucky State University, 400 E Main St, Frankfort, KY, 40601-2355. Tel: 502-597-5946. Fax: 502-597-5068. p. 914

Hampton, Denita, Mgr, Access & Media Serv, Georgia State University Library, 100 Decatur St SE, Atlanta, GA, 30303-3202. Tel: 404-413-2822. Fax: 404-413-2701. p. 516

Hampton, James, Head, Circ, Ref, Jackson State University, 1325 J R Lynch St, Jackson, MS, 39217. Tel: 601-979-2123. Fax: 601-979-2239. p. 1303

Hampton, Joseph, Br Mgr, Louisville Free Public Library, Newburg, 3305 Northwestern Pkwy, Louisville, KY, 40212. Tel: 502-574-1744. Fax: 502-776-9947. p. 924

Hampton, Lee, Dr, Exec Dir, Amistad Research Center, Tulane University, Tilton Hall, 6823 St Charles Ave, New Orleans, LA, 70118. Tel: 504-862-3222. Fax: 504-862-8961. p. 959

Hampton, Lily, Dir, Glenns Ferry Public Library, 298 S Lincoln, Glenns Ferry, ID, 83623. Tel: 208-366-2045. Fax: 208-366-2238. p. 574

Hampton, Liz G, Prog Coordr, Copper Queen Library, Six Main St, Bisbee, AZ, 85603. Tel: 520-432-4232. Fax: 520-432-7061. p. 58

Hampton, Lori, Br Coordr, Montrose Regional Library District, Paradox Branch, 21501 Six Mile Rd, Paradox, CO, 81429. Tel: 970-859-7236. Fax: 970-859-7235. p. 319

Hampton, Margaret Evans, Mgr, Free Will Baptist Bible College, 3630 W End Ave, Nashville, TN, 37205. Tel: 615-844-5284. Fax: 615-269-6028. p. 2256

Hampton, T Kae, Dir, Irion County Library, PO Box 766, Mertzon, TX, 76941-0766. Tel: 325-835-2704. Fax: 325-835-2008. p. 2362

Hampton, Tammy, Librn, Leonardville City Library, 117 N Erpelding, Leonardville, KS, 66449. Tel: 785-293-5606. p. 879

Hampton, Todd, Ref, Norwalk Community College, 188 Richards Ave, Norwalk, CT, 06854-1655. Tel: 203-857-7200. Fax: 203-857-7380. p. 362

Hamrick, Cherry, Dir, Delta Township District Library, 5130 Davenport Dr, Lansing, MI, 48917-2040. Tel: 517-321-4014. Fax: 517-321-2080. p. 1200

Hamrick, Leona, Ch, Leslie County Public Library, 22065 Main St, Hyden, KY, 41749. Tel: 606-672-2460. Fax: 606-672-4213. p. 918

Hamrick, Lisa, Br Mgr, Public Library of Cincinnati & Hamilton County, North Central, 11109 Hamilton Ave, Cincinnati, OH, 45231. Tel: 513-369-6068. Fax: 513-369-4459. p. 1872

Hamrick, Sarah, Dir, Pub Serv, Gallaudet University Library, 800 Florida Ave NE, Washington, DC, 20002-3095. Tel: 202-651-5214. p. 401

Hamrick, Sharon, ILL Tech, Sofia University Library, 1069 E Meadow Circle, Palo Alto, CA, 94303. Tel: 650-493-4430, Ext 221. Fax: 650-852-9780. p. 205

Hams, Teri, Librn, Minnesota Department of Corrections, 2305 Minnesota Blvd SE, Saint Cloud, MN, 56304. Tel: 320-240-3071. p. 1276

Hamson, Susan, Curator of Ms & Univ Archivist, Columbia University, Archives, Butler Library, 6th Flr, 114th St, MC 1127, New York, NY, 10027. Tel: 212-854-1331. Fax: 212-854-1365. p. 1674

Hamson, Susan, Curator of Manuscripts, Univ Archivist, Columbia University, Rare Book & Manuscript, Butler Library, 6th Flr E, 535 W 114th St, New York, NY, 10027. Tel: 212-854-1331. Fax: 212-854-1365. p. 1675

Han, Hong Gyu, Automation Spec, Northwest Missouri State University, 800 University Dr, Maryville, MO, 64468-6001. Tel: 660-562-1192. Fax: 660-562-1049. p. 1344

Han, Jiao, Cat, Oakland Public Library, 125 14th St, Oakland, CA, 94612. Tel: 510-238-2217. Fax: 510-238-6722. p. 197

Han, Qiming, Syst Librn, Housatonic Community College Library, 900 Lafayette Blvd, Bridgeport, CT, 06604. Tel: 203-332-5073. Fax: 203-332-5252. p. 332

Hanania, Dee Dee, Actg Librn, San Juan Bautista City Library, 801 Second St, San Juan Bautista, CA, 95045. Tel: 831-623-4687. Fax: 831-623-4701. p. 252

Hanawalt, Victoria L, Dir, Reed College, 3203 SE Woodstock Blvd, Portland, OR, 97202-8199. Tel: 503-777-7702. Fax: 503-777-7786. p. 2014

Hanaway, Wayne, Exec Dir, Spiro Public Library, 208 S Main, Spiro, OK, 74959. Tel: 918-962-3461. Fax: 918-962-5320. p. 1978

Hanblin, Jennifer, Ref Serv, Glenbow Museum Library, 130 Ninth Ave SE, Calgary, AB, T2G 0P3, CANADA. Tel: 403-268-4197. Fax: 403-232-6569. p. 2691

Hance, Jennifer, Dir, Natick Historical Society, 58 Eliot St, Natick, MA, 01760. Tel: 508-647-4841. p. 1108

Hancks, Jeff, Archives & Spec Coll Librn, Western Illinois University Libraries, One University Circle, Macomb, IL, 61455. Tel: 309-298-2718. Fax: 309-298-2791. p. 668

Hancock, Audrey, Dir, Osage Public Library, 406 Main St, Osage, IA, 50461-1125. Tel: 641-732-3323. Fax: 641-732-4419. p. 837

Hancock, Cheryl, Dir, Harney County Library, 80 West D St, Burns, OR, 97720-1299. Tel: 541-573-6670. Fax: 541-573-1571. p. 1993

Hancock, Don, Librn, Southwest Research & Information Center Library, 105 Stanford SE, Albuquerque, NM, 87106-3537. Tel: 505-262-1862. Fax: 505-262-1864. p. 1550

Hancock, Dorothy S, Ch, Chesterfield County Library, 119 W Main St, Chesterfield, SC, 29709-1512. Tel: 843-623-7489. Fax: 843-623-3295. p. 2186

Hancock, Holly, Dir, Bridgton Public Library, One Church St, Bridgton, ME, 04009. Tel: 207-647-2472. Fax: 207-647-5660. p. 979

Hancock, Joyce, Librn, Wetumpka Public Library, 212 S Main St, Wetumpka, AL, 36092. Tel: 334-567-1308. Fax: 334-567-1309. p. 40

Hancock, Julianne, Mgr, Communications & Libr Innovation, Salt Lake City Public Library, 210 E 400 S, Salt Lake City, UT, 84111-3280. Tel: 801-524-8219. Fax: 801-322-8194. p. 2413

Hancock, Kathy, Librn, Addie Davis Memorial Library, 301 N Fourth St, Mountain View, OK, 73062. Tel: 580-347-2397. Fax: 580-347-2397. p. 1969

Hancock, Kim, Dir, Libr Serv, Western Memorial Regional Hospital, West Valley Rd, Corner Brook, NL, A2H 6J7, CANADA. Tel: 709-637-5000, Ext 5395, 709-637-5395. Fax: 709-637-5268. p. 2770

Hancock, Lisa, Curator of Coll, Aspen Historical Society Library, 620 W Bleeker St, Aspen, CO, 81611. Tel: 970-925-3721, Ext 110. Fax: 970-925-5347. p. 288

Hancock, Molly, Coordr, Youth Serv, Pollard Memorial Library, 401 Merrimack St, Lowell, MA, 01852. Tel: 978-970-4120. Fax: 978-970-4117. p. 1100

Hancock, Pam, Br Head, Toronto Public Library, Forest Hill, 700 Eglinton Ave W, Toronto, ON, M5N 1B9, CANADA. Tel: 416-393-7706. Fax: 416-393-7611. p. 2861

Hancock, Pat, Dir, Salem Baptist Church Library, 103 N Broad St, Salem, VA, 24153. Tel: 540-387-0416. Fax: 540-375-6412. p. 2496

Hancock, Sharon, Head, Circ, Lincoln Parish Library, 910 N Trenton St, Ruston, LA, 71270-3328. Tel: 318-513-6406. Fax: 318-251-5045. p. 966

Hancock, Valerie, Dir, Morgan County Library, 50 N 100 W, Morgan, UT, 84050. Tel: 801-829-3481. Fax: 801-829-6176. p. 2408

Hancox, Amanda, Exec Dir, Dancer Transition Resource Centre, The Lynda Hamilton Centre, 250 The Esplanade, Ste 500, Toronto, ON, M5A 1J2, CANADA. Tel: 416-595-5655. Fax: 416-595-0009. p. 2852

Hancox, Terry, Dir, Cuyahoga Community College, Eastern Campus Library, 4250 Richmond Rd, Highland Hills, OH, 44122-6195. Tel: 216-987-2087. Fax: 216-987-2054. p. 1879

Hand, Amy, Ch, Camden Public Library, 55 Main St, Camden, ME, 04843-1703. Tel: 207-236-3440. Fax: 207-236-6673. p. 980

Hand, Linda Marie, Law Librn, Jefferson County Law Library, Jefferson County Court House, 716 Richard Arrington Jr Blvd N, Ste 530, Birmingham, AL, 35203. Tel: 205-325-5628. Fax: 205-322-5915. p. 8

Hand, Max, Dir, Cullman County Public Library System, 200 Clark St NE, Cullman, AL, 35055. Tel: 256-734-1068. Fax: 256-734-6902. p. 13

Hand, Rita, Cat, Amherst County Public Library, 382 S Main St, Amherst, VA, 24521. Tel: 434-946-9488. Fax: 434-946-9348. p. 2447

Hand, Rose, Ch, Colebrook Public Library, 126 Main St, Colebrook, NH, 03576. Tel: 603-237-4808. p. 1442

Hand, Troy, Librn, Paul D Camp Community College Library, Hobbs Suffolk Campus, 271 Kenyon Rd, Suffolk, VA, 23434. Tel: 757-925-6339. Fax: 757-925-6374. p. 2465

Handerson, Arlene, Mgr, Memphis Public Library, Frayser Branch, 3712 Argonne, Memphis, TN, 38127-4414. Tel: 901-357-4115. Fax: 901-358-0360. p. 2250

Handfield, Amy, Access Serv, Manhattan College, 4513 Manhattan College Pkwy, Riverdale, NY, 10471. Tel: 718-862-7166. Fax: 718-862-8028. p. 1728

Handfield, Jerry, State Archivist, Washington State Office of Secretary of State, 1129 Washington St SE, Olympia, WA, 98504-2283. Tel: 360-586-1492. Fax: 360-664-8814. p. 2523

Handis, Mike, Head, Tech Serv, City University of New York, 365 Fifth Ave, New York, NY, 10016-4309. Tel: 212-817-7075. Fax: 212-817-2982. p. 1673

Handle, Kathy, Dir, Arab Public Library, 325 Second St NW, Arab, AL, 35016-1999. Tel: 256-586-3366. Fax: 256-586-5638. p. 4

Handler, Susan Benard, Coll Develop, Amityville Public Library, Oak & John Sts, Amityville, NY, 11701. Tel: 631-264-0567. Fax: 631-264-2006. p. 1573

Handley, Deanna, Librn, Greenville Hospital System, Roger C Peace Hospital Library, 701 Grove Rd, Greenville, SC, 29605. Tel: 864-455-7176. Fax: 864-455-5696. p. 2197

Handrow, Margaret, Dir, Copperas Cove Public Library, 501 S Main St, Copperas Cove, TX, 76522. Tel: 254-547-3826. Fax: 254-542-7279. p. 2301

Handsor, Susan, Br Head, Chatham-Kent Public Library, Wallaceburg Branch, 209 James St, Wallaceburg, ON, N8A 2N4, CANADA. Tel: 519-627-5292. Fax: 519-627-3039. p. 2799

Handville, Scott, Asst Dir, Gardiner Public Library, 152 Water St, Gardiner, ME, 04345. Tel: 207-582-3312. Fax: 207-582-6104. p. 986

Handwork, Joy, Librn, Chinook Regional Library, Cabri Branch, PO Box 18, Cabri, SK, S0N 0J0, CANADA. Tel: 306-587-2911. p. 2928

Handy, Christopher, Tech Serv, Saint Louis Art Museum, One Fine Arts Dr, Forest Park, Saint Louis, MO, 63110-1380. Tel: 314-655-5456. Fax: 314-721-6172. p. 1357

Handy, Irene, Tech Serv & Pub Serv Librn, Richard Bland College Library, 11301 Johnson Rd, Petersburg, VA, 23805. Tel: 804-862-6226. Fax: 804-862-6125. p. 2484

Handy, Nancy Eichelman, Dir, Libr Serv, LMI Library, 2000 Corporate Ridge, McLean, VA, 22102-7805. Tel: 703-917-7214. Fax: 703-917-7474. p. 2478

Hanel, Mary, Coordr, Local Hist & Genealogy, Santa Clara City Library, 2635 Homestead Rd, Santa Clara, CA, 95051. Tel: 408-615-2909. Fax: 408-247-9657. p. 262

Hanes-Ramos, Melanie, Asst Dir, Main Libr, University of South Carolina at Beaufort Library, One University Blvd, Bluffton, SC, 29909-6085. Tel: 843-208-8023. Fax: 843-208-8296. p. 2182

Haney, Chad, Dir, Libr Develop, Oklahoma State University Libraries, Oklahoma State University, Athletic Ave, Stillwater, OK, 74078-1071, Tel: 405-744-6323. Fax: 405-744-5183. p. 1978

Haney, D Barbara, Circ Supvr, ILL, Bellevue University, 1000 Galvin Rd S, Bellevue, NE, 68005. Tel: 402-557-7314. Fax: 402-557-5427. p. 1393

Haney, David, Tech Serv, Grand Forks Public Library, 2110 Library Circle, Grand Forks, ND, 58201-6324. Tel: 701-772-8116, Ext 16. Fax: 701-772-1379. p. 1842

Haney, Mary, Hub Supvr, Lake Agassiz Regional Library, Detroit Lakes Public Library, 1000 Washington Ave, Detroit Lakes, MN, 56501-3035. Tel: 218-847-2168. Fax: 218-847-2160. p. 1266

Haney, Mary L, Dir, Hennessey Public Library, 525 S Main, Hennessey, OK, 73742. Tel: 405-853-2073, Fax: 405-853-2073. p. 1965

Hanger, Teresa, Per, Freed-Hardeman University, 158 E Main St, Henderson, TN, 38340-2399. Tel: 731-989-6067. Fax: 731-989-6065. p. 2237

Hanif, Ibrahim, Coll Develop, Wofford College, 429 N Church St, Spartanburg, SC, 29303-3663. Tel: 864-597-4300. Fax: 864-597-4329. p. 2206

Hanify, Dana, Adminr, Harvard Library, 1341 Massachusetts Ave, Wadsworth House, Cambridge, MA, 02138. Tel: 617-495-3650. Fax: 617-495-0370. p. 1073

Hanify, Julie, Dept Head, Music, Film & Audio, Carnegie Library of Pittsburgh, 4400 Forbes Ave, Pittsburgh, PA, 15213-4080. Tel: 412-622-3119. Fax: 412-622-6278. p. 2122

Hanisch, Dianne, Youth Serv, Spanish Peaks Library District, 415 Walsen Ave, Walsenburg, CO, 81089. Tel: 719-738-2774. Fax: 719-738-2468. p. 325

Hanke, Diane, Tech Mgr, St Andrews University, 1700 Dogwood Mile, Laurinburg, NC, 28352. Tel: 910-277-5049. Fax: 910-277-5050. p. 1805

Hanke, Erica, Asst Dir, Marion Carnegie Library, 206 S Market St, Marion, IL, 62959-2519. Tel: 618-993-5935. Fax: 618-997-6485. p. 670

Hankel, Marilyn, Assoc Dean, Libr Serv, University of New Orleans, 2000 Lakeshore Dr, New Orleans, LA, 70148. Tel: 504-280-5563. Fax: 504-280-7277. p. 964

Hanken, Tamara, Dir of Tech Serv, University of Nevada, Las Vegas Libraries, 4505 Maryland Pkwy, Box 457001, Las Vegas, NV, 89154-7001. Tel: 702-895-2286. Fax: 702-895-2287. p. 1431

Hanken, Tamera, Mgr, Libr Operations & Tech, Tacoma Community College Library, 6501 S 19th St, Tacoma, WA, 98466-6100. Tel: 253-566-5091. Fax: 253-566-5398. p. 2540

Hankerson, Paulette, ILL, Suwannee River Regional Library, 1848 Ohio Ave S, Dr Martin Luther King Jr Ave S, Live Oak, FL, 32064-4517. Tel: 386-205-1531. Fax: 386-364-6071. p. 461

Hankey, Aleksandra, Res Librn, POS Pilot Plant Corp Library, 118 Veterinary Rd, Saskatoon, SK, S7N 2R4, CANADA. Tel: 306-978-2800, Ext 811, 306-978-2811. Fax: 306-975-3766. p. 2926

Hankins, Anne, Dir, Kuna Community Library, 457 N Locust, Kuna, ID, 83634-1926. Tel: 208-922-1025. Fax: 208-922-1026. p. 577

Hankins, Darrell, Access Serv Librn, United States Military Academy Library, Jefferson Hall Library & Learning Center, 758 Cullum Rd, West Point, NY, 10996. Tel: 845-938-3833. Fax: 845-938-4000. p. 1767

Hankins, Helen, In Charge, Klamath County Library Services District, Bonanza Branch, 31703 Hwy 70, Bonanza, OR, 97623-9751. Tel: 541-545-6944. Fax: 541-545-6944. p. 2002

Hankins, Judith, Librn, New Madrid County Library, Morehouse Service Center, 204 Beech St, Morehouse, MO, 63868. Tel: 573-379-3583. p. 1350

Hankins, Kim, Libr Spec, Santa Fe Community College, 3000 NW 83rd St, Bldg Y-100, Gainesville, FL, 32606. Tel: 352-395-5415. Fax: 352-395-5102. p. 449

Hankins, Ora, Asst Br Mgr, Dallas Public Library, Martin Luther King Jr Branch, 2922 Martin Luther King Jr Blvd, Dallas, TX, 75215-2393. Tel: 214-670-0344. Fax: 214-670-0319. p. 2307

Hankins, Rebecca, Curator, Texas A&M University Libraries, Cushing Memorial Library & Archives, 5000 TAMU, College Station, TX, 77843-5000. Tel: 979-845-1951. Fax: 979-845-1441. p. 2299

Hankins-Wilk, Isabel, Librn, Wapiti Regional Library, Tisdale Community Library, 800 - 101st St, Tisdale, SK, S0E 1T0, CANADA. Tel: 306-873-4767. p. 2922

Hankinson, Julie, Cat, Benjamin Franklin Institute of Technology, Franklin Union Blg., Rm. 114, 41 Berkeley St, Boston, MA, 02116. Tel: 617-423-4630, Ext 123. p. 1055

Hanks, Diane, Acq, Gavilan College Library, 5055 Santa Teresa Blvd, Gilroy, CA, 95020. Tel: 408-848-4812. Fax: 408-846-4927. p. 154

Hanks, Gail, Br Mgr, Cleveland Public Library, Union, 3463 E 93rd St, Cleveland, OH, 44104. Tel: 216-623-7088. Fax: 216-623-7082. p. 1878

Hanks, Gardner, Interim Dir, Marshall Public Library, 113 S Garfield, Pocatello, ID, 83204-5722. Tel: 208-232-1263, Ext 29. Fax: 208-232-9266. p. 582

Hanks, Marianne, Dir, Cravath Memorial Library, 243 N Main, Hay Springs, NE, 69347. Tel: 308-638-4541. p. 1401

Hanks, Mike, Dir of Libr Serv, Huxley Public Library, 3C's Bldg, 2nd Flr, 515 N Main Ave, Huxley, IA, 50124. Tel: 515-597-2552. Fax: 515-597-2554. p. 821

Hanks, Nancy, Head, Tech Serv, Loyola-Notre Dame Library, Inc, 200 Winston Ave, Baltimore, MD, 21212. Tel: 410-617-6800. Fax: 410-617-6895. p. 1015

Hanlan, Laura, User Serv, Worcester Polytechnic Institute, 100 Institute Rd, Worcester, MA, 01609-2280. Tel: 508-831-5410. Fax: 508-831-5829. p. 1145

Hanley, Gretchen, Ref Librn, YA Serv, Lincoln Public Library, 145 Old River Rd, Lincoln, RI, 02865. Tel: 401-333-2422. Fax: 401-333-4154. p. 2168

Hanley, Lynda, Educ Librn, Learning Res Coordr, Manhattanville College Library, 2900 Purchase St, Purchase, NY, 10577. Tel: 914-323-5314. Fax: 914-323-8139. p. 1724

Hanley, Russell, Br Head, Toronto Public Library, Cedarbrae, 545 Markham Rd, Toronto, ON, M1H 2A1, CANADA. Tel: 416-396-8850. Fax: 416-396-8864. p. 2860

Hanley, Susan, Librn, Falmouth Hospital, 100 Ter Heun Dr, Falmouth, MA, 02540. Tel: 508-457-3521. Fax: 508-457-3997. p. 1088

Hanley, Thomas L, Dir, University of Dayton School of Law, 300 College Park, Dayton, OH, 45469-2780. Tel: 937-229-2444. Fax: 937-229-2555. p. 1894

Hanlin, John, Supvr, Pub Serv, Tufts University, 145 Harrison Ave, Boston, MA, 02111-1843. Tel: 617-636-6706. Fax: 617-636-4039. p. 1068

Hanlon, Dan, Assoc Librn, American Psychological Association, 750 First St NE, Rm 3012, Washington, DC, 20002-4242. Tel: 202-336-5645. Fax: 202-336-5643. p. 392

Hann, Klyn, Cat, YA Serv, Newberg Public Library, 503 E Hancock St, Newberg, OR, 97132-2899. Tel: 503-538-7323. Fax: 503-538-9720. p. 2007

Hanna, Betsy, Coordr, Valencia Community College, 850 W Morse Blvd, Winter Park, FL, 32789. Tel: 407-582-6814. Fax: 407-582-6014. p. 505

Hanna, Colleen, Dep Librn, Rhode Island State Law Library, Frank Licht Judicial Complex, 250 Benefit St, Providence, RI, 02903. Tel: 401-222-3275. Fax: 401-222-3865. p. 2175

Hanna, Hildur, Assoc Dir, Michigan State University, 115 Law College Bldg, East Lansing, MI, 48824-1300. Tel: 517-432-6863. Fax: 517-432-6861. p. 1175

Hanna, Joyce, Librn, Washington State Library, Airway Heights Correction Center, 11919 W Sprague Ave, Airway Heights, WA, 99001. Tel: 509-244-6700, Ext 6239. Fax: 509-244-6727. p. 2544

Hanna, Mark, Dir, Amarillo College Library, 2201 S Washington, Amarillo, TX, 79109. Tel: 806-371-5400. Fax: 806-371-5470. p. 2274

Hanna, Philip, Dir, Lindsey Wilson College, 210 Lindsey Wilson St, Columbia, KY, 42728. Tel: 270-384-8102. Fax: 270-384-4188. p. 910

Hanna, Susan, Doc Delivery & Reserve Coordr, Lock Haven University of Pennsylvania, 401 N Fairview Ave, Lock Haven, PA, 17745-2390. Tel: 570-484-2311. Fax: 570-484-2506. p. 2082

Hannaford, Julie, Coll Develop, University of Toronto Libraries, 252 Bloor St W, Toronto, ON, M5S 1V6, CANADA. Tel: 416-978-1702. Fax: 416-926-4737. p. 2867

Hannagan, Charlotte, Librn, Institute of International Finance Library, 1333 H St NW, Ste 800E, Washington, DC, 20005-4770. Tel: 202-857-3600. Fax: 202-775-1430. p. 404

Hannah, Kathleen, Ref Serv Coordr, Menasha Public Library, 440 First St, Menasha, WI, 54952-3191. Tel: 920-967-3692. Fax: 920-967-5159. p. 2614

Hannah, Sonja, Br Mgr, Los Angeles Public Library System, Eagle Rock, 5027 Caspar Ave, Los Angeles, CA, 90041-1901. Tel: 323-258-8078. Fax: 323-478-9530. p. 173

Hannahs, Sandra, Dir, West Fargo Public Library, 109 Third St E, West Fargo, ND, 58078. Tel: 701-433-5460. Fax: 701-433-5479. p. 1849

Hannan, Catalina, Librn, Historic Hudson Valley Library, 639 Bedford Rd, Tarrytown, NY, 10591. Tel: 914-366-6901, 914-366-6902. Fax: 914-631-0089. p. 1754

Hannan, Frankie, Acq, United States Air Force, 55 FSS/FSDL, Bldg 73, 510 Custer Dr, Offutt AFB, NE, 68113-2150. Tel: 402-294-5276, 402-294-7506, DSN 271-7124. Fax: 402-294-7124. p. 1411

Hannan, Heather Groves, Head of Libr, George Mason University Libraries, Mercer Library, Prince William Campus, 10900 University Blvd, Occoquan Bldg, Rm 104, Manassas, VA, 20110-2203. Tel: 703-993-8344. Fax: 703-993-8349. p. 2462

Hannan, Joyce, Dir, Federal Reserve Bank of Boston, 600 Atlantic Ave, Boston, MA, 02210-2204. Tel: 617-973-3397. Fax: 617-973-4221. p. 1061

Hanneman, Josie, Commun Librn, Deschutes Public Library District, La Pine Branch, 16425 First St, La Pine, OR, 97739. Tel: 541-312-1090. Fax: 541-536-0752. p. 1992

Hanninen, Shelley, In Charge, Natural Resources Canada-Canadian Forest Service, 1219 Queen St E, Sault Ste. Marie, ON, P6A 2E5, CANADA. Tel: 705-541-5501. Fax: 705-541-5712. p. 2840

Hannon, Aline, Librn, Wapiti Regional Library, Debden Public Library, 3 204 Second Ave E, Debden, SK, S0J 0S0, CANADA. Tel: 306-724-2240. p. 2921

Hannon, Bronwyn, Acq, Hofstra University, Special Collections/Long Island Studies Institute, 032 Axinn Library, 123 Hofstra University, Hempstead, NY, 11549-1230. Tel: 516-463-6404, 516-463-6411. Fax: 516-463-6442. p. 1635

Hannon, Bronwyn, Asst Dir, Spec Coll, Hofstra University, 123 Hofstra University, Hempstead, NY, 11549. p. 1635

Hannon, Christine, Dep Dir, Smith College Libraries, Northampton, MA, 01063. Tel: 413-585-2911. Fax: 413-585-2904. p. 1113

Hannon, Dianne, Youth Serv, Union County Public Library, 175 W Main St, Lake Butler, FL, 32054-1639. Tel: 386-496-3432. Fax: 386-496-1285. p. 457

Hannon, Doreen, Dir, Salem-South Lyon District Library, 9800 Pontiac Trail, South Lyon, MI, 48178-1307. Tel: 248-437-6431, Ext 206. Fax: 248-437-6593. p. 1227

Hannon, Todd, Ref Librn, Oregon Health & Science University Library, 3181 SW Sam Jackson Park Rd, Portland, OR, 97239-3098. Tel: 503-494-3460. Fax: 503-494-3227. p. 2013

Hannotte, LeeAnn, Librn, Wapiti Regional Library, St Benedict Public Library, Center Street, Village Office, Saint Benedict, SK, S0K 3T0, CANADA. Tel: 306-289-2072. p. 2922

Hanns, Stephen, Pub Serv, Welland Public Library, 50 The Boardwalk, Welland, ON, L3B 6J1, CANADA. Tel: 905-734-6210. Fax: 905-734-8955. p. 2870

Hannula, Betsy, Coll Develop, Curator, Westminster Historical Society Library, 110 Main St, Westminster, MA, 01473. Tel: 978-874-5569. Fax: 978-874-5569. p. 1139

Hannula, Mia, Librn, Department of Veterans Affairs, 1660 S Columbian Way, Seattle, WA, 98108-1597. Tel: 206-277-3255. Fax: 206-764-2816. p. 2527

Hannum, Rachel, Prog & Communications Coordr, Cecil County Public Library, 301 Newark Ave, Elkton, MD, 21921-5441. Tel: 410-996-5600. Fax: 410-996-5604. p. 1027

Hanrahan, Clark, In Charge, Evaluation Associates Inc Library, 1350 Telegraph Rd, West Chester, PA, 19380. Tel: 610-692-7686. Fax: 610-692-7687. p. 2153

Hans, Margaret, Librn, Lenawee County Library, Britton Branch, 120 College Ave, Britton, MI, 49229-9705. Tel: 517-451-2860. Fax: 517-451-2860. p. 1147

Hans, Ruth, Br Mgr, Indianapolis-Marion County Public Library, Warren, 9701 E 21st St, Indianapolis, IN, 46229-1707. Tel: 317-275-4550. p. 754

Hanschu, Beth, Cat, Emporia State University, 1200 Commercial St, Box 4051, Emporia, KS, 66801. Tel: 620-341-5055. Fax: 620-341-5997. p. 866

Hanscom, Diane, Cat, Husson University, One College Circle, Bangor, ME, 04401-2999. Tel: 207-941-7187, 207-941-7188. Fax: 207-941-7989. p. 976

Hanscomb, Patricia, ILL Librn, Pease Public Library, One Russell St, Plymouth, NH, 03264-1414. Tel: 603-536-2616. Fax: 603-536-2369. p. 1462

Hanse, Anthoula, ILL, Jamestown College, 6070 College Lane, Jamestown, ND, 58405-0001. Tel: 701-252-3467. Fax: 701-253-4446. p. 1844

Hanselman, David, Dir, US Army Transportation Museum Library, Besson Hall, 300 Washington Blvd, Fort Eustis, VA, 23604-5260. Tel: 757-878-1115. Fax: 757-878-5656. p. 2465

Hanselman, Kara, Asst Librn, North Mankato Taylor Library, 1001 Belgrade Ave, North Mankato, MN, 56003. Tel: 507-345-5120. Fax: 507-345-1861. p. 1268

Hanselmann, Rayla, Info Serv Librn, Trine University, 720 Park Ave, Angola, IN, 46703. Tel: 260-665-4179. Fax: 260-665-4283. p. 724

Hansen, Beth, Dir, Info Res, Connecticut College, 270 Mohegan Ave, New London, CT, 06320-4196. Tel: 860-439-2681. Fax: 860-439-2871. p. 359

Hansen, Bruce N, Dir, Colonial Heights Public Library, 1000 Yacht Basin Dr, Colonial Heights, VA, 23834. Tel: 804-520-9384. Fax: 804-524-8740. p. 2457

Hansen, Carol, Coll Develop, Ref Serv, Bethel University Library, 3900 Bethel Dr, Saint Paul, MN, 55112. Tel: 651-638-6222. Fax: 651-638-6001. p. 1277

Hansen, Carol, Instrul Serv Librn, Weber State University, 2901 University Circle, Ogden, UT, 84408-2901. Tel: 801-626-8709. Fax: 801-626-7045. p. 2409

Hansen, Carol, Dir of Libr, Virginia Commonwealth University Libraries, 901 Park Ave, Richmond, VA, 23284-2033. Tel: 804-828-1110. Fax: 804-828-0151. p. 2492

Hansen, Charlie, Dir, Granville Public Library, 217 E Broadway, Granville, OH, 43023-1398. Tel: 740-587-0196. Fax: 740-587-0197. p. 1902

Hansen, Cheryl, Dir, Charlton Public Library, 40 Main St, Charlton, MA, 01507. Tel: 508-248-0452. Fax: 508-248-0456. p. 1079

Hansen, Cheryl A, Librn, Engineering Systems Inc Library, 4215 Campus Dr, Aurora, IL, 60504-7900. Tel: 630-851-4566, Ext 238. Fax: 630-851-4870. p. 591

Hansen, Debra, Ch, Huntington Memorial Library, 62 Chestnut, Oneonta, NY, 13820-2498. Tel: 607-432-1980. p. 1711

Hansen, Eileen, Dir, Mercy College of Health Sciences Library, 928 Sixth Ave, Des Moines, IA, 50309-1239. Tel: 515-643-6613. Fax: 515-643-6695. p. 810

Hansen, Elizabeth, Librn, Lilly Endowment Library, 2801 N Meridian St, Indianapolis, IN, 46208. Tel: 317-916-7316. Fax: 317-926-4431. p. 755

Hansen, Glenn, Librn, Douglas County Library System, Oakland Branch, 637 NE Locust St, Oakland, OR, 97462. Tel: 541-459-9784. Fax: 541-459-9784. p. 2016

Hansen, Harlene, ILL, Coe College, 1220 First Ave NE, Cedar Rapids, IA, 52402-5092. Tel: 319-399-8016. Fax: 319-399-8019. p. 800

Hansen, Jean, Head, Adult Serv, Waterford Township Public Library, 5168 Civic Center Dr, Waterford, MI, 48329. Tel: 248-674-4831. Fax: 248-674-1910. p. 1235

Hansen, Jill, Adult Serv, Ref Serv, Fremont Area District Library, 104 E Main, Fremont, MI, 49412. Tel: 231-928-0253. Fax: 231-924-2355. p. 1182

Hansen, Jon, Dir, Digital Commons/Copyright Mgt, Kennesaw State University, 1000 Chastain Rd, Kennesaw, GA, 30144. Tel: 770-423-6248. Fax: 770-423-6185. p. 537

Hansen, Joy, Librn, Middlesex Community College, 100 Training Hill Rd, Middletown, CT, 06457-4889. Tel: 860-343-5832. Fax: 860-343-5874. p. 351

Hansen, Julie, Librn, Wilcox Public Library, 121 S Main St, Wilcox, NE, 68982. Tel: 308-478-5554. p. 1423

Hansen, Julie E, Librn, William Penn University, 201 Trueblood Ave, Oskaloosa, IA, 52577. Tel: 641-673-1197. Fax: 641-673-1098. p. 837

Hansen, Kathy, Circ, Brigham Young University, Harold B Lee Library, 2060 HBLL, Provo, UT, 84602. Tel: 801-422-2927. Fax: 801-422-0466. p. 2411

Hansen, Kay, Youth Serv Librn, Waupun Public Library, 123 S Forest St, Waupun, WI, 53963. Tel: 920-324-7925. p. 2646

Hansen, Kristi, Head, Youth Serv, Salina Public Library, 301 W Elm St, Salina, KS, 67401. Tel: 785-825-4624. Fax: 785-823-0706. p. 893

Hansen, Laura, Ref Librn, University of Saint Thomas, Charles J Keffer Library, 1000 LaSalle Ave, MOH 206, Minneapolis, MN, 55403. Tel: 651-962-4646. Fax: 651-962-4648. p. 1282

Hansen, Laurie, Libr Dir, Mt Pleasant Public Library, 24 E Main St, Mount Pleasant, UT, 84647-1429. Tel: 435-462-3240. Fax: 435-462-9115. p. 2408

Hansen, Linda, Electronic Serv Librn, University of New Brunswick, Saint John Campus, 100 Tucker Park Rd, Saint John, NB, E2L 4L5, CANADA. Tel: 506-648-5710. Fax: 506-648-5701. p. 2767

Hansen, Lindsey, Dir, Centerville Community Library, 421 Florida, Centerville, SD, 57014. Tel: 605-563-2540. Fax: 605-563-2615. p. 2211

Hansen, Marianne, Actg Libr Dir, Salmo Public Library, 106 Fourth St, Salmo, BC, V0G 1Z0, CANADA. Tel: 250-357-2312. Fax: 250-357-2312. p. 2737

Hansen, Melissa, Dir, Willamina Public Library, 385 NE C St, Willamina, OR, 97396. Tel: 503-876-6182. Fax: 503-876-1121. p. 2023

Hansen, Morgan, Dir, Van Horn Public Library, 115 SE Third St, Pine Island, MN, 55963-6783. Tel: 507-356-8558. Fax: 507-356-8599. p. 1270

Hansen, Roland, Head, Access Serv, Columbia College Chicago Library, 624 S Michigan Ave, Chicago, IL, 60605-1996. Tel: 312-369-7431. Fax: 312-344-8062. p. 611

Hansen, Sally L, Head, Pub Serv, Todd Wehr Library, St Norbert College, 301 Third St, De Pere, WI, 54115. Tel: 920-403-3453. Fax: 920-403-4064, p. 2587

Hansen, Sandy, Librn, Tripp County Library-Grossenburg Memorial, 442 S Monroe St, Winner, SD, 57580. Tel: 605-842-0330. p. 2222

Hansen, Sara, Asst Dir, Operations, Ocean County Library, 101 Washington St, Toms River, NJ, 08753. Tel: 732-349-6200. p. 1534

Hansen, Sarah, Dir, Old Bridge Public Library, One Old Bridge Plaza, Old Bridge, NJ, 08857-2498. Tel: 732-721-5600, Ext 5042. Fax: 732-679-0556. p. 1516

Hansen, Susan, Librn, Shacknove - Saint John's Medical Staff Library, 2200 Santa Monica Blvd, Santa Monica, CA, 90404. Tel: 310-582-7141. Fax: 310-582-7353. p. 266

Hansen, Susan, Br Mgr, West Hartford Public Library, Bishop's Corner, 15 Starkel Rd, West Hartford, CT, 06117. Tel: 860-561-8210. p. 376

Hansen, Tom, Asst Dir, Ref Serv, La Marque Public Library, 1011 Bayou Rd, La Marque, TX, 77568-4195. Tel: 409-938-9270. Fax: 409-938-9277. p. 2352

Hansen-Peterson, Jenny, Circ Mgr, Cherry Valley Public Library District, 755 E State St, Cherry Valley, IL, 61016-9699. Tel: 815-332-5161, Ext 25. Fax: 815-332-2441. p. 604

Hansen-Smith, Karen, Commun Libr Mgr, Contra Costa County Library, Clayton Library, 6125 Clayton Rd, Clayton, CA, 94517. Tel: 925-673-0659. Fax: 925-673-0359. p. 209

Hansen-Smith, Karen, Sr Commun Libr Mgr, Contra Costa County Library, Martinez Library, 740 Court St, Martinez, CA, 94553-1218. Tel: 925-646-9900. p. 209

Hanshew, Jody, Electronic Res, Govt Doc Librn, Emory & Henry College, 30480 Armbrister Dr, Emory, VA, 24327. Tel: 276-944-6213. Fax: 276-944-4592. p. 2460

Hansmeier, Susan, Circ Librn, Keene Public Library, 60 Winter St, Keene, NH, 03431-3360. Tel: 603-352-0157. Fax: 866-743-0446. p. 1452

Hanson, Ashley, Res Support & Instruction Librn, Connecticut College, 270 Mohegan Ave, New London, CT, 06320-4196. Tel: 860-439-2653. Fax: 860-439-2871. p. 359

Hanson, Cecelia, Dir, Roy City Library, 122 Third St E, Roy, WA, 98580. Tel: 253-843-2331. Fax: 253-843-0279. p. 2527

Hanson, Charles, Dr, Dir, Kettering University Library, 1700 W University Ave, Flint, MI, 48504-4898. Tel: 810-762-7814. Fax: 810-762-9744. p. 1180

Hanson, Craig, Mgr, Harvard Musical Association Library, 57A Chestnut St, Boston, MA, 02108. Tel: 617-523-2897. Fax: 617-523-2897. p. 1062

Hanson, Curt, Head, Spec Coll, University of North Dakota, 3051 University Ave, Stop 9000, Grand Forks, ND, 58202-9000. Tel: 701-777-4626. Fax: 701-777-3319. p. 1843

Hanson, Daniel J, Librn, Davis Polk & Wardwell Library, 450 Lexington Ave, New York, NY, 10017. Tel: 212-450-4266. Fax: 212-450-5522. p. 1677

Hanson, Dave, Dir, Linwood Community Library, 19649 Linwood Rd, Linwood, KS, 66052. Tel: 913-723-3686. Fax: 913-723-3686. p. 880

Hanson, David B, Electronic Res, Drake University, Drake Law Library, Opperman Hall, 2615 Carpenter Ave, Des Moines, IA, 50311-4505. Tel: 515-271-2077. Fax: 515-271-2530. p. 809

Hanson, Ellen, Librn, Reed McClure Law Firm Library, 601 Union St, Ste 1500, Seattle, WA, 98101. Tel: 206-292-4900. Fax: 206-223-0152. p. 2528

Hanson, Fred, Assoc Librn, Davis Wright Tremaine LLP, 1201 Third Ave, Ste 2200, Seattle, WA, 98101-3045. Tel: 206-628-7606. Fax: 206-628-7699. p. 2527

Hanson, Georgia, Dir, Aspen Historical Society Library, 620 W Bleeker St, Aspen, CO, 81611. Tel: 970-925-3721, Ext 101. Fax: 970-925-5347. p. 288

Hanson, Grete, Info Spec, Thrivent Financial for Lutherans, 625 Fourth Ave S, Minneapolis, MN, 55415. Tel: 612-340-7269. Fax: 612-340-5898. p. 1261

Hanson, Jackie, Syst Librn, Northern State University, 1200 S Jay St, Aberdeen, SD, 57401-7198. Tel: 605-626-2645. Fax: 605-626-2473. p. 2209

Hanson, Jan, Ch, YA Serv, Longview Public Library, 1600 Louisiana St, Longview, WA, 98632-2993. Tel: 360-442-5323. Fax: 360-442-5954. p. 2520

Hanson, Jennifer, Ch, Jackson-Madison County Library, 433 E Lafayette St, Jackson, TN, 38301-6386. Tel: 731-425-8600. Fax: 731-425-8609. p. 2238

Hanson, Joanne, In Charge, Chatham Public Library, Canaan Branch, 1647 County Rte 5, Canaan, NY, 12029-3017. Tel: 518-781-3392. p. 1605

Hanson, John, Dir, USS Liberty Memorial Public Library, 1620 11th Ave, Grafton, WI, 53024-2404. Tel: 262-375-5315. Fax: 262-375-5317. p. 2594

Hanson, Julia Bowers, Educ Spec, Charlotte Mecklenburg Library, 310 N Tryon St, Charlotte, NC, 28202-2176. Tel: 704-416-0101. Fax: 704-416-0130. p. 1781

Hanson, Kasey, User Support Serv Coordr, University of North Dakota, 215 Centennial Dr, Grand Forks, ND, 58202. Tel: 701-777-2204. Fax: 701-777-2217. p. 1843

Hanson, Katherine, Ref Librn, Bartlesville Public Library, 600 S Johnstone, Bartlesville, OK, 74003. Tel: 918-338-4161. Fax: 918-337-5338. p. 1957

Hanson, Kathlene, Electronic Res Coordr, California State University-Monterey Bay, 100 Campus Ctr, Seaside, CA, 93955-8001. Tel: 831-582-3883. Fax: 831-582-3875. p. 268

Hanson, Kathryn A, Dir, Graham Public Library, 1215 Main St, Union Grove, WI, 53182-1303. Tel: 262-878-2910. Fax: 262-878-0213. p. 2643

Hanson, Kristan, Visual Res Mgr, School of the Art Institute of Chicago, 37 S Wabash Ave, Chicago, IL, 60603-3103. Tel: 312-899-5097. Fax: 312-899-1851. p. 624

Hanson, Loretta, Dir, Williamsburg Public Library, 214 W State St, Williamsburg, IA, 52361. Tel: 319-668-1195. Fax: 319-668-9621. p. 853

Hanson, Mary, Dir, Marengo-Union Library District, 200 S State St, Marengo, IL, 60152. Tel: 815-568-8236. Fax: 815-568-5209. p. 670

Hanson, Mary A, Librn, Saint Mary's Health Sciences Library, 200 Jefferson SE, Grand Rapids, MI, 49503. Tel: 616-752-6243. Fax: 616-752-6419. p. 1186

Hanson, Michael, Acq, Ser, Lafayette College, 710 Sullivan Rd, Easton, PA, 18042-1797. Tel: 610-330-5636. Fax: 610-252-0370. p. 2052

Hanson, Norma Sue, Spec Coll Librn, Case Western Reserve University, 11055 Euclid Ave, Cleveland, OH, 44106. Tel: 216-368-0189. Fax: 216-368-6950. p. 1876

Hanson, Robin, Head, Circ, Head, ILL, University of Alaska Anchorage, Consortium Library, 3211 Providence Dr, Anchorage, AK, 99508-8176. Tel: 907-786-1871. Fax: 907-786-1834. p. 45

Hanson, Ryan, Asst Dir, Newton Free Library, 330 Homer St, Newton Centre, MA, 02459-1429. Tel: 617-796-1360. Fax: 617-965-8457. p. 1110

Hanson, Sally, Circ, Ch, Bennington Public Library, 15505 Warehouse St, Bennington, NE, 68007. Tel: 402-238-2201. Fax: 402-238-2218. p. 1394

Hanson, Steve, Libr & Archive Prof 2, Washington State Library, Department of Labor & Industries, 7273 Linderson Way SW, Tumwater, WA, 98501. Tel: 360-902-5498. Fax: 360-902-6335. p. 2544

Hanson, Susan, Tech Serv Librn, Westland Public Library, 6123 Central City Pkwy, Westland, MI, 48185. Tel: 734-326-6123. Fax: 734-595-4612. p. 1236

Hanson, Susanah, Libr Dir, Trinity Episcopal School for Ministry Library, 311 11th St, Ambridge, PA, 15003. Tel: 724-266-3838. Fax: 724-266-4617. p. 2029

Hanson, Teresa, Librn, Department of Veterans Affairs North Texas Health Care System, 4500 S Lancaster Rd, Dallas, TX, 75216. Tel: 214-857-2169. p. 2307

Hanson, Theresa, Tech Spec, Anne Carlsen Learning Center, 701 Third St NW, Jamestown, ND, 58401-2971. Tel: 701-952-5169. Fax: 701-952-5154. p. 1844

Hanson-Wilcox, MaryAnne, Dir, Grand County Library District, 225 E Jasper Ave, Granby, CO, 80446. Tel: 970-887-2149. Fax: 970-887-3851. p. 310

Hantla, Danette, Mgr, Salt Lake County Library Services, Draper Branch, 1136 E Pioneer Rd, Draper, UT, 84020-9628. Tel: 801-944-7558. Fax: 801-619-9861. p. 2414

Hantz, Joan, Dir, Chief Dull Knife College, One College Dr, Lame Deer, MT, 59043. Tel: 406-477-8293. Fax: 406-477-6575. p. 1384

Hanus, Karen L, Asst Dir, Medical College of Wisconsin Libraries, Health Research Ctr, 3rd Flr, 8701 Watertown Plank Rd, Milwaukee, WI, 53226-0509. Tel: 414-955-8329. Fax: 414-955-6532. p. 2619

Hanus, Norine, Coll Develop, University of Prince Edward Island, 550 University Ave, Charlottetown, PE, C1A 4P3, CANADA. Tel: 902-566-0343. Fax: 902-628-4305. p. 2876

Hanus, Trudy, Sr Librn, Hennepin County Library, Plymouth, 15700 36th Ave N, Plymouth, MN, 55446. Tel: 612-543-5828. Fax: 612-543-5827. p. 1264

Hanusek, Denise, Dr, Cat, Emory University Libraries, Pitts Theology Library, Candler School of Theology, 505 S Kilgo Circle NE, Atlanta, GA, 30322-2810. Tel: 404-727-4166. Fax: 404-727-1219. p. 514

Hanusovsky, Vicki, ILL, Pequot Library, 720 Pequot Ave, Southport, CT, 06890-1496. Tel: 203-259-0346, Ext 19. Fax: 203-259-5602. p. 368

Hanway, Wayne, Exec Dir, Southeastern Public Library System of Oklahoma, 401 N Second St, McAlester, OK, 74501. Tel: 918-426-0456. Fax: 918-426-0543. p. 1968

Hanzazi, Mounia, Br Head, Toronto Public Library, Flemingdon Park, 29 St Dennis Dr, Toronto, ON, M3C 3J3, CANADA. Tel: 416-395-5820. Fax: 416-395-5438. p. 2861

Happ, Dianne, Ref Librn, Bradley University, 1501 W Bradley Ave, Peoria, IL, 61625. Tel: 309-677-2850. Fax: 309-677-2558. p. 690

Happ, Stacia, Librn, Waubonsee Community College, State Rte 47 at Waubonsee Dr, Sugar Grove, IL, 60554. Tel: 630-466-2400. Fax: 630-466-7799. p. 708

Haprian, James, Info Tech Dir, Cuyahoga County Public Library, 2111 Snow Rd, Parma, OH, 44134-2728. Tel: 216-398-1800. Fax: 216-398-1748. p. 1927

Haprian, Jim, Tech Serv, Medina County District Library, 210 S Broadway, Medina, OH, 44256. Tel: 330-722-6235, Ext 2950. Fax: 330-725-2053. p. 1916

Harada, Glenda, Head, Admin Serv, California State University, Fresno, Henry Madden Library, 5200 N Barton Ave, Mail Stop ML-34, Fresno, CA, 93740-8014. Tel: 559-278-2142. Fax: 559-278-6952. p. 150

Harada, Jason, Coordr, Heald College, 1500 Kapiolani Blvd, Honolulu, HI, 96814. Tel: 808-628-5525. Fax: 808-955-6964. p. 564

Harada, Violet, Prof, University of Hawaii, 2550 The Mall, Honolulu, HI, 96822. Tel: 808-956-7321. Fax: 808-956-5835. p. 2964

Harader, Janet, Head, Ref, Tulare County Library, 200 W Oak Ave, Visalia, CA, 93291-4993. Tel: 559-733-6954, Ext 229. Fax: 559-730-2524. p. 280

Harader, Janet, Librn IV, Tulare County Library, Visalia Headquarters Branch, 200 W Oak Ave, Visalia, CA, 93291. Tel: 559-713-2705. Fax: 559-737-4586. p. 281

Haralson, Michele, Dir, Samford University Library, Curriculum Materials Center, Beeson Education Bldg, 800 Lakeshore Dr, Birmingham, AL, 35229. Tel: 205-726-2558. Fax: 205-726-2068. p. 9

Harant, Andrew, Br Mgr, Cleveland Public Library, West Park, 3805 W 157th St, Cleveland, OH, 44111. Tel: 216-623-7102. Fax: 216-623-7104. p. 1878

Haraughty, Melissa, Mgr, United States Air Force, 27 SVS/SVMG, 107 Trident Ave, Bldg 75, Cannon AFB, NM, 88103-5211. Tel: 505-784-2786. Fax: 505-784-6929. p. 1552

Harbec, Amélie, Chef de Section, Bibliothèques de Montrèal, Mercier, 8105, rue Hochelaga, Montreal, QC, H1L 2K9, CANADA. Tel: 514-872-8737. Fax: 514-872-0524. p. 2890

Harber, Annette, Ser Librn, Trevecca Nazarene University, 73 Lester Ave, Nashville, TN, 37210-4227. Tel: 615-248-1338. Fax: 615-248-1452. p. 2259

Harber, Joy, Dir, Roann Paw Paw Township Public Library, 240 S Chippewa Rd, Roann, IN, 46974. Tel: 765-833-5231. Fax: 765-833-5231. p. 775

Harbin, Karen, Acq, Supvr, High Point University, 833 Montlieu Ave, High Point, NC, 27262-4221. Tel: 336-841-9100. Fax: 336-841-5123. p. 1802

Harbison, Andrew, Dir, Libr Serv, Argosy University, 2601-A Elliott Ave, Seattle, WA, 98121. Tel: 206-393-3576. Fax: 206-393-3579. p. 2527

Harbison, Andrew, Dir, Art Institute of Seattle Library, North Campus, 5th Flr, 2323 Elliott Ave, Seattle, WA, 98121. Tel: 206-239-2359. Fax: 206-441-3475. p. 2527

Harbison, John, Dir, Libr & Info Mgt, Covington & Burling LLP, 1201 Pennsylvania Ave NW, 11th Flr, Washington, DC, 20004-2401. Tel: 202-662-6000. Fax: 202-778-6658. p. 397

Harbison, Vanessa, Libr Assoc, Norris Public Library, 132 N Main, Rutherfordton, NC, 28139. Tel: 828-287-4981. Fax: 828-287-0660. p. 1821

Harbour, Beverly, Mgr, Cabell County Public Library, Salt Rock Branch, Salt Rock Community School, RFS No 1, Madison Creek Rd, Salt Rock, WV, 25559. Tel: 304-733-2186. Fax: 304-733-2186. p. 2561

Harcourt, Kate, Dir, Columbia University, Original & Special Materials Cataloging, 102 Butler Library, 535 W 114th St, New York, NY, 10027. Tel: 212-854-2714. Fax: 212-854-5167. p. 1675

Hardacre, Amber, Dir, Kensington Community-School Library, 203 S Jackson, Kensington, KS, 66951. Tel: 785-476-2219. Fax: 785-476-2215. p. 876

Hardacre, Mari, YA Serv, Allen County Public Library, 900 Library Plaza, Fort Wayne, IN, 46802. Tel: 260-421-1256. Fax: 260-421-1386. p. 740

Hardage, Scott, Sci/Tech Prog, Giles County Public Library, 122 S Second St, Pulaski, TN, 38478-3285. Tel: 931-363-2720. Fax: 931-424-7032. p. 2264

Hardee, Davis, Circ, Libr Tech, Grays Harbor College, 1620 Edward P Smith Dr, Aberdeen, WA, 98520-7599. Tel: 360-538-4050. Fax: 360-538-4294. p. 2507

Hardee, Patsy, Mgr, Leath Thomas Memorial Library, Hamlet Public, 302 Main St, Hamlet, NC, 28345-3304. Tel: 910-582-3477. Fax: 910-582-3478. p. 1820

Harden, Fred, Head, Ref, Daytona Beach College Library, 1200 W International Speedway Blvd, Daytona Beach, FL, 32114. Tel: 386-506-3608. Fax: 386-506-3008. p. 435

Harden, Holly, Librn, Johns Hopkins University Libraries, Carol J Gray Nursing Information Resource Center, 525 N Wolfe St, Rm 313, Baltimore, MD, 21202. Tel: 410-955-7559. p. 1014

Harden, Jennifer, Br Mgr, Prince William Public Library System, Dale City Neighborhood, 4249 Dale Blvd, Woodbridge, VA, 22193-2414. Tel: 703-792-5670. Fax: 703-670-6152. p. 2486

Harden, Kathy, Electronic Serv, Ref & Instrul Serv, Instr Coordr, University of Mary Hardin-Baylor, 900 College St, UMHB Sta, Box 8016, Belton, TX, 76513-2599. Tel: 254-295-4161. Fax: 254-295-4642. p. 2289

Harden, Kevin, Distance Educ, Electronic Serv, Ref Serv, Averett University Library, 344 W Main St, Danville, VA, 24541-2849. Tel: 434-791-5690. Fax: 434-791-5637. p. 2459

Harden, Lillian, Asst Librn, Albemarle Regional Library, Lawrence Memorial Public Library, 204 E Dundee St, Windsor, NC, 27983. Tel: 252-794-2244. Fax: 252-794-1546. p. 1835

Harden, Lynn A, Exec Dir, Brown County Public Library, 613 S High St, Mount Orab, OH, 45154. Tel: 937-444-0181. Fax: 937-444-6502. p. 1919

Harden, Maureen, Admin Dir, University of California, San Diego, 9500 Gilman Dr, Mail Code 0175G, La Jolla, CA, 92093-0175. Tel: 858-534-1277. Fax: 858-534-4970. p. 162

Harden, Robert, Dir, Sumter County Library, 111 N Harvin St, Sumter, SC, 29150. Tel: 803-773-7273. Fax: 803-773-4875. p. 2206

Hardenbergh, Melissa, Librn, NACCO Materials Handling Group, Inc, 4000 NE Blue Lake Rd, Fairview, OR, 97025. Tel: 503-721-6234. Fax: 503-721-1364. p. 1998

Hardenbrook, Joe, Instruction & Ref Librn, University of Wisconsin-Green Bay, 2420 Nicolet Dr, Green Bay, WI, 54311-7001. Tel: 920-465-2666. Fax: 920-465-2136. p. 2596

Harder, Adreena, Libr Mgr, Standard Municipal Library, PO Box 305, Standard, AB, T0J 3G0, CANADA. Tel: 403-644-3995. p. 2718

Harder, Kenette, Acq & Coll Develop Librn, Southwest Baptist University Libraries, 1600 University Ave, Bolivar, MO, 65613. Tel: 417-328-1625. Fax: 417-328-1652. p. 1320

Harder, Marilyn, Asst Librn, Southeast Regional Library, Gainsborough Branch, 401 Railway Ave, Gainsborough, SK, S0C 0Z0, CANADA. Tel: 306-685-2229. p. 2929

Harder, Marsha, Librn, Central Presbyterian Church Library, 125 N Seventh St, Terre Haute, IN, 47807-3195. Tel: 812-232-5049. p. 781

Harder, Michelle, Asst Librn, Harper Public Library, 1002 Oak St, Harper, KS, 67058-1233. Tel: 620-896-2959. Fax: 620-896-7832. p. 870

Harder, Trudy, Cent Libr Serv Mgr, Saskatoon Public Library, 311-23rd St E, Saskatoon, SK, S7K 0J6, CANADA. Tel: 306-975-7567. Fax: 306-975-7542. p. 2926

Harder-Gissing, Laureen, Librn & Archivist, Conrad Grebel University College Library, 140 Westmount Rd N, Waterloo, ON, N2L 3G6, CANADA. Tel: 519-885-0220, Ext 24238. Fax: 519-885-0014. p. 2869

Harders, Faith, Librn, University of Kentucky Libraries, Design Library, 200 Pence Hall, Lexington, KY, 40506-0041. Tel: 859-257-1533. Fax: 859-257-4305. p. 922

Hardesty, Katherine, Pub Relations Coordr, Cherry Hill Public Library, 1100 Kings Hwy N, Cherry Hill, NJ, 08034-1911. Tel: 856-903-1207. Fax: 856-667-9503. p. 1478

Hardgrave, Michelle, Librn, Fabian & Clendenin, 215 S State St, Ste 1200, Salt Lake City, UT, 84111-2323. Tel: 801-531-8900. Fax: 801-596-2814. p. 2412

Hardgrove, David, Head, Tech Serv, Saint Peter's College, 99 Glenwood Ave, Jersey City, NJ, 07306. Tel: 201-761-6453. Fax: 201-432-4117. p. 1493

Hardie, Margie, Circ, Clark Memorial Library, 39 N Ninth St, Clarkdale, AZ, 86324. Tel: 928-639-2480. Fax: 928-639-2489. p. 60

Hardiman, Elisia, Librn, Michigan Department of Corrections, Ernest C Brooks Correctional Facility Library, 2500 S Sheridan Rd, Muskegon, MI, 49444. Tel: 231-773-9200, Ext 1916. p. 1161

Hardiman, Mary Ellen, Dir, North Providence Union Free Library, 1810 Mineral Spring Ave, North Providence, RI, 02904. Tel: 401-353-5600. p. 2170

Hardiman, Thomas, Dir, Portsmouth Athenaeum, Six-Seven Market Sq, Portsmouth, NH, 03821. Tel: 603-431-2538. Fax: 603-431-7180. p. 1463

Hardin, Jennifer, Asst Librn, Cincinnati Art Museum, 953 Eden Park Dr, Cincinnati, OH, 45202-1557. Tel: 513-639-2978. Fax: 513-721-0129. p. 1868

Hardin, Lisa, Adminr, Tech Serv, Genealogy Serv, Purchasing, Meade County Public Library, 400 Library Pl, Brandenburg, KY, 40108-1045. Tel: 270-422-2094. Fax: 270-422-3133. p. 908

Hardin, Lowana, Circ, Sequoyah Regional Library System, 116 Brown Industrial Pkwy, Canton, GA, 30114-2899. Tel: 770-479-3090, Ext 221. Fax: 770-479-3069. p. 523

Hardin, Patricia A, Librn, Norris Public Library, 132 N Main, Rutherfordton, NC, 28139. Tel: 828-287-4981. Fax: 828-287-0660. p. 1821

Hardin, Steve, Ref/Instruction Librn, Indiana State University, 510 North 6 1/2 St, Terre Haute, IN, 47809. Tel: 812-237-7685. Fax: 812-237-3376. p. 781

Hardin, Sue, Asst Dir, Bus Operations & Human Res, Hayner Public Library District, 326 Belle St, Alton, IL, 62002. Tel: 618-462-0677. Fax: 618-462-0665. p. 588

Hardin, Vickie, Outreach Coordr, Bossier Parish Central Library, 2206 Beckett St, Bossier City, LA, 71111. Tel: 318-746-1693. Fax: 318-746-7768. p. 945

Hardina-Wilhelm, Nicole, Adult Serv, Neenah Public Library, 240 E Wisconsin Ave, Neenah, WI, 54956-3010. Tel: 920-886-6312. Fax: 920-886-6324. p. 2624

Harding, Becky, Media Spec, New Hampshire State Prison Library, 281 N State St, Concord, NH, 03301. Tel: 603-271-1929. Fax: 603-271-0401. p. 1443

Harding, Becky, Librn, New Hampshire Department of Corrections, 317 Mast Rd, Goffstown, NH, 03045. Tel: 603-668-6137. p. 1448

Harding, Elaine, Head, Tech Serv, Stow-Munroe Falls Public Library, 3512 Darrow Rd, Stow, OH, 44224. Tel: 330-688-3295. p. 1937

Harding, Joyce, Libr Tech, Shippensburg University, 1871 Old Main Dr, Shippensburg, PA, 17257-2299. Tel: 717-477-1123, Ext 3289. Fax: 717-477-1389. p. 2140

Harding, Judith, Coordr, Mount Ida College, National Center for Death Education Library, 777 Dedham St, Newton, MA, 02459. Tel: 617-928-4552. Fax: 617-928-4713. p. 1110

Harding, Judy, Assoc Dir, Libr Serv, Mount Ida College, Wadsworth Library, 777 Dedham St, Newton, MA, 02459. Tel: 617-928-4552. Fax: 617-928-4038. p. 1110

Harding, Mable, Dir, Florida Today Newspaper Library, One Gannett Plaza, Melbourne, FL, 32940. Tel: 321-242-3500. Fax: 321-242-6620. p. 463

Harding, Patricia, Dir, Burlingame Public Library, 480 Primrose Rd, Burlingame, CA, 94010-4083. Tel: 650-558-7401. Fax: 650-342-1948. p. 130

Harding, Paulette, Doc, Poplar Creek Public Library District, 1405 S Park Ave, Streamwood, IL, 60107-2997. Tel: 630-837-6800. Fax: 630-837-6823. p. 708

Harding, Ronni Renee, Dir, Bartley Public Library, 411 Commercial St, Bartley, NE, 69020. Tel: 308-692-3313. p. 1392

Harding, Susan, Supvr, Tech Serv, Mesquite Public Library, 300 W Grubb Dr, Mesquite, TX, 75149. Tel: 972-216-6220. Fax: 972-216-6740. p. 2362

Harding, Torrie, Tech Serv, Payson Public Library, 328 N McLane Rd, Payson, AZ, 85541. Tel: 928-474-9260. Fax: 928-474-2679. p. 70

Harding, Wendy, In Charge, Bunnvale Public Library, Seven Bunnvale Rd, Rte 513, Califon, NJ, 07830. Tel: 908-638-8884. p. 1476

Hardman, Joyce, In Charge, Klamath County Library Services District, Sprague River Branch, Sprague River Hwy, Sprague River, OR, 97639-8602. Tel: 541-533-2769. p. 2002

Hardnock, Irene, Librn, Ashland Public Library, 1229 Center St, Ashland, PA, 17921-1207. Tel: 570-875-3175. Fax: 570-875-2699. p. 2030

Hardrick, Sanema, Res Librn, Finnegan, Henderson, Farabow, Garrett & Dunner, 901 New York Ave NW, Washington, DC, 20001-4413. Tel: 202-216-5040. Fax: 202-408-4400. p. 400

Hardtke, Kristy, Tech Serv, Central Wyoming College Library, 2660 Peck Ave, Riverton, WY, 82501. Tel: 307-855-2109. Fax: 307-855-2094. p. 2659

Hardy, Beatriz B, Dr, Dean of Libr, Instrul Res, Salisbury University, 1101 Camden Ave, Salisbury, MD, 21801-6863. Tel: 410-543-6130. Fax: 410-543-6203. p. 1040

Hardy, Beatriz B, Dr, Dir, Spec Coll, College of William & Mary in Virginia, Earl Gregg Swem Library, One Landrum Dr, Williamsburg, VA, 23187. Tel: 757-221-3054. Fax: 757-221-5440. p. 2502

Hardy, Carla, Libr Mgr, Sweetwater County Library System, 300 N First East, Green River, WY, 82935. Tel: 307-875-3615, Ext 1410. Fax: 307-872-3203. p. 2655

Hardy, Cathy, Librn, Hanson Bridgett LLP, 425 Market St, 26th Flr, San Francisco, CA, 94105. Tel: 415-995-5855. Fax: 415-541-9366. p. 242

Hardy, Cheri, Asst Dir, Children's Prog, Hatfield Public Library, 39 Main St, Hatfield, MA, 01038. Tel: 413-247-9097. Fax: 413-247-9237. p. 1094

Hardy, Eileen, Mgr, Wellesley College, 106 Central St, Wellesley, MA, 02481-8275. Tel: 781-283-3317. Fax: 781-283-3690. p. 1135

Hardy, Erica, Access Serv/Reserves/Ref Librn, Agnes Scott College, 141 E College Ave, Decatur, GA, 30030-3770. Tel: 404-471-6337. Fax: 404-471-5037. p. 529

Hardy, Felecia, Mgr, Brunswick County Library, Rourk Library, 5068 Main St, Shallotte, NC, 28459. Tel: 910-754-6578. Fax: 910-754-6874. p. 1824

Hardy, Gladystine, In Charge, Florida Department of Corrections, 19000 SW 377th St, Florida City, FL, 33034-6409. Tel: 305-242-1800. Fax: 305-242-1881. p. 440

Hardy, Jan, Cat Spec, Carnegie Mellon University, Hunt Library, 4909 Frew St, Pittsburgh, PA, 15213-3890. Tel: 412-268-2446. Fax: 412-268-2793. p. 2123

Hardy, Jenafer, Youth Serv Librn, Pulaski County Public Library System, 60 W Third St, Pulaski, VA, 24301. Tel: 540-980-7770. Fax: 540-980-7775. p. 2486

Hardy, Lenore, Dir, Health Sci Libr, Dir, Libr Admin Serv, Drexel University Health Sciences Libraries, 245 N 15th St MS 449, Philadelphia, PA, 19102-1192. Tel: 215-762-7022. Fax: 215-762-8180. p. 2105

Hardy, Lenore, Dir, Libr Admin Serv, Drexel University Libraries, Hagerty Library, 33rd & Market Sts, Philadelphia, PA, 19104-2875. Tel: 215-895-2758. Fax: 215-895-2070. p. 2105

Hardy, Louann, Ref Librn, Pulaski County Public Library, 304 S Main St, Somerset, KY, 42501-1402. Tel: 606-679-8401. Fax: 606-679-1779. p. 935

Hardy, Mary, Head, Adult Serv, Howe Library, 13 South St, Hanover, NH, 03755. Tel: 603-643-4120. Fax: 603-643-0725. p. 1450

Hardy, Mary, ILL, Ithaca College Library, 953 Danby Rd, Ithaca, NY, 14850-7060. Tel: 607-274-3206. Fax: 607-274-1539. p. 1643

Hardy, Mechelle, Librn, Washtenaw County Metropolitan Planning Commission Library, 705 N Zeeb Rd, Ann Arbor, MI, 48107. Tel: 734-994-2435. Fax: 734-994-8284. p. 1153

Hardy, Paula, Libr Tech, Thompson Cariboo Shuswap Health Sciences Library, 311 Columbia St, Kamloops, BC, V2C 2T1, CANADA. Tel: 250-314-2342. Fax: 250-314-2189. p. 2729

Hardy, Ronald, Head, Coll & Tech Serv, University of Wisconsin Oshkosh, 801 Elmwood Ave, Oshkosh, WI, 54901. Tel: 920-424-2097. Fax: 920-424-7338. p. 2628

Hardy, Rosemary, Librn, United States Environmental Protection Agency, 75 Hawthorne St, 13th Flr, San Francisco, CA, 94105. Tel: 415-972-3657. Fax: 415-947-3553. p. 248

Hardy, Shaun J, Librn, Carnegie Institution of Washington, Department of Terrestrial Magnetism & Geophysical Laboratory, 5241 Broad Branch Rd NW, Washington, DC, 20015-1395. Tel: 202-478-7960. Fax: 202-478-8821. p. 395

Hardy, Yolanda T, Librn, Birmingham Public Library, Smithfield, One Eighth Ave W, Birmingham, AL, 35204. Tel: 205-324-8428. Fax: 205-254-8851. p. 7

Hare, Candace, Libr Dir, York Library Region, Nashwaaksis Public School Library, 324 Fulton Ave, Fredericton, NB, E3A 5J4, CANADA. Tel: 506-453-3241. Fax: 506-444-4129. p. 2765

Hare, Judith, Chief Exec Officer, Halifax Public Libraries, 60 Alderney Dr, Dartmouth, NS, B2Y 4P8, CANADA. Tel: 902-490-5744. Fax: 902-490-5762. p. 2779

Hare, Mary, Libr Dir, Carson County Public Library, 401 Main, Panhandle, TX, 79068. Tel: 806-537-3742. Fax: 806-537-3780. p. 2368

Hare, Peter, Ref Librn, Bank Street College of Education Library, 610 W 112th St, 5th Flr, New York, NY, 10025. Tel: 212-875-4455. Fax: 212-875-4558. p. 1669

Harer, John, Dr, Asst Prof, East Carolina University, 101 Umstead Residence Hall, Greenville, NC, 27858-4353. Tel: 252-328-4389. Fax: 252-328-4368. p. 2971

Harera, Patricia, Ch, Corpus Christi Public Libraries, 805 Comanche, Corpus Christi, TX, 78401. Tel: 361-880-7020. Fax: 361-826-7046. p. 2301

Harford, Alice, Dir, Anderson-Lee Library, 43 Main St, Silver Creek, NY, 14136. Tel: 716-934-3468. Fax: 716-934-3037. p. 1744

Harger, Danita, Librn, Arkansas River Valley Regional Library System, Logan County, 419 N Kennedy, Booneville, AR, 72927-3630. Tel: 479-675-2735. Fax: 479-675-2735. p. 97

Hargett, Amber, Ch, Neuse Regional Library, 510 N Queen St, Kinston, NC, 28501. Tel: 252-527-7066, Ext 133. Fax: 252-527-8220. p. 1805

Hargett, Brian, Head, Ref, Lee County Library, 219 N Madison St, Tupelo, MS, 38804-3899. Tel: 662-841-9027. Fax: 662-840-7615. p. 1316

Hargett, Dean, Acq, State Historical Society of Missouri Library, 1020 Lowry St, Columbia, MO, 65201-7298. Tel: 573-882-9369. Fax: 573-884-4950. p. 1324

Hargett, Debbie, Per, Ref Serv, Spec Coll, Wingate University, PO Box 219, Wingate, NC, 28174-1202. Tel: 704-233-8089. Fax: 704-233-8254. p. 1832

Hargett, Tony, Mgr, Robeson County Public Library, Hector MacLean Public, 106 S Main St, Fairmont, NC, 28340. Tel: 910-628-9331. Fax: 910-628-9331. p. 1808

Hargis, Beth, Ch, William Jeanes Memorial Library, 4051 Joshua Rd, Lafayette Hill, PA, 19444-1400. Tel: 610-828-0441. Fax: 610-828-4049. p. 2075

Hargis, Leah, Sr Librn, Carmelite Monastery, 1318 Dulaney Valley Rd, Baltimore, MD, 21286-1399. Tel: 410-823-7415. Fax: 410-823-7418. p. 1012

Hargis-Poston, Miriam, Dir, Ramsey Public Library, 401 S Superior St, Ramsey, IL, 62080. Tel: 618-423-2019. Fax: 618-423-2120. p. 693

Hargreaves, Connie, Mgr, Edmonton Public Library, Sprucewood, 11555 95th St, Edmonton, AB, T5G 1L5, CANADA. Tel: 780-496-1054. Fax: 780-496-7010. p. 2700

Hargrove, Dorothy, Dir, Englewood Public Library, 1000 Englewood Pkwy, Englewood, CO, 80110. Tel: 303-762-2560. Fax: 303-783-6890. p. 306

Hargrove, Fran, Dir, D Brown Memorial Library, 203 N Second St, Rosebud, TX, 76570. Tel: 254-583-2328. Fax: 254-583-2328. p. 2377

Hargrove, Jane, Vols Librn, Milton Public Library, 422 N Main St, Milton, IA, 52570. Tel: 641-656-4611. Fax: 641-656-4611. p. 832

Hargrove, Nancy, Children's & Teen Serv, Troy-Miami County Public Library, 419 W Main St, Troy, OH, 45373. Tel: 937-339-0502. Fax: 937-335-4880. p. 1941

Hargrove, Scott, Dir, Info Tech & Support Serv, Fraser Valley Regional Library, 34589 Delair Rd, Abbotsford, BC, V2S 5Y1, CANADA. Tel: 604-859-7141. Fax: 604-859-5701. p. 2723

Hargrove, Valerie, Circ Librn, Tombigbee Regional Library System, 338 Commerce, West Point, MS, 39773. Tel: 662-494-4872. Fax: 662-494-0300. p. 1317

Haricombe, Lorraine, Dean of Libr, University of Kansas Libraries, 1425 Jayhawk Blvd, Lawrence, KS, 66045-7544. Tel: 785-864-3956. Fax: 785-864-5311. p. 878

Haricombe, Lorraine, Dean, University of Kansas Libraries, Anschutz Library, 1301 Hoch Auditoria Dr, Lawrence, KS, 66045-7537. Tel: 785-864-4928. Fax: 785-864-5705. p. 878

Harke, Vic, Librn, Hillsborough Community College, Dale Mabry Campus Library, 4001 Tampa Bay Blvd, Tampa, FL, 33614-7820. Tel: 813-253-7381. Fax: 813-253-7400. p. 496

Harken, Shelby, Head, Tech Serv, University of North Dakota, 3051 University Ave, Stop 9000, Grand Forks, ND, 58202-9000. Tel: 701-777-4634. Fax: 701-777-3319. p. 1843

Harkins, Anna, Periodicals Librn, Board of Governors of The Federal Reserve System, Research Library, 20th & C St NW, MS 102, Washington, DC, 20551. Tel: 202-452-3333. Fax: 202-530-6222. p. 394

Harkins, Carmen, Chief Librn, Chandler Public Library, 1021 Manvel Ave, Chandler, OK, 74834. Tel: 405-258-3204. Fax: 405-258-3205. p. 1959

Harkins, Clarence, Computer Serv, Langston University, PO Box 1600, Langston, OK, 73050-1600. Tel: 405-466-3293. Fax: 405-466-3459. p. 1967

Harkins, Shirley, Librn, Madill City County Library, 500 W Overton St, Madill, OK, 73446. Tel: 580-795-2749. Fax: 580-795-2749. p. 1967

Harkins, Vickie, Librn, Talladega Public Library, 202 South St E, Talladega, AL, 35160. Tel: 256-362-4211. Fax: 256-362-0653. p. 37

Harkness, Alan, Asst State Librn, Libr Develop, Georgia Public Library Service, 1800 Century Place, Ste 150, Atlanta, GA, 30345-4304. Tel: 404-235-7134. Fax: 404-235-7201. p. 515

Harkness, Alan, Asst State Librn, Libr Develop, Georgia Online Database, c/o Public Library Services, 1800 Century Pl NE, Ste 150, Atlanta, GA, 30345-4304. Tel: 404-235-7134. Fax: 404-235-7201. p. 2941

Harkness, Amy, Acq Librn, Piedmont Healthcare, Inc, 1968 Peachtree Rd NW, Atlanta, GA, 30309. Tel: 404-605-3305. Fax: 404-609-6641. p. 517

Harkreader, Bruce, Supv Librn, Nevada Department of Corrections, 1200 Prison Rd, Lovelock, NV, 89419. Tel: 775-273-1300. Fax: 775-273-4277. p. 1431

Harlan, Jim, Dir, Wayne County, Indiana, Historical Museum Library, 1150 North A St, Richmond, IN, 47374. Tel: 765-962-5756. Fax: 765-939-0909. p. 775

Harlan, Sandy, Adult Serv, Ella M Everhard Public Library, 132 Broad St, Wadsworth, OH, 44281-1897. Tel: 330-334-5761. Fax: 330-334-6605. p. 1943

Harlen, Mallory, Teen Librn, Ossining Public Library, 53 Croton Ave, Ossining, NY, 10562-4903. Tel: 914-941-2416. Fax: 914-941-7464. p. 1712

Harley, Terri, Dir, Girard Public Library, 128 W Prairie Ave, Girard, KS, 66743-1498. Tel: 620-724-4317. Fax: 620-724-8374. p. 868

Harlin, Kenneth, Access Serv, Columbia University, C V Starr East Asian Library, 300 Kent Hall, MC 3901, 1140 Amsterdam Ave, New York, NY, 10027. Tel: 212-854-4318. Fax: 212-662-6286. p. 1675

Harloe, Bart, Exec Dir, Connect NY, Rochester Institute of Technology, 90 Lomb Memorial Dr, Rochester, NY, 14623. Tel: 585-475-2050. p. 2950

Harlow, Rebecca, Adult Serv, Ref, Case Memorial Library, 176 Tyler City Rd, Orange, CT, 06477-2498. Tel: 203-891-2170. Fax: 203-891-2190. p. 364

Harlow, Roxanne, ILL, Saint Luke's Health System Libraries, 190 E Bannock St, Boise, ID, 83712-6297. Tel: 208-381-2276. Fax: 208-381-4317. p. 572

Harlowe, Jeanette, Dir, American Hospital Association, 155 N Wacker Dr, 4th Flr, Chicago, IL, 60606. Tel: 312-422-2050. Fax: 312-422-4700. p. 605

Harma, Bonnie, Asst Librn, Aurora Public Library, 14 W Second Ave N, Aurora, MN, 55705-1314. Tel: 218-229-2021. p. 1240

Harman, Jean, Dir, Dutton Public Library, 22 Main St W, Dutton, MT, 59433. Tel: 406-476-3382. Fax: 406-476-3382. p. 1378

Harmata, Linda, Librn, Alberta Law Libraries, Departmental Library, 400A Bowker Bldg, North, 9833 - 109 St, Edmonton, AB, T5K 2E8, CANADA. Tel: 780-422-6264. Fax: 780-422-5912. p. 2699

Harmeling, Deborah, Sister, Archives Dir, St Walburg Monastery Archives, 2500 Amsterdam Rd, Villa Hills, KY, 41017. Tel: 859-331-6771. Fax: 859-331-2136. p. 936

Harmer, Bill, Head, Adult Serv, Chelsea District Library, 221 S Main St, Chelsea, MI, 48118-1267. Tel: 734-475-8732. Fax: 734-475-6190. p. 1163

Harmon, Amy, Ref Serv, Ad, Hudson Library & Historical Society, 96 Library St, Hudson, OH, 44236-5122. Tel: 330-653-6658. Fax: 330-650-3373. p. 1905

Harmon, Dianne, Assoc Dir, Joliet Public Library, 150 N Ottawa St, Joliet, IL, 60432-4192. Tel: 815-740-2660. Fax: 815-740-6161. p. 660

Harmon, E Glynn, Prof, University of Texas at Austin, One University Sta, D7000, Austin, TX, 78712-0390. Tel: 512-471-3821. Fax: 512-471-3971. p. 2975

Harmon, Marie, Asst Dir, Guntersville Public Library, 1240 O'Brig Ave, Guntersville, AL, 35976. Tel: 256-571-7595. Fax: 256-571-7596. p. 19

Harmon, Marlene, Ref Librn, University of California, Berkeley, Law, 225 Boalt Hall, Berkeley, CA, 94720. Tel: 510-642-4044. Fax: 510-643-5039. p. 128

Harmon, Mary A, Assoc Librn, Pikeville College, 147 Sycamore St, Pikeville, KY, 41501-9118. Tel: 606-218-5610. Fax: 606-218-5613. p. 933

Harmon, Patricia Ann, Mgr, Chemtura Corp, 199 Benson Rd, Middlebury, CT, 06749. Tel: 203-573-4508. Fax: 203-573-2890. p. 351

Harmon, Peg, Asst Dir, Kokomo-Howard County Public Library, 220 N Union St, Kokomo, IN, 46901-4614. Tel: 765-457-3242. Fax: 765-457-3683. p. 758

Harmon, Terry, Circ, Elkins-Randolph County Public Library, 416 Davis Ave, Elkins, WV, 26241. Tel: 304-637-0287. Fax: 304-637-0288. p. 2558

Harmony, Stephena, Dir, University of Cincinnati, Muntz Hall, Rm 115, 9555 Plainfield Rd, Cincinnati, OH, 45236-1096. Tel: 513-936-1547. Fax: 513-745-5767. p. 1873

Harms, Anna Leah, Librn, Canadian Environmental Law Association, 130 Spadina Ave, Ste 301, Toronto, ON, M5V 2L4, CANADA. Tel: 416-960-2284, Ext 210. Fax: 416-960-9392. p. 2851

Harms, Daniel, Bibliographer, Instrul Serv Librn, SUNY Cortland, 81 Prospect Terrace, Cortland, NY, 13045. Tel: 607-753-2525. Fax: 607-753-5669. p. 1611

Harms, Diane L, Dir, Benny Gambaiani Public Library, 104 S Cherry St, Shell Rock, IA, 50670. Tel: 319-885-4345. Fax: 319-885-6209. p. 842

Harms, Gay V, Mgr, Hussar Municipal Library, Hussar School, Hussar, AB, T0J 1S0, CANADA. Tel: 403-787-3781. Fax: 403-787-3922. p. 2707

Harms, Jenny, Ch, Burns Lake Public Library, 585 Government St, Burns Lake, BC, V0J 1E0, CANADA. Tel: 250-692-3192. Fax: 250-692-7488. p. 2726

Harms, Kristi, Dir, Switzerland County Public Library, 205 Ferry St, Vevay, IN, 47043. Tel: 812-427-3363. Fax: 812-427-3654. p. 784

Harms, Lisa, Assoc Mgr, Circ & Coll, Metropolitan Museum of Art, Thomas J Watson Library, 1000 Fifth Ave, New York, NY, 10028-0198. Tel: 212-650-2344. Fax: 212-570-3847. p. 1686

Harmsworth Dow, Joan, Librn, Regina-Qu'Appelle Health Region, Health Sciences Library-Wascana, 2180 23rd Ave, Regina, SK, S4S 0A5, CANADA. Tel: 306-766-5441. Fax: 306-766-5460. p. 2923

Harn, Rhonda, Dir, Westgate Public Library, Three Main St, Westgate, IA, 50681. Tel: 563-578-5151. Fax: 563-578-5151. p. 852

Harnegie, Mary Pat, Med Librn, South Pointe Hospital Library, 4110 Warrensville Center Rd, Warrensville Heights, OH, 44122. Tel: 216-491-7454. Fax: 216-491-7560. p. 1945

Harnett, Susan, Ref/Clinical Librn, Eastern Virginia Medical School, 740 W Olney Rd, Norfolk, VA, 23501. Tel: 757-446-5840. Fax: 757-446-5134. p. 2481

Harney, Resa, Acq, Automation Syst Coordr, Tech Serv, Agnes Scott College, 141 E College Ave, Decatur, GA, 30030-3770. Tel: 404-471-6339. Fax: 404-471-5037. p. 529

Harnish, Tracy, Dir, Ruth Hughes Memorial District Library, 211 N Almont Ave, Imlay City, MI, 48444-1004. Tel: 810-724-8043. Fax: 810-724-2602. p. 1193

Harnke, Deborah, Libr Tech, Bureau of Land Management Library, Denver Federal Center, Bldg 50, Sixth & Kipling, Denver, CO, 80225. Tel: 303-236-6648. Fax: 303-236-4810. p. 298

Harnois, Michel, Exec Dir, La Societe d'Histoire de Sherbrooke, 275, rue Dufferin, Sherbrooke, QC, J1H 4M5, CANADA. Tel: 819-821-5406. Fax: 819-821-5417. p. 2912

Harold, Fran Powell, Dir, Girl Scouts of the USA, 10 E Oglethorpe Ave, Savannah, GA, 31401. Tel: 912-233-4501. Fax: 912-233-4659. p. 550

Harold, Marlena, Youth Serv, Satellite Beach Public Library, 751 Jamaica Blvd, Satellite Beach, FL, 32937. Tel: 321-779-4004. Fax: 321-779-4036. p. 490

Haron, Nora, Mgr, Purchasing, Oakland Public Library, 125 14th St, Oakland, CA, 94612. Tel: 510-238-6572. Fax: 510-238-2232. p. 197

Harp, Kim, Legis Librn, State Library of Kansas, State Capitol Bldg, Topeka, KS, 66612. Tel: 785-296-3296. Fax: 785-296-6650. p. 896

Harp, Ramona K, Libr Mgr, Apache County Library District, Greer Memorial, 74A Main St, Greer, AZ, 85927. Tel: 928-735-7710. Fax: 928-735-7710. p. 80

Harp, Rebekah, Info Spec, Southwest Florida Regional Planning Council Library, 1926 Victoria Ave, Fort Myers, FL, 33901. Tel: 239-338-2550, Ext 217. Fax: 239-338-2560. p. 446

Harpell, Gisela, Head, Circ, Morris County Library, 30 E Hanover Ave, Whippany, NJ, 07981. Tel: 973-285-6948. p. 1544

Harper, Amy, Librn, University of Washington Libraries, K K Sherwood Medical Library, 104 Harborview Hall, 326 Ninth Ave, Box 359902, Seattle, WA, 98104-2499. Tel: 206-604-9876. Fax: 206-731-8673. p. 2535

Harper, Barbara, Circ Mgr, Ricks Memorial Library (Yazoo Library Association), 310 N Main St, Yazoo City, MS, 39194-4253. Tel: 662-746-5557. Fax: 662-746-7309. p. 1318

Harper, Beth, Tech Serv, Spanish Peaks Library District, 415 Walsen Ave, Walsenburg, CO, 81089. Tel: 719-738-2774. Fax: 719-738-2468. p. 325

Harper, Chris, Info Syst Spec, Longwood University, Redford & Race St, Farmville, VA, 23909. Tel: 434-395-2438. Fax: 434-395-2453. p. 2463

Harper, Cynthia, Syst Librn, Colgate University, 13 Oak Dr, Hamilton, NY, 13346-1398. Tel: 315-228-7300. Fax: 315-228-7934. p. 1633

Harper, Deborah, Dir, Groves Public Library, 5600 W Washington St, Groves, TX, 77619. Tel: 409-962-6281. Fax: 409-962-3379. p. 2330

Harper, Esma, In Charge, Oceanic Institute Library, 41-202 Kalanianeole Hwy, Waimanalo, HI, 96795. Tel: 808-259-3123. Fax: 808-259-5971. p. 568

Harper, Janet, Br Adminr, Noble County Public Library, West, 120 Jefferson St, Cromwell, IN, 46732-0555. Tel: 260-856-2119. Fax: 260-856-2119. p. 723

Harper, Jeanette, Br Mgr, Florence Public Library, 104 W Main St, Florence, MS, 39073. Tel: 601-845-6032. Fax: 601-845-4625. p. 1298

Harper, Joy, Dir, Darwin R Barker Library, Seven Day St, Fredonia, NY, 14063. Tel: 716-672-8051. Fax: 716-679-3547. p. 1624

Harper, Kenneth, Librn, University of Rochester, Laboratory for Laser Energetics Library, 250 E River Rd, Rochester, NY, 14623. Tel: 585-275-4479. Fax: 585-273-3663. p. 1733

Harper, Kimberly, Ref Spec, State Historical Society of Missouri Library, 1020 Lowry St, Columbia, MO, 65201-7298. Tel: 573-882-7083. Fax: 573-884-4950. p. 1324

Harper, Laura, Children's Serv Coordr, Montgomery County Memorial Library System, 104 I-45 N, Conroe, TX, 77301-2720. Tel: 936-788-8377, Ext 242. Fax: 936-788-8398. p. 2300

Harper, Linda, In Charge, Beauregard Parish Library, East Beauregard, 7580 Hwy 26, Dry Creek, LA, 70634. Tel: 337-463-6217. Fax: 337-462-5434. p. 948

Harper, Linda, Circ, Hingham Public Library, 66 Leavitt St, Hingham, MA, 02043. Tel: 781-741-1405. Fax: 781-749-0956. p. 1095

Harper, Linda, Br Mgr, Lord Fairfax Community College, 173 Skirmisher Lane, Middletown, VA, 22645-1745. Tel: 540-351-1554. Fax: 540-868-7171. p. 2479

Harper, Lu, Librn, University of Rochester, Charlotte Whitney Allen Library, Memorial Art Gallery, 500 University Ave, Rochester, NY, 14607. Tel: 585-276-8997. Fax: 585-473-6266. p. 1733

Harper, Mary, Exec Dir, Tuscaloosa Public Library, 1801 Jack Warner Pkwy, Tuscaloosa, AL, 35401-1027. Tel: 205-345-5820, Ext 204. Fax: 205-752-8300. p. 38

Harper, Mary Ann, Dir, Ouachita Technical College, One College Circle, Malvern, AR, 72104. Tel: 501-337-5000. Fax: 501-337-9382. p. 109

Harper, Megan, Dr, Asst Prof, Kent State University, 314 Library, Kent, OH, 44242-0001. Tel: 330-672-2782. Fax: 330-672-7965. p. 2972

Harper, Nancy L, Dir, White Cloud Community Library, 1038 Wilcox Ave, White Cloud, MI, 49349. Tel: 231-689-6631. Fax: 231-689-6699. p. 1236

Harper, Patti, Head, Archives & Res Coll, Carleton University Library, 1125 Colonel By Dr, Ottawa, ON, K1S 5B6, CANADA. Tel: 613-520-2600, Ext 8066. Fax: 613-520-2750. p. 2830

Harper, Shauna, Librn, Camden-Clark Memorial Hospital, 800 Garfield Ave, Parkersburg, WV, 26101. Tel: 304-424-2450. Fax: 304-424-2861. p. 2568

Harper, Susan, Mgr, Cobb County Public Library System, Acworth Branch, 4569 Dallas St, Acworth, GA, 30101. Tel: 770-917-5165. Fax: 770-917-5177. p. 542

Harper, Yvonne, Head, Circ, Oxnard Public Library, 251 South A St, Oxnard, CA, 93030. Tel: 805-385-7512. Fax: 805-385-7526. p. 202

Harpool, Lynn, Cat Librn, Free Public Library of Monroe Township, 713 Marsha Ave, Williamstown, NJ, 08094. Tel: 856-629-1212. Fax: 856-875-0191. p. 1544

Harpst, Chuck, Hist Coll Librn, Ref Librn, Tecumseh District Library, 215 N Ottawa St, Tecumseh, MI, 49286-1564. Tel: 517-423-2238. Fax: 517-423-5519. p. 1230

Harr, Grace, Br Mgr, Shreve Memorial Library, Blanchard Branch, 344 Alexander St, Blanchard, LA, 71009. Tel: 318-929-3163. Fax: 318-929-3163. p. 969

Harr, Jeffrey, Chair, Onondaga Community College, 4585 W Seneca Tpk, Syracuse, NY, 13215-4585. Tel: 315-498-2334. Fax: 315-498-7213. p. 1752

Harral, Lisa Jensen, Librn, Blackfoot Public Library, 129 N Broadway, Blackfoot, ID, 83221-2204. Tel: 208-785-8628. Fax: 208-782-9688. p. 569

Harrel, Melissa, Circ Mgr, Duke University Libraries, Divinity School Library, Gray Bldg, 102 Chapel Dr, Durham, NC, 27708. Tel: 919-660-3449. Fax: 919-681-7594. p. 1787

Harrell, Amy, Music & Media Librn, Trinity College Library, 300 Summit St, Hartford, CT, 06106. Tel: 860-297-2193. Fax: 860-297-2251. p. 347

Harrell, Anita, Br Mgr, Hampton Public Library, Phoebus Branch, One S Mallory St, Hampton, VA, 23663. Tel: 757-727-1149. Fax: 757-727-1047. p. 2468

Harrell, Anita, Coordr, Outreach Serv, Hampton Public Library, 4207 Victoria Blvd, Hampton, VA, 23669-4243. Tel: 757-727-1154. Fax: 757-727-1152. p. 2468

Harrell, Gail, Regional Libr Supvr, Wake County Public Library System, Southeast Regional Library, 908 Seventh Ave, Garner, NC, 27529. Tel: 919-662-2255. Fax: 919-662-2270. p. 1818

Harrell, Haywood, Superintendent, National Park Service, 1055 Pittsburg Landing Rd, Shiloh, TN, 38376. Tel: 731-689-5275. Fax: 731-689-5450. p. 2265

Harrell, Judy, Co-Mgr, Thomas County Public Library System, Boston Carnegie Public Library, 250 S Main St, Boston, GA, 31626-3674. Tel: 229-498-5101. Fax: 229-498-5101. p. 553

Harrell, Judy, Mgr, Eastern State Hospital, 4601 Ironbound Rd, Williamsburg, VA, 23188. Tel: 757-253-4310. Fax: 757-253-5192. p. 2503

Harrell, Karen, Ser, Nelson-Atkins Museum of Art, 4525 Oak St, Kansas City, MO, 64111-1873. Tel: 816-751-0408. Fax: 816-751-0498. p. 1340

Harrell, Leta, Librn, Hamilton City Library, 21 E Main St, Hamilton, KS, 66853-9768. Tel: 620-678-3646. Fax: 620-678-3646. p. 870

Harrell, Nick, Ref & Instrul Serv Librn, University of Miami, 1311 Miller Dr, Coral Gables, FL, 33146. Tel: 305-284-2251. Fax: 305-284-3554. p. 434

Harrell, Ruth O'Neal, Librn, Beaufort, Hyde & Martin County Regional Library, Mattamuskeet, 20418 US 264, Swan Quarter, NC, 27885. Tel: 252-926-0310. Fax: 252-926-0311. p. 1828

Harrell, Toni, Dir, Kansas State Library, ESU Memorial Union, 1200 Commercial, Box 4055, Emporia, KS, 66801-5087. Tel: 620-341-6280. p. 866

Harrell, Toni, Dir, Talking Bks, State Library of Kansas, State Capitol Bldg, Topeka, KS, 66612. Tel: 785-296-3296. Fax: 785-296-6650. p. 896

Harrell, Virginia, Librn, Fort Bend County Libraries, Cinco Ranch, 2620 Commercial Center Blvd, Katy, TX, 77494. Tel: 281-633-4600. Fax: 281-395-6377. p. 2375

Harrelson, Betty, Ch, Andalusia Public Library, 212 S Three Notch St, Andalusia, AL, 36420. Tel: 334-222-6612. Fax: 334-222-6612. p. 4

Harrelson, Margaret, Librn, Wellsville Public Library, 108 W Hudson St, Wellsville, MO, 63384. Tel: 573-684-6151. Fax: 573-684-6151. p. 1372

Harrigan, Mary, Head, Ref Serv, Crown Point Community Library, 214 S Court St, Crown Point, IN, 46307. Tel: 219-663-0270, 219-663-0271. Fax: 219-663-0403. p. 734

Harriger, Sherill Lynn, Libr Dir, Warner University, 13895 Hwy 27, Lake Wales, FL, 33859. Tel: 863-638-7674. Fax: 863-638-7675. p. 458

Harrill, Maureen G, Ch, Salem Public Library, 28 E Main St, Salem, VA, 24153. Tel: 540-375-3089. Fax: 540-389-7054. p. 2496

Harrington, Brenda, Adult Prog Coordr, Belfast Free Library, 106 High St, Belfast, ME, 04915. Tel: 207-338-3884. Fax: 207-338-3895. p. 977

Harrington, Daphne, Dir, Simmons College, 300 The Fenway, Boston, MA, 02115-5898. Tel: 617-521-2754. p. 1066

Harrington, Dianna, Acq, Herrick District Library, 300 S River Ave, Holland, MI, 49423-3290. Tel: 616-355-3100. p. 1190

Harrington, Donna, Mgr, Sequoyah Regional Library System, Pickens County Public, 100 Library Lane, Jasper, GA, 30143. Tel: 706-692-5411. Fax: 706-692-9518. p. 523

Harrington, Drew, Dir, University of Portland, 5000 N Willamette Blvd, Portland, OR, 97203-5743. Tel: 503-943-7111. Fax: 503-943-7491. p. 2015

Harrington, Heather, Asst Librn, Historic Deerfield Inc & Pocumtuck Valley Memorial Association Libraries, Six Memorial St, Deerfield, MA, 01342-9736. Tel: 413-775-7125. Fax: 413-775-7223. p. 1084

Harrington, Jason, ILL/Doc Delivery Serv, K&L Gates LLP, 1601 K St NW, L-3, Washington, DC, 20006. Tel: 202-661-3715. Fax: 202-778-9100. p. 406

Harrington, Jeri, Asst Librn, Albion Area Public Library, 111 E Pearl St, Albion, PA, 16401-1202. Tel: 814-756-5400. Fax: 814-756-5400. p. 2026

Harrington, Judy, Head, Pub Serv, Middle Georgia Regional Library System, 1180 Washington Ave, Macon, GA, 31201-1790. Tel: 478-744-0836. Fax: 478-742-3161. p. 541

Harrington, Kathleen, Dir, Nevada Supreme Court Library, Supreme Court Bldg, 201 S Carson St, Ste 100, Carson City, NV, 89701-4702. Tel: 775-684-1670. Fax: 775-684-1662. p. 1426

Harrington, Keran, Head, Tech Serv, The Urbana Free Library, 210 W Green St, Urbana, IL, 61801-5326. Tel: 217-367-4057. Fax: 217-367-4061. p. 713

Harrington, Liza, Librn, Greenfield Community College Library, One College Dr, Greenfield, MA, 01301-9739. Tel: 413-775-1836. Fax: 413-775-1838. p. 1092

Harrington, Marni, Librn, University of Western Ontario, North Campus Bldg, Rm 280, London, ON, N6A 5B7, CANADA. Tel: 519-661-2111, Ext 88489. Fax: 519-661-3848. p. 2819

Harrington, Matt, Dir, ILL, Tate & Lyle, 2200 E Eldorado St, Decatur, IL, 62525-1801. Tel: 217-421-2543. Fax: 217-421-2519. p. 634

Harrington, Micki, Libr Serv Supvr/Circ, Keene State College, 229 Main St, Keene, NH, 03435-3201. Tel: 603-358-2782. Fax: 603-358-2745. p. 1453

Harrington, Molly, Mgr, Saint Joseph's Hospital & Medical Center, 350 W Thomas Rd, Phoenix, AZ, 85013. Tel: 602-406-3299. Fax: 602-406-4171. p. 77

Harrington, Pam, Ch, Missoula Public Library, 301 E Main, Missoula, MT, 59802-4799. Tel: 406-721-2665. Fax: 406-728-5900. p. 1386

Harrington, Rebecca, Syst Librn, Orlando Health, 1414 Kuhl Ave, MP 28, Orlando, FL, 32806-2134. Tel: 321-841-5454. Fax: 321-843-6825. p. 477

Harrington, Ryan, Foreign & Intl Law Librn, Yale University Library, Lillian Goldman Library Yale Law School, 127 Wall St, New Haven, CT, 06511. Tel: 203-432-7371. Fax: 203-432-2112. p. 358

Harrington, Sherre N, Dir, Berry College, 2277 Martha Berry Hwy, Mount Berry, GA, 30149. Tel: 706-236-2285. p. 546

Harrington, Tracy, Database Librn, Belhaven University, 1500 Peachtree St, Jackson, MS, 39202. Tel: 601-968-5948. Fax: 601-968-5968. p. 1303

Harris, Abbie, Br Librn, Madison County Public Library, Berea Branch, 319 Chestnut St, Berea, KY, 40403. Tel: 859-986-7112. Fax: 859-986-7208. p. 934

Harris, Amy, Ref Librn, Horry-Georgetown Technical College, Georgetown Campus, 4003 S Fraser St, Georgetown, SC, 29440. Tel: 843-520-1423. Fax: 843-520-1462. p. 2192

Harris, Ann, Dir, Frances L Simek Memorial Library-Medford, 400 N Main, Medford, WI, 54451. Tel: 715-748-2505. Fax: 715-748-4160. p. 2614

Harris, Barbara, Librn, Lapeer District Library, Columbiaville Branch, 4718 First St, Columbiaville, MI, 48421-9143. Tel: 810-793-6100. Fax: 810-793-6243. p. 1202

Harris, Barbara, Librn, Lapeer District Library, Otter Lake Branch, 6361 Detroit St, Otter Lake, MI, 48464-9104. Tel: 810-793-6300. Fax: 810-793-7040. p. 1203

Harris, Belinda, Librn, Roanoke Times Library, 201 W Campbell Ave, Roanoke, VA, 24011. Tel: 540-981-3280. Fax: 540-981-3346. p. 2494

Harris, Beth, Cat, Prairie Skies Public Library District, 125 W Editor St, Ashland, IL, 62612. Tel: 217-476-3417. Fax: 217-476-8076. p. 590

Harris, Beth, Librn, Prairie Skies Public Library District, Pleasant Plains Branch, 555 Buckeye Rd, Pleasant Plains, IL, 62677. Tel: 217-626-1553. Fax: 217-626-2433. p. 590

Harris, Beth, Ch, Chester County Library, 100 Center St, Chester, SC, 29706. Tel: 803-377-8145. Fax: 803-377-8146. p. 2185

Harris, Beth R, Librn, Tech Serv, Paier College of Art, Inc Library, 20 Gorham Ave, Hamden, CT, 06514-3902. Tel: 203-287-3023. Fax: 203-287-3021. p. 343

Harris, Beth S, Spec Coll & Archives Librn, Hollins University, 7950 E Campus Dr, Roanoke, VA, 24020-1000. Tel: 540-362-6237. Fax: 540-362-6756. p. 2493

Harris, Beverly, Acq, Ser, Dillard University, 2601 Gentilly Blvd, New Orleans, LA, 70122-3097. Tel: 504-816-4784. Fax: 504-816-4787. p. 960

Harris, Boyd, Circ Mgr, Gardner-Webb University, 110 S Main St, Boiling Springs, NC, 28017. Tel: 704-406-4295. Fax: 704-406-4623. p. 1776

Harris, Brena, ILL, Clark County Law Library, 309 S Third St, Ste 400, Las Vegas, NV, 89155. Tel: 702-455-4696. Fax: 702-455-5120. p. 1428

Harris, Brenda, Ref, Stanly County Public Library, 133 E Main St, Albemarle, NC, 28001. Tel: 704-986-3759. Fax: 704-983-6713. p. 1773

Harris, Brenda, Librn, Lyons Public Library, 448 Cedar St, Lyons, OR, 97358-2122. Tel: 503-859-2366. p. 2004

Harris, Brian, Br Supvr, Chemung County Library District, Big Flats Library, 78 Canal St, Big Flats, NY, 14814. Tel: 607-562-3300. p. 1619

Harris, Carmen, Librn, National Institute on Aging, 5600 Nathan Shock Dr, Baltimore, MD, 21224-6825. Tel: 410-558-8125. Fax: 410-558-8224. p. 1016

Harris, Carol, Interim Dir, Beecher Community Library, 660 Penfield St, Beecher, IL, 60401. Tel: 708-946-9090. Fax: 708-946-2896. p. 593

Harris, Carol A, Dir, Libr Serv, Deborah Heart & Lung Center, 200 Trenton Rd, Browns Mills, NJ, 08015. Tel: 609-893-1200, Ext 4398. Fax: 609-893-1566. p. 1475

Harris, Charlene, Asst Dir, Caroline Library Inc, 17202 Richmond Tpk, Milford, VA, 22514. Tel: 804-633-5455. Fax: 804-633-9069. p. 2479

Harris, Colleen, Head, Access Serv, University of Tennessee at Chattanooga Library, 615 McCallie Ave, Dept 6456, Chattanooga, TN, 37403-2598. Tel: 423-425-4501. Fax: 423-425-4775. p. 2228

Harris, D J, Managing Librn, Austin Public Library, Windsor Park, 5833 Westminster Dr, Austin, TX, 78723. Tel: 512-974-9841. Fax: 512-974-9844. p. 2279

Harris, Darlene, Principal Librn, Tampa-Hillsborough County Public Library System, Robert W Saunders Sr Public Library, 1505 N Nebraska Ave, Tampa, FL, 33602-2899. Fax: 813-301-7119. p. 498

Harris, Dawn M, Asst Dir, Killeen City Library System, 205 E Church Ave, Killeen, TX, 76541. Tel: 254-501-8966. Fax: 254-501-7704. p. 2350

Harris, Debbie, Outreach Librn, Green County Public Library, 112 W Court St, Greensburg, KY, 42743. Tel: 270-932-7081. Fax: 270-932-7081. p. 915

Harris, Deborah, Br Mgr, Charleston County Public Library, Otranto Road Regional, 2261 Otranto Rd, North Charleston, SC, 29406. Tel: 843-572-4094. Fax: 843-572-4190. p. 2183

Harris, Diane, Circ Librn, Hyrum Library, 50 W Main, Hyrum, UT, 84319. Tel: 435-245-6411. Fax: 435-245-0180. p. 2406

Harris, Diane, Dir, Circ & Bldg Serv, Pacific Lutheran University, 12180 Park Ave S, Tacoma, WA, 98447-0001. Tel: 253-535-7500. Fax: 253-535-7315. p. 2539

Harris, Dinah, Dir, Everett Horn Public Library, 702 W Church St, Lexington, TN, 38351-1713. Tel: 731-968-3239. Fax: 731-968-4134. p. 2245

Harris, Eboni Ardell, Librn, Lake Park Public Library, 529 Park Ave, Lake Park, FL, 33403. Tel: 561-881-3330. p. 458

Harris, Edward, Dr, Dean, Southern Connecticut State University, 501 Crescent St, New Haven, CT, 06515. Tel: 203-392-5701. Fax: 203-392-5748. p. 2963

Harris, Essie, Br Mgr, Champaign Public Library, Douglass Branch, 504 E Grove St, Champaign, IL, 61820-3239. Tel: 217-403-2090, 217-403-4455. Fax: 217-356-9561. p. 603

Harris, Frances Jacobsen, Librn, University of Illinois Library at Urbana-Champaign, University Laboratory High School, 1212 W Springfield Ave, Rm 201, Urbana, IL, 61801. Tel: 217-333-1589. Fax: 217-333-4064. p. 713

Harris, Freida, Librn, Jewish Community Center on the Palisades, 411 E Clinton Ave, Tenafly, NJ, 07670. Tel: 201-569-7900, Ext 234. Fax: 201-569-7448. p. 1533

Harris, Geraldine, Dir, Allen Parish Libraries, 320 S Sixth St, Oberlin, LA, 70655. Tel: 337-639-4315. Fax: 337-639-2654. p. 965

Harris, Geraldine, Libr Tech, Michigan Department of Corrections, Ernest C Brooks Correctional Facility Library, 2500 S Sheridan Rd, Muskegon, MI, 49444. Tel: 231-773-9200, Ext 1916. p. 1161

Harris, Greg, Librn, New York State Department of Correctional Services, 1879 Davis St, Elmira, NY, 14901-1042. Tel: 607-734-3901. p. 1620

Harris Houk, Amy, Info Literacy, Ref Librn, University of North Carolina at Greensboro, 320 Spring Garden St, Greensboro, NC, 27402. Tel: 336-256-0275. Fax: 336-334-5399. p. 1798

Harris, Jane, Br Mgr, Jacksonville Public Library, Maxville, 8375 Maxville Rd, Jacksonville, FL, 32234-2748. Tel: 904-289-7563. Fax: 904-289-9285. p. 454

Harris, Jane, Br Mgr, Jacksonville Public Library, West Regional, 1425 Chaffee Rd S, Jacksonville, FL, 32221-1119. Tel: 904-693-1448. Fax: 904-693-1470. p. 454

Harris, Jane, Librn, Sugar Grove Free Library, Harmon & School Sts, Sugar Grove, PA, 16350. Tel: 814-489-7872. Fax: 814-489-7826. p. 2144

Harris, Janet, Prog & Vols Coordr, National Archives & Records Administration, 441 Freedom Pkwy, Atlanta, GA, 30307. Tel: 404-865-7114. Fax: 404-865-7102. p. 517

Harris, Jay, Acq, University of Alabama at Birmingham, Lister Hill Library of the Health Sciences, 1700 University Blvd, Birmingham, AL, 35294-0013. Tel: 205-934-5460. Fax: 205-934-3545. p. 10

Harris, Jean, Libr Mgr, Pikes Peak Library District, Monument Library, 1706 Lake Woodmoor Dr, Monument, CO, 80132-9074. Tel: 719-488-2370. p. 296

Harris, Jean, Libr Mgr, Pikes Peak Library District, Palmer Lake Library, 66 Lower Glenway, Palmer Lake, CO, 80133. Tel: 719-481-2587. p. 296

Harris, Jennifer, Asst Dir, Plymouth Public Library, 132 South St, Plymouth, MA, 02360-3309. Tel: 508-830-4250. Fax: 508-830-4258. p. 1118

Harris, Jennifer, Ch, Midland County Public Library, 301 W Missouri, Midland, TX, 79701. Tel: 432-688-4320. Fax: 432-688-4939. p. 2363

Harris, Jessica, Librn, University of Texas at Brownsville & Texas Southmost College Library, 80 Fort Brown St, Brownsville, TX, 78521. Tel: 956-882-7281. Fax: 956-882-5495. p. 2292

Harris, Joan, Br Librn, Sweetwater County Library System, Wamsutter Branch Library, 230 Tierney, Lot 44, Wamsutter, WY, 82336. Tel: 307-324-9121. Fax: 307-324-9121. p. 2656

Harris, Johnnie, Mgr, Pine Mountain Regional Library, Butler Public, 56 W Main St, Butler, GA, 31006-0508. Tel: 478-862-5428. Fax: 478-862-2924. p. 542

Harris, Judy, Dir, Libr Serv, Bryan Cave LLP, One Metropolitan Sq, 211 N Broadway, Ste 3600, Saint Louis, MO, 63102-2750. Tel: 314-259-2298. Fax: 314-259-2020. p. 1353

Harris, Julie, In Charge, Finley Hospital, 350 N Grandview Ave, Dubuque, IA, 52001. Tel: 563-589-2496. Fax: 563-557-2813. p. 811

Harris, Kathie, Br Mgr, Great River Regional Library, Myrtle Mabee Library, 324 Washburn Ave, Belgrade, MN, 56312. Tel: 320-254-8842. p. 1275

Harris, Kathryn M, Dir, Libr Serv, Illinois Historic Preservation Agency, 112 N Sixth St, Springfield, IL, 62701. Tel: 217-524-7219. Fax: 217-785-6250. p. 705

Harris, Katrina, Adminr, Head of Libr, Riverdale Public Library District, 208 W 144th St, Riverdale, IL, 60827-2788. Tel: 708-841-3311. Fax: 708-841-1805. p. 695

Harris, Kelly, Ch, YA Librn, Amagansett Free Library, 215 Main St, Amagansett, NY, 11930. Tel: 631-267-3810. Fax: 631-267-0087. p. 1573

Harris, Kerri-Lynn, Ch, Kimberly Public Library, 120 Madison St W, Kimberly, ID, 83341. Tel: 208-212-1565. Fax: 208-423-4556. p. 577

Harris, Kresta, Librn, Lake Placid Memorial Library, 205 W Interlake Blvd, Lake Placid, FL, 33852. Tel: 863-699-3705. Fax: 863-699-3713. p. 458

Harris, Laura, Ref Serv, Iliff School of Theology, 2201 S University Blvd, Denver, CO, 80210. Tel: 303-765-3173. Fax: 303-777-0164. p. 302

Harris, Laura, Ch, Johnson County Public Library, Trafalgar Branch, 424 Tower St, Trafalgar, IN, 46181. Tel: 317-878-9560. Fax: 317-878-4093. p. 744

Harris, LaVonda, Circ Supvr, Eastern Virginia Medical School, 740 W Olney Rd, Norfolk, VA, 23501. Tel: 757-446-5840. Fax: 757-446-5134. p. 2481

Harris, Lee, Asst Librn, Dorion Public Library, 170 Dorion Loop Rd, Dorion, ON, P0T 1K0, CANADA. Tel: 807-857-2289. Fax: 807-857-2203. p. 2802

Harris, Linda, Head, Ref, University of Alabama at Birmingham, Mervyn H Sterne Library, 917 13th St S, Birmingham, AL, 35205. Tel: 205-934-6364. p. 10

Harris, Linda, Librn, Cross Cancer Institute Library, 11560 University Ave, Edmonton, AB, T6G 1Z2, CANADA. Tel: 780-432-8593. Fax: 780-432-8886. p. 2700

Harris, Lorene B, Dir, University of South Carolina, Medford Library, 476 Hubbard Dr, Lancaster, SC, 29720. Tel: 803-313-7000, 803-313-7060. Fax: 803-313-7107. p. 2190

Harris, Lori-Lee, Librn, Southeast Regional Library, White City Branch, Community Ctr, 12 Ramm Ave, White City, SK, S4L 5B1, CANADA. Tel: 306-781-2118. p. 2931

Harris, Lorie, Exec Dir, Ontario Archaeological Society Library, 1444 Queen St E, Ste 102, Toronto, ON, M4A 2W1, CANADA. Tel: 416-406-5959. Fax: 416-406-5959. p. 2856

Harris, Lynn, Mgr, Littler Mendelson Library, 650 California St, 20th Flr, San Francisco, CA, 94108-2693. Tel: 415-399-8441. Fax: 415-399-8490. p. 243

Harris, Lynn, Actg Admin Officer, San Jose Public Library, 150 E San Fernando St, San Jose, CA, 95112-3580. Tel: 408-808-2152. p. 250

Harris, Lynne, Chair, Department of Community Services, Government of Yukon, Ross River Community, Ross River School, Ross River, YT, Y0B 1S0, CANADA. Tel: 867-969-2909. p. 2933

Harris, Maria, Libr Dir, Enosburgh Public Library, 241 Main St, Enosburg Falls, VT, 05450. Tel: 802-933-2328. p. 2423

Harris, Mark, Automation Syst Coordr, Ames Public Library, 515 Douglas Ave, Ames, IA, 50010. Tel: 515-239-5669. Fax: 515-233-9001. p. 792

Harris, Mark, Dir of Libr Serv, Texas A&M University Central Texas, 1901 S Clear Creek Rd, Killeen, TX, 76549. Tel: 254-526-1244, 254-526-1618, 254-526-1619. Fax: 254-526-1589, 254-526-1993. p. 2350

Harris, Mary, Librn, Shaw Library, Main St, Mercer, ME, 04957. Tel: 207-587-2529. Fax: 207-587-2529. p. 991

Harris, Mary Ann, Ch, Circ, Monroe County Public Library, 121 Pineville Rd, Monroeville, AL, 36460. Tel: 251-743-3818. Fax: 251-575-7357. p. 27

Harris, Mary Boden, Circ, Ref Asst, Grambling State University, 403 Main St, Grambling, LA, 71245. Tel: 318-274-2472. Fax: 318-274-3268. p. 950

Harris, Mary Ellen, Librn, International Society of Parametric Analysts, 6723 Odyssey Dr, Huntsville, AL, 35806. Tel: 256-971-6425. Fax: 256-971-6654. p. 22

Harris, Mary G, Ref Librn, Alcorn State University, 1000 ASU Dr, Alcorn State, MS, 39096-7500. Tel: 601-877-6357. Fax: 601-877-3885. p. 1293

Harris, Melanie, Head Librn, Lincoln Public Library, 49 Complex Dr, Lincoln, AL, 35096-5096. Tel: 205-763-7244. Fax: 205-763-7244. p. 23

Harris, Misti, Head, Youth Serv, Jennings County Public Library, 2375 N State Hwy 3, North Vernon, IN, 47265-1596. Tel: 812-346-2091. Fax: 812-346-2127. p. 769

Harris, Nicole, Asst Dir, Info Syst, George Washington University, Jacob Burns Law Library, 716 20th St NW, Washington, DC, 20052. Tel: 202-994-4225. Fax: 202-994-2874. p. 402

Harris, Nicole, Dir, Graettinger Public Library, 115 W Robins St, Graettinger, IA, 51342. Tel: 712-859-3592. Fax: 712-859-3197. p. 818

Harris, Olivia, Librn, St James Hospital & Health Centers, 1423 Chicago Rd, Chicago Heights, IL, 60411. Tel: 708-756-1000, Ext 6666. Fax: 708-709-2193. p. 628

Harris, Pam, Res Librn, Boeing Co, S034-1040, Saint Louis, MO, 63166. Tel: 314-387-8023. Fax: 314-777-2424. p. 1353

Harris, Pam, Outreach & Instruction Librn, Swarthmore College, 500 College Ave, Swarthmore, PA, 19081-1081. Tel: 610-690-2056. Fax: 610-328-7329. p. 2145

Harris, Paula, Chairperson, Didsbury Municipal Library, 2033 19th Ave, Didsbury, AB, T0M 0W0, CANADA. Tel: 403-335-3142. Fax: 403-335-3141. p. 2696

Harris, Rebecca, Circ, University of Charleston, 2300 MacCorkle Ave SE, Charleston, WV, 25304-1099. Tel: 304-357-4780. Fax: 304-357-4715. p. 2556

Harris, Robert A, Dir, Helen M Plum Memorial Public Library District, 110 W Maple St, Lombard, IL, 60148-2594. Tel: 630-627-0316. Fax: 630-627-0336. p. 667

Harris, Robin, Pub Serv Librn, University of Louisville Libraries, Brandeis School of Law Library, 2301 S Third St, Louisville, KY, 40208. Tel: 502-852-6083. Fax: 502-852-8906. p. 926

Harris, Rosalind, Assoc Librn, Concordia College, 1804 Green St, Selma, AL, 36703-3323. Tel: 334-874-5700, Ext 19745. Fax: 334-874-5755. p. 35

Harris, Ruth, Br Mgr, First Regional Library, Robert C Irwin Public Library, 1285 Kenny Hill Ave, Tunica, MS, 38676. Tel: 662-363-2162. Fax: 662-357-5929. p. 1301

Harris, Sally, Outreach Coordr, Menominee County Library, S319 Railroad St, Stephenson, MI, 49887. Tel: 906-753-6923. Fax: 906-753-4678. p. 1229

Harris, Sandra, Asst Dir, United Methodist Church - South Georgia Conference, Epworth-by-the-Sea, 100 Arthur Moore Dr, Saint Simons Island, GA, 31522. Tel: 912-638-4050. Fax: 912-638-9050. p. 549

Harris, Sandy, Libr Serv Supvr, Tronox LLC, 3301 NW 150th St, Oklahoma City, OK, 73134. Tel: 405-775-5012, Ext 5755. Fax: 405-775-5027. p. 1975

Harris, Sara, Exec Dir, Center for the Study of Aging Library, 196 Shaker Rd, Albany, NY, 12211-2028. Tel: 518-465-6927. p. 1568

Harris, Sarah, Librn, Fort Worth Library, Northside, 601 Park St, Fort Worth, TX, 76106. Tel: 817-626-8241. Fax: 817-625-0702. p. 2322

Harris, Sharlene, Syst Coordr, University of the Virgin Islands, Two John Brewers Bay, Saint Thomas, VI, 00802-9990. Tel: 340-693-1368. Fax: 340-693-1365. p. 2679

Harris, Sharon, Br Mgr, Prairie-River Library District, Nezperce Community, 602 Fourth Ave, Nezperce, ID, 83543. Tel: 208-937-2458. Fax: 208-937-2458. p. 577

Harris, Sherelle, Asst Dir, Norwalk Public Library, One Belden Ave, Norwalk, CT, 06850. Tel: 203-899-2780. Fax: 203-857-4410. p. 362

Harris, Sherri, Libr Serv Dir, Sandersville Technical College, 1189 Deepstep Rd, Sandersville, GA, 31082. Tel: 478-553-2070. Fax: 478-553-2117. p. 549

Harris, Stacey, Ref & Info Serv, Port Chester-Rye Brook Public Library, One Haseco Ave, Port Chester, NY, 10573. Tel: 914-939-6710. Fax: 914-939-4735. p. 1720

Harris, Stephanie, Ref Serv, Orlando Health, 1414 Kuhl Ave, MP 28, Orlando, FL, 32806-2134. Tel: 321-841-5454. Fax: 321-843-6825. p. 477

Harris, Susan, Dir, Holmes County Public Library, 303 N J Harvey Etheridge, Bonifay, FL, 32425. Tel: 850-547-3573. Fax: 850-547-2801. p. 429

Harris, Susan, Head, Circ, Easttown Library & Information Center, 720 First Ave, Berwyn, PA, 19312-1769. Tel: 610-644-0138. Fax: 610-251-9739. p. 2033

Harris, Susie, Libr Asst, Fisk University, Fisk University, 1000 17th Ave N, Nashville, TN, 37208-3051. Tel: 615-329-8640. Fax: 615-329-8761. p. 2256

Harris, Suzan, Librn, Bartram Trail Regional Library, Thomson-McDuffie County, 338 Main St, Thomson, GA, 30824. Tel: 706-595-1341. Fax: 706-597-9458. p. 556

Harris, Tammie, Tech Serv, Pine Bluff & Jefferson County Library System, Main Library, 200 E Eighth Ave, Pine Bluff, AR, 71601. Tel: 870-534-4802. Fax: 870-534-8707. p. 112

Harris, Terry, Circ, ILL, Cynthiana-Harrison County Public Library, 104 N Main St, Cynthiana, KY, 41031. Tel: 859-234-4881. Fax: 859-234-0059. p. 911

Harris, Tina, Br Mgr, Russell County Public Library, Honaker Community Library, Ten Library Dr, Honaker, VA, 24260. Tel: 276-873-6600. Fax: 276-873-5800. p. 2473

Harris, Toby, Head Librn, Temple De Hirsch Sinai Library, 1511 E Pike, Seattle, WA, 98122. Tel: 206-315-7398. Fax: 206-324-6772. p. 2532

Harris, Toby, Lead Librn, Temple De Hirsch Sinai Library, Bellevue Branch, 3850 156th Ave SE, Bellevue, WA, 98006. Tel: 206-323-8486, Ext 7481. p. 2532

Harris, Tonia, Mgr, Libr Serv, Spartanburg Regional Medical Center, 101 E Wood St, Spartanburg, SC, 29303. Tel: 864-560-6220. Fax: 864-560-6791. p. 2205

Harris, Wynn, Media Spec, Central New Mexico Community College Libraries, 525 Buena Vista SE, Albuquerque, NM, 87106-4023. Tel: 505-224-3284. Fax: 505-224-3321. p. 1548

Harris, Yvonne, Br Mgr, Prince George's County Memorial, Surratts-Clinton Branch, 9400 Piscataway Rd, Clinton, MD, 20735-3632. Tel: 301-868-9200. Fax: 301-856-9369. p. 1033

Harris-Jackman, Dionne, Libr Spec, Columbia University, Social Work Library, Columbia University School of Social Work, 1255 Amsterdam Ave, 2nd Flr, New York, NY, 10027. Tel: 212-851-2197. Fax: 212-851-2199. p. 1675

Harris-Wheatley, Janine, Chief Exec Officer, Essa Public Library, 8505 County Rd 10, Unit 1, Angus, ON, L0M 1B1, CANADA. Tel: 705-424-6531. Fax: 705-424-5521. p. 2792

Harris-Wheatley, Janine, Chief Exec Officer, Essa Public Library, Thornton Branch, 34 Robert St, Thornton, ON, L0L 2N0, CANADA. Tel: 705-424-6531. Fax: 705-458-1820. p. 2792

Harrison, April H, Librn, Pleasant Grove Public Library, 30 E Center St, Pleasant Grove, UT, 84062-2234. Tel: 801-785-3950. Fax: 801-785-9734. p. 2410

Harrison, Beryl, Ref, Cyrenius H Booth Library, 25 Main St, Newtown, CT, 06470. Tel: 203-426-4533. Fax: 203-426-2196. p. 361

Harrison, Beulah, Mgr, Northwest Regional Library System, Charles Whitehead Wewahitchka Public Library, 314 North Second St, Wewahitchka, FL, 32465. Tel: 850-639-2419. Fax: 850-639-3862. p. 481

Harrison, Bill, Head, Tech Serv, Parsippany-Troy Hills Free Public Library, 449 Halsey Rd, Parsippany, NJ, 07054. Tel: 973-887-5150. Fax: 973-887-0062. p. 1517

Harrison, Brenda, Librn, Bellevue Township Library, 212 N Main St, Bellevue, MI, 49021. Tel: 269-763-3369. Fax: 269-763-3369. p. 1156

Harrison, Cynthia, Sci/Eng Librn, Youngstown State University, One University Plaza, Youngstown, OH, 44555-0001. Tel: 330-941-3680. Fax: 330-941-3734. p. 1953

Harrison, Cynthia, Dir, Anacortes Public Library, 1220 Tenth St, Anacortes, WA, 98221-1922. Tel: 360-293-1926, Ext 23. Fax: 360-293-1929. p. 2507

Harrison, Cynthia L, Coordr, Tech Serv, Norfolk State University Library, 700 Park Ave, Norfolk, VA, 23504-8010. Tel: 757-823-2422. Fax: 757-823-2431. p. 2482

Harrison, Daniel, Syst Adminr, Henry Ford Community College, 5101 Evergreen Rd, Dearborn, MI, 48128-1495. Tel: 313-845-6376. Fax: 313-845-9795. p. 1167

Harrison, Danielle, Head Librn, MPR Associates, Inc, 320 King St, Alexandria, VA, 22314-3238. Tel: 703-519-0567. Fax: 703-519-0226. p. 2446

Harrison, Darrell, Librn, Osborn Correctional Institution, 335 Bilton Rd, Somers, CT, 06071. Tel: 860-566-7500, Ext 5471, 860-566-7500, Ext 5478. Fax: 860-763-3157. p. 367

Harrison, Dorothy, Br Mgr, Athens Regional Library System, Lay Park Community Resource Center, 297 Hoyt St, Athens, GA, 30601. Tel: 706-613-3667. Fax: 706-613-3667. p. 508

Harrison, Eva Jane, Reader Serv, Ch, Library for the Blind & Physically Handicapped, 900 W Capitol Ave, Ste 100, Little Rock, AR, 72201-3108. Tel: 501-682-2871. Fax: 501-682-1529. p. 106

Harrison, Fabian, Head Librn, SIAST-Saskatchewan Institute of Applied Science & Technology, ldylwyld Dr & 33rd St W, Saskatoon, SK, S7K 3R5, CANADA. Tel: 306-659-4240. Fax: 306-964-1222. p. 2927

Harrison, Gwen, Network Serv, Illinois State Library, Gwendolyn Brooks Bldg, 300 S Second St, Springfield, IL, 62701-9713. Tel: 217-785-5334. Fax: 217-785-4326. p. 705

Harrison, Heather, Br Mgr, East Baton Rouge Parish Library, Central, 11260 Joor Rd, Baton Rouge, LA, 70818. Tel: 225-262-2655. Fax: 225-262-2649. p. 943

Harrison, Isom, Dir, Lawrence Livermore National Laboratory Library, 7000 East Ave, Livermore, CA, 94550. Tel: 925-424-6105. Fax: 925-424-2921. p. 164

Harrison, Jann, Coordr, CHRISTUS Santa Rosa Health Care, 333 N Santa Rosa St, San Antonio, TX, 78207-3198. Tel: 210-704-2284. Fax: 210-704-3177. p. 2379

Harrison, Jeffrey C, Dir, Kraemer Library & Community Center, 910 Main St, Plain, WI, 53577. Tel: 608-546-4201. Fax: 608-546-4201. p. 2630

Harrison, Jerri, Cat, Paulina June & George Pollak Library, 800 N State College Blvd, Fullerton, CA, 92834. Tel: 714-278-2714. Fax: 714-278-2439. p. 154

Harrison, John C, Assoc Col Librn for Coll Develop & Bibliog Serv, Bates College, 48 Campus Ave, Lewiston, ME, 04240. Tel: 207-786-6270. Fax: 207-786-6055. p. 989

Harrison, Laura, Dir, Brooks County Public Library, 404 Barwick Rd, Quitman, GA, 31643. Tel: 229-263-4412. Fax: 229-263-8002. p. 547

Harrison, Laurie, Head, Ch, Riverhead Free Library, 330 Court St, Riverhead, NY, 11901-2885. Tel: 631-727-3228. Fax: 631-727-4762. p. 1728

Harrison, Linda, Coord, Ad Serv, ILL, Clovis-Carver Public Library, 701 N Main, Clovis, NM, 88101. Tel: 505-769-7840. Fax: 505-769-7842. p. 1553

Harrison, Linda, Br Mgr, Nashville Public Library, East, 206 Gallatin Rd, Nashville, TN, 37206-3240. Tel: 615-862-5860. Fax: 615-862-5807. p. 2257

Harrison, Lynn, Sr Asst Librn, Haldimand County Public Library, Dunnville Branch, 317 Chestnut St, Dunnville, ON, N1A 2H4, CANADA. Tel: 905-774-4240. Fax: 905-774-2530. p. 2803

Harrison, Marcia, Head, Tech Serv, Swampscott Public Library, 61 Burrill St, Swampscott, MA, 01907. Tel: 781-596-8867. Fax: 781-596-8826. p. 1130

Harrison, Margaret, Chief, Libr Serv, United States Army, Marquat Memorial Library, Bank Hall, Bldg D-3915, 3004 Ardennes St, Fort Bragg, NC, 28310-9610. Tel: 910-396-3958. Fax: 910-432-7788. p. 1794

Harrison, Margaret C, Coordr, Outreach Serv, State Library of Louisiana, 701 N Fourth St, Baton Rouge, LA, 70802. Tel: 225-342-0035. Fax: 225-342-6817. p. 944

Harrison, Marjorie, Dir, San Juan Island Library District, 1010 Guard St, Friday Harbor, WA, 98250-9612. Tel: 360-378-2798. Fax: 360-378-2706. p. 2516

Harrison, Mark, Librn, Saint Herman Theological Seminary Library, 414 Mission Rd, Kodiak, AK, 99615. Tel: 907-486-3524. Fax: 907-486-5935. p. 51

Harrison, Mary, Ch, Public Library for Union County, 255 Reitz Blvd, Lewisburg, PA, 17837-9211. Tel: 570-523-1172. Fax: 570-524-7771. p. 2081

Harrison, Paula, Asst Dir, Costilla County Library, Blanca-Ft Garland Branch, 17591 E Hwy 160, Blanca, CO, 81123. Tel: 719-379-3945. Fax: 719-379-3945. p. 322

Harrison, Randal, Web Developer, Michigan Technological University, 1400 Townsend Dr, Houghton, MI, 49931-1295. Tel: 906-487-1482. p. 1191

Harrison, Ray, Info Serv Librn, Richmond Heights Memorial Library, 8001 Dale Ave, Richmond Heights, MO, 63117. Tel: 314-645-6202. Fax: 314-781-3434. p. 1350

Harrison, Sally, Br Mgr, Ocean County Library, Waretown Branch, 112 Main St, Waretown, NJ, 08758-9252. Tel: 609-693-5133. Fax: 609-242-8784. p. 1535

Harrison, Scot, Dir, Saint Martin's University, 5300 Pacific Ave SE, Lacey, WA, 98503. Tel: 360-486-8808. Fax: 360-486-8810. p. 2519

Harrison, Shelley, Archives Mgr, Blue Earth County Historical Society, 415 E Cherry St, Mankato, MN, 56001. Tel: 507-345-5566. p. 1257

Harrison, Stewart, Head of Libr, Defence Research & Development Canada-Toronto Library, 1133 Sheppard Ave W, Toronto, ON, M3K 2C9, CANADA. Tel: 416-635-2070. Fax: 416-635-2104. p. 2852

Harrison, Tanja, Univ Librn, Mount Saint Vincent University Library, 166 Bedford Hwy, Halifax, NS, B3M 2J6, CANADA. Tel: 902-457-6108. Fax: 902-457-6445. p. 2781

Harrison, Terrence, Archivist, Mason City Public Library, 225 Second St SE, Mason City, IA, 50401. Tel: 641-421-3668. Fax: 641-423-2615. p. 830

Harrison, Tracey, Librn, Missouri Department of Corrections, Northeast Correctional Center, 13698 Airport Rd, Bowling Green, MO, 63334. Tel: 573-324-9975. Fax: 573-324-5028. p. 1335

Harrison-Cox, Lucinda, Assoc Law Librn, Roger Williams University, Ten Metacom Ave, Bristol, RI, 02809-5171. Tel: 401-254-4533. Fax: 401-254-4543. p. 2163

Harrison-Thomas, Suzanne, Ch, Milford Public Library, 57 New Haven Ave, Milford, CT, 06460. Tel: 203-783-3312. Fax: 203-877-1072. p. 352

Harriston, Victoria, Mgr, The National Academies, 500 Fifth St NW, Keck 304, Washington, DC, 20001-2721. Tel: 202-334-2125. Fax: 202-334-1651. p. 409

Harrod, Thomas, Librn, University of Maryland Libraries, White Memorial Chemistry Library, 1526 Chemistry Bldg, College Park, MD, 20742-7011. Tel: 301-405-9078. Fax: 301-405-9164. p. 1025

Harron, Laura, Ref Serv, Theresa Public Library, 290 Mayville St, Theresa, WI, 53091-0307. Tel: 920-488-2342. Fax: 920-488-2342. p. 2642

Harrow, Andrea, Managing Dir, Good Samaritan Hospital, 637 S Lucas Ave, Los Angeles, CA, 90017. Tel: 213-977-2047, 213-977-2323. Fax: 213-977-2325. p. 170

Harrow, Christopher, Librn, Chinook Regional Library, Swift Current Branch, R C Dahl Ctr, 411 Herbert St E, Swift Current, SK, S9H 1M5, CANADA. Tel: 306-778-2752. Fax: 306-773-8769. p. 2928

Harrow, Mary, Readers' Advisory, Peninsula Public Library, 280 Central Ave, Lawrence, NY, 11559. Tel: 516-239-3262. Fax: 516-239-8425. p. 1651

Harrow, Ruth, Asst Librn, Haynes Library, 33 Washburn Rd, Alexandria, NH, 03222-6532. Tel: 603-744-6529. p. 1437

Harry, Cindy, Syst Adminr, Cherokee County Public Library, 300 E Rutledge Ave, Gaffney, SC, 29340-2227. Tel: 864-487-2711. Fax: 864-487-2752. p. 2194

Harsh, Judith, Librn, Howard City Library, 126 S Wabash, Howard, KS, 67349. Tel: 620-374-2890. p. 872

Harshbarger, May, Head Librn, Mercy Health Center, 4300 W Memorial Rd, Oklahoma City, OK, 73120. Tel: 405-752-3390. Fax: 405-752-3670. p. 1972

Harshbarger, Tammy, Br Mgr, Clark County Public Library, Houston, Five W Jamestown St, South Charleston, OH, 45368. Tel: 937-462-8047. p. 1935

Harshfield, Susan, Librn, Genesee District Library, Montrose-Jennings Library, 241 Feher Dr, Montrose, MI, 48457. Tel: 810-639-6388. Fax: 810-639-3675. p. 1180

Harshman, Cheryl, Dir, West Liberty University, CSC No 135, West Liberty, WV, 26074. Tel: 304-336-8035. Fax: 304-336-8186. p. 2574

Harsin, Steven D, Exec VPres, Mus & Libr, Ironworld Discovery Center, 801 SW Hwy 169, Ste 1, Chisholm, MN, 55719. Tel: 218-254-1220. Fax: 218-254-7971. p. 1245

Harston, Julie, Ref Librn, Lipscomb University, One University Park Dr, Nashville, TN, 37204-3951. Tel: 615-966-5717. Fax: 615-966-5874. p. 2257

Harston, Lisa, Librn, Leeds & the Thousand Islands Public Library, Lyndhurst Branch, 426 Lyndhurst Rd, Lyndhurst, ON, K0E 1N0, CANADA. Tel: 613-928-2277. Fax: 613-928-2816. p. 2815

Hart, Barbara, Libr Tech, Department of Veterans Affairs, 1901 Veterans Memorial Dr, 14LIB-T, Temple, TX, 76504. Tel: 254-743-0607. Fax: 254-743-0183. p. 2390

Hart, Cynthia, Dir, La Marque Public Library, 1011 Bayou Rd, La Marque, TX, 77568-4195. Tel: 409-938-9270. Fax: 409-938-9277. p. 2352

Hart, Douglas, Librn, South University, 9801 Belvedere Rd, Royal Palm Beach, FL, 33411-3640. Tel: 561-273-6401. Fax: 561-273-6420. p. 485

Hart, Elizabeth, In Charge, California School for the Blind, 500 Walnut Ave, Fremont, CA, 94536. Tel: 510-794-3800, Ext 259. Fax: 510-794-3813. p. 149

Hart, Elizabeth, Librn, Logan-Hocking County District Library, Laurelville Branch, 16240 Maple St, Laurelville, OH, 43135. Tel: 740-332-4700. Fax: 740-332-1379. p. 1910

Hart, Emily, Health Sci Librn, Wayne State University Libraries, Vera P Shiffman Medical Library & Learning Resources Centers, Rackham Bldg Rm 044, 60 Farnsworth, Detroit, MI, 48202. Tel: 313-577-1088. Fax: 313-577-6668. p. 1173

Hart, George, Assoc Univ Librn, University of Massachusetts at Boston, 100 Morrissey Blvd, Boston, MA, 02125-3300. Tel: 617-287-5923. p. 1068

Hart, Holly, Ch, Onondaga Free Library, 4840 W Seneca Tpk, Syracuse, NY, 13215. Tel: 315-492-1727. Fax: 315-492-1323. p. 1753

Hart, James, Ref Librn, University of Cincinnati, 2540 Clifton Ave, Cincinnati, OH, 45219. Tel: 513-556-0160. Fax: 513-556-6265. p. 1874

Hart, Jan, Sr Archivist, Irving Public Library, 801 W Irving Blvd, Irving, TX, 75015. Tel: 972-721-3729. Fax: 972-721-2463. p. 2346

Hart, Jeff, Mgr, Dow Chemical Library, Business Intelligence Ctr, B-1210, 2301 Brazosport Blvd, Freeport, TX, 77541. Tel: 979-238-2011, 979-238-4854. p. 2325

Hart, Jennifer, Librn, University of Chicago Library, Eckhart Library, 1118 E 58th St, Chicago, IL, 60637. Tel: 773-702-8774. Fax: 773-702-7535. p. 627

Hart, Jennifer, Asst Librn, Vermont Regional Library for the Blind & Physically Handicapped, Vermont Dept of Libraries Special Services Unit, 578 Paine Turnpike N, Berlin, VT, 05602. Tel: 802-828-3273. Fax: 802-828-2199. p. 2419

Hart, Joan, Sr Librn, Kearny Public Library, 318 Kearny Ave, Kearny, NJ, 07032. Tel: 201-998-2666. Fax: 201-998-1141. p. 1493

Hart, Judith E, Dir, Lewis & Clark Library, 120 S Last Chance Gulch, Helena, MT, 59601. Tel: 406-447-1690. Fax: 406-447-1687. p. 1382

Hart, Julie, Libr Dir, McCracken County Public Library, 555 Washington St, Paducah, KY, 42003-1735. Tel: 270-442-2510, Ext 13. Fax: 270-443-9322. p. 932

Hart, Karen, Exec Dir, Mary Ball Washington Museum & Library, Inc, 8346 Mary Ball Rd, Lancaster, VA, 22503. Tel: 804-462-7280. Fax: 804-462-6107. p. 2473

Hart, Karen C, Ad, Choctaw County Public Library, 703 E Jackson St, Hugo, OK, 74743. Tel: 580-326-5591. Fax: 580-326-7388. p. 1966

Hart, Kathleen, Prog Coordr, Canterbury Public Library, One Municipal Dr, Canterbury, CT, 06331-1453. Tel: 860-546-9022. Fax: 860-546-1142. p. 333

Hart, Kim, Libr Tech, Billings Clinic, 2825 Eighth Ave N, Billings, MT, 59107. Tel: 406-238-2226. Fax: 406-238-2253. p. 1374

Hart, Kristin, Librn, Adelphi University, 75 Varick St, New York, NY, 10013. Tel: 212-965-8340. Fax: 212-965-8367. p. 1667

Hart, Lanette, Asst Dir, Sharon Public Library, 11 N Main St, Sharon, MA, 02067-1299. Tel: 781-784-1578. Fax: 781-784-4728. p. 1123

Hart, Lea, Mgr, Delta County Libraries, Delta Public Library, 211 W Sixth St, Delta, CO, 81416. Tel: 970-874-9630. Fax: 970-874-8605. p. 313

Hart, Loretta, Adult Serv, Fort Worth Library, 500 W Third St, Fort Worth, TX, 76102. Tel: 817-871-7701. Fax: 817-871-7734. p. 2321

Hart, Lorraine, Librn, R L Banks & Associates Inc Library, 2107 Wilson Blvd, Ste 750, Arlington, VA, 22201. Tel: 703-276-7522. Fax: 703-276-7732. p. 2449

Hart, Marilyn, Librn, City College, 177 Montgomery Rd, Altamonte Springs, FL, 32714-3129. Tel: 407-831-9816. Fax: 407-831-1147. p. 425

Hart, Mary K, Librn, San Diego Miramar College, 10440 Black Mountain Rd, San Diego, CA, 92126-2999. Tel: 619-388-7614. Fax: 619-388-7918. p. 235

Hart, Melanie Dawn, Libr Tech, Carnegie Public Library, South Fork Branch, 0031 Mall St, South Fork, CO, 81154. Tel: 719-873-5079. Fax: 719-873-5192. p. 318

Hart, Mildred, Supvr, Circ, Elko-Lander-Eureka County Library System, 720 Court St, Elko, NV, 89801. Tel: 775-738-3066. Fax: 775-738-8262. p. 1426

Hart, Patricia, Ref Librn, Chapman University School of Law, 370 N Glassell St, Rm 325, Orange, CA, 92866. Tel: 714-628-2537. p. 201

Hart, Patricia, Cat Librn, University of Washington Libraries, Marian Gould Gallagher Law Library, William H Gates Hall, Box 353025, Seattle, WA, 98195-3025. Tel: 206-543-6516. Fax: 206-685-2165. p. 2534

Hart, Paula, Br Asst, Los Angeles County Law Library, Torrance, S Bay County Bldg, Rm 110, 825 Maple Ave, Torrance, CA, 90503. Tel: 310-222-8816. Fax: 310-320-9734. p. 172

Hart, Regina, Librn, Michael Baker Jr, Inc Library, 4301 Dutch Ridge Rd, Beaver, PA, 15009. Tel: 724-495-4021. Fax: 724-495-4001. p. 2031

Hart, Richard, Info Serv Supvr, Forbes Library, 20 West St, Northampton, MA, 01060-3798. Tel: 413-587-1011. Fax: 413-587-1015. p. 1113

Hart, Richard L, Dir, Penn State Erie, 4951 College Dr, Erie, PA, 16563-4115. Tel: 814-898-6106. Fax: 814-898-6350. p. 2056

Hart, Sarah, Librn, Insurance Library Association of Boston, 156 State St, Boston, MA, 02109. Tel: 617-227-2087. Fax: 617-723-8524. p. 1062

Hart, Shery, Acq, Jefferson County Rural Library District, 620 Cedar Ave, Port Hadlock, WA, 98339-9514. Tel: 360-385-6544. Fax: 360-385-7921. p. 2524

Hart, Susan, Dir, Rushford Public Library, 101 N Mill St, Rushford, MN, 55971. Tel: 507-864-7600. Fax: 507-864-7003. p. 1273

Hart, Susan, Chief Exec Officer, Librn, Billings Township Public Library, 18 Upper St, Kagawong, ON, P0P 1J0, CANADA. Tel: 705-282-2944. p. 2812

Hart, Victoria, Dir, Tri-Township Public Library District, 209 S Main St, Troy, IL, 62294. Tel: 618-667-2133. Fax: 618-667-9866. p. 710

Hart, Virginia, Librn, Pilgrim Congregational Church, Four Watson St, Nashua, NH, 03064. Tel: 603-882-1801. Fax: 603-882-1801. p. 1459

Hartel, Lynda J, Head, Acq, Ohio State University LIBRARIES, John A Prior Health Sciences Library, 376 W Tenth Ave, Columbus, OH, 43210-1240. Tel: 614-292-4892. Fax: 614-292-1920. p. 1889

Harter, Christopher, Dir, Ref & Libr Serv, Amistad Research Center, Tulane University, Tilton Hall, 6823 St Charles Ave, New Orleans, LA, 70118. Tel: 504-862-3229. Fax: 504-862-8961. p. 959

Harter, Dale, Archivist, Curator, Bridgewater College, 402 E College St, Bridgewater, VA, 22812. Tel: 540-828-5457. Fax: 540-828-5482. p. 2452

Hartford, Brenda, Librn, Harvey Memorial Library, 771 State Hwy 150, Parkman, ME, 04443-3201. Tel: 207-876-3730. p. 995

Harthorn, Sandy, Curator, Boise Art Museum Library, 670 Julia Davis Dr, Boise, ID, 83702. Tel: 208-345-8330, Ext 19. Fax: 208-345-2247. p. 570

Hartig, Linda, Dr, Ref, Carroll College, 100 N East Ave, Waukesha, WI, 53186. Tel: 262-524-7179. Fax: 262-524-7377. p. 2644

Hartigan, Annette, Librn, US National Park Service, 107 Park Headquarters Rd, Gatlinburg, TN, 37738. Tel: 865-436-1296. Fax: 865-436-1220. p. 2235

Hartigan, Christine, Dir, Wood-Ridge Memorial Library, 231 Hackensack St, Wood-Ridge, NJ, 07075. Tel: 201-438-2455. Fax: 201-438-8399. p. 1546

Hartin, Linda, Circ, ILL, Morristown Centennial Library, Seven Richmond St, Morrisville, VT, 05661. Tel: 802-888-3853. p. 2430

Hartke, Lynn, Ref, Saint Louis University, Omer Poos Law Library, Morrissey Hall, 3700 Lindell Blvd, Saint Louis, MO, 63108-3478. Tel: 314-977-2756. Fax: 314-977-3966. p. 1361

Hartkorn, Stacy, Br Supvr, Spokane County Library District, Airway Heights Library, 1213 S Lundstrom, Airway Heights, WA, 99001-9000. Tel: 509-893-8250. Fax: 509-893-8473. p. 2537

Hartley, Bill, Dir, Media Serv, North Park University, Brandel Library, 5114 N Christiana Ave, Chicago, IL, 60625. Tel: 773-244-5579. Fax: 773-244-4891. p. 620

Hartley, Dorothy, Asst Librn, Buffalo Public Library, Hwy 79, Buffalo, TX, 75831. Tel: 903-322-4146. Fax: 903-322-3253. p. 2293

Hartley, Jeffery, Dir, National Archives & Records Administration, 8601 Adelphi Rd, Rm 2380, College Park, MD, 20740. Tel: 301-837-1795. Fax: 301-837-0459. p. 1024

Hartley, Kathy, Asst Librn, Lewis County Public Library, 52 Second St, Vanceburg, KY, 41179. Tel: 606-796-2532. Fax: 606-796-2532. p. 936

Hartley, Lauran, Coll Develop/Ref Librn, Columbia University, C V Starr East Asian Library, 300 Kent Hall, MC 3901, 1140 Amsterdam Ave, New York, NY, 10027. Tel: 212-854-4318. Fax: 212-662-6286. p. 1675

Hartley, Leslie, Adult Serv, Chillicothe & Ross County Public Library, 140 S Paint St, Chillicothe, OH, 45601. Tel: 740-702-4145. Fax: 740-702-4153. p. 1867

Hartley, Pam, Supvr, Circ, Tigard Public Library, 13500 SW Hall Blvd, Tigard, OR, 97223-8111. Tel: 503-684-6537, Ext 2510. Fax: 503-598-7515, 503-718-2797. p. 2021

Hartley, Shirley, Br Mgr, Cass District Library, Edwardsburg Branch, 26745 Church St, Edwardsburg, MI, 49112. Tel: 269-663-5875. Fax: 269-663-6215. p. 1161

Hartley, Susan, Ch, Cheshire Public Library, 104 Main St, Cheshire, CT, 06410-2499. Tel: 203-272-2245. Fax: 203-272-7714. p. 333

Hartman, Britni, Dir, Schmaling Memorial Public Library District, 501 Tenth Ave, Fulton, IL, 61252. Tel: 815-589-2045. Fax: 815-589-4483. p. 647

Hartman, Caroline, Dir, Cumberland Public Library, 119 Main St, Cumberland, IA, 50843-9900. Tel: 712-774-5334. Fax: 712-774-5334. p. 805

Hartman, Cathy, Assoc Dean, University of North Texas Libraries, PO Box 305190, Denton, TX, 76203-5190. Tel: 940-565-3269. Fax: 940-369-8760. p. 2313

Hartman, Chris, Syst & Distance Learning Librn, Central New Mexico Community College Libraries, 525 Buena Vista SE, Albuquerque, NM, 87106-4023. Tel: 505-224-3292. Fax: 505-224-3321. p. 1548

Hartman, Deborah, Br Mgr, Allegany County Library System, George's Creek, 76 Main St, Lonaconing, MD, 21539. Tel: 301-463-2629. Fax: 301-463-2485. p. 1026

Hartman, Fritz, Head, Tech Serv, Ser & Syst, Goshen College, Harold & Wilma Good Library, 1700 S Main, Goshen, IN, 46526-4794. Tel: 574-535-7423. Fax: 574-535-7438. p. 745

Hartman, Judy, Dir, Mechanicsville Public Library, 218 E First St, Mechanicsville, IA, 52306. Tel: 563-432-7135. Fax: 563-432-7135. p. 831

Hartman, Krista, Cataloger, Mohawk Valley Community College Library, 1101 Sherman Dr, Utica, NY, 13501-5394. Tel: 315-792-5399. Fax: 315-792-5666. p. 1759

Hartman, Lianne, Instrul Serv/Ref Librn, Gwynedd-Mercy College, 1325 Sumneytown Pike, Gwynedd Valley, PA, 19437. Tel: 215-646-7300, Ext 493. Fax: 215-641-5596. p. 2063

Hartman, Linda, Archivist, Wakarusa Public Library, 124 N Elkhart St, Wakarusa, IN, 46573. Tel: 574-862-2465. Fax: 574-862-4156. p. 785

Hartman, Lisa A, Govt Doc Coordr, Frostburg State University, One Stadium Dr, Frostburg, MD, 21532. Tel: 301-687-4734. Fax: 301-687-7069. p. 1029

Hartman, Lisa A, Ref/Instruction Librn, Harrisburg Area Community College, 2010 Pennsylvania Ave, York, PA, 17404. Tel: 717-718-0328, Ext 3556. Fax: 717-718-8967. p. 2159

Hartman, Lois R, Dir, Watervliet District Library, 333 N Main St, Watervliet, MI, 49098-9793. Tel: 269-463-6382. Fax: 269-463-3117. p. 1235

Hartman, Lori, Dir, Morrill Public Library, 119 E Webster, Morrill, NE, 69358. Tel: 308-247-2611. Fax: 308-247-2309. p. 1409

Hartman, Mary, Dir, Peabody Public Library, 1160 E Hwy Rd 205, Columbia City, IN, 46725. Tel: 260-244-5541. Fax: 260-244-5653. p. 733

Hartman, Mary, Adult Serv, Kendallville Public Library, 221 S Park Ave, Kendallville, IN, 46755-2248. Tel: 260-343-2010. Fax: 260-343-2011. p. 756

Hartman, Mary, Assoc Librn, Pub Serv, Clark University, 950 Main St, Worcester, MA, 01610-1477. Tel: 508-793-7711. Fax: 508-793-8871. p. 1143

Hartman, Matt, Sr Librn, California Department of Corrections Library System, Chuckawalla Valley State Prison, 19025 Wiley's Well Rd, Blythe, CA, 92225. Tel: 760-922-5300. Fax: 760-922-9755. p. 221

Hartman, Maureen, Coord Librn, Youth Learning/Literacy & Libr Mgt, Hennepin County Library, Eden Prairie, 565 Prairie Center Dr, Eden Prairie, MN, 55344-5319. Tel: 612-543-8141. Fax: 612-543-6277. p. 1263

Hartman, Maureen, Coord Librn, Youth Learning/Literacy & Libr Mgt, Hennepin County Library, Hopkins, 22 11th Ave N, Hopkins, MN, 55343-7575. Tel: 612-543-8141. Fax: 612-543-6402. p. 1263

Hartman, Maureen, Coordr Librn, Adult Learning/Literacy & Libr Mgt, Hennepin County Library, East Lake, 2727 E Lake St, Minneapolis, MN, 55406. Tel: 612-543-8141. Fax: 612-543-8427. p. 1263

Hartman, Maureen, Coord Librn, Youth Learning/Literacy & Libr Mgt, Hennepin County Library, Nokomis, 5100 34th Ave S, Minneapolis, MN, 55417-1545. Tel: 612-543-8141. Fax: 612-543-6802. p. 1264

Hartman, Maureen, Coord Librn, Youth Learning/Literacy & Libr Mgt, Hennepin County Library, Osseo, 415 Central Ave, Osseo, MN, 55369-1194. Tel: 612-543-8141. Fax: 612-543-5752. p. 1264

Hartman, Maureen, Coord Librn, Youth Learning/Literacy & Libr Mgt, Hennepin County Library, Saint Louis Park, 3240 Library Lane, Saint Louis Park, MN, 55426-4101. Tel: 612-543-8141. Fax: 612-543-6127. p. 1264

Hartman, Maureen, Coord Librn, Youth Learning/Literacy & Libr Mgt, Hennepin County Library, Southeast, 1222 4th St SE, Minneapolis, MN, 55414. Tel: 612-543-8141. Fax: 612-543-6727. p. 1264

Hartman, Maureen, Coord Librn, Youth Learning, Hennepin County Library, Maple Grove, 8001 Main St N, Maple Grove, MN, 55369-4617. Tel: 612-543-8141. Fax: 612-543-6452. p. 1264

Hartman, Nancy, Ref & Info Serv, Web Coordr, West Lafayette Public Library, 208 W Columbia St, West Lafayette, IN, 47906. Tel: 765-743-2261. Fax: 765-743-0540. p. 787

Hartman, Peg, Librn, Arizona State Schools for the Deaf & the Blind Library, 1200 W Speedway, Tucson, AZ, 85745. Tel: 520-770-3462. Fax: 520-770-3752. p. 85

Hartman, Rachael, Mgr, Geauga County Public Library, Middlefield Library, 16167 E High St, Middlefield, OH, 44062. Tel: 440-632-1961. Fax: 440-632-1407. p. 1867

Hartman, Regina, Mgr, Christ Hospital, 2139 Auburn Ave, Cincinnati, OH, 45219. Tel: 513-585-2737. Fax: 513-585-4353. p. 1868

Hartman, Robin R, Dir of Libr Serv, Hope International University, 2500 E Nutwood Ave, Fullerton, CA, 92831. Tel: 714-879-3901, Ext 1212. Fax: 714-681-7515. p. 154

Hartman, Rochelle, Head, Ref (Info Serv), La Crosse Public Library, 800 Main St, La Crosse, WI, 54601. Tel: 608-789-8191. Fax: 608-789-7161. p. 2603

Hartman, Sarah, Tech Serv, Middleton Public Library, 7425 Hubbard Ave, Middleton, WI, 53562-3117. Tel: 608-827-7421. Fax: 608-836-5724. p. 2616

Hartman, Shawn, Asst Dir, Pub Serv, Chadron State College, 300 E 12th St, Chadron, NE, 69337. Tel: 308-432-6271. p. 1395

Hartman, Shawn, Asst Prog Dir, Chadron State College, Reta King Library, 300 E 12th St, Chadron, NE, 69337-2675. Tel: 308-432-6271. Fax: 308-432-6409. p. 2969

Hartman, Stephanie, Info Serv, Massachusetts Institute of Technology Libraries, Barker Engineering, Bldg 10-500, 77 Massachusetts Ave, Cambridge, MA, 02139-4307. Tel: 617-253-9361. Fax: 617-258-5623. p. 1077

Hartman, Stephanie, Info Serv, Massachusetts Institute of Technology Libraries, Science, Bldg 14S-134, 77 Massachusetts Ave, Cambridge, MA, 02139-4307. Tel: 617-253-9361. Fax: 617-253-6365. p. 1078

Hartmann, Anna, Teen Librn, Council Bluffs Public Library, 400 Willow Ave, Council Bluffs, IA, 51503-4269. Tel: 712-323-7553, Ext 105. Fax: 712-323-1269. p. 805

Hartmann, Carey, Dep County Librn, Laramie County Library System, 2200 Pioneer Ave, Cheyenne, WY, 82001-3610. Tel: 307-773-7222. Fax: 307-634-2082. p. 2652

Hartmann, Eric J, Archivist, Catholic Archives of Texas, 1600 N Congress, Austin, TX, 78711. Tel: 512-476-6296. Fax: 512-476-3715. p. 2280

Hartmann, Jonathan, Hospital Informationist/Hospital Outreach Librn, Georgetown University, Dahlgren Memorial Library, Preclinical Science Bldg GM-7, 3900 Reservoir Rd NW, Washington, DC, 20007. Tel: 202-687-1308. Fax: 202-687-1862. p. 402

Hartmann, Sharon, Coordr, Acq, Goucher College Library, 1021 Dulaney Valley Rd, Baltimore, MD, 21204. Tel: 410-337-6409. Fax: 410-337-6419. p. 1014

Hartness, Ann, Head Librn, University of Texas Libraries, Nettie Lee Benson Latin American Collection, Sid Richardson Hall 1-108, Austin, TX, 78713-8916. Tel: 512-495-4520. Fax: 512-495-4568. p. 2283

Hartnett, Ann, Asst Dir, Hinsdale Public Library, 122 Brattleboro Rd, Hinsdale, NH, 03451. Tel: 603-336-5713. p. 1451

Hartnett, Tim, Assoc Librn, Coordr, Info Outreach, State University of New York College at Plattsburgh, Two Draper Ave, Plattsburgh, NY, 12901-2697. Tel: 518-564-5205. Fax: 518-564-5209. p. 1719

Hartog, John, II, Libr Dir, Faith Baptist Bible College & Theological Seminary, 1900 NW Fourth St, Ankeny, IA, 50023. Tel: 515-964-0601. Fax: 515-964-1638. p. 793

Harton, Jack, Ref Librn, Highline Community College Library, 2400 S 240th St, MS 25-4, Des Moines, WA, 98198. Tel: 206-878-3710, Ext 3806. Fax: 206-870-3776. p. 2514

Hartough, Joanne, ILL, University of Toledo, 2801 W Bancroft St, Mail Stop 509, Toledo, OH, 43606-3390. Tel: 419-530-2808. Fax: 419-530-2726. p. 1941

Hartsberg, Debra, Br Mgr, Bloomfield-Eastern Greene County Public Library, Owensburg, 11431 E Main St, Owensburg, IN, 47453. Tel: 812-863-2899. Fax: 812-863-2899. p. 726

Hartschuh, David, Network Adminr, Sheridan County Public Library System, 335 W Alger St, Sheridan, WY, 82801-3899. Tel: 307-674-8585, Ext 5. p. 2660

Hartse, Merri, Electronic Res, Gonzaga University School of Law, 721 N Cincinnati St, Spokane, WA, 99202. Tel: 509-323-5792. Fax: 509-323-5733. p. 2536

Hartsel, Sandra, Librn, Bettsville Public Library, 233 State St, Bettsville, OH, 44815-9999. Tel: 419-986-5198. Fax: 419-986-6012. p. 1859

Hartsell, Karen, In Charge, Stanly County Public Library, Locust Branch, 213 Towne Centre Dr, Locust, NC, 28097. Tel: 704-888-0103. p. 1773

Hartsell-Gundy, Jeffrey, Govt Info & Law Librn, Miami University Libraries, 225 King Library, Oxford, OH, 45056. Tel: 513-529-4139. Fax: 513-529-3110. p. 1926

Hartshorn, Lana C, Librn, Hartshorn Family Association Library, 1204 Fourth St Dr SE, Conover, NC, 28613-1847. Tel: 828-464-4981. Fax: 828-464-4981. p. 1785

Hartshorne, Darryl, Circ Mgr, Milton L Rock Resource Center, 1720 Locust St, Philadelphia, PA, 19103. Tel: 215-893-5265. Fax: 215-717-3170. p. 2115

Hartson, Melissa, Coll Develop Librn, Newport Beach Public Library, 1000 Avocado Ave, Newport Beach, CA, 92660-6301. Tel: 949-717-3827. Fax: 949-640-5648. p. 194

Hartsook, Bev, Storyhour Coordr, Russell Public Library, 126 E Sixth St, Russell, KS, 67665-2041. Tel: 785-483-2742. Fax: 785-483-6254. p. 892

Hartsook, Herb, Dir, University of South Carolina, South Carolina Political Collections, 720 College St, Columbia, SC, 29208. Tel: 803-777-0578. Fax: 803-777-0578. p. 2190

Hartung, John W, Dir, Kootenai-Shoshone Area Libraries, 8385 N Government Way, Hayden, ID, 83835-9280. Tel: 208-772-5612, Ext 16. Fax: 208-772-2498. p. 575

Hartung, John W, Fiscal Agent, Cooperative Information Network, 8385 N Government Way, Hayden, ID, 83835-9280. Tel: 208-772-5612, Ext 16. Fax: 208-772-2498. p. 2941

Hartung, Steven, Supv Librn, Pamunkey Regional Library, 7527 Library Dr, Hanover, VA, 23069. Tel: 804-537-6211. Fax: 804-537-6389. p. 2469

Hartwell, Lynette, Br Head, Toronto Public Library, Centennial, 578 Finch Ave W, Toronto, ON, M2R 1N7, CANADA. Tel: 416-395-5490. Fax: 416-395-5437. p. 2860

Hartwell, Teri, Librn, Selover Public Library, 31 State Rte 95, Chesterville, OH, 43317-0025. Tel: 419-768-3431. Fax: 419-768-2249. p. 1867

Hartwick, Cathy, Supvr, Ch Serv, Pickaway County District Public Library, 1160 N Court St, Circleville, OH, 43113-1725. Tel: 740-477-1644, Ext 228. Fax: 740-474-2855. p. 1875

Hartwick, Sue, Dir, Hoard Historical Museum Library, 401 Whitewater Ave, Fort Atkinson, WI, 53538. Tel: 920-563-7769. Fax: 920-568-3203. p. 2593

Hartwig, D Scott, Supvr, Gettysburg National Military Park Library, 1195 Baltimore Pike, Ste 100, Gettysburg, PA, 17325. Tel: 717-334-1124, Ext 1231. Fax: 717-334-1997. p. 2060

Hartwig, John P, Dir, Wisconsin Lutheran Seminary Library, 6633 W Wartburg Circle, Mequon, WI, 53092-1530. Tel: 262-242-8113. Fax: 262-242-8118. p. 2615

Hartwig, Laura, Coordr, ILL, Ref Librn, Meriden Public Library, 105 Miller St, Meriden, CT, 06450. Tel: 203-238-2347. Fax: 203-238-3647. p. 350

Harty, Kathleen, Acad Info Serv, Sacred Heart School of Theology, 7335 S Hwy 100, Franklin, WI, 53132. Tel: 414-425-8300, Ext 7278. Fax: 414-529-6992. p. 2593

Harty, Mary Masse, Ch, Barrington Public Library, 281 County Rd, Barrington, RI, 02806. Tel: 401-247-1920. Fax: 401-247-3763. p. 2163

Hartz, Brieann, Ref Librn, Northern Tier Library Association, 4015 Dickey Rd, Gibsonia, PA, 15044-9713. Tel: 724-449-2665. Fax: 724-443-6755. p. 2060

Hartz, Laurie, Support Librn, Recording for the Blind & Dyslexic, 20 Roszel Rd, Princeton, NJ, 08540. Tel: 609-452-0606. Fax: 609-520-7990, 609-987-8116. p. 1524

Hartzell, Gwen, Librn, Zion Mennonite Church & Public Library, 149 Cherry Lane, Souderton, PA, 18964. Tel: 215-723-3592. Fax: 215-723-0573. p. 2142

Hartzell, Lisa, Ch, Libr Asst III, Haywood County Public Library, Canton Branch, 11 Pennsylvania Ave, Canton, NC, 28716. Tel: 828-648-2924. Fax: 828-648-0377. p. 1829

Hartzell, Tami, Librn, Rochester General Hospital, 1425 Portland Ave, Rochester, NY, 14621. Tel: 585-922-4743. Fax: 585-544-1504. p. 1731

Hartzler, Valerie, Dir, Mechanicsburg Public Library, 60 S Main St, Mechanicsburg, OH, 43044. Tel: 937-834-2004. Fax: 937-834-3396. p. 1916

Harvan, Christine, Librn, Rawle & Henderson, The Widener Bldg, One S Penn Sq, 17th Fl, Philadelphia, PA, 19107. Tel: 215-575-4480. Fax: 215-563-2583. p. 2115

Harvel, Maureen J, Librn, Tombstone Reading Station-Tombstone City Library, Fourth & Toughnut Sts, Tombstone, AZ, 85638. Tel: 520-457-3612. Fax: 520-457-3612. p. 85

Harvell, Gloria G, Acq, Virginia State University, One Hayden Dr, Petersburg, VA, 23806-0001. Tel: 804-524-5740. Fax: 804-524-6959. p. 2484

Harvell, Laura, Librn, United States Army, Winn Army Community Hospital Medical Library, 1061 Harman Ave, Ste 2J11B, Fort Stewart, GA, 31314-5611. Tel: 912-435-6542. Fax: 912-435-5480. p. 533

Harvell, Tony, Head, Acq, University of California, San Diego, 9500 Gilman Dr, Mail Code 0175G, La Jolla, CA, 92093-0175. Tel: 858-534-3305. Fax: 858-534-1256. p. 162

Harvey, Aisha, Head, Coll Develop, Duke University Libraries, 411 Chapel Dr, Durham, NC, 27708. Tel: 919-660-7892. Fax: 919-660-5923. p. 1787

Harvey, Amanda, Libr Mgr, American Numismatic Association Library, 818 N Cascade Ave, Colorado Springs, CO, 80903-3279. Tel: 719-482-9821. Fax: 719-634-4085. p. 294

Harvey, Angie, Asst Dir, Pub Serv, University of Virginia's College at Wise, One College Ave, Wise, VA, 24293. Tel: 276-328-0150. Fax: 276-328-0105. p. 2504

Harvey, Audrey, Info Serv Librn, Northampton Community College, 3835 Green Pond Rd, Bethlehem, PA, 18020-7599. Tel: 610-861-5360. Fax: 610-861-5373. p. 2034

Harvey, Barbara, Health Sci Librn, University of South Dakota, Wegner Health Science Information Center, Sanford School of Medicine, 414 E Clark, Vermillion, SD, 57069-2390. Tel: 605-677-5348. Fax: 605-677-5124. p. 2221

Harvey, Barbara, Libr Tech, The Parrott Centre, 376 Wallbridge-Loyalist Rd, Belleville, ON, K8N 5B9, CANADA. Tel: 613-969-1913, Ext 2595. Fax: 613-969-5183. p. 2795

Harvey, Brenda, Circ Mgr, Rapides Parish Library, 411 Washington St, Alexandria, LA, 71301-8338. Tel: 318-442-2411. Fax: 318-445-6478. p. 940

Harvey, Carolyn, Eng Librn, Phys Sci Librn, North Dakota State University Libraries, 1201 Albrecht Blvd, Fargo, ND, 58108. Tel: 701-231-5912. Fax: 701-231-6128. p. 1841

Harvey, Diane, Head, Instruction & Outreach, Duke University Libraries, 411 Chapel Dr, Durham, NC, 27708. Tel: 919-613-6836. Fax: 919-660-5923. p. 1787

Harvey, Jacalynn, Asst Dir, Roseville Public Library, 29777 Gratiot Ave, Roseville, MI, 48066. Tel: 586-445-5407. Fax: 586-445-5499. p. 1223

Harvey, Jennifer, Curric/Nonbk Librn, University of Nebraska at Kearney, 2508 11th Ave, Kearney, NE, 68849-2240. Tel: 308-865-8276. Fax: 308-865-8722. p. 1403

Harvey, Julia L, Tech Serv, Lebanon Valley College, 101 N College Ave, Annville, PA, 17003-1400. Tel: 717-867-6971. Fax: 717-867-6979. p. 2029

Harvey, Kay Ellen, Head Librn, Pennsylvania State University, Greater Allegheny, 4000 University Dr, McKeesport, PA, 15132-7698. Tel: 412-675-9109. Fax: 412-675-9113. p. 2085

Harvey, Ken, Communications Dir, Sno-Isle Libraries, 7312 35th Ave NE, Tulalip, WA, 98271-7417. Tel: 360-651-7030. Fax: 360-651-7151. p. 2541

Harvey, Leah, Mgr, Whitebird Community Library, PO Box 33, Whitebird, ID, 83554-0033. Tel: 208-839-2805. p. 585

Harvey, Lesia, Acq, United Theological Seminary Library, 4501 Denlinger Rd, Trotwood, OH, 45426. Tel: 937-529-2201, Ext 3400. Fax: 937-529-2292. p. 1941

Harvey, Marikate, Tech Serv, Stevens County Library, 500 Monroe, Hugoton, KS, 67951-2639. Tel: 620-544-2301. Fax: 620-544-2322. p. 872

Harvey, Mark, State Archivist, Michigan Department of History, Arts & Libraries - Michigan Historical Center, 702 W Kalamazoo St, Lansing, MI, 48909-8240. Tel: 517-373-1408. Fax: 517-241-1658. p. 1201

Harvey, Melinda, Ref Librn, Gadsden State Community College, McClellan Center, 100 Gamecock Dr, Anniston, AL, 36205. Tel: 256-238-9352. p. 18

Hasting, Linda, Circ, Wilberforce University, 1055 N Bickett Rd, Wilberforce, OH, 45384-5801. Tel: 937-708-5630. Fax: 937-708-5771. p. 1948

Hastings, David W, Archivist, Washington State Office of Secretary of State, 1129 Washington St SE, Olympia, WA, 98504-2283. Tel: 360-753-1801. Fax: 360-664-8814. p. 2523

Hastings, Diana, Ref Librn, Talbot County Free Library, 100 W Dover St, Easton, MD, 21601-2620. Tel: 410-822-1626. Fax: 410-820-8217. p. 1027

Hastings, Joy, Circ Mgr, Palm Springs Public Library, 300 S Sunrise Way, Palm Springs, CA, 92262-7699. Tel: 760-323-8387. Fax: 760-320-9834. p. 203

Hastings, Karen, Asst Admin, Upper Merion Township Library, 175 W Valley Forge Rd, King of Prussia, PA, 19406-2399. Tel: 610-265-1196. Fax: 610-265-3398. p. 2074

Hastings, Pam, Mgr, Libr & Info Res, McLean Hospital, 115 Mill St, Mail Stop 203, Belmont, MA, 02478. Tel: 617-855-2460. Fax: 617-855-2414. p. 1053

Hastings, Pat, Dir, Argie Cooper Public Library, 100 S Main St, Shelbyville, TN, 37160-3984. Tel: 931-684-7323. Fax: 931-685-4848. p. 2265

Hastings, Robin, Syst Coordr, Missouri River Regional Library, 214 Adams St, Jefferson City, MO, 65101-3244. Tel: 573-634-6064, Ext 242. p. 1335

Hastings, Ruth Joye, Head, Circ, University of San Diego, Katherine M & George M Pardee Jr Legal Research Center, 5998 Alcala Park, San Diego, CA, 92110-2492. Tel: 619-260-7479. Fax: 619-260-4616. p. 239

Hastings, Samantha K, Dir, Prof, University of South Carolina, 1501 Greene St, Columbia, SC, 29208. Tel: 803-777-3858. Fax: 803-777-7938. p. 2973

Hastings, Susan, Access Serv, Virginia Military Institute, Letcher Ave, Lexington, VA, 24450. Tel: 540-464-7607. Fax: 540-464-7279. p. 2474

Hastings, William, Asst Dir, Tech Serv, YA Librn, DeWitt Community Library, Shoppingtown Mall, 3649 Erie Blvd E, DeWitt, NY, 13214. Tel: 315-446-3578. Fax: 315-446-1955. p. 1614

Hastler, Mary L, Dir, Harford County Public Library, 1221-A Brass Mill Rd, Belcamp, MD, 21017-1209. Tel: 410-273-5600, Ext 2252. Fax: 410-273-5606. p. 1020

Haston, Eugene, Br Mgr, Atlanta-Fulton Public Library System, Southwest Regional Library, 3665 Cascade Rd SW, Atlanta, GA, 30331. Tel: 404-699-6363. Fax: 404-699-6381. p. 512

Hastreiter, Michele, Dir, Humphrey Public Library, 307 Main St, Humphrey, NE, 68642. Tel: 402-923-0957. Fax: 402-923-0957. p. 1402

Hasty-Speed, Anita, Mgr, Durham County Library, Bragtown, 3200 Dearborn Dr, Durham, NC, 27704. Tel: 919-560-0210. p. 1788

Hatch, Alvin, Librn, Utah Department of Corrections, PO Box 898, Gunnison, UT, 84634-0898. Tel: 435-528-6000. Fax: 435-528-6234. p. 2406

Hatch, Carey, Asst Provost for Libr & Info Serv, SUNYConnect, Office of Library & Information Services, SUNY Plaza, Albany, NY, 12246. Tel: 518-443-5577. Fax: 518-443-5358. p. 2950

Hatch, Cathy, Librn, Old Perlican Public Library, PO Box 265, Old Perlican, NL, A0A 3G0, CANADA. Tel: 709-587-2028. p. 2770

Hatch, James, Archivist, Hatch-Billops Collection, Inc Library, 491 Broadway, 7th Flr, New York, NY, 10012. Tel: 212-966-3231. Fax: 212-966-3231. p. 1681

Hatch, Tina, Dir, Milford Public Library, 330 Family Dr, Milford, MI, 48381-2000. Tel: 248-684-0845. Fax: 248-684-2923. p. 1209

Hatchcock, Betty, Librn, Mid-Mississippi Regional Library System, Durant Public, 15338 N Jackson St, Durant, MS, 39063-3708. Tel: 662-653-3451. Fax: 662-653-3108. p. 1306

Hatchell, Sheila C, Dir, Minnesota Department of Transportation Library, 395 John Ireland Blvd, MS 155, Saint Paul, MN, 55155. Tel: 651-366-3733. Fax: 651-366-3789. p. 1279

Hatcher, Elizabeth, Info Researcher, Group Technology Library & Information Services, 150 W Warrenville Rd, MC F1, Naperville, IL, 60563. Tel: 630-420-4850. Fax: 630-420-3697. p. 678

Hatcher, Irene, Tech Serv, Daviess County Public Library, 2020 Frederica St, Owensboro, KY, 42301. Tel: 270-684-0211. Fax: 270-684-0218. p. 931

Hatcher, Jeanette, Ref Librn, Spec Coll Librn, Texas A&M International University, 5201 University Blvd, Laredo, TX, 78041-1900. Tel: 956-326-2404. Fax: 956-326-2399. p. 2354

Hatcher, Richard W, III, In Charge, US National Park Service, 1214 Middle St, Sullivan's Island, SC, 29482. Tel: 843-883-3123, Ext 22. Fax: 843-883-3910. p. 2206

Hatchett, Michael, Mgr, Henrico County Public Library, Fairfield Area Library, 1001 N Laburnum Ave, Henrico, VA, 23223-2705. Tel: 804-290-9300. Fax: 804-222-1958. p. 2471

Hatfield, Ella, Genealogy Librn, Citizens Library, 55 S College St, Washington, PA, 15301. Tel: 724-222-2400. Fax: 724-222-2606. p. 2151

Hatfield, Jean, Br Head, Wichita Public Library, Lionel Alford Regional, 3447 S Meridian, Wichita, KS, 67217-2151. Tel: 316-337-9119. Fax: 316-337-9118. p. 901

Hatfield, Jean, Br Mgr, Wichita Public Library, Linwood Park, 1901 S Kansas Ave, Wichita, KS, 67211. Tel: 316-337-9125. p. 901

Hatfield, Jennifer, Librn, Lockheed Martin, 9500 Godwin Dr, Manassas, VA, 20110. Tel: 703-367-6508. Fax: 703-367-4698. p. 2477

Hatfield, Kathy, Mgr, Tech Serv, Wilmington College, Pyle Ctr 1227, 1870 Quaker Way, Wilmington, OH, 45177-2473. Tel: 937-382-6661, Ext 398. Fax: 937-383-8571. p. 1949

Hatfield, Linda, Head, Adult Serv, Muskingum County Library System, 220 N Fifth St, Zanesville, OH, 43701-3587. Tel: 740-453-0391, Ext 132. Fax: 740-455-6937. p. 1953

Hatfield, Melissa, Adminr, Ohio Bureau of Worker's Compensation, 30 W Spring St, 3rd Flr, Columbus, OH, 43215-2256. Tel: 614-466-7388. Fax: 614-644-9634. p. 1886

Hatfield, Patricia M, Libr Dir, Smyth-Bland Regional Library, 118 S Sheffey St, Marion, VA, 24354. Tel: 276-783-2323. Fax: 276-783-5279. p. 2477

Hathaway, Althea, Librn, Whitman Memorial Library, Main St, Bryant Pond, ME, 04219. Tel: 207-665-2505. p. 980

Hathaway, Barbara, Dir, Bee Cave Public Library, 4000 Galleria Pkwy, Bee Cave, TX, 78738. Tel: 512-767-6624. Fax: 512-767-6629. p. 2288

Hathaway, Clio, Youth Serv Mgr, Hayward Public Library, 835 C St, Hayward, CA, 94541-5120. Tel: 510-881-7948. p. 157

Hathaway, Deborah, Acq, Supvr, University of Dallas, 1845 E Northgate Dr, Irving, TX, 75062-4736. Tel: 972-721-4122. Fax: 972-721-4010. p. 2347

Hathaway, Dianne, Dir, Goffstown Public Library, Two High St, Goffstown, NH, 03045-1910. Tel: 603-497-2102. Fax: 603-497-8437. p. 1448

Hathaway, Dianne, Chair, GMILCS, Inc, 1701B Hooksett Rd, Hooksett, NH, 03106. Tel: 603-485-4286. Fax: 603-485-4246. p. 2948

Hathaway, Ellen, Cat, Morgantown Public Library System, 373 Spruce St, Morgantown, WV, 26505. Tel: 304-291-7425. Fax: 304-291-7427. p. 2566

Hathaway, Karen, Ch, Shaler North Hills Library, 1822 Mount Royal Blvd, Glenshaw, PA, 15116. Tel: 412-486-0211. Fax: 412-486-8286. p. 2061

Hathaway, Laurence, Dir, Crawfordsville District Public Library, 205 S Washington St, Crawfordsville, IN, 47933. Tel: 765-362-2242. Fax: 765-362-7986. p. 734

Hathaway, Ruth A, Dir, Head Librn, Holbrook Public Library, Two Plymouth St, Holbrook, MA, 02343. Tel: 781-767-3644. Fax: 781-767-5721. p. 1095

Hathaway, Ted, Sr Librn, Hennepin County Library, Minneapolis Central, 300 Nicollet Mall, Minneapolis, MN, 55401. Tel: 612-543-8203. Fax: 612-543-8173. p. 1264

Hathaway, Teresa, Librn, United States Air Force, Hanscom Air Force Base Library FL2835, 66 SVS/SVMG, 98 Barksdale St, Bldg 1530, Hanscom AFB, MA, 01731-1807. Tel: 781-377-2177. Fax: 781-377-4482. p. 1093

Hathaway-Bell, Stacey, Reader Serv Mgr, Texas State Library & Archives Commission, 1201 Brazos, Austin, TX, 78711. Tel: 512-463-5458. Fax: 512-936-0685. p. 2283

Hathcock, Janice, Pub Info & Policy Coordr, The Library of Virginia, 800 E Broad St, Richmond, VA, 23219-8000. Tel: 804-692-3592. Fax: 804-692-3594. p. 2489

Hathcock, Kaye, Librn, Lenoir City Public Library, 100 W Broadway, Lenoir City, TN, 37771. Tel: 865-986-3210. p. 2245

Hatheway, Holly, Asst Dir, Access Serv, Yale University Library, Robert B Haas Family Arts Library, Loria Ctr, 180 York St, New Haven, CT, 06520. Tel: 203-432-2645. Fax: 203-432-0549. p. 358

Hathman, Laurie, Libr Dir, Rockhurst University, 1100 Rockhurst Rd, Kansas City, MO, 64110-2561. Tel: 816-501-4655. Fax: 816-501-4666. p. 1340

Hatleberg, Jenny, Librn, Montgomery College, Takoma Park Campus Library, 7600 Takoma Ave, Takoma Park, MD, 20912. Tel: 240-567-1685. Fax: 240-567-5820. p. 1037

Hatley, Alen, Automation Syst Coordr, Corpus Christi Public Libraries, 805 Comanche, Corpus Christi, TX, 78401. Tel: 361-826-7000. Fax: 361-826-7046. p. 2301

Hatnay, Rosemary, Info Spec, Towers Perrin Information Centre, South Tower, Ste 1501, 175 Bloor St E, Toronto, ON, M4W 3T6, CANADA. Tel: 416-960-7449. Fax: 416-960-2819. p. 2864

Hatt, Lisa, Cat, De Anza College, 21250 Stevens Creek Blvd, Cupertino, CA, 95014-5793. Tel: 408-864-8459. Fax: 408-864-8603. p. 138

Hatten, Christopher, Librn, Huntington Museum of Art Library, 2033 McCoy Rd, Huntington, WV, 25701. Tel: 304-529-2701, Ext 23. Fax: 304-529-7447. p. 2561

Hatterman, Cathy, Acq Librn, Nebraska Library Commission, The Atrium, 1200 N St, Ste 120, Lincoln, NE, 68508-2023. Tel: 402-471-4034. Fax: 402-471-2083. p. 1406

Hatterman, Gloria, Head Librn, Raymond A Whitwer Tilden Public Library, 202 S Center St, Tilden, NE, 68781. Tel: 402-368-5306. Fax: 402-368-5515. p. 1421

Hatton, Jason, Asst Dir, Bartholomew County Public Library, 536 Fifth St, Columbus, IN, 47201-6225. Tel: 812-379-1255. Fax: 812-379-1275. p. 733

Hau, Edward, Librn, Natural Resources Canada Library, 3303 33rd St NW, 2nd Flr, Calgary, AB, T2L 2A7, CANADA. Tel: 403-292-7165. Fax: 403-292-5377. p. 2692

Haubenstricker, Larry, Dir, Fairgrove District Library, 1959 Main St, Fairgrove, MI, 48733. Tel: 989-693-6050. Fax: 989-693-6446. p. 1177

Haubitz, Heiko, Dr, Instr, University of South Florida, 4202 Fowler Ave, CIS 1040, Tampa, FL, 33620-7800. Tel: 813-974-7650. Fax: 813-974-6840. p. 2964

Haubrich, Ann, Asst Librn, Chinook Regional Library, Hodgeville Branch, Main St, Hodgeville, SK, S0H 2B0, CANADA. Tel: 306-677-2223. p. 2928

Haubrich, Elizabeth, Librn, Chinook Regional Library, Hodgeville Branch, Main St, Hodgeville, SK, S0H 2B0, CANADA. Tel: 306-677-2223. p. 2928

Haubrich, Juliana, Circ Mgr, David & Joyce Milne Public Library, 1095 Main St, Williamstown, MA, 01267-2627. Tel: 413-458-5369. Fax: 413-458-3085. p. 1140

Hauck, Janet, Archivist, Whitworth University, 300 W Hawthorne Rd, Spokane, WA, 99251-0001. Tel: 509-777-4751. Fax: 509-777-3221. p. 2538

Hauck, William, Adminr, Correctional Institution for Women, PO Box 4004, Clinton, NJ, 08809-4004. Tel: 908-735-7111, Ext 3641. Fax: 908-735-0108. p. 1479

Hauck-Mah, Barb, Ref & Info Spec, Rockaway Township Free Public Library, 61 Mount Hope Rd, Rockaway, NJ, 07866. Tel: 973-627-2344. Fax: 973-627-7658. p. 1527

Hauck-Mah, Barbara, Dir, Lodi Memorial Library, One Memorial Dr, Lodi, NJ, 07644-1692. Tel: 973-365-4044. Fax: 973-365-0172. p. 1496

Hauck-Reif, Carol, Reader Serv, Deadwood Public Library, 435 Williams St, Deadwood, SD, 57732-1113. Tel: 605-578-2821. Fax: 605-578-2071. p. 2211

Haueisen, John, Librn, Worthington Historical Society Library, 50 W New England Ave, Worthington, OH, 43085-3536. Tel: 614-846-6494. Fax: 614-885-1040. p. 1950

Haueisen, Steffanie, Librn, Worthington Historical Society Library, 50 W New England Ave, Worthington, OH, 43085-3536. Tel: 614-885-1247. Fax: 614-885-1040. p. 1950

Hauenstein, Daniel, Human Res Dir, Cuyahoga County Public Library, 2111 Snow Rd, Parma, OH, 44134-2728. Tel: 216-398-1800. Fax: 216-398-1748. p. 1927

Hauf, Amy, In Charge, McLean-Mercer Regional Library, Max Branch, 215 Main St, Max, ND, 58759. Tel: 701-679-2263. p. 1848

Hauf, John, Cat, Dominican University of California, 50 Acacia Ave, San Rafael, CA, 94901-2298. Tel: 415-482-3522. Fax: 415-459-2309. p. 256

Haug, James, Librn, Smithsonian Libraries, John Wesley Powell Library of Anthropology, Nat Museum of Natural Hist, Rm 331, MRC 112, Tenth St & Constitution Ave NW, Washington, DC, 20560-0112. Tel: 202-633-1641. Fax: 202-357-1896. p. 415

Haug, Joan, Libr Tech, Jamestown Community College, Cattaraugus County, 260 N Union St, Olean, NY, 14760. Tel: 716-372-1661. Fax: 716-376-7032. p. 1647

Haug, Kathy, Ch, Richmond Public Library, 325 Civic Center Plaza, Richmond, CA, 94804-9991. Tel: 510-620-6555. Fax: 510-620-6850. p. 216

Haug, Lois, Asst Librn, Southeast Regional Library, Fort Qu'Appelle Branch, 140 Company Ave S, Fort Qu'Appelle, SK, S0G 1S0, CANADA. Tel: 306-332-6411. p. 2929

Haug, Thomas, Ref, Oakland Community College, 27055 Orchard Lake Rd, Bldg K, Farmington Hills, MI, 48334-4579. Tel: 248-522-3529. Fax: 248-522-3530. p. 1178

Haugaard, David, Dir, Res Serv, Historical Society of Pennsylvania, 1300 Locust St, Philadelphia, PA, 19107-5699. Tel: 215-732-6200, Ext 219. Fax: 215-732-2680. p. 2110

Hauge, Carol, Asst Librn, Elkader Public Library, 130 N Main St, Elkader, IA, 52043. Tel: 563-245-1446. Fax: 563-245-1446. p. 814

Hauge, Terri, Assoc Librn, Dakota College at Bottineau Library, 105 Simrall Blvd, Bottineau, ND, 58318. Tel: 701-228-5454. Fax: 701-228-5438. p. 1839

Haugen, Gene A, Mgr, North Dakota State Hospital, 2605 Circle Dr, Jamestown, ND, 58401-6905. Tel: 701-253-3679. Fax: 701-253-3204. p. 1844

Haugen, Gene A, Mgr, North Dakota State Hospital, Patients' Library, 2605 Circle Dr, Jamestown, ND, 58401-6905. Tel: 701-253-3678. p. 1844

Haugh, Amy, Dir, UPMC St Margaret, 815 Freeport Rd, Pittsburgh, PA, 15215. Tel: 412-784-4121, 412-784-4238. Fax: 412-784-4989. p. 2129

Haule, Laura, Mgr, Ref & Info Serv, St Charles Public Library District, One S Sixth Ave, Saint Charles, IL, 60174-2105. Tel: 630-584-0961, Ext 225. Fax: 630-584-3448. p. 699

Haulgren, Frank, Head, ILL & Assessment Coordr, Western Washington University, 516 High St, MS 9103, Bellingham, WA, 98225. Tel: 360-650-7639. Fax: 360-650-3044. p. 2509

Haumann, Ronda, Librn, Thomas County Library, 503 Main St, Thedford, NE, 69166. Tel: 308-645-2237. p. 1421

Haunton, Richard, Br Mgr, Catawba County Library, Claremont Branch, 3288 E Main St, Claremont, NC, 28610-1248. Tel: 828-459-9311. p. 1813

Haunty, Susan, Dir, Learning Serv, Florida State College at Jacksonville, Downtown Campus, 101 W State St, Jacksonville, FL, 32202-3056. Tel: 904-633-8368. Fax: 904-633-8328. p. 453

Haupt, Jon, Interim Dir, Music Librn, Southern Methodist University, Hamon Arts Library, 6101 N Bishop Blvd, Dallas, TX, 75275. Tel: 214-768-1855. Fax: 214-768-1800. p. 2310

Hauryski, Susan, Libr Tech, Department of Veterans Affairs, 76 Veterans Ave, Bath, NY, 14810. Tel: 607-664-4000, 607-664-4813. Fax: 607-664-4814. p. 1578

Hausburg, Jana, Mgr, Metropolitan Library System in Oklahoma County, Capitol Hill Library, 334 SW 26th St, Oklahoma City, OK, 73109-6711. Tel: 405-634-6308. Fax: 405-606-3244. p. 1972

Hauschildt, Jennifer, Pub Serv, United States Army, Casey Memorial Library, 72nd St & 761st Tank Battalion, Bldg 3202, Fort Hood, TX, 76544-5024. Tel: 254-287-0025. Fax: 254-288-4029. p. 2320

Hause, Joanna, Head, Tech Serv, Southeastern University, 1000 Longfellow Blvd, Lakeland, FL, 33801. Tel: 863-667-5062. Fax: 863-669-4160. p. 460

Hauser, Chris, Syst Adminr, Weber State University, 2901 University Circle, Ogden, UT, 84408-2901. Tel: 801-626-6104. Fax: 801-626-7045. p. 2409

Hauser, Jeanne, Chief Librn, Omaha World-Herald Library, 1314 Douglas St, Ste 700, Omaha, NE, 68102. Tel: 402-444-1012. Fax: 402-345-0183. p. 1414

Hauser, Valerie, Dir, Jefferson Public Library, 128 N Main St, Jefferson, OR, 97352. Tel: 541-327-3826. Fax: 541-327-3120. p. 2001

Hausinger, Shannon B, Libr Dir, Waller County Library, 2331 11th St, Hempstead, TX, 77445-6724. Tel: 979-826-7658. Fax: 979-826-7657. p. 2332

Hausler, Nancy, Dir, Union Public Library, 406 Commercial St, Union, IA, 50258. Tel: 641-486-5561. Fax: 641-486-2284. p. 848

Hausman, Sheri, Br Supvr, Scenic Regional Library of Franklin, Gasconade & Warren Counties, Hermann Branch, 601 Market St, Hermann, MO, 65041. Tel: 573-486-2024. p. 1369

Haustrate, Virginie, Mgr, Literary & Historical Society of Quebec Library, 44 Chaussee des Ecossais, Quebec, QC, G1R 4H3, CANADA. Tel: 418-694-9147. Fax: 418-694-0754. p. 2905

Haut, Adrian, Librn, Edward Chipman Public Library, 126 N Locust St, Momence, IL, 60954. Tel: 815-472-2581. Fax: 815-472-2581. p. 675

Hauver, Emily, Curator, University of Maryland, Baltimore County, 1000 Hilltop Circle, Baltimore, MD, 21250. Tel: 410-455-2356. Fax: 410-455-1567. p. 1018

Havard, Mahalya, Librn, CSSS de Gatineau - Hôpital Pierre-Janet, 20, rue Pharand, Gatineau, QC, J9A 1K7, CANADA. Tel: 819-771-7761, Ext 8380. Fax: 819-771-1506. p. 2883

Havel, Peter, Dir, Cedar Grove Free Public Library, One Municipal Plaza, Cedar Grove, NJ, 07009. Tel: 973-239-1447. Fax: 973-239-1275. p. 1478

Havemann, Gloria, Dir, Austin County Library System, 6730 Railroad, Wallis, TX, 77485. Tel: 979-478-6813. Fax: 979-478-6813. p. 2398

Haven, Karen, Tech Serv, Three Rivers Regional Library System, 208 Gloucester St, Brunswick, GA, 31520-7007. Tel: 912-267-1212. Fax: 912-267-9597. p. 522

Haven, Paula, Teen Serv Librn, Richmond Memorial Library, 19 Ross St, Batavia, NY, 14020. Tel: 585-343-9550. Fax: 585-344-4651. p. 1578

Havener, Peggy, Dir, Albert Lea Public Library, 211 E Clark St, Albert Lea, MN, 56007. Tel: 507-377-4355. Fax: 507-377-4339. p. 1239

Havener, W Michael, Dr, Prof, University of Rhode Island, Rodman Hall, 94 W Alumni Ave, Ste 2, Kingston, RI, 02881-0815. Tel: 401-874-4651. Fax: 401-874-4964. p. 2973

Havenga, Michelle, Ch, Sheridan County Public Library System, 335 W Alger St, Sheridan, WY, 82801-3899. Tel: 307-674-8585, Ext 5. p. 2660

Havens, Barret, Outreach Librn, Woodbury University Library, 7500 Glenoaks Blvd, Burbank, CA, 91510-1099. Tel: 818-252-5200. Fax: 818-767-4534. p. 130

Havens, Barret, Librn, Centralia College, 600 Centralia College Blvd, Centralia, WA, 98531. Tel: 360-736-9391, Ext 615. Fax: 360-330-7502. p. 2511

Havens, Patricia, City Historian, Dir, Simi Valley Historical Society & Museum, 137 Strathearn Pl, Simi Valley, CA, 93065-1605. Tel: 805-526-6453. Fax: 805-526-6462. p. 269

Havenstein-Coughlin, Rebecca, Head, Adult Serv, Canton Public Library, 1200 S Canton Center Rd, Canton, MI, 48188-1600. Tel: 734-397-0999. Fax: 734-397-1130. p. 1160

Haver, Connie, Librn, Depauville Free Library, 32333 County Rte 179, Depauville, NY, 13632. Tel: 315-686-3299. Fax: 315-686-3299. p. 1614

Haverhals, Valerie, Dir, Hawarden Public Library, 803 Tenth St, Hawarden, IA, 51023. Tel: 712-551-2244. Fax: 712-551-1720. p. 820

Haverkamp, Donna L, Libr Dir, Pinellas County Law Library, 324 S Ft Harrison Ave, Clearwater, FL, 33756-5165. Tel: 727-464-3411. Fax: 727-464-4571. p. 432

Haverkoch, Vanessa, Tech Serv Librn, Bennington College, One College Dr, Bennington, VT, 05201-6001. Tel: 802-440-4602. Fax: 802-440-4580. p. 2418

Havers, Rob, Dr, Exec Dir, Westminster College, National Churchill Museum, 501 Westminster Ave, Fulton, MO, 65251-1299. Tel: 573-592-5233. Fax: 573-592-5222. p. 1328

Havill, C J, Libr Dir, Bay De Noc Community College, 2001 N Lincoln Rd, Escanaba, MI, 49829-2511. Tel: 906-217-4055, 906-217-4076. Fax: 906-217-1657. p. 1177

Havrylik, Betty, Ref Serv, Ad, Cumberland Public Library, 1464 Diamond Hill Rd, Cumberland, RI, 02864-5510. Tel: 401-333-2552, Ext 201. Fax: 401-334-0578. p. 2165

Haw, Heather, Asst Librn, Alberta School for the Deaf Library, 6240 113 St, Edmonton, AB, T6H 3L2, CANADA. Tel: 780-436-0465. Fax: 780-436-5863. p. 2699

Hawamdeh, Suliman, Dr, Chair, Prof, University of North Texas, 1155 Union Circle, Denton, TX, 76203-5017. Tel: 940-565-2445. Fax: 940-565-3101. p. 2975

Hawco, Debbie, Tech Serv Librn, Department of Community Services, Government of Yukon, 1171 First Ave, Whitehorse, YT, Y1A 0G9, CANADA. Tel: 867-667-5239. Fax: 867-393-6333. p. 2933

Hawes, Beverly, Br Mgr, Atlanta-Fulton Public Library System, Carver Homes Library, 215 Lakewood Way, Ste 104, Atlanta, GA, 30315. Tel: 404-635-4012. Fax: 404-635-4016. p. 511

Hawes, Jennifer, Youth Serv, Boston Public Library, Lower Mills, 27 Richmond St, Dorchester, MA, 02124-5610. Tel: 617-298-7841. Fax: 617-296-2086. p. 1057

Hawes, Pat, Coll Develop, Smyrna Public Library, 100 Village Green Circle, Smyrna, GA, 30080-3478. Tel: 770-431-2860. Fax: 770-431-2862. p. 551

Hawes, Sandy, Digital Res Librn, Saint Leo University, 33701 State Rd 52, Saint Leo, FL, 33574. Tel: 352-588-8262. Fax: 352-588-8484. p. 487

Hawk, John, Rare Bks, University of San Francisco, 2130 Fulton St, San Francisco, CA, 94117-1080. Tel: 415-422-2036. Fax: 415-422-5949. p. 248

Hawk, Judy, Librn, Great River Medical Center Library, 1221 S Gear Ave, West Burlington, IA, 52655-1679. Tel: 319-768-4075. Fax: 319-768-4080. p. 852

Hawke, Nadine, Ref Serv Supvr, Bartlesville Public Library, 600 S Johnstone, Bartlesville, OK, 74003. Tel: 918-338-4166. Fax: 918-337-5338. p. 1957

Hawke, Susan, Assoc Librn, Concordia University Libraries, Counselling & Development, Career Resource Centre, 1455 de Maisonneuve Blvd W, H-440, Montreal, QC, H3G 1M8, CANADA. Tel: 514-848-2424, Local 3556. Fax: 514-848-4534. p. 2894

Hawkes, Linda, Electronic Res, Quinnipiac University, 275 Mount Carmel Ave, Hamden, CT, 06518. Tel: 203-582-8946. Fax: 203-582-3451. p. 343

Hawkes, Sarah, Mgr, Network Serv, Arkansas State Library, 900 W Capitol, Ste 100, Little Rock, AR, 72201-3108. Tel: 501-682-2053. Fax: 501-682-1529. p. 105

Hawkes, Warren, Dir, New York State Nurses Association Library, 11 Cornell Rd, Latham, NY, 12110. Tel: 518-782-9400, Ext 266. Fax: 518-782-7110. p. 1651

Hawkey, Linda, Dir, Kewanna Public Library, 210 E Main St, Kewanna, IN, 46939-9529. Tel: 574-653-2011. Fax: 574-653-2130. p. 757

Hawkins, Amorette, Dir, Rangely Regional Library, 109 E Main, Rangely, CO, 81648-2737. Tel: 970-675-8811. Fax: 970-675-8844. p. 321

Hawkins, Barbara, Ch Serv Librn, Fairfield Public Library, 1080 Old Post Rd, Fairfield, CT, 06824. Tel: 203-256-3155. p. 339

Hawkins, Charles, Dir, Historical Evaluation & Research Organization, 1407 Love Point Rd, Stevensville, MD, 21666. Tel: 410-643-8807. Fax: 410-643-8469. p. 1043

Hawkins, Cheryl, Librn, Hutchins-Atwell Public Library, 300 N Denton, Hutchins, TX, 75141-9404. Tel: 972-225-4711. Fax: 972-225-4593. p. 2346

Hawkins, Dennis, Exec Dir, Fund for Modern Courts Library, 351 W 54th St, New York, NY, 10019-5101. Tel: 212-541-6741. Fax: 212-541-7301. p. 1679

Hawkins, Diana, Coll Develop, Charles P Jones Memorial Library, 406 W Riverside St, Covington, VA, 24426. Tel: 540-962-3321. Fax: 540-962-8447. p. 2458

Hawkins, Gary, Digital Serv, Auburn University, Ralph Brown Draughon Library, 231 Mell St, Auburn, AL, 36849. Tel: 334-844-4500. Fax: 334-844-4424. p. 5

Hawkins, Helma, Dir, Youth Serv, The Kansas City Public Library, 14 W Tenth St, Kansas City, MO, 64105. Tel: 816-701-3450. Fax: 816-701-3401. p. 1338

Hawkins, Jeffrey, Interim Dir, Libr Mgr, Lassen Library District, 1618 Main St, Susanville, CA, 96130-4515. Tel: 530-251-8127. Fax: 530-257-8115. p. 274

Hawkins, John, Ref & Coll Develop Librn, Ossining Public Library, 53 Croton Ave, Ossining, NY, 10562-4903. Tel: 914-941-2416, Ext 316. Fax: 914-941-7464. p. 1712

Hawkins, Joseph, PhD, Dir, ONE Institute & Archives, 909 W Adams Blvd, Los Angeles, CA, 90007. Tel: 213-741-0094. p. 176

Hawkins, Lorianne, Librn, Harrison County Library System, Orange Grove Public, 12031 Mobile Ave, Gulfport, MS, 39503-3175. Tel: 228-832-6924. Fax: 228-832-6926. p. 1299

Hawkins, Lynn, Exec Dir, Mentor Public Library, 8215 Mentor Ave, Mentor, OH, 44060. Tel: 440-255-8811, Ext 232. Fax: 440-255-0520. p. 1917

Hawkins, Margaret, Info Literacy, Manatee Community College Library, 5840 26th St W, Bradenton, FL, 34207. Tel: 941-752-5305. Fax: 941-752-5308. p. 429

Hawkins, Margie, Librn, Holland & Knight LLP Orlando Library, 200 S Orange Ave, Ste 2600, Orlando, FL, 32801. Tel: 407-244-1153. Fax: 407-244-5288. p. 476

Hawkins, Marilyn, Curator, High Plains Museum Library, 413 Norris Ave, McCook, NE, 69001. Tel: 308-345-3661. p. 1408

Hawkins, Mary Ellen, Librn, Ozarka College, 218 College Dr, Melbourne, AR, 72556-8708. Tel: 870-368-7371. Fax: 870-368-2091. p. 109

Hawkins, Nina, Dir, Cambridge Community Library, Superior St, Cambridge, ID, 83610. Tel: 208-257-3434. p. 572

Hawkins, Paul, Dir, South Central Kansas Library System, 321 N Main St, South Hutchinson, KS, 67505-1146. Tel: 620-663-3211. Fax: 620-663-9797. p. 895

Hawkins, R, Ref, North Shore Public Library, 250 Rte 25A, Shoreham, NY, 11786-9677. Tel: 631-929-4488. Fax: 631-929-4551. p. 1743

Hawkins, Renee, Ch, Ricks Memorial Library (Yazoo Library Association), 310 N Main St, Yazoo City, MS, 39194-4253. Tel: 662-746-5557. Fax: 662-746-7309. p. 1318

Hawkins, Rich, Asst Dir, Lake Blackshear Regional Library System, 307 E Lamar St, Americus, GA, 31709-3633. Tel: 229-924-8091. Fax: 229-928-4445. p. 508

Hawkins, Roberta, Ref Serv, Compton Community College Library, 1111 E Artesia Blvd, Compton, CA, 90221. Tel: 310-900-1600, Ext 2175. Fax: 310-900-1693. p. 136

Hawkins, Shelley, Bus Mgr, Bus Serv, Iowa State University Library, 302 Parks Library, Ames, IA, 50011-2140. Tel: 515-294-1442, 515-294-1443. Fax: 515-294-5525. p. 793

Hawkins, Shirley, Actg Adminr, San Juan Bautista City Library, 801 Second St, San Juan Bautista, CA, 95045. Tel: 831-623-4687. Fax: 831-623-4701. p. 252

Hawkins, Shirley, Br Mgr, Lonesome Pine Regional Library, Haysi Public, 314 Main St, Haysi, VA, 24256. Tel: 276-865-4851. Fax: 276-865-5441. p. 2504

Hawkins, Suzan, Librn, New Gloucester Public Library, 379 Intervale Rd, New Gloucester, ME, 04260. Tel: 207-926-4840. p. 993

Hawkins, Tammy, Librn, De Soto Trail Regional Library, Baker County, Historical Court House, 100 Main St, Newton, GA, 39870. Tel: 229-734-3025. p. 522

Hawkins, Terry, Head, Reader Serv, United States Air Force, Air University - Muir S Fairchild Research Information Center, 600 Chennault Circle, Maxwell AFB, AL, 36112-6010. Tel: 334-953-2237. Fax: 334-953-2329. p. 24

Hawkins, Theresa, Dir, Edward F Owen Memorial Library, 1120 Willow Dr, Carter Lake, IA, 51510-1332. Tel: 712-347-5492. Fax: 712-347-5013. p. 799

Hawkins, Valencia, Assoc Dir, Cent Pub Serv, New Orleans Public Library, 219 Loyola Ave, New Orleans, LA, 70112-2044. Tel: 504-529-7323, 504-596-2570. Fax: 504-596-2609. p. 962

Hawks, Leota, Dir, Coalfield Public Library, 112 Jerry Jones, Coalfield, TN, 37719. Tel: 865-435-4275. Fax: 865-435-4275. p. 2230

Hawley, Anne, Ch, Deborah Rawson Memorial Library, Eight River Rd, Jericho, VT, 05465. Tel: 802-899-4962. Fax: 802-899-5257. p. 2426

Hawley, Betty, Circ, Pelham Library, Two S Valley Rd, Pelham, MA, 01002. Tel: 413-253-0657. Fax: 413-253-0594. p. 1117

Hawley, Corinne, Librn, North Loup Township Library, 112 South B St, North Loup, NE, 68859. Tel: 308-496-4230. p. 1410

Hawley, Dawn, Tech/eLearning, Bellingham Technical College Library, 3028 Lindbergh Ave, Bellingham, WA, 98225-1599. Tel: 360-752-8383. Fax: 360-752-8384. p. 2508

Hawley, George, PhD, Supv Librn, NJ Info Ctr, Newark Public Library, Five Washington St, Newark, NJ, 07101. Tel: 973-733-7775. Fax: 973-733-5648. p. 1511

Hawley, Heather, Med Librn, Northwestern Medical Center, 133 Fairfield St, Saint Albans, VT, 05478. Tel: 802-524-8448. Fax: 802-524-1250. p. 2434

Hawley, Jane, Ref Serv, Anderson University Library, 316 Boulevard, Anderson, SC, 29621. Tel: 864-231-2050. Fax: 864-231-2191. p. 2181

Hawley, Jeanne, Acq, Kent State University, 6000 Frank Ave NW, North Canton, OH, 44720-7548. Tel: 330-244-3321. Fax: 330-494-6212. p. 1923

Hawley, Kyle, Circ Mgr, Superior Public Library, 1530 Tower Ave, Superior, WI, 54880-2532. Tel: 715-394-8860. Fax: 715-394-8870. p. 2641

Hawley, Marge, Asst Librn, Aldrich Free Public Library, 299 Main St, Moosup, CT, 06354. Tel: 860-564-8760. Fax: 860-564-8491. p. 353

Hawn, Peggy, Br Support, Stormont, Dundas & Glengarry County Library, Morrisburg Branch, 28 Ottawa St (Arena SE), Morrisburg, ON, K0C 1X0, CANADA. Tel: 613-543-3384. Fax: 613-543-2427. p. 2802

Hawn, Peggy, Br Support, Stormont, Dundas & Glengarry County Library, South Mountain Branch, Main St, South Mountain, ON, K0E 1W0, CANADA. Tel: 613-989-2199. p. 2802

Hawney, Laura, Dir, North Shore Public Library, 250 Rte 25A, Shoreham, NY, 11786-9677. Tel: 631-929-4488. Fax: 631-929-4551. p. 1743

Haworth, Elizabeth, Dir, Pub Serv, James Madison University Libraries & Educational Technologies, 800 S Main St, Harrisonburg, VA, 22807-0001. Tel: 540-568-5730. Fax: 540-568-6339. p. 2470

Haworth, Laura, Assoc Dir/Librn, Denison Public Library, 300 W Gandy St, Denison, TX, 75020-3153. Tel: 903-465-1797. Fax: 903-465-1130. p. 2312

Hawrusik, Susan, Ref & Coll Develop Librn, Recording for the Blind & Dyslexic, 20 Roszel Rd, Princeton, NJ, 08540. Tel: 609-452-0606. Fax: 609-520-7990, 609-987-8116. p. 1524

Hawsey, Terri, Ch, Desoto Parish Library, Logansport Branch, 203 Hwy 5, Logansport, LA, 71049. Tel: 318-697-2311. Fax: 318-697-4081. p. 955

Hawthorne, Dalene, Dir, Arkansas City Public Library, 120 E Fifth Ave, Arkansas City, KS, 67005-2695. Tel: 620-442-1280. Fax: 620-442-4277. p. 856

Hawthorne, Keisha, Libr Asst, Our Lady of Holy Cross College Library, 4123 Woodland Dr, New Orleans, LA, 70131. Tel: 504-398-2101. Fax: 504-391-2421. p. 962

Hawthorne, Pathenia, Tech Serv, Department of Veterans Affairs, 508 Fulton St, Durham, NC, 27705. Tel: 919-286-6929, Ext 6654. Fax: 919-286-6859. p. 1787

Haxer, Laura, Digital Res Librn, Harrington College of Design Library, 200 W Madison St, Chicago, IL, 60606. Tel: 312-697-8020. Fax: 312-697-8115. p. 614

Haxton, Peter, Data Serv Coordr, State Library of Kansas, State Capitol Bldg, Topeka, KS, 66612. Tel: 785-296-3296. Fax: 785-296-6650. p. 896

Hay, Amy, Dir, Gilbert Public Library, 17 N Broadway, Gilbert, MN, 55741. Tel: 218-748-2230. Fax: 218-748-2229. p. 1252

Hay, Daniel, Circ Spec, Central New Mexico Community College Libraries, 525 Buena Vista SE, Albuquerque, NM, 87106-4023. Tel: 505-224-3280. Fax: 505-224-3321. p. 1548

Hay, Fred, Spec Coll Librn, Appalachian State University, 218 College St, Boone, NC, 28608. Tel: 828-262-2887. Fax: 828-262-3001. p. 1776

Hay, Fred J, Dr, Distinguished Prof & Librn, Appalachian State University, William Leonard Eury Appalachian Collection, Belk Library, 4th Flr, 218 College St, Boone, NC, 28608. Tel: 828-262-4041. Fax: 828-262-2553. p. 1777

Hay, Kathy, Librn, Harcourt Community Library, 106 W Second St, Harcourt, IA, 50544. Tel: 515-354-5391. Fax: 515-354-5391. p. 820

Hay, Marie, Head, Ser, Trinity International University, 2065 Half Day Rd, Deerfield, IL, 60015-1241. Tel: 847-317-4006. Fax: 847-317-4012. p. 635

Hay, Matthew, Cat/Ref/Libr Instruction, Allegany College of Maryland Library, 12401 Willowbrook Rd SE, Cumberland, MD, 21502-2596. Tel: 301-784-5366. Fax: 301-784-5017. p. 1026

Hay, Patricia, Continuing Educ Coordr, Northeast Florida Library Information Network, 2233 Park Ave, Ste 402, Orange Park, FL, 32073. Tel: 904-278-5620. Fax: 904-278-5625. p. 2940

Hay, Randy, In Charge, Bedford-Somerset Mental Health, 245 W Race St, Somerset, PA, 15501. Tel: 814-443-4891. Fax: 814-443-4898. p. 2141

Hayashi, Janet, Coll Mgt, Newbury College Library, 150 Fisher Ave, Brookline, MA, 02445-5796. Tel: 617-730-7070. Fax: 617-730-7239. p. 1071

Hayashi, Junie, Circ Librn, Leeward Community College Library, 96-045 Ala Ike, Pearl City, HI, 96782-3393. Tel: 808-455-0673. Fax: 808-453-6729. p. 567

Hayashi, Maris, Coll Develop, Florida Atlantic University, 777 Glades Rd, Boca Raton, FL, 33431. Tel: 561-297-4317. Fax: 561-297-2189. p. 428

Haydel, Lydia, Br Mgr, Iberville Parish Library, East Iberville, 5715 Monticello St, Saint Gabriel, LA, 70776. Tel: 225-642-8380. Fax: 225-642-8381. p. 966

Hayden, Carla D, Dr, Chief Exec Officer, Enoch Pratt Free Library, 400 Cathedral St, Baltimore, MD, 21201-4484. Tel: 410-396-5430. Fax: 410-396-1441. p. 1012

Hayden, Dolores, Automation Syst Coordr, Livonia Public Library, Civic Center, 32777 Five Mile Rd, Livonia, MI, 48154-3045. Tel: 734-466-2675. Fax: 734-458-6011. p. 1203

Hayden, Frances Diane, Actg Librn, North Carolina Office of Archives & History, North Carolina Maritime Museum, Charles R McNeill Maritime Library, 315 Front St, Beaufort, NC, 28516. Tel: 252-728-7317. Fax: 252-728-2108. p. 1808

Hayden, Jessica, Cat, University of Northern Colorado Libraries, 501 20th St, Greeley, CO, 80639. Tel: 970-351-2183. Fax: 970-351-2963. p. 312

Hayden, Karen, Dir, Little Dixie Regional Libraries, 111 N Fourth St, Moberly, MO, 65270-1577. Tel: 660-263-4426. Fax: 660-263-4024. p. 1345

Hayden, Meg, Electronic Res Librn, New Bedford Law Library, Superior Courthouse, 441 County St, New Bedford, MA, 02740. Tel: 508-992-8077. Fax: 508-991-7411. p. 1108

Hayden, Meridith, Ref & Instruction Librn, Ivy Technical Community College, 50 W Fall Creek Pkwy N Dr, Indianapolis, IN, 46208-5752. Tel: 317-921-4782. Fax: 317-921-4355. p. 755

Hayden, Ruth, Tech Serv, Smyrna Public Library, 100 Village Green Circle, Smyrna, GA, 30080-3478. Tel: 770-431-2860. Fax: 770-431-2862. p. 551

Hayden, Wallace, Hist Librn, Bacon Memorial District Library, 45 Vinewood, Wyandotte, MI, 48192-5221. Tel: 734-246-8357. Fax: 734-282-1540. p. 1237

Haydock, Jane, Acq, Ser, Yukon College Library, 500 College Dr, Whitehorse, YT, Y1A 5K4, CANADA. Tel: 867-668-8870. Fax: 867-668-8808. p. 2934

Haydu, Steve, Cataloger, Syst Librn, Alamogordo Public Library, 920 Oregon Ave, Alamogordo, NM, 88310. Tel: 575-439-4140. Fax: 575-439-4108. p. 1547

Hayek, Jennifer, Br Mgr, Chesterfield County Public Library, Enon, 1801 Enon Church Rd, Chester, VA, 23836. Tel: 804-530-3403. p. 2457

Hayek, Jennifer, Br Mgr, Chesterfield County Public Library, Ettrick-Matoaca, 4501 River Rd, Petersburg, VA, 23803. Tel: 804-526-8087. p. 2457

Hayek, Sonia, Librn, Iowa Veteran's Home Library, 1301 Summit St, Marshalltown, IA, 50158-5484. Tel: 641-753-4412. Fax: 641-753-4373. p. 830

Hayes, Andralee, AV, Per, Saddleback College, 28000 Marguerite Pkwy, Mission Viejo, CA, 92692. Tel: 949-582-4873. Fax: 949-364-0284. p. 187

Hayes, Andrea, Dir, Roosevelt County Library, 220 Second Ave S, Wolf Point, MT, 59201-1599. Tel: 406-653-2411. Fax: 406-653-1365. p. 1390

Hayes, Barbara, Ch, First United Methodist Church Library, 501 Howe St, Green Bay, WI, 54301. Tel: 920-437-9252. Fax: 920-437-0991. p. 2595

Hayes, Carrie, Tech Coordr, North Canton Public Library, 185 N Main St, North Canton, OH, 44720-2595. Tel: 330-499-4712. Fax: 330-499-7356. p. 1923

Hayes, Cindy, Br Mgr, Jefferson County Library, Northwest, 5680 State Rd PP, High Ridge, MO, 63049. Tel: 636-677-8186. Fax: 636-677-8243. p. 1331

Hayes, David, Univ Librn, Radford University, 801 E Main St, Radford, VA, 24142-0001. Tel: 540-831-5471. Fax: 540-831-6138. p. 2487

Hayes, David M, Archivist, University of Colorado Boulder, Archives & Special Collections, 1720 Pleasant St, Boulder, CO, 80309-0184. Tel: 303-492-6144, 303-492-7242. Fax: 303-492-1881. p. 291

Hayes, Elaine Jones, Spec Coll Librn, Laramie County Library System, 2200 Pioneer Ave, Cheyenne, WY, 82001-3610. Tel: 307-773-7232. Fax: 307-634-2082. p. 2652

Hayes, Elyse, Dir, Seminary of the Immaculate Conception Library, 440 W Neck Rd, Huntington, NY, 11743. Tel: 631-423-0483, Ext 141. Fax: 631-423-2346. p. 1639

Hayes, Eric, Tech Serv, Webmaster, Royal Oak Public Library, 222 E Eleven Mile Rd, Royal Oak, MI, 48067-2633. Tel: 248-246-3751. Fax: 248-246-3701. p. 1223

Hayes, Givane, Br Mgr, Ocean County Library, Barnegat Branch, 112 Burr St, Barnegat, NJ, 08005. Tel: 609-698-3331. Fax: 609-698-9592. p. 1534

Hayes, Gretchen, Head, Youth Serv, Mason City Public Library, 225 Second St SE, Mason City, IA, 50401. Tel: 641-421-3668. Fax: 641-423-2615. p. 830

Hayes, Helena, Dir, Big Rapids Community Library, 426 S Michigan Ave, Big Rapids, MI, 49307. Tel: 231-796-5234. Fax: 231-796-1078. p. 1158

Hayes, John, Imaging Tech, National Cowboy & Western Heritage Museum, 1700 NE 63rd St, Oklahoma City, OK, 73111. Tel: 405-478-2250, Ext 289. Fax: 405-478-6421. p. 1973

Hayes, Judith, Libr Mgr, Med Librn, Tuality Healthcare, Tuality Health Information Resource Center, 334 SE Eighth Ave, Hillsboro, OR, 97123-4201. Tel: 503-681-1702. Fax: 503-681-1761. p. 2000

Hayes, Judith, Librn, Tuality Healthcare, Health Sciences Library, 335 SE Eighth Ave, Hillsboro, OR, 97123. Tel: 503-681-1121. Fax: 503-681-1729. p. 2000

Hayes, Karen, Br Mgr, Harris County Public Library, Spring Branch Memorial, 930 Corbindale, Houston, TX, 77024. Tel: 713-464-1633. Fax: 713-973-2654. p. 2336

Hayes, Kathryn, Info Res Librn, Braille Institute Library Services, 741 N Vermont Ave, Los Angeles, CA, 90029-3514. Tel: 323-663-1111, Ext 1283. Fax: 323-662-2440. p. 168

Hayes, Linda, ILL, Cape May County Library, 30 Mechanic St, Cape May Court House, NJ, 08210. Tel: 609-463-6350. Fax: 609-465-3895. p. 1477

Hayes, Lisa, Ref Librn, Indiana Wesleyan University, 4201 S Washington St, Marion, IN, 46953. Tel: 513-881-3611. Fax: 765-677-2676. p. 762

Hayes, Lisa, Librn, South Carolina Historical Society Library, Fireproof Bldg, 100 Meeting St, Charleston, SC, 29401-2299. Tel: 843-723-3225, Ext 12. Fax: 843-723-8584. p. 2185

Hayes, Lois, Circ, Kent Memorial Library, 50 N Main St (Junction of Rtes 75 & 168), Suffield, CT, 06078-2117. Tel: 860-668-3896. Fax: 860-668-3895. p. 371

Hayes, Marion, Adult Serv, Manatee County Public Library System, 1301 Barcarrota Blvd W, Bradenton, FL, 34205. Tel: 941-748-5555. Fax: 941-749-7191. p. 429

Hayes, Mary, Asst Dir, San Francisco Law Library, Financial District, Monadnock Bldg, 685 Market St, Ste 420, San Francisco, CA, 94105. Tel: 415-882-9310. Fax: 415-882-9594. p. 245

Hayes, Mary Beth, Dir, Libr & Mus Serv, Arcadia Public Library, 20 W Duarte Rd, Arcadia, CA, 91006. Tel: 626-821-4364. Fax: 626-447-8050. p. 121

Hayes, Meredith, Asst Librn, Spruce Pine Public Library, 142 Walnut Ave, Spruce Pine, NC, 28777. Tel: 828-765-4673. p. 1825

Hayes, Michael, Librn, United States Court of Appeals, US Courthouse, 844 King St, Lock Box 43, Wilmington, DE, 19801. Tel: 302-573-5880, 302-573-5881. Fax: 302-573-6430. p. 389

Hayes, Patricia G, Dept Head, Pennsylvania State University, N Atherton St, State College, PA, 16801. Tel: 814-863-9940. Fax: 814-863-5568. p. 2143

Hayes, Rodney, Asst Librn, Randolph Public Library, 130 Durand Rd, Randolph, NH, 03593. Tel: 603-466-5408. p. 1463

Hayes, Sandy, Acq, Texas A&M University-Commerce, 2600 S Neal St, Commerce, TX, 75429. Tel: 903-886-5734. Fax: 903-886-5434. p. 2300

Hayes, Sharon, ILL, Carroll County Public Library, 115 Airport Dr, Westminster, MD, 21157. Tel: 410-386-4500. Fax: 410-386-4509. p. 1045

Hayes, Sheila, Sr Librn, Computer & Web-Based Res, Hartford Hospital, ERC Bldg-3, 80 Seymour St, Hartford, CT, 06102. Tel: 860-545-2416. Fax: 860-545-2572. p. 345

Hayes, Sheila, Librn, Portsmouth Regional Hospital, 333 Borthwick Ave, Portsmouth, NH, 03801. Tel: 603-433-4094. Fax: 603-433-5144. p. 1463

Hayes, Stephen M, Bus Librn, Hesburgh Libraries, Thomas J Mahaffey Jr Business Information Center, L001 Mendoza College of Business, Notre Dame, IN, 46556. Tel: 574-631-5268. Fax: 574-631-6367. p. 770

Hayes, Susan, Dir, Wetumpka Public Library, 212 S Main St, Wetumpka, AL, 36092. Tel: 334-567-1308. Fax: 334-567-1309. p. 40

Hayes, Susan, Cat, New York University, 70 Washington Sq S, New York, NY, 10012-1091. Tel: 212-998-2505. Fax: 212-995-4070. p. 1695

Hayes, Susan, Head, Tech Serv, Roanoke Public Libraries, 706 S Jefferson St, Roanoke, VA, 24016-5191. Tel: 540-853-2473. Fax: 540-853-1781. p. 2494

Hayes, Suzanne, Dir, Libr & Instrul Serv, Empire State College (Online Library), Three Union Ave, Saratoga Springs, NY, 12866. Tel: 518-587-2100. Fax: 518-581-9526. p. 1738

Hayes, Suzi, Dir, Parkland Library, 6620 University Dr, Parkland, FL, 33067. Tel: 954-757-4200. Fax: 954-753-5223. p. 481

Hayes, Tara, Info Res Coordr, Medical University of South Carolina Library, 171 Ashley Ave, Ste 300, Charleston, SC, 29425-0001. Tel: 843-792-9211. Fax: 843-792-7947. p. 2184

Hayes, Tempie, Weekend Librn, Barton College, 400 Atlantic Christian College Dr NE, Wilson, NC, 27893. Tel: 252-399-6500. Fax: 252-399-6571. p. 1831

Hayes, Teresa, Librn, Newton County Public Library, Hwy 7 S, Jasper, AR, 72641. Tel: 870-446-2983. Fax: 870-446-2983. p. 104

Hayes, Tim, Dir, Blue Earth County Library System, 100 E Main St, Mankato, MN, 56001. Tel: 507-304-4001. Fax: 507-304-4009. p. 1257

Hayes, Tracey J Hunter, Assoc Prof, Dir, Lincoln University, 1570 Old Baltimore Pike, Lincoln University, PA, 19352. Tel: 484-365-7370. Fax: 610-932-1206. p. 2082

Hayes, Vali, Br Mgr, Chickasaw Regional Library System, Healdton Public Library, 18 S Fourth, Healdton, OK, 73438. Tel: 580-229-0590. Fax: 580-229-0654. p. 1957

Hayes, Wendy Joy, Asst Dir, Town of Chester Public Library, 6307 State Rte 9, Chestertown, NY, 12817. Tel: 518-494-5384. Fax: 518-491-5171. p. 1606

Hayes-Hawkinson, Ann Marie, Curator, Figge Art Museum, 225 W Second St, Davenport, IA, 52801. Tel: 563-326-7804. Fax: 563-326-7876. p. 806

Hayes-Martin, Tonya, Librn, Fulton State Hospital, Patient's Library, 600 E Fifth St, Fulton, MO, 65251. Tel: 573-592-2261. Fax: 573-592-3011. p. 1328

Hayes-Martin, Tonya, Librn, Fulton State Hospital, Professional Library, 600 E Fifth St, Fulton, MO, 65251. Tel: 573-592-2261. Fax: 573-592-3011. p. 1328

Hayes-Zorn, Sheryln, Actg Dir, Curator of Manuscripts, Nevada Department of Cultural Affairs Division of Museums & History, 1650 N Virginia St, Reno, NV, 89503. Tel: 775-688-1191, Ext 222. Fax: 775-688-2917. p. 1432

Hayler, Carrie, Librn, McElroy, Deutsch, Mulvaney & Carpenter, LLP, Law Library, Three Gateway Ctr, 100 Mulberry St, Newark, NJ, 07102. Tel: 973-622-7711, Ext 2065. Fax: 973-622-5314. p. 1505

Hayles, Susan, Mgr, Res Syst, Leonard, Street & Deinard, 150 S Fifth St, Ste 2300, Minneapolis, MN, 55402. Tel: 612-335-1616. Fax: 612-335-1657. p. 1260

Hayman, Richard, Ref Librn, Grant MacEwan University Library, 10700 104th Ave, Edmonton, AB, T5J 4S2, CANADA. Tel: 780-497-5850. Fax: 780-497-5895. p. 2701

Haymes, Colin, Educ Coordr, Elisabet Ney Museum Library, 304 East 44th St, Austin, TX, 78751. Tel: 512-458-2255. Fax: 512-453-0638. p. 2281

Haymes, Don, Archives, Spec Coll, Christian Theological Seminary Library, 1000 W 42nd St, Indianapolis, IN, 46208. Tel: 317-931-2368. Fax: 317-931-2363. p. 750

Haymore, Teresa, Head Librn, Mountain Regional Library System, Fannin County Public Library, 400 W Main St, Ste 104, Blue Ridge, GA, 30513. Tel: 706-632-5263. Fax: 706-632-7719. p. 558

Haynes, Annie, Asst Dir, Claud H Gilmer Memorial Library, 206 N Hwy 377, Rocksprings, TX, 78880. Tel: 830-683-8130. Fax: 830-683-8131. p. 2376

Haynes, Bonita Gayle, Mgr, Libr Serv, John Van Puffelen Library of the Appalachian Bible College, 161 College Dr, Mount Hope, WV, 25880-1040. Tel: 304-877-6428, Ext 3211. Fax: 304-877-5983. p. 2567

Haynes, Cathy, Ref Serv, Ad, Coshocton Public Library, 655 Main St, Coshocton, OH, 43812-1697. Tel: 740-622-0956. Fax: 740-622-4331. p. 1891

Haynes, Debra, Dir, Youth Serv, Carthage Public Library, 612 S Garrison Ave, Carthage, MO, 64836. Tel: 417-237-7040. Fax: 417-237-7041. p. 1322

Haynes, Gene, Librn, Veterans Affairs Medical Center Library, 800 Zorn Ave, Louisville, KY, 40206-1499. Tel: 502-287-6240. Fax: 502-287-6134. p. 927

Haynes, Gene M, Head Librn, Kentucky Medical Library Association, VA Med Ctr, Libr Servs 142D, 800 Zorn Ave, Louisville, KY, 40206-1499. Tel: 502-287-6240, Ext 5584. Fax: 502-287-6134. p. 2944

Haynes, Linda, Librn, Mary Duncan Public Library, 100 W Main St, Benson, NC, 27504. Tel: 919-894-3724. Fax: 919-894-1283. p. 1776

Haynes, Richard, Dir, Harlan County Public Library, 107 N Third St, Harlan, KY, 40831. Tel: 606-573-5220. Fax: 606-573-5220. p. 916

Haynes, Sandra, Asst Dir, Teen Libns, Norelius Community Library, 1403 First Ave S, Denison, IA, 51442-2014. Tel: 712-263-9355. Fax: 712-263-8578. p. 808

Haynes, Suzanne, Ref & Instruction Librn, Tulsa Community College Learning Resources Center, Southeast Campus, 10300 E 81st St, Tulsa, OK, 74133-4513. Tel: 918-595-7704. Fax: 918-595-7706. p. 1983

Haynes, Theo, Bus Librn, Rutgers University Libraries, Paul Robeson Library, Camden, 300 N Fourth St, Camden, NJ, 08102-1404. Tel: 856-225-6033. Fax: 856-225-6428. p. 1477

Haynes, Wanda, Mgr, Pioneer Library System, McLoud Public, 133 N Main, McLoud, OK, 74851. Tel: 405-964-2960. Fax: 405-964-5389. p. 1970

Haynie, Donna, Librn, Slater Public Library, 201 N Main, Slater, MO, 65349. Tel: 660-529-3100. p. 1365

Haynie, Linda, Circ Supvr, LeTourneau University, 2100 S Mobberly Ave, Longview, TX, 75602-3524. Tel: 903-233-3268. Fax: 903-233-3263. p. 2357

Haynie, Steven, Br Mgr, Cuyahoga County Public Library, South Euclid-Lyndhurst Branch, 4645 Mayfield Rd, South Euclid, OH, 44121-4018. Tel: 216-382-4880. Fax: 216-382-4584. p. 1928

Hayreh, Shelley, Archivist, Columbia University, Avery Architectural & Fine Arts Library, 1172 Amsterdam Ave, MC 0301, New York, NY, 10027. Tel: 212-854-6199. Fax: 212-854-8904. p. 1674

Hays, Beth, Youth Serv Librn, Prairie du Sac Public Library, 560 Park Ave, Prairie du Sac, WI, 53578-1199. Tel: 608-643-8318. Fax: 608-643-4897. p. 2631

Hays, Fran, Br Mgr, Beaufort County Library, Beaufort Branch Library, 311 Scott St, Beaufort, SC, 29902-5591. Tel: 843-255-6456. Fax: 843-255-9426. p. 2181

Hays, Laura, Ref Serv, Ad, Carol Stream Public Library, 616 Hiawatha Dr, Carol Stream, IL, 60188. Tel: 630-653-0755. Fax: 630-653-6809. p. 601

Hays, Leigh, Dir, Le Bonheur Children's Medical Center, 50 N Dunlap Ave, Memphis, TN, 38103. Tel: 901-572-3167. Fax: 901-572-5290. p. 2249

Hays, Myrna, Librn, Wetumpka Public Library, 212 S Main St, Wetumpka, AL, 36092. Tel: 334-567-1308. Fax: 334-567-1309. p. 40

Hays, Sue, Libr Dir, Madison County Public Library, 507 W Main St, Richmond, KY, 40475. Tel: 859-623-6704. Fax: 859-623-2023. p. 934

Hays, Timothy, Chief Librn, United States Army, 696 Virginia Rd, Concord, MA, 01742-2751. Tel: 978-318-8349. Fax: 978-318-8693. p. 1083

Hayslett, Dawn, Pub Serv Mgr, Burlington Public Library, 210 Court St, Burlington, IA, 52601. Tel: 319-753-1647. Fax: 319-753-0789. p. 797

Hayslip, Paula, Ch, Little Dixie Regional Libraries, 111 N Fourth St, Moberly, MO, 65270-1577. Tel: 660-263-4426. Fax: 660-263-4024. p. 1345

Haythorn, J Denny, Dir, Whittier College, 3333 Harbor Blvd, Costa Mesa, CA, 92626. Tel: 714-444-4141. Fax: 714-444-3609. p. 137

Haythornthwaite, Caroline, Dir, Prof, University of British Columbia, The Irving K Barber Centre, 1961 E Mall, Ste 470, Vancouver, BC, V6T 1Z1, CANADA. Tel: 604-822-2404. Fax: 604-822-6006. p. 2977

Hayton, Greg, Chief Librn, Cambridge Libraries & Galleries, One North Sq, Cambridge, ON, N1S 2K6, CANADA. Tel: 519-621-0460. Fax: 519-621-2080. p. 2798

Hayward, Christine, Dir, Harrington Public Library, 110 Center St, Harrington, DE, 19952. Tel: 302-398-4647. Fax: 302-398-3847. p. 383

Hayward, Delvan, Libr Mgr, Miami Memorial-Gila County Library, 282 S Adonis Ave, Miami, AZ, 85539. Tel: 928-473-2621. Fax: 928-473-2567. p. 69

Hayward, Evelyn, Br Mgr, Willows Public Library, Elk Creek Branch, 455 Elm St, Elk Creek, CA, 95939. Tel: 530-968-5238. p. 284

Hayward, Karen L, Supvry Librn, United States Army, The Medal of Honor Memorial Library, 4418 Llewellyn Ave, Ste 5068, Fort George G. Meade, MD, 20755-5068. Tel: 301-677-4509, 301-677-5522. Fax: 301-677-2694. p. 1028

Hayward, Kenneth, Librn, Quail Botanical Gardens Foundation Inc Library, 230 Quail Gardens Dr, Encinitas, CA, 92024-0005. Tel: 760-436-3036. Fax: 760-632-0917. p. 146

Hayward, Lucille, ILL, Somerset County Library System, 11767 Beechwood St, Princess Anne, MD, 21853. Tel: 410-651-0852, Ext 11. Fax: 410-651-1388. p. 1036

Hayward, Mark, Dir, University of Texas Libraries, Population Research Center Library, Main Bldg 1800, G1800, Austin, TX, 78712. Tel: 512-471-8332. Fax: 512-471-4886. p. 2284

Hayward, Tracey, Head, ILL, Canal Fulton Public Library, 154 Market St NE, Canal Fulton, OH, 44614-1196. Tel: 330-854-4148. Fax: 330-854-9520. p. 1863

Haywood, Anne T, Dir, Bruton Memorial Library, 302 W McLendon St, Plant City, FL, 33563. Tel: 813-757-9215. Fax: 813-757-9217. p. 484

Haywood, Christy, Ch, Circ, Robertson County Public Library, 207 N Main St, Mount Olivet, KY, 41064. Tel: 606-724-5746. Fax: 606-724-5746. p. 930

Haywood, Felicia, Asst Dir, Bibliog Instr, Macon State College Library, 100 College Station Dr, Macon, GA, 31206-5144. Tel: 478-471-2867. Fax: 478-471-2869. p. 540

Haywood, Jean, Libr Mgr, Haut-Saint-Jean Regional Library, Dr Walter Chestnut Public Library, 395 Main St., Unit 1, Hartland, NB, E7P 2N3, CANADA. Tel: 506-375-4876. Fax: 506-375-6816. p. 2762

Hayword, Ann, Librn, Department of Corrections, 64 Base Rd, Machiasport, ME, 04655-0428. Tel: 207-255-1100, Ext 50262. Fax: 207-255-1176. p. 991

Hayworth, Eugene, Dir, Soc Sci, University of Colorado Boulder, 1720 Pleasant St, 184 UCB, Boulder, CO, 80309-0184. Tel: 303-492-7511. Fax: 303-492-3340. p. 291

Hayworth, Laura, Asst Dir, Johnson County Public Library, 219 N Church St, Mountain City, TN, 37683-1522. Tel: 423-727-6544. Fax: 423-727-0319. p. 2254

Hazard, Brenda, Dir, Hudson Valley Community College, 80 Vandenburgh Ave, Troy, NY, 12180. Tel: 518-629-7338. Fax: 518-629-7509. p. 1756

Hazel, Margaret, Virtual Br & Tech Innovation Mgr, Eugene Public Library, 100 W Tenth Ave, Eugene, OR, 97401. Tel: 541-682-5450. Fax: 541-682-5898. p. 1996

Hazelbaker, Joyce, Circ, Linn County Library District No 5, 904 Main St, Pleasanton, KS, 66075. Tel: 913-352-8554. Fax: 913-352-8554. p. 890

Hazelbaker, S Gayle, Dir, Tecumseh District Library, 215 N Ottawa St, Tecumseh, MI, 49286-1564. Tel: 517-423-2238. Fax: 517-423-5519. p. 1230

Hazelden, Joanna, Br Mgr, Chicago Public Library, Lincoln Park, 1150 W Fullerton Ave, Chicago, IL, 60614. Tel: 312-744-1926. Fax: 312-744-5018. p. 609

Hazeltine, Barb, Librn, Wapiti Regional Library, Christopher Lake Public Library, RM Office on Hwy 263, Christopher Lake, SK, S0J 0N0, CANADA. Tel: 306-982-4763. p. 2921

Hazelton, Flora, Asst Dir, Br Serv, Clayton County Library System, 865 Battlecreek Rd, Jonesboro, GA, 30236. Tel: 770-473-3850. Fax: 770-473-3858. p. 536

Hazelton, Penny A, Assoc Dean of Libr & Tech, University of Washington Libraries, Marian Gould Gallagher Law Library, William H Gates Hall, Box 353025, Seattle, WA, 98195-3025. Fax: 206-685-2165. p. 2534

Hazelwood, Wanda, Circ Librn, Marion County Public Library, 201 E Main St, Lebanon, KY, 40033-1133. Tel: 270-692-4698. Fax: 270-692-9555. p. 920

Hazen, Alice, Dir, Hopkins Public Library, 118 E Main St, Hopkins, MI, 49328-0366. Tel: 269-793-7516. Fax: 269-793-7047. p. 1191

Hazen, Dan C, Assoc Librn, Coll Develop, Harvard Library, Harvard College Library (Headquarters in Harry Elkins Widener Memorial Library), Widener Library, Rm 110, Cambridge, MA, 02138. Tel: 617-495-2401. Fax: 617-496-4750. p. 1075

Hazen, Ritza, Asst Librn, Chester County Law Library, Bar Association Bldg, 15 W Gay St, West Chester, PA, 19380-3014. Tel: 610-344-6166. Fax: 610-344-6994. p. 2153

Hazen, Ron, Cat, Tech Serv, Warren-Trumbull County Public Library, 444 Mahoning Ave NW, Warren, OH, 44483. Tel: 330-399-8807. Fax: 330-395-3988. p. 1944

Hazen, Teresa, Fac Librn, Mount Hood Community College Library, 26000 SE Stark St, Gresham, OR, 97030. Tel: 503-491-7161. Fax: 503-491-7389. p. 1999

Hazzan, Linda, Dir, Mkt & Communications, Toronto Public Library, 789 Yonge St, Toronto, ON, M4W 2G8, CANADA. Tel: 416-393-7131. Fax: 416-393-7229. p. 2860

He, Daqing, Asst Prof, University of Pittsburgh, 135 N Bellefield Ave, Pittsburgh, PA, 15260. Tel: 412-624-5230. Fax: 412-624-5231. p. 2973

He, Helen, Head of Libr, University of Toronto Libraries, Dentistry Library, 124 Edward St, Rm 267, Toronto, ON, M5G 1G6, CANADA. Tel: 416-979-4916, Ext 4371. Fax: 416-979-4936. p. 2865

He, Yan, Info Literacy Librn, Indiana University Kokomo Library, 2300 S Washington St, Kokomo, IN, 46904. Tel: 765-455-9265. Fax: 765-455-9276. p. 758

Heaberlin, J Charles, Archival Librn, Lexington Theological Seminary, 631 S Limestone, Lexington, KY, 40508. Tel: 859-280-1229. Fax: 859-281-6042. p. 921

Heacock, Mary Jo, Cat Librn, Villanova University, Law Library, Garey Hall, 299 N Spring Mill Rd, Villanova, PA, 19085. Tel: 610-519-7896. Fax: 610-519-7033. p. 2150

Heacox, Cindy, Br Mgr, Wilson County Public Library, Black Creek Branch, 103 Central Ave, Black Creek, NC, 27813. Tel: 252-237-3715. Fax: 252-237-3715. p. 1831

Head, Benjamin, Instruction Librn, Christian Brothers University, 650 E Pkwy South, Memphis, TN, 38104. Tel: 901-321-3432. Fax: 901-321-3219. p. 2248

Head, Carolyn, Exec Dir, Southwest Tennessee Community College, 170 Myrtle St, Memphis, TN, 38103. Tel: 901-333-5938. Fax: 901-333-5141. p. 2251

Head, Carolyn, Exec Dir, Southwest Tennessee Community College, George Freeman Library, 5983 Macon Cove, Memphis, TN, 38134. Tel: 901-333-4732. Fax: 901-333-4566. p. 2251

Head, Carolyn, Exec Dir, Southwest Tennessee Community College, Gill Library, 3833 Mountain Terrace, Memphis, TN, 38127. Tel: 901-333-5979. Fax: 901-333-5980. p. 2251

Head, Carolyn, Exec Dir, Southwest Tennessee Community College, Southeast Center Library, 5396 Mendenhall Mall, Memphis, TN, 38115. Tel: 901-333-6037. Fax: 901-333-6038. p. 2252

Head, Carolyn, Exec Dir, Southwest Tennessee Community College, Whitehaven Center Library, 3035 Directors Row, Bldg 6, Memphis, TN, 38131. Tel: 901-333-6442. Fax: 901-333-6441. p. 2252

Head, Connie, Instruction Librn, Gulf Coast State College Library, 5230 W Hwy 98, Panama City, FL, 32401. Tel: 850-872-3893. Fax: 850-872-3861. p. 480

Head, Daniel, Libr Asst, Neal, Gerber & Eisenberg LLP, Two N La Salle St, Ste 1700, Chicago, IL, 60602. Tel: 312-269-3091. Fax: 312-578-1793. p. 620

Head, Eric C, Asst Dir, Libr Serv, Citrus County Library System, 425 W Roosevelt Blvd, Beverly Hills, FL, 34465-4281. Tel: 352-746-9077. Fax: 352-746-9493. p. 427

Head, Joanne, Dep Dir, Western Counties Regional Library, 405 Main St, Yarmouth, NS, B5A 1G3, CANADA. Tel: 902-742-2486. Fax: 902-742-6920. p. 2786

Head, Karen, Supvr, Pub Serv, Northwest Christian University, 1188 Kincade, Eugene, OR, 97401. Tel: 541-684-7235. Fax: 541-684-7307. p. 1997

Head, Steve, Br Mgr, Hightower Sara Regional Library, Cave Spring Branch, 10-B Cedartown St, Cave Spring, GA, 30124-2702. Tel: 706-777-3346. Fax: 706-777-0947. p. 549

Head, Susan, Librn, Virginia Beach Public Library Department, Oceanfront Area, 700 Virginia Beach Blvd, Virginia Beach, VA, 23451. Tel: 757-385-2640. p. 2500

Headlam, Elizabeth, Sr Librn, Canadian Broadcasting Corp, Radio Archives, 205 Wellington St W, Toronto, ON, M5G 3G7, CANADA. Tel: 416-205-5880. Fax: 416-205-8602. p. 2850

Headley, Wanda, Libr Mgr, University of Colorado Boulder, Natural Hazard Center Library, 482 UCB, Boulder, CO, 80309-0482. Tel: 303-492-5787, 303-492-6818. Fax: 303-492-2151. p. 292

Headrick, Laura L, Br Coordr, Marathon County Public Library, Rothschild Branch, 211 Grand Ave, Rothschild, WI, 54474-1122. Tel: 715-359-6208. Fax: 715-359-6208. p. 2646

Headrick-York, Jennifer, Bus & Finance Mgr, Blount County Public Library, 508 N Cusick St, Maryville, TN, 37804-5714. Tel: 865-982-0981. Fax: 865-977-1142. p. 2246

Headtke, Kathy, Librn, Allan Hancock College, 800 S College Dr, Santa Maria, CA, 93454. Tel: 805-922-6966, Ext 5474. Fax: 805-735-1554. p. 265

Heady, Heather, Info Serv Librn, Cumberland County Public Library & Information Center, Spring Lake Branch, 101 Laketree Blvd, Spring Lake, NC, 28390-3189. Tel: 910-497-3650. Fax: 910-497-0523. p. 1793

Heady, Lisa, Asst Librn, Choctaw County Public Library, 703 E Jackson St, Hugo, OK, 74743. Tel: 580-326-5591. Fax: 580-326-7388. p. 1966

Heady, Liz, Youth Serv, Prairie Skies Public Library District, 125 W Editor St, Ashland, IL, 62612. Tel: 217-476-3417. Fax: 217-476-8076. p. 590

Heady, Mary, Asst Librn, Chair, Spec Coll & Archives, Ref Serv, University of Arkansas-Monticello Library, 514 University Dr, Monticello, AR, 71656. Tel: 870-460-1080. Fax: 870-460-1980. p. 110

Heagle, Heather, Exec Dir, Ontario Camps Association Library, 250 Merton St, Ste 301, Toronto, ON, M4S 1B1, CANADA. Tel: 416-485-0425. Fax: 416-485-0422. p. 2856

Heald, Phillip J, Librn, Lawrence County Law Library Association, Lawrence County Courthouse, 4th Flr Annex, 111 S Fourth St, Ironton, OH, 45638-1586. Tel: 740-533-0582. Fax: 740-533-1084. p. 1906

Healey, Jenny, Ref, New Jersey Department of Law & Public Safety, 25 Market St, West Wing, 6th Flr, Trenton, NJ, 08625. Tel: 609-292-4958. Fax: 609-633-6555. p. 1535

Healey, Patrick, Digital Projects Librn, NASA, Library, Bldg 21, Code 272, Greenbelt, MD, 20771. Tel: 301-286-0884. Fax: 301-286-1755. p. 1030

Healt, Kristin, Librn, West Leyden - Town of Lewis Library, 5213 Osceola Rd, West Leyden, NY, 13489. Tel: 315-942-6813. p. 1766

Healy, Edith, Bibliog Instr, Ref, Ecole de Technologie Superieure (Service de la bibliotheque), 1100 rue Notre-Dame Ouest, Montreal, QC, H3C 1K3, CANADA. Tel: 514-396-8946. Fax: 514-396-8633. p. 2895

Healy, Jane, Electronic Res Coordr, South Dakota State Library, 800 Governors Dr, Pierre, SD, 57501-2294. Tel: 605-773-3131. p. 2216

Healy, Judy Pat, Sister, ILL Librn, College of Saint Mary Library, 7000 Mercy Rd, Omaha, NE, 68106-2606. Tel: 402-399-2471. Fax: 402-399-2686. p. 1411

Healy, Karen, Br Librn, Upper Darby Township & Sellers Memorial Free Public Library, Municipal, 100 Garrett Rd, Upper Darby, PA, 19082. Tel: 610-734-7649. Fax: 610-734-5781. p. 2149

Healy, Mary, Librn, Anoka County Library, St Francis Branch, 3519 Bridge St NW, Saint Francis, MN, 55070-9754. Tel: 763-753-2131. Fax: 763-753-0085. p. 1241

Healy, Shawna, Ad, Rye Public Library, 581 Washington Rd, Rye, NH, 03870. Tel: 603-964-8401. Fax: 603-964-7065. p. 1464

Heaney, Janelle, Dir of Circ, Andover Public Library, 1511 E Central Ave, Andover, KS, 67002. Tel: 316-558-3500. Fax: 316-558-3503. p. 856

Heard, Allison, Dir, Dolton Public Library District, 14037 Lincoln, Dolton, IL, 60419-1091. Tel: 708-849-2385. Fax: 708-841-2725. p. 637

Heard, Ernest William, Dr, Dir, Belmont University, 1900 Belmont Blvd, Nashville, TN, 37212-3757. Tel: 615-460-6782. Fax: 615-460-5641. p. 2255

Heard, Rachell, Mgr, Cobb County Public Library System, Hattie G Wilson Branch, 350 Lemon St, Marietta, GA, 30060. Tel: 770-528-2526. Fax: 770-528-2591. p. 543

Heard, Thomas, Assoc Dir, Northern Kentucky University, Nunn Dr, Highland Heights, KY, 41099. Tel: 859-572-6482. Fax: 859-572-6529, 859-572-6664. p. 917

Hearn, Mike, Coordr, Libr Serv, Northern Essex Community College, Lawrence Campus Library, 45 Franklin St, Lawrence, MA, 01841. Tel: 978-738-7400. Fax: 978-738-7114. p. 1095

Hearne, Jane, Br Librn, Ritchie County Public Library, Pennsboro Branch, 411 Main St, Pennsboro, WV, 26415. Tel: 304-659-2197. Fax: 304-659-2197. p. 2560

Hearod, Marguerite, Head Librn, Seminole State College, Junction Hwy 9 & David L Boren Blvd, Seminole, OK, 74818. Tel: 405-382-9950, Ext 243. Fax: 405-382-9511. p. 1977

Hearst, Nancy, Librn, Harvard Library, Fairbank Center for Chinese Studies Collection, 625 Massachusetts Ave, Cambridge, MA, 02139. Tel: 617-495-5753. Fax: 617-495-9976. p. 1075

Heartwell, Alison, Dep Dir, Central Rappahannock Regional Library, 1201 Caroline St, Fredericksburg, VA, 22401-3761. Tel: 540-372-1144. Fax: 540-373-9411. p. 2465

Heath, Annette, Librn, Kern County Law Library, 1415 Truxtun Ave, Rm 301, Bakersfield, CA, 93301. Tel: 661-868-5320. Fax: 661-868-5368. p. 123

Heath, April, Br Assoc, Las Vegas-Clark County Library District, Moapa Valley Library, 36 N Moapa Valley Blvd, Overton, NV, 89040-0397. Tel: 702-397-2690. Fax: 702-397-2698. p. 1429

Heath, Catherine, Dir, Mary E Seymour Memorial Free Library, 22 N Main St, Stockton, NY, 14784-0432. Tel: 716-595-3323. Fax: 716-595-3323. p. 1749

Heath, Catherine, Dir, Seymour Mary E Memorial Free Library, Cassadaga Branch, 18 Maple Ave, Cassadaga, NY, 14718. Tel: 716-595-3822. Fax: 716-595-3822. p. 1749

Heath, Dale, Head, Ref Serv, Mount Prospect Public Library, Ten S Emerson St, Mount Prospect, IL, 60056. Tel: 847-253-5675. Fax: 847-253-0642. p. 677

Heath, Fred M, Dr, Vice Provost & Dir, University of Texas Libraries, 101 E 21st St, Austin, TX, 78713. Tel: 512-495-4350. Fax: 512-495-4296. p. 2283

Heath, Fred M, Dr, Vice Provost & Dir, University of Texas Libraries, Perry-Castaneda Library (Main Library), 101 E 21st St, Austin, TX, 78712-1266. Tel: 512-495-4350. p. 2284

Heath, Gary, Librn, Columbia Correctional Institution Library, 216 S E Corrections Way, Lake City, FL, 32025-2013. Tel: 386-754-1041, 386-754-7600. Fax: 386-754-7602. p. 457

Heath, Gayle R, Libr Dir, Tamaqua Public Library, 30 S Railroad St, Tamaqua, PA, 18252. Tel: 570-668-4660. Fax: 570-668-3047. p. 2145

Heath, Gord, Dr, Archives Dir, Canadian Baptist Archives, McMaster Divinity Col, 1280 Main St W, Hamilton, ON, L8S 4K1, CANADA. Tel: 905-525-9140, Ext 26409. Fax: 905-577-4782. p. 2808

Heath, Jackie, Dir, Belmont Public Library, 146 Main St, Belmont, NH, 03220-0308. Tel: 603-267-8331. Fax: 603-267-5924. p. 1438

Heath, Janet P, Coordr, Ser, East Carolina University, William E Laupus Health Sciences Library, 600 Moye Blvd, Health Sciences Bldg, Greenville, NC, 27834. Tel: 252-744-2234. Fax: 252-744-2672. p. 1799

Heath, Joan, Assoc VPres for Univ Libr, Texas State University-San Marcos, Wood & Talbot St, San Marcos, TX, 78666-4604. Tel: 512-245-2133. Fax: 512-245-3002. p. 2385

Heath, Kristin, Cat Librn, Music Librn, Carnegie Mellon University, Hunt Library, 4909 Frew St, Pittsburgh, PA, 15213-3890. Tel: 412-268-2446. Fax: 412-268-2793. p. 2123

Heath, Leila, Head, Adult Serv, Warrenville Public Library District, 28 W 751 Stafford Pl, Warrenville, IL, 60555. Tel: 630-393-1171. Fax: 630-393-1688. p. 715

Heath, Mabel, Librn, Thousand Island Park Library, Saint Lawrence Ave, Thousand Island Park, NY, 13692. Tel: 315-482-9098. Fax: 315-482-9098. p. 1755

Heath, Margaret M, Librn, Skadden, Arps, Slate, Meagher & Flom LLP, 1440 New York Ave NW, Washington, DC, 20005. Tel: 202-371-7760. Fax: 202-393-5760. p. 414

Heath, Patricia, Asst Librn, Wasaga Beach Public Library, 120 Glenwood Dr, Wasaga Beach, ON, L0L 2P0, CANADA. Tel: 705-429-5481. Fax: 705-429-5481. p. 2869

Heath, Phyllis, Circ, West Lafayette Public Library, 208 W Columbia St, West Lafayette, IN, 47906. Tel: 765-743-2261. Fax: 765-743-0540. p. 787

Heath, Rita, Ch, Converse County Library, Glenrock Branch, 518 S Fourth St, Glenrock, WY, 82637. Tel: 307-436-2573. Fax: 307-436-8525. p. 2654

Heath, Robert, Dean, Stillman College, 3601 Stillman Blvd, Tuscaloosa, AL, 35403. Tel: 205-366-8851. Fax: 205-247-8042. p. 38

Heath-Grunder, Wanda, Br Mgr, Plumas County Library, Chester Branch, 210 First Ave, Chester, CA, 96020-0429. Tel: 530-258-2742. Fax: 530-258-3725. p. 212

Heathcock, Kristin, Librn, Hillsborough Community College, Plant City Campus Learning Resources Center, 1206 N Park Rd, Plant City, FL, 33563. Tel: 813-757-2163. Fax: 813-757-2167. p. 496

Heathcote, Heather, Br Librn, London Public Library, East London, 2016 Dundas St, London, ON, N5V 1R1, CANADA. Tel: 519-451-7600. p. 2818

Heather, Cooke, Librn, Eastern Health, Addictions Services Library, Mount Pearl Sq, 760 Topsail Rd, St. John's, NL, A1B 4A4, CANADA. Tel: 709-752-4120, 709-752-4121. Fax: 709-752-4412. p. 2772

Heatherly, Carey, Archivist, Ref Librn, University of Montevallo, Station 6100, Montevallo, AL, 35115-6100. Tel: 205-665-6100. Fax: 205-665-6112. p. 27

Heaton, Daniel, Mgr, Tech Serv, Syst Mgr, Jefferson County Rural Library District, 620 Cedar Ave, Port Hadlock, WA, 98339-9514. Tel: 360-385-6544. Fax: 360-385-7921. p. 2524

Heaton, Katie, Adult Serv, Cat, Collinsville Memorial Public Library District, 408 W Main St, Collinsville, IL, 62234. Tel: 618-344-1112. Fax: 618-345-6401. p. 630

Heaton, Reba, Asst Dir, Haines Borough Public Library, PO Box 1089, Haines, AK, 99827-1089. Tel: 907-766-2545. Fax: 907-766-2551. p. 49

Heaton, Ruthanne, Children's Prog, Circ, Seneca Public Library District, 210 N Main St, Seneca, IL, 61360. Tel: 815-357-6566. Fax: 815-357-6568. p. 701

Heaton, Tony, Circ Mgr, Illinois Wesleyan University, One Ames Plaza, Bloomington, IL, 61701-7188. Tel: 309-556-3350. Fax: 309-556-3706. p. 595

Heavilin, Sharon, Dir, Moyer District Library, 618 S Sangamon, Gibson City, IL, 60936. Tel: 217-784-5343. Fax: 217-784-5373. p. 649

Heavin, Ernie, Mgr, ILL, Mgr, Per, Georgetown College, 400 E College St, Georgetown, KY, 40324. Tel: 502-863-8400. Fax: 502-868-7740. p. 915

Heavner, Ellen, Asst Law Librn, Collin County Law Library, Courthouse, Ste 10216, 2100 Bloomdale Rd, McKinney, TX, 75071. Tel: 972-548-4255. Fax: 972-547-5734. p. 2361

Hebblethwaite, Christopher, Coordr of Ref Serv, State University of New York at Oswego, SUNY Oswego, 7060 State Rte 104, Oswego, NY, 13126-3514. Tel: 315-312-3060. Fax: 315-312-3194. p. 1713

Hebel, John, Ref, Georgia Military College, 201 E Greene St, Milledgeville, GA, 31061. Tel: 478-445-2718. Fax: 478-445-5592. p. 544

Hebel, Sue, Dir, Cordova District Library, 402 Main Ave, Cordova, IL, 61242-9790. Tel: 309-654-2330. Fax: 309-654-2290. p. 631

Heberlein, Heather, Librn, Sheboygan Press Library, 632 Center Ave, Sheboygan, WI, 53081. Tel: 920-453-5110. Fax: 920-457-3573. p. 2637

Hebert, Anta Maria, Dir, Bladen County Public Library, 111 N Cyprus St, Elizabethtown, NC, 28337. Tel: 910-862-6990. Fax: 910-862-8777. p. 1791

Hebert, Bethany, Asst Librn, Walpole Town Library, Bridge Memorial Library, 48 Main St, Walpole, NH, 03608. Tel: 603-756-9806. Fax: 603-756-3140. p. 1466

Hébert, Carole, Libr Mgr, Chaleur Library Region, Mgr Paquet Public Library, 10A du Colisée St, Caraquet, NB, E1W 1A5, CANADA. Tel: 506-726-2681. Fax: 506-726-2685. p. 2761

Hebert, Carole, Acq, Circ, Centre de Documentation Collegiale, 1111 rue Lapierre, La Salle, QC, H8N 2J4, CANADA. Tel: 514-364-3320, Ext 241. Fax: 514-364-2627. p. 2885

Hebert, Geraldine, ILL, Bronx Community College Library & Learning Center, 106 Meister Hall, 2115 University Ave, Bronx, NY, 10453. Tel: 718-289-5947. Fax: 718-289-6063. p. 1586

Hebert, Gina, Br Mgr, Terrebonne Parish Library, 151 Library Dr, Houma, LA, 70360. Tel: 985-876-5861. Fax: 985-917-0582. p. 951

Hebert, Holly, Ref Librn, Spec Coll Librn, The Brentwood Library, 8109 Concord Rd, Brentwood, TN, 37027. Tel: 615-371-0090, Ext 8230. Fax: 615-371-2238. p. 2225

Hebert, Kathy, Circ Mgr, East Central Georgia Regional Library, Columbia County Public Library, 7022 Evans Town Center Blvd, Evans, GA, 30809. Tel: 706-447-7662. Fax: 706-868-3351. p. 519

Hebert, Kayla, Br Mgr, Ouachita Parish Public Library, Cpl J R Searcy Memorial Library, 5775 Jonesboro Rd, West Monroe, LA, 71292. Tel: 318-327-1240. Fax: 318-323-1565. p. 957

Hebert, Lisa, Asst Dir, Grayson County College Library, 6101 Grayson Dr, Denison, TX, 75020-8299. Tel: 903-463-8637. Fax: 903-465-4123. p. 2312

Hebert, Margaret Ann, Br Mgr, Terrebonne Parish Library, Montegut Branch, 1135 Hwy 55, Montegut, LA, 70377. Tel: 985-594-4390. Fax: 985-594-9512. p. 951

Hebert, Marianne, Automation Syst Librn, State University of New York College at Potsdam, 44 Pierrepont Ave, Potsdam, NY, 13676-2294. Tel: 315-267-3308. Fax: 315-267-2744. p. 1722

Hebert, Marianne, Coll Develop Coordr, Syst, State University of New York College at Potsdam, 44 Pierrepont Ave, Potsdam, NY, 13676-2294. Tel: 315-267-2485. Fax: 315-267-2744. p. 1722

Hebert, Robert, Mgt Librn, Wake Forest University, Professional Center Library, Worrell Professional Ctr for Law & Management, 1834 Wake Forest Rd, Winston-Salem, NC, 27106. Tel: 336-758-4567. Fax: 336-758-6077. p. 1834

Hébert, Sarah, Head, Ref Serv, Ref Librn, NHTI, Concord's Community College, 31 College Dr, Concord, NH, 03301-7425. Tel: 603-271-7219. Fax: 603-271-7189. p. 1443

Hebisen, Ann, Pub Serv Librn, South Plains College Library, 1401 S College Ave, Box E, Levelland, TX, 79336. Tel: 806-716-2298. Fax: 806-894-5274. p. 2355

Hecht, Alan S, Dir, General Conference of Seventh-Day Adventists, 12501 Old Columbia Pike, Silver Spring, MD, 20904. Tel: 301-680-6495. Fax: 301-680-6090. p. 1041

Hecht, Kathy, Ser, Washington Adventist University, 7600 Flower Ave, Takoma Park, MD, 20912-7796. Tel: 301-891-4216. Fax: 301-891-4204. p. 1043

Hecht, Kim, Head, Tech Serv, Worth Public Library District, 6917 W 111th St, Worth, IL, 60482. Tel: 708-448-2855. Fax: 708-448-9174. p. 721

Heck, Jeff J, Assoc Dir, Augusta State University, 2500 Walton Way, Augusta, GA, 30904-2200. Tel: 706-737-1745. Fax: 706-667-4415. p. 518

Heck, Melody, Dir, Galva Public Library District, 120 NW Third Ave, Galva, IL, 61434. Tel: 309-932-2180. Fax: 309-932-2280. p. 648

Heckaman, Denise, Tech Serv, Bourbon Public Library, 307 N Main St, Bourbon, IN, 46504-1596. Tel: 574-342-5655. Fax: 574-342-5001. p. 729

Heckaman, Rusty, Archivist, American Academy of Pediatrics, 141 Northwest Point Blvd, Elk Grove Village, IL, 60007-1098. Tel: 847-434-7093. Fax: 847-434-4993. p. 641

Heckart, Nick, Acad Serv Assoc, University of Denver, Morgridge College of Education, Katherine A Ruffatto Hall, 1999 E Evans Ave, Denver, CO, 80208. Tel: 303-871-2747. Fax: 303-871-2709. p. 2963

Heckathorn, Jean, Dir, Mercer County Law Library, 305 Mercer County Courthouse, Mercer, PA, 16137-0123. Tel: 724-662-3800, Ext 2302. Fax: 724-662-0620. p. 2088

Heckel, Debra, Circ, Jefferson County Library, Windsor, 7479 Metropolitian Blvd, Barnhart, MO, 63012. Tel: 636-461-1914. Fax: 636-461-1915. p. 1331

Heckel, Sherri, Librn, Owensboro Messenger-Inquirer Library, 1401 Frederica St, Owensboro, KY, 42301. Tel: 270-926-0123. Fax: 270-685-3446. p. 931

Hecker, Margaret, Cat/ILL Librn, Head, Coll Mgt, Kentucky State University, 400 E Main St, Frankfort, KY, 40601-2355. Tel: 502-597-6852. Fax: 502-597-5068. p. 914

Hecker, Mindy, Ref, American Occupational Therapy Foundation, 4720 Montgomery Lane, Bethesda, MD, 20814-5385. Tel: 301-652-6611, Ext 2557. Fax: 301-656-3620. p. 1021

Hecker, Tom, Sci Librn, University of Kentucky Libraries, Science Library, 211 King Bldg, Lexington, KY, 40506-0039. Tel: 859-257-8343. Fax: 859-323-3225. p. 922

Heckert, Dawn, Circ, Haverford College, 370 Lancaster Ave, Haverford, PA, 19041-1392. Tel: 610-896-1175. Fax: 610-896-1102. p. 2067

Heckford, J Ian, Chief Exec Officer, Oshawa Public Library, 65 Bagot St, Oshawa, ON, L1H 1N2, CANADA. Tel: 905-579-6111. Fax: 905-433-8107. p. 2827

Heckler, Marilyn, Ch, Rockaway Township Free Public Library, 61 Mount Hope Rd, Rockaway, NJ, 07866. Tel: 973-627-2344. Fax: 973-627-7658. p. 1527

Heckman, James, Circ Mgr, Village Library of Morgantown, 207 N Walnut St, Morgantown, PA, 19543. Tel: 610-286-1022. Fax: 610-286-1024. p. 2092

Heckman, Jan E, Librn, University of Connecticut at Avery Point Library, 1084 Shennecossett Rd, Groton, CT, 06340-6097. Tel: 860-405-9146. Fax: 860-405-9150. p. 342

Heckman, Lucy, Head, Ref, Saint John's University Library, 8000 Utopia Pkwy, Queens, NY, 11439. Tel: 718-990-6735. Fax: 718-380-0353. p. 1725

Heckman, Mary Ellen G, Dir, Libr Serv, Reading Area Community College, Ten S Second St, Reading, PA, 19602. Tel: 610-607-6237. Fax: 610-607-6254. p. 2133

Heckman, Sheila, Librn, Saint Louis Psychoanalytic Institute, 8820 Ladue Rd, 3rd Flr, Saint Louis, MO, 63124-2079. Tel: 314-361-7075, Ext 324. Fax: 314-361-6269. p. 1359

Heckor, Leesa, Dir, Chandler-Watts Memorial Library, 340 N Oak, Stratford, OK, 74872. Tel: 580-759-2684. Fax: 580-759-3121. p. 1979

Hector, Patricia, Br Mgr, Sonoma County Library, Central Library, 211 E St, Santa Rosa, CA, 95404. Tel: 707-545-0831, Ext 527. Fax: 707-575-0437. p. 267

Hedberg, Marilyn, Health Sci Librn, North Dakota State University Libraries, 1201 Albrecht Blvd, Fargo, ND, 58108. Tel: 701-231-7965. Fax: 701-231-6128. p. 1841

Hedberg, Marilyn, Health Sci Librn, North Dakota State University Libraries, Philip N Haakenson Health Sciences Library, 135 Sudro Hall, Fargo, ND, 58102. Tel: 701-231-7965. Fax: 701-231-7606. p. 1841

Hedberg, Ulf, Dir, Deaf Libr Coll & Archives, Gallaudet University Library, 800 Florida Ave NE, Washington, DC, 20002-3095. Tel: 202-651-5230. p. 401

Hedden, Gus, Dir, Parsons Memorial Library, 27 Saco Rd, Alfred, ME, 04002. Tel: 207-324-2001. Fax: 207-324-2001. p. 973

Hedden, Holly H, Tech Serv, Warren County Public Library, 1225 State St, Bowling Green, KY, 42101. Tel: 270-781-4882. Fax: 270-781-7323. p. 907

Heddinger, Linda, Asst Dir, South Charleston Public Library, 312 Fourth Ave, South Charleston, WV, 25303-1297. Tel: 304-744-6561. Fax: 304-744-8808. p. 2572

Hedger, Cynthia, Dir, Hadley-Luzerne Public Library, 19 Main St, Lake Luzerne, NY, 12846. Tel: 518-696-3423. Fax: 518-696-4263. p. 1650

Hedges, Nancy, Librn, Greene County Law Library, Court House, 3rd Flr, 45 N Detroit St, Xenia, OH, 45385. Tel: 937-562-5115. Fax: 937-562-5116. p. 1951

Hedges, Stephen, Exec Dir, Ohio Public Library Information Network, 2323 W Fifth Ave, Ste 130, Columbus, OH, 43204. Tel: 614-728-5252. Fax: 614-728-5256. p. 2952

Hedgespeth, Melanie, Tech Ctr Mgr, Salina Public Library, 301 W Elm St, Salina, KS, 67401. Tel: 785-825-4624. Fax: 785-823-0706. p. 893

Hedin, Jane, Ref, Michigan State University, 115 Law College Bldg, East Lansing, MI, 48824-1300. Tel: 517-432-6957. Fax: 517-432-6861. p. 1175

Hedlin, Carol, Dir, University of Alaska Southeast, 11120 Glacier Hwy, Juneau, AK, 99801-8676. Tel: 907-796-6467. Fax: 907-796-6249. p. 50

Hedquist, Pamela, Asst Archivist-Tech, Providence Archives, 4800 37th Ave SW, Seattle, WA, 98126. Tel: 509-474-2319. Fax: 206-923-4001. p. 2530

Hedrich, Johannes, Bur Chief, New Mexico Corrections Department, 4337 State Rd 14, Santa Fe, NM, 87508. Tel: 505-827-8503, 505-841-4282. Fax: 505-827-8548. p. 1562

Hedrick, Beth, Dir, Libr Serv, Lanier Technical College, 7745 Majors Rd, Cumming, GA, 30041. Tel: 770-531-6379. Fax: 770-781-6988. p. 527

Hedrick, Beth, Dir, Libr Syst, Lanier Technical College, 2990 Landrum Education Dr, Oakwood, GA, 30566. Tel: 770-531-6379. p. 547

Hedrick, Bruce, Dir, Cowley County Historical Society Museum Library, 1011 Mansfield, Winfield, KS, 67156-3557. Tel: 620-221-4811. p. 902

Hedrick, John, Dir, Northwestern Regional Library, 111 N Front St, Elkin, NC, 28621. Tel: 336-835-4894. Fax: 336-526-2270. p. 1791

Hedrick, Mary, Adminr, Harrison Regional Library System, 50 Lester St, Columbiana, AL, 35051. Tel: 205-669-3910. Fax: 205-669-3940. p. 13

Hedrick, Susan, Dir, Waunakee Public Library, 710 South St, Waunakee, WI, 53597-1638. Tel: 608-849-4217. Fax: 608-849-7817. p. 2645

Hedstrom, Gail, Coll Develop, Dir, Elbow Lake Public Library, 117 Central Ave N, Elbow Lake, MN, 56531. Tel: 218-685-6850. Fax: 218-685-6852. p. 1249

Hedstrom, John, ILL, Ref, High Point Public Library, 901 N Main St, High Point, NC, 27262. Tel: 336-883-8585. Fax: 336-883-3636. p. 1802

Hedstrom, Margaret, Assoc Prof, University of Michigan, 304 West Hall, 1085 S University, Ann Arbor, MI, 48109-1107. Tel: 734-763-2285. Fax: 734-764-2475. p. 2967

Heebner, Teresa, Youth Serv Librn, Bucks County Free Library, Bensalem Branch, 3700 Hulmeville Rd, Bensalem, PA, 19020-4449. Tel: 215-638-2030. Fax: 215-638-2192. p. 2050

Heeger-Brehm, Ned, Br Mgr, Public Library of Cincinnati & Hamilton County, Groesbeck, 2994 W Galbraith Rd, Cincinnati, OH, 45239. Tel: 513-369-4454. Fax: 513-369-4455. p. 1872

Heely, Tom, Libr Dir, Searsmont Town Library, 37 Main St S, Searsmont, ME, 04973. Tel: 207-342-5549. Fax: 207-342-3495. p. 1000

Heer, Diane, Dir, Kimball Library, Five Academy Ave, Atkinson, NH, 03811-2202. Tel: 603-362-5234. Fax: 603-362-6095. p. 1438

Heer, Toni M, Br Mgr, Pamunkey Regional Library, Atlee, 9161 Atlee Rd, Mechanicsville, VA, 23116. Tel: 804-559-0654. Fax: 804-559-0645. p. 2469

Heerema, Helen, Librn, Thunder Bay Law Association Library, District Courthouse Library, 277 Camelot St, Thunder Bay, ON, P7A 4B3, CANADA. Tel: 807-344-3481. Fax: 807-345-9091. p. 2849

Heesen, Erika, Interim Chief Exec Officer, Leeds & the Thousand Islands Public Library, 1B Jessie St, Lansdowne, ON, K0E 1L0, CANADA. Tel: 613-659-3885. Fax: 613-659-4192. p. 2815

Heezen, Ron, Dr, Dir, Shreve Memorial Library, 424 Texas St, Shreveport, LA, 71101. Tel: 318-226-5870. Fax: 318-226-4780. p. 969

Heezen, Ronald R, Br Mgr, Shreve Memorial Library, North Shreveport Branch, 4844 N Market St, Shreveport, LA, 71107. Tel: 318-674-8172. Fax: 318-868-9464. p. 970

Hefferle, Janet, Mgr, Libr Serv, Epstein, Becker & Green, 250 Park Ave, 12th Flr, New York, NY, 10177. Tel: 212-351-4695. Fax: 212-661-0989. p. 1677

Heffernan, Annette, Circ Mgr, Upper Arlington Public Library, 2800 Tremont Rd, Columbus, OH, 43221. Tel: 614-486-9621. Fax: 614-486-4530. p. 1891

Heffernan, Mary, ILL, Plattsburgh Public Library, 19 Oak St, Plattsburgh, NY, 12901-2810. Tel: 518-563-0921. Fax: 518-563-1681. p. 1719

Heffington, Elizabeth, Cat Librn, Lipscomb University, One University Park Dr, Nashville, TN, 37204-3951. Tel: 615-966-5803. Fax: 615-966-5874. p. 2256

Heffler, Howard, Bus Mgr, Finkelstein Memorial Library, 24 Chestnut St, Spring Valley, NY, 10977-5594. Tel: 845-352-5700. Fax: 845-352-2319. p. 1746

Heffner, Rosemary, Bus Librn, Annie Halenbake Ross Library, 232 W Main St, Lock Haven, PA, 17745-1241. Tel: 570-748-3321. Fax: 570-748-1050. p. 2082

Heffron, Susan, Instrul Serv Librn, Carroll College, 100 N East Ave, Waukesha, WI, 53186. Tel: 262-524-7674. Fax: 262-524-7377. p. 2644

Hefler, Barbara, Head, Pub Serv, Tufts University, 145 Harrison Ave, Boston, MA, 02111-1843. Tel: 617-636-2956. Fax: 617-636-4039. p. 1068

Hefley, Kay, In Charge, Texline Public Library, 517 S Second St, Texline, TX, 79087. Tel: 806-362-4849. p. 2392

Heflin, Bonnie, Dir, Nottawa Township Library, 685 E Main St, Centreville, MI, 49032-9603. Tel: 269-467-6289. Fax: 269-467-4422. p. 1162

Heflin, Shannon, Dir, Hooks Public Library, 108 W First St, Hooks, TX, 75561. Tel: 903-547-3365. p. 2333

Hefner, Sheryl, Ch, Allerton Public Library, 103 South Central Ave, Allerton, IA, 50008. Tel: 641-873-4575. p. 792

Hefner-Babb, Theresa, Govt Doc Librn, Lamar University, 211 Redbird Lane, Beaumont, TX, 77705. Tel: 409-880-2135. Fax: 409-880-2318. p. 2287

Hefney, Phyllis, Cat, ILL, Ser, York Technical College Library, 452 S Anderson Rd, Rock Hill, SC, 29730. Tel: 803-327-8025. Fax: 803-327-4535. p. 2203

Heft, Faye H, Ref Librn, Long Beach Public Library, 111 W Park Ave, Long Beach, NY, 11561-3326. Tel: 516-432-7201. Fax: 516-889-4641. p. 1654

Heft, Kim, Dir, Onarga Community Public Library District, 209 W Seminary St, Onarga, IL, 60955-1131. Tel: 815-268-7626. Fax: 815-268-4635. p. 685

Hegadorn, Robert, Ref Librn, Villanova University, Law Library, Garey Hall, 299 N Spring Mill Rd, Villanova, PA, 19085. Tel: 610-519-7021. Fax: 610-519-7033. p. 2150

Hegarty, Frances, Head, Tech Serv, Peabody Institute Library of Danvers, 15 Sylvan St, Danvers, MA, 01923-2735. Tel: 978-774-0554. Fax: 978-762-0251. p. 1083

Hegarty, William, Ref, Larchmont Public Library, 121 Larchmont Ave, Larchmont, NY, 10538. Tel: 914-834-2281. p. 1651

Hegedus, Cynthia, Br Mgr, Oakland Public Library, Brookfield, 9255 Edes Ave, Oakland, CA, 94603. Tel: 510-615-5725. Fax: 510-615-5862. p. 198

Hegedus, Mary Ellen, Dir of Libr Serv, Holy Cross College, 54515 State Rd 933 N, Box 308, Notre Dame, IN, 46556-0308. Tel: 574-239-8360. Fax: 574-239-8324. p. 771

Hegemann, Denise A, Acq, Asst Dir, Head, Pub Serv, Saint Vincent College & Seminary Library, 300 Fraser Purchase Rd, Latrobe, PA, 15650-2690. Tel: 724-805-2966. Fax: 724-805-2905. p. 2079

Hegemier, John, Dir, Albert & Bessie Mae Kronkosky Library of Bandera County, 515 Main St, Bandera, TX, 78003. Tel: 830-796-4213. Fax: 830-796-3449. p. 2286

Hegenbart, Barbara, Librn, University of California, Davis, 100 NW Quad, Davis, CA, 95616-5292. Tel: 530-752-6561. Fax: 530-752-3148. p. 139

Hegerat, Elisabeth, Assoc Dir, Pub Serv, Lethbridge Public Library, 810 Fifth Ave S, Lethbridge, AB, T1J 4C4, CANADA. Tel: 403-320-4187. Fax: 403-329-1478. p. 2709

Hegfors, Barbara, Librn, Scott County Library System, Shakopee Public Library, 235 S Lewis St, Shakopee, MN, 55379. Tel: 952-233-9590. Fax: 952-233-3851. p. 1284

Hegland, Betty Ann, Ref Serv, Douglas County Library, 720 Fillmore St, Alexandria, MN, 56308-1763. Tel: 320-762-3014. Fax: 320-762-3036. p. 1239

Hegr, Barbara E, Dir, Morton-James Public Library, 923 First Corso, Nebraska City, NE, 68410. Tel: 402-873-5609. Fax: 402-873-5601. p. 1409

Hehlke, Mary, Libr Asst, Camanche Public Library, 102 12th Ave, Camanche, IA, 52730. Tel: 563-259-1106. Fax: 563-259-1106. p. 798

Hehman, Anna, Ref, Taft, Stettinius & Hollister Library, 425 Walnut St, Ste 1800, Cincinnati, OH, 45202-3957. Tel: 513-381-2838. Fax: 513-381-0205. p. 1873

Hehman, Tom, Dir, Wicomico Public Library, 122 S Division St, Salisbury, MD, 21801. Tel: 410-749-3612, Ext 110. Fax: 410-548-2968. p. 1040

Hehr, Pamela, ILL, Ref Serv, Reading Public Library, 100 S Fifth St, Reading, PA, 19602. Tel: 610-655-6350. p. 2133

Heicher, Jeanne, Dir, Newport Public Library, 316 N Fourth St, Newport, PA, 17074-1203. Tel: 717-567-6860. Fax: 717-567-3373. p. 2097

Heid, Cheryl, Pub Serv, Johnston Public Library, 6700 Merle Hay Rd, Johnston, IA, 50131-0327. Tel: 515-278-5233. Fax: 515-278-4975. p. 824

Heid, Greg, Dir, Des Moines Public Library, 1000 Grand Ave, Des Moines, IA, 50309. Tel: 515-283-4288. Fax: 515-237-1654. p. 808

Heid, Jerri, Youth Serv, Ames Public Library, 515 Douglas Ave, Ames, IA, 50010. Tel: 515-239-5643. Fax: 515-233-9001. p. 792

Heidebrecht, Ruth, Tech Serv Team Leader, Hutchinson Public Library, 901 N Main, Hutchinson, KS, 67501-4492. Tel: 620-663-5441. Fax: 620-663-9506. p. 873

Heidecker, Cathy, Mgr, Agere Systems, Allentown Branch, 110 American Pkwy, Rm 12B-125, Allentown, PA, 18109. Tel: 610-712-6011. Fax: 610-712-6073. p. 2026

Heidecker, Kathleen, Adjunct Fac Librn, HACC Central Pennsylvania's Community College, 731 Old Harrisburg Rd, Gettysburg, PA, 17325. Tel: 717-337-1644. Fax: 717-337-2329. p. 2060

Heideman, John, Ch, North Chicago Public Library, 2100 Argonne Dr, North Chicago, IL, 60064. Tel: 847-689-0125. Fax: 847-689-9117. p. 682

Heidemann, Anne, Head, Children's, Tween & Teen Serv, Canton Public Library, 1200 S Canton Center Rd, Canton, MI, 48188-1600. Tel: 734-397-0999. Fax: 734-397-1130. p. 1160

Heidemann, Debra, Asst Librn, Benny Gambaiani Public Library, 104 S Cherry St, Shell Rock, IA, 50670. Tel: 319-885-4345. Fax: 319-885-6209. p. 842

Heidenblad, Carl, Dir, Nesmith Library, Eight Fellows Rd, Windham, NH, 03087. Tel: 603-432-7154. Fax: 603-537-0097. p. 1468

Heidenreich, Peggy, Asst Dir, Sauk City Public Library, 515 Water St, Sauk City, WI, 53583-1159. Tel: 608-643-8346. p. 2636

Heidenreich, Sheryl, ILL/Doc Delivery Serv, University of Nebraska at Kearney, 2508 11th Ave, Kearney, NE, 68849-2240. Tel: 308-865-8721. Fax: 308-865-8722. p. 1403

Heidenreich, Teresa, Dir, Washington Carnegie Public Library, 300 W Main St, Washington, IN, 47501-2698. Tel: 812-254-4586, Ext 222. Fax: 812-254-4585. p. 786

Heidenwolf, Terese, Head, Info Serv, Lafayette College, 710 Sullivan Rd, Easton, PA, 18042-1797. Tel: 610-330-5153. Fax: 610-252-0370. p. 2052

Heidi, Sandstrom, Assoc Dir, University of California Los Angeles Library, Louise M Darling Biomedical Library, 10833 LeConte Ave, 12-077 Center for the Health Sciences, Los Angeles, CA, 90095-1798. Tel: 310-825-1020. Fax: 310-825-0465. p. 178

Heidin, Lynn, Head, Tech Serv, Michigan State University, 115 Law College Bldg, East Lansing, MI, 48824-1300. Tel: 517-432-6864. Fax: 517-432-6861. p. 1175

Heidkamp, Rosemary, Dir, Wendell Free Library, Seven Wendell Depot Rd, Wendell, MA, 01379. Tel: 978-544-3559. Fax: 978-544-3559. p. 1135

Heidt, Carmen, Ref Serv, Clearwater Public Library System, Countryside, 2741 State Rd 580, Clearwater, FL, 33761. Tel: 727-562-4970. Fax: 727-669-1289. p. 432

Heidt, David, Circ Serv Mgr, Saint Joseph County Public Library, 304 S Main, South Bend, IN, 46601-2125. Tel: 574-282-4646. Fax: 574-280-2763. p. 779

Heiffner, Barbara, Automation Librn, Cat, Nicolet Area Technical College, 5364 College Dr, Rhinelander, WI, 54501. Tel: 715-365-4486. Fax: 715-365-4404. p. 2633

Height, Yvonne, In Charge, Arizona Department of Economic Security, 2800 N Hwy 87, Coolidge, AZ, 85228. Tel: 520-723-4151, Ext 1231. Fax: 520-723-7618. p. 60

Heighton, Olita, Asst Dir, Meigs County District Public Library, 216 W Main, Pomeroy, OH, 45769-1032. Tel: 740-992-5813. Fax: 740-992-6140. p. 1930

Heighton, Olita, Asst Dir, Meigs County District Public Library, Racine Branch, 210 Tyree Blvd, Racine, OH, 45771. Tel: 740-949-8200. Fax: 740-949-8300. p. 1930

Heikes, Gloria, Librn, Lenora Public Library, 125 1/2 E Washington St, Lenora, KS, 67645. Tel: 785-567-4432. p. 879

Heikkinen, Phil, Dir, Orcas Island Library District, 500 Rose St, Eastsound, WA, 98245-9453. Tel: 360-376-4985. Fax: 360-376-5750. p. 2514

Heil, Becky, Librn, Dubuque County Library, Epworth Branch, 110 Bierman Rd, Epworth, IA, 52045. Tel: 563-876-3388. Fax: 563-876-3388. p. 794

Heil, Becky, Librn, Dubuque County Library, Holy Cross Branch, 938 Church St, Holy Cross, IA, 52053. Tel: 563-870-2082. p. 794

Heil, Beth, Customer Serv Supvr, Evansville Vanderburgh Public Library, East Branch, 840 E Chandler, Evansville, IN, 47713. Tel: 812-428-8231. Fax: 812-436-7320. p. 738

Heil, Kathy, Librn, University of Maryland Center for Environmental Science, One Williams St, Solomons, MD, 20688. Tel: 410-326-7287. Fax: 410-326-7430. p. 1042

Heil, Lynn, Learning Res Asst, Cir/Reserve, Polk State College, Lakeland Campus Library, 3425 Winter Lake Rd, Sta 62, Lakeland, FL, 33803. Tel: 863-297-1042. Fax: 863-297-1064. p. 505

Heil, Rebecca S, Dir, Dubuque County Library, 5900 Saratoga Plaza, Ste 5, Asbury, IA, 52002. Tel: 563-582-0008. Fax: 563-582-0022. p. 794

Heil, Sara, Librn, Frenchtown Public Library, 29 Second St, Frenchtown, NJ, 08825. Tel: 908-996-4788. p. 1487

Heilbronner, Kathy, Asst Dir, Milwaukee Jewish Council for Community Relations Library, 1360 N Prospect Ave, 2nd Flr, Milwaukee, WI, 53202-3091. Tel: 414-390-5736. Fax: 414-390-5787. p. 2620

Heilbrunn, Lila, Dir, Libr & Media, Vancouver Community College, 250 W Pender St, Vancouver, BC, V6B 1S9, CANADA. Tel: 604-443-8566. Fax: 604-443-8588. p. 2743

Heilemann, Heidi, Assoc Dean, Knowledge Mgt, Dir, Stanford University Libraries, Lane Medical Library, Stanford University Medical Ctr, 300 Pasteur Dr, Rm L109, Stanford, CA, 94305-5123. Tel: 650-723-6831. Fax: 650-725-7471. p. 271

Heilenbach, Barbara, Head, Pub Serv, Warrenville Public Library District, 28 W 751 Stafford Pl, Warrenville, IL, 60555. Tel: 630-393-1171. Fax: 630-393-1688. p. 715

Heilig, Jean, Fiscal Officer, LSTA Coordr, Colorado State Library, 201 E Colfax Ave, Rm 309, Denver, CO, 80203-1799. Tel: 303-866-6731. Fax: 303-866-6940. p. 299

Heilik, Dena, Head Librn, Free Library of Philadelphia, Philbrick Popular Library, 1901 Vine St, Philadelphia, PA, 19103-1189. Tel: 215-686-5320. p. 2109

Heilman, Cheryl, Ch, North Baltimore Public Library, 230 N Main St, North Baltimore, OH, 45872-1125. Tel: 419-257-3621. Fax: 419-257-3859. p. 1923

Heim, Sarah, Res Serv Librn, Historical Society of Pennsylvania, 1300 Locust St, Philadelphia, PA, 19107-5699. Tel: 215-732-6200, Ext 261. Fax: 215-732-2680. p. 2110

Heiman, Anne, Dir, Libr Serv, BryanLGH College of the Health Sciences, 5035 Everett St, Lincoln, NE, 68506. Tel: 402-481-3908. Fax: 402-481-3138. p. 1404

Heiman, Paula, Librn, Pennsylvania Historical & Museum Commission, 400 North St, Plaza Level, Harrisburg, PA, 17120-0053. Tel: 717-783-9898. Fax: 717-214-2989. p. 2066

Heimbigner, Douglas, Instrul Serv Librn, Pace University, 861 Bedford Rd, Pleasantville, NY, 10570-2799. Tel: 917-773-3244. Fax: 914-773-3508. p. 1719

Heimburger, Bruce, Tech Adminr, Richland County Public Library, 1431 Assembly St, Columbia, SC, 29201-3101. Tel: 803-799-9084. Fax: 803-929-3448. p. 2188

Heimer, Gayle, Tech Serv, Austin Public Library, 323 Fourth Ave NE, Austin, MN, 55912-3370. Tel: 507-433-2391. Fax: 507-433-8787. p. 1240

Heimer, Marjorie, Support Serv Coordr, Athens Technical College Library, Greene County Campus, 1051 Athens Tech Dr, Greensboro, GA, 30642. Tel: 706-453-0536. p. 509

Heimer, Marjorie, Support Serv Coordr, Athens Technical College Library, Walton County Campus, 212 Bryant Rd, Monroe, GA, 30648. Tel: 770-207-3126. p. 509

Hein, Cindy, Dir, Rockville Public Library, 106 N Market St, Rockville, IN, 47872. Tel: 765-569-5544. Fax: 765-569-5546. p. 776

Hein, Jamison, Libr Asst, Clintonville Public Library, 75 Hemlock St, Clintonville, WI, 54929-1461. Tel: 715-823-4563. Fax: 715-823-7134. p. 2586

Hein, Karen, Actg Dir, Northampton Area Public Library, 1615 Laubach Ave, Northampton, PA, 18067-1597. Tel: 610-262-7537. Fax: 610-262-4356. p. 2100

Heinbuch, Lynn, Dir, Greenfield Public Library, 202 S First St, Greenfield, IA, 50849-1470. Tel: 641-743-6120. p. 819

Heindselman, Mark, Mgr, Knowledge Network & Info Serv, Emerson Process Management, RA Engel Technical Ctr, 1700 12th Ave, Marshalltown, IA, 50158. Tel: 641-754-2161. Fax: 641-754-3159. p. 830

Heiner, Marilyn, Librn, Lincoln County Library, Star Valley, 261 Washington, Afton, WY, 83110. Tel: 307-885-3158. Fax: 307-885-9651. p. 2656

Heines, Rodney M, Chief Librn, United States Air Force, Air Force Research Lab RIOIL, Bldg 3, 525 Brooks Rd, Rome, NY, 13441-4505. Tel: 315-330-7600. Fax: 315-330-3086. p. 1735

Heinicke, Jennifer, Pub Relations Coordr, Wichita Public Library, 223 S Main St, Wichita, KS, 67202. Tel: 316-261-8524. Fax: 316-262-4540. p. 901

Heinig, Cindy, Youth Serv, Cocoa Beach Public Library, 550 N Brevard Ave, Cocoa Beach, FL, 32931. Tel: 321-868-1104. Fax: 321-868-1107. p. 433

Heinlein, Jan, Bus Mgr, Nassau Library System, 900 Jerusalem Ave, Uniondale, NY, 11553-3039. Tel: 516-292-8920, Ext 246. Fax: 516-292-8944. p. 1758

Heinonen, Jan, Chief Exec Officer, South River-Machar Union Public Library, 63 Marie St, South River, ON, P0A 1X0, CANADA. Tel: 705-386-0222. Fax: 705-386-0222. p. 2842

Heinrich, Mark A, Librn, Dickinson Wright PLLC Library, 500 Woodward Ave, Ste 4000, Detroit, MI, 48226-3425. Tel: 313-223-3500. Fax: 313-223-3598. p. 1170

Heinrich, Rachel, Dir, Ely Public Library, 30 S First Ave E, Ely, MN, 55731. Tel: 218-365-5140. Fax: 218-365-6107. p. 1250

Heinrich, Suellen, Ch, Guilford Free Library, 67 Park St, Guilford, CT, 06437. Tel: 203-453-8282. Fax: 203-453-8288. p. 342

Heinrich, Virginia, Tech Serv, Minneapolis Community & Technical College Library, Wheelock Whitney Hall, 1501 Hennepin Ave, Minneapolis, MN, 55403. Tel: 612-659-6290. Fax: 612-659-6295. p. 1261

Heinrichs, John H, Dr, Assoc Prof, Wayne State University, 106 Kresge Library, Detroit, MI, 48202. Tel: 313-577-1825. Fax: 313-577-7563. p. 2967

Heinrichs, Wolfhart P, In Charge, Harvard Library, Hamilton A R Gibb Islamic Seminar Library, Widener Library, Rm Q, Harvard University, Cambridge, MA, 02138. Tel: 617-495-2437, 617-495-4310. Fax: 617-496-2902. p. 1075

Heinritz, Mrs Robert, Librn, Prince of Peace Lutheran Church Library, 4419 S Howell Ave, Milwaukee, WI, 53207. Tel: 414-483-3828. p. 2621

Heinson, Lillian, Digital Media Coordr, York University Libraries, Visual Arts Slide Library, York Campus, Phase II, 4700 Keele St, Ste 257, Toronto, ON, M3J 1P3, CANADA. Tel: 416-736-5534. Fax: 416-736-5447. p. 2868

Heinson, Lillian, In Charge, York University Libraries, Visual Resource Centre, Room 257 Goldfarb Centre of Fine Arts, 4700 Keele St, Toronto, ON, M3J 1P3, CANADA. Tel: 416-736-2100, Ext 33494. p. 2868

Heintz, Bridgette, Br Mgr, Hamburg Public Library, Lake Shore, 4857 Lake Shore Rd, Hamburg, NY, 14075. Tel: 716-627-3017. Fax: 716-627-6505. p. 1632

Heintz, Freda, Librn, Atlantic County Historical Society Library, 907 Shore Rd, Somers Point, NJ, 08244-2335. Tel: 609-927-5218. Fax: 609-927-5218. p. 1529

Heintz, John, Assoc Dir, Digital Initiatives, University of Saint Thomas, 2115 Summit Ave, Mail Box 5004, Saint Paul, MN, 55105. Tel: 651-962-5018. Fax: 651-962-5406. p. 1282

Heintz, Lucy, Acq of New Ser, Circ, Ref, Alberta Innovates-Technology Futures, 250 Karl Clark Rd, Edmonton, AB, T6N 134, CANADA. Tel: 780-450-5064. Fax: 780-450-8996. p. 2698

Heintzelman, Erich, Librn, Valencia Community College, East Campus, 701 N Econlockhatchee Trail, Orlando, FL, 32825. Tel: 407-582-2467. Fax: 407-582-8914. p. 478

Heintzman, Daniel, Tech Serv, United States Army, Morris J Swett Technical Library, Snow Hall 16, Bldg 730, Fort Sill, OK, 73503-5100. Tel: 580-442-4525. Fax: 580-442-7300. p. 1964

Heinz, Carol, Dir, Riverdale Public Library, 93 Newark Pompton Tpk, Riverdale, NJ, 07457. Tel: 973-835-5044. Fax: 973-835-2175. p. 1527

Heinz, Melanie, Circ, Front Range Community College, 3705 W 112th Ave, Westminster, CO, 80031-2140. Tel: 303-404-5587. Fax: 303-404-5144. p. 326

Heinzen, Judith, Actg Chief Exec Officer, Timmins Public Library, 320 Second Ave, Timmins, ON, P4N 4A8, CANADA. Tel: 705-360-2623. Fax: 705-360-2688. p. 2849

Heinzman, Mary B, Exec Dir, Info Res, Libr Dir, Saint Ambrose University Library, 518 W Locust St, Davenport, IA, 52803. Tel: 563-333-6241. Fax: 563-333-6248. p. 807

Heise, Candy, Ref Librn, Sanibel Public Library District, 770 Dunlop Rd, Sanibel, FL, 33957. Tel: 239-472-2483. Fax: 239-472-9524. p. 489

Heisel, Dawn, Ch, Virginia Public Library, 215 Fifth Ave S, Virginia, MN, 55792-2642. Tel: 218-748-7525. Fax: 218-748-7527. p. 1286

Heiser, John S, Historian, Gettysburg National Military Park Library, 1195 Baltimore Pike, Ste 100, Gettysburg, PA, 17325. Tel: 717-334-1124, Ext 1231. Fax: 717-334-1997. p. 2060

Heisey, Terry M, Dr, Librn, Evangelical School of Theology, 121 S College St, Myerstown, PA, 17067. Tel: 717-866-5775. Fax: 717-866-4667. p. 2094

Heisey, Wendy, Vols Serv Coordr, Milton-Union Public Library, 560 S Main St, West Milton, OH, 45383. Tel: 937-698-5515. Fax: 937-698-3774. p. 1946

Heisner, Ellen, Circ, Watertown Regional Library, 160 Sixth St NE, Watertown, SD, 57201-2778. Tel: 605-882-6220. Fax: 605-882-6221. p. 2221

Heiss, Deborah, Circ, ILL, Roselle Park, 404 Chestnut St, Roselle Park, NJ, 07204-1506. Tel: 908-245-2456. Fax: 908-245-9204. p. 1528

Heiss, Matt, Coll Develop, Church of Jesus Christ of Latter-Day Saints, Church History Library & Archives, 50 E North Temple, Salt Lake City, UT, 84150. Tel: 801-240-5944. Fax: 801-240-1845. p. 2412

Heistad, Kristy, Br Mgr, Antigo Public Library, Elton Branch, W4904, Hwy 64, Elton, WI, 54430-0046. Tel: 715-882-3881. p. 2578

Heister, Carla, Librn, Yale University Library, Forestry & Environmental Studies, Sage Hall, 205 Prospect St, 4th Flr, New Haven, CT, 06511. Tel: 203-432-5133. Fax: 203-432-5942. p. 357

Heitmeier, Kelly, Dir, Hillsboro Public Library, 100 W Commercial St, Hillsboro, IA, 52630. Tel: 319-253-4000. Fax: 319-253-4000. p. 821

Heitstuman, Phyllis, Librn, Denny Ashby Memorial Library, 856 Arlington St, Pomeroy, WA, 99347. Tel: 509-843-3710. p. 2523

Heitz, Sue, Br Mgr, Albuquerque-Bernalillo County Library System, Alamosa/Robert L Murphy Memorial Library, 6900 Gonzales Rd SW, Albuquerque, NM, 87105. Tel: 505-836-0684. Fax: 505-876-8779. p. 1548

Heitz, Sue, Mgr, Albuquerque-Bernalillo County Library System, Westgate, 1300 Delgado Dr SW, Albuquerque, NM, 87121. Tel: 505-833-6984. Fax: 505-833-6989. p. 1548

Heitzig, Carol, Dir, Watsonville Public Library, 310 Union St, Watsonville, CA, 95076. Tel: 831-768-3400. Fax: 831-763-4015. p. 282

Heitzman, Sandy, Circ, Forest Park Public Library, 7555 Jackson Blvd, Forest Park, IL, 60130. Tel: 708-366-7171. Fax: 708-366-7293. p. 646

Heitzman-Smith, Janet, Br Mgr, Mid-Continent Public Library, Liberty Branch, 1000 Kent St, Liberty, MO, 64068-2256. Tel: 816-781-9240. Fax: 816-781-5119. p. 1333

Heiz, Andrew, Electronic Serv, Orange County Community College Library, 115 South St, Middletown, NY, 10940. Tel: 845-341-4253. Fax: 845-341-4424. p. 1660

Hejl, Sheila, Info Serv Coordr, Calvert County Public Library, 850 Costley Way, Prince Frederick, MD, 20678. Tel: 410-535-0291. Fax: 410-535-3022. p. 1036

Helak, Barbara, Asst Dir, Stevens Memorial Community Library, 146 Main St, Attica, NY, 14011-1243. Tel: 585-591-2733. Fax: 585-591-3855. p. 1575

Helbert, Edith, Librn, Allen County Public Library, Hessen Cassel, 3030 E Paulding Rd, Fort Wayne, IN, 46816. Tel: 260-421-1330. Fax: 260-447-5978. p. 741

Helbing, Rachel R, Librn, Barberton Public Library, Community Health Library, Summa Barberton Hospital, 155 Fifth St NE, 1st Flr, Barberton, OH, 44203-3398. Tel: 330-615-3105. Fax: 330-615-3103. p. 1857

Held, Amy, Ch, Jefferson County Library, Arnold Branch, 1701 Missouri State Rd, Arnold, MO, 63010. Tel: 636-296-2204. Fax: 636-296-5975. p. 1331

Held, Tim, Ref & Instruction Librn, California State University, Stanislaus, One University Circle, Turlock, CA, 95382. Tel: 209-667-6555. p. 277

Helde, Karen, Dir of Libr, Lane Powell PC Library, 1420 Fifth Ave, Ste 4100, Seattle, WA, 98101-2388. Tel: 206-223-7741. Fax: 206-223-7107. p. 2528

Heldman, Judith, Librn, Harrington Park Public Library, Ten Herring St, Harrington Park, NJ, 07640. Tel: 201-768-5675. Fax: 201-768-7495. p. 1490

Heldt, John A, Ref, Lewis & Clark Library, 120 S Last Chance Gulch, Helena, MT, 59601. Tel: 406-447-1690, Ext 136. Fax: 406-447-1687. p. 1382

Helen, Hankins, In Charge, Klamath County Library Services District, South Suburbs, 3706 S Sixth St, Klamath Falls, OR, 97603. Tel: 541-273-3679. p. 2002

Helen, Marketta, Circ, University of Wisconsin-Fox Valley Library, 1478 Midway Rd, Menasha, WI, 54952-1297. Tel: 920-832-2672. Fax: 920-832-2874. p. 2614

Helfirch, Sharon, Dir, Andrew Bayne Memorial Library, 34 N Balph Ave, Bellevue, PA, 15202-3297. Tel: 412-766-7447. Fax: 412-766-3620. p. 2032

Helfrich, Gair, Libr Serv Mgr, Atlantic County Library System, 40 Farragut Ave, Mays Landing, NJ, 08330-1750. Tel: 609-625-2776. Fax: 609-625-8143. p. 1500

Helgeland, Pauline, Automation Syst Coordr, Northwest Regional Library, 210 LaBree Ave N, Thief River Falls, MN, 56701. Tel: 218-681-1066. Fax: 218-681-1095. p. 1286

Helgeson, Charlotte, Dir, East Grand Forks Campbell Library, 422 Fourth St NW, East Grand Forks, MN, 56721. Tel: 218-773-9121. Fax: 218-773-2645. p. 1249

Helgeson, Pamela, Dir, Dawson Public Library, 676 Pine St, Dawson, MN, 56232. Tel: 320-769-2069. Fax: 320-769-2170. p. 1247

Helicher, Karl, Dir, Upper Merion Township Library, 175 W Valley Forge Rd, King of Prussia, PA, 19406-2399. Tel: 610-205-8548. Fax: 610-265-3398. p. 2074

Heligas, Megan, Adminr, Flossmoor Public Library, 1000 Sterling Ave, Flossmoor, IL, 60422-1295. Tel: 708-798-3600. Fax: 708-798-3603. p. 646

Helik, Teresa, Chief Librn, Regis College Library, 100 Wellesley St W, Toronto, ON, M5S 2Z5, CANADA. Tel: 416-922-5474, Ext 235. Fax: 416-922-2898. p. 2857

Helle, John J, Dir, Fairfield Public Library, 261 Hollywood Ave, Fairfield, NJ, 07004. Tel: 973-227-3575. Fax: 973-227-7305. p. 1485

Hellenius, Shawna, Libr Dir, Alliant International University, 1000 S Fremont Ave, Unit 5, Alhambra, CA, 91803. Tel: 626-270-3270. Fax: 626-284-1682. p. 120

Heller, Amanda, Br Mgr, San Diego County Library, Casa de Oro, 9805 Campo Rd, No 180, Spring Valley, CA, 91977-1477. Tel: 619-463-3236. Fax: 619-463-8670. p. 233

Heller, Beth, Libr Dir, Presv Librn, American Alpine Club Library, 710 Tenth St, Ste 15, Golden, CO, 80401. Tel: 303-384-0110, Ext 13, 303-384-0112. p. 309

Heller, George F, Jr, Assoc Ref Librn, Youngstown State University, One University Plaza, Youngstown, OH, 44555-0001. Tel: 330-941-3675. Fax: 330-941-3734. p. 1953

Heller, James, Dir, College of William & Mary in Virginia, The Wolf Law Library, 613 S Henry St, Williamsburg, VA, 23187. Tel: 757-221-3252. Fax: 757-221-3051. p. 2502

Heller, Kary, Librn, Lankenau Hospital, 100 Lancaster Ave, Wynnewood, PA, 19096. Tel: 610-645-2698. Fax: 610-645-3425. p. 2158

Heller, Kay, Cat, Franklin County Library System, 101 Ragged Edge Rd S, Chambersburg, PA, 17202. Tel: 717-709-0282. Fax: 717-263-2248. p. 2043

Heller, Laura, Archivist/Librn, National Cowboy & Western Heritage Museum, 1700 NE 63rd St, Oklahoma City, OK, 73111. Tel: 405-478-2250. Fax: 405-478-6421. p. 1973

Heller, Lori, Ch, Emporia Public Library, 110 E Sixth Ave, Emporia, KS, 66801-3960. Tel: 620-340-6467. Fax: 620-340-6444. p. 865

Heller, Matthew, Ref Serv Librn, Ohio Dominican University Library, 1216 Sunbury Rd, Columbus, OH, 43219. Tel: 614-251-4585. Fax: 614-252-2650. p. 1886

Heller, Pat, Head of Libr, University of Pennsylvania Libraries, Leon Levy Dental Medicine Library, 240 S 40th St, Philadelphia, PA, 19104-6030. Tel: 215-898-8978. Fax: 215-898-7985. p. 2119

Heller, Rebecca, Ref, Roanoke College, 220 High St, Salem, VA, 24153. Tel: 540-375-2295. p. 2495

Heller, Susann, In Charge, Mill City Library, 260 SW Second Ave, Mill City, OR, 97360. Tel: 503-897-4143. p. 2006

Heller-Ross, Holly, Coordr, Instrul Serv, Interim Assoc Dean, Librn, State University of New York College at Plattsburgh, Two Draper Ave, Plattsburgh, NY, 12901-2697. Tel: 518-564-5192. Fax: 518-564-5209. p. 1719

Helling, Joyce, Librn, Florida Department of Corrections, 10650 SW 46th St, Jasper, FL, 32052-1360. Tel: 386-792-5151. Fax: 386-792-5504. p. 455

Helling, William, Head, Ref Serv, Crawfordsville District Public Library, 205 S Washington St, Crawfordsville, IN, 47933. Tel: 765-362-2242. Fax: 765-362-7986. p. 734

Hellman, Deena, Dir, Saint Matthew's & Saint Timothy's Neighborhood Center, Inc Library, 26 W 84th St, New York, NY, 10024. Tel: 212-362-6750, Ext 303. Fax: 212-362-8230. p. 1699

Hellman, Diane, Asst Librn, Bancroft Public Library, 208 E Ramsey St, Bancroft, IA, 50517. Tel: 515-885-2753. Fax: 515-885-2753. p. 795

Hellman, Kathy, Dir, Camp Verde Community Library, 130 Black Bridge Loop Rd, Camp Verde, AZ, 86322. Tel: 928-567-3414. Fax: 928-567-9583. p. 59

Hellmer, Michelle, Adult Serv, Carnegie-Stout Public Library, 360 W 11th St, Dubuque, IA, 52001. Tel: 563-589-4137. Fax: 563-589-4217. p. 811

Hellyer, Paul, Ref Serv, College of William & Mary in Virginia, The Wolf Law Library, 613 S Henry St, Williamsburg, VA, 23187. Tel: 757-221-3255. Fax: 757-221-3051. p. 2502

Helm, Dannie, Libr Mgr, University of Oregon Libraries, John E Jaqua Law Library, William W Knight Law Ctr, 2nd Flr, 1515 Agate St, Eugene, OR, 97403-1221. Tel: 541-346-8271. Fax: 541-346-1669. p. 1997

Helm, Glenn E, Libr Dir, Naval History & Heritage, 805 Kidder-Breese St SE, Washington, DC, 20374-5060. Tel: 202-433-4132. Fax: 202-433-9553. p. 411

Helm, Glenna, Admin Mgr, Grant MacEwan University Library, 10700 104th Ave, Edmonton, AB, T5J 4S2, CANADA. Tel: 780-497-5893. Fax: 780-497-5895. p. 2701

Helm, Grace G, Librn, Kingman Carnegie Public Library, 455 N Main St, Kingman, KS, 67068-1395. Tel: 620-532-3061. Fax: 620-532-2528. p. 876

Helm, Marly, Asst Librn, Cataloger, Arizona State Museum Library, University of Arizona, 1013 E University Blvd, Tucson, AZ, 85721-0026. Tel: 520-621-4695. Fax: 520-621-2976. p. 85

Helm, Sandra, Asst Librn, Chandler Public Library, 1021 Manvel Ave, Chandler, OK, 74834. Tel: 405-258-3204. Fax: 405-258-3205. p. 1959

Helm, Steve, Coordr, Info Tech, Radford University, 801 E Main St, Radford, VA, 24142-0001. Tel: 540-831-5471. Fax: 540-831-6138. p. 2487

Helm, Wilbur, ILL, Yakima Valley Genealogical Society Library, 1901 S 12th Ave, Union Gap, WA, 98903. Tel: 509-248-1328. p. 2545

Helman, Bill, Integrated Digital Serv Librn, University of Baltimore, 1420 Maryland Ave, Baltimore, MD, 21201. Tel: 410-837-4209. Fax: 410-837-4330. p. 1018

Helman, Deborah, Dir, University of Wisconsin-Madison, Kurt Wendt Engineering Library, 215 N Randall Ave, Madison, WI, 53706. Tel: 608-262-7980. Fax: 608-262-4739, 608-265-8751. p. 2610

Helmeci, Hollis, Dir, Bradford Memorial Library, 611 S Washington St, El Dorado, KS, 67042. Tel: 316-321-3363. Fax: 316-321-5546. p. 864

Helmen, Jennifer, Librn, Saint Joseph's Regional Medical Center, 801 E LaSalle, South Bend, IN, 46617. Tel: 574-237-7228. Fax: 574-472-6307. p. 779

Helmer, Geraldine, Librn, Chaplin Public Library, 130 Chaplin St, Chaplin, CT, 06235-2302. Tel: 860-455-9424. Fax: 860-455-0515. p. 333

Helmer, Holly, Cat Librn, Concordia University, 800 N Columbia Ave, Seward, NE, 68434-1595. Tel: 402-643-7254. Fax: 402-643-4218. p. 1419

Helmer, John, Exec Dir, Orbis Cascade Alliance, 2288 Oakmont Way, Eugene, OR, 97401-5519. Tel: 541-246-2470, Ext 205. Fax: 541-246-2477. p. 2953

Helmer, Joy, Librn, Hardtner Public Library, 102 E Central, Hardtner, KS, 67057. Tel: 620-296-4586. p. 870

Helmetsie, Carolyn, Mgr, NASA, Two W Durand St, Mail Stop 185, Hampton, VA, 23681-2199. Tel: 757-864-2356. Fax: 757-864-2375. p. 2468

Helmetsie, Elizabeth, Dir, Spencer Library, 41 N Main St, Spencer, NY, 14883-9100. Tel: 607-589-4496. Fax: 607-589-4271. p. 1746

Helmrich, Ed, Doc Delivery Mgr, Iona College, 715 North Ave, New Rochelle, NY, 10801-1890. Tel: 914-633-2351. Fax: 914-633-2136. p. 1666

Helmrick, Linda, Dir, Plainfield Public Library, 126 S Main St, Plainfield, WI, 54966-0305. Tel: 715-335-4523. Fax: 715-335-6712. p. 2630

Helms, Bernard, Per/Acq Librn, Andrews University, 1400 Library Rd, Berrien Springs, MI, 49104-1400. Tel: 269-471-3208. Fax: 269-471-6166. p. 1157

Helms, Caroline C, Libr Dir, Gonzales Public Library, 415 St Matthew, Gonzales, TX, 78629-4037. Tel: 830-672-6315. Fax: 830-672-8735. p. 2328

Helms, Cheryl V, Dir, Redwood Library & Athenaeum, 50 Bellevue Ave, Newport, RI, 02840-3292. Tel: 401-847-0292. Fax: 401-847-0192. p. 2169

Helms, Conrad A, Patron Serv, Saint Mary's College of Maryland Library, 18952 E Fisher Rd, Saint Mary's City, MD, 20686-3001. Tel: 240-895-3214. Fax: 240-895-4914. p. 1040

Helms, Cynthia, Head, Info Serv, Online Serv, Andrews University, 1400 Library Rd, Berrien Springs, MI, 49104-1400. Tel: 269-471-6260. Fax: 269-471-6166. p. 1157

Helms, Faye, Br Mgr, Kerkhoven Public Library, 208 N Tenth, Kerkhoven, MN, 56252. Tel: 320-264-2141. Fax: 320-264-2141. p. 1255

Helms, Judy, Ref Serv, Travis County Law Library, Travis City Admin Bldg, 314 W 11th, Rm 140, Austin, TX, 78701-2112. Tel: 512-854-9045. Fax: 512-473-9082. p. 2283

Helms, Linda, Dir, B F Jones Memorial Library, 663 Franklin Ave, Aliquippa, PA, 15001-3736. Tel: 724-375-2900. Fax: 724-375-3274. p. 2026

Helms, Lynn, Mgr, Libr Serv, Duke Energy Corp, 526 S Church St, NC EC06H, Charlotte, NC, 28202. Tel: 704-382-2803. Fax: 704-382-7826. p. 1783

Helms, Mary, Br Mgr, Martins Ferry Public Library, Bridgeport Branch, 661 Main St, Bridgeport, OH, 43912. Tel: 740-635-2563. Fax: 740-635-6974. p. 1914

Helms, Mary, Spec Coll Librn, Chattanooga-Hamilton County Bicentennial Library, 1001 Broad St, Chattanooga, TN, 37402-2652. Tel: 423-757-5317. Fax: 423-757-4994. p. 2226

Helms, Mary, Exec Secy, ICON Library Consortium, Univ of Nebr, McGoogan Libr of Med, Nebr Med Ctr, Box 986705, Omaha, NE, 68198-6705. Tel: 402-559-7099. Fax: 402-559-5498. p. 2948

Helms, Mary E, Assoc Dir, University of Nebraska Medical Center, 600 S 42nd St, Omaha, NE, 68198-6705. Tel: 402-559-7099. Fax: 402-559-5498. p. 1415

Helmstetter, Wendy, Dir, Info Res & Serv, Florida Institute of Technology, 150 W University Blvd, Melbourne, FL, 32901-6988. Tel: 321-674-8021. Fax: 321-724-2559. p. 463

Helmuth, Antje, Head Librn, Health & Human Services Library, British Columbia Ministry of Health, 1515 Blanshard St, Main Flr, Victoria, BC, V8W 3C8, CANADA. Tel: 250-952-2196. Fax: 250-952-2180. p. 2745

Helt, James F, Librn, San Diego Model Railroad Museum, 1649 El Prado, San Diego, CA, 92101. Tel: 619-696-0199. Fax: 619-696-0239. p. 235

Helton, Peggy, Br Mgr, Scott-Sebastian Regional Library, Lavaca Library, 100 S Davis, Lavaca, AR, 72941. p. 102

Heltshe-Steinhauer, Mary Ann, Commun Relations Mgr, Library System of Lancaster County, 1866 Colonial Village Lane, Ste 107, Lancaster, PA, 17601. Tel: 717-207-0500. Fax: 717-207-0504. p. 2077

Helwig, Rex, Automation Syst Coordr, Finger Lakes Library System, 119 E Green St, Ithaca, NY, 14850. Tel: 607-273-4074. Fax: 607-273-3618. p. 1642

Helwig-Rodriguez, Mary Louise, Ch, Little Falls Public Library, Eight Warren St, Little Falls, NJ, 07424. Tel: 973-256-2784. Fax: 973-256-6312. p. 1495

Hemen, Ruth, Ch, Huron Public Library, 521 Dakota Ave S, Huron, SD, 57350. Tel: 605-353-8530. Fax: 605-353-8531. p. 2213

Hemingson, Paula, ILL Supvr, Wartburg College Library, 100 Wartburg Blvd, Waverly, IA, 50677-0903. Tel: 319-352-8500. Fax: 319-352-8312. p. 851

Hemingson, Ruth, Librn, Anoka County Library, Northtown, 711 County Rd 10 NE, Blaine, MN, 55434-2398. Tel: 763-717-3267. Fax: 763-717-3259. p. 1241

Hemingway, Angela, Br Mgr, Horry County Memorial Library, Aynor Branch, 500 Ninth Ave, Aynor, SC, 29511. Tel: 843-358-3324. Fax: 843-358-1639. p. 2191

Hemingway, Gwenda, Librn, Horry County Memorial Library, Surfside Beach Branch, 410 Surfside Dr, Surfside Beach, SC, 29575. Tel: 843-238-0122. Fax: 843-238-4273. p. 2191

Hemingway, Melanie, Dir, Galax-Carroll Regional Library, Carroll County Public, 101 Beaver Dam Rd, Hillsville, VA, 24343. Tel: 276-236-2351. Fax: 276-236-5153. p. 2466

Hemleben, Kate, Fiscal Officer, Upper Arlington Public Library, 2800 Tremont Rd, Columbus, OH, 43221. Tel: 614-486-9621. Fax: 614-486-4530. p. 1891

Hemmasi, Harriette, Univ Librn, Brown University, Ten Prospect St, Box A, Providence, RI, 02912. Tel: 401-863-2167. Fax: 401-863-1272. p. 2172

Hemmat, Katherine, Ch, Collier County Public Library, Golden Gate, 2432 Lucerne Rd, Naples, FL, 34116. Tel: 239-455-1441. Fax: 239-455-8921. p. 471

Hemmelman, Brenda, Res Serv Librn, South Dakota State Library, 800 Governors Dr, Pierre, SD, 57501-2294. Tel: 605-773-3131. p. 2216

Hemmens, Ann, Head, Ref, Georgetown University, Georgetown Law Library (John Wolff & Edward Bennett Williams Libraries), 111 G St NW, Washington, DC, 20001. Tel: 202-662-9168. p. 403

Hemmig, William, Online Learning Librn, Bucks County Community College Library, 275 Swamp Rd, Newtown, PA, 18940-0999. Tel: 215-504-8611. Fax: 215-968-8142. p. 2097

Hemond, Jackie I, Dir, Salem Free Public Library, 264 Hartford Rd, Salem, CT, 06420. Tel: 860-859-1130. Fax: 860-859-9961. p. 366

Hemphill, Alisa, Mgr, ILL, Houston Academy of Medicine, 1133 John Freeman Blvd, Houston, TX, 77030. Tel: 713-795-4200. Fax: 713-790-7052. p. 2337

Hemphill, Andrea, Access Serv Tech-Libr Loans, Washtenaw Community College, 4800 E Huron River Dr, Ann Arbor, MI, 48105-4800. Tel: 734-973-3379. Fax: 734-973-3446. p. 1153

Hemphill, Joan, Youth Serv Spec, Linebaugh Public Library System of Rutherford County, 105 W Vine St, Murfreesboro, TN, 37130-3673. Tel: 615-893-4131. Fax: 615-848-5038. p. 2254

Hemphill, Lia, Head, Coll Develop, Nova Southeastern University Libraries, 3100 Ray Ferrero Jr Blvd, Fort Lauderdale, FL, 33314. Tel: 954-262-4633. Fax: 954-262-3805. p. 444

Hemphill, Ruth, Dir, Tennessee Regional Library for the Blind & Physically Handicapped, 403 Seventh Ave N, Nashville, TN, 37243-0313. Tel: 615-741-3917. Fax: 615-532-8856. p. 2258

Hempstead, Mark, Libr Tech-Mats, US Customs & Border Protection Library, 90 K St NE, 9th Flr, Washington, DC, 20004. Tel: 202-325-0171. Fax: 202-325-0170. p. 418

Hemrick, Robin, Regional Libr Supvr, Wake County Public Library System, North Regional Library, 7009 Harps Mill Rd, Raleigh, NC, 27615. Tel: 919-870-4021. Fax: 919-870-4007. p. 1818

Hemstock, Tom, Electronic Res Librn, University of New Hampshire School of Law, Two White St, Concord, NH, 03301. Tel: 603-228-1541, Ext 1130. Fax: 603-228-0388. p. 1443

Hemstreet, Carolyn, Dir, Hale County Public Library, 1103 Main St, Greensboro, AL, 36744. Tel: 334-624-3409. Fax: 334-624-3409. p. 19

Henard, Kevin, Librn, Hill College Library, Johnson County Campus, 2112 Mayfield Pkwy, Cleburne, TX, 76033. Tel: 817-760-5831. Fax: 817-556-2142. p. 2333

Henchey, Karen, YA Librn, Meredith Public Library, 91 Main St, Meredith, NH, 03253. Tel: 603-279-4303. Fax: 603-279-5352. p. 1457

Hendel, Chris, Div Mgr, Thousand Oaks Library, 1401 E Janss Rd, Thousand Oaks, CA, 91362-2199. Tel: 805-449-2660, Ext 7367. Fax: 805-373-6858. p. 275

Henders, Rosemary, Instrul Serv Librn, North Central College, 320 E School St, Naperville, IL, 60540. Tel: 630-637-5707. Fax: 630-637-5716. p. 679

Hendersen, Magi, Youth Serv, Glen Carbon Centennial Library, 198 S Main St, Glen Carbon, IL, 62034. Tel: 618-288-1212. Fax: 618-288-1205. p. 649

Hendershott, Carmen, Ref Serv, New School, Raymond Fogelman Library, 55 W 13th St, New York, NY, 10011. Tel: 212-229-5307, Ext 3053. Fax: 212-229-5306. p. 1688

Henderson, Alma J, Dir, Saddle Brook Free Public Library, 340 Mayhill St, Saddle Brook, NJ, 07663. Tel: 201-843-3287. Fax: 201-843-5512. p. 1528

Henderson, Alynza, Head, Cat, Hanover College, 121 Scenic Dr, Hanover, IN, 47243. Tel: 812-866-7165. Fax: 812-866-7172. p. 748

Henderson, Annie, Head, Access Serv, East Texas Baptist University, 1209 N Grove St, Marshall, TX, 75670-1498. Tel: 903-923-2256. Fax: 903-935-3447. p. 2359

Henderson, Barbara, Br Mgr, Saint Louis Public Library, Cabanne, 1106 Union Blvd, Saint Louis, MO, 63113. Tel: 314-367-0717. Fax: 314-367-7802. p. 1360

Henderson, Barbara, Mgr, Fort Worth Library, East Regional, 6301 Bridge St, Fort Worth, TX, 76105. Tel: 817-871-6436. Fax: 817-871-6440. p. 2322

Henderson, Beth, Librn, Monmouth County Library, Hazlet Branch, 251 Middle Rd, Hazlet, NJ, 07730. Tel: 732-264-7164. Fax: 732-739-1556. p. 1499

Henderson, Beverly, Dir, Stratton Public Library, 502 Bailey St, Stratton, NE, 69043. Tel: 308-276-2463. p. 1420

Henderson, Brooke, Art Librn, Wellesley College, Art Library, Jewett Arts Ctr, 106 Central St, Wellesley, MA, 02481. Tel: 781-283-2049. Fax: 781-283-3647. p. 1135

Henderson, Catherine, Ch, Greece Public Library, Two Vince Tofany Blvd, Greece, NY, 14612. Tel: 585-225-8951. Fax: 585-225-2777. p. 1630

Henderson, Christopher, Media Spec, Midwestern State University, 3410 Taft Ave, Wichita Falls, TX, 76308-2099. Tel: 940-397-4696. Fax: 940-397-4689. p. 2400

Henderson, Cindy, Br Mgr, Albemarle Regional Library, Ahoskie Public Library, 210 E Church St, Ahoskie, NC, 27910. Tel: 252-332-5500. Fax: 252-332-6435. p. 1835

Henderson, Connie, Mgr, Blackwater Regional Library, Carrollton Public, 14362 New Towne Haven Lane, Carrollton, VA, 23314. Tel: 757-238-2641. Fax: 757-238-3932. p. 2458

Henderson, Cynthia L, Dir, Howard University Libraries, Louis Stokes Health Sciences Library, 501 W St NW, Washington, DC, 20059. Tel: 202-884-1723. Fax: 202-884-1733. p. 404

Henderson, David W, Dir, Libr Serv, Eckerd College, 4200 54th Ave S, Saint Petersburg, FL, 33711. Tel: 727-864-8337. Fax: 727-864-8997. p. 488

Henderson, Diane J, Mgr, School of Ocean & Earth Science & Technology Library, 2525 Correa Rd, HIG 133, Honolulu, HI, 96822. Tel: 808-956-7040. Fax: 808-956-2538. p. 565

Henderson, Donna, Librn, South New Berlin Free Library, 3320 State Hwy 8, South New Berlin, NY, 13843. Tel: 607-859-2420. Fax: 607-859-2660. p. 1745

Henderson, Douglas, Dir, Charleston County Public Library, 68 Calhoun St, Charleston, SC, 29401. Tel: 843-805-6801. p. 2183

Henderson, Elizabeth, Instrul Serv Librn, Lynchburg College, 1501 Lakeside Dr, Lynchburg, VA, 24501-3199. Tel: 434-544-8204. Fax: 434-544-8499. p. 2476

Henderson, Francine, Adminr, Atlanta-Fulton Public Library System, Auburn Avenue Research Library on African-American Culture & History, 101 Auburn Ave NE, Atlanta, GA, 30303. Tel: 404-730-4001. Fax: 404-730-5879. p. 511

Henderson, Gwen, Acq, Texas Southern University, Thurgood Marshall School of Law Library, 3100 Cleburne Ave, Houston, TX, 77004. Tel: 713-313-1157. Fax: 713-313-4483. p. 2342

Henderson, Holly, Dir, Libr Serv, St John's Health System, 1235 E Cherokee St, Springfield, MO, 65804-2263. Tel: 417-820-2795. Fax: 417-820-5399. p. 1367

Henderson, Holly, Libr Dir, Saint John's Health System, Van K Smith Community Health Library, St John's Cancer Ctr, 2055 S Fremont, Springfield, MO, 65804-2263. Tel: 417-820-2539. Fax: 417-820-2587. p. 1367

Henderson, Ian, Mgr, Per, Otis College of Art & Design Library, 9045 Lincoln Blvd, Westchester, CA, 90045. Tel: 310-665-6800, Ext 6930. Fax: 310-665-6998. p. 283

Henderson, Jacqueline, Asst Librn, Cadwalader, Wickersham & Taft, 700 Sixth St NW, Suite 300, Washington, DC, 20001. Tel: 202-862-2217. Fax: 202-862-2400. p. 395

Henderson, Janet, Mat Mgr, Lubbock Public Library, 1306 Ninth St, Lubbock, TX, 79401. Tel: 806-775-2834. Fax: 806-775-2827. p. 2357

Henderson, Janice W, Dir, Northwest Florida State College, 100 College Blvd, Niceville, FL, 32578. Tel: 850-729-5392. Fax: 850-729-5295. p. 472

Henderson, Jarmila, Med Librn, United States Air Force, 5955 Zeamer Ave, 3MDG/SGSOL, Elmendorf AFB, AK, 99506-3700. Tel: 907-580-3024. Fax: 907-257-6768. p. 47

Henderson, Jason, Digitization & Virtual Ref Tech, Southwestern Oklahoma State University, 100 Campus Dr, Weatherford, OK, 73096-3002. Tel: 580-774-7024. Fax: 580-774-3112. p. 1985

Henderson, Joan G, Dir, Ferguson Municipal Public Library, 35 N Florissant Rd, Ferguson, MO, 63135. Tel: 314-521-1275. Fax: 314-521-1275. p. 1327

Henderson, Justin, Curator, Colorado Ski Museum-Ski Hall of Fame, 231 S Frontage Rd E, Vail, CO, 81657-3616. Tel: 970-476-1876. Fax: 970-476-1879. p. 324

Henderson, Kathrine, Instrul Serv Librn, Thunderbird School of Global Management, 15249 N 59th Ave, Glendale, AZ, 85306-6001. Tel: 602-978-7231. Fax: 602-978-7762. p. 64

Henderson, Kathy, Dir, Fremont County District Library, 925 Main, Ashton, ID, 83420. Tel: 208-652-7280. p. 569

Henderson, Kathy, Dir, Fremont County District Library, 420 N Bridge, Ste E, Saint Anthony, ID, 83445. Tel: 208-624-3192. Fax: 208-624-3192. p. 583

Henderson, Kim, Acq, Cat, Buffalo River Regional Library, 104 E Sixth St, Columbia, TN, 38401-3359. Tel: 931-388-9282. Fax: 931-388-1762. p. 2231

Henderson, Laurie, Librn, Saint Joseph Hospital, One Saint Joseph Dr, Lexington, KY, 40504. Tel: 859-313-1677. Fax: 859-313-3065. p. 921

Henderson, Lenni, Dir of Libr Serv, Richland College Library, 12800 Abrams Rd, Dallas, TX, 75243-2199. Tel: 972-238-6107. p. 2309

Henderson, Mantra, Dir, Mississippi Valley State University, 14000 Hwy 82 W, Itta Bena, MS, 38941. Tel: 662-254-3494. Fax: 662-254-3499. p. 1302

Henderson, Mary, Asst Dir, Morton Mandan Public Library, 609 W Main St, Mandan, ND, 58554. Tel: 701-667-5365. Fax: 701-667-5368. p. 1845

Henderson, Melissa, Ch, Glencoe Public Library, 320 Park Ave, Glencoe, IL, 60022-1597. Tel: 847-835-5056. Fax: 847-835-5648. p. 650

Henderson, Nancy, Health Sci Librn, Pacific University Library, 2043 College Way, Forest Grove, OR, 97116. Tel: 503-352-7208. Fax: 503-352-7230. p. 1998

Henderson, Nancy, Cat, Carnegie Library of McKeesport, 1507 Library Ave, McKeesport, PA, 15132-4796. Tel: 412-672-0625. Fax: 412-672-7860. p. 2085

Henderson, Rick, Asst Librn, Pennsylvania Academy of Fine Arts Library, 128 N Broad St, Philadelphia, PA, 19102. Tel: 215-972-7600, Ext 2030. Fax: 215-569-0153. p. 2113

Henderson, Robin, Ref Serv, Monroe County Public Library, 700 Fleming St, Key West, FL, 33040. Tel: 305-292-3595. Fax: 305-295-3626. p. 456

Henderson, Ron, Chief Exec Officer, Dir, Greater Sudbury Public Library, 74 MacKenzie St, Sudbury, ON, P3C 4X8, CANADA. Tel: 705-673-1155. Fax: 705-673-6145. p. 2846

Henderson, Rosy, YA Serv, New Brunswick Free Public Library, 60 Livingston Ave, New Brunswick, NJ, 08901-2597. Tel: 732-745-5108, Ext 22. Fax: 732-846-0226. p. 1508

Henderson, Ruth, Admin Serv, Maryland State Law Library, Courts of Appeal Bldg, 361 Rowe Blvd, Annapolis, MD, 21401-1697. Tel: 410-260-1430. Fax: 410-260-1572, 410-974-2063. p. 1010

Henderson, Sally, Librn, Mathematica Policy Research, Inc Library, 1100 First St NE, 12Flr, Washington, DC, 20002-4221. Tel: 202-484-4692. Fax: 202-863-1763. p. 408

Henderson, Sandra, Libr Dir, Lawson State Community College Library, 1100 Ninth Ave SW, Bessemer, AL, 35022. Tel: 205-929-3434, 205-929-6333. Fax: 205-925-3716. p. 6

Henderson, Sandra L, Dir, Lawson State Community College Library, 3060 Wilson Rd SW, Birmingham, AL, 35221. Tel: 205-925-2515, Ext 6333, 205-929-6333. Fax: 205-925-3716. p. 8

Henderson, Sarah, Access Serv, Minot State University, 500 University Ave W, Minot, ND, 58707. Tel: 701-858-3200. Fax: 701-858-3581. p. 1846

Henderson, Sharon, Br Mgr, Newport News Public Library System, Main Street, 110 Main St, Newport News, VA, 23601. Tel: 757-591-4858. Fax: 757-591-7425. p. 2480

Henderson, Sheila, Br Mgr, Live Oak Public Libraries, Port City Branch, 3501 Houlihan Ave, Savannah, GA, 31408. Tel: 912-964-8013. Fax: 912-966-5142. p. 550

Henderson, Sheila, Head Librn, Austin Community College, Round Rock Campus Library, 4400 College Park Dr, Round Rock, TX, 78665. Tel: 512-223-0116. Fax: 512-223-0903. p. 2278

Henderson, Steve, Syst Librn, Cerritos Library, 18025 Bloomfield Ave, Cerritos, CA, 90703. Tel: 562-916-1350. Fax: 562-916-1375. p. 133

Henderson, Terry, Cat, Warren County Memorial Library, 119 South Front St, Warrenton, NC, 27589. Tel: 252-257-4990. Fax: 252-257-4089. p. 1828

Henderson, Terry, Coll Develop, Warren County Memorial Library, 119 South Front St, Warrenton, NC, 27589. Tel: 252-257-4990. Fax: 252-257-4089. p. 1828

Henderson, Tom, Col Librn, Millsaps College, 1701 N State St, Jackson, MS, 39210-0001. Tel: 601-974-1075. Fax: 601-974-1082. p. 1303

Henderson, Tom, Adminr, Treas, Central Mississippi Library Council, c/o Millsaps College Library, 1701 N State St, Jackson, MS, 39210. Tel: 601-974-1070. Fax: 601-974-1082. p. 2947

Henderson, Vicki, Circ Mgr, Cheyenne Wells Public Library, 151 S First St W, Cheyenne Wells, CO, 80810. Tel: 719-767-5138. Fax: 719-767-5379. p. 294

Henderson, Vonda, Ref Serv, Truett-McConnell College, 100 Alumni Dr, Cleveland, GA, 30528-9799. Tel: 706-865-2134, Ext 153. Fax: 706-865-5130. p. 525

Henderson-Green, Gail, Dir, Internal Revenue Service, 1111 Constitution Ave NW, Rm 4324, Washington, DC, 20224. Tel: 202-622-8050, Ext 5822. Fax: 202-622-5844. p. 405

Henderstein, Amy, Dir, Warren Public Library, One City Sq, Ste 100, Warren, MI, 48093-2396. Tel: 586-574-4564. p. 1234

Hendon, Linda J, ILL/Tech Serv Librn, Ramapo Catskill Library System, 619 Rte 17M, Middletown, NY, 10940-4395. Tel: 845-343-1131, Ext 237. Fax: 845-343-1205. p. 1660

Hendren, Jo, Librn, Thompson Institute, 5650 Derry St, Harrisburg, PA, 17111. Tel: 717-564-4112, 717-901-5867. Fax: 717-558-1344. p. 2066

Hendrick, Cindy, Actg Librn, Benson Public Library, 200 13th St N, Benson, MN, 56215-1223. Tel: 320-842-7981. Fax: 320-843-4948. p. 1241

Hendrick, Karen, Head, Pub Serv, Abilene Christian University, 221 Brown Library, ACU Box 29208, Abilene, TX, 79699-9208. Tel: 325-674-2344. Fax: 325-674-2202. p. 2271

Hendrick, Linda, Ref Serv, Skagit Valley College, 2405 E College Way, Mount Vernon, WA, 98273-5899. Tel: 360-416-7606. Fax: 360-416-7698. p. 2521

Hendrick, Mary, Mgr, Youth Serv, North Madison County Public Library System, 1600 Main St, Elwood, IN, 46036. Tel: 765-552-5001. Fax: 765-552-0955. p. 737

Hendricks, Arthur, Humanities & Soc Sci Librn, Portland State University Library, 1875 SW Park Ave, Portland, OR, 97201-3220. Tel: 503-725-5879. Fax: 503-725-4524. p. 2014

Hendricks, Catherine, Coordr of Develop, Irvine Sullivan Ingram Library, University of West Georgia, 1601 Maple St, Carrollton, GA, 30118. Tel: 678-839-6498. Fax: 678-839-6511. p. 523

Hendricks, Frankie, Circ Supvr, Dallas Baptist University, 3000 Mountain Creek Pkwy, Dallas, TX, 75211-9299. Tel: 214-333-5213. Fax: 214-333-5323. p. 2305

Hendricks, Gail, Supvr, Riverside Public Library, Marcy Branch, 6927 Magnolia Ave, Riverside, CA, 92506. Tel: 951-826-2078. p. 218

Hendricks, John F, Dir, Phillips Public Library, 286 Cherry St, Phillips, WI, 54555-1240. Tel: 715-339-2868. p. 2629

Hendricks, John Milton, Asst Librn, United States District Court, 450 Golden Gate Ave, Box 36060, San Francisco, CA, 94102. Tel: 415-436-8130. Fax: 415-436-8134. p. 248

Hendricks, Kath Ann, YA Librn, Marshall Public Library, 113 S Garfield, Pocatello, ID, 83204-5722. Tel: 208-232-1263, Ext 28. Fax: 208-232-9266. p. 582

Hendricks, Kathy, Head, Admin Serv, University of Montana, Maureen & Mike Mansfield Library, 32 Campus Dr, No 9936, Missoula, MT, 59812-9936. Tel: 406-243-4583. Fax: 406-243-4067. p. 1386

Hendricks, Leta, Ref, Ohio State University LIBRARIES, Fine Arts, Wexner Center for the Arts, 1871 N High St, Columbus, OH, 43210. Tel: 614-292-6184. Fax: 614-292-4573. p. 1887

Hendricks, Lisa, Coll Develop Librn, Texas State Library & Archives Commission, 1201 Brazos, Austin, TX, 78711. Tel: 512-463-5458. Fax: 512-936-0685. p. 2283

Hendricks, Margaret, Ch, Grand Prairie of the West Public Library District, 142 W Jackson St, Virden, IL, 62690-1257. Tel: 217-965-3015. Fax: 217-965-3801. p. 714

Hendricks, Marilyn, Br Mgr, Green Tom County Library System, North Angelo, 3001 N Chadbourne, San Angelo, TX, 76904. Tel: 915-653-8412. p. 2378

Hendricks, Martha, Asst Dir, Clarksville-Montgomery County Public Library, 350 Pageant Lane, Ste 501, Clarksville, TN, 37040. Tel: 931-648-8826. Fax: 931-648-8831. p. 2229

Hendricks, Nancy, Dir, Texas State Technical College, 1902 N Loop 499, Harlingen, TX, 78550. Tel: 956-364-4609. Fax: 956-364-5149. p. 2331

Hendricks, Richard D, Dir, Dewitt, Ross & Stevens SC, Two E Mifflin St, Ste 600, Madison, WI, 53703. Tel: 608-283-5504. Fax: 608-252-9243. p. 2606

Hendricks, Robyn, Head, Circ, Decatur Public Library, 130 N Franklin St, Decatur, IL, 62523-1327. Tel: 217-421-9737. Fax: 217-233-4071. p. 634

Hendrickson, A Paige, Br Librn, Motlow State Community College Libraries, Smyrna Center Library, 5002 Motlow College Blvd, Smyrna, TN, 37167. Tel: 615-220-7815. p. 2267

Hendrickson, Anne, Dir, United States Patent & Trademark Office, 400 Dulany St, Rm 1D58, Alexandria, VA, 22314. Tel: 571-272-3547. Fax: 571-273-0048. p. 2446

Hendrickson, Catherine, Librn, Crafton Hills College Library, 11711 Sand Canyon Rd, Yucaipa, CA, 92399. Tel: 909-389-3323, 909-794-2161. Fax: 909-794-9524. p. 286

Hendrickson, Patricia, Librn, East Moline Correctional Center Library, 100 Hillcrest Rd, East Moline, IL, 61244. Tel: 309-755-4511, Ext 350. p. 638

Hendrickson, Philip, Dir, Libr Serv, Concordia University, 800 N Columbia Ave, Seward, NE, 68434-1595. Tel: 402-643-7254. Fax: 402-643-4218. p. 1419

Hendrickson, Susan, Rec Mgr, California Institute of Technology, 4800 Oak Grove Dr, MS 111-113, Pasadena, CA, 91109-8099. Tel: 818-354-3007. Fax: 818-393-6752. p. 206

Hendrickson, Susan Rhead, Librn, Natural Resources Research Institute, University of Minnesota - Duluth, 5013 Miller Trunk Hwy, Duluth, MN, 55811. Tel: 218-720-4235. Fax: 218-720-4219. p. 1248

Hendrickx, Cindy, Librn, Appleton Public Library, 322 W Schlieman Ave, Appleton, MN, 56208-1299. Tel: 320-289-1681. Fax: 320-289-1681. p. 1240

Hendrix, Dana, Head, Acq, Head, Coll Serv, Southwestern University, 1100 E University Ave, Georgetown, TX, 78626. Tel: 512-863-1241. Fax: 512-863-8198. p. 2327

Hendrix, Linda, Dir, Santa Rosa County Library System, 6275 Dogwood Dr, Milton, FL, 32570. Tel: 850-623-2043. Fax: 850-623-2138. p. 470

Hendrix, Nanci, Dir, Children's Prog, Hawkes Library, 100 W Eighth St, West Point, GA, 31833. Tel: 706-645-1549. Fax: 706-645-1549. p. 557

Hendrix, Page, ILL, York County Library, 138 E Black St, Rock Hill, SC, 29731. Tel: 803-981-5858. Fax: 803-981-5866. p. 2203

Hendrix, Sheryl, Tech Serv, Mount Vernon Nazarene University, 800 Martinsburg Rd, Mount Vernon, OH, 43050-9500. Tel: 740-397-9000, Ext 4240. Fax: 740-397-8847. p. 1919

Hendrix, Wanda, ILL, Decatur Public Library, 504 Cherry St NE, Decatur, AL, 35601. Tel: 256-353-2993. Fax: 256-350-6736. p. 14

Hendrixson, Barbara, Digital Serv, Ref Serv, Ball Memorial Hospital, 2401 W University Ave, Muncie, IN, 47303-3499. Tel: 765-747-3204. Fax: 765-747-0137. p. 766

Hendrixson, Kathy, Dir, Justin Potter Public Library, 101 S First St, Smithville, TN, 37166-1706. Tel: 615-597-4359. Fax: 615-597-4329. p. 2265

Hendry, David, Assoc Prof, University of Washington, Mary Gates Hall, Ste 370, Campus Box 352840, Seattle, WA, 98195-2840. Tel: 206-685-9937. Fax: 206-616-3152. p. 2976

Hendry, Julia, Spec Coll & Archives Librn, Wilfrid Laurier University Library, 75 University Ave W, Waterloo, ON, N2L 3C5, CANADA. Tel: 519-884-0710, Ext 3825. Fax: 519-884-3209. p. 2869

Hendryx, Betty, Dir, Garrison Public Library, 100 N Birch Ave, Garrison, IA, 52229. Tel: 319-477-5531. Fax: 319-477-5531. p. 817

Hendryx, Mike, Dir, Siskiyou County Museum Library, 910 S Main St, Yreka, CA, 96097. Tel: 530-842-3836. Fax: 530-842-3166. p. 285

Hendy, Nancy, Dir, Maxfield Public Library, Eight Rte 129, Loudon, NH, 03307. Tel: 603-798-5153. p. 1454

Heneghan, Constance, Br Mgr, Evanston Public Library, North, 2026 Central St, Evanston, IL, 60201. Tel: 847-866-0330. Fax: 847-866-0331. p. 643

Henely, Jen, Ref Asst, Crown College, 8700 College View Dr, Saint Bonifacius, MN, 55375-9002. Tel: 952-446-4240. Fax: 952-446-4149. p. 1274

Henfer, Paul, Tech Coordr, University of Wisconsin Center-Marathon County Library, 518 S Seventh Ave, Wausau, WI, 54401-5396. Tel: 715-261-6208. Fax: 715-261-6330. p. 2647

Henggeler, Wilma, Asst Dir, Maryville Public Library, 509 N Main, Maryville, MO, 64468. Tel: 660-582-5281. Fax: 660-582-2411. p. 1344

Hengst, Linda R, Dir, Ohioana Library, 274 E First Ave, Ste 300, Columbus, OH, 43201. Tel: 614-728-3044. Fax: 614-728-6974. p. 1890

Henika, Beth, Ch, North Shore Library, 6800 N Port Washington Rd, Glendale, WI, 53217. Tel: 414-351-3461. Fax: 414-351-3528. p. 2594

Hening, Joy, Coll Librn, Worcester Public Library, Three Salem Sq, Worcester, MA, 01608. Tel: 508-799-1655. Fax: 508-799-1652. p. 1145

Henion, Julie, Dir, Platte County Public Library, 904 Ninth St, Wheatland, WY, 82201-2699. Tel: 307-322-2689. Fax: 307-322-3540. p. 2661

Henitz, Mary Ellen, Head, Ref, Bergenfield Public Library, 50 W Clinton Ave, Bergenfield, NJ, 07621-2799. Tel: 201-387-4040, Ext 833. Fax: 201-387-9004. p. 1472

Henke, Jerry, Exec Dir, Fillmore County Historical Society, 202 County Rd, No 8, Fountain, MN, 55935. Tel: 507-268-4449. Fax: 507-268-4492. p. 1252

Henke, Mary, Librn, Hutchinson Public Library, 50 Hassan St SE, Hutchinson, MN, 55350-1881. Tel: 320-587-2368. Fax: 320-587-4286. p. 1254

Henkel, Harold, Ref Serv, Regent University Library, 1000 Regent University Dr, Virginia Beach, VA, 23464. Tel: 757-352-4198. Fax: 757-352-4167. p. 2499

Henkel, Judy, Dir, Lawrence County Public Library, Loretto Branch, 102 S Main St, Loretto, TN, 38469-2110. Tel: 931-853-7323. Fax: 931-853-7324. p. 2244

Henkel, Lynn, Tech Serv, Cranberry Public Library, 2525 Rochester Rd, Ste 300, Cranberry Township, PA, 16066-6423. Tel: 724-776-9100, Ext 1147. Fax: 724-776-2490. p. 2048

Henkin, Robert I, Chief Librn, Center for Molecular Nutrition & Sensory Disorders, 5125 MacArthur Blvd, Ste 20, Washington, DC, 20016. Tel: 202-364-4180. Fax: 202-364-9727. p. 396

Henler, Jeremy, Exec Dir, Lee & Dolores Hartzmark Library, 26000 Shaker Blvd, Beachwood, OH, 44122. Tel: 216-831-3233. Fax: 216-831-4216. p. 1858

Henley, Holly, Dir, Libr Develop, Arizona State Library, Archives & Public Records, 1700 W Washington, Rm 200, Phoenix, AZ, 85007. Tel: 602-926-4035. Fax: 602-256-7983. p. 72

Henley, Katherine, Electronic Serv Librn, Victoria Public Library, 302 N Main, Victoria, TX, 77901-6592. Tel: 361-485-3304. Fax: 361-485-3295. p. 2395

Henley, Michelle, In Charge, Saint Francis Memorial Hospital, 900 Hyde St, San Francisco, CA, 94109. Tel: 415-353-6320. Fax: 415-353-6323. p. 244

Henley, Regan, Br Librn, Park County Public Library, Guffey Branch, 1625 B County Rd 102, Guffey, CO, 80820. Tel: 719-689-9280. Fax: 719-689-9304. p. 289

Henn, Char, Dir, Goodhue County Historical Society Library, 1166 Oak St, Red Wing, MN, 55066-2447. Tel: 651-388-6024. Fax: 651-388-3577. p. 1271

Henne, Julie, Coordr, Communications & Fund Develop, Great River Regional Library, 1300 W St Germain St, Saint Cloud, MN, 56301-3667. Tel: 320-650-2532. Fax: 320-650-2501. p. 1274

Henne, Mark, Coll Develop, Tech Serv, Southington Public Library & Museum, 255 Main St, Southington, CT, 06489. Tel: 860-628-0947. Fax: 860-628-0488. p. 368

Hennedy, Jane, Dir, Hist Soc, Old Colony Historical Society, 66 Church Green, Taunton, MA, 02780. Tel: 508-822-1622. Fax: 508-880-6317. p. 1130

Henneman, Mary Lou, Librn, Boardman United Methodist Church Library, 6809 Market St, Boardman, OH, 44512. Tel: 330-758-4527. Fax: 330-758-7348. p. 1860

Hennemann, Amy, Libr Coordr, Nashville School of Law Library, 4013 Armory Oaks Dr, Nashville, TN, 37204. Tel: 615-256-3684. Fax: 615-244-2383. p. 2258

Hennen, Thomas J, Jr, Dir, Waukesha County Federated Library System, 831 N Grand Ave, Ste 220, Waukesha, WI, 53186-4822. Tel: 262-896-8080. Fax: 262-896-8086. p. 2645

Henner, Terry, Dir, University Medical Center of Southern Nevada, 2040 W Charleston Blvd, Ste 500, Las Vegas, NV, 89102. Tel: 702-383-2368. Fax: 702-383-2369. p. 1430

Henner, Terry, Dir, University of Nevada-Reno, Savitt Medical Library & IT Department, Pennington Medical Education Bldg, 1664 N Virginia St, Mail Stop 306, Reno, NV, 89557. Tel: 775-784-4625. Fax: 775-784-4489. p. 1433

Hennes, Teri, Adult Serv, Glencoe Public Library, 320 Park Ave, Glencoe, IL, 60022-1597. Tel: 847-835-5056. Fax: 847-835-5648. p. 650

Hennessey, Dennis, Librn, Community College of Allegheny County, 808 Ridge Ave, Pittsburgh, PA, 15212-6003. Tel: 412-237-2585. Fax: 412-237-6563. p. 2124

Hennessey, Diana, Br Mgr, Greenwood County Library, Ninety Six Branch, 100 S Cambridge St S, Ninety Six, SC, 29666. Tel: 864-543-4749. Fax: 864-543-4749. p. 2197

Hennessey, Jill, Access Serv Mgr, Salem State University Library, 352 Lafayette St, Salem, MA, 01970-5353. Tel: 978-542-6368. Fax: 978-542-6596. p. 1122

Hennessy, Patti, ILL, Williams & Connolly Library, 725 12th St NW, Washington, DC, 20005. Tel: 202-434-5302. Fax: 202-434-5029. p. 423

Hennessy, Thomas, Curator, Lock Museum of America, Inc Library, 230 Main St, Terryville, CT, 06786-5900. Tel: 860-589-6359. Fax: 860-589-6359. p. 372

Hennesy, Cody, Librn, Syst & Serv, California College of the Arts Libraries, 5212 Broadway, Oakland, CA, 94618. p. 196

Hennigan, Joan, Circ, Scott County Library System, 200 N Sixth Ave, Eldridge, IA, 52748. Tel: 563-285-4794. Fax: 563-285-4743. p. 813

Henniger, Juanita, Librn, Washington County Law Library, 205 Putnam St, Marietta, OH, 45750-3017. Tel: 740-373-6623, Ext 214. Fax: 740-373-2085. p. 1913

Henning, Arland, Cat Librn, Jacksonville State University Library, 700 Pelham Rd N, Jacksonville, AL, 36265. Tel: 256-782-5255. Fax: 256-782-5872. p. 22

Henning, Connie, Libr Tech, Minnesota West Community & Technical College, Jackson Campus, 401 West St, Jackson, MN, 56143. Tel: 507-847-3320. p. 1291

Henning, Coral, Dir, Sacramento County Public Law Library, 813 Sixth St, 1st Flr, Sacramento, CA, 95814-2403. Tel: 916-874-6013. Fax: 916-874-5691. p. 224

Henning, Coral, Pres, Northern California Association of Law Libraries, 268 Bush St, No 4006, San Francisco, CA, 94104. Tel: 916-874-6013. p. 2938

Henning, Jacqueline, Assoc Dean, Dean of Libr, LRC & Campus Tech, Libr Instruction, Broward College, 3501 SW Davie Rd, Davie, FL, 33314. Tel: 954-201-6648. Fax: 954-201-6490. p. 435

Henning, Joanne, Assoc Univ Librn, Coll Serv, Assoc Univ Librn, Info Serv, University of Victoria Libraries, McPherson Library, PO Box 1800, Victoria, BC, V8W 3H5, CANADA. Tel: 250-721-8211. Fax: 250-721-8215. p. 2746

Henning, Rebecca, Cat Librn, Amherst College, Amherst, MA, 01002. Fax: 413-542-2662. p. 1048

Henning-Sachs, Corinne, Youth Serv Librn, Walker Memorial Library, 800 Main St, Westbrook, ME, 04092. Tel: 207-854-0630. Fax: 207-854-0629. p. 1006

Hennings, Linda, Circ & Reserves Supvr, Wartburg College Library, 100 Wartburg Blvd, Waverly, IA, 50677-0903. Tel: 319-352-8524. Fax: 319-352-8312. p. 850

Hennrich, Christine, Mgr, Alcoa Technical Center Library, 100 Technical Dr, Alcoa Center, PA, 15069-0001. Tel: 724-337-2413. Fax: 724-337-2394. p. 2026

Henri, Gladys, Librn, Wapiti Regional Library, Leoville Public Library, Box 129, Leoville, SK, S0J 1N0, CANADA. Tel: 306-984-2057. p. 2921

Henri, Janine, Archit, Design & Digital Serv Librn, University of California Los Angeles Library, The Arts Library, 1400 Public Policy Bldg, Los Angeles, CA, 90095. Tel: 310-206-4587. Fax: 310-825-1303. p. 178

Henrich, Kristin, Head, Ref, University of Idaho Library, Rayburn St, Moscow, ID, 83844. Tel: 208-885-6514. Fax: 208-885-6817. p. 579

Henrich, Paul, Head Librn, New York State Supreme Court Library, Brooklyn, Supreme Court Bldg, Rm 349, 360 Adams St, Brooklyn, NY, 11201-3782. Tel: 347-296-1144. Fax: 718-643-2412. p. 1594

Henrich, Sharon, Mgr, Florida Hospital-Tampa, 3100 E Fletcher Ave, Tampa, FL, 33613-4688. Tel: 813-615-7236. Fax: 813-615-7854. p. 496

Henricks, Susan, Dir, Carnegie-Stout Public Library, 360 W 11th St, Dubuque, IA, 52001. Tel: 563-589-4126. Fax: 563-589-4217. p. 811

Henricksen, Misty, Mgr, Yarnell Public Library, 22278 N Hwy 89, Yarnell, AZ, 85362. Tel: 928-427-3191. Fax: 928-427-3191. p. 90

Henricksen-Georghiou, Heather, Doc, Newburgh Free Library, 124 Grand St, Newburgh, NY, 12550. Tel: 845-563-3600. Fax: 845-563-3602. p. 1705

Henrickson, Christy, Res Sharing Librn, University of Wisconsin-Madison, Kurt Wendt Engineering Library, 215 N Randall Ave, Madison, WI, 53706. Tel: 608-262-3493. Fax: 608-262-4739, 608-265-8751. p. 2610

Henriksson, Ann W, Ref Coordr, Shepherd University, 301 N King St, Shepherdstown, WV, 25443. Fax: 304-876-0731. p. 2571

Henry, Amy, In Charge, Avery Research Center, 2900 Bradley St, Pasadena, CA, 91107-1599. Tel: 626-398-2500, Ext 2567. Fax: 626-398-2540. p. 205

Henry, Andrew, Chief Librn, Department of Veterans Affairs, 1400 Black Horse Hill Rd, Coatesville, PA, 19320-2040. Tel: 610-383-0288, 610-384-7711. Fax: 610-383-0245. p. 2046

Henry, Angela, Asst Br Mgr, Evangeline Parish Library, Turkey Creek, 13951 Veterans Memorial Hwy, Ville Platte, LA, 70586. Tel: 337-461-2304. p. 971

Henry, Angela, Ref Serv, Clark State Community College Library, 570 E Leffel Lane, Springfield, OH, 45505. Tel: 937-328-6022. Fax: 937-328-6133. p. 1935

Henry, Anna, Br Mgr, Washington County Public Library, Barlow Branch, 8370 State Rte 339, Barlow, OH, 45712. Tel: 740-678-0103. Fax: 740-678-0046. p. 1914

Henry, Barbara, Commun Health Librn, Christiana Hospital Library, Christiana Hospital, 4755 Ogletown Stanton Rd, Newark, DE, 19718-0002. Tel: 302-733-1122. Fax: 302-733-1365. p. 385

Henry, Barbara, Commun Health Librn, Christiana Hospital Library, Wilmington Hospital Library, PO Box 1668, Wilmington, DE, 19899-1668. Tel: 302-623-4585. Fax: 302-428-2101. p. 385

Henry, Barbara, Mgr, Christiana Hospital Library, Junior Board Cancer Resource Library, 4701 Ogletown Stanton Rd, Newark, DE, 19713. Tel: 302-623-4580. Fax: 302-623-4589. p. 385

Henry, Barbara, Ad, Asst Dir, Wood Library Association of Canandaigua, 134 N Main St, Canandaigua, NY, 14424-1295. Tel: 585-394-1381. Fax: 585-394-2954. p. 1601

Henry, Brenna, Acq of New Ser, Coll Develop, Tech Serv Librn, Hillsdale College, 33 E College St, Hillsdale, MI, 49242. Tel: 517-607-2405. Fax: 517-607-2248. p. 1190

Henry, Cheryl, Librn, CalRecovery Inc Library, 2454 Stanwell Dr, Concord, CA, 94520. Tel: 925-356-3700. Fax: 925-356-7956. p. 136

Henry, Chriselle, Br Librn, Ascension Parish Library, Gonzales Branch, 708 S Irma Blvd, Gonzales, LA, 70737. Tel: 225-647-3955. Fax: 225-644-0063. p. 949

Henry, Chrissy, Syst Coordr, Spanish Fork Public Library, 49 S Main St, Spanish Fork, UT, 84660-2030. Tel: 801-804-4480. Fax: 801-798-5014. p. 2416

Henry, Christianne, Head of Libr, Walters Art Museum Library, 600 N Charles St, Baltimore, MD, 21201-5185. Tel: 410-547-9000, Ext 297. Fax: 410-752-4797. p. 1019

Henry, Deborah, Ref Librn, University of South Florida Saint Petersburg, 140 Seventh Ave S, POY118, Saint Petersburg, FL, 33701. Tel: 727-873-4401. Fax: 727-873-4196. p. 489

Henry, Elizabeth, Instruction & Ref/Electronic Res Librn, Gallaudet University Library, 800 Florida Ave NE, Washington, DC, 20002-3095. Tel: 202-651-5217. p. 401

Henry, Elizabeth C, Tech Serv Librn, Saint Leo University, 33701 State Rd 52, Saint Leo, FL, 33574. Tel: 352-588-8265. Fax: 352-588-8484. p. 487

Henry, Geneva, Exec Dir, Digital Scholarship Serv, Rice University, 6100 Main, MS-44, Houston, TX, 77005. Tel: 713-348-2480. Fax: 713-348-5258. p. 2341

Henry, Gwen, Librn, Florida Department of Children & Families, 800 E Cypress Dr, Pembroke Pines, FL, 33025-1499. Tel: 954-392-3000. p. 481

Henry, Helen, Assoc Univ Librn, University of California, Davis, 100 NW Quad, Davis, CA, 95616-5292. Tel: 530-752-6561. Fax: 530-752-3148. p. 139

Henry, Jackie, Admin Dir, Norwegian-American Historical Association Archives, 1510 St Olaf Ave, Northfield, MN, 55057. Tel: 507-786-3221. Fax: 507-786-3734. p. 1269

Henry, Jean, Ref, Ayer Library, 26 E Main St, Ayer, MA, 01432. Tel: 978-772-8250. Fax: 978-772-8251. p. 1051

Henry, Jeff, Automation Syst Coordr, Four County Library System, 304 Clubhouse Rd, Vestal, NY, 13850-3713. Tel: 607-723-8236, Ext 310. Fax: 607-723-1722. p. 1761

Henry, Jim, Libr Asst, Libby Memorial Library, 27 Staples St, Old Orchard Beach, ME, 04064. Tel: 207-934-4351. p. 994

Henry, Joan F, Dir, Dunellen Public Library, 100 New Market Rd, Dunellen, NJ, 08812. Tel: 732-968-4585. Fax: 732-424-1370. p. 1481

Henry, John, Automation Syst Coordr, Rogers Public Library, 711 S Dixieland Rd, Rogers, AR, 72758. Tel: 479-621-1152, Ext 13. Fax: 479-621-1165. p. 113

Henry, John B, III, Dir, Flint Institute of Arts, 1120 E Kearsley St, Flint, MI, 48503-1915. Tel: 810-237-7386. Fax: 810-234-1692. p. 1179

Henry, Jordie W, Librn, Toledo Blade-Library, 541 N Superior St, Toledo, OH, 43660. Tel: 419-724-6185. p. 1939

Henry, Laura, Mgr, Young Readers, Palos Verdes Library District, 701 Silver Spur Rd, Rolling Hills Estates, CA, 90274. Tel: 310-377-9584, Ext 206. Fax: 310-541-6807. p. 219

Henry, Lawrence, Dir, Computer Sciences Corporation, 655 15th St NW, Ste 500, Washington, DC, 20005. Tel: 202-741-4224. Fax: 202-628-3205. p. 2940

Henry, Lisa, Dir of Libr Operations, Kirkwood Public Library, 140 E Jefferson Ave, Kirkwood, MO, 63122. Tel: 314-821-5770, Ext 13. Fax: 314-822-3755. p. 1342

Henry, Lola, Librn, Williamson Public Library, 101 Logan St, Williamson, WV, 25661. Tel: 304-235-6029. Fax: 304-235-6029. p. 2575

Henry, Loreen, Head, Info Literacy, University of Texas at Dallas, 800 W Campbell Rd, Richardson, TX, 75080. Tel: 972-883-2126. Fax: 972-883-2473. p. 2374

Henry, Lynn, Coordr, Circ, Burton Public Library, 14588 W Park St, Burton, OH, 44021. Tel: 440-834-4466. Fax: 440-834-0128. p. 1862

Henry, Margaret H, Librn, Tampa General Hospital, PO Box 1289, Tampa, FL, 33601-1289. Tel: 813-844-7328. Fax: 813-844-7325. p. 497

Henry, Nancy, Head, Ref, Sonnenschein, Nath & Rosenthal, 8000 Sears Tower, 233 S Wacker Dr, Ste 7800, Chicago, IL, 60606-6404. Tel: 312-876-8000. Fax: 312-876-7934. p. 625

Henry, Nancy, Librn, Pennsylvania State University Libraries, Life Sciences, 401 Paterno Library, University Park, PA, 16802-1811. Tel: 814-865-3713. p. 2148

Henry, Priscilla B, Access Serv, Florida Agricultural & Mechanical University Libraries, 1500 S Martin Luther King Blvd, Tallahassee, FL, 32307-4700. Tel: 850-599-3370. Fax: 850-561-2293. p. 492

Henry, Renee, Librn, Newman Regional Library District, 108 W Yates St, Newman, IL, 61942. Tel: 217-837-2412. Fax: 217-837-2412. p. 680

Henry, Robin, Librn, Lovelace Respiratory Research Institute, 2425 Ridgecrest Dr SE, Albuquerque, NM, 87108-5127. Tel: 505-348-9178. Fax: 505-348-4978. p. 1549

Henry, Sean, Dr, Coordr, Libr Instruction, Webmaster, Frostburg State University, One Stadium Dr, Frostburg, MD, 21532. Tel: 301-687-4888. Fax: 301-687-7069. p. 1029

Henry, Shari, Br Mgr, Arlington County Department of Libraries, Westover, 1644 N McKinley Rd, Arlington, VA, 22205. Tel: 703-228-5261. Fax: 703-534-1240. p. 2449

Henry, Sheila, Dir, Rocky Ford Public Library, 400 S Tenth St, Rocky Ford, CO, 81067. Tel: 719-254-6641. Fax: 719-254-6647. p. 322

Henry, Stephen, Music Librn, University of Maryland Libraries, Michelle Smith Performing Arts Library, 2511 Clarice Smith Performing Arts Library, College Park, MD, 20742-1630. Tel: 301-405-9256. Fax: 301-314-7170. p. 1025

Henry, Sylvia, Dir, John Turgeson Public Library, 220 S Mound Ave, Belmont, WI, 53510. Tel: 608-762-5137. Fax: 608-762-5525. p. 2581

Henry, Youlana, Interim Assoc Dean, Florida State College at Jacksonville, North Campus, 4501 Capper Rd, Jacksonville, FL, 32218-4499. Tel: 904-766-6717. Fax: 904-766-6640. p. 453

Henry-Croom, Martha, Asst Dir, Access Serv, Kennesaw State University, 1000 Chastain Rd, Kennesaw, GA, 30144. Tel: 770-423-6511. Fax: 770-423-6185. p. 537

Henschel, Carol, Circ, Tech Serv, Milwaukee Area Technical College, 1200 S 71st St, Rm 213, West Allis, WI, 53214-3110. Tel: 414-456-5393. Fax: 414-456-5413. p. 2648

Henschel, Kathy, Asst Librn, Forest County Library, 106 Pine St, Marienville, PA, 16239. Tel: 814-927-8552. Fax: 814-927-8552. p. 2084

Hensel, Mike, Dir, London Public Library, 20 E First St, London, OH, 43140. Tel: 740-852-9543. Fax: 740-852-3691. p. 1911

Hensen, Janet, Circ, Shenandoah Public Library, 201 S Elm St, Shenandoah, IA, 51601. Tel: 712-246-2315. Fax: 712-246-5847. p. 843

Hensey, Mary, Dir, Northminster Presbyterian Church Library, 703 Compton Rd, Cincinnati, OH, 45231. Tel: 513-931-0243. Fax: 513-931-0260. p. 1871

Henshaw, Janice, Exec Dir, British Columbia Land Surveyors Foundation, No 301-2400 Bevan Ave, Sidney, BC, V8L 1W1, CANADA. Tel: 250-655-7222. Fax: 250-655-7223. p. 2737

Henshaw, Rod Neal, Dean of Libr, Drake University, 2725 University Ave, Des Moines, IA, 50311. Tel: 515-271-3993. Fax: 515-271-3933. p. 809

Henshaw, Rodney N, Pres, Iowa Private Academic Library Consortium, c/o Buena Vista University Library, 610 W Fourth St, Storm Lake, IA, 50588. Tel: 712-749-2127, 749-2203. Fax: 712-749-2033. p. 2943

Henslee, Holli, Librn, Southwest Baptist University Libraries, Springfield Campus Library, 4431 S Fremont, Springfield, MO, 65804-7307. Tel: 417-820-2103. Fax: 417-820-4847. p. 1320

Hensley, Angela, Actg Dir, Lincoln County Public Library, 201 Lancaster St, Stanford, KY, 40484. Tel: 606-365-7513. Fax: 606-365-5566. p. 935

Hensley, Barry, Librn, Tulsa City-County Library, Zarrow Regional Library, 2224 W 51st, Tulsa, OK, 74107. Tel: 918-591-4366. p. 1983

Hensley, Bill, Dir, Berwyn Public Library, 2701 Harlem Ave, Berwyn, IL, 60402. Tel: 708-795-8000. Fax: 708-795-8101. p. 594

Hensley, Craig, Br Mgr, Kansas City, Kansas Public Library, Mr & Mrs F L Schlagle, 4051 West Dr, Kansas City, KS, 66109. Tel: 913-299-2384. Fax: 913-299-9967. p. 875

Hensley, Dan, Ref & Instruction Librn, University of California, Berkeley, Thomas J Long Business & Economics Library, Haas School of Business, Rm S352, Berkeley, CA, 94720-6000. Tel: 510-642-0370. Fax: 510-643-5277. p. 128

Hensley, Elizabeth, Tech Serv, Culpeper County Library, 271 Southgate Shopping Ctr, Culpeper, VA, 22701-3215. Tel: 540-825-8691. Fax: 540-825-7486. p. 2459

Hensley, Evelyn, Dir, Southeast Kentucky Community & Technical College, Two Long Ave, Whitesburg, KY, 41858. Tel: 606-589-3334. p. 937

Hensley, Kelly, Head, Acq, East Tennessee State University, Sherrod Library, Seehorn Dr & Lake St, Johnson City, TN, 37614-0204. Tel: 423-439-5815. Fax: 423-439-4410. p. 2239

Hensley, Marian, Asst Dir, Maltman Memorial Public Library, 910 Main St, Wood River, NE, 68883. Tel: 308-583-2349. p. 1424

Hensley, Marilyn, Assoc Librn, Olmsted County Historical Society, 1195 W Circle Dr SW, Rochester, MN, 55902. Tel: 507-282-9447. Fax: 507-289-5481. p. 1272

Hensley, Monica, Br Mgr, Massanutten Regional Library, Elkton Community, 106 N Terrace Ave, Elkton, VA, 22827. Tel: monicah@mrlib.org. Fax: 540-298-0545. p. 2470

Hensley, Randy B, Coordr, Info Serv, Baruch College-CUNY, 151 E 25 St, Box H-0520, New York, NY, 10010-2313. Tel: 646-312-1609. p. 1670

Hensley, Tim, Ref, Pamunkey Regional Library, Atlee, 9161 Atlee Rd, Mechanicsville, VA, 23116. Tel: 804-559-0654. Fax: 804-559-0645. p. 2469

Hensman, Kathleen, Ref Librn, Delray Beach Public Library, 100 W Atlantic Ave, Delray Beach, FL, 33444. Tel: 561-819-6404. Fax: 561-266-9757. p. 437

Henson, Bruce, Assoc Dean, Res & Learning Serv, Georgia Institute of Technology Library, 704 Cherry St, Atlanta, GA, 30332-0900. Tel: 404-894-4501. Fax: 404-894-6084. p. 515

Henson, Olga, Circ, North Lake College Library, 5001 N MacArthur Blvd, Irving, TX, 75062. Tel: 972-273-3400. Fax: 972-273-3431. p. 2347

Henson, Patricia, Acq, Dougherty County Public Library, 300 Pine Ave, Albany, GA, 31701-2533. Tel: 229-420-3200. Fax: 229-420-3215. p. 507

Henson, Patricia, Br Mgr, Dougherty County Public Library, Southside, 2114 Habersham Rd, Albany, GA, 31705. Tel: 229-420-3260. p. 507

Henson, Sherry, Br Librn, Spartanburg County Public Libraries, Middle Tyger Library, 170 Groce Rd, Lyman, SC, 29365. Tel: 864-439-4759. p. 2205

Henthorn, Connie, Librn, Selover Public Library, 31 State Rte 95, Chesterville, OH, 43317-0025. Tel: 419-768-3431. Fax: 419-768-2249. p. 1867

Henthorn, Susan, Coordr, Berea Digital, Berea College, 100 Campus Dr, Berea, KY, 40404. Tel: 859-985-3268. Fax: 859-985-3912. p. 907

Henthorne, Nancy, ILL, Tennessee State University, 3500 John A Merritt Blvd, Nashville, TN, 37209. Tel: 615-963-5211. Fax: 615-963-5216. p. 2259

Hentz, Holly, Dir, Hamburg Township Library, 10411 Merrill Rd, Hamburg, MI, 48139. Tel: 810-231-1771. Fax: 810-231-1520. p. 1187

Hentz, Margaret B, Mgr, Dow Agrosciences, 9330 Zionsville Rd, Indianapolis, IN, 46268. Tel: 317-337-3517. Fax: 317-337-3245. p. 750

Hentzen, Jennifer, Adult Serv, Idaho Falls Public Library, 457 W Broadway, Idaho Falls, ID, 83402. Tel: 208-612-8460. Fax: 208-612-8467. p. 576

Henuset, Alana, Info Officer, Manitoba Agriculture, Food & Rural Initiatives, 810 Phillips St, Portage la Prairie, MB, R1N 3J9, CANADA. Tel: 204-239-3465. Fax: 204-239-3180. p. 2750

Hepker, Kathleen, Librn, Hudson Public Library, 205 S Market, Hudson, MI, 49247. Tel: 517-448-3801. Fax: 517-448-5095. p. 1192

Hepker, Theresa, Cat & Coll Librn, Whatcom County Library System, 5205 Northwest Dr, Bellingham, WA, 98226-9050. Tel: 360-384-3150. Fax: 360-384-4947. p. 2509

Hepler, Christine I, Assoc Dir, University of Maine School of Law, 246 Deering Ave, Portland, ME, 04102. Tel: 207-780-4827. Fax: 207-780-4913. p. 997

Hepp, David, Coordr, Extn Serv, Marion Public Library, Henkle-Holliday Memorial, 86 S High, La Rue, OH, 43332. Tel: 740-499-3066. p. 1914

Heppe, Jodi, Tech Serv, Louisville Public Library, 700 Lincoln Ave, Louisville, OH, 44641-1474. Tel: 330-875-1696. Fax: 330-875-3530. p. 1912

Her Many Horses, Kathi, Ref, Sinte Gleska University Library, E Hwy 18, Mission, SD, 57555. Tel: 605-856-8100, 605-856-8112. Fax: 605-856-2011. p. 2215

Herald, Dennis, Coordr, Rumberger, Kirk & Caldwell PA, 300 S Orange Ave, Ste 1400, Orlando, FL, 32801. Tel: 407-872-7300. Fax: 407-841-2133. p. 477

Herald, Glenna, Ref, Cincinnati Law Library Association, Hamilton County Court House, 1000 Main St, Rm 601, Cincinnati, OH, 45202. Tel: 513-946-5300, 513-946-5301. Fax: 513-946-5252. p. 1869

Heran, Anna, Archivist, Info Spec, Website Mgr, Lloyd Library & Museum, 917 Plum St, Cincinnati, OH, 45202. Tel: 513-721-3707. Fax: 513-721-6575. p. 1870

Heran, Maggie, Exec Dir, Lloyd Library & Museum, 917 Plum St, Cincinnati, OH, 45202. Tel: 513-721-3707. Fax: 513-721-6575. p. 1870

Heras, Elaine, Assoc Dir, Lewis & Clark College, Aubrey R Watzek Library, 0615 SW Palatine Hill Rd, Portland, OR, 97219-7899. Tel: 503-768-7277. Fax: 503-768-7282. p. 2011

Herb, Steven, Dir, Pa Ctr for the Bk, Head Librn, Pennsylvania State University Libraries, Education & Behavioral Sciences, 501 Paterno Library, University Park, PA, 16802-1812. Tel: 814-863-2141. p. 2148

Herberg, Robert, Ref, Alhambra Public Library, 101 S First St, Alhambra, CA, 91801-3432. Tel: 626-570-5008. Fax: 626-457-1104. p. 120

Herbert, Anita J, In Charge, Bradford Regional Medical Center, 116 Interstate Pkwy, Bradford, PA, 16701. Tel: 814-362-8572. Fax: 814-362-8632. p. 2037

Herbert, Barbara, Librn, Georgian Court University, 900 Lakewood Ave, Lakewood, NJ, 08701-2697. Tel: 732-987-2428. Fax: 732-987-2017. p. 1493

Herbert, Barry, Dep Circuit Librn, William J Campbell Library of the US Courts, 219 S Dearborn St, Rm 1637, Chicago, IL, 60604-1769. Tel: 312-435-5660. Fax: 312-408-5031. p. 607

Herbert, Bonita L, Head, Acq, Nicholls State University, 906 E First St, Thibodaux, LA, 70310. Tel: 985-448-4646, 985-448-4660. Fax: 985-448-4925. p. 971

Herbert, Candace, Ref, Fergus Falls Public Library, 205 E Hampden, Fergus Falls, MN, 56537-2930. Tel: 218-739-9387. Fax: 218-736-5131. p. 1251

Herbert, Dina, Circ Mgr, Johns Hopkins University School of Advanced International Studies, 1740 Massachusetts Ave NW, Washington, DC, 20036. Tel: 202-663-5900. Fax: 202-663-5916. p. 405

Herbert, Ethel, Librn, Shaw Library, Main St, Mercer, ME, 04957. Tel: 207-587-2529. Fax: 207-587-2529. p. 991

Herbert, Julia, Evening/Weekend Supvr, Snow College, 141 E Center St, Ephraim, UT, 84627. Tel: 435-283-7363. Fax: 435-283-7369. p. 2405

Herbert, Kelly, Dir, United States Army, Allen Memorial Library, Bldg 660, 7460 Colorado Ave, Fort Polk, LA, 71459-5000. Tel: 337-531-2665. Fax: 337-531-6687. p. 949

Herbert, Malveaux, Librn, Maryland Correctional Institution for Women Library, Rte 175, Box 535, Jessup, MD, 20794. Tel: 410-379-3828. Fax: 410-799-8867. p. 1033

Herbert, Mary, Asst Librn, Cazenovia Public Library, 100 Albany St, Cazenovia, NY, 13035. Tel: 315-655-9322. p. 1604

Herbert, Paul H, Exec Dir, Colonel Robert R McCormick Research Center, One S 151 Winfield Rd, Wheaton, IL, 60189-6097. Tel: 630-260-8186. Fax: 630-260-9298. p. 718

Herbert, Rose, Govt Doc, Micro, Southern University, Oliver B Spellman Law Library, 56 Roosevelt Steptoe, Baton Rouge, LA, 70813. Tel: 225-771-2194. Fax: 225-771-6254. p. 944

Herbert, Sandra, Librn, Cremona Municipal Library, 205 First St E, Cremona, AB, T0M 0R0, CANADA. Tel: 403-637-3762. Fax: 403-637-2101. p. 2696

Herbert, Sharon, ILL, Vermilion Parish Library, 405 E Saint Victor, Abbeville, LA, 70510-5101. Tel: 337-893-2655. Fax: 337-898-0526. p. 939

Herbert, Teri Lynn, Ref Librn, Medical University of South Carolina Library, 171 Ashley Ave, Ste 300, Charleston, SC, 29425-0001. Tel: 843-792-9211. Fax: 843-792-7947. p. 2184

Herbison, Tina, Reader Serv Mgr, Braille Institute Library Services, 741 N Vermont Ave, Los Angeles, CA, 90029-3514. Tel: 323-663-1111, Ext 1382. Fax: 323-662-2440. p. 168

Herbst, Joni, Tech Serv Librn, University of Oregon Libraries, John E Jaqua Law Library, William W Knight Law Ctr, 2nd Flr, 1515 Agate St, Eugene, OR, 97403-1221. Tel: 541-346-1655. Fax: 541-346-1669. p. 1997

Herbst, Lynne, Librn, Mount Holly Town Library, 26 Maple Hill Rd, Belmont, VT, 05730. Tel: 802-259-3707. p. 2418

Herc, Karen, Ch, Adams Memorial Library, 1112 Ligonier St, Latrobe, PA, 15650. Tel: 724-539-1972. Fax: 724-537-0338. p. 2078

Herd, Ellie, Head, Tech Serv, Dover Town Library, 56 Dedham St, Dover, MA, 02030-2214. Tel: 508-785-8113. Fax: 508-785-0138. p. 1085

Herdelin, Jamey, Mrs, Asst Prof, University of Kentucky, 320 Little Library Bldg, Lexington, KY, 40506-0224. Tel: 859-257-4161. Fax: 859-257-4205. p. 2966

Herder, Carolyn, Acq, US Department of Commerce, Radio Bldg, Rm 1202, 325 Broadway MC5, Boulder, CO, 80305-3328. Tel: 303-497-3271. Fax: 303-497-3890. p. 291

Herder, Melinda, Dir, Humboldt Public Library, 916 Bridge St, Humboldt, KS, 66748-1834. Tel: 620-473-2243. p. 873

Herdman, Rose, Librn, Flatbush Community Library, General Delivery, Flatbush, AB, T0G 0Z0, CANADA. Tel: 780-681-3756. p. 2704

Herdrich, Betty, Asst Librn, Feleti Barstow Public Library, PO Box 997687, Pago Pago, AS, 96799. Tel: 684-633-5816. Fax: 684-633-5823. p. 2666

Herdt, Tim, Syst Spec, United States Air Force, 28 FSS/FSDL, 2650 Doolittle Dr, Bldg 3910, Ellsworth AFB, SD, 57706-4820. Tel: 605-385-1686, 605-385-1688. Fax: 605-385-4467. p. 2212

Herendeen, Donna, Sci Librn, Lenhardt Library of the Chicago Botanic Garden, 1000 Lake Cook Rd, Glencoe, IL, 60022. Tel: 847-835-8273. Fax: 847-835-6885. p. 650

Heres, Simon, Mgr, Libr Info Tech, Biola University Library, 13800 Biola Ave, La Mirada, CA, 90639. Tel: 562-944-0351, Ext 5612. Fax: 562-903-4840. p. 162

Heretyk, Shelley, Chairperson, Washington Township Historical Society Library, Six Fairview Ave, Long Valley, NJ, 07853-3172. Tel: 908-876-9696. p. 1497

Herfurth, Kathy, Dir, Alger Public Library, 100 W Wagner St, Alger, OH, 45812. Tel: 419-757-7755. Fax: 419-757-7755. p. 1854

Hergert, Tom, Dr, Dir, Learning & Tech Res, Northern Virginia Community College Libraries, Manassas Campus, Colgan Hall, Rm 129, 6901 Sudley Rd, Manassas, VA, 20109-2399. Tel: 703-530-8259. Fax: 703-368-1069. p. 2447

Herick, Kathi, Head, Automation, Wright State University Libraries, 126 Dunbar Library, 3640 Colonel Glenn Hwy, Dayton, OH, 45435-0001. Tel: 937-775-3889. Fax: 937-775-4109. p. 1895

Herine, Sanford, Health Info Coordr, CHRISTUS St Mary Hospital, 3600 Gates Blvd, Port Arthur, TX, 77642-3850. Tel: 409-989-5150, 409-989-5804. Fax: 409-989-5137. p. 2371

Hering, Dawn, Dir, Strum Public Library, 114 Fifth Ave, Strum, WI, 54770. Tel: 715-695-3848. Fax: 715-695-3510. p. 2640

Hering, Karen, Ref Librn, Grant MacEwan University Library, 10700 104th Ave, Edmonton, AB, T5J 4S2, CANADA. Tel: 780-497-5850. Fax: 780-497-5895. p. 2701

Hering, Paula, Children's Prog Coordr, Covington-Veedersburg Public Library, Veedersburg Public, 408 N Main St, Veedersburg, IN, 47987. Tel: 765-294-2808. Fax: 765-294-4648. p. 734

Herkelman, Donna, Coordr, Mercy Medical Center Library, 1410 N Fourth St, Clinton, IA, 52732. Tel: 563-244-5555. Fax: 563-244-5592. p. 803

Herkovic, Andrew, Dir, Communications & Develop, Stanford University Libraries, 557 Escondido Mall, Stanford, CA, 94305-6004. Tel: 650-725-1064. p. 270

Herl, Vickie, Admin Mgr, Central Kansas Library System, 1409 Williams St, Great Bend, KS, 67530-4020. Tel: 620-792-4865. Fax: 620-792-5495. p. 869

Herlihy, Kit, Coordr, Cat, California State University, 333 S Twin Oaks Valley Rd, San Marcos, CA, 92096-0001. Tel: 760-750-4357. Fax: 760-750-3287. p. 254

Herlocker, Annie, Coll Develop Coordr, Linebaugh Public Library System of Rutherford County, 105 W Vine St, Murfreesboro, TN, 37130-3673. Tel: 615-893-4131. Fax: 615-848-5038. p. 2254

Hermalyn, Gary, Dr, Exec Dir, Bronx County Historical Society, 3309 Bainbridge Ave, Bronx, NY, 10467. Tel: 718-881-8900. Fax: 718-881-4827. p. 1586

Herman, Andrea, Dir, Adult Serv, Crandall Public Library, 251 Glen St, Glens Falls, NY, 12801-3593. Tel: 518-792-6508. Fax: 518-792-5251. p. 1629

Herman, Brian, Info Ctr Analyst, Emerson Process Management, RA Engel Technical Ctr, 1700 12th Ave, Marshalltown, IA, 50158. Tel: 641-754-2161. Fax: 641-754-3159. p. 830

Herman, Debbie, Electronic Res Librn, Central Connecticut State University, 1615 Stanley St, New Britain, CT, 06050. Tel: 860-832-2084. Fax: 860-832-3409. p. 353

Herman, Deborah, Ch, Oregon Public Library District, 300 Jefferson St, Oregon, IL, 61061. Tel: 815-732-2724. Fax: 815-732-6643. p. 686

Herman, Fred, Dir, Hamburg Center, Old Rte 22, Hamburg, PA, 19526. Tel: 610-562-6053. Fax: 610-562-6065. p. 2063

Herman, Justin, Ref Librn, Johnson & Wales University, 801 W Trade St, Charlotte, NC, 28202. Tel: 980-598-1607. p. 1783

Herman, Leslie, Mgr, John Peter Smith Hospital, 1500 S Main St, Fort Worth, TX, 76104. Tel: 817-921-3431, Ext 5088. Fax: 817-923-0718. p. 2323

Herman, Valerie, Adult Serv, Ref Librn, Somers Library, 80 Primrose St, Rte 139 & Reis Park, Somers, NY, 10589. Tel: 914-232-5717. Fax: 914-232-1035. p. 1745

Hermann, Bennett, In Charge, Temple Emanu-El, 455 Neptune Blvd, Long Beach, NY, 11561. Tel: 516-431-4060. Fax: 516-897-7465. p. 1654

Hermann, Carol, Librn, Lakeland Library Region, Hafford Branch, Box 520, Hafford, SK, S0J 1A0, CANADA. Tel: 306-549-2373. Fax: 306-549-2333. p. 2920

Hermann, Lew, Ref Serv, Queens University of Charlotte, 1900 Selwyn Ave, Charlotte, NC, 28274-0001. Tel: 704-337-2470. Fax: 704-337-2517. p. 1784

Hermes, Stacie, Dir, Potter Public Library, 333 Chestnut, Potter, NE, 69156. Tel: 308-879-4345. p. 1417

Hermiller, Ruth, Br Mgr, Putnam County District Library, Kalida Branch, 110 S Broad St, Kalida, OH, 45853-0183. Tel: 419-532-2129. p. 1926

Hermsen, Renee, Librn, Arizona Department of Corrections - Adult Institutions, 10000 S Wilmot Rd, Tucson, AZ, 85734. Tel: 520-574-0024, Ext 37919. Fax: 520-574-7308. p. 85

Hernandez, Alberto, Assoc Dir, Chief Librn, Hunter College Libraries, Centro - Center for Puerto Rican Studies Library, 2180 Third Ave, Rm 121, New York, NY, 10035. Tel: 212-396-7876. Fax: 212-396-7707. p. 1682

Hernandez, Anna, Librn, El Paso Community College Library, Northwest Campus-Jenna Welch & Laura Busch Community Library, 6701 S Desert Blvd, El Paso, TX, 79932. Tel: 915-831-8840. Fax: 915-831-8816. p. 2316

Hernandez, Carissa, Assoc Librn, Tech Serv, Cleveland Museum of Art, 11150 East Blvd, Cleveland, OH, 44106-1797. Tel: 216-707-6821. Fax: 216-421-0921. p. 1877

Hernandez, Carmen M, Dir, Alhambra Public Library, 101 S First St, Alhambra, CA, 91801-3432. Tel: 626-570-5079. Fax: 626-457-1104. p. 120

Hernandez, Cindy, Circ, El Centro College, 801 Main St, Dallas, TX, 75202-3605. Tel: 214-860-2174. Fax: 214-860-2440. p. 2308

Hernandez, Dawn, Head, Adult Serv, Marshall District Library, 124 W Green St, Marshall, MI, 49068. Tel: 269-781-7821. Fax: 269-781-7090. p. 1207

Hernandez, Frank, Libr Tech, United States Army, Institute of Surgical Research Library, 3698 Chambers Pass, Bldg 3611, Fort Sam Houston, TX, 78234-6315. Tel: 210-539-4559. Fax: 210-539-1460. p. 2321

Hernandez, Heather, Acq, Chabot College Library, 25555 Hesperian Blvd, Hayward, CA, 94545. Tel: 510-723-6763. p. 157

Hernandez, Heather, Tech Serv Librn, San Francisco Maritime Library, Fort Mason Ctr, Bldg E, 3rd Flr, San Francisco, CA, 94123. Tel: 415-561-7030. Fax: 415-556-1624. p. 245

Hernandez, Hector R, Br Mgr, Chicago Public Library, Rudy Lozano Library, 1805 S Loomis St, Chicago, IL, 60608. Tel: 312-746-4329. Fax: 312-746-4324. p. 609

Hernandez, Jeri, Librn, North Central Regional Library, Soap Lake Community, 32 E Main St, Soap Lake, WA, 98851. Tel: 509-246-1313. p. 2549

Hernandez, Jessica, Head, Coll Develop, Lehman College, City University of New York, 250 Bedford Park Blvd W, Bronx, NY, 10468-1589. Tel: 718-960-8582. Fax: 718-960-8952. p. 1587

Hernandez, Jessie, Supvr, Circ, Rancho Mirage Public Library, 71-100 Hwy 111, Rancho Mirage, CA, 92270. Tel: 760-341-7323. Fax: 760-341-5213. p. 213

Hernández, Jo Farb, Dir, Saving & Preserving Arts & Cultural Environments, 9053 Soquel Dr, Ste 205, Aptos, CA, 95003. Tel: 831-662-2907. Fax: 831-662-2918. p. 121

Hernandez, Josephine, Circ Coordr, Smith College Libraries, Anita O'K & Robert R Young Science Library, Clark Science Center, Bass Hall, Northampton, MA, 01063. Tel: 413-585-2881. Fax: 413-585-4480. p. 1114

Hernandez, Kerry, Librn, Arizona State Prison Complex Florence Libraries, 1305 E Butte Ave, Florence, AZ, 85232. Tel: 520-868-4011, Ext 6010. Fax: 520-868-8288. p. 63

Hernandez, Leonard, County Librn, San Bernardino County Library, 104 W Fourth St, San Bernardino, CA, 92415-0035. Tel: 909-387-5531. Fax: 909-387-5724. p. 228

Hernandez, Leticia M, Librn, Van Horn City County Library, 410 Crockett St, Van Horn, TX, 79855. Tel: 432-283-2855. Fax: 432-283-8316. p. 2395

Hernandez, Maria, Libr Serv Mgr, Mid-State Technical College, 2600 W Fifth St, Marshfield, WI, 54449. Tel: 715-422-5469. Fax: 715-422-5466. p. 2613

Hernandez, Maria, Libr Serv Mgr, Mid-State Technical College Library, 500 32nd St N, Wisconsin Rapids, WI, 54494. Tel: 715-422-5470. Fax: 715-422-5466. p. 2650

Hernandez, Mayra, Asst Dir, Port Chester-Rye Brook Public Library, One Haseco Ave, Port Chester, NY, 10573. Tel: 914-939-6710, Ext 111. Fax: 914-939-4735. p. 1720

Hernandez, Michele, Adult Serv, Winslow Public Library, 420 W Gilmore St, Winslow, AZ, 86047. Tel: 928-289-4982. Fax: 928-289-4182. p. 90

Hernandez, Patricia, Br Mgr, El Paso Public Library, Dorris Van Doren Regional, 551 Redd Rd, El Paso, TX, 79912. Tel: 915-875-0700. Fax: 915-585-1524. p. 2316

Hernandez, Pedro Juan, Sr Archivist, Hunter College Libraries, Centro - Center for Puerto Rican Studies Library, 2180 Third Ave, Rm 121, New York, NY, 10035. Tel: 212-772-5151. Fax: 212-396-7707. p. 1682

Hernandez, Philip, Syst Adminr, University of the Incarnate Word, 4301 Broadway, UPO Box 297, San Antonio, TX, 78209-6397. Tel: 210-829-3843. Fax: 210-829-6041. p. 2384

Hernandez, Steve, Dir, Oglala Lakota College, Pejuta Haka College Center, PO Box 370, Kyle, SD, 57752-0370. Tel: 605-455-2450. Fax: 605-455-2671. p. 2214

Hernandez, Terry, Librn, Arizona Department of Corrections - Adult Institutions, 4374 Butte Ave, Florence, AZ, 85232. Tel: 520-868-0201, Ext 4026. Fax: 520-868-8556. p. 63

Hernandez, Valeriano, Libr Mat Proc Spec, Laredo Community College, West End Washington St, Laredo, TX, 78040. Tel: 956-721-5279. Fax: 956-721-5447. p. 2353

Hernandez, Yvonne, Head, Circ, Brigham Young University-Hawaii, 55-220 Kulanui St, BYU-Hawaii, No 1966, Laie, HI, 96762-1294. Tel: 808-675-3850. Fax: 808-675-3877. p. 567

Hernandez-Delgado, Julio, Archivist, Hunter College Libraries, 695 Park Ave, New York, NY, 10065. Tel: 212-772-4149. Fax: 212-772-4142. p. 1682

Hernandez-Kurtulus, Susana, Librn, Veterans Health Administration, 1201 Broad Rock Blvd, Richmond, VA, 23249. Tel: 804-675-5142. Fax: 804-675-5252. p. 2492

Hernas, Pat, Access Serv, Mission College Library, 3000 Mission College Blvd, Santa Clara, CA, 95054-1897. Tel: 408-855-5167. Fax: 408-855-5462. p. 262

Hernden, Ken, Univ Librn, Algoma University College, 1520 Queen St E, Sault Ste. Marie, ON, P6A 2G4, CANADA. Tel: 705-949-2101. Fax: 705-949-6583. p. 2840

Herndon, Amy, Commun Coordr, Marion ISD Community Library, 500 Bulldog Blvd, Marion, TX, 78124. Tel: 830-914-2803, Ext 430, 830-914-4268. p. 2359

Herndon, Joel, PhD, Head, Data & GIS Serv, Duke University Libraries, 411 Chapel Dr, Durham, NC, 27708. Tel: 919-660-5946. Fax: 919-660-5923. p. 1787

Herndon, Kimmetha, Dir, Samford University Library, 800 Lakeshore Dr, Birmingham, AL, 35229. Tel: 205-726-2846. Fax: 205-726-4009. p. 9

Herndon, Laura, Per Asst, Clayton State University, 2000 Clayton State Blvd, Morrow, GA, 30260. Tel: 678-466-4335. Fax: 678-466-4349. p. 545

Herndon, Sylvia, Asst Librn, Wickenburg Public Library, 164 E Apache St, Wickenburg, AZ, 85390. Tel: 928-684-2665. p. 89

Herndon, Thomas, Coop Librn, ICF Consulting Inc, 630 K St, Ste 400, Sacramento, CA, 95814. Tel: 916-737-3000. Fax: 916-737-3030. p. 224

Herndon, Tom, Interim Dir, Claude Pepper Library, 636 W Call St, Tallahassee, FL, 32306-1123. Tel: 850-644-9305. Fax: 850-644-9350. p. 495

Hernon, Peter, Prof, Simmons College, 300 The Fenway, Boston, MA, 02115. Tel: 617-521-2800. Fax: 617-521-3192. p. 2967

Herold, Andrew D, Dir, Libr Serv, Logan-Hocking County District Library, 230 E Main St, Logan, OH, 43138. Tel: 740-385-2348. Fax: 740-385-9093. p. 1910

Herold, Doreen, Cat, Lehigh University, Fairchild-Martindale Library, Eight A E Packer Ave, Bethlehem, PA, 18015-3170. Tel: 610-758-2639. Fax: 610-758-6524. p. 2034

Herold, Irene M, Dean, Keene State College, 229 Main St, Keene, NH, 03435-3201. Tel: 603-358-2736. Fax: 603-358-2745. p. 1453

Herold, Kathy, Coordr, St Rita's Medical Center, 730 W Market St, Lima, OH, 45801-4667. Tel: 419-996-5842. Fax: 419-996-5166. p. 1910

Herold, Ken, Dir, Info Syst, Hamilton College, 198 College Hill Rd, Clinton, NY, 13323-1299. Tel: 315-859-4487. Fax: 315-859-4578. p. 1607

Herold, Philip, Asst Librn, University of Minnesota Libraries-Twin Cities, Forestry, B-50 Skok Hall, 2003 Upper Buford Circle, Saint Paul, MN, 55108. Tel: 612-624-3222. Fax: 612-624-3733. p. 1262

Herold, Tomi, Dir, Highland County Public Library, 31 N Water St, Monterey, VA, 24465. Tel: 540-468-2373. Fax: 540-468-2085. p. 2479

Herold, Tracy, Dir, Sun Prairie Public Library, 1350 Linnerud Dr, Sun Prairie, WI, 53590-2631. Tel: 608-825-7323. Fax: 608-825-3936. p. 2641

Heron, Christine, Sr Br Librn, Genesee District Library, Fenton-Jack R Winegarden Library, 200 E Caroline St, Fenton, MI, 48430. Tel: 810-629-7612. Fax: 810-629-0855. p. 1179

Herouart, Karen, Web Coordr, Greenburgh Public Library, 300 Tarrytown Rd, Elmsford, NY, 10523. Tel: 914-721-8217. Fax: 914-721-8201. p. 1620

Herr, Denise, Youth Serv Librn, South Milwaukee Public Library, 1907 Tenth Ave, South Milwaukee, WI, 53172. Tel: 414-768-8195. Fax: 414-768-8072. p. 2639

Herr, Jorene, Chief Librn, Bruun Memorial Public Library, 730 Third St, Humboldt, NE, 68376. Tel: 402-862-2914. p. 1402

Herr, Susan, Dir, Bulverde Area Rural Library District, 131 Bulverde Crossing, Bulverde, TX, 78163. Tel: 830-438-4864. Fax: 830-980-3362. p. 2293

Herrera, Alberto, Diversity Serv Librn, Marquette University Libraries, 1355 W Wisconsin Ave, Milwaukee, WI, 53233. Tel: 414-288-2140. Fax: 414-288-8821. p. 2618

Herrera, Gail, Asst Dean, Tech Serv, University of Mississippi, One Library Loop, University, MS, 38677. Tel: 662-915-5674. Fax: 662-915-5734. p. 1316

Herrera, Joy, Head, Youth Serv, Tarpon Springs Public Library, 138 E Lemon St, Tarpon Springs, FL, 34689. Tel: 727-943-4922. Fax: 727-943-4926. p. 499

Herrera, Luis, City Librn, San Francisco Public Library, 100 Larkin St, San Francisco, CA, 94102-4733. Tel: 415-557-4400. Fax: 415-557-4424. p. 246

Herrera, Lupe, Circ Coordr, Buda Public Library, 303 Main St, Buda, TX, 78610. Tel: 512-295-5899. Fax: 512-295-6525. p. 2293

Herrera, Martha, Br Mgr, El Paso Public Library, Irving Schwartz Branch, 1865 Dean Martin, El Paso, TX, 79936. Tel: 915-857-0594. Fax: 915-857-7218. p. 2316

Herrera, Norma, Dir, Dilley Public Library, 231 W FM 117, Dilley, TX, 78017. Tel: 830-965-1951. Fax: 830-965-4131. p. 2314

Herrgra, Claudra, Circ, Cerritos Library, 18025 Bloomfield Ave, Cerritos, CA, 90703. Tel: 562-916-1350. Fax: 562-916-1375, p. 133

Herrick, Amanda, Asst Dir, Mellinger Memorial Library, 11 Division St, Morning Sun, IA, 52640. Tel: 319-868-7505. Fax: 319-868-7505. p. 833

Herrick, Emily, Head, Ch, The Hampton Library, 2478 Main St, Bridgehampton, NY, 11932. Tel: 631-537-0015. Fax: 631-537-7229. p. 1585

Herrick, Janet, Head, Tech Serv, North Canton Public Library, 185 N Main St, North Canton, OH, 44720-2595. Tel: 330-499-4712. Fax: 330-499-7356. p. 1923

Herrick, Michael, Cataloger, Holy Trinity Orthodox Seminary Library, 1407 Robinson Rd, Jordanville, NY, 13361-0036. Tel: 315-858-3116. Fax: 315-858-0945. p. 1648

Herrick, Rebecca, Fiscal Officer, Burton Public Library, 14588 W Park St, Burton, OH, 44021. Tel: 440-834-4466. Fax: 440-834-0128. p. 1862

Herrick, Susan, Res, University of Maryland, Baltimore, Thurgood Marshall Law Library, 501 W Fayette St, Baltimore, MD, 21201-1768. Tel: 410-706-0793. Fax: 410-706-8354. p. 1019

Herridge, Fay, Librn, Fortune Public Library, Temple St, Fortune, NL, A0E 1P0, CANADA. Tel: 709-832-0232. Fax: 709-832-2210. p. 2770

Herries, Martina, Exec Dir, Bagaduce Music Lending Library, Five Music Library Lane, Blue Hill, ME, 04614. Tel: 207-374-5454. Fax: 207-374-2733. p. 978

Herriges, Jean, Sr Librn, San Jose Public Library, Rose Garden, 1580 Naglee Ave, San Jose, CA, 95126-2094. Tel: 408-808-3070. Fax: 408-999-0909. p. 251

Herriges, Jean, Sr Librn, San Jose Public Library, Willow Glen, 1157 Minnesota Ave, San Jose, CA, 95125-3324. Tel: 408-808-3045. Fax: 408-947-8901. p. 251

Herrin, Julie, Dir, Northville District Library, 212 W Cady St, Northville, MI, 48167-1560. Tel: 248-349-3020. Fax: 248-349-8250. p. 1214

Herring, Barbara, Libr Dir, Harry Benge Crozier Memorial Library, 184 W Moss St, Paint Rock, TX, 76866. Tel: 325-732-4320. p. 2367

Herring, Cathy, Supvr, Arkansas Department of Correction, Diagnostic Unit Library, 7500 Correction Circle, Pine Bluff, AR, 71603-1498. Tel: 870-267-6410. Fax: 870-267-6721. p. 112

Herring, Gary, Cat, Jones County Junior College, 900 S Court St, Ellisville, MS, 39437. Tel: 601-477-4055. Fax: 601-477-2600. p. 1298

Herring, Jenny, Libr Mgr, Three Rivers Regional Library System, St Simons Public Library, 530A Beachview Dr, Saint Simons Island, GA, 31522. Tel: 912-638-8234. Fax: 912-638-8254. p. 522

Herring, Jenny, Libr Mgr, Saint Simons Public Library, 530A Beachview Dr, Saint Simons Island, GA, 31522. Tel: 912-638-8234. Fax: 912-638-8254. p. 549

Herring, Joan, Tech Serv, Andalusia Public Library, 212 S Three Notch St, Andalusia, AL, 36420. Tel: 334-222-6612. Fax: 334-222-6612. p. 4

Herring, Mark Y, Dr, Dean, Libr Serv, Winthrop University, 824 Oakland Ave, Rock Hill, SC, 29733. Tel: 803-323-2232. Fax: 803-323-2215. p. 2203

Herring, Sherri, Interim Br Coordr, Shelby County Libraries, Jackson Center Memorial, 205 S Linden St, Jackson Center, OH, 45334. Tel: 937-596-5300. Fax: 937-596-5300. p. 1935

Herring, Susan, Dr, Cataloger/Ref Librn, Athens State University Library, 407 E Pryor St, Athens, AL, 35611. Tel: 256-233-8218. Fax: 256-233-6547. p. 5

Herring, William Dallas, Librn, Duplin County Historical Foundation, PO Box 130, Rose Hill, NC, 28458. Tel: 910-289-2430. p. 1821

Herrington, Cheryl, Libr Mgr, Community College of Beaver County Library, One Campus Dr, Monaca, PA, 15061-2588. Tel: 724-775-8561, Ext 316. Fax: 724-728-8024. p. 2090

Herrington, Deborah, Head, Circ, The Library of Hattiesburg, Petal, Forrest County, 329 Hardy St, Hattiesburg, MS, 39401-3496. Tel: 601-582-4461. Fax: 601-582-5338. p. 1300

Herrington, Joy, Ch, Shaler North Hills Library, 1822 Mount Royal Blvd, Glenshaw, PA, 15116. Tel: 412-486-0211. Fax: 412-486-8286. p. 2061

Herrington, Lori, Br Mgr, Saint Clair County Library System, Memphis Public, 34830 Potter St, Memphis, MI, 48041. Tel: 810-392-2980. Fax: 810-392-3206. p. 1219

Herrington, Lori, Br Mgr, Saint Clair County Library System, Yale Public, Two Jones St, Yale, MI, 48097. Tel: 810-387-2940. Fax: 810-387-2051. p. 1220

Herrington, Mimi, Dir, Bad Axe Area District Library, 200 S Hanselman, Bad Axe, MI, 48413. Tel: 989-269-8538. Fax: 989-269-2411. p. 1155

Herrity, Carol, Ref Librn, Lehigh County Historical Society, Lehigh Valley Heritage Museum, 432 W Walnut St, Allentown, PA, 18102-5428. Tel: 610-435-1074, Ext 12. Fax: 610-435-9812. p. 2026

Herrlein, Alex, Ref Librn, Lloyd Library & Museum, 917 Plum St, Cincinnati, OH, 45202. Tel: 513-721-3707. Fax: 513-721-6575. p. 1870

Herrlich, Katherine, Res & Instruction Librn, Northeastern University Libraries, Snell Library, 360 Huntington Ave, Boston, MA, 02115. Tel: 617-373-5305. p. 1065

Herrling, Leah W, Mkt, Southwest Wisconsin Library System, 1775 Fourth St, Fennimore, WI, 53809-1137. Tel: 608-822-2054. Fax: 608-822-6251. p. 2591

Herrmann, Ann, Youth Serv Mgr, Manitowoc Public Library, 707 Quay St, Manitowoc, WI, 54220. Tel: 920-686-3000. p. 2612

Herrmann, Becky, Dir, Chelmsford Public Library, 25 Boston Rd, Chelmsford, MA, 01824-3088. Tel: 978-256-5521. Fax: 978-256-8511. p. 1079

Herrmann, Ellen, Ref Serv, Ad, Crete Public Library District, 1177 N Main St, Crete, IL, 60417. Tel: 708-672-8017. Fax: 708-672-3529. p. 632

Herrmann, Gretchen, Bibliographer, SUNY Cortland, 81 Prospect Terrace, Cortland, NY, 13045. Tel: 607-753-2525. Fax: 607-753-5669. p. 1611

Herrmann, Stephanie, Dir, Union Parish Library, 202 W Jackson St, Farmerville, LA, 71241-2799. Tel: 318-368-9226, 318-368-9288. Fax: 318-368-9224. p. 949

Herron, Shelley, Ch, Albion District Library, 501 S Superior St, Albion, MI, 49224. Tel: 517-629-3993. Fax: 517-629-5354. p. 1148

Herron, Susan J, Br Mgr, Public Library Association of Annapolis & Anne Arundel County, Inc, Broadneck, 1275 Green Holly Dr, Annapolis, MD, 21401. Tel: 410-222-1905. Fax: 410-222-1908. p. 1010

Herrschaft, Winn, Res Librn, Washington County Historical Society & Museum Library, 17677 NW Springville Rd, Portland, OR, 97229. Tel: 503-645-5353. Fax: 503-645-5650. p. 2015

Hersberger, Julie, PhD, Dr, Assoc Prof, University of North Carolina at Greensboro, School of Education, 349 Curry Bldg, Greensboro, NC, 27402. Tel: 336-334-3482. Fax: 336-334-5060. p. 2971

Hersch, Carolyn A, Ref Librn, Neal, Gerber & Eisenberg LLP, Two N La Salle St, Ste 1700, Chicago, IL, 60602. Tel: 312-269-5275. Fax: 312-578-1793. p. 620

Hersch, Susan B, Librn, Hahn, Loeser & Parks, 200 Public Sq, Ste 3300, Cleveland, OH, 44114-2301. Tel: 216-621-0150. Fax: 216-241-2824. p. 1880

Herschberger, Seth, Asst Dir, Cass County Public Library, 400 E Mechanic, Harrisonville, MO, 64701. Tel: 816-380-4600. Fax: 816-884-2301. p. 1330

Herscovitch, Pearl, Chair, Mount Royal University Library, 4825 Mount Royal Gate SW, Calgary, AB, T3E 6K6, CANADA. Tel: 403-440-6022. Fax: 403-440-6758. p. 2692

Hersh, Daniel, Tech Serv & Automation, Oakland Public Library, 125 14th St, Oakland, CA, 94612. Tel: 510-238-3270. Fax: 510-238-2232. p. 197

Hersh, Daniel, Supv Librn, Cat & Coll Mgt, Oakland Public Library, Main Library, 125 14th St, Oakland, CA, 94612. Tel: 510-238-3134. Fax: 510-238-2232. p. 198

Hersh, Deborah, Ref Librn, Northborough Free Library, 34 Main St, Northborough, MA, 01532-1942. Tel: 508-393-5025. Fax: 508-393-5027. p. 1114

Hersh, Paul, Dir, Med Libr, Saint John's Riverside Hospital, Andrus Pavilion, Medical Library 4th Flr, 967 N Broadway, Yonkers, NY, 10701. Tel: 914-964-4281. Fax: 914-964-4971. p. 1771

Hersh, Tori, Principal Librn, Lee County Library System, Cape Coral-Lee County Public, 921 SW 39th Terrace, Cape Coral, FL, 33914-5721. Tel: 239-533-4500. p. 445

Hersh-Tudor, Andrew, Dir, Wenatchee Valley College, 1300 Fifth St, Wenatchee, WA, 98801. Tel: 509-682-6715. Fax: 509-682-6711. p. 2549

Hershberger, Judy, Dir, Oakdale Public Library, 406 Fifth St, Oakdale, NE, 68761. Tel: 402-776-2602. Fax: 402-776-2602. p. 1411

Hershfeld, Georgia, Cat, Chancellor Robert R Livingston Masonic Library of Grand Lodge, 71 W 23rd St, 14th Flr, New York, NY, 10010-4171. Tel: 212-337-6620. Fax: 212-633-2639. p. 1672

Hershman, Carol, Sr Librn, Tampa-Hillsborough County Public Library System, Austin Davis Public Library, 17808 Wayne Rd, Odessa, FL, 33556. Fax: 813-264-3903. p. 497

Hershoff, Nancy Sun, ILS Coordr/Planning Officer, Florida International University, 3000 NE 151st St, North Miami, FL, 33181-3600. Tel: 305-919-5727. Fax: 305-919-5914. p. 472

Hershorin, Jill, Archivist, Jewish Historical Society of Metrowest Library, 901 Rte 10 E, Whippany, NJ, 07981-1156. Tel: 973-929-2994, 973-929-2995. Fax: 973-428-8327. p. 1544

Hersin, Steve, Dir, Cook Public Library, 103 S River St, Cook, MN, 55723. Tel: 218-666-2210. p. 1246

Herston, Ken, Reader Serv, Alabama Public Library Service, 6030 Monticello Dr, Montgomery, AL, 36130-6000. Tel: 334-213-3906. Fax: 334-213-3993. p. 27

Hert, Darlene, Tech & Access Serv Librn, Montana State University, 1500 University Dr, Billings, MT, 59101-0298. Tel: 406-657-1661. Fax: 406-657-2037. p. 1374

Hertel, Tina, Dir, Muhlenberg College, 2400 Chew St, Allentown, PA, 18104-5586. Tel: 484-664-3550. Fax: 484-664-3511. p. 2027

Hertz, Ian, Bus Librn, Winston-Salem State University, 601 Martin Luther King Jr Dr, Winston-Salem, NC, 27110. Tel: 336-750-2532. Fax: 336-750-2459. p. 1834

Hertzler, Randy, Librn, Montgomery College, Rockville Campus Library, Macklin Tower, 51 Mannakee St, Rockville, MD, 20850. Tel: 240-567-7129. Fax: 240-567-7153. p. 1037

Hertzlinger, Helene, Head, Ref, Levittown Public Library, One Bluegrass Lane, Levittown, NY, 11756-1292. Tel: 516-731-5728. Fax: 516-735-3168. p. 1652

Hertzoff, Hilary, YA Serv, Mamaroneck Public Library District, 136 Prospect Ave, Mamaroneck, NY, 10543. Tel: 914-698-1250. Fax: 914-381-3088. p. 1657

Herwatic, Rebecca, Supvr, Access Serv, Pennsylvania State University, 1600 Woodland Rd, Abington, PA, 19001. Tel: 215-881-7431. Fax: 215-881-7423. p. 2025

Herz, Stephanie, Librn, Historical Society of Moorestown Library, 12 High St, Moorestown, NJ, 08057. Tel: 856-235-0353. p. 1504

Herzig, Stella, Ref, Saint Ambrose University Library, 518 W Locust St, Davenport, IA, 52803. Tel: 563-333-6056. Fax: 563-333-6248. p. 807

Herzig, Tara, Circ, Sunderland Public Library, 20 School St, Sunderland, MA, 01375. Tel: 413-665-2642. Fax: 413-665-1435. p. 1130

Herzinger, K, Archivist/Librn, Tryon Palace, 610 Pollock St, New Bern, NC, 28562-5614. Tel: 252-639-3500, 252-639-3537. Fax: 252-514-4876. p. 1812

Herzinger, Sandra, Librn, Christ United Methodist Church Library, 4530 A St, Lincoln, NE, 68510. Tel: 402-489-9618. Fax: 402-489-9675. p. 1404

Herzog, Brian, Head, Ref, Chelmsford Public Library, 25 Boston Rd, Chelmsford, MA, 01824-3088. Tel: 978-256-5521. Fax: 978-256-8511. p. 1079

Herzog, Dianne, Youth Serv Mgr, Council Bluffs Public Library, 400 Willow Ave, Council Bluffs, IA, 51503-4269. Tel: 712-323-7553, Ext 113. Fax: 712-323-1269. p. 805

Herzog, Fred, Computer Serv, Network Serv, Skene Memorial Library, 1017 Main St, Fleischmanns, NY, 12430. Tel: 845-254-4581. Fax: 845-254-4581. p. 1622

Herzog, Melinda, Exec Dir, Catawba County Historical Museum, 30 N College Ave, Newton, NC, 28658. Tel: 828-465-0383. Fax: 828-465-9813. p. 1813

Herzog, Sherri, Librn, Evansville Public Library, 602 S Public St, Evansville, IL, 62242. Fax: 618-853-2342. p. 645

Herzog, Susan, Info Literacy, Eastern Connecticut State University, 83 Windham St, Willimantic, CT, 06226-2295. Tel: 860-465-4470. Fax: 860-465-5521. p. 378

Herzstein, Barbara, Librn, Massachusetts Audubon Society, Ten Juniper Rd, Belmont, MA, 02478. Tel: 617-489-5050. Fax: 617-484-8664. p. 1053

Heser, Cheryl J, Dir, Rosebud County Library, 201 N Ninth Ave, Forsyth, MT, 59327. Tel: 406-346-7561. Fax: 406-346-7685. p. 1378

Heser, Steve, Adminr, Milwaukee County Federated Library System, 709 N Eighth St, Milwaukee, WI, 53233-2414. Tel: 414-286-5934. Fax: 414-286-3209. p. 2619

Heskett, Jeannine, Librn, Darien Public Library, 47 Park St, Darien, WI, 53114-0465. Tel: 262-882-5155. Fax: 262-882-5157. p. 2587

Hesler, June, Asst Libr Dir, Larchmont Public Library, 121 Larchmont Ave, Larchmont, NY, 10538. Tel: 914-834-2281. p. 1651

Heslin, Linda, Librn, New York Institute of Technology, Education Hall Library Art & Architecture Collection, PO Box 8000, Old Westbury, NY, 11568. Tel: 516-686-7422, 516-686-7579. Fax: 516-686-7814. p. 1710

Hess, Alex, III, Librn, University of North Carolina at Chapel Hill, Institute of Government, Knapp-Sanders Bldg, CB No 3330, Chapel Hill, NC, 27599-3330. Tel: 919-966-4172. Fax: 919-966-4762. p. 1781

Hess, Bettina, Cataloger, German Society of Pennsylvania, 611 Spring Garden St, Philadelphia, PA, 19123. Tel: 215-627-2332. Fax: 215-627-5297. p. 2110

Hess, Bradley, Tech Serv Librn, Concordia Seminary Library, 801 Seminary Pl, Saint Louis, MO, 63105-3199. Tel: 314-505-7042. Fax: 314-505-7046. p. 1353

Hess, Charlotte, Assoc Dean, Res, Coll & Scholarly Communication, Syracuse University Library, 222 Waverly Ave, Syracuse, NY, 13244-2010. Tel: 315-443-2573. p. 1754

Hess, Corrie, Ser, Louisiana State University Libraries, LSU School of Veterinary Medicine Library, Skip Bertman Dr, Baton Rouge, LA, 70803-8414. Tel: 225-578-9799. Fax: 225-578-9798. p. 944

Hess, Dave, Media Serv, Virginia Military Institute, Letcher Ave, Lexington, VA, 24450. Tel: 540-464-7228. Fax: 540-464-7279. p. 2474

Hess, Eric, Network Serv, Cleveland Law Library Association, One W Lakeside Ave, 4th Flr, Cleveland, OH, 44113-1023. Tel: 216-861-5070. Fax: 216-861-1606. p. 1877

Hess, Glenda, Ch, Paoli Public Library, Ten E Court, Paoli, IN, 47454. Tel: 812-723-3841. Fax: 812-723-3841. p. 772

Hess, Jackie, Dir, Mitchell Public Library, 221 N Duff St, Mitchell, SD, 57301-2596. Tel: 605-995-8480. Fax: 605-995-8482. p. 2215

Hess, Jen, Managing Librn, Columbus Metropolitan Library, Shepard Branch, 790 N Nelson Rd, Columbus, OH, 43219. Tel: 614-645-2275. Fax: 614-479-4229. p. 1885

Hess, Kate, Coordr, Kirkwood Community College Library, Iowa City Campus Library, 1816 Lower Muscatine Rd, Iowa City, IA, 52240. Tel: 319-887-3612. Fax: 319-887-3606. p. 800

Hess, Laura, Asst Librn, Stanton Public Library, 1009 Jackpine St, Stanton, NE, 68779. Tel: 402-439-2230. Fax: 402-439-2248. p. 1420

Hess, Marjorie, Cat Librn, Amherst College, Amherst, MA, 01002. Fax: 413-542-2662. p. 1048

Hess, Martha, Per, East Brunswick Public Library, Two Jean Walling Civic Center, East Brunswick, NJ, 08816-3599. Tel: 732-390-6950. Fax: 732-390-6796. p. 1481

Hess, Mary Louise, Dir, Wolf, Block, Schorr & Solis-Cohen LLP, 1650 Arch St, Philadelphia, PA, 19103. Tel: 215-977-2000. Fax: 215-977-2740. p. 2120

Hess, Mehta, Adult Serv, New London Public Library, 406 S Pearl St, New London, WI, 54961-1441. Tel: 920-982-8519. Fax: 920-982-8617. p. 2625

Hess, Paula, Librn, Dunlap Public Library, 102 S Tenth St, Dunlap, IA, 51529. Tel: 712-643-5311. Fax: 712-643-5311. p. 812

Hess, Sharon, Tech Spec, Clinton Public Library, 306 Eighth Ave S, Clinton, IA, 52732. Tel: 563-242-8441. Fax: 563-242-8162. p. 803

Hess, Stephanie, Acq, Nova Southeastern University Libraries, Shepard Broad Law Center Library, 3305 College Ave, Fort Lauderdale, FL, 33314. Tel: 954-262-6100. p. 444

Hess, Tamra, Dir, East Palestine Memorial Public Library, 309 N Market St, East Palestine, OH, 44413. Tel: 330-426-3778. Fax: 330-426-4950. p. 1897

Hess, Vineca, Librn, Mono County Free Library, June Lake, 90 W Granite Ave, June Lake, CA, 93529. Tel: 760-648-7284. Fax: 760-648-7284. p. 182

Hess, Wendy, Syst Coordr, Summa Health System, 55 N Arch, Ste G-3, Akron, OH, 44304. Tel: 330-375-3260. Fax: 330-375-3978. p. 1853

Hesse, Linda, Librn, Challis Public Library, 501 Sixth St, Challis, ID, 83226. Tel: 208-879-4267. Fax: 208-879-4267. p. 572

Hesse, Sunny, Human Res Coordr, Great River Regional Library, 1300 W St Germain St, Saint Cloud, MN, 56301-3667. Tel: 320-650-2511. Fax: 320-650-2501. p. 1274

Hesse, Susan, Dir, Wachtell, Lipton, Rosen & Katz, 51 W 52nd St, New York, NY, 10019. Tel: 212-403-1521. Fax: 212-403-2000. p. 1702

Hesselbein, Krista, Librn, Amos Press, Inc Library, 911 Vandemark Rd, Sidney, OH, 45365. Tel: 937-498-2111, Ext 276. p. 1934

Hesselink, Carolyn, ILL, Highlands County Library System, 319 W Center Ave, Sebring, FL, 33870-3109. Tel: 863-402-6716. Fax: 863-385-2883. p. 491

Hesselink, Joanne, Dir, Freeport District Library, 208 S State St, Freeport, MI, 49325-9759. Tel: 616-765-5181. Fax: 616-765-5181. p. 1182

Hessenauer, Jean, Dir, Tydings & Rosenberg LLP, 100 E Pratt St, 26th Flr, Baltimore, MD, 21202. Tel: 410-752-9700, 410-752-9804. Fax: 410-727-5460. p. 1018

Hessler, Celeste, Cataloger, Stony Brook University, Music, Melville Library, Rm W1530, Stony Brook, NY, 11794-3333. Tel: 631-632-7541. Fax: 631-632-1741. p. 1750

Hessling, Paul, Spec Coll/Chief Monographic Cataloger, University of North Carolina at Greensboro, 320 Spring Garden St, Greensboro, NC, 27402. Tel: 336-334-5880. Fax: 336-334-5399. p. 1798

Hessney-Moore, Susan, Mgr, Libr Operations, University of New Mexico, Fine Arts & Design Library, George Pearl Hall, 4th Flr, Albuquerque, NM, 87131. Tel: 505-277-5443. p. 1551

Hesson, Donna D, Mgr, Johns Hopkins University Libraries, William H Welch Medical Library, 1900 E Monument St, Baltimore, MD, 21205. Tel: 410-955-3028. Fax: 410-955-0200. p. 1015

Hesson, Linda, Ch, Lied Public Library, 508 Iowa St, Essex, IA, 51638. Tel: 712-379-3355. Fax: 712-379-3355. p. 815

Hesson, Michael, ILL, Olympic College, 1600 Chester Ave, Bremerton, WA, 98337. Tel: 360-475-7250. Fax: 360-475-7261. p. 2510

Hestand, Stephanie, Pub Serv Librn, Monroe County Public Library, 500 W Fourth St, Tompkinsville, KY, 42167. Tel: 270-487-5301. Fax: 270-487-5309. p. 936

Hester, Benjie, Youth Serv Mgr, Wake County Public Library System, Cameron Village Regional Library, 1930 Clark Ave, Raleigh, NC, 27605. Tel: 919-856-6725. Fax: 919-856-6722. p. 1817

Hester, Gloria, Acq, Circ, Jackson State Community College Library, 2046 North Pkwy, Jackson, TN, 38301. Tel: 731-425-3520, Ext 328. Fax: 731-425-2625. p. 2238

Hester, Mary, Dir, Libr Serv, Barton County Community College Library, 245 NE 30 Rd, Great Bend, KS, 67530. Tel: 620-792-9364. Fax: 620-792-3238. p. 869

Hester, Sandra, Dir, Fitzgerald-Ben Hill County Library, 123 N Main St, Fitzgerald, GA, 31750-2591. Tel: 229-426-5080. Fax: 229-426-5084. p. 532

Hesterberg, Anna, Cataloger, Columbia Public Library, 106 N Metter, Columbia, IL, 62236-2299. Tel: 618-281-4237. Fax: 618-281-6977. p. 631

Hesterberg, Sherry, Librn, Girard Township Library, 201 W Madison, Girard, IL, 62640-1550. Tel: 217-627-2414. Fax: 217-627-2093. p. 649

Heston, Lana L, Admin Mgr, Yuma County Library District, 2951 S 21st Dr, Yuma, AZ, 85364. Tel: 928-782-1871. Fax: 928-782-9420. p. 91

Heth, Leanna, Ch, Ottawa Library, 105 S Hickory St, Ottawa, KS, 66067-2306. Tel: 785-242-3080. Fax: 785-242-8789. p. 887

Hetherington, Ray, Tech Coordr, Greenville Public Library, 573 Putnam Pike, Greenville, RI, 02828-2195. Tel: 401-949-3630. Fax: 401-949-0530. p. 2166

Hetherton, Tim, Coordr, Ref Serv-Adult, Newport Beach Public Library, 1000 Avocado Ave, Newport Beach, CA, 92660-6301. Tel: 949-717-3819. Fax: 949-640-5681. p. 194

Hetrick, Lori, Dir, Limestone College, 1115 College Dr, Gaffney, SC, 29340. Tel: 864-488-4446. Fax: 864-487-4613. p. 2194

Hett, Bill, Chief Exec Officer, Norfolk County Public Library, 46 Colborne St S, Simcoe, ON, N3Y 4H3, CANADA. Tel: 519-426-3506, Ext 1253. Fax: 519-426-0657. p. 2841

Hettich, Dana, Ref Librn, University of Alabama at Birmingham, Mervyn H Sterne Library, 917 13th St S, Birmingham, AL, 35205. Tel: 205-934-6364. p. 10

Hettman, Lori, Br Mgr, Jackson County Library Services, Gold Hill Branch, 202 Dardanelles St, Gold Hill, OR, 97525-9771. Tel: 541-855-1994. Fax: 541-855-1994. p. 2005

Hétu, Dominique, Dir, Bibliotheque et Archives nationales du Quebec, 475 de Maisonneuve E, Montreal, QC, H2L 5C4, CANADA. Tel: 514-873-1101, Ext 3237. Fax: 514-873-9312. p. 2888

Hetu, Jean-Francois, Actg Br Mgr, Bibliotheques Publiques de Longueuil, 100 rue Saint-Laurent Ouest, Longueuil, QC, J4H 1M1, CANADA. Tel: 450-463-7180. Fax: 450-646-8080. p. 2886

Hetu, Sylvie, Librn, Fasken Martineau DuMoulin LLP, 800 Victoria Sq, Montreal, QC, H4Z 1E9, CANADA. Tel: 514-397-5154. Fax: 514-397-7600. p. 2895

Hetzel, Pat, Adminr, Escambia County Cooperative Library System, 700 E Church St, Atmore, AL, 36502. Tel: 251-368-4130. Fax: 251-368-4130. p. 5

Hetzler, Svetha, Ch, Middleton Public Library, 7425 Hubbard Ave, Middleton, WI, 53562-3117. Tel: 608-827-7411. Fax: 608-836-5724. p. 2616

Heu, Nancy, Dir, Windward Community College Library, 45-720 Keaahala Rd, Kaneohe, HI, 96744. Tel: 808-235-7435. Fax: 808-235-7344. p. 566

Heuer, Dan, Mgr, ILL & E-Res, Bucknell University, Interlibrary Loan, Library & Information Technology, Lewisburg, PA, 17837. Tel: 570-577-3249. p. 2080

Heusel, Karen, Res, Schulte Roth & Zabel LLP, 919 Third Ave, New York, NY, 10022. Tel: 212-756-2274. Fax: 212-593-5955. p. 1699

Heuser, Frederick J, Dir, Presbyterian Church (USA) Department of History, 425 Lombard St, Philadelphia, PA, 19147-1516. Tel: 215-627-1852. Fax: 215-627-0115. p. 2115

Heusinvelt, Ruth Ann, Adult Serv, Northminster Presbyterian Church Library, 703 Compton Rd, Cincinnati, OH, 45231. Tel: 513-931-0243. Fax: 513-931-0260. p. 1871

Heusser-Ladwig, Susan Ann, Librn, Perham Area Public Library, 225 Second Ave NE, Perham, MN, 56573-1819. Tel: 218-346-4892. Fax: 218-346-4906. p. 1270

Heuvel, Kathleen Vanden, Dir, University of California, Berkeley, Law, 225 Boalt Hall, Berkeley, CA, 94720. Tel: 510-642-4044. Fax: 510-643-5039. p. 128

Heverly, Jean, Librn, Colorado Department of Corrections, 12101 Hwy 61, Sterling, CO, 80751. Tel: 970-521-3403. Fax: 970-521-8905. p. 323

Heverly, Jean, Librn, Colorado Department of Corrections, Sterling Correctional Facility Library-East Side, 12101 Hwy 61, Sterling, CO, 80751. Tel: 970-521-3403. Fax: 970-521-8905. p. 323

Hevey, Cheryl Beth, Dir, Bonney Memorial Library, 36 Main St, Cornish, ME, 04020. Tel: 207-625-8083. Fax: 207-625-8083. p. 982

Hewes, Peggy, Librn, Baldwin Memorial Library, 33 Main St, Wells River, VT, 05081. Tel: 802-757-2693. p. 2438

Hewett, Nancy, Pub Serv, Coastal Carolina Community College, 444 Western Blvd, Jacksonville, NC, 28546-6877. Tel: 910-455-1221, 910-938-6237. Fax: 910-455-7027. p. 1803

Hewett-Beah, Rachel, Cat Mgr, University of New Mexico, 200 College Rd, Gallup, NM, 87301. Tel: 505-863-7552. Fax: 505-863-7624. p. 1556

Hewey, Brian, Syst Adminr, George H & Ella M Rodgers Memorial Library, 194 Derry Rd, Hudson, NH, 03051. Tel: 603-886-6030. Fax: 603-816-4501. p. 1452

Hewison, Nancy S, Assoc Dean, Planning & Admin, Purdue University Libraries, 504 W State St, West Lafayette, IN, 47907-2058. Tel: 765-494-2900. Fax: 765-494-0156. p. 786

Hewitt, Allison, Libr Mgr, Caroline Municipal Library, 5023 50th Ave, Caroline, AB, T0M 0M0, CANADA. Tel: 403-722-4060. Fax: 403-722-4070. p. 2694

Hewitt, Anita, Circ Librn, Gilford Public Library, 31 Potter Hill Rd, Gilford, NH, 03249-6803. Tel: 603-524-6042. Fax: 603-524-1218. p. 1448

Hewitt, Carolyn, Ch, Aurora Public Library, Eola, 555 S Eola Rd, Aurora, IL, 60504-8992. Tel: 630-264-3400. Fax: 630-898-5220. p. 591

Hewitt, Cindy, Br Mgr, Huntsville-Madison Public Library, Monrovia Public Library, 254 Allen Drake Dr, Huntsville, AL, 35806. Tel: 256-489-3392. p. 21

Hewitt, Dianne, Web Serv, Douglas College Library, 700 Royal Ave, New Westminster, BC, V3M 5Z5, CANADA. Tel: 604-527-5182. Fax: 604-527-5193. p. 2734

Hewitt, Douglas, Librn, Essex Law Association Law Library, Superior Courthouse, 245 Windsor Ave, Windsor, ON, N9A 1J2, CANADA. Tel: 519-252-8418. Fax: 519-252-9686. p. 2871

Hewitt, Kristen, Dir, Whitefish Bay Public Library, 5420 N Marlborough Dr, Whitefish Bay, WI, 53217. Tel: 414-964-4380. Fax: 414-964-5733. p. 2648

Hewitt, Robin, Dir, Finance & Fac, Hamilton Public Library, 55 York Blvd, Hamilton, ON, L8R 3K1, CANADA. Tel: 905-546-3200. Fax: 905-546-3202. p. 2808

Hewitt, Thomas, Dir, Skyline College Library, 3300 College Dr, San Bruno, CA, 94066-1698. Tel: 650-738-4311. Fax: 650-738-4149. p. 230

Hewitt, Tracy, Head Librn, Hazeltine Public Library, 891 Busti-Sugar Grove Rd, Jamestown, NY, 14701-9510. Tel: 716-487-1281. Fax: 716-487-0760. p. 1646

Hewitt, Virginia A, Dir, Brooks Free Library, 739 Main St, Harwich, MA, 02645. Tel: 508-430-7562. Fax: 508-430-7564. p. 1094

Hewlett, Carol, Dir, Jackson-George Regional Library System, 3214 Pascagoula St, Pascagoula, MS, 39567. Tel: 228-769-3099. Fax: 228-769-3146. p. 1310

Heyd, Michael, Dir, Susquehanna Health Medical Library, 777 Rural Ave, Williamsport, PA, 17701-3198. Tel: 570-321-2266. p. 2157

Heyde, Laura, Librn, Eau Claire Leader-Telegram Newsroom Library, 701 S Farwell St, Eau Claire, WI, 54702. Tel: 715-833-9200. Fax: 715-858-7308. p. 2589

Heye, Sam, Pub Serv, Dominican College Library, 480 Western Hwy, Blauvelt, NY, 10913-2000. Tel: 845-848-7505. Fax: 845-359-2525. p. 1583

Heyer, Kathy, Asst Dir, Manchester Public Library, 304 N Franklin St, Manchester, IA, 52057. Tel: 563-927-3719. Fax: 563-927-3058. p. 829

Heyer-Gray, Robert, Actg Head, Libr, University of California, Davis, Physical Sciences & Engineering Library, One Shields Ave, Davis, CA, 95616-8676. Tel: 530-752-0459. Fax: 530-752-4719. p. 140

Heyns, Erla P, Dr, Dir, Cornell University Library, Flower-Sprecher Veterinary Library, S2 160 Veterinary Education Ctr, Ithaca, NY, 14853-6401. Tel: 607-253-3515. Fax: 607-253-3080. p. 1641

Heytvelt, Lillian, Dir, Denny Ashby Memorial Library, 856 Arlington St, Pomeroy, WA, 99347. Tel: 509-843-3710. p. 2523

Heywood, Cheryl, Librn, Timberland Regional Library, Olympia Branch, 313 Eighth Ave SE, Olympia, WA, 98501-1307. Tel: 360-352-0595. Fax: 360-586-3207. p. 2543

Heywood, John, Ref Librn, American University, 4801 Massachusetts Ave NW, Washington, DC, 20016-8182. Tel: 202-274-4329. Fax: 202-274-4365. p. 393

Hezlett, Sibyl, Head, Tech Serv, Topsfield Town Library, One S Common St, Topsfield, MA, 01983-1496. Tel: 978-887-1528. Fax: 978-887-0185. p. 1131

Hiatt, Virginia M, Dir, Union City Public Library, 408 N Columbia St, Union City, IN, 47390-1404. Tel: 765-964-4748. Fax: 765-964-4748. p. 782

Hibbard, James, Head, Archives, University of Wisconsin - Platteville, One University Plaza, Platteville, WI, 53818. Tel: 608-342-1229. Fax: 608-342-1645. p. 2630

Hibbert, Kathleen, Ref, Attleboro Public Library, 74 N Main St, Attleboro, MA, 02703. Tel: 508-222-0157, 508-222-0159. Fax: 508-226-3326. p. 1050

Hibbert, Sarah, Circ Mgr, Estacada Public Library, 825 NW Wade St, Estacada, OR, 97023. Tel: 503-630-8273. Fax: 503-630-8282. p. 1996

Hibbert, Vicki, Dir, Clive Public Library, 1900 NW 114th St, Clive, IA, 50325. Tel: 515-453-2221. Fax: 515-453-2246. p. 803

Hibbett, Gloria, Head Librn, Free Library of Philadelphia, Regional Foundation Center, 1901 Vine St, Philadelphia, PA, 19103-1189. Tel: 215-686-5423. p. 2109

Hibbler, Elliott, Res/Fac Serv Librn, Western New England University, 1215 Wilbraham Rd, Springfield, MA, 01119-2689. Tel: 413-782-1454. Fax: 413-782-1745. p. 1128

Hibbler, Laura, Ref & Instruction Librn, College of the Holy Cross, One College St, Worcester, MA, 01610. Tel: 508-793-3886. Fax: 508-793-2372. p. 1143

Hibner, Holly, Adult Serv Coordr, Plymouth District Library, 223 S Main St, Plymouth, MI, 48170-1687. Tel: 734-453-0750, Ext 213. Fax: 734-453-0733. p. 1218

Hibpshman, Lawrence E, Archivist, Alaska State Archives, 141 Willoughby Ave, Juneau, AK, 99801-1720. Tel: 907-465-2270. Fax: 907-465-2465. p. 49

Hibshman, Dan, Dir, Mendocino County Law Library, Courthouse, Rm 307, 100 N State St, Ukiah, CA, 95482. Tel: 707-463-4201. Fax: 707-468-3459. p. 277

Hice, Linda, Librn, Lowgap Public Library, 9070 W Pine St, Lowgap, NC, 27024. Tel: 336-352-3000. Fax: 336-352-3000. p. 1807

Hick, Jo, Ch, Phillips Public Library, 286 Cherry St, Phillips, WI, 54555-1240. Tel: 715-339-2868. p. 2629

Hickam, Brian, Asst Dir, Libr Serv, Benedictine University Library, Charles E Becker Library, 1500 N Fifth St, Springfield, IL, 62702. Tel: 217-525-1420, Ext 221. Fax: 217-525-2651. p. 666

Hickam, Lennea, Cat, Kingsport Public Library & Archives, 400 Broad St, Kingsport, TN, 37660-4292. Tel: 423-229-9369. Fax: 423-224-2558. p. 2240

Hickerson, Thomas, Vice Provost for Libr, University of Calgary Library, 2500 University Dr NW, Calgary, AB, T2N 1N4, CANADA. Tel: 403-220-5953. Fax: 403-282-1218. p. 2693

Hickey, Colleen, Sister, Assoc Dir, University of Detroit Mercy Library, Kresge Law Library, 651 E Jefferson, Detroit, MI, 48226. Tel: 313-596-0239. Fax: 313-596-0245. p. 1172

Hickey, Daniel, Bus & Info Sci Librn, Pennsylvania State University Libraries, William & Joan Schreyer Business Library, 301 Paterno Library, University Park, PA, 16802-1810. Tel: 814-865-9645. Fax: 814-863-6370. p. 2148

Hickey, LadyJane, Coordr, Bibliog Serv, Austin College, 900 N Grand Ave, Ste 6L, Sherman, TX, 75090-4402. Tel: 903-813-2237. Fax: 903-813-2297. p. 2387

Hickey, Marcia, Ch, Wareham Free Library, 59 Marion Rd, Wareham, MA, 02571. Tel: 508-295-2343, Ext 1014. Fax: 508-295-2678. p. 1133

Hickey, Peggy, Br Mgr, Kern County Library, Kern River Valley Branch, 7054 Lake Isabella Blvd, Lake Isabella, CA, 93240-9205. Tel: 760-549-2083. p. 124

Hickey, Peggy, Br Supvr, Kern County Library, Kernville Branch, 48 Tobias St, Kernville, CA, 93238. Tel: 760-376-6180. p. 124

Hickey, Shirley, Ch, Margaret R Grundy Memorial Library, 680 Radcliffe St, Bristol, PA, 19007-5199. Tel: 215-788-7891. Fax: 215-788-4976. p. 2037

Hickey, Timothy, Access Serv/ILL Librn, Wagner College, One Campus Rd, Staten Island, NY, 10301-4495. Tel: 718-390-3401. Fax: 718-420-4218. p. 1748

Hickler, Nancy, Dir, Warwick Free Public Library, Four Hotel Rd, Warwick, MA, 01378-9311. Tel: 978-544-7866. Fax: 978-544-7866. p. 1133

Hicklin, Karen, Dir, Trails Regional Library, 432 N Holden St, Warrensburg, MO, 64093. Tel: 660-747-1699. Fax: 660-747-5774. p. 1371

Hickman, Brenda, Dir, Gassaway Public Library, 536 Elk, Gassaway, WV, 26624-1216. Tel: 304-364-8292. Fax: 304-364-8292. p. 2559

Hickman, D, Dir, Sara Hightower Regional Library, 205 Riverside Pkwy, Rome, GA, 30161-2922. Tel: 706-236-4601. Fax: 706-236-4605. p. 549

Hickman, Delana, Librn for Blind & Physically Handicapped, Hightower Sara Regional Library, Northwest Georgia Talking Book Library, 205 Riverside Pkwy, Rome, GA, 30161-2922. Tel: 706-236-4618. Fax: 706-236-4631. p. 549

Hickman, Josh, Digital Res Librn, Beloit College, 731 College St, Beloit, WI, 53511-5595. Tel: 608-363-2246. Fax: 608-363-2487. p. 2581

Hickman, Linda, Ch, Montague Public Libraries, 201 Ave A, Turners Falls, MA, 01376-1989. Tel: 413-863-3214. Fax: 413-863-3227. p. 1131

Hickman, Michael, Br Mgr, Atlanta-Fulton Public Library System, East Point Library, 2757 Main St, East Point, GA, 30344. Tel: 404-762-4842. Fax: 404-762-4844. p. 512

Hickman, Shelby, Ch, Youth Serv Librn, Mercer County Library, 601 Grant, Princeton, MO, 64673. Tel: 660-748-3725. Fax: 660-748-3723. p. 1350

Hickman, Valerie, Archivist, Tech Serv, Montana State University-Northern, 300 11th St W, Havre, MT, 59501. Tel: 406-265-3706. Fax: 406-265-3799. p. 1381

Hickner, Paula, Librn, University of Kentucky Libraries, Lucille Little Fine Arts Library & Learning Center, 160 Patterson Dr, Lexington, KY, 40506-0224. Tel: 859-257-4104. Fax: 859-257-4662. p. 922

Hickok, Barbara, Circ & ILL, Southern New Hampshire University, 2500 N River Rd, Manchester, NH, 03106-1045. Tel: 603-645-9605. Fax: 603-645-9685. p. 1456

Hickox, Jan Ellen, Head Librn, Casey Township Library, 307 E Main St, Casey, IL, 62420. Tel: 217-932-2105. Fax: 217-932-2105. p. 602

Hicks, Ava M, Dir, Arkansas Supreme Court Library, 625 Marshall St, Ste 1500, Little Rock, AR, 72201. Tel: 501-682-2147. Fax: 501-682-6877. p. 105

Hicks, Brenda, Br Supvr, Western Manitoba Regional Library, Hartney/Cameron Branch, 209 Airdrie St, Hartney, MB, R0M 0X0, CANADA. Tel: 204-858-2101. p. 2748

Hicks, Christina, YA Serv, Friendswood Public Library, 416 S Friendswood Dr, Friendswood, TX, 77546-3897. Tel: 281-482-7135. Fax: 281-482-2685. p. 2325

Hicks, Cindy, Media Serv, Oklahoma Baptist University, 500 W University, OBU Box 61310, Shawnee, OK, 74804-2504. Tel: 405-878-2253. Fax: 405-878-2256. p. 1977

Hicks, Colleen, Exec Dir, Museum of the American Indian Library, Miwok Park, 2200 Novato Blvd, Novato, CA, 94947. Tel: 415-897-4064. Fax: 415-892-7804. p. 196

Hicks, Deann, Libr Tech, VA North Texas Health Care System, 1201 E Ninth St, Bonham, TX, 75418. Tel: 903-583-6302. Fax: 903-583-6694. p. 2290

Hicks, Doris, YA Serv, Albany Public Library, 1390 Waverly Dr SE, Albany, OR, 97322. Tel: 541-917-7580, Ext 4704. Fax: 541-917-7586. p. 1989

Hicks, Elaine, Educ & Outreach Librn, Tulane University, Rudolph Matas Library of the Health Sciences, Tulane Health Sciences Campus, 1430 Tulane Ave, SL-86, New Orleans, LA, 70112-2699. Tel: 504-988-2785. Fax: 504-988-7417. p. 963

Hicks, Emily Anne, Dir, Info Acq & Organization, University of Dayton Libraries, 300 College Park Dr, Dayton, OH, 45469-1360. Tel: 937-229-1558. Fax: 937-229-4590. p. 1894

Hicks, Emma, Librn, West Blocton Public Library, 62 Walter Owens Dr, West Blocton, AL, 35184. Tel: 205-938-3570. Fax: 205-938-7803. p. 40

Hicks, George, Fac Supvr, Jones Library, Inc, 43 Amity St, Amherst, MA, 01002-2285. Tel: 413-259-3174. Fax: 413-256-4096. p. 1049

Hicks, Gloria, Head Librn, Tech Serv, World Data Center Glaciology, Boulder, CIRES, UCB 449, 1540 30th St, Boulder, CO, 80309-0449. Tel: 303-492-4004, 303-492-5774. Fax: 303-492-2468. p. 292

Hicks, Janet, Dir, Carnegie-Schuyler Library, 303 E Second St, Pana, IL, 62557. Tel: 217-562-2326. Fax: 217-562-2343. p. 688

Hicks, Kay, Tech Coordr, Barton County Library, 300 W Tenth St, Lamar, MO, 64759. Tel: 417-682-5355. Fax: 417-682-3206. p. 1343

Hicks, Kevin, Br Dir, Darlington County Library, Society Hill Branch, 473 S Main St, Society Hill, SC, 29593. Tel: 843-378-0026. Fax: 843-378-0026. p. 2192

Hicks, Kim, Dir, Madisonville Public Library, 4023 Hwy 411 N, Unit C, Madisonville, TN, 37354-1535. Tel: 423-442-4085. Fax: 423-442-8121. p. 2246

Hicks, Laurel R, Asst Dir, Gaston-Lincoln Regional Library, 1555 E Garrison Blvd, Gastonia, NC, 28054. Tel: 704-868-2164. Fax: 704-853-6012. p. 1794

Hicks, Lisa, Dir, Charles P Jones Memorial Library, 406 W Riverside St, Covington, VA, 24426. Tel: 540-962-3321. Fax: 540-962-8447. p. 2458

Hicks, Margaret, Br Mgr, Memphis Public Library, Levi, 3676 Hwy 61 S, Memphis, TN, 38109-8296. Tel: 901-789-3140. Fax: 901-789-3141. p. 2250

Hicks, Michael, Librn, Stanly Community College, Snyder Bldg, Albemarle, NC, 28001. Tel: 704-991-0261. Fax: 704-991-0112. p. 1773

Hicks, Minora, Dir, Clinton Junior College Library, 1029 Crawford Rd, Rock Hill, SC, 29730-5152. Tel: 803-327-7402, Ext 248. Fax: 803-324-2734. p. 2202

Hicks, Stephanie, Automation/Pub Serv Librn, Dyer Library, 371 Main St, Saco, ME, 04072. Tel: 207-283-3861. Fax: 207-283-0754. p. 999

Hicks, Trisha, Dir, Burt Public Library, 119 Walnut St, Burt, IA, 50522. Tel: 515-924-3680. Fax: 515-924-3681. p. 798

Hicks, Yvonne, Dir, C W Clark Memorial Library, 160 N Main St, Oriskany Falls, NY, 13425. Tel: 315-821-7850. Fax: 315-821-7850. p. 1712

Hickson, Dorothy, Transcript Coordr, NPR Library, 635 Massachusetts Ave NW, Washington, DC, 20001. Tel: 202-513-2351. Fax: 202-513-3056. p. 412

Hickson, Jamey, Head, Genealogical Serv, Lebanon Public Library, 104 E Washington St, Lebanon, IN, 46052. Tel: 765-482-3460. Fax: 317-873-5059. p. 761

Hickson-Stevenson, Pam, Asst Dir, Akron-Summit County Public Library, 60 S High St, Akron, OH, 44326. Tel: 330-643-9102. Fax: 330-643-9160. p. 1852

Hickson-Stevenson, Pamela, Asst Dir, Akron-Summit County Public Library, Odom Boulevard, 600 Vernon Odom Blvd, Akron, OH, 44307-1828. Tel: 330-434-8726. Fax: 330-434-3750. p. 1852

Hicok, Paul, Dir, Troy Public Library, Lansingburgh Branch, Fourth Ave & 114th St, Troy, NY, 12182. Tel: 518-235-5310. p. 1757

Hicok, Paul, Dir, Troy Public Library, Sycaway Branch, Hoosick St & Lee Ave, Troy, NY, 12180. Tel: 518-274-1822. p. 1757

Hicok, Paul, Exec Dir, Troy Public Library, 100 Second St, Troy, NY, 12180-4005. Tel: 518-274-7071. Fax: 518-271-9154. p. 1757

Hidalgo, Kleo, Librn, Howard College - San Angelo Library, 3501 N US Hwy 67, San Angelo, TX, 76905. Tel: 325-481-8300, Ext 309. Fax: 325-481-8321. p. 2379

Hidek, Lynn, Ch, Henry Carter Hull Library, Inc, Ten Killingworth Tpk, Clinton, CT, 06413. Tel: 860-669-2342. Fax: 860-669-8318. p. 334

Hieb, Linda, Ref, Caldwell Public Library, 1010 Dearborn, Caldwell, ID, 83605-4195. Tel: 208-459-3242. Fax: 208-459-7344. p. 572

Hiebert, Esther, Librn, Gem Jubilee Library, PO Box 6, Gem, AB, T0J 1M0, CANADA. Tel: 403-641-3245. Fax: 403-641-3245. p. 2705

Hiebert, Greta, ILL, Bethel College Library, 300 E 27th St, North Newton, KS, 67117-0531. Tel: 316-284-5361. Fax: 316-284-5843. p. 885

Hiebing, Dottie, Exec Dir, Metropolitan New York Library Council, 57 E 11th St, 4th Flr, New York, NY, 10003-4605. Tel: 212-228-2320. Fax: 212-228-2598. p. 2950

Hielscher, Christina, Circ, Librn Supvr, Lakeland Public Library, 100 Lake Morton Dr, Lakeland, FL, 33801-5375. Tel: 863-834-4280. Fax: 863-834-4293. p. 459

Hieronymus, Ruth Ann, Ch, Atlanta Public Library District, 100 Race St, Atlanta, IL, 61723. Tel: 217-648-2112. Fax: 217-648-5269. p. 590

Hiett, Debra, Dir, Hampstead Public Library, Nine Mary E Clark Dr, Hampstead, NH, 03841. Tel: 603-329-6411. Fax: 603-329-6036. p. 1449

Higa, Mori Lou, Coll Develop, Electronic Res, University of Texas Southwestern Medical Center Library, 5323 Harry Hines Blvd, Dallas, TX, 75390-9049. Tel: 214-648-2989. Fax: 214-648-2826. p. 2311

Higbee, Vicki, Librn, Lincoln County Library, Alamo Branch, 100 South First W, Alamo, NV, 89001. Tel: 775-725-3343. Fax: 775-725-3344. p. 1432

Higbie, Harmony, Libr Dir, McLean-Mercer Regional Library, Underwood Branch, 88 Lincoln Ave, Underwood, ND, 58576. Tel: 701-442-3441. Fax: 701-442-5481. p. 1848

Higdon, Barbara, Cat, Sheffield Public Library, 316 N Montgomery Ave, Sheffield, AL, 35660. Tel: 256-386-5633. Fax: 256-386-5608. p. 36

Higel, Jesse, Mrs, Weekend Supvr, Ohio State University LIBRARIES, Newark Campus Library, Warner Library & Student Center, 1179 University Dr, Newark, OH, 43055-1797. Tel: 740-366-9307. Fax: 740-366-9264. p. 1889

Higeons, Dana, Head, Cat & Computer Serv, Oral Roberts University Library, 7777 South Lewis Ave, Tulsa, OK, 74171. Tel: 918-495-6885. Fax: 918-495-6893. p. 1981

Higginbotham, Cecelia, Librn, United States Army, USA MEDDAC Medical Library, Fort Polk - Bayne-Jones Army Community Hospital, 1585 Third St, Bldg 285, Fort Polk, LA, 71459-5110. Tel: 337-531-3725, 337-531-3726. Fax: 337-531-3082. p. 949

Higginbotham, Hal F, Treas, Metropolitan New York Library Council, 57 E 11th St, 4th Flr, New York, NY, 10003-4605. Tel: 212-228-2320. Fax: 212-228-2598. p. 2950

Higginbotham, Gretchen, Head, Resource Sharing, California State University, Fresno, Henry Madden Library, 5200 N Barton Ave, Mail Stop ML-34, Fresno, CA, 93740-8014. Tel: 559-278-3032. Fax: 559-278-6952. p. 150

Higginbottom, Mary, Librn, Genesee District Library, Davison Area, 203 E Fourth St, Davison, MI, 48423. Tel: 810-653-2022. Fax: 810-653-7633. p. 1179

Higginbottom, Patricia, Pub Serv, University of Alabama at Birmingham, Lister Hill Library of the Health Sciences, 1700 University Blvd, Birmingham, AL, 35294-0013. Tel: 205-934-5460. Fax: 205-934-3545. p. 10

Higgins, Barbara, ILL, Free Library of Philadelphia, Library for the Blind & Physically Handicapped, 919 Walnut St, Philadelphia, PA, 19107-5289. Tel: 215-683-3213. Fax: 215-683-3211. p. 2108

Higgins, Carmen, Outreach Coordr, Westmont Public Library, 428 N Cass, Westmont, IL, 60559-1502. Tel: 630-969-5625. Fax: 630-969-6490. p. 717

Higgins, Deborah, Circ Supvr, Rutland Free Library, Ten Court St, Rutland, VT, 05701-4058. Tel: 802-773-1860. Fax: 802-773-1825. p. 2434

Higgins, Leila, Br Mgr, Orange County Library District, Windermere Branch, 530 Main St, Windermere, FL, 34786. p. 477

Higgins, Michael J, Dir, Libr & Archives, Metropolitan Club of the City of Washington Library, 1700 H St, NW, Washington, DC, 20006. Tel: 202-835-2556. p. 408

Higgins, Robin W, Libr Tech, Metropolitan Club of the City of Washington Library, 1700 H St, NW, Washington, DC, 20006. Tel: 202-835-2556. p. 408

Higgins, Shana, Coordr, Libr Instruction, Ref Librn, University of Redlands, 1200 E Colton Ave, Redlands, CA, 92374-3758. Tel: 909-748-8022. Fax: 909-335-5392. p. 215

Higgins, Susan, Chief Exec Officer, North Grenville Public Library, Norenberg Bldg, One Water St, Kemptville, ON, K0G 1J0, CANADA. Tel: 613-258-4711, Ext 6. Fax: 613-258-4134. p. 2812

Higgins, Thomas, VPres, K T Analytics Inc Library, 885 Rosemount Rd, Oakland, CA, 94610. Tel: 510-839-7702. Fax: 510-839-9887. p. 197

Higginson, Dawn, Dir, Oxford Public Library, 486 Oxford Rd, Oxford, CT, 06478. Tel: 203-888-6944. Fax: 203-888-2666. p. 364

Higginson, Laura, Br Mgr, Mississauga Library System, Frank McKechnie Branch, 310 Bristol Rd E, Mississauga, ON, L4Z 3V5, CANADA. Tel: 905-615-4660. Fax: 905-615-3625. p. 2823

Higgs, Nancy, Br Mgr, Evansville Vanderburgh Public Library, North Park, 960 Koehler Dr, Evansville, IN, 47710. Tel: 812-428-8408. Fax: 812-428-8243. p. 738

Higgs, Patricia, Archivist, Librn, Omohundro Institute of Early American History & Culture, Swem Library, One Landrum Dr, Williamsburg, VA, 23185. Tel: 757-221-1126. Fax: 757-221-1047. p. 2503

High, Roberta, Asst Librn, Twin Bridges Public Library, 206 S Main St, Twin Bridges, MT, 59754. Tel: 406-684-5416. Fax: 406-684-5260. p. 1389

High, Vicki, Libr Tech, Midwestern University, 20201 S Crawford, Olympia Fields, IL, 60461. Tel: 708-747-4000, Ext 1190. Fax: 708-747-0244. p. 685

Higham, Peter, Music Librn, Mount Allison University Libraries & Archives, Alfred Whitehead Music Library, 134 Main St, Sackville, NB, E4L 1A6, CANADA. Tel: 506-364-2561. p. 2766

Highfill, Laura, Br Mgr, Charlotte Mecklenburg Library, Matthews Branch, 230 Matthews Station St, Matthews, NC, 28105. Tel: 704-416-5000. Fax: 704-416-5100. p. 1782

Highler, Sharon, Dir, Shorewood-Troy Public Library District, 650 Deerwood Dr, Shorewood, IL, 60431. Tel: 815-725-1715. Fax: 815-725-1722. p. 702

Highsmith, Doug, Ref & Info Serv, Team Leader, California State University, East Bay Library, 25800 Carlos Bee Blvd, Hayward, CA, 94542-3052. Tel: 510-885-3610. Fax: 510-885-2049. p. 157

Highsmith, Ellen M, Dir, Morehouse Parish Library, 524 E Madison Ave, Bastrop, LA, 71220. Tel: 318-281-3696. Fax: 318-281-3683. p. 941

Highsmith, Rayne, Br Mgr, Live Oak Public Libraries, Springfield Branch, 810 Hwy 119 S, Springfield, GA, 31329. Tel: 912-754-3003. Fax: 912-754-9494. p. 550

Hight, Maryann, Ref & Instruction Librn, California State University, Stanislaus, One University Circle, Turlock, CA, 95382. Tel: 209-664-6553. p. 277

Hight, Sandra, Librn, Saint Alphonsus Health System, Central Tower, 1055 N Curtis Rd, 2nd Flr, Boise, ID, 83706. Tel: 208-367-3993. Fax: 208-367-2702. p. 571

Hightower, Brent, Dir, Libr Serv, Adams & Reese Law Library, One Shell Sq, 701 Poydras, Ste 4500, New Orleans, LA, 70139. Tel: 504-581-3234. Fax: 504-566-0210. p. 959

Hightower, Christy, Bibliographer, Librn, University of California, 1156 High St, Santa Cruz, CA, 95064. Tel: 831-459-4708. Fax: 831-459-8206. p. 264

Higle, Jane, Dir, Libr Serv, Kingswood University, 26 Western St, Sussex, NB, E4E 1E6, CANADA. Tel: 506-432-4400. Fax: 506-432-4425. p. 2767

Higley, Rita L, Dir, Horton Free Public Library, 809 First Ave E, Horton, KS, 66439-1898. Tel: 785-486-3326. Fax: 785-486-2116. p. 872

Hignett, Joan, Acq, Ashland University Library, 509 College Ave, Ashland, OH, 44805-3796. Tel: 419-289-5400. Fax: 419-289-5422. p. 1855

Hignite, Heather, Librn, The Arkansas Arts Center, MacArthur Park, 501 E Ninth St, Little Rock, AR, 72202. Tel: 501-396-0341. Fax: 501-375-8053. p. 105

Higo, Patricia, Archives & Spec Coll Librn, University of Detroit Mercy Library, 4001 W McNichols Rd, Detroit, MI, 48221-3038. Tel: 313-578-0435. Fax: 313-993-1780. p. 1172

Hiigel, Fletcher, Dir, Guthrie Memorial Library - Hanover's Public Library, Two Library Pl, Hanover, PA, 17331-2283. Tel: 717-632-5183. Fax: 717-632-7565. p. 2064

Hiigel, Sharon, Curator of Coll, Fresno City & County Historical Society Archives, 7160 W Kearney Blvd, Fresno, CA, 93706. Tel: 559-441-0862. Fax: 559-441-1372. p. 151

Hilbelink, Judy, Ch, ILL, Northwestern College, 101 Seventh St SW, Orange City, IA, 51041-1996. Tel: 712-707-7234. Fax: 712-707-7247. p. 836

Hilbun, Janet, Dr, Asst Prof, University of North Texas, 1155 Union Circle, Denton, TX, 76203-5017. Tel: 940-565-2445. Fax: 940-565-3101. p. 2975

Hildebrand, Jane, Regional Librn, Three Rivers Regional Library System, 208 Gloucester St, Brunswick, GA, 31520-7007. Tel: 912-267-1212. Fax: 912-267-9597. p. 522

Hildebrand, Janice, Librn, Sheboygan County Historical Research Center Library, 518 Water St, Sheboygan Falls, WI, 53085. Tel: 920-467-4667. Fax: 920-467-1395. p. 2638

Hildebrand, Julie, Asst Dir, Independence Public Library, 220 E Maple, Independence, KS, 67301-3899. Tel: 620-331-3030. Fax: 620-331-4093. p. 873

Hildebrand, Karen, Librn, Hendry County Library System, Barron Library, 461 N Main St, Labelle, FL, 33935. Tel: 863-675-0833. Fax: 863-675-7544. p. 433

Hildebrand, Melita, Librn, Lakeland Library Region, Rabbit Lake Branch, Box 146, Rabbit Lake, SK, S0M 2L0, CANADA. Tel: 306-824-2089. p. 2920

Hildebrand, Theresa, Circ Mgr, Fountaindale Public Library District, 300 W Briarcliff Rd, Bolingbrook, IL, 60440-2844. Tel: 630-759-2102, Ext 4151. Fax: 630-759-9519. p. 596

Hilderbrand, Barbara Y, Cat/Metadata Librn, Florida Southern College, 111 Lake Hollingsworth Dr, Lakeland, FL, 33801-5698. Tel: 863-680-4736. Fax: 863-680-4126. p. 459

Hilderbrand, Carol, Br Librn, Douglas County Library System, Canyonville Branch, 250 N Main St, Canyonville, OR, 97417. Tel: 541-839-4727. Fax: 541-839-4727. p. 2016

Hilderbrand, Morna, Head, ILL, Head, Info Serv, Rochester Institute of Technology, 90 Lomb Memorial Dr, Rochester, NY, 14623-5604. Tel: 585-475-2560. Fax: 585-475-7007. p. 1731

Hilderman, Janet, Librn, Regina Public Library, Sunrise, 3130 E Woodhams Dr, Regina, SK, S4V 2P9, CANADA. Tel: 306-777-6095. Fax: 306-949-7271. p. 2923

Hildreth, Brian M, Dir, David A Howe Public Library, 155 N Main St, Wellsville, NY, 14895. Tel: 585-593-3410. Fax: 585-593-4176. p. 1765

Hildreth, Elizabeth, Br Mgr, San Diego County Library, La Mesa Branch, 8074 Allison Ave, La Mesa, CA, 91941-5001. Tel: 619-469-2151. Fax: 619-697-3751. p. 234

Hildreth, Heather, Head, Circ, West Des Moines Public Library, 4000 Mills Civic Pkwy, West Des Moines, IA, 50265-2049. Tel: 515-222-3400. Fax: 515-222-3401. p. 852

Hildreth, WyLaina, Sr Librn, Denton Public Library, North Branch, 3020 N Locust, Denton, TX, 76209. Tel: 940-349-8774. Fax: 940-387-5367. p. 2312

Hile, Mary Anne, Coll Mgr, Johnson County Library, 9875 W 87th St, Overland Park, KS, 66212. Tel: 913-495-2434. Fax: 913-495-2460. p. 888

Hile, Sandra, Ch, Greenburgh Public Library, 300 Tarrytown Rd, Elmsford, NY, 10523. Tel: 914-721-8200. Fax: 914-721-8201. p. 1620

Hileman, Connie, Asst Dir, Rolla Public Library, 14 SE First St, Rolla, ND, 58367. Tel: 701-477-3849. Fax: 701-477-9633. p. 1848

Hiles, Rita, Coordr, Circ & Customer Serv, Fairfield County District Library, 219 N Broad St, Lancaster, OH, 43130-3098. Tel: 740-653-2745. Fax: 740-653-4199. p. 1908

Hiles, Roger, Mgr, Libr Serv, Santa Barbara Public Library, 40 E Anapamu St, Santa Barbara, CA, 93101-2722. Tel: 805-564-5611. p. 261

Hilger, Stephanie, Asst Librn, Chinook Regional Library, Leader Branch, 151 First St W, Leader, SK, S0N 1H0, CANADA. Tel: 306-628-3830. p. 2928

Hilgers, Laraine, Br Librn, John F Kennedy University Libraries, Berkeley Campus Library, 2956 San Pablo Ave, 2nd Flr, Berkeley, CA, 94702. Tel: 510-649-1008. Fax: 510-645-0910. p. 210

Hilkemann, Judy, Head, Ref, Syst Librn, Norfolk Public Library, 308 Prospect Ave, Norfolk, NE, 68701-4138. Tel: 402-844-2104. Fax: 402-844-2102. p. 1410

Hilkert, Judy, Librn, Hinds Community College, 505 E Main St, Raymond, MS, 39154. Tel: 601-857-3355. Fax: 601-857-3293. p. 1313

Hill, Amy, Dir, Libr & Info Serv, Waldorf College, 106 S Sixth St, Forest City, IA, 50436. Tel: 641-585-8672. Fax: 641-585-8111. p. 816

Hill, Amy, Dir, Melbourne Public Library, 603 Main St, Melbourne, IA, 50162. Tel: 641-482-3115. Fax: 641-482-3003. p. 831

Hill, Angel, Br Mgr, Harris County Public Library, Katy Branch, 5414 Franz Rd, Katy, TX, 77493. Tel: 281-391-3509. Fax: 281-391-1927. p. 2336

Hill, Ann Marie, Law Librn, Lewis County Law Library, 7660 State St, 2nd Flr, Lowville, NY, 13367. Tel: 315-376-5317, 315-376-5383. Fax: 315-376-4145. p. 1655

Hill, April, Libr Mgr, Plano Public Library System, Christopher A Parr Library, 6200 Windhaven Pkwy, Plano, TX, 75093. Tel: 972-769-4300. Fax: 972-769-4304. p. 2371

Hill, Barbara, Per Coordr, Christian Brothers University, 650 E Pkwy South, Memphis, TN, 38104. Tel: 901-321-3432. Fax: 901-321-3219. p. 2248

Hill, Barbara, ILL, Brown Public Library, 93 S Main St, Northfield, VT, 05663. Tel: 802-485-4621. Fax: 802-485-4990. p. 2431

Hill, Barbarie, Mgr, Cincinnati Children's Hospital, Sabin Education Ctr, D2 80, 3333 Burnet Ave, Cincinnati, OH, 45229-3039. Tel: 513-636-5490. Fax: 513-559-9669. p. 1868

Hill, Betty, Asst Br Mgr, Sullivan County Public Library, Colonial Heights Branch, 149 Pactolus Rd, Kingsport, TN, 37663. Tel: 423-239-1100. Fax: 423-239-1100. p. 2224

Hill, Byron C, Librn, Bowditch & Dewey, 311 Main St, Worcester, MA, 01608. Tel: 508-926-3331. Fax: 508-929-3140. p. 1143

Hill, Catherine, Libr Tech, Townsend Public Library, 276 Main St, Townsend, MA, 01469-1513. Tel: 978-597-1714. Fax: 978-597-2779. p. 1131

Hill, Cathy, Br Head, Chatham-Kent Public Library, Highgate Branch, 291 King St, Highgate, ON, N0P 1T0, CANADA. Tel: 519-678-3313. Fax: 519-678-3313. p. 2799

Hill, Christine M, Asst Libr Dir, Willingboro Public Library, Willingboro Town Ctr, 220 Willingboro Pkwy, Willingboro, NJ, 08046. Tel: 609-877-0476, 609-877-6668. Fax: 609-835-1699. p. 1544

Hill, Chuck, Univ Archivist, Eastern Kentucky University Libraries, 521 Lancaster Ave, Richmond, KY, 40475-3102. Tel: 859-622-1778. Fax: 859-622-1174. p. 933

Hill, Cindy, Mgr, Federal Reserve Bank of San Francisco, 101 Market St, San Francisco, CA, 94105-1579. Tel: 415-974-3216. Fax: 415-974-3429. p. 242

Hill, Constance, Sr Librn, Hennepin County Library, Minneapolis Central, 300 Nicollet Mall, Minneapolis, MN, 55401. Tel: 612-543-8124. Fax: 612-543-8173. p. 1264

Hill, Corinne, Asst Dir, Res Mgt Serv, Dallas Public Library, 1515 Young St, Dallas, TX, 75201-5499. Tel: 214-670-1774. Fax: 214-670-7839. p. 2306

Hill, Damon, Sr Librn, Marin County Free Library, Civic Center Branch, 3501 Civic Center Dr, Rm 427, San Rafael, CA, 94903-4177. Tel: 415-499-6056. p. 257

Hill, Darnelle, Chief Exec Officer, Hornepayne Public Library, 68 Front St, Hornepayne, ON, P0M 1Z0, CANADA. Tel: 807-868-2332. Fax: 807-868-3111. p. 2811

Hill, David, Br Mgr, Brampton Library, Chinguacousy Branch, 150 Central Park Dr, Brampton, ON, L6T 1B4, CANADA. Tel: 905-793-4636, Ext 4120. Fax: 905-793-0506. p. 2796

Hill, Debra, Ref Librn II, Humboldt County Library, Eureka (Main Library), 1313 Third St, Eureka, CA, 95501. Tel: 707-269-1900. p. 147

Hill, Diana, Br Mgr, Jackson District Library, Spring Arbor Branch, 113 E Main St, Spring Arbor, MI, 49283. Tel: 517-750-2030. Fax: 517-750-2030. p. 1196

Hill, Donna, Librn, First Assembly of God Library, 4501 Burrow Dr, North Little Rock, AR, 72116. Tel: 501-758-8553. Fax: 501-758-3830. p. 111

Hill, Elaine, Admin Serv, Vanderbilt University, Walker Management Library, Owen Graduate School of Management, 401 21st Ave S, Nashville, TN, 37203. Tel: 615-343-4109. Fax: 615-343-0061. p. 2261

Hill, Elizabeth, Dir, Libr, Media & eLearning, South Puget Sound Community College Library, 2011 Mottman Rd SW, Olympia, WA, 98512. Tel: 360-596-5271. Fax: 360-596-5714. p. 2522

Hill, Francie, Dir, Bickelhaupt Arboretum Library, 340 S 14th St, Clinton, IA, 52732-5432. Tel: 563-242-4771. Fax: 563-242-7373. p. 803

Hill, Gary, Dep Dir, Brigham Young University, Howard W Hunter Law Library, 256 JRCB, Provo, UT, 84602-8000. Tel: 801-422-3593. Fax: 801-422-0404. p. 2411

Hill, Graham, Dir, Knowledge Mgt, National Coffee Association Library, 45 Broadway, Ste 1140, New York, NY, 10006. Tel: 212-766-4007. Fax: 212-766-5815. p. 1687

Hill, Greg, Dir, Fairbanks North Star Borough Public Library & Regional Center, 1215 Cowles St, Fairbanks, AK, 99701. Tel: 907-459-1020. Fax: 907-459-1024. p. 47

Hill, J B, Dir, Pub Serv, University of Arkansas at Little Rock, 2801 S University Ave, Little Rock, AR, 72204. Tel: 501-569-3123. Fax: 501-569-3017. p. 107

Hill, Jackie, Br Mgr, Knox County Public Library System, Cedar Bluff Branch, 9045 Cross Park Dr, Cedar Bluff, TN, 37923. Tel: 865-470-7033. Fax: 865-470-0927. p. 2242

Hill, Jacob, Ref & Instruction Librn, Elmhurst College, 190 Prospect St, Elmhurst, IL, 60126. Tel: 630-617-3168. Fax: 630-617-3332. p. 642

Hill, James, Dir, Zumbrota Public Library, 100 West Ave, Zumbrota, MN, 55992. Tel: 507-732-5211. Fax: 507-732-1212. p. 1291

Hill, James, Br Mgr, Nelsonville Public Library, 95 W Washington, Nelsonville, OH, 45764-1177. Tel: 740-753-2118. Fax: 740-753-3543. p. 1920

Hill, Janene, YA Librn, Manhattan Public Library, 629 Poyntz Ave, Manhattan, KS, 66502-6086. Tel: 785-776-4741. Fax: 785-776-1545. p. 881

Hill, Janene, YA Serv, Grant County Library, 215 E Grant Ave, Ulysses, KS, 67880-2958. Tel: 620-356-1433. Fax: 620-356-1344. p. 898

Hill, Janet, Librn, City of Kawartha Lakes Public Library, Carden, 258 Lake Dalrymple Rd, Sebright, ON, L0K 1W0, CANADA. Tel: 705-833-2845. Fax: 705-832-2273. p. 2816

Hill, Jeanne, Sister, Librn, Holy Trinity Monastery Library, Hwy 80, Milepost 302, Saint David, AZ, 85630. Tel: 520-720-5174. Fax: 520-720-4202. p. 79

Hill, Joan, Librn, Wetumka Public Library, 202 N Main, Wetumka, OK, 74883. Tel: 405-452-3785. Fax: 405-452-5825. p. 1986

Hill, Joanna, Dir, Swedenborg Foundation Library, 320 N Church St, West Chester, PA, 19380. Tel: 610-430-3222. Fax: 610-430-7982. p. 2153

Hill, Judy, Acq, Mat, Plainfield-Guilford Township Public Library, 1120 Stafford Rd, Plainfield, IN, 46168-2230. Tel: 317-839-6602. Fax: 317-838-3805. p. 773

Hill, Judy, Dir, Binger Public Library, 217 W Main, Binger, OK, 73009. p. 1958

Hill, Julie, Br Mgr, Saint Joseph County Public Library, LaSalle Branch, 3232 W Ardmore, South Bend, IN, 46628-3232. Tel: 574-282-4633. p. 779

Hill, June, In Charge, City of Kawartha Lakes Public Library, Dalton, 13 Rumohr, RR 1, Sebright, ON, L0K 1W0, CANADA. Tel: 705-833-2858. Fax: 705-833-2752. p. 2816

Hill, Karen, AV Coordr, Virginia Wesleyan College, 1584 Wesleyan Dr, Norfolk, VA, 23502-5599. Tel: 757-455-3239. Fax: 757-455-2129. p. 2483

Hill, Kathryn, Libr Dir, Orange County Library, 146A Madison Rd, Orange, VA, 22960. Tel: 540-661-5444. Fax: 540-672-5040. p. 2483

Hill, Kathy, Admin Officer, Smithsonian Libraries, Nat Museum of Natural Hist, Rm 22, MRC154, Tenth St & Constitution Ave NW, Washington, DC, 20002. Tel: 202-633-1945. Fax: 202-633-7367. p. 414

Hill, Laura, Libr Mgr, McPherson Municipal Library, 5113 50 St, Ryley, AB, T0B 4A0, CANADA. Tel: 780-663-3999. Fax: 780-663-3909. p. 2715

Hill, Leslie, Librn, Shawano City-County Library, Wittenberg Public, 302 S Cherry St, Wittenberg, WI, 54499. Tel: 715-253-2936. p. 2637

Hill, Lola L, Librn, Stigler Public Library, 402 NE Sixth St, Stigler, OK, 74462. Tel: 918-967-4801. Fax: 918-967-4470. p. 1978

Hill, Margaret J, Law Librn, Barnstable Law Library, First District Court House, Barnstable, MA, 02630. Tel: 508-362-8539. Fax: 508-362-1374. p. 1051

Hill, Marguerite, Librn, Pine Plains Free Library, 7775 S Main St, Pine Plains, NY, 12567-5653. Tel: 518-398-1927. Fax: 518-398-6085. p. 1718

Hill, Michelle, Asst Med Librn, Primary Children's Medical Center Library, 100 N Mario Capecchi Dr, Salt Lake City, UT, 84113. Tel: 801-662-1390. Fax: 801-662-1393. p. 2413

Hill, Myra, Ref Librn, Jefferson County Library, Arnold Branch, 1701 Missouri State Rd, Arnold, MO, 63010. Tel: 636-296-2204. Fax: 636-296-5975. p. 1331

Hill, Nanci, Head, Reader Serv, Nevins Memorial Library, 305 Broadway, Methuen, MA, 01844-6898. Tel: 978-686-4080. Fax: 978-686-8669. p. 1105

Hill, Nancy, Asst Dir, Tech Serv/Cat, University of Texas at El Paso Library, 500 W University Ave, El Paso, TX, 79968-0582. Tel: 915-747-6722. Fax: 915-747-5345. p. 2317

Hill, Nancy, Coordr, Librn III, West Texas Library System, 1306 Ninth St, Lubbock, TX, 79401-2798. Tel: 806-775-2854. Fax: 806-775-2856. p. 2358

Hill, Nancy Milone, Dir, Boxford Town Library, Ten Elm St, Boxford, MA, 01921. Tel: 978-887-7323. Fax: 978-887-6352. p. 1069

Hill, Nelda, Cent Libr Mgr, Knox County Public Library System, 500 W Church Ave, Knoxville, TN, 37902-2505. Tel: 865-215-8729. Fax: 865-215-8742. p. 2241

Hill, Pam, Br & Extn Librn, Portage County Public Library, Almond Branch, Village Hall, 122 Main St, Almond, WI, 54909. Tel: 715-366-2151. Fax: 715-366-2151. p. 2640

Hill, Pam, Br & Extn Librn, Portage County Public Library, Plover Branch, 2151 Roosevelt Dr, Plover, WI, 54467. Tel: 715-341-4007. Fax: 715-346-1601. p. 2640

Hill, Pamela, Br & Extn Librn, Portage County Public Library, Charles M White Library Bldg, 1001 Main St, Stevens Point, WI, 54481-2860. Tel: 715-346-1544. Fax: 715-346-1239. p. 2640

Hill, Penny, Br Supvr, Fresno County Public Library, 2420 Mariposa St, Fresno, CA, 93721-2285. Tel: 559-600-7323. p. 151

Hill, Rebecca B, Head Librn, Rutherford B Hayes Presidential Center Library, Spiegel Grove, Fremont, OH, 43420-2796. Tel: 419-332-2081, Ext 231. Fax: 419-332-4952. p. 1900

Hill, Rebekah, Librn, Pittsburgh Institute of Mortuary Science, 5808 Baum Blvd, Pittsburgh, PA, 15206. Tel: 412-362-8500. Fax: 412-362-1684. p. 2127

Hill, Rudean, Ref Librn, Sumter County Library, 111 N Harvin St, Sumter, SC, 29150. Tel: 803-773-7273. Fax: 803-773-4875. p. 2206

Hill, Ruth, Pub Serv, National Library of Medicine, Bldg 38, Rm 2E-17B, 8600 Rockville Pike, Bethesda, MD, 20894. Tel: 301-496-6308. Fax: 301-496-4450. p. 1022

Hill, Ruth G, Res Coordr, St Mary's County Historical Society, 41680 Tudor Pl, Leonardtown, MD, 20650-0212. Tel: 301-475-2467. Fax: 301-475-2467. p. 1035

Hill, Ruth J, Dir, Libr Serv, Southern University, Oliver B Spellman Law Library, 56 Roosevelt Steptoe, Baton Rouge, LA, 70813. Tel: 225-771-2139, 225-771-2315. Fax: 225-771-6254. p. 944

Hill, Sandra D, Libr Dir, Villa Park Public Library, 305 S Ardmore Ave, Villa Park, IL, 60181-2698. Tel: 630-834-1164, Ext 111. Fax: 630-834-0489. p. 714

Hill, Sharon, Asst Dir, Palm Beach County Library System, 3650 Summit Blvd, West Palm Beach, FL, 33406-4198. Tel: 561-233-2724. Fax: 561-233-2692. p. 503

Hill, Sharon, Circ, Panola College, 1109 W Panola St, Carthage, TX, 75633. Tel: 903-693-1155. Fax: 903-693-1115. p. 2295

Hill, Shera, Librn, San Luis Obispo County Library, Cayucos Branch, 310 B St, Cayucos, CA, 93430. Tel: 805-995-3312. Fax: 805-995-0573. p. 254

Hill, Sonya, Librn, Indiana Veteran's Home, 3851 North River Rd, West Lafayette, IN, 47906. Tel: 765-463-1502, Ext 8200. p. 786

Hill, Steve, Librn, First Presbyterian Church of Flint, 746 S Saginaw St, Flint, MI, 48502-1508. Tel: 810-234-8673. Fax: 810-234-1643. p. 1179

Hill, Susan, Dir, Andover Public Library, 142 W Main St, Andover, OH, 44003-9318. Tel: 440-293-6792. Fax: 440-293-5720. p. 1854

Hill, Susan H, Dir, Brigham City Library, 26 E Forest, Brigham City, UT, 84302-2198. Tel: 435-723-5850. Fax: 435-723-2813. p. 2403

Hill, Theresa, Tech Serv, Northwest Regional Library System, 898 W 11 St, Panama City, FL, 32401. Tel: 850-522-2100. Fax: 850-522-2138. p. 480

Hill, Theresa, Dir, Hepburn Library of Waddington, 30 Main St, Waddington, NY, 13694. Tel: 315-388-4454. Fax: 315-388-4050. p. 1761

Hill, Thomas, Librn, Self Regional Healthcare, 1325 Spring St, Greenwood, SC, 29646. Tel: 864-725-4851. Fax: 864-725-4838. p. 2198

Hill, Thomas E, Librn, Vassar College Library, Art Library, 124 Raymon Ave, Poughkeepsie, NY, 12604-0022. Tel: 845-437-5790. p. 1723

Hill, Tonia, Libr Tech, Minnesota West Community & Technical College, Canby Campus, 1011 First St W, Canby, MN, 56220. Tel: 507-223-7252. Fax: 507-223-5291. p. 1291

Hill, Tracy, Librn, Lincoln Correctional Center Library, 1098 1350th St, Lincoln, IL, 62656-5094. Tel: 217-735-5411, Ext 368. Fax: 217-735-1361. p. 665

Hill, Trent, Sr Lecturer, University of Washington, Mary Gates Hall, Ste 370, Campus Box 352840, Seattle, WA, 98195-2840. Tel: 206-685-9937. Fax: 206-616-3152. p. 2976

Hill, Trudy, Ch, Springdale Public Library, 405 S Pleasant St, Springdale, AR, 72764. Tel: 479-750-8180. Fax: 479-750-8182. p. 115

Hill-Festa, Lisa, Coll Mgr, Nordic Heritage Museum, Walter Johnson Memorial Library, 3014 NW 67th St, Seattle, WA, 98117. Tel: 206-789-5707, Ext 18. Fax: 206-789-3271. p. 2529

Hille Cribbs, Elizabeth, Cat, Mercer County Community College Library, 1200 Old Trenton Rd, West Windsor, NJ, 08550. Tel: 609-570-3556. Fax: 609-570-3845. p. 1542

Hillegas, Judy, Dir, Everett Free Library, 137 E Main St, Everett, PA, 15537-1259. Tel: 814-652-5922. Fax: 814-652-5425. p. 2056

Hillemann, Eric, Archivist, Carleton College, One N College St, Northfield, MN, 55057-4097. Tel: 507-222-4270. Fax: 507-222-4087. p. 1269

Hillen, Charles, Head, Acq & Ser, Loyola Marymount University, One LMU Dr, MS 8200, Los Angeles, CA, 90045-2659. Tel: 310-338-4458. Fax: 310-338-4366. p. 175

Hiller Clark, Anne, Instrul Serv Librn, Shaw Hist Libr Librn, Oregon Institute of Technology Library, 3201 Campus Dr, Klamath Falls, OR, 97601-8801. Tel: 541-885-1686. Fax: 541-885-1777. p. 2002

Hiller, Kimberli, Br Mgr, Holmes County District Public Library, Walnut Creek Branch, 4877 Olde Pump St, Walnut Creek, OH, 44687. Tel: 330-893-3464. Fax: 330-893-8464. p. 1918

Hiller, Lois W, Dir, Mystic & Noank Library, Inc, 40 Library St, Mystic, CT, 06355. Tel: 860-536-7721. Fax: 860-536-2350. p. 353

Hiller, Marc, Head, Coll Develop, Ecole Polytechnique de Montreal Bibliotheque, 2500, chemin de Polytechnique, Montreal, QC, H3T 1J4, CANADA. Tel: 514-340-4666. Fax: 514-340-4026. p. 2895

Hiller, Paul, Exec Dir, ALS Society of British Columbia, 1600 W Sixth Ave, Ste 208, Vancouver, BC, V6J 1R3, CANADA. Tel: 604-685-0737. Fax: 604-685-0725. p. 2740

Hillesheim, Jodi, Asst Libr Dir, Upper Iowa University, 605 Washington St, Fayette, IA, 52142. Tel: 563-425-5270. Fax: 563-425-5271. p. 816

Hillhouse, Sharon, Mgr, Parker Public Library, Indian Hills, 66907 Indian Hills Way, Salome, AZ, 85348. Tel: 928-859-4271. Fax: 928-859-4364. p. 70

Hilliard, Susan, Librn, Pilot Rock Public Library, 144 N Alder Pl, Pilot Rock, OR, 97868. Tel: 541-443-3285. Fax: 541-443-2253. p. 2009

Hilliard-Bradley, Yvonne, Libr Dir, Blackwater Regional Library, 22511 Main St, Courtland, VA, 23837. Tel: 757-653-2821. Fax: 757-653-9374. p. 2458

Hillick, Amy, Circ, Ref Librn, Orange County Community College Library, 115 South St, Middletown, NY, 10940. Tel: 845-341-4253. Fax: 845-341-4424. p. 1660

Hillier, Katherine, Dir, Pease Public Library, One Russell St, Plymouth, NH, 03264-1414. Tel: 603-536-2616. Fax: 603-536-2369. p. 1462

Hilliker, Melisandre, Info Literacy, Ref, University of Tampa, 401 W Kennedy Blvd, Tampa, FL, 33606-1490. Tel: 813-253-6231. Fax: 813-258-7426. p. 499

Hillman, Cari, Pub Relations, Middletown Public Library, 125 S Broad St, Middletown, OH, 45044. Tel: 513-424-1251. Fax: 513-424-6585. p. 1917

Hillman, Carol, Asst Dir, Altoona Public Library, 1303 Lynn Ave, Altoona, WI, 54720-0278. Tel: 715-839-5029. Fax: 715-830-5119. p. 2577

Hillman, Constance, Ch, Warminster Township Free Library, 1076 Emma Lane, Warminster, PA, 18974. Tel: 215-672-4362. Fax: 215-672-3604. p. 2150

Hillman, Kathy, Assoc Prof & Dir, Cent Libr Spec Coll, Baylor University Libraries, Moody Memorial Library, 1312 S Third, Waco, TX, 76798. p. 2396

Hillman, Lia, Br Mgr, San Francisco Public Library, Potrero Branch Library, 1616 20th St, San Francisco, CA, 94107-2811. Tel: 415-355-2822. Fax: 415-401-8147. p. 246

Hillman, Robert, Head Archivist, Eastern Illinois University, 600 Lincoln Ave, Charleston, IL, 61920. Tel: 217-581-7552. Fax: 217-581-6409. p. 603

Hillner, Melanie, Sci Librn, University of Richmond, 28 Westhampton Way, Richmond, VA, 23173. Tel: 804-289-8262. Fax: 804-289-8757. p. 2491

Hillquist, Dorthe, Dir, Waterford Library Association, 663 Waterford Rd, Waterford, ME, 04088. Tel: 207-583-2050. p. 1005

Hills, Mable, Circ, Georgetown County Library, 405 Cleland St, Georgetown, SC, 29440-3200. Tel: 843-545-3300. Fax: 843-545-3395. p. 2194

Hillyer, Jean, Asst Dir, Baylor University Libraries, Mabel Peters Caruth Learning Resource Center, Louise Herrington School of Nursing, 3700 Worth St, Dallas, TX, 75246. Tel: 214-820-2100. Fax: 214-820-4770. p. 2396

Hillyer, Sharon, Librn, Brown County Public Library District, 143 W Main St, Mount Sterling, IL, 62353. Tel: 217-773-2013. Fax: 217-773-4723. p. 677

Hilron, Debra, Librn, Alaska State Court Law Library, Ketchikan Branch, 415 Main St, Rm 206, Ketchikan, AK, 99901. Tel: 907-225-0500. Fax: 907-225-7420. p. 44

Hiltbrunn, Margaret, Cataloger, ILL, Unity Library & Archives, 1901 NW Blue Pkwy, Unity Village, MO, 64065-0001. Tel: 816-251-3503, 816-524-3550, Ext 2370. p. 1370

Hilton, Bev, Ref/Clinical Librn, University of Kentucky Libraries, Medical Center Library, 800 Rose St, Lexington, KY, 40536-0298. Tel: 859-323-8008. Fax: 859-323-1040. p. 922

Hilton, Emma, Circ, Harvin Clarendon County Library, 215 N Brooks St, Manning, SC, 29102. Tel: 803-435-8633. Fax: 803-435-8101. p. 2199

Hilton, Jane, Dir, Elwood Public Library, 505 Ripley St, Elwood, NE, 68937. Tel: 308-785-2035. Fax: 308-785-2035. p. 1398

Hilton, Thomas, Dept Head, Ref Librn, Lyndhurst Free Public Library, 355 Valley Brook Ave, Lyndhurst, NJ, 07071. Tel: 201-804-2478. Fax: 201-939-7677. p. 1497

Hiltz, Darcy, Archives, Guelph Public Library, 100 Norfolk St, Guelph, ON, N1H 4J6, CANADA. Tel: 519-824-6220. Fax: 519-824-8342. p. 2807

Hiltz, Helen, Mgr, District of Columbia Public Library, Takoma Park, 416 Cedar St NW, Washington, DC, 20012. Tel: 202-576-7252. p. 399

Hilyard, Nann Blaine, Dir, Zion-Benton Public Library District, 2400 Gabriel Ave, Zion, IL, 60099. Tel: 847-872-4680, Ext 110. Fax: 847-872-4942. p. 722

Hilyerd, Will, Asst Prof, Ref, University of Louisville Libraries, Brandeis School of Law Library, 2301 S Third St, Louisville, KY, 40208. Tel: 502-852-6080. Fax: 502-852-8906. p. 926

Hime, Christina, Circ Mgr, Jackson County Public Library, 303 W Second St, Seymour, IN, 47274-2147. Tel: 812-522-3412, Ext 238. Fax: 812-522-5456. p. 777

Hime, Laurie, Librn, Miami Dade College, Kendall Campus Library, 11011 SW 104th St, Miami, FL, 33176-3393. Tel: 305-237-0996, 305-237-2015, 305-237-2291. Fax: 305-237-2923. p. 466

Himmel, Jane, Asst Dir, Pigeon District Library, 7236 Nitz St, Pigeon, MI, 48755. Tel: 989-453-2341. Fax: 989-453-2266. p. 1217

Himsel, Christian, Instrul Serv Librn, Ref, Concordia University Wisconsin, 12800 N Lake Shore Dr, Mequon, WI, 53097-2402. Tel: 262-243-4534. Fax: 262-243-4424. p. 2615

Hinch, George, Board Pres, Capitan Public Library, 101 E Second St, Capitan, NM, 88316. Tel: 575-354-3035. Fax: 575-354-3223. p. 1552

Hinch, Marsha, Dir, Choteau-Teton Public Library, 17 N Main, Choteau, MT, 59422. Tel: 406-466-2052. Fax: 406-466-2052. p. 1376

Hinchcliff, Marilou Z, Coordr, Cat, Bloomsburg University of Pennsylvania, 400 E Second St, Bloomsburg, PA, 17815-1301. Tel: 570-389-4224. Fax: 570-389-3066. p. 2035

Hinchcliffe, John, Cat, Ref Serv, Bloomfield College Library, Liberty St & Oakland Ave, Bloomfield, NJ, 07003. Tel: 973-748-9000, Ext 336. Fax: 973-743-3998. p. 1473

Hinck, Jonathan, Archivist, Ser Librn, Viterbo University, 900 Viterbo Dr, La Crosse, WI, 54601. Tel: 608-796-3262. Fax: 608-796-3275. p. 2603

Hinckley, Steven, Assoc Dean, Libr & Info Serv, Dir, Law Libr, Pennsylvania State University - Dickinson School of Law (University Libraries), 1170 Harrisburg Pike, Carlisle, PA, 17013-1617. Tel: 814-867-0390. Fax: 717-240-5127. p. 2042

Hindeleh, Nitsa, Dir, Libr Serv, Missouri Baptist University, One College Park Dr, Saint Louis, MO, 63141-8698. Tel: 314-392-2319. Fax: 314-392-2343. p. 1356

Hinderliter, Lori, Exec Dir, Butler Area Public Library, 218 N McKean St, Butler, PA, 16001-4971. Tel: 724-287-1715, Ext 106. Fax: 724-285-5090. p. 2039

Hinderliter, Nina, Librn, Soutar Memorial Library, 102 S Ellis, Boise City, OK, 73933. Tel: 580-544-2715. Fax: 580-544-2715. p. 1958

Hinders, Tom, Govt Doc, Ser, Oberlin College Library, 148 W College St, Oberlin, OH, 44074. Tel: 440-775-8285. Fax: 440-775-6586. p. 1924

Hindes, Debra, Ref, Flint Memorial Library, 147 Park St, North Reading, MA, 01864. Tel: 978-664-4942. Fax: 978-664-0812. p. 1113

Hindes, Kristen, Head, ILL & Coll Serv, Saint Michael's College, One Winooski Park, Box L, Colchester, VT, 05439-2525. Tel: 802-654-2400. Fax: 802-654-2630. p. 2422

Hinds, Bryan, Evening Circ Supvr, Saint Ambrose University Library, 518 W Locust St, Davenport, IA, 52803. Tel: 563-333-6475. Fax: 563-333-6248. p. 807

Hinds, Lorna, Tech Serv, Worcester County Library, 307 N Washington St, Snow Hill, MD, 21863. Tel: 410-632-2600. Fax: 410-632-1159. p. 1042

Hinds, Stuart, Mgr, Johnson County Library, Corinth, 8100 Mission Rd, Prairie Village, KS, 66208. Tel: 913-967-8653. Fax: 913-967-8663. p. 888

Hinds, Stuart, Dir, Spec Coll, University of Missouri-Kansas City Libraries, 800 E 51st St, Kansas City, MO, 64110. Tel: 816-235-1532. Fax: 816-333-5584. p. 1341

Hinds, Susan, Circ, Reserves, Auburn University, Ralph Brown Draughon Library, 231 Mell St, Auburn, AL, 36849. Tel: 334-844-1579. Fax: 334-844-4424. p. 5

Hindulak, Abby, Coll Develop Librn, Ella M Everhard Public Library, 132 Broad St, Wadsworth, OH, 44281-1897. Tel: 330-334-5761. Fax: 330-334-6605. p. 1943

Hine, Betsy N, Cat Librn, Indiana State University, 510 North 6 1/2 St, Terre Haute, IN, 47809. Tel: 812-237-2572. Fax: 812-237-3376. p. 781

Hines, Betty, Ref Serv, Muskogee Public Library, 801 W Okmulgee, Muskogee, OK, 74401. Tel: 918-682-6657. Fax: 918-682-9466. p. 1969

Hines, Bonnie, Dr, Coll Develop Coordr, Syst Adminr, Louisiana State University at Alexandria, 8100 Hwy 71 S, Alexandria, LA, 71302. Tel: 318-473-6438. Fax: 318-473-6556. p. 940

Hines, Brandon, YA Serv, Hays Public Library, 1205 Main, Hays, KS, 67601-3693. Tel: 785-625-9014. Fax: 785-625-8683. p. 871

Hines, Geneva, Genealogy/Local Hist Spec, Milton-Union Public Library, 560 S Main St, West Milton, OH, 45383. Tel: 937-698-5515. Fax: 937-698-3774. p. 1946

Hines, Jean, Br Coordr, Pratt Institute Libraries, 200 Willoughby Ave, Brooklyn, NY, 11205-3897. Tel: 212-647-7547. Fax: 718-399-4401. p. 1594

Hines, Jean, Coordr, Pratt Institute Libraries, Pratt Manhattan, 144 W 14th St, New York, NY, 10011-7301. Tel: 212-647-7539. Fax: 646-336-8797. p. 1594

Hines, Judy, LRC Supvr, Sandhills Community College, 3395 Airport Rd, Pinehurst, NC, 28374. Tel: 910-695-3890. Fax: 910-695-3947. p. 1814

Hines, Julie, Campus Librn, Golden Gate Baptist Theological Seminary Library, 2240 N Hayden Rd, Ste 101, Scottsdale, AZ, 85257-2801. Tel: 480-941-1993, Ext 213. Fax: 480-945-4199. p. 80

Hines, Linda, Ch, Wharton County Library, 1920 N Fulton, Wharton, TX, 77488. Tel: 979-532-8080. p. 2400

Hines Nobles, Bunny, Head of Libr, Monroe County Public Library, 121 Pineville Rd, Monroeville, AL, 36460. Tel: 251-743-3818. Fax: 251-575-7357. p. 27

Hines, Patricia A, Med Librn, Krohn Memorial Library, The Good Samaritan Hospital of Lebanon, Pennsylvania, Fourth & Walnut Sts, Lebanon, PA, 17042. Tel: 717-270-7826. Fax: 717-270-3882. p. 2079

Hines, Sarah, Ch, Vineyard Haven Public Library, 200 Main St, Vineyard Haven, MA, 02568-9710. Tel: 508-696-4211, Ext 14. Fax: 508-696-7495. p. 1132

Hines, Scott, Ref Librn, Palo Alto University, 1791 Arastradero Rd, Palo Alto, CA, 94304. Tel: 650-433-3808. Fax: 650-433-3888. p. 204

Hines, Susie, Librn, University of Maryland, PO Box 775, Cambridge, MD, 21613-0775. Tel: 410-221-8450. Fax: 410-221-8490. p. 1022

Hines, Tammy, Reader Serv Librn, Longwood University, Redford & Race St, Farmville, VA, 23909. Tel: 434-395-2444. Fax: 434-395-2453. p. 2463

Hines, Thomas Collier, Curator, Dir, South Union Shaker Village, 850 Shaker Museum Rd, Auburn, KY, 42206. Tel: 270-542-4167. Fax: 270-542-7558. p. 906

Hiney, Carole, Dir, DeTour Area School & Public Library, 202 S Division St, DeTour Village, MI, 49725. Tel: 906-297-2011. Fax: 906-297-3403. p. 1169

Hinger, Joseph P, Assoc Dir, Tech Serv, Saint John's University Library, Rittenberg Law Library, 8000 Utopia Pkwy, Queens, NY, 11439. Tel: 718-990-1582. Fax: 718-990-6649. p. 1725

Hink, Betty Jean, Dir, Greenwood Reading Center, Main St, Greenwood, NY, 14839. Tel: 607-225-4654. p. 1632

Hinkel, Joanne, Commun & Media Relations, Boise Public Library, 715 S Capitol Blvd, Boise, ID, 83702. Tel: 208-384-4372. p. 570

Hinkel, Stacy, In Charge, DLA Piper US LLP, 401 B St, Ste 1700, San Diego, CA, 92101-4297. Tel: 619-699-2700. Fax: 619-699-2701. p. 231

Hinken, Susan E, Head, Tech Serv, University of Portland, 5000 N Willamette Blvd, Portland, OR, 97203-5743. Tel: 503-943-7111. Fax: 503-943-7491. p. 2015

Hinkle, Arlene, Librn, Caprock Public Library, 104 N First, Quitaque, TX, 79255. Tel: 806-455-1225. Fax: 806-455-1225. p. 2373

Hinkle, Karyn, Reader Serv Librn, Bard Graduate Center Library, 38 W 86th St, New York, NY, 10024. Tel: 212-501-3035. Fax: 212-501-3098. p. 1669

Hinkle, Kendra, Adminr, US Department of the Interior, National Park Service, 121 Monument Ave, Greeneville, TN, 37743. Tel: 423-638-3711. Fax: 423-798-0754. p. 2236

Hinkle, Kristina, Ch, A Holmes Johnson Memorial Library, 319 Lower Mill Bay Rd, Kodiak, AK, 99615. Tel: 907-486-8683. Fax: 907-486-8681. p. 51

Hinkle, Mary Kay, Admin Librn, Cat Mgr, Head, ILL, Crawford County Library System, 201 Plum St, Grayling, MI, 49738. Tel: 989-348-9214. Fax: 989-348-9294. p. 1186

Hinkle, Terri-Leigh, Acq, Simmons College, 300 The Fenway, Boston, MA, 02115-5898. p. 1066

Hinkley, Cindy, Ch, Charles M Bailey Public Library, 39 Bowdoin St, Winthrop, ME, 04364. Tel: 207-377-8673. p. 1007

Hinkley, David, Dir, Montclair Free Public Library, 50 S Fullerton Ave, Montclair, NJ, 07042. Tel: 973-744-0500, Ext 2226. Fax: 973-744-5268. p. 1503

Hinkley, Heidi Lynn, Librn, Peabody Memorial Library, 621 Main St, Jonesport, ME, 04649. Tel: 207-497-3003. p. 988

Hinman, Charles R, Dir of Educ, USS Bowfin Submarine Museum & Park Library, 11 Arizona Memorial Dr, Honolulu, HI, 96818-3145. Tel: 808-423-1341. Fax: 808-422-5201. p. 566

Hinojosa, Angelina, Ref Serv, Saint Joseph College, 1678 Asylum Ave, West Hartford, CT, 06117-2791. Tel: 860-232-4571. Fax: 860-523-4356. p. 376

Hinojosa, Rogelio, Acq Librn, Texas A&M International University, 5201 University Blvd, Laredo, TX, 78041-1900. Tel: 956-326-2123. Fax: 956-326-2399. p. 2354

Hinrichs, Marjorie, AV, Ida Public Library, 320 N State St, Belvidere, IL, 61008-3299. Tel: 815-544-3838. Fax: 815-544-8909. p. 594

Hinrichs, Patrick, Ch, North Las Vegas Library District, 2300 Civic Center Dr, North Las Vegas, NV, 89030-5839. Tel: 702-633-1070. Fax: 702-649-2576. p. 1432

Hinrichsen, LaBerta, Ch, Moorhead Public Library, PO Box 33, Moorhead, IA, 51558-0033. Tel: 712-886-5211. p. 833

Hinse, Odette, Ref, Hopital Maisonneuve-Rosemont, 5415 boul de l'Assomption, Montreal, QC, H1T 2M4, CANADA. Tel: 514-252-3462. Fax: 514-252-3574. p. 2896

Hinshaw, Janet, Librn, Wilson Ornithological Society, Univ of Michigan Museum of Zoology, 1109 Geddes Ave, Ann Arbor, MI, 48109-1079. Tel: 734-764-0457. Fax: 734-763-4080. p. 1153

Hinson, Blair, Br Mgr, Oconee County Public Library, Seneca Branch, 300 E South Second St, Seneca, SC, 29678. Tel: 864-882-4855. Fax: 864-882-5559. p. 2207

Hinson, Delana, Br Mgr, Clarkesville-Habersham County Library, 178 E Green St, Clarkesville, GA, 30523. Tel: 706-754-4413. Fax: 706-754-3479. p. 524

Hinson, Doris, Cat Librn, Duke University Libraries, School of Law Library, 210 Science Dr, Durham, NC, 27708. Tel: 919-613-7117. Fax: 919-613-7237. p. 1788

Hinson, Neda, Dir, Hamilton Parks Public Library, 74 Parks Plaza, Trimble, TN, 38259-4106. Tel: 731-297-3601. p. 2267

Hinson, Pat, Librn, Lancaster County Library, Kershaw Memorial, 3855 Fork Hill Rd, Kershaw, SC, 29067. Tel: 803-475-2609. Fax: 803-475-4444. p. 2199

Hinton, Amy, Librn, Southeastern Baptist College, 4229 Hwy 15 N, Laurel, MS, 39440. Tel: 601-426-6346. Fax: 601-426-6347. p. 1307

Hinton, Joan, Br Mgr, Broward County Division of Libraries, North Lauderdale Saraniero Branch, 6901 Kimberly Blvd, North Lauderdale, FL, 33068. Tel: 954-968-3840. Fax: 954-968-3842. p. 442

Hinton, Martha, Librn, Dixie Regional Library System, Houlka Public, 201 Walker St, Houlka, MS, 38850-0275. Tel: 662-568-2747. Fax: 662-568-2747. p. 1312

Hinton, Natalie, Asst Dir, User Serv (ILL), Gettysburg College, 300 N Washington St, Gettysburg, PA, 17325. Tel: 717-337-7032. Fax: 717-337-7001. p. 2059

Hinton, Patricia, Ref Asst, Clinton Junior College Library, 1029 Crawford Rd, Rock Hill, SC, 29730-5152. Tel: 803-327-7402, Ext 228. Fax: 803-324-2734. p. 2202

Hinton, Patricia G, Head Librn, Louisburg College, 501 N Main St, Louisburg, NC, 27549-7704. Tel: 919-497-3269. Fax: 919-496-5444. p. 1807

Hintz, Gail, Ch, Chillicothe Public Library District, 430 N Bradley Ave, Chillicothe, IL, 61523-1920. Tel: 309-274-2719. Fax: 309-274-3000. p. 628

Hintz, Sarah, Ref Supvr, Pickaway County District Public Library, 1160 N Court St, Circleville, OH, 43113-1725. Tel: 740-477-1644, Ext 227. Fax: 740-474-2855. p. 1875

Hiott, Judith, Chief, Houston Area Library Automated Network, Houston Public Library, 500 McKinney Ave, Houston, TX, 77002. Tel: 832-393-1411. Fax: 832-393-1427. p. 2956

Hiott, Linda, Br Mgr, Anderson County Library, Lander Memorial Regional, 925 Greenville Dr, Williamston, SC, 29697. Tel: 864-847-5238. Fax: 864-847-5238. p. 2180

Hipke, Jenny, Librn, Marinette County Library System, Peshtigo Public Library, 331 French St, Peshtigo, WI, 54157-1219. Tel: 715-582-4905. Fax: 715-582-4905. p. 2612

Hipp, Caroline, Chief, Extn Serv, Richland County Public Library, 1431 Assembly St, Columbia, SC, 29201-3101. Tel: 803-799-9084. Fax: 803-929-3448. p. 2188

Hipp, Joan, Dir, Florham Park Public Library, 107 Ridgedale Ave, Florham Park, NJ, 07932. Tel: 973-377-2694. Fax: 973-377-2085. p. 1486

Hippen, Sharon, Dir, Buffalo Center Public Library, 221 N Main St, Buffalo Center, IA, 50424. Tel: 641-562-2546. Fax: 641-562-2546. p. 797

Hippenhammer, Craighton, Informatics Librn, Olivet Nazarene University, One University Ave, Bourbonnais, IL, 60914-2271. Tel: 815-939-5145. Fax: 815-939-5170. p. 596

Hipple, Diana, Coordr, Nebraska Department of Correctional Services, 2309 N Hwy 83, McCook, NE, 69001. Tel: 308-345-8405, Ext 224. Fax: 308-345-8407. p. 1408

Hipple, Thomas, Dir, Juniata County Library, Inc, 498 Jefferson St, Mifflintown, PA, 17059-1424. Tel: 717-436-6378. Fax: 717-436-9324. p. 2089

Hipps, Kathy, Info Literacy Librn, Tusculum College, Hwy 107, 60 Shiloh Rd, Greeneville, TN, 37743. Tel: 423-636-7320, Ext 5123. Fax: 423-787-8498. p. 2236

Hipsley, Christina, Cat, Ser, Stevenson University Library, 1525 Greenspring Valley Rd, Stevenson, MD, 21153. Tel: 443-334-2766. Fax: 410-486-7329. p. 1043

Hire, Tara, Librn, Monhegan Memorial Library, One Library Lane, Monhegan, ME, 04852. Tel: 207-596-0549. p. 992

Hiremath, Uma, Dr, Exec Dir, Ames Free Library, 53 Main St, North Easton, MA, 02356. Tel: 508-238-2000. Fax: 508-238-2980. p. 1112

Hirneisen, Deborah G, Libr Dir, Valley Forge Christian College, 1401 Charlestown Rd, Phoenixville, PA, 19460. Tel: 610-917-2003. Fax: 610-917-2008. p. 2120

Hirohata-Goto, Gayle, Br Mgr, Hawaii State Public Library System, Aiea Public Library, 99-143 Moanalua Rd, Aiea, HI, 96701-4009. Tel: 808-483-7333. Fax: 808-483-7336. p. 561

Hirooka, Kathleen, Supv Librn, Commun Relations, Oakland Public Library, 125 14th St, Oakland, CA, 94612. Tel: 510-238-6713. Fax: 510-238-4923. p. 197

Hirsch, Christina, Circ Serv, East Meadow Public Library, 1886 Front St, East Meadow, NY, 11554-1705. Tel: 516-794-2570. Fax: 516-794-1272. p. 1617

Hirsch, Gerald, Asst Dir, Info Syst & Ref Serv, State Historical Society of Missouri Library, 1020 Lowry St, Columbia, MO, 65201-7298. Tel: 573-884-7906. Fax: 573-884-4950. p. 1324

Hirsch, Lois, Librn, Congregation Rodeph Shalom, 615 N Broad St, Philadelphia, PA, 19123. Tel: 215-627-6747 (Philadelphia Center), 215-635-2500 (Elkins Park Center). Fax: 215-627-1313. p. 2104

Hirsch, Marga, Librn, Park Avenue Synagogue, 50 E 87th St, New York, NY, 10128. Tel: 212-369-2600, Ext 127. Fax: 212-410-7879. p. 1697

Hirsch-Shell, Livia, Acq, Huntington Library, 1151 Oxford Rd, San Marino, CA, 91108. Tel: 626-405-2185. Fax: 626-449-5720. p. 255

Hirschberg, Michael, Exec Dir, American Helicopter Society International Library, 217 N Washington St, Alexandria, VA, 22314. Tel: 703-684-6777. Fax: 703-739-9279. p. 2445

Hirschel, Aimee, Dir, Upper Skagit Library, 45770-B Main St, Concrete, WA, 98237. Tel: 360-853-7939. Fax: 360-853-7555. p. 2513

Hirschi, Cheryl, Br Mgr, Saint Johns County Public Library System, 6670 US 1 South, Saint Augustine, FL, 32086. Tel: 904-827-6918. Fax: 904-827-6905. p. 486

Hirschy, Margaret, Assoc Dir/Coll Mgr, The University of Findlay, 1000 N Main St, Findlay, OH, 45840-3695. Tel: 419-434-4262. p. 1899

Hirschy, Margaret, Dir, Winebrenner Theological Seminary Library, 950 N Main St, Findlay, OH, 45840-3652. Tel: 419-434-4260. Fax: 419-434-4267. p. 1899

Hirsekorn, Patricia, ILL, Gloucester County College Library, 1400 Tanyard Rd, Sewell, NJ, 08080. Tel: 856-468-5000, Ext 2250. Fax: 856-464-1695. p. 1529

Hirsh, Barbara, Dir, Info Res & Knowledge Mgt, National Economic Research Associates, Inc, 360 Hamilton Ave, 10th Flr, White Plains, NY, 10601. Tel: 914-448-4090. Fax: 914-448-4040. p. 1768

Hirsh, Kenneth, Dir, Law Libr & Info Tech, University of Cincinnati, 2540 Clifton Ave, Cincinnati, OH, 45219. Tel: 513-556-0163. Fax: 513-556-6265. p. 1874

Hirsh, Sandy, Dr, Dir, Prof, San Jose State University, One Washington Sq, San Jose, CA, 95192-0029. Tel: 408-924-2490. Fax: 408-924-2476. p. 2962

Hirshfield, Laura, AV, Evanston Public Library, 1703 Orrington, Evanston, IL, 60201. Tel: 847-448-8620. Fax: 847-866-0313. p. 643

Hirst, Jeff, Dir, Diocese of Pittsburgh, 2900 Noblestown Rd, Pittsburgh, PA, 15205. Tel: 412-928-5817. Fax: 412-928-5833. p. 2125

Hirt, Beverly, Dir, Smyrna Public Library, 107 S Main St, Smyrna, DE, 19977. Tel: 302-653-4579. Fax: 302-653-2650. p. 386

Hirten, Maureen, Dir, Capital Area District Libraries, 401 S Capitol Ave, Lansing, MI, 48933. Tel: 517-367-6341. Fax: 517-374-1068. p. 1200

Hirtle, Stephen, Assoc Prof, University of Pittsburgh, 135 N Bellefield Ave, Pittsburgh, PA, 15260. Tel: 412-624-5230. Fax: 412-624-5231. p. 2973

Hirtz, Carrie, Head Librn, Skadden, Arps, Slate, Meagher & Flom Library, Four Times Sq, New York, NY, 10036. Tel: 212-735-3000. Fax: 212-735-3244. p. 1700

Hirumi, Atsusi, Dr, Assoc Prof, University of Central Florida, College of Education, PO Box 161250, Orlando, FL, 32816. Tel: 407-823-1760. Fax: 407-823-4880. p. 2963

Hiser, Brigada, Dir, Mitchell County Public Library, 340 Oak St, Colorado City, TX, 79512. Tel: 325-728-3968. Fax: 325-728-3912. p. 2299

Hisky, Brigitte, Ref Asst, Howard Community College Library, 10901 Little Patuxent Pkwy, Columbia, MD, 21044. Tel: 443-518-4812. Fax: 443-518-4993. p. 1025

Hisle, W Lee, Librn of the Col, VPres for Info Serv, Connecticut College, 270 Mohegan Ave, New London, CT, 06320-4196. Tel: 860-439-2650. Fax: 860-439-2871. p. 359

Hislop, Gregory W, PhD, Assoc Prof, Drexel University, Rush Bldg, Rm 306, 30 N 33rd St, Philadelphia, PA, 19104-2875. Tel: 215-895-2474. Fax: 215-895-2494. p. 2972

Hist, Judy, Commun Libr Mgr, County of Los Angeles Public Library, Lancaster Library, 601 W Lancaster Blvd, Lancaster, CA, 93534. Tel: 661-948-5029. Fax: 661-945-0480. p. 142

Hitchcock, Eloise, Dean of Libr, Cumberland University, One Cumberland Sq, Lebanon, TN, 37087. Tel: 615-547-1351. Fax: 615-444-2569. p. 2244

Hitchcock, Jennifer, Youth Ref Librn, Fruitville Public Library, 100 Coburn Rd, Sarasota, FL, 34240. Tel: 941-861-2500. Fax: 941-861-2528. p. 489

Hitchcock, Ruth, Youth Serv Librn, Albany County Public Library, 310 S Eighth St, Laramie, WY, 82070-3969. Tel: 307-721-2580. Fax: 307-721-2584. p. 2657

Hitchcock, Vicki, Dir, Carbon County Library System, 215 W Buffalo St, Rawlins, WY, 82301. Tel: 307-328-2618. Fax: 307-328-2615. p. 2659

Hitchens, Connie, Librn, Central Citizens' Library District, 1134 E 3100 North Rd, Ste C, Clifton, IL, 60927-7088. Tel: 815-694-2800. Fax: 815-694-3200. p. 630

Hitchingham, Eileen, Dean of Libr, Virginia Polytechnic Institute & State University Libraries, Drill Field Dr, Blacksburg, VA, 24062-9001. Tel: 540-231-5595. Fax: 540-231-3946. p. 2451

Hitchings, Robert, Genealogy Librn, Local Hist Librn, Norfolk Public Library, 235 E Plume St, Norfolk, VA, 23510-1706. Tel: 757-664-7485. Fax: 757-441-5863. p. 2481

Hitchings, Tina, ILL, Kinnelon Public Library, 132 Kinnelon Rd, Kinnelon, NJ, 07405-2393. Tel: 973-838-1321. Fax: 973-838-0741. p. 1493

Hite, Jay, Tech Coordr, McCracken County Public Library, 555 Washington St, Paducah, KY, 42003-1735. Tel: 270-442-2510, Ext 13. Fax: 270-443-9322. p. 932

Hite, Katy, Ref/Instruction & Distance Learning Librn, Roosevelt University, 430 S Michigan Ave, Chicago, IL, 60605. Fax: 312-341-2425. p. 623

Hite, Maggie, Circ Librn, Chapel Hill Public Library, 100 Library Dr, Chapel Hill, NC, 27514. Tel: 919-968-2947. Fax: 919-968-2838. p. 1780

Hite, Marilyn, Dir, Defiance Public Library, 320 Fort St, Defiance, OH, 43512-2186. Tel: 419-782-1456. Fax: 419-782-6235. p. 1895

Hitt, Wendy, Librn, Church of the Holy Faith, Episcopal, 311 E Palace Ave, Santa Fe, NM, 87501. Tel: 505-982-4447, Ext 113. p. 1562

Hittle, Cindy, Br Dir, Morton County Library, Rolla Branch, 202 Third St, Rolla, KS, 67954. Tel: 620-593-4328. Fax: 620-593-4276. p. 865

Hittle, Gayle, Law Librn, Berliner Cohen Law Library, Ten Almaden Blvd, 11th Flr, San Jose, CA, 95113-2233. Tel: 408-938-2458. Fax: 408-998-5388. p. 249

Hittner, Jackie, Libr Serv Mgr, American Association of Orthodontists, 401 N Lindbergh Blvd, Saint Louis, MO, 63141. Tel: 314-292-6542. Fax: 314-997-1745. p. 1353

Hitzelberger, Michael, Circ Serv, Volunteer State Community College Library, 1480 Nashville Pike, Gallatin, TN, 37066-3188. Tel: 615-230-3400, Ext 3409. Fax: 615-230-3410. p. 2235

Hively, Charley, Pub Serv Dir, Clarksburg-Harrison Public Library, 404 W Pike St, Clarksburg, WV, 26301. Tel: 304-627-2236. Fax: 304-627-2239. p. 2557

Hively, Charley, Coordr, Ref & Instrul Serv, Fairmont State University, 1201 Locust Ave, Fairmont, WV, 26554. Tel: 304-367-4617. Fax: 304-367-4677. p. 2559

Hively, Todd, Ref, Temple College, 2600 S First St, Temple, TX, 76504. Tel: 254-298-8426. Fax: 254-298-8430. p. 2391

Hives, Chris, Archivist, University of British Columbia Library, University Archives, Irving K Barber Learning Centre, 1961 East Mall, Vancouver, BC, V6T 1Z1, CANADA. Tel: 604-827-3951. p. 2743

Hixson, Carol, Dean of Libr, University of South Florida Saint Petersburg, 140 Seventh Ave S, POY118, Saint Petersburg, FL, 33701. Tel: 727-873-4401. Fax: 727-873-4196. p. 489

Hixson, Cheryl, AV, Whitehall Township Public Library, 3700 Mechanicsville Rd, Whitehall, PA, 18052-3399. Tel: 610-432-4339. Fax: 610-432-9387. p. 2155

Hixson, Kim, Dir, Yakima Valley Libraries, 102 N Third St, Yakima, WA, 98901-2759. Tel: 509-452-8541. Fax: 509-575-2093. p. 2550

Hixson, Sandy, Cat, Cleveland State Community College Library, 3535 Adkisson Dr, Cleveland, TN, 37312-2813. Tel: 423-478-6209. Fax: 423-478-6255. p. 2229

Hlavsa, Larry, Dir, Saint Helena Public Library, 1492 Library Lane, Saint Helena, CA, 94574-1143. Tel: 707-963-5244. Fax: 707-963-5264. p. 226

Hlavsa, Larry B, Libr Dir, Webmaster, New Ulm Public Library, 17 N Broadway, New Ulm, MN, 56073-1786. Tel: 507-359-8331. Fax: 507-354-3255. p. 1268

Hlushko, Tonya, Asst Librn, Ashmont Community Library, PO Box 330, Ashmont, AB, T0A 0C0, CANADA. Tel: 780-726-3793, 780-726-3877. Fax: 780-726-3777. p. 2684

Hnatuik, Jeanine, Asst Librn, Massey & Township Public Library, 185 Grove, Massey, ON, P0P 1P0, CANADA. Tel: 705-865-2641. Fax: 705-865-1781. p. 2820

Hnetkovsky, Barbara, Asst Dir, Circ Mgr, Manhattan-Elwood Public Library District, 240 Whitson St, Manhattan, IL, 60442. Tel: 815-478-3987. Fax: 815-478-3988. p. 669

Ho, Agnes W, Dir, Neuse Regional Library, 510 N Queen St, Kinston, NC, 28501. Tel: 252-527-7066, Ext 131. Fax: 252-527-8220. p. 1805

Ho, Cora C, Dep Dir, Tufts University, 145 Harrison Ave, Boston, MA, 02111-1843. Fax: 617-636-4039. p. 1068

Ho, Huyen, Access Serv, Samuel Merritt College, 400 Hawthorne Ave, Oakland, CA, 94609. Tel: 510-869-8694. Fax: 510-869-6633. p. 199

Ho, James K, Assoc Dir, Howard University Libraries, Founders & Undergraduate Library, 500 Howard Pl NW, Washington, DC, 20059. Tel: 202-806-5669. p. 404

Ho, Jeanette, Cat, Texas A&M University Libraries, 5000 TAMU, College Station, TX, 77843-5000. Tel: 979-845-5438. Fax: 979-845-6238. p. 2298

Ho, Maria, Tech Serv, Tyndale University College & Seminary, 25 Ballyconnor Ct, Toronto, ON, M2M 4B3, CANADA. Tel: 416-226-6380. Fax: 416-218-6765. p. 2864

Ho, May Lein, Dir, Middlesex Public Library, 1300 Mountain Ave, Middlesex, NJ, 08846. Tel: 732-356-6602. Fax: 732-356-8420. p. 1501

Ho, Michael, Mrg, Admin Serv, Surrey Public Library, 10350 University Dr, Surrey, BC, V3T 4B8, CANADA. Tel: 604-598-7303. Fax: 604-598-7310. p. 2739

Ho, Pui-Ching, Commun Libr Mgr, County of Los Angeles Public Library, San Dimas Library, 145 N Walnut Ave, San Dimas, CA, 91773-2603. Tel: 909-599-6738. Fax: 909-592-4490. p. 143

Ho, SuHui, Digital Serv Librn, University of California, San Diego, Science & Engineering, 9500 Gilman Dr, Dept 0175E, La Jolla, CA, 92093-0175. Tel: 858-534-4579. Fax: 858-534-5583. p. 162

Hoadley, Deb, Dir, Langley-Adams Library, 185 Main St, Groveland, MA, 01834-1314. Tel: 978-372-1732. Fax: 978-374-6590. p. 1093

Hoadley, Sue A, Dir, Westerlo Public Library, 604 State Rte 143, Westerlo, NY, 12193. Tel: 518-797-3415. Fax: 518-797-3415. p. 1767

Hoag, Edward, Dir, Somerset County Library System, Hillsborough Public, Hillsborough Municipal Complex, 379 S Branch Rd, Hillsborough, NJ, 08844. Tel: 908-369-2200. Fax: 908-369-8242. p. 1475

Hoag, Katherine, Asst Librn, Dalton Free Public Library, 462 Main St, Dalton, MA, 01226. Tel: 413-684-6112. Fax: 413-684-4750. p. 1083

Hoagland, Denise, Syst Coordr, University of Rochester, River Campus Libraries, 755 Library Rd, Rochester, NY, 14627-0055. Tel: 585-275-4461. Fax: 585-273-5309. p. 1733

Hoagstrom, Maggie, Librn, Nebraska Department of Natural Resources Library, State Office Bldg, 4th Flr, 301 Centennial Mall S, Lincoln, NE, 68509-4676. Tel: 402-471-2081. Fax: 402-471-2900. p. 1405

Hoang, Ann, Asst Univ Librn, New Jersey Institute of Technology, University Heights, Newark, NJ, 07102-1982. Tel: 973-596-3206. Fax: 973-643-5601. p. 1511

Hoang, Ha, ILL, Ref, John Tyler Community College Library, Moyar Hall, M216, 13101 Jefferson Davis Hwy, Chester, VA, 23831-5316. Tel: 804-706-5195. Fax: 804-796-4238. p. 2456

Hoar, Mary, Pres, Yonkers Historical Society, 1500 Central Park Ave, Yonkers, NY, 10710. Tel: 914-961-8940. Fax: 914-961-8945. p. 1771

Hoar, Susan, Librn, Taft Public Library, 18 Main St, Mendon, MA, 01756. Tel: 508-473-3259. Fax: 508-473-7049. p. 1105

Hoar, Susan, Ser, Thomas Nelson Community College Library, Wythe Hall 228, 99 Thomas Nelson Dr, Hampton, VA, 23666. Tel: 757-825-3529. Fax: 757-825-2870. p. 2469

Hoare, Betty, Asst Libr Mgr, Claresholm Public Library, 211 49th Ave W, Claresholm, AB, T0L 0T0, CANADA. Tel: 403-625-4168. Fax: 403-625-2939. p. 2695

Hobbins, Joanna, Info Spec, McGill University Libraries, Walter Hitschfeld Geographic Information Centre, Burnside Hall, Rm 524, 805 Sherbrooke St W, Montreal, QC, H3A 2K6, CANADA. Tel: 514-398-7453, 514-398-8095. Fax: 514-398-7437. p. 2898

Hobbins, John, Law Librn, McGill University Libraries, Nahum Gelber Law Library, 3660 Peel St, Montreal, QC, H3A 1W9, CANADA. Tel: 514-398-4715. Fax: 514-398-3585. p. 2898

Hobbs, Angie, Ref Coordr, Wake Forest University, Professional Center Library, Worrell Professional Ctr for Law & Management, 1834 Wake Forest Rd, Winston-Salem, NC, 27106. Tel: 336-758-5438. Fax: 336-758-6077. p. 1834

Hobbs, Bonnie, Tech Serv & Syst Mgr, Thomas Branigan Memorial Library, 200 E Picacho Ave, Las Cruces, NM, 88001-3499. Tel: 575-528-4043. Fax: 575-528-4030. p. 1557

Hobbs, Janet L, Mgr, Libr Serv, Cedars-Sinai Medical Center, South Tower, Rm 2815, 8700 Beverly Blvd, Los Angeles, CA, 90048-1865. Tel: 310-423-3751. Fax: 310-423-0138. p. 169

Hobbs, Jim, Online Serv Coordr, Loyola University New Orleans, 6363 Saint Charles Ave, New Orleans, LA, 70118-6195. Tel: 504-864-7111. Fax: 504-864-7247. p. 961

Hobbs, Lynn, Dir, Pendleton Community Library, 595 E Water St, Pendleton, IN, 46064-1070. Tel: 765-778-7527, Ext 107. Fax: 765-778-7529. p. 772

Hobbs, Rose, Sister, Dir, Maria College of Albany Library, 700 New Scotland Ave, Albany, NY, 12208. Tel: 518-438-3111, Ext 215. Fax: 518-453-1366. p. 1569

Hobbs, Sandie, Libr Dir, Willows Public Library, 201 N Lassen St, Willows, CA, 95988-3010. Tel: 530-934-5156. Fax: 530-934-2225. p. 284

Hobbs, Susan T, Br Mgr, Chesapeake Public Library, Major Hillard Library, 824 Old George Washington Hwy N, Chesapeake, VA, 23323-2214. Tel: 757-410-7084. Fax: 757-410-7088, 757-410-7089. p. 2456

Hobeck, Jenny, Circ, Sparta Public Library, 211 W Broadway, Sparta, IL, 62286. Tel: 618-443-5014. Fax: 618-443-2952. p. 704

Hoberecht, Toni, Ref & Instruction Librn, University of Oklahoma, Schusterman Ctr, 4502 E 41st St, Tulsa, OK, 74135. Tel: 918-660-3220. Fax: 918-660-3215. p. 1984

Hoberg, Kathy, Libr Dir, Logan County Public Library, 317 Main St, Stapleton, NE, 69163. Tel: 308-636-2343. p. 1420

Hobgood, Jill, ILL, Ref Librn, Saint Mary's College, Notre Dame, IN, 46556-5001. Tel: 574-284-4804. Fax: 574-284-4791. p. 771

Hochstatter, Heather, Info Spec, Kaye Scholer LLP, 425 Park Ave, New York, NY, 10022. Tel: 212-836-8000, 212-836-8312. Fax: 212-836-6613. p. 1684

Hochstein, Sandra, Info Literacy, Douglas College Library, 700 Royal Ave, New Westminster, BC, V3M 5Z5, CANADA. Tel: 604-777-6135. Fax: 604-527-5193. p. 2734

Hochstetler, Adam, ILL, Ref, Pickaway County District Public Library, 1160 N Court St, Circleville, OH, 43113-1725. Tel: 740-477-1644. Fax: 740-474-2855. p. 1875

Hochstetler, Donald, Dr, Dir, Worcester State College, 486 Chandler St, Worcester, MA, 01602-2597. Tel: 508-929-8511. Fax: 508-929-8198. p. 1145

Hochstetler, Marcus L, Dir, King County Law Library, W 621 King County Courthouse, 516 Third Ave, Seattle, WA, 98104. Tel: marcus.hochstetler@metrokc.gov. Fax: 206-205-0513. p. 2528

Hochstetler, Ruth, Day Circ Mgr, Goshen College, Harold & Wilma Good Library, 1700 S Main, Goshen, IN, 46526-4794. Tel: 574-535-7427. Fax: 574-535-7438. p. 745

Hock, Janice (Jenny), Acq Librn, Angelo State University Library, 2025 S Johnson, San Angelo, TX, 76904-5079. Tel: 325-486-6525. Fax: 325-942-2198. p. 2378

Hock, Paula, Commun Libr Mgr, County of Los Angeles Public Library, San Fernando Library, 217 N Maclay Ave, San Fernando, CA, 91340-2433. Tel: 818-365-6928. Fax: 818-365-3820. p. 143

Hock, Paula, Commun Libr Mgr, Santa Clarita Public Library, Newhall Library, 22704 W Ninth St, Santa Clarita, CA, 91321. Tel: 661-259-0750. Fax: 661-254-5760. p. 263

Hockenberry, Benjamin, Syst Librn, Saint John Fisher College, 3690 East Ave, Rochester, NY, 14618-3599. Tel: 585-385-8382. Fax: 585-385-8445. p. 1732

Hockenberry, Doreen, Head, Govt Doc, Ohio University Libraries, 30 Park Pl, Athens, OH, 45701-2978. Tel: 740-593-2718. Fax: 740-593-2708. p. 1856

Hockensmith, Joshua, Libr Tech, University of North Carolina at Chapel Hill, Joseph Curtis Sloane Art Library, 102 Hanes Art Ctr, CB No 3405, Chapel Hill, NC, 27599-3405. Tel: 919-962-2397. Fax: 919-962-0722. p. 1781

Hocking, Connie, ILL, Salina Public Library, 301 W Elm St, Salina, KS, 67401. Tel: 785-825-4624. Fax: 785-823-0706. p. 893

Hocking, Kimberly, Head, Access Serv, Campbell University, Norman Adrian Wiggins School of Law Library, 225 Hillsborough St, Ste 203, Raleigh, NC, 27603. Tel: 919-865-5869. Fax: 919-865-5995. p. 1778

Hoctor, Stephanie, Ch, Clinton Public Library, 313 S Fourth St, Clinton, IN, 47842-2398. Tel: 765-832-8349. Fax: 765-832-3823. p. 732

Hodapp, Patricia C, Dir of Libr, Santa Fe Public Library, 145 Washington Ave, Santa Fe, NM, 87501. Tel: 505-955-6788. Fax: 505-955-6676. p. 1563

Hodd, Becky, Ref Librn, County College of Morris, 214 Center Grove Rd, Randolph, NJ, 07869-2086. p. 1525

Hodder, Dorothy, Sr Librn, New Hanover County Public Library, 201 Chestnut St, Wilmington, NC, 28401. Tel: 910-798-6323. Fax: 910-798-6312. p. 1830

Hodel, Mary Anne, Dir, Orange County Library District, 101 E Central Blvd, Orlando, FL, 32801. Tel: 407-835-7323. p. 476

Hodge, Barbara, Supvr, Tech Serv, Pickaway County District Public Library, 1160 N Court St, Circleville, OH, 43113-1725. Tel: 740-477-1644, Ext 222. Fax: 740-474-2855. p. 1875

Hodge, Bernadette, Librn, New York Center for Agricultural Medicine & Health Library, One Atwell Rd, Cooperstown, NY, 13326. Tel: 607-547-6023, Ext 233. Fax: 607-547-6087. p. 1610

Hodge, Dennis, Head Librn, Lewis Dana Hill Memorial Library, 2079 Main St, Center Lovell, ME, 04231-9702. Tel: 207-928-2301. p. 982

Hodge, Jonathan, Cat, Fairfield University, 1073 N Benson Rd, Fairfield, CT, 06430-5195. Tel: 203-254-4044. Fax: 203-254-4135. p. 339

Hodge, Kerry, Acq & Ser Spec, Washington State University Libraries, 14204 NE Salmon Creek Ave, Vancouver, WA, 98686. Tel: 360-546-9684. Fax: 360-546-9039. p. 2546

Hodge, Megan, Asst Br Mgr, Chesterfield County Public Library, LaPrade, 9000 Hull St Rd, Richmond, VA, 23236. Tel: 804-276-7755. p. 2457

Hodge, Mildred, Dir of Libr Serv, Three Rivers Community College, 574 New London Tpk, Norwich, CT, 06360-6598. Tel: 860-892-5727. Fax: 860-886-0691. p. 363

Hodge, Miriam, Br Mgr, Pointe Coupee Parish Library, Morganza Branch, 221 S Louisiana, Hwy 1, Morganza, LA, 70759. Tel: 225-694-2428. Fax: 225-694-2428. p. 964

Hodge, Susan, Sr Dir, Commun Engagement, University of South Carolina Upstate Library, 800 University Way, Spartanburg, SC, 29303. Tel: 864-503-5275. Fax: 864-503-5601. p. 2205

Hodge-Bodart, Catherine, Cat/Metadata Librn, Muhlenberg College, 2400 Chew St, Allentown, PA, 18104-5586. Tel: 484-664-3575. Fax: 484-664-3511. p. 2027

Hodgen, Doris, Cat, ILL, University of South Dakota, McKusick Law Library, 414 E Clark St, Vermillion, SD, 57069-2390. Tel: 605-677-5259. Fax: 605-677-5417. p. 2220

Hodgen, Shirley, Ch, Thorntown Public Library, 124 N Market St, Thorntown, IN, 46071-1144. Tel: 765-436-7348. Fax: 765-436-7011. p. 782

Hodges, Addie, Circ Supvr, Sampson-Clinton Public Library, 217 Graham St, Clinton, NC, 28328. Tel: 910-592-4153. Fax: 910-590-3504. p. 1784

Hodges, Ann C, Librn, Carmody & Torrance, 50 Leavenworth St, Waterbury, CT, 06702. Tel: 203-573-1200. Fax: 203-575-2600. p. 374

Hodges, Bill, Mgr, Network Serv, University of Tennessee, Taylor Law Center, 1505 W Cumberland Ave, Knoxville, TN, 37996-1800. Tel: 865-974-2547. Fax: 865-974-6571, 865-974-6595. p. 2243

Hodges, Catherine, Mgr, Florida State College at Jacksonville, Nassau Center Library, 76346 William Burgess Blvd, Yulee, FL, 32097. Tel: 904-548-4468. Fax: 904-548-4427. p. 453

Hodges, Dean, Librn, Adult Serv, Haltom City Public Library, 4809 Haltom Rd, Haltom City, TX, 76117-3622. Tel: 817-222-7758. Fax: 817-834-1446. p. 2330

Hodges, Doreen, Head Librn, Valdez Consortium Library, 212 Fairbanks St, Valdez, AK, 99686. Tel: 907-835-4632. Fax: 907-835-4876. p. 55

Hodges, James, Dr, Cataloger, Florida College, 119 N Glen Arven Ave, Temple Terrace, FL, 33617-5578. Tel: 813-988-5131, Ext 210. p. 500

Hodges, Judy, Asst Dir, Meredith Public Library, 91 Main St, Meredith, NH, 03253. Tel: 603-279-4303. Fax: 603-279-5352. p. 1457

Hodges, Melinda, Dir, Buda Public Library, 303 Main St, Buda, TX, 78610. Tel: 512-295-5899. Fax: 512-295-6525. p. 2293

Hodges, Ruth A, Dr, Asst Prof, Ref & Info Spec, South Carolina State University, 300 College St NE, Orangeburg, SC, 29115-4427. Tel: 803-536-7045. Fax: 803-536-8902. p. 2202

Hodges, Sharon, Dir, Petersburgh Public Library, 69 Main St, Petersburgh, NY, 12138-5010. Tel: 518-658-2927. Fax: 518-658-2927. p. 1717

Hodges-Humble, Laurie, Librn, Innisfail Public Library, 5300A 55th St Close, Innisfail, AB, T4G 1R6, CANADA. Tel: 403-227-4407. Fax: 403-227-3122. p. 2707

Hodgin, Chuck, Ref Librn, University of Mobile, 5735 College Pkwy, Mobile, AL, 36613-2842. Tel: 251-442-2242. Fax: 251-442-2515. p. 26

Hodgins, David, Circ, Methodist College, 5400 Ramsey St, Fayetteville, NC, 28311. Tel: 910-630-7618. Fax: 910-630-7119. p. 1793

Hodgkinson, Amanda, AV, Ch, Orillia Public Library, 36 Mississaga St W, Orillia, ON, L3V 3A6, CANADA. Tel: 705-325-2338. Fax: 705-327-1744. p. 2826

Hodgson, Bea, In Charge, City of Kawartha Lakes Public Library, Norland Branch, 3448 County Rd 45, Norland, ON, K0M 2L0, CANADA. Tel: 705-454-8552. Fax: 705-454-9749. p. 2816

Hodgson, Lori, Dir, Burlington Public Library, 22 Sears St, Burlington, MA, 01803. Tel: 781-270-1690. Fax: 781-229-0406. p. 1072

Hodgson, William, Dir, Trent University, Media Services/Information Technology, Thomas J Bata Library, No 105, 1600 W Bank Dr, Peterborough, ON, K9J 7B8, CANADA. Tel: 705-748-1011, Ext 7458. p. 2836

Hodis, Haydee, Mgr, Springfield City Library, East Springfield Branch, 21 Osborne Terrace, Springfield, MA, 01104. Tel: 413-263-6840. Fax: 413-263-6842. p. 1127

Hodis, Haydee, Mgr, Springfield City Library, Liberty Branch, 773 Liberty St, Springfield, MA, 01104. Tel: 413-263-6849. Fax: 413-263-6851. p. 1127

Hodis, Haydee, Supvr, Springfield City Library, Brightwood Branch, 359 Plainfield St, Springfield, MA, 01107. Tel: 413-263-6805. Fax: 413-263-6810. p. 1127

Hodos, Susan, Br Mgr, Broward County Division of Libraries, Margate-Catharine Young Branch, 5810 Park Dr, Margate, FL, 33063. Tel: 954-968-3800. Fax: 954-968-3803. p. 442

Hodosy, Ken, Librn, New York State Department of Correctional Services, 23147 Swan Rd, Watertown, NY, 13601-9340. Tel: 315-782-7490, Ext 4600. Fax: 315-782-7490, Ext 2099. p. 1763

Hodson, Sara S, Curator, Huntington Library, 1151 Oxford Rd, San Marino, CA, 91108. Tel: 626-405-2205. Fax: 626-449-5720. p. 255

Hoecherl, Vickie, Br Mgr, Otsego County Library, Johannesburg Branch, 10900 East M-32, Johannesburg, MI, 49751. Tel: 989-732-3928. Fax: 989-731-3365. p. 1182

Hoedel, Bonnie, Libr Asst, Manistique School & Public Library, 100 N Cedar St, Manistique, MI, 49854-1293. Tel: 906-341-4316. Fax: 906-341-6751. p. 1206

Hoef, Gail, Mgr, Monsanto Company, 800 N Lindbergh Blvd, Saint Louis, MO, 63167. Tel: 314-694-4747. Fax: 314-694-8748. p. 1356

Hoefer, Stephen P, Operations & Bus Mgr, The Nyack Library, 59 S Broadway, Nyack, NY, 10960. Tel: 845-358-3370, Ext 33. Fax: 845-358-1363. p. 1708

Hoehamer, Matt, Dir, Hull Public Library, 1408 Main St, Hull, IA, 51239. Tel: 712-439-1321. Fax: 712-439-1534. p. 821

Hoehl, Susan, Dir, Allegheny General Hospital, 320 E North Ave, Pittsburgh, PA, 15212-4772. Tel: 412-359-3040. Fax: 412-359-4420. p. 2121

Hoek, D J, Head Music Libr, Northwestern University Library, Music, 1970 Campus Dr, Evanston, IL, 60208-2300. Tel: 847-491-2884. Fax: 847-467-7574. p. 644

Hoekstra, Cheryl, Dir, Alton Public Library, 605 Tenth St, Alton, IA, 51003. Tel: 712-756-4516. Fax: 712-756-4140. p. 792

Hoekstra, Maurie, County Librn, Calaveras County Library, 891 Mountain Ranch Rd, San Andreas, CA, 95249. Tel: 209-754-6701. Fax: 209-754-6512. p. 226

Hoekstra, Maurie, County Librn, Calaveras County Library, Angels Camp Branch, 426 N Main St, Angels Camp, CA, 95222. Tel: 209-736-2198. p. 227

Hoekstra, Ruth, Asst Librn, Ocheyedan Public Library, 874 Main St, Ocheyedan, IA, 51354. Tel: 712-758-3352. Fax: 712-758-3352. p. 836

Hoelscher, Connie, Librn, First Presbyterian Church, Five W Montgomery Ave, Ardmore, PA, 19003. Tel: 610-642-6650. Fax: 610-645-0517. p. 2029

Hoelscher, Elisa, Web Serv, Group Health Cooperative, 201 16th Ave E, Seattle, WA, 98112. Tel: 206-326-4985. Fax: 206-326-2629. p. 2527

Hoelter, Laura, Cat & Syst Librn, College of Saint Scholastica Library, 1200 Kenwood Ave, Duluth, MN, 55811-4199. Tel: 218-723-6141. Fax: 218-723-5948. p. 1247

Hoeltzel, Elaine, Dir, Olivet College Library, 333 S Main St, Olivet, MI, 49076-9730. Tel: 269-749-7582. Fax: 269-749-7121. p. 1215

Hoelzel, Linda, Dir, Dudley-Tucker Library, Six Epping St, Raymond, NH, 03077. Tel: 603-895-2633. Fax: 603-895-0904. p. 1463

Hoelzen, Randall, Doc Delivery, ILL, Ref Serv, University of Wisconsin-La Crosse, 1631 Pine St, La Crosse, WI, 54601-3748. Tel: 608-785-8398. Fax: 608-785-8639. p. 2603

Hoenig, Lisa, Dir, Redford Township District Library, 25320 W Six Mile, Redford, MI, 48240. Tel: 313-531-6900. Fax: 313-531-1721. p. 1220

Hoeper, Ronna, Instrul Serv Librn, Ref Serv, University of Wisconsin-Whitewater Library, 800 W Main St, Whitewater, WI, 53190. Tel: 262-472-5522. Fax: 262-472-5727. p. 2649

Hoepker, Sharon, Libr Mgr, ICF Consulting Inc, 630 K St, Ste 400, Sacramento, CA, 95814. Tel: 916-737-3000. Fax: 916-737-3030. p. 224

Hoeppner, Christopher, Assoc Dir, Admin Serv, DePaul University Libraries, 2350 N Kenmore, Chicago, IL, 60614. Tel: 773-325-3725, 773-325-7862. Fax: 773-325-7870. p. 612

Hoerman, Heidi L, Instr, University of South Carolina, 1501 Greene St, Columbia, SC, 29208. Tel: 803-777-3858. Fax: 803-777-7938. p. 2973

Hoerner, Kristina L, Adult Serv, Champaign Public Library, 200 W Green St, Champaign, IL, 61820-5193. Tel: 217-403-2050. Fax: 217-403-2053. p. 602

Hoesly, Jody, Coll & Scholarly Communications, Librn, University of Wisconsin-Madison, Kurt Wendt Engineering Library, 215 N Randall Ave, Madison, WI, 53706. Tel: 608-262-3493. Fax: 608-262-4739, 608-265-8751. p. 2610

Hoesman, Pam, Dir, Birchard Public Library of Sandusky County, 423 Croghan St, Fremont, OH, 43420. Tel: 419-334-7101. Fax: 419-334-4788. p. 1900

Hoey, Agnes, Mgr, Canton Free Library, Rensselaer Falls Branch, 212 Rensselaer St, Rensselaer Falls, NY, 13680. Tel: 315-344-7406. Fax: 315-344-7406. p. 1602

Hoey, Ann, Youth Serv Librn II, New Hampshire State Library, 20 Park St, Concord, NH, 03301-6314. Tel: 603-271-2865. Fax: 603-271-2205, 603-271-6826. p. 1443

Hoey, Suzanne M, Head Law Librn, Massachusetts Trial Court, 184 Main St, Worcester, MA, 01608. Tel: 508-831-2525. Fax: 508-754-9933. p. 1144

Hofacket, Jean, County Librn, Alameda County Library, 2450 Stevenson Blvd, Fremont, CA, 94538-2326. Tel: 510-745-1500. Fax: 510-793-2987. p. 149

Hofbauer, Ann, Electronic & Ad, Amityville Public Library, Oak & John Sts, Amityville, NY, 11701. Tel: 631-264-0567. Fax: 631-264-2006. p. 1573

Hofer, Amy, Distance Learning Librn, Portland State University Library, 1875 SW Park Ave, Portland, OR, 97201-3220. Tel: 503-725-9939. Fax: 503-725-4524. p. 2014

Hofer, Hanna, Pub Relations, Canby Public Library, 292 N Holly St, Canby, OR, 97013-3732. Tel: 503-266-3394. Fax: 503-266-1709. p. 1993

Hofer, Shannon, Acq, Circ, ILL, Mayville State University, 330 Third St NE, Mayville, ND, 58257. Tel: 701-788-4815. Fax: 701-788-4846. p. 1846

Hoff, Laura, Mgr, Association for Research & Enlightenment, 215 67th St, Virginia Beach, VA, 23451. Tel: 757-428-3588, Ext 7141. Fax: 757-422-4631. p. 2498

Hoffbeck, Sandy, Acq, Per, Southwest Minnesota State University Library, 1501 State St, Marshall, MN, 56258. Tel: 507-537-6134. Fax: 507-537-6200. p. 1258

Hoffecker, Lilian, Librn, Colorado Council of Medical Librarians, PO Box 101058, Denver, CO, 80210-1058. Tel: 303-724-2124. Fax: 303-724-2154. p. 2939

Hoffenberg, Ruth, Dir, Mount Sinai Services-Queens Hospital Center Affiliation, 82-68 164th St, Jamaica, NY, 11432. Tel: 718-883-4021. Fax: 718-883-6125. p. 1643

Hoffer, Charlene, Dir, Vandergrift Public Library Association, 128C Washington Ave, Vandergrift, PA, 15690-1214. Tel: 724-568-2212. Fax: 724-568-3862. p. 2149

Hoffer, Stephanie, Chief Financial Officer, St Marys Community Public Library, 140 S Chestnut St, Saint Marys, OH, 45885-2307. Tel: 419-394-7471. Fax: 419-394-7291. p. 1933

Hofferle, Margaret, Libr Tech, Saint Xavier University, 3700 W 103rd St, Chicago, IL, 60655-3105. Tel: 773-298-3362. Fax: 773-779-5231. p. 623

Hoffius, Susan, Curator, Medical University of South Carolina Library, Waring Historical Library, 175 Ashley Ave, Charleston, SC, 29425-0001. Tel: 843-792-2288. Fax: 843-792-8619. p. 2185

Hoffler, Katy, Music Libr Mgr, Davidson College, 209 Ridge Rd, Davidson, NC, 28035-0001. Tel: 704-894-2721. Fax: 704-894-2625. p. 1786

Hoffman, A P, Dir, Wallace Community College, 1141 Wallace Dr, Dothan, AL, 36303. Tel: 334-556-2225, 334-983-3521, Ext 2225. Fax: 334-556-2283. p. 15

Hoffman, Anne Marie, Circ, Mastics-Moriches-Shirley Community Library, 407 William Floyd Pkwy, Shirley, NY, 11967. Tel: 631-399-1511. Fax: 631-281-4442. p. 1743

Hoffman, Barbara, Circ, Lehigh Carbon Community College Library, 4525 Education Park Dr, Schnecksville, PA, 18078-9372. Tel: 610-799-1196. Fax: 610-779-1159. p. 2136

Hoffman, Carol, Ch, Laurens Public Library, 273 N Third St, Laurens, IA, 50554. Tel: 712-841-4612. Fax: 712-841-4612. p. 827

Hoffman, Catherine, Dir, Farmer City Public Library, 105 E Green St, Farmer City, IL, 61842-1508. Tel: 309-928-9532. Fax: 309-928-2540. p. 645

Hoffman, Cheryl, Dir, Spies Public Library, 940 First St, Menominee, MI, 49858-3296. Tel: 906-863-2900. Fax: 906-863-5000. p. 1208

Hoffman, Deena, Dir, Moravia Public Library, 100 E Chariton, Moravia, IA, 52571-9530. Tel: 641-724-3440. Fax: 641-724-3440. p. 833

Hoffman, Douglas, Librn, Tyrrell County Public Library, 414 Main St, Columbia, NC, 27925. Tel: 252-796-3771. Fax: 252-796-1167. p. 1785

Hoffman, Francine, Chef de Div, Bibliothèques de Montrèal; Saint-Pierre, 183, rue des Érables, Montreal, QC, H8R 1B1, CANADA. Tel: 514-634-3471, Ext 304. Fax: 514-634-8194. p. 2891

Hoffman, Francine, Chef de Div, Bibliothèques de Montrèal, Saul-Bellow, 3100, rue Saint-Antoine, Montreal, QC, H8S 4B8, CANADA. Tel: 514-634-3471, Ext 304. Fax: 514-634-8194. p. 2892

Hoffman, Germaine, Dir, French-Canadian Genealogical Society of Connecticut, Inc Library, 53 Tolland Green, Tolland, CT, 06084. Tel: 860-623-8721. p. 372

Hoffman, Jacqueline, Head, Circ, Southbury Public Library, 100 Poverty Rd, Southbury, CT, 06488. Tel: 203-262-0626. Fax: 203-262-6734. p. 368

Hoffman, James, Cat, University of Tulsa Libraries, 2933 E Sixth St, Tulsa, OK, 74104-3123. Tel: 918-631-3486. Fax: 918-631-3791. p. 1984

Hoffman, Jana, Ch, Ledding Library of Milwaukie, 10660 SE 21st Ave, Milwaukie, OR, 97222. Tel: 503-786-7585. Fax: 503-659-9497. p. 2006

Hoffman, Jane, Ch, Islip Public Library, 71 Monell Ave, Islip, NY, 11751-3999. Tel: 631-581-5933. Fax: 631-277-8429. p. 1641

Hoffman, Jay, Co-Dir, Coll Develop, Ref Serv, University of Maine at Augusta Libraries, 46 University Dr, Augusta, ME, 04330-9410. Tel: 207-621-3349. Fax: 207-621-3311. p. 975

Hoffman, Jennifer, Dir, Pub Libr Serv, Lackawanna Public Library, 560 Ridge Rd, Lackawanna, NY, 14218. Tel: 716-823-0630. Fax: 716-827-1997. p. 1650

Hoffman, Jennifer J, Mgr, Bks & Borrowing, Denver Public Library, Ten W 14th Ave Pkwy, Denver, CO, 80204-2731. Tel: 720-865-2034. Fax: 720-865-1477. p. 300

Hoffman, Jill, Libr Tech, Allen Community College Library, 1801 N Cottonwood, Iola, KS, 66749-1648. Tel: 620-365-5116, Ext 208. Fax: 620-365-3284. p. 873

Hoffman, Kathryn, Br Mgr, Fairfax County Public Library, City of Fairfax Regional Library, 10360 North St, Fairfax, VA, 22030-2514. Tel: 703-293-6227. p. 2461

Hoffman, Kimberly, Coordr of Sci Libr, Catholic University of America, Engineering-Architecture & Mathematics Library, 200 Pangborn Hall, 620 Michigan Ave NE, Washington, DC, 20064. Tel: 202-319-6178. Fax: 202-319-4485. p. 395

Hoffman, Kimberly, Coordr of Sci Libr, Catholic University of America, Physics Library, 101 Hannan Hall, 620 Michigan Ave NE, Washington, DC, 20064. Tel: 202-319-5320. Fax: 202-319-4485. p. 396

Hoffman, Kristin, Ref & Instruction Librn, Biola University Library, 13800 Biola Ave, La Mirada, CA, 90639. Tel: 562-944-0351, Ext 5154. Fax: 562-903-4840. p. 162

Hoffman, Lila, Circ, Centralia Regional Library District, Ralph W & Bernice S Sprehe Library, 103 S Broadway, Hoffman, IL, 62250. Tel: 618-495-9955. Fax: 618-495-9955. p. 602

Hoffman, Lynn M, Operations Mgr, Brown County Library, 515 Pine St, Green Bay, WI, 54301. Tel: 920-448-5808. Fax: 920-448-4376. p. 2595

Hoffman, Lynne, Dir, Libr Develop, Pierce County Library System, 3005 112th St E, Tacoma, WA, 98446-2215. Tel: 253-548-3456. Fax: 253-537-4600. p. 2539

Hoffman, Michael B, Librn, Torys Law Library, 237 Park Ave, 20th Flr, New York, NY, 10017. Tel: 212-880-6177. Fax: 212-682-0200. p. 1701

Hoffman, Nadine, Law Librn, University of Calgary Library, Law Library, 2500 University Dr NW, Calgary, AB, T2N 1N4, CANADA. Tel: 403-220-8392. Fax: 403-282-3000. p. 2693

Hoffman, Nancy, Asst Dir, Robert W Barlow Memorial Library, 921 Washington Ave, Iowa Falls, IA, 50126. Tel: 641-648-2872. Fax: 641-648-2872. p. 824

Hoffman, Nicholas James, Dir, Elkhart County Historical Society, Inc, 304 W Vistula, Bristol, IN, 46507. Tel: 574-848-4322. Fax: 574-848-5703. p. 729

Hoffman, Olwen, Librn, Parkland Regional Library, Spalding Branch, PO Box 37, Spalding, SK, S0K 4C0, CANADA. Tel: 306-872-2184. p. 2932

Hoffman, Ruth, Dir, Congregation Mikveh Israel Archives, Independence Mall E, 44 N Fourth St, Philadelphia, PA, 19106. Tel: 215-922-5446. Fax: 215-922-1550. p. 2104

Hoffman, Shane Ian, Info Tech Supvr, Pickaway County District Public Library, 1160 N Court St, Circleville, OH, 43113-1725. Tel: 740-477-1644, Ext 232. Fax: 740-474-2855. p. 1875

Hoffman, Stephanie, Librn, Peninsula Temple Beth El Library, 1700 Alameda de Las Pulgas, San Mateo, CA, 94403. Tel: 650-341-7701. Fax: 650-570-7183. p. 255

Hoffman, Sue, Br Head, Toronto Public Library, City Hall, Nathan Phillips Sq, 100 Queen St W, Toronto, ON, M5H 2N3, CANADA. Tel: 416-393-7650. Fax: 416-393-7421. p. 2861

Hoffman, Susan, Admin Librn, Chandler Public Library, Sunset, 4930 W Ray Rd, Chandler, AZ, 85226-6219. Tel: 480-782-2800. Fax: 480-782-2848. p. 60

Hoffman, Susan, Head, Ch, Newmarket Public Library, 438 Park Ave, Newmarket, ON, L3Y 1W1, CANADA. Tel: 905-953-5110. Fax: 905-953-5104. p. 2824

Hoffman, Valeria, Br Coordr, Sheppard Memorial Library, Margaret Little Blount Library, 201 Ives St, Bethel, NC, 27812. Tel: 252-825-0782. Fax: 252-825-0782. p. 1799

Hoffman, Valeria, Br Coordr, Sheppard Memorial Library, Winterville Public, 2613 Railroad St, Winterville, NC, 28590-9760. Tel: 252-756-1786. Fax: 252-355-0287. p. 1799

HoffmanHill, Chris, Br Mgr, Walla Walla County Rural Library District, Burbank Library, 875 Lake Rd, Burbank, WA, 99323. Tel: 509-545-6549. Fax: 509-545-6549. p. 2547

Hoffmann, Diane, Librn, Leeds Public Library, PO Box 295, Leeds, ND, 58346. Tel: 701-466-2930. p. 1845

Hoffmann, Frank, Dr, Prof, Sam Houston State University, 1921 Ave J, Huntsville, TX, 77340. Tel: 936-294-1289. Fax: 936-294-1153. p. 2974

Hoffmann, John, Librn, University of Illinois Library at Urbana-Champaign, Illinois History & Lincoln Collections, 322 Main Library, 1408 W Gregory Dr, Urbana, IL, 61801. Tel: 217-333-1777. p. 712

Hoffmann, Lynn, Ref & Access Serv Librn, Slippery Rock University of Pennsylvania, Slippery Rock, PA, 16057-9989. Tel: 724-738-2666. Fax: 724-738-2661. p. 2140

Hoffmann, Thomas E, Librn, Kalmbach Publishing Co Library, 21027 Crossroads Circle, Waukesha, WI, 53186. Tel: 262-796-8776, Ext 423. Fax: 262-796-6468. p. 2645

Hoffmaster, Sharlene, Libr Dir, Crockett Public Library, 709 E Houston Ave, Crockett, TX, 75835-2124. Tel: 936-544-3089. Fax: 936-544-4139. p. 2303

Hoffmeister, Elizabeth, Librn, United States Army, 72 Lyme Rd, Hanover, NH, 03755-1290. Tel: 603-646-4338. Fax: 603-646-4712. p. 1450

Hoffmeyer, Joann E, Dir, Lenox Township Library, 58976 Main St, New Haven, MI, 48048-2685. Tel: 586-749-3430. Fax: 586-749-3245. p. 1214

Hoffpauir, Georgia V, Cat, Circ, Coll Develop, Quitman Public Library, 202 East Goode St, Quitman, TX, 75783-2533. Tel: 903-763-4191. Fax: 903-763-2532. p. 2373

Hofland, Hope, Dir, Hospers Public Library, 213 Main St, Hospers, IA, 51238. Tel: 712-752-8400. Fax: 712-752-8601. p. 821

Hofmann, Patricia, Dir, Calvert County Public Library, 850 Costley Way, Prince Frederick, MD, 20678. Tel: 410-535-0291. Fax: 410-535-3022. p. 1036

Hofmeister, Craig, Dir, Human Res, East Bonner County Free Library District, 1407 Cedar St, Sandpoint, ID, 83864-2052. Tel: 208-263-6930, Ext 201. Fax: 208-263-8320. p. 583

Hofstee, Sharon, Librn, Christian Reformed Church Library, PO Box 3, New Holland, SD, 57364. Tel: 605-243-2346. p. 2216

Hogan, Carol, Br Mgr, Memphis Public Library, North, 1192 Vollintine, Memphis, TN, 38107-2899. Tel: 901-276-6631. Fax: 901-726-0731. p. 2250

Hogan, D Sean, Res Mgt Coordr, Austin Peay State University, 601 E College St, Clarksville, TN, 37044. Tel: 931-221-1325. Fax: 931-221-7296. p. 2228

Hogan, DeAnna, Dir, Winthrop Public Library, 354 W Madison, Winthrop, IA, 50682. Tel: 319-935-3374. Fax: 319-935-3574. p. 853

Hogan, Denise, ILL, Warren County-Vicksburg Public Library, 700 Veto St, Vicksburg, MS, 39180-3595. Tel: 601-636-6411. Fax: 601-634-4809. p. 1317

Hogan, Diane, Ref Serv, East Greenwich Free Library, 82 Peirce St, East Greenwich, RI, 02818. Tel: 401-884-9510. Fax: 401-884-3790. p. 2165

Hogan, Eddy, Coordr, Coll Develop, California State University-Monterey Bay, 100 Campus Ctr, Seaside, CA, 93955-8001. Tel: 831-582-3794. Fax: 831-582-3875. p. 268

Hogan, Gail, Librn, Law Society of Newfoundland Library, 196-198 Water St, St. John's, NL, A1C 1A9, CANADA. Tel: 709-753-7770. Fax: 709-753-0054. p. 2772

Hogan, Geneva, Br Mgr, Sumter County Library, South Sumter Branch, 337 Manning Ave, Sumter, SC, 29150. Tel: 803-775-7132. Fax: 803-775-7132. p. 2206

Hogan, Gerard, ILL, Ref, Central Washington University, 400 E University Way, Ellensburg, WA, 98926-7548. Tel: 509-963-1901. Fax: 509-963-3684. p. 2514

Hogan, Kathleen, Doc Librn, United States Army, Bldg 465, Rm 113, White Sands Missile Range, NM, 88002-5039. Tel: 575-678-1774. Fax: 575-678-2270. p. 1566

Hogan, Kay, Dir, North Florida Community College Library, 325 NW Turner Davis Dr, Madison, FL, 32340-1699. Tel: 850-973-9422. p. 462

Hogan, Lisa, ILL, Palm Beach State College, 3160 PGA Blvd, Palm Beach Gardens, FL, 33410-2893. Tel: 561-207-5800. Fax: 561-207-5805. p. 479

Hogan, Mary, Dir, Cora J Belden Library, 33 Church St, Rocky Hill, CT, 06067-1568. Tel: 860-258-7621. p. 365

Hogan, Nancy, ILL, Westwood Public Library, 668 High St, Westwood, MA, 02090. Tel: 781-320-1049. Fax: 781-326-5383. p. 1139

Hogan, Pam, Librn, Perkins, Thompson Library, One Canal Plaza, Portland, ME, 04112. Tel: 207-774-2635, Ext 278. Fax: 207-871-8026. p. 997

Hogan, Patricia Marie, Admin Librn, Poplar Creek Public Library District, 1405 S Park Ave, Streamwood, IL, 60107-2997. Tel: 630-483-4917. Fax: 630-837-6823. p. 708

Hogan, Sarah, Govt Doc, Micro, Boston College Libraries, Thomas P O'Neill Jr Library (Central Library), 140 Commonwealth Ave, Chestnut Hill, MA, 02467. Tel: 617-552-3306. Fax: 617-552-0599. p. 1081

Hogan, Walter, Tech Serv, Eastern Michigan University, 955 W Circle Dr Library, Rm 200, Ypsilanti, MI, 48197. Tel: 734-487-0020, Ext 2054. p. 1238

Hogan-Vidal, Pat, Media Cat Serv Librn, Valparaiso University, 1410 Chapel Dr, Valparaiso, IN, 46383-6493. Tel: 219-464-6128. p. 783

Hogans, Debra, In Charge, Walton County Public Library System, North Walton County - Gladys N Milton Memorial, 261 Flowersview Blvd, Laurel Hill, FL, 32567. Tel: 850-834-5383. Fax: 850-834-5487. p. 437

Hoganson, Ben, Ref & Instrul Serv, Instr Coordr, Battelle Energy Alliance, LLC, 1776 Science Center Dr, MS 2300, Idaho Falls, ID, 83415-2300. Tel: 208-526-1185. Fax: 208-526-0211. p. 576

Hogben, Ben, Mgr, Access Serv, Ithaca College Library, 953 Danby Rd, Ithaca, NY, 14850-7060. Tel: 607-274-1689. Fax: 607-274-1539. p. 1643

Hogenboom, Janice, Ref, Patterson Library, 40 S Portage St, Westfield, NY, 14787. Tel: 716-326-2154. Fax: 716-326-2554. p. 1768

Hogenson, Becky, Dir, Howe Community Library, 315 S Collins Freeway, Howe, TX, 75459. Tel: 903-532-3350. Fax: 903-532-3351. p. 2345

Hogg, Gordon, Libr Dir, University of Kentucky Libraries, Special Collections, King Bldg, Lexington, KY, 40506-0039. Tel: 859-257-1949. Fax: 859-257-6311. p. 922

Hoglund, Bethany, Ch, Bellingham Public Library, 210 Central Ave, CS-9710, Bellingham, WA, 98227-9710. Tel: 360-778-7323. p. 2508

Hogue, Amanda, Ch, Hollis Social Library, Two Monument Sq, Hollis, NH, 03049. Tel: 603-465-7721. Fax: 603-465-3507. p. 1451

Hogue, Bonnie, Dir, Johnsonburg Public Library, 520 Market St, Johnsonburg, PA, 15845-0240. Tel: 814-965-4110. Fax: 814-965-3320. p. 2073

Hogue, Deborah, Br Mgr, Anythink Libraries, Anythink Commerce City, 7185 Monaco St, Commerce City, CO, 80022. Tel: 303-287-0063. Fax: 303-289-6313. p. 324

Hogue, Edwina, Asst Librn, East Mississippi Community College, Golden Triangle Campus Library, 8731 S Frontage Rd, Mayhew, MS, 39753. Tel: 662-243-1914. Fax: 662-243-1952. p. 1314

Hoheisel, Eric, Head, Circ, Thomas M Cooley Law School Libraries, 300 S Capitol Ave, Lansing, MI, 48901. Tel: 517-371-5140, Ext 3311. Fax: 517-334-5715, 517-334-5717. p. 1202

Hoheisel, Tim, Dir, Augustana College, Center for Western Studies, 2201 S Summit Ave, Sioux Falls, SD, 57197. Tel: 605-274-4007. Fax: 605-274-4999. p. 2218

Hohensee, Sherry, Dir, Iowa Central Community College, Eagle Grove, 316 NW Third St, Eagle Grove, IA, 50533. Tel: 515-448-4723. Fax: 515-448-2800. p. 817

Hohenstein, Jenny, Res Serv Mgr, Jenkins Law Library, 833 Chestnut St, Ste 1220, Philadelphia, PA, 19107-4429. Tel: 215-574-7941. Fax: 215-574-7920. p. 2111

Hohertz, Cherie, Access Serv, Syst Librn, University of Dallas, 1845 E Northgate Dr, Irving, TX, 75062-4736. Tel: 972-721-5328. Fax: 972-721-4010. p. 2347

Hohl, Robert, Ref & Instruction Librn, Saint Mary's College, Notre Dame, IN, 46556-5001. Tel: 219-284-5287. Fax: 574-284-4791. p. 771

Hohl, Ruth, Librn, Wauneta Public Library, 319 N Tecumseh Ave, Wauneta, NE, 69045. Tel: 308-394-5243. Fax: 308-394-5243. p. 1422

Hohl, Sukey, Asst Dir, Sublette County Library, 155 S Tyler Ave, Pinedale, WY, 82941. Tel: 307-367-4115. Fax: 307-367-6722. p. 2658

Hohlbein, Mary, Br Head, Mackinaw Area Public Library, Bliss Branch, 265 Sturgeon Bay Trail, Levering, MI, 49755. Tel: 231-537-2927. p. 1205

Hohmeister, Cay, Dir, LeRoy Collins Leon County Public Library System, 200 W Park Ave, Tallahassee, FL, 32301-7720. Tel: 850-606-2665. Fax: 850-606-2601. p. 492

Hohn, Robin, Youth Serv, John C Fremont Library District, 130 Church Ave, Florence, CO, 81226. Tel: 719-784-4649. Fax: 719-784-4937. p. 307

Hohnadel, Sonia, In Charge, Tri-College University Libraries Consortium, NDSU Downtown Campus, 650 NP Ave, No 110, Fargo, ND, 58102. Tel: 701-231-8170. Fax: 701-231-7205. p. 2951

Hohner, Debbie, Dir, Mercer Public Library, 2648 W Margaret St, Mercer, WI, 54547. Tel: 715-476-2366. Fax: 715-476-2366. p. 2616

Hohner, Michael, Coordr, Info Tech, University of Winnipeg Library, 515 Portage Ave, Winnipeg, MB, R3B 2E9, CANADA. Tel: 204-786-9801. Fax: 204-783-8910. p. 2759

Hoiland, Charleen, Media Spec, Oregon School for the Deaf Library, 999 Locust St NE, Salem, OR, 97301-0954. Tel: 503-378-3825, 503-378-6779. Fax: 503-378-3378. p. 2018

Hoiles, Mary, Librn, Greenville Public Library, 414 W Main St, Greenville, IL, 62246-1615. Tel: 618-664-3115. Fax: 618-664-9442. p. 652

Hoins, Denise, Dir, Sumner Public Library, 206 N Railroad St, Sumner, IA, 50674. Tel: 563-578-3324. Fax: 563-578-3324. p. 847

Hokanson, Ann, Dir, Austin Public Library, 323 Fourth Ave NE, Austin, MN, 55912-3370. Tel: 507-433-2391. Fax: 507-433-8787. p. 1240

Hokanson, Sherry Ann, Dir, United States Air Force, Two W Castle St, Fairchild AFB, WA, 99011-8532. Tel: 509-247-5228, 509-247-5556. Fax: 509-247-3365. p. 2515

Hoke, Carol, Children's & Prog Serv Mgr, Cedar Rapids Public Library West, 2600 Edgewood Rd SW, Ste 330, Cedar Rapids, IA, 52404. Tel: 319-398-5123. Fax: 319-398-0476. p. 800

Hoke, Debra, Circ, Colorado College, 1021 N Cascade Ave, Colorado Springs, CO, 80903-3252. Tel: 719-389-6658. Fax: 719-389-6082. p. 294

Hoke, Tamara, Head Librn, Jay-Niles Memorial Library, 983 Main St, North Jay, ME, 04262. Tel: 207-645-4062. p. 994

Hokit, Karla, Supvr, Per, Carroll College, 1601 N Benton Ave, Helena, MT, 59625. Tel: 406-447-4340. Fax: 406-447-4525. p. 1381

Hoks, Heidi, Br Mgr, Carver County Library, Norwood Young America Branch, 314 Elm St W, Norwood Young America, MN, 55397. Tel: 952-467-2665. Fax: 952-467-4219. p. 1245

Hoks, Heidi, Br Mgr, Carver County Library, Waconia Branch, 217 S Vine St, Waconia, MN, 55387-1337. Tel: 952-442-4714. Fax: 952-856-4242. p. 1245

Hoks, Heidi, Br Mgr, Carver County Library, Watertown Branch, 309 Lewis Ave, Watertown, MN, 55388-0277. Tel: 952-955-2939. Fax: 952-955-2939. p. 1245

Holahan, Sara, Dep Dir, Mount Vernon City Library, 315 Snoqualmie St, Mount Vernon, WA, 98273. Tel: 360-336-6209. Fax: 360-336-6259. p. 2521

Holba, Carrie, Ref Serv Coordr, Alaska Resources Library & Information Services, Library Bldg, 3211 Providence Dr, Ste 111, Anchorage, AK, 99508-4614. Tel: 907-786-7660. Fax: 907-786-7652. p. 43

Holbach, Marilyn, Ref, Minot Public Library, 516 Second Ave SW, Minot, ND, 58701-3792. Tel: 701-852-1045. Fax: 701-852-2595. p. 1846

Holberg, Constance, Dir, State University of New York - Jefferson Community College, 1220 Coffeen St, Watertown, NY, 13601-1897. Tel: 315-786-2224. Fax: 315-788-0716. p. 1764

Holberg, John E, Res & Ref Librn, Covenant College, 14049 Scenic Hwy, Lookout Mountain, GA, 30750. Tel: 706-419-1430. Fax: 706-419-3480. p. 539

Holbert, Barb, In Charge, Lansing Community Library, 27 Auburn Rd, Lansing, NY, 14882. Tel: 607-533-4939. Fax: 607-533-7196. p. 1651

Holbert, Gentry L, Dir, Spring Hill College, 4000 Dauphin St, Mobile, AL, 36608. Tel: 251-380-3870. Fax: 251-460-2107. p. 26

Holbert, Terry, Dir, Electra Public Library, 401 N Waggoner St, Electra, TX, 76360. Tel: 940-495-2208. Fax: 940-495-4143. p. 2317

Holbrook, Deb, Govt Doc, Northland Pioneer College Libraries, PO Box 610, Holbrook, AZ, 86025. Tel: 928-289-6523. p. 65

Holbrook, Deborah, Chief Librn, Coll Develop, Coordr, Libr Serv, Coconino Community College, 2800 S Lone Tree Rd, Flagstaff, AZ, 86001-2701. Tel: 928-226-4272. Fax: 928-226-4103. p. 62

Holbrook, Diane L, Br Mgr, Kinchafoonee Regional Library System, Webster County Library, 572 Washington St, Preston, GA, 31824-0316. Tel: 229-828-5740. Fax: 229-828-5740. p. 529

Holbrook, Juliana, Cat, Hingham Public Library, 66 Leavitt St, Hingham, MA, 02043. Tel: 781-741-1405. Fax: 781-749-0956. p. 1095

Holcomb, Jo, Lit Spec/Librn, Guthrie Theater Foundation, 818 Second St S, Minneapolis, MN, 55415. Tel: 612-225-6117. p. 1260

Holcomb, Jolynn, Asst Br Mgr, Chesterfield County Public Library, Midlothian, 521 Coalfield Rd, Midlothian, VA, 23114. Tel: 804-768-7907. p. 2457

Holcomb, Linda, Computer Lab Tech, Ivy Tech State Community College-Northwest, 1440 E 35th Ave, Gary, IN, 46409-1499. Tel: 219-981-4410. Fax: 219-981-4415. p. 745

Holcomb, Mary, Head, Coll Serv, University of Arizona, Arizona Health Sciences Library, 1501 N Campbell Ave, Tucson, AZ, 85724. Tel: 520-626-2924. Fax: 520-626-2922. p. 88

Holcomb, Shirley, Librn, Federal Law Enforcement Training Center Library, Bldg 262, 1131 Chapel Crossing Rd, Glynco, GA, 31524. Tel: 912-267-2320. p. 535

Holcomb, Trinna, Youth Serv Coordr, Lafourche Parish Public Library, South Lafourche Public Library, 16241 East Main St, CutOff, LA, 70345. Tel: 985-632-7140. Fax: 985-632-4963. p. 971

Holcomb-Densmore, Kendra, Asst Librn, Nazarene Theological Seminary, 1700 E Meyer Blvd, Kansas City, MO, 64131. Tel: 816-268-5473. Fax: 816-822-9025. p. 1340

Holcombe, Eric, Circ Spec, Western Nevada Community College, 2201 W College Pkwy, Carson City, NV, 89703. Tel: 775-445-3229. Fax: 775-445-3363. p. 1426

Holczer, Lolita, Head, Pub Serv, Butt-Holdsworth Memorial Library, 505 Water St, Kerrville, TX, 78028. Tel: 830-257-8422. Fax: 830-792-5552. p. 2349

Holda, Brian, Instrul Serv Librn, Cornerstone University, 1001 E Beltline Ave NE, Grand Rapids, MI, 49525. Tel: 616-949-5300. Fax: 616-222-1405. p. 1184

Holdaway, Loyette, Librn, Emery County Library, Cleveland Branch, 45 W Main, Cleveland, UT, 84518. Tel: 435-653-2204. Fax: 435-653-2104. p. 2403

Holden, Carol, Borrower Serv Librn, Palmer Public Library, 1455 N Main St, Palmer, MA, 01069. Tel: 413-283-3330. Fax: 413-283-9970. p. 1116

Holden, Hugh A, Coordr, Off Campus User Serv, Piedmont College, 165 Central Ave, Demorest, GA, 30535. Tel: 706-776-0111. Fax: 706-776-3338. p. 530

Holden, Irina, Outreach & Instruction Librn, Ref Librn, University at Albany, State University of New York, Science Library, 1400 Washington Ave, Albany, NY, 12222. Tel: 518-437-3948. Fax: 518-437-3952. p. 1571

Holden, Laura, Head, Spec Coll, Anderson County Library, 300 N McDuffie St, Anderson, SC, 29621-5643. Tel: 864-260-4500. Fax: 864-260-4510. p. 2180

Holden, Martha H, Dir, Peabody Institute Library, 82 Main St, Peabody, MA, 01960-5592. Tel: 978-531-0100. Fax: 978-532-1797. p. 1116

Holden, Susan, Ref Serv, YA, Harborfields Public Library, 31 Broadway, Greenlawn, NY, 11740-1382. Tel: 631-757-4200. Fax: 631-757-7216. p. 1631

Holden, Teresa, Dir, Middletown Fallcreek Township Public Library, 780 High St, Middletown, IN, 47356-1399. Tel: 765-354-4071. Fax: 765-354-9578. p. 765

Holden, Theresa, Interim Dir, Palestine Public Library, 2000 S Loop 256, Ste 42, Palestine, TX, 75801. Tel: 903-729-4121. Fax: 903-729-4062. p. 2368

Holder, Ann, Librn, Tennessee Valley Authority, 1101 Market St, LP 4A-C, Chattanooga, TN, 37402. Tel: 423-751-4913. Fax: 423-751-4914. p. 2228

Holder, Ann H, Dir, Sam Houston State University, 1830 Bobby K Marks Dr, Huntsville, TX, 77340. Tel: 936-294-1614. Fax: 936-294-3780. p. 2345

Holder, Barbara, Librn, Forintek Canada Corp, 2665 East Mall, Vancouver, BC, V6T 1W5, CANADA. Tel: 604-224-3221, Ext 668. Fax: 604-222-5690. p. 2741

Holder, Eugene, Dir, Southwestern Assemblies of God University, 1200 Sycamore, Waxahachie, TX, 75165-2342. Tel: 972-825-4761. Fax: 972-923-0488. p. 2398

Holder, Nell, Libr Assoc, Desoto Parish Library, Stonewall Branch, 808 Hwy 171, Stonewall, LA, 71078. Tel: 318-925-9191. Fax: 318-925-3392. p. 956

Holder, Stacy, Adult Serv, Malden Public Library, 36 Salem St, Malden, MA, 02148-5291. Tel: 781-324-0218. Fax: 781-324-4467. p. 1102

Holderfield, Alison, Dir, Dongola Public Library District, 114 NE Front St, Dongola, IL, 62926-2345. Tel: 618-827-3622. p. 637

Holderied, Rachel, Media Cat Serv Librn, University of North Carolina at Pembroke, Faculty Row, Pembroke, NC, 28372. Tel: 910-521-6516. Fax: 910-521-6547. p. 1814

Holderman, Sharon, Libr Dir, Ohio State University LIBRARIES, Agricultural Technical Institute Library, Halterman Hall, 1328 Dover Rd, Wooster, OH, 44691-4000. Tel: 330-287-1224. Fax: 330-287-1333. p. 1887

Holdhusen, Deedra, Instruction Librn, University of South Dakota, 414 E Clark St, Vermillion, SD, 57069. Tel: 605-677-5371. Fax: 605-677-6834. p. 2220

Holding, Nancy, Librn, Parsons State Hospital & Training Center, 2601 Gabriel, Parsons, KS, 67357-2399. Tel: 620-421-6550, Ext 1781. p. 889

Holdman, Virginia May, Circ, Rushville Public Library, 130 W Third St, Rushville, IN, 46173-1899. Tel: 765-932-3496. Fax: 765-932-4528. p. 776

Holdorf, Marilyn, Co-Librn, Big Springs Public Library, 400 Pine St, Big Springs, NE, 69122. Tel: 308-889-3482. p. 1394

Holdredge, Faith, Regional Mgr, Tennessee State Library & Archives, 403 Seventh Ave N, Nashville, TN, 37243-0312. Tel: 931-836-2209. Fax: 615-532-2472, 615-741-6471. p. 2259

Holdredge, Faith A, Dir, Falling Water River Regional Library, 208 E Minnear St, Cookeville, TN, 38501-3949. Tel: 931-526-4016. Fax: 931-528-3311. p. 2231

Holdried, Anthony, Instrul Serv/Ref Librn, University of North Carolina at Pembroke, Faculty Row, Pembroke, NC, 28372. Tel: 910-521-6516. Fax: 910-521-6547. p. 1814

Holehan, Tom, Pub Relations, Stratford Library Association, 2203 Main St, Stratford, CT, 06615. Tel: 203-385-4162. Fax: 203-381-2079. p. 371

Holekamp, Melissa, Genealogy Librn, Lee County Library, 219 N Madison St, Tupelo, MS, 38804-3899. Tel: 662-841-9027. Fax: 662-840-7615. p. 1316

Holeman, Cheryle, Circ/Reserves, Oral Roberts University Library, 7777 South Lewis Ave, Tulsa, OK, 74171. Tel: 918-495-6028. Fax: 918-495-6893. p. 1981

Holeton, Richard, Dir, Acad Computing Serv, Stanford University Libraries, 557 Escondido Mall, Stanford, CA, 94305-6004. Tel: 650-725-1064. p. 270

Holian, Dzwinka, Assoc Dir, Cleveland Health
Sciences Library, Allen Memorial Library,
11000 Euclid Ave, Cleveland, OH, 44106-7130.
Tel: 216-368-3643. p. 1876

Holian, Dzwinka, Assoc Dir, Cleveland Health
Sciences Library, School of Medicine,
Robbins Bldg, 2109 Adelbert Rd, Cleveland,
OH, 44106-4914. Tel: 216-368-3642. Fax:
216-368-3008, 216-368-6421. p. 1876

Holida, Carrie, Fiscal Officer, Willard Memorial
Library, Six W Emerald St, Willard, OH,
44890-1498. Tel: 419-933-8564. Fax:
419-933-4783. p. 1948

Holiday, Christine L, Librn, United States Army,
Bldg 35, One C Tree Rd, McAlester, OK,
74501. Tel: 918-420-8772. Fax: 918-420-8473.
p. 1968

Holiday, Connie, Librn, Wilsonville Public Library,
203 Iva St, Wilsonville, NE, 69046. Tel:
308-349-4367. p. 1423

Holkesvig, Wendy, Librn, Northwood City Library,
420 Trojan Rd, Northwood, ND, 58267-3001.
Tel: 701-587-5221. Fax: 701-587-5423. p. 1847

Holl, Deborah, Syst Adminr, Tech Serv, Widener
University, One University Pl, Chester,
PA, 19013-5792. Tel: 610-499-4299. Fax:
610-499-4588. p. 2044

Holl, Justin, Dir, Farallones Marine Sanctuary
Association, Bldg 991, Old Coast Guard Sta,
Marine Dr, San Francisco, CA, 94129. Tel:
415-561-6625. Fax: 415-561-6616. p. 242

Holland, Adelle, Librn, Holly Community Library,
1620 FM 2869, Teaching Library, Hawkins, TX,
75765. Tel: 903-769-5142. p. 2331

Holland, Amy, Ch & Youth Librn, Hamlin
Public Library, 422 Clarkson Hamlin TL Rd,
Hamlin, NY, 14464. Tel: 585-964-2320. Fax:
585-964-2374. p. 1633

Holland, Bruce, Exec Dir, UNI-Bell PVC Pipe
Association Library, 2711 LBJ Freeway, Ste
1000, Dallas, TX, 75234. Tel: 972-243-3902.
Fax: 972-243-3907. p. 2311

Holland, Debbie, Librn, United States Department of
Housing & Urban Development, 801 Cherry St
Unit 45, Ste 2500, Fort Worth, TX, 76102. Tel:
817-978-5924. Fax: 817-978-5563. p. 2324

Holland, Douglas L, Dir, Missouri Botanical Garden
Library, 4500 Shaw Blvd, Saint Louis, MO,
63110. Tel: 314-577-0842. Fax: 314-577-0840.
p. 1356

Holland, Elizabeth M, Exhibits Curator, Spec Coll,
Chicago Public Library, Special Collections &
Preservation Division, 400 S State St, Chicago,
IL, 60605. Tel: 312-747-4883. p. 609

Holland, Glenda, Dr, Assoc Dean, University of
Louisiana at Monroe, 306 Strauss Hall, 700
University Ave, Monroe, LA, 71209. Tel:
318-342-1246. Fax: 318-342-1213. p. 2966

Holland, Gretchen, Br Mgr, Stark County
District Library, Sandy Valley Branch, 9754
Cleveland Ave SE, Magnolia, OH, 44643. Tel:
330-866-3366. Fax: 330-866-9859. p. 1865

Holland, Heidi, Dir, Flagstaff City-Coconino
County Public Library System, 300 W Aspen,
Flagstaff, AZ, 86001. Tel: 928-213-2331. Fax:
928-774-9573. p. 62

Holland, Janet E, Libr Tech, Virginia State Law
Library, Supreme Court Bldg, 2nd Flr, 100 N
Ninth St, Richmond, VA, 23219-2335. Tel:
804-786-2075. Fax: 804-786-4542. p. 2493

Holland, Jeanie, Br Mgr, Live Oak Public Libraries,
Pooler Branch, 216 S Rogers St, Pooler, GA,
31322. Tel: 912-748-0471. Fax: 912-748-4947.
p. 550

Holland, Joseph, Librn, Sturdy Memorial Hospital,
211 Park St, Attleboro, MA, 02703. Tel:
508-236-7920. Fax: 508-236-7909. p. 1050

Holland, Karen, Cat, Manville Public Library,
100 S Tenth Ave, Manville, NJ, 08835. Tel:
908-722-9722. Fax: 908-722-0631. p. 1499

Holland, Kindra, Librn, Erie City Public Library,
204 S Butler, Erie, KS, 66733-1349. Tel:
620-244-5119. Fax: 620-244-5119. p. 866

Holland, Kylie, In Charge, Multnomah County
Library, Rockwood, 17917 SE Stark St,
Portland, OR, 97233-4825. Tel: 503-988-5396.
Fax: 503-988-5178. p. 2012

Holland, Leslie, Head of Libr, Memphis College of
Art, 1930 Poplar Ave, Memphis, TN, 38104.
Tel: 901-272-5131. Fax: 901-272-5104. p. 2249

Holland, Linda, Asst Librn, Christopher Public
Library, 204 E Market St, Christopher,
IL, 62822-1759. Tel: 618-724-7534. Fax:
618-724-7534. p. 629

Holland, Lisa, Archivist, Wagner College, One
Campus Rd, Staten Island, NY, 10301-4495. Tel:
718-390-3401. Fax: 718-420-4218. p. 1748

Holland, Lissa, Br Mgr, Lancaster Public Library,
Lancaster Public Library West - Mountville
Branch, 120 College Ave, Mountville, PA,
17554. Tel: 717-285-3231. p. 2077

Holland, Lori, Br Mgr, Kent District Library, Library
for the Blind & Physically Handicapped, 3350
Michael Ave SW, Wyoming, MI, 49509. Tel:
616-647-3988. Fax: 616-647-3984. p. 1166

Holland, Lori, Br Mgr, Kent District Library,
Wyoming Branch, 3350 Michael Ave SW,
Wyoming, MI, 49509. Tel: 616-784-2007. Fax:
616-647-3984. p. 1166

Holland, Martha, Mgr, Ref & Info Serv, Bucknell
University, Research Services, Library &
Information Technology, Lewisburg, PA, 17837.
Tel: 570-577-1673. p. 2080

Holland, Mary, Mgr, National Semiconductor Corp,
2900 Semiconductor Dr, MS-DT-05, Santa
Clara, CA, 95052-8090. Tel: 408-721-3810. Fax:
408-721-7060. p. 262

Holland, Mary Jane, Ch, Teen Serv, Boulder Public
Library, 1001 Arapahoe Rd, Boulder, CO,
80302. Tel: 303-441-3100. Fax: 303-442-1808.
p. 290

Holland, Michael, Univ Archivist, University
of Missouri-Columbia, Elmer Ellis Library,
Ellis Library Bldg, Rm 104, Columbia,
MO, 65201-5149. Tel: 573-882-4602. Fax:
573-882-8044. p. 1325

Holland, Nancy, Dir, Huntingdon County Library,
330 Penn St, Huntingdon, PA, 16652-1487. Tel:
814-643-0200. Fax: 814-643-0132. p. 2070

Holland, Tom, Support Serv, Santa Fe Community
College, 3000 NW 83rd St, Bldg Y-100,
Gainesville, FL, 32606. Tel: 352-395-5103. Fax:
352-395-5102. p. 449

Holland, Yasma, Dir, Kaufman County Library, 3790
S Houston St, Kaufman, TX, 75142-2033. Tel:
972-932-6222. Fax: 972-932-0681. p. 2349

Holland, Zettie, Librn, Arkansas State
University-Searcy, 1800 E Moore, Searcy,
AR, 72143-4710. Tel: 501-207-4031. Fax:
501-268-0263. p. 114

Hollander, David, Law Librn, Princeton University,
Politics & Law Collections, Firestone Library,
A-17-J-1, One Washington Rd, Princeton, NJ,
08544. Tel: 609-258-3209, 609-258-3701.
p. 1524

Hollander, Gail, Ref & Info Literacy Librn, Howard
Community College Library, 10901 Little
Patuxent Pkwy, Columbia, MD, 21044. Tel:
443-518-4633. Fax: 443-518-4993. p. 1025

Hollenbach, Marybeth, Br Mgr, Mid-Continent
Public Library, Buckner Branch, 19 E
Jefferson St, Buckner, MO, 64016-9713. Tel:
816-650-3212. Fax: 816-650-6780. p. 1332

Hollenbeck, Leo, ILL, Social Security
Administration Library, Annex Bldg
1520, Baltimore, MD, 21235-6401. Fax:
410-966-2027. p. 1017

Hollenberg, Linda, Librn, Warren County Public
Library District, Kirkwood Branch, PO Box 249,
Kirkwood, IL, 61447-0249. Tel: 309-768-2173.
p. 675

Hollendonner, Diane, Outreach Serv Librn,
Jacksonville Public Library, 201 W College
Ave, Jacksonville, IL, 62650-2497. Tel:
217-243-5435. Fax: 217-243-2182. p. 659

Hollens, Deborah, Govt Doc, Southern Oregon
University, 1250 Siskiyou Blvd, Ashland,
OR, 97520-5076. Tel: 541-552-6850. Fax:
541-552-6429. p. 1990

Holler, Ginger, Ch, Orange County Public Library,
137 W Margaret Lane, Hillsborough, NC,
27278. Tel: 919-245-2525. Fax: 919-644-3003.
p. 1802

Holler, Leah, Coordr, Search Serv, Nestle Purina Pet
Care Co, Checkerboard Sq 2S, Saint Louis, MO,
63164. Tel: 314-982-2056. Fax: 314-982-3259.
p. 1357

Holler, Mary Ehret, Dir, Protection Township
Library, 404 N Broadway, Protection, KS,
67127. Tel: 620-622-4886. Fax: 620-622-4492.
p. 891

Holler, Wendy, Dir, Marysville-Rye Library, 198
Overcrest Rd, Marysville, PA, 17053-1157. Tel:
717-957-2851. Fax: 717-957-3054. p. 2084

Hollerich, Mary, Dir, Lewis University Library,
One University Pkwy, Unit 300, Romeoville,
IL, 60446-2200. Tel: 815-836-5300. Fax:
815-838-9456. p. 698

Hollers, Judith, Dir, Indianola Public Library,
122 N Fourth St, Indianola, NE, 69034. Tel:
308-364-9259. p. 1403

Holles, Melanie, Extn Serv, Stanly County Public
Library, 133 E Main St, Albemarle, NC, 28001.
Tel: 704-986-3759. Fax: 704-983-6713. p. 1773

Holleufer, Jill, Head, YA, Baldwin Public Library,
2385 Grand Ave, Baldwin, NY, 11510-3289. Tel:
516-223-6228. Fax: 516-623-7991. p. 1577

Holley, Amber, Br Mgr, Jacksonville Public
Library, Argyle, 7973 Old Middleburg
Rd S, Jacksonville, FL, 32222-1817. Tel:
904-573-3164. Fax: 904-573-3162. p. 453

Holley, Beth, Head, Acq, University of Alabama,
University Libraries, University of Alabama
Campus, Capstone Dr, Tuscaloosa, AL, 35487.
Tel: 205-348-1493. Fax: 205-348-6358. p. 38

Holley, Leta, Dir, Federal Election Commission, 999
E St NW, Rm 801, Washington, DC, 20463. Tel:
202-694-1516. Fax: 202-208-3579. p. 400

Holley, Margaret, Librn, Filer Public Library,
219 Main St, Filer, ID, 83328-5349. Tel:
208-326-4143. p. 574

Holley, Robert P, Dr, Prof, Wayne State University,
106 Kresge Library, Detroit, MI, 48202. Tel:
313-577-1825. Fax: 313-577-7563. p. 2967

Holley, Shelley, Ch, Southington Public Library &
Museum, 255 Main St, Southington, CT, 06489.
Tel: 860-628-0947. Fax: 860-628-0488. p. 368

Holley, Shelley, Dir, Libr Serv, Frisco Public
Library, 6101 Frisco Square Blvd, Ste 3000,
Frisco, TX, 75034-3000. Tel: 972-292-5669.
Fax: 972-292-5699. p. 2325

Holley, Vashti, Asst Librn, Albemarle Regional
Library, Lawrence Memorial Public Library,
204 E Dundee St, Windsor, NC, 27983. Tel:
252-794-2244. Fax: 252-794-1546. p. 1835

Holley-Hall, Heather, Mgr, Br Serv, Alamance
County Public Libraries, Graham Public Library,
211 S Main St, Graham, NC, 27253. Tel:
336-570-6730. Fax: 336-570-6732. p. 1779

Holley-Harris, Nzinga, Coll Develop, Webmaster,
United States Department of Justice, MCB No 4,
Quantico, VA, 22135. Tel: 703-632-3218. Fax:
703-632-3214. p. 2487

Holliday, Deloice, Head of Libr, Indiana University
Bloomington, Neal-Marshall Black Culture
Center Library, Neal-Marshall Ctr, Rm A113,
275 N Jordan, Bloomington, IN, 47405. Tel:
812-855-3237. Fax: 812-856-4558. p. 728

Holliday, Diane, Archives, Dowling College Library,
150 Idle Hour Blvd, Oakdale, NY, 11769-1999.
Tel: 631-244-3397. Fax: 631-244-3374. p. 1709

Hollier, Pam, Head, Circ, Montrose Regional
Library District, 320 S Second St, Montrose,
CO, 81401-3909. Tel: 970-249-9656. Fax:
970-240-1901. p. 318

Hollifield, Allison, Ch, McDowell County Public
Library, 90 W Court St, Marion, NC, 28752.
Tel: 828-652-3858. Fax: 828-652-2098. p. 1808

Holliger, Carol, Archivist, Ohio Wesleyan University, 43 Rowland, Delaware, OH, 43015-2370. Tel: 740-368-3285. Fax: 740-368-3222. p. 1896

Hollin, Connie, Assoc Librn, Tech Serv, Western Wyoming Community College, 2500 College Dr, Rock Springs, WY, 82902. Tel: 307-382-1702. Fax: 307-382-7665. p. 2659

Hollinger, LaShannon, Dir, Alabama Southern Community College, 2800 S Alabama Ave, Monroeville, AL, 36460. Tel: 251-575-3156, Ext 8271. Fax: 251-575-5116. p. 26

Hollinger, LaShannon, Dir, Alabama Southern Community College, Gilbertown Campus, 251 College St, Gilbertown, AL, 36908. Tel: 251-575-3156, Ext 8271. Fax: 334-843-2420. p. 27

Hollinger, LaShannon, Dir, Alabama Southern Community College, Thomasville Campus-Kathryn Tucker Windham Museum Library, 30755 Hwy 43, Thomasville, AL, 36784-2519. Tel: 251-575-3156, Ext 8271. Fax: 334-636-1478. p. 27

Hollinger, Richard, Spec Coll, University of Maine, 5729 Fogler Library, Orono, ME, 04469-5729. Fax: 207-581-1653. p. 995

Hollingshead, Jessica, Acq/Ser Librn, Harvard Library, Dumbarton Oaks Research Library, 1703 32nd St NW, Washington, MA, 20007. Tel: 202-339-6400. Fax: 202-625-0279. p. 1074

Hollingshead, Sue, Info Tech Serv Mgr, Laramie County Library System, 2200 Pioneer Ave, Cheyenne, WY, 82001-3610. Tel: 307-773-7234. Fax: 307-634-2082. p. 2652

Hollingsworth, Cheryl, Adult Ref Librn, AV Librn, Mesquite Public Library, 300 W Grubb Dr, Mesquite, TX, 75149. Tel: 972-216-6220. Fax: 972-216-6740. p. 2362

Hollingsworth, David, Librn, Pine Forest Regional Library, R E Blackwell Memorial, 403 S Fir Ave, Collins, MS, 39428. Tel: 601-765-8582. Fax: 601-765-8582. p. 1314

Hollingsworth, Dena, Chief Librn, Gibson, Dunn & Crutcher, 333 S Grand Ave, Los Angeles, CA, 90071-3197. Tel: 213-229-7000. Fax: 213-229-7520. p. 170

Hollingsworth, Diane, Tech Serv, Gordon College Library, 419 College Dr, Barnesville, GA, 30204. Tel: 770-358-5078. Fax: 770-358-5240. p. 521

Hollingsworth, Erin, Youth Serv, Tuzzy Consortium Library, 5421 North Star St, Barrow, AK, 99723. Tel: 907-852-4050. Fax: 907-852-4059. p. 46

Hollingsworth, Erin, Cat, Pinellas Park Public Library, 7770 52nd St, Pinellas Park, FL, 33781-3498. Tel: 727-541-0718. Fax: 727-541-0818. p. 483

Hollingsworth, Janet, Coordr, Humber College, Lakeshore Campus Library, 3199 Lakeshore Blvd W, Toronto, ON, M8V 1K8, CANADA. Tel: 416-675-6622, Ext 3250. Fax: 416-252-0918. p. 2854

Hollingsworth, Janet L, Dir, Herrick Memorial Library, 101 Willard Memorial Sq, Wellington, OH, 44090-1342. Tel: 440-647-2120. Fax: 440-647-2103. p. 1945

Hollingsworth, Melba, Dir, Gordo Public Library, 287 Main St, Gordo, AL, 35466. Tel: 205-364-7148. Fax: 205-364-7148. p. 19

Hollingsworth, Penny, Mgr, Acq Serv, Mgr, Ser, Louisiana College, 1140 College Blvd, Pineville, LA, 71359. Tel: 318-487-7201. Fax: 318-487-7143. p. 965

Hollingsworth, Rebecca, Info Serv Librn, Lafayette Public Library, 301 W Congress, Lafayette, LA, 70501-6866. Tel: 337-261-5775. Fax: 337-261-5782. p. 952

Hollins, Lydia W, Librn Assoc, Bishop State Community College, Southwest Campus, 925 Dauphin Island Pkwy, Mobile, AL, 36605-3299. Tel: 251-665-4091. Fax: 251-479-7091. p. 25

Hollis, Bobby Allen, In Charge, Robert B Jones Memorial Library, 135 Main St, Lynnville, TN, 38472. Tel: 931-273-3466. p. 2246

Hollis, Charlotte, Head Librn, El Paso Community College Library, Rio Grande Campus Library, 1111 N Oregon, El Paso, TX, 79902. Tel: 915-831-4019. p. 2316

Hollis, Deborah, Assoc Prof, Head, Spec Coll, University of Colorado Boulder, 1720 Pleasant St, 184 UCB, Boulder, CO, 80309-0184. Tel: 303-492-3910. Fax: 303-492-3340. p. 291

Hollis, Deborah R, Head, Spec Coll, University of Colorado Boulder, Archives & Special Collections, 1720 Pleasant St, Boulder, CO, 80309-0184. Tel: 303-492-3910. Fax: 303-492-1881. p. 291

Hollis, Heather, Head, Circ, Kewanee Public Library District, 102 S Tremont St, Kewanee, IL, 61443. Tel: 309-852-4505. Fax: 309-852-4466. p. 661

Hollis, Heather, Youth Serv, Toulon Public Library District, 306 W Jefferson, Toulon, IL, 61483. Tel: 309-286-5791. Fax: 309-286-4481. p. 710

Hollis, Linda Sue, Librn, Colorado Department of Corrections, 12750 Hwy 96, Lane 13, Crowley, CO, 81034. Tel: 719-267-3520, Ext 3251. Fax: 719-267-5024. p. 297

Hollis, Sandra, Libr Mgr, National Association of Insurance Commissioners, 1100 Walnut St, Ste 1500, Kansas City, MO, 64106-2197. Tel: 816-783-8252. Fax: 816-460-7682. p. 1340

Hollis, Wendy, Head, Ch, Louis Bay 2nd Library, 345 Lafayette Ave, Hawthorne, NJ, 07506-2599. Tel: 973-427-5745, Ext 21. Fax: 973-427-5269. p. 1490

Hollman, Patrice, Br Mgr, Albany Public Library, Delaware, 331 Delaware Ave, Albany, NY, 12209. Tel: 518-463-0254. p. 1568

Hollman, Patrice, Outreach Serv Librn, Albany Public Library, 161 Washington Ave, Albany, NY, 12210. Tel: 518-427-4325. Fax: 518-449-3386. p. 1568

Holloman, Donna, Coll Develop, Temple Public Library, 100 W Adams Ave, Temple, TX, 76501-7641. Tel: 254-298-5284. Fax: 254-298-5328. p. 2391

Holloman, Gayle, Br Mgr, Atlanta-Fulton Public Library System, Dr Robert E Fulton Regional at Ocee, 5090 Abbotts Bridge Rd, Alpharetta, GA, 30005-4601. Tel: 770-360-8897. Fax: 770-360-8892. p. 512

Hollow Horn Bear, Elsie, Circ, Sinte Gleska University Library, E Hwy 18, Mission, SD, 57555. Tel: 605-856-8100, 605-856-8112. Fax: 605-856-2011. p. 2215

Hollowak, Thomas, Assoc Dir, Spec Coll & Archives, University of Baltimore, 1420 Maryland Ave, Baltimore, MD, 21201. Tel: 410-837-4268. Fax: 410-837-4330. p. 1018

Holloway, Grace, Dir, Gwinnett County Law Library, 75 Langley Dr, Lawrenceville, GA, 30046. Tel: 770-822-8571. Fax: 770-822-8570. p. 538

Holloway, Kristine, Sr Asst Librn, California State University, 9001 Stockdale Hwy, Bakersfield, CA, 93311-1022. Tel: 661-654-5072. Fax: 661-654-3238. p. 123

Holloway, Lynne Thorn, Dir, Augusta Public Library, 1609 State St, Augusta, KS, 67010-2098. Tel: 316-775-2681. Fax: 316-775-7692. p. 857

Holloway, Patricia, Dir, West Hartford Public Library, 20 S Main St, West Hartford, CT, 06107-2432. Tel: 860-561-6950. Fax: 860-561-6976. p. 376

Holloway, Patricia, Learning Res Ctr Spec, Florida State University Libraries, College of Nursing, Learning Resource Center, 102 College of Nursing, Tallahassee, FL, 32306-4310. Tel: 850-644-1291. Fax: 850-644-7660. p. 494

Holloway, Sharon, Cat, Tech Serv, Benton Harbor Public Library, 213 E Wall St, Benton Harbor, MI, 49022-4499. Tel: 269-926-6139. Fax: 269-926-1674. p. 1156

Holloway, Tami, AV, Fulton County Public Library, 320 W Seventh St, Rochester, IN, 46975-1332. Tel: 574-223-2713. Fax: 574-223-5102. p. 776

Holloway, Tami, ILL, Fulton County Public Library, 320 W Seventh St, Rochester, IN, 46975-1332. Tel: 574-223-2713. Fax: 574-223-5102. p. 776

Holloway, Veronica, Libr Commun Serv Mgr, Richmond Public Library, East End, 1200 N 25th St, Richmond, VA, 23223-5250. Tel: 804-646-4474. Fax: 804-646-0104. p. 2490

Hollowell, Bob, Med Librn, Swedish Medical Center Library, First Hill Campus, 747 Broadway, Seattle, WA, 98122-4307. Tel: 206-386-2484. Fax: 206-215-3081. p. 2532

Hollowell, Elaine, Youth Serv Suprv, Burlington County Library, Cinnaminson Branch, 1619 Riverton Rd, Cinnaminson, NJ, 08077. Tel: 856-829-9340. Fax: 856-829-2243. p. 1543

Holly, Janet S, Doc, Ref Serv, Virginia Military Institute, Letcher Ave, Lexington, VA, 24450. Tel: 540-464-7296. Fax: 540-464-7279. p. 2474

Holly, Kathi, Br Mgr, New Britain Public Library, Jefferson, 140 Horse Plain Rd, New Britain, CT, 06053. Tel: 860-225-4700. Fax: 860-832-9521. p. 354

Holm, Adrian, Librn, Colville Confederated Tribe Library, Inchelium Resource Center, 12 Community Loop Rd, Inchelium, WA, 99138. Tel: 509-722-7037. Fax: 509-533-7040. p. 2521

Holm, Adrian, Librn, Colville Confederated Tribe Library, Keller Library, 11673 S Hwy 21, Keller, WA, 99140. Tel: 509-634-2802. p. 2521

Holm, Carolyn, Admin Serv, Crescent Hill Baptist Church Library, 2800 Frankfort Ave, Louisville, KY, 40206. Tel: 502-896-4425. Fax: 502-896-9855. p. 923

Holm, Jen, Librn, Massachusetts Society for the Prevention of Cruelty to Animals (MSPCA) Library, 350 S Huntington Ave, Boston, MA, 02130. Tel: 617-522-7400, Ext 5322. Fax: 617-522-4885. p. 1064

Holm, John, Electronic Res Librn, Norwich University, 23 Harmon Dr, Northfield, VT, 05663. Tel: 802-485-2523. Fax: 802-485-2173. p. 2431

Holm, Peggy, Dir, Kodiak College, 117 Benny Benson Dr, Kodiak, AK, 99615-6643. Tel: 907-486-1238. Fax: 907-486-1257. p. 51

Holm, Vanessa, Chief Exec Officer, Bancroft Public Library, 14 Flint Ave, Bancroft, ON, K0L 1C0, CANADA. Tel: 613-332-3380. Fax: 613-332-5473. p. 2793

Holman, Deb, Head of Br Serv, Licking County Library, Emerson R Miller Branch, 990 W Main St, Newark, OH, 43055. Tel: 740-344-2155. Fax: 740-344-4271. p. 1922

Holman, Jenifer, Acq, University of Wisconsin-La Crosse, 1631 Pine St, La Crosse, WI, 54601-3748. Tel: 608-785-8395. Fax: 608-785-8634. p. 2603

Holman, Jos N, County Librn, Tippecanoe County Public Library, 627 South St, Lafayette, IN, 47901-1470. Tel: 765-429-0100. Fax: 765-429-0150. p. 759

Holman, Joyce, Cataloger, Tech Serv, Miles College, 5500 Myron Massey Blvd, Fairfield, AL, 35064. Tel: 205-929-1713. Fax: 205-929-1635. p. 16

Holman, Kathleen, Dir, Forsyth Township Public Library, 184 W Flint St, Gwinn, MI, 49841. Tel: 906-346-3433. Fax: 906-346-3433. p. 1187

Holman, Kimberly, Pub Serv, Cochise County Library District, Old High School, 2nd Flr, 100 Clawson, Bisbee, AZ, 85603. Tel: 520-432-8930. Fax: 520-432-7339. p. 58

Holman, Kristina, Libr Tech, Nova Scotia Department of Education Library, 2021 Brunswick St, Halifax, NS, B3J 2S9, CANADA. Tel: 902-424-4920. Fax: 902-424-0519. p. 2782

Holman, Lucy, Dir, University of Baltimore, 1420 Maryland Ave, Baltimore, MD, 21201. Tel: 410-837-4333. Fax: 410-837-4330. p. 1018

Holman, Lynn, Per, Montreat College, 310 Gaither Circle, Montreat, NC, 28757. Tel: 828-669-8012, Ext 3504. Fax: 828-350-2083. p. 1810

Holman, Mark, Librn, Sitting Bull College Library, 1341 92nd St, Fort Yates, ND, 58538. Tel: 701-854-3861, Ext 8024. Fax: 701-854-3403. p. 1842

Holman, Mark, Ref Serv, University of Texas Libraries, Jamail Center for Legal Research, University of Texas School of Law, 727 E Dean Keeton St, Austin, TX, 78705-3224. Tel: 512-471-7726. Fax: 512-471-0243. p. 2284

Holman, Rita, Librn, Wapiti Regional Library, Choiceland Public Library, 116 First St E, Choiceland, SK, S0J 0M0, CANADA. Tel: 306-428-2216. p. 2921

Holman, Ruby, Ref Serv, Tombigbee Regional Library System, Amory Municipal Library, 401 Second Ave N at Fourth St, Amory, MS, 38821. Tel: 662-256-5261. Fax: 662-256-6321. p. 1318

Holman, Stephanie, Ch, Monroe County Public Library, Ellettsville Branch, 600 W Temperance St, Ellettsville, IN, 47429. Tel: 812-876-1272. Fax: 812-876-2515. p. 728

Holmberg, James, Curator, Filson Historical Society Library, 1310 S Third St, Louisville, KY, 40208. Tel: 502-635-5083. Fax: 502-635-5086. p. 923

Holmberg, Linda, Sch Librn, Centerville Community Library, 421 Florida, Centerville, SD, 57014. Tel: 605-563-2540. Fax: 605-563-2615. p. 2211

Holmberg, Ruth, Librn, CancerCare Manitoba Library, 4005 675 McDermot Ave, Winnipeg, MB, R3E 0V9, CANADA. Tel: 204-787-2136. Fax: 204-787-4761. p. 2755

Holme, Heather, Ref, Summa Health System, 55 N Arch, Ste G-3, Akron, OH, 44304. Tel: 330-375-3260. Fax: 330-375-3978. p. 1853

Holmer, Paul, Spec Coll Librn, Southern Connecticut State University, 501 Crescent St, New Haven, CT, 06515. Tel: 203-392-5746. Fax: 203-392-5775. p. 356

Holmer, Susan, Dir, Menlo Park Public Library, 800 Alma St, Alma & Ravenswood, Menlo Park, CA, 94025-3455. Tel: 650-330-2500. Fax: 650-327-7030. p. 185

Holmes, Anne, Asst Librn, Skidompha Public Library, 184 Main St, Damariscotta, ME, 04543-4670. Tel: 207-563-5513. Fax: 207-563-1941. p. 983

Holmes, B Joey, Asst Librn, ILL Librn, Dunbar Free Library, 401 Rte 10 S, Grantham, NH, 03753. Tel: 603-863-2172. Fax: 603-863-2172. p. 1448

Holmes, Barry, Chief Exec Officer, Greater Victoria Public Library Board, 735 Broughton St, Victoria, BC, V8W 3H2, CANADA. Tel: 250-382-7241. Fax: 250-382-7125. p. 2745

Holmes, Barry, Chief Exec Officer, Windsor Public Library, 850 Ouellette Ave, Windsor, ON, N9A 4M9, CANADA. Tel: 519-255-6770, Ext 4425. Fax: 519-255-7207. p. 2872

Holmes, Colette, Mgt Librn, Rensselaer Libraries, Rensselaer Polytechnic Inst, 110 Eighth St, Troy, NY, 12180-3590. Tel: 518-276-8300. Fax: 518-276-2044. p. 1756

Holmes, Craig, Info Serv, Southington Public Library & Museum, 255 Main St, Southington, CT, 06489. Tel: 860-628-0947. Fax: 860-628-0488. p. 368

Holmes, David, Training/Coll Librn, Foundation Center-Cleveland Library, 1422 Euclid Ave, Ste 1600, Cleveland, OH, 44115-2001. Tel: 216-861-1934. Fax: 216-861-1936. p. 1880

Holmes, Debbie, Dean of Libr, College of Coastal Georgia, One College Way, Brunswick, GA, 31520-3644. Tel: 912-279-5700. p. 521

Holmes, Denise, Libr Dir, Banks Public Library, 111 Market St, Banks, OR, 97106-9019. Tel: 503-324-1382. Fax: 503-324-9132. p. 1991

Holmes, Edwin, Librn, Edwin T Holmes Law Library, 146 South St, Rockport, MA, 01966. Tel: 978-546-3478. Fax: 978-546-6785. p. 1121

Holmes, Elizabeth, Coll Develop, Saint Anselm College, 100 Saint Anselm Dr, Manchester, NH, 03102-1310. Tel: 603-641-7300. Fax: 603-641-7345. p. 1456

Holmes, Frances, Head, Pub Serv, Montana Tech Library, 1300 W Park St, Butte, MT, 59701-8997. Tel: 406-496-4222. Fax: 406-496-4133. p. 1376

Holmes, Gail, Dir, Dallam-Hartley County Library, 420 Denrock Ave, Dalhart, TX, 79022. Tel: 806-244-2761. Fax: 806-244-2761. p. 2304

Holmes, Gerald, Diversity Coordr, Ref Librn, University of North Carolina at Greensboro, 320 Spring Garden St, Greensboro, NC, 27402. Tel: 336-256-0273. Fax: 336-334-5399. p. 1798

Holmes, Haley, Br Mgr, San Antonio Public Library, Parman, 20735 Wilderness Oak, San Antonio, TX, 78258. Tel: 210-207-2703. Fax: 210-207-2703. p. 2382

Holmes, Heidi, Br Mgr, Oconee County Public Library, 501 W South Broad St, Walhalla, SC, 29691. Tel: 864-638-4133. Fax: 864-638-4132. p. 2207

Holmes, James, Tech & Media Res, Reed College, 3203 SE Woodstock Blvd, Portland, OR, 97202-8199. Tel: 503-777-7702. Fax: 503-777-7786. p. 2014

Holmes, Jamie, Instruction Librn, Northeastern State University, Broken Arrow Campus Library, Bldg E Library, 3100 E New Orleans St, Broken Arrow, OK, 74014. Tel: 918-449-6456. Fax: 918-449-6454. p. 1979

Holmes, Jason, Dr, Asst Prof, Kent State University, 314 Library, Kent, OH, 44242-0001. Tel: 330-672-2782. Fax: 330-672-7965. p. 2972

Holmes, Katherine, Asst Dir, Lesley University, 89 Brattle St, Cambridge, MA, 02138-2790. Tel: 617-349-8840. Fax: 617-349-8849. p. 1077

Holmes, Linda, Librn, Louisiana State Penitentiary Library, Main Prison Library, A Bldg, Angola, LA, 70712. Tel: 225-655-2031. Fax: 225-655-2585. p. 941

Holmes, Linda, Assoc Librn, Brooklyn Law School Library, 250 Joralemon St, Brooklyn, NY, 11201. Tel: 718-780-7973. Fax: 718-780-0369. p. 1590

Holmes, Margo, Dir, Orthopaedic Hospital, 2400 S Flower St, Los Angeles, CA, 90007. Tel: 213-742-1000. Fax: 213-742-1100. p. 176

Holmes, Nancy, Cat Librn, Piedmont Regional Library, 189 Bell View St, Winder, GA, 30680-1706. Tel: 770-867-2762. Fax: 770-867-7483. p. 557

Holmes, Pamela V, Asst Dir, East Orange Public Library, 21 S Arlington Ave, East Orange, NJ, 07018-3892. Tel: 973-266-5600. Fax: 973-674-1991. p. 1482

Holmes, Pat, Acq Librn, Keene Public Library, 60 Winter St, Keene, NH, 03431-3360. Tel: 603-352-0157. Fax: 866-743-0446. p. 1452

Holmes, Sandra, Librn, Braille Philosophers Library & Press, 516 N Lucas Dr, Santa Maria, CA, 93454-3828. Tel: 805-614-4977. Fax: 805-614-4977. p. 265

Holmes, Sandra J, Dir, Ozark-Dale County Public Library, Inc, 416 James St, Ozark, AL, 36360. Tel: 334-774-2399, 334-774-5480. p. 33

Holmes, Sue, Tech Serv, North Palm Beach Public Library, 303 Anchorage Dr, North Palm Beach, FL, 33408. Tel: 561-841-3383. Fax: 561-848-2874. p. 473

Holmes, Susan, Dir, Lauri Ann West Memorial Library, 1220 Powers Run Rd, Pittsburgh, PA, 15238-2618. Tel: 412-828-9520. Fax: 412-828-4960. p. 2129

Holmes, Wendy, Ref Serv, Davis & Co, 666 Burrard St, Ste 2800, Vancouver, BC, V6C 2Z7, CANADA. Tel: 604-643-6425. Fax: 604-605-3598. p. 2740

Holmquist, Jane, Librn, Princeton University, Astrophysics, Peyton Hall, Ivy Lane, Princeton, NJ, 08544-1001. Tel: 609-258-3150. Fax: 609-258-1020. p. 1523

Holmquist, Kimberly J, Dir, Gibbon Public Library, 1050 Adams Ave, Gibbon, MN, 55335. Tel: 507-834-6640. Fax: 507-834-6640. p. 1252

Holmquist, Norma, ILL, University of Connecticut, 99 E Main St, Waterbury, CT, 06702-2311. Tel: 203-236-9900. Fax: 203-236-9905. p. 375

Hols, Frances, Libr Mgr, Willingdon Public Library, 4911-52 Ave, Willingdon, AB, T0B 4R0, CANADA. Tel: 780-367-2146, 780-367-2642. p. 2722

Holsey, Nancy, Law Librn, Lassen County Law Library, 2610 Riverside Dr, Susanville, CA, 96130. Tel: 530-251-8353. p. 274

Holshouser, Deanne W, Dir, Librn, Edwardsville Public Library, 112 S Kansas St, Edwardsville, IL, 62025. Tel: 618-692-7556. Fax: 618-692-9566. p. 639

Holsomback, Jimmy, Bus Mgr, Rapides Parish Library, 411 Washington St, Alexandria, LA, 71301-8338. Tel: 318-445-6436, Ext 1004. Fax: 318-445-6478. p. 940

Holst, Bruce, Dir, Marie Selby Botanical Gardens Research Library, 811 S Palm Ave, Sarasota, FL, 34236-7726. Tel: 941-955-7553, Ext 312. Fax: 941-951-1474. p. 490

Holst, Kathryn, Dir, Huntington City Township Public Library, 200 W Market St, Huntington, IN, 46750-2655. Tel: 260-356-0824. Fax: 260-356-3073. p. 748

Holst, Kathryn, Dir, Huntington City Township Public Library, Markle Public Library, 197 E Morse St, Markle, IN, 46770. Tel: 260-758-3332. Fax: 260-758-3332. p. 748

Holst, Kathy, Asst Dir, Hudson Public Library, 401 Fifth St, Hudson, IA, 50643. Tel: 319-988-4217. p. 821

Holst, Ruth, Assoc Dir, National Network of Libraries of Medicine Greater Midwest Region, c/o Library of Health Sci, Univ Illinois at Chicago, 1750 W Polk St, M/C 763, Chicago, IL, 60612-4330. Tel: 312-996-2464. Fax: 312-996-2226. p. 2942

Holste, Jean, Ch, Humboldt Public Library, 30 Sixth St N, Humboldt, IA, 50548. Tel: 515-332-1925. Fax: 515-332-1926. p. 821

Holstein, Susanna, Fac & Security Mgr, Kanawha County Public Library, 123 Capitol St, Charleston, WV, 25301. Tel: 304-343-4646. Fax: 304-348-6530. p. 2556

Holsten, Virginia, Dir, Vinton Public Library, 510 Second Ave, Vinton, IA, 52349. Tel: 319-472-4208. Fax: 319-472-2548. p. 849

Holster, Debra, Br Mgr, Grand Prairie Public Library System, Betty Warmack Branch Library, 760 Bardin Rd, Grand Prairie, TX, 75052. Tel: 972-237-5772. Fax: 972-237-5779. p. 2329

Holster, Elaine, Librn, Clover Park Technical College Library, 4500 Steilacoom Blvd SW, Bldg 15, Lakewood, WA, 98499-4098. Tel: 253-589-5628. Fax: 253-589-5726. p. 2519

Holt, Barb, Librn, Lakeland Library Region, Marshall Branch, 13 Main St, Marshall, SK, S0M 1R0, CANADA. Tel: 306-387-6155. p. 2920

Holt, Barbara, Dir, Perkins Coie, 1120 NW Couch St, 10th Flr, Portland, OR, 97209-4128. Tel: 206-359-8444. Fax: 206-359-9000. p. 2013

Holt, Caleb, Coordr, Heald College, 1605 E March Lane, Stockton, CA, 95210. Tel: 209-473-5200. Fax: 209-473-5287. p. 272

Holt, Cheryl, Librn, Parkland Regional Library, Rose Valley Branch, 300 Centre St, Rose Valley, SK, S0E 1M0, CANADA. Tel: 306-322-2001. p. 2932

Holt, Chris, Mgr, Libr Serv, Public Library of Cincinnati & Hamilton County, 800 Vine St, Cincinnati, OH, 45202-2009. Tel: 513-369-4417. Fax: 513-369-6993. p. 1871

Holt, Cynthia, Head, Coll Develop, Presv, George Mason University Libraries, 4400 University Dr, MSN 2FL, Fairfax, VA, 22030-4444. Tel: 703-993-2250. Fax: 703-993-2200. p. 2462

Holt, Cynthia, Assoc Univ Librn, Coll Serv, Concordia University Libraries, 1400 de Maisonneuve Blvd W, LB 209, Montreal, QC, H3G 1M8, CANADA. Tel: 514-848-2424, Ext 5255. Fax: 514-848-2882. p. 2894

Holt, David A, Librn, Hardin Memorial Hospital, 913 N Dixie Ave, Elizabethtown, KY, 42701-2503. Tel: 270-706-1688. Fax: 270-706-1336. p. 912

Holt, Dianne, Cat, Chippewa River District Library, 301 S University Ave, Mount Pleasant, MI, 48858-2597. Tel: 989-772-3488, Ext 24. Fax: 989-772-3280. p. 1211

Holt, Fianna D, Tech Serv, Albright College, 13th & Exeter Sts, Reading, PA, 19604. Tel: 610-921-7201. Fax: 610-921-7509. p. 2132

Holt, Jack E, Br Mgr, Augusta County Library, Churchville Branch, 3714 Churchville Ave, Churchville, VA, 24421. Tel: 540-245-5287. Fax: 540-245-5290. p. 2464

Holt, Janifer, Ref Librn, Dartmouth College Library, Feldberg Business Administration & Engineering Library, 6193 Murdough Ctr, Hanover, NH, 03755-3560. Tel: 603-646-2191. Fax: 603-646-2384. p. 1450

Holt, Laura J, Librn, School for Advanced Research Library, 660 Garcia St, Santa Fe, NM, 87505. Tel: 505-954-7234. Fax: 505-954-7214. p. 1564

Holt, Margaret, Libr Asst, Bastyr University Library, 14500 Juanita Dr NE, Kenmore, WA, 98028. Tel: 425-602-3023. Fax: 425-602-3188. p. 2518

Holt, Marilyn, Dept Head, Pennsylvania Dept, Carnegie Library of Pittsburgh, 4400 Forbes Ave, Pittsburgh, PA, 15213-4080. Tel: 412-622-3154. Fax: 412-578-2569. p. 2122

Holt, Mary, Mgr, Cobb County Public Library System, Lewis A Ray Branch, 4500 Oakdale Rd, Smyrna, GA, 30080. Tel: 770-801-5335. Fax: 770-801-5316. p. 543

Holt, Mary, Coordr, Info Serv, Tulane University, Rudolph Matas Library of the Health Sciences, Tulane Health Sciences Campus, 1430 Tulane Ave, SL-86, New Orleans, LA, 70112-2699. Tel: 504-988-2062. Fax: 504-988-7417. p. 963

Holt, Mary, Asst Dir, Dillon City Library, 121 S Idaho, Dillon, MT, 59725-2500. Tel: 406-683-4544. p. 1378

Holt, Mary, Librn, Berlin Township Library, 201 Veteran's Ave, West Berlin, NJ, 08091. Tel: 856-767-0439. Fax: 856-753-6729. p. 1540

Holt, Ronda, Info Tech Librn, Butler Community College Libraries, 901 S Haverhill Rd, El Dorado, KS, 67042-3280. Tel: 316-323-6410. Fax: 316-322-3315. p. 864

Holt, Ross A, Dir, Randolph County Public Library, 201 Worth St, Asheboro, NC, 27203. Tel: 336-318-6800. Fax: 336-318-6823. p. 1774

Holt, Sally, Ref & Teen Librn, Auburn Public Library, 49 Spring St, Auburn, ME, 04210. Tel: 207-333-6640. Fax: 207-333-6644. p. 974

Holt, Sharon Ann, Dr, Exec Dir, Sandy Spring Museum Library, 17901 Bentley Rd, Sandy Spring, MD, 20860. Tel: 301-774-0022. Fax: 301-774-8149. p. 1041

Holt, Susan, Tech Serv Supvr, Brentwood Public Library, 8765 Eulalie Ave, Brentwood, MO, 63144. Tel: 314-963-8632. Fax: 314-962-8675. p. 1320

Holt, Tom, Cat Mgr, California State University, East Bay Library, 25800 Carlos Bee Blvd, Hayward, CA, 94542-3052. Tel: 510-885-2429. Fax: 510-885-2049. p. 157

Holt, Wayne, Actg Librn, Pasadena Public Library, 1201 Jeff Ginn Memorial Dr, Pasadena, TX, 77506-4895. Tel: 713-477-0276. Fax: 713-475-7005. p. 2368

Holt, William, Circ, Atlanta University Center, 111 James P Brawley Dr SW, Atlanta, GA, 30314. Tel: 404-978-2048. Fax: 404-577-5158. p. 513

Holt-Dalziel, Leslie, Res Ctr Mgr, Holland College Library Services, 140 Weymouth St, Charlottetown, PE, C1A 4Z1, CANADA. Tel: 902-566-9635. Fax: 902-566-9522. p. 2875

Holtcamp, Virginia, Dir, Starkville-Oktibbeha County Public Library System, 326 University Dr, Starkville, MS, 39759. Tel: 662-323-2766, 662-323-2783. Fax: 662-323-9140. p. 1315

Holten, Noreen G, Librn, Cathlamet Public Library, 100 Main St, Cathlamet, WA, 98612. Tel: 360-795-3254. Fax: 360-795-8500. p. 2511

Holterhoff, Sally, Govt Info/Ref Librn, Valparaiso University, School of Law Library, 656 S Greenwich St, Valparaiso, IN, 46383. Tel: 219-465-7827. Fax: 219-465-7917. p. 784

Holtgrave, Diane, Asst Librn, Breese Public Library, 530 N Third St, Breese, IL, 62230. Tel: 618-526-7361. Fax: 618-526-0143. p. 597

Holthaus, Karen E, Libr Dir, Seneca Free Library, 606 Main St, Seneca, KS, 66538. Tel: 785-336-2377. Fax: 785-336-3699. p. 894

Holthof, Ben, Curator, Marine Museum of the Great Lakes at Kingston, 55 Ontario St, Kingston, ON, K7L 2Y2, CANADA. Tel: 613-542-2261. Fax: 613-542-0043. p. 2814

Holtman, Dawn, ILL, Charles A Ransom District Library, 180 S Sherwood Ave, Plainwell, MI, 49080-1896. Tel: 269-685-8024. Fax: 269-685-2266. p. 1218

Holtman, Tracy, Asst Dir, Coll Mgt, Tarleton State University Library, 201 Saint Felix, Stephenville, TX, 76401. Tel: 254-968-9246. Fax: 254-968-9467. p. 2389

Holtmann, Libby, Mgr, Plano Public Library System, W O Haggard Jr Library, 2501 Coit Rd, Plano, TX, 75075. Tel: 972-769-4250. Fax: 972-769-4256. p. 2370

Holton, Jill, Head of Mkt & Communications, Licking County Library, 101 W Main St, Newark, OH, 43055-5054. Tel: 740-349-5541. Fax: 740-349-5535. p. 1922

Holton, Tommy S, Dean of Libr, Dillard University, 2601 Gentilly Blvd, New Orleans, LA, 70122-3097. Tel: 504-816-4784. Fax: 504-816-4787. p. 960

Holtry Curtis, Cara, Librn, Cumberland County Historical Society, 21 N Pitt, Carlisle, PA, 17013-2945. Tel: 717-249-7610. Fax: 717-258-9332. p. 2041

Holtz, Elizabeth, Librn, Washington County Free Library, Sharpsburg Public, 106 E Main St, Sharpsburg, MD, 21782. Tel: 301-432-8825. p. 1031

Holtz, Jerry, Automation Sys Supvr, Woodbridge Public Library, George Frederick Plaza, Woodbridge, NJ, 07095. Tel: 732-634-4450. p. 1545

Holtz, Margie, Librn, Ashley Public Library District, 70 N Second St, Ashley, IL, 62808. Tel: 618-485-2295. Fax: 618-485-2295. p. 590

Holtz, Ruth, Ref, Bracebridge Public Library, 94 Manitoba St, Bracebridge, ON, P1L 2B5, CANADA. Tel: 705-645-4171. Fax: 705-645-6551. p. 2796

Holtzclaw, John W, Mgr, Libr Serv, Nationwide Library, One Nationwide Plaza 1-01-05, Columbus, OH, 43215. Tel: 614-249-6414. Fax: 614-249-2218. p. 1886

Holtzclaw, Shari, Syst Coordr, Webmaster, North Georgia College & State University, 238 Georgia Circle, Dahlonega, GA, 30597-3001. Tel: 706-864-1327. p. 527

Holtze, Terri, Head, Web Serv, University of Louisville Libraries, William F Ekstrom Library, Belknap Campus, 2215 S Third St, Louisville, KY, 40292. Tel: 502-852-4477. Fax: 502-852-7394. p. 927

Holtzman, Douglas, Asst Libr Dir, Monterey Public Library, 625 Pacific St, Monterey, CA, 93940-2866. Tel: 831-646-3745. Fax: 831-646-5618. p. 190

Holtzman, Matthew, Librn, Monhegan Memorial Library, One Library Lane, Monhegan, ME, 04852. Tel: 207-596-0549. p. 992

Holub, Donna, Asst Librn, Schulenburg Public Library, 310 Simpson, Schulenburg, TX, 78956. Tel: 979-743-3345. p. 2385

Holveck, Leanne, Libr Asst II, Christiana Hospital Library, Christiana Hospital, 4755 Ogletown Stanton Rd, Newark, DE, 19718-0002. Tel: 302-428-2201. Fax: 302-733-1365. p. 385

Holvenstot, Suzanne, Circ, Northeast Wisconsin Technical College Library, 2740 W Mason St, Green Bay, WI, 54303-4966. Tel: 920-498-5732. Fax: 920-498-6910. p. 2596

Holwick, Diane, Asst Dir, Fort Smith Public Library, 3201 Rogers Ave, Fort Smith, AR, 72903. Tel: 479-783-0229. Fax: 479-782-8571. p. 100

Holyfield, Erin, Asst Librn, Henderson County, 121 S Prairieville, Athens, TX, 75751. Tel: 903-677-7295. Fax: 903-677-7275. p. 2277

Holyoke, Francesca, Dept Head, Archives, University of New Brunswick Libraries, Five Macaulay Dr, Fredericton, NB, E3B 5H5, CANADA. Tel: 506-453-4965. Fax: 506-453-4595. p. 2763

Holz, Dayna, Librn, Berkeley Public Library, 2090 Kittredge St, Berkeley, CA, 94704. Tel: 510-981-6100. Fax: 510-981-6111. p. 126

Holz, Karen, Br Mgr, Bloomfield-Eastern Greene County Public Library, Eastern, 11453 East St, Rd 54, Bloomfield, IN, 47424. Tel: 812-825-2677. Fax: 812-825-2677. p. 726

Holz, Sandra, Librn, Whitefield Public Library, Eight Lancaster Rd, Whitefield, NH, 03598. Tel: 603-837-2030. Fax: 603-837-3124. p. 1468

Holzhauer, Gretchen, Sr Librn, Franklin Correctional Facility, 62 Bare Hill Rd, Malone, NY, 12953. Tel: 518-483-6040. Fax: 518-483-6040, Ext 2099. p. 1656

Holzman, Melody, Interim Head of Tech Serv, County of Los Angeles Public Library, 7400 E Imperial Hwy, Downey, CA, 90242-3375. Tel: 562-940-8543. Fax: 562-803-3032. p. 140

Holzmann, Robert, Syst Librn, Tulsa Community College Learning Resources Center, Metro Campus, 909 S Boston Ave, Tulsa, OK, 74119-2011. Tel: 918-595-7173. Fax: 918-595-7179. p. 1983

Holzwarth, Evelyn, Adminr, Hastings Public Library, 227 E State St, Hastings, MI, 49058-1817. Tel: 269-945-4263. Fax: 269-948-3874. p. 1189

Hom, Linda, Head Law Librn, Middlesex Law Library at Cambridge, Superior Courthouse, 40 Thorndike St, Cambridge, MA, 02141. Tel: 617-494-4148. Fax: 617-225-0026. p. 1078

Hom, Sharon, Br Mgr, US Courts Library, Byron Rogers Courthouse, 1929 Stout St, Rm 430, Denver, CO, 80294. Tel: 303-844-3591. Fax: 303-844-5958. p. 303

Homa, Frances, Ch, Rocky River Public Library, 1600 Hampton Rd, Rocky River, OH, 44116-2699. Tel: 440-333-7610. Fax: 440-333-4184. p. 1932

Homan, Evelyn, Dir, Lexington Public Library District, 207 S Cedar St, Lexington, IL, 61753. Tel: 309-365-7801. Fax: 309-365-9028. p. 665

Homan, Rebecca, Archivist, Bibliographer, Gainesville State College, 3820 Mundy Mill Rd, Oakwood, GA, 30566. Tel: 678-717-3656. Fax: 770-718-3657. p. 547

Homan, Scott, Ad, Burlington County Library, Cinnaminson Branch, 1619 Riverton Rd, Cinnaminson, NJ, 08077. Tel: 856-829-9340. Fax: 856-829-2243. p. 1543

Homant, Susan, Head, Ref, University of Detroit Mercy Library, 4001 W McNichols Rd, Detroit, MI, 48221-3038. Tel: 313-578-0577. Fax: 313-993-1780. p. 1172

Homer, Starr, Librn, Northwest Regional Library, Clyde Nix Public Library, 350 Bexar Ave W, Hamilton, AL, 35570. Tel: 205-921-4290. Fax: 205-921-4290. p. 40

Homick, Ronald, Chairperson, Houston Community College Central College, Central Campus Library, 1300 Holman, Houston, TX, 77004. Tel: 713-718-6133. Fax: 713-718-6154. p. 2337

Homme, Kathy, Dir, Arlington Public Library, 321 W Main St, Arlington, MN, 55307-0391. Tel: 507-964-2490. Fax: 507-964-2490. p. 1240

Hommel, Maggie, Reader Serv Mgr, Park Ridge Public Library, 20 S Prospect, Park Ridge, IL, 60068-4188. Tel: 847-720-3282. Fax: 847-825-0001. p. 688

Hommerding, Leroy, Dr, Dir, Fort Myers Beach Public Library, 2755 Estero Blvd, Fort Myers Beach, FL, 33931. Tel: 239-765-8162. Fax: 239-463-8776. p. 446

Homolka, Linda, Dir, J H Robbins Memorial Library, 219 N Lincoln, Ellsworth, KS, 67439-3313. Tel: 785-472-3969. Fax: 785-472-4191. p. 865

Homolka, Susie, Dir, Dvoracek Memorial Library, 419 W Third, Wilber, NE, 68465. Tel: 402-821-2832. p. 1423

Honchell, Ann, Br Mgr, Garfield County Public Library System, New Castle Branch, 402 W Main, New Castle, CO, 81647. Tel: 970-984-2346. Fax: 970-984-2081. p. 319

Honea, Barbara, Head, Tech Serv, Corsicana Public Library, 100 N 12th St, Corsicana, TX, 75110. Tel: 903-654-4810, 903-654-4813. Fax: 903-654-4814. p. 2302

Honea, Roxanna, Br Mgr, Avoyelles Parish Library, Plaucheville Branch, Town Hall, Gin St, Plaucheville, LA, 71362. Tel: 318-359-1016. p. 956

Honesto, Nora, Asst Librn, Hockley County Memorial Library, 811 Austin St, Levelland, TX, 79336. Tel: 806-894-6750. Fax: 806-894-6917. p. 2355

Honeycutt, Heather, Asst Librn, Harnett County Public Library, Erwin Public, 110 West F St, Erwin, NC, 28339. Tel: 910-897-5780. Fax: 910-897-4474. p. 1807

Honeysett, Kathleen, Info Tech Coordr, San Diego County Library, 5560 Overland Ave, Ste 110, San Diego, CA, 92123. Tel: 858-694-2483. Fax: 858-495-5981. p. 233

Hong, E K, Cat, Society of the Cincinnati Library, 2118 Massachusetts Ave NW, Washington, DC, 20008. Tel: 202-785-2040, Ext 411. Fax: 202-785-0729. p. 416

Hong, Paul, Syst Mgr, Whittier College, Bonnie Bell Wardman Library, 7031 Founders Hill Rd, Whittier, CA, 90608-9984. Tel: 562-907-4247. Fax: 562-698-7168. p. 283

Honn, Rosemary, Circ, Webmaster, Ottawa Library, 105 S Hickory St, Ottawa, KS, 66067-2306. Tel: 785-242-3080. Fax: 785-242-8789. p. 887

Honnold, RoseMary, YA Serv, Coshocton Public Library, 655 Main St, Coshocton, OH, 43812-1697. Tel: 740-622-0956. Fax: 740-622-4331. p. 1891

Honold, Carole, Dir, Bagley Public Library, 117 Main, Bagley, IA, 50026. Tel: 712-999-5621. Fax: 641-427-5214. p. 795

Honor, Naomi Goldberg, Head, Adult Serv, Haverstraw Kings Daughters Public Library, Ten W Ramapo Rd, Garnerville, NY, 10923. Tel: 845-786-3800. Fax: 845-786-3791. p. 1626

Honsey, Nora, Coll Coordr, Chinook Regional Library, 1240 Chaplin St W, Swift Current, SK, S9H 0G8, CANADA. Tel: 306-773-3186. Fax: 306-773-0434. p. 2927

Hony, Candace, Circ Supvr, Mgr, ILL, Greenwood-Leflore Public Library System, 405 W Washington St, Greenwood, MS, 38930-4297. Tel: 662-453-3634. Fax: 662-453-0683. p. 1299

Hoobler, Janice M, Acad Res Coordr/Med Librn, St Mary's Medical Center, Catholic Healthcare West, 2235 Hayes St, 4th flr, San Francisco, CA, 94117. Tel: 415-750-5795. Fax: 415-750-8149. p. 244

Hood, Carolyn, Head, ILL, Gonzaga University School of Law, 721 N Cincinnati St, Spokane, WA, 99202. Tel: 509-323-3749. Fax: 509-323-5733. p. 2536

Hood, Carroll, Librn, Monroe City Public Library, 109A Second St, Monroe City, MO, 63456. Tel: 573-735-2665. Fax: 573-735-4943. p. 1347

Hood, Daniel, Ref/Outreach Librn, Indian River State College, 3209 Virginia Ave, Fort Pierce, FL, 34981-5599. Tel: 772-462-7588. Fax: 772-462-4780. p. 446

Hood, Darleen, Circ Mgr, Hagaman Memorial Library, 227 Main St, East Haven, CT, 06512-3003. Tel: 203-468-3890. Fax: 203-468-3892. p. 337

Hood, John, Librn, Ecology & Environment Inc, Library, 368 Pleasantview Dr, Lancaster, NY, 14086-1316. Tel: 716-684-8060. Fax: 716-684-0844. p. 1651

Hood, Martha, Assoc Dir, Tech Serv, University of Houston - Clear Lake, 2700 Bay Area Blvd, Houston, TX, 77058-1098. Tel: 281-283-3920. Fax: 281-283-3937. p. 2343

Hood, Mary D, Dir, Law Libr, Santa Clara University, Heafey Law Library, School of Law, 500 El Camino Real, Santa Clara, CA, 95053-0430. Tel: 408-554-2732. Fax: 408-554-5318. p. 263

Hood, Nona, Dir, Prairie Community Library, 506 King St, Cottonwood, ID, 83522. Tel: 208-962-3714. p. 573

Hood, Patricia, Ref/Outreach Librn, Indian River State College, 2229 NW Ninth Ave, Okeechobee, FL, 34972. Tel: 772-462-7600, 863-824-6000. p. 474

Hood, Sabrina, Dir, Aztec Public Library, 319 S Ash, Aztec, NM, 87410. Tel: 505-334-7658. Fax: 505-334-7659. p. 1551

Hood, Sarah, User Serv, Columbia College, 1301 Columbia College Dr, Columbia, SC, 29203-9987. Tel: 803-786-3703. Fax: 803-786-3700. p. 2187

Hood, Saundra, Librn, Georgia Department of Corrections, Office of Library Services, 3001 Gordon Hwy, Grovetown, GA, 30813. Tel: 706-855-4882. Fax: 706-855-4924. p. 536

Hood, Yolanda, Bibliographer, YA Serv, University of Northern Iowa Library, 1227 W 27th St, Cedar Falls, IA, 50613-3675. Tel: 319-273-6167. Fax: 319-273-2913. p. 799

Hooee, Cordelia, Dir, Zuni Public Library, 27 E Chavez Circle, Zuni, NM, 87327. Tel: 505-782-4575. Fax: 505-782-7210. p. 1566

Hoofnagle, Bumpy, Ch, Lake Alfred Public Library, 195 E Pomelo St, Lake Alfred, FL, 33850. Tel: 863-291-5378. Fax: 863-965-6386. p. 457

Hooft, Robert, Video Bookings, ILL & Overdues, Justice Institute of British Columbia Library, 715 McBride Blvd, New Westminster, BC, V3L 5T4, CANADA. Tel: 604-528-5598. Fax: 604-528-5593. p. 2734

Hoogakker, David, Librn, National Louis University Library & Learning Support, Lisle, 850 Warrenville Rd, Lisle, IL, 60532. Tel: 630-874-4608. Fax: 630-960-4608. p. 619

Hoogeveen, Sonja, Br Mgr, Tulare County Library, Three Rivers Branch, 42052 Eggers Dr, Three Rivers, CA, 93271-9774. Tel: 559-561-4564. Fax: 559-561-7318. p. 281

Hoogland, Margaret, Distance Support Librn, A T Still University of Health Sciences, Kirksville Campus, 800 W Jefferson St, Kirksville, MO, 63501. Tel: 660-626-2340. Fax: 660-626-2031, 660-626-2333. p. 1342

Hook, Alexandra, Librn, Aurora College, 50 Conibear St, Fort Smith, NT, X0E 0P0, CANADA. Tel: 867-872-7544. Fax: 867-872-4511. p. 2775

Hook, Bill, Assoc Dean, Vanderbilt University, 419 21st Ave S, Nashville, TN, 37203-2427. Tel: 615-322-7100. Fax: 615-343-8279. p. 2260

Hook, Bill, Dir, Vanderbilt University, Central Library, 419 21st Ave S, Nashville, TN, 37203-2427. Tel: 615-322-2800. Fax: 615-343-7451. p. 2260

Hook, Bill, Interim Dir, Vanderbilt University, The Peabody Library, 230 Appleton Pl, PBM 135, Nashville, TN, 37203. Tel: 615-322-8096. Fax: 615-343-7923. p. 2261

Hook, Marilyn, Pub Serv, Midlands Technical College Library, 1260 Lexington Dr, West Columbia, SC, 29170-2176. Tel: 803-822-3535. Fax: 803-822-3670. p. 2207

Hook, Mary, Dir, Manistique School & Public Library, 100 N Cedar St, Manistique, MI, 49854-1293. Tel: 906-341-4316. Fax: 906-341-6751. p. 1206

Hook, Olivia, Night Supvr, California State University Dominguez Hills, 1000 E Victoria St, Carson, CA, 90747. Tel: 310-243-3407. Fax: 310-516-4219. p. 132

Hook, William, Dir, Vanderbilt University, Divinity Library, 419 21st Ave S, Nashville, TN, 37203-2427. Tel: 615-322-2865. Fax: 615-343-8279. p. 2260

Hooker, Alice, In Charge, Berea College, Science Research, CPO 2191, Berea, KY, 40404. Tel: 859-985-3351. Fax: 859-985-3303. p. 907

Hooker, Celia, Dir, Rankin Public Library, 310 E Tenth St, Rankin, TX, 79778. Tel: 432-693-2881. Fax: 432-693-2667. p. 2373

Hooker, Mary Kaye, Head Librn, Bauder College Library, 384 Northyards Blvd NW, Ste 190, Atlanta, GA, 30313. Tel: 404-443-1807, 404-443-1808. Fax: 404-237-1619. p. 513

Hookham, Kathleen, Dir, Powers Memorial Library, 115 Main St, Palmyra, WI, 53156. Tel: 262-495-4605. Fax: 262-495-8617. p. 2629

Hooks, Denise, Dir, Mideastern Michigan Library Cooperative, 503 S Saginaw St, Ste 839, Flint, MI, 48502. Tel: 810-232-7119. Fax: 810-232-6639. p. 2946

Hooks, Glenda, Br Librn, Duplin County Library, Emily S Hill Library, 106 Park Circle Dr, Faison, NC, 28341. Tel: 910-267-0601. Fax: 910-267-0601. p. 1804

Hooks, James, Dr, Librn, Indiana University of Pennsylvania, Northpointe Regional Campus Library, 167 Northpointe Blvd, Freeport, PA, 16229. Tel: 724-294-3306. Fax: 724-294-3307. p. 2071

Hooks, Leocadia, Ser, Texas Southern University, 3100 Cleburne Ave, Houston, TX, 77004. Tel: 713-313-4423. Fax: 713-313-1080. p. 2342

Hooks, Vera, Ser, Fayetteville State University, 1200 Murchison Rd, Fayetteville, NC, 28301-4298. Tel: 910-672-1539. Fax: 910-672-1746. p. 1793

Hookway, Judith, Adult Serv, Rodman Public Library, 215 E Broadway St, Alliance, OH, 44601-2694. Tel: 330-821-2665. Fax: 330-821-5053. p. 1854

Hooley, Mary, Dir, LaGrange County Public Library, 203 W Spring St, LaGrange, IN, 46761-1845. Tel: 260-463-2841. Fax: 260-463-2843. p. 759

Hoolihan, Joan, Head, Teen Serv, New York State Judicial Department, M Dolores Denman Courthouse, 50 East Ave, Ste 100, Rochester, NY, 14604-2214. Tel: 585-530-3250. Fax: 585-530-3270. p. 1731

Hooper, Angel, Pub Serv, University of Texas, School of Public Health Library, 1200 Herman Pressler Blvd, Houston, TX, 77030-3900. Tel: 713-500-9121. Fax: 713-500-9125. p. 2344

Hooper, Anthony, Br Mgr, Hawaii State Public Library System, Wahiawa Public Library, 820 California Ave, Wahiawa, HI, 96786. Tel: 808-622-6345. Fax: 808-622-6348. p. 563

Hooper, Candice, Curator, Coronado Public Library, 640 Orange Ave, Coronado, CA, 92118-1526. Tel: 619-522-2476. Fax: 619-435-4205. p. 137

Hooper, Gailene, Librn, North Central Regional Library, Republic Community, 794 S Clark Ave, Republic, WA, 99166-8823. Tel: 509-775-3328. p. 2549

Hooper, J Leon, Dir, Woodstock Theological Center Library, Georgetown University, Lauinger Library, PO Box 571170, Washington, DC, 20057-1170. Tel: 202-687-4250. Fax: 202-687-7473. p. 423

Hooper, Jim, Librn, Fingerlakes Developmental Disabilities Service Office Monroe Developmental Center, 620 Westfall Rd, Rochester, NY, 14620-4610. Tel: 585-461-8978. Fax: 585-461-8974. p. 1729

Hooper, JoAnn, Head Librn, Edson Public Library, 4726-8 Avenue, Edson, AB, T7E 1S8, CANADA. Tel: 780-723-6691. Fax: 780-723-9728. p. 2703

Hooper, Leon, Fr, Head, Woodstock Theol Ctr Libr, Georgetown University, 37th & N St NW, Washington, DC, 20057-1174. Tel: 202-687-4250. Fax: 202-687-7501. p. 402

Hooper, Marjorie, Assoc State Librn, Idaho Commission for Libraries, 325 W State St, Boise, ID, 83702-6072. Tel: 208-334-2150. Fax: 208-334-4016. p. 571

Hooper, Michael, Electronic Res Librn, Austin Peay State University, 601 E College St, Clarksville, TN, 37044. Tel: 931-221-7092. Fax: 931-221-7296. p. 2228

Hooper, Peg, Mgr, Jefferson County Public Library, Golden Library, 1019 Tenth St, Golden, CO, 80401. p. 315

Hoornaert, Pat, Head, Youth Serv, Mokena Community Public Library District, 11327 W 195th St, Mokena, IL, 60448. Tel: 708-479-9663. Fax: 708-479-9684. p. 674

Hoover, Anna R, Asst Dir, Piedmont Regional Library, 189 Bell View St, Winder, GA, 30680-1706. Tel: 770-867-2762. Fax: 770-867-7483. p. 557

Hoover, Barbara, Head, Ref, Anderson University, Robert A Nicholson Library, 1100 E Fifth St, Anderson, IN, 46012-3495. Tel: 765-641-4281. Fax: 765-641-3850. p. 724

Hoover, Cathy, Mgr, Charlestown-Clark County Public Library, Sellersburg Branch, 430 N Indiana Ave, Sellersburg, IN, 47172. Tel: 812-246-4493. Fax: 812-246-4382. p. 731

Hoover, Cheryl, ILL Tech, Montana State University, 1500 University Dr, Billings, MT, 59101-0298. Tel: 406-657-2262. Fax: 406-657-2037. p. 1374

Hoover, Clarke, Info Tech, Orem Public Library, 58 N State St, Orem, UT, 84057-5596. Tel: 801-229-7050. Fax: 801-229-7130. p. 2409

Hoover, Danise, Pub Serv, Hunter College Libraries, 695 Park Ave, New York, NY, 10065. Tel: 212-772-4190. Fax: 212-772-4142. p. 1682

Hoover, Douglas A, Dean, Libr Serv, California University of Pennsylvania, 250 University Ave, California, PA, 15419-1394. Tel: 724-938-4091. Fax: 724-938-5901. p. 2040

Hoover, Jodi, Digital Media Librn, University of Maryland, Baltimore County, 1000 Hilltop Circle, Baltimore, MD, 21250. Tel: 410-455-2356. p. 1018

Hoover, John Neal, Dir, Saint Louis Mercantile Library at the University of Missouri-St Louis, Thomas Jefferson Library Bldg, One University Blvd, Saint Louis, MO, 63121-4400. Tel: 314-516-7245. Fax: 314-516-7241. p. 1359

Hoover, Khaki, Libr Instr, Outreach Prog, Amarillo College Library, 2201 S Washington, Amarillo, TX, 79109. Tel: 806-371-5400. Fax: 806-371-5470. p. 2274

Hoover, Lynda, Admin Assoc, Montana State University, 1500 University Dr, Billings, MT, 59101-0298. Tel: 406-657-2262. Fax: 406-657-2037. p. 1374

Hoover, Nancy, Univ Librn, Marylhurst University, 17600 Pacific Hwy (Hwy 43), Marylhurst, OR, 97036-7036. Tel: 503-699-6261, Ext 3372. Fax: 503-636-1957. p. 2004

Hoover, Rachiel, Ref Librn, Thomas Ford Memorial Library, 800 Chestnut Ave, Western Springs, IL, 60558. Tel: 708-246-0520. Fax: 708-246-0403. p. 717

Hoover, Terry, Head, Archives & Ms, The Henry Ford, 20900 Oakwood Blvd, Dearborn, MI, 48124-5029. Tel: 313-982-6087. Fax: 313-982-6244. p. 1167

Hoover, Valarie, Br Mgr, Loudoun County Public Library, Sterling Branch, 120 Enterprise St, Sterling, VA, 20164. Tel: 703-430-9500. Fax: 703-430-5935. p. 2474

Hoover, Venita L, Dir, Oklahoma County Law Library, 321 Park Ave, Rm 247, Oklahoma City, OK, 73102-3695. Tel: 405-713-1353. Fax: 405-713-1852. p. 1974

Hopcroft, Ginny, Govt Doc Librn, Bowdoin College Library, 3000 College Sta, Brunswick, ME, 04011-8421. Tel: 207-725-3298. p. 979

Hope, Anne Scott, Tech Serv Librn, National University of Health Sciences Learning Resource Center, 200 E Roosevelt Rd, Bldg C, Lombard, IL, 60148-4583. Tel: 630-889-6538. Fax: 630-495-6658. p. 667

Hope, Ben, Br Chief, National Institutes of Health Library, 10 Center Dr, Rm 1L25A, Bethesda, MD, 20892. Tel: 301-594-6473. Fax: 301-402-0254. p. 1021

Hope, Cathy, Asst Br Mgr, Ch, Atlanta-Fulton Public Library System, East Atlanta Library, 400 Flat Shoals Ave SE, Atlanta, GA, 30318-1938. Tel: 404-730-5438. Fax: 404-730-5436. p. 512

Hope, Elizabeth, Ch, Chesapeake Public Library, Russell Memorial, 2808 Taylor Rd, Chesapeake, VA, 23321-2210. Tel: 757-410-7027. Fax: 757-410-7029. p. 2456

Hope, Eve, Chief Librn, Hazelton District Public Library, 4255 Government St, Hazelton, BC, V0J 1Y0, CANADA. Tel: 250-842-5961. Fax: 250-842-2176. p. 2729

Hope, Kin, Circ, Pacific Oaks College, 55 Eureka St, Pasadena, CA, 91103. Tel: 626-529-8451. p. 206

Hope, Laura, Assoc Dean, Chaffey College Library, 5885 Haven Ave, Rancho Cucamonga, CA, 91737-3002. Tel: 909-652-6800. Fax: 909-466-2821. p. 212

Hope, Patricia, Circ Supvr, Waycross College Library, 2001 S Georgia Pkwy, Waycross, GA, 31503. Tel: 912-449-7646. Fax: 912-449-7611. p. 557

Hope, Sheila, Readers' Advisory Coordr, Westmont Public Library, 428 N Cass, Westmont, IL, 60559-1502. Tel: 630-969-5625. Fax: 630-969-6490. p. 717

Hopf, Mary, Br Mgr, Los Angeles Public Library System, Palisades Branch, 861 Alma Real Dr, Pacific Palisades, CA, 90272-3797. Tel: 310-459-2754. Fax: 310-454-3198. p. 174

Hopkins, Anita, Dir, Hancock County Public Library, 138 Willow St, Sneedville, TN, 37869. Tel: 423-733-2020. p. 2266

Hopkins, Barry C, Assoc Librn, Pub Serv, Lutheran School of Theology at Chicago & McCormick Theological Seminary, 1100 E 55th St, Chicago, IL, 60615-5199. Tel: 773-256-0738. Fax: 773-256-0737. p. 618

Hopkins, Brigitte, Interim Dir, West Warwick Public Library, 1043 Main St, West Warwick, RI, 02893. Tel: 401-828-3750. Fax: 401-828-8493. p. 2178

Hopkins, Carolyn, Librn, Copper Mountain College, 6162 Rotary Way, Joshua Tree, CA, 92252. Tel: 760-366-3791, Ext 5293. Fax: 760-366-5256. p. 161

Hopkins, Cinnamon, Circ, ILL, Converse County Library, 300 Walnut St, Douglas, WY, 82633. Tel: 307-358-3644. Fax: 307-358-6743. p. 2654

Hopkins, Claudia, Dir & Librn, Oxford Public Library, 115 S Sumner St, Oxford, KS, 67119. Tel: 620-455-2221. Fax: 620-455-2221. p. 889

Hopkins, Donna K, Res Librn, Champion Technologies Technical Library, 3130 FM 521 Rd, Fresno, TX, 77545. Tel: 281-710-9401. Fax: 281-710-9415. p. 2325

Hopkins, Edith, Libr Dir, Clarington Public Library, 163 Church St, Bowmanville, ON, L1C 1T7, CANADA. Tel: 905-623-7322. Fax: 905-623-9905. p. 2796

Hopkins, Elizabeth, Commun Relations Librn, Helen Hall Library, 100 W Walker, League City, TX, 77573-3899. Tel: 281-554-1106. Fax: 281-554-1118. p. 2354

Hopkins, Freda, Mgr, Memphis Public Library, Raleigh Branch, 3157 Powers Rd, Memphis, TN, 38128. Tel: 901-386-5333. Fax: 901-371-9495. p. 2250

Hopkins, Greg, Librn, Kansas Department of Corrections, PO Box 8098, Topeka, KS, 66608-0098. Tel: 785-354-9800. Fax: 785-354-9798. p. 896

Hopkins, Jane L, Dir, Greenville College, 301 N Elm, Greenville, IL, 62246. Tel: 618-664-6603. Fax: 618-664-9578. p. 652

Hopkins, Jeri Kay, Librn, US Court Library - Eighth Circuit, 111 S 18th Plaza, Ste 4104, Omaha, NE, 68102-1322. Tel: 402-661-7590. Fax: 402-661-7591. p. 1414

Hopkins, Joan, Instruction Librn, Benedictine University Library, 5700 College Rd, Lisle, IL, 60532-0900. Tel: 630-829-6050. Fax: 630-960-9451. p. 666

Hopkins, John, Assoc Dir, Info Tech, University of Cincinnati, 2540 Clifton Ave, Cincinnati, OH, 45219. Tel: 513-556-0153. Fax: 513-556-6265. p. 1874

Hopkins, Joyce, Asst Librn, Lincoln Heritage Public Library, 105 Wallace St, Dale, IN, 47523-9267. Tel: 812-937-7170. Fax: 812-937-7102. p. 735

Hopkins, Joyce, Librn, Stella Hill Memorial Library, 158 W San Antonio St, Alto, TX, 75925. Tel: 936-858-4343. p. 2273

Hopkins, Karen, Dir, Converse County Library, 300 Walnut St, Douglas, WY, 82633. Tel: 307-358-3644. Fax: 307-358-6743. p. 2654

Hopkins, Lana, Activity Spec, Kansas Department of Corrections, 1318 KS Hwy 264, Larned, KS, 67550. Tel: 620-285-6249. Fax: 620-285-8070. p. 877

Hopkins, Linda, Ref Serv, United States Marine Corps, 1401 West Rd, Bldg 1220, Camp Lejeune, NC, 28547-2539. Tel: 910-451-5724. Fax: 910-451-1871. p. 1779

Hopkins, Mary Catherine, Dir, Sussex County Department of Libraries, Milton Public, 121 Union St, Milton, DE, 19968. Tel: 302-684-8856. Fax: 302-684-8956. p. 383

Hopkins, Mary Catherine, Dir, Milton Public Library, 23 S Front St, Milton, PA, 17847. Tel: 570-742-7111. Fax: 570-742-7137. p. 2090

Hopkins, Melissa, Cat, Mineral Area College, 5270 Flat River Rd, Park Hills, MO, 63601. Tel: 573-518-2277. Fax: 573-518-2162. p. 1349

Hopkins, Michele, Br Mgr, Region of Waterloo Library, Ayr Branch, 137 Stanley St, Ayr, ON, N0B 1E0, CANADA. Tel: 519-632-7298. p. 2793

Hopkins, Pat, Ref Serv, Washington State Office of Secretary of State, 1129 Washington St SE, Olympia, WA, 98504-2283. Tel: 360-586-4894. Fax: 360-664-8814. p. 2523

Hopkins, Rose M, Br Mgr, Shreve Memorial Library, Oil City Branch, 102 Allen, Oil City, LA, 71061. Tel: 318-995-7975. Fax: 318-995-7975. p. 970

Hopkins, Susan, Network Serv, Central & Western Massachusetts Automated Resource Sharing, 67 Millbrook St, Ste 201, Worcester, MA, 01606. Tel: 508-755-3323, Ext 18. Fax: 508-755-3721. p. 2945

Hopkins, Tammy, Dir, Pike Library, 65 Main St, Pike, NY, 14130. Tel: 585-493-5900. Fax: 585-493-5900. p. 1717

Hopkins, Tony R, Dir, Ohio University-Zanesville/Zane State College, 1425 Newark Rd, Zanesville, OH, 43701. Tel: 740-588-1409. Fax: 740-453-0706. p. 1954

Hopkins, Wayne, Libr Serv Mgr, Palmer Theological Seminary, Six Lancaster Ave, Wynnewood, PA, 19096. Tel: 610-645-9318. p. 2158

Hopkinson, Caroline, Ref & Instruction Librn, Armstrong Atlantic State University, 11935 Abercorn St, Savannah, GA, 31419. Tel: 912-344-3027. Fax: 912-344-3457. p. 549

Hopkinson, Dawn, Libr Serv Mgr, Bellevue Medical Library, 462 First Ave & 27th St, 14N12, New York, NY, 10016. Tel: 212-562-8181. Fax: 212-562-3506. p. 1670

Hoppe, Frank, Ref Librn, Imperial Valley College, 380 E Ira Aten Rd, Imperial, CA, 92251. Tel: 760-355-6193. Fax: 760-355-1090. p. 159

Hopper, Deana, Circ/Per, Graves County Public Library, 601 N 17th St, Mayfield, KY, 42066. Tel: 270-247-2911. Fax: 270-247-2991. p. 928

Hopper, Laura, Librn, Schroeder Public Library, 93 Main St, Keystone, IA, 52249. Tel: 319-442-3329. Fax: 319-442-3327. p. 825

Hopper, Michael, Librn, Harvard Library, Hamilton A R Gibb Islamic Seminar Library, Widener Library, Rm Q, Harvard University, Cambridge, MA, 02138. Tel: 617-495-2437, 617-495-4310. Fax: 617-496-2902. p. 1075

Hopper, Rosita, Dean of Libr, Johnson & Wales University Library, 111 Dorrance St, Providence, RI, 02903. Tel: 401-598-1145. Fax: 401-598-1834. p. 2172

Hopper, Toni, Ref Serv, Elsie Quirk Public Library of Englewood, 100 W Dearborn St, Englewood, FL, 34223-3309. Tel: 941-861-1211. p. 439

Hoppman, Andrew, Dir, Lied Public Library, 100 E Garfield St, Clarinda, IA, 51632. Tel: 712-542-2416. Fax: 712-542-3590. p. 802

Hopson, Allan, Dir, New York State Veterans Home Library, 4211 St Hwy 220, Oxford, NY, 13830. Tel: 607-843-3100. Fax: 607-843-3199. p. 1714

Hopson, Debbie, Mgr, Mason County Library System, 508 Viand St, Point Pleasant, WV, 25550-1199. Tel: 304-675-0894. Fax: 304-675-0895. p. 2570

Hopson, Donna, Br Mgr, Rockford Public Library, Rockton Centre, 3112 N Rockton Ave, Rockford, IL, 6110-2837. Tel: 815-965-7606, Ext 778. Fax: 815-963-8855. p. 698

Hopson, Dunarene, Asst Mgr, Circ, Rockford Public Library, 215 N Wyman St, Rockford, IL, 61101-1023. Tel: 815-965-7606. Fax: 815-965-0866. p. 697

Hopson, Mike, Educ Spec, University of Hawaii Center, West Hawaii, 81-964 Halekii St, Kealakekua, HI, 96750. Tel: 808-322-4858, 808-322-4862. Fax: 808-322-4859. p. 566

Hopwood, Susan, Outreach Librn, Marquette University Libraries, 1355 W Wisconsin Ave, Milwaukee, WI, 53233. Tel: 414-288-5995. Fax: 414-288-7813. p. 2618

Hoque, Edwinna, Librn, Starkville-Oktibbeha County Public, Maben Branch, 831 Second Ave, Maben, MS, 39750-9742. Tel: 662-263-5619. Fax: 662-263-5619. p. 1315

Hor, Annie, Interim Dean, Libr Serv, California State University, Stanislaus, One University Circle, Turlock, CA, 95382. Tel: 209-667-3607. p. 277

Horacek, Louis, Asst Dir, Head, Tech Serv, Ohio County Public Library, 52 16th St, Wheeling, WV, 26003-3696. Tel: 304-232-0244. Fax: 304-232-6848. p. 2574

Horacek, Tamara, Managing Librn, Dolby Laboratories, Inc, 100 Potrero Ave, San Francisco, CA, 94103. Tel: 415-558-0268. Fax: 415-863-1373. p. 242

Horah, Jan L, Dir, Gulf Beaches Public Library, 200 Municipal Dr, Madeira Beach, FL, 33708. Tel: 727-391-2828. Fax: 727-399-2840. p. 462

Horah, Richard, Head, Media Serv, Armstrong Atlantic State University, 11935 Abercorn St, Savannah, GA, 31419. Tel: 912-344-3027. Fax: 912-344-3457. p. 549

Horak, Beula, Librn, St Joseph Hospital Library, 2901 Squalicum Pkwy, Bellingham, WA, 98225. Tel: 360-738-6786. Fax: 360-715-4106. p. 2509

Horak, Maureen, Assoc Dean, Libr Serv, Massachusetts College of Liberal Arts, 375 Church St, Ste 9250, North Adams, MA, 01247. Tel: 413-662-5321. Fax: 413-662-5286. p. 1111

Horan, Kate, Asst Dir, Pub Serv, McAllen Memorial Library, 601 N Main, McAllen, TX, 78501-4666. Tel: 956-688-3300. Fax: 956-688-3301. p. 2360

Horan, Krista, Syst Adminr, Neptune Public Library, 25 Neptune Blvd, Neptune, NJ, 07753-1125. Tel: 732-775-8241. Fax: 732-774-1132. p. 1507

Horan, Mary, Librn, Theda Clark Medical Center, 130 Second St, Neenah, WI, 54956-2883. Tel: 920-729-2190. Fax: 920-729-2321. p. 2624

Horanzy, Erin, Circ, Saint Joseph College, 1678 Asylum Ave, West Hartford, CT, 06117-2791. Tel: 860-232-4571. Fax: 860-523-4356. p. 376

Horat, Linda, Circ, Southern California University of Health Sciences, 16200 E Amber Valley Dr, Whittier, CA, 90604-4098. Tel: 562-902-3368. Fax: 562-902-3323. p. 283

Horbal, Andrew, Access Serv Librn, McDaniel College, Two College Hill, Westminster, MD, 21157-4390. Tel: 410-857-2281. Fax: 410-857-2748. p. 1046

Horbatt, Shirley, Librn, Kean University, 1000 Morris Ave, Union, NJ, 07083. Tel: 908-737-4600. Fax: 908-737-4620. p. 1537

Horchem, Debbie, Librn, Forman Valley Public Library District, 404 1/2 S Harrison, Manito, IL, 61546. Tel: 309-968-6093. Fax: 309-968-7120. p. 670

Hord, Bill, Librn, Houston Community College - Southwest College, Stafford Campus Library, 9910 Cash Rd, Stafford, TX, 77477-4405. Tel: 713-718-7823. Fax: 713-718-6723. p. 2338

Horgan, Laura, Syst Coordr, Middlesex Community College, Bldg 1-ARC, Springs Rd, Bedford, MA, 01730. Tel: 781-280-3702. Fax: 781-280-3771. p. 1052

Horgan, Laura, Coordr, Middlesex Community College, Federal Bldg, E Merrimack St, Lowell, MA, 01852. Tel: 978-937-5454. Fax: 978-656-3031. p. 1100

Horgan, Maureen E, Assoc Dir, Admin Serv, Teachers College, Columbia University, 525 W 120th St, New York, NY, 10027-6696. Tel: 212-678-3446. p. 1701

Horgan, Thomas R, Pres, New Hampshire College & University Council, Three Barrell Ct, Ste 100, Concord, NH, 03301-8543. Tel: 603-225-4199. Fax: 603-225-8108. p. 2948

Horio, Molly, Dir, Bromenn Healthcare, 1304 Franklin Ave, Normal, IL, 61761. Tel: 309-827-4321, Ext 5281. Fax: 309-268-5953. p. 681

Horn, Beth, Dir, Geneva Public Library, 244 Main St, Geneva, NY, 14456-2370. Tel: 315-789-5303. Fax: 315-789-9835. p. 1627

Horn, Bonnie, ILL & Distance Libr Serv Spec, Lincoln University, 1570 Old Baltimore Pike, Lincoln University, PA, 19352. Tel: 484-365-7356. Fax: 610-932-1206. p. 2082

Horn, Claudia, Head, Spec Coll & Archives, Chapman University, One University Dr, Orange, CA, 92866-1099. Tel: 714-532-7756. Fax: 714-532-7743. p. 200

Horn, David, Archivist, Boston College Libraries, John J Burns Library of Rare Books & Special Collections, 140 Commonwealth Ave, Chestnut Hill, MA, 02467. Tel: 617-552-3698. Fax: 617-552-2465. p. 1080

Horn, Dee, Librn, Northeast Regional Library, George E Allen Library, 500 W Church St, Booneville, MS, 38829-3353. Tel: 662-728-6553. Fax: 662-728-4127. p. 1297

Horn, Gina, Br Coordr, Branch District Library, Sherwood Branch, 118 E Sherman St, Sherwood, MI, 49089. Tel: 517-741-7976. Fax: 517-741-7976. p. 1165

Horn, Gini, Librn, Mount Nittany Medical Center, 1800 E Park Ave, State College, PA, 16803. Tel: 814-234-6191. Fax: 814-231-7031. p. 2143

Horn, James, Dir, Colonial Williamsburg Foundation, 313 First St, Williamsburg, VA, 23185-4306. Tel: 757-565-8501. Fax: 757-565-8508. p. 2502

Horn, Karen, Circ Supvr, Sturgis Library, 3090 Main St, Barnstable, MA, 02630. Tel: 508-362-6636. Fax: 508-362-5467. p. 1051

Horn, Katherine Lee, Dir, Elma Ross Public Library, 1011 E Main St, Brownsville, TN, 38012-2652. Tel: 731-772-9534. Fax: 731-772-5416. p. 2225

Horn, Linda, Dir, Didymus Thomas Library, 9639 Main St, Remsen, NY, 13438. Tel: 315-831-5651. Fax: 315-831-5651. p. 1726

Horn, Mary, Ref Librn, West Virginia State University, Campus Box L17, Institute, WV, 25112. Tel: 304-766-3162. Fax: 304-766-4103. p. 2562

Horn, Maureen, Librn, Massachusetts Horticultural Society Library, 900 Washington St, Rte 16, Wellesley, MA, 02482. Tel: 617-933-4910. Fax: 617-933-4901. p. 1134

Horn, Sarah C, Dir, Lyons Public Library, 4209 Joliet Ave, Lyons, IL, 60534-1597. Tel: 708-447-3577. Fax: 708-447-3589. p. 668

Horn, Theresa, Mgr, Ch Serv, Saint Joseph County Public Library, 304 S Main, South Bend, IN, 46601-2125. Tel: 574-282-4646. Fax: 574-280-2763. p. 779

Hornbach, Ann, Head of Libr, Free Library of Philadelphia, Torresdale Branch, 3079 Holme Ave, Philadelphia, PA, 19136-1101. Tel: 215-685-0494. Fax: 215-685-0495. p. 2109

Hornbaker, Eileen, Tech Info Spec, United States Fish & Wildlife Service, 698 Conservation Way, Shepherdstown, WV, 25443. Tel: 304-876-7687. Fax: 304-876-7213. p. 2571

Hornbeck, Charles, Libr Syst Support Tech, Keene State College, 229 Main St, Keene, NH, 03435-3201. Tel: 603-358-2739. Fax: 603-358-2745. p. 1453

Hornberger, Gretchen, Librn, Coconino County Law Library & Self-Help Center, 200 N San Francisco St, Flagstaff, AZ, 86001. Tel: 928-779-6656. p. 62

Hornbuckle, Del, Head Librn, Montgomery College, 51 Mannakee St, Rockville, MD, 20850. Tel: 240-567-4244. p. 1037

Hornbuckle, Del, Head Librn, Montgomery College, Rockville Campus Library, Macklin Tower, 51 Mannakee St, Rockville, MD, 20850. Tel: 240-567-5067, 240-567-7117. Fax: 240-567-7153. p. 1037

Hornbuckle, Sharon, Asst Librn, Wagoner City Public Library, 302 N Main, Wagoner, OK, 74467-3834. Tel: 918-485-2126. Fax: 918-485-0179. p. 1985

Hornby, Kathryn, Interim Head Librn, University of British Columbia Library, Woodward Biomedical Library, 2198 Health Sciences Mall, Vancouver, BC, V6T 1Z3, CANADA. Tel: 604-822-4970. Fax: 604-822-5596. p. 2743

Horne, Laura, Soc Sci Librn, University of Richmond, 28 Westhampton Way, Richmond, VA, 23173. Tel: 804-289-8851. Fax: 804-289-8757. p. 2491

Horneck, Kathy, ILL, California Lutheran University, 60 W Olsen Rd, Thousand Oaks, CA, 91360-2787. Tel: 805-493-3250. Fax: 805-493-3842. p. 274

Horner, Kelly, Youth Serv, Guthrie Memorial Library - Hanover's Public Library, Two Library Pl, Hanover, PA, 17331-2283. Tel: 717-632-5183. Fax: 717-632-7565. p. 2064

Horner, Lana, Head, Circ, Wichita Falls Public Library, 600 11th St, Wichita Falls, TX, 76301-4604. Tel: 940-767-0868, Ext 225. Fax: 940-720-6672. p. 2401

Horner, Nancy, Adult Serv Mgr, Eugene Public Library, 100 W Tenth Ave, Eugene, OR, 97401. Tel: 541-682-5450. Fax: 541-682-5898. p. 1996

Horner, Patricia, Asst Dir, Lucas County Law Library, Lucas County Family Court Center, 905 Jackson St, Toledo, OH, 43604-5512. Tel: 419-213-4747. Fax: 419-213-4287. p. 1939

Horner, Tom, ILL & Presv Librn, Covenant College, 14049 Scenic Hwy, Lookout Mountain, GA, 30750. Tel: 706-419-1430. Fax: 706-419-3480. p. 539

Hornick, Linda, Br Mgr, Wellington County Library, Rockwood Branch, 85 Christie St, Rockwood, ON, N0B 2K0, CANADA. Tel: 519-856-4851. Fax: 519-856-2990. p. 2805

Horning, Kathleen T, Dir, University of Wisconsin-Madison, Cooperative Children's Book Center, 4290 Helen C White Hall, 600 N Park St, Madison, WI, 53706. Tel: 608-263-3721. Fax: 608-262-4933. p. 2608

Hornsby, Cynthia, Librn, Pearl River County Library System, Poplarville Public, 202 W Beers St, Poplarville, MS, 39470. Tel: 601-795-8411. Fax: 601-795-8411. p. 1311

Hornsby, Karen, Dir, Chico Public Library Inc, 106 W Jacksboro, Chico, TX, 76431. Tel: 940-644-2330. Fax: 940-644-2330. p. 2297

Horodecki, Linda, Res Coordr, Volunteer Manitoba, Five Donald St S, 4th Flr, Winnipeg, MB, R3L 2T4, CANADA. Tel: 204-477-5180, Ext 223. Fax: 204-453-6198. p. 2759

Horonic, Josip, Syst Mgr, Andrews University, 1400 Library Rd, Berrien Springs, MI, 49104-1400. Tel: 269-471-3865. Fax: 269-471-6166. p. 1157

Horowitz, Marc David, Dir, North Babylon Public Library, 815 Deer Park Ave, North Babylon, NY, 11703-3812. Tel: 631-669-4020. Fax: 631-669-3432. p. 1706

Horowitz, Sarah, Spec Coll Librn, Augustana College Library, 3435 9 1/2 Ave, Rock Island, IL, 61201-2296. Tel: 309-794-7266. Fax: 309-794-7640. p. 696

Horrell, Jeff, Dean of Libr, Dartmouth College Library, 6025 Baker Berry Library, Rm 115, Hanover, NH, 03755-3525. Tel: 603-646-2236. Fax: 603-646-3702. p. 1450

Horrell, Jeffrey, Col Librn, Dean of Libr, Dartmouth College Library, Baker-Berry Library, 6025 Baker-Berry Library, Hanover, NH, 03755-3525. Tel: 603-646-2236. Fax: 603-646-2167. p. 1450

Horrigan, Bebhinn, Librn, Faith Evangelical Seminary Library, 3504 N Pearl St, Tacoma, WA, 98407-2607. Tel: 253-752-2020, Ext 32. Fax: 253-759-1790. p. 2538

Horrocks, David, Archivist, National Archives & Records Administration, 1000 Beal Ave, Ann Arbor, MI, 48109-2114. Tel: 734-205-0562. Fax: 734-205-0571. p. 1151

Horrocks, Marlee, Asst Dir, Saline District Library, 555 N Maple Rd, Saline, MI, 48176. Tel: 734-429-5450. Fax: 734-944-0600. p. 1225

Horrocks, Sandra, Libr Tech, Buena Vista Correctional Complex Library, 15125 Hwys 24 & 285, Buena Vista, CO, 81211. Tel: 719-395-7254. Fax: 719-395-7214. p. 293

Horrocks, Sherma, Dir, Richland Township Library, 8821 Third St, Vestaburg, MI, 48891. Tel: 989-268-5044. Fax: 989-268-5629. p. 1233

Horsch, Sonya, Librn, Andale District Library, 328 Main St, Andale, KS, 67001. Tel: 316-444-2363. Fax: 316-444-2363. p. 855

Horsfall, Susan, Budget Officer, Stanford University Libraries, 557 Escondido Mall, Stanford, CA, 94305-6004. Tel: 650-725-1064. p. 270

Horsley, Barb, Librn, Wessington Springs Carnegie Library, 109 W Main St, Wessington Springs, SD, 57382. Tel: 605-539-1803. p. 2222

Horsley, Jordon, Coordr, Media Serv, Marymount Manhattan College, 221 E 71st St, New York, NY, 10021. Tel: 212-774-4854. p. 1685

Horst, Irene, Librn, Passionist Academic Institute Library, 5700 N Harlem Ave, Chicago, IL, 60631. Tel: 773-631-1686, Ext 237. Fax: 773-631-1705, 773-631-8059. p. 622

Horst, Pam, Librn, Alaska Bible College Library, 200 College Dr, Glennallen, AK, 99588. Tel: 907-822-3201. Fax: 907-822-5027. p. 48

Horst, Rita, Ref Serv, Kearney Public Library, 2020 First Ave, Kearney, NE, 68847. Tel: 308-233-3282. Fax: 308-233-3291. p. 1403

Horst, Victoria, Head Librn, Coastal Plain Regional Library, Tifton-Tift County Public, 163 S Virginia Ave, Tifton, GA, 31794. Tel: 229-386-7148. Fax: 229-386-7205. p. 554

Hortin, Rita, Head Librn, Albion Public Library, Six N Fourth St, Albion, IL, 62806. Tel: 618-445-3314. p. 587

Hortman, Melinda, Mgr, Pine Mountain Regional Library, Reynolds Community, 208 N Winston St, Reynolds, GA, 31076. Tel: 478-847-3468. Fax: 478-847-4553. p. 542

Horton, Clara Jo, Dir, Alexander Memorial Library, 201 S Center St, Cotulla, TX, 78014-2255. Tel: 830-879-2601. Fax: 830-879-2601. p. 2303

Horton, James H, VPres, Info Tech, Polk State College, 999 Ave H NE, Winter Haven, FL, 33881-4299. Tel: 863-297-1041. Fax: 863-297-1065. p. 504

Horton, Janelle, Librn, Newton County Public Library, Deweyville Public Library, 212 State Hwy 272, Deweyville, TX, 77614. Tel: 409-746-0222. Fax: 409-746-9955. p. 2366

Horton, Jennifer, Cat, Oral Roberts University Library, 7777 South Lewis Ave, Tulsa, OK, 74171. Tel: 918-495-6881. Fax: 918-495-6893. p. 1981

Horton, Jenny, Ref & Libr Instruction, King College, 1350 King College Rd, Bristol, TN, 37620. Tel: 423-652-6325. Fax: 423-652-4871. p. 2225

Horton, John, Assoc Prof, Librn, Cuyahoga Community College, Metropolitan Campus Library, 2900 Community College Ave, Cleveland, OH, 44115. Tel: 216-987-3607. Fax: 216-987-4404. p. 1879

Horton, Johnna, Dir of Libr Serv, South Central College, 1920 Lee Blvd, North Mankato, MN, 56003-2504. Tel: 507-389-7223, 507-389-7245. Fax: 507-625-7534. p. 1268

Horton, Julie, Coordr of Ref Serv, Greenwood County Library, 600 S Main St, Greenwood, SC, 29646. Tel: 864-941-3042. Fax: 864-941-4651. p. 2197

Horton, Lia, Ref & Info Literacy Librn, Saint Joseph's College, 278 Whites Bridge Rd, Standish, ME, 04084-5263. Tel: 207-893-7725. Fax: 207-893-7883. p. 1002

Horton, Marcia, Info Serv, New Port Richey Public Library, 5939 Main St, New Port Richey, FL, 34652. Tel: 727-853-1279. Fax: 727-853-1280. p. 472

Horton, Mary Alice, Dir, Aurora Public Library District, 414 Second St, Aurora, IN, 47001-1384. Tel: 812-926-0646. Fax: 812-926-0665. p. 725

Horton, Mary Alice, Librn, Aurora Public Library District, Dillsboro Public, 10151 Library Lane, Dillsboro, IN, 47018. Tel: 812-432-5200. Fax: 812-432-5209. p. 725

Horton, Mary C, Admin Dir, University of South Carolina, 1322 Greene St, Columbia, SC, 29208-0103. Tel: 803-777-3142. p. 2189

Horton, Pat, Youth Serv Librn, Blue Hill Public Library, Five Parker Point Rd, Blue Hill, ME, 04614-0821. Tel: 207-374-5515. Fax: 207-374-5254. p. 978

Horton, Peggy, Youth Serv Librn, Monon Town & Township Public Library, 427 N Market, Monon, IN, 47959. Tel: 219-253-6517. Fax: 219-253-8373. p. 765

Horton, Russell P, Ref & Outreach Archivist, Wisconsin Department of Veterans Affairs, 30 W Mifflin St, Ste 300, Madison, WI, 53703. Tel: 608-267-1790. Fax: 608-264-7615. p. 2610

Horton, Ryan, Res, Public Policy Forum, 633 W Wisconsin Ave, Ste 406, Milwaukee, WI, 53203. Tel: 414-276-8240. Fax: 414-276-9962. p. 2621

Horton, Stanley W, Asst Dean, Grays Harbor College, 1620 Edward P Smith Dr, Aberdeen, WA, 98520-7599. Tel: 360-538-4050. Fax: 360-538-4294. p. 2507

Horton, Steve, Mgr, ILL, Mgr, Tech Serv, East Texas Baptist University, 1209 N Grove St, Marshall, TX, 75670-1498. Tel: 903-923-2256. Fax: 903-935-3447. p. 2359

Horton, Susan, Dir, Trumbull Library, 33 Quality St, Trumbull, CT, 06611. Tel: 203-452-5197. Fax: 203-452-5125. p. 373

Horton, Tina, Librn, Chaffee Public Library, 202 Wright Ave, Chaffee, MO, 63740. Tel: 573-887-3298. Fax: 573-887-3298. p. 1323

Horton, Travis, Br Mgr, Wake County Public Library System, Green Road Community Library, 4101 Green Rd, Raleigh, NC, 27604. Tel: 919-790-3242. Fax: 919-790-3250. p. 1818

Horton, Valerie, Dir, Minitex Library Information Network, Univ Minn Twin Cities, 15 Andersen Library, 222 21st Ave S, Minneapolis, MN, 55455-0439. Tel: 612-624-2839. Fax: 612-624-4508. p. 2947

Horvath, Diane M, Librn, Sacred Heart Hospital, 421 Chew St, Allentown, PA, 18102. Tel: 610-776-4747. Fax: 610-606-4422. p. 2027

Horvath, Elizabeth, Librn, Mid-Hudson Forensic Psychiatric Center Library, 2834 Rte 17M, New Hampton, NY, 10958-5011. Tel: 845-374-8700, Ext 3625, 845-374-8842. Fax: 845-374-8853. p. 1665

Horvath, Irene, Br Mgr, Hawaii State Public Library System, Kailua-Kona Public Library, 75-138 Hualalai Rd, Kailua-Kona, HI, 96740-1704. Tel: 808-327-4327. Fax: 808-327-4326. p. 562

Horvath, Jessica, Head, Tech Serv, Eisenhower Public Library District, 4613 N Oketo Ave, Harwood Heights, IL, 60706. Tel: 708-867-7828. Fax: 708-867-1535. p. 654

Horvath, Joyce, Tech Serv, Northbrook Public Library, 1201 Cedar Lane, Northbrook, IL, 60062-4581. Tel: 847-272-6224. Fax: 847-272-5362. p. 682

Horvath, Patricia, Tech Serv, Duquesne University, Center for Legal Information, 900 Locust St, Pittsburgh, PA, 15282. Tel: 412-396-5016. Fax: 412-396-6294. p. 2125

Horvath, Robert T, Dir, Talbot County Free Library, 100 W Dover St, Easton, MD, 21601-2620. Tel: 410-822-1626. Fax: 410-820-8217. p. 1027

Horvay, Henrietta C, Curator, Pres, Goshen Historical Society Library, 21 Old Middle St, Goshen, CT, 06756-2001. Tel: 860-491-3129. p. 341

Horwath, Jenn, Digital Serv Librn, Mohawk College Library, 135 Fennell Ave W, Hamilton, ON, L9C 1E9, CANADA. Tel: 905-575-1212, Ext 3194. Fax: 905-575-2011. p. 2810

Horwath, Nancy, Adult Serv, Bethlehem Area Public Library, South Side, 400 Webster St, Bethlehem, PA, 18015. Tel: 610-867-7852. Fax: 610-867-9821. p. 2034

Hosegood, Shirley, Librn, Lakeland Library Region, Radisson Branch, Box 161, Radisson, SK, S0K 3L0, CANADA. Tel: 306-827-4521. p. 2920

Hosein, Sharida, Head Librn, University of Manitoba Libraries, William R Newman Library (Agriculture), 66 Dafoe Rd, Winnipeg, MB, R3T 2N2, CANADA. Tel: 204-474-6334. Fax: 204-474-7527. p. 2759

Hosey, Edward, Dep Dir, United States Courts for the Ninth Circuit Library, 95 Seventh St, San Francisco, CA, 94103. Tel: 415-556-9500. Fax: 415-556-9927. p. 247

Hosey, Sheila, Librn, Mount Olive Correctional Complex Library, One Mountainside Way, Mount Olive, WV, 25185. Tel: 304-442-7213. Fax: 304-442-7227. p. 2567

Hosford, Debbie, Librn, Catawba County Library, Saint Stephens, 3225 Springs Rd, Hickory, NC, 28601-9700. Tel: 828-256-3030. Fax: 828-256-6029. p. 1813

Hosford, John, Visual Res Curator, Alfred University, Scholes Library of Ceramics, New York State College of Ceramics at Alfred University, Two Pine St, Alfred, NY, 14802-1297. p. 1572

Hoskin, Michelle, Circ, Altadena Library District, 600 E Mariposa St, Altadena, CA, 91001. Tel: 626-798-0833. Fax: 626-798-5351. p. 120

Hoskins, Holly, Ch, Burlington County Library, Evesham Branch, Evesham Municipal Complex, 984 Tuckerton Rd, Marlton, NJ, 08053. Tel: 856-983-1444. Fax: 856-983-4939. p. 1543

Hoskins, Michelle, ILL, Altadena Library District, 600 E Mariposa St, Altadena, CA, 91001. Tel: 626-798-0833. Fax: 626-798-5351. p. 120

Hoskins, Nellie, Librn, Galena Public Library, 315 W Seventh St, Galena, KS, 66739-1293. Tel: 620-783-5132. Fax: 620-783-5030. p. 868

Hoskins, Sue, Asst Dir, Wilton Public Library, 106 E Fourth St, Wilton, IA, 52778. Tel: 563-732-2583. Fax: 563-732-2593. p. 853

Hoskins, Susan, Exec Dir, Pipestone County Historical Society, 113 S Hiawatha, Pipestone, MN, 56164. Tel: 507-825-2563. Fax: 507-825-2563. p. 1271

Hoskins, Susan Paige, Circ Librn/Ser, Mountain State University Library, 609 S Kanawha St, Beckley, WV, 25801. Tel: 304-929-1369. Fax: 304-929-1665. p. 2553

Hoskins, William J, Dir, Siouxland Heritage Museums, 200 W Sixth St, Sioux Falls, SD, 57104. Tel: 605-367-4210. Fax: 605-367-6004. p. 2218

Hoskinson-Dean, Mary, Asst Dir, Children & Teen Librn, Mark Twain Library, Rte 53 & Diamond Hill Rd, Redding, CT, 06896. Tel: 203-938-2545. Fax: 203-938-4026. p. 365

Hosko, George, Fr, ILL Librn, University of Saint Thomas, 1100 W Main, Houston, TX, 77006. Tel: 713-525-2192. Fax: 713-525-3886. p. 2344

Hosny, Hany, Lending Serv Librn, Roanoke College, 220 High St, Salem, VA, 24153. Tel: 540-375-2295. p. 2495

Hossfeld, Linda, Tech Serv Librn, Sheridan County Public Library System, 335 W Alger St, Sheridan, WY, 82801-3899. Tel: 307-674-8585, Ext 5. p. 2660

Hosteler, Jennifer, Actg Dir, Argosy University, Heritage Sq, 5001 Lyndon B Johnson Freeway, Dallas, TX, 75244. Tel: 214-459-2215. Fax: 214-672-8106. p. 2304

Hosterman, Denise A, Ch, West End Library, 1724 State Rte 235, Laurelton, PA, 17835. Tel: 570-922-4773. Fax: 570-922-1162. p. 2079

Hostetler, Linda D, Dir, Butler County Law Library Association, Ten Journal Sq, Ste 200, Hamilton, OH, 45011. Tel: 513-887-3455. Fax: 513-887-3696. p. 1903

Hostetler, Theodore J, Dir, Randolph College, 2500 Rivermont Ave, Lynchburg, VA, 24503. Tel: 434-947-8133. Fax: 434-947-8134. p. 2476

Hostetter, Diana, Off Mgr/Circ Supvr, Germantown Community Library, 1925 Exeter Rd, Germantown, TN, 38138-2815. Tel: 901-757-7323. Fax: 901-756-9940. p. 2235

Hostetter, Sylvia-Michelle, Cat, Germantown Community Library, 1925 Exeter Rd, Germantown, TN, 38138-2815. Tel: 901-757-7323, Ext 7476. Fax: 901-756-9940. p. 2235

Hosticka, Carolyn, Head Librn, Holland & Knight LLP, 131 S Dearborn, 30th Flr, Chicago, IL, 60603. Tel: 312-578-6616. Fax: 312-578-6666. p. 614

Hosto, April, Librn, Hanson Professional Services, Inc, 1525 S Sixth St, Springfield, IL, 62703-2886. Tel: 217-788-2450. Fax: 217-747-9416. p. 704

Hostutler, Justin, Libr Tech, Trinity Episcopal School for Ministry Library, 311 11th St, Ambridge, PA, 15003. Tel: 724-266-3838. Fax: 724-266-4617. p. 2029

Hotchkiss, Patricia, Dir, Cochise College Library, 4190 W Hwy 80, Douglas, AZ, 85607. Tel: 520-417-4082. Fax: 520-417-4120. p. 61

Hotchkiss, Patricia, Dir, Cochise College Library, Andrea Cracchiolo Library, 901 N Colombo Ave, Sierra Vista, AZ, 85635. Tel: 520-515-5320. Fax: 520-515-5464. p. 61

Hotchkiss, Valerie, Librn, University of Illinois Library at Urbana-Champaign, Rare Book & Manuscript Library, 346 Main Library, MC-522, 1408 W Gregory Dr, Urbana, IL, 61801. Tel: 217-333-3777. Fax: 217-244-1755. p. 713

Hoth, Brian, Librn, Buffalo & Erie County Public Library System, Riverside, 820 Tonawanda, Buffalo, NY, 14207-1448. Tel: 716-875-0562. Fax: 716-875-0562. p. 1597

Hott, Joann, Asst Librn, Henryetta Public Library, 518 W Main, Henryetta, OK, 74437. Tel: 918-652-7377. Fax: 918-652-2796. p. 1965

Hotton, Charlotte, Tech Serv Mgr, Wicomico Public Library, 122 S Division St, Salisbury, MD, 21801. Tel: 410-749-3612, Ext 118. Fax: 410-548-2968. p. 1040

Hotz, Laurie, Youth Serv Dir, Fort Dodge Public Library, 424 Central Ave, Fort Dodge, IA, 50501. Tel: 515-573-8167, Ext 244. Fax: 515-573-5422. p. 817

Houbeck, Robert L, Jr, Dir, University of Michigan-Flint, 303 E Kearsley St, Flint, MI, 48502-1950. Tel: 810-762-3018. Fax: 810-762-3133. p. 1181

Houchens, Tracy, Cat, Logan County Public Library, 201 W Sixth St, Russellville, KY, 42276. Tel: 270-726-6129. Fax: 270-726-6127. p. 934

Houchin, David, Curator, Clarksburg-Harrison Public Library, 404 W Pike St, Clarksburg, WV, 26301. Tel: 304-627-2236. Fax: 304-627-2239. p. 2557

Houchins, Pat, Librn, Warren County Public Library, Smiths Grove Branch, 127 S Main St, Smiths Grove, KY, 42171-8130. Tel: 270-563-6651. Fax: 270-563-6651. p. 907

Houck, Michael, Librn, Johns Hopkins University Libraries, School of Professional Studies in Business & Education, Ten N Charles St, Baltimore, MD, 21201. Tel: 410-516-0700. Fax: 410-659-8210. p. 1014

Houck, Michael, Librn, Johns Hopkins University Libraries, 6740 Alexander Bell Dr, Columbia, MD, 21040. Tel: 301-621-3377, 410-290-1777. Fax: 410-290-0007. p. 1026

Houck, Tisa, Access Serv, Chattanooga State Community College, 4501 Amnicola Hwy, Chattanooga, TN, 37406-1097. Tel: 423-697-4448. Fax: 423-697-4409. p. 2227

Houde, Lisa, Head, Youth Serv, Rye Public Library, 581 Washington Rd, Rye, NH, 03870. Tel: 603-964-8401. Fax: 603-964-7065. p. 1464

Houge, Meredith, Dir, Galesville Public Library, 16787 S Main St, Galesville, WI, 54630. Tel: 608-582-2552. p. 2593

Hough, Elizabeth, Pub Relations Mgr, Hedberg Public Library, 316 S Main St, Janesville, WI, 53545. Tel: 608-758-6607. Fax: 608-758-6583. p. 2600

Hough, Gary, Head, Cat, University of Massachusetts Amherst, 154 Hicks Way, Amherst, MA, 01003-9275. Tel: 413-545-6856. Fax: 413-545-6873. p. 1049

Hough, Joan, Dir, Mount Carroll Township Public Library, 208 N Main St, Mount Carroll, IL, 61053-1022. Tel: 815-244-1751. Fax: 815-244-5203. p. 676

Hough, Kendra, Supvr, Iowa Lakes Community College, 800 21st St, Spirit Lake, IA, 51360. Tel: 712-336-3439, 712-336-6564. Fax: 712-336-1357. p. 845

Houghtaling, Jeanne, Ref Librn, Alamogordo Public Library, 920 Oregon Ave, Alamogordo, NM, 88310. Tel: 575-439-4140. Fax: 575-439-4108. p. 1547

Houghtaling, June, Dir, Towanda Public Library, 104 Main St, Towanda, PA, 18848-1895. Tel: 570-265-2470. Fax: 570-265-7212. p. 2146

Houghtaling, Shirley, Head, Pub Serv, West Des Moines Public Library, 4000 Mills Civic Pkwy, West Des Moines, IA, 50265-2049. Tel: 515-222-3400. Fax: 515-222-3401. p. 852

Houghton, Angie, Dir, Susquehanna County Historical Society & Free Library Association, Hallstead-Great Bend Branch Library, 135 Franklin Ave, Hallstead, PA, 18822. Tel: 570-879-2227. Fax: 570-879-0982. p. 2092

Houghton, Carol, Law & Politics Coll Mgr, Princeton University, Politics & Law Collections, Firestone Library, A-17-J-1, One Washington Rd, Princeton, NJ, 08544. Tel: 609-258-3209, 609-258-3701. p. 1524

Houghton, Mary, Hist Coll Librn, Albion District Library, 501 S Superior St, Albion, MI, 49224. Tel: 517-629-3993. Fax: 517-629-5354. p. 1148

Houghton, Patricia, ILL, Queen Anne's County Free Library, 121 S Commerce St, Centreville, MD, 21617. Tel: 410-758-0980. Fax: 410-758-0614. p. 1023

Houghton-Kiel, Claire, Interim Dir, Haledon Free Public Library, 510 Bellmont Ave, Haledon, NJ, 07508-1396. Tel: 973-790-3808. p. 1490

Houghton-Theall, Joan, Assoc Dir, King & Spalding, 1180 Peachtree St NE, Flr 17, Atlanta, GA, 30309. Tel: 404-572-4600, Ext 3300. Fax: 404-572-5123. p. 516

Hougland, Mary, Dir, Jennings County Public Library, 2375 N State Hwy 3, North Vernon, IN, 47265-1596. Tel: 812-346-2091. Fax: 812-346-2127. p. 769

Houk, Barb, Spec Serv Librn, Crown Point Community Library, 214 S Court St, Crown Point, IN, 46307. Tel: 219-663-0270, 219-663-0271. Fax: 219-663-0403. p. 734

Houk, Deborah, Tech Serv Librn, McKendree University, 701 College Rd, Lebanon, IL, 62254-1299. Tel: 618-537-6951. Fax: 618-537-8411. p. 664

Houk, Sarah, Head, Tech Serv, Fayetteville Public Library, 401 W Mountain St, Fayetteville, AR, 72701. Tel: 479-856-7000. Fax: 479-571-0222. p. 99

Houke, Billy, Med Librn, Charlie Norwood VA Medical Center Library, One Freedom Way, Augusta, GA, 30904-6285. Tel: 706-733-0188, Ext 2813. Fax: 706-823-3920. p. 520

Houlahan, John, Dir, Pioneerland Library System, 410 Fifth St SW, Willmar, MN, 56201. Tel: 320-235-6106, Ext 27. Fax: 320-214-0187. p. 1288

Houlden, Melanie G, Chief Librn, Surrey Public Library, 10350 University Dr, Surrey, BC, V3T 4B8, CANADA. Tel: 604-598-7305. Fax: 604-598-7310. p. 2739

Houle, Anne, Ch, Youth Serv, Whitchurch-Stouffville Public Library, 30 Burkholder St, Stouffville, ON, L4A 4K1, CANADA. Tel: 905-642-7323. Fax: 905-640-1384. p. 2845

Houle, Carmen, Doc, Centre Canadien d'etudes et de Cooperation Internationale, 3000 Omer-Lavallee, Montreal, QC, H1Y 3R8, CANADA. Tel: 514-875-9911, Ext 288. Fax: 514-875-6469. p. 2892

Houle, Louis, Assoc Dir, Client Serv, Sci, Health & Eng, McGill University Libraries, 3459 McTavish St, Montreal, QC, H3A 1Y1, CANADA. Tel: 514-398-4763. Fax: 514-398-3903. p. 2898

Houle, Louis, Librn, McGill University Libraries, Schulich Library of Science & Engineering, Macdonald Stewart Library Bldg, 809 Sherbrooke St W, Montreal, QC, H3A 2K6, CANADA. Tel: 514-398-4769. Fax: 514-398-3903. p. 2899

Houle, Louise, Media Spec, Bibliotheques de Trois-Rivieres, Bibliotheque de Pointe-du-Lac (Simone-L-Roy), 500 rue de la Grande-Allee, Trois-Rivieres, QC, G0X 1Z0, CANADA. Tel: 819-377-4289. Fax: 819-377-7116. p. 2914

Houle, Maurice, Chef de Section, Bibliothèques de Montrèal, Roxboro, 110, rue Cartier, Montreal, QC, H8Y 1G8, CANADA. Tel: 514-620-4181, Ext 2212. Fax: 514-684-8563. p. 2891

Houlihan, Laurie, Dir, Plaistow Public Library, 85 Main St, Plaistow, NH, 03865. Tel: 603-382-6011. Fax: 603-382-0202. p. 1462

Houlne, Celina, Dir, Rockingham Free Public Library, 65 Westminster St, Bellows Falls, VT, 05101. Tel: 802-463-4270. Fax: 802-463-1566. p. 2418

Houmard, Joanne, Ser, Mount Union College Library, 1972 Clark Ave, Alliance, OH, 44601-3993. Tel: 330-823-3844. Fax: 330-823-3963. p. 1854

Hounshell, Janet, Librn, Cisco Public Library, 600 Ave G, Cisco, TX, 76437. Tel: 254-442-1020. p. 2297

Hounshell, JoAnn, Assoc Dir, Illinois Institute of Technology, Chicago-Kent College of Law Library, 565 W Adams St, Chicago, IL, 60661. Tel: 312-906-5675. Fax: 312-906-5679. p. 615

Houpt, Helen, Librn, Tech Serv, Harrisburg Hospital Library at PinnacleHealth System, Main Bldg, 2nd Flr, 111 S Front St, Harrisburg, PA, 17101-2099. Tel: 717-657-7247. Fax: 717-657-7248. p. 2065

Houpt, Helen L, Librn, PinnacleHealth Library Services, 4300 Londonderry Rd, Harrisburg, PA, 17103. Tel: 717-657-7247. Fax: 717-657-7248. p. 2066

Hourahan, Richard, Archivist, Rye Historical Society Library, One Purchase St, Rye, NY, 10580. Tel: 914-967-8657. Fax: 914-967-6253. p. 1736

Hourigan, Lynn, Adult Serv, Lee County Library System, East County Regional, 881 Gunnery Rd N, Lehigh Acres, FL, 33971. Tel: 239-461-7314. Fax: 239-461-7321. p. 445

House, Carol, Circ, Environmental Protection Agency - R S Kerr Environmental Research Center, 919 Kerr Lab Research Dr, Ada, OK, 74820. Tel: 580-436-8800. Fax: 580-436-8503. p. 1955

House, Edward, Dir, Beaverton City Library, 12375 SW Fifth St, Beaverton, OR, 97005-2883. Tel: 503-526-3705. Fax: 503-526-2636. p. 1991

House, Elizabeth, Dir, McDowell County Public Library, 90 W Court St, Marion, NC, 28752. Tel: 828-652-3858. Fax: 828-652-2098. p. 1808

House, Lisa, In Charge, Essent Corp, 865 DeShong Dr, Paris, TX, 75462-2097. Fax: 903-782-2802. p. 2368

House, Luise, Dir, Mountain Home Public Library, 790 N Tenth E, Mountain Home, ID, 83647-2830. Tel: 208-587-4716. Fax: 208-587-6645. p. 580

House, Martin, Asst Dir, Pub Serv, Central Piedmont Community College Library, 1201 Elizabeth Ave, Charlotte, NC, 28235. Tel: 704-330-6752. Fax: 704-330-6887. p. 1781

House, Paula, Head, Info Serv, Muskego Public Library, S73 W16663 Janesville Rd, Muskego, WI, 53150. Tel: 262-971-2109. Fax: 262-971-2115. p. 2623

House, Rod, State Archivist, Idaho State Historical Society, Idaho History Ctr, 2205 Old Penitentiary Rd, Boise, ID, 83712. Tel: 208-334-3356. Fax: 208-334-3198. p. 571

House, Sara, Mgr, Calgary Public Library, Shawnessy, South Fish Creek Complex, 333 Shawville Blvd SE, Calgary, AB, T2Y 4H3, CANADA. p. 2690

Housel, Mary, City Librn, Santa Maria Public Library, 421 S McClelland St, Santa Maria, CA, 93454-5116. Tel: 805-925-0994. Fax: 805-922-2330. p. 265

Houser, Gabe, Tech Serv Coordr, University of California, Merced Library, 5200 N Lake Rd, Merced, CA, 95343-5001. Tel: 209-631-0953. Fax: 209-228-4271. p. 186

Houser, Kay, Librn, Southeastern Community College Library, 4564 Chadbourne Hwy, Whiteville, NC, 28472. Tel: 910-642-7141, Ext 219. Fax: 910-642-4513. p. 1830

Houser, Maxine, Chief Librn, Golconda Public Library, 126 W Main St, Golconda, IL, 62938. Tel: 618-683-6531. Fax: 618-683-6531. p. 651

Housley, Harold, Archivist, Yellowstone National Park, Yellowstone Heritage & Research Ctr, 200 Old Yellowstone Trail, Gardiner, MT, 59030. Tel: 307-344-2563. Fax: 406-848-9958. p. 1379

Houssiere, Barbara, Asst Prof, Res Librn, McNeese State University, 4205 Ryan St, Lake Charles, LA, 70609. Tel: 337-475-5732. Fax: 337-475-5719, 337-475-5727. p. 954

Housten, Frances, Sr Librn, YA Serv, Cranford Free Public Library, 224 Walnut Ave, Cranford, NJ, 07016-2931. Tel: 908-709-7272. Fax: 908-709-1658. p. 1480

Houston, Alan, Ref Librn, Chappaqua Public Library, 195 S Greeley Ave, Chappaqua, NY, 10514. Tel: 914-238-4779. Fax: 914-238-3597. p. 1605

Houston, Anne, Head, Pub Serv, Tulane University, 7001 Freret St, New Orleans, LA, 70118-5682. Tel: 504-314-7822. Fax: 504-865-6773. p. 963

Houston, Christina, Dep Dir, Lyndon Baines Johnson Library & Museum, 2313 Red River St, Austin, TX, 78705. Tel: 512-721-0206. p. 2281

Houston, Cynthia, Dr, Asst Prof, Western Kentucky University, School of Teacher Education, 1092 Gary A Ransdell Hall, Normal St, WKU No 61030, Bowling Green, KY, 42101-1030. Tel: 270-745-4662. Fax: 270-745-6322. p. 2966

Houston, Diane, Librn, Central Oklahoma Juvenile Center Library, 700 S Ninth, Tecumseh, OK, 74893. Tel: 405-598-4146. Fax: 405-598-4158. p. 1980

Houston, James S, Dep Dir, Art Circle Public Library, Cumberland County, 154 E First St, Crossville, TN, 38555-4696. Tel: 931-484-6790, Ext 228. Fax: 931-707-8956. p. 2232

Houston, Jean, Circ, National Humanities Center Library, Seven Alexander Dr, Research Triangle Park, NC, 27709. Tel: 919-549-0661. Fax: 919-990-8535. p. 1819

Houston, Karla, Dir, Lisbon Public Library, 45 School St, Lisbon, NH, 03585. Tel: 603-838-6615. Fax: 603-838-6615. p. 1454

Houston, Lorna, Chief Librn, Township of Cramahe Public Library, Six King St, Colborne, ON, K0K 1S0, CANADA. Tel: 905-355-3722. Fax: 905-355-3430. p. 2800

Houston, Merle, Dir, Chipola College Library, 3094 Indian Circle, Marianna, FL, 32446. Tel: 850-718-2272. Fax: 850-718-2349. p. 462

Houston, Mike, Br Mgr, San Bernardino County Library, Chino Branch, 13180 Central Ave, Chino, CA, 91710. Tel: 909-465-5280. Fax: 909-465-5240. p. 228

Houston, Nainsi J, Ref & Instruction Librn, Heidelberg University, 10 Greenfield St, Tiffin, OH, 44883-2420. Tel: 419-448-2104. Fax: 419-448-2578. p. 1938

Houston, Tammy, Admin Serv Coordr, Saint John the Baptist Parish Library, 2920 New Hwy 51, LaPlace, LA, 70068. Tel: 985-652-2225, 985-652-6857. Fax: 985-652-8005. p. 954

Houston, Vincent, Chief Financial Officer, Dir of Admin Serv Div, Texas State Library & Archives Commission, 1201 Brazos St, Austin, TX, 78701. Tel: 512-463-5460. p. 2282

Houtler, Kris, Youth Serv Librn, Reedsburg Public Library, 370 Vine St, Reedsburg, WI, 53959-1917. Tel: 608-524-3316, 608-768-7323. Fax: 608-524-9024. p. 2633

Houts, Cheryl, Commun Librn, Santa Clara County Library District, Campbell Public, 77 Harrison Ave, Campbell, CA, 95008-1409. Tel: 408-866-1991. Fax: 408-866-1433. p. 181

Houtz, Thomas, Libr Dir, Tower-Porter Community Library, 230 E Grand Ave, Tower City, PA, 17980-1124. Tel: 717-647-4900. p. 2146

Hovan, Maryann, Youth Serv Coordr, Hoyt Library, 284 Wyoming Ave, Kingston, PA, 18704-3597. Tel: 570-287-2013. Fax: 570-283-2081. p. 2074

Hovanic, Katie, Circ, Clackamas Community College, 19600 S Molalla Ave, Oregon City, OR, 97045. Tel: 503-657-6958, Ext 2464. Fax: 503-655-8925. p. 2009

Hovda, Bethany, Circ Supvr, Moody Bible Institute, 820 N La Salle Blvd, Chicago, IL, 60610-3284. Tel: 312-329-4136. Fax: 312-329-8959. p. 619

Hovde, Anne, Acq, University of Minnesota Duluth Library, 416 Library Dr, Duluth, MN, 55812. Tel: 218-726-7887. Fax: 218-726-8019. p. 1248

Hovde, Roberta, Res, Star Tribune, 425 Portland Ave, Minneapolis, MN, 55488. Tel: 612-673-4375. Fax: 612-673-4459. p. 1261

Hovden, Cathy, Asst Dir, Le Mars Public Library, 46 First St SW, Le Mars, IA, 51031-3696. Tel: 712-546-5004. Fax: 712-546-5797. p. 827

Hovekamp, Tina, Assoc Col Librn, Info & Access Serv Librn, Central Oregon Community College Barber Library, 2600 NW College Way, Bend, OR, 97701-5998. Tel: 541-383-7295. Fax: 541-383-7406. p. 1991

Hover, Kelly, Dir, Smith-Welch Memorial Library, 105 W Fifth St, Hearne, TX, 77859. Tel: 979-279-5191. Fax: 979-279-6212. p. 2331

Hovermale, Karen, Librn, Federal Reserve Bank of Minneapolis, 90 Hennepin Ave, Minneapolis, MN, 55401-2171. Tel: 612-204-5509. p. 1259

Hoverson, Sharon, Dir, Concordia College, 901 S Eighth St, Moorhead, MN, 56562. Tel: 218-299-4642. Fax: 218-299-4253. p. 1265

Hovey, Diane, Dir, Gorham Free Library, 2664 Main St, Gorham, NY, 14461. Tel: 585-526-6655. Fax: 585-526-6995. p. 1629

Hovey, Jacqueline, Mgr, Gowanda Free Library, 56 W Main St, Gowanda, NY, 14070-1390. Tel: 716-532-3451. Fax: 716-532-3415. p. 1630

Hovey, Mark, Network Tech, Deschutes Public Library District, 507 NW Wall St, Bend, OR, 97701-2698. Tel: 541-312-1040. Fax: 541-389-2982. p. 1992

Hovey, Melissa, Circ Mgr, Alma College Library, 614 W Superior St, Alma, MI, 48801. Tel: 989-463-7229. Fax: 989-463-8694. p. 1149

Hovinga, Hillary, Pub Relations Mgr, Herrick District Library, 300 S River Ave, Holland, MI, 49423-3290. Tel: 616-355-3728. p. 1190

Hovis, Debra, Librn, Catawba County Library, Conover Express Branch, 101 First St E, Conover, NC, 28613. Tel: 828-466-5108. Fax: 828-466-5109. p. 1813

Hovland, Arlyss, Cataloger, Marshall-Lyon County Library, 301 W Lyon St, Marshall, MN, 56258. Tel: 507-537-7003. p. 1258

Howanitz, Nancy, Ch, Monroe County Public Library, 700 Fleming St, Key West, FL, 33040. Tel: 305-292-3595. Fax: 305-295-3626. p. 456

Howard, Alison, Br Mgr, Wilson County Public Library, Lucama Branch, 103 E Spring St, Lucama, NC, 27851. Tel: 252-239-0046. Fax: 252-239-0046. p. 1831

Howard, Allaina, Head, Archives, Librn, World Data Center Glaciology, Boulder, CIRES, UCB 449, 1540 30th St, Boulder, CO, 80309-0449. Tel: 303-492-4004, 303-492-5774. Fax: 303-492-2468. p. 292

Howard, Allison, Cat, University of South Florida, Hinks & Elaine Shimberg Health Sciences Library, 12901 Bruce B Downs Blvd, MDC Box 31, Tampa, FL, 33612-4799. Tel: 813-974-2399. Fax: 813-974-3605, 813-974-4930. p. 498

Howard, Angela, Acq Librn, Nelson County Public Library, 201 Cathedral Manor, Bardstown, KY, 40004-1515. Tel: 502-348-3714. Fax: 502-348-5578. p. 906

Howard, Anice, Librn, Boonville-Warrick County Public Library, Lynnville Branch, 211 N Main, Lynnville, IN, 47619. Tel: 812-922-5409. p. 729

Howard, Anjah, Chairperson, Camrose Public Library, 4710 50th Ave, Camrose, AB, T4V 0R8, CANADA. Tel: 780-672-4214. Fax: 780-672-9165. p. 2694

Howard, Ann-Marie, Asst Librn, New Ipswich Library, Six Main St, New Ipswich, NH, 03071. Tel: 603-878-4644. p. 1459

Howard, Beth, Broadcast Librn, NPR Library, 635 Massachusetts Ave NW, Washington, DC, 20001. Fax: 202-513-3056. p. 412

Howard, Brian J, Exec Dir, Oneida County Historical Society Library, 1608 Genesee St, Utica, NY, 13502. Tel: 315-735-3642. Fax: 315-732-0806. p. 1759

Howard, Bryan, Ad, London Public Library, 20 E First St, London, OH, 43140. Tel: 740-852-9543. Fax: 740-852-3691. p. 1911

Howard, Cathy, ILL, Ref Librn, Greene County Public Library, 120 N 12th St, Paragould, AR, 72450. Tel: 870-236-8711. Fax: 870-236-1442. p. 111

Howard, Christine, Ch, Jasper-Dubois County Contractual Public Library, 1116 Main St, Jasper, IN, 47546-2899. Tel: 812-482-2712. Fax: 812-482-7123. p. 756

Howard Clayton, Mary, Br Mgr, Coastal Plain Regional Library, Carrie Dorsey Perry Memorial, 315 W Marion Ave, Nashville, GA, 31639. Tel: 229-686-2782. Fax: 229-686-2782. p. 554

Howard, Dan, Dir, Pub Libr Support Serv, North Central Regional Library, 16 N Columbia St, Wenatchee, WA, 98801-8103. Tel: 509-663-1117, Ext 122. Fax: 509-662-8060. p. 2548

Howard, Deanna, Dir, Plano Community Library District, 15 W North St, Plano, IL, 60545. Tel: 630-552-2009. Fax: 630-552-1008. p. 691

Howard, Dianne, Mgr, Libr Serv, Lord Corporation, 2000 W Grandview Blvd, Erie, PA, 16514. Tel: 814-868-0924, Ext 3510. Fax: 814-866-6323. p. 2056

Howard, Dorinda, Tech Serv, Rochester Public Library, 65 S Main St, Rochester, NH, 03867-2707. Tel: 603-332-1428. Fax: 603-335-7582. p. 1464

Howard, Gabriella, ILL, University of Maine at Augusta Libraries, 46 University Dr, Augusta, ME, 04330-9410. Tel: 207-621-3349. Fax: 207-621-3311. p. 975

Howard, Jack, Librn, Royal Ontario Museum, 100 Queen's Park, Toronto, ON, M5S 2C6, CANADA. Tel: 416-586-5718. Fax: 416-586-5519. p. 2858

Howard, Janet, Dir, Carlinville Public Library, 510 N Broad St, Carlinville, IL, 62626-1019. Tel: 217-854-3505. Fax: 217-854-5349. p. 600

Howard, Janet, Automation Syst Coordr, Altus Public Library, 421 N Hudson, Altus, OK, 73521. Tel: 580-477-2890. Fax: 580-477-3626. p. 1955

Howard, Jenifer, Ref & Digital Librn, Kentucky Historical Society, 100 W Broadway, Frankfort, KY, 40601. Tel: 502-564-1792. Fax: 502-564-4701. p. 913

Howard, Jessica, Ref Librn, Greenwood County Library, 600 S Main St, Greenwood, SC, 29646. Tel: 864-941-4650. Fax: 864-941-4651. p. 2197

Howard, Joanne, Youth Serv, Clearwater Public Library System, 100 N Osceola Ave, Clearwater, FL, 33755. Tel: 727-562-4970. Fax: 727-562-4977. p. 432

Howard, Judith, Br Librn, Kemper-Newton Regional Library System, Scooba Branch, 1016 Kemper St, Scooba, MS, 39358. Tel: 662-476-8452. p. 1316

Howard, Judith, Media Serv, Augustana College, 2001 S Summit Ave, Sioux Falls, SD, 57197-0001. Tel: 605-274-4920. Fax: 605-274-5447. p. 2218

Howard, Judy, Media Spec, Grand Ledge Area District Library, 131 E Jefferson St, Grand Ledge, MI, 48837-1534. Tel: 517-627-7014. Fax: 517-627-6276. p. 1183

Howard, Judy, Br Mgr, Wellington County Library, Fergus Branch, 190 St Andrew St W, Fergus, ON, N1M 1N5, CANADA. Tel: 519-843-1180. Fax: 519-843-5743. p. 2805

Howard, Karol, Res Librn, Bryan Cave LLP, 120 Broadway, Ste 300, Santa Monica, CA, 90401. Tel: 310-576-2100. Fax: 310-576-2200. p. 265

Howard, Kirk, Pub Serv, Marylhurst University, 17600 Pacific Hwy (Hwy 43), Marylhurst, OR, 97036-7036. Tel: 503-699-6261, Ext 3375. Fax: 503-636-1957. p. 2004

Howard, Linda May, Librn, Bohdan Lesack Memorial Library, 13750 96th Ave, Surrey, BC, V3V 1Z2, CANADA. Tel: 604-585-5666, Ext 772467. Fax: 604-585-5540. p. 2738

Howard, Martha, Librn, Thetford Historical Society Library, 16 Library Rd, Thetford, VT, 05074. Tel: 802-785-2068. p. 2437

Howard, Mary, Supv Librn, Dearborn Heights City Libraries, Caroline Kennedy Library, 24590 George St, Dearborn Heights, MI, 48127. Tel: 313-791-3824. Fax: 313-791-3801. p. 1168

Howard, Michelle, Librn, Kaplan, McLaughlin & Diaz Architects Library, 222 Vallejo St, San Francisco, CA, 94111. Tel: 415-398-5191. Fax: 415-394-7158. p. 243

Howard, Miranda, Head of Libr, Western Michigan University, Visual Resources, 2213 Sangren Hall, 2nd Flr, Kalamazoo, MI, 49008. Tel: 269-387-4113. Fax: 269-387-4114. p. 1198

Howard, Mollie, Mgr, Memphis Public Library, Raleigh Branch, 3157 Powers Rd, Memphis, TN, 38128. Tel: 901-386-5333. Fax: 901-371-9495. p. 2250

Howard, Mykie, Ser/Govt Doc Librn, Morehead State University, 150 University Blvd, Morehead, KY, 40351. Tel: 606-783-5116. Fax: 606-783-5037. p. 929

Howard, Patsy, Mgr, Currituck County Public Library, Moyock Public Library, 126 Campus Dr, Moyock, NC, 27958. Tel: 252-435-6419. Fax: 252-435-0680. p. 1776

Howard, Paul, Librn, Salem Hospital Community Education Center, 890 Oak St SE, Salem, OR, 97301. Tel: 503-814-1598. Fax: 503-814-1599. p. 2018

Howard, Peter, Ref Librn, State of Oregon Law Library, Supreme Court Bldg, 1163 State St, Salem, OR, 97301-2563. Tel: 503-986-5640. Fax: 503-986-5623. p. 2018

Howard, Sandra, Cat, Pittsburgh Theological Seminary, 616 N Highland Ave, Pittsburgh, PA, 15206-2596. Tel: 412-924-1359. Fax: 412-362-2329. p. 2127

Howard, Sara Catherine, Instr, Sam Houston State University, 1921 Ave J, Huntsville, TX, 77340. Tel: 936-294-4641. Fax: 936-294-1153. p. 2974

Howard, Sarah, Mgr, Ch & Youth Serv, Daniel Boone Regional Library, 100 W Broadway, Columbia, MO, 65203. Tel: 573-443-3161. Fax: 573-443-3281. p. 1324

Howard, Sheryl, Extended Day Librn, Lawson State Community College Library, 1100 Ninth Ave SW, Bessemer, AL, 35022. Tel: 205-929-3434, 205-929-6333. Fax: 205-925-3716. p. 6

Howard, Stephen R, Curator, Longyear Museum Library, 1125 Boylston St, Chestnut Hill, MA, 02467. Tel: 617-278-9000. Fax: 617-278-9003. p. 1081

Howard, Susannah, Ref, Oak Ridge Public Library, 1401 Oak Ridge Tpk, Oak Ridge, TN, 37830-6224. Tel: 865-425-3455. Fax: 865-425-3429. p. 2262

Howard, Tony, Serv Area Mgr, Columbus Metropolitan Library, Karl Road, 5590 Karl Rd, Columbus, OH, 43229. Tel: 614-645-2275. Fax: 614-479-4259. p. 1884

Howard, Tony, Managing Librn, Columbus Metropolitan Library, Northern Lights, 4093 Cleveland Ave, Columbus, OH, 43224. Tel: 614-645-2275. Fax: 614-479-4249. p. 1885

Howard, Virginia Anne, Pub Serv Mgr, Southwest Tennessee Community College, George Freeman Library, 5983 Macon Cove, Memphis, TN, 38134. Tel: 901-333-4706. Fax: 901-333-4566. p. 2251

Howard, Vivian, Lecturer, Dalhousie University, 6100 University Ave, Halifax, NS, B3H 3J5, CANADA. Tel: 902-494-3656. Fax: 902-494-2451. p. 2978

Howard, William, Ref, Virginia Intermont College, 1013 Moore St, Bristol, VA, 24201. Tel: 276-466-7958. p. 2453

Howard-Kelley, Jennifer, Ch, Harvin Clarendon County Library, 215 N Brooks St, Manning, SC, 29102. Tel: 803-435-8633. Fax: 803-435-8101. p. 2199

Howarth, Annette, Librn, Yachats Public Library, 560 W Seventh, Yachats, OR, 97498. Tel: 541-547-3741. Fax: 541-547-3741. p. 2023

Howarth, Lynne, Assoc Dean, Res, University of Toronto, 140 St George St, Toronto, ON, M5S 3G6, CANADA. Tel: 416-978-3234. Fax: 416-978-5762. p. 2978

Howarth, Rachel, Assoc Librn, Pub Serv, Harvard Library, Houghton Library-Rare Books & Manuscripts, Houghton Library, Cambridge, MA, 02138. Tel: 617-495-2441. Fax: 617-495-1376. p. 1075

Howatson, Beverley, Br Head, Toronto Public Library, Locke, 3083 Yonge St, Toronto, ON, M4N 2K7, CANADA. Tel: 416-393-7730. Fax: 416-393-7581. p. 2862

Howd, Dean, Coll Develop, Western Illinois University Libraries, One University Circle, Macomb, IL, 61455. Tel: 309-298-2736. Fax: 309-298-2791. p. 669

Howden, Norman, Dr, Asst Dean, El Centro College, 801 Main St, Dallas, TX, 75202-3605. Tel: 214-860-2176. Fax: 214-860-2440. p. 2307

Howe, Carol, Librn, Worcester County Library, Snow Hill Branch, 307 N Washington St, Snow Hill, MD, 21863. Tel: 410-632-3495. Fax: 410-632-1159. p. 1042

Howe, Carol, Ref, Immaculata University, 1145 King Rd, Immaculata, PA, 19345-0705. Tel: 610-647-4400, Ext 3832. Fax: 610-640-5828. p. 2071

Howe, Carol, Dr, Info Serv Librn, University of Arizona, Arizona Health Sciences Library, 1501 N Campbell Ave, Tucson, AZ, 85724. Tel: 520-626-2739. Fax: 520-626-2922. p. 88

Howe, Cynthia C, Asst Dir, Maynard Public Library, 77 Nason St, Maynard, MA, 01754-2316. Tel: 978-897-1010. Fax: 978-897-9884. p. 1103

Howe, Donna, Pub Serv, Big Horn County Public Library, 419 N Custer Ave, Hardin, MT, 59034. Fax: 406-665-1804. p. 1381

Howe, Fran, Librn, Candor Free Library, Two Bank St, Candor, NY, 13743-1510. Tel: 607-659-7258. Fax: 607-659-7500. p. 1602

Howe, Kristi, Libr Dir, Beloit Public Library, 605 Eclipse Blvd, Beloit, WI, 53511. Tel: 608-364-2917. Fax: 608-364-2907. p. 2581

Howe, Leni, In Charge, Dallas County Historical Society, 224 Hemlock Dr, Buffalo, MO, 65622-8649. Tel: 417-345-7297. Fax: 417-345-7297. p. 1321

Howe, Marilyn, Libr Dir, Mount Pulaski Public Library District, 320 N Washington St, Mount Pulaski, IL, 62548. Tel: 217-792-5919. Fax: 217-792-3449. p. 677

Howe, Nancy, County Librn, Santa Clara County Library District, 14600 Winchester Blvd, Los Gatos, CA, 95032. Tel: 408-293-2326. Fax: 408-364-0161. p. 180

Howe, Nancy J, Tech Coordr, Baldwinsville Public Library, 33 E Genesee St, Baldwinsville, NY, 13027-2575. Tel: 315-635-5631. Fax: 315-635-6760. p. 1577

Howe, Patricia, Head, Tech Serv, Longwood University, Redford & Race St, Farmville, VA, 23909. Tel: 434-395-2443. Fax: 434-395-2453. p. 2463

Howe, Sara, Circ, Bixby Memorial Free Library, 258 Main St, Vergennes, VT, 05491. Tel: 802-877-2211. Fax: 802-877-2411. p. 2437

Howell, Amber, Librn, Potwin Public Library, 126 N Randall, Potwin, KS, 67123. Tel: 620-752-3421. Fax: 620-752-3421. p. 890

Howell, Carole, Librn, White River Regional Library, Fulton County-Mammoth Spring Branch, 315 Main St, Mammoth Spring, AR, 72554. Tel: 870-625-3205. p. 94

Howell, Catherine, Archivist, Central Piedmont Community College Library, 1201 Elizabeth Ave, Charlotte, NC, 28235. Tel: 704-330-6373. Fax: 704-330-6887. p. 1781

Howell, Charles, Curator, University of Maryland Libraries, Broadcast Pioneers Library of American Broadcasting, Hornbake Library, College Park, MD, 20742. Tel: 301-405-9160. Fax: 301-314-2634. p. 1025

Howell, Darlene, Libr Adminr, West Florida Public Library, 200 W Gregory, Pensacola, FL, 32502. Tel: 850-436-5060. p. 482

Howell, Donna W, Dir, Mountain Regional Library System, 698 Miller St, Young Harris, GA, 30582. Tel: 706-379-3732. Fax: 706-379-2047. p. 558

Howell, Jan, Curator, Cherry County Historical Society Library, Box 284, Valentine, NE, 69201-0284. Tel: 402-376-2015. p. 1422

Howell, Jeanne, Librn, Canada Department of National Defence, Royal Artillery Park, Bldg No 3, 5460 Royal Artillery Court, Halifax, NS, B3J 0A8, CANADA. Tel: 902-427-4494. Fax: 902-427-4495. p. 2780

Howell, Jenny, Outreach Serv Librn, Musser Public Library, 304 Iowa Ave, Muscatine, IA, 52761-3875. Tel: 563-263-3065. Fax: 563-264-1033. p. 834

Howell, Judy K, Ref, Big Sandy Community & Technical College, One Bert T Combs Dr, Prestonsburg, KY, 41653. Tel: 606-889-4750. Fax: 606-886-8683. p. 933

Howell, Julie, Librn, East Parker County Library, 201 FM 1187 N, Aledo, TX, 76008. Tel: 817-441-6545. Fax: 817-441-5787. p. 2273

Howell, Linda, Tech Serv, Waco-McLennan County Library System, 1717 Austin Ave, Waco, TX, 76701-1794. Tel: 254-750-5993. Fax: 254-750-5940. p. 2397

Howell, Linda, Syst Librn, Union Institute & University, 62 Ridge St, Ste 2, Montpelier, VT, 05602. Tel: 802-828-8747. Fax: 802-828-8748. p. 2429

Howell, Marie, Dir, Rhoads Memorial Library, 103 SW Second St, Dimmitt, TX, 79027. Tel: 806-647-3532. Fax: 806-647-1038. p. 2314

Howell, Mark E, Librn, RTI International, 3040 Cornwallis Rd, Research Triangle Park, NC, 27709. Tel: 919-541-6364. Fax: 919-541-1221. p. 1820

Howell, Mary, Librn, Florida Office of Financial Regulation, Fletcher Bldg, 101 E Gaines St, Ste 526, Tallahassee, FL, 32399-0379. Tel: 850-410-9896. Fax: 850-410-9645. p. 494

Howell, Ora Mims, Sr Librn, United States Environmental Protection Agency, Region 4 Library, Atlanta Federal Center, 61 Forsyth St SW, Atlanta, GA, 30303-3104. Tel: 404-562-8125. Fax: 404-562-8114. p. 518

Howell, Polly, Ref, Wabash Carnegie Public Library, 188 W Hill St, Wabash, IN, 46992-3048. Tel: 260-563-2972. Fax: 260-563-0222. p. 785

Howell, Rachel, Asst Mgr, Dallas Public Library, 1515 Young St, Dallas, TX, 75201-5499. Tel: 214-670-1400. Fax: 214-670-7839. p. 2306

Howell, Ramona, Librn, White County Regional Library System, Beebe Public, 115 W Illinois, Beebe, AR, 72012-3245. Tel: 501-882-3235. Fax: 501-882-3235. p. 114

Howell, Sherita, Librn, Northeast Mississippi Community College, 101 Cunningham Blvd, Booneville, MS, 38829. Tel: 662-720-7583. Fax: 662-728-2428. p. 1294

Howerton, Linda, Dir, Person County Public Library, 319 S Main St, Roxboro, NC, 27573. Tel: 336-597-7881. Fax: 336-597-5081. p. 1821

Howerton, Nancy, Librn, Gabbs Community Library, 602 Third St, Gabbs, NV, 89409. Tel: 775-285-2686. p. 1428

Howerton, Ramona, Ref Librn, United States Department of the Treasury, United States Department of the Treasury, 250 E St SW, Washington, DC, 20219. Tel: 202-874-4719. Fax: 202-874-5138. p. 419

Howerton, Ramona, Mgr, Libr Serv, Duff & Phelps, 311 S Wacker Dr, Ste 4200, Chicago, IL, 60606. Tel: 312-697-4672. Fax: 312-697-4609. p. 613

Howerton, Virginia, Pub Serv Res Mgr, Seminole County Public Library System, 215 N Oxford Rd, Casselberry, FL, 32707. Tel: 407-665-1545. Fax: 407-665-1510. p. 431

Howes, Barbara, Librn, Butler University Libraries, Ruth Lilly Science Library, 740 W 46th St, Indianapolis, IN, 46208-3485. Tel: 317-940-9401. Fax: 317-940-9519. p. 749

Howes, Suzan, Regional Librn, Volusia County Public Library, Ormond Beach Public, 30 S Beach St, Ormond Beach, FL, 32174. Tel: 386-676-4191. Fax: 386-676-4194. p. 436

Howie, Judy, Head, Ref, Midwestern Baptist Theological Seminary Library, 5001 N Oak Trafficway, Kansas City, MO, 64118-4620. Tel: 816-414-3729. Fax: 816-414-3790. p. 1339

Howie, Mary Ann, Librn, Rochester General Hospital, 1425 Portland Ave, Rochester, NY, 14621. Tel: 585-922-4743. Fax: 585-544-1504. p. 1731

Howitt-Covalt, Tammy, Dir, Bridgeport Public Library, 722 Main St, Bridgeport, NE, 69336. Tel: 308-262-0326. Fax: 308-262-1412. p. 1394

Howk, Cynthia, Coordr, Landmark Society of Western New York, Inc, 133 S Fitzhugh St, Rochester, NY, 14608-2204. Tel: 585-546-7029, Ext 24. Fax: 585-546-4788. p. 1730

Howland, Jane, Assoc Teaching Prof, University of Missouri-Columbia, 303 Townsend Hall, Columbia, MO, 65211. Tel: 573-882-4546. Fax: 573-884-2917. p. 2969

Howland, Joan, Head, Circ, Dover Town Library, 56 Dedham St, Dover, MA, 02030-2214. Tel: 508-785-8113. Fax: 508-785-0138. p. 1085

Howland, Joan, Assoc Dean, Info Tech, University of Minnesota Libraries-Twin Cities, Law, 120 Law Bldg, 229 19th Ave S, Minneapolis, MN, 55455. Tel: 612-625-4300. Fax: 612-625-3478. p. 1262

Howland, Joanie, Dir, Cortez Public Library, 202 N Park, Cortez, CO, 81321-3300. Tel: 970-565-8117. Fax: 970-565-8720. p. 297

Howland, Louise, Dir, Beaman Memorial Public Library, Eight Newton St, West Boylston, MA, 01583. Tel: 508-835-3711. Fax: 508-835-4770. p. 1136

Howland, Nancy, Dir, Riverside Regional Library, 1997 E Jackson Blvd, Jackson, MO, 63755-1949. Tel: 573-243-8141. Fax: 573-243-8142. p. 1334

Howlett, Jackie, Cataloger, Coll Develop Librn, Kalamazoo Valley Community College Libraries, 6767 West O Ave, Kalamazoo, MI, 49003. Tel: 269-488-4328, 269-488-4380. Fax: 269-488-4488. p. 1197

Howlett, Lee Ann, Ser, University of South Florida, Hinks & Elaine Shimberg Health Sciences Library, 12901 Bruce B Downs Blvd, MDC Box 31, Tampa, FL, 33612-4799. Tel: 813-974-2399. Fax: 813-974-3605, 813-974-4930. p. 498

Howlett-Soltysiak, Sheila, Br Mgr, Caledon Public Library, Inglewood Branch, 15825 McLaughlin Rd, Inglewood, ON, L7C 1H4, CANADA. Tel: 905-838-3324. p. 2795

Howley, Susan, Pub Policy Dir, National Center for Victims of Crime Library, 2000 M St NW, Ste 480, Washington, DC, 20036. Tel: 202-467-8722. Fax: 202-467-8701. p. 409

Howren, Laurie, Coordr, Georgia Northwestern Technical College, Polk County Campus Library, 466 Brock Rd, Rockmart, GA, 30153. Tel: 678-757-2043. Fax: 678-757-1673. p. 548

Howrey, Mary, Dr, Dir, Libr Serv, DeVry University, 2300 SW 145th Ave, Miramar, FL, 33027-4150. Tel: 954-499-9619. Fax: 954-499-9659. p. 470

Howsare, Vicki, Ch, Moundsville-Marshall County Public Library, 700 Fifth St, Moundsville, WV, 26041-1993. Tel: 304-845-6911. Fax: 304-845-6912. p. 2567

Howse, David, Info Serv Librn, University of Arizona, Arizona Health Sciences Library, 1501 N Campbell Ave, Tucson, AZ, 85724. Tel: 520-626-2934. Fax: 520-626-2922. p. 88

Howze, Rebecca, Head, ILL, United States Air Force, Air University - Muir S Fairchild Research Information Center, 600 Chennault Circle, Maxwell AFB, AL, 36112-6010. Tel: 334-953-2606. p. 24

Hoxie, David E, Dir, Alderson-Broaddus College, College Hill Rd, Philippi, WV, 26416. Tel: 304-457-6229. Fax: 304-457-6239. p. 2569

Hoxmeier, Kathy, Per Coordr, Southern Oregon University, 1250 Siskiyou Blvd, Ashland, OR, 97520-5076. Tel: 541-552-6844. Fax: 541-552-6429. p. 1990

Hoxworth, Sharon, Librn, Holmes County District Public Library, Killbuck Branch, 160 W Front St, Killbuck, OH, 44637. Tel: 330-276-0882. Fax: 330-276-0882. p. 1918

Hoy, Charlotte, Librn, Elizabethtown-Kitley Township Public Library, Kitley Branch, 424 Hwy 29, Toledo, ON, K0E 1Y0, CANADA. Fax: 613-345-7235. p. 2791

Hoy, Edana, Head, Youth Serv, Bethlehem Area Public Library, 11 W Church St, Bethlehem, PA, 18018. Tel: 610-867-3761, Ext 218. Fax: 610-867-2767. p. 2034

Hoy, Edna, Ch Serv Librn, Bucks County Free Library, James A Michener Branch, 401 W Mill St, Quakertown, PA, 18951-1248. Tel: 215-536-3306. Fax: 215-536-8397. p. 2050

Hoy, Isabel M, Dir, Goshen County Library, 2001 East A St, Torrington, WY, 82240-2898. Tel: 307-532-3411. Fax: 307-532-2169. p. 2661

Hoy, Matt, Supvr, Mayo Clinic Health System, 1221 Whipple St, Eau Claire, WI, 54702-4105. Tel: 715-838-3248. Fax: 715-838-3289. p. 2590

Hoyer, Edward, Per, Southern Connecticut State University, 501 Crescent St, New Haven, CT, 06515. Tel: 203-392-5731. Fax: 203-392-5775. p. 356

Hoyer, John, Music Libr Assoc, Hope College, Van Wylen Library, 53 Graves Pl, Holland, MI, 49422. Tel: 616-395-7659. Fax: 616-395-7965. p. 1191

Hoyer, Meredith, Adult Serv, Somerset County Library System, Mary Jacobs Memorial, 64 Washington St, Rocky Hill, NJ, 08553. Tel: 609-924-7073. Fax: 609-924-7668. p. 1475

Hoying, Karen, Librn, Mercer County District Library, Zahn-Marion Township Branch, Five East Franklin St, Chickasaw, OH, 45826. Tel: 419-925-4966. Fax: 419-925-4227. p. 1866

Hoyle, Gary, Dir, Albemarle Regional Library, 303 W Tryon St, Winton, NC, 27986. Tel: 252-358-7832. Fax: 252-358-7868. p. 1835

Hoyle, Karen Nelson, Curator, University of Minnesota Libraries-Twin Cities, Children's Literature Research Collections, Elmer L Andersen Library, 222 21st Ave S, Ste 113, Minneapolis, MN, 55455. Tel: 612-624-4576. Fax: 612-626-0377. p. 1262

Hoyle, Norman, Ref Serv, Tri-County Technical College Library, 7900 Hwy 76, Pendleton, SC, 29670. Tel: 864-646-1750. Fax: 864-646-1543. p. 2202

Hoyle, Ruth, Dir, Davie County Public Library, Cooleemee Branch, 7796 NC Hwy 801 S, Cooleemee, NC, 27014. Tel: 336-751-2023. Fax: 336-284-2805. p. 1810

Hoyle, Ruth A, Dir, Davie County Public Library, 371 N Main St, Mocksville, NC, 27028-2115. Tel: 336-753-6030. Fax: 336-751-1370. p. 1809

Hoyne, Kathleen, Co-Dir, Cabot Public Library, 3084 Main St, Cabot, VT, 05647. Tel: 802-563-2721. p. 2421

Hoyt, Karen, Librn, Nationwide Library, One Nationwide Plaza 1-01-05, Columbus, OH, 43215. Tel: 614-249-6414. Fax: 614-249-2218. p. 1886

Hoyt, Karen, Cataloger, Piedmont Technical College Library, 620 N Emerald Rd, Bldg K, Greenwood, SC, 29646. Tel: 864-941-8659. Fax: 864-941-8558. p. 2198

Hoyt, Linda, Dir, Horicon Free Public Library, 6604 State Rte 8, Brant Lake, NY, 12815. Tel: 518-494-4189. Fax: 518-494-3852. p. 1584

Hoyt, Virginia, Dir, Elmwood Public Library, 124 West D St, Elmwood, NE, 68349. Tel: 402-994-4125. Fax: 402-994-4125. p. 1398

Hoyt Wickes, Nancy, Librn, Society of Mayflower Descendants in the State of California Library, 405 14th St, Terrace Level, Oakland, CA, 94612. Tel: 510-451-9599. p. 199

Hozak, Jeanne, Dir, Adult Serv, Hall County Library System, 127 Main St NW, Gainesville, GA, 30501-3699. Tel: 770-532-3311. Fax: 770-532-4305. p. 534

Hrabina, Sharon, Librn, Pocono Medical Center, 206 E Brown St, East Stroudsburg, PA, 18301. Tel: 570-476-3515. Fax: 570-476-3472. p. 2051

Hrabina, Sharon, Chairperson, Cooperating Hospital Libraries of the Lehigh Valley Area, Saint Luke's Hospital, Estes Library, 801 Ostrum St, Bethlehem, PA, 18015. Tel: 570-476-3515. Fax: 610-954-4651. p. 2954

Hradecky, Rachel, Outreach/Pub Serv Librn, University of Maryland, Baltimore, Thurgood Marshall Law Library, 501 W Fayette St, Baltimore, MD, 21201-1768. Tel: 410-706-0784. Fax: 410-706-8354. p. 1019

Hranjec, Stephanie, Ref Serv, Monroe Community College, Damon City Campus Library, 228 E Main St, 4th Flr 4-101, Rochester, NY, 14604. Tel: 585-262-1413. Fax: 585-262-1516. p. 1730

Hren, Richard, Head, Tech Serv, Carthage College, 2001 Alford Park Dr, Kenosha, WI, 53140-1900. Tel: 262-551-5900. Fax: 262-551-5904. p. 2601

Hricko, Mary, Dir, Kent State University, 11411 Claridon-Troy Rd, Burton, OH, 44021-9535. Tel: 440-834-3722. Fax: 440-834-0919. p. 1862

Hristov, Nathalie, Librn, University of Tennessee, Knoxville, George F DeVine Music Library, 301 Music Bldg, 1741 Volunteer Blvd, Knoxville, TN, 37996-2600. Tel: 865-974-9893. Fax: 865-974-0564. p. 2244

Hrivnak, David, Dir, Peoples Library, 880 Barnes St, New Kensington, PA, 15068. Tel: 724-339-1021, Ext 12. Fax: 724-339-2027. p. 2097

Hrobsky, Anne, Head, Youth Serv, Worcester Public Library, Three Salem Sq, Worcester, MA, 01608. Tel: 508-799-1672. Fax: 508-799-1652. p. 1145

Hronchek, Jessica, Ref & Instrul Serv Librn, Hope College, Van Wylen Library, 53 Graves Pl, Holland, MI, 49422. Tel: 616-395-7124. Fax: 616-395-7965. p. 1190

Hronek, Beth, Pub Serv, Lake Superior State University, 906 Ryan Ave, Sault Sainte Marie, MI, 49783. Tel: 906-635-2815. Fax: 906-635-2193. p. 1226

Hronek, Debbie, Dir, Joliet Public Library, 211 E Front Ave, Joliet, MT, 59041. Tel: 406-962-3013. p. 1383

Hruska, Brad, Ch, Columbus Public Library, 2504 14th St, Columbus, NE, 68601-4988. Tel: 402-564-7116. Fax: 402-563-3378. p. 1396

Hruska, Martha, Assoc Univ Librn, Coll Serv, University of California, San Diego, 9500 Gilman Dr, Mail Code 0175G, La Jolla, CA, 92093-0175. Tel: 858-534-1235. Fax: 858-534-4970. p. 162

Hrycelak, M, Dr, Archivist, Dir, Ukrainian Medical Association of North America, 2247 W Chicago Ave, Ste 206, Chicago, IL, 60622. Tel: 773-278-6262. p. 625

Hryciw-Wing, Carol, Head, Tech Serv, Rhode Island College, 600 Mt Pleasant Ave, Providence, RI, 02908-1924. Tel: 401-456-8126. Fax: 401-456-9646. p. 2174

Hryshko, Jane, ILL, Bard College, One Library Rd, Annandale-on-Hudson, NY, 12504. Tel: 845-758-7502. Fax: 845-758-5801. p. 1574

Hseih, Ma Lei, Instrul Serv Librn, Rider University, 2083 Lawrenceville Rd, Lawrenceville, NJ, 08648-3099. Tel: 609-896-5241. Fax: 609-896-8029. p. 1494

Hshieh-Yee, Ingrid, Dr, Dean, Catholic University of America, Marist Hall, 228, 620 Michigan Ave NE, Washington, DC, 20064. Tel: 202-319-5085. Fax: 202-319-5574. p. 2963

Hsiao, Dori, Operations Mgr, University of California, Berkeley, Environmental Design, 210 Wurster Hall, Berkeley, CA, 94720-6000. Tel: 510-643-7222. Fax: 510-642-8266. p. 127

Hsieh, Fang-Lan, Dr, Librn, Southwestern Baptist Theological Seminary Libraries, Kathryn Sullivan Bowld Music Library, 1809 W Broadus, Rm 113, Fort Worth, TX, 76115-2157. Tel: 817-923-1921, Ext 2070. Fax: 817-921-8762. p. 2323

Hsieh, Haowei, Dr, Asst Prof, University of Iowa, 3087 Main Library, Iowa City, IA, 52242-1420. Tel: 319-335-5707. Fax: 319-335-5374. p. 2965

Hsieh, Margaret, Med Librn, ValleyCare Health System, 5725 W Las Positas Blvd, Ste 270, Pleasanton, CA, 94588. Tel: 925-734-3315. Fax: 925-734-3372. p. 211

Hsiung, Lai-Ying, Head, Tech Serv, University of California, 1156 High St, Santa Cruz, CA, 95064. Tel: 831-459-5166. Fax: 831-459-8206. p. 264

Hsu, Kwei-Feng, Dir, Libr Serv, Wharton County Junior College, 911 Boling Hwy, Wharton, TX, 77488-3298. Tel: 979-532-6953. Fax: 979-532-6527. p. 2399

Hsu, Mona, Operations Librn, San Diego Christian College, 2100 Greenfield Dr, El Cajon, CA, 92019-1161. Tel: 619-201-8681. Fax: 619-201-8799. p. 145

Hsu, Peter, Commun Libr Mgr, County of Los Angeles Public Library, Lennox Library, 4359 Lennox Blvd, Lennox, CA, 90304-2398. Tel: 310-674-0385. Fax: 310-673-6508. p. 142

Hsueh-Ying, Wang, Cat, Monterey Institute of International Studies, 425 Van Buren St, Monterey, CA, 93940. Tel: 831-647-4136. Fax: 831-647-3518. p. 190

Hu, Chengren, Dr, Dir, Tech & Info Serv, Chicago State University, 9501 S Martin Luther King Jr Dr, LIB 440, Chicago, IL, 60628-1598. Tel: 773-995-3983. Fax: 773-995-3772. p. 610

Hu, Estelle, Med Librn, Silver Cross Hospital Medical Library, 1200 Maple Rd, Joliet, IL, 60432-9988. Tel: 815-300-7477. Fax: 815-300-3567. p. 660

Hu, Mei-Xiang, Cat Librn, Tennessee Technological University, 1100 N Peachtree Ave, Cookeville, TN, 38505. Tel: 931-372-3326. Fax: 931-372-6112. p. 2231

Hu, Qian, Librn, Rutgers University Libraries, Physics Library, Serin Physics Laboratory, 136 Frelinghuysen Rd, Piscataway, NJ, 08854-8019. Tel: 732-445-3526, Ext 315. Fax: 732-445-4964. p. 1509

Hu, Robert H, Dir, Saint Mary's University, Sarita Kennedy East Law Library, One Camino Santa Maria, San Antonio, TX, 78228-8605. Tel: 210-431-2056. Fax: 210-436-3240. p. 2381

Hu, Sheila, ILL, Pace University, 861 Bedford Rd, Pleasantville, NY, 10570-2799. Tel: 914-773-3853. Fax: 914-773-3508. p. 1720

Hu, Suxiao, Head, Coll Develop & Acq Develop, Montclair State University, One Normal Ave, Montclair, NJ, 07043-1699. Tel: 973-655-7151. Fax: 973-655-7780. p. 1503

Hu, Xiaohua Tony, PhD, Assoc Prof, Drexel University, Rush Bldg, Rm 306, 30 N 33rd St, Philadelphia, PA, 19104-2875. Tel: 215-895-2474. Fax: 215-895-2494. p. 2972

Hu, Yasha, Commun Libr Mgr, Queens Borough Public Library, Elmhurst Community Library, 86-01 Broadway, Elmhurst, NY, 11373. Tel: 718-271-1020. Fax: 718-699-8069. p. 1644

Hua, Julia, Commun Libr Mgr, Queens Borough Public Library, Fresh Meadows Community Library, 193-20 Horace Harding Expressway, Fresh Meadows, NY, 11365. Tel: 718-454-7272. Fax: 718-454-5820. p. 1644

Huaman, Theresa, Cat Librn, College of the Holy Cross, One College St, Worcester, MA, 01610. Tel: 508-793-2638. Fax: 508-793-2372. p. 1143

Huang, Chao, Syst & Cat Librn, Christian Theological Seminary Library, 1000 W 42nd St, Indianapolis, IN, 46208. Tel: 317-924-1331. Fax: 317-931-2363. p. 750

Huang, Harriet, Coll Develop, Pace University, 861 Bedford Rd, Pleasantville, NY, 10570-2799. Tel: 914-773-3240. Fax: 914-773-3508. p. 1720

Huang, Hong, Dr, Asst Prof, University of South Florida, 4202 Fowler Ave, CIS 1040, Tampa, FL, 33620-7800. Tel: 813-974-6361. Fax: 813-974-6840. p. 2964

Huang, Jian, Br Mgr, Brooklyn Public Library, Canarsie, 1580 Rockaway Pkwy, Brooklyn, NY, 11236. Tel: 718-257-6547. Fax: 718-257-6557. p. 1591

Huang, Jintao, Tech Coordr, Pickerington Public Library, 201 Opportunity Way, Pickerington, OH, 43147-1296. Tel: 614-837-4104. Fax: 614-837-8425. p. 1930

Huang, Joyce, Dir, University of Wisconsin-Whitewater Library, 800 W Main St, Whitewater, WI, 53190. Tel: 262-472-5516. Fax: 262-472-5727. p. 2649

Huang, Mary-Ann S, Head, Tech Serv, Aldrich Public Library, Six Washington St, Barre, VT, 05641-4227. Tel: 802-476-7550. Fax: 802-479-0450 (Call before sending fax). p. 2418

Hubal, Barbara, Librn, OMNOVA Solutions Inc, 2990 Gilchrist Rd, Akron, OH, 44305. Tel: 330-794-6382. Fax: 330-794-6375. p. 1853

Hubbard, Amanda, Tech Serv, Hinds Community College, Utica Campus Learning Resources/Library, Hwy 18 W, Utica, MS, 39175-9599. Tel: 601-885-7035. p. 1313

Hubbard, Beth, Librn, Martinsville Public Library District, 120 E Cumberland, Martinsville, IL, 62442-1000. Tel: 217-382-4113. Fax: 217-382-4113. p. 671

Hubbard, Brian, Head, Ref (Info Serv), Westfield State University, 577 Western Ave, Westfield, MA, 01085-2580. Tel: 413-572-5482. Fax: 413-572-5520. p. 1138

Hubbard, Christine, Dir, Lostant Community Library, 102 W Third St, Lostant, IL, 61334. Tel: 815-368-3530. Fax: 815-368-8035. p. 668

Hubbard, Erin, Acq, New Hampshire Law Library, Supreme Court Bldg, One Charles Doe Dr, Concord, NH, 03301-6160. Tel: 603-271-3777. Fax: 603-513-5450. p. 1443

Hubbard, Etta, Asst Librn, Shaw Public Library, Nine Lily Bay Rd, Greenville, ME, 04441. Tel: 207-695-3579. Fax: 207-695-0310. p. 987

Hubbard, J Stephen, Ref, Fargo Public Library, 102 N Third St, Fargo, ND, 58102. Tel: 701-241-1472. Fax: 701-241-8581. p. 1841

Hubbard, Jason, Info Tech, Bethune-Cookman College, 640 Mary McLeod Bethune Blvd, Daytona Beach, FL, 32114. Tel: 386-481-2186. Fax: 386-481-2182. p. 435

Hubbard, Joan, Univ Librn, Weber State University, 2901 University Circle, Ogden, UT, 84408-2901. Tel: 801-626-6405. Fax: 801-626-7045. p. 2409

Hubbard Krimmer, Susanna, Chief Exec Officer, Chief Librn, London Public Library, 251 Dundas St, London, ON, N6A 6H9, CANADA. Tel: 519-661-5143. Fax: 519-663-9013. p. 2817

Hubbard, Margaret, Tech Serv Assoc, Wartburg College Library, 100 Wartburg Blvd, Waverly, IA, 50677-0903. Tel: 319-352-8500. Fax: 319-352-8312. p. 851

Hubbard, Marlis, Librn, Concordia University Libraries, Counselling & Development, Career Resource Centre, 1455 de Maisonneuve Blvd W, H-440, Montreal, QC, H3G 1M8, CANADA. Tel: 514-848-2424, Local 7385. Fax: 514-848-4534. p. 2894

Hubbard, Marty, Asst Librn, Ledyard Public Libraries, 718 Colonel Ledyard Hwy, Ledyard, CT, 06339. Tel: 860-464-9912. Fax: 860-464-9927. p. 349

Hubbard, Quatro, Archivist, Virginia Department of Historic Resources, 2801 Kensington Ave, Richmond, VA, 23221. Tel: 804-367-2323, Ext 124. Fax: 804-367-2391. p. 2492

Hubble, Ann, Bibliographer, Librn, University of California, 1156 High St, Santa Cruz, CA, 95064. Tel: 831-459-4974. Fax: 831-459-8206. p. 264

Hubbs, Dan, Adult Serv, Saratoga Springs Public Library, 49 Henry St, Saratoga Springs, NY, 12866. Tel: 518-584-7860. Fax: 518-584-7866. p. 1738

Hubbs, Guy, Archivist, Ref Librn, Birmingham-Southern College, 900 Arkadelphia Rd, Birmingham, AL, 35254. Tel: 205-226-4752. Fax: 205-226-4743. p. 8

Hubener, Hal, Dir, Blue Ridge Regional Library, 310 E Church St, Martinsville, VA, 24112-2999. Tel: 276-403-5435. Fax: 276-632-1660. p. 2477

Hubenschmidt, Carl, Ref Librn, Lindenwood University, 209 S Kingshighway, Saint Charles, MO, 63301. Tel: 636-949-4758. Fax: 636-949-4822. p. 1351

Huber, Anne, Inst Librn, University of Illinois Library at Urbana-Champaign, Prairie Research Institute Library, 1816 S Oak St, Champaign, IL, 61820. Tel: 217-333-5110. Fax: 217-244-0802. p. 713

Huber, Dale, Actg Br Mgr, Hawaii State Public Library System, Hilo Public Library, 300 Waianuenue Ave, Hilo, HI, 96720-2447. Tel: 808-933-8888. Fax: 808-933-8895. p. 562

Huber, Daniel, YA Serv, Oyster Bay-East Norwich Public Library, 89 E Main St, Oyster Bay, NY, 11771. Tel: 516-922-1212. Fax: 516-922-6453. p. 1714

Huber, Jeffrey T, Dr, Dir, University of Kentucky, 320 Little Library Bldg, Lexington, KY, 40506-0224. Tel: 859-257-8876. Fax: 859-257-4205. p. 2966

Huber, Kathy, Librn, Tulsa City-County Library, Genealogy Center, 2901 S Harvard, Tulsa, OK, 74114. Tel: 918-746-5222. p. 1983

Huber, Marie, Librn, Bruning Public Library, 141 Main St, Bruning, NE, 68322. p. 1394

Huber, Rahn, Librn, Vanderbilt University, Walker Management Library, Owen Graduate School of Management, 401 21st Ave S, Nashville, TN, 37203. Tel: 615-343-4084. Fax: 615-343-0061. p. 2261

Hubers, Barb, Dir, Thornapple Kellogg School & Community Library, 3885 Bender Rd, Middleville, MI, 49333-9273. Tel: 269-795-5434. Fax: 269-795-8997. p. 1208

Hubert, Lisa, Librn, Wapiti Regional Library, Wakaw Public Library, 121 Main St, Wakaw, SK, S0K 4P0, CANADA. Tel: 306-233-5552. p. 2922

Hubert, Mimi, In Charge, Lashly & Baer PC, 714 Locust St, Saint Louis, MO, 63101. Tel: 314-621-2939, Ext 1017. Fax: 314-621-6844. p. 1355

Hubert, Tina, Dir, Six Mile Regional Library District, 2001 Delmar St, Granite City, IL, 62040-4590. Tel: 618-452-6238. Fax: 618-876-6317. p. 651

Hubert, Warren, Librn, Hunt Correctional Center Library, 6925 Hwy 74, Saint Gabriel, LA, 70776. Tel: 225-319-4507. Fax: 225-319-4596. p. 967

Hubick, Lisa, Pub Relations Librn, Kwantlen Polytechnic University Library, 12666 72 Ave., Surrey, BC, V3W 2M8, CANADA. Tel: 604-599-3404. Fax: 604-599-3202. p. 2738

Hubsher, Robert, Exec Dir, Ramapo Catskill Library System, 619 Rte 17M, Middletown, NY, 10940-4395. Tel: 845-343-1131, Ext 242. Fax: 845-343-1205. p. 1660

Huch, Cathryn, Ch, Livonia Public Library, Alfred Noble Branch, 32901 Plymouth Rd, Livonia, MI, 48150-1793. Tel: 734-421-6600. Fax: 734-421-6606. p. 1203

Huchinson, Diane, Circ Supvr, Covina Public Library, 234 N Second Ave, Covina, CA, 91723-2198. Tel: 626-384-5301. Fax: 626-384-5315. p. 137

Huckaby, Gale, Co-Dir, Real County Public Library, 225 Main St, Leakey, TX, 78873. Tel: 830-232-5199. Fax: 830-232-5913. p. 2354

Huckaby, Lillie, Ch, Chickasha Public Library, 527 W Iowa Ave, Chickasha, OK, 73018. Tel: 405-222-6075. Fax: 405-222-6072. p. 1959

Hucker, Tracy, Circ Mgr, Fremont Public Library District, 1170 N Midlothian Rd, Mundelein, IL, 60060. Tel: 847-566-8702. Fax: 847-566-0204. p. 678

Huckfeldt, Robert, Dir, University of California, Davis, Institute of Governmental Affairs Library & Data Archive, Shields Library, Rm 360, One Shields Ave, Davis, CA, 95616-8617. Tel: 530-752-2042. Fax: 530-752-2835. p. 139

Huckle, Norman, Head of Doc Delivery, University of Nevada-Reno, Savitt Medical Library & IT Department, Pennington Medical Education Bldg, 1664 N Virginia St, Mail Stop 306, Reno, NV, 89557. Tel: 775-784-4625. Fax: 775-784-4489. p. 1433

Hudak, Andrew F, Jr, Dir, St Andrew's Abbey, 10510 Buckeye Rd, Cleveland, OH, 44104. Tel: 216-721-5300, Ext 294. Fax: 216-791-8268. p. 1881

Hudak, Joseph, Br Mgr, Central Arkansas Library System, Dee Brown Branch, 6325 Baseline, Little Rock, AR, 72209-4810. Tel: 501-568-7494. p. 106

Hudak, Milly, Curator, In Charge, Winchester Historical Society Library, 225 Prospect St, Winsted, CT, 06098-1942. Tel: 860-379-8433. p. 380

Hudak, Susan, Bibliog Instr, Carnegie Library of Pittsburgh, 4400 Forbes Ave, Pittsburgh, PA, 15213-4080. Tel: 412-920-4524. Fax: 412-920-4531. p. 2122

Huddleston, Brian, Sr Ref Librn, Loyola University New Orleans, Loyola Law Library, School of Law, 7214 St Charles Ave, New Orleans, LA, 70118. Tel: 504-861-5539. Fax: 504-861-5895. p. 961

Huddleston, Carmen, Librn, Stanford Health Library, Stanford Hospital, E303 Stanford Hospital, 300 Pasteur Dr, Palo Alto, CA, 94305. Tel: 650-725-8100. Fax: 650-725-8102. p. 205

Huddleston, Charlotte, Tech Serv, Carnegie Public Library, 114 Delta Ave, Clarksdale, MS, 38614-4212. Tel: 662-624-4461. Fax: 662-627-4344. p. 1295

Huddleston, Joyce, Asst Librn, Macon County Public Library, 311 Church St, Lafayette, TN, 37083-1607. Tel: 615-666-4340. Fax: 615-666-8932. p. 2244

Huddy, John, Br Mgr, Loudoun County Public Library, Ashburn Branch, 43316 Hay Rd, Ashburn, VA, 20147. Tel: 703-737-8100. Fax: 703-737-8101. p. 2473

Huddy, Lorraine, Librn, Collaborative Pojects, CTW Library Consortium, Olin Memorial Library, Wesleyan University, Middletown, CT, 06459-6065. Tel: 860-685-3844. Fax: 860-685-2661. p. 2939

Hudec, Rebecca, Asst Librn, Chinook Regional Library, Fox Valley Branch, 85 Centre St E, Fox Valley, SK, S0N 0V0, CANADA. Tel: 306-666-2045. p. 2928

Hudgens, Jan B, Librn, Bergen Regional Medical Center Library, 230 E Ridgewood Ave, Paramus, NJ, 07652. Tel: 201-967-4065. p. 1517

Hudgins, Donna, Ser, University of Mary Washington, 1801 College Ave, Fredericksburg, VA, 22401-4665. Tel: 540-654-1762. Fax: 540-654-1067. p. 2466

Hudgins, Edie, Librn, Haynesville Correctional Center, 241 Barnfield Rd, Haynesville, VA, 22472. Tel: 804-333-3577, Ext 4713. Fax: 804-333-1295. p. 2471

Hudgins, Nelda B, Dir, Aliceville Public Library, 416 Third Ave NE, Aliceville, AL, 35442. Tel: 205-373-6691. Fax: 205-373-3731. p. 4

Hudgins, Robin, Ref Librn, Middle Georgia Regional Library System, 1180 Washington Ave, Macon, GA, 31201-1790. Tel: 478-744-0838. Fax: 478-742-3161. p. 541

Hudgson, Wendy, Asst Librn, Miles Community College Library, 2715 Dickinson, Miles City, MT, 59301. Tel: 406-874-6105. Fax: 406-874-6282. p. 1386

Hudner, Stephanie, Asst Head, Res Mgt, Metadata & Operations, Northeastern University Libraries, Snell Library, 360 Huntington Ave, Boston, MA, 02115. Tel: 617-373-8778. p. 1065

Hudner, Stephanie, Metadata Librn, Northeastern University School of Law Library, 400 Huntington Ave, Boston, MA, 02115. Tel: 617-373-3716. Fax: 617-373-8705. p. 1066

Hudock, Sandy, Dept Chair, Head, Pub Serv, Colorado State University Pueblo Library, 2200 Bonforte Blvd, Pueblo, CO, 81001-4901. Tel: 719-549-2527. Fax: 719-549-2738. p. 320

Hudon, Michele, Assoc Prof, Universite de Montreal, 3150, rue Jean-Brillant, bur C-2004, Montreal, QC, H3T 1N8, CANADA. Tel: 514-343-6044. Fax: 514-343-5753. p. 2979

Hudon, Rachelle, Tech Serv, Bibliotheque Municipale d'Alma, 500 Collard, Alma, QC, G8B 1N2, CANADA. Tel: 418-669-5139. Fax: 418-669-5089. p. 2879

Hudson, Alexia, Ref Librn, Pennsylvania State University, 30 E Swedesford Rd, Malvern, PA, 19355. Tel: 610-648-3364. Fax: 610-725-5223. p. 2083

Hudson, Beth, Dir, Libr Serv, Walla Walla Public Library, 238 E Alder, Walla Walla, WA, 99362. Tel: 509-524-4433. Fax: 509-524-7950. p. 2547

Hudson, Bill, Adminr, Library System of Lancaster County, 1866 Colonial Village Lane, Ste 107, Lancaster, PA, 17601. Tel: 717-207-0500. Fax: 717-207-0504. p. 2077

Hudson, Brandon, Fac Coordr, Georgetown University, Dahlgren Memorial Library, Preclinical Science Bldg GM-7, 3900 Reservoir Rd NW, Washington, DC, 20007. Tel: 202-687-1448. Fax: 202-687-1862. p. 402

Hudson, Carlyn, Outreach Coordr, Young Adult Serv Coordr, Somerville Library, 35 West End Ave, Somerville, NJ, 08876. Tel: 908-725-1336. Fax: 908-231-0608. p. 1530

Hudson, Christopher, Govt Doc, Emory University School of Law, 1301 Clifton Rd, Atlanta, GA, 30322. Tel: 404-727-0452. Fax: 404-727-2202. p. 514

Hudson, Diane, Br Mgr, Greene County Public Library, Cedarville Community Library, 20 S Miller St, Cedarville, OH, 45314-8556. Tel: 937-352-4006. Fax: 937-766-2847. p. 1951

Hudson, Freddy, Br Mgr, Central Arkansas Library System, John Gould Fletcher Branch, 823 N Buchanan St, Little Rock, AR, 72205-3211. Tel: 501-663-5457. p. 106

Hudson, Helen, Br Mgr, Dare County Library, Hatteras Branch, PO Box 309, Hatteras, NC, 27943-0309. Tel: 252-986-2385. Fax: 252-986-2952. p. 1808

Hudson, Homer, Libr Tech, Saint Louis Public Library, Saint Louis Marketplace, 6548 Manchester Ave, Saint Louis, MO, 63139. Tel: 314-647-0939. Fax: 314-647-1062. p. 1360

Hudson, Jamie, Librn, Western Plains Library System, Weatherford Public Library, 219 E Frankin, Weatherford, OK, 73096-5134. Tel: 580-772-3591. Fax: 580-772-3591. p. 1961

Hudson, Jane, Mgr, Greensboro Public Library, Hemphill, 2301 W Vandalia Rd, Greensboro, NC, 27407. Tel: 336-373-2925. Fax: 336-855-6635. p. 1796

Hudson, Jessica, Br Mgr, County Librn, Nevada County Library, 980 Helling Way, Nevada City, CA, 95959. Tel: 530-265-7078. p. 193

Hudson, Joan, Librn, Shibley Righton LLP, 250 University Ave, Ste 700, Toronto, ON, M5H 3E5, CANADA. Tel: 416-214-5294. Fax: 416-214-5400. p. 2858

Hudson, Julie, Ch, Clearwater Public Library System, Countryside, 2741 State Rd 580, Clearwater, FL, 33761. Tel: 727-562-4970. Fax: 727-669-1289. p. 432

Hudson, Karen, Librn, Salt Spring Island Public Library, 129 McPhillips Ave, Salt Spring Island, BC, V8K 2T6, CANADA. Tel: 250-537-4666. Fax: 250-537-4666. p. 2737

Hudson, Kathy, Mgr, Jefferson County Library System, Wadley Public, 11 W College Ave, Wadley, GA, 30477. Tel: 478-252-1366. Fax: 478-252-1337. p. 540

Hudson, Kay M, Dir, Milford Public Library, 11 SE Front St, Milford, DE, 19963. Tel: 302-422-8996. Fax: 302-422-9269. p. 384

Hudson, M Janet, Dir, Ligonier Valley Library Association, Inc, 120 W Main St, Ligonier, PA, 15658-1243. Tel: 724-238-6451. Fax: 724-238-6989. p. 2081

Hudson, Marge, Head, Circ, Touro College, 225 Eastview Dr, Central Islip, NY, 11722-4539. Tel: 631-761-7158. Fax: 631-761-7159. p. 1605

Hudson, Marilyn A, Dir, Southwestern Christian University Library, C H Springer Bldg, 7210 NW 39th Expressway, Bethany, OK, 73008. Tel: 405-789-7661, Ext 3451. Fax: 405-495-0078. p. 1958

Hudson, Mark, Adult Serv, Monroeville Public Library, 4000 Gateway Campus Blvd, Monroeville, PA, 15146-3381. Tel: 412-372-0500, Ext 13. Fax: 412-372-1168. p. 2091

Hudson, Michelle, Ref Serv Mgr, Jackson/Hinds Library System, Eudora Welty Library (Main Library), 300 North State St, Jackson, MS, 39201-1705. Tel: 601-968-5803, Ext 5809. Fax: 601-968-5806. p. 1303

Hudson, Nancy, Acq, Tech Serv, Hinshaw & Culbertson Library, 222 N LaSalle, Ste 300, Chicago, IL, 60601-1081. Tel: 312-704-3000. Fax: 312-704-3951. p. 614

Hudson, Norma, Asst Librn, Alexander Hamilton Memorial Free Library, 13676 Monterey Lane, Blue Ridge Summit, PA, 17214. Tel: 717-794-2240. Fax: 717-794-5929. p. 2036

Hudson, Robert, Univ Librn, Boston University Libraries, Mugar Memorial Library, 771 Commonwealth Ave, Boston, MA, 02215. Tel: 617-353-3710. Fax: 617-353-2084. p. 1058

Hudson, Ruth, Ch, Chase Library, Seven Main St, West Harwich, MA, 02671-1041. Tel: 508-432-2610. p. 1137

Hudson, Sarah, Asst Dir, Davidson County Public Library System, Thomasville Public, 14 Randolph St, Thomasville, NC, 27360-4638. Tel: 336-474-2690. Fax: 336-472-4690. p. 1806

Hudson, Sarah H, Asst Dir, Davidson County Public Library System, 602 S Main St, Lexington, NC, 27292. Tel: 336-474-2696. Fax: 336-472-4690. p. 1806

Hudson, Sigrid, Ch, City of Commerce Public Library, 5655 Jillson St, Commerce, CA, 90040-1485. Tel: 323-722-6660, Ext 2829. Fax: 323-724-1978. p. 136

Hudson, Tracy, Circ Librn, Sullivan City Public Library, Two W Water St, Sullivan, IL, 61951. Tel: 217-728-7221. Fax: 217-728-2215. p. 708

Hudspeth, Guy, Libr Mgr, Alachua County Library District, Archer Branch, 13266 SW State Rd 45, Archer, FL, 32618-5524. Tel: 352-495-3367. Fax: 352-495-3061. p. 448

Hudziec, Linda, Vols Librn, Gilmanton Corner Public Library, 503 Province Rd, Gilmanton, NH, 03237-9205. Tel: 603-267-6200. p. 1448

Huebener, Becky, Librn, Brighton Memorial Library, 110 N Main, Brighton, IL, 62012. Tel: 618-372-8450. Fax: 618-372-7450. p. 597

Huebschen, Cynthia, Ref Librn, University of Wisconsin Oshkosh, 801 Elmwood Ave, Oshkosh, WI, 54901. Tel: 920-424-7327. Fax: 920-424-7338. p. 2628

Huebschman, Richard, Ref Librn, Moraine Park Technical College, 2151 N Main St, West Bend, WI, 53090-1598. Tel: 262-334-3413, Ext 5759. Fax: 262-335-5829. p. 2648

Huelsbeck, Julie, Asst Dir, Mohave County Library District, 3269 N Burbank St, Kingman, AZ, 86402-7000. Tel: 928-692-5711. p. 66

Huelsman, Betty, Librn, McLean-Mercer Regional Library, Turtle Lake Public Library, City Hall, Turtle Lake, ND, 58575. Tel: 701-448-9170. p. 1848

Huen, Janet, Asst Dir, Poughkeepsie Public Library District, 93 Market St, Poughkeepsie, NY, 12601. Tel: 845-485-3445, Ext 3308. Fax: 845-485-3789. p. 1723

Hueneke, Lisa, Info Assoc, Academy for Educational Development, 1825 Connecticut Ave NW, Washington, DC, 20009-5721. Tel: 202-884-8000, 202-884-8118. Fax: 202-884-8491. p. 391

Huenneke, Judith A, Sr Res Spec, The Mary Baker Eddy Library, Lending & Reference Services, 200 Massachusetts Ave, P02-10, Boston, MA, 02115-3017. Tel: 617-450-7111. p. 1060

Huerkamp, Diane, Dir, Mooresville Public Library, 220 W Harrison St, Mooresville, IN, 46158-1633. Tel: 317-831-7323. Fax: 317-831-7383. p. 766

Huerta, Deborah, Librn, Colgate University, George R Cooley Science Library, 13 Oak Dr, Hamilton, NY, 13346-1338. Tel: 315-228-7311. Fax: 315-228-7029. p. 1633

Huerta, Deborah, Sci, Colgate University, 13 Oak Dr, Hamilton, NY, 13346-1398. Tel: 315-228-7300. Fax: 315-228-7934. p. 1633

Huerta, Regan, Mrs, Archives Coordr, Pajaro Valley Historical Association, 332 E Beach St, Watsonville, CA, 95076. Tel: 831-722-0305. Fax: 831-722-5501. p. 282

Huesmann, James, Dean of Libr, University of Alaska Fairbanks, 310 Tanana Dr, Fairbanks, AK, 99775. Tel: 907-474-7224. Fax: 907-474-6841. p. 48

Huestis, Jeff, Assoc Univ Librn, Networked Info Res, Washington University Libraries, One Brookings Dr, Campus Box 1061, Saint Louis, MO, 63130-4862. Tel: 314-935-5951. Fax: 314-935-4045. p. 1362

Huestis, Laurie, Librn, RCMP Centennial Library, 264 24th St, Fort Macleod, AB, T0L 0Z0, CANADA. Tel: 403-553-3880. p. 2704

Huetig, Maggie, Dir, Laurel Community Learning Center, 502 Wakefield St, Laurel, NE, 68745-0248. Tel: 402-256-3431. Fax: 402-256-9465. p. 1403

Huey, Nola, Children's & Youth Serv, Great Falls Public Library, 301 Second Ave N, Great Falls, MT, 59401-2593. Tel: 406-453-0349, Ext 215. Fax: 406-453-0181. p. 1380

Huff, Alice, Syst Adminr, Gettysburg College, 300 N Washington St, Gettysburg, PA, 17325. Tel: 717-337-7020. Fax: 717-337-7001. p. 2059

Huff, Amy, Dir, Dadeville Public Library, 205 N West St, Dadeville, AL, 36853. Tel: 256-825-7820. Fax: 256-825-7820. p. 14

Huff, Brenda, Dir, Corbin Public Library, 305 Roy Kidd Ave, Corbin, KY, 40701. Tel: 606-528-6366. Fax: 606-523-1895. p. 910

Huff, Chris, Assoc Dir, Univ Libr, Irvine Sullivan Ingram Library, University of West Georgia, 1601 Maple St, Carrollton, GA, 30118. Tel: 678-839-6498. Fax: 678-839-6511. p. 523

Huff, Dee, Ch, Hollis & Helen Baright Public Library, 5555 S 77th St, Ralston, NE, 68127-2899. Tel: 402-331-7636. Fax: 402-331-1168. p. 1417

Huff, Diana, Dir, Bronson Public Library, 509 Clay St, Bronson, KS, 66716. Tel: 620-939-4910. Fax: 620-939-4569. p. 858

Huff, Elizabeth, Asst Dir, Storm Lake Public Library, 609 Cayuga St, Storm Lake, IA, 50588. Tel: 712-732-8026. Fax: 712-732-7609. p. 846

Huff, Evelyn, Librn, Roberts County Library, 300 W Commercial St, Miami, TX, 79059. Tel: 806-868-4791. p. 2363

Huff, Heidi, Coordr, Instrul Serv, Indiana University East Campus Library, 2325 Chester Blvd, Richmond, IN, 47374. Tel: 765-973-8434. Fax: 765-973-8315. p. 775

Huff, Jackie, Br Mgr, Mercer County Library System, Ewing Branch, 61 Scotch Rd, Ewing, NJ, 08628. Tel: 609-882-3130. Fax: 609-538-0212. p. 1494

Huff, James, Instruction Librn, Goucher College Library, 1021 Dulaney Valley Rd, Baltimore, MD, 21204. Tel: 410-337-6340. Fax: 410-337-6419. p. 1014

Huff, Joanne, Tech Asst, Western Oklahoma State College, 2801 N Main St, Altus, OK, 73521. Tel: 580-477-7948. Fax: 580-477-7777. p. 1956

Huff, Mary, Librn, American Watchmakers-Clockmakers Institute Library, 701 Enterprise Dr, Harrison, OH, 45030-1696. Tel: 513-367-9800. Fax: 513-367-1414. p. 1904

Huff, Michael, Coll & Merchandising Dir, Mid-Columbia Libraries, 405 S Dayton, Kennewick, WA, 99336. Tel: 509-582-4745. Fax: 509-737-6349. p. 2518

Huff, Pamela, Pub Serv, Troup-Harris Regional Library System, 115 Alford St, La Grange, GA, 30240-3041. Tel: 706-882-7784, Ext 32. Fax: 706-883-7342. p. 537

Huff, Sue, Br Librn, Community District Library, Corunna/Caledonia Township Branch, 210 E Corunna Ave, Corunna, MI, 48817. Tel: 989-743-4800. Fax: 989-743-5502. p. 1166

Huff, Theresa, Asst Mgr, Dallas Public Library, 1515 Young St, Dallas, TX, 75201-5499. Tel: 214-670-1400. Fax: 214-670-7839. p. 2306

Huff-Eibl, Robyn, Head, Circ, University of Arizona, 1510 E University Blvd, Tucson, AZ, 85721. Tel: 520-621-6441. p. 88

Huffines, Beth, Dir, Librn, Roodhouse Public Library, 220 W Franklin St, Roodhouse, IL, 62082-1412. Tel: 217-589-5123. p. 698

Huffman, Anne, Head, Instrul Serv, Head, Pub Serv, University of Kansas Medical Center, 2100 W 39th Ave, Kansas City, KS, 66160-7180. Tel: 913-588-7322. Fax: 913-588-7304. p. 876

Huffman, Ben, Dir, Barryton Public Library, 198 Northern Ave, Barryton, MI, 49305. Tel: 989-382-5288. Fax: 989-382-9073. p. 1155

Huffman, Brian R, County Law Librn, Washington County Library, Washington County Law Library, Washington County Courthouse, 14949 62nd St N, Rm 1005, Stillwater, MN, 55082. Tel: 651-430-6954. Fax: 651-430-6331. p. 1290

Huffman, Isaac, Libr Mgr, Providence Saint Peter Hospital, 413 Lilly Rd NE, Olympia, WA, 98506. Tel: 360-493-7222. Fax: 360-493-5696. p. 2522

Huffman, Katie, Adult Serv, Head, Ref, Wilmington Memorial Library, 175 Middlesex Ave, Wilmington, MA, 01887-2779. Tel: 978-658-2967. Fax: 978-658-9699. p. 1141

Huffman, Margie, Dir, Auburn Public Library, 749 E Thach Ave, Auburn, AL, 36830. Tel: 334-501-3190. p. 5

Huffman, Melissa, Instrul Serv Librn, Rose State College, 6420 SE 15th St, Midwest City, OK, 73110. Tel: 405-733-7538. Fax: 405-736-0260. p. 1968

Huffman, Paul, Archivist, Lindenwood University, 209 S Kingshighway, Saint Charles, MO, 63301. Tel: 636-949-4823. Fax: 636-949-4822. p. 1351

Huffman, Selina, Ch, Wayne County Public Library, 1200 Oak St, Kenova, WV, 25530-1335. Tel: 304-453-2462. Fax: 304-453-2462. p. 2563

Huffman, Stephanie, Dr, Coordr, University of Central Arkansas, College of Education, PO Box 4918, Conway, AR, 72032-5001. Tel: 501-450-5430. Fax: 501-450-5680. p. 2962

Huffman, Susan, Ch, Massanutten Regional Library, 174 S Main St, Harrisonburg, VA, 22801. Tel: 540-434-4475. Fax: 540-434-4382. p. 2470

Huffstetter, John, Ref Librn, Oak Creek Public Library, 8620 S Howell Ave, Oak Creek, WI, 53154. Tel: 414-764-4400. Fax: 414-768-6583. p. 2626

Huftalen, Alison L, Head Librn, Toledo Museum of Art, 2445 Monroe St, Toledo, OH, 43620. Tel: 419-255-8000. Fax: 419-255-5638. p. 1940

Hug, Rita, Head, Tech Serv, University of Colorado at Colorado Springs, 1420 Austin Bluffs Pkwy, Colorado Springs, CO, 80918. Tel: 719-255-3291. Fax: 719-528-5227. p. 296

Hugar, Carol, Dir, Womelsdorf Community Library, 203 W High St, Womelsdorf, PA, 19567-1307. Tel: 610-589-1424. Fax: 610-589-5022. p. 2157

Huget, Trudy, Adminr, Alberta Committee of Citizens with Disabilities Library, 106-10423 178 St NW, Edmonton, AB, T5S 1R5, CANADA. Tel: 780-488-9088. Fax: 780-488-3757. p. 2697

Huggard, Kara, Electronic Res, Logan Library, 255 N Main, Logan, UT, 84321-3914. Tel: 435-716-9123. Fax: 435-716-9145. p. 2407

Huggins, Annelle R, Assoc Dean, University Libraries, University of Memphis, 126 Ned R McWherter Library, Memphis, TN, 38152-3250. Tel: 901-678-4482. p. 2252

Huggins, Heather, Ref Serv, YA, Middletown Public Library, 700 W Main Rd, Middletown, RI, 02842-6391. Tel: 401-846-1573. Fax: 401-846-3031. p. 2168

Huggins, Marvin A, Archivist, Concordia Historical Institute Library, 804 Seminary Pl, Saint Louis, MO, 63105-3014. Tel: 314-505-7900. Fax: 314-505-7901. p. 1353

Huggins, Melanie, Exec Dir, Richland County Public Library, 1431 Assembly St, Columbia, SC, 29201-3101. Tel: 803-799-9084. Fax: 803-929-3448. p. 2188

Huggins, Rebecca, Dir, Fairfield Public Library, 104 W Adams, Fairfield, IA, 52556. Tel: 641-472-6551. Fax: 641-472-3249. p. 815

Hugh, Dawn, Ref, Historical Association of Southern Florida, 101 W Flagler St, Miami, FL, 33130. Tel: 305-375-1492. Fax: 305-372-6313. p. 465

Hugh, Howard, Chief Librn, United States Department of State, 2201 C St NW, Rm 3239, Washington, DC, 20520-2442. Tel: 202-647-1099. Fax: 202-647-2971. p. 419

Hughbanks, Julie, Mgr, Parkview Hospital, 2200 Randallia Dr, Fort Wayne, IN, 46805. Tel: 260-373-3690. Fax: 260-373-3692. p. 742

Hughbanks, Kelly, Youth Serv Coordr, Milwaukee Public Library, 814 W Wisconsin Ave, Milwaukee, WI, 53233-2385. Tel: 414-286-3000. Fax: 414-286-2794. p. 2620

Hughes, Amy, Circuit Librn, Community Health Network Library, 1500 N Ritter Ave, Indianapolis, IN, 46219. Tel: 317-621-5811. Fax: 317-351-7816. p. 750

Hughes, Ann C, Dir, Brewton-Parker College, 201 David-Eliza Fountain Circle, Mount Vernon, GA, 30445. Tel: 912-583-3230. Fax: 912-583-3454. p. 546

Hughes, Anne, Dir, Glen Carbon Centennial Library, 198 S Main St, Glen Carbon, IL, 62034. Tel: 618-288-1212. Fax: 618-288-1205. p. 649

Hughes, Annie, Info Serv Librn, University of Southern California Libraries, Jennifer Ann Wilson Dental Library & Learning Center, 925 W 34th St, DEN 21, University Park - MC 0641, Los Angeles, CA, 90089-0641. Tel: 213-740-6476. Fax: 213-748-8565. p. 179

Hughes, Brian, Dr, Assoc Dir, Head, Media Design Ctr, Teachers College, Columbia University, 525 W 120th St, New York, NY, 10027-6696. Tel: 212-678-3069. p. 1701

Hughes, Carol Ann, Assoc Univ Librn, Pub Serv, University of California Library, PO Box 19557, Irvine, CA, 92623-9557. Tel: 949-824-9753. p. 160

Hughes, Carole, Librn, Saint John West Shore Hospital, 29000 Center Ridge Rd, Westlake, OH, 44145. Tel: 440-827-5569. Fax: 440-827-5573. p. 1947

Hughes, Carolyn C, Head, Ser, University of Southern Maine, 314 Forest Ave, Portland, ME, 04104. Tel: 207-780-4671. Fax: 207-780-4042. p. 998

Hughes, Charles, Coordr, Tech Serv, University of Louisiana at Monroe Library, 700 University Ave, Monroe, LA, 71209-0720. Tel: 318-342-3051. Fax: 318-342-1075. p. 958

Hughes, Cheryl, Br Mgr, Anderson County Library, Jennie Erwin Branch, 318 Shirley Ave, Honea Path, SC, 29654. Tel: 864-369-7751. Fax: 864-369-7751. p. 2180

Hughes, Cynthia D, Cat, Mount Olive College, 634 Henderson St, Mount Olive, NC, 28365-1699. Tel: 919-658-7869, Ext 1414. Fax: 919-658-8934. p. 1811

Hughes, Diane, Librn, Morrisville Free Library Association, 300 N Pennsylvania Ave, Morrisville, PA, 19067-6621. Tel: 215-295-4850. Fax: 215-295-4851. p. 2093

Hughes, Donald A, Jr, Dir, Capital University, Law School Library, 303 E Broad St, Columbus, OH, 43215. Tel: 614-236-6464. Fax: 614-236-6957. p. 1883

Hughes, Ed, Dir, Rhinelander District Library, 106 N Stevens St, Rhinelander, WI, 54501-3193. Tel: 715-365-1070. Fax: 715-365-1076. p. 2633

Hughes, Elaine, Coll Mgr, Museum of Northern Arizona-Harold S Colton Memorial Library, 3101 N Fort Valley Rd, Flagstaff, AZ, 86001. Tel: 928-774-5211, Ext 228. Fax: 928-779-1527. p. 62

Hughes, Elaine, Librn, Broadlawns Medical Center, 1801 Hickman Rd, Des Moines, IA, 50314. Tel: 515-282-2394. Fax: 515-282-5634. p. 808

Hughes, Elaine, Treas, Polk County Biomedical Consortium, c/o Broadlawns Medical Center Library, 1801 Hickman Rd, Des Moines, IA, 50314. Tel: 515-282 2394. Fax: 515-282 5634. p. 2943

Hughes, Elizabeth, Tech Serv, Lyndhurst Free Public Library, 355 Valley Brook Ave, Lyndhurst, NJ, 07071. Tel: 201-804-2478. Fax: 201-939-7677. p. 1497

Hughes, Erdene, Librn, Logan County Public Library, Auburn Branch, 433 W Main St, Auburn, KY, 42206. Tel: 270-542-8180. Fax: 270-542-8180. p. 934

Hughes, Gary, Dir, Hartnell College, 411 Central Ave, Salinas, CA, 93901. Tel: 831-755-6700. Fax: 831-759-6084. p. 2962

Hughes, Glenda, Pub Serv, Tech Serv, University of Charleston, 2300 MacCorkle Ave SE, Charleston, WV, 25304-1099. Tel: 304-357-4917. Fax: 304-357-4715. p. 2556

Hughes, Jane, Automation & Tech Serv Mgr, Kanawha County Public Library, 123 Capitol St, Charleston, WV, 25301. Tel: 304-343-4646. Fax: 304-348-6530. p. 2556

Hughes, Janet, Librn, Pennsylvania State University Libraries, Life Sciences, 401 Paterno Library, University Park, PA, 16802-1811. Tel: 814-865-3705. p. 2148

Hughes, Jean, Ref Librn, Atlanta-Fulton Public Library System, Northeast-Spruill Oaks Regional Library, 9560 Spruill Rd, Alpharetta, GA, 30022. Tel: 770-360-8820. Fax: 770-360-8823. p. 512

Hughes, Jeanine, Libr Asst II, Montgomery City-County Public Library System, Pike Road Branch Library, 9585 Vaughn Rd, Pike Road, AL, 36064. Tel: 334-244-8679. Fax: 334-240-4887. p. 30

Hughes, Jennifer, Access Serv Librn, Coastal Carolina University, 755 Hwy 544, Conway, SC, 29526. Tel: 843-349-2415. Fax: 843-349-2412. p. 2191

Hughes, John, Dir of Libr, Psychological Studies Institute, 2055 Mount Paran Rd NW, Atlanta, GA, 30327. Tel: 404-233-3949, Ext 110. Fax: 404-239-9460. p. 518

Hughes, Julie, Exec Dir, Bartholomew County Historical Society, 524 Third St, Columbus, IN, 47201. Tel: 812-372-3541. Fax: 812-372-3113. p. 733

Hughes, Julie, Dir, Coplay Public Library, 49 S Fifth, Coplay, PA, 18037-1398. Tel: 610-262-7351. Fax: 610-262-4937. p. 2047

Hughes, Kathleen, Head, Cat, Metadata & Archival Serv, Montclair State University, One Normal Ave, Montclair, NJ, 07043-1699. Tel: 973-655-7077. Fax: 973-655-7780. p. 1503

Hughes, Kelly, Br Supvr, Flint River Regional Library, Barnesville-Lamar County Library, 401 Thomaston St, Barnesville, GA, 30204. Tel: 770-358-3270. p. 535

Hughes, Kristen, Librn, Bent Northrop Memorial Library, 164 Park St, Fairfield, VT, 05455. Tel: 802-827-3945. Fax: 802-827-3604. p. 2424

Hughes, Kristin, Cat, California Lutheran University, 60 W Olsen Rd, Thousand Oaks, CA, 91360-2787. Tel: 805-493-3250. Fax: 805-493-3842. p. 274

Hughes, Leslie, Librn, East Central Community College, 275 E Broad St, Decatur, MS, 39327. Tel: 601-635-2111, Ext 219, 601-635-2111, Ext 220, 601-635-6219. Fax: 601-635-2150. p. 1298

Hughes, Lindsey, Tech Serv, Youth Serv Librn, Marstons Mills Public Library, 2160 Main St, Marstons Mills, MA, 02648. Tel: 508-428-5175. Fax: 508-420-5194. p. 1103

Hughes, Lisa, Mgr, Baltimore County Public Library, Towson Branch, 320 York Rd, Towson, MD, 21204-5179. Tel: 410-887-6166. Fax: 410-887-3170. p. 1044

Hughes, Lori, Circ, University of Wisconsin-Superior, PO Box 2000, Belknap & Catlin, Superior, WI, 54880-2000. Tel: 715-394-8343. Fax: 715-394-8462. p. 2641

Hughes, Marcy, Libr Assoc, Lima Public Library, Lafayette Branch, 225 E Sugar St, Lafayette, OH, 45854. Tel: 419-649-6482. Fax: 419-649-9488. p. 1910

Hughes, Marianne, Curator, Henry County Historical Society, 606 S 14th St, New Castle, IN, 47362. Tel: 765-529-4028. p. 768

Hughes, Marilyn, Librn, Wallowa County Library, Troy Library Station, 66247 Redmond Grade, Enterprise, OR, 97828. Tel: 541-828-7788. Fax: 541-828-7748. p. 1996

Hughes, Mary, Librn, Dickson Mounds Museum Library, 10956 N Dickson Mounds Rd, Lewistown, IL, 61542. Tel: 309-547-3721. Fax: 309-547-3189. p. 665

Hughes, Marylou, ILL, Free Library of Springfield Township, 1600 Paper Mill Rd, Wyndmoor, PA, 19038. Tel: 215-836-5300. Fax: 215-836-2404. p. 2158

Hughes, Meg, Dir, Archives & Photographic Serv, Valentine Richmond History Center, 1015 E Clay St, Richmond, VA, 23219-1590. Tel: 804-649-0711. Fax: 804-643-3510. p. 2491

Hughes, Melanie, Coordr, Automation & Tech Serv, Indiana University Southeast Library, 4201 Grant Line Rd, New Albany, IN, 47150. Tel: 812-941-2262. Fax: 812-941-2656. p. 767

Hughes, Melissa, Dir, Midland Park Memorial Library, 250 Godwin Ave, Midland Park, NJ, 07432. Tel: 201-444-2390. Fax: 201-444-2813. p. 1502

Hughes, Michelle, Head, Adult Serv, Dover Public Library, 45 S State St, Dover, DE, 19901. Tel: 302-736-7030. Fax: 302-736-5087. p. 382

Hughes, Michelle, Circ Supvr, Washington County Library System, 88 West 100 South, Saint George, UT, 84770-3490. Tel: 435-634-5737. Fax: 435-634-5741. p. 2412

Hughes, Nancy, Br Coordr, Kern County Library, 701 Truxtun Ave, Bakersfield, CA, 93301-4816. Tel: 661-868-0700. Fax: 661-868-0799. p. 124

Hughes, Nancy B, Br Mgr, Albemarle Regional Library, Lawrence Memorial Public Library, 204 E Dundee St, Windsor, NC, 27983. Tel: 252-794-2244. Fax: 252-794-1546. p. 1835

Hughes, Nicole, Commun Relations & Mkt Mgr, Palm Beach County Library System, 3650 Summit Blvd, West Palm Beach, FL, 33406-4198. Tel: 561-233-2768. Fax: 561-233-2692. p. 503

Hughes, Patti, Librn, Lyme Free Library, 12165 Main St, Chaumont, NY, 13622-9603. Tel: 315-649-5454. Fax: 315-649-2911. p. 1605

Hughes, Patty, Librn, Nebraska Department of Corrections, 2725 N Hwy 50, Tecumseh, NE, 68450. Tel: 402-335-5998. Fax: 402-335-5115. p. 1421

Hughes, Ruth, Chief Cataloger, Syst Librn, Library Company of Philadelphia, 1314 Locust St, Philadelphia, PA, 19107-5698. Tel: 215-546-3181. Fax: 215-546-5167. p. 2112

Hughes, Sandra, Supvr, Circ, Tigard Public Library, 13500 SW Hall Blvd, Tigard, OR, 97223-8111. Tel: 503-684-6537, Ext 2515. Fax: 503-598-7515, 503-718-2797. p. 2021

Hughes, Sandra Hammond, Libr Dir, Charleston Southern University, 9200 University Blvd, Charleston, SC, 29406. Tel: 843-863-7933. Fax: 843-863-7947. p. 2183

Hughes, Scott, City Librn, Bridgeport Public Library, 925 Broad St, Bridgeport, CT, 06604. Tel: 203-576-7403. Fax: 203-576-8255. p. 331

Hughes, Sharon, Ser, San Juan College Library, 4601 College Blvd, Farmington, NM, 87402. Tel: 505-566-3691. Fax: 505-566-3381. p. 1555

Hughes, Susan, Acq, Purchasing, North Georgia College & State University, 238 Georgia Circle, Dahlonega, GA, 30597-3001. Tel: 706-864-1524. p. 527

Hughes, Tracey, Librn, Colorado Mountain College, 1330 Bob Adams Dr, Steamboat Springs, CO, 80487. Tel: 970-870-4451. Fax: 970-870-4490. p. 322

Hughes, Trella, Librn, McGinley Memorial Public Library, 317 S Main St, McGregor, TX, 76657. Tel: 254-840-3732. Fax: 254-840-2624. p. 2361

Hughes, Virginia, Librn, Miller & Martin PLLC, Volunteer Bldg, Ste 1000, 832 Georgia Ave, Chattanooga, TN, 37402-2289. Tel: 423-756-6600. Fax: 423-785-8480. p. 2227

Hughes, Woodson, Br Mgr, Halifax County-South Boston Regional Library, South Boston Public Library, 509 Broad St, South Boston, VA, 24592. Tel: 434-575-4228. Fax: 434-575-4229. p. 2467

Hughes-Oldenburg, Donna, Head, Bibliog Instr, Old Dominion University Libraries, 4427 Hampton Blvd, Norfolk, VA, 23529-0256. Tel: 757-683-4153. Fax: 757-683-5767. p. 2482

Hughey, Susan, Ch, Somerset Public Library, 1464 County St, Somerset, MA, 02726. Tel: 508-646-2829. Fax: 508-646-2831. p. 1124

Hughsam, Larry, Dir of Finance, Toronto Public Library, 789 Yonge St, Toronto, ON, M4W 2G8, CANADA. Tel: 416-393-7131. Fax: 416-393-7229. p. 2860

Hughson, Patty, ILL, Regent University Library, 1000 Regent University Dr, Virginia Beach, VA, 23464. Tel: 757-352-4185. Fax: 757-352-4167. p. 2499

Hughston, Milan R, Chief Librn, Museum of Modern Art Library, 11 W 53rd St, New York, NY, 10019-5498. Tel: 212-708-9409. Fax: 212-333-1122. p. 1687

Hugie, Todd, Info Tech, Utah State University, 3000 Old Main Hill, Logan, UT, 84322-3000. Tel: 435-797-2638. Fax: 435-797-2880. p. 2407

Hugley, Lori, Br Mgr, Kokomo-Howard County Public Library, South Branch, 1755 E Center Rd, Kokomo, IN, 46902-5322. Tel: 765-453-4150. Fax: 765-453-6677. p. 758

Hugo, Marianne, Mgr, Libr Serv, Anaheim Public Library, Canyon Hills, 400 Scout Trail, Anaheim, CA, 92807-4763. Tel: 714-974-7630. p. 120

Hugo, Terri, Coll Develop Librn, McLennan Community College Library, 1400 College Dr, Waco, TX, 76708-1498. Tel: 254-299-8389. Fax: 254-299-8026. p. 2397

Hugus, Susan, Br Head, Jones Library, Inc, 43 Amity St, Amherst, MA, 01002-2285. Tel: 413-259-3095. Fax: 413-256-4096. p. 1048

Hugus, Susan, Br Head, Jones Library, Inc, Munson Memorial, 1046 S East St, South Amherst, MA, 01002. Tel: 413-259-3095. p. 1049

Hui, Cecilia, Syst Librn, De Anza College, 21250 Stevens Creek Blvd, Cupertino, CA, 95014-5793. Tel: 408-864-8383. Fax: 408-864-8603. p. 138

Hui, Frances, Ref Serv, Las Positas College Library, 3000 Campus Hill Dr, Livermore, CA, 94551-7623. Tel: 925-424-1150. Fax: 925-606-7249. p. 164

Hui, Katherina, Librn, City of Edmonton, Sustainable Development Library, HSBC, 5th Flr, 10250 101 St, Edmonton, AB, T5J 3P4, CANADA. Tel: 780-496-6165. Fax: 780-496-6054. p. 2700

Hui, Mimi, Dir, Free Public Library of Hasbrouck Heights, 320 Boulevard, Hasbrouck Heights, NJ, 07604. Tel: 201-288-0484, 201-288-0488. Fax: 201-288-5467. p. 1490

Hui, Shun-Ken, Br Mgr, Chicago Public Library, Rogers Park, 6907 N Clark St, Chicago, IL, 60626. Tel: 312-744-0156. Fax: 312-744-7591. p. 609

Hui, Stella, Librn, Autism Society of British Columbia Library, 3701 E Hastings, Ste 303, Burnaby, BC, V5C 2H6, CANADA. Tel: 604-434-0880. Fax: 604-434-0801. p. 2725

Hui, Timothy K, Dir, Cairn University, 200 Manor Ave, Langhorne, PA, 19047. Tel: 215-702-4370. Fax: 215-702-4374. p. 2078

Huie, Teresa, ILL, Ref, Sr Info Res Spec, Federal Reserve Bank of Boston, 600 Atlantic Ave, Boston, MA, 02210-2204. Tel: 617-973-3397. Fax: 617-973-4221. p. 1061

Huiner, Leslie, Librn, Victor Valley Community College Library, 18422 Bear Valley Rd, Victorville, CA, 92395-5850. Tel: 760-245-4271, Ext 2262. Fax: 760-245-4373. p. 280

Huisken, Darrel, Librn, Theological School of Protestant Reformed Churches Library, 4949 Ivanrest Ave SW, Grandville, MI, 49418-9709. Tel: 616-531-1490. Fax: 616-531-3033. p. 1186

Huisman, Melissa Ann, Dir, Gary Byker Memorial Library, 3338 Van Buren St, Hudsonville, MI, 49426. Tel: 616-669-7172, Ext 5. Fax: 616-669-5150. p. 1192

Huisman, Nancy, Dir, Aplington Legion Memorial Library, 929 Parrot St, Aplington, IA, 50604. Tel: 319-347-2432. Fax: 319-347-2432. p. 794

Huisman, Rhonda, ILL, Northwest Iowa Community College Library, 603 W Park St, Sheldon, IA, 51201. Tel: 712-324-5061. Fax: 712-324-4157. p. 842

Hujsak, Mary, Assessment Librn, Ref Librn, Oklahoma State University - Tulsa Library, 700 N Greenwood Ave, Tulsa, OK, 74106-0700. Tel: 918-594-8453. Fax: 918-594-8145. p. 1981

Hukill, Debra, Br Mgr, Hutchinson County Library, Stinnett Branch, 500 S Main St, Stinnett, TX, 79083. Tel: 806-878-4013. Fax: 806-878-4014. p. 2290

Hukill, Kim, Librn, American Institute of Physics, One Physics Ellipse, College Park, MD, 20740-3843. Tel: 301-209-3177. Fax: 301-209-3144. p. 1024

Hulbert, Linda A, Assoc Dir, Tech Serv, University of Saint Thomas, 2115 Summit Ave, Mail Box 5004, Saint Paul, MN, 55105. Tel: 651-962-5016. Fax: 651-962-5406. p. 1282

Hulbert, Steven W, Librn, Claremont School of Theology Library, Center for Process Studies, 1325 N College Ave, Claremont, CA, 91711-3154. Tel: 909-447-2533, 909-621-5330. Fax: 909-621-2760. p. 135

Hulett, Elizabeth, Head, Adult Serv, Washington County Free Library, 100 S Potomac St, Hagerstown, MD, 21740. Tel: 301-739-3250. Fax: 301-739-7603. p. 1031

Hulgus, Caryl, Br Mgr, Ohio Township Public Library System, Newburgh Library, 30 W Water St, Newburgh, IN, 47630. Tel: 812-858-1437. Fax: 812-858-9390. p. 768

Huling, Nancy, Head, Ref & Res Serv, University of Washington Libraries, Allen Library, 4th Flr, Rm 482, Box 352900, Seattle, WA, 98195-2900. Tel: 206-685-2211. Fax: 206-685-8727. p. 2533

Hull, Andrea, Cat, Pacifica Foundation, 3729 Cahuenga Blvd W, North Hollywood, CA, 91604. Tel: 818-506-1077, Ext 265. Fax: 818-506-1084. p. 194

Hull, Betsy, Head Librn, Capital Area District Libraries, Hope Borbas Okemos Library, 4321 Okemos Rd, Okemos, MI, 48864. Tel: 517-347-2021. Fax: 517-347-2034. p. 1200

Hull, Caitlin, Adult Serv, Cresskill Public Library, 53 Union Ave, Cresskill, NJ, 07626. Tel: 201-567-3521. Fax: 201-567-5067. p. 1480

Hull, Carol, Br Mgr, Defiance Public Library, Sherwood Branch, 117 Harrison St, Sherwood, OH, 43556. Tel: 419-899-4343. Fax: 419-899-4343. p. 1895

Hull, Carol, Dir, Schuylkill Haven Free Public Library, 104 Saint John St, Schuylkill Haven, PA, 17972-1614. Tel: 570-385-0542. Fax: 570-385-2523. p. 2136

Hull, Deborah, Univ Librn, Pacific States University Library, 3450 Wilshire Blvd, Ste 500, Los Angeles, CA, 90010. Tel: 323-731-2383. Fax: 323-731-7276. p. 176

Hull, Denise, Dir, Hope Community Library, 216 N Main St, Hope, KS, 67451. Tel: 785-366-7219. p. 872

Hull, Diane, Circ Mgr, Summit Free Public Library, 75 Maple St, Summit, NJ, 07901-9984. Tel: 908-273-0350. Fax: 908-273-0031. p. 1532

Hull, Douglas, Ref Librn, Miller Nash LLP Library, 111 SW Fifth Ave, 3400 US Bancorp Tower, Portland, OR, 97204-3699. Tel: 503-224-5858. Fax: 503-224-0155. p. 2011

Hull, Jane, Librn, Mississippi State Hospital, Medical Library, Whitfield Rd, Whitfield, MS, 39193. Tel: 601-351-8000, Ext 4278. p. 1318

Hull, Jane, Librn, Mississippi State Hospital, Patient Library, Whitfield Rd, Whitfield, MS, 39193. Tel: 601-351-8000, Ext 4278. p. 1318

Hull, Jennifer, Commun Librn, Fort Vancouver Regional Library District, White Salmon Valley Community Library, 77 NE Wauna Ave, White Salmon, WA, 98672. Tel: 509-493-1132. Fax: 509-493-2943. p. 2546

Hull, Nina, Commun Libr Mgr, County of Los Angeles Public Library, Agoura Hills Library, 29901 Ladyface Ct, Agoura Hills, CA, 91301. Tel: 818-889-2278. Fax: 818-991-5019. p. 140

Hull, Pat, ILL, Pub Serv Spec, Gaston College, 201 Hwy 321 S, Dallas, NC, 28034-1499. Tel: 704-922-6359. Fax: 704-922-2342. p. 1786

Hull, Robert, Dir, North Branford Library Department, Edward Smith Branch, Three Old Post Rd, Northford, CT, 06472. Tel: 203-484-0469. Fax: 203-484-6024. p. 361

Hull, Robert V, Dir, North Branford Library Department, 1720 Foxon Rd, North Branford, CT, 06471. Tel: 203-315-6020. Fax: 203-315-6021. p. 361

Hull, Sara, Info Res Coordr, Empire State College (Online Library), Three Union Ave, Saratoga Springs, NY, 12866. Tel: 518-587-2100. Fax: 518-581-9526. p. 1738

Hull, Sarah, Librn, Washington County Free Library, Keedysville Branch, Taylor Park, Keedysville, MD, 21756. Tel: 301-432-5795. p. 1031

Hull, Sarah, Archivist/Head of Local Hist, Plainfield Public Library, 800 Park Ave, Plainfield, NJ, 07060-2594. Tel: 908-757-1111, Ext 136. Fax: 908-754-0063. p. 1521

Hull, Sharon, Head, Spec Coll, Tennessee State University, 3500 John A Merritt Blvd, Nashville, TN, 37209. Tel: 615-963-5219. Fax: 615-963-5216. p. 2259

Hull, Tracy, Assoc Dean, Texas Christian University, 2913 Lowden St, TCU Box 298400, Fort Worth, TX, 76129. Tel: 817-257-7106. Fax: 817-257-7282. p. 2323

Hull, Trish, Mgr, Salt Lake County Library Services, Magna Branch, 8339 W 3500 South, Magna, UT, 84044-1870. Tel: 801-944-7657. Fax: 801-250-6927. p. 2414

Hull, Vernelle, Br Mgr, Mexico-Audrain County Library District, Farber Branch, 113 W Front St, Farber, MO, 63345. Tel: 573-249-2761. Fax: 573-249-2012. p. 1345

Hull, Vicky, Head, Adult Serv, Paulding County Carnegie Library, 205 S Main St, Paulding, OH, 45879-1492. Tel: 419-399-2032. Fax: 419-399-2114. p. 1928

Hull, Yvonne, Br Head, East Baton Rouge Parish Library, Jones Creek Regional, 6222 Jones Creek Rd, Baton Rouge, LA, 70817. Tel: 225-756-1180. Fax: 225-756-1153. p. 943

Hullberg, Helen, Asst Dir, Menomonie Public Library, 600 Wolske Bay Rd, Menomonie, WI, 54751. Tel: 715-232-2164. Fax: 715-232-2324. p. 2614

Hullinger, Jane, Asst Libr Dir, Humeston Public Library, 302 Broad St, Humeston, IA, 50123. Tel: 641-877-4811. p. 821

Hulme, Dale, In Charge, Saint Olaf Lutheran Church, 2901 Emerson Ave N, Minneapolis, MN, 55411. Tel: 612-529-7726. Fax: 612-529-4385. p. 1261

Huls, Sheila, Asst Librn, Bern Community Library, 401 Main St, Bern, KS, 66408. Tel: 785-336-3000. Fax: 785-336-3000. p. 858

Hulse, Bruce, Dir, Info Serv, Washington Research Library Consortium, 901 Commerce Dr, Upper Marlboro, MD, 20774. Tel: 301-390-2000. Fax: 301-390-2020. p. 2945

Hulse, Jacqueline, Asst Librn, Andrews Public Library, 871 Main St, Andrews, NC, 28901. Tel: 828-321-5956. Fax: 828-321-3256. p. 1773

Hulse, Michelle, Dir, Fredonia Public Library, 807 Jefferson, Fredonia, KS, 66736. Tel: 620-378-2863. Fax: 620-378-2645. p. 868

Hulseberg, Anna, Electronic Res Librn, Gustavus Adolphus College, 800 W College Ave, Saint Peter, MN, 56082. Tel: 507-933-7566. Fax: 507-933-6292. p. 1283

Hulsebus, Sage, Res, Pew Charitable Trusts Library, 901 E St NW, Washington, DC, 20004. Tel: 202-540-6374. p. 413

Hulsebus, Sage, Sr Librn, Freedom Forum World Center Library, 9893 Brewers Ct, Laurel, MD, 20723. Tel: 301-957-3215. Fax: 301-957-3281. p. 1034

Hulsey, Rick, Dir, Willard Library, Seven W Van Buren St, Battle Creek, MI, 49017-3009. Tel: 269-968-8166. Fax: 269-968-3284. p. 1155

Hulsey, Rick, Dir, Southwest Michigan Library Cooperative, 305 Oak St, Paw Paw, MI, 49079-1364. Tel: 269-968-8166. Fax: 269-657-4494. p. 2946

Hulslander, Nancy, Asst Librn, Ch, Neponset Public Library, 201 W Commercial St, Neponset, IL, 61345. Tel: 309-594-2204. Fax: 309-594-2204. p. 679

Hulst, Carolyn, Bus Mgr, Herrick District Library, 300 S River Ave, Holland, MI, 49423-3290. Tel: 616-355-3100. p. 1190

Hulston, Nancy, Archivist, Kansas University Medical Center, 1020-1030 Robinson Bldg, 3901 Rainbow Blvd, Kansas City, KS, 66160-7311. Tel: 913-588-7243. Fax: 913-588-7060. p. 875

Hultberg, Jane, Dir, College of the Atlantic, 109 Eden St, Bar Harbor, ME, 04609-1198. Tel: 207-288-5015, Ext 210. Fax: 207-288-2328. p. 976

Hultine, Mary, Circ Mgr, Oregon Health & Science University Library, 3181 SW Sam Jackson Park Rd, Portland, OR, 97239-3098. Tel: 503-494-3460. Fax: 503-494-3227. p. 2013

Hulting, Fred, Dir, Knowledge Discovery Serv, General Mills, Inc, James Ford Bell Library & Information Services, 9000 Plymouth Ave N, Minneapolis, MN, 55427. Tel: 763-764-6460. Fax: 763-764-3166. p. 1260

Hultman, Cindy, Adult Serv, Minocqua Public Library, 415 Menominee St, Minocqua, WI, 54548. Tel: 715-356-4437. Fax: 715-358-2873. p. 2622

Hultquist, Sharon Shurtz, Dir, Ivy Tech Community College of Indiana, Northeast, 3800 N Anthony Blvd, Fort Wayne, IN, 46805-1430. Tel: 260-480-4172, 260-482-9171. Fax: 260-480-4121. p. 742

Hults, Patricia, Mgr, Tech Serv, Rensselaer Libraries, Rensselaer Polytechnic Inst, 110 Eighth St, Troy, NY, 12180-3590. Tel: 518-276-8300. Fax: 518-276-2044. p. 1756

Hultz, Karen, Br Mgr, Irondequoit Public Library, Helen McGraw Branch, 2180 Ridge Rd E, Rochester, NY, 14622. Tel: 585-336-6060. Fax: 585-336-6067. p. 1730

Humay, Dawn, Librn, Banner Boswell Medical Center, 10401 W Thunderbird Blvd, Sun City, AZ, 85351. Tel: 623-832-6668. Fax: 623-832-5574. p. 82

Humber, Alliah, Curator, Howard University Libraries, Architecture, 2366 Sixth St NW, Washington, DC, 20059. Tel: 202-806-7773. Fax: 202-806-4441. p. 404

Humber, Amy, Head, Adult Serv, Tompkins County Public Library, 101 E Green St, Ithaca, NY, 14850-5613. Tel: 607-272-4557, Ext 247. Fax: 607-272-8111. p. 1643

Humberston, Margaret, Head of Libr & Archives, Connecticut Valley Historical Museum, The Quadrangle, Edwards St, Springfield, MA, 01103. Tel: 413-263-6800, Ext 311. Fax: 413-263-6898. p. 1127

Humbert, Betty, Libr Dir, Twin Bridges Public Library, 206 S Main St, Twin Bridges, MT, 59754. Tel: 406-684-5416. Fax: 406-684-5260. p. 1389

Humble, Todd, Tech Serv, North Richland Hills Public Library, 9015 Grand Ave, North Richland Hills, TX, 76180. Tel: 817-427-6822. Fax: 817-427-6808. p. 2366

Humburg, Patricia, Supvr, Circ, Greensboro College, 815 W Market St, Greensboro, NC, 27401. Tel: 336-272-7102, Ext 377. Fax: 336-217-7233. p. 1796

Hume, Tina, Asst Dir, Nora Sparks Warren Library, 210 N Willow St, Pauls Valley, OK, 73075. Tel: 405-238-5188. Fax: 405-238-5188. p. 1976

Humenic, Susan, Head, Circ, Free Public Library of Bayonne, 697 Avenue C, Bayonne, NJ, 07002. Tel: 201-858-6970. Fax: 201-437-6928. p. 1470

Humerickhouse, Russ, Fiscal Officer, Stark County District Library, 715 Market Ave N, Canton, OH, 44702-1018. Tel: 330-458-2690. Fax: 330-455-9596. p. 1864

Humes, Robert W, Head, Ref, United States Air Force Academy Libraries, 2354 Fairchild Dr, Ste 3A10, USAF Academy, CO, 80840-6214. Tel: 719-333-4406. Fax: 719-333-4754. p. 324

Humes, Rosanne, Per, Nassau Community College, One Education Dr, Garden City, NY, 11530-6793. Tel: 516-572-7400. Fax: 516-572-7846. p. 1626

Humeston, Dale, Ch, Saint Clair Shores Public Library, 22500 11 Mile Rd, Saint Clair Shores, MI, 48081-1399. Tel: 586-771-9020. Fax: 586-771-8935. p. 1224

Humeston, Dale, Youth Serv, Saint Clair Shores Public Library, 22500 11 Mile Rd, Saint Clair Shores, MI, 48081-1399. Tel: 586-771-9020. Fax: 586-771-8935. p. 1224

Humiston, Claudia, Cataloger, ILL, Northwestern Regional Library, 111 N Front St, Elkin, NC, 28621. Tel: 336-835-4894. Fax: 336-526-2270. p. 1791

Hummel, Diane, Librn, Richard R Smith Medical Library, 1840 Wealthy St SE, Grand Rapids, MI, 49506. Tel: 616-774-7931. Fax: 616-774-5290. p. 1186

Hummel, Diane, Mgr, Spectrum Health, A Level West Bldg, 100 Michigan St NE, Grand Rapids, MI, 49503-2560. Tel: 616-391-1655. Fax: 616-391-3527. p. 1186

Hummel, Jennifer L, Adjunct Fac Librn, Harrisburg Area Community College, 2010 Pennsylvania Ave, York, PA, 17404. Tel: 717-718-0328, Ext 3520. Fax: 717-718-8967. p. 2159

Hummel, Pat, Br Mgr, US Courts Library, Byron Rogers Courthouse, 1929 Stout St, Rm 430, Denver, CO, 80294. Tel: 303-844-3591. Fax: 303-844-5958. p. 303

Hummel, Patricia, Librn, United States Courts Library, US Courthouse, Rm 201, 350 S Main St, Salt Lake City, UT, 84101. Tel: 801-524-3505. Fax: 801-524-5375. p. 2414

Hummel, Patty, Dir, Allison Public Library, 412 Third St, Allison, IA, 50602. Tel: 319-267-2562. Fax: 319-267-2562. p. 792

Hummel, Penny, Dir, Canby Public Library, 292 N Holly St, Canby, OR, 97013-3732. Tel: 503-266-3394. Fax: 503-266-1709. p. 1993

Hummel, Sandra, Br Mgr, Mifflin County Library, Rothrock Branch, Ten N Queen St, McVeytown, PA, 17051. Tel: 717-899-6851. Fax: 717-899-6851. p. 2081

Hummel-Shea, Linda, Dir, Northern Essex Community College, 100 Elliott St, Haverhill, MA, 01830. Tel: 978-556-3423. Fax: 978-556-3738. p. 1094

Hummel-Shea, Linda, Dir, Libr Serv, Northern Essex Community College, Lawrence Campus Library, 45 Franklin St, Lawrence, MA, 01841. Tel: 978-556-3423. Fax: 978-738-7114. p. 1095

Hummer, Laura, ILL, Ser, Nashotah House Library, 2777 Mission Rd, Nashotah, WI, 53058-9793. Tel: 262-646-6535. Fax: 262-646-6504. p. 2624

Hummons, Heather, Circ Mgr, DePaul University Libraries, Vincent G Rinn Law Library, 25 E Jackson Blvd, 5th Flr, Chicago, IL, 60604-2287. Tel: 312-362-8958. Fax: 312-362-6908. p. 612

Humpal, Cathy, Dir, Lawler Public Library, 412 E Grove, Lawler, IA, 52154. Tel: 563-238-2191. Fax: 563-238-2191. p. 827

Humpherey, David, Dir, San Francisco Performing Arts Library & Museum, 401 Van Ness Ave, 4th Flr, San Francisco, CA, 94102. Tel: 415-255-4800. Fax: 415-255-1913. p. 246

Humphrey, Cathy, Supvr, Essex County Library, Harrow Branch, 140 King St W, Harrow, ON, N0R 1G0, CANADA. Tel: 226-946-1529, Ext 260. p. 2804

Humphrey, Ellen, Dep Chief Exec Officer, Calgary Public Library, 616 Macleod Trail SE, Calgary, AB, T2G 2M2, CANADA. Tel: 403-260-2600. Fax: 403-237-5393. p. 2688

Humphrey, Guy W, Res, Preble County District Library, 450 S Barron St, Eaton, OH, 45320-2402. Tel: 937-456-4250. Fax: 937-456-4774. p. 1897

Humphrey, Holden, Tech Serv Dir, Aiken-Bamberg-Barnwell-Edgefield Regional Library System, 314 Chesterfield St SW, Aiken, SC, 29801-7171. Tel: 803-642-7575. Fax: 803-642-7597. p. 2179

Humphrey, Josh, Dir, Kearny Public Library, 318 Kearny Ave, Kearny, NJ, 07032. Tel: 201-998-2666. Fax: 201-998-1141. p. 1493

Humphrey, Josh, Dir, Kearny Public Library, Kearny Branch, 759 Kearny Ave, Kearny, NJ, 07032. Tel: 201-955-7988. p. 1493

Humphrey, Joy, Tech Serv, Pepperdine University Libraries, School of Law-Jerene Appleby Harnish Law Library, 24255 Pacific Coast Hwy, Malibu, CA, 90263. Tel: 310-506-4643. Fax: 310-506-4836. p. 182

Humphrey, Julie, Ref Librn, Tech Serv Librn, Durham Technical Community College, 1637 Lawson St, Durham, NC, 27703. Tel: 919-536-7211. Fax: 919-686-3471. p. 1788

Humphrey, Louise, Dir of Libr, Appalachian Regional Library, 215 Tenth St, North Wilkesboro, NC, 28659. Tel: 336-838-2818. Fax: 336-667-2638. p. 1813

Humphrey, Marie, Spec Coll Librn, Midland County Public Library, 301 W Missouri, Midland, TX, 79701. Tel: 432-688-4320. Fax: 432-688-4939. p. 2363

Humphrey, Mary V, Med Librn, University of Wyoming Family Medicine Residency Program, 1522 East A St, Casper, WY, 82601. Tel: 307-233-6055. Fax: 307-473-1284. p. 2652

Humphrey, Richard E, Ref Librn, Indiana University, Ruth Lilly Law Library, 530 W New York St, Indianapolis, IN, 46202-3225. Tel: 317-274-3884, 317-274-4028. Fax: 317-274-8825. p. 752

Humphrey, Robin K, Pub Access Librn, Centenary College of Louisiana, 2834 Woodlawn St, Shreveport, LA, 71104-3335. Tel: 318-869-5047. Fax: 318-869-5004. p. 967

Humphrey, T, Circ Mgr, Educ Res Assoc, Ohio University-Zanesville/ Zane State College, 1425 Newark Rd, Zanesville, OH, 43701. Tel: 740-588-1405. Fax: 740-453-0706. p. 1954

Humphrey, Tom, Dir, Gadsden State Community College, Pierce C Cain Learning Resource Center, 1801 Coleman Rd, Anniston, AL, 36207-6858. Tel: 256-835-5435. Fax: 256-835-5476. p. 18

Humphreys, Alexandra, Instruction Librn, Arizona State University Libraries, Downtown Phoenix Campus Library, UCENT Bldg, Ste L1-62, 411 N Central Ave, Phoenix, AZ, 85004-1213. Tel: 602-496-1188. Fax: 602-496-0312. p. 83

Humphreys, Carlos, Librn, El Paso Community College Library, Transmountain Campus Library, 9570 Gateway Blvd N, El Paso, TX, 79924. Tel: 915-831-5092. p. 2316

Humphreys, Glenn, Head, Spec Coll, Chicago Public Library, Special Collections & Preservation Division, 400 S State St, Chicago, IL, 60605. Tel: 312-747-1941. p. 609

Humphreys, Jean Marie, Libr Assoc, Prince George's County Memorial, Baden Branch, 13603 Baden-Westwood Rd, Brandywine, MD, 20613-8167. Tel: 301-888-1152. p. 1032

Humphreys, Kristin, Ref Serv, Squire, Sanders & Dempsey Library, 1201 Pennsylvania Ave NW, Ste 500, Washington, DC, 20044. Tel: 202-626-6708. Fax: 202-626-6780. p. 416

Humphreys, Patricia, Head, Ad Ref Serv, YA Serv, Katonah Village Library, 26 Bedford Rd, Katonah, NY, 10536-2121. Tel: 914-232-3508. Fax: 914-232-0415. p. 1648

Humphries, Amy, Asst Dir, Head, Adult Serv, Wallingford Public Library, 200 N Main St, Wallingford, CT, 06492-3791. Tel: 203-284-6422. Fax: 203-269-5698. p. 373

Humphries, Jimmy J, Librn, Media Spec, Itawamba Community College, 602 W Hill St, Fulton, MS, 38843. Tel: 662-862-8381. Fax: 662-862-8410. p. 1298

Humphries, LaJean, Mgr, Schwabe, Williamson & Wyatt Library, Pacwest Ctr, 1211 SW Fifth Ave, Ste 1500, Portland, OR, 97204-3795. Tel: 503-796-2071. Fax: 503-796-2900. p. 2014

Humphries, Norma, Dir, Jack McConnico Memorial Library, 225 Oak Grove Rd, Selmer, TN, 38375. Tel: 731-645-5571. Fax: 731-645-4874. p. 2265

Humphries, Rose M, Head, Adult Serv, Bremen Public Library, 304 N Jackson St, Bremen, IN, 46506. Tel: 574-546-2849. Fax: 574-546-4938. p. 729

Humphries, Sherry, Br Mgr, Darlington County Library, Lamar Branch, 103 E Main St, Lamar, SC, 29069. Tel: 843-326-5524. Fax: 843-326-7302. p. 2192

Humrich, Kathy, Dir, Jackson County Public Library, 412 Fourth St, Walden, CO, 80480. Tel: 970-723-4602. Fax: 970-723-4602. p. 325

Hund, June, Tech Serv Librn, Case Western Reserve University, Lillian F & Milford J Harris Library, Mandel School of Applied Social Sciences, 11235 Bellflower Rd, Cleveland, OH, 44106-7164. Tel: 216-368-2302. Fax: 216-368-2106. p. 1876

Hundemer, Thomas, Dir, Hurley Music Libr, Centenary College of Louisiana, 2834 Woodlawn St, Shreveport, LA, 71104-3335. Tel: 318-689-5247. Fax: 318-869-5248. p. 967

Hundey, Jane, Br Mgr, Huron County Library, Exeter Branch, 330 Main St, Exeter, ON, N0M 1S6, CANADA. Tel: 519-235-1890. p. 2799

Hundey, Jane, Br Mgr, Huron County Library, Kirkton Branch, 70497 Perth Rd 164, Kirkton, ON, N0K 1K0, CANADA. Tel: 519-229-8854. p. 2800

Hundley, Cheryl, ILL, Ferrum College, 150 Wiley Dr, Ferrum, VA, 24088. Tel: 540-365-4426. Fax: 540-365-4423. p. 2463

Hundt, Lindsey, Mgr, Montgomery County Public Libraries, Potomac Library, 10101 Glenolden Dr, Potomac, MD, 20854-5052. Tel: 240-777-0690. Fax: 301-983-4479. p. 1039

Hung, Kwei, Acq Librn, Howard University Libraries, Law Library, 2929 Van Ness St NW, Washington, DC, 20008. Tel: 202-806-8051. Fax: 202-806-8400. p. 404

Hungerford, Garrett, Network Adminr, Salem-South Lyon District Library, 9800 Pontiac Trail, South Lyon, MI, 48178-1307. Tel: 248-437-6431, Ext 208. Fax: 248-437-6593. p. 1227

Hungerman, Marie Gabriel, Sister, Admin Dir, IHM Library/Resource Center, 610 W Elm Ave, Monroe, MI, 48162-7909. Tel: 734-240-9713. Fax: 734-240-8347. p. 1209

Hunn, Debbie, ILL, Ref, Dallas Theological Seminary, 3909 Swiss Ave, Dallas, TX, 75204. Tel: 214-841-3752. Fax: 214-841-3745. p. 2307

Hunn, Marvin, Dir, Dallas Theological Seminary, 3909 Swiss Ave, Dallas, TX, 75204. Tel: 214-841-3751. Fax: 214-841-3745. p. 2307

Hunnefeld, Christine, Coll Develop Librn, Framingham Public Library, 49 Lexington St, Framingham, MA, 01702-8278. Tel: 508-879-5570, Ext 4359. Fax: 508-820-7210. p. 1090

Hunnicutt, Susan, Spec Projects Librn, University of Texas Health Science Center at San Antonio Libraries, 7703 Floyd Curl Dr, MSC 7940, San Antonio, TX, 78229-3900. Tel: 210-567-2400. Fax: 210-567-2490. p. 2383

Hunsaker, Marci, Co-Unit Head, Ref, San Jose State University, One Washington Sq, San Jose, CA, 95192-0028. Tel: 408-808-2094. Fax: 408-808-2141. p. 251

Hunsaker, Theresa, Dir, Grundy County-Jewett Norris Library, 1331 Main St, Trenton, MO, 64683. Tel: 660-359-3577. Fax: 660-359-6220. p. 1368

Hunsberger, Amy, Mgr, Ser, Middle Tennessee State University, Center for Popular Music, John Bragg Mass Communication Bldg, Rm 140, 1301 E Main St, Murfreesboro, TN, 37132. Tel: 615-898-2755. Fax: 615-898-5829. p. 2254

Hunsicker, Jennifer, Br Mgr, Nashville Public Library, Goodlettsville Branch, 205 Rivergate Pkwy, Goodlettsville, TN, 37072. Tel: 615-862-5862. Fax: 615-862-5798. p. 2257

Hunt, Amber, Ref Librn, Tech Librn, Marlboro College, 64 Dalrymple Rd, Marlboro, VT, 05344-0300. Tel: 802-258-9221. Fax: 802-451-7550. p. 2428

Hunt, Andrew, Dir, Cleveland Bradley County Public Library, 795 Church St NE, Cleveland, TN, 37311-5295. Tel: 423-472-2163. Fax: 423-339-9791. p. 2229

Hunt, Ann, Dir, New London Public Library, 406 S Pearl St, New London, WI, 54961-1441. Tel: 920-982-8519. Fax: 920-982-8617. p. 2625

Hunt, Barbara, Mgr, Penns Grove-Carney's Point Public Library, 222 S Broad St, Penns Grove, NJ, 08069. Tel: 856-299-4255. Fax: 856-299-4552. p. 1519

Hunt, Chance, Dir, Prog & Serv Develop, The Seattle Public Library, 1000 Fourth Ave, Seattle, WA, 98104-1109. Tel: 206-386-4097. p. 2531

Hunt, Cheryl R, Br Librn, Providence Community Library, Wanskuck Library, 233 Veazie St, Providence, RI, 02904. Tel: 401-274-4145. p. 2173

Hunt, Christopher, Mgr, Oakwood Hospital Medical Library, 18101 Oakwood Blvd, Dearborn, MI, 48124-2500. Tel: 313-593-7685. Fax: 313-436-2699. p. 1167

Hunt, Deb, Assoc Dir, Lancaster Bible College Library, 901 Eden Rd, Lancaster, PA, 17601-5036. Tel: 717-560-8250. Fax: 717-560-8265. p. 2076

Hunt, Diana C, Asst Dir, Briggs Lawrence County Public Library, 321 S Fourth St, Ironton, OH, 45638. Tel: 740-377-2288. Fax: 740-377-9290. p. 1906

Hunt, Diana J, Librn, Miller Stratvert PA, 500 Marquette Ave NW, Ste 100, Albuquerque, NM, 87102-5326. Tel: 505-842-1950. Fax: 505-243-4408. p. 1549

Hunt, Diane C, Dir, Hardee County Public Library, 315 N Sixth Ave, Ste 114, Wauchula, FL, 33873. Tel: 863-773-6438. Fax: 863-767-1091. p. 502

Hunt, Elizabeth, Librn, Rollins College, 1000 Holt Ave, Campus Box 2744, Winter Park, FL, 32789-2744. Tel: 407-691-6431. Fax: 407-646-1515. p. 505

Hunt, Glenda, Dir, Adair County Public Library, One Library Lane, Kirksville, MO, 63501. Tel: 660-665-6038. Fax: 660-627-0028. p. 1342

Hunt, Jennie, Tech Serv, Greensboro College, 815 W Market St, Greensboro, NC, 27401. Tel: 336-272-7102, Ext 230. Fax: 336-217-7233. p. 1796

Hunt, Jennifer, Dir, The Boston Conservatory, Eight The Fenway, Boston, MA, 02215-4099. Tel: 617-912-9132. Fax: 617-912-9101. p. 1056

Hunt, Jessica, Ch, White Cloud Community Library, 1038 Wilcox Ave, White Cloud, MI, 49349. Tel: 231-689-6631. Fax: 231-689-6699. p. 1236

Hunt, Judith Lin, Dr, Dean, Montclair State University, One Normal Ave, Montclair, NJ, 07043-1699. Tel: 973-655-4301. Fax: 973-655-7780. p. 1503

Hunt, Karla, Dir, Fort Sumner Public Library, 235 W Sumner Ave, Fort Sumner, NM, 88119. Tel: 505-355-2832. Fax: 505-355-7732. p. 1555

Hunt, Kim, Bus Mgr, McCracken County Public Library, 555 Washington St, Paducah, KY, 42003-1735. Tel: 270-442-2510, Ext 13. Fax: 270-443-9322. p. 932

Hunt, Lois, Circ Supvr, Spring Arbor University, 106 E Main St, Spring Arbor, MI, 49283. Tel: 800-968-9103, Ext 1442. Fax: 517-750-2108. p. 1229

Hunt, Maria, Head, Scholarly Res, University of Utah, Marriott Library, 295 S 1500 East, Salt Lake City, UT, 84112-0860. Tel: 801-581-7741. Fax: 801-585-7185. p. 2415

Hunt, Marsha, Dep Chief Exec Officer, Pelham Public Library, 43 Pelham Town Sq, Fonthill, ON, L0S 1E0, CANADA. Tel: 905-892-6443. Fax: 905-892-3392. p. 2805

Hunt, Mary, Mgr, Albuquerque-Bernalillo County Library System, Lomas-Tramway, 908 Eastridge NE, Albuquerque, NM, 87123. Tel: 505-291-6295. Fax: 505-291-6299. p. 1548

Hunt, Nina, Head, Youth Serv, Bellingham Public Library, 100 Blackstone St, Bellingham, MA, 02019. Tel: 508-966-1660. Fax: 508-966-3189. p. 1052

Hunt, Patty, Bibliog Instr, Ref, Minot State University, 500 University Ave W, Minot, ND, 58707. Tel: 701-858-3200. Fax: 701-858-3581. p. 1846

Hunt, Steve, Syst Librn, Santa Monica College Library, 1900 Pico Blvd, Santa Monica, CA, 90405-1628. Tel: 310-434-4334, 310-434-4692. Fax: 310-434-4387. p. 266

Hunt, Susan, Dir, Carthage Public Library District, 500 Wabash Ave, Carthage, IL, 62321. Tel: 217-357-3232. Fax: 217-357-2392. p. 601

Hunt, Susan, Dir, Colchester District Library, 203 Macomb St, Colchester, IL, 62326. Tel: 309-776-4861. Fax: 309-776-4099. p. 630

Hunt, Susan, Librn, Allen County Public Library, Aboite, 5630 Coventry Lane, Fort Wayne, IN, 46804. Tel: 260-421-1310. Fax: 260-432-2394. p. 740

Hunt, Teresa, In Charge, Fossil Public Library, 401 Main St, Fossil, OR, 97830. Tel: 541-763-2046. Fax: 541-763-2124. p. 1998

Hunt, Val, Librn, Bauder College Library, 384 Northyards Blvd NW, Ste 190, Atlanta, GA, 30313. Tel: 404-443-1807, 404-443-1808. Fax: 404-237-1619. p. 513

Hunt, Valdoshia, Ch, Atlanta-Fulton Public Library System, Mechanicsville Library, 400 Formwalt St SW, Atlanta, GA, 30312. Tel: 404-730-4779. p. 512

Hunt-Coffey, Nancy, Asst Dir, Commun Serv, City Librn, Beverly Hills Public Library, 444 N Rexford Dr, Beverly Hills, CA, 90210-4877. Tel: 310-288-2220. Fax: 310-278-3387. p. 129

Hunt-McCain, Pearl, Sr Librn, Hennepin County Library, Oxboro, 8801 Portland Ave S, Bloomington, MN, 55420-2997. Tel: 612-543-5778. Fax: 612-543-5777. p. 1264

Hunter, Amy, Mgr, Hamilton Public Library, Ancaster, 300 Wilson St E, Ancaster, ON, L9G 2B9, CANADA. Tel: 905-546-3200, Ext 3463. p. 2808

Hunter, Benjamin, Head, Cat & Coll, University of Idaho Library, Rayburn St, Moscow, ID, 83844. Tel: 208-885-5813. Fax: 208-885-6817. p. 579

Hunter, Carol, Assoc Univ Librn, Coll & Serv, University of North Carolina at Chapel Hill, Davis Library, 208 Raleigh St, Campus Box 3900, Chapel Hill, NC, 27514-8890. p. 1780

Hunter, Carol, Assoc Univ Librn, Pub Serv & Coll, University of Virginia, PO Box 400114, Charlottesville, VA, 22904-4114. Tel: 434-924-3021. Fax: 434-924-1431. p. 2454

Hunter, Cheri, Librn, Decatur Genealogical Society Library, 1255 W South Side Dr, Decatur, IL, 62521-4024. Tel: 217-429-0135. p. 633

Hunter, Cindy, Librn, Bashaw Public Library, 5020 52 St, Bashaw, AB, T0B 0H0, CANADA. Tel: 780-372-4055. Fax: 780-372-4055. p. 2684

Hunter, Clyde, Jr, Br Mgr, Chesapeake Public Library, Russell Memorial, 2808 Taylor Rd, Chesapeake, VA, 23321-2210. Tel: 757-410-7028. Fax: 757-410-7029. p. 2456

Hunter, Cynthia, Asst Dir, Cent Libr Serv, Asst Dir, Commun Libr Serv, Clayton County Library System, 865 Battlecreek Rd, Jonesboro, GA, 30236. Tel: 770-473-3850. Fax: 770-473-3858. p. 536

Hunter, Dalena E, Librn, University of California, Los Angeles, Ralph J Bunche Center for African-American Studies Library & Media Center, 135 Haines Hall, Box 951545, Los Angeles, CA, 90095-1545. Tel: 310-825-6060. Fax: 310-825-5019. p. 179

Hunter, David, Librn, University of Texas Libraries, Fine Arts, Doty Fine Arts Bldg 3-200, 23rd & Trinity, Austin, TX, 78713. Tel: 512-495-4475. Fax: 512-495-4490. p. 2284

Hunter, Deann, Ad, Laconia Public Library, 695 Main St, Laconia, NH, 03246-2780. Tel: 603-524-4775. Fax: 603-527-1277. p. 1453

Hunter, Diane, Head, Teaching & Learning Serv, University of Missouri-Kansas City Libraries, 800 E 51st St, Kansas City, MO, 64110. Tel: 816-235-1537. Fax: 816-333-5584. p. 1341

Hunter, Diane, Circ, Rider University, 2083 Lawrenceville Rd, Lawrenceville, NJ, 08648-3099. Tel: 609-896-5111. Fax: 609-896-8029. p. 1494

Hunter, Elaine, Acq, Innovation, Energy & Mines, 1395 Ellice Ave, Ste 360, Winnipeg, MB, R3G 3P2, CANADA. Tel: 204-945-4154. Fax: 204-945-8427. p. 2756

Hunter, Eleanor, Ref Librn, Atlanta-Fulton Public Library System, Auburn Avenue Research Library on African-American Culture & History, 101 Auburn Ave NE, Atlanta, GA, 30303. Tel: 404-730-4001, Ext 199. Fax: 404-730-5879. p. 511

Hunter, Greg, Librn, Oregon State Correctional Institution Library, 3405 Deer Park Dr SE, Salem, OR, 97310-3985. Tel: 503-373-7523. Fax: 503-378-8919. p. 2018

Hunter, Gregory, Dr, Dir, PhD Prog, Prof, Long Island University, C W Post Campus, 720 Northern Blvd, Brookville, NY, 11548-1300. Tel: 516-299-7171. Fax: 516-299-4168. p. 2969

Hunter, James, Curator, Huronia Museum, 549 Little Lake Park Rd, Midland, ON, L4R 4P4, CANADA. Tel: 705-526-2844. Fax: 705-527-6622. p. 2821

Hunter, Joan, Librn, Windom Public Library, 904 Fourth Ave, Windom, MN, 56101-1639. Tel: 507-831-6131. p. 1289

Hunter, John, Co-Dir, Ref Librn, Ozark Christian College, 1111 N Main, Joplin, MO, 64801-4804. Tel: 417-626-1234, Ext 2708. Fax: 417-624-0090. p. 1336

Hunter, John, Acq, Cat, Woodburn Public Library, 280 Garfield St, Woodburn, OR, 97071-4698. Tel: 503-982-5257. Fax: 503-982-2808. p. 2023

Hunter, Judy, Librn, Lancaster County Library, 313 S White St, Lancaster, SC, 29720. Tel: 803-285-1502. Fax: 803-285-6004. p. 2198

Hunter, Julie, Assoc Dir, Pub Serv, Broward County Division of Libraries, 100 S Andrews Ave, Fort Lauderdale, FL, 33301. Tel: 954-357-6592. Fax: 954-357-5733. p. 440

Hunter, Karen, Asst Librn, Tech Serv, North Carolina Central University, School of Law Library, 1512 S Alston Ave, Durham, NC, 27707. Tel: 919-530-7180. Fax: 919-530-7926. p. 1789

Hunter, Kate, Librn, Orwell Free Library, 473 Main St, Orwell, VT, 05670. Tel: 802-948-2041. p. 2431

Hunter, Kathy, Librn, Westminster Presbyterian Church Library, 2701 Cameron Mills Rd, Alexandria, VA, 22302. Tel: 703-549-4766. Fax: 703-548-1505. p. 2447

Hunter, Kerry, Br Mgr, Louisville Free Public Library, Western, 604 S Tenth St, Louisville, KY, 40203. Tel: 502-574-1779. Fax: 502-589-9937. p. 925

Hunter, Kimberly, Bibliographer, United States Air Force, Air University - Muir S Fairchild Research Information Center, 600 Chennault Circle, Maxwell AFB, AL, 36112-6010. Tel: 334-953-9811. p. 24

Hunter, Leah, Librn, Delia Municipal Library, 205 Third Ave N, Delia, AB, T0J 0W0, CANADA. Tel: 403-364-3777. Fax: 403-364-3805. p. 2696

Hunter, Linda, Dir, Butler Public Library, 100 W Atkinson, Butler, MO, 64730. Tel: 660-679-4321. Fax: 660-679-4321. p. 1321

Hunter, Lynda, Ch, Delray Beach Public Library, 100 W Atlantic Ave, Delray Beach, FL, 33444. Tel: 561-266-0197. Fax: 561-266-9757. p. 437

Hunter, Lynne, Adult Serv, Wilton Free Public Library, Six Goodspeed St, Wilton, ME, 04294. Tel: 207-645-4831. Fax: 207-645-9417. p. 1007

Hunter, Mark, Acq, Roselle Free Public Library, 104 W Fourth Ave, Roselle, NJ, 07203. Tel: 908-245-5809. Fax: 908-298-8881. p. 1527

Hunter, Mary Ann, Head, Circ, Head, Tech Serv, Saratoga Springs Public Library, 49 Henry St, Saratoga Springs, NY, 12866. Tel: 518-584-7860. Fax: 518-584-7866. p. 1738

Hunter, Michael, Info Syst Tech, Southern West Virginia Community & Technical College, Rte 97, Saulsville, WV, 25876. Tel: 304-294-8346. Fax: 304-294-8534. p. 2571

Hunter, Mike, Librn, Brigham Young University, Harold B Lee Library, 2060 HBLL, Provo, UT, 84602. Tel: 801-422-2927. Fax: 801-422-0466. p. 2411

Hunter, Nancy, Pub Serv Mgr, University of Cincinnati, 4200 Clermont College Dr, Batavia, OH, 45103-1785. Tel: 513-732-5233. Fax: 513-732-5237. p. 1858

Hunter, Pam, Dir, Sedalia Public Library, 311 W Third St, Sedalia, MO, 65301-4399. Tel: 660-826-1314. Fax: 660-826-0396. p. 1365

Hunter, Paul, Evening Supvr, Drexel University Health Sciences Libraries, 245 N 15th St MS 449, Philadelphia, PA, 19102-1192. Fax: 215-762-8180. p. 2105

Hunter, Rachael, Acq, Admin Coordr, Louisiana State University at Alexandria, 8100 Hwy 71 S, Alexandria, LA, 71302. Tel: 318-473-6438. Fax: 318-473-6556. p. 940

Hunter, Shannon, Chief Exec Officer, North Kawartha Public Library, 175 Burleigh St, Apsley, ON, K0L 1A0, CANADA. Tel: 705-656-4333. Fax: 705-656-2538. p. 2792

Hunter, Shauna, Asst Dir, Hampden Sydney College, 257 Via Sacra, HSC Box 7, Hampden Sydney, VA, 23943. Tel: 434-223-6194. Fax: 434-223-6351. p. 2468

Hunter, Shauna, Pub Serv, Hampden Sydney College, 257 Via Sacra, HSC Box 7, Hampden Sydney, VA, 23943. Tel: 434-223-6193. Fax: 434-223-6351. p. 2468

Hunter, Sue, Head, Ref Serv, Pace University Library, New York Civic Ctr, One Pace Plaza, New York, NY, 10038-1502. Tel: 212-346-1331. Fax: 212-346-1615. p. 1696

Hunter, Tiah, Res, Nevada Power Co Library, 6226 W Sahara Ave, Las Vegas, NV, 89151. Tel: 702-367-5055. Fax: 702-227-2023. p. 1430

Hunter, Timothy, Coordr, Libr Sci, Rowan-Cabarrus Community College, South Campus, 1531 Trinity Church Rd, Concord, NC, 28027-7601. Tel: 704-216-3694. Fax: 704-788-2169. p. 1822

Hunter, Tonja, Librn, Lawson State Community College Library, 1100 Ninth Ave SW, Bessemer, AL, 35022. Tel: 205-929-3434, 205-929-6333. Fax: 205-925-3716. p. 6

Hunter, Tonja, Ref, Lawson State Community College Library, 3060 Wilson Rd SW, Birmingham, AL, 35221. Tel: 205-925-2515, Ext 6333, 205-929-6333. Fax: 205-925-3716. p. 8

Hunter, Vera, Librn, Shiloh Baptist Church, 1510 Ninth St NW, Washington, DC, 20001. Tel: 202-232-4288. Fax: 202-234-6235. p. 414

Hunter, Wanda, Genealogy Serv, Cumberland County Public Library & Information Center, 300 Maiden Lane, Fayetteville, NC, 28301-5000. Tel: 910-483-7727. Fax: 910-486-5372. p. 1792

Hunter-Beatty, Betty, Asst Librn, Patterson, Belknap, Webb & Tyler LLP Library, 1133 Avenue of the Americas, New York, NY, 10036. Tel: 212-336-2930, Ext 2326. Fax: 212-336-2955. p. 1697

Hunter-Brodhead, Rhea, Circ, Waubonsee Community College, State Rte 47 at Waubonsee Dr, Sugar Grove, IL, 60554. Tel: 630-466-2401. Fax: 630-466-7799. p. 708

Huntington, Claire, Librn, Geisinger Health System, 100 N Academy Ave, Danville, PA, 17822-2101. Tel: 570-271-6288. Fax: 570-271-5738. p. 2049

Huntington, Debbie, Syst/Tech Proc Librn, Pearl River Community College, 101 Hwy 11 N, Poplarville, MS, 39470. Tel: 601-403-1331. Fax: 601-403-1135. p. 1312

Huntington, Linda, ILL, Pierson Library, 5376 Shelburne Rd, Shelburne, VT, 05482. Tel: 802-985-5124. Fax: 802-985-5129. p. 2435

Huntington, Lucas, Access Serv Librn, Our Lady of the Lake College Library, 5329 Didesse St, Baton Rouge, LA, 70808. Tel: 225-768-0803. Fax: 225-761-7303. p. 944

Huntington, Marilyn, Librn, Hartford Conservatory, 834 Asylum Ave, Hartford, CT, 06105. Tel: 860-246-2588, Ext 11. Fax: 860-249-6330. p. 345

Huntington, Stan, Dir, Maywood Public Library District, 121 S Fifth Ave, Maywood, IL, 60153. Tel: 703-343-1847, Ext 28. Fax: 708-343-2115. p. 672

Huntley, Aimee, ILL, Per, Mount Marty College Library, 1105 W Eighth St, Yankton, SD, 57078-3724. Tel: 605-668-1555. Fax: 605-668-1357. p. 2222

Huntley, Nancy, Dir, Lincoln Library, 326 S Seventh St, Springfield, IL, 62701. Tel: 217-753-4900, Ext 219. Fax: 217-753-5329. p. 706

Huntley, Shelly, Dir, Shedd-Porter Memorial Library, Main St, Alstead, NH, 03602. Tel: 603-835-6661. p. 1437

Huntley, Teresa, Mgr, Dayton Metro Library, Kettering-Moraine, 3496 Far Hills Ave, Kettering, OH, 45429. Tel: 937-496-8938. Fax: 937-496-4338. p. 1893

Huntsha, Lisa, Archivist, Librn, Swenson Swedish Immigration Research Center, Augustana College, 3520 Seventh Ave, Rock Island, IL, 61201. Tel: 309-794-7496. Fax: 309-794-7443. p. 696

Huntsman, Mary Taylor, Pub Serv Librn, Somerset Community College Library, Harold B Strunk Learning Resource Ctr, 808 Monticello St, Somerset, KY, 42501. Tel: 606-451-6710. Fax: 606-679-5139. p. 935

Huntsman, Patricia, Cat, Vinson & Elkins, 3055 First City Tower, 1001 Fannin, Houston, TX, 77002-6760. Tel: 713-758-2678. Fax: 713-615-5211. p. 2345

Hunziker, John, Communications Mgr, Rochester Public Library, 101 Second St SE, Rochester, MN, 55904-3776. Tel: 507-328-2343. Fax: 507-328-2384. p. 1273

Hupp, Julie, Librn, State of Ohio Department of Corrections, 15708 Collinsville Rd, Caldwell, OH, 43724. Tel: 740-748-5188. Fax: 740-748-5010. p. 1863

Hupp, Marcia, Ch, Mamaroneck Public Library District, 136 Prospect Ave, Mamaroneck, NY, 10543. Tel: 914-698-1250. Fax: 914-381-3088. p. 1657

Hupp, Stephen, Dir, West Virginia University, 300 Campus Dr, Parkersburg, WV, 26104. Tel: 304-424-8260. Fax: 304-424-8349. p. 2568

Hurd, Cynthia, Br Mgr, Charleston County Public Library, Saint Andrews Regional, 1735 N Woodmere Dr, Charleston, SC, 29407. Tel: 843-766-2546. Fax: 843-766-2762. p. 2183

Hurd, Jennifer, Br Mgr, Round Lake Library, Malta Community Center, One Bayberry Dr, Malta, NY, 12020. Tel: 518-682-2495. Fax: 518-682-2492. p. 1736

Hurd, Kay, Dir, Almont District Library, 213 W St Clair St, Almont, MI, 48003-8476. Tel: 810-798-3100. Fax: 810-798-2208. p. 1149

Hurd, Sue, Circ, Hot Springs County Library, 344 Arapahoe, Thermopolis, WY, 82443-0951. Tel: 307-864-3104. Fax: 307-864-5416. p. 2661

Hurlbert, Dianne, Librn, Mississippi Gulf Coast Community College, 2226 Switzer Rd, Gulfport, MS, 39507. Tel: 228-897-3880. Fax: 228-896-2521. p. 1300

Hurlbert, Janet M, Assoc Dean, Dir, Libr Serv, Lycoming College, 700 College Pl, Williamsport, PA, 17701-5192. Tel: 570-321-4082. Fax: 570-321-4090. p. 2156

Hurlbert, Terry, Head, Cat, Carnegie Mellon University, Hunt Library, 4909 Frew St, Pittsburgh, PA, 15213-3890. Tel: 412-268-2446. Fax: 412-268-2793. p. 2123

Hurlburt, Leeanne, Librn, Palliser Regional Library, Elbow Branch, 402 Minto St, Elbow, SK, S0H 1J0, CANADA. Tel: 306-854-2220. p. 2918

Hurlburt, Thomas, Assoc Dir, Ch, Rhinelander District Library, 106 N Stevens St, Rhinelander, WI, 54501-3193. Tel: 715-365-1073. Fax: 715-365-1076. p. 2633

Hurlbut, Joe, Operating Syst/Network Analyst, Oregon Institute of Technology Library, 3201 Campus Dr, Klamath Falls, OR, 97601-8801. Tel: 541-885-1772. Fax: 541-885-1777. p. 2002

Hurley, Bernie, Dir, University of California, Berkeley, Technical Services, 250 Moffit Library, Berkeley, CA, 94720-6000. Tel: 510-643-8239. Fax: 510-642-8331. p. 128

Hurley, Dorothy, Ch, Westborough Public Library, 55 W Main St, Westborough, MA, 01581. Tel: 508-366-3050. Fax: 508-366-3049. p. 1138

Hurley, John, Syst Adminr, National Archives & Records Administration, 1000 Beal Ave, Ann Arbor, MI, 48109-2114. Tel: 734-205-0553. Fax: 734-205-0571. p. 1151

Hurley, John, Tech Support, Fordham University Libraries, 441 E Fordham Rd, Bronx, NY, 10458-5151. Tel: 718-817-3570. Fax: 718-817-3582. p. 1586

Hurley, Kathie, Pub Info Officer, New Haven Free Public Library, 133 Elm St, New Haven, CT, 06510. Tel: 203-946-8130. Fax: 203-946-8140. p. 355

Hurley, Lauren, Br Coordr, Vance-Granville Community College, Warren Campus, 210 W Ridgeway St, Warrenton, NC, 27589-1838. Tel: 252-738-3685. Fax: 252-257-3612. p. 1800

Hurley, Linda, In Charge, Springfield Hospital Library, 25 Ridgewood Rd, Springfield, VT, 05156-3057. Tel: 802-885-2151. Fax: 802-885-3959. p. 2436

Hurley, Michael, Instrul Tech, Allegheny College Library, 555 N Main St, Meadville, PA, 16335. Tel: 814-332-2890. Fax: 814-337-5673. p. 2086

Hurley, Nancy, Br Mgr, Montgomery County Public Library, Mount Gilead Branch, 110 W Allenton St, Mount Gilead, NC, 27306. Tel: 910-439-6651. Fax: 910-439-6651. p. 1827

Hurley, Terri, AV, Dir, Pub Relations, Pub Serv, Great Bend Public Library, 1409 Williams St, Great Bend, KS, 67530-4090. Tel: 620-792-2409. Fax: 620-792-5495, 620-793-7270. p. 869

Hurley, Theresa, Ch, Lynn Public Library, Five N Common St, Lynn, MA, 01902. Tel: 781-595-0567. Fax: 781-592-5050. p. 1101

Hursh, David, Head Librn, East Carolina University, Music Library, A J Fletcher Music Ctr, Rm A110, Greenville, NC, 27858. Tel: 252-328-1239. Fax: 252-328-1243. p. 1799

Hurst, Chris, Actg Univ Librn, Automation Syst Coordr, Brandon University, 270 18th St, Brandon, MB, R7A 6A9, CANADA. Tel: 204-727-9687. Fax: 204-727-1072. p. 2747

Hurst, Eloise, Principal Librn, Tampa-Hillsborough County Public Library System, SouthShore Regional Library, 15816 Beth Shields Way, Ruskin, FL, 33573-4093. Fax: 813-372-1150. p. 498

Hurst, Emily, Tech Coordr, National Network of Libraries of Medicine South Central Region, c/o HAM-TMC Library, 1133 John Freeman Blvd, Houston, TX, 77030-2809. Tel: 713-799-7189. Fax: 713-790-7030. p. 2956

Hurst, Martha, Librn, Schering-Plough Health Care, Inc, 3030 Jackson Ave, Memphis, TN, 38112-2020. Tel: 901-320-2702. Fax: 901-320-3017. p. 2251

Hurst, Ruth, Team Leader, Nevada Power Co Library, 6226 W Sahara Ave, Las Vegas, NV, 89151. Tel: 702-367-5055. Fax: 702-227-2023. p. 1430

Hurst, Vicki, Tech Serv, Letcher County Public Libraries, 220 Main St, Whitesburg, KY, 41858. Tel: 606-633-7547. Fax: 606-633-3407. p. 937

Hurt, Lynn, Acq & Cat, Interim Dir, Virginia Western Community College, 3095 Colonial Ave SW, Roanoke, VA, 24015-4705. Tel: 540-857-6445. Fax: 540-857-6058. p. 2495

Hurt, Tara, Archivist, Spec Coll Librn, Eastern Connecticut State University, 83 Windham St, Willimantic, CT, 06226-2295. Tel: 860-465-5563. Fax: 860-465-5521. p. 378

Hurtado, Cassandra, Librn, Endometriosis Association Library & Reading Room, 8585 N 76th Pl, Milwaukee, WI, 53223-2692. Tel: 414-355-2200. Fax: 414-355-6065. p. 2618

Hurtado, Lezlee, Youth Serv, Lompoc Public Library, 501 E North Ave, Lompoc, CA, 93436-3498. Tel: 805-875-8781. Fax: 805-736-6440. p. 165

Hurteau, Rebecca, Head of Libr, De Leon City County Library, 125 E Reynosa St, De Leon, TX, 76444-1862. Tel: 254-893-2417. Fax: 254-893-4915. p. 2311

Hurtienne, Naomi, Ref Librn, Lafourche Parish Public Library, Martha Sowell Utley Memorial (Main Library), 314 St Mary St, Thibodaux, LA, 70301-2620. Tel: 985-447-4119. Fax: 985-449-4128. p. 971

Hurwitz, Donna, Dir, Marymount Manhattan College, 221 E 71st St, New York, NY, 10021. Tel: 212-774-4801. Fax: 212-458-8207. p. 1685

Hurwitz, Michael, Libr Asst, Smithers Public Library, 3817 Alfred Ave, Box 55, Smithers, BC, V0J 2N0, CANADA. Tel: 250-847-3043. Fax: 250-847-1533. p. 2737

Hurwood, Gilbert Arthur, Librn, State of Ohio Department of Corrections, 1580 State Rte 56 SW, London, OH, 43140. Tel: 740-852-2454. Fax: 740-852-1591. p. 1911

Huryta, Karrie, Libr Dir, Ravenna Public Library, 121 W Seneca St, Ravenna, NE, 68869-1362. Tel: 308-452-4213. Fax: 308-452-4210. p. 1417

Husband, Patricia, Asst Dir, Br Serv, East Baton Rouge Parish Library, 7711 Goodwood Blvd, Baton Rouge, LA, 70806-7625. Tel: 225-231-3785. Fax: 225-231-3788. p. 942

Husband, Susan, Managing Librn, Pima County Public Library, Santa Rosa Learning Center, 1075 S Tenth Ave, Tucson, AZ, 85701. Tel: 520-594-5260. Fax: 520-594-5481. p. 87

Husch, Barbara, Br Mgr, Door County Library, Forestville Branch, 123 Hwy 42 S, Forestville, WI, 54213. Tel: 920-856-6886. p. 2641

Huseboe, Arthur R, Exec Dir, Augustana College, Center for Western Studies, 2201 S Summit Ave, Sioux Falls, SD, 57197. Tel: 605-274-4007. Fax: 605-274-4999. p. 2218

Husher, Brent, Coordr, Virtual Libr, University of Missouri-Kansas City Libraries, 800 E 51st St, Kansas City, MO, 64110. Tel: 816-235-1281. Fax: 816-333-5584. p. 1341

Huska, Deb, Dir, Carnegie Public Library, 513 N Orleans Ave, Dell Rapids, SD, 57022-1637. Tel: 605-428-3280. p. 2211

Huska, Miranda, Br Head, Toronto Public Library, Parkdale, 1303 Queen St W, Toronto, ON, M6K 1L6, CANADA. Tel: 416-393-7686. Fax: 416-393-7705. p. 2862

Huske, Nancy, Circ Librn, Silver Lake Library, 203 Railroad St, Silver Lake, KS, 66539. Tel: 785-582-5141. Fax: 785-582-4282. p. 894

Huskey, Julie, Librn, Central Georgia Technical College Library, 3300 Macon Tech Dr, Macon, GA, 31206-3628. Tel: 478-757-3549. Fax: 478-757-3545. p. 540

Husman, Sheri, Med Librn, Doctors Medical Center, 1441 Florida Ave, Modesto, CA, 95352-4418. Tel: 209-576-3782. Fax: 209-576-3595. p. 187

Husom, Valerie J, Dir of Libr, Black Creek Village Library, 507 S Maple St, Black Creek, WI, 54106-9304. Tel: 920-984-3094. Fax: 920-984-3559. p. 2582

Huss, Jane, Head, Tech Serv, Tiffin-Seneca Public Library, 77 Jefferson St, Tiffin, OH, 44883. Tel: 419-447-3751. Fax: 419-447-3045. p. 1938

Hussain, Mohamed, Asst Dir, Res Mgt Serv, State University of New York Downstate Medical Center, 395 Lenox Rd, Brooklyn, NY, 11203. Tel: 718-270-7450. Fax: 718-270-7413, 718-270-7468. p. 1595

Hussain, Rownak P, Dir, Hopkinton Public Library, 13 Main St, Hopkinton, MA, 01748. Tel: 508-497-9777. Fax: 508-497-9778. p. 1096

Husser, Kathy, Br Mgr, Phoenix Public Library, Ironwood Library, 4333 E Chandler Blvd, Phoenix, AZ, 85048. p. 76

Hussey, Julia, Librn, World Resources Institute, Ten G St NE, Ste 800, Washington, DC, 20002. Tel: 202-729-7602. Fax: 202-729-7610. p. 423

Hussey, Kip, Ref & Instrul Serv Librn, Notre Dame de Namur University Library, 1500 Ralston Ave, Belmont, CA, 94002-1908. Tel: 650-508-3712. Fax: 650-508-3697. p. 126

Hussey, Lisa, Asst Prof, Simmons College, 300 The Fenway, Boston, MA, 02115. Tel: 617-521-2800. Fax: 617-521-3192. p. 2967

Hussey-Arntson, K, Dir, Wilmette Historical Museum, 609 Ridge Rd, Wilmette, IL, 60091-2721. Tel: 847-853-7666. Fax: 847-853-7706. p. 719

Hust, Carolyn, Tech Serv, Rose State College, 6420 SE 15th St, Midwest City, OK, 73110. Tel: 405-736-0204. Fax: 405-736-0260. p. 1968

Husted, Amy, Ch, Norton Public Library, One Washington Sq, Norton, KS, 67654-1615. Tel: 785-877-2481. p. 885

Huston, Celia, Dr, Librn, San Bernardino Valley College Library, 701 S Mount Vernon Ave, San Bernardino, CA, 92410. Tel: 909-384-8574. p. 229

Huston, Dale, Ref, Champlain Regional College, 900 Riverside Dr, Saint Lambert, QC, J4P 3P2, CANADA. Tel: 450-672-7360. Fax: 450-672-2152. p. 2908

Huston, Dawn, Dir, Dunbar Free Library, 401 Rte 10 S, Grantham, NH, 03753. Tel: 603-863-2172. Fax: 603-863-2172. p. 1448

Huston, Rebekah, Asst Librn, Houston Public Library, 3150 14th St, Houston, BC, V0J 1Z0, CANADA. Tel: 250-845-2256. Fax: 250-845-2088. p. 2729

Hutchens, Jim, Asst Univ Librn, Head of Doc Delivery, Nova Southeastern University Libraries, 3100 Ray Ferrero Jr Blvd, Fort Lauderdale, FL, 33314. Tel: 954-262-4648. Fax: 954-262-3805. p. 444

Hutchens, Karen, Librn, Eastern Health, Centre for Nursing Studies Learning Resource Centre, 100 Forest Rd, St. John's, NL, A1A 1E5, CANADA. Tel: 709-777-8189. Fax: 709-777-8193. p. 2772

Hutchens, Laura, Dir, Coll Develop, Blount County Public Library, 508 N Cusick St, Maryville, TN, 37804-5714. Tel: 865-982-0981. Fax: 865-977-1142. p. 2246

Hutchens, Susan, Librn, East Bend Public Library, 332 W Main St, East Bend, NC, 27018. Tel: 336-699-3890. Fax: 336-699-2359. p. 1790

Hutcherson, Bartholomew, Fr, Dir, Newman Catholic Student Center, 1615 E Second St, Tucson, AZ, 85719. Tel: 520-327-6662. Fax: 520-327-6559. p. 86

Hutcherson, Norm, Sr Asst Librn, California State University, 9001 Stockdale Hwy, Bakersfield, CA, 93311-1022. Tel: 661-654-2061. Fax: 661-654-3238. p. 123

Hutcheson, Beth, Ref Librn, Homewood Public Library, 1721 Oxmoor Rd, Homewood, AL, 35209-4085. Tel: 205-332-6625. Fax: 205-802-6424. p. 20

Hutcheson, Margie, Dir, Sumter County Library System, 201 Monroe St, Livingston, AL, 35470. Tel: 205-652-2349. p. 24

Hutcheson, Margie, Dir, Ruby Pickens Tartt Public Library, 201 Monroe St, Livingston, AL, 35470. Tel: 205-652-2349. Fax: 205-652-6688. p. 24

Hutcheson, Sandria, Librn, Missouri Department of Corrections, Southeast Correctional Center, Hwy 105, Charleston, MO, 63834. Tel: 573-683-4409. Fax: 573-683-7022. p. 1335

Hutchings, Carol, Ch, Morris Area Public Library District, 604 Liberty St, Morris, IL, 60450. Tel: 815-942-6880. Fax: 815-942-6415. p. 675

Hutchings, Jessica, Asst Prof, Res Librn, McNeese State University, 4205 Ryan St, Lake Charles, LA, 70609. Tel: 337-475-5546. Fax: 337-475-5719, 337-475-5727. p. 954

Hutchings, Laura, Librn, Parkland Regional Library, Saltcoats Branch, 117 Allen Ave, Saltcoats, SK, S0A 3R0, CANADA. Tel: 306-744-2911. p. 2932

Hutchins, Carol, Librn, New York University, Courant Institute of Mathematical Sciences, 251 Mercer St, 12th Flr, New York, NY, 10012-1185. Tel: 212-998-3315. Fax: 212-995-4808. p. 1695

Hutchins, Debbie, In Charge, Merced County Library, Irwin-Hilmar Branch, 20041 W Falke St, Hilmar, CA, 95324-0970. Tel: 209-632-0746. p. 186

Hutchins, Donna, Dir, Odem Public Library, 516 Voss Ave, Odem, TX, 78370. Tel: 361-368-7388. Fax: 361-368-7388. p. 2366

Hutchins, Geri, Tech Serv, Rio Rancho Public Library, 755 Loma Colorado Dr NE, Rio Rancho, NM, 87124. Tel: 505-891-5013. Fax: 502-892-4782. p. 1561

Hutchins, Julia, Youth/Young Adult Librn, Leesburg Public Library, 100 E Main St, Leesburg, FL, 34748. Tel: 352-728-9790. Fax: 352-728-9794. p. 461

Hutchins, Linda, Youth Serv, Normal Public Library, 206 W College Ave, Normal, IL, 61761. Tel: 309-452-1757. Fax: 309-452-5312. p. 681

Hutchins, Margaret, Youth Serv, Rye Public Library, 581 Washington Rd, Rye, NH, 03870. Tel: 603-964-8401. Fax: 603-964-7065. p. 1464

Hutchins, Ron, Sr Ref Librn, Webmaster, University of Texas, M D Anderson Cancer Center Research Medical Library, 1400 Pressler St, Houston, TX, 77030-3722. Tel: 713-745-4334. Fax: 713-563-3650. p. 2344

Hutchins, Thelma, Dir of Libr, Fairmont State University, 1201 Locust Ave, Fairmont, WV, 26554. Tel: 304-367-4733. Fax: 304-367-4677. p. 2559

Hutchins, Thelma, Dir of Libr Serv, Fairmont State College, School of Education, 1201 Locust Ave, Fairmont, WV, 26554. Tel: 304-367-4122. Fax: 304-367-4677. p. 2976

Hutchinson, Amy, Dir, Lake County Library District, 513 Center St, Lakeview, OR, 97630-1582. Tel: 541-947-6019. Fax: 541-947-6034. p. 2003

Hutchinson, Beck, Head, Cat, Head, Coll Develop, Florida Hospital College of Health Sciences, 671 Winyah Dr, Orlando, FL, 32803. Tel: 407-303-7747, Ext 9882. Fax: 407-303-9622. p. 475

Hutchinson, Cheryl, Librn, Manitoba Department of Finance, 910-386 Broadway, Winnipeg, MB, R3C 3R6, CANADA. Tel: 204-945-3757, 204-945-8329. Fax: 204-945-5051. p. 2756

Hutchinson, Cindy, Asst Librn, Macsherry Library, 112 Walton St, Alexandria Bay, NY, 13607. Tel: 315-482-2241. Fax: 315-482-2241. p. 1572

Hutchinson, Corrie, Dir, Stephens College, 1200 E Broadway, Columbia, MO, 65215. Tel: 573-876-7182. Fax: 573-876-7264. p. 1325

Hutchinson, Ditha, Mgr, Bureau of Land Management Library, 5100 E Winnemucca Blvd, Winnemucca, NV, 89445. Tel: 775-623-1500. Fax: 775-623-1503. p. 1435

Hutchinson, Holly, Youth Serv Librn, Atchison Public Library, 401 Kansas Ave, Atchison, KS, 66002-2495. Tel: 913-367-1902. Fax: 913-367-2717. p. 856

Hutchinson, Jonathan C, Archives Librn, Syst Adminr, Pfeiffer University, 48380 US Hwy 52 N, Misenheimer, NC, 28109. Tel: 704-463-3361. Fax: 704-463-3356. p. 1809

Hutchinson, Kyle, Pharm Librn, Western New England University, 1215 Wilbraham Rd, Springfield, MA, 01119. Tel: 413-782-1534. Fax: 413-796-2011. p. 1128

Hutchinson, Laurie, Info Spec, Hickory Public Library, 375 Third St NE, Hickory, NC, 28601-5126. Tel: 828-304-0500, Ext 7281. Fax: 828-304-0023. p. 1801

Hutchinson, Lynn, Librn, Topeka Genealogical Society Library, 2717 SE Indiana Ave, Topeka, KS, 66605-1440. Tel: 785-233-5762. p. 897

Hutchinson, Lynn, Librn, First Baptist Church Library, 1701 Winchester Ave, Ashland, KY, 41101. Tel: 606-324-3109. Fax: 606-324-4344. p. 906

Hutchinson, Natalie, Dir, Central College, Campus Box 6500, 812 University St, Pella, IA, 50219-1999. Tel: 641-628-5220. Fax: 641-628-5327. p. 838

Hutchinson, Pamela, Dir, Giddings Public Library, 276 N Orange St, Giddings, TX, 78942-3317. Tel: 979-542-2716. Fax: 979-542-1879. p. 2328

Hutchinson, Robin, Acq, Coll Develop, Doc, St Lawrence University, 23 Romoda Dr, Canton, NY, 13617. Tel: 315-229-5331. Fax: 315-229-5729. p. 1602

Hutchinson, Susan, Dir, University of Northern Colorado, McKee Hall 518, 501 20th St, Greeley, CO, 80639. Tel: 970-351-2816. Fax: 970-351-1622. p. 2963

Hutchinson, Terri, Literacy Coordr, Alachua County Library District, 401 E University Ave, Gainesville, FL, 32601-5453. Tel: 352-334-3929. Fax: 352-334-3918. p. 448

Hutchinson, William, III, YA Serv, Atlanta-Fulton Public Library System, Southwest Regional Library, 3665 Cascade Rd SW, Atlanta, GA, 30331. Tel: 404-699-6363. Fax: 404-699-6381. p. 512

Hutchison, Angel, Tech Serv, Springdale Public Library, 405 S Pleasant St, Springdale, AR, 72764. Tel: 479-750-8180. Fax: 479-750-8182. p. 115

Hutchison, Ann, Tech Dir, Akron-Summit County Public Library, 60 S High St, Akron, OH, 44326. Tel: 330-643-9000. Fax: 330-643-9160. p. 1852

Hutchison, David, Dir, Libr Serv, Umpqua Community College Library, 1140 Umpqua College Rd, Roseburg, OR, 97470. Tel: 541-440-4638. Fax: 541-440-4637. p. 2017

Hutchison, Donna, Dir, Media Serv, First Baptist Church, 209 E South, Longview, TX, 75601. Tel: 903-758-0681, Ext 117. Fax: 903-753-0936. p. 2356

Hutchison, Jane B, Prog Chair, William Paterson University, College of Education, 1600 Valley Rd, Wayne, NJ, 07470. Tel: 973-720-2331, 973-720-2980. Fax: 973-720-2585. p. 2969

Hutchison, Kathleen, Coll Develop, Dir, Mississippi College, 101 W College St, Clinton, MS, 39058. Tel: 601-925-3870. Fax: 601-925-3435. p. 1296

Hutchison, Kathleen, Mgr, Mississippi Electronic Libraries Online, Mississippi State Board for Community & Junior Colleges, 3825 Ridgewood Rd, Jackson, MS, 39211. Tel: 601-432-6518. Fax: 601-432-6363. p. 2947

Hutchison, Katie, Asst Librn, Archives & Spec Coll, Walsh University, 2020 E Maple St NW, North Canton, OH, 44720-3336. Tel: 330-244-4968. Fax: 330-490-7270. p. 1923

Hutchison, Robin, Coll Mgt Lectr, Texas A&M University Libraries, Cushing Memorial Library & Archives, 5000 TAMU, College Station, TX, 77843-5000. Tel: 979-845-1951. Fax: 979-845-1441. p. 2299

Hutchson, Kim, Librn, Georgia Department of Corrections, Office of Library Services, Hwy 107 S, Mount Vernon, GA, 30445. Tel: 912-583-3600. Fax: 912-583-3667. p. 546

Huth, Barb, Head, Tech Serv, Kendallville Public Library, 221 S Park Ave, Kendallville, IN, 46755-2248. Tel: 260-343-2010. Fax: 260-343-2011. p. 756

Huth, Nancy, Educ Curator, Taft Museum of Art Library, 316 Pike St, Cincinnati, OH, 45202-4293. Tel: 513-241-0343. Fax: 513-241-2266. p. 1873

Hutslar, Jack, Dr, Dir, North American Youth Sport Institute, 4985 Oak Garden Dr, Kernersville, NC, 27284-9520. Tel: 336-784-4926. Fax: 336-784-5546. p. 1804

Hutson, Ashley, Br Mgr, Washington County Free Library, Smithsburg Branch, 66 W Water St, Smithsburg, MD, 21783-1604. Tel: 301-824-7722. p. 1031

Hutson, James H, Chief Librn, Library of Congress, Manuscript Division, James Madison Memorial Bldg, Rms 101-102, 101 Independence Ave SE, Washington, DC, 20540. p. 407

Hutson, Jeffrey, Assoc Dir, Pub Serv, University of Baltimore, 1420 Maryland Ave, Baltimore, MD, 21201. Tel: 410-837-4298. Fax: 410-837-4330. p. 1018

Hutson, Mical, ILL, Bud Werner Memorial Library, 1289 Lincoln Ave, Steamboat Springs, CO, 80487. Tel: 970-879-0240. Fax: 970-879-3476. p. 323

Hutson, Regina, Librn, Puckett Public Library, 118 Cemetery Rd, Puckett, MS, 39151. Tel: 601-824-0180. p. 1312

Hutte, Carol, Bibliog Instr, Ref, Chaffey College Library, 5885 Haven Ave, Rancho Cucamonga, CA, 91737-3002. Tel: 909-652-6800. Fax: 909-466-2821. p. 212

Huttenhower, James, Tech Serv, Bethel Park Public Library, 5100 W Library Ave, Bethel Park, PA, 15102. Tel: 412-831-6800, Ext 262, 412-851-2465. Fax: 412-835-9360. p. 2033

Huttenlock, Terry, Syst Coordr, Wheaton College, 510 Irving Ave, Wheaton, IL, 60187-5593. Tel: 630-752-5352. Fax: 630-752-5855. p. 718

Hutto, Annette, Librn, Camp Wood Public Library, 117 S Nueces, Camp Wood, TX, 78833-0828. Tel: 830-597-3208. Fax: 830-597-3208. p. 2294

Hutto, Dena, Head, Ref (Info Serv), Reed College, 3203 SE Woodstock Blvd, Portland, OR, 97202-8199. Tel: 503-777-7702. Fax: 503-777-7786. p. 2014

Hutto, Rebecca, Cat, Samford University Library, Lucille Stewart Beeson Law Library, 800 Lakeshore Dr, Birmingham, AL, 35229. Tel: 205-726-2714. Fax: 205-726-2644. p. 9

Hutton, Ann, Exec Dir, Southeastern Libraries Cooperating, 2600 19th St NW, Rochester, MN, 55901-0767. Tel: 507-288-5513. Fax: 507-288-8697. p. 2947

Hutton, Cathy, Asst Librn, Circ, Nyssa Public Library, 319 Main St, Nyssa, OR, 97913-3845. Tel: 541-372-2978. Fax: 541-372-3278. p. 2008

Hutton, E J, Managing Librn, Young Public Library, 150 Community Center Rd, Young, AZ, 85554. Tel: 928-462-3588. Fax: 928-462-3588. p. 90

Hutton, Jacquelyn, Circ, University of Medicine & Dentistry of New Jersey, 30 12th Ave, Newark, NJ, 07103-2706. Tel: 973-972-4580. p. 1513

Hutton, Jane, Electronic Res, Web Serv, West Chester University, 25 W Rosedale Ave, West Chester, PA, 19383. Tel: 610-436-3453. p. 2153

Hutton, Theresa, Librn, Centre County Library & Historical Museum, Holt Memorial, Nine W Pine St, Philipsburg, PA, 16866. Tel: 814-342-1987. Fax: 814-342-0530. p. 2032

Hutton-hughes, Emily, Head, Coll Develop, Colgate University, 13 Oak Dr, Hamilton, NY, 13346-1398. Tel: 315-228-7300. Fax: 315-228-7934. p. 1633

Hutzel, Martha, Br Mgr, Central Rappahannock Regional Library, Porter Branch, 2001 Parkway Blvd, Stafford, VA, 22554-3972. Tel: 540-659-4909. Fax: 540-659-4359. p. 2466

Huwe, Beth, Librn, Herzing College Library, 5218 E Terrace Dr, Madison, WI, 53718-8340. Tel: 608-663-0816. Fax: 608-249-8593. p. 2606

Huwe, Jane, Info Serv Librn, Siouxland Libraries, 200 N Dakota Ave, Sioux Falls, SD, 57104. Tel: 605-367-8722. Fax: 605-367-4312. p. 2218

Huwe, Terence, Librn, University of California, Berkeley, Institute for Research on Labor & Employment Library, 2521 Channing Way, MC 5555, Berkeley, CA, 94720-5555. Tel: 510-642-1705. Fax: 510-642-6432. p. 128

Huwieler, Cara, Ref & Teen Librn, The Brentwood Library, 8109 Concord Rd, Brentwood, TN, 37027. Tel: 615-371-0090, Ext 8130. Fax: 615-371-2238. p. 2225

Huxley, Carleen, Ref Serv, State University of New York - Jefferson Community College, 1220 Coffeen St, Watertown, NY, 13601-1897. Tel: 315-786-2225. Fax: 315-788-0716. p. 1764

Huxley, Kelly L, Librn, Onoway Public Library, 4708 Lac Sainte Anne Trail, Onoway, AB, T0E 1V0, CANADA. Tel: 780-967-2445. Fax: 888-467-1309. p. 2713

Huxtable, Michael, Ref Librn, Portsmouth Public Library, 175 Parrott Ave, Portsmouth, NH, 03801-4452. Tel: 603-766-1722. Fax: 603-433-0981. p. 1463

Huyck, Sharlyn S, Dir, Ovid Public Library, 206 N Main St, Ovid, MI, 48866. Tel: 989-834-5800. Fax: 989-834-5113. p. 1216

Huynh, Angelica M, Chief Human Res Officer, Queens Borough Public Library, 89-11 Merrick Blvd, Jamaica, NY, 11432. Tel: 718-990-0737. p. 1643

Huynh, Hai, Acq of Monographs, Cat, Notre Dame de Namur University Library, 1500 Ralston Ave, Belmont, CA, 94002-1908. Tel: 650-508-3486. Fax: 650-508-3697. p. 126

Huynh, Loc, ILL, Beverly Hills Public Library, 444 N Rexford Dr, Beverly Hills, CA, 90210-4877. Tel: 310-288-2220. Fax: 310-278-3387. p. 129

Hwang, Amy, Info Serv, Eastern Nazarene College, 23 E Elm Ave, Quincy, MA, 02170. Tel: 617-745-3850. Fax: 617-745-3913. p. 1119

Hwang, Peter, Dr, Officer, American Rhinologic Society Library, PO Box 495, Warwick, NY, 10990-0495. Tel: 845-988-1631. Fax: 845-986-1527. p. 1762

Hwang, Yunmi, Chief Exec Officer, St Mary's Public Library, 15 Church St N, St. Marys, ON, N4X 1B4, CANADA. Tel: 519-284-3346. Fax: 519-284-2630. p. 2844

Hyatt, Jason, Libr Mgr, Charlotte Mecklenburg Library, ImaginOn: The Joe & Joan Martin Center, 300 E Seventh St, Charlotte, NC, 28202. Tel: 704-416-4601. Fax: 704-416-4700. p. 1782

Hyatt, Jenny, Ch, Cynthiana-Harrison County Public Library, 104 N Main St, Cynthiana, KY, 41031. Tel: 859-234-4881. Fax: 859-234-0059. p. 911

Hyatt, Lillian, Librn, Fluor, 100 Fluor Daniel Dr, Greenville, SC, 29607-2762. Tel: 864-281-4799. Fax: 864-281-6480. p. 2195

Hyatt, Linda, Librn, Colorado Territorial Correctional Facility Library, PO Box 1010, Canon City, CO, 81215-1010. Tel: 719-275-4181, Ext 3167. Fax: 719-269-4115. p. 294

Hyatt, Mary Ann, Dir, University of Oregon Libraries, John E Jaqua Law Library, William W Knight Law Ctr, 2nd Flr, 1515 Agate St, Eugene, OR, 97403-1221. Tel: 541-346-3097. Fax: 541-346-1669. p. 1997

Hyatt, Maryjane, Youth Serv, St Pete Beach Public Library, 365 73rd Ave, Saint Pete Beach, FL, 33706-1996. Tel: 727-363-9238. Fax: 727-552-1760. p. 487

Hyde, Anne S, Asst Librn, Keyser-Mineral County Public Library, Fort Ashby Public, PO Box 74, Fort Ashby, WV, 26719-0064. Tel: 304-298-4493. Fax: 304-298-4014. p. 2563

Hyde, Debra, Adult Serv, Park Falls Public Library, 121 N Fourth Ave, Park Falls, WI, 54552. Tel: 715-762-3121. Fax: 715-762-2286. p. 2629

Hyde, Loree, Ref Librn, Oregon Health & Science University Library, 3181 SW Sam Jackson Park Rd, Portland, OR, 97239-3098. Tel: 503-494-3460. Fax: 503-494-3227. p. 2013

Hyde, Mary A, Dir, American College of Obstetricians & Gynecologists, 409 12th St SW, Washington, DC, 20024-2188. Tel: 202-863-2518. Fax: 202-484-1595. p. 392

Hyde, Rachel, Librn, Parkersburg & Wood County Public Library, South Parkersburg, 1713 Blizzard Dr, Parkersburg, WV, 26101. Tel: 304-428-7041. Fax: 304-428-7041. p. 2568

Hyde, Rebecca, Coordr, Info Literacy, Saint Louis University, 3650 Lindell Blvd, Saint Louis, MO, 63108-3302. Tel: 314-977-3106. Fax: 314-977-3108. p. 1360

Hyder-Darlington, Louise M, Access Serv Librn, Elizabethtown College, One Alpha Dr, Elizabethtown, PA, 17022-2227. Tel: 717-361-1454. Fax: 717-361-1167. p. 2053

Hyer, Cassandra, Librn, United States Court of Appeals, 600 Camp St, Rm 106, New Orleans, LA, 70130. Tel: 504-310-7797. Fax: 504-310-7578. p. 964

Hyfler, Amy, Asst Dir, Ruth L Rockwood Memorial Library, Ten Robert Harp Dr, Livingston, NJ, 07039. Tel: 973-992-4600. Fax: 973-994-2346. p. 1496

Hyland, Douglas, Dir, New Britain Museum of American Art Library, 56 Lexington St, New Britain, CT, 06052. Tel: 860-229-0257. Fax: 860-229-3445. p. 354

Hyland, Evelyn, Asst Librn, Groveton Public Library, 126 W First, Groveton, TX, 75845. Tel: 936-642-2483. p. 2330

Hyland, Judy, Dir, Serv Delivery, Burlington Public Library, 2331 New St, Burlington, ON, L7R 1J4, CANADA. Tel: 905-639-3611. Fax: 905-681-7277. p. 2797

Hyland, Maureen, Coll Develop, Per, Humber College, 205 Humber College Blvd, Toronto, ON, M9W 5L7, CANADA. Tel: 416-675-6622, Ext 4501. Fax: 416-675-7439. p. 2854

Hyland, Sheryl, Br Head, Toronto Public Library, Maryvale, Parkway Mall, 85 Ellesmere Rd, Toronto, ON, M1R 4B9, CANADA. Tel: 416-396-8931. Fax: 416-396-3603. p. 2862

Hyland, Stephanie, In Charge, Connecticut Society of Genealogists, Inc Library, 175 Maple St, East Hartford, CT, 06118-2364. Tel: 860-569-0002. Fax: 860-569-0339. p. 337

Hylen, Sandra, Dir, Ontario Public Library, 1850 Ridge Rd, Ontario, NY, 14519. Tel: 315-524-8381. Fax: 315-524-5838. p. 1711

Hyles, Linda, Mkt Coordr, Chattahoochee Valley Libraries, 3000 Macon Rd, Columbus, GA, 31906-2201. Tel: 706-243-2673. Fax: 706-243-2710. p. 525

Hylton, Andrea, Syst Librn, Johnson C Smith University, 100 Beatties Ford Rd, Charlotte, NC, 28216. Tel: 704-371-6740. Fax: 704-378-1191. p. 1783

Hylton, Candess, Mgr, Lonesome Pine Regional Library, Coeburn Community, 111 Third St, Coeburn, VA, 24230. Tel: 276-395-6152. Fax: 276-395-3563. p. 2504

Hylton, Lesley, Circ, Taylor County Public Library, 200 Beech St, Grafton, WV, 26354. Tel: 304-265-6121. Fax: 304-265-6122. p. 2559

Hylton, Mary Agnes, Br Mgr, Indianapolis-Marion County Public Library, Eagle, 3325 Lowry Rd, Indianapolis, IN, 46222-1240. Tel: 317-275-4340. p. 754

Hylton, Ramona, Govt Doc Librn, East Stroudsburg University, 216 Normal St, East Stroudsburg, PA, 18301-2999. Tel: 570-422-3150. Fax: 570-422-3151. p. 2051

Hyman, Mark, Dir, Alan Wofsy Fine Arts Reference Library, 1109 Geary Blvd, San Francisco, CA, 94109. Tel: 415-292-6500. Fax: 415-292-6594. p. 249

Hyman, Ruth, Head of Libr, Free Library of Philadelphia, Paschalville Branch, 6942 Woodland Ave, Philadelphia, PA, 19142-1823. Tel: 215-685-2662, 215-685-2663. Fax: 215-685-2656. p. 2108

Hyman, Ryan, Curator, Macculloch Hall Historical Museum Archives, 45 Macculloch Ave, Morristown, NJ, 07960. Tel: 973-538-2404. Fax: 973-538-9428. p. 1505

Hymel, Melissa, Dir, Pointe Coupee Parish Library, 201 Claiborne St, New Roads, LA, 70760-3403. Tel: 225-638-7593. Fax: 225-638-9847. p. 964

Hymes, Judith I, Tech Serv Dir, Washington College, 300 Washington Ave, Chestertown, MD, 21620-1197. Tel: 410-778-7278. Fax: 410-778-7288. p. 1023

Hynd, Joanna, Actg Dir, Thomaston Public Library, 60 Main St, Thomaston, ME, 04861. Tel: 207-354-2453. p. 1003

Hynes, Deborah, Br Coordr, Nashville Public Library, Watkins Community, 612 17th Ave N, Nashville, TN, 37203-2878. Tel: 615-862-5872. Fax: 615-862-6746. p. 2258

Hynes, Deborah, Br Mgr, Nashville Public Library, Richland Park, 4711 Charlotte Ave, Nashville, TN, 37209-3404. Tel: 615-862-5870. Fax: 615-862-5897. p. 2258

Hynes, Donna, ILL, YA Serv, Rochester Public Library, 65 S Main St, Rochester, NH, 03867-2707. Tel: 603-332-1428. Fax: 603-335-7582. p. 1464

Hynes, Michelle, Circ, C W Clark Memorial Library, 160 N Main St, Oriskany Falls, NY, 13425. Tel: 315-821-7850. Fax: 315-821-7850. p. 1712

Hynson, Judith S, Dir, Libr & Res Serv, Jessie Ball Dupont Memorial Library, Stratford Hall, 483 Great House Rd, Stratford, VA, 22558. Tel: 804-493-8038, Ext 8572. Fax: 804-493-8006. p. 2497

Hypher, Monica, Tech Librn, University of Toronto Libraries, Industrial Relations Centre, Jean & Dorothy Newman Library, 121 Saint George St, Toronto, ON, M5S 1A1, CANADA. Tel: 416-978-2928. Fax: 416-978-5694. p. 2866

Hypio, Mike, Librn, West Shore Community College, 3000 N Stiles Rd, Scottville, MI, 49454. Tel: 231-843-5529, 231-845-6211. Fax: 231-845-2007. p. 1226

Hyres, Ann Marie, Tech Serv, Northwestern Connecticut Community College Library, Park Pl E, Winsted, CT, 06098. Tel: 860-738-6479. Fax: 860-379-4995. p. 379

Hysiuk, Jenna, Librn, Palliser Regional Library, Mossbank Branch, 310 Main St, Mossbank, SK, S0H 3G0, CANADA. Tel: 306-354-2474. Fax: 306-354-2646. p. 2919

Hyslop, Colleen, In Charge, Canadian Wildlife Federation, 350 Michael Cowpland Dr, Kanata, ON, K2M 2W1, CANADA. Tel: 613-599-9594. Fax: 613-599-4428. p. 2812

Hyslop, Colleen F, Assoc Dir, Human Res, Michigan State University Library, 100 Library, East Lansing, MI, 48824-1048. Tel: 517-884-6390. Fax: 517-432-3532. p. 1175

Hyson, Gay, YA Serv, Medford Public Library, 111 High St, Medford, MA, 02155. Tel: 781-395-7950. Fax: 781-391-2261. p. 1104

Hysong, Gabriel, Librn, Rolls-Royce, Mail Code S5, 2001 S Tibbs Ave, Indianapolis, IN, 46241. Tel: 317-230-4751. Fax: 317-230-8901. p. 755

Iacobucci, Marisa, Adult Serv, Outreach Serv Librn, Finger Lakes Library System, 119 E Green St, Ithaca, NY, 14850. Tel: 607-273-4074. Fax: 607-273-3618. p. 1642

Iacone, Audrey, Mgr, Carnegie Library of Pittsburgh, Beechview, 1910 Broadway Ave, Pittsburgh, PA, 15216. Tel: 412-563-2900. p. 2122

Iandoli, Michael, Dir, Larz Anderson Auto Museum Library & Archives, Larz Anderson Park, 15 Newton St, Brookline, MA, 02445. Tel: 617-522-6547. Fax: 617-524-0170. p. 1071

Iannaccone, Leonard, Librn, North Jersey Media Group Library, 150 River St, Hackensack, NJ, 07601. Tel: 201-646-4000. Fax: 201-646-4737. p. 1489

Iannino, Jill, Cat, Kinnelon Public Library, 132 Kinnelon Rd, Kinnelon, NJ, 07405-2393. Tel: 973-838-1321. Fax: 973-838-0741. p. 1493

Iannuzzelli, Jennifer, Actg Libr Mgr, Chaleur Library Region, Petit-Rocher Public Library, 702 Principale St, Office 110, Petit-Rocher, NB, E8J 1V1, CANADA. Tel: 506-542-2744. Fax: 506-542-2745. p. 2761

Iannuzzi, Patricia, Dean, Univ Libr, University of Nevada, Las Vegas Libraries, 4505 Maryland Pkwy, Box 457001, Las Vegas, NV, 89154-7001. Tel: 702-895-2286. Fax: 702-895-2287. p. 1430

Iantorno, Joanne, Head, Info Serv, Radnor Memorial Library, 114 W Wayne Ave, Wayne, PA, 19087-4098. Tel: 610-687-1124. Fax: 610-687-1454. p. 2152

Iavorskaia, Irina, Librn, Royal Victoria Hospital, Women's Pavilion Library, 687 Pine Ave W, Rm F 4-24, Montreal, QC, H3A 1A1, CANADA. Tel: 514-934-1934, Ext 34738. Fax: 514-843-1678. p. 2901

Ibanez, Florante, Computing Serv Librn, Loyola Law School, 919 S Albany St, Los Angeles, CA, 90015-1211. Tel: 213-736-1431. Fax: 213-487-2204. p. 175

Ibararran, Megan, Ch & Youth Librn, Nutley Free Public Library, 93 Booth Dr, Nutley, NJ, 07110-2782. Tel: 973-667-0405. p. 1515

Ibarra, Monica, Ser, California State University, 9001 Stockdale Hwy, Bakersfield, CA, 93311-1022. Tel: 661-664-3249. Fax: 661-654-3238. p. 123

Ibarra, San Juanita, Circ Asst, Laredo Community College, Senator Judith Zaffirini Library (South Library), 5500 S Zapata Hwy, Laredo, TX, 78046. Fax: 956-794-4375. p. 2353

Ibaugh, Phila, Dir, Ransomville Free Library, 3733 Ransomville Rd, Ransomville, NY, 14131. Tel: 716-791-4073. Fax: 716-791-4073. p. 1726

Iberer, Stephanie, Dir, Lincoln Park Public Library, 12 Boonton Tpk, Lincoln Park, NJ, 07035. Tel: 973-694-8283. Fax: 973-694-5515. p. 1495

Ibey, Dawn, Br Head, Vancouver Public Library, Oakridge, 650 W 41st Ave, No 191, Vancouver, BC, V5Z 2M9, CANADA. Tel: 604-665-3980. Fax: 604-665-3932. p. 2744

Ibold, Mike, Librn, Calaveras County Law Library, Government Center, 891 Mountain Ranch Rd, San Andreas, CA, 95249. Tel: 209-754-6314. p. 226

Ibraheem, Abiodum, Cat, Robert Morris University Library, 6001 University Blvd, Moon Township, PA, 15108-1189. Tel: 412-397-6875. Fax: 412-397-4288. p. 2092

Ice, Catherine, Pres, Greater Oklahoma Area Health Sciences Library Consortium, Mercy Memorial Health Ctr-Resource Ctr, 1011 14th Ave NW, Ardmore, OK, 73401. Tel: 580-220-6625. Fax: 580-220-6599. p. 2953

Ice, Nolamae S, Dir, Holly Public Library, 302 S Main, Holly, CO, 81047-9149. Tel: 719-537-6520. Fax: 719-537-6621. p. 313

Ice, Priscilla, Mgr, Info Tech, Spokane County Library District, 4322 N Argonne Rd, Spokane, WA, 99212-1868. Tel: 509-893-8450. Fax: 509-893-8478. p. 2536

Icenhour, Linda, Dir, Johnson County Public Library, 219 N Church St, Mountain City, TN, 37683-1522. Tel: 423-727-6544. Fax: 423-727-0319. p. 2254

Icenhower, Jackie, Librn, Atlanta Public Library, 101 W Hiram St, Atlanta, TX, 75551. Tel: 903-796-2112. Fax: 903-799-4067. p. 2277

Ichihana, Anne, Circ, Mohawk Valley Community College Library, 1101 Sherman Dr, Utica, NY, 13501-5394. Tel: 315-731-5735. Fax: 315-792-5666. p. 1759

Ichinaga, Moon, Ref/Electronic Res Librn, El Camino College, 16007 S Crenshaw Blvd, Torrance, CA, 90506. Tel: 310-660-3525. Fax: 310-660-3513. p. 159

Ichord, Jane, Info Serv Librn, Tufts University, 145 Harrison Ave, Boston, MA, 02111-1843. Fax: 617-636-4039. p. 1068

Icolari, Letty, Dir, Admin Serv, Denver Public Library, Ten W 14th Ave Pkwy, Denver, CO, 80204-2731. Tel: 720-865-1111. Fax: 720-865-2087. p. 300

Ideson, Lindsay, Head of Libr, Jefferson-Madison Regional Library, Northside, 300 Albemarle Sq, Charlottesville, VA, 22901-1466. Tel: 434-973-7893. Fax: 434-973-5876. p. 2454

Idsvoog, Eric, In Charge, Harvard Library, Child Memorial & English Tutorial Library, Widener, Rm Z, Cambridge, MA, 02138. Tel: 617-495-4681. p. 1074

Ien, Erica, Head, Ch, Victoria Public Library, 302 N Main, Victoria, TX, 77901-6592. Tel: 361-485-3304. Fax: 361-485-3295. p. 2395

Ierardi, Julia, Sr Librn, Malden Public Library, 36 Salem St, Malden, MA, 02148-5291. Tel: 781-324-0218. Fax: 781-324-4467. p. 1102

Iferd, Nadine, Acq, Ser, Naval Surface Warfare Center, 110 Vernon Ave, Panama City, FL, 32407-7001. Tel: 850-234-4848. Fax: 850-234-4844. p. 480

Iffergan, Christi, Br Supvr, Gaston County Public Library, Union Road, 5800 Union Rd, Gastonia, NC, 28056. Tel: 704-852-4073. Fax: 704-852-9631. p. 1794

Iglesias, Edward, Syst Librn, Central Connecticut State University, 1615 Stanley St, New Britain, CT, 06050. Tel: 860-832-2082. Fax: 860-832-3409. p. 353

Iglesias, Estrella, Dir, Miami Dade College, North Campus Learning Resources, 11380 NW 27th Ave, Miami, FL, 33167. Tel: 305-237-1471. Fax: 305-237-8276. p. 466

Ignatowicz, Norma, Circ, Canton Public Library, 40 Dyer Ave, Canton, CT, 06019. Tel: 860-693-5800. Fax: 860-693-5804. p. 333

Igoe, James, Law Librn, Social Security Administration Library, Annex Bldg 1520, Baltimore, MD, 21235-6401. Fax: 410-966-2027. p. 1017

Iheanacho, Morris, Cat, Tech Serv, Oakwood College, 7000 Adventist Blvd, Huntsville, AL, 35896. Tel: 256-726-7246. Fax: 256-726-7538. p. 22

Ihlenfeldt, Kay, Librn, Wisconsin Department of Public Instruction, DPI Professional Library, GEF 3 Bldg, 3rd Flr, 125 S Webster St, Madison, WI, 53703. Tel: 608-266-3108. Fax: 608-266-2529. p. 2610

Ihnat, Bertha, Ref, Ohio State University LIBRARIES, Archives, 2700 Kenny Rd, Columbus, OH, 43210. Tel: 614-292-2409. Fax: 614-688-4150. p. 1887

Ihnen, Amy, Dir, Chatham Area Public Library District, 600 E Spruce St, Chatham, IL, 62629. Tel: 217-483-2713. Fax: 217-483-2361. p. 604

Ihrig, Elizabeth, Librn, The Bakken - A Library & Museum of Electricity in Life, 3537 Zenith Ave S, Minneapolis, MN, 55416. Tel: 612-926-3878. Fax: 612-927-7265. p. 1259

Iida-Cordon, Ayumi, Archivist, Pinellas County Government, 11909 125th St N, Largo, FL, 33774. Tel: 727-582-2123. Fax: 727-582-2455. p. 460

Ijams, Sally, Head, Knowledge & Learning Serv, Darien Library, 1441 Post Rd, Darien, CT, 06820-5419. Tel: 203-669-5229. Fax: 203-655-1547. p. 336

Ikeda, Anne, Mgr, Lang Michener LLP Library, 1500-1055 W Georgia St, Vancouver, BC, V6E 4N7, CANADA. Tel: 604-689-9111. Fax: 604-685-7084. p. 2741

Ikemoto, Karen, Br Mgr, Hawaii State Public Library System, Hanapepe Public Library, 4490 Kona Rd, Hanapepe, HI, 96716. Tel: 808-335-8418. Fax: 808-335-2120. p. 561

Ikuta, Kay, Head, Adult Serv, Inglewood Public Library, 101 W Manchester Blvd, Inglewood, CA, 90301-1771. Tel: 310-412-5397. Fax: 310-412-8848. p. 159

Iles, Barbara, ILL, Tombigbee Regional Library System, 338 Commerce, West Point, MS, 39773. Tel: 662-494-4872. Fax: 662-494-0300. p. 1317

Iles, Teresa, Br Mgr, Nelsonville Public Library, Chauncey Public, 29 Converse St, Chauncey, OH, 45719. Tel: 740-797-2512. Fax: 740-797-2512. p. 1920

Ilgar, Guo, Adult Serv, Uniondale Public Library, 400 Uniondale Ave, Uniondale, NY, 11553-1995. Tel: 516-489-2220, Ext 208. Fax: 516-489-4005. p. 1758

Ilievski, Fannie, Librn, Methodist Hospital, 600 Grant St, Gary, IN, 46402. Tel: 219-886-4554. Fax: 219-886-4271. p. 745

Ille, Jon, Archivist, Little Big Horn College Library, One Forestry Lane, Crow Agency, MT, 59022. Tel: 406-638-3182. Fax: 406-638-3170. p. 1377

Illick, E Ralph, Ref Serv, Ad, Pauline Haass Public Library, N64 W23820 Main St, Sussex, WI, 53089-3120. Tel: 262-246-5180. Fax: 262-246-5236. p. 2642

Illick, Ralph, Dir, Marathon County Public Library, 300 N First St, Wausau, WI, 54403-5405. Tel: 715-261-7211. Fax: 715-261-7204. p. 2646

Illingworth, Mary-Ellen, Librn, Saskatchewan Labour Relations & Workplace Safety Library, 300 - 1870 Albert St, Regina, SK, S4P 4W1, CANADA. Tel: 306-787-2429. Fax: 306-798-5190. p. 2924

Illis, Diane C, Communications Coordr, Northern Tier Library Association, 4015 Dickey Rd, Gibsonia, PA, 15044-9713. Tel: 724-449-2665. Fax: 724-443-6755. p. 2060

Illobachie, Nonyem, Commun Libr Mgr, Queens Borough Public Library, Whitestone Community Library, 151-10 14th Rd, Whitestone, NY, 11357. Tel: 718-767-8010. Fax: 718-357-3086. p. 1645

Im, Kui-Bin, Syst Librn, University of Michigan-Flint, 303 E Kearsley St, Flint, MI, 48502-1950. Tel: 810-762-3199. Fax: 810-762-3133. p. 1181

Imbeau, Lynn, Librn, Greater Sudbury Public Library, Capreol Branch, Nine Morin St, Capreol, ON, P0M 1H0, CANADA. Tel: 705-688-3958. Fax: 705-858-1085. p. 2846

Imboden, Lynnette, Librn, East Central Arkansas Regional Library, Hickory Ridge Branch, 135 S Front, Hickory Ridge, AR, 72347. Tel: 870-697-2201. Fax: 870-697-2201. p. 117

Imhoff, Heather, Head, Pub Info, Des Plaines Public Library, 1501 Ellinwood St, Des Plaines, IL, 60016-4553. Tel: 847-376-2792. Fax: 847-827-7974. p. 636

Imig, Lois, Br Mgr, Omaha Public Library, Millard, 13214 Westwood Lane, Omaha, NE, 68144. Tel: 402-444-4848. Fax: 402-444-6623. p. 1414

Imler, Bonnie, Info Tech, Pennsylvania State University, Altoona College, 3000 Ivyside Park, Altoona, PA, 16601-3760. Tel: 814-949-5499. Fax: 814-949-5246, 814-949-5520. p. 2028

Imm-Stroukoff, Eumie, Asst Dir, Librn, Georgia O'Keeffe Museum, 217 Johnson St, Santa Fe, NM, 87501. Tel: 505-946-1011. Fax: 505-946-1093. p. 1563

Immel, Debbie, Circ, ILL, Saddleback College, 28000 Marguerite Pkwy, Mission Viejo, CA, 92692. Tel: 949-582-4523. Fax: 949-364-0284. p. 187

Immen, Patricia A, Dir, Concord Public Library, 45 Green St, Concord, NH, 03301-4294. Tel: 603-230-3680. Fax: 603-230-3693. p. 1442

Immler, Frank, Head, Coll Develop, Temple University Libraries, 1210 W Berks St, Philadelphia, PA, 19122-6088. Tel: 215-204-9244. Fax: 215-204-5201. p. 2117

Immroth, Barbara F, Prof, University of Texas at Austin, One University Sta, D7000, Austin, TX, 78712-0390. Tel: 512-471-3821. Fax: 512-471-3971. p. 2975

Imparato, Martha, Spec Coll Librn, Washburn University, 1700 SW College Ave, Topeka, KS, 66621. Tel: 785-670-1981. Fax: 785-670-3223. p. 897

Imperial, Robin, Mgr, District of Columbia Public Library, Petworth, 4200 Kansas Ave NW, Washington, DC, 20011. Tel: 202-541-6300. p. 398

Imperial, Robin, Librn, Cumberland County Public Library & Information Center, Bordeaux, 3711 Village Dr, Fayetteville, NC, 28304-1530. Tel: 910-424-4008. Fax: 910-423-1456. p. 1792

Impullitti, Cathy, Sr Br Mgr, OC Public Libraries, Ladera Ranch Library, 29551 Sienna Pkwy, Ladera Ranch, CA, 92694. Tel: 949-234-5940. Fax: 949-347-1330. p. 258

Imrie, Diane, Exec Dir, Northwestern Ontario Sports Hall of Fame Library, 219 May St S, Thunder Bay, ON, P7E 1B5, CANADA. Tel: 807-622-2852. Fax: 807-622-2736. p. 2848

Inaba, Guy, Ref Serv, Kapiolani Community College Library, 4303 Diamond Head Rd, Honolulu, HI, 96816. Tel: 808-734-9206. Fax: 808-734-9453. p. 564

Inabinet, Sherry, Coll Develop, Exec Dir, Middlesex County Public Library, 150 Grace St, Urbanna, VA, 23175. Tel: 804-758-5717. Fax: 804-758-5910. p. 2498

Inagi, Yoko, Head, Cat, City College of the City University of New York, North Academic Ctr, 160 Convent Ave, New York, NY, 10031. Tel: 212-650-7623. Fax: 212-650-7604. p. 1672

Indalecio, Laurel, Coordr, Ch Serv, El Paso Public Library, 501 N Oregon St, El Paso, TX, 79901. Tel: 915-543-5470. Fax: 915-543-5410. p. 2316

Indarjit, Mahendra, Div Mgr, Queens Borough Public Library, Business, Science & Technology Division, 89-11 Merrick Blvd, Jamaica, NY, 11432. Tel: 718-990-8674. Fax: 718-658-8342. p. 1644

Ineguez, Heidi, Computer Spec, Yakama Nation Library, Yakama Nation Cultural Ctr, Hwy 97 at Fort Rd, Toppenish, WA, 98948. Tel: 509-865-2800, Ext 6, 509-865-5121, Ext 4721, 509-865-5121, Ext 4747. Fax: 509-865-6101. p. 2541

Infante, Adele, Dir, Grafton - Midview Public Library, 983 Main St, Grafton, OH, 44044-1492. Tel: 440-926-3317. Fax: 440-926-3000. p. 1902

Infante, Jean, Librn, Southborough Public Library, 25 Main St, Southborough, MA, 01772. Tel: 508-485-5031. Fax: 508-229-4451. p. 1126

Infantine, Patricia W, Dir, Manlius Library, One Arkie Albanese Ave, Manlius, NY, 13104. Tel: 315-682-6400. Fax: 315-682-4490. p. 1657

Ingall, Andrew, Asst Curator, The Jewish Museum, 1109 Fifth Ave, New York, NY, 10128. Tel: 212-423-3234. Fax: 212-423-3232. p. 1683

Ingalls, Amy, Ch Mgr, Manhattan-Elwood Public Library District, 240 Whitson St, Manhattan, IL, 60442. Tel: 815-478-3987. Fax: 815-478-3988. p. 669

Ingalls, Kate, Librn, Beverly Public Library, Beverly Farms, 24 Vine St, Beverly, MA, 01915-2208. Tel: 978-921-6066. Fax: 978-927-9239. p. 1053

Ingalls, Maureen, Asst Librn, Bancroft Public Library, 208 E Ramsey St, Bancroft, IA, 50517. Tel: 515-885-2753. Fax: 515-885-2753. p. 795

Ingegno, Megan, Circ, Franklin Township Free Public Library, 485 DeMott Lane, Somerset, NJ, 08873. Tel: 732-873-8700. Fax: 732-873-0746. p. 1529

Ingelson, Allan, Exec Dir, Canadian Institute of Resources Law, University of Calgary, Murray Fraser Hall, Rm 3353, Calgary, AB, T2N 1N4, CANADA. Tel: 403-220-3200. Fax: 403-282-6182. p. 2691

Ingersoll, Lynne, Mgr, Ref & Tech Serv, Blue Island Public Library, 2433 York St, Blue Island, IL, 60406-2011. Tel: 703-388-1078, Ext 19. Fax: 708-388-1143. p. 596

Ingle, Alicia, Spec Coll Librn, Yuma County Library District, 2951 S 21st Dr, Yuma, AZ, 85364. Tel: 928-373-6498. Fax: 928-782-9420. p. 91

Ingles, Ernie, Dir, University of Alberta, 3-20 Rutherford S, Edmonton, AB, T6G 2J4, CANADA. Tel: 780-492-4578. Fax: 780-492-2430. p. 2977

Inglis, Amy, Dir, Barrington Public Library, 105 Ramsdell Lane, Barrington, NH, 03825. Tel: 603-664-9715. Fax: 603-664-5219. p. 1438

Inglis, Carol-Anne, Acq & Coll, Vanier College Library, 821 Ave Sainte-Croix, Saint Laurent, QC, H4X 3L9, CANADA. Tel: 514-744-7500, Ext 7540. Fax: 514-744-7545. p. 2909

Inglis, Leslie, Pub Serv Librn, Franklin Pierce University Library, 40 University Dr, Rindge, NH, 03461-3114. Tel: 603-899-1141. Fax: 603-899-4375. p. 1463

Ingman, Kristin, Libr Assoc, Johnson & Wales University, 1701 NE 127th St, North Miami, FL, 33181. Tel: 305-892-7043. p. 472

Ingmire, Andrea, Libr Dir, Greensburg-Decatur County Public Library, 1110 E Main St, Greensburg, IN, 47240. Tel: 812-663-2826. Fax: 812-663-5617. p. 746

Ingold, Cindy, Librn, University of Illinois Library at Urbana-Champaign, Social Sciences, Health & Education Library, 100 Main Library, MC-522, 1408 W Gregory Dr, Urbana, IL, 61801. Tel: 217-333-7998. Fax: 217-333-2214. p. 713

Ingold, Jane, Archives, Ref Serv, Penn State Erie, 4951 College Dr, Erie, PA, 16563-4115. Tel: 814-898-6106. Fax: 814-898-6350. p. 2056

Ingold, Meb, Ch, La Grange Park Public Library District, 555 N LaGrange Rd, La Grange Park, IL, 60526-5644. Tel: 708-352-0100. Fax: 708-352-1606. p. 662

Ingolfsland, Dennis, Dr, Dir, Crown College, 8700 College View Dr, Saint Bonifacius, MN, 55375-9002. Tel: 952-446-4240. Fax: 952-446-4149. p. 1274

Ingraham, Brenda, Librn, Tifereth Israel Synagogue Library, 3219 Sheridan Blvd, Lincoln, NE, 68502. Tel: 402-423-8569. p. 1406

Ingram, Carolyn, Cat, Ref, Central Alabama Community College, 1675 Cherokee Rd, Alexander City, AL, 35010. Tel: 256-215-4291. Fax: 256-234-0384. p. 3

Ingram, Catherine E, Head, Adult Serv, Elmhurst Public Library, 125 S Prospect, Elmhurst, IL, 60126-3298. Tel: 630-279-8696. Fax: 630-279-0636. p. 642

Ingram, Cathy, Curator, US National Park Service, 1411 W St SE, Washington, DC, 20020. Tel: 202-426-5961. Fax: 202-426-0880. p. 420

Ingram, Cindy, Dir, Satsuma Public Library, 5466 Old Hwy 43, Satsuma, AL, 36572. Tel: 251-679-0700. Fax: 251-679-0973. p. 35

Ingram, Cindy, Cat, Alberta Department of Environment Library, 9920 108th St, 6th Flr, Edmonton, AB, T5K 2M4, CANADA. Tel: 780-427-3920. Fax: 780-422-0170. p. 2698

Ingram, David, Coordr, Info Tech, Cleveland Bradley County Public Library, 795 Church St NE, Cleveland, TN, 37311-5295. Tel: 423-472-2163. Fax: 423-339-9791. p. 2229

Ingram, Julie, Librn, Lonoke Prairie County Regional Library Headquarters, Devalls Bluff Public, 173 Market St, Devalls Bluff, AR, 72041. Tel: 870-998-7010. Fax: 870-998-7010. p. 108

Ingram, June, Libr Asst, Connecticut College, Greer Music Library, 270 Mohegan Ave, Box 5234, New London, CT, 06320-4196. Tel: 860-439-2711. Fax: 860-439-2871. p. 360

Ingram, Kim, Dir, Southampton Free Library, 947 Street Rd, Southampton, PA, 18966. Tel: 215-322-1415. Fax: 215-396-9375. p. 2142

Ingram, Laurie, Youth Serv, Jerseyville Public Library, 105 N Liberty St, Jerseyville, IL, 62052-1512. Tel: 618-498-9514. Fax: 618-498-3036. p. 659

Ingram, Lisa, Br Mgr, Memphis Public Library, Poplar-White Station, 5094 Poplar, Memphis, TN, 38117-7629. Tel: 901-415-2777. Fax: 901-682-8975. p. 2250

Ingram, Michael, Syst Coordr, Tech Serv, High Point University, 833 Montlieu Ave, High Point, NC, 27262-4221. Tel: 336-841-9152. Fax: 336-841-5123. p. 1802

Ingram, Nadia, YA Serv, Selby Public Library, 1331 First St, Sarasota, FL, 34236-4899. Tel: 941-861-1100. Fax: 941-316-1188. p. 490

Ingram, Rebecca, Youth Serv Mgr, Fremont Public Library District, 1170 N Midlothian Rd, Mundelein, IL, 60060. Tel: 847-566-8702. Fax: 847-566-0204. p. 678

Ingram, Tamela, Librn, Poinsett County Public Library, Lepanto Branch, 240 Greenwood St, Lepanto, AR, 72354. Tel: 870-475-6144. Fax: 870-475-6144. p. 102

Ingram, Vicky, Librn, University of Virginia, Physics, 323 Physics Bldg, Charlottesville, VA, 22903-2458. Tel: 434-924-6589. p. 2455

Ingrassia, Barbara, Assoc Dir, Strategic Initiatives & Workforce Develop, University of Massachusetts Medical School, 55 Lake Ave N, Worcester, MA, 01655-2397. Tel: 508-856-1041. Fax: 508-856-5039. p. 1145

Ingrassia, Dawn, Librn, Worcester County Library, Pocomoke City Branch, 301 Market St, Pocomoke City, MD, 21851. Tel: 410-957-0878. Fax: 410-957-4773. p. 1042

Ings, Catherine, Librn, Correctional Service of Canada-Pacific Region, 4732 Cemetery Rd, Agassiz, BC, V0M 1A0, CANADA. Tel: 604-796-2121, Ext 4329. Fax: 604-796-4500. p. 2724

Ingvaldsen, Caroline, Br Head, Toronto Public Library, Dufferin/St Clair, 1625 Dufferin St, Toronto, ON, M6H 3L9, CANADA. Tel: 416-393-7712. Fax: 416-393-7410. p. 2861

Inman, Denise, Br Mgr, East Providence Public Library, Rumford, 1392 Pawtucket Ave, East Providence, RI, 02916. Tel: 401-434-8559. Fax: 401-434-1808. p. 2166

Inman, Gail, Adult Serv, Coll Develop, Lincolnwood Public Library District, 4000 W Pratt Ave, Lincolnwood, IL, 60712. Tel: 847-677-5277. Fax: 847-677-1937. p. 666

Inman, Mary, Youth Serv Librn, Lemont Public Library District, 50 E Wend St, Lemont, IL, 60439-6439. Tel: 630-257-6541. Fax: 630-257-7737. p. 664

Inman, Nora, Acq of Monographs, Oklahoma Baptist University, 500 W University, OBU Box 61310, Shawnee, OK, 74804-2504. Tel: 405-878-2268. Fax: 405-878-2256. p. 1977

Inman, Phillip, Dir, Jacob Sears Memorial Library, 23 Center St, East Dennis, MA, 02641. Tel: 508-385-8151. p. 1086

Inman, Ruth A, Res Mgt Librn, Kennedy-King College, City Colleges of Chicago Library, 6403 S Halsted, Chicago, IL, 60621. Tel: 773-602-5449. Fax: 773-602-5450. p. 616

Inman, Teresa, Archivist, Spec Coll Librn, Presbyterian College, 211 E Maple St, Clinton, SC, 29325. Tel: 864-833-8525. Fax: 864-833-8315. p. 2186

Innes, Genevieve, Educ Librn, Pub Serv, Western Connecticut State University, 181 White St, Danbury, CT, 06810. Tel: 203-837-9100. Fax: 203-837-9108. p. 335

Innes, Jane Ellen, Dir, Univ Libr, Cleary University Library, 3750 Cleary Dr, Howell, MI, 48843. Tel: 734-332-4477, Ext 3320. Fax: 517-548-2170. p. 1192

Innes, Jane Ellen, Dir, Univ Libr, Cleary University Library, Washtenaw Campus, 3601 Plymouth Rd, Ann Arbor, MI, 48105-2659. Tel: 734-332-4477, Ext 3320. Fax: 734-332-4646. p. 1192

Innes, Tim, Ref & Outreach, Thomas M Cooley Law School Libraries, 300 S Capitol Ave, Lansing, MI, 48901. Tel: 517-371-5140, Ext 3303. Fax: 517-334-5715, 517-334-5717. p. 1202

Inniger, Alyssa, Electronic Res & Ref Librn, Bethany Lutheran College Memorial Library, 700 Luther Dr, Mankato, MN, 56001-4490. Tel: 507-344-7000. Fax: 507-344-7376. p. 1257

Ino, Darla, Dir, White County Regional Library System, 113 E Pleasure Ave, Searcy, AR, 72143-7798. Tel: 501-268-2449, 501-279-2870. Fax: 501-268-5682. p. 114

Insalaco, Robin, Acq/Archives Librn, Tyler Junior College, 1327 S Baxter St, Tyler, TX, 75701. Tel: 903-510-2549. Fax: 903-510-2639. p. 2393

Inscore, Cathy, Libr Spec, Copper Mountain College, 6162 Rotary Way, Joshua Tree, CA, 92252. Tel: 760-366-3791, Ext 5901. Fax: 760-366-5256. p. 161

Insetta, Debra, Br Coordr, Parsippany-Troy Hills Free Public Library, Mount Tabor Branch, 31 Trinity Park, Mount Tabor, NJ, 07878. Tel: 973-627-9508. p. 1518

Inskeep, Carroll, Libr Assoc, Morrison & Mary Wiley Library District, 206 W Main St, Elmwood, IL, 61529-9641. Tel: 309-742-2431. Fax: 309-742-8298. p. 642

Insler, Stanley, Curator, Yale University Library, American Oriental Society, 329 Sterling Memorial Library, New Haven, CT, 06520. Tel: 203-432-2455. Fax: 203-432-4087. p. 356

Insley, Diane, Mgr, Patron Serv, San Marcos Public Library, 625 E Hopkins, San Marcos, TX, 78666. Tel: 512-393-8200. p. 2384

Interiano, Luis, Ad, West Baton Rouge Parish Library, 830 N Alexander Ave, Port Allen, LA, 70767-2327. Tel: 225-342-7920. Fax: 225-342-7915. p. 966

Intravia, Toni, Tech Serv Supvr, Massapequa Public Library, 40 Harbor Lane, Massapequa Park, NY, 11762. Tel: 516-799-0770. Fax: 516-795-7528. p. 1658

Inzerilla, Tina, Ref, Las Positas College Library, 3000 Campus Hill Dr, Livermore, CA, 94551-7623. Tel: 925-424-1150. Fax: 925-606-7249. p. 164

Ioanid, Aurora S, Head, Tech Serv, Monmouth University, 400 Cedar Ave, West Long Branch, NJ, 07764. Tel: 732-571-3450, Ext 5364. Fax: 732-263-5124. p. 1541

Ioannidou, Arsi, Asst Dir, New School, Harry Scherman Library, 150 W 85th St, New York, NY, 10024-4499. Tel: 212-580-0210, Ext 4827. Fax: 212-580-1738. p. 1688

Iobst, Barbara J, Dir, Lehigh Valley Hospital, Cedar Crest & I-78, Allentown, PA, 18105. Tel: 610-402-8410. Fax: 610-402-8409. p. 2027

Iobst, Barbara J, Dir, Lehigh Valley Hospital, Health Library & Learning Center, 17th & Chew, Allentown, PA, 18105. Tel: 610-402-8410. Fax: 610-402-8409. p. 2027

Iobst, Barbara J, Dir, Lehigh Valley Hospital, Muhlenberg Medical Library, 2545 Schoenersville Rd, Bethlehem, PA, 18017. Tel: 610-402-8410. Fax: 610-402-8409. p. 2027

Iodice, Anthony, Mgr, Ctr for the Enhancement of Learning & Teaching, Iona College, 715 North Ave, New Rochelle, NY, 10801-1890. Tel: 914-633-2347. Fax: 914-633-2136. p. 1666

Iodice, Tony, Ref Serv, Fordham University Westchester Library, 400 Westchester Ave, West Harrison, NY, 10604. Tel: 914-367-3426. p. 1766

Ionin, Raisa, Librn, Argosy University, 1550 Wilson Blvd, Ste 600, Arlington, VA, 22209. Fax: 703-243-5682. p. 2448

Iorio, Edward J, Dir, Marine Products Library, Ten Furnace Brook Pkwy, Quincy, MA, 02169. Tel: 617-268-0758. Fax: 617-472-9359. p. 1119

Ioselev, Boris, Librn, Brooklyn Public Library, Gravesend, 303 Ave X, Brooklyn, NY, 11223. Tel: 718-382-5792. Fax: 718-382-5926. p. 1591

Ip, Lina, Cat, College of Mount Saint Vincent, 6301 Riverdale Ave, Bronx, NY, 10471-1093. Tel: 718-405-3395. Fax: 718-601-2091. p. 1586

Ip, Phillip, Electronic Serv, United States Department of the Army, CEHEC-ZL Casey Bldg, 7701 Telegraph Rd, Alexandria, VA, 22315-3860. Tel: 703-428-6388. Fax: 703-428-6310. p. 2446

Ippoliti, Cinthya, Assessment Librn, Instrul Serv Librn, Paradise Valley Community College Library, 18401 N 32nd St, Phoenix, AZ, 85032-1200. Tel: 602-787-7209. Fax: 602-787-7205. p. 75

Ippoliti, Cinthya, Terrapin Learning Commons & Student Support Serv, University of Maryland Libraries, Theodore R McKeldin Library, College Park, MD, 20742-7011. Tel: 301-314-7224. Fax: 301-314-9408. p. 1025

Ipsen, Patricia, Dir, New Hampton Public Library, 20 W Spring St, New Hampton, IA, 50659. Tel: 641-394-2184. Fax: 641-394-5482. p. 834

Ipsen-Tompkins, Bernie, Outreach Serv Librn, Iredell County Public Library, 201 N Tradd St, Statesville, NC, 28677. Tel: 704-878-3099. Fax: 704-878-5449. p. 1825

Irace, Jo-Ann, Head, Access Serv, Williams College, 55 Sawyer Library Dr, Williamstown, MA, 01267. Tel: 413-597-2920. Fax: 413-597-4106. p. 1140

Irby, Patricia, Librn, Baptist College of Health Sciences, 1003 Monroe, Memphis, TN, 38104. Tel: 901-572-2677. Fax: 901-572-2674. p. 2247

Ireland, Ashley, Res & Instruction Librn, Murray State University, 205 Waterfield Library, Dean's Office, Murray, KY, 42071-3307. Tel: 270-809-4819. Fax: 270-809-3736. p. 930

Ireland, Faye, Tech Serv, Surry Community College, 630 S Main St, Dobson, NC, 27017-8432. Tel: 336-386-3501. Fax: 336-386-3692. p. 1787

Ireland, Lois, Mgr, Freddie Mac Corporate Information Resource Center, 8200 Jones Branch Dr, MS 251, McLean, VA, 22102. Tel: 703-903-3335. Fax: 703-903-2755. p. 2478

Ireland, Terry, ILL, Libr Assoc, Carnegie Mellon University, Software Engineering Institute Library, 4500 Fifth Ave, Pittsburgh, PA, 15213-2612. Tel: 412-268-7733. Fax: 412-268-1340. p. 2124

Irey, Sayumi, Librn, Bellevue College, 3000 Landerholm Circle SE, Bellevue, WA, 98007-6484. Tel: 425-564-2354. Fax: 425-564-6186. p. 2508

Irish, Elizabeth, Asst Dir, Albany Medical College, 47 New Scotland Ave, MC 63, Albany, NY, 12208. Tel: 518-262-4980. Fax: 518-262-5820. p. 1568

Irish, Mark, Ref, Islip Public Library, 71 Monell Ave, Islip, NY, 11751-3999. Tel: 631-581-5933. Fax: 631-277-8429. p. 1641

Irish, Molly, Commun Serv Coordr, Lighthouse for the Blind & Visually Impaired, 214 Van Ness Ave, San Francisco, CA, 94102. Tel: 415-694-7320. Fax: 415-863-7568. p. 243

Irizarry, Christine, Mgr, Ref Serv, Spec Coll & Archives Librn, Tennessean Library & Archives, 1100 Broadway, Nashville, TN, 37203. Tel: 615-259-8000. p. 2258

Irizarry, Patty, Head, Circ, Demarest Public Library, 90 Hardenburgh Ave, Demarest, NJ, 07627-2197. Tel: 201-768-8714. Fax: 201-767-8094. p. 1481

Irizarry-Vazquez, Esther, Dir, Pontifical Catholic University Of Puerto Rico, Encarnacion Valdes Library, 2250 Avenida Las Americas, Ste 509, Ponce, PR, 00717-0777. Tel: 787-841-2000, Ext 1801, 787-841-2000, Ext 1802. Fax: 787-284-0235. p. 2674

Irmscher, Laura, Coll Develop Mgr, Boston Public Library, 700 Boylston St, Boston, MA, 02117-0286. Tel: 617-536-5400. Fax: 617-236-4306. p. 1056

Irons, Carol, Librn, Fairfax Public Library, 158 E Elm, Fairfax, OK, 74637. Tel: 918-642-5535. Fax: 918-642-3350. p. 1963

Irons, Lynda R, Instrul Serv & Res Librn, Pacific University Library, 2043 College Way, Forest Grove, OR, 97116. Tel: 503-352-1409. Fax: 503-352-1416. p. 1998

Irons, Nicholas, Info Tech, Brooklyn College Library, 2900 Bedford Ave, Brooklyn, NY, 11210-2889. Tel: 718-951-4634. Fax: 718-951-4540. p. 1589

Irvin, Corinne, Librn, Woodbury County Library, Hornick Branch, 510 Main St, Hornick, IA, 51026. Tel: 712-874-3616. p. 834

Irvin, Gena, Mgr, Outreach Serv, Laurel County Public Library District, 120 College Park Dr, London, KY, 40741. Tel: 606-864-5759. Fax: 606-862-8057. p. 922

Irvin, Kim, Circ, Jacksonville Public Library, 201 W College Ave, Jacksonville, IL, 62650-2497. Tel: 217-243-5435. Fax: 217-243-2182. p. 659

Irvin, Linda, In Charge, United States Department of Justice, 209 S LaSalle, Ste 600, Chicago, IL, 60604. Tel: 312-353-7530. Fax: 312-353-1046. p. 625

Irvin, Nicole, Librn, Yutan Public Library, 502 Third St, Yutan, NE, 68073. Tel: 402-625-2111. Fax: 402-625-2111. p. 1424

Irvin, Patricia, Circ Mgr, Highland Park Public Library, 494 Laurel Ave, Highland Park, IL, 60035-2690. Tel: 847-432-0216. Fax: 847-432-9139. p. 655

Irvin, Sally, Assoc Dir, Wake Forest University, Professional Center Library, Worrell Professional Ctr for Law & Management, 1834 Wake Forest Rd, Winston-Salem, NC, 27106. Tel: 336-758-5442. Fax: 336-758-6077. p. 1834

Irvin-Craig, Linda, Exec Dir, Washington County Historical Society, 135 W Washington St, Hagerstown, MD, 21740. Tel: 301-797-8782. Fax: 240-625-9498. p. 1031

Irvine, Dora, Librn, Prairie Crocus Regional Library, 137 Main St, Rivers, MB, R0K 1X0, CANADA. Tel: 204-328-7613. p. 2751

Irving, Catherine, Libr Spec, Saint Francis Xavier University, Marie Michael Library, Coady International Institute, PO Box 5000, Antigonish, NS, B2G 2W5, CANADA. Tel: 902-867-3964. Fax: 902-867-3907. p. 2777

Irving, Dale, Info Syst, Middleborough Public Library, 102 N Main St, Middleborough, MA, 02346. Tel: 508-946-2470. Fax: 508-946-2473. p. 1105

Irving, Dave, Librn, Palo Alto City Library, Mitchell Park, 3700 Middlefield Rd, Palo Alto, CA, 94303. Fax: 650-856-7925. p. 204

Irving, Diane, Commun Libr Mgr, Queens Borough Public Library, Saint Albans Community Library, 191-05 Linden Blvd, Saint Albans, NY, 11412. Tel: 718-528-8196. p. 1645

Irving, Jamie, Asst Librn, Stewart Free Library, Eight Levi Stewart Dr, Corinna, ME, 04928. Tel: 207-278-2454. Fax: 207-278-5200. p. 982

Irving, Kathleen, Libr Mgr, Milk River Municipal Library, PO Box 579, Milk River, AB, T0K 1M0, CANADA. Tel: 403-647-3793. p. 2711

Irving, Steven, Electronic Res Librn, Southern Utah University, 351 W University Blvd, Cedar City, UT, 84720. Tel: 435-586-5480. Fax: 435-865-8152. p. 2404

Irving, Susan, Br Mgr, Louisville Free Public Library, St Matthews-Eline Branch, 3940 Grandview Ave, Louisville, KY, 40207. Tel: 502-574-1771. Fax: 502-894-8709. p. 924

Irwin, Elaine, Asst Dir, Tech Serv, Upper Darby Township & Sellers Memorial Free Public Library, 76 S State Rd, Upper Darby, PA, 19082. Tel: 610-789-4440. p. 2149

Irwin, Gail J, Librn, Ainsworth Public Library, 445 N Main St, Ainsworth, NE, 69210. Tel: 402-387-2032. Fax: 402-387-0209. p. 1391

Irwin, Kathy M, Dir of Libr Serv, Mott Community College, 1401 E Court St, Flint, MI, 48503. Tel: 810-762-0415. Fax: 810-762-0407. p. 1180

Irwin, Ken, Ref Librn, Wittenberg University, 807 Woodlawn Ave, Springfield, OH, 45504. Tel: 937-327-7594. Fax: 937-327-6139. p. 1936

Irwin, Rebecca, Head, Coll, Head, Digital Libr Initiatives, Head, Per, Middlebury College Library, 110 Storrs Ave, Middlebury, VT, 05753-6007. Tel: 802-443-5499. Fax: 802-443-2074, 802-443-5698. p. 2428

Irwin, Susan, Interim Dir, Arizona Historical Foundation, Arizona State University, Rm 412, Box 871006, Tempe, AZ, 85287-1006. Tel: 480-965-3283. Fax: 480-966-1077. p. 83

Irwin, Susan K, Asst Dir, Williams County Public Library, 107 E High St, Bryan, OH, 43506-1702. Tel: 419-636-6734. Fax: 419-636-3970. p. 1862

Irwin-Smiler, Kate, Ref Librn, Wake Forest University, Professional Center Library, Worrell Professional Ctr for Law & Management, 1834 Wake Forest Rd, Winston-Salem, NC, 27106. Tel: 336-758-4009. Fax: 336-758-6077. p. 1834

Isaac, Kim, Univ Librn, University of the Fraser Valley, 33844 King Rd, Abbotsford, BC, V2S 7M8, CANADA. Tel: 604-504-7441. Fax: 604-853-8055. p. 2724

Isaac, Kim, Univ Librn, University of the Fraser Valley, Chilliwack Campus, Library, Bldg A, 45190 Caen Ave, Chilliwack, BC, V2R 0N3, CANADA. Tel: 604-792-0025, 604-795-2824. Fax: 604-792-8550. p. 2724

Isaacs, Jane, Pub Serv, Plain City Public Library, 305 W Main St, Plain City, OH, 43064-1148. Tel: 614-873-4912, Ext 28. Fax: 614-873-8364. p. 1930

Isaacs, Judith, Dir, Jemez Springs Public Library, 30 Jemez Plaza, Jemez Springs, NM, 87025. Tel: 505-829-9155. Fax: 505-829-3339. p. 1557

Isaacs, Sarah, Dir, Illinois Early Intervention Clearinghouse, Univ of Illinois-Urbana-Champaign, Children's Research Center, 51 Gerty Dr, Champaign, IL, 61820. Tel: 217-333-1386. Fax: 217-244-7732. p. 603

Isaacson, Kathy, Syst Coordr, Lawrence University, 113 S Lawe St, Appleton, WI, 54911-5683. Fax: 920-832-6967. p. 2578

Isaacson, Linda, Head, Adult Serv, Lyons Public Library, 4209 Joliet Ave, Lyons, IL, 60534-1597. Tel: 708-447-3577. Fax: 708-447-3589. p. 668

Isabell, Erin, Ch, Platteville Public Library, 65 S Elm, Platteville, WI, 53818. Tel: 608-348-7441. Fax: 608-348-9923. p. 2630

Isacson, Barbara, Dir, Bloomfield College Library, Media Center, 80 Oakland Ave, Bloomfield, NJ, 07003. Tel: 973-748-9000, Ext 370. Fax: 973-566-9483. p. 1473

Isacson, Barbara, Media Spec, Bloomfield College Library, Liberty St & Oakland Ave, Bloomfield, NJ, 07003. Tel: 973-748-9000, Ext 370. Fax: 973-743-3998. p. 1473

Isadore, Harold, Ref Serv, Southern University, Oliver B Spellman Law Library, 56 Roosevelt Steptoe, Baton Rouge, LA, 70813. Tel: 225-771-2139, 225-771-2315. Fax: 225-771-6254. p. 944

Isakson, Kirk, Dir, Multimedia Serv, Pacific Lutheran University, 12180 Park Ave S, Tacoma, WA, 98447-0001. Tel: 253-535-7500. Fax: 253-535-7315. p. 2539

Isakson, Nikki J, Dir, Paw Paw Public Library District, 362 Chicago Rd, Paw Paw, IL, 61353. Tel: 815-627-9396. Fax: 815-627-3707. p. 689

Isbell, Anne M, Dir, Lake Blackshear Regional Library System, 307 E Lamar St, Americus, GA, 31709-3633. Tel: 229-924-8091. Fax: 229-928-4445. p. 508

Isbell, Dennis, Libr Dir, Arizona State University Libraries, Fletcher Library, 4701 W Thunderbird Rd, Glendale, AZ, 85306. Tel: 602-543-8508. Fax: 602-543-8540. p. 83

Isbell, Linda, Asst Librn, Crosby County Library, Ralls Branch, 813 Main St, Ralls, TX, 79357. Tel: 806-253-2755. Fax: 806-253-2755. p. 2303

Iscrupe, Shirley G, Archivist, Ligonier Valley Library Association, Inc, 120 W Main St, Ligonier, PA, 15658-1243. Tel: 724-238-6451. Fax: 724-238-6989. p. 2081

Iseminger, Damian, Cat, New England Conservatory of Music, 33 Gainsborough St, Boston, MA, 02115. Tel: 617-585-1254. Fax: 617-585-1245. p. 1064

Isenberg, Laurie, Access Serv & Syst, California State University, East Bay Library, 25800 Carlos Bee Blvd, Hayward, CA, 94542-3052. Tel: 510-885-3664. Fax: 510-885-2049. p. 157

Isgett, Kim, Br Mgr, Chesterfield County Library, Fannie D Lowry Memorial, PO Box 505, Jefferson, SC, 29718-0505. Tel: 843-658-3966. Fax: 843-658-6695. p. 2186

Isgett, Kim, Br Mgr, Chesterfield County Library, McBee Depot Library, PO Box 506, McBee, SC, 29101. Tel: 843-335-7515. Fax: 843-335-6219. p. 2186

Ishibashi, Jane, Circ Librn, Fullerton College, 321 E Chapman Ave, Fullerton, CA, 92832-2095. Tel: 714-992-7378. Fax: 714-992-9961. p. 153

Isho, Awayah, Librn, Assyrian Universal Alliance Foundation, 7055 N Clark St, Chicago, IL, 60626. Tel: 773-274-9262. Fax: 773-274-5866. p. 606

Isicson, Robin, Principal Librn, Tech Serv, San Diego County Library, 5560 Overland Ave, Ste 110, San Diego, CA, 92123. Tel: 858-694-2439. Fax: 858-495-5981. p. 233

Iskenderian, Marguerite, Music, Brooklyn College Library, 2900 Bedford Ave, Brooklyn, NY, 11210-2889. Tel: 718-951-5347. Fax: 718-951-4540. p. 1589

Isleb, Karyn, Head, Ch, Manchester City Library, 405 Pine St, Manchester, NH, 03104-6199. Tel: 603-624-6550. Fax: 603-624-6559. p. 1455

Isler, Melinda, Spec Coll & Archives Librn, Ferris State University Library, 1010 Campus Dr, Big Rapids, MI, 49307-2279. Tel: 231-591-3500. Fax: 231-591-3724. p. 1158

Isles, Marie, Br Mgr, Potter Justin Public Library, Alexandria Branch, 109 Public Sq, Alexandria, TN, 37012-2141. Tel: 615-529-4124. Fax: 615-529-4124. p. 2266

Isley, Cary, Sr Cat Librn, Tulsa Community College Learning Resources Center, Metro Campus, 909 S Boston Ave, Tulsa, OK, 74119-2011. Tel: 918-595-7177. Fax: 918-595-7179. p. 1983

Isley, Lisa, Cat, Coll Develop, Blue Ridge Regional Library, 310 E Church St, Martinsville, VA, 24112-2999. Tel: 276-403-5451. Fax: 276-632-1660. p. 2477

Ismail, Lizah, Ref & Instrul Serv, Instr Coordr, College of Misericordia, 301 Lake St, Dallas, PA, 18612-1098. Tel: 570-674-6231. Fax: 570-674-6342. p. 2048

Ismail, Lizah, Outreach & Instruction Librn, Limestone College, 1115 College Dr, Gaffney, SC, 29340. Tel: 864-488-4612. Fax: 864-487-4613. p. 2194

Ismail, Matthew I, Dir, Coll Develop, Central Michigan University, Park 407, Mount Pleasant, MI, 48859. Tel: 989-774-2143. Fax: 989-774-2179. p. 1211

Ison, Mitch, Ref Librn, Nevada State Library & Archives, 100 N Stewart St, Carson City, NV, 89701-4285. Tel: 775-684-3348. Fax: 775-684-3330. p. 1426

Ison, Robin Singer, Dir, Mercer County Public Library, 109 W Lexington St, Harrodsburg, KY, 40330-1542. Tel: 859-734-3680. Fax: 859-734-7524. p. 916

Ispahany, Rafat, Coll Develop/Tech Serv Librn, Tenafly Public Library, 100 Riveredge Rd, Tenafly, NJ, 07670-2087. Tel: 201-568-8680. Fax: 201-568-5475. p. 1533

Israel, Jackie, Mgr, Satilla Regional Library, Pearson Public Library, 202 E Bullard Ave, Pearson, GA, 31642-9277. Tel: 912-422-3500. Fax: 912-422-3500. p. 531

Israel, Philip, Dir, Westfield Memorial Library, 550 E Broad St, Westfield, NJ, 07090. Tel: 908-789-4090. Fax: 908-789-0921. p. 1543

Istace, Jean, Librn, Parkland Regional Library, Spy Hill Branch, 316 Main St, Spy Hill, SK, S0A 3W0, CANADA. Tel: 306-534-2122. p. 2932

Ito, Jennifer, Exec Dir, Foothills Art Center, 809 15th St, Golden, CO, 80401. Tel: 303-279-3922. Fax: 303-279-9470. p. 309

Ito, Shirley S, Syst Adminr, Webmaster, LA84 Foundation, 2141 W Adams Blvd, Los Angeles, CA, 90018. Tel: 323-730-4646. Fax: 323-730-0546. p. 171

Ito, Todd, Ref Librn, University of Chicago Library, D'Angelo Law Library, 1121 E 60th St, Chicago, IL, 60637-2786. Tel: 773-702-9617. Fax: 773-702-2889. p. 626

Ivaldi, Janet, Ad, Mark Twain Library, Rte 53 & Diamond Hill Rd, Redding, CT, 06896. Tel: 203-938-2545. Fax: 203-938-4026. p. 365

Ivanick, Peter, Head, Libr Syst, Drexel University Libraries, Hagerty Library, 33rd & Market Sts, Philadelphia, PA, 19104-2875. Tel: 215-895-2090. Fax: 215-895-2070. p. 2105

Ivanis, Draica, ILL, Chelsea Public Library, 569 Broadway, Chelsea, MA, 02150-2991. Tel: 617-466-4350. Fax: 617-466-4359. p. 1080

Ivankovic, Anthony Karl, Librn for Deaf, Spec Coll Librn, California State University, Northridge, National Center on Deafness-PEPNet Resource Center, 18111 Nordhoff St, Northridge, CA, 91330-8267. Tel: 818-435-8174. Fax: 818-677-7963. p. 195

Ivanoff, Doris, Librn, Ticasuk Library, PO Box 28, Unalakleet, AK, 99684-0028. Tel: 907-624-3053. Fax: 907-624-3130. p. 54

Ivany, Kathryn, Archivist, City of Edmonton, Archives, 10440 - 108 Ave, 2nd Flr, Prince of Wales Armouries Heritage Centre, Edmonton, AB, T5H 3Z9, CANADA. Tel: 780-496-8721. Fax: 780-496-8732. p. 2699

Ivarra, Lulu, Dir, Tri-Community Library, 6910 Hwy 80, Prairie Lea, TX, 78661. Tel: 512-488-2164. Fax: 512-488-9006. p. 2372

Ivaskewitz, Marie, Br Supvr, Marion County Public Library System, Fort McCoy Public Library, 14660 NE Hwy 315, Fort McCoy, FL, 32134. Tel: 352-438-2560. Fax: 352-438-2562. p. 474

Ivers, Brenda, Bkmobile/Outreach Serv, Transylvania County Library, 212 S Gaston, Brevard, NC, 28712. Tel: 828-884-3151, Ext 246. Fax: 828-877-4230. p. 1777

Ivers, Kimberley, Dir, Southborough Public Library, 25 Main St, Southborough, MA, 01772. Tel: 508-485-5031. Fax: 508-229-4451. p. 1126

Iversen, David, Cat, Minot State University, 500 University Ave W, Minot, ND, 58707. Tel: 701-858-3200. Fax: 701-858-3581. p. 1846

Iversen, Mary, Actg Librn, Everson Museum of Art Library, 401 Harrison St, Syracuse, NY, 13202. Tel: 315-474-6064. Fax: 315-474-6943. p. 1751

Iversen, Teresa, Head, Info Serv/Readers Advisory, DeKalb Public Library, 309 Oak St, DeKalb, IL, 60115-3369. Tel: 815-756-9568. Fax: 815-756-7837. p. 635

Iverson, Debbie, Prog Coordr, Young Adult Serv Coordr, Sheridan County Public Library System, 335 W Alger St, Sheridan, WY, 82801-3899. Tel: 307-674-8585, Ext 5. p. 2660

Iverson, Sandra, Mgr, St Michael's Hospital, 209 Victoria St, Toronto, ON, M5B 1W8, CANADA. Tel: 416-864-6060, Ext 77694. Fax: 416-864-5296. p. 2858

Ives, Joey, Adult Serv, Comstock Township Library, 6130 King Hwy, Comstock, MI, 49041. Tel: 269-345-0136. Fax: 269-345-0138. p. 1165

Ivey, Ann, Libr Mgr, Fruitville Public Library, 100 Coburn Rd, Sarasota, FL, 34240. Tel: 941-861-2500. Fax: 941-861-2528. p. 489

Ivey, David, Dir, Logansport-Cass County Public Library, 616 E Broadway, Logansport, IN, 46947-3187. Tel: 574-753-6383. Fax: 574-722-5889. p. 761

Ivey, Jennifer, Ch Serv Spec, Athens Regional Library System, Madison County, 1315 Hwy 98 W, Danielsville, GA, 30633. Tel: 706-795-5597. Fax: 706-795-0830. p. 509

Ivy, Estelle, Br Mgr, Dixie Regional Library System, Okolona Carnegie Branch, 321 Main St, Okolona, MS, 38860. Tel: 662-447-2401. Fax: 662-447-2401. p. 1312

Ivy, Helen A, Librn, Marine Resources Library, 217 Ft Johnson Rd, Charleston, SC, 29412. Tel: 843-953-9370. Fax: 843-953-9371. p. 2184

Ivy, Helen Anita, Librn II, College of Charleston, Marine Resources, 217 Fort Johnson Rd, Bldg 8, Charleston, SC, 29412. Tel: 843-953-9370. Fax: 843-953-9371. p. 2184

Ivy, Lynne, Ref, Pahrump Community Library, 701 E St, Pahrump, NV, 89048-2164. Tel: 775-727-5930. Fax: 775-727-6209. p. 1432

Iwala, Cecilia, Syst Librn, Grambling State University, 403 Main St, Grambling, LA, 71245. Tel: 318-274-7367. Fax: 318-274-3268. p. 950

Iwami, Russell, Ref Librn, National University of Health Sciences Learning Resource Center, 200 E Roosevelt Rd, Bldg C, Lombard, IL, 60148-4583. Tel: 630-889-6612. Fax: 630-495-6658. p. 667

Iwan, Irene, Assoc Librn, Info Tech Serv, Hartford Public Library, 500 Main St, Hartford, CT, 06103-3075. Tel: 860-695-6350. Fax: 860-722-6900. p. 346

Iwan, Martha, Media Spec, Ad, Music & Media Librn, Mount Kisco Public Library, 100 E Main St, Mount Kisco, NY, 10549. Tel: 914-864-1150. Fax: 914-666-3899. p. 1663

Iwanec, Peter, Br Mgr, Chicago Public Library, Oriole Park, 7454 W Balmoral Ave, Chicago, IL, 60656. Tel: 312-744-1965. Fax: 312-744-7853. p. 609

Iwanickyj, Judith, Tech Serv, The Hampton Library, 2478 Main St, Bridgehampton, NY, 11932. Tel: 631-537-0015. Fax: 631-537-7229. p. 1585

Iwanowicz, Susan L, Dir, Libr Serv, Albany College of Pharmacy & Health Sciences, 106 New Scotland Ave, Albany, NY, 12208. Tel: 518-694-7217. Fax: 518-694-7300. p. 1567

Iwanowski, Carol, Adult Serv, Sun Prairie Public Library, 1350 Linnerud Dr, Sun Prairie, WI, 53590-2631. Tel: 608-825-7323. Fax: 608-825-3936. p. 2641

Iyer, Hemalata, Dr, Assoc Prof, University at Albany, State University of New York, Draper 116, 135 Western Ave, Albany, NY, 12222. Tel: 518-442-5116. Fax: 518-442-5367. p. 2970

Izatt, James, Librn, Worcester Public Library, Worcester Talking Book Library, Three Salem Sq, Worcester, MA, 01608-2015. Tel: 508-799-1655, 508-799-1730. Fax: 508-799-1676, 508-799-1734. p. 1145

Izaurralde, Arthur B, Info Res, Librn, Association for Financial Professionals, 4520 East-West Hwy, Ste 750, Bethesda, MD, 20814. Tel: 301-961-8811. p. 1021

Izbicki, Donna R, Librn, Connecticut Judicial Branch Law Libraries, Putnam Law Library, Putnam Courthouse, 155 Church St, Putnam, CT, 06260. Tel: 860-928-3716. Fax: 860-963-7531. p. 344

Izbicki, Thomas, Actg Assoc Univ Librn, Coll Develop, Rutgers University Libraries, 169 College Ave, New Brunswick, NJ, 08901-1163. Tel: 732-932-7129, Ext 125. Fax: 732-932-7637. p. 1508

Izon, Robin, Adminr, Libr Operations, California Institute of Technology, 1200 E California Blvd, M/C 1-32, Pasadena, CA, 91125-3200. Tel: 626-395-6411. Fax: 626-792-7540. p. 205

Izor, Gillian, Asst Dir, Germantown Public Library, 51 N Plum St, Germantown, OH, 45327. Tel: 937-855-4001. Fax: 937-855-6098. p. 1901

Izzi, Beverly, Youth Serv Coordr, Calvert County Public Library, 850 Costley Way, Prince Frederick, MD, 20678. Tel: 410-535-0291. Fax: 410-535-3022. p. 1036

Izzo, David, Mgr, Computing & Media Serv, Dartmouth College Library, Biomedical Libraries (Dana Biomedical & Matthews-Fuller Health Sciences Library), Dana Biomedical Library/HB 6168, 64 College St, Hanover, NH, 03755-3563. Tel: 603-650-1663. p. 1450

Jabido, Penelope, Supv Librn, Cat, Newark Public Library, Five Washington St, Newark, NJ, 07101. Tel: 973-733-7737. Fax: 973-733-5648. p. 1511

Jablonski, Judith, Asst Prof, University of Pittsburgh, 135 N Bellefield Ave, Pittsburgh, PA, 15260. Tel: 412-624-5230. Fax: 412-624-5231. p. 2973

Jablonski, Shelly, Librn, Montgomery College, Rockville Campus Library, Macklin Tower, 51 Mannakee St, Rockville, MD, 20850. Tel: 240-567-7174. Fax: 240-567-7153. p. 1037

Jabusch, Kay, Librn, Irene Ingle Public Library, 124 Second Ave, Wrangell, AK, 99929. Tel: 907-874-3535. Fax: 907-874-2520. p. 55

Jaby, Ruby, Mgr, Public Library Association of Annapolis & Anne Arundel County, Inc, Crofton, 1681 Riedel Rd, Crofton, MD, 21114. Tel: 410-222-7915. Fax: 410-222-7269. p. 1010

Jach, Cecille, Dir, Epilepsy Foundation, 8301 Professional Pl, Landover, MD, 20785. Tel: 301-459-3700, Ext 3737. Fax: 301-577-4941. p. 1034

Jacinto, Florence, Br Mgr, Los Angeles Public Library System, Panorama City Branch, 14345 Roscoe Blvd, Panorama City, CA, 91402-4222. Tel: 818-894-4071. Fax: 818-891-5960. p. 174

Jacinto, Marguerite, Ref Librn, Taunton Public Library, 12 Pleasant St, Taunton, MA, 02780. Tel: 508-821-1410. Fax: 508-821-1414. p. 1130

Jacisin, Marek, Educ Media Coodr, New England College of Optometry Library, 424 Beacon St, Boston, MA, 02115. Tel: 617-587-5654. Fax: 617-587-5573. p. 1064

Jaciw, Kim, Libr Tech, Department of Veterans Affairs Medical Center Library, 385 Tremont Ave, East Orange, NJ, 07018-1095. Tel: 908-647-0180, Ext 4545, 973-676-1000, Ext 1969. Fax: 973-395-7234. p. 1482

Jaciw, Kim, ILL, Department of Veterans Affairs, Lyons Campus Medical Library, 151 Knollcroft Rd, Lyons, NJ, 07939. Tel: 908-647-0180, Ext 4545, 973-676-1000. Fax: 908-604-5837. p. 1497

Jack, Debbie, Dir, Parkland Community Library, 4422 Walbert Ave, Allentown, PA, 18104-1619. Tel: 610-398-1361. Fax: 610-398-3538. p. 2027

Jack, Frieda, Tech Syst & Proc Mgr, Cecil County Public Library, 301 Newark Ave, Elkton, MD, 21921-5441. Tel: 410-996-5600. Fax: 410-996-5604. p. 1027

Jack, Jill, Ref, Coe College, 1220 First Ave NE, Cedar Rapids, IA, 52402-5092. Tel: 319-399-8017. Fax: 319-399-8019. p. 800

Jack, Nancy, Dir, Maltman Memorial Public Library, 910 Main St, Wood River, NE, 68883. Tel: 308-583-2349. p. 1424

Jackamore, Cori, Br Mgr, Denver Public Library, Athmar Park, 1055 S Tejon St, Denver, CO, 80223. Tel: 303-935-0721. Fax: 303-934-9388. p. 301

Jackamore, Cori, Br Mgr, Denver Public Library, Decker, 1501 S Logan, Denver, CO, 80210-2632. Tel: 303-733-7584. Fax: 303-733-8665. p. 301

Jackamore, Cori, Br Mgr, Denver Public Library, Eugene Field, 810 S University Blvd, Denver, CO, 80209-4725. Tel: 303-777-2301. Fax: 303-722-7331. p. 301

Jackamore, Cori, Br Mgr, Denver Public Library, Park Hill, 4705 Montview Blvd, Denver, CO, 80207-3760. Tel: 303-331-4063. Fax: 303-388-2335. p. 301

Jackamore, Cori, Br Mgr, Denver Public Library, Virginia Village, 1500 S Dahlia St, Denver, CO, 80222. Tel: 303-757-6662. Fax: 303-692-0721. p. 301

Jackel, Gloria, Librn, Holocaust Memorial & Tolerance Center of Nassau County, Welwyn Preserve, 100 Crescent Beach Rd, Glen Cove, NY, 11542. Tel: 516-571-8043. Fax: 516-571-8041. p. 1628

Jackel, Marsha, Coll Mgt, Govt Doc, Graceland University, One University Pl, Lamoni, IA, 50140. Tel: 641-784-5301. Fax: 641-784-5497. p. 826

Jackie, Hasson, Libr Coordr, Dix Hills Jewish Center Library, 555 Vanderbilt Pkwy, Dix Hills, NY, 11746. Tel: 631-499-6644. Fax: 631-499-6092. p. 1614

Jackiw, Michael, Computer Serv Mgr, Indian Trails Public Library District, 355 S Schoenbeck Rd, Wheeling, IL, 60090. Tel: 847-459-4100. Fax: 847-459-4760. p. 719

Jackman, Doreen, Libr Mgr, View Royal Reading Centre, 103B-1497 Admirals Rd, Victoria, BC, V9A 2P8, CANADA. Tel: 250-479-2723. Fax: 250-479-2723. p. 2746

Jackman, Kara, Archivist & Spec Coll Librn, Boston University Libraries, School of Theology Library, 745 Commonwealth Ave, 2nd Flr, Boston, MA, 02215. Tel: 617-353-3034. Fax: 617-358-0699. p. 1058

Jacknis, Norman J, VPres, Metropolitan New York Library Council, 57 E 11th St, 4th Flr, New York, NY, 10003-4605. Tel: 212-228-2320. Fax: 212-228-2598. p. 2950

Jacks, Belinda, Dir, Farmers Branch Manske Library, 13613 Webb Chapel, Farmers Branch, TX, 75234-3756. Tel: 972-247-2511. Fax: 972-247-9606. p. 2319

Jacks, Jamie, Distance Educ, California State University, 9001 Stockdale Hwy, Bakersfield, CA, 93311-1022. Tel: 661-654-3372. Fax: 661-654-3238. p. 123

Jacks, Steve, Dir, Kingston Public Library, 10004 Bradford Way, Kingston, TN, 37763. Tel: 865-376-9905. Fax: 865-376-2301. p. 2241

Jackson, A Ashley, Bldg Mgr & Librn, Duke University Libraries, 411 Chapel Dr, Durham, NC, 27708. Tel: 919-660-7860. Fax: 919-660-5923. p. 1787

Jackson, A Craig, Head, Tech Serv, Mechanics' Institute Library, 57 Post St, San Francisco, CA, 94104-5003. Tel: 415-393-0104. Fax: 415-421-4192. p. 243

Jackson, Alisa, ILL, The Rockefeller University, 1222 York Ave, Welch Hall, New York, NY, 10065. Tel: 212-327-8904. Fax: 212-327-8802. p. 1698

Jackson, Amanda, Dir, Libr Serv, Gadsden Public Library, 254 College St, Gadsden, AL, 35901. Tel: 256-549-4699. p. 18

Jackson, Andrew, Exec Dir, Queens Borough Public Library, Langston Hughes Community Library, 100-01 Northern Blvd, Corona, NY, 11368-1938. Tel: 718-651-1100. Fax: 718-651-6258. p. 1644

Jackson, Andrew, Librn, United States Courts Library, 515 Rusk Ave, Rm 6311, Houston, TX, 77002. Tel: 713-250-5696. Fax: 713-250-5091. p. 2343

Jackson, Anita, Br Mgr, Saint Clair County Library System, G Lynn Campbell Branch, 1955 N Allen Rd, Kimball, MI, 48074. Tel: 810-982-9171. Fax: 810-987-9689. p. 1219

Jackson, Ann, Mgr, Tech Serv, Rocky River Public Library, 1600 Hampton Rd, Rocky River, OH, 44116-2699. Tel: 440-333-7610. Fax: 440-333-4184. p. 1932

Jackson, Ann, Tech Serv, Rocky River Public Library, 1600 Hampton Rd, Rocky River, OH, 44116-2699. Tel: 440-333-7610. Fax: 440-333-4184. p. 1932

Jackson, Arlyne Ann, Head of Librn, Boston University Libraries, Frederic S Pardee Management Library, Boston University School of Management, 595 Commonwealth Ave, Boston, MA, 02215. Tel: 617-353-4310. Fax: 617-353-4307. p. 1058

Jackson, Aurelia, Cataloger, Northwest Kansas Library System, Two Washington Sq, Norton, KS, 67654-1615. Tel: 785-877-5148. Fax: 785-877-5697. p. 885

Jackson, Barbara L, Circ & Tech Serv Asst, Lawrence Technological University Library, 21000 W Ten Mile Rd, Southfield, MI, 48075-1058. Tel: 248-204-3000. Fax: 248-204-3005. p. 1228

Jackson, Beatheia, Info Serv, Pasquotank-Camden Library, 100 E Colonial Ave, Elizabeth City, NC, 27909. Tel: 252-335-2473, 252-335-7536. Fax: 252-331-7449. p. 1791

Jackson, Betty Ann, Librn, Columbia County Library, Taylor Public Library, 101 W Pope, Taylor, AR, 71861. Tel: 870-694-2051. p. 108

Jackson, Bonnie, Pres, Coin Public Library, 115 Main St, Coin, IA, 51636. Tel: 712-583-3684. p. 803

Jackson, Brian, Ref Librn, Grant MacEwan University Library, 10700 104th Ave, Edmonton, AB, T5J 4S2, CANADA. Tel: 780-497-5850. Fax: 780-497-5895. p. 2701

Jackson, Carleton L, Head, Nonprint Media Serv, University of Maryland Libraries, R Lee Hornbake Library, 0300 Hornbake Library Bldg, North Wing, College Park, MD, 20742-7011. Tel: 301-405-9226. Fax: 301-314-9419. p. 1025

Jackson, Carol, Dir, Culver-Union Township Public Library, 107 N Main St, Culver, IN, 46511-1595. Tel: 574-842-2701, 574-842-2941. Fax: 574-842-3441. p. 735

Jackson, Carol, Br Mgr, Ramsey County Library, North Saint Paul Branch, 2290 N First St, North Saint Paul, MN, 55109. Tel: 651-747-2700. Fax: 651-747-2705. p. 1284

Jackson, Carol, Dir, Beaver Falls Library, 9607 Lewis St, Beaver Falls, NY, 13305. Tel: 315-346-6216. Fax: 315-346-6216. p. 1579

Jackson, Cassandra, Ref & Circ Librn, LeMoyne-Owen College, 807 Walker Ave, Memphis, TN, 38126. Tel: 901-435-1355. Fax: 901-435-1374. p. 2249

Jackson, Cheryl, Mgr, Info Serv, Division of Legislative Services Reference Center, General Assembly Bldg, 2nd Flr, 910 Capitol St, Richmond, VA, 23219. Tel: 804-786-3591. Fax: 804-371-0169, 804-371-8705. p. 2488

Jackson, Chris, Commun Outreach Mgr, Monroe County Public Library, 303 E Kirkwood Ave, Bloomington, IN, 47408. Tel: 812-349-3050. Fax: 812-349-3051. p. 728

Jackson, Cindy, Ch, Otterbein Public Library, 23 E First St, Otterbein, IN, 47970. Tel: 765-583-2107. Fax: 765-583-2337. p. 772

Jackson, Daphne L, Ref Librn, Chappaqua Public Library, 195 S Greeley Ave, Chappaqua, NY, 10514. Tel: 914-238-4779. Fax: 914-238-3597. p. 1605

Jackson, Darla, Head, Ref, Oklahoma City University, Law Library, 2501 N Blackwelder, Oklahoma City, OK, 73106. Tel: 405-208-5271. Fax: 405-208-5172. p. 1974

Jackson, Darlene, Ch, Niles District Library, 620 E Main St, Niles, MI, 49120. Tel: 269-683-8545, Ext 109. Fax: 269-683-0075. p. 1214

Jackson, Darlene, Librn, Galeton Public Library, Five Park Ln, Galeton, PA, 16922. Tel: 814-435-2321. Fax: 814-435-2321. p. 2059

Jackson, Darlene, Head of Libr, Charleston County Public Library, 68 Calhoun St, Charleston, SC, 29401. Tel: 843-805-6808. p. 2183

Jackson, David, Librn II, Arlington Public Library System, Southeast, 900 SE Green Oaks Blvd, Arlington, TX, 76018-1708. Tel: 817-459-6395. Fax: 817-472-6495. p. 2276

Jackson, David, Chmn, First Baptist Church Library, 2709 Monument Ave, Richmond, VA, 23220. Tel: 804-355-8637, Ext 20. Fax: 804-359-4000. p. 2488

Jackson, David W, Dir, Jackson County Historical Society, 112 W Lexington Ave, Ste 103, Independence, MO, 64050-3700. Tel: 816-252-7454. Fax: 816-461-1510. p. 1332

Jackson, Debbie, Librn, Tulsa World, 315 S Boulder Ave, Tulsa, OK, 74103-3401. Tel: 918-582-0921. Fax: 918-581-8425. p. 1984

Jackson, Debra, Chief Exec Officer, Haldimand County Public Library, 111 Broad St E, Dunnville, ON, N1A 2X5, CANADA. Tel: 905-318-3272. Fax: 905-774-4294. p. 2802

Jackson, Delilah, Dir, Washington Municipal Library, 418 N Main St, Washington, LA, 70589. Tel: 337-826-7336. Fax: 337-826-7521. p. 971

Jackson, Diane, Ref Librn, Three Rivers Regional Library System, 208 Gloucester St, Brunswick, GA, 31520-7007. Tel: 912-267-1212. Fax: 912-267-9597. p. 522

Jackson, Donna Lee, Librn, Wakefield Library Association, 2699 Wakefield Rd, Wakefield, NH, 03872. Tel: 603-522-3032. p. 1466

Jackson, Elise, Circ Coordr, Tech Serv Coordr, Palmyra Public Library, Borough Bldg, 325 S Railroad St, Palmyra, PA, 17078-2492. Tel: 717-838-1347. Fax: 717-838-1236. p. 2101

Jackson, Gerald D, Librn, Calhoun Community College, Huntsville Campus Learning Resource Center, 102-B Wynn Dr, Huntsville, AL, 35805. Tel: 256-890-4771. Fax: 256-230-1143. p. 14

Jackson, Gerard, Br Mgr, Broward County Division of Libraries, Hollywood Beach-Bernice P Oster Reading Center, 1301 S Ocean Dr, Hollywood, FL, 33019. Tel: 954-926-2437. Fax: 954-926-2438. p. 441

Jackson, Jackie, Ch, Atlanta-Fulton Public Library System, College Park Library, 3647 Main St, College Park, GA, 30337. Tel: 404-762-4061. Fax: 404-762-4062. p. 511

Jackson, Jean, Circ, Pellissippi State Technical Community College, 10915 Harding Valley Rd, Knoxville, TN, 37933. Tel: 865-539-7047. Fax: 865-694-6625. p. 2243

Jackson, Jeff, Dir, Milwaukee Area Technical College, 700 W State St, Milwaukee, WI, 53233-1443. Tel: 414-297-6946. Fax: 414-297-6798. p. 2619

Jackson, Jennie, Br Mgr, Riverside County Library System, Mission Trail Library, 34303 Mission Trail, Wildomar, CA, 92595. Tel: 951-471-3855. Fax: 951-471-0188. p. 218

Jackson, Jennifer, Pub Serv, Tarrant County College, Jenkins Garrett Library-South Campus, 5301 Campus Dr, Fort Worth, TX, 76119. Tel: 817-515-4524. Fax: 817-515-4436. p. 2323

Jackson, Jennifer, Dir, Libr Serv, University of the Virgin Islands, RR 2, Box 10000, Kingshill, VI, 00850-9781. Tel: 340-692-4000. Fax: 340-692-4005. p. 2679

Jackson, Joe, Cat & Syst Librn, Winona State University, 175 W Mark St, Winona, MN, 55987-5838. Tel: 507-457-5152. p. 1290

Jackson, Joe, Tech Serv Librn, Paris Junior College, 2400 Clarksville St, Paris, TX, 75460. Tel: 903-782-0437. Fax: 903-782-0356. p. 2368

Jackson, Johnny W, Dir, Central State University, 1400 Brush Row Rd, Wilberforce, OH, 45384. Tel: 937-376-6372. Fax: 937-376-6132. p. 1948

Jackson, Joshua T, Ref Librn, Emerson College Library, 120 Boylston St, Boston, MA, 02116-4624. Tel: 617-824-8334. Fax: 617-824-7817. p. 1060

Jackson, Joyce, Dir, Centralia Regional Library District, 515 E Broadway, Centralia, IL, 62801. Tel: 618-532-5222. Fax: 618-532-8578. p. 602

Jackson, Judith, Assoc Law Librn, Harris County Law Library, Congress Plaza, 1019 Congress, 17th Flr, Houston, TX, 77002. Tel: 713-755-5183. p. 2335

Jackson, Judy, Asst Libr Dir, Bullitt County Public Library, 127 N Walnut St, Shepherdsville, KY, 40165-6083. Tel: 502-543-7675. Fax: 502-543-5487. p. 935

Jackson, Julia, Law Librn, Brinks, Hofer, Gilson & Lione, NBC Tower, 455 N Cityfront Plaza Dr, Ste 3600, Chicago, IL, 60611-5599. Tel: 312-321-4200. Fax: 312-321-4299. p. 607

Jackson, Karla, Librn, Georgia Department of Corrections, Office of Library Services, 200 Gulfstream Rd, Garden City, GA, 31418. Tel: 912-965-6330. Fax: 912-966-6799. p. 535

Jackson, Kathie, Ch, Sr Librn, Peoria Public Library, Sunrise Mountain, 21109 N 98th Ave, Peoria, AZ, 85382. Tel: 623-773-8667. Fax: 623-773-8670. p. 71

Jackson, Kathy, Info Res Spec, Washington Group International, 7800 E Union Ave, Ste 100, Denver, CO, 80237. Tel: 303-843-3536. Fax: 303-843-2208. p. 304

Jackson, Kay, Librn, Fort Meade Public Library, 75 E Broadway, Fort Meade, FL, 33841-2998. Tel: 863-285-8287. Fax: 863-285-9159. p. 444

Jackson, Kayla, Ch, Moore Memorial Public Library, 1701 Ninth Ave N, Texas City, TX, 77590. Tel: 409-643-5979. Fax: 409-948-1106. p. 2392

Jackson, Kim, Acq, Cat, Tech Serv, Bethel University, 325 Cherry Ave, McKenzie, TN, 38201. Tel: 731-352-4083. Fax: 731-352-4070. p. 2247

Jackson, Kim, Pres, International Parking Institute, 701 Kenmore Ave, Fredericksburg, VA, 22401-5737. Tel: 540-371-7535. Fax: 540-371-8022. p. 2466

Jackson, Lane, Rural Br Supvr, Lakeland Library Region, 1302 100 St, North Battleford, SK, S9A 0V8, CANADA. Tel: 306-445-6108. Fax: 306-445-5717. p. 2919

Jackson, Lisa, Coll Develop Officer, Pasadena Public Library, 1201 Jeff Ginn Memorial Dr, Pasadena, TX, 77506-4895. Tel: 713-477-0276. Fax: 713-475-7005. p. 2368

Jackson, Lori, Head Librn, Manning Municipal & District Library, 311 Fourth Ave SE, Manning, AB, T0H 2M0, CANADA. Tel: 780-836-3054. p. 2711

Jackson, Lori, Ref, Kenora Public Library, 24 Main St S, Kenora, ON, P9N 1S7, CANADA. Tel: 807-467-2081. Fax: 807-467-2085. p. 2812

Jackson, Lorraine, Dir, Salem Public Library, 370 Essex St, Salem, MA, 01970-3298. Tel: 978-744-0860. Fax: 978-745-8616. p. 1122

Jackson, Lue Dean, Br Mgr, Pamunkey Regional Library, King & Queen, 450 Newtown Rd, Saint Stephens Church, VA, 23148. Tel: 804-769-1623. Fax: 804-769-9286. p. 2469

Jackson, Maggi, Br Mgr, Public Library of Cincinnati & Hamilton County, West End, 805 Ezzard Charles Dr, Cincinnati, OH, 45203. Tel: 513-369-6026. Fax: 513-369-4536. p. 1873

Jackson, Marian D, Dir, Libr Serv, Tyler Junior College, 1327 S Baxter St, Tyler, TX, 75701. Tel: 903-510-2502, 903-510-2503. Fax: 903-510-2639. p. 2393

Jackson, Marie, Adult Serv, Shaler North Hills Library, 1822 Mount Royal Blvd, Glenshaw, PA, 15116. Tel: 412-486-0211. Fax: 412-486-8286. p. 2061

Jackson, Mark, ILL, Online Serv, Ref Serv, Bloomfield College Library, Liberty St & Oakland Ave, Bloomfield, NJ, 07003. Tel: 973-748-9000, Ext 714. Fax: 973-743-3998. p. 1473

Jackson, Martha, Dir, Leighton Township Public Library, 4451 12th St, Moline, MI, 49335. Tel: 616-877-4143. Fax: 616-877-4484. p. 1209

Jackson, Mary, Dir, Burnet County Library System, Marble Falls Public Branch, 101 Main St, Marble Falls, TX, 78654. Tel: 830-693-3023. Fax: 830-693-3987. p. 2293

Jackson, Mary Beth, Ch, Merriam-Gilbert Public Library, Three W Main St, West Brookfield, MA, 01585. Tel: 508-867-1410. Fax: 508-867-1409. p. 1137

Jackson, Melissa, ILL Librn, Armstrong Atlantic State University, 11935 Abercorn St, Savannah, GA, 31419. Tel: 912-344-3027. Fax: 912-344-3457. p. 549

Jackson, Melissa, Admin Mgr, Bethel University, 325 Cherry Ave, McKenzie, TN, 38201. Tel: 731-352-4083. Fax: 731-352-4070. p. 2247

Jackson, Melody, Chief Librn, Grant County Library, 507 S Canyon Blvd, John Day, OR, 97845-1050. Tel: 541-575-1992. p. 2001

Jackson, Michelle, Mgr, Columbus Metropolitan Library, Outreach Division, 96 S Grant St, Columbus, OH, 43215-4781. Tel: 614-645-2275. Fax: 614-849-1390. p. 1885

Jackson, Morris, Res Librn, Jones Day, 325 John H McConnell Blvd, Ste 600, Columbus, OH, 43215-2673. Tel: 614-469-3939. Fax: 614-461-4198. p. 1886

Jackson, Muriel, Head of Libr, Middle Georgia Regional Library System, Genealogical & Historical Room & Georgia Archives, 1180 Washington Ave, Macon, GA, 31201-1790. Tel: 478-744-0821. Fax: 478-744-0840. p. 541

Jackson, Needra, Tech Serv, University of Missouri-Columbia, Law Library, 203 Hulston Hall, Columbia, MO, 65211-4190. Tel: 573-882-9675. Fax: 573-882-9676. p. 1326

Jackson, P, Head, Tech Serv, Public Safety Canada, 340 Laurier Ave W, 10A, Ottawa, ON, K1A 0P8, CANADA. Tel: 613-991-2784. Fax: 613-941-6171. p. 2832

Jackson, Pam, Dir, Spanish Fork Public Library, 49 S Main St, Spanish Fork, UT, 84660-2030. Tel: 801-804-4480. Fax: 801-798-5014. p. 2416

Jackson, Pamela, Info Literacy, San Diego State University Library & Information Access, 5500 Campanile Dr, San Diego, CA, 92182-8050. Tel: 619-594-3809. Fax: 619-594-3270. p. 237

Jackson, Pat, Pub Serv, The Ferguson Library, One Public Library Plaza, 96 Broad St, Stamford, CT, 06904. Tel: 203-964-1000, Ext 8223. Fax: 203-357-9098. p. 369

Jackson, Patsy, ILL, Yavapai College Library, 1100 E Sheldon St, Bldg 19, Prescott, AZ, 86301. Tel: 928-776-2260. Fax: 928-776-2275. p. 78

Jackson, Paul, Bibliog Instr, Pub Serv, Aims Community College, College Ctr, 5401 W 20th St, 750.1, Greeley, CO, 80634-3002. Tel: 970-6339-6618. Fax: 970-506-6937. p. 311

Jackson, Raphael, Circ Librn, Ref Librn, Kentucky State University, 400 E Main St, Frankfort, KY, 40601-2355. Tel: 502-597-5930. Fax: 502-597-5068. p. 914

Jackson, Rebecca, Humanities & Soc Sci Librn, Iowa State University Library, 302 Parks Library, Ames, IA, 50011-2140. Tel: 515-294-1442, 515-294-1443. Fax: 515-294-5525. p. 793

Jackson, Rhonda, Librn, Central Arizona College, 273 E Old West Hwy (US 60), Apache Junction, AZ, 85219-5231. Tel: 480-677-7747. Fax: 480-677-7738. p. 57

Jackson, Rhonda, Librn, Central Arizona College, 8470 N Overfield Rd, Coolidge, AZ, 85128. Tel: 520-494-5286. Fax: 520-494-5284. p. 60

Jackson, Richard, Cat, Huntington Library, 1151 Oxford Rd, San Marino, CA, 91108. Tel: 626-405-2384. Fax: 626-449-5720. p. 255

Jackson, Ron, Ref Librn, United States Army, John L Throckmorton Library, IMSE-BRG-MWR-L Bldg 1-3346, Randolph St, Fort Bragg, NC, 28310-5000. Tel: 910-396-2665. Fax: 910-907-2274. p. 1794

Jackson, Ruth M, Dr, Univ Librn, University of California, Riverside Libraries, 900 University Ave, Riverside, CA, 92521. p. 218

Jackson, Samuel, Jr, Tech Coordr, Montgomery City-County Public Library System, 245 High St, Montgomery, AL, 36104. Tel: 334-240-4986. Fax: 334-240-4977. p. 29

Jackson, Scott, Dir, Fac & Syst, University of North Texas Libraries, PO Box 305190, Denton, TX, 76203-5190. Tel: 940-565-3024. Fax: 940-369-8760. p. 2313

Jackson, Sharon, Tech Serv, Mount Hood Community College Library, 26000 SE Stark St, Gresham, OR, 97030. Tel: 503-491-7161. Fax: 503-491-7389. p. 1999

Jackson, Sheila, Asst Dir, Main Libr Serv, Carnegie Library of Pittsburgh, 4400 Forbes Ave, Pittsburgh, PA, 15213-4080. Tel: 412-622-3110. Fax: 412-622-3141. p. 2122

Jackson, Sherry, Law Librn, Dinsmore & Shohl Library, 255 E Fifth St, 1900 Chemed Ctr, Cincinnati, OH, 45202-3172. Tel: 513-977-8435. Fax: 513-977-8141. p. 1870

Jackson, Stephen M, Librn, Tennessee State Law Library, Law Library, Supreme Ct Bldg, 401 Seventh Ave N, Nashville, TN, 37219-1407. Tel: 615-741-2016. Fax: 615-741-7186. p. 2259

Jackson, Steven J, Asst Prof, University of Michigan, 304 West Hall, 1085 S University, Ann Arbor, MI, 48109-1107. Tel: 734-763-2285. Fax: 734-764-2475. p. 2967

Jackson, Suzanne, Librn, Saint Louis Psychiatric Rehabilitation Center, 5300 Arsenal St, Saint Louis, MO, 63139. Tel: 314-877-6500. p. 1359

Jackson, Terry, Dir, San Bruno Public Library, 701 Angus Ave W, San Bruno, CA, 94066-3490. Tel: 650-616-7078. Fax: 650-876-0848. p. 230

Jackson, Tisa, Ch, Atlanta-Fulton Public Library System, East Point Library, 2757 Main St, East Point, GA, 30344. Tel: 404-762-4842. Fax: 404-762-4844. p. 512

Jackson, Tish, Ch, Bellevue Public Library, 106 N Third St, Bellevue, IA, 52031. Tel: 563-872-4991. Fax: 563-872-4094. p. 796

Jackson, Tremain, Br Mgr, Abilene Public Library, South Branch Library, 1401 S Danville, Abilene, TX, 79605. Tel: 325-698-7378. Fax: 325-698-7621. p. 2272

Jackson, Viveca, Librn, Middle Georgia Regional Library System, West Bibb Branch, Northwest Commons, 5580 Thomaston Rd, Macon, GA, 31220-8118. Tel: 478-744-0818. Fax: 478-744-0819. p. 541

Jackson-Beck, Lauren, Info Serv Librn, Aurora University, 315 S Gladstone, Aurora, IL, 60506-4877. Tel: 630-844-5525. Fax: 630-844-3848. p. 591

Jackson-Brown, Grace, Head of Libr, Indiana University Bloomington, Weil Journalism Library, Ernie Pyle Hall, 940 E Seventh St, Bloomington, IN, 47405-7108. Tel: 812-855-9247. Fax: 812-855-0901. p. 728

Jackson-Darling, Andi, Libr Dir, Falmouth Memorial Library, Five Lunt Rd, Falmouth, ME, 04105-1292. Tel: 207-781-2351. Fax: 207-781-4094. p. 985

Jackson-Reno, Nancy, Coordr, New Hampshire Department of Health & Human Services, State Office Park S, Main Bldg, 3rd flr N, 105 Pleasant St, Concord, NH, 03301. Tel: 603-271-2677. Fax: 603-271-6105. p. 1442

Jackson-Sow, Tasha, Br Mgr, First Regional Library, Jessie J Edwards Public Library, 610 E Central Ave, Coldwater, MS, 38618. Tel: 662-622-5573. Fax: 662-622-5846. p. 1301

Jacky, Noreen, Libr Supvr-Popular Libr, University of Washington Libraries, Architecture-Urban Planning, 334 Gould Hall, Box 355730, Seattle, WA, 98195-5730. Tel: 206-543-4067. p. 2533

Jacob, Ann, Br Mgr, Mississauga Library System, Mississauga Valley, 1275 Mississauga Valley Blvd, Mississauga, ON, L5A 3R8, CANADA. Tel: 905-615-4670. Fax: 905-615-4671. p. 2823

Jacob, Barbara, Dir, Cuero Public Library, 207 E Main St, Cuero, TX, 77954. Tel: 361-275-2864. Fax: 361-275-2864. p. 2304

Jacob, Diane, Head, Archives, Head, Rec Mgt, Virginia Military Institute, Letcher Ave, Lexington, VA, 24450. Tel: 540-464-7566. Fax: 540-464-7279. p. 2474

Jacob, Joanne, Regional Dir, Haut-Saint-Jean Regional Library, 15, rue de l'Église St, Ste 102, Edmundston, NB, E3V 1J3, CANADA. Tel: 506-735-2074. Fax: 506-735-2193. p. 2762

Jacob, John, Archivist, Washington & Lee University, Wilbur C Hall Law Library, Lewis Hall, E Denny Circle, Lexington, VA, 24450. Tel: 540-458-8969. Fax: 540-458-8967. p. 2474

Jacob, Kathryn, Curator, Harvard Library, Arthur & Elizabeth Schlesinger Library on the History of Women in America, Three James St, Cambridge, MA, 02138-3766. Tel: 617-495-8530. Fax: 617-496-8340. p. 1076

Jacob, Lisa, Mgr, Advocate Illinois Masonic Medical Center, 836 W Wellington Ave, Rm 7501, Chicago, IL, 60657. Tel: 773-296-5084. p. 605

Jacob, Nora, Dir, Libr Serv, Orange Public Library & History Center, 407 E Chapman Ave, Orange, CA, 92866-1509. Tel: 714-288-2400. Fax: 714-771-6126. p. 201

Jacob, Susan, Dir, Saint Lucie County Library System, 101 Melody Lane, Fort Pierce, FL, 34950-4402. Tel: 772-462-1615. Fax: 772-462-2750. p. 447

Jacobek, Phyllis A, Dir, Mokena Community Public Library District, 11327 W 195th St, Mokena, IL, 60448. Tel: 708-479-9663. Fax: 708-479-1690. p. 674

Jacobi, Kristin M, Head, Cat, Eastern Connecticut State University, 83 Windham St, Willimantic, CT, 06226-2295. Tel: 860-465-4508. Fax: 860-465-5523. p. 378

Jacobi, Laura, Supvr, Instruction & Ref, Gallaudet University Library, 800 Florida Ave NE, Washington, DC, 20002-3095. Tel: 202-651-5239. p. 401

Jacobowitz, Reina, Ref Serv Librn, Roseland Free Public Library, 20 Roseland Ave, Roseland, NJ, 07068-1235. Tel: 973-226-8636. Fax: 973-226-6429. p. 1527

Jacobs, Barb, Ch, North Suburban Library District, 6340 N Second St, Loves Park, IL, 61111. Tel: 815-633-4247. Fax: 815-633-4249. p. 668

Jacobs, Bev, Pub Serv, Carleton A Friday Memorial Library, 155 E First St, New Richmond, WI, 54017. Tel: 715-243-0431. Fax: 715-246-2691. p. 2625

Jacobs, Candee, Dir, Beck Bookman Library, 420 W Fourth St, Holton, KS, 66436-1572. Tel: 785-364-3532. Fax: 785-364-5402. p. 872

Jacobs, Carla, Dir, Hatchie River Regional Library, 63 Executive Dr, Jackson, TN, 38305. Tel: 731-668-0710. Fax: 731-668-6663. p. 2238

Jacobs, Carla, Regional Mgr, Tennessee State Library & Archives, 403 Seventh Ave N, Nashville, TN, 37243-0312. Tel: 731-668-0710. Fax: 615-532-2472, 615-741-6471. p. 2259

Jacobs, Carolyn, Dr, Head, Ref, Lone Star College System, North Harris College Library, 2700 W W Thorne Dr, Houston, TX, 77073. Tel: 281-618-5487. Fax: 281-618-5695. p. 2340

Jacobs, Daniel, Dr, Dir, Boston Psychoanalytic Society & Institute, Inc, 169 Herrick Rd, Newton, MA, 02459. Tel: 617-266-0953, Ext 104. Fax: 857-255-3253. p. 1109

Jacobs, Deborah, Librn, Scott County Library System, Walcott Branch, 207 S Main St, Walcott, IA, 52773. Tel: 563-284-6612. Fax: 563-284-6612. p. 814

Jacobs, Donald W, Chief Info Officer, Bucks County Law Library, Court House, 55 E Court St, First Flr, Doylestown, PA, 18901. Tel: 215-343-6023, 215-348-6000. Fax: 215-348-6827. p. 2050

Jacobs, Dorothy, Libr Asst, H J Nugen Public Library, 103 E Main St, New London, IA, 52645. Tel: 319-367-7704. Fax: 319-367-7710. p. 835

Jacobs, Gloria, Br Head, Toronto Public Library, Bloor/Gladstone, 1101 Bloor St W, Toronto, ON, M6H 1M7, CANADA. Tel: 416-393-7674. Fax: 416-393-7502. p. 2860

Jacobs, Janice, Librn, East Berlin Library Association, 80 Main St, East Berlin, CT, 06023. Tel: 860-828-3123. p. 337

Jacobs, Janine, Ch, Fullerton Public Library, 353 W Commonwealth Ave, Fullerton, CA, 92832-1796. Tel: 714-738-6343. Fax: 714-447-3280. p. 154

Jacobs, Jude, Ch, Orchard Park Public Library, S-4570 S Buffalo St, Orchard Park, NY, 14127. Tel: 716-662-9851. Fax: 716-667-3098. p. 1712

Jacobs, Kathy, Dir, Yankton Community Library, 515 Walnut, Yankton, SD, 57078-4042. Tel: 605-668-5275. Fax: 605-668-5277. p. 2222

Jacobs, Kelley, Mgt Analyst, Salem Public Library, 585 Liberty St SE, Salem, OR, 97301. Tel: 503-588-6064. Fax: 503-588-6055. p. 2018

Jacobs, Laura, Archivist/Librn, Ref & Info Literacy Librn, University of Wisconsin-Superior, PO Box 2000, Belknap & Catlin, Superior, WI, 54880-2000. Tel: 715-394-8359. Fax: 715-394-8462. p. 2641

Jacobs, Laura, Assoc Prof, University of Wisconsin-Superior, Belknap & Catlin, PO Box 2000, Superior, WI, 54880. Tel: 715-394-8359. Fax: 715-394-8462. p. 2977

Jacobs, Laureen, Ch, Arlington Public Library System, Northeast, 1905 Brown Blvd, Arlington, TX, 76006-4605. Tel: 817-277-5573. Fax: 817-276-8649. p. 2276

Jacobs, Laureen, Early Childhood Librn, Arlington Public Library System, 101 E Abram St, MS 10-0100, Arlington, TX, 76010-1183. Tel: 817-459-6900. Fax: 817-459-6936. p. 2276

Jacobs, Leslie, Br Mgr, Clermont County Public Library, Batavia-Doris Wood Branch, 180 S Third St, Batavia, OH, 45103-2806. Tel: 513-732-2128. Fax: 513-732-2498. p. 1858

Jacobs, Lisa, Dir, Riverhead Free Library, 330 Court St, Riverhead, NY, 11901-2885. Tel: 631-727-3228. Fax: 631-727-4762. p. 1728

Jacobs, Mark, Exec Dir, Washington Research Library Consortium, 901 Commerce Dr, Upper Marlboro, MD, 20774. Tel: 301-390-2000. Fax: 301-390-2020. p. 2945

Jacobs, Marty, Curator, Museum of the City of New York, 1220 Fifth Ave, New York, NY, 10029. Tel: 212-534-1672, Ext 3380. Fax: 212-534-5974. p. 1687

Jacobs, Relly, Librn, Drinker Biddle & Reath, 500 Campus Dr, Florham Park, NJ, 07932. Tel: 973-360-1100. Fax: 973-360-9831. p. 1486

Jacobs, Sheila, Br Supvr, Lincoln City Libraries, Dan A Williams Branch, 5000 Mike Scholl St, Lincoln, NE, 68524. Tel: 402-441-4252. p. 1405

Jacobs, Sheila, Br Supvr, Lincoln City Libraries, Loren Corey Eiseley Branch, 1530 Superior St, Lincoln, NE, 68521. Tel: 402-441-4250. Fax: 402-441-4253. p. 1405

Jacobs, Warren, Ref & Instruction Librn, California State University, Stanislaus, One University Circle, Turlock, CA, 95382. Tel: 209-664-6565. p. 277

Jacobsen, Aurora, Ad, Winona Public Library, 151 W Fifth St, Winona, MN, 55987-3170. Tel: 507-452-4582. Fax: 507-452-5842. p. 1290

Jacobsen, Donald, Dir, Englewood Public Library, 31 Engle St, Englewood, NJ, 07631. Tel: 201-568-2215, Ext 222. Fax: 201-568-6895. p. 1484

Jacobsen, LaVonne, Head, Coll Access & Mgt Serv/Dept Co-Chair, San Francisco State University, 1630 Holloway Ave, San Francisco, CA, 94132-4030. Tel: 415-338-6953. Fax: 415-338-0534. p. 247

Jacobsen, Lynne, Assoc Univ Librn, Coll Serv, Pepperdine University Libraries, 24255 Pacific Coast Hwy, Malibu, CA, 90263. Tel: 310-506-4252. Fax: 310-506-7225. p. 182

Jacobsma, Kelly, Dir, Hope College, Van Wylen Library, 53 Graves Pl, Holland, MI, 49422. Tel: 616-395-7790. Fax: 616-395-7965. p. 1190

Jacobsohn, Dan, Chief Info Officer, Dir, University of Wisconsin-Madison, MERIT Library (Media, Education Resources & Information Technology), 225 N Mills St, Madison, WI, 53706. Tel: 608-263-4755. Fax: 608-262-6050. p. 2609

Jacobson, Alan, Br Mgr, Everett Public Library, Evergreen, 9512 Evergreen Way, Everett, WA, 98204. Tel: 425-257-8270. Fax: 425-257-8265. p. 2515

Jacobson, Beverly, Dir, Hazel Mackin Community Library, 107 W Main St, Roberts, WI, 54023. Tel: 715-749-3849. p. 2635

Jacobson, Claudia, In Charge, Milwaukee Public Museum, 800 W Wells St, Milwaukee, WI, 53233. Tel: 414-278-2736. Fax: 414-278-6100. p. 2620

Jacobson, David, Br Head, Winnipeg Public Library, St John's, 500 Salter St, Winnipeg, MB, R2W 4M5, CANADA. Tel: 204-986-4689. Fax: 204-986-7123. p. 2760

Jacobson, Eileen, Asst Librn, Caledonia Public Library, 231 E Main St, Caledonia, MN, 55921-1321. Tel: 507-725-2671. Fax: 507-725-5258. p. 1243

Jacobson, Karen, Br Asst, Marathon County Public Library, Hatley Branch, 435 Curtis Ave, Hatley, WI, 54440. Tel: 715-446-3537. Fax: 715-446-3537. p. 2646

Jacobson, Kristen, Ref Serv, Ch, Westchester Public Library, 10700 Canterbury St, Westchester, IL, 60154. Tel: 708-562-3573. Fax: 708-562-1298. p. 717

Jacobson, Lucille, Asst Dir, ILL, McIntosh Memorial Library, 118 E Jefferson St, Viroqua, WI, 54665. Tel: 608-637-7151. Fax: 608-637-8608. p. 2643

Jacobson, Michelle, Ref, Kurth Memorial Library, 706 S Raguet, Lufkin, TX, 75904. Tel: 936-630-0560. Fax: 936-639-2487. p. 2358

Jacobson, Pamela, Dir, Rowley Public Library, 141 Main St, Rowley, MA, 01969. Tel: 978-948-2850. Fax: 978-948-2266. p. 1121

Jacobson, Patty, Asst Librn, Menlo Public Library, Menlo Community Bldg, 504 Fifth St, Menlo, IA, 50164. Tel: 641-524-4201. Fax: 641-524-2682. p. 831

Jacobson, Phyllis, Asst Librn, Fontanelle Public Library, 303 Washington St, Fontanelle, IA, 50846. Tel: 641-745-4981. Fax: 641-745-3017. p. 816

Jacobson, Renee, ILL, Per, University of Minnesota Medical Center - Fairview, Library, 2450 Riverside Ave, Minneapolis, MN, 55454. Tel: 612-273-6546. Fax: 612-273-2675. p. 1262

Jacobson, Sandy, Librn, Jones Day, 77 W Wacker Dr, Ste 3500, Chicago, IL, 60601-1692. Tel: 312-269-4128. Fax: 312-782-8585. p. 616

Jacobson, Terra, Mgr, Libr Serv, Moraine Valley Community College Library, 9000 W College Pkwy, Palos Hills, IL, 60465. Tel: 708-974-5467. Fax: 708-974-1184. p. 687

Jacobson, Vickie, Mgr, United States Navy, 500 Moffett Ave, No 104, Kingsville, TX, 78363-5034. Tel: 361-516-6271. Fax: 361-516-6971. p. 2351

Jacobson-Carroll, Liz, Dir, Buckland Public Library, 30 Upper St, Shelburne Falls, MA, 01370. Tel: 413-625-9412. Fax: 413-625-9412. p. 1123

Jacoby, Beth, Coll Develop, York College of Pennsylvania, 441 Country Club Rd, York, PA, 17403-3651. Tel: 717-815-1950. Fax: 717-849-1608. p. 2160

Jacoby, Robert, Sr Legal Res Librn, University of Toledo, LaValley Law Library, Mail Stop 508, 2801 W Bancroft St, Toledo, OH, 43606-3390. Tel: 419-530-2733. Fax: 419-530-5121. p. 1941

Jacoby, Shirley, Dir, Council for Relationships Library, 4025 Chestnut St, 1st Flr, Philadelphia, PA, 19104. Tel: 215-382-6680. Fax: 215-386-1743. p. 2105

Jacox, Corinne, Cat, Ref, Creighton University, Klutznick Law Library - McGrath, North, Mullin & Kratz Legal Research Center, School of Law, 2500 California Plaza, Omaha, NE, 68178-0340. Tel: 402-280-2251, 402-280-2875. Fax: 402-280-2244. p. 1412

Jacques, Charlotte, Librn, Baiting Hollow Free Library, Four Warner Dr, Calverton, NY, 11933. Tel: 631-727-8765. p. 1600

Jacques, Danielle, Dir, Agriculture & Agri-Food Canada, Tower 6, 1341 Baseline Rd, Ottawa, ON, K1A 0C5, CANADA. Tel: 613-773-1400. Fax: 613-773-1499. p. 2827

Jacques, Dorais, Dir, Div Archives, Les Archives de la Ville de Quebec, 350 rue Saint Joseph E, 4th Flr, Quebec, QC, G1K 3B2, CANADA. Tel: 418-641-6214. Fax: 418-641-6702. p. 2905

Jacques, Nicole, Pub Serv Librn, Wesleyan College, 4760 Forsyth Rd, Macon, GA, 31210-4462. Tel: 478-757-5203. Fax: 478-757-3898. p. 541

Jacques, Sandra, Librn, College Bart Bibliotheque, 751 cote d'Abraham, Quebec, QC, G1R 1A2, CANADA. Tel: 418-522-3906. Fax: 418-522-5456. p. 2904

Jacquet, Roberta C, Dr, Dir, Cabrini College Library, 610 King of Prussia Rd, Radnor, PA, 19087-3698. Tel: 610-902-8260. Fax: 610-902-8539. p. 2132

Jacquot, Maureen, Librn, Missouri Court of Appeals, One Old Post Office Sq, Rm 304, 815 Olive St, Saint Louis, MO, 63101. Tel: 314-539-4300. Fax: 314-539-4324. p. 1356

Jacso, Peter, Prof, University of Hawaii, 2550 The Mall, Honolulu, HI, 96822. Tel: 808-956-7321. Fax: 808-956-5835. p. 2964

Jadlos, Melissa, Dir, Saint John Fisher College, 3690 East Ave, Rochester, NY, 14618-3599. Tel: 585-385-8165. Fax: 585-385-8445. p. 1732

Jaeger, Bret, Dir, Waupun Public Library, 123 S Forest St, Waupun, WI, 53963. Tel: 920-324-7925. p. 2646

Jaeger, John, Ref Librn, Dallas Baptist University, 3000 Mountain Creek Pkwy, Dallas, TX, 75211-9299. Tel: 214-333-5212. Fax: 214-333-5323. p. 2305

Jaegers, Linda, Librn, Illinois Department of Corrections, 2021 Kentville Rd, Kewanee, IL, 61443. Tel: 309-852-4601, Ext 3331. Fax: 309-852-4617. p. 661

Jaehn, Tomas, Curator, Museum of New Mexico, Palace of the Governors-Fray Angelico Chavez History Library, 120 Washington Ave, Santa Fe, NM, 87501. Tel: 505-476-5090. Fax: 505-476-5053. p. 1562

Jaet, Julia, Ref Serv, Marquette University, Sensenbrenner Hall, 1103 W Wisconsin Ave, Milwaukee, WI, 53233-2313. Tel: 414-288-7092. Fax: 414-288-5914. p. 2618

Jaeyong, Chang, Librn, University of California, Berkeley, C V Starr East Asian Library, Berkeley, CA, 94720-6000. Tel: 510-642-2556. Fax: 510-642-3817. p. 128

Jaffe, Eileen, Bibliog Database Mgr, Pinal County Library District, 92 W Butte Ave, Florence, AZ, 85132. Tel: 520-866-6457. Fax: 520-866-6533. p. 63

Jaffe, John G, Dir, Sweet Briar College, 134 Chapel Rd, Sweet Briar, VA, 24595-1200. Tel: 434-381-6138. Fax: 434-381-6173. p. 2497

Jaffe, Lee, Librn, University of California, 1156 High St, Santa Cruz, CA, 95064. Tel: 831-459-3297. Fax: 831-459-8206. p. 264

Jaffe, Marina, Circ Coordr, Maryville College, 502 E Lamar Alexander Pkwy, Maryville, TN, 37804-5907. Tel: 865-981-8256. Fax: 865-981-8267. p. 2247

Jaffee, John, Dir, Virginia Independent College & University Library Association, c/o Mary Helen Cochran Library, Sweet Briar College, Sweet Briar, VA, 24595. Tel: 434-381-6139. Fax: 434-381-6173. p. 2957

Jaffee, John G, Dir, Lynchburg Information Online Network, 2315 Memorial Ave, Lynchburg, VA, 24503. Tel: 434-381-6139. Fax: 434-381-6173. p. 2957

Jager, Teresa, Br Mgr, Wayne County Public Library, Dalton Branch, 127 S Church St, Dalton, OH, 44618. Tel: 330-828-8486. Fax: 330-828-0255. p. 1950

Jaggard, Jane, Librn, Wyoming Public Library District, 119 N Seventh St, Wyoming, IL, 61491. Tel: 309-695-2241. Fax: 309-695-2241. p. 722

Jaggars, Damon, Assoc Univ Librn, Coll Develop, Bibliog Serv, Columbia University, Butler Library, Rm 517, 535 W 114th St, New York, NY, 10027. Tel: 212-854-0025. Fax: 212-854-9099. p. 1674

Jagger, Toni L, Dir, Alvah N Belding Memorial Library, 302 E Main St, Belding, MI, 48809-1799. Tel: 616-794-1450. Fax: 616-794-3510. p. 1156

Jaggers, Karen, Dir, Libr Serv, Eastern Arizona College, 615 N Stadium Ave, Thatcher, AZ, 85552. Tel: 928-428-8308. Fax: 928-428-8390. p. 84

Jagos, Maureen, Interim Dir, Chester Public Library, 1784 Kings Hwy, Chester, NY, 10918. Tel: 845-469-4252. Fax: 845-469-7583. p. 1606

Jaguszewski, Janice, Interim Dir, University of Minnesota Libraries-Twin Cities, Health Sciences Libraries, Diehl Hall, 505 Essex St SE, Minneapolis, MN, 55455. Tel: 612-626-0998. Fax: 612-626-5822. p. 1262

Jahlas, LuAnn, Dir, Brooklyn Public Library, 306 Jackson St, Brooklyn, IA, 52211. Tel: 641-522-9272. Fax: 641-522-9272. p. 797

Jahncke, Marjie, Br Mgr, Saint Tammany Parish Library, Bush Branch, 81597 Hwy 41, Bush, LA, 70431. Tel: 985-886-3588. Fax: 985-886-3588. p. 948

Jahr, Joanne, Librn, WKH/LWW American Journal of Nursing, 333 Seventh Flr, New York, NY, 10001. Tel: 646-674-6601. Fax: 212-886-1206. p. 1703

Jakich, Lisa, Br Mgr, Starke County Public Library System, San Pierre Branch, 103 Broadway, San Pierre, IN, 46374. Tel: 219-828-4352. p. 758

Jakoboski, Jean, Dir, Aldrich Free Public Library, 299 Main St, Moosup, CT, 06354. Tel: 860-564-8760. Fax: 860-564-8491. p. 353

Jaksic, Victoria, Ch, Atlanta-Fulton Public Library System, Roswell Regional Library, 115 Norcross St, Roswell, GA, 30075. Tel: 770-640-3075. Fax: 770-640-3077. p. 512

Jakub, William, Dir, Franciscan University of Steubenville, 1235 University Blvd, Steubenville, OH, 43952-1763. Tel: 740-283-6208. Fax: 740-284-7239. p. 1936

Jakubcin, Margaret, Asst Dir, North Olympic Library System, 2210 S Peabody St, Port Angeles, WA, 98362-6536. Tel: 360-417-8500, Ext 7714. Fax: 360-457-3125. p. 2523

Jakubowski, Barbara, Asst Dean, Info & Tech Mgt, University of Texas at San Antonio Libraries, One UTSA Circle, San Antonio, TX, 78249-0671. Tel: 210-458-5509. p. 2383

Jakubowski, Mary Jean, Dir, Buffalo & Erie County Public Library System, One Lafayette Sq, Buffalo, NY, 14203-1887. Tel: 716-858-8900. Fax: 716-858-6211. p. 1596

Jakubowski, Robert, Acq Tech, Palo Alto College, 1400 W Villaret St, San Antonio, TX, 78224-2499. Tel: 210-486-3562. Fax: 210-486-9184. p. 2380

Jakubs, Deborah, PhD, Univ Librn & Vice Provost for Libr Affairs, Duke University Libraries, 411 Chapel Dr, Durham, NC, 27708. Tel: 919-660-5800. Fax: 919-660-5923. p. 1787

Jakus, Florence, Br Mgr, Las Vegas-Clark County Library District, West Charleston Library, 6301 W Charleston Blvd, Las Vegas, NV, 89146-1124. Tel: 702-507-3940. Fax: 702-507-3950. p. 1430

Jalley, Joanne, Electronic Res, Ser, Illinois Valley Community College, 815 N Orlando Smith Ave, Oglesby, IL, 61348-9692. Tel: 815-224-0237. Fax: 815-224-9147. p. 685

Jalowiec, Tammi, Br Librn, Lake Agassiz Regional Library, Fosston Public Library, 421 Foss Ave N, Fosston, MN, 56542. Tel: 218-435-1320. Fax: 218-435-1320. p. 1266

Jalowka, Claudia, Law Librn, Connecticut Judicial Branch Law Libraries, 90 Washington St, Third Flr, Hartford, CT, 06106. Tel: 860-706-5145. Fax: 860-706-5086. p. 344

Jamal, Arif, Head Librn, University of Pittsburgh, African-American Collection, Hillman Library, 1st Flr, Pittsburgh, PA, 15260. Tel: 412-648-7759. Fax: 412-648-7733. p. 2128

Jamal, Arif, Librn, University of Pittsburgh, Buhl Library of Social Work, Hillman Library, 1st Flr, Pittsburgh, PA, 15260. Tel: 412-648-7759. p. 2128

Jamasb, Shirin, Head Librn, Delaware Technical & Community College, PO Box 630, Sea Shore Hwy, Georgetown, DE, 19947-0630. Tel: 302-856-9033. Fax: 302-858-5462. p. 383

James, Bernetta, Br Supvr, Jackson/Hinds Library System, Margaret Walker Alexander Library, 2525 Robinson Rd, Jackson, MS, 39209-6256. Tel: 601-354-8911. Fax: 601-354-8912. p. 1303

James, Beverly A, Exec Dir, Greenville County Library System, 25 Heritage Green Pl, Greenville, SC, 29601-2034. Tel: 864-527-9231. Fax: 864-235-8375. p. 2196

James, Carla Louise, Dir of Libr, Roanoke Higher Education Center Library, 108 N Jefferson St, Ste 216, Roanoke, VA, 24016. Tel: 540-767-6010. Fax: 540-767-6012. p. 2494

James, Carrie, Adult Serv, Harvin Clarendon County Library, 215 N Brooks St, Manning, SC, 29102. Tel: 803-435-8633. Fax: 803-435-8101. p. 2199

James, Cathy, Dir, Northeast Missouri Library Service, 207 W Chestnut, Kahoka, MO, 63445-1489. Tel: 660-727-2327. Fax: 660-727-2327. p. 1336

James, Cathy, Dir, Northeast Missouri Library Service, Knox County Public, 120 S Main St, Edina, MO, 63537-1427. Tel: 660-397-2460. Fax: 660-397-2460. p. 1336

James, Charles, Librn, University of California, Berkeley, NISEE-PEER Earthquake Engineering Library, 453 Richmond Field Sta, 1301 S 46th St, Richmond, CA, 94804. Tel: 510-665-3419. Fax: 510-665-3456. p. 128

James, Charles, Dir, Bluegrass Community & Technical College, Oswald Bldg, 470 Cooper Dr, Lexington, KY, 40506-0235. Tel: 859-246-6393. Fax: 859-246-4675. p. 920

James, Chris, Law Librn, Muskogee Law Library Association, Muskogee County Court House, Muskogee, OK, 74401. Tel: 918-682-7873. p. 1969

James, Dean, Assoc Dir, Coll Develop, Houston Academy of Medicine, 1133 John Freeman Blvd, Houston, TX, 77030. Tel: 713-799-7122. Fax: 713-790-7052. p. 2337

James, Delane, Dir, Buckham Memorial Library, 11 Division St E, Faribault, MN, 55021-6000. Tel: 507-334-2089. Fax: 507-384-0503. p. 1250

James, Delo, Chief Librn, Department of Veterans Affairs Medical Center Library, 385 Tremont Ave, East Orange, NJ, 07018-1095. Tel: 908-647-0180, Ext 4412. Fax: 973-395-7234. p. 1482

James, Donna, Dir, Libr Serv, Distance Educ, Info Literacy, Valley City State University Library, 101 College St SW, Valley City, ND, 58072-4098. Tel: 701-845-7276. Fax: 701-845-7437. p. 1848

James, Donna V, Dir, Valley City State University, 101 College St SW, Valley City, ND, 58072-4098. Tel: 701-845-7276. Fax: 701-845-7437. p. 2971

James, Evelyn L, Librn, Historical Society of Dauphin County Library, 219 S Front St, Harrisburg, PA, 17104. Tel: 717-233-3462. Fax: 717-233-6059. p. 2065

James, Heather, Head, Res & Instrul Serv, Marquette University Libraries, 1355 W Wisconsin Ave, Milwaukee, WI, 53233. Tel: 414-288-7214. Fax: 414-288-7813. p. 2618

James, Janet, Electronic Res, Fried, Frank, Harris, Shriver & Jacobson LLP, 1001 Pennsylvania Ave NW, Ste 800, Washington, DC, 20004. Tel: 202-639-7293. Fax: 202-639-7008. p. 401

James, Janet, Acq, Rhodes College, 2000 North Pkwy, Memphis, TN, 38112-1694. Tel: 901-843-3903. Fax: 901-843-3404. p. 2251

James, Jennifer, Librn, Institute of American Indian & Alaska Native Culture & Arts Development Library, 83 Avan Nu Po Rd, Santa Fe, NM, 87508. Tel: 505-424-5715. Fax: 505-424-3131. p. 1562

James, John R, Assoc Librn, Dartmouth College Library, 6025 Baker Berry Library, Rm 115, Hanover, NH, 03755-3525. Tel: 603-646-2236. Fax: 603-646-3702. p. 1450

James, Joyce, Asst Dir, Bollinger County Library, 302 Conrad St, Marble Hill, MO, 63764. Tel: 573-238-2713. Fax: 573-238-2879. p. 1344

James, Julie, Br Mgr, Raleigh Public Library, 150 Main St, Raleigh, MS, 39153. Tel: 601-782-4277. Fax: 601-782-4400. p. 1313

James, Kathleen, Dir, Saint Clair County Community College, 323 Erie St, Port Huron, MI, 48060. Tel: 810-984-3881, 810-989-5640. Fax: 810-984-2852. p. 1219

James, Kelly, Tech Serv Librn, Rockford College, 5050 E State St, Rockford, IL, 61108-2393. Tel: 815-394-5045. Fax: 815-226-4084. p. 697

James, Leslie, Br Mgr, Hall County Library System, Spout Springs Branch, 6488 Spout Springs Rd, Flowery Branch, GA, 30542. Tel: 770-532-3311, Ext 191. p. 534

James, Linda, Dir, Lynnville Public Library, 301 South St, Lynnville, IA, 50153. Tel: 641-527-2590. Fax: 641-527-2592. p. 828

James, Lynsey, Br Mgr, West Georgia Regional Library, Paulding County Public Library, 1010 E Memorial Dr, Dallas, GA, 30132. Tel: 770-445-5680. Fax: 770-443-7626. p. 524

James, Maneia, Libr Asst I, Montgomery City-County Public Library System, Juliette Hampton Morgan Memorial Library (Main Library), 245 High St, Montgomery, AL, 36104. Tel: 334-240-4999. Fax: 334-240-4980. p. 30

James, Maureen, Coll Develop Librn, University of Arkansas at Little Rock, 2801 S University Ave, Little Rock, AR, 72204. Tel: 501-569-8816. Fax: 501-569-8128. p. 107

James, Nicole, Br Mgr, Indianapolis-Marion County Public Library, College Avenue, 4180 N College Ave, Indianapolis, IN, 46205. Tel: 317-275-4325. p. 754

James, Paula, Dir, Adel Public Library, 303 S Tenth St, Adel, IA, 50003-1797. Tel: 515-993-3512. Fax: 515-993-3191. p. 791

James, Paula, Dir of Finance, South Carolina State Library, 1430-1500 Senate St, Columbia, SC, 29201. Tel: 803-734-8917. Fax: 803-734-8676. p. 2189

James, Phyllis, Librn, Parkland Regional Library, Semans Branch, 103 King St, Semans, SK, S0A 3S0, CANADA. Tel: 306-524-2224. p. 2932

James, Rachel, Prog Coordr/Ch, Seward Community Library Museum, 239 Six Ave, Seward, AK, 99664. Tel: 907-224-4082. Fax: 907-224-3521. p. 53

James, Randall, Libr Dir, American InterContinental University, Buckhead Campus Library, 3330 Peachtree Rd NE, Atlanta, GA, 30326. Tel: 404-965-6547. Fax: 404-965-5705. p. 510

James, Rebecca I, Asst Br Librn, Lexington County Public Library System, Irmo Branch, 6251 St Andrews Rd, Columbia, SC, 29212-3152. Tel: 803-798-7880. Fax: 803-798-8570. p. 2199

James, Robert, Asst Dir, Adm Serv, East Carolina University, J Y Joyner Library, E Fifth St, Greenville, NC, 27858-4353. Tel: 252-328-6114. Fax: 252-328-6892. p. 1798

James, Sally, Br Mgr, Harrison County Library System, Pass Christian Public, War Memorial Park, 324 E Second St, Pass Christian, MS, 39571. Tel: 228-452-4596. Fax: 228-452-1111. p. 1299

James, Scott, Archivist, Arts & Letters Club Library, 14 Elm St, Toronto, ON, M5G 1G7, CANADA. Tel: 416-597-0223. Fax: 416-597-9544. p. 2850

James, Sherryl, Commun Serv Librn, East Central Georgia Regional Library, 902 Greene St, Augusta, GA, 30901. Tel: 706-821-2600. Fax: 706-724-6762. p. 519

James, Shery, Asst Mgr, Ref Spec, First Regional Library, B J Chain Public Library, 6619 Hwy 305 N, Olive Branch, MS, 38654. Tel: 662-895-5900. Fax: 662-895-9171. p. 1301

James, Susan, Asst Dir, Ref, Bayliss Public Library, 541 Library Dr, Sault Sainte Marie, MI, 49783. Tel: 906-632-9331. Fax: 906-635-0210. p. 1226

James, Ting, Head, Tech Serv, Saint Louis University, Omer Poos Law Library, Morrissey Hall, 3700 Lindell Blvd, Saint Louis, MO, 63108-3478. Tel: 314-977-3356. Fax: 314-977-3966. p. 1361

James, Trina, Br Mgr, Jasper-Dubois County Contractual Public Library, Ferdinand Branch, 243 W Tenth St, Ferdinand, IN, 47542. Tel: 812-367-1671. Fax: 812-367-1063. p. 756

James, Vivian, Dir, Museum of Early Trades & Crafts Library, Nine Main St, Madison, NJ, 07940. Tel: 973-377-2982, Ext 11. Fax: 973-377-7358. p. 1498

James, William, Dir, Villanova University, Law Library, Garey Hall, 299 N Spring Mill Rd, Villanova, PA, 19085. Tel: 610-519-7023. Fax: 610-519-7033. p. 2150

James-Herron, Ann, Slide Librn, Regis University, 3333 Regis Blvd, Denver, CO, 80221-1099. Tel: 303-458-4030. Fax: 303-964-5497. p. 303

James-Jenkin, Connie, Ref Librn, Elgin Community College, 1700 Spartan Dr, Elgin, IL, 60123. Tel: 847-214-7337. p. 641

James-Vigil, Allyson, Ser, Central New Mexico Community College Libraries, Montoya Campus Library, J Bldg, Rm 123, 4700 Morris NE, Albuquerque, NM, 87111. Tel: 505-224-5731. Fax: 505-224-5727. p. 1548

Jameson, Cynthia, Br Mgr, Athens Regional Library System, Bogart Branch, 200 S Burson Ave, Bogart, GA, 30622. Tel: 770-725-9443. Fax: 770-725-9443. p. 508

Jameson, Jodi, Nursing Librn, University of Toledo, Health Science Campus, Mail Stop 1061, 3000 Arlington Ave, Toledo, OH, 43614-5805. Tel: 419-383-4223. Fax: 419-383-6146. p. 1940

Jameson, Wanda, Librn, Kirwin City Library, First & Main, Kirwin, KS, 67644. Tel: 785-543-6652. Fax: 785-543-6168. p. 876

Jamgochian, Dana, Dir, Epworth United Methodist Church Library, 3077 Valleyview Dr, Toledo, OH, 43615-2237. Tel: 419-531-4236. Fax: 419-531-7487. p. 1939

Jamieson, Steve, Assoc Librn, Pub Serv, Covenant Theological Seminary, 12330 Conway Rd, Saint Louis, MO, 63141. Tel: 314-392-4100, 314-434-4044. Fax: 314-392-4116, 314-434-4819. p. 1354

Jamison, Charles A, Acq, Dir, Ursinus College Library, 601 E Main St, Collegeville, PA, 19426. Tel: 610-409-3607. Fax: 610-489-0634. p. 2046

Jamison, Jackie, Dir, Camargo Township District Library, 14 N Main St, Villa Grove, IL, 61956. Tel: 217-832-5211. Fax: 217-832-7203. p. 714

Jamison, James, Electronic Res, Pennsylvania State University Libraries, 510 Paterno Library, University Park, PA, 16802. Tel: 814-867-0886. Fax: 814-865-3665. p. 2148

Jamison, Janine, Br Mgr, Fort Smith Public Library, 3201 Rogers Ave, Fort Smith, AR, 72903. Tel: 479-785-0405. Fax: 479-785-0431. p. 100

Jamison, Janine, Br Mgr, Fort Smith Public Library, Windsor Drive, 4701 Windsor Dr, Fort Smith, AR, 72904. Tel: 479-785-0405. Fax: 479-785-0431. p. 101

Jamison, Joanie, Dir, Colo Public Library, 309 Main St, Colo, IA, 50056. Tel: 641-377-2900. Fax: 641-377-2468. p. 804

Jamison, Ruth, Chairperson, Irma Municipal Library, 5012 51st Ave, Irma, AB, T0B 2H0, CANADA. Tel: 780-754-3746. Fax: 780-754-3802. p. 2707

Jamison, Sandra Lee, Librn, The HealthCare Chaplaincy, 307 E 60th St, New York, NY, 10022. Tel: 212-644-1111, Ext 235. Fax: 212-486-7060. p. 1681

Jan, Deborah, Head of Librn, University of California, Berkeley, Sheldon Margen Public Health Library, One University Hall, Berkeley, CA, 94720-7360. Tel: 510-642-2511. Fax: 510-642-7623. p. 128

Janda, Linda, Med Librn, United States Army, General Leonard Wood Army Community Hospital Medical Library, 126 Missouri Ave, Fort Leonard Wood, MO, 65473-5700. Tel: 573-596-0131, Ext 69110. Fax: 573-596-5359. p. 1328

Jander, Karen, Ser, E-Res, University of Wisconsin-Milwaukee Libraries, 2311 E Hartford Ave, Milwaukee, WI, 53211. Tel: 414-229-4785, 414-229-6202. Fax: 414-229-6766. p. 2622

Jandreau, Dale, Dir, Skowhegan Public Library, Nine Elm St, Skowhegan, ME, 04976. Tel: 207-474-9072. p. 1000

Janec, Judy, Archivist, JFCS Holocaust Center, 2245 Post St, San Francisco, CA, 94115. Tel: 415-777-9060, Ext 206. Fax: 415-449-3720. p. 243

Janega, Sheila, Br Mgr, Fairfax County Public Library, Patrick Henry Branch, 101 Maple Ave E, Vienna, VA, 22180-5794. Tel: 703-938-0405. p. 2461

Janes, Joseph, Assoc Prof, University of Washington, Mary Gates Hall, Ste 370, Campus Box 352840, Seattle, WA, 98195-2840. Tel: 206-685-9937. Fax: 206-616-3152. p. 2976

Janes, Judy, Dir, University of California, Davis, Mabie Law Library, 400 Mrak Hall Dr, Davis, CA, 95616. Tel: 530-752-3327. Fax: 530-752-8766. p. 140

Janes, Lisa, ILL, Pub Serv, Union Theological Seminary & Presbyterian School of Christian Education, 3401 Brook Rd, Richmond, VA, 23227. Tel: 804-278-4310. Fax: 804-278-4375. p. 2490

Janet, Kaye, Ref Serv, Ad, Niles District Library, 620 E Main St, Niles, MI, 49120. Tel: 269-683-8545, Ext 115. Fax: 269-683-0075. p. 1214

Janeth, Oster, Youth Serv Librn, Bulverde Area Rural Library District, 131 Bulverde Crossing, Bulverde, TX, 78163. Tel: 830-438-4864. Fax: 830-980-3362. p. 2293

Janewski, Tim, Dir of Libr Serv, The King's University College, 9125 50th St, Edmonton, AB, T6B 2H3, CANADA. Tel: 780-465-8304. Fax: 780-465-3534. p. 2701

Janice, Hebbard, Librn, Baca County Public Library, Walsh Branch, 400 N Colorado St, Walsh, CO, 81090. Tel: 719-324-5349. Fax: 719-324-5349. p. 322

Janik, Toni, Dir, Hotel-Dieu Grace Hospital, 1030 Ouellette Ave, Windsor, ON, N9A 1E1, CANADA. Tel: 519-973-4411, Ext 3178, 519-973-4411, Ext 3528. Fax: 519-973-0642. p. 2871

Janis, James, Librn, Hicksville Public Library, 169 Jerusalem Ave, Hicksville, NY, 11801. Tel: 516-931-1417. Fax: 516-822-5672. p. 1636

Janish, Rose, Bibliog Instr, Erie Community College-City Campus, 121 Ellicott St, Buffalo, NY, 14203. Tel: 716-851-1074. Fax: 716-270-5987. p. 1598

Jank, David, Info Instruction, Distance Learning, Dowling College Library, 150 Idle Hour Blvd, Oakdale, NY, 11769-1999. Tel: 631-244-3081. Fax: 631-244-3374. p. 1709

Jank, Donna, Librn, Southeast Regional Library, Balgonie Branch, 129 Railway St E, Balgonie, SK, S0G 0E0, CANADA. Tel: 306-771-2332. p. 2929

Janke, Karen, Libr Dir, Erikson Institute, 451 N LaSalle St, Ste 210, Chicago, IL, 60654. Tel: 312-893-7210. Fax: 312-893-7213. p. 613

Janko, Denise, Librn, Beaver County Pioneer Library, 201 Douglas St, Beaver, OK, 73932. Tel: 580-625-3076. Fax: 580-625-3076. p. 1958

Jankowska, Ewa, Dir, Clinton-Essex-Franklin Library System, 33 Oak St, Plattsburgh, NY, 12901-2810. Tel: 518-563-5190, Ext 11. Fax: 518-563-0421. p. 1718

Jankowski, Carol, Dir, Duxbury Free Library, 77 Alden St, Duxbury, MA, 02332. Tel: 781-934-2721, Ext 104. Fax: 781-934-0663. p. 1085

Jankowski, Janice, Br Mgr, Manistee County Library, Arcadia Branch, 3586 Glovers Lake Rd, Arcadia, MI, 49613. Tel: 231-889-4230. Fax: 231-889-4230. p. 1205

Jankowski, Lee, Dir, North Pike District Library, 119 S Corey St, Griggsville, IL, 62340. Tel: 217-833-2633. Fax: 217-833-2283. p. 653

Jankowski, Pamela, Br Mgr, Cuyahoga County Public Library, North Olmsted Branch, 27403 Lorain Rd, North Olmsted, OH, 44070-4037. Tel: 440-777-6211. Fax: 440-777-4312. p. 1927

Jankowski, Pamela, Br Mgr, Cuyahoga County Public Library, Olmsted Falls Branch, 8100 Mapleway Dr, Olmsted Falls, OH, 44138. Tel: 440-235-1150. Fax: 440-235-0954. p. 1927

Janku, David, Head, Computer Serv, Rogers Memorial Library, 91 Coopers Farm Rd, Southampton, NY, 11968. Tel: 631-283-0774. Fax: 631-287-6539. p. 1746

Janney, Faith, Archives, Circ & ILL, Virginia Western Community College, 3095 Colonial Ave SW, Roanoke, VA, 24015-4705. Tel: 540-857-6332. Fax: 540-857-6058. p. 2495

Janngula, Suzan, Dir, Linton Public Library, 101 First St NE, Linton, ND, 58552-7123. Tel: 701-254-4737. p. 1845

Janok, Linda, Br Coordr, San Mateo Public Library, Hillsdale, 205 W Hillsdale Blvd, San Mateo, CA, 94403-4217. Tel: 650-522-7880. Fax: 650-522-7881. p. 256

Janoski-Haehlen, Emily M, Assoc Dean, Valparaiso University, School of Law Library, 656 S Greenwich St, Valparaiso, IN, 46383. Tel: 219-465-7827. Fax: 219-465-7917. p. 784

Janosko, Joann, Ser, Indiana University of Pennsylvania, 431 S 11th St, Indiana, PA, 15705-1096. Tel: 724-357-6106. Fax: 724-357-4891. p. 2071

Janosko, Shelly Hypes, Dir, Libr Serv, Danville Public Library, 511 Patton St, Danville, VA, 24541. Tel: 434-799-5195. Fax: 434-792-5172. p. 2459

Janota, Claudine, Librn, Goliad County Library, 320 S Commercial St, Goliad, TX, 77963. Tel: 361-645-2291. Fax: 361-645-8956. p. 2328

Janour, Vera, Tech Serv, Cooley Godward Kronish LLP Library, 101 California St, 5th Flr, San Francisco, CA, 94111. Tel: 415-693-2000. Fax: 415-693-2222. p. 241

Janovicz, Juli, Asst Dir & Head, Adult Serv, Interim Dir, Winnetka-Northfield Public Library District, 768 Oak St, Winnetka, IL, 60093-2583. Tel: 847-446-7220. Fax: 847-446-5085. p. 720

Janower, Lori, Libr Serv Coordr, Innovation, Energy & Mines, 1395 Ellice Ave, Ste 360, Winnipeg, MB, R3G 3P2, CANADA. Tel: 204-945-6569. Fax: 204-945-8427. p. 2756

Jans, Daniel, Circ, Simon Fraser University Vancouver Library, 515 W Hastings St, Vancouver, BC, V6B 5K3, CANADA. Tel: 778-782-5050. Fax: 778-782-5052. p. 2742

Jans, Pat, Dir, Schroeder Public Library, 93 Main St, Keystone, IA, 52249. Tel: 319-442-3329. Fax: 319-442-3327. p. 825

Jans-Duffy, Kathy, Coll Mgt, Seneca Falls Historical Society Library, 55 Cayuga St, Seneca Falls, NY, 13148. Tel: 315-568-8412. Fax: 315-568-8426. p. 1742

Jansa, Marilyn, Tech Serv, Richard C Sullivan Public Library of Wilton Manors, 500 NE 26th St, Wilton Manors, FL, 33305. Tel: 954-390-2195. Fax: 954-390-2183. p. 504

Jansen, Amy, Bus & Web Experience Ref Librn, Sacred Heart University, 5151 Park Ave, Fairfield, CT, 06825-1000. Tel: 203-365-4818. Fax: 203-374-9968. p. 339

Jansen, Jean, Asst Head, Youth Serv, Villa Park Public Library, 305 S Ardmore Ave, Villa Park, IL, 60181-2698. Tel: 630-834-1164. Fax: 630-834-0489. p. 714

Jansen, Kathy, Asst Librn, Mayville District Public Library, 6090 Fulton St, Mayville, MI, 48744. Tel: 989-843-6522. Fax: 989-843-0078. p. 1207

Jansen, Kitty, In Charge, Eiteljorg Museum of American Indians & Western Art, 500 W Washington St, Indianapolis, IN, 46204-2707. Tel: 317-636-9378, Ext 1346. Fax: 317-264-1446. p. 750

Jansen, Mike, Commun Librn, Fort Vancouver Regional Library District, Three Creeks Community Library, 800 C NE Tenney Rd, Vancouver, WA, 98685. Tel: 360-517-9696. Fax: 360-574-6429. p. 2546

Jansen, Raymond, Librn, Cuyahoga Community College, Western Campus Library, 11000 Pleasant Valley Rd, Parma, OH, 44130-5199. Tel: 216-987-5411. Fax: 216-987-5050. p. 1879

Jansen, Robert H, Asst Dir, Star Tribune, 425 Portland Ave, Minneapolis, MN, 55488. Tel: 612-673-4375. Fax: 612-673-4459. p. 1261

Janson, Barbara, Chief Librn, Johnson & Wales University Library, Culinary Library, 321 Harborside Blvd, Providence, RI, 02905. Tel: 401-598-1466. p. 2172

Jansons, Andre, Evening Ref Librn, Bethune-Cookman College, 640 Mary McLeod Bethune Blvd, Daytona Beach, FL, 32114. Tel: 386-481-2186. Fax: 386-481-2182. p. 435

Janssen, Barbara, Head, Pub Serv, Security Public Library, 715 Aspen Dr, Security, CO, 80911-1807. Tel: 719-391-3190. Fax: 719-392-7641. p. 322

Janssen, Ian, Dir, University of Delaware Library, Archives, 002 Pearson Hall, Newark, DE, 19716. Tel: 302-831-2750. Fax: 302-831-6903. p. 386

Janssens, Hennie, Ch, Township of Athens Public Library, Five Central St, Athens, ON, K0E 1B0, CANADA. Tel: 613-924-2048. p. 2792

Jantz, Julie, Librn, Odessa Public Library, 21 E First St, Odessa, WA, 99159. Tel: 509-982-2903. Fax: 509-982-2410. p. 2522

Jantz, Verda, In Charge, Merced County Library, William J George Branch, 401 Lesher Dr, Ste E, Merced, CA, 95340. Tel: 209-725-3909. p. 185

Jantzi, Leanna, Pub Serv, Okanagan College Library, 1000 KLO Rd, Kelowna, BC, V1Y 4X8, CANADA. p. 2730

Janus, Denise, Head, Support Serv, Auburn Hills Public Library, 3400 E Seyburn Dr, Auburn Hills, MI, 48326-2759. Tel: 248-370-9466. Fax: 248-370-9364. p. 1154

Janutolo, Trish, Spec Coll Librn, Anderson University, Robert A Nicholson Library, 1100 E Fifth St, Anderson, IN, 46012-3495. Tel: 765-641-4271. Fax: 765-641-3850. p. 724

Janyk, Roen, Web Serv Librn, Okanagan College Library, 1000 KLO Rd, Kelowna, BC, V1Y 4X8, CANADA. p. 2730

Janz, Marie, Syst Librn, Saint Joseph's Hospital, 611 Saint Joseph Ave, Marshfield, WI, 54449. Tel: 715-346-5090. Fax: 715-343-3246. p. 2613

Janzen, Deborah, Support Serv Mgr, Fresno County Public Library, 2420 Mariposa St, Fresno, CA, 93721-2285. Tel: 559-600-7323. p. 151

Janzen, Donna, Chairperson, Rosemary Community Library, 622 Dahlia St, Rosemary, AB, T0J 2W0, CANADA. Tel: 403-378-4493, Ext 150. Fax: 403-378-4388. p. 2715

Janzen, Grant, Coordr, Alberta Law Libraries, Court House, 320 Fourth St S, Lethbridge, AB, T1J 1Z8, CANADA. Tel: 403-381-5639. Fax: 403-381-5703. p. 2709

Janzen, Jane, Dir, Western Plains Library System, 501 S 28th St, Clinton, OK, 73601-3996. Tel: 580-323-0974. Fax: 580-323-1190. p. 1960

Janzen, Junie C, Tech Serv Librn, University of Oklahoma, Schusterman Ctr, 4502 E 41st St, Tulsa, OK, 74135. Tel: 918-660-3224. Fax: 918-660-3215. p. 1984

Jaque, Diana, Head, Acq, Head, Coll Develop, University of Southern California Libraries, Asa V Call Law Library, 699 Exposition Blvd, LAW 202, MC 0072, Los Angeles, CA, 90089-0072. Tel: 213-740-6482. Fax: 213-740-7179. p. 179

Jaquess, Joe, ILL, University of Wisconsin-Whitewater Library, 800 W Main St, Whitewater, WI, 53190. Tel: 262-472-1881. Fax: 262-472-5727. p. 2649

Jaquette, James, ILL, Thomas Crane Public Library, 40 Washington St, Quincy, MA, 02269-9164. Tel: 617-376-1300. Fax: 617-376-1313. p. 1119

Jaquith, Matthew, Prog Coordr, Springfield City Library, 220 State St, Springfield, MA, 01103. Tel: 413-263-6828, Ext 221. Fax: 413-263-6817. p. 1127

Jaramillo, George, Dir, Taos Public Library, 402 Camino de La Placita, Taos, NM, 87571. Tel: 575-737-2587. Fax: 575-737-2586. p. 1566

Jaramillo, Sandra, In Charge, Commission of Public Records, 1209 Camino Carlos Rey, Santa Fe, NM, 87507. Tel: 505-476-7902. Fax: 505-476-7901. p. 1562

Jardine, Carolyn, Ref, Antioch University New England Library, 40 Avon St, Keene, NH, 03431-3516. Tel: 603-283-2400. Fax: 603-357-7345. p. 1452

Jardine, Marjory, Ref & Instruction Librn, Justice Institute of British Columbia Library, 715 McBride Blvd, New Westminster, BC, V3L 5T4, CANADA. Tel: 604-528-5592. Fax: 604-528-5593. p. 2734

Jardine, Spencer, Coordr, Instruction, Idaho State University, Idaho State University, 850 S Ninth Ave, Pocatello, ID, 83209-8089. Tel: 208-282-5609. Fax: 208-282-5847. p. 581

Jareo, Peter, Br Mgr, Charlotte Mecklenburg Library, Plaza Midwood Branch, 1623 Central Ave, Charlotte, NC, 28205. Tel: 704-416-6200. Fax: 704-416-6300. p. 1782

Jarigese, Jeannie, Head Librn, Mason Memorial Public Library, 104 W Main St, Buda, IL, 61314. Tel: 309-895-7701. Fax: 309-895-7701. p. 598

Jarman, Charles, Br Mgr, San Diego County Library, Lakeside Branch, 9839 Vine St, Lakeside, CA, 92040-3199. Tel: 619-443-1811. Fax: 619-443-8002. p. 234

Jarmusz, Ruth, Br Mgr, San Bernardino County Library, Yucaipa Branch, 12040 Fifth St, Yucaipa, CA, 92399. Tel: 909-790-3146. Fax: 909-790-3151. p. 229

Jaroch, Diane, Dir, Watertown Public Library, 100 S Water St, Watertown, WI, 53094-4320. Tel: 920-262-4090. Fax: 920-261-8943. p. 2644

Jarocki, Martha Olson, Librn, Pesticide Action Network North American Regional Center, 49 Powell St, Ste 500, San Francisco, CA, 94102. Tel: 415-981-1771. Fax: 415-981-1991. p. 244

Jarog, Patricia, Br Mgr, White Oak Library District, 121 E Eighth St, Lockport, IL, 60441. Tel: 815-838-0755. p. 667

Jarombek, Kathy, Dir, Youth Serv, Perrot Memorial Library, 90 Sound Beach Ave, Old Greenwich, CT, 06870. Tel: 203-637-8802. Fax: 203-698-2620. p. 363

Jarrell, Carolyn G, Asst Dir, Sabina Public Library, 11 E Elm St, Sabina, OH, 45169-1330. Tel: 937-584-2751. Fax: 937-584-2751. p. 1932

Jarrell, Elizabeth, Asst Dir, East Morgan County Library District, 500 Clayton St, Brush, CO, 80723-2110. Tel: 970-842-4596. Fax: 970-842-2450. p. 293

Jarrell, Holly, Tech Serv, Uncle Remus Regional Library System, 1121 East Ave, Madison, GA, 30650. Tel: 706-342-4974, Ext 18. Fax: 706-342-4510. p. 541

Jarrett, Ann, Acq, Blue Island Public Library, 2433 York St, Blue Island, IL, 60406-2011. Tel: 708-388-1078, Ext 18. Fax: 708-388-1143. p. 596

Jarrett, Gina, Coordr, Acq, Wake Forest University, Professional Center Library, Worrell Professional Ctr for Law & Management, 1834 Wake Forest Rd, Winston-Salem, NC, 27106. Tel: 336-758-5438. Fax: 336-758-6077. p. 1834

Jarrett, Peggy, Coll Develop/Ref Librn, University of Washington Libraries, Marian Gould Gallagher Law Library, William H Gates Hall, Box 353025, Seattle, WA, 98195-3025. Fax: 206-685-2165. p. 2534

Jarson, Jennifer, Head, Pub Outreach & Info Literacy Serv, Muhlenberg College, 2400 Chew St, Allentown, PA, 18104-5586. Tel: 484-664-3552. Fax: 484-664-3511. p. 2027

Jarush, Sharon, Ref, East Hartford Public Library, 840 Main St, East Hartford, CT, 06108. Tel: 860-289-6429. Fax: 860-291-9166. p. 337

Jarvi, Betty, Librn, Tyson Library, 286 Dublin Rd, Ludlow, VT, 05149. Tel: 802-228-8037. p. 2427

Jarvis, BettyJo, Dir, Stones River Regional Library, 2118 E Main St, Murfreesboro, TN, 37130. Tel: 615-893-3380. Fax: 615-895-6727. p. 2255

Jarvis, BettyJo, Regional Mgr, Tennessee State Library & Archives, 403 Seventh Ave N, Nashville, TN, 37243-0312. Tel: 615-893-3380. Fax: 615-532-2472, 615-741-6471. p. 2259

Jarvis, Bill, Tech Serv Mgr, Harris County Public Library, 8080 El Rio, Houston, TX, 77054. Tel: 713-749-9040. Fax: 713-749-9090. p. 2335

Jarvis, Dow, Hist Coll Librn, Oxnard Public Library, 251 South A St, Oxnard, CA, 93030. Tel: 805-385-7531. Fax: 805-385-7526. p. 202

Jarvis, E J, Coordr, Libr Serv, Beth El Hebrew Congregation Library & Information Center, 3830 Seminary Rd, Alexandria, VA, 22304. Tel: 703-370-9400. Fax: 703-370-7730. p. 2445

Jarvis, Helen, Ref Tech, Gowling Lafleur Henderson LLP, One First Canadian Pl, 100 King St W, Ste 1600, Toronto, ON, M5X 1G5, CANADA. Tel: 416-862-5735. Fax: 416-862-7661. p. 2854

Jarvis, Julie, Librn, MacDonald, Dettwiler & Associates Library, 13800 Commerce Pkwy, Richmond, BC, V6V 2J3, CANADA. Tel: 604-278-3411, Ext 2447. Fax: 604-278-2117. p. 2736

Jarvis, Katherine, Mgr, Palo Alto Research Center (PARC), 3333 Coyote Hill Rd, Palo Alto, CA, 94304-1314. Tel: 650-812-4903. p. 204

Jarvis, Kathleen, Librn, Jerome Public Library, 600 Clark St, Jerome, AZ, 86331. Tel: 928-639-0574. Fax: 928-639-0574. p. 66

Jarvis, Rebekah, Dir, Arvilla E Diver Memorial Library, 136 Main St, Schaghticoke, NY, 12154. Tel: 518-753-4344. Fax: 518-753-4344. p. 1740

Jarzemsky, Timothy, Dir, Bloomingdale Public Library, 101 Fairfield Way, Bloomingdale, IL, 60108-1579. Tel: 630-529-3120. Fax: 630-529-3243. p. 595

Jarzombek, Scott C, Libr Dir, Pawling Free Library, 11 Broad St, Pawling, NY, 12564. Tel: 845-855-3444. Fax: 845-855-8138. p. 1716

Jascha, Jill, Acq & Ser Librn, Mgt Team, North Idaho College Library, 1000 W Garden Ave, Coeur d'Alene, ID, 83814-2199. Tel: 208-769-3236. Fax: 208-769-3428. p. 573

Jasinski, Jennifer, YA Librn, Nashua Public Library, Two Court St, Nashua, NH, 03060. Tel: 603-589-4600. Fax: 603-594-3457. p. 1458

Jasinski, Margaret, Mgr, Coll Serv, Arlington Heights Memorial Library, 500 N Dunton Ave, Arlington Heights, IL, 60004-5966. Tel: 847-506-2643. Fax: 847-506-2650. p. 589

Jaskot, Virginia, Mgr, Cabell County Public Library, Gallaher Village, 368 Norway Ave, Huntington, WV, 25705. Tel: 304-528-5696. Fax: 304-528-5696. p. 2561

Jaskowski, Selma K, Asst Dir, Info Serv & Digital Initiatives, University of Central Florida Libraries, 4000 Central Florida Blvd, Bldg 2, Orlando, FL, 32816-2666. Tel: 407-823-5444. Fax: 407-823-4627. p. 477

Jaskula, Gary, Firmwide Libr Mgr, Cooley LLP, 1114 Avenue of the Americas, New York, NY, 10036. Tel: 212-479-6000. Fax: 212-479-6275. p. 1676

Jaskula, Sharon, Literacy Prog Mgr, Jacksonville Public Library, 303 N Laura St, Jacksonville, FL, 32202-3505. Tel: 904-630-2426. Fax: 904-630-2431. p. 453

Jasmine deVlas, Akke, Asst Librn, David M Hunt Library, 63 Main St, Falls Village, CT, 06031. Tel: 860-824-7424. p. 339

Jason, Andrea, Librn, Newport Beach Public Library, Balboa Branch, 100 E Balboa Blvd, Balboa, CA, 92661. Tel: 949-644-3076. Fax: 949-675-8524. p. 194

Jason, Darryl, In Charge, Tobacco Merchants Association of the United States, 231 Clarksville Rd, Princeton, NJ, 08543. Tel: 609-275-4900. Fax: 609-275-8379. p. 1524

Jassin, Ray, Dir, Mendes & Mount, LLP, 750 Seventh Ave, New York, NY, 10019-6829. Tel: 212-261-8000, 212-261-8338. Fax: 212-261-8750. p. 1686

Jasso, Liz, Computer Lab Tech, Wharton County Junior College, 911 Boling Hwy, Wharton, TX, 77488-3298. Tel: 979-532-6332. Fax: 979-532-6527. p. 2399

Jastrzebski, Luke, Assoc Libr Dir, Pub Serv, University of Texas at El Paso Library, 500 W University Ave, El Paso, TX, 79968-0582. Tel: 915-747-6723. Fax: 915-747-5345. p. 2317

Jasumback, John, Br Mgr, Mid-Continent Public Library, South Independence Branch, 13700 E 35th St, Independence, MO, 64055-2464. Tel: 816-461-2050. Fax: 816-461-4759. p. 1333

Jatropelli, Giovanna, Actg Dir, Italian Cultural Institute, 1200 Dr Penfield Ave, Montreal, QC, H3A 1A9, CANADA. Tel: 514-849-3473. Fax: 514-849-2569. p. 2897

Jatulis, V A, Librn, Thomas Aquinas College, 10000 N Ojai Rd, Santa Paula, CA, 93060-9980. Tel: 805-525-4417. Fax: 805-525-9342. p. 267

Jaudon, Buddy, Res Coordr, Tampa Tribune Co, 200 S Parker St, Tampa, FL, 33606. Tel: 813-259-7965. Fax: 813-259-8199. p. 498

Jauquet, Tricia, Tech Serv Librn, Purdue University North Central Library, Library-Student-Faculty (LSF) Bldg, 2nd Flr, 1401 S US Hwy 421, Westville, IN, 46391. Tel: 219-785-5234. Fax: 219-785-5501. p. 787

Jauquet-Kalinoski, Barbara, Regional Dir, Northwest Regional Library, 210 LaBree Ave N, Thief River Falls, MN, 56701. Tel: 218-681-1066. Fax: 218-681-1095. p. 1286

Javorski, Susanne, Librn, Wesleyan University, Art Library, 301 High St, Middletown, CT, 06459-3199. Tel: 860-685-3327. p. 352

Javorsky, Mary, Ref Librn, YA Librn, New Hartford Public Library, Two Library Lane, New Hartford, NY, 13413-2815. Tel: 315-733-1535. Fax: 315-733-0795. p. 1665

Jaworski, Mary, Dir, Port Austin Township Library, 114 Railroad St, Port Austin, MI, 48467. Tel: 989-738-7212. Fax: 989-738-7983. p. 1219

Jax, John, Coll Develop, University of Wisconsin-La Crosse, 1631 Pine St, La Crosse, WI, 54601-3748. Tel: 608-785-8567. Fax: 608-785-8639. p. 2603

Jay, Dianne, Librn, Paxton Public Library, 108 N Oak St, Paxton, NE, 69155. Tel: 308-239-4763. p. 1416

Jay, Marjorie, Dir, Libr & Res Serv, Greenberg Glusker Fields Claman & Machtinger LLP Library, 1900 Avenue of the Stars, Ste 2100, Los Angeles, CA, 90067. Tel: 310-553-3610. Fax: 310-553-0687. p. 170

Jayasuriya, Kumar, Assoc Law Librn, Patron Serv, Georgetown University, Georgetown Law Library (John Wolff & Edward Bennett Williams Libraries), 111 G St NW, Washington, DC, 20001. Fax: 202-662-9168. p. 403

Jaycox, Emily, Librn, Missouri History Museum, 225 S Skinker Blvd, Saint Louis, MO, 63105. Tel: 314-746-4500. Fax: 314-746-4548. p. 1356

Jayes, Linda, Tech Serv Supvr, New Hampshire State Library, 20 Park St, Concord, NH, 03301-6314. Tel: 603-271-2429. Fax: 603-271-2205, 603-271-6826. p. 1443

Jayko, Holli, Ch, Adams Free Library, 92 Park St, Adams, MA, 01220-2096. Tel: 413-743-8345. Fax: 413-743-8344. p. 1047

Jayne, JoAnn, Dir, Vaughn College Library, 8601 23rd Ave, Flushing, NY, 11369. Tel: 718-429-6600, Ext 184. Fax: 718-478-7066. p. 1623

Jayne, Zina, Dir, Becket Athenaeum, Inc Library, 3367 Main St, Becket, MA, 01223. Tel: 413-623-5483. p. 1051

Jaynes, Courtney, Circ Mgr, North Central Regional Library, Wenatchee Public (Headquarters), 310 Douglas St, Wenatchee, WA, 98801-2864. Tel: 509-662-5021. Fax: 509-663-9731. p. 2549

Jeakins, Kathy, Bus Mgr, Bloomington Public Library, 205 E Olive St, Bloomington, IL, 61701. Tel: 309-828-6091. Fax: 309-828-7312. p. 595

Jean, Gilbert, Head, Circ, Buchanan County Public Library, Rte 2, Poetown Rd, Grundy, VA, 24614-9613. Tel: 276-935-6581. Fax: 276-935-6292. p. 2467

Jean, Jill, Libr Dir, Kitsap Regional Library, 1301 Sylvan Way, Bremerton, WA, 98310-3498. Tel: 360-405-9136. Fax: 360-405-9156. p. 2510

Jean, Natalie, Asst Univ Librn, Florida State University Libraries, The Career Center Library, Dunlap Success Ctr 1200, 100 S Woodward Ave, Tallahassee, FL, 32304. Tel: 850-644-9779. Fax: 850-644-3273. p. 494

Jean-Pierre, Peguy, Tech Serv Supvr, Columbia University, Lehman Library, 420 W 118th St, New York, NY, 10027. Tel: 212-854-3794. Fax: 212-854-2495. p. 1675

Jeannotte, Helene, Acq, Asst Librn, Cegep de Jonquiere, 2505 rue St Hubert, Jonquiere, QC, G7X 7W2, CANADA. Tel: 418-547-2191. Fax: 418-547-0917. p. 2884

Jebbie, Nicole, Ch, Saint Johns County Public Library System, Anastasia Island Branch, 124 Seagrove Main St, Saint Augustine Beach, FL, 32080. Tel: 904-209-3732. Fax: 904-209-3735. p. 487

Jeche, Lynn, Curator, Klamath County Museum & Baldwin Hotel Museum, 1451 Main St, Klamath Falls, OR, 97601. Tel: 541-883-4208. Fax: 541-883-5170. p. 2002

Jedry, Micheline, VPres for Info Serv, Wellesley College, 106 Central St, Wellesley, MA, 02481-8275. Tel: 781-283-2166. Fax: 781-283-3904. p. 1135

Jedrzejczak, Bozena, Acq, Ser, Johns Hopkins University-Peabody Conservatory of Music, 21 E Mount Vernon Pl, Baltimore, MD, 21202-2397. Tel: 410-659-8100, Ext 1159. Fax: 410-685-0657. p. 1015

Jedziniak, Christina, Br Mgr, Bartow County Public Library System, Emmie Nelson Branch, 108 Covered Bridge Rd SW, Cartersville, GA, 30120. Tel: 770-382-2057. Fax: 770-382-6316. p. 524

Jeeves, Sharon, Librn, Southeast Regional Library, Wolseley Branch, 500 Front St, Wolseley, SK, S0G 5H0, CANADA. Tel: 306-698-2221. p. 2931

Jefferds, Carrie, Dir, Belmont Literary & Historical Society Free Library, Two Willets Ave, Belmont, NY, 14813. Tel: 585-268-5308. Fax: 585-268-5308. p. 1580

Jefferies, Deborah, Dir, North Carolina Central University, School of Law Library, 1512 S Alston Ave, Durham, NC, 27707. Tel: 919-530-6113. Fax: 919-530-7926. p. 1789

Jefferies, Marie, ILL, Ref, Lexington County Public Library System, 5440 Augusta Rd, Lexington, SC, 29072. Tel: 803-785-2686. Fax: 803-785-2601. p. 2199

Jeffers, Christine, Asst Dir, Pawtucket Public Library, 13 Summer St, Pawtucket, RI, 02860. Tel: 401-725-3714. Fax: 401-728-2170. p. 2171

Jeffers, Inez, Head of Libr, Volusia County Public Library, John H Dickerson Heritage, 411 S Keech St, Daytona Beach, FL, 32114. Tel: 386-239-6478. p. 436

Jefferson, Ashley, Br Mgr, Alexandria Library, Ellen Coolidge Burke Branch, 4701 Seminary Rd, Alexandria, VA, 22304. Tel: 703-746-1704. Fax: 703-746-1775. p. 2444

Jefferson, Jerin, Computer Tech, Elizabeth City State University, 1704 Weeksville Rd, Elizabeth City, NC, 27909. Tel: 252-335-3905. Fax: 252-335-3446. p. 1790

Jefferson, Karen, Archivist, Atlanta University Center, 111 James P Brawley Dr SW, Atlanta, GA, 30314. Tel: 404-978-2045. Fax: 404-577-5158. p. 513

Jefferson, Lila, Acq, Coll Develop, University of Louisiana at Monroe Library, 700 University Ave, Monroe, LA, 71209-0720. Tel: 318-342-1053. Fax: 318-342-1075. p. 958

Jefferson, Marva, Acq, Black & Veatch, 11401 Lamar, Overland Park, KS, 66211. Tel: 913-458-7884. Fax: 913-458-2934. p. 887

Jefferson, Micah, Tech Serv, Roosevelt University, Robert R McCormick Tribune Foundation Library, 1400 N Roosevelt Blvd, Schaumburg, IL, 60173. Tel: 847-619-7980. Fax: 847-619-7983. p. 623

Jefferson, Richard, Librn, Oak Grove Lutheran Church, 7045 Lyndale Ave S, Richfield, MN, 55423-3099. Tel: 612-869-4917. p. 1272

Jefferson, Sharon, Br Mgr, Cleveland Public Library, Glenville, 11900 St Clair Ave, Cleveland, OH, 44108. Tel: 216-623-6983. Fax: 216-623-6985. p. 1878

Jefferson, Terressa, Br Mgr, Hickory Public Library, Ridgeview, 706 First St SW, Hickory, NC, 28602. Tel: 828-345-6037, Ext 7285. Fax: 828-267-0485. p. 1801

Jeffery, Darren, Prov Libr Serv Supvr, Thousand Oaks Library, 1401 E Janss Rd, Thousand Oaks, CA, 91362-2199. Tel: 805-449-2660, Ext 7350. Fax: 805-373-6858. p. 275

Jeffery, Linda, Mgr, UPMC Hamot, 201 State St, Erie, PA, 16550. Tel: 814-877-3628. Fax: 814-877-6188. p. 2056

Jeffery, Susan, Dir, North Pocono Public Library, 113 Van Brunt St, Moscow, PA, 18444-9254. Tel: 570-842-4700. Fax: 570-842-1304. p. 2093

Jeffrey, Beryl, Pub Serv Mgr, Richmond Public Library, 100-7700 Minoru Gate, Richmond, BC, V6Y 1R9, CANADA. Tel: 604-231-6417. Fax: 604-273-0459. p. 2736

Jeffrey, Betty, Instrul Serv Librn, University of Prince Edward Island, 550 University Ave, Charlottetown, PE, C1A 4P3, CANADA. Tel: 902-566-0343. Fax: 902-628-4305. p. 2876

Jeffrey, Cathy, Assoc Dean, Coll & Res Mgt Chair, Clayton State University, 2000 Clayton State Blvd, Morrow, GA, 30260. Tel: 678-466-4325. Fax: 678-466-4349. p. 545

Jeffrey, Doug, Sr Librn, California Department of Corrections Library System, San Quentin State Prison Library, 100 Main St, San Quentin, CA, 94964. Tel: 415-454-1460, Ext 3384. Fax: 415-455-5049. p. 222

Jeffrey, Jackie, Librn, Banner Good Samaritan Medical Center, Grace Middlebrook Family Learning Center, 1111 E McDowell Rd, Phoenix, AZ, 85006. Tel: 602-239-4970. Fax: 602-239-4971. p. 72

Jeffrey, Jamey, Syst Adminr, Laurel County Public Library District, 120 College Park Dr, London, KY, 40741. Tel: 606-864-5759. Fax: 606-862-8057. p. 922

Jeffrey, Laura, Transcript Coordr, NPR Library, 635 Massachusetts Ave NW, Washington, DC, 20001. Fax: 202-513-3056. p. 412

Jeffrey, Linda, Librn, Allen County Public Library, New Haven Branch, 648 Green St, New Haven, IN, 46774. Tel: 260-421-1345. Fax: 260-493-0130. p. 741

Jeffrey, Lorraine, Mgr, Salt Lake County Library Services, Ruth V Tyler Branch, 8041 S Wood St, 55 West, Midvale, UT, 84047-7559. Tel: 801-944-7608. Fax: 801-565-8012. p. 2414

Jeffrey, Phillip, Mgr, Hamilton Wentworth Catholic District School Board, 44 Hunt St, Hamilton, ON, L8R 3R1, CANADA. Tel: 905-525-2930. Fax: 905-523-0247. p. 2810

Jeffries, Alex, Tech & Ref, Chillicothe Public Library District, 430 N Bradley Ave, Chillicothe, IL, 61523-1920. Tel: 309-274-2719. Fax: 309-274-3000. p. 628

Jeffries, Carrie, Dir of Circ, Glen Ellyn Public Library, 400 Duane St, Glen Ellyn, IL, 60137-4508. Tel: 630-469-0879. Fax: 630-469-1086. p. 650

Jeffries, Freddie, AV, Ref Serv, Rust College, 150 E Rust Ave, Holly Springs, MS, 38635. Tel: 662-252-8000, Ext 4100. Fax: 662-252-8873. p. 1302

Jeffries, Janet, Archivist, Pub Serv, Doane College, 1014 Boswell Ave, Crete, NE, 68333-2421. Tel: 402-826-8565. Fax: 402-826-8199. p. 1396

Jeffries, Kathleen, Outreach Librn, New Brunswick Legislative Library, Legislative Bldg, 706 Queen St, Fredericton, NB, E3B 1C5, CANADA. Tel: 506-453-8345. Fax: 506-444-5889. p. 2763

Jeffries, Scott, Asst Dir, Ref Librn, Dallas Baptist University, 3000 Mountain Creek Pkwy, Dallas, TX, 75211-9299. Tel: 214-333-5211. Fax: 214-333-5323. p. 2305

Jeffries, Shellie, Co-Dir, Electronic Serv, Aquinas College, 1607 Robinson Rd SE, Grand Rapids, MI, 49506-1799. Tel: 616-632-2137. Fax: 616-732-4534. p. 1183

Jeffries, Susan, Dir, Libr Serv, Northwestern Oklahoma State University, 709 Oklahoma Blvd, Alva, OK, 73717. Tel: 580-327-8570. Fax: 580-327-8501. p. 1956

Jeffries, Susan, Dir, Northwestern Oklahoma State University Libraries, 2929 E Randolph, Enid, OK, 73701. Tel: 580-327-8570. Fax: 580-213-3140. p. 1963

Jeffs, Kay, Asst Librn, Emery County Library, Huntington Branch, 92 S Main, Huntington, UT, 84528. Tel: 435-687-9590. Fax: 435-687-9510. p. 2404

Jelen, Andrew, Acq Librn, Head, Coll Develop, Wichita Falls Public Library, 600 11th St, Wichita Falls, TX, 76301-4604. Tel: 940-767-0868, Ext 228. Fax: 940-720-6672. p. 2401

Jelks, Towanna, Libr Tech, Department of Veterans Affairs, PO Box 5000-142D, Hines, IL, 60141-5142. Tel: 708-202-2000. Fax: 708-202-2719. p. 656

Jelley, Dave, Librn, Osram Sylvania, 71 Cherry Hill Dr, Beverly, MA, 01915. Tel: 978-750-1725. Fax: 978-750-1797. p. 1054

Jellinger, Susan, Ref Librn, State Historical Society of Iowa-Des Moines Library, 600 E Locust, Des Moines, IA, 50319-0290. Tel: 515-281-6200. Fax: 515-282-0502. p. 810

Jellison, Connie, Librn, Burrell Township Library, Willow St & Park Dr, Black Lick, PA, 15716. Tel: 724-248-7122. Fax: 724-248-7122. p. 2035

Jemison, Keith, Librn, Tulsa City-County Library, Rudisill Regional Library, 1520 N Hartford, Tulsa, OK, 74106. Tel: 918-596-7280. Fax: 918-596-7283. p. 1983

Jemison, Kyla, Music Librn, Banff Centre, 107 Tunnel Mountain Dr, Banff, AB, T1L 1H5, CANADA. Tel: 403-762-6221. Fax: 403-762-6266. p. 2684

Jen, Obermaier, Sr Librn, Tampa-Hillsborough County Public Library System, C Blythe Andrews, Jr Public Library, 2607 E Martin Luther King Blvd, Tampa, FL, 33610-7770. Fax: 813-276-2989. p. 497

Jenerette, Kim, Br Mgr, Columbus County Public Library, Rube McCray Memorial, 301 Flemington Dr, Lake Waccamaw, NC, 28450. Tel: 910-646-4616. Fax: 910-646-4747. p. 1829

Jeng, Ling Hwey, Dr, Dir, Prof, Texas Woman's University, PO Box 425438, Denton, TX, 76204-5438. Tel: 940-898-2602. Fax: 940-898-2611. p. 2974

Jeng-Chu, Wei, Head, Tech, Worcester Public Library, Three Salem Sq, Worcester, MA, 01608. Tel: 508-799-1655. Fax: 508-799-1652. p. 1145

Jeng-Chu, Wei, Interim Head Librn, Worcester Public Library, Three Salem Sq, Worcester, MA, 01608. Tel: 508-799-1655. Fax: 508-799-1652. p. 1145

Jenicke, Alice, Coll Develop, Chippewa River District Library, 301 S University Ave, Mount Pleasant, MI, 48858-2597. Tel: 989-772-3488, Ext 20. Fax: 989-772-3280. p. 1211

Jenison, Priscilla, Law Librn, Rhode Island Department of Corrections, Maximum Security Library, 40 Howard Ave, Cranston, RI, 02920. Tel: 401-462-2636. Fax: 401-462-2526. p. 2165

Jenison, Priscilla, Law Librn, Rhode Island Department of Corrections, Medium Moran Security Library, PO Box 8274, Cranston, RI, 02920-0274. Tel: 401-462-3700. Fax: 401-462-1161. p. 2165

Jenkins, Anita, Libr Mgr, Alachua County Library District, Library Partnership: A Neighborhood Resource Center, 1130 NE 16th Ave, Gainesville, FL, 32601. Tel: 352-334-0165. Fax: 352-334-0167. p. 448

Jenkins, Anne Cushing, Librn, Harvard Library, Belfer Center for Science & International Affairs Library, John F Kennedy School of Government, 79 John F Kennedy St, Cambridge, MA, 02138. Tel: 617-495-1408. Fax: 617-495-8963. p. 1074

Jenkins, Barb, Librn, Water of Life Evangelical Friends Church Library, 3750 Sullivant Ave, Columbus, OH, 43228. Tel: 614-274-5131. Fax: 614-274-5920. p. 1891

Jenkins, Carol, Librn, Fayette Public Library, 855 S Jefferson, La Grange, TX, 78945. Tel: 979-968-3765. Fax: 979-968-5357. p. 2351

Jenkins, Carol G, Dir, University of North Carolina at Chapel Hill, Health Sciences, 355 S Columbia St, Chapel Hill, NC, 27599. Tel: 919-966-2111. Fax: 919-966-5592. p. 1781

Jenkins, Charmaine, Br Supvr, Bruce County Public Library, Tiverton Branch, 56 King St, Tiverton, ON, N0G 2T0, CANADA. Tel: 519-368-5655. p. 2837

Jenkins, Charmaine, Librn, Bruce County Public Library, Kincardine Branch, 727 Queen St, Kincardine, ON, N2Z 1Z9, CANADA. Tel: 519-396-3289. Fax: 519-396-3289. p. 2837

Jenkins, Christine, Assoc Prof, University of Illinois at Urbana-Champaign, Library & Information Science Bldg, 501 E Daniel St, Champaign, IL, 61820-6211. Tel: 217-333-3280. Fax: 217-244-3302. p. 2965

Jenkins, Dana S, Dir, South Jefferson Public Library, 49 Church St, Summit Point, WV, 25446. Tel: 304-725-6227. Fax: 304-728-2586. p. 2572

Jenkins, Diana, Admin Librn, James Memorial Library, 300 W Scioto St, Saint James, MO, 65559. Tel: 573-265-7211. Fax: 573-265-8771. p. 1352

Jenkins, Itaski, Circ & ILL, Trident Technical College, Main Campus Learning Resources Center, LR-M, PO Box 118067, Charleston, SC, 29423-8067. Tel: 843-574-6089. Fax: 843-574-6484. p. 2185

Jenkins, James, Computer Serv, North Babylon Public Library, 815 Deer Park Ave, North Babylon, NY, 11703-3812. Tel: 631-669-4020. Fax: 631-669-3432. p. 1706

Jenkins, Jennifer, Mgr, Greenville County Library System, Simpsonville (Hendricks) Branch, 626 NE Main St, Simpsonville, SC, 29681. Tel: 864-963-9031. Fax: 864-228-0986. p. 2196

Jenkins, Jonah, Supvr, Massachusetts Institute of Technology Libraries, Rotch Library-Architecture & Planning, Bldg 7-238, 77 Massachusetts Ave, Cambridge, MA, 02139-4307. Tel: 617-258-5588. Fax: 617-253-9331. p. 1078

Jenkins, Joseph, Exec Dir, Briggs Lawrence County Public Library, 321 S Fourth St, Ironton, OH, 45638. Tel: 740-532-1124. Fax: 740-532-4948. p. 1906

Jenkins, Julia-Ann, Br Mgr, Librn III, Montgomery City-County Public Library System, E L Lowder Regional Branch Library, 2590 Bell Rd, Montgomery, AL, 36117. Tel: 334-244-5717. Fax: 334-240-4893. p. 30

Jenkins, Karen, Educ Coordr, Alaska State Department of Corrections, 9101 Hesterberg Rd, Eagle River, AK, 99577. Tel: 907-694-9511. Fax: 907-694-4507. p. 47

Jenkins, Karla, Libr Supvr-Popular Libr, College of the Ozarks, Lyons Memorial Library, One Opportunity Ave, Point Lookout, MO, 65726. Tel: 417-690-3411. Fax: 417-334-3085. p. 1349

Jenkins, Katherine, Asst Dir, Operations & Personnel, Monroe Community College, LeRoy V Good Library, 1000 E Henrietta Rd, Rochester, NY, 14692. Tel: 585-292-2320. p. 1730

Jenkins, Kevin, Librn, Ontario Workplace Tribunals Library, 505 University Ave, 7th Flr, Toronto, ON, M5G 2P2, CANADA. Tel: 416-314-8959. Fax: 416-326-5164. p. 2857

Jenkins, LaTanya, Doc Librn, Ref Librn, Morgan State University, 1700 E Cold Spring Lane, Baltimore, MD, 21251. Tel: 443-885-1719. p. 1016

Jenkins, Laverne C, Head, Tech Serv, Cuyahoga Community College, Library Technical Services, 2900 Community College Ave, MRC30, Cleveland, OH, 44115-3123. Tel: 216-987-3437. Fax: 216-987-3352. p. 1879

Jenkins, Linda, Circ, Bastrop Public Library, 1100 Church St, Bastrop, TX, 78602. Tel: 512-321-5441. Fax: 512-321-3163. p. 2286

Jenkins, Marli, Dir, Taylor County Public Library, 200 Beech St, Grafton, WV, 26354. Tel: 304-265-6121. Fax: 304-265-6122. p. 2559

Jenkins, Martha A, Librn, Benton County Law Library, 559 NW Monroe Ave, Corvallis, OR, 97330. Tel: 541-766-6673. Fax: 541-766-6014. p. 1994

Jenkins, Marty, Head, Tech Serv, Wright State University Libraries, 126 Dunbar Library, 3640 Colonel Glenn Hwy, Dayton, OH, 45435-0001. Tel: 937-775-4983. Fax: 937-775-4109. p. 1895

Jenkins, Mary, Dir, Cincinnati Law Library Association, Hamilton County Court House, 1000 Main St, Rm 601, Cincinnati, OH, 45202. Tel: 513-946-5300, 513-946-5301. Fax: 513-946-5252. p. 1869

Jenkins, Natasha, Info Literacy, ILL, Alabama State University, 915 S Jackson St, Montgomery, AL, 36104. Tel: 334-229-4106, 334-229-6890. Fax: 334-229-4911, 334-229-4940. p. 28

Jenkins, Nathaniel, Web Serv Coordr, Whatcom County Library System, 5205 Northwest Dr, Bellingham, WA, 98226-9050. Tel: 360-384-3150. Fax: 360-384-4947. p. 2509

Jenkins, Pam, Ch, New Bern-Craven County Public Library, 400 Johnson St, New Bern, NC, 28560-4098. Tel: 252-638-7815. Fax: 252-638-7817. p. 1812

Jenkins, Pamela, Asst Libr Dir, Youth Serv Mgr, Brunswick Public Library Association, 23 Pleasant St, Brunswick, ME, 04011-2295. Tel: 207-725-5242. Fax: 207-725-6313. p. 979

Jenkins, Patricia, Librn III, San Diego Public Library, 820 E St, San Diego, CA, 92101-6478. Tel: 619-236-5830. Fax: 619-238-6639. p. 235

Jenkins, Paul Owen, Dir, Libr Serv, College of Mount Saint Joseph, 5701 Delhi Rd, Cincinnati, OH, 45233-1671. Tel: 513-244-4351. Fax: 513-244-4355. p. 1869

Jenkins, Randy, Mgr, Libr Depository, West Virginia University Libraries, WVU Libraries, 1549 University Ave, Morgantown, WV, 26506. Tel: 304-293-4040. Fax: 304-293-6638. p. 2566

Jenkins, Roger, Adminr, Nikolai Public Library, PO Box 90, Nikolai, AK, 99691-0090. Tel: 907-293-2427. Fax: 907-293-2115. p. 52

Jenkins, Ruth, Librn, Florida Department of Corrections, 4455 Sam Mitchell Dr, Chipley, FL, 32428. Tel: 850-773-6100. Fax: 850-773-6252. p. 431

Jenkins, Sandra, Instr, University of Central Missouri, Dept of Educational Leadership & Human Development, Lovinger 4101, Warrensburg, MO, 64093. Tel: 660-543-4150. Fax: 660-543-4164. p. 2968

Jenkins, Sharon, Librn, Cape Fear Valley Health System, 1638 Owen Dr, Fayetteville, NC, 28304. Tel: 910-609-6601. Fax: 910-609-7710. p. 1792

Jenkins, Susan J, Dir, Driftwood Public Library, 801 SW Hwy 101, Ste 201, Lincoln City, OR, 97367-2720. Tel: 541-996-2277. Fax: 541-996-1262. p. 2004

Jenkins, Tammy, Libr Dir, Eastern Kentucky Health Science Information Network, c/o Camden-Carroll Library, Morehead State University, Morehead, KY, 40351. Tel: 606-783-6860. Fax: 606-784-2178. p. 2944

Jenkins, Thomas E, Dir, Thomas Beaver Free Library, 205 Ferry St, Danville, PA, 17821-1939. Tel: 570-275-4180. Fax: 570-275-8480. p. 2049

Jenkins, Trish, Br Mgr, Riverside County Library System, Canyon Lake Library, 31516 Railroad Canyon Rd, Canyon Lake, CA, 92587. Tel: 951-244-9181. Fax: 951-244-7382. p. 217

Jenkins, Vickie, Admin Serv, Belmont Abbey College, 100 Belmont-Mt Holly Rd, Belmont, NC, 28012. Tel: 704-461-6748. Fax: 704-461-6743. p. 1776

Jenkins, Vince, Tech Serv, University of Wisconsin-Madison, MERIT Library (Media, Education Resources & Information Technology), 225 N Mills St, Madison, WI, 53706. Tel: 608-262-7301. Fax: 608-262-6050. p. 2609

Jenkins, Yvonne, Dir, Randolph Public Library, 130 Durand Rd, Randolph, NH, 03593. Tel: 603-466-5408. p. 1463

Jenkinson, Ellan, Br Mgr, Richland County Public Library, John Hughes Cooper Branch, 5317 N Trenholm Rd, Columbia, SC, 29206. Tel: 803-787-3462. Fax: 803-787-8040. p. 2188

Jenkinson, Victor, Syst Librn, University of South Carolina, School of Medicine, 6311 Garners Ferry Rd, Columbia, SC, 29209. Tel: 803-733-3351. Fax: 803-733-1509. p. 2190

Jenkinson, Victor, Tech Prog Dir, Partnership Among South Carolina Academic Libraries, 1333 Main St, Ste 305, Columbia, SC, 29201. Tel: 803-734-0911. Fax: 803-734-0901. p. 2955

Jenks, Ann, State Archivist, State Historical
Society of North Dakota, North Dakota
Heritage Ctr, 612 E Boulevard Ave, Bismarck,
ND, 58505-0830. Tel: 701-328-2668. Fax:
701-328-2650. p. 1838

Jenks, Ann, Head Univ Archivist, Bowling Green
State University Libraries, Center for Archival
Collections, Jerome Library, 5th Flr, Bowling
Green, OH, 43403. Tel: 419-372-2411. Fax:
419-372-0155. p. 1861

Jenks, Kelly, Instruction Coordr, Gonzaga
University, 502 E Boone Ave, Spokane,
WA, 99258-0095. Tel: 509-313-3829. Fax:
509-323-5904. p. 2536

Jenks, Margaret D, Librn, Oregon Department of
Geology & Mineral Industries Library, Ste
965, No 28, 800 NE Oregon St, Portland,
OR, 97232-2162. Tel: 971-673-1546. Fax:
971-673-1562. p. 2013

Jenks, Matt, Cat Librn, University of New
Hampshire School of Law, Two White St,
Concord, NH, 03301. Tel: 603-228-1541, Ext
1130. Fax: 603-228-0388. p. 1443

Jenks, Pamelia, Libr Dir, Oakley Library District,
185 E Main, Oakley, ID, 83346. Tel:
208-862-3434. p. 581

Jenks, Theresa, Asst Librn, Oakley Library
District, 185 E Main, Oakley, ID, 83346. Tel:
208-862-3434. p. 581

Jenne, Shawn, Librn, Santiam Correctional
Institution Library, 4005 Aumsville Hwy, Salem,
OR, 97317. Tel: 503-378-3678, Ext 522. Fax:
503-378-8520. p. 2018

Jenner, Anne, Archives Dir, North Park University,
Brandel Library, 5114 N Christiana Ave,
Chicago, IL, 60625. Tel: 773-244-6224. Fax:
773-244-4891. p. 620

Jenner, Anne, Archivist, Dir, Spec Coll Librn, North
Park University, Covenant Archives & Historical
Library, Archives of North Park University, 3225
W Foster Ave, Chicago, IL, 60625-4895. Tel:
773-244-6223. Fax: 773-244-4891. p. 620

Jenner, Anne, Archivist, North Park University,
Swedish-American Archives of Greater Chicago,
3225 W Foster Ave, Chicago, IL, 60625. Tel:
773-244-6224. p. 620

Jenness, Adrienne, Circ Librn, Ref Librn, Drexel
University Libraries, Queen Lane Library, 2900
Queen Lane, Philadelphia, PA, 19129. Tel:
215-991-8740. Fax: 215-843-0840. p. 2105

Jennette, Sharon, Cat, Rare Bks, Freed-Hardeman
University, 158 E Main St, Henderson,
TN, 38340-2399. Tel: 731-989-6067. Fax:
731-989-6065. p. 2237

Jennifer, Roades, Br Mgr, Western Sullivan Public
Library, 45 Lower Main St, Callicoon, NY,
12723. Tel: 845-887-4040. Fax: 845-887-8957.
p. 1600

Jennings, Anita N, Librn IV, Newport News Public
Library System, Pearl Bailey Branch, 2510
Wickham Ave, Newport News, VA, 23607. Tel:
757-247-8677. Fax: 757-247-2321. p. 2480

Jennings, Brenda, Librn, Missouri Department of
Corrections, Maryville Treatment Center, 30227
US Hwy 136, Maryville, MO, 64468-8353. Tel:
660-582-6542. Fax: 660-582-8071. p. 1334

Jennings, Connie, In Charge, Mid-Columbia
Libraries, Kahlotus Branch, E 225 Weston,
Kahlotus, WA, 99335. Tel: 509-282-3493. Fax:
509-282-3493. p. 2518

Jennings, Cynthia, Dir, Old Town Public Library,
46 Middle St, Old Town, ME, 04468. Tel:
207-827-3972. Fax: 207-827-3978. p. 994

Jennings, David, Dir, Cent Libr Serv, Akron-Summit
County Public Library, 60 S High St,
Akron, OH, 44326. Tel: 330-643-9100. Fax:
330-643-9160. p. 1852

Jennings, Diane, Coll Develop, Catawba County
Library, 115 West C St, Newton, NC, 28658.
Tel: 828-465-8664. Fax: 828-465-8983. p. 1813

Jennings, Donald W, Brother, Librn, Church of Jesus
Christ of Latter-Day Saints, Boca Raton Family
History Center, 1530 W Camino Real, Boca
Raton, UT, 33486. Tel: 561-395-6644. Fax:
561-395-8957. p. 2412

Jennings, Eric, Ref Librn, University of
Wisconsin-Eau Claire, 105 Garfield Ave, Eau
Claire, WI, 54702-4004. Tel: 715-836-3715. Fax:
715-836-2949. p. 2590

Jennings, Gary L, Librn, Botanical Research
Institute of Texas Library, 500 E Fourth St, Fort
Worth, TX, 76102. Tel: 817-332-4441. Fax:
817-332-4112. p. 2321

Jennings, Janet I, Dir, Superior Public Library, 1530
Tower Ave, Superior, WI, 54880-2532. Tel:
715-394-8860. Fax: 715-394-8870. p. 2641

Jennings, John, Tech Serv, Pierce College Library,
Puyallup Campus, 1601 39th Ave SE,
Puyallup, WA, 98374. Tel: 253-840-8309. Fax:
253-840-8316. p. 2520

Jennings, Karlene N, Dir, Libr Develop, College of
William & Mary in Virginia, Earl Gregg Swem
Library, One Landrum Dr, Williamsburg, VA,
23187. Tel: 757-221-7779. Fax: 757-221-2635.
p. 2502

Jennings, Lawerence, Dir, Human Res, Brooklyn
Public Library, Grand Army Plaza, Brooklyn,
NY, 11238-5698. Tel: 718-230-2155. Fax:
718-783-7443. p. 1590

Jennings, Linda, Assoc Librn, Wilkinsburg
Public Library, 605 Ross Ave, Pittsburgh,
PA, 15221-2195. Tel: 412-244-2942. Fax:
412-243-6943. p. 2130

Jennings, Linda, Assoc Librn, Wilkinsburg Public
Library, Eastridge, 1900 Graham Blvd,
Pittsburgh, PA, 15235. Tel: 412-342-0056.
p. 2130

Jennings, Mariann, Dir, Prospect Park Free Library,
720 Maryland Ave, Prospect Park, PA, 19076.
Tel: 610-532-4643. Fax: 610-532-5648. p. 2132

Jennings, Marie, YA Serv, United States Navy,
Base Library, Naval Submarine Base New
London, Bldg 164, Groton, CT, 06349.
Tel: 860-694-2578, 860-694-3723. Fax:
860-694-2578. p. 342

Jennings, Mary Jo, Dir, Garfield Public Library,
500 Midland Ave, Garfield, NJ, 07026. Tel:
973-478-3800. Fax: 973-478-7162. p. 1487

Jennings, Mike, Coordr, Syst & Digital Initiatives,
Tulane University, Rudolph Matas Library of
the Health Sciences, Tulane Health Sciences
Campus, 1430 Tulane Ave, SL-86, New Orleans,
LA, 70112-2699. Tel: 504-988-5157. Fax:
504-988-7417. p. 963

Jennings, Pam, Br Mgr, Akron-Summit County
Public Library, Odom Boulevard, 600 Vernon
Odom Blvd, Akron, OH, 44307-1828. Tel:
330-434-8726. Fax: 330-434-3750. p. 1852

Jennings, Pat, In Charge, First United Methodist
Church, Epworth Library & Susannah Wesley
Media Center, 419 NE First St, Gainesville, FL,
32601. Tel: 352-372-8523. Fax: 352-372-2524.
p. 449

Jennings, Sharon, Dir, Beatty Library District,
400 N Fourth St, Beatty, NV, 89003. Tel:
775-553-2257. Fax: 775-553-2257. p. 1425

Jennings, Susan L, Dean, Chattanooga State
Community College, 4501 Amnicola
Hwy, Chattanooga, TN, 37406-1097. Tel:
423-697-2576. Fax: 423-697-4409. p. 2227

Jennings, Thomasine Z, Ch, Dir, Ilion Free Public
Library, 78 West St, Ilion, NY, 13357-1797. Tel:
315-894-5028. Fax: 315-894-9980. p. 1640

Jennings, Troy S, Tech Serv, Sioux City Public
Library, 529 Pierce St, Sioux City, IA,
51101-1203. Tel: 712-255-2933. p. 844

Jens, Megan, Ref Librn, Hamline University, School
of Law Library, 1536 Hewitt Ave, Saint Paul,
MN, 55104-1237. Tel: 651-523-2379. Fax:
651-523-2863. p. 1278

Jensen, Aaron, Brother, Librn, Assumption Abbey
Library, 418 Third Ave W, Richardton,
ND, 58652-7100. Tel: 701-974-3315. Fax:
701-974-3317. p. 1847

Jensen, Barb, Librn, Soldier Public Library, 108 Oak
St, Soldier, IA, 51572-6237. Tel: 712-884-2266.
Fax: 712-884-2264. p. 845

Jensen, Becky, Dir, Peacham Library, 656
Bayley Hazen Rd, Peacham, VT, 05862. Tel:
802-592-3216. p. 2431

Jensen, Dale R, Dir of Libr/Media Serv, Evangel
University, 1111 N Glenstone Ave, Springfield,
MO, 65802. Tel: 417-865-2815, Ext 7268.
p. 1366

Jensen, Denise, Dir, Berlin Public Library, 270 Main
St, Berlin, NH, 03570. Tel: 603-752-5210. Fax:
603-752-8568. p. 1439

Jensen, Denise, Ch, Normal Memorial Library,
301 N Eagle St, Fayette, OH, 43521. Tel:
419-237-2115. Fax: 419-237-2002. p. 1899

Jensen, Diane, Archives Librn, Tech Serv Librn,
Peace College, 15 E Peace St, Raleigh,
NC, 27604-1194. Tel: 919-508-2305. Fax:
919-508-2769. p. 1816

Jensen, Dianne, Tech Serv, North Platte Public
Library, 120 W Fourth St, North Platte,
NE, 69101-3993. Tel: 308-535-8036. Fax:
308-535-8296. p. 1410

Jensen, Doris, Dir, Sidney Public Library, 1112 12th
Ave, Sidney, NE, 69162. Tel: 308-254-3110.
Fax: 308-254-3710. p. 1419

Jensen, Faye, Exec Dir, South Carolina Historical
Society Library, Fireproof Bldg, 100 Meeting St,
Charleston, SC, 29401-2299. Tel: 843-723-3225,
Ext 10. Fax: 843-723-8584. p. 2185

Jensen, Florence, Librn, First United Methodist
Church Library, 625 Hamilton Ave, Palo
Alto, CA, 94301. Tel: 650-323-6167. Fax:
650-323-3923. p. 204

Jensen, Gertrude, Dir, Armstrong Public Library,
308 Sixth St, Armstrong, IA, 50514. Tel:
712-868-3353. Fax: 712-868-3779. p. 794

Jensen, Imogene, Dir, Rock River Library District,
105 Eighth St, Silvis, IL, 61282-1199. Tel:
309-755-3393. Fax: 309-755-1816. p. 702

Jensen, Joanne, Ref, Bull, Houser & Tupper
Library, 3000 Royal Centre, 1055 W Georgia
St, Vancouver, BC, V6E 3R3, CANADA. Tel:
604-641-4965. Fax: 604-646-2643. p. 2740

Jensen, John, Acq Librn, University of the District
of Columbia, David A Clarke School of Law,
Charles N & Hilda H M Mason Law Library,
Bldg 39, Rm B-16, 4200 Connecticut Ave NW,
Washington, DC, 20008. Tel: 202-274-5214.
Fax: 202-274-7311. p. 421

Jensen, Judy, Youth Serv, Baldwin Public Library,
400 Cedar St, Baldwin, WI, 54002-0475. Tel:
715-684-3813. Fax: 715-684-5115. p. 2580

Jensen, Karen, Coll Develop Officer, University of
Alaska Fairbanks, 310 Tanana Dr, Fairbanks,
AK, 99775. Tel: 907-474-6695. Fax:
907-474-6841. p. 48

Jensen, Karen, Dir, Hagaman Memorial Library, 227
Main St, East Haven, CT, 06512-3003. Tel:
203-468-3890. Fax: 203-468-3892. p. 337

Jensen, Karen, Librn, Ohio Bureau of Worker's
Compensation, 30 W Spring St, 3rd Flr,
Columbus, OH, 43215-2256. Tel: 614-466-7388.
Fax: 614-644-9634. p. 1886

Jensen, Kate, Librn, Juvenile Correction Center
Library, 2220 E 600 North, Saint Anthony, ID,
83445. Tel: 208-624-3462. Fax: 208-624-0973.
p. 583

Jensen, Kathy, Circ, Waupun Public Library,
123 S Forest St, Waupun, WI, 53963. Tel:
920-324-7925. p. 2646

Jensen, Kelly, ILL, Libr Asst, California Academy
of Sciences Library, Golden Gate Park, 55
Music Concourse Dr, San Francisco, CA, 94118.
Tel: 415-379-5484. Fax: 415-379-5729. p. 240

Jensen, Kristi, Head of Libr, University of
Minnesota Libraries-Twin Cities, John R
Borchert Map Library, S-76 Wilson Library, 309
19th Ave S, Minneapolis, MN, 55455. Tel:
612-624-4549. Fax: 612-626-9353. p. 1262

Jensen, Lauren, Pub Serv Librn, Monmouth College,
700 E Broadway, Monmouth, IL, 61462-1963.
Tel: 309-457-2190. Fax: 309-457-2226. p. 675

Jensen, Louise, Br Mgr, Placer County Library,
Kings Beach Branch, 301 Secline Dr, Kings
Beach, CA, 96143. Tel: 530-546-2021. Fax:
530-546-2126. p. 123

Jensen, Mary, Circ/Reserves, Supvr, University of Washington Libraries, Music, 113 Music Bldg, Box 353450, Seattle, WA, 98195-3450. Tel: 206-543-1159, 206-543-1168. p. 2534

Jensen, Mattie, Libr Mgr, Delburne Municipal Library, 2210 Main St, Delburne, AB, T0M 0V0, CANADA. Tel: 403-749-3848. Fax: 403-749-2800. p. 2696

Jensen, Nancy, Dir, Lincoln Carnegie Library, 203 S Third, Lincoln, KS, 67455. Tel: 785-524-4034. p. 879

Jensen, Patricia, Ad, Putnam Public Library, 225 Kennedy Dr, Putnam, CT, 06260-1691. Tel: 860-963-6826. Fax: 860-963-6828. p. 365

Jensen, R Bruce, Info Commons/Voices & Choices Ctr, Kutztown University, 15200 Kutztown Rd, Bldg 5, Kutztown, PA, 19530-0735. Tel: 610-683-4484. Fax: 610-683-4747. p. 2075

Jensen, Renee, Develop Officer, Rockford Public Library, 215 N Wyman St, Rockford, IL, 61101-1023. Tel: 815-965-7606. Fax: 815-965-0866. p. 697

Jensen, Richard, Sci, Brigham Young University, Harold B Lee Library, 2060 HBLL, Provo, UT, 84602. Tel: 801-422-2927. Fax: 801-422-0466. p. 2411

Jensen, Robert, Circ, Fordham University Westchester Library, 400 Westchester Ave, West Harrison, NY, 10604. Tel: 914-367-3426. p. 1766

Jensen, Robert, Network Adminr, Southern Oregon Library Information System, 724 S Central Ave, Ste 112, Medford, OR, 97501. Tel: 541-772-2141. Fax: 541-772-2144. p. 2953

Jensen, Sandra, Dir, United States Marine Corps, Library Services, Bldg 1146, Camp Pendleton, CA, 92055. Tel: 760-725-5104, 760-725-5669. Fax: 760-725-6569. p. 131

Jensen, Shannon, Dir, Evansdale Public Library, 123 N Evans Rd, Evansdale, IA, 50707. Tel: 319-232-5367. Fax: 319-232-5367. p. 815

Jensen, Sue, Adult Serv, Welles-Turner Memorial Library, 2407 Main St, Glastonbury, CT, 06033. Tel: 860-652-7730. Fax: 860-652-7721. p. 340

Jensen, Teresa, Libr Serv Adminr, San Antonio Public Library, 600 Soledad, San Antonio, TX, 78205-2786. Tel: 210-207-2829. Fax: 210-207-2603. p. 2382

Jensen, Valerie, County Librn, Chambers County Library System, 202 Cummings St, Anahuac, TX, 77514. Tel: 409-267-8261. Fax: 409-267-3783. p. 2274

Jensen, Valerie, County Librn, Chambers County Library System, Chambers County Library, 202 Cummings St, Anahuac, TX, 77514. Tel: 409-267-2554. Fax: 409-267-5181. p. 2275

Jenson, Carol, Br Mgr, Riverside County Library System, Valle Vista Library, 25757 Fairview Ave, Hemet, CA, 92544. Tel: 951-927-2611. Fax: 951-927-7902. p. 218

Jenson, Jeff, Col Archivist/Librn, Gustavus Adolphus College, 800 W College Ave, Saint Peter, MN, 56082. Tel: 507-933-7572. Fax: 507-933-6292. p. 1283

Jenson, Linda, Dir, Libr Serv, Tarrant County College, Jenkins Garrett Library-South Campus, 5301 Campus Dr, Fort Worth, TX, 76119. Tel: 817-515-4524. Fax: 817-515-4436. p. 2323

Jenson, Patria, Dir, Linn Grove Public Library, 110 Weaver St, Linn Grove, IA, 51033-1019. Tel: 712-296-3919. Fax: 712-296-3919. p. 828

Jenson, Rob, Archivist, Montgomery County Historical Society Library, 111 W Montgomery Ave, Rockville, MD, 20850. Tel: 301-340-2974. Fax: 301-340-2871. p. 1038

Jent, Neloa, Asst Librn, Johnston City Public Library, 506 Washington Ave, Johnston City, IL, 62951-1697. Tel: 618-983-6359. Fax: 618-983-6359. p. 659

Jenynak, Jeremy, Dir, Morris Automated Information Network, c/o Morris County Library, 30 East Hanover Ave, Whippany, NJ, 07981. Tel: 973-631-5353. Fax: 973-631-5366. p. 2949

Jepko, Kathryn, Circ, ILL, The College of Idaho, 2112 Cleveland Blvd, Caldwell, ID, 83605-4432. Tel: 208-459-5506. Fax: 208-459-5299. p. 572

Jeppesen, Bruce, Assoc Dir, Cleveland State University, University Library, Rhodes Tower, 2121 Euclid Ave, Cleveland, OH, 44115-2214. Tel: 216-687-2475. Fax: 216-687-9380. p. 1879

Jeppesen, Sheila, Librn, Sugar-Salem School Community Library, One Digger Dr, Sugar City, ID, 83448-9999. Tel: 208-356-0271. Fax: 208-359-3167. p. 584

Jerabek, Ann, ILL Librn, Sam Houston State University, 1830 Bobby K Marks Dr, Huntsville, TX, 77340. Tel: 936-294-3528. Fax: 936-294-1597. p. 2345

Jerard, Jacques, Dir, Commission Scolaire de la Capitale, Louis-Jolliet, 1201 De Le Pointe-Aux-Lievres, Quebec, QC, G1N 4M1, CANADA. Tel: 418-525-8230. Fax: 418-525-8772. p. 2904

Jercinovic, Kay, Asst Librn, Moriarty Community Library, 202 S Broadway, Moriarty, NM, 87035. Tel: 505-832-2513. Fax: 505-832-8296. p. 1560

Jeremiah, Jacob, Head, Access Serv, Roosevelt University, 430 S Michigan Ave, Chicago, IL, 60605. Tel: 312-341-6965. Fax: 312-341-2425. p. 623

Jeremic, Ana, Libr Serv Mgr, Saint Joseph's Health Centre, 30 The Queensway, Toronto, ON, M6R 1B5, CANADA. Tel: 416-530-6726. Fax: 416-530-6244. p. 2858

Jergovic, Daniel, Metadata Librn, Northeastern University Libraries, Snell Library, 360 Huntington Ave, Boston, MA, 02115. Tel: 617-373-7102. p. 1065

Jerla, Jackie, Librn, Yellowstone National Park, Yellowstone Heritage & Research Ctr, 200 Old Yellowstone Trail, Gardiner, MT, 59030. Tel: 307-344-2264. Fax: 406-848-9958. p. 1379

Jermann, Mary, Librn, Jamestown Community College, Cattaraugus County, 260 N Union St, Olean, NY, 14760. Tel: 716-376-7594. Fax: 716-376-7032. p. 1647

Jernigan, Diane, In Charge, South Georgia Regional Library System, Talking Book Center, 300 Woodrow Wilson Dr, Valdosta, GA, 31602. Tel: 229-333-7658. Fax: 229-333-0774. p. 555

Jernigan, Diane, Librn for Blind & Physically Handicapped, South Georgia Regional Library System, 300 Woodrow Wilson Dr, Valdosta, GA, 31602-2592. Tel: 229-333-0086. Fax: 229-333-7669. p. 555

Jernigan, Douglas, Bibliog Instr, Meridian Community College, 910 Hwy 19 N, Meridian, MS, 39307. Tel: 601-484-8762. Fax: 601-482-3936. p. 1308

Jernigan Hutcherson, Marsha, Dir, Irving Meek Jr Memorial Library, 204 W Main St, Adamsville, TN, 38310. Tel: 731-632-3572. Fax: 731-632-3572. p. 2223

Jernigan, Kristen, Learning Res Asst, Ser & ILL, Polk State College, Lakeland Campus Library, 3425 Winter Lake Rd, Sta 62, Lakeland, FL, 33803. Tel: 863-297-1042. Fax: 863-297-1064. p. 505

Jernigan, William W, Dr, Dean, Learning Res, Theological Librn, Oral Roberts University Library, 7777 South Lewis Ave, Tulsa, OK, 74171. Tel: 918-495-6723. Fax: 918-495-6893. p. 1981

Jernigan-Pedrick, Velora, Librn, Department of Mental Health, St Elizabeths Hospital, 1100 Alabama Ave SE, Washington, DC, 20032. Tel: 202-299-5997. p. 397

Jerome, Judith, Dir, Dunham Public Library, 76 Main St, Whitesboro, NY, 13492. Tel: 315-736-9734. Fax: 315-736-3265. p. 1769

Jerose, Terese, Asst Dir, Ref, Southeastern Baptist Theological Seminary Library, 114 N Wingate St, Wake Forest, NC, 27587. Tel: 919-556-3104. Fax: 919-863-8150. p. 1827

Jerrido, Margaret, Archivist, Temple University Libraries, 1210 W Berks St, Philadelphia, PA, 19122-6088. Tel: 215-204-6639. Fax: 215-204-5201. p. 2117

Jersey, Patricia J, Ref Serv, East Stroudsburg University, 216 Normal St, East Stroudsburg, PA, 18301-2999. Tel: 570-422-3157. Fax: 570-422-3151. p. 2051

Jersyk, Julie, Res & Instruction Librn, Northeastern University Libraries, Snell Library, 360 Huntington Ave, Boston, MA, 02115. Tel: 617-373-2458. p. 1065

Jeser-Skaggs, Sharlee, Instrul Serv Librn, Richland College Library, 12800 Abrams Rd, Dallas, TX, 75243-2199. Tel: 972-238-6081. p. 2309

Jeske, Margo, Dir, University of Ottawa Libraries, Brian Dickson Law Library, Fauteux Hall, 57 Louis Pasteur, Ottawa, ON, K1N 6N5, CANADA. Tel: 613-562-5845. Fax: 613-562-5279. p. 2834

Jeske, Michelle, Dir, Coll & Tech, Denver Public Library, Ten W 14th Ave Pkwy, Denver, CO, 80204-2731. Tel: 720-865-1111. Fax: 720-865-2087. p. 300

Jespersen, Pamela, Adult Serv, Crook County Library, Moorcroft Branch, 105 E Converse, Moorcroft, WY, 82721. Tel: 307-756-3232. Fax: 307-756-3232. p. 2661

Jesse, Patricia, Info Spec, Metropolitan Area Planning Agency, 2222 Cuming St, Omaha, NE, 68102-4328. Tel: 402-444-6866. Fax: 402-342-0949. p. 1413

Jessee, Lee Ann, Dir, Adair County Public Library, 307 Greensburg St, Columbia, KY, 42728-1488. Tel: 270-384-2472. Fax: 270-384-9446. p. 910

Jesseman, Deborah, Dr, Asst Prof, Prog Coordr, Minnesota State University, Mankato, College of Education, Armstrong Hall AH 313, Mankato, MN, 56001-8400. Tel: 507-389-5662. Fax: 507-389-5751. p. 2968

Jesseph, May, Librn, University Center Rochester, 851 30 Ave SE, Rochester, MN, 55904. Tel: 507-285-7233. Fax: 507-281-7772. p. 1273

Jessie, Pamela, Librn, Birmingham Public Library, Woodlawn, 5709 First Ave N, Birmingham, AL, 35212. Tel: 205-595-2001. Fax: 205-595-9654. p. 8

Jessop, Nancy, Br Head, Toronto Public Library, College-Shaw, 766 College St, Toronto, ON, M6G 1C4, CANADA. Tel: 416-393-7668. Fax: 416-393-7418. p. 2861

Jessup, Margaret, Digital Serv Archivist, Smith College Libraries, Sophia Smith Collection, Seven Neilson Dr, Northampton, MA, 01063. Tel: 413-585-2985. Fax: 413-585-2886. p. 1114

Jessup, Rhinnon, Bus Librn, University of Calgary Library, Business Library, Haskayne School of Business, Scurfield Hall, Rm 301, Calgary, AB, T2N 1N4, CANADA. Tel: 403-220-4410. Fax: 403-220-0120. p. 2693

Jester, Valerie, Br Mgr, Timberland Regional Library, W H Abel Memorial Library, 125 Main St S, Montesano, WA, 98563-3794. Tel: 360-249-4211. Fax: 360-249-4203. p. 2543

Jestrab, Carol, Circ Tech, Montana State University, 1500 University Dr, Billings, MT, 59101-0298. Tel: 406-657-2262. Fax: 406-657-2037. p. 1374

Jestrab, Carol, Circ, Doc, Montana State University-Northern, 300 11th St W, Havre, MT, 59501. Tel: 406-265-3706. Fax: 406-265-3799. p. 1381

Jesudason, Sarah, Supvr, Ad Serv, Tigard Public Library, 13500 SW Hall Blvd, Tigard, OR, 97223-8111. Tel: 503-684-6537, Ext 2649. Fax: 503-598-7515, 503-718-2797. p. 2021

Jesus, Margaret, Asst Dir, Payson Public Library, 328 N McLane Rd, Payson, AZ, 85541. Tel: 928-474-9260. Fax: 928-474-2679. p. 70

Jeter, Ann H, Librn, Jackson Walker LLP, 901 Main St, Ste 6000, Dallas, TX, 75202. Tel: 214-953-6038. Fax: 214-953-5822. p. 2308

Jeter, Kelli, Asst Dir, Benson Public Library, 300 S Huachuca, Benson, AZ, 85602-6650. Tel: 520-586-9535. Fax: 520-586-3224. p. 58

Jeter, Virginia, Mgr, Lake Blackshear Regional Library System, Byromville Public, 452 Main St, Byromville, GA, 31007-2500. Tel: 478-433-5100. p. 508

Jett, Denise, Govt Doc, Ser, Oklahoma Baptist University, 500 W University, OBU Box 61310, Shawnee, OK, 74804-2504. Tel: 405-878-2284. Fax: 405-878-2256. p. 1977

Jett, Zeny, Dir, Libr Serv, Panola College, 1109 W Panola St, Carthage, TX, 75633. Tel: 903-693-2005. Fax: 903-693-1115. p. 2295

Jette, Karen, Dir, Libr Serv, Grand Canyon University, 3300 W Camelback Rd, Phoenix, AZ, 85017-3030. Tel: 602-639-6641. Fax: 602-639-7835. p. 73

Jetter, Rose, Br Mgr, Pierce County Library System, South Hill, 15420 Meridian E, Puyallup, WA, 98375. Tel: 253-548-3303. Fax: 253-841-4692. p. 2539

Jeuell, Carol Ann, Ref Librn, Ann & Robert H Lurie Children's Hospital of Chicago, 225 E Chicago Ave, Box 12, Chicago, IL, 60611-2605. Tel: 312-227-4707. Fax: 312-227-9707. p. 618

Jevine, Janine, Dir, Airdrie Public Library, 111-304 Main St SE, Airdrie, AB, T4B 3C3, CANADA. Tel: 403-948-0600. Fax: 403-912-4002. p. 2683

Jewell, Connie, Dir, Mercer Area Library, 143 N Pitt St, Mercer, PA, 16137-1283. Tel: 724-662-4233. Fax: 724-662-8893. p. 2088

Jewell, Cynthia, Br Mgr, Williams County Public Library, Edon Branch, 103 N Michigan St, Edon, OH, 43518. Tel: 419-272-2839. Fax: 419-272-2839. p. 1862

Jewell, Elisabeth, Circ, NHTI, Concord's Community College, 31 College Dr, Concord, NH, 03301-7425. Tel: 603-271-7186. Fax: 603-271-7189. p. 1443

Jewell, Geneva, Libr Coordr, Jefferson Community & Technical College, Jefferson Technical Campus, 727 W Chestnut St, Louisville, KY, 40203. Tel: 502-213-4167. p. 924

Jewell, Robert, Pres, Brookgreen Gardens Library, 1931 Brookgreen Dr, Murrells Inlet, SC, 29576. Tel: 843-235-6000. Fax: 843-235-6003. p. 2201

Jewell, Susan, Dir, Wolbach Community Library, 610 Kingston St, Wolbach, NE, 68882. Tel: 308-246-5232. Fax: 308-246-5234. p. 1423

Jewett, Carol, Regional Librn, Community College of Philadelphia Library, 1700 Spring Garden St, Philadelphia, PA, 19130. Tel: 215-751-8000. Fax: 215-751-8762. p. 2104

Jewett, Cynthia, Librn, Orlando Campus, Keiser University Library System, 1500 NW 49th St, Fort Lauderdale, FL, 33309. Tel: 954-351-4035. Fax: 954-351-4051. p. 443

Jewkes, Becky, Asst Librn, Emery County Library, Ferron Branch, 55 N 200 West, Ferron, UT, 84523. Tel: 435-384-2637. Fax: 435-384-2876. p. 2404

Jewkes, Sylvia, Librn, Southeast Regional Library, Wawota Branch, 308 Railway Ave, Wawota, SK, S0G 5A0, CANADA. Tel: 306-739-2375. p. 2931

Jeyanayagam, Renuka, Br Head, Toronto Public Library, Taylor Memorial, 1440 Kingston Rd, Toronto, ON, M1N 1R3, CANADA. Tel: 416-396-8939. Fax: 416-396-3601. p. 2863

Jezik, Katherine, Cat/Syst Librn, Orange County Community College Library, 115 South St, Middletown, NY, 10940. Tel: 845-341-4256. Fax: 845-341-4424. p. 1660

Jhagroo, Pansey, Circ, Indian River County Library System, 1600 21st St, Vero Beach, FL, 32960. Tel: 772-770-5060. Fax: 772-770-5066. p. 501

Jhingan, Edwina, In Charge, Lockheed Martin Systems Integration - Owego, 1801 State Rte 17C, Maildrop 0409, Owego, NY, 13827. Tel: 607-751-2128. Fax: 607-751-6171. p. 1713

Jia, Peijun Jeffrey, Reserves & Syst Librn, Queensborough Community College, City University of New York, 222-05 56th Ave, Bayside, NY, 11364-1497. Tel: 718-281-5594. Fax: 718-281-5012. p. 1579

Jia, Ying, Mrg, Tech Res, New York Academy of Medicine Library, 1216 Fifth Ave, New York, NY, 10029-5293. Tel: 212-822-7334. Fax: 212-423-0266. p. 1688

Jiabin, Wang, Librn, University of Toronto Libraries, Engineering & Computer Science Library, Sandford Fleming Bldg, Rm 2402, Ten King's College Rd, Toronto, ON, M5S 1A5, CANADA. Tel: 416-978-6494. Fax: 416-971-2091. p. 2865

Jiang, Shali Y, Med Librn, American Red Cross Holland Laboratory, 15601 Crabbs Branch Way, Rockville, MD, 20855-2743. Tel: 301-738-0640. Fax: 301-738-0660. p. 1037

Jiang, Yumin, Tech Serv Librn, University of Colorado Boulder, The William A Wise Law Library, 2450 Kittredge Loop Dr, 402 UCB, Boulder, CO, 80309-0402. Tel: 303-492-2706. Fax: 303-492-2707. p. 292

Jiao, Shuqin, Asst Univ Librn, Access Serv, Saint Louis University, 3650 Lindell Blvd, Saint Louis, MO, 63108-3302. Tel: 314-977-3086. Fax: 314-977-3108. p. 1360

Jim, Stewart, Network Serv, Syst, Middlebury College Library, 110 Storrs Ave, Middlebury, VT, 05753-6007. Tel: 802-443-5490. Fax: 802-443-2074, 802-443-5698. p. 2428

Jimenez, Abby, Dir, Cedarbrake Library, 5602 State Hwy 317 N, Belton, TX, 76513. Tel: 254-780-2436. Fax: 254-780-2436. p. 2289

Jimenez, Ivonne, Dep Dir of Libr - Spec Projects, El Paso Public Library, 501 N Oregon St, El Paso, TX, 79901. Tel: 915-543-5412. Fax: 915-543-5410. p. 2316

Jimenez, Janie, Co-Librn, Big Springs Public Library, 400 Pine St, Big Springs, NE, 69122. Tel: 308-889-3482. p. 1394

Jimenez, Jennifer, Distance Learning Librn, Coastal Bend College, 1814 S Brahma Blvd, Kingville, TX, 78363. Tel: 361-592-1615. p. 2351

Jimenez, Jimmy, Mgr, San Antonio Public Library, Forest Hills, 5245 Ingram, San Antonio, TX, 78228. Tel: 210-431-2544. Fax: 210-434-3524. p. 2382

Jimenez, Jimmy, Mgr, San Antonio Public Library, Memorial, 3222 Culebra, San Antonio, TX, 78228. Tel: 210-432-6783. Fax: 210-435-5471. p. 2382

Jimenez, Lilly, Literacy Coordr, Covina Public Library, 234 N Second Ave, Covina, CA, 91723-2198. Tel: 626-384-5280. Fax: 626-384-5315. p. 137

Jimenez, Rita, Dir, Neighborhood Libr, Multnomah County Library, 205 NE Russell St, Portland, OR, 97212-3796. Tel: 503-988-5402. Fax: 503-988-5441. p. 2011

Jimenez, Teresa, Asst Librn, American Society of Anesthesiologists, 520 N Northwest Hwy, Park Ridge, IL, 60068-2573. Tel: 847-825-5586. Fax: 847-825-1692. p. 688

Jin, Guojia, Tech Serv, Ohoopee Regional Library System, 610 Jackson St, Vidalia, GA, 30474-2835. Tel: 912-537-9283. Fax: 912-537-3735. p. 555

Jin, Tao, Asst Prof, Louisiana State University, 267 Coates Hall, Baton Rouge, LA, 70803. Tel: 225-578-3158. Fax: 225-578-4581. p. 2966

Jin, Young Lark, Br Mgr, Brampton Library, Cyril Clark Branch, 20 Loafers Lake Lane, Brampton, ON, L6Z 1X9, CANADA. Tel: 905-793-4636, Ext 4404. Fax: 905-846-4278. p. 2796

Jinks, Mary L, Dir of Tech Serv, University of the Incarnate Word, 4301 Broadway, UPO Box 297, San Antonio, TX, 78209-6397. Tel: 210-829-3839. Fax: 210-829-6041. p. 2384

Jinmook, Kim, Asst Prof, University of South Carolina, 1501 Greene St, Columbia, SC, 29208. Tel: 803-777-3858. Fax: 803-777-7938. p. 2973

Jirges, Donna Mae, Dir, New England Public Library, 726 McKenzie Ave, New England, ND, 58647-7105. Tel: 701-579-4223. p. 1847

Jiricek, Laurie, Acq, Mount Angel Abbey Library, One Abbey Dr, Saint Benedict, OR, 97373. Tel: 503-845-3303, 503-845-3317. Fax: 503-845-3500. p. 2017

Jirik, Sarah, Acq, Faegre & Benson, LLP, 2200 Wells Fargo Ctr, 90 South Seventh St, Minneapolis, MN, 55402-3901. Tel: 612-766-7000. Fax: 612-766-1600. p. 1259

Jirsa, Bev, Per, Wheaton Public Library, 225 N Cross St, Wheaton, IL, 60187-5376. Tel: 630-868-7573. Fax: 630-668-8950. p. 719

Jizba, Richard, Head, Info Serv, Creighton University, Health Sciences Library-Learning Resource Center, 2770 Webster St, Omaha, NE, 68178-0210. Tel: 402-280-5142. Fax: 402-280-5134. p. 1412

Jo, Clifford, Dir of Finance, Pierce County Library System, 3005 112th St E, Tacoma, WA, 98446-2215. Tel: 253-548-3453. Fax: 253-537-4600. p. 2539

Joachim, Anthony, Ref Librn, William Paterson University of New Jersey, 300 Pompton Rd, Wayne, NJ, 07470. Tel: 973-720-3665. Fax: 973-720-3171. p. 1540

Joanne, Obrand, Supvr, Circ, New Westminster Public Library, 716 Sixth Ave, New Westminster, BC, V3M 2B3, CANADA. Tel: 604-527-4660. Fax: 604-527-4674. p. 2734

Job, Ann, Ch, Montville Township Public Library, 90 Horseneck Rd, Montville, NJ, 07045-9626. Tel: 973-402-0900. Fax: 973-402-0592. p. 1504

Job, Eric Jon, Info Tech Mgr, Johnson City Public Library, 100 W Millard St, Johnson City, TN, 37604. Tel: 423-434-4468. Fax: 423-434-4469. p. 2240

Job, Maris, Asst Dir, Massapequa Public Library, 40 Harbor Lane, Massapequa Park, NY, 11762. Tel: 516-798-4607, Ext 303. Fax: 516-795-7528. p. 1658

Job, Maris, Asst Dir, Massapequa Public Library, Central Avenue, 523 Central Ave, Massapequa, NY, 11758. Tel: 516-798-4607, Ext 303. Fax: 516-798-2804. p. 1658

Job, Sam, Librn, Crafton Hills College Library, 11711 Sand Canyon Rd, Yucaipa, CA, 92399. Tel: 909-389-3322. Fax: 909-794-9524. p. 286

Jobari, Tiyebeh, Tech Serv, Butte College Library, 3536 Butte Campus Dr, Oroville, CA, 95965-8399. Tel: 530-879-4022. p. 201

Jobe, David, Librn, Buckingham Correctional Center, 1349 Correctional Center Rd, Dillwyn, VA, 23936. Tel: 434-391-5980, Ext 5508. Fax: 434-983-1296. p. 2460

Jobe, Jane, Cat, Lynchburg Public Library, 2315 Memorial Ave, Lynchburg, VA, 24501. Tel: 434-455-6300. p. 2476

Jobe, Janita, Admin Serv, University of Nevada-Reno, 1664 N Virginia St, Mailstop 0322, Reno, NV, 89557-0322. Tel: 775-682-5688. Fax: 775-784-4529. p. 1433

Jobe, Margaret, Head, Govt Info, University of Colorado Boulder, 1720 Pleasant St, 184 UCB, Boulder, CO, 80309-0184. Tel: 303-492-8834. Fax: 303-492-3340. p. 291

Jobe, Peggy, Head, Govt Info, University of Colorado Boulder, Government Information, Norlin Library, 1720 Pleasant St, Boulder, CO, 80309. Tel: 303-492-4682. Fax: 303-492-1881. p. 292

Jobst, Gayle L, Librn, Warminster Township Free Library, 1076 Emma Lane, Warminster, PA, 18974. Tel: 215-672-4362. Fax: 215-672-3604. p. 2150

Jochem, Christine, Archivist, Spec Coll Librn, The Morristown & Morris Township Library, One Miller Rd, Morristown, NJ, 07960. Tel: 973-538-6161. Fax: 973-267-4064. p. 1505

Jochem, Christine, Dept Head, Morristown & Morris Township Library, North Jersey History & Genealogy Center, One Miller Rd, Morristown, NJ, 07960. Tel: 973-538-3473. Fax: 973-267-4064. p. 1505

Jocius, Chris, Head, Ref, Curtis Laws Wilson Library, 400 W 14th St, Rolla, MO, 65409-0060. Tel: 573-341-7842. Fax: 573-341-4233. p. 1351

Jockinson, Doug, Sr Librn, California Department of Corrections Library System, California Correctional Institution, 24900 Hwy 202, Tehachapi, CA, 93561. Tel: 661-822-4402. Fax: 661-823-3358, 661-823-5016. p. 221

Jodoin, Louise, Librn, Bibliotheque Mallaig Library, 3110 First St E, Mallaig, AB, T0A 2K0, CANADA. Tel: 780-635-3858. Fax: 780-635-3938. p. 2710

Jodoin, Luc, Chief, Info Tech Serv, Planning & Develop Librn, Bibliothèques de Montrèal, 801, rue Brennan, 5e Etage, Bureau 5206, Montreal, QC, H3C 0G4, CANADA. Tel: 514-872-2918. Fax: 514-872-0530. p. 2889

Jodon, Kris, Dir, Chapelwood United Methodist Church, 11140 Greenbay St, Houston, TX, 77024-6798. Tel: 713-465-3467, Ext 127. Fax: 713-365-2808. p. 2334

Joe, Linda, Webmaster, West Hempstead Public Library, 500 Hempstead Ave, West Hempstead, NY, 11552. Tel: 516-481-6591. Fax: 516-481-2608. p. 1766

Joe, McSharry, Pres, Natural History Society of Maryland, Inc Library, 6908 Belair Rd, Baltimore, MD, 21206. Tel: 410-882-5376. p. 1017

Joe, Rowenhorst, Asst Librn, Merrill Public Library, 321 Fourth St, Merrill, IA, 51038. Tel: 712-938-2503. Fax: 712-938-2503. p. 832

Joens, David, Dir, Illinois State Archives, Two W Margaret Cross Norton Bldg, Springfield, IL, 62756. Tel: 217-782-3492. Fax: 217-524-3930. p. 705

Joerg, DeAnn, AV, Liberty Municipal Library, 1710 Sam Houston Ave, Liberty, TX, 77575-4741. Tel: 936-336-8901. Fax: 936-336-2414. p. 2355

Joffrion, Elizabeth, Dir, Heritage Res, Western Washington University, 516 High St, MS 9103, Bellingham, WA, 98225. Tel: 360-650-3283. Fax: 360-650-3044. p. 2509

Johal, Jinder, Br Head, Vancouver Public Library, Fraserview, 1950 Argyle Dr, Vancouver, BC, V5P 2A8, CANADA. Tel: 604-665-3957. Fax: 604-665-3431. p. 2744

Johal, Rajiv, Librn, McGill University Libraries, Howard Ross Library of Management, Samuel Bronfman Bldg, 1001 Sherbrooke St W, 2nd Flr, Montreal, QC, H3A 1G5, CANADA. Tel: 514-398-4690. Fax: 514-398-5046. p. 2899

Johal, Rashmi, Tech Serv, Solano Community College Library, 4000 Suisun Valley Rd, Fairfield, CA, 94534. Tel: 707-864-7132. Fax: 707-864-7231. p. 148

Johanningmeier, Jen, Libr Asst, Farmersburg Public Library, 208 S Main St, Farmersburg, IA, 52047. Tel: 563-536-2229. Fax: 563-536-2229. p. 815

Johansen, Krista, Libr Mgr, Albert-Westmorland-Kent Regional Library, Dorchester Public, 3516 Cape Rd, Dorchester, NB, E4K 2X5, CANADA. Tel: 506-379-3032. Fax: 506-379-3033. p. 2765

Johansen, Norma, In Charge, Tillamook County Library, Garibaldi Branch, City Hall, Garibaldi, OR, 97118. Tel: 503-322-2100. Fax: 503-322-2100. p. 2021

Johansen, Peggy, Dir, Livingston Manor Free Library, 92 Main St, Livingston Manor, NY, 12758-5113. Tel: 845-439-5440. Fax: 845-439-3141. p. 1653

Johanson, Al, Archivist, Illinois Railway Museum, 7000 Olson Rd, Union, IL, 60180. Tel: 815-923-2020. Fax: 815-923-2006. p. 711

Johanson, Melissa, Asst Dir, Lake Mills Public Library, 102 S Lake St, Lake Mills, IA, 50450. Tel: 641-592-0092. Fax: 641-592-0093. p. 826

Johanson, Mirja, Tech Serv, Perrot Memorial Library, 90 Sound Beach Ave, Old Greenwich, CT, 06870. Tel: 203-637-1066. Fax: 203-698-2620. p. 363

John, Amy, In Charge, Milwaukee Academy of Medicine Library, 8701 Watertown Plank Rd, Milwaukee, WI, 53226. Tel: 414-456-8249. Fax: 414-456-6537. p. 2619

John, Laurie, Dir, Saint Patrick's Seminary, 320 Middlefield Rd, Menlo Park, CA, 94025. Tel: 650-289-3348. Fax: 650-323-5447. p. 185

John, Sheela, Librn, McLaren Oakland, 50 N Perry St, Pontiac, MI, 48342-2217. Tel: 248-338-5000, Ext 3155. Fax: 248-338-5025. p. 1218

John, Tessymol, Librn, Bronxville Public Library, 201 Pondfield Rd, Bronxville, NY, 10708. Tel: 914-337-7680. Fax: 914-337-0332. p. 1588

John, Walden, Dir, Abbott Library, 542 Rte 11, Sunapee, NH, 03782. Tel: 603-763-5513. Fax: 603-763-8765. p. 1466

John-Williams, Melissa, Music, YA Serv, Somerset County Library System, Peapack & Gladstone Public, School St, Peapack, NJ, 07977. Tel: 908-234-0598. Fax: 908-719-2236. p. 1475

Johnas, Julia, Adult Serv, Highland Park Public Library, 494 Laurel Ave, Highland Park, IL, 60035-2690. Tel: 847-432-0216. Fax: 847-432-9139. p. 655

Johner, Carol, Commun Relations Librn, Saskatoon Public Library, 311-23rd St E, Saskatoon, SK, S7K 0J6, CANADA. Tel: 306-975-7530. Fax: 306-975-7542. p. 2926

Johns, Deborah, Asst Dir, Seminole Tribe of Florida, Rte 6, Box 668, Okeechobee, FL, 34974-8912. Tel: 863-763-4236, 863-763-5520. Fax: 863-763-0679. p. 474

Johns, Heather, Librn, Black Watch Memorial Library, 99 Montcalm St, Ticonderoga, NY, 12883. Tel: 518-585-7380. Fax: 518-585-3209. p. 1755

Johns, Jennifer, Curator, Librn & Archivist, Ruthmere Museum, 302 E Beardsley Ave, Elkhart, IN, 46514. Tel: 574-264-0330. Fax: 574-266-0474. p. 737

Johns, Julia, Librn, Brumback Library, Middle Point Branch, 102 Railroad St, Middle Point, OH, 45863. Tel: 419-968-2553. p. 1943

Johns, Martha, Youth Serv, Way Public Library, 101 E Indiana Ave, Perrysburg, OH, 43551. Tel: 419-874-3135, Ext 127. Fax: 419-874-6129. p. 1929

Johns, Mary, Dir, Evanston Public Library, 1703 Orrington, Evanston, IL, 60201. Tel: 847-448-8600, 847-866-0300. Fax: 847-866-0313. p. 643

Johns, Mary, Electronic Serv Librn, Louisiana State University Libraries, Paul M Hebert Law Center, One E Campus Dr, Baton Rouge, LA, 70803-1000. Tel: 225-578-6530. Fax: 225-578-5773. p. 944

Johns, Mary, Dir, Siouxland Libraries, 200 N Dakota Ave, Sioux Falls, SD, 57104. Tel: 605-367-8700. Fax: 605-367-4312. p. 2218

Johns, Nancy, Librn, Lakeland Hospital-Niles, 31 N St Joseph Ave, Niles, MI, 49120. Tel: 269-683-5510. p. 1214

Johns, Nancy, Coordr, Lakeland Hospital - Saint Joseph, 1234 Napier Ave, Saint Joseph, MI, 49085-2158. Tel: 616-982-4904. Fax: 616-982-4993. p. 1225

Johns, Susan, Librn, Belle Center Free Public Library, 103 S Elizabeth St, Belle Center, OH, 43310. Tel: 937-464-3611. Fax: 937-464-3611. p. 1858

Johns, Valarie, Librn, Douglas County Library System, Mildred Whipple Library, 205 West A Ave, Drain, OR, 97435. Tel: 541-836-2648. Fax: 541-836-2304. p. 2016

Johns, Virginia, Librn, Missouri School for the Deaf, 505 E Fifth St, Fulton, MO, 65251-1703. Tel: 573-592-2513. Fax: 573-592-2570. p. 1328

Johns, Warren, Cat Librn, Loma Linda University, 11072 Anderson St, Loma Linda, CA, 92350-0001. Tel: 909-558-4581. Fax: 909-558-4121. p. 165

Johns-Masten, Kathryn, Head, Cat & Ser, State University of New York at Oswego, SUNY Oswego, 7060 State Rte 104, Oswego, NY, 13126-3514. Tel: 315-312-3553. Fax: 315-312-3194. p. 1713

Johns-Smith, Susan, Syst Coordr, Pittsburg State University, 1605 S Joplin St, Pittsburg, KS, 66762-5889. Tel: 620-235-4115. Fax: 620-235-4090. p. 890

Johnsen, Leigh, Dr, Librn & Archivist, San Joaquin County Historical Museum, 11793 N Micke Grove Rd, Lodi, CA, 95241. Tel: 209-331-2055. Fax: 209-331-2057. p. 165

Johnsen, Linda, Br Mgr, Lake County Public Library, Cedar Lake Branch, 10010 W 133rd Ave, Cedar Lake, IN, 46303. Tel: 219-374-7121. Fax: 219-374-6333. p. 764

Johnsen, Mary Kay, Spec Coll Librn, Carnegie Mellon University, Hunt Library, 4909 Frew St, Pittsburgh, PA, 15213-3890. Tel: 412-268-6622. Fax: 412-268-2793. p. 2123

Johnsen, Sheila, Asst Librn, Raymond A Sapp Memorial Township Library, 103 E Main St, Wyanet, IL, 61379. Tel: 815-699-2342. Fax: 815-699-2342. p. 721

Johnson, Aaron, Network Adminr, Juneau Public Libraries, 292 Marine Way, Juneau, AK, 99801. Tel: 907-586-5324. Fax: 907-586-3419. p. 50

Johnson, Abby, Ch, New Albany-Floyd County Public Library, 180 W Spring St, New Albany, IN, 47150-3692. Tel: 812-944-8464. Fax: 812-949-3532. p. 768

Johnson, Aileen, Br Mgr, Montgomery County-Norristown Public Library, Perkiomen Valley, 290 Second St, Schwenksville, PA, 19473. Tel: 610-287-8360. Fax: 610-287-8360. p. 2098

Johnson, Alice, Dr, Dean, Learning Res, San Antonio College, 1001 Howard St, San Antonio, TX, 78212. Tel: 210-486-0554. p. 2381

Johnson, Alison, Asst Libr Dir, Indiana Wesleyan University, 4201 S Washington St, Marion, IN, 46953. Tel: 765-677-2383. Fax: 765-677-2676. p. 762

Johnson, Allan R, Dir, Southeast Regional Library, 49 Bison Ave, Weyburn, SK, S4H 0H9, CANADA. Tel: 306-848-3101. Fax: 306-842-2665. p. 2929

Johnson, Allen R, Admin Dir, Pocahontas County Free Libraries, 500 Eighth St, Marlinton, WV, 24954-1227. Tel: 304-799-6000. Fax: 304-799-3988. p. 2564

Johnson, Alvina, Librn, Woodbury County Library, Pierson Branch, 321 Fourth St, Pierson, IA, 51048. Tel: 712-375-5022. p. 834

Johnson, Amy, Libr Develop Coordr, Florida Department of State, Division of Library & Information Services, R A Gray Bldg, 500 S Bronough St, Tallahassee, FL, 32399-0250. Tel: 850-245-6622. Fax: 850-245-6735. p. 493

Johnson, Andrea, Head, Youth Serv, Northbrook Public Library, 1201 Cedar Lane, Northbrook, IL, 60062-4581. Tel: 847-272-6224. Fax: 847-272-5362. p. 682

Johnson, Angela, Supvr, Coll Develop, Pickaway County District Public Library, 1160 N Court St, Circleville, OH, 43113-1725. Tel: 740-477-1644, Ext 229. Fax: 740-474-2855. p. 1875

Johnson, Anita, Supvr, Essex County Library, Tecumseh Branch, 13675 St Gregory's Rd, Tecumseh, ON, N8N 3E4, CANADA. Tel: 226-946-1529, Ext 230. p. 2804

Johnson, Ann Kinken, Librn, Virginian-Pilot Library, 150 W Brambleton Ave, Norfolk, VA, 23510-2018. Tel: 757-446-2242. Fax: 757-446-2974. p. 2483

Johnson, Anna, Br Mgr, Martins Ferry Public Library, Powhatan Point Branch, 339 N State Rte 7, Powhatan Point, OH, 43942. Tel: 740-795-4624. Fax: 740-795-4624. p. 1914

Johnson, Anna, Fac Librn, Mount Hood Community College Library, 26000 SE Stark St, Gresham, OR, 97030. Tel: 503-491-7686. Fax: 503-491-7389. p. 1999

Johnson, Anna Marie F, Head, Ref & Info Literacy Serv, University of Louisville Libraries, William F Ekstrom Library, Belknap Campus, 2215 S Third St, Louisville, KY, 40292. Tel: 502-852-1491. Fax: 502-852-7394. p. 927

Johnson, Anne, Asst Dir, Eagle Valley Library District, 600 Broadway, Eagle, CO, 81631. Tel: 970-328-8800. Fax: 970-328-6901. p. 305

Johnson, Anne, Ch, Libr Asst, Evansdale Public Library, 123 N Evans Rd, Evansdale, IA, 50707. Tel: 319-232-5367. Fax: 319-232-5367. p. 815

Johnson, Anne, Librn, Rockbridge Regional Library, Buena Vista Public, 2110 Magnolia Ave, Buena Vista, VA, 24416. Tel: 540-261-2715. Fax: 540-261-4822. p. 2474

Johnson, Audrey, Dir, Mazomanie Free Library, 102 Brodhead St, Mazomanie, WI, 53560. Tel: 608-795-2104. Fax: 608-795-2102. p. 2614

Johnson, Barbara, Commun Libr Mgr, County of Los Angeles Public Library, Wiseburn Library, 5335 W 135th St, Hawthorne, CA, 90250-4948. Tel: 310-643-8880. Fax: 310-536-0749. p. 144

Johnson, Barbara, Asst Librn, Alvan Bolster Ricker Memorial Library, 1211 Maine St, Poland, ME, 04274. Tel: 207-998-4390. Fax: 207-998-2120. p. 996

Johnson, Barbara, Local Hist Librn, Northport-East Northport Public Library, 151 Laurel Ave, Northport, NY, 11768. Tel: 631-261-6930. Fax: 631-261-6718. p. 1707

Johnson, Barbara, Tech Serv, Edmonds Community College Library, 20000 68th Ave W, Lynnwood, WA, 98036. Tel: 425-640-1529. p. 2520

Johnson, Barbara Ann, Mgr, Cincinnati Children's Hospital Medical Center Division of Developmental & Behavioral Pediatrics, 3430 Burnet Ave, MOB 2 MLC 3000, Cincinnati, OH, 45229. Tel: 513-636-4626. Fax: 513-636-0107. p. 1868

Johnson, Barbara Glassford, Tech Serv Mgr, Bedford Public Library, 2424 Forest Ridge Dr, Bedford, TX, 76021. Tel: 817-952-2360. Fax: 817-952-2396. p. 2288

Johnson, Ben, Electronic Res, Vermont Technical College, Main St, Randolph Center, VT, 05061. Tel: 802-728-1237. Fax: 802-728-1506. p. 2433

Johnson, Benjamin, Fac Librn, Vermont Technical College, Main St, Randolph Center, VT, 05061. Tel: 802-728-1237. Fax: 802-728-1506. p. 2433

Johnson, Benjamin, AV/Multimedia Spec, Longwood University, Redford & Race St, Farmville, VA, 23909. Tel: 434-395-2456. Fax: 434-395-2453. p. 2463

Johnson, Bernadette J, Govt Doc, Francis Marion University, 4822 East Palmetto St, Florence, SC, 29506. Tel: 843-661-1313. Fax: 843-661-1309. p. 2194

Johnson, Beth, Head, Access Serv, Radford University, 801 E Main St, Radford, VA, 24142-0001. Tel: 540-831-6648. Fax: 540-831-6138. p. 2487

Johnson, Bethanne, Adult Serv, Ref Serv, Southwest Public Libraries, SPL Admin, 3359 Park St, Grove City, OH, 43123. Tel: 614-875-6716. Fax: 614-875-2219. p. 1903

Johnson, Betsy, Head, Youth Serv, Henderson District Public Libraries, 280 S Green Valley Pkwy, Henderson, NV, 89012. Tel: 702-492-7252. Fax: 702-492-1711. p. 1428

Johnson, Betty, Genealogy Serv, Cherokee Regional Library System, 305 S Duke St, LaFayette, GA, 30728-2936. Tel: 706-638-4912. Fax: 706-638-3979. p. 538

Johnson, Betty, Librn, Griswold Memorial Library, Main St, Colrain, MA, 01340. Tel: 413-624-3619. Fax: 413-624-3619. p. 1082

Johnson, Betty W, Librn, National College, 1813 E Main St, Salem, VA, 24153-4598. Tel: 540-444-4189, 540-986-1800, Ext 189. Fax: 540-444-4195. p. 2495

Johnson, Bev, Tech Serv, Town of Vail Public Library, 292 W Meadow Dr, Vail, CO, 81657. Tel: 970-479-2184. Fax: 970-479-2192. p. 325

Johnson, Bev, Asst Librn, Southwestern Manitoba Regional Library, 149 Main St, Melita, MB, R0M 1L0, CANADA. Tel: 204-522-3923. Fax: 204-522-3923. p. 2749

Johnson, Bill, Asst Dir, Winter Park Public Library, 460 E New England Ave, Winter Park, FL, 32789-4493. Tel: 407-623-3496. Fax: 407-623-3489. p. 505

Johnson, Bill M, Dir of Educ, Crescent Hill Baptist Church Library, 2800 Frankfort Ave, Louisville, KY, 40206. Tel: 502-896-4425. Fax: 502-896-9855. p. 923

Johnson, Brandi Woods, Librn, Wiregrass Georgia Technical College Library, 1676 Elm St, Rm 112, Sparks, GA, 31647. Tel: 229-549-7368. Fax: 229-549-6286. p. 552

Johnson, Brandi Woods, Librn, Wiregrass Georgia Technical College Library, 4089 Val Tech Rd, Valdosta, GA, 31602. Tel: 229-259-5177. Fax: 229-259-5179. p. 555

Johnson, Brenda, Br Coordr, Forsyth County Public Library, Sharon Forks, 2820 Old Atlanta Rd, Cumming, GA, 30041. Tel: 770-781-9840. p. 527

Johnson, Brenda, Dean, Indiana University, Ruth Lilly Medical Library, 975 W Walnut St, IB 100, Indianapolis, IN, 46202-5121. Tel: 317-274-7182. Fax: 317-278-2349. p. 752

Johnson, Brenda, Librn, Palmyra Memorial Library, 525 Illinois Pl, Palmyra, NE, 68418. Tel: 402-780-5344. Fax: 402-780-5344. p. 1416

Johnson, Brenda, Br Mgr, Fairfield County District Library, Bremen Rushcreek Memorial Branch, 200 School St, Bremen, OH, 43107. Tel: 740-569-7246. p. 1908

Johnson, Brenda, Br Mgr, Fairfield County District Library, Johns Memorial Branch, 116 E High St, Amanda, OH, 43102. Tel: 740-969-2785. p. 1908

Johnson, Brent, Ref Serv, Widener University, Harrisburg Campus Law Library, 3800 Vartan Way, Harrisburg, DE, 17110. Tel: 717-541-3984. Fax: 717-541-3998. p. 389

Johnson, Bri, YA Serv, Barrington Public Library, 281 County Rd, Barrington, RI, 02806. Tel: 401-247-1920. Fax: 401-247-3763. p. 2163

Johnson, Bridgett, Dir, Libr Serv, Lewistown Public Library, 701 W Main St, Lewistown, MT, 59457. Tel: 406-538-5212. Fax: 406-538-3920. p. 1384

Johnson, Bruce, Librn IV, San Diego Public Library, 820 E St, San Diego, CA, 92101-6478. Tel: 619-236-5830. Fax: 619-238-6639. p. 235

Johnson, Bruce S, Assoc Dean, Info, Ohio State University LIBRARIES, Michael E Moritz Law Library, 55 W 12th Ave, Columbus, OH, 43210-1391. Tel: 614-292-2964. Fax: 614-292-3202. p. 1888

Johnson, Candy, ILL, Emporia State University, 1200 Commercial St, Box 4051, Emporia, KS, 66801. Tel: 620-341-5207. Fax: 620-341-5997. p. 866

Johnson, Carla Conrad, Dean of Libr, Libr Dir, Alfred University, Scholes Library of Ceramics, New York State College of Ceramics at Alfred University, Two Pine St, Alfred, NY, 14802-1297. p. 1572

Johnson, Carol, Chair, Head, Circ, Head, Per, Normandale Community College Library, 9700 France Ave S, Bloomington, MN, 55431. Tel: 952-487-8298. Fax: 952-487-8101. p. 1241

Johnson, Carol A, Dir, Marcellus Free Library, Two Slocombe St, Marcellus, NY, 13108. Tel: 315-673-3221. Fax: 315-673-0148. p. 1657

Johnson, Carol P, Dir, Saint Catherine University, 2004 Randolph Ave, Mail F-10, Saint Paul, MN, 55105-1794. Tel: 651-690-6650. Fax: 651-690-8636. p. 1281

Johnson, Carolyn, Dir, Oak Grove Baptist Church Library, 2829 Oak Grove Church Rd, Carrollton, GA, 30117. Tel: 770-834-7019. Fax: 770-834-8218. p. 523

Johnson, Carolyn, Coordr, Pub Serv, North Shore Community College Library, One Ferncroft Rd, Danvers, MA, 01923-4093. Tel: 978-739-6245. Fax: 978-739-5500. p. 1083

Johnson, Carolyn, Info Librn, Northwest Missouri State University, 800 University Dr, Maryville, MO, 64468-6001. Tel: 660-562-1192. Fax: 660-562-1049. p. 1344

Johnson, Carolyn A, Music Librn, Connecticut College, Greer Music Library, 270 Mohegan Ave, Box 5234, New London, CT, 06320-4196. Tel: 860-439-2711. Fax: 860-439-2871. p. 360

Johnson, Catherine, Curator, Librn, National Park Service, 800 S San Marcial, El Paso, TX, 79905. Tel: 915-532-7273, Ext 110. Fax: 915-532-7240. p. 2317

Johnson, Cathy, Br Mgr, Glendale Public Library, Foothills, 19055 N 57th Ave, Glendale, AZ, 85308. Tel: 623-930-3867. Fax: 623-930-3855. p. 64

Johnson, Charles, Coll Develop, Museum of Ventura County, 100 E Main St, Ventura, CA, 93001. Tel: 805-794-0594. Fax: 805-653-5267. p. 279

Johnson, Cheryl, Head, Res Serv, James Prendergast Library Association, 509 Cherry St, Jamestown, NY, 14701. Tel: 716-484-7135. Fax: 716-487-1148. p. 1647

Johnson, Cheryl, Ch, Newport Public Library, 316 N Fourth St, Newport, PA, 17074-1203. Tel: 717-567-6860. Fax: 717-567-3373. p. 2097

Johnson, Cheryl A, Dir, Hanna Municipal Library, PO Box 878, Hanna, AB, T0J 1P0, CANADA. Tel: 403-854-3865. Fax: 403-854-2772. p. 2706

Johnson, Christina, Circ, Muscle Shoals Public Library, 1918 E Avalon, Muscle Shoals, AL, 35661. Tel: 256-386-9212. Fax: 256-386-9211. p. 32

Johnson, Christina, Head, Children's Dept, Lebanon Public Library, 104 E Washington St, Lebanon, IN, 46052. Tel: 765-483-2570. Fax: 317-873-5059. p. 761

Johnson, Christine, In Charge, California State Polytechnic University Library, College of Environmental Design Library, Bldg 7, 3801 W Temple Ave, Pomona, CA, 91768. Tel: 909-869-2665. p. 211

Johnson, Christine, Adult Serv Coordr, Westminster Public Library, 3705 W 112th Ave, Westminster, CO, 80031. Tel: 303-658-2620. Fax: 303-404-5135. p. 326

Johnson, Christopher, Ref Serv, Webster Groves Public Library, 301 E Lockwood Ave, Webster Groves, MO, 63119-3102. Tel: 314-961-7277. Fax: 314-961-4233. p. 1372

Johnson, Connelly, Assoc Librn, Davis Wright Tremaine LLP, 1201 Third Ave, Ste 2200, Seattle, WA, 98101-3045. Tel: 206-628-7604. Fax: 206-628-7699. p. 2527

Johnson, Connie, Dir, Logan Public Library, 121 E Sixth St, Logan, IA, 51546. Tel: 712-644-2551. Fax: 712-644-2551. p. 828

Johnson, Cyntha, Asst Dir, Faulkner-Van Buren Regional Library System, 1900 Tyler St, Conway, AR, 72032. Tel: 501-327-7482. Fax: 501-327-9098. p. 96

Johnson, Cynthia, Actg Dir, University of California Library, Grunigen Medical Library, Bldg 22A Rt 81, 101 The City Dr S, Orange, CA, 92868. Tel: 714-456-5585. p. 160

Johnson, Cynthia, Head, Ref, Cary Memorial Library, 1874 Massachusetts Ave, Lexington, MA, 02420. Tel: 781-862-6288, Ext 232. Fax: 781-862-7355. p. 1099

Johnson, Cynthia F, Dir, Rowayton Library, 33 Highland Ave, Rowayton, CT, 06853. Tel: 203-838-5038. Fax: 203-523-0438, 928-437-5038. p. 366

Johnson, Dan, Head Librn, University of South Carolina, PO Box 617, Allendale, SC, 29810-0617. Tel: 803-584-3446, Ext 153. Fax: 803-584-5038. p. 2180

Johnson, Daniel J, Dir, Hull Public Library, Nine Main St, Hull, MA, 02045-1199. Tel: 781-925-2295. Fax: 781-925-0867. p. 1096

Johnson, Daphne, In Charge, Florida Department of Corrections, 10980 Demilley Rd, Polk City, FL, 33868. Tel: 863-984-9173, Ext 300. p. 484

Johnson, Darla, Dir, Plover Public Library, 301 Main St, Plover, IA, 50573. Tel: 712-857-3532. p. 839

Johnson Dashnaw, Linda, Ch, Shrewsbury Public Library, 609 Main St, Shrewsbury, MA, 01545. Tel: 508-841-8537. Fax: 508-841-8540. p. 1124

Johnson, David, Exec Dir, Fayetteville Public Library, 401 W Mountain St, Fayetteville, AR, 72701. Tel: 479-856-7100. Fax: 479-571-0222. p. 99

Johnson, David Jeffrey, Archivist, Casemate Museum Library, 20 Bernard Rd, Fort Monroe, VA, 23651-1004. Tel: 757-788-3935. Fax: 757-788-3886. p. 2465

Johnson, Deanna, Br Mgr, Librn, Monsanto-Calgene Campus Library, 1920 Fifth St, Davis, CA, 95616. Tel: 530-753-6313. Fax: 530-792-2453. p. 139

Johnson, Deanna, Actg Head, Health Sci Libr, University of California, Davis, Loren D Carlson Health Sciences Library, Med Sci 1B, One Shields Ave, Davis, CA, 95616-5291. Tel: 530-752-3271. Fax: 530-752-4718. p. 139

Johnson, Debora, Ch, Pocahontas County Free Libraries, 500 Eighth St, Marlinton, WV, 24954-1227. Tel: 304-799-6000. Fax: 304-799-3988. p. 2564

Johnson, Deborah, Libr Mgr, Mercy College of Ohio Library, 2221 Madison Ave, Toledo, OH, 43604. Tel: 419-251-1821. Fax: 419-251-1730. p. 1939

Johnson, Deborah G, Libr Tech, University of Arkansas for Medical Sciences South Arkansas Library, 460 W Oak, El Dorado, AR, 71730. Tel: 870-881-4403, 870-881-4404. Fax: 870-862-0570. p. 98

Johnson, Deborah Lazare, ILL, University of Louisiana at Lafayette, PO Box 40199, Lafayette, LA, 70504-0199. Tel: 337-482-6036. Fax: 337-482-6399. p. 953

Johnson, Deborah S, Dir, East Morgan County Library District, 500 Clayton St, Brush, CO, 80723-2110. Tel: 970-842-4596. Fax: 970-842-2450. p. 293

Johnson, Dee, II, Dir, Central Community College, 4500 63rd St, Columbus, NE, 68601. Tel: 402-562-1202. Fax: 402-562-1227. p. 1396

Johnson, Deirdre, Youth Serv, Mount Kisco Public Library, 100 E Main St, Mount Kisco, NY, 10549. Tel: 914-864-0039. Fax: 914-666-3899. p. 1663

Johnson, Demi, Teen Librn, Humboldt Public Library, 30 Sixth St N, Humboldt, IA, 50548. Tel: 515-332-1925. Fax: 515-332-1926. p. 821

Johnson, Denise, Ref/Govt Doc Librn, Bradley University, 1501 W Bradley Ave, Peoria, IL, 61625. Tel: 309-677-2850. Fax: 309-677-2558. p. 690

Johnson, Diana, Dir, Stromsburg Public Library, 230 Central St, Stromsburg, NE, 68666. Tel: 402-764-7681. Fax: 402-764-7681. p. 1420

Johnson, Diane, Sr Librn, California Department of Corrections Library System, Valley State Prison for Women, 21633 Ave 24, Chowchilla, CA, 93610. Tel: 559-665-6100, Ext 6066. p. 222

Johnson, Diane, Libr Mgr, Nassau County Public Library System, Yulee Branch, 76346 William Burgess Blvd, Yulee, FL, 32097. Tel: 904-548-4465. Fax: 904-548-4426. p. 440

Johnson, Diane, Librn, Waterville Historical Society Library, 62 Silver St, Unit B, Waterville, ME, 04901. Tel: 207-872-9439. p. 1005

Johnson, Diane, Asst Dir, Charles County Public Library, Two Garrett Ave, La Plata, MD, 20646-5959. Tel: 301-934-9001. Fax: 301-934-2297. p. 1033

Johnson, Diane, Ser, State University of New York College at Geneseo, SUNY Geneseo, One College Circle, Geneseo, NY, 14454-1498. p. 1627

Johnson, Diane M, Tech Serv, Kauai Community College, 3-1901 Kaumualii Hwy, Lihue, HI, 96766. Tel: 808-245-8240. Fax: 808-245-8294. p. 567

Johnson, Donna, Asst Dir, Ruthven Public Library, 1301 Gowrie St, Ruthven, IA, 51358. Tel: 712-837-4820. Fax: 712-837-4820. p. 841

Johnson, Donna, Cat, Leicester Public Library, 1136 Main St, Leicester, MA, 01524-0389. Tel: 508-892-7020. Fax: 508-892-7045. p. 1098

Johnson, Donna, Dir, Mabel Public Library, 110 E Newburg, Mabel, MN, 55954. Tel: 507-493-5336. Fax: 507-493-3336. p. 1256

Johnson, Doris, Dir, Southwestern Christian College, Hogan Steward Learning Ctr, 200 Bowser St, Terrell, TX, 75160-3400. Tel: 972-524-3341, Ext 141. Fax: 972-563-7133. p. 2391

Johnson, Doris E, Govt Doc Coordr, Ref & Info Spec, South Carolina State University, 300 College St NE, Orangeburg, SC, 29115-4427. Tel: 803-536-8642. Fax: 803-536-8902. p. 2202

Johnson, Dorothy, Asst Dir, Mitchellville Public Library, 204 Center Ave N, Mitchellville, IA, 50169. Tel: 515-967-3339. Fax: 515-967-1868. p. 832

Johnson, Dorothy, Circ Mgr, Hackley Public Library, 316 W Webster Ave, Muskegon, MI, 49440. Tel: 231-722-7276, Ext 231. Fax: 231-726-5567. p. 1212

Johnson, Elaine, Per, Crown College, 8700 College View Dr, Saint Bonifacius, MN, 55375-9002. Tel: 952-446-4240. Fax: 952-446-4149. p. 1274

Johnson, Elizabeth, Extn Serv Mgr, La Porte County Public Library, 904 Indiana Ave, La Porte, IN, 46350-3435. Tel: 219-362-6156. Fax: 219-362-6158. p. 758

Johnson, Elizabeth, Coord, Ad Serv, Cranston Public Library, 140 Sockanosset Cross Rd, Cranston, RI, 02920-5539. Tel: 401-943-9080. Fax: 401-946-5079. p. 2164

Johnson, Elizabeth, Libr Mgr, Vancouver Island Regional Library, Courtenay Branch, 300 Sixth St, Courtenay, BC, V9N 9V9, CANADA. Tel: 250-334-3369. Fax: 250-334-0910. p. 2732

Johnson, Elizabeth, Acq, Toronto Rehab, 550 University Ave, Toronto, ON, M5G 2A2, CANADA. Tel: 416-597-3422, Ext 3050. Fax: 416-591-6515. p. 2864

Johnson, Elizabeth Benson, Asst Dir, University of Minnesota Duluth Library, 416 Library Dr, Duluth, MN, 55812. Tel: 218-726-6561. Fax: 218-726-8019. p. 1248

Johnson, Elvernoy, State Librn, The State Library of Massachusetts, State House, Rm 341, 24 Beacon St, Boston, MA, 02133. Tel: 617-727-2592. Fax: 617-727-5819. p. 1067

Johnson, Eric, Dir, Southeastern Louisiana University, SLU Box 10896, 1211 SGA Dr, Hammond, LA, 70402. Tel: 985-549-3860. Fax: 985-549-3995. p. 950

Johnson, Eric, Web Serv Librn, Thomas Jefferson Foundation Inc, 1329 Kenwood Farm Lane, Charlottesville, VA, 22902. Tel: 434-984-7540. Fax: 434-984-7546. p. 2454

Johnson, Evelyn, Adult Serv, Mgr, Ref Serv, Watauga County Public Library, 140 Queen St, Boone, NC, 28607. Tel: 828-264-8784. Fax: 828-264-1794. p. 1777

Johnson, Faith M, Dir, Town of Ulster Public Library, 860 Ulster Ave, Kingston, NY, 12401. Tel: 845-338-7881. Fax: 845-338-7884. p. 1650

Johnson, Frances, Br Head, Toronto Public Library, Guildwood, Guildwood Plaza, 123 Guildwood Pkwy, Toronto, ON, M1E 4V2, CANADA. Tel: 416-396-8872. Fax: 416-396-3610. p. 2861

Johnson, Fred, Prog Coordr, National Cotton Council of America Library, 7193 Goodlett Farms Pkwy, Cordova, TN, 38016. Tel: 901-274-9030. Fax: 901-725-0510. p. 2232

Johnson, Frederic, Librn, Campton Public Library, 1110 New Hampshire, Rte 175, Campton, NH, 03223. Tel: 603-726-4877. Fax: 603-726-4877. p. 1440

Johnson, Frederic P, Pres, Waterville Historical Society Library, 62 Silver St, Unit B, Waterville, ME, 04901. Tel: 207-872-6286. p. 1005

Johnson, Gary, Access Serv, University of California, Santa Barbara, Santa Barbara, CA, 93106-9010. Tel: 805-893-3386. Fax: 805-893-7010. p. 261

Johnson, Gary L, Adminr, Shelby County Law Library, Shelby County Courthouse, 140 Adams Ave, Rm 334, Memphis, TN, 38103. Tel: 901-527-7041. Fax: 901-522-8936. p. 2251

Johnson, Gay, Dir, Piggott Public Library, 361 W Main, Piggott, AR, 72454. Tel: 870-598-3666. Fax: 870-598-3666. p. 112

Johnson, Georgene Timko, Dir, Libr Serv, Washington State Community College, 710 Colegate Dr, Marietta, OH, 45750. Tel: 740-374-8716, Ext 3107. Fax: 740-373-7496. p. 1914

Johnson, Gerald B, Librn, Naples Daily News Library, 1100 Immokalee Rd, Naples, FL, 34110-4810. Tel: 239-263-4796. Fax: 239-263-4816. p. 471

Johnson, Glen, Libr Instruction, Pub Serv, Shelton State Community College, 9500 Old Greensboro Rd, Tuscaloosa, AL, 35405. Tel: 205-391-2327. Fax: 205-391-3926. p. 38

Johnson, Heidi, First Year/Info Literacy Librn, College of Saint Scholastica Library, 1200 Kenwood Ave, Duluth, MN, 55811-4199. Tel: 218-723-6488. Fax: 218-723-5948. p. 1247

Johnson, Helen, Br Head, Cullman County Public Library System, Tom Bevill Public, 151 Byars Rd, Hanceville, AL, 35077. Tel: 256-287-1573. Fax: 256-287-1573. p. 13

Johnson, Holly, Librn, Chinook Regional Library, Frontier Branch, First St W, Frontier, SK, S0N 0W0, CANADA. Tel: 306-296-4667. p. 2928

Johnson, Holly A, Dir IT, Data Serv & Mat Proc, Howard County Library System, 6600 Cradlerock Way, Columbia, MD, 21045-4912. Tel: 410-313-7750. Fax: 410-313-7742. p. 1026

Johnson, Hope, Asst Dir, Academy of Art University Library, 180 New Montogomery, 6th Flr, San Francisco, CA, 94105. Tel: 415-618-3894. Fax: 415-618-3981. p. 240

Johnson, Ingrid, Sr Librn, Ch Serv, Rancho Mirage Public Library, 71-100 Hwy 111, Rancho Mirage, CA, 92270. Tel: 760-341-7323. Fax: 760-341-5213. p. 213

Johnson, Ivan G, Mat Develop, Braille Institute Library Services, 741 N Vermont Ave, Los Angeles, CA, 90029-3514. Tel: 323-663-1111, Ext 1388. Fax: 323-662-2440. p. 168

Johnson, Jacqueline, Info Res Spec, Edison Electric Institute, 701 Pennsylvania Ave NW, 3rd Flr, Washington, DC, 20004-2696. Tel: 202-508-5623. p. 399

Johnson, Jacqueline, Archivist, Miami University Libraries, Western College Memorial Archives, Peabody Hall, Oxford, OH, 45056. Tel: 513-529-9695. p. 1926

Johnson, Jacqueline Fessard, Head, Coll Develop & Spec Coll, Indiana University Southeast Library, 4201 Grant Line Rd, New Albany, IN, 47150. Tel: 812-941-2262. Fax: 812-941-2656. p. 767

Johnson, James R, Librn, VA Pittsburgh Healthcare System, Medical Library Heinz Division, 1010 Delafield Rd, Pittsburgh, PA, 15215. Tel: 412-784-3747. Fax: 412-784-3508. p. 2129

Johnson, Jan, Dir, Daviess County Library, 306 W Grand, Gallatin, MO, 64640-1132. Tel: 660-663-3222. Fax: 660-663-3250. p. 1329

Johnson, Jan, Br Assoc, Las Vegas-Clark County Library District, Moapa Town Library, 1340 E Hwy 168, Moapa, NV, 89025. Tel: 702-864-2438. Fax: 702-864-2467. p. 1429

Johnson, Jane, Ch, Topsfield Town Library, One S Common St, Topsfield, MA, 01983-1496. Tel: 978-887-1528. Fax: 978-887-0185. p. 1131

Johnson, Janet, Dir, Benton Public Library, 48 W Main St, Benton, WI, 53803-0026. Tel: 608-759-2665. p. 2581

Johnson, Janice, Mgr, Youth Serv, Princeton Public Library, 65 Witherspoon St, Princeton, NJ, 08542. Tel: 609-924-9529, Ext 243. Fax: 609-924-6109. p. 1522

Johnson, Jayne, Head, Circ, Bacon Memorial District Library, 45 Vinewood, Wyandotte, MI, 48192-5221. Tel: 734-246-8357. Fax: 734-282-1540. p. 1237

Johnson, Jeanne, Br Cluster Mgr, Fresno County Public Library, 2420 Mariposa St, Fresno, CA, 93721-2285. Tel: 559-600-7323. p. 151

Johnson, Jeannie, Dir, Mesquite Public Library, 300 W Grubb Dr, Mesquite, TX, 75149. Tel: 972-216-6220. Fax: 972-216-6740. p. 2362

Johnson, Jennifer, Librn, Ohioana Library, 274 E First Ave, Ste 300, Columbus, OH, 43201. Tel: 614-466-3831. Fax: 614-728-6974. p. 1890

Johnson, Jennifer, Vols Serv Coordr, Beaverton City Library, 12375 SW Fifth St, Beaverton, OR, 97005-2883. Tel: 503-526-3703. Fax: 503-526-2636. p. 1991

Johnson, Jennifer I, Assoc Archivist, Cargill, Inc, 15407 McGinty Rd W, Wayzata, MN, 55391. Tel: 952-742-6498. Fax: 952-742-6062. p. 1287

Johnson, Jenny Marie, Head Librn, University of Illinois Library at Urbana-Champaign, Map & Geography, 1408 W Gregory Dr, 418 Main Library, Mc-522, Urbana, IL, 61801. Tel: 217-333-0827. Fax: 217-333-2214. p. 712

Johnson, Jerry, Youth Serv Librn, Fitchburg Public Library, 610 Main St, Fitchburg, MA, 01420-3146. Tel: 978-345-9637. Fax: 978-345-9631. p. 1089

Johnson, Jessica, Asst Librn, The Morning Call, 101 N Sixth St, Allentown, PA, 18101. Tel: 610-820-6500. Fax: 610-820-6693. p. 2027

Johnson, Jill, Librn, Wapiti Regional Library, Kinistino Public Library, 210 Kinistino Ave, Kinistino, SK, S0J 1H0, CANADA. Tel: 306-864-2537. p. 2921

Johnson, Jim, Circ Asst, SRI International, Life Sciences Library, 333 Ravenswood Ave, Menlo Park, CA, 94025. Tel: 650-859-3549. p. 185

Johnson, Jo Anne, Librn, Krotz Springs Municipal Public Library, 216 Park St, Krotz Springs, LA, 70570. Tel: 337-566-8190. Fax: 337-566-2233. p. 952

Johnson, Joan, Dep Dir, Pub Serv, Milwaukee Public Library, 814 W Wisconsin Ave, Milwaukee, WI, 53233-2385. Tel: 414-286-3000. Fax: 414-286-2794. p. 2620

Johnson, Jocelyn, Ser, Saint Thomas University Library, Law Library, 16401 NW 37th Ave, Miami Gardens, FL, 33054. Tel: 305-623-2338. Fax: 305-623-2337. p. 469

Johnson, Jody, Tech Serv, University of Wisconsin-Superior, PO Box 2000, Belknap & Catlin, Superior, WI, 54880-2000. Tel: 715-394-8343. Fax: 715-394-8462. p. 2641

Johnson, Johanna, Head, Govt Info, Dallas Public Library, 1515 Young St, Dallas, TX, 75201-5499. Tel: 214-670-1468. Fax: 214-670-1451. p. 2306

Johnson, John, Adult Serv, ILL Librn, Keene Public Library, 60 Winter St, Keene, NH, 03431-3360. Tel: 603-352-0157. Fax: 866-743-0446. p. 1452

Johnson, Johnny, Dr, Head, Access Serv, Oklahoma State University Libraries, Oklahoma State University, Athletic Ave, Stillwater, OK, 74078-1071. Tel: 405-744-9729. Fax: 405-744-5183. p. 1978

Johnson, Joy, Ref Librn, South College Library, 3904 Lonas Dr, Knoxville, TN, 37909. Tel: 865-251-1750, 865-251-1832. p. 2243

Johnson, Joyce, Asst Dir, Pub Serv, Florida Agricultural & Mechanical University Libraries, 1500 S Martin Luther King Blvd, Tallahassee, FL, 32307-4700. Tel: 850-599-3370. Fax: 850-561-2293. p. 492

Johnson, Joyce, Circ, William Madison Randall Library, 601 S College Rd, Wilmington, NC, 28403-5616. Tel: 910-962-3000. Fax: 910-962-3078. p. 1831

Johnson, Judy, Librn, Southwest Arkansas Regional Library, Glenwood Branch, 210 Second St, Ste L, Glenwood, AR, 71943. Tel: 870-356-4643. Fax: 870-356-4643. p. 103

Johnson, Judy, ILL, Iowa Lakes Community College Library, 3200 College Dr, Emmetsburg, IA, 50536. Tel: 712-852-5317. Fax: 712-852-3094. p. 814

Johnson, Judy, Librn, Flint Institute of Arts, 1120 E Kearsley St, Flint, MI, 48503-1915. Tel: 810-237-7386. Fax: 810-234-1692. p. 1179

Johnson, Judy, Librn, Colonial Library, 160 Main St, Richburg, NY, 14774. Tel: 585-928-2694. Fax: 585-928-2694. p. 1727

Johnson, Judy, Ref/Bibliog Instruction Librn, Clark State Community College Library, 570 E Leffel Lane, Springfield, OH, 45505. Tel: 937-328-7968. Fax: 937-328-6133. p. 1935

Johnson, Julie, Br Mgr, Enoch Pratt Free Library, Roland Park, 5108 Roland Ave, Baltimore, MD, 21210-2132. Tel: 410-396-6099. Fax: 410-396-6116. p. 1013

Johnson, Julie, Exec Dir, Kinderhook Memorial Library, 18 Hudson St, Kinderhook, NY, 12106-2003. Tel: 518-758-6192. p. 1649

Johnson, Julie, Librn, Annapolis Valley Regional Library, Kentville Branch, 95 Cornwallis St, Kentville, NS, B4N 3X7, CANADA. Tel: 902-679-2544. Fax: 902-679-2544. p. 2778

Johnson, K R, Dir, Libr & Media Serv, Purdue University North Central Library, Library-Student-Faculty (LSF) Bldg, 2nd Flr, 1401 S US Hwy 421, Westville, IN, 46391. Tel: 219-785-5248. Fax: 219-785-5501. p. 787

Johnson, Karen, Head, Syst, University of San Francisco, 2130 Fulton St, San Francisco, CA, 94117-1080. Tel: 415-422-2759. Fax: 415-422-5949. p. 248

Johnson, Karen, Adult Serv Mgr, Cedar Rapids Public Library West, 2600 Edgewood Rd SW, Ste 330, Cedar Rapids, IA, 52404. Tel: 319-398-5123. Fax: 319-398-0476. p. 800

Johnson, Karen, Circ Mgr, Morningside College, 1601 Morningside Ave, Sioux City, IA, 51106. Tel: 712-274-5195. Fax: 712-274-5224. p. 844

Johnson, Karen A, Dir, Avon Public Library, 280 W Main St, Avon, MA, 02322. Tel: 508-583-0378. Fax: 508-580-2757. p. 1051

Johnson, Karen J, Dir, Bridgeville Public Library, 600 S Cannon St, Bridgeville, DE, 19933-1126. Tel: 302-337-7401. Fax: 302-337-3270. p. 381

Johnson, Karen J, Librn, United States Courts Library, Walter E Hoffman US Courthouse, 600 Granby St, Rm 319, Norfolk, VA, 23510. Tel: 757-222-7044. Fax: 757-222-7047. p. 2483

Johnson, Karen S, Mgr, Henrico County Public Library, Tuckahoe Area Library, 1901 Starling Dr, Henrico, VA, 23229-4564. Tel: 804-290-9100. Fax: 804-270-2293. p. 2471

Johnson, Katherine, Dir, Dowagiac District Library, 211 Commercial St, Dowagiac, MI, 49047-1728. Tel: 269-782-3826. Fax: 269-782-9798. p. 1174

Johnson, Katherine, Head Librn, Capital Area District Libraries, Downtown Lansing Library, 401 S Capitol Ave, Lansing, MI, 48933. Tel: 517-367-6322. Fax: 517-374-1068. p. 1200

Johnson, Katherine Burger, Dr, Archivist, Assoc Prof, Curator, University of Louisville Libraries, University Archives & Records Center, Ekstrom Library, 2215 S Third St, Louisville, KY, 40208. Tel: 502-852-6674. Fax: 502-852-6673. p. 927

Johnson, Kathryn W, Acq, Laurens County Library, 1017 W Main St, Laurens, SC, 29360. Tel: 864-681-7323. Fax: 864-681-0598. p. 2199

Johnson, Kathy, Ref, Alaska Department of Natural Resources, Public Information Center, 550 W Seventh Ave, Ste 1260, Anchorage, AK, 99501. Tel: 907-269-8413. Fax: 907-269-8901. p. 43

Johnson, Kathy, Libr Asst, Benzonia Public Library, 891 Michigan Ave, Benzonia, MI, 49616-9784. Tel: 231-882-4111. Fax: 231-882-4111. p. 1157

Johnson, Kathy, Br Mgr, Pasadena Public Library, Fairmont, 4330 Fairmont, Pasadena, TX, 77504-3306. Tel: 281-998-1095. Fax: 281-998-1583. p. 2368

Johnson, Kathy Spence, Archivist, United Methodist Church, 122 W Franklin Ave, Ste 400, Minneapolis, MN, 55404. Tel: 612-230-6149. Fax: 612-870-1260. p. 1261

Johnson, Katie, Ch, Andover Free Library, 40 Main St, Andover, NY, 14806. Tel: 607-478-8442. Fax: 607-478-5056. p. 1574

Johnson, Katie, Ch, Spooner Memorial Library, 421 High St, Spooner, WI, 54801-1431. Tel: 715-635-2792. Fax: 715-635-2147. p. 2639

Johnson, Kay, Coordr, Tech Serv, Radford University, 801 E Main St, Radford, VA, 24142-0001. Tel: 540-831-5703. Fax: 540-831-6138. p. 2487

Johnson, Kelli, Res & Instruction Librn, Marshall University Libraries, One John Marshall Dr, Huntington, WV, 25755-2060. Tel: 304-696-6567. Fax: 304-696-5858. p. 2561

Johnson, Ken, Ref & Instrul Serv Librn, Saint Olaf College, Rolvaag Memorial Library, Glasoe Science Library, Halvorson Music Library, 1510 Saint Olaf Ave, Northfield, MN, 55057-1097. Tel: 507-786-3793. Fax: 507-786-3734. p. 1269

Johnson, Kenneth Paul, Dir, Halifax County-South Boston Regional Library, 177 S Main St, Halifax, VA, 24558. Tel: 434-476-3357. Fax: 434-476-3359. p. 2467

Johnson, Kim, Librn, Anoka County Library, Rum River, 4201 Sixth Ave N, Anoka, MN, 55303. Tel: 763-576-4695. Fax: 763-576-4699. p. 1241

Johnson, Kim, Asst Dir, Madisonville Public Library, 4023 Hwy 411 N, Unit C, Madisonville, TN, 37354-1535. Tel: 423-442-4085. Fax: 423-442-8121. p. 2246

Johnson, Kim, Libr Mgr, Calmar Public Library, 4705 50th Ave, Calmar, AB, T0C 0V0, CANADA. Tel: 780-985-3472. Fax: 780-985-2859. p. 2694

Johnson, Kim, Librn, Catalina Public Library, PO Box 69, Catalina, NL, A0C 1J0, CANADA. Tel: 709-469-3045. Fax: 709-469-3045. p. 2769

Johnson, Kimberly, Mgr, Tulsa City-County Library, South Broken Arrow, 3600 S Chestnut, Broken Arrow, OK, 74011. Tel: 918-451-0002. Fax: 918-451-0118. p. 1983

Johnson, Kimberly, Coordr, Archives & Spec Coll, Texas Woman's University Libraries, 304 Administration Dr, Denton, TX, 76204. Tel: 940-898-3743. Fax: 940-898-3764. p. 2312

Johnson, Kristynn, Tech Serv Mgr, Eugene Public Library, 100 W Tenth Ave, Eugene, OR, 97401. Tel: 541-682-5450. Fax: 541-682-5898. p. 1996

Johnson, Latesha, Br Librn, Bolivar County Library System, Field Memorial Library, 132 N Peeler Ave, Shaw, MS, 38773. Tel: 662-754-4597. Fax: 662-754-4597. p. 1296

Johnson, Laura, Dep Dir, Pub Serv, Indianapolis-Marion County Public Library, 2450 N Meridian St, Indianapolis, IN, 46208. Tel: 317-275-4012. Fax: 317-269-5300. p. 753

Johnson, Laura, Children's & YA Librn, Green County Public Library, 112 W Court St, Greensburg, KY, 42743. Tel: 270-932-7081. Fax: 270-932-7081. p. 915

Johnson, Lauren, Dir, Temple Israel Libraries & Media Center, 5725 Walnut Lake Rd, West Bloomfield, MI, 48323. Tel: 248-661-5700. Fax: 248-661-1302. p. 1236

Johnson, Lavonne, ILL, Pub Serv, Bryan College Library, 585 Bryan Dr, Dayton, TN, 37321. Tel: 423-775-7228. Fax: 423-775-7309. p. 2232

Johnson, Layne, Br Mgr, Livingston Parish Library, Watson Branch, 36581 Outback Rd, Denham Springs, LA, 70706. Tel: 225-664-3963. Fax: 225-664-1949. p. 955

Johnson, Leann, Asst Dir, Peoria Public Library, 107 NE Monroe St, Peoria, IL, 61602-1070. Tel: 309-497-2139. Fax: 309-497-2007. p. 690

Johnson, Lela, Br Mgr, Lonesome Pine Regional Library, Rose Hill Community, Main St, Rose Hill, VA, 24281. Tel: 276-445-5329. Fax: 276-445-5329. p. 2504

Johnson, Linda, Librn I, YA Librn, Montgomery City-County Public Library System, Juliette Hampton Morgan Memorial Library (Main Library), 245 High St, Montgomery, AL, 36104. Tel: 334-240-4983. Fax: 334-240-4980. p. 30

Johnson, Linda, Dir, Mancelona Township Library, 202 W State St, Mancelona, MI, 49659. Tel: 231-587-9451. p. 1205

Johnson, Linda, Doc, University of New Hampshire Library, 18 Library Way, Durham, NH, 03824. Tel: 603-862-2453. Fax: 603-862-3403. p. 1445

Johnson, Linda, Dir, Kilgore Public Library, 301 Henderson Blvd, Kilgore, TX, 75662-2799. Tel: 903-984-1529. Fax: 903-983-1779. p. 2350

Johnson, Linda, Head, Circ, University of Calgary Library, Doucette Library of Teaching Resources, 370 Education Block, 2500

University Dr NW, Calgary, AB, T2N 1N4, CANADA. Tel: 403-220-3982. Fax: 403-220-8211. p. 2693

Johnson, Linda E, Pres & Chief Exec Officer, Brooklyn Public Library, Grand Army Plaza, Brooklyn, NY, 11238-5698. Tel: 718-230-2100. Fax: 718-398-3947. p. 1590

Johnson, Linda Sue, Assoc Librn, Perry Memorial Library, 22 SE Fifth Ave, Perryton, TX, 79070. Tel: 806-435-5801. Fax: 806-435-4266. p. 2369

Johnson, Lisa, Exec Dir, The Stanley Whitman House Library, 37 High St, Farmington, CT, 06032. Tel: 860-677-9222. Fax: 860-677-7758. p. 340

Johnson, Lisa, Librn, Balmertown Public Library, 12 Fifth St, Balmertown, ON, P0V 1C0, CANADA. Tel: 807-735-2110. Fax: 807-735-2110. p. 2793

Johnson, Liz M, Ref Librn, Wake Forest University, Professional Center Library, Worrell Professional Ctr for Law & Management, 1834 Wake Forest Rd, Winston-Salem, NC, 27106. Tel: 336-758-5438. Fax: 336-758-6077. p. 1834

Johnson, Lois, Asst Br Supvr, Region of Waterloo Library, St Clements Branch, 3605 Lobsinger Line, St. Clements, ON, N0B 2M0, CANADA. Tel: 519-699-4341. p. 2793

Johnson, Lori, Cat, Curric Center Librn, Tech Serv Librn, Moody Bible Institute, 820 N La Salle Blvd, Chicago, IL, 60610-3284. Tel: 312-329-4102. Fax: 312-329-8959. p. 619

Johnson, Lori, Head of Libr, Visual Res, Oregon College of Art & Craft Library, 8245 SW Barnes Rd, Portland, OR, 97225. Tel: 503-297-5544, Ext 119. Fax: 503-297-9651. p. 2012

Johnson, Lorrinda, Br Mgr, Satilla Regional Library, 200 S Madison Ave, Ste D, Douglas, GA, 31533. Tel: 912-384-4667. Fax: 912-389-4365. p. 530

Johnson, Lou Vonne, Archives, Bryan College Station Public Library System, Carnegie History Center, 111 S Main St, Bryan, TX, 77803. Tel: 979-209-5630. p. 2292

Johnson, Luann P, Computer Serv, West Liberty University, CSC No 135, West Liberty, WV, 26074. Tel: 304-336-8035. Fax: 304-336-8186. p. 2574

Johnson, Lydia, Librn, South Mountain Community College Library, 7050 S 24th St, Phoenix, AZ, 85042. Tel: 602-243-8187. Fax: 602-243-8180. p. 77

Johnson, Lyle C, Dir, Acadia Parish Library, 1125 N Parkerson Ave, Crowley, LA, 70526. Tel: 337-788-1880, 337-788-1881. Fax: 337-788-3759. p. 948

Johnson, Lyn, Libr Spec, New Mexico State University at Alamogordo, 2400 N Scenic Dr, Alamogordo, NM, 88310. Tel: 575-439-3653. Fax: 575-439-3657. p. 1547

Johnson, Lynn, Youth Serv, Carol Stream Public Library, 616 Hiawatha Dr, Carol Stream, IL, 60188. Tel: 630-653-0755. Fax: 630-653-6809. p. 601

Johnson, M Douglas, Head, Electronic Syst, United States Air Force Academy Libraries, 2354 Fairchild Dr, Ste 3A10, USAF Academy, CO, 80840-6214. Tel: 719-333-4406. Fax: 719-333-4754. p. 324

Johnson, Mancil, Archivist, Tennessee Technological University, 1100 N Peachtree Ave, Cookeville, TN, 38505. Tel: 931-372-3326. Fax: 931-372-6112. p. 2231

Johnson, Marcia, Dir, Miami Public Library, 200 N Main, Miami, OK, 74354. Tel: 918-541-2292. Fax: 918-542-9363. p. 1968

Johnson, Marcia G, Librn, Minnesota West Community & Technical College Libraries, 1450 College Way, Worthington, MN, 56187-3024. Tel: 507-372-3462. p. 1291

Johnson, Margaret F, Librn, Delaware County Historical Society, 408 Avenue of the States, Chester, PA, 19013. Tel: 610-872-0502. Fax: 610-872-0503. p. 2044

Johnson, Marie, Media Spec, University of Alaska Fairbanks, 310 Tanana Dr, Fairbanks, AK, 99775. Tel: 907-474-7024. Fax: 907-474-6841. p. 48

Johnson, Marilyn, Dir, Luverne Public Library, 117 DeWitt St, Luverne, IA, 50560. Tel: 515-882-3436. Fax: 515-882-3436. p. 828

Johnson, Marilyn, Cat, Dir, National Society of Sons of Utah Pioneers, 3301 E 2920 S, Salt Lake City, UT, 84109. Tel: 801-484-4441. Fax: 801-484-2067. p. 2413

Johnson, Marjorie, Librn, Southeast Regional Library, Carnduff Branch, 506 Anderson Ave, Carnduff, SK, S0C 0S0, CANADA. Tel: 306-482-3255. p. 2929

Johnson, Marjorie, Librn, Southeast Regional Library, Gainsborough Branch, 401 Railway Ave, Gainsborough, SK, S0C 0Z0, CANADA. Tel: 306-685-2229. p. 2929

Johnson, Mark, Dir, Info Tech, Nassau County Public Library System, 25 N Fourth St, Fernandina Beach, FL, 32034-4123. Tel: 904-491-7393. Fax: 904-277-7366. p. 439

Johnson, Martha, Head, Registration Serv, Mount Prospect Public Library, Ten S Emerson St, Mount Prospect, IL, 60056. Tel: 847-253-5675. Fax: 847-253-0642. p. 677

Johnson, Mary, Dir, Albert City Public Library, 215 Main, Albert City, IA, 50510. Tel: 712-843-2012. Fax: 712-843-2058. p. 791

Johnson, Mary, Asst Dir, Dakota County Library System, 1340 Wescott Rd, Eagan, MN, 55123-1099. Tel: 651-450-2929. Fax: 651-450-2915. p. 1249

Johnson, Mary, In Charge, Nebraska Indian Community College, PO Box 428, Macy, NE, 68039-0428. Tel: 402-837-5078. Fax: 402-837-4183. p. 1408

Johnson, Mary, In Charge, Nebraska Indian Community College Library, 425 Frazier Ave N, Ste 1, Niobrara, NE, 68760. Tel: 402-857-2434. Fax: 402-857-2543. p. 1409

Johnson, Mary, Head, Ch, Woodbury Public Library, 33 Delaware St, Woodbury, NJ, 08096. Tel: 856-845-2611. p. 1545

Johnson, Mary, YA Serv, North Castle Public Library, 19 Whippoorwill Rd E, Armonk, NY, 10504. Tel: 914-273-3887. Fax: 914-273-5572. p. 1575

Johnson, Mary, Sch Libr Coordr, South Dakota State Library, 800 Governors Dr, Pierre, SD, 57501-2294. Tel: 605-773-3131. p. 2216

Johnson, Mary Jean, Dir, Bluffton University, One University Dr, Bluffton, OH, 45817-2104. Tel: 419-358-3396. Fax: 419-358-3384. p. 1860

Johnson, Matina, Coordr, Hoover Public Library, 200 Municipal Dr, Hoover, AL, 35216. Tel: 205-444-7810. Fax: 205-444-7878. p. 20

Johnson, Max, Tech Serv, Coastal Plain Regional Library, 2014 Chestnut Ave, Tifton, GA, 31794. Tel: 229-386-3400. Fax: 229-386-7007. p. 554

Johnson, Megan, Br Mgr, Stark County District Library, Plain Community Branch, 1803 Schneider St NE, Canton, OH, 44721. Tel: 330-494-3399. Fax: 330-497-0466. p. 1865

Johnson, Melanie, Mgr, Coll Serv, Johnson County Public Library, 401 State St, Franklin, IN, 46131-2545. Tel: 317-738-2833. Fax: 317-738-9635. p. 744

Johnson, Melanie, Ser Librn, Bristol Community College, 777 Elsbree St, Fall River, MA, 02720. Tel: 508-678-2811, Ext 2458. Fax: 508-730-3270. p. 1088

Johnson, Melanie, Mgr, Edmonton Public Library, Highlands, 6516 118th Ave, Edmonton, AB, T5W 1G6, CANADA. Tel: 780-496-1806. Fax: 780-496-7012. p. 2700

Johnson, Melissa, Coll Develop Librn, Lynn University Library, 3601 N Military Trail, Boca Raton, FL, 33431-5598. Tel: 561-237-7056. Fax: 561-237-7074. p. 428

Johnson, Melissa, Electronic Serv, Ser, Abilene Christian University, 221 Brown Library, ACU Box 29208, Abilene, TX, 79699-9208. Tel: 325-674-2344. Fax: 325-674-2202. p. 2271

Johnson, Melissa, Coordr, ILL, Coordr, Youth Serv, United States Army Dugway Proving Ground, 5124 Kister Ave, IMWE-DUG-MWL MS1, Dugway, UT, 84022-1097. Tel: 435-831-2178. Fax: 435-831-3543. p. 2404

Johnson, Melvin, In Charge, New York State Office of Parks, Recreation & Historic Preservation, 84 Liberty St, Newburgh, NY, 12550-5603. Tel: 845-562-1195. Fax: 845-561-1789. p. 1705

Johnson Melvin, L Rebecca, Head, Ms & Archives, University of Delaware Library, 181 S College Ave, Newark, DE, 19717-5267. Tel: 302-831-2231. Fax: 302-831-1046. p. 386

Johnson, Merrill, Dir, George Fox University, 416 N Meridian St, Newberg, OR, 97132. Tel: 503-554-2410. Fax: 503-554-3599. p. 2007

Johnson, Michele, Mgr, Three Rivers Regional Library System, Hog Hammock Community Library, 1023 Hillery Ln, Sapelo Island, GA, 31327. Tel: 912-485-2186, 912-485-2215. Fax: 912-485-2263. p. 522

Johnson, Michelle, Dir, Hammond Community Library, 850 Davis St, Hammond, WI, 54015. Tel: 715-796-2281. Fax: 715-796-2332. p. 2597

Johnson, Mildred, Librn, Northwest Library on Deaf Culture & History, 1609 19th Ave, Seattle, WA, 98122. Tel: 206-322-5551. Fax: 206-720-3251. p. 2529

Johnson, Miriam J, Asst Dir, Bedford Public Library, Three Meetinghouse Rd, Bedford, NH, 03110-5406. Tel: 603-472-2300, 603-472-3023. Fax: 603-472-2978. p. 1438

Johnson, Molly, Asst Dir, Head, Youth Serv, Charlton Public Library, 40 Main St, Charlton, MA, 01507. Tel: 508-248-0452. Fax: 508-248-0456. p. 1079

Johnson, Nancy, Dir, Azusa City Library, 729 N Dalton Ave, Azusa, CA, 91702-2586. Tel: 626-812-5232. Fax: 626-334-4368. p. 123

Johnson, Nancy, County Librn, Riverside County Library System, 1335 Spruce St, Riverside, CA, 92507. Tel: 951-955-1158. Fax: 951-955-8916. p. 217

Johnson, Nancy, Assoc Dean, Libr & Info Serv, Georgia State University Library, College of Law Library, 140 Decatur St, Atlanta, GA, 30302. Tel: 404-651-4140. Fax: 404-651-1112. p. 516

Johnson, Nancy, Librn, C A Rolloff Law Library, Chippewa County Courthouse, 11th St & Hwy 7, Montevideo, MN, 56265. Tel: 320-269-8550. Fax: 320-269-7733. p. 1265

Johnson, Nancy, Cat, Logan-Hocking County District Library, 230 E Main St, Logan, OH, 43138. Tel: 740-385-2348. Fax: 740-385-9093. p. 1910

Johnson, Nancy B, Dir, Brighton District Library, 100 Library Dr, Brighton, MI, 48116. Tel: 810-229-6571, Ext 203. Fax: 810-229-3161. p. 1159

Johnson, Nicole, Head, Ref (Info Serv), North Suburban Library District, 6340 N Second St, Loves Park, IL, 61111. Tel: 815-633-4247. Fax: 815-633-4249. p. 668

Johnson, Nikki, Librn, International Business College Library, 7205 Shadeland Sta, Indianapolis, IN, 46256. Tel: 317-841-6400, Ext 194. Fax: 317-841-6419. p. 754

Johnson, Nikki, Librn, Logan County Libraries, Rushsylvania Branch, 113 N Sandusky, Rushsylvania, OH, 43347. Tel: 937-468-9963. p. 1859

Johnson, Norma, Ref Librn, University of Arkansas Libraries, 365 N McIlroy Ave, Fayetteville, AR, 72701-4002. Tel: 479-575-3498. Fax: 479-575-6656. p. 99

Johnson, Pam, Dir of Libr Serv, Recording for the Blind & Dyslexic, 20 Roszel Rd, Princeton, NJ, 08540. Tel: 609-520-8028. Fax: 609-520-7990, 609-987-8116. p. 1524

Johnson, Pam, Dir, Libr Serv, DeVry University, 1140 Virginia Dr, Fort Washington, PA, 19034. Tel: 215-591-5700, Ext 5786. Fax: 215-591-5754. p. 2058

Johnson, Pam, Cat, Pocahontas County Free Libraries, 500 Eighth St, Marlinton, WV, 24954-1227. Tel: 304-799-6000. Fax: 304-799-3988. p. 2564

Johnson, Pamela, Circ Spec, ILL Spec, Sutton Free Public Library, Four Uxbridge Rd, Sutton, MA, 01590. Tel: 508-865-8752. Fax: 508-865-8751. p. 1130

Johnson, Patricia, Head, Tech Serv, Wallingford Public Library, 200 N Main St, Wallingford, CT, 06492-3791. Tel: 203-265-6754. Fax: 203-269-5698. p. 373

Johnson, Patricia, ILL, Outreach Librn, Chautauqua-Cattaraugus Library System, 106 W Fifth St, Jamestown, NY, 14701. Tel: 716-484-7136. p. 1646

Johnson, Patricia J, Archivist, Sacramento Archives & Museum Collection Center, 551 Sequoia Pacific Blvd, Sacramento, CA, 95814-0229. Tel: 916-264-7072. Fax: 916-264-7582. p. 224

Johnson, Patsy, Br Mgr, Pine Bluff & Jefferson County Library System, Redfield Public Library, 310 Brodie St, Redfield, AR, 72132. Tel: 501-397-5070. Fax: 501-397-5070. p. 112

Johnson, Paul, AV Coordr, Coll Develop, Media Spec, Ontario City Library, 215 East C St, Ontario, CA, 91764. Tel: 909-395-2217. Fax: 909-395-2043. p. 200

Johnson, Paul, Evening Supvr, Assumption College, 500 Salisbury St, Worcester, MA, 01609. Tel: 508-767-7271. Fax: 508-767-7374. p. 1143

Johnson, Paula, Librn, Poland Public Library, 8849 Main St, Poland, NY, 13431. Tel: 315-826-3112. Fax: 315-826-5677. p. 1720

Johnson, Paula E, Dir, Osceola Public Library, 131 N Main, Osceola, NE, 68651. Tel: 402-747-4301. Fax: 402-747-4991. p. 1415

Johnson, Paulette, Admin Officer, Tufts University, 35 Professors Row, Medford, MA, 02155-5816. Tel: 617-627-3345. Fax: 617-627-3002. p. 1104

Johnson, Paulette L, Acq, Dir, Oakwood College, 7000 Adventist Blvd, Huntsville, AL, 35896. Tel: 256-726-7250. Fax: 256-726-7538. p. 22

Johnson, Peg, Libr Dir, Santa Fe Community College Library, 6401 Richards Ave, Santa Fe, NM, 87508-4887. Tel: 505-428-1506. Fax: 505-428-1288. p. 1563

Johnson, Peggy, Librn, Chocorua Public Library, 125 Deer Hill Rd, Chocorua, NH, 03817. Tel: 603-323-8610. p. 1441

Johnson, Peggy, Dir, Rolla Public Library, 14 SE First St, Rolla, ND, 58367. Tel: 701-477-3849. Fax: 701-477-9633. p. 1848

Johnson, Peggy, Dir, Oak Hill Public Library, 226 S Front St, Oak Hill, OH, 45656. Tel: 740-682-6457. Fax: 740-682-3522. p. 1924

Johnson, Peggy Jane, Dir, Elbert County Public Library, 345 Heard St, Elberton, GA, 30635. Tel: 706-283-5375. Fax: 706-283-5456. p. 532

Johnson, Penny, Sr Librn, Hennepin County Library, Penn Lake, 8800 Penn Ave S, Bloomington, MN, 55431-2022. Tel: 612-543-5803. Fax: 612-543-5802. p. 1264

Johnson, Perry, Dean, Instruction Support Serv, Northeastern Technical College Library, 1201 Chesterfield Hwy, Cheraw, SC, 29520-7015. Tel: 843-921-6955. Fax: 843-921-6987. p. 2185

Johnson, Peter E, Tech Librn, Mountain Regional Library System, 698 Miller St, Young Harris, GA, 30582. Tel: 706-379-3732. Fax: 706-379-2047. p. 558

Johnson, Philip M, Dr, Dir, Multnomah University, 8435 NE Glisan St, Portland, OR, 97220-5898. Tel: 503-251-5323. Fax: 503-254-1268. p. 2012

Johnson, Phyllis, Govt Doc, University of Mary Washington, 1801 College Ave, Fredericksburg, VA, 22401-4665. Tel: 540-654-1759. Fax: 540-654-1067. p. 2466

Johnson, Priscilla, Asst Dir, Floyd Memorial Library, 539 First St, Greenport, NY, 11944-1399. Tel: 631-477-0660. Fax: 631-477-2647. p. 1631

Johnson, Priscilla, Commun Libr Mgr, Queens Borough Public Library, Rochdale Village Community Library, 169-09 137th Ave, Jamaica, NY, 11434. Tel: 718-723-4440. p. 1645

Johnson, Priscilla, Circ Mgr, Roanoke County Public Library, 3131 Electric Rd SW, Roanoke, VA, 24018-6496. Tel: 540-772-7507. Fax: 540-989-3129. p. 2494

Johnson, Rafe A, Asst Dir, Jefferson Community & Technical College, Southwest Campus Library, 1000 Community College Dr, Louisville, KY, 40272. Tel: 502-213-7291. Fax: 502-935-8653. p. 924

Johnson, Rebecca, Libr Asst, Cascade Public Library, 310 First Ave W, Cascade, IA, 52033. Tel: 563-852-3201. Fax: 563-852-6011. p. 799

Johnson, Rebecca, Mgr, San Antonio Public Library, Pan American, 1122 W Pyron Ave, San Antonio, TX, 78221. Tel: 210-924-8164. Fax: 210-932-1489. p. 2382

Johnson, Regina, Dir, Phoenicia Library, 48 Main St, Phoenicia, NY, 12464-5213. Tel: 845-688-7811. p. 1717

Johnson, Regina, Head of Libr, Free Library of Philadelphia, Wyoming Branch, 231 E Wyoming Ave, Philadelphia, PA, 19120-4439. Tel: 215-685-9158. Fax: 215-685-9159. p. 2109

Johnson Renvall, Poppy, Assoc Dir, Central New Mexico Community College Libraries, 525 Buena Vista SE, Albuquerque, NM, 87106-4023. Tel: 505-224-3292. Fax: 505-224-3321. p. 1548

Johnson, Rhonda, Head, Access Serv, Hostos Community College Library, 475 Grand Concourse, A-207, Bronx, NY, 10451. Tel: 718-518-4214. Fax: 718-518-4206. p. 1587

Johnson, Richard, Librn, Cook County Law Library, Bridgeview Branch, 10220 S 76th Ave, Bridgeview, IL, 60455. Tel: 708-974-6201. Fax: 708-974-6053. p. 612

Johnson, Rita, Dir of Libr Serv, Lenoir-Rhyne University Library, 625 7th Ave NE, Hickory, NC, 28601. Tel: 828-328-7235. Fax: 828-328-7338. p. 1801

Johnson, Roberta, Head, Adult Serv, Des Plaines Public Library, 1501 Ellinwood St, Des Plaines, IL, 60016-4553. Tel: 847-827-5551. Fax: 847-827-7974. p. 636

Johnson, Rosina, Dir, Newbury Public Library, 933 Rte 103, Newbury, NH, 03255-5803. Tel: 603-763-5803. Fax: 603-763-5803. p. 1460

Johnson, Ruby, Circ, Dine College, PO Box 1000, Tsaile, AZ, 86556. Tel: 928-724-6758. p. 85

Johnson, Ruth Ann, Dir, Cushing Public Library, 215 N Steele, Cushing, OK, 74023-3319. Tel: 918-225-4188. Fax: 918-225-6201. p. 1961

Johnson, Ryan, Head, Ref (Info Serv), University of Mississippi, One Library Loop, University, MS, 38677. Tel: 662-915-5877. Fax: 662-915-5734. p. 1316

Johnson, Samantha, Head, Tech Proc, Moore Memorial Public Library, 1701 Ninth Ave N, Texas City, TX, 77590. Tel: 409-643-5979. Fax: 409-948-1106. p. 2392

Johnson, Sandra, Librn, Copiah-Jefferson Regional Library System, 223 S Extension St, Hazlehurst, MS, 39083-3339. Tel: 601-894-1681. Fax: 601-894-1672. p. 1301

Johnson, Sarah, Ref Librn, Eastern Illinois University, 600 Lincoln Ave, Charleston, IL, 61920. Tel: 217-581-7538. p. 603

Johnson, Sarah H, Dir, Info Tech Develop Serv, Polk State College, 999 Ave H NE, Winter Haven, FL, 33881-4299. Tel: 863-297-1040. Fax: 863-297-1065. p. 504

Johnson, Sarah-Lynda, Supvr, Ser, Marylhurst University, 17600 Pacific Hwy (Hwy 43), Marylhurst, OR, 97036-7036. Tel: 503-699-6261. Fax: 503-636-1957. p. 2004

Johnson, Shari, Doc, University of West Florida, 11000 University Pkwy, Pensacola, FL, 32514-5750. Tel: 850-474-2711. Fax: 850-474-3338. p. 482

Johnson, Sharon, Librn, Tallassee Community Library, 99 S Freeman Ave, Tallassee, AL, 36078. Tel: 334-283-2732. Fax: 334-283-2732. p. 37

Johnson, Sharon, Commun Libr Mgr, County of Los Angeles Public Library, Compton Library, 240 W Compton Blvd, Compton, CA, 90220-3109. Tel: 310-637-0202. Fax: 310-537-1141. p. 141

Johnson, Sharon, Dir, Kiowa County Public Library District, 1305 Goff St, Eads, CO, 81036. Tel: 719-438-5581. Fax: 719-438-6581. p. 305

Johnson, Sharon, Instruction Librn, Austin Peay State University, 601 E College St, Clarksville, TN, 37044. Tel: 931-221-7914. Fax: 931-221-7296. p. 2228

Johnson, Sharon, Circ, Nicolet Area Technical College, 5364 College Dr, Rhinelander, WI, 54501. Tel: 715-365-4479. Fax: 715-365-4404. p. 2633

Johnson, Sharon E, Govt Doc, Ref Librn, United States Air Force Academy Libraries, 2354 Fairchild Dr, Ste 3A10, USAF Academy, CO, 80840-6214. Tel: 719-333-2223. Fax: 719-333-4754. p. 324

Johnson, Sharron, Br Mgr, Colusa County Free Library, Maxwell Branch, 34 Oak St, Maxwell, CA, 95955. Tel: 530-438-2250. Fax: 530-438-2250. p. 136

Johnson, Sheila Grant, Dean of Libr, Oklahoma State University Libraries, Oklahoma State University, Athletic Ave, Stillwater, OK, 74078-1071. Tel: 405-744-9729. Fax: 405-744-5183. p. 1978

Johnson, Shelby, Circ Librn, Wythe-Grayson Regional Library, Fries Public, 105 W Main St, Fries, VA, 24330. Tel: 276-744-3160. Fax: 276-744-3160. p. 2472

Johnson, Sheraze, Asst Librn, Gadsen Correctional Institution Library, 6044 Greensboro Hwy, Quincy, FL, 32351. Tel: 850-875-9701, Ext 2261. Fax: 850-875-9710. p. 485

Johnson, Sherry, Coord, Ad Serv, Highland Park Public Library, 31 N Fifth Ave, Highland Park, NJ, 08904. Tel: 732-572-2750. Fax: 732-819-9046. p. 1490

Johnson, Shirley, Br Mgr, Enoch Pratt Free Library, Edmondson Avenue, 4330 Edmondson Ave, Baltimore, MD, 21229-1615. Tel: 410-396-0946. Fax: 410-396-0947. p. 1013

Johnson, Shirley, Br Mgr, Enoch Pratt Free Library, Pennsylvania Avenue, 1531 W North Ave, Baltimore, MD, 21217-1735. Tel: 410-396-0399. Fax: 410-396-0025. p. 1013

Johnson, Shirley M, Cataloger, Librn, Tech Serv Coordr, Clarion University of Pennsylvania, 840 Wood St, Clarion, PA, 16214. Tel: 814-393-2746. Fax: 814-393-2344. p. 2045

Johnson, Sidnye, Per, Spec Coll Librn, West Texas A&M University, University Dr & 26th St, Canyon, TX, 79016. Tel: 806-651-2209. Fax: 806-651-2213. p. 2294

Johnson, Sigrid, Librn, University of Manitoba Libraries, Elizabeth Dafoe Library, 25 Chancellor's Circle, Winnipeg, MB, R3T 2N2, CANADA. Tel: 204-474-9544. Fax: 204-474-7577. p. 2758

Johnson, Sonya, Asst Librn, Belle Plaine Community Library, 904 12th St, Belle Plaine, IA, 52208-1711. Tel: 319-444-2902. Fax: 319-444-2902. p. 796

Johnson, Stan, Mgr, Access Serv, University of North Dakota, 3051 University Ave, Stop 9000, Grand Forks, ND, 58202-9000. Tel: 701-777-2617. Fax: 701-777-6745. p. 1843

Johnson, Stephanie, Asst Dir, Guilford Free Library, 67 Park St, Guilford, CT, 06437. Tel: 203-453-8282. Fax: 203-453-8288. p. 342

Johnson, Stephanie, Coordr, Access Serv, Lyme Academy College of Fine Arts, 84 Lyme St, Old Lyme, CT, 06371-2333. Tel: 860-434-5232, Ext 130. Fax: 860-434-2095. p. 363

Johnson, Stephen, Bus Serv, Distance Educ, Librn, University of South Dakota, 414 E Clark St, Vermillion, SD, 57069. Tel: 605-677-5371. Fax: 605-677-6834. p. 2220

Johnson, Steve, Syst Coordr, Alaska Resources Library & Information Services, Library Bldg, 3211 Providence Dr, Ste 111, Anchorage, AK, 99508-4614. Tel: 907-786-7661. Fax: 907-786-7652. p. 43

Johnson, Steven, Librn, TRW Automotive Library, 12075 Tech Center Dr, Ste 2, Livonia, MI, 48150-2172. Tel: 734-855-2304. Fax: 734-855-2367. p. 1204

Johnson, Susan, Librn, Cornwall Free Public Library, 2629 Rte 30, Cornwall, VT, 05753-9340. Tel: 802-462-3615. Fax: 802-462-2606. p. 2422

Johnson, Susan, Dir, Winter Public Library, 5129 N Main St, Winter, WI, 54896. Tel: 715-266-2144. p. 2650

Johnson, Suzanne, Ref, Valencia Community College, Raymer Maguire Jr Learning Resources Center, West Campus, 1800 S Kirkman Rd, Orlando, FL, 32811. Tel: 407-582-1210. Fax: 407-582-1686. p. 478

Johnson, Suzanne, Youth Serv Librn, George F Johnson Memorial Library, 1001 Park St, Endicott, NY, 13760. Tel: 607-757-5350. Fax: 607-757-2491. p. 1621

Johnson, Suzanne, Asst Dir, Longwood Public Library, 800 Middle Country Rd, Middle Island, NY, 11953. Tel: 631-924-6400. Fax: 631-924-7538. p. 1660

Johnson, Tally, Br Mgr, Chester County Library, Great Falls Branch, 39 Calhoun St, Great Falls, SC, 29055. Tel: 803-482-2149. Fax: 803-482-3531. p. 2186

Johnson, Tamara, Ch, Patrick Henry School District Public Library, 208 NE Ave, Deshler, OH, 43516. Tel: 419-278-3616. Fax: 419-278-3616. p. 1896

Johnson, Tammy, Tech Serv, Columbia Theological Seminary, 701 Columbia Dr, Decatur, GA, 30030. Tel: 404-687-4549. Fax: 404-687-4687. p. 529

Johnson, Tammy, Dir, Kirbyville Public Library, 210 S Elizabeth St, Kirbyville, TX, 75956. Tel: 409-423-4653. Fax: 409-423-5545. p. 2351

Johnson, Tammy, Supvr, Middlesex County Library, Komoka Branch, One Tunks Lane, Komoka, ON, N0L 1R0, CANADA. Tel: 519-657-1461. p. 2845

Johnson, Tara, Dir, West Union Community Library, 210 N Vine St, West Union, IA, 52175. Tel: 563-422-3103. Fax: 563-422-3103. p. 852

Johnson, Teresa, Br Coordr, Siskiyou County Public Library, Fort Jones Branch, 119 Sixty E, Fort Jones, CA, 96032-0446. Tel: 530-468-2383. p. 286

Johnson, Teresa, Asst Dir, Webster County Public Library, 101 State Rte 132 E, Dixon, KY, 42409. Tel: 270-639-9171. Fax: 270-639-6207. p. 911

Johnson, Teresa, Librn, Dyersburg State Community College, 1510 Lake Rd, Dyersburg, TN, 38024. Tel: 731-286-3352. Fax: 731-286-3228. p. 2233

Johnson, Teresa J, Asst Librn, Sedro-Woolley Public Library, 802 Ball Ave, Sedro-Woolley, WA, 98284-2008. Tel: 360-855-1166. p. 2535

Johnson, Terry, In Charge, Illinois Department of Natural Resources, 1308 E Fifth St, Metropolis, IL, 62960. Tel: 618-524-4712. Fax: 618-524-9321. p. 673

Johnson, Therese, Youth Serv, Fox Lake Public District Library, 255 E Grand Ave, Fox Lake, IL, 60020-1697. Tel: 847-587-0198. Fax: 847-587-9493. p. 646

Johnson, Tim, In Charge, Northwest Geophysical Associates Inc Library, PO Box 1063, Corvallis, OR, 97339. Tel: 541-757-7231. Fax: 541-757-7331. p. 1994

Johnson, Timmy, Health Sci Librn, University of South Dakota, Wegner Health Science Information Center, Sanford School of Medicine, 414 E Clark, Vermillion, SD, 57069-2390. Tel: 605-677-5348. Fax: 605-677-5124. p. 2221

Johnson, Timothy, Assoc Librn, Curator, University of Minnesota Libraries-Twin Cities, Special Collections & Rare Books, Elmer L Andersen

Library, 222 21st Ave S, Ste 111, Minneapolis, MN, 55455. Tel: 612-626-9166. Fax: 612-625-5525. p. 1262

Johnson, Tina, Ch, Kettleson Memorial Library, 320 Harbor Dr, Sitka, AK, 99835-7553. Tel: 907-747-8708. Fax: 907-747-8755. p. 53

Johnson, Toni, Dir, Lake Mills Public Library, 102 S Lake St, Lake Mills, IA, 50450. Tel: 641-592-0092. Fax: 641-592-0093. p. 826

Johnson, Tonya, Br Mgr, Live Oak Public Libraries, Forest City Branch, 1501 Stiles Ave, Savannah, GA, 31415. Tel: 912-238-0614. Fax: 912-236-8879. p. 550

Johnson, Tracey, Librn, Shawnee Community College Library, 8364 Shawnee College Rd, Ullin, IL, 62992. Tel: 618-634-3271. Fax: 618-634-3215. p. 711

Johnson, Troy, Ref/Electronic Serv Librn, Creighton University, Klutznick Law Library - McGrath, North, Mullin & Kratz Legal Research Center, School of Law, 2500 California Plaza, Omaha, NE, 68178-0340. Tel: 402-280-2251, 402-280-2875. Fax: 402-280-2244. p. 1412

Johnson, Valerie, ILL Supvr, Montgomery County-Norristown Public Library, 1001 Powell St, Norristown, PA, 19401-3817. Tel: 610-278-5100. p. 2098

Johnson, Valerie, Supvr, ILL, Montgomery County-Norristown Public Library, 1001 Powell St, Norristown, PA, 19401-3817. Tel: 610-278-5100, Ext 120. p. 2098

Johnson Varney, Suzanne, Tech Serv, Shawnee State University, 940 Second St, Portsmouth, OH, 45662-4344. Tel: 740-351-3410. Fax: 740-351-3432. p. 1931

Johnson, Victoria, Br Mgr, Prince George's County Memorial, Spauldings Branch, 5811 Old Silver Hill Rd, District Heights, MD, 20747-2108. Tel: 301-817-3750. p. 1033

Johnson, Victoria, Syst Adminr, Web Developer, Drury University, 900 N Benton Ave, Springfield, MO, 65802. Tel: 417-873-7348. Fax: 417-873-7432. p. 1366

Johnson, Virginia, Dir, Morton County Library, 410 Kansas, Elkhart, KS, 67950. Tel: 620-697-2025. Fax: 620-697-4205. p. 865

Johnson, Virginia, Ref Librn, Taunton Public Library, 12 Pleasant St, Taunton, MA, 02780. Tel: 508-821-1410. Fax: 508-821-1414. p. 1130

Johnson, Wanda, Librn, Greenville County Planning Department, 301 University Ridge, Ste 400, Greenville, SC, 29601. Tel: 864-467-7270. Fax: 864-467-5962. p. 2196

Johnson, Wendy, Dir, Libr Serv, River Parishes Community College Library, 7384 John LeBlanc Blvd (Hwy 22), Sorrento, LA, 70778. Tel: 225-675-0230. Fax: 225-675-8595. p. 970

Johnson, William, Ref Serv, Monroe Community College, Damon City Campus Library, 228 E Main St, 4th Flr 4-101, Rochester, NY, 14604. Tel: 585-262-1413. Fax: 585-262-1516. p. 1730

Johnson, Willie J, Br Mgr, Enoch Pratt Free Library, Patterson Park, 158 N Linwood Ave, Baltimore, MD, 21224-1255. Tel: 410-396-0983. Fax: 410-396-5215. p. 1013

Johnson, Winnie, Mgr, Dayton Metro Library, Madden Hills, 2542 Germantown St, Dayton, OH, 45408. Tel: 937-496-8942. Fax: 937-496-4342. p. 1893

Johnson, Yvonne, Librn, Ridgewater College Library, Two Century Ave, Hutchinson, MN, 55350. Tel: 320-234-8567. Fax: 320-234-8640. p. 1254

Johnson-Bignotti, Darlene, Ref, Oakland Community College, 739 S Washington, Bldg C, Royal Oak, MI, 48067-3898. Tel: 248-246-2526. Fax: 248-246-2520. p. 1223

Johnson-Corcoran, Lynn, Coll Develop, Central Connecticut State University, 1615 Stanley St, New Britain, CT, 06050. Tel: 860-832-2059. Fax: 860-832-3409. p. 353

Johnson-Craig, Kay, Librn, Ford City Library, E Eighth St, Ford, KS, 67842-0108. Tel: 620-369-2820. Fax: 620-369-2216. p. 867

Johnson-Grau, Glenn, Head, Coll Develop, Loyola Marymount University, One LMU Dr, MS 8200, Los Angeles, CA, 90045-2659. Tel: 310-338-6063. Fax: 310-338-4366. p. 175

Johnson-Houston, Debbie Delafoisse, Asst Prof, Dir, McNeese State University, 4205 Ryan St, Lake Charles, LA, 70609. Tel: 337-475-5716. Fax: 337-475-5719, 337-475-5727. p. 954

Johnson-Spence, Jennifer, Dir, Cooke County Library, 200 S Weaver St, Gainesville, TX, 76240-4790. Tel: 940-668-5530. Fax: 940-668-5533. p. 2326

Johnsrud, Karin, Head, Ref, Fordham University School of Law, 140 W 62nd St, New York, NY, 10023-7485. Tel: 212-636-7968. Fax: 212-930-8818. p. 1678

Johnston, Alice, Br Librn, Hamlin-Lincoln County Public Library, Branchland Outpost Library, PO Box 278, Branchland, WV, 25506-0278. Tel: 304-778-7315. Fax: 304-778-3840. p. 2560

Johnston, Andrew, Asst Dir, Archives, Winthrop University, 824 Oakland Ave, Rock Hill, SC, 29733. Tel: 803-323-2302. Fax: 803-323-2215. p. 2203

Johnston, Ann, Grad Sch Tech Librn, Olivet Nazarene University, One University Ave, Bourbonnais, IL, 60914-2271. Tel: 815-939-5061. Fax: 815-939-5170. p. 596

Johnston, Ann T, Cat Librn, Mgt Team, North Idaho College Library, 1000 W Garden Ave, Coeur d'Alene, ID, 83814-2199. Tel: 208-769-3240. Fax: 208-769-3428. p. 573

Johnston, Anna, Assoc Dean, Libr & Learning, Mohawk College Library, 135 Fennell Ave W, Hamilton, ON, L9C 1E9, CANADA. Tel: 905-540-1212, Ext 2737. Fax: 905-575-2011. p. 2810

Johnston, Anny, Br Asst, Huron County Library, Bayfield Branch, 20 Main St, Bayfield, ON, N0M 1G0, CANADA. Tel: 519-565-2886. p. 2799

Johnston, Barbara, Ch, Washington County Library System, 341 Main St, Greenville, MS, 38701-4097. Tel: 662-335-2331. Fax: 662-390-4758. p. 1298

Johnston, BJ, Assoc Univ Librn, Coll Serv, Washington University Libraries, One Brookings Dr, Campus Box 1061, Saint Louis, MO, 63130-4862. Tel: 314-935-5468. Fax: 314-935-4045. p. 1362

Johnston, Bruce, Syst Librn, Eastern Connecticut State University, 83 Windham St, Willimantic, CT, 06226-2295. Tel: 860-465-5552. Fax: 860-465-5521. p. 378

Johnston, Bruce, ILL, Robert Morris University Library, 6001 University Blvd, Moon Township, PA, 15108-1189. Tel: 412-397-6877. Fax: 412-397-4288. p. 2092

Johnston, Chris, Asst Br Mgr, Dorchester County Library, Summerville Branch, 76 Old Trolley Rd, Summerville, SC, 29485. Tel: 843-871-5075. Fax: 843-875-4811. p. 2204

Johnston, Christine, Dir, Robertson Memorial Library, 849 Greenfield Rd, Leyden, MA, 01301-9419. Tel: 413-773-9334. Fax: 413-772-0146. p. 1099

Johnston, Claire, Curator, Historic Charlton Park Village & Museum Library, 2545 S Charlton Park Rd, Hastings, MI, 49058-8102. Tel: 269-945-3775, Ext 102. Fax: 269-945-0390. p. 1189

Johnston, Courtenay, Librn, Pouce Coupe Public Library, 5000-49th Ave, Pouce Coupe, BC, V0C 2C0, CANADA. Tel: 250-786-5765. Fax: 250-786-5765. p. 2735

Johnston, Diana, Youth Serv Coordr, Herbert Wescoat Memorial Library, 120 N Market St, McArthur, OH, 45651-1218. Tel: 740-596-5691. Fax: 740-596-2477. p. 1916

Johnston, Eva M, Interim Dir, Chattanooga-Hamilton County Bicentennial Library, 1001 Broad St, Chattanooga, TN, 37402-2652. Tel: 423-757-5310. Fax: 423-757-4994. p. 2226

Johnston, Gail, Assoc Dir, Texas A&M University-Commerce, 2600 S Neal St, Commerce, TX, 75429. Tel: 903-886-5715. Fax: 903-886-5434. p. 2300

Johnston, Gordon, Dir, Three Rivers Community College Library, 2080 Three Rivers Blvd, Poplar Bluff, MO, 63901. Tel: 573-840-9654. Fax: 573-840-9659. p. 1349

Johnston, Grace, Asst Librn, Kaiser-Permanente Medical Center, 9961 Sierra Ave, Fontana, CA, 92335. Tel: 909-427-5086. Fax: 909-427-6288. p. 148

Johnston, Hannah, Librn, Spring Grove Hospital Center, Isidore Tuerk Bldg, 55 Wade Ave, Catonsville, MD, 21228. Tel: 410-402-7824. Fax: 410-402-7732. p. 1023

Johnston, Jackie J, Acq, University of Dayton School of Law, 300 College Park, Dayton, OH, 45469-2780. Tel: 937-229-2314. Fax: 937-229-2555. p. 1894

Johnston, James R, Dir, Joliet Public Library, 150 N Ottawa St, Joliet, IL, 60432-4192. Tel: 815-740-2660. Fax: 815-740-6161. p. 660

Johnston, Janette, Mgr, Ch Serv, Round Rock Public Library, 216 E Main St, Round Rock, TX, 78664. Tel: 512-218-7002. Fax: 512-218-7061. p. 2377

Johnston, Janis, Dir, University of Illinois Library at Urbana-Champaign, Law, 142 Law Bldg, 504 E Pennsylvania Ave, Champaign, IL, 61820. Tel: 217-244-3046. Fax: 217-244-8500. p. 712

Johnston, Jay, Dir, Farmington Library, Barney Branch, 71 Main St, Farmington, CT, 06032. Tel: 860-673-6791, Ext 2, p. 340

Johnston, Jay, Dir, The Farmington Library, Six Monteith Dr, Farmington, CT, 06032. Tel: 860-673-6791. Fax: 860-675-7148. p. 340

Johnston, Jean, Br Mgr, Fairfax County Public Library, Pohick Regional, 6450 Sydenstricker Rd, Burke, VA, 22015-4274. Tel: 703-644-7333. p. 2461

Johnston, Jeff, Br Mgr, Knox County Public Library System, Burlington Branch, 4614 Asheville Hwy, Knoxville, TN, 37914. Tel: 865-525-5431. Fax: 865-525-4648. p. 2242

Johnston, Jill, Br Head, Winnipeg Public Library, Westwood, 66 Allard Ave, Winnipeg, MB, R3K 0T3, CANADA. Tel: 204-986-4742. Fax: 204-986-3799. p. 2760

Johnston, Jo Ellen, Ref Serv, Salem Public Library, 821 E State St, Salem, OH, 44460-2298. Tel: 330-332-0042. Fax: 330-332-4488. p. 1934

Johnston, John, Librn, Victoria Conservatory of Music, 907 Pandora Ave, Victoria, BC, V8V 3P4, CANADA. Tel: 250-386-5311, Ext 234. Fax: 250-386-6602. p. 2746

Johnston, Joyce, Cat, Ref, Jackson State Community College Library, 2046 North Pkwy, Jackson, TN, 38301. Tel: 731-424-3520, Ext 325. Fax: 731-425-2625. p. 2238

Johnston, Judy, Librn, North Central Regional Library, Brewster Public Library, 108 S Third St, Brewster, WA, 98812. Tel: 509-689-4046. Fax: 509-689-4046. p. 2548

Johnston, Kate, Ch, Naples Public Library, 940 Roosevelt Trail, Naples, ME, 04055. Tel: 207-693-6841. Fax: 207-693-7098. p. 993

Johnston, Kathryn, Dir, University of Wisconsin-Fond du Lac Library, 400 University Dr, Fond du Lac, WI, 54935-2950. Tel: 920-929-3617. Fax: 920-929-7640. p. 2592

Johnston, Kathy, Dir, Baldwin City Library, 800 Seventh St, Baldwin City, KS, 66006. Tel: 785-594-3411. Fax: 785-594-3411. p. 857

Johnston, Kit, Librn, National Marine Fisheries Service, 110 Shaffer Rd, Santa Cruz, CA, 95060-5730. Tel: 831-420-3962. Fax: 831-420-3978. p. 264

Johnston, Layla, Libr Dir, Pontiac Public Library, 211 E Madison St, Pontiac, IL, 61764. Tel: 815-844-7229. Fax: 815-844-3475. p. 692

Johnston, Lindsay, Pub Serv Mgr, University of Alberta, Rutherford (Humanities & Social Sciences) Library, 1-01 Rutherford South, Edmonton, AB, T6G 2J8, CANADA. Tel: 780-492-0598. Fax: 780-492-5083. p. 2702

Johnston, Lisa, Assoc Dir, Sweet Briar College, 134 Chapel Rd, Sweet Briar, VA, 24595-1200. Tel: 434-381-6138. Fax: 434-381-6173. p. 2497

Johnston, Lowanda, Librn, Sesser Public Library, 303 W Franklin St, Sesser, IL, 62884. Tel: 618-625-6566. Fax: 618-625-6566. p. 701

Johnston, M Elizabeth, Dir, Sherborn Library, Four Sanger St, Sherborn, MA, 01770-1499. Tel: 508-653-0770. Fax: 508-650-9243. p. 1123

Johnston, Margaret, Circ Serv Supvr, Geneva Public Library District, 127 James St, Geneva, IL, 60134. Tel: 630-232-0780. Fax: 630-232-0881. p. 649

Johnston, Melissa, Asst Prof, University of Alabama, 514 Main Library, Tuscaloosa, AL, 35487. Tel: 205-348-4610. Fax: 205-348-3746. p. 2961

Johnston, Nathalie, Supv Librn, Klamath County Library Services District, 126 S Third St, Klamath Falls, OR, 97601-6394. Tel: 541-882-8894. Fax: 541-882-6166. p. 2001

Johnston, Penny, Asst Librn, Cochise County Library District, Myrtle Kraft Library, 2393 S Rock House Rd, Portal, AZ, 85632. Tel: 520-558-2468. Fax: 520-558-2468. p. 58

Johnston, Penny, Librn, Marion Lawrance Memorial Library, 15 E Franklin St, Gratis, OH, 45330. Tel: 937-787-3502. Fax: 937-787-3502. p. 1903

Johnston, Rebecca, Dir, Info Access Libr Serv, Southern Regional Area Health Education Center, 1601 Owen Dr, Fayetteville, NC, 28304. Tel: 910-678-7270. Fax: 910-323-4007. p. 1793

Johnston, Robert C, Dir, Le Moyne College, 1419 Salt Springs Rd, Syracuse, NY, 13214-1301. Tel: 315-445-4321. Fax: 315-445-4642. p. 1751

Johnston, Roy, Mgr, Computer Info Service, Cedar Rapids Public Library West, 2600 Edgewood Rd SW, Ste 330, Cedar Rapids, IA, 52404. Tel: 319-398-5123. Fax: 319-398-0476. p. 800

Johnston, Sarah, Syst & Web Develop Librn, Saint Olaf College, Rolvaag Memorial Library, Glasoe Science Library, Halvorson Music Library, 1510 Saint Olaf Ave, Northfield, MN, 55057-1097. Tel: 507-786-3771. Fax: 507-786-3734. p. 1269

Johnston, Sharla, Circ, Cleveland Law Library Association, One W Lakeside Ave, 4th Flr, Cleveland, OH, 44113-1023. Tel: 216-861-5070. Fax: 216-861-1606. p. 1877

Johnston, Susan, Supv Librn, Stockton-San Joaquin County Public Library, 605 N El Dorado St, Stockton, CA, 95202. Tel: 209-937-8312. Fax: 209-937-8683. p. 272

Johnston, Suzie, Dir, Louisiana House of Representatives, PO Box 94012, Baton Rouge, LA, 70804-9012. Tel: 225-342-2430. Fax: 225-342-2431. p. 943

Johnston, Tina, Ch, Circ Serv, Bonne Terre Memorial Library, Five SW Main St, Bonne Terre, MO, 63628. Tel: 573-358-2260. Fax: 573-358-5941. p. 1320

Johnston, Virginia, Circ, Castleton State College, 178 Alumni Dr, Castleton, VT, 05735. Tel: 802-468-1256. Fax: 802-468-1475. p. 2421

Johnston, William Christopher, Br Librn, Berkeley County Library System, Daniel Island, 2301 Daniel Island Dr, Charleston, SC, 29492. Tel: 843-471-2952. p. 2200

Johnston, William L, Interim Dir, University of Wisconsin-Stout Library, 315 Tenth Ave, Menomonie, WI, 54751-0790. Tel: 715-232-1184. Fax: 715-232-1783. p. 2615

Johnstone, Aureole, Br Mgr, Sacramento Public Library, Del Paso Heights Library, 920 Grand Ave, Sacramento, CA, 95838. p. 224

Johnstone, Brian, Digital Res Librn, Bucks County Community College Library, 275 Swamp Rd, Newtown, PA, 18940-0999. Tel: 215-504-8554. Fax: 215-968-8142. p. 2097

Johnstone, Jay, Librn, Yolo County Library, Davis Branch, 315 E 14th St, Davis, CA, 95616. Tel: 530-757-5593. Fax: 530-757-5590. p. 284

Johnstone, Jo, Youth Serv Coordr, Tye Preston Memorial Library, 16311 S Access Rd, Canyon Lake, TX, 78133-5301. Tel: 830-964-3744. Fax: 830-964-3126. p. 2295

Johnstone, Kay L, In Charge, Geisinger Wyoming Valley Medical Center Library, 1000 E Mountain Dr, Wilkes-Barre, PA, 18711. Tel: 570-826-7809. Fax: 570-826-7682. p. 2155

Johnstone, Morgan, Libr Mgr, Radway & District Municipal Library, PO Box 220, Radway, AB, T0A 2V0, CANADA. Tel: 780-736-3548. Fax: 780-736-3858. p. 2714

Johnstone, Paige, Mgr, Spec Coll, School of the Art Institute of Chicago, 37 S Wabash Ave, Chicago, IL, 60603-3103. Tel: 312-899-5097. Fax: 312-899-1851. p. 624

Johnting, Wendell, Cat & Govt Doc Librn, Indiana University, Ruth Lilly Law Library, 530 W New York St, Indianapolis, IN, 46202-3225. Tel: 317-274-3884, 317-274-4028. Fax: 317-274-8825. p. 752

Joiner, Mary Jo, Dir, Kenai Community Library, 163 Main St Loop, Kenai, AK, 99611-7723. Tel: 907-283-4378. Fax: 907-283-2266. p. 50

Joiner, Sara, Children's Coordr, Brazoria County Library System, 451 N Velasco, Ste 250, Angleton, TX, 77515. Tel: 979-864-1826. Fax: 979-864-1298. p. 2275

Jokhi, Rusi, Libr Mgr, Vancouver Island Regional Library, Sooke Branch, 2065 Anna Marie Rd, Sooke, BC, V0S 1N0, CANADA. Tel: 250-642-3022. Fax: 250-642-3994. p. 2733

Jolin, Louise, Ref, CHU Sainte-Justine, 3175 Chemin Cote-Sainte-Catherine, Montreal, QC, H3T 1C5, CANADA. Tel: 514-345-4681. Fax: 514-345-4806. p. 2893

Jolley, Daniel, Libr Syst Mgr, Gardner-Webb University, 110 S Main St, Boiling Springs, NC, 28017. Tel: 704-406-4297. Fax: 704-406-4623. p. 1776

Jolliffe, Bette, Dir, Marathon Public Library, 306 W Attica St, Marathon, IA, 50565. Tel: 712-289-2200. p. 829

Jolliffe, Frank, Dept Head, Tech Serv, Bank Street College of Education Library, 610 W 112th St, 5th Flr, New York, NY, 10025. Tel: 212-875-4455. Fax: 212-875-4558. p. 1669

Jolliffe, Louise, Youth Serv Librn, Orono Public Library, 39 Pine St, Orono, ME, 04473. Tel: 207-866-5060. p. 994

Jolly, Deanne Marie, Dir, Collins Public Library, 212 Main St, Collins, IA, 50055. Tel: 641-385-2464. Fax: 641-385-2205. p. 803

Jolly, Terri, Acq, Amarillo Public Library, 413 E Fourth Ave, Amarillo, TX, 79101. Tel: 806-378-3054. Fax: 806-378-9327. p. 2274

Joly, Bob, ILL, Saint Johnsbury Athenaeum, 1171 Main St, Saint Johnsbury, VT, 05819-2289. Tel: 802-748-8291. Fax: 802-748-8086. p. 2435

Joly, Robert, Dir, Woodbury Community Library, 69 Valley Lake Rd, Woodbury, VT, 05681. Tel: 802-472-5710. p. 2440

Jonas, Donna, Dir, Kendalia Public Library, 2610-B Hwy 473, Kendalia, TX, 78027-2010. Tel: 830-336-2002. Fax: 830-336-2002. p. 2349

Jonas, James, Electronic Res, Info Serv, University of Wisconsin-Madison, MERIT Library (Media, Education Resources & Information Technology), 225 N Mills St, Madison, WI, 53706. Tel: 608-263-4934. Fax: 608-262-6050. p. 2609

Jonassen, David H, Prof, University of Missouri-Columbia, 303 Townsend Hall, Columbia, MO, 65211. Tel: 573-882-4546. Fax: 573-884-2917. p. 2968

Jonathan, Sunitha, Br Librn, Brooklyn Public Library, Gerritsen Beach, 2808 Gerritsen Ave, Brooklyn, NY, 11229. Tel: 718-368-1435. Fax: 718-368-1506. p. 1591

Joncyk, Erica, Dir, David M Hunt Library, 63 Main St, Falls Village, CT, 06031. Tel: 860-824-7424. p. 339

Jones, Alice, Dir, Frankfort City Library, 104 E Second St, Frankfort, KS, 66427-1403. Tel: 785-292-4320. p. 867

Jones, Alison R, Instrul Serv/Ref Librn, Carson-Newman College, 1634 Russell Ave, Jefferson City, TN, 37760. Tel: 865-471-3340. Fax: 865-471-3450. p. 2239

Jones, Ami, Youth Serv Librn, Alamogordo Public Library, 920 Oregon Ave, Alamogordo, NM, 88310. Tel: 575-439-4140. Fax: 575-439-4108. p. 1547

Jones, Andrea, Circ, ILL, Hartford Seminary Library, 77 Sherman St, Hartford, CT, 06105-2260. Tel: 860-509-9561. Fax: 860-509-9509. p. 346

Jones, Ann, Semmes Found Head Librn, McNay Art Museum Library, 6000 N New Braunfels Ave, San Antonio, TX, 78209. Tel: 210-805-1727. Fax: 210-824-0218. p. 2380

Jones, Annie O, Librn, The Repository Library, 500 Market Ave S, Canton, OH, 44702. Tel: 330-580-8300. Fax: 330-454-5745. p. 1864

Jones, April, Libr Assoc, Georgia Power Co-Southern Co, 241 Ralph McGill Blvd NE, Bin 10044, Atlanta, GA, 30308. Tel: 404-506-6633. Fax: 404-506-6652. p. 515

Jones, Avis, Br Mgr, Wake County Public Library System, Southgate Community Library, 1601-14 Cross Link Rd, Raleigh, NC, 27610. Tel: 919-856-6691. Fax: 919-856-6762. p. 1818

Jones, Barbara, Mgr, Suwannee River Regional Library, Jasper Public Library, 311 Hatley St NE, Jasper, FL, 32052. Tel: 386-792-2285. Fax: 386-792-1966. p. 461

Jones, Barbara, Govt Doc Librn, ILL, Dalton State College, 650 College Dr, Dalton, GA, 30720-3778. Tel: 706-272-4585. Fax: 706-272-4511. p. 528

Jones, Barbara, Libr Assoc, Desoto Parish Library, Pelican Branch, 145 Jackson Ave, Pelican, LA, 71063-2803. Tel: 318-755-2353. Fax: 318-755-2031. p. 956

Jones, Bethany E, Youth Serv Librn, Waynesboro Public Library, 600 S Wayne Ave, Waynesboro, VA, 22980. Tel: 540-942-6746. Fax: 540-942-6753. p. 2501

Jones, Beverly, Prof, North Carolina Central University, 1801 Fayetteville St, Durham, NC, 27707. Tel: 919-530-6485. Fax: 919-530-6402. p. 2971

Jones, Bobbi, Dir, Denmark Technical College, 500 Solomon Blatt Blvd, Denmark, SC, 29042. Tel: 803-793-5213. Fax: 803-793-5942. p. 2192

Jones, Bobbie, Br Mgr, Washington Parish Library System, Franklinton Branch, 825 Free St, Franklinton, LA, 70438. Tel: 985-839-7805. Fax: 985-839-7808. p. 950

Jones, Bonnie, Cataloger, South Puget Sound Community College Library, 2011 Mottman Rd SW, Olympia, WA, 98512. Tel: 360-596-5271. Fax: 360-596-5714. p. 2522

Jones, Brenda, Pub Serv Librn, Ref Serv, Glendale Community College Library, 1500 N Verdugo Rd, Glendale, CA, 91208-2894. Tel: 818-240-1000, Ext 5574. Fax: 818-246-5107. p. 155

Jones, Brenda, Tech Serv, Albemarle Regional Library, 303 W Tryon St, Winton, NC, 27986. Tel: 252-358-7854. Fax: 252-358-7868. p. 1835

Jones, Brenda K, Ref, Samford University Library, Lucille Stewart Beeson Law Library, 800 Lakeshore Dr, Birmingham, AL, 35229. Tel: 205-726-2714. Fax: 205-726-2644. p. 9

Jones, Camille S, Libr Assoc, Wildman, Harrold, Allen & Dixon LLP, 225 W Wacker Dr, Ste 3000, Chicago, IL, 60606. Tel: 312-201-2363. Fax: 312-201-2555. p. 628

Jones, Candace, Asst Librn, Louisburg College, 501 N Main St, Louisburg, NC, 27549-7704. Tel: 919-497-3237. Fax: 919-496-5444. p. 1807

Jones, Carol, Head, Doc Delivery/ILL, Yale University Library, Sterling Memorial Library, 120 High St, New Haven, CT, 06520. Tel: 203-432-2080. Fax: 203-432-1294. p. 359

Jones, Carol, Dir, Jonesboro Public Library, 124 E Fourth St, Jonesboro, IN, 46938-1105. Tel: 765-677-9080. p. 756

Jones, Carol Elizabeth, Head, Youth Serv, Rockbridge Regional Library, 138 S Main St, Lexington, VA, 24450-2316. Tel: 540-463-4324. Fax: 540-464-4824. p. 2474

Jones, Casey, Actg Br Mgr, Hawaii State Public Library System, Waianae Public Library, 85-625 Farrington Hwy, Waianae, HI, 96792. Tel: 808-697-7868. Fax: 808-697-7870. p. 563

Jones, Cassie, Br Mgr, Live Oak Public Libraries, Port Wentworth Branch, 102 Aberfeldy St, Port Wentworth, GA, 31407. Tel: 912-964-0371. Fax: 912-964-0371. p. 550

Jones, Cassie, YA Librn, Morgan County Public Library, 110 S Jefferson St, Martinsville, IN, 46151. Tel: 765-342-3451. Fax: 765-342-9992. p. 763

Jones, Cerrelda, Dir, Br Serv, Cook County Law Library, 2900 Richard J Daley Ctr, 50 W Washington, Chicago, IL, 60602. Tel: 312-603-2435. Fax: 312-603-9706. p. 611

Jones, Charlene, Dir, Carroll Public Library, 506 Main St, Carroll, NE, 68723. Tel: 402-585-4586. p. 1395

Jones, Charlene, Dir, Virden Public Library, 209 Church St, Virden, NM, 85534. Tel: 505-358-2544. Fax: 505-358-2544. p. 1566

Jones, Cheryl, Assoc Prof, Dir, Curric Res Ctr, Missouri State University, Duane G Meyer Library, 901 S National Ave, Springfield, MO, 65897. Tel: 417-836-4525. Fax: 417-836-4764. p. 2968

Jones, Christine, Br Mgr, Fairfax County Public Library, Centreville Regional, 14200 Saint Germain Dr, Centreville, VA, 20121-2299. Tel: 703-830-2223. p. 2461

Jones, Cindy, Head, Mat Mgt, Howard County Library System, 6600 Cradlerock Way, Columbia, MD, 21045-4912. Tel: 410-313-7750. Fax: 410-313-7742. p. 1026

Jones, Claire, Dir, Mid-South Community College, Donald W Reynolds Ctr, 2000 W Broadway, West Memphis, AR, 72301-3829. Tel: 870-733-6768. Fax: 870-733-6719. p. 117

Jones, Claudia, Tech Serv, Institut de Recherches Cliniques de Montreal Library, 110 Pine Ave W, Rm 2340, Montreal, QC, H2W 1R7, CANADA. Tel: 514-987-5598. Fax: 514-987-5675. p. 2896

Jones, Connie, Curric Center Librn, Concordia College, 901 S Eighth St, Moorhead, MN, 56562. Tel: 218-299-3238. Fax: 218-299-4253. p. 1265

Jones, Craig Arvid, Librn, Allegheny Valley Hospital, 1301 Carlisle St, Natrona Heights, PA, 15065. Tel: 724-226-7092. Fax: 724-226-7303. p. 2094

Jones, Cyndi, ILL & Ser, West Baton Rouge Parish Library, 830 N Alexander Ave, Port Allen, LA, 70767-2327. Tel: 225-342-7920. Fax: 225-342-7918. p. 966

Jones, Cynthia, Dir, Phelps Dunbar LLP, 365 Canal St, Ste 2000, New Orleans, LA, 70130-6534. Tel: 504-566-1311, Ext 1287. Fax: 504-568-9130. p. 963

Jones, Cynthia, Librn, Phelps Dunbar, LLP, 4270 Interstate 55 N, Jackson, MS, 39211-6391. Tel: 601-352-2300. Fax: 601-360-9777. p. 1305

Jones, Cynthia E, Regional Mgr, Saint Louis Public Library, Carpenter, 3309 S Grand Ave, Saint Louis, MO, 63118. Tel: 314-772-6586. Fax: 314-772-1871. p. 1360

Jones, D Carol, Interim Dir, Charleston Library Society, 164 King St, Charleston, SC, 29401. Tel: 843-723-9912. Fax: 843-723-3500. p. 2183

Jones, D R, Dep Dir, Case Western Reserve University, School of Law Library, 11075 East Blvd, Cleveland, OH, 44106-7148. Tel: 216-368-2794. Fax: 216-368-1002. p. 1876

Jones, D R, Asst Prof of Law, Assoc Dean, Info, Dir, Law Libr, The University of Memphis, One N Front St, Memphis, TN, 38103. Tel: 901-678-3244. Fax: 901-678-5293. p. 2252

Jones, Darcel, In Charge, Contra Costa County Library, Bay Point Library, 205 Pacifica Ave, Bay Point, CA, 94565. Tel: 925-458-9597. p. 209

Jones, Darci, Coll Develop Librn, Dir, Mercyhurst College, 501 E 38th St, Erie, PA, 16546. Tel: 814-824-2237. Fax: 814-824-2219. p. 2056

Jones, Darla, Asst Ch, Gallatin County Public Library, 209 W Market St, Warsaw, KY, 41095. Tel: 859-567-2786. Fax: 859-567-4750. p. 936

Jones, Darren, Dir, Maple Springs Baptist Bible College & Seminary Library, 4130 Belt Rd, Capitol Heights, MD, 20743. Tel: 301-736-3631. Fax: 301-735-6507. p. 1023

Jones, Dave, Head, Ref, Westhampton Free Library, Seven Library Ave, Westhampton Beach, NY, 11978-2697. Tel: 631-288-3335. Fax: 631-288-5715. p. 1768

Jones, David, Ref Serv, Dawson College Library, 3040 Sherbrooke St W, Westmount, QC, H3Z 1A4, CANADA. Tel: 514-931-8731, Ext 1734. Fax: 514-931-3567. p. 2915

Jones, David L, Cataloger, University of Alberta, William C Wonders Map Collection, 1-55 Cameron Library, Edmonton, AB, T6G 2J8, CANADA. Tel: 780-492-3433. Fax: 780-492-2721. p. 2703

Jones, David M, Libr Dir, Jacksonville University, 2800 University Blvd N, Jacksonville, FL, 32211-3394. Tel: 904-256-7267. Fax: 904-256-7259. p. 454

Jones, Debbie Majoue, Acq, Cat, Instrul Serv Librn, York Technical College Library, 452 S Anderson Rd, Rock Hill, SC, 29730. Tel: 803-325-2883. Fax: 803-327-4535. p. 2203

Jones, Debra, Assoc Law Librn, Bibliog/Ser Control, Pennsylvania State University - Dickinson School of Law (University Libraries), 1170 Harrisburg Pike, Carlisle, PA, 17013-1617. Tel: 717-240-5222. Fax: 717-240-5127. p. 2042

Jones, Dee, Head, Cat, Louisiana State University Health Sciences Center, 1501 Kings Hwy, Shreveport, LA, 71130. Tel: 318-675-5458. Fax: 318-675-5442. p. 968

Jones, Diane, Ch, Coshocton Public Library, 655 Main St, Coshocton, OH, 43812-1697. Tel: 740-622-0956. Fax: 740-622-4331. p. 1891

Jones, Dianne, Librn, Lincoln-Lawrence-Franklin Regional Library, Lawrence County Public Library, 142 Courthouse Sq, Monticello, MS, 39654-6014. Tel: 601-587-2471. Fax: 601-587-7582. p. 1295

Jones, Dixie A, Librn, Department of Veterans Affairs, 510 E Stoner Ave, Shreveport, LA, 71101-4295. Tel: 318-990-5181. Fax: 318-990-5570. p. 968

Jones, Donna, Cat, Thomas County Public Library System, 201 N Madison St, Thomasville, GA, 31792-5414. Tel: 229-225-5252. Fax: 229-225-5258. p. 553

Jones, Donna, Youth Serv Coordr, Duplin County Library, 107 Bowden Dr, Kenansville, NC, 28349-0930. Tel: 910-296-2117. Fax: 910-296-2172. p. 1804

Jones, Donna, Head, Circ, Haverford Township Free Library, 1601 Darby Rd, Havertown, PA, 19083-3798. Tel: 610-446-3082, Ext 201. Fax: 610-853-3090. p. 2067

Jones, Doris, Asst Librn, Horse Cave Free Public Library, 111 Higbee St, Horse Cave, KY, 42749-1110. Tel: 270-786-1130. p. 918

Jones, Doris, Dir, Pub Serv, Greenville Technical College Library, 620 S Pleasantburg Dr, Greenville, SC, 29607. Tel: 864-250-8018. Fax: 864-250-8506. p. 2197

Jones, Doug, Dir, Wakulla County Public Library, 4330 Crawfordville Hwy, Crawfordville, FL, 32327. Tel: 850-926-7415. Fax: 850-926-4513. p. 434

Jones, Doug, Ref Serv, Clackamas County Library, Clackamas Corner, 11750 SE 82nd Ave, Ste D, Portland, OR, 97086. Tel: 503-722-6222. p. 2008

Jones, Ed, Assoc Dir, Assessment & Tech Serv, National University Library, 9393 Lightwave Ave, San Diego, CA, 92123-1447. Tel: 858-541-7920. Fax: 858-541-7994. p. 232

Jones, Elizabeth, Syst & Ser Librn, Oklahoma City University, Dulaney-Browne Library, 2501 N Blackwelder, Oklahoma City, OK, 73106. Tel: 405-208-5068. Fax: 405-208-5291. p. 1974

Jones, Ellen, Cat, Ocmulgee Regional Library System, 535 Second Ave, Eastman, GA, 31023. Tel: 478-374-4711. Fax: 478-374-5646. p. 531

Jones, Ellen, Ref, University of Iowa Libraries, Law Library, 200 Boyd Law Bldg, Iowa City, IA, 52242-1166. Tel: 319-335-9068. Fax: 319-335-9039. p. 824

Jones, Ellen, Circ Librn, ILL, Barrington Public Library, 105 Ramsdell Lane, Barrington, NH, 03825. Tel: 603-664-9715. Fax: 603-664-5219. p. 1438

Jones, Eric, Dir, Badger Public Library, 211 First Ave SE, Badger, IA, 50516. Tel: 515-545-4793. Fax: 515-545-4440. p. 795

Jones, Esther, ILL, Volusia County Public Library, 1290 Indian Lake Rd, Daytona Beach, FL, 32124. Tel: 386-248-1745. Fax: 386-248-1746. p. 436

Jones, Esther, Librn, Marshall County Library System, Ruth B French Library, 161 S Hwy 309, Byhalia, MS, 38611. Tel: 662-838-4024. Fax: 662-838-6900. p. 1302

Jones, Evi, Dir, Cheaha Regional Library, 935 Coleman St, Heflin, AL, 36264. Tel: 256-463-7125. Fax: 256-463-7125. p. 20

Jones, Faye, Dir, Florida State University Libraries, College of Law Library, 425 W Jefferson St, Tallahassee, FL, 32306. Tel: 850-644-4578. Fax: 850-644-5216. p. 494

Jones, Gail, Sr Librn, Mill Valley Public Library, 375 Throckmorton Ave, Mill Valley, CA, 94941-2698. Tel: 415-389-4292, Ext 133. Fax: 415-388-8929. p. 186

Jones, Gary, Librn, Southeastern Illinois College, 3575 College Rd, Harrisburg, IL, 62946. Tel: 618-252-5400, Ext 2260, 618-252-5400, Ext 2261. Fax: 618-252-2713. p. 653

Jones, Genie, Youth Serv, Fairhope Public Library, 501 Fairhope Ave, Fairhope, AL, 36532. Tel: 251-928-7483. Fax: 251-928-9717. p. 16

Jones, Georgia, Ch, Carleton A Friday Memorial Library, 155 E First St, New Richmond, WI, 54017. Tel: 715-243-0431. Fax: 715-246-2691. p. 2625

Jones, Gregory, Cat & Tech Serv Librn, University of Rio Grande, 218 N College Ave, Rio Grande, OH, 45674. Tel: 740-245-7459. Fax: 740-245-7096. p. 1931

Jones, Gwendolyn, Tech Serv, Rust College, 150 E Rust Ave, Holly Springs, MS, 38635. Tel: 662-252-8000, Ext 4100. Fax: 662-252-8873. p. 1302

Jones, Heather M, Asst Dir, Swaledale Public Library, 504 Main St, Swaledale, IA, 50477. Tel: 641-995-2352. Fax: 641-995-2352. p. 847

Jones, Helen, Ref Librn, University of Massachusetts Lowell Libraries, 61 Wilder St, Lowell, MA, 01854-3098. Tel: 978-934-4581. Fax: 978-934-3015. p. 1100

Jones, J Karen, Librn, Vienna Correctional Center Library, 6695 State Rte 146 E, Vienna, IL, 62995. Tel: 618-658-8371, Ext 270. p. 714

Jones, Jacqueline L, Assoc Dean, Learning Res, Baton Rouge Community College, 201 Community College Dr, Baton Rouge, LA, 70806. Tel: 225-216-8170. Fax: 225-216-8712. p. 942

Jones, James B, Ref Librn, Atlanta-Fulton Public Library System, South Fulton Regional Library, 4055 Flatshoals Rd SW, Union City, GA, 30291. Tel: 770-306-3092. Fax: 770-306-3127. p. 512

Jones, Jami, Dr, Asst Prof, East Carolina University, 101 Umstead Residence Hall, Greenville, NC, 27858-4353. Tel: 252-328-6621. Fax: 252-328-4368. p. 2971

Jones, Jan, Dir, Castleton Free Library, Main St, Castleton, VT, 05735. Tel: 802-468-5574. p. 2421

Jones, Jane, Chief Librn, Radium Hot Springs Public Library, PO Box 293, Radium Hot Springs, BC, V0A 1M0, CANADA. Tel: 250-347-9131. p. 2736

Jones, Janice, Dir, Yates Center Public Library, 218 N Main, Yates Center, KS, 66783-1424. Tel: 620-625-3341. Fax: 620-625-3035. p. 903

Jones, Janice, Dir, Maury County Public Library, Mount Pleasant Branch, 200 Hay Long Ave, Mount Pleasant, TN, 38474. Tel: 931-379-3752. Fax: 931-379-3774. p. 2231

Jones, Jean, Circ, East Lyme Public Library, Inc, 39 Society Rd, Niantic, CT, 06357-1100. Tel: 860-739-6926. Fax: 860-691-0020. p. 361

Jones, Jean, Asst Librn, Neligh Public Library, 710 Main St, Neligh, NE, 68756-1246. Tel: 402-887-5140. Fax: 402-887-4530. p. 1409

Jones, Jeanette, Ref Librn, College of Southern Nevada, 6375 W Charleston Blvd, W10I, Las Vegas, NV, 89146. Tel: 702-651-5085. Fax: 702-651-5718. p. 1429

Jones, Jeanette, Ref Librn, College of Southern Nevada, Henderson Campus, 700 S College Dr, H1A, Henderson, NV, 89002. Tel: 702-651-3066. Fax: 702-651-3513. p. 1429

Jones, Jeanne, Librn, Jackson-George Regional Library System, Ocean Springs Municipal Library, 525 Dewey Ave, Ocean Springs, MS, 39564. Tel: 228-875-1193. Fax: 228-875-1535. p. 1310

Jones, Jeannette, Children's Serv Coordr, Libr Tech, Powell River Public Library, 4411 Michigan Ave, Powell River, BC, V8A 2S3, CANADA. Tel: 604-485-8625. Fax: 604-485-5320. p. 2735

Jones, Jennie, In Charge, Abraham Lincoln Birthplace National Historic Site Library, 2995 Lincoln Farm Rd, Hodgenville, KY, 42748. Tel: 270-358-3137, 270-358-3138. Fax: 270-358-3874. p. 918

Jones, Jennifer, Br Mgr, Harford County Public Library, Aberdeen Branch, 21 Franklin St, Aberdeen, MD, 21001-2495. Tel: 410-273-5608. Fax: 410-273-5610. p. 1020

Jones, Jennifer, Youth Serv Librn, Plymouth Public Library, Manomet Branch, 12 Strand Ave, Manomet, MA, 02345. Tel: 508-830-4185. p. 1118

Jones, Jennifer, Coll Develop, Minnesota Historical Society Library, 345 Kellogg Blvd W, Saint Paul, MN, 55102-1906. Tel: 651-259-3246. Fax: 651-297-7436. p. 1280

Jones, Jennifer B, Head, Tech Serv, Bismarck Veterans Memorial Public Library, 515 N Fifth St, Bismarck, ND, 58503-4081. Tel: 701-355-1488. Fax: 701-221-3729. p. 1837

Jones, Jerry, Youth Serv Coordr, Natrona County Public Library, 307 E Second St, Casper, WY, 82601. Tel: 307-237-4935, Ext 129. Fax: 307-266-3734. p. 2652

Jones, Jim, Media Spec, Troy University, 502 University Dr, Dothan, AL, 36304. Tel: 334-983-6556, Ext 1393. Fax: 334-983-6327. p. 15

Jones, Jo Ann K, Librn, Pike-Amite-Walthall Library System, Magnolia Branch, 230 S Cherry St, Magnolia, MS, 39652. Tel: 601-783-6565. p. 1308

Jones, Joanne E, Dir, Massasoit Community College Library, One Massasoit Blvd, Brockton, MA, 02302. Tel: 508-588-9100, Ext 1944. Fax: 508-427-1265. p. 1071

Jones, Joel, Dep Dir, Br, The Kansas City Public Library, 14 W Tenth St, Kansas City, MO, 64105. Tel: 816-701-3504. Fax: 816-701-3401. p. 1338

Jones, John A, Librn, Ozark Regional Library, Sainte Genevieve Branch, 21388 Hwy 32, Sainte Genevieve, MO, 63670. Tel: 573-883-3358. p. 1333

Jones, Judith, Br Mgr, Toledo-Lucas County Public Library, Mott, 1085 Dorr St, Toledo, OH, 43607. Tel: 419-259-5230. Fax: 419-255-4237. p. 1940

Jones, Judy, Tech Serv, Bullitt County Public Library, 127 N Walnut St, Shepherdsville, KY, 40165-6083. Tel: 502-543-7675. Fax: 502-543-5487. p. 935

Jones, Julia D, ILL, Librn, Bath County Memorial Library, 24 W Main St, Owingsville, KY, 40360. Tel: 606-674-2531. Fax: 606-674-2531. p. 931

Jones, Karen, Librn, Iva Jane Peek Public Library, 121 N Main St, Decatur, AR, 72722. Tel: 479-752-7323. Fax: 479-752-7323. p. 97

Jones, Karen, Circ, Clovis Community College Library, 417 Schepps Blvd, Clovis, NM, 88101. Tel: 575-769-4080. Fax: 575-769-4190. p. 1553

Jones, Karyn, Pub Serv, San Jacinto College North, 5800 Uvalde Rd, Houston, TX, 77049-4599. Tel: 281-459-7116. Fax: 281-459-7166. p. 2342

Jones, Katherin, Dir, McLouth Public Library, 215 S Union, McLouth, KS, 66054. Tel: 913-796-2225. Fax: 913-796-2230. p. 882

Jones, Kathleen, Dir, Art Institutes of California, San Francisco, 1170 Market St, San Francisco, CA, 94102-4908. Tel: 415-276-4010. Fax: 415-863-1121. p. 240

Jones, Kathy, Librn, Arkansas River Valley Regional Library System, Johnson County, Two Taylor Circle, Clarksville, AR, 72830-3653. Tel: 479-754-3135. Fax: 479-754-6343. p. 97

Jones, Kathy, Br Mgr, Calcasieu Parish Public Library, Westlake Branch, 937 Mulberry St, Westlake, LA, 70669. Tel: 337-721-7113. Fax: 337-437-3571. p. 954

Jones, Kathy, Curator, Cambria County Historical Society Library, 615 N Center St, Ebensburg, PA, 15931. Tel: 814-472-6674. p. 2052

Jones, Kathy, Librn, Parkland Regional Library, Jansen Branch, Main St, Jansen, SK, S0K 2B0, CANADA. Tel: 306-364-2122. p. 2932

Jones, Kay, Librn, Foothill College, 12345 El Monte Rd, Los Altos Hills, CA, 94022-4599. Tel: 650-949-7602. Fax: 650-949-7123. p. 167

Jones, Kay, Librn, Foothill College, 12345 El Monte Rd, Los Altos Hills, CA, 94022-4599. Tel: 650-949-7086. Fax: 650-949-7123. p. 2962

Jones, Kevin, Head Cataloger, Librn, Alternative Press Center Library, 2040 N Milwaukee Ave, 2nd Flr, Chicago, IL, 60647. Tel: 312-451-8133. Fax: 773-772-4180. p. 605

Jones, Kevin R, Dir, United States Navy, Bldg 160, 2601E Paul Jones St, Great Lakes, IL, 60088-2845. Tel: 847-688-4617. Fax: 847-688-3602. p. 652

Jones, Koala, Libr Asst, Claremont School of Theology Library, 1325 N College Ave, Claremont, CA, 91711. Tel: 909-447-2589. p. 134

Jones, Kristen, Asst Dean, Linn-Benton Community College Library, 6500 SW Pacific Blvd, Albany, OR, 97321-3799. Tel: 541-917-4638. Fax: 541-917-4659. p. 1989

Jones, Kristine, Dir, York Technical College Library, 452 S Anderson Rd, Rock Hill, SC, 29730. Tel: 803-981-7075. Fax: 803-327-4535. p. 2203

Jones, LaShawn M, Mgr, Access Serv, Purdue University, 2200 169th St, Hammond, IN, 46323-2094. Tel: 219-989-2138. Fax: 219-989-2070. p. 747

Jones, LaTonya, Circ, Craighead County Jonesboro Public Library, 315 W Oak Ave, Jonesboro, AR, 72401-3513. Tel: 870-935-5133. Fax: 870-935-7987. p. 104

Jones, Laura, Br Mgr, Cherokee County Public Library, Blacksburg Branch, 201 S Rutherford St, Blacksburg, SC, 29702. Tel: 864-839-2630. Fax: 864-839-2572. p. 2194

Jones, Leigh, Eng Librn, Tuskegee University, Hollis Burke Frissell Bldg, 1200 W Old Montgomery Rd, Tuskegee, AL, 36088. Tel: 334-727-8901. Fax: 334-727-9282. p. 39

Jones, Lenisa, Br Mgr, Marshall County Public Library System, 1003 Poplar St, Benton, KY, 42025. Tel: 270-527-9969. Fax: 270-527-0506. p. 907

Jones, Lesliediana, Head, Doc Serv, George Washington University, Jacob Burns Law Library, 716 20th St NW, Washington, DC, 20052. Tel: 202-994-9017. Fax: 202-994-2874. p. 402

Jones, Lillie, Br Mgr, Gadsden Public Library, East Gadsden, 919 Wilson St, Gadsden, AL, 35903. Tel: 256-549-4691. p. 18

Jones, Linda, Dir, Shoals Public Library, 404 N High St, Shoals, IN, 47581. Tel: 812-247-3838. Fax: 812-247-3838. p. 778

Jones, Linda, Bibliog Instr, Ref, Roberts Wesleyan College & Northeastern Seminary, 2301 Westside Dr, Rochester, NY, 14624-1997. Tel: 585-594-6044. Fax: 585-594-6543. p. 1731

Jones, Linda, Dir, Scurry County Library, 1916 23rd St, Snyder, TX, 79549-1910. Tel: 325-573-5572. Fax: 325-573-1060. p. 2388

Jones, Linda T, Head, Tech Serv, Columbus State University Libraries, 4225 University Ave, Columbus, GA, 31907. Tel: 706-565-3556. Fax: 706-568-2084. p. 526

Jones, Lisa, Dir, Grayson County Public Library, 130 E Market St, Leitchfield, KY, 42754-1439. Tel: 270-259-5455. Fax: 270-259-4552. p. 920

Jones, Lisa, Br Mgr, Terrebonne Parish Library, North Terrebonne, 4130 W Park Ave, Gray, LA, 70359. Tel: 985-868-3050. Fax: 985-868-3051. p. 951

Jones, Lizbeth A, Head, Cat, United States Air Force Academy Libraries, 2354 Fairchild Dr, Ste 3A10, USAF Academy, CO, 80840-6214. Tel: 719-333-4783. Fax: 719-333-4754. p. 324

Jones, Lois, Dir, Massanutten Regional Library, 174 S Main St, Harrisonburg, VA, 22801. Tel: 540-434-4475. Fax: 540-434-4382. p. 2470

Jones, Lonnie, Head, Circ Serv, Homewood Public Library, 1721 Oxmoor Rd, Homewood, AL, 35209-4085. Tel: 205-332-6611. Fax: 205-802-6424. p. 20

Jones, Louise, Functional Team Dir, Spec Coll & Libr, Kentucky Historical Society, 100 W Broadway, Frankfort, KY, 40601. Tel: 502-564-1792. Fax: 502-564-4701. p. 913

Jones, Lucy, Circ, Libr Asst, Greenwood-Leflore Public Library System, 405 W Washington St, Greenwood, MS, 38930-4297. Tel: 662-453-3634. Fax: 662-453-0683. p. 1299

Jones, Lynette, Info Serv, Carrollton Public Library, 1700 Keller Springs Rd, Carrollton, TX, 75006. Tel: 972-466-4814. Fax: 972-466-4265. p. 2295

Jones, Lynn, Circ, ILL, Juniata College, 1815 Moore St, Huntingdon, PA, 16652-2120. Tel: 814-641-3450. Fax: 814-641-3435. p. 2070

Jones, Maple, Br Mgr, Morehouse Parish Library, Dunbar, 1102 Perry St, Bastrop, LA, 71220. Tel: 318-281-1137. p. 941

Jones, Marcie, Br Mgr, Los Angeles Public Library System, Washington Irving Branch, 4117 W Washington Blvd, Los Angeles, CA, 90018-1053. Tel: 323-734-6303. Fax: 323-731-2416. p. 173

Jones, Margaret Faye, Dean, Learning Res, Nashville State Technical Community College, 120 White Bridge Rd, Nashville, TN, 37209-4515. Tel: 615-353-3556. Fax: 615-353-3558. p. 2258

Jones, Margarette, Librn, El Centro College, 801 Main St, Dallas, TX, 75202-3605. Tel: 214-860-2174. Fax: 214-860-2440. p. 2308

Jones, Marie, Asst Dean, Grad Prog Librn, East Tennessee State University, Sherrod Library, Seehorn Dr & Lake St, Johnson City, TN, 37614-0204. Tel: 423-439-4336. Fax: 423-439-5222. p. 2239

Jones, Marie, Dir, Minor Hill Public Library, PO Box 69, Minor Hill, TN, 38473. Tel: 931-565-3699. p. 2253

Jones, Marilyn, Br Mgr, Enoch Pratt Free Library, Forest Park Branch, 3023 Garrison Blvd, Baltimore, MD, 21216. Tel: 410-396-0942. Fax: 410-396-0945. p. 1013

Jones, Marilyn, Br Mgr, Knox County Public Library System, Farragut Branch, 417 N Campbell Station Rd, Farragut, TN, 37922. Tel: 865-777-1750. Fax: 865-777-1751. p. 2242

Jones, Mark H, State Archivist, Connecticut State Library, 231 Capitol Ave, Hartford, CT, 06106. Tel: 860-757-6595. Fax: 860-757-6542. p. 345

Jones, Martha, Head, Mat Mgt, Morse Institute Library, 14 E Central St, Natick, MA, 01760. Tel: 508-647-6400, Ext 1534. Fax: 508-647-6527. p. 1107

Jones, Marva, Circ, Wissahickon Valley Public Library, 650 Skippack Pike, Blue Bell, PA, 19422. Tel: 215-643-1320. Fax: 215-643-6611. p. 2036

Jones, Mary, Br Mgr, Saint Martin Parish Library, Cecilia Branch, 2460 Cecilia Sr High School Hwy, Cecilia, LA, 70521. Tel: 337-667-7411. Fax: 337-667-7411. p. 967

Jones, Mary B, Librn, United States Courts Library, 517 E Wisconsin Ave, Rm 516, Milwaukee, WI, 53202. Tel: 414-297-1698. Fax: 414-297-1695. p. 2621

Jones, Mary L, Br Mgr, Chicago Public Library, Brainerd, 1350 W 89th St, Chicago, IL, 60620. Tel: 312-747-6291. Fax: 312-747-1319. p. 608

Jones, Mary Lynne, Ch, Marion County Sub-District Library, 212 S Main St, Palmyra, MO, 63461. Tel: 573-769-2830. Fax: 573-769-0405. p. 1348

Jones, Maryhelen, Contractor Librn, Mgr, United States Air Force, AFRL/RVIL, 3550 Aberdeen Ave SE Bldg 570, Kirtland AFB, NM, 87117-5776. Tel: 505-846-4767. Fax: 505-846-4790. p. 1557

Jones, Matthew, Librn, LTG Associates Library, 6930 Carrol Ave, Ste 700, Takoma Park, MD, 20912. Tel: 301-270-0882. Fax: 301-270-1966. p. 1043

Jones, Maureeen, ILL Librn, Mark Twain Library, Rte 53 & Diamond Hill Rd, Redding, CT, 06896. Tel: 203-938-2545. Fax: 203-938-4026. p. 365

Jones, Maureen, Librn, Bay Correctional Facility Library, 5400 Bay Line Dr, Panama City, FL, 32404. Tel: 850-769-1455, Ext 243. Fax: 850-769-1942. p. 480

Jones, Mavis, Ch, Dillon County Library, 600 E Main St, Dillon, SC, 29536. Tel: 843-774-0330. Fax: 843-774-0733. p. 2192

Jones, Maya N, Br Head, Librn, Birmingham Public Library, West End, 1348 Tuscaloosa Ave SW, Birmingham, AL, 35211. Tel: 205-226-4089. Fax: 205-785-6260. p. 8

Jones, Melissa, Ch, Schaumburg Township District Library, 130 S Roselle Rd, Schaumburg, IL, 60193. Tel: 847-923-3427. Fax: 847-923-3131. p. 701

Jones, Melissa, Br Supvr, Barry-Lawrence Regional Library, Purdy Branch, 403 Hwy C, Purdy, MO, 65734. Tel: 417-442-7314. Fax: 417-442-7314. p. 1347

Jones, Melissa, In Charge, Osterhout Free Library, South, Two Airy St, Wilkes-Barre, PA, 18702. Tel: 570-823-5544. Fax: 570-823-5544. p. 2156

Jones, Michelle, Coordr, ILL, Columbus State University Libraries, 4225 University Ave, Columbus, GA, 31907. Tel: 706-568-2042. Fax: 706-568-2084. p. 526

Jones, Misty, Dep Dir, Cent Div, San Diego Public Library, 820 E St, San Diego, CA, 92101-6478. Tel: 619-236-5873. Fax: 619-238-6639. p. 235

Jones, Molly Lank, Dir, Sherman & Ruth Weiss Community Library, 10788 State Hwy 77 W, Hayward, WI, 54843. Tel: 715-634-2161. Fax: 715-634-5257. p. 2598

Jones, Muriel, Ref Librn, Goucher College Library, 1021 Dulaney Valley Rd, Baltimore, MD, 21204. Tel: 410-337-3289. Fax: 410-337-6419. p. 1014

Jones, Muriel, Ref Serv, Goucher College Library, 1021 Dulaney Valley Rd, Baltimore, MD, 21204. Tel: 410-337-6360. Fax: 410-337-6419. p. 1014

Jones, Myra, Dir, Lytton Public Library, 118 Main St, Lytton, IA, 50561. Tel: 712-466-2522. Fax: 712-466-2522. p. 828

Jones, Nancy, Br Coordr, Motlow State Community College Libraries, McMinnville Center Library, 225 Cadillac Lane, McMinnville, TN, 37110. Tel: 931-815-2113. Fax: 931-668-2172. p. 2267

Jones, Nick, Head Librn, Milwaukee Area Technical College, 5555 W Highland Rd, Rm A282, Mequon, WI, 53092-1199. Tel: 262-238-2212. p. 2615

Jones, Pamela, Dir, Medaille College Library, 18 Agassiz Circle, Buffalo, NY, 14214. Tel: 716-880-2283. Fax: 716-884-9638. p. 1598

Jones, Pamela, Coordr, Ser, Greensboro College, 815 W Market St, Greensboro, NC, 27401. Tel: 336-272-7102, Ext 328. Fax: 336-217-7233. p. 1796

Jones, Patricia, Dir of Tech Serv, Oklahoma Historical Society, 2401 N Laird Ave, Oklahoma City, OK, 73105-4997. Tel: 405-522-4025. Fax: 405-522-0644. p. 1974

Jones, Patrick Michael, Dir, East Hartford Public Library, 840 Main St, East Hartford, CT, 06108. Tel: 860-289-6429. Fax: 860-291-9166. p. 337

Jones, Paul, Circ, Wofford College, 429 N Church St, Spartanburg, SC, 29303-3663. Tel: 864-597-4300. Fax: 864-597-4329. p. 2206

Jones, Peggy Jo, Ch, Jacksonville Public Library, 502 S Jackson St, Jacksonville, TX, 75766. Tel: 903-586-7664. Fax: 903-586-3397. p. 2347

Jones, Phil, Bus Mgr, Northern New York Library Network, 6721 US Hwy 11, Potsdam, NY, 13676. Tel: 315-265-1119. Fax: 315-265-1881. p. 2950

Jones, Philip, Coll Develop, Central Arkansas Library System, 100 Rock St, Little Rock, AR, 72201-4698. Tel: 501-918-3070. p. 106

Jones, Phillip, Reader Serv Librn, Grinnell College Libraries, 1111 Sixth Ave, Grinnell, IA, 50112-1770. Tel: 641-269-3355. Fax: 641-269-4283. p. 819

Jones, Phillip J, Head of Libr, University of Arkansas Libraries, Fine Arts, 104 Fine Arts Bldg, Fayetteville, AR, 72701. Tel: 479-575-3081. p. 100

Jones, Plummer Alson, Jr, Dr, Prof, East Carolina University, 101 Umstead Residence Hall, Greenville, NC, 27858-4353. Tel: 252-328-6803. Fax: 252-328-4368. p. 2971

Jones, Precious, Ref Serv Supvr, Carnegie Mellon University, Hunt Library, 4909 Frew St, Pittsburgh, PA, 15213-3890. Tel: 412-268-2446. Fax: 412-268-2793. p. 2123

Jones, Rachel, Librn, Glen Elder Library, 105 S Mill, Glen Elder, KS, 67446. Tel: 785-545-3632. p. 868

Jones, Rane, Head Librn, Pima Public Library, 50 S 200 West, Pima, AZ, 85543. Tel: 928-485-2822. Fax: 928-485-0701. p. 77

Jones, Rebekka, Coll Develop Coordr, Scottsdale Public Library, 3839 N Drinkwater Blvd, Scottsdale, AZ, 85251-4467. Tel: 480-312-7323. Fax: 480-312-7993. p. 81

Jones, Richard, Circ, University of California Los Angeles Library, College Library, Powell Library Bldg, Los Angeles, CA, 90095. Tel: 310-825-5756. Fax: 310-206-9312. p. 178

Jones, Robbie F, Media Spec, Georgia Military College, 201 E Greene St, Milledgeville, GA, 31061. Tel: 478-445-2718. Fax: 478-445-5592. p. 544

Jones, Robert, Asst Tech Serv Librn, Armstrong Atlantic State University, 11935 Abercorn St, Savannah, GA, 31419. Tel: 912-344-3027. Fax: 912-344-3457. p. 549

Jones, Robert, YA Serv, Illinois State Library, Gwendolyn Brooks Bldg, 300 S Second St, Springfield, IL, 62701-9713. Tel: 217-785-1168. Fax: 217-785-4326. p. 705

Jones, Robert A, Dir, Milton-Freewater Public Library, Eight SW Eighth Ave, Milton-Freewater, OR, 97862-1501. Tel: 541-938-8246. Fax: 541-938-8254. p. 2006

Jones, Ronald, Electronic Serv/Ref Librn, University of Cincinnati, 2540 Clifton Ave, Cincinnati, OH, 45219. Tel: 513-556-0158. Fax: 513-556-6265. p. 1874

Jones, Ryan, Libr Assoc, Maine State Law
& Legislative Reference Library, 43 State
House Sta, Augusta, ME, 04333-0043. Tel:
207-287-1600. Fax: 207-287-6467. p. 974

Jones, Salena, Br Mgr, Mexico-Audrain County
Library District, Ed French Memorial, 204
E Second St, Laddonia, MO, 63352. Tel:
573-373-2393. Fax: 573-373-2393. p. 1345

Jones, Sallie, Librn, Orange County RDMD
Technical Library, 300 N Flower St, Santa Ana,
CA, 92703-5001. Tel: 714-834-3497. Fax:
714-834-5188. p. 259

Jones, Sally, Ref & Instruction Coordr, McDaniel
College, Two College Hill, Westminster,
MD, 21157-4390. Tel: 410-857-2287. Fax:
410-857-2748. p. 1046

Jones, Sam, AV, Amarillo Public Library, 413
E Fourth Ave, Amarillo, TX, 79101. Tel:
806-378-3054. Fax: 806-378-9327. p. 2274

Jones, Sam, Br Mgr, Amarillo Public Library,
Northwest Branch, 6100 W Ninth, Amarillo,
TX, 79106-0700. Tel: 806-359-2035. Fax:
806-359-2037. p. 2274

Jones, Sandra, Br Mgr, Anythink Libraries, Anythink
Wright Farms, 5877 E 120th Ave, Thornton,
CO, 80602. Tel: 303-405-3200. p. 324

Jones, Sara, Librn, South County Law Library, 200
W Atlantic Ave, Delray Beach, FL, 33444. Tel:
561-274-1440. p. 438

Jones, Sara, Dir, Carson City Library, 900 N Roop
St, Carson City, NV, 89701. Tel: 775-887-2244.
Fax: 775-887-2273. p. 1425

Jones, Sara, Asst Librn, Freeport Area Library,
428 Market St, Freeport, PA, 16229-1122. Tel:
724-295-3616. Fax: 724-295-3616. p. 2059

Jones, Sarah, Acq, Elizabethtown Community
& Technical College Library, 600 College
Street Rd, Elizabethtown, KY, 42701. Tel:
270-706-8812. Fax: 270-769-1618. p. 912

Jones, Sarah, Ref Librn, Tidewater Community
College, 1700 College Crescent, Virginia Beach,
VA, 23453. Fax: 757-427-0327. p. 2500

Jones, Scott, Asst Dir, Weber County Library
System, 2464 Jefferson Ave, Ogden, UT,
84401-2464. Tel: 801-337-2617. Fax:
801-337-2615. p. 2408

Jones, Shannon, Coordr, Outreach Serv, Virginia
Commonwealth University Libraries,
Tompkins-McCaw Library, Medical College of
Virginia Campus, 509 N 12th St, Richmond,
VA, 23298-0582. Tel: 804-828-0626. Fax:
804-828-6089. p. 2492

Jones, Sharain, Dir, Sam Waller Museum
Library, 306 Fischer Ave, The Pas, MB, R9A
1K4, CANADA. Tel: 204-623-3802. Fax:
204-623-5506. p. 2753

Jones, Sharon, Librn, Genoa Public Library,
421 Willard Ave, Genoa, NE, 68640. Tel:
402-993-2943. p. 1399

Jones, Shelly, Librn, Greater West Central Public
Library District, Golden Branch, 309 Quincy
St, Golden, IL, 62339. Tel: 217-696-2428. Fax:
217-696-2428. p. 591

Jones, Starla T, Mgr, Rapides Parish Library, Martin
Luther King Jr Memorial, 3311 Third St,
Alexandria, LA, 71301. Tel: 318-445-3912. Fax:
318-445-8953. p. 940

Jones, Stephanie, Asst Dir, Libr Communications,
Memphis Public Library & Information Center,
3030 Poplar Ave, Memphis, TN, 38111-3527.
Tel: 901-415-2847. Fax: 901-323-7108. p. 2249

Jones, Stephen, Head, Access Serv, Yale University
Library, Beinecke Rare Book & Manuscript,
121 Wall St, New Haven, CT, 06520. Tel:
203-432-2973. Fax: 203-432-4047. p. 356

Jones, Stephen, Info Tech Serv Mgr, University
of Maryland, Baltimore County, 1000
Hilltop Circle, Baltimore, MD, 21250. Tel:
410-455-2356. p. 1018

Jones, Susan, Info Syst Spec, Grant MacEwan
University Library, 10700 104th Ave, Edmonton,
AB, T5J 4S2, CANADA. Tel: 780-497-5850.
Fax: 780-497-5895. p. 2701

Jones, Susan, Info Serv Librn, Nova Scotia
Barristers' Society, 1815 Upper Water St, 7th
Flr, Halifax, NS, B3J 1S7, CANADA. Tel:
902-425-2665. Fax: 902-422-1697. p. 2781

Jones, Suzanne, Coll Mgt, Florida Institute of
Technology, 150 W University Blvd, Melbourne,
FL, 32901-6988. Tel: 321-674-8021. Fax:
321-724-2559. p. 463

Jones, Suzanne, Actg Univ Librn, University of
Prince Edward Island, 550 University Ave,
Charlottetown, PE, C1A 4P3, CANADA. Tel:
902-566-0460. Fax: 902-628-4305. p. 2876

Jones, Sydney, Dir, Centre for Addiction & Mental
Health Library, 33 Russell St, Toronto, ON,
M5S 2S1, CANADA. Tel: 416-535-8501, Ext
6999. Fax: 416-595-6601. p. 2852

Jones, Tamara, Coordr, Tech Serv, Central
Mississippi Regional Library System, 104
Office Park Dr, Brandon, MS, 39042-2404. Tel:
601-825-0100. Fax: 601-825-0199. p. 1294

Jones, Tami, Mgr, Briggs Lawrence County Public
Library, Northern, 14860 State Rd 141, Willow
Wood, OH, 45696. Tel: 740-643-2086. Fax:
740-643-2086. p. 1906

Jones, Tanisha, Br Mgr, Broward County Division of
Libraries, Carver Ranches, 4735 SW 18th St,
West Park, FL, 33023. Tel: 954-985-1945. Fax:
954-985-1947. p. 441

Jones, Tanya, Librn, Sand Hill Public Library,
698 Pisgah Rd, Sand Hill, MS, 39161. Tel:
601-829-1653. Fax: 601-829-1653. p. 1314

Jones, Terry, Asst Librn, Jonesboro Public Library,
124 E Fourth St, Jonesboro, IN, 46938-1105.
Tel: 765-677-9080. p. 756

Jones, Theresa, Br Mgr, Putnam County District
Library, Continental Branch, 301 S Sixth St,
Continental, OH, 45831. Tel: 419-596-3727.
p. 1926

Jones, Thomas, Dir, Middle Georgia Regional
Library System, 1180 Washington Ave, Macon,
GA, 31201-1790. Tel: 478-744-0850. Fax:
478-742-3161. p. 540

Jones, Thomas, Actg Mgr, Memphis Public
Library, History & Travel, 3030 Poplar Ave,
Memphis, TN, 38111. Tel: 901-415-2742. Fax:
901-323-7981. p. 2250

Jones, Tianne, Br Mgr, Otsego County Library,
Vanderbilt Branch, 8170 Mill St, Vanderbilt, MI,
49795. Tel: 989-983-3600. Fax: 989-983-3105.
p. 1182

Jones, Todd, Ad, Johnson County Public Library,
Trafalgar Branch, 424 Tower St, Trafalgar, IN,
46181. Tel: 317-878-9560. Fax: 317-878-4093.
p. 744

Jones, Tracy, Librn, Southeast Regional Library,
Fillmore Branch, 51 Main St, Fillmore, SK, S0G
1N0, CANADA. Tel: 306-722-3369. p. 2929

Jones, Travis, Mgr, Info Tech, Florida Institute of
Technology, 150 W University Blvd, Melbourne,
FL, 32901-6988. Tel: 321-674-8021. Fax:
321-724-2559. p. 463

Jones, Vanessa, Coll Mgt Librn, Blue Mountain
College, 201 W Main St, Blue Mountain,
MS, 38610. Tel: 662-685-4771, Ext 142. Fax:
662-685-9519. p. 1294

Jones, Velma, Tech Serv, Norfolk State
University Library, 700 Park Ave, Norfolk,
VA, 23504-8010. Tel: 757-823-2429. Fax:
757-823-2431. p. 2482

Jones, Vickie, Tech Serv, Georgetown County
Library, 405 Cleland St, Georgetown,
SC, 29440-3200. Tel: 843-545-3300. Fax:
843-545-3395. p. 2194

Jones, Victor T, Jr, Spec Coll Librn, New
Bern-Craven County Public Library, 400
Johnson St, New Bern, NC, 28560-4098. Tel:
252-638-7808. Fax: 252-638-7817. p. 1812

Jones, Virginia Purefoy, Univ Librn, North
Carolina Central University, School of Library
& Information Sciences, James E Shepard
Memorial Library, 3rd Flr, 1801 Fayetteville St,
Durham, NC, 27707. Tel: 919-530-7323. Fax:
919-530-6402. p. 1789

Jones, Virginia Purefoy, Librn, North Carolina
Central University, 1801 Fayetteville St,
Durham, NC, 27707. Tel: 919-530-6485. Fax:
919-530-6402. p. 2971

Jones, Wayne, Assoc Univ Librn, Carleton
University Library, 1125 Colonel By Dr, Ottawa,
ON, K1S 5B6, CANADA. Tel: 613-520-2600,
Ext 8008. Fax: 613-520-2750. p. 2830

Jones, William, Adminr, Coler Goldwater Specialty
Hospital & Nursing Facility, Roosevelt Island,
One Main St, New York, NY, 10044. Tel:
212-318-4353. Fax: 212-848-4628. p. 1674

Jones, William, Dir, Goldwater Memorial Hospital,
900 Main, Roosevelt Island, New York, NY,
10001. Tel: 212-318-4800. Fax: 212-318-4628.
p. 1680

Jones, Wilma, Tech Serv, Powell County Public
Library, 725 Breckenridge St, Stanton, KY,
40380. Tel: 606-663-4511. Fax: 606-663-4346.
p. 936

Jones, Wilma L, Chief Librn, College of Staten
Island Library, 2800 Victory Blvd, 1L, Staten
Island, NY, 10314-6609. Tel: 718-982-4001.
Fax: 718-982-4002. p. 1747

Jones, Yolanda, Asst Dir, Computer Serv, Villanova
University, Law Library, Garey Hall, 299 N
Spring Mill Rd, Villanova, PA, 19085. Tel:
610-519-7235. Fax: 610-519-7033. p. 2150

Jones-Quartey, Theo S, Mgr, W R Grace & Co,
7500 Grace Dr, Columbia, MD, 21044. Tel:
410-531-4146. Fax: 410-531-4546. p. 1025

Jones-Rhoades, Melinda, Ref Librn, YA Librn,
Galesburg Public Library, 40 E Simmons St,
Galesburg, IL, 61401-4591. Tel: 309-343-6118.
Fax: 309-343-4877. p. 648

Jongeling, Tom, Ref, Black & Veatch, 11401 Lamar,
Overland Park, KS, 66211. Tel: 913-458-7884.
Fax: 913-458-2934. p. 887

Jonkel, Elizabeth, Asst Dir, Missoula Public Library,
301 E Main, Missoula, MT, 59802-4799. Tel:
406-721-2665. Fax: 406-728-5900. p. 1386

Jonna, Davis, Dir, Bogota Public Library, 375 Larch
Ave, Bogota, NJ, 07603. Tel: 201-488-7185.
Fax: 201-342-2094. p. 1473

Jons, Lajeane, Tech Serv, Mitchell Public Library,
221 N Duff St, Mitchell, SD, 57301-2596. Tel:
605-995-8480. Fax: 605-995-8482. p. 2215

Joorfetz, Clara, Info Serv Librn, State of Mississippi
Judiciary, Carroll Gartin Justice Bldg, 450 High
St, Jackson, MS, 39201. Tel: 601-359-3672. Fax:
601-359-2912. p. 1305

Joos, Phyllis, Dir, Hancock Community Library,
662 Sixth St, Hancock, MN, 56244-9998. Tel:
320-392-5666. Fax: 320-392-5132. p. 1253

Jorbin, Lesley, Librn, Cleveland State University,
University Library, Rhodes Tower, 2121
Euclid Ave, Cleveland, OH, 44115-2214. Tel:
216-687-6997. Fax: 216-687-9380. p. 1879

Jordan, Alyssa, Multimedia Ctr Librn, Youngstown
State University, One University Plaza,
Youngstown, OH, 44555-0001. Tel:
330-941-2382. Fax: 330-941-3734. p. 1953

Jordan, Alysse, Interim Dir, Columbia University,
The Burke Library at Union Theological
Seminary, 3041 Broadway, New York, NY,
10027. Tel: 212-851-2195. Fax: 212-851-5613.
p. 1674

Jordan, Alysse, Head of Libr, Librn, Columbia
University, Social Work Library, Columbia
University School of Social Work, 1255
Amsterdam Ave, 2nd Flr, New York, NY, 10027.
Tel: 212-851-2195. Fax: 212-851-2199. p. 1675

Jordan, Anne, Dir, Staatsburg Library, 72 Old Post
Rd, Staatsburg, NY, 12580. Tel: 845-889-4683.
Fax: 845-889-8414. p. 1747

Jordan, Barbara B, Librn, Tuscaloosa Public Library,
Subregional Library for the Blind & Physically
Handicapped, 1801 Jack Warner Pkwy,
Tuscaloosa, AL, 35401-1009. Tel: 205-345-3994.
Fax: 205-752-8300. p. 38

Jordan, Carol Walker, Dr, Univ Librn, Queens
University of Charlotte, 1900 Selwyn Ave,
Charlotte, NC, 28274-0001. Tel: 704-337-2400.
Fax: 704-337-2517. p. 1784

Jordan, Caroline, Acq, Peter White Public Library, 217 N Front St, Marquette, MI, 49855. Tel: 906-228-9510. Fax: 906-226-1783. p. 1207

Jordan, Cindy, Librn, Moline Public Library, 107 N Main, Moline, KS, 67353. Tel: 620-647-3310. Fax: 620-647-3310. p. 884

Jordan, Courtney, Interim Br Mgr, Boyd County Public Library, Catlettsburg Branch, 2704 Louisa St, Catlettsburg, KY, 41129. Tel: 606-739-8332. Fax: 606-739-5907. p. 905

Jordan, J, Head, Ch, Aurora Public Library, 15145 Young St, Aurora, ON, L4G 1M1, CANADA. Tel: 905-727-9493. Fax: 905-727-9374. p. 2793

Jordan, Jack, Librn, Patricia Romanko Public Library, 121 N Third St, Parma, ID, 83660. Tel: 208-722-6605. p. 581

Jordan, Jenny, Br Mgr, Palo Alto City Library, Children's, 1276 Harriet St, Palo Alto, CA, 94301. Tel: 659-463-4961. Fax: 650-463-4964. p. 204

Jordan, Joan, Acq, Mitchell Community College, 500 W Broad St, Statesville, NC, 28677. Tel: 704-878-3249. p. 1826

Jordan, Katherine, Chief Librn, United States Consumer Product Safety Commission Library, 4330 East West Hwy, Rm 701, Bethesda, MD, 20814. Tel: 301-504-7622. Fax: 301-504-0403. p. 1022

Jordan, Katherine, Head, Circ, Longview Public Library, 222 W Cotton St, Longview, TX, 75601-6348. Tel: 903-237-1355. Fax: 903-237-1327. p. 2357

Jordan, Kathy, Asst Dir, Perry Cook Memorial Public Library, 7406 County Rd 242, Shauck, OH, 43349. Tel: 419-362-7181. Fax: 419-362-1518. p. 1934

Jordan, Linda, Br Mgr, Atlanta-Fulton Public Library System, Mechanicsville Library, 400 Formwalt St SW, Atlanta, GA, 30312. Tel: 404-730-4779. p. 512

Jordan, Louis, Assoc Librn, Hesburgh Libraries, 221 Hesburgh Library, University of Notre Dame, Notre Dame, IN, 46556. Tel: 574-631-5252. Fax: 574-631-6772. p. 770

Jordan, Louis, Head, Spec Coll, Hesburgh Libraries, Medieval Institute Library, 715 Hesburgh Library, Notre Dame, IN, 46556-5629. Tel: 574-631-3778. Fax: 574-631-8644. p. 770

Jordan, Mark, Head, Syst, Simon Fraser University Library, 8888 University Dr, Burnaby, BC, V5A 1S6, CANADA. Tel: 778-782-5753. Fax: 778-782-3023. p. 2726

Jordan, Matt, Librn, University of Tennessee, Knoxville, George F DeVine Music Library, 301 Music Bldg, 1741 Volunteer Blvd, Knoxville, TN, 37996-2600. Tel: 865-974-4051. Fax: 865-974-0564. p. 2244

Jordan, Meg, Coordr, Heald College, 1605 E March Lane, Stockton, CA, 95210. Tel: 209-473-5200. Fax: 209-473-5287. p. 272

Jordan, Nancy, Dir, Long Island Community Library, Seven Gorham St, Long Island, ME, 04050. Tel: 207-766-2530. Fax: 207-766-2530. p. 990

Jordan, Natalie, Acq Asst, University of Saint Mary of the Lake - Mundelein Seminary, 1000 E Maple Ave, Mundelein, IL, 60060. Tel: 847-970-4820. Fax: 847-566-5229. p. 678

Jordan, Orlando, Asst Br Mgr, Atlanta-Fulton Public Library System, Dr Robert E Fulton Regional at Ocee, 5090 Abbotts Bridge Rd, Alpharetta, GA, 30005-4601. Tel: 770-360-8897. Fax: 770-360-8892. p. 512

Jordan, Pamela, Dir, Ashland Public Library, 207 N 15th St, Ashland, NE, 68003-1816. Tel: 402-944-7430. Fax: 402-944-7430. p. 1392

Jordan, Pamela A, Dir, Ashland Public Library, 224 Claremont Ave, Ashland, OH, 44805. Tel: 419-289-8188, Ext 17. Fax: 419-281-8552. p. 1855

Jordan, Patricia, Libr Dir, Spartanburg Community College Library, 800 Brisack Rd, Spartanburg, SC, 29305. Tel: 864-592-4615. Fax: 864-592-4762. p. 2205

Jordan, Rebecca, Librn, Redington-Fairview General Hospital, 46 Fairview Ave, Skowhegan, ME, 04976. Tel: 207-474-5121, Ext 419. Fax: 207-858-2314. p. 1000

Jordan, Rene, Planning, Res Projects Coordr, Knox County Public Library System, 500 W Church Ave, Knoxville, TN, 37902-2505. Tel: 865-215-8716. Fax: 865-215-8742. p. 2241

Jordan, Robert, ILL, Cerro Coso Community College Library, 3000 College Heights Blvd, Ridgecrest, CA, 93555-9571. Tel: 760-384-6131. Fax: 760-384-6139. p. 216

Jordan Russell, Candace, Librn, Roswell Museum & Art Center Library, 100 W 11th St, Roswell, NM, 88201. Tel: 575-624-6744, Ext 25. Fax: 575-624-6765. p. 1561

Jordan, Sharon, Br Mgr, Mesa County Public Library District, Collbran Branch, 111 Main St, Collbran, CO, 81624-9900. Tel: 970-487-3545. Fax: 970-487-3716. p. 311

Jordan, Stephen, Ref, Vanderbilt University, Alyne Queener Massey Law Library, 131 21st Ave S, Nashville, TN, 37203. Tel: 615-322-3814. Fax: 615-343-1265. p. 2261

Jordan, Tamara, Acq, Cat Tech, Pierce College Library, Puyallup Campus, 1601 39th Ave SE, Puyallup, WA, 98374. Tel: 253-840-8310. Fax: 253-840-8316. p. 2520

Jordan, Thelma, ILL, Sweet Briar College, 134 Chapel Rd, Sweet Briar, VA, 24595-1200. Tel: 434-381-6138. Fax: 434-381-6173. p. 2497

Jordan-Hubbard, Cynthia, Res, Chicago Urban League, 4510 S Michigan Ave, Chicago, IL, 60653. Tel: 773-285-1500. Fax: 773-285-7772. p. 611

Jordebrek, Jennifer, Dir, Ely Public Library, 1595 Dows St, Ely, IA, 52227. Tel: 319-848-7616. Fax: 319-848-4056. p. 814

Jordon, Donna, Br Mgr, Linebaugh Public Library System of Rutherford County, Eagleville Bicentennial Branch, 317 Hwy 99 E, Eagleville, TN, 37060. Tel: 615-274-2626. Fax: 615-274-2626. p. 2254

Jordon, Erika, Dir, Kezar Falls Circulating Library, Two Wadleigh St, Parsonsfield, ME, 04047. Tel: 207-625-2424. p. 995

Jordon, Jay, Pres & Chief Exec Officer, OCLC Online Computer Library Center, Inc, 6565 Kilgour Pl, Dublin, OH, 43017-3395. Tel: 614-764-6000. Fax: 614-718-1017. p. 2952

Jordon, Joan, Tech Serv, Ontario City Library, 215 East C St, Ontario, CA, 91764. Tel: 909-395-2234. Fax: 909-395-2043. p. 200

Jordon, Linda, Librn, Wilkes Memorial Library, Sixth St, Hubbard, TX, 76648. Tel: 254-576-2527. Fax: 785-899-6411. p. 2345

Jordon, Patty, Interim Head, Spec Coll & Archives, George Mason University Libraries, 4400 University Dr, MSN 2FL, Fairfax, VA, 22030-4444. Tel: 703-993-2250. Fax: 703-993-2200. p. 2462

Jordy, Janet, Br Mgr, Calcasieu Parish Public Library, DeQuincy Branch, 102 W Harrison St, DeQuincy, LA, 70633. Tel: 337-721-7087. Fax: 337-786-4213. p. 953

Jordy, Janet, Br Mgr, Calcasieu Parish Public Library, Starks Branch, 113 S Hwy 109, Starks, LA, 70661-4362. Tel: janet@calcasieu.lib.la.us. Fax: 337-743-6560. p. 954

Joress, Beth, Assoc Dir, Info Serv, Emerson College Library, 120 Boylston St, Boston, MA, 02116-4624. Tel: 617-824-8331. Fax: 617-824-7817. p. 1060

Jorge, Barbara, Ref Librn, Austin Community College, Pinnacle Campus Library, 7748 Hwy 290 W, Austin, TX, 78736. Tel: 512-223-8091. Fax: 512-223-8223. p. 2278

Jorge, Sanchez, Outreach Serv Librn, Fort Bend County Libraries, 1001 Golfview Dr, Richmond, TX, 77469-5199. Tel: 281-344-3818. Fax: 281-341-2688. p. 2374

Jorgensen, Barb, Dir, Schaller Public Library, 103 S Main St, Schaller, IA, 51053. Tel: 712-275-4741. p. 842

Jorgensen, Cheryl, Asst Dir, Dorothy Bramlage Public Library, 230 W Seventh, Junction City, KS, 66441-3097. Tel: 785-238-4311. Fax: 785-238-7873. p. 874

Jorgensen, Corinne, Dr, Dir, Prof, Florida State University, College of Communication & Information, 142 Collegiate Loop, Tallahassee, FL, 32306-2100. Tel: 850-644-8116. Fax: 850-644-9763. p. 2963

Jorgensen, Daphne, Asst to the Chair, University at Albany, State University of New York, Draper 116, 135 Western Ave, Albany, NY, 12222. Tel: 518-442-5110. Fax: 518-442-5367. p. 2970

Jorgensen, Herb, Archivist, Librn, The Blackhawk Museum, 3700 Blackhawk Plaza Circle, Danville, CA, 94506. Tel: 925-736-2277, Ext 254. Fax: 925-736-4818. p. 139

Jorgensen, John, Head, Circ, Head, Digital Planning, Rutgers University Libraries, Camden Law Library, 217 N Fifth St, Camden, NJ, 08102-1203. Tel: 856-225-6460. p. 1477

Jorgensen, Peter E, Dr, Dir, Acad & Res Tech, Florida State University, College of Communication & Information, 142 Collegiate Loop, Tallahassee, FL, 32306-2100. Tel: 850-644-4139. Fax: 850-644-9763. p. 2963

Jorgensen, Rachel, Info Literacy Librn, University of the District of Columbia, Learning Resources Division, 4200 Connecticut Ave NW, Washington, DC, 20008. Tel: 202-274-6370. Fax: 202-274-6012. p. 421

Jorgensen, Roy E, Actg Div Chief, Archives Dir, Ref Mgr, Fishkill Historical Society, 504 Rte 9, Fishkill, NY, 12524-2248. Tel: 845-896-9560. p. 1622

Jorgensen, Susan, Br Mgr, Chicago Public Library, Portage-Cragin, 5108 W Belmont Ave, Chicago, IL, 60641. Tel: 312-744-0152. Fax: 312-744-3776. p. 609

Jorgenson, Jan, Govt Doc, Central Washington University, 400 E University Way, Ellensburg, WA, 98926-7548. Tel: 509-963-1901. Fax: 509-963-3684. p. 2514

Joriner, Mary, Asst Librn, Patton Public Library, 444 Magee Ave, Patton, PA, 16668-1210. Tel: 814-674-8231. Fax: 814-674-6188. p. 2101

Jorns, Dixie, Br Mgr, Door County Library, Egg Harbor Branch, 7860 Hwy 42, Egg Harbor, WI, 54209. Tel: 920-868-2664. p. 2640

Jorrey, Sue, Librn, Kirby Free Library of Salisbury Center, 105 Rte 29A, Salisbury Center, NY, 13454. Tel: 315-429-9006. Fax: 315-429-9006. p. 1737

Jorstad, Cynthia, Librn, Northland Community & Technical College Library, 1101 Hwy One E, Thief River Falls, MN, 56701. Tel: 218-681-0756, 218-681-0757. p. 1285

Josefiak, Melissa, Asst Dir, Wethersfield Historical Society, 150 Main St, Wethersfield, CT, 06109. Tel: 860-529-7656. Fax: 860-563-2609. p. 377

Josefiak, Melissa, Interim Dir, Wethersfield Historical Society, 150 Main St, Wethersfield, CT, 06109. Tel: 860-529-7656. Fax: 860-563-2609. p. 377

Joseph, Angelina G, Head, Cat, Marquette University, Sensenbrenner Hall, 1103 W Wisconsin Ave, Milwaukee, WI, 53233-2313. Tel: 414-288-7092. Fax: 414-288-5914. p. 2618

Joseph, Arah, Libr Coordr, Blank Rome LLP Library, Chrysler Bldg, 15th Fl, 405 Lexington Ave, New York, NY, 10174. Tel: 212-885-5000. Fax: 212-885-5001. p. 1670

Joseph, Carol, In Charge, North Shore Synagogue, 83 Muttontown Rd, Syosset, NY, 11791. Tel: 516-921-2282. Fax: 516-921-2393. p. 1751

Joseph, Carol, Librn, City Hospital, Inc, 2500 Hospital Dr, Martinsburg, WV, 25401. Tel: 304-264-1246. Fax: 304-264-1381. p. 2565

Joseph, Claire, Dir, South Nassau Communities Hospital, One Healthy Way, Oceanside, NY, 11572. Tel: 516-632-3452. Fax: 516-766-3857. p. 1709

Joseph, Jennifer, Govt Doc, Head, Ref, New Castle Public Library, 207 E North St, New Castle, PA, 16101-3691. Tel: 724-658-6659. Fax: 724-658-7209. p. 2096

Joseph, Lawrence, PhD, Syst Adminr, Howard University Libraries, 500 Howard Pl NW, Washington, DC, 20059. Tel: 202-806-4096. Fax: 202-806-5903. p. 403

Joseph, Louise, Librn, McHenry County Law Library, 2200 N Seminary Ave, Woodstock, IL, 60098. Tel: 815-334-4166. Fax: 815-334-1005. p. 721

Joseph, Lura, Librn, University of Illinois Library at Urbana-Champaign, Geology, 223 Natural History Bldg, 1301 W Green St, Urbana, IL, 61801. Tel: 217-333-1266. Fax: 217-244-4319. p. 712

Joseph, Maria, Dir, Moon Township Public Library, 1700 Beaver Grade Rd, Ste 100, Moon Township, PA, 15108-2984. Tel: 412-269-0334. Fax: 412-269-0136. p. 2092

Joseph, Michael, Rare Bk Librn, Rutgers University Libraries, Special Collections & University Archives, 169 College Ave, New Brunswick, NJ, 08901-1163. Tel: 848-932-6153. Fax: 732-932-7012. p. 1509

Joseph, Mildred, Librn, Houston Community College Northeast College, North Forest Campus Library, 7525 Tidwell Rd, Houston, TX, 77016-4413. Tel: 713-635-0427. p. 2338

Joseph, Otis, Librn, Grant Thornton LLP, 175 W Jackson Blvd, 20th Flr, Chicago, IL, 60604. Tel: 312-602-8828. Fax: 312-565-4719. p. 625

Joseph, Stephen, Dean of Libr Serv, Butler County Community College, College Dr, Oak Hills, Butler, PA, 16002. Tel: 724-284-8511. Fax: 724-285-6047. p. 2040

Joseph, Susan, Bus Librn, Info Spec, International Flavors & Fragrances, Inc, 1515 Hwy 36, Union Beach, NJ, 07735. Tel: 732-335-2687. Fax: 732-335-2657. p. 1537

Joseph, Susan, Coll Develop, Eastern University, 1300 Eagle Rd, Saint Davids, PA, 19087. Tel: 610-225-5038. Fax: 610-341-1375. p. 2135

Joseph-Smith, Karen, Br Supvr, Berkeley Public Library, Claremont Branch, 2940 Benvenue Ave, Berkeley, CA, 94705. Tel: 510-981-6280. Fax: 510-843-1603. p. 126

Josephine, Helen, Head, Eng Libr, Stanford University Libraries, Engineering Library, Terman Engineering Ctr, 2nd Flr, Stanford, CA, 94305-4029. Tel: 650-723-0001. Fax: 650-725-1096. p. 271

Josephs, Ann-Marie R, Commun Libr Mgr, Queens Borough Public Library, Glendale Community Library, 78-60 73rd Pl, Glendale, NY, 11385. Tel: 718-821-4980. Fax: 718-821-7160. p. 1644

Josephson, Joyce, Br Head, Greater Victoria Public Library Board, Nellie McClung Branch, 3950 Cedar Hill Rd, Victoria, BC, V8P 3Z9, CANADA. Tel: 250-477-7111. Fax: 250-477-4257. p. 2745

Joshi, James, Asst Prof, University of Pittsburgh, 135 N Bellefield Ave, Pittsburgh, PA, 15260. Tel: 412-624-5230. Fax: 412-624-5231. p. 2973

Joshi, Keren, Ch, Wilmette Public Library District, 1242 Wilmette Ave, Wilmette, IL, 60091-2558. Tel: 847-256-6940. Fax: 847-256-6943. p. 719

Joshi, Lynne, Ref Librn, Nova Southeastern University, 3200 S University Dr, Fort Lauderdale, FL, 33328. Tel: 954-262-3106. Fax: 954-262-1821. p. 443

Joshua, Tiffany, Head, Circ, Scarborough Public Library, 48 Gorham Rd, Scarborough, ME, 04074. Tel: 207-883-4723. Fax: 207-883-9728. p. 1000

Joslin, Ann, State Librn, Idaho Commission for Libraries, 325 W State St, Boise, ID, 83702-6072. Tel: 208-334-2150. p. 571

Joslin, Ann, State Librn, Idaho Commission for Libraries, 325 W State St, Boise, ID, 83702-6072. Tel: 208-334-2150. Fax: 208-334-4016. p. 571

Joslin, Ann, Pres, Western Council of State Libraries, Inc, Idaho Commission for Libraries, 325 W State St, Boise, ID, 83702-6055. Tel: 208-334-2150. Fax: 208-334-4016. p. 2941

Joslin, J, Librn, Regional Treatment Centre/Pacific Institution Library, 33344 King Rd, Abbotsford, BC, V2S 4P4, CANADA. Tel: 604-870-7700, Ext 3399. Fax: 604-870-7746. p. 2724

Joslin, Janice, Librn, Kentucky Correctional Institution for Women Library, 3000 Ash Ave, Pewee Valley, KY, 40056. Tel: 502-241-8454, Ext 2224. Fax: 502-241-0372. p. 932

Joslin, Vickie, Libr Serv Mgr, Lake Worth Public Library, 15 North M St, Lake Worth, FL, 33460. Tel: 561-533-7354. Fax: 561-586-1651. p. 459

Joslyn, Amy, Ch, Fairport Public Library, One Fairport Village Landing, Fairport, NY, 14450. Tel: 585-223-9091. Fax: 585-223-3998. p. 1621

Jost, Carol, Fiscal Agent, Utah Academic Library Consortium, University of Utah, 295 S 1500 E, Salt Lake City, UT, 84112-0860. Tel: 801-581-3852, 801-581-7701. Fax: 801-585-7185. p. 2956

Jost, Katy, Ch, Fremont County Library System, Riverton Branch, 1330 W Park, Riverton, WY, 82501. Tel: 307-856-3556. Fax: 307-857-3722. p. 2657

Jost, Richard, Info Syst Coordr, University of Washington Libraries, Marian Gould Gallagher Law Library, William H Gates Hall, Box 353025, Seattle, WA, 98195-3025. Tel: 206-685-4980. Fax: 206-685-2165. p. 2534

Joudrey, Daniel, Asst Prof, Simmons College, 300 The Fenway, Boston, MA, 02115. Tel: 617-521-2800. Fax: 617-521-3192. p. 2967

Jouett, Patti, Tech Serv, Vernon College, 4400 College Dr, Vernon, TX, 76384. Tel: 940-552-6291, Ext 2220. Fax: 940-552-0288. p. 2395

Jourdain, Jan, Head, Info Tech, Amherst College, Amherst, MA, 01002. Fax: 413-542-2662. p. 1048

Jourdan, Carrie, Tech Serv Librn, Fox Lake Public District Library, 255 E Grand Ave, Fox Lake, IL, 60020-1697. Tel: 847-587-0198. Fax: 847-587-9493. p. 646

Jourdan, Rosemary, Librn, United Lodge of Theosophists, 347 E 72nd St, New York, NY, 10021. Tel: 212-535-2230. Fax: 212-628-3430. p. 1702

Jourdan-Caruso, Linda, Librn, C Berger Group, Inc Library, 327 E Gundersen Dr, Carol Stream, IL, 60188-2421. Tel: 630-653-1115. Fax: 630-653-1691. p. 601

Journey, Lawanna, Br Mgr, Middle Georgia Regional Library System, Montezuma Public Library, 506 N Dooly St, Montezuma, GA, 31063-1308. Tel: 478-472-6095. Fax: 478-472-6095. p. 541

Jouthas, Lee, Br Mgr, Alameda County Library, Dublin Branch, 200 Civic Plaza, Dublin, CA, 94568. Tel: 925-828-1315. Fax: 925-828-9296. p. 149

Joy, Graham, Coordr, San Francisco Biomedical Library Network, San Franscisco General Hospital UCSF/ Barnett-Briggs Medical Library, 1001 Potrero Ave, Bldg 30, First Fl, San Francisco, CA, 94110. Tel: 415-206-6639. p. 2938

Joyal, Paula, Bus & Finance Mgr, Lynn Public Library, Five N Common St, Lynn, MA, 01902. Tel: 781-595-0567. Fax: 781-592-5050. p. 1101

Joyce, Amy, Librn, Bryant & Stratton Business College, 465 Main St, Ste 400, Buffalo, NY, 14203. Tel: 716-884-9120, Ext 261. Fax: 716-884-0091. p. 1596

Joyce, Betty, Coordr, Bethany Presbyterian Church Library, 3000 Dewey Ave, Rochester, NY, 14616. Tel: 585-663-3000. Fax: 585-663-5325. p. 1728

Joyce, Candis, Dir, Swans Island Educational Society, 451 Atlantic Rd, Swans Island, ME, 04685. Tel: 207-526-4330. p. 1003

Joyce, Dan, Dir, Kenosha Public Museums Library, 5500 First Ave, Kenosha, WI, 53140. Tel: 262-653-4427. Fax: 262-653-4437. p. 2601

Joyce, Donald J, Fr, Dir, Donald E O'Shaughnessy Library, Oblate School of Theology, 285 Oblate Dr, San Antonio, TX, 78216-6693. Tel: 210-341-1368. Fax: 210-979-6520. p. 2380

Joyce, Eleanor, Asst Librn, Josiah Carpenter Library, 41 Main St, Pittsfield, NH, 03263. Tel: 603-435-8406. p. 1462

Joyce, Kelly, Head, ILL, Head, Ser, Hanover College, 121 Scenic Dr, Hanover, IN, 47243. Tel: 812-866-7166. Fax: 812-866-7172. p. 748

Joyce, Lisa, Curator, SUNY Cortland, Art Slide, Dowd Fine Arts Ctr, Cortland, NY, 13045. Tel: 607-753-5519. p. 1612

Joyce, Marie, Ch, Free Public Library of Hasbrouck Heights, 320 Boulevard, Hasbrouck Heights, NJ, 07604. Tel: 201-288-8911. Fax: 201-288-5467. p. 1490

Joyce, Martha, Pub Serv, Fanshawe College, 1001 Fanshawe College Blvd, London, ON, N5Y 5R6, CANADA. Tel: 519-452-4240. Fax: 519-452-4473. p. 2817

Joyce, Mary K, Mgr, Morristown Memorial Hospital Medical Library, 100 Madison Ave, Morristown, NJ, 07962. Tel: 973-971-8926. Fax: 973-290-7045. p. 1505

Joyce, Megan, Ref, High Point Public Library, 901 N Main St, High Point, NC, 27262. Tel: 336-883-3646. Fax: 336-883-3636. p. 1802

Joyce, Steve, Dir, Gillespie Public Library, 201 W Chestnut, Gillespie, IL, 62033. Tel: 217-839-3614. Fax: 217-839-4854. p. 649

Joyner, Joseph, Tech Coordr, Adams Memorial Library, 1112 Ligonier St, Latrobe, PA, 15650. Tel: 724-539-1972. Fax: 724-537-0338. p. 2078

Joyner, Lottie N, Circ, Pitt Community College, Hwy 11 S, Greenville, NC, 27835. Tel: 252-321-4350. Fax: 252-321-4404. p. 1799

Joyner, Susanna, Libr Dir, United States Army, Woodworth Consolidated Library/Fort Gordon Post Library, 549 Rice Rd, Bldg 33500, Fort Gordon, GA, 30905-5081. Tel: 706-791-7323. Fax: 706-791-3282. p. 533

Joyner, Tammy, Libr Asst, Wiregrass Georgia Technical College, 706 Baker Hwy, Douglas, GA, 31533. Tel: 912-389-2226. Fax: 912-389-4308. p. 531

Joynes, Roy, Br Mgr, Prince George's County Memorial, Laurel Branch, 507 Seventh St, Laurel, MD, 20707-4013. Tel: 301-776-6790. p. 1032

Jozwiak, Clare, Head, Ch, Marion Public Library, 600 S Washington St, Marion, IN, 46953-1992. Tel: 765-668-2900. Fax: 765-668-2911. p. 763

Jozwiak, Kathleen, Dir, Orrville Public Library, 230 N Main St, Orrville, OH, 44667. Tel: 330-683-1065. Fax: 330-683-1984. p. 1925

Jozwiak, Kathleen L, Dir, Henderson Memorial Public Library Association, 54 E Jefferson St, Jefferson, OH, 44047-1198. Tel: 440-576-3761. Fax: 440-576-8402. p. 1906

Ju, Boryung, Dr, Assoc Prof, Louisiana State University, 267 Coates Hall, Baton Rouge, LA, 70803. Tel: 225-578-3158. Fax: 225-578-4581. p. 2966

Juarbe, Dulce M, Head, Adult Serv, Eastchester Public Library, 11 Oak Ridge Pl, Eastchester, NY, 10709. Tel: 914-793-5055. Fax: 914-793-7862. p. 1618

Juárez-Ponce, María, Puerto Rican Coll Librn, Inter-American University of Puerto Rico, San German Campus, Ave Inter-American University, Rd 102, K 30 6, San German, PR, 00683-9801. Tel: 787-264-1912, Ext 7536. Fax: 787-264-2544. p. 2675

Jubb, Jane, Head, Ref, Northland Public Library, 300 Cumberland Rd, Pittsburgh, PA, 15237-5455. Tel: 412-366-8100, Ext 110. Fax: 412-366-2064. p. 2126

Jubinsky, Walter, Regional Librn, Volusia County Public Library, New Smyrna Beach Public, 1001 S Dixie Freeway, New Smyrna Beach, FL, 32168. Tel: 386-424-2910. Fax: 386-424-2913. p. 436

Jubitz, Molly, Librn, Levy County Public Library System, Cedar Key Public, 460 Second St, Cedar Key, FL, 32625. Tel: 352-543-5777. Fax: 352-543-5777. p. 430

Jucko, JoAnn, Circ Tech, Head, ILL, Normandale Community College Library, 9700 France Ave S, Bloomington, MN, 55431. Tel: 952-487-8290. Fax: 952-487-8101. p. 1242

Judas, Phyllis, Asst Librn, Shellsburg Public Library, 110 Main St, Shellsburg, IA, 52332. Tel: 319-436-2112. Fax: 319-436-2112. p. 843

Judd, Rebecca, Br Mgr, Kitsap Regional Library, Bainbridge Island Branch, 1270 Madison Ave N, Bainbridge Island, WA, 98110-2747. Tel: 206-842-4162, Ext 9802. Fax: 206-780-5310. p. 2510

Judd, Yvonne, Br Mgr, Summit County Library, Coalville Branch, 10 N Main, Coalville, UT, 84017. Tel: 435-336-3070. Fax: 435-336-2062. p. 2410

Jude, Drema, Exec Dir, Martin County Public Library, 180 E Main St, Inez, KY, 41224. Tel: 606-298-7766. Fax: 606-298-0680. p. 918

Jude, Sandi, Circ Supvr, Umatilla Public Library, 412 Hatfield Dr, Umatilla, FL, 32784-8913. Tel: 352-669-3284. Fax: 352-669-2927. p. 501

Judell, David, Dir, Rib Lake Public Library, 645 Pearl St, Rib Lake, WI, 54470. Tel: 715-427-5769. Fax: 715-427-5368. p. 2633

Judge, April L, Dir, West Caldwell Public Library, 30 Clinton Rd, West Caldwell, NJ, 07006. Tel: 973-226-5441. Fax: 973-228-7572. p. 1540

Judge, Doreen, Cataloger, Hubbard Free Library, 115 Second St, Hallowell, ME, 04347. Tel: 207-622-6582. p. 987

Judge, Pat, Acq, Skokie Public Library, 5215 Oakton St, Skokie, IL, 60077-3680. Tel: 847-673-7774. Fax: 847-673-7797. p. 703

Judith, Lihosit, Head, Pub Serv, University of San Diego, Katherine M & George M Pardee Jr Legal Research Center, 5998 Alcala Park, San Diego, CA, 92110-2492. Tel: 619-260-4766. Fax: 619-260-4616. p. 239

Judkins, Dolores, Head, Instruction & Outreach, Head, Res Serv, Oregon Health & Science University Library, 3181 SW Sam Jackson Park Rd, Portland, OR, 97239-3098. Tel: 503-494-3478. Fax: 503-494-3227. p. 2013

Judson, Anne C, Librn, Belding Memorial Library, 344 Main St, Ashfield, MA, 01330. Tel: 413-628-4414. p. 1050

Judt, Ted, Access Serv Librn, East Stroudsburg University, 216 Normal St, East Stroudsburg, PA, 18301-2999. Tel: 570-422-3544. Fax: 570-422-3151. p. 2051

Judy, Christine, Librn, Southeast Regional Library, Broadview Branch, 515 Main St, Broadview, SK, S0G 0K0, CANADA. Tel: 306-696-2414. p. 2929

Judy, Deborah, Ref, Maryland State Law Library, Courts of Appeal Bldg, 361 Rowe Blvd, Annapolis, MD, 21401-1697. Tel: 410-260-1430. Fax: 410-260-1572, 410-974-2063. p. 1010

Juel, Tracy, Dir, Black Bridge Library, 1079 S F Austin Blvd, Dime Box, TX, 77853. Tel: 979-884-0124. Fax: 979-884-0106. p. 2314

Juergens, Bonnie, Pres & Chief Exec Officer, Amigos Library Services, Inc, 14400 Midway Rd, Ste 200, Dallas, TX, 75244-3509. Tel: 972-340-2820. Fax: 972-991-6061. p. 2955

Juergens, David, Coll Develop, University of Mississippi Medical Center, 2500 N State St, Jackson, MS, 39216-4505. Tel: 601-984-1270. Fax: 601-984-1251. p. 1305

Juhasz, Anne, Mgr, Outreach Serv, Massillon Public Library, 208 Lincoln Way E, Massillon, OH, 44646-8416. Tel: 330-832-9831, Ext 329. Fax: 330-830-2182. p. 1915

Juhl, Beth, Head, Web Serv, University of Arkansas Libraries, 365 N McIlroy Ave, Fayetteville, AR, 72701-4002. Tel: 479-575-4665. Fax: 479-575-6656. p. 99

Juillet, Yves, Cat, Centre de Documentation Collegiale, 1111 rue Lapierre, La Salle, QC, H8N 2J4, CANADA. Tel: 514-364-3320, Ext 241. Fax: 514-364-2627. p. 2885

Julagay, Janelle, Bus Librn, University of Redlands, 1200 E Colton Ave, Redlands, CA, 92374-3758. Tel: 909-748-8022. Fax: 909-335-5392. p. 215

Julian, Alicia, Res, Williams & Connolly Library, 725 12th St NW, Washington, DC, 20005. Tel: 202-434-5312. Fax: 202-434-5029. p. 423

Julian, Barbara, ILL, Wheeling Jesuit University, 316 Washington Ave, Wheeling, WV, 26003-6295. Tel: 304-243-2226. Fax: 304-243-2466. p. 2575

Julian, Carol, Asst Chief Librn, Tribune Co, 501 N Calvert St, Baltimore, MD, 21202-3604. Tel: 410-332-6255. Fax: 410-332-6918. p. 1018

Julian, Elaine, Libr Mgr, Vancouver Island Regional Library, Campbell River Branch, 1240 Shopper's Row, Campbell River, BC, V9W 2C8, CANADA. Tel: 250-287-3655. Fax: 250-287-2119. p. 2732

Julian, Gail, Head, Acq, Clemson University Libraries, Box 343001, Clemson, SC, 29634-3001. Tel: 864-656-1114. Fax: 864-656-0758. p. 2186

Julian, Kristin, Archivist, Richard Nixon Library & Birthplace, 18001 Yorba Linda Blvd, Yorba Linda, CA, 92886. Tel: 714-993-5075. p. 285

Julian, Linda, Librn, University of Arkansas Community College at Morrilton, Kirk Bldg, 1537 University Blvd, Morrilton, AR, 72110-9601. Tel: 501-977-2033. Fax: 501-977-2134. p. 110

Julian, Ron, Supvr, Gutenberg College, 1883 University St, Eugene, OR, 97403. Tel: 541-683-5141. Fax: 541-683-6997. p. 1996

Julian, Tiea, Br Coordr, Indiana University Bloomington, Chemistry Library, Chemistry C003, 800 E Kirkwood Ave, Bloomington, IN, 47405-7102. Tel: 812-855-9452. p. 727

Julian-Milas, Sharon, Dir, Pleasant Hills Public Library, 302 Old Clairton Rd, Pleasant Hills, PA, 15236-4399. Tel: 412-655-2424. Fax: 412-655-2292. p. 2130

Juliano, Kathy, Head, ILL, Drew University Library, 36 Madison Ave, Madison, NJ, 07940. Tel: 973-408-3125. Fax: 973-408-3770. p. 1497

Juliano, Vincent, Asst Dir, Russell Library, 123 Broad St, Middletown, CT, 06457. Tel: 860-347-2528, Ext 144. p. 352

Julien, Heidi, Dir, Prof, University of Alabama, 514 Main Library, Tuscaloosa, AL, 35487. Tel: 205-348-4610. Fax: 205-348-3746. p. 2961

Julien, Paula, Access Serv Coordr, OCLC Library, 6565 Kilgour Pl, Dublin, OH, 43017. Tel: 614-764-6000. Fax: 614-793-8707. p. 1896

Julius, Carole A, Dir, Carver Public Library, Two Meadowbrook Way, Carver, MA, 02330-1278. Tel: 508-866-3415. Fax: 508-866-3416. p. 1079

Julius, Rachel, Pub Serv Librn, Art Center College of Design, 1700 Lida St, Pasadena, CA, 91103. Tel: 626-396-2231. Fax: 626-568-0428. p. 205

Julson, Ginny, Dir, Boyceville Public Library, 903 Main St, Boyceville, WI, 54725-9595. Tel: 715-643-2106. p. 2583

Julson, Marci, ILL, Minot Public Library, 516 Second Ave SW, Minot, ND, 58701-3792. Tel: 701-852-1045. Fax: 701-852-2595. p. 1846

Jumonville, Florence, Chair, Spec Coll, University of New Orleans, 2000 Lakeshore Dr, New Orleans, LA, 70148. Tel: 504-280-7275. Fax: 504-280-7277. p. 964

Jumonville, Judy, Dir, Capital City Press, 7290 Bluebonnet Blvd, Baton Rouge, LA, 70810. Tel: 225-388-0328. Fax: 225-388-0329. p. 942

Jump, Joan, Assoc Librn, New Mexico Military Institute, Toles Learning Center, 101 W College Blvd, Roswell, NM, 88201-5173. Tel: 575-624-8387. Fax: 575-624-8390. p. 1561

Jump, Margie, Librn, Coalgate Public Library, 115 W Ohio St, Coalgate, OK, 74538. Tel: 580-927-3103. Fax: 580-927-3846. p. 1961

June, Mary, ILL, Lake Superior State University, 906 Ryan Ave, Sault Sainte Marie, MI, 49783. Tel: 906-635-2815. Fax: 906-635-2193. p. 1226

Juneau, Ann, Librn, Smithsonian Libraries, National Museum of Natural History Library, Nat Museum of Natural Hist, Rm 51, MRC 154, Tenth St & Constitution Ave NW, Washington, DC, 20013-0712. Tel: 202-633-4939. Fax: 202-357-1896. p. 415

Jung, George R, Ref Serv, United States Army, Casey Memorial Library, 72nd St & 761st Tank Battalion, Bldg 3202, Fort Hood, TX, 76544-5024. Tel: 254-287-0025. Fax: 254-288-4029. p. 2320

Jung, Heidi, YA Serv, Gates Public Library, 902 Elmgrove Rd, Rochester, NY, 14624. Tel: 585-247-6446. Fax: 585-426-5733. p. 1729

Jung, Karen, Music Librn, Bowdoin College Library, Beckwith Music Library, Gibson Hall, 1st Flr, 9210 College Sta, Brunswick, ME, 04011. Tel: 207-725-3311. p. 979

Jung, Mary Kay, Dir, Thompson Coburn LLP, One US Bank Plaza, Saint Louis, MO, 63101. Tel: 314-552-6000. Fax: 314-552-7275. p. 1361

Jung, Rebecca, Teen Librn, Belvedere-Tiburon Library, 1501 Tiburon Blvd, Tiburon, CA, 94920. Tel: 415-789-2665. Fax: 415-789-2650. p. 275

Junik, Kristin, Librn, The Art Institute of Tennessee-Nashville Library, 100 Centerview Dr, Ste 250, Nashville, TN, 37214. Tel: 615-874-1067. Fax: 615-874-3530. p. 2255

Junior, Diana, Librn, Susquehanna County Historical Society & Free Library Association, Forest City Branch, 531 Main St, Forest City, PA, 18421-1421. Tel: 570-785-5590. Fax: 570-785-4822. p. 2092

Juniper, Wendy, Electronic Res, Moravian College & Moravian Theological Seminary, 1200 Main St, Bethlehem, PA, 18018-6650. Tel: 610-861-1546. Fax: 610-861-1577. p. 2034

Junius, Adrianne, Dir, Youth Serv, Hall County Library System, 127 Main St NW, Gainesville, GA, 30501-3699. Tel: 770-532-3311. Fax: 770-532-4305. p. 534

Junk, Carol, Circ Supvr, Grand Forks Public Library, 2110 Library Circle, Grand Forks, ND, 58201-6324. Tel: 701-772-8116. Fax: 701-772-1379. p. 1842

Junyk, Myra, Coordr, Libr Serv, Toronto Catholic District School Board, 80 Sheppard Ave E, Toronto, ON, M2N 6E8, CANADA. Tel: 416-222-8282, Ext 5324. Fax: 416-229-5392. p. 2859

Juorio, Alex, Dir, John M Cuelenaere Public Library, 125 12th St E, Prince Albert, SK, S6V 1B7, CANADA. Tel: 306-763-4150. Fax: 306-763-3816. p. 2920

Jurasek, Karen A, Serv Quality & Training Coordr, Drake University, 2725 University Ave, Des Moines, IA, 50311. Tel: 515-271-2903. Fax: 515-271-3933. p. 809

Juraska, Laura, Assoc Col Librn, Ref Serv, Bates College, 48 Campus Ave, Lewiston, ME, 04240. Tel: 207-786-8324. Fax: 207-786-6055. p. 989

Jurcik, Moira, Health Educator, Northwestern Memorial Hospital, 250 E Superior-Prentice Women's Hospital, First Floor, Room 2104, Chicago, IL, 60611. Tel: 312-472-3841. Fax: 312-472-3836. p. 621

Jurecek, Lisa, Librn, Salinas Alicia City of Alice Public Library, Orange Grove School & Public Library, PO Box 534, Orange Grove, TX, 78372. Tel: 361-384-2330, Ext 505, 361-384-2461. p. 2273

Jurecki, Hanna, Supvr, Ad Serv, Richardson Public Library, 900 Civic Center Dr, Richardson, TX, 75080. Tel: 972-744-4377. Fax: 972-744-5806. p. 2374

Jurey, Debra, Librn, San Luis Obispo County Library, Santa Margarita Branch, 9630 Murphy Ave, Santa Margarita, CA, 93453. Tel: 805-438-5622. Fax: 805-438-4879. p. 254

Jurgena, Melissa, Dr, Exec Dir, Liberty Hall Historic Site Library, 202 Wilkinson St, Frankfort, KY, 40601. Tel: 502-227-2560. Fax: 502-227-3348. p. 914

Jurgens, Jane, Ref Serv, Minneapolis Community & Technical College Library, Wheelock Whitney Hall, 1501 Hennepin Ave, Minneapolis, MN, 55403. Tel: 612-659-6287. Fax: 612-659-6295. p. 1261

Jurgenson, Jamie, Mgr, Dakota County Library System, Robert Trail, 14395 S Robert Trail, Rosemount, MN, 55068. Tel: 651-480-1205. Fax: 651-480-1212. p. 1249

Jurich, Cathy, Head, Youth Serv, Dexter District Library, 3255 Alpine St, Dexter, MI, 48130. Tel: 734-426-4477. Fax: 734-426-1217. p. 1174

Juris, Gail, Ref, Highland Park Public Library, 494 Laurel Ave, Highland Park, IL, 60035-2690. Tel: 847-432-0216. Fax: 847-432-9139. p. 655

Jurkins, Jacquelyn, Law Librn, Multnomah Law Library, County Courthouse, 4th Flr, 1021 SW Fourth Ave, Portland, OR, 97204. Tel: 503-988-3394. Fax: 503-988-3395. p. 2012

Jurkis, Marissa, Br Librn, Cisco College, Abilene Educational Center Library, 717 E Industrial Blvd, Abilene, TX, 79602. Tel: 325-794-4466. p. 2297

Jurkovic, Doreen, Librn, Southeast Regional Library, Maryfield Branch, 201 Barrows St, Maryfield, SK, S0G 3K0, CANADA. Tel: 306-646-2148. p. 2930

Jurney, Nancy, Ref, Southern Nazarene University, 4115 N College, Bethany, OK, 73008. Tel: 405-491-6350. Fax: 405-491-6355. p. 1958

Jurries, Elaine, Electronic Access/Sci & Eng Coll Develop Librn, Auraria Library, 1100 Lawrence St, Denver, CO, 80204-2095. Tel: 303-556-2622. Fax: 303-556-3528. p. 298

Jushchyshyn, Caroline, Br Librn, Upper Darby Township & Sellers Memorial Free Public Library, Primos Branch, 409 Ashland Rd, Secane, PA, 19018. Tel: 610-622-8091. Fax: 484-461-9026. p. 2149

Jusic, Jasmina, Ref Serv, Ad, Park City Library, 1255 Park Ave, Park City, UT, 84060. Tel: 435-615-5602. Fax: 435-615-4903. p. 2410

Jusino, Arleyn D, Asst Librn, Pontifical Catholic University Of Puerto Rico, Encarnacion Valdes Library, 2250 Avenida Las Americas, Ste 509, Ponce, PR, 00717-0777. Tel: 787-841-2000, Ext 1801, 787-841-2000, Ext 1802. Fax: 787-284-0235. p. 2674

Juskiewicz, Scott, Ref Librn, Montana Tech Library, 1300 W Park St, Butte, MT, 59701-8997. Tel: 406-496-4523. Fax: 406-496-4133. p. 1376

Just, Anne, Dir, Mason Library, 231 Main St, Great Barrington, MA, 01230. Tel: 413-528-2403. p. 1092

Just, Irena, Asst Dir, Asst Librn, Ch, Herrin City Library, 120 N 13th St, Herrin, IL, 62948-3233. Tel: 618-942-6109. Fax: 618-942-4165. p. 655

Justice, Adam, Curator, Polk Museum of Art, 800 E Palmetto St, Lakeland, FL, 33801-5529. Tel: 863-688-7743, Ext 241. Fax: 863-688-2611. p. 459

Justice, Diana, Ref Librn, Caldwell County Public Library, 120 Hospital Ave, Lenoir, NC, 28645-4454. Tel: 828-757-1270. Fax: 828-757-1413. p. 1806

Justice, Ellen, Head, Ref, Christiana Hospital Library, Christiana Hospital, 4755 Ogletown Stanton Rd, Newark, DE, 19718-0002. Tel: 302-733-1115. Fax: 302-733-1365. p. 385

Justice, Mike, Tech Serv, Southeast Kentucky Community & Technical College, 1300 Chichester Ave, Middlesboro, KY, 40965. Tel: 606-248-0443. Fax: 606-248-3233. p. 929

Justice, Terri, Dean, Broward College, South Campus Library LRC, 7300 Hollywood, Pembroke Pines, FL, 33024. Tel: 954-201-8827. Fax: 954-201-0282. p. 435

Justie, Kevin, Asst Dir, Syst & Tech, Morton Grove Public Library, 6140 Lincoln Ave, Morton Grove, IL, 60053-2989. Tel: 847-929-5110. Fax: 847-965-7903. p. 676

Justin, Megahan, Electronic Res & Ref Librn, Fontbonne University, 6800 Wydown Blvd, Saint Louis, MO, 63105. Tel: 314-719-8088. Fax: 314-719-8040. p. 1354

Justis, Lara, Libr Tech, Goucher College Library, 1021 Dulaney Valley Rd, Baltimore, MD, 21204. Tel: 410-337-6360. Fax: 410-337-6419. p. 1014

Justiss, Larry D, Dir, Tom Green County Library System, 113 W Beauregard, San Angelo, TX, 76903. Tel: 915-655-7321. Fax: 915-659-4027. p. 2378

Justsen, Marlene, Archivist, National Press Club, 529 14th St NW, 13th Flr, Washington, DC, 20045. Tel: 202-662-7598. Fax: 202-879-6725. p. 411

Justus, Sharon, Librn, Two Rivers Correctional Institute Library, 82911 Beach Access Rd, Umatilla, OR, 97882. Tel: 541-922-2177. p. 2022

Jutzi, Alan, Curator, Huntington Library, 1151 Oxford Rd, San Marino, CA, 91108. Tel: 626-405-2178. Fax: 626-449-5720. p. 255

Jwacu, Thulani, Circ, ILL, Libr Tech, Minneapolis Community & Technical College Library, Wheelock Whitney Hall, 1501 Hennepin Ave, Minneapolis, MN, 55403. Tel: 612-659-6294. Fax: 612-659-6295. p. 1261

Kaan, Linda, Youth Serv Coordr, Strasburg-Heisler Library, 143 Precision Ave, Strasburg, PA, 17579. Tel: 717-687-8969. Fax: 717-687-9795. p. 2143

Kaas, Mary Ellen, Dir, McElroy, Deutsch, Mulvaney & Carpenter, LLP, 1300 Mt Kemble Ave, Morristown, NJ, 07962. Tel: 973-425-8810. Fax: 973-425-0161. p. 1505

Kaatrude, Peter B, Dean of Libr, Lamar State College, 317 Stilwell Blvd, Port Arthur, TX, 77640. Tel: 409-984-6216. Fax: 409-984-6008. p. 2371

Kaba, Shawn, Libr Dir, Monroe College, 2468 Jerome Ave, Bronx, NY, 10468. Tel: 718-933-6700, Ext 8334. Fax: 718-584-4242. p. 1588

Kaback, Susann, Ch, James H Johnson Memorial Library, 670 Ward Dr, Deptford, NJ, 08096. Tel: 856-848-9149. Fax: 856-848-1813. p. 1481

Kaban, Melody, Libr Mgr, Smoky Lake Municipal Library, 5010-50 St, Smoky Lake, AB, T0A 3C0, CANADA. Tel: 780-656-4212. Fax: 780-656-4212. p. 2717

Kabara, Joseph, Asst Prof, University of Pittsburgh, 135 N Bellefield Ave, Pittsburgh, PA, 15260. Tel: 412-624-5230. Fax: 412-624-5231. p. 2973

Kabat, Jennean, Librn, Delta College Library, 1961 Delta Rd, University Center, MI, 48710. Tel: 989-686-9822. Fax: 989-686-4131. p. 1232

Kabelac, Julie, Coordr, Tech Serv, Syst, Wells College, 170 Main St, Aurora, NY, 13026-0500. Tel: 315 364-3357. Fax: 315-364-3412. p. 1576

Kabler, Debra, Dir, Barneveld Public Library, 107 W Orbison St, Barneveld, WI, 53507-9400. Tel: 608-924-3711. Fax: 608-924-3711. p. 2580

Kabrud, Jack A, Curator, Historical Society of Hennepin County, 2303 Third Ave S, Minneapolis, MN, 55404-3599. Tel: 612-870-1329. Fax: 612-870-1320. p. 1260

Kaceli, Stephanie S, Asst Dir, Automation Syst Coordr, Head, Tech Serv, Cairn University, 200 Manor Ave, Langhorne, PA, 19047. Tel: 215-702-4370. Fax: 215-702-4374. p. 2078

Kachaturian, Andrew, Librn, Newport Beach Public Library, Corona del Mar Branch, 420 Marigold Ave, Corona del Mar, CA, 92625. Tel: 949-717-3800. Fax: 949-673-4917. p. 194

Kaczmarczyk, Linda, Clinical Librn, Pediatrics, Hartford Hospital, ERC Bldg-3, 80 Seymour St, Hartford, CT, 06102. Tel: 860-545-2422. Fax: 860-545-2572. p. 345

Kaczmarek, Mary, Librn, The Alliance for Children & Families, 11700 W Lake Park Dr, Milwaukee, WI, 53224. Tel: 414-359-1040, Ext 3615. Fax: 414-359-1074. p. 2616

Kaczmarek, Susan, Asst City Librn, Oak Creek Public Library, 8620 S Howell Ave, Oak Creek, WI, 53154. Tel: 414-764-4400. Fax: 414-768-6583. p. 2626

Kaczmarski, Bill, Res, Kalsec, Inc, 3713 W Main St, Kalamazoo, MI, 49006. Tel: 269-382-3342. Fax: 269-382-3060. p. 1197

Kaczmarski, Brenda J, Dir, Deer Park Public Library, 112 Front St W, Deer Park, WI, 54007. Tel: 715-269-5464. Fax: 715-269-5464. p. 2588

Kaczor, Sue, Bibliographer, Ref Librn, University at Albany, State University of New York, Science Library, 1400 Washington Ave, Albany, NY, 12222. Tel: 518-437-3948. Fax: 518-437-3952. p. 1571

Kaczorowski, David, Ser, University of Medicine & Dentistry of New Jersey, Academic Ctr, One Medical Center Dr, Stratford, NJ, 08084. Tel: 856-566-6800. Fax: 856-566-6380. p. 1532

Kaczorowski, Monice M, Dir, Libr Serv & Competitive Intelligence, Neal, Gerber & Eisenberg LLP, Two N La Salle St, Ste 1700, Chicago, IL, 60602. Tel: 312-269-5220. Fax: 312-578-1793. p. 620

Kadel, Andrew, Fr, Dir, General Theological Seminary, 440 West 21st St, New York, NY, 10011. Tel: 212-243-5150. Fax: 212-924-6304. p. 1679

Kadhum, Ana, Ref, Uncle Remus Regional Library System, 1121 East Ave, Madison, GA, 30650. Tel: 706-342-4974, Ext 19. Fax: 706-342-4510. p. 541

Kading, Sue, Ch, Benton Harbor Public Library, 213 E Wall St, Benton Harbor, MI, 49022-4499. Tel: 269-926-6139. Fax: 269-926-1674. p. 1156

Kadiyala, Madhu, Ref Librn, Henderson District Public Libraries, 280 S Green Valley Pkwy, Henderson, NV, 89012. Tel: 702-492-7252. Fax: 702-492-1711. p. 1428

Kaeser, Rick, Doc Delivery, Webster University, 101 Edgar Rd, Saint Louis, MO, 63119. Tel: 314-968-5994. Fax: 314-968-7113. p. 1363

Kafasis, Beth Anne, Operations Adminr, Cranbury Public Library, 23 N Main St, Cranbury, NJ, 08512. Tel: 609-655-0555. Fax: 609-655-2858. p. 1480

Kafczynski, Kathy, Asst Librn, Michigan Department of Corrections, PO Box 236, Marenisco, MI, 49947. Tel: 906-787-2217. Fax: 906-787-2324. p. 1206

Kaffenberger, Betty, Archives Coordr, University of Saint Thomas, 1100 W Main, Houston, TX, 77006. Tel: 713-525-3895. Fax: 713-525-2117. p. 2344

Kafut, Mary Beth, Dir, Eveleth Public Library, 614 Pierce St, Eveleth, MN, 55734-1697. Tel: 218-744-7499. Fax: 218-742-9635. p. 1250

Kagan, Alan, Head Librn, Hebrew Theological College, Anne Blitstein Teachers Institute, 2600 Toughy Ave, Chicago, IL, 60645. Tel: 773-973-0241. Fax: 773-973-1627. p. 703

Kagen, Sarah, Ref, Proskauer Rose LLP Library, 1585 Broadway, Concourse Level, New York, NY, 10036. Tel: 212-969-5001. Fax: 212-969-2931. p. 1698

Kager, Jeff, Chief Librn, Department of Veterans Affairs, 508 Fulton St, Durham, NC, 27705. Tel: 919-286-6929. Fax: 919-286-6859. p. 1787

Kahan, Bobbi, Coordr, Mountain States Health Alliance, 400 N State of Franklin Rd, Johnson City, TN, 37604-6094. Tel: 423-431-1691. Fax: 423-431-1692. p. 2240

Kahan, Jane, Ch, Wixom Public Library, 49015 Pontiac Trail, Wixom, MI, 48393-2567. Tel: 248-624-2512. Fax: 248-624-0862. p. 1237

Kahelahela, Kipapa, Actg Br Mgr, Hawaii State Public Library System, Kealakekua Public Library, 81-6619 Mamalahoa Hwy, Kealakekua, HI, 96750. Tel: 808-323-7585. Fax: 808-323-7586. p. 562

Kahelin, Donna, Pub Serv Asst, Florida Southern College, 111 Lake Hollingsworth Dr, Lakeland, FL, 33801-5698. Tel: 863-616-6453. Fax: 863-680-4126. p. 459

Kahkola, Lynn, Ref Serv, Clear Creek Baptist Bible College, 300 Clear Creek Rd, Pineville, KY, 40977. Tel: 606-337-3196. Fax: 606-337-2372. p. 933

Kahl, Jeanne, Asst Dir, Balsam Lake Public Library, 404 Main St, Balsam Lake, WI, 54810-7261. Tel: 715-485-3215. Fax: 715-485-3215. p. 2580

Kahl, Karen, Dir, Union County Public Library, Two E Seminary St, Liberty, IN, 47353-1398. Tel: 765-458-5355, 765-458-6227. Fax: 765-458-9375. p. 761

Kahl, Kathleen, Youth Serv, Way Public Library, 101 E Indiana Ave, Perrysburg, OH, 43551. Tel: 419-874-3135, Ext 113. Fax: 419-874-6129. p. 1929

Kahlden, Cindy, Libr Dir, Weimar Public Library, One Jackson Sq, Weimar, TX, 78962-2019. Tel: 979-725-6608. Fax: 979-725-9033. p. 2399

Kahle, Cathy, Asst Librn, Sinclairville Free Library, 15 Main St, Sinclairville, NY, 14782. Tel: 716-962-5885. Fax: 716-962-5885. p. 1744

Kahle, Richard, In Charge, Ralph Stone & Co, Inc, 10954 Santa Monica Blvd, Los Angeles, CA, 90025. Tel: 310-478-1501. Fax: 310-478-7359. p. 177

Kahler, David, Syst Librn, Pittsylvania County Public Library, 24 Military Dr, Chatham, VA, 24531. Tel: 434-432-3271. Fax: 434-432-1405. p. 2455

Kahler, Tracie, Pres, Central Pennsylvania Health Sciences Library Association, Office for Research Protections, the Pennsylvania State University, 212 Kern Graduate Bldg, University Park, PA, 16802. Tel: 814-863-8699. Fax: 814-863-8699. p. 2953

Kahn, Deborah, Librn, Warren Public Library, 413 Main St, Warren, VT, 05674. Tel: 802-496-3913. Fax: 802-496-2418. p. 2438

Kahn, Leslie, Supv Librn, Ref, Newark Public Library, Five Washington St, Newark, NJ, 07101. Tel: 973-733-7784, 973-733-7800. Fax: 973-733-5648. p. 1511

Kahn, Martha, Ref Librn, South Huntington Public Library, 145 Pidgeon Hill Rd, Huntington Station, NY, 11746. Tel: 631-549-4411. Fax: 631-549-1266. p. 1639

Kahn, Natasha, Ref Librn, Fitchburg State College, 160 Pearl St, Fitchburg, MA, 01420. Tel: 978 665-4869. Fax: 978-665-3069. p. 1089

Kahn, Patricia, Librn, Pen Bay Medical Center, Six Glen Cove Dr, Rockport, ME, 04856. Tel: 207-596-8456. Fax: 207-593-5281. p. 999

Kahn, Sheila, Asst Librn, The Gunnery, 99 Green Hill Rd, Washington, CT, 06793. Tel: 860-868-7334, Ext 224. Fax: 860-868-0859. p. 374

Kahn, Susan, Exec Dir, National Tay-Sachs & Allied Diseases Association Library, 2001 Beacon St, Ste 204, Brighton, MA, 02135. Tel: 617-277-4463. Fax: 617-277-0134. p. 1070

Kahnhauser, Joan, Head, Adult Serv, Emma S Clark Memorial Library, 120 Main St, Setauket, NY, 11733-2868. Tel: 631-941-4080. Fax: 631-941-4541. p. 1742

Kaida, Nancy, Ref Serv, Northwest Vista College, Redbud Hall, 3535 N Ellison Dr, San Antonio, TX, 78251. Tel: 210-486-4571. Fax: 210-486-9105. p. 2380

Kaido, Debra, Librn, State Supreme Court, Hale Kaulike Bldg, 777 Kilauea Ave, Hilo, HI, 96720-4212. Tel: 808-961-7438. Fax: 808-961-7416. p. 559

Kaimowitz, Jeffrey H, Head Librn, Trinity College Library, Watkinson Library, 300 Summit St, Hartford, CT, 06106. Tel: 860-297-2268. p. 347

Kain, Peggy, Electronic Res, University of Alabama at Birmingham, Mervyn H Sterne Library, 917 13th St S, Birmingham, AL, 35205. Tel: 205-934-9939. p. 10

Kain-Breese, April, Dir, University of Wisconsin-Fox Valley Library, 1478 Midway Rd, Menasha, WI, 54952-1297. Tel: 920-832-2675. Fax: 920-832-2874. p. 2614

Kaip, Sarah, Librn, South Puget Sound Community College Library, 2011 Mottman Rd SW, Olympia, WA, 98512. Tel: 360-596-5271. Fax: 360-596-5714. p. 2522

Kairis, Rob, Dir, Kent State University, 6000 Frank Ave NW, North Canton, OH, 44720-7548. Tel: 330-244-3326. Fax: 330-494-6212. p. 1923

Kaiser, Blanka, ILL Tech, Alberta Government Library, 10025 Jasper Ave, 15th Flr, Edmonton, AB, T5J 2N3, CANADA. Tel: 780-427-8720. Fax: 780-422-9694. p. 2698

Kaiser, Carole, Circ, Fairhope Public Library, 501 Fairhope Ave, Fairhope, AL, 36532. Tel: 251-928-7483. Fax: 251-928-9717. p. 16

Kaiser, Gina, Coordr, Tech Serv, University of the Sciences in Philadelphia, 4200 Woodland Ave, Philadelphia, PA, 19104-4491. Tel: 215-596-8963. Fax: 215-596-8760. p. 2120

Kaiser, Helen, Br Mgr, North Vancouver District Public Library, Parkgate, 3675 Banff Ct, North Vancouver, BC, V7G 2A6, CANADA. Tel: 604-929-3727. Fax: 604-929-0758. p. 2734

Kaiser, Jan D, Mkt Mgr, Des Moines Public Library, 1000 Grand Ave, Des Moines, IA, 50309. Tel: 515-283-4103. Fax: 515-237-1654. p. 808

Kaiser, Liana, Br Supvr, Western Manitoba Regional Library, Neepawa Branch, 280 Davidson St, Neepawa, MB, R0J 1H0, CANADA. Tel: 204-476-5648. p. 2748

Kaiser, Louella, Dir, WaKeeney Public Library, 610 Russell Ave, WaKeeney, KS, 67672-2135. Tel: 785-743-2960. Fax: 785-743-5802. p. 899

Kaiser, Marceile, Tech & Syst Librn, Columbiana Public Library, 332 N Middle St, Columbiana, OH, 44408. Tel: 330-482-5509. Fax: 330-482-9669. p. 1883

Kaiser, Marcia, Libr Coordr, Monroe Clinic, 515 22nd Ave, Monroe, WI, 53566. Tel: 608-324-1590. Fax: 608-324-2499. p. 2623

Kaiser, Michael, Exec Dir, Lehigh Valley Planning Commission Library, 961 Marcon Blvd, Ste 310, Allentown, PA, 18109-9397. Tel: 610-264-4544. Fax: 610-264-2616. p. 2027

Kaiser, Nancy, Sr Asst Librn, State University of New York Institute of Technology, Rte 12 N & Horatio St, Utica, NY, 13502. Tel: 315-792-7307. Fax: 315-792-7517. p. 1759

Kaiser, Patricia, Asst Admin, Hudson Valley Community College, 80 Vandenburgh Ave, Troy, NY, 12180. Tel: 518-629-7330. Fax: 518-629-7509. p. 1756

Kaiser, Rita, Head, Ref, King County Law Library, W 621 King County Courthouse, 516 Third Ave, Seattle, WA, 98104. Tel: 206-296-0940. Fax: 206-205-0513. p. 2528

Kaiser, Sandy, Youth Serv, Linebaugh Public Library System of Rutherford County, Smyrna Public, 400 Enon Springs Rd W, Smyrna, TN, 37167. Tel: 615-459-4884. Fax: 615-459-2370. p. 2254

Kajiwara, Robert M, Head Librn, Kauai Community College, 3-1901 Kaumualii Hwy, Lihue, HI, 96766. Tel: 808-245-8233. Fax: 808-245-8294. p. 567

Kajner, Anita, Librn, Lakeland Library Region, Pierceland Branch, PO Box 250, Pierceland, SK, S0M 2K0, CANADA. Tel: 306-839-2166. p. 2920

Kakavis, Betty, Acq, Shaler North Hills Library, 1822 Mount Royal Blvd, Glenshaw, PA, 15116. Tel: 412-486-0211. Fax: 412-486-8286. p. 2061

Kakekagumick, Paula, Librn, Sucker Creek First Nations Public Library, RR 1, Box 21, Little Current, ON, P0P 1K0, CANADA. Tel: 705-368-2228, 705-368-3696. Fax: 705-368-3563. p. 2816

Kakuske, Tina, Circ Mgr, Beloit Public Library, 605 Eclipse Blvd, Beloit, WI, 53511. Tel: 608-364-5766. Fax: 608-364-2907. p. 2581

Kakuske, Tina, Adult Serv, Eager Free Public Library, 39 W Main St, Evansville, WI, 53536. Tel: 608-882-2260, 608-882-2275. Fax: 608-882-2261. p. 2591

Kalafut, Deborah, ILL, Bedford Park Public Library District, 7816 W 65th Pl, Bedford Park, IL, 60501. Tel: 708-458-6826. Fax: 708-458-9827. p. 593

Kalat, Mary, Br Librn, Community District Library, Bancroft-Shiawassee Township Branch, 625 Grand River Rd, Bancroft, MI, 48414. Tel: 989-743-5689. Fax: 989-634-5689. p. 1166

Kalathas, Diane, ILL, Shippensburg University, 1871 Old Main Dr, Shippensburg, PA, 17257-2299. Tel: 717-477-1463. Fax: 717-477-1389. p. 2140

Kalavaza, Gwen, Electronic Serv Mgr, Los Alamos County Library System, 2400 Central Ave, Los Alamos, NM, 87544. Tel: 505-662-8240. Fax: 505-662-8245. p. 1559

Kalb, Christine, Ch, Marvin Memorial Library, 29 W Whitney Ave, Shelby, OH, 44875-1252. Tel: 419-347-5576. Fax: 419-347-7285. p. 1934

Kalb, Rosalind, Dir, National Multiple Sclerosis Society, 733 Third Ave, New York, NY, 10017. Tel: 212-986-3240. Fax: 212-986-7981. p. 1688

Kalchthaler, Ingrid, Coordr, Ch Serv, Bethel Park Public Library, 5100 W Library Ave, Bethel Park, PA, 15102. Tel: 412-831-6800, Ext 262, 412-851-2465. Fax: 412-835-9360. p. 2033

Kalchthaler, Ingrid, Ch, Shaler North Hills Library, 1822 Mount Royal Blvd, Glenshaw, PA, 15116. Tel: 412-486-0211. Fax: 412-486-8286. p. 2061

Kalchthaler, Robert, Ref Serv, Ad, Bethel Park Public Library, 5100 W Library Ave, Bethel Park, PA, 15102. Tel: 412-831-6800, Ext 262, 412-851-2465. Fax: 412-835-9360. p. 2033

Kaldan, Janina, Librn, Robert Wood Johnson University Hospital Rahway, 865 Stone St, Rahway, NJ, 07065. Tel: 732-381-4200. p. 1524

Kale, Julie, Librn, Infineum USALP, 1900 E Linden Ave, Linden, NJ, 07036-1111. Tel: 908-474-2351. Fax: 908-474-2020. p. 1495

Kalemaris, Stanley, Outreach Serv Librn, South Huntington Public Library, 145 Pidgeon Hill Rd, Huntington Station, NY, 11746. Tel: 631-549-4411. Fax: 631-549-1266. p. 1639

Kaler, Sue, ILL, Wellesley Free Library, 530 Washington St, Wellesley, MA, 02482. Tel: 781-235-1610, Ext 1112. Fax: 781-235-0495. p. 1135

Kaleva, Debbie, Campus Librn, Nova Scotia Community College, 39 Acadia Ave, Stellarton, NS, B0K 1S0, CANADA. Tel: 902-755-7201. Fax: 902-755-7289. p. 2784

Kalfatovic, Martin, Assoc Dir, Digital Serv, Prog Dir, Biodiversity Heritage Libr, Smithsonian Libraries, Nat Museum of Natural Hist, Rm 22, MRC154, Tenth St & Constitution Ave NW, Washington, DC, 20002. Tel: 202-633-1705. Fax: 202-633-4315. p. 414

Kaliher, Michael, Librn II, Arizona Department of Corrections, Arizona State Prison Complex-Safford, NW Sulphur Springs Valley, Graham County, Fort Grant, AZ, 85643. Tel: 928-828-3393, Ext 4217. p. 63

Kalil, Katy, Br Mgr, Huntsville-Madison Public Library, Elizabeth Carpenter Public Library of New Hope, 5498 Main St, New Hope, AL, 35760. Tel: 256-723-2995. p. 21

Kalin, Amelia, Dir, Valley Cottage Free Library, 110 Rte 303, Valley Cottage, NY, 10989. Tel: 845-268-7700. Fax: 845-268-7760. p. 1760

Kalina, Kris, ILL, Librn, Conemaugh Memorial Medical Center, 1086 Franklin St, Johnstown, PA, 15905-4398. Tel: 814-534-5960, 814-534-9111. Fax: 814-534-3244. p. 2073

Kalinka, George, Adult Serv, YA Serv, Woodridge Public Library, Three Plaza Dr, Woodridge, IL, 60517-5014. Tel: 630-964-7899. Fax: 630-964-0175. p. 721

Kalinowsk, Sue, Circ Supvr, Rossford Public Library, 720 Dixie Hwy, Rossford, OH, 43460-1289. Tel: 419-666-0924. Fax: 419-666-1989. p. 1932

Kalinski, Peter, Archivist, The Henry Ford, 20900 Oakwood Blvd, Dearborn, MI, 48124-5029. Tel: 313-982-6100, Ext 2538. Fax: 313-982-6244. p. 1167

Kalisz, Lorraine M, ILL, Adams Free Library, 92 Park St, Adams, MA, 01220-2096. Tel: 413-743-8345. Fax: 413-743-8344. p. 1047

Kalka, Justine, Head Librn, DLA Piper US LLP, 1251 Avenue of Americas, 45th Flr, New York, NY, 10020-1104. Tel: 212-776-3940. p. 1677

Kalkbrenner, Jane, Cent Libr Mgr, Onondaga County Public Library, The Galleries of Syracuse, 447 S Salina St, Syracuse, NY, 13202-2494. Fax: 315-435-8533. p. 1752

Kalla, June, Archivist, Ref, Stearns History Museum, 235 33rd Ave S, Saint Cloud, MN, 56301-3752. Tel: 320-253-8424. Fax: 320-253-2172. p. 1276

Kallas, Diane L, Circ Mgr, Tech Serv Mgr, Mead Public Library, 710 N Eighth St, Sheboygan, WI, 53081-4563. Tel: 920-459-3400, Ext 3403. Fax: 920-459-0204. p. 2637

Kallas, Kathy, Circ, Uinta County Library, 701 Main St, Evanston, WY, 82930. Tel: 307-789-2770. Fax: 307-789-0148. p. 2655

Kallas, Michelle, Ch, Uinta County Library, 701 Main St, Evanston, WY, 82930. Tel: 307-789-1329. Fax: 307-789-0148. p. 2655

Kallberg, Cheryl, Head, Ch, Manhasset Public Library, 30 Onderdonk Ave, Manhasset, NY, 11030. Tel: 516 627-2300, Ext 305. Fax: 516-627-4339. p. 1657

Kallem, Ayers, Reserves, Middlebury College Library, 110 Storrs Ave, Middlebury, VT, 05753-6007. Tel: 802-443-5490. Fax: 802-443-2074, 802-443-5698. p. 2428

Kaller, Reuben, Ref, St Philip's College, 1801 Martin Luther King Dr, San Antonio, TX, 78203-2098. Tel: 210-486-2330. Fax: 210-486-2335. p. 2381

Kallfisch, Doreen, Head, Tech Serv, Middletown Public Library, 55 New Monmouth Rd, Middletown, NJ, 07748. Tel: 732-671-3700, Ext 328. Fax: 732-671-5839. p. 1501

Kallies, James, Ref, Utica Public Library, 303 Genesee St, Utica, NY, 13501. Tel: 315-735-2279. Fax: 315-734-1004. p. 1760

Kallista, Fay, Ref & ILL Librn, Argosy University of Chicago Library, 225 N Michigan Ave, Chicago, IL, 60601. Tel: 312-777-7653. Fax: 312-777-7749. p. 606

Kalloway, Kalla, Teen Serv, Dakota County Library System, 1340 Wescott Rd, Eagan, MN, 55123-1099. Tel: 651-450-2941. Fax: 651-450-2915. p. 1249

Kallunki, Sandy J, Supvr, Pub Serv, Brown County Library, 515 Pine St, Green Bay, WI, 54301. Tel: 920-448-5844. Fax: 920-448-6253. p. 2595

Kallusky, Barb, Head, Pub Serv, Hamline University, School of Law Library, 1536 Hewitt Ave, Saint Paul, MN, 55104-1237. Tel: 651-523-2379. Fax: 651-523-2863. p. 1278

Kalman, Georgia, Librn, Temple Israel Library, 2324 Emerson Ave S, Minneapolis, MN, 55405-2695. Tel: 612-374-0338. Fax: 612-377-6630. p. 1261

Kalman, Jay, Admin Dir, Ref Serv, Ad, Harvey Public Library District, 15441 Turlington Ave, Harvey, IL, 60426-3683. Tel: 708-331-0757, Ext 205. Fax: 708-331-2835. p. 654

Kalman, Sharon, Ch, Paramus Public Library, E 116 Century Rd, Paramus, NJ, 07652-4398. Tel: 201-599-1300. Fax: 201-599-0059. p. 1517

Kalmanson, Kathryn, Instruction/Coll Mgt Spec, Salisbury University, 1101 Camden Ave, Salisbury, MD, 21801-6863. Tel: 410-543-6130. Fax: 410-543-6203. p. 1040

Kalnins, Karen, Memphis Satellite Librn, US Court of Appeals for the Sixth Circuit Library, 312 Potter Stewart US Courthouse, Cincinnati, OH, 45202. Tel: 901-495-1357. Fax: 513-564-7329. p. 1873

Kalogeros-Chattan, Charlie, Libr Mgr, Los Alamos County Library System, 2400 Central Ave, Los Alamos, NM, 87544. Tel: 505-662-8242. Fax: 505-662-8245. p. 1559

Kalra, Aarash, Dr, Librn, SNC-Lavalin Inc Library, 195 West Mall, Toronto, ON, M9C 5K1, CANADA. Tel: 416-252-5311. Fax: 416-231-5356. p. 2858

Kalteis, Natasha, Exec Dir, General Federation of Women's Clubs, 1734 N St NW, Washington, DC, 20036-2990. Tel: 202-347-3168. Fax: 202-835-0246. p. 401

Kaltenbach, Ryan, Dep Dir, Saginaw Art Museum, 1126 N Michigan Ave, Saginaw, MI, 48602-4763. Tel: 989-754-2491. Fax: 989-754-9387. p. 1224

Kalter, Bruce, Dir, Donna Public Library, 301 S Main St, Donna, TX, 78537. Tel: 956-464-2221. Fax: 956-464-2172. p. 2314

Kaluzny, Mary, Head, Tech Serv, Clinton-Macomb Public Library, 40900 Romeo Plank Rd, Clinton Township, MI, 48038-2955. Tel: 586-226-5061. Fax: 586-226-5008. p. 1164

Kaluzny, Neal, Br Mgr, Milwaukee Public Library, Tippecanoe, 3912 S Howell Ave, Milwaukee, WI, 53207. Tel: 414-286-3085. Fax: 414-286-8405. p. 2620

Kalvee, Debbie, Assoc Univ Librn, Serv & Facilities, Brock University, 500 Glenridge Ave, St. Catharines, ON, L2S 3A1, CANADA. Tel: 905-688-5550, Ext 3198. Fax: 905-988-5490. p. 2842

Kalvig, Loraine, Librn, Grafton Public Library, 203 Fourth Ave, Grafton, IA, 50440-0025. Tel: 641-748-2735. Fax: 641-748-2739. p. 818

Kalvoda, Laura, Circ, Bismarck State College Library, 1500 Edwards Ave, Bismarck, ND, 58501. Tel: 701-224-5483. Fax: 701-224-5551. p. 1837

Kalyan, Sulekha, Acq Librn, Seton Hall University Libraries, Walsh Libary Bldg, 400 S Orange Ave, South Orange, NJ, 07079. Tel: 973-761-9438. Fax: 973-761-9432. p. 1530

Kamada, Hitoshi, Assoc Librn, University of Arizona, East Asian Collection, 1510 E University Blvd, Tucson, AZ, 85720. Tel: 520-307-2772. Fax: 520-621-3655. p. 89

Kamaraczewski, Mary, Res, Kirkland & Ellis LLP Library, 300 N LaSalle St, 11th Flr, Chicago, IL, 60654. Tel: 312-862-6528. Fax: 312-862-2200. p. 616

Kamarei, Zahra, Librn, University of North Carolina at Chapel Hill, Brauer (Math-Physics), 365 Phillips Hall, CB No 3250, Chapel Hill, NC, 27599-3250. Tel: 919-962-2323. Fax: 919-962-2568. p. 1780

Kamarei, Zari, Librn, University of North Carolina at Chapel Hill, Kenan (Chemistry), Wilson Library, 2nd Level, CB No 3290, Chapel Hill, NC, 27599. Tel: 919-962-1188. Fax: 919-962-2388. p. 1781

Kamau, Nellie, Electronic Res Librn, United States Agency for International Development, 1300 Pennsylvania Ave NW, Rm M01-010, Washington, DC, 20523-1000. Tel: 202-712-0579. Fax: 202-216-3515. p. 417

Kambic, Sandy, Librn, Provena Saint Mary's Hospital, 500 W Court St, Kankakee, IL, 60901. Tel: 815-937-2477. Fax: 815-937-2466. p. 661

Kambitsch, Timothy, Exec Dir, Dayton Metro Library, 215 E Third St, Dayton, OH, 45402-2103. Tel: 937-463-2665. Fax: 937-496-4300. p. 1892

Kambule, Addis, Librn, Roxbury Correctional Institution Library, 18701 Roxbury Rd, Hagerstown, MD, 21746. Tel: 240-420-3000, Ext 5290. Fax: 301-733-2672. p. 1031

Kamecke, Debra, Librn, Cairo Public Library, 512 Main St, Cairo, NY, 12413-3007. Tel: 518-622-9864. Fax: 518-622-9874. p. 1600

Kamego, Claire, Acq, Texas Health Harris Methodist Fort Worth Hospital, 1301 Pennsylvania Ave, Fort Worth, TX, 76104. Tel: 817-250-2118. Fax: 817-250-5119. p. 2324

Kamennof-Sine, Lana, Regional Librn, Annapolis Valley Regional Library, Lawrencetown Branch, 50 Elliot Rd, Lawrencetown, NS, B0S 1M0, CANADA. Tel: 902-584-2102. Fax: 902-584-2085. p. 2778

Kamennof-Sine, Lana, Campus Librn, Nova Scotia Community College, 236 Belcher St, Kentville, NS, B4N 0A6, CANADA. Tel: 902-679-7380. Fax: 902-679-5187. p. 2783

Kamens, Carol, Librn, Trumbull Memorial Hospital, 1350 E Market St, Warren, OH, 44482. Tel: 330-841-9379. Fax: 330-841-1949. p. 1944

Kameoka, Dorothy, ILL, New Hampshire Hospital, 36 Clinton St, Concord, NH, 03301-3861. Tel: 603-271-5420. Fax: 603-271-5415. p. 1442

Kamer, Jessica, Br Mgr, Portsmouth Public Library, Vernal G Riffe Branch, 3850 Rhodes Ave, New Boston, OH, 45662. Tel: 740-456-4412. Fax: 740-456-4047. p. 1931

Kamerman, Jeannie, Head, Curric Mat Ctr, University of West Florida, 11000 University Pkwy, Pensacola, FL, 32514-5750. Tel: 850-474-2439. Fax: 850-474-3338. p. 482

KamHong, Brittaney, Managing Librn, National Concrete Masonry Association Library, 13750 Sunrise Valley Dr, Herndon, VA, 20171-3499. Tel: 703-713-1900. Fax: 703-713-1910. p. 2471

Kamikawa, Julie, Dir, Mount Mary College, 2900 N Menomonee River Pkwy, Milwaukee, WI, 53222-4597. Tel: 414-258-4810, Ext 190. Fax: 414-256-1205. p. 2621

Kamikawaji, Harold, Dir, Human Res, Vancouver Island Regional Library, 6250 Hammond Bay Rd, Nanaimo, BC, V9R 5N3, CANADA. Tel: 250-729-2306. Fax: 250-758-2482. p. 2732

Kamilos, Charlie, Librn, George Fox University, Portland Center Library, Hampton Plaza, 12753 SW 68th Ave, Portland, OR, 97223. Tel: 503-554-6131. Fax: 503-554-6134. p. 2007

Kamin, Linda, Br Mgr, Broward County Division of Libraries, Tamarac Branch, 8701 W Commercial Blvd, Tamarac, FL, 33351. Tel: 954-720-2282. Fax: 954-720-2285. p. 442

Kamin, Rachel, Librn, North Suburban Synagogue Beth El, 1175 Sheridan Rd, Highland Park, IL, 60035. Tel: 847-432-8900. Fax: 847-432-9242. p. 656

Kaminsk, Dorothy, Librn, Marinette County Library System, Coleman Public Library, 123 W Main St, Coleman, WI, 54112. Tel: 920-897-2400. Fax: 920-897-2400. p. 2612

Kaminski, Carla, Circ Supvr, Hope College, Van Wylen Library, 53 Graves Pl, Holland, MI, 49422. Tel: 616-395-7889. Fax: 616-395-7965. p. 1190

Kaminski, Ellen, Tech Serv, Newburyport Public Library, 94 State St, Newburyport, MA, 01950-6619. Tel: 978-465-4428, Ext 230. Fax: 978-463-0394. p. 1109

Kaminski, Greg, Supvr, Center for Naval Analyses Library, 4825 Mark Center Dr, Alexandria, VA, 22311-1846. Tel: 703-824-2173. Fax: 703-824-2200. p. 2445

Kaminski, Lynn, Ref Librn, Englewood Public Library, 31 Engle St, Englewood, NJ, 07631. Tel: 201-568-2215. Fax: 201-568-6895. p. 1484

Kaminski, Michael, Mgr, San Antonio Public Library, Landa, 233 Bushnell Ave, San Antonio, TX, 78212. Tel: 210-732-8369. Fax: 210-737-9662. p. 2382

Kaminski, Michael, Mgr, San Antonio Public Library, Westfall, 6111 Rosedale Ct, San Antonio, TX, 78201. Tel: 210-344-2373. Fax: 210-344-4699. p. 2382

Kaminsky, AnnMarie, Mgr, Libr Serv, Lawrence & Memorial Hospital, 365 Montauk Ave, New London, CT, 06320. Tel: 860-442-0711, Ext 2238. Fax: 860-271-4302. p. 360

Kammer, Dan, Dir, Libr Serv, New Mexico State University at Alamogordo, 2400 N Scenic Dr, Alamogordo, NM, 88310. Tel: 575-439-3806. Fax: 575-439-3657. p. 1547

Kammer, Dick, Coordr, Menorah Medical Center, 5721 W 119th St, Overland Park, KS, 66209. Tel: 913-498-6625. Fax: 913-498-6642. p. 888

Kammer, Gail, Coop Librn, Burns & McDonnell Engineering Co, 9400 Ward Pkwy, Kansas City, MO, 64114. Tel: 816-822-3550. Fax: 816-822-3409. p. 1337

Kammer, Sandy, Librn, Saint Clair County Mental Health Service Library, 311 Electric Ave, Port Huron, MI, 48060. Tel: 810-985-8900. Fax: 810-985-7620. p. 1220

Kammerdiner, Paul, Govt Doc, Ferris State University Library, 1010 Campus Dr, Big Rapids, MI, 49307-2279. Tel: 231-591-3500. Fax: 231-591-3724. p. 1158

Kammerer, James, Supvr, Libr & Info Serv, Montana State Library, 1515 E Sixth Ave, Helena, MT, 59620-1800. Tel: 406-444-5432. Fax: 406-444-0266. p. 1383

Kammerlocher, Lisa, Librn, Arizona State University Libraries, Fletcher Library, 4701 W Thunderbird Rd, Glendale, AZ, 85306. Tel: 602-543-5718. Fax: 602-543-8540. p. 83

Kammerman, Amy, Bibliog Instruction Coordr, William Rainey Harper College Library, 1200 W Algonguin Rd, Palatine, IL, 60067. Tel: 847-925-6555. Fax: 847-925-6164. p. 687

Kammeyer, Scott, Circ, Pataskala Public Library, 101 S Vine St, Pataskala, OH, 43062. Tel: 740-927-9986. Fax: 740-964-6204. p. 1928

Kammradt, Doris, Head Librn, Coll, Res & Instruction, Trinity College Library, 300 Summit St, Hartford, CT, 06106. Tel: 860-297-5352. Fax: 860-297-2251. p. 347

Kamoche, Njambi, Dean, William Rainey Harper College Library, 1200 W Algonguin Rd, Palatine, IL, 60067. Tel: 847-925-6584. Fax: 847-925-6164. p. 687

Kamoche, Njambi, Dir, Langston University, PO Box 1600, Langston, OK, 73050-1600. Tel: 405-466-3293. Fax: 405-466-3459. p. 1967

Kamoe, Marilynn, Librn, Rigby Public Library, 110 N State St, Rigby, ID, 83442. Tel: 208-745-8231. Fax: 208-745-8231. p. 582

Kamon, Karen, Ch, Nichols Memorial Library, 169 Main St, Kingston, NH, 03848-0128. Tel: 603-642-3521. Fax: 603-642-3135. p. 1453

Kamp, Donna, Br Coordr, Upper Dublin Public Library, North Hills Community Center, 212 Girard Ave, North Hills, PA, 19038. Tel: 215-884-4760. p. 2058

Kampen, Jeanette, Asst Dir, Six Mile Regional Library District, 2001 Delmar St, Granite City, IL, 62040-4590. Tel: 618-452-6238. Fax: 618-876-6317. p. 651

Kampenhout, Carol, Bus & Human Res Mgr, Latah County Library District, 110 S Jefferson, Moscow, ID, 83843-2833. Tel: 208-882-3925. Fax: 208-882-5098. p. 579

Kampnich, Joan, Dir, Croghan Free Library, Main St, Croghan, NY, 13327. Tel: 315-346-6521. Fax: 315-346-6521. p. 1612

Kamrud, Pat, In Charge, Wayzata Community Church Library, 125 E Wayzata Blvd, Wayzata, MN, 55391. Tel: 952-473-8877. Fax: 952-473-2695. p. 1288

Kamtman, Leslie, Music Librn, University of North Carolina School of the Arts, 1533 S Main St, Winston-Salem, NC, 27127. Tel: 336-770-3270. Fax: 336-770-3271. p. 1833

Kan, Winnie, Circ Coordr, Regent College, 5800 University Blvd, Vancouver, BC, V6T 2E4, CANADA. Tel: 604-221-3369. Fax: 604-224-3097. p. 2742

Kanabar, Dina, Head, Tech Serv, Syst Programmer, J V Fletcher Library, 50 Main St, Westford, MA, 01886-2599. Tel: 978-399-2308. Fax: 978-692-4418. p. 1138

Kanady, Catherine, Asst Dir, Northeast Regional Library, 1023 Fillmore St, Corinth, MS, 38834-4199. Tel: 662-287-7311. Fax: 662-286-8010. p. 1297

Kanal-Scott, Borany, Libr Tech, Harrisburg Area Community College, One HACC Dr, Harrisburg, PA, 17110-2999. Tel: 717-780-2460. Fax: 717-780-2462. p. 2065

Kanaley, Steven, Libr Tech, United States Holocaust Memorial Museum Library, 100 Raoul Wallenberg Pl SW, Washington, DC, 20024. Tel: 202-479-9717. Fax: 202-479-9726. p. 420

Kanalley, William, Coll Develop, Siena College, 515 Loudon Rd, Loudonville, NY, 12211-1462. Tel: 518-783-2522. Fax: 518-783-2570. p. 1655

Kanarr, Maryellen, Adult Serv, Parkland Community Library, 4422 Walbert Ave, Allentown, PA, 18104-1619. Tel: 610-398-1361. Fax: 610-398-3538. p. 2027

Kanarski, Kathleen, Managing Librn, Austin Public Library, North Village, 2505 Steck Ave, Austin, TX, 78757. Tel: 512-974-9960. Fax: 512-974-9965. p. 2279

Kanciruk, Barbara, Librn, Parkland Regional Library, Lemberg Branch, PO Box 339, Lemberg, SK, S0A 2B0, CANADA. Tel: 306-335-2267. p. 2932

Kandel, Marlene, Tech Serv Coordr, John Jay College of Criminal Justice, 899 Tenth Ave, New York, NY, 10019. Tel: 212-237-8237. Fax: 212-237-8221. p. 1684

Kane, Andrea, Circ Mgr, Stillwater Public Library, 1107 S Duck St, Stillwater, OK, 74074. Tel: 405-372-3633, Ext 114. Fax: 405-624-0552. p. 1978

Kane, Angelika, Head Librn, Pittsburgh Post Gazette, 34 Blvd of the Allies, Pittsburgh, PA, 15222. Tel: 412-263-1397. Fax: 412-471-1987. p. 2127

Kane, Beth, Libr Dir, Norway Memorial Library, 258 Main St, Norway, ME, 04268. Tel: 207-743-5309. Fax: 207-744-0111. p. 994

Kane, Deborah, Asst Dir, Tech Serv, Hudson Public Library, Three Washington St at The Rotary, Hudson, MA, 01749-2499. Tel: 978-568-9644. Fax: 978-568-9646. p. 1096

Kane, Julie, Head, Tech Serv, Sweet Briar College, 134 Chapel Rd, Sweet Briar, VA, 24595-1200. Tel: 434-381-6138. Fax: 434-381-6173. p. 2497

Kane, Katherine, Dir, Harriet Beecher Stowe Center Library, 77 Forest St, Hartford, CT, 06105-3296. Tel: 860-522-9258, Ext 313. Fax: 860-522-9259. p. 347

Kane, Kathleen, Pub Serv, Medford Public Library, 111 High St, Medford, MA, 02155. Tel: 781-395-7950. Fax: 781-391-2261. p. 1104

Kane, Laura, Asst Dir, Info Serv, University of South Carolina, School of Medicine, 6311 Garners Ferry Rd, Columbia, SC, 29209. Tel: 803-733-3344. Fax: 803-733-1509. p. 2190

Kane, Laura, Asst Dir, Info Serv, Columbia Area Medical Librarians' Association, University of South Carolina, School of Medicine Library, 6311 Garner's Ferry Rd, Columbia, SC, 29209. Tel: 803-733-3361. Fax: 803-733-1509. p. 2955

Kane, Mary L, Adult Serv, Ringwood Public Library, 30 Cannici Dr, Ringwood, NJ, 07456. Tel: 973-962-6256. Fax: 973-962-7799. p. 1526

Kane, Melissa A, Dir, Cascade Public Library, 310 First Ave W, Cascade, IA, 52033. Tel: 563-852-3201. Fax: 563-852-6011. p. 799

Kane, Patrice, Head, Spec Coll & Archives, Fordham University Libraries, 441 E Fordham Rd, Bronx, NY, 10458-5151. Tel: 718-817-3570. Fax: 718-817-3582. p. 1586

Kane, Pera, Librn, Birmingham Temple Library, 28611 W Twelve Mile Rd, Farmington Hills, MI, 48334. Tel: 248-477-1410. Fax: 248-477-9014. p. 1177

Kane, Renee, Circ, Lakeland Public Library, Larry R Jackson Branch, 1700 N Florida Ave, Lakeland, FL, 33805. Tel: 863-834-4288. Fax: 863-834-4327. p. 459

Kane, Sue, Actg Commun Libr Mgr, County of Los Angeles Public Library, Alondra Library, 11949 Alondra Blvd, Norwalk, CA, 90650-7108. Tel: 562-868-7771. Fax: 562-863-8620. p. 140

Kane, Sue, Commun Libr Mgr, County of Los Angeles Public Library, Norwalk Library, 12350 Imperial Hwy, Norwalk, CA, 90650-3199. Tel: 562-868-0775. Fax: 562-929-1130. p. 142

Kane, Tricia, Br Mgr, Rock Island Public Library, Southwest, 9010 Ridgewood Rd, Rock Island, IL, 61201. Tel: 309-732-7364. Fax: 309-732-7337. p. 696

Kane, Tricia, Br Mgr, Rock Island Public Library, Thirty-Thirty-One Branch, 3059 30th St, Rock Island, IL, 61201. Tel: 309-732-7364. Fax: 309-732-7371. p. 696

Kane, Tricia L, Dir, Br Serv, Rock Island Public Library, 401 19th St, Rock Island, IL, 61201. Tel: 309-732-7364. Fax: 309-732-7342. p. 696

Kanenwisher, Jenilee, Librn, Fargo Public Library, Northport, 2714 Broadway, Fargo, ND, 58102. Tel: 701-476-4026. p. 1841

Kaneshalingam, Mythili, Coordr, Librn, Algonquin College Learning Resource Centre, Ottawa Valley, 315 Pembroke St E, Pembroke, ON, K8A 3K2, CANADA. Tel: 613-735-4700, Ext 2707. Fax: 613-735-8801. p. 2828

Kaneshiro, Kellie, Biomedical Librn, Indiana University, Ruth Lilly Medical Library, 975 W Walnut St, IB 100, Indianapolis, IN, 46202-5121. Tel: 317-274-1612. Fax: 317-278-2349. p. 752

Kang, Byung, Cat Librn, Palomar College Library - Media Center, 1140 W Mission Rd, San Marcos, CA, 92069-1487. Tel: 760-744-1150, Ext 2848. Fax: 760-761-3500. p. 254

Kang, Li, Librn, GateWay Community College Library, 108 N 40th St, Phoenix, AZ, 85034-1704. Tel: 602-286-8461. Fax: 602-286-8459. p. 73

Kang, Mikyung, Librn, Harvard Library, Harvard-Yenching Library, Two Divinity Ave, Cambridge, MA, 02138. Tel: 617-495-2756. Fax: 617-496-6008. p. 1075

Kang, Tae, Coordr, Acq, Assemblies of God Theological Seminary, 1435 N Glenstone Ave, Springfield, MO, 65802-2131. Tel: 417-268-1062. Fax: 417-268-1001. p. 1365

Kangas, Jim, Pub Serv Librn, Kettering University Library, 1700 W University Ave, Flint, MI, 48504-4898. Tel: 810-762-7818. Fax: 810-762-9744. p. 1180

Kaniaris, Debbie, Tech Serv Librn, Oconee County Public Library, 501 W South Broad St, Walhalla, SC, 29691. Tel: 864-638-4133. Fax: 864-638-4132. p. 2207

Kaniaris, Debra, Coll Develop, Pickens County Library System, 304 Biltmore Rd, Easley, SC, 29640. Tel: 864-850-7077. Fax: 864-850-7088. p. 2193

Kaniewski, Patricia, Br Mgr, Branch District Library, Union Township Branch, 221 N Broadway St, Union City, MI, 49094-1153. Tel: 517-741-5061. Fax: 517-741-5061. p. 1165

Kanigan-Fairen, Joan, Exec Dir, Brant Historical Society Library, 57 Charlotte St, Brantford, ON, N3T 2W6, CANADA. Tel: 519-752-2483. Fax: 519-752-1931. p. 2796

Kannady, Pam, Dir, Human Res, The Kansas City Public Library, 14 W Tenth St, Kansas City, MO, 64105. Tel: 816-701-3517. Fax: 816-701-3401. p. 1338

Kanne, Lynn, Librn, Seattle Central Community College, 1701 Broadway, 2BE2101, Seattle, WA, 98122. Tel: 206-587-4072. Fax: 206-587-3878. p. 2530

Kanner, Amber, Digital Res Librn, Instruction Librn, American International College, 1000 State St, Springfield, MA, 01109. Tel: 413-205-3225. Fax: 413-205-3904. p. 1126

Kanno, Faith C, Head, Breckinridge Libr Br, Library of the Marine Corps, Gray Research Ctr, 2040 Broadway St, Quantico, VA, 22134-5107. Tel: 703-784-0459. Fax: 703-784-4089. p. 2486

Kannwischer, Nancy, Circ, Conyers-Rockdale Library System, 864 Green St, Conyers, GA, 30012. Tel: 770-388-5040. Fax: 770-388-5043. p. 527

Kanouff, Jean, Librn, William E Anderson Library of Penn Hills, 1037 Stotler Rd, Pittsburgh, PA, 15235-2099. Tel: 412-795-3507. Fax: 412-798-2186. p. 2121

Kanouse, Elizabeth L, Dir, Denville Free Public Library, 121 Diamond Spring Rd, Denville, NJ, 07834. Tel: 973-627-6555. Fax: 973-627-1913. p. 1481

Kantner, Audrey, Youth Serv Coordr, Easton Area Public Library & District Center, 515 Church St, Easton, PA, 18042-3587. Tel: 610-258-2917. Fax: 610-253-2231. p. 2052

Kantner, Christine L, ILL, Albright College, 13th & Exeter Sts, Reading, PA, 19604. Tel: 610-921-7517. Fax: 610-921-7509. p. 2132

Kantola, Anne, Dir, McCall Public Library, 218 E Park St, McCall, ID, 83638. Tel: 208-634-5522. p. 578

Kantor, Joseph, Librn, Leechburg Public Library, 215 First St, Leechburg, PA, 15656-1375. Tel: 724-845-1911. p. 2080

Kantor, Paul, Prof, Rutgers, The State University of New Jersey, Four Huntington St, New Brunswick, NJ, 08901-1071. Tel: 732-932-7500, Ext 8955. Fax: 732-932-2644. p. 2969

Kantor, Scott, Coll Mgt Librn, Gainesville State College, 3820 Mundy Mill Rd, Oakwood, GA, 30566. Tel: 678-717-3664. Fax: 770-718-3657. p. 547

Kapa, Dubravka, Dir, Vanier Libr, Concordia University Libraries, 1400 de Maisonneuve Blvd W, LB 209, Montreal, QC, H3G 1M8, CANADA. Tel: 514-848-2424, Ext 7721. Fax: 514-848-2804. p. 2894

Kapetanakis, Kathryn, Librn, Winston-Salem Journal Library, 418 N Marshall St, Winston-Salem, NC, 27101. Tel: 336-727-7275. Fax: 336-727-4095. p. 1834

Kapke, Julie, Br Librn, Duluth Public Library, Mount Royal, 105 Mount Royal Shopping Circle, Duluth, MN, 55803. Tel: 218-730-4290. Fax: 218-723-3846. p. 1248

Kaplan, Amy, Ch, Teen Librn, Briarcliff Manor Public Library, One Library Rd, Briarcliff Manor, NY, 10510. Tel: 914-733-3612. Fax: 914-941-7091. p. 1585

Kaplan, Dianne, Admin Officer, Hofstra University Law Library, 122 Hofstra University, Hempstead, NY, 11549-1220. Tel: 516-463-5898. Fax: 516-463-5129. p. 1635

Kaplan, Janice, Dir, New York Academy of Medicine Library, 1216 Fifth Ave, New York, NY, 10029-5293. Tel: 212-822-7327. Fax: 212-423-0266. p. 1688

Kaplan, Judith, Mgr, Baltimore County Public Library, Pikesville, 1301 Reisterstown Rd, Baltimore, MD, 21208-4195. Tel: 410-887-1234. Fax: 410-486-2782. p. 1044

Kaplan, Lesly, Managing Librn I, Sno-Isle Libraries, Edmonds Community Library, 650 Main St, Edmonds, WA, 98020. Tel: 425-771-1933. Fax: 425-771-1977. p. 2542

Kaplan, Mark, Br Mgr, Chicago Public Library, Bezazian, 1226 W Ainslie St, Chicago, IL, 60640. Tel: 312-744-0019. Fax: 312-744-9881. p. 608

Kaplan, Paul, Head, Adult Serv, Lake Villa District Library, 1001 E Grand Ave, Lake Villa, IL, 60046. Tel: 847-356-7711, Ext 230. Fax: 847-265-9595. p. 663

Kaplan, Penelope, Asst Dir, Maurice M Pine Free Public Library, 10-01 Fair Lawn Ave, Fair Lawn, NJ, 07410. Tel: 201-796-3400. Fax: 201-794-6344. p. 1485

Kaplan, Richard, Dir, Massachusetts College of Pharmacy & Health Sciences, 179 Longwood Ave, Boston, MA, 02115-5896. Tel: 617-732-2803. Fax: 617-278-1566. p. 1063

Kaplan, Richard, Asst Mgr, Main Libr Serv, Mgr, Ref Serv, Carnegie Library of Pittsburgh, 4400 Forbes Ave, Pittsburgh, PA, 15213-4080. Tel: 412-622-1964. Fax: 412-622-3141. p. 2122

Kaplan, Sue, Head, Ch, Sunnyvale Public Library, 665 W Olive Ave, Sunnyvale, CA, 94086-7622. Tel: 408-730-7300. Fax: 408-735-8767. p. 273

Kaplan, Susan, Dir, Sayreville Public Library, 1050 Washington Rd, Parlin, NJ, 08859. Tel: 732-727-0212. Fax: 732-553-0775. p. 1517

Kaplowitz, Joan, Head, Ref, University of California Los Angeles Library, Louise M Darling Biomedical Library, 10833 LeConte Ave, 12-077 Center for the Health Sciences, Los Angeles, CA, 90095-1798. Tel: 310-825-4904. Fax: 310-825-0465. p. 178

Kapoun, Jim, Assoc Dir, Info Serv, Youngstown State University, One University Plaza, Youngstown, OH, 44555-0001. Tel: 330-941-1478. Fax: 330-941-3734. p. 1953

Kapoun, Jim M, Dir, Libr & Info Serv, Antioch College, One Morgan Pl, Yellow Springs, OH, 45387-1694. Tel: 937-769-1238. Fax: 937-769-1239. p. 1952

Kapp, Amy, Coordr, National Recreation & Park Association, 22377 Belmont Ridge Rd, Ashburn, VA, 20148. Tel: 703-858-2151, 703-858-2192. Fax: 703-858-0794. p. 2450

Kappanadze, Margaret, Info Serv Librn, Elmira College, One Park Pl, Elmira, NY, 14901. Tel: 607-735-1867. Fax: 607-735-1158. p. 1620

Kappel, Kathleen, Dir, Carnegie Library of Pittsburgh, Leonard C Staisey Bldg, 4724 Baum Blvd, Pittsburgh, PA, 15213-1321. Tel: 412-687-2440. Fax: 412-687-2442. p. 2123

Kappenberg, Marilyn, Dir, Plainedge Public Library, 1060 Hicksville Rd, Massapequa, NY, 11758. Tel: 516-735-4133. Fax: 516-735-4192. p. 1658

Kappenman, Karen, Dir, Richard Salter Storrs Library, 693 Longmeadow St, Longmeadow, MA, 01106. Tel: 413-565-4181. Fax: 413-565-4183. p. 1100

Kappenman, Karen, Dir, Edwards Public Library, 30 East St, Southampton, MA, 01073-9324. Tel: 413-527-9480. Fax: 413-527-9480. p. 1126

Kappmeyer, Lori O, Cat, Iowa State University Library, 302 Parks Library, Ames, IA, 50011-2140. Tel: 515-294-1442, 515-294-1443. Fax: 515-294-5525. p. 793

Kappus, Theresa, Distance Learning Librn, Ref & ILL Librn, Gonzaga University, 502 E Boone Ave, Spokane, WA, 99258-0095. Tel: 509-313-6534. Fax: 509-323-5904. p. 2536

Kapranos, Aubrey, Tech Serv Librn, Lamar State College-Orange Library, 410 Front St, Orange, TX, 77630-5796. Tel: 409-882-3953. Fax: 409-883-7552. p. 2367

Kapture, Lawrence, Head, Adult Serv, Portage District Library, 300 Library Lane, Portage, MI, 49002. Tel: 269-329-4542, Ext 710. Fax: 269-324-9222. p. 1220

Kapusta, Linda, Br Mgr, Ref Librn, North Suburban Library District, Roscoe Branch, 5562 Clayton Circle, Roscoe, IL, 61073. Tel: 815-623-6266. Fax: 815-623-8591. p. 668

Kapusta, Linda, Ref Librn, North Suburban Library District, 6340 N Second St, Loves Park, IL, 61111. Tel: 815-633-4247. Fax: 815-633-4249. p. 668

Kapustka, Mary Ann, Librn, Carson City Hospital, 406 E Elm, Carson City, MI, 48811-9693. Tel: 989-584-3131, Ext 243. Fax: 989-584-6165. p. 1161

Karabon, Leslie, Librn, Bethany-Calvary United Methodist Church Library, 7265 W Center St, Wauwatosa, WI, 53210-1129. Tel: 414-258-2868. Fax: 414-258-4171. p. 2647

Karageorge, Elizabeth, Adult Serv, Cumberland Public Library, 1464 Diamond Hill Rd, Cumberland, RI, 02864-5510. Tel: 401-333-2552. Fax: 401-334-0578. p. 2165

Karain, Catherine, Access Serv Tech-Reserves, Washtenaw Community College, 4800 E Huron River Dr, Ann Arbor, MI, 48105-4800. Tel: 734-477-8709. Fax: 734-973-3446. p. 1153

Karanja, James, Br Head, Toronto Public Library, Jane/Dundas, 620 Jane St, Toronto, ON, M6S 4A6, CANADA. Tel: 416-394-1014. Fax: 416-394-1025. p. 2862

Karanovich, Judy, YA Serv, Clinton Public Library, 313 S Fourth St, Clinton, IN, 47842-2398. Tel: 765-832-8349. Fax: 765-832-3823. p. 732

Karas, Laura, Archives Coordr, Pub Serv Librn, University of South Carolina Upstate Library, 800 University Way, Spartanburg, SC, 29303. Tel: 864-503-5637. Fax: 864-503-5601. p. 2205

Karas, Timothy, Dir of Libr Serv, Mission College Library, 3000 Mission College Blvd, Santa Clara, CA, 95054-1897. Tel: 408-855-5164. Fax: 408-855-5462. p. 262

Karasinski, Cindy M, Dir, Cobleigh Public Library, 14 Depot St, Lyndonville, VT, 05851. Tel: 802-626-5475. Fax: 802-626-1167. p. 2427

Karass, Alan, Librn, College of the Holy Cross, Fenwick Music Library, Fenwick Bldg, Worcester, MA, 01610-2394. Tel: 508-793-2295. p. 1144

Karatsu, Robert, Libr Dir, Rancho Cucamonga Public Library, 7368 Archibald Ave, Rancho Cucamonga, CA, 91730. Tel: 909-477-2720, Ext 5022. Fax: 909-477-2721. p. 213

Karcich, Grant, Head Librn, Iqaluit Centennial Library, Bag 189A, Iqaluit, NU, X0A 0H0, CANADA. Tel: 867-979-5400. Fax: 867-979-1373. p. 2789

Karczewski, Lesley, Dir, Chester Library, 250 W Main St, Chester, NJ, 07930. Tel: 908-879-7612. Fax: 908-879-8695. p. 1478

Karczewski, Val, Libr Dir, Lake Park Public Library, 905 S Market St, Lake Park, IA, 51347. Tel: 712-832-9505. Fax: 712-832-9507. p. 826

Kardon, Ellen, ILL, West Nyack Free Library, 65 Strawtown Rd, West Nyack, NY, 10994. Tel: 845-358-6081. Fax: 845-358-4071. p. 1766

Karel, Thomas A, Coll Develop, Franklin & Marshall College, 450 College Ave, Lancaster, PA, 17603-3318. Tel: 717-291-3845. Fax: 717-291-4160. p. 2076

Karell, Julia, Br Mgr, Arlington County Department of Libraries, Cherrydale, 2190 N Military Rd, Arlington, VA, 22207. Tel: 703-228-6331. Fax: 703-516-4568. p. 2448

Karen, Lehmkuhl, Cat Librn, Maryland Department of Legislative Services Library, 90 State Circle, Annapolis, MD, 21401. Tel: 410-946-5400. Fax: 410-946-5405. p. 1010

Karen, MacArthur, Cat Librn, BCC-UCF Joint Use Library, 1519 Clearlake Rd, Cocoa, FL, 32922. Tel: 321-433-7266. Fax: 321-433-7678. p. 433

Karen, Merritt, Librn, Public Library of Steubenville & Jefferson County, Tiltonsville Branch, 702 Walden Ave, Tiltonsville, OH, 43963. Tel: 740-859-5163. Fax: 740-859-0603. p. 1937

Karen, Neely, Br Mgr, Boone Daniel Regional Library, Southern Boone County Public Library, 117 E Broadway, Ashland, MO, 65010. Tel: 573-817-7090. Fax: 573-499-0191. p. 1324

Kargacin, Kevin, Head, Info Serv, University of New Mexico, 1919 Las Lomas NE, Albuquerque, NM, 87106. Tel: 505-277-3038. Fax: 505-277-2773. p. 1550

Kargut, Sigrid, AV Coll & Instrul Librn, Kwantlen Polytechnic University Library, 12666 72 Ave., Surrey, BC, V3W 2M8, CANADA. Tel: 604-599-2378. Fax: 604-599-2106. p. 2738

Karhoff, Brenton, Pres, Knox County Historical Society Library, 107 N Fourth, Edina, MO, 63537-1470. Tel: 660-397-2349. Fax: 660-397-3331. p. 1327

Kariel, Douglas, Head, Tech Serv & Syst, Athabasca University Library, One University Dr, Athabasca, AB, T9S 3A3, CANADA. Tel: 780-675-6261. Fax: 780-675-6478. p. 2684

Karim, Lisa, Dir, La Grange Association Library, 488 Freedom Plains Rd, Ste 109, Poughkeepsie, NY, 12603. Tel: 845-452-3141. Fax: 845-452-1974. p. 1722

Karimi, Hassan, Asst Prof, University of Pittsburgh, 135 N Bellefield Ave, Pittsburgh, PA, 15260. Tel: 412-624-5230. Fax: 412-624-5831. p. 2973

Karimkhani, Denise, Dir, University of Mary Hardin-Baylor, 900 College St, UMHB Sta, Box 8016, Belton, TX, 76513-2599. Tel: 254-295-4636. Fax: 254-295-4642. p. 2289

Karimushan, Fareeza, Librn, Golder Associates, Ltd, 4260 Still Creek Dr, 5th Flr, Burnaby, BC, V5C 6C6, CANADA. Tel: 604-298-6623, Ext 4349. Fax: 604-298-5253. p. 2725

Karius, Janet, Asst Dir, Carver County Library, Four City Hall Plaza, Chaska, MN, 55318-1963. Tel: 952-448-9395. Fax: 952-448-9392. p. 1245

Karius, Janet, Br Mgr, Carver County Library, Chaska Branch, Three City Hall Plaza, Chaska, MN, 55318. Tel: 952-448-3886. Fax: 952-279-5216. p. 1245

Karkoff, Liz, Ch, Harrison Public Library, West Harrison Branch, Two E Madison St, West Harrison, NY, 10604. Tel: 914-948-2092. Fax: 914-948-4350. p. 1634

Karle, Lisa, Circ, Saint Mary's College, Notre Dame, IN, 46556-5001. Tel: 574-284-5396. Fax: 574-284-4791. p. 771

Karlin, Tricia, Tech Serv Coordr, Lawrence Public Library, 707 Vermont St, Lawrence, KS, 66044-2371. Tel: 785-843-3833, Ext 109. Fax: 785-843-3368. p. 878

Karlinchak, Stephen, Info Spec, Pittsburgh Post Gazette, 34 Blvd of the Allies, Pittsburgh, PA, 15222. Tel: 412-263-2585. Fax: 412-471-1987. p. 2127

Karlinsey, Lee, Librn, Roberts Public Library, 659 N 2870 East, Roberts, ID, 83444-5069. Tel: 208-228-2210. p. 583

Karlsberger, Mindy, Br Mgr, Grand Canyon-Tusayan Community Library, 11 Navajo St, Grand Canyon, AZ, 86023. Tel: 928-638-2718. Fax: 928-638-2718. p. 65

Karman, Christi, Head, Tech Serv, Carroll Community College, 1601 Washington Rd, Westminster, MD, 21157-6944. Tel: 410-386-8337. Fax: 410-386-8331. p. 1045

Karmes-Jesonis, Erica, E-Br Mgr & Graphic Designer, Cecil County Public Library, 301 Newark Ave, Elkton, MD, 21921-5441. Tel: 410-996-5600. Fax: 410-996-5604. p. 1027

Karn-Carmichael, Kathy, Doc Librn, University of South Carolina Aiken, 471 University Pkwy, Aiken, SC, 29801. Tel: 803-641-3320. Fax: 803-641-3302. p. 2180

Karney, James A, Dir, Waco-McLennan County Library System, 1717 Austin Ave, Waco, TX, 76701-1794. Tel: 254-750-5941. Fax: 254-750-5940. p. 2397

Karnib, Nidaa, Head, Archives & Patient Info, Maimonides Hospital Geriatric Centre, 5795 Caldwell Ave, Montreal, QC, H4W 1W3, CANADA. Tel: 514-483-2121, Ext 2299. Fax: 514-483-1086. p. 2898

Karnold, Sandra, Lead Librn, Aurora West Allis Medical Center, 8901 W Lincoln Ave, West Allis, WI, 53227-0901. Tel: 414-328-7910. Fax: 414-328-7912. p. 2647

Karns, Denise, Librn, Norris City Memorial Public Library District, 603 S Division St, Norris City, IL, 62869. Tel: 618-378-3713. Fax: 618-378-3713. p. 681

Karns, Lori, West Region & Youth Serv Mgr, Ventura County Library, 5600 Everglades St, Ste A, Ventura, CA, 93003. Tel: 805-677-7156. Fax: 805-677-7173. p. 279

Karoblis, Dalija P, Asst Dir, Public Library of Brookline, 361 Washington St, Brookline, MA, 02445. Tel: 617-730-2370. Fax: 617-730-2160. p. 1071

Karolyn, Nance, Dir, Fox River Grove Public Library District, 407 Lincoln Ave, Fox River Grove, IL, 60021-1406. Tel: 847-639-2274. Fax: 847-639-0300. p. 646

Karp, Susan, Circ Supvr, Woodstock Theological Center Library, Georgetown University, Lauinger Library, PO Box 571170, Washington, DC, 20057-1170. Tel: 202-687-7513. Fax: 202-687-7473. p. 423

Karp-Opperer, Margi, Asst Dir, Pub Serv, Novi Public Library, 45245 W Ten Mile Rd, Novi, MI, 48375. Tel: 248-349-0720. Fax: 248-349-6520. p. 1214

Karpel, Barbara E, Tech Serv, Library Company of the Baltimore Bar, 100 N Calvert St, Rm 618, Baltimore, MD, 21202-1723. Tel: 410-727-0280. Fax: 410-685-4791. p. 1015

Karpiel, Sharon, Head, Kids' Librn, Elmhurst Public Library, 125 S Prospect, Elmhurst, IL, 60126-3298. Tel: 630-279-8696. Fax: 630-279-0636. p. 642

Karpuk, Susan, Principal Cataloger, Yale University Library, Lillian Goldman Library Yale Law School, 127 Wall St, New Haven, CT, 06511. Tel: 203-432-1600. Fax: 203-432-2112. p. 358

Karr, Enid, Librn, Boston College Libraries, Catherine B O'Connor Library, Weston Observatory, 381 Concord Rd, Weston, MA, 02193-1340. Tel: 617-552-4477. Fax: 617-552-8388. p. 1081

Karr, Holly, Librn, Itawamba Community College, 602 W Hill St, Fulton, MS, 38843. Tel: 662-862-8378. Fax: 662-862-8410. p. 1298

Karr, Kristin, Electronic Serv, Wyoming Supreme Court, Supreme Court Bldg, 2301 Capitol Ave, Cheyenne, WY, 82002-0450. Tel: 307-777-6487. Fax: 307-777-7240. p. 2653

Karr, Roger N, Librn, Federal Judicial Center, One Columbus Circle NE, Washington, DC, 20002-8003. Tel: 202-502-4153. Fax: 202-502-4077. p. 400

Karr, Ronald, Ref Librn, University of Massachusetts Lowell Libraries, 61 Wilder St, Lowell, MA, 01854-3098. Tel: 978-934-4590. Fax: 978-934-3015. p. 1100

Karr, Sharon, Mgr, Edmonton Public Library, Mill Woods, 601 Mill Woods Town Centre, 2331 66 St, Edmonton, AB, T6K 4B5, CANADA. Tel: 780-496-7077. Fax: 780-496-1450. p. 2700

Karre, David J, Exec Dir, Four County Library System, 304 Clubhouse Rd, Vestal, NY, 13850-3713. Tel: 607-723-8236, Ext 301. Fax: 607-723-1722. p. 1761

Karrell, Julia, Mgr, District of Columbia Public Library, Francis A Gregory Branch, 3660 Alabama Ave SE, Washington, DC, 20020. Tel: 202-645-4297. p. 398

Karren, Susan, Dir, National Archives & Records Administration, 6125 Sand Point Way NE, Seattle, WA, 98115-7999. Tel: 206-336-5141. Fax: 206-336-5112. p. 2529

Karrick, Gayla, Dir, Williamsfield Public Library District, 111 W Gale St, Williamsfield, IL, 61489. Tel: 309-639-2630. Fax: 309-639-2611. p. 719

Karrow, Robert, Curator, Spec Coll, Newberry Library, 60 W Walton St, Chicago, IL, 60610-3305. Tel: 312-255-3554. p. 620

Karrs, Kevin, Dir of Info Support Serv, Charlotte Campus, Pfeiffer University, Pfeiffer Library at Charlotte, 4701 Park Rd, Charlotte, NC, 28209. Tel: 704-945-7305. Fax: 704-521-8617. p. 1809

Karshmer, Elana, Instruction Prog & Info Literacy Librn, Saint Leo University, 33701 State Rd 52, Saint Leo, FL, 33574. Tel: 352-588-8412. Fax: 352-588-8484. p. 487

Karshner, Mary, Dir, Head, Youth & Teen Serv, Royal Oak Public Library, 222 E Eleven Mile Rd, Royal Oak, MI, 48067-2633. Tel: 248-246-3710. Fax: 248-246-3701. p. 1223

Karstadt, Bruce N, Chief Exec Officer, Pres, American Swedish Institute, 2600 Park Ave, Minneapolis, MN, 55407. Tel: 612-870-3348. Fax: 612-871-8682. p. 1258

Karsten, Eileen, Head, Tech Serv, Lake Forest College, 555 N Sheridan, Lake Forest, IL, 60045. Tel: 847-735-5066. Fax: 847-735-6297. p. 663

Karwoski, Carolyn, Programming, The Ferguson Library, One Public Library Plaza, 96 Broad St, Stamford, CT, 06904. Tel: 203-964-1000, Ext 8220. Fax: 203-357-0660. p. 369

Kasabian, Janet, Librn, Cox, Castle & Nicholson LLP Library, 2049 Century Park E, 28th Flr, Los Angeles, CA, 90067. Tel: 310-277-4222, Ext 2444. Fax: 310-277-7889. p. 169

Kasacavage, Karen, Dir, Woodford County Library, 115 N Main St, Versailles, KY, 40383-1289. Tel: 859-873-5191. Fax: 859-873-1542. p. 936

Kasak, Laura, Br Mgr, Saint Louis County Library, Florissant Valley Branch, 195 New Florissant Rd S, Florissant, MO, 63031. Tel: 314-921-7200. p. 1358

Kasamatsu, Mary, Dir, Waterbury Public Library, 28 N Main St, Waterbury, VT, 05676. Tel: 802-244-7036. p. 2438

Kasbohm, Kristine E., Libr Dir, Canisius College, 2001 Main St, Buffalo, NY, 14208-1098. Tel: 716-888-2900. Fax: 716-888-8420. p. 1597

Kascus, Marie, Assoc Dir, Coll Develop & Acq Librn, Champlain College Library, 163 S Willard St, Burlington, VT, 05401. Tel: 802-860-2718. p. 2420

Kasdan, Harriet M, Asst Librn, Mills Law Library, 220 Montgomery St, Ste 116, San Francisco, CA, 94104. Tel: 415-781-2665. Fax: 415-781-1116. p. 244

Kash-Holley, Melissa, Ref & Instruction, Oklahoma State University - Center for Health Sciences, 1111 W 17th St, Tulsa, OK, 74107-1898. Tel: 918-561-8457. Fax: 918-561-8412. p. 1981

Kashner, Beth, Dir, Pawlet Public Library, 141 School St, Pawlet, VT, 05761. Tel: 802-325-3123. p. 2431

Kasirer, Katherine, Librn, National Film Board of Canada, 3155 Cote de Liesse, Montreal, QC, H4N 2N4, CANADA. Tel: 514-283-9045. Fax: 514-283-9811. p. 2900

Kaske, Neal, Dir, Libr & Info Serv, National Oceanic & Atmospheric Administration, 1315 East West Hwy, 2nd Flr, Silver Spring, MD, 20910. Tel: 301-713-2600, Ext 157. Fax: 301-713-4598. p. 1042

Kaskey, Sid, Dir, Libr Serv, Squire Sanders & Dempsey LLC Library, 200 S Biscayne Blvd, Ste 4000, Miami, FL, 33131. Tel: 305-577-2932. Fax: 305-577-7001. p. 468

Kasling, Tess, Syst Librn, Saint John's University, 2835 Abbey Plaza, Collegeville, MN, 56321. Tel: 320-363-3280. Fax: 320-363-2126. p. 1246

Kasling, Tess, Syst Librn, College of Saint Benedict, 37 S College Ave, Saint Joseph, MN, 56374. Tel: 320-363-3280. Fax: 320-363-5197. p. 1277

Kasmier, Martha, Ch, Bolivar-Harpers Ferry Public Library, 151 Polk St, Harpers Ferry, WV, 25425. Tel: 304-535-2301. Fax: 304-535-2301. p. 2560

Kaspar, Carol, Librn, Newkirk Public Library, 116 N Maple St, Newkirk, OK, 74647-4011. Tel: 580-362-3934. Fax: 580-362-1028. p. 1970

Kasper, Barbara, Dr, Librn, Miami Correctional Facility, Phase II Library, 3038 W 850 S, Bunker Hill, IN, 46914. Tel: 765-689-8920. Fax: 765-689-5964. p. 730

Kasper, Debbie, Asst Librn, Greensboro Free Library, 53 Wilson St, Greensboro, VT, 05841. Tel: 802-533-2531. p. 2425

Kasper, Jacquelyn, Govt Doc, University of Arizona, James E Rogers College of Law Library, PO Box 210176, Tucson, AZ, 85721-0176. Tel: 520-621-1413. Fax: 520-621-3138. p. 89

Kasper, Michael, Coordr, Coll Develop, Ref Librn, Amherst College, Amherst, MA, 01002. Fax: 413-542-2662. p. 1048

Kasperek, Sheila M, Ref, Mansfield University, Mansfield, PA, 16933. Tel: 570-662-4675. Fax: 570-662-4993. p. 2084

Kasprowicz, Frank, Dir, Reading Public Library, 100 S Fifth St, Reading, PA, 19602. Tel: 610-655-6350. p. 2133

Kass, Scott, Head, Reader Serv, Florida International University, 3000 NE 151st St, North Miami, FL, 33181-3600. Tel: 305-919-5933. Fax: 305-919-5914. p. 472

Kassana, Charles, Res Librn, Saint Thomas University Library, Law Library, 16401 NW 37th Ave, Miami Gardens, FL, 33054. Tel: 305-623-2330. Fax: 305-623-2337. p. 469

Kassebaum, Jessica, Asst Librn, Silver City Public Library, 408 Main St, Silver City, IA, 51571. Tel: 712-525-9053. Fax: 712-525-9053. p. 843

Kassman, Rachel, Archivist, Librn, Jewish Museum of Maryland, 15 Lloyd St, Baltimore, MD, 21202. Tel: 410-732-6400, Ext 18. Fax: 410-732-6451. p. 1014

Kassner, Deborah, Youth Serv, Albany County Public Library, 310 S Eighth St, Laramie, WY, 82070-3969. Tel: 307-721-2580. Fax: 307-721-2584. p. 2657

Kasten, Ulla, Curator, Yale University Library, Babylonian Collection, 130 Wall St, New Haven, CT, 06520. Tel: 203-432-1837. Fax: 203-432-7231. p. 356

Kastigar, Amy, Adult Serv, Head, Ref, Ohio County Public Library, 52 16th St, Wheeling, WV, 26003-3696. Tel: 304-232-0244. Fax: 304-232-6848. p. 2574

Kastin, Shelli, Head, Cat, Washington University Libraries, One Brookings Dr, Campus Box 1061, Saint Louis, MO, 63130-4862. Tel: 314-935-5400. Fax: 314-935-4045. p. 1362

Kastner, Shirley, Librn, Glen Ullin Public Library, 114 S Main St, Glen Ullin, ND, 58631. Tel: 701-348-3951. p. 1842

Kastrinsky, Joan, Librn, American Institute of Food Distribution Inc, 10 Mountainview Rd, Ste F125, Upper Saddle River, NJ, 07458. Tel: 201-791-5570, Ext 25. Fax: 201-791-5222. p. 1537

Kasuba, Karen, Supv Librn, California Energy Commission Library, 1516 Ninth St, MS10, Sacramento, CA, 95814-5512. Tel: 916-654-4292. Fax: 916-654-4046. p. 222

Kasuboski, Anne, Distance Educ Librn, University of Wisconsin-Green Bay, 2420 Nicolet Dr, Green Bay, WI, 54311-7001. Tel: 920-465-2543. Fax: 920-465-2136. p. 2596

Kasulaitis, Mary, Managing Librn, Pima County Public Library, Caviglia-Arivaca, 17050 W Arivaca Rd, Arivaca, AZ, 85601. Tel: 520-594-5235. Fax: 520-594-5236. p. 87

Kasun, Leo J, Head, Dept of Educ Res, National Gallery of Art Library, Department of Education Resources, Fourth St & Constitution Ave NW, Washington, DC, 20565. Tel: 202-842-6280. Fax: 202-842-6935. p. 409

Kaszyski, Melissa, Br Mgr, Chicago Public Library, Dunning, 7455 W Cornelia Ave, Chicago, IL, 60634. Tel: 312-743-0480. p. 608

Katafiasz, Carl, Ref Serv, Ad, Livonia Public Library, Civic Center, 32777 Five Mile Rd, Livonia, MI, 48154-3045. Tel: 734-466-2480. Fax: 734-458-6011. p. 1203

Katelnikoff, Justina, Librn, Ouzinkie Tribal Council, 130 Third St, Ouzinkie, AK, 99644. Tel: 907-680-2323. Fax: 907-680-2214. p. 52

Katherine, Griffin, Info Serv Mgr, Yuma County Library District, 2951 S 21st Dr, Yuma, AZ, 85364. Tel: 928-373-6480. Fax: 928-782-9420. p. 91

Kathryn, Kulpa, Ref Serv, Fall River Public Library, 104 N Main St, Fall River, MA, 02720. Tel: 508-324-2700. Fax: 508-324-2707. p. 1088

Kathryn, Pike, Librn Dir, Davenport Public Library, 505 Seventh St, Davenport, WA, 99122. Tel: 509-725-4355. p. 2513

Kathy, Nixon, Mgr, Sonoma County Library, Santa Rosa Northwest Regional, 150 Coddingtown Ctr, Santa Rosa, CA, 95401. Tel: 707-546-2265. Fax: 707-546-2510. p. 268

Kati, Rebekah, Info Tech Librn, Walden University Library, 100 Washington Ave S, Ste 900, Minneapolis, MN, 55401. p. 1262

Katich, Carmel, Doc, Mount Union College Library, 1972 Clark Ave, Alliance, OH, 44601-3993. Tel: 330-823-3844. Fax: 330-823-3963. p. 1854

Katopol, Patricia, Dr, Asst Prof, University of Iowa, 3087 Main Library, Iowa City, IA, 52242-1420. Tel: 319-335-5707. Fax: 319-335-5374. p. 2965

Katsh, Sara, Dir, AORN Center for Library Services & Archives, 2170 S Parker Rd, Ste 400, Denver, CO, 80231-5711. Tel: 303-755-6304, Ext 288. Fax: 303-368-4460. p. 298

Katsouleas, Linda, Dir, Newport Beach Public Library, 1000 Avocado Ave, Newport Beach, CA, 92660-6301. Tel: 949-717-3810. Fax: 949-640-5681. p. 194

Katte, Jill, Digital Coll Prog Coordr, Duke University Libraries, 411 Chapel Dr, Durham, NC, 27708. Tel: 919-660-5911. Fax: 919-660-5923. p. 1787

Kattelman, Beth, Assoc Curator, Ohio State University LIBRARIES, Jerome Lawrence & Robert E Lee Theatre Research Institute Library, 1430 Lincoln Tower, 1800 Cannon Dr, Columbus, OH, 43210-1230. Tel: 614-292-6614. Fax: 614-688-8417. p. 1888

Kattie, Rosa, Adult Prog Coordr, Carnegie Public Library, 712 Sixth St, Charleston, IL, 61920. Tel: 217-345-4913. Fax: 217-348-5616. p. 603

Katz, Alexander, Head of Libr, Foundation for Student Communication, Princeton University, 48 University Pl, Rm 305, Princeton, NJ, 08540. Tel: 609-258-1111. Fax: 609-258-1222. p. 1522

Katz, Bill, Ref, Troutman Sanders LLP, 1001 Haxall Point, Richmond, VA, 23219. Tel: 804-697-1200. Fax: 804-697-1339. p. 2490

Katz, Bonnie, Adult Ref Librn, Media Spec, Ossining Public Library, 53 Croton Ave, Ossining, NY, 10562-4903. Tel: 914-941-2416. Fax: 914-941-7464. p. 1712

Katz, Bonnie A, Dir, Libr Serv, Solano County Library, 1150 Kentucky St, Fairfield, CA, 94533-5799. Fax: 707-421-7474. p. 148

Katz, Charna, Librn, Bolsters Mills Village Library, 659 Bolsters Mills Rd, Harrison, ME, 04040. Tel: 207-583-6421. p. 987

Katz, Gary, Adminr, Kripke Jewish Federation Library, 333 S 132nd St, Omaha, NE, 68154. Tel: 402-334-6461. Fax: 402-334-6464. p. 1413

Katz, Helen, Mgr, Ontario Ministry of Finance, 95 Grosvenor St, 1st Flr, Toronto, ON, M7A 1Y8, CANADA. Tel: 416-325-1253. Fax: 416-325-1212. p. 2856

Katz, Jeffrey, Dir of Libr, Bard College, One Library Rd, Annandale-on-Hudson, NY, 12504. Tel: 845-758-6822. Fax: 845-758-5801. p. 1574

Katz, Linda M, Assoc Dir, Health Sci Libr, Drexel University Health Sciences Libraries, 245 N 15th St MS 449, Philadelphia, PA, 19102-1192. Tel: 215-762-7632. Fax: 215-762-8180. p. 2105

Katz, Margery, Librn, Wisconsin Department of Employee Trust Funds Library, 801 W Badger Rd, Madison, WI, 53713-2526. Tel: 608-267-2926. Fax: 608-267-4549. p. 2610

Katz, Milagros, Head of Libr, Bridgton Academy Library, Chadbourne Hill Rd, North Bridgton, ME, 04057. Tel: 207-647-2121. Fax: 207-647-3146. p. 993

Katz, Rose, Reader Serv Librn, Jewish Community Library, 1835 Ellis St, San Francisco, CA, 94115. Tel: 415-567-3327, Ext 706. p. 243

Katz, Stephen, Educ Mat Ctr Librn, University of Wisconsin Oshkosh, 801 Elmwood Ave, Oshkosh, WI, 54901. Tel: 920-424-2320. Fax: 920-424-7338. p. 2628

Katz, Toni, Asst Dir, Coll Mgt, Colby College Libraries, 5100 Mayflower Hill, Waterville, ME, 04901. Tel: 207-859-5142. Fax: 207-859-5105. p. 1005

Katzarkov, Roumiana, Dir, Miami Children's Hospital Medical Library, 3100 SW 62nd Ave, Miami, FL, 33155-3009. Tel: 305-666-6511, Ext 4470. Fax: 305-284-1145. p. 466

Katzenstein, Susan, Asst Dir, Memorial Hall Library, Two N Main St, Andover, MA, 01810. Tel: 978-623-8401. Fax: 978-623-8407. p. 1049

Katzenstein, Susan, Asst Dir, Haverhill Public Library, 99 Main St, Haverhill, MA, 01830-5092. Tel: 978-373-1586, Ext 641. Fax: 978-372-8508. p. 1094

Katzif, Dale, Mgr, Wellesley College, 106 Central St, Wellesley, MA, 02481-8275. Tel: 781-283-2109. Fax: 781-283-3690. p. 1135

Katzman, Dexter, Mgr, San Antonio Public Library, Guerra, 7978 Military Dr W, San Antonio, TX, 78227. Tel: 210-673-1492. Fax: 210-673-3862. p. 2382

Katzoff, Beth, Archivist, Pub Serv, Columbia University, C V Starr East Asian Library, 300 Kent Hall, MC 3901, 1140 Amsterdam Ave, New York, NY, 10027. Tel: 212-854-4318. Fax: 212-662-6286. p. 1675

Kauble, Jackie, Librn, Audrain County Historical Society, 501 S Muldrow St, Mexico, MO, 65265. Tel: 573-581-3910. Fax: 573-581-7155. p. 1345

Kauffman, Ann, Coll Develop Coordr, Head, Ref Serv, Goshen Public Library, 601 S Fifth St, Goshen, IN, 46526-3994. Tel: 574-533-9531. Fax: 574-533-5211. p. 746

Kauffman, Connie, Head, Youth Serv, Princeton Public Library, 698 E Peru St, Princeton, IL, 61356. Tel: 815-875-1331. Fax: 815-872-1376. p. 692

Kauffman, Fern, Librn, Missoula Public Library, Swan Valley Community, 6811 Hwy 83, Condon, MT, 59826. Tel: 406-754-2521. p. 1386

Kauffman, Jeanne, Ch, Upper Merion Township Library, 175 W Valley Forge Rd, King of Prussia, PA, 19406-2399. Tel: 610-265-4806. Fax: 610-265-3398. p. 2074

Kauffman, Laura C, Ch, Exeter Community Library, 4569 Prestwick Dr, Reading, PA, 19606. Tel: 610-406-9431. Fax: 610-406-9415. p. 2133

Kauffman, Linda, Librn, Iosco-Arenac District Library, Au Gres Community, 230 N MacKinaw, Au Gres, MI, 48703. Tel: 989-876-8818. Fax: 989-876-8818. p. 1176

Kauffman, Maggie, Coordr, California State Department of Transportation, 1120 N St, Rm 1315, Sacramento, CA, 95812. Tel: 916-654-2630, Ext 3179. Fax: 916-654-6128. p. 222

Kauffman, S Blair, Dir, Yale University Library, Lillian Goldman Library Yale Law School, 127 Wall St, New Haven, CT, 06511. Tel: 203-432-1600. Fax: 203-432-2112. p. 358

Kaufman, Amy, Head of Libr, Queen's University, Law Library, Macdonald Hall, 128 Union St, Kingston, ON, K7L 3N6, CANADA. Tel: 613-533-2842. Fax: 613-533-2594. p. 2814

Kaufman, Billie Jo, Dean, Info Serv, Dir, American University, 4801 Massachusetts Ave NW, Washington, DC, 20016-8182. Tel: 202-274-4374. Fax: 202-274-4365. p. 393

Kaufman, Debi, Acq, Whitworth University, 300 W Hawthorne Rd, Spokane, WA, 99251-0001. Tel: 509-777-4485. Fax: 509-777-3221. p. 2538

Kaufman, Debra, Mgr, PerkinElmer, 710 Bridgeport Ave, Shelton, CT, 06484. Tel: 203-402-1840. Fax: 203-944-4923. p. 367

Kaufman, Delora, Ch, Hillsboro Public Library, 120 E Grand, Hillsboro, KS, 67063-1598. Tel: 620-947-3827. Fax: 620-947-3810. p. 872

Kaufman, Janet, Res Serv, University of Guelph, 50 Stone Rd E, Guelph, ON, N1G 2W1, CANADA. Tel: 519-824-4120, Ext 52075, 519-824-4120, Ext 52181. Fax: 519-824-6931. p. 2807

Kaufman, Jean, Mgr, Brandywine Hundred Library, 1300 Foulk Rd, Wilmington, DE, 19803. Tel: 302-477-3150. Fax: 302-477-4545. p. 387

Kaufman, Kimberly, Acq/Ser Librn, Geneva College, 3200 College Ave, Beaver Falls, PA, 15010-3599. Tel: 724-847-6563. Fax: 724-847-6687. p. 2031

Kaufman, Leah, ILL, Stevens Institute of Technology, Castle Point on Hudson, Hoboken, NJ, 07030. Tel: 201-216-5200. Fax: 201-216-8319. p. 1491

Kaufman, LeAnn L, Dir, Freeman Public Library, 322 S Main St, Freeman, SD, 57029. Tel: 605-925-7003. Fax: 605-925-7127. p. 2212

Kaufman, Lois, Br Mgr, Saint Clair County Library System, Marine City Public, 300 S Parker Rd, Marine City, MI, 48039. Tel: 810-765-5233. Fax: 810-765-4376. p. 1219

Kaufman, Michelle Sarjeant, Dir, Marin History Museum Library, 1125 B St, San Rafael, CA, 94901. Tel: 415-454-8538. Fax: 415-454-6137. p. 257

Kaufman, Pamela, Law Librn, Connecticut Judicial Branch Law Libraries, Stamford Law Library, Stamford Courthouse, 123 Hoyt St, Stamford, CT, 06905. Tel: 203-965-5377. Fax: 203-965-5784. p. 344

Kaufman, Patricia, Dir, Mahopac Public Library, 668 Rte 6, Mahopac, NY, 10541. Tel: 845-628-2009. Fax: 845-628-0672. p. 1656

Kaufman, Paula, Dean, Libr & Univ Librn, University of Illinois Library at Urbana-Champaign, 1408 W Gregory Drive, Urbana, IL, 61801. Tel: 217-333-2290. p. 711

Keach, Jennifer, Head, Digital Libr Serv, James Madison University Libraries & Educational Technologies, 800 S Main St, Harrisonburg, VA, 22807-0001. Tel: 540-568-8749. Fax: 540-568-6339. p. 2470

Keally, Jillian, Assoc Dean, University of Tennessee, Knoxville, 1015 Volunteer Blvd, Knoxville, TN, 37996-1000. Tel: 865-974-6600. Fax: 865-974-4259. p. 2243

Kean, Carol, Librn, John G Smith Memorial Public Library, 517 Ridge St, Dawson, NE, 68337. Tel: 402-855-4815. p. 1397

Keane, Edward, Ref/Instruction Librn, Long Island University, One University Plaza, Brooklyn, NY, 11201-9926. Tel: 718-488-1081. Fax: 718-780-4057. p. 1593

Keane, Ellen, Head, Access Serv, University of Massachusetts Lowell Libraries, 61 Wilder St, Lowell, MA, 01854-3098. Tel: 978-934-4594. Fax: 978-934-3015. p. 1100

Keane, Ellen, Head, Access Serv, University of Massachusetts Lowell Libraries, Lydon Library, 84 University Ave, Lowell, MA, 01854-2896. Tel: 978-934-3203. Fax: 978-934-3014. p. 1101

Keane, Patrice, Exec Dir, American Society for Psychical Research Inc Library, Five W 73rd St, New York, NY, 10023. Tel: 212-799-5050. Fax: 212-496-2497. p. 1668

Kearley, Jamie, Head, Res & Instruction, University of Wyoming Libraries, 13th & Ivinson, Laramie, WY, 82071. Tel: 307-766-3425. Fax: 307-766-2510. p. 2658

Kearley, Tim, Librn, University Of Wyoming, Dept 3035, 1000 E University Ave, Laramie, WY, 82071. Tel: 307-766-2210. Fax: 307-766-4044. p. 2657

Kearn, Debbie, Actg Libr Dir, Jamestown City Library, 311 D Walnut St, Jamestown, KS, 66948. Tel: 785-439-6258. p. 874

Kearn, Jerry, AV, Yukon College Library, 500 College Dr, Whitehorse, YT, Y1A 5K4, CANADA. Tel: 867-668-8870. Fax: 867-668-8808. p. 2934

Kearney, Eileen, Circ Mgr, Computer Serv, ILL, Lynn Public Library, Five N Common St, Lynn, MA, 01902. Tel: 781-595-0567. Fax: 781-592-5050. p. 1101

Kearney, Jeannie, Librn, Riverland Community College, 1600 Eighth Ave NW, Austin, MN, 55912. Tel: 507-433-0533. Fax: 507-433-0515. p. 1240

Kearney, Jennifer, ILL, Florida College, 119 N Glen Arven Ave, Temple Terrace, FL, 33617-5578. Tel: 813-988-5131, Ext 210. p. 500

Kearney, Maeghan, Govt Pub Librn, Alaska State Library, 333 Willoughby Ave, State Office Bldg, 8th Flr, Juneau, AK, 99801. Tel: 907-465-2910. Fax: 907-465-2151. p. 49

Kearney, Richard, Electronic Res, Ref, William Paterson University of New Jersey, 300 Pompton Rd, Wayne, NJ, 07470. Tel: 973-720-2165. Fax: 973-720-3171. p. 1540

Kearney, Susan, Dir, Lakota Public Library, 204 Third St, Lakota, IA, 50451-7084. Tel: 515-886-2312. Fax: 515-886-2312. p. 826

Kearns, Amy, Asst Dir, Head, Ad Ref Serv, Middletown Public Library, 55 New Monmouth Rd, Middletown, NJ, 07748. Tel: 732-671-3700, Ext 330. Fax: 732-671-5839. p. 1501

Kearns, Andrew, Coordr, Instruction, Pub Serv Librn, University of South Carolina Upstate Library, 800 University Way, Spartanburg, SC, 29303. Tel: 864-503-5403. Fax: 864-503-5601. p. 2205

Kearns, Jodi, Instr, Kent State University, 314 Library, Kent, OH, 44242-0001. Tel: 330-672-2782. Fax: 330-672-7965. p. 2972

Kearns, Karen, Head, Spec Coll, Idaho State University, Idaho State University, 850 S Ninth Ave, Pocatello, ID, 83209-8089. Tel: 208-282-3608. Fax: 208-282-5847. p. 581

Kearns, Sheila, Dir, Tech & Info Serv, State of Vermont Department of Libraries, 109 State St, Montpelier, VT, 05609-0601. Tel: 802-828-6952. Fax: 802-828-2199. p. 2429

Kearns, Trish, Head, Cat, College of William & Mary in Virginia, Earl Gregg Swem Library, One Landrum Dr, Williamsburg, VA, 23187. Tel: 757-221-1940. Fax: 757-221-2635. p. 2502

Kearns-Kaplan, Mary, Adult Serv & Outreach Coordr, New Jersey State Library, Talking Book & Braille Center, 2300 Stuyvesant Ave, Trenton, NJ, 08618. Tel: 609-406-7179, Ext 834. Fax: 609-406-7181. p. 1536

Kearns-Padgett, Mary Jane, Librn, Hamilton Law Association Library, 45 Main St E, Ste 500, Hamilton, ON, L8N 2B7, CANADA. Tel: 905-522-1563. Fax: 905-572-1188. p. 2808

Kearsey, Debra, Librn, Eastern Health, Waterford Hospital Library & Information Services, Waterford Bridge Rd, St. John's, NL, A1E 4J8, CANADA. Tel: 709-777-3368. Fax: 709-777-3319. p. 2772

Keating, Carolyn A, Dir, Westhampton Public Library, One North Rd, Westhampton, MA, 01027. Tel: 413-527-5386. p. 1139

Keating, Denise, Librn, Central Piedmont Community College Library, 1201 Elizabeth Ave, Charlotte, NC, 28235. Tel: 704-330-4418. Fax: 704-330-6887. p. 1781

Keating, Denise, Campus Librn, ECPI University, 250 Berryhill Rd, Ste 300, Columbia, SC, 29210. Tel: 803-772-3333. p. 2187

Keating, Julie, Head, Adult Serv, Bloomingdale Public Library, 101 Fairfield Way, Bloomingdale, IL, 60108-1579. Tel: 630-529-3120. Fax: 630-529-3243. p. 595

Keating, Kevin, Govt Doc Librn, Alaska Resources Library & Information Services, Library Bldg, 3211 Providence Dr, Ste 111, Anchorage, AK, 99508-4614. Tel: 907-786-7688. Fax: 907-786-7652. p. 43

Keating, Kevin, Ref & Instruction, University of Alaska Anchorage, Consortium Library, 3211 Providence Dr, Anchorage, AK, 99508-8176. Tel: 907-786-1871. Fax: 907-786-1834. p. 45

Keating, Lorreen, Asst Dir, Ch & Youth Librn, North Hampton Public Library, 237A Atlantic Ave, North Hampton, NH, 03862-2341. Tel: 603-964-6326. Fax: 603-964-1107. p. 1461

Keating, Maura, Ref Librn, Bryant University, 1150 Douglas Pike, Smithfield, RI, 02917-1284. Tel: 401-232-6125. Fax: 401-232-6126. p. 2176

Keating-Hadlock, Lark, Archives, University of Wisconsin-Eau Claire, 105 Garfield Ave, Eau Claire, WI, 54702-4004. Tel: 715-836-3715. Fax: 715-836-2949. p. 2590

Keaton, Bernice, Librn, Auditor General's Library, Claude Pepper Bldg, Rm G-78, 111 W Madison St, Tallahassee, FL, 32399-1450. Tel: 850-448-5534. Fax: 850-488-6975. p. 492

Keaton, Dottie, Librn, First Presbyterian Church Library, 399 S Trimble Rd, Mansfield, OH, 44906. Tel: 419-756-7066. p. 1912

Keaton, Phyllis, Dir, Howland Public Library, 313 Main St, Beacon, NY, 12508. Tel: 845-831-1134. Fax: 845-831-1165. p. 1579

Keays, Thomas H, Electronic Syst & Res Librn, Le Moyne College, 1419 Salt Springs Rd, Syracuse, NY, 13214-1301. Tel: 315-445-4322. Fax: 315-445-4642. p. 1751

Kebabian, Ann, Head, Cat, Colgate University, 13 Oak Dr, Hamilton, NY, 13346-1398. Tel: 315-228-7300. Fax: 315-228-7934. p. 1633

Kebede, Yodit, Head, Acq, Teachers College, Columbia University, 525 W 120th St, New York, NY, 10027-6696. Tel: 212-678-3440. p. 1701

Kebert, Joyce M, Ser, Grove City College, 300 Campus Dr, Grove City, PA, 16127-2198. Tel: 724-458-3821. Fax: 724-458-2181. p. 2063

Keck, Andy, Assoc Dir, Duke University Libraries, Divinity School Library, Gray Bldg, 102 Chapel Dr, Durham, NC, 27708. Tel: 919-660-3549. Fax: 919-681-7594. p. 1787

Keck, Kerry, Asst Univ Librn, Res Serv, Rice University, 6100 Main, MS-44, Houston, TX, 77005. Tel: 713-348-2926. Fax: 713-348-5258. p. 2341

Kedley, Jane, Dir, The Frances Banta Waggoner Community Library, 505 Tenth St, DeWitt, IA, 52742-1335. Tel: 563-659-5523. Fax: 563-659-2901. p. 810

Kee, Cheryl, Asst Librn, Albemarle Regional Library, Northampton Memorial Library, 207 W Jefferson St, Jackson, NC, 27845. Tel: 252-534-3571. Fax: 252-534-1017. p. 1835

Kee, Karen, Head, Circ, Helen M Plum Memorial Public Library District, 110 W Maple St, Lombard, IL, 60148-2594. Tel: 630-627-0316. Fax: 630-627-0336. p. 667

Keefe, Ann, Mgr, Coll Develop, Mgr, Tech Serv, Springfield City Library, 220 State St, Springfield, MA, 01103. Tel: 413-263-6828, Ext 294. Fax: 413-263-6817. p. 1127

Keefe, Betsy, Cat, Fairfax County Public Library, 12000 Government Center Pkwy, Ste 324, Fairfax, VA, 22035-0012. Tel: 703-324-3100. Fax: 703-324-8365. p. 2461

Keefe, Jeanne, Media & Digital Assets Librn, Rensselaer Libraries, Rensselaer Polytechnic Inst, 110 Eighth St, Troy, NY, 12180-3590. Tel: 518-276-8300. Fax: 518-276-2044. p. 1756

Keefe, Kathleen, Dir, Westmoreland County Community College, 400 Armbrust Rd, Youngwood, PA, 15697-1895. Tel: 724-925-4100. Fax: 724-925-1150. p. 2160

Keefe, Susanne, Dir, Sussex County Department of Libraries, South Coastal Public Library, 43 Kent Ave, Bethany Beach, DE, 19930. Tel: 302-539-5231. Fax: 302-537-9106. p. 383

Keefe, Thomas, Instrul Serv Librn, The John Marshall Law School, 315 S Plymouth Ct, Chicago, IL, 60604. Tel: 312-427-2737. Fax: 312-427-8307. p. 618

Keefer, Kelly, AV, Burlingame Public Library, 480 Primrose Rd, Burlingame, CA, 94010-4083. Tel: 650-558-7415. Fax: 650-342-1948. p. 130

Keefer, Kelly, Sr Librn, Ch Serv, San Leandro Public Library, 300 Estudillo Ave, San Leandro, CA, 94577. Tel: 510-577-3954. Fax: 510-577-3967. p. 252

Keefer, Monica, Librn, Parkland Regional Library, Muenster Branch, 307 Railway St, Muenster, SK, S0K 2Y0, CANADA. Tel: 306-682-5252. p. 2932

Keefer, Pat, Asst Libr Dir, Morrison & Mary Wiley Library District, 206 W Main St, Elmwood, IL, 61529-9641. Tel: 309-742-2431. Fax: 309-742-8298. p. 642

Keefer, Sue, Dir, Otero Junior College, 20 Pinon Ave, La Junta, CO, 81050-3347. Tel: 719-384-6882. p. 314

Keefer, Susan, Librn, Synergy Medical Education Alliance, Saint Mary's Branch, 800 S Washington, 2nd Flr, Saginaw, MI, 48601-2551. Tel: 989-907-8204. Fax: 989-907-8616. p. 1224

Keegan, Paula, Br Head, Bridgeport Public Library, North, 3455 Madison Ave, Bridgeport, CT, 06606. Tel: 203-576-8021. Fax: 203-576-7752. p. 331

Keehber, James, Dir, Libr Serv, Piscataway Township Free Public Library, 500 Hoes Lane, Piscataway, NJ, 08854. Tel: 732-463-1633. Fax: 732-463-9022. p. 1520

Keehleer, James, Dir, Piscataway Township Free Public Library, Johanna W Westergard Library, 20 Murray Ave, Piscataway, NJ, 08854. Tel: 732-752-1166. Fax: 732-752-1951. p. 1520

Keehr, Karen, Curator, Stuhr Museum of the Prairie Pioneer, 3133 W Hwy 34, Grand Island, NE, 68801-7280. Tel: 308-385-5316. Fax: 308-385-5028. p. 1400

Keel, Connie, Dir, Memorial Hospital at Gulfport, 4500 13th St, Gulfport, MS, 39501. Tel: 228-867-5366. Fax: 228-865-3214. p. 1300

Keeler, Barbara, Head Librn, Capital Area District Libraries, Leslie Library, 201 Pennsylvania St, Leslie, MI, 49251. Tel: 517-589-9400. Fax: 517-589-0536. p. 1200

Keeler, Cheryl, Br Mgr, Massanutten Regional Library, Grottoes Branch, 601 Dogwood Ave, Grottoes, VA, 24441. Tel: 540-249-3436. Fax: 540-249-8307. p. 2470

Keeler, Hali R, Dir, Bill Memorial Library, 240 Monument St, Groton, CT, 06340. Tel: 860-445-0392. Fax: 860-449-8971. p. 342

Keeler, Janice, Mgr, Knowledge Mgt, National Economic Research Associates, Inc, 360 Hamilton Ave, 10th Flr, White Plains, NY, 10601. Tel: 312-573-2813. Fax: 914-448-4040. p. 1768

Keeler, Jeannie, Circ, Marshall Memorial Library, 110 S Diamond St, Deming, NM, 88030-3698. Tel: 505-546-9202. Fax: 505-546-9649. p. 1554

Keeler, Justin, Commun Librn, Fort Vancouver Regional Library District, La Center Community Library, 1411 NE Lockwood Creek Rd, La Center, WA, 98629. Tel: 360-619-1800. p. 2546

Keeler, William, Archivist, Librn, Rochester Historical Society Library, 115 South Ave, Rochester, NY, 14604. Tel: 716-428-8470. Fax: 716-588-8478. p. 1731

Keeley, Kurt, Database Mgr, American Water Works Association, 6666 W Quincy Ave, Denver, CO, 80235. Tel: 303-347-6171. Fax: 303-795-7603. p. 298

Keelin, Russell W, Asst Librn, Hillsboro City Library, 118 S Waco St, Hillsboro, TX, 76645. Tel: 254-582-7385. Fax: 254-582-7765. p. 2333

Keeling, B Roger, Pub Serv, Saint Paul's College, 115 College Dr, Lawrenceville, VA, 23868-1299. Tel: 434-848-1835. Fax: 434-848-1861. p. 2473

Keeling, Mary Ann, Law Librn, US Customs & Border Protection Library, 90 K St NE, 9th Flr, Washington, DC, 20004. Tel: 202-325-0162. Fax: 202-325-0170. p. 418

Keely, Alan, Assoc Dir, Wake Forest University, Professional Center Library, Worrell Professional Ctr for Law & Management, 1834 Wake Forest Rd, Winston-Salem, NC, 27106. Tel: 336-758-5438. Fax: 336-758-6077. p. 1834

Keely, Susan, Bibliog Instr, Ref, University of North Carolina School of the Arts, 1533 S Main St, Winston-Salem, NC, 27127. Tel: 336-770-3270. Fax: 336-770-3271. p. 1834

Keen, Jennifer, Asst Dir, Head, Tech Serv, YA Librn, Holliston Public Library, 752 Washington St, Holliston, MA, 01746. Tel: 508-429-0617. Fax: 508-429-0625. p. 1095

Keen, Machelle, Coll Mgr, Vanderbilt University, Science & Engineering, 3200 Stevenson Ctr, 419 21st Ave S, Nashville, TN, 37240-0007. Tel: 615-322-4165. Fax: 615-343-7249. p. 2261

Keen, Richard C, Librn, Pennsylvania Department of Conservation & Natural Resources, 3240 Schoolhouse Rd, Middletown, PA, 17057-3534. Tel: 717-702-2020. Fax: 717-702-2065. p. 2089

Keena, Katherine Knapp, Prog Mgr, Archival Coll, Girl Scouts of the USA, 10 E Oglethorpe Ave, Savannah, GA, 31401. Tel: 912-233-4501. Fax: 912-233-4659. p. 550

Keenan, Kathleen, Asst Dir, Stevens Memorial Library, 345 Main St, North Andover, MA, 01845. Tel: 978-688-9505. Fax: 978-688-9507. p. 1112

Keenan, Marsha, Head, Syst, Texas A&M University-Commerce, 2600 S Neal St, Commerce, TX, 75429. Tel: 903-886-5727. Fax: 903-886-5434. p. 2300

Keenan, Phyllis, Dir, Osburn Public Library, 921 E Mullan, Osburn, ID, 83849. Tel: 208-752-9711. Fax: 208-753-8585. p. 581

Keenan, Rebecca H, Dir of Tech Serv, Interim Dir, Libr Serv, Librn, Washington & Jefferson College Library, 60 S Lincoln St, Washington, PA, 15301. Tel: 724-223-6069. Fax: 724-223-5272. p. 2151

Keenan, Susan S, Ch, Pitkin County Library, 120 N Mill St, Aspen, CO, 81611. Tel: 970-925-4025. Fax: 970-925-3935. p. 288

Keenan, Teressa, Head, Metadata & Continuing Res Section of Bibliog Mgt Serv, University of Montana, Maureen & Mike Mansfield Library, 32 Campus Dr, No 9936, Missoula, MT, 59812-9936. Tel: 406-243-4592. Fax: 406-243-4067. p. 1386

Keene, Deborah, Assoc Dean, George Mason University Libraries, School of Law, 3301 N Fairfax Dr, Arlington, VA, 22201-4426. Tel: 703-993-8110. Fax: 703-993-8113. p. 2462

Keene, Lee P, Head, Instrul & Res Serv, Whitman College, 345 Boyer Ave, Walla Walla, WA, 99362. Tel: 509-527-5917. Fax: 509-527-5900. p. 2547

Keenehan, Deborah, Head, Circ, Lima Public Library, 650 W Market St, Lima, OH, 45801. Tel: 419-228-5113. Fax: 419-224-2669. p. 1910

Keeney, Charlotte Kay, Dir, Pulaski County Public Library, 304 S Main St, Somerset, KY, 42501-1402. Tel: 606-679-8401. Fax: 606-679-1779. p. 935

Keeney, Debbie, Circ, Pub Serv, Polk State College, 999 Ave H NE, Winter Haven, FL, 33881-4299. Tel: 863-297-1040. Fax: 863-297-1065. p. 504

Keeney, Diane, Br Mgr, Crown Point Community Library, Winfield, 10645 Randolph St, Crown Point, IN, 46307. Tel: 219-662-4039. Fax: 219-662-4068. p. 734

Keeney, Donald E, Dir, Episcopal Theological Seminary of the Southwest, 501 E 32nd St, Austin, TX, 78705. Tel: 512-472-4133, 512-478-5212. Fax: 512-472-4620. p. 2280

Keeney, Mary Ellen, Ch, Ridley Park Public Library, 107 E Ward St, Ridley Park, PA, 19078-3097. Tel: 610-583-7207. Fax: 610-583-2160. p. 2134

Keeney, Scott, Ch, Albany Public Library, 1390 Waverly Dr SE, Albany, OR, 97322. Tel: 541-917-7591. Fax: 541-917-7586. p. 1989

Keepper, Michael, Acq Librn, Cat Mgr, Dir, Herrin City Library, 120 N 13th St, Herrin, IL, 62948-3233. Tel: 618-942-6109. Fax: 618-942-4165. p. 655

Keeran, Peggy, Ref, University of Denver, 2150 E Evans Ave, Denver, CO, 80208-2007. Tel: 303-871-3441. Fax: 303-871-2290. p. 304

Keesler, Lenoir C, Jr, Chief Exec Officer, Charlotte Mecklenburg Library, 310 N Tryon St, Charlotte, NC, 28202-2176. Tel: 704-416-0101. Fax: 704-416-0130. p. 1781

Keesler, Toni, Librn, Preble County District Library, Camden, 104 S Main St, Eaton, OH, 45311. Tel: 937-452-3142. Fax: 937-452-7365. p. 1897

Keesling, Kurt, Librn III, Site Supvr, Orange Public Library & History Center, Taft Branch, 740 E Taft Ave, Orange, CA, 92865-4406. Tel: 714-288-2440. Fax: 714-282-8663. p. 201

Keetch, Jean, Librn, Rimbey Municipal Library, 4938 50th Ave, Rimbey, AB, T0C 2J0, CANADA. Tel: 403-843-2841. p. 2715

Keeton, Kendrick, Virtual Librn, Dona Ana Community College Library, East Mesa Campus, 2800 N Sonoma Ranch Blvd, Las Cruces, NM, 88011. Tel: 575-528-7260. Fax: 575-528-7422. p. 1558

Keever, Cynthia D, Dir, Livingstone College, Hood Theological Seminary Library, 1810 Lutheran Synod Dr, Salisbury, NC, 28144. Tel: 704-636-6779, 704-636-6840. Fax: 704-636-7699. p. 1822

Keever, Mary, Circ Mgr, Friendswood Public Library, 416 S Friendswood Dr, Friendswood, TX, 77546-3897. Tel: 281-482-7135. Fax: 281-482-2685. p. 2325

Keever, Selina, Br Mgr, Lincoln County Public Library, West Lincoln, 5545 W Hwy 27, Vale, NC, 28168. Tel: 704-276-9946. Fax: 704-276-9946. p. 1807

Keffer, Debbie, Librn, Roachdale-Franklin Township Public Library, 100 E Washington, Roachdale, IN, 46172. Tel: 765-522-1491. Fax: 765-522-1491. p. 775

Kegler, Lydia, Dr, Libr Dir, Columbia County Traveling Library Authority, 702 Sawmill Rd, Ste 101, Bloomsburg, PA, 17815. Tel: 570-387-8782. p. 2036

Kegley, Jay, Managing Librn, Columbus Metropolitan Library, 96 S Grant Ave, Columbus, OH, 43215-4781. Tel: 614-645-2275. Fax: 614-849-1157. p. 1884

Kegley, Jay, Managing Librn, Columbus Metropolitan Library, Main Library, 96 S Grant Ave, Columbus, OH, 43215-4781. Tel: 614-645-2275. Fax: 614-849-1389. p. 1885

Kehlenbrink, Laura, Human Res Mgr, Wayne Township Library, 80 N Sixth St, Richmond, IN, 47374-3079. Tel: 765-966-8291. Fax: 765-962-1318. p. 775

Kehler, Bill, Libr Dir, Rocky Mountain College, 1511 Poly Dr, Billings, MT, 59102-1796. Tel: 406-657-1140. Fax: 406-657-1085. p. 1374

Kehm, Colin, Digital Serv Spec, Bellevue University, 1000 Galvin Rd S, Bellevue, NE, 68005. Tel: 402-557-7299. Fax: 402-557-5427. p. 1393

Kehn, Jana, Adult Serv, Lied Scottsbluff Public Library, 1809 Third Ave, Scottsbluff, NE, 69361-2493. Tel: 308-630-6250. Fax: 308-630-6293. p. 1418

Kehnast, Anna, Per, Gloucester County College Library, 1400 Tanyard Rd, Sewell, NJ, 08080. Tel: 856-468-5000, Ext 2250. Fax: 856-464-1695. p. 1529

Kehoe, Crystal, Youth Serv Librn, Scott County Library System, 200 N Sixth Ave, Eldridge, IA, 52748. Tel: 563-285-4794. Fax: 563-285-4743. p. 813

Kehoe, Kathleen, Librn, Columbia University, Mathematics-Science, 303 Mathematics, 2990 Broadway, MC 4702, New York, NY, 10027. Tel: 212-854-4182. Fax: 212-854-8849. p. 1675

Kehoe, Lauren, Acq, Instruction & Ref Serv, Saint Joseph's College, 222 Clinton Ave, Brooklyn, NY, 11205-3697. Tel: 718-940-5877. Fax: 718-636-7250. p. 1594

Kehoe, Michelle, Dir, Boone Area Library, 129 N Mill St, Birdsboro, PA, 19508-2340. Tel: 610-582-5666. Fax: 610-582-6826. p. 2035

Kehoe, Susan, Circ/ILL Librn, Sandown Public Library, 305 Main St, Sandown, NH, 03873. Tel: 603-887-3428. Fax: 603-887-0590. p. 1465

Kehoe-Robinson, Colleen, Ref & Info Serv, Web Coordr, Mohawk Valley Community College Library, 1101 Sherman Dr, Utica, NY, 13501-5394. Tel: 315-731-5737. Fax: 315-792-5666. p. 1759

Kehr, Rosemary, Librn, Ozark Regional Library, Steelville Branch, 210 S Fourth St, Steelville, MO, 65565. Tel: 573-775-2338. p. 1333

Kehrt, Edna, Libr Serv Mgr, Indiana Baptist College Library, 1301 W County Line Rd, Greenwood, IN, 46142. Tel: 317-882-2327, 317-882-2345. Fax: 317-885-2960. p. 747

Keigley, Helen, AV Spec, Circ Spec, London Public Library, 20 E First St, London, OH, 43140. Tel: 740-852-9543. Fax: 740-852-3691. p. 1911

Keims, Carol, Asst Dir, Mahanoy City Public Library, 17-19 W Mahanoy Ave, Mahanoy City, PA, 17948-2615. Tel: 570-773-1610. p. 2083

Keinsley, Jason, Agr Librn, University of Kentucky Libraries, Agricultural Information Center, N24 Agricultural Sciences Ctr N, Lexington, KY, 40546-0091. Tel: 859-257-2758. Fax: 859-323-4719. p. 922

Keiper, Sonia, Adult Serv, Media Spec, Ref, Altoona Area Public Library, 1600 Fifth Ave, Altoona, PA, 16602-3693. Tel: 814-946-0417, Ext 147. Fax: 814-946-3230. p. 2028

Keirstead, Robin, Univ Archivist, Western University - Libraries, 1151 Richmond St, Ste 200, London, ON, N6A 3K7, CANADA. Tel: 519-661-2111, Ext 87289. Fax: 519-661-3493. p. 2819

Keirstead, Robin, Univ Archivist, Western University - Libraries, Western Archives, Archives & Research Collection Centre (ARCC), 1151 Richmond St, Ste 2, London, ON, N6A 3K7, CANADA. Tel: 519-661-2111, Ext 87289. Fax: 519-850-2979. p. 2819

Keiser, Barbara J, Dir, Eastern Monroe Public Library, 1002 N Ninth St, Stroudsburg, PA, 18360. Tel: 570-421-0800. Fax: 570-421-0212. p. 2143

Keiser, Barbie, Ref Librn, NPR Library, 635 Massachusetts Ave NW, Washington, DC, 20001. Fax: 202-513-3056. p. 412

Keiser, Helen, Librn, Snyder County Historical Society, Inc Library, 30 E Market St, Middleburg, PA, 17842-1017. Tel: 570-837-6191. Fax: 570-837-4282. p. 2089

Keiser, Jennifer, ILL, Rodale Inc, 400 S Tenth St, Emmaus, PA, 18098. Tel: 610-967-8729, 610-967-8880. Fax: 610-967-8100. p. 2054

Keisha, Parks, Ch, Cleveland Bradley County Public Library, 795 Church St NE, Cleveland, TN, 37311-5295. Tel: 423-472-2163. Fax: 423-339-9791. p. 2229

Keisling, Bruce, Librn, Theological Education Association of Mid America, Southern Baptist Theological Seminary, 2825 Lexington Rd, Louisville, KY, 40280. Tel: 502-897-4807. Fax: 502-897-4600. p. 2944

Keisling, Bruce L, Dir, Southern Baptist Theological Seminary, 2825 Lexington Rd, Louisville, KY, 40280-0294. p. 925

Keissling, Marie, Reader Serv, YA Serv, Free Library of Springfield Township, 1600 Paper Mill Rd, Wyndmoor, PA, 19038. Tel: 215-836-5300. Fax: 215-836-2404. p. 2158

Keith, Betsy, Ch, Library of Graham, 910 Cherry St, Graham, TX, 76450-3547. Tel: 940-549-0600. Fax: 940-549-8624. p. 2329

Keith, Bingham F, Archives, Cheyney University, 1837 University Circle, Cheyney, PA, 19319. Tel: 610-399-2203. Fax: 610-399-2491. p. 2044

Keith, Bonnie, Youth Serv Librn, Helen Hall Library, 100 W Walker, League City, TX, 77573-3899. Tel: 281-554-1112. Fax: 281-554-1118. p. 2354

Keith, Brian W, Asst Dean, Human & Financial Res, University of Florida Libraries, 535 Library W, Gainesville, FL, 32611-7000. Tel: 352-273-2595. Fax: 352-392-4538. p. 449

Keith, Carole, Head, Cat, University of Nevada-Reno, Savitt Medical Library & IT Department, Pennington Medical Education Bldg, 1664 N Virginia St, Mail Stop 306, Reno, NV, 89557. Tel: 775-784-4625. Fax: 775-784-4489. p. 1433

Keith, Hilary Gordon, Dir of Libr Serv, Santa Fe Springs City Library, 11700 E Telegraph Rd, Santa Fe Springs, CA, 90670-3600. Tel: 562-868-7738. Fax: 562-929-3680. p. 265

Keith, Jim, Librn, Lester Public Library of Rome, 1157 Rome Center Dr, Nekoosa, WI, 54457. Tel: 715-325-8990. Fax: 715-325-8993. p. 2624

Keith, Latrina, Tech Serv Librn, New York Academy of Medicine Library, 1216 Fifth Ave, New York, NY, 10029-5293. Tel: 212-822-7331. Fax: 212-423-0266. p. 1688

Keith, Linda, Acq, Coll Develop, ILL, Northwest Kansas Library System, Two Washington Sq, Norton, KS, 67654-1615. Tel: 785-877-5148. Fax: 785-877-5697. p. 885

Keith, Lisa, Adult Serv, Gardendale Martha Moore Public Library, 995 Mt Olive Rd, Gardendale, AL, 35071. Tel: 205-631-6639. Fax: 205-631-0146. p. 18

Keith, Marcia, Circ Mgr, Calumet College of Saint Joseph, 2400 New York Ave, Whiting, IN, 46394. Tel: 219-473-4375. Fax: 219-473-4259. p. 787

Keith, Ronna, Ch, Old Lyme, Two Library Lane, Old Lyme, CT, 06371. Tel: 860-434-1684. Fax: 860-434-9547. p. 363

Keith, Tammy, Head, Coll Mgt, Kokomo-Howard County Public Library, 220 N Union St, Kokomo, IN, 46901-4614. Tel: 765-457-3242. Fax: 765-457-3683. p. 758

Keith, Vicki, ILL Spec, Lakeshores Library System, 725 Cornerstone Crossing, Ste C, Waterford, WI, 53185. Tel: 262-514-4500, Ext 64. Fax: 262-514-4544. p. 2644

Keith-Henry, Alex, ILL, United States Air Force, 55 FSS/FSDL, Bldg 73, 510 Custer Dr, Offutt AFB, NE, 68113-2150. Tel: 402-294-5276, 402-294-7506, DSN 271-7124. Fax: 402-294-7124. p. 1411

Keizer, Colleen, Br Mgr, West Lincoln Public Library, Wellandport Branch, 5042 Canborough Rd, Wellandport, ON, L0R 2J0, CANADA. Tel: 905-386-6792. p. 2842

Kelchlin, Kelly, Librn, Phoenix College, 1202 W Thomas Rd, Phoenix, AZ, 85013. Tel: 602-285-7457. Fax: 602-285-7368. p. 76

Kelchner, Gina, Periodicals Librn, Rodale Inc, 400 S Tenth St, Emmaus, PA, 18098. Tel: 610-967-7569. Fax: 610-967-8100. p. 2054

Keleher, Jean, Coll Develop, United States Senate Library, SRB-15 Senate Russell Bldg, Washington, DC, 20510-7112. Tel: 202-224-7106. Fax: 202-224-0879. p. 421

Keleman, Aubri, Coordr, Teen Serv, Whatcom County Library System, 5205 Northwest Dr, Bellingham, WA, 98226-9050. Tel: 360-384-3150. Fax: 360-384-4947. p. 2509

Kelemen, Jennifer, Adult Serv, River Edge Free Public Library, 685 Elm Ave, River Edge, NJ, 07661. Tel: 201-261-1663. Fax: 201-986-0214. p. 1526

Kelien, Becky, Adult Serv, Jeffersonville Township Public Library, 211 E Court Ave, Jeffersonville, IN, 47130. Tel: 812-285-5630. Fax: 812-285-5639. p. 756

Kelker, Signe, Ref Librn, Shippensburg University, 1871 Old Main Dr, Shippensburg, PA, 17257-2299. Tel: 717-477-1289. Fax: 717-477-1389. p. 2140

Kellam, Lynda, Data Serv & Govt Info Librn, University of North Carolina at Greensboro, 320 Spring Garden St, Greensboro, NC, 27402. Tel: 336-334-5241. Fax: 336-334-5399. p. 1798

Kellar, Ed, Asst Dir, Jennings County Public Library, 2375 N State Hwy 3, North Vernon, IN, 47265-1596. Tel: 812-346-2091. Fax: 812-346-2127. p. 769

Kelleher, Angie, Access Serv, Alma College Library, 614 W Superior St, Alma, MI, 48801. Tel: 989-463-7345. Fax: 989-463-8694. p. 1149

Kelleher, Carolyn B, Librn, Ridgewater College Library, 2101 15th Ave NW, Willmar, MN, 56201. Tel: 320-222-7537. Fax: 320-222-7539. p. 1289

Kelleher, Christian, Archivist, University of Texas Libraries, Nettie Lee Benson Latin American Collection, Sid Richardson Hall 1-108, Austin, TX, 78713-8916. Tel: 512-495-4520. Fax: 512-495-4568. p. 2283

Kelleher, Laura, Br Mgr, Louisville Free Public Library, Bon Air Regional, 2816 Del Rio Pl, Louisville, KY, 40220. Tel: 502-574-1795. Fax: 502-454-0169. p. 924

Kelleher, Mary, Dr, Chair, University of Saint Thomas, Cardinal Beran Library at Saint Mary's Seminary, 9845 Memorial Dr, Houston, TX, 77024-3498. Tel: 713-686-4345, Ext 248, 713-686-4345, Ext 265. Fax: 713-681-7550. p. 2344

Kellen, Chris, Syst Mgr, Carnegie Mellon University, Hunt Library, 4909 Frew St, Pittsburgh, PA, 15213-3890. Tel: 412-268-2446. Fax: 412-268-2793. p. 2123

Keller, A, Librn, Thurber Engineering Library, 1281 W Georgia St, Ste 900, Vancouver, BC, V6E 3J7, CANADA. Tel: 604-684-4384. Fax: 604-684-5124. p. 2742

Keller, Allie, Actg Dir, Rochester College, 800 W Avon Rd, Rochester Hills, MI, 48307. Tel: 248-218-2268. Fax: 248-218-2265. p. 1222

Keller, Anne, Teen Librn, Tecumseh District Library, 215 N Ottawa St, Tecumseh, MI, 49286-1564. Tel: 517-423-2238. Fax: 517-423-5519. p. 1230

Keller, Bernice, Librn, Wapiti Regional Library, Pilger Public Library, 622 Main St, Pilger, SK, S0K 3G0, CANADA. Tel: 306-367-4809. p. 2921

Keller, Carla, Libr Spec, Maysville Community & Technical College Library, Licking Valley Campus Library, 319 Webster Ave, Cynthiana, KY, 41031. Tel: 859-234-8626, Ext 66417. p. 928

Keller, Colleen A, Ref Librn, Web Coordr, Girard Free Library, 105 E Prospect St, Girard, OH, 44420-1899. Tel: 330-545-2508. Fax: 330-545-8213. p. 1902

Keller, Connie, Coordr, Tech Serv & Syst, Elon University, 308 N O'Kelly Ave, Elon, NC, 27244-0187. Tel: 336-278-6578. Fax: 336-278-6637. p. 1791

Keller, Deborah E, Eng Librn, United States Department of the Army, CEHEC-ZL Casey Bldg, 7701 Telegraph Rd, Alexandria, VA, 22315-3860. Tel: 703-428-6388. Fax: 703-428-6310. p. 2446

Keller, Dena, Circ & Reserves Supvr, Washington State University Libraries, 14204 NE Salmon Creek Ave, Vancouver, WA, 98686. Tel: 360-546-9685. Fax: 360-546-9039. p. 2546

Keller, Denise, Dir, Pinal County Library District, 92 W Butte Ave, Florence, AZ, 85132. Tel: 520-866-6457. Fax: 520-866-6533. p. 63

Keller, Donna, Asst Librn, Owensville Carnegie Public Library, 110 S Main St, Owensville, IN, 47665. Tel: 812-724-3335. Fax: 812-724-3336. p. 772

Keller, Dorothy, Librn, Boston Public Library, Faneuil, 419 Faneuil St, Brighton, MA, 02135-1699. Tel: 617-782-6705. Fax: 617-787-3654. p. 1057

Keller, Elise, Satellite Librn, Ralph M Freeman Memorial Library for the US Courts, 436 US Courthouse, 231 W Lafayette Blvd, Detroit, MI, 48226-2719. Tel: 313-234-5255. Fax: 313-234-5383. p. 1171

Keller, Elise, Detroit Satellite Librn, US Court of Appeals for the Sixth Circuit Library, 312 Potter Stewart US Courthouse, Cincinnati, OH, 45202. Tel: 313-234-5255. Fax: 513-564-7329. p. 1873

Keller, Faith, ILL Librn, South Carolina State Library, 1430-1500 Senate St, Columbia, SC, 29201. Tel: 803-734-8851. Fax: 803-734-8676. p. 2189

Keller, Irma, ILL, Tomah Public Library, 716 Superior Ave, Tomah, WI, 54660-2098. Tel: 608-374-7470. Fax: 608-374-7471. p. 2642

Keller, Janet, Librn, Washington Public Library, 116 E Second St, Washington, KS, 66968-1916. Tel: 785-325-2114. p. 899

Keller, Karen, Dir, Anchorage Public Library, 3600 Denali St, Anchorage, AK, 99503. Tel: 907-343-2892. Fax: 907-343-2930. p. 44

Keller, Kathy, Br Mgr, Putnam County Library System, Algood Branch, 125 Fourth Ave, Algood, TN, 38506-5224. Tel: 931-537-3240. Fax: 931-372-8517. p. 2231

Keller, Kim, Dir, Bryan-Bennett Library, 315 S Maple, Salem, IL, 62881. Tel: 618-548-3006. Fax: 618-548-3096. p. 700

Keller, Kit, Dir, Planning & Data Serv, Nebraska Library Commission, The Atrium, 1200 N St, Ste 120, Lincoln, NE, 68508-2023. Tel: 402-471-3216. Fax: 402-471-2083. p. 1406

Keller, Leigh Cregan, Pub Serv, Ramapo College of New Jersey, 505 Ramapo Valley Rd, Mahwah, NJ, 07430-1623. Tel: 201-684-7316. p. 1498

Keller, Linda, Head, ILL, Arkansas State University, 322 University Loop West Circle, State University, AR, 72401. Tel: 870-972-3077. Fax: 870-972-3199. p. 115

Keller, Michael A, Dir, Acad Info Res, Univ Librn, Stanford University Libraries, 557 Escondido Mall, Stanford, CA, 94305-6004. Tel: 650-723-5553. p. 270

Keller, Noelle, Tech Serv Librn, Adrian College, 110 S Madison St, Adrian, MI, 49221. Tel: 517-265-5161, Ext 4229. Fax: 517-264-3748. p. 1147

Keller, Rita, Cat, North Central Regional Library, 16 N Columbia St, Wenatchee, WA, 98801-8103. Tel: 509-663-1117, Ext 110. Fax: 509-662-8060. p. 2548

Keller, Ruth, Libr Assoc, Washington State Library, Natural Resources Building, PO Box 47000, Olympia, WA, 98504-7000. Tel: 360-902-2992. Fax: 360-902-2607. p. 2545

Keller, Susan C, Acq Librn, Asst Dean, Coll Develop Librn, Western Piedmont Community College, 1001 Burkemont Ave, Morganton, NC, 28655-4504. Tel: 828-448-6037. Fax: 828-448-6173. p. 1811

Keller, Susan J, Dir, Culpeper County Library, 271 Southgate Shopping Ctr, Culpeper, VA, 22701-3215. Tel: 540-825-8691. Fax: 540-825-7486. p. 2459

Keller, Timothy, Tech Serv, Baldwin Wallace University, Jones Music Library, 49 Seminary St, Berea, OH, 44017-1905. Tel: 440-826-2375. p. 1859

Keller, William, Fine Arts Librn, University of Pennsylvania Libraries, Fisher Fine Arts Library, Furness Bldg, 220 S 34th St, Philadelphia, PA, 19104-6308. Tel: 215-898-8325. Fax: 215-573-2066. p. 2119

Keller, William J, VPres, Libr & Info Serv, Railway Mail Service Library, Inc, 117 E Main St, Boyce, VA, 22620-9639. Tel: 540-837-9090. p. 2452

Keller, Yvonne, Librn, Waterloo-Cedar Falls Courier, 501 Commercial St, Waterloo, IA, 50701. Tel: 319-291-1477. Fax: 319-291-2069. p. 850

Keller-Raber, Candace, Dr, Dir, DeVry University, 4000 Millenia Blvd, Orlando, FL, 32839. Tel: 407-355-4809. Fax: 407-355-4777. p. 475

Kellerman, Carol, Librn, Lapeer District Library, Metamora Branch, 4018 Oak St, Metamora, MI, 48455. Tel: 810-678-2991. Fax: 810-678-3253. p. 1202

Kellerman, Karen, Pub Serv, Penticton Public Library, 785 Main St, Penticton, BC, V2A 5E3, CANADA. Tel: 250-770-7786. Fax: 250-770-7787. p. 2735

Kellerman, Larry M, Librn, Central Lakes College Library, 501 W College Dr, Brainerd, MN, 56401. Tel: 218-855-8178. Fax: 218-855-8179. p. 1242

Kellerman, Sue, Head, Digitization & Presv Dept, Pennsylvania State University Libraries, 510 Paterno Library, University Park, PA, 16802. Tel: 814-865-0401. Fax: 814-865-3665. p. 2148

Kelley, Alyce, Dir, Emmett Public Library, 275 S Hayes, Emmett, ID, 83617-2972. Tel: 208-365-6057. Fax: 208-365-6060. p. 574

Kelley, Amy, Librn, Livingston Correctional Facility Library, PO Box 49, Sonyea, NY, 14556. Tel: 585-658-3710. Fax: 585-658-4841. p. 1745

Kelley, Beverely, Asst Dir, Central Christian College of Kansas, 1200 S Main, McPherson, KS, 67460. Tel: 620-241-0723, Ext 359. Fax: 620-241-6032. p. 883

Kelley, Brian C, Dir, Libr Serv, Palm Beach State College, 4200 Congress Ave, Mail Sta 17, Lake Worth, FL, 33461. Tel: 561-868-3706. Fax: 561-868-3708. p. 459

Kelley, Carol M, Assoc Libr Dir, Coll & Bibliog Serv, University of Texas at El Paso Library, 500 W University Ave, El Paso, TX, 79968-0582. Tel: 915-747-6710. Fax: 915-747-5345. p. 2317

Kelley, Christina, Teen Librn, Bartholomew County Public Library, 536 Fifth St, Columbus, IN, 47201-6225. Tel: 812-379-1288. Fax: 812-379-1275. p. 733

Kelley, Colleen, Libr Tech, Lois Wagner Memorial Library, 35200 Division Rd, Richmond, MI, 48062. Tel: 586-727-2665. Fax: 586-727-3774. p. 1221

Kelley, Dan, Fac Outreach Librn, Lewis & Clark College, Aubrey R Watzek Library, 0615 SW Palatine Hill Rd, Portland, OR, 97219-7899. Tel: 503-768-7274. Fax: 503-768-7282. p. 2011

Kelley, Deborah, Mgr, White County Public Library, Helen Branch, 90 Petes Park Rd, Helen, GA, 30545. Tel: 706-878-2438. Fax: 706-878-1479. p. 525

Kelley, Emily, Ref Librn, Porter, Wright, Morris & Arthur, LLP, Huntington Ctr, 41 S High St, Columbus, OH, 43215-6194. Tel: 614-227-2152. Fax: 614-227-2100. p. 1890

Kelley, Gloria, Dean, Central Piedmont Community College Library, 1201 Elizabeth Ave, Charlotte, NC, 28235. Tel: 704-330-6441. Fax: 704-330-6887. p. 1781

Kelley, Gwen, Br Mgr, Jefferson Parish Library, Rosedale, 4036 Jefferson Hwy, Jefferson, LA, 70121. Tel: 504-838-4350. Fax: 504-838-1129. p. 957

Kelley, Ina, Ref Librn, Central Texas College, Bld 102, 6200 W Central Texas Expressway, Killeen, TX, 76549. Tel: 254-526-1237. Fax: 254-526-1878. p. 2350

Kelley, Jamie D, Dir, Marysville Public Library, 1009 Broadway, Marysville, KS, 66508-1814. Tel: 785-562-2491. Fax: 785-562-4086. p. 882

Kelley, Jan, Librn, New Hope Christian College, 2155 Bailey Hill Rd, Eugene, OR, 97405. Tel: 541-485-1780, Ext 3309. Fax: 541-343-5801. p. 1997

Kelley, Jennifer, Ref, College of DuPage Library, 425 Fawell Blvd, Glen Ellyn, IL, 60137-6599. Tel: 630-942-2383. Fax: 630-858-8757. p. 649

Kelley, Jennifer, Outreach Librn, Kershaw County Library, Bethune Public, 206 S Main St, Bethune, SC, 29009. Tel: 843-334-8420. Fax: 843-334-6981. p. 2182

Kelley, Kathleen, ILL, Saint Joseph College, 1678 Asylum Ave, West Hartford, CT, 06117-2791. Tel: 860-232-4571. Fax: 860-523-4356. p. 376

Kelley, Lana, Acq, Carrollton Public Library, 1700 Keller Springs Rd, Carrollton, TX, 75006. Tel: 972-466-4704. Fax: 972-466-4265. p. 2295

Kelley, Linda, Librn, Thompson-Nicola Regional District Library System, Barriere Branch, 4511 Barriere Town Rd, Barriere, BC, V0E 1E0, CANADA. Tel: 250-672-5811. Fax: 250-672-5811. p. 2729

Kelley, Margaret, Coll Coordr, Nodaway County Historical Society/Mary H Jackson Research Center, 110 N Walnut St, Maryville, MO, 64468-2251. Tel: 660-582-8176. Fax: 660-562-3377. p. 1344

Kelley, Martha, Acq Mgr, Mgr, ILL, Mgr, Ser, Martin Methodist College, 433 W Madison St, Pulaski, TN, 38478-2799. Tel: 931-363-9844. Fax: 931-363-9844. p. 2264

Kelley, Mary, Acq, Indiana State Library, 315 W Ohio St, Indianapolis, IN, 46202. Tel: 317-232-1939. Fax: 317-232-0002. p. 752

Kelley, Mary Beth, Tech Serv, Fox Valley Technical College, 1825 N Bluemound Dr, Appleton, WI, 54914. Tel: 920-735-4836. Fax: 920-735-4870. p. 2578

Kelley, Mary G, Head, Ref (Info Serv), Woodbridge Town Library, Ten Newton Rd, Woodbridge, CT, 06525. Tel: 203-389-3433. Fax: 203-389-3457. p. 380

Kelley, Melanie A, Dir of Libr Serv, Ice Miller LLP, One American Sq, Ste 2900, Indianapolis, IN, 46282-0020. Tel: 317-236-2414. Fax: 317-592-4207. p. 751

Kelley, Michelle, ILL Assoc, Hope College, Van Wylen Library, 53 Graves Pl, Holland, MI, 49422. Tel: 616-395-7794. Fax: 616-395-7965. p. 1191

Kelley, Nancy, Br Supvr, Licking County Library, Hebron Branch, 934 W Main St, Hebron, OH, 43025. Tel: 740-928-3923. Fax: 740-928-9437. p. 1922

Kelley, Nick, Tech Mgr, Avon Lake Public Library, 32649 Electric Blvd, Avon Lake, OH, 44012-1669. Tel: 440-933-8128. Fax: 440-933-5659. p. 1857

Kelley, Patte, Head, Children's Dept, Carnegie Library of Pittsburgh, 4400 Forbes Ave, Pittsburgh, PA, 15213-4080. Tel: 412-622-1924. Fax: 412-578-2595. p. 2122

Kelley, Rhona, Head of Ref & Instrul Serv, Southern Illinois University School of Medicine Library, 801 N Rutledge, Springfield, IL, 62702. Tel: 217-545-2658. Fax: 217-545-0988. p. 706

Kelley, Robert, PhD, Br Mgr, Ouachita Parish Public Library, Louise Williams Branch, 140 Bayou Oaks Dr, Monroe, LA, 71203. Tel: 318-327-5422. Fax: 318-343-3476. p. 958

Kelley, Susan, Mgr, Welchs, 749 Middlesex Tpk, Billerica, MA, 01821. Tel: 978-670-8506. Fax: 978-670-8539. p. 1054

Kelley, Susan, Youth Serv, Snow Library, 67 Main St, Orleans, MA, 02653-2413. Tel: 508-240-3760. Fax: 508-255-5701. p. 1116

Kelley, Timothy A, Dir, Oxford Free Library, 339 Main St, Oxford, MA, 01540. Tel: 508-987-6003. Fax: 508-987-3896. p. 1116

Kelley, Todd D, Assoc Provost, Univ Librn, University of the South, 735 University Ave, Sewanee, TN, 37383-1000. Tel: 931-598-1777. Fax: 931-598-1702. p. 2265

Kellner, Amy, Adult Serv, Zelienople Area Public Library, 227 S High St, Zelienople, PA, 16063-1319. Tel: 724-452-9330. Fax: 724-452-9318. p. 2160

Kellogg, Betty, Assoc Dir, Coll & Acces Serv, National University Library, 9393 Lightwave Ave, San Diego, CA, 92123-1447. Tel: 858-541-7944. Fax: 858-541-7994. p. 232

Kellogg, Jeremiah, In Charge, State of Vermont Department of Libraries, Midstate Library Service Center, 578 Paine Tpk N, Berlin, VT, 05602. Tel: 802-828-2320. p. 2429

Kellogg, Kim, Dir, Polk City Community Library, 1500 W Broadway St, Polk City, IA, 50226-2001. Tel: 515-984-6119. Fax: 515-984-9273. p. 839

Kellogg, Melody, Mgr, Metropolitan Library System in Oklahoma County, Edmond Library, Ten S Blvd, Edmond, OK, 73034. Tel: 405-341-9282. Fax: 405-606-3411. p. 1972

Kellsey, Charlene, Head, Acq, University of Colorado Boulder, 1720 Pleasant St, 184 UCB, Boulder, CO, 80309-0184. Tel: 303-492-3921. Fax: 303-492-3340. p. 291

Kellum, Becky, Info Serv Supvr, State Library of Ohio, SEO Library Center, 40780 Marietta Rd, Caldwell, OH, 43724. Tel: 740-783-5705. p. 1890

Kelly, Andrew, Tech Serv Librn, Paul Smiths College of Arts & Sciences, Rte's 30 & 86, Paul Smiths, NY, 12970. Tel: 518-327-6354. Fax: 518-327-6350. p. 1715

Kelly, Angela, Asst Dir, North Mankato Taylor Library, 1001 Belgrade Ave, North Mankato, MN, 56003. Tel: 507-345-5120. Fax: 507-345-1861. p. 1268

Kelly, Anne, Ch, YA Serv, Brockway Memorial Library, 10021 NE Second Ave, Miami Shores, FL, 33138. Tel: 305-758-8107. p. 470

Kelly, Barbara, Dir, Faulkner University, 5345 Atlanta Hwy, Montgomery, AL, 36109-3398. Tel: 334-386-7207. Fax: 334-386-7481. p. 28

Kelly, Barbara, Acq, Franklin Square Public Library, 19 Lincoln Rd, Franklin Square, NY, 11010. Tel: 516-488-3444. Fax: 516-354-3368. p. 1624

Kelly, Betsy, Assoc Dir, Digital Initiatives, Washington University Libraries, Bernard Becker Medical Library, 660 S Euclid Ave, Campus Box 8132, Saint Louis, MO, 63110. Tel: 314-362-2783. Fax: 314-367-9534. p. 1362

Kelly, Betty, Acq/Coll Develop Librn, Furman University Libraries, 3300 Poinsett Hwy, Greenville, SC, 29613-4100. Tel: 864-294-2712. Fax: 864-294-3004. p. 2195

Kelly, Carol, Librn, IHM Library/Resource Center, 610 W Elm Ave, Monroe, MI, 48162-7909. Tel: 734-240-9713. Fax: 734-240-8347. p. 1209

Kelly, Cheryl, Head, Ch, Salem Public Library, 821 E State St, Salem, OH, 44460-2298. Tel: 330-332-0042. Fax: 330-332-4488. p. 1934

Kelly, Clarice, Ref Librn, Lawrence County Public Library, 102 W Main & Jefferson, Louisa, KY, 41230. Tel: 606-638-0554, 606-638-4497. Fax: 606-638-1293. p. 923

Kelly, Darlene, Dir, Learning Res, CDU Health Sciences Library, 1731 E 120th St, Los Angeles, CA, 90059. Tel: 323-563-4869. Fax: 323-563-4861. p. 169

Kelly, David, Brother, Dir, Saint Vincent College & Seminary Library, 300 Fraser Purchase Rd, Latrobe, PA, 15650-2690. Tel: 724-805-2966. Fax: 724-805-2905. p. 2079

Kelly, Donna, Librn, Saint Petersburg College, Clearwater Campus Library, 2465 Drew St, Clearwater, FL, 33765. Tel: 727-341-3771. Fax: 727-791-2601. p. 483

Kelly, Donna, Dir, Millinocket Regional Hospital, 200 Somerset St, Millinocket, ME, 04462-1298. Tel: 207-723-5161, Ext 298. Fax: 207-723-4913. p. 992

Kelly, Donna, Br Librn, Supvr, Lorain Public Library System, Avon Branch, 37485 Harvest Dr, Avon, OH, 44011-2812. Tel: 440-934-4743. Fax: 440-934-4165. p. 1911

Kelly, Dorothy, Tech Serv Librn, United States Department of Veterans Affairs, Library Service (142D), 13000 Bruce B Downs Blvd, Tampa, FL, 33612. Tel: 813-972-2000, Ext 6571. Fax: 813-978-5917. p. 498

Kelly, Elizabeth, Digital Initiatives Librn, Loyola University New Orleans, 6363 Saint Charles Ave, New Orleans, LA, 70118-6195. Tel: 504-864-7111. Fax: 504-864-7247. p. 961

Kelly Fischer, Cheryl, Ref Librn, University of California Los Angeles Library, Hugh & Hazel Darling Law Library, 112 Law Bldg, Box 951458, 385 Charles E Young Dr E, Los Angeles, CA, 90095-1458. Tel: 310-825-7826. Fax: 310-825-1372. p. 178

Kelly, Frances, ILL, Quinnipiac University, 275 Mount Carmel Ave, Hamden, CT, 06518. Tel: 203-582-8635. Fax: 203-582-3451. p. 343

Kelly, Gae, Cat, Ref Serv, Concordia University Wisconsin, 12800 N Lake Shore Dr, Mequon, WI, 53097-2402. Tel: 262-243-4402. Fax: 262-243-4424. p. 2615

Kelly, Gina, Dir, Libr Serv, Argosy Education Group, 2233 W Dunlap Ave, Ste 150, Phoenix, AZ, 85021. Tel: 602-216-3124. Fax: 602-216-3150. p. 71

Kelly, Harriet, Dir, Ohio Valley Medical Center, 2000 Eoff St, Wheeling, WV, 26003. Tel: 304-234-8771. Fax: 304-234-8330. p. 2574

Kelly, Helen, Ch, Cambridge Libraries & Galleries, One North Sq, Cambridge, ON, N1S 2K6, CANADA. Tel: 519-621-0460. Fax: 519-621-2080. p. 2798

Kelly, James, Bibliographer, University of Massachusetts Amherst, 154 Hicks Way, Amherst, MA, 01003-9275. Tel: 413-545-3981. Fax: 413-545-6873. p. 1049

Kelly, James, Access Serv, Vanderbilt University, Alyne Queener Massey Law Library, 131 21st Ave S, Nashville, TN, 37203. Tel: 615-343-0208. Fax: 615-343-1265. p. 2261

Kelly, Jane, Coordr, Williams County Public Library, 107 E High St, Bryan, OH, 43506-1702. Tel: 419-636-6734. Fax: 419-636-3970. p. 1862

Kelly, Janice, Exec Dir, NN/LM SE/ARMLS, University of Maryland, Baltimore, Health Sciences & Human Services Library, 601 W Lombard St, Baltimore, MD, 21201. Tel: 410-706-2855. Fax: 410-706-3101. p. 1019

Kelly, Jean, Circ, ILL, Hanson Public Library, 132 Maquan St, Hanson, MA, 02341. Tel: 781-293-2151. Fax: 781-293-6801. p. 1093

Kelly, Jenna, Br Mgr, Monterey County Free Libraries, Big Sur Branch, Hwy 1 at Ripplewood Resort, Big Sur, CA, 93920. Tel: 831-667-2537. Fax: 831-667-0708. p. 183

Kelly, Joyce, Librn, Arizona Department of Corrections - Adult Institutions, 2014 N Citrus Rd, Goodyear, AZ, 85338. Tel: 623-853-0304, Ext 25574. Fax: 623-853-0304. p. 65

Kelly, Judy, Dir, Hubbard Memorial Library, 24 Center St, Ludlow, MA, 01056-2795. Tel: 413-583-3408. Fax: 413-583-5646. p. 1101

Kelly, Judy, Cat Mgr, Martin Methodist College, 433 W Madison St, Pulaski, TN, 38478-2799. Tel: 931-363-9844. Fax: 931-363-9844. p. 2264

Kelly, Judy M, Dir of Tech Serv, New College of Florida University of South Florida Sarasota Manatee, 5800 Bay Shore Rd, Sarasota, FL, 34243-2109. Tel: 941-487-4413. Fax: 941-487-4307. p. 490

Kelly, Karen, Libr Mgr, West Caldwell Public Library, 30 Clinton Rd, West Caldwell, NJ, 07006. Tel: 973-226-5441. Fax: 973-228-7572. p. 1540

Kelly, Kate, Head, Info Serv, Tufts University, 145 Harrison Ave, Boston, MA, 02111-1843. Fax: 617-636-4039. p. 1068

Kelly, Kathy, Librn, Lockridge, Grindal, Nauen PLLP, 100 Washington Ave S, Ste 2200, Minneapolis, MN, 55401. Tel: 612-339-6900. Fax: 612-339-0981. p. 1260

Kelly, Kay, Mgr, Electronic Res, Drake University, 2725 University Ave, Des Moines, IA, 50311. Tel: 515-271-2119. Fax: 515-271-3933. p. 809

Kelly, Kurtis, Adult Serv Supvr, Estes Park Public Library, 335 E Elkhorn Ave, Estes Park, CO, 80517. Tel: 970-586-8116. Fax: 970-586-0189. p. 306

Kelly, Kyle, Tech Serv, New England School of Law Library, 154 Stuart St, Boston, MA, 02116-5687. Tel: 617-422-7214. Fax: 617-422-7303. p. 1065

Kelly, Lauri, Librn, Touro College Libraries, 43 W 23rd St, Fifth Fl, New York, NY, 10010. Tel: 212-463-0400, Ext 5321. Fax: 212-627-3696. p. 1701

Kelly, Leslie, Dir, Info Serv, University of Maine at Fort Kent, 23 University Dr, Fort Kent, ME, 04743. Tel: 207-834-7528. Fax: 207-834-7518. p. 986

Kelly, Linda, Ch, Evans Public Library District, 215 S Fifth St, Vandalia, IL, 62471-2703. Tel: 618-283-2824. Fax: 618-283-4705. p. 713

Kelly, Lisa, Dir, Info Serv, Nebraska Library Commission, The Atrium, 1200 N St, Ste 120, Lincoln, NE, 68508-2023. Tel: 402-471-4015. Fax: 402-471-2083. p. 1406

Kelly, Louise R, Coll Develop, Dir, Volunteer State Community College Library, 1480 Nashville Pike, Gallatin, TN, 37066-3188. Tel: 615-230-3400, Ext 3412. Fax: 615-230-3410. p. 2235

Kelly, Lynn S, Dir, Libr Serv, Waycross College Library, 2001 S Georgia Pkwy, Waycross, GA, 31503. Tel: 912-449-7516. Fax: 912-449-7611. p. 557

Kelly, Madeline, Ref, Berkshire Athenaeum, One Wendell Ave, Pittsfield, MA, 01201-6385. Tel: 413-499-9480. Fax: 413-499-9489. p. 1117

Kelly, Madelon, Librn, Gibbs Library, 40 Old Union Rd, Washington, ME, 04574. Tel: 207-845-2663. p. 1005

Kelly, Margaret, Librn, Boston Public Library, East Boston, 276 Meridian St, Boston, MA, 02128-1654. Tel: 617-569-0271. Fax: 617-569-6665. p. 1057

Kelly, Marge, YA Serv, Garden City Public Library, 60 Seventh St, Garden City, NY, 11530-2891. Tel: 516-742-8405. Fax: 516-742-2675. p. 1626

Kelly, Marie, Ch, Rochester Public Library, 65 S Main St, Rochester, NH, 03867-2707. Tel: 603-332-1428. Fax: 603-335-7582. p. 1464

Kelly, Martin, Asst Dir, Digital & Spec Coll, Digital Coll Librn, Colby College Libraries, 5100 Mayflower Hill, Waterville, ME, 04901. Tel: 207-859-5162. Fax: 207-859-5105. p. 1005

Kelly, Mary, Br Mgr, Huntington Public Library, Huntington Station Branch, 1335 New York Ave, Huntington Station, NY, 11746. Tel: 631-421-5053. Fax: 631-421-3488. p. 1639

Kelly, Mary, Librn, McMillan Birch Mendelsohn Library, 1000 Sherbrooke St W, 27th Flr, Montreal, QC, H3A 3G4, CANADA. Tel: 514-987-5000, 514-987-5043. Fax: 514-987-1213. p. 2899

Kelly, Maureen, Br Mgr, Atlanta-Fulton Public Library System, Georgia-Hill Library, 250 Georgia Ave SE, Atlanta, GA, 30312. Tel: 404-730-5427. Fax: 404-730-5429. p. 512

Kelly, Maureen, Extended Campus Librn, Head Librn, Oregon State University, 2600 NW College Way, Bend, OR, 97701-5998. Tel: 541-322-3110. Fax: 541-383-7507. p. 1992

Kelly, Meghan, Tech Serv, Laramie County Community College Library, 1400 E College Dr, Cheyenne, WY, 82007-3204. Tel: 307-778-1201. Fax: 307-778-1399. p. 2652

Kelly, Melissa, Support Serv Coordr, Newport Beach Public Library, 1000 Avocado Ave, Newport Beach, CA, 92660-6301. Tel: 949-717-3852. Fax: 949-640-5681. p. 194

Kelly, Mike, Head, Archives & Spec Coll, Amherst College, Amherst, MA, 01002. Fax: 413-542-2662. p. 1048

Kelly, Mike, Asst Dean, University of New Mexico-University Libraries, 1900 Roma NE, Albuquerque, NM, 87131-0001. Tel: 505-277-6451. p. 1550

Kelly, Myla Stokes, Chair, MiraCosta College Library, One Barnard Dr, Oceanside, CA, 92056-3899. Tel: 760-634-7836. Fax: 760-795-6723. p. 199

Kelly, Myla Stokes, Librn, MiraCosta College Library, San Elijo Campus, 3333 Manchester Ave, Cardiff, CA, 92007-1516. Tel: 760-634-7836. Fax: 760-634-7890. p. 199

Kelly, Nancy, Cat, Ventress Memorial Library, 15 Library Plaza, Marshfield, MA, 02050. Tel: 781-834-5535. Fax: 781-837-8362. p. 1103

Kelly, Nina, Asst Librn, Niagara Health System, 142 Queenston St, St. Catharines, ON, L2R 7C6, CANADA. Tel: 905-378-4647, Ext 44354. Fax: 905-704-4767. p. 2843

Kelly, Pamela, Adult Info Serv Mgr, Wethersfield Public Library, 515 Silas Deane Hwy, Wethersfield, CT, 06109. Tel: 860-529-2665. Fax: 860-257-2822. p. 378

Kelly, Patricia, Head, Ref Serv, Lynnfield Public Library, 18 Summer St, Lynnfield, MA, 01940-1837. Tel: 781-334-5411. Fax: 781-334-2164. p. 1101

Kelly, Paula, Dir, Whitehall Public Library, 100 Borough Park Dr, Pittsburgh, PA, 15236-2098. Tel: 412-882-6622. Fax: 412-882-9556. p. 2130

Kelly, Rene, Info Tech Dir, Delaware County Library System, 340 N Middletown Rd, Bldg 19, Media, PA, 19063-5597. Tel: 610-891-8622. Fax: 610-891-8641. p. 2087

Kelly, Robert, Coordr, Libr Serv, Hutchinson Community College, 1300 N Plum St, Hutchinson, KS, 67501. Tel: 620-665-3548. Fax: 620-665-3392. p. 873

Kelly, Robert, Dir, Coll Develop, Redwood Library & Athenaeum, 50 Bellevue Ave, Newport, RI, 02840-3292. Tel: 401-847-0292. Fax: 401-847-0192. p. 2169

Kelly, Robert, Mgr, Waco-McLennan County Library System, South Waco, 2737 S 18th St, Waco, TX, 76706. Tel: 254-750-8621. Fax: 254-750-8606. p. 2398

Kelly, Robin, Youth Serv, Fort Smith Public Library, 3201 Rogers Ave, Fort Smith, AR, 72903. Tel: 479-783-0229. Fax: 479-782-8571. p. 100

Kelly, Rosann, Asst Dir, Saint John's University, Saint Augustine Hall, Rm 408, 8000 Utopia Pkwy, Jamaica, NY, 11439. Tel: 718-990-1457. Fax: 718-990-2071. p. 2970

Kelly, Sandra, Tech Serv, Destin Library, 150 Sibert Ave, Destin, FL, 32541-1523. Tel: 850-837-8572. Fax: 850-837-5248. p. 438

Kelly, Savannah L, Instrul Serv Librn, Westmont College, 955 La Paz Rd, Santa Barbara, CA, 93108-1099. Tel: 805-565-6000, 805-565-6147. Fax: 805-565-6220. p. 262

Kelly, Siobhan, Circ, Norwood Public Library, 198 Summit St, Norwood, NJ, 07648-1835. Tel: 201-768-9555. Fax: 201-767-2176. p. 1515

Kelly, Steven, Pres, West Hennepin County Pioneers Association Library, 1953 W Wayzata Blvd, Long Lake, MN, 55356-9362. Tel: 952-473-6557. p. 1256

Kelly, Sue, Asst Librn, Multnomah University, 8435 NE Glisan St, Portland, OR, 97220-5898. Tel: 503-251-5324. Fax: 503-254-1268. p. 2012

Kelly, Timothy, Head, Pub Serv, Ref, Willamette University, J W Long Law Library, 245 Winter St SE, Salem, OR, 97301. Tel: 503-370-6386. Fax: 503-375-5426. p. 2019

Kelly, William, Br Mgr, Cuyahoga County Public Library, Beachwood Branch, 25501 Shaker Blvd, Beachwood, OH, 44122-2306. Tel: 216-831-6868. Fax: 216-831-0412. p. 1927

Kelly-Jones, Nancy, Dir, Illinois School for the Deaf, 125 Webster, Jacksonville, IL, 62650. Tel: 217-479-4240. Fax: 217-479-4244. p. 658

Kelm, Bill, Syst Librn, Willamette University, 900 State St, Salem, OR, 97301. Tel: 503-375-5332. Fax: 503-370-6141. p. 2019

Kelman, Deb, Librn, Minnesota State Community & Technical College, 1414 College Way, Fergus Falls, MN, 56537-1000. Tel: 218-736-1650. Fax: 218-736-1510. p. 1251

Kelman, Elizabeth, City Librn, Blair Memorial Library, 416 N Main St, Clawson, MI, 48017-1599. Tel: 248-588-5500. Fax: 248-588-3114. p. 1163

Kelmelis, Jessica, Librn, Tolland Public Library, 22 Clubhouse Rd, Tolland, MA, 01034-9551. Tel: 413-258-4201. p. 1131

Kelmelis, Judy, ILL, Ref Librn, Groton Public Library, 52 Newtown Rd, Groton, CT, 06340. Tel: 860-441-6750. Fax: 860-448-0363. p. 342

Kelpin, Susan, Ch, Cresskill Public Library, 53 Union Ave, Cresskill, NJ, 07626. Tel: 201-567-3521. Fax: 201-567-5067. p. 1480

Kelsall-Dempsey, Julie, Dir, Highland Public Library, 30 Church St, Highland, NY, 12528. Tel: 845-691-2275. Fax: 845-691-6302. p. 1636

Kelsch, Laurel A, Librn, Grande Cache Municipal Library, 10601 Shand Ave, Grande Cache, AB, T0E 0Y0, CANADA. Tel: 780-827-2081. Fax: 780-827-3112. p. 2705

Kelsey, Deborah, Libr Dir, Medfield Memorial Public Library, 468 Main St, Medfield, MA, 02052-2008. Tel: 508-359-4544. Fax: 508-359-8124. p. 1103

Kelsey, Jan, Head, Ref, Fordham University Libraries, 441 E Fordham Rd, Bronx, NY, 10458-5151. Tel: 718-817-3570. Fax: 718-817-3582. p. 1586

Kelsey, Laura, Ref/Instruction Librn, Indiana Wesleyan University, 4201 S Washington St, Marion, IN, 46953. Tel: 765-677-2403. p. 762

Kelsey, Laura, Supvr, Youth Serv, Muncie Center Township Public Library, 2005 S High St, Muncie, IN, 47302. Tel: 765-747-8229. Fax: 765-747-8211. p. 767

Kelsey, Marie, Dir, College of Saint Scholastica, 1200 Kenwood Ave, Duluth, MN, 55811-4199. Tel: 218-723-6155. Fax: 218-723-6709. p. 2968

Kelso, Julia, Dir, Big Horn County Library, 430 West C St, Basin, WY, 82410. Tel: 307-568-2388. Fax: 307-568-2011. p. 2651

Kelto, Kathy, Librn, Traverse Area District Library, Subregional Library for the Blind & Physically Handicapped, 610 Woodmere, Traverse City, MI, 49686. Tel: 231-932-8558. Fax: 231-932-8578. p. 1231

Kelton, Kathleen, Circ Serv Mgr, Mission Viejo Library, 100 Civic Ctr, Mission Viejo, CA, 92691. Tel: 949-830-7100, Ext 5130. Fax: 949-586-8447. p. 187

Kemble, Camille, Asst Librn, Panora Public Library, 102 N First St, Panora, IA, 50216. Tel: 641-755-2529. Fax: 641-755-3009. p. 838

Kemble, Rita, Supvr, Ch Serv, Mishawaka-Penn-Harris Public Library, Bittersweet, 602 Bittersweet Rd, Mishawaka, IN, 46544-4155. Tel: 574-259-0392, Ext 306. Fax: 574-259-0399. p. 765

Kemen, Shannon, Ref Librn, University of Cincinnati, 2540 Clifton Ave, Cincinnati, OH, 45219. Tel: 513-556-6407. Fax: 513-556-6265. p. 1874

Kemi, Karen, Dir, Carlton Public Library, 310 Chestnut Ave, Carlton, MN, 55718. Tel: 218-384-3322. Fax: 218-384-4229. p. 1244

Kemm, Jessica, Br Mgr, Tangipahoa Parish Library, Amite Branch, 761 W Oak St, Amite, LA, 70422. Tel: 985-748-7151. Fax: 985-748-5476. p. 941

Kemp, Ada, Dir, Hesser College, Three Sundial Ave, Manchester, NH, 03103. Tel: 603-296-6333. Fax: 603-666-4722. p. 1455

Kemp, Barbara E, Head, Ref & Instruction, United States Naval Academy, 589 McNair Rd, Annapolis, MD, 21402-5029. Tel: 410-293-6900. Fax: 410-293-6909. p. 1011

Kemp, Bill, Archivist/Librn, McLean County Museum of History, 200 N Main, Bloomington, IL, 61701. Tel: 309-827-0428. Fax: 309-827-0100. p. 595

Kemp, Gina, Dir, Saint Ignace Public Library, 110 W Spruce St, Saint Ignace, MI, 49781-1649. Tel: 906-643-8318. Fax: 906-643-9809. p. 1224

Kemp, Jan, Asst Dean, Pub Serv, University of Texas at San Antonio Libraries, One UTSA Circle, San Antonio, TX, 78249-0671. Tel: 210-458-7506. p. 2383

Kemp, Karen, Ch, Lunenburg Public Library, 1023 Massachusetts Ave, Lunenburg, MA, 01462. Tel: 978-582-4140. Fax: 978-582-4141. p. 1101

Kemp, Kathi Lee, Dir, Eager Free Public Library, 39 W Main St, Evansville, WI, 53536. Tel: 608-882-2278. Fax: 608-882-2261. p. 2591

Kemp, Leatrice, Archivist, Librn, Rochester Museum & Science Center, 657 East Ave, Rochester, NY, 14607. Tel: 585-271-4320, Ext 315. Fax: 585-271-0492. p. 1732

Kemp, Linda, Chief Librn, Texas Education Agency, 1701 N Congress Ave, Austin, TX, 78701-1494. Tel: 512-463-9050. Fax: 512-475-3447. p. 2282

Kemp, Nan, ILL, Amarillo College Library, 2201 S Washington, Amarillo, TX, 79109. Tel: 806-371-5400. Fax: 806-371-5470. p. 2274

Kemp, Roberta, Sr Librn, Hennepin County Library, Ridgedale, 12601 Ridgedale Dr, Minnetonka, MN, 55305-1909. Tel: 612-543-8568. Fax: 612-543-8819. p. 1264

Kemp, Tracy, Ref Supvr, Columbus State Community College Library, 550 E Spring St, Columbus, OH, 43215. Tel: 614-287-5380. Fax: 614-287-6029. p. 1885

Kemp, Victoria, Mgr, Tech Serv, Flower Mound Public Library, 3030 Broadmoor Lane, Flower Mound, TX, 75022. Tel: 972-874-6154. Fax: 972-874-6466. p. 2319

Kempa, Kathy, Head, Circ, Head, ILL, Southeastern University, 1000 Longfellow Blvd, Lakeland, FL, 33801. Tel: 863-667-5089. Fax: 863-669-4160. p. 460

Kemparaju, Arathi, Librn, Maryland State Division of Labor & Industry, 312 Marshall Ave, Ste 600, Laurel, MD, 20707. Tel: 410-880-4970. Fax: 301-483-8332. p. 1035

Kempe, Deborah, Coll Mgt, The Frick Collection, Ten E 71st St, New York, NY, 10021. Tel: 212-288-8700. Fax: 212-879-2091. p. 1679

Kemper, Ann L, Dir, Harrisburg Area Community College, 2010 Pennsylvania Ave, York, PA, 17404. Tel: 717-718-0328, Ext 3546. Fax: 717-718-8967. p. 2159

Kemper, Linda, Asst Librn, New Straitsville Public Library, 102 E Main St, New Straitsville, OH, 43766. Tel: 740-394-2717. Fax: 740-394-2817. p. 1921

Kemper, Paula, Bus Mgr, North Kansas City Public Library, 2251 Howell St, North Kansas City, MO, 64116. Tel: 816-221-3360. Fax: 816-221-8298. p. 1348

Kemper, R Crosby, III, Dir, The Kansas City Public Library, 14 W Tenth St, Kansas City, MO, 64105. Tel: 816-701-3516. Fax: 816-701-3401. p. 1338

Kemper, Terry, Dir of Libr Serv, Waukesha County Technical College Library, 800 Main St, Pewaukee, WI, 53072. Tel: 262-695-3459. Fax: 262-695-3402. p. 2629

Kempke, Ann, Tech Serv, Northwestern Health Sciences University, 2501 W 84th St, Bloomington, MN, 55431-1599. Tel: 952-885-5419 Ext 221. Fax: 952-884-3318. p. 1242

Kenaley, Maggie, Ref Librn, Verona Public Library, 500 Silent St, Verona, WI, 53593. Tel: 608-845-7180. Fax: 608-845-8917. p. 2643

Kenaley, Patricia, Circ, Attleboro Public Library, 74 N Main St, Attleboro, MA, 02703. Tel: 508-222-0157, 508-222-0159. Fax: 508-226-3326. p. 1050

Kenan, Sharon K, Sr Librn, Ref, McLennan Community College Library, 1400 College Dr, Waco, TX, 76708-1498. Tel: 254-299-8343. Fax: 254-299-8026. p. 2397

Kenausis, Veronica, Syst Librn, Western Connecticut State University, 181 White St, Danbury, CT, 06810. Tel: 203-837-8818. Fax: 203-837-9108. p. 335

Kendall, Adam, Coll Mgr, Grand Lodge Free & Accepted Masons of California, 1111 California St, San Francisco, CA, 94108. Tel: 415-292-9137. Fax: 415-776-0483. p. 242

Kendall, Barbara, Bus Mgr, Sweetwater County Library System, 300 N First East, Green River, WY, 82935. Tel: 307-875-3615. Fax: 307-872-3203. p. 2655

Kendall, Bonnie, Ser, Alberta Department of Environment Library, 9920 108th St, 6th Flr, Edmonton, AB, T5K 2M4, CANADA. Tel: 780-422-7214. Fax: 780-422-0170. p. 2698

Kendall, Charles, Head, Coll Serv, Alexandrian Public Library, 115 W Fifth St, Mount Vernon, IN, 47620. Tel: 812-838-3286. Fax: 812-838-9639. p. 766

Kendall, Diane, Br Mgr, Mississauga Library System, Lorne Park, 1474 Truscott Dr, Mississauga, ON, L5J 1Z2, CANADA. Tel: 905-615-4845. Fax: 905-615-4846. p. 2823

Kendall, Grace, Managing Librn, Columbus Metropolitan Library, Hilliard Branch, 4772 Cemetery Rd, Hilliard, OH, 43026. Tel: 614-645-2275. Fax: 614-479-4149. p. 1884

Kendall, Karl, Dep Dir, Coll & Prog, Phoenix Public Library, 1221 N Central Ave, Phoenix, AZ, 85004-1820. Tel: 602-262-4636. Fax: 602-261-8836. p. 76

Kendall, Lori, Assoc Prof, University of Illinois at Urbana-Champaign, Library & Information Science Bldg, 501 E Daniel St, Champaign, IL, 61820-6211. Tel: 217-333-3280. Fax: 217-244-3302. p. 2965

Kendall, Patricia, Mgr, New Jersey Natural Gas Co Library, 1415 Wyckoff Rd, Wall, NJ, 07719. Tel: 732-938-1000. Fax: 732-938-2134. p. 1539

Kendall, Sandra, Dir, Mount Sinai Hospital, 600 University Ave, Rm 18-234, Toronto, ON, M5G 1X5, CANADA. Tel: 416-586-4800, Ext 4614. Fax: 416-586-4998. p. 2855

Kendall, Susan, Coordr, Coll Develop, San Jose State University, One Washington Sq, San Jose, CA, 95192-0028. Tel: 408-808-2039. Fax: 408-808-2141. p. 251

Kendall, Susan, Mgr, Cobb County Public Library System, Vinings, 4290 Paces Ferry Rd NW, Atlanta, GA, 30339. Tel: 770-801-5330. Fax: 770-801-5319. p. 543

Kendoziorski, Rhonda, Dir, Extn Serv, McCreary County Public Library District, Six N Main St, Whitley City, KY, 42653. Tel: 606-376-8738. Fax: 606-376-3631. p. 937

Kendrach, Michael G, Dir, Samford University Library, Global Drug Information Center McWhorter School of Pharmacy, Ingalls Bldg, 800 Lakeshore Dr, Birmingham, AL, 35229. Tel: 205-726-2161, 205-726-2891. Fax: 205-726-4012. p. 9

Kendrick, Audrey, Tech Serv, Jamestown Public Library, 200 W Main St, Jamestown, NC, 27282. Tel: 336-454-4815. Fax: 336-454-0630. p. 1803

Kendrick, Beth, Librn, Double Springs Public Library, 637 Blake Dr, Double Springs, AL, 35553. Tel: 205-489-2412. Fax: 205-489-2412. p. 15

Kendrick, Cherie, Ref Serv, Weatherford Public Library, 1014 Charles St, Weatherford, TX, 76086-5098. Tel: 817-598-4150. Fax: 817-598-4161. p. 2399

Kendrick, Cheryl, Circ, Shelbina Carnegie Public Library, 102 N Center, Shelbina, MO, 63468. Tel: 573-588-2271. Fax: 573-588-2271. p. 1365

Kendrick, Dawn, Ref Serv, Washington State Law Library, Temple of Justice, Olympia, WA, 98504. Tel: 360-357-2136. Fax: 360-357-2143. p. 2523

Kendrick, Elizabeth Ann, Libr Asst, Everman Public Library, 100 N Race St, Everman, TX, 76140. Tel: 817-551-0726. Fax: 817-551-1999. p. 2318

Kendrick, Emily, Ch, Van Alstyne Public Library, 151 W Cooper St, Van Alstyne, TX, 75495. Tel: 903-482-5991. Fax: 903-482-1316. p. 2395

Kendrick, Joyce, Assoc Libr, Concordia College, 1804 Green St, Selma, AL, 36703-3323. Tel: 334-874-5700, Ext 19734. Fax: 334-874-5755. p. 35

Kendrick, Kaetrena D, Ref Coordr, University of South Carolina Aiken, 471 University Pkwy, Aiken, SC, 29801. Tel: 803-641-3282. Fax: 803-641-3302. p. 2180

Kendrick, Kaetrena Davis, Asst Libr, University of South Carolina, Medford Library, 476 Hubbard Dr, Lancaster, SC, 29720. Tel: 803-313-7061. Fax: 803-313-7107. p. 2190

Kendrick, Marta, Ref Librn, Indian River State College, 6155 College Lane, Vero Beach, FL, 32966. Tel: 772-226-2544. Fax: 772-226-2542. p. 502

Kendrick, Sherri, Ref Librn, Cliffside Park Free Public Library, 505 Palisade Ave, Cliffside Park, NJ, 07010. Tel: 201-945-2867. Fax: 201-945-1016. p. 1479

Kendricks, Marian, Ref, Tiverton Library Services, 238 Highland Rd, Tiverton, RI, 02878. Tel: 401-625-6796. Fax: 401-625-5499. p. 2176

Kendze, Deborah, Libr Dir, Northern Lakes College Library, Mission St, Grouard, AB, T0G 1C0, CANADA. Tel: 780-849-8671. Fax: 780-751-3386. p. 2706

Kendze, Deborah, Dir, Libr Serv, Northern Lakes College Library, 1201 Main St SE, Slave Lake, AB, T0G 2A3, CANADA. Tel: 780-849-8670. Fax: 780-849-2570. p. 2716

Keneally, Claire, Librn, Shriners Hospital for Children, 12502 USF Pine Dr, Tampa, FL, 33612-9411. Tel: 813-972-2250, Ext 7608. Fax: 813-975-7125. p. 497

Kenealy, Jane, Archivist, San Diego Historical Society, Balboa Park, 1649 El Prado, Ste 3, San Diego, CA, 92101. Tel: 619-232-6203. Fax: 619-232-1059. p. 235

Kenerson, Murle, Dr, Asst Dir, Pub Serv, Tennessee State University, 3500 John A Merritt Blvd, Nashville, TN, 37209. Tel: 615-963-5203. Fax: 615-963-5216. p. 2259

Keninger, Karen, Dir, Library of Congress, National Library Service for the Blind & Physically Handicapped, 1291 Taylor St NW, Washington, DC, 20542. Tel: 202-707-5100. Fax: 202-707-0712. p. 407

Kenison, Connie, Dir, Northwood Public Library, 906 First Ave S, Northwood, IA, 50459. Tel: 641-324-1340. p. 836

Kenkel, Glenda, Br Librn, Riverside Regional Library, Scott City Branch, 2016 Main St, Scott City, MO, 63780. Tel: 573-264-2413. Fax: 573-264-2413. p. 1334

Kenkel, Kevin J, Dir, Learning Res, Dakota Wesleyan University, 1201 McGovern Ave, Mitchell, SD, 57301. Tel: 605-995-2617. Fax: 605-995-2893. p. 2215

Kennard, Miriam, Librn, University of North Carolina at Chapel Hill, Geological Sciences, 121 Mitchell Hall, CB No 3315, Chapel Hill, NC, 27599-3315. Tel: 919-962-0681. Fax: 919-966-4519. p. 1781

Kenne, Ann M, Univ Archivist, University of Saint Thomas, 2115 Summit Ave, Mail Box 5004, Saint Paul, MN, 55105. Tel: 651-962-5461. Fax: 651-962-5406. p. 1282

Kennedy, Amy, Dir, Wheeler Library, 101 Main St, North Stonington, CT, 06359. Tel: 860-535-0383. p. 362

Kennedy, Angela, Mgr, Libr Serv, K&L Gates Library, 1717 Main St, Ste 2800, Dallas, TX, 75201. Tel: 214-939-5510. Fax: 214-939-5849. p. 2309

Kennedy, Ann, Circ, Newburgh Free Library, 124 Grand St, Newburgh, NY, 12550. Tel: 845-563-3600. Fax: 845-563-3602. p. 1705

Kennedy, Ann Keith, Ref Librn, Drexel University Libraries, Hagerty Library, 33rd & Market Sts, Philadelphia, PA, 19104-2875. Tel: 215-895-2772. Fax: 215-895-2070. p. 2105

Kennedy, Ann L, Dir, Carol Stream Public Library, 616 Hiawatha Dr, Carol Stream, IL, 60188. Tel: 630-344-6101. Fax: 630-653-6809. p. 601

Kennedy, Anne McCarthy, Automation Serv, Newburgh Free Library, 124 Grand St, Newburgh, NY, 12550. Tel: 845-563-3600. Fax: 845-563-3602. p. 1705

Kennedy, Beth, Br Head, Grey Highlands Public Library, Walter Harris Memorial Library, 75 Walker St, Markdale, ON, N0C 1H0, CANADA. Tel: 519-986-3436. Fax: 519-986-4799. p. 2805

Kennedy, Bethany, Head, Access Serv, Washtenaw Community College, 4800 E Huron River Dr, Ann Arbor, MI, 48105-4800. Tel: 734-477-8723. Fax: 734-973-3446. p. 1153

Kennedy, Charlene, Br Coordr, Cochise County Library District, Elfrida Library, 10552 N Hwy 191, Elfrida, AZ, 85610-9021. Tel: 520-642-1744. Fax: 520-642-1744. p. 58

Kennedy, Cheryl, Adult Serv Mgr, Info Tech Mgr, Glendale Public Library, 5959 W Brown St, Glendale, AZ, 85302-1248. Tel: 623-930-3546. Fax: 623-842-4209. p. 64

Kennedy, Chris, Mgr, Metropolitan Library System in Oklahoma County, Midwest City Library, 8143 E Reno, Midwest City, OK, 73110-3999. Tel: 405-732-4828. Fax: 405-606-3451. p. 1973

Kennedy, Christina, Libr Assoc, Canizaro Library at Ave Maria University, 5251 Avila Ave, Ave Maria, FL, 34142. Tel: 239-280-2428. p. 426

Kennedy, Dale, In Charge, City of Kawartha Lakes Public Library, Omemee Branch, One Kings St W, Omemee, ON, K0L 2W0, CANADA. Tel: 705-799-5711. Fax: 705-799-6498. p. 2816

Kennedy, Dan, Ref, DeVry University, 4000 Millenia Blvd, Orlando, FL, 32839. Tel: 407-355-4807. Fax: 407-355-4777. p. 475

Kennedy, Deborah, Br Head, Chatham-Kent Public Library, Thamesville Branch, Three London Rd, Thamesville, ON, N0P 2K0, CANADA. Tel: 519-692-4251. Fax: 519-692-5915. p. 2799

Kennedy, Donna, Res & Instruction Librn, Northeastern University Libraries, Snell Library, 360 Huntington Ave, Boston, MA, 02115. Tel: 617-373-3197. p. 1065

Kennedy, Eddie, Mgr, Alexander Graham Bell National Historic Site of Canada, 559 Chebucto St, Baddeck, NS, B0E 1B0, CANADA. Tel: 902-295-2069. Fax: 902-295-3496. p. 2777

Kennedy, Elizabeth, Libr Dir, Cazenovia Public Library, 100 Albany St, Cazenovia, NY, 13035. Tel: 315-655-9322. p. 1604

Kennedy, Eric, Circ Supvr, Birmingham-Southern College, 900 Arkadelphia Rd, Birmingham, AL, 35254. Tel: 205-226-4740. Fax: 205-226-4743. p. 8

Kennedy, Eric, Admin Librn, Thomas M Cooley Law School Libraries, 300 S Capitol Ave, Lansing, MI, 48901. Tel: 517-371-5140, Ext 3306. Fax: 517-334-5715, 517-334-5717. p. 1202

Kennedy, Evelyn, Regional Librn, Charlotte County Library System, 2050 Forrest Nelson Blvd, Port Charlotte, FL, 33952. Tel: 941-613-3190. Fax: 941-613-3196. p. 484

Kennedy, Evelyn, Regional Librn, Charlotte County Library System, Mid-County Regional Library, 2050 Forrest Nelson Blvd, Port Charlotte, FL, 33952. Tel: 941-613-3191. Fax: 941-613-3177. p. 484

Kennedy, Heather, Libr Tech II, Pinal County Library District, 92 W Butte Ave, Florence, AZ, 85132. Tel: 520-866-6457. Fax: 520-866-6533. p. 63

Kennedy, Helen, Assoc Dir, Austin Presbyterian Theological Seminary, 100 E 27th St, Austin, TX, 78705-5797. Tel: 512-472-6736. Fax: 512-322-0901. p. 2278

Kennedy, Helen Kay, Br Mgr, Kent District Library, Spencer Township Branch, 14960 Meddler Ave, Gowen, MI, 49326. Tel: 616-784-2007. Fax: 616-647-3964. p. 1166

Kennedy, James, Re/Ser Librn, Hinds Community College, 505 E Main St, Raymond, MS, 39154. Tel: 601-857-3254. Fax: 601-857-3293. p. 1313

Kennedy, James R, Univ Librn, Buena Vista University Library, 610 W Fourth St, Storm Lake, IA, 50588. Tel: 712-749-2127. Fax: 712-749-2059. p. 846

Kennedy, Jane, Dir, Maplewood Memorial Library, 51 Baker St, Maplewood, NJ, 07040-2618. Tel: 973-762-1622. Fax: 973-762-0762. p. 1499

Kennedy, Jean, Libr Dir, Fayette County Library System, c/o Smithfield Public Library, 14 Water St, Smithfield, PA, 15478. Tel: 724-569-1777. Fax: 724-569-1772. p. 2141

Kennedy, Jean, Librn, Smithfield Public Library, 14 Water St, Smithfield, PA, 15478. Tel: 724-569-1777. p. 2141

Kennedy, Jean, Supv Librn, Department of Veterans Affairs, 1970 Roanoke Blvd, Salem, VA, 24153. Tel: 540-982-2463, Ext 2380. Fax: 540-983-1079. p. 2495

Kennedy, Jeanne, Cat, Southwestern Baptist Theological Seminary Libraries, 2001 W Seminary Dr, Fort Worth, TX, 76115-2157. Tel: 817-923-1921, Ext 4000. Fax: 817-921-8765. p. 2323

Kennedy, Jessie, Librn, Arlington City Library, PO Box 396, Arlington, KS, 67514-0396. Tel: 620-538-2471. p. 856

Kennedy, Joanne, Dir, Libr Serv, Saint John's Regional Medical Center, 1600 N Rose Ave, Oxnard, CA, 93030. Tel: 805-988-2820. Fax: 805-981-4419. p. 203

Kennedy, Jocelyn, Dir, Libr Serv, University of Connecticut, 39 Elizabeth St, Hartford, CT, 06105-2287. Tel: 860-570-5098. Fax: 860-570-5104. p. 348

Kennedy, John, Ref Librn, Media-Upper Providence Free Library, One E Front St, Media, PA, 19063. Tel: 610-566-1918. Fax: 610-566-9056. p. 2087

Kennedy, Joshua, Ch, Boxford Town Library, Ten Elm St, Boxford, MA, 01921. Tel: 978-887-7323. Fax: 978-887-6352. p. 1069

Kennedy, Joy, Chief Librn, Coll Develop, Northwest Community Hospital, 800 W Central Rd, Arlington Heights, IL, 60005-2392. Tel: 847-618-5180. Fax: 847-618-5189. p. 590

Kennedy, Judy, Network Serv, Elk Grove Village Public Library, 1001 Wellington Ave, Elk Grove Village, IL, 60007-3391. Tel: 847-439-0447. Fax: 847-439-0475. p. 641

Kennedy, Karol, Dep Libr Dir, Waukesha Public Library, 321 Wisconsin Ave, Waukesha, WI, 53186-4786. Tel: 262-524-3746. Fax: 262-524-3677. p. 2645

Kennedy, Kathleen, Ref Librn, Massachusetts Eye & Ear Infirmary Libraries, 243 Charles St, Boston, MA, 02114. Tel: 617-573-3196. Fax: 617-573-3370. p. 1063

Kennedy, Kay, Dir of Develop, Amarillo Museum of Art, 2200 S Van Buren St, Amarillo, TX, 79109-2407. Tel: 806-371-5050. Fax: 806-373-9235. p. 2274

Kennedy, Kelli, AV, Librn, Texas Department of State Health Services, 1100 W 49th St, Austin, TX, 78756-3199. Tel: 512-776-7260. Fax: 512-776-7474 (AV Library), 512-776-7683. p. 2282

Kennedy, Kristin, Br Mgr, Bossier Parish Central Library, Benton Branch, 115 Courthouse Dr, Benton, LA, 71006. Tel: 318-965-2751. Fax: 318-965-4379. p. 946

Kennedy, Laurine, Br Mgr, Handley Regional Library, Clarke County Library, 101 Chalmers Ct, Berryville, VA, 22611. Tel: 540-955-5144. Fax: 540-955-3655. p. 2503

Kennedy, Liam, Librn, Eastern Correctional Institution, East Library, 30420 Revells Neck Rd, Westover, MD, 21890-3358. Tel: 410-845-4000, Ext 6227. Fax: 410-845-4208. p. 1046

Kennedy, Linda, Mgr, Albuquerque-Bernalillo County Library System, Tony Hillerman Branch, 8205 Apache Ave NE, Albuquerque, NM, 87110. Tel: 505-291-6264. Fax: 505-291-6275. p. 1548

Kennedy, Linda M, Head, Pub Serv, University of California, Davis, 100 NW Quad, Davis, CA, 95616-5292. Tel: 530-752-6561. Fax: 530-752-3148. p. 139

Kennedy, Linn, Dir, Baldwin Cabin Public Library, Cibola National Forest, Forest Rd 100, Datil, NM, 87821. Tel: 575-772-5230. p. 1554

Kennedy, Lynda, Pub Serv, College of Coastal Georgia, One College Way, Brunswick, GA, 31520-3644. Tel: 912-279-5700. p. 521

Kennedy, Lynne, Head, Ref, Sachem Public Library, 150 Holbrook Rd, Holbrook, NY, 11741. Tel: 631-588-5024. Fax: 631-588-5064. p. 1637

Kennedy Madole, Amber, Ref Librn, Loyola Law School, 919 S Albany St, Los Angeles, CA, 90015-1211. Tel: 213-736-8389. Fax: 213-487-2204. p. 175

Kennedy, Margaret, Pub Serv, Laurens County Library, 1017 W Main St, Laurens, SC, 29360. Tel: 864-681-7323. Fax: 864-681-0598. p. 2199

Kennedy, Marie, Head, Metadata & Content Mgt, University of Southern California Libraries, Norris Medical Library, 2003 Zonal Ave, Los Angeles, CA, 90089-9130. Tel: 323-442-1134. Fax: 323-221-1235. p. 179

Kennedy, Mary, Ref & Instrul Serv, Instr Coordr, Alliant International University, 10455 Pomerado Rd, San Diego, CA, 92131-1799. Tel: 858-635-4677. Fax: 858-635-4599. p. 230

Kennedy, Mary, Cat, Joint Free Public Library of the Chathams, 214 Main St, Chatham, NJ, 07928. Tel: 973-635-0603. Fax: 973-635-7827. p. 1478

Kennedy, Maureen, ILL Supvr, Indiana University South Bend, 1700 Mishawaka Ave, South Bend, IN, 46615. Tel: 574-520-4449. Fax: 574-520-4472. p. 778

Kennedy, Mikel, Tech Serv, Blackfeet Community College, US Hwy Two & 89, Browning, MT, 59417. Tel: 406-338-5441. Fax: 406-338-5454. p. 1376

Kennedy, Mona, Librn, Reverend Martin Bieber Public Library, 1075 N Third Ave, Bowdle, SD, 57428. Tel: 605-285-6464. p. 2210

Kennedy, Nancy, Tech Serv Librn, Niagara County Community College, 3111 Saunders Settlement Rd, Sanborn, NY, 14132. Tel: 716-614-6792. Fax: 716-614-6816, 716-614-6828. p. 1737

Kennedy, Nicole, Ch, Clearwater Public Library System, East, 2251 Drew St, Clearwater, FL, 33765. Tel: 727-562-4970. p. 432

Kennedy, Nora, Ref, Albert-Westmorland-Kent Regional Library, 644 Main St, Ste 201, Moncton, NB, E1C 1E2, CANADA. Tel: 506-869-6032. Fax: 506-869-6022. p. 2765

Kennedy, Patrick, Archivist, Troy-Miami County Public Library, 419 W Main St, Troy, OH, 45373. Tel: 937-339-0502. Fax: 937-335-4880. p. 1941

Kennedy, Patty, Dir, Sunshine Hall Free Library, 14 Proctor Rd, Eldred, NY, 12732-5207. Tel: 845-557-6258. Fax: 845-557-0578. p. 1618

Kennedy, Samantha, Librn, Hepler City Library, 105 S Prairie, Hepler, KS, 66746. Tel: 620-368-4379. Fax: 620-368-4379. p. 871

Kennedy, Sandy, Dir, Bedford Public Library, 507 Jefferson, Bedford, IA, 50833-1314. Tel: 712-523-2828. p. 796

Kennedy, Sara, ILL, Delaware County District Library, 84 E Winter St, Delaware, OH, 43015. Tel: 740-362-3861. Fax: 740-369-0196. p. 1895

Kennedy, Scott, Dir, Res Serv, University of Connecticut Library, 369 Fairfield Rd, Storrs, CT, 06269-1005. Tel: 860-486-2219. Fax: 860-486-0584. p. 370

Kennedy, Sue, Br Mgr, Indianapolis-Marion County Public Library, Irvington, 5625 E Washington St, Indianapolis, IN, 46219-6411. Tel: 317-275-4450. p. 754

Kennedy, Terri, Tech Serv Librn, Yarmouth Town Libraries, South Yarmouth Branch, 312 Old Main St, South Yarmouth, MA, 02664. Tel: 508-760-4820. Fax: 508-760-2699. p. 1126

Kennedy, Terry, Dir, Providence University College & Seminary Library, Ten College Crescent, Otterburne, MB, R0A 1G0, CANADA. Tel: 204-433-7488. Fax: 204-433-7158. p. 2750

Kennedy, Tonya, Librn, New Market Public Library, 407 Main St, New Market, IA, 51646. Tel: 712-585-3467. p. 835

Kennedy, William, Govt Doc, Humanities Librn, University of Redlands, 1200 E Colton Ave, Redlands, CA, 92374-3758. Tel: 909-748-8022. Fax: 909-335-5392. p. 215

Kennedy-Brunner, Kathy, Br Mgr, Public Library of Cincinnati & Hamilton County, Madeira Branch, 7200 Miami Ave, Madeira, OH, 45243. Tel: 513-369-6028. Fax: 513-369-4501. p. 1872

Kennedy-Grant, Pat, Readers' Serv Manager, Bernardsville Public Library, One Anderson Hill Rd, Bernardsville, NJ, 07924. Tel: 908-766-0118. Fax: 908-766-2464. p. 1472

Kennedy-Witthar, Shawna, Dir, West Texas A&M University, University Dr & 26th St, Canyon, TX, 79016. Tel: 806-651-2227. Fax: 806-651-2213. p. 2294

Kennel, Sara, Librn, Potomac Public Library, 110 E State St, Potomac, IL, 61865. Tel: 217-987-6457. Fax: 217-987-6457. p. 692

Kenner, Myra, Bus Off Mgr, Duluth Public Library, 520 W Superior St, Duluth, MN, 55802. Tel: 218-730-4223. Fax: 218-723-3815, 218-723-3822. p. 1247

Kennerly, Holly, Tech Serv, Hamilton East Public Library, One Library Plaza, Cumberland Rd, Noblesville, IN, 46060-5639. Tel: 317-770-3220. Fax: 317-776-6936. p. 769

Kennerly, John F, Dir, Erskine College & Theological Seminary, One Depot St, Due West, SC, 29639. Tel: 864-379-8788. Fax: 864-379-2900. p. 2193

Kennerly, Joyce Claypool, V, Pub Info Officer, Fort Bend County Libraries, 1001 Golfview Dr, Richmond, TX, 77469-5199. Tel: 281-341-2611. Fax: 281-341-2688. p. 2375

Kenneth, Marsha Harpole, Circ Librn, Mississippi Delta Community College, 414 Hwy 3 South, Moorhead, MS, 38761. Tel: 662-246-6376. Fax: 662-246-8627. p. 1309

Kennett, Dorothy, In Charge, Second Presbyterian Church, 313 N East St, Bloomington, IL, 61701. Tel: 309-828-6297. Fax: 309-828-7038. p. 596

Kennett, Karen, Librn, Halton County Law Association, 491 Steeles Ave E, Milton, ON, L9T 1Y7, CANADA. Tel: 905-878-1272. Fax: 905-878-8298. p. 2822

Kennett, Marilyn, Dir, Drake Community Library, 930 Park St, Grinnell, IA, 50112-2016. Tel: 641-236-2661. Fax: 641-236-2667. p. 819

Kennett, Rachel, Br Supvr, Spokane County Library District, Cheney Library, 610 First St, Cheney, WA, 99004-1688. Tel: 509-893-8280. Fax: 509-893-8475. p. 2537

Kenney, Anne R, Univ Librn, Cornell University Library, 201 Olin Library, Ithaca, NY, 14853-5301. Tel: 607-255-3393. Fax: 607-255-6788. p. 1641

Kenney, Anne R, Univ Librn, Cornell University Library, Olin, Kroch, Uris Libraries, 201 Olin Library, Ithaca, NY, 14853. Fax: 607-255-6788. p. 1642

Kenney, Barbara Ferrer, Instrul Serv Librn, Roger Williams University Library, One Old Ferry Rd, Bristol, RI, 02809. Tel: 401-254-3359. Fax: 401-254-3631. p. 2164

Kenney, Brian, Dir, White Plains Public Library, 100 Martine Ave, White Plains, NY, 10601-2599. Tel: 914-422-1406. Fax: 914-422-1462. p. 1769

Kenney, Donald, Assoc Dean, Head, Circ, Virginia Polytechnic Institute & State University Libraries, Drill Field Dr, Blacksburg, VA, 24062-9001. Tel: 540-231-6170. Fax: 540-231-3946. p. 2451

Kenney, Donna, Ch, Lincoln-Lawrence-Franklin Regional Library, 100 S Jackson St, Brookhaven, MS, 39601-3347. Tel: 601-833-3369, 601-833-5038. Fax: 601-833-3381. p. 1294

Kenney, Jennifer, Ch, Phillipsburg City Library, 888 Fourth St, Phillipsburg, KS, 67661. Tel: 785-543-5325. Fax: 785-543-5374. p. 890

Kenney, Jo Ellen, Dir, Carnegie Library of McKeesport, 1507 Library Ave, McKeesport, PA, 15132-4796. Tel: 412-672-0625. Fax: 412-672-7860. p. 2085

Kenney, Kristine, Info Serv, Palatine Public Library District, 700 N North Ct, Palatine, IL, 60067-8159. Tel: 847-358-5881. p. 686

Kenney, Yuri, Coord, Ad Serv, Santa Clarita Public Library, 18601 Soledad Canyon Rd, Santa Clarita, CA, 91351. Tel: 661-251-2720. Fax: 661-298-7137. p. 263

Kennick Brown, Sylvia, Col Archivist & Spec Coll Librn, Williams College, 55 Sawyer Library Dr, Williamstown, MA, 01267. Tel: 413-597-2596. Fax: 413-597-4106. p. 1141

Kennison, Brian, Syst, Western Connecticut State University, 181 White St, Danbury, CT, 06810. Tel: 203-837-8847. Fax: 203-837-9108. p. 335

Kennison, John P, Librn, Bryan-Lang Historical Library, Fourth St at Camden Ave, Woodbine, GA, 31569. Tel: 912-576-5841. Fax: 912-576-5841. p. 557

Kennon, Tony, Dir, Riverside Public Library, 3581 Mission Inn Ave, Riverside, CA, 92501. Tel: 951-826-5201. Fax: 951-788-1528. p. 218

Kenny, Andrea, Head, Pub Serv, Edgewood College Library, 1000 Edgewood College Dr, Madison, WI, 53711-1997. Tel: 608-663-3300. Fax: 608-663-6778. p. 2606

Kenny, Ann M, In Charge, Ernst & Young, 200 Clarendon St, 47th Flr, Boston, MA, 02116. Tel: 617-859-6307. Fax: 617-859-6205. p. 1061

Kenny, Anne, Head, ILL, Boston College Libraries, Thomas P O'Neill Jr Library (Central Library), 140 Commonwealth Ave, Chestnut Hill, MA, 02467. Tel: 617-552-6937. Fax: 617-552-0599. p. 1081

Kenny, Bonnie Jean, Librn, Playboy Enterprises, Inc, Photo Library, 680 N Lake Shore Dr, Chicago, IL, 60611. Tel: 312-751-8000, Ext 2730. Fax: 312-751-2818. p. 622

Kenny, Gerard P, Librn, Sargent & Lundy, LLC, 55 E Monroe St, 24F60, Chicago, IL, 60603. Tel: 312-269-3525. Fax: 312-269-3757. p. 624

Kenny, Kathleen, Ch, Waterville Public Library, 73 Elm St, Waterville, ME, 04901-6078. Tel: 207-872-5433. Fax: 207-873-4779. p. 1006

Kenny, Line, Cat, Cegep de Jonquiere, 2505 rue St Hubert, Jonquiere, QC, G7X 7W2, CANADA. Tel: 418-547-2191. Fax: 418-547-0917. p. 2884

Kenny, Pat, Ref & Tech Librn, Harmony Library, 195 Putnam Pike, Harmony, RI, 02829. Tel: 401-949-2850. Fax: 401-949-2868. p. 2167

Kenny, Thomas J, Head, Pub Serv, Saint Peter's College, 99 Glenwood Ave, Jersey City, NJ, 07306. Tel: 201-761-6453. Fax: 201-432-4117. p. 1493

Keno, Sandy, Librn, Providence Regional Medical Center Everett, 1321 Colby Ave, Everett, WA, 98201. Tel: 509-474-3094. Fax: 509-474-4475. p. 2515

Kenreich, Mary Ellen, Head, Acq & Presv, Portland State University Library, 1875 SW Park Ave, Portland, OR, 97201-3220. Tel: 503-725-5780. Fax: 503-725-4524. p. 2014

Kent, Ada G, Librn, Ohio School for the Deaf Library, 500 Morse Rd, Columbus, OH, 43214. Tel: 614-728-1414. Fax: 614-728-4060. p. 1887

Kent, Amber, Mgr, Casa Grande Public Library, Vista Grande Library, 1556 N Arizola Rd, Casa Grande, AZ, 85122. Tel: 520-421-8652. Fax: 520-836-0819. p. 59

Kent, Amber, Prog Dir, Madison Library District, 73 N Center, Rexburg, ID, 83440-1539. Tel: 208-356-3461. p. 582

Kent, April, Head, Pub Serv, New Mexico Highlands University, Ninth & National Ave, Las Vegas, NM, 87701. Tel: 505-454-3401. Fax: 505-454-0026. p. 1559

Kent, Caroline, Dir, Res Support & Instruction, Connecticut College, 270 Mohegan Ave, New London, CT, 06320-4196. Tel: 860-439-2444. Fax: 860-439-2871. p. 359

Kent, Cynthia, Automation Syst Coordr, Lexington County Public Library System, 5440 Augusta Rd, Lexington, SC, 29072. Tel: 803-785-2644. Fax: 803-785-2601. p. 2199

Kent, David, Dir, Village Library of Cooperstown, 22 Main St, Cooperstown, NY, 13326-1331. Tel: 607-547-8344. Fax: 607-547-5487. p. 1610

Kent, David, Librn, Peninsula College Library, 1502 E Lauridsen Blvd, Port Angeles, WA, 98362-6698. Tel: 360-417-6285. Fax: 360-417-6295. p. 2524

Kent, Elizabeth, Dir, Oakwood Public Library District, 110 E Finley, Oakwood, IL, 61858. Tel: 217-354-4777. Fax: 217-354-4782. p. 684

Kent, Jean, Asst Librn, Dodge Center Public Library, 13 First Ave NW, Dodge Center, MN, 55927. Tel: 507-374-2275. Fax: 507-374-2694. p. 1247

Kent, Karen, In Charge, City of Kawartha Lakes Public Library, Kinmount Branch, 3980 County Rd 121, Kinmount, ON, K0M 2A0, CANADA. Tel: 705-488-3199. Fax: 705-488-1108. p. 2816

Kent Kunkel, Leslie Ann, Asst Dir, University of Arizona, 1515 E First St, Tucson, AZ, 85719. Tel: 520-621-3565. Fax: 520-621-3279. p. 2962

Kent, Linda, Librn II, New Hampshire State Library, 20 Park St, Concord, NH, 03301-6314. Tel: 603-271-2392. Fax: 603-271-2205, 603-271-6826. p. 1443

Kent, Linda, Chief Librn, City of Kawartha Lakes Public Library, 190 Kent St W, Lindsay, ON, K9V 2Y6, CANADA. Tel: 705-324-9411, Ext 1291. Fax: 705-878-1859. p. 2816

Kent, Liz, Electronic Res, Sweet Briar College, 134 Chapel Rd, Sweet Briar, VA, 24595-1200. Tel: 434-381-6138. Fax: 434-381-6173. p. 2497

Kent, Mary, Acq, Tulsa Community College Learning Resources Center, Metro Campus, 909 S Boston Ave, Tulsa, OK, 74119-2011. Tel: 918-595-7175. Fax: 918-595-7179. p. 1983

Kent, Paula, Dir, Haverhill Library Association, 67 Court St, Haverhill, NH, 03765. Tel: 603-989-5578. p. 1451

Kent, Susan, YA Serv, Wilbraham Public Library, 25 Crane Park Dr, Wilbraham, MA, 01095-1799. Tel: 413-596-6141. Fax: 413-596-5090. p. 1140

Kent, Susan, Ref Serv, Skagit Valley College, 2405 E College Way, Mount Vernon, WA, 98273-5899. Tel: 360-416-7607. Fax: 360-416-7698. p. 2521

Kent, Suzanne D, Adult Serv, Harper Woods Public Library, 19601 Harper, Harper Woods, MI, 48225-2001. Tel: 313-343-2575. Fax: 313-343-2127. p. 1188

Kent-Traore, Emma, Evening/Weekend Supvr, Hostos Community College Library, 475 Grand Concourse, A-207, Bronx, NY, 10451. Tel: 718-518-4224. Fax: 718-518-4206. p. 1587

Kentner, Susan, Chairperson, Rural Municipality of Argyle Public Library, 627 Elizabeth Ave, Baldur, MB, R0K 0B0, CANADA. Tel: 204-535-2314. Fax: 204-535-2242. p. 2747

Kenton, Linda M, Town Librn, San Anselmo Public Library, 110 Tunstead Ave, San Anselmo, CA, 94960-2617. Tel: 415-258-4656. Fax: 415-258-4666. p. 227

Kenvyn, Lettie, Br Mgr, Parish Allen Libraries, Kinder Branch, 833 Fourth Ave, Kinder, LA, 70648. Tel: 318-491-4514. Fax: 337-738-4213. p. 965

Kenworthy, Katherine, Assoc Dir, Cravath, Swaine & Moore LLP, 825 Eighth Ave, New York, NY, 10019. Tel: 212-474-3500. Fax: 212-474-3556. p. 1676

Kenworthy, Steve, Head, Tech Serv, Longmont Public Library, 409 Fourth Ave, Longmont, CO, 80501-6006. Tel: 303-651-8470. Fax: 303-651-8911. p. 317

Kenyon, Bethany, Access Serv Librn, University of New England Libraries, Josephine S Abplanalp Library, Portland Campus, 716 Stevens Ave, Portland, ME, 04103. Tel: 207-221-4325. Fax: 207-221-4893. p. 978

Kenyon, Lisa, Dir, Info Res, Mitchell College Library, 437 Pequot Ave, New London, CT, 06320-4498. Tel: 860-701-5156. Fax: 860-701-5099. p. 360

Kenyon, Sharon, Librn, Trinity Lutheran Church Library, 1904 Winnebago St, Madison, WI, 53704. Tel: 608-249-8527. Fax: 608-249-9070. p. 2608

Kenz, William, Govt Doc, Minnesota State University Moorhead, 1104 Seventh Ave S, Moorhead, MN, 56563. Tel: 218-477-2922. Fax: 218-477-5924. p. 1266

Keogan, William, Ref Librn, Saint John's University Library, 8000 Utopia Pkwy, Queens, NY, 11439. Tel: 718-990-6735. Fax: 718-380-0353. p. 1725

Keogh, Patricia, Head, Cat, Long Island University, One University Plaza, Brooklyn, NY, 11201-9926. Tel: 718-488-1081. Fax: 718-780-4057. p. 1593

Keohane, Jennifer, Bus Librn, Simsbury Public Library, 725 Hopmeadow St, Simsbury, CT, 06070. Tel: 860-658-7663. Fax: 860-658-6732. p. 367

Keohane, Jennifer, Exec Dir, Connecticut Library Consortium, 234 Court St, Middletown, CT, 06457-3304. Tel: 860-344-8777. Fax: 860-344-9199. p. 2939

Keon, Dan, Dir, Human Res, Toronto Public Library, 789 Yonge St, Toronto, ON, M4W 2G8, CANADA. Tel: 416-393-7131. Fax: 416-393-7229. p. 2860

Keough, Anne, Br Mgr, Chicago Public Library, Blackstone, 4904 S Lake Park Ave, Chicago, IL, 60615. Tel: 312-747-0511. Fax: 312-747-5821. p. 608

Keough, Brian, Head, Spec Coll & Archives, University at Albany, State University of New York, 1400 Washington Ave, Albany, NY, 12222-0001. Tel: 518-437-3931. Fax: 518-442-3088. p. 1570

Keough, Nancy, Librn, Swan Hills Municipal Library, 5536 Main St, Swan Hills, AB, T0G 2C0, CANADA. Tel: 780-333-4505. Fax: 780-333-4551. p. 2719

Keown, Vera, Librn, University of Manitoba Libraries, Sciences & Technology Library, 211 Machray Hall, Winnipeg, MB, R3T 2N2, CANADA. Tel: 204-474-8302. Fax: 204-474-7627. p. 2759

Kepler, Christy, Ch, Oswego Public Library District, 32 W Jefferson St, Oswego, IL, 60543. Tel: 630-554-3150. Fax: 630-978-1307. p. 686

Kepley, Cyndi, Tech Serv, New Albany-Floyd County Public Library, 180 W Spring St, New Albany, IN, 47150-3692. Tel: 812-944-8464. Fax: 812-949-3532. p. 768

Kepley, Vance, Dir, University of Wisconsin-Madison, Wisconsin Center for Film & Theater Research, 816 State St, Madison, WI, 53706. Tel: 608-264-6466. Fax: 608-264-6472. p. 2610

Kepner, Linda Tiernan, Asst Dir, Tech Librn, Peterborough Town Library, Two Concord St, Peterborough, NH, 03458. Tel: 603-924-8040. Fax: 603-924-8041. p. 1462

Keppel, Bea, Librn, Community Memorial Hospital, W180 N8085 Town Hall Rd, Menomonee Falls, WI, 53051-3558. Tel: 262-257-3440. Fax: 262-257-3311. p. 2614

Kepper, Angela, In Charge, AMEC, 5681-70 St, Edmonton, AB, T6B 3P6, CANADA. Tel: 780-436-2152. Fax: 780-435-8425. p. 2699

Kepple, Jennifer, Adult Serv, Fort Walton Beach Library, 185 Miracle Strip Pkwy SE, Fort Walton Beach, FL, 32548. Tel: 850-833-9590. Fax: 850-833-9659. p. 447

Kepple, Todd, Mgr, Klamath County Museum & Baldwin Hotel Museum, 1451 Main St, Klamath Falls, OR, 97601. Tel: 541-883-4208. Fax: 541-883-5170. p. 2002

Kerber, Sheila, Br Mgr, Douglas County Libraries, Highlands Ranch Library, 9292 Ridgeline Blvd, Highlands Ranch, CO, 80129. Tel: 303-791-7323. Fax: 720-348-9510. p. 294

Kerber, Sheila, Mgr, Douglas County Libraries, Roxborough, 8357 N Rampart Range Rd, Ste 200, Littleton, CO, 80125. Tel: 303-791-7323. p. 294

Kerbstat, Christa, Circ, Chino Valley Public Library, 1020 W Palomino Rd, Chino Valley, AZ, 86323-5500. Tel: 928-636-2687. Fax: 928-636-9129. p. 60

Kerby, Ramona N, Dr, Coordr, McDaniel College, Graduate Studies, Two College Hill, Westminster, MD, 21157-4390. Tel: 410-857-2507. Fax: 410-857-2515. p. 2967

Kerckhof, Goedele, Librn, Anne Chorney Public Library, 5125-51 St, Waskatenau, AB, T0A 3P0, CANADA. Tel: 780-358-2777. Fax: 780-358-2777. p. 2721

Kerdegari, Behjat, Ref Serv, Lodi Public Library, 201 W Locust St, Lodi, CA, 95240. Tel: 209-333-5566. Fax: 209-367-5944. p. 165

Kerdolff, Kathryn E, Ref, Louisiana State University Health Sciences Center, 433 Bolivar St, Box B3-1, New Orleans, LA, 70112-2223. Tel: 504-568-6100. Fax: 504-568-7718. p. 961

Kerestes, Sharon, Curric Center Librn, Cedarville University, 251 N Main St, Cedarville, OH, 45314-0601. Tel: 937-766-7840. Fax: 937-766-2337. p. 1865

Kerfoot, Barbara, Libr Mgr, Vancouver Island Regional Library, Chemainus Branch, 2592 Legion St, Chemainus, BC, V0R 1K0, CANADA. Tel: 250-246-9471. Fax: 250-246-9411. p. 2732

Kerfoot, Barbara, Libr Mgr, Vancouver Island Regional Library, Cowichan Lake, 38 King George, Lake Cowichan, BC, V0R 2G0, CANADA. Tel: 250-749-3431. Fax: 250-749-3401. p. 2732

Kerfoot, Barbara, Libr Mgr, Vancouver Island Regional Library, Cumberland Branch, 2724 Dunsmuir Ave, Cumberland, BC, V0R 1S0, CANADA. Tel: 250-336-8121. Fax: 250-336-8100. p. 2732

Kerfoot, Barbara, Libr Mgr, Vancouver Island Regional Library, Union Bay Branch, 5527 Island Hwy, Union Bay, BC, V0R 3B0, CANADA. Tel: 250-335-2433. Fax: 250-335-2492. p. 2733

Kerins, Mellie, Outreach Serv Librn, Augusta State University, 2500 Walton Way, Augusta, GA, 30904-2200. Tel: 706-737-1745. Fax: 706-667-4415. p. 518

Keriotis, Clara, Dir, Dreyfus Corp Library, 200 Park Ave, 7th Flr, New York, NY, 10166. Tel: 212-922-6087. Fax: 212-922-7018. p. 1677

Kerkvliet, Deb, Cat, Hamline University, Bush Memorial Library, 1536 Hewitt, Saint Paul, MN, 55104. Tel: 651-523-2375. Fax: 651-523-2199. p. 1278

Kerley, Izoro Dathane, Librn, Connors State College, Muskogee Campus Library, 201 Court St, Muskogee, OK, 74401. Tel: 918-684-5408. Fax: 918-684-0404. p. 1985

Kern, Alex, Asst Librn, Stanislaus County Law Library, 1101 13th St, Modesto, CA, 95354. Tel: 209-558-7759. Fax: 209-558-8284. p. 189

Kern, Alexander, In Charge, Short, Cressman & Burgess, 999 Third Ave, Ste 3000, Seattle, WA, 98104-4008. Tel: 206-682-3333, Ext 5555, 206-682-3333, Ext 5873. Fax: 206-340-8856. p. 2532

Kern, Barbara, Co-Dir, Pub Serv, Head of Librn, University of Chicago Library, John Crerar Library, 5730 S Ellis Ave, Chicago, IL, 60637. Tel: 773-702-8717. p. 626

Kern, Barbara, Co-Dir, Sci Libr, Head, Pub Serv, University of Chicago Library, 1100 E 57th St, Chicago, IL, 60637-1502. Tel: 773-702-8717. Fax: 773-702-3317. p. 626

Kern, Brian, Head, Tech Serv, Allegheny College Library, 555 N Main St, Meadville, PA, 16335. Tel: 814-332-3792. Fax: 814-337-5673. p. 2086

Kern, Carol H, Dir/Chief Exec Officer, Western Pocono Community Library, 2000 Pilgrim Way, Brodheadsville, PA, 18322. Tel: 570-992-7934. Fax: 570-992-7915. p. 2038

Kern, Deb, Dir, Dickinson Memorial Library, 115 Main St, Northfield, MA, 01360. Tel: 413-498-2455. Fax: 413-498-5111. p. 1114

Kern, Kristen, Fine & Performing Arts Librn, Portland State University Library, 1875 SW Park Ave, Portland, OR, 97201-3220. Tel: 503-725-5218. Fax: 503-725-4524. p. 2014

Kern, Linda, Asst Dir, Bolivar County Library System, 104 S Leflore Ave, Cleveland, MS, 38732. Tel: 662-843-2774. Fax: 662-843-4701. p. 1295

Kern, Lisa, Librn, College Church in Wheaton Library, 332 E Seminary Ave, Wheaton, IL, 60187. Tel: 630-668-0878, Ext 138. Fax: 630-668-0984. p. 718

Kern, Lisa, Br Mgr, Bucks County Free Library, Bensalem Branch, 3700 Hulmeville Rd, Bensalem, PA, 19020-4449. Tel: 215-638-2030. Fax: 215-638-2192. p. 2050

Kern, Lucy, Librn, Pennsylvania German Heritage Library, 22 Luckenbill Rd, Kutztown, PA, 19530. Tel: 484-646-4165. p. 2075

Kern, Pat, Librn, Palco Public Library, 311 Main St, Palco, KS, 67657. Tel: 785-737-4286. p. 889

Kern, Ralph, Dir of Libr Serv, Brigham Young University-Idaho, 525 S Center St, Rexburg, ID, 83460-0405. Tel: 208-496-9510. Fax: 208-496-9503. p. 582

Kern, Thomas D, Dir, Wauconda Area Public Library District, 801 N Main St, Wauconda, IL, 60084. Tel: 847-526-6225, Ext 209. Fax: 847-526-6244. p. 716

Kern, Verletta, Music Res Librn, University of Washington Libraries, Music, 113 Music Bldg, Box 353450, Seattle, WA, 98195-3450. Tel: 206-543-1159, 206-543-1168. p. 2534

Kern-Simirenko, Cheryl, Dean, Univ Libr, University of Akron Libraries, 315 Buchtel Mall, Akron, OH, 44325-1701. Tel: 330-972-7507. Fax: 330-972-5106. p. 1853

Kerner, Susie, Dir, Tecumseh Public Library, 170 Branch St, Tecumseh, NE, 68450. Tel: 402-335-2060. Fax: 402-335-2069. p. 1421

Kernicky, Greta, Coll Develop & Tech Serv Mgr, Manheim Township Public Library, 595 Granite Run Dr, Lancaster, PA, 17601. Tel: 717-560-6441. Fax: 717-560-0570. p. 2077

Kerns, Carla, Ref Serv, Seminole Community Library, 9200 113th St N, Seminole, FL, 33772. Tel: 727-394-6905. Fax: 727-398-3113. p. 491

Kerns, Julie, Mgr, Outreach Serv, Westerville Public Library, 126 S State St, Westerville, OH, 43081-2095. Tel: 614-882-7277, Ext 2144. Fax: 614-882-4160. p. 1947

Kerns, Kathy, Curator, Educ Res, Head of Libr, Stanford University Libraries, Cubberley Education Library, Education Bldg, Rm 202-205, Stanford, CA, 94305-3096. Tel: 650-723-2121. Fax: 650-736-0536. p. 271

Kerns, Lori Brown, Librn, United States Navy, 1002 Balch Blvd, Bldg 1003, Stennis Space Center, MS, 39522-5001. Tel: 228-688-4706. Fax: 228-688-4191. p. 1315

Kerns, Resa, Assoc Law Librn, University of Missouri-Columbia, Law Library, 203 Hulston Hall, Columbia, MO, 65211-4190. Tel: 573-882-5108. Fax: 573-882-9676. p. 1326

Kerns, Ritch, Tech Serv Librn, Antioch College, One Morgan Pl, Yellow Springs, OH, 45387-1694. Tel: 937-769-1238. Fax: 937-769-1239. p. 1952

Kerns, Rose Ann, ILL, Shelby County Libraries, 230 E North St, Sidney, OH, 45365-2785. Tel: 937-492-8354. Fax: 937-492-9229. p. 1934

Kerr, Anne, Librn, Marks-Quitman County Library, 315 E Main St, Marks, MS, 38646. Tel: 662-326-7141. Fax: 662-326-7369. p. 1307

Kerr, Barbara E, Asst Dir, Media Spec, Medford Public Library, 111 High St, Medford, MA, 02155. Tel: 781-395-7950. Fax: 781-391-2261. p. 1104

Kerr, Beth, Librn, University of Texas Libraries, Fine Arts, Doty Fine Arts Bldg 3-200, 23rd & Trinity, Austin, TX, 78713. Tel: 512-495-4482. Fax: 512-495-4490. p. 2284

Kerr, Donna, Br Mgr, Mendocino County Library District, Willits Branch, 390 E Commercial St, Willits, CA, 95490. Tel: 707-459-5908. Fax: 707-459-7819. p. 278

Kerr, Ellen, Br Supvr, Bruce County Public Library, Chesley Branch, 72 Second Ave SE, Chesley, ON, N0G 1L0, CANADA. Tel: 519-363-2239. Fax: 519-363-0726. p. 2837

Kerr, Ellen, Br Supvr, Bruce County Public Library, Paisley Branch, 274 Queen St N, Paisley, ON, N0G 2N0, CANADA. Tel: 519-353-7225. Fax: 519-353-7225. p. 2837

Kerr, Ellen, Supvr, Bruce County Public Library, Tara Branch, 67 Yonge St N, Tara, ON, N0H 2N0, CANADA. Tel: 519-934-2626. p. 2837

Kerr, Holly, Pub Serv & ILL, Louisiana State University Libraries, LSU School of Veterinary Medicine Library, Skip Bertman Dr, Baton Rouge, LA, 70803-8414. Tel: 225-578-9797. Fax: 225-578-9798. p. 944

Kerr, John Eddie, Librn, Wellington Law Association Library, Court House, 74 Woolwich St, Guelph, ON, N1H 3T9, CANADA. Tel: 519-763-6365. Fax: 519-763-6847. p. 2807

Kerr, Karalee, Asst Dir, Grimes Public Library, 200 N James, Grimes, IA, 50111. Tel: 515-986-3551. Fax: 515-986-9553. p. 819

Kerr, Katie, Assoc Dir, Pepperdine University Libraries, School of Law-Jerene Appleby Harnish Law Library, 24255 Pacific Coast Hwy, Malibu, CA, 90263. Tel: 310-506-4643. Fax: 310-506-4836. p. 182

Kerr, Kelly S, Tech Serv, Norfolk State University Library, 700 Park Ave, Norfolk, VA, 23504-8010. Tel: 757-823-2423. Fax: 757-823-2431. p. 2482

Kerr, Kimberly, Info Librn, Keyano College Library, 8115 Franklin Ave, Fort McMurray, AB, T9H 2H7, CANADA. Tel: 780-791-8911. Fax: 780-791-1555. p. 2704

Kerr, Marla, Circ Mgr, Sioux City Public Library, Perry Creek Branch Library, 2912 Hamilton Blvd, Sioux City, IA, 51104-2410. Tel: 712-255-2926. p. 844

Kerr, Marla, Circ, Sioux City Public Library, 529 Pierce St, Sioux City, IA, 51101-1203. Tel: 712-255-2933. p. 844

Kerr, Nancy, Mgr, Santa Clarita Public Library, Valencia Library, 23743 W Valencia Blvd, Santa Clarita, CA, 91355. Tel: 661-259-8332. Fax: 616-259-9654. p. 264

Kerr, Norwood A, Ref Archivist, Alabama Department of Archives & History Research Room, 624 Washington Ave, Montgomery, AL, 36130-0100. Tel: 334-242-4435. Fax: 334-240-3433. p. 27

Kerr, Paul, Dir, Beloit Historical Society, Lincoln Ctr, 845 Hackett St, Beloit, WI, 53511. Tel: 608-365-7835. Fax: 608-365-5999. p. 2581

Kerr, Perian P, Br Mgr, Librn, Starkville-Oktibbeha County Public, Sturgis Public Library, 2732 Hwy 12 W, Sturgis, MS, 39769. Tel: 662-465-7493. Fax: 662-465-7493. p. 1315

Kerr, Susan, Syst Librn, Davidson College, 209 Ridge Rd, Davidson, NC, 28035-0001. Tel: 704-894-2331. Fax: 704-894-2625. p. 1786

Kerrick, Beth, Ch, Marshall County Public Library System, 1003 Poplar St, Benton, KY, 42025. Tel: 270-527-9969. Fax: 270-527-0506. p. 907

Kerrigan, Beth, Head, Ch, Memorial Hall Library, Two N Main St, Andover, MA, 01810. Tel: 978-623-8401. Fax: 978-623-8407. p. 1049

Kerrigan, Gena, Dir, Rachel Kohl Community Library, 687 Smithbridge Rd, Glen Mills, PA, 19342-1225. Tel: 610-358-3445. Fax: 610-558-0693. p. 2061

Kerrigan, Helen, Br Mgr, Riverside County Library System, Desert Hot Springs Library, 11691 West Dr, Desert Hot Springs, CA, 92240. Tel: 760-329-5926. Fax: 760-329-3593. p. 217

Kersey, Carol, Br Mgr, Linebaugh Public Library System of Rutherford County, Smyrna Public, 400 Enon Springs Rd W, Smyrna, TN, 37167. Tel: 615-459-2700. Fax: 615-459-2370. p. 2254

Kersey, Jeff, AV, Library for the Blind & Physically Handicapped, 900 W Capitol Ave, Ste 100, Little Rock, AR, 72201-3108. Tel: 501-682-2858. Fax: 501-682-1529. p. 106

Kershaw, Alicia, Dir, J C Wheeler Library, 1593 S Main St, Martin, MI, 49070-9728. Tel: 269-672-7875. p. 1207

Kershner, Mary, Asst Dir, Whiting Public Library, 1735 Oliver St, Whiting, IN, 46394-1794. Tel: 219-473-4700, 219-659-0269. Fax: 219-659-5833. p. 788

Kershner, Seth, Pub Serv, Ref Librn, Northwestern Connecticut Community College Library, Park Pl E, Winsted, CT, 06098. Tel: 860-738-6481. Fax: 860-379-4995. p. 379

Kershner, Stephen, Dir, Cook Memorial Public Library District, 413 N Milwaukee Ave, Libertyville, IL, 60048-2280. Tel: 847-362-2330. Fax: 847-362-2354. p. 665

Kerslake, Pat, Librn, Middleburg Heights Community Church Library, 7165 Big Creek Pkwy, Middleburg Heights, OH, 44130. Tel: 440-842-7743. Fax: 440-842-7745. p. 1917

Kersten, Chris, ILL, Henderson County Public Library, 301 N Washington St, Hendersonville, NC, 28739. Tel: 828-697-4725. Fax: 828-692-8449, 828-697-4700. p. 1801

Kersten, Lynne, Dir, Thompson Falls Public Library, 911 Main St, Thompson Falls, MT, 59873. Tel: 406-827-3547. p. 1389

Kersten, Nicholas J, Dir, Librarian-Historian, Seventh Day Baptist Historical Society Library, 3120 Kennedy Rd, Janesville, WI, 53545-0225. Tel: 608-752-5055. Fax: 608-752-7711. p. 2600

Kerstens, Elizabeth Kelley, Exec Dir, Plymouth Historical Museum Archives, 155 S Main St, Plymouth, MI, 48170-1635. Tel: 734-455-8940. Fax: 734-455-7797. p. 1218

Kerstetter, Judy, Ref, South Country Library, 22 Station Rd, Bellport, NY, 11713. Tel: 631-286-0818. Fax: 631-286-4873. p. 1580

Kerul, Linda, Br Mgr, Toledo-Lucas County Public Library, Holland Branch, 1032 S McCord Rd, Holland, OH, 43528. Tel: 419-259-5240. Fax: 419-865-6706. p. 1939

Kervin, Nancy, Sr Ref Librn, United States Senate Library, SRB-15 Senate Russell Bldg, Washington, DC, 20510-7112. Tel: 202-224-7106. Fax: 202-224-0879. p. 421

Kerwin, Brenda, Syst Librn, Webmaster, Huntingdon College, 1500 E Fairview Ave, Montgomery, AL, 36106. Tel: 334-833-4529. Fax: 334-263-4465. p. 29

Kerwin, Jackie, Dir, Silverton Public Library, 1111 Reese, Silverton, CO, 81433. Tel: 970-387-5770. Fax: 970-387-0217. p. 322

Kesel, Barbara, Automation Syst Coordr, Washington County Cooperative Library Services, 111 NE Lincoln St, No 230-L MS58, Hillsboro, OR, 97124-3036. Tel: 503-846-3238. Fax: 503-846-3220. p. 2000

Kesler, Cynthia, Principal Librn, New York State Unified Court System, 401 Montgomery St, Syracuse, NY, 13202. Tel: 315-671-1150. Fax: 315-671-1160. p. 1752

Kesler, Leslie, Curator, Historian, Charlotte Museum of History, 3500 Shamrock Dr, Charlotte, NC, 28215. Tel: 704-568-1774. Fax: 704-566-1817. p. 1782

Kesler, Susan, Cat, Glen Carbon Centennial Library, 198 S Main St, Glen Carbon, IL, 62034. Tel: 618-288-1212. Fax: 618-288-1205. p. 649

Kessel, Kathleen, Pub Serv Librn, Wake Technical Community College, Health Sciences, 2901 Holston Lane, Raleigh, NC, 27610-2092. Tel: 919-747-0013. p. 1818

Kessell, Susan, Tech Serv, Blauvelt Free Library, 541 Western Hwy, Blauvelt, NY, 10913. Tel: 845-359-2811. Fax: 845-398-0017. p. 1583

Kesselman, Martin, Librn, Rutgers University Libraries, Stephen & Lucy Chang Science Library, Walter E Foran Hall, 59 Dudley Rd, New Brunswick, NJ, 08901-8520. Tel: 732-932-0305, Ext 163. Fax: 732-932-0311. p. 1508

Kessie, Darci, Dir, South Whitley-Cleveland Township Public Library, 201 E Front St, South Whitley, IN, 46787-1315. Tel: 260-723-5321. Fax: 260-723-5326. p. 780

Kessinger, Pam, Fac Librn-Rock Creek Campus, Portland Community College Library, 12000 SW 49th AV, Portland, OR, 97219. Tel: 971-722-7051. Fax: 971-722-8397. p. 2013

Kessler, Barbara, Dir, Jericho Public Library, One Merry Lane, Jericho, NY, 11753. Tel: 516-935-6790. Fax: 516-433-9581. p. 1647

Kessler, Carl, Ref Librn, Caplin & Drysdale Library, One Thomas Circle, NW, Ste 1100, Washington, DC, 20005. Tel: 202-862-7835. Fax: 202-429-3301. p. 395

Kessler, Christie, Dir, Cass County Public Library, 400 E Mechanic, Harrisonville, MO, 64701. Tel: 816-380-4600. Fax: 816-884-2301. p. 1330

Kessler, Nicole, Dir, Baker College, 4500 Enterprise Dr, Allen Park, MI, 48101-3033. Tel: 313-425-3713. Fax: 313-425-3777. p. 1149

Kessler, Thomas, Acq, Bibliographer, University of Northern Iowa Library, 1227 W 27th St, Cedar Falls, IA, 50613-3675. Tel: 319-273-2737. Fax: 319-273-2913. p. 799

Kesten, Priscilla, Ch, Peninsula Public Library, 280 Central Ave, Lawrence, NY, 11559. Tel: 516-239-3262. Fax: 516-239-8425. p. 1651

Kestenbaum, Joy, Dir, New School, Adam & Sophie Gimbel Design Library, Two W 13th St, 2nd Flr, New York, NY, 10011. Tel: 212-229-8914. Fax: 212-229-2806. p. 1688

Kester, Matt, Archivist, Brigham Young University-Hawaii, 55-220 Kulanui St, BYU-Hawaii, No 1966, Laie, HI, 96762-1294. Tel: 808-675-3869. Fax: 808-675-3877. p. 567

Kesterman, M'Lissa, Mgr, Ref Serv, Cincinnati Museum Center At Union Terminal, 1301 Western Ave, Cincinnati, OH, 45203. Tel: 513-287-7030. Fax: 513-287-7095. p. 1869

Kesterson, Cathy, Acq, Delphi Public Library, 222 E Main St, Delphi, IN, 46923. Tel: 765-564-2929. Fax: 765-564-4746. p. 735

Kestler, Ulrike, Pub Serv Librn, Kwantlen Polytechnic University Library, 12666 72 Ave., Surrey, BC, V3W 2M8, CANADA. Tel: 604-599-3199. Fax: 604-599-2106. p. 2738

Ketabchi, Mary Anne, Head, Ch, River Vale Free Public Library, 412 Rivervale Rd, River Vale, NJ, 07675. Tel: 201-391-2323. Fax: 201-391-6599. p. 1526

Ketcham, Maria, Dept Head, Detroit Institute of Arts, 5200 Woodward Ave, Detroit, MI, 48202. Tel: 313-833-3460. Fax: 313-833-6405. p. 1169

Ketcham, Russell, Dir, Eloy Public Library, 100 E Seventh St, Eloy, AZ, 85231. Tel: 520-466-3814. Fax: 520-466-4433. p. 62

Ketcham, Steve, Br Mgr, West Bloomfield Township Public Library, 4600 Walnut Lake Rd, West Bloomfield, MI, 48323. Tel: 248-363-4022. Fax: 248-363-7243. p. 1236

Ketchan, Steve, Br Mgr, West Bloomfield Township Public Library, Westacres, 7321 Commerce Rd, West Bloomfield, MI, 48324. Tel: 248-232-2401. Fax: 248-363-7243. p. 1236

Ketchum, Bill, Ref Serv, University of La Verne, 320 E D St, Ontario, CA, 91764. Tel: 909-460-2063. Fax: 909-460-2083. p. 200

Ketchum, Deb, Head, Circ, Capital Area District Libraries, Downtown Lansing Library, 401 S Capitol Ave, Lansing, MI, 48933. Tel: 517-367-6315. Fax: 517-374-1068. p. 1200

Ketchum, Judi, Tech Serv, Greenfield Community College Library, One College Dr, Greenfield, MA, 01301-9739. Tel: 413-775-1859. Fax: 413-775-1838. p. 1092

Ketchum, Susan, Ref, Long Island University, 100 Second Ave, Brentwood, NY, 11717. Tel: 631-273-5112. Fax: 631-273-5198. p. 1584

Ketelsen, Terry, State Archivist, Colorado Division of State Archives & Public Records Library, 1313 Sherman St, Rm 1B20, Denver, CO, 80203-2236. Tel: 303-866-4900. Fax: 303-866-2257. p. 299

Ketner, Elizabeth S, Librn, Stella Community Library, Third & Main St, Stella, NE, 68442. Tel: 402-883-2232. Fax: 402-883-2232. p. 1420

Ketner, Saundra, Librn, Joslin Diabetes Center, Inc, One Joslin Pl, Boston, MA, 02215. Tel: 617-732-2400 (Main), 617-732-2641 (Library). Fax: 617-732-2542. p. 1062

Kettel, James, Supvr, Genealogy Serv, Boyd County Public Library, 1740 Central Ave, Ashland, KY, 41101. Tel: 606-329-0090. Fax: 606-329-0578. p. 905

Kettell, Elizabeth, Librn, University of Rochester Medical Center, Basil G Bibby Library, Eastman Dental, 625 Elmwood Ave, Rochester, NY, 14620. Tel: 585-275-5010. Fax: 585-273-1230. p. 1734

Ketterer, Jan, Youth Serv, Mark Skinner Library, 48 West Rd, Manchester, VT, 05254. Tel: 802-362-2607. p. 2427

Ketterman, Elizabeth, Coll Develop/E-Res Librn, East Carolina University, William E Laupus Health Sciences Library, 600 Moye Blvd, Health Sciences Bldg, Greenville, NC, 27834. Tel: 252-744-3056. Fax: 252-744-2080. p. 1799

Kettler, Lynda, Dir, Libr Serv, Rogue Community College, Wiseman Ctr, 3345 Redwood Hwy, Grants Pass, OR, 97527. Tel: 541-956-7500, Ext 7147. Fax: 541-471-3588. p. 1999

Kettler, Pamela, Asst Librn, Valley Park Community Library, 320 Benton St, Valley Park, MO, 63088. Tel: 636-225-5608. Fax: 636-825-0079. p. 1370

Kettles, Patricia, Librn, Library Mgr, New York Public Library - Astor, Lenox & Tilden Foundations, Port Richmond Branch, 75 Bennett St, (@ Heberton Ave), Staten Island, NY, 10302. Tel: 718-442-0158. Fax: 718-447-2851. p. 1692

Kettling Law, Elys, Ref & Instruction Librn, The College of Wooster Libraries, 1140 Beall Ave, Wooster, OH, 44691-2364. Tel: 330-263-2443. Fax: 330-263-2253. p. 1949

Kettling, Martin, Actg Adminr, Lit Spec/Librn, Eugene O'Neill Theater Center, 305 Great Neck Rd, Waterford, CT, 06385. Tel: 860-443-5378, Ext 227. Fax: 860-443-9653. p. 375

Kettner, Megan, Cat, Memphis Theological Seminary Library, 168 E Parkway S, Memphis, TN, 38104. Tel: 901-334-5825. Fax: 901-452-4051. p. 2250

Kettner, Sandy, Librn, Chinook Regional Library, Gull Lake Branch, 1377 Conrad Ave, Gull Lake, SK, S0N 1A0, CANADA. Tel: 306-672-3277. p. 2928

Kettner, Susan, ILL, Cheltenham Township Library System, Glenside Free Library, 215 S Keswick Ave, Glenside, PA, 19038-4420. Tel: 215-885-0455. Fax: 215-885-1019. p. 2061

Keuneke, Beth, Coord, Ad Serv, St Marys Community Public Library, 140 S Chestnut St, Saint Marys, OH, 45885-2307. Tel: 419-394-7471. Fax: 419-394-7291. p. 1933

Keutzer, Gail, Ref Serv, Maryville University Library, 650 Maryville University Dr, Saint Louis, MO, 63141. Tel: 314-529-9494. Fax: 314-529-9941. p. 1356

Kevil, Tim, Dir of Libr, Navarro College, 3200 W Seventh Ave, Corsicana, TX, 75110-4899. Tel: 903-875-7442. Fax: 903-875-7449. p. 2303

Keville, Kathi, Dir, American Herb Association Library, PO Box 1673, Nevada City, CA, 95959. Tel: 530-265-9552. Fax: 530-274-3140. p. 193

Key, Cathy, Br Mgr, Shreve Memorial Library, Higginbotham/Bryson Branch, 9359 Greenwood Rd, Greenwood, LA, 71033. Tel: 318-938-1451. Fax: 318-938-1451. p. 969

Key, Charlet, Dir, Black Hawk College, 6600 34th Ave, Moline, IL, 61265. Tel: 309-796-5700. Fax: 309-796-0393. p. 674

Key, Delissa, Head, Circ, Washington County Free Library, 100 S Potomac St, Hagerstown, MD, 21740. Tel: 301-739-3250, Ext 126. Fax: 301-739-7603. p. 1031

Key, Dorothy M, Dir, Elizabeth Public Library, 11 S Broad St, Elizabeth, NJ, 07202. Tel: 908-354-6060. Fax: 908-354-5845. p. 1483

Keyes, Charles, Instruction & Outreach, Fiorello H LaGuardia Community College Library, 31-10 Thomson Ave, Long Island City, NY, 11101. Tel: 718-482-5421. Fax: 718-482-5444, 718-609-2011. p. 1654

Keyes, Christy, Dir, Lighthouse Point Library, 2200 NE 38th St, Lighthouse Point, FL, 33064-3913. Tel: 954-946-6398. Fax: 954-781-1950. p. 461

Keyes, Michele, Libr Tech, Cascade Public Library, 105 Front St, Cascade, ID, 83611. Tel: 208-382-4757. Fax: 208-382-4757. p. 572

Keyes, Patricia, ILL, Oakley Public Library, 700 W Third St, Oakley, KS, 67748-1256. Tel: 785-671-4776. Fax: 785-671-3868. p. 885

Keyes, Robert Lord, Archivist, Pelham Library, Two S Valley Rd, Pelham, MA, 01002. Tel: 413-253-0657. Fax: 413-253-0594. p. 1117

Keys, Anne, Br Head, Toronto Public Library, Mount Dennis, 1123 Weston Rd, Toronto, ON, M6N 3S3, CANADA. Tel: 416-394-1008. Fax: 416-394-1036. p. 2862

Keys, Daphene, Librn, Houston Community College - Southwest College, Missouri City (Sienna) Campus, 5855 Sienna Springs Way, Missouri City, TX, 77459. Tel: 713-718-2942. Fax: 713-718-2474. p. 2338

Keys, Linda, Acq, Supvr, Ser, Marquette University, Sensenbrenner Hall, 1103 W Wisconsin Ave, Milwaukee, WI, 53233-2313. Tel: 414-288-7092. Fax: 414-288-5914. p. 2618

Keys, Ronald, Ref Librn, Texas Southern University, 3100 Cleburne Ave, Houston, TX, 77004. Tel: 713-313-4424. Fax: 713-313-1080. p. 2342

Keyser, Jessica, Dir, Ferndale Public Library, 222 E Nine Mile Rd, Ferndale, MI, 48220. Tel: 248-546-2504. Fax: 248-545-5840. p. 1178

Keyser, Marcia, Instrul Serv Librn, Drake University, 2725 University Ave, Des Moines, IA, 50311. Tel: 515-271-3989. Fax: 515-271-3933. p. 809

Keysor, Betty, Librn, Glendive Public Library, Richey Public Library, 223 S Main St, Richey, MT, 59259. Tel: 406-773-5585. p. 1379

Khader, Majed, Dr, Assoc Univ Librn, Dir, Morrow Libr, Marshall University Libraries, One John Marshall Dr, Huntington, WV, 25755-2060. Tel: 304-696-3121. Fax: 304-696-5858. p. 2561

Khamouna, Mo, Curator, Nebraska College of Technical Agriculture Library, 404 E Seventh St, Curtis, NE, 69025. Tel: 308-367-4124, 308-367-5213. Fax: 308-367-5209. p. 1397

Khamphavong, Megan, Cat, Ref Serv, Ser/ILL, RMH Healthcare, 2010 Health Campus Dr, Harrisonburg, VA, 22801-3293. Tel: 540-689-1777. Fax: 540-689-1770. p. 2471

Khan, Karim, Mgr, Loudoun County Public Library, Rust Branch, 380 Old Waterford Rd NW, Leesburg, VA, 20176. Tel: 703-777-0323. Fax: 703-771-5620. p. 2474

Khan, Mohammed A, PhD, Dr, Admin Librn, Chief Librn, US Army Chaplain Center & School Library, 10100 Lee Rd, Fort Jackson, SC, 29207. Tel: 803-751-8828. Fax: 803-751-8393. p. 2194

Khan, Mumtaz, Tech Serv, Sinclair Community College Library, 444 W Third St, Dayton, OH, 45402-1460. Tel: 937-512-4513. Fax: 937-512-4564. p. 1894

Khan, Shabeer, Dir, Kaye Scholer LLP, 425 Park Ave, New York, NY, 10022. Tel: 212-836-8000, 212-836-8312. Fax: 212-836-6613. p. 1684

Kharouba, Dianne, Dir, University of Ottawa Libraries, Health Sciences, 451 Smyth Rd, Ottawa, ON, K1H 8M5, CANADA. Tel: 613-562-5407. p. 2834

Khatun, Taslima, Libr Spec, Northern Virginia Community College Libraries, Woodbridge Library, 15200 Neabsco Mills Rd, Seefeldt 427, Woodbridge, VA, 22191. Tel: 703-878-5727. Fax: 703-670-8433. p. 2448

Khayat, Gwen, Dir, Baxter County Library, Gassville Branch, 6469 Hwy 62 W, Gassville, AR, 72635. Tel: 870-435-2180. p. 110

Khayat, Gwen, Librn, Baxter County Library, 300 Library Hill, Mountain Home, AR, 72653. Tel: 870-580-0987. Fax: 870-580-0935. p. 110

Khipple, Lucia, Asst Libr Dir, Dir, Youth Serv, Rolling Meadows Library, 3110 Martin Lane, Rolling Meadows, IL, 60008. Tel: 847-259-6050. Fax: 847-259-5319. p. 698

Khoo, Michael, PhD, Asst Prof, Drexel University, Rush Bldg, Rm 306, 30 N 33rd St, Philadelphia, PA, 19104-2875, Tel: 215-895-2474. Fax: 215-895-2494. p. 2972

Khosrowpour, Shahrzad, Cat, Colorado State University Pueblo Library, 2200 Bonforte Blvd, Pueblo, CO, 81001-4901. Tel: 719-549-2361. Fax: 719-549-2738. p. 320

Khost, Deborah, Children's Programmer, Caldwell Public Library, 268 Bloomfield Ave, Caldwell, NJ, 07006-5198. Tel: 973-226-1636. Fax: 973-403-8606. p. 1476

Khoubesserian, Anny, Admin Mgr, Cornell University Library, The Samuel J Wood Library & The C V Starr Biomedical Information Center, 1300 York Ave, C115, Box 67, New York, NY, 10065-4896. Tel: 212-746-6050. Fax: 212-746-6494. p. 1642

Khouri, Anastasia, Coordr, Electronic Res, McGill University Libraries, Walter Hitschfeld Geographic Information Centre, Burnside Hall, Rm 524, 805 Sherbrooke St W, Montreal, QC, H3A 2K6, CANADA. Tel: 514-398-7453, 514-398-8095. Fax: 514-398-7437. p. 2898

Khouri, Anastassia, Dir, Archives Nationales du Quebec Bibliotheque, Cite Universitaire, Pavillon Louis Jacques Casault, CP 10450, Sainte-Foy, QC, G1V 4N1, CANADA. Tel: 418-644-4797. Fax: 418-646-4254. p. 2910

Khouvongsavanh, Laura, Electronic Ref Librn, Res & Instrul Serv, Sr Ref Librn, George Washington University, Virginia Science & Technology Campus Library, 44983 Knoll Sq, Ste 179, Ashburn, DC, 20147-2604. Tel: 703-726-3775. Fax: 703-726-8237. p. 402

Khwaja, Tariq, Ref Librn, Sullivan & Cromwell LLP, 125 Broad St, New York, NY, 10004. Tel: 212-558-3780. Fax: 212-558-3346. p. 1700

Kia, Mitra, Librn, Occidental Oil & Gas Corp Library, Five Greenway Plaza, Ste B-1, Houston, TX, 77046. Tel: 713-215-7667. Fax: 713-215-7528. p. 2341

Kiang, Agnes, Law Librn, United States Court of Appeals for the Armed Forces Library, 450 E St NW, Washington, DC, 20442-0001. Tel: 202-761-1466. p. 417

Kibiridge, Harry M, Prof, Queens College of the City University of New York, Benjamin Rosenthal Library, Rm 254, 65-30 Kissena Blvd, Flushing, NY, 11367. Tel: 718-997-3790. Fax: 718-997-3797. p. 2970

Kibler, Christopher, Access Serv, Circ Serv, La Salle University, 1900 W Olney Ave, Philadelphia, PA, 19141-1199. Tel: 215-951-1287. Fax: 215-951-1595. p. 2111

Kibler, Daniel, Br Mgr, Jacksonville Public Library, Dallas James Graham Branch, 2304 N Myrtle Ave, Jacksonville, FL, 32209-5099. Tel: 904-630-0922. Fax: 904-630-0439. p. 453

Kibler, Kathy, Br Mgr, Stark County District Library, Jackson Township Branch, 7487 Fulton Dr NW, Massillon, OH, 44646. Tel: 330-833-1010. Fax: 330-833-3491. p. 1864

Kibler, M Robin, Head, Coll Mgt, Williams College, 55 Sawyer Library Dr, Williamstown, MA, 01267. Tel: 413-597-3047. Fax: 413-597-4106. p. 1140

Kibreah, Golam, Pub Serv Mgr, Hancock County Public Library, 900 W McKenzie Rd, Greenfield, IN, 46140-1741. Tel: 317-462-5141. Fax: 317-462-5711. p. 746

Kickham-Samy, Mary, Electronic Serv Librn, Macomb Community College Libraries, J-Bldg, 14500 E 12 Mile Rd, Warren, MI, 48088-3896. Tel: 586-445-7419. Fax: 586-445-7157. p. 1234

Kickles, Christine, Bus Librn, College of DuPage Library, 425 Fawell Blvd, Glen Ellyn, IL, 60137-6599. Tel: 630-942-2021. Fax: 630-858-8757. p. 649

Kidd, Alyce, Br Coordr, Franklin County Library, Bunn Branch, 610 Main St, Bunn, NC, 27508. Tel: 919-496-6764. Fax: 919-497-5821. p. 1807

Kidd, Alyce, Br Coordr, Franklin County Library, Franklinton Branch, Nine W Mason St, Franklinton, NC, 27525. Tel: 919-494-2736. Fax: 919-494-2466. p. 1807

Kidd, Alyce, Br Coordr, Franklin County Library, Youngsville Branch, 218 US 1A Hwy S, Youngsville, NC, 27596. Tel: 919-556-1612. Fax: 919-556-9633. p. 1807

Kidd, Ann L, Dir, Haston Free Public Library, 161 N Main St, North Brookfield, MA, 01535. Tel: 508-867-0208. Fax: 508-867-0216. p. 1112

Kidd, Betty, Br Mgr, Mobile Public Library, Parkway, 1924-B Dauphin Island Pkwy, Mobile, AL, 36605-3004. Tel: 251-470-7712. Fax: 251-470-7766. p. 25

Kidd, Christine, VPres, Info Res, Palo Alto University, 1791 Arastradero Rd, Palo Alto, CA, 94304. Tel: 650-433-3808. Fax: 650-433-3888. p. 204

Kiddell, Dawn, Chief Exec Officer, Chief Librn, Cornwall Public Library, 45 Second St E, Cornwall, ON, K6H 1Y2, CANADA. Tel: 613-932-4796. Fax: 613-932-2715. p. 2801

Kidner, Rhonda, Mgr, Lubrizol Library & Research Center, 29400 Lakeland Blvd, Mail Drop 152L, Wickliffe, OH, 44092. Tel: 440-347-2971. Fax: 440-347-4713. p. 1947

Kidney, Sharon, Librn, Newmarket Public Library, One Elm St, Newmarket, NH, 03857-1201. Tel: 603-659-5311. Fax: 603-659-8849. p. 1460

Kidwell, Eric A, Dir, Libr Serv, Huntingdon College, 1500 E Fairview Ave, Montgomery, AL, 36106. Tel: 334-833-4421. Fax: 334-263-4465. p. 29

Kiebuzinski, Ksenya, PhD, Dr, Head of Libr, University of Toronto Libraries, Petro Jacyk Central & East European Resource Centre, 130 St George St, Rm 3008, Toronto, ON, M5S 1A5, CANADA. Tel: 416-978-0588. Fax: 416-971-2636. p. 2866

Kieczykowski, Ed, City Librn, Santa Clarita Public Library, 18601 Soledad Canyon Rd, Santa Clarita, CA, 91351. Tel: 661-251-2720. Fax: 661-298-7137. p. 263

Kiedrowski, Cathy, Ref, Cambridge Libraries & Galleries, One North Sq, Cambridge, ON, N1S 2K6, CANADA. Tel: 519-621-0460. Fax: 519-621-2080. p. 2798

Kiefer, Curtis, Youth Serv Mgr, Corvallis-Benton County Public Library, 645 NW Monroe Ave, Corvallis, OR, 97330. Tel: 541-766-6962. p. 1994

Kiefer, Kurt, Asst State Superintendent, Wisconsin Department of Public Instruction, 125 S Webster St, Madison, WI, 53707. Tel: 608-266-2205. Fax: 608-266-8770. p. 2610

Kieffer, Mary, Dir, McCord Memorial Library, 32 W Main St, North East, PA, 16428. Tel: 814-725-4057. p. 2099

Kieft, Robert, Col Librn, Occidental College Library, 1600 Campus Rd, Los Angeles, CA, 90041. Tel: 323-259-2504. Fax: 323-341-4991. p. 176

Kiegel, Joseph A, Head, Monographic Serv, University of Washington Libraries, Allen Library, 4th Flr, Rm 482, Box 352900, Seattle, WA, 98195-2900. Tel: 206-685-2298. Fax: 206-685-8782. p. 2533

Kiehl, Carole, Dean of Libr, University of Southern Mississippi Library, 118 College Dr, No 5053, Hattiesburg, MS, 39406. Tel: 601-266-4362. Fax: 601-266-6033. p. 1300

Kiehl, Gregg, Libr Dir, Tompkins Cortland Community College, 170 North St, Dryden, NY, 13053-8504. Tel: 607-844-8222. Fax: 607-844-6540. p. 1615

Kiekhaefer, Katie, Head, Youth Serv, Community Library, 24615 89th St, Salem, WI, 53168. Tel: 262-843-3348. Fax: 262-843-3144. p. 2636

Kiel, Becky, Libr Dir, Cottey College, 225 S College St, Nevada, MO, 64772-2892. Tel: 417-667-8181, Ext 2153. Fax: 417-448-1040. p. 1347

Kiel, Diana, Coll Develop, Coordr, Tech Serv, Iona College, 715 North Ave, New Rochelle, NY, 10801-1890. Tel: 914-633-2417. Fax: 914-633-2136. p. 1666

Kielar, Donna M, Dir, Thorp Reed & Armstrong, LLP Library, One Oxford Ctr, 301 Grant St, Ste 14, Pittsburgh, PA, 15219-1425. Tel: 412-394-2358, 412-394-7711. Fax: 412-394-2555. p. 2128

Kielb, Beth, Libr Dir, SullivanMunce Cultural Center, 225 W Hawthorne St, Zionsville, IN, 46077. Tel: 317-873-4900. p. 789

Kielbasa, Andrea, Head, Ch, East Islip Public Library, 381 E Main St, East Islip, NY, 11730-2896. Tel: 631-581-9200. Fax: 631-581-2245. p. 1617

Kieler, Kathy, Asst Librn, Kraemer Library & Community Center, 910 Main St, Plain, WI, 53577. Tel: 608-546-4201. Fax: 608-546-4201. p. 2630

Kielian, Anna, Circ & Stacks Coordr, University of Saint Mary of the Lake - Mundelein Seminary, 1000 E Maple Ave, Mundelein, IL, 60060. Tel: 847-970-4820. Fax: 847-566-5229. p. 678

Kielley, Liz Y, Tech Serv Coordr, Messiah College, One College Ave, Ste 3002, Mechanicsburg, PA, 17055. Tel: 717-691-6006, Ext 3850. Fax: 717-691-2356. p. 2087

Kieltyka, Marcus, Instruction & Outreach, Central Washington University, 400 E University Way, Ellensburg, WA, 98926-7548. Tel: 509-963-1901. Fax: 509-963-3684. p. 2514

Kieltyka, Theresa, Dir, Melvindale Public Library, 18650 Allen Rd, Melvindale, MI, 48122. Tel: 313-429-1090. Fax: 313-388-0432. p. 1208

Kiely, Daniel, Electronic Access, Diablo Valley College Library, 321 Golf Club Rd, Pleasant Hill, CA, 94523-1576. Tel: 925-685-1230, Ext 2393. Fax: 925-798-3588. p. 210

Kiely, Judith, Dir, Operations, Anthroposophical Society in America, 65 Fern Hill Rd, Ghent, NY, 12075. Tel: 518-672-7690. Fax: 518-672-5827. p. 1628

Kiely, Paula, Libr Dir, Milwaukee Public Library, 814 W Wisconsin Ave, Milwaukee, WI, 53233-2385. Tel: 414-286-3000. Fax: 414-286-2794. p. 2620

Kiene, Andrea, Librn, Aon Fire Protection Engineeering Corp Library, 1000 Milwaukee Ave, 5th Flr, Glenview, IL, 60025. Tel: 847-953-7700. p. 650

Kienenberger, Karen, Librn, Timberland Regional Library, McCleary Branch, 121 S Fourth St, McCleary, WA, 98557. Tel: 360-495-3368. Fax: 360-495-4496. p. 2543

Kientz, Julie, Asst Prof, University of Washington, Mary Gates Hall, Ste 370, Campus Box 352840, Seattle, WA, 98195-2840. Tel: 206-685-9937. Fax: 206-616-3152. p. 2976

Kier, Margaret, Div Chief, Chicago Public Library, Social Science & History Division, 400 S State St, Chicago, IL, 60605. Tel: 312-747-4608. p. 609

Kieraldo, John, Online Serv, Harold Washington College Library, City Colleges of Chicago, 30 E Lake St, 5th Flr, Chicago, IL, 60601-9996. Tel: 312-553-5761. Fax: 312-553-5783. p. 614

Kierans, Mary, Mgr, Support Serv, Fraser Valley Regional Library, 34589 Delair Rd, Abbotsford, BC, V2S 5Y1, CANADA. Tel: 604-859-7141. Fax: 604-859-5701. p. 2723

Kiesinger, Karson, Ref Librn, Bennington Free Library, 101 Silver St, Bennington, VT, 05201. Tel: 802-442-9051. p. 2418

Kiesling, Linda, Asst Circ Mgr, Central Baptist Theological Seminary, 22074 W 66th St, Shawnee, KS, 66226. Tel: 913-422-5789. Fax: 913-371-8110. p. 894

Kiesner, Pamela Nyberg, Dir, Bellingham Public Library, 210 Central Ave, CS-9710, Bellingham, WA, 98227-9710. Tel: 360-778-7221. p. 2508

Kiesowapy, Merissa, Asst Librn, Parkland Regional Library, Melville Branch, 444 Main St, Melville, SK, S0A 2P0, CANADA. Tel: 306-728-2171. p. 2932

Kietzer, Jane, Dir, Lomira Public Library, 1038 Main St, Lomira, WI, 53048-9515. Tel: 920-269-4115. Fax: 920-269-4115. p. 2605

Kietzman, William, Ref/Spec Projects Librn, Plymouth State University, Highland St, Plymouth, NH, 03264-1595. Tel: 603-535-2258. Fax: 603-535-2445. p. 1462

Kievit-Mason, Barbara A, Archivist, Sam Houston State University, 1830 Bobby K Marks Dr, Huntsville, TX, 77340. Tel: 936-294-3699. Fax: 936-294-3780. p. 2345

Kifer, Ruth, Dean, Univ Libr, San Jose State University, One Washington Sq, San Jose, CA, 95192-0028. Tel: 408-808-2419. Fax: 408-808-2141. p. 251

Kift, Judith, Librn, NEMI Public Library, 50 Meredith St, Little Current, ON, P0P 1K0, CANADA. Tel: 705-368-2444. Fax: 705-368-0708. p. 2816

Kight, Dawn, Mgr, Syst & Tech, Southern University, 167 Roosevelt Steptoe Ave, Baton Rouge, LA, 70813-0001. Tel: 225-771-4934. Fax: 225-771-4113. p. 944

Kiguchi Shin, Lisa, Assoc Librn, Sidley Austin LLP Library, 555 W Fifth St, Ste 4000, Los Angeles, CA, 90013. Tel: 213-896-6193. Fax: 213-896-6600. p. 177

Kiiskinen, Kim, Ref Serv, Ad, River Falls Public Library, 140 Union St, River Falls, WI, 54022. Tel: 715-425-0905, Ext 104. Fax: 715-425-0914. p. 2634

Kijak, Janice R, Dir, Info Syst, Kenyon College Library & Information Services, 103 College Dr, Gambier, OH, 43022-9624. Tel: 740-427-5186. Fax: 740-427-5272. p. 1901

Kilbert, Linda, Mgr, Ad Serv, Johnson County Public Library, 401 State St, Franklin, IN, 46131-2545. Tel: 317-738-2833. Fax: 317-738-9635. p. 744

Kilborne, Hugh, Dir, Rimrock Foundation Library, 1231 N 29th St, Billings, MT, 59101. Tel: 406-248-3175. Fax: 406-248-3821. p. 1374

Kilbridge, Rosemary, Dir, Chippewa Falls Public Library, 105 W Central, Chippewa Falls, WI, 54729-2397. Tel: 715-723-1146. Fax: 715-720-6922. p. 2585

Kilburn, Linda, Mgr, Coll Develop, Sequoyah Regional Library System, 116 Brown Industrial Pkwy, Canton, GA, 30114-2899. Tel: 770-479-3090, Ext 221. Fax: 770-479-3069. p. 523

Kilby, Cynthia, Asst Dir, Pine Mountain Regional Library, 218 Perry St NW, Manchester, GA, 31816-1317. Tel: 706-846-3851. Fax: 706-846-8455, 706-846-9632. p. 542

Kilby, Cynthia, Librn, Pine Mountain Regional Library, Hightower Memorial, 800 W Gordon St, Thomaston, GA, 30286-3417. Tel: 706-647-8649. Fax: 706-647-3977. p. 542

Kilby, Janet R, Tech Serv, Wilkes County Public Library, 215 Tenth St, North Wilkesboro, NC, 28659. Tel: 336-838-2818. Fax: 336-667-2638. p. 1813

Kilby, Tara, Cat, Blackhawk Technical College Library, 6004 S County Rd G, Janesville, WI, 53547. Tel: 608-743-4515. Fax: 608-743-4518. p. 2599

Kilcullen, Maureen, Ref, Kent State University, 6000 Frank Ave NW, North Canton, OH, 44720-7548. Tel: 330-244-3322. Fax: 330-494-6212. p. 1923

Kilday, Michele Squier, Dir, Phenix City-Russell County Library, 1501 17th Ave, Phenix City, AL, 36867. Tel: 334-664-1700. Fax: 334-298-8452. p. 33

Kildow, Deb, Acq, Western Nebraska Community College Library, 1601 E 27th NE, Scottsbluff, NE, 69361-1899. Tel: 308-635-6040. Fax: 308-635-6086. p. 1418

Kile, Barbara, Dir, Yavapai County Free Library District, 172 E Merritt St, Ste E, Prescott, AZ, 86301. Tel: 928-771-3191. Fax: 928-771-3113. p. 79

Kiley, Susan, Br Serv Coordr, Hernando County Public Library System, 238 Howell Ave, Brooksville, FL, 34601. Tel: 352-754-4043. Fax: 352-754-4044. p. 430

Kiley, Susan, Br Serv Coordr, Hernando County Public Library System, Istachatta Library Station, 16257 Lingle Rd, Istachatta, FL, 34601. Tel: 352-540-4304. p. 430

Kiley, Susan, Br Serv Coordr, Hernando County Public Library System, West Hernando, 6335 Blackbird Ave, Brooksville, FL, 34613. Tel: 352-754-4043. Fax: 352-592-5609. p. 430

Kilfoil, Sarah, Regional Dir, Chaleur Library Region, 113A Roseberry St, Campbellton, NB, E3N 2G6, CANADA. Tel: 506-789-6599. Fax: 506-789-7318. p. 2761

Kilgallen, Caitlin, Assoc Dir, School of Visual Arts, 380 Second Ave, 2nd Flr, New York, NY, 10010-3994. Tel: 212-592-2663. Fax: 212-592-2655. p. 1699

Kilgore, Donna, Br Mgr, Baker County Public Library, Haines Branch, Cole St between 3rd & 4th, Haines, OR, 97833. Tel: 541-856-3309. p. 1991

Kilhefner, John, Librn, Florida Department of Corrections, 691 Institution Rd, De Funiak Springs, FL, 32433-1831. Tel: 850-951-1437. Fax: 850-892-3691. p. 437

Kilian, Beth, Human Res Mgr, Contra Costa County Library, 1750 Oak Park Blvd, Pleasant Hill, CA, 94523-4497. Tel: 925-646-6434. Fax: 925-646-6461. p. 208

Kilimann, Joy, Br Mgr, Milwaukee Public Library, Mill Road, 6431 N 76th St, Milwaukee, WI, 53223. Tel: 414-286-3088. Fax: 414-286-8454. p. 2620

Killam, Lane, District Librn, United States Army Corps of Engineers, 803 Front St, Norfolk, VA, 23510-1096. Tel: 757-201-7562. Fax: 757-201-7870. p. 2483

Killebrew, Amy, Online Serv, Schaumburg Township District Library, 130 S Roselle Rd, Schaumburg, IL, 60193. Tel: 847-923-3328. Fax: 847-923-3131. p. 701

Killebrew, Rachel, Librn, Community of Christ Library, The Temple, 201 S River, Independence, MO, 64050-3689. Tel: 816-833-1000, Ext 2399. Fax: 816-521-3087. p. 1331

Killeen, Patricia, Ref Serv, Holmes Public Library, 470 Plymouth St, Halifax, MA, 02338. Tel: 781-293-2271. Fax: 781-294-8518. p. 1093

Killeen, Robin, Ch, Audubon Public Library, 401 N Park Pl, Audubon, IA, 50025-1258. Tel: 712-563-3301. Fax: 712-563-2580. p. 795

Killen, Susanne, Tech Asst, California Department of Corrections Library System, Avenal State Prison, One Kings Way, Avenal, CA, 93204. Tel: 559-386-0587, Ext 6644. p. 221

Killens, Caroline, Head, Acq, University of Georgia Libraries, Athens, GA, 30602-1641. Tel: 706-542-0594. Fax: 706-542-4144. p. 510

Killgore, Sarah, Asst Dir, Rippey Public Library, 224 Main St, Rippey, IA, 50235. Tel: 515-436-7714. Fax: 515-436-7485. p. 840

Killian, Cindy, Asst Librn, Thomaston Public Library, 248 Main St, Thomaston, CT, 06787. Tel: 860-283-4339. Fax: 860-283-4330. p. 372

Killian, David, Ref & Coll Develop Librn, George Washington University, Eckles Library, 2100 Foxhall Rd NW, Washington, DC, 20007-1199. Tel: 202-242-6623. Fax: 202-242-6632. p. 402

Killian, Hannah, Youth Serv, Parkland Community Library, 4422 Walbert Ave, Allentown, PA, 18104-1619. Tel: 610-398-1361. Fax: 610-398-3538. p. 2027

Killian, Mary, Coord, Ad Serv, West Bloomfield Township Public Library, 4600 Walnut Lake Rd, West Bloomfield, MI, 48323. Tel: 248-232-2307. Fax: 248-232-2291. p. 1236

Killian, Thomas R, Librn, City of Detroit, First National Bldg, 660 Woodward Ave, Ste 1650, Detroit, MI, 48226. Tel: 313-224-4550, Ext 23150. Fax: 313-224-5505. p. 1169

Killick, Michael, Br Mgr, Thompson-Nicola Regional District Library System, North Kamloops Branch, 795 Tranquille Rd, Kamloops, BC, V2B 3J3, CANADA. Tel: 250-554-1124. Fax: 250-376-3825. p. 2730

Killie, Mark, Dir, Berthoud Public Library, 236 Welch Ave, Berthoud, CO, 80513. Tel: 970-532-2757. Fax: 970-532-4372. p. 289

Killinger, Melissa A, Ch, Bosler Free Library, 158 W High St, Carlisle, PA, 17013-2988. Tel: 717-243-4642. Fax: 717-243-8281. p. 2041

Killinger, Tina, Bus & Finance Mgr, Annie Halenbake Ross Library, 232 W Main St, Lock Haven, PA, 17745-1241. Tel: 570-748-3321. Fax: 570-748-1050. p. 2082

Killingsworth, Elizabeth, Head, Info Literacy & Outreach, University of Central Florida Libraries, 4000 Central Florida Blvd, Bldg 2, Orlando, FL, 32816-2666. Tel: 407-823-5880. Fax: 407-823-2529. p. 477

Killion, Vicki, Head of Libr, Purdue University Libraries, Life Sciences, Lilly Hall of Life Sciences, Rm 2400, 915 W State St, West Lafayette, IN, 47907-2058. Tel: 765-494-1417. p. 786

Killion, Vicki, Head of Libr, Purdue University Libraries, Pharmacy, Nursing & Health Sciences, Heine Pharmacy Bldg 272, 575 Stadium Mall Dr, West Lafayette, IN, 47907-2058. Tel: 765-494-1417. p. 787

Killips, Lisa, Assoc Librn, University of Wisconsin-Richland, 1200 US Hwy 14 W, Richland Center, WI, 53581-1399. Tel: 608-647-6186, Ext 220. Fax: 608-647-6225. p. 2634

Killmon, Charles W, Libr Spec, Media & Tech Serv, Eastern Shore Community College, 29300 Lankford Hwy, Melfa, VA, 23410. Tel: 757-789-1722. Fax: 757-789-1739. p. 2478

Killough, Aaron, Coordr, Cat, Metadata Coordr, University of Central Oklahoma, 100 N University Dr, Edmond, OK, 73034. Tel: 405-974-2872. Fax: 405-974-3806, 405-974-3874. p. 1962

Killough, Angel, Ch, Hopkins County-Madisonville Public Library, 31 S Main St, Madisonville, KY, 42431. Tel: 270-825-2680. Fax: 270-825-2777. p. 927

Killoy, Tracy, Librn, Clark Fork & Blackfoot LLC, 40 E Broadway, Butte, MT, 59701. Tel: 406-497-2130. Fax: 406-497-2451. p. 1376

Killpack, Barbara, Outreach Librn, Sweetwater County Library System, 300 N First East, Green River, WY, 82935. Tel: 307-875-3615, Ext 1440. Fax: 307-872-3203. p. 2655

Kilmain, Pat, Dir, Palmer Public Library, 655 S Valley Way, Palmer, AK, 99645. Tel: 907-745-4690. Fax: 907-746-3570. p. 52

Kilman, Leigh, Head Librn, Austin Community College, Pinnacle Campus Library, 7748 Hwy 290 W, Austin, TX, 78736. Tel: 512-223-8114. Fax: 512-223-8223. p. 2278

Kilman, Marcus, Head, Circ Serv, University of Central Florida Libraries, 4000 Central Florida Blvd, Bldg 2, Orlando, FL, 32816-2666. Tel: 407-823-2527. Fax: 407-823-2529. p. 477

Kilmartin, Valerie, Dir, Durham Public Library, Seven Maple Ave, Durham, CT, 06422. Tel: 860-349-9544. Fax: 860-349-1897. p. 336

Kilmer, Glenda, Librn, Tulsa City-County Library, Herman & Kate Kaiser Library, 5202 S Hudson Ave, Tulsa, OK, 74135. Tel: 918-549-7542. Fax: 918-549-7545. p. 1983

Kilmer, Kevin, Assoc Dir, Elkhart Public Library, Dunlap, 58485 E County Rd 13, Elkhart, IN, 46516. Tel: 574-875-3100. Fax: 574-875-5512. p. 737

Kilmer, Loretta, Bus & Finance Mgr, La Crosse Public Library, 800 Main St, La Crosse, WI, 54601. Tel: 608-789-7147. Fax: 608-789-7106. p. 2603

Kilmer, Sue, Librn, Mabel C Fry Public Library, 1200 Lakeshore Dr, Yukon, OK, 73099. Tel: 405-354-8232. Fax: 405-350-7928. p. 1987

Kilmon, Joan, Br Mgr, Calvert County Public Library, Twin Beaches Branch, 3819 Harbor Rd, Chesapeake Beach, MD, 20732. Tel: 410-257-2411. Fax: 410-257-0663. p. 1036

Kilpatrick, Mary, Ref Serv, Massachusetts School of Law Library, 500 Federal St, Andover, MA, 01810. Tel: 978-681-0800. Fax: 978-681-6330. p. 1049

Kilpatrick, Sandra, Coordr, Acq, Elon University, 308 N O'Kelly Ave, Elon, NC, 27244-0187. Tel: 336-278-6600. Fax: 336-278-6637. p. 1791

Kilroy, Ardemis, Br Mgr, Cambridge Public Library, Valente Branch, 826 Cambridge St, Cambridge, MA, 02141. Tel: 617-349-4015. Fax: 617-349-4416. p. 1073

Kilsby, M, Archivist, Librn, Barkerville Historic Town Library & Archives, 14301 Hwy 26 E, Barkerville, BC, V0K 1B0, CANADA. Tel: 250-994-3332, Ext 26. Fax: 250-994-3435. p. 2725

Kilzer, Rebekah, Emerging Tech Librn, Drexel University Libraries, Hagerty Library, 33rd & Market Sts, Philadelphia, PA, 19104-2875. Tel: 215-895-6783. Fax: 215-895-2070. p. 2105

Kim, Angela, Dir, Louis Latzer Memorial Public Library, 1001 Ninth St, Highland, IL, 62249. Tel: 618-654-5066. Fax: 618-654-1324. p. 655

Kim, Chang Suk, Dr, Assoc Prof, Southern Connecticut State University, 501 Crescent St, New Haven, CT, 06515. Tel: 203-392-5191. Fax: 203-392-5780. p. 2963

Kim, ChanMin, PhD, Asst Prof, University of Georgia, College of Education, 224 River's Crossing, Athens, GA, 30602-7144. Tel: 706-542-4110. Fax: 706-542-4032. p. 2964

Kim, Colleen, Ch, Berlin Free Library, 834 Worthington Ridge, Berlin, CT, 06037-3203. Tel: 860-828-3344. p. 330

Kim, Daniel, Librn, Korean Cultural Center Library, 5505 Wilshire Blvd, Los Angeles, CA, 90036. Tel: 323-936-7141. Fax: 323-936-5712. p. 171

Kim, HaeSook, Cat, Golden Gate Baptist Theological Seminary Library, 201 Seminary Dr, Mill Valley, CA, 94941. Tel: 415-380-1300. Fax: 415-380-1652. p. 186

Kim, Hak Joon, Dr, Assoc Prof, Southern Connecticut State University, 501 Crescent St, New Haven, CT, 06515. Tel: 203-392-5764. Fax: 203-392-5780. p. 2963

Kim, Hana, Coll & Res Librn, University of Toronto Libraries, Cheng Yu Tung East Asian Library, John P Robarts Research Library, 130 St George St, Rm 8049, Toronto, ON, M5S 1A5, CANADA. Tel: 416-978-3300. Fax: 416-978-0863. p. 2865

Kim, Helen, Assoc Librn, Munger, Tolles & Olson LLP, 355 S Grand Ave, 35th Flr, Los Angeles, CA, 90071-1560. Tel: 213-683-9100. Fax: 213-683-5173. p. 176

Kim, Hyesoon H, Tech Serv Librn, United States Army, Van Noy Library, 5966 12th St, Bldg 1024, Fort Belvoir, VA, 22060-5554. Tel: 703-806-0093. p. 2464

Kim, Jeannie, Head, Ref (Info Serv), Southampton Free Library, 947 Street Rd, Southampton, PA, 18966. Tel: 215-322-1415. Fax: 215-396-9375. p. 2142

Kim, Jeffrey, Sr Lecturer, University of Washington, Mary Gates Hall, Ste 370, Campus Box 352840, Seattle, WA, 98195-2840. Tel: 206-685-9937. Fax: 206-616-3152. p. 2976

Kim, Jeonghyun Annie, Dr, Asst Prof, University of North Texas, 1155 Union Circle, Denton, TX, 76203-5017. Tel: 940-565-2445. Fax: 940-565-3101. p. 2975

Kim, Joanne Y, Fac Librn, Pasadena City College Library, 1570 E Colorado Blvd, Pasadena, CA, 91106-2003. Tel: 626-585-7837. Fax: 626-585-7913. p. 206

Kim, June, Sr Ref Librn, University of California Los Angeles Library, Hugh & Hazel Darling Law Library, 112 Law Bldg, Box 951458, 385 Charles E Young Dr E, Los Angeles, CA, 90095-1458. Tel: 310-825-7826. Fax: 310-825-1372. p. 178

Kim, Jung, Librn, United States Army, 180 Fifth St E, Saint Paul, MN, 55101-1600. Tel: 651-290-5680. Fax: 651-290-5256. p. 1282

Kim, Kiwon, Libr Asst, Cresskill Public Library, 53 Union Ave, Cresskill, NJ, 07626. Tel: 201-567-3521. Fax: 201-567-5067. p. 1480

Kim, Kungwha, Tech Serv Mgr, Lamar State College-Orange Library, 410 Front St, Orange, TX, 77630-5796. Tel: 409-882-3080. Fax: 409-883-7552. p. 2367

Kim, Kyung, Tech Serv, Plainsboro Free Public Library, 9 Van Doren St, Plainsboro, NJ, 08536. Tel: 609-275-2899. Fax: 609-799-5883. p. 1521

Kim, Kyung-Sun, Asst Prof, University of Wisconsin-Madison, 4217 H C White Hall, 600 N Park St, Madison, WI, 53706. Tel: 608-263-2941. Fax: 608-263-4849. p. 2976

Kim, Mi-Seon, Cat, Ref, Queensborough Community College, City University of New York, 222-05 56th Ave, Bayside, NY, 11364-1497. Tel: 718-631-5721. Fax: 718-281-5012. p. 1579

Kim, Michael, Head, Cat, University of Miami Libraries, 1300 Memorial Dr, Coral Gables, FL, 33146. Tel: 305-284-3233. Fax: 305-284-4027. p. 434

Kim, Patricia, Librn, Algonquin College Learning Resource Centre, Ottawa Valley, 315 Pembroke St E, Pembroke, ON, K8A 3K2, CANADA. Tel: 613-735-4700, Ext 2779. Fax: 613-735-8801. p. 2828

Kim, Popma, Supvr, University of Texas Libraries, Serials Acquisitions Unit, PO Box P, Austin, TX, 78713-8916. Tel: 512-495-4222. Fax: 512-495-4296. p. 2285

Kim, Sophia, Librn, Aria Health, School of Nursing Library, 4918 Penn St, Philadelphia, PA, 19124. Tel: 215-831-6740, Ext 132. Fax: 215-831-6782. p. 2103

Kim, Sujin, Dr, Assoc Prof, University of Kentucky, 320 Little Library Bldg, Lexington, KY, 40506-0224. Tel: 859-281-0110. Fax: 859-257-4205. p. 2966

Kim, Yanghee, Acq Librn, West Valley Community College Library, 14000 Fruitvale Ave, Saratoga, CA, 95070-5698. Tel: 408-741-2484. Fax: 408-741-2134. p. 268

Kim, Yong-Mi, PhD, Dr, Asst Prof, University of Oklahoma, Bizzell Memorial Library, 401 W Brooks, Rm 120, Norman, OK, 73019-6032. Tel: 918-660-3364. Fax: 405-325-7648. p. 2972

Kim, Youn-In, Ref, Cedar Crest College, 100 College Dr, Allentown, PA, 18104-6196. Tel: 610-606-4666, Ext 3387. Fax: 610-740-3769. p. 2026

Kim-Prieto, Dennis, Ref Serv, Rutgers University Library for the Center for Law & Justice, 123 Washington St, Newark, NJ, 07102-3094. Tel: 973-353-3037. Fax: 973-353-1356. p. 1513

Kimakwa, Sarah, Monographic Acq Coordr, Chicago State University, 9501 S Martin Luther King Jr Dr, LIB 440, Chicago, IL, 60628-1598. Tel: 773-995-3780. Fax: 773-995-3772. p. 610

Kimball, Audra, Dir, Mississippi Electronic Libraries Online, Mississippi State Board for Community & Junior Colleges, 3825 Ridgewood Rd, Jackson, MS, 39211. Tel: 601-432-6518. Fax: 601-432-6363. p. 2947

Kimball, Gregg, Dir, Pub Serv & Outreach, The Library of Virginia, 800 E Broad St, Richmond, VA, 23219-8000. Tel: 804-692-3722. Fax: 804-692-3594. p. 2489

Kimball, Jay, Cataloger/Ref Librn, US Customs & Border Protection Library, 90 K St NE, 9th Flr, Washington, DC, 20004. Tel: 202-325-0169. Fax: 202-325-0170. p. 418

Kimball, Lesley, Dir, Wiggin Memorial Library, Ten Bunker Hill Ave, Stratham, NH, 03885. Tel: 603-772-4346. p. 1465

Kimball, Melanie, Asst Prof, Simmons College, 300 The Fenway, Boston, MA, 02115. Tel: 617-521-2800. Fax: 617-521-3192. p. 2967

Kimball, Melanie, Dr, Asst Prof, University at Buffalo, State University of New York, 534 Baldy Hall, Buffalo, NY, 14260. Tel: 716-645-2412. Fax: 716-645-3775. p. 2971

Kimball, Susan J, Sci & Electronic Serv Librn, Amherst College, Amherst, MA, 01002. Fax: 413-542-2662. p. 1048

Kimball, Susan J, Sci & Electronic Serv Librn, Amherst College, Keefe Science Library, Amherst, MA, 01002. Tel: 413-542-2076. p. 1048

Kimball, Tevis, Curator, Spec Coll, Jones Library, Inc, 43 Amity St, Amherst, MA, 01002-2285. Tel: 413-259-3182. Fax: 413-256-4096. p. 1049

Kimball, Theresa, Circ Supvr, Davis County Library, North Branch, 562 S 1000 East, Clearfield, UT, 84015. Tel: 801-825-6662. p. 2405

Kimball, Tracey, Sr Legis Librn, Legislative Council Service Library, 411 State Capitol, Santa Fe, NM, 87501. Tel: 505-986-4600. Fax: 505-986-4680. p. 1562

Kimbelton, William, Syst Adminr, University of Cincinnati, 2540 Clifton Ave, Cincinnati, OH, 45219. Tel: 513-556-0430. Fax: 513-556-6265. p. 1874

Kimber, Cindy, Br Serv Coordr, Ajax Public Library, 55 Harwood Ave S, Ajax, ON, L1S 2H8, CANADA. Tel: 905-683-4000, Ext 8902. Fax: 905-683-6960. p. 2791

Kimber, Cindy, Br Serv Coordr, Ajax Public Library, McLean Branch, 95 Magill Dr, Ajax, ON, L1T 4M5, CANADA. Tel: 905-683-4000, Ext 8902. Fax: 905-428-3743. p. 2791

Kimber, Cindy, Br Serv Coordr, Ajax Public Library, Village Branch, 58 Church St N, Ajax, ON, L1T 2W6, CANADA. Tel: 905-619-2529, Ext 8902. Fax: 905-683-1140. p. 2791

Kimber, Deaun, Acq, Dixie State College of Utah, 225 S 700 E, Saint George, UT, 84770. Tel: 435-652-7721. Fax: 435-656-4169. p. 2411

Kimber, Georgina, Asst Librn, Chinook Regional Library, Maple Creek Branch, 205 Jasper St, Maple Creek, SK, S0N 1N0, CANADA. Tel: 306-662-3522. p. 2928

Kimber, Jeanne, In Charge, EnCana Corporation, 150 Ninth Ave SW, Calgary, AB, T2P 2S5, CANADA. Tel: 403-645-7644. Fax: 403-645-7649. p. 2691

Kimber, Sharon Kae, Dir, DeMary Memorial Library, 417 Seventh St, Rupert, ID, 83350-1692. Tel: 208-436-3874. Fax: 208-436-9719. p. 583

Kimber-Durr, Barbara, Per, Midland County Public Library, 301 W Missouri, Midland, TX, 79701. Tel: 432-688-4320. Fax: 432-688-4939. p. 2363

Kimberly, Laura, Chief Mem Serv Officer, Amigos Library Services, Inc, 14400 Midway Rd, Ste 200, Dallas, TX, 75244-3509. Tel: 972-340-2864. Fax: 972-991-6061. p. 2956

Kimble, Kathleen, Ch, Elma Public Library, 1860 Bowen Rd, Elma, NY, 14059. Tel: 716-652-2719. Fax: 716-652-0381. p. 1619

Kimbler, Jewel, Librn, Adair County Public Library, 307 Greensburg St, Columbia, KY, 42728-1488. Tel: 270-384-2472. Fax: 270-384-9446. p. 910

Kimborowicz, Holly, Librn, Lake Health, 7590 Auburn Rd, Concord Twp, OH, 44077. Tel: 440-639-4387 (East), 440-953-9600, Ext 33123 (West). p. 1891

Kimbrel, Kevin, Tech Serv, McHenry Public Library District, 809 N Front St, McHenry, IL, 60050. Tel: 815-385-0036. Fax: 815-385-7085. p. 672

Kimbrel, Nancy, ILL, Dodge City Community College, 2501 N 14th, Dodge City, KS, 67801. Tel: 620-225-1321, Ext 287, 620-227-9287. Fax: 620-225-0918. p. 863

Kimbro, Ellen, Evening Circ Supvr, Union University, 1050 Union University Dr, Jackson, TN, 38305-3697. Tel: 731-661-5070. Fax: 731-661-5175. p. 2238

Kimbrough, Jane, Mgr, Pioneer Library System, Blanchard Public, 200 NE Tenth St, Blanchard, OK, 73010. Tel: 405-485-2275. Fax: 405-485-9452. p. 1970

Kimbrough, Julie, Asst Dir, Coll Serv, University of North Carolina at Chapel Hill, Kathrine R Everett Law Library, UNC Law Library, 160 Ridge Rd, CB No 3385, Chapel Hill, NC, 27599-3385. Tel: 919-962-1199. Fax: 919-962-2294. p. 1781

Kimbrough, Marie, Ch, Dripping Springs Community Library, 501 Sportsplex Dr, Dripping Springs, TX, 78620. Tel: 512-858-7825. Fax: 512-858-2639. p. 2314

Kime, Lauren, Coll Access & Support Serv, Pennsylvania State University, College of Medicine, Penn State Hershey, Harrell Health Sciences Library, 500 University Dr, Hershey, PA, 17033. Tel: 717-531-8640. Fax: 717-531-8635. p. 2069

Kimley, Susan, Electronic Res Librn, Ser, Columbia University, Augustus C Long Health Sciences Library, 701 W 168th St, Lobby Level, New York, NY, 10032. Tel: 212-305-3605. Fax: 212-234-0595. p. 1675

Kimlinger, Julie, Coordr, Libr Serv, University of Saint Thomas, 2115 Summit Ave, Mail Box 5004, Saint Paul, MN, 55105. Tel: 651-962-5001. Fax: 651-962-5406. p. 1282

Kimmel, Jody, Asst Librn, Sullivan County Public Library, 109 E Second St, Milan, MO, 63556. Tel: 660-265-3911. Fax: 660-265-3911. p. 1345

Kimmel, Margaret, Prof, University of Pittsburgh, 135 N Bellefield Ave, Pittsburgh, PA, 15260. Tel: 412-624-5230. Fax: 412-624-5231. p. 2973

Kimmer, Melissa, Ch, Berkley Public Library, Three N Main St, Berkley, MA, 02779. Tel: 508-822-3329. Fax: 508-824-2471. p. 1053

Kimmet, Dennis, Librn, Van Wert County Law Library Association, Court House, 3rd Flr, 121 Main St, Van Wert, OH, 45891. Tel: 419-238-6935. Fax: 419-238-2874. p. 1943

Kimmet, Janet, Head, Exten Serv, Tiffin-Seneca Public Library, 77 Jefferson St, Tiffin, OH, 44883. Tel: 419-447-3751. Fax: 419-447-3045. p. 1938

Kimok, Debra, Info Outreach, Sr Asst Librn, Spec Coll Librn, State University of New York College at Plattsburgh, Two Draper Ave, Plattsburgh, NY, 12901-2697. Tel: 518-564-5206. Fax: 518-564-5325. p. 1719

Kimok, William, Rec Mgr, Univ Archivist, Ohio University Libraries, Mahn Center for Archives & Special Collections, Vernon R Alden Library, 30 Park Pl, Fifth Flr, Athens, OH, 45701-2978. Tel: 740-593-2712. Fax: 740-593-2708. p. 1856

Kimsey, Sofia, Head, Pub Serv, Head, Ref, Music, Oxnard Public Library, 251 South A St, Oxnard, CA, 93030. Tel: 805-385-7529. Fax: 805-385-7526. p. 202

Kimura, Jeanne, Webmaster, University of Puget Sound, 1500 N Warner St, Campus Mail Box 1021, Tacoma, WA, 98416-1021. Tel: 253-879-2958. Fax: 253-879-3670. p. 2541

Kimura, Sherise, Ref Serv, University of San Francisco, 2130 Fulton St, San Francisco, CA, 94117-1080. Tel: 415-422-5379. Fax: 415-422-5949. p. 248

Kinahan-Ockay, Mary, Archivist, Saint Peter's College, 99 Glenwood Ave, Jersey City, NJ, 07306. Tel: 201-761-6453. Fax: 201-432-4117. p. 1493

Kinamon, Ellen, Libr Tech, Lake Washington Technical College, 11605 132nd Ave NE, Kirkland, WA, 98034-8505. Tel: 425-739-8100, Ext 503. Fax: 425-739-8198. p. 2519

Kincade, William Luis, Dean of Libr, Howard County Junior College, 1001 Birdwell Lane, Big Spring, TX, 79720. Tel: 432-264-5092. Fax: 432-264-5094. p. 2289

Kincaid, Courtney, Libr Dir, Hood County Public Library, 222 N Travis, Granbury, TX, 76048. Tel: 817-573-3569. Fax: 817-573-3969. p. 2329

Kincaid, Janet, Librn, Fayette County Public Libraries, Meadow Bridge Branch, 53 Montrado St, Meadow Bridge, WV, 25976. Tel: 304-484-7942. Fax: 304-484-7942. p. 2568

Kincheloe, John, Head, Media Serv, Meredith College, 3800 Hillsborough St, Raleigh, NC, 27607-5298. Tel: 919-760-8457. Fax: 919-760-2830. p. 1815

Kinchla, Julie A, Head, Ref (Info Serv), Winchester Public Library, 80 Washington St, Winchester, MA, 01890. Tel: 781-721-7171, Ext 23. Fax: 781-721-7170. p. 1142

Kind, Jule, Off-Campus Libr Serv Dir, Indiana Wesleyan University, 4201 S Washington St, Marion, IN, 46953. Tel: 765-672-2980. Fax: 765-677-2676. p. 762

Kinder, Sean, Humanities & Soc Sci Librn, Western Kentucky University Libraries, Helm-Cravens Library Complex, 1906 College Heights Blvd, No 11067, Bowling Green, KY, 42101-1067. Tel: 270-745-2905. Fax: 270-745-6422. p. 908

Kinder, Vanessa J, Dr, Exec Dir, South Cook ISC4 Library, 253 W Joe Orr Rd, Chicago Heights, IL, 60411. Tel: 708-754-6600. Fax: 708-754-8687. p. 628

Kindilien, Maureen, Fac Librn, Manhattanville College Library, 2900 Purchase St, Purchase, NY, 10577. Tel: 914-323-3132. Fax: 914-323-8139. p. 1724

Kindle, Bonnie, Librn, Grays Harbor County, 102 W Broadway, Rm 203, Montesano, WA, 98563. Tel: 360-249-5311. Fax: 360-249-6391. p. 2521

Kindle, Tera, Dir, Waterville Public Library, 129 E Commercial St, Waterville, KS, 66548. Tel: 785-363-2769. Fax: 785-363-2778. p. 899

Kindle, Victoria, Br Mgr, Macon County Public Library, Red Boiling Springs Branch, 335 E Main St, Red Boiling Springs, TN, 37150-0033. Tel: 615-699-3701. Fax: 615-699-3777. p. 2244

Kindon, Rebecca, Info Res Mgr, SUNY Upstate Medical University, 766 Irving Ave, Syracuse, NY, 13210-1602. Tel: 315-464-7193. Fax: 315-464-4584. p. 1753

Kindschi, Amy, Head, Fac & Student Serv, University of Wisconsin-Madison, Kurt Wendt Engineering Library, 215 N Randall Ave, Madison, WI, 53706. Tel: 608-262-3493. Fax: 608-262-4739, 608-265-8751. p. 2610

Kindstedt, Susan, Archivist, Portsmouth Athenaeum, Six-Seven Market Sq, Portsmouth, NH, 03821. Tel: 603-431-2538. Fax: 603-431-7180. p. 1463

Kindt, Clare, Libr Supvr, Brown County Library, Kress Family Branch, 333 N Broadway, De Pere, WI, 54115. Tel: 920-448-4407. Fax: 920-448-4406. p. 2595

King, Abe, Br Mgr, Washington County Library System, Santa Clara Branch, 1099 N Lava Flow Dr, Saint George, UT, 84770-0999. Tel: 435-256-6327. Fax: 435-986-0436. p. 2412

King, Alan, Mgr, Milwaukee Journal Sentinel, PO Box 661, Milwaukee, WI, 53201-0661. Tel: 414-224-2171. p. 2620

King, Albert C, Ms Curator, Rutgers University Libraries, Special Collections & University Archives, 169 College Ave, New Brunswick, NJ, 08901-1163. Tel: 848-932-6153. Fax: 732-932-7012. p. 1509

King, Andrew, Coordr, Access Serv, University of Hartford Libraries, Mildred P Allen Memorial, 200 Bloomfield Ave, West Hartford, CT, 06117-0395. Tel: 860-768-4840. Fax: 860-768-5295. p. 376

King, Aneatra, Br Mgr, Broward County Division of Libraries, Lauderhill Towne Centre Library, 6399 W Oakland Park Blvd, Lauderhill, FL, 33313. Tel: 954-497-1630. Fax: 954-497-1632. p. 441

King, Angelynn, Dir, University of Maine at Machias, 116 O'Brien Ave, Machias, ME, 04654-1397. Tel: 207-255-1234. Fax: 207-255-1356. p. 991

King, Ann, Dir, Windsor-Severance Library, 720 Third St, Windsor, CO, 80550-5109. Tel: 970-686-5603, Ext 302. Fax: 970-686-2502. p. 326

King, Ann, Asst Librn, Ladd Public Library District, 125 N Main St, Ladd, IL, 61329. Tel: 815-894-3254. Fax: 815-894-3254. p. 662

King, Ann, Br Mgr, Saint Charles City County Library District, Kathryn Linnemann Branch, 2323 Elm St, Saint Charles, MO, 63301. Tel: 636-723-0232, 636-946-6294. Fax: 636-947-0692. p. 1364

King, Anne, Pres, Learning Disabilites Association of Yukon, 107 Main St, Whitehorse, YT, Y1A 2A7, CANADA. Tel: 867-668-5167. Fax: 867-668-6504. p. 2934

King, April, Mgr, District of Columbia Public Library, Southeast, 403 Seventh St SE, Washington, DC, 20003. Tel: 202-698-3377. p. 398

King, Barbara, Dir, Oklahoma City Community College, 7777 S May Ave, Oklahoma City, OK, 73159. Tel: 405-682-7564. Fax: 405-682-7585. p. 1973

King, Barrett, Dep Dir, Admin & Finance, Jacksonville Public Library, 303 N Laura St, Jacksonville, FL, 32202-3505. Tel: 904-630-1171. Fax: 904-630-2450. p. 453

King, Betsy, Librn, CAE USA, Inc Library, 4908 Tampa West Blvd, Tampa, FL, 33634. Tel: 813-887-1658. Fax: 813-901-6417. p. 496

King, Bointa, Coordr, Libr Serv, Gaston College, Harvey A Jonas Library, 511 S Aspen St, Lincolnton, NC, 28092. Tel: 704-748-1050. Fax: 704-748-1068. p. 1786

King, Christine, Assoc Dean, Ref & Instruction, Iowa State University Library, 302 Parks Library, Ames, IA, 50011-2140. Tel: 515-294-1442, 515-294-1443. Fax: 515-294-5525. p. 793

King, Christine, Head, Circ, The Hampton Library, 2478 Main St, Bridgehampton, NY, 11932. Tel: 631-537-0015. Fax: 631-537-7229. p. 1585

King, Christine H, Dir, Willingboro Public Library, Willingboro Town Ctr, 220 Willingboro Pkwy, Willingboro, NJ, 08046. Tel: 609-877-0476, 609-877-6668. Fax: 609-877-7941. p. 1544

King, Christopher, Pub Serv, Appalachian School of Law Library, 1221 Edgewater Dr, Grundy, VA, 24614-7062. Tel: 276-935-6688, Ext 1314. Fax: 276-935-7138. p. 2467

King, Claire, Asst Law Librn, Ref, Kansas Supreme Court, Kansas Judicial Ctr, 301 SW Tenth St, Topeka, KS, 66612-1502. Tel: 785-296-3257. Fax: 785-296-1863. p. 896

King, Cornelia S, Chief of Ref, Library Company of Philadelphia, 1314 Locust St, Philadelphia, PA, 19107-5698. Tel: 215-546-3181. Fax: 215-546-5167. p. 2112

King, Dale, Asst Dean, Admin Serv, Syracuse University Library, 222 Waverly Ave, Syracuse, NY, 13244-2010. Tel: 315-443-2573. p. 1754

King, Danielle, Br Mgr, Orange County Library District, Alafaya, 12000 E Colonial Dr, Orlando, FL, 32826. p. 476

King, Darlene, Dir, Winfield Library, 24961 Scott Hwy, Winfield, TN, 37892. Tel: 423-569-9047. Fax: 423-569-2569. p. 2269

King, David, Librn, Mount San Jacinto College, 1499 N State St, San Jacinto, CA, 92583-2399. Tel: 951-487-6752, Ext 1582. Fax: 951-654-8387. p. 249

King, David, Ref Serv, Widener University, School of Law Library, 4601 Concord Pike, Wilmington, DE, 19803. Tel: 302-477-2063. Fax: 302-477-2240. p. 389

King, David Lee, Digital Br & Serv Mgr, Topeka & Shawnee County Public Library, 1515 SW Tenth Ave, Topeka, KS, 66604-1374. Tel: 785-580-4400. Fax: 785-580-4496. p. 897

King, Debbie, Br Coordr, Fairfax County Public Library, 12000 Government Center Pkwy, Ste 324, Fairfax, VA, 22035-0012. Tel: 703-324-3100. Fax: 703-324-8365. p. 2461

King, Diana, Film, Television & Theater Librn, University of California Los Angeles Library, The Arts Library, 1400 Public Policy Bldg, Los Angeles, CA, 90095. Tel: 310-206-4823. Fax: 310-825-1303. p. 178

King, Dianna, Dir, Swayzee Public Library, 301 S Washington, Swayzee, IN, 46986. Tel: 765-922-7526. Fax: 765-922-4538. p. 780

King, Dwight, Head, Res Serv, University of Notre Dame, 2345 Biolchini Hall of Law, Notre Dame, IN, 46556-4640. Tel: 574-631-7024. Fax: 574-631-6371. p. 771

King, Elsie R, Librn, Noxubee County Library System, Brooksville Branch, 100 W Main St, Brooksville, MS, 39739. Tel: 662-738-4559. p. 1307

King, Emma, Circ, Midland College, 3600 N Garfield, Midland, TX, 79705. Tel: 432-685-4560. Fax: 432-685-6710. p. 2363

King, Eric, Tech Serv, Mayland Community College, 200 Mayland Dr, Spruce Pine, NC, 28777. Tel: 828-765-7351, Ext 243. Fax: 828-765-0728. p. 1825

King, Faye, Cat, Tech Serv, Columbus County Public Library, 407 N Powell Blvd, Whiteville, NC, 28472. Tel: 910-642-3116. Fax: 910-642-3839. p. 1829

King, Florence, Asst Univ Librn, University of Georgia Libraries, Athens, GA, 30602-1641. Tel: 706-542-0629. Fax: 706-542-4144. p. 510

King, Gail, Librn, Brigham Young University, Harold B Lee Library, 2060 HBLL, Provo, UT, 84602. Tel: 801-422-2927. Fax: 801-422-0466. p. 2411

King, Gary, Dir, Harvard Library, Harvard-MIT Data Center, CGIS Knafel Bldg, 1737 Cambridge St, Cambridge, MA, 02138. Tel: 617-495-4734. Fax: 617-496-5149. p. 1075

King, Gennice W, Assoc Dir, Xavier University of Louisiana, One Drexel Dr, New Orleans, LA, 70125-1098. Tel: 504-520-7606. Fax: 504-520-7940. p. 964

King, Gerry, Lead Librn, Canadian Lesbian & Gay Archives, 34 Isabella St, Toronto, ON, M4Y 1N1, CANADA. Tel: 416-777-2755. p. 2851

King, Glonette, Br Mgr, Farmington Public Library, Shiprock Branch Library, 2101 Farmington Ave, Farmington, NM, 87401. Tel: 505-368-3804. Fax: 505-599-1257. p. 1555

King, Helen, Asst Librn, Ballston Spa Public Library, 21 Milton Ave, Ballston Spa, NY, 12020. Tel: 518-885-5022. p. 1577

King, Irene, Instrul Serv Librn, Vancouver Community College, 250 W Pender St, Vancouver, BC, V6B 1S9, CANADA. Tel: 604-871-7225. Fax: 604-443-8588. p. 2743

King, Jackie, Dir, East Albemarle Regional Library, 100 E Colonial Ave, Elizabeth City, NC, 27909-0303. Tel: 252-335-2511. Fax: 252-335-2386. p. 1790

King, Jackie, Dir, Pasquotank-Camden Library, 100 E Colonial Ave, Elizabeth City, NC, 27909. Tel: 252-335-2473, 252-335-7536. Fax: 252-331-7440. p. 1791

King, Jae Luree, Librn, Mother Whiteside Memorial Library, 525 W High St, Grants, NM, 87020-2526. Tel: 505-287-4793. Fax: 505-285-6024. p. 1556

King, Jamie E, Youth Serv, Palestine Public Library, 2000 S Loop 256, Ste 42, Palestine, TX, 75801. Tel: 903-729-4121. Fax: 903-729-4062. p. 2368

King, Jane, Librn, Our Lady Queen of Martyrs Church, 32340 Pierce St, Beverly Hills, MI, 48025. Tel: 248-644-8620. Fax: 248-644-8623. p. 1158

King, Janet, Br Mgr, Uncle Remus Regional Library System, W H Stanton Memorial Library, 1045 W Hightower Trail, Social Circle, GA, 30025. Tel: 770-464-2444. Fax: 770-464-1596. p. 542

King, Jean, Circ Supvr, West Hempstead Public Library, 500 Hempstead Ave, West Hempstead, NY, 11552. Tel: 516-481-6591. Fax: 516-481-2608. p. 1766

King, Jennifer Gunter, Archivist, Dir, Spec Coll, Mount Holyoke College Library, 50 College St, South Hadley, MA, 01075-1423. Tel: 413-538-2441. Fax: 413-538-2370. p. 1125

King, Joan S, Dir, Wyomissing Public Library, Nine Reading Blvd, Wyomissing, PA, 19610-2084. Tel: 610-374-2385. Fax: 610-374-8424. p. 2159

King, John P, Treas, Malden Historical Society, c/o Malden Public Library, 36 Salem St, Malden, MA, 02148-5291. Tel: 781-338-9365. Fax: 781-324-4467. p. 1102

King, Joseph, Librn, Outreach Serv Librn, Pub Serv, San Jose City College Library, 2100 Moorpark Ave, San Jose, CA, 95128-2799. Tel: 408-298-2181, Ext 3115. Fax: 408-293-4728. p. 250

King, Justin, Youth Serv Librn, Hernando County Public Library System, 238 Howell Ave, Brooksville, FL, 34601. Tel: 352-754-4043. Fax: 352-754-4044. p. 430

King, Karen, Dir, University of Virginia, Darden Graduate School of Business-Camp Library, Student Services Bldg, 100 Darden Blvd, Charlottesville, VA, 22903. Tel: 434-924-7321. Fax: 434-924-3533. p. 2455

King, Karlie, Librn, Lakeland Library Region, Edam Branch, 1000 Main St, Edam, SK, S0M 0V0, CANADA. Tel: 306-397-2223. Fax: 306-397-2626. p. 2920

King, Kathy, Librn, Chinook Regional Library, Stewart Valley Branch, Box 1, Stewart Valley, SK, S0N 2P0, CANADA. Tel: 334-588-2384. Fax: 334-588-2384. p. 2928

King, Kelly, Asst Dir, McGregor-McKinney Public Library, 101 E Fulton St, Hartford, AL, 36344. Tel: 334-588-2384. Fax: 334-588-2384. p. 20

King, Kevin, Head, Patron Serv, Kalamazoo Public Library, 315 S Rose St, Kalamazoo, MI, 49007-5264. Tel: 269-553-7881. Fax: 269-553-7969. p. 1197

King, Kresta L, Dir, Okeechobee County Public Library, 206 SW 16th St, Okeechobee, FL, 34974. Tel: 863-763-3536. Fax: 863-763-5368. p. 474

King, Laura, Br Coordr, Pemberville Public Library, Stony Ridge Branch, 5805 Fremont Pike, Stony Ridge, OH, 43463. Tel: 419-837-5948. Fax: 419-837-5948. p. 1928

King, Laurel, Cat, Owens Community College Library, 30335 Oregon Rd, Perrysburg, OH, 43551. Tel: 567-661-7030. Fax: 567-661-7021. p. 1929

King, Lu, Dir, Pawhuska Public Library, 1801 Lynn Ave, Pawhuska, OK, 74056. Tel: 918-287-3989. Fax: 918-287-3989. p. 1976

King, Lynne, Dir, Libr Serv, Schenectady County Community College, 78 Washington Ave, Schenectady, NY, 12305. Tel: 518-381-1235. Fax: 518-381-1252. p. 1740

King, Marge, Circ, Magee Public Library, 120 First St NW, Magee, MS, 39111. Tel: 601-849-3747. Fax: 601-849-6609. p. 1307

King, Marianne, Br Librn, Holyrood Public Library, Witless Bay Access Rd, Holyrood, NL, A0A 2R0, CANADA. Tel: 709-229-7852. Fax: 709-229-7852. p. 2770

King, Martina, Dir, Ute Mountain Tribal Library, Education Ctr, 450 Sunset, Towaoc, CO, 81334. Tel: 970-564-5348. Fax: 970-564-5342. p. 324

King, Mary, Librn, Moore Memorial Library, 59 Genesee St, Greene, NY, 13778-1298. Tel: 607-656-9349. Fax: 607-656-9349. p. 1631

King, Mary Jo, Ch, Elko-Lander-Eureka County Library System, 720 Court St, Elko, NV, 89801. Tel: 775-738-3066. Fax: 775-738-8262. p. 1426

King, Maxie, Dir, Imperial Public Library, 223 W Farm Rd 11, Imperial, TX, 79743. Tel: 432-536-2236. Fax: 432-536-2236. p. 2346

King, Melanie Starr, Dir, Shamrock Public Library, 712 N Main St, Shamrock, TX, 79079. Tel: 806-256-3921. Fax: 806-256-3921. p. 2386

King, Michelle, Br Mgr, Onslow County Public Library, Swansboro Branch, 1460 W Corbett Ave, Swansboro, NC, 28584. Tel: 910-326-4888. Fax: 910-326-6682. p. 1803

King, Mikey, Head, Spec Coll Cat, University of Arkansas Libraries, 365 N McIlroy Ave, Fayetteville, AR, 72701-4002. Tel: 479-575-4657. Fax: 479-575-6656. p. 99

King, Muriel, Head, Circ, Head, Ref, Archbold Community Library, 205 Stryker St, Archbold, OH, 43502-1142. Tel: 419-446-2783. Fax: 419-446-2142. p. 1854

King, Nathaniel, Info Literacy Librn, Guilford College, 5800 W Friendly Ave, Greensboro, NC, 27410-4175. Tel: 336-316-2450. Fax: 336-316-2950. p. 1796

King, Pambanisha, Doc Delivery, Auburn University, Ralph Brown Draughon Library, 231 Mell St, Auburn, AL, 36849. Tel: 334-844-4500. Fax: 334-844-4424. p. 5

King, Patricia, Circ Librn, Rockland Public Library, 80 Union St, Rockland, ME, 04841. Tel: 207-594-0310. Fax: 207-594-0333. p. 999

King, Patricia, Dir, Topinabee Public Library, 1576 Straits Hwy, Topinabee, MI, 49791. Tel: 231-238-7514. Fax: 231-238-2112. p. 1231

King, Paul, Re/Ser Librn, Peace College, 15 E Peace St, Raleigh, NC, 27604-1194. Tel: 919-508-2302. Fax: 919-508-2769. p. 1816

King, Paula, Dir, The Scripps Research Institute, 10550 N Torrey Pines Rd, La Jolla, CA, 92037. Tel: 858-784-8705. Fax: 858-784-2035. p. 161

King, Polly, Librn, Leighton Public Library, 8740 Main St, Leighton, AL, 35646. Tel: 256-446-5380. Fax: 256-446-5380. p. 23

King, Reabeka, Bibliog Instr, Electronic Res, Kingsborough Community College, 2001 Oriental Blvd, Brooklyn, NY, 11235. Tel: 718-368-5429. Fax: 718-368-5482. p. 1592

King, Richard, Ref, Vincennes University, Shake Learning Resources Center, 1002 N First St, Vincennes, IN, 47591. Tel: 812-888-5411. Fax: 812-888-5471. p. 784

King, Robin, Govt Doc Asst, Indiana University Southeast Library, 4201 Grant Line Rd, New Albany, IN, 47150. Tel: 812-941-2262. Fax: 812-941-2656. p. 767

King, Rosa, Mgr, Three Rivers Regional Library System, Ida Hilton Library, 1105 Northway, Darien, GA, 31305. Tel: 912-437-2124. Fax: 912-437-5113. p. 522

King, Rose, Br Mgr, Williams County Public Library, Pioneer Branch, 106 Baubice St, Pioneer, OH, 43554. Tel: 419-737-2833. Fax: 419-737-2833. p. 1862

King, Rosemary, Dir, Paola Free Library, 101 E Peoria, Paola, KS, 66071-1798. Tel: 913-259-3655. Fax: 913-259-3656. p. 889

King, Sandra, Br Mgr, Dallas Public Library, Arcadia Park, 1302 N Justin Ave, Dallas, TX, 75211-1142. Tel: 214-670-6446. Fax: 214-670-7502. p. 2306

King, Sandra, Br Mgr, Dallas Public Library, Mountain Creek, 6102 Mountain Creek Pkwy, Dallas, TX, 75249. Tel: 214-670-6704. Fax: 214-670-6780. p. 2307

King, Sandra, Ch, Brooks Memorial Library, 224 Main St, Brattleboro, VT, 05301. Tel: 802-254-5290. Fax: 802-257-2309. p. 2420

King, Sarah, Ref Serv, Jessamine County Public Library, 600 S Main St, Nicholasville, KY, 40356-1839. Tel: 859-885-3523. Fax: 859-885-5164. p. 931

King, Signe, Mrg, Admin Serv, University of Kansas Medical Center, 2100 W 39th Ave, Kansas City, KS, 66160-7180. Tel: 913-588-7302. Fax: 913-588-7360. p. 876

King, Sonia I, Pres, Hawaii Library Consortium, c/o Hawaii Business Research Library, 590 Lipoa Pkwy, No 136, Kihei, HI, 96753. Tel: 808-875-2408. p. 2941

King, Stephanie, Ch, Nelson County Public Library, 201 Cathedral Manor, Bardstown, KY, 40004-1515. Tel: 502-348-3714. Fax: 502-348-5578. p. 906

King, Sue, Adult Serv Mgr, Wayne Township Library, 80 N Sixth St, Richmond, IN, 47374-3079. Tel: 765-966-8291. Fax: 765-962-1318. p. 775

King, Sue, Supvr, Middlesex County Library, Melbourne Branch, 6570 Longwoods Rd, Melbourne, ON, N0L 1T0, CANADA. Tel: 519-289-2405. Fax: 519-289-0191. p. 2845

King, Susan, Ch, Fort Bend County Libraries, 1001 Golfview Dr, Richmond, TX, 77469-5199. Tel: 281-341-2634. Fax: 281-341-2688. p. 2374

King, Thomas, ILL, Fried, Frank, Harris, Shriver & Jacobson LLP, 1001 Pennsylvania Ave NW, Ste 800, Washington, DC, 20004. Tel: 202-639-7104. Fax: 202-639-7008. p. 401

King, Tina, Br Mgr, Evangeline Parish Library, Turkey Creek, 13951 Veterans Memorial Hwy, Ville Platte, LA, 70586. Tel: 337-461-2304. p. 971

King, Vanessa, Ref, Emory University School of Law, 1301 Clifton Rd, Atlanta, GA, 30322. Tel: 404-712-7093. Fax: 404-727-2202. p. 515

King-Sloan, Meg, Dir, Comstock Township Library, 6130 King Hwy, Comstock, MI, 49041. Tel: 269-345-0136. Fax: 269-345-0138. p. 1165

Kingcade, Rachel, Chief Ref Librn, Library of the Marine Corps, Gray Research Ctr, 2040 Broadway St, Quantico, VA, 22134-5107. Tel: 703-784-4409. Fax: 703-784-4306. p. 2486

Kingery, Laurie, Head, Circ, Crown Point Community Library, 214 S Court St, Crown Point, IN, 46307. Tel: 219-663-0270, 219-663-0271. Fax: 219-663-0403. p. 734

Kingma, David, Archivist, Jesuit Oregon Province Archives & Library, Gonzaga University, Special Coll, Foley Ctr, Spokane, WA, 99258-0001. Tel: 509-323-3814. Fax: 509-324-5904. p. 2536

Kingseed, Libby, Archivist, Prog Officer, Kettering Foundation Library, 200 Commons Rd, Dayton, OH, 45459. Tel: 937-439-9806. Fax: 937-439-9837. p. 1893

Kingsford, Genene, Librn, Joseph City Library, 201 N Main, Joseph, OR, 97846. Tel: 541-432-0141. Fax: 541-432-3832. p. 2001

Kingsland, Jane, Ref Librn, County College of Morris, 214 Center Grove Rd, Randolph, NJ, 07869-2086. p. 1525

Kingsley, Candace, Br Mgr, Henderson District Public Libraries, James I Gibson Library, 100 W Lake Mead Pkwy, Henderson, NV, 89015. Tel: 702-565-8402. Fax: 702-565-8832. p. 1428

Kingsley, Ilana, Web Librn, University of Alaska Fairbanks, 310 Tanana Dr, Fairbanks, AK, 99775. Tel: 907-474-7518. Fax: 907-474-6841. p. 48

Kingsley, Nancy, E-Res & Journals, Colby-Sawyer College, 541 Main St, New London, NH, 03257-4648. Tel: 603-526-3169. Fax: 603-526-3777. p. 1459

Kingstad, Dawn, ILL, Glendive Public Library, 200 S Kendrick, Glendive, MT, 59330. Tel: 406-377-3633. Fax: 406-377-4568. p. 1379

Kingston, Bob, Fac Librn-Sylvania Campus, Portland Community College Library, 12000 SW 49th AV, Portland, OR, 97219. Tel: 971-722-4962. Fax: 971-722-8397. p. 2013

Kinkus, Mary, Br Mgr, Toledo-Lucas County Public Library, Locke, 703 Miami St, Toledo, OH, 43605. Tel: 419-259-5310. Fax: 419-691-3237. p. 1940

Kinman, Virginia, Electronic Res Librn, Longwood University, Redford & Race St, Farmville, VA, 23909. Tel: 434-395-2441. Fax: 434-395-2453. p. 2463

Kinna, Lisa, Teen Serv, Jervis Public Library Association, Inc, 613 N Washington St, Rome, NY, 13440-4296. Tel: 315-336-4570. p. 1734

Kinnaman, Allen Jon, Librn, The James E Nichols Memorial Library, 35 Plymouth St, Center Harbor, NH, 03226-3341. Tel: 603-253-6950. Fax: 603-253-7219. p. 1440

Kinnaman, Tracey A, Ch, ILL, Hot Springs County Library, 344 Arapahoe, Thermopolis, WY, 82443-0951. Tel: 307-864-3104. Fax: 307-864-5416. p. 2661

Kinnamon, Michele, Librn, Estacada Public Library, 825 NW Wade St, Estacada, OR, 97023. Tel: 503-630-8273. Fax: 503-630-8282. p. 1996

Kinnear, Lynn, Dir, Smith Memorial Library, 21 Miller Ave, Chautauqua, NY, 14722. Tel: 716-357-6296. Fax: 716-357-3657. p. 1606

Kinnee, Brenda, Cat Tech, Alberta Government Library, 10025 Jasper Ave, 15th Flr, Edmonton, AB, T5J 2N3, CANADA. Tel: 780-415-0226. Fax: 780-422-9694. p. 2698

Kinneer, James, Librn, Indiana Regional Medical Center, 835 Hospital Rd, Indiana, PA, 15701. Tel: 724-357-7055. Fax: 724-357-7094. p. 2071

Kinner, Laura, Tech Serv Dir, University of Toledo, 2801 W Bancroft St, Mail Stop 509, Toledo, OH, 43606-3390. Tel: 419-530-8532. Fax: 419-530-2726. p. 1941

Kinnersley, Ruth, Assoc Prof, Trevecca Nazarene University, School of Education, 333 Murfreesboro Rd, Nashville, TN, 37210-2877. Tel: 615-248-1201, 615-248-1205. Fax: 615-248-1597. p. 2974

Kinnersley, Ruth T, Dir, Libr Serv, Trevecca Nazarene University, 73 Lester Ave, Nashville, TN, 37210-4227. Tel: 615-248-1491. Fax: 615-248-1452. p. 2259

Kinney, Daniel, Assoc Dir, Coll & Tech Serv, Stony Brook University, W-1502 Melville Library, John S Toll Rd, Stony Brook, NY, 11794-3300. Tel: 631-632-7100. Fax: 631-632-7116. p. 1749

Kinney, Erin, Digital Initiatives Librn, Wyoming State Library, 2800 Central Ave, Cheyenne, WY, 82002. Tel: 307-777-6333. Fax: 307-777-6289. p. 2653

Kinney, Juanita, Br Mgr, Muskingum County Library System, Roseville Branch, 41 N Main, Roseville, OH, 43777. Tel: 740-697-0237. p. 1954

Kinney, Margaret, Head, Circ, Huntingdon College, 1500 E Fairview Ave, Montgomery, AL, 36106. Tel: 334-833-4422. Fax: 334-263-4465. p. 29

Kinney, Megan, Sr Librn, Denver Public Library, Ford-Warren Branch, 2825 High St, Denver, CO, 80205-4545. Tel: 720-865-0920. Fax: 720-865-0925. p. 301

Kinney, Paula, Dir, Iowa Wesleyan College, 107 W Broad St, Mount Pleasant, IA, 52641. Tel: 319-385-6316. Fax: 319-385-6324. p. 833

Kinney, Richmond, Ref Librn, Oak Creek Public Library, 8620 S Howell Ave, Oak Creek, WI, 53154. Tel: 414-764-4400. Fax: 414-768-6583. p. 2626

Kinney, Robert, Ref Librn, Windsor Public Library, 323 Broad St, Windsor, CT, 06095. Tel: 860-285-1910. Fax: 860-285-1889. p. 379

Kinney, Sheri, Dir, Yavapai College Library, Verde Valley Campus, 601 Black Hills Dr, Clarkdale, AZ, 86324. Tel: 928-634-6541. Fax: 928-634-6543. p. 79

Kinney, Sherry, Librn, Christian Life College Library, 9023 West Lane, Stockton, CA, 95210. Tel: 209-476-7840. Fax: 209-476-7868. p. 272

Kinney-Murphy, Rebekah, In Charge, Mid-Columbia Libraries, Benton City Branch, 810 Horne Rd, Benton City, WA, 99320. Tel: 509-588-6471. Fax: 509-588-4153. p. 2518

Kinnick, Chery, Supvr, University of Washington Libraries, Natural Sciences, Allen Library S, Ground & First Flrs, Box 352900, Seattle, WA, 98195-2900. Tel: 206-685-2127. Fax: 206-685-1665. p. 2534

Kinnin, Wade, Pub Serv, Howard Payne University, 1000 Fisk Ave, Brownwood, TX, 76801. Tel: 325-649-8095. Fax: 325-649-8904. p. 2292

Kinnison, Gloria, Librn, Ovid Public Library, 400 Main St, Ovid, CO, 80744-9500. p. 319

Kinnison, Phyllis, Archivist, Ouachita Baptist University, 410 Ouachita, OBU Box 3742, Arkadelphia, AR, 71998-0001. Tel: 870-245-5332. Fax: 870-245-5245. p. 93

Kinoshita, Silke, Br Mgr, Long Beach Public Library, Alamitos, 1836 E Third St, Long Beach, CA, 90802. Tel: 562-570-1037. p. 167

Kinsella, Kristen, Head, Circ, Lake Forest College, 555 N Sheridan, Lake Forest, IL, 60045. Tel: 847-735-5056. Fax: 847-735-6297. p. 663

Kinseth, Ramona, Dir, Kinney Memorial Library, 214 Main St, Hanlontown, IA, 50444. Tel: 641-896-2888. Fax: 641-896-2890. p. 820

Kinsey, Darleen, Coll Develop, Uintah County Library, 204 E 100 N, Vernal, UT, 84078-2695. Tel: 435-789-0091, Ext 15. Fax: 435-789-6822. p. 2416

Kinsey, Jackie, Librn, San Luis Obispo County Library, Morro Bay Branch, 625 Harbor St, Morro Bay, CA, 93442. Tel: 805-772-6394. Fax: 805-772-6396. p. 254

Kinsey, Shelby, Dir, Blossburg Memorial Library, 307 Main St, Blossburg, PA, 16912. Tel: 570-638-2197. Fax: 570-638-2197. p. 2036

Kinsinger, Patti, Head, Ref (Info Serv), Wilmington College, Pyle Ctr 1227, 1870 Quaker Way, Wilmington, OH, 45177-2473. Tel: 937-382-6661, Ext 441. Fax: 937-383-8571. p. 1949

Kinslow, Barbara A, Librn, ITT Corp, 5009 Centennial Blvd, Colorado Springs, CO, 80919-2401. Tel: 719-599-1500. Fax: 719-599-1942. p. 295

Kinslow, Brenda, Ch, Colfax Public Library, 207 S Clark St, Colfax, IN, 46035. Tel: 765-324-2915, Ext 103. Fax: 765-324-2689. p. 732

Kinslow, Carmela, Head, Access Serv, University of Notre Dame, 2345 Biolchini Hall of Law, Notre Dame, IN, 46556-4640. Tel: 574-631-5990. Fax: 574-631-6371. p. 771

Kintop, Jeffrey, Archivist, Nevada State Library & Archives, Archives & Records, 100 N Stewart St, Carson City, NV, 89701-4285. Tel: 775-684-3313. Fax: 775-684-3311. p. 1426

Kintzle, Angie, Librn, Swea City Public Library, 208 Third St N, Swea City, IA, 50590. Tel: 515-272-4216. Fax: 515-272-4216. p. 847

Kinyatti, Njoki-Wa-, Chief Librn, York College Library, 94-20 Guy R Brewer Blvd, Jamaica, NY, 11451. Tel: 718-262-2034. Fax: 718-262-2027, 718-262-2997. p. 1646

Kinyon, Sue, Dir, Brownsville Public Library, 379 Main St, Brownsville, WI, 53006-0248. Tel: 920-583-4325. Fax: 920-583-4325. p. 2583

Kinzel, Lori, Asst Dir, Head, Circ, Bridgeview Public Library, 7840 W 79th St, Bridgeview, IL, 60455-1496. Tel: 708-458-2880, Ext 101. Fax: 708-458-3553. p. 597

Kinzie, Karen, Circ Supvr, Salem Public Library, 585 Liberty St SE, Salem, OR, 97301. Tel: 503-588-6090. Fax: 503-588-6055. p. 2018

Kinzie, Lenora, Dir, Stormont-Vail Healthcare, 1500 SW Tenth St, Topeka, KS, 66604-1353. Tel: 785-354-5800. Fax: 785-354-5059. p. 897

Kinzle, Jane, Asst Librn, Palacios Library, Inc, 326 Main St, Palacios, TX, 77465. Tel: 361-972-3234. Fax: 361-972-2142. p. 2368

Kinzler, Milt, Librn, Northland Community & Technical College Library, 2022 Central Ave NE, East Grand Forks, MN, 56721. Tel: 218-773-4526. Fax: 218-773-4502. p. 1249

Kinzy, Marjorie, Ch, Mount Clemens Public Library, 150 Cass Ave, Mount Clemens, MI, 48043. Tel: 586-469-6200. Fax: 586-469-6668. p. 1210

Kipfmiller, Sara, Dir, Merrill District Library, 321 W Saginaw, Merrill, MI, 48637. Tel: 989-643-7300. Fax: 989-643-7300. p. 1208

Kiphart, Joyce, Lead Libr Tech, Department of Veterans Affairs, 4815 N Assembly St, Spokane, WA, 99205-2697. Tel: 509-434-7575. Fax: 509-434-7103. p. 2535

Kipnes, Ian R, Acq & Budget Control Librn, California Western School of Law Library, 290 Cedar St, San Diego, CA, 92101. Tel: 619-515-1512. Fax: 619-685-2918. p. 231

Kipp, Janette, Asst Librn, Carson City Public Library, 102 W Main St, Carson City, MI, 48811-0699. Tel: 989-584-3680. Fax: 989-584-3680. p. 1161

Kipp, Merida, Dir, Tech & Info Serv, Yakama Nation Library, Yakama Nation Cultural Ctr, Hwy 97 at Fort Rd, Toppenish, WA, 98948. Tel: 509-865-2800, Ext 6, 509-865-5121, Ext 4721, 509-865-5121, Ext 4747. Fax: 509-865-6101. p. 2541

Kipp, Sara, Dir, Stillwater Free Library, 72 S Hudson Ave, Stillwater, NY, 12170. Tel: 518-664-6255. Fax: 518-664-6826. p. 1749

Kiraly, Mike, Dir, Operations, Sonoma State University Library, 1801 E Cotati Ave, Rohnert Park, CA, 94928-3609. Tel: 707-664-2397. Fax: 707-664-2090. p. 219

Kirby, Adrienne, Dir, Hamlin Public Library, 422 Clarkson Hamlin TL Rd, Hamlin, NY, 14464. Tel: 585-964-2320. Fax: 585-964-2374. p. 1633

Kirby, Alexander, Info Literacy & eLearning Librn, Pennsylvania Highlands Community College Library, 101 Community College Way, Johnstown, PA, 15904. Tel: 814-262-6484. Fax: 814-269-9744. p. 2073

Kirby, Chris, Librn, Adult Serv & Tech, Ilsley Public Library, 75 Main St, Middlebury, VT, 05753. Tel: 802-388-4095. Fax: 802-388-4367. p. 2428

Kirby, Colleen, Asst State Librn, Access Serv, South Dakota State Library, 800 Governors Dr, Pierre, SD, 57501-2294. Tel: 605-773-3131. p. 2216

Kirby, Colleen, Asst State Librn, Access Serv, South Dakota State Library, Braille & Talking Book Program, McKay Bldg, 800 Governors Dr, Pierre, SD, 57501-2294. Tel: 605-773-5051. p. 2216

Kirby, Deborah, Dir, Pulaski Technical College Library, 3000 W Scenic Dr, North Little Rock, AR, 72118-3347. Tel: 501-812-2272. Fax: 501-812-2315. p. 111

Kirby, Diana, Pub Serv, North Palm Beach Public Library, 303 Anchorage Dr, North Palm Beach, FL, 33408. Tel: 561-841-3383. Fax: 561-848-2874. p. 473

Kirby, Frederick J, Dir, Benton Harbor Public Library, 213 E Wall St, Benton Harbor, MI, 49022-4499. Tel: 269-926-6139. Fax: 269-926-1674. p. 1156

Kirby, Janet, Tech Serv Librn, Emory & Henry College, 30480 Armbrister Dr, Emory, VA, 24327. Tel: 276-944-6207. Fax: 276-944-4592. p. 2460

Kirby, Karla, Youth Serv - Prog, Rapides Parish Library, Westside Regional, 5416 Provine Pl, Alexandria, LA, 71303. Tel: 318-442-2483, Ext 1904. Fax: 318-442-7678. p. 940

Kirby, Martha, Libr Coordr, Drexel University Libraries, Queen Lane Library, 2900 Queen Lane, Philadelphia, PA, 19129. Tel: 215-991-8740. Fax: 215-843-0840. p. 2105

Kirby, Michael, Head Librn, Dakota County Technical College Library, 1300 E 145th St, Rosemount, MN, 55068. Tel: 651-423-8366. Fax: 651-423-8043. p. 1273

Kirby, Rosemary, Ch, Quinte West Public Library, Seven Creswell Dr, Trenton, ON, K8V 6X5, CANADA. Tel: 613-394-3381. Fax: 613-394-2079. p. 2868

Kirby, Tim, Br Mgr, Jefferson Parish Library, Grand Isle Branch, 2757 La Hwy 1, Grand Isle, LA, 70358-9727. Tel: 985-787-3450. Fax: 985-787-2715. p. 956

Kirch, Kathy, Dir, Cadillac-Wexford Public Library, 411 S Lake St, Cadillac, MI, 49601. Tel: 231-775-6541. Fax: 231-775-6778. p. 1160

Kirch, Nancy, Coordr, Circ, Chesapeake Public Library, 298 Cedar Rd, Chesapeake, VA, 23322-5512. Tel: 757-410-7155. Fax: 757-410-7112. p. 2456

Kirchartz, Melanie, Circ & Stacks Coordr, Point Park University Library, 414 Wood St, Pittsburgh, PA, 15222. Tel: 412-392-3165. Fax: 412-392-3168. p. 2127

Kirchfeld, Friedhelm, Librn, National College of Naturopathic Medicine Library, 049 SW Porter, Portland, OR, 97201. Tel: 503-552-1542. Fax: 503-219-9709. p. 2012

Kirchgasser, Susanne, Librn, Austrian Cultural Forum Library, 11 E 52nd St, New York, NY, 10022. Tel: 212-319-5300. Fax: 212-644-8660. p. 1669

Kirchgesler, Kristen J, Ref & Instrul Serv Librn, Case Western Reserve University, Lillian F & Milford J Harris Library, Mandel School of Applied Social Sciences, 11235 Bellflower Rd, Cleveland, OH, 44106-7164. Tel: 216-368-2302. Fax: 216-368-2106. p. 1876

Kirchhoff, Debra, Br Mgr, Trails Regional Library, Concordia Branch, 813 S Main, Concordia, MO, 64020. Tel: 660-463-2277. p. 1371

Kirchhoff, Erin, Ad, Johnson County Public Library, White River Library, 1664 Library Blvd, Greenwood, IN, 46142. Tel: 317-885-1330. Fax: 317-882-4117. p. 744

Kirchmeier, Michael, Mgr, Jackson County Historical Society Library, 307 N Hwy 86, Lakefield, MN, 56150. Tel: 507-662-5505. p. 1255

Kirchmeyer, Judy, Ser, Mount Union College Library, 1972 Clark Ave, Alliance, OH, 44601-3993. Tel: 330-823-3844. Fax: 330-823-3963. p. 1854

Kirchner, Allison, Archivist, Southwestern Baptist Theological Seminary Libraries, 2001 W Seminary Dr, Fort Worth, TX, 76115-2157. Tel: 817-923-1921, Ext 4000. Fax: 817-921-8765. p. 2323

Kirchner, Janet, ILL, Iowa Lakes Community Colleges Library, 300 S 18th St, Estherville, IA, 51334. Tel: 712-362-7936. Fax: 712-362-5970. p. 815

Kirchner, Kathleen, Circ Supvr, Milford Town Library, 80 Spruce St, Milford, MA, 01757. Tel: 508-473-0651, 508-473-2145. Fax: 508-473-8651. p. 1105

Kirchner, Steve D, Assoc Dir, Harford County Public Library, 1221-A Brass Mill Rd, Belcamp, MD, 21017-1209. Tel: 410-273-5600, Ext 2250. Fax: 410-273-5606. p. 1020

Kirchner, Terry, Exec Dir, Westchester Library System, 540 White Plains Rd, Ste 200, Tarrytown, NY, 10591-5110. Tel: 914-674-3600. Fax: 914-674-4185. p. 1755

Kirchof, Gwen, In Charge, Southwest Health Center, 1400 E Side Rd, Platteville, WI, 53818. Tel: 608-831-4444. Fax: 608-831-3334. p. 2630

Kirchoff, Lori, Tech Serv, Campbell County Public Library System, 2101 S 4-J Rd, Gillette, WY, 82718-5205. Tel: 307-687-0009. Fax: 307-686-4009. p. 2655

Kirchoffer, Joyce, Br Librn, Clearwater Public Library System, Beach, 69 Bay Esplanade, Clearwater, FL, 33767. Tel: 727-562-4970. p. 432

Kirdahy, Carolyn, Sr Curator, Mus Coll, Lyman Library, Museum of Science, One Science Park, Boston, MA, 02114-1099. Tel: 617-589-0170. Fax: 617-589-0494. p. 1063

Kiriakova, Maria, Coll Develop Librn, John Jay College of Criminal Justice, 899 Tenth Ave, New York, NY, 10019. Tel: 212-237-8260. Fax: 212-237-8221. p. 1684

Kirk, Andrea, Mgr, Rohm & Haas Co, 727 Norristown Rd, Spring House, PA, 19477-0439. Fax: 215-641-7811. p. 2142

Kirk, Artemis, Univ Librn, Georgetown University, 37th & N St NW, Washington, DC, 20057-1174. Tel: 202-687-7425. Fax: 202-687-7501. p. 402

Kirk, Christopher, Circ Coordr, University of Dallas, 1845 E Northgate Dr, Irving, TX, 75062-4736. Tel: 972-721-4128. Fax: 972-721-4010. p. 2347

Kirk, Cristi Anne, Librn, Woodruff, Spradlin & Smart Library, 555 Anton Blvd, Ste 1200, Costa Mesa, CA, 92626-7670. Tel: 714-558-7000. p. 137

Kirk, Darcy, Assoc Dean of Libr & Tech, University of Connecticut, 39 Elizabeth St, Hartford, CT, 06105-2287. Tel: 860-570-5200. Fax: 860-570-5104. p. 348

Kirk, Dolores, Librn, Mid-Mississippi Regional Library System, Duck Hill Public, 127 N State St, Duck Hill, MS, 38925-9287. Tel: 662-565-2391. Fax: 662-565-2391. p. 1306

Kirk, Elizabeth, Assoc Librn, Dartmouth College Library, 6025 Baker Berry Library, Rm 115, Hanover, NH, 03755-3525. Tel: 603-646-2236. Fax: 603-646-3702. p. 1450

Kirk, Elizabeth, Assoc Librn, Dartmouth College Library, Baker-Berry Library, 6025 Baker-Berry Library, Hanover, NH, 03755-3525. Tel: 603-646-2560. Fax: 603-646-2167. p. 1450

Kirk, Eve G, Exec Dir, Cherry Valley Public Library District, 755 E State St, Cherry Valley, IL, 61016-9699. Tel: 815-332-5161, Ext 27. Fax: 815-332-2441. p. 604

Kirk, Jay, Coll Develop Librn, Marquette University Libraries, 1355 W Wisconsin Ave, Milwaukee, WI, 53233. Tel: 414-288-5213. Fax: 414-288-7813. p. 2618

Kirk, Judy, Librn, Florida State University Libraries, Center for Demography & Population Health, 606 Bellamy Bldg, Tallahassee, FL, 32306-2240. Tel: 850-644-1762. Fax: 850-644-8818. p. 494

Kirk, Kathleen, Librn, Department of Veterans Affairs, PO Box 5000-142D, Hines, IL, 60141-5142. Tel: 708-202-2000. Fax: 708-202-2719. p. 656

Kirk, Maresa, Circ Mgr, Eugene Public Library, 100 W Tenth Ave, Eugene, OR, 97401. Tel: 541-682-5450. Fax: 541-682-5898. p. 1996

Kirk, Mary, Access Serv & Syst, Rose State College, 6420 SE 15th St, Midwest City, OK, 73110. Tel: 405-736-0268. Fax: 405-736-0260. p. 1968

Kirk, Mike, Dir, Mount Gilead Public Library, 41 E High St, Mount Gilead, OH, 43338-1429. Tel: 419-947-5866. Fax: 419-947-9252. p. 1918

Kirk, Rachel, Acq Librn, Middle Tennessee State University, MTSU, PO Box 13, Murfreesboro, TN, 37132. Tel: 615-904-8518. p. 2254

Kirk, Simone, Br Mgr, Southeast Arkansas Regional Library, Star City Branch, 200 E Wiley, Star City, AR, 71667. Tel: 870-628-4711. Fax: 870-628-4711. p. 110

Kirkbride, Kathy, Br Mgr, Muskingum County Library System, Duncan Falls-Philo Branch, PO Box 472, Duncan Falls, OH, 43734-0472. Tel: 740-674-7100. p. 1954

Kirkendall, Beverly, Ch, Hurst Public Library, 901 Precinct Line Rd, Hurst, TX, 76053. Tel: 817-788-7300. Fax: 817-590-9515. p. 2345

Kirker, Susan, Circ Mgr, Howard Community College Library, 10901 Little Patuxent Pkwy, Columbia, MD, 21044. Tel: 443-518-4812. Fax: 443-518-4993. p. 1025

Kirkham, Phebe, Head, Info Serv, Head, Reader Serv, New Canaan Library, 151 Main St, New Canaan, CT, 06840. Tel: 203-594-5000. Fax: 203-594-5026. p. 354

Kirkland, Jane, Ser Librn, Cleveland Museum of Art, 11150 East Blvd, Cleveland, OH, 44106-1797. Tel: 216-707-2530. Fax: 216-421-0921. p. 1877

Kirkland, Karen, Librn, Grant Public Library, 5379 Main St, Grant, AL, 35747. Tel: 256-728-5128. Fax: 256-728-5128. p. 19

Kirkland, Laura, Cat, Stetson University, 421 N Woodland Blvd, Unit 8418, DeLand, FL, 32723. Tel: 386-822-4027. p. 437

Kirkland, Sarah, Evening Circ Supvr, Olivet Nazarene University, One University Ave, Bourbonnais, IL, 60914-2271. Tel: 815-939-5354. Fax: 815-939-5170. p. 596

Kirkman, Emily, Ch, Paris Public Library, 326 S Main St, Paris, TX, 75460. Tel: 903-785-8531. Fax: 903-784-6325. p. 2368

Kirkpatrick, Ann, Circ Serv, Volunteer State Community College Library, 1480 Nashville Pike, Gallatin, TN, 37066-3188. Tel: 615-230-3400, Ext 3402. Fax: 615-230-3410. p. 2235

Kirkpatrick, Brett, Dir, University of Texas Medical Branch, 301 University Blvd, Galveston, TX, 77555-1035. Tel: 409-772-2371. Fax: 409-762-9782. p. 2326

Kirkpatrick, Geoffrey, Asst Dir, Interim Dir, Bethlehem Public Library, 451 Delaware Ave, Delmar, NY, 12054-3042. Tel: 518-439-9314. Fax: 518-478-0901. p. 1614

Kirkpatrick, Keri, Media Spec, De Anza College, 21250 Stevens Creek Blvd, Cupertino, CA, 95014-5793. Tel: 408-864-8581. Fax: 408-864-8603. p. 138

Kirkpatrick, Kristie, Dir, Whitman County Rural Library District, 102 S Main St, Colfax, WA, 99111-1863. Tel: 509-397-4366. Tel: 509-397-6156. p. 2512

Kirkpatrick, Sierra, Librn, Walnut Public Library, 511 W Robbins, Walnut, KS, 66780. Tel: 620-354-6794. Fax: 620-354-6795. p. 899

Kirkpatrick, Stephen, Dir, State University of New York, 223 Store Hill Rd, Old Westbury, NY, 11568. Tel: 516-876-3156. Fax: 516-876-3325. p. 1710

Kirkwood, Kae Hirschy, Archivist, Geneva College, 3200 College Ave, Beaver Falls, PA, 15010-3599. Tel: 724-847-6694. Fax: 724-847-6687. p. 2031

Kirkwood, Marilyn, Dir, Valley Public Library, 210 N Locust St, Valley, NE, 68064. Tel: 402-359-9924. Fax: 402-359-9924. p. 1422

Kirkwood, Patricia, Eng & Math Librn, University of Arkansas Libraries, 365 N McIlroy Ave, Fayetteville, AR, 72701-4002. Tel: 479-575-2480. Fax: 479-575-6656. p. 99

Kirkwood, Sonya, ILL, Online Serv, Ref, Sinclair Community College Library, 444 W Third St, Dayton, OH, 45402-1460. Tel: 937-512-3005. Fax: 937-512-4564. p. 1894

Kirlin, George Bernard, Librn, Van Ness Feldman Library, 1050 Thomas Jefferson St NW, Washington, DC, 20007. Tel: 202-298-1800. Fax: 202-338-2416. p. 422

Kiron, Arthur, Curator, University of Pennsylvania Libraries, 3420 Walnut St, Philadelphia, PA, 19104-6206. Tel: 215-238-1290, Ext 202. Fax: 215-898-0559. p. 2118

Kiron, Arthur, Dr, Curator, Center for Advanced Judaic Studies Library, 420 Walnut St, Philadelphia, PA, 19106-3703. Tel: 215-238-1290. Fax: 215-238-1540. p. 2103

Kirouac, Diana, Acq/Cat Tech, Public Safety Canada, 340 Laurier Ave W, 10A, Ottawa, ON, K1A 0P8, CANADA. Tel: 613-991-5677. Fax: 613-941-6171. p. 2832

Kirpatrick, Nancy, Dir, Marian College, 3200 Cold Spring Rd, Indianapolis, IN, 46222. Tel: 317-955-6224. Fax: 317-955-6418. p. 755

Kirsch, Breanne, Pub Serv Librn, University of South Carolina Upstate Library, 800 University Way, Spartanburg, SC, 29303. Tel: 864-503-5613. Fax: 864-503-5601. p. 2205

Kirsch, Carol, Head Librn, State Historical Society of Iowa-Des Moines Library, 600 E Locust, Des Moines, IA, 50319-0290. Tel: 515-281-6200. Fax: 515-282-0502. p. 810

Kirsch, Carol, Head Librn, State Historical Society of Iowa, 402 Iowa Ave, Iowa City, IA, 52240-1806. Tel: 319-335-3916. Fax: 319-335-3935. p. 823

Kirsch, Leslie, Br Mgr, Middle Georgia Regional Library System, Marshallville Public Library, Main St, Marshallville, GA, 31057. Tel: 478-967-2413. Fax: 478-967-2413. p. 541

Kirsch, Marita David, Sister, Archivist, Immaculata University, 1145 King Rd, Immaculata, PA, 19345-0705. Tel: 610-647-4400, Ext 3828. Fax: 610-640-5828. p. 2071

Kirschbaum, Bae Ruth, Asst Librn, Eckstein Memorial Library, 1034 E Dewey St, Cassville, WI, 53806. Tel: 608-725-5838. Fax: 608-725-5152. p. 2584

Kirschen, Norma, Admin Dir, Center for Jewish History, 15 W 16 St, New York, NY, 10011-6301. Tel: 212-744-6400. Fax: 212-988-1305. p. 1671

Kirsh, Julie, Mgr, Sun Media, 333 King St E, Toronto, ON, M5A 3X5, CANADA. Tel: 416-947-2257. Fax: 416-947-2043. p. 2858

Kirsten, Holly, Head, Youth Serv, Chesterfield Township Library, 50560 Patricia Ave, Chesterfield, MI, 48051-3804. Tel: 586-598-4900. Fax: 586-598-7900. p. 1163

Kirton, Robena, Chief Librn, Gravenhurst Public Library, 180 Sharpe St W, Gravenhurst, ON, P1P 1J1, CANADA. Tel: 705-687-3382. Fax: 705-687-7016. p. 2806

Kirven, Barbara, Dir, Human Res, District of Columbia Public Library, 901 G St NW, Washington, DC, 20001-4599. Tel: 202-727-1131. Fax: 202-727-1129. p. 398

Kirven, Christine, Tech Serv, Rodman Public Library, 215 E Broadway St, Alliance, OH, 44601-2694. Tel: 330-821-2665. Fax: 330-821-5053. p. 1854

Kirven, Melissa, Asst Librn, Lee County Public Library, 200 N Main St, Bishopville, SC, 29010. Tel: 803-484-5921. Fax: 803-484-4177. p. 2182

Kirwin, Darla, Ch, Grand Rapids Area Library, 140 NE Second St, Grand Rapids, MN, 55744-2601. Tel: 218-326-7640. Fax: 218-326-7644. p. 1253

Kisby, Cynthia, Head, Regional Campus Libr, University of Central Florida Libraries, 4000 Central Florida Blvd, Bldg 2, Orlando, FL, 32816-2666. Tel: 407-823-2890. Fax: 407-823-2529. p. 477

Kiscaden, Elizabeth, Librn, Mercy Medical Center-North Iowa, 1000 Fourth St SW, Mason City, IA, 50401. Tel: 641-422-7699. Fax: 641-422-7698. p. 831

Kiser, Patricia, Automation Librn, Library Connection, Inc, 599 Matianuck Ave, Windsor, CT, 06095-3567. Tel: 860-298-5322. Fax: 860-298-5328. p. 2939

Kiser, Rick, Br Mgr, Hall County Library System, Clermont Branch, 197 King St, Clermont, GA, 30527. Tel: 770-532-3311, Ext 181. Fax: 770-983-1469. p. 534

Kiser, Rick, Mgr, Hall County Library System, Murrayville Branch, 4796 Thompson Bridge Rd, Murrayville, GA, 30507. Tel: 770-532-3311, Ext 171. Fax: 770-503-9298. p. 534

Kiser, Teresa, Syst Librn, Public Library of Anniston-Calhoun County, 108 E Tenth St, Anniston, AL, 36201. Tel: 256-237-8501, 256-237-8503. Fax: 256-238-0474. p. 4

Kiser Tudor, Joann, Br Mgr, Clermont County Public Library, Milford-Miami Township Branch, 1099 State Rte 131, Milford, OH, 45150-2700. Tel: 513-248-0700. Fax: 513-248-4579. p. 1858

Kish, Anne, Librn, University of Montana Western, 710 S Atlantic St, Dillon, MT, 59725. Tel: 406-683-7494. Fax: 406-683-7493. p. 1378

Kish, Linda, Circ, Sallie Logan Public Library, 1808 Walnut St, Murphysboro, IL, 62966. Tel: 618-684-3271. Fax: 618-684-2392. p. 678

Kishel, Deane, Syst Coordr, Bemidji State University, 1500 Birchmont Dr NE, Box 4, Bemidji, MN, 56601-2600. Tel: 218-755-3342. Fax: 218-755-2051. p. 1241

Kishel, Hans, Ref Librn, University of Wisconsin-Eau Claire, 105 Garfield Ave, Eau Claire, WI, 54702-4004. Tel: 715-836-3715. Fax: 715-836-2949. p. 2590

Kiskaddon, Wendie, Outreach & Vols Coordr, Way Public Library, 101 E Indiana Ave, Perrysburg, OH, 43551. Tel: 419-874-3135, Ext 107. Fax: 419-874-6129. p. 1929

Kisko, Jocelyne, Libr Mgr, Rockyford Municipal Library, Community Centre, 412 Serviceberry Trail, Rockyford, AB, T0J 2R0, CANADA. Tel: 403-533-3964. p. 2715

Kisler, Elizabeth Ann, Dir, John Mosser Public Library District, 106 W Meek St, Abingdon, IL, 61410-1451. Tel: 309-462-3129. Fax: 309-462-3129. p. 587

Kisler, Kristy, Br Mgr, Chicago Public Library, Independence, 3548 W Irving Park Rd, Chicago, IL, 60618. Tel: 312-744-0900. Fax: 312-744-7420. p. 609

Kisling, Vernon, Chair, Marston Sci Libr, University of Florida Libraries, 535 Library W, Gainesville, FL, 32611-7000. Tel: 352-273-2851. Fax: 352-392-4787. p. 449

Kisner, Diane, Br Mgr, Enlow Ruth Library of Garrett County, Kitzmiller Branch, PO Box 100, Kitzmiller, MD, 21538-0100. Tel: 301-453-3368. Fax: 301-453-3368. p. 1036

Kissack, Kathy, Youth Serv Mgr, Mohave County Library District, 3269 N Burbank St, Kingman, AZ, 86402-7000. Tel: 928-692-5716. p. 66

Kissel, Kelly, Librn, Evansville State Hospital, Patient Library, 3400 Lincoln Ave, Evansville, IN, 47714. Tel: 812-469-6800, Ext 4215. Fax: 812-469-6824. p. 738

Kissel, Laura, Archivist, Ohio State University LIBRARIES, Archives, 2700 Kenny Rd, Columbus, OH, 43210. Tel: 614-688-8173. Fax: 614-688-4150. p. 1887

Kissick, Barbara, Ch, Confederation Centre Public Library, Queen & Richmond St, Charlottetown, PE, C1A 8G8, CANADA. Tel: 902-368-4642. Fax: 902-368-4652. p. 2875

Kissinger, John, Pub Serv Librn, College of Coastal Georgia, Camden Center Learning Resources Center, 8001 Lakes Blvd, Kingsland, GA, 31548. Tel: 912-510-3331. p. 521

Kissler, Brian, Mat, Norwin Public Library Association Inc, 100 Caruthers Ln, Irwin, PA, 15642. Tel: 724-863-4700. Fax: 724-863-6195. p. 2072

Kister, Mark, Circ, Pub Serv, Ref Serv, Shelby County Libraries, 230 E North St, Sidney, OH, 45365-2785. Tel: 937-492-8354. Fax: 937-492-9229. p. 1934

Kistler, Janice, Ref Librn/Genealogy, Morgan County Public Library, 110 S Jefferson St, Martinsville, IN, 46151. Tel: 765-342-3451. Fax: 765-342-9992. p. 763

Kistner, Laura, Libr Tech, US Department of Commerce, Radio Bldg, Rm 1202, 325 Broadway MC5, Boulder, CO, 80305-3328. Tel: 303-497-3271. Fax: 303-497-3890. p. 291

Kiszka, Jennifer, Mgr, Hinshaw & Culbertson Library, 222 N LaSalle, Ste 300, Chicago, IL, 60601-1081. Tel: 312-704-3000. Fax: 312-704-3951. p. 614

Kitch, Gary, Librn, Gadsen Correctional Institution Library, 6044 Greensboro Hwy, Quincy, FL, 32351. Tel: 850-875-9701, Ext 2261. Fax: 850-875-9710. p. 485

Kitchel, Ann C, Assoc Dir, Creighton University, Klutznick Law Library - McGrath, North, Mullin & Kratz Legal Research Center, School of Law, 2500 California Plaza, Omaha, NE, 68178-0340. Tel: 402-280-2251, 402-280-2875. Fax: 402-280-2244. p. 1412

Kitchell, Catherine A, Ref Librn, Bureau of National Affairs, Inc Library, 1801 S Bell St, Rm 3200, Arlington, VA, 22202. Tel: 703-341-3311. Fax: 703-341-1636. p. 2449

Kitchell, Marilyn, Librn, Louisiana House of Representatives, PO Box 94012, Baton Rouge, LA, 70804-9012. Tel: 225-342-2430. Fax: 225-342-2431. p. 943

Kitchen, Amy, Commun Relations Coordr, Johnson County Public Library, 401 State St, Franklin, IN, 46131-2545. Tel: 317-738-2957. Fax: 317-738-9635. p. 744

Kitchen, David, Automation Syst Coordr, ILL, Albert Einstein Healthcare Network, 5501 Old York Rd, Philadelphia, PA, 19141. Tel: 215-456-6345. Fax: 215-456-8267. p. 2106

Kitchen, Jeremy, Br Mgr, Chicago Public Library, Richard J Daley Library, 3400 S Halsted St, Chicago, IL, 60608. Tel: 312-747-8990. Fax: 312-747-0939. p. 608

Kitchen, Rod, Supvr, Chain of Lakes Correctional Facility Library, 3516 E 75th S, Albion, IN, 46701. Tel: 206-636-3114. p. 723

Kitchens, Amy, Librn, Barton Library, Norphlet Public, City Hall Bldg, 101 E Padgett St, Norphlet, AR, 71759. Tel: 870-546-2274. Fax: 870-546-2274. p. 98

Kitchens, Denise, Chief, United States Army, 3909 Halls Ferry Rd, Vicksburg, MS, 39180-6199. Tel: 601-634-4120. Fax: 601-634-2306. p. 1317

Kitchens, Karen, Intellectual Property Librn, Wyoming State Library, 2800 Central Ave, Cheyenne, WY, 82002. Tel: 307-777-7281. Fax: 307-777-6289. p. 2653

Kitchens, Linda, Librn, Douglas County Library System, Glendale Branch, Third & Willis, Glendale, OR, 97442. Tel: 541-832-2360. Fax: 541-832-2360. p. 2016

Kitchens, Rhonda, Ref & Instruction Librn, Manatee Community College Library, Venice Campus, 8000 S Tamiami Trail, Venice, FL, 34293. Tel: 941-408-1435. Fax: 941-408-1445. p. 429

Kitchin, Ann, Bibliog Serv Librn, Southwest Baptist University Libraries, 1600 University Ave, Bolivar, MO, 65613. Tel: 417-328-1626. Fax: 417-328-1652. p. 1320

Kite, Kate, Asst Dir, Cat, Ch, Wood River Public Library, 326 E Ferguson Ave, Wood River, IL, 62095-2098. Tel: 618-254-4832. Fax: 618-254-4836. p. 721

Kitlas, Marilyn, Ref & Ad Serv Librn, Canterbury Public Library, One Municipal Dr, Canterbury, CT, 06331-1453. Tel: 860-546-9022. Fax: 860-546-1142. p. 333

Kitt, Valerie, Circ Supvr, Gonzaga University, 502 E Boone Ave, Spokane, WA, 99258-0095. Tel: 509-313-6540. Fax: 509-323-5904. p. 2536

Kittay, Mindy, Financial Dir, Anythink Libraries, 5877 E 120th Ave, Thornton, CO, 80602. Tel: 303-288-2001. Fax: 303-451-0190. p. 323

Kittendorf, Dale R, Main Libr Coordr, Mkt Coordr, Saint Clair County Library System, 210 McMorran Blvd, Port Huron, MI, 48060-4098. Tel: 810-987-7323, Ext 128. Fax: 810-966-2961. p. 1219

Kitterman, Jayne, Ref & Instruction Librn, Blinn College Library, 800 Blinn Blvd, Brenham, TX, 77833. Tel: 979-830-4250. Fax: 979-830-4222. p. 2291

Kittle, Paul, Electronic Ref Librn, Mt San Antonio College Library, 1100 N Grand Ave, Walnut, CA, 91789. Tel: 909-274-4260. Fax: 909-468-4011. p. 282

Kittle, Phyllis, Asst Librn, Washington County Library, Washington County Law Library, Washington County Courthouse, 14949 62nd St N, Rm 1005, Stillwater, MN, 55082. Tel: 651-430-6330. Fax: 651-430-6331. p. 1290

Kittler, Christine A, ILL, Department of Veterans Affairs, 1201 NW 16th St, Miami, FL, 33125-1673. Tel: 305-575-3187. Fax: 305-575-3118. p. 465

Kitts, Royce, Educ Librn, Washburn University, 1700 SW College Ave, Topeka, KS, 66621. Tel: 785-670-1956. Fax: 785-670-3223. p. 897

Kitzmann, Diane M, Dir, Montezuma Public Library, 500 E Main St, Montezuma, IA, 50171. Tel: 641-623-3417. Fax: 641-623-3339. p. 833

Kitzmiller, Kathleen, Cat Librn, South College Library, 3904 Lonas Dr, Knoxville, TN, 37909. Tel: 865-251-1750, 865-251-1832. p. 2243

Kitzul, Valerie, Asst Librn, Southeast Regional Library, Whitewood Branch, 731 Lalonde St, Whitewood, SK, S0G 5C0, CANADA. Tel: 306-735-4233. Fax: 306-735-4233. p. 2931

Kivel, Andy, Interim Dir, Libr Serv, Diablo Valley College Library, 321 Golf Club Rd, Pleasant Hill, CA, 94523-1576. Tel: 925-685-1230, Ext 2237. Fax: 925-798-3588. p. 210

Kizlyk, Kim, Librn, Parkland Regional Library, Kelvington Branch, 201 Main St, Kelvington, SK, S0A 1W0, CANADA. Tel: 306-327-4322. p. 2932

Klaas, Tyler, Br Mgr, Riverside County Library System, San Jacinto Library, 500 Idyllwild Dr, San Jacinto, CA, 92583. Tel: 951-654-8635. Fax: 951-487-8069. p. 218

Klaessig, Janet, Instrul Serv Librn, Delaware Valley College of Science & Agriculture, 700 E Butler Ave, Doylestown, PA, 18901-2699. Tel: 215-489-4957. Fax: 215-230-2967. p. 2050

Klager, Kathy B, Dir, Pauline Haass Public Library, N64 W23820 Main St, Sussex, WI, 53089-3120. Tel: 262-246-5180. Fax: 262-246-5236. p. 2642

Klaich, Mitchell, Dir, Jenner & Block Library, 353 N Clark St, Ste 4300, Chicago, IL, 60654. Tel: 312-222-9350. Fax: 312-527-0484. p. 616

Klais, Madge Hildebrandt, Asst Prof, University of Wisconsin-Madison, 4217 H C White Hall, 600 N Park St, Madison, WI, 53706. Tel: 608-263-2943. Fax: 608-263-4849. p. 2976

Klajbor, Diane, Acq/Res Mgt Asst, Alverno College Library, 3401 S 39th St, Milwaukee, WI, 53215. Tel: 414-382-6056. Fax: 414-382-6354. p. 2617

Klang, Jennifer, Dep Project Mgr, United States Department of the Interior Library, 1849 C St NW, Rm 1151, Washington, DC, 20240. Tel: 202-208-3396. Fax: 202-208-6773. p. 419

Klapes, Jeffrey M, Head, Info Serv, Lucius Beebe Memorial Library, 345 Main St, Wakefield, MA, 01880-5093. Tel: 781-246-6334. Fax: 781-246-6385. p. 1132

Klapperich, Barb, Librn, Stacyville Public Library, 106 N Broad St, Stacyville, IA, 50476. Tel: 641-710-2531. Fax: 641-710-2531. p. 845

Klappersack, Dennis, Chairperson, Houston Community College - Southwest College, Alief Center, 2811 Hayes Rd, Houston, TX, 77082. Tel: 713-718-6941. Fax: 713-718-6932. p. 2338

Klappersack, Dennis, Chairperson, Houston Community College - Southwest College, Alief Continuing Education Center, 13803 Bissonnet, Houston, TX, 77083. Tel: 713-718-5447. p. 2338

Klappersack, Dennis, Chairperson, Houston Community College - Southwest College, Missouri City (Sienna) Campus, 5855 Sienna Springs Way, Missouri City, TX, 77459. Tel: 713-718-2942. Fax: 713-718-2474. p. 2338

Klappersack, Dennis, Chairperson, Houston Community College - Southwest College, Stafford Campus Library, 9910 Cash Rd, Stafford, TX, 77477-4405. Tel: 713-718-7823. Fax: 713-718-6723. p. 2338

Klappersack, Dennis, Chairperson, Houston Community College - Southwest College, West Loop Center Library, 5601 West Loop S, Houston, TX, 77081-2221. Tel: 713-718-7880. Fax: 713-718-7881. p. 2338

Klapperstuck, Karen, Virtual Br Mgr, Monroe Township Public Library, Four Municipal Plaza, Monroe Township, NJ, 08831-1900. Tel: 732-521-5000, Ext 105. Fax: 732-521-4766. p. 1503

Klasey, John M, Sr Mgr, Libr Admin, DLA Piper US LLP, 203 N LaSalle St, Ste 1900, Chicago, IL, 60601. Tel: 312-984-5222. Fax: 312-251-5845. p. 612

Klassen, Anneliese, Circ, Lethbridge College, 3000 College Dr S, Lethbridge, AB, T1K 1L6, CANADA. Tel: 403-320-3352. p. 2709

Klassen, Barbara, Lead Librn, Bureau of Land Management Library, Denver Federal Center, Bldg 50, Sixth & Kipling, Denver, CO, 80225. Tel: 303-236-6650. Fax: 303-236-4810. p. 298

Klassen, Sandy, Chairperson, Czar Municipal Library, PO Box 127, Czar, AB, T0B 0Z0, CANADA. Tel: 780-857-3740. Fax: 780-857-2223. p. 2696

Klassen, Tim, Head of Libr, Cameron Science & Technology Library, University of Alberta, Science & Technology Library (Cameron), Edmonton, AB, T6G 2J8, CANADA. Tel: 780-492-7918. p. 2699

Klassen, Tim, Actg Head Librn, University of Alberta, Science & Technology Library, Cameron Library, Edmonton, AB, T6G 2J8, CANADA. Tel: 780-492-7918. Fax: 780-492-2721. p. 2702

Klatt, Gabriella, Dir, American Correctional Association, 206 N Washington St, Alexandria, VA, 22314. Tel: 703-224-0194. Fax: 703-224-0179. p. 2445

Klaudinyi, Jen, Ref Serv, Lane Community College Library, 4000 E 30th Ave, Eugene, OR, 97405-0640. Tel: 541-463-5357. Fax: 541-463-4150. p. 1996

Klaue, Mary, Ref Serv, Public Library for Union County, 255 Reitz Blvd, Lewisburg, PA, 17837-9211. Tel: 570-523-1172. Fax: 570-524-7771. p. 2081

Klaus, John, Ref Librn, William J Campbell Library of the US Courts, 219 S Dearborn St, Rm 1637, Chicago, IL, 60604-1769. Tel: 312-435-5660. Fax: 312-408-5031. p. 607

Klawansky, Susan, Librn, Seattle Children's Hospital, 4800 Sand Point Way NE, W-6850, Seattle, WA, 98105. Tel: 206-987-2098. Fax: 206-987-3838. p. 2530

Klawitter, Michael, Archivist, Ref Serv, Grand Rapids Community College, 140 Ransom NE Ave, Grand Rapids, MI, 49503. Tel: 616-234-3473. Fax: 616-234-3878. p. 1185

Klawitter, Roswitha, Br Head Librn, Okanagan Regional Library, 1430 KLO Rd, Kelowna, BC, V1W 3P6, CANADA. Tel: 250-860-4033. Fax: 250-861-8696. p. 2730

Klayman, Joyce, Librn, Ashland, Inc, 5200 Blazer Pkwy, Dublin, OH, 43017. Tel: 614-790-3281. Fax: 614-790-4269. p. 1896

Kleback, Cynthia, Br Mgr, Enoch Pratt Free Library, Southeast Anchor, 3601 Eastern Ave, Baltimore, MD, 21224-4109. Tel: 410-396-1580. Fax: 443-984-3941. p. 1013

Kleban, Nancy, Br Mgr, Sonoma County Library, Rohnert Part-Cotati Regional, 6250 Lynne Conde Way, Rohnert, CA, 94928. Tel: 707-584-9121. Fax: 707-584-8561. p. 268

Klecka, Diane, Head, Circ, Addison Public Library, Four Friendship Plaza, Addison, IL, 60101. Tel: 630-458-3322. Fax: 630-543-6645. p. 587

Klecker, Anita N, Librn, Online Serv, Torrance Memorial Medical Center, 3330 W Lomita Blvd, Torrance, CA, 90505. Tel: 310-517-4720. p. 276

Klecker, Rob, Librn, Monona Public Library, 1000 Nichols Rd, Monona, WI, 53716-2531. Tel: 608-222-6127. Fax: 608-222-8590. p. 2623

Kleckner, Karen, Head, Reader Serv, Deerfield Public Library, 920 Waukegan Rd, Deerfield, IL, 60015. Tel: 847-945-3311. Fax: 847-945-3402. p. 634

Klee, Rosita, Cat, Dine College, PO Box 1000, Tsaile, AZ, 86556. Tel: 928-724-6758. p. 85

Kleemann, Karen M, Youth Spec, Westmont Public Library, 428 N Cass, Westmont, IL, 60559-1502. Tel: 630-969-5625. Fax: 630-969-6490. p. 717

Kleen, Linda, Librn, Brookhaven College, 3939 Valley View, Farmers Branch, TX, 75244-4997. Tel: 972-860-4854. Fax: 972-860-4675. p. 2319

Klehn, Victoria L, Dir, Libr Serv, Marion & Ed Hughes Public Library, 2712 Nederland Ave, Nederland, TX, 77627-7015. Tel: 409-722-1255. Fax: 409-721-5469. p. 2365

Kleiderman, Kate, Archivist, Colonel Robert R McCormick Research Center, One S 151 Winfield Rd, Wheaton, IL, 60189-6097. Tel: 630-260-8186. Fax: 630-260-9298. p. 718

Kleier, Margie, Operations & Bus Mgr, Lawrenceburg Public Library District, 150 Mary St, Lawrenceburg, IN, 47025-1995. Tel: 812-537-2775. Fax: 812-537-2810. p. 760

Kleier, Margie, Asst Librn, Carbondale City Library, 234 Main St, Carbondale, KS, 66414-9635. Tel: 785-836-7638. Fax: 785-836-7789. p. 859

Kleim, Richard, Coll Develop, Tech Serv, New Port Richey Public Library, 5939 Main St, New Port Richey, FL, 34652. Tel: 727-853-1279. Fax: 727-853-1280. p. 472

Kleiman, Rhonda, Econ Develop Mgr & Consult, Library System of Lancaster County, 1866 Colonial Village Lane, Ste 107, Lancaster, PA, 17601. Tel: 717-207-0500. Fax: 717-207-0504. p. 2077

Klein, Adaire J, Dir, Simon Wiesenthal Center & Museum of Tolerance, 1399 S Roxbury Dr, Los Angeles, CA, 90035-4709. Tel: 310-772-7605. Fax: 310-277-6568. p. 177

Klein, Alan, Head, Tech Serv, Juilliard School, 60 Lincoln Center Plaza, New York, NY, 10023-6588. Tel: 212-799-5000, Ext 265. Fax: 212-769-6421. p. 1684

Klein, Bonnie, Br Coordr, Blue Earth County Library System, Mapleton Branch, 104 First Ave, Mapleton, MN, 56065. Tel: 507-524-3513. Fax: 507-524-4536. p. 1257

Klein, Christine, Head, Youth Serv, Portage District Library, 300 Library Lane, Portage, MI, 49002. Tel: 269-329-4542, Ext 721. Fax: 269-324-9222. p. 1220

Klein, Deborah, Librn, Pomona Valley Hospital Medical Center, 1798 N Garey Ave, Pomona, CA, 91767. Tel: 909-865-9878. Fax: 909-865-9770. p. 211

Klein, Gaale, Asst Librn, Shedd-Porter Memorial Library, Main St, Alstead, NH, 03602. Tel: 603-835-6661. p. 1437

Klein, Gary, Bus Librn, Willamette University, 900 State St, Salem, OR, 97301. Tel: 503-370-6743. Fax: 503-370-6141. p. 2019

Klein, Jason, Curator, Westchester County Department of Parks, Recreation & Conservation, Ward Pound Ridge Reservation, Rte 121 S & 35, Cross River, NY, 10518. Tel: 914-864-7322. Fax: 914-864-7323. p. 1612

Klein, Joseph, Librn, Roanoke Public Libraries, Law Library, City of Roanoke Courthouse, 315 Church Ave SW, Ste B, Roanoke, VA, 24016. Tel: 540-853-2268. Fax: 540-853-5474. p. 2494

Klein, Karyl, Archivist, Cardinal Stafford Library, Archives of the Catholic Archdiocese of Denver, 1300 S Steele St, Denver, CO, 80210. Tel: 303-520-9986. p. 298

Klein, Laura, Mgr, Ch Serv, Massillon Public Library, 208 Lincoln Way E, Massillon, OH, 44646-8416. Tel: 330-832-9831, Ext 319. Fax: 330-830-2182. p. 1915

Klein, Leib, Librn, Touro College Libraries, 43 W 23rd St, Fifth Fl, New York, NY, 10010. Tel: 718-871-6187, Ext 17. Fax: 718-686-7071. p. 1701

Klein, Martha F, Sr Res Librn, McKenna, Long & Aldridge LLP, 1900 K St NW, Washington, DC, 20006. Tel: 202-496-7844. Fax: 202-496-7756. p. 408

Klein, Pam, Adult Serv, San Rafael Public Library, 1100 E St, San Rafael, CA, 94901-1900. Tel: 415-485-3323. Fax: 415-485-3112. p. 257

Klein, Penelope J, Exec Dir, Central New York Library Resources Council, 6493 Ridings Rd, Syracuse, NY, 13206-1195. Tel: 315-446-5446. Fax: 315-446-5590. p. 2950

Klein, Rachel, Dir, Wilson Memorial Library, 109 E Washington Ave, Keota, IA, 52248. Tel: 641-636-3850. Fax: 641-636-3850. p. 825

Klein, Robert, Fla/Genealogy Dept Mgr, Miami-Dade Public Library System, 101 W Flagler St, Miami, FL, 33130-1523. Tel: 305-375-5023. Fax: 305-375-3048. p. 466

Klein, Sandra, Acq/Coll Develop Librn, University of Notre Dame, 2345 Biolchini Hall of Law, Notre Dame, IN, 46556-4640. Tel: 574-631-8447. Fax: 574-631-6371. p. 771

Klein, Stephen, Syst, City University of New York, 365 Fifth Ave, New York, NY, 10016-4309. Tel: 212-817-7074. Fax: 212-817-2982. p. 1673

Klein, Steve, Librn, Libbie A Cass Memorial Library, 757 Main St, Springfield, NH, 03284. Tel: 603-763-4381. Fax: 603-763-4381. p. 1465

Klein-Fedyshin, Michele, Mgr, Libr Serv, University of Pittsburgh Medical Center Shadyside, 5230 Centre Ave, Pittsburgh, PA, 15232. Tel: 412-623-2441. Fax: 412-623-4155. p. 2129

Kleinberg, Janet, Youth Serv Dir, Mark Skinner Library, 48 West Rd, Manchester, VT, 05254. Tel: 802-362-2607. p. 2427

Kleiner, Donna, Acq Librn, NASA Ames Research Center, Technical Library, Bldg 202, Mail Stop 202-3, Moffett Field, CA, 94035-1000. Tel: 650-604-6325. Fax: 650-604-4988. p. 189

Kleiner, Ida, Res Coordr, Radgowski Correctional Institution Library, 982 Norwich-New London Tpk, Uncasville, CT, 06382. Tel: 860-848-5070. Fax: 860-848-5097. p. 373

Kleingartner, Jeff, Communications Mgr, Timberland Regional Library, 415 Tumwater Blvd SW, Tumwater, WA, 98501-5799. Tel: 360-943-5001, Ext 2507. Fax: 360-586-6838. p. 2543

Kleinle, Roy, Librn, Monroe County Law Library, Court House, Stroudsburg, PA, 18360. Tel: 570-420-3642. p. 2144

Kleinmann, Lisa, Children's & YA Librn, Durham Public Library, Seven Mill Rd, Unit H, Durham, NH, 03824-0954. Tel: 603-868-6699. Fax: 603-868-9944. p. 1445

Kleinschmidt, Loreen, Mgr, University of California, Davis, Toxicology Documentation Center, Environ Toxicology Dept, One Shield Ave, Davis, CA, 95616-8588. Tel: 530-752-2587. Fax: 530-752-3394. p. 140

Kleinschmidt, Mary, Librn, Petersburg Public Library, 220 S Sixth St, Petersburg, IL, 62675. Tel: 217-632-2807. Fax: 217-632-2833. p. 691

Kleinsorge, Judy, Ch, Pioneer Memorial Library, 375 W Fourth St, Colby, KS, 67701-2197. Tel: 785-460-4470. Fax: 785-460-4472. p. 861

Klemann, Gail, Librn, Marion Public Library, 120 N Main, Marion, WI, 54950. Tel: 715-754-5368. Fax: 715-754-4610. p. 2613

Klemarczyk, Laurice, Librn, Fuss & O'Neill Inc, 146 Hartford Rd, Manchester, CT, 06040-5992. Tel: 860-646-2469, Ext 5367. Fax: 860-533-5143. p. 349

Klement, Ruth, Br Mgr, Great Neck Library, Lakeville, 475 Great Neck Rd, Great Neck, NY, 11021. Tel: 516-466-8055, Ext 231. Fax: 516-466-7863. p. 1630

Klemm, David, Med Illustration/Digital Imaging & Graphics Mgr, Georgetown University, Dahlgren Memorial Library, Preclinical Science Bldg GM-7, 3900 Reservoir Rd NW, Washington, DC, 20007. Tel: 202-687-1148. Fax: 202-687-1862. p. 402

Klemm, Erin, Dir, Bigelow Free Public Library, 54 Walnut St, Clinton, MA, 01510. Tel: 978-365-4160. Fax: 978-365-4161. p. 1082

Klemm, JoTisa, Librn, Tarrant County College, 2100 Southeast Pkwy, Arlington, TX, 76018. Tel: 817-515-3388. Fax: 817-515-3183. p. 2277

Klemm, Marlene, Librn, Frances L Simek Memorial Library-Medford, 400 N Main, Medford, WI, 54451. Tel: 715-748-2505. Fax: 715-748-4160. p. 2614

Klemme, Rhonda, Cataloger, Mayville Public Library, 111 N Main St, Mayville, WI, 53050. Tel: 920-387-7910. Fax: 920-387-7917. p. 2613

Klemmer, Sara, Librn, Charlotte Observer Newsroom Library, 600 S Tryon, Charlotte, NC, 28202. Tel: 704-358-5212. Fax: 704-358-5203. p. 1782

Klemundt, Mary, Cat/Ref Librn, Elgin Community College, 1700 Spartan Dr, Elgin, IL, 60123. Tel: 847-214-7337. p. 641

Klenklen, Jonathan Andrew, Acq, Wesley Theological Seminary Library, 4500 Massachusetts Ave NW, Washington, DC, 20016-5690. Tel: 202-885-8692. Fax: 202-885-8691. p. 422

Klenov, Catherine, Circ Supvr, Longy School of Music, One Follen St, Cambridge, MA, 02138. Tel: 617-876-0956, Ext 540. Fax: 617-354-8841. p. 1077

Klenowski, Molly, Circ Librn, Norton Public Library, 68 E Main St, Norton, MA, 02766. Tel: 508-285-0265. Fax: 508-285-0266. p. 1114

Klepacz, Kristina, Archivist, Dayton Art Institute, 456 Belmonte Park N, Dayton, OH, 45405-4700. Tel: 937-223-5277, Ext 354. Fax: 937-223-3140. p. 1892

Klepich, Dave, Ref, Battelle Energy Alliance, LLC, 1776 Science Center Dr, MS 2300, Idaho Falls, ID, 83415-2300. Tel: 208-526-1185. Fax: 208-526-0211. p. 576

Klepich, David, Info Res Librn, Idaho National Laboratory, 1765 N Yellowstone Hwy, Idaho Falls, ID, 83415-2300. Tel: 208-526-1682. Fax: 208-526-1697. p. 576

Klepitsch, Heather, Libr Dir, OSF Saint Anthony Medical Center, 5666 E State St, Rockford, IL, 61108-2472. Tel: 815-227-2558. Fax: 815-227-2904. p. 697

Kleppe-Lembo, Karen, Dir, Caldwell Public Library, 268 Bloomfield Ave, Caldwell, NJ, 07006-5198. Tel: 973-403-4649. Fax: 973-403-8606. p. 1476

Klepper, Micheal, Communications & Publ Librn, University of Virginia, Arthur J Morris Law Library, 580 Massie Rd, Charlottesville, VA, 22903-1789. Tel: 434-924-3495. Fax: 434-982-2232. p. 2455

Klepser, Gerry, Librn, Second Congregational United Church of Christ Library, 525 Cheshire Dr NE, Grand Rapids, MI, 49505. Tel: 616-361-2629. Fax: 616-361-8181. p. 1186

Klesse, Pam, Dir, Fenton Free Library, 1062 Chenango St, Binghamton, NY, 13901-1736. Tel: 607-724-8649. p. 1582

Kleszcz, Emily, Head, Circ, Dearborn Heights City Libraries, Caroline Kennedy Library, 24590 George St, Dearborn Heights, MI, 48127. Tel: 313-791-3805. Fax: 313-791-3801. p. 1168

Kleszynski, Margaret, Coll Develop Librn, Colorado State University Pueblo Library, 2200 Bonforte Blvd, Pueblo, CO, 81001-4901. Tel: 719-549-2361. Fax: 719-549-2738. p. 320

Klett, Rex E, Dir, Mitchell Community College, 500 W Broad St, Statesville, NC, 28677. Tel: 704-878-3206. p. 1826

Klett, Yvonne Pauline, Actg Exec Dir, Cantril Public Library, 104 W Third, Cantril, IA, 52542. Tel: 319-397-2366. Fax: 319-397-2366. p. 798

Kleven, Judith, Dir, Elizabeth Taber Library, Eight Spring St, Marion, MA, 02738. Tel: 508-748-1252. Fax: 508-748-0939. p. 1102

Klieman, Janet, Librn, United States Army, Lane Medical Library - Evans Army Community Hospital, 1650 Cochrane Circle, Fort Carson, CO, 80913-4604. Tel: 719-526-7285. Fax: 719-526-7113. p. 307

Kliemann, Joyce, Dir, Genevieve Miller Hitchcock Public Library, 8005 Barry Ave, Hitchcock, TX, 77563-3238. Tel: 409-986-7814. Fax: 409-986-6353. p. 2333

Klien, Lori, Ref Serv, National Library of Medicine, Bldg 38, Rm 2E-17B, 8600 Rockville Pike, Bethesda, MD, 20894. Tel: 301-496-6308. Fax: 301-496-4450. p. 1022

Klima, John, Access Serv Librn, Palmer College of Chiropractic-Davenport Campus, 1000 Brady St, Davenport, IA, 52803-5287. Tel: 563-884-5465. Fax: 563-884-5897. p. 806

Klima, John, Asst Libr Dir, Waukesha Public Library, 321 Wisconsin Ave, Waukesha, WI, 53186-4786. Tel: 262-524-3688. Fax: 262-524-3677. p. 2645

Klimchak, Linda, Sr Librn, New York State Department of Correctional Services, State Campus, Bldg 2, Library Services, 1220 Washington Ave, Albany, NY, 12226-2050. Tel: 518-485-7109. Fax: 518-402-1742. p. 1569

Klimczak, Aimee, Asst Teaching Prof, University of Missouri-Columbia, 303 Townsend Hall, Columbia, MO, 65211. Tel: 573-882-4546. Fax: 573-884-2917. p. 2969

Kliment, Lisa, Dir, Access Serv, ILL, Silver Lake College, 2406 S Alverno Rd, Manitowoc, WI, 54220. Tel: 920-686-6174. Fax: 920-684-7082. p. 2612

Klimiades, Mario Nick, Dir, Heard Museum, 2301 N Central Ave, Phoenix, AZ, 85004-1323. Tel: 602-251-0228. Fax: 602-252-9757. p. 73

Klimitchek, Rose, Dir, Jones Public Library, 801 South Cleveland, Ste A, Dayton, TX, 77535. Tel: 936-258-7060. Fax: 936-258-7634. p. 2311

Klimmek, Kelly, Ref Serv, Plunkett & Cooney, 38585 Woodward Ave, Bloomfield Hills, MI, 48304. Tel: 248-901-4090. Fax: 248-901-4040. p. 1159

Klimowicz, Judith, Asst Dir, Cranford Free Public Library, 224 Walnut Ave, Cranford, NJ, 07016-2931. Tel: 908-709-7272. Fax: 908-709-1658. p. 1480

Klimschot, Patricia Lynn, Dir, Libr & Info Serv, James Sprunt Community College Library, Boyette Bldg, 133 James Sprunt Dr, Kenansville, NC, 28349-0398. Tel: 910-296-2474. Fax: 910-296-6038. p. 1804

Kline, Carl, Head, Circ, Bexley Public Library, 2411 E Main St, Bexley, OH, 43209. Tel: 614-231-9709. p. 1860

Kline, Eve, Adminr, Somerset County Federated Library System, 6022 Glades Pike, Ste 120, Somerset, PA, 15501-0043. Tel: 814-445-5907. Fax: 814-443-0650. p. 2141

Kline, Eve, Admin Dir, Somerset County Library, 6022 Glades Pike, Ste 120, Somerset, PA, 15501-4300. Tel: 814-445-2556. Fax: 814-443-0650. p. 2141

Kline, Kathy D, Dir, Extn Serv, North Trails Public Library, 1553 W Sunbury Rd, West Sunbury, PA, 16061-1211. Tel: 724-476-1006. Fax: 724-637-2700. p. 2154

Kline, Meredith Moyer, Coordr, ILL, Dir, Head, Ser Acq, Gordon-Conwell Theological Seminary, 130 Essex St, South Hamilton, MA, 01982-2317. Tel: 978-646-4074. Fax: 978-646-4567. p. 1125

Kline, Pauline, Librn, Winkler County Library, Wink Branch, 207 Roy Orbison Dr, Wink, TX, 79789. Tel: 432-527-3691. p. 2349

Kline, Sims D, Res Librn, Stetson University, 421 N Woodland Blvd, Unit 8418, DeLand, FL, 32723. Tel: 386-822-7176. p. 437

Kline, Vickie, Syst, York College of Pennsylvania, 441 Country Club Rd, York, PA, 17403-3651. Tel: 717-815-1459. Fax: 717-849-1608. p. 2160

Klinefelter, Anne, Dir, University of North Carolina at Chapel Hill, Kathrine R Everett Law Library, UNC Law Library, 160 Ridge Rd, CB No 3385, Chapel Hill, NC, 27599-3385. Tel: 919-962-1321. p. 1781

Klinefelter, Diane, Libr Dir, Andrew Carnegie Free Library & Music Hall, 300 Beechwood Ave, Carnegie, PA, 15106-2699. Tel: 412-276-3456, Ext 5. Fax: 412-276-9472. p. 2042

Klinepeter, Pamela, Acq/Ser Librn, Ashland Community & Technical College, 1400 College Dr, Ashland, KY, 41101. Tel: 606-326-2254. Fax: 606-326-2186. p. 905

Kling, Maria, Dir, Gordon City Library, 101 W Fifth St, Gordon, NE, 69343. Tel: 308-282-1198. Fax: 308-282-0417. p. 1400

Kling, Susan, Asst Librn, Bandon Public Library, 1204 11th St SW, Bandon, OR, 97411. Tel: 541-347-3221. Fax: 541-347-9363. p. 1991

Kling, Susan S, Dir, Marion Public Library, 1095 Sixth Ave, Marion, IA, 52302. Tel: 319-377-3412. Fax: 319-377-0113. p. 830

Klingbeil, Joshua, Dir, Info Tech, Wisconsin Valley Library Service, 300 N First St, Wausau, WI, 54403. Tel: 715-261-7250. Fax: 715-261-7259. p. 2647

Klingbeil, Joshua, IT Dir, Wisconsin Valley Library Service, 300 N First St, Wausau, WI, 54403. Tel: 715-261-7252. Fax: 715-261-7259. p. 2958

Klingelsmith, Joyce, Dir, Archbold Community Library, 205 Stryker St, Archbold, OH, 43502-1142. Tel: 419-446-2783. Fax: 419-446-2142. p. 1854

Klingensmith, Marilyn, Dir, Plum Borough Community Library, 445 Center-New Texas Rd, Plum Borough, PA, 15239. Tel: 412-798-7323. Fax: 412-798-9245. p. 2130

Klingenstein, Leslie, Dir, North Dakota Vision Services-School for the Blind, 500 Stanford Rd, Grand Forks, ND, 58203. Tel: 701-795-2709. Fax: 701-795-2727. p. 1842

Klinger, Lorraine, Librn, Wellington Management Co, LLP, Two Radnor Corporate Ctr, Ste 300, Radnor, PA, 19087-8613. Tel: 610-631-3500. Fax: 610-631-3505. p. 2132

Klinger, Suzanne, Head, Ref Serv, University of Washington Libraries, Tacoma Library, 1900 Commerce St, Box 358460, Tacoma, WA, 98402-3100. Tel: 253-692-4443. Fax: 253-692-4445. p. 2535

Klingle, Philip A, Principal Law Librn, Supreme Court Library, Richmond County Court House, 25 Hyatt St, Rm 515, Staten Island, NY, 10301-1968. Tel: 718-675-8711. Fax: 718-447-6104. p. 1748

Klingler, Tom, Asst Dean, Tech Serv, Kent State University Libraries, 1125 Risman Dr, Kent, OH, 44242. Tel: 330-672-1646. Fax: 330-672-4811. p. 1907

Klink, Carol, Asst Dir, Acq, Asst Dir, Cat, Asst Dir, Ser, Loyola University Chicago Libraries, Law School Library, 25 E Pearson St, 3rd Flr, Chicago, IL, 60611. Tel: 312-915-7131, 312-915-7200, 312-915-7202. Fax: 312-915-6797. p. 617

Klinkow Hartmann, Margaret G, Dir, Oak Brook Public Library, 600 Oak Brook Rd, Oak Brook, IL, 60523. Tel: 630-368-7706. Fax: 630-368-7707. p. 683

Klinkow Hartmann, Margaret G, Libr Dir, South Holland Public Library, 16250 Wausau Ave, South Holland, IL, 60473. Tel: 708-331-5262. Fax: 708-331-6557. p. 704

Klint, Lars, Acq Librn, Harvard Library, Tozzer Library, 21 Divinity Ave, Cambridge, MA, 02138. Tel: 617-495-1481, 617-495-2253. Fax: 617-496-2741. p. 1076

Klinzman, Holly, Br Mgr, Garfield County Public Library System, Parachute Branch, 244 Grand Valley Way, Parachute, CO, 81635-9608. Tel: 970-285-9870. Fax: 970-285-7477. p. 319

Klippel, Lynne, Dir, Depaul Health Center, 12303 DePaul Dr, Bridgeton, MO, 63044-2588. Tel: 314-344-6397. Fax: 314-344-6035. p. 1320

Klipsch, Pamela R, Dir, Jefferson County Library, 5678 State Rd PP, High Ridge, MO, 63049-2216. Tel: 636-677-8689. Fax: 636-677-1769. p. 1330

Kloc, Leah, Ch, Sayreville Public Library, 1050 Washington Rd, Parlin, NJ, 08859. Tel: 732-727-0212. Fax: 732-553-0775. p. 1517

Klocek, Carole A, Librn, Mount Pleasant Free Public Library, 120 S Church St, Mount Pleasant, PA, 15666-1879. Tel: 724-547-3850. Fax: 724-547-0324. p. 2093

Klockenkemper, Jean, Dir of Financial Affairs, Libr, Vanderbilt University, 419 21st Ave S, Nashville, TN, 37203-2427. Tel: 615-322-7100. Fax: 615-343-8279. p. 2260

Klocko, Kay, Ref Serv, Upper Dublin Public Library, 805 Loch Alsh Ave, Fort Washington, PA, 19034. Tel: 215-628-8744. p. 2058

Kloda, Lori, Instrul Serv Librn, McGill University Libraries, Life Sciences Library, McIntyre Medical Science Bldg, 3655 Promenade Sir William Osler, Montreal, QC, H3G 1Y6, CANADA. Tel: 514-398-4475, Ext 09528. Fax: 514-398-3890. p. 2898

Kloempken, Mark, Pub Serv, Washington University Libraries, Law Library, Washington Univ Sch Law, Anheuser-Busch Hall, One Brookings Dr, Campus Box 1171, Saint Louis, MO, 63130. Tel: 314-935-7124. Fax: 314-935-7125. p. 1363

Kloepper, Cindy, ILL, Atchison Public Library, 401 Kansas Ave, Atchison, KS, 66002-2495. Tel: 913-367-1902. Fax: 913-367-2717. p. 856

Kloepperk, Krista, ILL Coordr, Lisle Library District, 777 Front St, Lisle, IL, 60532-3599. Tel: 630-971-1675. Fax: 630-971-1701. p. 666

Kloetzer, Beth, Mgr, Claymont Public Library, 3303 Green St, Claymont, DE, 19703. Tel: 302-798-4164. Fax: 302-798-6329. p. 381

Kloetzer, Beth, Mgr, Elsmere Public Library, 30 Spruce Ave, Wilmington, DE, 19805. Tel: 302-892-2210. Fax: 302-892-2213. p. 387

Kloiber, Deborah, Head, Spec Coll, Univ Archivist, Saint Catherine University, 2004 Randolph Ave, Mail F-10, Saint Paul, MN, 55105-1794. Tel: 651-690-6599. Fax: 651-690-8636. p. 1281

Klone, Amanda, Circ, Lewis-Clark State College Library, 500 Eighth Ave, Lewiston, ID, 83501. Tel: 208-792-2830. Fax: 208-792-2831. p. 578

Klooster, Darcy, Tech Coordr, Holmes Public Library, 470 Plymouth St, Halifax, MA, 02338. Tel: 781-293-2271. Fax: 781-294-8518. p. 1093

Klopf, Donna, Mgr, Boulder Public Library, Meadows, 4800 Baseline Rd, Ste C112, Boulder, CO, 80303-2678. Tel: 303-441-4390. p. 290

Klopfer, Jerry, Dir, New Mexico Military Institute, Toles Learning Center, 101 W College Blvd, Roswell, NM, 88201-5173. Tel: 575-624-8381. Fax: 575-624-8390. p. 1561

Klopfer, Rosemarie, ILL, Per, Roswell Public Library, 301 N Pennsylvania Ave, Roswell, NM, 88201. Tel: 575-622-7101. Fax: 575-622-7107. p. 1561

Kloppenborg, David, Librn, Missouri Veterans' Home Library, 1600 S Hickory, Mount Vernon, MO, 65712-2045. Tel: 417-466-7103. Fax: 417-466-4040. p. 1347

Klopper, Susan, Bus Librn, Emory University Libraries, Robert W Woodruff Library, 540 Asbury Circle, Atlanta, GA, 30322-2870. Tel: 404-727-0177. Fax: 404-727-1641. p. 514

Klos, Candy, Circ, Todd Wehr Library, St Norbert College, 301 Third St, De Pere, WI, 54115. Tel: 920-403-3280. Fax: 920-403-4064. p. 2587

Klos, Joanna, Operations Mgr, Wood Dale Public Library District, 520 N Wood Dale Rd, Wood Dale, IL, 60191. Tel: 630-766-6762. Fax: 630-766-5715. p. 721

Klos, Sheila, Dir, Harvard Library, Dumbarton Oaks Research Library, 1703 32nd St NW, Washington, MA, 20007. Tel: 202-339-6400. Fax: 202-625-0279. p. 1074

Kloszewski, Mark, Ref Serv, Indiana Free Library, Inc, 845 Philadelphia St, Indiana, PA, 15701-3908. Tel: 724-465-8841. Fax: 724-465-9902. p. 2071

Klotz, Michael K, Admin Librn, United States Environmental Protection Agency Region 3, 1650 Arch St, 3PM52, Philadelphia, PA, 19103. Tel: 215-814-5382. Fax: 215-814-5253. p. 2118

Klotzbucher, Enza, ILL, Widener University, School of Law Library, 4601 Concord Pike, Wilmington, DE, 19803. Tel: 302-477-2292. Fax: 302-477-2240. p. 389

Klovning, Tove, Govt Doc, Washington University Libraries, Law Library, Washington Univ Sch Law, Anheuser-Busch Hall, One Brookings Dr, Campus Box 1171, Saint Louis, MO, 63130. Tel: 314-935-6443. Fax: 314-935-7125. p. 1363

Klubek, Peter, Ref Librn, Baton Rouge Community College, 201 Community College Dr, Baton Rouge, LA, 70806. Tel: 225-216-8505. Fax: 225-216-8712. p. 942

Kludt, Dawn, Librn, Viborg City Public Library, 110 Main St, Viborg, SD, 57070. Tel: 605-326-5481. p. 2221

Kluetz, Penny, Librn, United States Department of Agriculture, 5985 Hwy K, Rhinelander, WI, 54501. Tel: 715-362-7474. Fax: 715-362-1166. p. 2633

Kluever, Joanna, Dir, Julia Hull District Library, 100 Library Lane, Stillman Valley, IL, 61084. Tel: 815-645-8611. Fax: 815-645-1341. p. 708

Klump, Holly, Coordr, ILL, Rivier College, 420 S Main St, Nashua, NH, 03060-5086. Tel: 603-897-8255. Fax: 603-897-8889. p. 1459

Klute, Kris, Circ Mgr, Ref Mgr, Sweetwater County Library System, Rock Springs Library, 400 C St, Rock Springs, WY, 82901-6221. Tel: 307-352-6667, Ext 2220. Fax: 307-352-6657. p. 2655

Klyczek, James J, Digital Serv & Info Tech Coordr, Batavia Public Library District, Ten S Batavia Ave, Batavia, IL, 60510-2793. Tel: 630-879-1393. Fax: 630-879-9118. p. 593

Kmetz, Tom, Coordr of Res Serv, Morehead State University, 150 University Blvd, Morehead, KY, 40351. Tel: 606-783-5111. Fax: 606-783-5037. p. 929

Knaack, Diane, In Charge, Cherokee Mental Health Institute, 1251 W Cedar Loop, Cherokee, IA, 51012. Tel: 712-225-6919. Fax: 712-225-6974. p. 801

Knaack, Linda, Instrul Serv Librn, Rensselaer at Hartford, 275 Windsor St, Hartford, CT, 06120-2991. Tel: 860-548-2490. Fax: 860-548-7904. p. 347

Knab, Sheryl, Exec Dir, Western New York Library Resources Council, 4455 Genesee St, Buffalo, NY, 14225. Tel: 716-633-0705. Fax: 716-633-1736. p. 2951

Knack, Kathy, Dir, Madison Valley Public Library, 210 Main St, Ennis, MT, 59729. Tel: 406-682-7244. Fax: 406-682-7669. p. 1378

Knackstedt, Sandra, Libr Dir, Whitehouse Community Library, Inc, 107 Bascom Rd, Whitehouse, TX, 75791-3230. Tel: 903-839-2949. p. 2400

Knaff, Diane, Cat, Preble County District Library, 450 S Barron St, Eaton, OH, 45320-2402. Tel: 937-456-4250. Fax: 937-456-6092. p. 1897

Knaggs, Gail, Librn, Markham Stouffville Hospital Library, 381 Church St, Markham, ON, L3P 7P3, CANADA. Tel: 905-472-7061. Fax: 905-472-7590. p. 2820

Knape, Kenneth, Br Mgr, Cleveland Public Library, Eastman, 11602 Lorain Ave, Cleveland, OH, 44111. Tel: 216-623-6955. Fax: 216-623-6957. p. 1878

Knape, Sherie, Dir, Fayette Public Library, 855 S Jefferson, La Grange, TX, 78945. Tel: 979-968-3765. Fax: 979-968-5357. p. 2351

Knapik, Bonnie, Asst Ch, Woodbury Public Library, 269 Main St S, Woodbury, CT, 06798. Tel: 203-263-3502. Fax: 203-263-0571. p. 380

Knapik, Elizabeth, Head, Info Literacy Programs, Sacred Heart University, 5151 Park Ave, Fairfield, CT, 06825-1000. Tel: 203-365-4816. Fax: 203-374-9968. p. 339

Knapik, Robert, Circ, Case Memorial Library, 176 Tyler City Rd, Orange, CT, 06477-2498. Tel: 203-891-2170. Fax: 203-891-2190. p. 364

Knapik-Fields, Sheila, Cat, Victorian Village Health Center, 1087 Dennison Ave, Columbus, OH, 43201. Tel: 614-544-5819. Fax: 614-299-2475. p. 1891

Knapmiller, Carol, Ch, La Crosse County Library, Administration Ctr, 103 State St, Holmen, WI, 54636. Tel: 608-526-4641. Fax: 608-526-3299. p. 2598

Knapp, Alice, Dir, New Canaan Library, 151 Main St, New Canaan, CT, 06840. Tel: 203-594-5000. Fax: 203-594-5026. p. 354

Knapp, Carolyn, Adult Serv, Three Rivers Regional Library System, 208 Gloucester St, Brunswick, GA, 31520-7007. Tel: 912-267-1212. Fax: 912-267-1544. p. 522

Knapp, Cary, ILL, Pub Serv, College of Coastal Georgia, One College Way, Brunswick, GA, 31520-3644. Tel: 912-279-5700. p. 521

Knapp, David, Tech Serv Librn, Oberlin College Library, Mary M Vial Music Library, Oberlin Conservatory of Music, 77 W College St, Oberlin, OH, 44074-1588. Tel: 440-775-8280. Fax: 440-775-8203. p. 1925

Knapp, Ernie, AV, Southwestern Michigan College, 58900 Cherry Grove Rd, Dowagiac, MI, 49047. Tel: 269-782-1341. Fax: 269-782-9575. p. 1174

Knapp, Jean, Librn, Bala-Cynwyd Library, 131 Old Lancaster Rd, Bala Cynwyd, PA, 19004-3037. Tel: 610-664-1196. Fax: 610-664-5534. p. 2030

Knapp, Jeff, Asst Librn, Coordr, Instruction, Pennsylvania State University, Altoona College, 3000 Ivyside Park, Altoona, PA, 16601-3760. Tel: 814-949-5493. Fax: 814-949-5246, 814-949-5520. p. 2028

Knapp, Kelli, Extn Serv, Warren Library Association, 205 Market St, Warren, PA, 16365. Tel: 814-723-4650. Fax: 814-723-4521. p. 2151

Knapp, Krista, Ref Serv Librn, Salisbury University, 1101 Camden Ave, Salisbury, MD, 21801-6863. Tel: 410-543-6130. Fax: 410-543-6203. p. 1040

Knapp, Laura, Mgr, Knowledge Mgt Serv, Ontario Securities Commission Library, 20 W Queen St, 20th Flr, Toronto, ON, M5H 3S8, CANADA. Tel: 416-593-2303. Fax: 416-593-3661. p. 2857

Knapp, Lorraine, Librn, New York State Supreme Court Sixth District Law Library, Five W Main St, Norwich, NY, 13815-1899. Tel: 607-334-9463. p. 1708

Knapp, Maureen, Ref, Louisiana State University Health Sciences Center, 433 Bolivar St, Box B3-1, New Orleans, LA, 70112-2223. Tel: 504-568-6100. Fax: 504-568-7718. p. 961

Knapp, Molly, Ref & Educ Librn, Tulane University, Rudolph Matas Library of the Health Sciences, Tulane Health Sciences Campus, 1430 Tulane Ave, SL-86, New Orleans, LA, 70112-2699. Tel: 504-988-5155. Fax: 504-988-7417. p. 963

Knapp, Patricia, Asst Commun Librn, Hartford Public Library, Camp Field, 30 Campfield Ave, Hartford, CT, 06114. Tel: 860-695-7440. Fax: 860-722-6874. p. 346

Knapp, Peter, Archivist, Trinity College Library, 300 Summit St, Hartford, CT, 06106. Tel: 860-297-2269. Fax: 860-297-2251. p. 347

Knapp, Sally, Chairperson, First Unitarian Universalist Society of Albany, 405 Washington Ave, Albany, NY, 12206. Tel: 518-463-7135. Fax: 518-463-1429. p. 1569

Knapp, Sandra J, Librn, Canadian Copper & Brass Development Association Library, 49 The Donway West, Ste 415, North York, ON, M3C 3M9, CANADA. Tel: 416-391-5599. Fax: 416-391-3823. p. 2825

Knapp, Steven, Coordr, Kansas City Library Service Program, Kansas City Public Library, 14 W Tenth St, Kansas City, MO, 64105-1702. Tel: 816-701-3551. Fax: 816-701-3401. p. 2947

Knapp, Tracey, Br Mgr, Bruce County Public Library, Walkerton Branch, 253 Durham St, Walkerton, ON, N0G 2V0, CANADA. Tel: 519-881-3240. Fax: 519-881-3240. p. 2837

Knapp, Tracey, Supvr, Bruce County Public Library, Cargill Branch, Major St, Cargill, ON, N0G 1J0, CANADA. Tel: 519-366-9990. Fax: 519-366-9990. p. 2837

Knapp, Wendy, Assoc Dir, Statewide Serv, Indiana State Library, 315 W Ohio St, Indianapolis, IN, 46202. Tel: 317-232-3691. Fax: 317-232-0002. p. 752

Knappenberger, Ginny, Librn, The State Botanical Garden of Georgia Library, 2450 S Milledge Ave, Athens, GA, 30605. Tel: 706-542-3977. Fax: 706-542-3091. p. 509

Knapton, Rachel, Youth Serv, Dundee Library, 32 Water St, Dundee, NY, 14837. Tel: 607-243-5938. Fax: 607-243-7733. p. 1616

Knauer, Roberta, Ref Librn, Wyckoff Public Library, 200 Woodland Ave, Wyckoff, NJ, 07481. Tel: 201-891-4866. Fax: 201-891-3892. p. 1546

Knauss, Dianne, Librn, The Morning Call, 101 N Sixth St, Allentown, PA, 18101. Tel: 610-820-6500. Fax: 610-820-6693. p. 2027

Knauth, Michael G, Dir, Farmingdale State College of New York, 2350 Broadhollow Rd, Farmingdale, NY, 11735-1021. Tel: 631-420-2040. Fax: 631-420-2473. p. 1622

Knecht, Bob, Curator, Kansas State Historical Society, 6425 SW Sixth Ave, Topeka, KS, 66615-1099. Tel: 785-272-8681. Fax: 785-272-8682. p. 896

Knecht, Elaine, Dir, Info Res, Hiscock & Barclay LLP, 1100 M&T Ctr, Three Fountain Plaza, Buffalo, NY, 14203. Tel: 716-856-5400. Fax: 716-846-1222. p. 1598

Knecht, Margaret, Head Librn, Kansas State Historical Society, 6425 SW Sixth Ave, Topeka, KS, 66615-1099. Tel: 785-272-8681. Fax: 785-272-8682. p. 896

Knecht, Michael, Libr Dir, Henderson Community College, 2660 S Green St, Henderson, KY, 42420. Tel: 270-831-9760. Fax: 270-831-9765. p. 917

Knecht, Thomas Peter, Dir, Parkesburg Free Library, 105 West St, Parkesburg, PA, 19365-1499. Tel: 610-857-5165. Fax: 610-857-1193. p. 2101

Knechtmann, James Allen, Ref Librn, Naval History & Heritage, 805 Kidder-Breese St SE, Washington, DC, 20374-5060. Tel: 202-433-7837. Fax: 202-433-9553. p. 411

Knee, Michael, Bibliographer, Ref Librn, University at Albany, State University of New York, Science Library, 1400 Washington Ave, Albany, NY, 12222. Tel: 518-437-3948. Fax: 518-437-3952. p. 1571

Kneeland, Angela, Supvr, Rogers Corporation, One Technology Dr, Rogers, CT, 06263. Tel: 860-779-5726. Fax: 860-779-5760. p. 366

Kneeland, Eve Engle, Ch, Auburn Public Library, 749 E Thach Ave, Auburn, AL, 36830. Tel: 334-501-3190. p. 5

Knefel, Mary Anne, Univ Librn, University of Dubuque Library, 2000 University Ave, Dubuque, IA, 52001. Tel: 563-589-3100. Fax: 563-589-3722. p. 812

Kneipp, Donna, Adult Serv, Williams County Public Library, 107 E High St, Bryan, OH, 43506-1702. Tel: 419-636-6734. Fax: 419-636-3970. p. 1862

Kneisler, Kelly, Ch, Weyauwega Public Library, 301 S Mill St, Weyauwega, WI, 54983. Tel: 920-867-3742. Fax: 920-867-3741. p. 2648

Kneiss, Joan, Ch, Allentown Public Library, 1210 Hamilton St, Allentown, PA, 18102. Tel: 610-820-2400. Fax: 610-820-0640. p. 2026

Knepp, Amy R, Dir, Oscoda County Library, 430 W Eighth St, Mio, MI, 48647. Tel: 989-826-3613. Fax: 989-826-5461. p. 1209

Knepp, April, Tech Serv, United States Agency for International Development, 1300 Pennsylvania Ave NW, Rm M01-010, Washington, DC, 20523-1000. Tel: 202-712-0579. Fax: 202-216-3515. p. 417

Knepper, Pixie, Ch, Clay Center Carnegie Library, 706 Sixth St, Clay Center, KS, 67432-2997. Tel: 785-632-3889. p. 861

Knesel, Susan, YA Serv, Campbell County Public Library System, 2101 S 4-J Rd, Gillette, WY, 82718-5205. Tel: 307-687-9227. Fax: 307-686-4009. p. 2655

Kness, Idelle, Principal, Department of Human Services-Youth Corrections, 1417 W Rio Grande, Colorado Springs, CO, 80906-1297. Tel: 719-329-6931. Fax: 719-633-5302. p. 295

Knettel, Colleen, ILL, University of Wisconsin-Superior, PO Box 2000, Belknap & Catlin, Superior, WI, 54880-2000. Tel: 715-394-8343. Fax: 715-394-8462. p. 2641

Knibbs, Barbara, Syst Mgr, The Farmington Library, Six Monteith Dr, Farmington, CT, 06032. Tel: 860-673-6791. Fax: 860-675-7148. p. 340

Knicely, Brian, Exec Dir, Stonewall National Museum & Archives, 1717 N Andrew Ave, Fort Lauderdale, FL, 33311. Tel: 954-763-8565. Fax: 866-929-5694. p. 444

Knieriem, Lesley, Reader Serv, Rogers Public Library, 711 S Dixieland Rd, Rogers, AR, 72758. Tel: 479-621-1152, Ext 22. Fax: 479-621-1165. p. 113

Knies, Michael, Archives, Spec Coll, University of Scranton, Monroe & Linden, Scranton, PA, 18510-4634. Tel: 570-941-6341. Fax: 570-941-7817. p. 2138

Knievel, Jennifer, Assoc Prof, Dir, Arts & Humanities, University of Colorado Boulder, 1720 Pleasant St, 184 UCB, Boulder, CO, 80309-0184. Tel: 303-492-8887. Fax: 303-492-3340. p. 291

Knight, Ann, Dir, Wayland Free Public Library, Five Concord Rd, Wayland, MA, 01778. Tel: 508-358-2311. Fax: 508-358-5249. p. 1134

Knight, Ayana, Libr Asst, Shaw University, 118 E South St, Raleigh, NC, 27601. Tel: 919-582-4985. Fax: 919-831-1161. p. 1817

Knight, Barbara, Asst Dir, University of North Dakota, School of Medicine and Health Sciences, 501 N Columbia Rd, Stop 9002, Grand Forks, ND, 58202-9002. Tel: 701-777-4129. Fax: 701-777-4790. p. 1842

Knight, Carley, Ref Librn, Jacksonville State University Library, 700 Pelham Rd N, Jacksonville, AL, 36265. Tel: 256-782-5255. Fax: 256-782-5872. p. 22

Knight, Carolyne, Dir, Bledsoe County Public Library, 478 Cumberland Ave, Pikeville, TN, 37367. Tel: 423-447-2817. Fax: 423-447-3002. p. 2263

Knight, Catherine, Librn, First United Methodist Church Library, 211 N School St, Normal, IL, 61761. Tel: 309-452-2096. Fax: 309-452-1327. p. 681

Knight, Cheryl DuBois, Librn, Brandywine Community Library, 60 Tower Dr, Topton, PA, 19562-1301. Tel: 610-682-7115. Fax: 610-682-7385. p. 2146

Knight, Chris, Tech Coordr, Otsego County Library, 700 S Otsego Ave, Gaylord, MI, 49735-1723. Tel: 989-732-5841. Fax: 989-732-9401. p. 1182

Knight, Collette, Coordr, Circ, Defiance College, 201 College Pl, Defiance, OH, 43512-1667. Tel: 419-783-2482. Fax: 419-783-2594. p. 1895

Knight, Erin, Libr Mgr, National Institute of Environmental Health Sciences Library, 111 TW Alexander Dr, Bldg 101, Research Triangle Park, NC, 27709. Tel: 919-541-3426. Fax: 919-541-0669. p. 1819

Knight, Jane, Ch, Rockport Public Library, 17 School St, Rockport, MA, 01966. Tel: 978-546-6934. Fax: 978-546-1011. p. 1121

Knight, Jane, Br Mgr, Surrey Public Library, Guildford, 15105 105th Ave, Surrey, BC, V3R 7G8, CANADA. Tel: 604-598-7370. Fax: 604-598-7361. p. 2739

Knight, Jane, Br Mgr, Surrey Public Library, Port Kells, 18885 88th Ave, Surrey, BC, V4N 3G5, CANADA. Tel: 604-598-7440. Fax: 604-598-7441. p. 2739

Knight, Janice, Librn, Boston Public Library, Codman Square, 690 Washington St, Dorchester, MA, 02124-3598. Tel: 617-436-8214. Fax: 617-436-0941. p. 1057

Knight, Janice, Asst Librn, Charleston Library Society, 164 King St, Charleston, SC, 29401. Tel: 843-723-9912. Fax: 843-723-3500. p. 2183

Knight, Jo Ann, Librn, United States Army, Morris J Swett Technical Library, Snow Hall 16, Bldg 730, Fort Sill, OK, 73503-5100. Tel: 580-442-4525. Fax: 580-442-7300. p. 1964

Knight, Joan, Dir, Jaffrey Public Library, 38 Main St, Jaffrey, NH, 03452-1196. Tel: 603-532-7301. Fax: 603-532-7301. p. 1452

Knight, Joanne E, Sr Ref Librn, United States Army, Combined Arms Research Library, US Army Command & General Staff College, Eisenhower Hall, 250 Gibbon Ave, Fort Leavenworth, KS, 66027-2314. Tel: 913-758-3001. Fax: 913-758-3014. p. 867

Knight, Jolene M, Head, Multimedia, Nicholls State University, 906 E First St, Thibodaux, LA, 70310. Tel: 985-448-4646, 985-448-4660. Fax: 985-448-4925. p. 971

Knight, Judy, Librn, Akron General Medical Center, 400 Wabash Ave, Akron, OH, 44307. Tel: 330-344-6242. Fax: 330-344-1834. p. 1851

Knight, Kimberly, Br Mgr, Arlington County Department of Libraries, Shirlington, 4200 Campbell Ave, Arlington, VA, 22206. Tel: 703-228-6546. Fax: 703-379-6728. p. 2448

Knight, Linda, Ref Serv, Ottawa Library, 105 S Hickory St, Ottawa, KS, 66067-2306. Tel: 785-242-3080. Fax: 785-242-8789. p. 887

Knight, Lorelle, Res Tech, Oglala Lakota College, Three Mile Creek Rd, Kyle, SD, 57752. Tel: 605-455-6069. Fax: 605-455-6070. p. 2213

Knight, Lorrie, Ref Librn, University of the Pacific Library, 3601 Pacific Ave, Stockton, CA, 95211. Tel: 209-946-2434. Fax: 209-946-2805. p. 273

Knight, Lydia F, Dir, Dalton State College, 650 College Dr, Dalton, GA, 30720-3778. Tel: 706-272-4585. Fax: 706-272-4511. p. 528

Knight, Merrie, Librn, Mississippi Delta Community College, Drew Library, 153 N Mail St, Drew, MS, 38737. Tel: 662-745-6322. Fax: 662-745-0194. p. 1309

Knight, Merrie, Librn, Mississippi Delta Community College, Greenwood Library, 207 West Park Ave, Greenwood, MS, 38930. Tel: 662-453-7377. Fax: 662-453-2043. p. 1309

Knight, Patricia, Mgr, Tech Serv, Essex County Library, 360 Fairview Ave W, Ste 101, Essex, ON, N8M 1Y3, CANADA. Tel: 519-776-5241. Fax: 519-776-6851. p. 2804

Knight, R Cecilia, Cat Librn, Grinnell College Libraries, 1111 Sixth Ave, Grinnell, IA, 50112-1770. Tel: 641-269-3368. Fax: 641-269-4283. p. 819

Knight, Robert, Chief Exec Officer, Tucson Museum of Art, 140 N Main Ave, Tucson, AZ, 85701-8290. Tel: 520-624-2333, Ext 122. Fax: 520-624-7202. p. 88

Knight, Rose, Bus Mgr, Eastern Washington University, 816 F St, 100 LIB, Cheney, WA, 99004-2453. Tel: 509-359-2306. Fax: 509-359-6456. p. 2512

Knight, Sharon, Ser, University of Wisconsin-Whitewater Library, 800 W Main St, Whitewater, WI, 53190. Tel: 262-472-5515. Fax: 262-472-5727. p. 2649

Knight, Shirley, Pub Serv, Ramapo College of New Jersey, 505 Ramapo Valley Rd, Mahwah, NJ, 07430-1623. Tel: 201-684-7315. p. 1498

Knight, Simon, Mgr, Intertek Testing Services, 1500 Brigantine Dr, Coquitlam, BC, V3K 7C1, CANADA. Tel: 604-520-3321. Fax: 604-524-9186. p. 2727

Knight, Stacey, Assoc Dir, Syst & Metadata, Saint Michael's College, One Winooski Park, Box L, Colchester, VT, 05439-2525. Tel: 802-654-2400. Fax: 802-654-2630. p. 2422

Knight, Tanith, Br Mgr, Jefferson-Madison Regional Library, Nelson Memorial, 8521 Thomas Nelson Hwy, Lovingston, VA, 22949. Tel: 434-263-5904. Fax: 434-263-5988. p. 2454

Knight, Tim, Head, Tech Serv, York University Libraries, Osgoode Hall Law School Library, One Scholar's Walk, York University, Toronto, ON, M3J 1P3, CANADA. Tel: 416-650-8403. Fax: 416-736-5298. p. 2868

Knight, Twyla, Br Mgr, Region of Waterloo Library, Wellesley Branch, 1137 Henry St, Wellesley, ON, N0B 2T0, CANADA. Tel: 519-656-2001. p. 2793

Knight, Valerie, Distance Learning Librn, Wayne State College, 1111 Main St, Wayne, NE, 68787. Tel: 402-375-7443. Fax: 402-375-7538. p. 1423

Knight-Davis, Stacey, Ref Librn, Eastern Illinois University, 600 Lincoln Ave, Charleston, IL, 61920. Tel: 217-581-7548. p. 603

Knight-Davis, Stacey, Mgr, East Central Illinois Consortium, Eastern Illinois University, Booth Library, 600 LincolnAve, Charleston, IL, 61920. Tel: 217-581-7549. Fax: 217-581-7534. p. 2942

Knighten, Roberta, Dir, Upland Public Library, 450 N Euclid Ave, Upland, CA, 91786-4732. Tel: 909-931-4200. Fax: 909-931-4209. p. 278

Knights, Angie, Librn, Augusta Township Public Library, 4500 County Rd 15, RR 2, Brockville, ON, K6V 5T2, CANADA. Tel: 613-926-2449. Fax: 613-702-0441. p. 2797

Knights, Diane, Assoc Dir, Pub Serv, University of Saint Thomas, 2115 Summit Ave, Mail Box 5004, Saint Paul, MN, 55105. Tel: 651-962-5026. Fax: 651-962-5406. p. 1282

Knippel, Deb, Asst Librn, Saint Michael's Hospital, 900 Illinois Ave, Stevens Point, WI, 54481. Tel: 715-346-5091. Fax: 715-343-3246. p. 2640

Knisely, Jane, Libr Dir, Claysburg Area Public Library, 957 Bedford St, Claysburg, PA, 16625. Tel: 814-239-8647. Fax: 814-239-2782. p. 2045

Knisely, Susan, Online Serv Librn, Nebraska Library Commission, The Atrium, 1200 N St, Ste 120, Lincoln, NE, 68508-2023. Tel: 402-471-3849. Fax: 402-471-2083. p. 1406

Knispel, Todd, Dir, Dawson Community College Library, 300 College Dr, Glendive, MT, 59330. Tel: 406-377-9413. Fax: 406-377-8132. p. 1379

Knobel, Sara L, Dir, Groton Public Library, 112 E Cortland St, Groton, NY, 13073. Tel: 607-898-5055. Fax: 607-898-5055. p. 1632

Knoch, Daniel L, Dir, Hillsdale College, 33 E College St, Hillsdale, MI, 49242. Tel: 517-607-2401. Fax: 517-607-2248. p. 1190

Knoch, Jessica, Ref Librn, Grant MacEwan University Library, 10700 104th Ave, Edmonton, AB, T5J 4S2, CANADA. Tel: 780-497-5850. Fax: 780-497-5895. p. 2701

Knoche, Becky, Asst Dir/Ch, West Branch Public Library, 300 N Downey, West Branch, IA, 52358. Tel: 319-643-2633. Fax: 319-643-2845. p. 852

Knoche, Charlotte M, Dr, Dir, Concordia University, 1282 Concordia Ave, Saint Paul, MN, 55104. Tel: 651-641-8278. Fax: 651-641-8782. p. 1278

Knockel, Ruth, Head of Libr, Volusia County Public Library, Orange City Public, 148 Albertus Way, Orange City, FL, 32763. Tel: 386-775-5270. p. 436

Knode, Jennifer, Libr Mgr, New York Public Library - Astor, Lenox & Tilden Foundations, Grand Central Library, 135 E 46th St, New York, NY, 10017. Tel: 212-621-0670. p. 1691

Knode, Marilu, Dir, Laumeier Sculpture Park Library & Archive, 12580 Rott Rd, Saint Louis, MO, 63127. Tel: 314-615-5280. Fax: 314-615-5283. p. 1355

Knodel, Karyl, Ser, University of South Dakota, McKusick Law Library, 414 E Clark St, Vermillion, SD, 57069-2390. Tel: 605-677-5259. Fax: 605-677-5417. p. 2220

Knoer, Susan, Archivist/Librn, Ohio University Libraries, Mahn Center for Archives & Special Collections, Vernon R Alden Library, 30 Park Pl, Fifth Flr, Athens, OH, 45701-2978. Tel: 740-593-2711. Fax: 740-593-2708. p. 1856

Knoll, Darla, Mgr, Wellington Management Co, LLP, Two Radnor Corporate Ctr, Ste 300, Radnor, PA, 19087-8613. Tel: 610-631-3500. Fax: 610-631-3505. p. 2132

Knoll, Deb, Ch, Loudonville Public Library, 122 E Main St, Loudonville, OH, 44842-1267. Tel: 419-994-5531. Fax: 419-994-4321. p. 1911

Knoll, LaNell, Librn, Colony City Library, 339 Cherry St, Colony, KS, 66015. Tel: 620-852-3530. Fax: 620-852-3107. p. 862

Knoll, Marilyn, Librn, Greater Sudbury Public Library, Copper Cliff Centennial Branch, 11 Balsam St, Copper Cliff, ON, P0M 1N0, CANADA. Tel: 705-688-3954. Fax: 705-682-0484. p. 2846

Knoll, Norleen, Ch, Hays Public Library, 1205 Main, Hays, KS, 67601-3693. Tel: 785-625-5916. Fax: 785-625-8683. p. 871

Knoop, Michael, In Charge, Express News Corp, 301 Ave E, San Antonio, TX, 78205. Tel: 210-250-3279. Fax: 210-250-3157. p. 2379

Knop, Kay, Circ, Enterprise Public Library, 101 E Grubbs St, Enterprise, AL, 36330. Tel: 334-347-2636. Fax: 334-393-6477. p. 15

Knop, Paula, Librn, Saint John's Lutheran Church Library, 512 N Wilhelm, Ellinwood, KS, 67526. Tel: 620-564-2044. p. 865

Knopf, Keith S, Librn, Kegler, Brown, Hill & Ritter, 65 E State St, Ste 1800, Columbus, OH, 43215. Tel: 614-255-5502. Fax: 614-464-2634. p. 1886

Knopf, Marieta, Ref, Metropolitan Community College, Maple Woods Community College Library, 2601 NE Barry Rd, Kansas City, MO, 64156. Tel: 816-604-3080. Fax: 816-437-3082. p. 1339

Knoppert, Diane, Br Librn, London Public Library, Sherwood Forest, Sherwood Forest Mall, 1225 Wonderland Rd N, London, ON, N6G 2V9, CANADA. Tel: 519-473-9965. p. 2818

Knorr, Emily, Ch, Bloomfield Public Library, 90 Broad St, Bloomfield, NJ, 07003. Tel: 973-566-6200, Ext 212. Fax: 973-566-6217. p. 1473

Knorr, Susan, Dir, Newtown Public Library, 201 Bishop Hollow Rd, Newtown Square, PA, 19073-4176. Tel: 610-353-1022. Fax: 610-353-2611. p. 2098

Knoth, Kathleen, Libr Dir, University of New Mexico, Taos Campus, 115 Civic Plaza Dr, Taos, NM, 87571. Tel: 575-737-6243. Fax: 575-737-6292. p. 1551

Knott, Angelina, Librn, New York State Supreme Court Library, Greene County Courthouse, 80 Woodland Ave, Catskill, NY, .12414. Tel: 518-943-3130. Fax: 518-943-7763. p. 1603

Knott, Christopher A, Dir, University of Maine School of Law, 246 Deering Ave, Portland, ME, 04102. Tel: 207-780-4828. Fax: 207-780-4913. p. 997

Knott, Diane, Dir, Coggon Public Library, 216 E Main St, Coggon, IA, 52218-0182. Tel: 319-435-2542. Fax: 319-435-2542. p. 803

Knott, Karen, Br Head, Toronto Public Library, Pleasant View, 575 Van Horne Ave, Toronto, ON, M2J 4S8, CANADA. Tel: 416-395-5940. Fax: 416-395-5419. p. 2863

Knott, Margie, Dir, Federal Trade Commission Library, 600 Pennsylvania Ave NW, Rm 630, Washington, DC, 20580. Tel: 202-326-2395. Fax: 202-326-2732. p. 400

Knott-Rogers, Hannah, Pub Serv, Mercer University Atlanta, 3001 Mercer University Dr, Atlanta, GA, 30341. Tel: 678-547-6272. Fax: 678-547-6270. p. 517

Knouse, Nola R, Dr, Dir, Moravian Music Foundation, 457 S Church St, Winston-Salem, NC, 27101. Tel: 336-725-0651. Fax: 336-725-4514. p. 1833

Knouse, Tracey, Mgr, San Antonio Public Library, Oakwell, 4134 Harry Wurzbach, San Antonio, TX, 78209. Tel: 210-828-2569. Fax: 210-821-6923. p. 2382

Knowland, Stephanie, Cat, Acton Memorial Library, 486 Main St, Acton, MA, 01720. Tel: 978-264-9641. Fax: 978-635-0073. p. 1047

Knowler, Tony, Chairperson, Lloydminster Public Library, 5010 49th St, Lloydminster, AB, T9V 0K2, CANADA. Tel: 780-875-0850. Fax: 780-875-6523. p. 2710

Knowles, Anne, Dir, Rampart Public Library District, 218 E Midland, Woodland Park, CO, 80863. Tel: 719-687-9281. Fax: 719-687-6631. p. 326

Knowles, Faye, Libr Dir, Flomaton Public Library, 436 Houston St, Flomaton, AL, 36441. Tel: 251-296-3552. Fax: 251-296-3355. p. 17

Knowles, Jane, Archivist, Harvard Library, Arthur & Elizabeth Schlesinger Library on the History of Women in America, Three James St, Cambridge, MA, 02138-3766. Tel: 617-495-8662. Fax: 617-496-8340. p. 1076

Knowles, Judi, Ch, Moultonborough Public Library, Four Holland St, Moultonborough, NH, 03254. Tel: 603-476-8895. p. 1458

Knowles, Marjorie, ILL Librn, Plaistow Public Library, 85 Main St, Plaistow, NH, 03865. Tel: 603-382-6011. Fax: 603-382-0202. p. 1462

Knowles, Sandy, Dir, South Carolina State Library, 1430 Senate St, Columbia, SC, 29201-3710. Tel: 803-734-4611. Fax: 803-734-4610. p. 2189

Knowlton, Carolyn, Libr Mgr, Haut-Saint-Jean Regional Library, Plaster Rock Public-School Library, 290-A Main St, Plaster Rock, NB, E7G 2C6, CANADA. Tel: 506-356-6018. Fax: 506-356-6019. p. 2762

Knowlton, Daniel, Bus & Finance Mgr, San Diego County Library, 5560 Overland Ave, Ste 110, San Diego, CA, 92123. Tel: 858-694-2471. Fax: 858-495-5981. p. 233

Knowlton, Ellen, Head, Ref & Adult Serv, Merrimack Public Library, 470 Daniel Webster Hwy, Merrimack, NH, 03054-3694. Tel: 603-424-5021. Fax: 603-424-7312. p. 1457

Knowlton, James, Dir, Mark Skinner Library, 48 West Rd, Manchester, VT, 05254. Tel: 802-362-2607. p. 2427

Knowlton, Lauren, Head Librn, Georgia Piedmont Technical College, Bldg B, Rm 109, 16200 Alcovy Rd, Covington, GA, 30014. Tel: 770-786-9522, Ext 3212, 770-786-9522, Ext 3233. p. 527

Knowlton, Sean, Librn, Columbia University, Area Studies, 307 International Affairs Bldg, 420 W 118th St, New York, NY, 10027. Tel: 212-854-3630. Fax: 212-854-3834. p. 1674

Knowlton, Steven, Coll Develop Librn, University Libraries, University of Memphis, 126 Ned R McWherter Library, Memphis, TN, 38152-3250. Tel: 901-678-8234. p. 2252

Knownton, Sean, Librn, Columbia University, Latin American & Iberian Studies, 307 International Affairs Bldg, 420 W 118th St, New York, NY, 10027. Tel: 212-854-3630. Fax: 212-854-3834. p. 1675

Knox, Brenda Christine, Dir, Donnellson Public Library, 500 Park St, Donnellson, IA, 52625. Tel: 319-835-5545. Fax: 319-835-5545. p. 811

Knox, Claire, In Charge, Florida State University Libraries, Radzinowicz Criminology Reading Room, 201 Hecht House, Tallahassee, FL, 32306-1127. Tel: 850-644-9845. Fax: 850-644-9614. p. 495

Knox, Emily, Asst Prof, University of Illinois at Urbana-Champaign, Library & Information Science Bldg, 501 E Daniel St, Champaign, IL, 61820-6211. Tel: 217-333-3280. Fax: 217-244-3302. p. 2965

Knox, Karen, Dir, Orion Township Public Library, 825 Joslyn Rd, Lake Orion, MI, 48362. Tel: 248-693-3000, Ext 305. Fax: 248-693-3009. p. 1199

Knox, Kathy, Assoc Dir, Pueblo City-County Library District, 100 E Abriendo Ave, Pueblo, CO, 81004-4290. Tel: 719-562-5627. Fax: 719-562-5619. p. 320

Knox, Keith, Mgr, User Serv, Kentucky Department for Libraries & Archives, 300 Coffee Tree Rd, Frankfort, KY, 40601. Tel: 502-564-8300. Fax: 502-564-5773. p. 913

Knox, Margaret, Acq, Coll Develop, Ref Serv, Mountain View College, 4849 W Illinois, Dallas, TX, 75211-6599. Tel: 214-860-8669. Fax: 214-860-8667. p. 2309

Knox, Sheryl Cormicle, Tech Dir, Capital Area District Libraries, 401 S Capitol Ave, Lansing, MI, 48933. Tel: 517-367-6347. Fax: 517-374-1068. p. 1200

Knuckle, Jacquelyn, Access Serv, Dept Chair, Community College of Philadelphia Library, 1700 Spring Garden St, Philadelphia, PA, 19130. Tel: 215-751-8000. Fax: 215-751-8762. p. 2104

Knuckle, Jacquelyn B, Librn, Chestnut Hill Hospital, 8835 Germantown Ave, Philadelphia, PA, 19118. Tel: 215-248-8206. Fax: 215-248-8240. p. 2104

Knudsen, Helen, Librn, Wind River Tribal College Library, 533 Ethete Rd, Ethete, WY, 82520. Tel: 307-335-8243. Fax: 307-335-8148. p. 2654

Knudsen, Johanna, Supvr, Access Serv, Seattle Pacific University Library, 3307 Third Ave W, Seattle, WA, 98119. Tel: 206-281-2789. Fax: 206-281-2936. p. 2530

Knudsen, Kay Horton, Res Librn, Colorado Division of Wildlife, 317 W Prospect Rd, Fort Collins, CO, 80526-2097. Tel: 970-472-4353. Fax: 970-472-4457. p. 307

Knudson, Norma, Dir, Info Res, Faegre & Benson, LLP, 2200 Wells Fargo Ctr, 90 South Seventh St, Minneapolis, MN, 55402-3901. Tel: 612-766-7000. Fax: 612-766-1600. p. 1259

Knueven, Joe, Dir, Germantown Public Library, 51 N Plum St, Germantown, OH, 45327. Tel: 937-855-4001. Fax: 937-855-6098. p. 1901

Knupp, Blaine E, Ref, Indiana University of Pennsylvania, 431 S 11th St, Indiana, PA, 15705-1096. Tel: 724-357-2338. Fax: 724-357-4891. p. 2071

Knupp, Linda, Dir, Manhattan Public Library, 629 Poyntz Ave, Manhattan, KS, 66502-6086. Tel: 785-776-4741. Fax: 785-776-1545. p. 881

Knupp, Linda, Dir, North Central Kansas Libraries System, 629 Poyntz Ave, Manhattan, KS, 66502-6086. Tel: 785-776-4741, Ext 129. Fax: 785-776-1545. p. 881

Knutel, Phillip, Dir, Bentley College, 175 Forest St, Waltham, MA, 02452-4705. Tel: 781-891-2168. Fax: 781-891-2830. p. 1132

Knuth, Charles M, Dir, Libr Serv, Foley & Lardner LLP, 3000 K St NW, 4th Flr, Washington, DC, 20007. Tel: 202-672-5315. Fax: 202-672-5399. p. 400

Knuth, Mary Elizabeth, Dir, Wautoma Public Library, 410 W Main St, Wautoma, WI, 54982-5415. Tel: 920-787-2988. Fax: 920-787-7786. p. 2647

Knuth, Patricia E, Syst Adminr, United States Army, Combined Arms Research Library, US Army Command & General Staff College, Eisenhower Hall, 250 Gibbon Ave, Fort Leavenworth, KS, 66027-2314. Tel: 913-758-3019. Fax: 913-758-3014. p. 867

Knuth, Rebecca, Prof, University of Hawaii, 2550 The Mall, Honolulu, HI, 96822. Tel: 808-956-7321. Fax: 808-956-5835. p. 2964

Knutsen, Deb, ILL, University of Alaska Fairbanks, 310 Tanana Dr, Fairbanks, AK, 99775. Tel: 907-474-6691. Fax: 907-474-6841. p. 48

Knutsen, Keith, Managing Librn, Pierce County Library System, Parkland-Spanaway, 13718 Pacific Ave S, Tacoma, WA, 98444. Tel: 253-548-3304. Fax: 253-536-3789. p. 2539

Knutson, Dave, Dean, Great Lakes Bible College Library, 470 Glenelm Crescent, Waterloo, ON, N2L 5C8, CANADA. Tel: 519-342-3040. p. 2869

Knutson, Jennifer, Circ, University of Sioux Falls, 1101 W 22nd St, Sioux Falls, SD, 57105-1699. Tel: 605-331-6660. p. 2219

Knutson, Loes, Librn, Moreno Valley Public Library, 25480 Alessandro Blvd, Moreno Valley, CA, 92553. Tel: 951-413-3880. Fax: 951-413-3895. p. 191

Knyaz, Olga, Tech Serv Librn, Troy University, 502 University Dr, Dothan, AL, 36304. Tel: 334-983-6556, Ext 1325. Fax: 334-983-6327. p. 15

Ko, Andrew, Asst Prof, University of Washington, Mary Gates Hall, Ste 370, Campus Box 352840, Seattle, WA, 98195-2840. Tel: 206-685-9937. Fax: 206-616-3152. p. 2976

Ko, Ellen, Librn Supvr, Coppell Public Library, 177 N Hertz Rd, Coppell, TX, 75019. Tel: 972-304-3656. Fax: 972-304-3622. p. 2301

Ko, Lin, Br Mgr, Richland County Public Library, Saint Andrews Regional, 2916 Broad River Rd, Columbia, SC, 29210. Tel: 803-772-6675. p. 2188

Kobak, Alicia, Mgr, Globe Institute of Technology, 500 Seventh Ave, New York, NY, 10018. Tel: 212-349-4330. p. 1680

Kobayashi, Vivian, Librn, Cogswell Polytechnical College Library, 1175 Bordeaux Dr, Sunnyvale, CA, 94089. Tel: 408-541-0100. Fax: 408-747-0764. p. 273

Kobbe, Marianne, Adult Serv, Coll Develop, Ref, Baldwin Public Library, 2385 Grand Ave, Baldwin, NY, 11510-3289. Tel: 516-223-6228. Fax: 516-623-7991. p. 1577

Kobe, Marianne, Circ, University of St Francis, 500 Wilcox St, Joliet, IL, 60435. Tel: 815-740-5041. Fax: 815-740-3364. p. 660

Kober, Shirlee-Ann, Head, Commun Serv, Lucy Robbins Welles Library, 95 Cedar St, Newington, CT, 06111-2645. Tel: 860-665-8707. Fax: 860-667-1255. p. 361

Kobialka, Kris, Archivist, Boston Architectural College, 320 Newbury St, Boston, MA, 02115. Tel: 617-585-0133. Fax: 617-585-0151. p. 1055

Kobiela, Kelly, Syst Librn, Colby-Sawyer College, 541 Main St, New London, NH, 03257-4648. Tel: 603-526-3799. Fax: 603-526-3777. p. 1459

Kobiela, Kelly, Syst Librn, Ohio Northern University, 525 S Main St, Ada, OH, 45810. Tel: 419-772-2183. Fax: 419-772-1927. p. 1851

Koblenz, Esther, Librn, Baker & Hostetler, Washington Sq, Ste 1100, 1050 Connecticut Ave NW, Washington, DC, 20036. Tel: 202-861-1578. Fax: 202-861-1783. p. 394

Koblick, Rebecca, Librn, City College of the City University of New York, Music Library, Shepard Hall, Rm 160, 160 Convent Ave, New York, NY, 10031. Tel: 212-650-7120. Fax: 212-650-7231. p. 1673

Koboldt, Marje, Asst Librn, Earlham Public Library, 120 S Chestnut St, Earlham, IA, 50072. Tel: 515-758-2121. Fax: 515-758-2121. p. 813

Koborg, Nicole, Cat, Tech Serv, Clarkson College Library, 101 S 42nd St, Omaha, NE, 68131-2739. Tel: 402-552-3387. Fax: 402-552-2899. p. 1411

Kobrin, Lisa, Head, Ref (Info Serv), Alamance County Public Libraries, May Memorial Library, 342 S Spring St, Burlington, NC, 27215. Tel: 336-229-3588. Fax: 336-229-3592. p. 1779

Kobritz, Barbara, Instruction Librn, Tompkins Cortland Community College, 170 North St, Dryden, NY, 13053-8504. Tel: 607-844-8222, Ext 4362. Fax: 607-844-6540. p. 1615

Kobs, Sharon, Circ, Willard Library, Seven W Van Buren St, Battle Creek, MI, 49017-3009. Tel: 269-968-8166. Fax: 269-968-3284. p. 1155

Kobulnicky, Michael, Dir, Kent State University, 330 University Dr NE, New Philadelphia, OH, 44663-9403. Tel: 330-339-3391, Ext 47471. Fax: 330-339-7888. p. 1921

Kobulnicky, Paul, Exec Dir, Youngstown State University, One University Plaza, Youngstown, OH, 44555-0001. Tel: 330-941-3676. Fax: 330-941-3734. p. 1953

Kobyljanec, Kathy, Access Serv, John Carroll University, 20700 N Park Blvd, University Heights, OH, 44118. Tel: 216-397-1646. Fax: 216-397-4256. p. 1942

Kocevar-Weidinger, Liz, Instrul & Ref Librn, Longwood University, Redford & Race St, Farmville, VA, 23909. Tel: 434-395-2445. Fax: 434-395-2453. p. 2463

Koch, Anna, Libr Experience Mgr, San Mateo County Library, Library Administration, 125 Lessingia Ct, San Mateo, CA, 94402-4000. Tel: 650-312-5205. Fax: 650-312-5382. p. 255

Koch, Barbara, Cat, Walsh College, 3838 Livernois Rd, Troy, MI, 48083-5066. Tel: 248-823-1228. Fax: 248-689-9066. p. 1232

Koch, Diane, Spec Coll & Archives Librn, Muhlenberg College, 2400 Chew St, Allentown, PA, 18104-5586. Tel: 484-664-3694. Fax: 484-664-3511. p. 2027

Koch, Kate, Librn, Lomond Municipal Library, Two Railway Ave N, Lomond, AB, T0L 1G0, CANADA. Tel: 403-792-3934. Fax: 403-792-3934. p. 2710

Koch, Katherine, Librn, Barnesville Hutton Memorial Library, 308 E Main St, Barnesville, OH, 43713-1410. Tel: 740-425-1651. Fax: 740-425-3504. p. 1857

Koch, Katherine, Head of Libr, University of Alberta, Herbert T Coutts Education & Physical Education Library, Educations Bldg, Edmonton, AB, T6G 2G5, CANADA. Tel: 780-492-1460. Fax: 780-492-8367. p. 2702

Koch, Kathy J, Archivist, Librn, American Association of Nurse Anesthetists, 222 S Prospect Ave, Park Ridge, IL, 60068-4001. Tel: 847-655-1106. Fax: 847-692-6968. p. 688

Koch, Linda, Genealogy & Hist Librn, Ref Serv, Ad, Allegan District Library, 331 Hubbard St, Allegan, MI, 49010. Tel: 269-673-4625. Fax: 269-673-8661. p. 1148

Koch, Mary, Dir, Gothenburg Public Library, 1104 Lake Ave, Gothenburg, NE, 69138-1903. Tel: 308-537-2591. Fax: 308-537-3667. p. 1400

Koch, Pat, Libr Asst, Oaklyn Memorial Library, 602 Newton Ave, Oaklyn, NJ, 08107. Tel: 856-858-8226. p. 1515

Koch, Pat, Ad, Marion County Public Library, Mannington Public, 109 Clarksburg St, Mannington, WV, 26582. Tel: 304-986-2803. Fax: 304-986-3425. p. 2559

Koch, Pat G, Ad, Marion County Library, 101 E Court St, Marion, SC, 29571-3699. Tel: 843-423-8300. Fax: 843-423-8302. p. 2200

Koch, Paul, Cat, Syst Coordr, Marian University, 45 S National Ave, Fond du Lac, WI, 54935. Tel: 920-923-7641, 920-923-8725. Fax: 920-923-7154. p. 2592

Koch, Phyllis, Asst Librn, Kiowa County Public Library District, 1305 Goff St, Eads, CO, 81036. Tel: 719-438-5581. Fax: 719-438-6581. p. 305

Koch, PJ, ILL, Saint Louis University, Medical Center Library, 1402 S Grand Blvd, Saint Louis, MO, 63104. Tel: 314-977-8806. Fax: 314-977-5573. p. 1361

Koch, Ramona, Librn, Eustis Public Library, 108 N Morton St, Eustis, NE, 69028. Tel: 308-486-2651. p. 1398

Koch, Shirley, Supvr, Maillibr, Meridian-Lauderdale County Public Library, 2517 Seventh St, Meridian, MS, 39301. Tel: 601-486-2263. Fax: 601-486-2260. p. 1308

Koch, Siobhan, Dir, Norwood Public Library, 198 Summit St, Norwood, NJ, 07648-1835. Tel: 201-768-9555. Fax: 201-767-2176. p. 1515

Koch, Suzanne, Dir, Oyster Bay-East Norwich Public Library, 89 E Main St, Oyster Bay, NY, 11771. Tel: 516-922-1212. Fax: 516-922-6453. p. 1714

Koch, Teri, Coordr, Acq, Coordr, Electronic Res, Coordr, Ser, Drake University, 2725 University Ave, Des Moines, IA, 50311. Tel: 515-271-2941. Fax: 515-271-3933. p. 809

Koch, Victoria, Librn, Billings Clinic, 2825 Eighth Ave N, Billings, MT, 59107. Tel: 406-238-2226. Fax: 406-238-2253. p. 1374

Kochan, Carol, Coordr, ILL, Utah State University, 3000 Old Main Hill, Logan, UT, 84322-3000. Tel: 435-797-2676. Fax: 435-797-2880. p. 2407

Kochan, Roman V, Dean, California State University, Long Beach, 1250 N Bellflower Blvd, Long Beach, CA, 90840. Tel: 562-985-4047. Fax: 562-985-8131. p. 165

Kochersperger, Sandra, Mgr, Eastern State Hospital, 4601 Ironbound Rd, Williamsburg, VA, 23188. Tel: 757-253-5457. Fax: 757-253-7078. p. 2503

Kochheiser, Wendy, Dir, Show Low Public Library, 180 N Ninth St, Show Low, AZ, 85901. Tel: 928-532-4073. Fax: 928-532-4079. p. 82

Kochi, Julia, Dir, Digital Libr & Coll, University of California San Francisco, 530 Parnassus Ave, San Francisco, CA, 94143-0840. Tel: 415-502-7539. p. 248

Kochik, Lisa, Ch, Newburgh Free Library, 124 Grand St, Newburgh, NY, 12550. Tel: 845-563-3600. Fax: 845-563-3602. p. 1705

Kochtanek, Tom, Assoc Prof, University of Missouri-Columbia, 303 Townsend Hall, Columbia, MO, 65211. Tel: 573-882-4546. Fax: 573-884-2917. p. 2968

Kociemba, Karen, Br Supvr, Marion County Public Library System, Dunnellon Public Library, 20351 Robinson Rd, Dunnellon, FL, 34431. Tel: 352-438-2520. Fax: 352-438-2522. p. 474

Kocin, Valerie, Br Mgr, Cuyahoga County Public Library, Independence Branch, 6361 Selig Dr, Independence, OH, 44131-4926. Tel: 216-447-0160. Fax: 216-447-1371. p. 1927

Kocis, Nancy, Dir, Riverton Village Library, 1200 E Riverton Rd, Riverton, IL, 62561-8200. Tel: 217-629-6353. Fax: 217-629-6353. p. 695

Kocken, Greg, Archivist, Rec Mgr, University of Wisconsin-Eau Claire, 105 Garfield Ave, Eau Claire, WI, 54702-4004. Tel: 715-834-3873. Fax: 715-836-2949. p. 2590

Kocour, Bruce G, Dean, Carson-Newman College, 1634 Russell Ave, Jefferson City, TN, 37760. Tel: 865-471-3336. Fax: 865-471-3450. p. 2239

Kocovsky, Jill, Asst Librn, Neuschafer Community Library, 317 Wolf River Dr, Fremont, WI, 54940-9054. Tel: 920-446-2474. Fax: 920-446-2480. p. 2593

Kocylowsky, Maria, Head of Libr, Fairleigh Dickinson University, Dickinson Hall, 140 University Plaza Dr, Hackensack, NJ, 07601. Tel: 201-692-2608. Fax: 201-692-7048. p. 1489

Kodiak, Diana, Archivist, National Archives & Records Administration, 654 W Third Ave, Anchorage, AK, 99501-2145. Tel: 907-261-7809. Fax: 907-261-7813. p. 45

Kodzis, Anthony, Acq Mgr, Tufts University, 35 Professors Row, Medford, MA, 02155-5816. Tel: 617-627-3595. Fax: 617-627-3002. p. 1104

Koebel, Nancy, YA Serv, Birchard Public Library of Sandusky County, 423 Croghan St, Fremont, OH, 43420. Tel: 419-334-7101. Fax: 419-334-4788. p. 1900

Koechley, Bob, Dir, Promega Corp, 2800 Woods Hollow Rd, Madison, WI, 53711. Tel: 608-274-4330. Fax: 608-277-2601. p. 2607

Koehl, Nancy, Interim Dir, Nesbitt Memorial Library, 529 Washington St, Columbus, TX, 78934-2326. Tel: 979-732-5514. Fax: 979-732-3392. p. 2299

Koehler, Amy E C, Pub Serv Adminr, Moody Bible Institute, 820 N La Salle Blvd, Chicago, IL, 60610-3284. Tel: 312-329-4139. Fax: 312-329-8959. p. 619

Koehler, Boyd, Instrul Serv Librn, Ref Serv, Augsburg College, 2211 Riverside Ave, Minneapolis, MN, 55454. Tel: 612-330-1604. Fax: 612-330-1436. p. 1259

Koehler, Jacob, Vis Acq, The College of Wooster Libraries, 1140 Beall Ave, Wooster, OH, 44691-2364. Tel: 330-263-2487. Fax: 330-263-2253. p. 1949

Koehler, Keri, Coll Mgr, San Francisco Maritime Library, Fort Mason Ctr, Bldg E, 3rd Flr, San Francisco, CA, 94123. Tel: 415-561-7030. Fax: 415-556-1624. p. 245

Koehler, Pam, Ch, West Lafayette Public Library, 208 W Columbia St, West Lafayette, IN, 47906. Tel: 765-743-2261. Fax: 765-743-0540. p. 787

Koehler, Robert, Librn, Meriter Hospital, Two Atrium, 202 S Park St, Madison, WI, 53715. Tel: 608-417-5900. Fax: 608-267-6007. p. 2607

Koehler, Sarah, Br Mgr, Whatcom County Library System, Ferndale Branch, 2007 Cherry St, Ferndale, WA, 98248. Tel: 360-384-3647. Fax: 360-384-6224. p. 2509

Koehler, Shelley, Dir, Shelbyville Free Public Library, 154 N Broadway St, Shelbyville, IL, 62565-1698. Tel: 217-774-4432. Fax: 217-774-2634. p. 702

Koehler, Wallace C, Dr, Dir, Prof, Valdosta State University, Odum Library - MLIS, 1500 N Patterson St, Valdosta, GA, 31698-0144. Tel: 229-245-3732. Fax: 229-259-5055. p. 2964

Koehn, Brent, Tech Serv Librn, Associated Mennonite Biblical Seminary Library, 3003 Benham Ave, Elkhart, IN, 46517. Tel: 574-296-6211. Fax: 574-295-0092. p. 737

Koehn, Michael, Actg Libr Dir, Head, Tech Serv, Columbia University, Augustus C Long Health Sciences Library, 701 W 168th St, Lobby Level, New York, NY, 10032. Tel: 212-305-9216. Fax: 212-234-0595. p. 1675

Koehnen, Julie, Librn, Cincinnati Law Library Association, Hamilton County Court House, 1000 Main St, Rm 601, Cincinnati, OH, 45202. Tel: 513-946-5300, 513-946-5301. Fax: 513-946-5252. p. 1869

Koehnk, Kris, Dir, Montgomery Memorial Library, 711 Main St, Jewell, IA, 50130. Tel: 515-827-5112. Fax: 515-827-5112. p. 824

Koelker, June, Dr, Dean, Texas Christian University, 2913 Lowden St, TCU Box 298400, Fort Worth, TX, 76129. Tel: 817-257-7106. Fax: 817-257-7282. p. 2323

Koelling, Holly, Mgr, Outreach Serv, King County Library System, 960 Newport Way NW, Issaquah, WA, 98027. Tel: 425-369-3200. Fax: 425-369-3255. p. 2516

Koelsch, Beth Ann, Curator, Women Vet Hist Project, University of North Carolina at Greensboro, 320 Spring Garden St, Greensboro, NC, 27402. Tel: 336-334-5880. Fax: 336-334-5399. p. 1798

Koen, Diane, Assoc Dir, Planning & Res, McGill University Libraries, 3459 McTavish St, Montreal, QC, H3A 1Y1, CANADA. Tel: 514-398-2149. Fax: 514-398-3561. p. 2898

Koenig, Donna, Librn, Land O'Lakes Inc Library, PO Box 64101, Saint Paul, MN, 55164-0101. Tel: 651-481-2691. Fax: 651-481-2002. p. 1278

Koenig, Jessica, Dir, Island Trees Public Library, 38 Farmedge Rd, Island Trees, NY, 11756-5200. Tel: 516-731-2211. Fax: 516-731-2395, 516-731-3798. p. 1640

Koenig, Lynn, Adult Serv Coordr, Lawrence Public Library, 707 Vermont St, Lawrence, KS, 66044-2371. Tel: 785-843-3833, Ext 113. Fax: 785-843-3368. p. 877

Koenig, Michael, Dr, Prof, Long Island University, C W Post Campus, 720 Northern Blvd, Brookville, NY, 11548-1300. Tel: 516-299-2176. Fax: 516-299-4168. p. 2969

Koenig, Sue, Dir, Clearwater Public Library, 109 E Ross St, Clearwater, KS, 67026-7824. Tel: 620-584-6474. Fax: 620-584-2995. p. 861

Koenig, Sue, Coll Develop, Newton Public Library, 720 N Oak, Newton, KS, 67114. Tel: 316-283-2890. Fax: 316-283-2916. p. 884

Koenig, Tracy, Dir, Athenaeum of Ohio, 6616 Beechmont Ave, Cincinnati, OH, 45230-2091. Tel: 513-233-6135. Fax: 513-231-3254. p. 1868

Koenigs, Lee, Dir, ILL, Libby Memorial Library, 27 Staples St, Old Orchard Beach, ME, 04064. Tel: 207-934-4351. p. 994

Koenigs, Mary Jane, Sister, ILL, Tech Serv, Briar Cliff University, 3303 Rebecca St, Sioux City, IA, 51104-2324. Tel: 712-279-5535. Fax: 712-279-1723. p. 843

Koenigsfeld, Julie, Librn, Missouri Department of Corrections, Algoa Correctional Center, 8501 No More Victims Rd, Jefferson City, MO, 65101-4567. Tel: 573-751-3911, Ext 640. Fax: 573-751-7375. p. 1334

Koeninger, Larry D, Dir, Libr Serv, Bryan College Station Public Library System, 201 E 26th St, Bryan, TX, 77803-5356. Tel: 979-209-5611. Fax: 979-209-5610. p. 2292

Koepf, Linda S, Dir, Texas State Technical College, 3801 Campus Dr, Waco, TX, 76705. Tel: 254-867-4846. Fax: 254-867-2339. p. 2397

Koepke, Jill M, Ref Librn, Dolton Public Library District, 14037 Lincoln, Dolton, IL, 60419-1091. Tel: 708-849-2385. Fax: 708-841-2725. p. 637

Koepke, Leanne A, Pub Serv, Carleton A Friday Memorial Library, 155 E First St, New Richmond, WI, 54017. Tel: 715-243-0431. Fax: 715-246-2691. p. 2625

Koeppe, Andrea, Ref Librn, University of Saint Thomas, Charles J Keffer Library, 1000 LaSalle Ave, MOH 206, Minneapolis, MN, 55403. Tel: 651-962-4647. Fax: 651-962-4648. p. 1282

Koerner, Norma, Asst Librn, Chatsworth Township Library, 432 E Locust St, Chatsworth, IL, 60921. Tel: 815-635-3004. Fax: 815-635-3004. p. 604

Koerner, Phil, Librn, Phenomenex Library, 411 Madrid Ave, Torrance, CA, 90501. Tel: 310-212-0555. Fax: 310-328-7768. p. 276

Koester, Judith, Librn, North Dakota School for the Deaf Library, 1401 College Dr N, Devils Lake, ND, 58301. Tel: 701-665-4433. Fax: 701-665-4409. p. 1839

Koestner, Lynne, Ref Serv, Missouri Baptist University, One College Park Dr, Saint Louis, MO, 63141-8698. Tel: 314-434-1115. Fax: 314-392-2343. p. 1356

Koetzner, John, Head Librn, Mendocino College Library, 1000 Hensley Creek Rd, Ukiah, CA, 95482-7821. Tel: 707-468-3053. Fax: 707-468-3056. p. 277

Koff, Jacob, Librn, Mills Law Library, 220 Montgomery St, Ste 116, San Francisco, CA, 94104. Tel: 415-781-2665. Fax: 415-781-1116. p. 244

Kofoot, M, Asst Librn, Nissen Public Library, 217 W Fifth, Saint Ansgar, IA, 50472-0040. Tel: 641-713-2218. Fax: 641-713-4716. p. 842

Kofron, Denise, Youth Serv Librn, Hopkinton Public Library, 13 Main St, Hopkinton, MA, 01748. Tel: 508-497-9777. Fax: 508-497-9778. p. 1096

Koger, Jane, Br Mgr, Warren Public Library, Maybelle Burnette Branch, 22005 Van Dyke Ave, Warren, MI, 48089. Tel: 586-758-2115. p. 1234

Koh, Kyungwon, PhD, Dr, Asst Prof, University of Oklahoma, Bizzell Memorial Library, 401 W Brooks, Rm 120, Norman, OK, 73019-6032. Tel: 405-325-3921. Fax: 405-325-7648. p. 2972

Kohane, Isaac, PhD, Dir, Harvard Library, Francis A Countway Library of Medicine, Boston Med Libr-Harvard Med Libr, Ten Shattuck St, Boston, MA, 02115. Tel: 617-432-4807. p. 1074

Kohl, Allan, Visual Res, Minneapolis College of Art & Design Library, 2501 Stevens Ave, Minneapolis, MN, 55404-3593. Tel: 612-874-3781. Fax: 612-874-3704. p. 1260

Kohl, Janelle M, Dir, Frank B Koller Memorial Library, 51S02 Hwy 51, Manitowish Waters, WI, 54545. Tel: 715-543-2700. Fax: 715-543-2700. p. 2611

Kohl, Kristi, Cat, Ref/Electronic Res/Web Librn, Centenary College of Louisiana, 2834 Woodlawn St, Shreveport, LA, 71104-3335. Tel: 318-869-5047. Fax: 318-869-5004. p. 967

Kohl, Laura, Head, Ref, Bryant University, 1150 Douglas Pike, Smithfield, RI, 02917-1284. Tel: 401-232-6125. Fax: 401-232-6126. p. 2176

Kohl, Mardell, Dir, Meadow Grove Public Library, 205 Main St, Meadow Grove, NE, 68752. Tel: 402-634-2266. Fax: 402-634-2266. p. 1408

Kohl, Michael, Head, Spec Coll, Clemson University Libraries, Box 343001, Clemson, SC, 29634-3001. Tel: 864-656-5176. Fax: 864-656-0758. p. 2186

Kohl, Michael, Head, Spec Coll, Clemson University Libraries, Special Collections Unit, Strom Thurmond Inst Bldg, Special Collections Box 343001, Clemson, SC, 29634-3001. Tel: 864-656-5176. Fax: 864-656-0233. p. 2186

Kohl, Rebecca, Photo Archivist, Montana Historical Society, 225 N Roberts St, Helena, MT, 59601-4514. Tel: 406-444-3317. Fax: 406-444-5297. p. 1382

Kohl, Sharon, Br Mgr, New Orleans Public Library, Children's Resource Center, 913 Napoleon Ave, New Orleans, LA, 70115-2862. Tel: 504-596-2628. Fax: 504-596-2669. p. 962

Kohlbuss, Terry, Exec Dir, Tri County Regional Planning Commission Library, 411 Hamilton Blvd, Ste 2001, Peoria, IL, 61602. Tel: 309-673-9330, Ext 231. Fax: 309-673-9802. p. 690

Kohlenberg, Jane, Dir, Pemberville Public Library, 375 E Front St, Pemberville, OH, 43450. Tel: 419-287-4012. Fax: 419-287-4620. p. 1928

Kohlenberg, Sally, Head, Circ, Huntington Woods Public Library, 26415 Scotia, Huntington Woods, MI, 48070-1198. Tel: 248-543-9720. Fax: 248-543-2559. p. 1193

Kohler, Dale, Dir, Libr Info Tech, California Polytechnic State University, One Grand Ave, San Luis Obispo, CA, 93407. Tel: 805-756-1922. Fax: 805-756-2346. p. 253

Kohler, Ellie, Supvr, Pub Serv, Rockhurst University, 1100 Rockhurst Rd, Kansas City, MO, 64110-2561. Tel: 816-501-4121. Fax: 816-501-4666. p. 1340

Kohler, Ruth DeYoung, Dir, John Michael Kohler Arts Center, 608 New York Ave, Sheboygan, WI, 53081-4507. Tel: 920-458-6144. Fax: 920-458-4473. p. 2637

Kohli, Ann, Librn, Lomira Public Library, 1038 Main St, Lomira, WI, 53048-9515. Tel: 920-269-4115. Fax: 920-269-4115. p. 2605

Kohli, Gary, Librn, Ottawa County Law Library Association, 315 Madison St, Port Clinton, OH, 43452. Tel: 419-734-6763. p. 1930

Kohli, Kate, Syst Coordr, Bloomfield College Library, Liberty St & Oakland Ave, Bloomfield, NJ, 07003. Tel: 973-748-9000, Ext 332. Fax: 973-743-3998. p. 1473

Kohli, Martin, In Charge, United States Department of Labor, 201 Varick St, Rm 808, New York, NY, 10014. Tel: 646-264-3600. Fax: 212-337-2532. p. 1702

Kohutiak, Bohdan, Dir, US Army War College Library, 122 Forbes Ave, Carlisle, PA, 17013-5220. Tel: 717-245-4300. Fax: 717-245-3323. p. 2042

Koier, Susan, ILL, Baldwin County Library Cooperative, Inc, 22251 Palmer St, Robertsdale, AL, 36567. Tel: 251-970-4010. Fax: 251-970-4011. p. 35

Koile, Rene, Children's Coordr, Claymont Public Library, 215 E Third St, Uhrichsville, OH, 44683. Tel: 740-922-3626. Fax: 740-922-3500. p. 1942

Kois, Debra, Patron Serv, Bennington Public Library, 15505 Warehouse St, Bennington, NE, 68007. Tel: 402-238-2201. Fax: 402-238-2218. p. 1394

Kok, Patrick, Acq, ILL, Redeemer College Library, 777 Garner Rd E, Ancaster, ON, L9K 1J4, CANADA. Tel: 905-648-2131. Fax: 905-648-2134. p. 2792

Kok, Victoria, Br Head, Virginia Polytechnic Institute & State University Libraries, Drill Field Dr, Blacksburg, VA, 24062-9001. Tel: 540-231-6610. Fax: 540-231-3946. p. 2451

Kok, Victoria T, Librn, Virginia Polytechnic Institute & State University Libraries, Veterinary Medicine, Phase III Duck Pond Dr, Blacksburg, VA, 24061-0442. Tel: 540-231-6610. Fax: 540-231-7367. p. 2451

Koke, Audrey M, Ref Librn, Endicott College Library, 376 Hale St, Beverly, MA, 01915. Tel: 978-232-2273. Fax: 978-232-2700. p. 1054

Kokes, Debra H, Libr Serv Dir, Art Circle Public Library, Cumberland County, 154 E First St, Crossville, TN, 38555-4696. Tel: 931-484-6790, Ext 221. Fax: 931-484-2350. p. 2232

Kokjer, Dean, Dr, Head of Libr, Calvary Presbyterian Church USA Library, 4495 Magnolia Ave, Riverside, CA, 92501. Tel: 951-686-0761. Fax: 951-686-1488. p. 216

Kokochak, Mary Jo, Librn, Lenawee County Library, Onsted Branch, 261 S Main St, Onsted, MI, 49265-9749. Tel: 517-467-2623. Fax: 517-467-6298. p. 1147

Kokocinski, Cynthia, Libr Tech, United States Courts Library, 940 Front St, Rm 3185, San Diego, CA, 92101-8920. Tel: 619-557-5387. Fax: 619-557-5077. p. 238

Kokodoko, Ajoke, Br Mgr, Oakland Public Library, Martin Luther King Branch, 6833 International Blvd, Oakland, CA, 94621. Tel: 510-615-5728. Fax: 510-615-5739. p. 198

Kokola, Melody B, Dir, Metuchen Public Library, 480 Middlesex Ave, Metuchen, NJ, 08840. Tel: 732-632-8526. Fax: 732-632-8535. p. 1501

Kokolus, Cait, Dir, Libr Serv, Anthony Cardinal Bevilacqua Theological Research Center, 100 E Wynnewood Rd, Wynnewood, PA, 19096. Tel: 610-785-6274. Fax: 610-664-7913. p. 2158

Kokoris, John, Pub Relations Coordr, Addison Public Library, Four Friendship Plaza, Addison, IL, 60101. Tel: 630-458-3303. Fax: 630-543-6645. p. 587

Kokot, Barbara, Ref Serv, Scarsdale Public Library, 54 Olmsted Rd, Scarsdale, NY, 10583. Tel: 914-722-1300. Fax: 914-722-1305. p. 1739

Kokot, Tammy, Dir, Twentieth Century Club Library, Main St, Almond, NY, 14804. Tel: 607-276-6311. Fax: 607-276-6311. p. 1572

Kokus, Marcia, Circ, Mount Aloysius College Library, 7373 Admiral Peary Hwy, Cresson, PA, 16630-1999. Tel: 814-886-6445. Fax: 814-886-5767. p. 2048

Kolaczynski, Cindy, Dir, Maricopa County Library District, 2700 N Central Ave, Ste 700, Phoenix, AZ, 85004. Tel: 602-652-3030. Fax: 602-652-3079. p. 74

Kolak, Lorie, Access Serv, ILL, DePaul University Libraries, Loop, One E Jackson Blvd, 10th Flr, Chicago, IL, 60604. Tel: 312-362-5403. Fax: 312-362-6186. p. 612

Kolatch, Joel, Info Tech Coordr, Lawrence Public Library, 707 Vermont St, Lawrence, KS, 66044-2371. Tel: 785-843-3833, Ext 106. Fax: 785-843-3368. p. 878

Kolaya, Meg, Dir, Scotch Plains Public Library, 1927 Bartle Ave, Scotch Plains, NJ, 07076-1212. Tel: 908-322-5007. Fax: 908-322-0490. p. 1528

Kolb, Bill, Sr Commun Libr Mgr, Contra Costa County Library, Concord Library, 2900 Salvio St, Concord, CA, 94519-2597. Tel: 925-646-5455. Fax: 925-646-5453. p. 209

Kolb, Dan, Dir, Saint Meinrad Archabbey & School of Theology, 200 Hill Dr, Saint Meinrad, IN, 47577. Tel: 812-357-6401. Fax: 812-357-6398. p. 777

Kolber, Denise, Adult Serv, Margaret R Grundy Memorial Library, 680 Radcliffe St, Bristol, PA, 19007-5199. Tel: 215-788-7891. Fax: 215-788-4976. p. 2037

Kolber, Eric N, Librn, United States Army, 1776 Niagara St, Buffalo, NY, 14201-3199. Tel: 716-879-4178. Fax: 716-879-6468. p. 1599

Kolda, Sarah, Asst Dir, Libr Serv, Holy Cross College, 54515 State Rd 933 N, Box 308, Notre Dame, IN, 46556-0308. Tel: 574-239-8391. Fax: 574-239-8324. p. 771

Kolderup, Davin, Digital Serv Librn, Johnson County Public Library, White River Library, 1664 Library Blvd, Greenwood, IN, 46142. Tel: 317-885-1330. Fax: 317-882-4117. p. 744

Kolenbrander, Nancy, Interim Assoc Dir, Western Carolina University, 176 Central Dr, Cullowhee, NC, 28723. Tel: 828-227-3421. Fax: 828-227-7015. p. 1786

Kolesar, Jenny, Bus & Finance Mgr, Hendrick Hudson Free Library, 185 Kings Ferry Rd, Montrose, NY, 10548. Tel: 914-739-5654. Fax: 914-739-5659. p. 1663

Kolesar, Patricia M, Asst Legis Librn, Saskatchewan Legislative Library, 234-2405 Legislative Dr, Regina, SK, S4S 0B3, CANADA. Tel: 306-787-9379. Fax: 306-787-5856. p. 2924

Kolisch, Frances, Librn, Mineral County Regional Library, 308 La Garita Ave, Creede, CO, 81130. Tel: 719-658-2313. Fax: 719-658-2942. p. 297

Kolk, Barbara, Librn, American Kennel Club Inc Library, 260 Madison Ave, 4th Flr, New York, NY, 10016. Tel: 212-696-8245, 212-696-8246. Fax: 212-696-8281. p. 1668

Kolker, Zinaida, Libr Asst, Raritan Bay Medical Center, 530 New Brunswick Ave, Perth Amboy, NJ, 08861. Tel: 732-324-5087. Fax: 732-324-4676. p. 1519

Kollar, Kathryn, Head, Acq, Centre Canadien d'Architecture/Canadian Centre for Architecture, 1920 rue Baile, Montreal, QC, H3H 2S6, CANADA. Tel: 514-939-7000. Fax: 514-939-7020. p. 2892

Kollar, Mary Ellen, Librn, Cleveland Psychoanalytic Center Library, 2460 Fairmount Blvd, Ste 312, Cleveland Heights, OH, 44106. Tel: 216-229-5959. Fax: 216-229-7321. p. 1882

Kollar, Rose Marie, Cat, Ref, Oakland Public Library, Two Municipal Plaza, Oakland, NJ, 07436. Tel: 201-337-3742. Fax: 201-337-0261. p. 1515

Koller, Betty, Head Librn, Big Horn County Library, Greybull Branch, PO Box 226, Greybull, WY, 82426-0226. Tel: 307-765-2551. p. 2651

Koller, Kathleen, Librn, Connecticut Judicial Branch Law Libraries, Waterbury Law Library, Waterbury Courthouse, 300 Grand St, Waterbury, CT, 06702. Tel: 203-591-3338. Fax: 203-596-4137. p. 344

Koller, Rita, Govt Doc, Ref Librn, Ser, Lake Forest College, 555 N Sheridan, Lake Forest, IL, 60045. Tel: 847-735-5065. Fax: 847-735-6297. p. 663

Koller, Sheryl, Asst Librn, Arapahoe Public Library, 302 Nebraska Ave, Arapahoe, NE, 68922. Tel: 308-962-7806. Fax: 308-962-3806. p. 1391

Kollins, Eileen, Librn, Suburban Temple, 22401 Chagrin Blvd, Beachwood, OH, 44122-5345. Tel: 216-991-0700. Fax: 216-991-0705. p. 1858

Kolman-Weber, Michele, Cataloger, Librn I, Louisville Public Library, 951 Spruce St, Louisville, CO, 80027. Tel: 303-335-4849. Fax: 303-335-4833. p. 317

Kolo, Vicky, Head, Tech Serv, ILL Coordr, Burlington County Library, Five Pioneer Blvd, Westampton, NJ, 08060. Tel: 609-267-9660, Ext 3020. Fax: 609-267-4091. p. 1542

Kolojaco, Leslie, Pub Serv Librn, Wharton County Junior College, 911 Boling Hwy, Wharton, TX, 77488-3298. Tel: 979-532-6356. Fax: 979-532-6527. p. 2399

Kolonay, Brittany, Emerging Tech Librn, University of the District of Columbia, David A Clarke School of Law, Charles N & Hilda H M Mason Law Library, Bldg 39, Rm B-16, 4200 Connecticut Ave NW, Washington, DC, 20008. Tel: 202-274-7310. Fax: 202-274-7311. p. 421

Kolosionek, Diane, Librn, Cleveland State University, University Library, Rhodes Tower, 2121 Euclid Ave, Cleveland, OH, 44115-2214. Tel: 216-802-3358. Fax: 216-687-9380. p. 1879

Kolsrud, Kelli, Dir, Info Serv/Publ, International Foundation of Employee Benefit Plans, 18700 W Bluemound Rd, Brookfield, WI, 53045-2936. Tel: 262-786-6710, Ext 5. Fax: 262-786-8780. p. 2583

Kolsto, Laura, Asst Librn, Girard Township Library, 201 W Madison, Girard, IL, 62640-1550. Tel: 217-627-2414. Fax: 217-627-2093. p. 649

Koltutsky, Laura, Actg Dir, University of Calgary Library, Doucette Library of Teaching Resources, 370 Education Block, 2500 University Dr NW, Calgary, AB, T2N 1N4, CANADA. Tel: 403-220-6295. Fax: 403-220-8211. p. 2693

Kolvek, Mike, Tech Serv, Cinema Arts, Inc, 207 Lincoln Green Lane, Newfoundland, PA, 18445. Tel: 570-676-4145. Fax: 570-676-9194. p. 2097

Koman, Cynthia, Ser, Albany Medical College, 47 New Scotland Ave, MC 63, Albany, NY, 12208. Tel: 518-262-6058. Fax: 518-262-5820. p. 1568

Koman, Cynthia, Ref Librn, Hudson Valley Community College, 80 Vandenburgh Ave, Troy, NY, 12180. Tel: 518-629-7336. Fax: 518-629-7509. p. 1756

Komara, Edward, Music Librn, State University of New York College at Potsdam, Julia E Crane Memorial Library, Crane School of Music, 44 Pierrepont Ave, Potsdam, NY, 13676-2294. Tel: 315-267-3227. Fax: 315-267-3115. p. 1722

Komernicky, Sue, Dir, Glendale Public Library, 5959 W Brown St, Glendale, AZ, 85302-1248. Tel: 623-930-3562. Fax: 623-842-4209. p. 64

Kominiarek, Martina, Exec Dir, Bucks County Free Library, 150 S Pine St, Doylestown, PA, 18901-4932. Tel: 215-348-0332, Ext 1101. Fax: 215-348-4760. p. 2050

Kominowski, James, Coll Develop, University of Manitoba Libraries, Elizabeth Dafoe Library, 25 Chancellor's Circle, Winnipeg, MB, R3T 2N2, CANADA. Tel: 204-474-9544. Fax: 204-474-7577. p. 2758

Komljenovic, Milan, Tech Coordr, Duquesne University, Center for Legal Information, 900 Locust St, Pittsburgh, PA, 15282. Tel: 412-396-5533. Fax: 412-396-6294. p. 2125

Komma, Pavanaja, Ch, Atlanta-Fulton Public Library System, Dr Robert E Fulton Regional at Ocee, 5090 Abbotts Bridge Rd, Alpharetta, GA, 30005-4601. Tel: 770-360-8897. Fax: 770-360-8892. p. 512

Kommer, Joen, Librn, San Luis Obispo County Library, Cambria Branch, 900 Main St, Cambria, CA, 93428. Tel: 805-927-4336. Fax: 805-927-3524. p. 254

Komorowski, Louis, Ref Mgr, Monroe County Library System, Ellis Reference & Information Center, 3700 S Custer Rd, Monroe, MI, 48161-9716. Tel: 734-241-5277. Fax: 734-242-9037. p. 1210

Komorowski, Walter, Head, Libr Syst, Williams College, 55 Sawyer Library Dr, Williamstown, MA, 01267. Tel: 413-597-2084. Fax: 413-597-4106. p. 1140

Kompanik, Linda, Dir, Logan County Public Library, 201 W Sixth St, Russellville, KY, 42276. Tel: 270-726-6129. Fax: 270-726-6127. p. 934

Komraus, Joyce, Dir, Michael Nivison Public Library, 90 Swallow Pl, Cloudcroft, NM, 88317. Tel: 575-682-1111. Fax: 575-682-1111. p. 1553

Konazeski, Raina, In Charge, Vigo County Public Library, West Terre Haute Branch, 626 National Ave, West Terre Haute, IN, 47885. Tel: 812-232-1113, Ext 287. Fax: 812-478-9602. p. 782

Koncz, Judith, Tech Serv, Morrill Memorial Library, 33 Walpole St, Norwood, MA, 02062-1206. Tel: 781-769-0200. Fax: 781-769-6083. p. 1115

Konczey, Tiffany L, Acq Librn, United States Army, Combined Arms Research Library, US Army Command & General Staff College, Eisenhower Hall, 250 Gibbon Ave, Fort Leavenworth, KS, 66027-2314. Tel: 913-758-3013. Fax: 913-758-3014. p. 867

Konda, Kaisha, Asst Librn, Colwich Community Library, 432 W Colwich, Colwich, KS, 67030. Tel: 316-796-1521. p. 862

Kondos, Paulette, Supvr, Per, Santa Clara City Library, 2635 Homestead Rd, Santa Clara, CA, 95051. Tel: 408-615-2985. Fax: 408-247-9657. p. 262

Konerding, Erhard, Doc, Wesleyan University, 252 Church St, Middletown, CT, 06459-3199. Tel: 860-685-3844. Fax: 860-685-2661. p. 352

Kong, Fanying, Mgr, Federal Reserve Bank of Dallas Library, 2200 N Pearl, Dallas, TX, 75201. Tel: 214-922-6000. Fax: 214-922-5222. p. 2308

Kong, Les, Head, Pub Serv, California State University, San Bernardino, 5500 University Pkwy, San Bernardino, CA, 92407-2318. Tel: 909-537-5111. Fax: 909-537-7048. p. 227

Kong, Martin, Syst Coordr, Chicago State University, 9501 S Martin Luther King Jr Dr, LIB 440, Chicago, IL, 60628-1598. Tel: 773-995-3908. Fax: 773-995-3772. p. 610

Kong, Randal, Assoc Dir, Hawaii Pacific University Libraries, 1060 Bishop St, Honolulu, HI, 96813-3192. Tel: 808-544-1162. Fax: 808-521-7998. p. 560

Kong, Richard, Digital Serv Mgr, Arlington Heights Memorial Library, 500 N Dunton Ave, Arlington Heights, IL, 60004-5966. Tel: 847-506-2674. Fax: 847-506-2650. p. 589

Kong, Seth, Circ Supvr, Indiana University-Purdue University, Herron Art Library, Herron School of Art & Design, 735 W New York St, Indianapolis, IN, 46202. Tel: 317-278-9434. Fax: 317-278-9497. p. 753

Kongchum, Laddawan, Supvr, Ser, Baton Rouge Community College, 201 Community College Dr, Baton Rouge, LA, 70806. Tel: 225-216-8017. Fax: 225-216-8712. p. 942

Konieczko, David, Computer Serv, Venable LLP Library, 575 Seventh St, NW, Washington, DC, 20004-1601. Tel: 202-344-4612. Fax: 202-344-8300. p. 422

Konig, Rhonda, Head, Ref Serv, Wayne County Public Library, 1001 E Ash St, Goldsboro, NC, 27530. Tel: 919-735-1824. Fax: 919-731-2889. p. 1795

Konin, Peter, Head Librn, Joslyn Art Museum, 2200 Dodge St, Omaha, NE, 68102-1296. Tel: 402-661-3300. Fax: 402-342-2376. p. 1413

Konius, Susan, Dir, National Archives & Records Administration, 210 Parkside Dr, West Branch, IA, 52358-9685. Tel: 319-643-5301. Fax: 319-643-6045. p. 851

Konkel, Mary S, Tech Serv Mgr, College of DuPage Library, 425 Fawell Blvd, Glen Ellyn, IL, 60137-6599. Tel: 630-942-2662. Fax: 630-858-8757. p. 649

Konn, Karen, Librn, Readington Township Library, 255 Main St, Whitehouse Station, NJ, 08889. Tel: 908-534-4421. Fax: 908-534-4421. p. 1544

Konny, Genya, Br Librn, Brooklyn Public Library, Jamaica Bay, 9727 Seaview Ave, Brooklyn, NY, 11236. Tel: 718-241-3571. Fax: 718-241-1981. p. 1591

Konomos, Philip, Assoc Univ Librn & Chief Tech Officer, Arizona State University Libraries, 300 E Orange Mall Dr, Tempe, AZ, 85287-1006. Tel: 480-965-9654. Fax: 480-965-9169. p. 83

Konopitski, Linda, Librn, Apache Junction Public Library, 1177 N Idaho Rd, Apache Junction, AZ, 85219. Tel: 480-474-8555. Fax: 480-983-4540. p. 57

Konoski, Robert, Ref (Adult Prog), Port Jefferson Free Library, 100 Thompson St, Port Jefferson, NY, 11777-1897. Tel: 631-473-0022. Fax: 631-473-4765. p. 1721

Konovalov, Yuri, Cat, Ferris State University Library, 1010 Campus Dr, Big Rapids, MI, 49307-2279. Tel: 231-591-3500. Fax: 231-591-3724. p. 1158

Konovitz, Lynn Alan, Dir, Grand Island Memorial Library, 1715 Bedell Rd, Grand Island, NY, 14072. Tel: 716-773-7124. Fax: 716-774-1146. p. 1630

Konrad, Shauna-Lee, Clinical Librn, Children's Hospital of Western Ontario, 800 Commissioners Rd E, London, ON, N6A 4G5, CANADA. Tel: 519-685-8500. Fax: 519-685-8103. p. 2817

Konsorada, Rose, Librn, Lamont Public Library, 4811 50 Ave, Lamont, AB, T0B 2R0, CANADA. Tel: 780-895-2299. Fax: 780-895-2600. p. 2709

Kontopoulos, Ourania, Ref, Delaware County Community College Library, 901 S Media Line Rd, Media, PA, 19063-1094. Tel: 610-359-5149, 610-359-5326. Fax: 610-359-5272. p. 2087

Kontowicz, Pamela, Ref & Ser Librn, Monmouth College, 700 E Broadway, Monmouth, IL, 61462-1963. Tel: 309-457-2278. Fax: 309-457-2226. p. 675

Kontrovitz, Eileen R, Head, Automation, Ouachita Parish Public Library, 1800 Stubbs Ave, Monroe, LA, 71201. Tel: 318-327-1490. Fax: 318-327-1373. p. 957

Konyari, Alexander, Mgr, Budget & Fac, Concordia University Libraries, 1400 de Maisonneuve Blvd W, LB 209, Montreal, QC, H3G 1M8, CANADA. Tel: 514-848-2424, Ext 7761. Fax: 514-848-2882. p. 2894

Konz, Shirley, Librn, Exira Public Library, 114 W Washington St, Exira, IA, 50076. Tel: 712-268-5489. Fax: 712-268-5489. p. 815

Koo, David, Sr Res Librn, Bridgestone/Firestone Research LLC, 1200 Firestone Pkwy, Akron, OH, 44317. Tel: 330-379-7630. Fax: 330-379-7530. p. 1852

Koob, Kelli, Coord Librn, Cap Projects, Hennepin County Library, 12601 Ridgedale Dr, Minnetonka, MN, 55305-1909. Tel: 612-543-8621. Fax: 612-543-8600. p. 1263

Koob, Marian, Mgr, Hoffmann-La Roche, Inc, 340 Kingsland St, Bldg 76/3, Nutley, NJ, 07110-1199. Tel: 973-235-2060. Fax: 973-235-5477. p. 1515

Koob, Mary, Asst Dir, Ch, New Milford Public Library, 200 Dahlia Ave, New Milford, NJ, 07646-1812. Tel: 201-262-1221. Fax: 201-262-5639. p. 1510

Kooiker, Diane, Br Mgr, Herrick District Library, North Side, 155 Riley St, Holland, MI, 49424-1884. Tel: 616-738-4364. Fax: 616-738-4359. p. 1190

Koonce, Danny, Pub Info Spec, Arkansas State Library, 900 W Capitol, Ste 100, Little Rock, AR, 72201-3108. Tel: 501-682-1525. Fax: 501-682-1529. p. 105

Koontz, Sandra, Libr Dir, United States Air Force, 375 FSS/FSDL, 510 Ward Dr, Scott AFB, IL, 62225-5360. Tel: 618-256-5100. Fax: 618-256-4558. p. 701

Koontz, Sylvia, Cataloger, University of North Carolina School of the Arts, 1533 S Main St, Winston-Salem, NC, 27127. Tel: 336-770-3270. Fax: 336-770-3271. p. 1834

Koonz, Peter, Dir, College of Saint Rose, 392-396 Western Ave, Albany, NY, 12203. Tel: 518-454-5180. Fax: 518-454-2897. p. 1568

Koopman, Ann, Web Coordr, Thomas Jefferson University, 1020 Walnut St, Philadelphia, PA, 19107. Tel: 215-503-0441. Fax: 215-923-3203. p. 2118

Koopmans-de Bruijn, Ria, Coll Develop/Ref Librn, Columbia University, C V Starr East Asian Library, 300 Kent Hall, MC 3901, 1140 Amsterdam Ave, New York, NY, 10027. Tel: 212-854-4318. Fax: 212-662-6286. p. 1675

Koos, Greg, Exec Dir, McLean County Museum of History, 200 N Main, Bloomington, IL, 61701. Tel: 309-827-0428. Fax: 309-827-0100. p. 595

Kootman, Danielle, Head, Ch, Middletown Public Library, 55 New Monmouth Rd, Middletown, NJ, 07748. Tel: 732-671-3700, Ext 323. Fax: 732-671-5839. p. 1501

Kooy, Diana, Librn, Jasper County Public Library, Wheatfield Branch, 350 S Bierma St, Wheatfield, IN, 46392. Tel: 219-956-3774. Fax: 219-956-4808. p. 774

Kopak, Richard, Asst Prof, University of British Columbia, The Irving K Barber Centre, 1961 E Mall, Ste 470, Vancouver, BC, V6T 1Z1, CANADA. Tel: 604-822-2404. Fax: 604-822-6006. p. 2977

Kopcha, Theodore J, PhD, Asst Prof, University of Georgia, College of Education, 224 River's Crossing, Athens, GA, 30602-7144. Tel: 706-542-4110. Fax: 706-542-4032. p. 2964

Kopczynski, Mary, Adult Serv, AV, Pittsford Community Library, 24 State St, Pittsford, NY, 14534. Tel: 585-248-6275. Fax: 585-248-6259. p. 1718

Kope, Linda, Asst Librn, Terra Alta Public Library, 701-B E State Ave, Terra Alta, WV, 26764-1204. Tel: 304-789-2724. Fax: 304-789-2724. p. 2572

Kopecky, Carle, Dir, Schoharie County Historical Society, 145 Fort Rd, Schoharie, NY, 12157. Tel: 518-295-7192. Fax: 518-295-7187. p. 1741

Kopecky, Linda, Res & Instrul Serv, University of Wisconsin-Milwaukee Libraries, 2311 E Hartford Ave, Milwaukee, WI, 53211. Tel: 414-229-4785, 414-229-6202. Fax: 414-229-6766. p. 2622

Kopecky, Melissa, Dir, South Orange Public Library, 65 Scotland Rd, South Orange, NJ, 07079. Tel: 973-762-0230. Fax: 973-762-1469. p. 1531

Kopenis, Lawrence, Coordr, Wilkes University, 187 S Franklin St, Wilkes-Barre, PA, 18766-0998. Tel: 570-408-4250. Fax: 570-408-7823. p. 2156

Koperski, Lynn, Librn, Kutak Rock LLP, 1650 Farnam St, Omaha, NE, 68102-2186. Tel: 402-346-6000. Fax: 402-346-1148. p. 1413

Kopf, L J, Ch, Richmond Free Library, 201 Bridge St, Richmond, VT, 05477. Tel: 802-434-3036. Fax: 802-434-3223. p. 2434

Kopine, Beth, Dir, Investigative Reporters & Editors Inc, University of Missouri, School of Journalism, 138 Neff Annex, Columbia, MO, 65211. Tel: 573-882-6668. Fax: 573-882-5431. p. 1324

Koplan, Stephen, Dr, Coordr, Educ Initiatives, Georgia Perimeter College, Dunwoody Campus Library, 2101 Womack Rd, Dunwoody, GA, 30338-4497. Tel: 770-274-5088. Fax: 770-274-5090. p. 525

Koplitz, Peggy, Adult Serv, First Congregational Church Library, 2101 16th St, Greeley, CO, 80631. Tel: 970-353-0828. Fax: 970-353-8447. p. 311

Koplitz, Peggy, Librn, Nichols Professional Library, 4701 Seminary Rd, Alexandria, VA, 22304. Tel: 703-461-4040. Fax: 703-370-7704. p. 2446

Kopp, Dana, Librn, The Learning Center, 500 W Broadway, Missoula, MT, 59802-4587. Tel: 406-329-5711. Fax: 406-329-5688. p. 1386

Kopp, James, Coll Mgr, New Britain Museum of American Art Library, 56 Lexington St, New Britain, CT, 06052. Tel: 860-229-0257. Fax: 860-229-3445. p. 354

Kopp, Kathleen, Asst Curator, Ohio State University LIBRARIES, Jerome Lawrence & Robert E Lee Theatre Research Institute Library, 1430 Lincoln Tower, 1800 Cannon Dr, Columbus, OH, 43210-1230. Tel: 614-292-6614. Fax: 614-688-8417. p. 1888

Kopp, Melinda, Librn, Stockton-San Joaquin County Public Library, Ripon Branch, 333 W Main St, Ripon, CA, 95336. Tel: 209-599-3326. Fax: 209-599-5530. p. 273

Kopp, Patricia, Tech Serv Mgr, Daniel Boone Regional Library, 100 W Broadway, Columbia, MO, 65203. Tel: 573-443-3161. Fax: 573-443-3281. p. 1324

Kopp, Sue, Dir, Libr Serv, Warner Pacific College, 2219 SE 68th Ave, Portland, OR, 97215-4099. Tel: 503-517-1032. Fax: 503-517-1351. p. 2015

Koppang, Diana J, Ref Librn, Neal, Gerber & Eisenberg LLP, Two N La Salle St, Ste 1700, Chicago, IL, 60602. Tel: 312-269-5219. Fax: 312-578-1793. p. 620

Koppe, Karen, Dir, Letts Public Library, 135 S Cherry St, Letts, IA, 52754. Tel: 319-726-5121. Fax: 319-726-5121. p. 827

Kopper, Ginny, Cat, Faulkner-Van Buren Regional Library System, 1900 Tyler St, Conway, AR, 72032. Tel: 501-327-7482. Fax: 501-327-9098. p. 96

Kopperud, Candace, Prog Coordr, Youth Serv Coordr, Palmer Public Library, 655 S Valley Way, Palmer, AK, 99645. Tel: 907-745-4690. Fax: 907-746-3570. p. 52

Kopplin, Barbara A, Dir, Flagg-Rochelle Public Library District, 619 Fourth Ave, Rochelle, IL, 61068. Tel: 815-562-3431. Fax: 815-562-3432. p. 695

Kopplin, William, Per, University of Texas Libraries, Perry-Castaneda Library (Main Library), 101 E 21st St, Austin, TX, 78712-1266. Tel: 512-495-4350. p. 2284

Kopren, Eileen, Asst Dir, Dickinson State University, 291 Campus Dr, Dickinson, ND, 58601. Tel: 701-483-2136. Fax: 701-483-2006. p. 1840

Kopriva, Rayna, Librn, Gove City Library, 519 Broad St, Gove, KS, 67736. Tel: 785-938-2242. p. 869

Korah, Abraham, Automation Syst Coordr, San Jacinto College, 8060 Spencer Hwy, Pasadena, TX, 77505. Tel: 281-476-1850. Fax: 281-478-2734. p. 2369

Korajczyk, Lisa, Librn, Steger-South Chicago Heights Public Library District, 54 E 31st St, Steger, IL, 60475. Tel: 708-755-5040. Fax: 708-755-2504. p. 707

Korber, Nancy, Librn, Fairchild Tropical Botanic Garden, 11935 Old Cutler Rd, Miami, FL, 33156. Tel: 305-667-1651, Ext 3424. Fax: 305-669-4074. p. 465

Korenic, Lynette, Dir, University of Wisconsin-Madison, Kohler Art Library, 800 University Ave, Madison, WI, 53706. Tel: 608-263-2256. Fax: 608-263-2255. p. 2609

Korenowsky, Christopher, Exec Dir, New Haven Free Public Library, 133 Elm St, New Haven, CT, 06510. Tel: 203-946-8139. Fax: 203-946-8140. p. 355

Korenuk, Denise, Dir, Western Taylor County Public Library, 380 E Main St, Gilman, WI, 54433. Tel: 715-447-5486. Fax: 715-447-8134. p. 2594

Koretsky, Nicholas, Pres, Museum of Russian Culture, Inc Library, 2450 Sutter St, San Francisco, CA, 94115. Tel: 415-921-4082. Fax: 415-921-4082. p. 244

Koretzky, Henry, Per, Pennsylvania State University-Harrisburg Library, 351 Olmsted Dr, Middletown, PA, 17057-4850. Tel: 717-948-6563. Fax: 717-948-6757. p. 2089

Korga, Iwona, In Charge, Pilsudski Institute of America Library, 180 Second Ave, New York, NY, 10003-5778. Tel: 212-505-9077. Fax: 212-505-9052. p. 1697

Korhun, Halyna L, Mgr, VA Healthcare Network - Upstate New York, 113 Holland Ave, 142D, Albany, NY, 12208. Tel: 518-626-6219. Fax: 518-626-5957. p. 1571

Korinchak, Shirley A, Coordr, Tech Serv, Pensacola State College, 1000 College Blvd, Pensacola, FL, 32504-8998. Tel: 850-484-2096. Fax: 850-484-1991. p. 482

Korklan, Michael, Librn, Metropolitan Community College, Penn Valley Community College Library, 3201 SW Trafficway, Kansas City, MO, 64111-2764. Tel: 816-759-4090. p. 1339

Korman, Jeanne S, Dir of Libr Serv, Stearns, Weaver, Miller, Weissler, Alhadeff & Sitterson, 2200 Museum Tower, 150 W Flagler St, Miami, FL, 33130. Tel: 305-789-3251. Fax: 305-789-3395. p. 468

Korn, Jennifer, Mgr, Public Library of Cincinnati & Hamilton County, TeenSpot, North Bldg, 2nd Flr, 800 Vine St, Cincinnati, OH, 45202-2009. Tel: 513-369-6960. Fax: 513-369-3123. p. 1873

Korn, Martin, Head Librn, Sheppard, Mullin, Richter & Hampton Library, 333 S Hope, 42nd flr, Los Angeles, CA, 90071. Tel: 213-617-4127. Fax: 213-620-1398. p. 177

Kornblau, Alan, Dir, Delray Beach Public Library, 100 W Atlantic Ave, Delray Beach, FL, 33444. Tel: 561-266-0194. Fax: 561-266-9757. p. 437

Kornblau, Amy, Head, Syst, Florida Atlantic University, 777 Glades Rd, Boca Raton, FL, 33431. Tel: 561-297-6762. Fax: 561-297-2189. p. 428

Kornegay, Becky, Head, Ref, Western Carolina University, 176 Central Dr, Cullowhee, NC, 28723. Tel: 828-227-3417. Fax: 828-227-7015. p. 1786

Kornegay, Holt, Dir, Franklin County Library, 906 N Main St, Louisburg, NC, 27549-2199. Tel: 919-496-2111. Fax: 919-496-1339. p. 1807

Kornkven, Kelly, Dir, Mayville State University, 330 Third St NE, Mayville, ND, 58257-1299. Tel: 701-788-2301. Fax: 701-788-4846. p. 2971

Korns, Tammy, Pub Relations Coordr, Plano Public Library System, Library Administration, 2501 Coit Rd, Plano, TX, 75075. Tel: 972-769-4211. Fax: 972-769-4269. p. 2370

Koroghlanian, Carol, Dr, Asst Prof, University of Wisconsin-Eau Claire, 105 Garfield Ave, Eau Claire, WI, 54702. Tel: 715-836-2635. Fax: 715-836-5099. p. 2976

Koronowski, Sue, Libr Mgr, Montgomery County Public Libraries, Twinbrook Library, 202 Meadow Hall Dr, Rockville, MD, 20851-1551. Tel: 240-777-0249. Fax: 240-777-0258. p. 1039

Koroscik, Alexandra, Ref Serv, Milwaukee Area Technical College, 5555 W Highland Rd, Rm A282, Mequon, WI, 53092-1199. Tel: 262-238-2301. p. 2615

Korpal, Nancy, Chief Financial Officer, Saint Joseph County Public Library, 304 S Main, South Bend, IN, 46601-2125. Tel: 574-282-4646. Fax: 574-280-2763. p. 779

Korpanty, Karen, Dir, Elma Public Library, 1860 Bowen Rd, Elma, NY, 14059. Tel: 716-652-2719. Fax: 716-652-0381. p. 1619

Korpieski, Amy, Ref/Bibliog Instruction Librn, Clark State Community College Library, 570 E Leffel Lane, Springfield, OH, 45505. Tel: 937-328-6022. Fax: 937-328-6133. p. 1935

Korstvedt, Paul, Asst Dir, Gale Free Library, 23 Highland St, Holden, MA, 01520-2599. Tel: 508-210-5560. Fax: 508-829-0232. p. 1095

Kortbein, Karen, Librn, Marinette County Library System, Wausaukee Public Library, 911 Cedar St, Wausaukee, WI, 54177. Tel: 715-856-5995. Fax: 715-856-5995. p. 2612

Korte, Beth, Br Mgr, Putnam County District Library, Leipsic Memorial, 305 W Main St, Leipsic, OH, 45856. Tel: 419-943-2604. p. 1926

Kortfelt, Jennifer, Head, Digital Libr Tech, Dartmouth College Library, Baker-Berry Library, 6025 Baker-Berry Library, Hanover, NH, 03755-3525. Tel: 603-646-2560. Fax: 603-646-2167. p. 1450

Korth, Melissa, Librn, Hay Lakes Municipal Library, PO Box 69, Hay Lakes, AB, T0B 1W0, CANADA. Tel: 780-878-2665. p. 2706

Kortright, Ceinnie, Librn, Lakeland Library Region, Cut Knife Branch, Box 595, Cut Knife, SK, S0M 0N0, CANADA. Tel: 306-398-2342. p. 2920

Kortus, Nickie, Pub Relations Mgr, Alachua County Library District, 401 E University Ave, Gainesville, FL, 32601-5453. Tel: 352-334-3909. Fax: 352-334-3918. p. 448

Kos, Ed, PhD, Univ Archivist, Rockhurst University, 1100 Rockhurst Rd, Kansas City, MO, 64110-2561. Tel: 816-501-4161. Fax: 816-501-4666. p. 1340

Kosakowski, David, Coll Develop, California State University, 9001 Stockdale Hwy, Bakersfield, CA, 93311-1022. Tel: 661-654-3259. Fax: 661-654-3238. p. 123

Kosakowski, John, Acq/Cat/Syst Adminr, Landmark College Library, River Rd S, Putney, VT, 05346. Tel: 802-387-6785. Fax: 802-387-6896. p. 2432

Koschik, Douglas, Dir, Baldwin Public Library, 300 W Merrill St, Birmingham, MI, 48009-1483. Tel: 248-647-1700. Fax: 248-647-6393. p. 1158

Koscielniak, Kim, Law Librn, Library of Michigan, 702 W Kalamazoo St, Lansing, MI, 48915. Tel: 517-373-4697. Fax: 517-373-5700. p. 1201

Koscielniak, Kimberly, Librn, Honigman Miller Schwartz & Cohn LLP, 2290 First National Bldg, 660 Woodward Ave, Detroit, MI, 48226-3583. Tel: 313-465-7169. Fax: 313-465-8000. p. 1171

Koscielniak, Kimberly, Law Librn, Library of Michigan, 702 W Kalamazoo, Lansing, MI, 48909. Tel: 517-373-0630. Fax: 517-373-3915. p. 1201

Koscielniak, Lucy, Librn, Frederick Memorial Hospital, 400 W Seventh St, Frederick, MD, 21701. Tel: 240-566-3459. Fax: 240-566-3650. p. 1029

Kosco, Sheilah, Asst Dir, Bastrop Public Library, 1100 Church St, Bastrop, TX, 78602. Tel: 512-321-5441. Fax: 512-321-3163. p. 2286

Kosecki, Stan, Actg Assoc Dir, Info Products, United States Department of Agriculture, 10301 Baltimore Ave, Beltsville, MD, 20705-2351. Tel: 301-504-7114. Fax: 301-504-5472. p. 1020

Kosek, Peggy, Asst Librn, Thompson Home Public Library, 125 W Center St, Ithaca, MI, 48847. Tel: 989-875-4184. Fax: 989-875-3374. p. 1194

Kosharek, Susan, Ad, Ref Librn, Oregon Public Library, 256 Brook St, Oregon, WI, 53575. Tel: 608-835-3656. Fax: 608-835-2856. p. 2627

Kosher, Helene, Sr Librn, California Department of Corrections Library System, California State Prison-Solano, 2100 Peabody Rd, Vacaville, CA, 95696. Tel: 707-451-0182. Fax: 707-454-3244. p. 221

Koshinsky, Deborah, Head of Libr, Arizona State University Libraries, Architecture & Environmental Design Library, 810 Forest Mall, Design N Bldg, Tempe, AZ, 85287-1705. Tel: 480-965-6400. Fax: 480-727-6965. p. 83

Koshman, Sherry, Asst Prof, University of Pittsburgh, 135 N Bellefield Ave, Pittsburgh, PA, 15260. Tel: 412-624-5230. Fax: 412-624-5231. p. 2973

Kosick, Kerry, Br Mgr, Kearny Public Library, Kearny Branch, 759 Kearny Ave, Kearny, NJ, 07032. Tel: 201-955-7988. p. 1493

Kosick, Kerry, Sr Librn, Kearny Public Library, 318 Kearny Ave, Kearny, NJ, 07032. Tel: 201-998-2666. Fax: 201-998-1141. p. 1493

Kosins, Cheryl, Ref Serv, Sequoyah Regional Library System, 116 Brown Industrial Pkwy, Canton, GA, 30114-2899. Tel: 770-479-3090, Ext 221. Fax: 770-479-3069. p. 523

Kosinski, Inez, Librn, Didsbury Municipal Library, 2033 19th Ave, Didsbury, AB, T0M 0W0, CANADA. Tel: 403-335-3142. Fax: 403-335-3141. p. 2696

Kosinski, Janet, Head, Ch, Tiverton Library Services, 238 Highland Rd, Tiverton, RI, 02878. Tel: 401-625-6796, Ext 14. Fax: 401-625-5499. p. 2176

Kositany-Buckner, Cheptoo, Dep Exec Dir, The Kansas City Public Library, 14 W Tenth St, Kansas City, MO, 64105. Tel: 816-701-3508. Fax: 816-701-3401. p. 1338

Kositzky, Joey, Br Mgr, Flathead County Library, Whitefish Branch, Nine Spokane Ave, Whitefish, MT, 59937. Tel: 406-862-6657. Fax: 406-863-2312. p. 1384

Koskie, Lynne, Acq Mgr, Roger & Peggy Madigan Library, 999 Hagan Way, Williamsport, PA, 17701. Tel: 570-327-4523. Fax: 570-327-4503. p. 2156

Koskinen, Susan, Librn, University of California, Berkeley, Physics-Astronomy Library, 351 LeConte Hall, Berkeley, CA, 94720-6000. Tel: 510-643-7662. Fax: 510-642-8350. p. 128

Kosko, Fran, Circ, Monmouth Public Library, 168 S Ecols St, Monmouth, OR, 97361. Tel: 503-838-1932. Fax: 503-838-3899. p. 2006

Koslov, Marcia J, Exec Dir, Los Angeles County Law Library, Mildred L Lillie Bldg, 301 W First St, Los Angeles, CA, 90012-3100. Tel: 213-785-2529. Fax: 213-613-1329. p. 171

Kosowan, Johane, Mrs, Mgr, Libr Serv, Kapuskasing Public Library, 24 Mundy Ave, Kapuskasing, ON, P5N 1P9, CANADA. Tel: 705-335-3363. Fax: 705-335-2464. p. 2812

Kosowski, Ania, Circ Mgr, Hamtramck Public Library, 2360 Caniff St, Hamtramck, MI, 48212. Tel: 313-365-7050. Fax: 313-365-0160. p. 1187

Koss, Donald, Chairperson, Richard J Daley College, 7500 S Pulaski Rd, Chicago, IL, 60652-1200. Tel: 773-838-7674. Fax: 773-838-7670. p. 623

Koss, Lynn, Curator, African American Museum & Library, 55 12th Ave SE, Cedar Rapids, IA, 52401. Tel: 319-862-2101, Ext 227. Fax: 319-862-2105. p. 800

Kosson, Roger, Soc Sci Liaison Librn, Denison University Libraries, 400 W Loop, Granville, OH, 43023. Tel: 740-587-6389. Fax: 740-587-6285. p. 1902

Kost, D Susan, Librn, Schuylkill County Law Library, Schuylkill County Court House, 401 N Second St, Pottsville, PA, 17901. Tel: 570-628-1235. Fax: 570-628-1017. p. 2131

Kost, Timi, Dir, Worthington West Franklin Community Library, 214 E Main St, Worthington, PA, 16262. Tel: 724-297-3762. Fax: 724-297-3762. p. 2157

Koste, Jodi, Fac Mgr, Spec Coll & Archives Librn, Virginia Commonwealth University Libraries, Tompkins-McCaw Library, Medical College of Virginia Campus, 509 N 12th St, Richmond, VA, 23298-0582. Tel: 804-828-9898. Fax: 804-828-6089. p. 2492

Koste, Ken, Jr, Head, Circ & Ref, Collinsville Memorial Public Library District, 408 W Main St, Collinsville, IL, 62234. Tel: 618-344-1112. Fax: 618-345-6401. p. 630

Kostechka, Patricia, Libr Asst, Wisconsin School for the Deaf, 309 W Walworth Ave, Delavan, WI, 53115. Tel: 262-728-7127, Ext 7133. Fax: 262-728-7129. p. 2588

Kostelecky, Sarah, Dir, Institute of American Indian & Alaska Native Culture & Arts Development Library, 83 Avan Nu Po Rd, Santa Fe, NM, 87508. Tel: 505-424-5715. Fax: 505-424-3131. p. 1562

Kostelnik, Linda, Br Mgr, Guernsey County District Public Library, Byesville Branch, 100 Glass Ave, Byesville, OH, 43723. Tel: 740-685-2236. Fax: 740-685-6105. p. 1863

Kostencki, Robert, Br Mgr, Chicago Public Library, West Belmont, 3104 N Narragansett Ave, Chicago, IL, 60634. Tel: 312-746-5142. Fax: 312-746-9477. p. 610

Koster, Daniel, Pub Serv/Ref Librn, Mars Hill College, 124 Cascade St, Mars Hill, NC, 28754. Tel: 828 689-1454. p. 1809

Koster, Stacy, Dir, Cawker City Public Library, 802 Locust, Cawker City, KS, 67430. Tel: 785-781-4925. p. 859

Kostin, Sarah, Youth Serv, Bud Werner Memorial Library, 1289 Lincoln Ave, Steamboat Springs, CO, 80487. Tel: 970-879-0240. Fax: 970-879-3476. p. 323

Kostinko, Gail, Ref Librn, GRA Inc Library, 115 West Ave, Ste 201, Jenkintown, PA, 19046. Tel: 215-884-7500. Fax: 215-884-1385. p. 2072

Kostka, Tracy, Librn, Stratford Public Library, 74 Main St, North Stratford, NH, 03590. Tel: 603-922-9016. p. 1461

Kostnik, Chuck, Actg Dir, Nottoway County Public Libraries, Crewe Branch, 400 Tyler St, Crewe, VA, 23930. Tel: 434-645-8688. Fax: 434-645-8688. p. 2458

Kostova, Gergana, Ref & Instruction Librn, University of Maryland, Baltimore County, 1000 Hilltop Circle, Baltimore, MD, 21250. Tel: 410-455-2356. p. 1018

Kostrzewski, Marilyn, Dir, Libr Serv, Oakwood Hospital Medical Library, 18101 Oakwood Blvd, Dearborn, MI, 48124-2500. Tel: 313-593-7685. Fax: 313-436-2699. p. 1167

Koszalka, Michael, Dir, West Allis Public Library, 7421 W National Ave, West Allis, WI, 53214-4699. Tel: 414-302-8503. Fax: 414-302-8545. p. 2648

Kot, Malgorzata, Head Librn, Polish Museum of America Library, 984 N Milwaukee Ave, Chicago, IL, 60642-4101. Tel: 773-384-3352, Ext 101. Fax: 773-384-3799. p. 622

Kotarba, Susan, Dir, Pub Serv, Denver Public Library, Ten W 14th Ave Pkwy, Denver, CO, 80204-2731. Tel: 720-865-1111. Fax: 720-865-2087. p. 300

Kotarba, Susan, Br Mgr, Denver Public Library, Westwood, 1000 S Lowell Blvd, Denver, CO, 80219-3339. Tel: 303-936-8808. Fax: 303-937-4454. p. 301

Kotarski, Janet, Bk Coordr, Lake County Public Library, 1919 W 81st Ave, Merrillville, IN, 46410-5488. Tel: 219-769-3541. Fax: 219-756-9358. p. 763

Koteles, Colin, Web Coordr, College of DuPage Library, 425 Fawell Blvd, Glen Ellyn, IL, 60137-6599. Tel: 630-942-2923. Fax: 630-858-8757. p. 649

Kothman, Ann, Librn, Inyo County Free Library, Bishop Branch, 210 Academy Ave, Bishop, CA, 93514-2693. Tel: 760-873-5115. Fax: 760-873-5356. p. 159

Kotlanger, Michael SJ, Archivist, University of San Francisco, 2130 Fulton St, San Francisco, CA, 94117-1080. Tel: 415-422-5932. Fax: 415-422-5949. p. 248

Kotow, Nickolas, Librn, Alcoa Technical Center Library, 100 Technical Dr, Alcoa Center, PA, 15069-0001. Tel: 724-337-2396, 724-337-5300. Fax: 724-337-2394. p. 2026

Kott, Linda, Info Serv, South Dakota State University, 1300 N Campus Dr, Box 2115, Brookings, SD, 57007-1098. Tel: 605-688-5957. Fax: 605-688-6133. p. 2211

Kottkamp, Gretchen, Ref Serv Mgr, Park Ridge Public Library, 20 S Prospect, Park Ridge, IL, 60068-4188. Tel: 847-720-3245. Fax: 847-825-0001. p. 688

Kottke, Brad, Circ Supvr, Johnson & Wales University, College of Business, 7150 Montview Blvd, Denver, CO, 80220. Tel: 303-256-9519. Fax: 303-256-9459. p. 302

Kotulis-Carter, Karen, Dir, Bloomfield Township Public Library, 1099 Lone Pine Rd, Bloomfield Township, MI, 48302-2410. Tel: 248-642-5800. Fax: 248-258-2555. p. 1159

Kotusky, Linda, Asst Dir, Elkins Public Library, Nine Center Rd, Canterbury, NH, 03224. Tel: 603-783-4386. Fax: 603-783-4817. p. 1440

Kotwick, Michael, Librn, Baker College of Flint, 1050 W Bristol Rd, Flint, MI, 48507-5508. Tel: 810-766-4237. Fax: 810-766-2013. p. 1179

Koukol, Mark, Tech Librn, Arrowhead Library System, 5528 Emerald Ave, Mountain Iron, MN, 55768-2069. Tel: 218-741-3840. Fax: 218-748-2171. p. 1267

Koulikov, Mikhail, Res Librn, New York Law Institute Library, 120 Broadway, Rm 932, New York, NY, 10271-0043. Tel: 212-732-8720. Fax: 212-406-1204. p. 1689

Kource, Pamela, Br Mgr, Cumberland County Public Library & Information Center, Cliffdale, 6882 Cliffdale Rd, Fayetteville, NC, 28314-1936. Tel: 910-864-3800. Fax: 910-487-9090. p. 1792

Kouril, Gail, Br Mgr, RAND Corporation Library, 1776 Main St, M1LIB, Santa Monica, CA, 90407. Tel: 703-413-1100. Fax: 310-451-7029. p. 266

Kouril, Gail, Libr Mgr, RAND Corp, 1200 S Hayes St, Arlington, VA, 22202. Tel: 703-413-1100, Ext 5330. Fax: 703-414-4729. p. 2450

Kouse, Cara, Br Mgr, Dayton Metro Library, Wilmington-Stroop, 3980 Wilmington Pike, Dayton, OH, 45429. Tel: 937-496-8966. Fax: 937-496-4366. p. 1893

Koutnik, Charles, Dir, Appomattox Regional Library, 209 E Cawson St, Hopewell, VA, 23860. Tel: 804-458-6329, 804-861-0322. Fax: 804-458-4349. p. 2472

Kovach, Fran, Ref & Instrul Serv Librn, Southern Illinois University School of Medicine Library, 801 N Rutledge, Springfield, IL, 62702. Tel: 217-545-2658. Fax: 217-545-0988. p. 706

Kovach, John, Col Archivist, Saint Mary's College, Notre Dame, IN, 46556-5001. Tel: 574-284-5282. Fax: 574-284-4791. p. 771

Kovach, Nancy, Circ, Shelby County Public Library, 309 Eighth St, Shelbyville, KY, 40065. Tel: 502-633-3803. Fax: 502-633-4025. p. 935

Kovach, Terri, Head, Tech Serv, Ref, Monroe County Community College, 1555 S Raisinville Rd, Monroe, MI, 48161. Tel: 734-384-4161. Fax: 734-384-4160. p. 1209

Kovacic, Ellen S, Sr Assoc Librn for Tech Serv, Hebrew Union College-Jewish Institute of Religion, HUC-JIR, 3101 Clifton Ave, Cincinnati, OH, 45220-2488. Tel: 513-487-3298. Fax: 513-221-0519. p. 1870

Kovacs, Danielle, Curator of Ms & Univ Archivist, University of Massachusetts Amherst, 154 Hicks Way, Amherst, MA, 01003-9275. Tel: 413-545-2784. Fax: 413-545-6873. p. 1049

Kovacs, Dawn, Tech Serv, Wheaton Public Library, 225 N Cross St, Wheaton, IL, 60187-5376. Tel: 630-668-1374. Fax: 630-668-8950. p. 719

Kovacs, Mary, Librn, Lorain County Law Library, 226 Middle Ave, Elyria, OH, 44035. Tel: 440-329-5567. Fax: 440-322-1724. p. 1898

Kovalcik, Justin, Syst Librn, United States Military Academy Library, Jefferson Hall Library & Learning Center, 758 Cullum Rd, West Point, NY, 10996. Tel: 845-938-3833. Fax: 845-938-4000. p. 1767

Kovalcin, Mary, Libr Syst Coordr, University of Scranton, Monroe & Linden, Scranton, PA, 18510-4634. Tel: 570-941-6135. Fax: 570-941-7817. p. 2138

Kovalenko, Donna L, Curator of Coll, Frye Art Museum Library, 704 Terry Ave, Seattle, WA, 98104. Tel: 206-622-9250. Fax: 206-223-1707. p. 2527

Kovarik, Jennifer, Registrar, Vesterheim Norwegian-American Museum, 502 W Water St, Decorah, IA, 52101. Tel: 563-382-9681. Fax: 563-382-8828. p. 807

Kovarik, Rochelle, Librn, Park River Public Library, 605 Sixth St W, Park River, ND, 58270. Tel: 701-284-6116. p. 1847

Koveleskie, Judith, Per, Seton Hill University, One Seton Hill Dr, Greensburg, PA, 15601. Tel: 724-838-7828. Fax: 724-838-4203. p. 2062

Kovell, Lorrie, Librn II, North Olympic Library System, 2210 S Peabody St, Port Angeles, WA, 98362-6536. Tel: 360-417-8500. Fax: 360-457-3125. p. 2523

Kovis, Jessie, Br Mgr, Mid-Columbia Libraries, Prosser Branch, 902 Seventh St, Prosser, WA, 99350. Tel: 509-786-2533. Fax: 509-786-7341. p. 2518

Kowal, Jan, YA Librn, Berkeley County Library System, 1003 Hwy 52, Moncks Corner, SC, 29461. Tel: 843-719-4278. p. 2200

Kowal, Ronnie, Asst Regional Libr Mgr, Broward County Division of Libraries, North Regional-BC, 1100 Coconut Creek Blvd, Coconut Creek, FL, 33066. Tel: 954-201-2607. Fax: 954-201-2650. p. 442

Kowal, Ruth, Dir, Admin & Finance, Boston Public Library, 700 Boylston St, Boston, MA, 02117-0286. Tel: 617-536-5400. Fax: 617-236-4306. p. 1056

Kowalcheck, Michael A, Dir, North Versailles Public Library, 1401 Greensburg Ave, North Versailles, PA, 15137. Tel: 412-823-2222. Fax: 412-823-2012. p. 2099

Kowalewski, Denis S, Head Librn, Chapman & Cutler, 111 W Monroe, Chicago, IL, 60603-4096. Tel: 312-845-3749. Fax: 312-701-6620. p. 607

Kowalewski, Donna, Dir, Galesburg Memorial Library, 188 E Michigan Ave, Galesburg, MI, 49053. Tel: 269-665-7839. Fax: 269-665-7788. p. 1182

Kowalewski, Jean, Br Head, Toronto Public Library, S Walter Stewart Branch, 170 Memorial Park Ave, Toronto, ON, M4J 2K5, CANADA. Tel: 416-396-3975. Fax: 416-396-3842. p. 2863

Kowalewski, Rosanna, Head, Pub Serv, University of Massachusetts Lowell Libraries, 61 Wilder St, Lowell, MA, 01854-3098. Tel: 978-934-4580. Fax: 978-934-3015. p. 1100

Kowalewski-Ward, Julie, Head, Access Serv, San Jose State University, One Washington Sq, San Jose, CA, 95192-0028. Tel: 408-808-2343. Fax: 408-808-2141. p. 251

Kowalik, Steven, Head Librn, Art Slide Libr, Hunter College Libraries, 695 Park Ave, New York, NY, 10065. Tel: 212-772-5054. Fax: 212-772-4142. p. 1682

Kowalski, Diana, Libr Assoc, North Dakota State University Libraries, Philip N Haakenson Health Sciences Library, 135 Sudro Hall, Fargo, ND, 58102. Tel: 701-231-7748. Fax: 701-231-7606. p. 1841

Kowalski, Jane, Dir, Carter County Library District, 403 Ash St, Van Buren, MO, 63965. Tel: 573-323-4315. Fax: 573-323-0188. p. 1370

Kowalski, Nicholas, Coll Develop Librn, University of Saint Thomas, 1100 W Main, Houston, TX, 77006. Tel: 713-525-2182. Fax: 713-525-2186. p. 2344

Kowalski, Richard, Sr Res Librn, Consumer Electronics Association, 1919 S Eads St, Arlington, VA, 22202. Tel: 703-907-7763. p. 2449

Kowalski, Sherry, Head, Ref, Broome County Public Library, 185 Court St, Binghamton, NY, 13901-3503. Tel: 607-778-6423. Fax: 607-778-6429. p. 1582

Kowalsky, Michelle, Prof, William Paterson University, College of Education, 1600 Valley Rd, Wayne, NJ, 07470. Tel: 973-720-2331, 973-720-2980. Fax: 973-720-2585. p. 2969

Kowell, Carole, Dir, Medina County District Library, 210 S Broadway, Medina, OH, 44256. Tel: 330-725-0588. Fax: 330-725-2053. p. 1916

Kownover, Margaret, Head, Ch, Goshen Public Library, 601 S Fifth St, Goshen, IN, 46526-3994. Tel: 574-533-9531. Fax: 574-533-5211. p. 746

Kownslar, Edward, Assoc Dir, Texas A&M University-Corpus Christi, Mary & Jeff Bell Library, 6300 Ocean Dr, Corpus Christi, TX, 78412-5501. Tel: 361-825-2643. Fax: 361-825-5973. p. 2302

Kox, Christopher, Chair, City College of San Francisco, 50 Phelan Ave, Rm 517, San Francisco, CA, 94112. Tel: 415-452-5519. Fax: 415-452-5478. p. 2962

Koyama, Gary, Mgr, Leo A Daly Co Library, America Saving Bldg, Ste 1230, 1357 Kapiolani Blvd, Honolulu, HI, 96814. Tel: 808-521-8889. Fax: 808-521-3757. p. 560

Koz, Olga, Ref, Largo Public Library, 120 Central Park Dr, Largo, FL, 33771. Tel: 727-587-6715. Fax: 727-586-7353. p. 460

Koza, John, Coordr, Tech Serv, North Shore Community College Library, One Ferncroft Rd, Danvers, MA, 01923-4093. Tel: 978-739-5413. Fax: 978-739-5500. p. 1083

Kozaczka, Stanley J, Dir, Libr Serv, Cazenovia College, Lincklaen St, Cazenovia, NY, 13035. Tel: 315-655-7132. Fax: 315-655-8675. p. 1603

Kozak, Anne, Dir, Thomas Ford Memorial Library, 800 Chestnut Ave, Western Springs, IL, 60558. Tel: 708-246-0520. Fax: 708-246-0403. p. 717

Kozak, Jeffrey S, Archivist, Asst Librn, George C Marshall Foundation Research Library, 1600 VMI Parade, Lexington, VA, 24450-1600. Tel: 540-463-7103, Ext 122. Fax: 540-464-5229. p. 2474

Kozak, Reka, Librn, Barnes-Jewish Hospital, 216 S Kingshighway Blvd, Mail Stop 90-32-639, Saint Louis, MO, 63110. Tel: 314-454-7208. Fax: 314-454-5301. p. 1353

Kozak-Selby, Gay, Chief Librn, County of Brant Public Library, 12 William St, Paris, ON, N3L 1K7, CANADA. Tel: 519-442-2433. Fax: 519-442-7582. p. 2835

Kozakiewicz, Scott, Coordr, Media Serv, Glendale Community College, 6000 W Olive Ave, Glendale, AZ, 85302. Tel: 623 845-3115. Fax: 623-845-3102. p. 64

Kozakowski, Kathleen, Ad, Wayne Public Library, 3737 S Wayne Rd, Wayne, MI, 48184. Tel: 734-721-7832. Fax: 734-721-0341. p. 1235

Kozel-La Ha, Sheree, Exec Dir, Homer Township Public Library District, 14320 W 151st St, Homer Glen, IL, 60491. Tel: 708-301-7908. Fax: 708-301-4535. p. 657

Kozelka, Van, Dir, Katonah Village Library, 26 Bedford Rd, Katonah, NY, 10536-2121. Tel: 914-232-3508. Fax: 914-232-0415. p. 1648

Kozey, Corene, Info Serv, Lethbridge College, 3000 College Dr S, Lethbridge, AB, T1K 1L6, CANADA. Tel: 403-320-3352. p. 2709

Kozikowski, Chester G, III, Educ Tech Spec, Boston College, 885 Centre St, Newton Centre, MA, 02459. Tel: 617-552-8606. Fax: 617-552-2889. p. 1110

Koziol, Margaret, Circ, Cold Spring Harbor Library, 95 Harbor Rd, Cold Spring Harbor, NY, 11724. Tel: 631-692-6820. Fax: 631-692-6827. p. 1609

Koziolek, Debbie, Asst Libr Dir, Wells Public Library, 54 First St SW, Wells, MN, 56097-1913. Tel: 507-553-3702. Fax: 507-553-6141. p. 1288

Kozlowski, Barbara A, Commun Serv, Pub Serv, Skokie Public Library, 5215 Oakton St, Skokie, IL, 60077-3680. Tel: 847-673-7774. Fax: 847-673-7797. p. 703

Kozlowski, Diane, Asst Dir, Webster Public Library, Webster Plaza, 980 Ridge Rd, Webster, NY, 14580. Tel: 585-872-7075. p. 1765

Kozlowski, Kazimiera, Curator, Connecticut Commission on Culture & Tourism, One S Canterbury Rd, Rte 14 & 169, Canterbury, CT, 06331. Tel: 860-546-7800. Fax: 860-546-7803. p. 333

Kozlowski, Ken, Dir, Supreme Court of Ohio, 65 S Front St, 11th Flr, Columbus, OH, 43215-3431. Tel: 614-387-9666. Fax: 614-387-9689. p. 1890

Kozubenko, Ven, Data & Web Serv Adminr, Spokane County Library District, 4322 N Argonne Rd, Spokane, WA, 99212-1868. Tel: 509-893-8453. Fax: 509-893-8472. p. 2536

Kozup, Kathleen, Mgr, Portage County District Library, Garrettsville Branch, 10482 South St, Garrettsville, OH, 44231. Tel: 330-527-4378. Fax: 330-527-4370. p. 1901

Kraat, Susan, Coordr, Libr Instruction, State University of New York College at New Paltz, 300 Hawk Dr, New Paltz, NY, 12561-2493. Tel: 845-257-3705. p. 1666

Krack, Hazel, Librn, Cando Community Library, 523 Main St, Cando, ND, 58324. Tel: 701-968-4549. p. 1839

Kraemer, Amy, Librn, Davis Public Library, 1391 Rte 123 N, Stoddard, NH, 03464. Tel: 603-446-6251. p. 1465

Kraemer, David, Dr, Librn, Jewish Theological Seminary Library, 3080 Broadway, New York, NY, 10027. Tel: 212-678-8075. Fax: 212-678-8891, 212-678-8998. p. 1683

Kraemer, Judy, Dir, Long Beach Memorial/Miller Children's Hospital Long Beach, 2801 Atlantic Ave, Long Beach, CA, 90806-1737. Tel: 562-933-3841. Fax: 562-933-3847. p. 166

Kraepel, Kathryn, Head, Tech Serv, Springfield Township Library, 12000 Davisburg Rd, Davisburg, MI, 48350. Tel: 248-846-6550. Fax: 248-846-6555. p. 1167

Krafft, Dean, Chief Tech Strategist, Cornell University Library, 201 Olin Library, Ithaca, NY, 14853-5301. Tel: 607-255-9214. Fax: 607-255-6788. p. 1641

Krafft, Leah, Librn, Absecon Public Library, 305 New Jersey Ave, Absecon, NJ, 08201. Tel: 609-646-2228. Fax: 609-383-8992. p. 1469

Krafft, Scott, Curator, Spec Coll, Northwestern University Library, 1970 Campus Dr, Evanston, IL, 60208-2300. Tel: 847-491-7658. p. 644

Kraft, Brian, Coll Mgr, Washington County Library, 8595 Central Park Pl, Woodbury, MN, 55125-9453. Tel: 651-275-8500. Fax: 651-275-8509. p. 1290

Kraft, Cheryl, Adult Serv, Neenah Public Library, 240 E Wisconsin Ave, Neenah, WI, 54956-3010. Tel: 920-886-6314. Fax: 920-886-6324. p. 2624

Kraft, Edward, Dir, Shellsburg Public Library, 110 Main St, Shellsburg, IA, 52332. Tel: 319-436-2112. Fax: 319-436-2112. p. 843

Kraft, Juliann, Acq, Buena Vista University Library, 610 W Fourth St, Storm Lake, IA, 50588. Tel: 712-749-2091. Fax: 712-749-2033. p. 846

Kraft, Lindsey, Youth Serv Mgr, Forest Park Public Library, 7555 Jackson Blvd, Forest Park, IL, 60130. Tel: 708-366-7171. Fax: 708-366-7293. p. 646

Kraft, Lindsey, Dir, Youth Serv, Lisle Library District, 777 Front St, Lisle, IL, 60532-3599. Tel: 630-971-1675. Fax: 630-971-1701. p. 666

Kraft, Michelle, Pres, Ohio Health Sciences Library Association, South Pointe Hospital, Medical Library, 20000 Harvard Rd, Warrensville Heights, OH, 44122. Tel: 216-491-7454. Fax: 216-491-7650. p. 2952

Kraft, Ned, Info Res, United States Department of State, 2201 C St NW, Rm 3239, Washington, DC, 20520-2442. Tel: 202-647-2196. Fax: 202-647-2971. p. 419

Kraft, Steve, Adult Info Serv Mgr, Circ, Guelph Public Library, 100 Norfolk St, Guelph, ON, N1H 4J6, CANADA. Tel: 519-824-6220. Fax: 519-824-8342. p. 2807

Kragness, Janice, Assoc Dir, Res & Instruction, University of Saint Thomas, 2115 Summit Ave, Mail Box 5004, Saint Paul, MN, 55105. Tel: 651-962-4645. Fax: 651-962-5406. p. 1282

Kragness, Janice, Assoc Dir, Res & Instruction, University of Saint Thomas, Charles J Keffer Library, 1000 LaSalle Ave, MOH 206, Minneapolis, MN, 55403. Tel: 651-962-4645. Fax: 651-962-4648. p. 1282

Krahn, Amy, Librn, Whitefish Bay Public Library, 5420 N Marlborough Dr, Whitefish Bay, WI, 53217. Tel: 414-964-4380. Fax: 414-964-5733. p. 2648

Krahn, Vonda, Adminr, Lanier Library Association, Inc, 72 Chestnut St, Tryon, NC, 28782. Tel: 828-859-9535. p. 1827

Kraimer, Elaine, Ch, Bancroft Memorial Library, 50 Hopedale St, Hopedale, MA, 01747-1799. Tel: 508-634-2209. Fax: 508-634-8095. p. 1096

Krajcar, Angela, Ch, Orangeburg Library, 20 S Greenbush Rd, Orangeburg, NY, 10962-1311. Tel: 845-359-2244. Fax: 845-359-8692. p. 1711

Krajewski, Rex, Head, Info Serv, Simmons College, 300 The Fenway, Boston, MA, 02115-5898. p. 1066

Krajnak, Patricia, Dir, Res & Ref Serv, International Foundation of Employee Benefit Plans, 18700 W Bluemound Rd, Brookfield, WI, 53045-2936. Tel: 262-786-6710, Ext 5. Fax: 262-786-8780. p. 2583

Krake, Erin, Librn, Roslyn Public Library, 201 S First, Roslyn, WA, 98941. Tel: 509-649-3420. Fax: 509-649-3420. p. 2526

Krakora, Ed, Dir, Ashland University Library, 509 College Ave, Ashland, OH, 44805-3796. Tel: 419-289-5401. Fax: 419-289-5422. p. 1855

Krakovec, Beverly, Asst Dir, White Oak Library District, 121 E Eighth St, Lockport, IL, 60441. Tel: 815-838-0755. p. 667

Krakovec, Beverly Jean, Br Mgr, White Oak Library District, Romeoville Branch, 201 W Normantown Rd, Romeoville, IL, 60446. Tel: 815-886-2030. p. 667

Kral, Jennifer, Librn, Capital Health Regional Medical Center, 750 Brunswick Ave, Trenton, NJ, 08638. Tel: 609-394-6065. Fax: 609-278-1882. p. 1535

Kralik, Casey, Tech Serv Librn, Bellevue University, 1000 Galvin Rd S, Bellevue, NE, 68005. Tel: 402-557-7309. Fax: 402-557-5427. p. 1393

Kralisz, Victor, Mgr, Dallas Public Library, 1515 Young St, Dallas, TX, 75201-5499. Tel: 214-670-1643, 670-1668. Fax: 214-670-1654. p. 2306

Kraljevich, Lisa, Children's/Teen Coordr, Boone Area Library, 129 N Mill St, Birdsboro, PA, 19508-2340. Tel: 610-582-5666. Fax: 610-582-6826. p. 2035

Kraljic, Mary, Access Serv, South Dakota State University, 1300 N Campus Dr, Box 2115, Brookings, SD, 57007-1098. Tel: 605-688-4049. Fax: 605-688-6133. p. 2210

Kraljic, Mary, Head, Pub Serv, South Dakota State University, 1300 N Campus Dr, Box 2115, Brookings, SD, 57007-1098. Tel: 605-688-4049. Fax: 605-688-6133. p. 2210

Krall, Robert, Dir for Departmental Libr, Res Sharing, & Delivery Serv, University of Pennsylvania Libraries, 3420 Walnut St, Philadelphia, PA, 19104-6206. Tel: 215-573-3626. Fax: 215-898-0559. p. 2118

Kram, Lauri, Dir, Edmonds Community College Library, 20000 68th Ave W, Lynnwood, WA, 98036. Tel: 425-640-1529. p. 2520

Kramar, Joyce, Acq, Sweet Briar College, 134 Chapel Rd, Sweet Briar, VA, 24595-1200. Tel: 434-381-6138. Fax: 434-381-6173. p. 2497

Kramek, Tara, Libr Tech, The Hospital of Central Connecticut, 100 Grand St, New Britain, CT, 06050. Tel: 860-224-5900, Ext 2570, 860-224-5900, Ext 2571. Fax: 860-224-5970. p. 354

Kramer, Becky, Libr Tech, Colorado Mountain College, 3000 County Rd 114, Glenwood Springs, CO, 81601. Tel: 970-947-8271. Fax: 970-947-8288. p. 309

Kramer, Beth, Dir, West Tisbury Free Public Library, 1042 State Rd, West Tisbury, MA, 02575. Tel: 508-693-3366. Fax: 508-696-0130. p. 1138

Kramer, Charla, Librn, Northwestern Michigan College, 1701 E Front St, Traverse City, MI, 49686-3061. Tel: 231-995-1973. Fax: 231-995-1056. p. 1231

Kramer, Charlene, Librn, Sasktel Corporate Library, 2121 Saskatchewan Dr, 12th Flr, Regina, SK, S4P 3Y2, CANADA. Tel: 306-777-2899. Fax: 306-359-9022. p. 2924

Kramer, Debbi, Librn, Three Forks Community Library, 607 Main St, Three Forks, MT, 59752. Tel: 406-285-3747. p. 1389

Kramer, Debby, ILL Coordr, Holy Family University Library, 9801 Frankford Ave, Philadelphia, PA, 19114. Tel: 267-341-3315, 267-341-3316. Fax: 215-632-8067. p. 2111

Kramer, Deeann, Librn, York Township Public Library, 1005 W Main St, Thomson, IL, 61285. Tel: 815-259-2480. Fax: 815-259-2480. p. 709

Kramer, Ed, Dir, Housing Advocates, Inc, 3655 Prospect Ave E, Cleveland, OH, 44115. Tel: 216-391-5444. Fax: 216-391-5404. p. 1880

Kramer, Ilene, Circ, Canton Public Library, 786 Washington St, Canton, MA, 02021-3029. Tel: 781-821-5027. Fax: 781-821-5029. p. 1079

Kramer, Jacqueline, Circ Mgr, Ref Mgr, Sweetwater County Library System, 300 N First East, Green River, WY, 82935. Tel: 307-875-3615, Ext 1120. Fax: 307-872-3203. p. 2655

Kramer, Jason, Exec Dir, New York State Higher Education Initiative, 22 Corporate Woods Blvd, Albany, NY, 12211-2350. Tel: 518-443-5444. Fax: 518-432-4346. p. 2950

Kramer, Jean, Tech Serv, Minnesota State University Moorhead, 1104 Seventh Ave S, Moorhead, MN, 56563. Tel: 218-477-2922. Fax: 218-477-5924. p. 1266

Kramer, Karen, Syst Librn, Gateway Community College, 20 Church St, New Haven, CT, 06510. Tel: 203-285-2140. Fax: 203-285-2055. p. 355

Kramer, Karen, Br Head, Somerville Public Library, West, 40 College Ave, Somerville, MA, 02144. Tel: 617-623-5000, Ext 2975. p. 1124

Kramer, Kathleen, Librn, Harrison Village Library, Four Front St, Harrison, ME, 04040. Tel: 207-583-2970. p. 987

Kramer, Larry, Access Serv, Avila University, 11901 Wornall Rd, Kansas City, MO, 64145. Tel: 816-501-3712. Fax: 816-501-2456. p. 1336

Kramer, Linda, Head Librn, Bowling Green State University Libraries, Curriculum Resource Center, Jerome Library, Bowling Green State University, Bowling Green, OH, 43403-0178. Tel: 419-372-2956. p. 1861

Kramer, Linda, Pub Serv Librn, Johnson State College Library, 337 College Hill, Johnson, VT, 05656. Tel: 802-635-1275. Fax: 802-635-1294. p. 2426

Kramer, Maria, Div Mgr, Redwood City Public Library, 1044 Middlefield Rd, Redwood City, CA, 94063-1868. Tel: 650-780-7018. Fax: 650-780-7069. p. 215

Kramer, Maric, E-Learning & Ref Librn, Wheelock College Library, 132 The Riverway, Boston, MA, 02215-4815. Tel: 617-879-1141. Fax: 617-879-2408. p. 1068

Kramer, Mary, Mgr, Xerox Corporation, 800 Phillips Rd, Bldg 0105-66C, Webster, NY, 14580. Tel: 585-422-3505. Fax: 585-422-8299. p. 1765

Kramer, Matthew, Librn, Massachusetts School of Professional Psychology Library, 221 Rivermoor St, Boston, MA, 02132. Tel: 617-327-6777, Ext 220. Fax: 617-327-4447. p. 1063

Kramer, Melissa, Dir, Planning & Communication, Bryn Mawr College, 101 N Merion Ave, Bryn Mawr, PA, 19010-2899. Tel: 610-527-5287. Fax: 610-526-7480. p. 2039

Kramer, Sally, Br Mgr, Public Library of Cincinnati & Hamilton County, Loveland Branch, 649 Loveland-Madeira Rd, Loveland, OH, 45140. Tel: 513-369-4476. Fax: 513-369-4477. p. 1872

Kramer, Sandra, Asst Dir for Serv, University of Arizona, Arizona Health Sciences Library, 1501 N Campbell Ave, Tucson, AZ, 85724. Tel: 520-626-6438. Fax: 520-626-2922. p. 88

Kramer, Wendy, Head, Youth Serv, Montgomery County-Norristown Public Library, Upper Perkiomen Valley, 350 Main St, Red Hill, PA, 18076. Tel: 215-679-2020. p. 2099

Krampfert, Paula, Acq, Southern New Hampshire University, 2500 N River Rd, Manchester, NH, 03106-1045. Tel: 603-645-9605. Fax: 603-645-9685. p. 1456

Kranis, Janet, Librn, Monmouth County Library, Eastern, 1001 Rte 35, Shrewsbury, NJ, 07702. Tel: 732-683-8980. Fax: 732-219-0140. p. 1499

Krantz, Jane, Exec Dir, Kehillat Israel Reconstructionist Congregation of Pacific Palisades, 16019 Sunset Blvd, Pacific Palisades, CA, 90272. Tel: 310-459-2328. Fax: 310-573-2098. p. 203

Krantz, Linda L, Dir, Rockbridge Regional Library, 138 S Main St, Lexington, VA, 24450-2316. Tel: 540-463-4324. Fax: 540-464-4824. p. 2474

Kranz, Mary, Librn, Mount Saint Mary's College, Doheny Campus Library, Ten Chester Pl, Los Angeles, CA, 90007. Tel: 213-477-2750. Fax: 213-749-8111. p. 175

Krapohl, Robert H, Dr, Libr Dir, Trinity International University, 2065 Half Day Rd, Deerfield, IL, 60015-1241. Tel: 847-317-4000. Fax: 847-317-4012. p. 635

Kraska, Leni, Br Support, Stormont, Dundas & Glengarry County Library, Lancaster Branch, (Main St) 195 Military St, Lancaster, ON, K0C 1N0, CANADA. Tel: 613-347-2311. Fax: 613-347-9088. p. 2801

Krasner, Stephanie, Librn, Temple Israel of New Rochelle, 1000 Pinebrook Blvd, New Rochelle, NY, 10804. Tel: 914-235-1800. Fax: 914-235-1854. p. 1667

Krasnesky, Lori, ILL Coordr, Mercyhurst College, 501 E 38th St, Erie, PA, 16546. Tel: 814-824-2234. Fax: 814-824-2219. p. 2056

Krasniewicz, Erin, Ref Serv, Pew Charitable Trusts Library, One Commerce Sq, 2005 Market St, Ste 1700, Philadelphia, PA, 19103-7017. Tel: 215-575-4814. Fax: 215-575-4939. p. 2114

Krasnodebski, Renita, Ref, College of Saint Elizabeth, Two Convent Rd, Morristown, NJ, 07960-6989. Tel: 973-290-4237. Fax: 973-290-4226. p. 1504

Kratchman, Julie, Mgr, Libr Serv, Educational Information & Resource Center, 107 Dilbreth Pkwy, Ste 200, Mullica Hill, NJ, 08062. Tel: 856-582-7000, Ext 140. Fax: 856-582-4206. p. 1506

Kratz, Charles E, Dean, University of Scranton, Monroe & Linden, Scranton, PA, 18510-4634. Tel: 570-941-4000, 570-941-4008. Fax: 570-941-7817. p. 2138

Kratzer, Lona, Archives, Hancock County Public Library, 240 Court Sq, Hawesville, KY, 42348. Tel: 270-927-6760. Fax: 270-927-6847. p. 916

Kratzer, Lona, Librn, Hancock County Public Library, Lewisport Branch, 403 Second St, Lewisport, KY, 42351. Tel: 270-295-3765. p. 916

Kraus, Aniza, Curator, Ukrainian Museum-Archives Inc, 1202 Kenilworth Ave, Cleveland, OH, 44113. Tel: 216-781-4329. p. 1881

Kraus, Darla Jean, Dir, Lakeview Community Library, 112 Butler St, Random Lake, WI, 53075-1708. Tel: 920-994-4825. Fax: 920-994-2230. p. 2632

Kraus, Holly, Dir, Wagner Community Library, 111 N Main St, Falls City, OR, 97344-9776. Tel: 503-787-3521, Ext 319. Fax: 503-787-1507. p. 1998

Kraus, Jan, Dir, Aspirus Wausau Hospital, 333 Pine Ridge Blvd, Wausau, WI, 54401. Tel: 715-847-2184. Fax: 715-847-2183. p. 2646

Kraus, Joe, Ref, University of Denver, 2150 E Evans Ave, Denver, CO, 80208-2007. Tel: 303-871-3441. Fax: 303-871-2290. p. 304

Krause, Edward, Fr, Dir, Catholic Central Verein of America, 3835 Westminster Pl, Saint Louis, MO, 63108. Tel: 314-371-1653. Fax: 314-371-0889. p. 1353

Krause, Orva, Librn, Lidgerwood City Library, 15 Wiley Ave S, Lidgerwood, ND, 58053-4001. Tel: 701-538-4669. p. 1845

Krause, Rebecca, Dir, Children & YA, Phoenixville Public Library, 183 Second Ave, Phoenixville, PA, 19460-3420. Tel: 610-933-3013, Ext 27. Fax: 610-933-4338. p. 2120

Krause, Rick, Coordr, Electronic Res, University of Wisconsin-Parkside Library, 900 Wood Rd, Kenosha, WI, 53141. Tel: 262-595-2356. Fax: 262-595-2545. p. 2602

Krause, Rose, Curator, Spec Coll, Northwest Museum of Art & Culture-Eastern Washington State Historical Society, 2316 W First Ave, Spokane, WA, 99201-1099. Tel: 509-363-5342. Fax: 509-363-5303. p. 2536

Krause, Sara, Librn, Dodge Correctional Institution Library, One W Lincoln St, Waupun, WI, 53963. Tel: 920-324-5577, Ext 6570. Fax: 920-324-6297. p. 2646

Krause, Susan, Tech Serv, Virginia Public Library, 215 Fifth Ave S, Virginia, MN, 55792-2642. Tel: 218-748-7525. Fax: 218-748-7527. p. 1286

Krause, Wendy M, Dir, Honeoye Public Library, 8708 Main St, Honeoye, NY, 14471. Tel: 585-229-5020. Fax: 585-229-5881. p. 1637

Kraushaar, Katie, Info Serv Mgr, Quincy Public Library, 526 Jersey St, Quincy, IL, 62301-3996. Tel: 217-223-1309. Fax: 217-222-5672. p. 693

Kraushaar, Liz, Circ, ILL, Rossford Public Library, 720 Dixie Hwy, Rossford, OH, 43460-1289. Tel: 419-666-0924. Fax: 419-666-1989. p. 1932

Krauspe, Claudia, Head, Youth Serv, Helen M Plum Memorial Public Library District, 110 W Maple St, Lombard, IL, 60148-2594. Tel: 630-627-0316. Fax: 630-627-0336. p. 667

Krauss, Bob, Electronic Res, Ser, Biola University Library, 13800 Biola Ave, La Mirada, CA, 90639. Tel: 562-903-4837. Fax: 562-903-4840. p. 162

Krauss, Rose Marie, Librn, Media Spec, United States Marine Corps, PO Box 5018, Elrod Ave, Beaufort, SC, 29906-5018. Tel: 843-228-7682. Fax: 843-228-7596. p. 2181

Krauss, Rose Marie, Librn, Media Spec, United States Marine Corps, Blvd DeFrance, Bldg 283, Parris Island, SC, 29905-0070. Tel: 843-228-1671. Fax: 843-228-3840. p. 2202

Krauth, Diane K, Dir, Franklin County Library, 105 S Porter St, Winchester, TN, 37398-1546. Tel: 931-967-3706. Fax: 931-962-1477. p. 2269

Krautheim, Anne, Dir, Dwight D Eisenhower Public Library, 537 Totowa Rd, Totowa, NJ, 07512-1699. Tel: 973-790-3265, Ext 11. Fax: 973-790-0306. p. 1535

Krautler, Charles, Dir, Atlanta Regional Commission Information Center, 40 Courtland St NE, Atlanta, GA, 30303. Tel: 404-463-3100. Fax: 404-463-3105. p. 513

Krautter, Mary, Head of Ref & Instrul Serv, University of North Carolina at Greensboro, 320 Spring Garden St, Greensboro, NC, 27402. Tel: 336-334-5880. Fax: 336-334-5399. p. 1798

Kravig, Janet, Archives & Spec Coll Librn, Cat Librn, Tech Serv Librn, Oklahoma Panhandle State University, 409 W Sewell St, Goodwell, OK, 73939. Tel: 580-349-1546. Fax: 580-349-1541. p. 1964

Krawchuk, Kathleen, Librn, University of Florida, 3200 E Palm Beach Rd, Belle Glade, FL, 33430. Tel: 561-993-1517. Fax: 561-993-1582. p. 427

Krawczak, Joyce, ILL, Ref Serv, Cheboygan Area Public Library, 100 S Bailey St, Cheboygan, MI, 49721-1661. Tel: 231-627-2381. Fax: 231-627-9172. p. 1162

Krawczyk, Christina, Mgt Librn, UOP Knowledge & Library Services, 25 E Algonquin Rd, Des Plaines, IL, 60016. Tel: 847-391-1483. Fax: 847-391-3330. p. 636

Krawczyk, Richard, Head of Libr, Free Library of Philadelphia, Katharine Drexel Branch, 11099 Knights Rd, Philadelphia, PA, 19154-3516. Tel: 215-685-9383. Fax: 215-685-9384. p. 2107

Krazmien, Mindy, Exec Dir, Putnam County Historical Society & Foundry School Museum Library, 63 Chestnut St, Cold Spring, NY, 10516. Tel: 845-265-4010. Fax: 845-265-2884. p. 1608

Krebsbach, Suzanne, Librn, South Carolina Public Service Authority, One Riverwood Dr, Moncks Corner, SC, 29461. Tel: 843-761-4072. Fax: 843-761-4112. p. 2200

Krefting, Judy, Librn, Jasper Municipal Library, 500 Robson St, Jasper, AB, T0E 1E0, CANADA. Tel: 780-852-3652. Fax: 780-852-5841. p. 2707

Kregel, Charlie, Chief Librn, Powell River Public Library, 4411 Michigan Ave, Powell River, BC, V8A 2S3, CANADA. Tel: 604-485-8661. Fax: 604-485-5320. p. 2735

Kregstein, Phyllis, Dir, Libr Serv, New Mexico VA Health Care System, 1501 San Pedro SE, Albuquerque, NM, 87108. Tel: 505-256-2786. Fax: 505-256-2870. p. 1549

Kreher, Jan, Circ, C E Brehm Memorial Public Library District, 101 S Seventh St, Mount Vernon, IL, 62864. Tel: 618-242-6322. Fax: 618-242-0810. p. 677

Krei, Nancy, Dir, Fontana Public Library, 166 Second Ave, Fontana, WI, 53125. Tel: 262-275-5107. Fax: 262-275-2179. p. 2592

Kreig-Sigman, Kelly, Dir, La Crosse Public Library, 800 Main St, La Crosse, WI, 54601. Tel: 608-789-7100. Fax: 608-789-7106. p. 2603

Kreiger, Tanis, Covering Supvr, Pub Serv & Acq, Electronic Res Librn, Rensselaer Libraries, Rensselaer Polytechnic Inst, 110 Eighth St, Troy, NY, 12180-3590. Tel: 518-276-8300. Fax: 518-276-2044. p. 1756

Kreiling, Jeffrey, Librn, Buchanan Ingersoll & Rooney PC, Two Liberty Pl, 50 S 16th St, Ste 3200, Philadelphia, PA, 19102-2555. Tel: 215-665-5311. Fax: 215-665-8760. p. 2103

Kreimeier, Danis, Dir, Napa City-County Library, 580 Coombs St, Napa, CA, 94559-3396. Tel: 707-253-4241. Fax: 707-253-4615. p. 192

Kreinbring, Mary, Dir, American Dental Association Department of Library Services, 211 E Chicago Ave, 6th Flr, Chicago, IL, 60611-2678. Tel: 312-440-2642. Fax: 312-440-2774. p. 605

Kreiner, Mary Beth, Librn, Cranbrook Academy of Art Library, 39221 Woodward Ave, Bloomfield Hills, MI, 48304. Tel: 248-645-3477. Fax: 248-645-3464. p. 1158

Kreinik, Doug, Pres, Temple B'Nai Israel Library, 1703 20th St, Parkersburg, WV, 26101. Tel: 304-485-6729. p. 2568

Kreinus, Anthony, Brother, Asst Librn, ILL, Divine Word College, 102 Jacoby Dr SW, Epworth, IA, 52045-0380. Tel: 563-876-3353, Ext 207. p. 814

Kreis, Ellen, Ref, Sidley Austin LLP, 1501 K St NW, Washington, DC, 20005. Tel: 202-736-8525. Fax: 202-736-8711. p. 414

Kreiser, Nancy, Actg Sr Commun Libr Mgr, Contra Costa County Library, Dougherty Station Library, 17017 Bollinger Canyon Rd, San Ramon, CA, 94582. Tel: 925-973-3380. p. 209

Kreiser, Nancy, Actg Sr Commun Libr Mgr, Contra Costa County Library, San Ramon Library, 100 Montgomery St, San Ramon, CA, 94583-4707. Tel: 925-973-2850. Fax: 925-866-6720. p. 209

Krekovich, Gale, YA Serv, Calumet City Public Library, 660 Manistee Ave, Calumet City, IL, 60409. Tel: 708-862-6220, Ext 233. Fax: 708-862-0872. p. 599

Kreller, Kayla, Dir, Phillipsburg City Library, 888 Fourth St, Phillipsburg, KS, 67661. Tel: 785-543-5325. Fax: 785-543-5374. p. 890

Kremer, Brenda, Dir, Eldon Public Library, 608 W Elm St, Eldon, IA, 52554. Tel: 641-652-7517. Fax: 641-652-7517. p. 813

Kremer, Gary R, Dr, Exec Dir, State Historical Society of Missouri Library, 1020 Lowry St, Columbia, MO, 65201-7298. Tel: 573-882-7083. Fax: 573-884-4950. p. 1324

Kremer, Jacalyn, Outreach Librn, Sr Librn, Ref, Fairfield University, 1073 N Benson Rd, Fairfield, CT, 06430-5195. Tel: 203-254-4044. Fax: 203-254-4135. p. 339

Kremer, Lori, Ref Serv, Alhambra Public Library, 101 S First St, Alhambra, CA, 91801-3432. Tel: 626-570-5008. Fax: 626-457-1104. p. 120

Kremer-Wright, Garret B, Archivist, Orange County Regional History Center, 65 E Central Blvd, Orlando, FL, 32801. Tel: 407-836-8584. Fax: 407-836-8550. p. 477

Kren, MaryBeth, Librn, Robert Wood Johnson Foundation, Rte 1 & College Rd E, Princeton, NJ, 08543. Tel: 609-627-5895. Fax: 609-627-6421. p. 1522

Kreneck, Thomas, Dr, Archivist, Spec Coll Librn, Texas A&M University-Corpus Christi, Mary & Jeff Bell Library, 6300 Ocean Dr, Corpus Christi, TX, 78412-5501. Tel: 361-825-2643. Fax: 361-825-5973. p. 2302

Krenz, Bonnie, Dir, Griggs County Public Library, 902 Burrell Ave, Cooperstown, ND, 58425. Tel: 701-797-2214. p. 1839

Krenzke, Tom, Ref & Instruction Librn, Concordia University, 800 N Columbia Ave, Seward, NE, 68434-1595. Tel: 402-643-7254. Fax: 402-643-4218. p. 1419

Krepps, Wilma, Br Mgr, New Oxford Area Library, 122 N Peter St, New Oxford, PA, 17350-1229. Tel: 717-624-2182. Fax: 717-624-1358. p. 2097

Kreps, Dennis, Librn, Kalamazoo Institute of Arts, 314 S Park St, Kalamazoo, MI, 49007-5102. Tel: 269-349-7775, Ext 3165. Fax: 269-349-9313. p. 1197

Kresh, Diane, Dir, Arlington County Department of Libraries, 1015 N Quincy St, Arlington, VA, 22201. Tel: 703-228-3346, 703-228-3348. Fax: 703-228-3354. p. 2448

Kreshak, Cari, In Charge, National Park Service, PO Box 100, Mineral, CA, 96063-0100. Tel: 530-595-4444. Fax: 530-595-3408. p. 187

Kresich, Anton, Sr Res Spec, Clausen Miller Research Services Dept, Ten S LaSalle St, 16th Flr, Chicago, IL, 60603-1098. Tel: 312-606-7887. Fax: 312-606-7777. p. 611

Kress, Nancy, Head, Access Serv & Doc Delivery, ILL, University of Nevada, Las Vegas Libraries, 4505 Maryland Pkwy, Box 457001, Las Vegas, NV, 89154-7001. Tel: 702-895-2286. Fax: 702-895-2287. p. 1431

Kress, Nancy, Head, Access & Delivery Serv, North Carolina State University Libraries, Two Broughton Dr, Raleigh, NC, 27695. Tel: 919-515-7188. Fax: 919-515-3628. p. 1816

Kress-Dunn, Pam, Librn, Mercy Medical Center - Dubuque, 250 Mercy Dr, Dubuque, IA, 52001-7398. Tel: 563-589-9620. Fax: 563-589-8185. p. 812

Kressal, Linda J, Dir, Tri-County Community College, 4600 E Hwy 64, Murphy, NC, 28906. Tel: 828-835-4314, 828-837-6810. Fax: 828-837-0028. p. 1812

Kresse, Kerry, Dir, Physics & Astronomy Libr, University of Wisconsin-Madison, Woodman Astronomical Library, 6515 Sterling Hall, 475 N Charter St, Madison, WI, 53706. Tel: 608-262-8696. Fax: 608-236-6386. p. 2610

Kresse, Kerry L, Dir, Physics & Astronomy Libr, University of Wisconsin-Madison, Physics Library, 4220 Chamberlin Hall, 1150 University Ave, Madison, WI, 53706. Tel: 608-262-8696. Fax: 608-265-2754. p. 2609

Kressler, Tara, Br Mgr, Public Library of Cincinnati & Hamilton County, Symmes Township, 11850 E Enyart Rd, Loveland, OH, 45140. Tel: 513-369-6001. Fax: 513-369-4481. p. 1873

Krestine, L J, Librn, Otis Community Library, 121 S Main, Otis, KS, 67565. Tel: 785-387-2287. p. 887

Kretser, Sheila A, Dir, Greenville Area Public Library, 330 Main St, Greenville, PA, 16125-2619. Tel: 724-588-5490. Fax: 724-588-5481. p. 2063

Krett, Carol, Dir, Arcadia Free Public Library, 406 E Main St, Arcadia, WI, 54612-1396. Tel: 608-323-7505. Fax: 608-323-7505. p. 2579

Krettler, Kandice, Head, Circ & Tech Serv, Bloomingdale Public Library, 101 Fairfield Way, Bloomingdale, IL, 60108-1579. Tel: 630-529-3120. Fax: 630-529-3243. p. 595

Kretz, Chris, Digital Res Librn, Dowling College Library, 150 Idle Hour Blvd, Oakdale, NY, 11769-1999. Tel: 631-244-3396. Fax: 631-244-3374. p. 1709

Kretzmer, Kathy, Ch, Vestal Public Library, 320 Vestal Pkwy E, Vestal, NY, 13850-1632. Tel: 607-754-4243. Fax: 607-754-7936. p. 1761

Kreuger, William, Asst Librn, Grand Lodge of Iowa, AF & AM, 813 First Ave SE, Cedar Rapids, IA, 52406. Tel: 319-365-1438. Fax: 319-365-1439. p. 800

Kreutter, Lisa, Teen Librn, Boynton Beach City Library, 208 S Seacrest Blvd, Boynton Beach, FL, 33435. Tel: 561-742-6390. Fax: 561-742-6381. p. 429

Kreutzer-Hodson, Teresa, Curator, Hastings Museum of Natural & Cultural History Library, 1330 N Burlington, Hastings, NE, 68901. Tel: 402-461-2399. Fax: 402-461-2379. p. 1401

Kreymer, Oleg, Syst Librn, Metropolitan Museum of Art, Thomas J Watson Library, 1000 Fifth Ave, New York, NY, 10028-0198. Tel: 212-650-2438. Fax: 212-570-3847. p. 1686

Kriberney, Karen, Per, Spokane Falls Community College, 3410 Ft George Wright Dr, MS 3020, Spokane, WA, 99224-5288. Tel: 509-533-3800. Fax: 509-533-3144. p. 2537

Krichbaum, Kelly, Purchasing, Ashland Public Library, 224 Claremont Ave, Ashland, OH, 44805. Tel: 419-289-8188, Ext 20. Fax: 419-281-8552. p. 1855

Krichel, Thomas, Dr, Asst Prof, Long Island University, C W Post Campus, 720 Northern Blvd, Brookville, NY, 11548-1300. Tel: 516-299-2843. Fax: 516-299-4168. p. 2970

Krichko, Lorraine, Circ, Wake Technical Community College, 9101 Fayetteville Rd, Raleigh, NC, 27603-5696. Tel: 919-866-5644. Fax: 919-662-3575. p. 1818

Krick, Robert, Historian, National Park Service, 3215 E Broad St, Richmond, VA, 23223. Tel: 804-226-1981. Fax: 804-771-8522. p. 2489

Krieb, Dennis, Dir, Lewis & Clark Community College, 5800 Godfrey Rd, Godfrey, IL, 62035. Tel: 618-468-4330. Fax: 618-468-4301. p. 651

Krieger, Eric, Br Mgr, Jefferson Parish Library, Live Oak, 125 Acadia Dr, Waggaman, LA, 70094. Tel: 504-736-8475. Fax: 504-431-0653. p. 956

Krieger, Martin, Librn, Battle Creek Health System, 165 N Washington Ave, Battle Creek, MI, 49017. Tel: 269-966-8331. Fax: 269-966-8332. p. 1155

Krieger, Mary, Ref Serv, Saint Louis University, Medical Center Library, 1402 S Grand Blvd, Saint Louis, MO, 63104. Tel: 314-977-8810. Fax: 314-977-5573. p. 1361

Kriegh, David, Tech Serv Librn, Saint Patrick's Seminary, 320 Middlefield Rd, Menlo Park, CA, 94025. Tel: 650-321-5655. Fax: 650-323-5447. p. 185

Kriegisch, Ann, Ch, Wauwatosa Public Library, 7635 W North Ave, Wauwatosa, WI, 53213-1718. Tel: 414-471-8484. Fax: 414-479-8984. p. 2647

Krig, Robin O, Instr, Sam Houston State University, 1921 Ave J, Huntsville, TX, 77340. Tel: 936-294-1151. Fax: 936-294-1153. p. 2974

Krige, Ansie, Br Mgr, Cobb County Public Library System, Mountain View, 3320 Sandy Plains Rd, Marietta, GA, 30066. Tel: 770-509-2725. Fax: 770-509-2726. p. 543

Kriigel, Barbara, Assoc Dir, University of Michigan-Dearborn, 4901 Evergreen Rd, Dearborn, MI, 48128-2406. Tel: 313-593-5614. Fax: 313-593-5478. p. 1168

Kripal, Dixie, Pres, Nancy Fawcett Memorial Library, 724 Oberfelder St, Lodgepole, NE, 69149-0318. Tel: 308-483-5714. p. 1407

Krippel, Beth, Br Mgr, Harris County Public Library, Atascocita, 19520 Pinehurst Trails Dr, Humble, TX, 77346. Tel: 281-812-2162. Fax: 281-812-2135. p. 2335

Kripple, Lynn, Coordr, Saint Joseph Health Center, 300 First Capitol Dr, Saint Charles, MO, 63301. Tel: 314-344-6397. p. 1352

Kris, Duke, Br Mgr, Kern County Library, Tehachapi Branch, 1001 W Tehachapi Blvd, Ste A-400, Tehachapi, CA, 93561-2551. Tel: 661-822-4938. Fax: 661-823-8406. p. 125

Krishnamurthy, Prashant, Asst Prof, University of Pittsburgh, 135 N Bellefield Ave, Pittsburgh, PA, 15260. Tel: 412-624-5230. Fax: 412-624-5231. p. 2973

Krishnaswami, Julie, Ref Serv, Yale University Library, Lillian Goldman Library Yale Law School, 127 Wall St, New Haven, CT, 06511. Tel: 203-432-1600. Fax: 203-432-2112. p. 358

Krishnaswamy, Vidya, Pub Serv Librn, Tarrant County College, 2100 Southeast Pkwy, Arlington, TX, 76018. Tel: 817-515-3086. Fax: 817-515-3183. p. 2277

Krisko, Janet, ILL, George F Johnson Memorial Library, 1001 Park St, Endicott, NY, 13760. Tel: 607-757-5350. Fax: 607-757-2491. p. 1621

Krispli, Suzanna, Dir, Hampton Community Library, Shoppers Plaza, Ste 8, 4960 Rte 8, Allison Park, PA, 15101-2354. Tel: 724-444-0040. Fax: 724-444-0040. p. 2028

Kriss, Don, Exec Dir, Shaare Emeth Temple, 11645 Ladue Rd, Saint Louis, MO, 63141. Tel: 314-569-0010. Fax: 314-569-0271. p. 1361

Krissoff, Alan, Interim Dir, Mount Sinai School of Medicine, One Gustave L Levy Pl, New York, NY, 10029. Tel: 212-241-7892. Fax: 212-831-2625. p. 1687

Krist, Dawn, Librn, North Memorial Health Care, 3300 Oakdale N, Robbinsdale, MN, 55422. Tel: 763-520-5673. Fax: 763-520-1453. p. 1272

Krist, Dawn, Cat Librn, Northwestern College, 3003 Snelling Ave N, Saint Paul, MN, 55113. Tel: 651-631-5241. Fax: 651-631-5598. p. 1280

Krist, Lisa, In Charge, Institute of Internal Auditors Library, 247 Maitland Ave, Altamonte Springs, FL, 32701-4201. Tel: 407-937-1362. Fax: 407-937-1101. p. 425

Kristapsons, Maris, Librn, IBM Corp, 2070 Rte 52, Hopewell Junction, NY, 12533. Tel: 845-894-3198. Fax: 845-892-6399. p. 1638

Kristen, Hewitt, Adminr, Lakeshores Library System, 725 Cornerstone Crossing, Ste C, Waterford, WI, 53185. Tel: 262-514-4500, Ext 66. Fax: 262-514-4544. p. 2644

Kristianson, Lynn, ILL, Arlington County Department of Libraries, 1015 N Quincy St, Arlington, VA, 22201. Tel: 703-228-3346, 703-228-3348. Fax: 703-228-3354. p. 2448

Kristof, Cindy, Head, Access Serv, Kent State University Libraries, 1125 Risman Dr, Kent, OH, 44242. Tel: 330-672-1641. Fax: 330-672-4811. p. 1907

Kriter, Gillian, Supvr, Child & Parent Resource Institute, 600 Sanatorium Rd, London, ON, N6H 3W7, CANADA. Tel: 519-858-2774, Ext 2076. Fax: 519-858-3913. p. 2817

Kritikos, Chris, Ch, Carnegie Library of McKeesport, 1507 Library Ave, McKeesport, PA, 15132-4796. Tel: 412-672-0625. Fax: 412-672-7860. p. 2085

Krivda, Marita J, Med Librn, Temple University Hospital, Episcopal Campus, Front St & Lehigh Ave, Philadelphia, PA, 19125. Tel: 215-707-0286. Fax: 215-707-0291. p. 2117

Krivesti, Robin, Media Libr Mgr, Ohio University Libraries, 30 Park Pl, Athens, OH, 45701-2978. Tel: 740-593-2665. Fax: 740-593-2708. p. 1856

Krivick, Mary Ann, Librn, Connecticut Judicial Branch Law Libraries, Bridgeport Law Library, Bridgeport Courthouse, 1061 Main St, Bridgeport, CT, 06604. Tel: 203-579-7244. Fax: 203-579-7298. p. 344

Krober, Alfred, Dir, Libr Serv, Roberts Wesleyan College & Northeastern Seminary, 2301 Westside Dr, Rochester, NY, 14624-1997. Tel: 585-594-6501. Fax: 585-594-6543. p. 1731

Kroc, Gloria, Librn, Gottlieb Memorial Hospital, 701 W North Ave, Melrose Park, IL, 60160. Tel: 708-681-3200, Ext 1173. Fax: 708-681-3973. p. 673

Kroeckel, Carol, Librn, Little Dixie Regional Libraries, Madison Branch, 113 E Broadway, Madison, MO, 65263. Tel: 660-291-3695. Fax: 660-291-8695. p. 1346

Kroeff-Streng, Kay, Tech Serv Librn, Minneapolis College of Art & Design Library, 2501 Stevens Ave, Minneapolis, MN, 55404-3593. Tel: 612-874-3734. Fax: 612-874-3704. p. 1260

Kroes, Mary Susan, Tech Serv, Hackley Public Library, 316 W Webster Ave, Muskegon, MI, 49440. Tel: 231-722-7276, Ext 237. Fax: 231-726-5567. p. 1212

Kroesche, Sue, Dir, Le Mars Public Library, 46 First St SW, Le Mars, IA, 51031-3696. Tel: 712-546-5004. Fax: 712-546-5797. p. 827

Kroessler, Jeffrey, Circ Librn, John Jay College of Criminal Justice, 899 Tenth Ave, New York, NY, 10019. Tel: 212-237-8236. Fax: 212-237-8221. p. 1683

Kroh, Ryan, Head, Info Tech, North Dakota State Library, Library Memorial Bldg, 604 East Blvd Ave, Dept 250, Bismarck, ND, 58505-0800. Tel: 701-328-4658. Fax: 701-328-2040. p. 1838

Krohle, Frederick, Circ Asst, Wilkes University, 187 S Franklin St, Wilkes-Barre, PA, 18766-0998. Tel: 570-408-4250. Fax: 570-408-7823. p. 2156

Krohle, Jean, Supvr, Wilkes University, 187 S Franklin St, Wilkes-Barre, PA, 18766-0998. Tel: 570-408-4250. Fax: 570-408-7823. p. 2156

Krohn, Geri, Ref Serv, Travis County Law Library, Travis City Admin Bldg, 314 W 11th, Rm 140, Austin, TX, 78701-2112. Tel: 512-854-9273. Fax: 512-473-9082. p. 2283

Krohn, Joy, Ch, Avoca Public Library, 213 N Elm St, Avoca, IA, 51521. Tel: 712-343-6358. Fax: 712-343-6358. p. 795

Krohnen, Michael, Librn, Krishnamurti Foundation of America Library, 1098 McAndrew Rd, Ojai, CA, 93023. Tel: 805-646-4948. p. 200

Krois, Jerome W, Dir, Eaton Public Library, 132 Maple Ave, Eaton, CO, 80615-3441. Tel: 970-454-2189. Fax: 970-454-2958. p. 305

Krol, Danielle, Libr District Dir, Mohave County Library District, 3269 N Burbank St, Kingman, AZ, 86402-7000. p. 66

Krol, Katie, Dir, Monson Free Library, Two High St, Monson, MA, 01057-1095. Tel: 413-267-9035. Fax: 413-267-5496. p. 1106

Krol, Katie, Info Serv Supvr, Forbes Library, 20 West St, Northampton, MA, 01060-3798. Tel: 413-587-1011. Fax: 413-587-1015. p. 1113

Kroll, Anna Lois, Cat Librn, The Master's Seminary Library, 13248 Roscoe Blvd, Sun Valley, CA, 91352. Tel: 818-909-5634. Fax: 818-909-5680. p. 273

Kroll, Jim, Mgr, Spec Coll, Denver Public Library, Ten W 14th Ave Pkwy, Denver, CO, 80204-2731. Tel: 720-865-1820. Fax: 720-865-1880. p. 300

Kroll, Jim, Western Hist & Genealogy Mgr, Denver Public Library, Blair-Caldwell African American Research Library, 2401 Welton St, Denver, CO, 80205-3015. Tel: 720-865-2401. Fax: 720-865-2418. p. 301

Kroll, Karen, Ch, La Crosse County Library, Administration Ctr, 103 State St, Holmen, WI, 54636. Tel: 608-526-9600. Fax: 608-526-3299. p. 2598

Kroll, Kim Adele, Dir, Lena Armstrong Public Library, 301 E First Ave, Belton, TX, 76513. Tel: 254-933-5830. Fax: 254-933-5831. p. 2288

Kroll, Lynn, Dir, Sea Girt Library, Railroad Station at the Plaza, Sea Girt, NJ, 08750. Tel: 732-449-1099. Fax: 732-449-4138. p. 1529

Kroll, Mark A, Cataloger, Benedictine University Library, 5700 College Rd, Lisle, IL, 60532-0900. Tel: 630-829-6050. Fax: 630-960-9451. p. 666

Kroll, Susan M, Dir, Ohio State University LIBRARIES, John A Prior Health Sciences Library, 376 W Tenth Ave, Columbus, OH, 43210-1240. Tel: 614-292-4852. Fax: 614-292-1920. p. 1889

Krompf, Steve, Librn, American Institute for Cancer Research Library, 1759 R St NW, Washington, DC, 20009. Tel: 202-328-7744. Fax: 202-328-7226. p. 392

Kron, Judith, Dir, Ruth L Rockwood Memorial Library, Ten Robert Harp Dr, Livingston, NJ, 07039. Tel: 973-992-4600. Fax: 973-994-2346. p. 1496

Kron, Sue, Asst Librn, Phillips County Library, Ten S Fourth St E, Malta, MT, 59538. Tel: 406-654-2407. Fax: 406-654-2407. p. 1385

Kronberg, Kay, Media Spec, Nebraska Department of Corrections, 1107 Recharge Rd, York, NE, 68467-8003. Tel: 402-362-3317, Ext 260. Fax: 402-362-3892. p. 1424

Krone, Robin, Dir, Prairie Skies Public Library District, 125 W Editor St, Ashland, IL, 62612. Tel: 217-476-3417. Fax: 217-476-8076. p. 590

Krone, Robin, Dir, Prairie Skies Public Library District, Pleasant Plains Branch, 555 Buckeye Rd, Pleasant Plains, IL, 62677. Tel: 217-626-1553. Fax: 217-626-2433. p. 590

Kronen, Steven, Librn, Miami Dade College, Kendall Campus Library, 11011 SW 104th St, Miami, FL, 33176-3393. Tel: 305-237-0996, 305-237-2015, 305-237-2291. Fax: 305-237-2923. p. 466

Kronenberg, Karen, Ref Librn, Florida Coastal School of Law, 8787 Baypine Rd, Jacksonville, FL, 32256. Tel: 904-256-1112. Fax: 904-680-7677. p. 452

Kronenbitter, Jennifer, Coordr, Bibliog Serv, SUNY Cortland, 81 Prospect Terrace, Cortland, NY, 13045. Tel: 607-753-2525. Fax: 607-753-5669. p. 1611

Kronenfeld, Michael R, Dir, A T Still University, 5850 E Still Circle, Mesa, AZ, 85206-6091. Tel: 480-219-6091. Fax: 480-219-6100. p. 68

Kronewitter, Barbara, Coll Develop, Washington County Free Library, 100 S Potomac St, Hagerstown, MD, 21740. Tel: 301-739-3250. Fax: 301-739-7603. p. 1031

Kroon, Linda, Dir, University of Iowa, Sojourner Truth Library, 130 N Madison, Iowa City, IA, 52242. Tel: 319-335-1486. Fax: 319-353-1985. p. 823

Kropf, Joan R, Curator, Librn, Salvador Dali Foundation Inc, 1000 Third St S, Saint Petersburg, FL, 33701. Tel: 727-823-3767. Fax: 727-823-8532. p. 487

Kropf, Linda K, Libr Dir, Shelbina Carnegie Public Library, 102 N Center, Shelbina, MO, 63468. Tel: 573-588-2271. Fax: 573-588-2271. p. 1365

Kropf, Valerie, Res Librn, DLA Piper US LLP, 203 N LaSalle St, Ste 1900, Chicago, IL, 60601. Tel: 312-984-5703. Fax: 312-251-5845. p. 612

Kropninski, Sherry, Circ, Coll Develop, Ref, North Island College, 3699 Roger St, Port Alberni, BC, V9Y 8E3, CANADA. Tel: 250-724-8717. Fax: 250-724-8700. p. 2735

Krost, Sandra J, Head, Ch, Bremen Public Library, 304 N Jackson St, Bremen, IN, 46506. Tel: 574-546-2849. Fax: 574-546-4938. p. 729

Krotenberg, Joan, Assoc Dir, 1st Cerebral Palsy of New Jersey, Seven Sanford Ave, Belleville, NJ, 07109. Tel: 973-751-0200. Fax: 973-751-4635. p. 1471

Krotz, Leah, Dir, Belleville Public Library, 1327 19th St, Belleville, KS, 66935-2296. Tel: 785-527-5305. Fax: 785-527-5305. p. 857

Kruckenberg, Cathy, Dir, Independence Public Library, 23688 Adams St, Independence, WI, 54747. Tel: 715-985-3616. Fax: 715-985-2530. p. 2599

Kruckenberg, Molly, Dir, Montana Historical Society, 225 N Roberts St, Helena, MT, 59601-4514. Tel: 406-444-2681. Fax: 406-444-5297. p. 1382

Kruegel, Leslie, Ref, Maurice M Pine Free Public Library, 10-01 Fair Lawn Ave, Fair Lawn, NJ, 07410. Tel: 201-796-3400. Fax: 201-794-6344. p. 1485

Krueger, Amy, Sr Librn, Tel Ref, Lee County Library System, 2345 Union St, Fort Myers, FL, 33901-3917. Tel: 239-533-4800. Fax: 239-485-1100. p. 445

Krueger, Bonnie, Adult Serv, Ref, Owatonna Public Library, 105 N Elm Ave, Owatonna, MN, 55060-2405. Tel: 507-444-2460. Fax: 507-444-2465. p. 1270

Krueger, Bruce, Archives Assoc, State Historical Society of Iowa-Des Moines Library, 600 E Locust, Des Moines, IA, 50319-0290. Tel: 515-281-6200. Fax: 515-282-0502. p. 810

Krueger, Charity, Exec Dir, Aullwood Audubon Center & Farm, 1000 Aullwood Rd, Dayton, OH, 45414. Tel: 937-890-7360. Fax: 937-890-2382. p. 1892

Krueger, Cynthia, Tech Serv, St Vincent de Paul Regional Seminary Library, 10701 S Military Trail, Boynton Beach, FL, 33436-4811. Tel: 561-732-4424, Ext 173. Fax: 561-737-2205. p. 429

Krueger, Debbie, Youth Serv Coordr, Castroville Public Library, 802 London St, Castroville, TX, 78009. Tel: 830-931-4095. Fax: 830-931-9050. p. 2295

Krueger, Gudrun, Ref Librn, College of the Holy Cross, One College St, Worcester, MA, 01610. Tel: 508-793-2640. Fax: 508-793-2372. p. 1143

Krueger, Heidi, Electronic Serv Librn, St Charles Public Library District, One S Sixth Ave, Saint Charles, IL, 60174-2105, Tel: 630-584-0076, Ext 256. Fax: 630-584-3448. p. 699

Krueger, Karl, Coll Develop, Dir, Lutheran Theological Seminary, 7301 Germantown Ave, Philadelphia, PA, 19119-1794. Tel: 215-248-6330. Fax: 215-248-6327. p. 2112

Krueger, Karla, Interim Coordr, University of Northern Iowa, Library 121, Rod Library, Cedar Falls, IA, 50613. Tel: 319-273-7241. Fax: 319-273-2913. p. 2965

Krueger, Martha, Circ Librn, Yarmouth Town Libraries, South Yarmouth Branch, 312 Old Main St, South Yarmouth, MA, 02664. Tel: 508-760-4820. Fax: 508-760-2699. p. 1126

Krueger, Richard, Dir, United States Air Force, 436 SVS/SVMG, 262 Chad St, Dover AFB, DE, 19902-7235. Tel: 302-677-3992, 302-677-3995. Fax: 302-677-5490. p. 383

Krueger, Rochelle, Govt Doc Librn, University of Nebraska at Kearney, 2508 11th Ave, Kearney, NE, 68849-2240. Tel: 308-865-8542. Fax: 308-865-8722. p. 1403

Krueger, Sperry, Res, North Carolina Biotechnology Center Library, 15 Alexander Dr, Research Triangle Park, NC, 27709. Tel: 919-541-9366. Fax: 919-990-9521. p. 1820

Krueger, Vicki, Br Mgr, Saint Louis County Library, Jamestown Bluffs Branch, 4153 Hwy 67, Florissant, MO, 63034. Tel: 314-741-6800. p. 1359

Kruempel, DeAnn, Ch, Missouri Valley Public Library, 420 E Huron St, Missouri Valley, IA, 51555. Tel: 712-642-4111. Fax: 712-642-4172. p. 832

Kruer, June, Mgr, Charlestown-Clark County Public Library, Henryville Branch, 214 E Main St, Henryville, IN, 47126. Tel: 812-294-4246. Fax: 812-294-1078. p. 731

Krug, Amy, Archives Librn, Electronic Res Librn, Howard Community College Library, 10901 Little Patuxent Pkwy, Columbia, MD, 21044. Tel: 443-518-4788. Fax: 443-518-4993. p. 1025

Kruger, Jodi, Ref, Pepperdine University Libraries, School of Law-Jerene Appleby Harnish Law Library, 24255 Pacific Coast Hwy, Malibu, CA, 90263. Tel: 310-506-4643. Fax: 310-506-4836. p. 182

Kruger, Marilyn, Br Head, Toronto Public Library, Armour Heights, 2140 Avenue Rd, Toronto, ON, M5M 4M7, CANADA. Tel: 416-395-5430. Fax: 416-395-5433. p. 2860

Kruger, Rebecca P, Tech Serv, Wilkes Community College, 1328 Collegiate Dr, Wilkesboro, NC, 28697. Tel: 336-838-6514. Fax: 336-838-6515. p. 1830

Kruger, Susan, Youth Serv Librn, Albion Public Library, 437 S Third St, Albion, NE, 68620. Tel: 402-395-2021. p. 1391

Kruger, Suzanne, Dir, Mount Hope-Funks Grove Townships Library District, 111 S Hamilton St, McLean, IL, 61754-7624. Tel: 309-874-2291. Fax: 309-874-2291. p. 672

Kruk, Pauline A, Librn, Connecticut Valley Hospital, Hallock Medical Library, Page Hall, Silver St, Middletown, CT, 06457. Tel: 860-262-5059. Fax: 860-262-5049. p. 351

Krukoff, John, Dir, National Association of Realtors, 430 N Michigan Ave, Chicago, IL, 60611-4087. Tel: 312-329-8200. Fax: 312-329-5960. p. 619

Krul, Kathy, Principal Librn, Lee County Library System, East County Regional, 881 Gunnery Rd N, Lehigh Acres, FL, 33971. Tel: 239-461-7315. Fax: 239-461-7321. p. 445

Krulisch, Lee, Exec Dir, Scientists Center for Animal Welfare Library, 7833 Walker Dr, Ste 410, Greenbelt, MD, 20770. Tel: 301-345-3500. Fax: 301-345-3503. p. 1030

Krull, Jeffrey R, Dir, Allen County Public Library, 900 Library Plaza, Fort Wayne, IN, 46802. Tel: 260-421-1201. Fax: 260-421-1386. p. 740

Krull, Rob, Ref Serv, Palm Beach State College, 4200 Congress Ave, Mail Sta 17, Lake Worth, FL, 33461. Tel: 561-868-3800. Fax: 561-868-3708. p. 459

Krull, Rose, Head, Circ, Fulton County Public Library, 320 W Seventh St, Rochester, IN, 46975-1332. Tel: 574-223-2713. Fax: 574-223-5102. p. 776

Krumnow, Stacy G, Libr Mgr, Piedmont Regional Library, Banks County Public, 226 Hwy 51 S, Homer, GA, 30547. Tel: 706-677-3164. Fax: 706-677-3164. p. 557

Krumper, Deirdre S, Dir, Bandon Public Library, 1204 11th St SW, Bandon, OR, 97411. Tel: 541-347-3221. Fax: 541-347-9363. p. 1991

Krumwiede, Richard, Dir, Outagamie Waupaca Library System, 225 N Oneida, Appleton, WI, 54911-4780. Tel: 920-832-6190. Fax: 920-832-6422. p. 2578

Krupp, Cindy, Librn, Indian River County Library System, Law, 2000 16th Ave, Ste 119, Vero Beach, FL, 32960. Tel: 772-770-5157. Fax: 772-770-5158. p. 502

Krupp, Edwin C, Dr, Dir, Griffith Observatory Library, 2800 E Observatory Rd, Los Angeles, CA, 90027. Tel: 213-473-0800. Fax: 213-473-0818. p. 170

Krupp, Robert A, Dr, Head of Libr, Western Seminary, 5511 SE Hawthorne Blvd, Portland, OR, 97215-3367. Tel: 503-517-1838. Fax: 503-517-1801. p. 2015

Kruse, Carrie, Dir, University of Wisconsin-Madison, College (Undergraduate) Library, 600 N Park St, Madison, WI, 53706. Tel: 608-262-3245. Fax: 608-262-4631. p. 2608

Kruse, Christian, Dir, Live Oak Public Libraries, 2002 Bull St, Savannah, GA, 31401. Tel: 912-652-3601. Fax: 912-652-3638. p. 550

Kruse, Dave, Superintendent, National Park Service, One Indian Well Headquarters, Tulelake, CA, 96134. Tel: 530-667-8113, 530-667-8119. Fax: 530-667-2737. p. 276

Kruse, David, Librn, New Windsor Public Library District, 412 Main St, New Windsor, IL, 61465. Tel: 309-667-2515. Fax: 309-667-2515. p. 680

Kruse, Donna, Genealogy Serv, Fort Worth Library, 500 W Third St, Fort Worth, TX, 76102. Tel: 817-871-7740. Fax: 817-871-7734. p. 2321

Kruse, Edward, Librn, Athens County Law Library, Court House, 4th Flr, Athens, OH, 45701. Tel: 740-593-8893. Fax: 740-592-3282. p. 1856

Kruse, Elizabeth A, Dir, Clatskanie Library District, 11 Lillich St, Clatskanie, OR, 97016. Tel: 503-728-3732. p. 1993

Kruse, Emily, Dir, Osgood Public Library, 136 W Ripley St, Osgood, IN, 47037-0235. Tel: 812-689-4011. Fax: 812-689-5062. p. 771

Kruse, Ken, Ch, Russell Library, 123 Broad St, Middletown, CT, 06457. Tel: 860-347-2528. p. 352

Kruse, Mary E, Asst Dir, Pataskala Public Library, 101 S Vine St, Pataskala, OH, 43062. Tel: 740-927-9986. Fax: 740-964-6204. p. 1928

Kruse, Michael J, Dir, Batesville Memorial Public Library, 131 N Walnut St, Batesville, IN, 47006. Tel: 812-934-4706. Fax: 812-934-6288. p. 725

Kruse, Robert, Tech Serv, Boston Athenaeum, 10 1/2 Beacon St, Boston, MA, 02108-3777. Tel: 617-227-0270. Fax: 617-227-5266. p. 1056

Kruse, Ted, Assoc Dir, Tech Serv, University of Baltimore, 1420 Maryland Ave, Baltimore, MD, 21201. Tel: 410-837-4260. Fax: 410-837-4330. p. 1018

Kruser, Barbara, AV, Reader Serv, Niles Public Library District, 6960 Oakton St, Niles, IL, 60714. Tel: 847-663-1234. Fax: 847-663-1350. p. 680

Krushell, Cathy, Supvr, Ventura County Library, Fillmore Library, 502 Second St, Fillmore, CA, 93015. Tel: 805-524-3355. Fax: 808-524-4636. p. 279

Krusling, James S, Assoc Dean, Libr & Learning Res, Glendale Community College Library, 1500 N Verdugo Rd, Glendale, CA, 91208-2894. Tel: 818-240-1000, Ext 5574. Fax: 818-246-5107. p. 155

Kruthoffer, Betsy, Asst Librn, Cat Librn, Ser, Lloyd Library & Museum, 917 Plum St, Cincinnati, OH, 45202. Tel: 513-721-3707. Fax: 513-721-6575. p. 1870

Kruy, Martha, Ref Librn, Norwalk Community College, 188 Richards Ave, Norwalk, CT, 06854-1655. Tel: 203-857-7208. Fax: 203-857-7380. p. 362

Kruzich, Michael J, Dir, Ferris State University, 17 Fountain St NW, 2nd Flr, Grand Rapids, MI, 49503-3002. Tel: 616-451-1868, Ext 1122. Fax: 616-831-9689. p. 1184

Krydick, Dana, Syst Librn, Seton Hill University, One Seton Hill Dr, Greensburg, PA, 15601. Tel: 724-838-4291. Fax: 724-838-4203. p. 2062

Krysak, Nikki, Head, Instrul Serv, Norwich University, 23 Harmon Dr, Northfield, VT, 05663. Tel: 802-485-2168. Fax: 802-485-2173. p. 2431

Krystopowicz, Catherine, Head of Libr, Free Library of Philadelphia, Bushrod Branch, 6304 Castor Ave, Philadelphia, PA, 19149-2731. Tel: 215-685-1471, 215-685-1472. Fax: 215-685-1079. p. 2107

Krystyniak, Claudine, Cataloger, Cliffside Park Free Public Library, 505 Palisade Ave, Cliffside Park, NJ, 07010. Tel: 201-945-2867. Fax: 201-945-1016. p. 1479

Krzanowski, Robert, Tech Serv, Slippery Rock University of Pennsylvania, Slippery Rock, PA, 16057-9989. Tel: 724-738-2058. Fax: 724-738-2661. p. 2140

Krzysko, Nina, Br Mgr, Howard County Library System, Central Branch, 10375 Little Patuxent Pkwy, Columbia, MD, 21044-3499. Tel: 410-313-7800. Fax: 410-313-7864. p. 1026

Ku, Shirley, YA Serv, Fullerton Public Library, 353 W Commonwealth Ave, Fullerton, CA, 92832-1796. Tel: 714-773-5719. Fax: 714-447-3280. p. 154

Kuba, Jenifer, Asst Dir, Essex County Historical Society, 7590 Court St, Elizabethtown, NY, 12932. Tel: 518-873-6466. Fax: 518-873-6466. p. 1618

Kubala, Carol, Adult Serv, Saxton B Little Free Library, Inc, 319 Rte 87, Columbia, CT, 06237-1143. Tel: 860-228-0350. Fax: 860-228-1569. p. 334

Kubala, Linda, Web Serv & Ref Librn, Saint Joseph's University, Francis A Drexel Library, 5600 City Ave, Philadelphia, PA, 19131-1395. Tel: 610-660-1531. Fax: 610-660-1916. p. 2116

Kuban, Lori, Ad, Elm Grove Public Library, 13600 W Juneau Blvd, Elm Grove, WI, 53122-1679. Tel: 262-782-6717. Fax: 262-780-4827. p. 2591

Kubash, Emily, Br Mgr, Clinton-Macomb Public Library, North, 16800 24 Mile Rd, Macomb Township, MI, 48042. Tel: 586-226-5081. Fax: 586-226-5088. p. 1164

Kubiak, Michelle Lee, Librn, United States Department of Labor, 1301 Airport Rd, Beaver, WV, 25813-9426. Tel: 304-256-3233. Fax: 304-256-3372. p. 2553

Kubic, Craig, Dr, Dir, Midwestern Baptist Theological Seminary Library, 5001 N Oak Trafficway, Kansas City, MO, 64118-4620. Tel: 816-414-3729. Fax: 816-414-3790. p. 1339

Kubik, Adam, Head, Monographic Cat, Clayton State University, 2000 Clayton State Blvd, Morrow, GA, 30260. Tel: 678-466-4337. Fax: 678-466-4349. p. 545

Kubik, Angela, Libr Dir, Fort Saskatchewan Public Library, 10011 102nd St, Fort Saskatchewan, AB, T8L 2C5, CANADA. Tel: 780-998-4288. Fax: 780-992-3255. p. 2704

Kubista, Mary, Librn, Scott County Library System, Jordan Public Library, 230 S Broadway, Jordan, MN, 55352-1508. Tel: 952-492-2500. Fax: 952-492-2500. p. 1284

Kubota, Charleen, Head Librn, California State Department of Health Services, 1515 Clay St, 16th Flr, Oakland, CA, 94612. Tel: 510-622-3204. Fax: 510-622-3197. p. 196

Kubow, Wendy, Circ, Palmer College of Chiropractic-West Campus Library, 90 E Tasman Dr, San Jose, CA, 95134. Tel: 408-944-6142. Fax: 408-944-6181. p. 250

Kuchan, Barbara, Assoc Dir, Temple University Libraries, Health Science Center Libraries, 3440 N Broad St, Philadelphia, PA, 19140. Tel: 215-707-3738. Fax: 215-707-4135. p. 2117

Kucharski, Christine, Ref Librn, SUNY Upstate Medical University, 766 Irving Ave, Syracuse, NY, 13210-1602. Tel: 315-464-7199. Fax: 315-464-4584. p. 1753

Kucharski, Kathleen, Dir, United States Air Force, 21 SVS/SVMG, 201 W Stewart Ave, Bldg 1171, Peterson AFB, CO, 80914-1600. Tel: 719-556-7463. Fax: 719-556-6752. p. 320

Kucher, Patricia, Cat, Acorn Public Library District, 15624 S Central Ave, Oak Forest, IL, 60452-3204. Tel: 708-687-3700. Fax: 708-687-3712. p. 683

Kucher, Sue Ann, Asst Dir, Reedsburg Public Library, 370 Vine St, Reedsburg, WI, 53959-1917. Tel: 608-524-3316, 608-768-7323. Fax: 608-524-9024. p. 2633

Kuchieski, Ann, Head, Circ & Ref, Clapp Memorial Library, 19 S Main St, Belchertown, MA, 01007-0627. Tel: 413-323-0417. Fax: 413-323-0453. p. 1052

Kuchinsky, Scott, Adult Literacy Coordr, Plainfield Public Library, 800 Park Ave, Plainfield, NJ, 07060-2594. Tel: 908-757-1111, Ext 120. Fax: 908-754-0063. p. 1521

Kuchmay, Laura, Ad, Middletown Free Library, 21 N Pennell Rd, Lima, PA, 19037. Tel: 610-566-7828. Fax: 610-892-0880. p. 2082

Kuchta, Irene, Access Serv, Ramapo College of New Jersey, 505 Ramapo Valley Rd, Mahwah, NJ, 07430-1623. Tel: 201-684-7577. p. 1498

Kuchta, Julie, Mgr, Carnegie Library of Pittsburgh, Carrick, 1811 Brownsville Rd, Pittsburgh, PA, 15210-3906. Tel: 412-882-3897. p. 2122

Kuchta, Peter, Dir, Jefferson Carnegie Library, 301 W Lafayette, Jefferson, TX, 75657. Tel: 903-665-8911. Fax: 903-665-8911. p. 2348

Kucsak, Michael, Dir, Libr Syst & Tech, University of North Florida, Bldg 12-Library, One UNF Dr, Jacksonville, FL, 32224-2645. Tel: 904-620-2552. Fax: 904-620-2719. p. 455

Kucynski, Lucy, Libr Spec, Harrisburg Area Community College, One HACC Dr, Harrisburg, PA, 17110-2999. Tel: 717-780-2460. Fax: 717-780-2462. p. 2065

Kuczerepa, Paul, Mgr, Baxter International, 25212 W Illinois Rte 120, RLT 22, Round Lake, IL, 60073. Tel: 847-270-5360. Fax: 847-270-5381. p. 699

Kuczinski, Dale, Circ, ILL, University of Southern Maine, 51 Westminster St, Lewiston, ME, 04240. Tel: 207-753-6540. Fax: 207-753-6543. p. 990

Kuczma, Michelle, Dir, Libr Serv, Buchalter Nemer, 1000 Wilshire Blvd, Ste 1500, Los Angeles, CA, 90017. Tel: 213-891-0700. Fax: 213-896-0400. p. 169

Kuczynski, Peter, Head, Circ, Orland Park Public Library, 14921 Ravinia Ave, Orland Park, IL, 60462. Tel: 708-428-5100. Fax: 708-349-8322. p. 686

Kude, Peggy, Circ Supvr, Carroll College, 1601 N Benton Ave, Helena, MT, 59625. Tel: 406-447-4340. Fax: 406-447-4525. p. 1381

Kuden, Jodee, Acq, Head, Coll Develop, University of Alaska Anchorage, Consortium Library, 3211 Providence Dr, Anchorage, AK, 99508-8176. Tel: 907-786-1875. Fax: 907-786-1834. p. 45

Kuderewko, Angela, Librn, Parkland Regional Library, Strasbourg Branch, 113 Pearson St, Strasbourg, SK, S0G 4V0, CANADA. Tel: 306-725-3239. p. 2932

Kudrna, Kelly, Libr Dir, Stanley Public Library, 116 Main St, Stanley, ND, 58784-4051. Tel: 701-628-2223. p. 1848

Kuebel, Jan, Br Mgr, Riverside County Library System, Home Gardens Library, 3785 Neece St, Corona, CA, 92879. Tel: 951-279-2148. Fax: 951-734-3170. p. 217

Kuebler, Margot, Br Mgr, Fairfield County Library, Ridgeway Branch, 175 S Palmer St, Ridgeway, SC, 29130. Tel: 803-337-2068. Fax: 803-337-2068. p. 2207

Kuechenmeister, Lynn, Circ, Chippewa Falls Public Library, 105 W Central, Chippewa Falls, WI, 54729-2397. Tel: 715-723-1146. Fax: 715-720-6922. p. 2585

Kuechle, Pat, Admin Serv, Autism Treatment Services of Saskatchewan, Inc Library, 609 25th St E, Saskatoon, SK, S7K 0L7, CANADA. Tel: 306-665-7013. Fax: 306-665-7011. p. 2925

Kuechmann, Christopher, County Librn, Val Verde County Library, 300 Spring St, Del Rio, TX, 78840. Tel: 830-774-7595. Fax: 830-774-7607. p. 2312

Kuehhas, Thomas A, Dir, Oyster Bay Historical Society Library, 20 Summit St, Oyster Bay, NY, 11771. Tel: 516-922-5032. Fax: 516-922-6892. p. 1714

Kuehl, Debra, Ch, Smiths Falls Public Library, 81 Beckwith St N, Smiths Falls, ON, K7A 2B9, CANADA. Tel: 613-283-2911. Fax: 613-283-9834. p. 2842

Kuehl, Heidi Frostestad, Foreign Comparative & Intl Law Librn, Northwestern University, Chicago, Pritzker Legal Research Center, 375 E Chicago Ave, Chicago, IL, 60611. Tel: 312-503-4725. Fax: 312-503-9230. p. 621

Kuehn, Bobbie, Supvr, Brown County Library, East Branch, 2255 Main St, Green Bay, WI, 54302-3743. Tel: 920-391-4600. Fax: 920-391-4601. p. 2595

Kuehn, Mary, Asst Librn, Harrie P Woodson Memorial Library, 704 W Hwy 21, Caldwell, TX, 77836-1129. Tel: 979-567-4111. Fax: 979-567-4962. p. 2294

Kuehne, Janet, Dir, Trinity College, 2430 Welbilt Blvd, Trinity, FL, 34655. Tel: 727-376-6911. Fax: 727-376-0781. p. 500

Kuenzi, Vicki, Med Librn, Waukesha Memorial Hospital, 725 American Ave, Waukesha, WI, 53188-9982. Tel: 262-928-2150. Fax: 262-928-2514. p. 2645

Kuester, Earlene, Asst Dir, Head, Pub Serv, Stetson University College of Law Library, 1401 61st St S, Gulfport, FL, 33707. Tel: 727-562-7826. Fax: 727-345-8973. p. 450

Kueter, Andrea, Archives Coordr, University of Puget Sound, 1500 N Warner St, Campus Mail Box 1021, Tacoma, WA, 98416-1021. Tel: 253-879-2875. Fax: 253-879-3670. p. 2541

Kuhl, Brandy, Asst Librn, San Francisco Botanical Garden Society at Strybing Arboretum, 1199 Ninth Ave, (Ninth Ave at Lincoln Way), San Francisco, CA, 94122-2384. Tel: 415-661-1316, Ext 303. Fax: 415-661-3539. p. 244

Kuhl, Jason, Exec Dir, Arlington Heights Memorial Library, 500 N Dunton Ave, Arlington Heights, IL, 60004-5966. Tel: 847-506-2612. Fax: 847-506-2650. p. 589

Kuhl, Nancy, Curator, Coll of Am Lit, Yale University Library, Beinecke Rare Book & Manuscript, 121 Wall St, New Haven, CT, 06520. Tel: 203-432-2966. Fax: 203-432-4047. p. 356

Kuhl, Patricia L, Mgr, Client Res & Info Serv, Aon Hewitt Library, Four Overlook Point, Lincolnshire, IL, 60069. Tel: 847-295-5000. p. 666

Kuhlman, Cindy, Dir, Athens First United Methodist Church Library, 327 N Lumpkin St, Athens, GA, 30601. Tel: 706-543-1442. Fax: 706-546-4797. p. 508

Kuhlman, Robin, Mgr, Geauga County Public Library, Thompson Library Station, 16700 Thompson Rd, Thompson, OH, 44086. Tel: 440-298-3831. Fax: 440-298-3921. p. 1867

Kuhlmann, Connie, Regional Mgr, North Central Regional Library, Moses Lake Community, 418 E Fifth Ave, Moses Lake, WA, 98837-1797. Tel: 509-765-3489. Fax: 509-766-0286. p. 2549

Kuhlmann, Doreen, Bus Mgr, Nebraska Library Commission, The Atrium, 1200 N St, Ste 120, Lincoln, NE, 68508-2023. Fax: 402-471-2083. p. 1406

Kuhlmeier, Sylvia, Dir of Libr Serv, Missouri State University-West Plains, 304 W Trish Knight St, West Plains, MO, 65775. Tel: 417-255-7945. Fax: 417-255-7944. p. 1372

Kuhlthau, Carol C, Prof, Rutgers, The State University of New Jersey, Four Huntington St, New Brunswick, NJ, 08901-1071. Tel: 732-932-7500, Ext 8955. Fax: 732-932-2644. p. 2969

Kuhn, Betty, Circ, Lester Public Library, 1001 Adams St, Two Rivers, WI, 54241. Tel: 920-793-8888. Fax: 920-793-7150. p. 2643

Kuhn, Charles L, Dir, Lynn University Library, 3601 N Military Trail, Boca Raton, FL, 33431-5598. Tel: 561-237-7067. Fax: 561-237-7065. p. 428

Kuhn, Charlotte, Br Librn, Wapiti Regional Library, Alvena Public Library, Business/Commerce Complex, 101 Main St, Alvena, SK, S0K 0E0, CANADA. Tel: 306-943-2003. p. 2921

Kuhn, Christine, Dir, Westmont Public Library, 428 N Cass, Westmont, IL, 60559-1502. Tel: 630-969-5625. Fax: 630-969-6490. p. 717

Kuhn, Eric, Mgr, Bear Library, 101 Governors Pl, Bear, DE, 19701. Tel: 302-838-3300. Fax: 302-838-3307. p. 381

Kuhn, Jim, Head, Coll Info Serv, Folger Shakespeare Library, 201 E Capitol St SE, Washington, DC, 20003-1094. Tel: 202-544-4600. Fax: 202-544-4623. p. 400

Kuhn, Kathy, ILL & Distance Libr Serv Spec, Joseph & Elizabeth Shaw Public Library, One S Front St, Clearfield, PA, 16830. Tel: 814-765-3271. Fax: 814-765-6316. p. 2046

Kuhn, Phil, Br Mgr, Lawrenceburg Public Library District, North Dearborn Branch, 25969 Dole Rd, West Harrison, IN, 47060. Tel: 812-637-0777. Fax: 812-637-0797. p. 760

Kuhns, Amanda, Ref & Instruction Librn, Tulsa Community College Learning Resources Center, West Campus Library, 7505 W 41st St, Tulsa, OK, 74107-8633. Tel: 918-595-8012. Fax: 918-595-8016. p. 1984

Kuhns, Barbara, Asst Dir, Tech, Dayton Metro Library, 215 E Third St, Dayton, OH, 45402-2103. Tel: 937-463-2665. Fax: 937-496-4300. p. 1892

Kuhns, Eleanor, Asst Dir, Head, Adult Serv, Goshen Free Public Library, 42 Main St, Goshen, MA, 01032-9608. Tel: 413-268-7033. p. 1091

Kuhns, Judy, Tech Serv & Syst Librn, Ulster County Community College, Stone Ridge, NY, 12484. Tel: 845-687-5213. Fax: 845-687-5220. p. 1749

Kuhr, Vera, Dir, Mead Public Library, 316 S Vine, Mead, NE, 68041. Tel: 402-624-6605. Fax: 402-624-6605. p. 1408

Kuiken, Anita, Coordr, ILL, Per & Stack Maintenance, SUNY Cortland, 81 Prospect Terrace, Cortland, NY, 13045. Tel: 607-753-2525. Fax: 607-753-5669. p. 1611

Kuiper, Rhonda, Ref & Info Supvr, Westbank Community Library District, 1309 Westbank Dr, Austin, TX, 78746. Tel: 512-327-3045. Fax: 512-327-3074. p. 2285

Kujawa, Christine, Head, Circ Serv, Syst Librn, Bismarck Veterans Memorial Public Library, 515 N Fifth St, Bismarck, ND, 58503-4081. Tel: 701-355-1496. Fax: 701-221-3729. p. 1837

Kujawa, Josephine F, Librn, Lexington College Library, 310 S Peoria, Chicago, IL, 60607. Tel: 312-226-6294. Fax: 312-226-6405. p. 616

Kukainis, Beate N, Tech Serv, University of Louisiana at Lafayette, PO Box 40199, Lafayette, LA, 70504-0199. Tel: 337-482-6033. Fax: 337-482-6399. p. 953

Kukil, Karen, Assoc Curator, Smith College Libraries, Mortimer Rare Book Room, Northampton, MA, 01063. Tel: 413-585-2908. Fax: 413-585-4486. p. 1114

Kukil, Karen, Ref Archivist, Smith College Libraries, Sophia Smith Collection, Seven Neilson Dr, Northampton, MA, 01063. Tel: 413-585-2988. Fax: 413-585-2886. p. 1114

Kuklinski, Joan, Exec Dir, Central & Western Massachusetts Automated Resource Sharing, 67 Millbrook St, Ste 201, Worcester, MA, 01606. Tel: 508-755-3323, Ext 30. Fax: 508-755-3721. p. 2945

Kukreja, Neera, Dir, Cook County Hospital Libraries, 1900 W Polk St, 2nd fl, Chicago, IL, 60612. Tel: 312-864-0502. p. 611

Kula, Norma, Dir of Libr, Monroe County Public Library, 700 Fleming St, Key West, FL, 33040. Tel: 305-853-7349. Fax: 305-853-7311. p. 456

Kulchycki, Ashley, Supvr, Ch Serv, Collingwood Public Library, 55 St Marie St, Collingwood, ON, L9Y 0W6, CANADA. Tel: 705-445-1571, Ext 6234. Fax: 705-445-3704. p. 2800

Kulczak, Deb, Head, Music Cat/Database Maintenance, University of Arkansas Libraries, 365 N McIlroy Ave, Fayetteville, AR, 72701-4002. Tel: 479-575-4811. Fax: 479-575-6656. p. 99

Kulesa, Dianne, Librn, Rothgerber, Johnson & Lyons, One Tabor Ctr, Ste 3000, 1200 17th St, Denver, CO, 80202. Tel: 303-623-9000. Fax: 303-623-9222. p. 303

Kulieke, Mark, Librn, Green Bay Correctional Institution Library, PO Box 19033, Green Bay, WI, 54307-9033. Tel: 920-432-4877, Ext 3457. Fax: 920-432-5388. p. 2595

Kulikowski, Leah, Dir, Wamego Public Library, 431 Lincoln, Wamego, KS, 66547-1620. Tel: 785-456-9181. Fax: 785-456-8986. p. 899

Kulikowsky, Vicky, Ch, Long Hill Township Public Library, 917 Valley Rd, Gillette, NJ, 07933. Tel: 908-647-2088. Fax: 908-647-2098. p. 1488

Kull, Christine, Archivist, Monroe County Historical Museum, 126 S Monroe St, Monroe, MI, 48161. Tel: 734-240-7787. Fax: 734-240-7788. p. 1209

Kullas, Janice, Dir, Serv Develop, Oakville Public Library, 120 Navy St, Oakville, ON, L6J 2Z4, CANADA. Tel: 905-815-2035. Fax: 905-815-2024. p. 2825

Kullman, David, Ref, Saint Louis University, Omer Poos Law Library, Morrissey Hall, 3700 Lindell Blvd, Saint Louis, MO, 63108-3478. Tel: 314-977-3947. Fax: 314-977-3966. p. 1361

Kulmatiski, Andrew, Dir, Schenectady County Public Library, 99 Clinton St, Schenectady, NY, 12305-2083. Tel: 518-388-4543. Fax: 518-386-2241. p. 1740

Kulp, Louise A, Visual Res, Franklin & Marshall College, 450 College Ave, Lancaster, PA, 17603-3318. Tel: 717-291-4242. Fax: 717-291-4160. p. 2076

Kulzy, Maryellen, Ch, Librn, Lyndhurst Free Public Library, 355 Valley Brook Ave, Lyndhurst, NJ, 07071. Tel: 201-804-2478. Fax: 201-939-7677. p. 1497

Kuma, Johnson, Ref Librn, Eastern Illinois University, 600 Lincoln Ave, Charleston, IL, 61920. Tel: 217-581-7550. p. 603

Kumagai, Gillian, Librn, Stanford Health Library, Stanford Comprehensive Cancer Center, 875 Blake Wilbur Dr, Stanford, CA, 94305. Tel: 650-736-1713. Fax: 650-736-7157. p. 205

Kumar, Sangeeta, Librn, South Suburban College Library, 15800 S State St, Rm 1249, South Holland, IL, 60473-1200. Tel: 708-596-2000, Ext 2574. Fax: 708-210-5755. p. 704

Kumar, Suhasini, Govt Doc, University of Toledo, 2801 W Bancroft St, Mail Stop 509, Toledo, OH, 43606-3390. Tel: 419-530-4485. Fax: 419-530-2726. p. 1941

Kumar, Susan, Dir, Palisades Park Free Public Library, 257 Second St, Palisades Park, NJ, 07650. Tel: 201-585-4150. Fax: 201-585-2151. p. 1517

Kumasi, Kafi, Dr, Asst Prof, Wayne State University, 106 Kresge Library, Detroit, MI, 48202. Tel: 313-577-1825. Fax: 313-577-7563. p. 2968

Kumher, Linnea, Librn, Hundred Public Library, Rte 250, Hundred, WV, 26575. Tel: 304-775-5161. Fax: 304-775-5161. p. 2560

Kump, Cindy, Pub Serv, Ref Librn, University of Saint Francis, 201 Pope John Paul II Ctr, 2701 Spring St, Fort Wayne, IN, 46808. Tel: 260-399-7700, Ext 6056. Fax: 260-399-8166. p. 742

Kump, Sandy, Circ, Titusville Public Library, 2121 S Hopkins Ave, Titusville, FL, 32780. Tel: 321-264-5026. Fax: 321-264-5030. p. 500

Kun, JaEun, Librn, University of California Los Angeles Library, Richard C Rudolph East Asian Library, 21617 Research Library YRL, Los Angeles, CA, 90095-1575. Tel: 310-825-9535. Fax: 310-206-4960. p. 179

Kun, Susan A, Br Mgr, Oakville Public Library, Woodside, 1274 Rebecca St, Oakville, ON, L6L 1Z2, CANADA. Tel: 905-815-5954. Fax: 905-815-2036. p. 2826

Kundert-Cameron, Elizabeth, Librn, Whyte Museum of the Canadian Rockies, 111 Bear St, Banff, AB, T1L 1A3, CANADA. Tel: 403-762-2291, Ext 335. Fax: 403-762-2339. p. 2684

Kung, Wendy, Tech Serv, Malden Public Library, 36 Salem St, Malden, MA, 02148-5291. Tel: 781-324-0218. Fax: 781-324-4467. p. 1102

Kunk, Patricia, Librn, Mercer County District Library, Saint Henry Granville Township, 200 E Main St, Saint Henry, OH, 45883. Tel: 419-678-3128. Fax: 419-678-3128. p. 1866

Kunkel, Karen, In Charge, East West Gateway Council of Governments Library, One Memorial Dr, Ste 1600, Saint Louis, MO, 63102. Tel: 314-421-4220, Ext 201. Fax: 314-231-6120. p. 1354

Kunkel, Lilith R, Dir, Kent State University, 2491 State Rte 45-S, Salem, OH, 44460-9412. Tel: 330-337-4213. Fax: 330-337-4144. p. 1933

Kunkel, Marita, Dir, Univ Librn, Pacific University Library, 2043 College Way, Forest Grove, OR, 97116. Tel: 503-352-1401. Fax: 503-352-1416. p. 1998

Kunkel, Nance M, Librn, Blackduck Community Library, 72 First St SE, Blackduck, MN, 56630. Tel: 218-835-6600. Fax: 218-835-6600. p. 1241

Kunkel-Coryell, Lori, Asst Dir, Ypsilanti District Library, 5577 Whittaker Rd, Ypsilanti, MI, 48197. Tel: 734-482-4110. Fax: 734-482-0047. p. 1238

Kunkle, Dan R, Exec Dir, Wildlife Information Center, 8844 Paint Mill Rd, Slatington, PA, 18080. Tel: 610-760-8889. Fax: 610-760-8889. p. 2140

Kunkle, Judie, Fac Coordr, Collingwood Library & Museum on Americanism, 8301 East Blvd Dr, Alexandria, VA, 22308. Tel: 703-765-1652. Fax: 703-765-8390. p. 2445

Kunkler, Jennifer, Cat Librn, Ohio Northern University, 525 S Main St, Ada, OH, 45810. Tel: 419-772-2181. Fax: 419-772-1927. p. 1851

Kunnapas, Tiia, Librn, Bauder College Library, 384 Northyards Blvd NW, Ste 190, Atlanta, GA, 30313. Tel: 404-443-1807, 404-443-1808. Fax: 404-237-1619. p. 513

Kunnapas, Tila, Libr Dir, DeVry University, One West Court Sq, Ste 100, Decatur, GA, 30030. Tel: 404-270-2702. p. 530

Kunsch, Kelly, Ref, Seattle University, School of Law Library, Sullivan Hall, 901 12th Ave, Seattle, WA, 98122-4411. Tel: 206-398-4221. Fax: 206-398-4194. p. 2532

Kuntz, Angelika, Head, Circ, Mount Laurel Library, 100 Walt Whitman Ave, Mount Laurel, NJ, 08054. Tel: 856-234-7319. Fax: 856-234-6916. p. 1506

Kuntz, Barbara, Pres, Lillian Perdido Bay Library, 12634 Ickler Ave, Lillian, AL, 36549. Tel: 251-962-4700. Fax: 251-962-4700. p. 23

Kuntz, Betty, Br Librn, Southeast Regional Library, Vibank Branch, 101 Second Ave, Vibank, SK, S0G 4Y0, CANADA. Tel: 306-762-2270. p. 2931

Kuntz, Christina, Br Mgr, Carroll County Public Library, Westminster Branch, 50 E Main St, Westminster, MD, 21157-5097. Tel: 410-386-4490. Fax: 410-386-4487. p. 1046

Kuntz, J, Asst Librn, Nissen Public Library, 217 W Fifth, Saint Ansgar, IA, 50472-0040. Tel: 641-713-2218. Fax: 641-713-4716. p. 842

Kuntz, Jennifer, Librn, United States Army, Womack Army Medical Center, Medical Library, WAMC Stop A, 2817 Reilly Rd, Fort Bragg, NC, 28310-7301. Tel: 910-907-7323. Fax: 910-907-7449. p. 1794

Kuntz, Jerry, Electronic Res Consult, Ramapo Catskill Library System, 619 Rte 17M, Middletown, NY, 10940-4395. Tel: 845-343-1131, Ext 246. Fax: 845-343-1205. p. 1660

Kuntz, Marsha, Dir, Nissen Public Library, 217 W Fifth, Saint Ansgar, IA, 50472-0040. Tel: 641-713-2218. Fax: 641-713-4716. p. 842

Kuntz, Rita, Librn, Lakeland Library Region, Battleford Branch, 201 22nd St W, Battleford, SK, S0M 0E0, CANADA. Tel: 306-937-2646. Fax: 306-937-6631. p. 2920

Kuntz, Robert, Mgr, Info Tech, Web Librn, Carroll County Public Library, 115 Airport Dr, Westminster, MD, 21157. Tel: 410-386-4500. Fax: 410-386-4509. p. 1045

Kuntz, Tina, Pub Serv, Dickinson Area Public Library, Billings County Resource Center, PO Box 307, Medora, ND, 58645-0307. Tel: 701-623-4604. Fax: 701-623-4941. p. 1840

Kuntzelman, Carol, Head, Coll Develop, Tech Serv, Hedberg Public Library, 316 S Main St, Janesville, WI, 53545. Tel: 608-758-6611. Fax: 608-758-6583. p. 2599

Kunz, Karen, Interim Dir, Oregon Institute of Technology Library, 3201 Campus Dr, Klamath Falls, OR, 97601-8801. Tel: 541-885-1769. Fax: 541-885-1777. p. 2002

Kunze, Janice, Librn, Keewatin Public Library, 125 W Third Ave, Keewatin, MN, 55753. Tel: 218-778-6377. Fax: 218-778-6193. p. 1255

Kunzinger, Jeannie, Asst City Librn, Helen Hall Library, 100 W Walker, League City, TX, 77573-3899. Tel: 281-554-1116. Fax: 281-554-1118. p. 2354

Kuo, Andrew, Librn, Contra Costa College Library, 2600 Mission Bell Dr, San Pablo, CA, 94806-3195. Tel: 510-235-7800, Ext 4449. Fax: 510-234-8161. p. 256

Kuo, Jiun, Head, Cat & Metadata Serv, Rice University, 6100 Main, MS-44, Houston, TX, 77005. Tel: 713-348-2568. Fax: 713-348-5258. p. 2341

Kuon, Tricia, Dr, Assoc Prof, Sam Houston State University, 1921 Ave J, Huntsville, TX, 77340. Tel: 936-294-3365. Fax: 936-294-1153. p. 2974

Kuonen, Cheryl, Br Mgr, Willoughby-Eastlake Public Library, Willowick Branch, 263 E 305th St, Willowick, OH, 44095. Tel: 440-943-4151. Fax: 440-944-6901. p. 1949

Kupas, David, Access Serv Librn, University of Pittsburgh, Johnstown Campus, 450 Schoolhouse Rd, Johnstown, PA, 15904. Tel: 814-269-1983. Fax: 814-269-7286. p. 2073

Kupchinski, Marie, Librn, Parkland Regional Library, Buchanan Branch, 315 Central, Buchanan, SK, S0A 0J0, CANADA. Tel: 306-592-2137. p. 2931

Kupec, Christopher, Asst Libr Dir, Chelmsford Public Library, 25 Boston Rd, Chelmsford, MA, 01824-3088. Tel: 978-256-5521. Fax: 978-256-8511. p. 1079

Kuperberg, Sandy, Circ, Social Security Administration Library, Annex Bldg 1520, Baltimore, MD, 21235-6401. Fax: 410-966-2027. p. 1017

Kupersmith, Peter, Dir, Delaware Valley College of Science & Agriculture, 700 E Butler Ave, Doylestown, PA, 18901-2699. Tel: 215-489-2254. Fax: 215-230-2967. p. 2050

Kupferberg, Natalie, Head of Libr, Ohio State University LIBRARIES, Biological Sciences & Pharmacy, 102 Riffe Bldg, 496 W 12th Ave, Columbus, OH, 43210-1214. Tel: 614-292-1744. Fax: 614-688-3123. p. 1887

Kupiec, Brian, Head, Tech & Digital Assets, Yale University Library, Beinecke Rare Book & Manuscript, 121 Wall St, New Haven, CT, 06520. Tel: 203-432-2965. Fax: 203-432-4047. p. 356

Kuppens, Mother Lucia, Librn, Abbey of Regina Laudis Library, Flanders Rd, Bethlehem, CT, 06751. Tel: 203-266-7727. p. 330

Kupper, Gary, Br Mgr, Saint Clair County Library System, Ira Township, 7013 Meldrum Rd, Fair Haven, MI, 48023. Tel: 586-725-9081. Fax: 586-725-1256. p. 1219

Kupsky, Carol, Asst Librn, Chilton Public Library, 221 Park St, Chilton, WI, 53014. Tel: 920-849-4414. Fax: 920-849-2370. p. 2585

Kurashige, Vicki, Dir, North Chatham Free Library, PO Box 907, North Chatham, NY, 12132-0907. Tel: 518-766-3211. Fax: 518-766-3211. p. 1706

Kurasz, Susan, In Charge, Mallinckrodt Baker, Inc, 1904 J T Baker Way, Phillipsburg, NJ, 08865. Tel: 908-859-2151, Ext 9418. Fax: 908-859-9454. p. 1519

Kurchenko, Victoria, In Charge, Research & Documentation Center of the Ukranian Institute of America, Two E 79th St, New York, NY, 10021. Tel: 212-288-8660. Fax: 212-288-2918. p. 1698

Kurhan, Scott, III, Ref Serv, Chesapeake Public Library, Russell Memorial, 2808 Taylor Rd, Chesapeake, VA, 23321-2210. Tel: 757-410-7020. Fax: 757-410-7029. p. 2456

Kuric, Keith, Head, Circ, La Porte County Public Library, 904 Indiana Ave, La Porte, IN, 46350-3435. Tel: 219-362-6156. Fax: 219-362-6158. p. 758

Kurkjian, Luella H, Br Chief, Hawaii State Archives, Iolani Palace Grounds, 364 S King St, Honolulu, HI, 96813. Tel: 808-586-0329. Fax: 808-586-0330. p. 561

Kurmas, Gaye, Dir, Hollis Social Library, Two Monument Sq, Hollis, NH, 03049. Tel: 603-465-7721. Fax: 603-465-3507. p. 1451

Kurosman, Kathleen, Ref Librn, Vassar College Library, 124 Raymond Ave, Maildrop 20, Poughkeepsie, NY, 12604-0020. Tel: 845-437-5760. Fax: 845-437-5864. p. 1723

Kurpiers, Ron, Coll Mgt, Augsburg College, 2211 Riverside Ave, Minneapolis, MN, 55454. Tel: 612-330-1604. Fax: 612-330-1436. p. 1259

Kurtenbach, Julie, Libr Dir, Piper City Public Library District, 39 W Main, Piper City, IL, 60959. Tel: 815-686-9234. Fax: 815-686-9234. p. 691

Kurth, Linda, Dir, Raymond A Sapp Memorial Township Library, 103 E Main St, Wyanet, IL, 61379. Tel: 815-699-2342. Fax: 815-699-2342. p. 721

Kurtti, James N, Dir, Findlandia University, Finnish American Heritage Center & Historical Archive, 435 Quincy St, Hancock, MI, 49930-1845. Tel: 906-487-7347. Fax: 906-487-7557. p. 1188

Kurtz, Becky, Dir, Wheatland Township Library, 207 Michigan Ave, Remus, MI, 49340. Tel: 989-967-8271. Fax: 989-967-8271. p. 1221

Kurtz Debra, Head, Digital Projects, Duke University Libraries, 411 Chapel Dr, Durham, NC, 27708. Tel: 919-660-5888. Fax: 919-668-2578. p. 1787

Kurtz, Diane, Head, Info Tech Serv, Stratford Library Association, 2203 Main St, Stratford, CT, 06615. Tel: 203-385-4161. Fax: 203-381-2079. p. 371

Kurtz, Holly, Br Mgr, Ontario City Library, Colony High, 3850 E Riverside Dr, Ontario, CA, 91761-1623. Tel: 909-395-2014. Fax: 909-930-0836. p. 200

Kurtz, Jeffery, Exec Dir, Cedar Falls Historical Society Archives, 308 W Third St, Cedar Falls, IA, 50613. Tel: 319-266-5149. Fax: 319-268-1812. p. 799

Kurtz, Tony, Mgr, Univ Rec Ctr, Western Washington University, 516 High St, MS 9103, Bellingham, WA, 98225. Tel: 360-650-3124. Fax: 360-650-3044. p. 2509

Kurtz-Shaw, Georgann, Head, Pub Serv, Greenville College, 301 N Elm, Greenville, IL, 62246. Tel: 618-664-6603. Fax: 618-664-9578. p. 652

Kuryliw, Ken, Librn, Red River North Regional Library, 303 Main St, Selkirk, MB, R1A 1S7, CANADA. Tel: 204-482-3522. Fax: 204-482-6166. p. 2751

Kurylowski, Linda, Asst Commun Librn, Hartford Public Library, Blue Hills, 649 Blue Hills Ave, Hartford, CT, 06112. Tel: 860-695-7420. Fax: 860-722-6907. p. 346

Kurz, Robin, Dr, Asst Prof, Louisiana State University, 267 Coates Hall, Baton Rouge, LA, 70803. Tel: 225-578-3158. Fax: 225-578-4581. p. 2966

Kurzmann, Susan, Pub Serv, Ramapo College of New Jersey, 505 Ramapo Valley Rd, Mahwah, NJ, 07430-1623. Tel: 201-684-7199. p. 1498

Kurzontkowski, Laura, Head, Circ, Holliston Public Library, 752 Washington St, Holliston, MA, 01746. Tel: 508-429-0617. Fax: 508-429-0625. p. 1095

Kurzum, Narmin, Librn, HackensackUMC Mountainside, One Bay Ave, Montclair, NJ, 07042-4898. Tel: 973-429-6240. Fax: 973-680-7850. p. 1503

Kusack, James, Dr, Prof, Southern Connecticut State University, 501 Crescent St, New Haven, CT, 06515. Tel: 203-392-5706. Fax: 203-392-5780. p. 2963

Kuserk, Evelyn, Chief Librn, ECRI Institute Library, 5200 Butler Pike, Plymouth Meeting, PA, 19462. Tel: 610-825-6000, Ext 5309. Fax: 610-834-7366. p. 2130

Kushmaul, Elaine, Sr Librn, Central Piedmont Community College Library, 1201 Elizabeth Ave, Charlotte, NC, 28235. Tel: 704-330-6113. Fax: 704-330-6887. p. 1781

Kushmeder, Michele, Ch, Hazleton Area Public Library, 55 N Church St, Hazleton, PA, 18201-5893. Tel: 570-454-2961. Fax: 570-454-0630. p. 2068

Kushner, Scott, Dir, LaFayette Public Library, Rte 11 N, LaFayette, NY, 13084. Tel: 315-677-3782. Fax: 315-677-0211. p. 1650

Kushnerick, Heather, Spec Coll Librn, South Texas College of Law, 1303 San Jacinto St, Houston, TX, 77002-7000. Tel: 713-646-1711. Fax: 713-659-2217. p. 2342

Kuske, Terry, Coordr, Tech Serv, ILL, Kiel Public Library, 511 Third St, Kiel, WI, 53042. Tel: 920-894-7122. Fax: 920-894-4023. p. 2602

Kusmik, Jennifer, Tech Serv, Johns Hopkins University School of Advanced International Studies, 1740 Massachusetts Ave NW, Washington, DC, 20036. Tel: 202-663-5958. Fax: 202-663-5916. p. 405

Kusmik, Rachel, Res Serv Librn, Jones Day, 901 Lakeside Ave, Cleveland, OH, 44114. Tel: 216-586-3939. Fax: 216-579-0212. p. 1880

Kuss, Kurt, Cat Librn, Aiso Library, 543 Lawton Rd, Ste 617A, Monterey, CA, 93944-3214. Tel: 831-242-5572. Fax: 831-242-5816. p. 189

Kussman, Barbara, Info Spec, Lakeshore Technical College Library, 1290 North Ave, Cleveland, WI, 53015. Tel: 920-693-1149. Fax: 920-693-8966. p. 2585

Kuster, Shanna, Ch, Winter Park Public Library, 460 E New England Ave, Winter Park, FL, 32789-4493. Tel: 407-623-3300. Fax: 407-623-3489. p. 505

Kuta, Nancy, Ch, Logan County Libraries, 220 N Main St, Bellefontaine, OH, 43311-2228. Tel: 937-599-4189. Fax: 937-599-5503. p. 1859

Kutaka, Aileen, In Charge, Walt Disney Imagineering, 1401 Flower St, Glendale, CA, 91201. Tel: 818-544-6594. Fax: 818-544-7845. p. 155

Kutcher, Teresa, Br Mgr, Tuscarawas County Public Library, Bolivar Branch, 455 W Water St SW, Bolivar, OH, 44612-9224. Tel: 330-874-2720. Fax: 330-874-1410. p. 1921

Kutolowski, Terry, Regional Libr Mgr, Broward County Division of Libraries, West Regional, 8601 W Broward Blvd, Plantation, FL, 33324. Tel: 954-382-5860, Ext 263. Fax: 954-382-5873. p. 442

Kuttler, Sharon, Mgr, Tech Serv, Provo City Library, 550 N University Ave, Provo, UT, 84601-1618. Tel: 801-852-6676. Fax: 801-852-6688. p. 2411

Kutulas, Nan, Ref, United States Army, Marquat Memorial Library, Bank Hall, Bldg D-3915, 3004 Ardennes St, Fort Bragg, NC, 28310-9610. Tel: 910-432-8920. Fax: 910-432-7788. p. 1794

Kutz, Ed, Sr Librn, Denver Public Library, Eugene Field, 810 S University Blvd, Denver, CO, 80209-4725. Tel: 303-777-2301. Fax: 303-722-7331. p. 301

Kutzik, George, Mgr, Eastman Chemical, State Hwy 837, West Elizabeth, PA, 15088-0567. Tel: 412-384-2520. Fax: 412-384-9634. p. 2154

Kuusinen, Jackie, Ref Librn, Bud Werner Memorial Library, 1289 Lincoln Ave, Steamboat Springs, CO, 80487. Tel: 970-879-0240. Fax: 970-879-3476. p. 323

Kuykendall, Francis, Dir, South Arkansas Community College, 300 Summit, El Dorado, AR, 71730. Tel: 870-864-7116. Fax: 870-864-7134. p. 98

Kuykendall, Tom, Ref, San Antonio College, 1001 Howard St, San Antonio, TX, 78212. Tel: 210-486-0554. p. 2381

Kuyper-Rushing, Lois, Head of Libr, Louisiana State University Libraries, Carter Music Resources Center, 202 Middleton Library, Baton Rouge, LA, 70803-3300. Tel: 225-578-4674. Fax: 225-578-6825. p. 943

Kuzma, David, Ref Curator, Rutgers University Libraries, Special Collections & University Archives, 169 College Ave, New Brunswick, NJ, 08901-1163. Tel: 848-932-6151. Fax: 732-932-7012. p. 1509

Kuzma, Scott, Archivist, Ironworld Discovery Center, 801 SW Hwy 169, Ste 1, Chisholm, MN, 55719. Tel: 218-254-1229. Fax: 218-254-7971. p. 1245

Kuzyk, Rachelle, Mgr, Libr Serv, Wetaskiwin Public Library, 5002 51st Ave, Wetaskiwin, AB, T9A 0V1, CANADA. Tel: 780-361-4446. Fax: 780-352-3266. p. 2721

Kvaracein, Kim, Asst Librn, Warren Public Library, 934 Main St, Warren, MA, 01083-0937. Tel: 413-436-7690. Fax: 413-436-7690. p. 1133

Kvasnicka, Kara, Sr Br Librn, Genesee District Library, Grand Blanc Area (McFarlen Public Library), 515 Perry Rd, Grand Blanc, MI, 48439. Tel: 810-694-5310. Fax: 810-694-5313. p. 1180

Kvenild, Cass, Interim Head of Libr, University of Wyoming Libraries, Learning Resource Center, Dept 3374, 1000 E University Ave, Laramie, WY, 82071. Tel: 307-766-5119. p. 2658

Kvill, Randy, Curator, Reynolds-Alberta Museum Reference Centre, Two KMS W Hwy 13, Wetaskiwin, AB, T9A 2G1, CANADA. Tel: 780-361-1351, Ext 254, 780-361-1351, Ext 255. Fax: 780-361-1239. p. 2721

Kvinnesland, Lynne, Pub Serv, DeSales University, 2755 Station Ave, Center Valley, PA, 18034. Tel: 610-282-1100, Ext 1266. Fax: 610-282-2342. p. 2043

Kwak, Gail S, Govt Doc, Head, Ref, Ref Librn, Northwestern State University Libraries, 913 University Pkwy, Natchitoches, LA, 71497. Tel: 318-357-4477. Fax: 318-357-4470. p. 958

Kwan, Anita, Commun Serv Coordr, Learning Disabilities Association of British Columbia-Vancouver Chapter, 3292 E Broadway, Vancouver, BC, V5M 1Z8, CANADA. Tel: 604-873-8139. Fax: 604-873-8140. p. 2741

Kwan, Connie, Med Librn, Santa Clara Valley Medical Center, 751 S Bascom Ave, Rm 2E063, San Jose, CA, 95128. Tel: 408-885-5651. Fax: 408-885-5655. p. 252

Kwant, Genevieve, Librn, Brantford Public Library, St Paul Avenue Branch, 441 St Paul Ave, Brantford, ON, N3R 4N8, CANADA. Tel: 519-753-2179. Fax: 519-753-3557. p. 2796

Kwant, Genevieve, Mgr, Br & Popular Serv, Brantford Public Library, 173 Colborne St, Brantford, ON, N3T 2G8, CANADA. Tel: 519-756-2220, Ext 324. Fax: 519-756-4979. p. 2796

Kwasik, Hanna, Head, Cat, Head, Ser, Louisiana State University Health Sciences Center, 433 Bolivar St, Box B3-1, New Orleans, LA, 70112-2223. Tel: 504-568-6106. Fax: 504-568-7718. p. 961

Kwasikpui, Shirley, Asst Librn, Albemarle Regional Library, Elizabeth Sewell Parker Memorial Library, 213 E Main, Murfreesboro, NC, 27855. Tel: 252-398-4494. Fax: 252-398-5724. p. 1835

Kwasnicki, Amy, Evening/Weekend Ref Librn, Drexel University Libraries, Hagerty Library, 33rd & Market Sts, Philadelphia, PA, 19104-2875. Tel: 215-895-2750. Fax: 215-895-2070. p. 2105

Kwasnik, Steve, Info Serv Librn, Bridgeport Public Library, 925 Broad St, Bridgeport, CT, 06604. Tel: 203-576-7403. Fax: 203-576-8255. p. 331

Kwedar, Melinda, Archivist, Curator, Kenilworth Historical Society, 415 Kenilworth Ave, Kenilworth, IL, 60043-1134. Tel: 847-251-2565. Fax: 847-251-2565. p. 661

Kwembe, Azungwe, Coordr, Ser, Chicago State University, 9501 S Martin Luther King Jr Dr, LIB 440, Chicago, IL, 60628-1598. Tel: 995-821-2848. Fax: 773-995-3772. p. 610

Kwiat, Chris, Libr Mgr, American Academy of Pediatrics, 141 Northwest Point Blvd, Elk Grove Village, IL, 60007-1098. Tel: 847-434-7635. Fax: 847-434-4993. p. 641

Kwiatkowski, Karen, Dir, Northwestern Technical College Library, 265 Bicentennial Trail, Rock Spring, GA, 30739. Tel: 706-764-3533. Fax: 706-764-3567. p. 548

Kwiatkowski, Karyn L, Cat Librn, Carlow University, 3333 Fifth Ave, Pittsburgh, PA, 15213. Tel: 412-578-6143. Fax: 412-578-6242. p. 2122

Kwik, Marilyn, Head, Adult Serv, Westland Public Library, 6123 Central City Pkwy, Westland, MI, 48185. Tel: 734-326-6123. Fax: 734-595-4612. p. 1236

Kwok, Borree, Dean of Libr, Campbell University, 113 Main St, Buies Creek, NC, 27506. Tel: 910-893-1460. Fax: 910-893-1470. p. 1778

Kwok, Hueyduan, Br Mgr, Hawaii State Public Library System, Aina Haina Public Library, 5246 Kalanianaole Hwy, Honolulu, HI, 96821. Tel: 808-377-2456. Fax: 808-377-2455. p. 561

Kwok, Meggy, In Charge, Canadian Bible Society Library, Ten Carnforth Rd, Toronto, ON, M4A 2S4, CANADA. Tel: 416-757-4171. Fax: 416-757-3376. p. 2850

Kwon, Maria V, Dir, Nyack Hospital, 160 N Midland Ave, Nyack, NY, 10960. Tel: 845-348-2514, 854-348-2000. Fax: 845-348-2515. p. 1708

Kwong, Bella, Med Librn, Los Angeles County-University of Southern California, Medical Center, Inpatient Tower -3K111, 2051 Marengo St, Los Angeles, CA, 90033. Tel: 323-409-7006. Fax: 323-441-8291. p. 172

Kwong, Vincci, Head, Web Serv, Indiana University South Bend, 1700 Mishawaka Ave, South Bend, IN, 46615. Tel: 574-520-4444. Fax: 574-520-4472. p. 778

Kyes Leab, Katharine, Dir, American Book Prices Current Library, PO Box 1236, Washington, CT, 06793. Tel: 860-868-7408. p. 374

Kyhnsen, Sophita, Dir, Bosque Farms Public Library, 1455 W Bosque Loop, Bosque Farms, NM, 87068. Tel: 505-869-2227. Fax: 505-869-3342. p. 1552

Kyle, Cathy, Teen Serv, Chili Public Library, 3333 Chili Ave, Rochester, NY, 14624-5494. Tel: 585-889-2200. Fax: 585-889-5819. p. 1729

Kyle, Nadine, Tech Serv, Iowa Wesleyan College, 107 W Broad St, Mount Pleasant, IA, 52641. Tel: 319-385-6319. Fax: 319-385-6324. p. 833

Kyle, Rita, Librn, Southeast Regional Library, Carlyle Branch, 119 Souris W, Carlyle, SK, S0C 0R0, CANADA. Tel: 306-453-6120. Fax: 306-453-6120. p. 2929

Kyle, Rita, Librn, Southeast Regional Library, Manor Branch, 23 Main St, Manor, SK, S0C 1R0, CANADA. Tel: 306-448-2266. Fax: 306-448-2266. p. 2930

Kyle, Sabrina, Librn, Sistersville Public Library, 518 Wells St, Sistersville, WV, 26175. Tel: 304-652-6701. Fax: 304-652-6701. p. 2572

Kyle, Todd, Chief Exec Officer, Newmarket Public Library, 438 Park Ave, Newmarket, ON, L3Y 1W1, CANADA. Tel: 905-953-5110. Fax: 905-953-5104. p. 2824

Kyles, Aurelia, Asst Dir, Outreach & Spec Projects, Memphis Public Library & Information Center, 3030 Poplar Ave, Memphis, TN, 38111-3527. Tel: 901-415-2871. Fax: 901-323-7108. p. 2249

Kynard, Pauline, Asst Mgr, Toledo-Lucas County Public Library, Sanger, 3030 W Central Ave, Toledo, OH, 43606. Tel: 419-259-5370. Fax: 419-536-9573. p. 1940

Kynard, Pauline, Br Mgr, Toledo-Lucas County Public Library, Sylvania Branch, 6749 Monroe St, Sylvania, OH, 43560. Tel: 419-882-2089. Fax: 419-882-8993. p. 1940

Kynast, Mary, Dir, Maud Preston Palenske Memorial Library, 500 Market St, Saint Joseph, MI, 49085. Tel: 269-983-7167, Ext 12. Fax: 269-983-5804. p. 1225

Kyprios, Linda, Exec Dir, Collin College, 2800 E Spring Creek Pkwy, Plano, TX, 75074. Tel: 972-881-5726. Fax: 972-881-5911. p. 2370

Kyriakis, Demetri, Head, Ref, Morse Institute Library, 14 E Central St, Natick, MA, 01760. Tel: 508-647-6400, Ext 1527. Fax: 508-647-6527. p. 1107

Kyriakodis, Harry, Librn, American Law Institute Library, 4025 Chestnut St, Philadelphia, PA, 19104. Tel: 215-243-1654. Fax: 215-243-1636. p. 2102

Kyrios, Terry, Dir, Salisbury Public Library, 17 Elm St, Salisbury, MA, 01952. Tel: 978-465-5071. p. 1122

Kyrios, Terry, Mgr, Libr Serv, EMH Regional Healthcare System, 630 E River St, Elyria, OH, 44035. Tel: 440-326-4321. Fax: 440-329-7405. p. 1898

Kyser, Carol, Dir, Oshkosh Public Library, 307 W First St, Oshkosh, NE, 69154. Tel: 308-772-4554. Fax: 308-772-4492. p. 1415

L'Helgouach, Véronique, Bibliothecaire Responsable, Bibliothèques de Montréal, La Petite-Patrie, 6707, avenue De Lorimier, Montreal, QC, H2G 2P8, CANADA. Tel: 514-872-1734. Fax: 514-872-0526. p. 2890

L'Heureux, Angele, Librn, Federation des Medecins Specialistes du Quebec Bibliotheque, Two Complexe Desjardins, Ste 3000, Montreal, QC, H5B 1G8, CANADA. Tel: 514-350-5000. Fax: 514-350-5100. p. 2895

L'Heureux, Sonia, Dir, Library of Parliament, Parliament Bldgs, Ste 677F, Ottawa, ON, K1A 0A9, CANADA. Tel: 613-992-3122. p. 2831

L'Hommebieu, Ann Marie, Doc Delivery, Albany Medical College, 47 New Scotland Ave, MC 63, Albany, NY, 12208. Tel: 518-262-5569. Fax: 518-262-5820. p. 1568

La Barre, Kathryn, Assoc Prof, University of Illinois at Urbana-Champaign, Library & Information Science Bldg, 501 E Daniel St, Champaign, IL, 61820-6211. Tel: 217-333-3280. Fax: 217-244-3302. p. 2965

La Belle, Anne, Ref, Hudson Valley Community College, 80 Vandenburgh Ave, Troy, NY, 12180. Tel: 518-629-7384. Fax: 518-629-7509. p. 1756

La Bossiere, Holly, Dir, Ponca City Library, 515 E Grand, Ponca City, OK, 74601. Tel: 580-767-0345. Fax: 580-767-0377. p. 1976

La Chapelle, Jennifer, Chief Exec Officer, Clearview Public Library, 201 Huron St, Stayner, ON, L0M 1S0, CANADA. Tel: 705-428-3595. Fax: 705-428-3595. p. 2844

La Chapelle, Jennifer, Chief Exec Officer, Clearview Public Library, Sunnidale Branch, 5237 Simcoe County Rd 9, New Lowell, ON, L0M 1N0, CANADA. Tel: 705-424-6288. Fax: 705-424-6288. p. 2845

La Fleur, Robbie, Dir, Minnesota Legislative Reference Library, 645 State Office Bldg, 100 Rev Dr Martin Luther King Jr Blvd, Saint Paul, MN, 55155-1050. Tel: 651-296-8310. Fax: 651-296-9731. p. 1280

La Force, Gina, Chief Librn/CEO, Thunder Bay Public Library, 285 Red River Rd, Thunder Bay, ON, P7B 1A9, CANADA. Tel: 807-684-6802. Fax: 807-345-8727. p. 2849

La Forter, Susan, Pres, Western Massachusetts Health Information Consortium, Baystate Medical Ctr Health Sciences Library, 759 Chestnut St, Springfield, MA, 01199. Tel: 413-787-2053. Fax: 413-794-1974. p. 2946

La Macchia, James, II, Tech Coordr, Michigan State University, 115 Law College Bldg, East Lansing, MI, 48824-1300. Tel: 517-432-6866. Fax: 517-432-6861. p. 1175

La, Mibong, Head Librn, Passaic County Community College, One College Blvd, Paterson, NJ, 07505. Tel: 973-684-5885. Fax: 973-684-6675. p. 1518

La Riviere, Marguerite, Dir, Kegoayah Kozga Public Library, 223 Front St, Nome, AK, 99762. Tel: 907-443-6628. Fax: 907-443-3762. p. 52

La Rocca, Kelly, Br Mgr, Saint Tammany Parish Library, Slidell Branch, 555 Robert Blvd, Slidell, LA, 70458. Tel: 985-646-6470. Fax: 985-645-3553. p. 948

La Rue, Eva, Asst Curator, Central Nevada Museum & Historical Society, 1900 Logan Field Rd, Tonopah, NV, 89049. Tel: 775-482-9676. Fax: 775-482-5423. p. 1434

La Spina, Anita, Ch, Rockville Centre Public Library, 221 N Village Ave, Rockville Centre, NY, 11570. Tel: 516-766-6257. Fax: 516-766-6090. p. 1734

La Valle, Dawn, Asst Dir, Admin Serv, Fairfield Public Library, 1080 Old Post Rd, Fairfield, CT, 06824. Tel: 203-256-3154. p. 339

La Valle, Dawn, Dir, Libr Develop, Connecticut State Library, 231 Capitol Ave, Hartford, CT, 06106. Tel: 860-757-6665. Fax: 860-757-6503. p. 345

La Verna, Lewis, Cat, Southside Virginia Community College Libraries, 109 Campus Dr, Alberta, VA, 23821. Tel: 434-949-1064. Fax: 434-949-0013. p. 2444

Laakso, Barbara, Librn, Rackemann, Sawyer & Brewster Library, 160 Federal St, Boston, MA, 02110-1700. Tel: 617-542-2300. Fax: 617-542-7437. p. 1066

Laas, Kelly, Librn, Illinois Institute of Technology, Center for the Study of Ethics in the Professions Library, Hermann Union Bldg/Mezzanine, Rm 205, 3241 S Federal St, Chicago, IL, 60616. Tel: 312-567-6913. Fax: 312-567-3016. p. 615

LaBadia, Maria, Youth Serv, Montclair Free Public Library, 50 S Fullerton Ave, Montclair, NJ, 07042. Tel: 973-744-0500, Ext 2226. Fax: 973-744-5268. p. 1503

LaBarge, Mary, Assoc Librn, Moorpark College Library, 7075 Campus Rd, Moorpark, CA, 93021-1695. Tel: 805-378-1450. Fax: 805-378-1470. p. 191

LaBarrett, Joye, Managing Dir, The Texas State Museum of Asian Cultures & Educational Center, 1809 N Chaparral, Corpus Christi, TX, 78401. Tel: 361-882-2641. Fax: 361-882-5718. p. 2302

LaBatto, Marianne, Archivist, Brooklyn College Library, 2900 Bedford Ave, Brooklyn, NY, 11210-2889. Tel: 718-951-5346. Fax: 718-951-4540. p. 1589

Labbe, Charlotte, Head, ILL, Fordham University Libraries, 441 E Fordham Rd, Bronx, NY, 10458-5151. Tel: 718-817-3570. Fax: 718-817-3582. p. 1586

Labbe, Charlotte, ILL, Fordham University Libraries, 441 E Fordham Rd, Bronx, NY, 10458-5151. Tel: 718-817-3570. Fax: 718-817-3582. p. 1586

Labbe, Johanne, Circ, Cegep St Jean Sur Richelieu Bibliotheque, 30 boul du Seminaire, CP 1018, Saint-Jean-Sur-Richelieu, QC, J3B 7B1, CANADA. Tel: 450-347-5301, Ext 2333. Fax: 450-347-3329, 450-358-9350. p. 2911

Labbe, Teresa M, Dir, Okemah Public Library, 301 S Second, Okemah, OK, 74859. Tel: 918-623-1915. Fax: 918-623-0489. p. 1971

Labeaune, Inga, Circ, Reader Serv, Monterey Public Library, 625 Pacific St, Monterey, CA, 93940-2866. Tel: 831-646-3477. Fax: 831-646-5618. p. 190

Labedz, Elizabeth, Libr Mgr, K&L Gates LLP, State Street Financial Ctr, One Lincoln St, Boston, MA, 02111-2950. Tel: 617-951-9160. Fax: 617-261-3175. p. 1062

LaBelle, Catherine, Head, Coll Serv, West Orange Free Public Library, 46 Mount Pleasant Ave, West Orange, NJ, 07052-4903. Tel: 973-736-0198. Fax: 973-736-1655. p. 1541

LaBelle, Darlene, Dir, Macomb County Library, 16480 Hall Rd, Clinton Township, MI, 48038-1132. Tel: 586-412-5999. Fax: 586-286-8951. p. 1164

Labelle, Jacqueline, Exec Dir, Centre Regional de Services aux Bibliotheques Publiques de la Monteregie, 275 rue Conrad-Pelletier, La Prairie, QC, J5R 4V1, CANADA. Tel: 450-444-5433. Fax: 450-659-3364. p. 2885

LaBelle, S, Librn, Vancouver Holocaust Education Centre Library & Archives, 50-950 W 41st Ave, Vancouver, BC, V5Z 2N7, CANADA. Tel: 604-264-0499. Fax: 604-264-0497. p. 2743

LaBelle, Shannon, Libr Res Serv Mgr, Audrey & Harry Hawthorn Library & Archives at the UBC Museum of Anthropology, 6393 NW Marine Dr, Vancouver, BC, V6T 1Z2, CANADA. Tel: 604-822-4834. Fax: 604-822-2974. p. 2741

Laberge, Linda, Librn, Bibliotheque de l'Institut Nazareth et Louis-Braille, 1111 St Charles St W, Longueuil, QC, J4K 5G4, CANADA. Tel: 450-463-1710. Fax: 450-463-0243. p. 2886

LaBerge, Valerie, Youth Serv, Sandwich District Library, 107 E Center St, Sandwich, IL, 60548-1603. Tel: 815-786-8308. Fax: 815-786-9231. p. 700

Labonte, Alison, Sr Librn, Data Contracts, Board of Governors of The Federal Reserve System, Research Library, 20th & C St NW, MS 102, Washington, DC, 20551. Tel: 202-452-3333. Fax: 202-530-6222. p. 394

Labonte, Alison, Ref Serv, RAND Corp, 1200 S Hayes St, Arlington, VA, 22202. Tel: 703-413-1100, Ext 5330. Fax: 703-414-4729. p. 2450

Labonte, Chantal, Libr Tech, Health Canada, 1001 Boul St Laurent Ouest, Longueuil, QC, J4K 1C7, CANADA. Tel: 450-928-4189. Fax: 450-928-4102. p. 2887

LaBonte, Dale, Re/Ser Librn, Quinsigamond Community College, 670 W Boylston St, Worcester, MA, 01606-2092. Tel: 508-854-7472. Fax: 508-854-4204. p. 1144

Labonte, George, Librn, Worcester Telegram & Gazette Library, 20 Franklin St, Worcester, MA, 01608-1904. Tel: 508-793-9277. Fax: 508-793-9281. p. 1146

Labonte, Patricia, Librn, Niagara College of Applied Arts & Technology, 300 Woodlawn Rd, Welland, ON, L3C 7L3, CANADA. Tel: 905-735-2211, Ext 7767. Fax: 905-736-6021. p. 2870

Labory, Marie-Helene, Coll Develop Librn, Ref Librn, Universite du Quebec en Outaouais, 283, Blvd Alexandre-Tache, Case postale 1250, succ Hull, Gatineau, QC, J8X 3X7, CANADA. Tel: 819-595-3900, Ext 1856. Fax: 819-773-1669. p. 2884

Labosky, Ted, Ser, Tech Serv, Forsyth Technical Community College Library, 2100 Silas Creek Pkwy, Winston-Salem, NC, 27103. Tel: 336-734-7508. Fax: 336-761-2465. p. 1833

Labovitch, Lisa, Dir, Libr & Archives, Union League Club of Chicago Library, 65 W Jackson Blvd, Chicago, IL, 60604. Tel: 312-435-4818. p. 625

Labow, Marilyn, Librn, Whitewater Region, 20 Cameron St, Beachburg, ON, K0J 1C0, CANADA. Tel: 613-582-7090. p. 2794

Labra, Luis, Br Mgr, Prince George's County Memorial, Bowie Branch, 15210 Annapolis Rd, Bowie, MD, 20715. Tel: 301-262-7000. Fax: 301-809-2792. p. 1032

LaBranch, Nicole, Ch, William Fogg Library, 116 Old Rd, Eliot, ME, 03903. Tel: 207-439-9437. Fax: 207-439-9437. p. 984

LaBrash, Beverley, Br Mgr, Elizabethtown-Kitley Township Public Library, Lyn Branch, 14 Main St, Lyn, ON, K0E 1M0, CANADA. Tel: 613-345-0033. p. 2791

Labrecque, Julie, In Charge, Bibliotheque Municipale de Levis, Seven Mgr Gosselin, Levis, QC, G6V 5J9, CANADA. Tel: 418-838-4126. Fax: 418-838-4124. p. 2886

LaBree, Janie, Regional Supvr, Great River Regional Library, 1300 W St Germain St, Saint Cloud, MN, 56301-3667. Tel: 320-650-2544. Fax: 320-650-2501. p. 1274

LaBrie, Darlene, Dir, New Berlin Library, 15 S Main St, New Berlin, NY, 13411-2905. Tel: 607-847-8564. Fax: 607-847-8564. p. 1664

LaBrosse, Dawn, Youth Serv Mgr, Washington County Library, 8595 Central Park Pl, Woodbury, MN, 55125-9453. Tel: 651-275-8500. Fax: 651-275-8509. p. 1290

Labrum, Dana, Br Mgr, Saint Joseph County Public Library, Roger B Francis Branch, 52655 N Ironwood Rd, South Bend, IN, 46635. Tel: 574-282-4641. p. 779

Labsan, C, Acq, Cat, United States Army, Marquat Memorial Library, Bank Hall, Bldg D-3915, 3004 Ardennes St, Fort Bragg, NC, 28310-9610. Tel: 910-432-6503. Fax: 910-432-7788. p. 1794

Labuda, Joseph, Dir, Pima Community College, 2202 W Anklam Rd, Tucson, AZ, 85709-0001. Tel: 520-206-6821. Fax: 520-206-3059. p. 86

Labuda, Joseph, Dir, Pima Community College, District Library Services, 4905B E Broadway Blvd, Tucson, AZ, 85709-1140. Tel: 520-206-6821. Fax: 520-206-6821. p. 86

LaBuda, Kathy, Dir, Antioch Public Library District, 757 Main St, Antioch, IL, 60002. Tel: 847-395-0874. Fax: 847-395-5399. p. 589

Lac, Tiffany, Br Mgr, San Francisco Public Library, Ortega Branch Library, 3223 Ortega St, San Francisco, CA, 94122-4053. Tel: 415-355-5700. Fax: 415-655-5942. p. 246

Lacasse, Lucinda, Dir, Jackman Public Library, 604 Main St, Jackman, ME, 04945. Tel: 207-668-2110. p. 988

Lacayanga, Tiffany, Br Mgr, Glendale Public Library, Chevy Chase, 3301 E Chevy Chase Dr, Glendale, CA, 91206-1416. Tel: 818-548-2047. Fax: 818-548-7713. p. 155

Lacayanga, Tiffany, Br Mgr, Glendale Public Library, Montrose-Crescenta Branch, 2465 Honolulu Ave, Montrose, CA, 91020-1803. Tel: 818-548-2048. Fax: 818-248-6987. p. 155

Lacayo, Carmela G, Dr, Pres, National Association for Hispanic Elderly Library, 234 E Colorado Blvd, Ste 300, Pasadena, CA, 91101. Tel: 626-564-1988. Fax: 626-564-2659. p. 206

Lace-Robb, Marilynn, Dir, Georgetown County Library, Carvers Bay, 13048 Choppee Rd, Hemingway, SC, 29554-3318. Tel: 843-558-6654. Fax: 843-558-6680. p. 2195

Lacelle, Dominique, Dir, Plantagenet Village Library System, 550 Albert St, Plantagenet, ON, K0B 1L0, CANADA. Tel: 613-679-4928. Fax: 613-673-2051. p. 2836

LaCentra, Allie, Info Serv, Saint Helena Public Library, 1492 Library Lane, Saint Helena, CA, 94574-1143. Tel: 707-963-5244. Fax: 707-963-5264. p. 226

Lacey, Angela, Dir, Poinsett County Public Library, 200 N East St, Harrisburg, AR, 72432. Tel: 870-578-4465. Fax: 870-578-4466. p. 102

Lacey, Dona, Br Mgr, Scott County Public Library, 108 S Main St, Scottsburg, IN, 47170. Tel: 812-752-2751. Fax: 812-752-2878. p. 777

Lacey, Donna, Br Mgr, Scott County Public Library, Austin Branch, 26 Union Ave, Austin, IN, 47102-1344. Tel: 812-794-2721. Fax: 812-794-4550. p. 777

Lacey, Pat, Libr Tech, United States Army Corps of Engineers, 2902 Newmark Dr, Champaign, IL, 61822. Tel: 217-373-7217. Fax: 217-373-7258. p. 603

Lach, Mary Ann, Dir, New York Eye & Ear Infirmary, 310 E 14th St, New York, NY, 10003. Tel: 212-979-4000. Fax: 212-979-4179. p. 1689

Lachance, Annie, ILL, Ref, Ministere de la Sante et des Services Sociaux, 1075, Chemin Ste-Foy, 5e etage, Quebec, QC, G1S 2M1, CANADA. Tel: 418-266-7018. Fax: 418-266-7024. p. 2905

Lachance, Barbara, Dir, Sandown Public Library, 305 Main St, Sandown, NH, 03873. Tel: 603-887-3428. Fax: 603-887-0590. p. 1465

Lachance, Gilles, Pub Serv, Ref, Commission des Valeurs Mobilieres du Quebec Bibliotheque, 800 Square Victoria, 22nd Flr, CP 246, Montreal, QC, H4Z 1G3, CANADA. Tel: 514-940-2199, Ext 4494. Fax: 514-873-3090. p. 2894

Lachance, Johanne, Librn, FPInnovations-Forintek, 319 rue Franquet, Quebec, QC, G1P 4R4, CANADA. Tel: 418-659-2647. Fax: 418-659-2922. p. 2905

Lachance, Lise, Asst Dir, Chambre des Notaires du Quebec, Tour Bourse 800 Victoria Pl, Montreal, QC, H4Z 1L8, CANADA. Tel: 514-879-1793, Ext 240. Fax: 514-879-1697. p. 2893

LaChapelle, Jennifer, Chief Exec Officer, Clearview Public Library, Creemore Branch, 165 Library St, Creemore, ON, L0M 1G0, CANADA. Tel: 705-466-3011. Fax: 705-466-3011. p. 2845

Lachatanere, Diana, Asst Dir, Coll Serv, New York Public Library - Astor, Lenox & Tilden Foundations, Schomburg Center for Research in Black Culture, 515 Malcolm X Blvd, New York, NY, 10037-1801. Tel: 212-491-2225. Fax: 212-491-6760. p. 1693

Lachemayer, Diane, Dir, Hunterdon Developmental Center Library, 40 Pittstown Rd, Clinton, NJ, 08809. Tel: 908-735-4031, Ext 1147. Fax: 908-730-1359. p. 1479

Lachine-Caron, Kim, Admin Serv, Chatham-Kent Public Library, 120 Queen St, Chatham, ON, N7M 2G6, CANADA. Tel: 519-354-2940. Fax: 519-354-7366. p. 2799

Lachoff, Irwin, Assoc Univ Archivist, Xavier University of Louisiana, One Drexel Dr, New Orleans, LA, 70125-1098. Tel: 504-520-7305. Fax: 504-520-7940. p. 964

Lackey, Polly, Dr, Dir, Wayland Baptist University, 1900 W Seventh, Plainview, TX, 79072-6957. Tel: 806-291-3700. Fax: 806-291-1964. p. 2370

Lackie, Robert, Instrul Serv Librn, Rider University, 2083 Lawrenceville Rd, Lawrenceville, NJ, 08648-3099. Tel: 609-895-5626. Fax: 609-896-8029. p. 1494

Lackovic, Randy, Librn, University of Maine, 193 Clarks Cove Rd, Walpole, ME, 04573. Tel: 207-563-8193. Fax: 207-563-3119. p. 1004

LaClaire, Terri, Asst Librn, Alvan Bolster Ricker Memorial Library, 1211 Maine St, Poland, ME, 04274. Tel: 207-998-4390. Fax: 207-998-2120. p. 996

Lacomb, Mike, Librn, United States Army, Aberdeen Area Garrison Library, Bldg 3326, Aberdeen Proving Ground, MD, 21005-5001. Tel: 410-278-3417. Fax: 410-278-5684. p. 1009

Lacono, Anthony, Br Mgr, Salinas Public Library, El Gabilan, 1400 N Main St, Salinas, CA, 93906. Tel: 831-758-7302. Fax: 831-442-0817. p. 226

LaCourse, Patricia C, Sci/Eng Librn, Alfred University, Scholes Library of Ceramics, New York State College of Ceramics at Alfred University, Two Pine St, Alfred, NY, 14802-1297. Tel: 607-871-2943. p. 1572

Lacoursiere, Michel, Dir, Bibliotheques de Trois-Rivieres, 1425 Place de l'Hotel de Ville, CP 1713, Trois-Rivieres, QC, G9A 5L9, CANADA. Tel: 819-372-4645. Fax: 819-693-1892. p. 2913

Lacouture, Helen, Assoc Law Librn, Access & Organization, Boston College, 885 Centre St, Newton Centre, MA, 02459. Tel: 617-552-8609. Fax: 617-552-2889. p. 1110

Lacouture, Marge, Librn, United States Navy, Naval Undersea Warfare Center Division, Newport Technical Library, 1176 Howell St, Bldg 101, Newport, RI, 02841. Tel: 401-832-4338. Fax: 401-832-3699. p. 2170

LaCroix, Christian, Coll Develop, Managing Librn, Purchasing, College de Levis, Nine rue Mgr Gosselin, Levis, QC, G6V 5K1, CANADA. Tel: 418-833-1249, Ext 140. Fax: 418-833-1974. p. 2886

Lacroix, Johanne, Mgr, Societe Radio-Canada Bibliotheque, 1400 est boul Rene-Levesque, Montreal, QC, H2L 2M2, CANADA. Tel: 514-597-4804. Fax: 514-597-6236. p. 2901

LaCroix, Michael J, Dir, Creighton University, 2500 California Plaza, Omaha, NE, 68178-0209. Tel: 402-280-2217. Fax: 402-280-2435. p. 1412

Lacy, Pamela, Librn, Lord Corp, 110 Lord Dr, Cary, NC, 27511-7900. Tel: 919-469-2500. Fax: 919-460-9648. p. 1779

Lacy, Teresa, Dir, Alabama Institute for the Deaf & Blind, 705 South St, Talladega, AL, 35160. Tel: 256-761-3237. Fax: 256-761-3561. p. 36

Ladarola, Phyllis, Mgr, ILL, Mgr, Per, Arapahoe Community College, 5900 S Santa Fe Dr, Littleton, CO, 80160. Fax: 303-798-4173. p. 316

Ladd, Dennis, Ref, Southwestern Law School, 3050 Wilshire Blvd, Los Angeles, CA, 90010. Tel: 213-738-5771. Fax: 213-738-5792. p. 177

Ladd, Ken, Assoc Dean of Libr, University of Saskatchewan Libraries, Murray Library, Three Campus Dr, Saskatoon, SK, S7N 5A4, CANADA. Tel: 306-966-5946. Fax: 306-966-6040. p. 2927

Ladd, Lisa, Coll Spec, Dartmouth College Library, Kresge Physical Sciences Library, 6115 Fairchild Hall, Hanover, NH, 03755-3571. Tel: 603-646-3563. Fax: 603-646-3681. p. 1450

Ladd, Margaret, Librn, Piermont Public Library, 130 Rte 10, Piermont, NH, 03779-3205. Tel: 603-272-4967. Fax: 603-272-4947. p. 1462

Ladd, Nancy, Libr Dir, Tech Librn, Pillsbury Free Library, 18 E Main St, Warner, NH, 03278. Tel: 603-456-2289. Fax: 603-456-3177. p. 1467

Ladewig, Aimee, Dir, Bellville Public Library, 12 W Palm, Bellville, TX, 77418-1446. Tel: 979-865-3731. Fax: 979-865-2060. p. 2288

Ladika, Tina, Ch, South Kingstown Public Library, 1057 Kingstown Rd, Peace Dale, RI, 02879-2434. Tel: 401-783-4085, 401-789-1555. Fax: 401-782-6370. p. 2171

Ladner, Elizabeth, Access Serv, University of North Carolina at Charlotte, 9201 University City Blvd, Charlotte, NC, 28223-0001. Tel: 704-687-4295. Fax: 704-687-3050. p. 1784

Ladner, Sandra, Br Mgr, Hancock County Library System, Kiln Public Library, 17065 Hwy 603, Kiln, MS, 39556. Tel: 228-255-1724. Fax: 228-255-0644. p. 1293

Ladner, Sharyn, Dir, Access & Info Serv, University of Miami Libraries, 1300 Memorial Dr, Coral Gables, FL, 33146. Tel: 305-284-5254. Fax: 305-284-4027. p. 434

Ladson, Barbara, Ch, Perry Carnegie Library, 302 N Seventh St, Perry, OK, 73077. Tel: 580-336-4721. Fax: 580-336-5497. p. 1976

Ladwig, Parker, Math & Life Sci Librn, Hesburgh Libraries, O'Meara Mathematics Library, 001 Hayes-Healy Ctr, Notre Dame, IN, 46556-5641. Tel: 574-631-7278. Fax: 574-631-9660. p. 770

LaFaver, DeAnna, Librn, Bremond Public Library & Visitors Center, 115 S Main St, Bremond, TX, 76629. Tel: 254-746-7752. Fax: 254-746-7065. p. 2291

Lafaye, Cary, Pub Serv, Midlands Technical College Library, Beltline Library, 316 S Beltline Blvd, 2nd Flr, Columbia, SC, 29205. Tel: 803-738-7762. Fax: 803-738-7719. p. 2207

Lafazan, Bonnie, Dir, Berkeley College, Middlesex Campus, 430 Rahway Ave, Woodbridge, NJ, 07095. Tel: 732-750-1800, Ext 2200. Fax: 732-726-9286. p. 1545

LaFever, Susan, Coordr, Bibliog Control & Libr Automation, Tennessee Technological University, 1100 N Peachtree Ave, Cookeville, TN, 38505. Tel: 931-372-6110. Fax: 931-372-6112. p. 2231

Lafferty, Becky, Pub Serv, Vermont Technical College, Main St, Randolph Center, VT, 05061. Tel: 802-728-1237. Fax: 802-728-1506. p. 2433

Lafferty, Julie, Ch, Kirklin Public Library, 115 N Main, Kirklin, IN, 46050. Tel: 765-279-8308. Fax: 765-279-8258. p. 757

Lafferty, Rebecca, Head, Ref, Clarksburg-Harrison Public Library, 404 W Pike St, Clarksburg, WV, 26301. Tel: 304-627-2236. Fax: 304-627-2239. p. 2557

Lafferty, Robert, Tech Serv, Broadview Public Library District, 2226 S 16th Ave, Broadview, IL, 60155-4000. Tel: 708-345-1325. Fax: 708-345-5024. p. 597

Lafferty, Sheila A, Dir/Ref Librn, University of Connecticut - Torrington Regional Campus Library, 855 University Dr, Torrington, CT, 06790. Tel: 806-626-6841. Fax: 860-626-6817. p. 372

Laffey, Jim, Prof, University of Missouri-Columbia, 303 Townsend Hall, Columbia, MO, 65211. Tel: 573-882-4546. Fax: 573-884-2917. p. 2968

Laffond, Debra, Ch Serv Librn, Pelham Public Library, 24 Village Green, Pelham, NH, 03076. Tel: 603-635-7581. Fax: 603-635-6952. p. 1461

LaFine Rhoads, Debi, Librn, Iroquois County Genealogical Society Library, Old Courthouse Museum, 103 W Cherry St, Watseka, IL, 60970-1524. Tel: 815-432-3730. Fax: 815-432-3730. p. 716

Lafionatis, Lydia, Head, Access Serv, Northeastern University School of Law Library, 400 Huntington Ave, Boston, MA, 02115. Tel: 617-373-5482. Fax: 617-373-8705. p. 1066

LaFleche, Life, Librn, College Militaire Royal de Saint-Jean Library, 15 rue Jaques-Cartier Nord, Saint-Jean-Sur-Richelieu, QC, J3B 8R8, CANADA. Tel: 450-358-6608. Fax: 450-358-6929. p. 2911

Lafleur, LeRoy, Ref, University of Rochester, River Campus Libraries, 755 Library Rd, Rochester, NY, 14627-0055. Tel: 585-275-4461. Fax: 585-273-5309. p. 1733

LaFleur, LeRoy J, Head of Libr, George Mason University Libraries, Arlington Campus, 3401 N Fairfax Dr, Arlington, VA, 22201. Tel: 703-993-8268. Fax: 703-993-8142. p. 2462

LaFleur, Thomas Walter, Libr Dir, Laredo Community College, Senator Judith Zaffirini Library (South Library), 5500 S Zapata Hwy, Laredo, TX, 78046. Tel: 956-721-5816. Fax: 956-721-5447. p. 2353

LaFleur, Thomas Walter, Libr Dir, Laredo Community College, West End Washington St, Laredo, TX, 78040. Tel: 956-721-5283. Fax: 956-721-5447. p. 2353

LaFond, Brigitte, Head of Libr, Canadian Museum of Civilization Library, 100 Laurier St, Gatineau, QC, K1A 0M8, CANADA. Tel: 819-776-7151. Fax: 819-776-7152. p. 2883

LaFond, Christine, Librn, Clear Lake Public Library, 350 Fourth Ave, Clear Lake, WI, 54005. Tel: 715-263-2802. p. 2585

LaFond, Margaret, Dir, Rehoboth Beach Public Library, 226 Rehoboth Ave, Rehoboth Beach, DE, 19971-2141. Tel: 302-227-8044. Fax: 302-227-0597. p. 386

LaFond, Pierrette, Tech Serv, Musee de la Civilisation - Bibliotheque du Seminaire de Quebec, Nine rue de l'Universite, Quebec, QC, G1R 5K1, CANADA. Tel: 418-643-2158. Fax: 418-692-5206. p. 2906

Lafonde, Linda C, ILL Coordr, Quinte West Public Library, Seven Creswell Dr, Trenton, ON, K8V 6X5, CANADA. Tel: 613-394-3381, Ext 3316. Fax: 613-394-2079. p. 2868

Lafont, Ann, Librn, Quebec Ministere De L'Agriculture Des Pecheries Et De L'Alimentation Bibliotheque, 200 Chemin Sainte-Foy, 1er etage, Quebec, QC, G1R 4X6, CANADA. Tel: 418-380-2100, Ext 3504. Fax: 418-380-2175. p. 2906

LaFontain, Darbie, Ch, Duncan Public Library, 2211 N Hwy 81, Duncan, OK, 73533. Tel: 580-255-0636. Fax: 580-255-6136. p. 1961

LaForce, Claire, Librn, Rutland Regional Medical Center, 160 Allen St, Rutland, VT, 05701. Tel: 802-747-3777. Fax: 802-747-3955. p. 2434

Laforest, Joanne, Librn, Cegep Riviere du-Loup-Bibliotheque, 80 rue Frontenac, Riviere-du-Loup, QC, G5R 1R1, CANADA. Tel: 418-862-6903, Ext 2238. Fax: 418-862-4959. p. 2907

LaForge, John, Dir, Progressive Foundation, 740 Round Lake Rd, Luck, WI, 54853. Tel: 715-472-4185. Fax: 715-472-4184. p. 2606

LaForge, Ruth, Br Librn, Wapiti Regional Library, Arborfield Public Library, 201 Main St, Arborfield, SK, S0E 0A0, CANADA. Tel: 306-769-8533. p. 2921

Lafortune, Sylvie, Chair, Dept of Libr & Archives, Laurentian University, 935 Ramsey Lake Rd, Sudbury, ON, P3E 2C6, CANADA. Tel: 705-675-1151, Ext 3302. Fax: 705-675-4877. p. 2846

Laframboise, Carole, Asst Librn, Britt Area Library, 841 Riverside Dr, Britt, ON, P0G 1A0, CANADA. Tel: 705-383-2292. Fax: 705-383-0077. p. 2797

LaFrance, Denise, Ref Librn, Dover Public Library, 73 Locust St, Dover, NH, 03820-3785. Tel: 603-516-6050. Fax: 603-516-6053. p. 1445

Lafrance, Isabelle, Dir, Bibliotheque et Archives nationales du Quebec, 475 de Maisonneuve E, Montreal, QC, H2L 5C4, CANADA. Tel: 514-873-1101, Ext 3203. Fax: 514-873-9312. p. 2888

LaFrance, Liselle, Dir, Van Rensselaer - Rankin Family Historic Cherry Hill Museum & Library, 523 1/2 S Pearl St, Albany, NY, 12202. Tel: 518-434-4791. Fax: 518-434-4806. p. 1571

LaFrance, Lucie, Cat, Pub Serv, Tech Serv, Commission des Valeurs Mobilieres du Quebec Bibliotheque, 800 Square Victoria, 22nd Flr, CP 246, Montreal, QC, H4Z 1G3, CANADA. Tel: 514-940-2199, Ext 4494. Fax: 514-873-3090. p. 2894

LaFrance, Peg, Mgr, Orrick, Herrington & Sutcliffe LLP, The Orrick Bldg, 405 Howard St, San Francisco, CA, 94105-2669. Tel: 415-773-5700. Fax: 415-773-5759. p. 244

LaFrance, Ruth, Youth Serv Librn, Lenox Library Association, 18 Main St, Lenox, MA, 01240. Tel: 413-637-0197. Fax: 413-637-2115. p. 1098

Lafreniere, Cheryl, Chief Exec Officer, Head Librn, Teck Centennial Library, Ten Kirkland St E, Kirkland Lake, ON, P2N 1P1, CANADA. Tel: 705-567-7966. Fax: 705-568-6303. p. 2814

Lagace, Michel, Librn, Office Franco-Quebecois pour la Jeunesse Library, 11 Rene Levesque E, Montreal, QC, H2X 3Z6, CANADA. Tel: 514-873-4255. Fax: 514-873-0067. p. 2900

Laganosky, Jessica, Librn, Harbaugh-Thomas Library, 50 W York St, Biglerville, PA, 17307. Tel: 717-677-6257. Fax: 717-677-6357. p. 2035

Laganosky, Jessica, Librn, Littlestown Library, 46 E King St, Rm 3, Littlestown, PA, 17340. Tel: 717-359-0446. Fax: 717-359-1359. p. 2082

Lage, Kathryn, Actg Head, Earth Sci & Map Libr, University of Colorado Boulder, 1720 Pleasant St, 184 UCB, Boulder, CO, 80309-0184. Tel: 303-735-4917. Fax: 303-492-3340. p. 291

Lage, Kathryn, Actg Head, Earth Sci & Map Libr, University of Colorado Boulder, Jerry Crail Johnson Earth Sciences & Map Library, 2200 Colorado Ave, 184 UCB, Boulder, CO, 80309-0184. Tel: 303-735-4917. Fax: 303-735-4879. p. 292

Lager, Darla, Ch, Owatonna Public Library, 105 N Elm Ave, Owatonna, MN, 55060-2405. Tel: 507-444-2460. Fax: 507-444-2465. p. 1270

Lager, Mark, Support Serv Mgr, Ventura County Library, 5600 Everglades St, Ste A, Ventura, CA, 93003. Tel: 805-677-7150. Fax: 805-677-7173. p. 279

Lagerman, Susan M, Communications & Libr Prog Mgr, Brown County Library, 515 Pine St, Green Bay, WI, 54301. Tel: 920-448-5806. Fax: 920-448-4376. p. 2595

Lagermann, Patty, Ch, Jefferson County Library, Windsor, 7479 Metropolitian Blvd, Barnhart, MO, 63012. Tel: 636-461-1914. Fax: 636-461-1915. p. 1331

Lagerstrom, Jill, Chief Librn, Space Telescope Science Institute Library, 3700 San Martin Dr, Baltimore, MD, 21218. Tel: 410-338-4961. Fax: 410-338-4767. p. 1017

Lageschulte, Denise, Asst Dir, Ida Grove Public Library, 100 E Second St, Ida Grove, IA, 51445. Tel: 712-364-2306. Fax: 712-364-3228. p. 822

Lagios, Melina, Youth Serv, San Juan Island Library District, 1010 Guard St, Friday Harbor, WA, 98250-9612. Tel: 360-378-2798. Fax: 360-378-2706. p. 2516

Lagomarsino, Pam, Br Librn, Mariposa County Library, Red Cloud, 10332-C Fiske Rd, Coulterville, CA, 95311. Tel: 209-878-3692. p. 184

Lagonia, Maria, Managing Librn, Rye Free Reading Room, 1061 Boston Post Rd, Rye, NY, 10580. Tel: 914-231-3165. Fax: 914-967-5522. p. 1736

LaGore, David, Librn, First Baptist Church Library, 300 Saint Francis St, Kennett, MO, 63857. Tel: 573-888-4689. Fax: 573-888-4680. p. 1342

LaGore, Sara, Librn, First Baptist Church Library, 300 Saint Francis St, Kennett, MO, 63857. Tel: 573-888-4689. Fax: 573-888-4680. p. 1342

Lagoy, Heather, Electronic Res Librn, Syst, Webmaster, Nazareth College of Rochester Library, 4245 East Ave, Rochester, NY, 14618-3790. Tel: 585-389-2121. Fax: 585-389-2145. p. 1730

Lagraize, L, Br Mgr, New Orleans Public Library, East New Orleans Branch, 5641 Read Blvd, New Orleans, LA, 70127-3105. Tel: 504-596-0200. p. 962

LaGrange, Mary, Dir, Springville Memorial Library, 264 Broadway St, Springville, IA, 52336. Tel: 319-854-6444. Fax: 319-854-6443. p. 845

Lagree, Sara, ILL, DeKalb County Public Library, Administrative Office, 215 Sycamore St, 4th Flr, Decatur, GA, 30030. Tel: 404-370-3070, Ext 2016. Fax: 404-370-3073. p. 529

LaGrew, Gina, Dir, Mazinaigan Waakaaigant - Red Cliff Public Library, 88850 Church Rd, Bayfield, WI, 54814-4604. Tel: 715-779-3764. Fax: 715-779-5093. p. 2580

LaGro, Elizabeth A, Mgr, Libr Serv, Hollister Incorporated, 2000 Hollister Dr, Libertyville, IL, 60048. Tel: 847-918-3890. Fax: 847-918-3453. p. 665

LaGuardia, Cheryl, Res Librn, Harvard Library, Harvard College Library (Headquarters in Harry Elkins Widener Memorial Library), Widener Library, Rm 110, Cambridge, MA, 02138. Tel: 617-495-2401. Fax: 617-496-4226. p. 1075

Lague, Carole, Head Librn, Bibliotheque Municipale de Gatineau, Édifice Pierre Papin, CP 1970 Succ. Hull, Gatineau, QC, J8X 3Y9, CANADA. p. 2882

Laguë, Carole, Chief Librn, Bibliotheque Municipale de Gatineau, 144, boul de l'Hôpital, local 317, Gatineau, QC, J8T 7S7, CANADA. Tel: 819-243-2345, Ext 2548. Fax: 819-243-2399. p. 2882

Lague, Mark, Dir, Canton Public Library, 786 Washington St, Canton, MA, 02021-3029. Tel: 781-821-5027. Fax: 781-821-5029. p. 1079

LaGue, Mary D, Coll Mgr, Taubman Museum of Art, 110 Salem Ave SE, Roanoke, VA, 24011. Tel: 540-342-5760. Fax: 540-342-5798. p. 2494

Lagumina, Ann, Br Mgr, Las Vegas-Clark County Library District, Whitney Library, 5175 E Tropicana Ave, Las Vegas, NV, 89122. Tel: 702-507-4010. Fax: 702-507-4026. p. 1430

Lah, Barbara, Law Librn, University of New Mexico, Law Library, 1117 Stanford Dr NE, Albuquerque, NM, 87131-1441. Tel: 505-277-6236. Fax: 505-277-0068. p. 1551

Laherty, Jennifer, Coll Develop, California State University, East Bay Library, 25800 Carlos Bee Blvd, Hayward, CA, 94542-3052. Tel: 510-885-2555. Fax: 510-885-2049. p. 157

Lahey, Cynde Bloom, Asst Dir, New Canaan Library, 151 Main St, New Canaan, CT, 06840. Tel: 203-594-5021. Fax: 203-594-5026. p. 354

Lahey, Sue, Ref Serv, Albany Medical College, 47 New Scotland Ave, MC 63, Albany, NY, 12208. Tel: 518-262-5531. Fax: 518-262-5820. p. 1568

Lahiri, Amar, Head, Cat, Robert L Carothers Library & Learning Commons, 15 Lippitt Rd, Kingston, RI, 02881. Tel: 401-874-2660. Fax: 401-874-4608. p. 2168

Lahmann, Jenie, Pub Relations/Mkt/Web Site, Wayne Township Library, 80 N Sixth St, Richmond, IN, 47374-3079. Tel: 765-966-8291. Fax: 765-962-1318. p. 775

Lahmon, Jo, Br Mgr, Cobb County Public Library System, South Cobb, 805 Clay Rd, Mableton, GA, 30126. Tel: 678-398-5828. Fax: 678-398-5833. p. 543

Lahn, Betty, Dir, Learning Commons, Williston State College Library, 1410 University Ave, Williston, ND, 58801. Tel: 701-774-4226. Fax: 701-774-4547. p. 1849

Lahr, Mary, Dir, Delhi Public Library, 316A Franklin St, Delhi, IA, 52223-9602. Tel: 563-922-2037. Fax: 563-922-2037. p. 807

Lahti, Gail K, Librn, Palos Community Hospital, 12251 S 80th Ave, Palos Heights, IL, 60463. Tel: 708-923-4640. Fax: 708-923-4674. p. 687

LaHue, Dorothy, Br Coordr, Siskiyou County Public Library, Happy Camp Branch, 143 Buckhorn Rd, Happy Camp, CA, 96039. Tel: 530-493-2964. p. 286

Lai, Diane, Pub Serv Librn, Mechanics' Institute Library, 57 Post St, San Francisco, CA, 94104-5003. Tel: 415-393-0118. Fax: 415-421-4192. p. 243

Lai, Francesco, Head of Libr, Environment Canada Library, Burlington, 867 Lakeshore Rd, Burlington, ON, L7R 4A6, CANADA. Tel: 905-336-4982. Fax: 905-336-4428. p. 2798

Lai, Grace, Librn, State University of New York Educational Opportunity Center, 100 New St, Syracuse, NY, 13202. Tel: 315-472-0130, Ext 116. Fax: 315-472-1241. p. 1753

Lai, Patricia, Archivist, Hawaii State Archives, Iolani Palace Grounds, 364 S King St, Honolulu, HI, 96813. Tel: 808-586-0329. Fax: 808-586-0330. p. 561

Lai, Weiliang, Dir, West New York Public Library, 425 60th St, West New York, NJ, 07093-2211. Tel: 201-295-5135. Fax: 201-662-1473. p. 1541

Laier, Caroline, Pub Serv, Schenectady County Community College, 78 Washington Ave, Schenectady, NY, 12305. Tel: 518-381-1235. Fax: 518-381-1252. p. 1740

Laieski, Cheryl, Syst Programmer, Maricopa County Community College District, 2411 W 14th St, Tempe, AZ, 85281-6942. Tel: 480-731-8918. Fax: 480-731-8787. p. 2937

Laing, Brenda, Asst Librn, Ashaway Free Library, 15 Knight St, Ashaway, RI, 02804-1410. Tel: 401-377-2770. Fax: 401-377-2770. p. 2163

Laing, Carol, Regional Libr Supvr, Wake County Public Library System, East Regional Library, 946 Steeple Square Ct, Knightdale, NC, 27545. Tel: 919-217-5305. Fax: 919-217-5327. p. 1817

Laing, Michele, Br Head, University of Waterloo Library, Musagetes Architecture Library, Seven Melville St S, Cambridge, ON, N1S 2H4, CANADA. p. 2870

Laing, Sue, Circ Mgr, Crandall Public Library, 251 Glen St, Glens Falls, NY, 12801-3593. Tel: 518-792-6508. Fax: 518-792-5251. p. 1629

Laiosa, Joyce, Youth Serv, Voorheesville Public Library, 51 School Rd, Voorheesville, NY, 12186. Tel: 518-765-2791. Fax: 518-765-3007. p. 1761

Laird, Cathryn, Br Mgr, Manatee County Public Library System, Braden River, 4915 53rd Ave E, Bradenton, FL, 34203. Tel: 941-727-6079. Fax: 941-727-6059. p. 430

Laird, Danielle, Dir, Librn, Mounds Public Library, 418 First St, Mounds, IL, 62964. Tel: 618-745-6610. p. 676

Laird, Ralph, Librn, Niagara College of Applied Arts & Technology, Glendale, 135 Taylor Rd, RR 4, Niagara on the Lake, ON, L0S 1J0, CANADA. Tel: 905-641-2252, Ext 4402. Fax: 905-988-4313. p. 2870

Laird, Sandra, Br Mgr, Mississauga Library System, Streetsville, 112 Queen St S, Mississauga, ON, L5M 1K8, CANADA. Tel: 905-615-4785. p. 2823

Laite, Berkley, Chair, Shippensburg University, 1871 Old Main Dr, Shippensburg, PA, 17257-2299. Tel: 717-477-1473. Fax: 717-477-1389. p. 2140

Laity, Amy, Dir, Harris-Elmore Public Library, 328 Toledo St, Elmore, OH, 43416. Tel: 419-862-2482. Fax: 419-862-2123. p. 1898

LaJesse, Vicky, Ch, Atlanta-Fulton Public Library System, Stewart-Lakewood Library, 2893 Lakewood Ave SW, Atlanta, GA, 30315. Tel: 404-762-4054. Fax: 404-762-4056. p. 512

Lajoie, Linda, Ch, Springfield City Library, 220 State St, Springfield, MA, 01103. Tel: 413-263-6828, Ext 201. Fax: 413-263-6817. p. 1127

Lajoie, Marie-Claire, Archivist, Fall River Historical Society Museum, 451 Rock St, Fall River, MA, 02720. Tel: 508-679-1071. Fax: 508-675-5754. p. 1088

Lajoie, Paul, ILL Access & Serv Mgr/Evening, Fashion Institute of Technology-SUNY, Seventh Ave at 27th St, New York, NY, 10001-5992. Tel: 212-217-4362. Fax: 212-217-4371. p. 1678

Lakatos, Holly, Librn, California Court of Appeal Third Appellate District Library, 914 Capitol Mall, 10th Flr, Sacramento, CA, 95814. Tel: 916-653-0207. Fax: 916-653-0322. p. 220

Lakatos, Jackie, Circ, Lemont Public Library District, 50 E Wend St, Lemont, IL, 60439-6439. Tel: 630-257-6541. Fax: 630-257-7737. p. 664

Lake, Edward, Librn, Thayer Public Library, Three Main St, Ashuelot, NH, 03441-2616. Tel: 603-239-4099. p. 1438

Lake, Laurie, Ref, Cleveland Institute of Music, 11021 East Blvd, Cleveland, OH, 44106-1776. Tel: 216-795-3151. Fax: 216-791-3063. p. 1877

Lake, Lin C, Coll Develop, Columbia College, 1301 Columbia College Dr, Columbia, SC, 29203-9987. Tel: 803-786-3042. Fax: 803-786-3700. p. 2187

Lake, Linda, Curator, Historic Courthouse Museum Library, 255 N Main St, Lakeport, CA, 95453. Tel: 707-263-4555. Fax: 707-263-7918. p. 163

Lake, Scharron, Librn, Endeavor Public Library, 125 Park S, Endeavor, WI, 53930. Tel: 608-587-2902. Fax: 608-587-2902. p. 2591

Lakie, Patricia, Ch, Woodland Public Library, 250 First St, Woodland, CA, 95695-3411. Tel: 530-661-5980. Fax: 530-666-5408. p. 284

Lalancette, Christian, Archivist, Le Seminaire Saint-Joseph de Trois-Rivieres, 858 rue Laviolette, local 221, Trois-Rivieres, QC, G9A 5S3, CANADA. Tel: 819-376-4459, Ext 135. Fax: 819-378-0607. p. 2914

Lalevee, Marie, Head Librn, The Library of the French Cultural Center Alliance Francaise of Boston, 53 Marlborough St, Boston, MA, 02116-2099. Tel: 617-912-0400 ext 419. Fax: 617-912-0450. p. 1062

Laliberte, Sylvie, ILL, Ministere des Ressources naturelles et de la Faune, 5700 4e Ave Ouest, B-201, Quebec, QC, G1H 6R1, CANADA. Tel: 418-627-8686, Ext 3554. Fax: 418-644-1124. p. 2906

Lalla, Nadia, Coordr, Coll & Info Serv, University of Michigan, A Alfred Taubman Health Sciences Library, 1135 E Catherine, Ann Arbor, MI, 48109-2038. Tel: 734-764-1210. p. 1153

Lalley, Sandee, Ch, Oil City Library, Two Central Ave, Oil City, PA, 16301-2795. Tel: 814-678-3072. Fax: 814-676-8028. p. 2100

Lalli, Patricia, Ch, Joshua Hyde Public Library, 306 Main St, Sturbridge, MA, 01566-1242. Tel: 508-347-2512. Fax: 508-347-2872. p. 1129

Lalli, Robert, Ref, Utica Public Library, 303 Genesee St, Utica, NY, 13501. Tel: 315-735-2279. Fax: 315-734-1034. p. 1760

Lalli, Stephen J, Circ, Fordham University Westchester Library, 400 Westchester Ave, West Harrison, NY, 10604. Tel: 914-367-3426. p. 1766

Lally, Sharon, Acq, Southern New Hampshire University, 2500 N River Rd, Manchester, NH, 03106-1045. Tel: 603-645-9605. Fax: 603-645-9685. p. 1456

Lalmansingh, Anne Marie, Br Mgr, Enoch Pratt Free Library, Waverly, 400 E 33rd St, Baltimore, MD, 21218-3401. Tel: 410-396-6053. Fax: 410-396-6150. p. 1013

Lalonde, Betty, Librn, Wabamun Public Library, 5132 53rd Ave, Wabamun, AB, T0E 2K0, CANADA. Tel: 780-892-2713. Fax: 780-892-7294. p. 2721

Lalonde, Daniel, Dir, Bibliotheque Commemorative Desautels, 1801 DuPont St, Marieville, QC, J3M 1J7, CANADA. Tel: 450-460-4444, Ext 271. Fax: 450-460-3526. p. 2887

Lalonde, Denise, Librn, Greater Sudbury Public Library, Azilda Branch, 120 Ste-Agnus St, Azilda, ON, P0M 1B0, CANADA. Tel: 705-983-3955. Fax: 705-983-4119. p. 2846

Lalonde, Nathalie, Libr Tech, Bruyere Continuing Care Library, 43 Bruyere St, Ottawa, ON, K1N 5C8, CANADA. Tel: 613-562-6262, Ext 4054. Fax: 613-562-4237. p. 2828

LaLonde-Reaume, Michelle, Asst Detroit Satellite Librn, US Court of Appeals for the Sixth Circuit Library, 312 Potter Stewart US Courthouse, Cincinnati, OH, 45202. Tel: 513-564-7321. Fax: 513-564-7329. p. 1873

Laluzerne, Tony, Circ, Todd Wehr Library, St Norbert College, 301 Third St, De Pere, WI, 54115. Tel: 920-403-3280. Fax: 920-403-4064. p. 2587

LaLuzerne, Tony, Cataloger, University of Wisconsin-Green Bay, 2420 Nicolet Dr, Green Bay, WI, 54311-7001. Tel: 920-465-2785. Fax: 920-465-2136. p. 2596

Lalwani, Leena, Coll Develop, Ref, University of Michigan, Art, Architecture & Engineering Library, Duderstadt Ctr, 2281 Bonnisteel Blvd, Ann Arbor, MI, 48109-2094. Tel: 734-647-5747. Fax: 734-764-4487. p. 1152

Lam, Carolyn, Assoc Dir, Mgr, Seneca College of Applied Arts & Technology, Newnham Campus (Main), 1750 Finch Ave E, North York, ON, M2J 2X5, CANADA. Tel: 416-491-5050, Ext 22100. Fax: 416-491-3349. p. 2813

Lam, Henry, Info Spec, Sunnybrook Health Sciences Centre - Library Services, 2075 Bayview Ave, Rm EG-29, Toronto, ON, M4N 3M5, CANADA. Tel: 416-480-6100, Ext 2562. Fax: 416-480-6848. p. 2859

Lam, Janet, Br Mgr, Librn IV, Hawaii State Public Library System, North Kohala Public Library, 54-3645 Akoni Pule Hwy, Kapaau, HI, 96755. Tel: 808-889-6655. Fax: 808-889-6656. p. 563

Lam, Judy, Librn, Cook County Law Library, Rolling Meadows Branch, 2121 Euclid, Rolling Meadows, IL, 60008. Tel: 847-818-2290. Fax: 847-818-2025. p. 612

Lam, Kwan-Yau, Pub Serv, Truman College, 1145 W Wilson Ave, Chicago, IL, 60640-5691. Tel: 773-907-4869. Fax: 773-907-6803. p. 625

Lam, Linda, Managing Librn, Pima County Public Library, Salazar-Ajo Branch, 33 Plaza, Ajo, AZ, 85321. Tel: 520-387-6075. Fax: 520-387-5345. p. 87

Lam, Mimi, Digital Librn, Union of British Columbia Indian Chiefs, 342 Water St, 4th Flr, Vancouver, BC, V6B 1B6, CANADA. Tel: 604-684-0231. Fax: 604-684-5726. p. 2742

Lam, Pauline P, Dir, Cedar Park Public Library, 550 Discovery Blvd, Cedar Park, TX, 78613. Tel: 512-401-5600. Fax: 512-259-5236. p. 2296

Lam, Tracy, Acq, De Anza College, 21250 Stevens Creek Blvd, Cupertino, CA, 95014-5793. Tel: 408-864-8439. Fax: 408-864-8603. p. 138

Lama, Maureen, Acq, Barry University, 11300 NE Second Ave, Miami, FL, 33161. Tel: 305-899-3760. Fax: 305-899-4792. p. 464

Lamade, Dawn A, Dir, Young Harris College, One College St, Young Harris, GA, 30582. Tel: 706-379-4313. Fax: 706-379-4314. p. 558

Lamaire, Raymond, Pres, French-Canadian Genealogical Society of Connecticut, Inc Library, 53 Tolland Green, Tolland, CT, 06084. Tel: 860-643-7231. p. 372

Laman, James, Circ Supvr, Lander University, 320 Stanley Ave, Greenwood, SC, 29649-2099. Tel: 864-388-8365. Fax: 864-388-8816. p. 2197

LaMar, Alethea, Dir, Mellinger Memorial Library, 11 Division St, Morning Sun, IA, 52640. Tel: 319-868-7505. Fax: 319-868-7505. p. 833

LaMar, LaRee, ILL, St John's Health System, 1235 E Cherokee St, Springfield, MO, 65804-2263. Tel: 417-820-2795. Fax: 417-820-5399. p. 1367

Lamar, Sandra, Computer Serv, New England School of Law Library, 154 Stuart St, Boston, MA, 02116-5687. Tel: 617-422-7282. Fax: 617-422-7303. p. 1065

LaMarche, Jenna, Br Support, Stormont, Dundas & Glengarry County Library, Crysler Branch, 16 Third St, Crysler, ON, K0C 1G0, CANADA. Tel: 613-987-2090. p. 2801

LaMarche, Sherry, Circ, Hudson Valley Community College, 80 Vandenburgh Ave, Troy, NY, 12180. Tel: 518-629-7985. Fax: 518-629-7509. p. 1756

LaMark, Tina, Asst Dir, Tech & Access Serv, Carnegie Library of Pittsburgh, 4400 Forbes Ave, Pittsburgh, PA, 15213-4080. Tel: 412-920-4520. Fax: 412-920-4531. p. 2122

LaMay, Thomasin, ILL Mgr, Goucher College Library, 1021 Dulaney Valley Rd, Baltimore, MD, 21204. Tel: 410-337-6031. Fax: 410-337-6419. p. 1014

Lamb, Audree, Librn, Village Library of Morris, 152 Main St, Morris, NY, 13808. Tel: 607-263-2080. Fax: 607-263-2080. p. 1663

Lamb, Beth, Ref Serv, Stevenson University Library, 1525 Greenspring Valley Rd, Stevenson, MD, 21153. Tel: 410-486-7000, 443-334-2233. Fax: 410-486-7329. p. 1043

Lamb, Connie, Librn, Brigham Young University, Harold B Lee Library, 2060 HBLL, Provo, UT, 84602. Tel: 801-422-2927. Fax: 801-422-0466. p. 2411

Lamb, Debbie, Asst Dir, Mary Esther Public Library, 100 Hollywood Blvd W, Mary Esther, FL, 32569-1957. Tel: 850-243-5731. Fax: 850-243-4931. p. 463

Lamb, Dorothy, Ch, Linden Public Library, 131 S Main, Linden, IA, 50146. Tel: 641-744-2124. p. 828

Lamb, Heather, Ref Librn, Belvedere-Tiburon Library, 1501 Tiburon Blvd, Tiburon, CA, 94920. Tel: 415-789-2665. Fax: 415-789-2650. p. 275

Lamb, Holly Ward, Youth Serv, Howell Carnegie District Library, 314 W Grand River Ave, Howell, MI, 48843. Tel: 517-546-0720. Fax: 517-546-1494. p. 1192

Lamb, Jamey, Access Serv Librn, Media Serv Librn, Oklahoma State University - Center for Health Sciences, 1111 W 17th St, Tulsa, OK, 74107-1898. Tel: 918-561-1114. Fax: 918-561-8412. p. 1981

Lamb, Jonas, Electronic Serv, Juneau Public Libraries, 292 Marine Way, Juneau, AK, 99801. Tel: 907-586-5324. Fax: 907-586-3419. p. 50

Lamb, Sandra, Libr Mgr, Sally Ploof Hunter Memorial Library, 101 Public Works Dr, Black River, NY, 13612. Tel: 315-773-5163. Fax: 315-775-1224. p. 1583

Lamb, Therese, Head, Ref, Henderson District Public Libraries, James I Gibson Library, 100 W Lake Mead Pkwy, Henderson, NV, 89015. Tel: 702-565-8402. Fax: 702-565-8832. p. 1428

Lambe, Catherine V, Librn, Williams Mullen Library, 301 Fayetteville St, Ste 1700, Raleigh, NC, 27601. Tel: 919-981-4038. Fax: 919-981-4300. p. 1819

Lambert, Abby, Adult/YA Librn Supvr, Durango Public Library, 1900 E Third Ave, Durango, CO, 81301. Tel: 970-375-3387. Fax: 970-375-3398. p. 304

Lambert, Beverly, Dir, Prosser Public Library, One Tunxis Ave, Bloomfield, CT, 06002-2476. Tel: 860-243-9721. Fax: 860-242-1629. p. 330

Lambert, Brent L, Dir, National Model Railroad Association, 4121 Cromwell Rd, Chattanooga, TN, 37421-2119. Tel: 423-894-8144. Fax: 423-899-4869. p. 2228

Lambert, Damian, Br Mgr, New Orleans Public Library, Nix Branch, 1401 S Carrollton Ave, New Orleans, LA, 70118-2809. Tel: 504-596-2630. Fax: 504-596-2672. p. 962

Lambert, David, Circ, Capilano College Library, 2055 Purcell Way, North Vancouver, BC, V7J 3H5, CANADA. Tel: 604-986-1911, Ext 2108. Fax: 604-984-1728. p. 2734

Lambert, David Allen, Virtual Ref, New England Historic Genealogical Society Library, 99-101 Newbury St, Boston, MA, 02116-3007. Tel: 617-226-1239. Fax: 617-536-7307. p. 1065

Lambert, Debra K, Dir, Hillsboro Public Library, 819 High Ave, Hillsboro, WI, 54634. Tel: 608-489-2192. p. 2598

Lambert, Donna L, Dir, Stewart Free Library, Eight Levi Stewart Dr, Corinna, ME, 04928. Tel: 207-278-2454. Fax: 207-278-5200. p. 982

Lambert, Elizabeth, Br Mgr, Broward County Division of Libraries, Century Plaza, 1856A W Hillsboro Blvd, Deerfield Beach, FL, 33442. Tel: 954-360-1330. Fax: 954-360-1332. p. 441

Lambert, Frank, Asst Prof, Kent State University, 314 Library, Kent, OH, 44242-0001. Tel: 330-672-2782. Fax: 330-672-7965. p. 2972

Lambert, Harold, Jr, In Charge, Harold M Lambert Studios, 239 M Madison Ave, Warminster, PA, 18974. Tel: 215-328-9464. Fax: 215-328-9465. p. 2150

Lambert, Jan, Coordr, Libr Serv, Malvern-Hot Spring County Library, 202 E Third St, Malvern, AR, 72104. Tel: 501-332-5441. Fax: 501-332-6679. p. 108

Lambert, Jan, Soc Work Librn, University of Connecticut Library, Harleigh B Trecker Library, 1800 Asylum Ave, West Hartford, CT, 06117. Tel: 860-570-9035. Fax: 860-570-9036. p. 371

Lambert, Joshua, Head, Access Serv, Missouri State University, 850 S John Q Hammons Pkwy, Springfield, MO, 65807. Tel: 417-836-3183. Fax: 417-836-4764. p. 1367

Lambert, Joshua, Asst Prof, Missouri State University, Duane G Meyer Library, 901 S National Ave, Springfield, MO, 65897. Tel: 417-836-4525. Fax: 417-836-4764. p. 2968

Lambert, Karen, Dir, North Branch Township Library, 3714 Huron St (M-90), North Branch, MI, 48461-8117. Tel: 810-688-2282. Fax: 810-688-3165. p. 1214

Lambert, Leigh, Dir, Southside Regional Library, 316 Washington St, Boydton, VA, 23917. Tel: 434-738-6580. Fax: 434-738-6070. p. 2452

Lambert, Linda, Instrul Serv Librn, Taylor University, 236 W Reade Ave, Upland, IN, 46989-1001. Tel: 765-998-5270. Fax: 765-998-5569. p. 783

Lambert, Linda, Dir, Whatcom Community College Library, 237 W Kellogg Rd, Bellingham, WA, 98226. Tel: 360-383-3300. p. 2509

Lambert, Linda, Access Serv & Syst, College Bourget Bibliotheque, 65 rue Saint Pierre, Rigaud, QC, J0P 1P0, CANADA. Tel: 450-451-0815. Fax: 450-451-4171. p. 2907

Lambert, Lindalee M, Co-Dir, Tuftonboro Free Library, 221 Middle Rd, Center Tuftonboro, NH, 03816. Tel: 603-569-4256. Fax: 603-569-5885. p. 1441

Lambert, Marjory, In Charge, Furnas County Law Library, Courthouse, 912 R St, Beaver City, NE, 68926. Tel: 308-268-4025. p. 1393

Lambert, Mark, In Charge, Texas General Land Office, Stephen F Austin Bldg, 1700 N Congress Ave, Austin, TX, 78701. Tel: 512-463-5277. Fax: 512-475-4619. p. 2282

Lambert, Michael, Dep Dir, Libr Serv, San Mateo County Library, Library Administration, 125 Lessingia Ct, San Mateo, CA, 94402-4000. Tel: 650-312-5251. Fax: 650-312-5382. p. 255

Lambert, Michael, Exec Dir, Distance Education & Training Council, 1601 18th St NW, Ste 2, Washington, DC, 20009. Tel: 202-234-5100, Ext 101. Fax: 202-332-1386. p. 398

Lambert, Nancy, Asst Dean, Pub Serv Librn, University of South Carolina Upstate Library, 800 University Way, Spartanburg, SC, 29303. Tel: 864-503-5615. Fax: 864-503-5601. p. 2205

Lambert, Paulette, Acq, Ser, University of King's College Library, 6350 Coburg Rd, Halifax, NS, B3H 2A1, CANADA. Tel: 902-422-1271. Fax: 902-423-3357. p. 2783

Lambert, Raymond, In Charge, Harold M Lambert Studios, 239 M Madison Ave, Warminster, PA, 18974. Tel: 215-328-9464. Fax: 215-328-9465. p. 2150

Lambert, Tamatha, Librn, Northern Virginia Community College Libraries, Loudoun Campus, 1000 Harry Flood Byrd Hwy, Sterling, VA, 20164-8699. Tel: 703-450-2642. Fax: 703-404-7374. p. 2447

Lambert, Toni, Asst Dir, Pub Serv, Austin Public Library, 800 Guadalupe St, Austin, TX, 78701. Tel: 512-974-7466. p. 2278

Lambertson, David, Fac Supvr, New England Bible College Library, 879 Sawyer St, South Portland, ME, 04116. Tel: 207-799-5979. Fax: 207-799-6586. p. 1001

Lambertson, Harold, Tech Coordr, Knox County Public Library, 502 N Seventh St, Vincennes, IN, 47591-2119. Tel: 812-886-4380. Fax: 812-886-0342. p. 784

Lambly, Peter D, Res Coordr, Nova Scotia Legal Aid Library, 5475 Spring Garden Rd, Ste 401, Halifax, NS, B3J 3T2, CANADA. Tel: 902-420-6590. Fax: 902-428-5736. p. 2782

Lamborn, Joan, Assoc Dean, University of Northern Colorado Libraries, 501 20th St, Greeley, CO, 80639. Tel: 970-351-2601. Fax: 970-351-2963. p. 312

Lamborn, John, Dir, Wabash College, PO Box 352, Crawfordsville, IN, 47933. Tel: 765-361-6081. Fax: 765-361-6295. p. 734

Lamborne, Sean, Adult Serv, Librn I, Louisville Public Library, 951 Spruce St, Louisville, CO, 80027. Tel: 303-335-4849. Fax: 303-335-4833. p. 317

Lambousy, Greg, Dir of Coll, Louisiana State Museum, 751 Chartres St, New Orleans, LA, 70176. Tel: 504-568-7882, 504-568-8214. Fax: 504-599-1950. p. 960

Lambousy, Greg, Dir of Coll, Louisiana State Museum, New Orleans Jazz Club Collection, Old US Mint, 400 Esplanade Ave, New Orleans, LA, 70176. Tel: 504-568-6968. Fax: 504-568-4995. p. 960

Lambrecht, Jay H, Assoc Univ Librn, University of Illinois at Chicago, MC 234, 801 S Morgan St, Chicago, IL, 60607. Tel: 312-996-2716. Fax: 312-413-0424. p. 627

Lambrecht, RoJean, Cat, Columbus Public Library, 2504 14th St, Columbus, NE, 68601-4988. Tel: 402-564-7116. Fax: 402-563-3378. p. 1396

Lambright, Donovan, Automation Librn, Southeastern Libraries Cooperating, 2600 19th St NW, Rochester, MN, 55901-0767. Tel: 507-288-5513. Fax: 507-288-8697. p. 2947

Lambropoulos, Mary, Libr Mgr, York Library Region, Minto Public Library, 420 Pleasant Dr, Unit 2, Minto, NB, E4B 2T3, CANADA. Tel: 506-327-3220. Fax: 506-327-3041. p. 2764

Lambrou, Angella, Computer Serv, McGill University Libraries, Life Sciences Library, McIntyre Medical Science Bldg, 3655 Promenade Sir William Osler, Montreal, QC, H3G 1Y6, CANADA. Tel: 514-398-4475, Ext 09184. Fax: 514-398-3890. p. 2898

Lambson, Steven, Sr Res Librn, University of Missouri-Columbia, Law Library, 203 Hulston Hall, Columbia, MO, 65211-4190. Tel: 573-882-6464. Fax: 573-882-9676. p. 1326

LaMear, Arline, Librn, Columbia River Maritime Museum Library, 1792 Marine Dr, Astoria, OR, 97103. Tel: 503-325-2323. Fax: 503-325-2331. p. 1990

LaMee, James, Coordr, Libr Support for Distance Educ, Pub Serv Librn, University of South Carolina Upstate Library, 800 University Way, Spartanburg, SC, 29303. Tel: 864-503-5991. Fax: 864-503-5601. p. 2205

LaMee, James, Coordr, Pub Serv Librn, University of South Carolina Upstate Library, University Center of Greenville Library, 225 S Pleasantburg Dr, Greenville, SC, 29607-2544. Tel: 864-503-5991. Fax: 864-250-8905. p. 2206

Lamere, Cathie, Genealogy & Local Hist Mgr, Hayner Public Library District, 326 Belle St, Alton, IL, 62002. Tel: 618-462-0677. Fax: 618-462-0665. p. 588

Lamie, Therese, Mgr, Info Serv, Nova Scotia Government, 5151 Terminal Rd, Halifax, NS, B3J 2L7, CANADA. Tel: 902-424-7699. Fax: 902-424-1730. p. 2782

Lamis, Karen, Mgr, Harford County Public Library, Joppa Branch, 655 Towne Center Dr, Joppa, MD, 21085-4497. Tel: 410-612-1600. Fax: 410-612-1662. p. 1020

Lamkin, Charles, Libr Tech, Saint Louis Public Library, Charing Cross, 356 N Skinker Blvd, Saint Louis, MO, 63130. Tel: 314-726-2653. Fax: 314-726-6541. p. 1360

Lamkin, John R, II, Dir, University of Maryland-Eastern Shore, Music Learning Resources, PAC Bldg, Princess Anne, MD, 21853. Tel: 410-651-2200, Ext 6570. Fax: 410-651-7688. p. 1037

Lamm, Spencer, Head, Digital Libr Prog & Tech Planning, Swarthmore College, 500 College Ave, Swarthmore, PA, 19081-1081. Tel: 610-328-8541. Fax: 610-328-7329. p. 2145

Lammers, Deborah, Mgr, Henrico County Public Library, Dumbarton Area, 6800 Staples Mill Rd, Henrico, VA, 23228-4930. Tel: 804-290-9400. Fax: 804-266-8986. p. 2471

Lammers, Glenda, Dir, Brewton Public Library, 206 W Jackson St, Brewton, AL, 36426. Tel: 251-867-4626, Ext 1743. Fax: 251-809-1749. p. 10

Lammers, Glenda, Dir, Marion Military Institute, 1101 Washington St, Marion, AL, 36756. Tel: 334-683-2371. p. 24

Lammers, Keith, Dir, Pennsylvania College of Optometry, 8360 Old York Rd, Elkins Park, PA, 19027. Tel: 215-780-1260. Fax: 215-780-1263. p. 2054

Lammers, Tim, Librn, Dekalb Medical Center, 2701 N Decatur Rd, Decatur, GA, 30033. Tel: 404-501-5638. Fax: 404-501-1052. p. 530

Lammert, Richard A, Tech Serv Librn, Concordia Theological Seminary, 6600 N Clinton St, Fort Wayne, IN, 46825. Tel: 260-452-2145. Fax: 260-452-2126. p. 741

Lammie, Hannah, Br Mgr, Toledo-Lucas County Public Library, Washington, 5560 Harvest Lane, Toledo, OH, 43623. Tel: 419-259-5330. Fax: 419-472-4991. p. 1940

Lammrish, Beth, Br Mgr, Clermont County Public Library, Union Township, 4462 Mt Carmel-Tobasco Rd, Cincinnati, OH, 45244-2224. Tel: 513-528-1744. Fax: 513-528-0539. p. 1858

Lamon, Patricia, Ch, Tech Serv, Walter E Olson Memorial Library, 203 N Main St, Eagle River, WI, 54521. Tel: 715-479-8070, Ext 22. Fax: 715-479-2435. p. 2589

Lamont, Elizabeth, Chief Librn, Montreal General Hospital, 1650 Cedar Ave, Rm E6-157, Montreal, QC, H3G 1A4, CANADA. Tel: 514-934-1934, Ext 35293, 514-934-1934, Ext 43057. Fax: 514-934-8250. p. 2900

Lamont, Elizabeth, Chief Librn, Royal Victoria Hospital, Medical Library, 687 Pine Ave W, Rm H4-01, Montreal, QC, H3A 1A1, CANADA. Tel: 514-934-1934, Ext 35290. Fax: 514-843-1483. p. 2901

Lamont, Loraine, Tech Serv, Shaker Heights Public Library, 16500 Van Aken Blvd, Shaker Heights, OH, 44120-5318. Tel: 216-991-2030. Fax: 216-991-5951. p. 1934

Lamont, Lynn, Ch, Brewster Public Library, 79 Main St, Brewster, NY, 10509. Tel: 845-279-6421. Fax: 845-279-0043. p. 1584

Lamont, Sharon, Dir, Organizational Serv, University of Waterloo Library, 200 University Ave W, Waterloo, ON, N2L 3G1, CANADA. Tel: 519-888-4567, Ext 33519. Fax: 519-888-4320. p. 2869

Lamont, Sheila, Librn, Parkland Regional Library, Raymore Branch, PO Box 244, Raymore, SK, S0A 3J0, CANADA. Tel: 306-746-2166. p. 2932

Lamontagne, Nancie, Pub Serv, College Edouard-Montpetit Bibliotheque, 945 Chemin de Chambly, Longueuil, QC, J4H 3M6, CANADA. Tel: 450-679-2631, Ext 2461. Fax: 450-677-2945. p. 2887

Lamoreaux, Kellie, Librn, Umatilla Public Library, 911 Seventh St, Umatilla, OR, 97882-9507. Tel: 541-922-5704. Fax: 541-922-5708. p. 2022

Lamothe, Alain, Electronic Res Librn, Laurentian University, 935 Ramsey Lake Rd, Sudbury, ON, P3E 2C6, CANADA. Tel: 705-675-1151, Ext 3304. Fax: 705-675-4877. p. 2846

Lamothe, Janis, Chief Exec Officer, Librn, Manitouwadge Public Library, Community Ctr, Two Manitou Rd, Manitouwadge, ON, P0T 2C0, CANADA. Tel: 807-826-3913. Fax: 807-826-4640. p. 2820

Lamothe, Joanne, Dir, Sandwich Public Library, 142 Main St, Sandwich, MA, 02563. Tel: 508-888-0625. Fax: 508-833-1076. p. 1122

Lamoureux, Isabelle, Head Librn, Simone de Beauvoir Library, Concordia Univ, Simone de Beauvoir Inst, MU-401, 2170 Bishop St, Montreal, QC, H3G 1M8, CANADA. Tel: 514-848-2424, Ext 2377. p. 2901

Lampert, Lori, Govt Doc, Ref Serv, State University of New York College at Brockport, 350 New Campus Dr, Brockport, NY, 14420-2997. Tel: 585-395-5191. Fax: 585-395-5651. p. 1585

Lamphere, Avonelle, Ch, Durand Public Library, 604 Seventh Ave E, Durand, WI, 54736. Tel: 715-672-8730. p. 2589

Lamphere, Dawn, Dir, Margaret Reaney Memorial Library, 19 Kingsbury Ave, Saint Johnsville, NY, 13452. Tel: 518-568-7822. Fax: 518-568-7822. p. 1737

Lamphier, Susan, Head, AV, Somerville Public Library, 79 Highland Ave, Somerville, MA, 02143. Tel: 617-623-5000, Ext 2836. Fax: 617-628-4052. p. 1124

Lamson, Evangeline, Chmn of Libr Board, Hanna Municipal Library, PO Box 878, Hanna, AB, T0J 1P0, CANADA. Tel: 403-854-3865. Fax: 403-854-2772. p. 2706

Lamson, Karen, Librn, United Memorial Medical Center, 127 North St, Batavia, NY, 14020-1697. Tel: 585-344-5273. Fax: 585-344-7461. p. 1578

Lamy, Mary Anne, Coordr, Border Regional Library, 312 Seventh Ave, Virden, MB, R0M 2C0, CANADA. Tel: 204-748-3862. Fax: 204-748-3862. p. 2753

Lamy, Rudolf, Ref, Maryland State Law Library, Courts of Appeal Bldg, 361 Rowe Blvd, Annapolis, MD, 21401-1697. Tel: 410-260-1430. Fax: 410-260-1572, 410-974-2063. p. 1010

Lamy, Suzanne, Doc, Quebec Conseil de la Famille et de l'Enfance, 900 Rene-Levesque Blvd E, 8e etage, Quebec, QC, G1R 6B5, CANADA. Tel: 418-646-5865. Fax: 418-643-9832. p. 2906

Lancaster, Adrianna, Dr, Dir, East Central University, 1100 E 14th St, Ada, OK, 74820-6999. Tel: 580-310-5375. Fax: 580-436-3242. p. 1955

Lancaster, Gail, Librn, Saint Petersburg College, Saint Petersburg-Gibbs Campus Library, 6605 Fifth Ave N, Saint Petersburg, FL, 33710. Tel: 727-341-4793. Fax: 727-341-7188. p. 483

Lancaster, Jeanine, Br Mgr, Humboldt County Library, Rio Dell Branch, 715 Wildwood Ave, Rio Dell, CA, 95562-1321. Tel: 707-764-3333. p. 147

Lancaster, Joyce, Tech Serv, Shelby County Public Library, 309 Eighth St, Shelbyville, KY, 40065. Tel: 502-633-3803. Fax: 502-633-4025. p. 935

Lancaster, Kathy, Pub Serv, Shelton State Community College, 9500 Old Greensboro Rd, Tuscaloosa, AL, 35405. Tel: 205-391-2226. Fax: 205-391-3926. p. 38

Lancaster, Scott, Educ Librn, Texas A&M University-Commerce, 2600 S Neal St, Commerce, TX, 75429. Tel: 903-468-8139. Fax: 903-886-5434. p. 2300

Lancaster, Therese, Cat Librn, Mercyhurst College, 501 E 38th St, Erie, PA, 16546. Tel: 814-824-2231. Fax: 814-824-2219. p. 2056

Lancaster, William, Info Tech Spec, Louisiana Tech University, Everett St at The Columns, Ruston, LA, 71272. Tel: 318-257-3555. Fax: 318-257-2579. p. 966

Lance, Kayla, ILL, Libr Tech, University of Arkansas for Medical Sciences, 300 E Sixth St, Texarkana, AR, 71854. Tel: 870-779-6023. Fax: 870-779-6050. p. 116

Lance, Nancy, Ch, North Manchester Public Library, 405 N Market St, North Manchester, IN, 46962. Tel: 260-982-4773. Fax: 260-982-6342. p. 769

Lancester, Gail, Br Mgr, Kern County Library, Holloway-Gonzales Branch, 506 E Brundage Lane, Bakersfield, CA, 93307-3337. Tel: 661-861-2083. p. 124

Lanchang, Javier, Syst Serv Dir, Bucks County Free Library, 150 S Pine St, Doylestown, PA, 18901-4932. Tel: 215-348-0332, Ext 1103. Fax: 215-348-4760. p. 2050

Land, Barbara Jane, Librn, The Book Club of California, 312 Sutter St, Ste 510, San Francisco, CA, 94108-4320. Tel: 415-781-7532. Fax: 415-781-7537. p. 240

Land, Elaine, ILL, Ozark-Dale County Public Library, Inc, 416 James St, Ozark, AL, 36360. Tel: 334-774-2399, 334-774-5480. p. 33

Land, Jennifer, Coordr, Web Serv, Spartanburg County Public Libraries, 151 S Church St, Spartanburg, SC, 29306-3241. Tel: 864-596-3500. Fax: 864-596-3518. p. 2205

Land, Mary, Br Librn, Halton Hills Public Library, Acton Branch, 17 River St, Acton, ON, L7J 1C2, CANADA. Tel: 519-853-0301. Fax: 519-853-3110. p. 2806

Land, Mary Elizabeth, Dir, Abbeville County Library System, 201 S Main St, Abbeville, SC, 29620. Tel: 864-459-4009. Fax: 864-459-4009. p. 2179

Landa, Keith, Dir, Teaching, Learning & Tech Ctr, State University of New York, 735 Anderson Hill Rd, Purchase, NY, 10577-1400. Tel: 914-251-6450. Fax: 914-251-6437. p. 1724

Landau, Bill, Br Mgr, Flagstaff City-Coconino County Public Library System, East Flagstaff Community Library, 3000 N Fourth St, Flagstaff, AZ, 86004. Tel: 928-213-2365. p. 62

Landau, Cynthia, Asst Dir, Law Libr, University of New Hampshire School of Law, Two White St, Concord, NH, 03301. Tel: 603-228-1541, Ext 1130. Fax: 603-228-0388. p. 1443

Landau, Elvita, Dir, Brookings Public Library, 515 Third St, Brookings, SD, 57006. Tel: 605-692-9407. Fax: 605-692-9386. p. 2210

Landau, Herbert B, Exec Dir, Lancaster Public Library, 125 N Duke St, Lancaster, PA, 17602-2883. Tel: 717-394-2651. Fax: 717-394-3083. p. 2077

Landau, Rebecca, Librn, Penn Presbyterian Medical Center, 39th & Market St, Philadelphia, PA, 19104. Tel: 215-662-9575. Fax: 215-243-3200. p. 2113

Landauer, Debbie, Town Librn, Fairfax Community Library, 75 Hunt St, Fairfax, VT, 05454. Tel: 802-849-2420. Fax: 802-849-2611. p. 2424

Landavazo, Jim, Librn, Ohlone College, 43600 Mission Blvd, Fremont, CA, 94539. Tel: 510-659-6163. Fax: 510-659-6265. p. 149

Landeck, Gary, Dir, Atchison Public Library, 401 Kansas Ave, Atchison, KS, 66002-2495. Tel: 913-367-1902, Ext 208. Fax: 913-367-2717. p. 856

Lander, Beth, Dir, Manor College, 700 Fox Chase Rd, Jenkintown, PA, 19046-3399. Tel: 215-885-2360. Fax: 215-576-6564. p. 2072

Landers, Alison B, Dep Dir, Pub Serv, Sacramento Public Library, 828 I St, Sacramento, CA, 95814. Tel: 916-264-2747. Fax: 916-264-2755. p. 224

Landers, Barb, Mgr, Ch Serv, Wayne County Public Library, 220 W Liberty St, Wooster, OH, 44691-3593. Tel: 330-804-4664. Fax: 330-262-1352. p. 1950

Landers, Teresa, Dir of Libr, Santa Cruz City-County Library System Headquarters, 117 Union St, Santa Cruz, CA, 95060-3873. Tel: 831-427-7706, Ext 7612. Fax: 831-427-7720. p. 264

Landers, Teresa, Asst Dir, Corvallis-Benton County Public Library, Philomath Community Library, 1050 Applegate St, Philomath, OR, 97370. Tel: 541-766-6995. Fax: 541-929-5934. p. 1994

Landeryou, Sarah, Mgr, Pub Serv, San Miguel County Public Library District 1, 100 W Pacific Ave, Telluride, CO, 81435-2189. Tel: 970-728-4519. Fax: 970-728-3340. p. 323

Landes, Sonja, Circ, ILL, State University of New York College at Geneseo, SUNY Geneseo, One College Circle, Geneseo, NY, 14454-1498. p. 1627

Landesman, Shulamis, Electronic Coll Librn, Yeshiva University Libraries, Pollack Library-Landowne Bloom Library, Wilf Campus, 2520 Amsterdam Ave, New York, NY, 10033. Tel: 212-960-5378, 212-960-5379, 212-960-5380. Fax: 212-960-0066. p. 1704

Landgraf, Kathy, Asst Librn, Albert City Public Library, 215 Main, Albert City, IA, 50510. Tel: 712-843-2012. Fax: 712-843-2058. p. 791

Landgrebe, Randall E, Dir, Iowa Regional Library for the Blind & Physically Handicapped, 524 Fourth St, Des Moines, IA, 50309-2364. Tel: 515-281-1291. Fax: 515-281-1378. p. 810

Landheer, Diane, Br Head, Muskegon Area District Library, Ravenna Branch, 12278 Stafford, Ravenna, MI, 49451-9410. Tel: 231-853-6975. Fax: 231-737-6307. p. 1213

Landi, DebbieLee, Spec Coll & Archives Librn, Furman University Libraries, 3300 Poinsett Hwy, Greenville, SC, 29613-4100. Tel: 864-294-2714. Fax: 864-294-3004. p. 2195

Landin, Roxanne, Youth Serv, Fremont Area District Library, 104 E Main, Fremont, MI, 49412. Tel: 231-928-2049. Fax: 231-924-2355. p. 1182

Landino, Tracy, Coll Mgr, Country Music Hall of Fame & Museum, 222 Fifth Ave S, Nashville, TN, 37203. Tel: 615-416-2036. Fax: 615-255-2245. p. 2255

Landis, Andrea, Ch, Hartford City Public Library, 314 N High St, Hartford City, IN, 47348-2143. Tel: 765-348-1720. Fax: 765-348-5090. p. 748

Landis, Bruce, Tech Coordr, Chillicothe & Ross County Public Library, 140 S Paint St, Chillicothe, OH, 45601. Tel: 740-702-4145. Fax: 740-702-4153. p. 1867

Landis, Dennis, Curator, John Carter Brown Library, Brown University, George & Brown Sts, Providence, RI, 02912. Tel: 401-863-2725. Fax: 401-863-3477. p. 2171

Landis, Kate, Ref, North Arlington Free Public Library, 210 Ridge Rd, North Arlington, NJ, 07031. Tel: 201-955-5640. Fax: 201-991-7850. p. 1514

Landis, Katie, Ch, Boundary County District Library, 6370 Kootenai St, Bonners Ferry, ID, 83805. Tel: 208-267-3750. Fax: 208-267-5231. p. 572

Landis, Larry, Head, Univ Archives, Oregon State University Libraries, 121 The Valley Library, Corvallis, OR, 97331-4501. Tel: 541-737-0540. Fax: 541-737-0541. p. 1994

Landis, Larry A, Head, Archives & Spec Coll, Oregon State University Libraries, University Archives & Special Collections, 121 Valley Library, Corvallis, OR, 97331-4501. Tel: 541-737-0540. Fax: 541-737-3453. p. 1994

Landis, Linn, Dir, Desoto Parish Library, 109 Crosby St, Mansfield, LA, 71052. Tel: 318-872-6100. Fax: 318-872-6120. p. 955

Landis-McFeeley, Melissa, Head, Tech Serv, Kankakee Public Library, 201 E Merchant St, Kankakee, IL, 60901. Tel: 815-939-4564. Fax: 815-939-9057. p. 661

Landon, LaDawn, Dir, Lewisville Public Library, 117 E Main St, Lewisville, ID, 83431. Tel: 208-754-8608. p. 578

Landow, Janet, Chairperson, Unitarian Universalist Congregation, 183 Riverside Dr, Binghamton, NY, 13905. Tel: 607-729-1641. Fax: 607-729-1899. p. 1582

Landreth, Barbara B, Librn, Centers for Disease Control & Prevention Public Health Library & Information Center, 1095 Willowdale Rd, Mailstop L-1055, Morgantown, WV, 26505-2888. Tel: 304-285-5887. Fax: 304-285-6085. p. 2566

Landreth, Susan, Head Librn, Bunker Hill Public Library District, 220 E Warren St, Bunker Hill, IL, 62014. Tel: 618-585-4736. Fax: 618-585-6073. p. 598

Landrigan, Billy, Asst Librn, Pearl River Community College, Forest County Center Library, 5448 US Hwy 49 S, Hattiesburg, MS, 39401. Tel: 601-554-5522. Fax: 601-554-5470. p. 1312

Landrum, Cynthia, Asst Dir, Mt Lebanon Public Library, 16 Castle Shannon Blvd, Pittsburgh, PA, 15228-2252. Tel: 412-531-1912. Fax: 412-531-1161. p. 2126

Landrum, Janet, Librn, William Carey University Libraries, 3939 Gentilly Blvd, Box 308, New Orleans, LA, 70126. Tel: 504-286-3292. p. 964

Landry, Abbie V, Dir of Libr, Northwestern State University Libraries, 913 University Pkwy, Natchitoches, LA, 71497. Tel: 318-357-4477. Fax: 318-357-4470. p. 958

Landry, Constance, Asst Dir, Gorham Public Library, 35 Railroad St, Gorham, NH, 03581. Tel: 603-466-2525. p. 1448

Landry, Dan, Tech Coordr, Santa Cruz City-County Library System Headquarters, 117 Union St, Santa Cruz, CA, 95060-3873. Tel: 831-427-7706, Ext 7768. Fax: 831-427-7720. p. 264

Landry, Diane, Librn, WCAX-TV Library, PO Box 4508, Burlington, VT, 05406-4508. Tel: 802-652-6300. Fax: 802-652-6399. p. 2421

Landry, Francis R, AV Coordr, Med Librn & Coordr Med Educ, HealthAlliance Hospital-Leominster Campus, Hospital Rd, Leominster, MA, 01453-8004. Tel: 978-466-4035. Fax: 978-466-4038. p. 1098

Landry, Frank, Coordr, Correctional Services of Canada, 4902 A Main St, Dorchester, NB, E4K 2Y9, CANADA. Tel: 506-379-4502, 506-379-4550. Fax: 506-379-4616. p. 2762

Landry, Helene, Libr Tech, College des Medecins du Quebec, 2170 Rene-Levesque Blvd W, Montreal, QC, H3H 2T8, CANADA. Tel: 514-933-4441, Ext 5253, 514-933-4441, Ext 5254. Fax: 514-933-9112. p. 2894

Landry, Jeremy A, Head, Automation, Nicholls State University, 906 E First St, Thibodaux, LA, 70310. Tel: 985-448-4646, 985-448-4660. Fax: 985-448-4925. p. 971

Landry, Mary, Pub Serv, Ref Librn, Eastern Counties Regional Library, 390 Murray St, Mulgrave, NS, B0E 2G0, CANADA. Tel: 902-747-2597. Fax: 902-747-2500. p. 2783

Landry, Pierre B, Head, Coll Serv, Res, Musee national des beaux-arts du Quebec Bibliotheque, Parc des Champs-de-Bataille, Quebec, QC, G1R 5H3, CANADA. Tel: 418-644-6460. Fax: 418-643-2478. p. 2906

Landry, Ted, Asst Dir, Acadia Parish Library, 1125 N Parkerson Ave, Crowley, LA, 70526. Tel: 337-788-1880, 337-788-1881. Fax: 337-788-3759. p. 948

Landsburg, Alex, Dir of Tech Serv, Society of Naval Architects & Marine Engineers Library, 601 Pavonia Ave, Jersey City, NJ, 07306. Tel: 202-548-8932. Fax: 201-798-4975. p. 1493

Landsness, Martha, Librn, Sioux Rapids Memorial Library, 215 Second St, Sioux Rapids, IA, 50585. Tel: 712-283-2064. Fax: 712-283-2064. p. 844

Landstreet, Steve, Head Librn, Free Library of Philadelphia, Music, 1901 Vine St, Philadelphia, PA, 19103-1189. Tel: 215-686-5316. p. 2108

Landy, Gail P, Dir, Levi Heywood Memorial Library, 55 W Lynde St, Gardner, MA, 01440. Tel: 978-632-5298. Fax: 978-630-2864. p. 1090

Landy, Lorraine, Asst Librn, Saul Brodsky Jewish Community Library, 12 Millstone Campus Dr, Saint Louis, MO, 63146-5776. Tel: 314-442-3720. Fax: 314-432-1277. p. 1353

Lane, Ann Marie, Librn, American Heritage Center, Centennial Complex, Dept 3924, 1000 E University Ave, Laramie, WY, 82071. Tel: 307-766-2565. Fax: 307-766-5511. p. 2657

Lane, Anna, Dir, Marshall Public Library, 300 S Alamo Blvd, Marshall, TX, 75670. Tel: 903-935-4465. Fax: 903-935-4463. p. 2360

Lane, Barbara, Circ, Dorothy Alling Memorial Library, 21 Library Lane, Williston, VT, 05495. Tel: 802-878-4918. Fax: 802-878-3964. p. 2440

Lane, Barbara, Info Res Spec, Talisman Energy Inc, 2000, 888 Third St SW, Calgary, AB, T2P 5C5, CANADA. Tel: 403-237-1429. Fax: 403-231-2823. p. 2693

Lane, Beverly S, Asst Librn, Pontifical College Josephinum, 7625 N High St, Columbus, OH, 43235-1498. Tel: 614-985-2295. Fax: 614-885-2307. p. 1890

Lane, Daniel, Head, Pub Serv, Tenafly Public Library, 100 Riveredge Rd, Tenafly, NJ, 07670-2087. Tel: 201-568-8680. Fax: 201-568-5475. p. 1533

Lane, David, Youth Serv, Clearwater Public Library System, 100 N Osceola Ave, Clearwater, FL, 33755. Tel: 727-562-4970. Fax: 727-562-4977. p. 432

Lane, David, Librn, University of New Hampshire Library, Biological Sciences, Kendall Hall, 129 Main St, Durham, NH, 03824-3590. Tel: 603-862-1018. Fax: 603-862-2789. p. 1445

Lane, Emily, Managing Librn, Pima County Public Library, El Rio, 1390 W Speedway, Tucson, AZ, 85745. Tel: 520-594-5245. Fax: 520-594-5246. p. 87

Lane, Helen Taylor, Head, Res & Instrul Serv, Fashion Institute of Technology-SUNY, Seventh Ave at 27th St, New York, NY, 10001-5992. Tel: 212-217-4407. Fax: 212-217-4371. p. 1678

Lane, Judy, Asst Librn, Law Society of New Brunswick Library, Justice Bldg, Fredericton, NB, E3B 5H1, CANADA. Tel: 506-453-2500. Fax: 506-453-9438. p. 2763

Lane, Karen E, Dir, Aldrich Public Library, Six Washington St, Barre, VT, 05641-4227. Tel: 802-476-7550, Ext 307. Fax: 802-479-0450 (Call before sending fax). p. 2418

Lane, Kathy, Head, Youth Serv, Marshall District Library, 124 W Green St, Marshall, MI, 49068. Tel: 269-781-7821, Ext 16. Fax: 269-781-7090. p. 1207

Lane, Lori, Librn, Andale District Library, 328 Main St, Andale, KS, 67001. Tel: 316-444-2363. Fax: 316-444-2363. p. 855

Lane, Mary, Mgr, Lorillard Tobacco Co, 420 N English St, Greensboro, NC, 27405-7310. Tel: 336-335-6896. Fax: 336-335-6640. p. 1797

Lane, Mike, AV, Circ, West Florida Public Library, 200 W Gregory, Pensacola, FL, 32502. Tel: 850-436-5060. p. 482

Lane, Myra, Circ, Lawrence Library, 15 Main St, Pepperell, MA, 01463. Tel: 978-433-0330. Fax: 978-433-0317. p. 1117

Lane, Patricia S, Ref Librn, Library of the Marine Corps, Gray Research Ctr, 2040 Broadway St, Quantico, VA, 22134-5107. Tel: 703-784-4409. Fax: 703-784-4306. p. 2486

Lane, Renita, Admin Librn, Hinds Community College, Rankin Campus Learning Resources/Library, 3805 Hwy 80 E, Pearl, MS, 39208-4295. Tel: 601-936-5538. Fax: 601-936-5542. p. 1313

Lane, Rhonda, Mgr, Cobb County Public Library System, Sweetwater Valley, 5000 Austell-Powder Springs Rd, Ste 123, Austell, GA, 30106. Tel: 770-819-3290. Fax: 770-819-3293. p. 543

Lane, Sandra, Head, Ref, North Canton Public Library, 185 N Main St, North Canton, OH, 44720-2595. Tel: 330-499-4712. Fax: 330-499-7356. p. 1923

Lane, Sharon, Asst Librn, Beck Bookman Library, 420 W Fourth St, Holton, KS, 66436-1572. Tel: 785-364-3532. Fax: 785-364-5402. p. 872

Lane, Theresa, Br Mgr, Morristown-Hamblen Library, Davis Homes Branch Library, 1149 Kennedy Circle, Morristown, TN, 37814-5406. Tel: 423-581-3413. p. 2253

Laney, Dena, Syst Librn, Long Beach City College, 4901 E Carson St, Long Beach, CA, 90808. Tel: 562-938-4714. Fax: 562-938-3062, 562-938-4777. p. 166

Lanfear, Candy, Dir, Cascade Foothills Library, 39095 Dexter Rd, Dexter, OR, 97431. Tel: 541-937-2625. p. 1995

Lang, Albert, Archivist, Spec Coll, Carson-Newman College, 1634 Russell Ave, Jefferson City, TN, 37760. Tel: 865-471-3542. Fax: 865-471-3450. p. 2239

Lang, Beth, Head, Res & Instrul Serv, University of Massachusetts Amherst, 154 Hicks Way, Amherst, MA, 01003-9275. Tel: 413-545-6890. Fax: 413-545-6873. p. 1049

Lang, Celine, Dr, Dean of Libr, Florida Institute of Technology, 150 W University Blvd, Melbourne, FL, 32901-6988. Tel: 321-674-7111. Fax: 321-724-2559. p. 463

Lang, Cheryl, Ref Librn, Webmaster, Mid-Continent Public Library, Midwest Genealogy Center, 3440 S Lee's Summit Rd, Independence, MO, 64055-1923. Tel: 816-252-7228. Fax: 816-254-7146. p. 1333

Lang, Cheryl A, Dir, Carnegie Public Library, 101 W Clay, Albany, MO, 64402. Tel: 660-726-5615. Fax: 660-726-4213. p. 1319

Lang, Christa, Librn, Sidley, Austin, Brown & Wood LLP, 787 Seventh Ave, 24th Flr, New York, NY, 10019. Tel: 212-839-5300. Fax: 212-839-5599. p. 1700

Lang, David W, Librn, Dechert LLP, 1775 I St NW, Washington, DC, 20006-2401. Tel: 202-261-7909. Fax: 202-261-3333. p. 397

Lang, Deborah, Ref, Fordham University Library at Lincoln Center, Leon Lowenstein Bldg, 113 W 60th St, New York, NY, 10023-7480. Tel: 212-636-6050. Fax: 212-636-6766. p. 1678

Lang, Erica, AV, Ref, Hempstead Public Library, 115 Nichols Ct, Hempstead, NY, 11550-3199. Tel: 516-481-6990. Fax: 516-481-6719. p. 1634

Lang, Isa, Head, Info Serv, Chapman University School of Law, 370 N Glassell St, Rm 325, Orange, CA, 92866. Tel: 714-628-2537. p. 200

Lang, Isobel, Br Head, Toronto Public Library, Wychwood, 1431 Bathurst St, Toronto, ON, M5R 3J2, CANADA. Tel: 416-393-7683. Fax: 416-393-7665. p. 2863

Lang, Jacqueline, Tech Serv, Fargo Public Library, 102 N Third St, Fargo, ND, 58102. Tel: 701-241-6673. Fax: 701-241-8581. p. 1841

Lang, Karla, Spec Coll Librn, Palestine Public Library, 2000 S Loop 256, Ste 42, Palestine, TX, 75801. Tel: 903-729-4121. Fax: 903-729-4062. p. 2368

Lang, Katherine, Actg Head, Circ, United States Naval Academy, 589 McNair Rd, Annapolis, MD, 21402-5029. Tel: 410-293-6900. Fax: 410-293-6909. p. 1011

Lang, Kathy, Curator, Jean Lafitte National Historical Park & Preserve, 419 Decatur St, New Orleans, LA, 70130. Tel: 504-589-2636. Fax: 504-589-3851. p. 960

Lang, Kem, Curator, Corporate Heritage, OCLC Library, 6565 Kilgour Pl, Dublin, OH, 43017. Tel: 614-761-5217. Fax: 614-793-8707. p. 1896

Lang, Melissa, YA Serv, Cumberland County Public Library & Information Center, 300 Maiden Lane, Fayetteville, NC, 28301-5000. Tel: 910-483-7727. Fax: 910-486-5372. p. 1792

Lang, Michelle, Grad Ref Librn, Pace University, 861 Bedford Rd, Pleasantville, NY, 10570-2799. Tel: 914-422-4384. Fax: 914-773-3508. p. 1719

Lang, Nancy C, Librn, Dunbarton Public Library, 1004 School St, Dunbarton, NH, 03046-4816. Tel: 603-774-3546. Fax: 603-774-5563. p. 1445

Lang, Robin D, Outreach & Res Serv Librn, Westmont College, 955 La Paz Rd, Santa Barbara, CA, 93108-1099. Tel: 805-565-6000, 805-565-6147. Fax: 805-565-6220. p. 262

Lang, Sharon, Dir, Comfrey Public Library, 306 Brown St W, Comfrey, MN, 56019-1167. Tel: 507-877-6600. Fax: 507-877-3492. p. 1246

Lang, Sumer, Libr Assoc, Georgia Highlands College Libraries, 3175 Cedartown Hwy SE, Rome, GA, 30161. Tel: 706-295-6318. Fax: 706-295-6365. p. 548

Lang, Victoria A, Dir, Holderness Library, 866 US Rte 3, Holderness, NH, 03245. Tel: 603-968-7066. p. 1451

Langan, Bonnie, Br Mgr, Harris County Public Library, Baldwin Boettcher Branch, 22248 Aldine Westfield Rd, Humble, TX, 77338. Tel: 281-821-1320. Fax: 281-443-8068. p. 2335

Langan, James, Ref Librn, University of Pittsburgh, Johnstown Campus, 450 Schoolhouse Rd, Johnstown, PA, 15904. Tel: 814-269-7300. Fax: 814-269-7286. p. 2073

Langberg, Margaret, Acq, ILL, Harcum College Library, 750 Montgomery Ave, Bryn Mawr, PA, 19010-3476. Tel: 610-526-6085. Fax: 610-526-6086. p. 2039

Langdon, Hedy, Librn, Phillips Public Library, 96 Main St, Phillips, ME, 04966. Tel: 207-639-2665. Fax: 207-639-2665. p. 995

Langdon, Joseph, Br Mgr, United States Geological Survey Library, 345 Middlefield Rd, Bldg 15 (MS-955), Menlo Park, CA, 94025-3591. Tel: 650-329-5013. Fax: 650-329-5132. p. 185

Lange, Eleanor, Head Librn, Interlochen Center for the Arts, Frederick & Elizabeth Ludwig Fennell Music Library, 4000 Hwy M-137, Interlochen, MI, 49643. Tel: 231-276-7230. Fax: 231-276-7882. p. 1193

Lange, Janice P, Head, Tech Serv, Sam Houston State University, 1830 Bobby K Marks Dr, Huntsville, TX, 77340. Tel: 936-294-1620. Fax: 936-294-3780. p. 2345

Lange, Karen, Dir, Laramie County Community College Library, 1400 E College Dr, Cheyenne, WY, 82007-3204. Tel: 307-778-1204. Fax: 307-778-1399. p. 2652

Lange, Linda, Libr Assoc, Marshall-Lyon County Library, 301 W Lyon St, Marshall, MN, 56258. Tel: 507-537-7003. p. 1258

Lange, Margaret, Librn, North Central Regional Library, Tonasket Community, 209 A Whitcomb Ave, Tonasket, WA, 98855-8818. Tel: 509-486-2366. Fax: 509-486-2366. p. 2549

Lange, Pamela, Dir, Bureau County Historical Society Museum & Library, 109 Park Ave W, Princeton, IL, 61356-1927. Tel: 815-875-2184. p. 692

Lange, Sami, Libr Spec, Sonoma State University Library, 1801 E Cotati Ave, Rohnert Park, CA, 94928-3609. Tel: 707-664-2397. Fax: 707-664-2090. p. 219

Lange, Sue, Fiscal Mgr, Lee County Library System, 2345 Union St, Fort Myers, FL, 33901-3917. Tel: 239-533-4820. Fax: 239-485-1100. p. 445

Lange, Thomas, Librn, Somesville Library Association, 116 Main St, Mount Desert, ME, 04660. Tel: 207-244-7404. p. 992

Langendoerfer, Amanda, Spec Coll & Archives Librn, Truman State University, 100 E Normal, Kirksville, MO, 63501-4211. Tel: 660-785-7546. p. 1342

Langendorfer, Jeanne, Coordr, Ser, Bowling Green State University Libraries, 204 Wm T Jerome Library, Bowling Green, OH, 43403-0170. p. 1861

Langenkamp, Stephanie, Dir of Libr, San Marcos Public Library, 625 E Hopkins, San Marcos, TX, 78666. Tel: 512-393-8200. p. 2384

Langenwalter, Laurel, Tech Serv, Albany Public Library, 1390 Waverly Dr SE, Albany, OR, 97322. Tel: 541-917-7580, Ext 4700. Fax: 541-917-7586. p. 1989

Langer, Helen, Dir, Spalding Public Library, 141 Saint Joseph St, Spalding, NE, 68665. Tel: 308-497-2695. p. 1420

Langerman, Joanne, Patron Serv, Southern Maine Community College Library, Two Fort Rd, South Portland, ME, 04106. Tel: 207-741-5521. Fax: 207-741-5522. p. 1002

Langevin, Ann, Librn, Lake Mead National Recreation Area Library, Alan Bible Visitor Ctr, Intersection of Hwys 93 & 166, Boulder City, NV, 89005. Tel: 702-293-8990. Fax: 702-293-8029. p. 1425

Langevin, Cheryl, Acq Librn, Century College Library, 3300 N Century Ave, White Bear Lake, MN, 55110. Tel: 651-779-3969. Fax: 651-779-3963. p. 1288

Langfitt, Leann, Dir, Primghar Public Library, 320 First St NE, Primghar, IA, 51245. Tel: 712-957-8981. Fax: 712-957-8981. p. 839

Langford, Kay, Librn, Columbus-Lowndes Public Library, Caledonia Public, 754 Main St, Caledonia, MS, 39740. Tel: 662-356-6384. Fax: 662-356-6384. p. 1297

Langford, Lari, Head, Access Serv, Head, Info Serv, University of Toronto Libraries, Robarts Library, 130 St George St, Toronto, ON, M5S 1A5, CANADA. Tel: 416-978-2898. Fax: 416-978-1608. p. 2867

Langford, Meller, Dep Dir, Pub Serv, Houston Public Library, 500 McKinney Ave, Houston, TX, 77002-2534. Tel: 832-393-1329. Fax: 832-393-1324. p. 2338

Langford, Scott, Librn, United States National Park Service-Fort Vancouver National Historic Site-Library, 1001 E Fifth St, Vancouver, WA, 98661. Tel: 360-696-7659, Ext 18. Fax: 360-696-7657. p. 2546

Langham, William C, Dir, Orangeburg Library, 20 S Greenbush Rd, Orangeburg, NY, 10962-1311. Tel: 845-359-2244. Fax: 845-359-8692. p. 1711

Langhans, Eliza, Dir, Hatfield Public Library, 39 Main St, Hatfield, MA, 01038. Tel: 413-247-9097. Fax: 413-247-9237. p. 1094

Langhart, Nick, Dir, Boylston Public Library, 695 Main St, Boylston, MA, 01505-1399. Tel: 508-869-2371. Fax: 508-869-6195. p. 1069

Langhart, Nick, Dir, Forbush Memorial Library, 118 Main St, Westminster, MA, 01473. Tel: 978-874-7416. Fax: 978-874-7424. p. 1139

Langhoff, Mary, Libr Asst, Suring Area Public Library, 604 E Main St, Suring, WI, 54174. Tel: 920-842-4451. p. 2641

Langhoff, Pam, ILL, Lincoln Library, 326 S Seventh St, Springfield, IL, 62701. Tel: 217-753-4900. Fax: 217-753-5329. p. 706

Langhurst, Andrea, Acq, Tech Serv, General Electric Global Research, One Research Circle, Niskayuna, NY, 12309. Tel: 518-387-4952, 518-387-5000. p. 1706

Langkabel, Carol, Ch, Plymouth Public Library, 130 Division St, Plymouth, WI, 53073-1802. Tel: 920-892-4416. Fax: 920-892-6295. p. 2631

Langlais, Jean, Outreach & Develop Mgr, St Charles Public Library District, One S Sixth Ave, Saint Charles, IL, 60174-2105. Tel: 630-584-0076, Ext 219. Fax: 630-584-3448. p. 699

Langland, Laurie, Univ Archivist, Dakota Wesleyan University, 1201 McGovern Ave, Mitchell, SD, 57301. Tel: 605-995-2134. Fax: 605-995-2893. p. 2215

Langley, Dawn, Head Librn, Woodsville Free Public Library, 14 School Lane, Woodsville, NH, 03785. Tel: 603-747-3483. p. 1468

Langley, Jean M, Dir, Northborough Free Library, 34 Main St, Northborough, MA, 01532-1942. Tel: 508-393-5025. Fax: 508-393-5027. p. 1114

Langley, Leslie, Head Librn, Wister Public Library, 101 Caston, Wister, OK, 74966. Tel: 918-655-7654. Fax: 918-655-3267. p. 1986

Langley, Megan, Br Head, Vancouver Public Library, Strathcona, 592 E Pender St, Vancouver, BC, V6A 1V5, CANADA. Tel: 604-665-3967. Fax: 604-665-3549. p. 2744

Langley, Monica, Acq, Ser, Charleston Southern University, 9200 University Blvd, Charleston, SC, 29406. Tel: 843-863-7911. Fax: 843-863-7947. p. 2183

Langley, Nancy, Acq, Colby-Sawyer College, 541 Main St, New London, NH, 03257-4648. Tel: 603-526-3684. Fax: 603-526-3777. p. 1459

Langley, Nicole, Librn Supvr, Charlotte County Library System, Punta Gorda Public, 424 W Henry St, Punta Gorda, FL, 33950. Fax: 941-833-5463. p. 485

Langley, Paula, Circ Mgr, Towson University, 8000 York Rd, Towson, MD, 21252-0001. Tel: 410-704-3442. Fax: 410-704-3760. p. 1045

Langlois, Ann, Asst Dir, Tech Serv, Lapeer District Library, 201 Village West Dr S, Lapeer, MI, 48446-1699. Tel: 810-664-9521. Fax: 810-664-8527. p. 1202

Langlois, Georges, Librn, College Montmorency Bibliotheque, 475 Boul de L Avenir, Laval, QC, H7N 5H9, CANADA. Tel: 450-975-6274. Fax: 450-381-2263. p. 2886

Langlois, Jennifer, Ref, Black & Veatch, 11401 Lamar, Overland Park, KS, 66211. Tel: 913-458-7884. Fax: 913-458-2934. p. 887

Langlois, Jessica, Librn, West Dennis Free Public Library, 260 Main St, West Dennis, MA, 02670. Tel: 508-398-2050. Fax: 508-394-6279. p. 1137

Langlois, Linda, Dir, Bibliotheque Municipale de Amos, 222 Front St E, Amos, QC, J9T 1H3, CANADA. Tel: 819-732-6070. Fax: 819-732-3242. p. 2879

Langloss, Mary, Ch, Illiopolis-Niantic Public Library District, Sixth & Mary Sts, Illiopolis, IL, 62539. Tel: 217-486-5561. Fax: 217-486-7811. p. 658

Langmo, Jim, Tech Serv Mgr, Washington County Library, 8595 Central Park Pl, Woodbury, MN, 55125-9453. Tel: 651-275-8500. Fax: 651-275-8509. p. 1290

Lango-Salmon, Enethenia, Br Mgr, Tampa-Hillsborough County Public Library System, Norma & Joseph Robinson Partnership Library@Sulphur Springs, 8412 N 13th St, Tampa, FL, 33604-1899. Tel: 813-273-3652. Fax: 813-975-7372. p. 498

Langreck, Lois Ann, Dir, Waucoma Public Library, 103 First Ave, Waucoma, IA, 52171. Tel: 563-776-9971. Fax: 563-776-4042. p. 850

Langstaff, Anna L, Asst Dir, Beverly Public Library, 32 Essex St, Beverly, MA, 01915-4561. Tel: 978-921-6062. Fax: 978-922-8329. p. 1053

Langston, Barbara, Librn, Formoso Public Library, 204 Main St, Formoso, KS, 66942-9802. Tel: 785-794-2424. p. 867

Langston, Janine, Info Literacy, Birmingham Public Library, 2100 Park Pl, Birmingham, AL, 35203. Tel: 205-322-6371. Fax: 205-322-7739. p. 7

Langston, Jeanette, Tech Serv, Whitworth University, 300 W Hawthorne Rd, Spokane, WA, 99251-0001. Tel: 509-777-4226. Fax: 509-777-3221. p. 2538

Langston, Lizbeth, Dr, Head, Ref & Info Serv, University of California, Riverside Libraries, Raymond L Orbach Science Library, 900 University Ave, Riverside, CA, 92521. Tel: 951-827-3529. p. 219

Langston, Marc, Head, Coll Mgt & Tech Serv, California State University, Chico, 400 W First St, Chico, CA, 95929-0295. Tel: 530-898-4587. Fax: 530-898-4443. p. 133

Langston, Mary, Head, Acq, Southeast Missouri State University, One University Plaza, Mail Stop 4600, Cape Girardeau, MO, 63701. Tel: 573-651-2746. Fax: 573-651-2666. p. 1322

Langston, Roxann, Dir, Huntsville Memorial Hospital, 110 Memorial Hospital Dr, Huntsville, TX, 77340. Tel: 936-435-7520. Fax: 936-291-4218. p. 2345

Langston, Tom, Tech Serv, Germantown Community Library, 1925 Exeter Rd, Germantown, TN, 38138-2815. Tel: 901-757-7323. Fax: 901-756-9940. p. 2235

Langston, Vikki, Librn, Southwest Arkansas Regional Library, Tollette Branch, 205 Town Hall Dr, Tollette, AR, 71851. Tel: 870-287-7166. p. 103

Langton, Sherri, Tech Serv, Northwestern College, 101 Seventh St SW, Orange City, IA, 51041-1996. Tel: 712-707-7234. Fax: 712-707-7247. p. 836

Lanham, Allen, Dr, Dean, Libr Serv, Eastern Illinois University, 600 Lincoln Ave, Charleston, IL, 61920. p. 603

Lanham, Catherine, ILL, United States Air Force, 744 Douhet Dr, Bldg 4244, Barksdale AFB, LA, 71110. Tel: 318-456-4182. Fax: 318-752-0509. p. 941

Lanier, Heather, Circ Serv Supvr, The Brentwood Library, 8109 Concord Rd, Brentwood, TN, 37027. Tel: 615-371-0090, Ext 8600. Fax: 615-371-2238. p. 2225

Lanier, Jill, Tech Serv, O'Melveny & Myers LLP, Times Square Tower, Seven Times Sq, New York, NY, 10036. Tel: 212-326-2022. Fax: 212-326-2061. p. 1696

Lanier, Terri, Br Coordr, Duplin County Library, 107 Bowden Dr, Kenansville, NC, 28349-0930. Tel: 910-296-2117. Fax: 910-296-2172. p. 1804

Lanigan, Carrie, Libr Tech, St Lawrence College Library, 2288 Parkedale Ave, Brockville, ON, K6V 5X3, CANADA. Tel: 613-345-0660, Ext 3104. p. 2797

Lanigan, Janet, Fac Librn, Quincy College, Newport Hall, Rm 103, 150 Newport Ave, Quincy, MA, 02171. Tel: 617-984-1680. Fax: 617-984-1782. p. 1119

Lanigan, Karen, Circ Supvr, Tech Serv Supvr, Plumb Memorial Library, 65 Wooster St, Shelton, CT, 06484. Tel: 203-924-1580. Fax: 203-924-8422. p. 367

Laning, Melissa, Assoc Dean, Assessment, Personnel & Res, University of Louisville Libraries, 2215 S Third St, Louisville, KY, 40292. Tel: 502-852-6745. Fax: 502-852-7394. p. 926

Laning, Melissa, Assoc Dean, Assessment, Personnel & Res, University of Louisville Libraries, William F Ekstrom Library, Belknap Campus, 2215 S Third St, Louisville, KY, 40292. Tel: 502-852-8726. Fax: 502-852-7394. p. 927

Lank, Robin, Ch, Milford Public Library, 11 SE Front St, Milford, DE, 19963. Tel: 302-422-8996. Fax: 302-422-9269. p. 384

Lankford, Shirley, Instrul Serv Librn, Irvine Sullivan Ingram Library, University of West Georgia, 1601 Maple St, Carrollton, GA, 30118. Tel: 678-839-6498. Fax: 678-839-6511. p. 523

Lankfort, Nora, Librn, Danbury Public Library, 1104 Main St, Danbury, NC, 27016. Tel: 336-593-2419. Fax: 336-593-3232. p. 1786

Lanman, Jane, Acq/Syst Librn, University of California Los Angeles Library, Hugh & Hazel Darling Law Library, 112 Law Bldg, Box 951458, 385 Charles E Young Dr E, Los Angeles, CA, 90095-1458. Tel: 310-825-7826. Fax: 310-825-1372. p. 178

Lann, Jennifer, Dir of Libr Serv, Landmark College Library, River Rd S, Putney, VT, 05346. Tel: 802-387-1648. Fax: 802-387-6896. p. 2432

Lanning, Scott W, Access Serv, Ref Librn, Southern Utah University, 351 W University Blvd, Cedar City, UT, 84720. Tel: 435-865-8156. Fax: 435-865-8152. p. 2404

Lannom, Lee Ann, Librn, Vanderbilt University, The Peabody Library, 230 Appleton Pl, PBM 135, Nashville, TN, 37203. Tel: 615-343-2915. Fax: 615-343-7923. p. 2261

Lannon, Amber, Head Librn, McGill University Libraries, Howard Ross Library of Management, Samuel Bronfman Bldg, 1001 Sherbrooke St W, 2nd Flr, Montreal, QC, H3A 1G5, CANADA. Tel: 514-398-4690. Fax: 514-398-5046. p. 2899

Lannon, Amy, Asst Dir, Reading Public Library, 64 Middlesex Ave, Reading, MA, 01867-2550. Tel: 781-944-0840. Fax: 781-942-9106. p. 1120

Lannon, John, Assoc Dir, Boston Athenaeum, 10 1/2 Beacon St, Boston, MA, 02108-3777. Tel: 617-227-0270. Fax: 617-227-5266. p. 1056

Lanoue, Margaret, Head, Ref, Guilderland Public Library, 2228 Western Ave, Guilderland, NY, 12084-9701. Tel: 518-456-2400. Fax: 518-456-0923. p. 1632

Lanouette, Francine, Head of Libr, Ecole Nationale d'Administration Publique Libraries, Bibliotheque (Montreal Campus), 4750 Ave Henri-Julien, 5e etage, Montreal, QC, H2T 3E5, CANADA. Tel: 514-849-3989. Fax: 514-849-3369. p. 2905

Lanouette, Jennifer, Med Librn, Charlton Memorial Hospital, 363 Highland Ave, Fall River, MA, 02720. Tel: 508-679-7196. Fax: 508-679-7458. p. 1088

Lanphier, Connie, Dir, Utopia Memorial Library, 800 Main St, Utopia, TX, 78884. Tel: 830-966-3448. Fax: 830-966-3412. p. 2394

Lansdell, Diane, Supvr, City of Kawartha Lakes Public Library, 190 Kent St W, Lindsay, ON, K9V 2Y6, CANADA. Tel: 705-324-9411, Ext 1291. Fax: 705-878-1859. p. 2816

Lansdell, Diane, Supvr, City of Kawartha Lakes Public Library, Lindsay Branch, 190 Kent St W, Lindsay, ON, K9V 2Y6, CANADA. Tel: 705-324-5632. Fax: 705-324-7140. p. 2816

Lansdown, Erica, Br Mgr, Long Beach Public Library, Burnett, 560 E Hill St, Long Beach, CA, 90806. Tel: 562-570-1041. p. 167

Lanser, Karen, Br Supvr, Hesburgh Libraries, O'Meara Mathematics Library, 001 Hayes-Healy Ctr, Notre Dame, IN, 46556-5641. Tel: 574-631-7278. Fax: 574-631-9660. p. 770

Lansing, Kathy, Adminr, Baptist Joint Committee Library, 200 Maryland Ave NE, Washington, DC, 20002. Tel: 202-544-4226. Fax: 202-544-2094. p. 394

Lanto, Ellen, Acq of New Ser, Tech Serv, San Bernardino Public Library, 555 W Sixth St, San Bernardino, CA, 92410-3001. Tel: 909-381-8215. Fax: 909-381-8229. p. 229

Lantz, Arden, Librn, Margaret S Sterck School for the Deaf Library, 620 E Chestnut Hill Rd, Newark, DE, 19713. Tel: 302-454-2301. Fax: 302-454-3493. p. 385

Lantz, Cathy, Ch, Pataskala Public Library, 101 S Vine St, Pataskala, OH, 43062. Tel: 740-927-9986. Fax: 740-964-6204. p. 1928

Lantz, Elizabeth A, Dir, Libr & Archives, Cleveland Museum of Art, 11150 East Blvd, Cleveland, OH, 44106-1797. Tel: 216-707-2530. Fax: 216-421-0921. p. 1877

Lanum, Marian, Circ Asst, Little Elm Public Library, 100 W Eldorado Pkwy, Little Elm, TX, 75068. Tel: 214-975-0430. Fax: 972-377-5546. p. 2356

Lanxon, Robert, Ref Serv, Ledding Library of Milwaukie, 10660 SE 21st Ave, Milwaukie, OR, 97222. Tel: 503-786-7580. Fax: 503-659-9497. p. 2006

Lanz, Jesse, Commun Libr Mgr, County of Los Angeles Public Library, Diamond Bar Library, 1061 S Grand Ave, Diamond Bar, CA, 91765-2299. Tel: 909-861-4978. Fax: 909-860-3054. p. 141

Lanza-Galindo, Oscar, Libr Dir, SIT Graduate Institute/SIT Study Abroad, One Kipling Rd, Brattleboro, VT, 05302. Tel: 802-258-3354. Fax: 802-258-3248. p. 2420

Lanzhen, Tian, Info Spec, Burlington County College Library, 601 Pemberton-Browns Mills Rd, Pemberton, NJ, 08068. Fax: 609-894-4189. p. 1519

Lapayover, Alan, Asst Librn, Reconstructionist Rabbinical College Library, 1299 Church Rd, Wyncote, PA, 19095. Tel: 215-576-0800, Ext 232. Fax: 215-576-6143. p. 2158

LaPee, Tiffany, Dir, Chetopa City Library, 312 Maple, Chetopa, KS, 67336-0206. Tel: 620-236-7194. p. 860

LaPenn, Ronna, Tech Serv Librn, Whipple Free Library, Two Central Sq, New Boston, NH, 03070. Tel: 603-487-3391. Fax: 603-487-2886. p. 1459

LaPenna, Cynthia, Ref Serv, Mount Olive Public Library, 202 Flanders-Drakestown Rd, Flanders, NJ, 07836. Tel: 973-691-8686. Fax: 973-691-8542. p. 1485

LaPenotiere, Beth, Br Mgr, Harford County Public Library, Bel Air Branch, 100 E Pennsylvania Ave, Bel Air, MD, 21014-3799. Tel: 410-638-3151. Fax: 410-638-3155. p. 1020

LaPenotiere, David, Mgr, Baltimore County Public Library, White Marsh, 8133 Sandpiper Circle, Baltimore, MD, 21236-4973. Tel: 410-887-5097. Fax: 410-931-9229. p. 1045

Lapenta, Nicole, Archivist, The Mary Baker Eddy Library, Lending & Reference Services, 200 Massachusetts Ave, P02-10, Boston, MA, 02115-3017. Tel: 617-450-7325. p. 1060

Laper, Eugene, ILL, Lehman College, City University of New York, 250 Bedford Park Blvd W, Bronx, NY, 10468-1589. Tel: 718-960-8577. Fax: 718-960-8090. p. 1587

LaPerla, Susan, Dir of Develop, New Canaan Library, 151 Main St, New Canaan, CT, 06840. Tel: 203-594-5000. Fax: 203-594-5026. p. 354

Laperriere, Celine, Head Librn, Bibliotheque Publique de Pointe-Claire, 100 av Douglas-Shand, Pointe-Claire, QC, H9R 4V1, CANADA. Tel: 514-630-1217. Fax: 514-630-1261. p. 2902

LaPerriere, Jenny, Sr Librn, Denver Public Library, Schlessman, 100 Poplar St, Denver, CO, 80220-4522. Tel: 720-865-0000. Fax: 720-865-0047. p. 301

Laphen, Mary Kate, Librn, Merrickville Public Library, 446 Main St W, Merrickville, ON, K0G 1N0, CANADA. Tel: 613-269-3326. Fax: 613-269-3326. p. 2821

Lapidow, Amy, Info Serv Librn, Tufts University, 145 Harrison Ave, Boston, MA, 02111-1843. Fax: 617-636-4039. p. 1068

Lapienyte-Bareikiene, Kristina, Head, Per, Lithuanian Research & Studies Center, Inc, 5600 S Claremont Ave, Chicago, IL, 60636-1039. Tel: 773-434-4545. Fax: 773-434-9363. p. 617

LaPier, Ethel, Br Mgr, Albany Public Library, John Howe Library, 105 Schuyler St, Albany, NY, 12202. Tel: 518-482-7911, Ext 20. Fax: 518-472-9406. p. 1568

LaPier, Ethel, Br Mgr, Albany Public Library, New Scotland, 369 New Scotland Ave, Albany, NY, 12208. Tel: 518-482-7911, Ext 20. p. 1568

LaPier, Ethel, Br Mgr, Albany Public Library, Pine Hills, 517 Western Ave, Albany, NY, 12203. Tel: 518-482-7911, Ext 20. Fax: 518-482-7916. p. 1568

LaPier, Ethel, Br Supvr, Albany Public Library, 161 Washington Ave, Albany, NY, 12210. Tel: 518-482-7911, Ext 20. Fax: 518-449-3386. p. 1568

LaPier, Ethel, Br Supvr, Albany Public Library, North Albany Branch, 616 N Pearl St, Albany, NY, 12204. Tel: 518-482-7911, Ext 20. p. 1568

LaPierre, Danielle, ILL, Bibliotheque Municipale de Saint Felicien, 1209 Blvd Sacre-Coeur, Saint Felicien, QC, G8K 2R5, CANADA. Tel: 418-679-5334. Fax: 418-679-2178. p. 2908

Lapierre, Diane, Dir, Commun Relations, Denver Public Library, Ten W 14th Ave Pkwy, Denver, CO, 80204-2731. Tel: 720-865-1111. Fax: 720-865-2087. p. 300

LaPierre, Kathleen, Asst Librn, Colebrook Public Library, 126 Main St, Colebrook, NH, 03576. Tel: 603-237-4808. p. 1442

Lapierre, Rhona, Coop Librn, Manitoba Hydro Library, 360 Portage Ave, Winnipeg, MB, R3C 30G8, CANADA. Tel: 204-360-3212. Fax: 204-360-6104. p. 2756

Lapina, MaryAnn, Dir, Medina County Law Library Association, 93 Public Sq, Medina, OH, 44256. Tel: 330-725-9744. Fax: 330-723-9608. p. 1917

Lapins, Michael, Supvr, Media Ctr, San Diego State University Library & Information Access, 5500 Campanile Dr, San Diego, CA, 92182-8050. Tel: 619-594-8241. Fax: 619-594-3270. p. 237

Lapinski, Rena, Head, Circ, South Hadley Public Library, 27 Bardwell St, South Hadley, MA, 01075. Tel: 413-538-5045. Fax: 413-539-9250. p. 1125

Lapis, Susan, Asst Dir, Prescott Valley Public Library, 7401 E Civic Circle, Prescott Valley, AZ, 86314. Tel: 928-759-3040. Fax: 928-759-3121. p. 79

Laplante, Audrey, Asst Prof, Universite de Montreal, 3150, rue Jean-Brillant, bur C-2004, Montreal, QC, H3T 1N8, CANADA. Tel: 514-343-6044. Fax: 514-343-5753. p. 2979

LaPlante, Bea, Librn, Shaw Library, Main St, Mercer, ME, 04957. Tel: 207-587-2529. Fax: 207-587-2529. p. 991

LaPlante, Debbie, Asst Librn, Drumheller Public Library, 224 Centre St, Drumheller, AB, T0J 0Y2, CANADA. Tel: 403-823-1371. Fax: 403-823-3651. p. 2697

LaPlante, Isabelle, Librn, Centre de Documentation Collegiale, 1111 rue Lapierre, La Salle, QC, H8N 2J4, CANADA. Tel: 514-364-3320, Ext 241. Fax: 514-364-2627. p. 2885

LaPlante, Jane, Bibliog Instr, Ref, Minot State University, 500 University Ave W, Minot, ND, 58707. Tel: 701-858-3200. Fax: 701-858-3581. p. 1846

LaPlante, Kim, Mgr, Product Res & Libr Serv, Northeast Wisconsin Technical College Library, 2740 W Mason St, Green Bay, WI, 54303-4966. Tel: 920-498-5487. Fax: 920-498-6910. p. 2596

LaPoint, Virginia, Librn, Allen Correctional Institution Library, 2338 N West St, Lima, OH, 45801. Tel: 419-224-8000, Ext 3006. Fax: 419-998-5618. p. 1909

LaPoint, Virginia A, Librn II, Oakwood Correctional Facility Library, 3200 N West St, Lima, OH, 45801-2048. Tel: 419-225-8052, Ext 2263. Fax: 419-225-8000. p. 1910

LaPointe, Amy, Dir, Amherst Town Library, 14 Main St, Amherst, NH, 03031-2930. Tel: 603-673-2288. Fax: 603-672-6063. p. 1437

LaPointe, Celine, AV, Cegep de Jonquiere, 2505 rue St Hubert, Jonquiere, QC, G7X 7W2, CANADA. Tel: 418-547-2191. Fax: 418-547-0917. p. 2884

Lapointe, Julie, Librn, Southeast Regional Library, Sedley Branch, 224 Broadway Ave, Sedley, SK, S0G 4K0, CANADA. Tel: 306-885-4505. Fax: 306-885-4506. p. 2931

LaPointe, Linda, Tech Serv, Moravian College & Moravian Theological Seminary, 1200 Main St, Bethlehem, PA, 18018-6650. Tel: 610-861-1547. Fax: 610-861-1577. p. 2034

Lapointe, Lisa A, Instrul Serv Librn, Florida Southern College, 111 Lake Hollingsworth Dr, Lakeland, FL, 33801-5698. Tel: 863-616-6451. Fax: 863-680-4126. p. 459

Lapointe, Lois, Asst Librn, Whitingham Free Public Library, 2948 Vt Rte 100, Jacksonville, VT, 05342. Tel: 802-368-7506. p. 2426

Lapointe, Lucette, Circ, Ecole de Technologie Superieure (Service de la bibliotheque), 1100 rue Notre-Dame Ouest, Montreal, QC, H3C 1K3, CANADA. Tel: 514-396-8946. Fax: 514-396-8633. p. 2895

LaPolla, Jackie, Dir, Keyport Free Public Library, 109 Broad St, Keyport, NJ, 07735. Tel: 732-264-0543. Fax: 732-264-0875. p. 1493

Laporte, Betty Ann, Librn, Rich Valley Public Library, RR 1, Gunn, AB, T0E 1A0, CANADA. Tel: 780-967-0502. p. 2706

Laporte, Jonathan, Syst Librn, Hopital Hotel-Dieu du CHUM, 3840 rue St-Urbain, Montreal, QC, H2W 1T8, CANADA. Tel: 514-890-8000, Ext 27217. p. 2896

LaPorte, Michelle, Mgr, Libr Serv, Lerners LLP Library, 85 Dufferin Ave, London, ON, N6A 4G4, CANADA. Tel: 519-640-6355. Fax: 519-932-3355. p. 2817

LaPorte, Toni, Br Librn, Livonia Public Library, Carl Sandburg Branch, 30100 W Seven Mile Rd, Livonia, MI, 48152-1918. Tel: 248-893-4010. Fax: 248-476-6230. p. 1204

LaPorte, Toni, Br Librn, Livonia Public Library, Vest Pocket, 15128 Farmington Rd, Livonia, MI, 48154-5417. Tel: 734-466-2559. p. 1204

Lapp, Diane, Libr Mgr, Christian Library of Lancaster County, 1873 Lincoln Hwy E, Lancaster, PA, 17602. Tel: 717-393-0300. p. 2076

Lappin, Amy, Ch, Lebanon Public Library, Nine E Park St, Lebanon, NH, 03766. Tel: 603-448-2459. p. 1454

Laprade, Michelle, Asst Librn, Bracken Memorial Library, 57 Academy Rd, Woodstock, CT, 06281. Tel: 860-928-0046. Fax: 860-928-2117. p. 380

LaPratt, Linda, Librn, Charlotte County Library, Phenix Branch, Charlotte St, Phenix, VA, 23959. Tel: 434-542-4654. p. 2453

LaPrelle, Robert H, Exec Dir, Museum of the American Railroad, Fair Park, 1105 Washington St, Dallas, TX, 75210. Tel: 214-428-0101. Fax: 214-426-1937. p. 2309

LaPrelle, Robin, Br Supvr, Wythe-Grayson Regional Library, Rural Retreat Public, 119 N Greever St, Rural Retreat, VA, 24368-2450. Tel: 276-686-8337. Fax: 276-686-8337. p. 2472

LaPrise, Joanne, Librn, Bibliotheque Municipale de Saint Felicien, 1209 Blvd Sacre-Coeur, Saint Felicien, QC, G8K 2R5, CANADA. Tel: 418-679-5334. Fax: 418-679-2178. p. 2908

Lapsansky, Emma, Curator, Haverford College, 370 Lancaster Ave, Haverford, PA, 19041-1392. Tel: 610-896-1274. Fax: 610-896-1102. p. 2067

Lapsansky, Phillip, Curator of African Americana, Library Company of Philadelphia, 1314 Locust St, Philadelphia, PA, 19107-5698. Tel: 215-546-3181. Fax: 215-546-5167. p. 2112

Lapsley, Andrea, Dir of Develop, Colorado State University Libraries, Morgan Library, 1201 Center Avenue Mall, Fort Collins, CO, 80523-. Tel: 970-491-1838. Fax: 970-491-1195. p. 307

Lapsley, Diane, Asst Dir, Sparta Public Library, 22 Woodport Rd, Sparta, NJ, 07871. Tel: 973-729-3101. Fax: 973-729-1755. p. 1531

Laptich, Chloe, Libr Mgr, Rainbow Lake Municipal Library, PO Box 266, Rainbow Lake, AB, T0H 2Y0, CANADA. Tel: 780-956-3656. Fax: 780-956-3858. p. 2714

Lara, Elena, Head, Outreach Serv, Round Lake Area Public Library District, 906 Hart Rd, Round Lake, IL, 60073. Tel: 847-546-7060, Ext 122. Fax: 847-546-7104. p. 699

Lara, Rosa, Librn, National Park Service, 100 Lady Bird Lane, Johnson City, TX, 78636. Tel: 830-868-7128, Ext 260. Fax: 830-868-7863. p. 2348

Larade, Sharon, Archives Dir, United Church of Canada, 95 Charles St W, Toronto, ON, M5S 1K7, CANADA. Tel: 416-585-4563. Fax: 416-585-4584. p. 2864

Laramie, Susan, Librn, Laconia Public Library, Lakeport (Ossian Wilbur Goss Reading Room), 188 Elm St, Laconia, NH, 03246. Tel: 603-524-3808. p. 1453

Laramie, Xenda, Ch, Rowley Public Library, 141 Main St, Rowley, MA, 01969. Tel: 978-948-2850. Fax: 978-948-2266. p. 1121

Larash, Frances A, Dir, Emmaus Public Library, 11 E Main St, Emmaus, PA, 18049. Tel: 610-965-9284. Fax: 610-965-6446. p. 2054

Larcom, Leslie, Asst Librn, Monroeton Public Library, 110 College Ave, Monroeton, PA, 18832. Tel: 570-265-2871. Fax: 570-265-7995. p. 2091

Large, Anna, Libr Instruction, Ref Serv, Jacksonville University, 2800 University Blvd N, Jacksonville, FL, 32211-3394. Tel: 904-256-7263. Fax: 904-256-7259. p. 454

Large, Cathy, Librn, Salt River Project Library, 1600 N Priest Dr, Tempe, AZ, 85281-1213. Tel: 602-236-2259. Fax: 602-236-2664. p. 84

Large, J Andrew, Prof, McGill University, 3661 Peel St, Montreal, QC, H3A 1X1, CANADA. Tel: 514-398-3360. Fax: 514-398-7193. p. 2979

Largent, Judy, Librn, Rosiclare Memorial Public Library, Main St, Rosiclare, IL, 62982. Tel: 618-285-6213. Fax: 618-285-6213. p. 699

Largent, Mary, Dir, Crowder College, 601 Laclede Ave, Neosho, MO, 64850. Tel: 417-455-5610. Fax: 417-451-4280. p. 1347

Largo, Lora, Instruction Librn, South Mountain Community College Library, 7050 S 24th St, Phoenix, AZ, 85042. Tel: 602-243-8345. Fax: 602-243-8180. p. 77

Larimer, Cindy, Circ/Reserves, Ser, University of Maryland Libraries, Architecture Library, College Park, MD, 20742-7011. Tel: 301-405-6317. Fax: 301-314-9583. p. 1025

Larimore, Nola, Librn, Saint Elmo Public Library District, Beecher City Branch, 108 N James St, Beecher City, IL, 62414. Tel: 618-487-9400. p. 700

Larison, Phyllis, Dep Dir, Edwin A Bemis Public Library, 6014 S Datura St, Littleton, CO, 80120-2636. Tel: 303-795-3961. Fax: 303-795-3996. p. 316

Larke, Julia, Libr Assoc, Mendocino County Library District, Coast Community, 225 Main St, Point Arena, CA, 95468. Tel: 707-882-3114. Fax: 707-882-3114. p. 277

Larkin, Annie, Coll Mgr, Bisbee Mining & Historical Museum, Five Copper Queen Plaza, Bisbee, AZ, 85603. Tel: 520-432-7071. Fax: 520-432-7800. p. 58

Larkin, Jack, Dir, Old Sturbridge Village, One Old Sturbridge Village Rd, Sturbridge, MA, 01566. Tel: 508-347-3362. Fax: 508-347-0375. p. 1129

Larkin, Joan, Br Coordr, Lennox & Addington County Public Library, Tamworth Branch, One Ottawa St, Tamworth, ON, K0K 3G0, CANADA. Tel: 613-379-3082. p. 2824

Larkin, Linda F, Libr Dir, North Country Community College Library, 23 Santanoni Ave, Saranac Lake, NY, 12983-2046. Tel: 518-891-2915, Ext 218. p. 1738

Larkin, Mary Jo, Dean of Libr, Chestnut Hill College, 9601 Germantown Ave, Philadelphia, PA, 19118-2695. Tel: 215-248-7055. Fax: 215-248-7056. p. 2104

Larner, Caren, In Charge, E I du Pont Canada Co, 7070 Mississauga Rd, Mississauga, ON, L5N 5M8, CANADA. Tel: 905-821-5782. Fax: 905-821-5519. p. 2822

LaRocca-Fels, Karen, Dir, Cornwall Public Library, 395 Hudson St, Cornwall, NY, 12518-1552. Tel: 845-534-8282. Fax: 845-534-3827. p. 1611

LaRocca-Fels, Karen, Asst Dir, Finkelstein Memorial Library, 24 Chestnut St, Spring Valley, NY, 10977-5594. Tel: 845-352-5700. Fax: 845-352-2319. p. 1746

Laroche, Pierre, Mgr, Lab Chrysotile, Inc, Rte 112, Thetford Mines, QC, G6H 2M9, CANADA. Tel: 418-338-7500, Ext 644. Fax: 418-338-7664. p. 2913

LaRochelle, Stephen, Dir, Kennebec Valley Community College, 92 Western Ave, Fairfield, ME, 04937-1367. Tel: 207-453-5004. Fax: 207-453-5194. p. 985

LaRock, Tami, Asst Dir, Tech Serv Dir, Goodwin Library, 422 Main St, Farmington, NH, 03835-1519. Tel: 603-755-2944. Fax: 603-755-2944. p. 1447

Larocque, Rebecca, Head, Info Serv, North Bay Public Library, 271 Worthington St E, North Bay, ON, P1B 1H1, CANADA. Tel: 705-474-4830. Fax: 705-495-4010. p. 2825

LaRonge-Mohr, Connie, Librn, Southeast Regional Library, Pilot Butte Branch, Third St & Second Ave, Pilot Butte, SK, S0G 3Z0, CANADA. Tel: 306-781-3403. p. 2930

Laroque, Claudette, Info Spec, Learning Disabilities Association of Canada Library, 1188 Wellington St W, Ste 201, Ottawa, ON, K1Y 2Z5, CANADA. Tel: 613-238-5721. Fax: 613-235-5391. p. 2831

LaRosa, Mary, Adult Serv, YA Serv, Franklin Square Public Library, 19 Lincoln Rd, Franklin Square, NY, 11010. Tel: 516-488-3444. Fax: 516-354-3368. p. 1624

LaRosa, Sharon, Outreach Serv Librn, Plymouth Public Library, 132 South St, Plymouth, MA, 02360-3309. Tel: 508-830-4250. Fax: 508-830-4258. p. 1118

LaRose, Debbie, Circ, The William K Sanford Town Library, 629 Albany Shaker Rd, Loudonville, NY, 12211-1196. Tel: 518-458-9274. Fax: 518-438-0988. p. 1655

LaRose, Leslie, Dir, Augusta Memorial Public Library, 113 N Stone St, Augusta, WI, 54722-6000. Tel: 715-286-2070. Fax: 715-286-5367. p. 2579

Larose, Lorie, In Charge, Yukon Women's Directorate Library, 404 Hanson St, Ste 1, Whitehorse, YT, Y1A 1Y8, CANADA. Tel: 867-667-3030. Fax: 867-393-6270. p. 2934

LaRose, Michele Dill, Access Serv Librn, Vermont Law School, 68 North Windsor, South Royalton, VT, 05068. Tel: 802-831-1403. Fax: 802-763-7159. p. 2436

LaRose, Patricia, Head, Ref, Newport Public Library, 300 Spring St, Newport, RI, 02840. Tel: 401-847-8720. Fax: 401-842-0841. p. 2169

LaRose, Suzanna, Sr Ref Librn, Gowling Lafleur Henderson LLP, One First Canadian Pl, 100 King St W, Ste 1600, Toronto, ON, M5X 1G5, CANADA. Tel: 416-862-4282. Fax: 416-862-7661. p. 2854

Larouche, Alain, Librn, Bibliotheque de Sorel Tracy, 3015, up Leisure, Recreation, De Sorel Tracy, QC, J3P 7K1, CANADA. Tel: 450-742-8321. Fax: 450-764-8894. p. 2881

LaRouche, Ellen, Head, Circ, Goodrich Memorial Library, 202 Main St, Newport, VT, 05855. Tel: 802-334-7902. Fax: 802-334-3890. p. 2430

Larouche, Helene, Dir, Universite du Quebec en Outaouais, 283, Blvd Alexandre-Tache, Case postale 1250, succ Hull, Gatineau, QC, J8X 3X7, CANADA. Tel: 819-595-3900, Ext 1790. Fax: 819-773-1669. p. 2884

Larouche, Monique, Tech Serv, Chateauguay Municipal Library, 25 Maple Blvd, Chateauguay, QC, J6J 3P7, CANADA. Tel: 450-698-3085. Fax: 450-698-3109. p. 2880

Larouche, Renee-Claude, Ref, College LaSalle, Bureau 4100, 2000 Saint Catherine St W, Montreal, QC, H3H 2T2, CANADA. Tel: 514-939-2006, Ext 4503. Fax: 514-939-7292. p. 2894

LaRoux, Christopher, Dir, Greenville Public Library, 573 Putnam Pike, Greenville, RI, 02828-2195. Tel: 401-949-3630. Fax: 401-949-0530. p. 2166

Larrabee, MaryPat, Dir, Saint Albans Free Library, 11 Maiden Lane, Saint Albans, VT, 05478. Tel: 802-524-1507. Fax: 802-524-1514. p. 2434

Larrabee, Pat, Librn, Maine Charitable Mechanic Association Library, 519 Congress St, Portland, ME, 04101. Tel: 207-773-8396. p. 996

Larrance, Anneke J, Exec Dir, Associated Colleges of the Saint Lawrence Valley, SUNY Potsdam, 288 Van Housen Extension, Potsdam, NY, 13676-2299. Tel: 315-267-3331. Fax: 315-267-2389. p. 2949

Larribeau, Lisa, Acq, United States Courts for the Ninth Circuit Library, 95 Seventh St, San Francisco, CA, 94103. Tel: 415-556-9500. Fax: 415-556-9927. p. 247

Larrington, Jane, Law Ref Librn/Instruction & Outreach Spec, University of San Diego, Katherine M & George M Pardee Jr Legal Research Center, 5998 Alcala Park, San Diego, CA, 92110-2492. Tel: 619-260-4752. Fax: 619-260-4616. p. 239

Larrison, Roben Jack, Curator, Western Oregon University, Jensen Arctic Museum - Western Research Library, 590 W Church St, Monmouth, OR, 97361. Tel: 503-838-8468. Fax: 503-838-8289. p. 2006

Larrow, Heather, Librn, Great Meadow Correctional Facility Library, 11739 State Rte 22, Comstock, NY, 12821. Tel: 518-639-5516, Ext 4601. Fax: 518-639-5516, Ext 2099. p. 1609

Larry, Judy, Dir, Philippi Public Library, 102 S Main St, Philippi, WV, 26416-1317. Tel: 304-457-3495. Fax: 304-457-5569. p. 2569

Larry, Tietze, Syst Librn, United States Military Academy Library, Jefferson Hall Library & Learning Center, 758 Cullum Rd, West Point, NY, 10996. Tel: 845-938-3833. Fax: 845-938-4000. p. 1767

Larsen, Alison, Ser, Siena College, 515 Loudon Rd, Loudonville, NY, 12211-1462. Tel: 518-782-6765. Fax: 518-783-2570. p. 1655

Larsen, Carole, Dir, Emery County Library, Orangeville Branch, 125 S Main, Orangeville, UT, 84537. Tel: 435-748-2726. Fax: 435-748-2736. p. 2404

Larsen, Carolyn C, Adult Serv, Warminster Township Free Library, 1076 Emma Lane, Warminster, PA, 18974. Tel: 215-672-4362. Fax: 215-672-3604. p. 2150

Larsen, Deborah J, Asst Dir, Mount Clemens Public Library, 150 Cass Ave, Mount Clemens, MI, 48043. Tel: 586-469-6200. Fax: 586-469-6668. p. 1210

Larsen, Julie, Asst Dir, Southern Virginia University, One University Hill Dr, Buena Vista, VA, 24416. Tel: 540-261-8440. Fax: 540-261-8496. p. 2453

Larsen, Lynda, Ref, Paul, Hastings, Janofsky & Walker LLP, 515 S Flower, 25th Flr, Los Angeles, CA, 90071. Tel: 213-683-5092. Fax: 213-627-0705. p. 176

Larsen, Mary, Librn, Fernbank Science Center Library, 156 Heaton Park Dr NE, Atlanta, GA, 30307-1398. Tel: 678-874-7116. Fax: 678-874-7110. p. 515

Larsen, Rodney, In Charge, Patterson, Palmer, Hunt & Murphy Law Library, One Brunswick Sq, Ste 1500, Saint John, NB, E2L 4H8, CANADA. Tel: 506-632-8900. Fax: 506-632-8809. p. 2767

Larsen, Ronald L, Dean, University of Pittsburgh, 135 N Bellefield Ave, Pittsburgh, PA, 15260, Tel: 412-624-5230. Fax: 412-624-5231. p. 2973

Larsen, Susan, Br Mgr, North Vancouver District Public Library, Capilano, 3045 Highland Blvd, North Vancouver, BC, V7R 2X4, CANADA. Tel: 604-987-4471. Fax: 604-987-0956. p. 2734

Larsen, Tom, Head, Monographic Cat, Portland State University Library, 1875 SW Park Ave, Portland, OR, 97201-3220. Tel: 503-725-8179. Fax: 503-725-4524. p. 2014

Larson, April, Ch, Hibbing Public Library, 2020 E Fifth Ave, Hibbing, MN, 55746-1702. Tel: 218-362-5959. Fax: 218-312-9779. p. 1254

Larson, April K, Libr Dir, Buhl Public Library, 400 Jones Ave, Buhl, MN, 55713. Tel: 218-258-3391. Fax: 218-258-3391. p. 1243

Larson, Barbara, Librn, Northwest Regional Library, Warroad Public Library, 202 Main Ave NW, Warroad, MN, 56763. Tel: 218-386-1283. Fax: 218-386-3408. p. 1286

Larson, Bob, Lecturer, University of Washington, Mary Gates Hall, Ste 370, Campus Box 352840, Seattle, WA, 98195-2840. Tel: 206-685-9937. Fax: 206-616-3152. p. 2976

Larson, Cara, Br Mgr, Riverside County Library System, Paloma Valley Library, 31375 Bradley Rd, Menifee, CA, 92584. Tel: 951-301-3682. Fax: 951-301-8423. p. 218

Larson, Carolyn, Head, Ref, Library of Congress, 101 Independence Ave at First St SE, Washington, DC, 20540. Tel: 202-707-5000. Fax: 202-707-1925. p. 406

Larson, Carolyn, Br Mgr, Hawaii State Public Library System, Lihue Public Library, 4344 Hardy St, Lihue, HI, 96766. Tel: 808-241-3222. Fax: 808-241-3225. p. 562

Larson, Christine, Mgr, Buckeye Public Library, 310 N Sixth St, Buckeye, AZ, 85326-2439. Tel: 623-349-6300. Fax: 623-349-6310. p. 58

Larson, Craig, Librn, North Hennepin Community College Library, 7411 85th Ave N, Brooklyn Park, MN, 55445-2298. Tel: 763-424-0733. Fax: 763-493-3569. p. 1243

Larson, Dana, Librn, Comfrey Public Library, 306 Brown St W, Comfrey, MN, 56019-1167. Tel: 507-877-6600. Fax: 507-877-3492. p. 1246

Larson, Danielle, Circ Librn, Silver Lake Library, 203 Railroad St, Silver Lake, KS, 66539. Tel: 785-582-5141. Fax: 785-582-4282. p. 894

Larson, David, Librn, Cochrane Public Library, 405 Railway St W, Cochrane, AB, T4C 2E2, CANADA. Tel: 403-932-4353. Fax: 403-932-4385. p. 2695

Larson, Dian, Ser, Northwestern Health Sciences University, 2501 W 84th St, Bloomington, MN, 55431-1599. Tel: 952-885-5419. Fax: 952-884-3318. p. 1242

Larson, Donna, Libr Asst, North Valley Public Library, 208 Main St, Stevensville, MT, 59870. Tel: 406-777-5061. Fax: 406-777-5061. p. 1388

Larson, Eric, Head, Digital & Computer Serv, University of Wisconsin-Madison, Kurt Wendt Engineering Library, 215 N Randall Ave, Madison, WI, 53706. Tel: 608-262-3493. Fax: 608-262-4739, 608-265-8751. p. 2610

Larson, Erma, Circ, University of South Dakota, McKusick Law Library, 414 E Clark St, Vermillion, SD, 57069-2390. Tel: 605-677-5259. Fax: 605-677-5417. p. 2220

Larson, Gaylene, Dir, Dixon Township Library, 120 W Walnut, Argonia, KS, 67004. Tel: 620-435-6979. p. 856

Larson, Inga C, Curator, North Andover Historical Society Library, 153 Academy Rd, North Andover, MA, 01845. Tel: 978-686-4035. Fax: 978-686-6616. p. 1111

Larson, Jane A, Dir, Vermillion Public Library, 18 Church St, Vermillion, SD, 57069-3093. Tel: 605-677-7060. Fax: 605-677-7160. p. 2221

Larson, Janet, Libr Asst, Oaklyn Memorial Library, 602 Newton Ave, Oaklyn, NJ, 08107. Tel: 856-858-8226. p. 1515

Larson, Janice, Dir, Ransom Memorial Public Library, 110 E Main St, Altona, IL, 61414-9998. Tel: 309-484-6193. p. 588

Larson, Jean, Ad, Lake Forest Library, 360 E Deerpath Ave, Lake Forest, IL, 60045-2252. Tel: 847-810-4613. Fax: 847-234-1453. p. 663

Larson, Judith, Asst Libr Dir, Our Lady of the Lake University, 411 SW 24th St, San Antonio, TX, 78207-4689. Tel: 210-434-6711, Ext 2324. Fax: 210-436-1616. p. 2380

Larson, Judy, Dir, Winslow Public Library, 136 Halifax St, Winslow, ME, 04901. Tel: 207-872-1978. Fax: 207-872-1979. p. 1007

Larson, Julie, Dir, Titonka Public Library, 136 Main St N, Titonka, IA, 50480. Tel: 515-928-2509. Fax: 515-928-2509. p. 847

Larson, Kendall, Coll Mgt, Winona State University, 175 W Mark St, Winona, MN, 55987-5838. Tel: 507-457-5367. p. 1290

Larson, Kimberly, Exec Dir, Eugene Field House & Saint Louis Toy Museum, 634 S Broadway, Saint Louis, MO, 63102. Tel: 314-421-4689. Fax: 314-588-9468. p. 1354

Larson, Laura, Ch, Russell Library, 123 Broad St, Middletown, CT, 06457. Tel: 860-347-2528. p. 352

Larson, Leah, Librn, Irma Municipal Library, 5012 51st Ave, Irma, AB, T0B 2H0, CANADA. Tel: 780-754-3746. Fax: 780-754-3802. p. 2707

Larson, Margaret, Dir, Jordaan Memorial Library, 724 Broadway, Larned, KS, 67550-3051. Tel: 620-285-2876. Fax: 620-285-7275. p. 877

Larson, Mary Alice, Libr Tech, Wisconsin Indianhead Technical College, 1900 College Dr, Rice Lake, WI, 54868. Tel: 715-234-7082, Ext 5424. Fax: 715-234-5172. p. 2634

Larson, Molly, Dir, Rockport Public Library, One Limerock St, Rockport, ME, 04856-6141. Tel: 207-236-3642. Fax: 207-236-3642. p. 999

Larson, Nicole, Librn, Veteran Municipal Library, 201 Lucknow St, Veteran, AB, T0C 2S0, CANADA. Tel: 403-575-3915. Fax: 403-575-3870. p. 2720

Larson, Nicole, Librn, Parkland Regional Library, Kamsack Branch, 235 Second St, Kamsack, SK, S0A 1S0, CANADA. Tel: 306-542-3787. p. 2932

Larson, Pam, Asst Librn, ILL, Chester Public Library, 21 W Main St, Chester, CT, 06412. Tel: 860-526-0018. p. 334

Larson, Pamela, Exec VPres, National Academy of Social Insurance Library, 1776 Massachusetts Ave NW, Ste 615, Washington, DC, 20036. Tel: 202-452-8097. Fax: 202-452-8111. p. 409

Larson, Pansilee, Curator, North Central Nevada Historical Society, Maple Ave & Jungo Rd, Winnemucca, NV, 89446. Tel: 775-623-2912. Fax: 775-623-5640. p. 1435

Larson, Pat, Librn, Woonsocket Community Library, PO Box 428, Woonsocket, SD, 57385-0428. Tel: 605-796-1412. p. 2222

Larson, Peggy, Head, Info Serv, Arizona-Sonora Desert Museum Library, 2021 N Kinney Rd, Tucson, AZ, 85743. Tel: 520-883-1380, Ext 264. Fax: 520-883-2500. p. 85

Larson, Randy, Pres, Swedish Historical Society of Rockford, 404 S Third St, Rockford, IL, 61104. Tel: 815-963-5559. Fax: 815-963-5559. p. 698

Larson, Reid, Ref Librn, Hamilton College, 198 College Hill Rd, Clinton, NY, 13323-1299. Tel: 315-859-4480. Fax: 315-859-4578. p. 1607

Larson, Ronald J, Dir, Wisconsin State Journal - Capital Times Library, 1901 Fish Hatchery Rd, Madison, WI, 53713. Tel: 608-252-6412. Fax: 608-252-6119. p. 2611

Larson, Roxanne, Dir, Baudette Public Library, 110 First Ave SW, Baudette, MN, 56623. Tel: 218-634-2329. Fax: 218-634-2329. p. 1240

Larson, Ruth, Info Res, United States Olympic Committee, 1750 E Boulder, Colorado Springs, CO, 80909. Tel: 719-866-4622. Fax: 719-632-5352. p. 296

Larson, Scott, Librn, Beveridge & Diamond, PC Library, 1350 I St NW, Ste 700, Washington, DC, 20005-3311. Tel: 202-789-6000. Fax: 202-789-6190. p. 394

Larson, Sharyl, Librn, Slayton Public Library, 2451 Broadway Ave, Slayton, MN, 56172. Tel: 507-836-8778. Fax: 507-836-8778. p. 1284

Larson, Signe E, Librn, Information Masters Library, 37980 Reed Rd, Manzanita, OR, 97130. Tel: 503-368-6990. Fax: 503-368-7118. p. 2004

Larson, Sue, Head, Youth Serv, Warrenville Public Library District, 28 W 751 Stafford Pl, Warrenville, IL, 60555. Tel: 630-393-1171. Fax: 630-393-1688. p. 715

Larson, Susan, Head, Pub Serv, Minnesota State Law Library, Minnesota Judicial Ctr, Rm G25, 25 Rev Dr Martin Luther King Jr Blvd, Saint Paul, MN, 55155. Tel: 651-296-2775. Fax: 651-296-6740. p. 1280

Larson, Susan, Br Mgr, Fairfax County Public Library, Lorton Branch, 9520 Richmond Hwy, Lorton, VA, 22079-2124. Tel: 703-339-7385. p. 2461

Larson, Thomas, Web Coordr, State University of New York at Oswego, SUNY Oswego, 7060 State Rte 104, Oswego, NY, 13126-3514. Tel: 315-312-3539. Fax: 315-312-3194. p. 1713

Larson, Vaughn, Librn, Utah State University, Ann Carroll Moore Children's Library, 6700 Old Main Hill, Logan, UT, 84322. Tel: 435-797-3093. p. 2407

Larson, Vici, Librn, Sussex County Library System, E Louise Childs Memorial, 21 Sparta Rd, Stanhope, NJ, 07874. Tel: 973-770-1000. Fax: 973-770-0094. p. 1514

Larson, Vicki, Acq, Clarke University, 1550 Clarke Dr, Dubuque, IA, 52001. Tel: 563-588-6424. Fax: 563-588-8160. p. 811

Larson, Victoria, Mgr, Info Serv, Empire State Development Library, Albany, NY, 12245. Tel: 518-292-5238. Fax: 518-292-5805. p. 1569

Larson, Wendy, Librn, Rice Memorial Hospital Library, 301 Becker Ave SW, Willmar, MN, 56201. Tel: 320-231-4248. Fax: 320-231-4463. p. 1289

Larson-Troyer, Rebecca, Local Hist Librn, Barberton Public Library, 602 W Park Ave, Barberton, OH, 44203-2458. Tel: 330-745-1194. Fax: 330-745-8261. p. 1857

LaRue, Amy, Asst Librn, Susquehanna County Historical Society & Free Library Association, Two Monument Sq, Montrose, PA, 18801-1115. Tel: 570-278-1881. Fax: 570-278-9336. p. 2092

LaRue, Daniel, Dir, Hamburg Public Library, 35 N Third St, Hamburg, PA, 19526-1502. Tel: 610-562-2843. Fax: 610-562-8136. p. 2064

LaRue, Jamie, Dir, Douglas County Libraries, 100 S Wilcox, Castle Rock, CO, 80104. Tel: 303-688-7654. Fax: 303-688-7655. p. 294

LaRue, Karen, Librn, Townshend Public Library, 1971 Rte 30, Townshend, VT, 05353. Tel: 802-365-4039. p. 2437

LaRue, Linda, Mgr, Cabell County Public Library, Barboursville Branch, 728 Main St, Barboursville, WV, 25504. Tel: 304-736-4621. Fax: 304-736-6240. p. 2561

LaSala, Rosemary, Ref/Govt Doc Librn, Saint John's University Library, Rittenberg Law Library, 8000 Utopia Pkwy, Queens, NY, 11439. Tel: 718-990-1896. Fax: 718-990-6649. p. 1725

Lasansky, Jeannette, Coll Develop, Union County Historical Society Library, Union County Courthouse, S Second & St Louis Sts, Lewisburg, PA, 17837. Tel: 570-524-8666. Fax: 570-524-8743. p. 2081

LaSasso, Richard, Librn, Tonkon Torp LLP, 888 SW Fifth Ave, Ste 1600, Portland, OR, 97204-2099. Tel: 503-802-2089. Fax: 503-972-3789. p. 2014

LaSata, Julie, Librn, Bakerville Library, Six Maple Hollow Rd, New Hartford, CT, 06057. Tel: 860-482-8806. Fax: 860-482-8806. p. 355

LaScala, Gale, Librn, Hamilton Memorial Library, 195 Rte 20, Chester, MA, 01011-9648. Tel: 413-354-7808. p. 1080

Lascar, Claudia, Librn, City College of the City University of New York, Science-Engineering, Marshak Bldg, Rm 29, 160 Convent Ave, New York, NY, 10031. Tel: 212-650-6826. Fax: 212-650-7626. p. 1673

Lascola, Gail, Librn, VA Connecticut Health Care System, 950 Campbell Ave, West Haven, CT, 06516-5247. Tel: 203-932-5711, Ext 2898. Fax: 203-937-3822. p. 377

Lasek, Mark, Librn, Bryant & Stratton College Library, 1259 Central Ave, Albany, NY, 12205. Tel: 518-437-1802. Fax: 518-437-1048. p. 1568

Lasell, Jennifer, Libr Tech, Butte College Library, 3536 Butte Campus Dr, Oroville, CA, 95965-8399. p. 201

Lash, Anna, Dir, West Routt Library District, 201 E Jefferson Ave, Hayden, CO, 81639. Tel: 970-276-3777. Fax: 970-276-3778. p. 313

Lash, Julie, Youth Serv Librn, Casa Grande Public Library, 449 N Dry Lake, Casa Grande, AZ, 85222. Tel: 520-421-8710, Ext 5150. Fax: 520-421-8701. p. 59

Lash, Metta, Librn, Montgomery College, Germantown Campus Library, 20200 Observation Dr, Germantown, MD, 20876. Tel: 240-567-7857. Fax: 301-353-7859. p. 1037

Lash, Virginia, Tech Serv, Reading Public Library, 100 S Fifth St, Reading, PA, 19602. Tel: 610-655-6350. p. 2133

Lasha, Suzanne, Pub Serv, Canon City Public Library, 516 Macon Ave, Canon City, CO, 81212-3380. Tel: 719-269-9020. Fax: 719-269-9031. p. 293

Lashbrook, Brian, Info Tech, Daviess County Public Library, 2020 Frederica St, Owensboro, KY, 42301. Tel: 270-684-0211. Fax: 270-684-0218. p. 931

Lasher, Allie, Librn, Clark Memorial Library, 21713 Cussewago St, Venango, PA, 16440. Tel: 814-398-9956. p. 2149

Lasher, Marie, Librn, The College of Saint Mary Magdalen, 511 Kearsarge Mountain Rd, Warner, NH, 03278. Tel: 603-456-2656. Fax: 603-456-2660. p. 1467

Lasher-Sommers, Clai, Asst Librn, Westmoreland Public Library, 33 S Village Rd, Westmoreland, NH, 03467. Tel: 603-399-7750. p. 1468

Lashley, Eric P, Dir, Libr Serv, Georgetown Public Library, 402 W Eighth St, Georgetown, TX, 78626-5503. Fax: 512-930-3764. p. 2327

Lashley, Pat, Br Mgr, Spencer County Public Library, Parker Branch, PO Box 361, Hatfield, IN, 47617-0361. Tel: 812-359-4030. p. 776

Lashway, Colleen, Br Mgr, Hawaii State Public Library System, Hawaii Kai Public Library, 249 Lunalilo Home Rd, Honolulu, HI, 96825. Tel: 808-397-5833. Fax: 808-397-5832. p. 561

Lasiewski, Erik, Libr Supvr, California School for the Deaf Library, 3044 Horace St, Riverside, CA, 92506. Tel: 951-248-7700, Ext 4138. p. 216

LaSita, Laura, Outreach Serv Librn, YA Serv, Riverhead Free Library, 330 Court St, Riverhead, NY, 11901-2885. Tel: 631-727-3228. Fax: 631-727-4762. p. 1728

Laskaris, Lisa, Instruction/Info Lit Librn, University of Bridgeport, 126 Park Ave, Bridgeport, CT, 06604-5620. Tel: 203-576-4408. Fax: 203-576-4791. p. 332

Lasker, Polly, Librn, Smithsonian Libraries, National Zoological Park Library, Nat Zoological Park, Education Bldg-Visitor Ctr, MRC 551, 3000 Block of Connecticut Ave NW, Washington, DC, 20008-0551. Tel: 202-633-1702. Fax: 202-673-4900. p. 415

Lasker, Polly, Ref Serv, Smithsonian Libraries, National Museum of Natural History Library, Nat Museum of Natural Hist, Rm 51, MRC 154, Tenth St & Constitution Ave NW, Washington, DC, 20013-0712. Tel: 202-633-1702. Fax: 202-357-1896. p. 415

Laskin, Miriam, Dr, Coordr, Instrul Serv, Info Literacy Librn, Hostos Community College Library, 475 Grand Concourse, A-207, Bronx, NY, 10451. Tel: 718-518-4207. Fax: 718-518-4206. p. 1587

Laskowski, Nancy, Head Librn, Free Library of Philadelphia, Access Services, 1901 Vine St, Philadelphia, PA, 19103-1189. Tel: 215-686-5412. Fax: 215-686-5353. p. 2106

Laskowski, Nancy, Interim Adminr, Free Library of Philadelphia, Library for the Blind & Physically Handicapped, 919 Walnut St, Philadelphia, PA, 19107-5289. Tel: 215-683-3213. Fax: 215-683-3211. p. 2108

Lasky, Kate, Exec Dir, Josephine Community Libraries, Inc, 200 NW C St, Grants Pass, OR, 97526-2094. Tel: 541-476-0571. Fax: 541-479-0685. p. 1999

Lasleur, Lise, Librn, Bibliotheque Municipale de Greenfield Park, 225 rue Empire, Greenfield Park, Longueuil, QC, J4V 1T9, CANADA. Tel: 450-463-7140. Fax: 450-466-8112. p. 2886

Lasner, Robert, Evening Librn, Weekend Librn, Saint Joseph's College, 222 Clinton Ave, Brooklyn, NY, 11205-3697. Fax: 718-636-7250. p. 1594

Lasnick, Karen, Mgr, Libr Serv, Bryan Cave LLP, 120 Broadway, Ste 300, Santa Monica, CA, 90401. Tel: 310-576-2100. Fax: 310-576-2200. p. 265

Laspee, Laura, Dir, Clymer Library, 115 Firehouse Rd, Pocono Pines, PA, 18350-9705. Tel: 570-646-0826. Fax: 570-646-6181. p. 2131

LasQuety, Mary, Asst Librn, Saints Mary & Elizabeth Medical Center, 2233 W Division St, Chicago, IL, 60622. Tel: 312-770-2219. Fax: 312-770-2221. p. 624

Lass, Diane, Head, Circ, Baldwin Public Library, 2385 Grand Ave, Baldwin, NY, 11510-3289. Tel: 516-223-6228. Fax: 516-623-7991. p. 1577

Lass, Vickie, Asst Librn, Western Dakota Technical Institute Library, 800 Mickelson Dr, Rapid City, SD, 57703. Tel: 605-718-2904. Fax: 605-718-2537. p. 2217

Lassell, Jeannette, Librn, Bloomfield Public Library, 333 S First St, Bloomfield, NM, 87413-6221. Tel: 505-632-8315. Fax: 505-632-0876. p. 1552

Lassen, Christie P, Dir, Pub Relations, Howard County Library System, 6600 Cradlerock Way, Columbia, MD, 21045-4912. Tel: 410-313-7750. Fax: 410-313-7742. p. 1026

Lassen, Karen, Br Mgr, Las Vegas-Clark County Library District, Laughlin Library, 2840S Needles Hwy, Laughlin, NV, 89029. Tel: 702-507-4070. Fax: 702-507-4067. p. 1429

Lassiter, Amy, Dir, Winchester Public Library, 203 Fourth St, Winchester, KS, 66097. Tel: 913-774-4967. Fax: 913-774-4967. p. 902

Lassiter, Kathy, Br Mgr, Dare County Library, Kill Devil Hills Branch, 400 Mustian St, Kill Devil Hills, NC, 27948. Tel: 252-441-4331. Fax: 252-441-0608. p. 1808

Lassiter, Kay, Dir, Delaware Township Library, 421 Mary St, No A, Valley Falls, KS, 66088. Tel: 785-945-3990. Fax: 785-945-3341. p. 898

Lasson, Lori, Circ Mgr, Three Rivers Regional Library System, 208 Gloucester St, Brunswick, GA, 31520-7007. Tel: 912-267-1212. Fax: 912-267-9597. p. 522

Lassonde, Agnès, Bibliothecaire Responsable, Bibliothèques de Montréal, Saint-Laurent, 1380, rue de l'Église, Montreal, QC, H4L 2H2, CANADA. Tel: 514-855-6000. Fax: 514-855-6129. p. 2891

Last, Kimberly, Head, Tech Serv, Prospect Heights Public Library District, 12 N Elm St, Prospect Heights, IL, 60070-1450. Tel: 847-259-3500. Fax: 847-259-4602. p. 692

Laster, Emma, Ch, Atlanta-Fulton Public Library System, Adamsville-Collier Heights, 3424 Martin Luther King Dr, Atlanta, GA, 30331. Tel: 404-699-4206. Fax: 404-699-6380. p. 511

Lastra, Sarai, Vice Chancellor of Info Serv, Universidad del Turabo, PO Box 3030, Gurabo, PR, 00778-3030. Tel: 787-743-7979, Ext 4501. Fax: 787-743-7924. p. 2673

Lastra, Sarai, Instr, University of Puerto Rico, Rio Piedras Campus, PO Box 21906, San Juan, PR, 00931-1906. Tel: 787-764-0000, Ext 1286, 787-764-0000, Ext 5028. Fax: 787-764-2311. p. 2977

Lastres, Steven A, Dir, Libr Serv, Debevoise & Plimpton, 919 Third Ave, New York, NY, 10022. Tel: 212-909-6279. Fax: 212-909-1025. p. 1677

Laszlo, Krisztina, Archivist, Audrey & Harry Hawthorn Library & Archives at the UBC Museum of Anthropology, 6393 NW Marine Dr, Vancouver, BC, V6T 1Z2, CANADA. Tel: 604-822-4834. Fax: 604-822-2974. p. 2741

Latan, Graciela, Info Officer, Toronto Public Health Library, 277 Victoria St, 6th Flr, Toronto, ON, M5B 1W2, CANADA. Tel: 416-338-7862. Fax: 416-338-0489. p. 2859

Latanision, Nancy, Instr, Kutztown University, Kutztown, PA, 19530. Tel: 610-683-4300. Fax: 610-683-1326. p. 2973

Latch, Patricia, Prog Coordr, Cobb County Public Library System, 266 Roswell St, Marietta, GA, 30060-2004. Tel: 770-528-2342. Fax: 770-528-2349. p. 542

Later, Sarah, Dir, Anderson City, Anderson, Stony Creek & Union Townships Public Library, 111 E 12th St, Anderson, IN, 46016-2701. Tel: 765-641-2454. Fax: 765-641-2197. p. 723

Laterza, Patricia, Ch, North Haven Memorial Library, 17 Elm St, North Haven, CT, 06473. Tel: 203-239-5803. Fax: 203-234-2130. p. 362

Latham, Bethany, Electronic Res Librn, Jacksonville State University Library, 700 Pelham Rd N, Jacksonville, AL, 36265. Tel: 256-782-5255. Fax: 256-782-5872. p. 22

Latham, Clara M, Dir, Midwestern State University, 3410 Taft Ave, Wichita Falls, TX, 76308-2099. Fax: 940-397-4689. p. 2400

Latham, Kevin, Asst Librn, Per & Reserve Serv Librn, University of Guam, UOG Sta, Mangilao, GU, 96923. Tel: 671-735-2335. Fax: 671-734-6882. p. 2667

Latham, Lana, Dir, San Juan County Library, Blanding Branch, 25 W 300 South, Blanding, UT, 84511-3829. Tel: 435-678-2335. Fax: 435-678-2335. p. 2408

Latham, Laurie, Br Mgr, Blackwater Regional Library, Agnes Taylor Gray Branch, 125 Bank St, Waverly, VA, 23890-3235. Tel: 804-834-2192. Fax: 804-834-8671. p. 2458

Latham, Laurie, Br Mgr, Blackwater Regional Library, Troxler Memorial, 100 Wilson Ave, Wakefield, VA, 23888. Tel: 757-899-6500. Fax: 757-899-2400. p. 2458

Latham, Ronald B, Dir, Berkshire Athenaeum, One Wendell Ave, Pittsfield, MA, 01201-6385. Tel: 413-499-9480. Fax: 413-499-9489. p. 1117

Latham, William, Circ Librn, University of Miami, 1311 Miller Dr, Coral Gables, FL, 33146. Tel: 305-284-2251. Fax: 305-284-3554. p. 434

Lathrop, Ben, Br Mgr, Public Library of Cincinnati & Hamilton County, Covedale, 4980 Glenway Ave, Cincinnati, OH, 45238. Tel: 513-369-4460. Fax: 513-369-4461. p. 1871

Lathrop, Janice, Ref, Anne Arundel Community College, 101 College Pkwy, Arnold, MD, 21012-1895. Tel: 410-777-2211. Fax: 410-777-2652. p. 1011

Lathrop, Norman, Mgr, Norman Lathrop Enterprises Library, 2342 Star Dr, Wooster, OH, 44691-9019. Tel: 330-262-5587. p. 1950

Lathrop, Sue, Dir, Idaho Springs Public Library, 219 14th Ave, Idaho Springs, CO, 80452. Tel: 303-569-2403. Fax: 303-567-2020. p. 313

Latimer, Jo Ann, Cat, Tech Serv, Sandwich Public Library, 142 Main St, Sandwich, MA, 02563. Tel: 508-888-0625. Fax: 508-833-1076. p. 1122

Latimer, Michele H, Supvr, Access Serv, Boston College, 885 Centre St, Newton Centre, MA, 02459. Tel: 617-552-8605. Fax: 617-552-2889. p. 1110

Latini, Joseph, Dir, South Huntington Public Library, 145 Pidgeon Hill Rd, Huntington Station, NY, 11746. Tel: 631-549-4411. Fax: 631-549-1266. p. 1639

Latiolais, Lester, Br Mgr, Saint Martin Parish Library, Breaux Bridge Branch, 102 Courthouse St, Breaux Bridge, LA, 70517. Tel: 337-332-2733. Fax: 337-332-2733. p. 967

LaTouche, Carmen, Br Head, Toronto Public Library, Amesbury Park, 1565 Lawrence Ave W, Toronto, ON, M6L 1A8, CANADA. Tel: 416-395-5420. Fax: 416-395-5432. p. 2860

Latour, John, Info Spec, Artexte Information Centre, 460 Saint-Catherine W, Ste 508, Montreal, QC, H3B 1A7, CANADA. Tel: 514-874-0049. p. 2888

Latour, Terry S, Dr, Dean, Clarion University of Pennsylvania, 840 Wood St, Clarion, PA, 16214. Tel: 814-393-1931. Fax: 814-393-2344. p. 2045

LaTronica, M Starr, Ch, Four County Library System, 304 Clubhouse Rd, Vestal, NY, 13850-3713. Tel: 607-723-8236, Ext 350. Fax: 607-723-1722. p. 1761

Latshaw, Hayley, Mgr, San Antonio Public Library, Cody, 11441 Vance Jackson, San Antonio, TX, 78230. Tel: 210-696-6396. Fax: 210-696-6273. p. 2382

Latshaw, Jack, Dir, Geisinger Health System, 100 N Academy Ave, Danville, PA, 17822-2101. Tel: 570-271-8197. Fax: 570-271-5738. p. 2049

Latta-Guthrie, Leslie, Exec Dir, Alberta Culture, 8555 Roper Rd, Edmonton, AB, T6E 5W1, CANADA. Tel: 780-427-1750. Fax: 780-427-4646. p. 2697

Lattanzio, Effie, Head, Circ, St Thomas Public Library, 153 Curtis St, St. Thomas, ON, N5P 3Z7, CANADA. Tel: 519-631-6050. Fax: 519-631-1987. p. 2844

Lattimer, Jamie, Coordr, Cat, Urbana University, 579 College Way, Urbana, OH, 43078-2091. Tel: 937-484-1336. Fax: 937-653-8551. p. 1942

Latto, Steve, Librn, Arizona Department of Corrections - Adult Institutions, 26700 S Hwy 85, Buckeye, AZ, 85326. Tel: 623-386-6160, Ext 4908. Fax: 623-386-6160, Ext 4910. p. 58

Latulippe, Tina, Cat, Tech Serv, College Merici - Bibliotheque, 755 Grande Allée Ouest, Quebec, QC, G1S 1C1, CANADA. Tel: 418-683-2104, Ext 2249. Fax: 418-682-8938. p. 2904

Laturnus, Caralee, Librn, Chinook Regional Library, Pennant Branch, PO Box 10, Pennant, SK, S0N 1X0, CANADA. Tel: 306-626-3316. p. 2928

Latuszek, Thomas, Cat, Florida Coastal School of Law, 8787 Baypine Rd, Jacksonville, FL, 32256. Tel: 904-680-7637. Fax: 904-680-7677. p. 452

Latyszewskyj, Maria, Head, EC Libr Downsview, Environment Canada Library, Downsview, 4905 Dufferin St, Toronto, ON, M3H 5T4, CANADA. Tel: 416-739-4828. Fax: 416-739-4212. p. 2853

Latzel, Teresa, Librn, Rankin Public Library, Midkiff Public, 12701 No FM 2401, Midkiff, TX, 79755. Tel: 432-535-2311. Fax: 432-535-2312. p. 2373

Lau, Clement Chu-Sing, Tech Serv, University of Baltimore, Law Library, 1415 Maryland Ave, Baltimore, MD, 21201. Tel: 410-837-4554. Fax: 410-837-4570. p. 1018

Lau, Kevin, Head, Instrul Tech & Libr Info Serv, Harvard Library, Frances Loeb Library, Harvard Graduate School of Design, 48 Quincy St, Gund Hall, Cambridge, MA, 02138. Tel: 617-495-9163. p. 1076

Lau, Tammy, Spec Coll Librn, California State University, Fresno, Henry Madden Library, 5200 N Barton Ave, Mail Stop ML-34, Fresno, CA, 93740-8014. Tel: 559-278-2595. Fax: 559-278-6952. p. 150

Lau, Tracy, Libr Tech, Orlando Health, 1414 Kuhl Ave, MP 28, Orlando, FL, 32806-2134. Tel: 321-841-5454. Fax: 321-843-6825. p. 477

Lau, Winson, Ref & Instruction Librn, Berkeley College Library, Three E 43rd St, New York, NY, 10017. Tel: 212-986-4343. Fax: 212-661-2940. p. 1670

Laubacher, Marilyn R, Dir, Baldwinsville Public Library, 33 E Genesee St, Baldwinsville, NY, 13027-2575. Tel: 315-635-5631. Fax: 315-635-6760. p. 1577

Laube, Irene H, Asst Dean of Libr, Durham Technical Community College, 1637 Lawson St, Durham, NC, 27703. Tel: 919-536-7211. Fax: 919-686-3471. p. 1788

Laubenstein, Janice, Sr Coll Adminr, J J Keller & Associates, Inc, 3003 W Breezewood Lane, Neenah, WI, 54956-9611. Tel: 920-722-7271. Fax: 920-720-7741. p. 2624

Lauber, Melissa, Acq, Pub Serv Librn, Virginia Union University, 1500 N Lombardy St, Richmond, VA, 23220. Tel: 804-278-4112. Fax: 804-257-5818. p. 2493

Laubersheimer, John, Coll Develop Librn, Info Spec, University of Bridgeport, 126 Park Ave, Bridgeport, CT, 06604-5620. Tel: 203-576-4508. Fax: 203-576-4791. p. 332

Laubner, Nathaniel, Chief Librn, United States Air Force, Wright-Patterson Air Force Base Library FL2300, 88 MSG/SVMG, Bldg 1226, 5435 Hemlock St, Wright-Patterson AFB, OH, 45433-5420. Tel: 937-257-4340, 937-257-4815. Fax: 937-656-1776. p. 1951

Lauchner, Sharon, Br Adminr, Frederick County Public Libraries, Walkersville Branch, 57 W Frederick St, Walkersville, MD, 21793. Tel: 301-845-8880. Fax: 301-845-5759. p. 1029

Lauchner, Sharon, Br Mgr, Frederick County Public Libraries, Middletown Branch, 101 Prospect, Middletown, MD, 21769. Tel: 301-371-7560. p. 1029

Lauck, Jennifer, Dir, Bloomfield Public Library, 121 S Broadway, Bloomfield, NE, 68718. Tel: 402-373-4588. Fax: 402-373-2601. p. 1394

Laud, Tim, Dir, Zenith Electronics LLC, 2000 Millbrook Dr, Lincolnshire, IL, 60069. Tel: 847-941-8000. Fax: 847-941-8555. p. 666

Laudenslager, Georgia, Ref & Outreach, Roger & Peggy Madigan Library, 999 Hagan Way, Williamsport, PA, 17701. Tel: 570-327-4523. Fax: 570-327-4503. p. 2156

Lauder, Tracey, Asst Dean, Libr Admin, University of New Hampshire Library, 18 Library Way, Durham, NH, 03824. Tel: 603-862-3041. Fax: 603-862-0247. p. 1445

Lauderdale, Sarah, Head, Ref, Hamilton-Wenham Public Library, 14 Union St, South Hamilton, MA, 01982. Tel: 978-468-5577. Fax: 978-468-5535. p. 1125

Laudone, Charisse, Head, Tech Serv, Stinson Memorial Public Library District, 409 S Main St, Anna, IL, 62906. Tel: 618-833-2521. Fax: 618-833-3560. p. 589

Lauer, Anita, Head, Cat, Teachers College, Columbia University, 525 W 120th St, New York, NY, 10027-6696. Tel: 212-678-3424. p. 1701

Lauer, Anna, Librn, Cuyahoga Community College, Eastern Campus Library, 4250 Richmond Rd, Highland Hills, OH, 44122-6195. Tel: 216-987-2091. Fax: 216-987-2054. p. 1879

Lauer, Chris, Ref Asst, Lompoc Public Library, 501 E North Ave, Lompoc, CA, 93436-3498. Tel: 805-875-8775. Fax: 805-736-6440. p. 165

Lauer, Gina, Circ, Stevenson University Library, 1525 Greenspring Valley Rd, Stevenson, MD, 21153. Tel: 410-486-7000, 443-334-2233. Fax: 410-486-7329. p. 1043

Lauer, Heather, Asst Librn, Argosy University, 5250 17th St, Sarasota, FL, 34235. Tel: 941-379-0404, Ext 229. Fax: 941-379-9464. p. 489

Lauer, Jonathan D, Dir, Messiah College, One College Ave, Ste 3002, Mechanicsburg, PA, 17055. Tel: 717-691-6006, Ext 3820. Fax: 717-691-2356. p. 2087

Lauer, Joseph, Librn, Michigan State University Library, Area Studies, 100 Library, East Lansing, MI, 48824. Tel: 517-884-6392. Fax: 517-432-3532. p. 1175

Lauer, Judy A, Dir, NYS Supreme Court Library - Binghamton, Broome County Courthouse, Rm 107, 92 Court St, Binghamton, NY, 13901-3301. Tel: 607-778-2119. Fax: 212-457-2958. p. 1582

Lauer, Tracy, Librn, Anheuser-Busch Co, Inc, One Busch Pl, Saint Louis, MO, 63118. Tel: 314-577-2000. p. 1353

Lauer-Bader, Michele, Dir, Half Hollow Hills Community Library, 55 Vanderbilt Pkwy, Dix Hills, NY, 11746. Tel: 631-421-4530. Fax: 631-421-0730. p. 1615

Lauerman, Jill, Reader Serv, Poplar Creek Public Library District, 1405 S Park Ave, Streamwood, IL, 60107-2997. Tel: 630-837-6800. Fax: 630-837-6823. p. 708

Laughlin, Gregory, Bus Mgr, Goshen Public Library, 601 S Fifth St, Goshen, IN, 46526-3994, Tel: 574-533-9531. Fax: 574-533-5211. p. 746

Laughlin, Gregory K, Dir, Samford University Library, Lucille Stewart Beeson Law Library, 800 Lakeshore Dr, Birmingham, AL, 35229. Tel: 205-726-2714. Fax: 205-726-2644. p. 9

Laughlin, Jennifer, Curator, Wyandotte County Museum, 631 N 126th St, Bonner Springs, KS, 66012. Tel: 913-721-1078. Fax: 913-721-1394. p. 858

Laughlin, Marcia, Asst Librn, Barryton Public Library, 198 Northern Ave, Barryton, MI, 49305. Tel: 989-382-5288. Fax: 989-382-9073. p. 1155

Laughlin, Mary, Asst Dir, Mobile Public Library, 700 Government St, Mobile, AL, 36602. Tel: 251-208-7106. Fax: 251-208-5865. p. 25

Laughlin, Mary, Interim Dir, Mobile Public Library, 700 Government St, Mobile, AL, 36602. Tel: 251-208-7106. Fax: 251-208-5865. p. 25

Laughlin, Michelle, Br Librn, Preble County District Library, West Alexandria Branch, 16 N Main St, West Alexandria, OH, 45381. Tel: 937-839-4915. Fax: 937-839-4209. p. 1898

Laughlin, Patricia, Dir, Hales Corners Library, 5885 S 116th St, Hales Corners, WI, 53130-1707. Tel: 414-529-6150. Fax: 414-529-6154. p. 2597

Laughlin, Riva, Librn, Haynes & Boone LLP, 2323 Victory Ave, Ste 700, Dallas, TX, 75219. Tel: 713-547-2828. p. 2308

Laughlin, Sara, Dir, Monroe County Public Library, 303 E Kirkwood Ave, Bloomington, IN, 47408. Tel: 812-349-3050. Fax: 812-349-3051. p. 728

Laughlin, Sherry, Assoc Univ Librn, University of Southern Mississippi Library, 118 College Dr, No 5053, Hattiesburg, MS, 39406. Tel: 601-266-4270. Fax: 601-266-6033. p. 1300

Laughlin, Sherry, Assoc Dean, University of Southern Mississippi Library, William David McCain Library & Archives, 118 College Dr, No 5148, Hattiesburg, MS, 39406. Tel: 601-266-4270. Fax: 601-226-6269. p. 1301

Laughlin, Sherry, Dir of Libr, William Carey University Libraries, 498 Tuscan Ave, Box 5, Hattiesburg, MS, 39401. Tel: 601-318-6169. Fax: 601-318-6171. p. 1301

Laughlin, Steve, Ref Librn, Birmingham-Southern College, 900 Arkadelphia Rd, Birmingham, AL, 35254. Tel: 205-226-4740. Fax: 205-226-4743. p. 8

Laughlin, Tania, Dir, Crystal City Public Library, 736 Mississippi Ave, Crystal City, MO, 63019-1646. Tel: 636-937-7166. Fax: 636-937-3193. p. 1327

Laughner, Lynn, Librn, Morgantown Public Library, Clinton District Library, 2005 Grafton Rd, Morgantown, WV, 26508. Tel: 304-291-0703. Fax: 304-291-0703. p. 2566

Laukhuf, Valerie, Youth Serv, Putnam County District Library, The Educational Service Ctr, 124 Putnam Pkwy, Ottawa, OH, 45875-1471. Tel: 419-523-3747. Fax: 419-523-6477. p. 1926

Laul, Karen, Cat, Albert Einstein College of Medicine, 1300 Morris Park Ave, Bronx, NY, 10461. Tel: 718-430-3114. Fax: 718-430-8795. p. 1586

Lauland, Regina, Asst Dir, Lafourche Parish Public Library, 303 W Fifth St, Thibodaux, LA, 70301-3123. Tel: 985-446-1163. Fax: 985-446-3848. p. 970

Lauman, Ruth, Dir, Hamburg Public Library, 1301 Main St, Hamburg, IA, 51640. Tel: 712-382-1395. Fax: 712-382-1405. p. 820

Laumas, Elizabeth R, Cat Spec, Transylvania University Library, 300 N Broadway, Lexington, KY, 40508. Tel: 859-233-8225. Fax: 859-233-8779. p. 921

Laumeister, Virginia, Dir, First Reformed Church of Schenectady, Eight N Church St, Schenectady, NY, 12305-1699. Tel: 518-377-2201. Fax: 518-374-4098. p. 1740

Laun, Carol, Librn, Salmon Brook Historical Society, 208 Salmon Brook St, Granby, CT, 06035-2402. Tel: 860-653-9713. p. 341

Laun, Mary Ann, Dir, Pasadena City College Library, 1570 E Colorado Blvd, Pasadena, CA, 91106-2003. Tel: 626-585-7833. Fax: 626-585-7913. p. 206

Laun, Susan, Ch, Portsmouth Public Library, 175 Parrott Ave, Portsmouth, NH, 03801-4452. Tel: 603-766-1742. Fax: 603-433-0981. p. 1463

Laundy, Katherine, Mgr, Info Mgt, Public Service Labour Relations Board Library, West Tower, 6th Flr, 240 Sparks St, Ottawa, ON, K1P 5V2, CANADA. Tel: 613-990-1800. Fax: 613-990-1849. p. 2833

Laura, Beswick, Libr Mgr, Vancouver Island Regional Library, Port Alice Branch, Marine Dr, Port Alice, BC, V0N 2N0, CANADA. Tel: 250-284-3554. Fax: 250-284-3557. p. 2733

Laura, Dixon, ILL, Mary Imogene Bassett Hospital, One Atwell Rd, Cooperstown, NY, 13326. Tel: 607-547-3115. Fax: 607-547-3006. p. 1609

Laura, Honaker, Br Mgr, Knox County Public Library System, Norwood Branch, 1110 Merchants Dr, Knoxville, TN, 37912-4704. Tel: 865-688-2454. Fax: 865-688-0677. p. 2242

Laurell, RoseAleta, Dir, Bell-Whittington Public Library, 2400 Memorial Pkwy, Portland, TX, 78374. Tel: 361-777-0921. Fax: 361-643-6411. p. 2372

Lauren, Robin, Adult Serv, Tinley Park Public Library, 7851 Timber Dr, Tinley Park, IL, 60477-3398. Tel: 708-532-0160, Ext 1. Fax: 708-532-2981. p. 709

Laurendine, Terry, Tech Serv, Museum of Western Art Library, 1550 Bandera Hwy, Kerrville, TX, 78028-9547. Tel: 830-896-2553. Fax: 830-257-5206. p. 2349

Laurenzi, Joseph, Libr Mgr, San Luis Obispo County Library, Los Osos Branch, 2075 Palisades Ave, Los Osos, CA, 93402. Tel: 805-528-1862. Fax: 805-528-7835. p. 254

Laurette, Sandra, Educ Curator, Art Museum of Southeast Texas Library, 500 Main St, Beaumont, TX, 77701. Tel: 409-832-3432. Fax: 409-832-8508. p. 2287

Lauricella, Susan, Head, Teen Serv, Wilton Library Association, 137 Old Ridgefield Rd, Wilton, CT, 06897-3019. Tel: 203-762-3950. Fax: 203-834-1166. p. 378

Lauricio, Ariel, ILL, California State University, 9001 Stockdale Hwy, Bakersfield, CA, 93311-1022. Tel: 661-664-3189. Fax: 661-654-3238. p. 123

Laurie, Carol, Br Librn, Monroe County Library System, Erie Branch, 2065 Erie Rd, Erie, MI, 48133-9757. Tel: 734-848-4420. Fax: 734-848-4420. p. 1210

Laurie, Carol, Br Librn, Monroe County Library System, Rasey Memorial, 4349 Oak St, Luna Pier, MI, 48157. Tel: 734-848-4572. Fax: 734-848-4572. p. 1210

Laurie, Mary, Librn, Hamburg Public Library, 35 N Third St, Hamburg, PA, 19526-1502. Tel: 610-562-2843. Fax: 610-562-8136. p. 2064

Laurito, Gerry, Circ/Adult Serv, Camp Verde Community Library, 130 Black Bridge Loop Rd, Camp Verde, AZ, 86322. Tel: 928-567-3414. Fax: 928-567-9583. p. 59

Lauritsen, Aimee, Circ, College of Eastern Utah Library, 451 E & 400 N, Price, UT, 84501. Tel: 435-613-5646. Fax: 435-613-5863. p. 2410

Lauritsen, David, Coll Develop, Dir, Montevideo-Chippewa County Public Library, 224 S First St, Montevideo, MN, 56265-1425. Tel: 320-269-6501. Fax: 320-269-8696. p. 1265

Lauritzen, Brenda, Ref Librn, County of Carleton Law Library, Ottawa Court House, 2004-161 Elgin St, Ottawa, ON, K2P 2K1, CANADA. Tel: 613-233-7386. Fax: 613-238-3788. p. 2830

Lauritzen, Heidi, Coordr, Circ, Iowa City Public Library, 123 S Linn St, Iowa City, IA, 52240. Tel: 319-887-6020. Fax: 319-356-5494. p. 822

Laursen, Irene, Instrul Serv Librn, Res, Wellesley College, Science Library, Science Ctr, 106 Central St, Wellesley, MA, 02481. Tel: 781-283-3084. Fax: 781-283-3642. p. 1135

Laursen, Janet, Librn, Aurelia Public Library, 232 Main St, Aurelia, IA, 51005. Tel: 712-434-5330. Fax: 712-434-5330. p. 795

Lausten, Heather, Librn, Grand Canyon University, 3300 W Camelback Rd, Phoenix, AZ, 85017-3030. Tel: 602-639-6641. Fax: 602-639-7835. p. 73

Laut, Chris, III, Dir, Law Libr, Liberty Mutual Group, 175 Berkeley St, 7th Flr, Boston, MA, 02116-5066. Tel: 617-357-9500, Ext 44192. Fax: 617-574-5830. p. 1062

Lautemann, Eva, Dir, Georgia Perimeter College, 555 N Indian Creek Dr, Clarkston, GA, 30021-2396. Tel: 678-891-3633. Fax: 404-298-4919. p. 525

Lautenslager, Theresa, Br Mgr, Whitman County Rural Library District, Rosalia Branch, 402 S Whitman Ave, Rosalia, WA, 99170. Tel: 509-523-3109. p. 2513

Lauver, Bonnie, Librn, Blackwater Regional Library, Windsor Public, 18 Duke St, Windsor, VA, 23487. Tel: 757-242-3046. Fax: 757-242-3726. p. 2458

Lauzier, Martine, Tech Serv, Institut de Recherches Cliniques de Montreal Library, 110 Pine Ave W, Rm 2340, Montreal, QC, H2W 1R7, CANADA. Tel: 514-987-5596. Fax: 514-987-5675. p. 2896

Lauzier, Renee, Ref Serv, Norton Rose Canada LLP Library, One Place Ville Marie, Ste 2500, Montreal, QC, H3B 1R1, CANADA. Tel: 514-847-4701. Fax: 514-286-5474. p. 2900

Lauzon, Helene, Chief Librn, Hopital Maisonneuve-Rosemont, 5415 boul de l'Assomption, Montreal, QC, H1T 2M4, CANADA. Tel: 514-252-3462. Fax: 514-252-3574. p. 2896

Lauzon, Marcelle, Ref Serv, College de Limoilou-Campus de Charlesbourg, 7600 Third Ave E, Charlesbourg, QC, G1H 7L4, CANADA. Tel: 418-647-6600, Ext 3611. p. 2880

Lauzon, Natalie, Circ, Per, Tech Serv, Morneau Sobeco Library, 500 Rene-Levesque Blvd W, Ste 1200, Montreal, QC, H2Z 1W7, CANADA. Tel: 514-878-9090, Ext 8299. Fax: 514-875-2673. p. 2900

Lauzon, Patti, Dir of Advan, Canadian Mental Health Association, 1400 Windsor Ave, Windsor, ON, N8X 3L9, CANADA. Tel: 519-255-7440. Fax: 519-255-7817. p. 2871

Lauzon, Sheila, Circ Librn, Libby Memorial Library, 27 Staples St, Old Orchard Beach, ME, 04064. Tel: 207-934-4351. p. 994

Lauzon-Albert, Angèle, Librn, Bibliotheque Publique de Moonbeam, 53 St-Aubin Ave, CP 370, Moonbeam, ON, P0L 1V0, CANADA. Tel: 705-367-2462. Fax: 705-367-2120. p. 2823

LaValla, Daniel, Dir of Libr Serv, Biblical Theological Seminary Library, 200 N Main St, Hatfield, PA, 19440-2499. Tel: 215-368-5000, Ext 123. Fax: 215-368-6906. p. 2067

LaValla, Daniel, Chair, Southeastern Pennsylvania Theological Library Association, c/o Biblical Seminary, 200 N Main St, Hatfield, PA, 19440. Tel: 215-368-5000, Ext 234. p. 2954

LaValle, Lise, Libr Tech, Agriculture Canada, 430 Gouin Blvd, Saint-Jean-Sur-Richelieu, QC, J3B 3E6, CANADA. Tel: 450-346-4494. Fax: 450-346-7740. p. 2911

LaVallee, Cindy, Librn, Manitoba Indigenous Culture-Educational Center, 119 Sutherland Ave, Winnipeg, MB, R2W 3C9, CANADA. Tel: 204-942-0228. Fax: 204-947-6564. p. 2756

LaVallee, Connie, Ch, Lebanon Public Library, 101 S Broadway, Lebanon, OH, 45036. Tel: 513-932-2665. Fax: 513-932-7323. p. 1909

Lavallee, Julie, Ref Serv, Norton Rose Canada LLP Library, One Place Ville Marie, Ste 2500, Montreal, QC, H3B 1R1, CANADA. Tel: 514-847-4701. Fax: 514-286-5474. p. 2900

LaVallee, Martha, Asst Dir, Woodbury Public Library, 16 County Rte 105, Highland Mills, NY, 10930-9802. Tel: 845-928-6162. Fax: 845-928-3079. p. 1636

Lavallee, Steven, In Charge, Brown University, Sciences Library, 201 Thayer St, Providence, RI, 02912. Tel: 401-863-3333. Fax: 401-863-9639. p. 2172

Lavelle, Mary Kay, Ref Serv, East Stroudsburg University, 216 Normal St, East Stroudsburg, PA, 18301-2999. Tel: 570-422-3154. Fax: 570-422-3151. p. 2051

Lavender, Beth, Ref Serv, Ad, Smiths Falls Public Library, 81 Beckwith St N, Smiths Falls, ON, K7A 2B9, CANADA. Tel: 613-283-2911. Fax: 613-283-9834. p. 2842

Laverdure, Paul, Coll Develop, Dir, University of Sudbury Library, 935 Ramsey Lake Rd, Sudbury, ON, P3E 2C6, CANADA. Tel: 705-673-5661, Ext 208. Fax: 705-673-4912. p. 2847

Lavergne, Yvonne, Asst Br Mgr, Evangeline Parish Library, Chataignier Branch, 6215 Charles Armand Jr St, Chataignier, LA, 70524. Tel: 337-885-2028. Fax: 337-885-2028. p. 971

Laverty, Bruce, Curator of Archit, Athenaeum of Philadelphia, 219 S Sixth St, East Washington Square, Philadelphia, PA, 19106-3794. Tel: 215-925-2688. Fax: 215-925-3755. p. 2103

Laverty, Corrine, Head, Educ Libr, Queen's University, Education Library, Duncan McArthur Hall, 511 Union St at Sir John A Macdonald Blvd, Kingston, ON, K7M 5R7, CANADA. Tel: 613-533-2191. Fax: 613-533-2010. p. 2814

Lavery, Linda, Dir, Eagle Free Library, 3413 School St, Bliss, NY, 14024. Tel: 585-322-7701. Fax: 585-322-7701. p. 1583

Lavigne, Diane, Librn, Bibliotheques Publiques de Longueuil, Succursale Georges-Dor, 2760 Chemin de Chambly, Longueuil, QC, J4L 1M7, CANADA. Tel: 450-463-7180. p. 2887

Lavigne, Guylaine, Libr Tech, College des Medecins du Quebec, 2170 Rene-Levesque Blvd W, Montreal, QC, H3H 2T8, CANADA. Tel: 514-933-4441, Ext 5253, 514-933-4441, Ext 5254. Fax: 514-933-9112. p. 2894

LaVigueur, Lynn, Tech Serv, Department of Veterans Affairs, 11201 Benton St, Loma Linda, CA, 92357. Tel: 909-422-3000, Ext 2970. Fax: 909-422-3164. p. 165

Lavigueur, Philippe, Librn, College Montmorency Bibliotheque, 475 Boul de L Avenir, Laval, QC, H7N 5H9, CANADA. Tel: 450-975-6274. Fax: 450-381-2263. p. 2886

Lavin, Lucianne, Dr, Dir, Institute for American Indian Studies, 38 Curtis Rd, Washington, CT, 06793-0260. Tel: 860-868-0518. Fax: 860-868-1649. p. 374

Lavin, Susan, Br Mgr, Kitsap Regional Library, Downtown Bremerton Branch, 612 Fifth St, Bremerton, WA, 98337-1416. Tel: 360-377-3955. Fax: 360-479-8206. p. 2510

LaVista, Susan, Dir, Hampton Bays Public Library, 52 Ponquogue Ave, Hampton Bays, NY, 11946-0207. Tel: 631-728-6241. Fax: 631-728-0166. p. 1633

Lavoie, Amy, Br Mgr, Catahoula Parish Library, Jonesville Branch, 205 Pond St, Jonesville, LA, 71343. Tel: 318-339-7070. Fax: 318-339-7073. p. 951

Lavoie, Julie, Librn, Bibliothèque Allard Regional Library, 104086 PTH 11, Saint Georges, MB, R0E 1V0, CANADA. Tel: 204-367-8443. Fax: 204-367-1780. p. 2751

LaVoie, Leah, Dir, Garfield County Library, 228 E Main St, Jordan, MT, 59337. Tel: 406-557-2297. p. 1384

Lavoie, Lisa, Dr, Dir of Libr Serv, Tunxis Community College Library, 271 Scott Swamp Rd, Farmington, CT, 06032. Tel: 860-255-3786. Fax: 860-255-3808. p. 340

Lavoie, Marie, Librn, Bibliotheque de St Isidore, PO Box 1168, St. Isidore, AB, T0H 3B0, CANADA. Tel: 780-624-8192. Fax: 780-624-8192. p. 2717

Lavoie, Marie, Dir, Bibliotheque d'Albert Rousseau, 711 ave Albert Rousseau, Sainte-Etienne, QC, G6J 1Z7, CANADA. Tel: 418-831-6492. Fax: 418-831-6107. p. 2910

Lavoie, Michele, Librn, Ministere des Finances Bibliotheque, 12 rue St Louis, Bureau 2-12, Quebec, QC, G1R 5L3, CANADA. Tel: 418-691-2256. Fax: 418-643-9911. p. 2906

Lavoie, Mireille, Asst Librn, Bibliotheque Publique de Fermont, 130 Le Carrefour CP 10, Fermont, QC, G0G 1J0, CANADA. Tel: 418-287-3227. Fax: 418-287-3274. p. 2882

Lavoie, Murielle, Adminr, Centre Hospitalier Robert-Giffard - Institut Universitaire en Sante Mentale, 2601 rue de la Canardiere, Quebec, QC, G1J 2G3, CANADA. Tel: 418-663-5000, Ext 6607. Fax: 418-666-9416. p. 2904

Lavoie, Odette, Sr Info Spec, Business Development Bank of Canada Research & Information Center, Five Place Ville Marie, 3rd Flr, Montreal, QC, H3B 5E7, CANADA. Tel: 514-283-7632. Fax: 514-283-0439. p. 2892

Lavoie, Rachel, Tech Serv Librn, Haut-Saint-Jean Regional Library, 15, rue de l'Église St, Ste 102, Edmundston, NB, E3V 1J3, CANADA. Tel: 506-735-2074. Fax: 506-735-2193. p. 2762

Lavoie, S, In Charge, Hopital Sainte-Anne, 305 boul des Anciens-Combattants, Sainte-Anne-de-Bellevue, QC, H9X 1Y9, CANADA. Tel: 514-457-3440. Fax: 514-457-2761. p. 2909

Lavoie, Steve, Actg Br Mgr, Oakland Public Library, Asian, 388 Ninth St, Ste 190, Oakland, CA, 94612. Tel: 510-238-3400. Fax: 510-238-4732. p. 198

Lavoie, Yvon, Libr Tech, Institut de Recherche d'Hydro-Quebec Bibliotheque, 1800 Lionel-Boulet Blvd, CP 1000, Varennes, QC, J3X 1S1, CANADA. Tel: 450-652-8999. Fax: 450-652-8040. p. 2914

Lavoie-Dohn, Rachael, Br Mgr, Ocean County Library, Island Heights Branch, 121 Central Ave, Island Heights, NJ, 08732. Tel: 732-270-6266. Fax: 732-270-0308. p. 1534

Law, Christine, Tech Serv Librn, Roosevelt University, 430 S Michigan Ave, Chicago, IL, 60605. Tel: 312-341-3642. Fax: 312-341-2425. p. 623

Law, Darnell, Librn, Appomattox Regional Library, Burrowsville, 18701 James River Dr, Disputanta, VA, 23842. Tel: 757-866-0659. p. 2472

Law, Darnell, Librn, Appomattox Regional Library, Carson Branch, 16101 Halligan Park Rd, Carson, VA, 23830. Tel: 434-246-2900. p. 2472

Law, Darnell, Librn, Appomattox Regional Library, Dinwiddie Branch, 14103 Boydton Plank Rd, Dinwiddie, VA, 23841. Tel: 804-469-9450. Fax: 804-469-9450. p. 2472

Law, Darnell, Librn, Appomattox Regional Library, McKenney Branch, 20707 First St, McKenney, VA, 23872-2703. Tel: 804-478-4866. Fax: 804-478-4866. p. 2472

Law, Darnell, Librn, Appomattox Regional Library, Rohoic, 7301 Boydton Plank Rd, Petersburg, VA, 23803. Tel: 804-732-4119. Fax: 804-732-4119. p. 2472

Law, Jill, Circ Librn, Marion Public Library, 1095 Sixth Ave, Marion, IA, 52302. Tel: 319-377-3412. Fax: 319-377-0113. p. 830

Law, John, Dir, Libr Serv, Aurora University, 315 S Gladstone, Aurora, IL, 60506-4877. Tel: 630-844-5437, 630-892-6431. Fax: 630-844-3848. p. 591

Law, Kendra, Librn, Rock Falls Public Library District, 1007 Seventh Ave, Rock Falls, IL, 61071. Tel: 815-626-3958. Fax: 815-626-8750. p. 696

Law, Mary Alice, Librn, Portage County Law Library, 241 S Chestnut St, Ravenna, OH, 44266. Tel: 330-297-3661. p. 1931

Law, Nancy, Ref Librn, YA Librn, Pease Public Library, One Russell St, Plymouth, NH, 03264-1414. Tel: 603-536-2616. Fax: 603-536-2369. p. 1462

Lawal, Linda D, Librn, East Central Regional Hospital, 100 Myrtle Blvd, Gracewood, GA, 30812. Tel: 706-790-2011, Ext 2183. Fax: 706-790-2247. p. 535

Lawal, Linda D, Librn, East Central Regional Hospital, Augusta Campus Library, 3405 Mike Padgett Hwy, Augusta, GA, 30906. Tel: 706-792-7227, 706-792-7228. p. 535

Lawler, Linda, Bus Mgr, North Country Library System, 22072 County Rte 190, Watertown, NY, 13601-1066. Tel: 315-782-5540. Fax: 315-782-6883. p. 1763

Lawler, Sylvia, Dir, Kimble County Library, 208 N Tenth St, Junction, TX, 76849. Tel: 325-446-2342. Fax: 325-446-3615. p. 2348

Lawless, Alan, Dir, Rogers State University Library, 1701 W Will Rogers Blvd, Claremore, OK, 74017-3252. Tel: 918-343-7716. Fax: 918-343-7897. p. 1960

Lawless, Deborah, Med Librn, Saint Vincent's Medical Center, One Shircliff Way, Jacksonville, FL, 32204. Tel: 904-308-8165. Fax: 904-308-2976. p. 454

Lawless, Jane, Dir, Curry College, 1071 Blue Hill Ave, Milton, MA, 02186-9984. Tel: 617-333-2245. Fax: 617-333-2164. p. 1106

Lawless, Lenard, Librn, Cape Breton University Library, 1250 Grand Lake Rd, Sydney, NS, B1P 6L2, CANADA. Tel: 902-563-1421. Fax: 902-563-1826. p. 2785

Lawless, Nichole, Dir, Madison Public Library, 208 W Third St, Madison, NE, 68748. Tel: 402-454-3500. Fax: 402-454-3376. p. 1408

Lawley, Jennifer, Cat Librn, West Georgia Regional Library, 710 Rome St, Carrollton, GA, 30117. Tel: 770-836-6711. Fax: 770-836-4787. p. 523

Lawlor, Susan, Cat, Thomas Nelson Community College Library, Wythe Hall 228, 99 Thomas Nelson Dr, Hampton, VA, 23666. Tel: 757-825-3530. Fax: 757-825-2870. p. 2468

Lawrence, Bethany, Mgr, Whedon Cancer Foundation Library, 30 S Scott St, Sheridan, WY, 82801-6308. Tel: 307-672-2941. Fax: 307-672-7273. p. 2660

Lawrence, Betty, Asst Dir, Cent Libr Serv, Rochester Public Library, 115 South Ave, Rochester, NY, 14604-1896. Tel: 585-428-8393. Fax: 585-428-8353. p. 1732

Lawrence, Cecelia C, Dir, North Platte Public Library, 120 W Fourth St, North Platte, NE, 69101-3993. Tel: 308-535-8036. Fax: 308-535-8296. p. 1410

Lawrence, Dan H, Dir, Prevention Information Center Library, Rocky Mountain Center for Health Promotion & Education, 7525 W 10th Ave, Lakewood, CO, 80214. Tel: 303-239-8633. Fax: 303-239-8428. p. 315

Lawrence, Deirdre E, Principal Librn, Brooklyn Museum of Art, Libraries & Archives, 200 Eastern Pkwy, Brooklyn, NY, 11238. Tel: 718-501-6307. Fax: 718-501-6125. p. 1590

Lawrence, Delores, Librn, Greensboro Public Library, McGirt-Horton, 2509 Phillips Ave, Greensboro, NC, 27405. Tel: 336-373-5810. Fax: 336-332-6458. p. 1796

Lawrence, Donna, Dir, Bristow Public Library, 111 W Seventh Ave, Bristow, OK, 74010-2401. Tel: 918-367-6562. Fax: 918-367-1156. p. 1959

Lawrence, Evonne Kelly, Circ Coordr, Loyola University New Orleans, 6363 Saint Charles Ave, New Orleans, LA, 70118-6195. Tel: 504-864-7111. Fax: 504-864-7247. p. 961

Lawrence, James, Dir, Mid-Michigan Library League, 210 1/2 N Mitchell, Cadillac, MI, 49601-1835. Tel: 231-775-3037. Fax: 231-775-1749. p. 2946

Lawrence, Janice, Dir, Zelienople Area Public Library, 227 S High St, Zelienople, PA, 16063-1319. Tel: 724-452-9330. Fax: 724-452-9318. p. 2160

Lawrence, Janna, Asst Dir, University of Iowa Libraries, Hardin Library for the Health Sciences, 600 Newton Rd, Iowa City, IA, 52242. Tel: 319-335-9871. Fax: 319-353-3752. p. 823

Lawrence, Jimmet G, Coordr, Lamar State College, 317 Stilwell Blvd, Port Arthur, TX, 77640. Tel: 409-984-6222. Fax: 409-984-6008. p. 2371

Lawrence, Justin, Librn, University of Texas at Brownsville & Texas Southmost College Library, 80 Fort Brown St, Brownsville, TX, 78521. Tel: 956-882-8221. Fax: 956-882-5495. p. 2292

Lawrence, Kathy, Librn, Woodgate Free Library, Woodgate Dr, Woodgate, NY, 13494. Tel: 315-392-4814. Fax: 315-392-4814. p. 1770

Lawrence, LaVonna, Librn, Florence Township Public Library, 1350 Hornberger Ave, Roebling, NJ, 08554. Tel: 609-499-0143. Fax: 609-499-0551. p. 1527

Lawrence, Lesley, Chairperson, Libr Media Serv Head Librn, John Abbott College, 21,275 Lakeshore Rd, Sainte-Anne-de-Bellevue, QC, H9X 3L9, CANADA. Tel: 514-457-6610, Ext 5335. p. 2910

Lawrence, Linda, Tech Serv, Reading Area Community College, Ten S Second St, Reading, PA, 19602. Tel: 610-372-4721, Ext 5033. Fax: 610-607-6254. p. 2133

Lawrence, Lisa, Dir, Franklin County Library, 100 Main St, Mount Vernon, TX, 75457. Tel: 903-537-4916. Fax: 903-537-4319. p. 2364

Lawrence, Lori, Access Serv Librn, Tyler Public Library, 201 S College Ave, Tyler, TX, 75702-7381. Tel: 903-593-7323. Fax: 903-531-1329. p. 2394

Lawrence, Mark, Actg Dir, Roxbury Community College Library, Academic Bldg, Rm 211, 1234 Columbus Ave, Boston, MA, 02120-3400. Tel: 617-541-5323. Fax: 617-933-7476. p. 1066

Lawrence, Mary Beth, Librn, New Mexico Rehabilitation Center Library, 31 Gail Harris Ave, Roswell, NM, 88203. Tel: 575-347-3467. Fax: 575-347-5177. p. 1561

Lawrence, Niki, Br Head, Toronto Public Library, Riverdale, 370 Broadview Ave, Toronto, ON, M4K 2M8, CANADA. Tel: 416-393-7720. Fax: 416-393-7424. p. 2863

Lawrence, Norine, Dir, Clifton Public Library, 101 School St, Clifton, AZ, 85533. Tel: 928-865-2461. Fax: 928-865-3014. p. 60

Lawrence, Patricia, Circ Asst, Hanover College, 121 Scenic Dr, Hanover, IN, 47243. Tel: 812-866-7176. Fax: 812-866-7172. p. 748

Lawrence, Peg, Syst Librn, Minnesota State University, Mankato, ML3097, Mankato, MN, 56001. Tel: 507-389-5952. Fax: 507-389-5155. p. 1257

Lawrence, Rhonda, Head, Cat, University of California Los Angeles Library, Hugh & Hazel Darling Law Library, 112 Law Bldg, Box 951458, 385 Charles E Young Dr E, Los Angeles, CA, 90095-1458. Tel: 310-825-7826. Fax: 310-825-1372. p. 178

Lawrence, Susie, Dir of Libr Serv, Lexington Public Library, 140 E Main St, Lexington, KY, 40507-1376. Tel: 859-231-5533. Fax: 859-231-5598. p. 920

Lawrence, Thomas A, Exec Dir, Poughkeepsie Public Library District, 93 Market St, Poughkeepsie, NY, 12601. Tel: 845-485-3445. Fax: 845-485-3789. p. 1723

Lawrence, Thomas E, Librn, New York State Department of Correctional Services, One Correction Way, Ogdensburg, NY, 13669. Tel: 315-393-0281. Fax: 315-393-0281, Ext 3299. p. 1709

Lawrimore, Erin, Univ Archivist, University of North Carolina at Greensboro, 320 Spring Garden St, Greensboro, NC, 27402. Tel: 336-334-5880. Fax: 336-334-5399. p. 1798

Lawruk, Michelle, Cat, YA Serv, Seneca Public Library District, 210 N Main St, Seneca, IL, 61360. Tel: 815-357-6566. Fax: 815-357-6568. p. 701

Lawry, Beth, Mgr, Customer Serv, Carnegie Library of Pittsburgh, 4400 Forbes Ave, Pittsburgh, PA, 15213-4080. Tel: 412-622-3150. Fax: 412-622-6278. p. 2122

Laws, Cindy, Dir, Peterstown Public Library, 23 College Ave, Peterstown, WV, 24963. Tel: 304-753-9568. Fax: 304-753-9684. p. 2569

Lawson, Brenda, Coll Serv, Massachusetts Historical Society Library, 1154 Boylston St, Boston, MA, 02215-3695. Tel: 617-646-0502. Fax: 617-859-0074. p. 1063

Lawson, Deb, Librn, Hayes Center Public Library, 402 Troth St, Hayes Center, NE, 69032. Tel: 308-286-3411. p. 1401

Lawson, Dianne, Librn, Platt Memorial Library, 279 Main St, Shoreham, VT, 05770-9759. Tel: 802-897-2647. p. 2435

Lawson, Dianne, Asst Librn, Bixby Memorial Free Library, 258 Main St, Vergennes, VT, 05491. Tel: 802-877-2211. Fax: 802-877-2411. p. 2437

Lawson, Dorothy, ILL/Doc Delivery Serv, McGill University Libraries, Howard Ross Library of Management, Samuel Bronfman Bldg, 1001 Sherbrooke St W, 2nd Flr, Montreal, QC, H3A 1G5, CANADA. Tel: 514-398-4690. Fax: 514-398-5046. p. 2899

Lawson, Gerry, Coordr, Oral Hist Lang Lab, Audrey & Harry Hawthorn Library & Archives at the UBC Museum of Anthropology, 6393 NW Marine Dr, Vancouver, BC, V6T 1Z2, CANADA. Tel: 604-822-4834. Fax: 604-822-2974. p. 2741

Lawson, Glenn, Circ, Massachusetts College of Liberal Arts, 375 Church St, Ste 9250, North Adams, MA, 01247. Tel: 413-662-5321. Fax: 413-662-5286. p. 1111

Lawson, Harla, Br Mgr, Delaware County District Library, 84 E Winter St, Delaware, OH, 43015. Tel: 740-666-1410. Fax: 740-369-0196. p. 1895

Lawson, Harla, Br Mgr, Delaware County District Library, Ostrander Branch, 75 N Fourth St, Ostrander, OH, 43061. Tel: 740-666-1410. Fax: 740-666-1437. p. 1895

Lawson, Heather, Br Head, First Regional Library, Hernando Public Library, 370 W Commerce St, Hernando, MS, 38632-2130. Tel: 662-429-4439. Fax: 662-429-8625. p. 1301

Lawson, Jennifer, Teen Serv, Grandview Heights Public Library, 1685 W First Ave, Columbus, OH, 43212. Tel: 614-486-2951. Fax: 614-481-7021. p. 1886

Lawson, Karen, Assoc Dean, Coll & Tech Serv, Iowa State University Library, 302 Parks Library, Ames, IA, 50011-2140. Tel: 515-294-1442, 515-294-1443. Fax: 515-294-5525. p. 793

Lawson, Keith, Dr, Asst Prof, Dalhousie University, 6100 University Ave, Halifax, NS, B3H 3J5, CANADA. Tel: 902-494-3656. Fax: 902-494-2451. p. 2978

Lawson, Kristen, Ch, Allerton Public Library District, 201 N State St, Monticello, IL, 61856. Tel: 217-762-4676. Fax: 217-762-2021. p. 675

Lawson, Laura, Librn, Mid-Mississippi Regional Library System, Lexington Public, 208 Tchula St, Lexington, MS, 39095-3134. Tel: 662-834-2571. Fax: 662-834-4578. p. 1306

Lawson, Maggie, Br Supvr, Madison County Library System, Flora Public Library, 168 Carter St No C, Flora, MS, 39071. Tel: 601-879-8835. Fax: 601-879-8835. p. 1295

Lawson, Maggie, Pub Serv Dir, Webmaster, Madison County Library System, 102 Priestley St, Canton, MS, 39046-4599. p. 1295

Lawson, Martha, Br Librn, Bolivar County Library System, Gunnison Public Library, 404 Main St, Gunnison, MS, 38746. Tel: 662-747-2201. p. 1296

Lawson, Martha, Br Librn, Bolivar County Library System, Rosedale Public Library, 702 Front St, Rosedale, MS, 38769. Tel: 662-759-6632. Fax: 662-759-6332. p. 1296

Lawson, Matthew, Head, Tech Serv, Info Tech, Fayetteville State University, 1200 Murchison Rd, Fayetteville, NC, 28301-4298. Tel: 910-672-1546. Fax: 910-672-1746. p. 1793

Lawson, Michele B, Br Mgr, Tech Serv, Middlesborough-Bell County Public Library, 126 S 20th St, Middlesboro, KY, 40965-1212. Tel: 606-248-4812. Fax: 606-248-8766. p. 929

Lawson, Mildred, Br Librn, Russell County Public Library, 94 N Main, Jamestown, KY, 42629. Tel: 270-866-5200. Fax: 270-343-2019. p. 919

Lawson, Mildred, Br Librn, Russell County Public Library, Russell Springs Branch, 512 Main St, Russell Springs, KY, 42642-4356. Tel: 270-866-5200. Fax: 270-866-5201. p. 919

Lawson, Rhea, PhD, Dr, Dir, Houston Public Library, 500 McKinney Ave, Houston, TX, 77002-2534. Tel: 832-393-1313. Fax: 832-393-1324. p. 2338

Lawson, Rickey, Tech Serv, Mountain Empire Community College, 3441 Mountain Empire Rd, Big Stone Gap, VA, 24219. Tel: 276-523-2400, Ext 267. Fax: 276-523-8220. p. 2451

Lawson, Roger, Admin Librn, National Gallery of Art Library, Fourth St & Constitution Ave NW, Washington, DC, 20565. Tel: 202-842-6511. Fax: 202-789-3068. p. 409

Lawson, Rose, Acq, Ser, Kenrick-Glennon Seminary, 5200 Glennon Dr, Saint Louis, MO, 63119. Tel: 314-792-6131. Fax: 314-792-6503. p. 1355

Lawson, Sabrina, Librn, Shoshoni Public Library, 216 Idaho St, Shoshoni, WY, 82649. Tel: 307-876-2777. Fax: 307-876-2777. p. 2660

Lawson, Scott, Dir, Plumas County Museum Library, 500 Jackson St, Quincy, CA, 95971. Tel: 530-283-6320. Fax: 530-283-6081. p. 212

Lawson, Sharon, Librn, Fowler Public Library, 114 E Cranston Ave, Fowler, CO, 81039-1198. Tel: 719-263-4472. Fax: 719-263-5845. p. 308

Lawson, Wayne, Archivist, Washington State Office of Secretary of State, 1129 Washington St SE, Olympia, WA, 98504-2283. Tel: 360-753-1684. Fax: 360-664-2803. p. 2523

Lawton, Amy, Tech Serv, Swansea Free Public Library, 69 Main St, Swansea, MA, 02777. Tel: 508-674-9609. Fax: 508-675-5444. p. 1130

Lawton, Catherine, Head, Pub Serv, Memorial University of Newfoundland, Fisheries & Marine Institute - Dr C R Barrett Library, 155 Ridge Rd, St. John's, NL, A1C 5R3, CANADA. Tel: 709-778-0662. Fax: 709-778-0316. p. 2772

Lawton, Kelley, Head, Lilly Libr, Duke University Libraries, 411 Chapel Dr, Durham, NC, 27708. Tel: 919-660-5990. Fax: 919-660-5999. p. 1787

Lawton, LaRoi, Media Spec, Bronx Community College Library & Learning Center, 106 Meister Hall, 2115 University Ave, Bronx, NY, 10453. Tel: 718-289-5348. Fax: 718-289-6471. p. 1586

Lawton, Sarah, Teen Serv Librn, San Miguel County Public Library District 1, 100 W Pacific Ave, Telluride, CO, 81435-2189. Tel: 970-728-4519. Fax: 970-728-3340. p. 323

Lawton, Sarah, Youth Serv Librn, Ilsley Public Library, 75 Main St, Middlebury, VT, 05753. Tel: 802-388-4097. Fax: 802-388-4367. p. 2428

Lawver, Denise, Libr Dir, Wahoo Public Library, 637 N Maple St, Wahoo, NE, 68066-1673. Tel: 402-443-3871. Fax: 402-443-3877. p. 1422

Laxdal, Brenda, Librn, Parkland Regional Library, Wynyard Branch, 431 Bosworth St, Wynyard, SK, S0A 4T0, CANADA. Tel: 306-554-3321. p. 2932

Laxminarayan, Ishwar, Dir, Jackson District Library, 290 W Michigan Ave, Jackson, MI, 49201. Tel: 517-788-4099, Ext 1309. Fax: 517-782-8635. p. 1195

Laxton, Julie, Human Res Dir, Capital Area District Libraries, 401 S Capitol Ave, Lansing, MI, 48933. Tel: 517-367-6349. Fax: 517-374-1068. p. 1200

Lay, Lynn B, Librn, Byrd Polar Research Center, 176 Scott Hall, 1090 Carmack Rd, Columbus, OH, 43210-1002. Tel: 614-292-6715. Fax: 614-292-4697. p. 1883

Lay, Nora, Br Head, Toronto Public Library, Evelyn Gregory, 120 Trowell Ave, Toronto, ON, M6M 1L7, CANADA. Tel: 416-394-1006. Fax: 416-394-1035. p. 2861

Lay, Shirley, Librn, Harbor Hospital Center, S Main Bldg, Rm 112, 3001 S Hanover St, Baltimore, MD, 21225-1290. Tel: 410-350-3419. Fax: 410-350-2032. p. 1014

Lay, Tracy Elizabeth, Lead Librn, West Desert Technical Information Center, TEDT-DPW-DST, MS No 5, 4531 B St, Rm 116, Dugway, UT, 84022-5005. Tel: 435-831-5009. Fax: 435-831-3813. p. 2405

Laybourn, Connie, ILL, Deer Park Public Library, 3009 Center St, Deer Park, TX, 77536-5099. Tel: 281-478-7208. Fax: 281-478-7212. p. 2311

Laycock, Mary, Librn, National Park Service, 26611 US Hwy 385, Hot Springs, SD, 57747. Tel: 605-745-4600. Fax: 605-745-4207. p. 2213

Layden, James E, Dir, Ohio Dominican University Library, 1216 Sunbury Rd, Columbus, OH, 43219. Tel: 614-251-4758. Fax: 614-252-2650. p. 1886

Layel, Gaye, Librn, Boonville Community Public Library, 121 W Main St, Boonville, NC, 27011-9125. Tel: 336-367-7737. Fax: 336-367-7767. p. 1777

Laygues, Donna, Circ, Harrison Public Library, Bruce Ave, Harrison, NY, 10528. Tel: 914-835-0324. Fax: 914-835-1564. p. 1634

Layland, Deen, Br Mgr, La Crosse County Library, Holmen Area, 103 State St, Holmen, WI, 54636. Tel: 608-526-4198. Fax: 608-526-3299. p. 2598

Layman, Eileen, Librn, Iona College, Rockland Graduate Center, Two Blue Hill Plaza, Concourse Level, Pearl River, NY, 10965. Tel: 845-620-1350. Fax: 845-620-1260. p. 1666

Layne, Alison, Librn, Charlotte County Library System, Port Charlotte Public, 2280 Aaron St, Port Charlotte, FL, 33952. Fax: 941-764-5571. p. 484

Layne, Ashley, Dir, Multimedia & Adult Serv, Spartanburg County Public Libraries, 151 S Church St, Spartanburg, SC, 29306-3241. Tel: 864-596-3500. Fax: 864-596-3518. p. 2205

Layne, Linda, Asst Librn, Cameron Public Library, 304 E Third St, Cameron, TX, 76520. Tel: 254-697-2401. Fax: 254-697-2401. p. 2294

Laynor, Barbara, Extn Serv, Camden County College Library, Rohrer E-Library, 1889 Rte 70 E, Cherry Hill, NJ, 08003. Tel: 856-874-6001, 856-874-6002. Fax: 856-874-6049. p. 1473

Laytham, Jenne, Asst Dir, Basehor Community Library District 2, 1400 158th St, Basehor, KS, 66007. Tel: 913-724-2828. Fax: 913-724-2898. p. 857

Layton, Beth, Dir, Northeastern Ohio Universities College of Medicine, 4209 State Rd 44, Rootstown, OH, 44272. Tel: 330-325-6611. Fax: 330-325-0522. p. 1932

Layton, Colleen, Dir, Michigan Municipal League Library, 1675 Green Rd, Ann Arbor, MI, 48105. Tel: 734-669-6320. Fax: 734-662-8083. p. 1151

Layton, Jennifer, Librn, Libr Dir, Gateway Medical Center Health Science Library, 651 Dunlop Lane, Clarksville, TN, 37040. Tel: 931-502-2085. Fax: 931-502-2086. p. 2229

Layton, Julia, Librn, Grace Grebing Public Library, 110 N Main, Dell City, TX, 79837. Tel: 915-964-2468, 915-964-2495, Ext 3000. Fax: 915-964-2468. p. 2312

Layton, Renee, Br Mgr, Sabine Parish Library, Pleasant Hill Branch, 8434 Bridges St, Pleasant Hill, LA, 71065. Tel: 318-796-2595. p. 956

Laz, Susan, Circ, Hudson Valley Community College, 80 Vandenburgh Ave, Troy, NY, 12180. Tel: 518-629-7336. Fax: 518-629-7509. p. 1756

Lazar, Tom, Libr Tech, Vancouver Community College, 250 W Pender St, Vancouver, BC, V6B 1S9, CANADA. Tel: 604-443-8566. Fax: 604-443-8588. p. 2743

Lazaris, Christine, Cat, Skokie Public Library, 5215 Oakton St, Skokie, IL, 60077-3680. Tel: 847-673-7774. Fax: 847-673-7797. p. 703

Lazidis, Jennifer, Ref Serv, Ad, Elmwood Park Public Library, 210 Lee St, Elmwood Park, NJ, 07407. Tel: 201-796-8888. Fax: 201-703-1425. p. 1484

Lazorwitz, Sharon, Asst Circ Librn, Texas Chiropractic College, 5912 Spencer Hwy, Pasadena, TX, 77505. Tel: 281-998-6049. Fax: 281-487-4168. p. 2369

Lazouskas, Lorraine, Coordr, Bibliog Control, Chicago State University, 9501 S Martin Luther King Jr Dr, LIB 440, Chicago, IL, 60628-1598. Tel: 773-995-2561. Fax: 773-995-3772. p. 610

Lazovi, Dorothy, Asst Librn, Schuylkill County Law Library, Schuylkill County Court Hourse, 401 N Second St, Pottsville, PA, 17901. Tel: 570-628-1235. Fax: 570-628-1017. p. 2131

Lazration, Herb, Br Head, Bridgeport Public Library, Old Mill Green, 1677-81 E Main St, Bridgeport, CT, 06608. Tel: 203-576-7634. p. 331

Lazration, Herb, Info Serv Librn, Bridgeport Public Library, 925 Broad St, Bridgeport, CT, 06604. Tel: 203-576-7403. Fax: 203-576-8255. p. 331

Lazun, Mary Jo, Head, Electronic & Non-Bk Serv, Maryland State Law Library, Courts of Appeal Bldg, 361 Rowe Blvd, Annapolis, MD, 21401-1697. Tel: 410-260-1430. Fax: 410-260-1572, 410-974-2063. p. 1010

Lazzari, Susan, Circ Supvr, Wyckoff Public Library, 200 Woodland Ave, Wyckoff, NJ, 07481. Tel: 201-891-4866. Fax: 201-891-3892. p. 1546

Le, Binh P, Assoc Librn, Pennsylvania State University, 1600 Woodland Rd, Abington, PA, 19001. Tel: 215-881-7426. Fax: 215-881-7423. p. 2025

Le Blanc, Lorraine, Ref, Cinematheque Quebecoise, 335 boul de Maisonneuve est, Montreal, QC, H2X 1K1, CANADA. Tel: 514-842-9768, Ext 262. Fax: 514-842-1816. p. 2893

Le, Christine, Mgr, Federal Reserve Bank of Philadelphia, 100 N Sixth St, 4th Flr, Philadelphia, PA, 19106. Tel: 215-574-6540. Fax: 215-574-3847. p. 2106

le Conge, Monique, Dir, Palo Alto City Library, 1213 Newell Rd, Palo Alto, CA, 94303-2907. Tel: 650-329-2436. Fax: 650-327-2033. p. 204

Le, Julie, In Charge, Metropolitan Museum of Art, The Irene Lewisohn Costume Reference Library, Costume Institute, 1000 Fifth Ave, New York, NY, 10028. Tel: 212-396-5233, 212-650-2723. Fax: 212-570-3970. p. 1686

Le, Loan, Tech Serv, United States District Court, 450 Golden Gate Ave, Box 36060, San Francisco, CA, 94102. Tel: 415-436-8130. Fax: 415-436-8134. p. 248

Le, Marianne, Coll Develop, Pub Serv, Everett Community College, 2000 Tower St, Everett, WA, 98201-1352. Tel: 425-388-9351. Fax: 425-388-9144. p. 2515

Le Veque, Anne, Dir, United States Conference of Catholic Bishops Library, 3211 Fourth St NE, Washington, DC, 20017-1194. Tel: 202-541-3193. Fax: 202-541-3322. p. 417

Lea, Eileen, Librn, Jarvie Public Library, PO Box 119, Jarvie, AB, T0G 1H0, CANADA. Tel: 780-954-3935. Fax: 780-954-3885. p. 2707

Lea, Joe, Media Spec, York Correctional Institution Library, 201 W Main St, Niantic, CT, 06357. Tel: 860-691-6810, 860-691-6814. Fax: 860-691-6864. p. 361

Leach, Alexandra, User Serv, Columbia College, 1301 Columbia College Dr, Columbia, SC, 29203-9987. Tel: 803-786-3338. Fax: 803-786-3700. p. 2187

Leach, Barbara, Automation Syst Coordr, Cumberland County Library System, 19 S West St, Carlisle, PA, 17013-2839. Tel: 717-240-7735. p. 2041

Leach, Bruce A, Head, Sci Libr, Ohio State University LIBRARIES, Biological Sciences & Pharmacy, 102 Riffe Bldg, 496 W 12th Ave, Columbus, OH, 43210-1214. Tel: 614-292-1744. Fax: 614-688-3123. p. 1887

Leach, Carol, Head, Ref, ILL, South Huntington Public Library, 145 Pidgeon Hill Rd, Huntington Station, NY, 11746. Tel: 631-549-4411. Fax: 631-549-1266. p. 1639

Leach, Cynthia J, Pub Serv Librn, Rowan County Public Library, 175 Beacon Hill Dr, Morehead, KY, 40351. Tel: 606-784-7137. Fax: 606-784-2130. p. 929

Leach, Gillian K, Exec Dir, Pioneer Historical Society of Bedford County Inc, 6441 Lincoln Hwy, Bedford, PA, 15522. Tel: 814-623-2011. Fax: 814-623-2011. p. 2032

Leach, Janet, Librn, Presence Mercy Medical Center, 1325 N Highland Ave, Aurora, IL, 60506. Tel: 630-801-2686. Fax: 630-801-2687. p. 592

Leach, Karen, Librn, Wheeling Hospital, Inc, One Medical Park, Wheeling, WV, 26003. Tel: 304-243-3308. Fax: 304-243-3329. p. 2575

Leach, Laura, Med Librn, Charlotte AHEC Library, Medical Education Bldg, 1000 Blythe Blvd, Charlotte, NC, 28203. Tel: 704-355-3129. Fax: 704-355-7138. p. 1781

Leach, Laura Mae, Br Mgr, Riverside County Library System, Louis Robidoux Library, 5840 Mission Blvd, Jurupa Valley, CA, 92509. Tel: 951-682-5485. Fax: 951-682-8641. p. 218

Leach, Leslie Corey, Head Librn, Skadden, Arps, Slate, Meagher & Flom LLP Library, One Rodney Sq, 7th Flr, 920 N King St, Wilmington, DE, 19801. Tel: 302-651-3224. Fax: 302-651-3001. p. 388

Leach, Martha, Librn, Halifax County Library, Scotland Neck Memorial, 1600 Main St, Scotland Neck, NC, 27874-1438. Tel: 252-826-5578. Fax: 252-826-5037. p. 1799

Leach, Michael, Coll Develop, Harvard Library, Godfrey Lowell Cabot Science Library, Science Center, One Oxford St, Cambridge, MA, 02138. Tel: 617-495-7091. Fax: 617-495-5324. p. 1074

Leach, Michael, Head, Coll Develop, Harvard Library, History of Science Library - Cabot Science Library, Science Center, One Oxford St, Cambridge, MA, 02138. Tel: 617-495-5355. Fax: 617-495-5324. p. 1075

Leach, Nellie, Dir, Paw Paw Public Library, 250 Moser Ave, Paw Paw, WV, 25434-9500. Tel: 304-947-7013. Fax: 304-947-7013. p. 2569

Leach, Pat, Libr Dir, Lincoln City Libraries, 136 S 14th St, Lincoln, NE, 68508-1899. Tel: 402-441-8510. Fax: 402-441-8586. p. 1404

Leach, Sandra, Br Mgr, University of Tennessee, Knoxville, Agriculture-Veterinary Medicine, A-113 Veterinary Teaching Hospital, 2407 Joe Johnson Dr, Knoxville, TN, 37996-4541. Tel: 865-974-7922. Fax: 865-974-4732. p. 2244

Leach-Murray, Susan, Tech & Technical Serv Librn, Franklin College, 101 Branigin Blvd, Franklin, IN, 46131-2623. Tel: 317-738-8164. Fax: 317-738-8787. p. 743

Leache, Kathryn, Head, Ad Ref Serv, Lucius E & Elsie C Burch Library, 501 Poplar View Pkwy, Collierville, TN, 38017. Tel: 901-457-2600. Fax: 901-854-5893. p. 2230

Leachman, Chelsea, Teen Serv, Whitman County Rural Library District, 102 S Main St, Colfax, WA, 99111-1863. Tel: 509-397-4366. Fax: 509-397-6156. p. 2512

Leachman, Deanna, Actg Commun Libr Mgr, Contra Costa County Library, Antioch Community Library, 501 W 18th St, Antioch, CA, 94509-2292. Tel: 925-757-9224. Fax: 925-427-8540. p. 209

Leadbetter, Laurie, Ref, Carolina Population Center Library, University of North Carolina at Chapel Hill, 302 University Sq E, 123 W Franklin St, Chapel Hill, NC, 27516-2524. Tel: 919-962-3081. Fax: 919-962-7217. p. 1780

Leader, Jeanne, Dean, Arts & Learning Res, Everett Community College, 2000 Tower St, Everett, WA, 98201-1352. Tel: 425-388-9502. Fax: 425-388-9144. p. 2515

Leader, Katharine M, Circ Mgr, Lancaster Public Library, 125 N Duke St, Lancaster, PA, 17602-2883. Tel: 717-394-2651, Ext 102. Fax: 717-394-2651. p. 2077

Leader, Linda, Librn, Niobrara Public Library, 25414 Park Ave, Ste 3, Niobrara, NE, 68760. Tel: 402-857-3565. Fax: 402-857-3824. p. 1409

Leader, Shelley, City Librn, Helen Hall Library, 100 W Walker, League City, TX, 77573-3899. Tel: 281-554-1109. Fax: 281-554-1118. p. 2354

Leahey, Thomas, Lead Libr Tech, University of Washington Libraries, Engineering Library, Engineering Library Bldg, Box 352170, Seattle, WA, 98195-2170. Tel: 206-543-5107. Fax: 206-543-3305. p. 2533

Leahy, Germaine, Head, Ref, George Washington University, Jacob Burns Law Library, 716 20th St NW, Washington, DC, 20052. Tel: 202-994-8551. Fax: 202-994-2874. p. 402

Leahy, Kathleen, Head, Ref, Hingham Public Library, 66 Leavitt St, Hingham, MA, 02043. Tel: 781-741-1405. Fax: 781-749-0956. p. 1095

Leak, Carl, Assoc Dir, Res & Instruction, Winston-Salem State University, 601 Martin Luther King Jr Dr, Winston-Salem, NC, 27110. Tel: 336-750-2453. Fax: 336-750-2459. p. 1834

Leal, Adria, Librn, Miami Dade College, Wolfson Campus Library, 300 NE Second Ave, Miami, FL, 33132. Tel: 305-237-3144. Fax: 305-237-3707. p. 466

Leal, Betty, Br Mgr, Dallas Public Library, Paul Laurence Dunbar Lancaster-Kiest Branch, 2008 E Kiest St, Dallas, TX, 75216-4448. Tel: 214-670-1952. Fax: 214-670-0588. p. 2306

Leal, Betty, Br Mgr, Dallas Public Library, Highland Hills, 3624 Simpson Stuart Rd, Dallas, TX, 75241-4399. Tel: 214-670-0987. Fax: 214-670-0318. p. 2307

Leal, Maria Angela, Asst Curator, Catholic University of America, Oliveira Lima Library, 22 Mullen Library, 620 Michigan Ave NE, Washington, DC, 20064. Tel: 202-319-5059. Fax: 202-319-4735. p. 396

Leal, Monika, Dir, Info Serv, The Miami Herald, One Herald Plaza, Miami, FL, 33132. Tel: 305-376-3665. Fax: 305-376-4424, 305-995-8183. p. 467

Leali, Sharon, Youth Serv, Jackson City Library, 21 Broadway St, Jackson, OH, 45640-1695. Tel: 740-286-4111. Fax: 740-286-3438. p. 1906

Leamon, Lois, Librn, Downey Avenue Christian Church Library, 111 S Downey Ave, Indianapolis, IN, 46219. Tel: 317-359-5304. p. 750

Leane, Judy, Children's/Ref Librn, Florham Park Public Library, 107 Ridgedale Ave, Florham Park, NJ, 07932. Tel: 973-377-2694. Fax: 973-377-2085. p. 1486

Leap, Steven, Librn, United States Army, Moncrief Army Hospital Medical Library, 4500 Stuart St, Fort Jackson, SC, 29207-5720. Tel: 803-751-2149. Fax: 803-751-2012. p. 2194

Leaper, Margaret, Chief Exec Officer, Cobalt Public Library, 30 Lang St, Cobalt, ON, P0J 1C0, CANADA. Tel: 705-679-8120. Fax: 705-679-8120. p. 2800

Lear, Bernadette A, Behav Sci & Educ Ref Librn, Coordr, Instruction & Outreach, Pennsylvania State University-Harrisburg Library, 351 Olmsted Dr, Middletown, PA, 17057-4850. Tel: 717-948-6360. Fax: 717-948-6757. p. 2089

Lear, Brett W, Libr Dir, Martin County Library System, 2351 SE Monterey Rd, Stuart, FL, 34996. Tel: 772-221-1410. Fax: 772-219-4959. p. 491

Lear, Joy, Br Mgr, Ada Community Library, Star Branch, 10706 W State St, Star, ID, 83669. Tel: 208-286-9755. Fax: 208-286-9755. p. 570

Lear, Paul, Mgr, New York State Office of Parks, Recreation & Historic Preservation, One E Fourth St, Oswego, NY, 13126. Tel: 315-343-4711. Fax: 315-343-1430. p. 1713

Leard, Sharon, Libr Tech, Prince Edward Island Public Library Service, Borden-Carleton Public, 244 Borden Ave, Borden, PE, C0B 1X0, CANADA. Tel: 902-437-6492. p. 2876

Learned, Elizabeth Peck, Assoc Dean, Libr Serv, Roger Williams University Library, One Old Ferry Rd, Bristol, RI, 02809. Tel: 401-254-3625. Fax: 401-254-3631. p. 2164

Leary, Christopher, Head, Ref, Delray Beach Public Library, 100 W Atlantic Ave, Delray Beach, FL, 33444. Tel: 561-819-6406. Fax: 561-266-9757. p. 437

Leary, Deborah, Head, Circ, Closter Public Library, 280 High St, Closter, NJ, 07624-1898. Tel: 201-768-4197. Fax: 201-768-4220. p. 1479

Leary, Debra, Br Mgr, Rochester Public Library, Arnett, 310 Arnett Blvd, Rochester, NY, 14619. Tel: 585-428-8214. p. 1732

Leary, Dianne, Ch, Melbourne Beach Public Library, 324 Ocean Ave, Melbourne Beach, FL, 32951. Tel: 321-956-5642. Fax: 321-953-6942. p. 464

Leary, Margaret A, Dir, University of Michigan, Law Library, 801 Monroe St, Ann Arbor, MI, 48109-1210. Tel: 734-764-9322. Fax: 734-615-0178. p. 1152

Leary, Patricia, Pub Serv, Lindenhurst Memorial Library, One Lee Ave, Lindenhurst, NY, 11757-5399. Tel: 631-957-7755. Fax: 631-957-7114. p. 1652

Leary, Pauline, Librn, Transamerica Occidental Life Insurance, 1150 S Olive St, Ste T-2100, Los Angeles, CA, 90015-2211. Tel: 213-742-5237. Fax: 213-741-6623. p. 178

Leary, Roman, Asst Dir, Ref Librn, Edgecombe County Memorial Library, 909 Main St, Tarboro, NC, 27886. Tel: 252-823-1141. Fax: 252-823-7699. p. 1826

Leath, Janis, Librn, University of Wyoming Libraries, Rocky Mountain Herbarium Reference Collection, Dept 3262, 1000 E University Ave, Laramie, WY, 82071. Tel: 307-766-2236. Fax: 307-766-5588. p. 2658

Leathe, Agnes, Librn, Massachusetts Trial Court, 57 Providence Hwy, Norwood, MA, 02062. Tel: 781-769-7483. Fax: 781-769-7836. p. 1115

Leather, Anne, Asst Mgr, Libr Serv, Jones Day, 2727 N Harwood St, Dallas, TX, 75201-1515. Tel: 214-969-4823. Fax: 214-969-5100. p. 2308

Leatherman, Rita, Librn, Amarillo Globe-News Library, 900 Harrison, Amarillo, TX, 79166-2091. Tel: 806-345-3331. Fax: 806-373-0810. p. 2274

Leathley, Alison, Sr Libr Assoc, KPMG LLP, 355 S Grand Ave, Ste 2000, Los Angeles, CA, 90017-1568. Tel: 213-972-4000. Fax: 213-622-1217. p. 171

Leathorn, Jeanette, Dir, Ogemaw District Library, 107 W Main St, Rose City, MI, 48654. Tel: 989-685-3300. Fax: 989-685-3647. p. 1223

Leavens, Dorothy, Ch, Greene Public Library, 231 W Traer, Greene, IA, 50636-9406. Tel: 641-816-5642. Fax: 641-816-4838. p. 819

Leaver, Pauline, Ch, Greenville Public Library, 573 Putnam Pike, Greenville, RI, 02828-2195. Tel: 401-949-3630. Fax: 401-949-0530. p. 2166

Leavins, Ann, Asst Dir, Holmes County Public Library, 303 N J Harvey Etheridge, Bonifay, FL, 32425. Tel: 850-547-3573. Fax: 850-547-2801. p. 429

Leavitt, Carolynn, Br Assoc, Las Vegas-Clark County Library District, Bunkerville Library, Ten W Virgin St, Bunkerville, NV, 89007. Tel: 702-346-5238. Fax: 702-346-5784. p. 1429

Leavitt, John, Librn, Washington County Community College Library, One College Dr, Calais, ME, 04619. Tel: 207-454-1000. Fax: 207-454-1053. p. 980

Leavitt, Laura, Coordr, Michigan State University Library, Labor & Industrial Relations, 50 College Law Bldg, East Lansing, MI, 48824. Tel: 517-355-4647. Fax: 517-353-6648. p. 1175

Leavy, Claire, Dir, Lee County Public Library, 245 Walnut Ave S, Leesburg, GA, 31763-4367. Tel: 229-759-2369. Fax: 229-759-2326. p. 539

Leazer, Gregory, Chair, University of California, Los Angeles, 2320 Moore Hall, Mail Box 951521, Los Angeles, CA, 90095-1521. Tel: 310-825-8799. Fax: 310-206-3076. p. 2962

LeBar, Diane E, Sr Ref Librn, Oakwood Hospital Medical Library, 18101 Oakwood Blvd, Dearborn, MI, 48124-2500. Tel: 313-593-7685. Fax: 313-436-2699. p. 1167

LeBaron, C Frederick, Head, Coll Develop, Head, Fac Serv, Loyola University Chicago Libraries, Law School Library, 25 E Pearson St, 3rd Flr, Chicago, IL, 60611. Tel: 312-918-6842. Fax: 312-915-6797. p. 617

LeBaron, Tonya, Br Mgr, Winn Parish Library, Dodson Branch, 206 E Gresham, Dodson, LA, 71422. Tel: 318-628-2821. p. 972

Lebby, Kathleen, Head, Ch, New Castle Public Library, 207 E North St, New Castle, PA, 16101-3691. Tel: 724-658-6659. Fax: 724-658-7209. p. 2096

LeBeau, Chris, Asst Teaching Prof, Kans City, University of Missouri-Columbia, 303 Townsend Hall, Columbia, MO, 65211. Tel: 573-882-4546. Fax: 573-884-2917. p. 2969

Lebeau, Nicole, Support Serv Coordr, Martin County Library System, 2351 SE Monterey Rd, Stuart, FL, 34996. Tel: 772-221-1404. Fax: 772-221-1404. p. 491

LeBeau, Tamera, Asst Dir, Livermore Public Library, 1188 S Livermore Ave, Livermore, CA, 94550. Tel: 925-373-5500. Fax: 925-373-5503. p. 164

Lebeba, Betty, Librn, Medford Public Library, 123 S Main St, Medford, OK, 73759. Tel: 580-395-2801. Fax: 580-395-2342. p. 1968

Lebel, Anne, Dir, Bibliotheque Municipale de la Baie, 1911 Sixth Ave, La Baie, QC, G7B 1S1, CANADA. Tel: 418-697-5085. Fax: 418-697-5087. p. 2885

Lebel, Clement, Dir of Tech Serv, Assemblee Nationale du Quebec Bibliotheque, 1035 Rue des Parlementaires, Edifice Pamphile-Lemay, Quebec, QC, G1A 1A3, CANADA. Tel: 418-528-1262. Fax: 418-646-4873. p. 2903

Lebel, Elisabeth, Librn, College LaSalle, Bureau 4100, 2000 Saint Catherine St W, Montreal, QC, H3H 2T2, CANADA. Tel: 514-939-2006, Ext 4470. Fax: 514-939-7292. p. 2894

Lebele, Marc, Dept Head, Montreal City Hall, 275 Notre Dame St E, R-113, Montreal, QC, H2Y 1C6, CANADA. Tel: 514-872-9092. Fax: 514-872-3475. p. 2899

Leber, Terese, Syst Librn, East-West Center, 1601 East-West Rd, Honolulu, HI, 96848-1601. Tel: 808-944-7405. Fax: 808-944-7600. p. 560

LeBert-Corbello, Linda, PhD, Dir, Jefferson Davis Parish Library, 118 W Plaquemine St, Jennings, LA, 70546-5856. Tel: 337-824-1210. Fax: 337-824-5444. p. 952

Lebish, Alan, Assoc Libr Dir, Kennesaw State University, 1000 Chastain Rd, Kennesaw, GA, 30144. Tel: 770-423-6192. Fax: 770-423-6185. p. 537

LeBlanc, Anne, In Charge, Eastern Counties Regional Library, Coady & Tompkins Memorial, 7972 Cabot Trail Hwy, General Delivery, Margaree Forks, NS, B0E 2A0, CANADA. Tel: 902-248-2821. Fax: 902-248-2821. p. 2783

LeBlanc, Claire, Ref Serv, Ad, Oldsmar Library, 400 St Petersburg Dr E, Oldsmar, FL, 34677. Tel: 813-749-1178. Fax: 813-854-1881. p. 474

LeBlanc, Diana, Tech Serv Librn, Wadleigh Memorial Library, 49 Nashua St, Milford, NH, 03055-3753. Tel: 603-673-2408. Fax: 603-672-6064. p. 1457

LeBlanc, Donald, Ref, Friendswood Public Library, 416 S Friendswood Dr, Friendswood, TX, 77546-3897. Tel: 281-482-7135. Fax: 281-482-2685. p. 2325

LeBlanc, Donna, Librn, Rapides Parish Library, Mildred B Martin Branch, 801 W Shamrock, Pineville, LA, 71360. Tel: 318-442-7575. Fax: 318-449-4946. p. 940

Leblanc, Gabrielle, Libr Mgr, Albert-Westmorland-Kent Regional Library, Shediac Public, 337 Main St, Unit 100, Shediac, NB, E4P 2B1, CANADA. Tel: 506-532-7000, Ext 244. Fax: 506-532-8400. p. 2765

LeBlanc, Jocelyne, Libr Mgr, Albert-Westmorland-Kent Regional Library, Memramcook Public, 540 Centrale St, Unit 1, Memramcook, NB, E4K 3S6, CANADA. Tel: 506-758-4029. Fax: 506-758-4079. p. 2765

LeBlanc, Joshua R, Info Tech Mgr, Vermilion Parish Library, 405 E Saint Victor, Abbeville, LA, 70510-5101. Tel: 337-893-2655. Fax: 337-898-0526. p. 939

LeBlanc, Linda, Access Serv, Fitchburg State College, 160 Pearl St, Fitchburg, MA, 01420. Tel: 978-665-3062. Fax: 978-665-3069. p. 1089

Leblanc, Louise, Librn, Centre Hospitalier de Charlevoix, 74 Blvd Ambroise-Fafard, Baie Saint-Paul, QC, G3Z 2J6, CANADA. Tel: 418-435-5150. Fax: 418-435-0212, 418-435-6451. p. 2879

LeBlanc, Michel, Librn, Bibliotheque Municipale Come-Saint-Germain, 545 rue des Ecoles, Drummondville, QC, J2B 1J6, CANADA. Tel: 819-474-8841, 819-478-6573. Fax: 819-478-0399. p. 2881

LeBlanc, Shelly, Librn, Onebane Law Firm APC, 1200 Camellia Blvd, Ste 300, Lafayette, LA, 70508. Tel: 337-237-2660, Ext 1152. Fax: 337-266-1232. p. 953

LeBlanc, Sylvie, Libr Mgr, Albert-Westmorland-Kent Regional Library, Bibliotheque Publique Gerald-Leblanc de Bouctouche, 84 boul Irving, Unite 100, Bouctouche, NB, E4S 3L4, CANADA. Tel: 506-743-7263. Fax: 506-743-7263. p. 2765

Leblant, Nicole, ILL, Mattawa Public Library, 370 Pine St, Mattawa, ON, P0H 1V0, CANADA. Tel: 705-744-5550. Fax: 705-744-1714. p. 2821

Leblond, Lyse, Asst Dir, Bibliotheque Municipale de Saint-Simeon, 502 St-Laurent, Saint-Simeon, QC, G0T 1X0, CANADA. Tel: 418-638-2691. p. 2911

LeBoeuf, Mary Cosper, Dir, Terrebonne Parish Library, 151 Library Dr, Houma, LA, 70360. Tel: 985-876-5861. Fax: 985-917-0582. p. 951

LeBoeuf, Nicole, Ser & Electronic Res Librn, Adams State University, 208 Edgemont Ave, Alamosa, CO, 81101-2373. Tel: 719-587-7173. Fax: 719-587-7590. p. 287

LeBouef, Susanna, Dir, Lafourche Parish Public Library, 303 W Fifth St, Thibodaux, LA, 70301-3123. Tel: 985-446-1163. Fax: 985-446-3848. p. 970

Lebowitz, Ruth, Librn, Long Beach Medical Center, 455 E Bay Dr, Long Beach, NY, 11561. Tel: 516-897-1012. Fax: 516-897-1077. p. 1654

Lebreche, Anne, Outreach Serv Librn, Plymouth State University, Highland St, Plymouth, NH, 03264-1595. Tel: 603-535-2258. Fax: 603-535-2445. p. 1462

LeBreton, Jonathan, Sr Assoc Univ Librn, Temple University Libraries, 1210 W Berks St, Philadelphia, PA, 19122-6088. Tel: 215-204-3184. Fax: 215-204-5201. p. 2117

Lebrunn, Corinne, Exec Dir, Alliance for Innovation in Science & Technology Information, 369 Montezuma Ave, No 237, Santa Fe, NM, 87501. p. 2949

Lechner, Judith, Prof, Auburn University, 4036 Haley Ctr, Auburn, AL, 36849-5221. Tel: 334-844-4460. Fax: 334-844-3072. p. 2961

Leckie, Gloria, Dr, Prog Coordr, University of Western Ontario, Faculty of Information & Media Studies, North Campus Bldg, Rm 240, London, ON, N6A 5B7, CANADA. Tel: 519-661-4017. Fax: 519-661-3506. p. 2978

Lecky, Joanne, Libr Dir, McCarthy Tetrault Library, 777 Dunsmuir St, No 1300, Vancouver, BC, V7Y 1K2, CANADA. Tel: 604-643-7100. Fax: 604-643-7900. p. 2741

LeClair, Andrea, Ref, Richard Salter Storrs Library, 693 Longmeadow St, Longmeadow, MA, 01106. Tel: 413-565-4181. Fax: 413-565-4183. p. 1100

LeClair, Jocelyne, Librn, Bibliotheque Municipale JR L'Heureux, 14 Comeau St, Maniwaki, QC, J9E 2R8, CANADA. Tel: 819-449-2738. p. 2887

Leclair, Julie, Bibliothecaire Responsable, Bibliothèques de Montrèal, Saint-Léonard, 8420, boulevard Lacordaire, Montreal, QC, H1R 3G5, CANADA. Tel: 514-328-8500, Ext 8521. Fax: 514-328-7002. p. 2891

LeClair, Marcy, Dir, Keene Public Library, Main St, Keene, NY, 12942. Tel: 518-576-2200. Fax: 518-576-2200. p. 1648

LeClair, Susan, Librn, Elkins Public Library, Nine Center Rd, Canterbury, NH, 03224. Tel: 603-783-4386. Fax: 603-783-4817. p. 1440

Leclair-Marzolf, Marsha, Assoc Dir, Coll Mgt, Salt Lake County Library Services, 2197 E Fort Union Blvd, Salt Lake City, UT, 84121-3139. Tel: 801-943-4636. Fax: 801-942-6323. p. 2413

LeClaire, Sarah, In Charge, Caribou Law Library, 144 Sweden, Caribou, ME, 04736. Tel: 207-762-2244. p. 981

LeClerc, Joyce, Librn, Androscoggin Valley Hospital, 59 Page Hill Rd, Berlin, NH, 03570. Tel: 603-326-5833. Fax: 603-752-2501. p. 1439

Leclerc, Manon, Coordr, Institut de la Statistique du Quebec, 200 Chemin Ste Foy, 3e etage, Quebec, QC, G1R 5T4, CANADA. Tel: 418-691-2401. Fax: 418-643-4129. p. 2905

LeClevc, Jocelyne, Info Spec, Pfizer Canada, Inc, 17300 Trans-Canada Hwy, Pointe-Claire, QC, H9J 2M5, CANADA. Tel: 514-426-7060. Fax: 514-426-7558. p. 2903

Lecnar, Kathy, Dir, Colfax Public Library, 25 W Division St, Colfax, IA, 50054. Tel: 515-674-3625. p. 803

Lecompte, Louis-Luc, Head of Libr, CHU Sainte-Justine, 3175 Chemin Cote-Sainte-Catherine, Montreal, QC, H3T 1C5, CANADA. Tel: 514-345-4681. Fax: 514-345-4806. p. 2893

LeCroy, Emma, Br Mgr, Athens Regional Library System, Lavonia-Carnegie Branch, 28 Hartwell Rd, Lavonia, GA, 30553. Tel: 706-356-4307. Fax: 706-356-4307. p. 508

Ledbetter, Deborah, Tech Serv, Washington County Public Library, 205 Oak Hill St, Abingdon, VA, 24210. Tel: 276-676-6340. Fax: 276-676-6235. p. 2443

Ledbetter, Krista, Dir, Morgan County Public Library, 110 S Jefferson St, Martinsville, IN, 46151. Tel: 765-342-3451. Fax: 765-342-9992. p. 763

Ledbetter, Molly Dahlstrom, Ref Librn, Austin Community College, Cypress Creek Campus Library, 1555 Cypress Creek Rd, Cedar Park, TX, 78613. Tel: 512-223-2137. Fax: 512-223-2035. p. 2278

Ledbetter, Sherry, Chairperson, Acq, Coll & Tech Proc, Harold Washington College Library, City Colleges of Chicago, 30 E Lake St, 5th Flr, Chicago, IL, 60601-9996. Tel: 312-553-5762. Fax: 312-553-5783. p. 614

Ledden, Stacie, Communications Mgr, Anythink Libraries, 5877 E 120th Ave, Thornton, CO, 80602. Tel: 303-288-2001. Fax: 303-451-0190. p. 323

Leddy, Brian, Adult Serv, Ref, New Milford Public Library, 200 Dahlia Ave, New Milford, NJ, 07646-1812. Tel: 201-262-1221. Fax: 201-262-5639. p. 1510

Leddy, Diane, Ref Librn, Hauppauge Public Library, 601 Veterans Memorial Hwy, Hauppauge, NY, 11788. Tel: 631-979-1600. Fax: 631-979-5457. p. 1634

Ledeboer, Nancy, Dir, Spokane County Library District, 4322 N Argonne Rd, Spokane, WA, 99212-1868. Tel: 509-893-8200. Fax: 509-893-8472. p. 2536

Ledee, Mikel, Libr Assoc, Louisiana State University Libraries, Carter Music Resources Center, 202 Middleton Library, Baton Rouge, LA, 70803-3300. Tel: 225-578-4674. Fax: 225-578-6825. p. 943

Leder, Susan, Librn, Phillips Community College of the University of Arkansas, 2807 Hwy 165 S, Box A, Stuttgart, AR, 72160. Tel: 870-673-4201, Ext 1819. Fax: 870-673-8166. p. 116

Ledermann, Molly, Ref Librn, Missoula Public Library, 301 E Main, Missoula, MT, 59802-4799. Tel: 406-721-2665. Fax: 406-728-5900. p. 1386

Ledet, Henry J, Dir, Lincoln-Lawrence-Franklin Regional Library, 100 S Jackson St, Brookhaven, MS, 39601-3347. Tel: 601-833-3369, 601-833-5038. Fax: 601-833-3381. p. 1294

Ledet, Sylvia, Br Mgr, Washington Parish Library System, Thomas, 30369 Hwy 424, Franklinton, LA, 70438. Tel: 985-848-7061. p. 950

Ledford, Barbara, Asst Br Mgr, Louisville Free Public Library, Crescent Hill, 2762 Frankfort Ave, Louisville, KY, 40206. Tel: 502-574-1793. Fax: 502-894-8505. p. 924

Ledford, Brandie, Dir, Sac City Public Library, 1001 W Main St, Sac City, IA, 50583. Tel: 712-662-7276. Fax: 712-662-7802. p. 841

Ledford, Brenda, Librn, McCoy Memorial Library, 118 S Washington St, McLeansboro, IL, 62859. Tel: 618-643-2125. Fax: 618-643-2207. p. 672

Ledford, Darlene, Br Librn, Carson County Public Library, Skellytown Branch, N Main St, Skellytown, TX, 79080. Tel: 806-848-2551. Fax: 806-848-2551. p. 2368

Ledford, Lisa, Librn, Madison County Public Library, Hot Springs Branch, 88 Bridge St, Hot Springs, NC, 28743-9645. Tel: 828-622-3584. Fax: 828-622-3584. p. 1809

Ledgerwood, Georgeanna E, Med Librn, Krohn Memorial Library, The Good Samaritan Hospital of Lebanon, Pennsylvania, Fourth & Walnut Sts, Lebanon, PA, 17042. Tel: 717-270-7826. Fax: 717-270-3882. p. 2079

Ledingham, Lori, Outreach Serv, Pub Relations, Meaford Public Library, 15 Trowbridge St W, Meaford, ON, N4L 1V4, CANADA. Tel: 519-538-1060, Ext 1123. Fax: 519-538-1808. p. 2821

Ledley, MacKenzie Inez, Exec Dir, Pulaski County Public Library, 121 S Riverside Dr, Winamac, IN, 46996-1596. Tel: 574-946-3432. Fax: 574-946-6598. p. 788

Ledoux, Louise, Dir, Crockett County Public Library, 1201 Ave G, Ozona, TX, 76943. Tel: 325-392-3565. Fax: 325-392-2941. p. 2367

LeDoux, Valinda D, Cat, Southern University, Oliver B Spellman Law Library, 56 Roosevelt Steptoe, Baton Rouge, LA, 70813. Tel: 225-771-2196. Fax: 225-771-6254. p. 944

Leduc, Colette, Librn, College Notre Dame Library, 3791 Queen Marie Rd, Montreal, QC, H3V 1A8, CANADA. Tel: 514-739-3371. Fax: 514-739-4833. p. 2894

Leduc, Isabelle, Circ, Ministere des Finances Bibliotheque, 12 rue St Louis, Bureau 2-12, Quebec, QC, G1R 5L3, CANADA. Tel: 418-644-7303. Fax: 418-643-9911. p. 2906

LeDuc, Janice, Asst Dir, Middlebury Public Library, 30 Crest Rd, Middlebury, CT, 06762. Tel: 203-758-2634. Fax: 203-577-4164. p. 351

Ledvina, Holly, Tech Serv Librn, College of Lake County, 19351 W Washington St, Grayslake, IL, 60030. Tel: 847-543-2461. Fax: 847-223-7690. p. 652

Ledvina, Holly, Cat Librn, Outagamie Waupaca Library System, 225 N Oneida, Appleton, WI, 54911-4780. Tel: 920-832-6190. Fax: 920-832-6422. p. 2578

Lee, Alex, Supvr, Circ, The Ferguson Library, One Public Library Plaza, 96 Broad St, Stamford, CT, 06904. Tel: 203-964-1000, Ext 8260. Fax: 203-357-9098. p. 369

Lee, Angela, Librn, University of Washington Libraries, Social Work, 252 Social Work Bldg, Box 354900, 15th Ave NE, Seattle, WA, 98195-4900. Tel: 206-685-2180. Fax: 206-685-7647. p. 2535

Lee, Anne, Mat Mgr, Free Library of Philadelphia, 1901 Vine St, Philadelphia, PA, 19103-1189. Tel: 215-686-5318. Fax: 215-563-3628. p. 2106

Lee, Annie, Dir, Hawkeye Public Library, 104 S Second St, Hawkeye, IA, 52147-0216. Tel: 563-427-5536. Fax: 563-427-5536. p. 820

Lee, Anthony E, Ref Librn, Seton Hall University Libraries, Walsh Libary Bldg, 400 S Orange Ave, South Orange, NJ, 07079. Tel: 973-761-9440. Fax: 973-761-9432. p. 1530

Lee, Ava K, Asst Libr Dir, Fauquier County Public Library, 11 Winchester St, Warrenton, VA, 20186-2825. Tel: 540-349-1856. Fax: 540-349-3278. p. 2500

Lee, Barbara, Coordr, Ref (Info Serv), Cullman County Public Library System, 200 Clark St NE, Cullman, AL, 35055. Tel: 256-734-1068. Fax: 256-734-6902. p. 13

Lee, Bertus, Librn, United States Nuclear Regulatory Commission, Law Library, 11555 Rockville Pike, Rockville, MD, 20852. Tel: 301-415-1526. Fax: 301-415-3725. p. 1040

Lee, Betty, ILL, Malheur County Library, 388 SW Second Ave, Ontario, OR, 97914. Tel: 541-889-6371. Fax: 541-889-4279. p. 2008

Lee, Bonnie, Dir, Orange Beach Public Library, 26267 Canal Rd, Orange Beach, AL, 36561-3917. Tel: 251-981-2923. Fax: 251-981-2920. p. 33

Lee, Brenda, Asst Librn, Sundridge-Strong Union Public Library, 110 Main St, Sundridge, ON, P0A 1Z0, CANADA. Tel: 705-384-7311. Fax: 705-384-7311. p. 2847

Lee, Bridgette, Libr Spec, ILL, Saint Louis Community College, Instructional Resources, 5460 Highland Park Dr, Saint Louis, MO, 63110. Tel: 314-644-9555. p. 1358

Lee, Carla, Dir, University of Virginia, Charles L Brown Science & Engineering Library, Clark Hall, Charlottesville, VA, 22903-3188. Tel: 434-924-3628. Fax: 434-924-4338. p. 2454

Lee, Carla H, Dir, University of Virginia, Astronomy, Charles L Brown Sci & Eng Library, 264 Astronomy Bldg, 530 McCormick Rd, Charlottesville, VA, 22904. Tel: 434-243-2390. Fax: 434-924-4337. p. 2454

Lee, Carol, Libr Asst, Neuse Regional Library, Trenton Public Library, 204 Lakeview Dr, Trenton, NC, 28585-0610. Tel: 252-448-4261. Fax: 252-448-4261. p. 1805

Lee, Catherine, Ser, National Semiconductor Corp, 2900 Semiconductor Dr, MS-DT-05, Santa Clara, CA, 95052-8090. Tel: 408-721-3810. Fax: 408-721-7060. p. 262

Lee, Catherine, Dir, Cape Fear Community College, 415 N Second St, Wilmington, NC, 28401-3993. Tel: 910-362-7030. Fax: 910-362-7005. p. 1830

Lee, Cathlean, Chief Exec Officer, Chief Librn, Meaford Public Library, 15 Trowbridge St W, Meaford, ON, N4L 1V4, CANADA. Tel: 519-538-1060, Ext 1123. Fax: 519-538-1808. p. 2821

Lee, Celina, Dept Head, Long Beach City College, 4901 E Carson St, Long Beach, CA, 90808. Tel: 562-938-3130. Fax: 562-938-3062, 562-938-4777. p. 166

Lee, Cheryl, Sr Librn, Palo Alto City Library, Children's, 1276 Harriet St, Palo Alto, CA, 94301. Fax: 650-463-4964. p. 204

Lee, Christopher, Dir, Roseland Free Public Library, 20 Roseland Ave, Roseland, NJ, 07068-1235. Tel: 973-226-8636. Fax: 973-226-6429. p. 1527

Lee, Chui-chun, Dean, State University of New York College at New Paltz, 300 Hawk Dr, New Paltz, NY, 12561-2493. p. 1666

Lee, Dan, Assoc Dir, Pub Serv, Presbyterian College, 211 E Maple St, Clinton, SC, 29325. Tel: 864-833-8437. Fax: 864-833-8315. p. 2186

Lee, Daniel, Asst Libr Mgr, Tech, Chandler Public Library, 22 S Delaware, Chandler, AZ, 85225. Tel: 480-782-2813. Fax: 480-782-2823. p. 59

Lee, Deanna, VPres, Communications, Mkt & Bus, The New York Public Library - Astor, Lenox & Tilden Foundations, 476 Fifth Ave, (@ 42nd St), New York, NY, 10018-2788. Tel: 212-592-7714. Fax: 212-592-7440. p. 1690

Lee, Desiree, Commun Libr Mgr, County of Los Angeles Public Library, Rowland Heights Library, 1850 Nogales St, Rowland Heights, CA, 91748-2945. Tel: 626-912-5348. Fax: 626-810-3538. p. 143

Lee, Diann, Dir, Evergreen-Conecuh County Public Library, 119 Cemetery Ave, Evergreen, AL, 36401. Tel: 251-578-2670. Fax: 251-578-2316. p. 16

Lee, Don, Monographs Cataloger, Academy of Motion Picture Arts & Sciences, 333 S La Cienega Blvd, Beverly Hills, CA, 90211. Tel: 310-247-3000, Ext 2207. Fax: 310-657-5193. p. 129

Lee, Doris, Librn, North Park Baptist Church Library, 2605 Rex Cruse Dr, Sherman, TX, 75092. Tel: 903-892-8429. Fax: 903-893-4463. p. 2387

Lee, E Christina, Tech Serv, Norfolk State University Library, 700 Park Ave, Norfolk, VA, 23504-8010. Tel: 757-823-9061. Fax: 757-823-2431. p. 2482

Lee, Earl W, Tech Serv Coordr, Pittsburg State University, 1605 S Joplin St, Pittsburg, KS, 66762-5889. Tel: 620-235-4885. Fax: 620-235-4090. p. 890

Lee, Erika, Dir, University of Minnesota Libraries-Twin Cities, Immigration History Research Center, Elmer L Andersen Library, 222 21st Ave S, Ste 311, Minneapolis, MN, 55455. Tel: 612-625-5573. Fax: 612-626-0018. p. 1262

Lee, Frances, Ch, Highland Park Public Library, 31 N Fifth Ave, Highland Park, NJ, 08904. Tel: 732-572-2750. Fax: 732-819-9046. p. 1490

Lee, Frank, Librn, Latham & Watkins LLP Library, 505 Montgomery St, Ste 1900, San Francisco, CA, 94111. Tel: 415-391-0600. Fax: 415-395-8095. p. 243

Lee, Georgia, Tech Serv Coordr, Marion County Library, 101 E Court St, Marion, SC, 29571-3699. Tel: 843-423-8300. Fax: 843-423-8302. p. 2200

Lee, Heath, Pub Serv Librn, Ocmulgee Regional Library System, 535 Second Ave, Eastman, GA, 31023. Tel: 478-374-4711. Fax: 478-374-5646. p. 531

Lee, Hsiao-Hung, Dr, Dir, Rock Valley College Library, Educational Resources Center, 3301 N Mulford Rd, Rockford, IL, 61114. Tel: 815-921-4627. Fax: 815-921-4629. p. 697

Lee, Irene, Br Mgr, San Francisco Public Library, Golden Gate Valley Branch Library, 1801 Green St, San Francisco, CA, 94123-4921. Tel: 415-355-5666. Fax: 415-561-0153. p. 246

Lee, Iris M, Head, Coll Serv, George Washington University, Jacob Burns Law Library, 716 20th St NW, Washington, DC, 20052. Tel: 202-994-2733. Fax: 202-994-2874. p. 402

Lee, Janet, Tech Serv, Regis University, 3333 Regis Blvd, Denver, CO, 80221-1099. Tel: 303-458-4030. Fax: 303-964-5497. p. 303

Lee, Janet, Ch, Ada Public Library, 124 S Rennie, Ada, OK, 74820. Tel: 580-436-8121. Fax: 580-436-0534. p. 1955

Lee, Janice, Head, ILL, Ottawa University, 1001 S Cedar, Ottawa, KS, 66067-3399. Tel: 785-242-5200, Ext 5444. Fax: 785-229-1012. p. 887

Lee, Janis, Pub Serv Asst, Vanderbilt University, Divinity Library, 419 21st Ave S, Nashville, TN, 37203-2427. Tel: 615-322-2865. Fax: 615-343-8279. p. 2260

Lee, Jean, Commun Libr Mgr, Queens Borough Public Library, Bayside Community Library, 214-20 Northern Blvd, Bayside, NY, 11361. Tel: 718-229-1834. Fax: 718-225-8547. p. 1644

Lee, Jean, Br Head, Toronto Public Library, St James Town, 495 Sherbourne St, Toronto, ON, M4X 1K7, CANADA. Tel: 416-393-7744. Fax: 416-393-7562. p. 2863

Lee, Jennifer, Br Mgr, McAllen Memorial Library, Lark, 2601 Lark Ave, McAllen, TX, 78504. Tel: 956-688-3320. Fax: 956-688-3346. p. 2361

Lee, Jennifer, Ref Librn, Torys LLP Library, 79 Wellington St W, Ste 3000, Toronto, ON, M5K 1N2, CANADA. Tel: 416-865-8159. Fax: 416-865-7380. p. 2864

Lee, Jennifer B, Curator, Performing Arts & Exhibitions, Columbia University, Rare Book & Manuscript, Butler Library, 6th Flr E, 535 W 114th St, New York, NY, 10027. Tel: 212-854-4048. Fax: 212-854-1365. p. 1675

Lee, Jin Ha, Asst Prof, University of Washington, Mary Gates Hall, Ste 370, Campus Box 352840, Seattle, WA, 98195-2840. Tel: 206-685-9937. Fax: 206-616-3152. p. 2976

Lee, Joan, Br Mgr, Rochester Public Library, Lincoln, 851 Joseph Ave, Rochester, NY, 14621. Tel: 585-428-8210. p. 1732

Lee, Joanne, IT Mgr, Yuma County Library District, 2951 S 21st Dr, Yuma, AZ, 85364. Tel: 928-782-1871. Fax: 928-782-9420. p. 91

Lee, John, Ref, Pace University, 861 Bedford Rd, Pleasantville, NY, 10570-2799. Tel: 914-773-3381. Fax: 914-773-3508. p. 1720

Lee, Jonathon, Cat, Chair, Ref Serv, Los Angeles Harbor College, 1111 Figueroa Pl, Wilmington, CA, 90744-2397. Tel: 310-233-4475. Fax: 310-233-4689. p. 284

Lee, Joye, Librn, Garfield County Library, 217 G St, Burwell, NE, 68823. Tel: 308-346-4711. Fax: 308-346-4711. p. 1395

Lee, Judy, Librn, E C Rowell Public Library, 85 E Central Ave, Webster, FL, 33597-4701. Tel: 352-568-1600. Fax: 352-568-1399. p. 502

Lee, Judy, Dr, Assoc Prof, University of Central Florida, College of Education, PO Box 161250, Orlando, FL, 32816. Tel: 407-823-5175. Fax: 407-823-4880. p. 2963

Lee, Julia, Ref, Russell Library, 123 Broad St, Middletown, CT, 06457. Tel: 860-347-2528. p. 352

Lee, Ken, Circ/Per, Prof, Libr Sci, Ref Librn, West Los Angeles College Library, 9000 Overland Ave, Culver City, CA, 90230. Tel: 310-287-4402. Fax: 310-287-4366. p. 138

Lee, Kristy, Circ, Info Serv, State University of New York College at New Paltz, 300 Hawk Dr, New Paltz, NY, 12561-2493. Tel: 845-257-3769. p. 1666

Lee, Laura, Librn, Montpelier Public Library, 301 S Main St, Montpelier, IN, 47359. Tel: 765-728-5969. Fax: 765-728-5969. p. 766

Lee, Laurie, Asst Librn, Titonka Public Library, 136 Main St N, Titonka, IA, 50480. Tel: 515-928-2509. Fax: 515-928-2509. p. 847

Lee, Lena, Ch, Blue Earth Community Library, 124 W Seventh St, Blue Earth, MN, 56013-1308. Tel: 507-526-5012. Fax: 507-526-4683. p. 1242

Lee, Leslie A, Asst Dir, Admin, George Washington University, Jacob Burns Law Library, 716 20th St NW, Washington, DC, 20052. Tel: 202-994-2385. Fax: 202-994-2874. p. 402

Lee, Levada, Cat, Pontiac Public Library, 211 E Madison St, Pontiac, IL, 61764. Tel: 815-844-7229. Fax: 815-844-3475. p. 692

Lee, Linda, Librn, Eriksdale Public Library, PO Box 219, Eriksdale, MB, R0C 0W0, CANADA. Tel: 204-739-2668. p. 2748

Lee, Lorie, Head Librn, Henderson County, 121 S Prairieville, Athens, TX, 75751. Tel: 903-677-7295. Fax: 903-677-7275. p. 2277

Lee, Lynn, Asst Librn, Rockville Public Library, 106 N Market St, Rockville, IN, 47872. Tel: 765-569-5544. Fax: 765-569-5546. p. 776

Lee, Marilyn, Head, Ser, Xavier University of Louisiana, One Drexel Dr, New Orleans, LA, 70125-1098. Tel: 504-520-5298. Fax: 504-520-7940. p. 964

Lee, Mark, Computer Serv, United States Air Force, 4FSS/FSDL, 1520 Goodson St, Bldg 3660, Seymour Johnson AFB, NC, 27531. Tel: 919-722-5825. Fax: 919-722-5835. p. 1823

Lee, Mark, Mgr, Carnegie Library of Pittsburgh, Sheraden, 720 Sherwood Ave, Pittsburgh, PA, 15204-1724. Tel: 412-331-1135. p. 2123

Lee, Mark, Mgr, Carnegie Library of Pittsburgh, West End, 47 Wabash Ave, Pittsburgh, PA, 15220-5422. Tel: 412-921-1717. p. 2123

Lee, Marsha, Dir, United States Air Force, 2555 Coman Ave, Eielson AFB, AK, 99702. Tel: 907-377-3174. Fax: 907-377-1683. p. 47

Lee, Marsha M, Undergrad Serv/Humanities & Sci Librn, University of Connecticut Library, Harleigh B Trecker Library, 1800 Asylum Ave, West Hartford, CT, 06117. Tel: 860-570-9030. Fax: 860-570-9036. p. 371

Lee, Martha, Head, Support Serv, Orion Township Public Library, 825 Joslyn Rd, Lake Orion, MI, 48362. Tel: 248-693-3000, Ext 304. Fax: 248-693-3009. p. 1199

Lee, Mary, Libr Asst I, Montgomery City-County Public Library System, Juliette Hampton Morgan Memorial Library (Main Library), 245 High St, Montgomery, AL, 36104. Tel: 334-240-4999. Fax: 334-240-4980. p. 30

Lee, Mary Kay, Tech Serv, Grant County Public Library, 207 E Park Ave, Milbank, SD, 57252-2497. Tel: 605-432-6543. Fax: 605-432-4635. p. 2215

Lee, Meghan, Archivist, Richard Nixon Library & Birthplace, 18001 Yorba Linda Blvd, Yorba Linda, CA, 92886. Tel: 714-993-5075. p. 285

Lee, Michele, Librn, Mercy College Libraries, Bronx Campus, 1200 Waters Pl, Bronx, NY, 10461. Tel: 718-678-8394. p. 1615

Lee, Michele, Librn, Mercy College Libraries, Manhattan Campus, 66 W 35th St, New York, NY, 10001. Tel: 212-615-3364. Fax: 212-967-6330. p. 1615

Lee, Nancy, Info/Ref Serv Mgr, Westfield Washington Public Library, 333 W Hoover St, Westfield, IN, 46074-9283. Tel: 317-896-9391. Fax: 317-896-3702. p. 787

Lee, Nancy, Librn, State Library of Iowa, 1112 E Grand Ave, Des Moines, IA, 50319. Tel: 515-281-4105. Fax: 515-281-6191. p. 810

Lee, Nancy, Br Mgr, Great River Regional Library, Big Lake Library, 160 Lake St N, Big Lake, MN, 55309. Tel: 763-263-6445. Fax: 763-263-6445. p. 1274

Lee, Nicole, Exec Dir, TransAfrica Forum, 1629 K St NW, Ste 1100, Washington, DC, 20006. Tel: 202-223-1960. Fax: 202-223-1966. p. 417

Lee, Nina, Head, Automation, Head, Tech Serv, Mercy College Libraries, 555 Broadway, Dobbs Ferry, NY, 10522. Tel: 914-674-7263. Fax: 914-674-7581. p. 1615

Lee, Norice, Assoc Dean, New Mexico State University Library, 2911 McFie Circle, Las Cruces, NM, 88003. Tel: 575-646-1508. Fax: 575-646-6940. p. 1558

Lee, Pier M, Admin Dir, Peters Township Public Library, 616 E McMurray Rd, McMurray, PA, 15317-3495. Tel: 724-941-9430. Fax: 724-941-9438. p. 2086

Lee, Regina, Head, Govt Pub, Maps & Micro, Tennessee Technological University, 1100 N Peachtree Ave, Cookeville, TN, 38505. Tel: 931-372-6105. Fax: 931-372-6112. p. 2231

Lee, Richard, Exec Dir, Waukegan Public Library, 128 N County St, Waukegan, IL, 60085. Tel: 847-623-2041. Fax: 847-623-2092, 847-623-2094. p. 716

Lee, Roderick, Br Mgr, East Central Georgia Regional Library, Diamond Lakes, 101 Diamond Lakes Way, Hephzibah, GA, 30815. Tel: 706-772-2432. Fax: 706-772-2433. p. 519

Lee, Rose, In Charge, Racine County Law Library, 730 Wisconsin Ave, Racine, WI, 53403-1247. Tel: 262-636-3773. Fax: 262-636-3341. p. 2632

Lee, Salina, Libr Asst, C G Jung Institute of San Francisco, 2040 Gough St, San Francisco, CA, 94109. Tel: 415-771-8055, Ext 207. Fax: 415-771-8926. p. 243

Lee, Sandra, Pub Serv, Birmingham Public Library, 2100 Park Pl, Birmingham, AL, 35203. Tel: 205-226-3742. Fax: 205-226-3743. p. 7

Lee, Sandra, Librn, Fermi National Accelerator Laboratory Library, Kirk & Wilson Sts, Batavia, IL, 60510. Tel: 630-840-3401. Fax: 630-840-4636. p. 593

Lee, Sandra, Adult & Tech Serv Mgr, Concord Public Library, 45 Green St, Concord, NH, 03301-4294. Tel: 603-230-3685. Fax: 603-230-3693. p. 1442

Lee, Sarah, Acq, Cat, Mobile Public Library, 700 Government St, Mobile, AL, 36602. Tel: 251-208-7106. Fax: 251-208-5865. p. 25

Lee, Sarah Hooke, Asst Dean, Dir, Northeastern University School of Law Library, 400 Huntington Ave, Boston, MA, 02115. Tel: 617-373-3394. Fax: 617-373-8705. p. 1066

Lee, Seong Heon, Asst Librn, Chicago Theological Seminary, 5757 S University Ave, Chicago, IL, 60637-1507. Tel: 773-322-0246. Fax: 773-752-7194. p. 611

Lee, Shari, PhD, Asst Prof, Saint John's University, Saint Augustine Hall, Rm 408, 8000 Utopia Pkwy, Jamaica, NY, 11439. Tel: 718-990-1451. Fax: 718-990-2071. p. 2970

Lee, Sharon, Br Mgr, Kitsap Regional Library, Poulsbo Branch, 700 N E Lincoln St, Poulsbo, WA, 98370-7688. Tel: 360-779-2915. Fax: 360-779-1051. p. 2510

Lee, Sheila, Librn, Sheridan County Library, 100 W Laurel Ave, Plentywood, MT, 59254. Tel: 406-765-2317. Fax: 406-765-2129. p. 1387

Lee, Sonja, Tech Serv, Calumet City Public Library, 660 Manistee Ave, Calumet City, IL, 60409. Tel: 708-862-6220, Ext 236. Fax: 708-862-0872. p. 599

Lee, Suki, Br Mgr, Howard County Library System, East Columbia, 6600 Cradlerock Way, Columbia, MD, 21045-4912. Tel: 410-313-7700. p. 1026

Lee, Susan M, Info Serv, University of Great Falls Library, 1301 20th St S, Great Falls, MT, 59405-4948. Tel: 406-791-5315. Fax: 406-791-5395. p. 1380

Lee, Thomas G, Librn, Michigan Department of Corrections, PO Box 236, Marenisco, MI, 49947. Tel: 906-787-2217. Fax: 906-787-2324. p. 1206

Lee, Tricia, Mgr, Jefferson County Public Library, Lakewood Library, 10200 W 20th Ave, Lakewood, CO, 80215. p. 315

Lee, Veronica, Actg Br Mgr, Oakland Public Library, Eastmont, Eastmont Town Ctr, Ste 211, 7200 Bancroft Ave, Oakland, CA, 94605. Tel: 510-615-5726. Fax: 510-615-5863. p. 198

Lee, Vickie, Br Mgr, Johnson County Public Library, Trafalgar Branch, 424 Tower St, Trafalgar, IN, 46181. Tel: 317-878-9560. Fax: 317-878-4093. p. 744

Lee, Vija, Libr Assoc, Lima Public Library, Cairo Branch, 108 W Main St, Unit R, Cairo, OH, 45820. Tel: 419-641-7744. Fax: 419-641-6274. p. 1910

Lee, Wai-Fong, Dean, Instrul Res Serv, Seattle Central Community College, 1701 Broadway, 2BE2101, Seattle, WA, 98122. Tel: 206-587-4062. Fax: 206-587-3878. p. 2530

Lee, Yan Ye, Syst & Tech Serv Librn, Wagner College, One Campus Rd, Staten Island, NY, 10301-4495. Tel: 718-420-4219. Fax: 718-420-4218. p. 1748

Lee, Young, Ref Serv, University of La Verne, 320 E D St, Ontario, CA, 91764. Tel: 909-460-2062. Fax: 909-460-2083. p. 200

Leech, Robin, Head Librn, Oklahoma State University Libraries, Digital Library Services, Edmon Low Library, Rm 215A, Stillwater, OK, 74078-1071. Tel: 405-744-9161. Fax: 405-744-5183. p. 1978

Leech, Robin, Head, Digital Libr Serv, Oklahoma State University Libraries, Oklahoma State University, Athletic Ave, Stillwater, OK, 74078-1071. Tel: 405-744-9729. Fax: 405-744-5183. p. 1978

Leedberg, Kristina, Ref, J V Fletcher Library, 50 Main St, Westford, MA, 01886-2599. Tel: 978-692-5555. Fax: 978-692-4418. p. 1138

Leedy, James, Archivist, Ref, Bluefield State College, 219 Rock St, Bluefield, WV, 24701. Tel: 304-327-4053. Fax: 304-327-4203. p. 2554

Leedy, Louise, Coordr, Tuolumne County Genealogical Society Library, 158 W Bradford St, Sonora, CA, 95370-4920. Tel: 209-532-1317. p. 269

Leedy, Stephanie, Head, Ref, Auburn Public Library, 749 E Thach Ave, Auburn, AL, 36830. Tel: 334-501-3190. p. 5

Leek, Kathy, Asst Librn, Emo Public Library, Jesse St, Emo, ON, P0W 1E0, CANADA. Tel: 807-482-2575. Fax: 807-482-2575. p. 2804

Leek, Max, Dir, Douglas County Library System, 1409 NE Diamond Lake Blvd, Roseburg, OR, 97470. Tel: 541-440-4305. Fax: 541-957-7798. p. 2016

Leek, Susan, Circ, Umpqua Community College Library, 1140 Umpqua College Rd, Roseburg, OR, 97470. Tel: 541-440-4640. Fax: 541-440-4637. p. 2017

Leeman, Lauren, Ref Spec, State Historical Society of Missouri Library, 1020 Lowry St, Columbia, MO, 65201-7298. Tel: 573-882-7083. Fax: 573-884-4950. p. 1324

Leeman, Sarah, Assoc Electronic Res Librn, Argonne National Laboratory, 9700 S Cass Ave, Bldg 240, Argonne, IL, 60439-4801. Tel: 630-252-4224. Fax: 630-252-5024. p. 589

Leembruggen, Patricia E, Librn, CoxHealth Libraries, Cox Medical Ctr N, 1423 N Jefferson Ave, J-200, Springfield, MO, 65802. Tel: 417-269-8892. Fax: 417-269-6140. p. 1366

Leembruggen, Patricia E, Librn, CoxHealth Libraries, David Miller Memorial Library, Cox Medical Ctr S, 3801 S National Ave, Springfield, MO, 65807. Tel: 417-269-3460. Fax: 417-269-3492. p. 1366

Leeney-Panagrossi, Anne, Dir, Albertus Magnus College Library, 700 Prospect St, New Haven, CT, 06511. Tel: 203-773-8594. Fax: 203-773-8588. p. 355

Leese, Carol, Acq Mgr, University of Montana, Maureen & Mike Mansfield Library, 32 Campus Dr, No 9936, Missoula, MT, 59812-9936. Tel: 406-243-5926. Fax: 406-243-4067. p. 1386

Leeson, Andrea, Librn, Annapolis Valley Regional Library, Kingston Branch, 671 Main St, Kingston, NS, B0P 1R0, CANADA. Tel: 902-765-3631. p. 2778

LeFager, Amy, Librn, National Louis University Library & Learning Support, Wheeling, 1000 Capitol Dr, Wheeling, IL, 60090-7201. Tel: 847-947-5335. Fax: 847-947-5335. p. 620

LeFaive, Lianne, Asst Librn, Chinook Regional Library, Gull Lake Branch, 1377 Conrad Ave, Gull Lake, SK, S0N 1A0, CANADA. Tel: 306-672-3277. p. 2928

Lefand, Ellie, Mat, Ivy Tech Community College of Indiana, Northeast, 3800 N Anthony Blvd, Fort Wayne, IN, 46805-1430. Tel: 260-480-2032. Fax: 260-480-4121. p. 742

Lefco, Kathy, Dir, Libr Serv, Winston & Strawn LLP Library, 35 W Wacker Dr, Chicago, IL, 60601. Tel: 312-558-5740. Fax: 312-558-5700. p. 628

Lefebvre, Gaye, Dir, Libr Serv, Davies, Ward, Phillips & Vineberg, 155 Wellington St W, Toronto, ON, M5V 3J7, CANADA. Tel: 416-863-0900. Fax: 416-863-0871. p. 2852

Lefebvre, Guy, Librn, Ministere de la Culture, 587 rue Radisson, Trois-Rivieres, QC, G9A 2C8, CANADA. Tel: 819-371-6748. Fax: 819-371-6955. p. 2914

Lefebvre, Melanie, Librn, Calumet Public Library, 932 Gary St, Calumet, MN, 55716. Tel: lefebvre@arrowhead.lib.mn.us. Fax: 218-247-3108. p. 1243

Lefebvre, Rodney, Network Tech, Montgomery City-County Public Library System, 245 High St, Montgomery, AL, 36104. Tel: 334-240-4985. Fax: 334-240-4977. p. 29

LeFevre, Cathy, Librn, Clarella Hackett Johnson Library, E 9311 County Rd I, Sand Creek, WI, 54765. Tel: 715-658-1269. p. 2636

Lefevre, Julie, Digital Serv Librn, University of California, Berkeley, Institute of Governmental Studies, 109 Moses Hall, Ground flr, 94720-2370, Berkeley, CA, 94720-2370. Tel: 510-642-1472. Fax: 510-643-0866. p. 128

LeFevre, Sue, Bus Operations Mgr, Indiana University South Bend, 1700 Mishawaka Ave, South Bend, IN, 46615. Tel: 574-520-4404. Fax: 574-520-4472. p. 778

Leffel, Leandra, Br Mgr, Muskingum County Library System, South Branch, 2530 Maysville Pike, South Zanesville, OH, 43701. Tel: 740-454-1511. p. 1954

Leffler, Cheryl, Assoc Librn, Pub Serv, Indian Hills Community College, 525 Grandview Ave, Bldg 10, Ottumwa, IA, 52501-1398. Tel: 641-683-5178. Fax: 641-683-5184. p. 837

Leffler, Mary, Mgr, Ref Serv, Marion Public Library, 600 S Washington St, Marion, IN, 46953-1992. Tel: 765-668-2900. Fax: 765-668-2911. p. 763

Leffler, Mary, Exec Dir, Southeast Regional Library System, 252 W 13th St, Wellston, OH, 45692. Tel: 740-384-2103, Ext 5. Fax: 740-384-2106. p. 2952

Leffler, Pam, Asst Dir, Carol Stream Public Library, 616 Hiawatha Dr, Carol Stream, IL, 60188. Tel: 630-344-6107. Fax: 630-653-6809. p. 601

Lefkowitz, Dale, Librn, Kings County Law Library, Kings County Govt Ctr, 1400 W Lacey Blvd, Hanford, CA, 93230. Tel: 559-582-3211, Ext 4430. p. 156

Lefkowitz, Kathleen, Br Mgr, Cleveland Public Library, Walz, 7910 Detroit Ave, Cleveland, OH, 44102. Tel: 216-623-7095. Fax: 216-623-7099. p. 1878

Lefkowitz, Paula, Head, Ch, Parsippany-Troy Hills Free Public Library, 449 Halsey Rd, Parsippany, NJ, 07054. Tel: 973-887-5150. Fax: 973-887-0062. p. 1517

LeFoll, Christine, Admin Librn, Godfrey Memorial Library, 134 Newfield St, Middletown, CT, 06457-2534. Tel: 860-346-4375. Fax: 860-347-9874. p. 351

Lefort, Christine, Reader Serv, Attleboro Public Library, 74 N Main St, Attleboro, MA, 02703. Tel: 508-222-0157, 508-222-0159. Fax: 508-226-3326. p. 1050

LeFort, Margarita, Circ, Hornepayne Public Library, 68 Front St, Hornepayne, ON, P0M 1Z0, CANADA. Tel: 807-868-2332. Fax: 807-868-3111. p. 2811

Lefrancois, Carol, Librn, Defence R&D Canada-Valcartier Library, 2459 Pie-XI Blvd N, Val-Belair, QC, G3J 1X5, CANADA. Tel: 418-844-4000, Ext 4244. Fax: 418-844-4624. p. 2914

Lefrancois, Emilie, Chief Librn, Haut-Saint-Jean Regional Library, Monseigneur W J Conway Public, 33 rue Irene, Edmundston, NB, E3V 1B7, CANADA. Tel: 506-735-4713. Fax: 506-737-6848. p. 2762

Lefrancois, Guy, Dir, University de Moncton, 165 boul Hebert, Edmundston, NB, E3V 2S8, CANADA. Tel: 506-737-5266. Fax: 506-737-5373. p. 2762

Leftokwitz, Ilene, Adult Serv, ILL, Ref, Denville Free Public Library, 121 Diamond Spring Rd, Denville, NJ, 07834. Tel: 973-627-6555. Fax: 973-627-1913. p. 1481

Leftwich, James B, Dir, Berkeley College, White Plains Campus, 99 Church St, White Plains, NJ, 10601. Tel: 914-694-1122, Ext 3370. p. 1545

Legarreta, Carol, Pub Serv Adminr, Br Operations, Montgomery County Public Libraries, 21 Maryland Ave, Ste 310, Rockville, MD, 20850. Tel: 240-777-0030. p. 1038

Legaspi, Lizeth, Ref Librn, Camarena Memorial Library, 850 Encinas Ave, Calexico, CA, 92231. Tel: 760-768-2170. Fax: 760-357-0404. p. 131

Legault, Daniel, Chef de Section, Bibliothèques de Montrèal, Marie-Uguay, 6052, rue Monk, Montreal, QC, H4E 3H6, CANADA. Tel: 514-872-2313. Fax: 514-872-0513. p. 2890

Legault, Daniel, Chef de Section, Bibliothèques de Montrèal, Saint-Henri, 4707, rue Notre-Dame Ouest, Montreal, QC, H4C 1S9, CANADA. Tel: 514-872-2313. Fax: 514-872-0512. p. 2891

Legendre, Esther, Librn, College Marie de France Library, 4635 chemin Queen Mary, Montreal, QC, H3W 1W3, CANADA. Tel: 514-737-1177. Fax: 514-737-0789. p. 2894

Léger, France, Acq & Develop, Asst Dir, Commun Outreach, Bibliotheque Publique de Chicoutimi, 155, rue Racine Est, Chicoutimi, QC, G7H 1R5, CANADA. Tel: 418-698-3000, Ext 4180. Fax: 418-698-5359. p. 2880

Leger, France, Dir, Bibliotheque Municipale de Jonquiere, 2850 Davis Pl, Jonquiere, QC, G7X 7W7, CANADA. Tel: 418-699-6068, 418-699-6069. Fax: 418-699-6046. p. 2884

Leger, Linda, Ref, Malaspina University-College Library, 900 Fifth St, Nanaimo, BC, V9R 5S5, CANADA. Tel: 250-753-3245, Ext 2347. Fax: 250-740-6473. p. 2732

Leger, Lori, Librn, Horizon Health Network, 135 MacBeath Ave, Moncton, NB, E1C 6Z8, CANADA. Tel: 506-870-2546. Fax: 506-857-5785. p. 2766

Leger, Paulette, Librn Mgr, Albert-Westmorland-Kent Regional Library, Saint-Antoine Public, 11 Ave Jeanne d'Arc, Saint Antoine, NB, E4V 1H2, CANADA. Tel: 506-525-4028. Fax: 506-525-4199. p. 2765

Leger-Hornby, Tracey, Dr, Asst VPres, Libr Serv, Worcester Polytechnic Institute, 100 Institute Rd, Worcester, MA, 01609-2280. Tel: 508-831-5410. Fax: 508-831-5829. p. 1145

Legere, Shelagh, Mgr, Access Serv, Mount Saint Vincent University Library, 166 Bedford Hwy, Halifax, NS, B3M 2J6, CANADA. Tel: 902-457-6204. Fax: 902-457-6445. p. 2781

Legg, Jeannette, Tech Serv, Plumas County Library, 445 Jackson St, Quincy, CA, 95971-9410. Tel: 530-283-6310. Fax: 530-283-3242. p. 212

Leggett, Erlinda, Libr Tech, Pamlico Community College, 5049 Hwy 306 S, Grantsboro, NC, 28529. Tel: 252-249-1851, Ext 3034. Fax: 252-249-2377. p. 1795

Leggett, Kim, Supvr II, Columbus State Community College Library, 550 E Spring St, Columbus, OH, 43215. Tel: 614-287-5879. Fax: 614-287-2457. p. 1885

Leggott, Mark, Univ Librn, University of Winnipeg Library, 515 Portage Ave, Winnipeg, MB, R3B 2E9, CANADA. Tel: 204-786-9801. Fax: 204-783-8910. p. 2759

Legleiter, Sharolyn, Govt Doc, Fort Hays State University, 600 Park St, Hays, KS, 67601-4099. Tel: 785-628-4431. Fax: 785-628-4096. p. 871

Lego, Amy, Dir, Rock Falls Public Library District, 1007 Seventh Ave, Rock Falls, IL, 61071. Tel: 815-626-3958. Fax: 815-626-8750. p. 696

LeGrande, Rae, In Charge, Amador County Library, Plymouth Branch, 9375 Main St, Plymouth, CA, 95669. Tel: 209-245-6476. p. 161

Legree, Jon, Info & Tech Serv Mgr, Yorba Linda Public Library, 18181 Imperial Hwy, Yorba Linda, CA, 92886-3437. Tel: 714-777-2873. Fax: 714-777-0640. p. 285

LeGrow, Nancy, Br Mgr, Oakville Public Library, Clearview Neighbourhood, 2860 Kingsway Dr, Oakville, ON, L6J 6R3, CANADA. Tel: 905-815-2033. Fax: 905-815-2034. p. 2825

LeGuern, Charles A, Coordr, Libr & Educ Serv, Memorial Hospital of South Bend, 615 N Michigan, South Bend, IN, 46601. Tel: 574-647-7389, 574-647-7491. Fax: 574-647-3319. p. 779

Leh, C, Librn, STV Inc Library, 205 W Welsh Dr, Douglassville, PA, 19518. Tel: 610-385-8200, 610-385-8280. Fax: 610-385-8501. p. 2049

Lehman, Carol, Librn, Mountain Lake Public Library, 1054 Fourth Ave, Mountain Lake, MN, 56159-1455. Tel: 507-427-2506. Fax: 507-427-2506. p. 1267

Lehman, Cecily, Assoc Librn, Madison Area Technical College, 3550 Anderson St, Rm 230, Madison, WI, 53704. Tel: 608-246-6634. Fax: 608-246-6644. p. 2606

Lehman, Debbie, Ch, Bayliss Public Library, 541 Library Dr, Sault Sainte Marie, MI, 49783. Tel: 906-632-9331. Fax: 906-635-0210. p. 1226

Lehman, Debra A, Dir, Nokomis Public Library, 22 S Cedar St, Ste 2, Nokomis, IL, 62075. Tel: 217-563-2734. Fax: 217-563-2740. p. 680

Lehman, Douglas K, Dir, Wittenberg University, 807 Woodlawn Ave, Springfield, OH, 45504. Tel: 937-327-7016. Fax: 937-327-6139. p. 1936

Lehman, Helen, Librn, First Church of the Brethren Library, 2710 Kingston Rd, York, PA, 17402-3799. Tel: 717-755-0307. p. 2159

Lehman, Janice, In Charge, Holy Trinity Lutheran Church Library, 2730 E 31st St, Minneapolis, MN, 55406. Tel: 612-729-8358. Fax: 612-729-6773. p. 1260

Lehman, Kathleen, Head of Libr, University of Arkansas Libraries, Physics, 102 Physics, Fayetteville, AR, 72701. Tel: 479-575-7048. p. 100

Lehman, Kim, Youth Serv Spec, Central Texas Library System, Inc, 5555 N Lamar Blvd, Ste L115, Austin, TX, 78751. Tel: 512-583-0704. Fax: 512-583-0709. p. 2280

Lehman, Lisa, Instruction Librn, University of Alaska Fairbanks, 310 Tanana Dr, Fairbanks, AK, 99775. Tel: 907-474-5350. Fax: 907-474-6841. p. 48

Lehman, Luann, Mgr, Libr Serv, Southern State Community College, 100 Hobart Dr, Hillsboro, OH, 45133-9487. Tel: 937-382-6645, Ext 4580. Fax: 937-382-8431. p. 1904

Lehman, Patti, Dir, Antlers Public Library, 104 SE Second St, Antlers, OK, 74523-4000. Tel: 580-298-5649. Fax: 580-298-3567. p. 1956

Lehman, Sarah, Pub Relations Coordr, Kansas City, Kansas Public Library, 625 Minnesota Ave, Kansas City, KS, 66101. Tel: 913-279-2106. Fax: 913-279-2033. p. 875

Lehmann, David, Ref Librn, University of South Carolina, Coleman Karesh Law Library, USC Law Ctr, 701 Main St, Columbia, SC, 29208. Tel: 803-777-5942. Fax: 803-777-9405. p. 2190

Lehmann, Karen, Info Literacy Librn, Wartburg College Library, 100 Wartburg Blvd, Waverly, IA, 50677-0903. Tel: 319-352-8460. Fax: 319-352-8312. p. 850

Lehmann, Kathleen, Actg Dir, Head, Ref, Louis Bay 2nd Library, 345 Lafayette Ave, Hawthorne, NJ, 07506-2599. Tel: 973-427-5745, Ext 17. Fax: 973-427-5269. p. 1490

Lehmann, Marie, ILL & Distance Libr Serv Spec, Athol Public Library, 568 Main St, Athol, MA, 01331. Tel: 978-249-9515. Fax: 978-249-7636. p. 1050

Lehmann, Sarah, Ref Serv, American River College Library, 4700 College Oak Dr, Sacramento, CA, 95841. Tel: 916-484-8455. Fax: 916-484-8018, 916-484-8657. p. 220

Lehner, John, Assoc Dean, Personnel Planning & Syst, University of Houston, M D Anderson Library, 114 University Libraries, Houston, TX, 77204-2000. Tel: 713-743-9800. Fax: 713-743-9811. p. 2343

Lehnerz, Greta, Bus Mgr, Natrona County Public Library, 307 E Second St, Casper, WY, 82601. Tel: 307-237-4935. Fax: 307-266-3734. p. 2652

Lehr, Brenda, Librn, New Baden Public Library, 210 N First St, New Baden, IL, 62265. Tel: 618-588-4554. Fax: 618-588-4554. p. 679

Lehr, Lore, Youth Serv, Southwest Public Libraries, SPL Admin, 3359 Park St, Grove City, OH, 43123. Tel: 614-875-6716. Fax: 614-875-2219. p. 1903

Lehr, Marcia Gold, Fac Serv Librn, Northwestern University, Chicago, Pritzker Legal Research Center, 375 E Chicago Ave, Chicago, IL, 60611. Tel: 312-503-4356. Fax: 312-503-9230. p. 621

Lehr, Miller, Br Mgr, Cecil County Public Library, Perryville Branch, 500 Coudon Blvd, Perryville, MD, 21903. Tel: 410-996-6070. p. 1027

Lehr, Scott, VPres, Mkt & Develop, International Franchise Association, 1501 K St NW, Ste 350, Washington, DC, 20005. Tel: 202-662-0785. Fax: 202-628-0812. p. 405

Lehr, Shirley, Dir, Owen Public Library, 414 Central Ave, Owen, WI, 54460-9777. Tel: 715-229-2939. Fax: 715-229-2939. p. 2628

Lehrer, Beverly, Librn, Montgomery College, Takoma Park Campus Library, 7600 Takoma Ave, Takoma Park, MD, 20912. Tel: 240-567-1559. Fax: 240-567-5820. p. 1037

Lehu, Peter, Head of Libr, Free Library of Philadelphia, Charles L Durham Branch, 3320 Haverford Ave, Philadelphia, PA, 19104-2021. Tel: 215-685-7436, 215-685-7677. Fax: 215-685-7439. p. 2107

Lei, Jean, Med Librn, Memorial Hospitals Association, 1800 Coffee Rd, Ste 43, Modesto, CA, 95355-2700. Tel: 209-569-7721. Fax: 209-569-7469. p. 187

Lei Zeng, Marcia, Dr, Prof, Kent State University, 314 Library, Kent, OH, 44242-0001. Tel: 330-672-2782. Fax: 330-672-7965. p. 2972

Leibbrandt, Pat, Librn, St Francis Public Library, 121 N Scott St, Saint Francis, KS, 67756. Tel: 785-332-3292. p. 892

Leibee, Nancy, Per, Tech Serv Librn, Saint Joseph's College, Hwy 231 S, Rensselaer, IN, 47978. Tel: 219-866-6390. Fax: 219-866-6135. p. 774

Leibergen, Leah, Acq, Govt Doc, University of Wisconsin-Green Bay, 2420 Nicolet Dr, Green Bay, WI, 54311-7001. Tel: 920-465-2382. Fax: 920-465-2136. p. 2596

Leibiger, Carol, Coordr, Info Literacy, Librn, University of South Dakota, 414 E Clark St, Vermillion, SD, 57069. Tel: 605-677-5371. Fax: 605-677-6834. p. 2220

Leibold, Sue, Libr Dir, Clarke University, 1550 Clarke Dr, Dubuque, IA, 52001. Tel: 563-588-6320. Fax: 563-588-8160. p. 811

Leibowitz, Gerald, Media Spec, Nassau Community College, One Education Dr, Garden City, NY, 11530-6793. Tel: 516-572-7400. Fax: 516-572-7846. p. 1626

Leibowitz, Ilene, Head, Ch, North Merrick Public Library, 1691 Meadowbrook Rd, North Merrick, NY, 11566. Tel: 516-378-7474. Fax: 516-378-0876. p. 1706

Leifer, Judith, Circ, ILL, Center for Advanced Judaic Studies Library, 420 Walnut St, Philadelphia, PA, 19106-3703. Tel: 215-238-1290. Fax: 215-238-1540. p. 2103

Leifheit, Carolyn, Adult Serv, Oswego Public Library District, 32 W Jefferson St, Oswego, IL, 60543. Tel: 630-554-3150. Fax: 630-978-1307. p. 686

Leigh, Arlett Hodges, ILL, FEMA/DHS Library, 500 C St SW, Rm 123, Washington, DC, 20472. Tel: 202-646-3769. Fax: 202-646-4295. p. 400

Leigh, Cheryl, Librn, Elizabeth City State University, 1704 Weeksville Rd, Elizabeth City, NC, 27909. Tel: 252-335-3586. Fax: 252-335-3446. p. 1790

Leigh, James, Circ Mgr, Malvern-Hot Spring County Library, 202 E Third St, Malvern, AR, 72104. Tel: 501-332-5441. Fax: 501-332-6679. p. 108

Leigh, Kathryn, Head, Access Serv, University of Massachusetts Amherst, 154 Hicks Way, Amherst, MA, 01003-9275. Tel: 413-577-0175. Fax: 413-545-6873. p. 1049

Leigh, Robin, Adult Serv, Ref, Safety Harbor Public Library, 101 Second St N, Safety Harbor, FL, 34695. Tel: 727-724-1525. Fax: 727-724-1533. p. 486

Leigh, Yvette, Br Mgr, Chicago Public Library, Toman, 2708 S Pulaski Rd, Chicago, IL, 60623. Tel: 312-745-1660. Fax: 312-745-1621. p. 609

Leighton, Ann, Br Mgr, Ruth Enlow Library of Garrett County, Six N Second St, Oakland, MD, 21550-1393. Tel: 301-334-3996, Ext 104. Fax: 301-334-4152. p. 1035

Leighton, Diana, Ch, Mark & Emily Turner Memorial Library, 39 Second St, Presque Isle, ME, 04769. Tel: 207-764-2571. Fax: 207-768-5756. p. 998

Leighton, Judith, Head, Tech Serv, Bangor Public Library, 145 Harlow St, Bangor, ME, 04401-1802. Tel: 207-947-8336. Fax: 207-945-6694. p. 975

Leighton, Lauren, Per, Saint Mary's University of Minnesota, 700 Terrace Heights, No 26, Winona, MN, 55987-1399. Tel: 507-457-1564. Fax: 507-457-1565. p. 1289

Leighton, Shann, Librn, Grand Valley Public Library, Four Amaranth St E, Grand Valley, ON, L0N 1G0, CANADA. Tel: 519-928-5622. Fax: 519-928-2586. p. 2806

Leighton, Vernon, Info Gallery Coordr, Winona State University, 175 W Mark St, Winona, MN, 55987-5838. Tel: 507-457-5148. p. 1290

Leighty, Linda, Br Mgr, Kendallville Public Library, Limberlost Public, 164 Kelly St, Rome City, IN, 46784. Tel: 260-854-2775. Fax: 260-854-3382. p. 757

Leighty, Linda C, Dir, Pitt Community College, Hwy 11 S, Greenville, NC, 27835. Tel: 252-321-4357. Fax: 252-321-4404. p. 1799

Leija, Leticia S, Dir, Dustin Michael Sekula Memorial Library, 1906 S Closner Blvd, Edinburg, TX, 78539. Tel: 956-383-6246. Fax: 956-318-3123. p. 2315

Leik, Susan, Librn, Colquitt Regional Medical Center, 3131 S Main St, Moultrie, GA, 31768. Tel: 229-890-3460. Fax: 229-891-9345. p. 545

Leik, Susan T, Librn, John D Archbold Memorial Hospital, PO Box 1018, Thomasville, GA, 31799-1018. Tel: 229-228-2063. p. 553

Leik, Susan T, Librn, South Georgia Medical Center, PO Box 1727, Valdosta, GA, 31603-1727. Tel: 229-259-4178. Fax: 229-245-6139. p. 555

Leimkuehler, Lynn, Dir, Brunswick Public Library, 115 W Broadway, Brunswick, MO, 65236. Tel: 660-548-1026, 660-548-3237. p. 1321

Leinaweaver, Alexa, Br Mgr, Charles County Public Library, Two Garrett Ave, La Plata, MD, 20646-5959. Tel: 301-934-9001. Fax: 301-934-2297. p. 1033

Leinbach, Helen, Dir, North Webster Community Public Library, 301 N Main St, North Webster, IN, 46555. Tel: 574-834-7122. Fax: 574-834-7122. p. 770

Leinheiser, Diane, Librn, Pottsville Hospital & Warne Clinic, 420 S Jackson St, Pottsville, PA, 17901. Tel: 570-621-5000, 570-621-5033. Fax: 570-621-5113. p. 2131

Leininger, Lea, Health Sci Ref Librn, University of North Carolina at Greensboro, 320 Spring Garden St, Greensboro, NC, 27402. Tel: 336-256-0215. Fax: 336-334-5399. p. 1798

Leino, Opal, Br Mgr, Clay County Public Library System, Middleburg Clay-Hill Branch, 2245 Aster Ave, Middleburg, FL, 32068. Tel: 904-541-5855. p. 475

Leipert, Kristen, Asst Archivist, Whitney Museum of American Art, 945 Madison Ave, New York, NY, 10021. Tel: 212-671-5335. p. 1703

Leisenring, Mindy, Dir, Cortland County Historical Society, 25 Homer Ave, Cortland, NY, 13045. Tel: 607-756-6071. p. 1611

Leisenring, Rick, Curator, Glenn H Curtiss Museum of Local History, 8419 State Rte 54, Hammondsport, NY, 14840-0326. Tel: 607-569-2160. Fax: 607-569-2040. p. 1633

Leiser, Amy, Exec Dir, Monroe County Historical Association, 900 Main St, Stroudsburg, PA, 18360. Tel: 570-421-7703. Fax: 570-421-9199. p. 2144

Leishman, Joan, Dir, University of Toronto Libraries, Gerstein Science Information Centre, Seven & Nine Kings College Circle, Toronto, ON, M5S 1A5, CANADA. Tel: 416-978-7662. Fax: 416-971-2848. p. 2866

Leisman, Patricia, In Charge, Merced County Library, Dos Palos Branch, 2002 Almond, Dos Palos, CA, 93620-2304. Tel: 209-392-2155. p. 185

Leisser, Traudi, Circ Asst, McGill University Libraries, Howard Ross Library of Management, Samuel Bronfman Bldg, 1001 Sherbrooke St W, 2nd Flr, Montreal, QC, H3A 1G5, CANADA. Tel: 514-398-4690, Ext 09272. Fax: 514-398-5046. p. 2899

Leist, Cindy, Ref Serv, Suntree/Viera Public Library, 902 Jordan Blass Dr, Melbourne, FL, 32940. Tel: 321-255-4404. Fax: 321-255-4406. p. 463

Leist, Cynthia, Dir, Melbourne Beach Public Library, 324 Ocean Ave, Melbourne Beach, FL, 32951. Tel: 321-956-5642. Fax: 321-953-6942. p. 464

Leist, Stephen, Circ Serv Supvr, Transylvania University Library, 300 N Broadway, Lexington, KY, 40508. Tel: 859-233-8225. Fax: 859-233-8779. p. 921

Leist, Stephen, Res Librn, Virginia Wesleyan College, 1584 Wesleyan Dr, Norfolk, VA, 23502-5599. Tel: 757-455-2131. Fax: 757-455-2129. p. 2483

Leister, Susan, Head, Metadata Serv, Georgetown University, 37th & N St NW, Washington, DC, 20057-1174. Tel: 202-687-1557. Fax: 202-687-7501. p. 402

Leite, Manny, Dir, East Bridgewater Public Library, 32 Union St, East Bridgewater, MA, 02333-1598. Tel: 508-378-1616. Fax: 508-378-1617. p. 1085

Leite, Manny, Asst Dir, Head, Ref, Tiverton Library Services, Union Public Library, 3832 Main Rd, Tiverton, RI, 02878-1321. Tel: 401-625-6799. p. 2177

Leiter, Dena, Dir of Libr, Union County College Libraries, 1033 Springfield Ave, Cranford, NJ, 07016. Tel: 908-709-7623. Fax: 908-709-7589. p. 1480

Leiter, Richard, Dir, University of Nebraska-Lincoln, Marvin & Virginia Schmid Law Library, 40 Fair St, Lincoln, NE, 68583. Tel: 402-472-5737. Fax: 402-472-8260. p. 1407

Leith, Christy, Librn, Davis Wright Tremaine LLP, 1201 Third Ave, Ste 2200, Seattle, WA, 98101-3045. Tel: 206-622-3150. Fax: 206-628-7699. p. 2527

Leiting, Peggy, Dir, The Lied Randolph Public Library, 111 N Douglas St, Randolph, NE, 68771-5510. Tel: 402-337-0046. Fax: 402-337-0046. p. 1417

Leitle, Kathy, Assoc Dep Dir, Saint Louis Public Library, 1415 Olive St, Saint Louis, MO, 63103-2315. Tel: 314-539-0300. Fax: 314-241-3840. p. 1359

Leitner, Lee, PhD, Assoc Teaching Prof, Drexel University, Rush Bldg, Rm 306, 30 N 33rd St, Philadelphia, PA, 19104-2875. Tel: 215-895-2474. Fax: 215-895-2494. p. 2972

Leitner, Mona, Br Mgr, Louisville Free Public Library, Highlands-Shelby Park, Mid-City Mall, 1250 Bardstown Rd, Louisville, KY, 40204. Tel: 502-574-1672. Fax: 502-451-0548. p. 924

Leitz, Robert, Dr, Curator, James Smith Noel Coll, Louisiana State University, One University Pl, Shreveport, LA, 71115-2399. Tel: 318-798-4161. Fax: 318-797-5156. p. 968

Leive, Cynthia, Head Librn, McGill University Libraries, Marvin Duchow Music Library, New Music Bldg, 3rd Flr, 527 Sherbrooke St W, Montreal, QC, H3A 1E3, CANADA. Tel: 514-398-4695. Fax: 514-398-8276. p. 2898

Leja, Ilga, Dir, Nova Scotia College of Art & Design Library, 5163 Duke St, Halifax, NS, B3J 3J6, CANADA. Tel: 902-494-8196. Fax: 902-425-1978. p. 2781

Leland, Christopher, Tech Serv Librn, Meredith Public Library, 91 Main St, Meredith, NH, 03253. Tel: 603-279-4303. Fax: 603-279-5352. p. 1457

Leland, Harriott Cheves, Archivist, Huguenot Society of South Carolina Library, 138 Logan St, Charleston, SC, 29401. Tel: 843-723-3235. Fax: 843-853-8476. p. 2184

Lelansky, Craig, Head, Access Serv, Georgetown University, Georgetown Law Library (John Wolff & Edward Bennett Williams Libraries), 111 G St NW, Washington, DC, 20001. Fax: 202-662-9168. p. 403

Lele, Pradeep, Dir, Lone Star College System, North Harris College Library, 2700 W W Thorne Dr, Houston, TX, 77073. Tel: 281-618-5497. Fax: 281-618-5695. p. 2340

Lelievre, Steve, Head, Eng Libr, University of New Brunswick Libraries, Engineering, Sir Edmund Head Hall, Rm C-15, 15 Dineen Dr, Fredericton, NB, E3B 5A3, CANADA. Tel: 506-453-4747. Fax: 506-453-4829. p. 2764

Lellig, Cynthia A, Dir, Jesup Public Library, 721 Sixth St, Jesup, IA, 50648-0585. Tel: 319-827-1533. Fax: 319-827-1580. p. 824

LeLoup, Amber, In Charge, Bureau of Land Management, 2550 N State St, Ukiah, CA, 95482-3023. Tel: 707-468-4000. Fax: 707-468-4027. p. 277

Lema, Mary Ann, Adult Serv, Prairie Trails Public Library District, 8449 S Moody, Burbank, IL, 60459-2525. Tel: 708-430-3688. Fax: 708-430-5596. p. 598

Lemaire, Helene, Ref Serv, Institut de Recherche d'Hydro-Quebec Bibliotheque, 1800 Lionel-Boulet Blvd, CP 1000, Varennes, QC, J3X 1S1, CANADA. Tel: 450-652-8022. Fax: 450-652-8040. p. 2914

Lemaire, Jean, Academy Librn, Bibliothèque Laurent-Michel-Vacher, 9155 rue St-Hubert, Montreal, QC, H2M 1Y8, CANADA. Tel: 514-389-5921, Ext 2240. Fax: 514-389-1422. p. 2888

LeMaistre, Tiffany, Acq/Coll Develop Librn, University of Texas at Tyler Library, 3900 University Blvd, Tyler, TX, 75799. Tel: 903-565-5614. Fax: 903-566-2513. p. 2394

Lemanua, Kolotita, Ch, Leavenworth Public Library, 417 Spruce St, Leavenworth, KS, 66048. Tel: 913-682-5666. Fax: 913-682-1248. p. 879

LeMarie, Deanna, Br Mgr, Davis Jefferson Parish Library, Lake Arthur Branch, 600 Fourth St, Lake Arthur, LA, 70549. Tel: 337-774-3661. Fax: 337-774-3657. p. 952

LeMaster, Charles, Pub Serv, Western Iowa Technical Community College, 4647 Stone Ave, Sioux City, IA, 51106. Tel: 712-274-8733, Ext 1239. Fax: 712-274-6423. p. 844

LeMaster, Kristin, Br Mgr, Clark County Public Library, Southern Village, 1123 Sunset Ave, Springfield, OH, 45505. Tel: 937-322-2226. p. 1935

Lemay, Anne, Youth Serv, Franklin Township Free Public Library, 485 DeMott Lane, Somerset, NJ, 08873. Tel: 732-873-8700. Fax: 732-873-0746. p. 1529

Lemay, Annie, Documentation Tech, CSSS d'Arthabaska-Erable, 5 rue des Hospitalieres, Victoriaville, QC, G6P 6N2, CANADA. Tel: 819-357-2030, Ext 2185. Fax: 819-357-6060. p. 2915

Lemay, Christine, Head Librn, Department of Fisheries & Oceans Canada, 850 route de la Mer, Mont-Joli, QC, G5H 3Z4, CANADA. Tel: 418-775-0552. Fax: 418-775-0538. p. 2887

Lemay, Denise, Media Spec, Bibliotheques de Trois-Rivieres, Bibliotheque Aline-Piche, 5575 boul Jean-XXIII, Trois-Rivieres, QC, G8Z 4A8, CANADA. Tel: 819-374-6525. Fax: 819-374-5126. p. 2913

Lemay, Janet G, Libr Mgr, High Prairie Municipal Library, 4723 53rd Ave, High Prairie, AB, T0G 1E0, CANADA. Tel: 780-523-3838. Fax: 780-523-3838. p. 2707

LeMay, Jill E, Libr Dir, Kennebunk Free Library, 112 Main St, Kennebunk, ME, 04043. Tel: 207-985-2173. Fax: 207-985-4730. p. 988

Lemay, N Curtis, Dir, University of Saint Thomas, Archbishop Ireland Memorial Library, 2260 Summit Ave, Mail No IRL, Saint Paul, MN, 55105. Tel: 651-962-5453. Fax: 651-962-5460. p. 1282

Lemay, Nicolle, Ref Librn, Grant MacEwan University Library, 10700 104th Ave, Edmonton, AB, T5J 4S2, CANADA. Tel: 780-497-5850. Fax: 780-497-5895. p. 2701

Lemay, Paul, Dir of Communications, Dir, Commun Develop, Dir, Cultural Serv, Bibliothèques de Laval, 1535 boul Chomedey, Laval, QC, H7V 3Z4, CANADA. Tel: 450-978-6888, Ext 5649. Fax: 450-978-5833. p. 2886

Lemay, Yvon, Asst Prof, Universite de Montreal, 3150, rue Jean-Brillant, bur C-2004, Montreal, QC, H3T 1N8, CANADA. Tel: 514-343-6044. Fax: 514-343-5753. p. 2979

Lembeck, Linda, Mgr, Wyoming Game & Fish Department Library, 3030 Energy Lane, Casper, WY, 82604. Tel: 307-473-3402. Fax: 307-473-3433. p. 2652

Lemberg, Richard, Coordr, Instrul Serv, Saint Mary's College Library, 1928 Saint Mary's Rd, Moraga, CA, 94575. Tel: 925-631-4229. Fax: 925-376-6097. p. 191

Lembke, Roberta, Interim Dir, Libr Serv, Saint Olaf College, Rolvaag Memorial Library, Glasoe Science Library, Halvorson Music Library, 1510 Saint Olaf Ave, Northfield, MN, 55057-1097. Tel: 507-786-3097. Fax: 507-786-3734. p. 1269

Lemen, Miriam, Librn, Federal Home Loan Bank of Indianapolis Library, 8250 Woodfield Crossing Blvd, Indianapolis, IN, 46240-7324. Tel: 317-465-0438. Fax: 317-465-0397. p. 751

Lemerande, Cynthia M, Librn, Edith Evans Community Library, 5216 Forest Ave, Laona, WI, 54541. Tel: 715-674-4751. Fax: 715-674-5904. p. 2605

Lemhouse, Ken, Ref, Brevard Community College, Philip F Nohrr Learning Resource Ctr, 3865 N Wickham Rd, Melbourne, FL, 32935-2399. Tel: 321-433-5575. Fax: 321-433-5619. p. 463

Lemhouse, Sherri, Dir, Brownsville Community Library, 146 Spaulding, Brownsville, OR, 97327. Tel: 541-466-5454. p. 1992

LeMieux, Chris, Youth Serv, Spokane Public Library, East Side, 524 S Stone Ave, Spokane, WA, 99202. Tel: 509-444-5377. Fax: 509-444-5369. p. 2537

LeMieux, Chris, Youth Serv, Spokane Public Library, Hillyard, 4005 N Cook Ave, Spokane, WA, 99207. Tel: 509-444-5382. Fax: 509-444-5370. p. 2538

LeMieux, Chris, Youth Serv, Spokane Public Library, Indian Trail, 4909 W Barnes Rd, Spokane, WA, 99208. Tel: 509-444-5397. Fax: 509-444-5399. p. 2538

LeMieux, Diane, Librn, Ministry of the Attorney General, Superior Law Courts, 800 Smithe St, Vancouver, BC, V6Z 2E1, CANADA. Tel: 604-660-2799. Fax: 604-660-1723. p. 2741

LeMieux, Mary, Asst Librn, Morristown Centennial Library, Seven Richmond St, Morrisville, VT, 05661. Tel: 802-888-3853. p. 2430

Lemieux, Victoria, Asst Prof, University of British Columbia, The Irving K Barber Centre, 1961 E Mall, Ste 470, Vancouver, BC, V6T 1Z1, CANADA. Tel: 604-822-2404. Fax: 604-822-6006. p. 2977

Lemin Lee, Jill, Circ Librn, Athenaeum of Philadelphia, 219 S Sixth St, East Washington Square, Philadelphia, PA, 19106-3794. Tel: 215-925-2688. Fax: 215-925-3755. p. 2103

Leming, Stefani, Head, Ch, Head, Youth Serv, Middletown Public Library, 125 S Broad St, Middletown, OH, 45044. Tel: 513-424-8042. Fax: 513-424-6585. p. 1917

Leming, Tracy, Pres, Colorado Association of Law Libraries, PO Box 13363, Denver, CO, 80201. Tel: 303-492-7535. Fax: 303-492-2707. p. 2939

Lemke, Christine, Youth Serv Librn, Jacksonville Public Library, 201 W College Ave, Jacksonville, IL, 62650-2497. Tel: 217-243-5435. Fax: 217-243-2182. p. 659

Lemke, Cynthia, Librn, Northrop Grumman Mission Systems, 12011 Sunset Hills Rd, Reston, VA, 20190. Tel: 703-345-7738. Fax: 703-345-7735. p. 2487

Lemke, Donald, Adminr, State University of New York Downstate Medical Center, 395 Lenox Rd, Brooklyn, NY, 11203. Tel: 718-270-7410. Fax: 718-270-7413, 718-270-7468. p. 1595

Lemke, Karen, Pub Relations, Teen Serv, Pine River Public Library District, 395 Bayfield Center Dr, Bayfield, CO, 81122. Tel: 970-884-2222. Fax: 970-884-7155. p. 289

Lemke, Susan K, Spec Coll & Archives Librn, US Department of Defense, Fort McNair, Marshall Hall, Washington, DC, 20319-5066. Tel: 202-685-3957. Fax: 202-685-3733. p. 418

Lemley, Cecile, Dir, Adamsville Public Library, 4825 Main St, Adamsville, AL, 35005-1947. Tel: 205-674-3399. Fax: 205-674-5405. p. 3

Lemme, Susan, Ref Librn, Middle Georgia Regional Library System, 1180 Washington Ave, Macon, GA, 31201-1790. Tel: 478-744-0839. Fax: 478-742-3161. p. 541

Lemmens, Laura, Head Librn, Alberta Department of Environment Library, 9920 108th St, 6th Flr, Edmonton, AB, T5K 2M4, CANADA. Tel: 780-427-5870. Fax: 780-422-0170. p. 2698

Lemmens, Tony, Syst Tech, University of Toronto Libraries, Faculty of Information Inforum, 140 Saint George St, 4th Flr, Toronto, ON, M5S 3G6, CANADA. Tel: 416-978-7168. Fax: 416-978-5769. p. 2866

Lemmer, Catherine, Head, Info Serv, Indiana University, Ruth Lilly Law Library, 530 W New York St, Indianapolis, IN, 46202-3225. Tel: 317-274-3884, 317-274-4028. Fax: 317-274-8825. p. 752

Lemmon, Alfred E, Dir, Historic New Orleans Collection, 410 Chartres St, New Orleans, LA, 70130-2102. Tel: 504-598-7124. Fax: 504-598-7168. p. 960

Lemmon, Lauren, Asst Dir, Ida Rupp Public Library, 310 Madison St, Port Clinton, OH, 43452. Tel: 419-732-3212. Fax: 419-734-9867. p. 1930

LeMoine, Norma Jean, Libr Dir, Rock Springs Public Library, 101 First St, Rock Springs, WI, 53961-8011. Tel: 608-522-5050. Fax: 608-522-5050. p. 2635

Lemon, Amanda, Electronic Serv/Ref Librn, Oklahoma City Community College, 7777 S May Ave, Oklahoma City, OK, 73159. Tel: 405-682-1611, Ext 7146. Fax: 405-682-7585. p. 1973

Lemon, Kate, Librn, Louisiana House of Representatives, PO Box 94012, Baton Rouge, LA, 70804-9012. Tel: 225-342-2430. Fax: 225-342-2431. p. 943

Lemon, Mary Ann, Dir, Ottumwa Public Library, 102 W Fourth St, Ottumwa, IA, 52501. Tel: 641-682-7563. Fax: 641-682-4970. p. 837

Lemon, Nancy, In Charge, Owens-Corning Corp, 2790 Columbus Rd, Rte 16, Granville, OH, 43023-1200. Tel: 740-321-5000. Fax: 740-321-7255. p. 1903

Lemon, Nancy, In Charge, Owens-Corning Science & Technology Center, 2790 Columbus Rd, Granville, OH, 43023. Tel: 614-430-3401. Fax: 740-321-7255. p. 1903

Lemon, Shanda, Electronic Res, Pub Serv Librn, Virginia Union University, 1500 N Lombardy St, Richmond, VA, 23220. Tel: 804-278-4120. Fax: 804-257-5818. p. 2493

Lemon, Susan, Libr Asst, Woodward Public Library, 118 S Main St, Woodward, IA, 50276. Tel: 515-438-2636. Fax: 515-438-2636. p. 854

LeMond, Liz, Librn, Crossroads Bible College, 601 N Shortridge Rd, Indianapolis, IN, 46219-4912. Tel: 317-352-8736. Fax: 317-352-9145. p. 750

LeMonde-McIntyre, Michelle, Commun Serv, Framingham Public Library, 49 Lexington St, Framingham, MA, 01702-8278. Tel: 508-879-5570, Ext 4347. Fax: 508-820-7210. p. 1090

Lemons, Evelyn, Librn, Fort Concho National Historic Landmark, 630 S Oakes St, San Angelo, TX, 76903-7099. Tel: 325-657-4442. Fax: 325-657-4531. p. 2378

Lempinen-Leedy, Nance, Ref Librn, Santa Fe Community College, 3000 NW 83rd St, Bldg Y-100, Gainesville, FL, 32606. Tel: 352-395-5406. Fax: 352-395-5102. p. 449

Lempke, Susan, Youth Serv, Niles Public Library District, 6960 Oakton St, Niles, IL, 60714. Tel: 847-663-1234. Fax: 847-663-1350. p. 680

Lemyre, Elizabeth, Head, Youth Serv, Bibliotheque de Kirkland, 17100 Hymus Blvd, Kirkland, QC, H9J 2W2, CANADA. Tel: 514-630-2726. Fax: 514-630-2716. p. 2884

Lence, Sheila K, Librn, Northeast Regional Library, Blue Mountain Public Library, 110 Mill St, Blue Mountain, MS, 38610. Tel: 662-685-4721. Fax: 662-685-4031. p. 1297

Lencka, Margaret, Asst Librn, OLI Systems, Inc Library, 108 American Rd, Morris Plains, NJ, 07950. Tel: 973-539-4996. Fax: 973-539-5922. p. 1504

Lenders, Taryn, Librn, Alberta Children's Hospital Knowledge Centre, 2888 Shaganappi Trail NW, A2-908, 2nd Flr, Calgary, AB, T3B 6AB, CANADA. Tel: 403-955-2722. Fax: 403-955-2799. p. 2687

Lenders, Taryn, Librn, Peter Lougheed Ctr Knowledge Ctr, University of Calgary Library, Health Sciences Library, Health Sci Ctr, 3330 Hospital Dr NW, Calgary, AB, T2N 4N1, CANADA. Tel: 403-943-4737. Fax: 403-210-9847. p. 2693

Lendis, Raychel, Br Assoc, Las Vegas-Clark County Library District, Mount Charleston Library, 75 Ski Chalet Pl, HCR 38, Box 269, Las Vegas, NV, 89124. Tel: 702-872-5585. Fax: 702-872-5631. p. 1429

Lendrum, Linda, Br Librn, Massey & Township Public Library, Webbwood Public, 16 Main St, Webbwood, ON, P0P 1P0, CANADA. Tel: 705-869-4147. Fax: 705-869-4147. p. 2820

Lenfesty, Tracy, Librn, Nova Scotia Department of Natural Resources Library, Founders Sq, 1701 Hollis St, 3rd Flr, Halifax, NS, B3J 3M8, CANADA. Tel: 902-424-8633. Fax: 902-424-7735. p. 2782

Lengellé, Fabien, Secy Gen & Dir Gen, Communications Bur, Library & Archives Canada, 550 De la Cité Blvd, Gatineau, QC, K1A 0N4, CANADA. Tel: 819-934-5717. Fax: 819-934-5839. p. 2883

Lenglet, Bianca, In Charge, Saint Anthony's Health Care Library, 1200 Seventh Ave N, Saint Petersburg, FL, 33705. Tel: 727-825-1286. Fax: 727-820-7877. p. 488

Lenihan, Marianne, Doc Delivery, Per, Rider University, 2083 Lawrenceville Rd, Lawrenceville, NJ, 08648-3099. Tel: 609-896-5111. Fax: 609-896-8029. p. 1494

Leninger, Jill, City Librn, Oak Creek Public Library, 8620 S Howell Ave, Oak Creek, WI, 53154. Tel: 414-768-6580. Fax: 414-768-6583. p. 2626

Lenio, Jennifer, Media Spec, Brighton Memorial Library, 2300 Elmwood Ave, Rochester, NY, 14618. Tel: 585-784-5300. Fax: 585-784-5333. p. 1728

Lenk, Mary Anne, Dir, Saint Thomas Aquinas College, 125 Rte 340, Sparkill, NY, 10976. Tel: 845-398-4219. Fax: 845-359-9537. p. 1746

Lenker, Mark, Asst Librn, Instruction & Ref, Longwood University, Redford & Race St, Farmville, VA, 23909. Tel: 434-395-2257. Fax: 434-395-2453. p. 2463

Lenkow, Tanya, Head, Circ, Kinnelon Public Library, 132 Kinnelon Rd, Kinnelon, NJ, 07405-2393. Tel: 973-838-1321. Fax: 973-838-0741. p. 1493

Lenkowski, Patricia, Instrul Serv Librn, West Chester University, 25 W Rosedale Ave, West Chester, PA, 19383. Tel: 610-436-3393. p. 2153

Lennertz Jetton, Lora, Head, Performing Arts & Media, University of Arkansas Libraries, 365 N McIlroy Ave, Fayetteville, AR, 72701-4002. Tel: 479-575-5514. Fax: 479-575-6656. p. 99

Lennig, Carol, Ref Librn, Prosser Public Library, One Tunxis Ave, Bloomfield, CT, 06002-2476. Tel: 860-243-9721. Fax: 860-242-1629. p. 330

Lennon, Vanessa, Cat Librn, North Carolina Central University, 1801 Fayetteville St, Durham, NC, 27707-3129. Tel: 919-530-7309. Fax: 919-530-7612. p. 1789

Lennox, Allison, Mgr, Canadian Broadcasting Corp, Radio Archives, 205 Wellington St W, Toronto, ON, M5G 3G7, CANADA. Tel: 416-205-5880. Fax: 416-205-8602. p. 2850

Lennox, Cheryl, Head Librn, Cordova District Library, 402 Main Ave, Cordova, IL, 61242-9790. Tel: 309-654-2330. Fax: 309-654-2290. p. 631

Lenoir, Brenda, Librn, Los Angeles County Department of Public Works, 900 S Fremont Ave, Alhambra, CA, 91803. Tel: 626-458-4978. Fax: 626-979-5379. p. 120

Lenon, Mary Ann, Dir, Morton Township Public Library, 110 S James, Mecosta, MI, 49332-9334. Tel: 231-972-8315. Fax: 231-972-4332. p. 1207

Lenore, Leila, Head, Circ, Media Spec, Chickasaw Regional Library System, 601 Railway Express, Ardmore, OK, 73401. Tel: 580-223-3164. Fax: 580-223-3280. p. 1957

Lenox, Glenna, Bus Mgr, Lebanon Public Library, 104 E Washington St, Lebanon, IN, 46052. Tel: 765-482-3460. Fax: 317-873-5059. p. 761

Lenroot-Ernt, Lois, Coord Librn, Cap Projects, Hennepin County Library, 12601 Ridgedale Dr, Minnetonka, MN, 55305-1909. Tel: 612-543-8555. Fax: 612-543-8600. p. 1263

Lensing, Robin, YA Serv, Pawtucket Public Library, 13 Summer St, Pawtucket, RI, 02860. Tel: 401-725-3714. Fax: 401-728-2170. p. 2171

Lent, Laura, Chief, Coll & Tech Serv, San Francisco Public Library, 100 Larkin St, San Francisco, CA, 94102-4733. Tel: 415-557-4220. Fax: 415-557-4424. p. 246

Lenth, Julie, In Charge, Hamilton Sundstrand, 4747 Harrison Ave, MS 268-6, Rockford, IL, 61108. Tel: 815-394-2911. Fax: 860-660-6303. p. 697

Lentine, Andy, Head, Admin Serv, Lake Villa District Library, 1001 E Grand Ave, Lake Villa, IL, 60046. Tel: 847-356-7711, Ext 211. Fax: 847-265-9595. p. 663

Lentini, Elaine, Librn, Saint-Gobain Abrasives Library, One New Bond St, Worcester, MA, 01606-2614. Tel: 508-795-2001. Fax: 508-795-5755. p. 1144

Lentz, Barbara, Libr Mgr, Washoe County Library System, Northwest Reno Library, 2325 Robb Dr, Reno, NV, 89523. Tel: 775-787-4117. Fax: 775-787-4127. p. 1434

Lentz, Gerald John, Fr, Librn, California Province of the Society of Jesus, 300 College Ave, Los Gatos, CA, 95030. Tel: 408-884-1700. Fax: 408-884-1747. p. 180

Lentz, Janet, Head, Monographic Acq, University of Pennsylvania Libraries, 3420 Walnut St, Philadelphia, PA, 19104-6206. Tel: 215-898-5932. Fax: 215-898-0559. p. 2118

Lentz, Jennifer, Head, Coll, Ref Librn, University of California Los Angeles Library, Hugh & Hazel Darling Law Library, 112 Law Bldg, Box 951458, 385 Charles E Young Dr E, Los Angeles, CA, 90095-1458. Tel: 310-825-7826. Fax: 310-825-1372. p. 178

Lenville, Jean, Asst Dean, University of Scranton, Monroe & Linden, Scranton, PA, 18510-4634. Tel: 570-941-4009. Fax: 570-941-7817. p. 2138

Lenz, Brian, Supvr, Student Computing Ctr, San Diego State University Library & Information Access, 5500 Campanile Dr, San Diego, CA, 92182-8050. Tel: 619-594-1652. Fax: 619-594-0487. p. 237

Lenz, Kelly, Dir, South Georgia Regional Library System, 300 Woodrow Wilson Dr, Valdosta, GA, 31602-2592. Tel: 229-333-0086. Fax: 229-333-7669. p. 555

Lenz, Vicki, Circ, Appleton Public Library, 225 N Oneida St, Appleton, WI, 54911-4780. Tel: 920-832-6170. Fax: 920-832-6182. p. 2578

Leo, Jennifer Alvino, Head, Lending/IT Coordr, Walker Memorial Library, 800 Main St, Westbrook, ME, 04092. Tel: 207-854-0630. Fax: 207-854-0629. p. 1006

Leo, Laurie, Dir, Scottsville Free Library, 28 Main St, Scottsville, NY, 14546. Tel: 585-889-2023. Fax: 585-889-7938. p. 1741

Leo, Laurie, Dir, Scottsville Free Library, Mumford Branch, 883 George St, Mumford, NY, 14511. Tel: 718-538-6124. p. 1742

Leon, Aixa, Spec Coll Librn, University of Puerto Rico Library, Cayey Campus, 205 Ave Antonio R Barcelo, Cayey, PR, 00736. Tel: 787-738-2161, Ext 2226. Fax: 787-263-2108. p. 2672

Leon, Andrea, Head, Circ/ILL, Washburn University, 1700 SW College Ave, Topeka, KS, 66621. Tel: 785-670-1179. Fax: 785-670-3223. p. 897

Leon, Anne, Pub Libr Serv, Broward County Division of Libraries, Alvin Sherman Library, Research & Information Technology Center at Nova Southeastern University, 3100 Ray Ferrero Jr Blvd, Fort Lauderdale, FL, 33314. Tel: 954-262-4601. Fax: 954-262-3805. p. 442

Leon, Kathy, Dir, Bucklin Public Library, 201 N Main, Bucklin, KS, 67834. Tel: 620-826-3223. Fax: 620-826-3794. p. 858

Leon, Lars, ILL, University of Kansas Libraries, 1425 Jayhawk Blvd, Lawrence, KS, 66045-7544. Tel: 785-864-3956. Fax: 785-864-5311. p. 878

Leonard, Aloysius, Head, Acq, University of Waterloo Library, 200 University Ave W, Waterloo, ON, N2L 3G1, CANADA. Tel: 519-888-4567, Ext 35430. Fax: 519-888-4320. p. 2869

Leonard, Amanda, Librn, Newton Public Library & Museum, 100 S Van Buren St, Newton, IL, 62448. Tel: 618-783-8141. Fax: 618-783-8149. p. 680

Leonard, Barbara, Dir, Ellenburg Center Library, 15 Brandy Brook Rd, Ellenburg Center, NY, 12934. Tel: 518-594-7489. p. 1618

Leonard, Ben, Dir, Nicollet County Historical Society, 1851 N Minnesota Ave, Saint Peter, MN, 56082. Tel: 507-934-2160. Fax: 507-934-8715. p. 1283

Leonard, David, Chief Tech Officer, Boston Public Library, 700 Boylston St, Boston, MA, 02117-0286. Tel: 617-536-5400. Fax: 617-236-4306. p. 1056

Leonard, David, Pres, Trebas Institute, East Tower, 6th Flr, 550 Sherbrooke St W, Montreal, QC, H3A 1B9, CANADA. Tel: 514-845-4141. Fax: 514-845-2581. p. 2902

Leonard, Donna, Librn, Springtown Public Library, 626 N Main St, Springtown, TX, 76082-2541. Tel: 817-523-5862. Fax: 817-523-5922. p. 2388

Leonard, Gloria, Coll Develop, Dir, Washington Talking Book & Braille Library, 2021 Ninth Ave, Seattle, WA, 98121-2783. Tel: 206-386-1254. Fax: 206-615-0437. p. 2535

Leonard, James, Dir, University of Alabama, School of Law Library, 101 Paul Bryant Dr, Tuscaloosa, AL, 35487. Tel: 205-348-5925. Fax: 205-348-1112. p. 38

Leonard, Julia, Assoc Prof, University of Iowa, 3087 Main Library, Iowa City, IA, 52242-1420. Tel: 319-335-5707. Fax: 319-335-5374. p. 2965

Leonard, Kevin, Univ Archivist, Northwestern University Library, 1970 Campus Dr, Evanston, IL, 60208-2300. Tel: 847-491-7658. p. 644

Leonard, Laura, Librn, Hillsdale Free Public Library, 509 Hillsdale Ave, Hillsdale, NJ, 07642. Tel: 201-358-5072. Fax: 201-358-5074. p. 1491

Leonard, Laura, Dir, Twinsburg Public Library, 10050 Ravenna Rd, Twinsburg, OH, 44087-1796. Tel: 330-425-4268, Ext 21. Fax: 330-425-3622. p. 1941

Leonard, Linda, Br Mgr, Vermilion Parish Library, Kaplan Branch, 815 N Cushing Ave, Kaplan, LA, 70548-2614. Tel: 337-643-7209. Fax: 337-643-7250. p. 939

Leonard, Lori, Libr Asst, Bridgeport Public Library, 722 Main St, Bridgeport, NE, 69336. Tel: 308-262-0326. Fax: 308-262-1412. p. 1394

Leonard, Mary, Librn, Dallas Museum of Art, 1717 N Harwood, Dallas, TX, 75201. Tel: 214-922-1277. Fax: 214-954-0174. p. 2306

Leonard, Mimi, In Charge, Newton Correctional Facility, Correctional Release Center Library, 307 S 60th Ave W, Newton, IA, 50208. Tel: 641-792-7552, Ext 357. Fax: 641-792-9288. p. 835

Leonard, Patricia, Ch, Brookline Public Library, 16 Main St, Brookline, NH, 03033. Tel: 603-673-3330. Fax: 603-673-0735. p. 1440

Leonard, Patt, Cat, University of Puget Sound, 1500 N Warner St, Campus Mail Box 1021, Tacoma, WA, 98416-1021. Tel: 253-879-2651. Fax: 253-879-3670. p. 2541

Leonard, Peter, Dir, Cedar Mill Community Library, 12505 NW Cornell Rd, Portland, OR, 97229. Tel: 503-644-0043. Fax: 503-644-3964. p. 2010

Leonard, Ronald P, Dir, Network of Alabama Academic Libraries, c/o Alabama Commission on Higher Education, 100 N Union St, Montgomery, AL, 36104. Tel: 334-242-2211. Fax: 334-242-0270. p. 2937

Leonard, Shannon, Ch, Ottawa Library, 105 S Hickory St, Ottawa, KS, 66067-2306. Tel: 785-242-3080. Fax: 785-242-8789. p. 887

Leonard, Sue, ILL, Blanchard-Santa Paula Public Library District, 119 N Eighth St, Santa Paula, CA, 93060-2709. Tel: 805-525-3615. Fax: 805-933-2324. p. 266

Leonard, Teresa G, Dir, News & Observer Publishing Co, 215 S McDowell St, Raleigh, NC, 27602. Tel: 919-829-4866. Fax: 919-829-8916. p. 1815

Leonard, Thomas C, Univ Librn, University of California, Berkeley, 255 Doe Library, Berkeley, CA, 94720-6000. Tel: 510-642-3773. Fax: 510-643-8179. p. 127

Leonard, Tina, Asst Dir, Head, Ch, Alma Public Library, 351 N Court, Alma, MI, 48801-1999. Tel: 989-463-3966, Ext 104. Fax: 989-466-5901. p. 1149

Leonardi, Sarah, Ref, Amherst Town Library, 14 Main St, Amherst, NH, 03031-2930. Tel: 603-673-2288. Fax: 603-672-6063. p. 1437

Leonardo, Dalia, Cat, City University of New York, 365 Fifth Ave, New York, NY, 10016-4309. Tel: 212-817-7067. Fax: 212-817-2982. p. 1673

Leonards, Shani, Ref Supvr, Berkeley Public Library, 2090 Kittredge St, Berkeley, CA, 94704. Tel: 510-981-6100. Fax: 510-981-6111. p. 126

Leone, Corinne, Sr Librn, New York State Department of Correctional Services, PO Box 350, Gowanda, NY, 14070-0350. Tel: 716-532-0177, Ext 4550. Fax: 716-532-0177. p. 1630

Leone, Gina, Youth Serv, Baldwin Borough Public Library, Wallace Bldg, 41 Macek Dr, Pittsburgh, PA, 15227-3638. Tel: 412-885-2255. Fax: 412-885-5255. p. 2121

Leone Winiewicz, RoseMarie, Dir, Atin Guha, MD Medical Library, Providence Hospital, 1150 Varnum St NE, Washington, DC, 20017. Tel: 202-269-7144. Fax: 202-269-7142. p. 403

Leonetti, John, Ref Librn, Naugatuck Valley Community College, 750 Chase Pkwy, Waterbury, CT, 06708. Tel: 203-575-8024. Fax: 203-575-8062. p. 375

Leong, Eric, Librn, Chaminade University of Honolulu, 3140 Waialae Ave, Honolulu, HI, 96816-1578. Tel: 808-735-4725. Fax: 808-735-4891. p. 560

Leong, Gail, Libr Tech, Providence Regional Medical Center Everett, 1321 Colby Ave, Everett, WA, 98201. Tel: 509-474-3094. Fax: 509-474-4475. p. 2515

Leong-Kurio, Nadine, Ref Serv, Tech Serv, Honolulu Community College Library, 874 Dillingham Blvd, Honolulu, HI, 96817-4598. Tel: 808-845-9198. Fax: 808-845-3618. p. 564

Leonhardt, Stacey, Br Mgr, Chestatee Regional Library System, Dawson County Library, 342 Allen St, Dawsonville, GA, 30534. Tel: 706-344-3690, Ext 21. Fax: 706-344-3691. p. 529

Leoni, Amy, Ref Librn, Belmont Technical College, 120 Fox-Shannon Pl, Saint Clairsville, OH, 43950-9735. Tel: 740-695-9500, Ext 1019. Fax: 740-695-2247. p. 1933

Leopold, Alan, Dir, Coll Serv, Newberry Library, 60 W Walton St, Chicago, IL, 60610-3305. Tel: 312-255-3629. p. 620

Leopold, Joan, Librn, United States Army, Fort Irwin Post Library, National Training Ctr, Bldg 331, Second St & F Ave, Fort Irwin, CA, 92310. Tel: 760-380-3462, 760-380-4337. Fax: 760-380-5071. p. 148

Lepage, Marc, Mgr, Canadian Police College Library, Canadian Police College, One Sandridge Rd, Bldg C, Ottawa, ON, K1G 3J2, CANADA. Tel: 613-993-3225. Fax: 613-993-2220. p. 2829

Lepage, Marc, Dir, Canadian International Development Agency, 200 Promenade du Portage, 8th Flr, Gatineau, QC, K1A 0G4, CANADA. Tel: 819-953-1035. Fax: 819-953-8132. p. 2882

LePage, Sharon, Dir, Chaminade University of Honolulu, 3140 Waialae Ave, Honolulu, HI, 96816-1578. Tel: 808-735-4725. Fax: 808-735-4891. p. 560

Lepine, Andree, Librn, Seminaire Des Peres Maristes Bibliotheque, 2315 Chemin St-Louis, Sillery, QC, G1T 1R5, CANADA. Tel: 418-651-4944. Fax: 418-651-6841. p. 2913

Lepionka, Nancy, Ch, Somerville Library, 35 West End Ave, Somerville, NJ, 08876. Tel: 908-725-1336. Fax: 908-231-0608. p. 1530

Lepkowski, Frank, Assoc Dean, Oakland University Library, 2200 N Squirrel Rd, Rochester, MI, 48309-4402. Tel: 248-370-4426. Fax: 248-370-2474. p. 1221

LePoer, Marja-Leena, Librn, Ashby Free Public Library, 812 Main St, Ashby, MA, 01431. Tel: 978-386-5377. Fax: 978-386-5377. p. 1050

Lepore, Alice, Dir, Sayville Library, 11 Collins Ave, Sayville, NY, 11782-3199. Tel: 631-589-4440. Fax: 631-589-6128. p. 1739

Lepore, Julie, Dir, North Scituate Public Library, 606 W Greenville Rd, North Scituate, RI, 02857. Tel: 401-647-5133. Fax: 401-647-2206. p. 2170

Lepore, Sue, Tech Serv, Troy-Miami County Public Library, 419 W Main St, Troy, OH, 45373. Tel: 937-339-0502. Fax: 937-335-4880. p. 1941

Leporini, Carolyn, Financial Dir, Martinsburg-Berkeley County Public Library, 101 W King St, Martinsburg, WV, 25401. Tel: 304-267-8933. Fax: 304-267-9720. p. 2565

LePors, Teresa, Coordr, Pub Serv & Ref Librn, Elon University, 308 N O'Kelly Ave, Elon, NC, 27244-0187. Tel: 336-278-6577. Fax: 336-278-6637. p. 1791

Leppanen, Audrey, Librn, Boston Public Library, Washington Village, 1226 Columbia Rd, South Boston, MA, 02127-3920. Tel: 617-269-7239. Fax: 617-268-7884. p. 1057

Leppert, Elaine, Dir, Caldwell Public Library, 1010 Dearborn, Caldwell, ID, 83605-4195. Tel: 208-459-3242. Fax: 208-459-7344. p. 572

Leprette, Hannah, Circ, ILL, Ref, North Island College, 3699 Roger St, Port Alberni, BC, V9Y 8E3, CANADA. Tel: 250-724-8717, 250-724-8760. Fax: 250-724-8700. p. 2735

Leraas, Jesse, Librn, Argosy University, 1515 Central Pkwy, Eagan, MN, 55121. Tel: 651-846-3351. Fax: 651-994-0105. p. 1249

Lerat, Phyllis, Head Librn, First Nations University of Canada, Saskatoon Campus Library, 226 20th St E, Saskatoon, SK, S7K 0A6, CANADA. Tel: 306-790-5950, Ext 3425. Fax: 306-931-1847. p. 2922

Lerat, Phyllis G, Univ Librn, First Nations University of Canada, One First Nations Way, Regina, SK, S4S 7K2, CANADA. Tel: 306-790-5950, Ext 3425. Fax: 306-790-5990. p. 2922

Lerch, Christopher, Mgr, Libr Tech Serv, Rochester Institute of Technology, 90 Lomb Memorial Dr, Rochester, NY, 14623-5604. Tel: 585-475-2050. Fax: 585-475-7007. p. 1731

Lerch, Maureen, Dir, Wayne College Library, University of Akron-Wayne College, 1901 Smucker Rd, Orrville, OH, 44667-9758. Tel: 330-684-8789. Fax: 330-683-1381. p. 1925

Lerczak, Nicki, Assoc Prof/Instrul Serv Librn, Genesee Community College, One College Rd, Batavia, NY, 14020-9704. Tel: 585-343-0055, Ext 6418. Fax: 585-345-6933. p. 1578

Lerdal, John, Dir, Pleasant Hill Public Library, 5151 Maple Dr, Pleasant Hill, IA, 50327-8456. Tel: 515-266-7815. Fax: 515-266-7793. p. 839

Lerg, Katherine, Dir, Human Res, Indianapolis-Marion County Public Library, 2450 N Meridian St, Indianapolis, IN, 46208. Tel: 317-275-4806. Fax: 317-269-5248. p. 753

Lerma, Valerie, Acq, Coll Develop, Superior Court Law Library, 101 W Jefferson, Phoenix, AZ, 85003. Tel: 602-506-1647. Fax: 602-506-2940. p. 77

Lerman, Linda, Dir, Norwalk Community College, 188 Richards Ave, Norwalk, CT, 06854-1655. Tel: 203-857-7200. Fax: 203-857-7380. p. 362

Lerman, Marc, Dir, Archives of the Roman Catholic Archdiocese of Toronto, 1155 Yonge St, Ste 505, Toronto, ON, M4T 1W2, CANADA. Tel: 416-934-3400, Ext 501. Fax: 416-934-3434. p. 2850

Lerman, Maria, Ref Serv, Bala-Cynwyd Library, 131 Old Lancaster Rd, Bala Cynwyd, PA, 19004-3037. Tel: 610-664-1196. Fax: 610-664-5534. p. 2030

Lerner, Bonnie, Electronic Serv, Ref Serv, Widener University, Harrisburg Campus Law Library, 3800 Vartan Way, Harrisburg, DE, 17110. Tel: 717-541-3944. Fax: 717-541-3998. p. 389

Leroux, Eric, Assoc Prof, Universite de Montreal, 3150, rue Jean-Brillant, bur C-2004, Montreal, QC, H3T 1N8, CANADA. Tel: 514-343-6044. Fax: 514-343-5753. p. 2979

Leroux, Jeanne, Chief Exec Officer, Nation Municipality Public Library, 25 Arena St, St. Isidore, ON, K0C 2B0, CANADA. Tel: 613-524-2252. Fax: 613-524-2545. p. 2843

Leroux, Jeanne, Chief Exec Officer, Nation Municipality Public Library, Limoges Branch, 205 Limoges Rd, Limoges, ON, K0A 2M0, CANADA. Tel: 613-443-1630. Fax: 613-443-9643. p. 2843

Leroux, Jeanne, Chief Exec Officer, Nation Municipality Public Library, St Albert Branch, 116 Principale St, Saint Albert, ON, K0A 3C0, CANADA. Tel: 613-987-2143. Fax: 613-987-2909. p. 2844

Leroy, Anne, Circ Supvr, Clark University, 950 Main St, Worcester, MA, 01610-1477. Tel: 508-793-7461. Fax: 508-793-8871. p. 1143

Leroy, Denise, Libr Mgr, Northern Forestry Centre, 5320 122nd St, Rm 052, Edmonton, AB, T6H 3S5, CANADA. Tel: 780-735-7324. Fax: 780-435-7356, 780-435-7359. p. 2702

Lerud-Heck, Joanne V, Dir, Colorado School of Mines, 1400 Illinois St, Golden, CO, 80401-1887. Tel: 303-273-3690. Fax: 303-273-3199. p. 309

Lerum, Traci, Circ Mgr, DeForest Area Public Library, 203 Library St, DeForest, WI, 53532. Tel: 608-846-5482. Fax: 608-846-6875. p. 2588

Les, Catherine, Supvr, Tech Serv, Sterling Heights Public Library, 40255 Dodge Park Rd, Sterling Heights, MI, 48313-4140. Tel: 586-446-2649. Fax: 586-276-4067. p. 1229

Lesa, Reupena, Ref, American Samoa Community College Library, Malaeimi Village, Malaeimi Rd, Mapusaga, AS, 96799. Tel: 684-699-5728. Fax: 684-699-5732. p. 2665

Lesage, Gilles, Exec Dir, La Societe Historique de Saint-Boniface Bibliotheque, 340 Provencher Blvd, Saint Boniface, MB, R2H 0G7, CANADA. Tel: 204-233-4888. Fax: 204-231-2562. p. 2751

Lesesne, Teri, Dr, Prof, Sam Houston State University, 1921 Ave J, Huntsville, TX, 77340. Tel: 936-294-3673. Fax: 936-294-1153. p. 2974

Lesh, Nancy, Ref Serv, University of Alaska Anchorage, Consortium Library, 3211 Providence Dr, Anchorage, AK, 99508-8176. Tel: 907-786-1871. Fax: 907-786-1834. p. 45

Leshendok, Maureen, Ref Librn, Truckee Meadows Community College, 7000 Dandini Blvd, Reno, NV, 89512-3999. Tel: 775-674-7600. Fax: 775-673-8231. p. 1432

Lesher, Anne, Librn, Catholic University of America, Reference & Instructional Services Division, 124 Mullen Library, 620 Michigan Ave NE, Washington, DC, 20064. Tel: 202-319-5068. Fax: 202-319-6054. p. 396

Lesher, Debbie, Dir, Randolph Public Library, 106 S Main St, Randolph, IA, 51649. Tel: 712-625-3561. Fax: 712-625-3561. p. 840

Lesher, Marcella, Per, Saint Mary's University, Louis J Blume Library, One Camino Santa Maria, San Antonio, TX, 78228-8608. Tel: 210-436-3441. Fax: 210-436-3782. p. 2381

Lesher, Pete, Chief Curator, Chesapeake Bay Maritime Museum Library, 213 N Talbot St, Saint Michaels, MD, 21663. Tel: 410-745-4971. Fax: 410-745-6088. p. 1040

Lesher, Robin, Dir, Adams County Library System, 140 Baltimore St, Gettysburg, PA, 17325-2311. Tel: 717-334-0163. Fax: 717-334-7992. p. 2059

Lesiak, Karen, Dir, Libr Serv, St Thomas Seminary & Archdiocesan Center, 467 Bloomfield Ave, Bloomfield, CT, 06002. Tel: 860-242-5573, Ext 2609. Fax: 860-242-4886, Library. p. 331

Lesieur, Denis J, Exec Dir, Lenox Library Association, 18 Main St, Lenox, MA, 01240. Tel: 413-637-2630. Fax: 413-637-2115. p. 1098

Lesley, Georgia, Br Mgr, Thompson-Nicola Regional District Library System, Lytton Branch, 121 Fourth St, Lytton, BC, V0K 1Z0, CANADA. Tel: 250-455-2521. Fax: 250-455-2521. p. 2729

Lesley, Kay, Ch, Muscle Shoals Public Library, 1918 E Avalon, Muscle Shoals, AL, 35661. Tel: 256-386-9212. Fax: 256-386-9211. p. 32

Lesley, Terri, Bus Mgr, Campbell County Public Library System, 2101 S 4-J Rd, Gillette, WY, 82718-5205. Tel: 307-687-0009. Fax: 307-686-4009. p. 2655

Lesley, Thomas M, Ref, Vestavia Hills Library in the Forest, 1112 Montgomery Hwy, Vestavia Hills, AL, 35216. Tel: 205-978-0155. Fax: 205-978-0156. p. 39

Leslie, Deborah J, Head, Cat, Folger Shakespeare Library, 201 E Capitol St SE, Washington, DC, 20003-1094. Tel: 202-544-4600. Fax: 202-544-4623. p. 400

Leslie, Glennda, Archivist, The City of Calgary, Corporate Records, Archives, 313 Seventh Ave SE, Calgary, AB, T2G 0J1, CANADA. Tel: 403-268-8180. Fax: 403-268-6731. p. 2691

Leslie, Laura J H, Circ Supvr, University of Washington Libraries, Engineering Library, Engineering Library Bldg, Box 352170, Seattle, WA, 98195-2170. Tel: 206-543-0740. Fax: 206-543-3305. p. 2533

Leslie, Melissa, Br Librn, Lake Agassiz Regional Library, Ada Public Library, 107 Fourth Ave E, Ada, MN, 56510-1302. Tel: 218-784-4480. Fax: 218-784-2594. p. 1265

Leslie, Su, Asst Librn, St Croix Falls Public Library, 230 S Washington St, Saint Croix Falls, WI, 54024. Tel: 715-483-1777. Fax: 715-483-1777. p. 2635

Lesnever, Arnold, Info Tech, Hopewell Public Library, 13 E Broad St, Hopewell, NJ, 08525. Tel: 609-466-1625. Fax: 609-466-1996. p. 1491

Lesnever, Elaine, ILL Coordr, Hopewell Public Library, 13 E Broad St, Hopewell, NJ, 08525. Tel: 609-466-1625. Fax: 609-466-1996. p. 1491

Lesniaski, David, PhD, Assoc Prof, Saint Catherine University, 2004 Randolph Ave, Mailstop No 4125, Saint Paul, MN, 55105. Tel: 651-690-6802. Fax: 651-690-8724. p. 2968

Lesperance, Lynn, Assoc Librn, Yarmouth Port Library, 297 Main St, Rte 6A, Yarmouth Port, MA, 02675. Tel: 508-362-3717. Fax: 508-362-6739. p. 1146

Lesperance-Caron, Lavone, Staff Develop Coordr, Manitoba Developmental Centre Memorial Library, 840 3rd St NE, Portage la Prairie, MB, R1N 3C6, CANADA. Tel: 204-856-4230. Fax: 204-856-4221. p. 2750

Lessard, Nancy, Access Serv, The Royal Society of Canada Library, 283 Sparks St, Ottawa, ON, K1R 7X9, CANADA. Tel: 613-991-6990. Fax: 613-991-6996. p. 2833

Lessard, Roger, Dir, Bibliotheque Municipale, 372A Ave Du College, East Broughton, QC, G0N 1G0, CANADA. Tel: 418-427-3408, 418-427-4900. Fax: 418-427-3478, 418-427-3514. p. 2882

Lessey, Holly, Circ Asst, Lancaster Bible College Library, 901 Eden Rd, Lancaster, PA, 17601-5036. Tel: 717-560-8250. Fax: 717-560-8265. p. 2076

Lessey, Lorri, Coll Develop, Ad, Fort Bend County Libraries, 1001 Golfview Dr, Richmond, TX, 77469-5199. Tel: 281-341-2640. Fax: 281-341-2688. p. 2374

Lesso, Elizabeth, Circ, Saint Joseph College, 1678 Asylum Ave, West Hartford, CT, 06117-2791. Tel: 860-232-4571. Fax: 860-523-4356. p. 376

Lessun, Walter, Jr, Dir, Gogebic Community College, E4946 Jackson Rd, Ironwood, MI, 49938. Tel: 906-932-4231, Ext 344. Fax: 906-932-0868. p. 1194

Lester, Alan, Curator, The Mary Baker Eddy Library, Lending & Reference Services, 200 Massachusetts Ave, P02-10, Boston, MA, 02115-3017. Tel: 617-450-7125. p. 1060

Lester, Charlotte, Head Librn, Magrath Public Library, Six N First St W, Magrath, AB, T0K 1J0, CANADA. Tel: 403-758-6498. Fax: 403-758-6442. p. 2710

Lester, David, Librn, Arnot Ogden Medical Center, 600 Roe Ave, Elmira, NY, 14905-1676. Tel: 607-737-4100, 607-737-4101. Fax: 607-737-4207. p. 1620

Lester, Denita, Libr Mgr, Muscle Shoals Public Library, 1918 E Avalon, Muscle Shoals, AL, 35661. Tel: 256-386-9212. Fax: 256-386-9211. p. 32

Lester, Frank, Bibliographer, Coordr, Media Serv, Webmaster, Vanderbilt University, Central Library, 419 21st Ave S, Nashville, TN, 37203-2427. Tel: 615-322-2838. Fax: 615-343-7451. p. 2260

Lester, Janice, Ref & Educ Librn, Long Island Jewish Medical Center, 270-05 76th Ave, New Hyde Park, NY, 11040. Tel: 718-470-7070. Fax: 718-470-6150. p. 1665

Lester, Mary, Librn, Winterport Memorial Library, 229 Main St, Winterport, ME, 04496. Tel: 207-223-5540. p. 1007

Lester, Noland, Mgr, Dayton Metro Library, Westwood, 3207 Hoover Ave, Dayton, OH, 45407. Tel: 937-496-8964. Fax: 937-496-4364. p. 1893

Lester, Sarah, Dir, Nutley Free Public Library, 93 Booth Dr, Nutley, NJ, 07110-2782. Tel: 973-667-0405. p. 1515

Lester, Stephen, Tech Serv, Center for Health, Environment & Justice, 150 S Washington St, Ste 300, Falls Church, VA, 22046. Tel: 703-237-2249. Fax: 703-237-8389. p. 2462

Lestini, Paula, Asst Librn, Wheeling Jesuit University, 316 Washington Ave, Wheeling, WV, 26003-6295. Tel: 304-243-2226. Fax: 304-243-2466. p. 2575

Lesur, Hollis, Sr Libr Asst, San Leandro Public Library, Mulford-Marina, 13699 Aurora Dr, San Leandro, CA, 94577-4036. Tel: 510-357-7976. p. 253

Lesur, Hollis, Sr Libr Asst, San Leandro Public Library, South, 14799 E 14th St, San Leandro, CA, 94578-2818. Tel: 510-577-7980. p. 253

Letalien, Jacqueline E, Br Mgr, Humboldt County Library, Kim Yerton Memorial Branch, Ten Loop Rd, Hoopa, CA, 95546. Tel: 530-625-5082. Fax: 530-625-5022. p. 147

Letendre, Jim, Coordr, Outreach Serv, Charleston County Public Library, 68 Calhoun St, Charleston, SC, 29401. Tel: 843-805-6883. p. 2183

Lethgo, Kelley, Youth Serv Librn, Tippecanoe County-Ivy Tech Library, 3101 S Creasy Lane, Lafayette, IN, 47903. Tel: 765-269-5392. Fax: 765-269-5383. p. 759

Letkeman, Susan, Asst Br Supvr, Region of Waterloo Library, St Jacobs Branch, 29 Queensway Dr, St. Jacobs, ON, N0B 2N0, CANADA. Tel: 519-664-3443. p. 2793

Letko, Heidi, Coll Coordr, Syst Coordr, Harvard Library, Blue Hill Meteorological Observatory Library, Pierce Hall, 29 Oxford St, Cambridge, MA, 02138. Tel: 617-495-2836. Fax: 617-495-9837. p. 1074

Leto, Susan, Circ, Grafton Public Library, 35 Grafton Common, Grafton, MA, 01519. Tel: 508-839-4649. Fax: 508-839-7726. p. 1091

Letourneau, Kelly, Librn, Wilson Community College Library, 902 Herring Ave, Wilson, NC, 27893. Tel: 252-246-1251. Fax: 252-243-7148. p. 1831

Letourneau, Therese, Dir, Cegep de Sherbrooke, 475 rue du Cegep, Sherbrooke, QC, J1E 4K1, CANADA. Tel: 819-564-6350, Ext 5231, 819-564-6350, Ext 5233. Fax: 819-564-4025. p. 2912

Lett, Kathleen M, Dir, Huntingburg Public Library, 419 N Jackson St, Huntingburg, IN, 47542. Tel: 812-683-2052. Fax: 812-683-2056. p. 748

Lett, Liz, Libr Coordr, Virginia Beach Public Library Department, South Rosemont Youth Library & Bookmobile, 1503 Competitor Ct, Virginia Beach, VA, 23456. Tel: 757-385-2650. p. 2500

Lett, Rosalind, Assoc Dir, Main Libr Pub Serv, Huntsville-Madison Public Library, 915 Monroe St, Huntsville, AL, 35801. Tel: 256-532-5946. Fax: 256-532-5997. p. 21

Letteri, Cynthia, Ref Serv, McHenry County College Library, 8900 US Hwy 14, Crystal Lake, IL, 60012-2738. Tel: 815-455-8533. Fax: 815-455-3999. p. 632

Lettieri, Diane, Youth & Multicultural Coll Develop, Lee County Library System, 2345 Union St, Fort Myers, FL, 33901-3917. Tel: 239-533-4800. Fax: 239-485-1100. p. 445

Lettieri, Diane, Coll Develop Librn, Lee County Library System, Processing Center, 881 Gunnery Rd N, Ste 2, Lehigh Acres, FL, 33971-1246. Tel: 239-461-7317. Fax: 239-461-7373. p. 446

Lettieri, Robin, Dir, Port Chester-Rye Brook Public Library, One Haseco Ave, Port Chester, NY, 10573. Tel: 914-939-6710, Ext 114. Fax: 914-939-4735. p. 1720

Lettofsky, Jean Loeb, Dir, Siegal College of Judaic Studies, 26500 Shaker Blvd, Cleveland, OH, 44122. Tel: 216-464-4050. Fax: 216-464-5827. p. 1881

Letts, Debra, Br Librn, Cadillac-Wexford Public Library, Manton Branch, 404 W Main St, Manton, MI, 49663. Tel: 231-824-3584. Fax: 231-824-3584. p. 1160

Leuck, Lisa, Dir, Elgin Public Library, 214 Main St, Elgin, IA, 52141. Tel: 563-426-5313. Fax: 563-426-5999. p. 814

Leung, Florence, Commun Libr Mgr, Queens Borough Public Library, East Elmhurst Community Library, 196-36 Northern Blvd, Flushing, NY, 11358. Tel: 718-357-6643. p. 1644

Leung, Rita, Librn, Fresno County Public Library, Cedar Clinton Neighborhood, 4150 E Clinton Ave, Fresno, CA, 93703-2520. Tel: 559-442-1770. p. 152

Leung, Rosina, Tech Serv Librn, Seneca College of Applied Arts & Technology, Newnham Campus (Main), 1750 Finch Ave E, North York, ON, M2J 2X5, CANADA. Tel: 416-491-5050, Ext 22391. Fax: 416-491-3349. p. 2813

Leupp, Stephanie, Ref Serv, Ad, Oklahoma Wesleyan University Library, 2201 Silver Lake Rd, Bartlesville, OK, 74006-6299. Tel: 918-335-6285. Fax: 918-335-6220. p. 1958

Leuthaeuser, Judy, Asst Dir, Pub Serv, Medina County District Library, 210 S Broadway, Medina, OH, 44256. Tel: 330-722-6235, Ext 2008. Fax: 330-725-2053. p. 1916

Lev, Yvonne, Distance Learning Librn, Goucher College Library, 1021 Dulaney Valley Rd, Baltimore, MD, 21204. Tel: 410-337-3289. Fax: 410-337-6419. p. 1014

Levac, Julie, Acq, National Gallery of Canada Library, 380 Sussex Dr, Ottawa, ON, K1N 9N4, CANADA. Tel: 613-990-0591. Fax: 613-990-9818. p. 2832

LeVan, Carolyn, Librn, Lyons Falls Free Library, 3918 High St, Lyons Falls, NY, 13368. Tel: 315-348-6180. Fax: 315-348-6180. p. 1656

Levang, Julie, Info Coordr, Ref Coordr, Duluth Public Library, 520 W Superior St, Duluth, MN, 55802. Tel: 218-730-4247. Fax: 218-723-3815, 218-723-3822. p. 1247

Levanovsky, Odelia, Access Serv Librn, Amherst College, Amherst, MA, 01002. Fax: 413-542-2662. p. 1048

LeVasseur, Alisha, Libr Supvr-Popular Libr, Jacksonville Public Library, 303 N Laura St, Jacksonville, FL, 32202-3505. Tel: 904-630-2982. Fax: 904-630-2431. p. 453

Levasseur, Denis, Librn, Webmaster, Ecole de Technologie Superieure (Service de la bibliotheque), 1100 rue Notre-Dame Ouest, Montreal, QC, H3C 1K3, CANADA. Tel: 514-396-8946. Fax: 514-396-8633. p. 2895

Levasseur, Stephanie, Dir, Baltimore County Circuit Court Library, 401 Bosley Ave, Towson, MD, 21204. Tel: 410-887-3086. Fax: 410-887-4807. p. 1044

Leveck, Jennifer, Youth Serv Librn, Solon Public Library, 320 W Main St, Solon, IA, 52333-9504. Tel: 319-624-2678. Fax: 319-624-5034. p. 845

Leven, Stuart, Pres, Western Philatelic Library, Bldg 6, Rm 6, 1500 Partridge Ave, Sunnyvale, CA, 94087. Tel: 408-733-0336. p. 274

Levenback, Karen L, Archivist/Librn, Franciscan Monastery Library, 1400 Quincy St NE, Washington, DC, 20017. Tel: 202-526-6800. Fax: 202-529-9889. p. 401

Levenberg, Nancy, Exec Dir, Napa County Historical Society, Goodman Library Bldg, 1219 First St, Napa, CA, 94559. Tel: 707-224-1739. p. 192

Levenhagen, Denise, Dir, John C Clegg Public Library, 137 Fourth St N, Central City, IA, 52214. Tel: 319-438-6685. Fax: 319-438-6685. p. 801

Levenson, David, In Charge, Florida State University Libraries, Department of Religion Library, 301-B Dodd Hall, Tallahassee, FL, 32306-1520. Tel: 850-644-1020. Fax: 850-644-7225. p. 494

Leventhal, Louis, Sr Res Librn, Parade Publications, Inc, 711 Third Avenue, 7th Flr, New York, NY, 10017-4014. Tel: 212-450-7000. Fax: 212-450-7283. p. 1697

Leventis, Laura, Reader Serv, South Carolina State Library, 1430 Senate St, Columbia, SC, 29201-3710. Tel: 803-734-4611. Fax: 803-734-4610. p. 2189

Lever, Carole, Mgr, Union Memorial Hospital, 201 E University Pkwy, Baltimore, MD, 21218. Tel: 410-554-2294. Fax: 410-554-2166. p. 1018

Lever, Victoria, Adult Serv, Babylon Public Library, 24 S Carll Ave, Babylon, NY, 11702. Tel: 631-669-1624. Fax: 631-669-7826. p. 1577

Leverance, Emily, ILL, Libr Asst, Globe Public Library, 339 S Broad St, Globe, AZ, 85501-1744. Tel: 928-425-6111. Fax: 928-425-3357. p. 65

Leverette, Opal, Librn, Pine Forest Regional Library, State Line Public, Eight Farrier St, State Line, MS, 39362. Tel: 601-848-7011. Fax: 601-848-7011. p. 1314

Leveridge, Jennifer, Commun Serv, Newmarket Public Library, 438 Park Ave, Newmarket, ON, L3Y 1W1, CANADA. Tel: 905-953-5110. Fax: 905-953-5104. p. 2824

Leverone, Antonia, Syst Serv, Tech Serv, Hanson Public Library, 132 Maquan St, Hanson, MA, 02341. Tel: 781-293-2151. Fax: 781-293-6801. p. 1093

Levers, Carol, Dir, Kansas City, Kansas Public Library, 625 Minnesota Ave, Kansas City, KS, 66101. Tel: 913-279-2219. Fax: 913-279-2033. p. 875

Leversee, Marcia, Dir, Antioch University New England Library, 40 Avon St, Keene, NH, 03431-3516. Tel: 603-283-2400. Fax: 603-357-7345. p. 1452

Levesque, Brian, Tech Coordr, Caribou Public Library, 30 High St, Caribou, ME, 04736. Tel: 207-493-4214. Fax: 207-493-4654. p. 981

Lévesque, Claudette, Actg Exec Dir, Canadian Heritage Information Network, 15 Eddy St, 4th Flr, Gatineau, QC, K1A 0M5, CANADA. Tel: 819-994-1200. Fax: 819-994-9555. p. 2960

Levesque, Gisele, Supvr, Essex County Library, Comber Branch, 6400 Main St, Comber, ON, N0P 1J0, CANADA. Tel: 226-946-1529, Ext 222. p. 2804

Levesque, Jeannine, Hist Coll Librn, Leominster Public Library, 30 West St, Leominster, MA, 01453. Tel: 978-534-7522. Fax: 978-840-3357. p. 1098

Levesque, Michel, Asst Librn, Societe d'Histoire et d'Archeologie des Monts, Inc, 675 Blvd Saint Anne Ouest, Sainte-Anne-des-Monts, QC, G4V 1T9, CANADA. Tel: 418-763-7871. p. 2910

Levesque, Nancy, Univ Librn, Thompson Rivers University, 900 McGill Rd, Kamloops, BC, V2C 5N3, CANADA. Tel: 250-828-5305. Fax: 250-828-5313. p. 2730

Levier, Lindsay, Pub Relations Coordr, Salem-South Lyon District Library, 9800 Pontiac Trail, South Lyon, MI, 48178-1307. Tel: 248-437-6431, Ext 209. Fax: 248-437-6593. p. 1227

Levin, Amy, Librn, Smithsonian Libraries, Museum Studies & Reference Library, Nat Museum of Natural Hist, Tenth St & Constitution Ave NW, Rm 27, MRC 154, Washington, DC, 20560. Tel: 202-633-1701. Fax: 202-786-2443. p. 415

Levin, Carie A, Educ Coordr, Morris County Historical Society, 68 Morris Ave, Morristown, NJ, 07960-4212. Tel: 973-267-3465. Fax: 973-267-8773. p. 1505

Levin, Dorothy, Mgr, Newsday, Inc Library, 235 Pinelawn Rd, Melville, NY, 11747-4250. Tel: 631-843-2333. Fax: 631-843-2065. p. 1659

Levin, M H, Dr, Librn, Environmental Research Associates Inc Library, PO Box 219, Villanova, PA, 19085-0219. Tel: 610-449-7400. Fax: 610-449-7404. p. 2149

Levin, Nancy S, Dir, Cleveland Heights-University Heights Public Library, 2345 Lee Rd, Cleveland Heights, OH, 44118-3493. Tel: 216-932-3600, Ext 240. Fax: 216-932-0932. p. 1882

Levine, Amy, Ref, US Courts Library, Byron Rogers Courthouse, 1929 Stout St, Rm 430, Denver, CO, 80294. Tel: 303-844-3591. Fax: 303-844-5958. p. 303

Levine, Amy, Dir, Rockland Public Library, 80 Union St, Rockland, ME, 04841. Tel: 207-594-0310. Fax: 207-594-0333. p. 999

Levine, Art, Librn, West Florida Hospital, 8383 N Davis Hwy, Pensacola, FL, 32514. Tel: 850-494-4490. Fax: 850-494-6060. p. 482

Levine, Chris, Libr Tech III, University of Colorado Boulder, Archives & Special Collections, 1720 Pleasant St, Boulder, CO, 80309-0184. Tel: 303-492-0381. Fax: 303-492-1881. p. 291

Levine, Cynthia, Tech Serv, Winston-Salem State University, 601 Martin Luther King Jr Dr, Winston-Salem, NC, 27110. Tel: 336-750-2123. Fax: 336-750-2459. p. 1834

Levine, Dennis, Automation Serv, Broward College, 3501 SW Davie Rd, Davie, FL, 33314. Tel: 954-201-6648. Fax: 954-201-6490. p. 435

Levine, Jane, Head, Tech Serv, Winnetka-Northfield Public Library District, 768 Oak St, Winnetka, IL, 60093-2583. Tel: 847-446-7220. Fax: 847-446-5085. p. 720

Levine, Jodi, Ch, Pelham Library, Two S Valley Rd, Pelham, MA, 01002. Tel: 413-253-0657. Fax: 413-253-0594. p. 1117

Levine, Kendra, Ref Librn, Institute of Transportation Studies Library, 412 McLaughlin Hall, MC 1720, Berkeley, CA, 94720-1720. Tel: 510-642-3604. Fax: 510-642-9180. p. 127

Levine, Lenora, Youth Serv Librn, Cotuit Library, 871 Main St, Cotuit, MA, 02635. Tel: 508-428-8141. Fax: 508-428-4636. p. 1083

Levine, Maureen, Cataloger, Ansonia Library, 53 S Cliff St, Ansonia, CT, 06401-1909. Tel: 203-734-6275. Fax: 203-732-4551. p. 329

Levine, Sharon, Ch, Lincolnwood Public Library District, 4000 W Pratt Ave, Lincolnwood, IL, 60712. Tel: 847-677-5277. Fax: 847-677-1937. p. 666

Levine-Clark, Michael, Coll Develop, University of Denver, 2150 E Evans Ave, Denver, CO, 80208-2007. Tel: 303-871-3441. Fax: 303-871-2290. p. 303

Levine-Clark, Michael, Ref, University of Denver, 2150 E Evans Ave, Denver, CO, 80208-2007. Tel: 303-871-3441. Fax: 303-871-2290. p. 304

Levinson, David, Syst Librn, Tech Spec, Lake Forest College, 555 N Sheridan, Lake Forest, IL, 60045. Tel: 847-735-5059. Fax: 847-735-6297. p. 663

Levitan, Jane, Head, Ch, Martinsburg-Berkeley County Public Library, 101 W King St, Martinsburg, WV, 25401. Tel: 304-267-8933. Fax: 304-267-9720. p. 2565

Levitt, Lisa, Acq Tech, University of Oregon Libraries, John E Jaqua Law Library, William W Knight Law Ctr, 2nd Flr, 1515 Agate St, Eugene, OR, 97403-1221. Tel: 541-346-3802. Fax: 541-346-1669. p. 1997

Levitt, Martin L, Dr, Librn, American Philosophical Society Library, 105 S Fifth St, Philadelphia, PA, 19106-3386. Tel: 215-440-3403. Fax: 215-440-3423. p. 2102

Levitt, Valerie, Libr Tech, Alameda Free Library, West End, 788 Santa Clara Ave, Alameda, CA, 94501-3334. Tel: 510-747-7767. Fax: 510-337-0877. p. 119

Levor, L Ruth, Assoc Dir, University of San Diego, Katherine M & George M Pardee Jr Legal Research Center, 5998 Alcala Park, San Diego, CA, 92110-2492. Tel: 619-260-4604. Fax: 619-260-4616. p. 239

Levy, Ann, Librn, Krieg DeVault LLP Library, One Indiana Sq, Ste 2800, Indianapolis, IN, 46204-2017. Tel: 317-636-4341. Fax: 317-636-1507. p. 750

Levy, April, Ref & Instrul Serv Librn, Columbia College Chicago Library, 624 S Michigan Ave, Chicago, IL, 60605-1996. Tel: 312-369-7072. Fax: 312-344-8062. p. 611

Levy, Carol, Coll Develop Mgr, Citizens Library, 55 S College St, Washington, PA, 15301. Tel: 724-222-2400. Fax: 724-222-2606. p. 2151

Levy, David, Prof, University of Washington, Mary Gates Hall, Ste 370, Campus Box 352840, Seattle, WA, 98195-2840. Tel: 206-685-9937. Fax: 206-616-3152. p. 2976

Levy, David B, Librn, Touro College Libraries, 43 W 23rd St, Fifth Fl, New York, NY, 10010. Tel: 212-287-3531. Fax: 212-627-3696. p. 1701

Levy, Enid, Librn, Glendale University, 220 N Glendale Ave, Glendale, CA, 91206. Tel: 818-247-0770. Fax: 818-247-0872. p. 155

Levy, June, Dir, Glendale Adventist Medical Center Library, 1509 Wilson Terrace, Glendale, CA, 91206. Tel: 818-409-8034. Fax: 818-546-5633. p. 155

Levy, June, Libr Dir, White Memorial Medical Center, 1720 Cesar E Chavez Ave, Los Angeles, CA, 90033-2462. Tel: 323-260-5715. Fax: 323-260-5748. p. 180

Levy, Karen, Librn, Vineland Developmental Center Hospital Library, 1676 E Landis Ave, Vineland, NJ, 08360. Tel: 856-794-5730. p. 1538

Levy, Laura, Head, Circ, Somerset County Library System, Peapack & Gladstone Public, School St, Peapack, NJ, 07977. Tel: 908-234-0598. Fax: 908-719-2236. p. 1475

Levy, Laura, Ref, Montclair State University, One Normal Ave, Montclair, NJ, 07043-1699. Tel: 973-655-7148. Fax: 973-655-7780. p. 1503

Levy, Lee, Br Mgr, Brooklyn Public Library, Homecrest, 2525 Coney Island Ave, Brooklyn, NY, 11223. Tel: 718-382-5924. Fax: 718-382-5955. p. 1591

Levy, Leslee, AV, Hewlett-Woodmere Public Library, 1125 Broadway, Hewlett, NY, 11557-0903. Tel: 516-374-1967. Fax: 516-569-1229. p. 1636

Levy, Leslie C, Exec Dir, Willa Cather Pioneer Memorial & Education Foundation, 413 N Webster St, Red Cloud, NE, 68970-2466. Tel: 402-746-2653. Fax: 402-746-2652. p. 1418

Levy, Michele, Info Serv Librn, Northampton Community College, 3835 Green Pond Rd, Bethlehem, PA, 18020-7599. Tel: 610-861-5360. Fax: 610-861-5373. p. 2034

Levy, Sarah, Access Serv, Rockland Community College Library, 145 College Rd, Suffern, NY, 10901. Tel: 845-574-4472. Fax: 845-574-4424. p. 1750

Lew, Charlotte, Coll Asst, Vanderbilt University, Divinity Library, 419 21st Ave S, Nashville, TN, 37203-2427. Tel: 615-322-2865. Fax: 615-343-8279. p. 2260

Lew, Ken, AV Coll, Franklin Lakes Free Public Library, 470 DeKorte Dr, Franklin Lakes, NJ, 07417. Tel: 201-891-2224. Fax: 201-891-5102. p. 1486

Lew, Margaret, Acq, Erie Community College-South Campus, 4041 Southwestern Blvd, Orchard Park, NY, 14127. Tel: 716-851-1772. Fax: 716-851-1778. p. 1712

Lewallen, John, Librn, Sedgwick County Law Library, 225 N Market St, Ste 210, Wichita, KS, 67202-2023. Tel: 316-263-2251, Ext 120. Fax: 316-263-0629. p. 900

Lewandoski, Jane, Pub Serv, Saint Clair County Community College, 323 Erie St, Port Huron, MI, 48060. Tel: 810-984-3881, 810-989-5640. Fax: 810-984-2852. p. 1219

Lewandowicz, Galina, Head of Libr & Archives, Cincinnati Art Museum, 953 Eden Park Dr, Cincinnati, OH, 45202-1557. Tel: 513-639-2978. Fax: 513-721-0129. p. 1868

Lewandowski, Jeff, Info & Tech Serv, Hinsdale Public Library, 20 E Maple St, Hinsdale, IL, 60521. Tel: 630-986-1976. Fax: 630-986-9654. p. 656

Lewek, Edward, Dir, Rochester General Hospital, 1425 Portland Ave, Rochester, NY, 14621. Tel: 585-922-4743. Fax: 585-544-1504. p. 1731

Lewellen, Rachel, Assessment Librn, University of Massachusetts Amherst, 154 Hicks Way, Amherst, MA, 01003-9275. Tel: 413-545-3343. Fax: 413-545-6873. p. 1049

Lewetag, Bonnie, Mgr, Healthsouth Harmarville Rehabilitation Hospital, Guys Run Rd, Pittsburgh, PA, 15238. Tel: 412-828-1300, Ext 7511. Fax: 412-826-6722. p. 2125

Lewin, Jackie, Exec Dir, St Joseph Museums Inc, 3406 Frederick Ave, Saint Joseph, MO, 64506. Tel: 816-232-8471. Fax: 816-232-8482. p. 1352

Lewis, Alison M, PhD, Asst Teaching Prof, Drexel University, Rush Bldg, Rm 306, 30 N 33rd St, Philadelphia, PA, 19104-2875. Tel: 215-895-2474. Fax: 215-895-2494. p. 2973

Lewis, Amy, Dir, Dine College, PO Box 580, Shiprock, NM, 87240-0580. Tel: 505-368-3543. Fax: 505-368-3519, 505-368-3539. p. 1565

Lewis, Ann, Dir, United States Air Force, Air Force Research Laboratory, Wright Research Site Technical Library, Det 1 AFRL/WSC, Bldg 642, Rm 1300, 2950 Hobson Way, Wright-Patterson AFB, OH, 45433-7765. Tel: 937-255-5511, Ext 4270. Fax: 937-656-7746. p. 1951

Lewis, Ann-Eliza, Dir, Columbia County Historical Society Library, Columbia County Museum, Five Albany Ave, Kinderhook, NY, 12106. Tel: 518-758-9265. Fax: 518-758-2499. p. 1649

Lewis, Anna, Asst Dir, University of Wisconsin-Madison, MERIT Library (Media, Education Resources & Information Technology), 225 N Mills St, Madison, WI, 53706. Tel: 608-263-4750. Fax: 608-262-6050. p. 2609

Lewis, Anne, Mgr, Latham & Watkins, 885 Third Ave, Ste 1000, New York, NY, 10022. Tel: 212-906-1200. Fax: 212-751-4864. p. 1685

Lewis, Arnold, Librn, Western Missouri Mental Health Center, 1000 E 24th St, Kansas City, MO, 64108. Tel: 816-512-7303. Fax: 816-512-7308. p. 1341

Lewis, Babrara, Mgr, Kinchafoonee Regional Library System, Calhoun County Library, 19379 E Hartford St, Edison, GA, 39846-5626. Tel: 229 835-2012. Fax: 229 835-2012. p. 528

Lewis, Barb, Librn, Cheney's Grove Township Library, 204 S State St, Saybrook, IL, 61770. Tel: 309-475-6131. Fax: 309-475-6131. p. 700

Lewis, Barbara, Ch, Free Library of Northampton Township, 25 Upper Holland Rd, Richboro, PA, 18954-1514. Tel: 215-357-3050. p. 2134

Lewis, Barry, Librn, San Luis Obispo County Law Library, County Government Ctr, Rm 125, 1050 Monterey St, San Luis Obispo, CA, 93408. Tel: 805-781-5855. Fax: 805-781-4172. p. 253

Lewis, Beth A, Dir, Talbot Research Library, 333 Cottman Ave, 3rd Flr, Philadelphia, PA, 19111-2497. Tel: 215-728-2711. Fax: 215-728-3655. p. 2117

Lewis, Betsy, Managing Librn I, Sno-Isle Libraries, Monroe Community Library, 1070 Village Way, Monroe, WA, 98272. Tel: 360-794-7851. Fax: 360-794-0292. p. 2542

Lewis, Betty, Per, Norwood Public Library, 198 Summit St, Norwood, NJ, 07648-1835. Tel: 201-768-9555. Fax: 201-767-2176. p. 1515

Lewis, Beverly, Dir, Rawlins Municipal Library, 1000 E Church St, Pierre, SD, 57501. Tel: 605-773-7421. Fax: 605-773-7423. p. 2216

Lewis, Brenda, Librn, White County Regional Library System, Bradford Branch, 302 W Walnut, Bradford, AR, 72020. Tel: 501-344-2558. Fax: 501-344-2558. p. 115

Lewis, Brian, County Librn, Tulare County Library, Visalia Headquarters Branch, 200 W Oak Ave, Visalia, CA, 93291. Tel: 559-713-2723. Fax: 559-737-4586. p. 281

Lewis, Brian G, County Librn, Tulare County Library, 200 W Oak Ave, Visalia, CA, 93291-4993. Tel: 559-733-6954, Ext 201. Fax: 559-730-2524. p. 280

Lewis, C Michael, Assoc Prof, University of Pittsburgh, 135 N Bellefield Ave, Pittsburgh, PA, 15260. Tel: 412-624-5230. Fax: 412-624-5231. p. 2973

Lewis, Candice, Doc Delivery, Libr Supvr-Popular Libr, University of Manitoba Libraries, Neil John Maclean Health Sciences Library, 223 Brodie Centre, 727 McDermot Ave, Winnipeg, MB, R3E 3P5, CANADA. Tel: 204-789-3345. Fax: 204-789-3922. p. 2759

Lewis, Carol, Ch, Speedway Public Library, 5633 W 25th St, Speedway, IN, 46224-3899. Tel: 317-243-8959. Fax: 317-243-9373. p. 780

Lewis, Carrie, Ref Librn, Midway College, 512 E Stephens St, Midway, KY, 40347-1120. Tel: 859-846-5744. Fax: 859-846-5333. p. 929

Lewis, Cathy, Dir, College of the Sequoias Library, 915 S Mooney Blvd, Visalia, CA, 93277. Tel: 559-730-3824. Fax: 559-737-4835. p. 280

Lewis, Chad, Coordr, ILL, Kenton County Public Library, 502 Scott Blvd, Covington, KY, 41011. Tel: 859-962-4060. Fax: 859-962-4096. p. 910

Lewis, Cheri, Br Mgr, Live Oak Public Libraries, Thunderbolt Branch, 2708 Mechanics Ave, Thunderbolt, GA, 31404. Tel: 912-354-5864. Fax: 912-354-5534. p. 550

Lewis, Christine, Acq Librn, Marshall University Libraries, One John Marshall Dr, Huntington, WV, 25755-2060. Tel: 304-696-4356. Fax: 304-696-5858. p. 2561

Lewis, Clayton D, Curator, University of Michigan, William L Clements Library, 909 S University Ave, Ann Arbor, MI, 48109-1190. Tel: 734-764-2347. Fax: 734-647-0716. p. 1152

Lewis, Clementine, ILL, Fiorello H LaGuardia Community College Library, 31-10 Thomson Ave, Long Island City, NY, 11101. Tel: 718-482-5421. Fax: 718-482-5444, 718-609-2011. p. 1654

Lewis, Connie, Asst Dir, Ref Serv, Hardin County Library, 1365 Pickwick St, Savannah, TN, 38372. Tel: 731-925-4314, 731-925-6848. Fax: 731-925-7132. p. 2264

Lewis, Courtney, Dir of Libr, Wyoming Seminary, 201 N Sprague Ave, Kingston, PA, 18704-3593. Tel: 570-270-2169. Fax: 570-270-2178. p. 2074

Lewis, Crissy, Dir, Sherman College of Straight Chiropractic, 2020 Springfield Rd, Spartanburg, SC, 29316-7251. Tel: 864-578-8770, Ext 253, 864-578-8770, Ext 254. Fax: 864-599-4860. p. 2204

Lewis, Cynthia, Librn, Vermont Law School, 68 North Windsor, South Royalton, VT, 05068. Tel: 802-831-1444. Fax: 802-763-7159. p. 2436

Lewis, Cynthia Patterson, Dir, King Library & Archives, 449 Auburn Ave NE, Atlanta, GA, 30312. Tel: 404-526-8986. Fax: 404-526-8914. p. 516

Lewis, Dan, Curator, Huntington Library, 1151 Oxford Rd, San Marino, CA, 91108. Tel: 626-405-2206. Fax: 626-449-5720. p. 255

Lewis, David, Dean, Indiana University-Purdue University Indianapolis, 755 W Michigan St, Indianapolis, IN, 46202-5195. Tel: 317-274-0493. Fax: 317-278-0368. p. 753

Lewis, Dawn, Br Mgr, Kent District Library, East Grand Rapids Branch, 746 Lakeside Dr SE, East Grand Rapids, MI, 49506. Tel: 616-784-2007. p. 1165

Lewis, Deanna, Tech Serv, Cape Fear Community College, 415 N Second St, Wilmington, NC, 28401-3993. Tel: 910-362-7039. Fax: 910-362-7005. p. 1830

Lewis, Debra, Br Mgr, Iberville Parish Library, Maringouin Branch, 77175 Ridgewood Dr, Maringouin, LA, 70757. Tel: 225-625-2743. Fax: 225-625-2743. p. 966

Lewis, Debra, Syst & Cat Librn, Fort Bend County Libraries, 1001 Golfview Dr, Richmond, TX, 77469-5199. Tel: 281-341-2633. Fax: 281-341-2688. p. 2374

Lewis, Delyn, Librn, Gladys Johnson Ritchie Library, 626 W College St, Jacksboro, TX, 76458-1655. Tel: 940-567-2240. Fax: 940-567-2240. p. 2347

Lewis, Derrick, Info Spec, United States Department of Transportation, National Highway Traffic Safety Administration-Technical Information Services, NPO-400, 1200 New Jersey Ave SE, Washington, DC, 20590. Fax: 202-493-2833. p. 420

Lewis, Donald, Supv Librn, Access Serv, Newark Public Library, Five Washington St, Newark, NJ, 07101. Tel: 973-733-7842. Fax: 973-733-5759. p. 1511

Lewis, Dorcas, Asst Dir, Brookline Public Library, 16 Main St, Brookline, NH, 03033. Tel: 603-673-3330. Fax: 603-673-0735. p. 1440

Lewis, Earnestine, Head of Libr, Southside Virginia Community College Libraries, 109 Campus Dr, Alberta, VA, 23821. Tel: 434-949-1064. Fax: 434-949-0013. p. 2444

Lewis, Eileen, Librn, Amity Public Library, 307 Trade St, Amity, OR, 97101. Tel: 503-835-8181. p. 1990

Lewis, Faye, Ref Serv, Dougherty County Public Library, 300 Pine Ave, Albany, GA, 31701-2533. Tel: 229-420-3200. Fax: 229-420-3215. p. 507

Lewis, Faye, Asst Dir, De Soto Trail Regional Library, 145 E Broad St, Camilla, GA, 31730-1842. Tel: 229-336-8372. Fax: 229-336-9353. p. 522

Lewis, Forest, Br Mgr, North Las Vegas Library District, Alexander Library, 1755 W Alexander Rd, North Las Vegas, NV, 89032. Tel: 702-633-2880. Fax: 702-399-9813. p. 1432

Lewis, Francene, Cat, Calvin College & Calvin Theological Seminary, 1855 Knollcrest Circle SE, Grand Rapids, MI, 49546-4402. Tel: 616-526-6308. Fax: 616-526-6470. p. 1184

Lewis, Gabrielle, Librn, Seyfarth Shaw, 131 S Dearborn St, Ste 2400, Chicago, IL, 60603-5577. Tel: 312-460-5000. Fax: 312-460-7000. p. 624

Lewis, Ginny, Div Mgr, Res Serv, High Point Public Library, 901 N Main St, High Point, NC, 27262. Tel: 336-883-3671. Fax: 336-883-3636. p. 1802

Lewis, Gregory, Libr Mgr, Metropolitan College of New York Library, 431 Canal St, 12th Flr, New York, NY, 10013. Tel: 212-343-1234, Ext 2007. Fax: 212-343-7398. p. 1686

Lewis, Howard, Exec Dir, The Institute of Business Appraisers, Inc Library, 6950 W Cypress Rd, Ste 209, Plantation, FL, 33317. Tel: 954-584-1144. Fax: 954-584-1184. p. 484

Lewis, Iveta, Libr Tech, University of Toronto Libraries, Family & Community Medicine Library, 500 University Ave, Toronto, ON, M5G 1V7, CANADA. Tel: 416-946-3071. Fax: 416-978-3912. p. 2866

Lewis, Jacqueline, Circ, ILL, University of Connecticut Health Center, 263 Farmington Ave, Farmington, CT, 06034. Tel: 860-679-2941. Fax: 860-679-4046. p. 340

Lewis, Jacqueline, Librn, Virginia Beach Public Library Department, Great Neck Area, 1251 Bayne Dr, Virginia Beach, VA, 23454. Tel: 757-385-2606. p. 2500

Lewis, Janet, Ch, Waldwick Public Library, 19-21 E Prospect St, Waldwick, NJ, 07463-2099. Tel: 201-652-5104. Fax: 201-652-6233. p. 1539

Lewis, Janice Steed, Assoc Dean, East Carolina University, J Y Joyner Library, E Fifth St, Greenville, NC, 27858-4353. Tel: 252-328-2267. Fax: 252-328-6892. p. 1798

Lewis, Jason, Webmaster, Teton County Library, 125 Virginian Lane, Jackson, WY, 83001. Tel: 307-733-2164, Ext 109. Fax: 307-733-4568. p. 2656

Lewis, Jean, Dir, Robert L F Sikes Public Library, 1445 Commerce Dr, Crestview, FL, 32539. Tel: 850-682-4432. Fax: 850-689-4788. p. 434

Lewis, Jean M, Librn, St John's Health System, 1235 E Cherokee St, Springfield, MO, 65804-2263. Tel: 417-820-2795. Fax: 417-820-5399. p. 1367

Lewis, Jennifer, Librn, Hamlin Memorial Library-Paris Hill, 16 Hannibal Hamlin Dr, South Paris, ME, 04281. Tel: 207-743-2980. p. 1001

Lewis, Jerry, Acq Librn, William J Campbell Library of the US Courts, 219 S Dearborn St, Rm 1637, Chicago, IL, 60604-1769. Tel: 312-435-5660. Fax: 312-408-5031. p. 607

Lewis, Jill, Dir, Maryland State Library for the Blind & Physically Handicapped, 415 Park Ave, Baltimore, MD, 21201-3603. Tel: 410-230-2424. Fax: 410-333-2095. p. 1016

Lewis, Jill H, Dir, Saratoga Hospital, 211 Church St, Saratoga Springs, NY, 12866. Tel: 518-583-8301. Fax: 518-580-4285. p. 1738

Lewis, Joanne, Dir, Global Issues Resource Center Library, Cuyahoga Community College, Education Ctr Bldg, Rm 115, 4250 Richmond Rd, Highland Hills, OH, 44122. Tel: 216-987-2224. Fax: 216-987-2133. p. 1904

Lewis, Jocelyn, Head, Tech Serv, Lebanon Public Library, 104 E Washington St, Lebanon, IN, 46052. Tel: 765-482-3460. Fax: 317-873-5059. p. 761

Lewis, Jodi, Br Librn, London Public Library, Jalna, 1119 Jalna Blvd, London, ON, N6E 3B3, CANADA. Tel: 519-685-6465. p. 2818

Lewis, Josh, Extn Spec, Metropolitan Library System in Oklahoma County, Jones Extension Library, 111 E Main, Jones, OK, 73049-0425. Tel: 405-399-5471. Fax: 405-399-3679. p. 1972

Lewis, Julia, Circ, Philadelphia College of Osteopathic Medicine, 4170 City Ave, Philadelphia, PA, 19131-1694. Tel: 215-871-6470. Fax: 215-871-6478. p. 2114

Lewis, Karen, Adult Serv, Charlotte Community Library, 226 S Bostwick St, Charlotte, MI, 48813-1801. Tel: 517-543-8859. Fax: 517-543-8868. p. 1162

Lewis, Karen, Conserv Librn, Res, Oregon Zoo Animal Management Library, 4001 SW Canyon Rd, Portland, OR, 97221. Tel: 503-220-5763. Fax: 503-226-0074. p. 2013

Lewis, Karen J, Chief Librn, United States Army, Seven Bernard Rd, Fort Monroe, VA, 23651-5124. Tel: 757-788-2967. Fax: 757-788-2931. p. 2465

Lewis, Kate, Dir, Carnegie Public Library, 314 McLeod St, Big Timber, MT, 59011. Tel: 406-932-5608. p. 1373

Lewis, Katherine, Asst Librn, Runnemede Free Public Library, Broadway & Black Horse Pike, Runnemede, NJ, 08078. Tel: 856-939-4688. Fax: 856-939-6371. p. 1528

Lewis Kempe, Gwen, Ser/Reserves Tech, University of Washington Libraries, Tacoma Library, 1900 Commerce St, Box 358460, Tacoma, WA, 98402-3100. Tel: 253-692-5748. Fax: 253-692-4445. p. 2535

Lewis, Ken, Br Mgr, Montgomery County Public Libraries, Little Falls Library, 5501 Massachusetts Ave, Bethesda, MD, 20816. Tel: 240-773-9526. Fax: 301-320-0164. p. 1038

Lewis, Ken, Dr, Dir, Child Custody Evaluation Services, Inc, PO Box 202, Glenside, PA, 19038-0202. Tel: 215-576-0177. p. 2062

Lewis, Layna L, Br Head, Brazoria County Library System, Angleton Branch, 401 E Cedar St, Angleton, TX, 77515-4652. Tel: 979-864-1519. Fax: 979-864-1518. p. 2275

Lewis, Lina, Librn, Washington County Library System, Greenland Branch Library, PO Box 67, 8 E Ross, Greenland, AR, 72737. Tel: 479-582-5992. p. 100

Lewis, Linda Carol, Head, Tech Serv, Jackson State University, 1325 J R Lynch St, Jackson, MS, 39217. Tel: 601-979-2123. Fax: 601-979-2239. p. 1303

Lewis, Lisa, Dir, Libr Serv, Huachuca City Public Library, 506 N Gonzales Blvd, Huachuca City, AZ, 85616-9610. Tel: 520-456-1063. Fax: 520-456-1063. p. 65

Lewis, Lucy, Br Mgr, Omaha Public Library, A V Sorensen Branch, 4808 Cass St, Omaha, NE, 68132-3031. Tel: 402-444-5274. Fax: 402-444-6592. p. 1414

Lewis, Marcia, Dir, Loveland Public Library, 300 N Adams Ave, Loveland, CO, 80537-5754. Tel: 970-962-2665. Fax: 970-962-2905. p. 317

Lewis, Marcia, Br Mgr, West Hartford Public Library, Julia Faxon Branch, 1073 New Britain Ave, West Hartford, CT, 06110. Tel: 860-561-8200. p. 376

Lewis, Margie, Ch, Faulkner-Van Buren Regional Library System, 1900 Tyler St, Conway, AR, 72032. Tel: 501-327-7482. Fax: 501-327-9098. p. 96

Lewis, Marilyn, Bibliog Serv, ILL, Virginia Institute of Marine Science, College of William & Mary, Rte 1208, Greate Rd, Gloucester Point, VA, 23062. Tel: 804-684-7116. Fax: 804-684-7113. p. 2467

Lewis, Marvin, Dir, Red River Parish Library, 2022 Alonzo, Coushatta, LA, 71019-9474. Tel: 318-932-5614. Fax: 318-932-6747. p. 947

Lewis, Mary Ann, YA Librn, Pocono Mountain Public Library, 5540 Memorial Blvd, Tobyhanna, PA, 18466. Tel: 570-894-8860. Fax: 570-894-8852. p. 2146

Lewis, Nancy, Ref, University of Maine, 5729 Fogler Library, Orono, ME, 04469-5729. Fax: 207-581-1653. p. 994

Lewis, Nancy, Interim Dir, Wood Place Library, 501 S Oak St, California, MO, 65018. Tel: 573-796-2642. Fax: 573-796-6108. p. 1321

Lewis, Nancy, Librn, Johnston Community College Library, Learning Resource Ctr, 245 College Rd, Smithfield, NC, 27577. Tel: 919-464-2251. p. 1824

Lewis, Nora, Dir, Libr & Archives, Georgia Historical Society Library, 501 Whitaker St, Savannah, GA, 31401. Tel: 912-651-2128. Fax: 912-651-2831. p. 550

Lewis, Ollie M, Circ/Reserves, Southern University, Oliver B Spellman Law Library, 56 Roosevelt Steptoe, Baton Rouge, LA, 70813. Tel: 225-771-2139, 225-771-2315. Fax: 225-771-6254. p. 944

Lewis, Omeria, Circ/AV Supvr, Jackson/Hinds Library System, Eudora Welty Library (Main Library), 300 North State St, Jackson, MS, 39201-1705. Tel: 601-968-5811. Fax: 601-968-5806. p. 1303

Lewis, Padgett, Mkt & Communications Mgr, Richland County Public Library, 1431 Assembly St, Columbia, SC, 29201-3101. Tel: 803-799-9084. Fax: 803-929-3448. p. 2188

Lewis, Pamela K, Mgr, Morrison & Foerster LLP, 5200 Republic Plaza Bldg, 370 17th St, Denver, CO, 80202. Tel: 303-592-2259. Fax: 303-592-1510. p. 302

Lewis, Patricia, Circ, Danville Public Library, 319 N Vermilion St, Danville, IL, 61832. Tel: 217-477-5220. Fax: 217-477-5230. p. 633

Lewis, Paula, In Charge, Abe & Esther Tenenbaum Library, Nine Lee Blvd, Savannah, GA, 31405. Tel: 912-352-4737. Fax: 912-352-3477. p. 551

Lewis, Peggy S, Doc Delivery, Frick Hospital, 508 S Church St, Mount Pleasant, PA, 15666. Tel: 724-547-1352. Fax: 724-547-1693. p. 2093

Lewis, Priscilla, Asst Dir, Fac Mgt & Develop, Interim Dir, Durham County Library, 300 N Roxboro St, Durham, NC, 27701. Tel: 919-560-0100. Fax: 919-560-0137. p. 1788

Lewis, Renette, Br Mgr, Live Oak Public Libraries, W W Law Branch, 909 E Bolton St, Savannah, GA, 31401. Tel: 912-236-8040. Fax: 912-236-8040. p. 550

Lewis, Rich, Dir, Prescott College Library, 217 Garden St, Prescott, AZ, 86301. Tel: 928-350-1300. p. 78

Lewis, Rita, Ch, Centralia Regional Library District, 515 E Broadway, Centralia, IL, 62801. Tel: 618-532-5222. Fax: 618-532-8578. p. 602

Lewis, Robert, Asst Librn, Encyclopaedia Britannica Inc, 331 N LaSalle, Chicago, IL, 60654. Tel: 312-347-7429. Fax: 312-294-2162. p. 613

Lewis, Robin, Dir, United States Department of Housing & Urban Development, 451 Seventh St SW, Rm 8141, Washington, DC, 20410. Tel: 202-708-2370. Fax: 202-708-1485. p. 419

Lewis, Roxanne, Br Mgr, Northeast Missouri Library Service, Lewis County Branch-LaBelle, 425 State St, LaBelle, MO, 63447. Tel: 660-213-3600. Fax: 660-462-3600. p. 1336

Lewis, Sabrina, Info Spec, Albemarle Corp Library, Information Services, 451 Florida St, 15th Flr, Baton Rouge, LA, 70801-1700. Tel: 225-388-7402 (customer serv). Fax: 225-388-7686. p. 942

Lewis, Sandy, Tech Info Spec, OSHA, 200 Constitution Ave NW, Rm N-2625, Washington, DC, 20210-2001. Tel: 202-693-2350. Fax: 202-693-1648. p. 412

Lewis, Sarah, Br Mgr, Putnam County Library System, Baxter Branch, Baxter City Hall, 200 Main St, Baxter, TN, 38544-0335. Tel: 931-858-1888. p. 2231

Lewis, Savannah, Libr Dir, Seldovia Public Library, 260 Seldovia St, Seldovia, AK, 99663. Tel: 907-234-7662. p. 52

Lewis, Sheri, Assoc Librn, Pub Serv, University of Chicago Library, D'Angelo Law Library, 1121 E 60th St, Chicago, IL, 60637-2786. Tel: 773-702-9614. Fax: 773-702-2889. p. 626

Lewis, Shirley, Asst Librn, Pub Serv, Walsh University, 2020 E Maple St NW, North Canton, OH, 44720-3336. Tel: 330-490-7187. Fax: 330-490-7270. p. 1923

Lewis, Shirley, Dir, Oglala Lakota College, He Sapa College Center, 127 Knollwood Dr, Rapid City, SD, 57709. Tel: 605-342-1513. Fax: 605-342-8547. p. 2214

Lewis, Sonia, Chief Exec Officer, Kitchener Public Library, 85 Queen St N, Kitchener, ON, N2H 2H1, CANADA. Tel: 519-743-0271. Fax: 519-743-1261. p. 2815

Lewis, Susan, Dir, Boston Architectural College, 320 Newbury St, Boston, MA, 02115. Tel: 617-585-0234. Fax: 617-585-0151. p. 1055

Lewis, Terri, Tech Serv Mgr, Boulder Public Library, 1001 Arapahoe Rd, Boulder, CO, 80302. Tel: 303-441-3100. Fax: 303-442-1808. p. 290

Lewis, Theresa A, Librn, Alden Balch Memorial Library, 24 E Main St, Lunenburg, VT, 05906. Tel: 802-892-5365. p. 2427

Lewis, Timothy A, Dir, State Law Librn, Alabama Supreme Court & State Law Library, Heflin-Torbert Judicial Bldg, 300 Dexter Ave, Montgomery, AL, 36104. Tel: 334-229-0578. Fax: 334-229-0543. p. 28

Lewis, TJ, Asst Archivist, City of Edmonton, Archives, 10440 - 108 Ave, 2nd Flr, Prince of Wales Armouries Heritage Centre, Edmonton, AB, T5H 3Z9, CANADA. Tel: 780-496-8722. Fax: 780-496-8732. p. 2699

Lewis, Valerie, Ref Librn, Atlanta-Fulton Public Library System, Southwest Regional Library, 3665 Cascade Rd SW, Atlanta, GA, 30331. Tel: 404-699-6363. Fax: 404-699-6381. p. 512

Lewis, Valerie, Librn, Suffolk Cooperative Library System, Long Island Talking Book Library, 627 N Sunrise Service Rd, Bellport, NY, 11713. Tel: 631-286-1600. Fax: 631-286-1647. p. 1580

Lewis, Valerie, Outreach Prog, Suffolk Cooperative Library System, 627 N Sunrise Service Rd, Bellport, NY, 11713. Tel: 631-286-1600. Fax: 631-286-1647. p. 1580

Lewis, Veronica, Libr Dir, Prairie Bible Institute, 330 Fourth Ave N, Three Hills, AB, T0M 2N0, CANADA. Tel: 403-443-5511, Ext 3343. Fax: 403-443-5540. p. 2719

Lewis, Vickie, Asst Dir, North Kansas City Public Library, 2251 Howell St, North Kansas City, MO, 64116. Tel: 816-221-3360. Fax: 816-221-8298. p. 1348

Lewis, Vivian, Actg Univ Librn, McMaster University Library, 1280 Main St W, Hamilton, ON, L8S 4L6, CANADA. Tel: 905-524-9140, Ext 23883. Fax: 905-524-9850. p. 2810

Lewis, William, Br Mgr, Brooklyn Public Library, Kensington, 410 Ditmas Ave, Brooklyn, NY, 11218. Tel: 718-435-9431. Fax: 718-435-9491. p. 1591

Lewis, Yuki, Br Mgr, Huntsville-Madison Public Library, Oscar Mason Library, 149 Mason Ct, Huntsville, AL, 35805. Tel: 256-535-2249. p. 21

Lewis-Brown, Lisa, Asst Librn, Spencer County Public Library, 168 Taylorsville Rd, Taylorsville, KY, 40071. Tel: 502-477-8137. Fax: 502-477-5033. p. 936

Lewis-Coker, Florence, District I Supvry Librn, Berkeley County Library System, 1003 Hwy 52, Moncks Corner, SC, 29461. Tel: 843-719-4228. p. 2200

Lewis-Somers, Susan, Assoc Librn, Pub Serv, American University, 4801 Massachusetts Ave NW, Washington, DC, 20016-8182. Tel: 202-274-4330. Fax: 202-274-4365. p. 393

Lewis-Spann, Julia, Dir, ITT Technical Institute, 3401 S University Dr, Fort Lauderdale, FL, 33328. Tel: 954-476-9300, Ext 141. p. 443

Lewis-Tidwell, Tara T, Circ, Hardin County Public Library, 100 Jim Owen Dr, Elizabethtown, KY, 42701. Tel: 270-769-6337. Fax: 270-769-0437. p. 912

Lewontin, Amy, Coll Develop Librn, Northeastern University Libraries, Snell Library, 360 Huntington Ave, Boston, MA, 02115. Tel: 617-373-2001. p. 1065

Lexow, Janet, Asst Librn, Mercyhurst College, Ridge Library - North East Campus, 16 W Division St, North East, PA, 16428. Tel: 814-725-6326. Fax: 814-725-6112. p. 2056

Leyko, Andrea K, Coordr, Pub Serv, Carlow University, 3333 Fifth Ave, Pittsburgh, PA, 15213. Tel: 412-578-6139. Fax: 412-578-6242. p. 2122

Leypunskaya, Anna, Librn, North Jersey Media Group Library, 150 River St, Hackensack, NJ, 07601. Tel: 201-646-4000. Fax: 201-646-4737. p. 1489

Leysen, Sherry, Ref Librn, University of Washington Libraries, Marian Gould Gallagher Law Library, William H Gates Hall, Box 353025, Seattle, WA, 98195-3025. Tel: 206-685-4084. Fax: 206-685-2165. p. 2534

Leyser, Lisa, Dir, Federal Communications Commission Library, 445 12th St SW, Washington, DC, 20554. Tel: 202-418-0450. Fax: 202-418-2805. p. 400

Leyva, Lupie, Br Mgr, Los Angeles Public Library System, Robert L Stevenson Branch, 803 Spence St, Los Angeles, CA, 90023-1728. Tel: 323-268-4710. Fax: 213-612-0425. p. 174

Lezenby, Chris, Ref, Bank of America Merrill Lynch & Co, 250 Vesey St, 24th Flr, New York, NY, 10080. Tel: 212-449-3814. Fax: 212-449-1379. p. 1669

Lhota, Robert, Dean, Dyersburg State Community College, 1510 Lake Rd, Dyersburg, TN, 38024. Tel: 731-286-3226. Fax: 731-286-3228. p. 2233

Li, Alec, Acq, Cat, Gordon College, 255 Grapevine Rd, Wenham, MA, 01984-1899. Tel: 978-867-4341. Fax: 978-867-4660. p. 1136

Li, Amy, Dir, Rockford Memorial Hospital, 2400 N Rockton Ave, Rockford, IL, 61103. Tel: 815-971-6287. Fax: 815-968-7007. p. 697

Li, Beverly, Tech Serv, Lee College Library, 150 Lee Dr, Baytown, TX, 77520. Tel: 281-425-6379. Fax: 281-425-6557. p. 2286

Li, Bin, Dr, Sr Lecturer, Wayne State University, 106 Kresge Library, Detroit, MI, 48202. Tel: 313-577-1825. Fax: 313-577-7563. p. 2968

Li, Danny, Col Lab Tech, Queensborough Community College, City University of New York, 222-05 56th Ave, Bayside, NY, 11364-1497. Tel: 718-631-6672. Fax: 718-281-5012. p. 1579

Li, Diane, Br Mgr, Howard County Library System, Savage Branch, 9125 Durness Lane, Laurel, MD, 20723-5991. Tel: 410-880-5975. Fax: 410-880-5999. p. 1026

Li, Jie, Asst Dir, Coll Mgt, University of South Alabama, Biomedical Library, Biomedical Library Bldg, 5791 USA Dr N, Mobile, AL, 36688-0002. Tel: 251-460-6890. Fax: 251-460-6958. p. 26

Li, Jiexun Jason, PhD, Asst Prof, Drexel University, Rush Bldg, Rm 306, 30 N 33rd St, Philadelphia, PA, 19104-2875. Tel: 215-895-2474. Fax: 215-895-2494. p. 2972

Li, Jing, Commun Libr Mgr, County of Los Angeles Public Library, City Terrace Library, 4025 E City Terrace Dr, Los Angeles, CA, 90063-1297. Tel: 323-261-0295. Fax: 323-261-1790. p. 141

Li, Lilian, Info & Tech Librn, Medicine Hat College Library, 299 College Dr SE, Medicine Hat, AB, T1A 3Y6, CANADA. Tel: 403-529-3869. Fax: 403-504-3634. p. 2711

Li, Lisa, Ref Librn, University of Arkansas at Little Rock, 2801 S University Ave, Little Rock, AR, 72204. Tel: 501-569-8811. Fax: 501-569-3017. p. 107

Li, Marjorie, Br Coordr, Oakland Public Library, 125 14th St, Oakland, CA, 94612. Tel: 510-238-3670. Fax: 510-238-2232. p. 197

Li, Meilling, Dir of Tech, Los Angeles County Law Library, Mildred L Lillie Bldg, 301 W First St, Los Angeles, CA, 90012-3100. Tel: 213-785-2529. Fax: 213-613-1329. p. 172

Li, Ping, Asst Prof, Queens College of the City University of New York, Benjamin Rosenthal Library, Rm 254, 65-30 Kissena Blvd, Flushing, NY, 11367. Tel: 718-997-3790. Fax: 718-997-3797. p. 2970

Li, Robert, Librn, Hawaii Community Correctional Center Library, 60 Punahele St, Hilo, HI, 96720. Tel: 808-969-3090. Fax: 808-969-3090. p. 559

Li, Robert, Librn, Kulani Correctional Facility Library, HC-01 Stainback Hwy, Hilo, HI, 96720. Tel: 808-935-9268. Fax: 808-935-9268. p. 559

Li, Sam, Law Librn, United States Attorney's Office Library, North Branch, 970 Broad St, Ste 700, Newark, NJ, 07102. Tel: 973-645-2709. p. 1513

Li, Sam, Law Librn, United States Attorney's Office Library, Trenton Branch, 402 E State St, Trenton, NJ, 08608. Tel: 973-645-2709. p. 1513

Li, Sam, Librn, United States Attorney's Office Library, 970 Broad St, Rm 700, Newark, NJ, 07102. Tel: 973-645-2700. Fax: 973-297-2007. p. 1513

Li, Xiaohua, Dir, Digital Libr Tech & Serv, Sacred Heart University, 5151 Park Ave, Fairfield, CT, 06825-1000. Tel: 203-371-7702. Fax: 203-374-9968. p. 339

Li, Xiaoli, Head, Cat & Metadata Serv, University of California, Davis, 100 NW Quad, Davis, CA, 95616-5292. Tel: 530-752-6561. Fax: 530-752-3148. p. 139

Li, Xin, Assoc Univ Librn, Cornell University Library, 201 Olin Library, Ithaca, NY, 14853-5301. Tel: 607-255-7026. Fax: 607-255-6788. p. 1641

Li, Ying, Pub Serv Mgr, St Charles Community College, 4601 Mid Rivers Mall Dr, Cottleville, MO, 63376. Tel: 636-922-8438. Fax: 636-922-8433. p. 1326

Li, Yubao, Instrul Librn, Dona Ana Community College Library, 3400 S Espina, Rm 260, Las Cruces, NM, 88003. Tel: 575-527-7556. Fax: 575-527-7636. p. 1558

Li, Yuxin, Head, Cat & Ser, University of Houston, The O'Quinn Law Library, 12 Law Library, Houston, TX, 77204-6054. Tel: 713-743-2300. Fax: 713-743-2296. p. 2343

Li-Bugg, W Cherry, Dr, Dean III, Learning Res & Educ Tech, Santa Rosa Junior College, 1501 Mendocino Ave, Santa Rosa, CA, 95401. Tel: 707-527-4392. Fax: 707-527-4545. p. 267

Liamos, Paul, Br Mgr, US Courts Library, Byron Rogers Courthouse, 1929 Stout St, Rm 430, Denver, CO, 80294. Tel: 303-844-3591. Fax: 303-844-5958. p. 303

Liang, Michael, Chief Info Officer, San Francisco Public Library, 100 Larkin St, San Francisco, CA, 94102-4733. Tel: 415-557-4340. Fax: 415-557-4424. p. 246

Liang, Shan, Br Mgr, Los Angeles Public Library System, Chinatown, 639 N Hill St, Los Angeles, CA, 90012-2317. Tel: 213-620-0925. Fax: 213-620-9956. p. 173

Liao, Jiaqing, Acq of Monographs, Acq of New Ser, Cat, Far Eastern Research Library, Nine First Ave NE, Plato, MN, 55370-0181. Tel: 320-238-2591, 612-926-6887. p. 1271

Liao, Shan, Web Librn, Environmental Protection Agency, 2000 Traverwood Dr, Ann Arbor, MI, 48105. Tel: 734-214-4435. Fax: 734-214-4525. p. 1151

Liao, Yan, Head, Cat & Metadata Serv, Georgetown University, Georgetown Law Library (John Wolff & Edward Bennett Williams Libraries), 111 G St NW, Washington, DC, 20001. Fax: 202-662-9168. p. 403

Liaw, Barbara, Cat, Tech Serv, Huntsville-Madison Public Library, 915 Monroe St, Huntsville, AL, 35801. Tel: 256-532-5976. Fax: 256-532-5997. p. 21

Libbey, George H, Assoc Dean, Pub Serv, University of Detroit Mercy Library, 4001 W McNichols Rd, Detroit, MI, 48221-3038. Tel: 313-993-1078. Fax: 313-993-1780. p. 1172

Libby, Donna, Dir, Klamath Community College, 7390 S Sixth St, Klamath Falls, OR, 97603. Tel: 541-880-2206, 541-882-3521. Fax: 541-885-7758. p. 2001

Libby, Eileen, Librn, University of Chicago Library, Social Service Administration, 969 E 60th St, Chicago, IL, 60637-2627. Tel: 773-702-1199. Fax: 773-702-0874. p. 627

Libby, Katy, Cat, East Tennessee State University, Sherrod Library, Seehorn Dr & Lake St, Johnson City, TN, 37614-0204. Tel: 423-439-6992. Fax: 423-439-4410. p. 2239

Libby, Sandy, Librn, The Frances Kibble Kenny Lake Public Library, Mile 5 Edgerton Hwy, Copper Center, AK, 99573-9703. Tel: 907-822-3015. Fax: 907-822-3015. p. 46

Liberato, Leslie, Outreach Serv Librn, Bluffton Public Library, 145 S Main St, Bluffton, OH, 45817. Tel: 419-358-5016. Fax: 419-358-9653. p. 1860

Liberovsky, Alexis, Archivist, Orthodox Church in America, 6850 Rte 25A, Syosset, NY, 11791. Tel: 516-922-0550. Fax: 516-922-0954. p. 1751

Libertini, Arleen, Mgr, Empire Health Services, 910 W Fifth Ave, Spokane, WA, 99204. Tel: 509-473-7398. Fax: 509-473-7790. p. 2535

Library, Director, Libr Dir, Northern Wayne Community Library, 11 Library Rd, Lakewood, PA, 18439. Tel: 570-798-2444. Fax: 570-798-2444. p. 2076

Licari-DeMay, Terri L, Dir, Condell Medical Center, 900 Garfield Ave, Libertyville, IL, 60048. Tel: 847-990-5265. Fax: 847-990-2806. p. 665

Lichtenstein, Art A, Dir, University of Central Arkansas, 201 Donaghey Ave, Conway, AR, 72035. Tel: 501-450-3174. Fax: 501-450-5208. p. 97

Lichtenwalner, Jenny, Ref Librn, Scotch Plains Public Library, 1927 Bartle Ave, Scotch Plains, NJ, 07076-1212. Tel: 908-322-5007. Fax: 908-322-0490. p. 1528

Lichter, Patricia, Br Mgr, Oakland Public Library, Rockridge, 5366 College Ave, Oakland, CA, 94618. Tel: 510-597-5017. Fax: 510-597-5067. p. 198

Lichtman, Cathy, Teen Librn, Plymouth District Library, 223 S Main St, Plymouth, MI, 48170-1687. Tel: 734-453-0750, Ext 230. Fax: 734-453-0733. p. 1218

Lichtsinn, Jill, Acad Tech Support Librn, Manchester College, 604 E College Ave, North Manchester, IN, 46962. Tel: 260-982-5015. Fax: 260-982-5362. p. 769

Lickfelt, Elaine, Br Mgr, Sandusky Library, Kelleys Island Branch, 528 Division St, Kelleys Island, OH, 43438. Tel: 419-746-9575. p. 1934

Licklider, Jane, Librn, Diagnostic & Evaluation Center Library, 3220 W Van Dorn St, Lincoln, NE, 68522-9278. Tel: 402-471-3330. Fax: 402-479-6368. p. 1404

Licks, Sandra, Dir, Tracy Memorial Library, 304 Main St, New London, NH, 03257-7813. Tel: 603-526-4656. Fax: 603-526-8035. p. 1460

Lickteig, Jessie, Dir, Cherryvale Public Library, 329 E Main, Cherryvale, KS, 67335-1413. Tel: 620-336-3460. Fax: 620-336-3460. p. 860

Liddicoat, Michael, Sr Librn, El Camino Los Gatos Health Library, 815 Pollard Rd, Los Gatos, CA, 95032. Tel: 408-866-4044. Fax: 408-866-3829. p. 180

Liddington, Elizabeth, Ch Serv Librn, Waterford Public Library, 117 Third St, Waterford, NY, 12188. Tel: 518-237-0891. Fax: 518-237-2568. p. 1763

Liddy, Elizabeth D, Dean, Syracuse University, Center for Science & Technology, Rm 4-206, Syracuse, NY, 13244-4100. Tel: 315-443-2911. Fax: 315-443-5673. p. 2970

Liddy, Martin, Campus Librn, Milwaukee Area Technical College, 1200 S 71st St, Rm 213, West Allis, WI, 53214-3110. Tel: 414-456-5392. Fax: 414-456-5413. p. 2648

Liddy, Mary Ellen, Adult Serv, YA Serv, Kinnelon Public Library, 132 Kinnelon Rd, Kinnelon, NJ, 07405-2393. Tel: 973-838-1321. Fax: 973-838-0741. p. 1493

Lidgren, Ann, Mgr, Calgary Public Library, Nose Hill, 1530 Northmount Dr NW, Calgary, AB, T2L 0G6, CANADA. p. 2690

Lidle, Barbara, Asst Dir, J Lewis Crozer Library, 620 Engle St, Chester, PA, 19013-2199. Tel: 610-494-3454. Fax: 610-494-8954. p. 2044

Lieb, Gretchen, Ref Librn, Vassar College Library, 124 Raymond Ave, Maildrop 20, Poughkeepsie, NY, 12604-0020. Tel: 845-437-5760. Fax: 845-437-5864. p. 1723

Lieber, Barb, Dir of Libr Serv, John Wood Community College Library, 1301 S 48th St, Quincy, IL, 62305. Tel: 217-641-4535, 217-641-4537. Fax: 217-641-4197. p. 693

Lieberman, Annie, Br Mgr, Flathead County Library, Bigfork Branch, 525 Electric Ave, Bigfork, MT, 59911. Tel: 406-837-6976. p. 1384

Lieberman, Faye, Ch, Franklin Square Public Library, 19 Lincoln Rd, Franklin Square, NY, 11010. Tel: 516-488-3444. Fax: 516-354-3368. p. 1624

Lieberson, Lisa, Dir, Village Library of Wrightstown, 727 Penns Park Rd, Wrightstown, PA, 18940-9605. Tel: 215-598-3322. Fax: 215-598-9659. p. 2158

Liebert, June, Dir, The John Marshall Law School, 315 S Plymouth Ct, Chicago, IL, 60604. Tel: 312-427-2737. Fax: 312-427-8307. p. 618

Liebert, Tobe, Asst Dir, University of Texas Libraries, Jamail Center for Legal Research, University of Texas School of Law, 727 E Dean Keeton St, Austin, TX, 78705-3224. Tel: 512-471-7726. Fax: 512-471-0243. p. 2284

Lieberthal, Susan, Libr Dir, Suffolk County Community College, 533 College Rd, Selden, NY, 11784-2899. Tel: 631-451-4800. Fax: 631-451-4697. p. 1742

Lieberthal, Susan, Head, ILL, Stony Brook University, W-1502 Melville Library, John S Toll Rd, Stony Brook, NY, 11794-3300. Tel: 631-632-7100. Fax: 631-632-7116. p. 1749

Liebl, Janet, Curator, Lac Qui Parle County Historical Society, 250 Eighth Ave S, Madison, MN, 56256. Tel: 320-598-7678. p. 1256

Liebler, Raizel, Res Serv Librn, The John Marshall Law School, 315 S Plymouth Ct, Chicago, IL, 60604. Tel: 312-427-2737. Fax: 312-427-8307. p. 618

Liebman, Judith, Dir, Mercy College Libraries, 555 Broadway, Dobbs Ferry, NY, 10522. Tel: 914-674-7260. Fax: 914-674-7581. p. 1615

Liebman, Karen, Dir, Syosset Public Library, 225 S Oyster Bay Rd, Syosset, NY, 11791-5897. Tel: 516-921-7161. Fax: 516-921-8771. p. 1751

Liebst, Anne, Dir of Tech Serv, Linda Hall Library, 5109 Cherry St, Kansas City, MO, 64110-2498. Tel: 816-926-8784. Fax: 816-926-8790. p. 1337

Liebst, Claire Anne, Dir, Tech & Tech Serv, University of Arkansas at Little Rock, 2801 S University Ave, Little Rock, AR, 72204. Tel: 501-569-3248. Fax: 501-569-8128. p. 107

Liechty, Melanie, Computer Serv, Logan Library, 255 N Main, Logan, UT, 84321-3914. Tel: 435-716-9123. Fax: 435-716-9145. p. 2407

Lieckfield, Bob, Dir, Clayton Group Services, Inc, 22345 Roethel Dr, Novi, MI, 48375-4710. Tel: 248-344-1770. Fax: 248-344-2654. p. 1214

Liedtka, Theresa, Dean, University of Tennessee at Chattanooga Library, 615 McCallie Ave, Dept 6456, Chattanooga, TN, 37403-2598. Tel: 423-425-4506. Fax: 423-425-4775. p. 2228

Liedtke, Julie, Br Mgr, Cuyahoga County Public Library, Orange Branch, 31300 Chagrin Blvd, Pepper Pike, OH, 44124-5916. Tel: 216-831-4282. Fax: 216-831-0714. p. 1927

Lieffers, Roxanne, Asst Br Mgr, Atlanta-Fulton Public Library System, Buckhead Library, 269 Buckhead Ave NE, Atlanta, GA, 30305. Tel: 404-814-3500. Fax: 404-814-3503. p. 511

Lieffrig, Celine, Head, Ch, Amityville Public Library, Oak & John Sts, Amityville, NY, 11701. Tel: 631-264-0567. Fax: 631-264-2006. p. 1573

Lien, Debra, Librn, Mary Gilkey City Library, 416 Ferry St, Dayton, OR, 97114-9774. Tel: 503-864-2221. Fax: 503-864-2956. p. 1995

Lien, Marlys, Circ & Adult Serv Mgr, Council Bluffs Public Library, 400 Willow Ave, Council Bluffs, IA, 51503-4269. Tel: 712-323-7553, Ext 118. Fax: 712-323-1269. p. 805

Lien, Pam, Sch Librn, Lac La Biche County Library Board, Plamondon Municipal Library, Ecole Plamondon, Plamondon, AB, T0A 2T0, CANADA. Tel: 780-798-3852. p. 2708

Liendo, Danniza, Cat, Saint Thomas University Library, Law Library, 16401 NW 37th Ave, Miami Gardens, FL, 33054. Tel: 305-623-2313. Fax: 305-623-2337. p. 469

Lienemann, Stacy, Asst Dir, Watonwan County Library, 125 Fifth St S, Saint James, MN, 56081. Tel: 507-375-1278. Fax: 507-375-5415. p. 1276

Lierman, Ashley, Info Tech/Technical Serv Librn, Rosemont College Library, 1400 Montgomery Ave, Rosemont, PA, 19010-1631. Tel: 610-527-0200, Ext 2287. Fax: 610-525-2930. p. 2135

Liesenbein, Barbara, Dir, Dutchess Community College Library, 53 Pendell Rd, Poughkeepsie, NY, 12601-1595. Tel: 845-431-8635. Fax: 845-431-8995. p. 1722

Liesinger, Bev, In Charge, Siouxland Libraries, Crooks Branch, 900 N West Ave, Crooks, SD, 57020-6402. Tel: 605-543-5296. Fax: 605-543-5297. p. 2219

Liesinger, Bev, In Charge, Siouxland Libraries, Garretson Branch, 649 Main St, Garretson, SD, 57030-0392. Tel: 605-594-6619. Fax: 605-594-6619. p. 2219

Liesman, Vanda, In Charge, Elkhart Public Library District, 121 E Bohan St, Elkhart, IL, 62634. Tel: 217-947-2313. Fax: 217-947-2313. p. 642

Liestman, Daniel, Libr Dir, DeVry University, 3600 S 344th Way, Federal Way, WA, 98001-9558. Tel: 253-943-2800. Fax: 253-943-3297. p. 2515

Lietz, Jeremy, Dr, Dir, Educational Leadership Institute Library, 424 Susan Lane, Thiensville, WI, 53092. Tel: 262-512-2875. p. 2642

Lietzan, Caitlin, Dir, Libr Serv, Williams & Connolly Library, 725 12th St NW, Washington, DC, 20005. Tel: 202-434-5306. Fax: 202-434-5029. p. 423

Lifka, Robert, Dir, North Riverside Public Library District, 2400 S DesPlaines Ave, North Riverside, IL, 60546. Tel: 708-447-0869, Ext 225. Fax: 708-447-0526. p. 682

Light, Betty, Chair, First Baptist Church, 122 Gaston St, Brevard, NC, 28712. Tel: 828-883-8251. Fax: 828-883-8573. p. 1777

Light, Brian, Head, Circ, University of California, Berkeley, Education Psychology, 2600 Tolman Hall, Berkeley, CA, 94720-6000. Tel: 510-642-4209. Fax: 510-642-8224. p. 127

Light, Karen, Coll Mgt Librn, Westerly Public Library, 44 Broad St, Westerly, RI, 02891. Tel: 401-596-2877, Ext 328. Fax: 401-596-5600. p. 2178

Light, Lin, Automation Syst Coordr, Tech Serv, Herrick District Library, 300 S River Ave, Holland, MI, 49423-3290. Tel: 616-355-3100. p. 1190

Light, Phoenix, Mgr, Henry County Public Library System, Fairview Public Library, 28 Austin Rd, Stockbridge, GA, 30281. Tel: 770-389-6277. Fax: 770-389-6282. p. 544

Lightbody, Melanie Webber, County Librn, Mendocino County Library District, 105 N Main St, Ukiah, CA, 95482. p. 277

Lightcap, Paul, Tech Serv Mgr, Salem Public Library, 585 Liberty St SE, Salem, OR, 97301. Tel: 503-588-6020. Fax: 503-588-6055. p. 2018

Lightfeldt, Diana, Head, Fac & Receiving, University of California, Riverside Libraries, 900 University Ave, Riverside, CA, 92521. Tel: 951-827-2849. p. 218

Lightfoot, Linda K, Tech Serv, Okefenokee Regional Library, 401 Lee Ave, Waycross, GA, 31501. Tel: 912-287-4978. Fax: 912-284-2533. p. 557

Lightfoot, Susan, Dir, Carrollton Public Library, One N Folger, Carrollton, MO, 64633. Tel: 660-542-0183. Fax: 660-542-0654. p. 1322

Lightner, Karen, Head Librn, Free Library of Philadelphia, Art, 1901 Vine St, Philadelphia, PA, 19103-1189. Tel: 215-686-5403. p. 2106

Lightner, Karen, Curator, Free Library of Philadelphia, Print & Picture, 1901 Vine St, Philadelphia, PA, 19103-1189. Tel: 215-686-5405. p. 2109

Lightner, Patricia, Cat, Juniata College, 1815 Moore St, Huntingdon, PA, 16652-2120. Tel: 814-641-3450. Fax: 814-641-3435. p. 2070

Lightwood, Marian, Librn, The Frances Kibble Kenny Lake Public Library, Mile 5 Edgerton Hwy, Copper Center, AK, 99573-9703. Tel: 907-822-3015. Fax: 907-822-3015. p. 46

Ligozio, Patricia, Electronic Res, Webster Public Library, Webster Plaza, 980 Ridge Rd, Webster, NY, 14580. Tel: 585-872-7075. p. 1765

Liimatainen, Susan, Asst Dir, Rutland Free Public Library, 280 Main St, Rutland, MA, 01543. Tel: 508-886-4108. Fax: 508-886-4141. p. 1121

Liles, Pam, Librn, Evening Post Publishing Co, 134 Columbus St, Charleston, SC, 29403. Tel: 843-937-5698. Fax: 843-937-5696. p. 2184

Liles, Twillia J, Br Mgr, Montgomery County Memorial Library System, R F Meador Branch, 709 W Montgomery, Willis, TX, 77378. Tel: 936-442-7740. Fax: 936-856-3360. p. 2300

Liliefeldt, Mariko, Chief Librn, Japan Foundation, 131 Bloor St W, Ste 213, Toronto, ON, M5S 1R1, CANADA. Tel: 416-966-1600, Ext 238, 416-966-2935. Fax: 416-966-0957. p. 2855

Liljequist, Karen, Med Librn, Children's Institute Library, 1405 Shady Ave, Pittsburgh, PA, 15217-1350. Tel: 412-420-2247. Fax: 412-420-2510. p. 2124

Lilla, Debbie, Circ, Libr Coordr, Winona Public Library, 151 W Fifth St, Winona, MN, 55987-3170. Tel: 507-452-4582. Fax: 507-452-5842. p. 1290

Lilla, Rick, Media Serv, Lock Haven University of Pennsylvania, 401 N Fairview Ave, Lock Haven, PA, 17745-2390. Tel: 570-484-2463. Fax: 570-484-2506. p. 2082

Lillard, Justin, Ref, Harding University, 915 E Market St, Searcy, AR, 72149-2267. Tel: 501-279-4251. p. 114

Lillegard, Jeanne M, Dir, Judith Basin County Free Library, 19 Third N, Stanford, MT, 59479. Tel: 406-566-2277, Ext 123. Fax: 406-566-2211. p. 1388

Lillejord, Connie, Librn, Parkland Regional Library, Southey Branch, 260 Keats St, Southey, SK, S0G 4P0, CANADA. Tel: 306-726-2907. p. 2932

Liller, Anne, Mgr, Urban Br, Public Library of Youngstown & Mahoning County, 305 Wick Ave, Youngstown, OH, 44503-1079. Tel: 330-744-8636. Fax: 330-744-3355. p. 1952

Lilles, Linda, Reserves, Washington State University, 600 N Riverpoint Blvd, Spokane, WA, 99202. Tel: 509-358-7930. Fax: 509-358-7928. p. 2538

Lilley, Phyllis J, Br Mgr, Palm Beach County Library System, Belle Glade Branch, 530 S Main St, Belle Glade, FL, 33430. Tel: 561-996-3453. Fax: 561-996-2304. p. 503

Lilley, Phyllis J, Br Mgr, Palm Beach County Library System, Clarence E Anthony Branch, 375 SW Second Ave, South Bay, FL, 33493. Tel: 561-992-8393. Fax: 561-996-5925. p. 503

Lilley, Phyllis J, Br Mgr, Palm Beach County Library System, Loula V York Branch, 525 Bacom Point Rd, Pahokee, FL, 33476. Tel: 561-924-5928. Fax: 561-924-2271. p. 503

Lilley, Rose, Tech Serv, California Baptist University, 8432 Magnolia Ave, Riverside, CA, 92504. Tel: 951-343-4353. p. 216

Lillie, Elizabeth L, Dir, Free Public Library of Monroe Township, 713 Marsha Ave, Williamstown, NJ, 08094. Tel: 856-629-1212. Fax: 856-875-0191. p. 1544

Lillis, Lorna, ILL, Scott County Library System, 200 N Sixth Ave, Eldridge, IA, 52748. Tel: 563-285-4794. Fax: 563-285-4743. p. 813

Lilly, Amy, Dir, Raleigh County Public Library, 221 N Kanawha St, Beckley, WV, 25801-4716. Tel: 304-255-0511. Fax: 304-255-9161. p. 2554

Lilly, Bonnie, Circ, Ref, Fort Sumner Public Library, 235 W Sumner Ave, Fort Sumner, NM, 88119. Tel: 505-355-2832. Fax: 505-355-7732. p. 1555

Lilly, Charles, Archivist, ILL, Concord University, 1000 Vermillion St, Athens, WV, 24712. Tel: 304-384-5371. Fax: 304-384-7955. p. 2553

Lilly, Elise, Assoc Dir, Willkie Farr & Gallagher LLP, 787 Seventh Ave, New York, NY, 10019. Tel: 212-728-8700. Fax: 212-728-3303. p. 1703

Lilly, Melanie, Asst Dir, Louisville Free Public Library, 301 York St, Louisville, KY, 40203-2205. Tel: 502-574-1845. Fax: 502-574-1666, 502-574-1693. p. 924

Lilton, Deborah, Bibliographer, Vanderbilt University, Central Library, 419 21st Ave S, Nashville, TN, 37203-2427. Tel: 615-343-4237. Fax: 615-343-7451. p. 2260

Lily, Galindo, Dir, Fort Hancock County Public Library, 101 School Dr, Fort Hancock, TX, 79839. Tel: 915-769-3811, Ext 1306. Fax: 915-769-3940. p. 2320

Lilyquist, Lisa, City Librn, Lakeland Public Library, 100 Lake Morton Dr, Lakeland, FL, 33801-5375. Tel: 863-834-4280. Fax: 863-834-4293. p. 459

Lim, Catherine, Ch, Lewisboro Library, 15 Main St, South Salem, NY, 10590-1413. Tel: 914-763-3857. Fax: 914-763-2193. p. 1745

Lim, Hoong, Librn, Fraser Health Authority, 3935 Kincaid St, Burnaby, BC, V5G 2X6, CANADA. Tel: 604-412-6255. Fax: 604-412-6177. p. 2725

Lim, James, Distance Educ, Electronic Serv, City College of San Francisco, 50 Phelan Ave, San Francisco, CA, 94112. Tel: 415-452-5430. Fax: 415-452-5588. p. 241

Lim, Myungcha Miki, Br Mgr, Los Angeles Public Library System, Pio Pico-Koreatown, 694 S Oxford, Los Angeles, CA, 90005-2872. Tel: 213-368-7282, 213-381-1453. Fax: 213-612-0433. p. 174

Lim, Sook, PhD, Assoc Prof, Saint Catherine University, 2004 Randolph Ave, Mailstop No 4125, Saint Paul, MN, 55105. Tel: 651-690-6802. Fax: 651-690-8724. p. 2968

Lim, Susan, Librn, Acuren Group, Inc, 7450 18th St, Edmonton, AB, T6P 1N8, CANADA. Tel: 780-440-2131. Fax: 780-440-1167. p. 2697

Lim-Sharpe, Judy, Chief Librn, United States Department of the Treasury, Treasury Library, 1500 Pennsylvania Ave NW, Rm 1428 MT, Washington, DC, 20220. Tel: 202-622-0990. Fax: 202-622-0018. p. 419

Lima, Robin A, ILL Tech, United States Naval War College Library, 686 Cushing Rd, Newport, RI, 02841-1207. Tel: 401-841-2641. Fax: 401-841-6491. p. 2169

Limacher, Michael, Coordr, Media Serv, Illinois Wesleyan University, One Ames Plaza, Bloomington, IL, 61701-7188. Tel: 309-556-3323. Fax: 309-556-3706. p. 595

Limb, Peter, Librn, Michigan State University Library, Area Studies, 100 Library, East Lansing, MI, 48824. Tel: 517-884-6392. Fax: 517-432-3532. p. 1175

Limbach, Letty, Librn, DC Court of Appeals Library, 430 E St NW, Rm 203, Washington, DC, 20001. Tel: 202-879-2767. Fax: 202-879-9912. p. 397

Limings, Debra, ILL/Per Spec, Mount Vernon Nazarene University, 800 Martinsburg Rd, Mount Vernon, OH, 43050-9500. Tel: 740-397-9000, Ext 4240. Fax: 740-397-8847. p. 1919

Limoges, Diane, Dir, Eastern Township Public Library, 206 W Main St, Crofton, NE, 68730. Tel: 402-388-4915. Fax: 402-388-4915. p. 1396

Limoges, Julie, Librn, Ministere des Affaires municipales et de Regions, 10 rue Pierre-Olivier-Chauveau, Sous-sol, Aile Chauveau, Quebec, QC, G1R 4J3, CANADA. Tel: 418-691-2018. Fax: 418-528-8970. p. 2905

Limond, Kim, Ref Librn, Clinton Public Library, 306 Eighth Ave S, Clinton, IA, 52732. Tel: 563-242-8441. Fax: 563-242-8162. p. 803

Limonez, Rocio, Circ, Waubonsee Community College, State Rte 47 at Waubonsee Dr, Sugar Grove, IL, 60554. Tel: 630-466-2943. Fax: 630-466-7799. p. 708

Limpitlaw, Amy, Res & Electronic Serv Librn, Yale University Library, Divinity School Library, 409 Prospect St, New Haven, CT, 06511-2108. Tel: 203-432-5290. Fax: 203-432-3906. p. 357

Limpitlaw, Amy, Head Librn, Boston University Libraries, School of Theology Library, 745 Commonwealth Ave, 2nd Flr, Boston, MA, 02215. Tel: 617-353-3034. Fax: 617-358-0699. p. 1058

Lin, Ann, Circ Serv Dir, Lisle Library District, 777 Front St, Lisle, IL, 60532-3599. Tel: 630-971-1675. Fax: 630-971-1701. p. 666

Lin, Emily S, Head, Digital Assets, University of California, Merced Library, 5200 N Lake Rd, Merced, CA, 95343-5001. Tel: 209-658-7146. Fax: 209-228-4271. p. 186

Lin, Hsiu-Ling, Ser Tech, Oregon Institute of Technology Library, 3201 Campus Dr, Klamath Falls, OR, 97601-8801. Tel: 541-885-1772. Fax: 541-885-1777. p. 2002

Lin, James K, Cat, Harvard Library, Harvard-Yenching Library, Two Divinity Ave, Cambridge, MA, 02138. Tel: 617-495-2756. Fax: 617-496-6008. p. 1075

Lin, Joanna, Librn, Department of Veterans Affairs - VA Maryland Health Care System, Ten N Greene St, BT/142D/LIB, Baltimore, MD, 21201. Tel: 410-605-7092. Fax: 410-605-7905. p. 1012

Lin, Joanna, Treas, Maryland Association of Health Science Librarians, VA Medical HealthCare System, Medical Library, Ten N Greene St, Baltimore, MD, 21201. Tel: 401-605-7093. p. 2944

Lin, Ken, Asst Prof, Libr Sci, Ref, Syst Librn, West Los Angeles College Library, 9000 Overland Ave, Culver City, CA, 90230. Tel: 310-287-4437. Fax: 310-287-4366. p. 138

Lin, Mingzhi, Acq of Monographs & Journals, Acq of New Ser, Far Eastern Research Library, Nine First Ave NE, Plato, MN, 55370-0181. Tel: 320-238-2591, 612-926-6887. p. 1271

Lin, Shao-Chen, Tech Serv, Lincolnwood Public Library District, 4000 W Pratt Ave, Lincolnwood, IL, 60712. Tel: 847-677-5277. Fax: 847-677-1937. p. 666

Lin, Shihmei, Librn, Anderson, McPharlin & Conners LLP Library, 444 S Flower St, No 3100, Los Angeles, CA, 90071. Tel: 213-236-1677. Fax: 213-622-7594. p. 168

Lin, Tony, Co-Chair, Irvine Valley College Library, 5500 Irvine Center Dr, Irvine, CA, 92618-4399. Tel: 949-451-5261. Fax: 949-451-5796. p. 160

Lin, Xia, PhD, Assoc Prof, Drexel University, Rush Bldg, Rm 306, 30 N 33rd St, Philadelphia, PA, 19104-2875. Tel: 215-895-2474. Fax: 215-895-2494. p. 2972

Lin, Ying, Electronic Res, Info Literacy Librn, Maryville University Library, 650 Maryville University Dr, Saint Louis, MO, 63141. Tel: 314-529-6879. Fax: 314-529-9941. p. 1356

Lin, Yongtao, Librn, Tom Baker Cancer Ctr Knowledge Ctr, Holy Cross Site, University of Calgary Library, Health Sciences Library, Health Sci Ctr, 3330 Hospital Dr NW, Calgary, AB, T2N 4N1, CANADA. Tel: 403-521-3285. Fax: 403-210-9847. p. 2693

Lin, Yu-Hung, Co-Dir, Federal Reserve Bank of New York, 33 Liberty St, Federal Reserve PO Sta, New York, NY, 10045. Tel: 212-720-5670, 212-720-8289. Fax: 212-720-1372. p. 1678

Linahan, Mary Ann, ILL, Yeshiva University Libraries, Pollack Library-Landowne Bloom Library, Wilf Campus, 2520 Amsterdam Ave, New York, NY, 10033. Tel: 212-960-5378, 212-960-5379, 212-960-5380. Fax: 212-960-0066. p. 1704

Linan, Robert, Br Mgr, Arlington Public Library System, Woodland West, 2837 W Park Row Dr, Arlington, TX, 76013-2261. Tel: 817-277-5265. Fax: 817-795-4741. p. 2277

Linares, Fernando, Br Mgr, Stanislaus County Free Library, Keyes Branch, 4420 Maud Ave, Keyes, CA, 95328-0367. Tel: 209-664-8006. Fax: 209-664-8006. p. 188

Linberger, Peter, Head, Coll Mgt, University of Akron Libraries, 315 Buchtel Mall, Akron, OH, 44325-1701. Tel: 330-972-8230. Fax: 330-972-5106. p. 1853

Lincheid, Julie, Circ, Watonwan County Library, Butterfield Branch, 111 Second St N, Butterfield, MN, 56120-0237. Tel: 507-956-2361. p. 1276

Lincicum, Shirley, Libr Instruction, Western Oregon University, Wayne & Lynn Hamersly Library, 345 N Monmouth Ave, Monmouth, OR, 97361-1396. Tel: 503-838-8890. Fax: 503-838-8399. p. 2006

Linck, Nancy, Dir, Barnes Reading Room, 640 Main St, Everest, KS, 66424. Tel: 785-548-7733. Fax: 785-548-7733. p. 866

Lincke-Fisseler, Brenda, Ch, Friench Simpson Memorial Library, 705 E Fourth St, Hallettsville, TX, 77964-2828. Tel: 361-798-3243. Fax: 361-798-5833. p. 2330

Lincoln, Beth, Asst Librn, Bartlett Public Library, Main St, Bartlett, NH, 03812. Tel: 603-374-2755. Fax: 603-374-2755. p. 1438

Lincoln, Christine L, Mgr, Res Serv, Aerospace Corp, 2360 E El Segundo Blvd, El Segundo, CA, 90245-4691. Tel: 310-336-6738. Fax: 310-336-0624. p. 146

Lincoln, Elizabeth, Dep Dir, Minnesota Legislative Reference Library, 645 State Office Bldg, 100 Rev Dr Martin Luther King Jr Blvd, Saint Paul, MN, 55155-1050. Tel: 651-296-0594. Fax: 651-296-9731. p. 1280

Lincoln, Gerald, Dir, Lancaster Bible College Library, 901 Eden Rd, Lancaster, PA, 17601-5036. Tel: 717-560-8250. Fax: 717-560-8265. p. 2076

Lincoln, Jacalyn, Ref Serv, YA, Ohio Township Public Library System, 4111 Lakeshore Dr, Newburgh, IN, 47630-2274. Tel: 812-853-5468. Fax: 812-853-0509. p. 768

Lincoln, Megumi Saito, Mgr, Libr Serv, Howard Hughes Medical Institute, 4000 Jones Bridge Rd, Chevy Chase, MD, 20815-6789. Tel: 301-215-8661. Fax: 301-215-8663. p. 1024

Lincoln, Nancy, Asst Dir, Weston Public Library, 56 Norfield Rd, Weston, CT, 06883-2225. Tel: 203-222-2665. Fax: 203-222-2560. p. 377

Lincoln, Tamara, Artic Bibliogr, Curator, Rare Bks & Maps, University of Alaska Fairbanks, 310 Tanana Dr, Fairbanks, AK, 99775. Tel: 907-474-6671. Fax: 907-474-6841. p. 48

Lincoln, Timothy D, Dir, Austin Presbyterian Theological Seminary, 100 E 27th St, Austin, TX, 78705-5797. Tel: 512-472-6736. Fax: 512-322-0901. p. 2278

Lincoln, Yolanda, Adminr, US National Park Service, PO Box 150, Ganado, AZ, 86505-0150. Tel: 928-755-3475. Fax: 928-755-3405. p. 64

Lind, Carolyn Sue, Asst Dir, Donnellson Public Library, 500 Park St, Donnellson, IA, 52625. Tel: 319-835-5545. Fax: 319-835-5545. p. 811

Lind, Debbie, Dir, Wallowa Public Library, 201 N Main, Wallowa, OR, 97885. Tel: 541-886-4265. p. 2022

Lind, Doug, Dir, Law Libr, Southern Illinois University Carbondale, Law Library, Lesar Law Bldg, 1150 Douglas Dr, Carbondale, IL, 62901. Tel: 618-453-8713. Fax: 618-453-8728. p. 600

Lind, Kari, Asst Librn, Challis Public Library, 501 Sixth St, Challis, ID, 83226. Tel: 208-879-4267. Fax: 208-879-4267. p. 572

Lind, Peggy, In Charge, Siouxland Libraries, Brandon Branch, 305 S Splitrock, Brandon, SD, 57005-1651. Tel: 605-582-2390. Fax: 605-582-8760. p. 2219

Lind, Stephanie, Dir, Cornelius Public Library, 1355 N Barlow St, Cornelius, OR, 97113-8912. Tel: 503-992-5307. Fax: 503-357-7775. p. 1994

Lind, Stephanie, Outreach Serv Librn, Washington County Cooperative Library Services, 111 NE Lincoln St, No 230-L MS58, Hillsboro, OR, 97124-3036. Tel: 503-617-6330. Fax: 503-846-3220. p. 2000

Lind, Werner, Asst Dir, Bluefield College, 3000 College Dr, Bluefield, VA, 24605. Tel: 276-326-4238. Fax: 276-326-4288. p. 2451

Lind-Sinanian, Gary, Curator, Armenian Library & Museum of America, Inc, 65 Main St, Watertown, MA, 02472. Tel: 617-926-2562, Ext 25. Fax: 617-926-0175. p. 1133

Lind-Sinanian, Susan, Curator, Armenian Library & Museum of America, Inc, 65 Main St, Watertown, MA, 02472. Tel: 617-926-2562. Fax: 617-926-0175. p. 1133

Linda, Avellar, Develop/Communications, The Ferguson Library, One Public Library Plaza, 96 Broad St, Stamford, CT, 06904. Tel: 203-964-1000, Ext 8208. Fax: 203-357-9098. p. 369

Linda, Crouch, Mgr, Tech Support, Dyersburg State Community College, 1510 Lake Rd, Dyersburg, TN, 38024. Tel: 731-286-3223. Fax: 731-286-3228. p. 2233

Linda, Farrell, In Charge, Woodland Park Zoo Library, 601 N 59th St, Seattle, WA, 98103. Tel: 206-684-4840. Fax: 206-233-2663. p. 2535

Linda, Helen, Libr Syst & Tech Serv Coordr, Goddard College, 123 Pitkin Rd, Plainfield, VT, 05667. Tel: 802-322-1602. p. 2432

Linda, Litzinger, Asst Dir, Southwest Public Libraries, SPL Admin, 3359 Park St, Grove City, OH, 43123. Tel: 614-875-6716. Fax: 614-875-2219. p. 1903

Linda, Seybold, Librn, Grove United Methodist Church Library, 490 W Boot Rd, West Chester, PA, 19380. Tel: 610-696-2663. Fax: 610-696-5625. p. 2153

Linda, Whitaker D, Archivist, Librn, Arizona Historical Society Museum Library & Archives, 1300 N College Ave, Tempe, AZ, 85281. Tel: 480-929-0292, Ext 127. Fax: 480-929-9973. p. 83

Lindahl, Susan, Libr Syst/Access Serv Mgr, University of Wisconsin-Stout Library, 315 Tenth Ave, Menomonie, WI, 54751-0790. Tel: 715-232-3382. Fax: 715-232-1783. p. 2615

Lindballe-Vincett, Penny, Chairperson, Galahad Public Library, PO Box 58, Galahad, AB, T0B 1R0, CANADA. Tel: 780-583-3917. Fax: 780-583-3917. p. 2705

Lindberg, Cecile, Ch, Beaman Memorial Public Library, Eight Newton St, West Boylston, MA, 01583. Tel: 508-835-3711. Fax: 508-835-4770. p. 1136

Lindberg, Donald A B, Dr, Dir, National Library of Medicine, Bldg 38, Rm 2E-17B, 8600 Rockville Pike, Bethesda, MD, 20894. Tel: 301-496-6308. Fax: 301-496-4450. p. 1022

Lindberg, Jane, Librn, Saratoga Hospital, 211 Church St, Saratoga Springs, NY, 12866. Tel: 518-583-8301. Fax: 518-580-4285. p. 1738

Lindbloom, Mary-Carol, Exec Dir, South Central Regional Library Council, Clinton Hall, 108 N Cayuga St, Ithaca, NY, 14850. Tel: 607-273-9106. Fax: 607-272-0740. p. 2950

Lindell, Ann, Head, Archit & Fine Arts Libr, University of Florida Libraries, 535 Library W, Gainesville, FL, 32611-7000. Tel: 352-273-2805. Fax: 352-846-2747. p. 450

Lindell, Cheryl, Br Mgr, Watonwan County Library, Lewisville Branch, 105 Lewis St W, Lewisville, MN, 56060. Tel: 507-435-2781. Fax: 507-435-2781. p. 1277

Lindell, Cheryl, Libr Asst, Watonwan County Library, Madelia Branch, 23 First St NW, Madelia, MN, 56062-1411. Tel: 507-642-3511. Fax: 507-642-8144. p. 1277

Lindell, Lisa, Cat, South Dakota State University, 1300 N Campus Dr, Box 2115, Brookings, SD, 57007-1098. Tel: 605-688-5561. Fax: 605-688-6133. p. 2210

Lindem, Margaret, Librn, University of Pennsylvania Libraries, Veterinary Library, 380 S University Ave, Philadelphia, PA, 19104-6008. Tel: 215-898-8874. Fax: 215-573-2007. p. 2119

Lindeman, Ian, YA Librn, Converse County Library, 300 Walnut St, Douglas, WY, 82633. Tel: 307-358-3644. Fax: 307-358-6743. p. 2654

Lindemann, Kathy, Actg Sr Librn, Los Angeles Public Library System, Westchester-Loyola Village, 7114 W Manchester Ave, Los Angeles, CA, 90045-3509. Tel: 310-348-1096. Fax: 310-348-1082. p. 174

Lindemann, Richard, Dir, Archives & Spec Coll, Bowdoin College Library, 3000 College Sta, Brunswick, ME, 04011-8421. Tel: 207-725-3288. p. 979

Lindemann, Ruth B, Dr, Instrul Serv Librn, Ref, Danville Area Community College Library, 2000 E Main St, Danville, IL, 61832-5199. Tel: 217-443-8735. Fax: 217-554-1623. p. 632

Lindemuth, Charlotte, Mgr, Seligman Public Library, 202 Floyd St, Seligman, AZ, 86337. Tel: 928-422-3633. Fax: 928-422-3633. p. 81

Linden, Danielle, Libr Mgr, Saint Joseph Hospital & Childrens Hospital of Orange County, 1100 W Stewart Dr, Orange, CA, 92863. Tel: 714-771-8291. Fax: 714-744-8533. p. 201

Linden, Jeremy, Archivist, State University of New York at Fredonia, 280 Central Ave, Fredonia, NY, 14063. Tel: 716-673-3181. Fax: 716-673-3185. p. 1624

Linden, Julie, Govt Doc, Yale University Library, Government Documents & Information Center, 38 Mansfield St, New Haven, CT, 06511. Tel: 203-432-3209. Fax: 203-432-3214. p. 358

Linden, Sara, Dir, Jay Johnson Public Library, 411 Main St, Quinter, KS, 67752. Tel: 785-754-2171. p. 891

Lindenbaum, Mitch, Librn, California Department of Corrections & Rehabilitation, Fifth St & Western Ave, Norco, CA, 92860. Tel: 951-737-2683, Ext 4202. Fax: 951-273-2380. p. 194

Lindenbaum, Mitch, Sr Librn, California Department of Corrections Library System, Sierra Conservation Center, 5100 O'Byrnes Ferry Rd, Jamestown, CA, 95327. Tel: 209-984-5291, Ext 5306. Fax: 209-984-4563. p. 222

Lindenfeld, Ellen, Regional Libr Mgr, Broward County Division of Libraries, Southwest Regional, 16835 Sheridan St, Pembroke Pines, FL, 33331. Tel: 954-538-9996, Ext 273. Fax: 954-538-9165. p. 442

Lindenmuth, Janet, Ref Serv, Widener University, School of Law Library, 4601 Concord Pike, Wilmington, DE, 19803. Tel: 302-477-2245. Fax: 302-477-2240. p. 389

Linder, Allison, Circ, Virginia Intermont College, 1013 Moore St, Bristol, VA, 24201. Tel: 276-466-7955. p. 2453

Linder, Lynda, Assoc Librn, Kansas Wesleyan University, 100 E Claflin Ave, Salina, KS, 67401-6100. Tel: 785-827-5541, Ext 4120. Fax: 785-827-0927. p. 893

Linderman, Eric, Adult Serv, Euclid Public Library, 631 E 222nd St, Euclid, OH, 44123-2091. Tel: 216-261-5300, Ext 134. Fax: 216-261-9559. p. 1898

Linderman, Kate, Br Mgr, Evansville Vanderburgh Public Library, Red Bank, 120 S Red Bank Rd, Evansville, IN, 47712. Tel: 812-428-8399. Fax: 812-428-8240. p. 738

Linderman, Mike, Mgr, Angel Mounds State Historic Site Library, 8215 Pollack Ave, Evansville, IN, 47715. Tel: 812-853-3956. Fax: 812-858-7686. p. 738

Linderman, Vivian, Ref Librn, California State University Dominguez Hills, 1000 E Victoria St, Carson, CA, 90747. Tel: 310-243-2308. Fax: 310-516-4219. p. 132

Linderman-Justice, Carol, Outreach Serv Librn, Cumberland County Library System, 19 S West St, Carlisle, PA, 17013-2839. Tel: 717-240-7771. p. 2041

Lindgren, Dianne J, Librn, Southwestern Community College Library, 447 College Dr, Sylva, NC, 28779. Tel: 828-586-4091, Ext 268. Fax: 828-586-3129. p. 1826

Lindgren, Marilyn, Dir, Kingsley Public Library, 220 Main St, Kingsley, IA, 51028. Tel: 712-378-2410. Fax: 712-378-2410. p. 825

Lindh, Rosella, Librn, Tulsa City-County Library, Kendall-Whittier Branch, 21 S Lewis St, Tulsa, OK, 74104. Tel: 918-596-7303. Fax: 918-596-7304. p. 1983

Lindley, Carolyn, Br Mgr, Vermillion County Public Library, Dana Branch, 140 Maple St, Dana, IN, 47847. Tel: 765-665-0365. p. 769

Lindley, Elizabeth A, Mgr, Tech Serv, Oakland Community College, Library Systems, 2900 Featherstone Rd, MTEC A210, Auburn Hills, MI, 48326. Tel: 248-232-4478. Fax: 248-232-4089. p. 1154

Lindmier, Connie, Curator, Laramie Plains Museum Association Inc Library, 603 Ivinson Ave, Laramie, WY, 82070-3299. Tel: 307-742-4448. p. 2657

Lindner, Kerstin (Kris), Ref Librn, Godfrey Memorial Library, 134 Newfield St, Middletown, CT, 06457-2534. Tel: 860-346-4375. Fax: 860-347-9874. p. 351

Lindner, Mary, Curric Libr Cataloger, College of Saint Rose, 392-396 Western Ave, Albany, NY, 12203. Tel: 518-337-4693. Fax: 518-454-2897. p. 1568

Lindner, Shawna, Youth Serv Coordr, Kearney Public Library, 2020 First Ave, Kearney, NE, 68847. Tel: 308-233-3284. Fax: 308-233-3291. p. 1403

Lindquist, April, Circ, Gateway Technical College, 3520 30th Ave, Kenosha, WI, 53144-1690. Tel: 262-564-2540. Fax: 262-564-2787. p. 2601

Lindquist, Christopher J, Dir, Westfield Athenaeum, Six Elm St, Westfield, MA, 01085-2997. Tel: 413-568-7833, Ext 81. Fax: 413-568-0988. p. 1138

Lindquist, Diane, Libr Asst, Northwestern College, Naperville Campus, 1809 N Mill St, Naperville, IL, 60563. Tel: 630-753-9091. Fax: 630-753-9823. p. 621

Lindquist, Janice, Head, Acq, Rice University, 6100 Main, MS-44, Houston, TX, 77005. Tel: 713-348-4023. Fax: 713-348-5258. p. 2341

Lindquist, Karen, Asst Dir, David M Hunt Library, 63 Main St, Falls Village, CT, 06031. Tel: 860-824-7424. p. 339

Lindquist, Kristen, Ref/Distance Learning Librn, Tech Librn, University of Wisconsin-Superior, PO Box 2000, Belknap & Catlin, Superior, WI, 54880-2000. Tel: 715-394-8343. Fax: 715-394-8462. p. 2641

Lindquist, Linda, Ref, New Ulm Public Library, 17 N Broadway, New Ulm, MN, 56073-1786. Tel: 507-359-8331. Fax: 507-354-3255. p. 1268

Lindquist, Virginia, Dir, Lincoln Township Library, 105 S Hampton, Wausa, NE, 68786. Tel: 402-586-2454. Fax: 402-586-2454. p. 1422

Lindsay, Amanda, Ref Librn, United States Air Force, Wright-Patterson Air Force Base Library FL2300, 88 MSG/SVMG, Bldg 1226, 5435 Hemlock St, Wright-Patterson AFB, OH, 45433-5420. Tel: 937-257-4340, 937-257-4815. Fax: 937-656-1776. p. 1951

Lindsay, Ann, Tech Serv, Schlow Centre Region Library, 211 S Allen St, State College, PA, 16801-4806. Tel: 814-237-6236. Fax: 814-238-8508. p. 2143

Lindsay, Charmaine, Chief Exec Officer, Cobourg Public Library, 200 Ontario St, Cobourg, ON, K9A 5P4, CANADA. Tel: 905-372-9271, Ext 6200. Fax: 905-372-4538. p. 2800

Lindsay, J Michael, Ser, Web Adminr, University of Tennessee Graduate School of Medicine, 1924 Alcoa Hwy, Box U-111, Knoxville, TN, 37920. Tel: 865-305-9528. Fax: 865-305-9527. p. 2243

Lindsay, Kim, Dir, Wimodaughsian Free Library, 19 W Main St, Canisteo, NY, 14823-1005. Tel: 607-698-4445. Fax: 607-698-4445. p. 1602

Lindsay, Lorin, Tech Serv, Arizona State Braille & Talking Book Library, 1030 N 32nd St, Phoenix, AZ, 85008. Tel: 602-255-5578. Fax: 602-286-0444. p. 72

Lindsay, Nina, Ch, Oakland Public Library, 125 14th St, Oakland, CA, 94612. Tel: 510-238-3282. Fax: 510-238-2232. p. 197

Lindsay, Nina, Supv Librn, Ch, Oakland Public Library, Main Library, 125 14th St, Oakland, CA, 94612. Tel: 510-238-3134. Fax: 510-238-2232. p. 198

Lindsay, Sharon, Librn, Rockbridge Regional Library, Bath County Public, 96 Courthouse Hill Rd, Warm Springs, VA, 24484. Tel: 540-839-7286. Fax: 540-839-3058. p. 2474

Lindsey, Almata, Librn, Glover Spencer Memorial Library, 100 S Sixth St, Corner SE Sixth & Blakely Ave, Rush Springs, OK, 73082. Tel: 580-476-2108. Fax: 580-476-2129. p. 1977

Lindsey, April, Dir, Laurel University Library, 1215 Eastchester Drive, High Point, NC, 27265-3197. Tel: 336-889-2262 Ext 146. Fax: 336-889-2261. p. 1802

Lindsey, Heidi, Librn, Southborough Public Library, 25 Main St, Southborough, MA, 01772. Tel: 508-485-5031. Fax: 508-229-4451. p. 1126

Lindsey, Jennifer, Ch, Chili Public Library, 3333 Chili Ave, Rochester, NY, 14624-5494. Tel: 585-889-2200. Fax: 585-889-5819. p. 1729

Lindsey, Kathy, ILL, Bastrop Public Library, 1100 Church St, Bastrop, TX, 78602. Tel: 512-321-5441. Fax: 512-321-3163. p. 2286

Lindsey, Kristi, Dir, Penrose Community Library, 35 Seventh Ave, Penrose, CO, 81240-0318. Tel: 719-372-6017. Fax: 719-372-6018. p. 320

Lindsey, Laura, Youth Serv, Grayson County Public Library, 130 E Market St, Leitchfield, KY, 42754-1439. Tel: 270-259-5455. Fax: 270-259-4552. p. 920

Lindsey, Lou, Assoc Dir, University of Tulsa Libraries, Mabee Legal Information Center, 3120 E Fourth Pl, Tulsa, OK, 74104-3189. Tel: 918-631-2404. Fax: 918-631-3556. p. 1984

Lindsey, Mary Bennett, Dir, Audubon Regional Library, 12220 Woodville St, Clinton, LA, 70722. Tel: 225-683-8753. Fax: 225-683-4634. p. 947

Lindsey, Rae, Ch, McCord Memorial Library, 32 W Main St, North East, PA, 16428. Tel: 814-725-4057. p. 2099

Lindsey, Robert, Ref Librn, Pittsburg State University, 1605 S Joplin St, Pittsburg, KS, 66762-5889. Tel: 620-235-4887. Fax: 620-235-4090. p. 890

Lindsey, Robert, Web Coordr, South Carolina State Library, 1430-1500 Senate St, Columbia, SC, 29201. Tel: 803-734-5831. Fax: 803-734-8676. p. 2189

Lindsey, Ronald, Libr Tech, Smithsonian Libraries, National Museum of Natural History Library, Nat Museum of Natural Hist, Rm 51, MRC 154, Tenth St & Constitution Ave NW, Washington, DC, 20013-0712. Tel: 202-633-1673. Fax: 202-357-1896. p. 415

Lindskog, Lauren, Prog Coordr, Exploratorium Learning Commons, 3601 Lyon St, San Francisco, CA, 94123. Tel: 415-561-0336. Fax: 415-561-0370. p. 242

Lindsey, Cheryl D, Circ, Per, Roanoke Bible College, 715 N Poindexter St, Elizabeth City, NC, 27909-4054. Tel: 252-334-2092. Fax: 252-334-2071. p. 1791

Lindsley, Luisa, Libr Dir, Tenney Memorial Library, Inc, 4886 Main St S, Newbury, VT, 05051. Tel: 802-866-5366. p. 2430

Lindsley, Robert E, Dir, Alfred H Baumann Free Public Library, Seven Brophy Lane, West Paterson, NJ, 07424-2733. Tel: 973-345-8120. Fax: 973-345-8196. p. 1542

Lindstrom, Annamarie, Ch, Roseville Public Library, 29777 Gratiot Ave, Roseville, MI, 48066. Tel: 586-445-5407. Fax: 586-445-5499. p. 1223

Lindstrom, Elaine, Mgr, Dayton Metro Library, Brookville Branch, 425 Rona Pkwy, Brookville, OH, 45309. Tel: 937-496-8922. Fax: 937-496-4322. p. 1893

Lindstrom, Janet, Exec Dir, New Canaan Historical Society Library, 13 Oenoke Ridge, New Canaan, CT, 06840. Tel: 203-966-1776. Fax: 203-972-5917. p. 354

Lindstrom, Mary Ellen, Actg Dir, Medina Community Library, 13948 State Hwy 16 N, Medina, TX, 78055. Tel: 830-589-2825. Fax: 830-589-7514. p. 2361

Lindstrom, Maureen A, Assoc Dir, Info Commons, State University of New York College at Buffalo, 1300 Elmwood Ave, Buffalo, NY, 14222-1095. Tel: 716-878-6236. Fax: 716-878-3134. p. 1599

Lindt, Jim, Mgr, Tech Serv, Wood Dale Public Library District, 520 N Wood Dale Rd, Wood Dale, IL, 60191. Tel: 630-766-6762. Fax: 630-766-5715. p. 721

Lindvall, Rachel, Dir, Sinte Gleska University Library, E Hwy 18, Mission, SD, 57555. Tel: 605-856-8100, 605-856-8112. Fax: 605-856-2011. p. 2215

Line, Faith A, Dir, Anderson County Library, 300 N McDuffie St, Anderson, SC, 29621-5643. Tel: 864-260-4500. Fax: 864-260-4510. p. 2180

Linehan, Katherine, Unit Mgr, Chicago Public Library, Popular Library, 400 S State St, Chicago, IL, 60605. Tel: 312-747-4100. p. 609

Linehan, Pat, Acq, Webster Groves Public Library, 301 E Lockwood Ave, Webster Groves, MO, 63119-3102. Tel: 314-961-3784. Fax: 314-961-4233. p. 1372

Ling, Amy, Asst Librn, North Valley Public Library, 208 Main St, Stevensville, MT, 59870. Tel: 406-777-5061. Fax: 406-777-5061. p. 1388

Ling, Molly, Info Spec, Ogilvy Public Relations Worldwide Information Center, 636 Eleventh Ave, New York, NY, 10036. Tel: 212-880-5200, 212-880-5319. Fax: 212-880-2880. p. 1696

Linge, Ken, Librn, Blake Memorial Library, 676 Village Rd, East Corinth, VT, 05040. Tel: 802-439-5338. Fax: 802-439-5338. p. 2423

Lingenfelter, Mike, Webmaster, Bellwood-Antis Public Library, 526 Main St, Bellwood, PA, 16617-1910. Tel: 814-742-8234. Fax: 814-742-8235. p. 2032

Linger, Kim, Tech Coordr, Beaver County Library System, One Campus Dr, Monaca, PA, 15061-2523. Tel: 724-728-3737. Fax: 724-728-8024. p. 2090

Linger, Mary, Dir, Cheatham County Public Library, 188 County Services Dr, Ste 200, Ashland City, TN, 37015-1726. Tel: 615-792-4828. Fax: 615-792-2054. p. 2223

Lingle, Jane, Head, Tech Serv, Oldsmar Library, 400 St Petersburg Dr E, Oldsmar, FL, 34677. Tel: 813-749-1178. Fax: 813-854-1881. p. 474

Lingo, Marci, Ref, Bakersfield College, 1801 Panorama Dr, Bakersfield, CA, 93305-1298. Tel: 661-395-4461. Fax: 661-395-4397. p. 123

Lingor, Pamla J, Dir, Alexander Mitchell Public Library, 519 S Kline St, Aberdeen, SD, 57401-4495. Tel: 605-626-7097. Fax: 605-626-3506. p. 2209

Linhares, Phil, Chief Curator, Oakland Museum of California Art Library, 1000 Oak St, Oakland, CA, 94607-4892. Tel: 510-238-3005. Fax: 510-238-6925. p. 197

Linhart, Sharon T, Br Librn, Elko-Lander-Eureka County Library System, Austin Branch, 88 Main St, Austin, NV, 89310. Tel: 775-964-2428. Fax: 775-964-2426. p. 1427

Link, Cathy, Mgr, Ch & Youth Serv, Frederick County Public Libraries, 110 E Patrick St, Frederick, MD, 21701. Tel: 301-600-1613. Fax: 301-600-3789. p. 1028

Link, Debbie, Libr Assoc, Saluda County Library, 101 S Main St, Saluda, SC, 29138. Tel: 864-445-2267, 864-445-9586. Fax: 864-445-2725. p. 2204

Link, Elizabeth, Br Mgr, Jefferson County Library, Arnold Branch, 1701 Missouri State Rd, Arnold, MO, 63010. Tel: 636-296-2204. Fax: 636-296-5975. p. 1331

Link, Jeanne, Online Searching & Outreach Coordr, Ref Librn, Library of Rush University Medical Center, Armour Academic Ctr, 600 S Paulina St, 5th Flr, Chicago, IL, 60612-3874. Tel: 312-942-6784. Fax: 312-942-3143. p. 617

Linke, Daniel, Curator, Univ Archivist, Princeton University, Seeley G Mudd Manuscript Library, 65 Olden St, Princeton, NJ, 08544. Tel: 609-258-6345. Fax: 609-258-3385. p. 1524

Linke, Dee, Circ Supvr, Philadelphia University, 4201 Henry Ave, Philadelphia, PA, 19144-5497. Tel: 215-951-2841. Fax: 215-951-2574. p. 2115

Linke, Erika, Assoc Dean, Carnegie Mellon University, Hunt Library, 4909 Frew St, Pittsburgh, PA, 15213-3890. Tel: 412-268-7800. Fax: 412-268-2793. p. 2123

Linker, Pat, Asst Librn, Northeast Medical Center, 920 Church St N, Concord, NC, 28025. Tel: 704-403-1726. Fax: 704-783-1776. p. 1785

Linkewich, Bernice, Asst Mgr, Edmonton Public Library, Highlands, 6516 118th Ave, Edmonton, AB, T5W 1G6, CANADA. Tel: 780-496-1806. Fax: 780-496-7012. p. 2700

Linkle, Stacie, Libr Asst, Hubbard Free Library, 115 Second St, Hallowell, ME, 04347. Tel: 207-622-6582. p. 987

Linko, Marjorie, Dir, Liberty Public Library, 189 N Main St, Liberty, NY, 12754-1828. Tel: 845-292-6070. Fax: 845-292-5609. p. 1652

Linkous, Kimberly, Acq, Coordr, Libr Serv, Saint Louis Community College, Instructional Resources, 5460 Highland Park Dr, Saint Louis, MO, 63110. Tel: 314-644-9559. p. 1358

Linkowski, Robin, Youth Serv Librn, Lyon Township Public Library, 27005 S Milford Rd, South Lyon, MI, 48178. Tel: 248-437-8800. Fax: 248-437-4621. p. 1227

Linn, Gary, Dr, Dir, Alvin C York Veterans Administration Medical Center, 3400 Lebanon Pike, Murfreesboro, TN, 37129. Tel: 615-893-1360, Ext 6142. Fax: 615-867-5778. p. 2255

Linn, Jeanne, Libr Tech, Colorado Department of Corrections, 30999 County Rd 15, Fort Lyon, CO, 81038. Tel: 719-456-2288, Ext 4252. Fax: 719-456-3211. p. 308

Linn, Mott, Archivist, Clark University, Archives & Special Collections, Downing & Woodland Sts, Worcester, MA, 01610-1477. Tel: 508-793-7572. Fax: 508-793-8871. p. 1143

Linnane, Mary Lu, Assoc Dir, Tech Serv, DePaul University Libraries, Vincent G Rinn Law Library, 25 E Jackson Blvd, 5th Flr, Chicago, IL, 60604-2287. Tel: 312-362-6895. Fax: 312-362-6908. p. 612

Linneman, Julie, Outreach Serv Librn, Prog Coordr, Wichita Public Library, 223 S Main St, Wichita, KS, 67202. Tel: 316-261-8590. Fax: 316-262-4540. p. 901

Linsday, Sharon, Br Mgr, Warren Public Library, Arthur J Miller Branch, 5460 Arden St, Ste 303, Warren, MI, 48092. Tel: 586-751-5377. p. 1234

Linse, Mary, Head, Tech Serv, Olathe Public Library, 201 E Park St, Olathe, KS, 66061. Tel: 913-971-6863. Fax: 913-971-6809. p. 886

Linskey-Deegan, Mara, Assoc Curator, Charles H MacNider Museum Library, 303 Second St SE, Mason City, IA, 50401-3925. Tel: 641-421-3666. Fax: 641-422-9612. p. 830

Linsmeier, Shawn, Pub Serv Asst, Silver Lake College, 2406 S Alverno Rd, Manitowoc, WI, 54220. Tel: 920-686-6145. Fax: 920-684-7082. p. 2612

Lintelmann, Susan, Ms Curator, United States Military Academy Library, Jefferson Hall Library & Learning Center, 758 Cullum Rd, West Point, NY, 10996. Tel: 845-938-3833. Fax: 845-938-4000. p. 1767

Lintleman, Sue, Ch, Circ, Liberty Municipal Library, 1710 Sam Houston Ave, Liberty, TX, 77575-4741. Tel: 936-336-8901. Fax: 936-336-2414. p. 2355

Lintner, Barbara, Dir, Ch Serv, The Urbana Free Library, 210 W Green St, Urbana, IL, 61801-5326. Tel: 217-367-4069. Fax: 217-367-4061. p. 713

Linton, Anne, Dir, George Washington University, Paul Himmelfarb Health Sciences Library, 2300 I St NW, Washington, DC, 20037. Tel: 202-994-1826. Fax: 202-994-4343. p. 402

Linton, Barbara, Head, Ref, Borough of Manhattan Community College Library, 199 Chambers St, New York, NY, 10007. Tel: 212-220-1448. Fax: 212-748-7466. p. 1671

Linton, Dorothy, Br Mgr, Washington County - Jonesborough Library, 200 Sabin Dr, Jonesborough, TN, 37659-1306. Tel: 423-753-1800. Fax: 423-753-1802. p. 2240

Linton, Henri, In Charge, University of Arkansas-Pine Bluff, Fine Arts, Art Department, Mail Slot 4925, Pine Bluff, AR, 71601. Tel: 870-575-8236. Fax: 870-575-4636. p. 113

Linton, Sylvia, Libr Instruction & Ref Spec, Gateway Technical College, 400 County Rd H, Elkhorn, WI, 53121. Tel: 262-741-8042, 262-741-8438. Fax: 262-741-8201. p. 2590

Linton, Walter, Libr Asst, New York Academy of Medicine Library, 1216 Fifth Ave, New York, NY, 10029-5293. Tel: 212-822-7362. Fax: 212-423-0266. p. 1688

Lintz, Laura, Librn, Public Library of Arlington, Edith M Fox Library & Community Center, 175 Massachusetts Ave, Arlington, MA, 02474. Tel: 781-316-3196. p. 1050

Linvill, Anne, Info & Access Serv Librn, Menlo College, 1000 El Camino Real, Atherton, CA, 94027-4300. Tel: 650-543-3826. Fax: 650-543-3833. p. 122

Linville, Dorothy, Br Librn, Mingo County Library, Kermit Branch, 138-B Main St, Kermit, WV, 25674. Tel: 304-393-4553. Fax: 304-393-4553. p. 2558

Linville, Patricia, Dir, Seward Community Library Museum, 239 Six Ave, Seward, AK, 99664. Tel: 907-224-4082. Fax: 907-224-3521. p. 53

Linxwiler, Gerald, Doc, Per, San Bernardino Public Library, 555 W Sixth St, San Bernardino, CA, 92410-3001. Tel: 909-381-8215. Fax: 909-381-8229. p. 229

Linz, Robert, Assoc Dir, Head, Pub Serv, University of Colorado Boulder, The William A Wise Law Library, 2450 Kittredge Loop Dr, 402 UCB, Boulder, CO, 80309-0402. Tel: 303-492-7534. Fax: 303-492-2707. p. 292

Linzmeyer, Jane, Dir, University of Wisconsin-Madison, Social Work Library, 1350 University Ave, Rm 236, Madison, WI, 53706. Tel: 608-263-3840. Fax: 608-265-2754. p. 2609

Linzner, Erika, Circ Supvr, Madison Area Technical College, 3550 Anderson St, Rm 230, Madison, WI, 53704. Tel: 608-246-6659. Fax: 608-246-6644. p. 2606

Liong, Jocelle, Ch, Cerritos Library, 18025 Bloomfield Ave, Cerritos, CA, 90703. Tel: 562-916-1350. Fax: 562-916-1375. p. 133

Lipa, Deborah, Librn, North Adams Regional Hospital, 71 Hospital Ave, North Adams, MA, 01247. Tel: 413-663-3701. Fax: 413-664-5016. p. 1111

Lipartito, Robert, Cat, Rowan University Library, Wilson Music Library, Main Campus, Rte 322, Glassboro, NJ, 08028. Tel: 856-256-4500, Ext 3542, 856-256-4799. Fax: 856-256-4644. p. 1488

LiPetri, Vickie, Head, Circ, Wantagh Public Library, 3285 Park Ave, Wantagh, NY, 11793. Tel: 516-221-1200. Fax: 516-826-9357. p. 1762

Lipfert, Nathan, Sr Curator, Maine Maritime Museum, 243 Washington St, Bath, ME, 04530. Tel: 207-443-1316, Ext 328. Fax: 207-443-1665. p. 976

Liphuysen, Hank, Chairperson, Empress Municipal Library, 613 Third Ave, Empress, AB, T0J 1E0, CANADA. Tel: 403-565-3936. Fax: 403-565-2010. p. 2703

Lipin, Libby, Cat, Webmaster, Athol Public Library, 568 Main St, Athol, MA, 01331. Tel: 978-249-9515. Fax: 978-249-7636. p. 1050

Lipinski, Brent, Br Mgr, Chicago Public Library, Wrightwood-Ashburn, 8530 S Kedzie Ave, Chicago, IL, 60652. Tel: 312-747-2696. Fax: 312-747-1937. p. 610

Lipinski, Carol, Ref Librn, Burlington County Library, Evesham Branch, Evesham Municipal Complex, 984 Tuckerton Rd, Marlton, NJ, 08053. Tel: 856-983-1444. Fax: 856-983-4939. p. 1543

Lipinski, Eileen, Libr Mgr, Legislative Reference Bureau, City Hall, Rm B-11, 200 E Wells St, Milwaukee, WI, 53202-3567. Tel: 414-286-8818. Fax: 414-286-3004. p. 2618

Lipinski, Katie, Youth Serv Mgr, Twinsburg Public Library, 10050 Ravenna Rd, Twinsburg, OH, 44087-1796. Tel: 330-425-4268. Fax: 330-425-3622. p. 1941

Lipke, Linda, Asst Dir, Galva Public Library District, 120 NW Third Ave, Galva, IL, 61434. Tel: 309-932-2180. Fax: 309-932-2280. p. 648

Lipkin, Gina, Youth Serv Librn, Langley-Adams Library, 185 Main St, Groveland, MA, 01834-1314. Tel: 978-372-1732. Fax: 978-374-6590. p. 1093

Lipman, Penny, Librn, Royal Canadian Military Institute Library, 426 University Ave, Toronto, ON, M5G 1S9, CANADA. Tel: 416-597-0286, Ext 128. Fax: 416-597-6919. p. 2858

Lipnitskaya, Inna, Dir, Lincoln Medical Center, 234 E 149th St, Bronx, NY, 10451. Tel: 718-579-5745. Fax: 718-579-5170. p. 1587

Lipof, Rita, Br Mgr, Broward County Division of Libraries, Riverland, 2710 W Davie Blvd, Fort Lauderdale, FL, 33312. Tel: 954-791-1085. Fax: 954-791-1087. p. 442

Lipomi, Deena, Access Serv, YA Serv, Brighton Memorial Library, 2300 Elmwood Ave, Rochester, NY, 14618. Tel: 585-784-5300. Fax: 585-784-5333. p. 1728

Lippard, Rodney, Dir, Learning Res, Rowan-Cabarrus Community College, 1333 Jake Alexander Blvd, Salisbury, NC, 28145. Tel: 704-216-3691. Fax: 704-216-3827. p. 1822

Lippert, David, Digital Serv, Portland Community College Library, 12000 SW 49th AV, Portland, OR, 97219. Tel: 971-722-8397. p. 2013

Lippert, Villa, Br Mgr, Lake Lillian Public Library, 450 Lakeview St, Lake Lillian, MN, 56253. Tel: 320-664-4514. Fax: 320-664-4514. p. 1255

Lippert, Villa, Librn, Raymond Public Library, 208 Cofield St N, Raymond, MN, 56282. Tel: 320-967-4411. p. 1271

Lippincott, Bertram, III, Librn, Newport Historical Society Library, 82 Touro St, Newport, RI, 02840. Tel: 401-846-0813. Fax: 401-846-1853. p. 2169

Lippincott, Marge, Dean, Info Tech & Learning Res, Mount Ida College, Wadsworth Library, 777 Dedham St, Newton, MA, 02459. Tel: 617-928-4596. Fax: 617-928-4038. p. 1110

Lippitt, Dana, Curator, Bangor Historical Society Library, 159 Union St, Bangor, ME, 04401. Tel: 207-942-1900, 207-942-5766. Fax: 207-942-1910. p. 975

Lippman, Robert, Dir, Banning Library District, 21 W Nicolet St, Banning, CA, 92220. Tel: 951-849-3192. p. 125

Lippman, Stephen, Ref, Bank of America Merrill Lynch & Co, 250 Vesey St, 24th Flr, New York, NY, 10080. Tel: 212-449-3814. Fax: 212-449-1379. p. 1669

Lippmann, Adrienne, Tech Serv, New York Institute of Technology, Northern Blvd, Old Westbury, NY, 11568-8000. Tel: 516-686-3743. Fax: 516-686-3709. p. 1710

Lippo, Amy, Asst Dir, Sullivan County Public Library, 1655 Blountville Blvd, Blountville, TN, 37617. Tel: 423-279-2716. Fax: 423-279-2836. p. 2224

Lippold, Karen, Head, Info Serv, Ref, Memorial University of Newfoundland, Queen Elizabeth II Library, 234 Elizabeth Ave, St. John's, NL, A1B 3Y1, CANADA. Tel: 709-737-7428. Fax: 709-737-2153. p. 2773

Lippold, Mary, Ref Serv, Ser, South Texas College of Law, 1303 San Jacinto St, Houston, TX, 77002-7000. Tel: 713-646-1711. Fax: 713-659-2217. p. 2342

Lippy, Brooke, Asst Librn, University of Hartford Libraries, Mildred P Allen Memorial, 200 Bloomfield Ave, West Hartford, CT, 06117-0395. Tel: 860-768-4404. Fax: 860-768-5295. p. 376

Lippy, Judith, Commun Serv Mgr, Richmond Public Library, Belmont Branch, 3100 Ellwood Ave, Richmond, VA, 23221. Tel: 804-646-1139. Fax: 804-646-1105. p. 2490

Lipscomb, Bobby, Librn, Huntsville-Madison Public Library, Subregional Library for the Blind & Physically Handicapped, 915 Monroe St, Huntsville, AL, 35801-5007. Tel: 256-532-5980. Fax: 256-532-5997. p. 21

Lipscomb Butsko, Carol L, Dir, Fairport Harbor Public Library, 335 Vine St, Fairport Harbor, OH, 44077-5799. Tel: 440-354-8191. Fax: 440-354-6059. p. 1899

Lipscomb, Georgia, Librn, Sardis City Public Library, 1310 Church St, Sardis City, AL, 35956-2200. Tel: 256-593-5634. Fax: 256-593-6258. p. 35

Lipscomb, Pam, Mgr, Miami University Libraries, Southwest Ohio Regional Depository (SWORD), Middletown Campus, Middletown, OH, 45042. Tel: 513-727-3474. Fax: 513-727-3478. p. 1926

Lipscomb, Robert, Dir, Harrison County Library System, 2600 24th Ave, No 6, Gulfport, MS, 39501-2081. Tel: 228-868-1383, Ext 22. Fax: 228-863-7433. p. 1299

Lipscombe, Joan M, Librn, Parks Canada - Ontario Service Centre Library, 111 Water St E, Cornwall, ON, K6H 6S3, CANADA. Tel: 613-938-5787. Fax: 613-938-5766. p. 2801

Lipsey, Kim, Librn, Washington University Libraries, Bernard Becker Medical Library, 660 S Euclid Ave, Campus Box 8132, Saint Louis, MO, 63110. Tel: 314-362-4733. Fax: 314-454-6606. p. 1362

Lipson, Susanne, Dir, Charlie Garrett Memorial Library, 103 S Fisher St, Gorman, TX, 76454. Tel: 254-734-3301, 254-734-4305. p. 2328

Liptax, Deborah, Develop Dir, Public Library of Youngstown & Mahoning County, 305 Wick Ave, Youngstown, OH, 44503-1079. Tel: 330-744-8636. Fax: 330-744-3355. p. 1952

Liranzo, Angelo, Br Mgr, Pasco County Library System, Hugh Embry Branch, 14215 Fourth St, Dade City, FL, 33523. Tel: 352-567-3576. Fax: 352-521-6670. p. 451

Lirocco, Sharon, Asst Librn, Fobes Memorial Library, Four Maple St, Oakham, MA, 01068. Tel: 508-882-3372. Fax: 508-882-3372. p. 1116

Lis, Janine, Mkt Mgr, Harford County Public Library, 1221-A Brass Mill Rd, Belcamp, MD, 21017-1209. Tel: 410-273-5600, Ext 2256. Fax: 410-273-5606. p. 1020

Lisa, Bjerken, Sr Librn, Hennepin County Library, Southeast, 1222 4th St SE, Minneapolis, MN, 55414. Tel: 612-543-6403. Fax: 612-543-6727. p. 1264

Lisa, Veronica, Librn, Department of Veterans Affairs, Lyons Campus Medical Library, 151 Knollcroft Rd, Lyons, NJ, 07939. Tel: 908-647-0180, Ext 4545, 973-676-1000. Fax: 908-604-5837. p. 1497

Lischke, Mike, Dir, Northwest AHEC Library Information Network, Wake Forest University School of Medicine, Medical Center Blvd, Winston-Salem, NC, 27157-1060. Tel: 336-713-7700. Fax: 336-713-7701. p. 2951

Lisefski, Alice, Librn, Hazleton Area Public Library, Nuremberg Branch, Mahanoy St, Nuremberg, PA, 18241. Tel: 570-384-4101. p. 2068

Lishia, Kimberly, Br Mgr, Enlow Ruth Library of Garrett County, Grantsville Branch, PO Box 237, Grantsville, MD, 21536-0237. Tel: 301-895-5298. Fax: 301-245-4411. p. 1036

Liska, Ruth C, Asst Dir, Mackinaw Area Public Library, 528 W Central Ave, Mackinaw City, MI, 49701-9681. Tel: 231-436-5451. Fax: 231-436-7344. p. 1205

Liskey, Patty, Tech Serv Mgr, Massanutten Regional Library, 174 S Main St, Harrisonburg, VA, 22801. Tel: 540-434-4475. Fax: 540-434-4382. p. 2470

Liskiewicz, Lisa M, Head of Libr, Herkimer County Law Library, 301 N Washington St, Ste 5511, Herkimer, NY, 13350-1299. Tel: 315-867-1172. Fax: 315-866-7991. p. 1635

Liskowiak, Zara, Dir, Champaign County Library, 1060 Scioto St, Urbana, OH, 43078. Tel: 937-653-3811. Fax: 937-653-5679. p. 1942

Liss, Katherine, YA Librn, Metuchen Public Library, 480 Middlesex Ave, Metuchen, NJ, 08840. Tel: 732-632-8526. Fax: 732-632-8535. p. 1501

Liss, Michael, Ref Serv, Fairleigh Dickinson University, 1000 River Rd, Teaneck, NJ, 07666-1914. Tel: 201-692-2279, Ext 2276. Fax: 201-692-9815. p. 1532

Liss, Nancy, Librn, Maryland Correctional Institution-Jessup Library, Rte 175, Jessup, MD, 20794. Tel: 410-799-7610, Ext 4314. Fax: 410-799-2859. p. 1033

Liss, Rick, Librn, East Jersey State Prison Library, Lock Bag R, Woodbridge Ave, Rahway, NJ, 07065. Tel: 732-396-2695. Fax: 732-499-5023. p. 1524

Lissak, Debra, Exec Dir, The Urbana Free Library, 210 W Green St, Urbana, IL, 61801-5326. Tel: 217-367-4057. Fax: 217-367-4061. p. 713

List, Barbara, Dir, Coll Develop, Columbia University, Butler Library, Rm 517, 535 W 114th St, New York, NY, 10027. Tel: 212-854-7309. Fax: 212-854-9099. p. 1674

List, Edith, Assoc Dir, Principia College, One Maybeck Pl, Elsah, IL, 62028-9703. Tel: 618-374-5076. Fax: 618-374-5107. p. 643

List, Kathleen L, Dir, Libr Serv, Ringling College of Art & Design, 2700 N Tamiami Trail, Sarasota, FL, 34234. Tel: 941-359-7582. Fax: 941-359-7632. p. 490

List, Mary Ann, Dir, Portsmouth Public Library, 175 Parrott Ave, Portsmouth, NH, 03801-4452. Tel: 603-766-1710. Fax: 603-433-0981. p. 1463

Liste, Rob, Circ, Warren-Trumbull County Public Library, 444 Mahoning Ave NW, Warren, OH, 44483. Tel: 330-399-8807. Fax: 330-395-3988. p. 1944

Lister, Lisa, Ref Serv, Colorado College, 1021 N Cascade Ave, Colorado Springs, CO, 80903-3252. Tel: 719-389-6658. Fax: 719-389-6082. p. 294

Listernick, Robert, Circ, Hebrew College, 160 Herrick Rd, Newton Centre, MA, 02459. Tel: 617-559-8750. Fax: 617-559-8751. p. 1110

Liston, Elaine, Archivist, NASA, Kennedy Space Center, FL, 32899. Tel: 321-867-3600. Fax: 321-867-4534. p. 455

Liston, Michele, Br Mgr, Enlow Ruth Library of Garrett County, Friendsville Branch, PO Box 57, Friendsville, MD, 21531-0057. Tel: 301-746-5663. Fax: 301-746-5663. p. 1035

Liston, Samuel, Tech Analyst, Oceanside Public Library, 330 N Coast Hwy, Oceanside, CA, 92054-2824. Tel: 760-435-5628. Fax: 760-435-9614. p. 199

Listrom, Judith, Cat Mgr, Mid-Continent Public Library, 15616 E US Hwy 24, Independence, MO, 64050-2098. Tel: 816-836-5200. Fax: 816-521-7253. p. 1332

Litchfield, Eileen, Librn, Greenville Law Library Association, 124 W Fifth St, Greenville, OH, 45331. Tel: 937-547-9741. Fax: 937-547-9743. p. 1903

Litherland, Linda, Dir, Perry Memorial Hospital, 530 Park Ave E, Princeton, IL, 61356. Tel: 815-875-2811, Ext 4479. Fax: 815-872-1257. p. 692

Litherland, Steven, Ref Librn, Tidewater Community College, 120 Campus Dr, Portsmouth, VA, 23701. Fax: 757-822-2149. p. 2485

Litjens, Marcie, Ch, Center Moriches Free Public Library, 235 Main St, Center Moriches, NY, 11934. Tel: 631-878-0940. p. 1604

Litke, Amy, Head, Ch, New Britain Public Library, 20 High St, New Britain, CT, 06051-4226. Tel: 860-224-3155. Fax: 860-223-6729. p. 354

Litland, Kimberly, Dir, Brookfield Public Library, 3609 Grand Blvd, Brookfield, IL, 60513. Tel: 708-485-6917. Fax: 708-485-5172. p. 598

Litland, Kimberly, Ref Serv, Melrose Park Public Library, 801 N Broadway, Melrose Park, IL, 60160. Tel: 708-343-3391. Fax: 708-531-5327. p. 673

Little, Alisha, Cat, University of Texas Libraries, Serials Acquisitions Unit, PO Box P, Austin, TX, 78713-8916. Tel: 512-495-4222. Fax: 512-495-4296. p. 2285

Little, Debby, Librn, Western Counties Regional Library, Yarmouth Branch, 405 Main St, Yarmouth, NS, B5A 1G3, CANADA. Tel: 902-742-5040. Fax: 902-742-6920. p. 2787

Little, Dena, Youth Serv Mgr, Upper Arlington Public Library, 2800 Tremont Rd, Columbus, OH, 43221. Tel: 614-486-9621. Fax: 614-486-4530. p. 1891

Little, Elaine, Librn, Chinook Regional Library, Hazlet Branch, Railway Ave, Hazlet, SK, S0N 1E0, CANADA. Tel: 306-678-2155. p. 2928

Little, Farrah, Librn, Ref & Copyright, Justice Institute of British Columbia Library, 715 McBride Blvd, New Westminster, BC, V3L 5T4, CANADA. Tel: 604-528-5893. Fax: 604-528-5593. p. 2734

Little, Floyd W, Jr, Asst Br Mgr, Ch, Librn I, Montgomery City-County Public Library System, Coliseum Boulevard Branch Library, 840 Coliseum Blvd, Montgomery, AL, 36109. Tel: 334-271-7005. Fax: 334-244-5754. p. 29

Little, Gelynn, Librn, Barton Library, Huttig Branch, Frost St, Huttig, AR, 71747. Tel: 870-943-3411. Fax: 870-943-3411. p. 98

Little, Honey, Pub Serv, Lewistown Public Library, 701 W Main St, Lewistown, MT, 59457. Tel: 406-538-5212. Fax: 406-538-3920. p. 1384

Little, Jennifer, Head, User Serv, Morehead State University, 150 University Blvd, Morehead, KY, 40351. Tel: 606-783-5352. Fax: 606-783-5037. p. 929

Little, Jennifer, Info Literacy, Instrul Serv Librn, Res Serv, State University of New York College at Brockport, 350 New Campus Dr, Brockport, NY, 14420-2997. Tel: 585-395-2482. Fax: 585-395-5651. p. 1585

Little, Jessica, Dir, Saint Louis Public Library, 312 Michigan Ave, Saint Louis, MI, 48880. Tel: 989-681-5141. Fax: 989-681-2077. p. 1225

Little, Karen, Dir, University of Louisville Libraries, Dwight Anderson Music Library, 105 W Brandeis Ave, Louisville, KY, 40208. Tel: 502-852-5659. Fax: 502-852-7701. p. 926

Little, Kathy, Br Coordr, Mesa Public Library, 64 E First St, Mesa, AZ, 85201-6768. Tel: 480-644-2726. Fax: 480-644-2991. p. 69

Little, Kathy, Mgr, Delta County Libraries, Crawford Public, 425 Hwy 92, Crawford, CO, 81415. Tel: 970-921-3500. Fax: 970-921-4500. p. 313

Little, Kitty, Dir, Rye Free Reading Room, 1061 Boston Post Rd, Rye, NY, 10580. Tel: 914-967-0480. Fax: 914-967-5522. p. 1736

Little, Lara B, ILL, Libr Dir, Ref Librn, Pfeiffer University, 48380 US Hwy 52 N, Misenheimer, NC, 28109. Tel: 704-463-3350. Fax: 704-463-3356. p. 1809

Little, Larry R, Chief Librn, Penticton Public Library, 785 Main St, Penticton, BC, V2A 5E3, CANADA. Tel: 250-770-7781. Fax: 250-770-7787. p. 2735

Little, Linda G, Br Supvr, Scenic Regional Library of Franklin, Gasconade & Warren Counties, Owensville Branch, 107 N First St, Owensville, MO, 65066. Tel: 573-437-2188. p. 1369

Little, Margaret, Ch, La Marque Public Library, 1011 Bayou Rd, La Marque, TX, 77568-4195. Tel: 409-938-9270. Fax: 409-938-9277. p. 2352

Little, Mary C, Dir of Tech Serv, Queens Borough Public Library, 89-11 Merrick Blvd, Jamaica, NY, 11432. Tel: 718-990-0733. p. 1643

Little, Micquel, Access Serv Librn, Saint John Fisher College, 3690 East Ave, Rochester, NY, 14618-3599. Tel: 585-385-8165. Fax: 585-385-8445. p. 1732

Little, Mike, Adminr, Delaware Correctional Center Law Library, 1181 Paddock Rd, Smyrna, DE, 19977. Tel: 302-653-9261, Ext 2450. Fax: 302-659-6687. p. 386

Little, Nancy, Br Mgr, Saint Tammany Parish Library, Mandeville Branch, 844 Girod St, Mandeville, LA, 70448. Tel: 985-626-4293. Fax: 985-624-4621. p. 948

Little, Naomi, Admin Serv, Contra Costa County Public Law Library, 1020 Ward St, 1st Flr, Martinez, CA, 94553-1360. Tel: 925-646-2783. Fax: 925-646-2438. p. 184

Little, Rachel, Ref Librn, Baylor University Libraries, Sheridan & John Eddie Williams Legal Research & Technology Center, 1114 S University Parks Dr, One Bear Pl, No 97128, Waco, TX, 76798-7128. Tel: 254-710-2168. Fax: 254-710-2294. p. 2397

Little, Sharon, Circ, Kingfisher Memorial Library, 505 W Will Rogers St, Kingfisher, OK, 73750. Tel: 405-375-3384. Fax: 405-375-3306. p. 1966

Little, Sheila, Circ Mgr, Saline District Library, 555 N Maple Rd, Saline, MI, 48176. Tel: 734-429-5450. Fax: 734-944-0600. p. 1225

Little, Sylvia, Ser, McGill University Libraries, Howard Ross Library of Management, Samuel Bronfman Bldg, 1001 Sherbrooke St W, 2nd Flr, Montreal, QC, H3A 1G5, CANADA. Tel: 514-398-8268. Fax: 514-398-5046. p. 2899

Little, Valerie, Actg Asst Principal Librn, Minnesota Orchestra Music Library, 1111 Nicollet Mall, Minneapolis, MN, 55403. Tel: 612-371-5663. Fax: 612-371-0838. p. 1261

Littlefield, Audrey, Libr Asst, Gardiner Public Library, 152 Water St, Gardiner, ME, 04345. Tel: 207-582-3312. Fax: 207-582-6104. p. 986

Littlefield, Barbara, Head, Youth Serv, Glenview Public Library, 1930 Glenview Rd, Glenview, IL, 60025-2899. Tel: 847-729-7500. Fax: 847-729-7558. p. 650

Littlefield, Erica, Head, Youth Serv, Twin Falls Public Library, 201 Fourth Ave E, Twin Falls, ID, 83301-6397. Tel: 208-733-2964. Fax: 208-733-2965. p. 584

Littlefield, Gary, Dir, Carnegie Regional Library, 49 W Seventh St, Grafton, ND, 58237. Tel: 701-352-2754. Fax: 701-352-2757. p. 1842

Littlefield, Mary W, Dir, Ogunquit Memorial Library, 166 Shore Rd, Ogunquit, ME, 03907. Tel: 207-646-9024. p. 994

Littlejohn, David, In Charge, Milliken & Company, 920 Milliken Rd, MS M-470, Spartanburg, SC, 29303. Tel: 864-503-1734. Fax: 864-503-2769. p. 2204

Littlejohn, Donna, Dir, Amarillo Public Library, 413 E Fourth Ave, Amarillo, TX, 79101. Tel: 806-378-3050. Fax: 806-378-9327. p. 2274

Littlejohn, Donna, Dir, Harrington Library Consortium, 413 E Fourth Ave, Amarillo, TX, 79101. Tel: 806-378-6037. Fax: 806-378-6038. p. 2956

Littlejohn, Timothy, Br Mgr, Hawaii State Public Library System, Waialua Public Library, 67-068 Kealohanui St, Waialua, HI, 96791. Tel: 808-637-8286. Fax: 808-637-8288. p. 563

Littlejohns, Carolyn, Head, Tech Serv, John Abbott College, 21,275 Lakeshore Rd, Sainte-Anne-de-Bellevue, QC, H9X 3L9, CANADA. Tel: 514-457-6610, Ext 5335. p. 2910

Littleton, Stanley, Asst Dir, Jackson County Public Library System, 2929 Green St, Marianna, FL, 32446. Tel: 850-482-9631. Fax: 850-482-9632. p. 462

Littman, Rebecca, Music Librn, University of Wisconsin-Milwaukee, 2311 E Hartford Ave, Milwaukee, WI, 53211. Tel: 414-229-4785, 414-229-6202. Fax: 414-229-6766. p. 2622

Litton, Jocelan, Tech Serv, Coquitlam Public Library, 575 Poirier St, Coquitlam, BC, V3J 6A9, CANADA. Tel: 604-937-4150. Fax: 604-931-6739. p. 2727

Littrel, Ellen, Asst Dir, Ch, Erie Public Library District, 802 Eighth Ave, Erie, IL, 61250. Tel: 309-659-2707. Fax: 309-659-2707. p. 643

Littrel, Sharon, Librn, Davenport Public Library, 109 N Maple Ave, Davenport, NE, 68335. Tel: 402-364-2147. p. 1397

Littrell, Deborah, Dir, Libr Develop & Networking, Texas State Library & Archives Commission, 1201 Brazos St, Austin, TX, 78701. Tel: 512-463-5456. Fax: 512-463-8800. p. 2282

Littrell, Stephen, Librn, University of Texas Libraries, Wasserman Public Affairs Library, Sid Richardson Hall 3.243, S5442, Austin, TX, 78712-1282. Tel: 512-495-4401. Fax: 512-471-4697. p. 2285

Litts, Douglas, Libr Dir, Smithsonian Libraries, Smithsonian American Art Museum/National Portrait Gallery Library, Victor Bldg, Rm 2100, MRC 975, 750 Ninth St NW, Washington, DC, 20560. Tel: 202-633-8230. Fax: 202-633-8232. p. 415

Litwack, Helen, Coll Develop, New England School of Law Library, 154 Stuart St, Boston, MA, 02116-5687. Tel: 617-422-7282. Fax: 617-422-7303. p. 1065

Litwiller, Denise, Dir, H A Peine Memorial Library, 202 N Main Ave, Minier, IL, 61759. Tel: 309-392-3220. Fax: 309-392-2697. p. 674

Litwinowicz, Anthony, Sr Librn, Fishkill Correctional Facility Library, Bldg 13, Beacon, NY, 12508. Tel: 845-831-4800, Ext 4600. Fax: 845-831-3199. p. 1579

Litwinowicz, Anthony, Sr Librn, New York Department of Correctional Services, 247 Harris Rd, Bedford Hills, NY, 10507-2499. Tel: 914-241-3100, Ext 4540. Fax: 914-241-3100. p. 1579

Litzer, Don, Asst Libr Dir, Head, Adult Serv, T B Scott Library, 106 W First St, Merrill, WI, 54452-2398. Tel: 715-536-7191. Fax: 715-536-1705. p. 2616

Liu, Chang, Dir, Loudoun County Public Library, Admin Offices, 908A Trailview Blvd SE, Leesburg, VA, 20175-4415. Tel: 703-777-0368. Fax: 703-771-5238, 703-771-5252. p. 2473

Liu, Frank Y, Dir, Allegheny County Law Library, 921 City-County Bldg, 414 Grant St, Pittsburgh, PA, 15219-2543. Tel: 412-396-5018. Fax: 412-350-5889. p. 2121

Liu, Frank Y, Dir, Duquesne University, Center for Legal Information, 900 Locust St, Pittsburgh, PA, 15282. Tel: 412-396-5018. Fax: 412-396-6294. p. 2125

Liu, Guoying (Grace), Syst Mgr, University of Windsor, 401 Sunset Ave, Windsor, ON, N9B 3P4, CANADA. Tel: 519-253-3000, Ext 3160. p. 2871

Liu, Hongbin, Web Serv Librn, Yale University Library, Harvey Cushing/John Hay Whitney Medical Library, Sterling Hall of Medicine, 333 Cedar St, L110 SHM, New Haven, CT, 06520. Tel: 203-785-5352. Fax: 203-785-5636. p. 358

Liu, Hongru, Libr Tech, First Nations University of Canada, Saskatoon Campus Library, 226 20th St E, Saskatoon, SK, S7K 0A6, CANADA. Tel: 306-931-1800, Ext 5425. Fax: 306-931-1847. p. 2922

Liu, Hope, Instructional Technologist, Cardinal Stritch University Library, 6801 N Yates Rd, Milwaukee, WI, 53207-3985. Tel: 414-410-4454. Fax: 414-410-4268. p. 2617

Liu, James, Media Coordr, Brooklyn College Library, 2900 Bedford Ave, Brooklyn, NY, 11210-2889. Tel: 718-951-4868. Fax: 718-951-4540. p. 1589

Liu, Jian, Head of Libr, Indiana University Bloomington, Public Health Library, 1025 E Seventh St, Bloomington, IN, 47405. Tel: 812-855-4420. Fax: 812-855-6778. p. 728

Liu, Jiang, Commun Libr Mgr, Queens Borough Public Library, Lefrak City Community Library, 98-30 57th Ave, Corona, NY, 11368. Tel: 718-592-7677. p. 1645

Liu, Kathleen, Ref, Collingswood Public Library, 771 Haddon Ave, Collingswood, NJ, 08108-3714. Tel: 856-858-0649. Fax: 856-858-5016. p. 1480

Liu, Lan, Dir, Middlesex Community College, 100 Training Hill Rd, Middletown, CT, 06457-4889. Tel: 860-343-5833. Fax: 860-343-5874. p. 351

Liu, Liz, Libr Serv Mgr, Quest Diagnostics, Inc, 33608 Ortega Hwy, San Juan Capistrano, CA, 92690-6130. Tel: 949-728-4689. Fax: 949-728-4047. p. 252

Liu, Min, Asst Dir, Long Island Library Resources Council, 627 N Sunrise Service Rd, Bellport, NY, 11713. Tel: 631-675-1570. p. 2950

Liu, Peter Y, Dir, Monterey Institute of International Studies, 425 Van Buren St, Monterey, CA, 93940. Tel: 831-647-4139. Fax: 831-647-3518. p. 190

Liu, Rosa, Mgr, Res Libr & Info Prog, National Institute of Standards & Technology Research Library, 100 Bureau Dr, Stop 2500, Gaithersburg, MD, 20899-2500. Tel: 301-975-2787. Fax: 301-869-8071. p. 1030

Liu, Simon, Dir, United States Department of Agriculture, 10301 Baltimore Ave, Beltsville, MD, 20705-2351. Tel: 301-504-5755. Fax: 301-504-5472. p. 1020

Liu, Victor, Dean, Learning Res, Washtenaw Community College, 4800 E Huron River Dr, Ann Arbor, MI, 48105-4800. Tel: 734-973-3379. Fax: 734-973-3446. p. 1153

Liu, Weilee, Ref, Teaneck Public Library, 840 Teaneck Rd, Teaneck, NJ, 07666. Tel: 201-837-4171. Fax: 201-837-0410. p. 1533

Liu, Yabin, Info Tech, Addison Public Library, Four Friendship Plaza, Addison, IL, 60101. Tel: 630-458-3350. Fax: 630-543-6645. p. 587

Liu, Yan Quan, Dr, Assoc Prof, Southern Connecticut State University, 501 Crescent St, New Haven, CT, 06515. Tel: 203-392-5763. Fax: 203-392-5780. p. 2963

Liu-Snyder, Jessie, Info Spec, Cigna Co Library, 900 Cottage Grove Rd, Bloomfield, CT, 06002. Tel: 860-226-4327. Fax: 860-226-5128. p. 330

Liudahl, Su, Dir, Lane Library District, 64 W Oregon Ave, Creswell, OR, 97426. Tel: 541-895-3053. Fax: 541-895-3507. p. 1995

Livas, Melinda, Distance Serv Librn, Winston-Salem State University, 601 Martin Luther King Jr Dr, Winston-Salem, NC, 27110. Tel: 336-750-8933. Fax: 336-750-2459. p. 1834

Lively, Dave B, Tech Serv, Jefferson County Law Library, Jefferson County Court House, 716 Richard Arrington Jr Blvd N, Ste 530, Birmingham, AL, 35203. Tel: 205-325-5628. Fax: 205-322-5915. p. 8

Lively, Doris, Dir, Grant Parish Library, 300 Main St, Colfax, LA, 71417-1830. Tel: 318-627-9920. Fax: 318-627-9900. p. 947

Lively, Katey, Librn, Gutekunst Public Library, 309 Second St SE, State Center, IA, 50247-0550. Tel: 641-483-2741. Fax: 641-483-2131. p. 846

Livergood, Ryan, Dir, Public Library of Arlington, 700 Massachusetts Ave, Arlington, MA, 02476. Tel: 781-316-3200, 781-316-3233. Fax: 781-316-3209. p. 1050

Livergood, Ryan, Asst Dir, Dover Town Library, 56 Dedham St, Dover, MA, 02030-2214. Tel: 508-785-8113. Fax: 508-785-0138. p. 1084

Livermore, Tracie, Dir, Nineveh Public Library of Colesville Township, 3029 NY State Hwy 7, Nineveh, NY, 13813. Tel: 607-693-1858. Fax: 607-693-1858. p. 1706

Livesay, Lisa, Dir, Stinson Memorial Public Library District, 409 S Main St, Anna, IL, 62906. Tel: 618-833-2521. Fax: 618-833-3560. p. 589

Livesay, Lori, Dir of Circ, Spartanburg County Public Libraries, 151 S Church St, Spartanburg, SC, 29306-3241. Tel: 864-596-3500. Fax: 864-596-3518. p. 2205

Livick, Martha, Circ, Blue Ridge Community College, One College Lane, Weyers Cave, VA, 24486. Tel: 540-453-2247. Fax: 540-234-9598. p. 2502

Livingston, Alayne, Librn, Oxford Public Library, 213 Choccolocco St, Oxford, AL, 36203. Tel: 256-831-1750. Fax: 256-835-6798. p. 33

Livingston, Anne, Tech Serv, Wenatchee Valley College, 1300 Fifth St, Wenatchee, WA, 98801. Tel: 509-682-6710. Fax: 509-682-6711. p. 2550

Livingston, Brenda, Br Head, Toronto Public Library, Downsview, 2793 Keele St, Toronto, ON, M3M 2G3, CANADA. Tel: 416-395-5720. Fax: 416-395-5727. p. 2861

Livingston, Bridget, Syst Librn, Treas, Columbia Area Medical Librarians' Association, University of South Carolina, School of Medicine Library, 6311 Garner's Ferry Rd, Columbia, SC, 29209. Tel: 803-733-3361. Fax: 803-733-1509. p. 2955

Livingston, Briget, Dir, Chapin Memorial Library, 400 14th Ave N, Myrtle Beach, SC, 29577-3612. Tel: 843-918-1275. Fax: 843-918-1288. p. 2201

Livingston, Christopher, Br Supvr, Kern County Library, Bryce C Rathbun Branch, 200 W China Grade Loop, Bakersfield, CA, 93308-1709. Tel: 661-393-6431. Fax: 661-393-6432. p. 124

Livingston, Edward M, AV, Northwest Florida State College, 100 College Blvd, Niceville, FL, 32578. Tel: 850-729-5392. Fax: 850-729-5295. p. 472

Livingston, Jami, Dir, Drake Public Library, 115 Drake Ave, Centerville, IA, 52544. Tel: 641-856-6676. Fax: 641-856-6135. p. 801

Livingston, Janet, Dir, Ekalaka Public Library, 115 Main St, Ekalaka, MT, 59324. Tel: 406-775-6336. Fax: 406-775-6325. p. 1378

Livingston, Martie, ILL, Ottawa Library, 105 S Hickory St, Ottawa, KS, 66067-2306. Tel: 785-242-3080. Fax: 785-242-8789. p. 887

Livingston, Sarah, Librn, Huntington Memorial Library, 62 Chestnut, Oneonta, NY, 13820-2498. Tel: 607-432-1980. p. 1711

Livingston, Shaney T, Dir, Alachua County Library District, 401 E University Ave, Gainesville, FL, 32601-5453. Tel: 352-334-3900. Fax: 352-334-3918. p. 448

Livingston, Susan, Librn, South Florida State College Library, 600 W College Dr, Avon Park, FL, 33825-9356. Tel: 863-784-7305. Fax: 863-452-6042. p. 426

Livingstone, Dorothy, Ref, Cape Canaveral Public Library, 201 Polk Ave, Cape Canaveral, FL, 32920-3067. Tel: 321-868-1101. Fax: 321-868-1103. p. 431

Livoti, Maria, Head, Circ, New Canaan Library, 151 Main St, New Canaan, CT, 06840. Tel: 203-594-5000. Fax: 203-594-5026. p. 354

Livsey, Barbara, ILL, Mamie Doud Eisenhower Public Library, Three Community Park Rd, Broomfield, CO, 80020-3781. Tel: 720-887-2300. Fax: 720-887-1384. p. 292

Livsey, Karen, Archivist, Fenton History Center-Library, 67 Washington St, Jamestown, NY, 14701-6697. Tel: 716-664-6256. Fax: 716-483-7524. p. 1646

Lixey, Carrie, Adult Serv Mgr, Yorba Linda Public Library, 18181 Imperial Hwy, Yorba Linda, CA, 92886-3437. Tel: 714-777-2873. Fax: 714-777-0640. p. 285

Lize, Joanne, Youth Serv, Venice Public Library, 300 S Nokomis Ave, Venice, FL, 34285-2416. Tel: 941-861-1330. Fax: 941-486-2345. p. 501

Lizotte, Isabelle, Res Serv Spec, Borden Ladner Gervais LLP Library, 1000 de la Gauchetiere W, Ste 900, Montreal, QC, H3B 5H4, CANADA. Tel: 514-954-3159. Fax: 514-954-1905. p. 2892

Ljungquist, Ross, ILL, State University of New York Downstate Medical Center, 395 Lenox Rd, Brooklyn, NY, 11203. Tel: 718-270-7400. Fax: 718-270-7413, 718-270-7468. p. 1595

Llamas, Lito, Librn, Shell Oil Co, 910 Louisiana St, Ste 4353, Houston, TX, 77002. Tel: 713-241-2155. Fax: 713-241-7029. p. 2342

Llerandi, Patricia, Adult Serv, Schaumburg Township District Library, 130 S Roselle Rd, Schaumburg, IL, 60193. Tel: 847-923-3215. Fax: 847-923-3428. p. 701

Llewellyn, Lisa, Br Mgr, San Bernardino County Library, Grand Terrace Branch, 22795 Barton Rd, Grand Terrace, CA, 92313. Tel: 909-783-0147. Fax: 909-783-1913. p. 228

Llewellyn, Muriel, Br Mgr, Collins LeRoy Leon County Public Library System, Northeast Branch, The Bruce J Host Center, 5513 Thomasville Rd, Tallahassee, FL, 32309. Tel: 850-606-2800. Fax: 850-606-2801. p. 492

Llewellyn, Penny, Pub Serv, Northwest Community College Library, 5331 McConnell Ave, Terrace, BC, V8G 4X2, CANADA. Tel: 250-638-5407. Fax: 250-635-1594. p. 2739

Llewllyn, Janet, Asst Librn, Nanty Glo Public Library, 942 Roberts St, Nanty Glo, PA, 15943-0296. Tel: 814-749-0111. Fax: 814-749-0111. p. 2094

Lloyd, Ann, Asst Librn, Chinook Regional Library, Central Butte Branch, Box 276, Central Butte, SK, S0H 0T0, CANADA. Tel: 306-796-4660. p. 2928

Lloyd, Darlene, Br Mgr, Monterey County Free Libraries, Bradley Branch, Dixie St, Bradley, CA, 93426. Tel: 805-472-9407. Fax: 805-472-9565. p. 183

Lloyd, Dawn, Acq Asst, Oklahoma Panhandle State University, 409 W Sewell, Goodwell, OK, 73939. Tel: 580-349-1548. Fax: 580-349-1541. p. 1964

Lloyd, Erin, Ch, Knox Public Library, 620 S Main St, Knox, PA, 16232. Tel: 814-797-1054. Fax: 814-797-1054. p. 2075

Lloyd, James H, Dir, Cincinnati Christian University, 2700 Glenway Ave, Cincinnati, OH, 45204-3200. Tel: 513-244-8138. Fax: 513-244-8434. p. 1869

Lloyd, Jane, Dir, Norwood Public Library, 513 Welcome Ave, Norwood, PA, 19074-1425. Tel: 610-534-0693. Fax: 610-532-8785. p. 2100

Lloyd, Jennifer, Head, ILL, Head, Info Tech, Louisiana State University Health Sciences Center, 433 Bolivar St, Box B3-1, New Orleans, LA, 70112-2223. Tel: 504-568-5550. Fax: 504-568-7718. p. 961

Lloyd, Jo, Dir, Lincoln County Library, 63 Main St, Pioche, NV, 89043. Tel: 775-962-5244. Fax: 775-962-5244. p. 1432

Lloyd, Kristi, Libr Tech, Colorado Department of Corrections, Arrowhead Correctional Center Library, US Hwy 50, Evans Blvd, Canon City, CO, 81215. Tel: 719-269-5601, Ext 3923. Fax: 719-269-5650. p. 293

Lloyd, Linda Lu, Librn, Nebraska Christian College, 12550 S 114th St, Papillion, NE, 68046. Tel: 402-935-9400. Fax: 402-935-9500. p. 1416

Lloyd, Marsha R, Br Librn, Kern County Library, Ridgecrest Branch, 131 E Las Flores Ave, Ridgecrest, CA, 93555-3648. Tel: 760-384-5870. Fax: 760-384-3211. p. 124

Lloyd, Peggy, Archives Mgr, Southwest Arkansas Regional Archives, Historic Washington State Park, 201 Hwy 195S, Washington, AR, 71862. Tel: 870-983-2633. Fax: 870-983-2636. p. 117

Lloyd, Rachel, Learning Res Coordr, Northeastern Oklahoma A&M College, 200 I NE, Miami, OK, 74354. Tel: 918-540-6381. Fax: 918-542-7065. p. 1968

Lloyd, Roberta, Dir, Stephen S Wise Temple Library, 15500 Stephen S Wise Dr, Los Angeles, CA, 90077. Tel: 310-889-2241. Fax: 310-476-2353. p. 180

Lloyd, Simon, Spec Coll Librn, University of Prince Edward Island, 550 University Ave, Charlottetown, PE, C1A 4P3, CANADA. Tel: 902-566-0343. Fax: 902-628-4305. p. 2876

Lloyd, Susan R, Res, FirstEnergy Corp, 76 S Main St, A-GO-17, Akron, OH, 44308. Tel: 330-384-4934. Fax: 330-255-1099. p. 1853

Lloyd, Toni, Ch, Wellsville Carnegie Public Library, 115 E Ninth St, Wellsville, OH, 43968-1431. Tel: 330-532-1526. Fax: 330-532-3127. p. 1946

Lo, Johanna, Ref, Palisades Free Library, 19 Closter Rd, Palisades, NY, 10964. Tel: 845-359-0136. Fax: 845-359-6124. p. 1714

Lo, Mei Ling, Librn, Rutgers University Libraries, Mathematical Sciences Library, Hill Ctr for Mathematical Sciences, 110 Frelinghuysen Rd, Piscataway, NJ, 08854-8019. Tel: 732-445-3735. Fax: 732-445-3064. p. 1509

Lo Presti, George, Circ, Farmingdale State College of New York, 2350 Broadhollow Rd, Farmingdale, NY, 11735-1021. Tel: 631-420-2040. Fax: 631-420-2473. p. 1622

Loader, Rebecca, Dir, Columbia Heights Public Library, 820 40th Ave NE, Columbia Heights, MN, 55421. Tel: 763-706-3690. Fax: 763-706-3691. p. 1246

Lobacz, Marsha, Asst Librn, University of North Carolina at Chapel Hill, Institute of Government, Knapp-Sanders Bldg, CB No 3330, Chapel Hill, NC, 27599-3330. Tel: 919-966-4172. Fax: 919-966-4762. p. 1781

Loban, Simon, Mgr, Ontario Ministry of Education, Mowat Block, 900 Bay St, 13th Flr, Toronto, ON, M7A 1L2, CANADA. Tel: 416-325-2654. Fax: 416-325-4235. p. 2856

Lobaugh, Susan, Ser, Virginia State University, One Hayden Dr, Petersburg, VA, 23806-0001. Tel: 804-542-5042. Fax: 804-524-6959. p. 2484

Lobaza, Cynthia, Asst Librn, Fox Lake Public District Library, 255 E Grand Ave, Fox Lake, IL, 60020-1697. Tel: 847-587-0198. Fax: 847-587-9493. p. 646

Lobdell, Patricia, Cat, Chino Valley Public Library, 1020 W Palomino Rd, Chino Valley, AZ, 86323-5500. Tel: 928-636-2687. Fax: 928-636-9129. p. 60

Lobe, Robert, Dir, Libr Serv, School of Visual Arts, 380 Second Ave, 2nd Flr, New York, NY, 10010-3994. Tel: 212-592-2661. Fax: 212-592-2655. p. 1699

Lober, Robin, Br Mgr, San Bernardino County Library, Adelanto Branch, 11497 Bartlett, Adelanto, CA, 92301. Tel: 760-246-5661. Fax: 760-246-4157. p. 228

Loberg, Emmie, Dir, George McCone Memorial County Library, 1101 C Ave, Circle, MT, 59215. Tel: 406-485-2350. p. 1377

Lobo, Sandra, Coordr, Patron Serv, Nichols College, 124 Center Rd, Dudley, MA, 01571. Tel: 508-213-2234. Fax: 508-213-2323. p. 1085

Lobrano, Kristi, Syst Librn, Bossier Parish Community College Library, 6220 E Texas St, Bossier City, LA, 71111. Tel: 318-678-6186. Fax: 318-678-6400. p. 946

Lobringier, Christopher, AV, Johns Hopkins University-Peabody Conservatory of Music, 21 E Mount Vernon Pl, Baltimore, MD, 21202-2397. Tel: 410-659-8100, Ext 1164. Fax: 410-685-0657. p. 1015

Locander, Susan, Ch, North Riverside Public Library District, 2400 S DesPlaines Ave, North Riverside, IL, 60546. Tel: 708-447-0869, Ext 224. Fax: 708-442-6566. p. 682

Locascio, Marian, Acq of New Ser, Ref Serv, Los Angeles Harbor College, 1111 Figueroa Pl, Wilmington, CA, 90744-2397. Tel: 310-233-4481. Fax: 310-233-4689. p. 284

Loch, Edward J, Brother, Archivist, Archdiocese of San Antonio, 2718 W Woodlawn, San Antonio, TX, 78228-5195. Tel: 210-734-1609, 210-734-2620, Ext 1103. p. 2379

Locher, Karen, Head, Pub Serv, University of Houston, 2602 N Ben Jordan St, Victoria, TX, 77901-5699. Tel: 361-570-4177. Fax: 361-570-4155. p. 2395

Locher, Sylvia L, Dir, Ashland Theological Seminary, 910 Center St, Ashland, OH, 44805. Tel: 419-289-5168. Fax: 419-289-5969. p. 1855

Lochhead, Mary, Head Librn, University of Manitoba Libraries, Architecture & Fine Arts Library, 206 Russell Bldg, 84 Curry Pl, Winnipeg, MB, R3T 2N2, CANADA. Tel: 204-474-9217. Fax: 204-474-7539. p. 2758

Lochhead, Sara, Univ Librn, Acadia University, 50 Acadia St, Wolfville, NS, B4P 2R6, CANADA. Tel: 902-585-1510. Fax: 902-585-1094. p. 2786

Lochner, Penny, Head, Coll Res Mgt, Muhlenberg College, 2400 Chew St, Allentown, PA, 18104-5586. Tel: 484-664-3561. Fax: 484-664-3511. p. 2027

Lock, Larry, Pres, Kewanee Historical Society Museum & Library, 211 N Chestnut St, Kewanee, IL, 61443. Tel: 309-854-9701. p. 661

Lock, Madeline, Dir, Everest University, Brandon Campus Library, Sabal Business Ctr, 3924 Coconut Palm Dr, Tampa, FL, 33619. Tel: 813-621-0041. Fax: 813-623-3183. p. 496

Lock, Mary Beth, Dir, Access Serv, Wake Forest University, PO Box 7777, Winston-Salem, NC, 27109-7777. Tel: 336-758-6140. Fax: 336-758-3694, 336-758-8831. p. 1834

Lockaby, Dorothy, Head, Access Serv, George Mason University Libraries, 4400 University Dr, MSN 2FL, Fairfax, VA, 22030-4444. Tel: 703-993-2250. Fax: 703-993-2200. p. 2462

Lockard, Anne, Music Cataloger, Cleveland Institute of Music, 11021 East Blvd, Cleveland, OH, 44106-1776. Tel: 216-795-3115. Fax: 216-791-3063. p. 1877

Locke, Carolyn, Librn, Reed Free Library, Eight Village Rd, Surry, NH, 03431-8314. Tel: 603-352-1761. p. 1466

Locke, James, Acq, AV, Cat, Saddleback College, 28000 Marguerite Pkwy, Mission Viejo, CA, 92692. Tel: 949-582-4874. Fax: 949-364-0284. p. 187

Locke, Jennifer, Libr Assoc, Maine State Law & Legislative Reference Library, 43 State House Sta, Augusta, ME, 04333-0043. Tel: 207-287-1600. Fax: 207-287-6467. p. 974

Locke, Jennifer, Librn, Milford Public Library, 40 Frenchtown Rd, Milford, NJ, 08848. Tel: 908-995-4072. p. 1502

Locke, Mary, ILL, Whipple Free Library, Two Central Sq, New Boston, NH, 03070. Tel: 603-487-3391. Fax: 603-487-2886. p. 1459

Locke, Sandy, Youth Serv, Washington County Library, 1444 Jackson Ave, Chipley, FL, 32428. Tel: 850-638-1314. Fax: 850-638-9499. p. 431

Locker, Ellen, Chief Librn, New York Daily News Library, 450 W 33rd St, New York, NY, 10001. Tel: 212-210-1509. Fax: 212-244-4033. p. 1689

Locker, Pamela, Br Mgr, Evansville Vanderburgh Public Library, Oaklyn, 3001 Oaklyn Dr, Evansville, IN, 47711. Tel: 812-428-8234, Ext 5403. Fax: 812-428-8245. p. 738

Lockerby, Robert William, Librn, Mazamas Library & Archives, 527 SE 43rd Ave, Portland, OR, 97215. Tel: 503-227-2345, Ext 2. Fax: 503-227-0862. p. 2011

Lockerby, Robin, Assoc Dir, Instruction, Outreach & Info Serv, National University Library, 9393 Lightwave Ave, San Diego, CA, 92123-1447. Tel: 858-541-7945. Fax: 858-541-7994. p. 232

Locket, Sonya, Dir of Libr Serv, Arkansas Baptist College Library, 1621 Martin Luther King Dr, Little Rock, AR, 72202. Tel: 501-244-5109. Fax: 501-244-5102. p. 105

Lockett, Nora, Dir, Bluefield College, 3000 College Dr, Bluefield, VA, 24605. Tel: 276-326-4237. Fax: 276-326-4288. p. 2451

Lockhart, David, Tech Serv, Richards Memorial Library, 118 N Washington St, North Attleboro, MA, 02760. Tel: 508-699-0122. Fax: 508-699-8075. p. 1112

Lockhart, Julie, Admin Serv, Chilton Clanton Library, Thorsby Public Library, City Hall, Hwy 31, Main St, Thorsby, AL, 35171. Tel: 205-646-3575. p. 12

Lockhart, Kevin, Bus Mgr, Niles Public Library District, 6960 Oakton St, Niles, IL, 60714. Tel: 847-663-1234. Fax: 847-663-1350. p. 680

Lockhart, Patricia, ILL, United States Army, 1794 Walker Ave SW, Fort McPherson, GA, 30330-1013. Tel: 404-464-2640, 404-464-2665. Fax: 404-464-3801. p. 533

Lockhart, Susan, Librn, Palestine Public Library District, 116 S Main St, Palestine, IL, 62451. Tel: 618-586-5317. Fax: 618-586-9711. p. 687

Lockhart, Trevor, Br Head, Winnipeg Public Library, Louis Riel Branch, 1168 Dakota St, Winnipeg, MB, R2N 3T8, CANADA. Tel: 204-986-4568. Fax: 204-986-3274. p. 2760

Lockhart, William M, Jr, Circ/Reserves, Southern University, Oliver B Spellman Law Library, 56 Roosevelt Steptoe, Baton Rouge, LA, 70813. Tel: 225-771-2139, 225-771-2315. Fax: 225-771-6254. p. 944

Locklear, Mattie, Mgr, Robeson County Public Library, Pembroke Public, 413 S Blaine St, Pembroke, NC, 28372. Tel: 910-521-1554. Fax: 910-521-1554. p. 1808

Locklear-Hunt, Marilyn, Dir, Robeson Community College Library, 5160 Fayetteville Rd, Lumberton, NC, 28360-2158. Tel: 910-272-3700, Ext 3321. Fax: 910-618-5685. p. 1807

Lockley, Lucy, Adult Coll Mgr, Saint Charles City County Library District, 77 Boone Hills Dr, Saint Peters, MO, 63376-0529. Tel: 636-441-2300. Fax: 636-441-3132. p. 1363

Lockman, Tim, Ref Librn, Kishwaukee College Library, 21193 Malta Rd, Malta, IL, 60150-9699. Tel: 815-825-2086, Ext 5660. Fax: 815-825-2072. p. 669

Locknar, Angela, Eng Librn, Instruction Coordr, Massachusetts Institute of Technology Libraries, Barker Engineering, Bldg 10-500, 77 Massachusetts Ave, Cambridge, MA, 02139-4307. Tel: 617-253-9230. Fax: 617-258-5623. p. 1077

Lockwood, Barbara, Dir, City of Calabasas Library, 200 Civic Center Way, Calabasas, CA, 91302. Tel: 818-225-7616. Fax: 818-225-7728. p. 131

Lockwood, Charles, Digital Serv, Loyola-Notre Dame Library, Inc, 200 Winston Ave, Baltimore, MD, 21212. Tel: 410-617-6800. Fax: 410-617-6895. p. 1015

Lockwood, Katie, Electronic Res Librn, University of Western States, 2900 NE 132nd Ave, Portland, OR, 97230-3099. Tel: 503-251-5752. Fax: 503-251-5759. p. 2015

Lockwood, Lynnn, Dir, Auburn Public Library, 49 Spring St, Auburn, ME, 04210. Tel: 207-333-6640. Fax: 207-333-6644. p. 974

Lockwood, Marsha, Librn, Buncombe County Public Libraries, South Buncombe Skyland, 260 Overlook Rd, Asheville, NC, 28803. Tel: 828-250-6488. p. 1774

Lockyer, Vicki, Librn, St Lawrence Public Library, PO Box 366, St. Lawrence, NL, A0E 2V0, CANADA. Tel: 709-873-2650. p. 2773

Locy, Steve, Head Librn, Oklahoma State University Libraries, Humanities & Social Sciences Division, Edmon Low Library, 3rd Flr, Stillwater, OK, 74078-1071. Tel: 405-744-6545. Fax: 405-744-5183. p. 1978

Locy, Steve, Head, Humanities & Soc Sci, Oklahoma State University Libraries, Oklahoma State University, Athletic Ave, Stillwater, OK, 74078-1071. Tel: 405-744-9729. Fax: 405-744-5183. p. 1978

Loder, Michael W, Librn, Pennsylvania State University, Schuylkill Campus, 240 University Dr, Schuylkill Haven, PA, 17972-2210. Tel: 570-385-6234. Fax: 570-385-6232. p. 2136

Lodge, Dan, Ref Librn, Garden City Public Library, 31735 Maplewood Rd, Garden City, MI, 48135. Tel: 734-793-1830. Fax: 734-793-1831. p. 1182

Lodge, Debra, Librn, Timrod Library, 217 Central Ave, Summerville, SC, 29483. Tel: 843-871-4600. Fax: 843-871-4600. p. 2206

Lodge, Melissa, Assoc State Librn, Libr Develop, State Library of Ohio, 274 E First Ave, Ste 100, Columbus, OH, 43201. Tel: 614-644-6914. Fax: 614-466-3584. p. 1890

Lodge, Sandra, Fiscal Officer, Licking County Library, 101 W Main St, Newark, OH, 43055-5054. Tel: 740-349-5505. Fax: 740-349-5535. p. 1922

Lodico, Nicolette, Mgr, Info Mgt, Ford Foundation Research Center, 320 E 43rd St, New York, NY, 10017. Tel: 212-573-5000. p. 1678

Lodico, Sally, Automation Syst Mgr, Knox County Public Library System, 500 W Church Ave, Knoxville, TN, 37902-2505. Tel: 865-215-8750. Fax: 865-215-8742. p. 2241

Lodwick, David, Libr Syst Coordr, Cleveland State University, University Library, Rhodes Tower, 2121 Euclid Ave, Cleveland, OH, 44115-2214. Tel: 216-687-6956. Fax: 216-687-9380. p. 1879

Loeb, Millie, Dir, Sherman Library Association, Rte 37 & 39, Sherman, CT, 06784. Tel: 860-354-2455. Fax: 860-354-7215. p. 367

Loechner, Cathy, YA Serv, Shelter Rock Public Library, 165 Searingtown Rd, Albertson, NY, 11507. Tel: 516-248-7343. p. 1571

Loeffel, Jennifer, Adult Serv, Franklin Public Library, 9151 W Loomis Rd, Franklin, WI, 53132. Tel: 414-425-8214. Fax: 414-425-9498. p. 2593

Loeffel, Pete, Dir, Muskego Public Library, S73 W16663 Janesville Rd, Muskego, WI, 53150. Tel: 262-971-2100. Fax: 262-971-2115. p. 2623

Loeffel, Pete, Adult Serv, Shorewood Public Library, 3920 N Murray Ave, Shorewood, WI, 53211-2385. Tel: 414-847-2670. p. 2638

Loeffler, Jane, Librn, Trinity Lutheran Church Library, 210 S Seventh St, Moorhead, MN, 56560-2794. Tel: 218-236-1333. Fax: 218-236-8918. p. 1266

Loeffler, Rosemary, Librn, La Ronge Public Library, 1212 Hildebrand Dr, La Ronge, SK, S0J 1L0, CANADA. Tel: 306-425-2160. Fax: 306-425-3883. p. 2918

Loehr, Eric, Libr Syst Mgr, Smith College Libraries, Northampton, MA, 01063. Tel: 413-585-2969. Fax: 413-585-2904. p. 1113

Loehr, Heather, Info Serv, Hanover College, 121 Scenic Dr, Hanover, IN, 47243. Tel: 812-866-7170. Fax: 812-866-7172. p. 748

Loehr, Joyce, Head Librn, Garden Plain Community Library, 502 N Main, Garden Plain, KS, 67050. Tel: 316-535-2990. Fax: 316-535-2990. p. 868

Loehr, Scott W, Chief Exec Officer, Delaware Historical Society Research Library, 505 N Market St, Wilmington, DE, 19801. Tel: 302-655-7161. Fax: 302-655-7844. p. 387

Loehrlein, Aaron, Asst Prof, University of British Columbia, The Irving K Barber Centre, 1961 E Mall, Ste 470, Vancouver, BC, V6T 1Z1, CANADA. Tel: 604-822-2404. Fax: 604-822-6006. p. 2977

Loeper, Lindsey, Archivist, University of Maryland, Baltimore County, 1000 Hilltop Circle, Baltimore, MD, 21250. Tel: 410-455-2356. Fax: 410-455-1567. p. 1018

Loeppky, Martha, Tech Serv, Providence University College & Seminary Library, Ten College Crescent, Otterburne, MB, R0A 1G0, CANADA. Tel: 204-433-7488. Fax: 204-433-7158. p. 2750

Loerke, Julie, Librn, British Columbia Courthouse Library Society, Court House, 250 George St, Prince George, BC, V2L 5S2, CANADA. Tel: 250-614-2763. Fax: 250-614-2788. p. 2736

Loesch, Martha M, Cat Librn, Seton Hall University Libraries, Walsh Libary Bldg, 400 S Orange Ave, South Orange, NJ, 07079. Tel: 973-761-9296. Fax: 973-761-9432. p. 1530

Loeser, Katherine, Br Mgr, Glendale Public Library, Casa Verdugo, 1151 N Brand Blvd, Glendale, CA, 91202-2503. Tel: 818-548-2047. Fax: 818-548-8052. p. 155

Loeser, Katherine, Br Mgr, Glendale Public Library, Grandview, 1535 Fifth St, Glendale, CA, 91201-1985. Tel: 818-548-2049. Fax: 818-549-0678. p. 155

Loest, Tylor S, Dir, Brandon Public Library, 117 E Main St, Brandon, WI, 53919. Tel: 920-346-2350. Fax: 920-346-5895. p. 2583

Loew, Janet S, Communications & Pub Relations Dir, Public Library of Youngstown & Mahoning County, 305 Wick Ave, Youngstown, OH, 44503-1079. Tel: 330-744-8636. Fax: 330-744-3355. p. 1952

Loewen, Iris, Chief Librn, Sechelt Public Library, 5797 Cowrie St, Sechelt, BC, V0N 3A0, CANADA. Tel: 604-885-3260. Fax: 604-885-5183. p. 2737

Lofgren, Debora, Assoc Librn, Stewartville Public Library, 110 Second St SE, Stewartville, MN, 55976-1306. Tel: 507-533-4902. Fax: 507-533-4746. p. 1285

Lofgren, Elizabeth, Ref Librn, Baker College of Muskegon Library, 1903 Marquette Ave, Muskegon, MI, 49442-3404. Tel: 231-777-5330. Fax: 231-777-5334. p. 1212

Lofgren, Lauran, Dir, Wayne Public Library, Robert B & Mary Y Benthack Library-Senior Ctr, 410 Pearl St, Wayne, NE, 68787. Tel: 402-375-3135. Fax: 402-375-5772. p. 1422

Loftin, Bob, Librn, Plano Public Library System, Municipal Reference, 1520 Ave K, Plano, TX, 75074. Tel: 972-941-7377. Fax: 972-941-7453. p. 2371

Loftin, Zelda, Asst Librn, Oak Grove Baptist Church Library, 2829 Oak Grove Church Rd, Carrollton, GA, 30117. Tel: 770-834-7019. Fax: 770-834-8218. p. 523

Loftis, Ben, Dir, Union County Carnegie Library, 300 E South St, Union, SC, 29379-2392. Tel: 864-427-7140. Fax: 864-427-4687. p. 2207

Loftis, Charissa, Coll Develop, Ref Librn, Wayne State College, 1111 Main St, Wayne, NE, 68787. Tel: 402-375-7729. Fax: 402-375-7538. p. 1423

Loftis, Kelley, Asst Dir, Tech Serv, Southern Pines Public Library, 170 W Connecticut Ave, Southern Pines, NC, 28387-4819. Tel: 910-692-8235. Fax: 910-695-1037. p. 1824

Loftis, Mary B, Librn, Metro Health Hospital, 5900 Byron Ctr Ave SW, Wyoming, MI, 49519. Tel: 616-252-7200. Fax: 616-252-7265. p. 1237

Loftis, Rebecca, Circ Serv, Volunteer State Community College Library, 1480 Nashville Pike, Gallatin, TN, 37066-3188. Tel: 615-230-3400, Ext 3409. Fax: 615-230-3410. p. 2235

Lofton, Holly, Dir, Lindsborg Community Library, 111 S Main St, Lindsborg, KS, 67456-2417. Tel: 785-227-2710. p. 880

Loftus, Danielle, Health Sci Librn, Tech Librn, University of South Dakota, 414 E Clark St, Vermillion, SD, 57069. Tel: 605-677-5371. Fax: 605-677-6834. p. 2220

Loftus, Elizabeth, Br Adminr, Onondaga County Public Library, The Galleries of Syracuse, 447 S Salina St, Syracuse, NY, 13202-2494. Fax: 315-435-8533. p. 1752

Loftus, Sydney, Dir, Madison County Historical Society Library, 435 Main St, Oneida, NY, 13421. Tel: 315-361-9735, 315-363-4136. p. 1710

Loga, Timothy, IT Dir, Mount Prospect Public Library, Ten S Emerson St, Mount Prospect, IL, 60056. Tel: 847-253-5675. Fax: 847-253-0642. p. 677

Logan, Chuck, Librn, United States Navy, Naval Undersea Warfare Center Division, Newport Technical Library, 1176 Howell St, Bldg 101, Newport, RI, 02841. Tel: 401-832-4338. Fax: 401-832-3699. p. 2170

Logan, Day, Mgr, Ser, The College of Wooster Libraries, 1140 Beall Ave, Wooster, OH, 44691-2364. Tel: 330-263-2130. Fax: 330-263-2253. p. 1949

Logan, Debbie, Br Coordr, Motlow State Community College Libraries, Fayetteville Center Library, 1802 Winchester Hwy, Fayetteville, TN, 37334. Tel: 931-438-0028. Fax: 931-438-0619. p. 2267

Logan, Doris, Tech Serv, Los Alamos County Library System, 2400 Central Ave, Los Alamos, NM, 87544. Tel: 505-662-8240. Fax: 505-662-8245. p. 1559

Logan, Elaine, Assoc Univ Librn, Eastern Michigan University, 955 W Circle Dr Library, Rm 200, Ypsilanti, MI, 48197. Tel: 734-487-0020 Ext 2222. p. 1238

Logan, Elaine M, Dir, University of Michigan-Dearborn, 4901 Evergreen Rd, Dearborn, MI, 48128-2406. Tel: 313-593-5445. Fax: 313-593-5478. p. 1168

Logan, John, Bibliographer, Princeton University, One Washington Rd, Princeton, NJ, 08544-2098. Tel: 609-258-3296. Fax: 609-258-0441. p. 1523

Logan, Kathy, Ch, Public Library of Enid & Garfield County, 120 W Maine, Enid, OK, 73701-5606. Tel: 580-234-6313. Fax: 580-249-9280. p. 1963

Logan, Kevin, Spec Coll Librn, Lakeland Public Library, 100 Lake Morton Dr, Lakeland, FL, 33801-5375. Tel: 863-834-4280. Fax: 863-834-4293. p. 459

Logan, Lynda Byrd, Dr, Dean, Prince George's Community College Library, 301 Largo Rd, Largo, MD, 20774-2199. Tel: 301-322-0466. Fax: 301-808-8847. p. 1034

Logan, Mary A, Mgr, Baltimore Metropolitan Council, 1500 Whetstone Way, Ste 300, Baltimore, MD, 21230. Tel: 410-732-9570. Fax: 410-732-9488. p. 1012

Logan, Penny A, Mgr, Libr Serv, Capital Health/Nova Scotia Hospital, Hugh Bell Bldg, Rm 200, 300 Pleasant St, Dartmouth, NS, B2Y 3Z9, CANADA. Tel: 902-473-4383. Fax: 902-464-4804. p. 2779

Logan Reid, Paula, Br Mgr, Cleveland Public Library, Memorial-Nottingham, 17109 Lake Shore Blvd, Cleveland, OH, 44110. Tel: 216-623-7039. Fax: 216-623-7042. p. 1878

Logan, Rochelle, Assoc Dir, Support Serv, Douglas County Libraries, 100 S Wilcox, Castle Rock, CO, 80104. Tel: 303-688-7603. Fax: 303-688-7655. p. 294

Logan, Sarah, Libr Tech, Department of Veterans Affairs, 510 E Stoner Ave, Shreveport, LA, 71101-4295. Tel: 318-990-5181. Fax: 318-990-5570. p. 968

Logan, Sharon, Librn, Miccosukee Community Library, Tamiami Sta, Miami, FL, 33144. Tel: 305-223-8380, Ext 2248. Fax: 305-223-1011. p. 467

Logan, Tracy, Dir, Reed City Public Library, 410 W Upton Ave, Reed City, MI, 49677-1152. Tel: 231-832-2131. Fax: 231-832-2131. p. 1221

Logan, Yvonne, Librn, San Carlos Public Library, 89 San Carlos Ave, San Carlos, AZ, 85550. Tel: 928-475-2611. Fax: 928-475-2611. p. 80

Logan-Peters, Kay, In Charge, University of Nebraska-Lincoln, Architecture Library, Architecture Hall, Rm 308, City Campus 0108, Lincoln, NE, 68588-0108. Tel: 402-472-1208. p. 1407

Loganbill, Nita, Dir, Morgan County Library, 600 N Hunter, Versailles, MO, 65084-1830. Tel: 573-378-5319. Fax: 573-378-6166. p. 1371

Loggins, Brenda, In Charge, Oklahoma Corporation Commission, Jim Thorpe Bldg, 2101 N Lincoln Blvd, Ste 400, Oklahoma City, OK, 73105-4904. Tel: 405-521-4257. Fax: 405-521-4150. p. 1974

Loggins, Greg, Libr Asst I, Montgomery City-County Public Library System, E L Lowder Regional Branch Library, 2590 Bell Rd, Montgomery, AL, 36117. Tel: 334-244-5717. Fax: 334-240-4893. p. 30

Logie, Diann, Supv Librn, Pueblo City-County Library District, Frank I Lamb Branch, 2525 S Pueblo Blvd, Pueblo, CO, 81005-2700. Tel: 719-562-5672. Fax: 719-562-5675. p. 321

Logsden, Kara, Adult Serv Coordr, Iowa City Public Library, 123 S Linn St, Iowa City, IA, 52240. Tel: 319-887-6007. Fax: 319-356-5494. p. 822

Logsdon, Clara, ILL, Ref Serv, St Catharine College Library, 2735 Bardstown Rd, Saint Catharine, KY, 40061. Tel: 859-336-5082, Ext 1260. Fax: 859-336-5031. p. 934

Logsdon, Mary, Libr Serv Coordr, Ames Public Library, 515 Douglas Ave, Ames, IA, 50010. Tel: 515-239-5633. Fax: 515-233-9001. p. 792

Logsdon, Paul, Dir/Ref Librn, Ohio Northern University, 525 S Main St, Ada, OH, 45810. Tel: 419-772-2181. Fax: 419-772-1927. p. 1851

Logsdon, Stephen, Archivist, Washington University Libraries, Bernard Becker Medical Library, 660 S Euclid Ave, Campus Box 8132, Saint Louis, MO, 63110. Tel: 314-362-4239. Fax: 314-454-6606. p. 1362

Logsdon, Vicki, Dir, Hart County Public Library, 500 E Union St, Munfordville, KY, 42765. Tel: 270-524-1953. Fax: 270-524-7323. p. 930

Logue, Joseph, Br Mgr, Cambridge Public Library, Collins Branch, 64 Aberdeen Ave, Cambridge, MA, 02138. Tel: 617-349-4021. Fax: 617-349-4423. p. 1073

Loh-Guan, Hilda, Commun Libr Mgr, County of Los Angeles Public Library, Chet Holifield Library, 1060 S Greenwood Ave, Montebello, CA, 90640-6030. Tel: 323-728-0421. Fax: 323-888-6053. p. 142

Lohman, Chris, Br Mgr, Kent District Library, Walker Branch, 4293 Remembrance Rd NW, Walker, MI, 49544. Tel: 616-784-2007. Fax: 616-647-3974. p. 1166

Lohman, Jody, Media Spec, High Point University, 833 Montlieu Ave, High Point, NC, 27262-4221. Tel: 336-841-9103. Fax: 336-841-5123. p. 1802

Lohman, Toni, Actg Mgr, Virginia Beach Public Library Department, Bldg 19, Municipal Ctr, 2nd Flr, 2416 Courthouse Dr, Virginia Beach, VA, 23456. Tel: 757-385-4321. Fax: 757-385-4220. p. 2500

Lohman, Toni, Librn, Virginia Beach Public Library Department, Collection Management, 4100 Virginia Beach Blvd, Virginia Beach, VA, 23452. Tel: 757-385-0170. p. 2500

Lohmeier, Mary, Librn, Legislative Reference Bureau, City Hall, Rm B-11, 200 E Wells St, Milwaukee, WI, 53202-3567. Tel: 414-286-2280. Fax: 414-286-3004. p. 2618

Lohoefener, Sharon, ILL, Ref, North Platte Public Library, 120 W Fourth St, North Platte, NE, 69101-3993. Tel: 308-535-8036. Fax: 308-535-8296. p. 1410

Lohr, Diane, Ref & Coll Develop Librn, Trident Technical College, Main Campus Learning Resources Center, LR-M, PO Box 118067, Charleston, SC, 29423-8067. Tel: 843-574-6089. Fax: 843-574-6484. p. 2185

Lohrer, Fred E, Librn, Archbold Biological Station Library, 123 Main Dr, Venus, FL, 33960. Tel: 863-465-2571. Fax: 863-699-1927. p. 501

Lohrstorfer, Martha, Lead Librn, Kalamazoo Public Library, Oshtemo, 7265 W Main St, Kalamazoo, MI, 49009. Tel: 269-553-7986. Fax: 269-375-6610. p. 1197

Lointier, Cécile, Chef de Div, Bibliothèques de Montrèal, Belleville, 10400, avenue de Belleville, Montreal, QC, H1H 4Z7, CANADA. Tel: 514-328-4000, Ext 4131 or 4128. Fax: 514-328-4298. p. 2889

Lointier, Cécile, Chef de Div, Bibliothèques de Montrèal, Charleroi, 4740, rue de Charleroi, Montreal, QC, H1H 1V2, CANADA. Tel: 514-328-4000, Ext 4131 or 4128. Fax: 514-328-4298. p. 2889

Lointier, Cécile, Chef de Div, Bibliothèques de Montrèal, Henri-Bourassa, 5400, boulevard Henri-Bourassa Est, Montreal, QC, H1G 2S9, CANADA. Tel: 514-328-4000, Ext 4131 or 4128. Fax: 514-328-4298. p. 2889

Lointier, Cécile, Chef de Div, Bibliothèques de Montrèal, Maison culturelle et communautaire, 12002, boulevard Rolland, Montreal, QC, H1G 3W1, CANADA. Tel: 514-328-4000, Ext 4131 or 4128. p. 2890

Lois, Nancy, Head, Tech Serv, Mount Holyoke College Library, 50 College St, South Hadley, MA, 01075-1423. Tel: 413-538-2225. Fax: 413-538-2370. p. 1125

Loiselle, Paul, Librn, New York Aquarium, W Eighth St & Surf Ave, Brooklyn, NY, 11224. Tel: 718-265-3406, 718-265-3437. Fax: 718-265-3420. p. 1593

Loizou, Mary Jane, ILL, New England Conservatory of Music, 33 Gainsborough St, Boston, MA, 02115. Tel: 617-585-1248. Fax: 617-585-1245. p. 1064

Lokey, Patricia, Dr, Dir, Scottsdale Community College Library, 9000 E Chaparral Rd, Scottsdale, AZ, 85256. Tel: 480-423-6653. Fax: 480-423-6666. p. 80

Lokken, Beth, Ch, YA Serv, Door County Library, Central Library, 107 S Fourth Ave, Sturgeon Bay, WI, 54235. p. 2640

Lokken, Sharon, Acq of Monographs, Libr Tech, Tech Serv, Polk State College, 999 Ave H NE, Winter Haven, FL, 33881-4299. Tel: 863-297-1040. Fax: 863-297-1065. p. 504

Lolich, Kathleen, Librn, Venable LLP Library, Rockville Office, One Church St, Ste 500, Rockville, MD, 20850. Tel: 301-217-5600. Fax: 301-217-5617. p. 1019

Lolich, Kathleen G, Librn, Venable LLP Library, 8010 Towers Crescent Dr, Ste 300, Vienna, VA, 22182. Tel: 703-760-1600, 703-760-1621. Fax: 703-821-8949. p. 2498

Lolis, John, Head, Tech Serv, White Plains Public Library, 100 Martine Ave, White Plains, NY, 10601-2599. Tel: 914-422-1400. Fax: 914-422-1462. p. 1769

Lomaki, Tammy, Librn, St Lawrence Supreme Court, 48 Court St, Canton, NY, 13617. Tel: 315-379-2279. Fax: 315-379-2424. p. 1602

Loman, Kris, Circ Supvr, Rosemary Garfoot Public Library, 2107 Julius St, Cross Plains, WI, 53528-9499. Tel: 608-798-3881. Fax: 608-798-0196. p. 2587

Loman, Scott Steven, Librn, Saint Johns Health System, 2015 Jackson St, Anderson, IN, 46016-4339. Tel: 765-646-8262. Fax: 765-646-8264. p. 724

Lomax, Denise W, Head of Libr, Federal Bureau of Prisons Library, 400 First St NW, 3rd Flr, Washington, DC, 20534. Tel: 202-307-3029. Fax: 202-307-5756. p. 400

Lomax, Georgia, Dep Dir, Pierce County Library System, 3005 112th St E, Tacoma, WA, 98446-2215. Tel: 253-548-3421. Fax: 253-537-4600. p. 2539

Lombard, Emmett, Outreach Librn, Gannon University, 109 University Sq, Erie, PA, 16541. Tel: 814-871-7557. Fax: 814-871-5666. p. 2055

Lombardi, Tara, Coll Develop/Ref Librn, Law Library of Louisiana, Louisiana Supreme Court, 2nd Flr, 400 Royal St, New Orleans, LA, 70130-2104. Tel: 504-310-2400. Fax: 504-310-2419. p. 960

Lombardo, Carol A, Dir, Garwood Free Public Library, 411 Third Ave, Garwood, NJ, 07027. Tel: 908-789-1670. Fax: 908-317-8146. p. 1487

Lombardo, Cindy, Dep Dir, COO, Cleveland Public Library, 325 Superior Ave, Cleveland, OH, 44114-1271. Tel: 216-623-2800. p. 1877

Lombardo, Julie, Head, Circ, Woodridge Public Library, Three Plaza Dr, Woodridge, IL, 60517-5014. Tel: 630-964-7899. Fax: 630-964-0175. p. 721

Lombardo, Sharon, Head Librn, ORC Worldwide, 500 Fifth Ave, 5th Flr, New York, NY, 10110. Tel: 212-852-0396. Fax: 212-398-1358. p. 1696

Lomedico, Kris, Br Mgr, Whatcom County Library System, Point Roberts Branch, Community Center, 1487 Gulf Rd, Point Roberts, WA, 98281. Tel: 360-945-6545. Fax: 360-945-6545. p. 2509

Lomeli, Maria, Br Mgr, Monterey County Free Libraries, San Ardo Branch, 62350 College St, San Ardo, CA, 93450. Tel: 831-627-2503. Fax: 831-627-4229. p. 183

Lomio, Paul, Dir, Stanford University Libraries, Robert Crown Law Library, Stanford Law School, 559 Nathan Abbott Way, Stanford, CA, 94305-8610. Tel: 650-723-2477. Fax: 650-723-1933. p. 271

Lommel, James, Dr, Access Serv & Syst, Syst Coordr, General Electric Global Research, One Research Circle, Niskayuna, NY, 12309. Tel: 518-387-6162. p. 1706

Lomoro, Jerry, Br Head, Toronto Public Library, Bayview, Bayview Village Shopping Ctr, 2901 Bayview Ave, Toronto, ON, M2K 1E6, CANADA. Tel: 416-395-5460. Fax: 416-395-5434. p. 2860

Lompe, Candy, Ch, Jesup Public Library, 721 Sixth St, Jesup, IA, 50648-0585. Tel: 319-827-1533. Fax: 319-827-1580. p. 824

Loncar, Carla, In Charge, Elko-Lander-Eureka County Library System, West Wendover Branch, 590 Camper Dr, West Wendover, NV, 89883. Tel: 775-664-2510. Fax: 775-664-2226. p. 1427

Lonchyna, Natalia J, Libr Dir, North Carolina Museum of Art, 2110 Blue Ridge Rd, Raleigh, NC, 27607-6494. Tel: 919-664-6769, 919-664-6770. Fax: 919-733-8034. p. 1815

Londensky, Andrea, Dir, South River Public Library, 55 Appleby Ave, South River, NJ, 08882-2499. Tel: 732-254-2488. Fax: 732-254-4116. p. 1531

London, Diana, Librn, Iosco-Arenac District Library, Robert J Parks Library - Oscoda Branch, 6010 Skeel St, Oscoda, MI, 48750. Tel: 989-739-9581. Fax: 989-739-9581. p. 1176

London, Jill S, Coll Support Serv Supvr, Mesa Public Library, 64 E First St, Mesa, AZ, 85201-6768. Tel: 480-644-3725. Fax: 480-644-2991. p. 69

London, Linda, Ref Librn, Oklahoma State University - Center for Health Sciences, 1111 W 17th St, Tulsa, OK, 74107-1898. Tel: 918-561-8466. Fax: 918-561-8412. p. 1981

London, Richard, Dir, University of Toronto Libraries, Thomas Fisher Rare Books Library, 120 St George St, Toronto, ON, M5S 1A5, CANADA. Tel: 416-978-6107. Fax: 416-978-1667. p. 2866

Lone, Chung, Head, Multi-Media Res Dept, Montclair State University, One Normal Ave, Montclair, NJ, 07043-1699. Tel: 973-655-7153. Fax: 973-655-7780. p. 1503

Lonergan, Bridget, Tech Serv, Foley & Hoag LLP Library, 155 Seaport Blvd, Boston, MA, 02210. Tel: 617-832-7070. Fax: 617-832-7000. p. 1061

Lonergan, Harriet, Br Mgr, Eastern Shore Public Library, Island Library, 4077 Main St, Chincoteague, VA, 23336. Tel: 757-336-3460. p. 2443

Lonergan, Penelope, Acq, Coll Develop, Dir, University of Saint Mary, 4100 S Fourth St Trafficway, Leavenworth, KS, 66048-5082. Tel: 913-758-6306. Fax: 913-758-6200. p. 879

Lonergan, RoseMarie, Med Librn, Bethesda Memorial Hospital, 2815 S Seacrest Blvd, Boynton Beach, FL, 33435-7934. Tel: 561-737-7733, Ext 4439. Fax: 561-735-7080. p. 429

Lonero, Mike, Dir, Law Tech, Loyola University Chicago Libraries, Law School Library, 25 E Pearson St, 3rd Flr, Chicago, IL, 60611. Tel: 315-915-7313. Fax: 312-915-6797. p. 617

Loney, Rebecca, Managing Librn II, Sno-Isle Libraries, Snohomish Community Library, 311 Maple Ave, Snohomish, WA, 98290. Tel: 360-568-2898. Fax: 360-568-6357. p. 2542

Loney, Stephanie, Pub Serv Mgr, Chula Vista Public Library, 365 F St, Chula Vista, CA, 91910-2697. Tel: 619-691-5288. Fax: 619-427-4246. p. 134

Long, Allison, Outreach Serv Librn, Haltom City Public Library, 4809 Haltom Rd, Haltom City, TX, 76117-3622. Tel: 817-222-7814. Fax: 817-834-1446. p. 2330

Long, Amber Roper, Librn, Birmingham News, 2201 Fourth Ave N, Birmingham, AL, 35203. Tel: 205-325-2408. Fax: 205-325-2495. p. 7

Long, Amy, Br Mgr, Douglas County Libraries, Parker Library, 10851 S Crossroads Dr, Parker, CO, 80134-9081. Tel: 303-841-6344. Fax: 303-841-7892. p. 294

Long, Amy, Br Mgr, Public Library of Cincinnati & Hamilton County, Greenhills, Seven Endicott St, Cincinnati, OH, 45218. Tel: 513-369-4441. Fax: 513-369-4535. p. 1872

Long, Annette, Br Mgr, Placer County Library, Applegate Branch, 18018 Applegate Rd, Applegate, CA, 95703. Tel: 530-878-2721. Fax: 530-878-2721. p. 123

Long, Betty, Dir, Roswell Public Library, 301 N Pennsylvania Ave, Roswell, NM, 88201. Tel: 575-622-7101. Fax: 575-622-7107. p. 1561

Long, Beverly, Asst Librn, Broome Community College, 907 Front St, Binghamton, NY, 13905-1328. Tel: 607-778-5701. Fax: 607-778-5108. p. 1581

Long, Bobbie, Exec Dir, Collin College, 2200 W University, McKinney, TX, 75071. Tel: 972-548-6860, 972-548-6868. Fax: 972-548-6844. p. 2361

Long, Brad, Ser, Thomas Jefferson University, 1020 Walnut St, Philadelphia, PA, 19107. Tel: 215-503-6994. Fax: 215-923-3203. p. 2118

Long, Carrie, Mgr, Res, Faegre & Benson, LLP, 2200 Wells Fargo Ctr, 90 South Seventh St, Minneapolis, MN, 55402-3901. Tel: 612-766-7000. Fax: 612-766-1600. p. 1259

Long, Casey, User Educ Librn, Agnes Scott College, 141 E College Ave, Decatur, GA, 30030-3770. Tel: 404-471-6343. Fax: 404-471-5037. p. 529

Long, Chris, Dir, Plain City Public Library, 305 W Main St, Plain City, OH, 43064-1148. Tel: 614-873-4912, Ext 23. Fax: 614-873-8364. p. 1930

Long, Chris Evan, Cat Librn, Indiana University, Ruth Lilly Law Library, 530 W New York St, Indianapolis, IN, 46202-3225. Tel: 317-274-3884, 317-274-4028. Fax: 317-274-8825. p. 752

Long, David, Librn, Defense Technical Information Center, 8725 John J Kingman Rd, Ste 944, Fort Belvoir, VA, 22060-6218. Tel: 703-767-8180. Fax: 703-767-9459. p. 2464

Long, Denise, Ref, Upper Merion Township Library, 175 W Valley Forge Rd, King of Prussia, PA, 19406-2399. Tel: 610-265-1196. Fax: 610-265-3398. p. 2074

Long, Diana, Dir, Altamonte Springs City Library, 281 N Maitland Ave, Altamonte Springs, FL, 32701. Tel: 407-571-8830. Fax: 407-571-8834. p. 425

Long, Donna, Circ Asst, South University Library, 5355 Vaughn Rd, Montgomery, AL, 36116-1120. Tel: 334-395-8800. Fax: 334-395-8859. p. 31

Long, Donna, Head, Ch, Anderson County Library, 300 N McDuffie St, Anderson, SC, 29621-5643. Tel: 864-260-4500. Fax: 864-260-4510. p. 2180

Long, E Terry, Librn, Virginia State Law Library, Supreme Court Bldg, 2nd Flr, 100 N Ninth St, Richmond, VA, 23219-2335. Tel: 804-786-2075. Fax: 804-786-4542. p. 2493

Long, Edna, Ser, Chipola College Library, 3094 Indian Circle, Marianna, FL, 32446. Tel: 850-718-2374. Fax: 850-718-2349. p. 462

Long, Elisabeth, Assoc Univ Librn, Digital Serv, University of Chicago Library, 1100 E 57th St, Chicago, IL, 60637-1502. Tel: 773-702-3732. Fax: 773-702-6623. p. 626

Long, Eloise, Dr, Dept Chair, Kutztown University, Kutztown, PA, 19530. Tel: 610-683-4300. Fax: 610-683-1326. p. 2973

Long, Heidi, Interim Librn, Los Gatos Public Library, 100 Villa Ave, Los Gatos, CA, 95030-6981. Tel: 408-354-6891. Fax: 408-399-6008. p. 180

Long, Hope, Dir of Libr, The Library at Birmingham Botanical Garden, 2612 Lane Park Rd, Birmingham, AL, 35223. Tel: 205-414-3931. Fax: 205-414-3922. p. 8

Long, Jane, Dean, Moraine Valley Community College Library, 9000 W College Pkwy, Palos Hills, IL, 60465. Tel: 708-974-5709. Fax: 708-974-1184. p. 687

Long, Jane, Circ Chief, Rockland Memorial Library, 20 Belmont St, Rockland, MA, 02370-2232. Tel: 781-878-1236. Fax: 781-878-4013. p. 1120

Long, Jane, Per & Govt Doc Librn, Southwestern Oklahoma State University, 100 Campus Dr, Weatherford, OK, 73096-3002. Tel: 580-774-3731. Fax: 580-774-3112. p. 1985

Long, Jennifer, Ref Librn, University of Alabama at Birmingham, Mervyn H Sterne Library, 917 11th St S, Birmingham, AL, 35205. Tel: 205-934-6364. p. 10

Long, Jennifer Lee, Asst Librn, Ch & Youth Librn, Haven Public Library, 121 N Kansas St, Haven, KS, 67543. Tel: 620-465-3524. Fax: 620-465-3524. p. 870

Long, Jessica, Pub Serv Librn, Kettering University Library, 1700 W University Ave, Flint, MI, 48504-4898. Tel: 810-762-9618. Fax: 810-762-9744. p. 1180

Long, Jessie, Asst Dir, White Cloud Community Library, 1038 Wilcox Ave, White Cloud, MI, 49349. Tel: 231-689-6631. Fax: 231-689-6699. p. 1236

Long, Jessie, Pub Serv Librn, Miami University-Middletown, 4200 N University Blvd, Middletown, OH, 45042-3497. Tel: 513-727-3225. p. 1917

Long, Jo-Ann, Asst Librn, South River-Machar Union Public Library, 63 Marie St, South River, ON, P0A 1X0, CANADA. Tel: 705-386-0222. Fax: 705-386-0222. p. 2842

Long, John, Coordr, Chittenden Regional Correctional Learning Center, Seven Farrell St, South Burlington, VT, 05403. Tel: 802-863-7356. Fax: 802-863-7473. p. 2435

Long, Judy, Ch, McDowell Public Library, 90 Howard St, Welch, WV, 24801. Tel: 304-436-3070. Fax: 304-436-8079. p. 2573

Long, Julie, Coll Develop, Saint Mary's College, Notre Dame, IN, 46556-5001. Tel: 574-284-5289. Fax: 574-284-4791. p. 771

Long, Katherine, Fiscal Officer, Wayne County Public Library, 220 W Liberty St, Wooster, OH, 44691-3593. Tel: 330-804-4680. Fax: 330-262-1352. p. 1950

Long, Kathy, Dir, Stanford University Libraries, Graduate School of Business Library, Knight Management Ctr, 655 Knight Way, Stanford, CA, 94305-7298. Tel: 650-725-2055. Fax: 650-723-0281. p. 271

Long, Linda, Librn, Lapeer District Library, Goodland, 2370 N Van Dyke Rd, Imlay City, MI, 48444. Tel: 810-724-1970. Fax: 810-724-5612. p. 1202

Long, Linda L, Acq, Northrop Grumman Corp, Integrated Systems Western Region Library, One Hornet Way, TS20/W7, El Segundo, CA, 90245. Tel: 310-331-7105. Fax: 310-332-5562. p. 176

Long, Lisa, Dir, Archives & Spec Coll, Redwood Library & Athenaeum, 50 Bellevue Ave, Newport, RI, 02840-3292. Tel: 401-847-0292. Fax: 401-847-0192. p. 2169

Long, Lorie, Br Mgr, Morgan County Public Library, Monrovia Branch, 145 S Chestnut St, Monrovia, IN, 46157. Tel: 317-996-4307. Fax: 317-996-3439. p. 763

Long, Marie, Circ, Ref, The LuEsther T Mertz Library, The New York Botanical Garden, 2900 Southern Blvd, Bronx, NY, 10458-5126. Tel: 718-817-8728. Fax: 718-817-8956. p. 1587

Long, Mary Beth, Librn, York County Library System, Redland Community, 48 Robin Hood Dr, Etters, PA, 17319. Tel: 717-938-5599. Fax: 717-938-5817. p. 2160

Long, Megan, Libr Mgr, Elliot Hospital, One Elliot Way, Manchester, NH, 03103. Tel: 603-663-2334. Fax: 603-663-3507. p. 1455

Long, Nina P, Archivist, Dir, Libr Serv, Wistar Institute Library, 3601 Spruce St, Rm 215, Philadelphia, PA, 19104-4268. Tel: 215-898-3826. Fax: 215-898-3856. p. 2120

Long, Pam, Admin Supvr, United States Military Academy Library, Jefferson Hall Library & Learning Center, 758 Cullum Rd, West Point, NY, 10996. Tel: 845-938-3833. Fax: 845-938-4000. p. 1767

Long, Paula, Librn, Grace Hall Memorial Library, 161 Main Rd, Montgomery, MA, 01085-9525. Tel: 413-862-3894. p. 1107

Long, Richard C, Dir, Florida Department of Transportation, Burns Bldg, 605 Suwannee St, Mail Sta 30, Tallahassee, FL, 32399. Tel: 850-414-4615. Fax: 850-414-4696. p. 494

Long, Rosalie A, Asst Dir, Annie Halenbake Ross Library, 232 W Main St, Lock Haven, PA, 17745-1241. Tel: 570-748-3321. Fax: 570-748-1050. p. 2082

Long, Roxanne, Libr Mgr, Vilna Municipal Library, 5431-50th St, Vilna, AB, T0A 3L0, CANADA. Tel: 780-636-2077. Fax: 780-636-3243. p. 2720

Long, Sandra, Ch, Wyandanch Public Library, 14 S 20th St, Wyandanch, NY, 11798. Tel: 631-643-4848. p. 1771

Long, Sandy, Dir, Whittemore Public Library, 405 Fourth St, Whittemore, IA, 50598. Tel: 515-884-2680. Fax: 515-884-2323. p. 853

Long, Shana, Librn, Muskingum County Law Library, 22 N Fifth St, Zanesville, OH, 43701. Tel: 740-455-7154. Fax: 740-588-4362. p. 1953

Long, Sharon, Dir, Libr & Media Serv, Newton County Public Library, 212 High St, Newton, TX, 75966. Tel: 409-379-8300. Fax: 409-379-2798. p. 2365

Long, Sherri, ILL, Bowling Green State University Libraries, 204 Wm T Jerome Library, Bowling Green, OH, 43403-0170. p. 1861

Long, Shirley, Dir, South Kingstown Public Library, 1057 Kingstown Rd, Peace Dale, RI, 02879-2434. Tel: 401-789-1555, Ext 102. Fax: 401-782-6370. p. 2171

Long, Stephen, Head, Tech Serv, Capital University, One College & Main, Columbus, OH, 43209. Tel: 614-236-6470. Fax: 614-236-6490. p. 1883

Long, Susan, Dir, Salmon River Public Library, 126 N Main, Riggins, ID, 83549. Tel: 208-628-3394. Fax: 208-628-3792. p. 583

Long, Susan Schweinsberg, Dir, Virginia Mason Medical Center Library, 925 Seneca, Seattle, WA, 98101. Tel: 206-223-6733. Fax: 206-223-2376. p. 2528

Long, Teresa Ann, Acq/Ser Supvr, Transylvania University Library, 300 N Broadway, Lexington, KY, 40508. Tel: 859-233-8225. Fax: 859-233-8779. p. 921

Longacre, Glenn, Archivist, National Archives & Records Administration, 7358 S Pulaski Rd, Chicago, IL, 60629-5898. Tel: 773-948-9001. Fax: 773-948-9050. p. 619

Longard, Monica, Chairperson, High Level Municipal Library, 10601 103 St, High Level, AB, T0H 1Z0, CANADA. Tel: 780-926-2097. Fax: 780-926-4268. p. 2706

Longbons, Dixie, Asst Librn, Albion Public Library, Six N Fourth St, Albion, IL, 62806. Tel: 618-445-3314. p. 587

Longbottom, Lauren, Ch, Ridley Township Public Library, 100 E MacDade Blvd, Folsom, PA, 19033-2592. Tel: 610-583-0593. Fax: 610-583-9505. p. 2057

Longbrake, Julia, Fac Librn, Mount Hood Community College Library, 26000 SE Stark St, Gresham, OR, 97030. Tel: 503-491-7693. Fax: 503-491-7389. p. 1999

Longcor, Donna, Dir, Holland Alexandria Free Public Library, 129 Spring Mills Rd, Milford, NJ, 08848. Tel: 908-995-4767. Fax: 908-995-4767. p. 1502

Longendelpher, Vicki, Dir, J R Clarke Public Library, 102 E Spring St, Covington, OH, 45318. Tel: 937-473-2226. Fax: 937-473-8118. p. 1892

Longhi, Melissa, Ser, City University of New York, 365 Fifth Ave, New York, NY, 10016-4309. Tel: 212-817-7040. Fax: 212-817-2982. p. 1673

Longino, Charlene, Head Librn, Harrison County Library System, Biloxi Central Library, 580 Howard Ave, Biloxi, MS, 39530-2303. Tel: 228-436-3095. Fax: 228-436-3097. p. 1299

Longino, Charlene, Head Librn, Harrison County Library System, Margaret Sherry Branch Library, 2141 Popps Ferry Rd, Biloxi, MS, 39532-4251. Tel: 228-388-1633. Fax: 228-388-0920. p. 1300

Longino, Charline, Head Librn, Harrison County Library System, West Biloxi Library, 2047 Pass Rd, Biloxi, MS, 39531-3125. Tel: 228-388-1633. Fax: 228-388-5652. p. 1300

Longley, Dana, Mgr, Libr Serv, Empire State College (Online Library), Three Union Ave, Saratoga Springs, NY, 12866. Tel: 518-587-2100. Fax: 518-581-9526. p. 1738

Longmuir, Kristin, Coll Develop Librn, Recording for the Blind & Dyslexic, 20 Roszel Rd, Princeton, NJ, 08540. Tel: 609-452-0606. Fax: 609-520-7990, 609-987-8116. p. 1524

Longo, Debora, Libr Dir, Somersworth Public Library, 25 Main St, Somersworth, NH, 03878-3198. Tel: 603-692-4587. Fax: 603-692-9110. p. 1465

Longo, Sandy, Youth Serv, Carbondale Public Library, Five N Main St, Carbondale, PA, 18407-2303. Tel: 570-282-4281. Fax: 570-282-7031. p. 2041

Longo-Salvador, Estela, Ref, West New York Public Library, 425 60th St, West New York, NJ, 07093-2211. Tel: 201-295-5135. Fax: 201-662-1473. p. 1541

Longoria, Pamela, Mgr, San Antonio Public Library, Collins Garden, 200 N Park, San Antonio, TX, 78204. Tel: 210-225-0331. p. 2382

Longoria, Shelly, Webmaster, Palm Springs Public Library, 300 S Sunrise Way, Palm Springs, CA, 92262-7699. Tel: 760-322-8389. Fax: 760-320-9834. p. 203

Longpre, Nicole, Librn, Bellevue College, 3000 Landerholm Circle SE, Bellevue, WA, 98007-6484. Tel: 425-564-3071. Fax: 425-564-6186. p. 2508

Longshore, Sue, Coll, Saint Lawrence County Historical Association Archives, Three E Main St, Canton, NY, 13617-0008. Tel: 315-386-8133. Fax: 315-386-8134. p. 1602

Longson, Shelly, Librn, Beaverlodge Public Library, 406 Tenth St, Beaverlodge, AB, T0H 0C0, CANADA. Tel: 780-354-2569. Fax: 780-354-3078. p. 2685

Longstaff, Rachel, Cat Librn, Saint Leo University, 33701 State Rd 52, Saint Leo, FL, 33574. Tel: 352-588-8586. Fax: 352-588-8484. p. 487

Longwell, Char, Mgr, Memorial Hospital, 1400 E Boulder, Rm 2406, Colorado Springs, CO, 80909-5599. Tel: 719-365-5182. Fax: 719-365-2642. p. 295

Longworth, Carolyn, Dir, Millicent Library, 45 Centre St, Fairhaven, MA, 02719. Tel: 508-992-5342. Fax: 508-993-7288. p. 1087

Lonnberg, Thomas R, Curator of Hist, Evansville Museum of Arts, History & Science Library, 411 SE Riverside Dr, Evansville, IN, 47713. Tel: 812-425-2406. Fax: 812-421-7509. p. 738

Lonon, Edyta, Circ Mgr, Harrisburg Area Community College, One HACC Dr, Harrisburg, PA, 17110-2999. Tel: 717-780-2460. Fax: 717-780-2462. p. 2065

Lonon, Vanessa Wallace, Tech Serv, Memorial Health University Medical Center, 4700 Waters Ave, Savannah, GA, 31403. Tel: 912-350-8345. p. 550

Loo, Alicia, Mgr, Legal Res & Client Serv, Supreme Court of Canada Library, 301 Wellington St, Ottawa, ON, K1A 0J1, CANADA. Tel: 613-996-7996. Fax: 613-952-2832. p. 2833

Looby, John, Head, Media Serv, Eastern Illinois University, 600 Lincoln Ave, Charleston, IL, 61920. Tel: 217-581-7564. Fax: 217-581-6993. p. 603

Looby, Judy, Coll Develop Librn, Carnegie Public Library, 712 Sixth St, Charleston, IL, 61920. Tel: 217-345-4913. Fax: 217-348-5616. p. 603

Loomis, Christy, Libr Dir, Marion ISD Community Library, 500 Bulldog Blvd, Marion, TX, 78124. Tel: 830-914-2803, Ext 430, 830-914-4268. p. 2359

Loomis, Evonne, Acq Librn, Northampton Community College, 3835 Green Pond Rd, Bethlehem, PA, 18020-7599. Tel: 610-861-5360. Fax: 610-861-5373. p. 2034

Loomis, Lucy E, Dir, Sturgis Library, 3090 Main St, Barnstable, MA, 02630. Tel: 508-362-8448. Fax: 508-362-5467. p. 1051

Loomis, Mary, Ch, Clarksburg-Harrison Public Library, 404 W Pike St, Clarksburg, WV, 26301. Tel: 304-627-2236. Fax: 304-627-2239. p. 2557

Loomis, Mary Kay, Bus Librn, Western Connecticut State University, Robert S Young Business Library, 181 White St, Danbury, CT, 06810-6885. Tel: 203-837-9139. Fax: 203-837-9135. p. 335

Looney, Beverly, Cat, Paola Free Library, 101 E Peoria, Paola, KS, 66071-1798. Tel: 913-259-3655. Fax: 913-259-3656. p. 889

Loop, Jackie, Web Coordr, Battelle Energy Alliance, LLC, 1776 Science Center Dr, MS 2300, Idaho Falls, ID, 83415-2300. Tel: 208-526-1185. Fax: 208-526-0211. p. 576

Lopatic, Paula, Ch, Vespasian Warner Public Library District, 310 N Quincy, Clinton, IL, 61727. Tel: 217-935-5174. Fax: 217-935-4425. p. 630

Loper, Kimberly, ILL, University of Miami, Louis Calder Memorial Library, Miller School of Medicine, 1601 NW Tenth Ave, Miami, FL, 33136. Tel: 305-243-6749. Fax: 305-325-8853. p. 469

Lopes, Claudia, Access Serv Coordr, University of Connecticut Library, Harleigh B Trecker Library, 1800 Asylum Ave, West Hartford, CT, 06117. Tel: 860-570-9040. Fax: 860-570-9036. p. 371

Lopes, Marlene, Spec Coll Librn, Rhode Island College, 600 Mt Pleasant Ave, Providence, RI, 02908-1924. Tel: 401-456-8126. Fax: 401-456-9646. p. 2174

Lopes, Sandra, Actg Chief, Audit & Evaluation Exec, Library & Archives Canada, 550 De la Cité Blvd, Gatineau, QC, K1A 0N4, CANADA. Tel: 613-897-8719. Fax: 819-934-7539. p. 2883

Lopes-Crocker, Jane, Dir, Gloucester County College Library, 1400 Tanyard Rd, Sewell, NJ, 08080. Tel: 856-468-5000, Ext 2250. Fax: 856-464-1695. p. 1529

Lopez, Andres, Spec Coll Librn, University of the Sacred Heart, Rosales St, PO Box 12383, Santurce, PR, 00914-0383. Tel: 787-728-1515, Ext 4353. Fax: 787-268-8868. p. 2678

Lopez, Antonio, Asst Instruction Librn, Occidental College Library, 1600 Campus Rd, Los Angeles, CA, 90041. Tel: 323-259-1487. Fax: 323-341-4991. p. 176

Lopez, Christina, Librn, Pitblado Law Library, 2500-360 Main St, Winnipeg, MB, R3C 4H6, CANADA. Tel: 204-956-0560. Fax: 204-957-0227. p. 2757

Lopez, Clara, Br Supvr, Harris County Public Library, South Houston Branch, 607 Ave A, South Houston, TX, 77587. Tel: 713-941-2385. Fax: 713-947-7389. p. 2336

Lopez, Danitza, Asst Librn, Nogales-Santa Cruz County Public Library, Rio Rico Library, 1060 Yavapai Dr, Rio Rico, AZ, 85648. Tel: 520-281-8067. p. 69

Lopez, Danitza, Ch, Nogales-Santa Cruz County Public Library, 518 N Grand Ave, Nogales, AZ, 85621. Tel: 520-287-3343. Fax: 520-287-4823. p. 69

Lopez, Debbie, Circ, Zephyrhills Public Library, 5347 Eighth St, Zephyrhills, FL, 33542. Tel: 813-780-0064. Fax: 813-780-0066. p. 505

Lopez, Eduardo, Dir, Hidalgo Public Library, 710 E Texano Dr, Hidalgo, TX, 78557. Tel: 956-843-2093. Fax: 956-843-8841. p. 2332

Lopez, Eleanor, Dir, Holland Hospital, 602 Michigan Ave, 3rd Flr, Holland, MI, 49423. Tel: 616-394-3107, 616-394-3109. Fax: 616-392-8448. p. 1190

Lopez, Eleanor, Dir, Holland Hospital, Health InfoSource Library, 3235 N Wellness Dr, Holland, MI, 49424. Tel: 616-394-3795. Fax: 616-394-3777. p. 1190

Lopez, Elizabeth, Br Mgr, Monterey County Free Libraries, Greenfield Branch, 315 El Camino Real, Greenfield, CA, 93927. Tel: 831-674-2614. Fax: 831-674-2688. p. 183

Lopez, Elsa M, PhD, Dr, Chief, Department of Veterans Affairs, Library Service 142D, Ten Calle Casia, San Juan, PR, 00921-3201. Tel: 787-641-3639. Fax: 787-641-4550. p. 2676

Lopez, Fabiana, Adult & Teen Serv, Bourbonnais Public Library District, 250 W John Casey Rd, Bourbonnais, IL, 60914. Tel: 815-933-1727. Fax: 815-933-1961. p. 596

Lopez, Frank, Librn, Palm Springs Art Museum Library, 101 Museum Dr, Palm Springs, CA, 92262. Tel: 760-322-4833. Fax: 760-327-5069. p. 203

Lopez, Gertie, Librn, San Xavier Library, 2018 W San Xavier Rd, Tucson, AZ, 85746. Tel: 520-807-8621. Fax: 520-807-8689. p. 88

Lopez, Jane, Br Mgr, Oakland Public Library, Cesar E Chavez Branch, 3301 E 12th St, Ste 271, Oakland, CA, 94601. Tel: 510-535-5620. Fax: 510-535-5622. p. 198

Lopez, Jane, Supv Librn, Br & Access Serv, Oakland Public Library, Main Library, 125 14th St, Oakland, CA, 94612. Tel: 510-238-3134. Fax: 510-238-2232. p. 198

Lopez, John Paul, Dir, Tolleson Public Library, 9555 W Van Buren St, Tolleson, AZ, 85353. Tel: 623-936-7111, Ext 2746. Fax: 623-936-9793. p. 84

Lopez, Jolanda, Eng Librn, Universidad del Turabo, PO Box 3030, Gurabo, PR, 00778-3030. Tel: 787-743-7979, Ext 4501. Fax: 787-743-7924. p. 2673

Lopez, Juan, Learning Res Ctr Dir, Ana G Mendez University System, 5601 Semoran Blvd, Ste 55, Orlando, FL, 32822. Tel: 407-207-3363, Ext 1813. Fax: 407-207-3373. p. 475

Lopez, Juanita, Libr Tech, Universidad Central Del Caribe, Avenida Laurel, Santa Juanita, Bayamon, PR, 00956. Tel: 787-798-3001, Ext 2307. Fax: 787-785-3425. p. 2672

Lopez, Lizette, Head, Acq, University of Puerto Rico, Law School Library, Avenidas Ponce de Leon & Gandara, San Juan, PR, 00931. Tel: 787-999-9703. Fax: 787-999-9680. p. 2676

Lopez, M, Dir, San Diego Family History Center, 4195 Camino Del Rio S, San Diego, CA, 92108. Tel: 619-584-7668. Fax: 619-584-1225. p. 234

Lopez, Maribel, Dir, Inter-American University of Puerto Rico, Bo Helechal, Carr 156 Intersiccion 719, Barranquitas, PR, 00794. Tel: 787-857-2585, 787-857-3600, Ext 2063. Fax: 787-857-2244. p. 2671

Lopez, Marli, Circ, City of Tavares Public Library, 314 N New Hampshire Ave, Tavares, FL, 32778. Tel: 352-742-6204. Fax: 352-742-6472. p. 499

Lopez, Mary, Adult Serv, Northlake Public Library District, 231 N Wolf Rd, Northlake, IL, 60164. Tel: 708-562-2301. Fax: 708-562-8120. p. 683

Lopez, Mary, Ref Librn, Hamilton Township Public Library, One Justice Samuel A Alito, Jr Way, Hamilton, NJ, 08619. Tel: 609-581-4060. Fax: 609-581-4067. p. 1490

Lopez, Mary, Librn, Temple Daily Telegram Library, Ten S Third St, Temple, TX, 76501-7619. Tel: 254-778-4444. Fax: 254-778-4444. p. 2391

Lopez, Mary Helen, Librn, Hayden Public Library, 520 Velasco Ave, Hayden, AZ, 85235. Tel: 520-356-7031. Fax: 520-356-7031. p. 65

Lopez, Mildred, Librn, Inter-American University of Puerto Rico, PO Box 20000, Aguadilla, PR, 00905. Tel: 787-891-0925. Fax: 787-882-3020. p. 2671

Lopez, Mildred, Cat, Pontifical Catholic University Of Puerto Rico, Encarnacion Valdes Library, 2250 Avenida Las Americas, Ste 509, Ponce, PR, 00717-0777. Tel: 787-841-2000, Ext 1821. Fax: 787-284-0235. p. 2675

Lopez, Monica, Coll Develop & Acq Librn, Cerritos College Library, 11110 Alondra Blvd, Norwalk, CA, 90650. Tel: 562-860-2451, Ext 2430. Fax: 562-467-5002. p. 195

Lopez, Patricia, Principal Librn, Adult Serv, Santa Ana Public Library, 26 Civic Center Plaza, Santa Ana, CA, 92701-4010. Tel: 714-647-5325. Fax: 714-647-5296. p. 259

Lopez, Rosa M, Libr Assoc, Salk Institute for Biological Studies, 10010 N Torrey Pines Rd, La Jolla, CA, 92037-1099. Tel: 858-453-4100, Ext 1235. Fax: 858-452-7472. p. 161

Lopez, Sallyann, Bus Operations & Res Mgr, University of Massachusetts at Boston, 100 Morrissey Blvd, Boston, MA, 02125-3300. Tel: 617-287-5917. p. 1068

López, Sigfredo, Tech Coordr, Amaury Veray Music Library, 350 Rafael Lamar, Hato Rey, PR, 00918. Tel: 787-751-0160, Ext 252. Fax: 787-754-5934. p. 2673

Lopez, Yolanda, Librn, Florida Department of Corrections, Everglades Correctional Institution Library, 1601 SW 187th Ave, Miami, FL, 33185. Tel: 305-228-2000, 305-228-2161. Fax: 305-228-2039. p. 465

Lopez-Fitzsimmons, Bernadette M, Cat, Manhattan College, 4513 Manhattan College Pkwy, Riverdale, NY, 10471. Tel: 718-862-7166. Fax: 718-862-8028. p. 1728

LoPinto, Leonard, Dir, Paramus Public Library, E 116 Century Rd, Paramus, NJ, 07652-4398. Tel: 201-599-1300. Fax: 201-599-0059. p. 1517

Lopresti, Rob, Interim Head, Map Libr, Ref Librn, Western Washington University, 516 High St, MS 9103, Bellingham, WA, 98225. Tel: 360-650-3342. Fax: 360-650-3044. p. 2509

LoPresti, Sara, Libr Asst, Burlington Public Library, 34 Library Lane, Burlington, CT, 06013. Tel: 860-673-3331. Fax: 860-673-0897. p. 333

Lopshire, Becky, Librn, Salina Public Library, 90 W Main St, Salina, UT, 84654. Tel: 435-529-7753. Fax: 435-529-1235. p. 2412

Lopuszynski, Cynthia, Head, Adult Serv, Crystal Lake Public Library, 126 Paddock St, Crystal Lake, IL, 60014. Tel: 815-459-1687. Fax: 815-459-9581. p. 632

Loranc, Lisa Marie, Asst Dir, Brazoria County Library System, 451 N Velasco, Ste 250, Angleton, TX, 77515. Tel: 979-864-1510. Fax: 979-864-1298. p. 2275

Lorbeer, Liz, Coll Mgt, University of Alabama at Birmingham, Lister Hill Library of the Health Sciences, 1700 University Blvd, Birmingham, AL, 35294-0013. Tel: 205-934-5460. Fax: 205-934-3545. p. 10

Lord, Ada, In Charge, Eastern Louisiana Mental Health Systems, Chapman Memorial Library, 4502 Hwy 951, Jackson, LA, 70748. Tel: 225-634-0560. Fax: 225-634-0188. p. 951

Lord, Charles, Assoc Dean, Univ Libr, Dir, Learning Res, University of Washington Libraries, Tacoma Library, 1900 Commerce St, Box 358460, Tacoma, WA, 98402-3100. Tel: 253-692-4444. Fax: 253-692-4445. p. 2535

Lord, Christine, Circ Mgr, Brewster Ladies' Library Association, 1822 Main St, Brewster, MA, 02631. Tel: 508-896-3913. Fax: 508-896-9372. p. 1069

Lord, Evelyn, Head Librn, Laney College, 900 Fallon St, Oakland, CA, 94607. Tel: 510-464-3493. Fax: 510-464-3264. p. 197

Lord, Hazel, Head, Access Serv, University of Southern California Libraries, Asa V Call Law Library, 699 Exposition Blvd, LAW 202, MC 0072, Los Angeles, CA, 90089-0072. Tel: 213-740-6482. Fax: 213-740-7179. p. 179

Lord, Kim, Asst Dir, Kent Memorial Library, 50 N Main St (Junction of Rtes 75 & 168), Suffield, CT, 06078-2117. Tel: 860-668-3896. Fax: 860-668-3895. p. 371

Lord, Linda H, State Librn, Maine State Library, LMA Bldg, 230 State St, Augusta, ME, 04333. Tel: 207-287-5600. Fax: 207-287-5615. p. 974

Lord, Lorraine, Br Mgr, Lubbock Public Library, Godeke, 6707 Slide Rd, Lubbock, TX, 79424. Tel: 806-775-3748. Fax: 806-767-3762. p. 2357

Lord, Michelle, Adult Serv, Southington Public Library & Museum, 255 Main St, Southington, CT, 06489. Tel: 860-628-0947. Fax: 860-628-0488. p. 368

Lord, Norma, Adult Serv, First Congregational Church Library, 2101 16th St, Greeley, CO, 80631. Tel: 970-353-0828. Fax: 970-353-8447. p. 311

Lord, Phil, Br Mgr, Howard County Library System, Elkridge Branch, 6540 Washington Blvd, Elkridge, MD, 21075. Tel: 410-313-5077. Fax: 410-313-5090. p. 1026

Lord, Ruth, Tech Serv, Wabash Carnegie Public Library, 188 W Hill St, Wabash, IN, 46992-3048. Tel: 260-563-2972. Fax: 260-563-0222. p. 785

Lorde, Karen, Br Librn, Brooklyn Public Library, New Lots, 665 New Lots Ave, Brooklyn, NY, 11207. Tel: 718-649-0311. Fax: 718-649-0719. p. 1591

Lorde, Karen, Supvr, Libr & Info Serv, Brooklyn Public Library, East Flatbush, 9612 Church Ave, Brooklyn, NY, 11212. Tel: 718-922-0927. Fax: 718-922-2394. p. 1591

Lore, Dorothy A, Librn, Washington County Library, 235 E High St, Potosi, MO, 63664. Tel: 573-438-4691. Fax: 573-438-6423. p. 1350

Lore, Rachel, ESL Coordr, Bergenfield Public Library, 50 W Clinton Ave, Bergenfield, NJ, 07621-2799. Tel: 201-387-4040, Ext 837. Fax: 201-387-9004. p. 1472

Loree, Erin, Tech Serv Librn, Amherst College, Amherst, MA, 01002. Fax: 413-542-2662. p. 1048

Lorence, David H, In Charge, National Tropical Botanical Garden Library, 3530 Papalina Rd, Kalaheo, HI, 96741. Tel: 808-332-7324, Ext 214. Fax: 808-332-9765. p. 566

Lorence, Luann, Dir, Eagle Nest Public Library, 74 N Tomboy Dr, Eagle Nest, NM, 87718. Tel: 505-377-0657. Fax: 505-377-2487. p. 1554

Lorensen, Angie, Adult & Tech Serv Coordr, Birchard Public Library of Sandusky County, 423 Croghan St, Fremont, OH, 43420. Tel: 419-334-7101. Fax: 419-334-4788. p. 1900

Lorenti, Mildred, Mgr, GE Asset Management, 3003 Summer St, Stamford, CT, 06905. Tel: 203-326-2404. p. 369

Lorenz, Becky, Asst Dir, Eastern Wyoming College Library, 3200 West C, Torrington, WY, 82240. Tel: 307-532-8210. Fax: 307-532-8225. p. 2661

Lorenz, Tammy, Dir, Karlen Memorial Library, 215 Blaine St, Beemer, NE, 68716. Tel: 402-528-3476. Fax: 402-528-3476. p. 1393

Lorenzen, Annemarie, Res, Schnader, Harrison, Segal & Lewis Library, 1600 Market St, Ste 3600, Philadelphia, PA, 19103. Tel: 215-751-2111. Fax: 215-751-2205. p. 2116

Lorenzen, Elizabeth, Ref/Instruction Librn, Indiana State University, 510 North 6 1/2 St, Terre Haute, IN, 47809. Tel: 812-237-4397. Fax: 812-237-3376. p. 781

Lorenzen, Michael, Assoc Dean, Pub Serv, Western Washington University, 516 High St, MS 9103, Bellingham, WA, 98225. Tel: 360-650-4449. Fax: 360-650-3044. p. 2509

Lorenzi, Lara, Dir, William Jeanes Memorial Library, 4051 Joshua Rd, Lafayette Hill, PA, 19444-1400. Tel: 610-828-0441. Fax: 610-828-4049. p. 2075

Lorenzo, Patricia, Serv Mgr, Outreach & Pub Awareness, Santa Clara County Library District, 14600 Winchester Blvd, Los Gatos, CA, 95032. Tel: 408-293-2326, Ext 3010. Fax: 408-364-0161. p. 180

Lorich, Linda, Acq, Schlow Centre Region Library, 211 S Allen St, State College, PA, 16801-4806. Tel: 814-237-6236. Fax: 814-238-8508. p. 2143

Lorimer, Katherine, Ref Serv, Goethe-Institut New York, 72 Spring St, 11th Flr, New York, NY, 10012. Tel: 212-439-8688. Fax: 212-439-8705. p. 1680

Loring, Christopher B, Dir of Libr, Smith College Libraries, Northampton, MA, 01063. Tel: 413-585-2910. Fax: 413-585-2904. p. 1113

Lorion, Johanne, Pub Serv, Cegep St Jean Sur Richelieu Bibliotheque, 30 boul du Seminaire, CP 1018, Saint-Jean-Sur-Richelieu, QC, J3B 7B1, CANADA. Tel: 450-347-5301, Ext 2333. Fax: 450-347-3329, 450-358-9350. p. 2911

Lorkovic, Tatjana, Curator, Yale University Library, Sterling Memorial Library, 120 High St, New Haven, CT, 06520. Tel: 203-432-1861. Fax: 203-432-1294. p. 359

Lorne, Lorraine, Asst Dir, Ref Serv Coordr, University of Arkansas Libraries, Robert A & Vivian Young Law Library, School of Law, Waterman Hall 107, Fayetteville, AR, 72701-1201. Tel: 479-575-5834. Fax: 479-575-2053. p. 100

Lorson, Amy, Ref Librn, Indiana Wesleyan University, 4201 S Washington St, Marion, IN, 46953. Tel: 502-261-5019. Fax: 765-677-2676. p. 762

LoRusso, Margaret, Ch, Harrison Public Library, Bruce Ave, Harrison, NY, 10528. Tel: 914-835-0324. Fax: 914-835-1564. p. 1634

Lorys, Jan, Dir, Polish Museum of America Library, 984 N Milwaukee Ave, Chicago, IL, 60642-4101. Tel: 773-384-3352, Ext 101. Fax: 773-384-3799. p. 622

Losana, Natalie, Dir, Belmar Public Library, 517 Tenth Ave, Belmar, NJ, 07719. Tel: 732-681-0775. Fax: 732-681-8419. p. 1471

LoSchiavo, Linda, Asst Dir, Fordham University Library at Lincoln Center, Leon Lowenstein Bldg, 113 W 60th St, New York, NY, 10023-7480. Tel: 212-636-6050. Fax: 212-636-6766. p. 1678

Losey, Debra A, Librn, United States Department of Commerce, National Oceanic & Atmospheric Administration, 8604 La Jolla Shores Dr, La Jolla, CA, 92037-1508. Tel: 858-546-7038, 858-546-7196. Fax: 858-546-5651. p. 161

Losinski, Jennifer, Asst Librn, Arcadia Free Public Library, 406 E Main St, Arcadia, WI, 54612-1396. Tel: 608-323-7505. Fax: 608-323-7505. p. 2579

Losinski, Patrick A, Exec Dir, Columbus Metropolitan Library, 96 S Grant Ave, Columbus, OH, 43215-4781. Tel: 614-645-2275. Fax: 614-849-1157. p. 1884

Losos, Elizabeth, Dr, Chief Exec Officer, Pres, Organization for Tropical Studies Library, Duke University, 410 Swift Ave, Durham, NC, 27705. Tel: 919-684-5774. Fax: 919-684-5661. p. 1789

Loter, Jim, Info Tech Dir, The Seattle Public Library, 1000 Fourth Ave, Seattle, WA, 98104-1109. Tel: 206-386-4662. p. 2531

Lothridge, Sherri, Cat, Ser, University of Pittsburgh at Bradford, 300 Campus Dr, Bradford, PA, 16701. Tel: 814-362-7610. Fax: 814-362-7688. p. 2037

Lotito, Amanda, YA Serv, Lindenhurst Memorial Library, One Lee Ave, Lindenhurst, NY, 11757-5399. Tel: 631-957-7755. Fax: 631-957-7114. p. 1652

Lotito, Katherine, Ref, Martin Luther College Library, 1995 Luther Ct, New Ulm, MN, 56073-3965. Tel: 507-354-8221, Ext 249 or 209. Fax: 507-233-9107. p. 1268

Lotspeich, Catherine, ILL/Doc Delivery Serv, Randolph College, 2500 Rivermont Ave, Lynchburg, VA, 24503. Tel: 434-947-8133. Fax: 434-947-8134. p. 2476

Lott, Linda, Rare Bk Librn, Harvard Library, Dumbarton Oaks Research Library, 1703 32nd St NW, Washington, MA, 20007. Tel: 202-339-6400. Fax: 202-625-0279. p. 1074

Lott, Lydia, Mgr, Satilla Regional Library, Ambrose Public Library, 1070 Cypress Ave, Ambrose, GA, 31512. Tel: 912-359-2536. Fax: 912-359-2536. p. 530

Lott, Sue, Acq, Greenwood-Leflore Public Library System, 405 W Washington St, Greenwood, MS, 38930-4297. Tel: 662-453-3634. Fax: 662-453-0683. p. 1299

Lott, Suzanne, Ch, Enfield Public Library, 104 Middle Rd, Enfield, CT, 06082. Tel: 860-763-7510. Fax: 860-763-7514. p. 338

Lott, Tyler C, Libr Serv Coordr, Ochsner Clinic Foundation, 1st Flr Hospital, 1514 Jefferson Hwy, New Orleans, LA, 70121-2429. Tel: 504-842-3760. Fax: 504-842-5339. p. 962

Lotton, Kristy, Dir, Sioux County Public Library, 182 W Third St, Harrison, NE, 69346. Tel: 308-668-9431. Fax: 308-668-2443. p. 1400

Lotz, Marsha, Ref, Matteson Public Library, 801 S School St, Matteson, IL, 60443-1897. Tel: 708-748-4431. Fax: 708-748-0510. p. 671

Lou Kurt, Mary, Asst Dir, Cascade Public Library, 310 First Ave W, Cascade, IA, 52033. Tel: 563-852-3201. Fax: 563-852-6011. p. 799

Loucks, Cami, Dir, Lancaster Veterans Memorial Library, 1600 Veterans Memorial Pkwy, Lancaster, TX, 75134. Tel: 972-227-1080. Fax: 972-227-5560. p. 2353

Loucks, Rhonda, Librn, Burns Public Library, 104 N Washington, Burns, KS, 66840. Tel: 620-726-5717. p. 859

Louden, William F, Univ Librn, University of Evansville, 1800 Lincoln Ave, Evansville, IN, 47722. Tel: 812-488-2376. Fax: 812-488-6996. p. 739

Loudenslager, Sarah, Bus Instrul Librn, Salisbury University, 1101 Camden Ave, Salisbury, MD, 21801-6863. Tel: 410-543-6130. Fax: 410-543-6203. p. 1040

Louderback, Art, Chief Librn, Historical Society of Western Pennsylvania, 1212 Smallman St, Pittsburgh, PA, 15222. Tel: 412-454-6360. Fax: 412-454-6028. p. 2125

Louderback, Chris, ILL, William Penn University, 201 Trueblood Ave, Oskaloosa, IA, 52577. Tel: 641-673-1096. Fax: 641-673-1098. p. 837

Louderback, Joseph, Libr Dir, DeVry University Library, 630 US Hwy One, North Brunswick, NJ, 08902. Tel: 732-729-3840. Fax: 732-729-3969. p. 1514

Louderback, Pamela, Dr, Info Serv Librn, Northeastern State University, Broken Arrow Campus Library, Bldg E Library, 3100 E New Orleans St, Broken Arrow, OK, 74014. Tel: 918-449-6453. Fax: 918-449-6454. p. 1979

Loudon, Lumi, Librn, Yakima County Law Library, Yakima County Courthouse, B33, 128 N Second St, Yakima, WA, 98901. Tel: 509-574-2692. p. 2550

Louge, Mary, Tech Serv Librn, Westmont College, 955 La Paz Rd, Santa Barbara, CA, 93108-1099. Tel: 805-565-6144. Fax: 805-565-6220. p. 262

Lougee, Wendy Pradt, Univ Librn, University of Minnesota Libraries-Twin Cities, 499 O Meredith Wilson Library, 309 19th Ave S, Minneapolis, MN, 55455-0414. Tel: 612-625-9148. Fax: 612-626-9353. p. 1262

Loughnane, Patricia, Admin Serv, Bergen County Cooperative Library System, 810 Main St, Hackensack, NJ, 07601. Tel: 201-489-1904. Fax: 201-489-4215. p. 2948

Loughran, Amy, Dir, United States Army Training & Doctrine Command, US Army Hq TRADOC, Seven Bernard Rd, Fort Monroe, VA, 23651. Tel: 757-788-2155. Fax: 757-788-5544. p. 2957

Louis, Marie, Cat, Southern University, Oliver B Spellman Law Library, 56 Roosevelt Steptoe, Baton Rouge, LA, 70813. Tel: 225-771-2196. Fax: 225-771-6254. p. 944

Louis-Jacques, Lyonette, Foreign & Intl Law Librn, University of Chicago Library, D'Angelo Law Library, 1121 E 60th St, Chicago, IL, 60637-2786. Tel: 773-702-9612. Fax: 773-702-2889. p. 626

Louisdhon-Louinis, Lucrece, Asst Dir, Miami-Dade Public Library System, 101 W Flagler St, Miami, FL, 33130-1523. Tel: 305-375-5501. Fax: 305-375-3048. p. 466

Lounsbery, Donna, Circ, Franklin College, 101 Branigin Blvd, Franklin, IN, 46131-2623. Tel: 317-738-8164. Fax: 317-738-8787. p. 743

Lounsbury, Valerie, Sci Res Mgr, National Aquarium in Baltimore, 501 E Pratt St, Baltimore, MD, 21202-3194. Tel: 410-659-4257. Fax: 410-576-1080. p. 1016

Lourenço, Mary, Libr Supvr-Popular Libr, McGill University Libraries, Nahum Gelber Law Library, 3660 Peel St, Montreal, QC, H3A 1W9, CANADA. Tel: 514-398-4715. Fax: 514-398-3585. p. 2898

Lourie, Joyce, Ref, Thomas Memorial Library, Six Scott Dyer Rd, Cape Elizabeth, ME, 04107. Tel: 207-799-1720. p. 980

Louros, Diana, Librn, New York Life Insurance Co, 51 Madison Ave, Rm 10-SB, New York, NY, 10010. Tel: 212-576-6458. Fax: 212-576-6886. p. 1690

Loutsch, Valerie, Co-Dir, Remsen Public Library, 211 Fulton, Remsen, IA, 51050. Tel: 712-786-2911. Fax: 712-786-3255. p. 840

Louwagie, Lacey, Teen Serv Librn, Marshall-Lyon County Library, 301 W Lyon St, Marshall, MN, 56258. Tel: 507-537-7003. p. 1258

Louzin, Brenna, Mgr, Legal & Bus Develop Res Serv, Foster Pepper PLLC, 1111 Third Ave, Ste 3400, Seattle, WA, 98101. Tel: 206-447-6287. Fax: 206-447-9700. p. 2529

Lovallo, Beth, Ref & Tech Librn, Woodbury Public Library, 269 Main St S, Woodbury, CT, 06798. Tel: 203-263-3502. Fax: 203-263-0571. p. 380

Lovan, Seng, Sr Commun Libr Mgr, Contra Costa County Library, Danville Library, 400 Front St, Danville, CA, 94526-3465. Tel: 925-837-4889. Fax: 925-831-1299. p. 209

Lovato, Barbara, Dr, Dir, University of New Mexico, Valencia Campus, 280 La Entrada, Los Lunas, NM, 87031. Tel: 505-925-8991. Fax: 505-925-8994. p. 1551

Lovatt, Holly, Adult Prog & Serv, Leduc Public Library, Two Alexandra Park, Leduc, AB, T9E 4C4, CANADA. Tel: 780-986-2637. Fax: 780-986-3462. p. 2709

Lovchik, Jennifer, Ref & Teen Serv, Bellingham Public Library, 210 Central Ave, CS-9710, Bellingham, WA, 98227-9710. Tel: 360-778-7323. p. 2508

Love, Alex, Syst Adminr, Warren County Public Library, 1225 State St, Bowling Green, KY, 42101. Tel: 270-781-4882. Fax: 270-781-7323. p. 907

Love, Anita, Asst Dir, Human Res & Coll Develop, Trails Regional Library, 432 N Holden St, Warrensburg, MO, 64093. Tel: 660-747-1699. Fax: 660-747-5774. p. 1371

Love, Barbara, Dir, Farmington Area Public Library District, 266 E Fort St, Farmington, IL, 61531-1276. Tel: 309-245-2175. Fax: 309-245-2294. p. 645

Love, Barbara, Dir, Br Operations, Kingston Frontenac Public Library, 130 Johnson St, Kingston, ON, K7L 1X8, CANADA. Tel: 613-549-8888, Ext 1180. Fax: 613-549-8476. p. 2813

Love, Bathsheba, Circ Serv, Murrell Memorial Library, Missouri Valley College, Tech Center Bldg, 500 E College St, Marshall, MO, 65340. Tel: 660-831-4180, 660-831-4181. Fax: 660-831-4068. p. 1344

Love, Brandolyn, Ref Librn, Sumter County Library, 111 N Harvin St, Sumter, SC, 29150. Tel: 803-773-7273. Fax: 803-773-4875. p. 2206

Love, Carina, Cat, Metadata Librn, Cuesta College Library, Hwy 1, San Luis Obispo, CA, 93401. Tel: 805-546-3100, Ext 2688. Fax: 805-546-3109. p. 253

Love, Emily, Librn, Hartselle Public Library, 152 NW Sparkman St, Hartselle, AL, 35640. Tel: 256-773-9880. Fax: 256-773-9884. p. 20

Love, Heather, Acq Librn, Slippery Rock University of Pennsylvania, Slippery Rock, PA, 16057-9989. Tel: 724-738-2058. Fax: 724-738-2661. p. 2140

Love, John, Librn, Gananoque Public Library, 100 Park St, Gananoque, ON, K7G 2Y5, CANADA. Tel: 613-382-2436. p. 2806

Love, Laurie, Circ Mgr, Wilkes County Public Library, 215 Tenth St, North Wilkesboro, NC, 28659. Tel: 336-838-2818. Fax: 336-667-2638. p. 1813

Love, Lisa M, Ref Librn, United States Air Force, Two W Castle St, Fairchild AFB, WA, 99011-8532. Tel: 509-247-5228, 509-247-5556. Fax: 509-247-3365. p. 2515

Love, Martha, Spec Projects Coordr/Vols Coordr, Springfield-Greene County Library District, 4653 S Campbell, Springfield, MO, 65810-1723. Tel: 417-882-0714. Fax: 417-883-9348. p. 1367

Love, Mike, Head, Media Serv, Carthage College, 2001 Alford Park Dr, Kenosha, WI, 53140-1900. Tel: 262-551-5900. Fax: 262-551-5904. p. 2601

Love, Toni, Ch, Choctaw County Public Library, 703 E Jackson St, Hugo, OK, 74743. Tel: 580-326-5591. Fax: 580-326-7388. p. 1966

Love, Vernitta, Circ Mgr, Pine Bluff & Jefferson County Library System, Main Library, 200 E Eighth Ave, Pine Bluff, AR, 71601. Tel: 870-534-4802. Fax: 870-534-8707. p. 112

Loveall, Sharron, Librn, North Central Regional Library, Leavenworth Community, 700 Hwy 2, Leavenworth, WA, 98826. Tel: 509-548-7923. Fax: 509-548-7923. p. 2549

Loveday, Laura, Libr Dir, Southwest Florida College, Learning Resource Center, Tampa Branch, 3910 Riga Blvd, Tampa, FL, 33619. Tel: 813-630-4401. Fax: 813-630-4272. p. 446

Lovejoy, Ellie, Librn, Mount Washington Public Library, Town Hall, 118 East St, Mount Washington, MA, 01258. Tel: 413-528-1798, 413-528-2839. Fax: 413-528-2839. p. 1107

Lovejoy, Suzanne Eggleston, Actg Librn, Pub Serv Librn, Yale University Library, Irving S Gilmore Music Library, 120 High St, New Haven, CT, 06520. Tel: 203-432-0492. Fax: 203-432-7339. p. 357

Lovelace, Diane, Dir, Libr Serv, Montgomery County Community College, 340 DeKalb Pike, Blue Bell, PA, 19422-0796. Tel: 215-641-6300, 215-641-6596. Fax: 215-619-7182. p. 2036

Lovelace, Kathleen, Ref/Instruction Librn, College of Lake County, 19351 W Washington St, Grayslake, IL, 60030. Tel: 847-543-2489. Fax: 847-223-7690. p. 652

Loveland, George, Head, Pub Serv, Ferrum College, 150 Wiley Dr, Ferrum, VA, 24088. Tel: 540-365-4426. Fax: 540-365-4423. p. 2463

Loveless, Janet W, Asst Dir, Nassau County Public Library System, 25 N Fourth St, Fernandina Beach, FL, 32034-4123. Tel: 904-548-4857. Fax: 904-277-7366. p. 439

Loveless, Laura, Br Mgr, Kansas City, Kansas Public Library, West Wyandotte, 1737 N 82nd St, Kansas City, KS, 66112. Tel: 913-596-5800, Ext 1001. Fax: 913-596-5806. p. 875

Lovelette, Scott, ILL, Kellogg-Hubbard Library, 135 Main St, Montpelier, VT, 05602. Tel: 802-223-3338. Fax: 802-223-3338. p. 2429

Lovell, Amy, Cat, Duquesne University, Center for Legal Information, 900 Locust St, Pittsburgh, PA, 15282. Tel: 412-396-6292. Fax: 412-396-6294. p. 2125

Lovell, Ann, Tech Serv, Green River Community College, 12401 SE 320th St, Auburn, WA, 98092-3699. Tel: 253-833-9111, Ext 2098. Fax: 253-288-3436, 253-288-3491. p. 2507

Lovell, Barbara, Librn, Nephi Public Library, 21 E First N, Nephi, UT, 84648-1501. Tel: 435-623-1312. Fax: 435-623-5443. p. 2408

Lovell, Carol, Curator, Stratford Historical Society Library, 967 Academy Hill, Stratford, CT, 06615. Tel: 203-378-0630. Fax: 203-378-2562. p. 371

Lovell, Chris, Digital Serv, Palm Beach Atlantic University, 300 Pembroke Pl, West Palm Beach, FL, 33401-6503. Tel: 561-803-2221. Fax: 561-803-2235. p. 503

Lovell, Cindy, Interim Exec Dir, Mark Twain Home Foundation, 120 N Main St, Hannibal, MO, 63401-3537. Tel: 573-221-9010, Ext 402. Fax: 573-221-7975. p. 1330

Lovell, Ellen, Libr Tech, Lamar Community College Library, Bowman Bldg, 2401 S Main St, Lamar, CO, 81052-3999. Tel: 719-336-1541. Fax: 719-336-2448. p. 315

Lovell, Judy, Librn, Faulkner-Van Buren Regional Library System, Greenbrier Branch, 13 Wilson Farm Rd, Greenbrier, AR, 72058. Tel: 501-679-6344. Fax: 501-679-6934. p. 96

Lovell, Lois, Dir, Sparta Township Library, 80 N Union St, Sparta, MI, 49345. Tel: 616-887-9937. Fax: 616-887-0179. p. 1229

Lovell, Mary, Librn, Seymour Public Library District, 176-178 Genesee St, Auburn, NY, 13021. Tel: 315-252-2571. Fax: 315-252-7985. p. 1576

Lovell, Mary, Tech Serv, Dickinson Area Public Library, 139 Third St W, Dickinson, ND, 58601. Tel: 701-456-7700. Fax: 701-456-7702. p. 1840

Lovell, Rita, Dir, Alpine County Library, 270 Laramie St, Markleeville, CA, 96120. Tel: 530-694-2120. Fax: 530-694-2408. p. 184

Lovell, Thoreau, Head, Info Tech, Head, Media Serv, San Francisco State University, 1630 Holloway Ave, San Francisco, CA, 94132-4030. Tel: 415-338-2285. p. 247

Lovelock, Marty, Chief Librn, Health Canada Library, Postal Locator 2202B, 251 Frederick Banting Driveway, Ottawa, ON, K1A 0K9, CANADA. Tel: 613-957-1545. Fax: 613-941-6957. p. 2831

Lovely, Lloyd, Dep Exec Dir, Finance & Support, Metropolitan Library System in Oklahoma County, 300 Park Ave, Oklahoma City, OK, 73102. Tel: 405-606-3725. Fax: 405-606-3722. p. 1972

Lovely, Rosemary, Br Mgr, Sacramento Public Library, Sylvan Oaks Community Library, 6700 Auburn Blvd, Citrus Heights, CA, 95621. p. 225

Lovely, Sandra, Mgr, Durham County Library, Parkwood, Parkwood Shopping Ctr, 5122 Revere Rd, Durham, NC, 27713. Tel: 919-560-0262. Fax: 919-560-0264. p. 1788

Loveman, Marcia, Coll Develop, ILL, Ref, Lake Wales Public Library, 290 Cypress Garden Lane, Lake Wales, FL, 33853. Tel: 863-678-4004. Fax: 863-678-4051. p. 458

Loveridge, Lucy, Ch, Framingham Public Library, 49 Lexington St, Framingham, MA, 01702-8278. Tel: 508-879-5570, Ext 4334. Fax: 508-820-7210. p. 1090

Lovering, Susan, Circ, ILL, Franklin Public Library, 310 Central St, Franklin, NH, 03235. Tel: 603-934-2911. Fax: 603-934-7413. p. 1447

Lovesey, Anthony, Automation Spec, New Brunswick Legislative Library, Legislative Bldg, 706 Queen St, Fredericton, NB, E3B 1C5, CANADA. Tel: 506-444-4997. Fax: 506-444-5889. p. 2763

Lovett, Deborah, Circ, Regis College Library, 235 Wellesley St, Weston, MA, 02493. Tel: 781-768-7300. Fax: 781-768-7323. p. 1139

Lovett, Deborah G, Libr Dir, Harrisburg Area Community College, 735 Cumberland St, Lebanon, PA, 17042. Tel: 717-270-6328. p. 2079

Lovett, Elizabeth, Librn, Williamson Public Library, 101 Logan St, Williamson, WV, 25661. Tel: 304-235-6029. Fax: 304-235-6029. p. 2574

Lovett, Heather, Mgr, William Sharpe Jr Hospital, 936 Sharpe Hospital Rd, Weston, WV, 26452. Tel: 304-269-1210, Ext 399. Fax: 304-269-6235. p. 2574

Lovett, John, Curator, University of Oklahoma, Western History Collection, Western History Collection, 452 MH, 630 Parrington Oval, Norman, OK, 73019. Tel: 405-325-3641. Fax: 405-325-6069. p. 1971

Lovewell, Heather L, Archivist, Saint Ambrose University Library, 518 W Locust St, Davenport, IA, 52803. Tel: 563-333-6444. Fax: 563-333-6248. p. 807

Loving, Joyce, Mgr, Saint Louis County Library, Special Collections Department, 1640 S Lindbergh Blvd, Saint Louis, MO, 63131-3598. Tel: 314-994-3300, Ext 241. Fax: 314-997-7602. p. 1359

Loving, Karen, Circ, Lincoln Memorial University, Cumberland Gap Pkwy, Box 2012, Harrogate, TN, 37752. Tel: 423-869-6219. Fax: 423-869-6426. p. 2236

Lovisolo, Lois, Dir, Bethpage Public Library, 47 Powell Ave, Bethpage, NY, 11714-3197. Tel: 516-931-3907. Fax: 516-931-3926. p. 1581

Low, Douglas, Head, Ref, University of West Florida, 11000 University Pkwy, Pensacola, FL, 32514-5750. Tel: 850-474-2264. Fax: 850-474-3338. p. 482

Low, Janet, Outreach Prog, Orem Public Library, 58 N State St, Orem, UT, 84057-5596. Tel: 801-229-7050. Fax: 801-229-7130. p. 2409

Low, Keith, Coordr, Teck Resources Limited, 3300-550 Burrard St, Vancouver, BC, V6C 0B3, CANADA. Tel: 604-699-4263. Fax: 604-699-4711. p. 2742

Lowden, Chris, Ref Librn, Dewey & LeBoeuf LLP Library, 1301 Avenue of the Americas, 22nd Flr, New York, NY, 10019. Tel: 212-259-8000. Fax: 212-259-6679. p. 1677

Lowden, Thomas, Dir, Beverly Free Library, 441 Cooper St, Beverly, NJ, 08010. Tel: 609-387-1259. Fax: 609-387-1259. p. 1472

Lowder, David, Head, Syst, Georgia Southern University, 1400 Southern Dr, Statesboro, GA, 30458. Tel: 912-478-0161. Fax: 912-478-0093. p. 552

Lowder, Patricia, Br Mgr, Cabarrus County Public Library, Harrisburg Branch, 201 Sims Pkwy, Harrisburg, NC, 28075. Tel: 704-920-2080. Fax: 704-455-2017. p. 1785

Lowe, Annie, Circ, Killeen City Library System, 205 E Church Ave, Killeen, TX, 76541. Tel: 254-501-8990. Fax: 254-501-7704. p. 2350

Lowe, Betty, Librn, History Museum & Historical Society of Western Virginia Library, One Market Sq, 3rd Flr, Roanoke, VA, 24011. Tel: 540-342-5770. Fax: 540-224-1256. p. 2493

Lowe, Carrie Beth, Dir, Johnson Bible College, 7900 Johnson Dr, Knoxville, TN, 37998. Tel: 865-251-2277. Fax: 865-251-2278. p. 2241

Lowe, David, Computer Serv, University of Alabama, School of Law Library, 101 Paul Bryant Dr, Tuscaloosa, AL, 35487. Tel: 205-348-5925. Fax: 205-348-1112. p. 38

Lowe, Elliott, Natural Res Mgr, Bureau of Land Management Library, 1150 University Ave, Fairbanks, AK, 99709-3844. Tel: 907-474-2307. Fax: 907-474-2280, 907-474-2282. p. 47

Lowe, Flora S, Dir, Ashford University Library, 400 N Bluff Blvd, Clinton, IA, 52732. Tel: 563-242-4023, Ext 3210. Fax: 563-242-2003. p. 803

Lowe, Karen, Instr, Appalachian State University, RCOE, Dept of LES, 311 Edwin Duncan Hall, Boone, NC, 28608. Tel: 828-262-7236. Fax: 828-262-6035. p. 2971

Lowe, Kathleen, Ref, University of Montevallo, Station 6100, Montevallo, AL, 35115-6100. Tel: 205-665-6100. Fax: 205-665-6112. p. 27

Lowe, Kathy, Asst Librn, Big Sandy Community & Technical College, One Bert T Combs Dr, Prestonsburg, KY, 41653. Tel: 606-889-4748. Fax: 606-886-8683. p. 933

Lowe, Louise, Circ, Mercer University Atlanta, 3001 Mercer University Dr, Atlanta, GA, 30341. Tel: 678-547-6207. Fax: 678-547-6270. p. 517

Lowe, Mary Ellen, Dir, Shamokin & Coal Township Public Library, Inc, 210 E Independence St, Shamokin, PA, 17872-6888. Tel: 570-648-3202. Fax: 570-648-4255. p. 2139

Lowe, Megan, Coordr, Pub Serv, University of Louisiana at Monroe Library, 700 University Ave, Monroe, LA, 71209-0720. Tel: 318-342-3041. Fax: 318-342-1075. p. 958

Lowe, Meredith, Head Librn, Museum of Flight, 9404 E Marginal Way S, Seattle, WA, 98108-4097. Tel: 206-768-7160. Fax: 206-764-5707. p. 2529

Lowe, Michele, Libr Mgr, Southwest Public Libraries, Westland Area Library, 4740 W Broad St, Columbus, OH, 43228. Tel: 614-878-1301. Fax: 614-878-3454. p. 1903

Lowe, Myra, Assoc Dean, West Virginia University Libraries, WVU Libraries, 1549 University Ave, Morgantown, WV, 26506. Tel: 304-293-4040. Fax: 304-293-6638. p. 2566

Lowe, Randall A, Acq, Coll Develop & Ser, Frostburg State University, One Stadium Dr, Frostburg, MD, 21532. Tel: 301-687-4313. Fax: 301-687-7069. p. 1029

Lowe, Rita, Br Coordr, Wayne County Public Library, 220 W Liberty St, Wooster, OH, 44691-3593. Tel: 330-804-4686. Fax: 330-262-1352. p. 1950

Lowe, Rob, Computer Serv, Webmaster, Prescott Public Library, 215 E Goodwin St, Prescott, AZ, 86303. Tel: 928-777-1522. Fax: 928-771-5829. p. 78

Lowe, Sidney, Head, Res Serv, University of Nevada, Las Vegas Libraries, 4505 Maryland Pkwy, Box 457001, Las Vegas, NV, 89154-7001. Tel: 702-895-2286. Fax: 702-895-2287. p. 1431

Lowe, Suzette, Dir, Jackson County Library, 208 N Church St, Ripley, WV, 25271-1204. Tel: 304-372-5343. Fax: 304-372-7935. p. 2570

Lowe-Wincentsen, Dawn, Portland Operations Librn, Oregon Institute of Technology Library, 3201 Campus Dr, Klamath Falls, OR, 97601-8801. Tel: 503-821-1258. Fax: 541-885-1777. p. 2002

Lowell, Cindy, Asst Dir, Brown Memorial Library, 53 Railroad St, Clinton, ME, 04927-3200. Tel: 207-426-8686. Fax: 207-426-8686. p. 982

Lowell, Patricia, Ref Serv, Sedona Public Library, 3250 White Bear Rd, Sedona, AZ, 86336. Tel: 928-282-7714. Fax: 928-282-5789. p. 81

Lowenberg, Darla, Libr Asst, Eston College, 730 First St SE, Eston, SK, S0L 1A0, CANADA. Tel: 306-962-3621. Fax: 306-962-3810. p. 2917

Lowenberg, Susan, Assoc Dean, California Institute of the Arts, 24700 McBean Pkwy, Valencia, CA, 91355. Tel: 661-253-7885. Fax: 661-254-4561. p. 278

Lowenstein, Betsy, Spec Coll Librn, The State Library of Massachusetts, State House, Rm 341, 24 Beacon St, Boston, MA, 02133. Tel: 617-727-2595, Ext 285. Fax: 617-727-5819. p. 1067

Lowenstein, Noah, Dir of Libr Serv, Saybrook University Library, 747 Front St, Third Flr, San Francisco, CA, 94111-1920. Tel: 415-394-5062. Fax: 415-433-9271. p. 247

Lowenstein, Noah, Phys Sci Librn, Dartmouth College Library, Kresge Physical Sciences Library, 6115 Fairchild Hall, Hanover, NH, 03755-3571. Tel: 603-646-3563. Fax: 603-646-3681. p. 1450

Lowenstein, Robyn, Bus Mgr, Plymouth District Library, 223 S Main St, Plymouth, MI, 48170-1687. Tel: 734-453-0750, Ext 215. Fax: 734-453-0733. p. 1218

Lowenthal, Lynn, Ch, Jackson County Public Library System, 2929 Green St, Marianna, FL, 32446. Tel: 850-482-9631. Fax: 850-482-9632. p. 462

Lowenthal, Mary, Tech Serv, Ellinwood School & Community Library, 210 N Schiller Ave, Ellinwood, KS, 67526-1651. Tel: 620-564-2306. Fax: 620-564-2848. p. 865

Lower, Wanda, Librn, Pennsylvania Joint State Government Commission Library, Finance Bldg, Rm G-16, Harrisburg, PA, 17120. Tel: 717-787-6803. Fax: 717-787-7020. p. 2066

Lowery, Anne, Dir, New London Public Library, 67 S Main St, New London, OH, 44851-1137. Tel: 419-929-3981. Fax: 419-929-0007. p. 1921

Lowery, Jenny, Dr, Instrul Serv Librn, Syst Librn, Union University, 1050 Union University Dr, Jackson, TN, 38305-3697. Tel: 731-661-5058. Fax: 731-661-5175. p. 2238

Lowery, Renee, Asst Dir, Owatonna Public Library, 105 N Elm Ave, Owatonna, MN, 55060-2405. Tel: 507-444-2460. Fax: 507-444-2465. p. 1270

Lowery, Tammy, Electronic Serv Librn, Aiso Library, 543 Lawton Rd, Ste 617A, Monterey, CA, 93944-3214. Tel: 831-242-5572. Fax: 831-242-5816. p. 189

Lowitz, Carolyn, Ch Serv Librn, Goodall City Library, 203 West A St, Ogallala, NE, 69153-2544. Tel: 308-284-4354. Fax: 308-284-6390. p. 1411

Lowman, Karen S, Sr Libr Tech, VA Puget Sound Health Care System, American Lake Div, 9600 Veterans Dr SW, Bldg 71, Tacoma, WA, 98493-5000. Tel: 253-583-1513. Fax: 253-589-4029. p. 2541

Lowman, L Susan, Libr Dir, Canton Public Library, 403 Lewis St, Canton, MO, 63435. Tel: 573-288-5279. Fax: 573-288-5279. p. 1321

Lowman, Sandra, Libr Mgr, Natural Resources Canada Library, Hugh John Flemming Forestry Centre, 1350 Regent St S, Fredericton, NB, E3B 5P7, CANADA. Tel: 506-452-3541, 506-452-3614. Fax: 506-452-3525. p. 2763

Lowman, Sara, Vice Provost & Univ Librn, Rice University, 6100 Main, MS-44, Houston, TX, 77005. Tel: 713-348-5113. Fax: 713-348-5258. p. 2341

Lowman Sheppard, Lisa, Libr Tech, Department of Veterans Affairs Medical Center Library, 385 Tremont Ave, East Orange, NJ, 07018-1095. Tel: 908-647-0180, Ext 4545, 973-676-1000, Ext 1969. Fax: 973-395-7234. p. 1482

Lowrey, Brandon S, Asst Librn, Northeast Regional Library, Corinth Public Library, 1023 Fillmore St, Corinth, MS, 38834-4199. Tel: 662-287-2441. Fax: 662-286-8010. p. 1297

Lowrey, Jim, Syst, University of Wisconsin-Milwaukee Libraries, 2311 E Hartford Ave, Milwaukee, WI, 53211. Tel: 414-229-4785, 414-229-6202. Fax: 414-229-6766. p. 2622

Lowrey, Patricia, Dir of Tech Serv, Cleveland Public Library, 325 Superior Ave, Cleveland, OH, 44114-1271. Tel: 216-623-2817. p. 1877

Lowrie, Jackie, Dir, Bowie Public Library, 301 Walnut St, Bowie, TX, 76230. Tel: 940-872-2681. Fax: 940-872-6418. p. 2290

Lowrie, Jackie, Dir, Libr Serv, Bridgeport Public Library, 2159 Tenth St, Bridgeport, TX, 76426. Tel: 940-683-4412. p. 2291

Lowrie, Reed, Ref Librn, Sci Librn, Harvard Library, History of Science Library - Cabot Science Library, Science Center, One Oxford St, Cambridge, MA, 02138. Tel: 617-495-5355. Fax: 617-495-5324. p. 1075

Lowrimore, Tom, Coord, Syst & Planning, Spartanburg County Public Libraries, 151 S Church St, Spartanburg, SC, 29306-3241. Tel: 864-596-3500. Fax: 864-596-3518. p. 2205

Lowry, Barbara, Coordr, Libr Syst & Mat Proc, Philadelphia University, 4201 Henry Ave, Philadelphia, PA, 19144-5497. Tel: 215-951-2842. Fax: 215-951-2574. p. 2115

Lowry, Dana, Librn, Jamaica Public Library, 316 Main St, Jamaica, IA, 50128. Tel: 641-429-3362. Fax: 641-429-3362. p. 824

Lowry, Linda, Bus Librn, Brock University, 500 Glenridge Ave, St. Catharines, ON, L2S 3A1, CANADA. Tel: 905-688-5550, Ext 4650. Fax: 905-988-5490. p. 2842

Lowry, Lucy, Dir, North Mankato Taylor Library, 1001 Belgrade Ave, North Mankato, MN, 56003. Tel: 507-345-5120. Fax: 507-345-1861. p. 1268

Lowry, Mary Ruth, Admin Librn, Ayer Public Library District, 208 Locust St, Delavan, IL, 61734. Tel: 309-244-8236. Fax: 309-244-8237. p. 636

Lowry, Raymon, Dir, Ennis Public Library, 501 W Ennis Ave, Ennis, TX, 75119-3803. Tel: 972-875-5360. Fax: 972-878-9649. p. 2318

Loy, Eva, Librn, Trinity Health Systems, 380 Summit Ave, Steubenville, OH, 43952. Tel: 740-283-7400. Fax: 740-283-7461. p. 1937

Loyd, Roger, Dir, Duke University Libraries, Divinity School Library, Gray Bldg, 102 Chapel Dr, Durham, NC, 27708. Tel: 919-660-3453. Fax: 919-681-7594. p. 1787

Loyer, Marsha, Coordr, Media Serv, Mishawaka-Penn-Harris Public Library, 209 Lincoln Way E, Mishawaka, IN, 46544-2084. Tel: 574-259-5277, Ext 200. Fax: 574-254-5585, 574-255-8489. p. 765

Loyo, Lisa, Mgr, Info Serv, National Academies, Transportation Research Board Library, 500 Fifth St NW, Washington, DC, 20001. Tel: 202-334-2989. Fax: 202-334-2527. p. 409

Loza, Lorraine, Cat, Clark Public Library, 303 Westfield Ave, Clark, NJ, 07066. Tel: 732-388-5999. Fax: 732-388-7866. p. 1479

Lozano, Eva, Librn, Crosby County Library, Ralls Branch, 813 Main St, Ralls, TX, 79357. Tel: 806-253-2755. Fax: 806-253-2755. p. 2303

Lozauskas, Eric, Info Tech, Bergen County Cooperative Library System, 810 Main St, Hackensack, NJ, 07601. Tel: 201-489-1904. Fax: 201-489-4215. p. 2948

Loze-Hudson, Erika, Libr Dir, USAIS, Bldg 9230, 8150 Marne Rd, Fort Benning, GA, 31905. Tel: 706-545-8591. Fax: 706-545-8590. p. 532

Lozen, Kathleen, Ch, Shelby Township Library, 51680 Van Dyke, Shelby Township, MI, 48316-4448. Tel: 586-739-7414. Fax: 586-726-0535. p. 1227

Lozito, Debora, Dir, Libr Serv, Edythe L Dyer Community Library, 269 Main Rd N, Hampden, ME, 04444. Tel: 207-862-3550. p. 987

Lrose, Lori, Supvr, Chester Mental Health Center, 1315 Lehmen Rd, Chester, IL, 62233-2542. Tel: 618-826-4571, Ext 463. Fax: 618-826-3581. p. 604

Lu, Aaron, Tech Serv, North Georgia College & State University, 238 Georgia Circle, Dahlonega, GA, 30597-3001. p. 528

Lu, Janet, Online Serv, Pub Serv, Nebraska Wesleyan University, 50th & St Paul, Lincoln, NE, 68504. Tel: 402-465-2400. Fax: 402-465-2189. p. 1406

Lu, Jennifer, Adminr, British Columbia Ministry of Energy & Mines, 1810 Blanshard St, Victoria, BC, V8W 9N3, CANADA. Tel: 250-952-0660. Fax: 250-952-0581. p. 2745

Lu, Mai, Br Mgr, Mississauga Library System, Cooksville, 3024 Hurontario St, Ste 212, Mississauga, ON, L5B 4M4, CANADA. Tel: 905-615-4855. p. 2823

Lu, Mai, Mgr, Mississauga Library System, Clarkson, 2475 Truscott Dr, Mississauga, ON, L5J 2B3, CANADA. Tel: 905-615-4840. Fax: 905-615-4841. p. 2823

Lu, Mei-Chen, Dir of Libr Serv, Dance Notation Bureau Library, 111 John St, Ste 704, New York, NY, 10038. Tel: 212-571-7011. Fax: 212-571-7012. p. 1676

Luba, Zakharov, Ref, Ser, Duke University Libraries, Divinity School Library, Gray Bldg, 102 Chapel Dr, Durham, NC, 27708. Tel: 919-660-3491. Fax: 919-681-7594. p. 1787

Lubansky, Marcia, Supv Librn, Tech Serv, Bernards Township Library, 32 S Maple Ave, Basking Ridge, NJ, 07920-1216. Tel: 908-204-3031. Fax: 908-766-1580. p. 1470

Lubbers, Chad, Mgr, Washington County Library, Newport Branch, 405 Seventh Ave, Newport, MN, 55055-1410. Tel: 651-459-9631. Fax: 651-459-9631. p. 1290

Lubbers, Chad, Mgr, Washington County Library, R H Stafford Branch, 8595 Central Park Pl, Woodbury, MN, 55125-9613. Tel: 651-731-1320. Fax: 651-275-8562. p. 1290

Lubbers, Chad, Mgr, Washington County Library, Valley Branch, 380 St Croix Trail S, Lakeland, MN, 55043. Tel: 651-436-5882. Fax: 651-436-5882. p. 1290

Lubeck, Rosalind, Dir, Jenkintown Library, 460 Old York Rd, Jenkintown, PA, 19046-2829. Tel: 215-884-0593. Fax: 215-884-2243. p. 2072

Lubenow, Janis, Libr Mgr, Marquette General Health System, East 84 Bldg, 3rd Flr, 580 W College Ave, Marquette, MI, 49855. Tel: 906-225-3429. Fax: 906-225-3524. p. 1206

Lubenow, Janis, Libr Mgr, Upper Peninsula of Michigan Health Science Library Consortium, c/o Marquette General Health System, 580 W College Ave, Marquette, MI, 49855. Tel: 906-225-3429. Fax: 906-225-3524. p. 2946

Luberda, Robert, Asst Librn, Chapman & Cutler, 111 W Monroe, Chicago, IL, 60603-4096. Tel: 312-845-3437. Fax: 312-701-6620. p. 607

Lubert, Renee, Librn, State Correctional Institution, 1120 Pike St, Huntingdon, PA, 16652. Tel: 814-643-6520. Fax: 814-506-1022. p. 2070

Lubert, Rose Ann, Dir, Girard Free Library, 105 E Prospect St, Girard, OH, 44420-1899. Tel: 330-545-2508. Fax: 330-545-8213. p. 1902

Lubetski, Edith, Head Librn, Yeshiva University Libraries, Hedi Steinberg Library, 245 Lexington Ave, New York, NY, 10016. Tel: 212-340-7720. Fax: 212-340-7808. p. 1704

Lubick, Marcia, Computer Support Spec, Montana Tech Library, 1300 W Park St, Butte, MT, 59701-8997. Tel: 406-496-4287. Fax: 406-496-4133. p. 1376

Lubienecki, Teresa, Cat, Dir, Online Serv, Christ the King Seminary Library, 711 Knox Rd, East Aurora, NY, 14052. Tel: 716-655-7098. Fax: 716-652-8903. p. 1616

Lubin, S Rebecca, Br Librn, Albany Public Library, Delaware, 331 Delaware Ave, Albany, NY, 12209. Tel: 518-463-0254. p. 1568

Lubkeman, Lynn, Archivist, Wisconsin Conference United Methodist Church, 750 Windsor St, Sun Prairie, WI, 53590. Tel: 608-837-7328, Ext 243. Fax: 608-837-8547. p. 2641

Lubovich, Linda, Ref, San Mateo Public Library, 1100 Park Ave, San Mateo, CA, 94403-7108. Tel: 650-522-7802. Fax: 650-522-7801. p. 256

Lubrecht, Alice, Dir, State Library of Pennsylvania, 607 South Dr, Forum Bldg, Harrisburg, PA, 17120-0600. Tel: 717-783-5968. Fax: 717-787-9127. p. 2066

Lubsen, Dani, Br Mgr, Anderson County Library, Pendleton Branch, 650 S Mechanic St, Pendleton, SC, 29670. Tel: 864-646-3045. Fax: 864-646-3046. p. 2181

Luc, Aubin, Librn, Bibliothèque Albert-le-Grand, 2715 Côte Ste-Catherine, Montreal, QC, H3T 1B6, CANADA. Tel: 514-731-3603, Ext 307. Fax: 514-731-0676. p. 2888

Lucareli, Christa, Head, Youth Serv, Farmingdale Public Library, 116 Merritts Rd, Farmingdale, NY, 11735. Tel: 516-249-9090, Ext 226. Fax: 516-694-9697. p. 1621

Lucas, Ann, Librn, Parkland Regional Library, Cupar Branch, 217 Stanley St, Cupar, SK, S0A 0Y0, CANADA. Tel: 306-723-4749. p. 2931

Lucas, Ann L, Librn, UPMC Northwest, 100 Fairfield Dr, Seneca, PA, 16346-2130. Tel: 814-437-7000, Ext 5331. p. 2139

Lucas, Aurea, Br Mgr, Adams Memorial Library, 1112 Ligonier St, Latrobe, PA, 15650. Tel: 724-539-1972. Fax: 724-537-0338. p. 2078

Lucas, Aurea, Br Mgr, Adams Memorial Library, Caldwell Memorial Library, 982 N Chestnut St Extension, Derry, PA, 15627. Tel: 724-694-5765. Fax: 724-694-8546. p. 2079

Lucas, Beverly, Dir, Librn, Kellyville Public Library, 230 E Buffalo, Kellyville, OK, 74039. Tel: 918-247-3740. Fax: 918-247-3740. p. 1966

Lucas, Carla, Librn, Fayette County Public Libraries, Ansted Public, 102 Oak St, Ansted, WV, 25812. Tel: 304-658-5472. Fax: 304-658-5472. p. 2568

Lucas, Chela, Commun Libr Mgr, Contra Costa County Library, San Pablo Library, 2300 El Portal Dr, Ste D, San Pablo, CA, 94806-4452. Tel: 510-374-3998. Fax: 510-374-3225. p. 209

Lucas, Cynthia Renee, Dir, Law Librn, Spokane County Law Library, Gardner Center Bldg, 1033 W Gardner, Spokane, WA, 99201. Tel: 509-477-3680. p. 2536

Lucas, Debra, Head, Ref, D'Youville College, 320 Porter Ave, Buffalo, NY, 14201-1084. Tel: 716-829-7764. Fax: 716-829-7770. p. 1597

Lucas, Doina, Head, Info Serv, Hamden Public Library, 2901 Dixwell Ave, Hamden, CT, 06518-3135. Tel: 203-287-2686. Fax: 203-287-2685. p. 343

Lucas, Gail, Br Mgr, Kings County Library, Hanford Branch, 401 N Douty St, Hanford, CA, 93230. Tel: 559-582-0261. Fax: 559-583-6163. p. 156

Lucas, Jody, Asst Librn, Luther Area Public Library, 115 State St, Luther, MI, 49656. Tel: 231-797-8006. Fax: 231-797-8010. p. 1204

Lucas, John, Ser, University of Mississippi Medical Center, 2500 N State St, Jackson, MS, 39216-4505. Tel: 601-984-1277. Fax: 601-984-1251. p. 1305

Lucas, Leandrea, Regional Mgr, Saint Louis Public Library, Schlafly, 225 N Euclid Ave, Saint Louis, MO, 63108. Tel: 314-367-4120. Fax: 314-367-4814. p. 1360

Lucas, Lewis, Tech & Syst Librn, Northeast Georgia Regional Library System, 204 Ellison St, Ste F, Clarkesville, GA, 30523. Tel: 706-754-0416. Fax: 706-754-0420. p. 524

Lucas, Lewis, Asst Dir, Info Tech, Clayton County Library System, 865 Battlecreek Rd, Jonesboro, GA, 30236. Tel: 770-473-3850. Fax: 770-473-3858. p. 536

Lucas, Marcy, Asst Librn, Finch Memorial Public Library, 205 N Walnut, Arnold, NE, 69120. Tel: 308-848-2219. Fax: 308-848-4729. p. 1392

Lucas, Mary Lea, Exec Dir, Clarion County Historical Society, 17 S Fifth Ave, Clarion, PA, 16214-1501. Tel: 814-226-4450. Fax: 814-226-7106. p. 2045

Lucas, Melanie, Asst Librn, Yukon Department of Environment Library, 10 Burns Rd, Whitehorse, YT, Y1A 4Y9, CANADA. Tel: 867-667-3029. Fax: 867-393-7197. p. 2934

Lucas, Michael, Librn, Canadian Friends of Soviet People Library, 280 Queen St W, Toronto, ON, M5V 2A1, CANADA. Tel: 416-977-5819. Fax: 416-593-0781. p. 2851

Lucas, Missy, Ch, Harrison County Library System, D'Iberville Public, 10391 AutoMall Pkwy, D'Iberville, MS, 39540. Tel: 228-392-2279. Fax: 228-396-9573. p. 1299

Lucas, Nancy, Head Librn, Michigan State University Library, William C Gast Business Library, DCLMSU & Business Library Bldg, East Lansing, MI, 48824. Tel: 517-355-3380. Fax: 517-353-6648. p. 1175

Lucas, Nina Baker, Circ Tech, Baltimore International College, 17 Commerce St, Baltimore, MD, 21202-3230. Tel: 410-752-4710, Ext 137 or 138. Fax: 410-752-6720. p. 1011

Lucas, Palma, Dir, New Year Shooters & Mummers Museum Library, 1100 S Second St, Philadelphia, PA, 19147. Tel: 215-336-3050. Fax: 215-389-5630. p. 2113

Lucas, Ruth, Br Librn, Brown County Public Library District, Versailles Branch, 211 N Chestnut, Versailles, IL, 62378. Tel: 217-225-3102. Fax: 217-225-9082. p. 677

Lucas, Shannon, Ref & Instrul Serv Librn, Mars Hill College, 124 Cascade St, Mars Hill, NC, 28754. Tel: 828-689-1391. p. 1809

Lucas, Sherry, Mgr, Pennsylvania Fish & Boat Commission, 1735 Shiloh Rd, State College, PA, 16801-8495. Tel: 814-355-4837. Fax: 814-355-8264. p. 2143

Lucas, Terri, Librn, Missouri Department of Corrections, Boonville Correctional Center, 1216 E Morgan St, Boonville, MO, 65233-1300. Tel: 660-882-6521, Ext 338. Fax: 660-882-3427. p. 1334

Lucas-Dunnom, Shawn, Ch, Mount Vernon Public Library, 28 S First Ave, Mount Vernon, NY, 10550. Tel: 914-668-1840. Fax: 914-668-1018. p. 1664

Lucas-Stannard, Paige, Librn, NASA, 21000 Brookpark Rd, MS 60-3, Cleveland, OH, 44135. Fax: 216-433-5777. p. 1880

Lucas-Youmans, Tasha, Libr Dir, Bethune-Cookman College, 640 Mary McLeod Bethune Blvd, Daytona Beach, FL, 32114. Tel: 368-481-2118. Fax: 386-481-2182. p. 435

Lucchesi, Sarah, Instruction & Learning Librn, Michigan Technological University, 1400 Townsend Dr, Houghton, MI, 49931-1295. Tel: 906-487-3379. p. 1191

Luce, Dena, Extended Serv, Faulkner University, 5345 Atlanta Hwy, Montgomery, AL, 36109-3398. Tel: 334-386-7482. Fax: 334-386-7481. p. 28

Luce, Jessica, Br Mgr, Toledo-Lucas County Public Library, Point Place, 2727 117th St, Toledo, OH, 43611. Tel: 419-259-5390. Fax: 419-729-5363. p. 1940

Luce, Marcia M, Tech Serv, Waltham Public Library, 735 Main St, Waltham, MA, 02451. Tel: 781-314-3436. Fax: 781-314-3426. p. 1133

Luce, Monica, Dean, Instrul Res, Highline Community College Library, 2400 S 240th St, MS 25-4, Des Moines, WA, 98198. Tel: 206-878-3710, Ext 3230. Fax: 206-870-3776. p. 2514

Luce, Monica, Dir, Highline Community College, 2400 S 240th St, Des Moines, WA, 98198. Tel: 206-878-3710, Ext 3230. Fax: 206-870-3776. p. 2975

Luce, Rick, Dean of Libr, University of Oklahoma, 401 W Brooks, Norman, OK, 73019. Tel: 405-325-2611. Fax: 405-325-7550. p. 1971

Lucero, Arlene, In Charge, National Atomic Museum Library, 1905 Mountain Rd NW, Albuquerque, NM, 87104. Tel: 505-245-2137. Fax: 505-242-4537. p. 1549

Lucero, Bella, Reader Serv, New Mexico State Library, Library for the Blind & Physically Handicapped, 1209 Camino Carlos Rey, Santa Fe, NM, 87507-5166. Tel: 505-476-9773. Fax: 505-476-9776. p. 1563

Lucey, Jean, Dir, Insurance Library Association of Boston, 156 State St, Boston, MA, 02109. Tel: 617-227-2087. Fax: 617-723-8524. p. 1062

Lucey, Jill, Dir, Four Star Public Library District, 132 W South St, Mendon, IL, 62351. Tel: 217-936-2131. Fax: 217-936-2132. p. 673

Lucey, Judith, Asst Archivist, New England Historic Genealogical Society Library, 99-101 Newbury St, Boston, MA, 02116-3007. Tel: 617-226-1223. Fax: 617-536-7307. p. 1065

Lucey, Kathleen, Educ Librn, Instrul Mat Coordr, Miami University Libraries, 225 King Library, Oxford, OH, 45056. Tel: 513-529-3340. Fax: 513-529-3110. p. 1926

Luchs, Manda L, Librn, Sewickley Township Public Library, 201 Highland Ave, Herminie, PA, 15637-1311. Tel: 724-446-9940. Fax: 724-446-9114. p. 2068

Lucht, Mary Anne, Dir, Ayer Library, 26 E Main St, Ayer, MA, 01432. Tel: 978-772-8250. Fax: 978-772-8251. p. 1051

Lucia, Joseph, Dir, Univ Librn, Villanova University, 800 Lancaster Ave, Villanova, PA, 19085. Tel: 610-519-4290. Fax: 610-519-5018. p. 2149

Lucia, Judith, Mgr, Outreach Serv, Jefferson County Rural Library District, 620 Cedar Ave, Port Hadlock, WA, 98339-9514. Tel: 360-385-6544. Fax: 360-385-7921. p. 2524

Luciano, Jean, Cat, ILL, University of Pittsburgh at Bradford, 300 Campus Dr, Bradford, PA, 16701. Tel: 814-362-7610. Fax: 814-362-7688. p. 2037

Lucik, Ronald, Asst Dir, Support Serv, Harris County Public Library, 8080 El Rio, Houston, TX, 77054. Tel: 713-749-9050. Fax: 713-749-9090. p. 2335

Lucio, Nettie, Circ Mgr, Saint Mary's University, Louis J Blume Library, One Camino Santa Maria, San Antonio, TX, 78228-8608. Tel: 210-436-3441. Fax: 210-436-3782. p. 2381

Luck, Carol, Dir, Alcona County Library System, 312 W Main, Harrisville, MI, 48740. Tel: 989-724-6796. Fax: 989-724-6173. p. 1188

Luck, Deborah Scott, Dean of Libr Serv, Randolph Community College, 629 Industrial Park Ave, Asheboro, NC, 27205-7333. Tel: 336-633-0272. Fax: 336-629-4695. p. 1773

Luck, Judy, Br Supvr, Spokane County Library District, Argonne Library, 4322 N Argonne Rd, Spokane, WA, 99212-1868. Tel: 509-893-8260. Fax: 509-893-8474. p. 2537

Luck, Lara, Br Head, Forsyth County Public Library, Rural Hall Branch, 7125 Broad St, Rural Hall, NC, 27045. Tel: 336-703-2970. Fax: 336-969-9401. p. 1832

Luckason, Barbara, Librn, Kensett Public Library, 214 Fifth St, Kensett, IA, 50448. Tel: 641-845-2222. Fax: 641-845-2222. p. 825

Lucken, Pam, Head, Ref, University of Miami, 1311 Miller Dr, Coral Gables, FL, 33146. Tel: 305-284-2251. Fax: 305-284-3554. p. 434

Lucker, Amy, Head Librn, New York University, Stephen Chan Library of Fine Arts, One E 78th St, New York, NY, 10021. Tel: 212-992-5825. Fax: 212-992-5807. p. 1695

Lucker, Amy, Tech Serv, New York University, 70 Washington Sq S, New York, NY, 10012-1091. Tel: 212-998-2505. Fax: 212-995-4070. p. 1695

Luckie, Caren Zentner, Law Librn, Jackson Walker Law Library, 1401 McKinney, Ste 1900, Houston, TX, 77010. Tel: 713-752-4479. Fax: 713-752-4221. p. 2345

Luckinbill, Eva, Exec Dir, Aurora Public Library, One E Benton St, Aurora, IL, 60505-4299. Tel: 630-264-4100. Fax: 630-896-3209. p. 591

Luckstead, Jon, Ref Librn, Austin Community College, Rio Grande Campus Library, 1212 Rio Grande, Austin, TX, 78701. Tel: 512-223-3089. Fax: 512-223-3430. p. 2278

Lucy, Castillo, Operations Coordr/Mgr, Washington Hospital Healthcare System, 2500 Mowry Ave, Fremont, CA, 94538. Tel: 510-494-7030. Fax: 510-742-9285. p. 150

Lucy, John, Dir, Trinity Baptist College Library, 800 Hammond Blvd, Jacksonville, FL, 32221-1342. Tel: 904-596-2508. Fax: 904-596-2531. p. 455

Lucy, Theodore, Ref, Florida State College at Jacksonville, Downtown Campus, 101 W State St, Jacksonville, FL, 32202-3056. Tel: 904-633-8368. Fax: 904-633-8328. p. 453

Luczywko, Maggie, Dir, St Francis Public Library, 4230 S Nicholson Ave, Saint Francis, WI, 53235. Tel: 414-481-7323. Fax: 414-481-8949. p. 2635

Luddy, Laurel, Educ Coordr, Wildwood Pre-Trial Facility Library, Five Chugach Ave, Kenai, AK, 99611. Tel: 907-260-7265. Fax: 907-260-7265. p. 50

Ludeman, Ross, Media Spec, Marylhurst University, 17600 Pacific Hwy (Hwy 43), Marylhurst, OR, 97036-7036. Tel: 503-699-6261, Ext 4443. Fax: 503-636-1957. p. 2004

Ludemann, Robert, Ref Serv, Merrick Library, 2279 Merrick Ave, Merrick, NY, 11566-4398. Tel: 516-377-6112. Fax: 516-377-1108. p. 1659

Luderitz, Mary Grace, Ref & ILL Librn, Long Hill Township Public Library, 917 Valley Rd, Gillette, NJ, 07933. Tel: 908-647-2088. Fax: 908-647-2098. p. 1488

Ludington, Colleen, Libr Serv Supvr, Hernando County Public Library System, Spring Hill Branch, 9220 Spring Hill Dr, Spring Hill, FL, 34608. Tel: 352-754-4043. Fax: 352-688-5038. p. 430

Ludington, Robin J, Cataloger, Ref Serv, Salem Public Library, 821 E State St, Salem, OH, 44460-2298. Tel: 330-332-0042. Fax: 330-332-4488. p. 1934

Ludlow, Heather, Info Serv Librn, Legislative Library of Nova Scotia, Province House, 2nd Flr, Halifax, NS, B3J 2P8, CANADA. Tel: 902-424-5932. Fax: 902-424-0220. p. 2781

Ludlow, Joan E, Dir, Hazel Park Memorial Library, 123 E Nine Mile Rd, Hazel Park, MI, 48030. Tel: 248-542-0940, 248-546-4095. Fax: 248-546-4083. p. 1189

Ludlow, Lori, YA Serv, Babylon Public Library, 24 S Carll Ave, Babylon, NY, 11702. Tel: 631-669-1624. Fax: 631-669-7826. p. 1577

Ludlum, Jean, Mgr, Youth Serv, Calgary Public Library, W R Castell Central Library, 616 Macleod Trail SE, Calgary, AB, T2G 2M2, CANADA. Tel: 403-260-2600. Fax: 403-237-5393. p. 2689

Ludlum, Mary, Dir, Grandview Heights Public Library, 1685 W First Ave, Columbus, OH, 43212. Tel: 614-486-2951. Fax: 614-481-7021. p. 1886

Ludovico, Carrie, Distance Educ, University of Richmond, 28 Westhampton Way, Richmond, VA, 23173. Tel: 804-287-6647. Fax: 804-289-8757. p. 2491

Ludvik, Anne, Chief Librn, Department of Veterans Affairs, Medical Library 142D, 4150 Clement St, San Francisco, CA, 94121. Tel: 415-221-4810, Ext 3302. Fax: 415-750-6919. p. 241

Ludwick, Bernie, Librn, Wallace Public Library, 415 River St, Wallace, ID, 83873-2260. Tel: 208-752-4571. Fax: 208-752-4571. p. 585

Ludwick, Pat, Tech Serv, Gulf Beaches Public Library, 200 Municipal Dr, Madeira Beach, FL, 33708. Tel: 727-391-2828. Fax: 727-399-2840. p. 462

Ludwig, Bobbi-Jean, Asst Cat Librn, Carthage College, 2001 Alford Park Dr, Kenosha, WI, 53140-1900. Tel: 262-551-5900. Fax: 262-551-5904. p. 2601

Ludwig, Deborah, Mgr, Ref Serv, Westlake Porter Public Library, 27333 Center Ridge Rd, Westlake, OH, 44145-3925. Tel: 440-871-2600. Fax: 440-871-6969. p. 1947

Ludwig, Kathleen, Asst Law Librn, Massachusetts Trial Court, Courthouse, 99 Main St, Ste 1, Northampton, MA, 01060. Tel: 413-586-2297. Fax: 413-584-0870. p. 1113

Ludwig, Katie, Asst Commissioner, Admin & Finance, Chicago Public Library, 400 S State St, Chicago, IL, 60605. Tel: 312-747-4030. Fax: 312-747-4522. p. 608

Ludwig, Lisa L, Dir, Colfax Public Library, 613 Main St, Colfax, WI, 54730. Tel: 715-962-4334. p. 2586

Ludwig, Marie, Dir, United States Air Force, Mitchell Memorial Library-Travis Air Force Base Library, 60 FSS/FSDL, 510 Travis Ave, Travis AFB, CA, 94535-2168. Tel: 707-424-4940. Fax: 707-424-3809. p. 276

Ludwig, Marie, Dir, United States Air Force, FL 4801, 596 Fourth St, Bldg 224, Holloman AFB, NM, 88330-8038. Tel: 575-572-3501. Fax: 575-572-5340. p. 1557

Ludwig, Michael, AV, University City Public Library, 6701 Delmar Blvd, University City, MO, 63130. Tel: 314-727-3150. Fax: 314-727-6005. p. 1370

Ludwig, Mike, Librn, California Department of Corrections Library System, Sierra Conservation Center, 5100 O'Byrnes Ferry Rd, Jamestown, CA, 95327. Tel: 209-984-5291, Ext 5306. Fax: 209-984-4563. p. 222

Ludwig, Vicky, Head, Coll Develop, Ref Coordr, Western New England University, 1215 Wilbraham Rd, Springfield, MA, 01119. Tel: 413-796-2265. Fax: 413-796-2011. p. 1128

Ludwig, Walter, Curator, Heisey Collectors of America, Inc, 169 W Church St, Newark, OH, 43055-0027. Tel: 740-345-2932. Fax: 740-345-9638. p. 1922

Ludwig, Zora, Head, Circ, Hammond Public Library, 564 State St, Hammond, IN, 46320-1532. Tel: 219-931-5100, Ext 331. Fax: 219-931-3474. p. 747

Ludwig-Ruppert, Susanna, Libr Dir, Galena Public Library District, 601 S Bench St, Galena, IL, 61036-2322. Tel: 815-777-0200. Fax: 815-777-1542. p. 647

Luebbe, Sharon, Br Supvr, Marathon County Public Library, Hatley Branch, 435 Curtis Ave, Hatley, WI, 54440. Tel: 715-446-3537. Fax: 715-446-3537. p. 2646

Luebchow, Elizabeth, Contractor Librn, United States Air Force, AFRL/RVIL, 3550 Aberdeen Ave SE Bldg 570, Kirtland AFB, NM, 87117-5776. Tel: 505-846-4767. Fax: 505-846-4790. p. 1557

Luebke, Betty, Cat, United States Army, Fort Wainwright Post Library, Santiago Ave, Bldg 3700, Fort Wainwright, AK, 99703-6600. Tel: 907-353-4137. Fax: 907-353-2609. p. 48

Luebke, Linda L, Librn, John Tyler Community College Library, Moyar Hall, M216, 13101 Jefferson Davis Hwy, Chester, VA, 23831-5316. Tel: 804-706-5202. Fax: 804-796-4238. p. 2456

Luebke, Pam, Circ, Aquinas College, 1607 Robinson Rd SE, Grand Rapids, MI, 49506-1799. Tel: 616-632-2127. Fax: 616-732-4534. p. 1183

Lueck, Sharry, Circ Librn, Syst Adminr, Watertown Public Library, 100 S Water St, Watertown, WI, 53094-4320. Tel: 920-262-4090, Ext 18. Fax: 920-261-8943. p. 2644

Luedke, Pamela A, Librn, Atwood Public Library, 102 S Sixth St, Atwood, KS, 67730-1998. Tel: 785-626-3805. Fax: 785-626-3805. p. 857

Luedtke, Cherry, Head Librn, Tech Serv & Automation, Austin Community College, 1212 Rio Grande, Austin, TX, 78701. Tel: 512-223-8682. Fax: 512-223-8611. p. 2278

Luehrs, Mary, Dir, Norton Public Library, One Washington Sq, Norton, KS, 67654-1615. Tel: 785-877-2481. p. 885

Luepke, Carol, Librn, Shawano City-County Library, Bonduel Public, 117 1/2 W Green Bay St, Bonduel, WI, 54107-8302. Tel: 715-758-2267. Fax: 715-758-6841. p. 2637

Luesing, Lois, Curator, Bethel College, 1001 W McKinley Ave, Mishawaka, IN, 46545. Tel: 574-257-3404. Fax: 574-257-3499. p. 765

Luetkehoelter, Mark, ILL Librn, Madison Area Technical College, 3550 Anderson St, Rm 230, Madison, WI, 53704. Tel: 608-246-6638. Fax: 608-246-6644. p. 2606

Luff, Mary, Librn, Richfield District Library, 105 S Main, Richfield, ID, 83349. Tel: 208-487-1242. p. 582

Lufkin, Ruth, Supv Librn, Ref, Bernards Township Library, 32 S Maple Ave, Basking Ridge, NJ, 07920-1216. Tel: 908-204-3031. Fax: 908-766-1580. p. 1470

Luft, Bill, Head, Ref, Macomb County Library, 16480 Hall Rd, Clinton Township, MI, 48038-1132. Tel: 586-286-6660. Fax: 586-412-5958. p. 1164

Lugo, Amado, Circ, Media Coordr, Saint Thomas University Library, Law Library, 16401 NW 37th Ave, Miami Gardens, FL, 33054. Tel: 305-623-2333. Fax: 305-623-2337. p. 469

Lugo, Angie, Dir, Ethel L Whipple Memorial Library, 402 W Ocean Blvd, Los Fresnos, TX, 78566. Tel: 956-233-5330. Fax: 956-233-3203. p. 2357

Lugo, Brenda S, Asst Dir, Controller, Palo Verde Valley Library District, 125 W Chanslorway, Blythe, CA, 92225-1293. Tel: 760-922-5371. Fax: 760-922-5334. p. 129

Lugo, Cecilia, Adminr, Pontifical Catholic University Of Puerto Rico, Encarnacion Valdes Library, 2250 Avenida Las Americas, Ste 509, Ponce, PR, 00717-0777. Tel: 787-841-2000, Ext 1801, 787-841-2000, Ext 1802. Fax: 787-284-0235. p. 2674

Lugo, Julia, ILL, Anchorage Public Library, 3600 Denali St, Anchorage, AK, 99503. Tel: 907-343-2839. Fax: 907-343-2930. p. 44

Lugo, Lelah, Electronic Res, University of Wisconsin-Stout Library, 315 Tenth Ave, Menomonie, WI, 54751-0790. Tel: 715-232-1552. Fax: 715-232-1783. p. 2615

Lugo-Gaylas, Norma, Ref, Wilbur Wright College North, 4300 N Narragansett Ave, Chicago, IL, 60634-1500. Tel: 773-481-8420. Fax: 773-481-8407. p. 627

Luh, Beatrice, Res, Yale University Library, Epidemiology & Public Health, Epidemiology & Public Health, 60 College St, New Haven, CT, 06520. Tel: 203-785-2835. Fax: 203-785-4998. p. 357

Luiken, Lois, Dir, Steamboat Rock Public Library, 511 Market St, Steamboat Rock, IA, 50672. Tel: 641-868-2300. Fax: 641-868-2300. p. 846

Luisi, Donald, Acq, Robert Morris University Library, 6001 University Blvd, Moon Township, PA, 15108-1189. Tel: 412-397-6865. Fax: 412-397-4288. p. 2092

Luizzi, Jacqueline, Dir, Delaware Valley Information Consortium, St Mary Medical Ctr Medical Library, 1201 Langhorne-Newtown Rd, Langhorne, PA, 19047. Tel: 215-710-2012. Fax: 215-710-4638. p. 2954

Lujan, Audrey, Actg City Librn, Anaheim Public Library, 500 W Broadway, Anaheim, CA, 92805-3699. Tel: 714-765-1880. p. 120

Lujan, Melverna, Dir, Santa Ana Pueblo Community Library, Two Dove Rd, Bernalillo, NM, 87004. Tel: 505-867-1623. Fax: 505-771-3849. p. 1552

Lukas, Janet, Libr Dir, Tomkins Cove Public Library, 419 Liberty Dr N, Tomkins Cove, NY, 10986. Tel: 845-786-3060. Fax: 845-947-5572. p. 1755

Lukas, Janet, VPres, Library Association of Rockland County, PO Box 917, New City, NY, 10956-0917. Tel: 845-786-3060. p. 2950

Lukas, Rosie, Head, Pub Serv, Huntley Area Public Library District, 11000 Ruth Rd, Huntley, IL, 60142-7155. Tel: 847-669-5386. Fax: 847-669-5439. p. 657

Lukas, Vicki, Cat, Kelley Library, 234 Main St, Salem, NH, 03079-3190. Tel: 603-898-7064. Fax: 603-898-8583. p. 1464

Lukasiewicz, Barbara, Dir, Henry Ford Community College, 5101 Evergreen Rd, Dearborn, MI, 48128-1495. Tel: 313-845-6379. Fax: 313-845-9795. p. 1167

Luke, Christine, Mgr, Satilla Regional Library, Willacoochee Public Library, 300 Fleetwood Ave, Willacoochee, GA, 31650-9653. Tel: 912-534-5252. Fax: 912-534-5252. p. 531

Luke, Keye, Sr Librn, San Jose Public Library, Alviso Branch, 5050 N First St, Alviso, CA, 95002. Tel: 408-263-3626. Fax: 408-956-9435. p. 251

Luke, Keye, Sr Librn, San Jose Public Library, Joyce Ellington Branch, 491 E Empire St, San Jose, CA, 95112-3308. Tel: 408-808-3043. Fax: 408-286-0664. p. 251

Luke, Terri, Regional Libr Supvr, Wake County Public Library System, West Regional Library, 4000 Louis Stephens Dr, Cary, NC, 27519. Tel: 919-463-8505. p. 1818

Luken, Deb, Br Mgr, Great River Regional Library, Monticello Library, 200 W Sixth St, Monticello, MN, 55362-8832. Tel: 763-295-2322. Fax: 763-295-8321. p. 1275

Lukenbill, W Bernard, Prof, University of Texas at Austin, One University Sta, D7000, Austin, TX, 78712-0390. Tel: 512-471-3821. Fax: 512-471-3971. p. 2975

Lukens, Nancy, Cat, Pender County Public Library, 103 S Cowan St, Burgaw, NC, 28425. Tel: 910-259-1234. Fax: 910-259-0656. p. 1778

Lukes, Ria, Tech Serv Librn, Indiana University Kokomo Library, 2300 S Washington St, Kokomo, IN, 46904. Tel: 765-455-9265. Fax: 765-455-9276. p. 758

Lukey, Brenda, Asst Librn, Chetwynd Public Library, 5012 46th St, Chetwynd, BC, V0C 1J0, CANADA. Tel: 250-788-2559. Fax: 250-788-2186. p. 2726

Lukkarila, Mary, Librn, Cloquet Public Library, 320 14th St, Cloquet, MN, 55720-2100. Tel: 218-879-1531. Fax: 218-879-6531. p. 1246

Lukomski, Jennifer, Asst Dir, Coll, University of Missouri, 23 Ellis Library, Columbia, MO, 65201-5149. Tel: 573-882-7231. Fax: 573-884-0345. p. 1325

Lukose, David, Br Mgr, Fort Bend County Libraries, Sienna Branch, 8411 Sienna Springs Blvd, Missouri City, TX, 77459. Tel: 281-238-2912. Fax: 281-238-2902. p. 2375

Lukow, Gregory, Div Chief, Library of Congress, Motion Picture, Broadcasting & Recorded Sound Division, Packard Campus for Audio-Visual Conservation, 19053 Mount Pony Rd, Culpeper, DC, 22701-7551. Tel: 202-707-5840. Fax: 202-707-0857. p. 407

Lukow, John, Cataloger, Fort Myers Beach Public Library, 2755 Estero Blvd, Fort Myers Beach, FL, 33931. Tel: 239-765-8162. Fax: 239-463-8776. p. 446

Luksa, Jennifer, Tech Serv, College of Misericordia, 301 Lake St, Dallas, PA, 18612-1098. Tel: 570-674-6231. Fax: 570-674-6342. p. 2048

Lull, David, Libr Supvr, Tech & Support Serv, Duluth Public Library, 520 W Superior St, Duluth, MN, 55802. Tel: 218-730-4251. Fax: 218-723-3815, 218-723-3822. p. 1247

Lull, Karen, ILL, Wartburg Theological Seminary, 333 Wartburg Pl, Dubuque, IA, 52003. Tel: 563-589-0267. Fax: 563-589-0333. p. 812

Lum, Raymond, Librn, Harvard Library, Harvard-Yenching Library, Two Divinity Ave, Cambridge, MA, 02138. Tel: 617-495-2756. Fax: 617-496-6008. p. 1075

Lumb, Alex, Librn, Camp, Dresser & Mckee, 50 Hampshire St, Cambridge, MA, 02139. Tel: 617-452-6822. Fax: 617-452-8006. p. 1073

Lumb, Paula, Ch, Edgecombe County Memorial Library, 909 Main St, Tarboro, NC, 27886. Tel: 252-823-1141. Fax: 252-823-7699. p. 1826

Lumbert, Lanier, Head, Tech Serv, University of Southern Maine, 314 Forest Ave, Portland, ME, 04104. Tel: 207-780-4670. Fax: 207-780-4042. p. 998

Lumetta, Joanne, Dir, Madonna University Library, 36600 Schoolcraft Rd, Livonia, MI, 48150-1173. Tel: 734-432-5689. Fax: 734-432-5687. p. 1204

Lumpe, Larry, Dir, Concordia Historical Institute Library, 804 Seminary Pl, Saint Louis, MO, 63105-3014. Tel: 314-505-7900. Fax: 314-505-7901. p. 1353

Lumpkin, Cornell, Librn, Christ Church Cathedral, 125 Monument Circle, Indianapolis, IN, 46204-2993. Tel: 317-636-4577. Fax: 317-635-1040. p. 750

Lumpkin, Lisa, Circ, Southwest Tennessee Community College, George Freeman Library, 5983 Macon Cove, Memphis, TN, 38134. Tel: 901-333-4105. Fax: 901-333-4566. p. 2251

Lumpkin, Terryll, Admin Officer, National Archives & Records Administration, 441 Freedom Pkwy, Atlanta, GA, 30307. Tel: 404-865-7119. Fax: 404-865-7102. p. 517

Lumumba, Jama, Media Spec, Jackson State University, 1325 J R Lynch St, Jackson, MS, 39217. Tel: 601-979-2123. Fax: 601-979-2239. p. 1303

Luna, Kristina, Mrg, Admin Serv, San Jose State University, One Washington Sq, San Jose, CA, 95192-0029. Tel: 408-924-2492. Fax: 408-924-2476. p. 2962

Luna, Marisa, ILL, Arrowhead Regional Medical Center, 400 N Pepper Ave, Colton, CA, 92324-1819. Tel: 909-580-1308. Fax: 909-580-1310. p. 135

Luna-Lamas, Sonia, Assoc Dir, Head, Tech Serv, Saint Thomas University Library, Law Library, 16401 NW 37th Ave, Miami Gardens, FL, 33054. Tel: 305-623-2387. Fax: 305-623-2337. p. 469

Lunce, Carol, Ref/Instruction Librn, Indiana State University, 510 North 6 1/2 St, Terre Haute, IN, 47809. Tel: 812-237-2058. Fax: 812-237-3376. p. 781

Lunce, Carol, Med Librn, Northern Virginia Community College Libraries, Medical Education Campus, 6699 Springfield Center Dr, Rm 341, Springfield, VA, 22150. Tel: 703-822-6684. Fax: 703-822-6612. p. 2447

Lunceford, Kenny, Adult Serv, Kenton County Public Library, William E Durr Branch, 1992 Walton-Nicholson Rd, Independence, KY, 41051. Tel: 859-962-4035. Fax: 859-962-4037. p. 910

Lund, Britton, Dir, Washington County Library System, 88 West 100 South, Saint George, UT, 84770-3490. Tel: 435-256-6331. Fax: 435-634-5741. p. 2412

Lund, Cynthia Wales, Spec Coll Librn, Saint Olaf College, Howard V & Edna H Hong Kierkegaard Library, 1510 Saint Olaf Ave, Northfield, MN, 55057-1097. Tel: 507-646-3846. Fax: 507-646-3858. p. 1269

Lund, Dean, Conserv Librn, Provincial Archives of New Brunswick, 23 Dineen Dr, Fredericton, NB, E3B 5A3, CANADA. Tel: 506-453-2122. Fax: 506-453-3288. p. 2763

Lund, Heidi, Librn, Veteran Affairs Canada Library, 125 Maple Hills Dr, Charlottetown, PE, C1C 0B6, CANADA. Tel: 902-368-0531. Fax: 902-370-4895. p. 2876

Lund, James, Commun Serv, Dir of Libr, Red
Wing Public Library, 225 East Ave, Red Wing,
MN, 55066-2298. Tel: 651-385-3646. Fax:
651-385-3644. p. 1272

Lund, Kathy, In Charge, Merced County Library,
Atwater Branch, 1600 Third St, Atwater, CA,
95301-3691. Tel: 209-358-6651. p. 185

Lund, Martha, Managing Librn, Columbus
Metropolitan Library, Main Library, 96 S
Grant Ave, Columbus, OH, 43215-4781. Tel:
614-645-2275. Fax: 614-849-1389. p. 1885

Lund, Tom, Librn, Edward A Block Family
Library, Riley Hospital, 702 Barnhill Dr,
Rm 1719, Indianapolis, IN, 46202-5128.
Tel: 317-274-1149, 317-278-1645. Fax:
317-278-1631. p. 749

Lundbech, Deborah, Librn, New Haven Community
Library, 78 North St, Ste 2, New Haven, VT,
05472. Tel: 802-453-4015. p. 2430

LundBorg, Joan, Dir, Hart Area Public Library,
415 S State St, Hart, MI, 49420-1228. Tel:
231-873-4476. Fax: 231-873-4476. p. 1188

Lunde, Daniel, Outreach & Develop Librn,
Minnesota State Law Library, Minnesota
Judicial Ctr, Rm G25, 25 Rev Dr Martin Luther
King Jr Blvd, Saint Paul, MN, 55155. Tel:
651-296-2775. Fax: 651-296-6740. p. 1280

Lunde, Diane, Coordr, Presv & Digital Serv,
Colorado State University Libraries, Morgan
Library, 1201 Center Avenue Mall, Fort
Collins, CO, 80523-. Tel: 970-491-1838. Fax:
970-491-1195. p. 307

Lunde, Sarah, Teen Serv, Burlington Public Library,
820 E Washington, Burlington, WA, 98233. Tel:
360-755-0760. Fax: 360-755-0717. p. 2511

Lundeen, Catherine, Chief Archivist, Coll Mgt &
Spec Projects, Archives of the Evangelical
Lutheran Church in America, 321 Bonnie
Lane, Elk Grove Village, IL, 60007.
Tel: 773-380-2818, 847-690-9410. Fax:
847-690-9502. p. 641

Lundeen, Gabriel, Dep Dir, Chattahoochee
Valley Libraries, 3000 Macon Rd, Columbus,
GA, 31906-2201. Tel: 706-243-2783. Fax:
706-243-2710. p. 525

Lundgren, Arlene, Librn, Briggs & Morgan, 2200
IDS Ctr, 80 S Elg, Minneapolis, MN, 55402.
Tel: 612-977-8400. p. 1259

Lundgren Perry, Martha, Libr Instruction, Bellarmine
University, 2001 Newburg Rd, Louisville,
KY, 40205-0671. Tel: 502-272-8139. Fax:
502-272-8038. p. 923

Lundgrin, Karen, Librn, Village Church Library,
6641 Mission Rd, Prairie Village, KS,
66208-1799. Tel: 913-262-4200. Fax:
913-262-0304. p. 891

Lundin, Anne, Assoc Prof, University of
Wisconsin-Madison, 4217 H C White Hall,
600 N Park St, Madison, WI, 53706. Tel:
608-265-4733. Fax: 608-263-4849. p. 2976

Lundquist, Cindy, Coordr, Pepperdine University
Libraries, West Los Angeles Graduate Campus
Library, 6100 Center Dr, Los Angeles, CA,
90045. Tel: 310-568-5717. Fax: 310-568-5789.
p. 182

Lundquist, Jane, Teen Librn, McGregor Public
Library, 334 Main St, McGregor, IA, 52157. Tel:
563-873-3318. Fax: 563-873-3318. p. 831

Lundquist, Jeanette, Dir, Deadwood Public Library,
435 Williams St, Deadwood, SD, 57732-1113.
Tel: 605-578-2821. Fax: 605-578-2071. p. 2211

Lundquist, Robert, Evening Librn, Art Center
College of Design, 1700 Lida St, Pasadena, CA,
91103. Tel: 626-396-2231. Fax: 626-568-0428.
p. 205

Lundstrom, Karin, Sr Librn, Alameda Free Library,
West End, 788 Santa Clara Ave, Alameda,
CA, 94501-3334. Tel: 510-747-7780. Fax:
510-337-0877. p. 119

Lundy, Deborah, Br Mgr, Harrison County Library
System, West Biloxi Library, 2047 Pass Rd,
Biloxi, MS, 39531-3125. Tel: 228-388-5696.
Fax: 228-388-5652. p. 1300

Lundy, M Winslow, Head, Monographic &
Spec Mat Cat Unit, University of Colorado
Boulder, 1720 Pleasant St, 184 UCB, Boulder,
CO, 80309-0184. Tel: 303-492-3918. Fax:
303-492-3340. p. 291

Luney, Kirtley, Circ, Dunedin Public Library,
223 Douglas Ave, Dunedin, FL, 34698. Tel:
727-298-3080, Ext 248. Fax: 727-298-3088.
p. 438

Lung, Mon Yin, Assoc Dir, University of Houston,
The O'Quinn Law Library, 12 Law Library,
Houston, TX, 77204-6054. Tel: 713-743-2300.
Fax: 713-743-2296. p. 2343

Lunghamer, Ann, Ch, Head, Ref, New Westminster
Public Library, 716 Sixth Ave, New
Westminster, BC, V3M 2B3, CANADA. Tel:
604-527-4678. Fax: 604-527-4674. p. 2734

Lungin, Lyudmila, Med Librn, Children's
Specialized Hospital, 150 New Providence Rd,
Mountainside, NJ, 07092. Tel: 908-233-3720,
Ext 5227. Fax: 908-301-5569. p. 1506

Lungren, John, Librn, Dodge Correctional Institution
Library, One W Lincoln St, Waupun, WI,
53963. Tel: 920-324-5577, Ext 6570. Fax:
920-324-6297. p. 2646

Lunn, Beth, Tech Coordr, Pioneerland Library
System, 410 Fifth St SW, Willmar, MN, 56201.
Tel: 320-235-6106. Fax: 320-214-0187. p. 1288

Lunn, Erna R, Dir Gen, Published Heritage, Ledyard
Public Library, 220 Edmunds St, Ledyard, IA,
50556. Tel: 515-646-3111. Fax: 515-646-3111.
p. 827

Lunn, Patricia, Dir, Woodbury Public Library,
269 Main St S, Woodbury, CT, 06798. Tel:
203-263-3502. Fax: 203-263-0571. p. 380

Lunsford, Brandon, Archival Serv Librn, Johnson
C Smith University, 100 Beatties Ford Rd,
Charlotte, NC, 28216. Tel: 704-371-6740. Fax:
704-378-1191. p. 1783

Lunsford, Mary, Adult Serv, Hinsdale Public
Library, 58 Maple St, Hinsdale, MA, 01235. Tel:
413-655-2303. Fax: 413-655-2303. p. 1095

Lunsford, Patricia A, Librn, Saint Elizabeth Regional
Health, 1701 S Creasy Lane, Lafayette, IN,
47905. Tel: 765-502-4010. Fax: 765-502-4011.
p. 759

Lunsford, Stacey L, Dir, Irvin L Young Memorial
Library, 431 W Center St, Whitewater,
WI, 53190-1915. Tel: 262-473-0530. Fax:
262-473-0539. p. 2649

Luo, Ronghua, Coordr, Wayne County Community
College District-Downriver Campus, 21000
North Line Rd, Taylor, MI, 48180-4798. Tel:
734-374-3228. Fax: 734-374-0240. p. 1230

Luo, Wei, Dir of Tech Serv, Washington University
Libraries, Law Library, Washington Univ Sch
Law, Anheuser-Busch Hall, One Brookings Dr,
Campus Box 1171, Saint Louis, MO, 63130.
Tel: 314-935-8045. Fax: 314-935-7125. p. 1363

Luokkanen, Pattie, Ser Librn, Michigan
Technological University, 1400 Townsend Dr,
Houghton, MI, 49931-1295. Tel: 906-487-2484.
p. 1191

Luopa, Laura, Ch, Caledon Public Library, 150
Queen St S, Bolton, ON, L7E 1E3, CANADA.
Tel: 905-857-1400. Fax: 905-857-8280. p. 2795

Luoto, Irene, Outreach Serv Librn, Coos County
Library Service District, Tioga Hall, 1988
Newmark Ave, Coos Bay, OR, 97420. Tel:
541-888-7273. Fax: 541-888-1529. p. 2953

Lupack, Alan, Dir, University of Rochester, Rossell
Hope Robbins Library, Rush Rhees Library, Rm
416, Rochester, NY, 14627. Tel: 585-275-0110.
p. 1733

Lupardus, Stephanie, Br Mgr, Pulaski County
Library District, Crocker Branch, 602 N
Commercial St, Crocker, MO, 65452. Tel:
573-736-5592. Fax: 573-736-5427. p. 1350

Lupas, Liana, Curator, American Bible Society
Library, 1865 Broadway, New York, NY,
10023-9980. Tel: 212-408-1204. Fax:
212-408-8724. p. 1667

Lupei, Barbara, Dir, United States Navy, One
Administration Circle, Stop 6203, China Lake,
CA, 93555-6100. Tel: 760-939-3389. Fax:
760-939-2431. p. 133

Lupo, Gianine, Libr Asst, Maine State Law
& Legislative Reference Library, 43 State
House Sta, Augusta, ME, 04333-0043. Tel:
207-287-1600. Fax: 207-287-6467. p. 974

Lupp, Denise, Dir, United States Army, Medical
Research Institute of Infectious Diseases
Library, Fort Detrick, 1425 Porter, Frederick,
MD, 21702-5011. Tel: 301-619-2717. Fax:
301-619-6059. p. 1029

Lupro, Linda, Br Mgr, Harford County Public
Library, Jarrettsville Branch, 3722 Norrisville
Rd, Jarrettsville, MD, 21084. Tel: 410-692-7887.
p. 1020

Lupton, Susan, Ref Librn, State Law Library
of Montana, 215 N Sanders, Helena, MT,
59601-4522. Tel: 406-444-3636. Fax:
406-444-3603. p. 1383

Lurie, Janice, Head Librn, Minneapolis Institute of
Arts, 2400 Third Ave S, Minneapolis, MN,
55404. Tel: 612-870-3117. Fax: 612-870-3004.
p. 1261

Lurvey, Susan A, Mgr, Libr Serv, EAA Library,
3000 Poberezny Rd, Oshkosh, WI, 54904. Tel:
920-426-4848. Fax: 920-426-4828. p. 2627

Lusak, Robert, Dir, Smithtown Library, One N
Country Rd, Smithtown, NY, 11787. Tel:
631-265-2072. Fax: 631-265-2044. p. 1744

Lusardi, Marion Ashen, Dir, Chesterfield Township
Library, 50560 Patricia Ave, Chesterfield,
MI, 48051-3804. Tel: 586-598-4900. Fax:
586-598-7900. p. 1163

Luscher, Betty, Tech Serv, Corona Public Library,
650 S Main St, Corona, CA, 92882. Tel:
951-736-2381. Fax: 951-736-2499. p. 136

Luscombe, Tawna, Asst Librn, Ch, Portales Public
Library, 218 S Ave B, Portales, NM, 88130. Tel:
505-356-3940. Fax: 505-356-3964. p. 1560

Luscombe, Tracy, Dir, Van Alstyne Public Library,
151 W Cooper St, Van Alstyne, TX, 75495. Tel:
903-482-5991. Fax: 903-482-1316. p. 2395

Lusey, Beverly A, Asst Dir, Ref, Bellevue
Public Library, 1003 Lincoln Rd, Bellevue,
NE, 68005-3199. Tel: 402-293-3157. Fax:
402-293-3163. p. 1393

Lusher, T J, Asst Dean, Automated Libr Serv,
Northern Illinois University Libraries, DeKalb,
IL, 60115-2868. Tel: 815-753-0521. p. 635

Lussier, Celine, Dir, Chateauguay Municipal
Library, 25 Maple Blvd, Chateauguay, QC,
J6J 3P7, CANADA. Tel: 450-698-3085. Fax:
450-698-3109. p. 2880

Lussier, Jacqueline, Librn, Benson Village Library,
2724 Stage Rd, Benson, VT, 05731. Tel:
802-537-4181. Fax: 802-537-2612. p. 2419

Lussier, Janet, Librn, Baystate Mary Lane
Hospital, 85 South St, Ware, MA, 01082. Tel:
413-967-2226. Fax: 413-967-2115. p. 1133

Lussier, Kathy, Asst Dir, Commun Relations
& Mkt, Jacksonville Public Library, 303 N
Laura St, Jacksonville, FL, 32202-3505. Tel:
904-630-7595. Fax: 904-630-2431. p. 453

Luster, Eddie, ILL, University of Alabama at
Birmingham, Mervyn H Sterne Library, 917
13th St S, Birmingham, AL, 35205. Tel:
205-934-6364. p. 10

Luster, Karen, Adult Serv, Glenside Public Library
District, 25 E Fullerton Ave, Glendale Heights,
IL, 60139-2697. Tel: 630-260-1550. Fax:
630-260-1433. p. 650

Luster, Louveller, Access Serv & Syst, Virginia
State University, One Hayden Dr, Petersburg,
VA, 23806-0001. Tel: 804-524-6945. Fax:
804-524-6959. p. 2484

Luster, Sean, Head, Info Serv, Bloomingdale Public
Library, 101 Fairfield Way, Bloomingdale,
IL, 60108-1579. Tel: 630-529-3120. Fax:
630-529-3243. p. 595

Lustiber, Kara, Dir, West Hurley Public Library,
42 Clover St, West Hurley, NY, 12491. Tel:
845-679-6405. Fax: 845-679-2144. p. 1766

Lustiger, Janice S, Librn, Norris, McLaughlin & Marcus, PA, 721 Rte 202-206 N, Bridgewater, NJ, 08807. Tel: 908-722-0700. Fax: 908-722-0755. p. 1474

Lutenske, Paul, Librn, Public Libraries of Saginaw, Butman-Fish, 1716 Hancock, Saginaw, MI, 48602. Tel: 989-799-9160. Fax: 989-799-8149. p. 1224

Luter, Zoe, Outreach Librn, Mesa Community College Library, 1833 W Southern Ave, Mesa, AZ, 85202. Tel: 480-461-7286. Fax: 480-461-7681. p. 68

Luteran, Camille, Mgr, Northern Onondaga Public Library, Brewerton Branch, 5437 Library St, Brewerton, NY, 13029-8719. Tel: 315-676-7484. Fax: 315-676-7463. p. 1707

Lutes, Joel, Pub Serv, Syst Coordr, Pacific Union College, One Angwin Ave, Angwin, CA, 94508-9705. Tel: 707-965-6674. Fax: 707-965-6504. p. 121

Luther, Dennis, Dir, Brentwood Library, 3501 Brownsville Rd, Pittsburgh, PA, 15227-3115. Tel: 412-882-5694. p. 2121

Luther, Doris, Br Librn, Stinson Memorial Public Library District, Cobden Branch, 100 S Front St, Cobden, IL, 62920. Tel: 618-893-4637. Fax: 618-893-4637. p. 589

Luther, Michelle, Dir, Fayetteville Publishing Co, 458 Whitfield St, Fayetteville, NC, 28306. Tel: 910-486-3584. Fax: 910-486-3545. p. 1793

Luther, Michelle, Res, Fayetteville Publishing Co, 458 Whitfield St, Fayetteville, NC, 28306. Tel: 910-486-3584. Fax: 910-486-3545. p. 1793

Luthje, Janet, Librn, Arcadia Township Library, 100 S Reynolds, Arcadia, NE, 68815. Tel: 308-789-6346. Fax: 308-789-6284. p. 1391

Lutke, Karen M, Dir, San Mateo County Law Library, 710 Hamilton St, Redwood City, CA, 94063. Tel: 650-363-4913. Fax: 650-367-8040. p. 216

Lutkenhaus, Rebecca, Ref Serv, Drake University, Drake Law Library, Opperman Hall, 2615 Carpenter Ave, Des Moines, IA, 50311-4505. Tel: 515-271-2141. Fax: 515-271-2530. p. 809

Luton, Lee, Acq, Tech Serv, Niceville Public Library, 206 N Partin Dr, Niceville, FL, 32578. Tel: 850-729-4070. Fax: 850-729-4053. p. 472

Luton, Sue, Br Librn, Grand County Library District, Juniper Library at Grand Lake, 316 Garfield St, Grand Lake, CO, 80447. Tel: 970-627-8353. Fax: 970-627-0929. p. 310

Luttmann, Georgene, Tech Serv Coordr, North Kingstown Free Library, 100 Boone St, North Kingstown, RI, 02852-5176. Tel: 401-294-3306. Fax: 401-294-1690. p. 2170

Luttmann, Stephen, Music, University of Northern Colorado Libraries, 501 20th St, Greeley, CO, 80639. Tel: 970-351-2281. Fax: 970-351-2963. p. 312

Luttrell, Amanda, Circ Mgr, Johnson County Public Library, Clark Pleasant Library, 530 Tracy Rd, Ste 250, New Whiteland, IN, 46184-9699. Tel: 317-535-6206. Fax: 317-535-6018. p. 744

Lutz, George, Librn, Citigroup Corporate Library, 666 Fifth Ave, 6th Fl, New York, NY, 10103. Tel: 212-559-9699. Fax: 212-783-6559. p. 1672

Lutz, James, Dir, Admin Serv, Texas Christian University, 2913 Lowden St, TCU Box 298400, Fort Worth, TX, 76129. Tel: 817-257-7106. Fax: 817-257-7282. p. 2323

Lutz, Jon, Electronic Res, Florida State University Libraries, College of Law Library, 425 W Jefferson St, Tallahassee, FL, 32306. Tel: 850-644-7488. Fax: 850-644-5216. p. 494

Lutz, Kimberly, Dr, Dir, Mkt & Outreach, University of North Carolina at Greensboro, 320 Spring Garden St, Greensboro, NC, 27402. Tel: 336-334-5880. Fax: 336-334-5399. p. 1798

Lutz, Sue, Libr Tech, Colorado Department of Corrections, Youth Offender Services, PO Box 35010, Pueblo, CO, 81003. Tel: 719-544-4800, Ext 3507. Fax: 719-583-5909. p. 320

Lutz, Violet, Dr, Spec Coll Librn, German Society of Pennsylvania, 611 Spring Garden St, Philadelphia, PA, 19123. Tel: 215-627-2332. Fax: 215-627-5297. p. 2110

Lutzel, John, Pub Serv, Owensboro Community & Technical College, 4800 New Hartford Rd, Owensboro, KY, 42303. Tel: 270-686-4574. Fax: 270-686-4594. p. 931

Lutzke, Amy, Asst Dir, Dwight Foster Public Library, 102 E Milwaukee Ave, Fort Atkinson, WI, 53538-2049. Tel: 920-563-7790. Fax: 920-563-7774. p. 2592

Lutzow, Eileen, Syst & Electronic Res, Charleston Southern University, 9200 University Blvd, Charleston, SC, 29406. Tel: 843-863-7951. Fax: 843-863-7947. p. 2183

Lutzweiler, Jim, Archivist, Southeastern Baptist Theological Seminary Library, 114 N Wingate St, Wake Forest, NC, 27587. Tel: 919-863-8249. Fax: 919-863-8150. p. 1827

Luu, Xinh, Intl & Foreign Law Librn, University of Virginia, Arthur J Morris Law Library, 580 Massie Rd, Charlottesville, VA, 22903-1789. Tel: 434-924-3970. Fax: 434-982-2232. p. 2455

Lux, Martha, Tech Serv, Oak Ridge Public Library, 1401 Oak Ridge Tpk, Oak Ridge, TN, 37830-6224. Tel: 865-425-3455. Fax: 865-425-3429. p. 2262

Luxenberg, Alan, VPres, Foreign Policy Research Institute Library, 1528 Walnut St, Ste 610, Philadelphia, PA, 19102. Tel: 215-732-3774, Ext 102. Fax: 215-732-4401. p. 2106

Luyben, Jean, Info Serv Librn, Trent University, 1600 West Bank Dr, Peterborough, ON, K9J 7B8, CANADA. Tel: 705-748-1011, Ext 1324. Fax: 705-748-1126. p. 2836

Luz, David W, Exec Dir, Schwenkfelder Library & Heritage Center, 105 Seminary St, Pennsburg, PA, 18073. Tel: 215-679-3103, Ext 11. Fax: 215-679-8175. p. 2102

Luzadder, Carla, Acq, ILL, Saint Joseph's College, Hwy 231 S, Rensselaer, IN, 47978. Tel: 219-866-6209. Fax: 219-866-6135. p. 774

Luzer, Nancy, Tech Serv, Castleton State College, 178 Alumni Dr, Castleton, VT, 05735. Tel: 802-468-1256. Fax: 802-468-1475. p. 2421

Luzier, Lisa, Librn, Federal Correctional Institution - Morgantown Library, PO Box 1000, Morgantown, WV, 26507-1000. Tel: 304-296-4416, Ext 351. Fax: 304-284-3622, 304-296-7549. p. 2566

Luzius, Jeff, Dr, Dir, United States Air Force, Air University - Muir S Fairchild Research Information Center, 600 Chennault Circle, Maxwell AFB, AL, 36112-6010. Tel: 334-953-2606. p. 24

Luzum, Cindy, Ch, Fort Atkinson Public Library, 302 Third St NW, Fort Atkinson, IA, 52144. Tel: 563-534-2222. Fax: 563-534-2222. p. 816

Lybarger, Lowell, Dr, Music & Media Librn, Arkansas Tech University, 305 West Q St, Russellville, AR, 72801-2222. Tel: 479-964-0584. Fax: 479-964-0559. p. 113

Lybecker, Linda, Asst Dir, Hillsboro Public Library, 2850 NE Brookwood Pkwy, Hillsboro, OR, 97124-5327. Tel: 503-615-6500. Fax: 503-615-6601. p. 2000

Lyczmanenko, Olga, Librn, New England Baptist Hospital, 125 Parker Hill Ave, Boston, MA, 02120-2847. Tel: 617-754-5155. Fax: 617-754-6414. p. 1064

Lydon, C Elspeth, Dir, Plumb Memorial Library, 65 Wooster St, Shelton, CT, 06484. Tel: 203-924-1580. Fax: 203-924-8422. p. 367

Lydon, Carla, Br Supvr, East Central Regional Library, Chisago Lakes Area Public Library, 11754 302nd St, Chisago City, MN, 55013. Tel: 651-257-2817. Fax: 651-257-2817. p. 1244

Lydon, Marie, Ref, Morrill Memorial Library, 33 Walpole St, Norwood, MA, 02062-1206. Tel: 781-769-0200. Fax: 781-769-6083. p. 1115

Lydon, Martina, Librn, Riverdale Presbyterian Church Library, 6513 Queens Chapel Rd, Hyattsville, MD, 20782-2197. Tel: mlydon@nal.usda.gov. Fax: 301-699-2156. p. 1033

Lydon, Mary, Librn, Massachusetts Water Resources Authority Library, Two Griffin Way, Chelsea, MA, 02150. Tel: 617-305-5584. Fax: 617-371-1610. p. 1080

Lyhane, Janice, ILL, Youth Serv, Marysville Public Library, 1009 Broadway, Marysville, KS, 66508-1814. Tel: 785-562-2491. Fax: 785-562-4086. p. 882

Lykens, Mary, Ch, Altoona Area Public Library, 1600 Fifth Ave, Altoona, PA, 16602-3693. Tel: 814-946-0417, Ext 123. Fax: 814-946-3230. p. 2028

Lykow, Jean, Res Ctr Mgr, Holland College Library Services, 140 Weymouth St, Charlottetown, PE, C1A 4Z1, CANADA. Tel: 902-888-6738. Fax: 902-566-9522. p. 2875

Lyle, Anna, Asst Dir, Support Serv, Forsyth County Public Library, 585 Dahlonega Rd, Cumming, GA, 30040-2109. Tel: 770-781-9840. Fax: 770-781-8089. p. 527

Lyle, Heather, Spec Coll Librn, Univ Archivist, Denison University Libraries, 400 W Loop, Granville, OH, 43023. Tel: 740-587-6399. Fax: 740-587-6285. p. 1902

Lyle, Stanley, Bibliographer, Ref Serv, University of Northern Iowa Library, 1227 W 27th St, Cedar Falls, IA, 50613-3675. Tel: 319-273-2843. Fax: 319-273-2913. p. 799

Lyle, Suzi, Dir, Selover Public Library, 31 State Rte 95, Chesterville, OH, 43317-0025. Tel: 419-768-3431. Fax: 419-768-2249. p. 1867

Lyles, Beth, Tech Serv, H Leslie Perry Memorial Library, 205 Breckenridge St, Henderson, NC, 27536. Tel: 252-438-3316. Fax: 252-438-3744. p. 1800

Lyles, Tina, Mgr, Publ & Mkt, Wyoming State Library, 2800 Central Ave, Cheyenne, WY, 82002. Tel: 307-777-6338. Fax: 307-777-6289. p. 2653

Lym, Brian, Sci Librn, Hunter College Libraries, 695 Park Ave, New York, NY, 10065. Tel: 212-772-4191. Fax: 212-772-4142. p. 1682

Lyman, Bibiane, Librn, International Institute of Integral Human Sciences Library, 1974 de Maisonneuve W, Montreal, QC, H3H 1K5, CANADA. Tel: 514-937-8359. Fax: 514-937-5380. p. 2897

Lyman, Cynthia, Access Serv, Carrollton Public Library, 1700 Keller Springs Rd, Carrollton, TX, 75006. Tel: 972-466-4812. Fax: 972-466-4265. p. 2295

Lyman, Jamie, Tech Serv Coordr, Sioux Center Public Library, 102 S Main Ave, Sioux Center, IA, 51250-1801. Tel: 712-722-2138. Fax: 712-722-1235. p. 843

Lyman, Jane, Ref Librn II, New Hampshire State Library, 20 Park St, Concord, NH, 03301-6314. Tel: 603-271-2392. Fax: 603-271-2205, 603-271-6826. p. 1443

Lyman, Monika, Syst Librn, Library of the Marine Corps, Gray Research Ctr, 2040 Broadway St, Quantico, VA, 22134-5107. Tel: 703-784-4409. Fax: 703-784-4306. p. 2486

Lyman, Platte, Dir, Blackfoot Public Library, 129 N Broadway, Blackfoot, ID, 83221-2204. Tel: 208-785-8628. Fax: 208-782-9688. p. 569

Lynagh, Pat, Asst Librn, Hillwood Estate, Museum & Gardens, 4155 Linnean Ave NW, Washington, DC, 20008. Tel: 202-243-3953. Fax: 202-966-7846. p. 403

Lynam-Davis, Nancy, Med Librn, Hillcrest Hospital, 6780 Mayfield Rd, Mayfield Heights, OH, 44124. Tel: 440-312-3250. Fax: 440-312-4799. p. 1915

Lynch, Anastasia Tarmann, Librn, Alaska State Library, 333 Willoughby Ave, State Office Bldg, 8th Flr, Juneau, AK, 99801. Tel: 907-465-2910. Fax: 907-465-2151. p. 49

Lynch, Anne, Acq, Coll Mgt, New England School of Law Library, 154 Stuart St, Boston, MA, 02116-5687. Tel: 617-422-7293. Fax: 617-422-7303. p. 1065

Lynch, Bernadette, Libr Spec, Harrisburg Area Community College, 1641 Old Philadelphia Pike, Lancaster, PA, 17602. Tel: 717-358-2986. Fax: 717-358-2952. p. 2076

Lynch, Bonnie, Dr, Exec Dir, Lehigh Valley Association of Independent Colleges, 130 W Greenwich St, Bethlehem, PA, 18018. Tel: 610-625-7892. Fax: 610-625-7891. p. 2954

Lynch, Brian, Circ Supvr, Saint John Fisher College, 3690 East Ave, Rochester, NY, 14618-3599. Tel: 585-385-8165. Fax: 585-385-8445. p. 1732

Lynch, Cheryl, Dir, Derry Public Library, 64 E Broadway, Derry, NH, 03038-2412. Tel: 603-432-6140. Fax: 603-432-6128. p. 1444

Lynch, Cynthia D, Dir, Libr Serv, Milwaukee Institute of Art & Design Library, 273 E Erie St, Milwaukee, WI, 53202-6003. Tel: 414-847-3340. Fax: 414-291-8077. p. 2619

Lynch, Dora, ILL, Kearny County Library, 101 E Prairie, Lakin, KS, 67860. Tel: 620-355-6674. Fax: 620-355-6801. p. 877

Lynch, Eva, Dir, Waterford Township Public Library, 2204 Atco Ave, Atco, NJ, 08004. Tel: 856-767-7727. Fax: 856-753-8998. p. 1469

Lynch, Frances, Admin Serv, Assoc Dir, Vanderbilt University, Annette & Irwin Eskind Biomedical Library, 2209 Garland Ave, Nashville, TN, 37232-8340. Tel: 615-936-2617. Fax: 615-936-1384. p. 2260

Lynch, Gina, Dir, Bingham McCutchen LLP, 150 Federal St, Boston, MA, 02110. Tel: 617-951-8313. Fax: 617-951-8543. p. 1055

Lynch, Grant C, Dir, Waukesha Public Library, 321 Wisconsin Ave, Waukesha, WI, 53186-4786. Tel: 262-524-3681. Fax: 262-524-3677. p. 2645

Lynch, James, Archivist, Bethel College Library, Mennonite Library & Archives, 300 E 27th St, North Newton, KS, 67117-0531. Tel: 316-284-5304. Fax: 316-284-5843. p. 885

Lynch, Jean-Marc, Coll Develop, Dir, Bibliotheque Municipale de Saint-Bruno-de-Montarville, 82 Seigneurial W, Saint Bruno-de-Montarville, QC, J3V 5N7, CANADA. Tel: 450-645-2950. Fax: 450-441-8485. p. 2908

Lynch, Katherine, Webmaster, Drexel University Libraries, Hagerty Library, 33rd & Market Sts, Philadelphia, PA, 19104-2875. Tel: 215-895-1344. Fax: 215-895-2070. p. 2105

Lynch, Kathy A, Dir, GateWay Community College Library, 108 N 40th St, Phoenix, AZ, 85034-1704. Tel: 602-286-8460. Fax: 602-286-8459. p. 73

Lynch, Liz, Actg Hub Supvr, Lake Agassiz Regional Library, Moorhead Public Library, 118 S Fifth St, Moorhead, MN, 56561-2756. Tel: 218-233-7594. Fax: 218-236-7405. p. 1266

Lynch, Marilyn, Dir, State Journal & Register, Copley Plaza, Springfield, IL, 62701. Tel: 217-788-1504. Fax: 217-788-1551. p. 707

Lynch, Mary, City Librn, Ventura County Library, Ojai Library, 111 E Ojai Ave, Ojai, CA, 93023. Tel: 805-646-1639. Fax: 805-646-4693. p. 280

Lynch, Mary McGuire, Dir, Samuels Public Library, 538 Villa Ave, Front Royal, VA, 22630. Tel: 540-635-3153, Ext 110. Fax: 540-635-7229. p. 2466

Lynch, Maureen, Ch, Rutland Free Public Library, 280 Main St, Rutland, MA, 01543. Tel: 508-886-4108. Fax: 508-886-4141. p. 1121

Lynch, Michael, Syst Librn, Quinebaug Valley Community College Library, 742 Upper Maple St, Danielson, CT, 06239. Tel: 860-412-7272. Fax: 860-412-7277. p. 335

Lynch, Michael J, Dir, John Marshall Law School, 1422 W Peachtree St NW, Atlanta, GA, 30309. Tel: 404-872-3593. Fax: 404-873-3802. p. 516

Lynch, Ruth, Ref, Whittier Public Library, 7344 S Washington Ave, Whittier, CA, 90602. Tel: 562-567-9900. Fax: 562-567-2880. p. 283

Lynch, Ruth, Supvr, Haliburton County Public Library, Dorset Branch, 1051 Main St, Dorset, ON, P0A 1E0, CANADA. Tel: 705-766-9969. p. 2807

Lynch, Terry R, Librn, California State Court of Appeal, 3389 12th St, Riverside, CA, 92501. Tel: 951-782-2485. Fax: 909-248-0235. p. 216

Lynch, Tim, Per, The Morristown & Morris Township Library, One Miller Rd, Morristown, NJ, 07960. Tel: 973-538-6161. Fax: 973-267-4064. p. 1505

Lynch, Virginia, Head, Tech Serv, Berkeley Heights Public Library, 290 Plainfield Ave, Berkeley Heights, NJ, 07922. Tel: 908-464-9333. Fax: 908-464-7098. p. 1472

Lynch, Wilma, In Charge, Fayette County Law Library, 120 N Limestone, Lexington, KY, 40507-1137. Tel: 859-246-2143. p. 920

Lynda, Buch, Br Head, Toronto Public Library, Jones, 118 Jones Ave, Toronto, ON, M4M 2Z9, CANADA. Tel: 416-393-7715. Fax: 416-393-7416. p. 2862

Lynde, Carol, Circ, Garden Valley District Library, 342 Village Circle, Garden Valley, ID, 83622-8040. Tel: 208-462-3317. Fax: 208-462-3758. p. 574

Lyne, Elayne, Circ Supvr, Thomas M Cooley Law School Libraries, 300 S Capitol Ave, Lansing, MI, 48901. Tel: 517-371-5140, Ext 3101. Fax: 517-334-5715, 517-334-5717. p. 1202

Lynn, Ann, Dir, Northwest Regional Library, 185 Ashwood Dr, Winfield, AL, 35594-5436. Tel: 205-487-2330. Fax: 205-487-4815. p. 40

Lynn, Barbara, Ch, Paterson Free Public Library, 250 Broadway, Paterson, NJ, 07501. Tel: 973-321-1223, Ext 2299. Fax: 973-321-1205. p. 1518

Lynn, Beth, Ch, Pub Serv, YA Serv, Thomas Beaver Free Library, 205 Ferry St, Danville, PA, 17821-1939. Tel: 570-275-4180. Fax: 570-275-8480. p. 2049

Lynn, Beth, Coll Develop Coordr, Union University, 1050 Union University Dr, Jackson, TN, 38305-3697. Tel: 731-661-5070. Fax: 731-661-5175. p. 2238

Lynn, Holly M, Dir, Ref Coordr, Burton Public Library, 14588 W Park St, Burton, OH, 44021. Tel: 440-834-4466. Fax: 440-834-0128. p. 1862

Lynn, Margaret, Assoc Dean, Coll Develop, Tech Serv, The College of New Rochelle, 29 Castle Pl, New Rochelle, NY, 10805-2308. Tel: 914-654-5345. Fax: 914-654-5884. p. 1666

Lynn, Marilyn, Chief, Quality Management & Educ, Department of Veterans Affairs, 1055 Clermont St, Denver, CO, 80220. Tel: 303-393-4644. Fax: 303-393-2829. p. 301

Lynn, Marsha, Dir, Odon Winkelpleck Public Library, 202 W Main St, Odon, IN, 47562. Tel: 812-636-4949. Fax: 812-636-4949. p. 771

Lynn, Mary Evelyn, Dir, Libr Serv, Cleveland State Community College Library, 3535 Adkisson Dr, Cleveland, TN, 37312-2813. Tel: 423-478-6209. Fax: 423-478-6255. p. 2229

Lynn, Michael Anne, Dir, Stonewall Jackson House, Stonewall Jackson House, Eight E Washington St, Lexington, VA, 24450. Tel: 540-463-2552. Fax: 540-463-4088. p. 2474

Lynn, Penee, Coordr, Salt Lake County Library Services, Alta Reading Room, Alta Community Ctr, Sandy, UT, 84092-6001. Tel: 801-742-2068. p. 2414

Lynn, Rebecca, Br Mgr, San Diego County Library, Solana Beach Branch, 157 Stevens Ave, Solana Beach, CA, 92075-1873. Tel: 858-755-1404. Fax: 858-755-9327. p. 234

Lynn, Ruth, Ch, Cary Memorial Library, 1874 Massachusetts Ave, Lexington, MA, 02420. Tel: 781-862-6288, Ext 172. Fax: 781-862-7355. p. 1099

Lynne, Linda, Librn, Waseca-Le Sueur Regional Library, New Richland Public, 129 S Broadway Ave, New Richland, MN, 56072. Tel: 507-465-3708. p. 1287

Lyon, Dee, Dir, Schleswig Public Library, 202 Cedar St, Schleswig, IA, 51461-0306. Tel: 712-676-3470. p. 842

Lyon, Havilah, Head, Circ Serv, Twin Falls Public Library, 201 Fourth Ave E, Twin Falls, ID, 83301-6397. Tel: 208-733-2964. Fax: 208-733-2965. p. 584

Lyon, Janet, Dir, Columbia County Rural Library District, 111 S Third St, Dayton, WA, 99328-1342. Tel: 509-382-4131. Fax: 509-382-1059. p. 2514

Lyon, Karis, Librn, Lorain County Historical Society, 509 Washington Ave, Elyria, OH, 44035. Tel: 440-322-3341. Fax: 440-322-2817. p. 1898

Lyon, Kate, Dir, Euless Public Library, 201 N Ector Dr, Euless, TX, 76039-3595. Tel: 817-685-1482. Fax: 817-267-1979. p. 2318

Lyon, Martha, Librn, Oswego School District Public Library, 120 E Second St, Oswego, NY, 13126. Tel: 315-341-5867. Fax: 315-216-6492. p. 1713

Lyon, Susan, Learning Engagement Mgr, Richland County Public Library, 1431 Assembly St, Columbia, SC, 29201-3101. Tel: 803-799-9084. Fax: 803-929-3448. p. 2188

Lyons, Audrey, Libr Asst, Alberta Innovates-Technology Futures, Vegreville Branch, Hwy 16A 75th St, Vegreville, AB, T9C 1T4, CANADA. Tel: 780-632-8417. Fax: 780-632-8300. p. 2698

Lyons, Carolyn, Librn, Medical Group Management Association, 104 Inverness Terrace E, Englewood, CO, 80112. Tel: 303-397-7887. Fax: 303-397-1823. p. 306

Lyons, Cheryl, Head Librn, Capital Area District Libraries, Holt-Delhi Library, 2078 Aurelius Rd, Holt, MI, 48842. Tel: 517-694-9351. Fax: 517-699-3865. p. 1200

Lyons, Christian, Librn, Colorado State Department of Natural Resources, 1580 Logan St, Ste 600, Denver, CO, 80203. Tel: 303-866-3549. Fax: 303-866-4474. p. 299

Lyons, Clare, Mgr, Cassels, Brock & Blackwell Library, Scotia Plaza, Ste 2100, 40 King St W, Toronto, ON, M5H 3C2, CANADA. Tel: 416-869-5436. Fax: 416-360-8877. p. 2852

Lyons, Curtis, Dir, Cornell University Library, Hospitality, Labor & Management Library, Ives Hall, Garden Ave, Ithaca, NY, 14853-3901. Tel: 607-255-2277. Fax: 607-255-9641. p. 1641

Lyons, Debbie, Head, Circ, McCreary County Public Library District, Six N Main St, Whitley City, KY, 42653. Tel: 606-376-8738. Fax: 606-376-3631. p. 937

Lyons, Denise, Dir, Libr Develop, South Carolina State Library, 1430-1500 Senate St, Columbia, SC, 29201. Tel: 803-734-6061. Fax: 803-734-8676. p. 2189

Lyons, Denise, Dir, Libr Develop, South Carolina Library Network, 1430 & 1500 Senate St, Columbia, SC, 29201. Tel: 803-734-8666. Fax: 803-734-8676. p. 2955

Lyons, Eric, Lead Children's Programmer, Missouri River Regional Library, 214 Adams St, Jefferson City, MO, 65101-3244. Tel: 573-634-6064, Ext 229. p. 1335

Lyons, Heather, Pub Serv, Provincial Archives of New Brunswick, 23 Dineen Dr, Fredericton, NB, E3B 5A3, CANADA. Tel: 506-453-2122. Fax: 506-453-3288. p. 2763

Lyons, Inez, Head, Govt Info, North Carolina Agricultural & Technical State University, 1601 E Market St, Greensboro, NC, 27411-0002. Tel: 336-334-7617, Ext 3223. Fax: 336-334-7783. p. 1797

Lyons, Jeff, Mgr, Knowledge Syst, Abbott, 100 Abbott Park Rd, AP 6B, Abbott Park, IL, 60064-6107. Tel: 847-934-4119. Fax: 847-937-6333. p. 587

Lyons, Judy, Coordr, Arrowhead Health Sciences Library Network, Wisconsin Indianhead Technical College, 505 Pine Ridge Dr, Shell Lake, WI, 54817. Tel: 715-468-2815, Ext 2298. Fax: 715-468-2819. p. 2958

Lyons, Kate, Info Tech Librn, Ref Serv, Hostos Community College Library, 475 Grand Concourse, A-207, Bronx, NY, 10451. Tel: 718-518-4213. Fax: 718-518-4206. p. 1587

Lyons, Kathleen, Asst Librn, Loyal Public Library, 214 N Main St, Loyal, WI, 54446. Tel: 715-255-8189. Fax: 715-255-8348. p. 2605

Lyons, Kay, Head, Youth Serv, Greenfield Public Library, 402 Main St, Greenfield, MA, 01301. Tel: 413-772-1544. Fax: 413-772-1589. p. 1092

Lyons, Ken, Assoc Librn, Bibliographer, University of California, 1156 High St, Santa Cruz, CA, 95064. Tel: 831-459-2593. Fax: 831-459-8206. p. 264

Lyons, Matthew, Dir, Archives & Coll Mgt, Historical Society of Pennsylvania, 1300 Locust St, Philadelphia, PA, 19107-5699. Tel: 215-732-6200, Ext 301. Fax: 215-732-2680. p. 2110

Lyons, Pamela, Assoc Dir, Birmingham Public Library, 2100 Park Pl, Birmingham, AL, 35203. Tel: 205-226-3613. Fax: 205-226-3743. p. 7

Lyons, Sean, Head, Pub Serv, Capital Area District Libraries, Hope Borbas Okemos Library, 4321 Okemos Rd, Okemos, MI, 48864. Tel: 517-347-2030. Fax: 517-347-2034. p. 1200

Lyons, Susan, Govt Doc, Rutgers University Library for the Center for Law & Justice, 123 Washington St, Newark, NJ, 07102-3094. Tel: 973-353-3092. Fax: 973-353-1356. p. 1513

Lyons, Susan, Cat, Murrysville Community Library, 4130 Sardis Rd, Murrysville, PA, 15668-1120. Tel: 724-327-1102. Fax: 724-327-7142. p. 2094

Lyons, Wendy, Librn, Akin, Gump, Strauss, Hauer & Feld Library, 1700 Pacific Ave, Ste 4100, Dallas, TX, 75201-4618. Tel: 214-969-4628. Fax: 214-969-4343. p. 2304

Lysenko, Rod, Coordr, ILL, Edgewood College Library, 1000 Edgewood College Dr, Madison, WI, 53711-1997. Tel: 608-663-3300. Fax: 608-663-6778. p. 2606

Lysiak, Lynne, Automation Syst Coordr, Appalachian State University, 218 College St, Boone, NC, 28608. Tel: 828-262-2794. Fax: 828-262-3001. p. 1776

Lyszak, Barbara, ILL, Chatham-Kent Public Library, 120 Queen St, Chatham, ON, N7M 2G6, CANADA. Tel: 519-354-2940. Fax: 519-354-7366. p. 2799

Lythgoe, Wenda, Chair, Department of Community Services, Government of Yukon, Haines Junction Community, Haines Junction Admininstration Bldg, Haines Junction, YT, Y0B 1L0, CANADA. Tel: 867-634-2215. Fax: 867-634-2400. p. 2933

Lytle, Cindy, Librn, Schulenburg Public Library, 310 Simpson, Schulenburg, TX, 78956. Tel: 979-743-3345. p. 2385

Lytle, Ray, Dean, Mid-Continent College, 99 Powell Rd E, Mayfield, KY, 42066-9007. Tel: 270-247-8521, Ext 275. Fax: 270-247-3115. p. 928

Lytle, Roane, Librn, State Correctional Institution, State Rte 2007, Houtzdale, PA, 16698. Tel: 814-378-1000, Ext 1556. Fax: 814-378-1030. p. 2070

Lytle, Steve, Archivist, Hartford Hospital, ERC Bldg-3, 80 Seymour St, Hartford, CT, 06102. Tel: 860-545-2421. Fax: 860-545-2572. p. 345

Lyttle, Lee, Dean, Libr Serv, Cooperating Libraries in Olympia, The Evergreen State College Library, L2300, Olympia, WA, 98505. Tel: 360-867-6260. Fax: 360-867-6790. p. 2957

Lytton, Ellen, Mgr, Libr Serv, Overseas Private Investment Corp Library, 1100 New York Ave NW, 11th Flr, Washington, DC, 20527. Tel: 202-336-8566. Fax: 202-408-9860. p. 412

Lyubimov, Andrei, Libr Mgr, Holy Trinity Orthodox Seminary Library, 1407 Robinson Rd, Jordanville, NY, 13361-0036. Tel: 315-858-3116. Fax: 315-858-0945. p. 1648

Ma, Ann, Librn, R B C Dominions Securities, Royal Bank Plaza, South Tower, 4th Flr, 200 Bay St, Toronto, ON, M5J 2W7, CANADA. Tel: 416-842-7574. Fax: 416-842-7555. p. 2857

Ma, Chunwei, Syst Coordr, Jersey Shore University Medical Center, 1945 Rte 33, Neptune, NJ, 07754-0397. Tel: 732-776-4265. Fax: 732-776-4530. p. 1507

Ma, Evelyn, Ref Librn, Yale University Library, Lillian Goldman Library Yale Law School, 127 Wall St, New Haven, CT, 06511. Tel: 203-432-1600. Fax: 203-432-2112. p. 358

Ma, Sharon, Info Spec, Ethicon, Inc, US Rte 22 W, Somerville, NJ, 08876. Tel: 908-218-0707, 908-218-3259. Fax: 908-218-3558. p. 1529

Ma, Tai-Loi, Dir, Princeton University, East Asian Library & The Gest Collection, 33 Frist Campus Ctr, Rm 317, Princeton, NJ, 08544-. Tel: 609-258-3183. Fax: 609-258-4573. p. 1523

Ma, Wei, Electronic Serv Librn, California State University Dominguez Hills, 1000 E Victoria St, Carson, CA, 90747. Tel: 310-243-2085. Fax: 310-516-4219. p. 132

Ma, Xiao-He, Librn, Harvard Library, Harvard-Yenching Library, Two Divinity Ave, Cambridge, MA, 02138. Tel: 617-495-2756. Fax: 617-496-6008. p. 1075

Ma, Yan, Dr, Prof, University of Rhode Island, Rodman Hall, 94 W Alumni Ave, Ste 2, Kingston, RI, 02881-0815. Tel: 401-874-2819. Fax: 401-874-4964. p. 2973

Ma, Yongli, Acq, Asst Dir, Southern Polytechnic State University, 1100 S Marietta Pkwy, Marietta, GA, 30060-2896. Tel: 678-915-7473. Fax: 678-915-4944. p. 543

Maas, Adrian, Dir of Finance, Vancouver Island Regional Library, 6250 Hammond Bay Rd, Nanaimo, BC, V9R 5N3, CANADA. Tel: 250-729-2319. Fax: 250-758-2482. p. 2732

Maas, Gwenn, Br Mgr, Henry Patrick School District Public Library, Malinta Branch, 204 N Henry St, Malinta, OH, 43535. Tel: 419-256-7223. Fax: 419-256-7223. p. 1896

Maas, Joan, Ch, Adair Public Library, 310 Audubon, Adair, IA, 50002. Tel: 641-742-3323. Fax: 641-742-3323. p. 791

Maas, Norman, Dir, Norfolk Public Library, 235 E Plume St, Norfolk, VA, 23510-1706. Tel: 757-664-7323. Fax: 757-441-5863. p. 2481

Maassen, Orlys, Librn, Bode Public Library, 114 Humboldt Ave, Bode, IA, 50519. Tel: 515-379-1258. Fax: 515-379-1486. p. 797

Maatta Smith, Stephanie, Dr, Asst Prof, Wayne State University, 106 Kresge Library, Detroit, MI, 48202. Tel: 313-577-1825. Fax: 313-577-7563. p. 2968

Mabe, Michael R, Dir, Chesterfield County Public Library, 9501 Lori Rd, Chesterfield, VA, 23832. Tel: 804-748-1601. Fax: 804-751-4679. p. 2457

Maben, Michael, Cat Librn, Indiana University, School of Law Library, Maurer School of Law, 211 S Indiana Ave, Bloomington, IN, 47405. Tel: 812-855-1882. Fax: 812-855-7099. p. 727

Maberly, Linda, Cat, Pacific Union College, One Angwin Ave, Angwin, CA, 94508-9705. Tel: 707-965-6640. Fax: 707-965-6504. p. 121

Maberry, Sue, Dir, Otis College of Art & Design Library, 9045 Lincoln Blvd, Westchester, CA, 90045. Tel: 310-665-6800, Ext 6930. Fax: 310-665-6998. p. 283

Mabie, Arlene, Dir, Librn, Hawkins Area Library, 709 Main St, Hawkins, WI, 54530-9557. Tel: 715-585-2311. Fax: 715-585-2311. p. 2597

Mabley, Pat, Asst Mgr, Valleyview Municipal Library, 4804 50th Ave, Valleyview, AB, T0H 3N0, CANADA. Tel: 780-524-3033. Fax: 780-524-4563. p. 2720

Mabry, Holly, Librn, Louisiana Public Library, 121 N Third St, Louisiana, MO, 63353. Tel: 573-754-4491. Fax: 573-754-4208. p. 1343

Mabry, Phil, Syst Mgr, Pickens County Library System, 304 Biltmore Rd, Easley, SC, 29640. Tel: 864-850-7077. Fax: 864-850-7088. p. 2193

Mabus, Lisa M, Librn, Hunterdon Developmental Center Library, 40 Pittstown Rd, Clinton, NJ, 08809. Tel: 908-735-4031, Ext 1028. Fax: 908-730-1311. p. 1479

Mabus, Vic, Cat, Computer Serv, Salida Regional Library, 405 E St, Salida, CO, 81201. Tel: 719-539-4826. p. 322

Mac, Lily, Librn, Gowling Lafleur Henderson LLP, One First Canadian Pl, 100 King St W, Ste 1600, Toronto, ON, M5X 1G5, CANADA. Tel: 416-862-3637. Fax: 416-862-7661. p. 2854

Mac Taggart, Mary, Commun Libr Mgr, County of Los Angeles Public Library, Lake Los Angeles Library, 16921 E Ave O, Ste A, Palmdale, CA, 93591. Tel: 661-264-0593. Fax: 661-264-0859. p. 142

MacAdam, Jeanette A, ILL, Rochester College, 800 W Avon Rd, Rochester Hills, MI, 48307. Tel: 248-218-2263. Fax: 248-218-2265. p. 1222

MacAndrew, Kathleen, Cat, Roger Williams University, Ten Metacom Ave, Bristol, RI, 02809-5171. Tel: 401-254-4538. Fax: 401-254-4543. p. 2163

MacArthur, Caroline, Dir, Southold Free Library, 53705 Main Rd, Southold, NY, 11971. Tel: 631-765-2077. Fax: 631-765-2197. p. 1746

MacAskill, Terry, Libr Syst Spec, University of Massachusetts at Boston, 100 Morrissey Blvd, Boston, MA, 02125-3300. Tel: 617-287-5914. p. 1068

Macaulay, Jennifer, Head, Syst, Stonehill College, 320 Washington St, Easton, MA, 02357-4015. Tel: 508-565-1238. Fax: 508-565-1424. p. 1086

Macaulay, Mary K, Librn, Polsinelli Shughart PC, 7733 Forsyth Blvd, Ste 1200, Saint Louis, MO, 63105. Tel: 314-727-7676, Ext 7151. Fax: 314-727-7166. p. 1357

MacBain, Christina, Ref Serv Coordr, Simcoe County Archives, 1149 Hwy 26, RR 2, Minesing, ON, L0L 1Y2, CANADA. Tel: 705-726-9300, Ext 1292. Fax: 705-725-5341. p. 2822

Macbeth, Douglas, Dir, Jackson Laboratory, 600 Main St, Bar Harbor, ME, 04609-1500. Tel: 207-288-6146. Fax: 207-288-6079. p. 976

MacBride, Katie, YA Librn, Mill Valley Public Library, 375 Throckmorton Ave, Mill Valley, CA, 94941-2698. Tel: 415-389-4292, Ext 129. Fax: 415-388-8929. p. 186

Maccall, Melinda, Librn, Sullivan University Library, Louisville Technical Institute Campus, 3901 Atkinson Square Dr, Louisville, KY, 40218. Tel: 502-456-6509. p. 926

MacCall, Steven, Assoc Prof, University of Alabama, 514 Main Library, Tuscaloosa, AL, 35487. Tel: 205-348-4610. Fax: 205-348-3746. p. 2961

MacCallum, Marcia, ILL Librn, Wiggin Memorial Library, Ten Bunker Hill Ave, Stratham, NH, 03885. Tel: 603-772-4346. p. 1465

MacCartney, Donna, ILL Spec, College of Lake County, 19351 W Washington St, Grayslake, IL, 60030. Tel: 847-543-2465. Fax: 847-223-7690. p. 652

MacConnell, Suzanne, Ch, Corona Public Library, 650 S Main St, Corona, CA, 92882. Tel: 951-736-2381. Fax: 951-736-2499. p. 136

MacCord, Erin, Dir of Develop, New Jersey State Library, Talking Book & Braille Center, 2300 Stuyvesant Ave, Trenton, NJ, 08618. Tel: 609-406-7179, Ext 816. Fax: 609-406-7181. p. 1536

MacCormick, Susan, Asst Librn, Aurora Free Library, 370 Main St, Aurora, NY, 13026. Tel: 315-364-8074. Fax: 315-364-8074. p. 1576

MacDonald, Alex, Br Mgr, Thompson-Nicola Regional District Library System, Kamloops Branch, 100-465 Victoria St, Kamloops, BC, V2C 2A9, CANADA. Tel: 250-372-5145. p. 2729

MacDonald, Anna, Libr Assoc II, Northwestern State University Libraries, 3329 University Pkwy, Leesville, LA, 71446. Tel: 337-392-3126. Fax: 337-392-3184. p. 955

MacDonald, Bertrum, Dr, Prof, Dalhousie University, 6100 University Ave, Halifax, NS, B3H 3J5, CANADA. Tel: 902-494-3656. Fax: 902-494-2451. p. 2978

MacDonald, Cathie, Libr Mgr, Rocky Mountain House Public Library, 4922 52nd St, Rocky Mountain House, AB, T4T 1B1, CANADA. Tel: 403-845-2042, 403-845-5775. Fax: 403-845-5633. p. 2715

MacDonald, Cathy, Libr Mgr, Albert-Westmorland-Kent Regional Library, Petitcodiac Public, Six Kay St, Ste 101, Petitcodiac, NB, E4Z 4K6, CANADA. Tel: 506-756-3144. Fax: 506-756-3142. p. 2765

MacDonald, Cathy, Librn, South Shore Public Libraries, 15442 Hwy Three, Hebbville, NS, B4V 6X6, CANADA. Tel: 902-543-2548. p. 2783

MacDonald, Corrie, Tech Coordr, Cranston Public Library, 140 Sockanosset Cross Rd, Cranston, RI, 02920-5539. Tel: 401-943-9080. Fax: 401-946-5079. p. 2164

MacDonald, Jamie, Cat, Taunton Public Library, 12 Pleasant St, Taunton, MA, 02780. Tel: 508-821-1410. Fax: 508-821-1414. p. 1131

MacDonald, Jean, Chief Librn, Pender Island Public Library, 4407 Bedwell Harbour Rd, Pender Island, BC, V0N 2M0, CANADA. Tel: 250-629-3722. Fax: 250-629-3788. p. 2735

Macdonald, Jeanette, Libr Tech, Nova Scotia Community College, 5685 Leeds St, Halifax, NS, B3J 3C4, CANADA. Tel: 902-491-4694. Fax: 902-491-2015. p. 2782

MacDonald, Joan, Chief Librn, Smith-Ennismore-Lakefield Public Library, 836 Charles St, Bridgenorth, ON, K0L 1H0, CANADA. Tel: 705-292-5065. Fax: 705-292-6695. p. 2797

MacDonald, John, Coordr, Nunavut Research Institute, PO Box 210, Igloolik, NU, X0A 0L0, CANADA. Tel: 867-934-2069. Fax: 867-934-2058. p. 2789

MacDonald, Joyce, Ref, Jefferson-Madison Regional Library, 201 E Market St, Charlottesville, VA, 22902-5287. Tel: 434-979-7151, Ext 206, 434-979-7151, Ext 207. Fax: 434-971-7035. p. 2453

MacDonald, Karen, Dir of Libr Operations, Provincetown Public Library, 356 Commercial St, Provincetown, MA, 02657-2209. Tel: 508-487-7094. p. 1119

MacDonald, Karen, Dir, Daland Memorial Library, Five N Main St, Mont Vernon, NH, 03057. Tel: 603-673-7888. Fax: 603-673-7888. p. 1458

MacDonald, Kathy, Liaison/Spec Librn, University of Waterloo Library, Witer Learning Resource Centre, Optometry Bldg, Rm 2101, Waterloo, ON, N2L 3G1, CANADA. Tel: 519-888-4567, Ext 38538. Fax: 519-725-0784. p. 2870

MacDonald, Kathy L, Dir, Bayport Public Library, 582 N Fourth St, Bayport, MN, 55003-1111. Tel: 651-275-4416. Fax: 651-275-4417. p. 1240

Macdonald, Kerry, Librn, University of Manitoba, Seven Oaks General Hospital Library, 2300 McPhillips St, Winnipeg, MB, R2V 3M3, CANADA. Tel: 204-632-3107. Fax: 204-694-8240. p. 2758

Macdonald, Kerry, Librn, University of Manitoba Libraries, Seven Oaks General Hospital Library, 2300 McPhillips St, Winnipeg, MB, R2V 3M3, CANADA. Tel: 204-632-3107. Fax: 204-694-8240. p. 2759

MacDonald, Kristine, Dir, Silverpeak Library, Goldfield Public Library, 233 Crook St, Goldfield, NV, 89013. Tel: 775-485-3236. Fax: 775-485-3236. p. 1434

MacDonald, Kristine, Dir, Silverpeak Library, Ten Montezuma St, Silverpeak, NV, 89047. Tel: 775-937-2215. Fax: 775-937-2215. p. 1434

Macdonald, Logan, Coll Develop Mgr, Anythink Libraries, 5877 E 120th Ave, Thornton, CO, 80602. Tel: 303-288-2001. Fax: 303-451-0190. p. 323

MacDonald, Nadine, Head, Access Serv, Pace University, 861 Bedford Rd, Pleasantville, NY, 10570-2799. Tel: 914-773-3854. Fax: 914-773-3508. p. 1719

MacDonald, Patricia, Ref, Loyola-Notre Dame Library, Inc, 200 Winston Ave, Baltimore, MD, 21212. Tel: 410-617-6800. Fax: 410-617-6895. p. 1015

MacDonald, Patricia, Assoc Univ Librn, Admin Serv, Towson University, 8000 York Rd, Towson, MD, 21252-0001. Tel: 410-704-2445. Fax: 410-704-3760. p. 1045

MacDonald, Patricia, Librn, Pouce Coupe Public Library, 5000-49th Ave, Pouce Coupe, BC, V0C 2C0, CANADA. Tel: 250-786-5765. Fax: 250-786-5765. p. 2735

MacDonald, Peter, Info Syst Spec, Hamilton College, 198 College Hill Rd, Clinton, NY, 13323-1299. Tel: 315-859-4493. Fax: 315-859-4578. p. 1607

MacDonald, Randall M, Libr Dir, Florida Southern College, 111 Lake Hollingsworth Dr, Lakeland, FL, 33801-5698. Tel: 863-680-4165. Fax: 863-680-4126. p. 459

MacDonald, Richard, Dir, Baraboo Public Library, 230 Fourth Ave, Baraboo, WI, 53913. Tel: 608-356-6166. Fax: 608-355-2779. p. 2580

MacDonald, Rose, Res Ctr Mgr, Holland College Library Services, 140 Weymouth St, Charlottetown, PE, C1A 4Z1, CANADA. Tel: 902-894-6837. Fax: 902-566-9522. p. 2875

MacDonald, Sara J, Pub Serv Librn, University of the Arts University Libraries, Anderson Hall, 1st Flr, 333 S Broad St, Philadelphia, PA, 19102. Tel: 215-717-6280. Fax: 215-717-6287. p. 2119

MacDonald, Susan, Ch, Weeks Public Library, 36 Post Rd, Greenland, NH, 03840-2312. Tel: 603-436-8548. Fax: 603-427-0913. p. 1449

MacDonald, Tim, Librn, Northwest Community College Library, 5331 McConnell Ave, Terrace, BC, V8G 4X2, CANADA. Tel: 250-638-5407. Fax: 250-635-1594. p. 2739

MacDonald, W James, Res Support & Instruction Librn, Connecticut College, 270 Mohegan Ave, New London, CT, 06320-4196. Tel: 860-439-2656. Fax: 860-439-2871. p. 359

MacDonald, Wendy, Chief Librn/CEO, Sioux Lookout Public Library, 21 Fifth Ave, Sioux Lookout, ON, P8T 1B3, CANADA. Tel: 807-737-3660. Fax: 807-737-4046. p. 2841

MacDonald, Yzonne, Dir, Fraser Milner Casgrain LLP, Barristers & Solicitors, 400 Toronto Dominion Ctr, 77 King St W, Toronto, ON, M5K 0A1, CANADA. Tel: 416-863-4581. Fax: 416-863-4592. p. 2853

MacDonell, Karen, Cat, College of Physicians & Surgeons of British Columbia, 100-1383 W Eighth Ave, Vancouver, BC, V6H 4C4, CANADA. Tel: 604-733-6671. Fax: 604-737-8582. p. 2740

MacDougall, Harriett, Dir, Nova Southeastern University Libraries, 3100 Ray Ferrero Jr Blvd, Fort Lauderdale, FL, 33314. Tel: 954-262-4600. Fax: 954-262-3805. p. 444

MacDougall, PJ, Librn, University of Toronto Libraries, Robertson Davies Library, Massey College, Four Devonshire Pl, Toronto, ON, M5S 2E1, CANADA. Tel: 416-978-2893. Fax: 416-978-1759. p. 2865

MacDougall, S Faye, Regional Librn, Cape Breton Regional Library, 50 Falmouth St, Sydney, NS, B1P 6X9, CANADA. Tel: 902-562-3279. Fax: 902-564-0765. p. 2785

MacDougall, Susan, Asst Librn, Keg River Community Library, NE 21-101-24-W5, Keg River, AB, T0H 2G0, CANADA. Tel: 780-981-2090. p. 2708

Mace, William D, Syst Librn, Aiso Library, 543 Lawton Rd, Ste 617A, Monterey, CA, 93944-3214. Tel: 831-242-5572. Fax: 831-242-5816. p. 189

Macek, Rosanne, Dir, Mountain View Public Library, 585 Franklin St, Mountain View, CA, 94041-1998. Tel: 650-903-6335. Fax: 650-962-0438. p. 192

MacEwan, Bonnie, Dean, Libr Serv, Auburn University, Ralph Brown Draughon Library, 231 Mell St, Auburn, AL, 36849. Tel: 334-844-1715. Fax: 334-844-4424. p. 5

MacEwen, Kathy, Libr Tech, Prince Edward Island Public Library Service, Souris Public, 75 Main St, Souris, PE, C0A 2B0, CANADA. Tel: 902-687-2157. p. 2876

MacFadden, Kimberly, Ch, Decatur Public Library, 504 Cherry St NE, Decatur, AL, 35601. Tel: 256-353-2993. Fax: 256-350-6736. p. 14

MacFarland, David, Operations Mgr, University of California, Berkeley, Anthropology, 230 Kroeber Hall, Berkeley, CA, 94720-6000. Tel: 510-642-2419. Fax: 510-643-9293. p. 127

MacFarland, Patty, Circ/Reserves Coordr, Lexington Theological Seminary, 631 S Limestone, Lexington, KY, 40508. Tel: 859-280-1229. Fax: 859-281-6042. p. 921

Macfarlane, Carrie M, Librn, Middlebury College Library, Armstrong Library, McCardell Bicentennial Hall, Middlebury, VT, 05753. Tel: 802-443-5018. Fax: 802-443-2016. p. 2428

MacFarlane, Karrie, Head of Ref & Instrul Serv, Middlebury College Library, 110 Storrs Ave, Middlebury, VT, 05753-6007. Tel: 802-443-5490. Fax: 802-443-2074, 802-443-5698. p. 2428

MacFarlane, Wilma, Librn, Farris Management Ltd, 700 W Georgia St, 26th Flr, Vancouver, BC, V7Y 1B3, CANADA. Tel: 604-684-9151. Fax: 604-661-9349. p. 2741

MacFate, Ann C, Dir, Needham Free Public Library, 1139 Highland Ave, Needham, MA, 02494-3298. Tel: 781-455-7559. Fax: 781-455-7591. p. 1108

MacFeiggan, Shelley, Tech Serv, Southern Tier Library System, 9424 Scott Rd, Painted Post, NY, 14870-9598. Tel: 607-962-3141. Fax: 607-962-5356. p. 1714

MacGowan, Sally, Acq Librn, University of Colorado Denver, 12950 E Montview Blvd, Aurora, CO, 80045. Tel: 303-724-2152. Fax: 303-724-2166. p. 289

MacGregor, Leslie, Dir, GEP Dodge Library, Two Main St, Bennington, NH, 03442-4109. Tel: 603-588-6585. Fax: 603-588-6585. p. 1439

MacGregor, Lynn, Librn, Atlantic Provinces Special Education Authority Library, 5940 South St, Halifax, NS, B3H 1S6, CANADA. Tel: 902-424-5639, 902-424-8524. Fax: 902-424-3808. p. 2780

MacGregor, Matthew, Pres, Testing Engineers International, Inc, 3455 S 500 West, South Salt Lake, UT, 84115-4234. Tel: 801-262-2332. Fax: 801-262-2363. p. 2416

MacGregor, Ray, Dir, Santa Barbara County Law Library, 312 E Cook St, Santa Maria, CA, 93454. Tel: 805-568-2296, 568-2297. Fax: 805-568-2299. p. 265

MacGregor, Raymond, Dir, McMahon Law Library of Santa Barbara County, County Court House, Santa Barbara, CA, 93101. Tel: 805-568-2296. Fax: 805-568-2299. p. 260

MacGuire, Mary Jane, Archives Coordr, Res Serv Librn, Landmark College Library, River Rd S, Putney, VT, 05346. Tel: 802-387-6755. Fax: 802-387-6896. p. 2432

Mach, Joan, Asst Librn, Saint Peter's College, Hudson Terrace, Englewood Cliffs, NJ, 07632. Tel: 201-985-2879. Fax: 201-568-6614. p. 1484

Machado, Julie, Libr Mgr, Washoe County Library System, Spanish Springs Library, 7100A Pyramid Lake Hwy, Sparks, NV, 89436-6669. Tel: 775-424-1844. Fax: 775-424-1840. p. 1434

Machalow, Robert, Head, Archives, Circ & Reserve, York College Library, 94-20 Guy R Brewer Blvd, Jamaica, NY, 11451. Tel: 718-262-2018. Fax: 718-262-2027, 718-262-2997. p. 1646

MacHart, Marlene, Librn, Daniels County Free Library, 203 Timmons St, Scobey, MT, 59263. Tel: 406-487-5502. Fax: 406-487-5502. p. 1388

Macheak, Carol, Head, Ref, University of Arkansas at Little Rock, 2801 S University Ave, Little Rock, AR, 72204. Tel: 501-569-8809. Fax: 501-569-3017. p. 107

MacHenry, David, Libr Asst, Licia & Mason Beekley Community Library, Ten Central Ave, New Hartford, CT, 06057. Tel: 860-379-7235. Fax: 860-379-5806. p. 355

Machlan, Rhonda, Res Sharing Spec, State Library of Kansas, State Capitol Bldg, Topeka, KS, 66612. Tel: 785-296-3296. Fax: 785-296-6650. p. 896

Macholz, Linda, Asst Dir, Ref Serv, Fairport Public Library, One Fairport Village Landing, Fairport, NY, 14450. Tel: 585-223-9091. Fax: 585-223-3998. p. 1621

Machones, Sherry, Librn, Edgerton Public Library, 101 Albion St, Edgerton, WI, 53534-1836. Tel: 608-884-4511. Fax: 608-884-7575. p. 2590

Macias, Irene, Dir, Santa Barbara Public Library, 40 E Anapamu St, Santa Barbara, CA, 93101-2722. Tel: 805-962-7623. p. 261

Macias, Irene, Dir, Santa Barbara Public Library, Central Library, 40 E Anapamu St, Santa Barbara, CA, 93101-2722. Tel: 805-962-7653. Fax: 805-564-5660. p. 261

Macias-Miller, Lily, Adminr, Phoenix VA Health Care System, 650 E Indian School Rd, Phoenix, AZ, 85012. Tel: 602-222-6411. Fax: 602-222-6472. p. 77

Maciejewski, Felice, Dir, Todd Wehr Library, St Norbert College, 301 Third St, De Pere, WI, 54115. Tel: 920-403-3280. Fax: 920-403-4064. p. 2587

Macinick, James, Ref, Farmingdale State College of New York, 2350 Broadhollow Rd, Farmingdale, NY, 11735-1021. Tel: 631-420-2040. Fax: 631-420-2473. p. 1622

MacInnis, Ann, Libr Tech, Prince Edward Island Public Library Service, St Peters Public, 1968 Cardigan Rd, St. Peters, PE, C0A 2A0, CANADA. Tel: 902-961-3415. p. 2876

MacInnis, Deborah A, Asst Dir, Edgartown Free Public Library, 58 N Water St, Edgartown, MA, 02539. Tel: 508-627-1373. p. 1087

MacInnis, Elaine, ILL, University of King's College Library, 6350 Coburg Rd, Halifax, NS, B3H 2A1, CANADA. Tel: 902-422-1271. Fax: 902-423-3357. p. 2783

MacInnis, Karen, Curator, Marblehead Museum & Historical Society Library, 170 Washington St, Marblehead, MA, 01945-3340. Tel: 781-631-1069. Fax: 781-631-0917. p. 1102

MacIntosh, Ian, Coll Librn, Cape Breton Regional Library, 50 Falmouth St, Sydney, NS, B1P 6X9, CANADA. Tel: 902-562-3279. Fax: 902-564-0765. p. 2785

MacIntosh, Maria, Exec Dir, AIDS Coalition of Nova Scotia Library, 1668 Barrington St, Halifax, NS, B3J 2A2, CANADA. Tel: 902-425-4882. Fax: 902-422-6200. p. 2780

MacIsaac, Jennifer, Cat, Nova Scotia Agricultural College Library, 135 College Rd, Truro, NS, B2N 5E3, CANADA. Tel: 902-893-4578. Fax: 902-895-0934. p. 2786

MacIver, Bonnie R, Dir, Leach Public Library, 417 Second Ave N, Wahpeton, ND, 58075. Tel: 701-642-5732. Fax: 701-642-5732. p. 1849

Mack, Betsy, Dir, Prospect Free Library, 915 Trenton Falls St, Prospect, NY, 13435. Tel: 315-896-2736. Fax: 315-896-4045. p. 1724

Mack, Cathi Cooper, Coordr, Coll Develop, South Carolina State University, 300 College St NE, Orangeburg, SC, 29115-4427. Tel: 803-536-8633. Fax: 803-536-8902. p. 2202

Mack, Cheryl, Dir, Air Force Research Laboratory, Technical Library, 203 W Eglin Blvd, Ste 300, Eglin AFB, FL, 32542-6843. Tel: 850-882-6849. Fax: 850-882-3214. p. 439

Mack, Cheryl, Info Spec, Air Force Research Laboratory, Munitions Directorate Technical Library, 203 W Eglin Blvd, Ste 300, Eglin AFB, FL, 32542-6843. Tel: 850-882-5586. Fax: 850-882-4476. p. 439

Mack, Cindy, Dir, Wixom Public Library, 49015 Pontiac Trail, Wixom, MI, 48393-2567. Tel: 248-624-2512. Fax: 248-624-0862. p. 1237

Mack, Diana, Librn, Metro Kalyn Community Library, 5017-49 St, Bag 250, Bruderheim, AB, T0B 0S0, CANADA. Tel: 780-796-3032. Fax: 780-796-3032. p. 2686

Mack, Helen, Acq, Lehigh University, Fairchild-Martindale Library, Eight A E Packer Ave, Bethlehem, PA, 18015-3170. Tel: 610-758-3035. Fax: 610-758-6524. p. 2034

Mack, Kara, ILL, Hale & Dorr Library, 60 State St, Boston, MA, 02109. Tel: 617-526-5900. Fax: 617-526-5000. p. 1061

Mack, Kari, Dir, Libr Serv, Ulster County Community College, Stone Ridge, NY, 12484. Tel: 845-687-5213. Fax: 845-687-5220. p. 1749

Mack, Kristin, Asst Dir, Ch, Blair Memorial Library, 416 N Main St, Clawson, MI, 48017-1599. Tel: 248-588-5500. Fax: 248-588-3114. p. 1163

Mack, Linda, Dir, Andrews University, Music Materials Center, 10230 Hamel Hall Rd, Berrien Springs, MI, 49104-0230. Tel: 269-471-3114. p. 1157

Mack, Mary Jo, Librn, John A Stahl Library, 330 N Colfax St, West Point, NE, 68788. Tel: 402-372-3831. Fax: 402-372-5931. p. 1423

Mack, Sue, ILL, Kent Memorial Library, 50 N Main St (Junction of Rtes 75 & 168), Suffield, CT, 06078-2117. Tel: 860-668-3896. Fax: 860-668-3895. p. 371

Mack-Harvin, Dionne, Dir, El Paso Public Library, 501 N Oregon St, El Paso, TX, 79901. Tel: 915-543-5413. Fax: 915-543-5410. p. 2316

MacKay, Camilla, Head of Libr, Bryn Mawr College, Rhys Carpenter Library for Art, Archaeology & Cities, 101 N Merion Ave, Bryn Mawr, PA, 19104-2899. Tel: 610-526-7910. Fax: 610-526-7975. p. 2039

MacKay, Crystal, Exec Dir, Farm & Food Care Ontario Library, 100 Stone Rd W, Ste 106, Guelph, ON, N1G 5L3, CANADA. Tel: 519-837-1326. Fax: 519-837-3209. p. 2806

MacKay, Gabrielle, Circ, Corona Public Library, 650 S Main St, Corona, CA, 92882. Tel: 951-736-2381. Fax: 951-736-2499. p. 136

MacKay, Johanna M, Info Literacy/Ref, Suffolk County Community College, 121 Speonk Riverhead Rd, Riverhead, NY, 11901-9990. Tel: 631-548-2569. Fax: 631-369-2641. p. 1728

Mackay, Kathy, Patient Educ Librn, Department of Veterans Affairs, One Veterans Dr, 142 D, Minneapolis, MN, 55417. Tel: 612-467-4212. Fax: 612-725-2046. p. 1259

MacKay, Pamela, Dir, Info Res, Huron University College Library, 1349 Western Rd, London, ON, N6G 1H3, CANADA. Tel: 519-438-7224, Ext 209. Fax: 519-438-3938. p. 2817

MacKellar, Laurie, Pub Serv, Elizabethtown Community & Technical College Library, 600 College Street Rd, Elizabethtown, KY, 42701. Tel: 270-706-8812. Fax: 270-769-1618. p. 912

Macken, Susan, Dir, Oelwein Public Library, 201 E Charles St, Oelwein, IA, 50662-1939. Tel: 319-283-1515. Fax: 319-283-6646. p. 836

Mackenzie, Annie, ILL, YA Serv, Fanwood Memorial Library, 14 Tillotson Rd, Fanwood, NJ, 07023-1399. Tel: 908-322-6400. Fax: 908-322-5590. p. 1485

Mackenzie, Barbara, Librn, Quesnel Library, 101 410 Kinchant St, Quesnel, BC, V2J 7J5, CANADA. Tel: 250-992-7912. Fax: 250-992-9882. p. 2736

MacKenzie, Dena, Librn, Wapiti Regional Library, Star City Public Library, 400 Fourth St, Star City, SK, S0E 1P0, CANADA. Tel: 306-863-4364. p. 2922

Mackenzie, Linda, Dir, Res & Ref Librn, Toronto Public Library, 789 Yonge St, Toronto, ON, M4W 2G8, CANADA. Tel: 416-393-7131. Fax: 416-393-7229. p. 2860

Mackenzie, Linda, Dir, Res & Ref Librn, Toronto Public Library, North York Central, 5120 Yonge St, Toronto, ON, M2N 5N9, CANADA. Tel: 416-395-5535. Fax: 416-395-5668. p. 2862

Mackenzie, Linda, Dir, Res & Ref Librn, Toronto Public Library, Toronto Reference Library, 789 Yonge St, Toronto, ON, M4W 2G8, CANADA. Tel: 416-395-5577. Fax: 416-393-7147. p. 2863

MacKenzie, Marjorie, Instrul Serv Librn, Green River Community College, 12401 SE 320th St, Auburn, WA, 98092-3699. Tel: 253-833-9111, Ext 2101. Fax: 253-288-3436, 253-288-3491. p. 2507

MacKenzie, Nancy, Sr Mgr, Calgary Public Library, W R Castell Central Library, 616 Macleod Trail SE, Calgary, AB, T2G 2M2, CANADA. Tel: 403-260-2600. Fax: 403-237-5393. p. 2689

MacKenzie, Richard, Coll Mgt, Maritime Museum of British Columbia Library, 28 Bastion Sq, Victoria, BC, V8W 1H9, CANADA. Tel: 250-385-4222, Ext 105. Fax: 250-382-2869. p. 2745

Mackenzie, Rosemary, Ch, Haston Free Public Library, 161 N Main St, North Brookfield, MA, 01535. Tel: 508-867-0208. Fax: 508-867-0216. p. 1112

Mackenzie, Sandy, Adult Serv, Dir, Human Res, Cross' Mills Public Library, 4417 Old Post Rd, Charlestown, RI, 02813. Tel: 401-364-6211. Fax: 401-364-0609. p. 2164

Mackenzie, Scott, Head, Access Serv, Simon Fraser University Library, 8888 University Dr, Burnaby, BC, V5A 1S6, CANADA. Tel: 778-782-4081. Fax: 778-782-3023. p. 2725

Mackereth, Anne, Pub Serv, Northwestern Health Sciences University, 2501 W 84th St, Bloomington, MN, 55431-1599. Tel: 952-885-5419 Ext 218. Fax: 952-884-3318. p. 1242

Mackes, Catrina L, Law Libr Asst, Berks County Law Library, Courthouse, Tenth Flr, 633 Court St, Reading, PA, 19601-4302. Tel: 610-478-3370. Fax: 610-478-6375. p. 2133

Mackesy-Karpoff, Eileen, Dir, Ridgefield Park Free Public Library, 107 Cedar St, Ridgefield Park, NJ, 07660. Tel: 201-641-0689. Fax: 201-440-1058. p. 1526

Mackey, Jill A, Dir, Crook County Library, 414 Main St, Sundance, WY, 82729. Tel: 307-283-1006, 307-283-1008. Fax: 307-283-1006. p. 2660

Mackey, Karen, Coop Librn, Donaldson Co, Inc, PO Box 1299, MS 301, Minneapolis, MN, 55440-1299. Tel: 952-887-3019. Fax: 952-887-3555. p. 1259

Mackey, Kay, Instrul Serv Librn, Yeshiva University Libraries, Dr Lillian & Dr Rebecca Chutick Law Library, Benjamin N Cardozo School of Law, 55 Fifth Ave, New York, NY, 10003-4301. Tel: 212-790-0223. Fax: 212-790-0236. p. 1703

Mackey, Kitty, Ref Librn (Info Serv), Clark College, Mail Stop LIB 112, 1933 Fort Vancouver Way, Vancouver, WA, 98663-3598. Tel: 360-992-2558. Fax: 360-992-2869. p. 2545

Mackey, Margaret, Dr, Prof & Grad Coordr, University of Alberta, 3-20 Rutherford S, Edmonton, AB, T6G 2J4, CANADA. Tel: 780-492-4578. Fax: 780-492-2430. p. 2977

Mackey, Michele, Libr Tech, Department of Veterans Affairs, One Veterans Dr, 142 D, Minneapolis, MN, 55417. Tel: 612-467-4200. Fax: 612-725-2046. p. 1259

Mackey, Neosha, Dean, Missouri State University, Duane G Meyer Library, 901 S National Ave, Springfield, MO, 65897. Tel: 417-836-4525. Fax: 417-836-4764. p. 2968

Mackey, Neosha A, Assoc Dean, Libr Serv, Missouri State University, 850 S John Q Hammons Pkwy, Springfield, MO, 65807. Tel: 417-836-4525. Fax: 417-836-4764. p. 1367

Mackey, Terry, Dir, Clackamas Community College, 19600 S Molalla Ave, Oregon City, OR, 97045. Tel: 503-657-6958, Ext 2289. Fax: 503-655-8925. p. 2009

Mackey-Russo, Denise, Ref, Russell Library, 123 Broad St, Middletown, CT, 06457. Tel: 860-347-2528. p. 352

Mackie, Christine, ILL, Ref Serv, Woodburn Public Library, 280 Garfield St, Woodburn, OR, 97071-4698. Tel: 503-982-5252. Fax: 503-982-2808. p. 2023

Mackie, Kelly, Librn, Craig Public Library, 504 Third St, Craig, AK, 99921. Tel: 907-826-3281. Fax: 907-826-3280. p. 46

Mackie, Lesley, Librn, University of Manitoba, Misericordia Health Centre LIbrary, 99 Cornish Ave, Winnipeg, MB, R3C 1A2, CANADA. Tel: 204-788-8109. Fax: 204-889-4174. p. 2758

Mackie, Lesley, Librn, University of Manitoba Libraries, Misericordia Health Care Library, 99 Cornish Ave, Winnipeg, MB, R3C 1A2, CANADA. Tel: 204-788-8109. Fax: 204-889-4174. p. 2759

Mackie, Lorraine, Asst Librn, Coaldale Public Library, 2014 18th St, Coaldale, AB, T1M 1M1, CANADA. Tel: 403-345-1340. Fax: 403-345-1342. p. 2695

Mackie, Patricia, Mgr, Hughenden Public Library, Seven McKenzie Ave, Hughenden, AB, T0B 2E0, CANADA. Tel: 780-856-2435. Fax: 780-856-2435. p. 2707

Mackie, Paula, Br Mgr, Huron County Library, Blyth Branch, 435 Queen St, Blyth, ON, N0M 1H0, CANADA. Tel: 519-523-4400. p. 2799

Mackie, Paula, Br Mgr, Huron County Library, Wingham Branch, 281 Edward St, Wingham, ON, N0G 2W0, CANADA. Tel: 519-357-3312. p. 2800

MacKie-Mason, Jeffrey, Assoc Dean, Prof, University of Michigan, 304 West Hall, 1085 S University, Ann Arbor, MI, 48109-1107. Tel: 734-763-2285. Fax: 734-764-2475. p. 2967

Mackiewicz, Patty, Librn, Levy & Droney, 74 Batterson Park Rd, Farmington, CT, 06032. Tel: 860-676-3000. Fax: 860-676-3200. p. 340

MacKillop, Clare, Br Supvr, Cape Breton Regional Library, Dominion Public, 78 Commercial St, Unit A, Dominion, NS, B1G 1B4, CANADA. Tel: 902-562-3279. p. 2785

MacKillop, Clare, Br Supvr, Cape Breton Regional Library, Donkin Public, 81 Centre Ave, Donkin, NS, B1A 6N4, CANADA. Tel: 902-737-1154. p. 2785

MacKillop, Clare, Br Supvr, Cape Breton Regional Library, Florence Public, 676 Bras d'or Florence Rd, Florence, NS, B1Y 1E4, CANADA. Tel: 902-736-7583. p. 2785

MacKillop, Clare, Br Supvr, Cape Breton Regional Library, Main-a-Dieu Public, 2886 Louisbourg-Main-a-Dieu Rd, Main-a-Dieu, NS, B1C 1X5, CANADA. Tel: 902-562-3279. p. 2785

MacKillop, Clare, Br Supvr, Cape Breton Regional Library, Martha Hollett Memorial, One Fraser Ave, Sydney Mines, NS, B1V 2B8, CANADA. Tel: 902-736-3219. p. 2785

MacKillop, Clare, Br Supvr, Cape Breton Regional Library, New Waterford Branch, 3390 Plummer Ave, New Waterford, NS, B1H 4K4, CANADA. Tel: 902-862-2892. p. 2785

MacKillop, Clare, Br Supvr, Cape Breton Regional Library, Tompkins Memorial, Tompkins Pl, 2249 Sydney Rd, Unit 3, Reserve Mines, NS, B1E 1J9, CANADA. Tel: 902-562-3279. p. 2785

MacKillop, Clare, Br Supvr, Cape Breton Regional Library, W W Lewis Memorial, Ten Upper Warren St, Louisbourg, NS, B1C 1M6, CANADA. Tel: 902-733-3608. p. 2785

MacKillop, Clare, Br Supvr, Cape Breton Regional Library, Wilfred Oram Centennial, 299 Commercial St, North Sydney, NS, B2A 1B9, CANADA. Tel: 902-794-3272. p. 2785

Mackin, Carol, Circ, Tech Serv & Automation, Swarthmore Public Library, Borough Hall, 121 Park Ave, Swarthmore, PA, 19081-1536. Tel: 610-543-0436, 610-543-3171. Fax: 610-328-6699. p. 2145

Mackin, Michael, Circ Coordr, Oregon Health & Science University Library, 3181 SW Sam Jackson Park Rd, Portland, OR, 97239-3098. Tel: 503-494-3460. Fax: 503-494-3227. p. 2013

MacKinney, Lisa, Asst Libr Dir, Hall County Library System, 127 Main St NW, Gainesville, GA, 30501-3699. Tel: 770-532-3311. Fax: 770-532-4305. p. 534

MacKinnon, Christy, Natl Dir, Libr & Info Serv, Bennett Jones LLP Library, 4500 Bankers Hall E, 855 Second St SW, Calgary, AB, T2P 4K7, CANADA. Tel: 403-298-3165. Fax: 403-265-7219. p. 2688

MacKinnon, Denise, Libr Coordr, Institute for Human Services Education, 60 Lorne St, Ste 1, Truro, NS, B2N 3K3, CANADA. Tel: 902-893-3342. Fax: 902-895-4487. p. 2786

MacKinnon, Janet, Mgr, Calgary Public Library, Shaganappi, Multi-Service Ctr, 3415 Eighth Ave SW, Calgary, AB, T3C 0E8, CANADA. p. 2690

MacKinnon, Janet, Mgr, Calgary Public Library, Thorn-Hill, 6617 Centre St N, Calgary, AB, T2K 4Y5, CANADA. p. 2691

MacKinnon, Jennifer, Libr Dir, Sundre Municipal Library, 310 Center St N, Sundre, AB, T0M 1X0, CANADA. Tel: 403-638-4000. Fax: 403-638-5755. p. 2718

MacKintosh, Pamela, Econ Librn, University of Michigan, Sumner & Laura Foster Library, 265 Lorch Hall, Ann Arbor, MI, 48109-1220. Tel: 734-763-6609. Fax: 734-764-2769. p. 1152

Mackisey, Gail, Circ Supvr, University of Manitoba Libraries, E K Williams Law Library, 401 Robson Hall, 224 Dysart Rd, Winnipeg, MB, R3T 2N2, CANADA. Tel: 204-474-9995. Fax: 204-474-7582. p. 2759

Macklin, Alexis, Dr, Dir, Historical Society of Western Pennsylvania, 1212 Smallman St, Pittsburgh, PA, 15222. Tel: 412-454-6364. Fax: 412-454-6028. p. 2125

Macklin, Christina, Libr Mgr, Treasure Valley Community College Library, 650 College Blvd, Ontario, OR, 97914-3423. Tel: 541-881-5928. Fax: 541-881-2724. p. 2009

Macklin, Gayle, Purchasing, Sedona Public Library, 3250 White Bear Rd, Sedona, AZ, 86336. Tel: 928-282-7714. Fax: 928-282-5789. p. 81

Macko, Lucinda, Med Librn, Saint Mary Medical Center, 1500 S Lake Park Ave, Hobart, IN, 46342. Tel: 219-947-6230. Fax: 219-947-6331. p. 748

MacLaren, Audra, Ad, Oliver Wolcott Library, 160 South St, Litchfield, CT, 06759-0187. Tel: 860-567-8030. Fax: 860-567-4784. p. 349

MacLauchlan, Meghan, Children's Serv Supvr, Youth Serv Coordr, Cherry Hill Public Library, 1100 Kings Hwy N, Cherry Hill, NJ, 08034-1911. Tel: 856-903-1230. Fax: 856-667-9503. p. 1478

MacLaughlin, Rhoda M, Dir, Libr Serv, Cowley County Community College, 131 S Third St, Arkansas City, KS, 67005. Tel: 620-441-5280. Fax: 620-441-5356. p. 856

MacLean, Barbara, Ref Serv, Harnett County Public Library, 601 S Main St, Lillington, NC, 27546-6107. Tel: 910-893-3446. Fax: 910-893-3001. p. 1806

MacLean, Barbara, ILL, Cape Breton Regional Library, 50 Falmouth St, Sydney, NS, B1P 6X9, CANADA. Tel: 902-562-3279. Fax: 902-564-0765. p. 2785

MacLean, Cathy, Mgr, Libr Serv, Royal Ottawa Health Care Group, 1145 Carling Ave, Ottawa, ON, K1Z 7K4, CANADA. Tel: 613-722-6521, Ext 6268. p. 2833

Maclean, Deborah, Head, Libr Syst, Head, Tech Serv, Ottawa Office of the Auditor General, West Tower, 240 Sparks St, 11th Flr, Ottawa, ON, K1A 0G6, CANADA. Tel: 613-995-3708. Fax: 613-952-5131. p. 2832

MacLean, Elaine, Tech Serv, Saint Francis Xavier University, West St, Antigonish, NS, B2G 2W5, CANADA. Tel: 902-867-2221. Fax: 902-867-5153. p. 2777

MacLean, Jim, Ref Serv, Capital Area District Libraries, Downtown Lansing Library, 401 S Capitol Ave, Lansing, MI, 48933. Tel: 517-367-6323. Fax: 517-374-1068. p. 1200

MacLean, Kay, Libr Tech, Prince Edward Island Public Library Service, Murray Harbour Public, 1381 Main St, Murray Harbour, PE, C0A 1V0, CANADA. Tel: 902-962-3875. p. 2876

MacLean, Kay, Libr Tech, Prince Edward Island Public Library Service, Murray River Leona Giddings Memorial Library, 1066 McInnis Rd, Murray River, PE, C0A 1V0, CANADA. Tel: 902-962-2667. p. 2876

MacLean, Lana, Librn, Nova Scotia Community College, 226 Reeves St, Port Hawkesbury, NS, B9A 2W2, CANADA. Tel: 902-625-4075. Fax: 902-625-0193. p. 2784

MacLean, Lana, Regional Librn, Nova Scotia Community College, 1240 Grand Lake Rd, Sydney, NS, B1P 6J7, CANADA. Tel: 902-563-2102. Fax: 902-563-0511. p. 2785

Maclean, Margaret, In Charge, Pictou - Antigonish Regional Library, River John Library, Main St, River John, NS, B0K 1N0, CANADA. Tel: 902-351-2599. p. 2784

MacLean, Pam, Circ Librn, Colby Memorial Library, Seven Colby Rd, Danville, NH, 03819-5104. Tel: 603-382-6733. Fax: 603-382-0487. p. 1444

MacLean, Robert, Dir, Tufts Library, 46 Broad St, Weymouth, MA, 02188. Tel: 781-337-1402. Fax: 781-682-6123. p. 1139

MacLean, Shelley, In Charge, Pictou - Antigonish Regional Library, Trenton Library, 122 Main St, Trenton, NS, B0K 1X0, CANADA. Tel: 902-752-5181. p. 2784

MacLean, Tanya, Librn, Clarenville Public Library, 98 Manitoba Dr, Clarenville, NL, A5A 1K7, CANADA. Tel: 709-466-7634. Fax: 709-466-7634. p. 2769

MacLehose, Stew, Dir, Libr Syst, University of New England Libraries, 11 Hills Beach Rd, Biddeford, ME, 04005. Tel: 207-221-4535. Fax: 207-602-5922. p. 978

MacLellan, Judith, Asst Librn, Josiah Carpenter Library, 41 Main St, Pittsfield, NH, 03263. Tel: 603-435-8406. p. 1462

MacLennan, Birdie, Head, Coll Mgt Serv, University of Vermont Libraries, 538 Main St, Burlington, VT, 05405-0036. Tel: 802-656-2016. Fax: 802-656-4038. p. 2421

MacLennan, Elise, Asst Dir, Wellesley Free Library, 530 Washington St, Wellesley, MA, 02482. Tel: 781-235-1610, Ext 1107. Fax: 781-235-0495. p. 1135

MacLennan, Rodrick, Ref Serv, Ad, Somerset County Library System, Peapack & Gladstone Public, School St, Peapack, NJ, 07977. Tel: 908-234-0598. Fax: 908-719-2236. p. 1475

MacLeod, Debbi, Dir, State Pub Libr, Colorado State Library, 201 E Colfax Ave, Rm 309, Denver, CO, 80203-1799. Tel: 303-866-6900. Fax: 303-866-6940. p. 299

MacLeod, Debbi, Dir, Colorado Talking Book Library, 180 Sheridan Blvd, Denver, CO, 80226. Tel: 303-727-9277. Fax: 303-727-9281. p. 300

MacLeod, John, Spec Coll & Archives Librn, Fort Malden National Historic Site of Canada Resource Centre, 100 Laird Ave, Amherstburg, ON, N9V 2Z2, CANADA. Tel: 519-736-5416. Fax: 519-736-6603. p. 2792

MacLeod, Ken, Dir, Bruce County Public Library, 1243 MacKenzie Rd, Port Elgin, ON, N0H 2C6, CANADA. Tel: 519-832-6935. Fax: 519-832-9000. p. 2837

MacLeod, Melissa, Ch, Carver Public Library, Two Meadowbrook Way, Carver, MA, 02330-1278. Tel: 508-866-3415. Fax: 508-866-3416. p. 1079

MacLeod, Suzanne, Asst Dir, Peabody Institute Library of Danvers, 15 Sylvan St, Danvers, MA, 01923-2735. Tel: 978-774-0554. Fax: 978-762-0251. p. 1083

MacLeod, Teresa, Libr Mgr, Fraser Valley Regional Library, Mission Library, 33247 Second Ave, Mission, BC, V2V 1J9, CANADA. Tel: 604-826-6610. Fax: 604-826-6614. p. 2724

Macmann, Carol, Br Mgr, Dayton Metro Library, New Lebanon Branch, 715 W Main St, New Lebanon, OH, 45345. Tel: 937-496-8948. p. 1893

MacMartin, Sue, Dir, Brown Public Library, 93 S Main St, Northfield, VT, 05663. Tel: 802-485-4621. Fax: 802-485-4990. p. 2431

MacMillan, Carol, Managing Librn, Pictou - Antigonish Regional Library, New Glasgow Library, 182 Dalhousie St, New Glasgow, NS, B2H 5E3, CANADA. Tel: 902-752-8233. Fax: 902-755-6775. p. 2784

MacMillan, Donald, Dir, Merrimac Public Library, 34 W Main St, Merrimac, MA, 01860. Tel: 978-346-9441. Fax: 978-346-8272. p. 1105

MacMillan, Gail, Dir, Digital Libr Prog, Virginia Polytechnic Institute & State University Libraries, Drill Field Dr, Blacksburg, VA, 24062-9001. Tel: 540-231-5252. Fax: 540-231-3946. p. 2451

MacMillan, Margaret, Librn, Winnipeg Free Press Library, 1135 Mountain Ave, Winnipeg, MB, R2X 3B6, CANADA. Tel: 204-697-7291. Fax: 204-697-7412. p. 2760

Macmillan, Phyllis, Dir, Pauline & Jane Chilton Memorial Public Library, 400 Oakes St, Marlin, TX, 76661. Tel: 254-883-6602. p. 2359

MacMorris, Leiza D, Mgr, Res Librn, Wilson, Sonsini, Goodrich & Rosati, 650 Page Mill Rd, Palo Alto, CA, 94304. Tel: 650-493-9300. Fax: 650-493-6811. p. 205

MacMullen, Scott, Syst Coordr, Western Counties Regional Library, 405 Main St, Yarmouth, NS, B5A 1G3, CANADA. Tel: 902-742-2486. Fax: 902-742-6920. p. 2786

MacMurray, Kathleen, Librn, Bryn Mawr Presbyterian Church, 625 Montgomery Ave, Bryn Mawr, PA, 19010-3599. Tel: 610-525-2821. p. 2039

Macnaughtan, Don, Ref Serv, Lane Community College Library, 4000 E 30th Ave, Eugene, OR, 97405-0640. Tel: 541-463-5359. Fax: 541-463-4150. p. 1996

MacNaughton, Ellen, Clinical Librn, Surgery, Hartford Hospital, ERC Bldg-3, 80 Seymour St, Hartford, CT, 06102. Tel: 860-545-2424. Fax: 860-545-2572. p. 345

MacNayr, Kerry, Asst Librn, Lisbon Public Library, 45 School St, Lisbon, NH, 03585. Tel: 603-838-6615. Fax: 603-838-6615. p. 1454

MacNeil, Heather, Assoc Dean, Acad, University of Toronto, 140 St George St, Toronto, ON, M5S 3G6, CANADA. Tel: 416-978-3234. Fax: 416-978-5762. p. 2978

MacNeil, Karen, Librn, Cape Breton Regional Library, Baddeck Public, 526 Chebucto St, Baddeck, NS, B0E 1B0, CANADA. Tel: 902-295-2055. p. 2785

MacNeil, Karen, Librn, Cape Breton Regional Library, Victoria North Regional, 36243 Cabot Trail, Ingonish, NS, B0C 1K0, CANADA. Tel: 902-285-2544. p. 2785

MacNeil, Rod, Dep Univ Librn, Thomas Jefferson University, 1020 Walnut St, Philadelphia, PA, 19107. Tel: 215-503-2827. Fax: 215-923-3203. p. 2118

MacNeill, Daniel S, Dir, Lexington County Public Library System, 5440 Augusta Rd, Lexington, SC, 29072. Tel: 803-785-2640. Fax: 803-785-2601. p. 2199

MacNeill, Molly, Bldg Mgr/Supvr, State University of New York College of Technology, 34 Cornell Dr, Canton, NY, 13617-1098. Tel: 315-386-7228. Fax: 315-386-7931. p. 1602

MacNeill, Sarah, YA Serv, Wells County Public Library, 200 W Washington St, Bluffton, IN, 46714-1999. Tel: 260-824-1612. Fax: 260-824-3129. p. 728

Macnicol, Laurie, Learning Res Coordr, Hillsborough Community College, Brandon Campus Learning Resources Center, 10414 E Columbus Dr, Tampa, FL, 33619-9640. Tel: 813-253-7935. p. 496

Macnutt, Glenn, Syst Librn, Salem State University Library, 352 Lafayette St, Salem, MA, 01970-5353. Tel: 978-542-6230. Fax: 978-542-6596. p. 1122

Macomber, Kimberly, Ref, Sacred Heart University, 5151 Park Ave, Fairfield, CT, 06825-1000. Tel: 203-371-7746. Fax: 203-374-9968. p. 339

Macomber, Nancy, Acq, Govt Doc, Queens College, Benjamin S Rosenthal Library, 65-30 Kissena Blvd, Flushing, NY, 11367-0904. Tel: 718-997-3700. Fax: 718-997-3753. p. 1623

MacPhail, Ann, Libr Tech, Operational Head, Algonquin College Learning Resource Centre, Heritage Institute, Seven Craig St, Perth, ON, K7H 1X7, CANADA. Tel: 613-267-2859, Ext 5607. Fax: 613-267-3950. p. 2828

MacPhail, Jessica, Libr Dir, Racine Public Library, 75 Seventh St, Racine, WI, 53403. Tel: 262-636-9252. Fax: 262-636-9260. p. 2632

MacPhee, Karen, Libr Supvr, Dartmouth College Library, Kresge Physical Sciences Library, 6115 Fairchild Hall, Hanover, NH, 03755-3571. Tel: 603-646-3563. Fax: 603-646-3681. p. 1450

MacPherson, Amy, Div Chair, Libr & Teaching & Learning Ctr, South Mountain Community College Library, 7050 S 24th St, Phoenix, AZ, 85042. Tel: 602-305-5714. Fax: 602-243-8180. p. 77

MacPherson, Erin, Ref, Nova Scotia Agricultural College Library, 135 College Rd, Truro, NS, B2N 5E3, CANADA. Tel: 902-893-6669. Fax: 902-895-0934. p. 2786

MacPherson, Grace, Cat, Saint Francis Xavier University, West St, Antigonish, NS, B2G 2W5, CANADA. Tel: 902-867-2267. Fax: 902-867-5153. p. 2777

MacPherson, Jean, Librn, Atlantic County Library System, Egg Harbor Township Branch, One Swift Dr, Egg Harbor Township, NJ, 08234. Tel: 609-927-8664. Fax: 609-927-4683. p. 1500

MacPherson, Karen, Ch, Youth Serv, Takoma Park Maryland Library, 101 Philadelphia Ave, Takoma Park, MD, 20912. Tel: 301-891-7259. Fax: 301-270-0814. p. 1043

MacPherson, Natalie, Info Res, Librn, Nova Scotia Environment Library, 5151 Terminal Rd, 5th Flr, Halifax, NS, B3J 1A1, CANADA. Tel: 902-722-1330. Fax: 902-424-0503. p. 2782

MacPherson, Ruthmary, Head, Tech Serv, Mount Allison University Libraries & Archives, 49 York St, Sackville, NB, E4L 1C6, CANADA. Tel: 506-364-2691. Fax: 506-364-2617. p. 2766

Macrae, Mairi, Pub Prog Librn, Department of Community Services, Government of Yukon, 1171 First Ave, Whitehorse, YT, Y1A 0G9, CANADA. Tel: 867-667-5228. Fax: 867-393-6333. p. 2933

Macready, Ward, Dir, Sunfield District Library, 112 Main St, Sunfield, MI, 48890. Tel: 517-566-8065. Fax: 517-566-8065. p. 1230

Macrellis, Susan, Dir, East Ridge City Library, 1517 Tombras Ave, East Ridge, TN, 37412-2716. Tel: 423-867-7323. p. 2233

Macrina, Alison, Circ Supvr, Moore College of Art & Design, 20th St & The Parkway, Philadelphia, PA, 19103-1179. Tel: 215-965-4054. Fax: 215-965-8544. p. 2112

MacRitchie, Andrea, Dean, Libr & Acad Support, Quinsigamond Community College, 670 W Boylston St, Worcester, MA, 01606-2092. Tel: 508-854-4366. Fax: 508-854-4204. p. 1144

Mactague, Nancy, Dr, Res & Electronic Resources Librn, Aurora University, 315 S Gladstone, Aurora, IL, 60506-4877. Tel: 630-844-5437, 630-892-6431. Fax: 630-844-3848. p. 591

Macuirles, Louise, Access Serv & Syst, Ref Serv, General Electric Global Research, One Research Circle, Niskayuna, NY, 12309. Tel: 518-387-4952, 518-387-5000. p. 1706

Macumber, Ann, Dir, Manilla Public Library, 447 Main St, Manilla, IA, 51454. Tel: 712-654-5192. p. 829

MacWaters, Cristi, Coordr, ILL, Colorado State University Libraries, Morgan Library, 1201 Center Avenue Mall, Fort Collins, CO, 80523-. Tel: 970-491-1838. Fax: 970-491-1195. p. 307

MacWatters, Kelly, Web Librn, The Sage Colleges, 140 New Scotland Ave, Albany, NY, 12208. Tel: 518-292-1784. Fax: 518-292-1904. p. 1570

MacWatters, Kelly, Ref Serv, Website Mgr, Siena College, 515 Loudon Rd, Loudonville, NY, 12211-1462. Tel: 518-783-2588. Fax: 518-783-2570. p. 1655

MacWatters, Kelly, Web Librn, The Sage Colleges, 45 Ferry St, Troy, NY, 12180. Tel: 518-292-1784. Fax: 518-244-2400. p. 1756

MacWhinnie, Laurie, Ref, University of Maine at Farmington, 116 South St, Farmington, ME, 04938-1990. Tel: 207-778-7210. Fax: 207-778-7223. p. 985

MacWithey, Brian, Libr Dir, Pioneer Memorial Library, 115 W Main St, Fredericksburg, TX, 78624. Tel: 830-997-6513. Fax: 830-997-6514. p. 2325

MacWithey, Mary, Asst Dir, Schreiner University, 2100 Memorial Blvd, Kerrville, TX, 78028-5697. Tel: 830-792-7313. Fax: 830-792-7448. p. 2350

Macy, Brenda G, Dir, Hardin County Public Library, 100 Jim Owen Dr, Elizabethtown, KY, 42701. Tel: 270-769-6337. Fax: 270-769-0437. p. 912

Madacsi, Nancy, Dir, Centenary College, 400 Jefferson St, Hackettstown, NJ, 07840. Tel: 908-852-1400, Ext 2345. Fax: 908-850-9528. p. 1489

Madaire, Patricia, Librn, Agriculture & Agri-Food Canada, Eastern Cereal & Oilseed Research Centre Library, K W Neatby Bldg, 930 Carling Ave, Ottawa, ON, K1A 0C6, CANADA. Tel: 613-759-1806. Fax: 613-759-1924. p. 2827

Madansingh, Kamini, Br Head, Winnipeg Public Library, Pembina Trail, 2724 Pembina Hwy, Winnipeg, MB, R3T 2H7, CANADA. Tel: 204-986-4370. Fax: 204-986-3290. p. 2760

Madara, Edward J, Prog Coordr, Saint Clare's Health Systems, 375 E McFarlan St, Dover, NJ, 07801. Tel: 973-989-1122. Fax: 973-989-1159. p. 1481

Madaras, Beckie, Tech Serv Mgr, Yavapai College Library, 1100 E Sheldon St, Bldg 19, Prescott, AZ, 86301. Tel: 928-776-2264. Fax: 928-776-2275. p. 78

Madaras, Becky, Librn, Cordes Lakes Public Library, 20445 E Quailrun Dr, Cordes Lakes, AZ, 86333. Tel: 928-632-5492. p. 61

Madaus, Richard, PhD, Exec Dir, College Center for Library Automation, 1753 W Paul Dirac Dr, Tallahassee, FL, 32310. Tel: 850-922-6044. Fax: 850-922-4869. p. 2940

Maddalena, Lisa, Ch, Sr Librn, Pacific Grove Public Library, 550 Central Ave, Pacific Grove, CA, 93950-2789. Tel: 831-648-5760, Ext 11. Fax: 831-373-3268. p. 203

Maddalena, Robin, Head, Access Serv, Pine Manor College, 400 Heath St, Chestnut Hill, MA, 02467. Tel: 617-731-7006. Fax: 617-731-7045. p. 1081

Madden, A, Circ Tech, Prairie State College Library, 202 S Halsted St, Chicago Heights, IL, 60411-8200. Tel: 708-709-3550. Fax: 708-709-3940. p. 628

Madden, Jan, Ch, Ozark County Library, 200 Elm St, Gainesville, MO, 65655. Tel: 417-679-4442. p. 1329

Madden, Karl, Info Literacy, Medgar Evers College, 1650 Bedford Ave, Brooklyn, NY, 11225-2010. Tel: 718-270-4874. Fax: 718-270-5182. p. 1593

Madden, Leslie, Instrul Serv Librn, Georgia State University Library, 100 Decatur St SE, Atlanta, GA, 30303-3202. Tel: 404-413-2807. Fax: 404-413-2701. p. 516

Madden, Linda, Libr Serv Supvr/ILL, Keene State College, 229 Main St, Keene, NH, 03435-3201. Tel: 603-358-2711. Fax: 603-358-2745. p. 1453

Madden, Lynne, Ch, Victor Free Library, 15 W Main, Victor, NY, 14564. Tel: 585-924-2637. Fax: 585-924-1893. p. 1761

Madden, Nancy, Libr Dir, Edison Community College Library, 1973 Edison Dr, Piqua, OH, 45356. Tel: 937-778-7955. Fax: 937-778-7958. p. 1930

Madden, Pamela, Archivist, Cat Librn, Wartburg College Library, 100 Wartburg Blvd, Waverly, IA, 50677-0903. Tel: 319-352-8461. Fax: 319-352-8312. p. 850

Madden, Richard, Dir, Martin Methodist College, 433 W Madison St, Pulaski, TN, 38478-2799. Tel: 931-363-9844. Fax: 931-363-9844. p. 2264

Madden, Shawn C, Dir, Southeastern Baptist Theological Seminary Library, 114 N Wingate St, Wake Forest, NC, 27587. Tel: 919-863-2250. Fax: 919-863-8150. p. 1827

Madden, Thomas, Dir, Durham Public Library, Seven Mill Rd, Unit H, Durham, NH, 03824-0954. Tel: 603-868-6699. Fax: 603-868-9944. p. 1445

Maddix, Jeanne, Dir, Universite de Moncton, Law Library, Moncton, NB, E1A 3E9, CANADA. Tel: 506-858-4547. Fax: 506-858-4518. p. 2766

Maddox, Cheryl Miller, Head, Pub Serv, Christian Theological Seminary Library, 1000 W 42nd St, Indianapolis, IN, 46208. Tel: 317-924-1331. Fax: 317-931-2363. p. 750

Maddox, Diane, Dir, Geraldine Public Library, 13543 Alabama Hwy 227, Geraldine, AL, 35974-0268. Tel: 256-659-6663. Fax: 256-659-6663. p. 18

Maddox, Eva, Instrul Serv Librn, University of the Virgin Islands, RR 2, Box 10000, Kingshill, VI, 00850-9781. Tel: 340-692-4137. Fax: 340-692-4135. p. 2679

Maddox, Peggy, Librn, Pea Ridge Community Library, 161 E Pickens Rd, Pea Ridge, AR, 72751-2306. Tel: 479-451-8442. p. 111

Maddox, Rebecca, Br Mgr, Louisville Free Public Library, Southwest Regional, 10375 Dixie Hwy, Louisville, KY, 40272. Tel: 502-933-0029. Fax: 502-933-2782. p. 925

Maddox, Sonja, Libr Asst/Tech, Nebraska Methodist College, 720 N 87th St, Omaha, NE, 68114. Tel: 402-354-7252. Fax: 402-354-7250. p. 1413

Maddux, Linda, Sci, Reed College, 3203 SE Woodstock Blvd, Portland, OR, 97202-8199. Tel: 503-777-7702. Fax: 503-777-7786. p. 2014

Madeau, Sylvie, Exec Dir, New Brunswick Public Library Service, 250 King St, Fredericton, NB, E3B 9M9, CANADA. Tel: 506-453-2354. Fax: 506-444-4064. p. 2763

Mader, Rob, Info Tech, Marshfield Public Library, 211 E Second St, Marshfield, WI, 54449. Tel: 715-387-8494, Ext 232. Fax: 715-387-6909. p. 2613

Mader, Sharon, Dr, Dean of Libr Serv, University of New Orleans, 2000 Lakeshore Dr, New Orleans, LA, 70148. Tel: 504-280-6556. Fax: 504-280-7277. p. 964

Madera, Amparo, Br Mgr, San Diego County Library, Lemon Grove Branch, 8073 Broadway, Lemon Grove, CA, 91945-2599. Tel: 619-463-9819. Fax: 619-463-8069. p. 234

Madera, Jeanette, Asst Dir, Monroe College, 2468 Jerome Ave, Bronx, NY, 10468. Tel: 718-933-6700, Ext 8342. Fax: 718-584-4242. p. 1588

Madero, Elizabeth, Ref Librn, Baltimore International College, 17 Commerce St, Baltimore, MD, 21202-3230. Tel: 410-752-4710, Ext 210. Fax: 410-752-6720. p. 1011

Madert, Margaret, Librn, Woodside United Methodist Church Library, 8900 Georgia Ave, Silver Spring, MD, 20910-2739. Tel: 301-587-1215. Fax: 301-589-6338. p. 1042

Madewell, Kaye, Dir, Clyde W Roddy Library, 371 First Ave, Dayton, TN, 37321-1499. Tel: 423-775-8406. Fax: 423-775-8422. p. 2232

Madigan, James, Asst Dir, Oak Park Public Library, 834 Lake St, Oak Park, IL, 60301. Tel: 708-697-6909. Fax: 708-697-6900. p. 684

Madigan, Melissa, Children's & Youth Serv, Merrill Memorial Library, 215 Main St, Yarmouth, ME, 04096. Tel: 207-846-4763. Fax: 207-846-2422. p. 1008

Madigan Pratt Ellen, Ref, Mount Wachusett Community College Library, 444 Green St, Gardner, MA, 01440. Tel: 978-630-9125. Fax: 978-630-9556. p. 1090

Madisen, Randi, Electronic Res Librn, Century College Library, 3300 N Century Ave, White Bear Lake, MN, 55110. Tel: 651-779-3292. Fax: 651-779-3963. p. 1288

Madison, Anne, Cent Libr Mgr, Bossier Parish Central Library, 2206 Beckett St, Bossier City, LA, 71111. Tel: 318-746-1693. Fax: 318-746-7768. p. 945

Madison, Jacqueline, Dir, Mooers Free Library, 2430 Rte 11, Mooers, NY, 12958. Tel: 518-236-7744. Fax: 518-236-7744. p. 1663

Madison, Lori, Customer Serv Supvr, Evansville Vanderburgh Public Library, Stringtown, 2100 Stringtown Rd, Evansville, IN, 47711. Tel: 812-428-8233. Fax: 812-426-9792. p. 738

Madison, Martha-Jean, Co-Dir, New Hampshire Family Voices Library, Dept Health & Human Servs, Spec Med Servs, Thayer Bldg, 129 Pleasant St, Concord, NH, 03301. Tel: 603-271-4525. Fax: 603-271-4902. p. 1442

Madison, Olivia M A, Dean of Libr, Iowa State University Library, 302 Parks Library, Ames, IA, 50011-2140. Tel: 515-294-1442, 515-294-1443. Fax: 515-294-5525. p. 793

Madison, Rhonda, Br Mgr, Terrebonne Parish Library, East Houma, 778 Grand Caillou Rd, Houma, LA, 70363. Tel: 985-876-7072. Fax: 985-876-9658. p. 951

Madonna, Barbara, Dir, Gloversville Public Library, 58 E Fulton St, Gloversville, NY, 12078. Tel: 518-725-2819. Fax: 518-773-0292. p. 1629

Madore, Greta, Librn, Barneveld Free Library Association, 118 Boon St, Barneveld, NY, 13304. Tel: 315-896-2096. p. 1578

Madorin, Sue, Head, Youth Serv, Oak Brook Public Library, 600 Oak Brook Rd, Oak Brook, IL, 60523. Tel: 630-368-7728. Fax: 630-368-7704, 630-990-4509. p. 683

Madorma, Valerie, Librn, Mary Fuller Frazier School Community Library, 142 Constitution St, Perryopolis, PA, 15473-1390. Tel: 724-736-8480. Fax: 724-736-8481. p. 2102

Madrak, Jan, Ch, Simsbury Public Library, 725 Hopmeadow St, Simsbury, CT, 06070. Tel: 860-658-7663. Fax: 860-658-6732. p. 367

Madray, Amrita, Ref Librn, Adelphi University Libraries, One South Ave, Garden City, NY, 11530. Tel: 516-877-3579. Fax: 516-877-3592. p. 1625

Madrid, Diane, ILL Coordr, Benedictine University Library, 5700 College Rd, Lisle, IL, 60532-0900. Tel: 630-829-6050. Fax: 630-960-9451. p. 666

Madrigal, Teresa, Br Mgr, Chicago Public Library, Little Village, 2311 S Kedzie Ave, Chicago, IL, 60623. Tel: 312-745-1862. p. 609

Madsen, Catherine, Bibliographer, National Yiddish Book Center, Harry & Jeanette Weinberg Bldg, 1021 West St, Amherst, MA, 01002-3375. Tel: 413-256-4900. Fax: 413-256-4700. p. 1049

Madsen, Laurie, Librn, First Regional Library, Senatobia Public Library, 222 Ward St, Senatobia, MS, 38668. Tel: 662-562-6791. Fax: 662-562-0414. p. 1302

Madsen, Leza, Ref Librn, Western Washington University, 516 High St, MS 9103, Bellingham, WA, 98225. Tel: 360-650-7583. Fax: 360-650-3044. p. 2509

Madsen, William W, Asst Dir, Matteson Public Library, 801 S School St, Matteson, IL, 60443-1897. Tel: 708-748-4431. Fax: 708-748-0510. p. 671

Madsen-Genszler, Elizabeth, Acq Librn, ILL, Ser Librn, Northland College, 1411 Ellis Ave, Ashland, WI, 54806-3999. Tel: 715-682-1279. Fax: 715-682-1693. p. 2579

Madson, Elizabeth, Coll Develop Mgr, Fargo Public Library, 102 N Third St, Fargo, ND, 58102. Tel: 701-241-1498. Fax: 701-241-8581. p. 1841

Madson, Philip W, Pres, Katzen International Inc Library, 2300 Wall St, Ste K, Cincinnati, OH, 45212-2789. Tel: 513-351-7500. Fax: 513-351-0810. p. 1870

Madway, Lorraine, Dr, Curator, Spec Coll & Univ Archives, Wichita State University Libraries, 1845 Fairmount, Wichita, KS, 67260-0068. Tel: 316-978-3590. Fax: 316-978-3048. p. 902

Madziarek, Andrea, Asst Dir, Smoky Valley Library District, 73 Hadley Circle, Round Mountain, NV, 89045. Tel: 775-377-2215. Fax: 775-377-2699. p. 1434

Maertens, Elizabeth, Acq, Ser, Adrian College, 110 S Madison St, Adrian, MI, 49221. Tel: 517-264-3900. Fax: 517-264-3748. p. 1147

Maerz, Kaye L, Dir, Libr & Info Serv, Law Librn, West Virginia Supreme Court of Appeals, Bldg 1, Rm E-404, 1900 Kanawha Blvd E, Charleston, WV, 25305-0833. Tel: 304-558-2607. Fax: 304-558-3673. p. 2557

Maestas, Marina, Head Librn, Theosophical Society in America, 1926 N Main St, Wheaton, IL, 60187. Tel: 630-668-1571, Ext 304. Fax: 630-668-4976. p. 718

Maeyama, Kikuko, Coll Develop, United Nations Dag Hammarskjold Library, United Nations, New York, NY, 10017. Tel: 917-367-9415. Fax: 212-263-2608. p. 1702

Maeyama, Kikuko, Coordr, United Nations System Electronic Information Acquisitions Consortium, c/o United Nations Library, 220 E 42nd St Rm, DN-2426, New York, NY, 10017. Tel: 212-963-2026. Fax: 212-963-2608. p. 2951

Maez, Janet, Acq Librn, Sweetwater County Library System, 300 N First East, Green River, WY, 82935. Tel: 307-352-6660. Fax: 307-872-3203. p. 2655

Maffeo, Steven E, Assoc Dir, United States Air Force Academy Libraries, 2354 Fairchild Dr, Ste 3A10, USAF Academy, CO, 80840-6214. Tel: 719-333-4406. Fax: 719-333-4754. p. 324

Magan, Deborah, Ref, Shelby County Public Library, 309 Eighth St, Shelbyville, KY, 40065. Tel: 502-633-3803. Fax: 502-633-4025. p. 935

Magariel, Dale, Dir, Stinson, Morrison, Hecker Library, 1201 Walnut St, No 2500, Kansas City, MO, 64106-2149. Tel: 816-842-8600. Fax: 816-691-3496. p. 1341

Magaw, Victoria, Br Mgr, Los Angeles Public Library System, Mid-Valley Regional, 16244 Nordhoff St, North Hills, CA, 91343. Tel: 818-895-3650. Fax: 818-895-3657. p. 173

Magazinnik, Tatyana, Commun Libr Mgr, Queens Borough Public Library, Broadway Community Library, 40-20 Broadway, Long Island City, NY, 11103. Tel: 718-721-2462. p. 1644

Magda, Mary Ann, Asst Librn, Seymour Public Library, 46 Church St, Seymour, CT, 06483. Tel: 203-888-3903. Fax: 203-888-4099. p. 366

Magedaz, Stacy, Coordr, Electronic Res, Ser, California State University, San Bernardino, 5500 University Pkwy, San Bernardino, CA, 92407-2318. Tel: 909-537-5103. Fax: 909-537-7048. p. 227

Magee, Colin, Librn, Madisonville Community College, 2000 College Dr, Madisonville, KY, 42431. Tel: 270-821-2250, Ext 8677. Fax: 270-825-8553. p. 927

Magee, Eileen, Asst Dir, Athenaeum of Philadelphia, 219 S Sixth St, East Washington Square, Philadelphia, PA, 19106-3794. Tel: 215-925-2688. Fax: 215-925-3755. p. 2103

Magee, Jen, Dir, Haxton Memorial Library, Three N Pearl St, Oakfield, NY, 14125. Tel: 585-948-9900. Fax: 585-948-9900. p. 1709

Magee, Jen, Libr Dir, Ogden Farmers' Library, 269 Ogden Center Rd, Spencerport, NY, 14559. Tel: 585-617-6181. Fax: 585-352-3406. p. 1746

Magee, Laurie, Asst Librn, La Harpe Carnegie Public Library District, 209 E Main St, La Harpe, IL, 61450. Tel: 217-659-7729. Fax: 217-659-7735. p. 662

Magee, Laurie, Ch, Oshkosh Public Library, 106 Washington Ave, Oshkosh, WI, 54901-4985. Tel: 920-236-5201, 920-236-5205. Fax: 920-236-5228. p. 2628

Magee, Margaret, Mgr, Highland County District Library, Greenfield Branch, 1125 W Jefferson St, Greenfield, OH, 45123. Tel: 937-981-3772. Fax: 937-981-5177. p. 1904

Magee, Marilyn, Asst Librn, Chinook Regional Library, Val Marie Branch, Val Marie Village Complex, Val Marie, SK, S0N 2T0, CANADA. Tel: 306-298-2133. p. 2929

Magee, Pat, Head, Ref, Elmont Public Library, 700 Hempstead Tpk, Elmont, NY, 11003-1896, Tel: 516-354-5280. Fax: 516-354-3276. p. 1620

Magee, Rhonda, Librn, Osawatomie State Hospital, 500 State Hospital Dr, Osawatomie, KS, 66064-1813. Tel: 913-755-7212. Fax: 913-755-7089. p. 886

Magee, William, Res & Instrul Serv, Regent University, 1000 Regent University Dr, Virginia Beach, VA, 23464-9800. Tel: 757-352-4098. Fax: 757-352-4451. p. 2499

Magelaner, Pamela, Circ Supvr, Denison University Libraries, 400 W Loop, Granville, OH, 43023. Tel: 740-587-5711. Fax: 740-587-6285. p. 1902

Magenau, Carol, Acq Librn, Dartmouth College Library, 6025 Baker Berry Library, Rm 115, Hanover, NH, 03755-3525. Tel: 603-646-2236. Fax: 603-646-3702. p. 1450

Magers, Linda, Dir, Fairmount Public Library, 217 S Main St, Fairmount, IN, 46928-1926. Tel: 765-948-3177. Fax: 765-948-3194. p. 739

Maggard, Suzanne, Ref/Coll Librn, University of Cincinnati Libraries, Archives & Rare Books, 808 Blegen Library, Cincinnati, OH, 45221. Tel: 513-556-7016. Fax: 513-556-2113. p. 1874

Maggert, Gillian, Mgr, Warrenton Community Library, 861 Pacific Dr, Hammond, OR, 97121. Tel: 503-861-3919. Fax: 503-861-2351. p. 2000

Maggio, Liz, Ch, Hamilton Township Public Library, One Justice Samuel A Alito, Jr Way, Hamilton, NJ, 08619. Tel: 609-581-4060. Fax: 609-581-4067. p. 1490

Maggio, Robert, Ref, Port Jefferson Free Library, 100 Thompson St, Port Jefferson, NY, 11777-1897. Tel: 631-473-0022. Fax: 631-473-4765. p. 1721

Maggio, Teri, Dr, Dir, Assumption Parish Library, 293 Napoleon Ave, Napoleonville, LA, 70390-2123. Tel: 985-369-7070. p. 958

Maghsoudi, Paymaneh, Dir, Whittier Public Library, 7344 S Washington Ave, Whittier, CA, 90602. Tel: 562-567-9900. Fax: 562-567-2880. p. 283

Magiel, Smith, Pub Serv, Northern Marianas College, Fina Sisu Lane, Bldg O, Saipan, MP, 96950. Tel: 670-234-3690, Ext 1122. Fax: 670-234-0759. p. 2669

Maginn, Julie, Circ, Ser, Raritan Valley Community College, 118 Lamington Rd, Branchburg, Somerville, NJ, 08876. Tel: 908-526-1200, Ext 8303. Fax: 908-526-2985. p. 1530

Maginnis, Ann, Head, Ref, Hood College, 401 Rosemont Ave, Frederick, MD, 21701. Tel: 301-696-3917. Fax: 301-696-3796. p. 1029

Maginnis, Valerie, Libr & Arts Dir, Boulder Public Library, 1001 Arapahoe Rd, Boulder, CO, 80302. Tel: 303-441-3100. Fax: 303-442-1808. p. 290

Magnavite, Lana, Per, Oak Lawn Public Library, 9427 S Raymond Ave, Oak Lawn, IL, 60453-2434. Tel: 708-422-4990. Fax: 708-422-5061. p. 683

Magness-Eubank, Eric, Dir, Alpena County Library, 211 N First St, Alpena, MI, 49707. Tel: 989-356-6188. Fax: 989-356-2765. p. 1150

Magnin, Emily, Librn, Limon Memorial Public Library, 205 E Ave, Limon, CO, 80828. Tel: 719-775-2163. Fax: 719-775-8808. p. 316

Magno, Rita, Libr Dir, Lone Rock Public Library, 234 N Broadway, Lone Rock, WI, 53556. Tel: 608-583-2034. Fax: 608-583-2034. p. 2605

Magnoni, Naomi, Librn, Southborough Public Library, 25 Main St, Southborough, MA, 01772. Tel: 508-485-5031. Fax: 508-229-4451. p. 1126

Magnus, Carolyn B, Dir, Portsmouth Free Public Library, 2658 E Main Rd, Portsmouth, RI, 02871. Tel: 401-683-9457. Fax: 401-683-5013. p. 2171

Magnuson, Diana L, Dr, Archivist, Baptist General Conference History Center, 3949 Bethel Dr, Saint Paul, MN, 55112-6940. Tel: 651-638-6282. Fax: 651-638-6001. p. 1277

Magnuson, Jake, Ref & Pub Serv Librn, MacMurray College, 447 E College Ave, Jacksonville, IL, 62650-2510. Tel: 217-479-7105. Fax: 217-245-5214. p. 659

Magnuson, Lauren, Info Serv Librn, Trine University, 720 Park Ave, Angola, IN, 46703. Tel: 260-665-4287. Fax: 260-665-4283. p. 724

Magnuson, Matthew, Librn, West Hills Community College, 300 Cherry Lane, Coalinga, CA, 93210. Tel: 559-934-2420. Fax: 559-935-2633. p. 135

Magnuson, Nancy, Dir, Libr Serv, Goucher College Library, 1021 Dulaney Valley Rd, Baltimore, MD, 21204. Tel: 410-337-6364. Fax: 410-337-6419. p. 1014

Magnuson, Rosalind, Archivist, The Brick Store Museum, 117 Main St, Kennebunk, ME, 04043. Tel: 207-985-4802. Fax: 207-985-6887. p. 988

Magnusson, Laura, Ch, Plaistow Public Library, 85 Main St, Plaistow, NH, 03865. Tel: 603-382-6011. Fax: 603-382-0202. p. 1462

Magnusson, Linda, Cataloger/Ref Librn, Sofia University Library, 1069 E Meadow Circle, Palo Alto, CA, 94303. Tel: 650-493-4430, Ext 263. Fax: 650-852-9780. p. 205

Magot, Seth, Dr, Assoc Prof, Long Island University, C W Post Campus, 720 Northern Blvd, Brookville, NY, 11548-1300. Tel: 516-299-2176. Fax: 516-299-4168. p. 2970

Magparangalan, Shawnee, ILL, Saint Louis University, 3650 Lindell Blvd, Saint Louis, MO, 63108-3302. Tel: 314-977-3100. Fax: 314-977-3108. p. 1360

Magruder, Katharine, Dir, Operations, Carriage Museum of America Library, 3915 Jay Trump Rd, Lexington, KY, 40511. Tel: 859-259-2933. Fax: 859-231-0973. p. 920

Magruder, Kerry, Librn, University of Oklahoma, History of Science Collections, Rm 521 NW, Norman, OK, 73019. Tel: 405-325-2741. p. 1971

Maguda, Joyce M, Dir, Eden Library, 2901 E Church St, Eden, NY, 14057. Tel: 716-992-4028. Fax: 716-992-4340. p. 1618

Maguire, Jean, Tech Serv Librn, New England Historic Genealogical Society Library, 99-101 Newbury St, Boston, MA, 02116-3007. Tel: 617-226-1229. Fax: 617-536-7307. p. 1065

Maguire, Mary, Libr Mgr, World Resources Institute, Ten G St NE, Ste 800, Washington, DC, 20002. Tel: 202-729-7602. Fax: 202-729-7610. p. 423

Maguire, Miranda, Adult Serv, Ref Serv, Fort McMurray Public Library, 151 MacDonald Dr, Fort McMurray, AB, T9H 5C5, CANADA. Tel: 780-743-7800. Fax: 780-743-7938. p. 2704

Mah, Karen, Head, Info Ctr, Agriculture & Agri-Food Canada, 5403 First Ave S, Lethbridge, AB, T1J 4B1, CANADA. Tel: 403-327-4561. Fax: 403-382-3156. p. 2709

Mah, Yoke Mei, Cat, Warren Wilson College, 701 Warren Wilson Rd, Swannanoa, NC, 28778. Tel: 828-771-3054. Fax: 828-771-7085. p. 1826

Mahaffey, Laurie, Dep Dir, Central Texas Library System, Inc, 5555 N Lamar Blvd, Ste L115, Austin, TX, 78751. Tel: 512-583-0704. Fax: 512-583-0709. p. 2280

Mahaffey, Renae, Libr Coordr, Lincoln Public Library, 485 Twelve Bridges Dr, Lincoln, CA, 95648. Tel: 916-434-2410. Fax: 919-409-9235. p. 164

Mahaffey, Stephanie, Mgr, Terrebonne Parish Library, Bourg Branch, 4405 Saint Andrew St, Bourg, LA, 70343-5431. Tel: 985-594-4717. Fax: 985-594-8392. p. 951

Mahaffie, Matthew B, Librn, Buchanan Ingersoll Rooney PC, 1700 K St NW, Ste 300, Washington, DC, 20006-3807. Tel: 202-452-7938. Fax: 202-452-7989. p. 395

Mahajan, Nalini, Dir, Med Libr, Marianjoy Rehabilitation Hospital, 26 W 171 Roosevelt Rd, Wheaton, IL, 60187. Tel: 630-909-7092. Fax: 630-260-0143. p. 718

Mahalko, Darlene, Asst Librn, Gallitzin Public Library, 411 Convent St, Ste 30, Gallitzin, PA, 16641-1234. Tel: 814-886-4041. Fax: 814-886-2125. p. 2059

Mahan, Dione, Head, Cat, Texas A&M University-Commerce, 2600 S Neal St, Commerce, TX, 75429. Tel: 903-886-5730. Fax: 903-886-5434. p. 2300

Mahan, Jeanne, Circ Mgr, Jefferson County Rural Library District, 620 Cedar Ave, Port Hadlock, WA, 98339-9514. Tel: 360-385-6544. Fax: 360-385-7921. p. 2524

Mahana, Sherry, Circ, Texas Chiropractic College, 5912 Spencer Hwy, Pasadena, TX, 77505. Tel: 281-998-6049. Fax: 281-487-4168. p. 2369

Mahaney, Colleen, Ch, Oxford Public Library, 48 S Second St, Oxford, PA, 19363-1377. Tel: 610-932-9625. Fax: 610-932-9251. p. 2101

Mahar, Kim, Ref Librn, Olean Public Library, 134 N Second St, Olean, NY, 14760-2583. Tel: 716-372-0200. Fax: 716-372-8651. p. 1710

Mahar, Tonya, Mgr, Scarborough Hospital, Health Information Resource Centre, Birchmount Campus, 3030 Birchmount Rd, Scarborough, ON, M1W 3W3, CANADA. Tel: 416-495-2437. Fax: 416-495-2562. p. 2841

Mahar, Tonya, Mgr, Scarborough Hospital, Health Sciences Library, 3050 Lawrence Ave E, Scarborough, ON, M1P 2V5, CANADA. Tel: 416-431-8114. Fax: 416-431-8232. p. 2841

Mahard, Martha, Prof of Practice, Simmons College, 300 The Fenway, Boston, MA, 02115. Tel: 617-521-2800. Fax: 617-521-3192. p. 2967

Mahardy, Alice, Librn, Richfield Springs Public Library, 102 Main St, Richfield Springs, NY, 13439. Tel: 315-858-0230. Fax: 315-858-0230. p. 1727

Mahendra, Sundeep, Evening Librn, Elon University, 308 N O'Kelly Ave, Elon, NC, 27244-0187. Tel: 336-278-6600. Fax: 336-278-6637. p. 1791

Maher, Abbi, Mgr, Libr Serv, Burns & Levinson, 125 Summer St, Boston, MA, 02110-1624. Tel: 617-345-3000. Fax: 617-345-3299. p. 1059

Maher, Diane, Spec Coll & Archives Librn, University of San Diego, Helen K & James S Copley Library, 5998 Alcala Park, San Diego, CA, 92110. Fax: 619-260-4617. p. 239

Maher, Meg, Librn, U-HAUL International, 2727 N Central Ave, Phoenix, AZ, 85036. Tel: 602-263-6011. p. 77

Maher, Michael, Res Librn, Nevada Department of Cultural Affairs Division of Museums & History, 1650 N Virginia St, Reno, NV, 89503. Tel: 775-688-1191. Fax: 775-688-2917. p. 1432

Maher, Stephen, Coll Develop, New York University School of Medicine, Medical Science Bldg 195, 550 First Ave, New York, NY, 10016-6450. Tel: 212-263-5397. Fax: 212-263-6534. p. 1696

Maher, Veronica, Media Res Librn, Roger Williams University Library, One Old Ferry Rd, Bristol, RI, 02809. Tel: 401-254-3114. Fax: 401-254-3631. p. 2164

Maher, William, Archivist, University of Illinois Library at Urbana-Champaign, University Archives, 19 Main Library, 1408 W Gregory Dr, Urbana, IL, 61801. Tel: 217-333-0798. Fax: 217-333-2868. p. 713

Maheux, Karen, Br Mgr, Mesa County Public Library District, Palisade Branch, 711 Iowa St, Palisade, CO, 81526. Tel: 970-464-7557. Fax: 970-464-7904. p. 311

Mahin, Carolyn, Dir, Pub Serv, University of Central Oklahoma, 100 N University Dr, Edmond, OK, 73034. Tel: 405-974-2595. Fax: 405-974-3806, 405-974-3874. p. 1962

Mahinske, Lar, Curator, Encyclopaedia Britannica Inc, 331 N LaSalle, Chicago, IL, 60654. Tel: 312-347-7429. Fax: 312-294-2162. p. 613

Mahler, Evangeline, In Charge, Mid-Columbia Libraries, Merrill's Corner, 5240 Eltopia W, Eltopia, WA, 99330. Tel: 509-297-4341. Fax: 509-297-4341. p. 2518

Mahmoud, Ibtisam M, Med Librn, Montreal Chest Institute, 3650 Saint Urbain St, J5 26, Montreal, QC, H2X 2P4, CANADA. Tel: 514-934-1934, Ext 32593. Fax: 514-849-3824. p. 2899

Mahmoud, Zahir M, Dir, Waynesboro Public Library, 600 S Wayne Ave, Waynesboro, VA, 22980. Tel: 540-942-6746. Fax: 540-942-6753. p. 2501

Mahnk, Karen H, Dir, Lake Park Public Library, 529 Park Ave, Lake Park, FL, 33403. Tel: 561-881-3331. p. 458

Mahnken, Christine, Librn, Alaska Oil & Gas Conservation Commission Library, 333 W Seventh Ave, Ste 100, Anchorage, AK, 99501. Tel: 907-279-1433. Fax: 907-276-7542. p. 43

Mahnken, Sherry, Ref Librn, Curtis Laws Wilson Library, 400 W 14th St, Rolla, MO, 65409-0060. Tel: 573-341-7843. Fax: 573-341-4233. p. 1351

Mahon, Penny, Ref/Media Serv Librn, Kansas City Kansas Community College Library, 7250 State Ave, Kansas City, KS, 66112-3098. Tel: 913-288-7650. Fax: 913-288-7606. p. 875

Mahon, Todd, Exec Dir, Anoka County History Center & Library, 2135 Third Ave N, Anoka, MN, 55303. Tel: 763-421-0600, Ext 104. Fax: 763-323-0218. p. 1239

Mahoney, Barb, Circ, Red Deer College Library, 100 College Blvd, Red Deer, AB, T4N 5H5, CANADA. Tel: 403-342-3344. Fax: 403-346-8500. p. 2714

Mahoney, Betsy, Law Librn, Madison County Law Library, 155 N Main St, Edwardsville, IL, 62025. Tel: 618-296-5921. Fax: 618-692-7475. p. 639

Mahoney, Brenda, Coordr, Librn, Algonquin College Learning Resource Centre, 1385 Woodroffe Ave, Ottawa, ON, K2G 1V8, CANADA. Tel: 613-727-4723, Ext 5284. Fax: 613-727-7642. p. 2827

Mahoney, Carol A, Dir, Greenwich Library, 101 W Putnam Ave, Greenwich, CT, 06830-5387. Tel: 203-622-7961. Fax: 203-622-7959. p. 341

Mahoney, Elizabeth, Ref Serv, Boston Herald, One Herald Sq, Boston, MA, 02118. Tel: 617-619-6680. Fax: 617-619-6450. p. 1056

Mahoney, Elizabeth T, Librn, University of Pittsburgh, Information Sciences, 135 N Bellefield Ave, Pittsburgh, PA, 15260. Tel: 412-624-4704. Fax: 412-624-4062. p. 2129

Mahoney, Geraldine, Dir, Briarcliff Manor Public Library, One Library Rd, Briarcliff Manor, NY, 10510. Tel: 914-733-3610. Fax: 914-941-7091. p. 1585

Mahoney, James J, Dir, The Nyack Library, 59 S Broadway, Nyack, NY, 10960. Tel: 845-358-3370. p. 1708

Mahoney, Jessica, Instruction & Ref Librn, Franklin College, 101 Branigin Blvd, Franklin, IN, 46131-2623. Tel: 317-738-8164. Fax: 317-738-8787. p. 743

Mahoney, Kathleen, Dir, Mashpee Public Library, 64 Steeple St, Mashpee, MA, 02649. Tel: 508-539-1435. Fax: 508-539-1437. p. 1103

Mahoney, Kevin, Dir, United States Department of Transportation, National Highway Traffic Safety Administration-Technical Information Services, NPO-400, 1200 New Jersey Ave SE, Washington, DC, 20590. Fax: 202-493-2833. p. 420

Mahoney, Mary Ann, In Charge, University of California, Berkeley, Chemistry, 100 Hildebrand Hall, Berkeley, CA, 94720-6000. Tel: 510-642-4345. Fax: 510-643-9041. p. 127

Mahoney, Ruth, Libr Assoc, Law Library of Louisiana, Louisiana Supreme Court, 2nd Flr, 400 Royal St, New Orleans, LA, 70130-2104. Tel: 504-310-2400. Fax: 504-310-2419. p. 960

Mahoney, Scott, Br Mgr, Metropolitan Community College Library, South Omaha Campus, Mahoney Bldg, 2909 Edward "Babe" Gomez Ave, Omaha, NE, 68107. Tel: 402-738-4506. Fax: 402-738-4738. p. 1413

Mahoney-Ayres, Brenda, Dir, Weston County Public Library, 23 W Main St, Newcastle, WY, 82701. Tel: 307-746-2206. Fax: 307-746-2218. p. 2658

Mahood, Ramona, Chair, Prof, University of Memphis, College of Education, 406 Ball Hall Educ Bldg, Memphis, TN, 38152. Tel: 901-678-2365. Fax: 901-678-3881. p. 2974

Mai, Brent, Univ Librn, Concordia University Library, 2811 NE Holman St, Portland, OR, 97211-6067. Tel: 503-493-6460. Fax: 503-280-8697. p. 2010

Maida, Maria, Ref, Proskauer Rose LLP Library, 1585 Broadway, Concourse Level, New York, NY, 10036. Tel: 212-969-5001. Fax: 212-969-2931. p. 1698

Maiello-Glucklich, Cindy, Circ, Tech Serv, Melrose Park Public Library, 801 N Broadway, Melrose Park, IL, 60160. Tel: 708-343-3391. Fax: 708-531-5327. p. 673

Maier, Cindy, Coll Develop, Corning Community College, One Academic Dr, Corning, NY, 14830. Tel: 607-962-9251. Fax: 607-962-9466. p. 1610

Maier, John, Head, Tech Serv, Pratt Institute Libraries, 200 Willoughby Ave, Brooklyn, NY, 11205-3897. Tel: 718-636-3659. Fax: 718-399-4401. p. 1594

Maier, Karen, Tech Serv, Presentation College Library, 1500 N Main, Aberdeen, SD, 57401-1299. Tel: 605-229-8498. Fax: 605-229-8430. p. 2209

Maier, Kyle, Ch, Alexandria Library, James M Duncan Jr Branch, 2501 Commonwealth Ave, Alexandria, VA, 22301. Tel: 703-746-1705. Fax: 703-746-1785. p. 2444

Maier, Martha S, Adult Serv, Providence Community Library, Rochambeau Library, 708 Hope St, Providence, RI, 02906. Tel: 401-272-3780. p. 2173

Maier, Robert C, Dir, Massachusetts Board of Library Commissioners, 98 N Washington St, Ste 401, Boston, MA, 02114. Tel: 617-725-1860. Fax: 617-725-0140. p. 1063

Maier, Robert C, Dir, Hyde Park Historical Society Archives, 35 Harvard Ave, Hyde Park, MA, 02136. Tel: 617-361-4398. Fax: 617-361-4398. p. 1097

Maier-O'Shea, Katie, Bibliog Instr, Coll Mgt, Head, Ref, North Park University, Brandel Library, 5114 N Christiana Ave, Chicago, IL, 60625. Tel: 773-244-5582. Fax: 773-244-4891. p. 620

Maiers, Michael, Librn, ITT Technical Institute, 4809 Memorial Hwy, Tampa, FL, 33634. Tel: 813-885-2244. Fax: 813-888-6078. p. 497

Maike, Amy, Cat, White Cloud Community Library, 1038 Wilcox Ave, White Cloud, MI, 49349. Tel: 231-689-6631. Fax: 231-689-6699. p. 1236

Maille, Chantal, Tech Serv, Bibliotheque H J Hemens, 339 Chemin Grande-Cote, Rosemere, QC, J7A 1K2, CANADA. Tel: 450-621-6132. Fax: 450-621-6131. p. 2907

Maillelle, Loretta, Dir, McGrath Community Library, 12 Chinana Ave, McGrath, AK, 99627. Tel: 907-524-3843. Fax: 907-524-3335. p. 51

Maillet, Lucienne, Dr, Prof, Long Island University, C W Post Campus, 720 Northern Blvd, Brookville, NY, 11548-1300. Tel: 516-299-2175. Fax: 516-299-4168. p. 2970

Maillet-Jones, Terry, Librn, Beaumont Enterprise Library, 380 Main St, Beaumont, TX, 77701-2331. Tel: 409-833-3311. Fax: 409-838-2857. p. 2287

Mailloux, Debbie, Mgr, Department of Veterans Affairs Library, 113 Comanche Rd, Fort Meade, SD, 57741-1099. Tel: 605-720-7055. Fax: 605-720-7054. p. 2212

Mailloux, Michele, Librn, Paul-Gerin-Lajoie-D'Outremont Library, 475 Bloomfield, Outremont, QC, H2V 3R9, CANADA. Tel: 514-276-3746. Fax: 514-276-9283. p. 2902

Main, Charlotte M, Librn, New Athens District Library, 201 N Van Buren St, New Athens, IL, 62264. Tel: 618-475-3255. Fax: 618-475-9384. p. 679

Main, Dorothy, Asst Librn, Mount Ayr Public Library, 121 W Monroe St, Mount Ayr, IA, 50854. Tel: 641-464-2159. Fax: 641-464-2159. p. 833

Main, Jenny, Asst Br Mgr, Lexington County Public Library System, Cayce-West Columbia Branch, 1500 Augusta Rd W, Columbia, SC, 29169. Tel: 803-794-6791. Fax: 803-926-5383. p. 2199

Main, Linda, Dr, Assoc Dir, Prof, San Jose State University, One Washington Sq, San Jose, CA, 95192-0029. Tel: 408-924-2490. Fax: 408-924-2476. p. 2962

Main, Lydia, Cat, East Lyme Public Library, Inc, 39 Society Rd, Niantic, CT, 06357-1100. Tel: 860-739-6926. Fax: 860-691-0020. p. 361

Main, Mary, Asst Librn, Chinook Regional Library, Abbey Branch, 133 Main St, Abbey, SK, S0N 0A0, CANADA. Tel: 306-689-2202. p. 2928

Maines, Barbara, Br Mgr, Central Rappahannock Regional Library, Montross Branch, 56 Polk St, Montross, VA, 22520-0308. Tel: 804-493-8194. Fax: 804-493-0446. p. 2466

Maingille, Shelly, Adminr, Agriculture & Agri-Food Canada, PO Box 29, Beaverlodge, AB, T0H 0C0, CANADA. Tel: 780-354-2212. Fax: 780-354-5150, 780-354-8171. p. 2685

Mainord, Sonya, Head Librn, Ballard-Carlisle-Livingston County Public Library, PO Box 428, Bardwell, KY, 42023-0428. Tel: 270-335-5059. p. 906

Mainprize, Grace, Head Librn, Oregon County Library District, Thayer Public, 121 N Second St, Thayer, MO, 65791. Tel: 417-264-3091. Fax: 417-264-3091. p. 1319

Mains, Megan, Circ Asst, Columbia International University, 7435 Monticello Rd, Columbia, SC, 29203-1599. Tel: 803-807-5115. Fax: 803-744-1391. p. 2187

Mainville, Carol, Librn, Plantagenet Village Library System, Curran, 791 Mill St, Curran, ON, K0B 1C0, CANADA. Tel: 613-673-2072. Fax: 613-673-2072. p. 2836

Mainville, Pamela, Dir, Vershire Community Library, Rte 113, Vershire, VT, 05079. Tel: 802-685-9982. p. 2438

Mainz, Rachel, Youth Serv Librn, Henderson District Public Libraries, James I Gibson Library, 100 W Lake Mead Pkwy, Henderson, NV, 89015. Tel: 702-565-8402. Fax: 702-565-8832. p. 1428

Maio, Kathleen, Asst Dir, Head, Access Serv, Suffolk University, 73 Tremont St, Boston, MA, 02108. Tel: 617-573-8535. Fax: 617-573-8756. p. 1067

Maio, Louise Procter, Chief Librn/CEO, Aurora Public Library, 15145 Young St, Aurora, ON, L4G 1M1, CANADA. Tel: 905-727-9493. Fax: 905-727-9374. p. 2793

Maio, Louise Procter, Chief Exec Officer, Richmond Hill Public Library, One Atkinson St, Richmond Hill, ON, L4C 0H5, CANADA. Tel: 905-884-9288. Fax: 905-770-0312, 905-884-6544. p. 2839

Maiolo, Gay, Librn, Willard-Cybulski Correctional Institution Library, 391 Shaker Rd, Enfield, CT, 06082. Tel: 860-763-6190, 860-763-6193, 860-763-6590. Fax: 860-763-6517. p. 338

Mair, Wendi, Curric Center Librn, Shaw University, 118 E South St, Raleigh, NC, 27601. Tel: 919-546-8555. Fax: 919-546-8554. p. 1817

Mairn, Chad, Librn, Saint Petersburg College, Saint Petersburg-Gibbs Campus Library, 6605 Fifth Ave N, Saint Petersburg, FL, 33710. Tel: 727-341-7188. Fax: 727-341-7188. p. 483

Maisel, Heather, Dir, Castlegar & District Public Library, 1005 Third St, Castlegar, BC, V1N 2A2, CANADA. Tel: 250-365-6611. Fax: 250-365-7765. p. 2726

Maisey, Elizabeth, Head, Tech Serv, Assumption College, 500 Salisbury St, Worcester, MA, 01609. Tel: 508-767-7384. Fax: 508-767-7374. p. 1143

Maisey, Lori, Doc Delivery, Tech Serv, Alberta Health Services, PO Box 1000, Ponoka, AB, T4J 1R8, CANADA. Tel: 403-783-7691. Fax: 403-783-7695. p. 2713

Maisey, Vivian, Br Mgr, Haverstraw Kings Daughters Public Library, Village Library, 85 Main St, Haverstraw, NY, 10927. Tel: 845-429-3445. Fax: 845-429-7313. p. 1627

Maisonet-Rodriguez, Aurea E, Head Librn, University of Puerto Rico Library System, Angel Quintero Alfaro Library (General Studies), Rio

Piedras Campus, Faculta de Estudios Generales, San Juan, PR, 00931. Tel: 787-764-0000, Ext 5196. Fax: 787-772-1479. p. 2677

Maitland, Jeri, Mgr, Calgary Public Library, W R Castell Central Library, 616 Macleod Trail SE, Calgary, AB, T2G 2M2, CANADA. Tel: 403-260-2600. Fax: 403-237-5393. p. 2689

Maitland, Jessica, Ch, Chesapeake Public Library, Indian River, 2320 Old Greenbrier Rd, Chesapeake, VA, 23325-4916. Tel: 757-410-7005. Fax: 757-410-7014. p. 2456

Maitra, Suchitra, Librn, Arlington County Department of Libraries, Homebound Service, 1015 N Quincy St, Arlington, VA, 22201. Tel: 703-228-5960. Fax: 703-228-5998. p. 2448

Maitzen, Peter, Fac Mgr, Glenview Public Library, 1930 Glenview Rd, Glenview, IL, 60025-2899. Tel: 847-729-7500. Fax: 847-729-7558. p. 650

Maj, Karen, Librn, Fresno County Public Library, Mendota Branch, 1246 Belmont Ave, Mendota, CA, 93640-2667. Tel: 559-600-9291. p. 152

Majahad, Carol, Dir, North Andover Historical Society Library, 153 Academy Rd, North Andover, MA, 01845. Tel: 978-686-4035. Fax: 978-686-6616. p. 1111

Majeau, Alison, Ser, Worcester State College, 486 Chandler St, Worcester, MA, 01602-2597. Tel: 508-929-8531. Fax: 508-929-8198. p. 1145

Majeski, Jeanne, Br Mgr, Door County Library, Baileys Harbor Branch, 2392 Hwy F, Baileys Harbor, WI, 54202. Tel: 920-839-2210. p. 2640

Majka, Deborah, Head, Tech Info Serv, Flossmoor Public Library, 1000 Sterling Ave, Flossmoor, IL, 60422-1295. Tel: 708-798-3600. Fax: 708-798-3603. p. 646

Major, Charlene, Info Literacy, Tuskegee University, Hollis Burke Frissell Bldg, 1200 W Old Montgomery Rd, Tuskegee, AL, 36088. Tel: 334-727-8676. Fax: 334-727-9282. p. 39

Major, Jacque, Libr Asst, Southwestern College, 3960 San Felipe Rd, Santa Fe, NM, 87507. Tel: 505-467-6825. Fax: 505-467-6826. p. 1564

Major, Kathy, Tech Serv, Gale Free Library, 23 Highland St, Holden, MA, 01520-2599. Tel: 508-210-5560. Fax: 508-829-0232. p. 1095

Major, Mary, Dir, Hinsdale Public Library, 122 Brattleboro Rd, Hinsdale, NH, 03451. Tel: 603-336-5713. p. 1451

Majors, Eva, Br Mgr, Lee County Public Library, Smithville Branch, 116 Main St, Smithville, GA, 31787. Tel: 229-846-6625. Fax: 229-846-6625. p. 539

Majors, Pamela, Head, Circ, Allegheny College Library, 555 N Main St, Meadville, PA, 16335. Tel: 814-332-3768. Fax: 814-337-5673. p. 2086

Majors, Rice, Dir, Libr Info Tech, University of Colorado Boulder, 1720 Pleasant St, 184 UCB, Boulder, CO, 80309-0184. Tel: 303-492-3965. Fax: 303-492-3340. p. 291

Majumdar, Manju, ILL Supvr, Norfolk State University Library, 700 Park Ave, Norfolk, VA, 23504-8010. Tel: 757-823-8517. Fax: 757-823-2431. p. 2482

Mak, Bonnie, Asst Prof, University of Illinois at Urbana-Champaign, Library & Information Science Bldg, 501 E Daniel St, Champaign, IL, 61820-6211. Tel: 217-333-3280. Fax: 217-244-3302. p. 2965

Mak, Judy, Br Head, Toronto Public Library, Cliffcrest, Cliffcrest Plaza, 3017 Kingston Rd, Toronto, ON, M1M 1P1, CANADA. Tel: 416-396-8916. Fax: 416-396-3605. p. 2861

Mak, Kevin, Ref Serv, Paterson Free Public Library, 250 Broadway, Paterson, NJ, 07501. Tel: 973-321-1223. Fax: 973-321-1205. p. 1518

Makala, Sheila, Tech Serv Coordr, Mishawaka-Penn-Harris Public Library, 209 Lincoln Way E, Mishawaka, IN, 46544-2084. Tel: 574-259-5277, Ext 278. Fax: 574-254-5585, 574-255-8489. p. 765

Makani, Joyline, Actg Head, Libr, Dalhousie University, 6225 University Ave, Halifax, NS, B3H 4H8, CANADA. p. 2780

Makarawicz, Grace, Dir, Langara College Library, 100 W 49th Ave, Vancouver, BC, V5Y 2Z6, CANADA. Tel: 604-323-5462. Fax: 604-323-5577. p. 2741

Makarewicz, Grace, Univ Librn, Capilano College Library, 2055 Purcell Way, North Vancouver, BC, V7J 3H5, CANADA. Tel: 604-984-4944. Fax: 604-984-1728. p. 2734

Makary, Paulette, ILL, Gadsden Public Library, 254 College St, Gadsden, AL, 35901. Tel: 256-549-4699. p. 18

Makepeace, Lyn, Ref, Malaspina University-College Library, 900 Fifth St, Nanaimo, BC, V9R 5S5, CANADA. Tel: 250-753-3245, Ext 2271. Fax: 250-740-6473. p. 2732

Maker, Paula, Librn, Sturdivant Public Library, 963 Main St, East Machias, ME, 04630. Tel: 207-255-0070. p. 984

Maki, Elizabeth, In Charge, National Park Service, PO Box Drawer 170, Moose, WY, 83012-0170. Tel: 307-739-3592. Fax: 307-739-3443. p. 2658

Maki, Judy, Acq, Colorado Mesa University, 1200 College Pl, Grand Junction, CO, 81501. Tel: 970-248-1436. Fax: 970-248-1930. p. 310

Maki, Karen E, Dep Dir, Gail Borden Public Library District, 270 N Grove Ave, Elgin, IL, 60120-5596. Tel: 847-429-5976. Fax: 847-742-0485. p. 640

Maki, Nancy, Asst Librn, Lyons Township District Library, 309 Bridge St, Lyons, MI, 48851. Tel: 989-855-3414. Fax: 989-855-2069. p. 1204

Makie, Peggy, Tech Info Spec, United States Army, Weed Army Community Hospital, Medical Library, PO Box 105109, Fort Irwin, CA, 92310-5109. Tel: 760-380-6889. Fax: 760-380-5734. p. 149

Makie, Peggy, Libr Mgr, Kaiser-Permanente Medical Center, 2025 Morse Ave, Sacramento, CA, 95825. Tel: 916-973-6944. Fax: 916-973-6999. p. 224

Makin, Mary, Librn, Ebensburg Cambria Public Library, 225 W Highland Ave, Ebensburg, PA, 15931-1507. Tel: 814-472-7957. Fax: 814-472-2037. p. 2052

Makkonen, Carol, Finance & Operations Mgr, Michigan Technological University, 1400 Townsend Dr, Houghton, MI, 49931-1295. Tel: 906-487-3535. p. 1191

Makley, Patricia, Dir, West Paris Public Library, 226 Main St, West Paris, ME, 04289. Tel: 207-674-2004. Fax: 207-674-2804. p. 1006

Makoujy, Janet, Head, Ch, New City Free Library, 220 N Main St, New City, NY, 10956. Tel: 845-634-4997. p. 1664

Makowsky, Elyse, Circ, Kemmerer Library Harding Township, 19 Blue Mill Rd, New Vernon, NJ, 07976. Tel: 973-267-2665. p. 1510

Maksin, Melanie, Soc Sci Librn, Swarthmore College, 500 College Ave, Swarthmore, PA, 19081-1081. Tel: 610-690-5786. Fax: 610-328-7329. p. 2145

Makstman, Alex, Bus Mgr, Winnetka-Northfield Public Library District, 768 Oak St, Winnetka, IL, 60093-2583. Tel: 847-446-7220. Fax: 847-446-5085. p. 720

Makuc, Mark, Dir, Monterey Library, 452 Main Rd, Monterey, MA, 01245. Tel: 413-528-3795. p. 1107

Makula, Amanda, Ref, Augustana College Library, 3435 9 1/2 Ave, Rock Island, IL, 61201-2296. Tel: 309-794-7266. Fax: 309-794-7640. p. 696

Malaguti, Jennifer, Asst Dir, Holbrook Public Library, Two Plymouth St, Holbrook, MA, 02343. Tel: 781-767-3644. Fax: 781-767-5721. p. 1095

Malahan, Patricia, Dir, First Church of Christ Congregational, 12 S Main St, West Hartford, CT, 06107. Tel: 860-232-3893. Fax: 860-232-8183. p. 376

Malak, Greg, Br Supvr, Marion County Public Library System, Forest Public Library, 905 S County 314A, Ocklawaha, FL, 32179. Tel: 352-438-2540. Fax: 352-438-2545. p. 474

Malak-McMullan, Elizabeth, Libr Coordr, Vaughan Public Libraries, Woodbridge Library, 150 Woodbridge Ave, Woodbridge, ON, L4L 2S7, CANADA. Tel: 905-653-7323. Fax: 905-851-2322. p. 2848

Malakoff, Dina, Commun Libr Mgr, County of Los Angeles Public Library, Live Oak Library, 4153-55 E Live Oak Ave, Arcadia, CA, 91006-5895. Tel: 626-446-8803. Fax: 626-446-9418. p. 142

Malamud, Judie, Dir, Albert Einstein College of Medicine, 1300 Morris Park Ave, Bronx, NY, 10461. Tel: 718-430-3108. Fax: 718-430-8795. p. 1585

Malanga, Kathleen, Asst Dir, Pub Serv, William Paterson University of New Jersey, 300 Pompton Rd, Wayne, NJ, 07470. Tel: 973-720-3189. Fax: 973-720-3171. p. 1540

Malar, John, Dir, Cranford Free Public Library, 224 Walnut Ave, Cranford, NJ, 07016-2931. Tel: 908-709-7272. Fax: 908-709-1658. p. 1480

Malarik, Susan, Head, Circ, Hudson Library & Historical Society, 96 Library St, Hudson, OH, 44236-5122. Tel: 330-653-6658. Fax: 330-650-3373. p. 1905

Malaschak, Donna, ILL, Edison State College, 8099 College Pkwy SW, Bldg J, Fort Myers, FL, 33919. Tel: 239-489-9376. Fax: 239-489-9095. p. 444

Malaterre, Natalie, ILL, Salish Kootenai College, PO Box 70, Pablo, MT, 59855. Tel: 406-275-4875. Fax: 406-275-4812. p. 1387

Malave, Marilda, In Charge, Paterson Free Public Library, South Paterson, 930 Main St, Paterson, NJ, 07503. Tel: 973-357-3020. p. 1518

Malavet, Carmen G, Actg Dir, Ponce School of Medicine Library, 395 Zona Industrial Reparada 2, Calle Dr Luis F Sala, Ponce, PR, 00716-2348. Tel: 787-840-2575. Fax: 787-844-3865. p. 2674

Malay, Rachel, Dir, Port Library, 1718 N Hersey, Beloit, KS, 67420. Tel: 785-738-3936. p. 857

Malbone, Danielle, Asst Librn, Art Institute of Indianapolis Library, 3500 Depauw Blvd, Indianapolis, IN, 46268. Tel: 317-613-4800, 317-613-4803. Fax: 317-613-4808. p. 749

Malbrough, Marilyn, Head, Circ, Great Bend Public Library, 1409 Williams St, Great Bend, KS, 67530-4090. Tel: 620-792-2409. Fax: 620-792-5495, 620-793-7270. p. 869

Malbrue, Barbara A, Dir, South St Landry Community Library, 235 Marie St, Sunset, LA, 70584. Tel: 337-662-3442, 337-662-3544. Fax: 337-662-3475. p. 970

Malcolm, Jane, Asst Dir, Pub Serv, Oral Roberts University Library, 7777 South Lewis Ave, Tulsa, OK, 74171. Tel: 918-495-7495. Fax: 918-495-6893. p. 1981

Malcolm, Mark A, Ch, Youth Serv, Maynard Public Library, 77 Nason St, Maynard, MA, 01754-2316. Tel: 978-897-1010. Fax: 978-897-9884. p. 1103

Malcolm, Melissa, Asst Dir, Pub Serv, Lapeer District Library, 201 Village West Dr S, Lapeer, MI, 48446-1699. Tel: 810-664-9521. Fax: 810-664-8527. p. 1202

Malcolm, Melissa, Asst Dir, Pub Serv, Lapeer District Library, Marguerite deAngeli Branch, 921 W Nepessing St, Lapeer, MI, 48446. Tel: 810-664-6971. Fax: 810-664-5581. p. 1202

Malcolm, Melissa, Dir of Libr Serv, Gloucester County Library, Point Branch, 1720 George Washington Memorial Hwy, Hayes, VA, 23072. Tel: 804-642-9790. Fax: 804-642-9853. p. 2467

Malcolm, Melissa, Dir, Libr Serv, Gloucester County Library, 6920 Main St, Gloucester, VA, 23061. Tel: 804-693-2998. Fax: 804-693-1477. p. 2467

Malcolm, Shannon, Res Librn, Greenberg Traurig LLP, 1221 Brickell Ave, Miami, FL, 33131. Tel: 305-579-0689. p. 465

Malcomb, Lou, Geology Librn, Indiana University Bloomington, Geology Library, Geology 603, 1001 E Tenth St, Bloomington, IN, 47405. Tel: 812-855-1494. Fax: 812-855-6614. p. 727

Malcomsom, Jeff, Archivist, Montana Historical Society, 225 N Roberts St, Helena, MT, 59601-4514. Tel: 406-444-7427. Fax: 406-444-5297. p. 1382

Maldonado, Cathy, Ref & Instruction, Saint Bonaventure University, 3261 W State Rd, Saint Bonaventure, NY, 14778. Tel: 716-375-2153. Fax: 716-375-2389. p. 1737

Maldonado, Fernando, Circ Supvr, Placentia Library District, 411 E Chapman Ave, Placentia, CA, 92870. Tel: 714-528-1906. Fax: 714-528-8236. p. 208

Maldonado, Ivette, Instruction Librn, University of Puerto Rico, Minillas Park, 170, 174 Rd, Bayamon, PR, 00959-1919. Tel: 787-993-0000, Ext 3222, 787-993-8857. Fax: 787-993-8914. p. 2672

Maldonado, Jadira, Bibliog Instr, University of Puerto Rico, 130 Ave Universidad, Arecibo, PR, 00612-3145. Tel: 787-815-0000, Ext 3151. Fax: 787-878-9363. p. 2671

Maldonado, Jose, Circ, Palatine Public Library District, 700 N North Ct, Palatine, IL, 60067-8159. Tel: 847-358-5881. p. 686

Maldonado, María del Carmen, Cat, Amaury Veray Music Library, 350 Rafael Lamar, Hato Rey, PR, 00918. Tel: 787-751-0160, Ext 247. Fax: 787-754-5934. p. 2673

Maldonado, Stephanie, Br Asst, Los Angeles County Law Library, Pomona, East District Superior Courts Bldg, 400 Civic Center Plaza, Rm 102, Pomona, CA, 91766. Tel: 909-784-1961. Fax: 909-623-9540. p. 172

Maldonando-Colombani, Judite, ESL Coordr, Pocono Mountain Public Library, 5540 Memorial Blvd, Tobyhanna, PA, 18466. Tel: 570-894-8860. Fax: 570-894-8852. p. 2146

Malec, Gloria, Dir, Windsor Locks Public Library, 28 Main St, Windsor Locks, CT, 06096. Tel: 860-627-1495. Fax: 860-627-1496. p. 379

Malec, Kathleen, Librn, Minnesota Pollution Control Agency Library, 520 Lafayette Rd, Saint Paul, MN, 55155-4194. Tel: 651-757-2547. Fax: 651-282-5446. p. 1280

Malecha, Deborah, Tech Serv, Delaware County District Library, 84 E Winter St, Delaware, OH, 43015. Tel: 740-362-3861. Fax: 740-369-0196. p. 1895

Malecki, Sharon, Ref Librn, Finger Lakes Community College, 4355 Lakeshore Dr, Canandaigua, NY, 14424-8395. Tel: 585-394-3500, Ext 7371. Fax: 585-394-8708. p. 1601

Malek, Tracy, Youth Serv, Scappoose Public Library, 52469 SE Second St, Scappoose, OR, 97056. Tel: 503-543-7123. Fax: 503-543-7161. p. 2019

Malenfant, Martine, Tech Serv, Musee de la Civilisation - Bibliotheque du Seminaire de Quebec, Nine rue de l'Universite, Quebec, QC, G1R 5K1, CANADA. Tel: 418-643-2158. Fax: 418-692-5206. p. 2906

Maler, Robyn, Librn, Royal Victoria Hospital, Medical Library, 687 Pine Ave W, Rm H4-01, Montreal, QC, H3A 1A1, CANADA. Tel: 514-934-1934, Ext 35290. Fax: 514-843-1483. p. 2901

Malerba, Douglas, Res Librn, McKenna, Long & Aldridge LLP, 1900 K St NW, Washington, DC, 20006. Tel: 202-496-7791. Fax: 202-496-7756. p. 408

Malesky, Kee, Librn, NPR Library, 635 Massachusetts Ave NW, Washington, DC, 20001. Fax: 202-513-3056. p. 412

Maley, Audrey, Librn, Moran Public Library, 335 N Cedar, Moran, KS, 66755. Tel: 620-237-4334. p. 884

Maley, Desmond, Librn, Laurentian University, 935 Ramsey Lake Rd, Sudbury, ON, P3E 2C6, CANADA. Tel: 705-675-1151, Ext 3323. Fax: 705-675-4877. p. 2846

Malgeri, Dina G, Dir, Malden Public Library, 36 Salem St, Malden, MA, 02148-5291. Tel: 781-324-0218. Fax: 781-324-4467. p. 1102

Malic, Tamar, Br Head, Chatham-Kent Public Library, Dresden Branch, 187 Brown St, Dresden, ON, N0P 1M0, CANADA. Tel: 519-683-4922. Fax: 519-683-1857. p. 2799

Malik, Jane, Chair, Coll Develop Librn, Oakton Community College Library, 1600 E Golf Rd, Rm 1410, Des Plaines, IL, 60016. Tel: 847-635-1715. Fax: 847-635-1987. p. 636

Malinowski, Donna, Librn, Jericho Town Library, Seven Jericho Ctr Green, Jericho Center, VT, 05465. Tel: 802-899-4686. p. 2426

Malinowski, Lisa, Adult Serv, Elk Grove Village Public Library, 1001 Wellington Ave, Elk Grove Village, IL, 60007-3391. Tel: 847-439-0447. Fax: 847-439-0475. p. 641

Malinowski, Marianne, Coll Develop, Ames Public Library, 515 Douglas Ave, Ames, IA, 50010. Tel: 515-239-5652. Fax: 515-233-9001. p. 792

Malinowski, Maureen, Librn, Hollister Incorporated, 2000 Hollister Dr, Libertyville, IL, 60048. Tel: 847-918-5805. Fax: 847-918-3453. p. 665

Malinowski, Ramona, Br Mgr, Henry Patrick School District Public Library, Hamler Branch, 230 Randolph St, Hamler, OH, 43524. Tel: 419-274-3821. Fax: 419-274-3821. p. 1896

Malinowski, Teresa, Ser, Paulina June & George Pollak Library, 800 N State College Blvd, Fullerton, CA, 92834. Tel: 714-278-2714. Fax: 714-278-2439. p. 154

Malizia, Kelly, Librn, East Lake Community Library, 4125 East Lake Rd, Palm Harbor, FL, 34685. Tel: 727-773-2665. Fax: 727-773-9583. p. 480

Malkowski, Elise, Principal Librn, Murrieta Public Library, Eight Town Sq, Murrieta, CA, 92562. Tel: 951-304-2665. Fax: 951-696-0165. p. 192

Malkowski, Eugene, Ref, Social Security Administration Library, Annex Bldg 1520, Baltimore, MD, 21235-6401. Tel: 410-965-6030. Fax: 410-966-2027. p. 1017

Malland, Kathy, Ref Serv, Ser, Concordia University Wisconsin, 12800 N Lake Shore Dr, Mequon, WI, 53097-2402. Tel: 262-243-4330, 262-243-4403. Fax: 262-243-4424. p. 2615

Mallard, Ann, Ref Serv, Georgia Perimeter College, 555 N Indian Creek Dr, Clarkston, GA, 30021-2396. Tel: 678-891-3634. Fax: 404-298-4919. p. 525

Mallari-Lee, George, Libr Tech, Royal Victoria Hospital, Medical Library, 687 Pine Ave W, Rm H4-01, Montreal, QC, H3A 1A1, CANADA. Tel: 514-934-1934, Ext 35290. Fax: 514-843-1483. p. 2901

Mallek, Arlene, Pub Serv, Riverdale Public Library District, 208 W 144th St, Riverdale, IL, 60827-2788. Tel: 708-841-3311. Fax: 708-841-1805. p. 695

Mallen, Bonnie, In Charge, Chemung County Library District, Van Etten Library, 83 Main St, Van Etten, NY, 14889. Tel: 607-589-4755. p. 1619

Mallen, Janet, Acq, Arcadia Public Library, 20 W Duarte Rd, Arcadia, CA, 91006. Tel: 626-294-4802. Fax: 626-447-8050. p. 121

Maller, Jane, Asst Librn, Crowheart Public Library, 33 Old Yellowstone Hwy, Crowheart, WY, 82512. Tel: 307-486-2280. p. 2654

Mallery, Mary, Assoc Dean, Tech Serv, Montclair State University, One Normal Ave, Montclair, NJ, 07043-1699. Tel: 973-655-7150. Fax: 973-655-7780. p. 1503

Malles, Evelyn, Head, Ch, Winter Park Public Library, 460 E New England Ave, Winter Park, FL, 32789-4493. Tel: 407-623-3300. Fax: 407-623-3489. p. 505

Mallet, Crystal, Asst Libr Dir, Silsbee Public Library, Santa Fe Park, Silsbee, TX, 77656. Tel: 409-385-4831. Fax: 409-385-7382. p. 2387

Mallet, Huguette, Info Serv, Ecole Polytechnique de Montreal Bibliotheque, 2500, chemin de Polytechnique, Montreal, QC, H3T 1J4, CANADA. Tel: 514-340-4666. Fax: 514-340-4026. p. 2895

Malley, Annie, Mgr, San Mateo County Library, Half Moon Bay Library, 620 Correas St, Half Moon Bay, CA, 94019. Tel: 650-726-2316. Fax: 650-726-9282. p. 256

Malley, Peggy, Dir, Ludden Memorial Library, 42 Main St, Dixfield, ME, 04224. Tel: 207-562-8838. Fax: 207-562-4311. p. 983

Malliett, Janet, Ser, Winston-Salem State University, 601 Martin Luther King Jr Dr, Winston-Salem, NC, 27110. Tel: 336-750-2440. Fax: 336-750-2459. p. 1834

Mallon, Melissa, Res & Info Serv Librn, Wichita State University Libraries, 1845 Fairmount, Wichita, KS, 67260-0068. Tel: 316-978-5077. Fax: 316-978-3048. p. 902

Mallon, Theresa, Support Serv Mgr, San Leandro Public Library, 300 Estudillo Ave, San Leandro, CA, 94577. Tel: 510-577-3942. Fax: 510-577-3967. p. 252

Mallonee, Mary Jane, Ref Serv, Widener University, School of Law Library, 4601 Concord Pike, Wilmington, DE, 19803. Tel: 302-477-2187. Fax: 302-477-2240. p. 389

Mallory, Mary, Librn, University of Illinois Library at Urbana-Champaign, Government Documents, 200-D Main Libr, 1408 W Gregory Dr, Urbana, IL, 61801. Tel: 217-244-4621. Fax: 217-333-2214. p. 712

Mallory, Patrick, Supvr, Libr Serv, Saint Louis Community College, Meramec Campus Library, 11333 Big Bend Rd, Saint Louis, MO, 63122-5720. Tel: 314-984-7615. Fax: 314-984-7225. p. 1358

Mallory, Tim, Adult Serv Coordr, Timberland Regional Library, 415 Tumwater Blvd SW, Tumwater, WA, 98501-5799. Tel: 360-943-5001, Ext 2502. Fax: 360-586-6838. p. 2543

Mallow, Sharon R, Dir, Tygart Valley Community Library, Rte 219-250, Mill Creek, WV, 26280. Tel: 304-335-6277. Fax: 304-335-6277. p. 2565

Malloy, L Joseph, ILL, Ref, Sweet Briar College, 134 Chapel Rd, Sweet Briar, VA, 24595-1200. Tel: 434-381-6138. Fax: 434-381-6173. p. 2497

Malloy, Loren, Dir, Danville-Center Township Public Library, 101 S Indiana St, Danville, IN, 46122-1809. Tel: 317-745-2604. Fax: 317-745-0756. p. 735

Malloy, Michele, Res Support Serv Coordr, Georgetown University, Dahlgren Memorial Library, Preclinical Science Bldg GM-7, 3900 Reservoir Rd NW, Washington, DC, 20007. Tel: 202-687-1783. Fax: 202-687-1862. p. 402

Malmanger, Julie, Br Librn, Lake Agassiz Regional Library, McIntosh Public Library, 115 Broadway NW, McIntosh, MN, 56556. Tel: 218-563-4555. Fax: 218-563-3042. p. 1266

Malmgren, Linda, Br Mgr, Door County Library, Ephraim Branch, 9996 Water St, Ephraim, WI, 54211. Tel: 920-854-2014. p. 2640

Malmon, Sandi-Jo, Coll Develop, Harvard Library, Eda Kuhn Loeb Music Library, Music Bldg, Harvard University, Cambridge, MA, 02138. Tel: 617-495-2794. Fax: 617-496-4636. p. 1076

Malmquist, Katherine, Br Mgr, Cuyahoga County Public Library, Chagrin Falls Branch, 100 E Orange St, Chagrin Falls, OH, 44022-2735. Tel: 440-247-3556. Fax: 440-247-0179. p. 1927

Malmquist, Katherine, Br Mgr, Cuyahoga County Public Library, Gates Mills Branch, 1491 Chagrin River Rd, Gates Mills, OH, 44040-9703. Tel: 440-423-4808. Fax: 440-423-1363. p. 1927

Malmros, Stephanie, Head, Archives & Ms, University of Texas Libraries, Center for American History, SRH 2-101, D1100, University of Texas at Austin, Austin, TX, 78712. Tel: 512-495-4515. Fax: 512-495-4542. p. 2284

Malofie, Agapapalagi, Librn, American Samoa Office of Library Services, Manulele, Nuiuuli Village, Pago Pago, AS, 96799. Tel: 684-699-9617. Fax: 684-633-4240. p. 2665

Malone, Allison, Dir, Southern Arkansas University Tech-Library, 6415 Spellman Rd, Camden, AR, 71701. Tel: 870-574-4518, 870-574-4544. Fax: 870-574-4568. p. 96

Malone, Chuck, Govt Doc, Western Illinois University Libraries, One University Circle, Macomb, IL, 61455. Tel: 309-298-2719. Fax: 309-298-2791. p. 669

Malone, Dana, Asst Librn, Latimer County Public Library, 301 W Ada Ave, Wilburton, OK, 74578. Tel: 918-465-3751. Fax: 918-465-4287. p. 1986

Malone, David, Archivist, Spec Coll Librn, Wheaton College, 510 Irving Ave, Wheaton, IL, 60187-5593. Tel: 630-752-5707. Fax: 630-752-5855. p. 718

Malone, David, Fine Arts Librn, Saint John's University, 2835 Abbey Plaza, Collegeville, MN, 56321. Tel: 320-363-2127. Fax: 320-363-2126. p. 1246

Malone, Debbie, Per, University of San Francisco, 2130 Fulton St, San Francisco, CA, 94117-1080. Tel: 415-422-5352. Fax: 415-422-5949. p. 248

Malone, Debbie, Dir, DeSales University, 2755 Station Ave, Center Valley, PA, 18034. Tel: 610-282-1100, Ext 1253. Fax: 610-282-2342. p. 2043

Malone, Denyce, Br Mgr, Indianapolis-Marion County Public Library, Flanner House, 2424 Dr Martin Luther King Jr St, Indianapolis, IN, 46208-5598. Tel: 317-275-4370. p. 754

Malone, Elizabeth, Br Librn, Copiah-Jefferson Regional Library System, 223 S Extension St, Hazlehurst, MS, 39083-3339. Tel: 601-894-1681. Fax: 601-894-1672. p. 1301

Malone, Kren, Mgr, Los Angeles Public Library System, Central Southern Area, 931 S Gaffey St, San Pedro, CA, 90731. Tel: 310-548-7785. Fax: 310-548-2096. p. 173

Malone, Linda, Adult Serv, Ref Serv, Ad, West Linn Public Library, 1595 Burns St, West Linn, OR, 97068-3231. Tel: 503-656-7853, Ext 3012. Fax: 503-656-2746. p. 2022

Malone, Sally, Genealogist, Morley Library, 184 Phelps St, Painesville, OH, 44077-3926. Tel: 440-352-3383, Ext 216. Fax: 440-352-2653. p. 1927

Malone, Todd, Br Coordr, Cochise County Library District, Myrtle Kraft Library, 2393 S Rock House Rd, Portal, AZ, 85632. Tel: 520-558-2468. Fax: 520-558-2468. p. 58

Malone, Verlon, Br Coordr, Nashville Public Library, Carnegie North, 1001 Monroe St, Nashville, TN, 37208-2543. Tel: 615-862-5858. Fax: 615-862-5749. p. 2257

Malone, Verlon, Br Mgr, Nashville Public Library, Bordeaux, 4000 Clarksville Pike, Nashville, TN, 37218-1912. Tel: 615-862-5856. Fax: 615-862-5748. p. 2257

Maloney, Ann, Ch, Chesapeake Public Library, Greenbrier, 1214 Volvo Pkwy, Chesapeake, VA, 23320-7600. Tel: 757-410-7065. Fax: 757-410-7071. p. 2456

Maloney, Christopher, Dir, Ocean City Free Public Library, 1735 Simpson Ave, Ste 4, Ocean City, NJ, 08226. Tel: 609-399-2434. Fax: 609-398-0751. p. 1515

Maloney, Clare, Admin Senior Librn, Greece Public Library, Two Vince Tofany Blvd, Greece, NY, 14612. Tel: 585-225-8951. Fax: 585-225-2777. p. 1630

Maloney, David, Network Adminr, Goshen Free Public Library, 42 Main St, Goshen, MA, 01032-9608. Tel: 413-268-7033. p. 1091

Maloney, Heather, Asst Dir, University of Cincinnati, Muntz Hall, Rm 115, 9555 Plainfield Rd, Cincinnati, OH, 45236-1096. Tel: 513-936-1541. Fax: 513-745-5767. p. 1873

Maloney, Julia, Dir, Jones College, 5353 Arlington Expressway, Rm 311, Jacksonville, FL, 32211. Tel: 904-743-1122, Ext 101. Fax: 904-743-4446. p. 454

Maloney, Krisellen, Dr, Dean of Libr, University of Texas at San Antonio Libraries, One UTSA Circle, San Antonio, TX, 78249-0671. Tel: 210-458-4889. p. 2383

Maloney, Laureen, Ch, Scranton Public Library, Albright Memorial Bldg, 500 Vine St, Scranton, PA, 18509-3298. Tel: 570-348-3000. Fax: 570-348-3020. p. 2138

Maloney, Laureen, Head, Ch, Scranton Public Library, Lackawanna County Children's Library, 520 Vine St, Scranton, PA, 18509-3298. Tel: 570-348-3000, Ext 3015. Fax: 570-348-3020. p. 2138

Maloney, Maureen, Br Librn, Duluth Public Library, West Duluth, 5830 Grand Ave, Duluth, MN, 55807. Tel: 218-730-4280. Fax: 218-723-3820. p. 1248

Maloney, S Timothy, Assoc Librn, University of Minnesota Libraries-Twin Cities, Music, 70 Ferguson Hall, 2106 S Fourth St, Minneapolis, MN, 55455. Tel: 612-624-5890. Fax: 612-625-6994. p. 1262

Malosh, Dan, Digital Ref Librn, Minnesota Braille & Talking Book Library, 388 SE Sixth Ave, Faribault, MN, 55021-6340. Tel: 507-384-6869. Fax: 507-333-4832. p. 1251

Malosh, Dan, Ad, Ref Coordr, Tech Coordr, Watertown Public Library, 100 S Water St, Watertown, WI, 53094-4320. Tel: 920-262-4090. Fax: 920-261-8943. p. 2644

Malott, John, Pres, Japan-American Society of Washington DC Library, 1819 L St NW, Level 1B, Washington, DC, 20036. Tel: 202-833-2210. Fax: 202-833-2456. p. 405

Malouin, Ashley, Ad, Jacob Edwards Library, 236 Main St, Southbridge, MA, 01550-2598. Tel: 508-764-5426. Fax: 508-764-5428. p. 1126

Maloy, Frances G, Dir, Union College, 807 Union St, Schenectady, NY, 12308. Tel: 518-388-6277. Fax: 518-388-6619, 518-388-6641. p. 1741

Maloy, Vicky, Acad Tech Librn, Mount Mercy University, 1330 Elmhurst Dr NE, Cedar Rapids, IA, 52402-4797. Tel: 319-368-6465. Fax: 319-363-9060. p. 801

Malski, Sue, In Charge, Alcona County Library System, Lincoln Branch, 330 Traverse Bay Rd, Lincoln, MI, 48742-0115. Tel: 989-724-6796. Fax: 989-736-3388. p. 1188

Maltais, Andre, Tech Serv, Ecole Polytechnique de Montreal Bibliotheque, 2500, chemin de Polytechnique, Montreal, QC, H3T 1J4, CANADA. Tel: 514-340-4666. Fax: 514-340-4026. p. 2895

Malthaner, Ann, Pub Relations & Mkt Mgr, Stow-Munroe Falls Public Library, 3512 Darrow Rd, Stow, OH, 44224. Tel: 330-688-3295. p. 1937

Malvasi-Haines, Martina, Syst Librn, Slippery Rock University of Pennsylvania, Slippery Rock, PA, 16057-9989. Tel: 724-738-2664. Fax: 724-738-2661. p. 2140

Malvaso, Diane, Br Mgr, Bucks County Free Library, James A Michener Branch, 401 W Mill St, Quakertown, PA, 18951-1248. Tel: 215-536-3306. Fax: 215-536-8397. p. 2050

Malveaux, Tanya, Br Mgr, Howard County Library System, Glenwood Branch, 2350 State Rte 97, Cooksville, MD, 21723. Tel: 410-313-5575. p. 1026

Malvoso, Dianne, Youth Serv Consult, Bucks County Free Library, 150 S Pine St, Doylestown, PA, 18901-4932. Tel: 215-348-0332, Ext 1135. Fax: 215-348-4760. p. 2050

Malynowsky-Rakowsky, Teresa, Lead Librn, Kalamazoo Public Library, Eastwood, 1112 Gayle St, Kalamazoo, MI, 49048. Tel: 269-553-7813. Fax: 269-345-6095. p. 1197

Malysa, Amy, Mgr, Youth Serv, Alsip-Merrionette Park Public Library District, 11960 S Pulaski Rd, Alsip, IL, 60803-1197. Tel: 708-371-5666. Fax: 708-371-5672. p. 588

Malyshev, Nina, Dir, Alaska Library Network, PO Box 100585, Anchorage, AK, 99501-0585. Tel: 907-269-6567. Fax: 907-269-6580. p. 2937

Malzacher, Valerie I, Dir, University of Wisconsin-River Falls, 410 S Third St, River Falls, WI, 54022. Tel: 715-425-3321. Fax: 715-425-0609. p. 2635

Mamaril, Al, Librn, Anoka-Ramsey Community College, 11200 Mississippi Blvd NW, Coon Rapids, MN, 55433. Tel: 763-433-1552. p. 1246

Maminski, Dolores, Assoc Dir, Frederick County Public Libraries, 110 E Patrick St, Frederick, MD, 21701. Tel: 301-600-1613. Fax: 301-600-3789. p. 1028

Mammone, David, Librn, North Jersey Media Group Library, 150 River St, Hackensack, NJ, 07601. Tel: 201-646-4000. Fax: 201-646-4737. p. 1489

Mammone, Sandra, Br Supvr, Whitby Public Library, Brooklin Branch, Eight Vipond Rd, Brooklin, ON, L1M 1B3, CANADA. Tel: 905-655-3191. p. 2871

Manahan, Becky, Ch, Saint Albans Free Library, 11 Maiden Lane, Saint Albans, VT, 05478. Tel: 802-524-1507. Fax: 802-524-1514. p. 2434

Manahan, Meghan, Dir of Tech Serv, George Mason University Libraries, 4400 University Dr, MSN 2FL, Fairfax, VA, 22030-4444. Tel: 703-993-2445. Fax: 703-993-2200. p. 2462

Manalli, Susan, Head, Tech Serv, Anderson County Library, 300 N McDuffie St, Anderson, SC, 29621-5643. Tel: 864-260-4500. Fax: 864-260-4510. p. 2180

Manasco, Brenna, Dir, Orange Public Library, 220 N Fifth St, Orange, TX, 77630. Tel: 409-883-1086. Fax: 409-883-1057. p. 2367

Manasco, James, Head, Coll Develop, University of Louisville Libraries, William F Ekstrom Library, Belknap Campus, 2215 S Third St, Louisville, KY, 40292. Tel: 502-852-8731. Fax: 502-852-7394. p. 927

Manasco, Michael, Ser, Samford University Library, Lucille Stewart Beeson Law Library, 800 Lakeshore Dr, Birmingham, AL, 35229. Tel: 205-726-2714. Fax: 205-726-2644. p. 9

Manase, Bessie, Asst Dir, American Samoa Office of Library Services, American Library Bldg, Pago Pago, AS, 96799. Tel: 684-699-2170. Fax: 684-633-4240, 684-699-2193. p. 2665

Mancill, Emily, Librn, Noxubee County Library System, Brooksville Branch, 100 W Main St, Brooksville, MS, 39739. Tel: 662-738-4559. p. 1307

Mancini, Abigail, Ref/Instruction Librn, Lesley University, 89 Brattle St, Cambridge, MA, 02138-2790. Tel: 617-349-8840. Fax: 617-349-8849. p. 1077

Mancini, Laura, Dir, Libr Serv, Adams-Pratt Oakland County Law Library, 1200 N Telegraph Rd, Bldg 14 E, Pontiac, MI, 48341-0481. Tel: 248-858-0012. Fax: 248-858-1536. p. 1218

Mancuso, Ellen, Customer Serv Mgr, Head, Tech Serv, Boynton Beach City Library, 208 S Seacrest Blvd, Boynton Beach, FL, 33435. Tel: 561-742-6390. Fax: 561-742-6381. p. 429

Mancuso, Mark, Sr Librn, Lexington County Public Library System, 5440 Augusta Rd, Lexington, SC, 29072. Tel: 803-785-2673. Fax: 803-785-2601. p. 2199

Mand, Karen, Cat, Todd Wehr Library, St Norbert College, 301 Third St, De Pere, WI, 54115. Tel: 920-403-3269. Fax: 920-403-4064. p. 2587

Mand, Karen E, Librn, Saint Norbert Abbey, 1016 N Broadway, De Pere, WI, 54115-2697. Tel: 920-337-4354. p. 2587

Mandaville, Lynn, Dir, Henika District Library, 149 S Main St, Wayland, MI, 49348-1208. Tel: 269-792-2891. Fax: 269-792-0399. p. 1235

Mandel, Andrea, Ch, Marple Public Library, 2599 Sproul Rd, Broomall, PA, 19008-2399. Tel: 610-356-1510. Fax: 610-356-3589. p. 2038

Mandel, Anne, Coordr, Ch Serv, Spec Serv Librn, Macomb County Library, Macomb Library for the Blind & Physically Handicapped, 16480 Hall Rd, Clinton Township, MI, 48038-1132. Tel: 586-286-1580. Fax: 586-286-0634. p. 1164

Mandel, Carol A, Dean of Libr, New York University, 70 Washington Sq S, New York, NY, 10012-1091. Tel: 212-998-2444. Fax: 212-995-4070. p. 1695

Mandel, Leila, Ref Librn, Community College of Beaver County Library, One Campus Dr, Monaca, PA, 15061-2588. Tel: 724-775-8561, Ext 113. Fax: 724-728-8024. p. 2090

Mandel, Mary, Dir, John Rogers Memorial Public Library, 703 Second St, Dodge, NE, 68633-3512. Tel: 402-693-2512. p. 1397

Mandell, Dorothy, Librn, Congregation B'Nai Jacob, Starr & Manavon Sts, Phoenixville, PA, 19460. Tel: 610-933-7474. Fax: 610-933-8197. p. 2120

Mandell, Edward, Dir, William E Anderson Library of Penn Hills, 1037 Stotler Rd, Pittsburgh, PA, 15235-2099. Tel: 412-795-3507. Fax: 412-798-2186. p. 2121

Mandella, Stephanie, Ch, Katonah Village Library, 26 Bedford Rd, Katonah, NY, 10536-2121. Tel: 914-232-1233. Fax: 914-232-0415. p. 1648

Mandelstam, Yael, Head, Cat, Fordham University School of Law, 140 W 62nd St, New York, NY, 10023-7485. Tel: 212-636-7971. Fax: 212-930-8818. p. 1678

Mandeville, Alison M, Dir, Champlain Memorial Library, 148 Elm St, Champlain, NY, 12919-5317. Tel: 518-298-8620. Fax: 518-298-8620. p. 1605

Mandeville-Gamble, Steven, Assoc Univ Librn, Coll & Scholarly Communication, The George Washington University, 2130 H St NW, Ste 201, Washington, DC, 20052. Tel: 202-994-6455. Fax: 202-994-6464. p. 401

Mandle, Denise, Coordr, Human Res, Saint Charles City County Library District, 77 Boone Hills Dr, Saint Peters, MO, 63376-0529. Tel: 636-441-2300. Fax: 636-441-3132. p. 1363

Mandracchia, James, Librn, Akin Free Library, 378 Old Quaker Hill Rd, Pawling, NY, 12564-3411. Tel: 860-354-2822. p. 1716

Mandrell, Beth, Ref Librn, Rend Lake College, 468 N Ken Gray Pkwy, Ina, IL, 62846. Tel: 618-437-5321. Fax: 618-437-5677. p. 658

Maner, Mary Linda, County Libr Mgr, East Central Georgia Regional Library, Columbia County Public Library, 7022 Evans Town Center Blvd, Evans, GA, 30809. Tel: 706-863-1946. Fax: 706-868-3351. p. 519

Maner, Sarah, Br Mgr, Richland County Public Library, Southeast Regional, 7421 Garners Ferry Rd, Columbia, SC, 29209. Tel: 803-776-0855. p. 2188

Manera, Karen, Br Mgr, York County Library, Fort Mill Public, 1818 Second Baxter Crossing, Fort Mill, SC, 29708. Tel: 803-547-4114. Fax: 803-547-4852. p. 2203

Maness, Chris, Cataloger, Jerseyville Public Library, 105 N Liberty St, Jerseyville, IL, 62052-1512. Tel: 618-498-9514. Fax: 618-498-3036. p. 659

Maness, Jack, Asst Prof, Dir, Sci, University of Colorado Boulder, 1720 Pleasant St, 184 UCB, Boulder, CO, 80309-0184. Tel: 303-492-4545. Fax: 303-492-3340. p. 291

Maness, Jack, Dir, Sci, University of Colorado Boulder, Gemmill Library of Engineering, Mathematics & Physics, Mathematics Bldg, Rm 135, 184 UCB, Boulder, CO, 80309-0184. Tel: 303-492-4545. Fax: 303-492-6488. p. 291

Maness, Sue, Dir, Tom Burnett Memorial Library, 400 W Alameda, Iowa Park, TX, 76367. Tel: 940-592-4981. Fax: 940-592-4664. p. 2346

Maney, Marilyn, Newark Br Mgr, Ref, New Jersey Department of Law & Public Safety, 25 Market St, West Wing, 6th Flr, Trenton, NJ, 08625. Tel: 973-648-3751. Fax: 973-648-7445. p. 1535

Mangan, Jean, Mgr, Ad Serv, Mgr, Youth Serv, Rockford Public Library, 215 N Wyman St, Rockford, IL, 61101-1023. Tel: 815-965-7606. Fax: 815-965-0866. p. 697

Mangan, Susan, Ch, Ellenville Public Library & Museum, 40 Center St, Ellenville, NY, 12428-1396. Tel: 845-647-5530. Fax: 845-647-3554. p. 1619

Mangano, Danielle, Cataloger, College of Saint Mary Library, 7000 Mercy Rd, Omaha, NE, 68106-2606. Tel: 402-399-2464. Fax: 402-399-2686. p. 1411

Mangel, Cindy, Br Dir, Somerset County Library System, Mary Jacobs Memorial, 64 Washington St, Rocky Hill, NJ, 08553. Tel: 609-924-7073. Fax: 609-924-7668. p. 1475

Manger, Ronelle, Librn, DLA Piper US LLP, 6225 Smith Ave, Baltimore, MD, 21209-3600. Tel: 410-580-4655. Fax: 410-580-3655. p. 1012

Manget, Deborah S, Dir, Conyers-Rockdale Library System, 864 Green St, Conyers, GA, 30012. Tel: 770-388-5040. Fax: 770-388-5043. p. 527

Mangin, Alicia, Youth Serv Librn, Hiawatha Public Library, 150 W Willman St, Hiawatha, IA, 52233. Tel: 319-393-1414. Fax: 319-393-6005. p. 821

Mangine, Ellen, Asst Dir, Marysville Public Library, 231 S Plum St, Marysville, OH, 43040-1596. Tel: 937-642-1876. Fax: 937-642-3457. p. 1915

Mangini, Mark, Ref Mgr, Upper Arlington Public Library, 2800 Tremont Rd, Columbus, OH, 43221. Tel: 614-486-9621. Fax: 614-486-2043. p. 1891

Mangino, Arlene, Librn/Mgr, Clara Maass Medical Center, One Clara Maass Dr, Belleville, NJ, 07109. Tel: 973-450-2294. Fax: 973-844-4390. p. 1471

Mangione, Kerrie, Head, Circ Serv, North Shore Community College Library, One Ferncroft Rd, Danvers, MA, 01923-4093. Tel: 978-739-6251. Fax: 978-739-5500. p. 1083

Mangner, Julia, Br Mgr, Saint Louis County Library, Prairie Commons Branch, 915 Utz Lane, Hazelwood, MO, 63042-2739. Tel: 314-895-1023. p. 1359

Mangold, Amy, Communications & Develop Officer, Evansville Vanderburgh Public Library, 200 SE Martin Luther King Jr Blvd, Evansville, IN, 47713-1604. Tel: 812-428-8242. p. 738

Mangrum, Shannon, Tech Coordr, Poplar Bluff Public Library, 318 N Main St, Poplar Bluff, MO, 63901. Tel: 573-686-8639. Fax: 573-785-6876. p. 1349

Mangrum, Suzanne, Coll Develop Librn, Middle Tennessee State University, MTSU, PO Box 13, Murfreesboro, TN, 37132. Tel: 615-904-8517. p. 2254

Mangum, Lillian, Distance Educ, University of Hawaii, 310 Kaahumanu Ave, Kahului, HI, 96732. Tel: 808-984-3584. Fax: 808-244-9644. p. 566

Mangum, Marian, Librn, Emery County Library, Emery Branch, 100 N Center, Emery, UT, 84522. Tel: 435-286-2474. Fax: 435-286-2434. p. 2404

Mangum, Nancy, Coll Develop, San Joaquin Delta College, 5151 Pacific Ave, Stockton, CA, 95207-6370. Tel: 209-954-5862. Fax: 209-954-5691. p. 272

Mangus, Kris, Circ Mgr, Saint Johns County Public Library System, 6670 US 1 South, Saint Augustine, FL, 32086. Tel: 904-827-6916. p. 486

Manhart, Lynn, Dir, Central City Public Library, 1604 15th Ave, Central City, NE, 68826. Tel: 308-946-2512. Fax: 308-946-3290. p. 1395

Manhart, Patty, Dir, Dodge County Historical Society, 1643 N Nye, Fremont, NE, 68025. Tel: 402-721-4515. Fax: 402-721-8354. p. 1399

Manhein, Louise, Dir, Bolivar-Hardeman County Library, 213 N Washington St, Bolivar, TN, 38008-2020. Tel: 731-658-3436. Fax: 731-658-4660. p. 2225

Manier, Daniel, Head, Tech Serv, University of Notre Dame, 2345 Biolchini Hall of Law, Notre Dame, IN, 46556-4640. Tel: 574-631-3939. Fax: 574-631-6371. p. 771

Manifold, Jana, Librn, Heavener Public Library, 203 E Ave C, Heavener, OK, 74937. Tel: 918-653-2870. Fax: 918-653-4805. p. 1965

Manildi, Donald, Curator, University of Maryland Libraries, Michelle Smith Performing Arts Library, 2511 Clarice Smith Performing Arts Library, College Park, MD, 20742-1630. Tel: 301-405-9217. Fax: 301-314-7170. p. 1025

Manion, Joe, Pub Serv Mgr, Washington County Library, 8595 Central Park Pl, Woodbury, MN, 55125-9453. Tel: 651-275-8500. Fax: 651-275-8509. p. 1290

Manion, Margaret, Ref Librn, University of Massachusetts Lowell Libraries, Lydon Library, 84 University Ave, Lowell, MA, 01854-2896. Tel: 978-934-3211. Fax: 978-934-3014. p. 1101

Maniotis, Charlene, Circ Coordr, Rivier College, 420 S Main St, Nashua, NH, 03060-5086. Tel: 603-897-8256. Fax: 603-897-8889. p. 1459

Maniquet, Scott, Libr Mgr, National Post Library, 300-1450 Don Mills Rd, Toronto, ON, M3B 3R5, CANADA. Tel: 416-383-2300. Fax: 416-442-2109. p. 2855

Maniscalco, Casey, Doc Delivery, ILL, Harvard Library, Blue Hill Meteorological Observatory Library, Pierce Hall, 29 Oxford St, Cambridge, MA, 02138. Tel: 617-495-2836. Fax: 617-495-9837. p. 1074

Manker, Roben, Head of Libr, Free Library of Philadelphia, Lucien E Blackwell West Philadelphia Regional, 125 S 52nd St, Philadelphia, PA, 19139-3408. Tel: 215-685-7424. Fax: 215-685-7438. p. 2107

Mankin, Carole, Res, Massachusetts General Hospital, Treadwell Library, Bartlett Hall Ext - I, 55 Fruit St, Boston, MA, 02114-2696. Tel: 617-726-8600. Fax: 617-726-6784. p. 1063

Mankin, Michlene D, Librn, Campbell County Memorial Hospital Library, 501 S Burma, Gillette, WY, 82716-3426. Tel: 307-688-1380. Fax: 307-688-1390. p. 2655

Manley, Betty, Br Mgr, Chickasaw Regional Library System, Wilson Public Library, 1087 US Hwy 70A, Wilson, OK, 73463. Tel: 580-668-2486. Fax: 580-668-9280. p. 1957

Manley, Cynthia, Tech Serv Team Leader, Oak Ridge National Laboratory, Bldg 4500N, MS-6191, Bethel Valley Rd, Oak Ridge, TN, 37830. Tel: 865-574-0082. Fax: 865-574-6915. p. 2262

Manley, Joe, Libr Tech, Bureau of National Affairs, Inc Library, 1801 S Bell St, Rm 3200, Arlington, VA, 22202. Tel: 703-341-3312. Fax: 703-341-1636. p. 2449

Manley, Patricia, Br Dir, Settlement Music School, Willow Grove Branch Library, 318 Davisville Rd, Willow Grove, PA, 19090. Tel: 215-320-2630. p. 2117

Mann, Caroline, Head, Pub Serv, University of Portland, 5000 N Willamette Blvd, Portland, OR, 97203-5743. Tel: 503-943-7111. Fax: 503-943-7491. p. 2015

Mann, Ginger, Tech Serv Librn, Texas A&M University-Texarkana, 7101 University Ave, Texarkana, TX, 75503. Tel: 903-223-3090. Fax: 903-334-6695. p. 2392

Mann, Grace, Ch, Washington County Library System, 88 West 100 South, Saint George, UT, 84770-3490. Tel: 435-256-6329. Fax: 435-634-5741. p. 2412

Mann, Jennifer D, Librn, Massachusetts State Laboratory Institute Library, Dept of Public Health, 305 South St, Jamaica Plain, MA, 02130. Tel: 617-983-6290. Fax: 617-983-6292. p. 1097

Mann, Karen, Br Mgr, Chesterfield County Public Library, Clover Hill, 6701 Deer Run Rd, Midlothian, VA, 23112. Tel: 804-318-8642. p. 2457

Mann, Kathleen, Regional Librn, Volusia County Public Library, DeLand Area Public, 130 E Howry Ave, DeLand, FL, 32724. Tel: 386-822-6430. Fax: 386-822-6435. p. 436

Mann, Laura, Exec Dir, Dawson City Museum & Historical Society, PO Box 303, Dawson City, YT, Y0B 1G0, CANADA. Tel: 867-993-5291 ext 24. Fax: 867-993-5839. p. 2933

Mann, Mary M, Librn, Ben Guthrie-Lac Du Flambeau Public Library, 622 Peace Pipe Rd, Lac Du Flambeau, WI, 54538. Tel: 715-588-7001. p. 2604

Mann, Paige, Phys Sci Librn, University of Redlands, 1200 E Colton Ave, Redlands, CA, 92374-3758. Tel: 909-748-8022. Fax: 909-335-5392. p. 215

Mann, Pamela, Librn, University of Texas Libraries, Nettie Lee Benson Latin American Collection, Sid Richardson Hall 1-108, Austin, TX, 78713-8916. Tel: 512-495-4520. Fax: 512-495-4568. p. 2283

Mann, Pamela E, Ref/Instruction/Outreach, Saint Mary's College of Maryland Library, 18952 E Fisher Rd, Saint Mary's City, MD, 20686-3001. Tel: 240-895-4285. Fax: 240-895-4914. p. 1040

Mann, Rita, Dir, Union City Public Library, 324 43rd St, Union City, NJ, 07087-5008. Tel: 201-866-7500. Fax: 201-866-0962. p. 1537

Mann, Sanjeet, Art Librn, Coordr, Electronic Res, University of Redlands, 1200 E Colton Ave, Redlands, CA, 92374-3758. Tel: 909-748-8022. Fax: 909-335-5392. p. 215

Mann, Shirley, Adult Serv, Huron Public Library, 333 Williams St, Huron, OH, 44839. Tel: 419-433-5009. Fax: 419-433-7228. p. 1906

Mann, Susan, Asst Dir, Pell City Library, 1923 First Ave N, Pell City, AL, 35125. Tel: 205-884-1015. Fax: 205-814-4798. p. 33

Mann, Susan S, Dir, Hillsboro City Library, 118 S Waco St, Hillsboro, TX, 76645. Tel: 254-582-7385. Fax: 254-582-7765. p. 2333

Mann, Valerie, ILL, Bethlehem Area Public Library, 11 W Church St, Bethlehem, PA, 18018. Tel: 610-867-3761. Fax: 610-867-2767. p. 2034

Manna, Luca, Cat & Training Librn, Bergen County Cooperative Library System, 810 Main St, Hackensack, NJ, 07601. Tel: 201-489-1904. Fax: 201-489-4215. p. 2948

Mannato, Hilda, Tech Spec Librn, Keuka College, 141 Central Ave, Keuka Park, NY, 14478-0038. Tel: 315-279-5224, 315-279-5632. Fax: 315-279-5334. p. 1649

Mannebach, Michelle, Asst Librn, Garden Plain Community Library, 502 N Main, Garden Plain, KS, 67050. Tel: 316-535-2990. Fax: 316-535-2990. p. 868

Manners, Katherine, Dir, Libr Serv, State Correctional Institution, 189 Fryock Rd, Indiana, PA, 15701. Tel: 724-465-9630. Fax: 724-464-5135. p. 2071

Manners, Lisa, Br Mgr, Broward County Division of Libraries, Deerfield Beach-Percy White Branch, 837 E Hillsboro Blvd, Deerfield Beach, FL, 33441. Tel: 954-360-1380. Fax: 954-360-1382. p. 441

Mannherz, Mary Jane, Dir, Margaret R Grundy Memorial Library, 680 Radcliffe St, Bristol, PA, 19007-5199. Tel: 215-788-7891. Fax: 215-788-4976. p. 2037

Mannigel, Lois, ILL, Ser, Concordia University, 800 N Columbia Ave, Seward, NE, 68434-1595. Tel: 402-643-7254. Fax: 402-643-4218. p. 1419

Manning, Audrey, Br Mgr, Shreve Memorial Library, West Shreveport Branch, 4380 Pines Rd, Shreveport, LA, 71119. Tel: 318-635-0883. Fax: 318-621-1056. p. 970

Manning, Brenda, Librn, Public Library of Anniston-Calhoun County, Carver Branch, 722 W 14th St, Anniston, AL, 36201. Tel: 256-237-7271. Fax: 256-237-7271. p. 4

Manning, Brian, Dep Dir, Cumberland County Public Library & Information Center, 300 Maiden Lane, Fayetteville, NC, 28301-5000. Tel: 910-483-7727. Fax: 910-486-5372. p. 1792

Manning, Carolyn, Dir, Wimberley Village Library, 400 FM 2325, Wimberley, TX, 78676-5096. Tel: 512-847-2188. Fax: 512-847-1467. p. 2401

Manning, Catreva, Archivist, Grout Museum of History & Science, 503 South St, Waterloo, IA, 50701. Tel: 319-234-6357. Fax: 319-236-0500. p. 850

Manning, Colleen, Assoc Dir, Pub Serv, Florida Coastal School of Law, 8787 Baypine Rd, Jacksonville, FL, 32256. Tel: 904-680-7615. Fax: 904-680-7677. p. 452

Manning, Diane, ILL Spec, Washington State University Libraries, 14204 NE Salmon Creek Ave, Vancouver, WA, 98686. Tel: 360-546-9154. Fax: 360-546-9039. p. 2546

Manning, Dorothy, Dir, Jourdanton Community Library, 1101 Campbell Ave, Jourdanton, TX, 78026. Tel: 830-769-3087. Fax: 830-769-4082. p. 2348

Manning, Geraldine, Ch, Forbush Memorial Library, 118 Main St, Westminster, MA, 01473. Tel: 978-874-7416. Fax: 978-874-7424. p. 1139

Manning, Jay, Tech Mgr, Jefferson County Library, 5678 State Rd PP, High Ridge, MO, 63049-2216. Tel: 636-677-8689. Fax: 636-677-1769. p. 1331

Manning, Jim, Exec Dir, Astronomical Society of the Pacific Library, 390 Ashton Ave, San Francisco, CA, 94112. Tel: 415-337-1100. Fax: 415-337-5205. p. 240

Manning, Karen, Dir, Maquoketa Public Library, 126 S Second St, Maquoketa, IA, 52060. Tel: 563-652-3874. p. 829

Manning, Kathryn, Libr Serv Supvr/Cat, Keene State College, 229 Main St, Keene, NH, 03435-3201. Tel: 603-358-2726. Fax: 603-358-2745. p. 1453

Manning, Kathy, Circ, Slippery Rock University of Pennsylvania, Slippery Rock, PA, 16057-9989. Tel: 724-738-2058. Fax: 724-738-2661. p. 2140

Manning, Kevin, Circ, Bridgewater State College, Ten Shaw Rd, Bridgewater, MA, 02325. Tel: 508-531-2005. Fax: 508-531-1349, 508-531-6103. p. 1070

Manning, Marilyn, Dir, Robinson Public Library District, 606 N Jefferson St, Robinson, IL, 62454-2665. Tel: 618-544-2917. Fax: 618-544-7172. p. 695

Manning, Mary, Ref Librn, Colonel Robert R McCormick Research Center, One S 151 Winfield Rd, Wheaton, IL, 60189-6097. Tel: 630-260-8186. Fax: 630-260-9298. p. 718

Manning, Mary, Asst Archivist, Spec Coll Librn, Adelphi University Libraries, One South Ave, Garden City, NY, 11530. Tel: 516-877-3818. Fax: 516-877-3592. p. 1625

Manning, Mary, Asst Univ Archivist, Texas A&M University Libraries, Cushing Memorial Library & Archives, 5000 TAMU, College Station, TX, 77843-5000. Tel: 979-845-1951. Fax: 979-845-1441. p. 2299

Manning, Maureen, Tech Serv, University Club Library, One W 54th St, New York, NY, 10019. Tel: 212-572-3418. Fax: 212-572-3452. p. 1702

Manning, Montie L, Dir, Alexandria-Monroe Public Library, 117 E Church St, Alexandria, IN, 46001-2005. Tel: 765-724-2196. Fax: 765-724-2204. p. 723

Manning, Robert, Asst Br Mgr, Ch, Atlanta-Fulton Public Library System, Fairburn Hobgood-Palmer Library, 60 Valley View Dr, Fairburn, GA, 30213. Tel: 770-306-3138. Fax: 770-306-3140. p. 512

Manning, Vicky, Circ Asst, Lee County Library, 219 N Madison St, Tupelo, MS, 38804-3899. Tel: 662-841-9027. Fax: 662-840-7615. p. 1316

Mannino, Caroll, Br Mgr, Jefferson County Public Library, Columbine, 7706 W Bowles Ave, Littleton, CO, 80123. p. 315

Mannino, Kathleen, ILL, Ref, The College of New Rochelle, 29 Castle Pl, New Rochelle, NY, 10805-2308. Tel: 914-654-5357. Fax: 914-654-5884. p. 1666

Mannion, Gail, Head, Lending Serv, Windsor Public Library, 323 Broad St, Windsor, CT, 06095. Tel: 860-285-1923. Fax: 860-285-1889. p. 379

Mannion, Robert, Head, Ref (Info Serv), Warner Library, 121 N Broadway, Tarrytown, NY, 10591. Tel: 914-631-7734. Fax: 914-631-2324. p. 1754

Mannix, Gina, Prog Dir, National Center for Law & Economic Justice, 275 Seventh Ave, Ste 1205, New York, NY, 10001-6708. Tel: 212-633-6967. Fax: 212-633-6371. p. 1687

Mannstedt, Kathy, Librn, USGS, 2630 Fanta Reed Rd, La Crosse, WI, 54603-1223. Tel: 608-781-6215. Fax: 608-783-6066. p. 2603

Manos, Rebecca, Librn, Boston Public Library, Parker Hill, 1497 Tremont St, Roxbury, MA, 02120-2995. Tel: 617-427-3820. Fax: 617-445-4321. p. 1057

Manouchehri, Elizabeth, Assoc Dir, Riverside County Law Library, 3989 Lemon St, Riverside, CA, 92501-4203. Tel: 951-368-0362. Fax: 951-368-0185. p. 217

Manriquez, Julio, Libr Asst II, Camarena Memorial Library, 850 Encinas Ave, Calexico, CA, 92231. Tel: 760-768-2170. Fax: 760-357-0404. p. 131

Mansbach, Judith, Dir, Edison Township Free Public Library, 340 Plainfield Ave, Edison, NJ, 08817. Tel: 732-287-2298. Fax: 732-819-9134. p. 1483

Mansbridge, Karen, Br Mgr, Public Library Association of Annapolis & Anne Arundel County, Inc, Severna Park, 45 McKinsey Rd, Severna Park, MD, 21146. Tel: 410-222-6290. Fax: 410-222-6297. p. 1011

Manseau, Pierre, Prof, College de Maisonneuve, 3800, rue Sherbrooke Est, Montreal, QC, H1X 2A2, CANADA. Tel: 514-254-7131. Fax: 514-251-9741. p. 2978

Mansen, Cheryl, Asst Dir, Mgr, Libr Develop, Utah State Library Division, 250 N 1950 West, Ste A, Salt Lake City, UT, 84116-7901. Tel: 801-715-6747. Fax: 801-715-6767. p. 2415

Mansfield, Bambi, Dir of Libr, Mgr Fac, Spec Coll Librn, Crawford County Library System, 201 Plum St, Grayling, MI, 49738. Tel: 989-348-9214. Fax: 989-348-9294. p. 1186

Mansfield, Judith, In Charge, Library of Congress, Bibliographic Access, 101 Independence Ave SE, Washington, DC, 20540. Tel: 202-707-2244. Fax: 202-707-5361. p. 406

Mansfield, Tara, Head, Circ, Hamilton-Wenham Public Library, 14 Union St, South Hamilton, MA, 01982. Tel: 978-468-5577. Fax: 978-468-5535. p. 1125

Mansfield-Egans, Cheryl, Ref, Lone Star College System, Montgomery College Library, 3200 College Park Dr, Conroe, TX, 77384. Tel: 936-273-7393. Fax: 936-273-7395. p. 2340

Manson, Bill, Chief Exec Officer, Caledon Public Library, 150 Queen St S, Bolton, ON, L7E 1E3, CANADA. Tel: 905-584-1456. Fax: 905-857-8280. p. 2795

Mansour, Mohamed, Dr, Dir, Palm Beach State College, 1977 College Dr, Belle Glade, FL, 33430. Tel: 561-993-1151. Fax: 561-993-1157. p. 427

Manstein, Robert, Librn, Gratz College, 7605 Old York Rd, Melrose Park, PA, 19027. Tel: 215-635-7300, Ext 127. Fax: 215-635-7320. p. 2088

Mansur, Helen, Tech Serv, Northern Essex Community College, 100 Elliott St, Haverhill, MA, 01830. Tel: 978-556-3425. Fax: 978-556-3738. p. 1094

Mantegna, Jean, Mgr, Human Res, Baltimore County Public Library, 320 York Rd, Towson, MD, 21204-5179. Tel: 410-887-6177. Fax: 410-887-6103. p. 1044

Mantei, Sheri, Circ Serv Team Leader, Sam Fore Jr Wilson County Public Library, One Library Lane, Floresville, TX, 78114. Tel: 830-393-7361. Fax: 830-393-7337. p. 2319

Manteuffel, Louise, Dir, Hotchkiss Library of Sharon, Inc, Ten Upper Main St, Sharon, CT, 06069. Tel: 860-364-5041. Fax: 860-364-6060. p. 367

Mantor-Ramirez, Cathy, Asst Dir, University of Texas Libraries, Jamail Center for Legal Research, University of Texas School of Law, 727 E Dean Keeton St, Austin, TX, 78705-3224. Tel: 512-471-7726. Fax: 512-471-0243. p. 2284

Mantrone, Tracey, Br Librn, Brooklyn Public Library, Mapleton, 1702 60th St, Brooklyn, NY, 11204. Tel: 718-256-2117. Fax: 718-256-1487. p. 1591

Mantrova, Katya, Dir, Biogen Idec Inc Library, 14 Cambridge Ctr, Cambridge, MA, 02142. Tel: 617-679-2000. Fax: 617-679-2306. p. 1072

Mantz, Nicole, Educ Curator, Cheyenne Mountain Zoological Park Library, 4250 Cheyenne Mountain Zoo Rd, Colorado Springs, CO, 80906. Tel: 719-633-9925, Ext 116. Fax: 719-633-2254. p. 294

Mantz, Stephen, Music Cat Librn, University of Colorado Boulder, Howard B Waltz Music Library, Imig Music Bldg, N250, 1720 Pleasant St, 184 UCB, Boulder, CO, 80309-0184. Tel: 303-492-0727. Fax: 303-735-0100. p. 292

Manuel, Larry, Dir, Wilmington Public Library, Tenth & Market St, Wilmington, DE, 19801. Tel: 302-571-7400. Fax: 302-654-9132. p. 389

Manuel, Larry L, Ref Librn, Wilmington University Library, 320 DuPont Hwy, New Castle, DE, 19720. Tel: 302-328-9401. Fax: 302-328-0914. p. 385

Manuel, Nancy, Dir, Bolivar-Harpers Ferry Public Library, 151 Polk St, Harpers Ferry, WV, 25425. Tel: 304-535-2301. Fax: 304-535-2301. p. 2560

Manuel, Shirley, Librn, Jackson County Library, Tuckerman Branch, 200 W Main St, Tuckerman, AR, 72473. Tel: 870-349-5336. Fax: 870-349-5336. p. 111

Manvell, Arthur, Honorary Librn, Royal Canadian Military Institute Library, 426 University Ave, Toronto, ON, M5G 1S9, CANADA. Tel: 416-597-0286, Ext 128. Fax: 416-597-6919. p. 2858

Manwarren, Carol, ILL, Guernsey Memorial Library, Three Court St, Norwich, NY, 13815. Tel: 607-334-4034. Fax: 607-336-3901. p. 1708

Manwiller, Linda, Dir, Myerstown Community Library, 199 N College St, Myerstown, PA, 17067. Tel: 717-866-2800. Fax: 717-866-5898. p. 2094

Many, Douglas, Mgr, Libr Syst, The Rockefeller University, 1222 York Ave, Welch Hall, New York, NY, 10065. Tel: 212-327-8906. Fax: 212-327-8802. p. 1698

Manz, William H, Sr Res Librn, Saint John's University Library, Rittenberg Law Library, 8000 Utopia Pkwy, Queens, NY, 11439. Tel: 718-990-6655. Fax: 718-990-6649. p. 1725

Manzella, Patricia A, Sr Librn, Newport News Public Library System, Virgil I Grissom Branch, 366 DeShazor Dr, Newport News, VA, 23608. Tel: 757-369-3190. Fax: 757-369-3198. p. 2480

Manzer, Constance, Dir, Springfield Memorial Library, 665 Main St, Springfield, NE, 68059. Tel: 402-253-2797. Fax: 402-253-2797. p. 1420

Manzer, Rachel, ILL, South Dakota State University, 1300 N Campus Dr, Box 2115, Brookings, SD, 57007-1098. Tel: 605-688-5573. Fax: 605-688-6133. p. 2211

Maounis, Nikki, Dir, Camden Public Library, 55 Main St, Camden, ME, 04843-1703. Tel: 207-236-3440. Fax: 207-236-6673. p. 980

Mapes, Justin, Dir, Ohio Public Library District, 112 N Main St, Ohio, IL, 61349. Tel: 815-376-5422. Fax: 815-376-5422. p. 685

Mapes, Marcy, Coll Develop Librn, Southwestern Assemblies of God University, 1200 Sycamore, Waxahachie, TX, 75165-2342. Tel: 972-825-4761. Fax: 972-923-0488. p. 2398

Maple, Amanda, Librn, Pennsylvania State University Libraries, George & Sherry Middlemas Arts & Humanities Library, Pennsylvania State University, W 202 Pattee Library, University Park, PA, 16802-1801. Tel: 814-863-1401. Fax: 814-863-7502. p. 2148

Maple, Connie, Mgr, ILL, Oklahoma Christian University, 2501 E Memorial Rd, Edmond, OK, 73013. Tel: 405-425-5312. Fax: 405-425-5313. p. 1962

Maples, Jody, Youth Serv Mgr, Lawrenceburg Public Library District, 150 Mary St, Lawrenceburg, IN, 47025-1995. Tel: 812-537-2775, Ext 23. Fax: 812-537-2810. p. 760

Maples, Judy, Br Mgr, West Georgia Regional Library, Lithia Springs Public Library, 7100 Junior High Dr, Lithia Springs, GA, 30122. Tel: 770-944-5931. Fax: 770-944-5932. p. 524

Mapue, Susie, In Charge, Legislative Assembly, 200 Vaughan St, Main Flr, Winnipeg, MB, R3C 1T5, CANADA. Tel: 204-945-3225. Fax: 204-945-6011. p. 2756

Mara, Mary, Dir of Libr Serv, City University of Seattle, 150-120th Ave NE, Bellevue, WA, 98005-3019. Tel: 425-709-3444. Fax: 425-709-3455. p. 2508

Marable, Antwanne G, Info Serv, Norfolk State University Library, 700 Park Ave, Norfolk, VA, 23504-8010. Tel: 757-823-8445. Fax: 757-823-2431. p. 2482

Maragliano, Kathryn, Coord of Libr Communications/Humanities Librn, Hilbert College, 5200 S Park Ave, Hamburg, NY, 14075. Tel: 716-649-7900, Ext 237. Fax: 716-648-6530. p. 1632

Maragno, Jean, Librn, Saint Joseph's Hospital, 50 Charlton Ave E, Hamilton, ON, L8N 4A6, CANADA. Tel: 905-522-4941, Ext 33410. Fax: 905-540-6504. p. 2811

Maragno, Jean, Coordr, Hamilton & District Health Library Network, c/o St Josephs Healthcare Hamilton, Sherman Libray, Rm T2305, 50 Charlton Ave E, Hamilton, ON, L8N 4A6, CANADA. Tel: 905-522-1155, Ext 3410. Fax: 905-540-6504. p. 2959

Marallo, Julie, Adult Serv, Nanuet Public Library, 149 Church St, Nanuet, NY, 10954. Tel: 845-623-4281. Fax: 845-623-2415. p. 1664

Maranda, Suzanne, Head of Libr, Queen's University, Bracken Health Sciences Library, Botterell Hall, Ground Flr, 18 Stuart St, Kingston, ON, K7L 3N6, CANADA. Tel: 613-533-6000, Ext 74522. Fax: 613-533-6892. p. 2814

Maranto, Robert, Mgr, Baltimore County Public Library, Essex, 1110 Eastern Blvd, Baltimore, MD, 21221-3497. Tel: 410-887-0295. Fax: 410-687-0075. p. 1044

Maranto, Robert, Mgr, Baltimore County Public Library, Sollers Point Branch, 323 Sollers Point Rd, Baltimore, MD, 21222-6169. Tel: 410-288-3123. Fax: 410-288-3125. p. 1044

Maravell, Daniel, Evening Res Serv Libr Spec, Landmark College Library, River Rd S, Putney, VT, 05346. Tel: 802-387-6763. Fax: 802-387-6896. p. 2433

Maravilla, Virginia, Dir, Huntley Area Public Library District, 11000 Ruth Rd, Huntley, IL, 60142-7155. Tel: 847-669-5386. Fax: 847-669-5439. p. 657

Marbella, Fidencio, Dir, Westchester Public Library, 10700 Canterbury St, Westchester, IL, 60154. Tel: 708-562-3573. Fax: 708-562-1298. p. 717

Marble, Lawrence, Dir, Garden City Public Library, 31735 Maplewood Rd, Garden City, MI, 48135. Tel: 734-793-1830. Fax: 734-793-1831. p. 1182

Marble, Neta, Librn, Floyd County Library, Lockney Branch, 124 S Main, Lockney, TX, 79241. Tel: 806-652-3561. p. 2319

Marcantel, Jerome, Asst Prof, Info Res Librn, McNeese State University, 4205 Ryan St, Lake Charles, LA, 70609. Tel: 337-475-5728. Fax: 337-475-5719, 337-475-5727. p. 954

Marceau, Louise, Reader Serv, Cegep de Sherbrooke, 475 rue du Cegep, Sherbrooke, QC, J1E 4K1, CANADA. Tel: 819-564-6350, Ext 5231, 819-564-6350, Ext 5233. Fax: 819-564-4025. p. 2912

Marcellus, Rhea, Librn, Blind River Public Library, Eight Woodward Ave, Blind River, ON, P0R 1B0, CANADA. Tel: 705-356-7616. Fax: 705-356-7343. p. 2795

March, Debra, Ref, Spec Coll Librn, Webmaster, Young Harris College, One College St, Young Harris, GA, 30582. Tel: 706-379-4313. Fax: 706-379-4314. p. 558

March, Gregory, Librn, University of Tennessee, Knoxville, Map Library, 15 Hoskins Bldg, Knoxville, TN, 37996-4006. Tel: 865-974-4315. Fax: 865-974-3925. p. 2244

March, Karen, Tech Serv, Department of Veterans Affairs, 2300 Ramsey St, Fayetteville, NC, 28301. Tel: 910-822-7072. p. 1793

March, Virginia Sharp, Dir, Perry Public Library, 3753 Main St, Perry, OH, 44081-9501. Tel: 440-259-3300. Fax: 440-259-3977. p. 1929

Marchand, Marc, Br Mgr, Arlington Public Library System, East Arlington, 1624 New York Ave, Arlington, TX, 76010-4795. Tel: 817-459-6792. Fax: 817-795-0726. p. 2276

Marchand, Marc, Br Mgr, Arlington Public Library System, Northeast, 1905 Brown Blvd, Arlington, TX, 76006-4605. Tel: 817-277-5573. Fax: 817-276-8649. p. 2276

Marchand, Marc, Libr Serv Mgr, Arlington Public Library System, 101 E Abram St, MS 10-0100, Arlington, TX, 76010-1183. Tel: 817-459-6900. Fax: 817-459-6936. p. 2276

Marchand, Marlene, Dir, Shelburne Public Library, 74 Village Rd, Shelburne, NH, 03581-3209. Tel: 603-466-2089. p. 1465

Marchand, Melinda, Mgr, Libr Serv, Emerson Hospital Medical Library, 133 Old Rd to Nine Acre Corner, Concord, MA, 01742. Tel: 978-287-3090. Fax: 978-287-3651. p. 1083

Marchand, Mike, Access Serv, Kearney Public Library, 2020 First Ave, Kearney, NE, 68847. Tel: 308-233-3285. Fax: 308-233-3291. p. 1403

Marchand, Nicole, Dir of Libr Serv, James J Hill Reference Library, 80 W Fourth St, Saint Paul, MN, 55102-1669. Tel: 651-265-5500. Fax: 651-265-5520. p. 1278

Marchand, Paul, Librn, Ecole de Technologie Superieure (Service de la bibliotheque), 1100 rue Notre-Dame Ouest, Montreal, QC, H3C 1K3, CANADA. Tel: 514-396-8946. Fax: 514-396-8633. p. 2895

Marchant, Susan, Mgr, Spec Coll, Topeka & Shawnee County Public Library, 1515 SW Tenth Ave, Topeka, KS, 66604-1374. Tel: 785-580-4400. Fax: 785-580-4496. p. 897

Marchbanks, Kathy, Librn, New Madrid County Library, New Madrid Memorial, 431 Mill St, New Madrid, MO, 63869. Tel: 573-748-2378. Fax: 573-748-7637. p. 1350

Marchefka, Nancy, Librn, S White Dickinson Memorial Library, 202 Chestnut Plain Rd, Whately, MA, 01093. Tel: 413-665-2170. p. 1140

Marchessault, Ellen, Tech Serv Dir, Carol Stream Public Library, 616 Hiawatha Dr, Carol Stream, IL, 60188. Tel: 630-653-0755. Fax: 630-653-6809. p. 601

Marchetti, Angie, ILL Librn, Littleton Public Library, 92 Main St, Littleton, NH, 03561-1238. Tel: 603-444-5741. Fax: 603-444-1706. p. 1454

Marchetti, Denise, Ch, Wyckoff Public Library, 200 Woodland Ave, Wyckoff, NJ, 07481. Tel: 201-891-4866. Fax: 201-891-3892. p. 1546

Marchino, Mark, Med Librn, Philadelphia VA Medical Center, 3900 Woodland Ave, Philadelphia, PA, 19104. Tel: 215-823-5860. Fax: 215-823-5108. p. 2115

Marchionini, Gary, Dr, Dean, University of North Carolina at Chapel Hill, CB No 3360, 100 Manning Hall, Chapel Hill, NC, 27599-3360. Tel: 919-962-8366. Fax: 919-962-8071. p. 2971

Marciano, Gina, Circ, North Providence Union Free Library, 1810 Mineral Spring Ave, North Providence, RI, 02904. Tel: 401-353-5600. p. 2170

Marciniak, Catherine, Ch, Fuller Public Library, 29 School St, Hillsboro, NH, 03244. Tel: 603-464-3595. Fax: 603-464-4572. p. 1451

Marciniak, Laura, Cat, Public Library of Johnston County & Smithfield, 305 E Market St, Smithfield, NC, 27577-3919. Tel: 919-934-8146. Fax: 919-934-8084. p. 1824

Marckmann, Kay, Dir, Fontanelle Public Library, 303 Washington St, Fontanelle, IA, 50846. Tel: 641-745-4981. Fax: 641-745-3017. p. 816

Marcks, Carol, Coll Develop, East Baton Rouge Parish Library, 7711 Goodwood Blvd, Baton Rouge, LA, 70806-7625. Tel: 225-231-3700. Fax: 225-231-3788. p. 942

Marco, Judy, Youth Librn, Central City Public Library, 1604 15th Ave, Central City, NE, 68826. Tel: 308-946-2512. Fax: 308-946-3290. p. 1395

Marcoline, Beverly, Dir of Libr, Utica College, 1600 Burrstone Rd, Utica, NY, 13502-4892. Tel: 315-792-3041. Fax: 315-792-3361. p. 1759

Marcondes, Michael, Tech Info Spec, Taunton Public Library, 12 Pleasant St, Taunton, MA, 02780. Tel: 508-821-1410. Fax: 508-821-1414. p. 1131

Marconnet, Donna, Instr, Madison Area Technical College, 3550 Anderson St, Rm 230, Madison, WI, 53704. Tel: 608-243-4085. Fax: 608-246-6644. p. 2606

Marcotte, Roland, Asst Libr Mgr, Venice Public Library, 300 S Nokomis Ave, Venice, FL, 34285-2416. Tel: 941-861-1330. Fax: 941-486-2345. p. 501

Marcoux, Elizabeth, Sr Lecturer, University of Washington, Mary Gates Hall, Ste 370, Campus Box 352840, Seattle, WA, 98195-2840. Tel: 206-685-9937. Fax: 206-616-3152. p. 2976

Marcoux, Julie, Pub Serv Librn, Universite de Moncton, 415 Ave de l'Universite, Moncton, NB, E1A 3E9, CANADA. Tel: 506-858-4012. Fax: 506-858-4086. p. 2766

Marcoux, Marie-Andree, Chef de Div, Bibliothèques de Montrèal, L'Octogone, 1080, avenue Dollard, Montreal, QC, H8N 2T9, CANADA. Tel: 514-367-6488. Fax: 514-367-6604. p. 2890

Marcoux, Sylvie, Libr Tech, Hospital du Saint-Sacrement, 1050, Chemin Sainte-Foy, Quebec, QC, G1S 4L8, CANADA. Tel: 418-682-7511, Ext 2128. Fax: 418-682-7730. p. 2905

Marcoux, Yves, Assoc Prof, Universite de Montreal, 3150, rue Jean-Brillant, bur C-2004, Montreal, QC, H3T 1N8, CANADA. Tel: 514-343-6044. Fax: 514-343-5753. p. 2979

Marcove, Nancy, Libr Serv Mgr, Robinson & Cole LLP Library, 280 Trumbull St, Hartford, CT, 06103-3597. Tel: 860-275-8200. Fax: 860-275-8299. p. 347

Marcum, James, Chair, Dir, Queens College of the City University of New York, Benjamin Rosenthal Library, Rm 254, 65-30 Kissena Blvd, Flushing, NY, 11367. Tel: 718-997-3790. Fax: 718-997-3797. p. 2970

Marcum, James W, Dr, Univ Librn, Fairleigh Dickinson University, 1000 River Rd, Teaneck, NJ, 07666-1914. Tel: 201-692-2276. Fax: 201-692-9815. p. 1532

Marcum, Lisa, Dir, Owsley County Public Library, Two Action Pl, Booneville, KY, 41314. Tel: 606-593-5700. Fax: 606-593-5708. p. 907

Marcum, Rebecca, Librn, Blount Memorial Hospital, 907 E Lamar Alexander Pkwy, Maryville, TN, 37804. Tel: 865-977-5520. Fax: 865-981-2473. p. 2247

Marcus, Cara, Dir, Brigham & Women's Faulkner Hospital, 1153 Centre St, Boston, MA, 02130. Tel: 617-983-7443. Fax: 617-983-7555. p. 1059

Marcus, Charles, Ref, University of California, 200 McAllister St, San Francisco, CA, 94102-4978. Tel: 415-565-4757. Fax: 415-581-8849. p. 248

Marcus, Elizabeth, Dir, Brockton Public Library System, 304 Main St, Brockton, MA, 02301-5390. Tel: 508-580-7890. Fax: 508-580-7898. p. 1070

Marcus, Elizabeth, Dir, Brockton Public Library System, East, 54 Kingman St, Brockton, MA, 02302. Tel: 508-580-7892. Fax: 508-580-7861. p. 1070

Marcus, Irene, Ref & ILL Librn, Tarpon Springs Public Library, 138 E Lemon St, Tarpon Springs, FL, 34689. Tel: 727-943-4922. Fax: 727-943-4926. p. 499

Marcus, Jaclyn, Ch, North Brunswick Free Public Library, 880 Hermann Rd, North Brunswick, NJ, 08902. Tel: 732-246-3545. Fax: 732-246-1341. p. 1514

Marcus, Ronald, Librn, Stamford Historical Society Library, 1508 High Ridge Rd, Stamford, CT, 06903-4107. Tel: 203-329-1183. Fax: 203-322-1607. p. 370

Marcus, Sandra, Coordr, Libr Pub Relations, Queensborough Community College, City University of New York, 222-05 56th Ave, Bayside, NY, 11364-1497. Tel: 718-281-5072. Fax: 718-281-5012. p. 1579

Marcuson, Karl, Ref/Info Tech Serv Librn, Longview Public Library, 1600 Louisiana St, Longview, WA, 98632-2993. Tel: 360-442-5300. Fax: 360-442-5954. p. 2520

Marder, Louis, Pres, The Shakespeare Data Bank, Inc Library, 1217 Ashland Ave, Evanston, IL, 60202-1103. Tel: 847-475-7550. p. 644

Marder, Olga, Head, Conserv & Presv, The LuEsther T Mertz Library, The New York Botanical Garden, 2900 Southern Blvd, Bronx, NY, 10458-5126. Tel: 718-817-8746. Fax: 718-817-8956. p. 1587

Mardis, Emily, Librn, United States Air Force, 102 Hall Blvd, No 2, San Antonio, TX, 78243-7168. Tel: 210-977-2804. Fax: 210-977-6621. p. 2383

Mardis, Lori, Info Librn, Northwest Missouri State University, 800 University Dr, Maryville, MO, 64468-6001. Tel: 660-562-1192. Fax: 660-562-1049. p. 1344

Mardis, Marcia, Dr, Asst Prof, Assoc Dir, PALM Ctr, Florida State University, College of Communication & Information, 142 Collegiate Loop, Tallahassee, FL, 32306-2100. Tel: 850-644-3392. Fax: 850-644-9763. p. 2963

Mare, Doris, In Charge, National Psychological Association for Psychoanalysis, Inc, 40 W 13th St, New York, NY, 10011. Tel: 212-924-7440. Fax: 212-989-7543. p. 1688

Mare, Ruth, Librn, Dix Dorothea Psychiatric Center, Patient Library, 656 State St, Bangor, ME, 04402. Tel: 207-941-4226. Fax: 207-941-4228. p. 975

Mare, Ruth, Librn, Dorothea Dix Psychiatric Center, 656 State St, Bangor, ME, 04402. Tel: 207-941-4226. Fax: 207-941-4444. p. 975

Maready, Teffiney, Head of Libr, Neuse Regional Library, Comfort Public Library, 4889 Hwy 41 W, Trenton, NC, 28585. Tel: 910-324-5061. p. 1805

Mares, Claire, In Charge, Eastern Nebraska Genealogical Society Library, PO Box 541, Fremont, NE, 68026-0541. Tel: 402-721-9553. p. 1399

Marez, Amanda, Asst Librn, Saint Mary Corwin Medical Center, 1008 Minnequa Ave, Pueblo, CO, 81004-9988. Tel: 719-560-5598. Fax: 719-560-4018. p. 321

Margaret, Edwards, Libr Tech, Charles B Danforth Public Library, 6208 VT Rte 12, Barnard, VT, 05031. Tel: 802-234-9408. p. 2417

Margarida, Danielle, Head, Ch, Sharon Public Library, 11 N Main St, Sharon, MA, 02067-1299. Tel: 781-784-1578. Fax: 781-784-4728. p. 1123

Margarita, Zambrano, Youth Serv, Ramsey Free Public Library, 30 Wyckoff Ave, Ramsey, NJ, 07446. Tel: 201-327-1445. Fax: 201-327-3687. p. 1525

Margerison, Sonja, Librn, Lakeland Library Region, Paynton Branch, 201 First St E, Paynton, SK, S0M 2J0, CANADA. Tel: 306-895-2175. p 2920

Marget, Wanda, Dir, Fairmont Public Library, 600 F St, Fairmont, NE, 68354. Tel: 402-268-6081. Fax: 402-268-6081. p. 1398

Margeton, Stephen, Dir, Catholic University of America, Judge Kathryn J DuFour Law Library, 3600 John McCormack Rd NE, Washington, DC, 20064-8206. Tel: 202-319-5116. Fax: 202-319-5581. p. 396

Margis, Amanda, ILL, Ref Serv, West Suburban Hospital Medical Center, Three Erie Court, Oak Park, IL, 60302. Tel: 708-763-6501. Fax: 708-383-8783. p. 684

Margolis, Bernard, State Librn, New York State Library, Cultural Education Center, 222 Madison Ave, Empire State Plaza, Albany, NY, 12230. Tel: 518-474-5961. Fax: 518-474-5786. p. 1570

Margolis, Katie, Ref & Instruction Librn, Harrisburg Area Community College, One HACC Dr, Harrisburg, PA, 17110-2999. Tel: 717-780-2460. Fax: 717-780-2462. p. 2065

Marhanka, Beth, Head, New Media Ctr, Georgetown University, 37th & N St NW, Washington, DC, 20057-1174. Tel: 202-687-7534. Fax: 202-687-7501. p. 402

Marhenke, Chris, Br Mgr, Broward County Division of Libraries, Miramar Branch Library & Education Center, 2050 Civic Center Pl, Miramar, FL, 33025. Tel: 954-437-1806, Ext 226. Fax: 954-437-2673. p. 441

Mari-Mutt, Jose A, PhD, Dr, Dir, University of Puerto Rico, Alfonso Valdes Ave, No 259 N, Mayaguez, PR, 00681. Tel: 787-265-3810, 787-832-4040. Fax: 787-265-5483. p. 2674

Maria, Ann, Ref Librn, Westbury Memorial Public Library, 445 Jefferson St, Westbury, NY, 11590. Tel: 516-333-0176. Fax: 516-333-1752. p. 1767

Mariani, Elsa, Actg Dir, Universidad del Este Library, Calle 190, Esquina 220 Bo Sabana Abajo, Carolina, PR, 00984-2010. Tel: 787-257-7373, Ext 2504. Fax: 787-257-7373, Ext 2516. p. 2672

Marich, Shannon, Ref Serv, Stoel Rives LLP, 900 SW Fifth Ave, Ste 2600, Portland, OR, 97204. Tel: 503-294-9576. Fax: 503-220-2480. p. 2014

Marichalar, Sylvia, Br Mgr, McAllen Memorial Library, Palm View, 3401 Jordan Ave, McAllen, TX, 78503. Tel: 956-688-3322. Fax: 956-688-3366. p. 2361

Marics, Joseph F, Jr, Dir, Libr Serv, Assemblies of God Theological Seminary, 1435 N Glenstone Ave, Springfield, MO, 65802-2131. Tel: 417-268-1060. Fax: 417-268-1001. p. 1365

Marietta, Phillips, Dir, Little Falls Public Library, Ten Waverly Pl, Little Falls, NY, 13365. Tel: 315-823-1542. Fax: 315-823-2995. p. 1652

Marietta, Terrie, Circ Coordr, Nesmith Library, Eight Fellows Rd, Windham, NH, 03087. Tel: 603-432-7154. Fax: 603-537-0097. p. 1468

Marihugh, Jody, Librn, Downs Carnegie Library, 504 S Morgan, Downs, KS, 67437-2019. Tel: 785-454-3821. Fax: 785-454-3821. p. 864

Marihugh, Shirley, Librn, Esbon Library, 168 Sunflower St, Esbon, KS, 66941. Tel: 785-725-3991. p. 866

Mariman, Devin, Coll Develop, Rider University, Katharine Houk Talbott Library, Westminster Choir College, 101 Walnut Lane, Princeton, NJ, 08540-3899. Tel: 609-921-7100, Ext 8298. Fax: 609-497-0243. p. 1494

Marin, Frank, Br Mgr, Broward County Division of Libraries, Hallandale Beach Branch, 300 S Federal Hwy, Hallandale, FL, 33009. Tel: 954-457-1750. Fax: 954-457-1753. p. 441

Marin, Mara, YA Serv, Elmont Public Library, 700 Hempstead Tpk, Elmont, NY, 11003-1896. Tel: 516-354-5280. Fax: 516-354-3276. p. 1620

Marina, Zhanna, Librn, Touro College Libraries, 43 W 23rd St, Fifth Fl, New York, NY, 10010. Tel: 212-463-0400, Ext 5321. Fax: 212-627-3696. p. 1701

Marinaccio, Gail M, Assoc Dir, Tech Serv, State University of New York College at Buffalo, 1300 Elmwood Ave, Buffalo, NY, 14222-1095. Tel: 716-878-6311. Fax: 716-878-4316. p. 1599

Marinaro, Sandy, Ref Serv, Stevenson University Library, 1525 Greenspring Valley Rd, Stevenson, MD, 21153. Tel: 410-486-7000, 443-334-2233. Fax: 410-486-7329. p. 1043

Marincola, John, Dr, Chmn of the Steering Comt, Florida State University Libraries, M Lynette Thompson Classics Library, 205 Dodd Hall, Tallahassee, FL, 32306-1510. Tel: 850-644-4259. p. 495

Marine, Stephen, Exec Dir, Winkler Ctr for the Hist of Health Professions, University of Cincinnati Libraries, Donald C Harrison Health Sciences Library, PO Box 670574, Cincinnati, OH, 45267-0574. Tel: 513-558-0166. Fax: 513-558-2682. p. 1874

Marine, Steve, Asst Dean, Spec Coll, University of Cincinnati Libraries, PO Box 210033, Cincinnati, OH, 45221-0033. Tel: 513-558-0166. Fax: 513-556-0325. p. 1874

Marinello, Vita, Adult Serv Mgr, Upper Arlington Public Library, 2800 Tremont Rd, Columbus, OH, 43221. Tel: 614-486-9621. Fax: 614-486-4530. p. 1891

Mariner, Erika, Ch, Converse County Library, 300 Walnut St, Douglas, WY, 82633. Tel: 307-358-3644. Fax: 307-358-6743. p. 2654

Mariner, Matthew, Digital Initiatives, Head, Spec Coll, Auraria Library, 1100 Lawrence St, Denver, CO, 80204-2095. Tel: 303-556-5817. Fax: 303-556-3528. p. 298

Marines, Annette, Assoc Librn, University of California, 1156 High St, Santa Cruz, CA, 95064. Tel: 831-459-3255. Fax: 831-459-8206. p. 264

Marini, Tom, Ref Serv Librn, University of Michigan, Kresge Business Administration Library, Stephen M Ross School of Business, 701 Tappan St, K3330, Ann Arbor, MI, 48109-1234. Tel: 734-764-4373. Fax: 734-764-3839. p. 1152

Marino, Debbie, Br Mgr, Troup-Harris Regional Library System, Harris County Public Library, 138 N College St, Hamilton, GA, 31811-6031. Tel: 706-628-4685. Fax: 706-628-4685. p. 538

Marino, Debbie, Mgr, Troup-Harris Regional Library System, Williams Memorial Library, 47 Mountain Hill Rd, Fortson, GA, 31808. Tel: 706-660-8796. Fax: 706-660-8796. p. 538

Marino, Donna, Bus Mgr, Yonkers Public Library, One Larkin Ctr, Yonkers, NY, 10701. Tel: 914-337-1500. Fax: 914-376-3004. p. 1771

Marino, Gordon, Curator, Saint Olaf College, Howard V & Edna H Hong Kierkegaard Library, 1510 Saint Olaf Ave, Northfield, MN, 55057-1097. Tel: 507-646-3609. Fax: 507-646-3858. p. 1269

Marino, Jane B, Dir, Great Neck Library, 159 Bayview Ave, Great Neck, NY, 11023-1938. Tel: 516-466-8055, Ext 200. Fax: 516-829-8297. p. 1630

Marino, Paolo, Librn, Italian Cultural Institute Library, 496 Huron St, Toronto, ON, M5R 2R3, CANADA. Tel: 416-921-3802. Fax: 416-962-2503. p. 2855

Marinus, Marilyn, Asst Librn, Pemberton & District Public Library, 7390 Cottonwood St, Pemberton, BC, V0N 2L0, CANADA. Tel: 604-894-6916. Fax: 604-894-6916. p. 2735

Marion, Berniece, Ch, Adams County Library, 103 N Sixth St, Hettinger, ND, 58639-7015. Tel: 701-567-2741. Fax: 701-567-2741. p. 1844

Marion, Carole, Mgr, Calgary Public Library, Forest Lawn, 4807 Eighth Ave SE, Calgary, AB, T2A 4M1, CANADA. p. 2689

Marion, Carole, Chief Exec Officer, West Nipissing Public Library, 225 rue Holditch, Ste 107, Sturgeon Falls, ON, P2B 1T1, CANADA. Tel: 705-753-2620. Fax: 705-753-2131. p. 2845

Marion, Guylaine, Librn, Laboratoire de Sciences Judiciaires et de Medicine Legale, Ministere de la Securite Publique Edifice Wilfrid Derome, 1701 rue Parthenais, 12th Flr, Montreal, QC, H2K 3S7, CANADA. Tel: 514-873-3301, Ext 61446. Fax: 514-873-4847. p. 2897

Marion, Joy, Librn, United States Army, WBAMC/MCHM, NTL, 5005 N Piedras St, Rm 2D01, El Paso, TX, 79920-5001. Tel: 915-742-2537, 915-742-2580. Fax: 915-742-1534. p. 2317

Marion, Linda S, PhD, Assoc Teaching Prof, Drexel University, Rush Bldg, Rm 306, 30 N 33rd St, Philadelphia, PA, 19104-2875. Tel: 215-895-2474. Fax: 215-895-2494. p. 2972

Marion, Phyllis, Dir of Libr, California Western School of Law Library, 290 Cedar St, San Diego, CA, 92101. Tel: 619-525-1429. Fax: 619-685-2918. p. 231

Maris, Arlene, Coll Develop Librn, Chatham-Kent Public Library, 120 Queen St, Chatham, ON, N7M 2G6, CANADA. Tel: 519-354-2940. Fax: 519-354-7366. p. 2799

Mariscotti, David, Head of Libr, Free Library of Philadelphia, Thomas F Donatucci Sr Branch, 1935 Shunk St, Philadelphia, PA, 19145-4234. Tel: 215-685-1653, 215-685-1755. Fax: 215-685-1652. p. 2107

Mariske, Linda A, Acq, Coll Develop, Foley & Lardner, 777 E Wisconsin Ave, Milwaukee, WI, 53202-5306. Tel: 414-271-2400. Fax: 414-297-4900. p. 2618

Marix, Mary L, Ref, Louisiana State University Health Sciences Center, 433 Bolivar St, Box B3-1, New Orleans, LA, 70112-2223. Tel: 504-568-6100. Fax: 504-568-7718. p. 961

Mark, Audrey, Dir, Pahkisimon Nuye?ah Library System, 118 Avro Pl, Air Ronge, CANADA. Tel: 306-425-4525. Fax: 306-425-4572. p. 2917

Mark, Beth L, Coordr, Instrul Serv, Messiah College, One College Ave, Ste 3002, Mechanicsburg, PA, 17055. Tel: 717-691-6006, Ext 3590. Fax: 717-691-2356. p. 2087

Mark, Cathy, Ref Serv, Cassels, Brock & Blackwell Library, Scotia Plaza, Ste 2100, 40 King St W, Toronto, ON, M5H 3C2, CANADA. Tel: 416-869-5436. Fax: 416-360-8877. p. 2852

Mark, David, Circ, Pub Serv, Polk State College, 999 Ave H NE, Winter Haven, FL, 33881-4299. Tel: 863-297-1040. Fax: 863-297-1065. p. 504

Mark, Joy, Res & Instrul Serv, Asbury Theological Seminary, 204 N Lexington Ave, Wilmore, KY, 40390-1199. Tel: 859-858-2233. Fax: 859-858-2330. p. 938

Mark, Karen, Librn, Cosmos Club Library, 2121 Massachusetts Ave NW, Washington, DC, 20008. Tel: 202-387-7783, Ext 333, 202-939-1525. Fax: 202-234-6817. p. 396

Mark, Susan, Statistics Librn, Wyoming State Library, 2800 Central Ave, Cheyenne, WY, 82002. Tel: 307-777-6333. Fax: 307-777-6289. p. 2653

Markees, Kathleen, Conserv Librn, Worcester Polytechnic Institute, 100 Institute Rd, Worcester, MA, 01609-2280. Tel: 508-831-5410. Fax: 508-831-5829. p. 1145

Markel, Bonnie, Ch, Merrick Library, 2279 Merrick Ave, Merrick, NY, 11566-4398. Tel: 516-277-6112, Ext 115. Fax: 516-377-1108. p. 1659

Markert, Joan W, Dir, Holland Public Library, 27 Sturbridge Rd, Unit 9, Holland, MA, 01521. Tel: 413-245-3607. p. 1095

Markey, Karen, Prof, University of Michigan, 304 West Hall, 1085 S University, Ann Arbor, MI, 48109-1107. Tel: 734-763-2285. Fax: 734-764-2475. p. 2967

Markey, Leslie, Cat, Tech Serv, Brooks Memorial Library, 224 Main St, Brattleboro, VT, 05301. Tel: 802-254-5290. Fax: 802-257-2309. p. 2420

Markey, Patricia, Asst Dir, Parkland Library, 6620 University Dr, Parkland, FL, 33067. Tel: 954-757-4200. Fax: 954-753-5223. p. 481

Markezich, Bev, Tech Serv, Three Rivers Public Library District, 25207 W Channon Dr, Channahon, IL, 60410-5028. Tel: 815-467-6200. Fax: 815-467-4012. p. 603

Markgraf, Jill, Distance Educ Coordr, Head, Res & Instruction, Ref Librn, University of Wisconsin-Eau Claire, 105 Garfield Ave, Eau Claire, WI, 54702-4004. Tel: 715-836-3715. Fax: 715-836-2949. p. 2590

Markgren, Susanne, Digital Serv Librn, State University of New York, 735 Anderson Hill Rd, Purchase, NY, 10577-1400. Tel: 914-251-6415. Fax: 914-251-6437. p. 1724

Markham, Barbara, Librn, Florida State College at Jacksonville, South Campus, 11901 Beach Blvd, Jacksonville, FL, 32246-6624. Tel: 904-646-2173. Fax: 904-646-2155. p. 453

Markham, Sherry, Br Mgr, San Diego County Library, Pine Valley Branch, 28804 Old Hwy 80, Pine Valley, CA, 91962. Tel: 619-473-8022. Fax: 619-473-9638. p. 234

Markham, Susan, Assoc Dir, Extn & Outreach Serv, Huntsville-Madison Public Library, 915 Monroe St, Huntsville, AL, 35801. Tel: 256-532-5961. Fax: 256-532-5997. p. 21

Markin, Doug, Librn, United States Army, Fort Detrick Post Library, Fort Detrick, 1520 Freedman Dr, Frederick, MD, 21702. Tel: 301-619-7519. Fax: 301-619-2884. p. 1029

Markinson, Andrea, Asst Dir, Educ Serv & Dir EBM Inst, State University of New York Downstate Medical Center, 395 Lenox Rd, Brooklyn, NY, 11203. Tel: 718-270-7400. Fax: 718-270-7413, 718-270-7468. p. 1595

Markland, Penny, Librn, Wapiti Regional Library, Melfort Public Library, 106 Crawford Ave W, Melfort, SK, S0E 1A0, CANADA. Tel: 306-752-2022. p. 2921

Markle, Betts, Dir, Libr & Info Serv, Argosy University, Bldg 2, Ste 400, 980 Hammond Dr, Atlanta, GA, 30328. Tel: 770-407-1047. Fax: 770-671-0418. p. 510

Markle, Betts, Dr, Libr Dir, Sierra Nevada College, 999 Tahoe Blvd, Incline Village, NV, 89450-9500. Tel: 775-831-1314, Ext 7511. Fax: 775-832-6134. p. 1428

Markle, Latricia, Ch, Tenafly Public Library, 100 Riveredge Rd, Tenafly, NJ, 07670-2087. Tel: 201-568-8680. Fax: 201-568-5475. p. 1533

Markle, Pat, Br Supvr, Bruce County Public Library, Mildmay-Carrick Branch, 51 Elora St, Mildmay, ON, N0G 2J0, CANADA. Tel: 519-367-2814. Fax: 519-367-2814. p. 2837

Markley, Andi, Mgr, Puget Sound Regional Council, 1011 Western Ave, Ste 500, Seattle, WA, 98104-1035. Tel: 206-464-7532. Fax: 206-587-4825. p. 2530

Markley, Andi, Res, Puget Sound Regional Council, 1011 Western Ave, Ste 500, Seattle, WA, 98104-1035. Tel: 206-464-7532. Fax: 206-587-4825. p. 2530

Markley, Chris, Librn, Public Library of Johnston County & Smithfield, Selma Public, 301 N Pollock, Selma, NC, 27576. Tel: 919-965-8613. p. 1824

Markley, Patricia, ILL, Siena College, 515 Loudon Rd, Loudonville, NY, 12211-1462. Tel: 518-783-4196. Fax: 518-783-2570. p. 1655

Markley, Susan, Librn, Bagdad Public Library, 100 Main St, Bagdad, AZ, 86321. Tel: 928-633-2325. Fax: 928-633-2054. p. 57

Markley, Susan, Acq, Villanova University, 800 Lancaster Ave, Villanova, PA, 19085. Tel: 610-519-6729. Fax: 610-519-5018. p. 2150

Markman, Rebecca, Librn, Fashion Institute of Design & Merchandising Library, 17590 Gillette Ave, Irvine, CA, 92614. Tel: 949-851-6200. Fax: 949-851-6808. p. 160

Marko, Mary, Ref Serv, Kapiolani Community College Library, 4303 Diamond Head Rd, Honolulu, HI, 96816. Tel: 808-734-9357. Fax: 808-734-9453. p. 564

Markoe, Glenn, Curator, Richmond Art Museum Library, 350 Hub Etchison Pkwy, Richmond, IN, 47374-0816. Tel: 765-966-0256. Fax: 765-973-3738. p. 775

Markov, Claudia, Mgr, Athens Regional Library System, Northeast Georgia Talking Book Center, 2025 Baxter St, Athens, GA, 30606-6331. Tel: 706-310-3650. Fax: 706-613-3660, 706-769-3952. p. 509

Markovich, Becky, Circ Serv Coordr, Albion College, 602 E Cass St, Albion, MI, 49224-1879. Tel: 517-629-0285. Fax: 517-629-0504. p. 1148

Markovich, Sharon, Circ, Mount Aloysius College Library, 7373 Admiral Peary Hwy, Cresson, PA, 16630-1999. Tel: 814-886-6445. Fax: 814-886-5767. p. 2048

Markovitz, Jean, Asst Librn, Burlington County Library, Riverton Free Branch, 306 Main St, Riverton, NJ, 08077. Tel: 856-829-2476. p. 1543

Markowitz, Barbara, Asst Dir, Oceanside Library, 30 Davison Ave, Oceanside, NY, 11572-2299. Tel: 516-766-2360. Fax: 516-766-1895. p. 1709

Marks, Debbie, Ref & Teen Serv, Arcadia Public Library, 20 W Duarte Rd, Arcadia, CA, 91006. Tel: 626-294-4801. Fax: 626-447-8050. p. 121

Marks, Ellen, Libr Dir, Univ Librn, Michigan Technological University, 1400 Townsend Dr, Houghton, MI, 49931-1295. Tel: 906-487-2508. p. 1191

Marks, Evelyn, In Charge, Rancho Los Amigos Medical Center, 7601 E Imperial Hwy, Rm 1109, Downey, CA, 90242-3456. Tel: 562-401-7696. p. 144

Marks, Francine, Mgr, Tech Serv, Long Branch Free Public Library, 328 Broadway, Long Branch, NJ, 07740. Tel: 732-222-3900. Fax: 732-222-3799. p. 1496

Marks, Howard, Dir, Libr & Media Serv, Western Texas College, 6200 S College Ave, Snyder, TX, 79549. Tel: 325-574-7678. Fax: 325-573-9321. p. 2388

Marks, J Lynn, Ref, Phoenix College, 1202 W Thomas Rd, Phoenix, AZ, 85013. Tel: 602-285-7457. Fax: 602-285-7368. p. 76

Marks, Jeanette, Teen/YA Librn, Brandon Township Public Library, 304 South St, Ortonville, MI, 48462. Tel: 248-627-1460. Fax: 248-627-9880. p. 1215

Marks, Jennifer, Circ Serv Mgr, Longmont Public Library, 409 Fourth Ave, Longmont, CO, 80501-6006. Tel: 303-651-8474. Fax: 303-651-8911. p. 317

Marks, Kim, Bibliog Instr, Ref Librn, Grove City College, 300 Campus Dr, Grove City, PA, 16127-2198. Tel: 724-450-1532. Fax: 724-458-2181. p. 2063

Marks, Lisa, Mgr, Libr Serv, Providence Saint Joseph Medical Center, 501 S Buena Vista St, Burbank, CA, 91505-4866. Tel: 818-847-3822. Fax: 818-847-3823. p. 130

Marks, Lynn, Circ Mgr, Newburyport Public Library, 94 State St, Newburyport, MA, 01950-6619. Tel: 978-465-4428, Ext 243. Fax: 978-463-0394. p. 1109

Marks, Mary, Assoc Univ Librn, Tech Serv, Fairleigh Dickinson University, 285 Madison Ave, M-LAO-03, Madison, NJ, 07940. Tel: 973-443-8520. Fax: 973-443-8525. p. 1497

Marks, Mary T, Dir, Learning Res, Manchester Community College, 1066 Front St, Manchester, NH, 03102. Tel: 603-668-6706, Ext 259. Fax: 603-668-5354. p. 1455

Marks, Pam, Mgr, Tech Libr Operations, Anderson County Public Library, 114 N Main St, Lawrenceburg, KY, 40342. Tel: 502-839-6420. Fax: 502-839-7243. p. 919

Marks, Patricia, Ch, Atlanta-Fulton Public Library System, Peachtree Library, 1315 Peachtree St NE, Atlanta, GA, 30309. Tel: 404-885-7830. Fax: 404-855-7833. p. 512

Marks, Paula, Librn, Chevron Global Library Houston, 3901 Briarpark Dr, Houston, TX, 77042. Tel: 713-954-6007. Fax: 713-954-6907. p. 2334

Markson, Teri, Librn, Stephen S Wise Temple Library, 15500 Stephen S Wise Dr, Los Angeles, CA, 90077. Tel: 310-889-2241. Fax: 310-476-2353. p. 180

Markus, Amy, Dir, Hancock Town Library, 25 Main St, Hancock, NH, 03449. Tel: 603-525-4411. p. 1449

Markus, Dan, Br Mgr, Saint Johns County Public Library System, Bartram Trail, 60 Davis Pond Blvd, Fruit Cove, FL, 32259-4390. Tel: 904-827-6961. Fax: 904-827-6965. p. 487

Markus, Jamie, Mgr, Libr Develop, Wyoming State Library, 2800 Central Ave, Cheyenne, WY, 82002. Tel: 307-777-5914. Fax: 307-777-6289. p. 2653

Markus, Lise, Circ Librn, Kellogg-Hubbard Library, 135 Main St, Montpelier, VT, 05602. Tel: 802-223-3338. Fax: 802-223-3338. p. 2429

Markus, Tim, Head, Cat, Evergreen State College, Library Bldg, Rm 2300, 2700 Evergreen Pkwy NW, Olympia, WA, 98505-0002. Tel: 360-867-6124. Fax: 360-867-6790. p. 2522

Markwalter, Mary, Dir, Mason City Public Library, 225 Second St SE, Mason City, IA, 50401. Tel: 641-421-3668. Fax: 641-423-2615. p. 830

Markworth, Linda, Br Mgr, Trails Regional Library, Corder Branch, 221 N Lafayette, Corder, MO, 64021. Tel: 660-394-2565. p. 1371

Marky, Anita, Br Mgr, Akron-Summit County Public Library, Ellet, 2470 E Market St, Akron, OH, 44312. Tel: 330-784-2019. Fax: 330-784-6692. p. 1852

Marlatt, Greta, Outreach & Coll Develop Mgr, Naval Postgraduate School, 411 Dyer Rd, Monterey, CA, 93943. Tel: 831-656-3500. Fax: 831-656-2050. p. 190

Marlatt, Tom, Tech Serv & Automation, Carnegie Public Library, 219 E Fourth St, East Liverpool, OH, 43920-3143. Tel: 330-385-2048. Fax: 330-385-7600. p. 1897

Marler, Janet, Dir, Marion City Library, 101 Library St, Marion, KS, 66861. Tel: 620-382-2442. p. 882

Marley, Judith, Asst Prof, University of South Carolina, 1501 Greene St, Columbia, SC, 29208. Tel: 803-777-3858. Fax: 803-777-7938. p. 2973

Marlin, Krista, Asst Librn, Chinook Regional Library, Sceptre Branch, 128 Kingsway, Sceptre, SK, S0N 2H0, CANADA. Tel: 306-623-4244. p. 2928

Marlin, Mike, Dir, California State Library, Braille & Talking Book Library, 900 N St, Sacramento, CA, 95814. Tel: 916-654-0640. Fax: 916-654-1119. p. 223

Marlino, Mary, Libr Dir, National Center for Atmospheric Research Library, 1850 Table Mesa Dr, Boulder, CO, 80305. Tel: 303-497-8350. Fax: 303-497-1170. p. 290

Marlor, Charles, Acq, Ser, Central Connecticut State University, 1615 Stanley St, New Britain, CT, 06050. Tel: 860-832-2073. Fax: 860-832-3409. p. 353

Marlow, Betty, Commun Libr Mgr, County of Los Angeles Public Library, East Rancho Dominguez Library, 4205 E Compton Blvd, East Rancho Dominguez, CA, 90221-3664. Tel: 310-632-6193. Fax: 310-608-0294. p. 141

Marlow, Cecilia Ann, Libr Dir, Cromaine District Library, 3688 N Hartland Rd, Hartland, MI, 48353. Tel: 810-632-5200, Ext 105. p. 1189

Marlow, Meme, Dir, Worch Memorial Public Library, 790 S Center St, Versailles, OH, 45380. Tel: 937-526-3416. Fax: 937-526-3990. p. 1943

Marlow, Neil, Br Head, Toronto Public Library, Mimico Centennial, 47 Station Rd, Toronto, ON, M8V 2R1, CANADA. Tel: 416-394-5330. Fax: 416-394-5338. p. 2862

Marlow, Nora, Tech Serv, Tidewater Community College Learning Resources Center, 300 Granby St, Norfolk, VA, 23510. Tel: 757-822-1105. Fax: 757-822-1105. p. 2483

Marlowe, Claudia, Cat Spec, San Francisco Art Institute, 800 Chestnut St, San Francisco, CA, 94133. Tel: 415-749-4562. p. 244

Marlowe, Richard, Dir, Media Serv, Mississippi Gulf Coast Community College, PO Box 548, Perkinston, MS, 39573-0011. Tel: 601-928-6354. Fax: 601-928-6359. p. 1311

Marlowe-Dziuk, Rosemary, Chief, Res & Info Serv, US Department of Defense, Fort McNair, Marshall Hall, Washington, DC, 20319-5066. Tel: 202-685-3511. Fax: 202-685-3733. p. 418

Marnatti, Janet, Dir, Coll Mgt, Bucks County Free Library, 150 S Pine St, Doylestown, PA, 18901-4932. Tel: 215-348-0332, Ext 1141. Fax: 215-348-4760. p. 2050

Marney, Bonnie, Librn, Phillips County Library, Dodson Branch, 121 Second St E, Dodson, MT, 59524. p. 1385

Marney, Dean, Dir, North Central Regional Library, 16 N Columbia St, Wenatchee, WA, 98801-8103. Tel: 509-663-1117, Ext 121. Fax: 509-662-8060. p. 2548

Maroff, Dorothy H, Acq, Ser, Webmaster, Case Western Reserve University, Lillian F & Milford J Harris Library, Mandel School of Applied Social Sciences, 11235 Bellflower Rd, Cleveland, OH, 44106-7164. Tel: 216-368-2293. Fax: 216-368-2106. p. 1876

Marone, Regina Kenny, Dir, Yale University Library, Harvey Cushing/John Hay Whitney Medical Library, Sterling Hall of Medicine, 333 Cedar St, L110 SHM, New Haven, CT, 06520. Tel: 203-785-5352. Fax: 203-785-5636. p. 358

Maroon, Jim, Pub Serv, Lawton Public Library, 110 SW Fourth St, Lawton, OK, 73501-4034. Tel: 580-581-3450. Fax: 580-248-0243. p. 1967

Marotta, Jan, Automation Syst Coordr, Ashland University Library, 509 College Ave, Ashland, OH, 44805-3796. Tel: 419-289-5400. Fax: 419-289-5422. p. 1855

Marotz, Karen, Head Librn, Simon Fraser University Vancouver Library, 515 W Hastings St, Vancouver, BC, V6B 5K3, CANADA. Tel: 778-782-5050. Fax: 778-782-5052. p. 2742

Marple, Karen, Head, Ch, Galesburg Public Library, 40 E Simmons St, Galesburg, IL, 61401-4591. Tel: 309-343-6118. Fax: 309-343-4877. p. 648

Marple, Susan, Librn, Portneuf District Library, 5210 Stuart Ave, Chubbuck, ID, 83202-2214. Tel: 208-237-2192. Fax: 208-237-2194. p. 573

Marquam, Barbara, Archives Dir, Mazamas Library & Archives, 527 SE 43rd Ave, Portland, OR, 97215. Tel: 503-227-2345, Ext 2. Fax: 503-227-0862. p. 2011

Marquardt, Cheryl, Librn, Waseca-Le Sueur Regional Library, Waldorf Branch, 109 Main St N, Waldorf, MN, 56091. Tel: 507-239-2248. p. 1287

Marquardt, Jennifer, Ch, Acorn Public Library District, 15624 S Central Ave, Oak Forest, IL, 60452-3204. Tel: 708-687-3700. Fax: 708-687-3712. p. 683

Marquardt, Larry, Dir, Des Moines University, 3300 Grand Ave, Des Moines, IA, 50312. Tel: 515-271-1537. Fax: 515-271-1625. p. 808

Marquardt, Marie, Librn, Alma Public Library, 312 Main St N, Alma, WI, 54610-0277. Tel: 608-685-3823. Fax: 608-685-4935. p. 2577

Marquardt, Mary, Dir, Cedarburg Public Library, W63 N583 Hanover Ave, Cedarburg, WI, 53012. Tel: 262-375-7640. Fax: 262-375-7618. p. 2585

Marquet, Cynthia, Librn, The Historical Society of the Cocalico Valley Library, 237 W Main St, Ephrata, PA, 17522. Tel: 717-733-1616. p. 2054

Marquez, Kesi, Librn, Woolworth Community Library, 100 E Utah Ave, Jal, NM, 88252. Tel: 505-395-3268. Fax: 505-395-2138. p. 1557

Marquez, Maggie, Asst Libr Dir, Marfa Public Library, 115 E Oak St, Marfa, TX, 79843. Tel: 432-729-4631. Fax: 432-729-3424. p. 2359

Marquez, Roberta, Commun Libr Mgr, County of Los Angeles Public Library, South El Monte Library, 1430 N Central Ave, South El Monte, CA, 91733-3302. Tel: 626-443-4158. Fax: 626-575-7450. p. 143

Marquis, Daniel, Acq, Librn, Pub Serv, Cegep de Granby Haute-Yamaska, 235 Saint Jacques St, Granby, QC, J2G 3N1, CANADA. Tel: 450-372-6614, Ext 1205. Fax: 450-372-6565. p. 2884

Marquis, Kathy, Pub Serv Librn, Albany County Public Library, 310 S Eighth St, Laramie, WY, 82070-3969. Tel: 307-721-2580, Ext 5438. Fax: 307-721-2584. p. 2657

Marquis, Luce, Head, Tech Serv, Bibliotheque Municipale Eva-Senecal, 450 Marquette St, Sherbrooke, QC, J1H 1M4, CANADA. Tel: 819-821-5861. Fax: 819-822-6110. p. 2912

Marr, Carolyn, Librn, Historical Society of Seattle &
King County, 2700 24th Ave E, Seattle, WA,
98112. Tel: 206-324-1126. Fax: 206-324-1346.
p. 2528

Marr, Jenny, Dir, Morrill Public Library, 431
Oregon, Hiawatha, KS, 66434-2290. Tel:
785-742-3831. Fax: 785-742-2054. p. 871

Marr, Norma, Librn, Calgary Herald Library, 215
16th St SE, Calgary, AB, T2P 0W8, CANADA.
Tel: 403-235-7361. Fax: 403-235-7379. p. 2688

Marr, Tracy, Adult Serv Mgr, Bellevue Public
Library, 224 E Main St, Bellevue, OH,
44811-1467. Tel: 419-483-4769. Fax:
419-483-0158. p. 1859

Marra, Chris, Circ Serv, Uniondale Public
Library, 400 Uniondale Ave, Uniondale, NY,
11553-1995. Tel: 516-489-2220, Ext 235. Fax:
516-489-4005. p. 1758

Marra, Rose, Prof, University of Missouri-Columbia,
303 Townsend Hall, Columbia, MO, 65211. Tel:
573-882-4546. Fax: 573-884-2917. p. 2968

Marra, Toshie, Librn, University of California Los
Angeles Library, Richard C Rudolph East Asian
Library, 21617 Research Library YRL, Los
Angeles, CA, 90095-1575. Tel: 310-825-2765.
Fax: 310-206-4960. p. 179

Marrall, Rebecca, Diversity & Disabilities Serv
Librn, Western Washington University, 516 High
St, MS 9103, Bellingham, WA, 98225. Tel:
360-650-4493. Fax: 360-650-3044. p. 2509

Marrapese, Jennifer, Exec Dir, Northeast Sustainable
Energy Association, 50 Miles St, Greenfield,
MA, 01301. Tel: 413-774-6051. Fax:
413-774-6053. p. 1093

Marrapodi, Elisabeth, Dir, Trinitas Hospital, 225
Williamson St, Elizabeth, NJ, 07207. Tel:
908-994-5488. Fax: 908-994-5099. p. 1483

Marrazas, Mariana, In Charge, ScottHulse, PC, 201
E Main Dr, Ste 1100, El Paso, TX, 79901. Tel:
915-533-2493. Fax: 915-546-8333. p. 2317

Marredeth, Gail, Librn, Cleveland State University,
University Library, Rhodes Tower, 2121
Euclid Ave, Cleveland, OH, 44115-2214. Tel:
216-687-2291. Fax: 216-687-9380. p. 1879

Marrero, Vanessa, Cataloger, Sam Fore Jr Wilson
County Public Library, One Library Lane,
Floresville, TX, 78114. Tel: 830-393-7361. Fax:
830-393-7337. p. 2319

Marrero, Yirah, Coordr, Jefferson County Library
District, 241 SE Seventh St, Madras, OR,
97741-1611. Tel: 541-475-3351. Fax:
541-475-7434. p. 2004

Marrese, Alicia, Circ Supvr, Saint John Fisher
College, 3690 East Ave, Rochester, NY,
14618-3599. Tel: 585-385-8165. Fax:
585-385-8445. p. 1732

Marrin, Alyson, Computer Librn, Britt Area
Library, 841 Riverside Dr, Britt, ON, P0G
1A0, CANADA. Tel: 705-383-2292. Fax:
705-383-0077. p. 2797

Marrin, Sara, Tech Serv Librn, Virginia Union
University, 1500 N Lombardy St, Richmond,
VA, 23220. Tel: 804-257-5823. Fax:
804-257-5818. p. 2493

Marriott, Karen, Mgr, Rodman Public Library, Town
Hall, Rodman, NY, 13682. Tel: 315-232-2522.
Fax: 315-232-3853. p. 1734

Marriott, Karen, Dep Exec Dir, Mat & Outreach,
Metropolitan Library System in Oklahoma
County, 300 Park Ave, Oklahoma City, OK,
73102. Tel: 405-606-3725. Fax: 405-606-3722.
p. 1972

Marrone, Andrew, Head, Circ, Elmwood Park Public
Library, 210 Lee St, Elmwood Park, NJ, 07407.
Tel: 201-796-2584. Fax: 201-703-1425. p. 1484

Marrone, Marie, Mgr, Weller Public Library,
41 W Main St, Mohawk, NY, 13407. Tel:
315-866-2983. Fax: 315-866-2983. p. 1662

Marrs, Kathleen, Mgr, Tulsa County Law Library,
500 S Denver Ave, Tulsa, OK, 74103. Tel:
918-596-5404. Fax: 918-596-4509. p. 1984

Marrs, Margaret, Dir, Rockwood Public Library, 117
N Front St, Rockwood, TN, 37854-2320. Tel:
865-354-1281. Fax: 865-354-4302. p. 2264

Marrufo, Suzanne, Br Mgr, El Paso Public Library,
Clardy Fox Branch, 5515 Robert Alva, El
Paso, TX, 79905. Tel: 915-772-0501. Fax:
915-772-7941. p. 2316

Marsala, Penny, Dir, Park Nicollet Institute, 3800
Park Nicollet Blvd, Saint Louis Park, MN,
55416. Tel: 952-993-5451. Fax: 952-993-1322.
p. 1277

Marsales, Rita, Cat, Menil Foundation, 1500 Branard
St, Houston, TX, 77006. Tel: 713-525-9424.
Fax: 713-525-9444. p. 2341

Marsch, Megan, Ref, Acorn Public Library
District, 15624 S Central Ave, Oak Forest,
IL, 60452-3204. Tel: 708-687-3700. Fax:
708-687-3712. p. 683

Marschall, Katherine, Cat Librn, Saint Mary's
College, Notre Dame, IN, 46556-5001. Tel:
574-284-4438. Fax: 574-284-4791. p. 771

Marsee, Patsy, Asst Dir, Marion County Public
Library System, 2720 E Silver Springs Blvd,
Ocala, FL, 34470. Tel: 352-671-8551. Fax:
352-368-4545. p. 474

Marsh, Ann, Librn, Northwest Point Reservoir
Library, 2230 Spillway Rd, Brandon, MS,
39047. Tel: 601-992-2539. Fax: 601-992-2539.
p. 1294

Marsh, Brenda, Dir, Lilly-Washington Public
Library, 520 Church St, Ste 1, Lilly, PA,
15938-1118. Tel: 814-886-7543. Fax:
814-886-3925. p. 2082

Marsh, Doris, Librn, Trinity Presbyterian Church,
367 Cranberry Rd, East Brunswick, NJ, 08816.
Tel: 732-257-6636. p. 1482

Marsh, Erin, Ch, Charles A Ransom District
Library, 180 S Sherwood Ave, Plainwell,
MI, 49080-1896. Tel: 269-685-8024. Fax:
269-685-2266. p. 1218

Marsh, Jamie, Learning Res Ctr Adminr, Florida
State University Libraries, College of Nursing,
Learning Resource Center, 102 College of
Nursing, Tallahassee, FL, 32306-4310. Tel:
850-644-1291. Fax: 850-644-7660. p. 494

Marsh, Janice, Pub Info Coordr, Warren-Newport
Public Library District, 224 N O'Plaine Rd,
Gurnee, IL, 60031. Tel: 847-244-5150. Fax:
847-244-3499. p. 653

Marsh, Kitty, Mgr, Davis Jefferson Parish Library,
Elton Branch, 813 Main St, Elton, LA, 70532.
Tel: 318-584-2640. Fax: 318-584-2236. p. 952

Marsh, Nicole Y, Head Librn, Lincoln University
Library, 401 15th St, Oakland, CA, 94612. Tel:
510-628-8011. Fax: 510-628-8012. p. 197

Marsh, Nyama, Patron Serv Mgr, Frank L
Weyenberg Library of Mequon-Thiensville,
11345 N Cedarburg Rd, Mequon, WI,
53092-1998. Tel: 262-242-2593. Fax:
262-478-3200. p. 2615

Marsh, Patty, Assoc Dir, Pub Serv, Stark County
District Library, 715 Market Ave N, Canton,
OH, 44702-1018. Tel: 330-458-2703. Fax:
330-455-9596. p. 1864

Marsh, Penny, Outreach Serv Mgr, Troy-Miami
County Public Library, 419 W Main St,
Troy, OH, 45373. Tel: 937-339-0502. Fax:
937-335-4880. p. 1941

Marsh, Sandra, Adult Serv, Palmdale City Library,
700 E Palmdale Blvd, Palmdale, CA, 93550.
Tel: 661-267-5600. Fax: 661-267-5606. p. 203

Marsh, Sue, Librn, National Fire Protection
Association, One Batterymarch Park, Quincy,
MA, 02169-7471. Tel: 617-984-7446. Fax:
617-984-7060. p. 1119

Marsh, Vicki, Br Mgr, Oldham County Public
Library, South Oldham, 6720 W Hwy 146,
Crestwood, KY, 40014. Tel: 502-241-1108. Fax:
502-241-1108. p. 919

Marsha, Webb, Genealogy Serv, C E Brehm
Memorial Public Library District, 101 S
Seventh St, Mount Vernon, IL, 62864. Tel:
618-242-6322. Fax: 618-242-0810. p. 677

Marshak, Bonnie, Pembroke Pines Campus Libr
Dir, Keiser University Library System, 1500
NW 49th St, Fort Lauderdale, FL, 33309. Tel:
954-351-4035. Fax: 954-351-4051. p. 443

Marshall, Brian, Librn, California Hospital Medical
Center Los Angeles, 1401 S Grand Ave, Los
Angeles, CA, 90015. Tel: 213-742-5872. Fax:
213-765-4046. p. 169

Marshall, Brian, Mgr, SM Stoller Corp, 4021
National Parks Hwy, Carlsbad, NM, 88220. Tel:
505-234-7625. Fax: 575-234-7076. p. 1553

Marshall, Carol Lynn, Ref Librn, Vassar College
Library, 124 Raymond Ave, Maildrop
20, Poughkeepsie, NY, 12604-0020. Tel:
845-437-5760. Fax: 845-437-5864. p. 1723

Marshall, Cathy, Librn, Libr Asn Pres, Sargentville
Library Association, 653 Reach Rd, Sargentville,
ME, 04673. Tel: 207-348-6404. p. 1000

Marshall, Cathy, Circ Mgr, Clinton-Macomb Public
Library, 40900 Romeo Plank Rd, Clinton
Township, MI, 48038-2955. Tel: 586-226-5024.
Fax: 586-226-5008. p. 1164

Marshall, Dale, Circ, First Baptist Church of West
Terre Haute Library, 205 S Fifth, West Terre
Haute, IN, 47885. Tel: 812-533-2016. p. 787

Marshall, Daniel, Librn, TCI College of Technology,
320 W 31st St, New York, NY, 10001. Tel:
212-594-4000, Ext 5279. Fax: 212-330-0894.
p. 1700

Marshall, Darlene, Librn, Mengle Memorial Library,
324 Main St, Brockway, PA, 15824-0324. Tel:
814-265-8245. Fax: 814-265-1125. p. 2037

Marshall, David, Head, Coll Develop, Georgetown
University, 37th & N St NW, Washington,
DC, 20057-1174. Tel: 202-687-7616. Fax:
202-687-7501. p. 402

Marshall, Denise, Dr, Instrul Serv Librn, Ref,
Fairleigh Dickinson University, 285 Madison
Ave, M-LAO-03, Madison, NJ, 07940. Tel:
973-443-8627. Fax: 973-443-8525. p. 1497

Marshall, Derek, Ref, Aiken-Bamberg-Barnwell-
Edgefield Regional Library System, Nancy
Carson - North Augusta Library, 135 Edgefield
Rd, North Augusta, SC, 29841-2423. Tel:
803-279-5767. Fax: 803-202-3588. p. 2179

Marshall, Dora, Dir, Baker College of Port
Huron Library, 3403 Lapeer Rd, Port Huron,
MI, 48060-2597. Tel: 810-989-2123. Fax:
810-985-6920. p. 1219

Marshall, Gwendoyln, Govt Doc, Per, Ursinus
College Library, 601 E Main St, Collegeville,
PA, 19426. Tel: 610-409-3000, Ext 2292. Fax:
610-489-0634. p. 2046

Marshall, Heidi L, Dir, Washington Hospital, 155
Wilson Ave, Washington, PA, 15301-3398. Tel:
724-223-3144. Fax: 724-223-4096. p. 2151

Marshall, Jackie, Librn, Wasaga Beach Public
Library, 120 Glenwood Dr, Wasaga Beach, ON,
L0L 2P0, CANADA. Tel: 705-429-5481. Fax:
705-429-5481. p. 2869

Marshall, Jeanne, Cat, Nassau County Public Library
System, 25 N Fourth St, Fernandina Beach,
FL, 32034-4123. Tel: 904-548-4865. Fax:
904-277-7366. p. 439

Marshall, Jeffrey, Spec Coll & Archives Librn,
University of Vermont Libraries, 538 Main St,
Burlington, VT, 05405-0036. Tel: 802-656-2595.
Fax: 802-656-4038. p. 2421

Marshall, Jennifer, Asst Prof, University of South
Carolina, 1501 Greene St, Columbia, SC, 29208.
Tel: 803-777-3858. Fax: 803-777-7938. p. 2973

Marshall, Jerilyn, Head, Ref, Instrul Serv Librn,
University of Northern Iowa Library, 1227 W
27th St, Cedar Falls, IA, 50613-3675. Tel:
319-273-3721. Fax: 319-273-2913. p. 799

Marshall, Jessica, Coll Mgt Librn, Dept Chair,
Slippery Rock University of Pennsylvania,
Slippery Rock, PA, 16057-9989. Tel:
724-738-2663. Fax: 724-738-2661. p. 2140

Marshall, Jessie W, Nonprofit Res Librn, Supvr,
Pub Serv, Memphis Public Library, Science,
Business, 3030 Poplar Ave, Memphis, TN,
38111. Tel: 901-415-2734. p. 2250

Marshall, Julia, Dir, Macon County Public Library,
311 Church St, Lafayette, TN, 37083-1607. Tel:
615-666-4340. Fax: 615-666-8932. p. 2244

Marshall, Karen, Asst Univ Librn, Info Res & Access, Western University - Libraries, 1151 Richmond St, Ste 200, London, ON, N6A 3K7, CANADA. Tel: 519-661-2111, Ext 84850. Fax: 519-661-3493. p. 2819

Marshall, Karri, Mgr, Dayton Metro Library, West Carrollton Branch, 300 E Central Ave, West Carrollton, OH, 45449. Tel: 937-496-8962. Fax: 937-496-4362. p. 1893

Marshall, Laura, Ref, Peru Public Library, 102 E Main St, Peru, IN, 46970-2338. Tel: 765-473-3069. Fax: 765-473-3060. p. 772

Marshall, Lavonne, Dir, Coopersville Area District Library, 333 Ottawa St, Coopersville, MI, 49404-1243. Tel: 616-837-6809. Fax: 616-837-7689. p. 1166

Marshall, Leslie, Librn, Hall of Flame, 6101 E Van Buren, Phoenix, AZ, 85008. Tel: 602-275-3473. Fax: 602-275-0896. p. 73

Marshall, Lois, Info Access Coordr, Lincoln University of Missouri, 712 Lee Dr, Jefferson City, MO, 65101. Tel: 573-681-5509. Fax: 573-681-5511. p. 1334

Marshall, Margaret, Dir, Public Library of Johnston County & Smithfield, 305 E Market St, Smithfield, NC, 27577-3919. Tel: 919-934-8146. Fax: 919-934-8084. p. 1824

Marshall, Mary, Ch, Addison Public Library, Four Friendship Plaza, Addison, IL, 60101. Tel: 630-543-3617. Fax: 630-543-6645. p. 587

Marshall, Mary, Librn, Keen Mountain Correctional Center, State Rd 629, Oakwood, VA, 24631. Tel: 276-498-7411, Ext 2055. Fax: 276-498-7341. p. 2483

Marshall, Nancy, Librn, Massachusetts General Hospital, Warren Library, 55 Fruit St, Boston, MA, 02114-2622. Tel: 617-726-2253. p. 1063

Marshall, Nancy, Info Serv, South Dakota State University, 1300 N Campus Dr, Box 2115, Brookings, SD, 57007-1098. Tel: 605-688-5093. Fax: 605-688-6133. p. 2211

Marshall, Nancy Hammeke, Exec Dir, Abington Township Public Library, 1030 Old York Rd, Abington, PA, 19001-4594. Tel: 215-885-5180, Ext 14. Fax: 215-885-9242. p. 2025

Marshall, Natalie, Acq Librn, Flint River Regional Library, 800 Memorial Dr, Griffin, GA, 30223. Tel: 770-412-4770. p. 535

Marshall, Nicole, Dir, Western University - Libraries, C B "Bud" Johnston Library, Richard Ivey School of Business, London, ON, N6A 3K7, CANADA. Tel: 519-661-2111, Ext 84842. Fax: 519-661-2158. p. 2819

Marshall, Patrick W, Dir, Jonathan Bourne Public Library, 19 Sandwich Rd, Bourne, MA, 02532-3699. Tel: 508-759-0644, Ext 107. Fax: 508-759-0647. p. 1068

Marshall, Paula J, Librn, Joseph & Elizabeth Shaw Public Library, One S Front St, Clearfield, PA, 16830. Tel: 814-765-3271. Fax: 814-765-6316. p. 2046

Marshall, Robert, Assoc Dir, University of Alabama, School of Law Library, 101 Paul Bryant Dr, Tuscaloosa, AL, 35487. Tel: 205-348-5925. Fax: 205-348-1112. p. 38

Marshall, Sandi, Librn, Sierra County Law Library, Courthouse, PO Box 457, Downieville, CA, 95936. Tel: 530-289-3269. Fax: 530-289-2822. p. 144

Marshall, Sharan D, Dir, Southern Maryland Regional Library Association, Inc, 37600 New Market Rd, Charlotte Hall, MD, 20622-3041. Tel: 301-843-3634, 301-884-0436, 301-934-9442. Fax: 301-884-0438. p. 1023

Marshall, Shirley, Ch, Parlin Ingersoll Public Library, 205 W Chestnut St, Canton, IL, 61520. Tel: 309-647-0328. Fax: 309-647-8117. p. 599

Marshall, Shirley, Youth Serv Librn, Helen Matthes Library, 100 E Market Ave, Effingham, IL, 62401-3499. Tel: 217-342-2464, Ext 6. Fax: 217-342-2413. p. 639

Marshall, Sibyl, Head, Pub Serv, University of Tennessee, Taylor Law Center, 1505 W Cumberland Ave, Knoxville, TN, 37996-1800. Tel: 865-974-5906. Fax: 865-974-6571, 865-974-6595. p. 2243

Marshall, Sue, Head Librn, Regina Leader-Post Ltd Library, 1964 Park St, Regina, SK, S4P 3G4, CANADA. Tel: 306-781-5234. Fax: 306-565-2588. p. 2923

Marshall, Susan, Info Spec, Central Washington Hospital, 1201 S Miller St, Wenatchee, WA, 98801. Tel: 509-664-3476. Fax: 509-665-6145. p. 2548

Marshall, Susan Bolda, Dir, American Academy of Pediatrics, 141 Northwest Point Blvd, Elk Grove Village, IL, 60007-1098. Tel: 847-434-4722. Fax: 847-434-4993. p. 641

Marshall, Vicki W, Coordr, Tech Serv, Flint River Regional Library, 800 Memorial Dr, Griffin, GA, 30223. Tel: 770-412-4770. p. 535

Marshbank-Murphy, Diane, Mgr, Acq Serv, Chicago Public Library, 400 S State St, Chicago, IL, 60605. Tel: 312-747-4659. Fax: 312-747-4078. p. 608

Marsicek, Kimberley, Head, Circ, Western Washington University, 516 High St, MS 9103, Bellingham, WA, 98225. Tel: 360-650-7776. Fax: 360-650-3044. p. 2509

Marsnik, Adam G, Head, Automation, Head, Cat, Normandale Community College Library, 9700 France Ave S, Bloomington, MN, 55431. Tel: 952-487-8297. Fax: 952-487-8101. p. 1242

Marson, Barbara M, Dr, Asst Prof, East Carolina University, 101 Umstead Residence Hall, Greenville, NC, 27858-4353. Tel: 252-328-6621. Fax: 252-328-4368. p. 2971

Marsteller, Karla J, Exec Dir, Palmyra Public Library, Borough Bldg, 325 S Railroad St, Palmyra, PA, 17078-2492. Tel: 717-838-1347. Fax: 717-838-1236. p. 2101

Marsteller, Matthew, Head, Sci Libr, Carnegie Mellon University, Engineering & Science Library, 4400 Wean Hall, Pittsburgh, PA, 15213-3890. Tel: 412-268-2426. Fax: 412-681-1998. p. 2123

Marsteller, Matthew, Head, Sci Libr, Carnegie Mellon University, Mellon Institute Library, 4400 Fifth Ave, 4th Flr, Pittsburgh, PA, 15213-3890. Tel: 412-268-3171. Fax: 412-268-6945. p. 2124

Marston, Lisa, Head of Libr, Leeds & the Thousand Islands Public Library, 1B Jessie St, Lansdowne, ON, K0E 1L0, CANADA. Tel: 613-659-3885. Fax: 613-659-4192. p. 2815

Marston, Marilyn S, Exec Mgr, Meherrin Regional Library, 133 W Hicks St, Lawrenceville, VA, 23868. Tel: 434-848-2418. Fax: 434-848-4786. p. 2473

Marszalek, Chris, Regional Mgr, South Region, Memphis Public Library & Information Center, 3030 Poplar Ave, Memphis, TN, 38111-3527. Tel: 901-415-2700. Fax: 901-323-7108. p. 2249

Marszycki, Kathleen, Dir, Libr Serv, Granby Public Library, 15 N Granby Rd, Granby, CT, 06035. Tel: 860-844-5275. Fax: 860-653-0241. p. 341

Marszycky, Kelly, Dir, Rathbun Free Memorial Library, 36 Main St, East Haddam, CT, 06423. Tel: 860-873-8210. Fax: 860-873-3601. p. 337

Mart, Susan Nevelow, Dir, University of Colorado Boulder, The William A Wise Law Library, 2450 Kittredge Loop Dr, 402 UCB, Boulder, CO, 80309-0402. Tel: 303-492-1233. Fax: 303-492-2707. p. 292

Mart-Rice, Jennifer, Head, Ser Acq, Northern Kentucky University, Nunn Dr, Highland Heights, KY, 41099. Tel: 859-572-5712. Fax: 859-572-6529, 859-572-6664. p. 917

Martel, Aline, Head Librn, Bibliotheque Publique de Fermont, 130 Le Carrefour CP 10, Fermont, QC, G0G 1J0, CANADA. Tel: 418-287-3227. Fax: 418-287-3274. p. 2882

Martel, Betsey, Ch, George H & Ella M Rodgers Memorial Library, 194 Derry Rd, Hudson, NH, 03051. Tel: 603-886-6030, Ext 4519. Fax: 603-816-4501. p. 1452

Martel, Donna, Adult Serv, Westborough Public Library, 55 W Main St, Westborough, MA, 01581. Tel: 508-366-3050. Fax: 508-366-3049. p. 1138

Martel, Francoise, Archivist, Canadian Centre for Ecumenism Library, 1819, René-Lévesque ouest, Bureau No 003, Montreal, QC, H3H 2P5, CANADA. Tel: 514-937-9176. Fax: 514-937-4986. p. 2892

Martel, Huguette, Tech Serv, Cegep de Jonquiere, 2505 rue St Hubert, Jonquiere, QC, G7X 7W2, CANADA. Tel: 418-547-2191. Fax: 418-547-0917. p. 2884

Martel, Marie-France, Tech Serv, Chateauguay Municipal Library, 25 Maple Blvd, Chateauguay, QC, J6J 3P7, CANADA. Tel: 450-698-3085. Fax: 450-698-3109. p. 2880

Martell, Elaine, Asst Librn, Zion Bible College Library, 27 Middle Hwy, Barrington, RI, 02806. Tel: 401-628-2117. Fax: 401-246-0906. p. 2163

Martell, Helvetia M, Ref Librn, Hunter College Libraries, Centro - Center for Puerto Rican Studies Library, 2180 Third Ave, Rm 121, New York, NY, 10035. Tel: 212-396-7874. Fax: 212-396-7707. p. 1682

Martell, Suzanne, Pub Serv Librn, Brooks Free Library, 739 Main St, Harwich, MA, 02645. Tel: 508-430-7562. Fax: 508-430-7564. p. 1094

Martello, Jean Marie, Archivist, Saint Lawrence County Historical Association Archives, Three E Main St, Canton, NY, 13617-0008. Tel: 315-386-8133. Fax: 315-386-8134. p. 1602

Marten, Carrie, ILL Librn, State University of New York, 735 Anderson Hill Rd, Purchase, NY, 10577-1400. Tel: 914-251-6400. Fax: 914-251-6437. p. 1724

Martens, Betsy Van der Veer, PhD, Dr, Asst Prof, University of Oklahoma, Bizzell Memorial Library, 401 W Brooks, Rm 120, Norman, OK, 73019-6032. Tel: 918-660-3376. Fax: 405-325-7648. p. 2972

Martens, Judy, Br Mgr, Garfield County Public Library System, Rifle Branch, 107 E Second St, Rifle, CO, 81650-2313. Tel: 970-625-3471. Fax: 970-625-3549. p. 319

Martens, Kathryn I, Dir, Crystal Lake Public Library, 126 Paddock St, Crystal Lake, IL, 60014. Tel: 815-459-1687. Fax: 815-459-9581. p. 632

Martens, Selena, Asst Librn, Parry Sound Public Library, 29 Mary St, Parry Sound, ON, P2A 1E3, CANADA. Tel: 705-746-9601. Fax: 705-746-9601. p. 2835

Martensen, Dan H, Metadata Librn, Syst Librn, Whitman College, 345 Boyer Ave, Walla Walla, WA, 99362. Tel: 509-527-5191. Fax: 509-527-5900. p. 2547

Marthaler, Bruce, Head, Tech Serv, College of Saint Elizabeth, Two Convent Rd, Morristown, NJ, 07960-6989. Tel: 973-290-4228. Fax: 973-290-4226. p. 1504

Martimucci, Edie, Ref, North Castle Public Library, 19 Whippoorwill Rd E, Armonk, NY, 10504. Tel: 914-273-3887. Fax: 914-273-5572. p. 1575

Martin, Aileen, Tech Serv, Patrick Henry Community College, 645 Patriot Ave, Martinsville, VA, 24115. Tel: 276-656-0439. Fax: 276-656-0327. p. 2478

Martin, Alyssa, ILL/Ref Librn, Troy University, Montgomery Campus, 252 Montgomery St, Montgomery, AL, 36104-3425. Tel: 334-241-9576. Fax: 334-241-9590. p. 31

Martin, Andrew, Librn, Odin, Feldman & Pittleman Library, 9302 Lee Hwy, Ste 1100, Fairfax, VA, 22031. Tel: 703-218-2100, 703-218-2362. Fax: 703-218-2160. p. 2462

Martin, Ann, Librn I, Ref Serv, Chesapeake Public Library, South Norfolk Memorial, 1100 Poindexter St, Chesapeake, VA, 23324-2447. Tel: 757-410-7053. Fax: 757-410-7055. p. 2456

Martin, Anne, Br Head, Vancouver Public Library, Collingwood, 2985 Kingsway, Vancouver, BC, V5R 5J4, CANADA. Tel: 604-665-3953. Fax: 604-665-3403. p. 2744

Martin, Anne Marie, Instrul Serv Librn, Anderson University Library, 316 Boulevard, Anderson, SC, 29621. Tel: 864-231-2050. Fax: 864-231-2191. p. 2181

Martin, Barbara, Librn, Tanana Community-School Library, 89 Front St, Tanana, AK, 99777. Tel: 907-366-7211. Fax: 907-366-7201. p. 54

Martin, Barbara, Librn, Pasadena Public Library, Santa Catalina, 999 E Washington Blvd, Pasadena, CA, 91104. Tel: 626-744-7272. p. 207

Martin, Basil D, Coordr, Info Literacy, Ref Librn, Clarion University of Pennsylvania, 840 Wood St, Clarion, PA, 16214. Tel: 814-393-2303. Fax: 814-393-2344. p. 2045

Martin, Bennie, Dir, Cook County Law Library, 2900 Richard J Daley Ctr, 50 W Washington, Chicago, IL, 60602. Tel: 312-603-5423. Fax: 312-603-4716. p. 611

Martin, Beth, Mgr, Ch Serv, Johnson County Public Library, White River Library, 1664 Library Blvd, Greenwood, IN, 46142. Tel: 317-885-1330. Fax: 317-882-4117. p. 744

Martin, Betty, Asst Dir, Octavia Fellin Public Library, 115 W Hill Ave, Gallup, NM, 87301. Tel: 505-863-1291. Fax: 505-722-5090. p. 1556

Martin, Beverly A, Dir, Johnson County Public Library, 401 State St, Franklin, IN, 46131-2545. Tel: 317-738-2833. Fax: 317-738-9635. p. 744

Martin, Brian, Librn, Wyoming Correctional Facility General Library, PO Box 501, Attica, NY, 14011. Tel: 585-591-1010, Ext 4600. Fax: 585-591-1010. p. 1575

Martin, Burrows, Jr, Mgr, District of Columbia Public Library, Chevy Chase, 5625 Connecticut Ave NW, Washington, DC, 20015. Tel: 202-282-0021. p. 398

Martin, C Suzanne, Dir of Admin Serv Div, University of Arkansas at Little Rock, 2801 S University Ave, Little Rock, AR, 72204. Tel: 501-569-8805. Fax: 501-569-3017. p. 107

Martin, Carl, Librn, Shriners' Hospitals for Children-Houston, Library, 6977 Main St, Houston, TX, 77030-3701. Tel: 713-793-3918. Fax: 713-793-3779. p. 2342

Martin, Carol, Circ, Harcum College Library, 750 Montgomery Ave, Bryn Mawr, PA, 19010-3476. Tel: 610-526-6085. Fax: 610-526-6086. p. 2039

Martin, Carol, Librn, Sherman & Ruth Weiss Community Library, 10788 State Hwy 77 W, Hayward, WI, 54843. Tel: 715-634-2161. Fax: 715-634-5257. p. 2598

Martin, Cathy L, Legis Librn, North Carolina Legislative Library, 500 Legislative Office Bldg, 300 N Salisbury St, Raleigh, NC, 27603-5925. Tel: 919-733-9390. Fax: 919-715-5460. p. 1815

Martin, Chase, Head, Circ, Lebanon Public Library, 104 E Washington St, Lebanon, IN, 46052. Tel: 765-482-3460. Fax: 317-873-5059. p. 761

Martin, Cheryl, Librn, United States Army Corps of Engineers, 109 Saint Joseph St, Mobile, AL, 36628-0001. Tel: 251-690-3182. Fax: 251-694-4350. p. 26

Martin, Cheryl, Asst Librn, Chinook Regional Library, Mankota Branch, Village Office Complex, First Ave, Mankota, SK, S0H 2W0, CANADA. Tel: 306-478-2401. p. 2928

Martin, Chris, Access Serv Librn, North Dakota State University Libraries, 1201 Albrecht Blvd, Fargo, ND, 58108. Tel: 701-231-8915. Fax: 701-231-6128. p. 1841

Martin, Christina, Circ Supvr, Mauney Memorial Library, 100 S Piedmont Ave, Kings Mountain, NC, 28086. Tel: 704-739-2371. Fax: 704-734-4499. p. 1804

Martin, Clara West, Librn, Wallace Community College, 3235 S Eufaula Ave, Eufaula, AL, 36027-3542. Tel: 334-687-3543, Ext 4202. Fax: 334-687-0255. p. 16

Martin, Clarice, ILL/Electronic Ref Serv Coordr, Tyler Junior College, 1327 S Baxter St, Tyler, TX, 75701. Tel: 903-510-2502, 903-510-2503. Fax: 903-510-2639. p. 2393

Martin, Curt, Librn, Greater Louisville, Inc, 614 W Main St, Louisville, KY, 40202. Tel: 502-625-0000. Fax: 502-625-0010. p. 923

Martin, Dana, Asst Librn, Stonewall County Library, 516 S Washington St, Aspermont, TX, 79502. Tel: 940-989-2730. Fax: 940-989-2730. p. 2277

Martin, Daniel W, Dir, Loyola Law School, 919 S Albany St, Los Angeles, CA, 90015-1211. Tel: 213-736-1197. Fax: 213-487-2204. p. 175

Martin, David, Adult Serv, Flossmoor Public Library, 1000 Sterling Ave, Flossmoor, IL, 60422-1295. Tel: 708-798-3600. Fax: 708-798-3603. p. 646

Martin, Dawna, Br Mgr, Carbon County Library System, Encampment Branch, 202 Rankin St, Encampment, WY, 82325. Tel: 307-327-5775. Fax: 307-327-5775. p. 2659

Martin, Debbie, Librn, Mills-Peninsula Health Services Library, 1501 Trousdale Dr, Burlingame, CA, 94010. Tel: 650-696-5621. Fax: 650-696-5484. p. 131

Martin, Debbie, Ch, New Braunfels Public Library, 700 E Common St, New Braunfels, TX, 78130-5689. Tel: 830-221-4313. Fax: 830-608-2151. p. 2365

Martin, Debbie, Managing Dir, Linden Municipal Library, 215-One St SE, Linden, AB, T0M 1J0, CANADA. Tel: 403-546-3757. Fax: 403-546-4220. p. 2710

Martin, Dennis M, Dir, Howard Miller Public Library, 14 S Church St, Zeeland, MI, 49464-1728. Tel: 616-772-0874. Fax: 616-772-3253. p. 1238

Martin, Dohn H, Assoc Dir, Oklahoma State University - Center for Health Sciences, 1111 W 17th St, Tulsa, OK, 74107-1898. Tel: 918-561-8449. Fax: 918-561-8412. p. 1981

Martin, Donald, Librn, Shady Grove Adventist Hospital, 9901 Medical Center Dr, Rockville, MD, 20850. Tel: 240-826-6101. Fax: 240-826-6500. p. 1039

Martin, Edwina, Libr Asst I, Montgomery City-County Public Library System, Rufus A Lewis Regional Branch Library, 3095 Mobile Hwy, Montgomery, AL, 36108. Tel: 334-240-4848. Fax: 334-240-4847. p. 30

Martin, Elaine, Dir, Libr Serv, University of Massachusetts Medical School, 55 Lake Ave N, Worcester, MA, 01655-2397. Tel: 508-856-2399. Fax: 508-856-5039. p. 1144

Martin, Elaine, Spec Coll Librn, Laurens County Library, 1017 W Main St, Laurens, SC, 29360. Tel: 864-681-7323. Fax: 864-681-0598. p. 2199

Martin, Elaine, Dir, National Network of Libraries of Medicine New England Region, University of Massachusetts Medical School, 222 Maple Ave, Shrewsbury, MA, 01545-2732. Tel: 508-856-5979. Fax: 508-856-5977. p. 2945

Martin, Elizabeth, Ref Serv, Compton Community College Library, 1111 E Artesia Blvd, Compton, CA, 90221. Tel: 310-900-1600, Ext 2175. Fax: 310-900-1693. p. 136

Martin, Elizabeth, ILL, Calaveras County Library, 891 Mountain Ranch Rd, San Andreas, CA, 95249. Tel: 209-754-6510. Fax: 209-754-6512. p. 226

Martin, Elizabeth, Head Librn, Finlandia University, 601 Quincy St, Hancock, MI, 49930-1882. Tel: 906-487-7252. Fax: 906-487-7297. p. 1187

Martin, Elizabeth, Dir, Cape Girardeau Public Library, 711 N Clark St, Cape Girardeau, MO, 63701. Tel: 573-334-5279. Fax: 573-334-8334. p. 1322

Martin, Emily, Dir, Larue County Public Library, 201 S Lincoln Blvd, Hodgenville, KY, 42748. Tel: 270-358-3851. Fax: 270-358-8647. p. 918

Martin, Erin L, Exec Dir, Historical Society of Rockland County Library, 20 Zukor Rd, New City, NY, 10956. Tel: 845-634-9629. Fax: 845-634-8690. p. 1664

Martin, Esther, Ref, Wofford College, 429 N Church St, Spartanburg, SC, 29303-3663. Tel: 864-597-4300. Fax: 864-597-4329. p. 2206

Martin, Francoise, Dir, Bibliotheque Municipale, 855 Ile-des-moulins, Terrebonne, QC, J6W 4N7, CANADA. Tel: 450-961-2001, Ext 1116. p. 2913

Martin, Gail, Admin Librn, Archivist, Internet Serv, Southwest Arkansas Regional Archives, Historic Washington State Park, 201 Hwy 195S, Washington, AR, 71862. Tel: 870-983-2633. Fax: 870-983-2636. p. 117

Martin, Glenn, Libr Asst, United States Navy, NAS Whidbey Island, 3535 Princeton St, Bldg 2510, Oak Harbor, WA, 98278. Tel: 360-257-2702. Fax: 360-257-3963. p. 2522

Martin, Greg, Ad, Wilsonville Public Library, 8200 SW Wilsonville Rd, Wilsonville, OR, 97070. Tel: 503-570-1591. Fax: 503-682-8685. p. 2023

Martin, Gregory, Coll Serv Librn, Cedarville University, 251 N Main St, Cedarville, OH, 45314-0601. Tel: 937-766-7840. Fax: 937-766-2337. p. 1865

Martin, Heath, Asst Head, Coll Develop, Western Carolina University, 176 Central Dr, Cullowhee, NC, 28723. Tel: 828-227-3729. Fax: 828-227-7015. p. 1786

Martin, Heather, Ref Librn, University of Alabama at Birmingham, Mervyn H Sterne Library, 917 13th St S, Birmingham, AL, 35205. Tel: 205-934-6364. p. 10

Martin, Heather, E-Learning & Reserves, University of Guelph, 50 Stone Rd E, Guelph, ON, N1G 2W1, CANADA. Tel: 519-824-4120, Ext 54701. Fax: 519-824-6931. p. 2807

Martin, J David, Head Librn, University of Iowa Libraries, Marvin A Pomerantz Business Library, 10 E Jefferson St, Iowa City, IA, 52242. Tel: 319-335-3077. Fax: 319-335-3752. p. 824

Martin, James, ILL, Troutman Sanders LLP, 600 Peachtree St NE, Ste 5200, Atlanta, GA, 30308-2216. Tel: 404-885-3196. Fax: 404-962-6783. p. 518

Martin, Jane, Regional Br Mgr, Lake County Library System, Cagan Crossings Community Library, 16729 Cagan Oaks, Clermont, FL, 34714. Tel: 352-243-1840. Fax: 352-243-3230. p. 500

Martin, Jane, Libr Dir, Winter Haven Public Library, 325 Ave A NW, Winter Haven, FL, 33881. Tel: 863-291-5880. Fax: 863-298-7708. p. 505

Martin, Jane, Libr Tech, Department of Fisheries & Oceans Canada, Central & Arctic Region, 501 University Crescent, Winnipeg, MB, R3T 2N6, CANADA. Tel: 204-983-5170. Fax: 204-984-4668. p. 2755

Martin, Janelle, Head, Circ, Dearborn Heights City Libraries, John F Kennedy Jr Library, 24602 Van Born Rd, Dearborn Heights, MI, 48125. Tel: 313-791-6055. Fax: 313-791-6051. p. 1168

Martin, Janelle, Head, Fiction, Lapeer District Library, 201 Village West Dr S, Lapeer, MI, 48446-1699. Tel: 810-664-9521. Fax: 810-664-8527. p. 1202

Martin, Jason, Dir, Alamance County Historic Properties Commission, 217 College St, Ste C, Graham, NC, 27253. Tel: 336-228-1312. Fax: 336-570-4055. p. 1795

Martin, Jef, Mgr, San Antonio Public Library, Maverick, 8700 Mistic Park, San Antonio, TX, 78254. Tel: 210-680-9346. Fax: 210-680-9311. p. 2382

Martin, Jeffrey, Librn, Pratt Memorial Library, 210 Cedar St, Fulton, MS, 38843. Tel: 662-862-4926. Fax: 662-862-2477. p. 1298

Martin, Jennifer, Info Serv Librn, University of Arizona, Arizona Health Sciences Library, 1501 N Campbell Ave, Tucson, AZ, 85724. Tel: 520-626-6344. Fax: 520-626-2922. p. 88

Martin, Jessica A, Circ Serv, Oakwood Hospital Medical Library, 18101 Oakwood Blvd, Dearborn, MI, 48124-2500. Tel: 313-593-7685. Fax: 313-436-2699. p. 1167

Martin, Jo Anne, Adult Serv, New Milford Public Library, 200 Dahlia Ave, New Milford, NJ, 07646-1812. Tel: 201-262-1221. Fax: 201-262-5639. p. 1510

Martin, Joan, Asst Librn, Swanton Public Library, One First St, Swanton, VT, 05488. Tel: 802-868-7656. p. 2437

Martin, Joan, Librn, Canada Agriculture & Agri-Food Canada, 107 Science Pl, Saskatoon, SK, S7N 0X2, CANADA. Tel: 306-956-7222. Fax: 306-956-7247. p. 2925

Martin, John, Res, Times Publishing Co, 490 First Ave S, Saint Petersburg, FL, 33701-4223. Tel: 727-893-8111. Fax: 727-893-8107. p. 488

Martin, John, Dir, Loutit District Library, 407 Columbus Ave, Grand Haven, MI, 49417. Tel: 616-842-5560, Ext 212. Fax: 616-847-0570. p. 1183

Martin, John, Regional Mgr, South Region, Mid-Continent Public Library, 15616 E US Hwy 24, Independence, MO, 64050-2098. Tel: 816-836-5200. Fax: 816-521-7253. p. 1332

Martin, Joy, Librn, Georgian College-Orillia Campus, 825 Memorial Ave, Orillia, ON, L3V 6S2, CANADA. Tel: 705-325-2740, Ext 3051. Fax: 705-329-3107. p. 2826

Martin, Joyce, Ch, Abbott Library, 542 Rte 11, Sunapee, NH, 03782. Tel: 603-763-5513. Fax: 603-763-8765. p. 1466

Martin, Julia, Dir, Schuylerville Public Library, 52 Ferry St, Schuylerville, NY, 12871. Tel: 518-695-6641. Fax: 518-695-6641. p. 1741

Martin, Juliette, Librn, Rolls-Royce (Canada) Library, 9500 Cote de Liesse, Lachine, QC, H8T 1A2, CANADA. Tel: 514-631-3541, Ext 2499. Fax: 514-636-9969. p. 2885

Martin, Karen, Archivist, Huntington Historical Society Library, 209 Main St, Huntington, NY, 11743. Tel: 631-427-7045, Ext 406. Fax: 631-427-7056. p. 1639

Martin, Katherine F, Head, Coll Mgt & Spec Serv, University of Northern Iowa Library, 1227 W 27th St, Cedar Falls, IA, 50613-3675. Tel: 319-273-7255. Fax: 319-273-2913. p. 799

Martin, Katherine R, Librn, Willamette Falls Hospital, 1500 Division St, Oregon City, OR, 97045. Tel: 503-650-6757. Fax: 503-650-6836. p. 2009

Martin, Kathi, Head of Libr, Timmins Public Library, Charles M Shields Centennial Library, 99 Bloor Ave, South Porcupine, ON, P0N 1H0, CANADA. Tel: 705-360-2623, Ext 8590. Fax: 705-360-2688. p. 2849

Martin, Kathleen, Dir, Montgomery County Circuit Court, Judicial Ctr, 50 Maryland Ave, Ste 326, Rockville, MD, 20850. Tel: 240-777-9121. Fax: 240-777-9126. p. 1038

Martin, Katie, In Charge, Lafayette Public Library, Youngsville Branch, Twin Oaks Plaza, 506 Lafayette St, Hwy 89, Ste C, Youngsville, LA, 70592. Tel: 337-856-9385. p. 953

Martin, Katy, Dir, Thorne Bay Public Library, 120 Freeman Dr, Thorne Bay, AK, 99919. Tel: 907-828-3303. p. 54

Martin, Kay K, Dir, Lebanon Public Library, 104 E Washington St, Lebanon, IN, 46052. Tel: 765-482-3460. Fax: 317-873-5059. p. 761

Martin, Kaye, Consumer Health Librn, Portland VA Medical Center Library, 3710 SW US Veterans Hospital Rd, P6LIB, Portland, OR, 97239-2964. Tel: 503-220-8262, Ext 55955. Fax: 503-721-7816. p. 2014

Martin, Keith, Ref Serv, National Institute of Standards & Technology Research Library, 100 Bureau Dr, Stop 2500, Gaithersburg, MD, 20899-2500. Tel: 301-975-2789. Fax: 301-869-8071. p. 1030

Martin, Kelley M, Libr Mgr, Sterne, Kessler, Goldstein & Fox Library, 1100 New York Ave NW, 8th Flr, Washington, DC, 20005-3934. Tel: 202-371-2600. Fax: 202-371-2540. p. 416

Martin, Kenna, Librn, Butler County Public Library, 116 W Ohio St, Morgantown, KY, 42261. Tel: 270-526-4722. Fax: 270-526-4722. p. 930

Martin, Kimberly A, Dir, Maple Park Public Library District, 302 Willow St, Maple Park, IL, 60151. Tel: 815-827-3362. Fax: 815-827-4072. p. 670

Martin, LaRuth, Computer Lab Mgr, Librn II, Webmaster, Montgomery City-County Public Library System, Juliette Hampton Morgan Memorial Library (Main Library), 245 High St, Montgomery, AL, 36104. Tel: 334-240-4994. Fax: 334-240-4980. p. 30

Martin, Laura, Dir, Pub Serv, Ref Serv, Oklahoma Historical Society, 2401 N Laird Ave, Oklahoma City, OK, 73105-4997. Tel: 402-522-5221. Fax: 405-522-0644. p. 1974

Martin, Linda, Librn, Nelson, Mullins, Riley & Scarborough, Beach First Ctr, 3751 Robert M Grissom Pkwy, Myrtle Beach, SC, 29577. Tel: 843-448-3500. Fax: 843-448-3437. p. 2201

Martin, Linda, Br Head, Toronto Public Library, Leaside, 165 McRae Dr, Toronto, ON, M4G 1S8, CANADA. Tel: 416-396-3835. Fax: 416-396-3840. p. 2862

Martin, Lora M, Head, Staff Educ & Training Dept, United States Navy, One Pickney Blvd, Beaufort, SC, 29902-6148. Tel: 843-228-5513. Fax: 843-228-5399. p. 2182

Martin, Lori D, Head of Libr, Bradley, Arant, Rose & White, One Federal Pl, 1819 Fifth Ave N, Birmingham, AL, 35203. Tel: 205-521-8000. Fax: 205-521-8800. p. 8

Martin, Lyn, Spec Coll Librn, Willard Library of Evansville, 21 First Ave, Evansville, IN, 47710-1294. Tel: 812-425-4309. Fax: 812-425-4303. p. 739

Martin, Lynn, ILL, Springfield College, 263 Alden St, Springfield, MA, 01109-3797. Tel: 413-748-3315. Fax: 413-748-3631. p. 1128

Martin, Lynn, Librn, New Lisbon Correctional Institution Library, 2000 Progress Rd, New Lisbon, WI, 53950. Tel: 608-562-7375. Fax: 608-562-6410. p. 2625

Martin, Lynne, Ch, Sheffield Public Library, 316 N Montgomery Ave, Sheffield, AL, 35660. Tel: 256-386-5633. Fax: 256-386-5608. p. 36

Martin, Mairead, Head, Digital Libr Tech, Pennsylvania State University Libraries, 510 Paterno Library, University Park, PA, 16802. Tel: 814-865-0401. Fax: 814-865-3665. p. 2148

Martin, Mandy, Ch, McPherson Public Library, 214 W Marlin, McPherson, KS, 67460-4299. Tel: 620-245-2570. Fax: 620-245-2567. p. 883

Martin, Marianne, AV, Colonial Williamsburg Foundation, John D Rockefeller Jr Library-Visual Resources, 313 First St, Williamsburg, VA, 23185-4306. Tel: 757-565-8541. Fax: 757-565-8548. p. 2502

Martin, Marie S, Librn, Voorhees College, 5480 Voorhees Rd, Denmark, SC, 29042. Tel: 803-793-3351, Ext 7095. Fax: 803-793-0471. p. 2192

Martin, Marilyn, Br Mgr, Lynchburg Public Library, Downtown, 900 Church St, Lynchburg, VA, 24504. Tel: 434-455-3820. Fax: 434-847-1403. p. 2476

Martin, Marion, ILL, Libr Tech, College of Southern Nevada, 6375 W Charleston Blvd, W10I, Las Vegas, NV, 89146. Tel: 702-651-5716. Fax: 702-651-5718. p. 1429

Martin, Marla, Teen Librn, Woodbury Public Library, 269 Main St S, Woodbury, CT, 06798. Tel: 203-263-3502. Fax: 203-263-0571. p. 380

Martin, Marna, Head, Ref, Cumberland County Public Library & Information Center, Cliffdale, 6882 Cliffdale Rd, Fayetteville, NC, 28314-1936. Tel: 910-864-3800. Fax: 910-487-9090. p. 1792

Martin, Martha, Dir, Pub Serv, Montreat College, 310 Gaither Circle, Montreat, NC, 28757. Tel: 828-669-8012, Ext 3503. Fax: 828-350-2083. p. 1810

Martin, Mary, Dir, Long Hill Township Public Library, 917 Valley Rd, Gillette, NJ, 07933. Tel: 908-647-2088. Fax: 908-647-2098. p. 1488

Martin, Melba, Librn, Houston Community College - Northwest College, Spring Branch Campus Library, 1010 W Sam Houston Pkwy N, Houston, TX, 77043-5008. Tel: 713-718-5656. Fax: 713-718-5745. p. 2338

Martin, Melissa, Librn IV, San Diego Public Library, 820 E St, San Diego, CA, 92101-6478. Tel: 619-238-6634. Fax: 619-238-6639. p. 235

Martin, Michael, Commun Libr Supvr, Yakima Valley Libraries, Selah Public Library, 106 South Second St, Selah, WA, 98942. Tel: 509-698-7345. Fax: 509-698-7345. p. 2551

Martin, Michalene, Br Mgr, Tuolumne County Free Library, Groveland Branch, 18990 Hwy 120, Groveland, CA, 95321. Tel: 209-962-6144. Fax: 209-962-5178. p. 269

Martin, Mies, Digital Res Coordr, Michigan Technological University, 1400 Townsend Dr, Houghton, MI, 49931-1295. Tel: 906-487-2135. p. 1191

Martin, Missy, Supvr, Access Serv, William Woods University, One University Ave, Fulton, MO, 65251. Tel: 573-592-4291. Fax: 573-592-1159. p. 1329

Martin, Mona, Dean, Santa Monica College Library, 1900 Pico Blvd, Santa Monica, CA, 90405-1628. Tel: 310-434-4334, 310-434-4692. Fax: 310-434-4387. p. 266

Martin, Mona, Asst Librn, Young Adult Serv, Caribou Public Library, 30 High St, Caribou, ME, 04736. Tel: 207-493-4214. Fax: 207-493-4654. p. 981

Martin, Neal, Syst Librn, Tech Serv, Mooresville Public Library, 304 S Main St, Mooresville, NC, 28115. Tel: 704-664-2927. Fax: 704-660-3292. p. 1810

Martin, Norene, Librn, Englewood Christian Church Library, 57 N Rural St, Indianapolis, IN, 46201. Tel: 317-639-1541. Fax: 317-639-3447. p. 751

Martin, Orville, Ref Librn, Ohio State University LIBRARIES, Jerome Lawrence & Robert E Lee Theatre Research Institute Library, 1430 Lincoln Tower, 1800 Cannon Dr, Columbus, OH, 43210-1230. Tel: 614-292-6614. Fax: 614-688-8417. p. 1888

Martin, Pam, Head, Prog, Syosset Public Library, 225 S Oyster Bay Rd, Syosset, NY, 11791-5897. Tel: 516-921-7161. Fax: 516-921-8771. p. 1751

Martin, Pamela, Mgr, Rapides Parish Library, Carl N Gunter Sr Branch, 5630 Holloway Rd, Pineville, LA, 71360. Tel: 318-443-7259. Fax: 318-443-1293. p. 940

Martin, Pat, Pub Info Coordr, Acterra Environmental Library, 3921 E Bayshore Rd, Palo Alto, CA, 94303. Tel: 650-962-9876, Ext 306. Fax: 650-962-8234. p. 204

Martin, Pat, Ref Serv Coordr, Supvr, ILL, Youth Serv, Red Wing Public Library, 225 East Ave, Red Wing, MN, 55066-2298. Tel: 651-385-3673. Fax: 651-385-3644. p. 1272

Martin, Patricia, Head, Circ, Carver Public Library, Two Meadowbrook Way, Carver, MA, 02330-1278. Tel: 508-866-3415. Fax: 508-866-3416. p. 1079

Martin, Paul, Ref, Pawtucket Public Library, 13 Summer St, Pawtucket, RI, 02860. Tel: 401-725-3714. Fax: 401-728-2170. p. 2171

Martin, Peggy, Mgr, Saint Gabriel's Hospital Library, 815 SE Second St, Little Falls, MN, 56345. Tel: 320-632-5441. Fax: 320-632-1190. p. 1256

Martin, Peggy, Dir, Simpson, Thacher & Bartlett, 425 Lexington Ave, New York, NY, 10017-3954. Tel: 212-455-2800. Fax: 212-455-2502. p. 1700

Martin, Penny, Librn, Prince George's Hospital Center, 3001 Hospital Dr, Cheverly, MD, 20785-1193. Tel: 301-618-2490. Fax: 301-618-2493. p. 1024

Martin, Randall, Exec Dir, Valley Library Consortium, 3210 Davenport Ave, Saginaw, MI, 48602-3495. Tel: 898-497-0925, Ext 5. Fax: 989-497-0918. p. 2946

Martin, Raymond, Dept Head, Librn, Community College of Allegheny County, 595 Beatty Rd, Monroeville, PA, 15146. Tel: 724-325-6796. Fax: 724-325-6696. p. 2091

Martin, Rebecca, Head, User Serv, Northern Illinois University Libraries, DeKalb, IL, 60115-2868. Tel: 815-753-9896. p. 635

Martin, Reed, Info Tech, Vernon Area Public Library District, 300 Olde Half Day Rd, Lincolnshire, IL, 60069-2901. Tel: 847-634-3650. Fax: 847-634-8449. p. 666

Martin, Renee, Head Librn, Calgary Board of Education, Second Flr Safran N, 1221 Eighth St SW, Calgary, AB, T2R 0L4, CANADA. Tel: 403-817-7814. Fax: 403-777-6027. p. 2688

Martin, Robert D, Dir, Libr & Media Serv, Molloy College, 1000 Hempstead Ave, Rockville Centre, NY, 11571. Tel: 516-678-5000, Ext 6819. Fax: 516-678-8908. p. 1734

Martin, Robin, Adult Serv, North Adams Public Library, 74 Church St, North Adams, MA, 01247. Tel: 413-662-3133. Fax: 413-662-3039. p. 1111

Martin, Rosa, Librn, Pasadena Public Library, Villa Parke Community Center, 363 E Villa St, Pasadena, CA, 91101. Tel: 626-744-6510. p. 207

Martin, Ruby, Dir, Lane County Library, 144 South Lane, Dighton, KS, 67839. Tel: 620-397-2808. Fax: 620-397-5937. p. 863

Martin, Russell, Dir, Southern Methodist University, DeGolyer Library of Special Collections, 6404 Robert S Hyer Lane, Dallas, TX, 75275. Tel: 214-768-3234. Fax: 214-768-1565. p. 2310

Martin, Ruth, Dir, Libr Serv, San Diego Christian College, 2100 Greenfield Dr, El Cajon, CA, 92019-1161. Tel: 619-201-8747. Fax: 619-201-8799. p. 145

Martin, Ruth, Libr Tech, Anoka-Ramsey Community College, 11200 Mississippi Blvd NW, Coon Rapids, MN, 55433. Tel: 763-433-1384. p. 1246

Martin, Sandra, Asst Dir, Wayne State University Libraries, Vera P Shiffman Medical Library & Learning Resources Centers, Rackham Bldg Rm 044, 60 Farnsworth, Detroit, MI, 48202. Tel: 313-577-6665. Fax: 313-577-6668. p. 1173

Martin, Sara, Head, Tech Serv, US Department of Commerce, Radio Bldg, Rm 1202, 325 Broadway MC5, Boulder, CO, 80305-3328. Tel: 303-497-3271. Fax: 303-497-3890. p. 291

Martin, Sara J K, Assoc Dean, Tech Serv & Libr Syst, University of Detroit Mercy Library, 4001 W McNichols Rd, Detroit, MI, 48221-3038. Tel: 313-993-1074. Fax: 313-993-1780. p. 1172

Martin, Sara L, Dir, World Food Logistics Organization Library, 1500 King St, Ste 201, Alexandria, VA, 22314. Tel: 703-373-4300. Fax: 703-373-4301. p. 2447

Martin, Saundra, Lead Libr Tech, University of Washington Libraries, Mathematics Research Library, C-306 Padelford Hall, Seattle, WA, 98195. Tel: 206-543-7296. p. 2534

Martin, Scott, Librn, University of Michigan, Museums, 2500 Museums Bldg, 1108 Geddes Rd, Ann Arbor, MI, 48109-1079. Tel: 734-936-2337. Fax: 734-764-3829. p. 1153

Martin, Sharon, Dir, Health One Presbyterian-Saint Luke's Medical Center, 1719 E 19th Ave, Denver, CO, 80218-1281. Tel: 303-839-6670. Fax: 303-869-1643. p. 302

Martin, Sharon, Br Mgr, Dallas Public Library, Park Forest, 3421 Forest Lane, Dallas, TX, 75234-7776. Tel: 214-670-6333. Fax: 214-670-6623. p. 2307

Martin, Shirley, ILL Coordr, Mooresville Public Library, 220 W Harrison St, Mooresville, IN, 46158-1633. Tel: 317-831-7323. Fax: 317-831-7383. p. 766

Martin, Shirley, Librn, Rapid City Regional Library, 425 Third Ave, Rapid City, MB, R0K 1W0, CANADA. Tel: 204-826-2732. p. 2750

Martin, Stephen H, Dir, Sheridan Public Library, 103 W First St, Sheridan, IN, 46069. Tel: 317-758-5201. Fax: 317-758-0045. p. 778

Martin, Sue, Libr Spec, Webmaster, Marstons Mills Public Library, 2160 Main St, Marstons Mills, MA, 02648. Tel: 508-428-5175. Fax: 508-420-5194. p. 1103

Martin, Susan, Asst Librn, Rosebud County Library, 201 N Ninth Ave, Forsyth, MT, 59327. Tel: 406-346-7561. Fax: 406-346-7685. p. 1378

Martin, Susan, Br Mgr, Cleveland Public Library, South Brooklyn, 4303 Pearl Rd, Cleveland, OH, 44109. Tel: 216-623-7067. Fax: 216-623-7069. p. 1878

Martin, Susan, Tech Serv Supvr, Smyth-Bland Regional Library, 118 S Sheffey St, Marion, VA, 24354. Tel: 276-783-2323, Ext 226. Fax: 276-783-5279. p. 2477

Martin, Susan H, Dir, Georgetown College, 400 E College St, Georgetown, KY, 40324. Tel: 502-863-8407. Fax: 502-868-7740. p. 915

Martin, Susanne, Head, Tech Serv, Easttown Library & Information Center, 720 First Ave, Berwyn, PA, 19312-1769. Tel: 610-644-0138. Fax: 610-251-9739. p. 2033

Martin, Suzanne, ILL, United States Department of Agriculture, 1100 Robert E Lee Blvd, New Orleans, LA, 70124. Tel: 504-286-4288. Fax: 504-286-4396. p. 964

Martin, Terri, Ch, Chickasaw Regional Library System, 601 Railway Express, Ardmore, OK, 73401. Tel: 580-223-3164. Fax: 580-223-3280. p. 1957

Martin, Tim, Adult Serv, Milton Public Library, 476 Canton Ave, Milton, MA, 02186-3299. Tel: 617-698-5757. Fax: 617-698-0441. p. 1106

Martin, Vanessa, Ref Librn, Greensburg-Decatur County Public Library, 1110 E Main St, Greensburg, IN, 47240. Tel: 812-663-2826. Fax: 812-663-5617. p. 746

Martin, Velvet, Head, Circ, Pierce College Library, 9401 Farwest Dr SW, Lakewood, WA, 98498. Tel: 253-964-6547. Fax: 253-964-6713. p. 2519

Martin, Vickie, Dir, Gilbreath Memorial Library, 916 N Main St, Winnsboro, TX, 75494. Tel: 903-342-6866. p. 2401

Martin, Virginia, Head, Circ, Rice University, 6100 Main, MS-44, Houston, TX, 77005. Tel: 713-348-2573. Fax: 713-348-5258. p. 2341

Martin, W Terry, Dir, Louisiana College, 1140 College Blvd, Pineville, LA, 71359. Tel: 318-487-7110. Fax: 318-487-7143. p. 965

Martin, Wilson G, Actg Dir, Prog Mgr, Utah State Historical Society, 300 Rio Grande, Salt Lake City, UT, 84101-1182. Tel: 801-533-3535. Fax: 801-533-3504. p. 2415

Martin, Wynell, Librn, De Soto Trail Regional Library, Pelham Carnegie Branch, 133 Hand Ave W, Pelham, GA, 31779. Tel: 229-294-6030. Fax: 229-294-6030. p. 523

Martin-Albright, K J, Dir, Wasilla Meta-Rose Public Library, 391 N Main St, Wasilla, AK, 99654-7085. Tel: 907-376-5913. Fax: 907-376-2347. p. 55

Martin-Diaz, Pamela, Librn, Allen County Public Library, Shawnee, 5600 Noll Ave, Fort Wayne, IN, 46806. Tel: 260-421-1355. Fax: 260-456-1871. p. 741

Martin-Schaff, Linda, Tech Serv Librn, Philadelphia Museum of Art Library, Ruth & Raymond G Perelman Bldg, 2525 Pennsylvania Ave, Philadelphia, PA, 19130. Tel: 215-684-7655. Fax: 215-236-0534. p. 2114

Martin-Woodard, Katie, Tech Serv, Pierson Library, 5376 Shelburne Rd, Shelburne, VT, 05482. Tel: 802-985-5124. Fax: 802-985-5129. p. 2435

Martindale, Bobbi, Librn, Van Buren District Library, Bangor Branch, 420 Division St, Bangor, MI, 49013-1112. Tel: 269-427-8810. Fax: 269-427-8810. p. 1168

Martindale, Peggy, Asst Dir, Tarrant County Law Library, 100 W Weatherford, Rm 420, Fort Worth, TX, 76196-0800. Tel: 817-884-1481. Fax: 817-884-1509. p. 2323

Martindill, Harvey, Mgr, Libr Serv, Golden Gate Baptist Theological Seminary Library, 251 S Randolph Ave, Ste A, Brea, CA, 92821-5759. Tel: 714-256-1311, Ext 27; 877-237-8478. Fax: 714-256-0292. p. 129

Martine, Renee, ILL/Doc Delivery Serv, Harrison Memorial Library, Ocean Ave & Lincoln St, Carmel, CA, 93921. Tel: 831-624-4629. Fax: 831-624-0407. p. 132

Martinek, Peter, Libr Supvr-Popular Libr, McGill University Libraries, Howard Ross Library of Management, Samuel Bronfman Bldg, 1001 Sherbrooke St W, 2nd Flr, Montreal, QC, H3A 1G5, CANADA. Tel: 514-398-4690, Ext 00864. Fax: 514-398-5046. p. 2899

Martinelli, Patricia, Adminr, Curator, Vineland Historical & Antiquarian Society Library, 108 S Seventh St, Vineland, NJ, 08360-4607. Tel: 856-691-1111. p. 1538

Martinengo, Laura, Commun Libr Mgr, Contra Costa County Library, Kensington Library, 61 Arlington Ave, Kensington, CA, 94707-1098. Tel: 510-524-3043. Fax: 510-528-2567. p. 209

Martinez, Alicia, Circ Mgr, Watsonville Public Library, 310 Union St, Watsonville, CA, 95076. Tel: 831-768-3400. Fax: 831-763-4015. p. 282

Martinez, Alma, Coordr, Carlsbad Medical Center, 2430 W Pierce St, Carlsbad, NM, 88220. Tel: 575-887-4100, Ext 4485. p. 1552

Martinez, Andrew, Archivist, Rhode Island School of Design Library, 15 Westminster St, Providence, RI, 02903. Tel: 401-709-5920. Fax: 401-709-5932. p. 2174

Martinez, Annette, Br Mgr, Anythink Libraries, Anythink Perl Mack, 7611 Hilltop Circle, Denver, CO, 80221. Tel: 303-428-3576. Fax: 303-428-1358. p. 324

Martinez, Arely Del, ILL, Tulane University, 7001 Freret St, New Orleans, LA, 70118-5682. Tel: 504-865-5131. Fax: 504-865-6773. p. 963

Martinez, Aurora, Br Mgr, Cleveland Heights-University Heights Public Library, University Heights, 13866 Cedar Rd, University Heights, OH, 44118-3201. Tel: 216-321-4700. Fax: 216-321-3049. p. 1882

Martinez, Bertha, Dir, Libr Serv, Dr Eugene Clark Public Library, 217 S Main St, Lockhart, TX, 78644-2742. Tel: 512-398-3223. Fax: 512-376-2258. p. 2356

Martinez, Betty, Dir, Everest University, 995 E Memorial Blvd, Ste 110, Lakeland, FL, 33801. Tel: 863-686-1444, Ext 131. Fax: 863-688-9881. p. 459

Martinez, Carmen L, Dir of Libr Serv, Oakland Public Library, Main Library, 125 14th St, Oakland, CA, 94612. Tel: 510-238-3281. Fax: 510-238-2232. p. 198

Martinez, Chris, Dir, Lewiston Public Library, 33 S Main, Lewiston, UT, 84320. Tel: 435-258-5515. Fax: 435-258-2141. p. 2407

Martinez, Christina, Head, User Serv, University of Colorado at Colorado Springs, 1420 Austin Bluffs Pkwy, Colorado Springs, CO, 80918. Tel: 719-255-3287. Fax: 719-528-5227. p. 296

Martinez, Claudia, Br Mgr, Los Angeles Public Library System, West Los Angeles Regional, 11360 Santa Monica Blvd, Los Angeles, CA, 90025-3152. Tel: 310-575-8323. Fax: 310-312-8309. p. 174

Martinez, David, Br Mgr, San Bernardino County Library, Kaiser Branch, 11155 Almond Ave, Fontana, CA, 92337. Tel: 909-357-5900, Ext 8029. Fax: 909-428-8494. p. 228

Martinez, Diane, Librn, The Shuter Library of Angel Fire, 11 S Angel Fire Rd, Angel Fire, NM, 87110. Tel: 575-377-6755. Fax: 575-377-3990. p. 1551

Martinez, Edward, Pub Serv Librn, El Camino College, 16007 S Crenshaw Blvd, Torrance, CA, 90506. Tel: 310-660-3525. Fax: 310-660-3513. p. 275

Martinez, Elizabeth, Dir, Salinas Public Library, 350 Lincoln Ave, Salinas, CA, 93901. Tel: 831-758-7311. Fax: 831-758-7336. p. 226

Martinez, Erma Jean, Br Mgr, Sabine Parish Library, Zwolle Branch, 2218 Port Arthur St, Zwolle, LA, 71486. Tel: 318-645-6955. p. 956

Martinez, Jose, Dir, Port Arthur Public Library, 4615 Ninth Ave, Port Arthur, TX, 77642. Tel: 409-985-8838, Ext 2234. Fax: 409-985-5969. p. 2371

Martinez, Karen, Dir, Northwest Area Health Education Center Library at Boone, Watauga Medical Ctr, 336 Deerfield Rd, Boone, NC, 28607-5008. Tel: 828-262-4300. Fax: 828-265-5048. p. 1777

Martinez, Karen Lee, Libr Coordr, Northwest Area Health Education Center Library at Hickory, Catawba Valley Medical Center, 810 Fairgrove Church Rd, Hickory, NC, 28602. Tel: 828-326-3482. Fax: 828-326-3484. p. 1802

Martinez, Karen Lee, Dir, Northwest AHEC Library at Hickory, Catawba Medical Ctr, 810 Fairgrove Church Rd, Hickory, NC, 28602. Tel: 828-326-3662. Fax: 828-326-3484. p. 2951

Martinez, Karina, Circ Serv, Fresno County Public Law Library, Fresno County Courthouse, Rm 600, 1100 Van Ness Ave, Fresno, CA, 93721-2017. Tel: 559-237-2227. Fax: 559-442-4960. p. 151

Martinez, Katharine, Dir, University of Arizona, Center for Creative Photography, 1030 N Olive Rd, Tucson, AZ, 85721-0001. Tel: 520-621-7993. Fax: 520-621-9444. p. 89

Martinez, Katharine, Librn, Harvard Library, Fine Arts Library, Fogg Art Museum, 32 Quincy St, Cambridge, MA, 02138. Tel: 617-495-3374. Fax: 617-496-4889. p. 1075

Martinez, Kelly, Outreach Serv Librn, Pub Serv, Hermiston Public Library, 235 E Gladys Ave, Hermiston, OR, 97838-1827. Tel: 541-567-2882. Fax: 541-667-5055. p. 2000

Martinez, Kristina, Ad, Columbiana Public Library, 332 N Middle St, Columbiana, OH, 44408. Tel: 330-482-5509. Fax: 330-482-9669. p. 1883

Martinez, Luis, Mgr, City of Commerce Public Library, Bristow Park Branch, 1466 S McDonnell Ave, Commerce, CA, 90040. Tel: 323-265-1787. Fax: 323-269-6608. p. 136

Martinez, Lyndsey, Asst Librn, Austin County Library System, 6730 Railroad, Wallis, TX, 77485. Tel: 979-478-6813. Fax: 979-478-6813. p. 2398

Martinez, M Claudia, Dir of Libr Operations, Free Library of Philadelphia, 1901 Vine St, Philadelphia, PA, 19103-1189. Tel: 215-686-5450. Fax: 215-563-3628. p. 2106

Martinez, Maribel, In Charge, Imperial County Law Library, Courthouse, 939 W Main St, 2nd Flr, El Centro, CA, 92243. Tel: 760-482-2271. Fax: 760-482-4530. p. 146

Martinez, Michael Mark, Libr Dir, Reinhardt University, 7300 Reinhardt Circle, Waleska, GA, 30183. Tel: 770-720-5995. Fax: 770-720-5944. p. 556

Martinez, Mike, Jr, Ref, Saint Mary's University, Sarita Kennedy East Law Library, One Camino Santa Maria, San Antonio, TX, 78228-8605. Tel: 210-436-3435, Ext 1374. Fax: 210-436-3240. p. 2381

Martinez, Miriam, Info Literacy Librn, Universidad del Turabo, PO Box 3030, Gurabo, PR, 00778-3030. Tel: 787-743-7979, Ext 4501. Fax: 787-743-7924. p. 2673

Martinez, Monique, ILL, Sadie Pope Dowdell Library of South Amboy, 100 Harold G Hoffman Plaza, South Amboy, NJ, 08879. Tel: 732-721-6060. Fax: 732-721-1054. p. 1530

Martinez, Nancy, Dir, Libr Serv, Lodi Public Library, 201 W Locust St, Lodi, CA, 95240. Tel: 209-333-5540. Fax: 209-367-5944. p. 165

Martinez, Noemi, Ch, University of Puerto Rico Library, Cayey Campus, 205 Ave Antonio R Barcelo, Cayey, PR, 00736. Tel: 787-738-2161, Ext 2069. Fax: 787-263-2108. p. 2672

Martinez, Nydia, Acq, Universidad Adventista de las Antillas, Carr 106 Km 2 Interior, Bo La Quinta, Mayaguez, PR, 00680. Tel: 787-834-9595, Ext 2311. Fax: 787-834-6015. p. 2674

Martinez, Pasha, Mgr, Carnegie Public Library, 500 National Ave, Las Vegas, NM, 87701. Tel: 505-426-3304. p. 1558

Martinez, Patty, Libr Tech-Mats, Alamosa Public Library, 300 Hunt Ave, Alamosa, CO, 81101. Tel: 719-589-6592. Fax: 719-589-3786. p. 287

Martinez, Paty, Weekend Librn, Val Verde County Library, 300 Spring St, Del Rio, TX, 78840. Tel: 830-774-7595. Fax: 830-774-7607. p. 2312

Martinez, Paul, Archivist, Cat Librn, Montclair State University, One Normal Ave, Montclair, NJ, 07043-1699. Tel: 973-655-3465. Fax: 973-655-7780. p. 1503

Martinez, Pilar, Exec Dir, Pub Serv, Edmonton Public Library, Seven Sir Winston Churchill Sq, Edmonton, AB, T5J 2V4, CANADA. Tel: 780-496-5522. Fax: 780-496-1885. p. 2700

Martinez, Raul, ILL, Dustin Michael Sekula Memorial Library, 1906 S Closner Blvd, Edinburg, TX, 78539. Tel: 956-383-6246. Fax: 956-318-3123. p. 2315

Martinez, Renee, Libr Mgr, Piedmont Regional Library, Pendergrass Public, 75 Glenn Gee Rd, Pendergrass, GA, 30567-4654. Tel: 706-693-4450. p. 557

Martinez, Rosa, Coll Librn, Tech Serv, Val Verde County Library, 300 Spring St, Del Rio, TX, 78840. Tel: 830-774-7595. Fax: 830-774-7607. p. 2312

Martinez, Sharon, Asst Dir, Nocona Public Library, Ten Cooke St, Nocona, TX, 76255. Tel: 940-825-6373. Fax: 940-825-4587. p. 2366

Martinez, Sherry, Br Mgr, Riverside County Library System, Perris Library, 163 E San Jacinto, Perris, CA, 92570. Tel: 951-657-2358. Fax: 951-657-9849. p. 218

Martinez, Sylvia, Librn, Gustavus Public Library, PO Box 279, Gustavus, AK, 99826-0279. Tel: 907-697-2350. Fax: 907-697-2249. p. 49

Martinez, Tammy, Automation Syst Coordr, Cat, Pontifical Catholic University Of Puerto Rico, Monseignor Fremiot Torres Oliver Legal Information & Research Center, 2250 Avenida Las Americas, Ste 544, Ponce, PR, 00717-9997. Tel: 787-841-2000, Ext 1858. Fax: 787-841-5354. p. 2675

Martinez, Teresa, Dir, Learning Res, Baptist University of the Americas, 8019 S Pan Am Expressway, San Antonio, TX, 78224-1397. Tel: 210-924-4338, Ext 233. Fax: 210-924-2701. p. 2379

Martinez, Trudy, Circ, Converse County Library, Glenrock Branch, 518 S Fourth St, Glenrock, WY, 82637. Tel: 307-436-2573. Fax: 307-436-8525. p. 2654

Martinez, Veronica, Librn, Contra Costa Times News Research Department, 2640 Shadelands Dr, Walnut Creek, CA, 94598. Tel: 510-208-6420. Fax: 925-943-8362. p. 282

Martinez, Zulima, Br Mgr, Main Libr, Columbia County Public Library, 308 NW Columbia Ave, Lake City, FL, 32055. Tel: 386-758-2101. Fax: 386-758-2135. p. 457

Martinez-Coyne, Fran, Head, Pub Serv, Benicia Public Library, 150 East L St, Benicia, CA, 94510-3281. Tel: 707-746-4343. Fax: 707-747-8122. p. 126

Martinez-Garcia Jr, Federico, Access Serv Mgr, Arizona State University Libraries, Downtown Phoenix Campus Library, UCENT Bldg, Ste L1-62, 411 N Central Ave, Phoenix, AZ, 85004-1213. Tel: 602-496-0318. Fax: 602-496-0312. p. 83

Martinez-Trigg, Claudia, Actg Librn, Shearing Plough BioPharma, 901 California Ave, Palo Alto, CA, 94304-1104. p. 204

Martini, Anne, Br Mgr, Public Library of Youngstown & Mahoning County, Boardman, 7680 Glenwood Ave, Youngstown, OH, 44512. Tel: 330-758-1414. Fax: 330-758-7918. p. 1952

Martinkus, Margaret, Curator, Princeton Public Library, 698 E Peru St, Princeton, IL, 61356. Tel: 815-875-1331. Fax: 815-872-1376. p. 692

Martino, Carmen, Br Head, Toronto Public Library, Perth/Dupont, 1589 Dupont St, Toronto, ON, M6P 3S5, CANADA. Tel: 416-393-7677. Fax: 416-393-7724. p. 2862

Martino, Cathy, Access Serv, Hood College, 401 Rosemont Ave, Frederick, MD, 21701. Tel: 301-696-3909. Fax: 301-696-3796. p. 1029

Martino, Marie, Syst & Cat Librn, Moraine Valley Community College Library, 9000 W College Pkwy, Palos Hills, IL, 60465. Tel: 708-974-5709. Fax: 708-974-1184. p. 687

Martino, Nancy, Chief Librn, Department of Veterans Affairs, 1601 Brenner Ave, Salisbury, NC, 28144. Tel: 704-638-9000, Ext 3403. Fax: 704-638-3483. p. 1822

Martino, William, Dir, Holmes County District Public Library, 3102 Glen Dr, Millersburg, OH, 44654. Tel: 330-674-5972, Ext 201. Fax: 330-674-1938. p. 1918

Martino, William, Exec Dir, Northeast Ohio Regional Library System, 4445 Mahoning Ave NW, Warren, OH, 44483. Tel: 330-847-7744. Fax: 330-847-7704. p. 2952

Martins, Michael, Curator, Fall River Historical Society Museum, 451 Rock St, Fall River, MA, 02720. Tel: 508-679-1071. Fax: 508-675-5754. p. 1088

Martinsen, Dan, PhD, Dir, McLennan Community College Library, 1400 College Dr, Waco, TX, 76708-1498. Tel: 254-299-8333. Fax: 254-299-8026. p. 2397

Martinsen, Laura, Dir, Saint Paul Library, 1301 Howard Ave, Saint Paul, NE, 68873-2021. Tel: 308-754-5223. p. 1418

Martinson, Doris, Archives Mgr, Archivist, Knox County Public Library System, 500 W Church Ave, Knoxville, TN, 37902-2505. Tel: 865-215-8804. Fax: 865-215-8742. p. 2241

Martinson, Gayle J, Archives Coll Mgr, Wisconsin Department of Veterans Affairs, 30 W Mifflin St, Ste 300, Madison, WI, 53703. Tel: 608-261-0536. Fax: 608-264-7615. p. 2610

Martinson, Mary, ILL, Saint Joseph's University, Francis A Drexel Library, 5600 City Ave, Philadelphia, PA, 19131-1395. Tel: 610-660-1905. Fax: 610-660-1916. p. 2116

Martinson, Melissa, Support Librn, Alamosa Public Library, 300 Hunt Ave, Alamosa, CO, 81101. Tel: 719-589-6592, Ext 2541. Fax: 719-589-3786. p. 287

Martocello, Anthony, Network & Syst Adminr, Northport-East Northport Public Library, 151 Laurel Ave, Northport, NY, 11768. Tel: 631-261-6930. Fax: 631-261-6718. p. 1707

Marton, Sandy, ILL, Collin College, 2800 E Spring Creek Pkwy, Plano, TX, 75074. Tel: 972-881-5931. Fax: 972-881-5866. p. 2370

Martone, Fran, Asst Librn, Georgia O'Keeffe Museum, 217 Johnson St, Santa Fe, NM, 87501. Tel: 505-946-1011. Fax: 505-946-1093. p. 1563

Martorana, Lorraine, Dir, Cecil College, One Seahawk Dr, North East, MD, 21901-1904. Tel: 410-287-1005. Fax: 410-287-1607. p. 1035

Martorella, Georgina, Chair, Ref Serv & Coll Develop, Hofstra University, 123 Hofstra University, Hempstead, NY, 11549. Tel: 516-463-4980. p. 1635

Marts, Michael, Libr Tech, Elizabeth City State University, 1704 Weeksville Rd, Elizabeth City, NC, 27909. Tel: 252-335-8514. Fax: 252-335-3446. p. 1791

Marty, Daryl, Librn, Historical Society of Old Yarmouth Library, 11 Strawberry Lane, Yarmouth Port, MA, 02675. Tel: 508-362-3021. p. 1146

Martyniak, Cathleen, Head, Presv Dept & Auxiliary Libr Fac, University of Florida Libraries, 535 Library W, Gainesville, FL, 32611-7000. Tel: 352-273-2830. Fax: 352-392-6597. p. 450

Martzel, Michele M, Promotional Serv Coordr, Batavia Public Library District, Ten S Batavia Ave, Batavia, IL, 60510-2793. Tel: 630-879-1393. Fax: 630-879-9118. p. 593

Maruscsak, Rich, Tech Serv Librn, Wichita Falls Public Library, 600 11th St, Wichita Falls, TX, 76301-4604. Tel: 940-767-0868, Ext 241. Fax: 940-720-6672. p. 2401

Marushin, James, Curator, Martin County Historical Society, Inc, 304 E Blue Earth Ave, Fairmont, MN, 56031. Tel: 507-235-5178. Fax: 507-235-5179. p. 1250

Maruskin, Jillian, Pub Serv Librn, Info Literacy, Ohio Wesleyan University, 43 Rowland, Delaware, OH, 43015-2370. Tel: 740-368-3237. Fax: 740-368-3222. p. 1896

Maruskin, John, Adult Serv, Clark County Public Library, 370 S Burns Ave, Winchester, KY, 40391-1876. Tel: 859-744-5661. Fax: 859-744-5993. p. 938

Maruskin, John, Chair, Bryant Free Library, 455 Berkshire Trail, Rte 9, Cummington, MA, 01026-9610. Tel: 413-634-0109. p. 1083

Maruskin, Julie, Dir, Clark County Public Library, 370 S Burns Ave, Winchester, KY, 40391-1876. Tel: 859-744-5661. Fax: 859-744-5993. p. 938

Marvan, Nancy, Bus Off Mgr, Hinsdale Public Library, 20 E Maple St, Hinsdale, IL, 60521. Tel: 630-986-1976. Fax: 630-986-9654. p. 656

Marve, Rodney, Asst Dir, Bay Shore-Brightwaters Public Library, One S Country Rd, Brightwaters, NY, 11718-1517. Tel: 631-665-4350. Fax: 631-665-4958. p. 1585

Marvin, Helena, Head, Govt Doc, Head, Ser, City College of the City University of New York, North Academic Ctr, 160 Convent Ave, New York, NY, 10031. Tel: 212-650-7604. Fax: 212-650-7604. p. 1672

Marvin, Kathie, Syst, West Chester University, 25 W Rosedale Ave, West Chester, PA, 19383. Tel: 610-436-1044. p. 2153

Marvin, Stephen, Ref Coordr, West Chester University, 25 W Rosedale Ave, West Chester, PA, 19383. Tel: 610-436-1068. p. 2153

Marx, Anthony W, Dr, Pres, The New York Public Library - Astor, Lenox & Tilden Foundations, 476 Fifth Ave, (@ 42nd St), New York, NY, 10018-2788. Tel: 212-930-0736. Fax: 212-930-9299. p. 1690

Marx, Mary Ann, Br Mgr, New Orleans Public Library, Alvar Branch, 913 Alvar St, New Orleans, LA, 70117-5409. Tel: 504-596-2667. Fax: 504-596-2667. p. 962

Marx, Richard, ILL, Iosco-Arenac District Library, 120 W Westover St, East Tawas, MI, 48730. Tel: 989-362-2651. Fax: 989-362-6056. p. 1175

Marx, Shereen, Gen Serv Librn, Baton Rouge Community College, 201 Community College Dr, Baton Rouge, LA, 70806. Tel: 225-216-8557. Fax: 225-216-8712. p. 942

Marx, Vicky, Outreach Librn, Antigo Public Library, 617 Clermont St, Antigo, WI, 54409-1894. Tel: 715-623-3724. Fax: 715-627-2317. p. 2578

Marx, Virginia, Librn, Owensboro Medical Health System, 811 E Parish Ave, Owensboro, KY, 42303. Tel: 270-688-2167. Fax: 270-688-2168. p. 931

Mary, Donald, Sister, Librn, Bolivar County Library System, Mound Bayou Public, 301 E Martin Luther King St, Mound Bayou, MS, 38762. Tel: 662-741-2559. Fax: 662-741-3494. p. 1296

Marzolla, Mary K, Head, Pub Serv, Widener University, School of Law Library, 4601 Concord Pike, Wilmington, DE, 19803. Tel: 302-477-2157. Fax: 302-477-2240. p. 389

Mas, Sabine, Asst Prof, Universite de Montreal, 3150, rue Jean-Brillant, bur C-2004, Montreal, QC, H3T 1N8, CANADA. Tel: 514-343-6044. Fax: 514-343-5753. p. 2979

Masat, Joan, Librn, Brunswick Public Library, 303 Franklin St, Brunswick, NE, 68720. Tel: 402-842-2105. p. 1395

Mascarenas, Sandra, ILL, Nogales-Santa Cruz County Public Library, 518 N Grand Ave, Nogales, AZ, 85621. Tel: 520-287-3343. Fax: 520-287-4823. p. 69

Maschmeier, Ruth, Assoc Librn, University of Wisconsin, 400 University Dr, West Bend, WI, 53095-3619. Tel: 262-335-5206. Fax: 262-335-5220. p. 2648

Mascia, Regina, Dir, West Hempstead Public Library, 500 Hempstead Ave, West Hempstead, NY, 11552. Tel: 516-481-6591. Fax: 516-481-2608. p. 1766

Mascia, Sara, Curator, Historical Society Serving Sleepy Hollow & Tarrytown, One Grove St, Tarrytown, NY, 10591. Tel: 914-631-8374. Fax: 914-631-8374. p. 1754

Mascus, Melissa, Circ & Ref, Addictions Foundation of Manitoba, 1031 Portage Ave, Winnipeg, MB, R3G 0R8, CANADA. Tel: 204-944-6279. Fax: 204-772-0225. p. 2753

Mase, Sheryl, Dir, Statewide Libr Serv, Library of Michigan, 702 W Kalamazoo St, Lansing, MI, 48915. Tel: 517-373-4331. Fax: 517-373-5700. p. 1201

Masek, Amy, ILL, Clarkson College Library, 101 S 42nd St, Omaha, NE, 68131-2739. Tel: 402-552-3387. Fax: 402-552-2899. p. 1411

Maseles, Judy Siebert, Librn, University of Missouri-Columbia, Engineering Library & Technology Commons, W2001 Lafferre Hall, Columbia, MO, 65211. Tel: 573-882-2715. Fax: 573-884-4499. p. 1325

Masen, Naunihal, Librn, Filion Wakely Thorup Angeletti LLP, 150 King St W, Ste 2601, Toronto, ON, M5H 4B6, CANADA. Tel: 416-408-5506. Fax: 416-408-4814. p. 2853

Masengale, Margaret, Librn, Northwest Regional Library, MCHS Community Library, 8115 US Hwy 43, Guin, AL, 35563. Tel: 205-468-2544. Fax: 205-468-2544. p. 40

Masenhimer, Tami, Commun Br Supvr, Pierce County Library System, DuPont Branch, 1540 Wilmington Dr, DuPont, WA, 98327. Tel: 253-548-3326. Fax: 253-964-4010. p. 2539

Maser, Michelle, Circ Mgr, Ref Mgr, Sweetwater County Library System, White Mountain Library, 2935 Sweetwater Dr, Rock Springs, WY, 82901-4331. Tel: 307-362-2665, Ext 3220. Fax: 307-352-6655. p. 2656

Mash, David, PhD, Dean of Libr Serv, Lander University, 320 Stanley Ave, Greenwood, SC, 29649-2099. Tel: 864-388-8035. Fax: 864-388-8816. p. 2197

Masheck, Kim, Librn, Kaplan University, 7009 Nordic Dr, Cedar Falls, IA, 50613. Tel: 319-277-0220. Fax: 319-268-0978. p. 799

Mashek, Kim, Dir, Libr Serv, Kaplan University, 2570 Fourth St SW - Plaza West, Mason City, IA, 50401. Tel: 641-423-2530. Fax: 641-423-7512. p. 830

Masih, Buddhwanti, Cat, Atlanta University Center, 111 James P Brawley Dr SW, Atlanta, GA, 30314. Tel: 404-978-2071. Fax: 404-577-5158. p. 513

Mask, Alan, Syst Librn, Wartburg College Library, 100 Wartburg Blvd, Waverly, IA, 50677-0903. Tel: 319-352-8244. Fax: 319-352-8312. p. 850

Maskell, Cathy, Assoc Dean of Libr, University of Windsor, 401 Sunset Ave, Windsor, ON, N9B 3P4, CANADA. Tel: 519-253-3000, Ext 3165. p. 2871

Masland, Anne, Ch, Hull Public Library, Nine Main St, Hull, MA, 02045-1199. Tel: 781-925-2295. Fax: 781-925-0867. p. 1096

Masler, Marilyn, In Charge, Memphis Brooks Museum of Art Library, Overton Park, 1934 Poplar Ave, Memphis, TN, 38104. Tel: 901-544-6200. Fax: 901-725-4071. p. 2249

Masloski, Karen, City Librn, Pembina City Library, Pembina Public School, 155 S Third St, Pembina, ND, 58271. Tel: 701-825-6217. p. 1847

Maslow, Linda, Res, Supreme Court of the United States Library, One First St NE, Washington, DC, 20543. Tel: 202-479-3037. Fax: 202-479-3477. p. 416

Maslowska, Magda, Acq, New Jersey Department of Law & Public Safety, 25 Market St, West Wing, 6th Flr, Trenton, NJ, 08625. Tel: 609-292-4958. Fax: 609-633-6555. p. 1535

Maslyn, David C, Dean, Robert L Carothers Library & Learning Commons, 15 Lippitt Rd, Kingston, RI, 02881. Tel: 401-874-2594. Fax: 401-874-4608. p. 2168

Masnik, Linda, Br Mgr, Fairfax County Public Library, Kings Park, 9000 Burke Lake Rd, Burke, VA, 22015-1683. Tel: 703-978-5600. p. 2461

Mason, Amanda, Librn, Albany Town Library, 530 Main St, Albany, VT, 05820. Tel: 802-755-6107. p. 2417

Mason, Andrew, Libr Asst, Nashville State Technical Community College, 120 White Bridge Rd, Nashville, TN, 37209-4515. Tel: 615-353-3555. Fax: 615-353-3558. p. 2258

Mason, Benita, Coordr, Electronic Res, Indiana University Southeast Library, 4201 Grant Line Rd, New Albany, IN, 47150. Tel: 812-941-2262. Fax: 812-941-2656. p. 767

Mason, Calvert, Extn Serv, Pub Serv, Rockingham County Public Library, 527 Boone Rd, Eden, NC, 27288. Tel: 336-627-1106. Fax: 336-623-1258. p. 1790

Mason, Diane, Youth Serv, Hewlett-Woodmere Public Library, 1125 Broadway, Hewlett, NY, 11557-0903. Tel: 516-374-1967. Fax: 516-569-1229. p. 1636

Mason, Donna, Asst Dir, Emmetsburg Public Library, 707 N Superior St, Emmetsburg, IA, 50536. Tel: 712-852-4009. Fax: 712-852-3785. p. 814

Mason, Eleanor, Dir, Twin Mountain Public Library, 92 School St, Carrol, NH, 03595. Tel: 603-846-5818. Fax: 603-846-5712. p. 1440

Mason, Elizabeth, Libr Tech, Long Beach Memorial/Miller Children's Hospital Long Beach, 2801 Atlantic Ave, Long Beach, CA, 90806-1737. Tel: 562-933-3841. Fax: 562-933-3847. p. 166

Mason, Emily, Libr Serv Supvr, Antioch University New England Library, 40 Avon St, Keene, NH, 03431-3516. Tel: 603-283-2400. Fax: 603-357-7345. p. 1452

Mason, Gail, Serv Mgr, Coll Develop & Reading Serv, Santa Clara County Library District, 14600 Winchester Blvd, Los Gatos, CA, 95032. Tel: 408-293-2326. Fax: 408-364-0161. p. 180

Mason, Jamie L, Dep Dir, Rocky River Public Library, 1600 Hampton Rd, Rocky River, OH, 44116-2699. Tel: 440-333-7610. Fax: 440-333-4184. p. 1932

Mason, Jeff, VPres, Canadian Health Libraries Association, 39 River St, Toronto, ON, M5A 3P1, CANADA. Tel: 416-646-1600. Fax: 416-646-9460. p. 2959

Mason, Jennifer, Ch, Fort McMurray Public Library, 151 MacDonald Dr, Fort McMurray, AB, T9H 5C5, CANADA. Tel: 780-743-7800. Fax: 780-743-7938. p. 2704

Mason, Joanne, AV, Harold Washington College Library, City Colleges of Chicago, 30 E Lake St, 5th Flr, Chicago, IL, 60601-9996. Tel: 312-553-5775. Fax: 312-553-5783. p. 614

Mason, Karen, Ser Librn, Medgar Evers College, 1650 Bedford Ave, Brooklyn, NY, 11225-2010. Tel: 718-270-4875. Fax: 718-270-5182. p. 1593

Mason, Karen, Evening Supvr, Slippery Rock University of Pennsylvania, Slippery Rock, PA, 16057-9989. Tel: 724-738-2058. Fax: 724-738-2661. p. 2140

Mason, Lida, Acq, Ser, Thiel College, 75 College Ave, Greenville, PA, 16125-2183. Tel: 724-589-2128. Fax: 724-589-2122. p. 2063

Mason, Liz, Tech Serv, Bismarck State College Library, 1500 Edwards Ave, Bismarck, ND, 58501. Tel: 701-224-5451. Fax: 701-224-5551. p. 1837

Mason, Lori, Actg Br Mgr, Brunswick County Library, Hickmans Crossroads Library, 1040 Calabash Rd, Calabash, NC, 28467. Tel: 910-575-0173. Fax: 910-575-0176. p. 1824

Mason, Lorre, Libr Mgr, Bingham McCutchen, Three Embarcadero Ctr, San Francisco, CA, 94111. Tel: 415-393-2560. Fax: 415-393-2286. p. 240

Mason, Lucinda, Ch, Bullitt County Public Library, 127 N Walnut St, Shepherdsville, KY, 40165-6083. Tel: 502-543-7675. Fax: 502-543-5487. p. 935

Mason, Mary Jane, Ch, Greensburg Hempfield Area Library, 237 S Pennsylvania Ave, Greensburg, PA, 15601-3086. Tel: 724-837-5620. Fax: 724-836-0160. p. 2062

Mason, Nicole, Agr & Biological Sci Librn, North Dakota State University Libraries, 1201 Albrecht Blvd, Fargo, ND, 58108. Tel: 701-231-8879. Fax: 701-231-6128. p. 1841

Mason, Patricia, Br Mgr, Uncle Remus Regional Library System, Putnam County Library, 309 N Madison Ave, Eatonton, GA, 31024. Tel: 706-485-6768. Fax: 706-485-5896. p. 542

Mason, Penny, Libr Mgr, San Bernardino County Library, Joshua Tree Branch, 6465 Park Blvd, Joshua Tree, CA, 92252. Tel: 760-366-8615. Fax: 760-366-8615. p. 228

Mason, Randall, Cat, Jonathan Bourne Public Library, 19 Sandwich Rd, Bourne, MA, 02532-3699. Tel: 508-759-0644, Ext 104. Fax: 508-759-0647. p. 1069

Mason, Robert, Assoc Dean, Res, Prof, University of Washington, Mary Gates Hall, Ste 370, Campus Box 352840, Seattle, WA, 98195-2840. Tel: 206-685-9937. Fax: 206-616-3152. p. 2976

Mason, Sally, Adult Serv, Asst Dir, Ref, Irvin L Young Memorial Library, 431 W Center St, Whitewater, WI, 53190-1915. Tel: 262-473-0530. Fax: 262-473-0539. p. 2649

Mason, Sandra, Chief Librn, Department of Veterans Affairs, 3200 Vine St, Cincinnati, OH, 45220-2213. Tel: 513-475-6315. Fax: 513-475-6454. p. 1870

Mason, Sharon, Librn, Black Heritage Library & Multicultural Center, 817 Harmon St, Findlay, OH, 45840. Tel: 419-423-4954. p. 1899

Mason, Sharon, Tech Serv Mgr, Findlay-Hancock County District Public Library, 206 Broadway, Findlay, OH, 45840-3382. Tel: 419-422-1712. Fax: 419-422-0638. p. 1899

Mason, Tim, Tech Serv Librn, University of North Texas Health Science Center at Fort Worth, 3500 Camp Bowie Blvd, Fort Worth, TX, 76107-2699. Tel: 817-735-2466. Fax: 817-763-0325. p. 2324

Mason, Tonia, Pub Relations, Providence Public Library, 150 Empire St, Providence, RI, 02903-3283. Tel: 401-455-8090. Fax: 401-455-8065, 401-455-8080. p. 2173

Masone, Valerie, Ser Librn, Iona College, 715 North Ave, New Rochelle, NY, 10801-1890. Tel: 914-633-2449. Fax: 914-633-2136. p. 1666

Masoni, Daniel, Dir, Unalaska Public Library, 64 Eleanor Dr, Unalaska, AK, 99685. Tel: 907-581-5060. Fax: 907-581-5266. p. 54

Massa, Jane M, Head, Adult Serv, Syst Coordr, Salem Public Library, 821 E State St, Salem, OH, 44460-2298. Tel: 330-332-0042. Fax: 330-332-4488. p. 1934

Massa, Mary Beth, Br Mgr, Colusa County Free Library, Princeton Branch, 232 Prince St, Princeton, CA, 95970. Tel: 530-439-2235. Fax: 530-439-2235. p. 136

Masschaele, Brain, Dir, Cultural Serv, Elgin County Public Library, 450 Sunset Dr, St. Thomas, ON, N5R 5V1, CANADA. Tel: 519-631-1460. Fax: 519-631-9209. p. 2844

Masserini, Margaret, Coordr, Salem County Library Commission, 900 Rte 45, Bldg 3, Pilesgrove, NJ, 08098. Tel: 856-769-1082. Fax: 856-769-2018. p. 1520

Massey, Cyn, Br Librn, Spartanburg County Public Libraries, Woodruff Library, 270 E Hayne St, Woodruff, SC, 29388. Tel: 864-476-8770. p. 2205

Massey, Jackie, Libr Coordr, Addictions Foundation of Manitoba, 1031 Portage Ave, Winnipeg, MB, R3G 0R8, CANADA. Tel: 204-944-6367. Fax: 204-772-0225. p. 2753

Massey, Regina, Ref, Southwest Tennessee Community College, 170 Myrtle St, Memphis, TN, 38103. Tel: 901-333-5140. Fax: 901-333-5141. p. 2251

Massey, Regina N, Per, Southwest Tennessee Community College, George Freeman Library, 5983 Macon Cove, Memphis, TN, 38134. Tel: 901-333-5140. Fax: 901-333-4566. p. 2251

Massey, Susan, Libr Tech, Lawrence & Memorial Hospital, 365 Montauk Ave, New London, CT, 06320. Tel: 860-442-0711, Ext 2238. Fax: 860-271-4302. p. 360

Massey, Will, Cent Libr Mgr, Nicholson Memorial Library System, 625 Austin St, Garland, TX, 75040-6365. Tel: 972-205-2500. Fax: 972-205-2523. p. 2327

Massie, Betty, Financial Serv, Albemarle Regional Library, 303 W Tryon St, Winton, NC, 27986. Tel: 252-358-7834. Fax: 252-358-7868. p. 1835

Massie, Rhonda, Mkt, Bloomington Public Library, 205 E Olive St, Bloomington, IL, 61701. Tel: 309-828-6091. Fax: 309-828-7312. p. 595

Massin, Susan, Dir, Fitzwilliam Town Library, 11 Templeton Tpk, Fitzwilliam, NH, 03447. Tel: 603-585-6503. Fax: 603-585-6738. p. 1447

Massingill, Carol S, Librn, First Lutheran Church, 415 Vine St, Johnstown, PA, 15901. Tel: 814-536-7521. Fax: 814-536-0855. p. 2073

Massis, Bruce, Dir, Columbus State Community College Library, 550 E Spring St, Columbus, OH, 43215. Tel: 614-287-5484. Fax: 614-287-2457. p. 1885

Massnick, Nancy, Dir, Hartland Public Library, 110 E Park Ave, Hartland, WI, 53029. Tel: 262-367-3350. Fax: 262-369-2251. p. 2597

Masson, Catherine, Br Tech, Monroe County Library System, Maybee Branch, 9060 Raisin St, Maybee, MI, 48159. Tel: 734-587-3680. Fax: 734-587-3680. p. 1210

Massoud, Mary, Br Head, Toronto Public Library, Woodside Square, Woodside Square Mall, 1571 Sandhurst Circle, Toronto, ON, M1V 1V2, CANADA. Tel: 416-396-8979. Fax: 416-395-3563. p. 2863

Massucco, Georgia A, Dir, Libr Serv, Lee Library Association, 100 Main St, Lee, MA, 01238-1688. Tel: 413-243-0385. Fax: 413-243-0381. p. 1098

Mast, Austin, Dr, Dir, Florida State University Libraries, Herbarium Library, 100 Biology I, Tallahassee, FL, 32306-4370. Tel: 850-644-6278. Fax: 850-644-0481. p. 495

Mast, Cheryl, Mgt Analyst, Carlsbad City Library, 1775 Dove Lane, Carlsbad, CA, 92011-4048. Tel: 760-602-2014. Fax: 760-602-7942. p. 132

Mast, Joanne, Ch, Indiana Free Library, Inc, 845 Philadelphia St, Indiana, PA, 15701-3908. Tel: 724-465-8841. Fax: 724-465-9902. p. 2071

Mast, Robert, Chief Librn, Info Spec, Federal Aviation Administration, Atlantic City International Airport, Atlantic City, NJ, 08405. Tel: 609-485-5124. Fax: 609-485-6088. p. 1470

Mast, Susan, Ch, Mount Pleasant Public Library, 307 E Monroe, Ste 101, Mount Pleasant, IA, 52641. Tel: 319-385-1490. Fax: 319-385-1491. p. 833

Mast, Susan B, Info Spec, Aerodyne Research, Inc, 45 Manning Rd, Billerica, MA, 01821-3976. Tel: 978-663-9500, Ext 257. Fax: 978-663-4918. p. 1054

Mastantuoni, Anthony, Acq, Supvr, Iona College, 715 North Ave, New Rochelle, NY, 10801-1890. Tel: 914-633-2028. Fax: 914-633-2136. p. 1666

Mastel, Bonnie, Tech Spec Librn, Legacy Emanuel Hospital & Health Center Library, 2801 N Gantenbein Ave, Portland, OR, 97227. Tel: 503-413-2558. Fax: 503-413-2544. p. 2011

Masten, Julie, Libr Tech/Archivist, Lake Michigan College, 2755 E Napier Ave, Benton Harbor, MI, 49022. Tel: 269-927-8100, Ext 5132. Fax: 269-927-6656. p. 1156

Masten, Lisa, Asst Dir, Lucy Robbins Welles Library, 95 Cedar St, Newington, CT, 06111-2645. Fax: 860-667-1255. p. 361

Masten, Nancy, Archivist, Miami County Museum, 51 N Broadway, Peru, IN, 46970. Tel: 765-473-9183. Fax: 765-473-3880. p. 772

Mastenbrook, Marianne, Archivist, Winona County Historical Society, 160 Johnson St, Winona, MN, 55987. Tel: 507-454-2723. Fax: 507-454-0006. p. 1290

Master, Laura, Ref, Kitchener Public Library, 85 Queen St N, Kitchener, ON, N2H 2H1, CANADA. Tel: 519-743-0271. Fax: 519-743-1261. p. 2815

Master, Sally, Tech Serv Dir, University City Public Library, 6701 Delmar Blvd, University City, MO, 63130. Tel: 314-727-3150. Fax: 314-727-6005. p. 1370

Masterpasqua, Alison, Access Serv, Circ, Swarthmore College, 500 College Ave, Swarthmore, PA, 19081-1081. Tel: 610-328-8478. Fax: 610-328-7329. p. 2145

Masters, Andrea, Librn, North Conway Public Library, 2719 White Mountain Hwy, North Conway, NH, 03860. Tel: 603-356-2961. p. 1460

Masters, Anne, Dir, Pioneer Library System, 225 N Webster Ave, Norman, OK, 73069-7133. Tel: 405-701-2642. Fax: 405-701-2649. p. 1970

Masters, Deborah C, Univ Librn, San Francisco State University, 1630 Holloway Ave, San Francisco, CA, 94132-4030. Tel: 415-338-1854. p. 247

Masters, Nancy, Libr Dir, Inyo County Free Library, 168 N Edwards St, Independence, CA, 93526. Tel: 760-878-0260. Fax: 760-878-0360. p. 159

Masters, Nancy, Law Libr Operations Mgr, Inyo County Law Library, 168 N Edwards St, Independence, CA, 93526. Tel: 760-878-0260. Fax: 760-878-0360. p. 159

Masterson, Amanda, In Charge, University of Texas Libraries, Bureau of Economic Geology, Publications Sales Office & Resource Center, 10100 Burnet Rd, Bldg 130, Austin, TX, 78758-4445. Tel: 512-471-2794. Fax: 512-471-0140. p. 2283

Masterson, Beth, Libr Tech, Colorado Department of Corrections, San Carlos Correctional Facility Library, 1410 W 13th St, Pueblo, CO, 81003-1961. Tel: 719-544-4800, Ext 3346. Fax: 719-583-5510. p. 320

Masterson, Nance, Dir, Webster Memorial Library, 20 Wentworth Village Rd, Wentworth, NH, 03282. Tel: 603-764-5818. p. 1467

Mastick, Elsie, Archivist, Moraga Historical Society Archives, 1500 Saint Mary's Rd, Moraga, CA, 94556-2037. Tel: 925-377-8734. p. 191

Mastragostino, Marlene, Adminr, McMaster University Library, 1280 Main St W, Hamilton, ON, L8S 4L6, CANADA. Tel: 905-525-9140, Ext 24355. Fax: 905-524-9850. p. 2810

Mastrangelo, Vito, Dir, Info Resources & Res, Illinois Appellate Court, 14th & Main Sts, Mount Vernon, IL, 62864. Tel: 618-242-6414. Fax: 618-242-9133. p. 678

Mastrodonato, Theresa M, Coordr of First Year Libr Instruction, Frostburg State University, One Stadium Dr, Frostburg, MD, 21532. Tel: 301-687-4425. Fax: 301-687-7069. p. 1029

Mastroianni, Dana, Dir, Moses Greeley Parker Memorial Library, 28 Arlington St, Dracut, MA, 01826. Tel: 978-454-5474. Fax: 978-454-9120. p. 1085

Mastroianni, Dana, Asst Dir, Needham Free Public Library, 1139 Highland Ave, Needham, MA, 02494-3298. Tel: 781-455-7559. Fax: 781-455-7591. p. 1108

Mastroianni, Rick, Mgr, Libr Serv, Freedom Forum World Center Library, 9893 Brewers Ct, Laurel, MD, 20723. Tel: 301-957-3210. Fax: 301-957-3281. p. 1034

Mastroinni, Dana, Ref, Chatham College, Woodland Rd, Pittsburgh, PA, 15232. Tel: 412-365-1602. Fax: 412-365-1465. p. 2124

Mastronardi, Mary, Supvr, Essex County Library, Essex Branch, 35 Gosfield Townline W, Essex, ON, N8M 0A1, CANADA. Tel: 226-946-1529, Ext 250. p. 2804

Masuchika, Glenn N, Info Literacy Librn, Pennsylvania State University Libraries, Library Learning Services, 305 Pattee Library, Tower, University Park, PA, 16802-1803. Tel: 814-867-2229. Fax: 814-865-3665. p. 2148

Masud-Paul, Janice, Info Tech, Camden County Library System, 203 Laurel Rd, Voorhees, NJ, 08043. Tel: 856-772-1636, Ext 3336. Fax: 856-772-6105. p. 1538

Mata, Lorena, Librn, Evergreen Valley College Library, 3095 Yerba Buena Rd, San Jose, CA, 95135. Tel: 408-274-7900, Ext 6743. Fax: 408-532-1925. p. 249

Mata, Nina, Br Assoc, Las Vegas-Clark County Library District, Blue Diamond Library, 14 Cottonwood Dr, Blue Diamond, NV, 89004. Tel: 702-875-4295. Fax: 702-875-4095. p. 1429

Matacio, Lauren, Instruction Librn, Andrews University, 1400 Library Rd, Berrien Springs, MI, 49104-1400. Tel: 269-471-6062. Fax: 269-471-6166. p. 1157

Mataloni, Constance Diane, Dir, Sibley Public Library, 406 Ninth St, Sibley, IA, 51249. Tel: 712-754-2888. Fax: 712-754-2590. p. 843

Matarazzo, James M, Prof, Simmons College, 300 The Fenway, Boston, MA, 02115. Tel: 617-521-2800. Fax: 617-521-3192. p. 2967

Matcau, Peter, LTA Supvr, Ser, Florida International University, 3000 NE 151st St, North Miami, FL, 33181-3600. Tel: 305-919-5716. Fax: 305-919-5914. p. 472

Matchett, Johnson, Libr Mgr, Atlanta Technical College, 1560 Metropolitan Pkwy SW, Atlanta, GA, 30310. Tel: 404-225-4595. Fax: 404-225-4658. p. 513

Matchinski, William L, Librn, Wyoming State Hospital Library, 831 Hwy 150 S, Evanston, WY, 82930-5340. Tel: 307-789-3464, Ext 785. Fax: 307-789-7373. p. 2655

Matczak, Jamie, Coordr, North East Wisconsin Intertype Libraries, Inc, 515 Pine St, Green Bay, WI, 54301. Tel: 920-448-4413. Fax: 920-448-4420. p. 2958

Mate, Paula, Syst Librn, Trevecca Nazarene University, 73 Lester Ave, Nashville, TN, 37210-4227. Tel: 615-248-7732. Fax: 615-248-1452. p. 2259

Matei, Daniela, Database Mgr, Syst Coordr, Fuller Theological Seminary, 135 N Oakland Ave, Pasadena, CA, 91182. Tel: 626-584-5218. Fax: 626-584-5613. p. 206

Mateika, Anton, Librn, New York State Supreme Court Library, Brooklyn, Supreme Court Bldg, Rm 349, 360 Adams St, Brooklyn, NY, 11201-3782. Tel: 347-296-1144. Fax: 718-643-2412. p. 1594

Matejic, Predrag, Dr, Curator, Ohio State University LIBRARIES, Hilandar Research Library & Research Center for Medieval Slavic Studies, 6065 Ackerman Library, 610-640 Ackerman Rd, Columbus, OH, 43202-4500. Tel: 614-292-0634. Fax: 614-292-7859. p. 1888

Mater, Dee, Dir, Abbott, 100 Abbott Park Rd, AP 6B, Abbott Park, IL, 60064-6107. Tel: 847-937-0425. Fax: 847-937-6333. p. 587

Mater, Emily, Asst Dir, Putnam District Library, 327 N Main St, Nashville, MI, 49073-9578. Tel: 517-852-9723. Fax: 517-852-9723. p. 1213

Matera, Cristina, Br Mgr, Chicago Public Library, Walker, 11071 S Hoyne Ave, Chicago, IL, 60643. Tel: 312-747-1920. Fax: 312-747-2929. p. 610

Maternowski, Lee James, Dir, Elk Grove Village Public Library, 1001 Wellington Ave, Elk Grove Village, IL, 60007-3391. Tel: 847-439-0447. Fax: 847-439-0475. p. 641

Mateyk, Rebekka, Dir, Stowe Free Library, 90 Pond St, Stowe, VT, 05672. Tel: 802-253-6145. Fax: 802-253-4808. p. 2436

Mathapo, Gail, Circ Librn, University of the District of Columbia, David A Clarke School of Law, Charles N & Hilda H M Mason Law Library, Bldg 39, Rm B-16, 4200 Connecticut Ave NW, Washington, DC, 20008. Tel: 202-274-7357. Fax: 202-274-7311. p. 421

Mathe, Peter, Librn, Saint Joseph's Hospital Health Center, 206 Prospect Ave, Syracuse, NY, 13203. Tel: 315-448-5053. Fax: 315-423-6804. p. 1753

Matheis, Bonnie, Ill Ctr for the Bk Coordr, Illinois State Library, Gwendolyn Brooks Bldg, 300 S Second St, Springfield, IL, 62701-9713. Tel: 217-558-2065. Fax: 217-785-4326. p. 705

Matheney, Bobbie, Youth Serv, Bolivar County Library System, 104 S Leflore Ave, Cleveland, MS, 38732. Tel: 662-843-2774. Fax: 662-843-4701. p. 1295

Mathenia, Brenda, Assoc Univ Librn, Client Serv & Fac, University of Lethbridge Library, 4401 University Dr, Lethbridge, AB, T1K 3M4, CANADA. Tel: 403-329-2261, 403-329-2263. Fax: 403-329-2234. p. 2710

Mather, Amy, Adult Serv Coordr, Omaha Public Library, 215 S 15th St, Omaha, NE, 68102-1629. Tel: 402-444-4800. Fax: 402-444-4504. p. 1414

Mather, Dave, Mgr, Pasco County Library System, South Holiday Branch, 4649 Mile Stretch Rd, Holiday, FL, 34690. Tel: 727-834-3331. Fax: 727-942-6740. p. 452

Mather, Diane, Ref Librn, University of Connecticut - Torrington Regional Campus Library, 855 University Dr, Torrington, CT, 06790. Tel: 860-626-6842. Fax: 860-626-6817. p. 372

Matherne, Diane, Br Mgr, Saint Mary Parish Library, Berwick Branch, 3527 Fourth St, Berwick, LA, 70342. Tel: 985-385-2943. Fax: 985-385-6474. p. 950

Mathers, Sandra, Tech Serv, Curry Public Library, 94341 Third St, Gold Beach, OR, 97444. Tel: 541-247-7246. Fax: 541-247-4411. p. 1999

Mathes, Holly, Ch, Grant County Library, 215 E Grant Ave, Ulysses, KS, 67880-2958. Tel: 620-356-1433. Fax: 620-356-1344. p. 898

Matheson, Iver, Br Mgr, Timberland Regional Library, Ocean Park Branch, 1308 256th Pl, Ocean Park, WA, 98640. Tel: 360-665-4184. Fax: 360-665-5983. p. 2543

Matheson, Kimberley, Circ Supvr, Davis County Library, South Branch, 725 S Main St, Bountiful, UT, 84010. Tel: 801-295-8732. p. 2405

Matheson, Molly, Ref Librn, Santa Rosa Junior College, 1501 Mendocino Ave, Santa Rosa, CA, 95401. Tel: 707-778-4162. Fax: 707-527-4545. p. 267

Matheson, Scott, Tech Serv, Yale University Library, Lillian Goldman Library Yale Law School, 127 Wall St, New Haven, CT, 06511. Tel: 203-432-1600. Fax: 203-432-2112. p. 358

Matheson, Sharon, Librn, Southeast Regional Library, Wapella Branch, 519 S Railway St, Wapella, SK, S0G 4Z0, CANADA. Tel: 306-532-4419. p. 2931

Matheuws, Katy, Circ Librn, Shawnee State University, 940 Second St, Portsmouth, OH, 45662-4344. Tel: 740-351-3492. Fax: 740-351-3432. p. 1931

Mathews, Alice, Br Mgr, La Porte County Public Library, Coolspring, 7089 W 400 N, Michigan City, IN, 46360. Tel: 219-879-3272. Fax: 219-879-3333. p. 758

Mathews, Ann E, Librn, Southwestern Virginia Mental Health Institute Library, 340 Bagley Circle, Marion, VA, 24354. Tel: 276-783-1200, Ext 161. Fax: 276-783-1247. p. 2477

Mathews, Barbara, Dir, Churchill County Library, 553 S Maine St, Fallon, NV, 89406-3387. Tel: 775-423-7581. Fax: 775-423-7766. p. 1427

Mathews, Carolyn, Acq, Worcester State College, 486 Chandler St, Worcester, MA, 01602-2597. Tel: 508-929-8647. Fax: 508-929-8198. p. 1145

Mathews, Janice, Soc Sci Librn, University of Connecticut Library, Harleigh B Trecker Library, 1800 Asylum Ave, West Hartford, CT, 06117. Tel: 860-570-9105. Fax: 860-570-9036. p. 371

Mathews, Janie, Tech Serv Librn, Spring Hill College, 4000 Dauphin St, Mobile, AL, 36608. Tel: 251-380-3870. Fax: jmathews@shc.edu. p. 26

Mathews, Mary, Bus Mgr, Catholic University of America, 620 Michigan Ave NE, 315 Mullen Library, Washington, DC, 20064. Tel: 202-319-5464. Fax: 202-319-4735. p. 395

Mathews, Nancy, Curator, Kenosha Public Museums Library, 5500 First Ave, Kenosha, WI, 53140. Tel: 262-653-4140, 262-653-4426. Fax: 262-653-4437. p. 2601

Mathews, Sandy, Principal Librn, Rancho Mirage Public Library, 71-100 Hwy 111, Rancho Mirage, CA, 92270. Tel: 760-341-7323. Fax: 760-341-5213. p. 213

Mathews, Susan, Tech Serv, Cochise County Library District, Old High School, 2nd Flr, 100 Clawson, Bisbee, AZ, 85603. Tel: 520-432-8930. Fax: 520-432-7339. p. 58

Mathews, Susan, Ref/Outreach Coordr, Harborfields Public Library, 31 Broadway, Greenlawn, NY, 11740-1382. Tel: 631-757-4200. Fax: 631-757-7216. p. 1631

Mathews, Wanda, Dir, Rush Oak Park Hospital Library, 520 S Maple, Oak Park, IL, 60304. Tel: 708-383-9300. Fax: 708-660-6480. p. 684

Mathewson, Amber, Managing Librn, Pima County Public Library, Joel D Valdez, 101 N Stone Ave, Tucson, AZ, 85701. Tel: 520-594-5500. Fax: 520-594-5501. p. 87

Mathewson, Kimberley, Librn, Middletown Springs Public Library, 39 West St, Middletown Springs, VT, 05757-4401. Tel: 802-235-2435. p. 2429

Mathias, Carol, Dir, Nicholls State University, 906 E First St, Thibodaux, LA, 70310. Tel: 985-448-4646, 985-448-4660. Fax: 985-448-4925. p. 971

Mathias, Molly, Coordr, Learning Commons, University of Wisconsin-Milwaukee Libraries, 2311 E Hartford Ave, Milwaukee, WI, 53211. Tel: 414-229-4785, 414-229-6202. Fax: 414-229-6766. p. 2622

Mathiasen, Elaine, Dir, Middleton Public Library, 307 Cornell St, Meridian, ID, 83644. Tel: 208-585-3931. p. 579

Mathies, Joyce, Br Librn, Pottawatomie Wabaunsee Regional Library, Alma Branch, 115 W Third St, Alma, KS, 66401. Tel: 785-765-3647. Fax: 785-765-3647. p. 892

Mathieson, Heather, ILL Supvr, University of Winnipeg Library, 515 Portage Ave, Winnipeg, MB, R3B 2E9, CANADA. Tel: 204-786-9801. Fax: 204-783-8910. p. 2759

Mathieu, Ann-Marie, Dep Dir, Planning & Support Serv, Saskatoon Public Library, 311-23rd St E, Saskatoon, SK, S7K 0J6, CANADA. Tel: 306-975-7586. Fax: 306-975-7542. p. 2926

Mathis, Eric, Adult Serv, South Georgia Regional Library System, 300 Woodrow Wilson Dr, Valdosta, GA, 31602-2592. Tel: 229-333-0086. Fax: 229-333-7669. p. 555

Mathis, Margaret, Librn, Vienna Carnegie Public Library, 401 Poplar St, Vienna, IL, 62995. Tel: 618-658-5051. Fax: 618-658-5051. p. 714

Mathis, Norma A, Dir, Oakdale Public Library, 212 Queen St, Oakdale, TN, 37829-3137. Tel: 423-369-2595, 423-369-3524. Fax: 423-369-2595. p. 2262

Mathis-Gleason, Lois, Employee Benefits Info Spec, International Foundation of Employee Benefit Plans, 18700 W Bluemound Rd, Brookfield, WI, 53045-2936. Tel: 262-786-6710, Ext 5. Fax: 262-786-8780. p. 2583

Mathis-Kull, Carlene, Librn, Deer Creek District Library, 205 First St, Deer Creek, IL, 61733. Tel: 309-447-6724. Fax: 309-447-6724. p. 634

Mathre, Valerie, Br Mgr, Clearwater Public Library System, North Greenwood, 905 N Martin Luther King Jr Ave, Clearwater, FL, 33755. Tel: 727-562-4970. p. 432

Mathur, Geeta, ILL, St Luke's-Roosevelt Hospital Center, 1111 Amsterdam Ave, New York, NY, 10025. Tel: 212-523-4315. Fax: 212-523-4313. p. 1699

Matiachuk, Richard, Pub Serv, Regent College, 5800 University Blvd, Vancouver, BC, V6T 2E4, CANADA. Tel: 604-221-3341. Fax: 604-224-3097. p. 2742

Matis, Lynn, Dir, State Transportation Library, Ten Park Plaza, Boston, MA, 02116. Tel: 617-973-8000. Fax: 617-973-7153. p. 1067

Matisko, Jody, Libr Asst II, New Hampshire State Library, Gallen State Office Park, Dolloff Bldg, 117 Pleasant St, Concord, NH, 03301-3852. Tel: 603-271-2417, 603-271-3429. Fax: 603-271-8370. p. 1443

Matkowski, Elizabeth, Info Serv Librn, Aurora University, 315 S Gladstone, Aurora, IL, 60506-4877. Tel: 630-844-5443. Fax: 630-844-3848. p. 591

Matlak, Andrea, Archivist, American Dental Association Department of Library Services, 211 E Chicago Ave, 6th Flr, Chicago, IL, 60611-2678. Tel: 312-440-2653. Fax: 312-440-2774. p. 605

Matlak, Jeff, Electronic Res Librn, Western Illinois University Libraries, One University Circle, Macomb, IL, 61455. Tel: 309-298-2720. Fax: 309-298-2791. p. 668

Matli, Becky, Br Supvr, Fresno County Public Library, 2420 Mariposa St, Fresno, CA, 93721-2285. Tel: 559-600-7323. p. 151

Matlin, Erin, Asst Dir, Amesbury Public Library, 149 Main St, Amesbury, MA, 01913. Tel: 978-388-8148. p. 1048

Matlin, Talitha, Assoc Dir, Libr Serv, Zoological Society of San Diego Library, Arnold & Mable Beckman Ctr for Conservation & Research for Endangered Species, San Diego, CA, 92112. Tel: 760-291-5479. Fax: 760-291-5478. p. 239

Matlow, Randy, Dir, Bullitt County Public Library, 127 N Walnut St, Shepherdsville, KY, 40165-6083. Tel: 502-543-7675. Fax: 502-543-5487. p. 935

Matney, Karen, Asst Br Mgr, Sullivan County Public Library, Bloomingdale Branch, 3230 Van Horn St, Kingsport, TN, 37660. Tel: 423-288-1310. Fax: 423-288-1310. p. 2224

Matochik, Michael J, Dir, Lee County Library, 107 Hawkins Ave, Sanford, NC, 27331-4399. Tel: 919-718-4665. Fax: 919-775-1832. p. 1823

Matos-Cabrera, Ana, Coll Develop Librn, Inter-American University of Puerto Rico, 104 Parque Industrial Turpeaux, Rd 1, Mercedita, PR, 00715-1602. Tel: 787-284-1912. Fax: 787-841-0103. p. 2674

Matott, Lynne H, Librn, Gouverneur Correctional Facility, Scott Settlement Rd, Gouverneur, NY, 13642. Tel: 315-287-7351, Ext 4600. Fax: 315-287-7351, Ext 3299. p. 1629

Matott, Roma, Syst Librn, Pioneer Library System, 2557 State Rte 21, Canandaigua, NY, 14424. Tel: 585-394-8260. Fax: 585-394-1935. p. 1601

Matott, Susan, Asst Dir, Ch, Pillsbury Free Library, 18 E Main St, Warner, NH, 03278. Tel: 603-456-2289. Fax: 603-456-3177. p. 1467

Matreci, Sandy, In Charge, Team Four, Inc Library, 14 N Newstead Ave, Saint Louis, MO, 63108. Tel: 314-533-2200. Fax: 314-533-2203. p. 1361

Matsil, Kathie, Ch, Meriden Public Library, 105 Miller St, Meriden, CT, 06450. Tel: 203-630-6347. Fax: 203-238-3647. p. 350

Matson, Christine, Ref & Instruction Librn, Guam Community College, One Sesame St, Mangilao, GU, 96921. Tel: 671-735-0231. p. 2667

Matson, Diana, Acq, SUNY Westchester Community College, 75 Grasslands Rd, Valhalla, NY, 10595-1693. Tel: 914-606-6819. Fax: 914-785-6513. p. 1760

Matsoukas, Konstantina, Educ Coordr, Head, Ref, Columbia University, Augustus C Long Health Sciences Library, 701 W 168th St, Lobby Level, New York, NY, 10032. Tel: 212-305-3605. Fax: 212-234-0595. p. 1675

Matsui, Dorothy, Ch, Everett Public Library, 2702 Hoyt Ave, Everett, WA, 98201-3556. Tel: 425-257-8030. Fax: 425-257-8017. p. 2515

Matsukawa, Norma, Info Literacy Librn, Leeward Community College Library, 96-045 Ala Ike, Pearl City, HI, 96782-3393. Tel: 808-455-0390. Fax: 808-453-6729. p. 567

Matsumoto, Lisa Anne, Librn, Hawaii State Hospital, 45-710 Keaahala Rd, Kaneohe, HI, 96744-3528. Tel: 808-236-8201. Fax: 808-247-7335. p. 566

Matsuoka-Motley, Nobue, Music & Performing Arts Librn, American University Library, Music Library, Katzen Arts Center, Rm 150, 4400 Massachusetts Ave NW, Washington, DC, 20016-8046. Tel: 202-885-3465. Fax: 202-885-3226. p. 393

Matsushita, Karl K, Dir, Japanese American National Library, 1619 Sutter St, San Francisco, CA, 94109. Tel: 415-567-5006. p. 243

Mattan, Erin, Pub Serv & IT, Troy-Miami County Public Library, 419 W Main St, Troy, OH, 45373. Tel: 937-339-0502. Fax: 937-335-4880. p. 1941

Matte, David, Ref Archivist, Idaho State Historical Society, Idaho History Ctr, 2205 Old Penitentiary Rd, Boise, ID, 83712. Tel: 208-334-3356. Fax: 208-334-3198. p. 571

Matte, Lisa M, Dir, Jervis Public Library Association, Inc, 613 N Washington St, Rome, NY, 13440-4296. Tel: 315-336-4570. p. 1734

Mattei, Coral, Tech Serv Supvr, Northwest Nazarene University, 623 University Blvd, Nampa, ID, 83686. Tel: 208-467-8605. Fax: 208-467-8610. p. 580

Mattei, Danielle, Head, Ch, Conant Public Library, Four Meetinghouse Hill Rd, Sterling, MA, 01564. Tel: 978-422-6409. Fax: 978-422-6643. p. 1128

Mattei, Janet A, Dr, Dir, American Association of Variable Star Observers, 25 Birch St, Cambridge, MA, 02138. Tel: 617-354-0484. Fax: 617-354-0665. p. 1072

Matteo, Christine, Chief, Admin, Ocean County Library, 101 Washington St, Toms River, NJ, 08753. Tel: 732-914-5402. p. 1534

Matter, Mary, ILL & Circ Spec, Whatcom County Library System, 5205 Northwest Dr, Bellingham, WA, 98226-9050. Tel: 360-384-3150. Fax: 360-384-4947. p. 2509

Mattern, Susan, ILL, Lehigh Carbon Community College Library, 4525 Education Park Dr, Schnecksville, PA, 18078-9372. Tel: 610-799-1163. Fax: 610-779-1159. p. 2136

Matteson, Miriam, Asst Prof, Kent State University, 314 Library, Kent, OH, 44242-0001. Tel: 330-672-2782. Fax: 330-672-7965. p. 2972

Mattfield, Marcia, Dir, Negaunee Public Library, 319 W Case St, Negaunee, MI, 49866. Tel: 906-475-9400, Ext 18. Fax: 906-475-4880. p. 1213

Mattheis, Mark E, Dir, Wilberforce University, 1055 N Bickett Rd, Wilberforce, OH, 45384-5801. Tel: 937-708-5024. Fax: 937-708-5771. p. 1948

Matthes, Marilyn, Dir, Collier County Public Library, 2385 Orange Blossom Dr, Naples, FL, 34109. Tel: 239-593-0334. Fax: 239-254-8167. p. 471

Matthew, Judy, Head, Per, William Paterson University of New Jersey, 300 Pompton Rd, Wayne, NJ, 07470. Tel: 973-720-2346. Fax: 973-720-3171. p. 1540

Matthew, Steven, Access Serv, Florida Atlantic University, 777 Glades Rd, Boca Raton, FL, 33431. Tel: 561-297-4027. Fax: 561-297-2189. p. 428

Matthewman, Anne C, Mgr, Toronto Lawyers Association Library, Courthouse, 361 University Ave, Toronto, ON, M5G 1T3, CANADA. Tel: 416-327-5700. Fax: 416-947-9148. p. 2859

Matthews, Allison, Educ & Ref Librn, SEAHEC Medical Library, 2131 S 17th St, Box 9025, Wilmington, NC, 28402-9025. Tel: 910-343-2180. Fax: 910-762-7600. p. 1831

Matthews, Barbara, Sr Cat Librn, Tulane University, Law Library, 6329 Freret St, New Orleans, LA, 70118-6231. Tel: 504-862-8867. Fax: 504-865-5917. p. 963

Matthews, Barbara, Circ Supvr, Memphis Public Library, Poplar-White Station, 5094 Poplar, Memphis, TN, 38117-7629. Tel: 901-415-2777. Fax: 901-682-8975. p. 2250

Matthews, Cheryl, Ch, Librn I, Dobbs Ferry Public Library, 55 Main St, Dobbs Ferry, NY, 10522. Tel: 914-693-6615. Fax: 914-693-4671. p. 1615

Matthews, Christine, Librn, Bread for the World Library, 425 Third St SW, Ste 1200, Washington, DC, 20024. Tel: 202-639-9400. p. 394

Matthews, David, Librn, Bear Lake County Free Library, Paris Branch, 62 S Main, Paris, ID, 83261. Tel: 208-945-2253. Fax: 208-945-1327. p. 579

Matthews, David, Ref/Instruction Librn, Fairmont State University, 1201 Locust Ave, Fairmont, WV, 26554. Tel: 304-367-4618. Fax: 304-367-4677. p. 2559

Matthews, Dawn, Br Mgr, Saint Joseph County Public Library, Centre Township Branch, 1150 E Kern Rd, South Bend, IN, 46614. Tel: 574-251-3700. p. 779

Matthews, Deborah, Adult Serv, Troy-Miami County Public Library, 419 W Main St, Troy, OH, 45373. Tel: 937-339-0502. Fax: 937-335-4880. p. 1941

Matthews, Deborah, Br Mgr, Troy-Miami County Public Library, Oakes-Beitman Memorial, 12 N Main St, Pleasant Hill, OH, 45359-0811. Tel: 937-676-2731. Fax: 937-676-2731. p. 1941

Matthews, Diana, Ref Librn, Santa Fe Community College, 3000 NW 83rd St, Bldg Y-100, Gainesville, FL, 32606. Tel: 352-395-5406. Fax: 352-395-5102. p. 449

Matthews, Donnajean, Dir, Libr Serv, Southern California College of Optometry, 2575 Yorba Linda Blvd, Fullerton, CA, 92831-1699. Tel: 714-449-7440. Fax: 714-879-0481. p. 154

Matthews, Elois, Ref, Moultrie-Colquitt County Library, 204 Fifth St SE, Moultrie, GA, 31768. Tel: 229-985-6540. Fax: 229-985-0936. p. 545

Matthews, Helen, Librn, Atlanta History Center, 3101 Andrews Dr NW, Atlanta, GA, 30305. Tel: 404-814-4048. Fax: 404-814-4175. p. 513

Matthews, James E, Coll Develop, Ref, Chabot College Library, 25555 Hesperian Blvd, Hayward, CA, 94545. p. 157

Matthews, Jane, Acq, Head, Cat, Peach Public Libraries, 315 Martin Luther King Jr Dr, Fort Valley, GA, 31030-4196. Tel: 478-825-1640. Fax: 478-825-2061. p. 533

Matthews, Jeannine, Circ Mgr, Pine Bluff & Jefferson County Library System, Main Library, 200 E Eighth Ave, Pine Bluff, AR, 71601. Tel: 870-534-4802. Fax: 870-534-8707. p. 112

Matthews, Joanne, Acq Librn, University of Northern British Columbia Library, 333 University Way, Prince George, BC, V2N 4Z9, CANADA. Tel: 250-960-6615. Fax: 250-960-6610. p. 2736

Matthews, Kathy, Librn, Elias, Matz, Tiernan & Herrick LLP, 734 15th St NW, 11th Flr, Washington, DC, 20005. Tel: 202-347-0300. Fax: 202-347-2172. p. 399

Matthews, Kimberley, Ch, Williamsburg County Library, 215 N Jackson, Kingstree, SC, 29556-3319. Tel: 843-355-9486. Fax: 843-355-9991. p. 2198

Matthews, Kimberly, Dir, Trenton Free Public Library, 120 Academy St, Trenton, NJ, 08608-1302. Tel: 609-392-7188. Fax: 609-396-7655. p. 1536

Matthews, Letitia M, Libr Tech, United States Army, Public Health Command Library, 5158 Blackhawk Rd, BLDG E-5158, Aberdeen Proving Ground, MD, 21010-5403. Tel: 410-436-4236. Fax: 410-436-4602. p. 1009

Matthews, Lisa, ILL, Robeson County Public Library, 101 N Chestnut St, Lumberton, NC, 28358-5639. Tel: 910-738-4859. Fax: 910-739-8321. p. 1808

Matthews, Lisa, Mgr, Robeson County Public Library, Rowland Public, 113 E Main St, Rowland, NC, 28383. p. 1808

Matthews, Lisa, Mgr, Rowland Public Library, 113 W Main St, Rowland, NC, 28383. Tel: 910-422-3996. p. 1821

Matthews, Londa L, Br Mgr, Audubon Regional Library, Jackson Branch, 3312 College St, Jackson, LA, 70748. Tel: 225-634-7408. Fax: 225-634-5896. p. 947

Matthews, Lucille, Librn, First Baptist Church, 218 N Magnolia, Luling, TX, 78648-2342. Tel: 830-875-2227. p. 2358

Matthews, Mary, Ref Serv Librn, Douglas College Library, 700 Royal Ave, New Westminster, BC, V3M 5Z5, CANADA. Tel: 604-527-5438. Fax: 604-527-5193. p. 2733

Matthews, Melinda, ILL, University of Louisiana at Monroe Library, 700 University Ave, Monroe, LA, 71209-0720. Tel: 318-342-1051. Fax: 318-342-1075. p. 958

Matthews, Michael E, Head, Ser & Media, ILL, Northwestern State University Libraries, 913 University Pkwy, Natchitoches, LA, 71497. Tel: 318-357-4406. Fax: 318-357-4470. p. 958

Matthews, Peggy, Br Mgr, Librn, Warner Public Library, 207 Eighth St, Warner, OK, 74469. Tel: 918-463-2363. Fax: 918-463-2711. p. 1985

Matthews, Ray, Govt Info Coordr, Utah State Library Division, 250 N 1950 West, Ste A, Salt Lake City, UT, 84116-7901. Tel: 801-715-6752. Fax: 801-715-6767. p. 2415

Matthews, Robert, Bibliog Instr, Hudson Valley Community College, 80 Vandenburgh Ave, Troy, NY, 12180. Tel: 518-629-7392. Fax: 518-629-7509. p. 1756

Matthews, Sarah, Ch, Wadsworth Library, 24 Center St, Geneseo, NY, 14454. Tel: 585-243-0440. Fax: 585-243-0429. p. 1627

Matthews, Sasha, Br Mgr, Chesapeake Public Library, Indian River, 2320 Old Greenbrier Rd, Chesapeake, VA, 23325-4916. Tel: 757-410-7007. Fax: 757-410-7014. p. 2456

Matthews, Shelley, Br Mgr, Rochester Public Library, Charlotte, 3557 Lake Ave, Rochester, NY, 14612. Tel: 585-428-8216. p. 1732

Matthews, Shelley, Br Mgr, Rochester Public Library, Maplewood, 1111 Dewey Ave, Rochester, NY, 14613. Tel: 585-428-8220. p. 1732

Matthews, Tansy, Assoc Dir, Virtual Library of Virginia, George Mason University, Fenwick B222, Fairfax, VA, 22030. Tel: 703-993-2694. Fax: 703-993-4662. p. 2957

Matthews, Vonnie, Dir, Santa Rosa Press Democrat, 427 Mendocino Ave, Santa Rosa, CA, 95401-6385. Tel: 707-526-8520. Fax: 707-521-5411. p. 267

Matthias, Jeffrey, Asst Dir, Jefferson Community & Technical College, 109 E Broadway, Louisville, KY, 40202. Tel: 502-213-2467. p. 924

Matthies, Brad, Access Serv, Butler University Libraries, 4600 Sunset Ave, Indianapolis, IN, 46208. Tel: 317-940-9549. Fax: 317-940-9711. p. 749

Matthies, Margo, Librn, Walnut Public Library, 224 Antique City Dr, Walnut, IA, 51577-0347. Tel: 712-784-3533. p. 849

Matticks, Rebecca, Dir, Hastings Museum of Natural & Cultural History Library, 1330 N Burlington, Hastings, NE, 68901. Tel: 402-461-2399. Fax: 402-461-2379. p. 1401

Mattimoe, Jean, Ref & Coll Develop Librn, University of Idaho Library, College of Law, 711 Rayburn St, Moscow, ID, 83844. Tel: 208-885-2162. Fax: 208-885-2743. p. 580

Mattingley, Will, Librn, Greenebaum, Doll & McDonald, 3500 National City Tower, Louisville, KY, 40202-3140. Tel: 502-589-4200. Fax: 502-587-3695. p. 923

Mattingly, Eric, Asst Dir, Breckinridge County Public Library, 112 S Main St, Hardinsburg, KY, 40143. Tel: 270-756-2323. Fax: 270-756-5634. p. 915

Mattingly, Melinda, Coll Mgr, Mgr, Ref Serv, Boulder Public Library, 1001 Arapahoe Rd, Boulder, CO, 80302. Tel: 303-441-3100. Fax: 303-442-1808. p. 290

Mattingly, Sue, Librn, Little Dixie Regional Libraries, Dulany Memorial, 101 N Main, Paris, MO, 65275-1398. Tel: 660-327-4707. Fax: 660-327-4094. p. 1346

Mattis, George, Asst Librn, Wytheville Community College Library, 1000 E Main St, Wytheville, VA, 24382. Tel: 276-223-4744. Fax: 276-223-4745. p. 2505

Mattison, Mark, Dir of Advan, University of Missouri-Kansas City Libraries, 800 E 51st St, Kansas City, MO, 64110. Tel: 816-235-5828. Fax: 816-333-5584. p. 1341

Mattix, Cathy, Genealogy Librn, Bartlett-Carnegie Sapulpa Public Library, 27 W Dewey, Sapulpa, OK, 74066. Tel: 918-224-5624. Fax: 918-224-3546. p. 1977

Mattlage, Alan, Head of Libr, University of Maryland Libraries, Architecture Library, College Park, MD, 20742-7011. Tel: 301-405-6317. Fax: 301-314-9583. p. 1025

Mattox, Gayle, Librn, Sargent Township Library, 504 Main St, Sargent, NE, 68874. Tel: 308-527-4241. p. 1418

Mattox, Sherie, Coordr, Alabama Power Co, 600 N 18th St, Birmingham, AL, 35203-2206. Tel: 205-257-4466. Fax: 205-257-2075. p. 6

Mattox, Zarita, Br Mgr, Ocean County Library, Lakewood Branch, 301 Lexington Ave, Lakewood, NJ, 08701. Tel: 732-363-1435. Fax: 732-363-1438. p. 1534

Matts, Constance, Dir, Res Serv, Faegre Baker Daniels Library, 300 N Meridian St, Ste 2700, Indianapolis, IN, 46204. Tel: 317-237-0300, Ext 1353. Fax: 317-237-1000. p. 751

Mattson, Bonnie, Dir, Lisbon Public Library, 409 Forest St, Lisbon, ND, 58054. Tel: 701-683-5174. Fax: 701-683-5174. p. 1845

Mattson, LaVonne, Librn, Ogema Public Library, W 5005 State Rd 86, Ogema, WI, 54459. Tel: 715-767-5130. Fax: 715-767-5130. p. 2627

Mattson, Leila, Head, Ref (Info Serv), Great Neck Library, 159 Bayview Ave, Great Neck, NY, 11023-1938. Tel: 516-466-8055. Fax: 516-829-8297. p. 1630

Mattson, Paul, Exec Dir, Libr & Info Serv, Luther College, 700 College Dr, Decorah, IA, 52101. Tel: 563-387-1717. Fax: 563-387-1657. p. 807

Mattson, Stuart, Dir, Prescott Valley Public Library, 7401 E Civic Circle, Prescott Valley, AZ, 86314. Tel: 928-759-3040. Fax: 928-759-3121. p. 79

Mattucci, Wilma, Mgr, Gilchrist County Public Library, 105 NE 11th Ave, Trenton, FL, 32693-3803. Tel: 352-463-3176. Fax: 352-463-3164. p. 500

Matty, Paul, Librn, Pima County Public Works Library, 201 N Stone Ave, Tucson, AZ, 85701. Tel: 520-740-6818. Fax: 520-623-5411. p. 87

Matucheski, Michele, Librn, Mercy Medical Center, 500 S Oakwood Rd, Oshkosh, WI, 54903. Tel: 920-223-0340. Fax: 920-223-0343. p. 2627

Matula, Richard A, Info Spec, Kenyon & Kenyon LLP, One Broadway, 10th Flr, New York, NY, 10004-1007. Tel: 212-908-6123. Fax: 212-908-6113. p. 1684

Matulewicz, Carolynn, Ch, Peninsula Public Library, 280 Central Ave, Lawrence, NY, 11559. Tel: 516-239-3262. Fax: 516-239-8425. p. 1651

Matulka, Carol, Dir, Librn, Pratt Community College, 348 NE State Rd 61, Pratt, KS, 67124. Tel: 620-450-2253. Fax: 620-672-2519. p. 891

Matulka, Denise, Cataloger, Librn, American Historical Society of Germans from Russia, 631 D St, Lincoln, NE, 68502-1199. Tel: 402-474-3363. Fax: 402-474-7229. p. 1404

Matulka, Denise I, Librn, Lincoln Journal Star Library, 926 P St, Lincoln, NE, 68508. Tel: 402-473-7297. Fax: 402-473-7291. p. 1405

Maturi, Donna, Head, Ref (Info Serv), Peabody Institute Library of Danvers, 15 Sylvan St, Danvers, MA, 01923-2735. Tel: 978-774-0554. Fax: 978-762-0251. p. 1083

Matusz, Anne M, Adult Serv, Peninsula Library & Historical Society, 6105 Riverview Rd, Peninsula, OH, 44264. Tel: 330-657-2291. Fax: 330-657-2311. p. 1928

Matuszak, Mary E, Dir, Libr Serv, New York County District Attorney's Office Library, One Hogan Pl, New York, NY, 10013. Tel: 212-335-4292. Fax: 212-335-4266. p. 1689

Matuszek, Michael, Mgr, King & Spalding, 1180 Peachtree St NE, Flr 17, Atlanta, GA, 30309. Tel: 404-572-4600, Ext 3300. Fax: 404-572-5123. p. 516

Matveyeva, Susan, Cat & Metadata, Wichita State University Libraries, 1845 Fairmount, Wichita, KS, 67260-0068. Tel: 316-978-5139. Fax: 316-978-3048. p. 902

Matyas, Cathy, Chief Exec Officer, Brampton Library, 65 Queen St E, Brampton, ON, L6W 3L6, CANADA. Tel: 905-793-4636, Ext 4311. Fax: 905-453-0810. p. 2796

Matyas, Cathy, Chief Librn, Waterloo Public Library, 35 Albert St, Waterloo, ON, N2L 5E2, CANADA. Tel: 519-886-1310. Fax: 519-886-7936. p. 2870

Matyas, Linda, Circ Serv, Per, Jacksonville University, 2800 University Blvd N, Jacksonville, FL, 32211-3394. Tel: 904-256-7274. Fax: 904-256-7259. p. 454

Matyn, Marian, Archivist, Central Michigan University, Clarke Historical Library, 250 E Preston, Mount Pleasant, MI, 48859. Tel: 989-774-3990. Fax: 989-774-2160. p. 1211

Matzen, George, Dir, Webermeier Memorial Public Library, 617 Second St, Milford, NE, 68405. Tel: 402-761-2937. Fax: 402-761-2937. p. 1408

Matzen, Nita, Dr, Prof, Appalachian State University, RCOE, Dept of LES, 311 Edwin Duncan Hall, Boone, NC, 28608. Tel: 828-262-7236. Fax: 828-262-6035. p. 2971

Mau, Catherine, Dep Dir, Durham County Library, 300 N Roxboro St, Durham, NC, 27701. Tel: 919-560-0168. Fax: 919-560-0137. p. 1788

Mau, Margaret, Chief Exec Officer, Pembroke Public Library, 237 Victoria St, Pembroke, ON, K8A 4K5, CANADA. Tel: 613-732-9178, Ext 3. Fax: 613-732-1116. p. 2835

Maubourquette, Stacy, Res Mgt Supvr, Northeastern University Libraries, Snell Library, 360 Huntington Ave, Boston, MA, 02115. Tel: 617-373-4974. p. 1065

Maud, Pam, Mgr, Lake County Public Library, Dyer-Schererville Branch, 1001 W Lincoln Hwy, Schererville, IN, 46375-1552. Tel: 219-322-4731. Fax: 219-865-5478. p. 764

Maud, Pam, Mgr, Lake County Public Library, Saint John Branch, 9450 Wicker Dr, Saint John, IN, 46373-9646. Tel: 219-365-5379. Fax: 219-365-5963. p. 764

Mauer, Bud, Dir, Duval County Law Library, 330 E Bay St, Rm 102, Jacksonville, FL, 32202. Tel: 904-630-2560. Fax: 904-630-2309. p. 452

Mauer, J David, Dir, University of Rio Grande, 218 N College Ave, Rio Grande, OH, 45674. Tel: 740-245-7005. Fax: 740-245-7096. p. 1931

Mauer, Judy, Acq, Chinook Regional Library, 1240 Chaplin St W, Swift Current, SK, S9H 0G8, CANADA. Tel: 306-773-3186. Fax: 306-773-0434. p. 2927

Mauer, Peg, Head Librn, Goff-Nelson Memorial Library, 41 Lake St, Tupper Lake, NY, 12986. Tel: 518-359-9421. Fax: 518-359-9421. p. 1757

Mauerhoff, Petra, Chief Librn, Eastern Counties Regional Library, 390 Murray St, Mulgrave, NS, B0E 2G0, CANADA. Tel: 902-747-2597. Fax: 902-747-2500. p. 2783

Maughan, Brian, Sr Librn, California Department of Corrections Library System, California Institution for Men, 14901 S Central Ave, Chino, CA, 91710. Tel: 909-597-1821, Ext 4350, 909-597-1821, Ext 4368. Fax: 909-606-7012. p. 221

Maughan, Brian, Sr Librn, California Department of Corrections Library System, California Institution for Women, 17656 Chino-Corona Rd, Corona, CA, 92880. Tel: 909-597-1771, Ext 6488. Fax: 909-606-4936. p. 221

Maughan, Christopher, Sr Librn, California Department of Corrections Library System, California Institution for Men, 14901 S Central Ave, Chino, CA, 91710. Tel: 909-597-1821, Ext 4350, 909-597-1821, Ext 4368. Fax: 909-606-7012. p. 221

Mauk, Janette, Spec Coll Librn, Pittsburg State University, 1605 S Joplin St, Pittsburg, KS, 66762-5889. Tel: 620-235-4883. Fax: 620-235-4090. p. 890

Mauldin, Patricia, Librn, Lexington County Public Library System, Chapin Branch, 129 NW Columbia Ave, Chapin, SC, 29036-9423. Tel: 803-345-5479. p. 2199

Mauldin-Ware, Alicia, Curator of Archives, United States Military Academy Library, Jefferson Hall Library & Learning Center, 758 Cullum Rd, West Point, NY, 10996. Tel: 845-938-3833. Fax: 845-938-4000. p. 1767

Maule, Susan, Dir, Mondamin Public Library, 201 Maple St, Mondamin, IA, 51557. Tel: 712-646-2888. p. 832

Maupin, Donald, Cat, Robert L Williams Public Library, 323 W Beech, Durant, OK, 74701. Tel: 580-924-3486. Fax: 580-924-8843. p. 1962

Maupin, Rita, Dir, Calhoun County Public Library, 17731 NE Pear St, Blountstown, FL, 32424. Tel: 850-674-8773. Fax: 850-674-2843. p. 427

Maura-Sardo, Mariano, Prof, University of Puerto Rico, Rio Piedras Campus, PO Box 21906, San Juan, PR, 00931-1906. Tel: 787-764-0000, Ext 1286, 787-764-0000, Ext 5028. Fax: 787-764-2311. p. 2977

Maurel, Dominique, Asst Prof, Universite de Montreal, 3150, rue Jean-Brillant, bur C-2004, Montreal, QC, H3T 1N8, CANADA. Tel: 514-343-6044. Fax: 514-343-5753. p. 2979

Maurer, Bradley, Br Librn, Davis County Library, Centerville Branch, 45 S 400 West, Centerville, UT, 84014. Tel: 801-294-4054. p. 2405

Maurer, David, Ad, Flat Rock Public Library, 25200 Gibraltar Rd, Flat Rock, MI, 48134. Tel: 734-782-2430. Fax: 734-789-8265. p. 1178

Maurer, Donna, Children's & Teen Serv Coordr, Larchwood Public Library, 1020 Broadway, Larchwood, IA, 51241. Tel: 712-477-2583. Fax: 712-477-2366. p. 827

Maurer, Jenny, Libr Tech Serv Mgr, Roger & Peggy Madigan Library, 999 Hagan Way, Williamsport, PA, 17701. Tel: 570-327-4523. Fax: 570-327-4503. p. 2156

Maurer, Margaret, Head, Cat, Kent State University Libraries, 1125 Risman Dr, Kent, OH, 44242. Tel: 330-672-1702. Fax: 330-672-4811. p. 1907

Maurer, Pat, Ref Serv, Venice Public Library, 300 S Nokomis Ave, Venice, FL, 34285-2416. Tel: 941-861-1330. Fax: 941-486-2345. p. 501

Maurer, Rozann, Dir, Rockford Carnegie Library, 162 S Main St, Rockford, OH, 45882-9260. Tel: 419-363-2630. Fax: 419-363-3723. p. 1932

Maurer, Willadean, Librn, Minatare Public Library, 309 Main St, Minatare, NE, 69356. Tel: 308-783-1414. Fax: 308-783-1414. p. 1408

Maurins, Arnold, Dir, Washoe County Library System, 301 S Center St, Reno, NV, 89501-2102. Tel: 775-327-8340. p. 1433

Mauro, Clare, Ref Librn, Torys LLP Library, 79 Wellington St W, Ste 3000, Toronto, ON, M5K 1N2, CANADA. Tel: 416-945-7704. Fax: 416-865-7380. p. 2864

Mauro, Sylvia, Ref Serv, Canadian Museum of Civilization Library, 100 Laurier St, Gatineau, QC, K1A 0M8, CANADA. Tel: 819-776-8479. Fax: 819-776-7152. p. 2883

Maus, Moira S, Dir, Curtis Township Library, 4884 Bamfield Rd, Glennie, MI, 48737. Tel: 989-735-2601. Fax: 989-735-2601. p. 1183

Maus, Nancy, Dir, Colwich Community Library, 432 W Colwich, Colwich, KS, 67030. Tel: 316-796-1521. p. 862

Maus, Patricia, Curator, Northeast Minnesota Historical Center, University of Minnesota-Duluth Library, 416 Library Dr, Annex 202, Duluth, MN, 55812. Tel: 218-726-8526. Fax: 218-726-6205. p. 1248

Maust, Patricia, Coordr, Youth Serv, Way Public Library, 101 E Indiana Ave, Perrysburg, OH, 43551. Tel: 419-874-3135, Ext 112. Fax: 419-874-6129. p. 1929

Mausteller, Bill, Asst Dir, Norwin Public Library Association Inc, 100 Caruthers Ln, Irwin, PA, 15642. Tel: 724-863-4700. Fax: 724-863-6195. p. 2072

Maute, Betty, Dir, Fulton Public Library, 160 S First St, Fulton, NY, 13069. Tel: 315-592-5159. Fax: 315-592-4504. p. 1625

Mauter, Gudion, Librn, Albuquerque-Bernalillo County Library System, South Broadway, 1025 Broadway Blvd SE, Albuquerque, NM, 87102. Tel: 505-764-1742. Fax: 505-764-1783. p. 1548

Mauzy, Carolyn, Ref, University of Dallas, 1845 E Northgate Dr, Irving, TX, 75062-4736. Tel: 972-721-5350. Fax: 972-721-4010. p. 2347

Mavodza, Judith, Head, Ref, ILL, Metropolitan College of New York Library, 431 Canal St, 12th Flr, New York, NY, 10013. Tel: 212-343-1234, Ext 2001. Fax: 212-343-7398. p. 1686

Mavor, Susan, Head, Spec Coll, University of Waterloo Library, 200 University Ave W, Waterloo, ON, N2L 3G1, CANADA. Tel: 519-888-4567, Ext 33122. Fax: 519-888-4320. p. 2869

Mavrinac, Mary Ann, Dean of Libr, Vice Provost, Andrew H & Janet Dayton Neilly, University of Rochester, River Campus Libraries, 755 Library Rd, Rochester, NY, 14627-0055. Tel: 585-275-4461. Fax: 585-273-5309. p. 1733

Mavrinac, Mary Ann, Dean, University of Rochester, Physics-Optics-Astronomy Library - River Campus, 374 Bausch & Lomb Hall, Rochester, NY, 14627-0171. Tel: 585-275-4469. Fax: 585-273-5321. p. 1733

Maw, Mary, Dir, Communications, Caledon Public Library, 150 Queen St S, Bolton, ON, L7E 1E3, CANADA. Tel: 905-857-1400. Fax: 905-857-8280. p. 2795

Mawby, Peg, Head Librn, Capital Area District Libraries, Webberville Library, 115 S Main St, Webberville, MI, 48892. Tel: 517-521-3643. Fax: 517-521-1079. p. 1200

Mawhinney, David, Univ Archivist, Mount Allison University Libraries & Archives, 49 York St, Sackville, NB, E4L 1C6, CANADA. Tel: 506-364-2691. Fax: 506-364-2617. p. 2766

Maxell, Alison, Exec Dir, Providence Athenaeum, 251 Benefit St, Providence, RI, 02903-2799. Tel: 401-421-6970. Fax: 401-421-2860. p. 2173

Maxey, Cindy, Librn, Rose Hill Public Library, 306 N Rose Hill Rd, Rose Hill, KS, 67133. Tel: 316-776-3013. p. 892

Maxey, Cindy, Head, Adult Serv, Shaker Heights Public Library, 16500 Van Aken Blvd, Shaker Heights, OH, 44120-5318. Tel: 216-991-2030. Fax: 216-991-5951. p. 1934

Maxfield, Cecil, Libr Serv Supvr/Cat, Keene State College, 229 Main St, Keene, NH, 03435-3201. Tel: 603-358-2758. Fax: 603-358-2745. p. 1453

Maxfield, Lisa, Supvr, Circ, Dartmouth College Library, Feldberg Business Administration & Engineering Library, 6193 Murdough Ctr, Hanover, NH, 03755-3560. Tel: 603-646-2191. Fax: 603-646-2384. p. 1450

Maxfield, Patrick, Tech Serv, New England Conservatory of Music, 33 Gainsborough St, Boston, MA, 02115. Tel: 617-585-1256. Fax: 617-585-1245. p. 1064

Maxfield, Sandy, Assoc Dean of Libr & Educ Tech, James Madison University Libraries & Educational Technologies, 800 S Main St, Harrisonburg, VA, 22807-0001. Tel: 540-568-6923. Fax: 540-568-6339. p. 2470

Maxfield-Ontko, Pamela, Librn, Holmes County Law Library, Court House, Ste 204, 1-E Jackson St, Millersburg, OH, 44654. Tel: 330-763-2956. Fax: 330-763-2957. p. 1918

Maxham, Judy, Ref Serv, Amherst County Public Library, 382 S Main St, Amherst, VA, 24521. Tel: 434-946-9488. Fax: 434-946-9348. p. 2447

Maxham, Marjorie P, Librn, Braintree Historical Society, Inc Library, 85 Quincey Ave, Braintree, MA, 02184-4416. Tel: 781-843-1518. Fax: 781-380-0731. p. 1069

Maxon, Nancy, YA Serv, Harper Woods Public Library, 19601 Harper, Harper Woods, MI, 48225-2001. Tel: 313-343-2575. Fax: 313-343-2127. p. 1188

Maxson, Adele, Campus Librn, Mohave Community College Library, Kingman Campus, 1971 Jagerson Ave, Kingman, AZ, 86401. Tel: 928-757-0802. Fax: 928-757-0871. p. 66

Maxson, Adele, Librn, Mohave Community College Library, 1971 Jagerson Ave, Kingman, AZ, 86409-1238. Tel: 928-757-4331. Fax: 928-757-0896. p. 66

Maxson, Kathleen, Ref Librn II, Nova Southeastern University Libraries, William S Richardson Library, Oceanographic Center, 8000 N Ocean Dr, Dania Beach, FL, 33004. Tel: 954-262-3643, 954-262-3681. Fax: 954-262-4021. p. 444

Maxson, Mike, Librn, Flat River Community Library, 200 W Judd St, Greenville, MI, 48838-2225. Tel: 616-754-6359. Fax: 616-754-1398. p. 1186

Maxstadt, John, Head, Pub Serv, Texas A&M International University, 5201 University Blvd, Laredo, TX, 78041-1900. Tel: 956-326-2116. Fax: 956-326-2399. p. 2354

Maxted, Lawrence, Coll Develop, Gannon University, 109 University Sq, Erie, PA, 16541. Tel: 814-871-7557. Fax: 814-871-5666. p. 2055

Maxwell, Brenda, Mgr, Cape Sable Historical Society Archives & Library, 2402 Hwy 3, Barrington, NS, B0W 1E0, CANADA. Tel: 902-637-2185. Fax: 902-637-2185. p. 2778

Maxwell, Caitlan, Electronic Rec Archivist, Montana Historical Society, 225 N Roberts St, Helena, MT, 59601-4514. Tel: 406-444-4770. Fax: 406-444-5297. p. 1382

Maxwell, Carol, Head, Tech Serv, Canizaro Library at Ave Maria University, 5251 Avila Ave, Ave Maria, FL, 34142. Tel: 239-280-1687. p. 426

Maxwell, Carol, ILL, Ref, Stevenson University Library, 1525 Greenspring Valley Rd, Stevenson, MD, 21153. Tel: 443-334-2535. Fax: 410-486-7329. p. 1043

Maxwell, Carol, Librn, Public Utility Commission of Texas Library, 1701 N Congress, 7th Flr, Austin, TX, 78701. Tel: 512-936-7075. Fax: 512-936-7079. p. 2281

Maxwell, Cathy, Head, Pub Serv, Bibliotheque de Beaconsfield, 303 Boulevard, Beaconsfield, QC, H9W 4A7, CANADA. Tel: 514-428-4460. Fax: 514-428-4477. p. 2880

Maxwell, Connie, Asst Dean, Libr, Texas Woman's University Libraries, 304 Administration Dr, Denton, TX, 76204. Tel: 940-898-3707. Fax: 940-898-3764. p. 2312

Maxwell, Daniel, Electronic Res, Southern Adventist University, 4851 Industrial Dr, Collegedale, TN, 37315. Tel: 423-236-2009. Fax: 423-236-1788. p. 2230

Maxwell, David, Info Tech, University of Northern Colorado Libraries, 501 20th St, Greeley, CO, 80639. Tel: 970-351-2601. Fax: 970-351-2963. p. 312

Maxwell, Donna, ILL, Waupun Public Library, 123 S Forest St, Waupun, WI, 53963. Tel: 920-324-7925. p. 2646

Maxwell, Gloria, Librn, Metropolitan Community College, Penn Valley Community College Library, 3201 SW Trafficway, Kansas City, MO, 64111-2764. Tel: 816-759-4290. p. 1339

Maxwell, J R, Librn, Delaware County Law Library Association, 20 W Central Ave, Delaware, OH, 43015. Tel: 740-833-2545. Fax: 740-833-2548. p. 1895

Maxwell, Jan, Asst Dean, Coll & Access, Ohio University Libraries, 30 Park Pl, Athens, OH, 45701-2978. Tel: 740-593-2707. Fax: 740-593-2708. p. 1856

Maxwell, Joan, Libr Mgr, Longview Municipal Library, 128 Morrison Pl, Longview, AB, T0L 1H0, CANADA. Tel: 403-558-3927. Fax: 403-558-3927. p. 2710

Maxwell, Judy, Tech Serv, Wells County Public Library, 200 W Washington St, Bluffton, IN, 46714-1999. Tel: 260-824-1612. Fax: 260-824-3129. p. 728

Maxwell, Littleton, Bus Librn, University of Richmond, 28 Westhampton Way, Richmond, VA, 23173. Tel: 804-289-8666. Fax: 804-289-8757. p. 2491

Maxwell, Lynne, Asst Dir, Pub Serv, Villanova University, Law Library, Garey Hall, 299 N Spring Mill Rd, Villanova, PA, 19085. Tel: 610-519-7236. Fax: 610-519-7033. p. 2150

Maxwell, Marge, Dr, Assoc Prof, Prog Coordr, Western Kentucky University, School of Teacher Education, 1092 Gary A Ransdell Hall, Normal St, WKU No 61030, Bowling Green, KY, 42101-1030. Tel: 270-745-2435, 270-745-5414. Fax: 270-745-6322. p. 2966

Maxwell, Nancy, Dir, Virginia Public Library, 215 Fifth Ave S, Virginia, MN, 55792-2642. Tel: 218-748-7525. Fax: 218-748-7527. p. 1286

Maxwell, Nancy, Librn, Grapevine Public Library, 1201 Municipal Way, Grapevine, TX, 76051. Tel: 817-410-3429. Fax: 817-410-3084. p. 2329

Maxwell, Nicole, Circ Supvr, Albany County Public Library, 310 S Eighth St, Laramie, WY, 82070-3969. Tel: 307-721-2580. Fax: 307-721-2584. p. 2657

Maxwell, Patricia, Syst Librn, State University of New York College at Brockport, 350 New Campus Dr, Brockport, NY, 14420-2997. Tel: 585-395-2578. Fax: 585-395-5651. p. 1585

Maxwell, Rebekah, Assoc Dir, Libr Operations, University of South Carolina, Coleman Karesh Law Library, USC Law Ctr, 701 Main St, Columbia, SC, 29208. Tel: 803-777-5942. Fax: 803-777-9405. p. 2190

Maxwell, Richard, Dir, Porter Adventist Hospital, 2525 S Downing St, Denver, CO, 80210-5241. Tel: 303-778-5656. Fax: 303-778-5608. p. 303

Maxwell, Sheila, Syst Adminr, Jasper County Public Library, 208 W Susan St, Rensselaer, IN, 47978. Tel: 219-866-5881. Fax: 219-866-7378. p. 774

Maxwell, Susan A, Dir, Nicholas P Sims Library, 515 W Main, Waxahachie, TX, 75165-3235. Tel: 972-937-2671. Fax: 972-937-4409. p. 2398

Maxymuk, John, Ref Serv, Rutgers University Libraries, Paul Robeson Library, Camden, 300 N Fourth St, Camden, NJ, 08102-1404. Tel: 856-225-6033. Fax: 856-225-6428. p. 1477

May, Alan, Electronic Res, University of Montevallo, Station 6100, Montevallo, AL, 35115-6100. Tel: 205-665-6100. Fax: 205-665-6112. p. 27

May, Anne, Media Serv, Manhasset Public Library, 30 Onderdonk Ave, Manhasset, NY, 11030. Tel: 516 627-2300, Ext 207. Fax: 516-627-4339. p. 1657

May, Barbara Jo, Adult Serv, Coll Develop, Okanagan Regional Library, 1430 KLO Rd, Kelowna, BC, V1W 3P6, CANADA. Tel: 250-860-4033. Fax: 250-861-8696. p. 2730

May, Caleb, Dir, Head Librn, Meade Public Library, 104 E West Plains, Meade, KS, 67864. Tel: 620-873-2522. Fax: 620-873-2522. p. 883

May, Carol, Librn, Davis Community Church Library, 412 C St, Davis, CA, 95616. Tel: 530-753-2894. Fax: 530-753-0182. p. 139

May, Carole, Librn, City of Kawartha Lakes Public Library, Kirkfield Service Centre Library, PO Box 246, 7 Monroe St, Kirkfield, ON, K0M 2B0, CANADA. Tel: 705-438-3331. Fax: 705-438-3138. p. 2816

May, Charles, Ref Serv, Nashville State Technical Community College, 120 White Bridge Rd, Nashville, TN, 37209-4515. Tel: 615-353-3557. Fax: 615-353-3558. p. 2258

May, Cinda, Dept Chair, Univ Digital & Archival Serv, Indiana State University, 510 North 6 1/2 St, Terre Haute, IN, 47809. Tel: 812-237-2534. Fax: 812-237-3376. p. 781

May, Daniel, Librn, Commodity Futures Trading Commission Library, 1155 21st St NW, Washington, DC, 20581. Tel: 202-418-5254. Fax: 202-418-5537. p. 396

May, David G, Dir of Libr Serv, Los Angeles Valley College Library, 5800 Fulton Ave, Valley Glen, CA, 91401-4096. Tel: 818-947-2754. Fax: 818-947-2751. p. 279

May, Dori, Coll Develop Librn, Maryville College, 502 E Lamar Alexander Pkwy, Maryville, TN, 37804-5907. Tel: 865-981-8074. Fax: 865-981-8267. p. 2247

May, Eleanor, Circ Serv, Ajax Public Library, 55 Harwood Ave S, Ajax, ON, L1S 2H8, CANADA. Tel: 905-683-4000, Ext 8821. Fax: 905-683-6960. p. 2791

May, Francine, Tech Serv, Mount Royal University Library, 4825 Mount Royal Gate SW, Calgary, AB, T3E 6K6, CANADA. Tel: 403-440-6128. Fax: 403-440-6758. p. 2692

May, George, Commun Libr Mgr, County of Los Angeles Public Library, La Verne Library, 3640 D St, La Verne, CA, 91750-3572. Tel: 909-596-1934. Fax: 909-596-7303. p. 142

May, Jackie, ILL, Jefferson County Library District, 241 SE Seventh St, Madras, OR, 97741-1611. Tel: 541-475-3351. Fax: 541-475-7434. p. 2004

May, Jeanne C, Dir, Helen Matthes Library, 100 E Market Ave, Effingham, IL, 62401-3499. Tel: 217-342-2464, Ext 5. Fax: 217-342-2413. p. 639

May, Jen, Dir, Secaucus Public Library, 1379 Patterson Plank Rd, Secaucus, NJ, 07094. Tel: 201-330-2083. Fax: 201-330-1741, 201-617-1695. p. 1529

May, Julie, Photo Archivist, Brooklyn Historical Society Othmer Library, 128 Pierrepont St, Brooklyn, NY, 11201-2711. Tel: 718-222-4111. Fax: 718-222-3794. p. 1590

May, Kimbel, Librn, St Philip's College, 1801 Martin Luther King Dr, San Antonio, TX, 78203-2098. Tel: 210-486-2330. Fax: 210-486-2335. p. 2381

May, Madonna, Dir, Neshoba County Public Library, 230 Beacon St, Philadelphia, MS, 39350. Tel: 601-656-4911. Fax: 601-656-6894. p. 1311

May, Margo, Asst Librn, Grace District Library, 204 S Main, Grace, ID, 83241. Tel: 208-425-3695. Fax: 208-425-3695. p. 575

May, Nick, Tech Mgr, Virginia Beach Public Library Department, Technology Services Division, Central Library, 4100 Virginia Beach Blvd, Virginia Beach, VA, 23452. Tel: 757-385-0170. p. 2500

May, Patricia, Dir, Saint Joseph's Regional Medical Center, 703 Main St, Paterson, NJ, 07503. Tel: 973-754-3590. Fax: 973-754-3593. p. 1519

May, Scott, Adult Serv, Roswell Public Library, 301 N Pennsylvania Ave, Roswell, NM, 88201. Tel: 575-622-7101. Fax: 575-622-7107. p. 1561

May, Sherri, Dir, Brownstown Public Library, 120 E Spring St, Brownstown, IN, 47220-1546. Tel: 812-358-2853. Fax: 812-358-4116. p. 730

Mayberry, Betty, Librn, Wright County Library, Mountain Grove Branch, 206 Green St, Mountain Grove, MO, 65711. Tel: 417-926-4453. Fax: 417-926-6240. p. 1330

Mayberry, Charles, Dir, Info Serv, SEFLIN - Southeast Florida Library Information Network, Inc, Wimberly Library, Office 452, Florida Atlantic University, 777 Glades Rd, Boca Raton, FL, 33431. Tel: 561-208-0984. Fax: 561-208-0995. p. 2940

Mayberry, Jill, Librn, Jacksonville Developmental Center Library, 1201 S Main St, Jacksonville, IL, 62650-3396. Fax: 217-479-2117. p. 659

Mayden, Linda, Dir, Pub Libr Serv, Blackwell Public Library, 123 W Padon, Blackwell, OK, 74631-2805. Tel: 580-363-1809. Fax: 580-363-7214. p. 1958

Mayer, Claudia, Head, Circ, Manchester City Library, 405 Pine St, Manchester, NH, 03104-6199. Tel: 603-624-6550. Fax: 603-624-6559. p. 1455

Mayer, Elaine, Libr Coordr, Alberta Law Libraries - Fort Saskatchewan, Courthouse, 10504-100th Ave, Fort Saskatchewan, AB, T8L 3S9, CANADA. Tel: 780-998-1200. Fax: 780-998-7222. p. 2704

Mayer, Gwen, Archives Mgr, Hudson Library & Historical Society, 96 Library St, Hudson, OH, 44236-5122. Tel: 330-653-6658. Fax: 330-650-3373. p. 1905

Mayer, Rita, Br Mgr, Fairfax County Public Library, Tysons-Pimmit Regional, 7584 Leesburg Pike, Falls Church, VA, 22043-2099. Tel: 703-790-8088. p. 2461

Mayer, Tina, Dir, Mount Arlington Public Library, 333 Howard Blvd, Mount Arlington, NJ, 07856-1196. Tel: 973-398-1516. Fax: 973-398-0171. p. 1506

Mayer, Will, Librn, Dallas Public Library, Pleasant Grove, 7310 Lake June Rd, Dallas, TX, 75217. Tel: 214-670-0965. p. 2307

Mayerson, Wendy, ILL Librn, Shelburne Public Library, 74 Village Rd, Shelburne, NH, 03581-3209. Tel: 603-466-2262. p. 1465

Mayes, Byron C, Head, Libr Syst & Tech, Temple University Libraries, 1210 W Berks St, Philadelphia, PA, 19122-6088. Tel: 215-204-5797. Fax: 215-204-5201. p. 2117

Mayes, Susan, Cat Librn, Belmont Abbey College, 100 Belmont-Mt Holly Rd, Belmont, NC, 28012. Tel: 704-461-6748. Fax: 704-461-6743. p. 1776

Mayeux, Ann, In Charge, Buncombe County Public Libraries, North Asheville, 1030 Merrimon Ave, Asheville, NC, 28804. Tel: 828-250-4752. p. 1774

Mayfield, Patricia Lynn, Jacksonville Campus Libr Dir, Keiser University Library System, 1500 NW 49th St, Fort Lauderdale, FL, 33309. Tel: 954-351-4035. Fax: 954-351-4051. p. 443

Mayfield, Pattie, Dir, Hall-Voyer Foundation, 500 N Sixth St, Honey Grove, TX, 75446. Tel: 903-378-2206. Fax: 903-378-2208. p. 2333

Mayfield, Peggy, Head Librn, Hartnell College Library, 411 Central Ave, Salinas, CA, 93901. Tel: 831-755-6898. Fax: 831-759-6084. p. 226

Mayfield, Robin, Libr Dir, Cascade Public Library, 105 Front St, Cascade, ID, 83611. Tel: 208-382-4757. Fax: 208-382-4757. p. 572

Mayfield, Sandra, Circ, Warren County-Vicksburg Public Library, 700 Veto St, Vicksburg, MS, 39180-3595. Tel: 601-636-6411. Fax: 601-634-4809. p. 1317

Mayfield, Toby, Br Mgr, Athens Regional Library System, Winterville Branch, 115 Marigold Lane, Winterville, GA, 30683. Tel: 706-742-7735. Fax: 706-742-7735. p. 509

Mayfield, W T, Librn, Northwest Mississippi Community College, 5197 WE Ross Pkwy, Southaven, MS, 38671. Tel: 662-280-6164. Fax: 662-280-6161. p. 1315

Mayhew, Catherine, Genealogy Serv, Martha's Vineyard Museum, Pease House, 59 School St, Edgartown, MA, 02539. Tel: 508-627-4441. Fax: 508-627-4436. p. 1087

Mayhew, Christina, Supvr, Elgin County Public Library, Aylmer Old Town Hall Branch, 38 John St S, Aylmer, ON, N5H 2C2, CANADA. Tel: 519-773-2439. Fax: 519-773-2420. p. 2844

Mayhood, Erin, Dir, University of Virginia, Music, Old Cabell Hall, Charlottesville, VA, 22904-4175. Tel: 434-924-7017. Fax: 434-924-6033. p. 2455

Mayhugh, Jean, Librn, Prescott City Public Library, 174 W Third, Prescott, KS, 66767. Tel: 913-471-4593. p. 891

Mayhugh, Steven, Br Mgr, Middletown Public Library, West Chester Branch, 9363 Centre Pointe Dr, West Chester, OH, 45069. Tel: 513-777-3717. Fax: 513-777-8452. p. 1917

Mayle, Rebecca, Ref/Outreach Coordr, Marion County Public Library, 321 Monroe St, Fairmont, WV, 26554-2952. Tel: 304-366-1210. Fax: 304-366-4831. p. 2559

Maylone, Theresa, Univ Librn, Saint John's University Library, 8000 Utopia Pkwy, Queens, NY, 11439. Tel: 718-990-6735. Fax: 718-380-0353. p. 1725

Maynard, Adele, Asst Librn, Central City Public Library, 1604 15th Ave, Central City, NE, 68826. Tel: 308-946-2512. Fax: 308-946-3290. p. 1395

Maynard, Clara, Br Mgr, Harris County Public Library, Aldine Branch, 11331 Airline Dr, Houston, TX, 77037. Tel: 281-445-5560. Fax: 281-445-8625. p. 2335

Maynard, Daniel, Bus Librn, Campbell University, 113 Main St, Buies Creek, NC, 27506. Tel: 910-893-1460. Fax: 910-893-1470. p. 1778

Maynard, Deborah, Dir, West Milford Township Library, 1490 Union Valley Rd, West Milford, NJ, 07480. Tel: 973-728-2820. Fax: 973-728-2106. p. 1541

Maynard, Felicia, Res Librn, United States Equal Employment Opportunity Commission Library, 131 M St NE, Rm 4SW16N, Washington, DC, 20507. Tel: 202-663-4630. Fax: 202-663-4629. p. 420

Maynard, Kay, ILL, Anderson University Library, 316 Boulevard, Anderson, SC, 29621. Tel: 864-231-2050. Fax: 864-231-2191. p. 2181

Maynard, Kim, Dir, Southern West Virginia Community & Technical College, 1601 Armory Dr, Williamson, WV, 25661. Tel: 304-236-7616. Fax: 304-235-6043. p. 2575

Maynard, Kimberly, Dir, Southern West Virginia Community & Technical College, Dempsey Branch Rd, Mount Gay, WV, 25637. Tel: 304-896-7378. Fax: 304-752-2837. p. 2567

Maynard, Leigh, Ch, Hopkinton Town Library, 61 Houston Dr, Contoocook, NH, 03229. Tel: 603-746-3663. Fax: 603-746-6799. p. 1444

Maynard, Marilyn, Librn, Tulare County Library, Pixley Branch, 300 N School, PO Box K, Pixley, CA, 93256. Tel: 559-757-3880. p. 281

Maynard, Michael, Librn, Arizona Department of Corrections - Adult Institutions, 2014 N Citrus Rd, Goodyear, AZ, 85338. Tel: 623-853-0304, Ext 24967. Fax: 623-853-0304. p. 65

Maynard, Quinn, Asst Dir, Shelby Area District Library, 189 Maple St, Shelby, MI, 49455-1134. Tel: 231-861-4565. Fax: 231-861-6868. p. 1227

Maynard, Roselee, Asst Librn, Cushing Public Library, 215 N Steele, Cushing, OK, 74023-3319. Tel: 918-225-4188. Fax: 918-225-6201. p. 1961

Maynard, Zora, Librn, United States Courts Library, 255 E Temple St, Rm 132, Los Angeles, CA, 90012. Tel: 213-894-8900. Fax: 213-894-8906. p. 178

Maynes, Judy, Head of Acq Serv, Dartmouth College Library, 6025 Baker Berry Library, Rm 115, Hanover, NH, 03755-3525. Tel: 603-646-2236. Fax: 603-646-3702. p. 1450

Maynes, Judy, Head, Acq, Dartmouth College Library, Baker-Berry Library, 6025 Baker-Berry Library, Hanover, NH, 03755-3525. Tel: 603-646-2560. Fax: 603-646-2167. p. 1450

Maynes, Warren, Ser Librn, Alberta Legislature Library, 216 Legislature Bldg, 10800-97 Ave, Edmonton, AB, T5K 2B6, CANADA. Tel: 780-427-0201. Fax: 780-427-6016. p. 2699

Maynor, Brielle, Mgr, Dayton Metro Library, Miamisburg Branch, 35 S Fifth St, Miamisburg, OH, 45342. Tel: 937-496-8946. Fax: 937-496-4346. p. 1893

Mayo, Alexa, Assoc Dir, Serv, Pub Serv, University of Maryland, Baltimore, Health Sciences & Human Services Library, 601 W Lombard St, Baltimore, MD, 21201. Tel: 410-706-1316. Fax: 410-706-3101. p. 1019

Mayo, Bob, Dir of Libr, Rensselaer Libraries, Rensselaer Polytechnic Inst, 110 Eighth St, Troy, NY, 12180-3590. Tel: 518-276-8300. Fax: 518-276-2044. p. 1756

Mayo, Douglas, Assoc Librn, Colonial Williamsburg Foundation, 313 First St, Williamsburg, VA, 23185-4306. Tel: 757-565-8521. Fax: 757-565-8538. p. 2502

Mayo, Douglas, Assoc Librn, Colonial Williamsburg Foundation, John D Rockefeller Jr Library-Special Collections, 313 First St, Williamsburg, VA, 23185-4306. Tel: 757-565-8521. Fax: 757-565-8528. p. 2502

Mayo, Justin, Dir, Washington County Public Library, 615 Fifth St, Marietta, OH, 45750-1973. Tel: 740-373-1057. p. 1913

Mayo, Kathy, Actg Literacy Contact, Mgr, Outreach Serv, Principal Librn, Lee County Library System, Outreach Services, 21100 Three Oaks Pkwy, Estero, FL, 33928. Tel: 239-390-3234. Fax: 239-498-6424. p. 446

Mayo, Lynn, Ref Librn, Hamilton College, 198 College Hill Rd, Clinton, NY, 13323-1299. Tel: 315-859-4746. Fax: 315-859-4578. p. 1607

Mayo, Martha, Dir, Spec Coll, University of Massachusetts Lowell Libraries, Center for Lowell History, Patrick J Mogan Cultural Ctr, 40 French St, Lowell, MA, 01852. Tel: 978-934-4998. Fax: 978-934-4995. p. 1101

Mayo, Patricia, Librn, Marystown Public Library, Columbia Dr, Marystown, NL, A0E 2M0, CANADA. Tel: 709-279-1507. Fax: 709-279-1507. p. 2770

Mayo, Rhonda, Cat, Reserves, Ser, University of Science & Arts of Oklahoma, 1901 S 17th St, Chickasha, OK, 73018. Tel: 405-574-1263. Fax: 405-574-1220. p. 1960

Mayo, Rosemary, Circ Coordr, Mooresville Public Library, 220 W Harrison St, Mooresville, IN, 46158-1633. Tel: 317-831-7323. Fax: 317-831-7383. p. 766

Mayo, Sheila, Web Developer, National Archives & Records Administration, 441 Freedom Pkwy, Atlanta, GA, 30307. Tel: 404-865-7120. Fax: 404-865-7102. p. 517

Mayon, Malisa, Librn, Morgan City Public Library, 220 Everett St, Morgan City, LA, 70380-3619. Tel: 985-380-4646. Fax: 985-380-4699. p. 958

Mayorga, Kay, Br Asst, Los Angeles County Law Library, Norwalk, SE Superior Courts Bldg, Rm 714, 12720 Norwalk Blvd, Norwalk, CA, 90650. Tel: 562-807-7310. Fax: 562-868-8936. p. 172

Mayr, Diane, Adult Serv, Asst Dir, Nesmith Library, Eight Fellows Rd, Windham, NH, 03087. Tel: 603-432-7154. Fax: 603-537-0097. p. 1468

Mayreis, Rex, Ref Librn, Crowell Public Library, 1890 Huntington Dr, San Marino, CA, 91108-2595. Tel: 626-300-0777, Ext 542. Fax: 626-284-0766. p. 254

Mays, Alan, Electronic Serv, Pennsylvania State University-Harrisburg Library, 351 Olmsted Dr, Middletown, PA, 17057-4850. Tel: 717-948-6070. Fax: 717-948-6757. p. 2089

Mays, Antje, Head, Monograph & AV Acq, Winthrop University, 824 Oakland Ave, Rock Hill, SC, 29733. Tel: 803-323-2131, 803-323-2274, 803-323-2311. Fax: 803-323-2215. p. 2203

Mays, Brenda, Ser, Mercer University, Jack Tarver Library, 1300 Edgewood Ave, Macon, GA, 31207. Tel: 478-301-2966. Fax: 478-301-2111. p. 540

Mays, Dorothy, Head, Pub Serv, Rollins College, 1000 Holt Ave, Campus Box 2744, Winter Park, FL, 32789-2744. Tel: 407-646-1533. Fax: 407-646-1515. p. 505

Mays, Florence, Interim Dir, Midlands Technical College Library, 1260 Lexington Dr, West Columbia, SC, 29170-2176. Tel: 803-822-3419. Fax: 803-822-3670. p. 2207

Mays, Florence, Interim Dir, Pub Serv, Midlands Technical College Library, Beltline Library, 316 S Beltline Blvd, 2nd Flr, Columbia, SC, 29205. Tel: 803-790-7512. Fax: 803-738-7719. p. 2207

Mays, Louis E, Bibliog Instr, Head Librn, Southern State Community College, 100 Hobart Dr, Hillsboro, OH, 45133-9487. Tel: 937-393-3431, Ext 2680, 937-695-0307, Ext 3580. Fax: 937-393-9370, 937-695-8093. p. 1904

Mayville, Gretchen, Circ Supvr, Springfield Township Library, 12000 Davisburg Rd, Davisburg, MI, 48350. Tel: 248-846-6550. Fax: 248-846-6555. p. 1167

Mayweather, Elaine, ILL, University of Medicine & Dentistry of New Jersey, Academic Ctr, One Medical Center Dr, Stratford, NJ, 08084. Tel: 856-566-6800. Fax: 856-566-6380. p. 1532

Mayweather, Elaine, Mgr, Kennedy Memorial Hospitals-University Medical Center, 435 Hurffville-Cross Keys Rd, Turnersville, NJ, 08012. Tel: 856-582-2675. Fax: 856-582-3190. p. 1537

Mazak, Thom, Prog & Youth Coordr, Lady Lake Public Library, 225 W Guava St, Lady Lake, FL, 32159. Tel: 352-753-2957. Fax: 352-753-3361. p. 457

Mazaros, Sue, Coll Mgt Librn, Belmont University, 1900 Belmont Blvd, Nashville, TN, 37212-3757. Tel: 615-460-6782. Fax: 615-460-5641. p. 2255

Mazer, Nancy, Bus Mgr, Bibliomation, 32 Crest Rd, Middlebury, CT, 06762. Tel: 203-577-4070, Ext 104. Fax: 203-577-4077. p. 2939

Mazerall, Anne, Info Officer, Canada Department of Fisheries & Oceans, One Challenger Dr, Dartmouth, NS, B2Y 4A2, CANADA. Tel: 902-426-3683. Fax: 902-496-1544. p. 2778

Maziar, Lucia, Libr Dir, United States Coast Guard Academy Library, 35 Mohegan Ave, New London, CT, 06320-4195. Tel: 860-444-8510. Fax: 860-444-8516. p. 360

Maziarz, Konrad, Syst Adminr, Hamtramck Public Library, 2360 Caniff St, Hamtramck, MI, 48212. Tel: 313-365-7050. Fax: 313-365-0160. p. 1187

Maziekien, Michael, Ref Librn/Bus Liaison, Nutley Free Public Library, 93 Booth Dr, Nutley, NJ, 07110-2782. Tel: 973-667-0405. p. 1515

Mazin, Beth, Dir, Memorial Hall Library, Two N Main St, Andover, MA, 01810. Tel: 978-623-8401. Fax: 978-623-8407. p. 1049

Mazor, Elizabeth, Ch, Gary Byker Memorial Library, 3338 Van Buren St, Hudsonville, MI, 49426. Tel: 616-669-7172, Ext 4. Fax: 616-669-5150. p. 1192

Mazour, Ruth, Ref Librn, Logan County Public Library, 201 W Sixth St, Russellville, KY, 42276. Tel: 270-726-6129. Fax: 270-726-6127. p. 934

Mazuk, Melody, Dir, Palmer Theological Seminary, Six Lancaster Ave, Wynnewood, PA, 19096. Tel: 610-645-9319. p. 2158

Mazur, Catherine, Librn, Connecticut Judicial Branch Law Libraries, Hartford Law Library, Hartford Courthouse, 95 Washington St, Hartford, CT, 06106. Tel: 860-548-2866. Fax: 860-548-2868. p. 344

Mazur, Tara, Libr Mgr, Daysland Public Library, 5130 50th St, Daysland, AB, T0B 1A0, CANADA. Tel: 780-679-7263. Fax: 780-374-2455. p. 2696

Mazur, Terry, Circ Supvr, Lorain County Community College, 1005 Abbe Rd N, North Elyria, OH, 44035-1691. Tel: 440-366-7289. Fax: 440-366-4127. p. 1924

Mazure, Sharon, Ref & ILL Librn, Fairmont State University, 1201 Locust Ave, Fairmont, WV, 26554. Tel: 304-367-4733. Fax: 304-367-4677. p. 2559

Mazure, Sharon, Asst Prof, Fairmont State College, School of Education, 1201 Locust Ave, Fairmont, WV, 26554. Tel: 304-367-4622. Fax: 304-367-4677. p. 2976

Mazure, Vicki, Dir, Harbor Beach Area District Library, 105 N Huron Ave, Harbor Beach, MI, 48441. Tel: 989-479-3417. Fax: 989-479-6818. p. 1188

Mazurek, Adam, Br Mgr, Public Library Association of Annapolis & Anne Arundel County, Inc, Linthicum, 400 Shipley Rd, Linthicum, MD, 21090. Tel: 410-222-6265. Fax: 410-222-6269. p. 1010

Mazurin, Judy, Librn, Parkland Regional Library, Pelly Branch, 300 W 2nd St, Pelly, SK, S0A 2Z0, CANADA. Tel: 306-595-2243. p. 2932

Mazurkiewicz, Elaine, ILL, Erie Community College-South Campus, 4041 Southwestern Blvd, Orchard Park, NY, 14127. Tel: 716-270-5358. Fax: 716-851-1778. p. 1712

Mazza, April, Youth Serv Librn, Wayland Free Public Library, Five Concord Rd, Wayland, MA, 01778. Tel: 508-358-2308. Fax: 508-358-5249. p. 1134

Mazza, April R, Ref Librn, Massachusetts Board of Library Commissioners, 98 N Washington St, Ste 401, Boston, MA, 02114. Tel: 617-725-1860. Fax: 617-725-0140. p. 1063

Mazzaccaro, Paul, Asst Dir & Chief Operating Officer, Westport Library Association, 20 Jesup Rd, Westport, CT, 06880. Tel: 203-291-4820. Fax: 203-227-3829. p. 377

Mazzella, Terri, Libr Asst II, Christiana Hospital Library, Christiana Hospital, 4755 Ogletown Stanton Rd, Newark, DE, 19718-0002. Tel: 302-623-4580. Fax: 302-733-1365. p. 385

Mazzolini, Deborah, Dir, Belvedere-Tiburon Library, 1501 Tiburon Blvd, Tiburon, CA, 94920. Tel: 415-789-2665. Fax: 415-789-2650. p. 275

Mazzone, Lois, Br Mgr, Warwick Public Library, Apponaug, 3267 Post Rd, Warwick, RI, 02886. Tel: 401-739-6411. p. 2177

Mazzu, Jennifer, Curator, Warren County Historical Society, 210 Fourth Ave, Warren, PA, 16365. Tel: 814-723-1795. Fax: 814-723-1795. p. 2150

Mbugua, Wambui, Ref & Info Serv, Borough of Manhattan Community College Library, 199 Chambers St, New York, NY, 10007. Tel: 212-220-1447. Fax: 212-748-7466. p. 1671

Mc Asey, Veronica, Dir, Southwestern College, 100 College St, Winfield, KS, 67156-2498. Tel: 620-229-6271. Fax: 620-229-6382. p. 902

McAbee, Rod K, Dir, Libr Syst, Oklahoma State University Libraries, Oklahoma State University, Athletic Ave, Stillwater, OK, 74078-1071. Tel: 405-744-5955. Fax: 405-744-5183. p. 1978

McAdam, Charlotte, Head, Libr Serv, Fisheries & Oceans Canada, 531 Brandy Cove Rd, Saint Andrews, NB, E5B 2L9, CANADA. Tel: 506-529-5909. Fax: 506-529-5862. p. 2766

McAdam, Paul Edward, Tech Serv Librn, Baltimore International College, 17 Commerce St, Baltimore, MD, 21202-3230. Tel: 410-752-4710, Ext 145. Fax: 410-752-6720. p. 1011

McAdams, Aimee, Libr Tech, Group Health Cooperative, Kathleen Hill Library, 320 Westlake Ave N, Ste 100, GHQ-E3S, Seattle, WA, 98109. Tel: 206-448-2542, 206-448-2771. Fax: 206-877-0687. p. 2528

McAdams, Barbara, Br Mgr, North Madison County Public Library, Frankton Community Library, 102 S Church St, Frankton, IN, 46044. Tel: 765-754-7116. Fax: 765-754-3312. p. 737

McAdams, Candy, Libr Dir, Ned R McWherter Weakley County Library, 341 Linden St, Dresden, TN, 38225-1400. Tel: 731-364-2678. Fax: 731-364-2599. p. 2233

McAdams, Kay, Librn, Van Buren District Library, Antwerp Sunshine Branch, 24823 Front Ave, Mattawan, MI, 49071. Tel: 269-668-2534. Fax: 269-668-2534. p. 1168

McAdams, Kisha, Mgr, Per, Columbia College, 1301 Columbia College Dr, Columbia, SC, 29203-9987. Tel: 803-786-3712. Fax: 803-786-3700. p. 2187

McAdams, Lauren Wade, Ref Librn, Baton Rouge Community College, 201 Community College Dr, Baton Rouge, LA, 70806. Tel: 225-216-8552. Fax: 225-216-8712. p. 942

McAdoo, Monty, Dr, Instrul Serv Librn, Online Serv, Edinboro University of Pennsylvania, 200 Tartan Ave, Edinboro, PA, 16444. Tel: 814-732-2779. Fax: 814-732-2883. p. 2053

McAfee, Dennis, Librn, West Lawn-Wyomissing Hills Library, 101 Woodside Ave, West Lawn, PA, 19609. Tel: 610-678-4888. Fax: 610-678-9210. p. 2154

McAfee, Mary, Asst Dir, Forsyth County Public Library, 660 W Fifth St, Winston-Salem, NC, 27101. Tel: 336-703-2979. Fax: 336-727-8128. p. 1832

McAfee, Travis, Syst Adminr, Way Public Library, 101 E Indiana Ave, Perrysburg, OH, 43551. Tel: 419-874-3135, Ext 103. Fax: 419-874-6129. p. 1929

McAfee, Yolanda, Tech Serv, University Park Public Library District, 1100 Blackhawk Dr, University Park, IL, 60466. Tel: 708-534-2580. Fax: 708-534-2583. p. 711

McAlexander, Sheila, Circ, McMinnville Public Library, 225 NW Adams St, McMinnville, OR, 97128-5425. Tel: 503-435-5562. Fax: 503-435-5560. p. 2005

McAlhany, Judy, Dir, Augusta Richmond County Historical Society Library, c/o Reese Library, Augusta State University, 2500 Walton Way, Augusta, GA, 30904-2200. Tel: 706-737-1532. Fax: 706-667-4415. p. 518

McAlister, Jenna, ILL Librn, Canaan Town Library, 1173 US Rte 4, Canaan, NH, 03741. Tel: 603-523-9650. p. 1440

McAlister, Mark, Adminr, Anthroposophical Society In Canada Library, 9100 Bathurst St, Lower Level Hesperus Fellowship Community, Thornhill, ON, L4J 8C7, CANADA. Tel: 905-886-5163. Fax: 905-886-4989. p. 2847

McAlister, Nadine, Head Librn, Department of Human Services-Youth Corrections, 13500 E Fremont Pl, Englewood, CO, 80112. Tel: 303-768-7529, 303-768-7566. Fax: 303-768-7525. p. 306

McAlister, Susan, Exec Dir, Minuteman Library Network, Ten Strathmore Rd, Natick, MA, 01760-2419. Tel: 508-655-8008. Fax: 508-655-1507. p. 2945

McAllister, Carla, Asst Librn, New Gloucester Public Library, 379 Intervale Rd, New Gloucester, ME, 04260. Tel: 207-926-4840. p. 993

McAllister, Hailey, Learning Res Ctr Asst, ITT Technical Institute, 9500 NE Cascades Pkwy, Portland, OR, 97220. Tel: 503-255-6500. Fax: 503-335-1715. p. 2011

McAllister, Jane, Local Hist Librn, Davie County Public Library, 371 N Main St, Mocksville, NC, 27028-2115. Tel: 336-753-6030. Fax: 336-751-1370. p. 1810

McAllister, Janet, Asst Dir, Glen Carbon Centennial Library, 198 S Main St, Glen Carbon, IL, 62034. Tel: 618-288-1212. Fax: 618-288-1205. p. 649

McAllister, Neil, Br Head, Greater Victoria Public Library Board, Oak Bay, 1442 Monterey Ave, Victoria, BC, V8S 4W1, CANADA. Tel: 250-592-2489. Fax: 250-370-0837. p. 2745

McAloon, Kate, Ref Serv, United States Trademark Office Law Library, 600 Dulany St, MDE 4B65, Alexandria, VA, 22314-5791. Tel: 571-272-9697. Fax: 571-273-9697. p. 2446

McAlorum, Shannon, Librn, College of the North Atlantic, Happy Valley-Goose Bay Campus, 219 Hamilton River Rd, Happy Valley-Goose Bay, NL, A0P 1E0, CANADA. Tel: 709-896-6772. Fax: 709-896-3733. p. 2771

McAlpin, Nancy, Dir, Saint Paris Public Library, 127 E Main St, Saint Paris, OH, 43072. Tel: 937-663-4349. Fax: 937-663-0297. p. 1933

McAlpin, Sara, Archives, Clarke University, 1550 Clarke Dr, Dubuque, IA, 52001. Tel: 563-588-6556. Fax: 563-588-8160. p. 811

McAlpine, Jo, Librn, Palliser Regional Library, Craik Branch, 611 First Ave, Craik, SK, S0G 0V0, CANADA. Tel: 306-734-2388. Fax: 306-734-2388. p. 2918

McAlvey, Michele, Dir, Walnut Public Library District, 101 Heaton, Walnut, IL, 61376. Tel: 815-379-2159. Fax: 815-379-2159. p. 715

McAmmond, Sharon, Pub Serv Coordr, Leduc Public Library, Two Alexandra Park, Leduc, AB, T9E 4C4, CANADA. Tel: 780-986-2637. Fax: 780-986-3462. p. 2709

McAnallen, Deborah K, Head, Cat, University of Georgia Libraries, Athens, GA, 30602-1641. Tel: 706-583-0705. Fax: 706-542-4144. p. 510

McAnally, Priscilla, Dir, Paris Public Library, 326 S Main St, Paris, TX, 75460. Tel: 903-785-8531. Fax: 903-784-6325. p. 2368

McAnaney, Evelyn, Tech Serv, Cape May County Library, 30 Mechanic St, Cape May Court House, NJ, 08210. Tel: 609-463-6350. Fax: 609-465-3895. p. 1477

McAndrew-Taylor, Marie, Head, Circ, Stevens Memorial Library, 345 Main St, North Andover, MA, 01845. Tel: 978-688-9505. Fax: 978-688-9507. p. 1112

McAnna, Suzanne, Circ, University of Texas Libraries, Perry-Castaneda Library (Main Library), 101 E 21st St, Austin, TX, 78712-1266. Tel: 512-495-4350. p. 2284

Mcaopine, Michael, Librn, Siskind, Cromarty, Ivey & Dowler, 680 Waterloo St, London, ON, N6A 3V8, CANADA. Tel: 519-672-2121. Fax: 519-672-6065. p. 2818

McAphee, Sylvia, Ser, University of Alabama at Birmingham, Lister Hill Library of the Health Sciences, 1700 University Blvd, Birmingham, AL, 35294-0013. Tel: 205-934-5460. Fax: 205-934-3545. p. 10

McArdell, Carol, Tech Serv, Pitkin County Library, 120 N Mill St, Aspen, CO, 81611. Tel: 970-925-4025. Fax: 970-925-3935. p. 288

McArdle, David, Dir, Gloucester, Lyceum & Sawyer Free Library, Two Dale Ave, Gloucester, MA, 01930-5906. Tel: 978-281-9763. Fax: 978-281-9770. p. 1091

McArdle, Janice, Youth Serv Librn, Granby Public Library, One Library Lane, Granby, MA, 01033-9416. Tel: 413-467-3320. Fax: 413-467-3320. p. 1091

McArdle, Karen L, ILL, University of Wisconsin Sheboygan, One University Dr, Sheboygan, WI, 53081-4789. Tel: 920-459-6625. Fax: 920-459-6602. p. 2637

McArdle, Nichole, ILL, Sullivan County Community College, 112 College Rd, Loch Sheldrake, NY, 12759-5108. Tel: 845-434-5750, Ext 4389. p. 1653

McArdle, Paula, Educ Curator, Tacoma Art Museum, 1701 Pacific Ave, Tacoma, WA, 98402. Tel: 253-272-4258, Ext 3026. Fax: 253-627-1898. p. 2540

McArdle Rojo, Christine, Dir, La Crosse County Library, Administration Ctr, 103 State St, Holmen, WI, 54636. Tel: 608-526-9600. Fax: 608-526-3299. p. 2598

McArthur, Diane, Syst Librn, Alabama A&M University, 4900 Meridian St, Huntsville, AL, 35762. Tel: 256-372-4715. Fax: 256-372-5768. p. 21

McArthur, Gillian, Circ, Chino Valley Public Library, 1020 W Palomino Rd, Chino Valley, AZ, 86323-5500. Tel: 928-636-2687. Fax: 928-636-9129. p. 60

McArthur, Lawrie, Pub Serv, Northwest Community College Library, 5331 McConnell Ave, Terrace, BC, V8G 4X2, CANADA. Tel: 250-638-5407. Fax: 250-635-1594. p. 2739

McArthur, Peter, Librn, Foster Associates, Inc Library, 4550 Montgomery Ave, Ste 350N, Bethesda, MD, 20814. Tel: 301-664-7800. Fax: 301-664-7810. p. 1021

McArthur, Rebecca, Librn, Greater Sudbury Public Library, New Sudbury, 1346 Lasalle Blvd, Sudbury, ON, P3A 1Z6, CANADA. Tel: 705-688-3952. p. 2846

McArthur, Rebecca, Librn, Greater Sudbury Public Library, South, 1991 Regent St S, Sudbury, ON, P3E 3Z9, CANADA. Tel: 705-688-3950. Fax: 705-522-7788. p. 2846

McArthur, Theresa, Head, Ch, Libr Assoc, West Milford Township Library, 1490 Union Valley Rd, West Milford, NJ, 07480. Tel: 973-728-2823. Fax: 973-728-2106. p. 1541

McArthur, W Neil, Dir, Libr Serv, Central Georgia Technical College Library, 3300 Macon Tech Dr, Macon, GA, 31206-3628. Tel: 478-757-3548. Fax: 478-757-3545. p. 540

McAskill, Bill, Librn, George Brown College of Applied Arts & Technology, 160 Kendal Ave, Toronto, ON, M5R 1M3, CANADA. Tel: 416-415-5000, Ext 4634. Fax: 416-415-4765. p. 2853

McAtee, Brian P, Dir, Southeastern Community College Library, 1500 W Agency Rd, West Burlington, IA, 52655. Tel: 319-752-2731, Ext 5091. Fax: 319-753-0322. p. 852

McAtee, Brian P, Librn, Southeastern Community College Library, Fred Karre Memorial Library-Keokuk Campus, 335 Messenger Rd, Keokuk, IA, 52632. Tel: 319-524-3221, Ext 8456. Fax: 319-524-6433. p. 852

McAteer, Mark, Assoc Dir, Circ, Saint Michael's College, One Winooski Park, Box L, Colchester, VT, 05439-2525. Tel: 802-654-2403. Fax: 802-654-2630. p. 2422

McAuliff, Steve, Librn, Telegraph Herald Library, 801 Bluff St, Dubuque, IA, 52001. Tel: 563-588-5770. Fax: 563-588-5745. p. 812

McAuliffe, Carol, Head, Map & Imagery Libr, University of Florida Libraries, 535 Library W, Gainesville, FL, 32611-7000. Tel: 352-273-2825. Fax: 352-392-4787. p. 450

McAuliffe, Gabriel C, Librn, Sierra Research Library, 1801 J St, Sacramento, CA, 95814. Tel: 916-444-6666. Fax: 916-444-8373. p. 225

McAuliffe, Lois, Ch, Ashland Public Library, 66 Front St, Ashland, MA, 01721-1606. Tel: 508-881-0134. Fax: 508-881-0135. p. 1050

McBee, Dana, Asst Dir, Support Serv, Austin Public Library, 800 Guadalupe St, Austin, TX, 78701. Tel: 512-974-7433. p. 2278

McBee, Joe David, Head, Ser, University of the South, 735 University Ave, Sewanee, TN, 37383-1000. Tel: 931-598-1574. Fax: 931-598-1702. p. 2265

McBeth, Becky, Dir, Lyons Public Library, 217 East Ave S, Lyons, KS, 67554-2721. Tel: 620-257-2961. p. 880

McBeth, Glen, Instrul Media, Washburn University, School of Law Library, 1700 SW College Ave, Topeka, KS, 66621. Tel: 785-670-1778. Fax: 785-670-3194. p. 897

McBeth, Leverne, Libr Spec, Spartanburg Community College Library, 800 Brisack Rd, Spartanburg, SC, 29305. Tel: 864-592-4615. Fax: 864-592-4762. p. 2205

McBeth, Susan, Dir, Nevada Public Library, 218 W Walnut, Nevada, MO, 64772-0931. Tel: 417-448-2770. Fax: 417-448-2771. p. 1348

McBoy, Janice, Librn, Lennox & Addington County Public Library, 4315 County Rd 1, Yarker, ON, K0K 3N0, CANADA. Tel: 613-377-1673. p. 2873

McBrady, Cindy, ILL, Lake Villa District Library, 1001 E Grand Ave, Lake Villa, IL, 60046. Tel: 847-356-7711, Ext 224. Fax: 847-265-9595. p. 663

McBrayer, Teresa, Mgr, White Settlement Public Library, 8215 White Settlement Rd, White Settlement, TX, 76108-1604. Tel: 817-367-0166. Fax: 817-246-8184. p. 2400

McBride, Amelia, Br Mgr, Clayton County Library System, Lovejoy, 1721 McDonough Rd, Hampton, GA, 30228. Tel: 770-472-8129. Fax: 770-472-8136. p. 537

McBride, Barbara, Youth Serv, Benzonia Public Library, 891 Michigan Ave, Benzonia, MI, 49616-9784. Tel: 231-882-4111. Fax: 231-882-4111. p. 1157

McBride, Carol, Circ, Sullivan County Community College, 112 College Rd, Loch Sheldrake, NY, 12759-5108. Tel: 845-434-5750, Ext 4389. p. 1653

McBride, Cheryl, Dir, North Brunswick Free Public Library, 880 Hermann Rd, North Brunswick, NJ, 08902. Tel: 732-246-3545. Fax: 732-246-1341. p. 1514

McBride, Christine H, Dir, University of Delaware Library, College of Education Resource Center, 012 Willard Hall Education Bldg, Newark, DE, 19716-2940. Tel: 302-831-2335. Fax: 302-831-8404. p. 386

McBride, Jerry, Head Librn, Stanford University Libraries, Music Library, Braun Music Ctr, 541 Lasuen Mall, Stanford, CA, 94305-3076. Tel: 650-723-1211. Fax: 650-725-1145. p. 271

McBride, John, Adult Serv, Metuchen Public Library, 480 Middlesex Ave, Metuchen, NJ, 08840. Tel: 732-632-8526. Fax: 732-632-8535. p. 1501

McBride, Kathleen, Dir, Mukwonago Community Library, 300 Washington Ave, Mukwonago, WI, 53149-1909. Tel: 262-363-6411. Fax: 262-363-6457. p. 2623

McBride, Kelly, Dir, Russell County Public Library, 248 W Main St, Lebanon, VA, 24266. Tel: 276-889-8044. Fax: 276-889-8045. p. 2473

McBride, Lee, Librn, Porter Memorial Library, 92 Court St, Machias, ME, 04654-2102. Tel: 207-255-3933. p. 991

McBride, Lenis, Cat, Alabama A&M University, 4900 Meridian St, Huntsville, AL, 35762. Tel: 256-372-4721. Fax: 256-372-5768. p. 21

McBride, Mary, Libr Tech, Mercer County Community College Library, 1200 Old Trenton Rd, West Windsor, NJ, 08550. Tel: 609-570-3179. Fax: 609-570-3845. p. 1542

McBride, Mary, Libr Tech, Mercer County Community College Library, James Kerney Campus, N Broad & Academy Sts, Trenton, NJ, 08690. Tel: 609-570-3179. Fax: 609-394-8167. p. 1542

McBride, Melanie, ILL, Rosemont College Library, 1400 Montgomery Ave, Rosemont, PA, 19010-1631. Tel: 610-527-0200, Ext 2271. Fax: 610-525-2930. p. 2135

McBride, Michael, Curator, Henry Whitfield State Museum Research Library, 248 Old Whitfield St, Guilford, CT, 06437-3459. Tel: 203-453-2457. Fax: 203-453-7544. p. 343

McBride, Noreen, Asst Dir, Youth Serv Librn, East Palestine Memorial Public Library, 309 N Market St, East Palestine, OH, 44413. Tel: 330-426-3778. Fax: 330-426-4950. p. 1897

McBride, P J, Dir, Zearing Public Library, 101 E Main, Zearing, IA, 50278. Tel: 641-487-7888. Fax: 641-487-7888. p. 854

McBride, Ray, Dir, Florence County Library System, 509 S Dargan St, Florence, SC, 29506. Tel: 843-662-8424. Fax: 843-661-7544. p. 2193

McBride, Regina, Dean of Libr, Southern Illinois University Edwardsville, Campus Box 1063, 30 Hairpin Circle, Edwardsville, IL, 62026-1063. Tel: 618-650-5198. Fax: 618-650-2717. p. 639

McBride, Robert C, Pres, United Empire Loyalists' Association of Canada Library, George Brown House, 202 - 50 Baldwin St, Toronto, ON, M5T 1L4, CANADA. Tel: 416-591-1783. p. 2864

McBride, Thomas D, Fac Mgr, Baach, Robinson & Lewis Library, 1201 F St NW, Ste 500, Washington, DC, 20004. Tel: 202-833-8900. Fax: 202-466-5738. p. 394

McBride, Trine, Dir, Ord Township Library, 1718 M St, Ord, NE, 68862. Tel: 308-728-3012. Fax: 308-728-3126. p. 1415

McBride, Tueredia, Dir, Lovington Public Library, 115 Main St, Lovington, NM, 88260. Tel: 575-396-3144, 575-396-6900. Fax: 575-396-7189. p. 1559

McBride-Brown, Sherry, Ref Librn, Boone Daniel Regional Library, Callaway County Public Library, 710 Court St, Fulton, MO, 65251. Tel: 573-642-7261. Fax: 573-642-4439. p. 1324

McBrien, Kate, Interim Exec Dir, Pejepscot Historical Society, 159 Park Row, Brunswick, ME, 04011. Tel: 207-729-6606. Fax: 207-729-6012. p. 980

McBryde, Allison Taylor, Coordr, Ch & Youth Serv, North Vancouver District Public Library, 1277 Lynn Valley Rd, North Vancouver, BC, V7J 2A1, CANADA. Tel: 604-990-5800. Fax: 604-984-7600. p. 2734

McBurney, Marlene, Librn, Palliser Regional Library, Coronach Branch, 111A Centre St, Coronach, SK, S0H 0Z0, CANADA. Tel: 306-267-3260. p. 2918

McBurney, Melissa, Libr Coordr, Med Librn, Columbia Basin College Library, 2600 N 20th Ave, Pasco, WA, 99301. Tel: 509-544-8336. Fax: 509-546-0401. p. 2523

McBurnie, Ann, Operations Mgr, Kwantlen Polytechnic University Library, 12666 72 Ave., Surrey, BC, V3W 2M8, CANADA. Tel: 604-599-3415. Fax: 604-599-2106. p. 2738

McCabe, Aliceann, Dir, Audrey Pack Memorial Library, 169 W Rhea Ave, Spring City, TN, 37381. Tel: 423-365-9757. Fax: 423-365-2198. p. 2266

McCabe, Bryan, Info Tech Serv Mgr, Saskatoon Public Library, 311-23rd St E, Saskatoon, SK, S7K 0J6, CANADA. Tel: 306-975-8136. Fax: 306-975-7542. p. 2926

McCabe, C Russell, Archivist, Delaware Public Archives, 121 Duke of York St, Dover, DE, 19901. Tel: 302-744-5000. Fax: 302-739-6710. p. 382

McCabe, Deborah M, Asst Dir, Portage County Public Library, Charles M White Library Bldg, 1001 Main St, Stevens Point, WI, 54481-2860. Tel: 715-346-1544. Fax: 715-346-1239. p. 2640

McCabe, Douglas, Curator of Manuscripts, Ohio University Libraries, Mahn Center for Archives & Special Collections, Vernon R Alden Library, 30 Park Pl, Fifth Flr, Athens, OH, 45701-2978. Tel: 740-593-2715. Fax: 740-593-2708. p. 1856

McCabe, Ellen, Bibliographer, Cataloger, SUNY Cortland, 81 Prospect Terrace, Cortland, NY, 13045. Tel: 607-753-2525. Fax: 607-753-5669. p. 1611

McCabe, James, Dr, Dir, Fordham University Library at Lincoln Center, Leon Lowenstein Bldg, 113 W 60th St, New York, NY, 10023-7480. Tel: 718-817-3570. Fax: 212-636-6766. p. 1678

McCabe, Jennifer, Dir, Libr Instruction, James Madison University Libraries & Educational Technologies, 800 S Main St, Harrisonburg, VA, 22807-0001. Tel: 540-568-3105. Fax: 540-568-6339. p. 2470

McCabe, Linda, Mgr, Lakeshore Technical College Library, 1290 North Ave, Cleveland, WI, 53015. Tel: 920-458-4183, Ext 130. Fax: 920-693-8966. p. 2585

McCabe, Michael M, Libr Dir, Brevard College, One Brevard College Dr, Brevard, NC, 28712-4283. Tel: 828-884-8248. p. 1777

McCabe, Murray, Chief Librn, Wellington County Library, 552 Wellington Rd 18, RR1, Fergus, ON, N1M 2W3, CANADA. Tel: 519-846-0918. Fax: 519-846-2066. p. 2805

McCabe, Nancy, Head, Tech Serv, Itasca Community Library, 500 W Irving Park Rd, Itasca, IL, 60143. Tel: 630-773-1699. Fax: 630-773-1707. p. 658

McCabe, Ronald, Dir, McMillan Memorial Library, 490 E Grand Ave, Wisconsin Rapids, WI, 54494-4898. Tel: 715-423-1040. Fax: 715-423-2665. p. 2650

McCafferty, Brian, Cat Librn, Wabash College, PO Box 352, Crawfordsville, IN, 47933. Tel: 765-361-6404. Fax: 765-361-6295. p. 734

McCafferty, Bridgit, Instruction & Ref Librn, Texas A&M University Central Texas, 1901 S Clear Creek Rd, Killeen, TX, 76549. Tel: 254-526-1617. Fax: 254-526-1589, 254-526-1993. p. 2350

McCafferty, Dominique, Sr Librn, Ch Serv, Covina Public Library, 234 N Second Ave, Covina, CA, 91723-2198. Tel: 626-384-5312. Fax: 626-384-5315. p. 137

McCafferty, Justine, Purchasing, Saint Mary's Public Library, 127 Center St, Saint Marys, PA, 15857. Tel: 814-834-6141. Fax: 814-834-9814. p. 2135

McCaffery, Michael, Dir, Libr Serv, Dearborn Heights City Libraries, Caroline Kennedy Library, 24590 George St, Dearborn Heights, MI, 48127. Tel: 313-791-3800. Fax: 313-791-3801. p. 1168

McCaffery, Rebecca, Ad, Hopkinton Public Library, 13 Main St, Hopkinton, MA, 01748. Tel: 508-497-9777. Fax: 508-497-9778. p. 1096

McCaffrey, Colin, Classics Librn, Yale University Library, Classics, Phelps Hall, 344 College St, Fifth Flr, New Haven, CT, 06511. Tel: 203-432-0854. p. 357

McCaffrey, Elaine, Mgr, Alexandria Library, Talking Books, 5005 Duke St, Alexandria, VA, 22304-2903. Tel: 703-746-1760. p. 2444

McCaffrey, Kate, Dir, Northern Onondaga Public Library, 100 Trolley Barn Lane, North Syracuse, NY, 13212. Tel: 315-458-6184. Fax: 315-458-7026. p. 1707

McCaffrey, Kate, Dir, Northern Onondaga Public Library, Brewerton Branch, 5437 Library St, Brewerton, NY, 13029-8719. Tel: 315-676-7484. Fax: 315-676-7463. p. 1707

McCaffrey, Kate, Dir, Northern Onondaga Public Library, Cicero Branch, 8686 Knowledge Lane, Cicero, NY, 13039. Tel: 315-699-2032. Fax: 315-699-2302. p. 1707

McCaffrey, Michele, Ref & Instruction, Ref Coordr, Saint Michael's College, One Winooski Park, Box L, Colchester, VT, 05439-2525. Tel: 802-654-2411. Fax: 802-654-2630. p. 2422

McCahey, Neely, Dir, Cutchogue-New Suffolk Free Library, 27550 Main Rd, Cutchogue, NY, 11935. Tel: 631-734-6360. Fax: 631-734-7010. p. 1613

McCahon, Paula, ILL, Manatee County Public Library System, 1301 Barcarrota Blvd W, Bradenton, FL, 34205. Tel: 941-748-5555. Fax: 941-749-7191. p. 429

McCain, Deborah V, ILL, University of Mississippi, Science, 1031 Natural Products Ctr, University, MS, 38677. Tel: 662-915-7381. Fax: 662-915-7549. p. 1316

McCain, Diana, Head, Res Ctr, Connecticut Historical Society Research Center, One Elizabeth St, Hartford, CT, 06105. Tel: 860-236-5621, Ext 213. Fax: 860-236-2664. p. 344

McCain, Katherine W, PhD, Prof, Drexel University, Rush Bldg, Rm 306, 30 N 33rd St, Philadelphia, PA, 19104-2875. Tel: 215-895-2474. Fax: 215-895-2494. p. 2972

McCain, Linda, Librn, Crittenden County Library, Earle Branch, 703 Commerce St, Earle, AR, 72331. Tel: 870-792-8500. p. 109

McCain, Mimi, Br Mgr, Phoenix Public Library, Harmon Library, 1325 S Fifth Ave, Phoenix, AZ, 85003-2661. p. 76

McCain, Nancy S, Dir, Lake County Public Library, 1115 Harrison Ave, Leadville, CO, 80461-3398. Tel: 719-486-0569. Fax: 719-486-3544. p. 316

McCain, Vivian, Dir, Lincoln Parish Library, 910 N Trenton St, Ruston, LA, 71270-3328. Tel: 318-513-6408. Fax: 318-513-6446. p. 966

McCall, Barbara, Info Res Spec, Allison Transmission Inc, m/c K09, One Allison Way, Indianapolis, IN, 46222-5200. Tel: 317-242-0470. Fax: 317-242-3626. p. 749

McCall, Bob, Br Mgr, Polk County Public Library, Saluda Branch, 44 W Main St, Saluda, NC, 28773-0398. Tel: 828-749-2117. Fax: 828-749-2118. p. 1785

McCall, Jayne, Dir, Nocona Public Library, Ten Cooke St, Nocona, TX, 76255. Tel: 940-825-6373. Fax: 940-825-4587. p. 2366

McCall, Kevin, Librn, Patton & Boggs LLP, 2550 M St NW, 8th Flr, Washington, DC, 20037. Tel: 202-457-6000. Fax: 202-457-6315. p. 412

McCall, Patti, Head, Pub Serv, Pratt Institute Libraries, 200 Willoughby Ave, Brooklyn, NY, 11205-3897. Tel: 718-399-4223. Fax: 718-399-4401. p. 1594

McCall, Tracey, Law Librn, Dauphin County Law Library, Dauphin County Courthouse, Front & Market Sts, 4th Flr, Harrisburg, PA, 17101. Tel: 717-780-6605. Fax: 717-780-6481. p. 2064

McCallips, Cheryl, Ref & Instruction Librn, Pennsylvania State University Libraries, News & Microforms Library, 21 Pattee Library, University Park, PA, 16802-1804. Tel: 814-863-1365. p. 2148

McCallister, Chris, Adult Serv, Otterbein Public Library, 23 E First St, Otterbein, IN, 47970. Tel: 765-583-2107. Fax: 765-583-2337. p. 772

McCallister, Deborah, Dir, West Newton Public Library, 124 N Water St, West Newton, PA, 15089. Tel: 724-872-8555. Fax: 724-872-8555. p. 2154

McCallister, Vicki, Dir, Dickinson Public Library, 4411 Hwy 3, Dickinson, TX, 77539. Tel: 281-534-3812. p. 2313

McCallon, Mark, Dr, Asst Dir, Abilene Christian University, 221 Brown Library, ACU Box 29208, Abilene, TX, 79699-9208. Tel: 325-674-2344. Fax: 325-674-2202. p. 2271

McCallum, Carolyn, Exec Dir, Jackson/Hinds Library System, 300 N State St, Jackson, MS, 39201-1705. Tel: 601-968-5810. p. 1303

McCallum, Melanie, Actg Sr Commun Libr Mgr, Contra Costa County Library, Moraga Library, 1500 Saint Mary's Rd, Moraga, CA, 94556-2099. Tel: 925-376-6852. Fax: 925-376-3034. p. 209

McCallum, Sheila, Youth Serv, Burlington Public Library, 34 Library Lane, Burlington, CT, 06013. Tel: 860-673-3331. Fax: 860-673-0897. p. 333

McCallum, Sophie, Librn, Peayamechikee Public Library, Box 160, Pinehouse Lake, SK, S0J 2B0, CANADA. Tel: 306-884-4888. Fax: 306-884-2164. p. 2920

McCambridge, Anne, Ch, London Public Library, Children's, 251 Dundas St, London, ON, N6A 6H9, CANADA. Tel: 519-661-4600. p. 2818

McCambridge, Sara, Asst Dir, Homer Township Public Library District, 14320 W 151st St, Homer Glen, IL, 60491. Tel: 708-301-7908. Fax: 708-301-4535. p. 657

McCammond-Watts, Heather, Ch Mgr, Oak Park Public Library, 834 Lake St, Oak Park, IL, 60301. Tel: 708-452-3425. Fax: 708-697-6900. p. 684

McCan, Cindy, Dir, Richland Public Library, 100 E Main St, Richland, IA, 52585. Tel: 319-456-6541. Fax: 319-456-6541. p. 840

McCance, John, Dir, University of the Southwest, 6610 Lovington Hwy, T-30, Hobbs, NM, 88240. Tel: 575-492-2141. Fax: 575-392-6006. p. 1557

McCandless, Margie, Ref, Bellevue University, 1000 Galvin Rd S, Bellevue, NE, 68005. Tel: 402-557-7302. Fax: 402-557-5427. p. 1393

McCandless, Sandra Sherman, Dir, Decatur Public Library, 504 Cherry St NE, Decatur, AL, 35601. Tel: 256-353-2993. Fax: 256-350-6736. p. 14

McCann, Darlene, Coordr, Br Serv, Clarington Public Library, Orono Branch, 127 Church St, Orono, ON, L0B 1M0, CANADA. Tel: 905-983-5507. p. 2796

McCann, Elva, Librn, Rideau Lakes Public Library, Newboro, Ten Brock St, Newboro, ON, K0G 1P0, CANADA. Tel: 613-272-0241. Fax: 613-272-0241. p. 2803

McCann, Heather, Pub Serv, Ref Coordr, Massachusetts Institute of Technology Libraries, Rotch Library-Architecture & Planning, Bldg 7-238, 77 Massachusetts Ave, Cambridge, MA, 02139-4307. Tel: 617-253-7098. Fax: 617-253-9331. p. 1078

McCann, Heidi, Coordr, Ref (Info Serv), Mount Wachusett Community College Library, 444 Green St, Gardner, MA, 01440. Tel: 978-630-9125. Fax: 978-630-9556. p. 1090

McCann, Jan, Tech Serv, Mary L Cook Public Library, 381 Old Stage Rd, Waynesville, OH, 45068. Tel: 513-897-4826. Fax: 513-897-9215. p. 1945

McCann, Jett, Assoc Dean, Knowledge Mgt, Dir, Georgetown University, Dahlgren Memorial Library, Preclinical Science Bldg GM-7, 3900 Reservoir Rd NW, Washington, DC, 20007. Tel: 202-687-1448. Fax: 202-687-1862. p. 402

McCann, John, Bus Librn, Albertus Magnus College Library, 700 Prospect St, New Haven, CT, 06511. Tel: 203-773-8594. Fax: 203-773-8588. p. 355

McCann, Julie, Br Mgr, Toledo-Lucas County Public Library, Birmingham, 203 Paine Ave, Toledo, OH, 43605. Tel: 419-259-5210. Fax: 419-691-8242. p. 1939

McCann, Linda, Dir, Libr Serv, Bucks County Community College Library, 275 Swamp Rd, Newtown, PA, 18940-0999. Tel: 215-968-8003. Fax: 215-968-8142. p. 2097

McCann, Maggie, Pub Serv Librn, Our Lady of the Lake College Library, 5329 Didesse St, Baton Rouge, LA, 70808. Tel: 225-768-1783. Fax: 225-761-7303. p. 944

McCann, Mary, Dir, Pennsylvania Hospital, Medical Library, Three Pine Ctr, 800 Spruce St, Philadelphia, PA, 19107-6192. Tel: 215-829-3998. Fax: 215-829-7155. p. 2113

McCann, Paul, Dir, Dexter District Library, 3255 Alpine St, Dexter, MI, 48130. Tel: 734-426-4477. Fax: 734-426-1217. p. 1173

McCann, Siobhan, Ch, Perry Public Library, 3753 Main St, Perry, OH, 44081-9501. Tel: 440-259-3300. Fax: 440-259-3977. p. 1929

McCann, Stephanie, Asst Dir, Shannon Medical Center Library, Pharmacy Dept Library, 120 E Harris, San Angelo, TX, 76903. Tel: 325-653-6741. Fax: 325-657-5401. p. 2379

McCann, Susan, Dir, Philipsburg Public Library, 102 S Sansome, Philipsburg, MT, 59858. Tel: 406-859-5030. Fax: 406-859-3821. p. 1387

McCann, Telce, Asst Librn, Ch, Stone Memorial Library, 1101 Main St, Conneautville, PA, 16406. Tel: 814-587-2142. Fax: 814-587-2142. p. 2047

McCann, Thelma, Dir, Hightower Memorial Library, 630 Ave A, York, AL, 36925. Tel: 205-392-2004. p. 41

McCann, Valerie S, Librn, United States Navy, Naval Operational Medicine Institute Library, 340 Hulse Rd, Pensacola, FL, 32508-1089. Tel: 850-452-2256. Fax: 850-452-2304. p. 482

McCanse, Rebecca, Dir, Mount Morris Public Library, 105 S McKendrie Ave, Mount Morris, IL, 61054. Tel: 815-734-4927. Fax: 815-734-6035. p. 677

McCardle, Alice, Librn, Calhoun County Public Library, Shelton's Park, 25008 NW State Rd 73, Altha, FL, 32421. Tel: 850-762-3992. Fax: 850-762-3992 (call first). p. 428

McCardle, Rachel, Dir, Hardy Wilson Memorial Hospital Library, 233 Magnolia St, Hazlehurst, MS, 39083-2200. Tel: 601-894-4541, Ext 6270. Fax: 601-894-5800. p. 1301

McCardwell, Kathy, Librn & Archivist, Colorado Railroad Historical Foundation, Inc, 17155 W 44th Ave, Golden, CO, 80403-1621. Tel: 303-279-4591. Fax: 303-279-4229. p. 309

McCargar, Glenna, Pres, Mosier Valley Library, 1003 Third Ave, Mosier, OR, 97040. Tel: 541-478-3495. p. 2007

McCarley, Amy, Dir, Karnes City Public Library, 302 S Panna Maria, Karnes City, TX, 78118. Tel: 830-780-2539. Fax: 830-780-3790. p. 2348

McCarrell, Kyle, Cat & Acq, Augusta State University, 2500 Walton Way, Augusta, GA, 30904-2200. Tel: 706-737-1745. Fax: 706-667-4415. p. 518

McCarrell, Sharon, Librn, Concord Free Public Library, Fowler Memorial, 1322 Main St, Concord, MA, 01742. Tel: 978-318-3350. Fax: 978-318-0906. p. 1082

McCarrier, Eileen, Mgr, Pillsbury Winthrop Shaw Pittman LLP, 1650 Tysons Blvd, McLean, VA, 22102. Tel: 703-770-7742. Fax: 703-770-7901. p. 2478

McCarroll, Colleen, Libr Dir, Shimer College Library, 3424 S State St, Chicago, IL, 60616-3893. Tel: 842-249-7898. p. 624

McCart, Janet, Librn, Missouri Department of Corrections, Western Reception & Diagnostic Correctional Center, 3401 Faraon St, Saint Joseph, MO, 64506-5101. Tel: 816-387-2158. Fax: 816-387-2217. p. 1335

McCart, Jessica, Ch, Bossier Parish Central Library, 2206 Beckett St, Bossier City, LA, 71111. Tel: 318-746-1693. Fax: 318-746-7768. p. 945

McCarter, Bernestine, Dir, Calumet Park Public Library, 1500 W 127th St, Calumet Park, IL, 60827. Tel: 708-385-5768. Fax: 708-385-8816. p. 599

McCarter, Deena, Asst Librn, Palliser Regional Library, Coronach Branch, 111A Centre St, Coronach, SK, S0H 0Z0, CANADA. Tel: 306-267-3260. p. 2918

McCarthy, Ann, Dir, River Vale Free Public Library, 412 Rivervale Rd, River Vale, NJ, 07675. Tel: 201-391-2323. Fax: 201-391-6599. p. 1526

McCarthy, Barbara, Dir, Virginia Department for the Blind & Vision Impaired, 395 Azalea Ave, Richmond, VA, 23227-3633. Tel: 804-371-3661. Fax: 804-371-3508. p. 2492

McCarthy, Carole, Librn, South Hampton Free Public Library, 3-1 Hilldale Ave, South Hampton, NH, 03827. Tel: 603-394-7319. Fax: 603-394-7319. p. 1465

McCarthy, Cheryl A, Dr, Prof, University of Rhode Island, Rodman Hall, 94 W Alumni Ave, Ste 2, Kingston, RI, 02881-0815. Tel: 401-874-4654. Fax: 401-874-4964. p. 2973

McCarthy, Daryl, Dir, North Greenbush Public Library, 141 Main Ave, Wynantskill, NY, 12198. Tel: 518-283-0303. Fax: 518-283-0303. p. 1771

McCarthy, Deborah, Head, Tech Serv, University of Wyoming Libraries, 13th & Ivinson, Laramie, WY, 82071. Tel: 307-766-4228. Fax: 307-766-5588. p. 2658

McCarthy, Diana, Commun Librn, Okanagan Regional Library, Falkland Branch, 5771 Hwy 97, Falkland, BC, V0E 1W0, CANADA. Tel: 250-379-2705. p. 2730

McCarthy, Evelyn, Mgr, L C Anderson Memorial Library, 50 S Kennedy St, Metter, GA, 30439-4442. Tel: 912-685-2455. Fax: 912-685-4462. p. 544

McCarthy, James, Instruction & Ref Librn, Gallaudet University Library, 800 Florida Ave NE, Washington, DC, 20002-3095. Tel: 866-954-7986. p. 401

McCarthy, Kathy, Librn, South Shore Hospital, 55 Fogg Rd at Rte 18, South Weymouth, MA, 02190. Tel: 781-340-8000, 781-340-8528. Fax: 781-331-0834. p. 1126

McCarthy, Kevin, Dir, Perrot Memorial Library, 90 Sound Beach Ave, Old Greenwich, CT, 06870. Tel: 203-637-1066. Fax: 203-698-2620. p. 363

McCarthy, Kristin, Assoc Dir, New England School of Law Library, 154 Stuart St, Boston, MA, 02116-5687. Tel: 617-422-7282. Fax: 617-422-7303. p. 1065

McCarthy, Lissa, Circ Supvr, Schoolcraft College, 18600 Haggerty Rd, Livonia, MI, 48152-2696. Tel: 734-462-4400, Ext 5326. Fax: 734-462-4495. p. 1204

McCarthy, Matthew, Mgr, Halifax Public Libraries, Captain William Spry Branch, Ten Kidston Rd, Halifax, NS, B3R 2J7, CANADA. Tel: 902-490-5734. Fax: 902-490-5741. p. 2779

McCarthy, Maureen, Head, Adult Serv, Head, Circ, Swampscott Public Library, 61 Burrill St, Swampscott, MA, 01907. Tel: 781-596-8867. Fax: 781-596-8826. p. 1130

McCarthy, Meaghan, Archivist, State Historical Society of Iowa-Des Moines, 600 E Locust, Des Moines, IA, 50319-0290. Tel: 515-281-6200. Fax: 515-282-0502. p. 810

McCarthy, Megan, Acq of New Ser, Saint Mary's University, 5429 Inglis St, Halifax, NS, B3H 3C3, CANADA. Tel: 902-491-6320. Fax: 902-420-5561. p. 2782

McCarthy, Meredith, Ref Librn, Jefferson County Library, Arnold Branch, 1701 Missouri State Rd, Arnold, MO, 63010. Tel: 636-296-2204. Fax: 636-296-5975. p. 1331

McCarthy, Patrick, Head of Libr, University of California, San Diego, Social Science & Humanities Library, 9500 Gilman Dr, Mail Code 0175R, La Jolla, CA, 92093-0175. Tel: 858-822-3943. Fax: 858-534-7548. p. 162

McCarthy, Patrick, Dir, Saint Louis University, Medical Center Library, 1402 S Grand Blvd, Saint Louis, MO, 63104. Tel: 314-977-8800. Fax: 314-977-5573. p. 1361

McCarthy, Patty, Dir of Develop, Iowa City Public Library, 123 S Linn St, Iowa City, IA, 52240. Tel: 319-356-5249. Fax: 319-356-5494. p. 822

McCarthy, Sandy, Librn, Washtenaw Community College, 4800 E Huron River Dr, Ann Arbor, MI, 48105-4800. Tel: 734-677-5293. Fax: 734-973-3446. p. 1153

McCarthy, Sean, Librn, Illinois Institute of Art - Chicago Library, 350 N Orleans St, Chicago, IL, 60654-1593. Tel: 312-777-8728, 312-777-8730. Fax: 312-777-8782. p. 615

McCarthy, Susan, Actg Assoc Dir, Knowledge Serv, United States Department of Agriculture, 10301 Baltimore Ave, Beltsville, MD, 20705-2351. Tel: 301-504-5510. Fax: 301-504-5472. p. 1020

McCarthy, Susan, Div Chief, Br Serv, Arlington County Department of Libraries, 1015 N Quincy St, Arlington, VA, 22201. Tel: 703-228-6334. Fax: 703-228-3354. p. 2448

McCarthy, Tammy, Automation Syst Coordr, Burlington Public Library, 166 E Jefferson St, Burlington, WI, 53105. Tel: 262-342-1134. Fax: 262-763-1938. p. 2584

McCarthy-Bond, Kate, Ch, Wallingford Public Library, 200 N Main St, Wallingford, CT, 06492-3791. Tel: 203-265-6754. Fax: 203-269-5698. p. 373

McCartney, D Steven, Dir, Libr Serv, Meridian-Lauderdale County Public Library, 2517 Seventh St, Meridian, MS, 39301. Tel: 601-693-6771. Fax: 601-486-2260. p. 1308

McCartney, Jane, Dir, North English Public Library, 123 S Main, North English, IA, 52316. Tel: 319-664-3725. Fax: 319-664-3725. p. 835

McCartney, Kate, Head, Youth Serv, Marysville Public Library, 231 S Plum St, Marysville, OH, 43040-1596. Tel: 937-642-1876. Fax: 937-642-3457. p. 1915

McCarty, Jennifer, Commun Libr Mgr, County of Los Angeles Public Library, La Mirada Library, 13800 La Mirada Blvd, La Mirada, CA, 90638-3098. Tel: 562-943-0277. Fax: 562-943-3920. p. 142

Mccarty, Jennifer J, Asst Curator, Alaska Heritage Museum & Library at Wells Fargo, 301 W Northern Lights Blvd, K3212-051, Anchorage, AK, 99503. Tel: 907-265-2834. Fax: 907-265-2860. p. 43

McCarty, Kim, Circ Supvr, Valdez Consortium Library, 212 Fairbanks St, Valdez, AK, 99686. Tel: 907-835-4632. Fax: 907-835-4876. p. 55

McCarty, Mac, Circ, Reformed Theological Seminary Library, 5422 Clinton Blvd, Jackson, MS, 39209-3099. Tel: 601-923-1623. Fax: 601-923-1621. p. 1305

McCarty, Veda, Dir, Prescott Public Library, 607 Second St, Prescott, IA, 50859-0177. Tel: 641-335-2238. Fax: 641-335-2238. p. 839

McCarville, Maria, Dir, Wayne County Regional Library for the Blind & Physically Handicapped, 30555 Michigan Ave, Westland, MI, 48186-5310. Tel: 734-727-7310. Fax: 734-727-7333. p. 1236

McCarville, Sarah, Coordr, Youth Serv, Grand Rapids Public Library, 111 Library St NE, Grand Rapids, MI, 49503-3268. Tel: 616-988-5400. Fax: 616-988-5419. p. 1185

McCary, Pat, Asst Dir, United States Air Force, 55 FSS/FSDL, Bldg 73, 510 Custer Dr, Offutt AFB, NE, 68113-2150. Tel: 402-294-5822. Fax: 402-294-7124. p. 1411

McCasland, Mary, Dir, Buena Park Library District, 7150 La Palma Ave, Buena Park, CA, 90620-2547. Tel: 714-826-4100. Fax: 714-826-5052. p. 129

McCasland, Terri, Dir, Swisher County Library, 127 SW Second St, Tulia, TX, 79088. Tel: 806-995-3447. Fax: 806-995-2206. p. 2393

McCaslin, David, Access & Fulfillment Serv Mgr, California Institute of Technology, 1200 E California Blvd, M/C 1-32, Pasadena, CA, 91125-3200. Tel: 626-395-6412. Fax: 626-792-7540. p. 205

McCaslin, David, Asst Law Librn, Access Serv, Pennsylvania State University - Dickinson School of Law (University Libraries), 1170 Harrisburg Pike, Carlisle, PA, 17013-1617. Tel: 814-865-8863. Fax: 717-240-5127. p. 2042

McCaslin, Nikki, Coll Develop, Res & Instruction Librn, Auraria Library, 1100 Lawrence St, Denver, CO, 80204-2095. Tel: 303-556-3390. Fax: 303-556-3528. p. 298

McCaslin, Sharon, Univ Librn, Fontbonne University, 6800 Wydown Blvd, Saint Louis, MO, 63105. Tel: 314-889-4567. Fax: 314-719-8040. p. 1354

McCaughan, Dolores, Circ Supvr, Saint Joseph's University, Francis A Drexel Library, 5600 City Ave, Philadelphia, PA, 19131-1395. Tel: 610-660-1926. Fax: 610-660-1916. p. 2116

McCaughtry, Dottie, Librn, Pullman & Comley, 90 Statehouse Sq, Flr 13, Hartford, CT, 06103-3711. Tel: 860-525-6645. Fax: 860-424-4370. p. 347

McCauley, Andrea, Ref Serv, Pew Charitable Trusts Library, One Commerce Sq, 2005 Market St, Ste 1700, Philadelphia, PA, 19103-7017. Tel: 215-575-4869. Fax: 215-575-4939. p. 2114

McCauley, Angela, Ch, Harnett County Public Library, 601 S Main St, Lillington, NC, 27546-6107. Tel: 910-893-3446. Fax: 910-893-3001. p. 1806

McCauley, Anne, Exec Dir, Longyear Museum Library, 1125 Boylston St, Chestnut Hill, MA, 02467. Tel: 617-278-9000. Fax: 617-278-9003. p. 1081

McCauley, Cindy, Tech Coordr, Springdale Public Library, 405 S Pleasant St, Springdale, AR, 72764. Tel: 479-750-8180. Fax: 479-750-8182. p. 115

McCauley, Diane, Libr Asst, Venice Public Library, 300 S Nokomis Ave, Venice, FL, 34285-2416. Tel: 941-861-1330. Fax: 941-486-2345. p. 501

McCauley, Diantha, Dir, Augusta County Library, 1759 Jefferson Hwy, Fishersville, VA, 22939. Tel: 540-885-3961, 540-949-6354. Fax: 540-943-5965. p. 2464

McCaulla, Sandra, Circ, Elizabeth Jones Library, 1050 Fairfield Ave, Grenada, MS, 38901-3605. Tel: 662-226-2072. Fax: 662-226-8747. p. 1299

McCawley, Christina, Dr, Head, Acq, Head, Ser, West Chester University, 25 W Rosedale Ave, West Chester, PA, 19383. Tel: 610-436-2167, 436-2656. Fax: 610-738-0555. p. 2153

McChesney, Berkeley, Ch, Edwards Public Library, 30 East St, Southampton, MA, 01073-9324. Tel: 413-527-9480. Fax: 413-527-9480. p. 1126

McChesney, Catherine, Librn, Huntington Free Library, Nine Westchester Sq, Bronx, NY, 10461-3513. Tel: 718-829-7770. Fax: 718-829-4875. p. 1587

McChesney, Elizabeth, Dir, Ch Serv, YA Serv, Chicago Public Library, 400 S State St, Chicago, IL, 60605. Tel: 312-747-4784. Fax: 312-747-4077. p. 608

McClain, Charlene, Head, Circ, Tennessee Technological University, 1100 N Peachtree Ave, Cookeville, TN, 38505. Tel: 931-372-3326. Fax: 931-372-6112. p. 2231

McClain, David, Cat Librn, Baptist Bible College, 730 E Kearney St, Springfield, MO, 65803. Tel: 417-268-6075. Fax: 417-268-6690. p. 1365

McClain, Judy, Librn, Iowa Genealogical Society Library, 628 E Grand Ave, Des Moines, IA, 50309-1924. Tel: 515-276-0287. Fax: 515-727-1824. p. 809

McClain, Karen, Dir, Newhall Public Library, 14 Main St, Newhall, IA, 52315. Tel: 319-223-5510. Fax: 319-223-5510. p. 835

McClain, Kesha, Libr Asst I, Montgomery City-County Public Library System, Coliseum Boulevard Branch Library, 840 Coliseum Blvd, Montgomery, AL, 36109. Tel: 334-271-7005. Fax: 334-244-5754. p. 29

McClain, Matt, Circ Librn, Silver Lake Library, 203 Railroad St, Silver Lake, KS, 66539. Tel: 785-582-5141. Fax: 785-582-4282. p. 894

McClain, Rebecca, Cat, Chillicothe & Ross County Public Library, 140 S Paint St, Chillicothe, OH, 45601. Tel: 740-702-4145. Fax: 740-702-4153. p. 1867

McClain, Tonya, AV, Kokomo-Howard County Public Library, 220 N Union St, Kokomo, IN, 46901-4614. Tel: 765-457-3242. Fax: 765-457-3683. p. 758

McClamma, Charlotte, Med Librn, Rady Children's Hospital - San Diego, 3020 Children's Way, Mailcode 5043, San Diego, CA, 92123-4282. Tel: 858-966-7474. Fax: 858-966-4934. p. 232

McClanahan, Mary Ellen, Teen Serv, Preble County District Library, 450 S Barron St, Eaton, OH, 45320-2402. Tel: 937-456-4250. Fax: 937-456-6092. p. 1897

McClanahan, Susan, Mgr, Access Serv, Guilford College, 5800 W Friendly Ave, Greensboro, NC, 27410-4175. Tel: 336-316-2251. Fax: 336-316-2950. p. 1796

McClary, Tiffany, Dir, Mkt, New Jersey State Library, 185 W State St, Trenton, NJ, 08618. Tel: 609-278-2640, Ext 122. Fax: 609-278-2652. p. 1536

McClay, Bruce, Librn, Walla Walla University Libraries, 10345 SE Market St, Portland, OR, 97216. Tel: 503-251-6115, Ext 7306. Fax: 503-251-6249. p. 2015

McClay, Bruce, Librn, Walla Walla University Libraries, 104 S College Ave, College Place, WA, 99324-1159. Tel: 503-251-7306. Fax: 509-527-2001. p. 2513

McClay, Doug, Electronic Res, Instruction Librn, Warner Pacific College, 2219 SE 68th Ave, Portland, OR, 97215-4099. Tel: 503-517-1118. Fax: 503-517-1351. p. 2015

McClayton, Barbara, Interim Mgr, Montgomery County Public Libraries, Gaithersburg Interim Library, Lakeforest Mall, 701 Russell Ave D201, Gaithersburg, MD, 20879. Tel: 240-773-9494. p. 1038

McCleary, Jill, Coll Develop Librn, Arizona Historical Society, 949 E Second St, Tucson, AZ, 85719. Tel: 520-617-1184. Fax: 520-629-8966. p. 85

McCleary, Kimberly, Librn, Boston Public Library, Fields Corner, 1520 Dorchester Ave, Dorchester, MA, 02122-1319. Tel: 617-436-2155. Fax: 617-282-2738. p. 1057

McCleery, Cheryl, Libr Dir, Strong Public Library, 14 S Main St, Strong, ME, 04983. Tel: 207-684-4003. Fax: 207-684-4004. p. 1003

McClellan, Cynthia, Dir, Lancaster General Hospital, 555 N Duke St, Lancaster, PA, 17602. Tel: 717-544-5697. Fax: 717-544-4923. p. 2077

McClellan, Cynthia, Coordr, Access Serv, University of the Sciences in Philadelphia, 4200 Woodland Ave, Philadelphia, PA, 19104-4491. Tel: 215-596-8961. Fax: 215-596-8760. p. 2120

McClellan, Margaret, Pub Serv, Midlands Technical College Library, 1260 Lexington Dr, West Columbia, SC, 29170-2176. Tel: 803-822-3674. Fax: 803-822-3670. p. 2207

McClellan, Margie, Librn, East Mississippi Regional Library System, Mary Weems Parker Memorial, 1016 N Pine Ave, Heidelberg, MS, 39439. Tel: 601-787-3857. Fax: 601-787-3857. p. 1313

McClellan, Michele, Head, Circ & Reserve, New Orleans Baptist Theological Seminary, 4110 Seminary Pl, New Orleans, LA, 70126. Tel: 504-816-8018. Fax: 504-816-8429. p. 961

McClelland, Rita, ILL, Slippery Rock University of Pennsylvania, Slippery Rock, PA, 16057-9989. Tel: 724-738-2058. Fax: 724-738-2661. p. 2140

McClements, Nancy, Ref, University of Wisconsin-Madison, 728 State St, Madison, WI, 53706. Tel: 608-262-3193. Fax: 608-265-2754. p. 2608

McClendon, Carolyn, Br Mgr, Orange County Library District, South Trail, 4600 S Orange Blossom Trail, Orlando, FL, 32839. p. 476

McClenney, Margaret, Access Serv, Norfolk State University Library, 700 Park Ave, Norfolk, VA, 23504-8010. Tel: 757-823-8445. Fax: 757-823-2431. p. 2482

McClenny, Bart, Admin Dir, Oklahoma Historical Society-Museum of the Western Prairie, 1100 Memorial Dr, Altus, OK, 73521. Tel: 580-482-1044. Fax: 580-482-0128. p. 1955

McClenon Grant, Marca, Ch, Larchmont Public Library, 121 Larchmont Ave, Larchmont, NY, 10538. Tel: 914-834-2281. p. 1651

McCleskey, Dawn, Librn, World Wildlife Fund-US Information Resource Center, 1250 24th St NW, Washington, DC, 20037-1125. Tel: 202-778-9636. Fax: 202-331-8836. p. 423

McCleskey, Sarah, Head, Access Serv, Interim Dir, Film & Media Libr, Hofstra University, 123 Hofstra University, Hempstead, NY, 11549. Tel: 516-463-5076. p. 1635

McClester, John, Acq, D'Youville College, 320 Porter Ave, Buffalo, NY, 14201-1084. Tel: 716-829-8129. Fax: 716-829-7770. p. 1597

McClintock, Susan Kincheloe, Head, Ref, Meredith College, 3800 Hillsborough St, Raleigh, NC, 27607-5298. Tel: 919-760-8382. Fax: 919-760-2830. p. 1815

McClish, Donna, Tech Info Spec, National Endowment for the Humanities Library, NEH Library, Rm 217, 1100 Pennsylvania Ave NW, Washington, DC, 20506. Tel: 202-606-8244. Fax: 202-606-8457. p. 409

McCloskey, Dan, Librn, Forsyth Institute, 140 The Fenway, Boston, MA, 02115-3799. Tel: 617-892-8245. Fax: 617-892-8470. p. 1061

McCloskey, Daniel, Syst Librn, New England College of Optometry Library, 424 Beacon St, Boston, MA, 02115. Tel: 617-587-5617. Fax: 617-587-5573. p. 1064

McCloskey, James M, Dir of Libr, Wilmington University Library, 320 DuPont Hwy, New Castle, DE, 19720. Tel: 302-328-9401. Fax: 302-328-0914. p. 384

McCloskey, Martha, Assoc Dir, Tom Green County Library System, 113 W Beauregard, San Angelo, TX, 76903. Tel: 915-655-7321. Fax: 915-659-4027. p. 2378

McCloskey, Maureen, Access Serv, ILL, Nicolet Area Technical College, 5364 College Dr, Rhinelander, WI, 54501. Tel: 715-365-4606. Fax: 715-365-4404. p. 2633

McCloskey, Richard, Tech Serv, Northwest Regional Library, 210 LaBree Ave N, Thief River Falls, MN, 56701. Tel: 218-681-1066. Fax: 218-681-1095. p. 1286

McCloskey, Ryan, IT Mgr, Bernards Township Library, 32 S Maple Ave, Basking Ridge, NJ, 07920-1216. Tel: 908-204-3031. Fax: 908-766-1580. p. 1470

McCloud, Alice, Br Mgr, San Francisco Public Library, Noe Valley/Sally Brunn Branch Library, 451 Jersey St, San Francisco, CA, 94114-3632. Tel: 415-355-5707. Fax: 415-282-8736. p. 246

McCloud, Bonnie M, Acq, Clackamas Community College, 19600 S Molalla Ave, Oregon City, OR, 97045. Tel: 503-657-6958, Ext 2466. Fax: 503-655-8925. p. 2009

McCloud, Jacquelyn, Digital Content Serv/Ref Librn, Cleveland State University, Cleveland-Marshall Law Library, Cleveland-Marshall College of Law, 1801 Euclid Ave, Cleveland, OH, 44115-2223. Tel: 216-523-7364. Fax: 216-687-6881. p. 1878

McCloud, Mary, Mgr, Department of Veterans Affairs, One Medical Center Dr, Clarksburg, WV, 26301. Tel: 304-623-7635. Fax: 304-623-7618. p. 2557

McCloud, Shirley, Libr Tech, Charlie Norwood VA Medical Center Library, One Freedom Way, Augusta, GA, 30904-6285. Tel: 706-733-0188, Ext 2820. Fax: 706-823-3920. p. 520

McCloy, Donna, ILL, Ref, Southern Arkansas University, 100 E University, Magnolia, AR, 71753-5000. Tel: 870-235-4178. Fax: 870-235-5018. p. 108

McCloy, E Keenon, Dir of Libr, Memphis Public Library & Information Center, 3030 Poplar Ave, Memphis, TN, 38111-3527. Tel: 901-415-2700. Fax: 901-323-7108. p. 2249

McCloy, Eric, Exec Dir, Arcadia University, 450 S Easton Rd, Glenside, PA, 19038-3295. Tel: 215-572-8521. Fax: 215-572-0240. p. 2061

McCluer, Debera, Ch, Hillsdale Community Library, 11 E Bacon St, Hillsdale, MI, 49242. Tel: 517-437-6473. Fax: 517-437-6477. p. 1190

McCluer, Molly, Nashville Satellite Librn, US Court of Appeals for the Sixth Circuit Library, 312 Potter Stewart US Courthouse, Cincinnati, OH, 45202. Tel: 513-564-7321. Fax: 513-564-7329. p. 1873

McClung, Anne, Librn, Rockbridge Regional Library, Goshen Public, 1124 Virginia Ave, Goshen, VA, 24439. Tel: 540-997-0351. Fax: 540-997-0019. p. 2474

McClung, Carol, Dir, Rupert Community Public Library, 602 Nicholas St, Rupert, WV, 25984. Tel: 304-392-6158. Fax: 304-392-5460. p. 2571

McClung, Larry, Librn, Brookhaven College, 3939 Valley View, Farmers Branch, TX, 75244-4997. Tel: 972-860-4854. Fax: 972-860-4675. p. 2319

McClung, Laura, Adult Serv, Goodland Public Library, 812 Broadway, Goodland, KS, 67735. Tel: 785-899-5461. Fax: 785-899-5461. p. 869

McClung, Mary, Dir, West Georgia Technical College Library, One College Circle, La Grange, GA, 30240. Tel: 770-537-6065. p. 538

McClung, Mary, Dir, Libr Serv, West Georgia Technical College, 176 Murphy Campus Blvd, Waco, GA, 30182. Tel: 770-537-6066. Fax: 770-537-7997. p. 556

McClung, Mary Jane, Circ Serv Librn, Monticello Union Township Public Library, 321 W Broadway, Monticello, IN, 47960-2047. Tel: 574-583-2665, 574-583-5643. Fax: 574-583-2782. p. 766

McClure, Charles, Dr, Dir, Info Inst, Prof, Florida State University, College of Communication & Information, 142 Collegiate Loop, Tallahassee, FL, 32306-2100. Tel: 850-644-8109. Fax: 850-644-9763. p. 2963

McClure, Heather, Archivist, Tech Serv, Saint John's College, 1160 Camino Cruz Blanca, Santa Fe, NM, 87505. Tel: 505-984-6045. Fax: 505-984-6004. p. 1563

McClure, Jonnica, Mgr, Lyon County Library System, Fernley Branch, 575 Silver Lace Blvd, Fernley, NV, 89408-8547. Tel: 775-575-3366. Fax: 775-575-3368. p. 1435

McClure, Karen D, Librn, Collins Public Library, 2341 Main St, Collins, NY, 14034-9799. Tel: 716-532-5129. Fax: 716-532-6210. p. 1609

McClure, Kate, Librn, San Luis Obispo County Library, Shell Beach Branch, 230 Leeward Ave, Shell Beach, CA, 93449. Tel: 805-773-2263. Fax: 805-773-2891. p. 254

McClure, Kathy, Ch, Eva K Bowlby Public Library, 311 N West St, Waynesburg, PA, 15370-1238. Tel: 724-727-9776, Ext 15. Fax: 724-852-1900. p. 2152

McClure, Kevin, Res/Govt Doc Librn, Illinois Institute of Technology, Chicago-Kent College of Law Library, 565 W Adams St, Chicago, IL, 60661. Tel: 312-906-5620. Fax: 312-906-5679. p. 615

McClure Kolk, Sarah, Instruction & Outreach, Calvin College & Calvin Theological Seminary, 1855 Knollcrest Circle SE, Grand Rapids, MI, 49546-4402. Tel: 616-526-6014. Fax: 616-526-6470. p. 1184

McClure, Rita, Circ, Meridian Community College, 910 Hwy 19 N, Meridian, MS, 39307. Tel: 601-484-8761. Fax: 601-482-3936. p. 1308

McClure, Tamara, Dir, Fuller Public Library, 29 School St, Hillsboro, NH, 03244. Tel: 603-464-3595. Fax: 603-464-4572. p. 1451

McClurg, Linda, Circ, Crestline Public Library, 324 N Thoman St, Crestline, OH, 44827-1410. Tel: 419-683-3909. Fax: 419-683-3022. p. 1892

McClurkan, Carolyn, Archivist, Kitsap County Historical Society, 280 Fourth St, Bremerton, WA, 98337-1813. Tel: 360-479-6226. Fax: 360-415-9294. p. 2510

McCluskey, Donna, Librn, Isaac F Umberhine Library, 164 Main St, Ste 3, Richmond, ME, 04357. Tel: 207-737-2770. p. 999

McCluskey, Eileen, Br Mgr, High Plains Library District, Carbon Valley Regional Library, Seven Park Ave, Firestone, CO, 80504. Tel: 720-685-5105. Fax: 720-685-5101. p. 311

McCluskey, Holly H, Curator, The Museums of Oglebay Institute Library, Oglebay Institute, The Burton Center, Wheeling, WV, 26003. Tel: 304-242-7272. Fax: 304-242-7287. p. 2574

McCluskey, Kathleen, Librn, Mountaineers Library, 300 Third Ave W, Seattle, WA, 98119. Tel: 206-284-6310, Ext 3014. Fax: 206-284-4977. p. 2528

McCluskey, Renee Andrews, Br Mgr, Webster Parish Library, Sarepta Branch, 24522 Hwy 371, Sarepta, LA, 71071. Tel: 318-847-4992. Fax: 318-847-4826. p. 957

McClusky, Duncan, Librn, University of Georgia College of Agricultural & Environmental Sciences, 4601 Research Way, Tifton, GA, 31793. Tel: 912-386-3447. Fax: 912-391-2501. p. 554

McColgan, Katherine, Prog Officer, Canadian Association of Research Libraries, 350 Albert St, Ste 600, Ottawa, ON, K1R 1B1, CANADA. Tel: 613-562-5800, Ext 2768. Fax: 613-562-5297. p. 2959

McColl, Terri, Dir, New Milford Public Library, 200 Dahlia Ave, New Milford, NJ, 07646-1812. Tel: 201-262-1221. Fax: 201-262-5639. p. 1510

McColley, Allyn, Pub Serv, Buckham Memorial Library, 11 Division St E, Faribault, MN, 55021-6000. Tel: 507-334-2089. Fax: 507-384-0503. p. 1250

McCollins, Sharon, Asst Mgr, Dallas Public Library, 1515 Young St, Dallas, TX, 75201-5499. Tel: 214-670-1400. Fax: 214-670-7839. p. 2306

McColloch, Mary, Librn, Dexter Public Library, 724 Marshall St, Dexter, IA, 50070. Tel: 515-789-4490. Fax: 515-789-4490. p. 810

McCollough, Kristy, Mgr, Thomas County Public Library System, Gladys H Clark Memorial Library, 1060 NE Railroad St, Ochlocknee, GA, 31773. Tel: 229-574-5884. Fax: 229-574-5884. p. 553

McCollough, Tamika Barnes, Librn, NOAA-EPA Partnership, MD-C 267-01, 109 T W Alexander Dr, Research Triangle Park, NC, 27711. Tel: 919-541-2777. Fax: 919-685-3110. p. 1819

McCollum, Cristine M, Info Spec, Federal Reserve Bank of Philadelphia, 100 N Sixth St, 4th Flr, Philadelphia, PA, 19106. Tel: 215-574-6626. Fax: 215-574-3847. p. 2106

McCollum, Dan E, Asst Dir, Doc Delivery, Info Serv, Vanderbilt University, Annette & Irwin Eskind Biomedical Library, 2209 Garland Ave, Nashville, TN, 37232-8340. Tel: 615-936-6176. Fax: 615-936-1384. p. 2260

McCollum, Julie, Libr Asst, Youth Serv, Barry-Lawrence Regional Library, Aurora Branch, 202 Jefferson, Aurora, MO, 65605. Tel: 417-678-2036. Fax: 417-678-2041. p. 1346

McCollum, Melissa, Commun Libr Mgr, County of Los Angeles Public Library, Lawndale Library, 14615 Burin Ave, Lawndale, CA, 90260-1431. Tel: 310-676-0177. Fax: 310-973-0498. p. 142

McCollum, Vicki, Librn, Yukon Department of Environment Library, 10 Burns Rd, Whitehorse, YT, Y1A 4Y9, CANADA. Tel: 867-667-3029. Fax: 867-393-7197. p. 2934

McComb, Debbie, In Charge, New Albany Community Library, 98 Front St, New Albany, PA, 18833. Tel: 570-363-2418. p. 2095

McCombie, Michaelene, Asst Libr Dir, ILL, Northern Cambria Public Library, 1030 Philadelphia Ave, Northern Cambria, PA, 15714-1399. Tel: 814-948-8222. Fax: 814-948-2813. p. 2100

McCombs, Gillian, Dean & Dir, Southern Methodist University, Central University Libraries, 6414 Robert S Hyer Lane, Dallas, TX, 75275. Tel: 214-768-2401. Fax: 214-768-3815. p. 2310

McCombs, Gillian, Dean, Dir, Southern Methodist University, Fondren Library, 6414 Robert S Hyer Lane, Dallas, TX, 75275. Tel: 214-768-2401. Fax: 214-768-3815. p. 2310

McCombs, Joyce, Dir, Delta Community Library, 2291 Deborah St, Delta Junction, AK, 99737. Tel: 907-895-4102. Fax: 907-895-4457. p. 47

McCombs, Wayne, Dir, J M Davis Arms & Historical Museum, 330 N JM Davis Blvd, Claremore, OK, 74017. Tel: 918-341-5707. Fax: 918-341-5771. p. 1960

McConaghy, Debra, Asst Librn, Phillips 66 Research Library, 122 PLB PRC, Bartlesville, OK, 74003-6670. Tel: 918-661-1950. Fax: 918-662-2171. p. 1958

McConchie, Corinne, Tech Serv Mgr, North Vancouver District Public Library, 1277 Lynn Valley Rd, North Vancouver, BC, V7J 2A1, CANADA. Tel: 604-990-5800. Fax: 604-984-7600. p. 2734

McConnel, Jon, Instruction & Ref Librn, Whatcom Community College Library, 237 W Kellogg Rd, Bellingham, WA, 98226. Tel: 360-383-3300. p. 2509

McConnell, Amanda, Circ Serv Coordr, Lawrence Public Library, 707 Vermont St, Lawrence, KS, 66044-2371. Tel: 785-843-3833, Ext 120. Fax: 785-843-3368. p. 877

McConnell, Barb, Librn, Lougheed Public Library, 5004 50 St, Lougheed, AB, T0B 2V0, CANADA. Tel: 780-386-2498. Fax: 780-386-2136. p. 2710

McConnell, Bridget, ILL, Monterey Public Library, 625 Pacific St, Monterey, CA, 93940-2866. Tel: 831-646-3932. Fax: 831-646-5618. p. 190

McConnell, Elaine, Curator, Rare Bks, United States Military Academy Library, Jefferson Hall Library & Learning Center, 758 Cullum Rd, West Point, NY, 10996. Tel: 845-938-3833. Fax: 845-938-4000. p. 1767

McConnell, Judy, Librn, Per & Fac Outreach, Roger & Peggy Madigan Library, 999 Hagan Way, Williamsport, PA, 17701. Tel: 570-327-4523. Fax: 570-327-4503. p. 2156

McConnell, Kathrin, Libr Dir, United States Food & Drug Administration Biosciences Library, WO2, Rm 3051, 10903 New Hampshire Ave, Silver Spring, MD, 20993. Tel: 301-796-2387. Fax: 301-796-9852. p. 1042

McConnell, Kathrin L, Dir, United States Department of Health & Human Services, Food & Drug Administration Biosciences Library, WO2, 3rd Flr, 10903 New Hampshire Ave, Silver Spring, MD, 20993. Tel: 301-796-2387. p. 1039

McConnell, Lucinda, Br Mgr, Wake County Public Library System, Fuquay-Varina Community Library, 133 S Fuquay Ave, Fuquay-Varina, NC, 27526. Tel: 919-557-2793. Fax: 919-557-2792. p. 1817

McConnell, Mallory, Asst Dir, Exeter Community Library, 4569 Prestwick Dr, Reading, PA, 19606. Tel: 610-406-9431. Fax: 610-406-9415. p. 2133

McConnell, Mary, Assoc Univ Librn, University of Calgary Library, 2500 University Dr NW, Calgary, AB, T2N 1N4, CANADA. Tel: 403-220-3725. Fax: 403-282-1218. p. 2693

McConnell, Mathew P, Dir, Brownwood Public Library, 600 Carnegie Blvd, Brownwood, TX, 76801-7038. Tel: 325-646-0155. Fax: 325-646-6503. p. 2292

McConnell, Penny, Dir, Danville Area Community College Library, 2000 E Main St, Danville, IL, 61832-5199. Tel: 217-443-8734. Fax: 217-554-1623. p. 632

McConnell, Rebecca, Librn, Pendleton County Library, 256 N Main St, Franklin, WV, 26807. Tel: 304-358-7038. Fax: 304-358-7038. p. 2559

McConnell, Sue, Ch, Southeast Steuben County Library, 300 Civic Center Plaza, Ste 101, Corning, NY, 14830. Tel: 607-936-3713, Ext 503. Fax: 607-936-1714. p. 1611

McCook, Kathleen de la Pena, Distinguished Univ Prof, University of South Florida, 4202 Fowler Ave, CIS 1040, Tampa, FL, 33620-7800. Tel: 813-974-3520. Fax: 813-974-6840. p. 2964

McCool, Gary, Ref Serv Coordr, Plymouth State University, Highland St, Plymouth, NH, 03264-1595. Tel: 603-535-2258. Fax: 603-535-2445. p. 1462

McCorcle, Mary, Librn, Dallas Public Library, Arcadia Park, 1302 N Justin Ave, Dallas, TX, 75211-1142. Tel: 214-670-6446. Fax: 214-670-7502. p. 2306

McCord, Helen, Dir, Kimberly Public Library, 120 Madison St W, Kimberly, ID, 83341. Tel: 208-423-4262. Fax: 208-423-4556. p. 577

McCord, Sarah, Head, Ref, Massachusetts College of Pharmacy & Health Sciences, 179 Longwood Ave, Boston, MA, 02115-5896. Tel: 617-735-1439. Fax: 617-278-1566. p. 1063

Mccord, Shirley, Tech Serv, John C Hart Memorial Library, 1130 Main St, Shrub Oak, NY, 10588. Tel: 914-245-5262. Fax: 914-245-2216. p. 1743

McCorkle, Kathleen, Librn, Sedan Public Library, 115 N Chautauqua St, Sedan, KS, 67361-1301. Tel: 620-725-3405. Fax: 620-725-3405. p. 894

McCorkle, Mary, Dir, Coll Serv, Louisiana Tech University, Everett St at The Columns, Ruston, LA, 71272. Tel: 318-257-3555. Fax: 318-257-2579. p. 966

McCorkle, Sharon, Librn, Illinois Department of Corrections, Rte 2, Box 36, Sumner, IL, 62466. Tel: 618-936-2064. Fax: 618-936-2842. p. 709

McCormack, Edward, Dir, University of Southern Mississippi, 730 E Beach Blvd, Long Beach, MS, 39560-2698. Tel: 228-266-4241. Fax: 228-865-4544. p. 1307

McCormack, Fatmata, Learning Res Ctr Spec, United States Agency for International Development, 1300 Pennsylvania Ave NW, Rm M01-010, Washington, DC, 20523-1000. Tel: 202-712-0579. Fax: 202-216-3515. p. 417

McCormack, Linda, Dir, Rock Rapids Public Library, 102 S Greene St, Rock Rapids, IA, 51246. Tel: 712-472-3541. Fax: 712-472-3541. p. 840

McCormack, Melanie, Asst Coordr, Adult Serv, Fairfield County District Library, 219 N Broad St, Lancaster, OH, 43130-3098. Tel: 740-653-2745. Fax: 740-653-4199. p. 1908

McCormack, Patsy, Librn, Trepassey Public Library, Molloy's Rd, Trepassey, NL, A0A 4B0, CANADA. Tel: 709-438-2224. Fax: 709-438-2224. p. 2773

McCormack, Rita, Media Serv Librn, Richmond Memorial Library, 19 Ross St, Batavia, NY, 14020. Tel: 585-343-9550. Fax: 585-344-4651. p. 1578

McCormack, Sarah, Head Librn, Brooks Public Library, 420 First Ave W, Brooks, AB, T1R 1B9, CANADA. Tel: 403-362-2947. Fax: 403-362-8111. p. 2686

McCormick, Agnes, Librn, Nottoway County Public Libraries, Burkeville Branch, 114 S Agnew, Burkeville, VA, 23922. Tel: 434-767-5555. Fax: 434-767-2652. p. 2458

McCormick, Beverly, Br Mgr, Seminole County Public Library System, Jean Rhein Central Library, 215 N Oxford Rd, Casselberry, FL, 32707. Tel: 407-665-1520. Fax: 407-665-1511. p. 431

McCormick, Bryan J, Dir, Hedberg Public Library, 316 S Main St, Janesville, WI, 53545. Tel: 608-758-6594. Fax: 608-758-6583. p. 2599

McCormick, Elizabeth, Cat, Radford University, 801 E Main St, Radford, VA, 24142-0001. Tel: 540-831-5635. Fax: 540-831-6138. p. 2487

McCormick, Evelyn, Coordr, Outreach Serv, Marysville Public Library, 231 S Plum St, Marysville, OH, 43040-1596. Tel: 937-642-1876. Fax: 937-642-3457. p. 1915

McCormick, Gail, Dir, General Federation of Women's Clubs, 1734 N St NW, Washington, DC, 20036-2990. Tel: 202-347-3168. Fax: 202-835-0246. p. 401

McCormick, Greg, Fiscal Officer, Illinois State Library, Gwendolyn Brooks Bldg, 300 S Second St, Springfield, IL, 62701-9713. Tel: 217-782-3504. Fax: 217-785-4326. p. 705

McCormick, Helen, Librn, Massachusetts Hospital School, Three Randolph St, Canton, MA, 02021. Tel: 781-830-8441. Fax: 781-830-8498. p. 1079

McCormick, Jennifer, Asst Archivist, Asst Librn, Charleston Museum Library, 360 Meeting St, Charleston, SC, 29403. Tel: 843-722-2996, Ext 244. Fax: 843-722-1784. p. 2183

McCormick, Kathleen, Assoc Dean, Spec Coll, Florida State University Libraries, Strozier Library Bldg, 116 Honors Way, Tallahassee, FL, 32306-0001. Tel: 850-644-2706. p. 494

McCormick, Linda, Cat, Duke University Libraries, Ford Library, One Towerview Rd, Durham, NC, 27708. Tel: 919-660-8016. Fax: 919-660-7950. p. 1787

McCormick, Lisa, Mgr, Libr Serv, Jewish Hospital, 4777 E Galbraith Rd, Cincinnati, OH, 45236. Tel: 513-686-5173. Fax: 513-686-5418. p. 1870

McCormick, Lynn, Literacy Serv, User Serv Librn, Tuolumne County Free Library, 480 Greenley Rd, Sonora, CA, 95370-5956. Tel: 209-533-5507. Fax: 209-533-0936. p. 269

McCormick, Marcella, Dir, Ridgeville Public Library, 308 N Walnut St, Ridgeville, IN, 47380. Tel: 765-857-2025. Fax: 765-857-2025. p. 775

McCormick, Margaret, Dir, Woods Hole Public Library, 581 Woods Hole Rd, Woods Hole, MA, 02543. Tel: 508-548-8961. Fax: 508-540-1969. p. 1142

McCormick, Mary, Pub Serv, Florida State University Libraries, College of Law Library, 425 W Jefferson St, Tallahassee, FL, 32306. Tel: 850-644-4578. Fax: 850-644-5216. p. 494

McCormick, Michael, In Charge, Harvard Library, History Department Library, Robinson Hall, Cambridge, MA, 02138. Tel: 617-495-2556. Fax: 617-496-3425. p. 1075

McCormick, Sheila, Dir, Clapp Memorial Library, 19 S Main St, Belchertown, MA, 01007-0627. Tel: 413-323-0417. Fax: 413-323-0453. p. 1052

McCormick, Sheila P, Dir, Sunderland Public Library, 20 School St, Sunderland, MA, 01375. Tel: 413-665-2642. Fax: 413-665-1435. p. 1130

McCormick, Yolanda Manning, Dir, Dillon County Library, 600 E Main St, Dillon, SC, 29536. Tel: 843-774-0330. Fax: 843-774-0733. p. 2192

McCorrison, Christine, Librn, Atkins Memorial Library, 419 Hudson Rd, Corinth, ME, 04427-3215. Tel: 207-285-7226. p. 982

McCoubrey, Katherine, Librn, Annapolis Valley Regional Library, Windsor Branch, 195 Albert St, Windsor, NS, B0N 2T0, CANADA. Tel: 902-798-5424. Fax: 902-798-0634. p. 2778

McCourry, Maurine, Acq of Monographs, Cat, Tech Serv & Syst Librn, Hillsdale College, 33 E College St, Hillsdale, MI, 49242. Tel: 517-607-2402. Fax: 517-607-2248. p. 1190

McCowin, Yvonne, In Charge, International Parking Institute, 701 Kenmore Ave, Fredericksburg, VA, 22401-5737. Tel: 540-371-7535. Fax: 540-371-8022. p. 2466

McCown, Alice, Assoc Librn, Columbus Technical College Library, 928 Manchester Expressway, Columbus, GA, 31904-6577. Tel: 706-649-1852. Fax: 706-649-1885. p. 526

McCown, Paula, Doc Delivery, Ball Memorial Hospital, 2401 W University Ave, Muncie, IN, 47303-3499. Tel: 765-741-1959. Fax: 765-747-0137. p. 766

McCoy, Barta, Librn, Northrop Grumman IT-TASC, 4801 Stonecroft Blvd, Chantilly, VA, 20151-3822. Tel: 703-633-8300, Ext 4654. Fax: 703-449-7648. p. 2453

McCoy, Betty, Librn, Latonia Baptist Church Library, 38th & Church Sts, Covington, KY, 41015. Tel: 859-431-8004. Fax: 859-431-1208. p. 910

McCoy, Brig, Network Serv Coordr, Kansas City, Kansas Public Library, 625 Minnesota Ave, Kansas City, KS, 66101. Tel: 913-279-2349. Fax: 913-279-2033. p. 875

McCoy, Cathleen, Head Librn, Cheltenham Township Library System, Elkins Park Free Library, 563 E Church Rd, Elkins Park, PA, 19027-2499. Tel: 215-635-5000. Fax: 215-635-5844. p. 2061

McCoy, Charlene, Librn, Hythe Public Library, PO Box 601, Hythe, AB, T0H 2C0, CANADA. Tel: 780-356-3014. Fax: 780-356-2009. p. 2707

McCoy, Eileen, Mgr, Ch Serv, East Central Georgia Regional Library, 902 Greene St, Augusta, GA, 30901. Tel: 706-821-2623. Fax: 706-724-6762. p. 519

McCoy, Erin, Circ, Eastern Nazarene College, 23 E Elm Ave, Quincy, MA, 02170. Tel: 617-745-3850. Fax: 617-745-3913. p. 1119

McCoy, Gina, Ref, Pepperdine University Libraries, School of Law-Jerene Appleby Harnish Law Library, 24255 Pacific Coast Hwy, Malibu, CA, 90263. Tel: 310-506-4643. Fax: 310-506-4836. p. 182

McCoy, Henry, Prog Coordr, Chattahoochee Valley Libraries, 3000 Macon Rd, Columbus, GA, 31906-2201. Tel: 706-243-2689. Fax: 706-243-2710. p. 525

McCoy, James, Librn, Ed & Hazel Richmond Public Library, 110 N Lamont St, Aransas Pass, TX, 78336-3698. Tel: 361-758-2350. p. 2276

McCoy, James, Automation Syst Coordr, Brownsville Public Library System, 2600 Central Blvd, Brownsville, TX, 78520-8824. Tel: 956-548-1055. Fax: 956-548-0684. p. 2292

McCoy, Kevin, Syst Librn, Suffolk County Community College, 533 College Rd, Selden, NY, 11784-2899. Tel: 631-451-4800. Fax: 631-451-4697. p. 1742

McCoy, Laureen, Adult Serv, Ref Serv, Ad, Altadena Library District, 600 E Mariposa St, Altadena, CA, 91001. Tel: 626-798-0833. Fax: 626-798-5351. p. 120

McCoy, Liberty, Instrul Serv/Ref Librn, Fielding Graduate University, 2020 De La Vina St, Santa Barbara, CA, 93105. Tel: 805-690-4373. p. 260

McCoy, Mary, Dir, Libr & Learning Res, Lamar State College-Orange Library, 410 Front St, Orange, TX, 77630-5796. Tel: 409-882-3083. Fax: 409-883-7552. p. 2367

McCoy, Michael, Adult Serv, Hastings-on-Hudson Public Library, Seven Maple Ave, Hastings-on-Hudson, NY, 10706. Tel: 914-478-3307. Fax: 914-478-4813. p. 1634

McCoy, Savannah, Youth Serv Coordr, Germantown Public Library, 51 N Plum St, Germantown, OH, 45327. Tel: 937-855-4001. Fax: 937-855-6098. p. 1901

McCoy, Shelly, Head, Student Multimedia Design Ctr, University of Delaware Library, 181 S College Ave, Newark, DE, 19717-5267. Tel: 302-831-2231. Fax: 302-831-1046. p. 386

McCoy, Stephanie, Dir, Pontiac Public Library, 60 E Pike St, Pontiac, MI, 48342. Tel: 248-758-3940. Fax: 248-758-3990. p. 1218

McCoy, Sydney, Br Mgr, Frederick County Public Libraries, C Burr Artz Public Library, 110 E Patrick St, Frederick, MD, 21701. Tel: 301-600-1630. Fax: 301-600-2905. p. 1029

McCoy, W Keith, Asst Dir, Somerset County Library System, One Vogt Dr, Bridgewater, NJ, 08807-2136. Tel: 908-526-4016, Ext 128. p. 1475

Mccoy-Lewis, Sandra, Admin Serv, US Customs & Border Protection Library, 90 K St NE, 9th Flr, Washington, DC, 20004. Tel: 202-325-0174. Fax: 202-325-0170. p. 418

McCracken, Jan, Librn, Akron Public Library, 302 Main, Akron, CO, 80720-1437. Tel: 970-345-6818. p. 287

McCracken, Linda, Dep Dir, Yakima Valley Libraries, 102 N Third St, Yakima, WA, 98901-2759. Tel: 509-452-8541. Fax: 509-575-2093. p. 2550

McCracken, Lois, Media Serv Librn, Housatonic Community College Library, 900 Lafayette Blvd, Bridgeport, CT, 06604. Tel: 203-332-5076. Fax: 203-332-5252. p. 331

McCracken, Lynn, Archives Mgr, Info Serv, ILL, The Parrott Centre, 376 Wallbridge-Loyalist Rd, Belleville, ON, K8N 5B9, CANADA. Tel: 613-969-1913, Ext 2339. Fax: 613-969-5183. p. 2795

McCracken, Vivian, Librn, Mount Carmel Area Public Library, 30 S Oak St, Mount Carmel, PA, 17851-2185. Tel: 570-339-0703. p. 2093

McCrackin, John, ILL Coordr, University of Wisconsin-Eau Claire, 105 Garfield Ave, Eau Claire, WI, 54702-4004. Tel: 715-836-3715. Fax: 715-836-2949. p. 2590

McCraney, Michelle, Assoc VPres & Dean, Daytona Beach College Library, 1200 W International Speedway Blvd, Daytona Beach, FL, 32114. Tel: 386-506-3055. Fax: 386-506-3008. p. 435

McCrank, Lawrence, Dr, Dean of Libr, Chicago State University, 9501 S Martin Luther King Jr Dr, LIB 440, Chicago, IL, 60628-1598. Tel: 773-995-2253. Fax: 773-995-3772. p. 610

McCrary, Linda, Mgr, ILL, Shreve Memorial Library, 424 Texas St, Shreveport, LA, 71101. Tel: 318-226-5897. Fax: 318-226-4780. p. 969

McCrary, Martha, Head, Tech Serv, United States Air Force, Air University - Muir S Fairchild Research Information Center, 600 Chennault Circle, Maxwell AFB, AL, 36112-6010. Tel: 334-953-7691. p. 24

McCrary, William Christopher, III, Libr Spec II, University of Missouri-Columbia, Math Sciences Library, 206 Math Sciences Bldg, Columbia, MO, 65211. Tel: 573-882-7286. Fax: 573-884-0058. p. 1326

McCray, Alexa T, Dep Dir, Harvard Library, Francis A Countway Library of Medicine, Boston Med Libr-Harvard Med Libr, Ten Shattuck St, Boston, MA, 02115. Tel: 617-432-4807. p. 1074

McCrea, Amber, Dir, Aram Public Library, 404 E Walworth Ave, Delavan, WI, 53115-1208. Tel: 262-728-3111. Fax: 262-728-3111. p. 2588

McCrea, Donna, Archives, Spec Coll Librn, University of Montana, Maureen & Mike Mansfield Library, 32 Campus Dr, No 9936, Missoula, MT, 59812-9936. Tel: 406-243-4403. Fax: 406-243-4067. p. 1386

McCreadie, Maureen, Dean, Learning Res, Bucks County Community College Library, 275 Swamp Rd, Newtown, PA, 18940-0999. Tel: 215-968-8004. Fax: 215-968-8142. p. 2097

McCreary, Alice, Ref Librn, Jenkins Law Library, 833 Chestnut St, Ste 1220, Philadelphia, PA, 19107-4429. Tel: 215-574-7942. Fax: 215-574-7920. p. 2111

McCreary, Karl R, Archivist, Oregon State University Libraries, University Archives & Special Collections, 121 Valley Library, Corvallis, OR, 97331-4501. Tel: 541-737-0539. Fax: 541-737-3453. p. 1995

McCree, Edward, Tech Coordr, Fort Worth Library, 500 W Third St, Fort Worth, TX, 76102. Tel: 817-871-8960. Fax: 817-871-7734. p. 2321

McCreless, Susan, Head, Tech Serv, University of Alabama in Huntsville, 301 Sparkman Dr NW, Huntsville, AL, 35899. Tel: 256-824-6537. Fax: 256-824-6083. p. 22

McCright, Hollis, Dir, Howard County Library, 500 Main St, Big Spring, TX, 79720-2532. Tel: 432-264-2260. Fax: 432-264-2263. p. 2289

McCrone, Kerry L, Dir, Newton Falls Public Library, 204 S Canal St, Newton Falls, OH, 44444-1694. Tel: 330-872-1282. Fax: 330-872-9153. p. 1922

McCrory, Nancy, Info Serv, Greenburgh Public Library, 300 Tarrytown Rd, Elmsford, NY, 10523. Tel: 914-721-8232. Fax: 914-721-8201. p. 1620

McCroskey, Marilyn, Prof, Missouri State University, Duane G Meyer Library, 901 S National Ave, Springfield, MO, 65897. Tel: 417-836-4525. Fax: 417-836-4764. p. 2968

McCroskey, Marilyn A, Head, Cat, Missouri State University, 850 S John Q Hammons Pkwy, Springfield, MO, 65807. Tel: 417-836-4541. Fax: 417-836-4764. p. 1367

McCrossen, Carol A, Head, Ref & YA Serv, Moffat Library of Washingtonville, Six W Main St, Washingtonville, NY, 10992. Tel: 845-496-5483. Fax: 845-496-6854. p. 1763

McCrum, Erin, Librn, Wapiti Regional Library, Saskatchewan Penitentiary, Box 160, Prince Albert, SK, S6V 5R6, CANADA. Tel: 306-765-8000, Ext 5643. p. 2922

McCruter, Mary B, Circ, ILL, Troy University, 502 University Dr, Dothan, AL, 36304. Tel: 334-983-6556, Ext 1320. Fax: 334-983-6327. p. 15

McCue, Amy, Br Mgr, Windsor Public Library, Wilson, 365 Windsor Ave, Windsor, CT, 06095-4550. Tel: 860-285-1931. Fax: 860-285-1931. p. 379

McCue, Diane, Libr Tech, Prince Edward Island Public Library Service, Tignish Public, 103 School St, Tignish, PE, C0B 2B0, CANADA. Tel: 902-882-7363. p. 2876

McCue, Don, Spec Coll Librn, A K Smiley Public Library, 125 W Vine St, Redlands, CA, 92373. Tel: 909-798-7632. Fax: 909-798-7566. p. 215

McCue, Janet, Assoc Univ Librn, Cornell University Library, 201 Olin Library, Ithaca, NY, 14853-5301. Tel: 607-255-5181. Fax: 607-255-6788. p. 1641

McCue, Michael, Dir, Teaneck Public Library, 840 Teaneck Rd, Teaneck, NJ, 07666. Tel: 201-837-4171. Fax: 201-837-0410. p. 1533

McCue, Nancy, Dir, Moultonborough Public Library, Four Holland St, Moultonborough, NH, 03254. Tel: 603-476-8895. p. 1458

McCuiston, Burl, Asst Dir, Coll Develop Instruction & Ref Librn, Lenoir-Rhyne University Library, 625 7th Ave NE, Hickory, NC, 28601. Tel: 828-328-7236. Fax: 828-328-7338. p. 1801

McCullar, Michele, Pub Serv, East Central University, 1100 E 14th St, Ada, OK, 74820-6999. Tel: 580-310-5370. Fax: 580-436-3242. p. 1955

McCullen, Elizabeth, Ref, Sampson-Clinton Public Library, 217 Graham St, Clinton, NC, 28328. Tel: 910-592-4153. Fax: 910-590-3504. p. 1784

McCulley, Carol, Librn, Linfield College, 900 S Baker St, McMinnville, OR, 97128. Tel: 503-883-2595. Fax: 503-883-2566. p. 2005

McCulley, Lucretia, Head, Ref, Instrul Serv Librn, Outreach Serv Librn, University of Richmond, 28 Westhampton Way, Richmond, VA, 23173. Tel: 804-289-8670. Fax: 804-289-8757. p. 2491

McCulley, Marcine, Dir, Rockwall County Library, 1215 E Yellowjacket Lane, Rockwall, TX, 75087. Tel: 972-204-7700. Fax: 972-204-7709. p. 2377

McCulloch, Adam, Archivist, Canadian Baptist Archives, McMaster Divinity Col, 1280 Main St W, Hamilton, ON, L8S 4K1, CANADA. Tel: 905-525-9140, Ext 23511. Fax: 905-577-4782. p. 2808

McCulloch, Alex, Head, Circ Serv, University of Waterloo Library, 200 University Ave W, Waterloo, ON, N2L 3G1, CANADA. Tel: 519-888-4567, Ext 35326. Fax: 519-888-4320. p. 2869

McCulloch, Andrew, Br Head, Winnipeg Public Library, Sir William Stephenson, 765 Keewatin St, Winnipeg, MB, R2X 3B9, CANADA. Tel: 204-986-7156. Fax: 204-986-7201. p. 2760

McCulloch, Patty, Mgr, Carbon County Library System, Sinclair Branch, 100 E Lincoln, Sinclair, WY, 82334. Tel: 307-324-6231. Fax: 307-324-6231. p. 2659

McCulloch, Steve, Librn, Raytheon Co, 1001 Boston Post Rd, Marlborough, MA, 01752-3789. Tel: 508-490-2288. Fax: 508-490-2017. p. 1103

McCullough, Andrea, Sr Res Librn, Faegre & Benson, LLP, 1900 15th St, Boulder, CO, 80302. Tel: 303-447-7700. Fax: 303-447-7800. p. 290

McCullough, Barbara, Br Mgr, Seminole County Public Library System, Northwest Branch, 580 Greenway Blvd, Lake Mary, FL, 32746. Tel: 407-665-1641. Fax: 407-665-1645. p. 431

McCullough, Barbara, Br Mgr, Seminole County Public Library System, West, 245 Hunt Club Blvd N, Longwood, FL, 32779. Tel: 407-665-1671. Fax: 407-665-1675. p. 431

McCullough, Barbara, Dir, William G Squires Library, 260 11th St NE, Cleveland, TN, 37311. Tel: 423-614-8567. Fax: 423-614-8555. p. 2230

McCullough, David, Ref Serv Coordr, Argosy University, Bldg 2, Ste 400, 980 Hammond Dr, Atlanta, GA, 30328. Tel: 770-407-1033. Fax: 770-671-0418. p. 510

McCullough, Deborah, Adult Serv Mgr, Public Library of Youngstown & Mahoning County, 305 Wick Ave, Youngstown, OH, 44503-1079. Tel: 330-744-8636. Fax: 330-744-3355. p. 1952

McCullough, Diana, Librn, Ranger City Library, 718 Pine St, Ranger, TX, 76470. Tel: 254-647-1880. Fax: 254-647-3070. p. 2373

McCullough, Doreen J, Dir, College of Saint Joseph, 71 Clement Rd, Rutland, VT, 05701. Tel: 802-776-5232. Fax: 802-776-5258. p. 2434

McCullough, Helen, Instrul Tech, Allegheny College Library, 555 N Main St, Meadville, PA, 16335. Tel: 814-332-3364. Fax: 814-337-5673. p. 2086

McCullough, Holly, Chief Curator, Telfair Museum of Art, 207 W York St, Savannah, GA, 31401. Tel: 912-790-8802. Fax: 912-790-8803. p. 551

McCullough, Holly, Mgr, Carnegie Library of Pittsburgh, Squirrel Hill, 5801 Forbes Ave, Pittsburgh, PA, 15217-1601. Tel: 412-422-9650. p. 2123

McCullough, Jane, Tech Serv, South Park Township Library, 2575 Brownsville Rd, South Park, PA, 15129-8527. Tel: 412-833-5585. Fax: 412-833-7368. p. 2142

McCullough, Jill, Ad, Clyde Public Library, 222 W Buckeye St, Clyde, OH, 43410. Tel: 419-547-7174. Fax: 419-547-0480. p. 1882

McCullough, Judy, Archives Mgr, Marshall County Historical Society Library, 123 N Michigan St, Plymouth, IN, 46563. Tel: 574-936-2306. Fax: 574-936-9306. p. 773

McCullough, Linda, Dir, Carthage Free Library, 412 Budd St, Carthage, NY, 13619. Tel: 315-493-2620. Fax: 315-493-2620. p. 1603

McCullough, Mark, Coordr, Ref (Info Serv), Minnesota State University, Mankato, ML3097, Mankato, MN, 56001. Tel: 507-389-5952. Fax: 507-389-5155. p. 1257

McCullough, Melissa, Ch, Louisville Free Public Library, Jeffersontown Branch, 10635 Watterson Trail, Jeffersontown, KY, 40299. Tel: 502-267-5713. Fax: 502-266-6569. p. 924

McCullough, Michael, Instrul Serv Librn, Monroe Community College, Damon City Campus Library, 228 E Main St, 4th Flr 4-101, Rochester, NY, 14604. Tel: 585-262-1413. Fax: 585-262-1516. p. 1730

McCullough, Ruth, Tech Serv, Kellogg-Hubbard Library, 135 Main St, Montpelier, VT, 05602. Tel: 802-223-3338. Fax: 802-223-3338. p. 2429

McCullough, Shirley, Coordr, Ser, Harris-Stowe State University Library, 3026 Laclede Ave, Saint Louis, MO, 63103-2199. Tel: 314-340-3621. Fax: 314-340-3630. p. 1355

McCullough, Suzy, Librn, Middle Georgia Regional Library System, Riverside Branch, Rivergate Shopping Ctr, 110 Holiday Dr N, Macon, GA, 31210. Tel: 478-757-8900. Fax: 478-757-1094. p. 541

McCullough, Tanga, Br Coordr, Dyersburg State Community College, 1510 Lake Rd, Dyersburg, TN, 38024. Tel: 731-475-3100. Fax: 901-475-0008. p. 2233

McCully, Kathleen, Bibliog Instr, Exec Dir, Isanti County Historical Society, 33525 Flanders St NE, Cambridge, MN, 55008. Tel: 763-689-4229. Fax: 763-552-0740. p. 1244

McCully, Melissa, Circ, Mount Wachusett Community College Library, 444 Green St, Gardner, MA, 01440. Tel: 978-630-9125. Fax: 978-630-9556. p. 1090

McCully, William, Exec Dir, Prospect Heights Public Library District, 12 N Elm St, Prospect Heights, IL, 60070-1450. Tel: 847-259-3500. Fax: 847-259-4602. p. 692

McCumsey, Liz, Librn, California Department of Corrections Library System, Pelican Bay State Prison, 5905 Lake Earl Dr, Crescent City, CA, 95532. Tel: 707-465-1000, Ext 7455. Fax: 707-465-9120. p. 222

McCune, Donna, Br Mgr, Riverside County Library System, Indio Library, 200 Civic Ctr Mall, Indio, CA, 92201. Tel: 760-347-2385. Fax: 760-347-3159. p. 217

McCune, Morgan, Cat, Tech Serv, Pittsburg State University, 1605 S Joplin St, Pittsburg, KS, 66762-5889. Tel: 620-235-4895. Fax: 620-235-4090. p. 890

McCurdy, Crystal, Br Mgr, Mexico-Audrain County Library District, Vandalia Branch, 309 S Main St, Vandalia, MO, 63382. Tel: 573-594-6600. Fax: 573-594-3590. p. 1345

McCurdy, Doris, Librn, Monroe County Public Library, 103 South St, Union, WV, 24983. Tel: 304-772-3038. Fax: 304-772-4052. p. 2573

McCurdy, Jane Byrd, Circ, Oyster Bay-East Norwich Public Library, 89 E Main St, Oyster Bay, NY, 11771. Tel: 516-922-1212. Fax: 516-922-6453. p. 1714

McCurdy, Lyn, Dir, AV, Wittenberg University, 807 Woodlawn Ave, Springfield, OH, 45504. Tel: 937-327-7325. Fax: 937-327-6139. p. 1936

McCurdy, Ollie, Br Mgr, Public Library of Youngstown & Mahoning County, Austintown, 600 S Raccoon Rd, Youngstown, OH, 44515. Tel: 330-792-6982. p. 1952

McCurdy, Ollie, Br Mgr, Public Library of Youngstown & Mahoning County, Lake Milton Branch, 1320 Grandview Ave, Lake Milton, OH, 44429. p. 1952

McCurdy, Ollie, Br Mgr, Public Library of Youngstown & Mahoning County, North Jackson Branch, 10775 Mahoning Ave Ext, North Jackson, OH, 44451. p. 1953

McCurdy, Sandra, Dir, Tarrant County College, Northwest Campus Walsh Library, 4801 Marine Creek Pkwy, Fort Worth, TX, 76179. Tel: 817-515-7725. Fax: 817-515-7720. p. 2323

McCurdy, Scott, Librn, United States Courts Libraries, 7A40 Mark O Hatfield, US Courthouse, 1000 SW Third Ave, Portland, OR, 97204. Tel: 503-326-8140. Fax: 503-326-8144. p. 2015

McCurdy, Scott M, Librn, US Court of Appeals Library, Pioneer Courthouse, 700 SW Sixth Ave, Ste 109, Portland, OR, 97204. Tel: 503-833-5310. Fax: 503-833-5315. p. 2015

McCurry, Cheryl, Youth Serv Librn, Oro Valley Public Library, 1305 W Naranja Dr, Oro Valley, AZ, 85737-9762. Tel: 520-229-5300. Fax: 520-229-5319. p. 70

McCusker, David, Ref Serv, American River College Library, 4700 College Oak Dr, Sacramento, CA, 95841. Tel: 916-484-8455. Fax: 916-484-8018, 916-484-8657. p. 220

McCusker, Kelly, Librn, University of Illinois Library at Urbana-Champaign, Social Sciences, Health & Education Library, 100 Main Library, MC-522, 1408 W Gregory Dr, Urbana, IL, 61801. Tel: 217-244-1868. Fax: 217-333-2214. p. 713

McCutchan, Sheila, Asst Librn, Doddridge County Public Library, 117 Court St, West Union, WV, 26456. Tel: 304-873-1941. Fax: 304-873-1324. p. 2574

McCutcheon, Barbara, Librn, Bonham Public Library, 305 E Fifth St, Bonham, TX, 75418-4002. Tel: 903-583-3128. Fax: 903-583-8030. p. 2290

McCutcheon, Camille, Coordr, Coll Mgt, Pub Serv Librn, University of South Carolina Upstate Library, 800 University Way, Spartanburg, SC, 29303. Tel: 864-503-5612. Fax: 864-503-5601. p. 2205

McCutcheon, Paul, Librn, Smithsonian Libraries, National Postal Museum Library, Two Massachusetts Ave NE, MRC 570, Washington, DC, 20560-0570. Tel: 202-633-5544. Fax: 202-633-9371. p. 415

McDade, Barbara Rice, Dir, Bangor Public Library, 145 Harlow St, Bangor, ME, 04401-1802. Tel: 207-947-8336. Fax: 207-945-6694. p. 975

McDade, Darlene, Asst Mgr, Atlanta-Fulton Public Library System, Southwest Regional Library, 3665 Cascade Rd SW, Atlanta, GA, 30331. Tel: 404-699-6363. Fax: 404-699-6381. p. 512

McDaid, Shirley, Dir, Adrian College, Educational Curriculum Center, 110 S Michigan St, Adrian, MI, 49221. Tel: 517-265-5161, Ext 4485. p. 1147

McDaniel, Doris, Head, Circ, Head, Per, University of North Alabama, One Harrison Plaza, Box 5028, Florence, AL, 35632-0001. Tel: 256-765-4241. Fax: 256-765-4438. p. 17

McDaniel, Gisele A, Ref & Instruction Librn, Tulsa Community College Learning Resources Center, Northeast Campus, 3727 E Apache St, Tulsa, OK, 74115-3150. Tel: 918-595-7502. Fax: 918-595-7504. p. 1983

McDaniel, Jon, Dir, Forsyth County Public Library, 585 Dahlonega Rd, Cumming, GA, 30040-2109. Tel: 770-781-9840. Fax: 770-781-8089. p. 527

McDaniel, Julie, Librn, Mercy Medical Center, 1343 N Fountain Blvd, Springfield, OH, 45501. Tel: 937-390-5000, Ext 2293. Fax: 937-390-5197. p. 1936

McDaniel, Julie, Dir, Libr Serv, Urbana University, 579 College Way, Urbana, OH, 43078-2091. Tel: 937-484-1335. Fax: 937-653-8551. p. 1942

McDaniel, Julie Ann, Librn, Community Hospital, 2615 E High St, Springfield, OH, 45505. Tel: 937-328-9468. Fax: 937-525-2314. p. 1936

McDaniel, Kathy, Librn, Glacier County Library, Browning Branch, PO Box 550, Browning, MT, 59417. Tel: 406-338-7105. Fax: 406-338-5436. p. 1377

McDaniel, Kelli, Libr Mgr, Piedmont Regional Library, Harold S Swindle Public Library, 5466 US Hwy 441 S, Nicholson, GA, 30565. Tel: 706-757-3577. Fax: 706-757-3246. p. 557

McDaniel, Mark, Circ Mgr, Reed College, 3203 SE Woodstock Blvd, Portland, OR, 97202-8199. Tel: 503-777-7702. Fax: 503-777-7786. p. 2014

McDaniel, Maureen, Dir, Stamps H B Memorial Library, Church Hill Branch, 302 E Main Blvd, Church Hill, TN, 37642. Tel: 423-357-4591. Fax: 423-357-8396. p. 2264

McDaniel, Michael W, Chief Librn, United States Army, Mickelsen Community Library, Mickelsen Library, Bldg 2E Sheridan Rd, Fort Bliss, TX, 79916. Tel: 915-568-6156. Fax: 915-568-5754. p. 2320

McDaniel, Rebecca, Br Head, Tombigbee Regional Library System, Weir Public Library, 123 Front St, Weir, MS, 39772. Tel: 662-547-6747. Fax: 662-547-6747. p. 1318

McDaniels, Kelly, Ch, Chickasaw Regional Library System, 601 Railway Express, Ardmore, OK, 73401. Tel: 580-223-3164. Fax: 580-223-3280. p. 1957

McDavid, Jo, Br Mgr, Sullivan County Public Library, Colonial Heights Branch, 149 Pactolus Rd, Kingsport, TN, 37663. Tel: 423-239-1100. Fax: 423-239-1100. p. 2224

McDavid, Jodi, Archivist, Cape Breton University Library, Beaton Institute, 1250 Grand Lake Rd, Sydney, NS, B1P 6L2, CANADA. Tel: 902-563-1690. Fax: 902-562-8899. p. 2785

McDermot, Leone, Chairperson, Truman College, 1145 W Wilson Ave, Chicago, IL, 60640-5691. Tel: 773-907-4877. Fax: 773-907-6803. p. 625

McDermott, Anne, Res Librn, Unilever HPC NA, Trumbull Corporate Park, 40 Merritt Blvd, Trumbull, CT, 06611. Tel: 203-377-8300, Ext 4312. p. 373

McDermott, April, Asst Dir, West Bridgewater Public Library, 80 Howard St, West Bridgewater, MA, 02379-1710. Tel: 508-894-1255. Fax: 508-894-1258. p. 1137

McDermott, Dona M, Archivist, United States National Park Service, 151 Library Lane, King of Prussia, PA, 19406. Tel: 610-296-2593. p. 2074

McDermott, Edward, Syst Librn, Clark University, 950 Main St, Worcester, MA, 01610-1477. Tel: 508-793-7651. Fax: 508-793-8871. p. 1143

McDermott, Ian, Asst Librn, Yale University Library, Center for British Art, 1080 Chapel St, New Haven, CT, 06520. Tel: 203-432-2848. Fax: 203-432-9613. p. 357

McDermott, Irene, Ref Librn, Crowell Public Library, 1890 Huntington Dr, San Marino, CA, 91108-2595. Tel: 626-300-0777, Ext 540. Fax: 626-284-0766. p. 254

McDermott, Janet, Cat, United Theological Seminary Library, 4501 Denlinger Rd, Trotwood, OH, 45426. Tel: 937-529-2201, Ext 3400. Fax: 937-529-2292. p. 1941

McDermott, Marie, Ch, New City Free Library, 220 N Main St, New City, NY, 10956. Tel: 845-634-4997. p. 1664

McDermott, Marilyn, Outreach & Instruction Librn, Mohawk College Library, 135 Fennell Ave W, Hamilton, ON, L9C 1E9, CANADA. Tel: 905-540-4247, Ext 26720. Fax: 905-528-5307. p. 2810

McDermott, Marilyn, Outreach & Instruction Librn, Mohawk College Library, IAHS (Institute for Applied Health Sciences) Library, 1400 Main St W, Hamilton, ON, L8S 1C7, CANADA. Tel: 905-540-4247, Ext 26720. Fax: 905-528-5307. p. 2810

McDermott, Monica, Ref Librn, Pollard Memorial Library, 401 Merrimack St, Lowell, MA, 01852. Tel: 978-970-4120. Fax: 978-970-4117. p. 1100

McDermott, Peggy, Head, Ref, Saint Louis University, Omer Poos Law Library, Morrissey Hall, 3700 Lindell Blvd, Saint Louis, MO, 63108-3478. Tel: 314-977-2739. Fax: 314-977-3966. p. 1361

McDermott, Samantha, Ch, Mount Angel Public Library, 290 E Charles St, Mount Angel, OR, 97362. Tel: 503-845-6401. Fax: 503-845-6261. p. 2007

McDevitt, Anna, Dir, Mallard Public Library, 605 Inman St, Mallard, IA, 50562. Tel: 712-425-3330. Fax: 712-425-3236. p. 829

McDevitt, Jeannette, Asst Librn, Carnegie Mellon University, Hunt Institute for Botanical Documentation, Hunt Library Bldg, 5th Flr, 4909 Frew St, Pittsburgh, PA, 15213-3890. Tel: 412-268-7301. Fax: 412-268-5677. p. 2124

McDevitt, Theresa, Dr, Spec Coll Librn, Indiana University of Pennsylvania, 431 S 11th St, Indiana, PA, 15705-1096. Tel: 724-357-3039. Fax: 724-357-4891. p. 2071

McDonald, Amanda, Tech Serv, Columbus-Lowndes Public Library, 314 N Seventh St, Columbus, MS, 39701. Tel: 662-329-5300. Fax: 662-329-5156. p. 1297

Mcdonald, Amy, In Charge, Annapolis Valley Regional Library, Robert Miller Memorial - Bridgetown Branch, 271 Granville St, Bridgetown, NS, B0S 1C0, CANADA. Tel: 902-665-2758. p. 2778

McDonald, Ann, Librn, Florida Hospital, 601 E Rollins, Orlando, FL, 32803. Tel: 407-303-1860. Fax: 407-303-1786. p. 475

McDonald, Antoinette, Libr Dir, Valerie Merrick Memorial Library, PO Box 479, Fort Totten, ND, 58335-0479. Tel: 701-766-1353. Fax: 701-766-1307. p. 1842

McDonald, Barbara, Assoc Univ Librn, Coll & Liaison Serv, Brock University, 500 Glenridge Ave, St. Catharines, ON, L2S 3A1, CANADA. Tel: 905-688-5550, Ext 3949. Fax: 905-988-5490. p. 2842

McDonald, Betty E, Media Spec, Columbia College, 1301 Columbia College Dr, Columbia, SC, 29203-9987. Tel: 803-786-3712. Fax: 803-786-3700. p. 2187

McDonald, Brenda, Dir, Cent Serv, Saint Louis Public Library, Central Library, 1301 Olive St, Saint Louis, MO, 63103. Tel: 314-241-2288. Fax: 314-539-0393. p. 1360

McDonald, Brenda, Dir, Cent Serv, Saint Louis Public Library, Compton Library, 1624 Locust St, Saint Louis, MO, 63103. p. 1360

McDonald, Brittany, Pub Serv, Lindsey Wilson College, 210 Lindsey Wilson St, Columbia, KY, 42728. Tel: 270-384-8251. Fax: 270-384-4188. p. 910

McDonald, Carolyn, Circ Supvr, Southwest Minnesota State University Library, 1501 State St, Marshall, MN, 56258. Tel: 507-537-6143. Fax: 507-537-6200. p. 1258

McDonald, Catherine, Asst Dir, Lucius Beebe Memorial Library, 345 Main St, Wakefield, MA, 01880-5093. Tel: 781-246-6334. Fax: 781-246-6385. p. 1132

McDonald, Christine, Dir, Crandall Public Library, 251 Glen St, Glens Falls, NY, 12801-3593. Tel: 518-792-6508. Fax: 518-792-5251. p. 1629

McDonald, Cynthia, Librn, Pine Forest Regional Library, Stone County, 242 Second St SE, Wiggins, MS, 39577. Tel: 601-928-4993. Fax: 601-928-4993. p. 1314

McDonald, Darla, Librn, Louisville Public Library, 217 Main St, Louisville, NE, 68037. Tel: 402-234-6265. p. 1407

McDonald, David, Info & Libr Tech Mgr, Legislative Library of Nova Scotia, Province House, 2nd Flr, Halifax, NS, B3J 2P8, CANADA. Tel: 902-424-5932. Fax: 902-424-0220. p. 2781

McDonald, David, Assoc Prof, University of Washington, Mary Gates Hall, Ste 370, Campus Box 352840, Seattle, WA, 98195-2840. Tel: 206-685-9937. Fax: 206-616-3152. p. 2976

McDonald, Dawna Gray, Asst Librn, Bette Winner Public Library, Recreation Ctr, Gillam, MB, R0B 0L0, CANADA. Tel: 204-652-2617. Fax: 204-652-2617. p. 2748

McDonald, Diane, Circ, Lyndhurst Free Public Library, 355 Valley Brook Ave, Lyndhurst, NJ, 07071. Tel: 201-804-2478. Fax: 201-939-7677. p. 1497

McDonald, Donna, Dir, Arkansas River Valley Regional Library System, Headquarters, 501 N Front St, Dardanelle, AR, 72834-3507. Tel: 479-229-4418. Fax: 479-229-2595. p. 97

McDonald, Donna, Asst Dir, Multimedia & Tech Serv, East Carolina University, William E Laupus Health Sciences Library, 600 Moye Blvd, Health Sciences Bldg, Greenville, NC, 27834. Tel: 252-744-2228. Fax: 252-744-3833. p. 1799

McDonald, Donna, Mgr, Henrico County Public Library, Sandston Branch Library, 23 East Williamsburg Rd, Sandston, VA, 23150-2011. Tel: 804-290-9700. Fax: 804-328-1041. p. 2471

McDonald, Dorothy, Librn, Annapolis Valley Regional Library, Annapolis Royal Branch, 285 Saint George St, Annapolis Royal, NS, B0S 1A0, CANADA. Tel: 902-532-2226. p. 2778

McDonald, Elizabeth, Head, Cat, University Libraries, University of Memphis, 126 Ned R McWherter Library, Memphis, TN, 38152-3250. Tel: 901-678-8237. p. 2252

McDonald, Ellen, Ref, Tufts University, Edwin Ginn Library, Mugar Bldg, 1st Flr, 160 Packard St, Medford, MA, 02155-7082. Tel: 617-627-3858. Fax: 617-627-3736. p. 1104

McDonald, Eva, Librn, Centennial College of Applied Arts & Technology, Progress Campus Library, 941 Progress Ave, Scarborough, ON, M1G 3T8, CANADA. Tel: 416-289-5000, Ext 2600. Fax: 416-289-5242. p. 2840

McDonald, Evelyn W, Libr Dir, Dimmit County Public Library, 200 N Ninth St, Carrizo Springs, TX, 78834. Tel: 830-876-1174. Fax: 830-876-3890. p. 2295

McDonald, Ginger, Librn, Zion Bible College Library, 27 Middle Hwy, Barrington, RI, 02806. Tel: 401-628-2117. Fax: 401-246-0906. p. 2163

McDonald, Jack, Pres, Rossland Historical Museum Association Archives, PO Box 26, Rossland, BC, V0G 1Y0, CANADA. Tel: 250-362-7722. Fax: 250-362-5379. p. 2737

McDonald, Jami, Br Mgr, Tazewell County Public Library, Richlands Branch, 102 Suffolk Ave, Richlands, VA, 24641-2435. Tel: 276-964-5282. Fax: 276-963-1107. p. 2498

McDonald, John, Dir, Claremont Colleges Library, 800 Dartmouth Ave, Claremont, CA, 91711. Tel: 909-621-8014. p. 134

McDonald, Joseph A, Dr, Dir of Libr Serv, Malone University, 2600 Cleveland Ave NW, Canton, OH, 44709-3897. Tel: 330-471-8377. Fax: 330-454-6977. p. 1863

McDonald, Julieta Lumbria, Coordr, Libr Serv, New Brunswick College of Craft & Design Library, 457 Queen St, 3rd Flr, Fredericton, NB, E3B 5H1, CANADA. Tel: 506-453-5938. Fax: 506-457-7352. p. 2763

McDonald, Kathryn, Libr Tech II, Pinal County Library District, 92 W Butte Ave, Florence, AZ, 85132. Tel: 520-866-6457. Fax: 520-866-6533. p. 63

McDonald, Krista, Dir, Miami University-Hamilton Campus, 1601 University Blvd, Hamilton, OH, 45011. Tel: 513-785-3235. Fax: 513-785-3231. p. 1904

McDonald, Margaret M, Acq, Coll Develop Librn, University of San Diego, Katherine M & George M Pardee Jr Legal Research Center, 5998 Alcala Park, San Diego, CA, 92110-2492. Tel: 619-260-4600, Ext 2541. Fax: 619-260-4616. p. 239

McDonald, Marianne Tomita, Circ/Reserves, University of California, Berkeley, Thomas J Long Business & Economics Library, Haas School of Business, Rm S352, Berkeley, CA, 94720-6000. Tel: 510-642-0371. Fax: 510-643-5277. p. 128

McDonald, Mary, Libr Dir, St Andrews University, 1700 Dogwood Mile, Laurinburg, NC, 28352. Tel: 910-277-5049. Fax: 910-277-5050. p. 1805

McDonald, Maureen, Head, Doc Delivery/ILL, University of Calgary Library, 2500 University Dr NW, Calgary, AB, T2N 1N4, CANADA. Tel: 403-220-7819. Fax: 403-282-1218. p. 2693

McDonald, Michael, Ref Serv, Internal Revenue Service, 1111 Constitution Ave NW, Rm 4324, Washington, DC, 20224. Tel: 202-622-8050. Fax: 202-622-5844. p. 405

McDonald, Mike, Dir, Franklin Ferguson Memorial Library, 410 N B St, Cripple Creek, CO, 80813. Tel: 719-689-2800. Fax: 719-689-3187. p. 297

McDonald, Nancy, Head, Outreach Serv, Waterford Township Public Library, 5168 Civic Center Dr, Waterford, MI, 48329. Tel: 248-674-4831. Fax: 248-674-1910. p. 1235

McDonald, Neil, Br Head, Toronto Public Library, Humber Summit, 2990 Islington Ave, Toronto, ON, M9L 2K6, CANADA. Tel: 416-395-5840. Fax: 416-395-5426. p. 2862

McDonald, Paula, Head, Circ, Head, ILL, Quinsigamond Community College, 670 W Boylston St, Worcester, MA, 01606-2092. Tel: 508-854-4366. Fax: 508-854-4204. p. 1144

McDonald, Peter, Dean, Libr Serv, California State University, Fresno, Henry Madden Library, 5200 N Barton Ave, Mail Stop ML-34, Fresno, CA, 93740-8014. Tel: 559-278-2403. Fax: 559-278-6952. p. 150

McDonald, Saddie, Librn, Mid-Mississippi Regional Library System, Pickens Public, 309 Hwy 51, Pickens, MS, 39146. Tel: 662-468-2391. Fax: 662-468-2392. p. 1306

McDonald, Sharon, Head, Ch, Bedford Free Public Library, Seven Mudge Way, Bedford, MA, 01730-2168. Tel: 781-275-9440. Fax: 781-275-3590. p. 1052

McDonald, Susan, Mgr, Charlotte Mecklenburg Library, South County Regional, 5801 Rea Rd, Charlotte, NC, 28277. Tel: 704-416-6600. p. 1782

McDonald, Tracy, AV Mgr, Westchester Public Library, 200 W Indiana Ave, Chesterton, IN, 46304-3122. Tel: 219-926-7696. Fax: 219-926-6424. p. 732

McDonnell, Dana, Circ Supvr, West Chester University, 25 W Rosedale Ave, West Chester, PA, 19383. Tel: 610-436-1098. p. 2153

McDonnell, Janice, Distance Educ, Lincoln Memorial University, Cumberland Gap Pkwy, Box 2012, Harrogate, TN, 37752. Tel: 423-869-7079. Fax: 423-869-6426. p. 2236

McDonnell, Leslie, Dir, Holliston Public Library, 752 Washington St, Holliston, MA, 01746. Tel: 508-429-0617. Fax: 508-429-0625. p. 1095

McDonnell, Michael, Head, Govt Doc & Maps, Western Michigan University, Arcadia at Vande Giessen St, Kalamazoo, MI, 49008-5353. Tel: 269-387-5187. Fax: 269-387-5012. p. 1198

McDonnell, R, Dir, Marysville Public Library, 231 S Plum St, Marysville, OH, 43040-1596. Tel: 937-642-1876. Fax: 937-642-3457. p. 1915

McDonnough, Charlene, Ad, Darlington County Library, Society Hill Branch, 473 S Main St, Society Hill, SC, 29593. Tel: 843-378-0026. Fax: 843-378-0026. p. 2192

McDonough, Beth, Ref Librn/Educ Liaison, Western Carolina University, 176 Central Dr, Cullowhee, NC, 28723. Tel: 828-227-3423. Fax: 828-227-7015. p. 1786

McDonough, Darren, Dir, Oberlin Public Library, 65 S Main St, Oberlin, OH, 44074-1626. Tel: 440-775-4790. Fax: 440-774-2880. p. 1925

McDonough, Debbie, Br Mgr, Massanutten Regional Library, Page Public, 100 Zerkel St, Luray, VA, 22835. Tel: 540-743-6867. p. 2470

McDonough, Douglas, Dir, Manchester Public Library, 586 Main St, Manchester, CT, 06040. Tel: 860-643-2471. Fax: 860-643-9453. p. 350

McDonough, Douglas, Dir, Manchester Public Library, Whiton Branch, 100 N Main St, Manchester, CT, 06040. Tel: 860-643-6892. Fax: 860-533-1251. p. 350

McDonough, Erin, Youth Serv Coordr, Waukee Public Library, 950 Warrior Lane, Waukee, IA, 50263. Tel: 515-987-1280. Fax: 515-987-5262. p. 850

McDonough, Jerome, Assoc Prof, University of Illinois at Urbana-Champaign, Library & Information Science Bldg, 501 E Daniel St, Champaign, IL, 61820-6211. Tel: 217-333-3280. Fax: 217-244-3302. p. 2965

McDonough, Kathleen, Ref, Holyoke Community College Library, Donahue Bldg, 2nd Flr, 303 Homestead Ave, Holyoke, MA, 01040-1099. Tel: 413-552-2598. Fax: 413-552-2729. p. 1095

McDonough, Kevin, Ref, Northern Michigan University, 1401 Presque Isle, Marquette, MI, 49855. Tel: 906-227-2118. Fax: 906-227-1333. p. 1207

McDonough, Kristin, Dir, New York Public Library - Astor, Lenox & Tilden Foundations, Science, Industry & Business Library, 188 Madison Ave, New York, NY, 10016-4314. Tel: 917-275-6975. Fax: 212-592-7082. p. 1693

McDonough, Lisa, Mgr, Vaughan Public Libraries, Kleinburg Library, 10341 Islington Ave N, Kleinburg, ON, L0J 1C0, CANADA. Tel: 905-653-7323. Fax: 905-893-2736. p. 2848

McDonough, Lisa, Mgr, Vaughan Public Libraries, Pierre Berton Resource Library, 4921 Rutherford Rd, Woodbridge, ON, L4L 1A6, CANADA. Tel: 905-653-7323. Fax: 905-856-5706. p. 2848

McDonough, Norma, Mgr, Portage County District Library, Brimfield Branch, 4064 Brimfield Plaza, Kent, OH, 44240. Tel: 330-677-5826. Fax: 330-677-5872. p. 1901

McDonough, Norma, Mgr, Portage County District Library, Randolph Branch, 1639 State Rte 44, Randolph, OH, 44265. Tel: 330-325-7003. Fax: 330-325-7740. p. 1901

McDonough, Timothy, Dir, Waterford Public Library, 117 Third St, Waterford, NY, 12188. Tel: 518-237-0891. Fax: 518-237-2568. p. 1763

McDougal, Marti, Dir/Librn, Linn County Library District No 1, 224 Main St, Parker, KS, 66072. Tel: 913-898-4650. Fax: 913-898-4650. p. 889

McDougal, Terri, Ch, Kanawha County Public Library, 123 Capitol St, Charleston, WV, 25301. Tel: 304-343-4646. Fax: 304-348-6530. p. 2556

McDougall, Donna, Librn, Parkland Regional Library, Wishart Branch, PO Box 48, Wishart, SK, S0A 4R0, CANADA. Tel: 306-576-2150. p. 2932

McDougall, Lynnda, Libr Asst, Smithers Public Library, 3817 Alfred Ave, Box 55, Smithers, BC, V0J 2N0, CANADA. Tel: 250-847-3043. Fax: 250-847-1533. p. 2737

McDowell, Bernadette, City Librn, Ventura County Library, Ray D Prueter Library, 510 Park Ave, Port Hueneme, CA, 93041. Tel: 805-486-5460. Fax: 805-487-9190. p. 280

McDowell, Cathryn, Dir, Snowflake-Taylor Public Library, 418 S Fourth W, Snowflake, AZ, 85937. Tel: 928-536-7103. Fax: 928-536-3057. p. 82

McDowell, Helen, Br Mgr, Charlotte Mecklenburg Library, Mountain Island Branch, 4420 Hoyt Galvin Way, Charlotte, NC, 28214. Tel: 704-416-5600. Fax: 704-416-5710. p. 1782

McDowell, Kate, Asst Prof, University of Illinois at Urbana-Champaign, Library & Information Science Bldg, 501 E Daniel St, Champaign, IL, 61820-6211. Tel: 217-333-3280. Fax: 217-244-3302. p. 2965

McDowell, Sharon, Dir, Montello Public Library, 128 Lake Ct, Montello, WI, 53949-9204. Tel: 608-297-7544. Fax: 608-297-2673. p. 2623

McDuffee, Diana, Dir, North Carolina Area Health Education Centers, Univ NC Health Sci Libr, CB 7585, Chapel Hill, NC, 27599-7585. Tel: 919-966-0963. p. 2951

McDuffie, Elaine, Youth Serv, Statesboro Regional Public Libraries, 124 S Main St, Statesboro, GA, 30458. Tel: 912-764-1344. Fax: 912-764-1348. p. 552

McDuffie-Smith, Zella, Ser Spec, Indian River State College, 3209 Virginia Ave, Fort Pierce, FL, 34981-5599. Tel: 772-462-7591. Fax: 772-462-4780. p. 446

McEachern, Felisha, Circ, Old Bridge Public Library, One Old Bridge Plaza, Old Bridge, NJ, 08857-2498. Tel: 732-721-5600, Ext 5012. Fax: 732-679-0556. p. 1516

McEachern, Josette, Info Res Mgr, Fraser Milner Casgrain LLP, 2900 Manulife Pl, 10180 - 101 St, Ste 2900, Edmonton, AB, T5J 3V5, CANADA. Tel: 780-423-7371. Fax: 780-423-7276. p. 2700

McEachern, Kristi, Librn, Mulvane Public Library, 101 E Main St, Mulvane, KS, 67110. Tel: 316-777-1211. Fax: 316-777-1755. p. 884

McEachern, Maria, Doc Delivery, ILL, Harvard-Smithsonian Center for Astrophysics Library, 60 Garden St, MS-56, Cambridge, MA, 02138. Tel: 617-495-7266. Fax: 617-495-7199. p. 1077

McEachern, Mark, Dir, Torrington Historical Society Library, 192 Main St, Torrington, CT, 06790. Tel: 860-482-8260. p. 372

McElhaney, Julie, Br Mgr, Licking County Library, Mary E Babcock Branch, 320 N Main St, Johnstown, OH, 43031. Tel: 740-967-2982. Fax: 740-967-0729. p. 1922

McElhenny, Andrea, Andrea, Coll Mgr, Libr Spec II, Northern Virginia Community College Libraries, Medical Education Campus, 6699 Springfield Center Dr, Rm 341, Springfield, VA, 22150. Tel: 703-822-6683. Fax: 703-822-6612. p. 2447

McElrath, Andrea, Ref, Saint John's University, Staten Island Campus, 300 Howard Ave, Staten Island, NY, 10301. Tel: 718-390-4456. Fax: 718-390-4290. p. 1748

McElroy, Anna, Br Mgr, Principal Librn, Oceanside Public Library, Mission Branch, 3861 B Mission Ave, Oceanside, CA, 92058. Tel: 760-435-5635. Fax: 760-433-6850. p. 200

McElroy, Deborah, Br Mgr, Palm Beach County Library System, Royal Palm Beach Branch, 500 Civic Center Way, Royal Palm Beach, FL, 33411. Tel: 407-790-6030. Fax: 407-790-6037. p. 503

McElroy, Emily, Head, Coll Develop, Head, Scholarly Communications, Oregon Health & Science University Library, 3181 SW Sam Jackson Park Rd, Portland, OR, 97239-3098. Tel: 503-494-6659. Fax: 503-494-3227. p. 2013

McElroy, Leanne, Libr Dir, Safford City-Graham County Library, 808 S Seventh Ave, Safford, AZ, 85546. Tel: 928-432-4151. Fax: 928-348-3209. p. 79

McElroy, Marcia, Librn, Las Animas - Bent County Public Library, 306 Fifth St, Las Animas, CO, 81054. Tel: 719-456-0111. Fax: 719-456-0112. p. 316

McElroy, Neil J, Dir, Lafayette College, 710 Sullivan Rd, Easton, PA, 18042-1797. Tel: 610-330-5150. Fax: 610-252-0370. p. 2052

McElroy, Richard, Acq, Ser, Massachusetts College of Art & Design, 621 Huntington Ave, Boston, MA, 02115-5882. Tel: 617-879-7112, 879-7106. Fax: 617-879-7110. p. 1063

McElroy-Boone, Adrienne, Dir, Smith, Gambrell & Russell, Prominade II, 1230 Peachtree St NE, Ste 3100, Atlanta, GA, 30309. Tel: 404-815-3538. Fax: 404-685-6838, 404-815-3509. p. 518

McElroy-Clark, Debby, Asst Dir, Support Serv, Memphis Public Library & Information Center, 3030 Poplar Ave, Memphis, TN, 38111-3527. Tel: 901-415-2700. Fax: 901-323-7108. p. 2249

McElveon, Pat, Librn II, Round Rock Public Library, 216 E Main St, Round Rock, TX, 78664. Tel: 512-218-7000, 512-218-7003. Fax: 512-218-7061. p. 2377

McElvey, Deborah, Acq Librn, Citrus County Library System, 425 W Roosevelt Blvd, Beverly Hills, FL, 34465-4281. Tel: 352-746-9077. Fax: 352-746-9493. p. 427

McEnany, Arthur E, Librn, Huey P Long Memorial Law Library, State Capitol, 900 N Third St, 14th Flr, Baton Rouge, LA, 70802. Tel: 225-342-2414. Fax: 225-342-2725. p. 943

McEntee, Heather, Dir, Bossier Parish Central Library, 2206 Beckett St, Bossier City, LA, 71111. Tel: 318-746-1693. Fax: 318-746-7768. p. 945

McEntire, Gerrye, Mem Discount Serv Mgr, Amigos Library Services, Inc, 14400 Midway Rd, Ste 200, Dallas, TX, 75244-3509. Tel: 972-340-2818. Fax: 972-991-6061. p. 2956

McEvers, Mike, Coordr, Circ, Colorado College, 1021 N Cascade Ave, Colorado Springs, CO, 80903-3252. Tel: 719-389-6658. Fax: 719-389-6082. p. 294

McEvoy, Jean, Info Literacy, Prince George's Community College Library, 301 Largo Rd, Largo, MD, 20774-2199. Tel: 301-322-0467. Fax: 301-808-8847. p. 1034

McEvoy, Tina, Asst Dir, Dir, Adult Serv, Lawrence Library, 15 Main St, Pepperell, MA, 01463. Tel: 978-433-0330. Fax: 978-433-0317. p. 1117

McEwen, Heather, Ref Librn, Northeastern Ohio Universities College of Medicine, 4209 State Rd 44, Rootstown, OH, 44272. Tel: 330-325-6600. Fax: 330-325-0522. p. 1932

McEwen, Janet, Librn, Western Plains Library System, Sentinel Public Library, 210 E Main, Sentinel, OK, 73664. Tel: 580-393-2244. p. 1961

McFadden, Carol, Ch, Patten Free Library, 33 Summer St, Bath, ME, 04530. Tel: 207-443-5141. Fax: 207-443-3514. p. 976

McFadden, David, Ref Librn, Southwestern Law School, 3050 Wilshire Blvd, Los Angeles, CA, 90010. Tel: 213-738-5771. Fax: 213-738-5792. p. 177

McFadden, Diane, ILL, Atlantic Public Library, 507 Poplar St, Atlantic, IA, 50022. Tel: 712-243-5466. Fax: 712-243-5011. p. 795

McFadden, Jacqueline, Doc, Winthrop University, 824 Oakland Ave, Rock Hill, SC, 29733. Tel: 803-323-2322. Fax: 803-323-2215. p. 2203

McFadden, Janet, Br Librn, Tay Township Public Library, Victoria Harbour Branch, 145 Albert St, Victoria Harbour, ON, L0K 2A0, CANADA. Tel: 705-534-3581. Fax: 705-534-3581. p. 2838

McFadden, Laurie, Access Serv, Archivist, Alfred University, Herrick Memorial Library, One Saxon Dr, Alfred, NY, 14802. Tel: 607-871-2385. Fax: 607-871-2299. p. 1572

McFadden, Riley, Dir, Westmoreland Reading Center, 50 Station Rd, Westmoreland, NY, 13490. Tel: 315-853-8001, Ext 5. p. 1768

McFadden, Robert, Archives, Pub Serv, Gordon-Conwell Theological Seminary, 130 Essex St, South Hamilton, MA, 01982-2317. Tel: 978-646-4074. Fax: 978-646-4567. p. 1125

McFadden, Sue, Ref, Louisiana Tech University, Everett St at The Columns, Ruston, LA, 71272. Tel: 318-257-3555. Fax: 318-257-2579. p. 966

McFadden, Sue A, Assoc Librn, Electronic Res, Indiana University East Campus Library, 2325 Chester Blvd, Richmond, IN, 47374. Tel: 765-973-8325. Fax: 765-973-8315. p. 775

McFadden, Timothy, Exec Dir, Boothbay Harbor Memorial Library, Four Oak St, Boothbay Harbor, ME, 04538. Tel: 207-633-3112. p. 978

McFadden, Timothy, Dir, Waldoboro Public Library, 908 Main St, Waldoboro, ME, 04572-0768. Tel: 207-832-4484. Fax: 207-832-4484. p. 1004

McFadden-Keesling, Allison, Librn, Oakland Community College, Woodland Hall, 7350 Cooley Lake Rd, Waterford, MI, 48327-4187. Tel: 248-942-3127. Fax: 248-942-3132. p. 1235

McFall, Linda, ILL, Coffeyville Public Library, 311 W Tenth, Coffeyville, KS, 67337-5816. Tel: 620-251-1370. Fax: 620-251-1512. p. 861

McFall, Lisa, Cat/Metadata Librn, Hamilton College, 198 College Hill Rd, Clinton, NY, 13323-1299. Tel: 859-4788. Fax: 315-859-4578. p. 1607

McFarlan, Ken, Librn, Lakeridge Health, One Hospital Ct, Oshawa, ON, L1G 2B9, CANADA. Tel: 905-576-8711, Ext 3334. Fax: 905-721-4759. p. 2827

McFarland, Anne L, Head, Bibliog & Digital Serv, State University of New York, College at Oneonta, 108 Ravine Pkwy, Oneonta, NY, 13820. Tel: 607-436-2727. Fax: 607-436-3081. p. 1711

McFarland, Denise, Dir, Sullivan Public Library, 436 Centre St, Sullivan, NH, 03445. Tel: 603-847-3458. Fax: 603-847-9154 (Town Hall). p. 1466

McFarland, Grace, Ser, United States Army, Brooke Army Medical Center Library, Medical Library MCHE-EDL, 3551 Roger Brooke Dr, Bldg 3600, Rm 371-17, Fort Sam Houston, TX, 78234-6200. Tel: 210-916-1119. Fax: 210-916-5709. p. 2320

McFarland, Marielle, Dir, Libr & Info Serv, University of Arkansas Community College at Hope, 2500 S Main St, Hope, AR, 71801. Tel: 870-722-8251. Fax: 870-777-8254. p. 104

McFarland, Robert, Dr, Librn, Washington University Libraries, Chemistry, 549 Louderman Hall, Campus Box 1134, Saint Louis, MO, 63130. Tel: 314-935-4818, 314-935-6591. Fax: 314-935-4778. p. 1362

McFarland, Seth I, Dir, Philmont Museum & Seton Memorial Library, Philmont Scout Ranch, 17 Deer Run Rd, Cimarron, NM, 87714. Tel: 575-376-2281, Ext 1256. Fax: 575-376-2602. p. 1553

McFarland, Tom, Dir, Admin Serv, Florida Institute of Technology, 150 W University Blvd, Melbourne, FL, 32901-6988. Tel: 321-674-8021. Fax: 321-724-2559. p. 463

McFarlane, Jackie, Ref, Oshawa Public Library, 65 Bagot St, Oshawa, ON, L1H 1N2, CANADA. Tel: 905-579-6111. Fax: 905-433-8107. p. 2827

McFarlin, Katie, Asst Librn, Aliceville Public Library, 416 Third Ave NE, Aliceville, AL, 35442. Tel: 205-373-6691. Fax: 205-373-3731. p. 4

McFarling, Pat, Dir, Kentucky Wesleyan College, 3000 Frederica St, Owensboro, KY, 42301. Tel: 270-852-3259. Fax: 270-926-3196. p. 931

McFarren, Jean, Admin Projects Mgr, Stark County District Library, 715 Market Ave N, Canton, OH, 44702-1018. Tel: 330-458-2702. Fax: 330-455-9596. p. 1864

McFaul, Mike, Librn, Laramie Soils Service Inc Library, 26 Six Bar E Rd, Centennial, WY, 82055. Tel: 307-742-4185. p. 2652

Mcferran, Noel S, Head, Pub Serv, University of Toronto Libraries, John M Kelly Library, University of Saint Michael's College, 113 Saint Joseph St, Toronto, ON, M5S 1J4, CANADA. Tel: 416-926-7114. Fax: 416-926-7262. p. 2866

McFerrin, Burke, Dir, Greenville-Butler County Public Library, 309 Ft Dale St, Greenville, AL, 36037. Tel: 334-382-3216. Fax: 334-382-9769. p. 19

McFerron, Jennifer, Head, Ref, Michigan City Public Library, 100 E Fourth St, Michigan City, IN, 46360-3393. Tel: 219-873-3476. Fax: 219-873-3068. p. 764

McFerron, Terice, Tech Serv, Indiana University of Pennsylvania, Harold S Orendorff Library, 101 Cogswell Hall, 422 S 11th St, Indiana, PA, 15705-1071. Tel: 724-357-2892. Fax: 724-357-4891. p. 2071

McGaffin, Rebecca, Head Librn, Young Men's Institute Library, 847 Chapel St, New Haven, CT, 06510. Tel: 203-562-4045. p. 359

McGaha, Vivian, Asst Dir, Coll Mgt, Pinellas Park Public Library, 7770 52nd St, Pinellas Park, FL, 33781-3498. Tel: 727-541-0718. Fax: 727-541-0818. p. 483

McGahee, Wanda, Mgr, Jefferson County Library System, McCollum Public, 405 N Main St, Wrens, GA, 30833-1142. Tel: 706-547-3484. Fax: 706-547-9358. p. 539

McGahey, Susan E, Head, Tech Serv, United States Court of Appeals, Burn Courthouse, 1st Flr, 601 Market St, Room 1609, Philadelphia, PA, 19106. Tel: 267-299-4300. Fax: 267-299-4328. p. 2118

McGahey, Yuni, Acq Asst, Saint Leo University, 33701 State Rd 52, Saint Leo, FL, 33574. Tel: 352-588-8419. Fax: 352-588-8484. p. 487

McGalliard, Mary, Libr Supvr, Southwest Baptist University Libraries, Mountain View Center Library, 209 W First St, Mountain View, MO, 65548. Tel: 417-934-5057. Fax: 417-934-5056. p. 1320

McGann, Bonnie, Br Mgr, Bruce County Public Library, Sauble Beach, 27 Community Centre Dr, RR 1, Box 11, Sauble Beach, ON, N0H 2G0, CANADA. Tel: 519-422-1283. Fax: 519-422-1283. p. 2837

McGann, Marcia, Dr, Dir, Marian Sutherland Kirby Library, 35 Kirby Ave, Mountain Top, PA, 18707-1214. Tel: 570-474-9313. Fax: 570-474-2587. p. 2093

McGannon, Diane, Outreach Serv Librn, National Sea Grant Library, Ocean Science & Exploration Ctr, URI-Bay Campus, Narragansett, RI, 02882-1197. Tel: 401-874-6114. p. 2168

McGarrell, Andrew, Tech Serv, Missouri Western State University, 4525 Downs Dr, Saint Joseph, MO, 64507-2294. Tel: 816-271-4368. Fax: 816-271-4574. p. 1352

McGarrity, Gayna, Asst Br Supvr, Region of Waterloo Library, Linwood Branch, 5279 Ament Line, Linwood, ON, N0B 2A0, CANADA. Tel: 519-698-2700. p. 2793

McGarrity, Patricia, Libr Tech, Mid-South Community College, Donald W Reynolds Ctr, 2000 W Broadway, West Memphis, AR, 72301-3829. Tel: 870-733-6768. Fax: 870-733-6719. p. 117

McGarvey, Marycatherine, Dir, Free Library of Springfield Township, 1600 Paper Mill Rd, Wyndmoor, PA, 19038. Tel: 215-836-5300. Fax: 215-836-2404. p. 2158

McGarvey, Nancy, Interim Dir, Syst/Ser/Ref Librn, Gwynedd-Mercy College, 1325 Sumneytown Pike, Gwynedd Valley, PA, 19437. Tel: 215-646-7300, Ext 493. Fax: 215-641-5596. p. 2063

McGary, Barbara, Youth Serv Coordr, Snyder County Libraries, Community Bldg, One N High St, Selinsgrove, PA, 17870-1599. Tel: 570-374-7163. Fax: 570-374-2120. p. 2138

McGauchie, Jackie M, Dir, Springtown Public Library, 626 N Main St, Springtown, TX, 76082-2541. Tel: 817-523-5862. Fax: 817-523-5922. p. 2388

McGaugh, Houston, Dir, Star of the Republic Museum Library, 23200 Park Rd 12, Washington, TX, 77880. Tel: 936-878-2461, Ext 234. Fax: 936-878-2462. p. 2398

McGavick, Mary H, Asst Dir, Public Library of Mount Vernon & Knox County, 201 N Mulberry St, Mount Vernon, OH, 43050-2413. Tel: 740-392-2665. Fax: 740-397-3866. p. 1919

McGeary, Timothy, Head, Libr Syst, University of North Carolina at Chapel Hill, Davis Library, 208 Raleigh St, Campus Box 3900, Chapel Hill, NC, 27514-8890. p. 1780

McGeath, Judy, ILL, Indianapolis-Marion County Public Library, 2450 N Meridian St, Indianapolis, IN, 46208. Tel: 317-275-4104. Fax: 317-269-5300. p. 753

McGeath, Kerry, Adminr, Southlake Public Library, 1400 Main St, Ste 130, Southlake, TX, 76092-7640. Tel: 817-748-8243. p. 2388

McGee, Angie, Br Mgr, Perry County Public Library, Lobelville Branch, 85 W Seventh St, Lobelville, TN, 37097. Tel: 931-593-3111. Fax: 931-593-2089. p. 2245

McGee, Cathy, Ch, Scott County Public Library, 104 S Bradford Lane, Georgetown, KY, 40324-2335. Tel: 502-863-3566. Fax: 502-863-9621. p. 915

McGee, Diane P, ILL, Harrison County Library System, 2600 24th Ave, No 6, Gulfport, MS, 39501-2081. Tel: 228-868-1383. Fax: 228-863-7433. p. 1299

McGee, Douglas, Librn, University of Pennsylvania Libraries, Engineering & Applied Science, 220 S 33rd St, Philadelphia, PA, 19104-6315. Tel: 215-898-8170. p. 2119

McGee, Gregg, Assoc Dir, Br Serv, Six Mile Regional Library District, District Branch Library, 2145 Johnson Rd, Granite City, IL, 62040. Tel: 618-452-6244. Fax: 618-452-6226. p. 651

McGee, John, Tech Coordr, University of North Alabama, One Harrison Plaza, Box 5028, Florence, AL, 35632-0001. Tel: 256-765-4454. Fax: 256-765-4438. p. 17

McGee, Loralei T, Librn, North Mississippi Medical Center, 830 S Gloster St, Tupelo, MS, 38801. Tel: 662-377-4399. Fax: 662-377-7239. p. 1316

McGee, Louise, Asst Librn, Woodsville Free Public Library, 14 School Lane, Woodsville, NH, 03785. Tel: 603-747-3483. p. 1468

McGee, Myrna, Asst Librn, Bella Vista Public Library, 11 Dickens Pl, Bella Vista, AR, 72714-4603. Tel: 479-855-1753. Fax: 479-855-4475. p. 94

McGee, Pat, Dir, Southeast Alabama Medical Center, 1108 Ross Clark Circle, Hwy 84 E, Dothan, AL, 36301-3024. Tel: 334-793-8102. p. 15

McGee, Patricia B, Coordr, Media Serv, Tennessee Technological University, 1100 N Peachtree Ave, Cookeville, TN, 38505. Tel: 931-372-3326. Fax: 931-372-6112. p. 2231

McGee, Sharon, Head, Archives & Spec Coll, Rec Librn, Kentucky State University, 400 E Main St, Frankfort, KY, 40601-2355. Tel: 502-597-6824. Fax: 502-597-5068. p. 914

McGee, Sherry A, Librn, Washoe Health System, 77 Pringle Way, Reno, NV, 89502-1474. Tel: 775-982-5693. Fax: 775-982-5735. p. 1434

McGee, Susan, Coordr, Circ, Jackson District Library, 290 W Michigan Ave, Jackson, MI, 49201. Tel: 517-788-4087, Ext 1345. Fax: 517-782-8635. p. 1195

McGee, Tony, Librn, Southwestern College Library, 900 Otay Lakes Rd, Chula Vista, CA, 91910-7299. Tel: 619-216-6619, 619-482-6373. Fax: 619-482-6417. p. 134

McGeehon, Carol, Tech Serv, Douglas County Library System, 1409 NE Diamond Lake Blvd, Roseburg, OR, 97470. Tel: 541-440-6005. Fax: 541-957-7798. p. 2016

McGehee, John, Dir of East Campus Libr, James Madison University Libraries & Educational Technologies, 800 S Main St, Harrisonburg, VA, 22807-0001. Tel: 540-568-3319. Fax: 540-568-6339. p. 2470

McGehee, Joy, Sci Outreach Librn, Benedictine University Library, 5700 College Rd, Lisle, IL, 60532-0900. Tel: 630-829-6050. Fax: 630-960-9451. p. 666

McGehee, Suzanne, Dir of Circ, Gulf Publishing Co Library, Two Green Plaza, Ste 1020, Houston, TX, 77046. Tel: 713-529-4301. Fax: 713-520-4433. p. 2335

McGeorge, Cindy, Youth Serv Librn, Middlesborough-Bell County Public Library, 126 S 20th St, Middlesboro, KY, 40965-1212. Tel: 606-248-4812. Fax: 606-248-8766. p. 929

McGhee, Devin, Mgr, Metropolitan Library System in Oklahoma County, Del City Library, 4509 SE 15th St, Del City, OK, 73115. Tel: 405-672-1377. Fax: 405-606-3292. p. 1972

McGhee, Ralph, Br Mgr, Knox County Public Library System, Mascot Branch, 2010 Library Rd, Mascot, TN, 37806-9999. Tel: 865-933-2620. Fax: 865-933-4239. p. 2242

McGiffin, Ginger, ILL, Libr Tech, Clarion University of Pennsylvania, 840 Wood St, Clarion, PA, 16214. Tel: 814-393-2343. Fax: 814-393-2344. p. 2045

McGill, Lesley, Prog & Res Coordr, Orangeville Public Library, One Mill St, Orangeville, ON, L9W 2M2, CANADA. Tel: 519-941-0610, Ext 5230. Fax: 519-941-4698. p. 2826

McGill, Sean, Commun Librn, Fort Vancouver Regional Library District, Ridgefield Community Library, 210 N Main Ave, Ridgefield, WA, 98642-9394. Tel: 360-887-8281. p. 2546

McGill, Sean, Commun Librn, Fort Vancouver Regional Library District, Washougal Community Library, 1661 C St, Washougal, WA, 98671. Tel: 360-835-5393. Fax: 360-835-9011. p. 2546

McGillan, Jennifer, Archivist, Columbia University, Augustus C Long Health Sciences Library, 701 W 168th St, Lobby Level, New York, NY, 10032. Tel: 212-305-3605. Fax: 212-234-0595. p. 1675

McGillis, Louise, Ref Serv, Memorial University of Newfoundland, Ferriss Hodgett Library, University Dr, Corner Brook, NL, A2H 6P9, CANADA. Tel: 709-637-6200, Ext 6122. Fax: 709-637-6273, 709-639-8125. p. 2772

McGillvary, Suzanne, Learning Res Coordr, Miami-Jacobs College, 110 N Patterson, Dayton, OH, 45402. Tel: 937-461-5174. p. 1893

McGillvray, Mathew R, ILL, Arkansas State University, Palm & Iowa Sts, Beebe, AR, 72012. Tel: 501-882-8976. Fax: 501-882-8833. p. 94

McGilvra, Doug, Res, Princeton University, Biology, Fine Hall Library, McDonnell Hall, One Washington Ave, Princeton, NJ, 08544. Tel: 609-258-3235. Fax: 609-258-2627. p. 1523

McGinn, Jane, Dr, Assoc Prof, Southern Connecticut State University, 501 Crescent St, New Haven, CT, 06515. Tel: 203-392-5086. Fax: 203-392-5780. p. 2963

McGinn, Kate, Archivist, Free Methodist Church of North America, 770 N High School Rd, Indianapolis, IN, 46214. Tel: 317-244-3660. Fax: 317-244-1247. p. 751

McGinnes, Teresa, Cataloger, Computer Tech, Bedford County Library, 240 S Wood St, Bedford, PA, 15522. Tel: 814-623-5010. p. 2031

McGinness, Paula, Dir, Honey Brook Community Library, 687 Compass Rd, Honey Brook, PA, 19344. Tel: 610-273-3303. Fax: 610-273-9382. p. 2069

McGinnis, Brenda, Dir, Lincoln County Library, 519 Emerald, Kemmerer, WY, 83101. Tel: 307-877-6961. Fax: 307-877-4147. p. 2656

McGinnis, Cela, Dir, Winchester Public Library, 2117 Lake St, Winchester, WI, 54557-9104. Tel: 715-686-2926. Fax: 715-686-2926. p. 2649

McGinnis, Daniel David, Syst Librn, The University of Texas-Pan American Library, 1201 W University Dr, Edinburg, TX, 78541-2999. Tel: 956-665-2878. Fax: 956-665-5396. p. 2315

McGinnis, Helen F, Curator, Moore College of Art & Design, 20th St & The Parkway, Philadelphia, PA, 19103-1179. Tel: 215-965-4058. Fax: 215-965-8544. p. 2112

McGinnis, Julia F, Tech Serv Librn, California University of Pennsylvania, 250 University Ave, California, PA, 15419-1394. Tel: 724-938-5472. Fax: 724-938-4490. p. 2040

McGinnis, Patricia, Br Mgr, Metropolitan Community College Library, Elkhorn Valley Campus, 204th & W Dodge Rd, Omaha, NE, 68022. Tel: 402-289-1206. Fax: 402-289-1286. p. 1413

McGinnis, Penny, Tech Serv Mgr, University of Cincinnati, 4200 Clermont College Dr, Batavia, OH, 45103-1785. Tel: 513-732-5206. Fax: 513-732-5237. p. 1858

McGinnis, Rhonda, Ref Librn, Wayne State University Libraries, Purdy-Kresge Library, 5265 Cass Ave, Detroit, MI, 48202. Tel: 313-577-8568. Fax: 313-577-3436. p. 1173

McGinniss, Jeremy, Assoc Librn, Baptist Bible College, 730 E Kearney St, Springfield, MO, 65803. Tel: 417-268-6075. Fax: 417-268-6690. p. 1365

Mcginniss, Katherine, Dir, Cape Fear Health Sciences Information Consortium, 1601 Owen Dr, Fayetteville, NC, 28301. Tel: 910-671-5046. Fax: 910-671-5337. p. 2951

McGinniss, Kathy, Dir, Southeastern Regional Medical Center, 300 W 27th St, Lumberton, NC, 28358. Tel: 910-671-5046. Fax: 910-671-5337. p. 1808

McGinty, Christine, Youth Serv, Bethlehem Public Library, 451 Delaware Ave, Delmar, NY, 12054-3042. Tel: 518-439-9314. Fax: 518-478-0901. p. 1614

McGinty, John W, Dir, Loyola-Notre Dame Library, Inc, 200 Winston Ave, Baltimore, MD, 21212. Tel: 410-617-6800. Fax: 410-617-6895. p. 1015

McGinty, Stephen, Bibliographer, University of Massachusetts Amherst, 154 Hicks Way, Amherst, MA, 01003-9275. Tel: 413-545-1871. Fax: 413-545-6873. p. 1049

McGirr, Diane, Librn, Greater Sudbury Public Library, Lionel Rheaume Public, 79 Main St, Dowling, ON, P0M 1R0, CANADA. Tel: 705-688-3956. Fax: 705-855-2591. p. 2846

McGirr, Kate, Assoc Dir, Admin Serv, University of California, 1156 High St, Santa Cruz, CA, 95064. Tel: 831-459-2076. Fax: 831-459-8206. p. 264

McGirt, Jacquelyn, Ref Librn, North Carolina Agricultural & Technical State University, 1601 E Market St, Greensboro, NC, 27411-0002. Tel: 336-334-7159, Ext 3214. Fax: 336-334-7783. p. 1797

McGiverin, Rolland, Dept Chair, Ref & Instruction, Indiana State University, 510 North 6 1/2 St, Terre Haute, IN, 47809. Tel: 812-237-2615. Fax: 812-237-3376. p. 781

McGivern, Kate, Ref, Bergen Community College, 400 Paramus Rd, Paramus, NJ, 07652-1595. Tel: 201-447-7980. Fax: 201-493-8167. p. 1517

McGivney, Jessica, ILL, City University of New York, 365 Fifth Ave, New York, NY, 10016-4309. Tel: 212-817-7040. Fax: 212-817-2982. p. 1673

McGivney, Peter, Ref, Howland Public Library, 313 Main St, Beacon, NY, 12508. Tel: 845-831-1134. Fax: 845-831-1165. p. 1579

McGlamery, Patrick, Dir, Libr Info Tech, University of Connecticut Library, 369 Fairfield Rd, Storrs, CT, 06269-1005. Tel: 860-486-2219. Fax: 860-486-0584. p. 370

McGlone, Victoria Mary, Librn, Florida State College at Jacksonville, North Campus, 4501 Capper Rd, Jacksonville, FL, 32218-4499. Tel: 904-766-6714. Fax: 904-766-6640. p. 453

McGlothlen, John M, Librn, Cedar Rapids Gazette Library, 500 Third Ave SE, Cedar Rapids, IA, 52406. Tel: 319-398-8328. Fax: 319-398-5846. p. 800

McGloughlin, Stephen, Dean of Libr, Cosumnes River College Library, 8401 Center Pkwy, Sacramento, CA, 95823. Tel: 916-691-7589. Fax: 916-691-7349. p. 223

McGlynn, Suzanne, Librn, Surf-Bal-Bay Library, 9301 Collins Ave, Surfside, FL, 33154. Tel: 305-865-2409. p. 492

McGoey, Richard P, Info & Res Mgr, Sutin, Thayer & Browne, Two Park Square Bldg, 10th Flr, 6565 Americas Pkwy NE, Albuquerque, NM, 87110. Tel: 505-883-2500. Fax: 505-888-6565. p. 1550

McGonagil, Ruthie, Ref, Proskauer Rose LLP Library, 1585 Broadway, Concourse Level, New York, NY, 10036. Tel: 212-969-5001. Fax: 212-969-2931. p. 1698

McGonagle, Patrick, Fiscal Officer, Granville Public Library, 217 E Broadway, Granville, OH, 43023-1398. Tel: 740-587-0196. Fax: 740-587-0197. p. 1903

McGonagle, Terry, Media Coordr, Whittier College, Bonnie Bell Wardman Library, 7031 Founders Hill Rd, Whittier, CA, 90608-9984. Tel: 562-907-4247. Fax: 562-698-7168. p. 283

McGonegal, Patrick, Webmaster, Juneau Public Libraries, 292 Marine Way, Juneau, AK, 99801. Tel: 907-586-5324. Fax: 907-586-3419. p. 50

McGoniagle, Paul, Access Serv, Newbury College Library, 150 Fisher Ave, Brookline, MA, 02445-5796. Tel: 617-738-2428. Fax: 617-730-7239. p. 1071

McGough, Annette, Tech Serv, Grand View Hospital, 700 Lawn Ave, Sellersville, PA, 18960. Tel: 215-453-4000, 215-453-4632. Fax: 215-453-4133. p. 2139

McGourty, Stacia, Coll Serv Librn, South Dakota State Library, 800 Governors Dr, Pierre, SD, 57501-2294. Tel: 605-773-3131. p. 2216

McGovern, Alice, Tech Serv, Dutchess Community College Library, 53 Pendell Rd, Poughkeepsie, NY, 12601-1595. Tel: 845-431-8640. Fax: 845-431-8995. p. 1722

McGovern, Chrissie, Head, Youth Serv, Matawan-Aberdeen Public Library, 165 Main St, Matawan, NJ, 07747. Tel: 732-583-9100. Fax: 732-583-9360. p. 1500

McGovern, Jane, Circ, Marian University, 45 S National Ave, Fond du Lac, WI, 54935. Tel: 920-923-7641, 920-923-8725. Fax: 920-923-7154. p. 2592

McGovern, Jerry, Librn, San Francisco Municipal Railway Library, 1145 Market St, Ste 402, San Francisco, CA, 94103-1545. Tel: 415-934-3977. Fax: 415-934-5747. p. 245

McGovern, Kim, Acq, Harrisburg Area Community College, 735 Cumberland St, Lebanon, PA, 17042. Tel: 717-780-2465. p. 2079

McGovern, Louise, Tech Serv, United States Army Research Laboratory, 2800 Powder Mill Rd, Adelphi, MD, 20783-1197. Tel: 301-394-2536. Fax: 301-394-1465. p. 1009

McGovern, Mary Grace, Dir, College of the Redwoods, 7351 Tompkins Hill Rd, Eureka, CA, 95501. Tel: 707-476-4264. Fax: 707-476-4432. p. 147

McGovern, Matthew, Ref Librn, Villanova University, Law Library, Garey Hall, 299 N Spring Mill Rd, Villanova, PA, 19085. Tel: 610-519-3893. Fax: 610-519-7033. p. 2150

McGowan, Anna Therese, Chief, Tech Info Ctr Section, United States Nuclear Regulatory Commission, Technical Library, 11545 Rockville Pike, T2C8, Rockville, MD, 20852-2738. Tel: 301-415-6239, 301-415-7204. Fax: 301-415-5365. p. 1040

McGowan, Christina, Head Ref Librn, Fairfield University, 1073 N Benson Rd, Fairfield, CT, 06430-5195. Tel: 203-254-4044. Fax: 203-254-4135. p. 339

McGowan, Courtney, Asst Curator, Telfair Museum of Art, 207 W York St, Savannah, GA, 31401. Tel: 912-790-8802. Fax: 912-790-8803. p. 551

Mcgowan, Edwin, Dir, Bear Mountain Trailside Museums Library, Bear Mountain State Park, Bear Mountain, NY, 10911-0427. Tel: 845-786-2701. Fax: 845-786-0496. p. 1579

McGowan, Jude, Ch, YA Serv, Forbes Library, 20 West St, Northampton, MA, 01060-3798. Tel: 413-587-1011. Fax: 413-587-1015. p. 1113

McGowan, Julie, Dir, Indiana University, Ruth Lilly Medical Library, 975 W Walnut St, IB 100, Indianapolis, IN, 46202-5121. Tel: 317-274-7183. Fax: 317-278-2349. p. 752

McGowan, Katie, Instruction Librn, Ref Librn, Harcum College Library, 750 Montgomery Ave, Bryn Mawr, PA, 19010-3476. Tel: 610-526-6085. Fax: 610-526-6086. p. 2039

McGowan, Marcella, Instrul Electronic Res, Ser, Johnson C Smith University, 100 Beatties Ford Rd, Charlotte, NC, 28216. Tel: 704-371-6740. Fax: 704-378-1191. p. 1783

Mcgowan, Rich, Dental Librn, New York University School of Medicine, John & Bertha E Waldmann Memorial Dental Library, 423 East 23rd St, 2nd Flr S, New York, NY, 10010. Tel: 212-998-9794. Fax: 212-995-3529. p. 1696

McGowan, Sandy, Circ Mgr, Prince Memorial Library, 266 Main St, Cumberland, ME, 04021-9754. Tel: 207-829-2215. Fax: 207-829-2221. p. 982

McGowan, Sharon L, Librn, C M Russell Museum Library, 400 13th St N, Great Falls, MT, 59401. Tel: 406-727-8787, Ext 348. Fax: 406-727-2402. p. 1380

McGowan, Susan, Mgr, Jefferson County Public Library, Standley Lake Library, 8485 Kipling St, Arvada, CO, 80005. p. 315

McGowen, Steve, Tech Serv, Denison Public Library, 300 W Gandy St, Denison, TX, 75020-3153. Tel: 903-465-1797. Fax: 903-465-1130. p. 2312

McGrane, Jane, Dir, Ionia Community Library, 101 W Iowa St, Ionia, IA, 50645-0130. Tel: 641-394-4803. Fax: 641-394-4803. p. 822

McGrane, Wendy, Libr Dir, Missouri Southern State University, 3950 E Newman Rd, Joplin, MO, 64801-1595. Tel: 417-625-9386. Fax: 417-625-9734. p. 1336

McGraner, Vic, Syst Coordr, Aiken-Bamberg-Barnwell-Edgefield Regional Library System, 314 Chesterfield St SW, Aiken, SC, 29801-7171. Tel: 803-642-7575. Fax: 803-642-7597. p. 2179

McGrath, Alicia, Acq, Supvr, Kentucky Department for Libraries & Archives, 300 Coffee Tree Rd, Frankfort, KY, 40601. Tel: 502-564-8300. Fax: 502-564-5773. p. 913

McGrath, Charlene, Dir, Libr & Info Serv, Gateway Community & Technical College, 790 Thomas More Pkwy, Rm E 213, Edgewood, KY, 41017. Tel: 859-442-4162. Fax: 859-341-6859. p. 911

McGrath, Deborah A, Asst Dir, Blount Library, Inc, Five N Main St, Franklinville, NY, 14737. Tel: 716-676-5715. Fax: 716-676-5715. p. 1624

McGrath, Eileen, Br Mgr, Middletown Public Library, Lincroft Branch, 730 Newman Springs Rd, Lincroft, NJ, 07738. Tel: 732-747-1140. p. 1501

McGrath, Genellen, Dir, Gold Coast Public Library, 50 Railroad Ave, Glen Head, NY, 11545. Tel: 516-759-8300. Fax: 516-759-8308. p. 1628

McGrath, Jeri, Br Mgr, Ocean County Library, Lacey Branch, Ten E Lacey Rd, Forked River, NJ, 08731-3626. Tel: 609-693-8566. Fax: 609-971-8973. p. 1534

McGrath, Jessica, Head, Adult Serv, Saline County Public Library, 1800 Smithers Dr, Benton, AR, 72015. Tel: 501-778-4766. Fax: 501-778-0536. p. 94

McGrath, Karen, Br Librn, Cranston Public Library, Auburn Branch, 396 Pontiac Ave, Cranston, RI, 02910-3322. Tel: 401-781-6116. p. 2165

McGrath, Kathryn, Asst Dir, Ref Librn, Dixon Homestead Library, 180 Washington Ave, Dumont, NJ, 07628. Tel: 201-384-2030. Fax: 201-384-5878. p. 1481

McGrath, Lance, Pub Serv Librn, Northwest Nazarene University, 623 University Blvd, Nampa, ID, 83686. Tel: 208-467-8613. Fax: 208-467-8610. p. 580

McGrath, Leslie, Br Head, Toronto Public Library, Osborne Collection of Early Children's Books, 239 College St, 4th Flr, Toronto, ON, M5T 1R5, CANADA. Tel: 416-393-7753. Fax: 416-393-7635. p. 2862

McGrath, Margaret, Ch, Plymouth Public Library, 132 South St, Plymouth, MA, 02360-3309. Tel: 508-830-4250. Fax: 508-830-4258. p. 1118

McGrath, Marsha, Ref, Clearwater Public Library System, 100 N Osceola Ave, Clearwater, FL, 33755. Tel: 727-562-4970. Fax: 727-562-4977. p. 432

McGrath, Michelle, Mgr, Oriskany Public Library, 621 Utica St, Oriskany, NY, 13424. Tel: 315-736-2532. Fax: 315-736-2532. p. 1712

McGrath, Mildred, Circ Mgr, Andrews University, 1400 Library Rd, Berrien Springs, MI, 49104-1400. Tel: 269-471-3976. Fax: 269-471-6166. p. 1157

McGrath, Natalie, YA Serv, Woodbridge Public Library, George Frederick Plaza, Woodbridge, NJ, 07095. Tel: 732-634-4450. p. 1545

McGrath, Renee, Mgr, Youth Serv, Nassau Library System, 900 Jerusalem Ave, Uniondale, NY, 11553-3039. Tel: 516-292-8920, Ext 230. Fax: 516-565-0950. p. 1758

McGrath, Renee Vaillancourt, Dir, North Valley Public Library, 208 Main St, Stevensville, MT, 59870. Tel: 406-777-5061. Fax: 406-777-5061. p. 1388

McGrattan, Alana, Libr Spec, Central New Mexico Community College Libraries, Rio Rancho Campus Library, 2601 Campus Blvd NE, Rm 112, Rio Rancho, NM, 87144. Tel: 505-224-4953. p. 1548

McGraw, Amy, Asst Dir, Independence Public Library, 805 First St E, Independence, IA, 50644. Tel: 319-334-2470. Fax: 319-332-0306. p. 822

McGraw, Brenda, Librn, Sarah Stewart Bovard Memorial Library, 156 Elm St, Tionesta, PA, 16353. Tel: 814-755-4454. Fax: 814-755-4333. p. 2145

McGraw, Dorothy, Ref Libr Assoc, Marshall University Libraries, One John Marshall Dr, Huntington, WV, 25755-2060. Tel: 304-746-8909. Fax: 304-696-5858. p. 2561

McGraw, John, Br Mgr, Central Arkansas Library System, Sidney S McMath Branch, 2100 John Barrow Rd, Little Rock, AR, 72204. Tel: 501-225-0066. p. 106

McGraw, John, Ref, Central Arkansas Library System, 100 Rock St, Little Rock, AR, 72201-4698. Tel: 501-918-3010. p. 106

McGraw, Shirley, Librn, Lonoke Prairie County Regional Library Headquarters, 204 E Second St, Lonoke, AR, 72086-2858. Tel: 501-676-6635. Fax: 501-676-7687. p. 108

McGraw, Shirley, Librn, Lonoke Prairie County Regional Library Headquarters, Marjorie Walker McCrary Memorial, 204 E Second St, Lonoke, AR, 72086. Tel: 501-676-6635. Fax: 501-676-7687. p. 108

McGreal, Pat, Ref Serv, DePaul University Libraries, Oak Forest, 16333 S Kilbourn Ave, Ste 5350, Oak Forest, IL, 60452. Tel: 630-636-3049. Fax: 708-633-9095. p. 612

McGreevy, Ronda, Br Mgr, Bayliss Public Library, Les Cheneaux Community, 75 E Hodeck St, Cedarville, MI, 49719. Tel: 906-484-3547. Fax: 906-484-3547. p. 1226

McGregor, Annette, Br Mgr, Dixie Regional Library System, 111 N Main St, Pontotoc, MS, 38863-2103. Tel: 662-489-3960. Fax: 662-489-7777. p. 1311

McGregor, Annette, Br Mgr, Dixie Regional Library System, Pontotoc County Library, 111 N Main St, Pontotoc, MS, 38863-2103. Tel: 662-489-3960. Fax: 662-489-7777. p. 1312

McGregor, B, Librn, Illinois Youth Center, 2848 W McDonough St, Joliet, IL, 60436. Tel: 815-725-1206. Fax: 815-725-9819. p. 659

McGregor, Tiffany, Interim Dir, Ref Librn, Neumann College Library, One Neumann Dr, Aston, PA, 19014-1298. Tel: 610-361-2487. Fax: 610-459-1370. p. 2030

McGrew, Fran M, Head Librn, Izard County Library, Nine Club Rd, Horseshoe Bend, AR, 72512-2717. Tel: 870-670-4318. p. 104

McGrew, Kevin W, Libr Dir, College of Saint Scholastica Library, 1200 Kenwood Ave, Duluth, MN, 55811-4199. Tel: 218-723-6198. Fax: 218-723-5948. p. 1247

McGrew, Paula L, Dir of Libr Serv, West Virginia Wesleyan College, 59 College Ave, Buckhannon, WV, 26201. Tel: 304-473-8059. Fax: 304-473-8888. p. 2555

McGrew, Susan, Librn, Geauga County Law Library Resources Board, 100 Short Court St, Ste BA, Chardon, OH, 44024. Tel: 440-279-2087. Fax: 440-285-3603. p. 1866

McGriff, Byron, Libr Tech, Alfred I Dupont Hospital for Children, 1600 Rockland Rd, Wilmington, DE, 19803. Tel: 302-651-5820. Fax: 302-651-5823. p. 387

McGriff, Delbra, Archivist, State Library of Florida, The Capitol, Rm 701, Tallahassee, FL, 32399. Tel: 850-245-6726. p. 495

McGriff, Marilyn, Tech Serv Librn, East Central Regional Library, 244 S Birch, Cambridge, MN, 55008-1588. Tel: 763-689-7390. Fax: 763-689-7389. p. 1243

McGriff-Powers, Kathleen, Cat, Erie Community College-City Campus, 121 Ellicott St, Buffalo, NY, 14203. Tel: 716-851-1074. Fax: 716-270-5987. p. 1598

McGrory, A, Ch, West Islip Public Library, Three Higbie Lane, West Islip, NY, 11795-3999. Tel: 631-661-7080. Fax: 631-661-7137. p. 1766

McGrory, Marilyn, Info Tech, Hamilton Spectator Library, 44 Frid St, Hamilton, ON, L8N 3G3, CANADA. Tel: 905-526-3315. p. 2810

McGuckin, Pat, Communications Mgr, Illinois State Library, Gwendolyn Brooks Bldg, 300 S Second St, Springfield, IL, 62701-9713. Tel: 217-558-4029. Fax: 217-785-4326. p. 705

McGugan, Debbie, Chief Librn, Grant MacEwan University Library, 10700 104th Ave, Edmonton, AB, T5J 4S2, CANADA. Tel: 780-497-5894. Fax: 780-497-5895. p. 2701

McGuigan, Glenn, Bus & Pub Admin Ref Librn, Ref & Pub Serv Coordr, Pennsylvania State University-Harrisburg Library, 351 Olmsted Dr, Middletown, PA, 17057-4850. Tel: 717-948-6078. Fax: 717-948-6757. p. 2089

McGuigan, Sharyn, Librn, Richardson Memorial Library, 1411 Main St, Sugar Hill, NH, 03585. Tel: 603-823-7001. p. 1465

McGuilberry, Kathy, Asst Librn, McAlester Public Library, 401 N Second St, McAlester, OK, 74501. Tel: 918-426-0930. Fax: 918-423-5731. p. 1968

McGuill, Tina, Librn, Dennis M O'Connor Public Library, 815 S Commerce St, Refugio, TX, 78377. Tel: 361-526-2608. Fax: 361-526-2608. p. 2373

McGuinness, Carol, Librn IV, Elaine Ione Sprauve Library, Enighed Estate, Cruz Bay, Saint John, VI, 00831. Tel: 340-776-6359. Fax: 340-776-6901. p. 2679

McGuinness, Phyllis, Prog Coordr, Bernards Township Library, 32 S Maple Ave, Basking Ridge, NJ, 07920-1216. Tel: 908-204-3031. Fax: 908-766-1580. p. 1470

McGuinness, Sue, Interim Dir, University of California, San Diego, Biomedical Library, 9500 Gilman Dr, 0699, La Jolla, CA, 92093-0699. Tel: 858-534-3418. Fax: 858-822-2219. p. 162

McGuire, Amy, Librn, Saint Joseph County Law Library, Court House, 101 S Main St, South Bend, IN, 46601. Tel: 574-235-9657. Fax: 574-235-9905. p. 779

McGuire, Angela, ILL, Thomas County Public Library System, 201 N Madison St, Thomasville, GA, 31792-5414. Tel: 229-225-5252. Fax: 229-225-5258. p. 553

McGuire, Bev, Mgr, Access Serv, Monmouth College, 700 E Broadway, Monmouth, IL, 61462-1963. Tel: 309-457-2190. Fax: 309-457-2226. p. 675

McGuire, Catherine, Outreach Serv Librn, Maryland State Law Library, Courts of Appeal Bldg, 361 Rowe Blvd, Annapolis, MD, 21401-1697. Tel: 410-260-1430. Fax: 410-260-1572, 410-974-2063. p. 1010

McGuire, Charlene, Tech Coordr, Southwest Kansas Library System, 100 Military Ave, Ste 210, Dodge City, KS, 67801-4484. Tel: 620-225-1231. Fax: 620-225-0252. p. 864

McGuire, Darwin, Tech Serv Mgr, Genesee District Library, G-4195 W Pasadena Ave, Flint, MI, 48504. Tel: 810-230-3329. Fax: 810-732-1161. p. 1179

McGuire, Dennis, Br Mgr, OC Public Libraries, West Garden Grove Branch, 11962 Bailey St, Garden Grove, CA, 92845-1104. Tel: 714-897-2594. Fax: 714-895-2761. p. 259

McGuire, Dennis, Head, Digital & Media Serv, Columbia College Chicago Library, 624 S Michigan Ave, Chicago, IL, 60605-1996. Tel: 312-369-7434. Fax: 312-344-8062. p. 611

Mcguire, Diane, Librn, Roanoke Public Libraries, Raleigh Court, 2112 Grandin Rd SW, Roanoke, VA, 24015. Tel: 540-853-2240. Fax: 540-853-1783. p. 2494

McGuire, Eva, Dir, Craft Memorial Library, 600 Commerce St, Bluefield, WV, 24701. Tel: 304-325-3943. Fax: 304-325-3702. p. 2555

McGuire, Ginger, Asst Mgr, Massachusetts Institute of Technology, 244 Wood St, Lexington, MA, 02420-9176. Tel: 781-981-2820. p. 1099

McGuire, Jane, Chief Exec Officer, Chief Librn, Prescott Public Library, 360 Dibble St W, Prescott, ON, K0E 1T0, CANADA. Tel: 613-925-4340. Fax: 613-925-0100, 613-925-4381. p. 2838

McGuire, Jean, Asst Librn, Carrollton Public Library, 509 S Main St, Carrollton, IL, 62016. Tel: 217-942-6715. Fax: 217-942-6005. p. 601

McGuire, Jean, Dir, Justice Public Library District, 7641 Oak Grove Ave, Justice, IL, 60458-1397. Tel: 708-496-1790. Fax: 708-496-1898. p. 660

McGuire, Jean, Dir, Metropolitan Council for Educational Opportunity Library, 40 Dimock St, Roxbury, MA, 02119. Tel: 617-427-1545. Fax: 617-541-0550. p. 1121

Mcguire, Jeffrey D, Librn, Gallagher & Kennedy, 2575 E Camelback Rd, Phoenix, AZ, 85016-4240. Tel: 602-530-8000, 602-530-8149. Fax: 602-530-8500. p. 73

McGuire, Kara, Asst Dir, Circ, ILL, Daemen College Library, Research & Information Commons, 4380 Main St, Amherst, NY, 14226-3592. Tel: 716-839-8243. Fax: 716-839-8475. p. 1573

McGuire, Leslie, Br Mgr, US Courts Library, Byron Rogers Courthouse, 1929 Stout St, Rm 430, Denver, CO, 80294. Tel: 303-844-3591. Fax: 303-844-5958. p. 303

McGuire, Leslie B, Librn, United States Court of Appeals, 333 W Fourth St, Tulsa, OK, 74103. Tel: 918-699-4744. Fax: 918-699-4743. p. 1984

McGuire, Marsha, Dir, Salado Public Library, 1151 N Main St, Salado, TX, 76571. Tel: 254-947-9191. Fax: 254-947-9146. p. 2378

McGuire, Mary, Dir, Lawrence County Public Library, 102 W Main & Jefferson, Louisa, KY, 41230. Tel: 606-638-0554, 606-638-4497, Fax: 606-638-1293. p. 923

McGuire, Michael, Dir, Traverse Area District Library, 610 Woodmere Ave, Traverse City, MI, 49686. Tel: 231-932-8500. Fax: 231-932-8538. p. 1231

McGuire, Michael C, Syst & Emerging Tech Librn, Colby College Libraries, 5100 Mayflower Hill, Waterville, ME, 04901. Tel: 207-859-5161. Fax: 207-859-5105. p. 1005

McGuire, Nancy, Instrul Serv Librn, Bob Jones University, 1700 Wade Hampton Blvd, Greenville, SC, 29614. Tel: 864-370-1800, Ext 6025. Fax: 864-232-1729. p. 2195

McGuire, Nancy, Circ Supvr, Waukesha Public Library, 321 Wisconsin Ave, Waukesha, WI, 53186-4786. Tel: 262-524-3693. Fax: 262-524-3677. p. 2645

McGuire, Noreen, Asst Univ Librn, Pace University, 861 Bedford Rd, Pleasantville, NY, 10570-2799. Tel: 914-773-3815. Fax: 914-773-3508. p. 1719

McGuire, Patricia, Tech Asst II - Media Spec, Potomac State College of West Virginia University, 101 Fort Ave, Keyser, WV, 26726. Tel: 304-788-6905. Fax: 304-788-6946. p. 2563

McGuire, Pauline, Librn, Van Buren District Library, Covert Branch, 33805 M-140 Hwy, Covert, MI, 49043. Tel: 269-764-1298. Fax: 269-764-1298. p. 1168

McGuire, Richard, Ref, Scranton Public Library, Albright Memorial Bldg, 500 Vine St, Scranton, PA, 18509-3298. Tel: 570-348-3000. Fax: 570-348-3020. p. 2138

McGuire, Ruth, Dir, Northwestern College, 3003 Snelling Ave N, Saint Paul, MN, 55113. Tel: 651-631-5241. Fax: 651-631-5598. p. 1280

Mcguire, Sarah, Circ, Keyser-Mineral County Public Library, 105 N Main St, Keyser, WV, 26726. Tel: 304-788-3222. Fax: 304-788-3222. p. 2563

McGuire, Serena, Readers' Advisor Librn, DC Regional Library for the Blind & Physically Handicapped, Adaptive Services Division, Rm 215, 901 G St NW, Washington, DC, 20001. Tel: 202-559-5368 (videophone), 202-727-2142. Fax: 202-727-0322. p. 397

McGuire, Suzanne, Dir, Berlin Public Library, 23 Carter St, Berlin, MA, 01503-1219. Tel: 978-838-2812. Fax: 978-838-2812. p. 1053

McGuire, Toby, Pub Relations, Aldrich Chemical Co, Inc Library, 6000 N Teutonia Ave, Milwaukee, WI, 53209-3645. Tel: 414-273-3850, Ext 5462. Fax: 414-298-7960. p. 2616

McGuire, Waller, Exec Dir, Saint Louis Public Library, 1415 Olive St, Saint Louis, MO, 63103-2315. Tel: 314-539-0300. Fax: 314-241-3840. p. 1359

McGuirl, Steve, Head, Acq, The New York Society Library, 53 E 79th St, New York, NY, 10075. Tel: 212-288-6900, Ext 247. Fax: 212-585-0227. p. 1694

McGurk, Pat, Chief Librn, Elliot Lake Public Library, Algo Centre Mall, 151 Ontario Ave, Elliot Lake, ON, P5A 2T2, CANADA. Tel: 705-848-2287, Ext 2800. Fax: 705-461-9464. p. 2803

McHale, Chris, Access Serv Librn, Fiorello H LaGuardia Community College Library, 31-10 Thomson Ave, Long Island City, NY, 11101. Tel: 718-482-5441. Fax: 718-482-5444, 718-609-2011. p. 1654

McHaney, Melba, Br Spec, Coalinga-Huron Library District, Huron Branch, 36050 O St, Huron, CA, 93234. Tel: 559-945-2284. Fax: 559-945-2855. p. 135

McHarg, Mary Ann, Mgr, Carnegie Library of Pittsburgh, Hazelwood, 4901 Second Ave, Pittsburgh, PA, 15207-1506. Tel: 412-421-2517. p. 2123

McHenry, Gayla, Supvr, Access Serv, Truman State University, 100 E Normal, Kirksville, MO, 63501-4211. Tel: 660-785-4037. p. 1342

McHenry, Kelley, Librn, Seattle Central Community College, 1701 Broadway, 2BE2101, Seattle, WA, 98122. Tel: 206-587-6336. Fax: 206-587-3878. p. 2530

McHenry, Melissa, Media Spec, Gates Public Library, 902 Elmgrove Rd, Rochester, NY, 14624. Tel: 585-247-6446. Fax: 585-426-5733. p. 1729

McHenry, Ruth, Librn, The Frances Kibble Kenny Lake Public Library, Mile 5 Edgerton Hwy, Copper Center, AK, 99573-9703. Tel: 907-822-3015. Fax: 907-822-3015. p. 46

McHenry, Wendie, Asst Univ Librn, University of Victoria Libraries, McPherson Library, PO Box 1800, Victoria, BC, V8W 3H5, CANADA. Tel: 250-721-8211. Fax: 250-721-8215. p. 2746

McHollin, Mattie, Archives Asst, Fisk University, Fisk University, 1000 17th Ave N, Nashville, TN, 37208-3051. Tel: 615-329-8838. Fax: 615-329-8761. p. 2256

McHone-Chase, Sarah, Unit Head, Info Delivery Serv, Northern Illinois University Libraries, DeKalb, IL, 60115-2868. Tel: 815-753-9860. p. 635

McHugh, Alicia, Br Mgr, Broward County Division of Libraries, Pembroke Pines Branch-Walter C Young Resource Center, 955 NW 129th Ave, Pembroke Pines, FL, 33028. Tel: 954-437-2635. Fax: 954-437-2624. p. 442

McHugh, Eileen, Dir, Cayuga Museum Library, 203 Genesee St, Auburn, NY, 13021. Tel: 315-253-8051. Fax: 315-253-9829. p. 1576

McHugh, Mel, Head Librn, South College Library, 3904 Lonas Dr, Knoxville, TN, 37909. Tel: 865-251-1750, 865-251-1832. p. 2243

McHugh, Michelle, Cat & Metadata, University of Scranton, Monroe & Linden, Scranton, PA, 18510-4634. Tel: 570-941-4004. Fax: 570-941-7818. p. 2138

McHugh, Valisa, Br Mgr, Amarillo Public Library, Southwest Branch, 6801 W 45th St, Amarillo, TX, 79109. Tel: 806-359-2094. Fax: 806-359-2096. p. 2274

McIlhenney, Joseph, Access Serv Librn, Asst Prof, Lincoln University, 1570 Old Baltimore Pike, Lincoln University, PA, 19352. Tel: 484-365-7366. Fax: 610-932-1206. p. 2082

McIlhenney, Joseph V, Dir, Harrisburg Area Community College, 1641 Old Philadelphia Pike, Lancaster, PA, 17602. Tel: 717-358-2222. Fax: 717-358-2952. p. 2076

McIlroy, Elaine R, Librn, Wellfleet Public Library, 55 W Main St, Wellfleet, MA, 02667. Tel: 508-349-0310, 508-349-0311. Fax: 508-349-0312. p. 1135

McIlvaine, Robert, In Charge, McIlvaine Co, 191 Waukegan Rd, Ste 208, Northfield, IL, 60093. Tel: 847-784-0012. Fax: 847-784-0061. p. 683

McIndoe, Tara-Lee, Head Librn, Southeast Regional Library, Midale Branch, Civic Ctr, 128 Haslem St, Midale, SK, S0C 1S0, CANADA. Tel: 306-458-2263. p. 2930

McInerney, Claire, Asst Prof, Rutgers, The State University of New Jersey, Four Huntington St, New Brunswick, NJ, 08901-1071. Tel: 732-932-7500, Ext 8955. Fax: 732-932-2644. p. 2969

McInerney, Gay, Dir, Bay County Historical Society, 321 Washington Ave, Bay City, MI, 48708. Tel: 989-893-5733. Fax: 989-893-5741. p. 1155

McInnis, Cathy, Adult Serv, Guelph Public Library, 100 Norfolk St, Guelph, ON, N1H 4J6, CANADA. Tel: 519-824-6220. Fax: 519-824-8342. p. 2807

McInnis, Dawn, Rare Bks, Kansas University Medical Center, 1020-1030 Robinson Bldg, 3901 Rainbow Blvd, Kansas City, KS, 66160-7311. Tel: 913-588-7244. Fax: 913-588-7060. p. 875

McInnis, Elaine, Univ Librn, Nova Scotia Agricultural College Library, 135 College Rd, Truro, NS, B2N 5E3, CANADA. Tel: 902-893-6669. Fax: 902-895-0934. p. 2786

McInnis, Juanita, Librn, Pine Forest Regional Library, Leakesville Public, 101 Lafayette St, Leakesville, MS, 39451. Tel: 601-394-6957. Fax: 601-394-6957. p. 1314

McIntee, Jocelyn, Head, Ref, Bayport-Blue Point Public Library, 203 Blue Point Ave, Blue Point, NY, 11715-1217. Tel: 631-363-6133. Fax: 631-363-6133. p. 1583

McIntosh, Claudia, Br Mgr, Montgomery County Public Library, Star Branch, 222 S Main St, Star, NC, 27356. Tel: 910-428-2338. Fax: 910-428-2338. p. 1827

McIntosh, Debra, Archivist, Millsaps College, 1701 N State St, Jackson, MS, 39210-0001. Tel: 601-974-1077. Fax: 601-974-1082. p. 1304

McIntosh, J, Actg Chief Librn, Environment Canada, Place Vincent Massey, 2nd Flr, 351 Saint Joseph Blvd, Gatineau, QC, K1A 0H3, CANADA. Tel: 819-953-1373. Fax: 819-997-5349. p. 2883

McIntosh, Karen F, Tech Serv, Amarillo College Library, 2201 S Washington, Amarillo, TX, 79109. Tel: 806-371-5400. Fax: 806-371-5470. p. 2274

McIntosh, Kathleen, Br Supvr, Gaston County Public Library, Lowell Branch, 203 McAdenville Rd, Lowell, NC, 28098. Tel: 704-824-1266. Fax: 704-824-1266. p. 1794

McIntosh, Linda, Br Mgr, Wadena City Library, 304 First St SW, Wadena, MN, 56482-1460. Tel: 218-631-2476. Fax: 218-631-2476. p. 1287

McIntosh, Lynn, Dir, Chickasaw Regional Library System, 601 Railway Express, Ardmore, OK, 73401. Tel: 580-223-3164. Fax: 580-223-3280. p. 1957

McIntosh, Marilyn, Dir, Monroe Free Library, 44 Millpond Pkwy, Monroe, NY, 10950. Tel: 845-783-4411. Fax: 845-782-4707. p. 1662

McIntosh, Mike, Ref Serv, Simon Fraser University Vancouver Library, 515 W Hastings St, Vancouver, BC, V6B 5K3, CANADA. Tel: 778-782-5050. Fax: 778-782-5052. p. 2742

McIntosh, Nancy, Dir, Ripley Free Library, 64 W Main St, Ripley, NY, 14775-0808. Tel: 716-736-3913. Fax: 716-736-3923. p. 1727

McIntosh-Doty, Mikail, Dir, Libr Serv, Concordia University Texas Library, 11400 Concordia University Dr, Austin, TX, 78726. Tel: 512-313-5050. p. 2280

McInturff, Connie, Adult Serv, Guthrie Memorial Library - Hanover's Public Library, Two Library Pl, Hanover, PA, 17331-2283. Tel: 717-632-5183. Fax: 717-632-7565. p. 2064

McIntyre, Ann, Librn, Warren County Public Library District, Roseville Branch, 145 W Penn Ave, Roseville, IL, 61473. Tel: 309-426-2336. p. 675

Mcintyre, Beth, Dir, Piedmont Regional Library, 189 Bell View St, Winder, GA, 30680-1706. Tel: 770-867-2762. Fax: 770-867-7483. p. 557

McIntyre, Catherine, Spec Coll, Utah Valley University Library, 800 W University Pkwy, Orem, UT, 84058-5999. Tel: 801-863-8821. Fax: 801-863-7065. p. 2409

McIntyre, Cynthia, Librn, Cape Breton Regional Library, Glace Bay Public, 121 Union St, Glace Bay, NS, B1A 2P8, CANADA. Tel: 902-849-8657. p. 2785

McIntyre, Elizabeth, Dir, Dublin Public Library, 1114 Main St, Dublin, NH, 03444. Tel: 603-563-8658. Fax: 603-563-8751. p. 1445

McIntyre, Elizabeth, Evening Ref Librn, Robeson Community College Library, 5160 Fayetteville Rd, Lumberton, NC, 28360-2158. Tel: 910-272-3700, Ext 3321. Fax: 910-618-5685. p. 1807

McIntyre, Mary, Asst Dir, Bad Axe Area District Library, 200 S Hanselman, Bad Axe, MI, 48413. Tel: 989-269-8538. Fax: 989-269-2411. p. 1155

McIntyre, Mary, Supvr, Middlesex County Library, Mount Brydges Branch, 22501 Adelaide Rd, Mount Brydges, ON, N0L 1W0, CANADA. Tel: 519-264-1061. p. 2845

McIntyre, Melissa, Libr Tech, New Mexico State University at Alamogordo, 2400 N Scenic Dr, Alamogordo, NM, 88310. Tel: 575-439-3803. Fax: 575-439-3657. p. 1547

McIntyre, Michelle, Dir, Roaring Spring Community Library, 320 E Main St, Roaring Spring, PA, 16673-1009. Tel: 814-224-2994. Fax: 814-224-4472. p. 2135

McIntyre, Olivia H, Coll Develop, Northeast Regional Library, 1023 Fillmore St, Corinth, MS, 38834-4199. Tel: 662-287-7311. Fax: 662-286-8010. p. 1297

McIntyre, Paula, Acq, Cat, Jacksonville University, 2800 University Blvd N, Jacksonville, FL, 32211-3394. Tel: 904-256-7265. Fax: 904-256-7259. p. 454

Mcintyre, Ronald, Librn, Cross City Correctional Institution Library, 568 NE 255th St, Cross City, FL, 32628. Tel: 352-498-4444, Ext 4372. Fax: 352-498-0194. p. 434

McIntyre, Rudy, Mgr, Masonic Public Library of Hawaii, 1611 Kewalo St, Honolulu, HI, 96822. Tel: 808-521-2070. Fax: 808-533-6493. p. 564

McIntyre, Sarah, Circ Mgr, Interim Co-Dir, West Linn Public Library, 1595 Burns St, West Linn, OR, 97068-3231. Tel: 503-656-7853, Ext 3019. Fax: 503-656-2746. p. 2022

McIntyre, Sue, Dir, Primrose Public Library, 229 Commercial St, Primrose, NE, 68655. p. 1417

McIntyre, Susie, Info Serv Supvr, Great Falls Public Library, 301 Second Ave N, Great Falls, MT, 59401-2593. Tel: 406-453-0349, Ext 232. Fax: 406-453-0181. p. 1380

McIntyre, William A, Dir, Learning Res, Nashua Community College, 505 Amherst St, Nashua, NH, 03063-1026. Tel: 603-882-6923, Ext 1567. Fax: 603-882-8690. p. 1458

McInvaill, Dwight, Dir, Georgetown County Library, 405 Cleland St, Georgetown, SC, 29440-3200. Tel: 843-545-3304. Fax: 843-545-3395. p. 2194

McIver, Kim, Br Head, Lee County Library, Broadway Branch, 206 S Main St, Broadway, NC, 27505. Tel: 919-258-6513. p. 1823

McIvor, Gloria, Librn, Chinook Regional Library, Lafleche Branch, 157 Main St, Lafleche, SK, S0H 2K0, CANADA. Tel: 306-472-5466. p. 2928

McKain, Joshua Van Kirk, Col Librn, Libr Dir, Fisher College Library, 118 Beacon St, Boston, MA, 02116. Tel: 617-236-8875. Fax: 617-670-4426. p. 1061

McKale, Bill, Dir, US Cavalry Museum, Bldg 263, Cameron Ave, Fort Riley, KS, 66442. Tel: 785-239-8234. Fax: 785-239-6243. p. 867

McKann, Helen, Librn, John Tyler Community College Library, Midlothian Campus, Hamel Hall, Rm H202, 800 Charter Colony Pkwy, Midlothian, VA, 23114-4383. Tel: 804-594-1523. Fax: 804-594-1525. p. 2456

McKanna, Patricia A, Librn, Honigman Miller Schwartz & Cohn LLP, 2290 First National Bldg, 660 Woodward Ave, Detroit, MI, 48226-3583. Tel: 313-465-7169. Fax: 313-465-8000. p. 1171

McKay, Darlene Harrington, Librn, Forrest College Library, 601 E River St, Anderson, SC, 29624. Tel: 864-225-7653. Fax: 864-261-7471. p. 2181

McKay, Devin, Dep Chief Librn/Fac Outreach Librn, Queensborough Community College, City University of New York, 222-05 56th Ave, Bayside, NY, 11364-1497. Tel: 718-281-5032. Fax: 718-281-5012. p. 1579

McKay, Kathy, Librn, Department of Veterans Affairs, Patient Education Center Library, One Veterans Dr, 142D1, Minneapolis, MN, 55417. Tel: 612-467-4212. Fax: 612-725-2046. p. 1259

McKay, Marilyn, Librn, Collier County Public Library, East Naples Branch, 8787 E Tamiami Trail, Naples, FL, 34113. Tel: 239-775-5592. Fax: 239-774-5148. p. 471

McKay, Michael, Chief Exec Officer, Scouts Canada, 1345 Baseline Rd, Ottawa, ON, K2C 0A7, CANADA. Tel: 613-224-5131. Fax: 613-224-3571. p. 2833

McKay, Myrna, Dir, Steele Public Library, 108 E Main St, Steele, MO, 63877-1528. Tel: 573-695-3561. Fax: 573-695-3021. p. 1368

McKay, Nellie, Libr Tech, United States Department of Energy, 1450 Queen Ave SW, Albany, OR, 97321-2152. Tel: 541-967-5864. Fax: 541-967-5936. p. 1989

McKay, Pamela R, Sr Librn, Ref, Worcester State College, 486 Chandler St, Worcester, MA, 01602-2597. Tel: 508-929-8528. Fax: 508-929-8198. p. 1145

McKay, Richard, Dir, San Jacinto College South, 13735 Beamer Rd, Houston, TX, 77089-6099. Tel: 281-922-3416. Fax: 281-922-3470. p. 2342

McKay, Sarah, Librn, Pacific Asia Museum Library, 46 N Los Robles Ave, Pasadena, CA, 91101-2009. Tel: 626-449-2742, Ext 24. Fax: 626-449-2754. p. 206

McKeag, Becky, Mgr, Douglas County Library System, 1409 NE Diamond Lake Blvd, Roseburg, OR, 97470. Tel: 541-440-4305. Fax: 541-957-7798. p. 2016

McKean, Jan, Dir, Wysox Township Library, 18 W Fifth St, Milledgeville, IL, 61051-9416. Tel: 815-225-7572. Fax: 815-225-7572. p. 674

McKean, Kitti, Mgr, Greenville County Library System, Augusta Road (Ramsey Family Branch), 100 Lydia St, Greenville, SC, 29605. Tel: 864-277-0161. Fax: 864-277-2673. p. 2196

McKean, Susan, Head, Youth Serv, Villa Park Public Library, 305 S Ardmore Ave, Villa Park, IL, 60181-2698. Tel: 630-834-1164, Ext 114. Fax: 630-834-0489. p. 714

McKeaney, Kristen, Ref Librn, Jenkins Law Library, 833 Chestnut St, Ste 1220, Philadelphia, PA, 19107-4429. Tel: 215-574-7943. Fax: 215-574-7920. p. 2111

McKearn, Anne, Cataloger, Aurora University, 315 S Gladstone, Aurora, IL, 60506-4877. Tel: 630-844-5653. Fax: 630-844-3848. p. 591

McKechnie, Sue, Automation Syst Coordr, ILL, Jefferson Public Library, 321 S Main St, Jefferson, WI, 53549-1772. Tel: 920-674-7733. Fax: 920-674-7735. p. 2600

McKee, Alison, Sr Commun Libr Mgr, Contra Costa County Library, Hercules Library, 109 Civic Dr, Hercules, CA, 94547. Tel: 510-245-2420. p. 209

McKee, Allyson, Head, Acq, West Virginia University Libraries, WVU Libraries, 1549 University Ave, Morgantown, WV, 26506. Tel: 304-293-4040. Fax: 304-293-6638. p. 2566

McKee, Anne, Prog Officer for Res Sharing, Greater Western Library Alliance, 5109 Cherry St, Kansas City, MO, 64110. Tel: 816-926-8765. Fax: 816-926-8790. p. 2947

McKee, Carrie, Librn, Lakeland Library Region, Denzil Branch, Box 188, Denzil, SK, S0L 0S0, CANADA. Tel: 306-358-2118. Fax: 306-358-4828. p. 2920

McKee, Denise, ILL, Gardner-Webb University, 110 S Main St, Boiling Springs, NC, 28017. Tel: 704-406-3050. Fax: 704-406-4623. p. 1776

McKee, Elizabeth, Educ Librn, University of Arkansas Libraries, 365 N McIlroy Ave, Fayetteville, AR, 72701-4002. Tel: 479-575-5313. Fax: 479-575-6656. p. 99

McKee, Genie V, Dr, Dean, Maryville University Library, 650 Maryville University Dr, Saint Louis, MO, 63141. Tel: 314-529-9509. Fax: 314-529-9941. p. 1356

McKee, Jennie, Access Serv, Reed College, 3203 SE Woodstock Blvd, Portland, OR, 97202-8199. Tel: 503-777-7702. Fax: 503-777-7786. p. 2014

McKee, Jimmy D, Dir, Caldwell County Public Library, 120 Hospital Ave, Lenoir, NC, 28645-4454. Tel: 828-757-1270. Fax: 828-757-1413. p. 1806

McKee, Laurie, Ref/Tech Serv Librn, Little Elm Public Library, 100 W Eldorado Pkwy, Little Elm, TX, 75068. Tel: 214-975-0430. Fax: 972-377-5546. p. 2356

McKee, Linda R, Head, Libr Serv, John & Mable Ringling Museum of Art Library, 5401 Bayshore Rd, Sarasota, FL, 34243. Tel: 941-359-5700, Ext 2701. Fax: 941-360-7370. p. 490

McKee, Mary, Dep Dir, Fordham University School of Law, 140 W 62nd St, New York, NY, 10023-7485. Tel: 212-636-6903. Fax: 212-930-8818. p. 1678

McKee, Maura, Youth Serv, Hillside Public Library, 405 N Hillside Ave, Hillside, IL, 60162-1295. Tel: 708-449-7510. Fax: 708-449-6119. p. 656

McKee, Sandra, Chief Exec Officer, Thessalon Public Library, 187 Main St, Thessalon, ON, P0R 1L0, CANADA. Tel: 705-842-2306. Fax: 705-842-5690. p. 2847

McKee, William, Br Mgr, Jefferson Parish Library, Gretna Branch, 102 Willow Dr, Gretna, LA, 70053. Tel: 504-364-2716. Fax: 504-364-2710. p. 956

McKeehan, Nancy C, Asst Dir, Syst, Medical University of South Carolina Library, 171 Ashley Ave, Ste 300, Charleston, SC, 29425-0001. Tel: 843-792-9211. Fax: 843-792-7947. p. 2184

McKeen, Valerie, Libr Tech, Network Adminr, Powell River Public Library, 4411 Michigan Ave, Powell River, BC, V8A 2S3, CANADA. Tel: 604-485-8663. Fax: 604-485-5320. p. 2735

McKeeth, Mari, Pub Relations, Normal Public Library, 206 W College Ave, Normal, IL, 61761. Tel: 309-452-1757. Fax: 309-452-5312. p. 681

McKeever, Judy Faye, Dir, Childress Public Library, 117 Ave B NE, Childress, TX, 79201-4509. Tel: 940-937-8421. Fax: 940-937-8421. p. 2297

McKeever, Karen, Asst Supvr, Access Serv, Judson University, 1151 N State St, Elgin, IL, 60123. Tel: 847-628-2030. Fax: 847-625-2045. p. 641

McKeever, Katie, Youth Serv, Alpha Park Public Library District, 3527 S Airport Rd, Bartonville, IL, 61607-1799. Tel: 309-697-3822, Ext 14. Fax: 309-697-9681. p. 592

McKeever, Kent, Dir, Columbia University, Arthur W Diamond Law Library, 435 W 116th St, New York, NY, 10027. Tel: 212-854-4228. Fax: 212-854-3295. p. 1674

McKeever, Libby, Youth Serv Librn, Whistler Public Library, 4329 Main St, Whistler, BC, V0N 1B4, CANADA. Tel: 604-935-8433. Fax: 604-935-8434. p. 2746

McKeich, Cynthia, Mgr, Seneca College of Applied Arts & Technology, 13990 Dufferin St N, King City, ON, L7B 1B3, CANADA. Tel: 416-491-5050. Fax: 905-833-1106. p. 2813

McKell, Jennifer, Dir, Chillicothe & Ross County Public Library, 140 S Paint St, Chillicothe, OH, 45601. Tel: 740-702-4145. Fax: 740-702-4153. p. 1867

McKellar, Norma S, Ch, Moultrie-Colquitt County Library, 204 Fifth St SE, Moultrie, GA, 31768. Tel: 229-985-6540. Fax: 229-985-0936. p. 545

McKellogg, James, Dir, Thomas More College Library, 333 Thomas More Pkwy, Crestview Hills, KY, 41017-2599. Tel: 859-344-3300. Fax: 859-344-3342. p. 910

McKelvey, Musette, Cataloger, Shaw University, 118 E South St, Raleigh, NC, 27601. Tel: 919-546-8406. Fax: 919-831-1161. p. 1817

McKelvy, Marcille, Librn, East Dallas Christian Church, 629 N Peak St, Dallas, TX, 75246. Tel: 214-824-8185. Fax: 214-824-8583. p. 2307

McKelvy, Nicole, Asst Dir, Hidalgo Public Library, 710 E Texano Dr, Hidalgo, TX, 78557. Tel: 956-843-2093. Fax: 956-843-8841. p. 2332

McKendry, Jean, Pub Serv Librn, Kwantlen Polytechnic University Library, 12666 72 Ave., Surrey, BC, V3W 2M8, CANADA. Tel: 604-599-3486. Fax: 604-599-2106. p. 2738

McKenna, Angie, Librn, Mildred Stevens Williams Memorial Library, 2916 Sennebec Rd, Appleton, ME, 04862. Tel: 207-785-5656. p. 973

McKenna, Anne, Distance Educ, Kauai Community College, 3-1901 Kaumualii Hwy, Lihue, HI, 96766. Tel: 808-245-8374. Fax: 808-245-8294. p. 567

McKenna, Donna, Dir, Williston Park Public Library, 494 Willis Ave, Williston Park, NY, 11596. Tel: 516-742-1820. Fax: 516-294-5004. p. 1770

McKenna, Frank J, Dir, Seaford Public Library, 2234 Jackson Ave, Seaford, NY, 11783. Tel: 516-221-1334. Fax: 516-826-8133. p. 1742

McKenna, Gerald M, Libr Dir, Henrico County Public Library, 1001 N Laburnum Ave, Henrico, VA, 23223-2705. Tel: 804-290-9000. Fax: 804-222-5566. p. 2471

McKenna, Jane, Pub Serv Librn, College of Alameda, 555 Ralph Appezzato Memorial Pkwy, Alameda, CA, 94501. Tel: 510-748-2366. Fax: 510-748-2380. p. 119

McKenna, Julie, Dep Dir, Regina Public Library, Library Directors Office, 2311 12th Ave, Regina, SK, S4P 0N3, CANADA. Tel: 306-777-6099. Fax: 306-949-7263. p. 2923

McKenna, Kristen, Educ Coordr, Edmonton Humane Society, 13620-163 St NW, Edmonton, AB, T5V 0B2, CANADA. Tel: 780-471-1774. Fax: 780-479-8946. p. 2700

McKenna, Ray, Dir, Oconomowoc Public Library, 200 South St, Oconomowoc, WI, 53066-5213. Tel: 262-569-2193. Fax: 262-569-2176. p. 2626

McKenna, Stephanie, Circ Supvr, Horsham Township Library, 435 Babylon Rd, Horsham, PA, 19044-1224. Tel: 215-443-2609, Ext 207. Fax: 215-443-2697. p. 2069

McKenna, Sue, Hist Coll Librn, Petroleum County Community Library, 205 S Broadway, Winnett, MT, 59087. Tel: 406-429-2451. Fax: 406-429-7631. p. 1390

McKenna-Tubbs, Tamara, Supvr, Circ, West Palm Beach Public Library, 411 Clematis St, West Palm Beach, FL, 33401. Tel: 561-868-7767. Fax: 561-868-7706. p. 504

McKenney, Janet, Dir of Develop, Maine State Library, LMA Bldg, 230 State St, Augusta, ME, 04333. Tel: 207-287-5603. Fax: 207-287-5615. p. 974

McKenney, Lisa, Pub Serv Coordr, Allegany County Library System, 31 Washington St, Cumberland, MD, 21502. Tel: 301-777-1200. Fax: 301-777-7299. p. 1026

McKenney, Susan, Libr Asst, Nassau County Public Library System, Bryceville Branch, 7280 Motes Rd, Bryceville, FL, 32009. Tel: 904-266-9813. Fax: 904-266-2271. p. 440

McKennon, Ed, Librn, Glendale Community College, 6000 W Olive Ave, Glendale, AZ, 85302. Tel: 623-845-3195. Fax: 623-845-3102. p. 64

McKenny, Susan, Br Mgr, Shreve Memorial Library, Rodessa Branch, 10093 Main St, Rodessa, LA, 71069. Tel: 318-223-4211. Fax: 318-223-4211. p. 970

McKensie, Marjorie, Adminr, Dauphin County Library System, East Shore Area Library, 4501 Ethel St, Harrisburg, PA, 17109. Tel: 717-652-9380, Ext 122. Fax: 717-545-3584. p. 2064

McKenzie, Ann, Commun Serv Mgr, Mgr, Ch Serv, St Catharines Public Library, 54 Church St, St. Catharines, ON, L2R 7K2, CANADA. Tel: 905-688-6103, Ext 226. Fax: 905-688-6292. p. 2843

McKenzie, Barbara, Dr, Chair, University of West Georgia, 1601 Maple St, Carrollton, GA, 30118. Tel: 678-839-6149. Fax: 678-839-6153. p. 2964

McKenzie, Chandra, Assoc Provost, Dir, Rochester Institute of Technology, 90 Lomb Memorial Dr, Rochester, NY, 14623-5604. Tel: 585-475-2566. Fax: 585-475-7007. p. 1731

McKenzie, Charlene, Br Mgr, Saint Paul Public Library, Rondo Community Outreach Library, 461 N Dale St, Saint Paul, MN, 55103. Tel: 651-266-7400. Fax: 651-266-7410. p. 1281

McKenzie, Daniel, Circ Mgr, Tyler Junior College, 1327 S Baxter St, Tyler, TX, 75701. Tel: 903-510-2502, 903-510-2503. Fax: 903-510-2639. p. 2393

McKenzie, Doyne, Coll Develop Mgr, Daniel Boone Regional Library, 100 W Broadway, Columbia, MO, 65203. Tel: 573-443-3161. Fax: 573-443-3281. p. 1324

McKenzie, Elizabeth, Dir, Suffolk University, John Joseph Moakley Law Library, 120 Tremont St, Boston, MA, 02108-4977. Tel: 617-573-8177. p. 1067

McKenzie, Grace Y, Librn, Sperry Marine, 1070 Seminole Trail, Charlottesville, VA, 22901. Tel: 434-974-2441. Fax: 434-974-2259. p. 2454

Mckenzie, James, Dept Head, Ref, University of New Brunswick Libraries, Five Macaulay Dr, Fredericton, NB, E3B 5H5, CANADA. Tel: 506-458-7056. Fax: 506-453-4595. p. 2763

McKenzie, Janis, Head, Info & Instrul Serv, Simon Fraser University Library, 8888 University Dr, Burnaby, BC, V5A 1S6, CANADA. Tel: 778-782-6865. Fax: 778-782-3023. p. 2726

McKenzie, Jean, Unit Head, Ref Librn, University of California, Berkeley, Kresge Engineering Library, 110 Bechtel Engineering Ctr, Berkeley, CA, 94720-6000. Tel: 510-642-3532. Fax: 510-643-6771. p. 128

McKenzie, Joe, Dir, Salina Public Library, 301 W Elm St, Salina, KS, 67401. Tel: 785-825-4624. Fax: 785-823-0706. p. 893

McKenzie, Karen, Chief Librn, Art Gallery of Ontario, 317 Dundas St W, Toronto, ON, M5T 1G4, CANADA. Tel: 416-979-6660. Fax: 416-979-6602. p. 2850

McKenzie, Ken, ILL, Pueblo City-County Library District, 100 E Abriendo Ave, Pueblo, CO, 81004-4290. Tel: 719-562-5637. Fax: 719-562-5619. p. 320

McKenzie, Lora, Libr Tech, United States Geological Survey, 11649 Leetown Rd, Kearneysville, WV, 25430. Tel: 304-724-4448. Fax: 304-724-4435. p. 2563

McKenzie, Marcia, Cat, Randolph College, 2500 Rivermont Ave, Lynchburg, VA, 24503. Tel: 434-947-8133. Fax: 434-947-8134. p. 2476

McKenzie, Marie-Carole, Asst Dir, Cegep Regional de Lanaudiere a Joliette, 20 rue Saint Charles Sud, Joliette, QC, J6E 4T1, CANADA. Tel: 450-759-1661. Fax: 450-759-4468, 450-759-7120. p. 2884

McKenzie, Pam, Dir, Allen Memorial Public Library, 121 E Blackbourn Ave, Hawkins, TX, 75765. Tel: 903-769-2241. p. 2331

McKenzie, Winston, Head Librn, Winston & Strawn Library, 200 Park Ave, New York, NY, 10166. Tel: 212-294-6885. Fax: 212-294-4700. p. 1703

McKeon, Debbie, Ch, Three Rivers Regional Library System, 208 Gloucester St, Brunswick, GA, 31520-7007. Tel: 912-267-1212. Fax: 912-267-9597. p. 522

McKeon, Taffy, Asst Dir, Libr Computing Serv, Georgetown University, Dahlgren Memorial Library, Preclinical Science Bldg GM-7, 3900 Reservoir Rd NW, Washington, DC, 20007. Tel: 202-687-1537. Fax: 202-687-1862. p. 402

McKeown, Deb, Dir, Norelius Community Library, 1403 First Ave S, Denison, IA, 51442-2014. Tel: 712-263-9355. Fax: 712-263-8578. p. 808

McKeown, Jonathan, Assoc Dir, Cobb County Public Library System, 266 Roswell St, Marietta, GA, 30060-2004. Tel: 770-528-2332. Fax: 770-528-2349. p. 542

McKeown, Terri, Fiscal Officer, Grandview Heights Public Library, 1685 W First Ave, Columbus, OH, 43212. Tel: 614-486-2951. Fax: 614-481-7021. p. 1886

McKeraghan, Amanda, Mgr, Colville Public Library, 195 S Oak St, Colville, WA, 99114-2845. Tel: 509-684-6620. Fax: 509-684-3911. p. 2513

McKerlie, Karen, Dir, Modeste Bedient Memorial Library, 3699 State Rte 54A, Branchport, NY, 14418. Tel: 315-595-2899. Fax: 315-595-2899. p. 1584

McKernan, Ro, Instruction & Ref Librn, Whatcom Community College Library, 237 W Kellogg Rd, Bellingham, WA, 98226. Tel: 360-383-3300. p. 2509

McKey, Kay D, Asst Dir, Cat, Saint John the Baptist Parish Library, 2920 New Hwy 51, LaPlace, LA, 70068. Tel: 985-652-2225, 985-652-6857. Fax: 985-652-8005. p. 954

McKibbens, Tangela, Mgr, Henry County Public Library System, Fortson Public Library, 61 McDonough St, Hampton, GA, 30228. Tel: 770-954-2812. Fax: 770-946-8349. p. 544

McKibbin, Barbara, Dir, Libr Serv, Cleveland Community College, 137 S Post Rd, Shelby, NC, 28152. Tel: 704-484-4116. Fax: 704-484-4036. p. 1823

McKibbon, Shelley, Librn, Maritimes Health Libraries Association, WK Kellogg Health Sciences Library, 5850 College St, Halifax, NS, B3H 1X5, CANADA. Tel: 902-494-2483. Fax: 902-494-3750. p. 2959

McKiel, Allen, Dr, Dean of Libr, Western Oregon University, Wayne & Lynn Hamersly Library, 345 N Monmouth Ave, Monmouth, OR, 97361-1396. Tel: 503-838-8886. Fax: 503-838-8399. p. 2006

McKiernan, Carole, Youth Serv Coordr, Burlington County Library, Five Pioneer Blvd, Westampton, NJ, 08060. Tel: 609-267-9660, Ext 3068. Fax: 609-267-4091. p. 1542

McKiernan, Kathleen, Co-Dir, Federal Reserve Bank of New York, 33 Liberty St, Federal Reserve PO Sta, New York, NY, 10045. Tel: 212-720-5670, 212-720-8289. Fax: 212-720-1372. p. 1678

McKillop, Christena, Dir, Western University - Libraries, Education, John George Althouse Faculty of Educ, 1137 Western Rd, London, ON, N6G 1G7, CANADA. Tel: 519-661-2111, Ext 88276. Fax: 519-661-3822. p. 2819

McKillop, Jocelyn, Archivist, Archives of Manitoba, 130-200 Vaughan St, Winnipeg, MB, R3C 1T5, CANADA. Tel: 204-945-3971. Fax: 204-948-2008. p. 2754

McKillop, Mary, Circ Librn, Ellsworth Public Library, 20 State St, Ellsworth, ME, 04605. Tel: 207-667-6363. Fax: 207-667-4901. p. 984

McKinley, Cathy, Dir, Atmore Public Library, 700 E Church St, Atmore, AL, 36502. Tel: 251-368-5234. Fax: 251-368-7064. p. 5

McKinley, Danielle, Librn, Canada Department of Fisheries & Oceans, 1190 Westmount Rd, Sydney, NS, B1P 6L1, CANADA. Tel: 902-564-3660, Ext 1164. Fax: 902-564-3672. p. 2784

McKinley, Deborah L, Tech Coordr, Scott County Library System, 13090 Alabama Ave S, Savage, MN, 55378-1479. Tel: 952-707-1760. Fax: 952-707-1775. p. 1283

McKinley, Glenda, Circ Supvr, Western Theological Seminary, 101 E 13th St, Holland, MI, 49423. Tel: 616-392-8555. p. 1191

McKinley, Jennifer, Asst Dir, Morgan County Public Library, 110 S Jefferson St, Martinsville, IN, 46151. Tel: 765-342-3451. Fax: 765-342-9992. p. 763

McKinley, Joyce, Circ Supvr, ILL, Thomas More College Library, 333 Thomas More Pkwy, Crestview Hills, KY, 41017-2599. Tel: 859-344-3300. Fax: 859-344-3342. p. 910

McKinley, Mary, Librn, George Junior Republic Library, 200 George Junior Rd, Grove City, PA, 16127. p. 2063

McKinney, Carol, Librn, Logan County Public Library, Adairville Branch, 101 Church St, Adairville, KY, 42202. Tel: 270-539-4601. Fax: 270-539-4601. p. 934

McKinney, David, Pub Serv, Shenandoah University, 1460 University Dr, Winchester, VA, 22601. Tel: 540-665-4634. Fax: 540-665-4609. p. 2503

McKinney, Fred, Ref Serv, Missouri Baptist University, One College Park Dr, Saint Louis, MO, 63141-8698. Tel: 314-434-1115. Fax: 314-392-2343. p. 1356

McKinney, Genette, Librn, Northeast Regional Library, Chalybeate Public Library, 2501-A Hwy 354, Walnut, MS, 38683-9762. Tel: 662-223-4621. p. 1297

McKinney, Jane, Br Librn, Prince Edward Island Public Library Service, Stratford Public, 57 Bunbury Rd, Stratford, PE, C1B 1T8, CANADA. Tel: 902-569-7441. p. 2876

McKinney, Janet, Electronic Res, Shook, Hardy & Bacon, 2555 Grand Blvd, 3rd Flr, Kansas City, MO, 64108-2613. Tel: 816-474-6550. Fax: 816-421-5547. p. 1341

McKinney, Karin L, Asst Dir, Trumbull County Law Library, 120 High St NW, Warren, OH, 44481. Tel: 330-675-2525. Fax: 330-675-2527. p. 1944

McKinney, Loretta, Dir of Libr Serv, Murrieta Public Library, Eight Town Sq, Murrieta, CA, 92562. Tel: 951-304-2665. Fax: 951-696-0165. p. 192

McKinney, Lorraine, Acq, Supvr, Connecticut College, 270 Mohegan Ave, New London, CT, 06320-4196. Tel: 860-439-2641. Fax: 860-439-2871. p. 359

McKinney, Mary, Managing Librn, Pima County Public Library, George Miller-Golf Links, 9640 E Golf Links Rd, Tucson, AZ, 85730. Tel: 520-594-5355. Fax: 520-770-4104. p. 87

McKinney, Rebekah, Acq, Missouri Baptist University, One College Park Dr, Saint Louis, MO, 63141-8698. Tel: 314-392-2336. Fax: 314-392-2343. p. 1356

McKinney, Rosie, Br Librn, Frankfort Community Public Library, Michigan Road Community Library, 2489 N St, Rd 29, Michigantown, IN, 46057-9566. Tel: 765-249-2303. Fax: 765-249-2303. p. 743

McKinney, Steve, Cat, Info Serv, Northwestern Regional Library, 111 N Front St, Elkin, NC, 28621. Tel: 336-835-4894. Fax: 336-526-2270. p. 1791

McKinney, Susan Dawn, Librn, St Joseph Township-Swearingen Memorial Library, 201 N Third, Saint Joseph, IL, 61873. Tel: 217-469-2159. Fax: 217-469-2159. p. 700

McKinney, Tammy, Outreach Serv Librn, Pike County Public Library, 1104 Main St, Petersburg, IN, 47567. Tel: 812-354-6257. Fax: 812-354-6259. p. 773

McKinnis, Kathy, Librn, Pawnee Public Library, 653 Illinois St, Pawnee, OK, 74058. Tel: 918-762-2138. Fax: 918-762-2101. p. 1976

McKinnon, Avis, Coordr, Mohave County Library District, South Mohave Valley Community Library, 8045 Hwy 95, Ste D, Mohave Valley, AZ, 86440. Tel: 928-768-1151. Fax: 928-768-1151. p. 67

McKinnon, Carey, In Charge, Santa Barbara Public Library, Los Olivos, Grange Hall, Santa Barbara, CA, 93102. p. 261

McKinnon, Carey, In Charge, Santa Barbara Public Library, Santa Ynez Branch, 3598 Sagunto St, Santa Ynez, CA, 93460. p. 261

McKinnon, Carey, In Charge, Santa Barbara Public Library, Solvang Branch, 1745 Mission Dr, Solvang, CA, 93463. Tel: 805-688-4214. p. 261

McKinnon, Chris, Acq, University of New England Libraries, Josephine S Abplanalp Library, Portland Campus, 716 Stevens Ave, Portland, ME, 04103. Tel: 207-221-4327. Fax: 207-221-4893. p. 978

McKinstry, Jill M, Dir, University of Washington Libraries, Odegaard Undergraduate Library, Box 353080, Seattle, WA, 98195-3080. Tel: 206-685-3933. Fax: 206-685-8485. p. 2534

McKinstry, Lesley, Dir, North Baltimore Public Library, 230 N Main St, North Baltimore, OH, 45872-1125. Tel: 419-257-3621. Fax: 419-257-3859. p. 1923

McKinstry, Mark, Br Mgr, Cuyahoga County Public Library, Bay Village Branch, 502 Cahoon Rd, Bay Village, OH, 44140-2179. Tel: 440-871-6392. Fax: 440-871-5320. p. 1927

McKinstry, Melissa, Librn, Haston Library, 5167 Main St, Franklin, VT, 05457. Tel: 802-285-6505. Fax: 802-285-2181. p. 2424

McKinstry, Richard, Dir, The Winterthur Library, 5105 Kennett Pike, Winterthur, DE, 19735. Tel: 302-888-4681. Fax: 302-888-3367. p. 389

McKinzie, Steve, Libr Dir, Catawba College, 2300 W Innes St, Salisbury, NC, 28144-2488. Tel: 704-637-4449. Fax: 704-637-4304. p. 1821

McKnelly, Michele, Govt Doc, Head, Tech Serv, University of Wisconsin-River Falls, 410 S Third St, River Falls, WI, 54022. Tel: 715-425-4482. Fax: 715-425-0609. p. 2635

McKnight, David, Dir, University of Pennsylvania Libraries, Rare Book & Manuscript Library, 3420 Walnut St, Philadelphia, PA, 19104. Tel: 215-746-5829. p. 2119

McKnight, Eleanor, Librn, Kean University, 1000 Morris Ave, Union, NJ, 07083. Tel: 908-737-4600. Fax: 908-737-4620. p. 1537

McKnight, Michelynn, Dr, Assoc Prof, Louisiana State University, 267 Coates Hall, Baton Rouge, LA, 70803. Tel: 225-578-3158. Fax: 225-578-4581. p. 2966

McKnight, Pamela, Pub Serv Librn, Pere Marquette District Library, 185 E Fourth St, Clare, MI, 48617. Tel: 989-386-7576. Fax: 989-386-3576. p. 1163

McKown, Kathy, Librn, Trimble County Public Library, 112 US Hwy 42 E, Bedford, KY, 40006-7622. Tel: 502-255-7362. Fax: 502-255-7491. p. 907

McKown, Teri, Ch, Butler Public Library, 340 S Broadway, Butler, IN, 46721. Tel: 260-868-2351. Fax: 260-868-5491. p. 730

McLachlan, Bonnie, Mgr, Connecticut Horticultural Society Library, 2433 Main St, Rocky Hill, CT, 06067-2539. Tel: 860-529-8713. Fax: 860-563-2217. p. 365

McLagan, Michelle A, Dir, Hepburn Library of Lisbon, 6899 County Rte 10, Lisbon, NY, 13658-4242. Tel: 315-393-0111. Fax: 315-393-0111. p. 1652

McLain, Guy, Dir, Connecticut Valley Historical Museum, The Quadrangle, Edwards St, Springfield, MA, 01103. Tel: 413-263-6800, Ext 230. Fax: 413-263-6898. p. 1127

McLamb, Jessica, ILL, Escanaba Public Library, 400 Ludington St, Escanaba, MI, 49829. Tel: 906-789-7323. Fax: 906-786-0942. p. 1177

McLane, Alec, Librn, Wesleyan University, Scores & Recordings Collection, 252 Church St, Middletown, CT, 06459-3199. Tel: 860-685-3898. p. 352

McLane, Curren, Dir, Azle Memorial Library, 333 W Main St, Azle, TX, 76020. Tel: 817-444-7216. Fax: 817-444-7064. p. 2285

McLaren, Cheri, Librn, Rural Municipality of Argyle Public Library, 627 Elizabeth Ave, Baldur, MB, R0K 0B0, CANADA. Tel: 204-535-2314. Fax: 204-535-2242. p. 2747

McLatchy, Kevin, Archives, Govt Doc, Slippery Rock University of Pennsylvania, Slippery Rock, PA, 16057-9989. Tel: 724-738-2058. Fax: 724-738-2661. p. 2140

McLaughlin, Amy, Reader Serv, Albany Public Library, 161 Washington Ave, Albany, NY, 12210. Tel: 518-427-4349. Fax: 518-449-3386. p. 1568

McLaughlin, Andrew E, Ref Serv, Melrose Public Library, 69 W Emerson St, Melrose, MA, 02176. Tel: 781-665-2313. Fax: 781-662-4229. p. 1105

McLaughlin, Anne, Ch, West Warwick Public Library, 1043 Main St, West Warwick, RI, 02893. Tel: 401-828-3750. Fax: 401-828-8493. p. 2178

McLaughlin, Brian, Ref, United States Senate Library, SRB-15 Senate Russell Bldg, Washington, DC, 20510-7112. Tel: 202-224-7106. Fax: 202-224-0879. p. 421

McLaughlin, Christianne, Dir, United States Air Force, F4D 3FA-30 SVX/SVMG, 100 Community Loop, Vandenberg AFB, CA, 93437-5223. Tel: 805-606-1110, Ext 69745. Fax: 805-734-8232, Ext 58941. p. 279

McLaughlin, Christine, Dir, Whitinsville Social Library, Inc, 17 Church St, Whitinsville, MA, 01588. Tel: 508-234-2151. p. 1140

McLaughlin, Daniel, Res, Weil, Gotshal & Manges Library, 767 Fifth Ave, New York, NY, 10153. Tel: 212-310-8626. Fax: 212-310-8007. p. 1702

McLaughlin, Debra, Asst Head, Coll Develop, Cobb County Public Library System, 266 Roswell St, Marietta, GA, 30060-2004. Tel: 770-528-2320. Fax: 770-528-2349. p. 542

McLaughlin, Debra, Outreach Serv Librn, Marlboro County Library, 200 John Corry Rd, Bennettsville, SC, 29512. Tel: 843-479-5630. Fax: 843-479-5645. p. 2182

McLaughlin, Grace, Dir, Clifford Chance LLP Library, 31 W 52nd St, New York, NY, 10019. Tel: 212-878-8095. Fax: 212-878-3474. p. 1673

McLaughlin, Hélène, Mgr, Universite de Moncton, 218 Blvd J-D-Gauthier, Shippagan, NB, E8S 1P6, CANADA. Tel: 506-336-3418, 506-336-3420. Fax: 506-336-3434. p. 2767

McLaughlin, Jean Castle, Ref Librn, New Milford Public Library, 200 Dahlia Ave, New Milford, NJ, 07646-1812. Tel: 201-262-1221. Fax: 201-262-5639. p. 1510

McLaughlin, Kathleen, Dir, Putnam Valley Free Library, 30 Oscawana Lake Rd, Putnam Valley, NY, 10579. Tel: 845-528-3242. Fax: 845-528-3297. p. 1725

McLaughlin, Kim, Ch, Libby Memorial Library, 27 Staples St, Old Orchard Beach, ME, 04064. Tel: 207-934-4351. p. 994

McLaughlin, Lauren, Asst Dir, Wilton Library Association, 137 Old Ridgefield Rd, Wilton, CT, 06897-3019. Tel: 203-762-3950. Fax: 203-834-1166. p. 378

McLaughlin, LaVerne, Dir, Albany State University, 504 College Dr, Albany, GA, 31705-2796. Tel: 229-430-4799. Fax: 229-430-4803. p. 507

McLaughlin, Mary Lee, Adult Serv, Ref Serv, Augsburg College, 2211 Riverside Ave, Minneapolis, MN, 55454. Tel: 612-330-1604. Fax: 612-330-1436. p. 1259

McLaughlin, Nancy, Head, Ch, Hamden Public Library, 2901 Dixwell Ave, Hamden, CT, 06518-3135. Tel: 203-230-3770. Fax: 203-287-2685. p. 343

Mclaughlin, Nancy, Dir, Chester Springs Library, 1685 A Art School Rd, Chester Springs, PA, 19425-1402. Tel: 610-827-9212. Fax: 610-827-1148. p. 2044

McLaughlin, Pamela, Dir, Communications & External Relations, Syracuse University Library, 222 Waverly Ave, Syracuse, NY, 13244-2010. Tel: 315-443-9788. p. 1754

McLaughlin, Patricia, Head of Libr, Free Library of Philadelphia, Joseph E Coleman Northwest Regional, 68 W Chelten Ave, Philadelphia, PA, 19144-2795. Tel: 215-685-2150. Fax: 215-848-7790. p. 2107

McLaughlin, Robert, Tech Serv, Finger Lakes Library System, 119 E Green St, Ithaca, NY, 14850. Tel: 607-273-4074. Fax: 607-273-3618. p. 1642

McLaughlin, Ryan, Ref & Web Res Librn, Muskingum University Library, 163 Stormont St, New Concord, OH, 43762-1199. Tel: 740-826-8157. Fax: 740-826-8404. p. 1920

McLaughlin, Sandra, Ch, Parkesburg Free Library, 105 West St, Parkesburg, PA, 19365-1499. Tel: 610-857-5165. Fax: 610-857-1193. p. 2101

McLaughlin, Terry, Librn, Howe Community Library, 315 S Collins Freeway, Howe, TX, 75459. Tel: 903-532-3350. Fax: 903-532-3351. p. 2345

McLauglin, Karen, Asst Dir, Davenport University, 6191 Kraft Ave SE, Grand Rapids, MI, 49512. Tel: 616-554-5612. Fax: 616-554-5226. p. 1184

McLaury, Linda L, Head, Access Serv, University of Northern Iowa Library, 1227 W 27th St, Cedar Falls, IA, 50613-3675. Tel: 319-273-3610. Fax: 319-273-2913. p. 799

McLean, Deb, Dir, Toronto Public Library, 107 W Main, Toronto, KS, 66777. Tel: 620-637-2661. Fax: 620-637-2661. p. 898

Mclean, Debbie, Asst Librn, Avery County Morrison Public Library, 150 Library Pl, Newland, NC, 28657. Tel: 828-733-9393. Fax: 828-682-6277. p. 1813

McLean, Elizabeth, Dir, Woods Memorial Presbyterian Church Library, 611 Baltimore-Annapolis Blvd, Severna Park, MD, 21146. Tel: 410-647-2550. Fax: 410-647-2781. p. 1041

McLean, Gale, Supvr, Per, Middle Tennessee State University, MTSU, PO Box 13, Murfreesboro, TN, 37132. Tel: 615-898-2819. p. 2254

McLean, J Stuart, Librn, Yarmouth County Museum & Archives, 22 Collins St, Yarmouth, NS, B5A 3C8, CANADA. Tel: 902-742-5539. Fax: 902-749-1120. p. 2787

McLean, Jennifer, Asst Librn, Tech Serv, North Carolina Supreme Court Library, 500 Justice Bldg, Two E Morgan St, Raleigh, NC, 27601-1428. Tel: 919-831-5709. Fax: 919-831-5732. p. 1816

McLean, Lisa, Asst Librn, AIB College of Business Library, 2500 Fleur Dr, Des Moines, IA, 50321-1749. Tel: 515-244-4221. Fax: 515-288-4366. p. 808

McLean, Mary, Br Mgr, Buncombe County Public Libraries, Leicester Branch, 1561 Alexander Rd, Leicester, NC, 28748. Tel: 828-250-6480. Fax: 828-683-8874. p. 1774

McLean, Rev Edward J, Dir, Archdiocese of Hartford, 125 Market St, Hartford, CT, 06103. Tel: 860-522-0602. Fax: 860-247-3490. p. 344

McLean, Rita, Ad, Wayne Public Library, Robert B & Mary Y Benthack Library-Senior Ctr, 410 Pearl St, Wayne, NE, 68787. Tel: 402-375-3135. Fax: 402-375-5772. p. 1422

McLean, Ursula, Ref, Johns Hopkins University-Peabody Conservatory of Music, 21 E Mount Vernon Pl, Baltimore, MD, 21202-2397. Tel: 410-659-8100, Ext 1162. Fax: 410-685-0657. p. 1015

McLean, Valla, Ref Librn, Grant MacEwan University Library, 10700 104th Ave, Edmonton, AB, T5J 4S2, CANADA. Tel: 780-497-5850. Fax: 780-497-5895. p. 2701

McLeish-Delgado, Karin, Librn, Lee County Library System, Talking Books, 13240 N Cleveland Ave, North Fort Myers, FL, 33903-4855. Tel: 239-995-2665. Fax: 239-995-1681. p. 446

McLeister, Kathy, Archives Dir, Theatre Historical Society of America, 152 N York Rd, 2nd Flr, Elmhurst, IL, 60126-2806. Tel: 630-782-1800. p. 642

McLeland, Courtenay, Govt Doc, University of North Florida, Bldg 12-Library, One UNF Dr, Jacksonville, FL, 32224-2645. Tel: 904-620-1529. Fax: 904-620-2719. p. 455

McLellan, David, Librn, Texas Department of State Health Services, 1100 W 49th St, Austin, TX, 78756-3199. Tel: 512-776-2882. Fax: 512-776-7474 (AV Library), 512-776-7683. p. 2282

McLellan, Donalda, Br Librn, Palliser Regional Library, Imperial Branch, 310 Royal St Town Office, Imperial, SK, S0G 2J0, CANADA. Tel: 306-963-2272. Fax: 306-963-2445. p. 2918

McLemore, Annette, Br Mgr, Bienville Parish Library, Ringgold Branch, 2078 Hall St, Ringgold, LA, 71068. Tel: 318-894-9770. Fax: 318-894-4339. p. 941

McLemore, Laura, Dr, Archivist, Louisiana State University, One University Pl, Shreveport, LA, 71115-2399. Tel: 318-797-5378. Fax: 318-797-5156. p. 968

McLemore, Lelan, Dr, Dir, Carroll College, 100 N East Ave, Waukesha, WI, 53186. Tel: 262-524-7177. Fax: 262-524-7377. p. 2644

McLemore, Mary, Br Mgr, Chickasaw Regional Library System, Mary E Parker Memorial, 500 W Broadway, Sulphur, OK, 73086. Tel: 580-622-5807. Fax: 580-622-6395. p. 1957

McLemore, Nancy J, Libr Dir, Copiah-Lincoln Community College, 11 Colin Circle, Natchez, MS, 39120. Tel: 601-446-1101. Fax: 601-446-1297. p. 1309

McLennan, Kathy, Circ, Perrot Memorial Library, 90 Sound Beach Ave, Old Greenwich, CT, 06870. Tel: 203-637-1066. Fax: 203-698-2620. p. 363

McLennan, Stacy, Librn, Doon Heritage Crossroads Library, Ten Huron Rd, Kitchener, ON, N2P 2R7, CANADA. Tel: 519-748-1914. Fax: 519-748-0009. p. 2815

McLeod, Anne, Head, Circ, Mount Allison University Libraries & Archives, 49 York St, Sackville, NB, E4L 1C6, CANADA. Tel: 506-364-3569. Fax: 506-364-2617. p. 2766

McLeod, Bill, Sr Librn, The National Academies, 500 Fifth St NW, Keck 304, Washington, DC, 20001-2721. Tel: 202-334-2125. Fax: 202-334-1651. p. 409

McLeod, Clara, Librn, Washington University Libraries, Earth & Planetary Science, EPSc Bldg, 3rd Flr, One Brookings Dr, Saint Louis, MO, 63130-4862. Tel: 314-935-4817. p. 1363

McLeod, Gillian, Libr Mgr, Fraser Valley Regional Library, George Mackie Library, 8440 - 112th St, Delta, BC, V4C 4W9, CANADA. Tel: 604-594-8155. Fax: 604-594-9364. p. 2724

McLeod, Gillian, Libr Mgr, Fraser Valley Regional Library, Ladner Pioneer Library, 4683 - 51st St, Delta, BC, V4K 2V8, CANADA. Tel: 604-946-6215. Fax: 604-946-7821. p. 2724

McLeod, Gillian, Libr Mgr, Fraser Valley Regional Library, Tsawwassen Library, 1321A - 56th St, Delta, BC, V4L 2A6, CANADA. Tel: 604-943-2271. Fax: 604-943-6941. p. 2724

Mcleod, Jan, Libr Tech, University of Manitoba Libraries, Victoria General Hospital Library, 2340 Pembina Hwy, Winnipeg, MB, R3T 2E8, CANADA. Tel: 204-477-3307. Fax: 204-269-7936. p. 2759

McLeod, Kathlyne, Asst Librn, Soldotna Public Library, 235 N Binkley St, Soldotna, AK, 99669. Tel: 907-262-4227. Fax: 907-262-6856. p. 54

McLeod, Krista I, Dir, Nevins Memorial Library, 305 Broadway, Methuen, MA, 01844-6898. Tel: 978-686-4080. Fax: 978-686-8669. p. 1105

McLeod, Laura, Librn, Lawrence County Library, Bobbi Jean Memorial, 102 Hendrix St, Imboden, AR, 72434. Tel: 870-869-2093. Fax: 870-869-2093. p. 116

McLeod, Laura, Librn, Boston Free Library, 9475 Boston State Rd, Boston, NY, 14025-9768. Tel: 716-941-3516. Fax: 716-941-0941. p. 1584

McLeod, Mary Alice, Librn, Cherokee-City-County Public Library, 123 S Grand Ave, Cherokee, OK, 73728. Tel: 580-596-2366. Fax: 580-596-2968. p. 1959

McLeod, Michael, Dr, Dean, Acad Support, South Florida State College Library, 600 W College Dr, Avon Park, FL, 33825-9356. Tel: 863-453-6661. Fax: 863-452-6042. p. 426

Mcleod, Pat, Asst Librn, Rotary Club of Slave Lake Public Library, 101 Main St SE, Slave Lake, AB, T0G 2A0, CANADA. Tel: 780-849-5250. Fax: 780-849-3275. p. 2716

McLeod, Patricia, Dir, David & Joyce Milne Public Library, 1095 Main St, Williamstown, MA, 01267-2627. Tel: 413-458-5369. Fax: 413-458-3085. p. 1140

McLeod, Sue, Head, Tech Serv, Horry County Memorial Library, Technical Services, Extension Bldg, 1603 Fourth Ave, Conway, SC, 29526. Tel: 843-248-1550. Fax: 843-248-1549. p. 2191

McLeod, Terry, Librn, Swan Lake Public Library, Milemarker 71 Hwy 83 S, Swan Lake, MT, 59911. Tel: 406-886-2086. Fax: 406-886-2086. p. 1389

McLonis, Kris, Govt Doc, University of Detroit Mercy Library, 4001 W McNichols Rd, Detroit, MI, 48221-3038. Tel: 313-578-0457. Fax: 313-993-1780. p. 1172

McLoughlin, Fran, Youth Serv Librn, Eastham Public Library, 190 Samoset Rd, Eastham, MA, 02642. Tel: 508-240-5950. Fax: 508-240-0786. p. 1086

McLoughlin, Laura, Ref & Instruction Librn, Roosevelt University, Robert R McCormick Tribune Foundation Library, 1400 N Roosevelt Blvd, Schaumburg, IL, 60173. Tel: 847-619-7980. Fax: 847-619-7983. p. 623

McLucas, Keri, Libr Tech, HACC Central Pennsylvania's Community College, 731 Old Harrisburg Rd, Gettysburg, PA, 17325. Tel: 717-337-1644. Fax: 717-337-2329. p. 2060

Mclughlin, Trevor, Librn, Southwestern Manitoba Regional Library, Napinka Branch, 57 Souris St, Napinka, MB, R0M 1N0, CANADA. Tel: 204-665-2282. p. 2750

McMahan, Carla, Dir, Libr Serv, North Greenville University, 7801 N Tigerville Rd, Tigerville, SC, 29688. Tel: 864-977-7091. Fax: 864-977-2126. p. 2206

McMahan, Diana, Br Coordr, Chickasaw Regional Library System, 601 Railway Express, Ardmore, OK, 73401. Tel: 580-223-3164. Fax: 580-223-3280. p. 1957

McMahan, Elizabeth, Cat Asst, Indiana University Southeast Library, 4201 Grant Line Rd, New Albany, IN, 47150. Tel: 812-941-2262. Fax: 812-941-2656. p. 767

McMahan, Maureen, Coordr, Tech Serv, University of Saint Francis, 201 Pope John Paul II Ctr, 2701 Spring St, Fort Wayne, IN, 46808. Tel: 260-399-7700, Ext 6059. Fax: 260-399-8166. p. 742

McMahan, Theresa, Dir, Sullivan County Public Library, 1655 Blountville Blvd, Blountville, TN, 37617. Tel: 423-279-2715. Fax: 423-279-2836. p. 2224

McMahill, Michalena, Youth Serv Librn, Mustang Public Library, 1201 N Mustang Rd, Mustang, OK, 73064. Tel: 405-376-2226. Fax: 405-376-9925. p. 1969

McMahon, Anne, Archivist, Santa Clara University, Archives, 500 El Camino Real, Santa Clara, CA, 95053-0500. Tel: 408-554-4117. Fax: 408-554-5179. p. 263

McMahon, Arlene, Mgr, Highland Public Library, Clintondale Branch, Crescent at Maple, Clintondale, NY, 12515. Tel: 845-883-5015. p. 1636

McMahon, Beth, Ref/Instruction Librn, Central College, Campus Box 6500, 812 University St, Pella, IA, 50219-1999. Tel: 641-628-5345. Fax: 641-628-5327. p. 838

McMahon, Cathy, Youth Serv, Sump Memorial Library, 222 N Jefferson St, Papillion, NE, 68046. Tel: 402-597-2040. Fax: 402-339-8019. p. 1416

McMahon, Dean, Librn, United Native Friendship Centre, 516 Portage Ave, Fort Frances, ON, P9A 3N1, CANADA. Tel: 807-274-8541. Fax: 807-274-4110. p. 2806

McMahon, Elisabeth, Communications, Advocacy & Outreach Serv Coordr, Grand Prairie Public Library System, 901 Conover Dr, Grand Prairie, TX, 75051. Tel: 972-237-5700. Fax: 972-237-5750. p. 2329

McMahon, Gerry, Dir, Franklin Lakes Free Public Library, 470 DeKorte Dr, Franklin Lakes, NJ, 07417. Tel: 201-891-2224. Fax: 201-891-5102. p. 1486

McMahon, Janette E, Dir, West Liberty Free Public Library, 400 N Spencer St, West Liberty, IA, 52776. Tel: 319-627-2084. Fax: 319-627-2135. p. 852

McMahon, Kevin, Mgr, Southern California Institute of Architecture, 960 E Third St, Los Angeles, CA, 90013. Tel: 213-613-2200, Ext 323. Fax: 213-613-2260. p. 177

McMahon, Mary W, Dir, Mary Riley Styles Public Library, 120 N Virginia Ave, Falls Church, VA, 22046. Tel: 703-248-5030. Fax: 703-248-5144. p. 2463

McMahon, Melody Layton, Libr Dir, Catholic Theological Union, 5416 S Cornell Ave, Chicago, IL, 60615-5698. Tel: 773-371-5464. Fax: 773-753-5340. p. 607

McMahon, Natalie, Dir, Southwest Mississippi Community College, Lakeside Dr, Summit, MS, 39666. Tel: 601-276-2004. Fax: 601-276-3748. p. 1315

McMahon, Patrick, Fr, Librn, Whitefriars Hall, 600 Webster St NE, Washington, DC, 20017. Tel: 202-526-1221, Ext 201. Fax: 202-526-9217. p. 422

McMahon, Patrick Thomas, Dir, The Carmelite Province of the Most Pure Heart of Mary, Whitefriars Hall, 1600 Webster St NE, Washington, DC, 20017. Tel: 202-526-1221, Ext 204. p. 395

McMain, Lynn M, Head, Ref, Sam Houston State University, 1830 Bobby K Marks Dr, Huntsville, TX, 77340. Tel: 936-294-3734. Fax: 936-294-3780. p. 2345

McMakin, Judy, Tech Serv, Richland Public Library, 955 Northgate Dr, Richland, WA, 99352-3539. Tel: 509-942-7604. Fax: 509-942-7442. p. 2526

McManman, Mary, Ref, Bay County Library System, 500 Center Ave, Bay City, MI, 48708. Tel: 989-893-9566. Fax: 989-893-9799. p. 1155

McManus, Alesia, Dir, Howard Community College Library, 10901 Little Patuxent Pkwy, Columbia, MD, 21044. Tel: 443-518-4812. Fax: 443-518-4993. p. 1025

McManus, Blanche, Tech Serv, South Park Township Library, 2575 Brownsville Rd, South Park, PA, 15129-8527. Tel: 412-833-5585. Fax: 412-833-7368. p. 2142

McManus, Heidi, Asst Dir, Utica Public Library, 303 Genesee St, Utica, NY, 13501. Tel: 315-735-2279. Fax: 315-734-1034. p. 1760

McManus, John L, Dir, Millinocket Memorial Library, Five Maine Ave, Millinocket, ME, 04462. Tel: 207-723-7020. Fax: 207-723-7020. p. 992

McManus, Karen, Librn, Alberta Law Libraries, Office of the Chief Medical Examiner Information Centre, 4070 Bowness Rd NW, Calgary, AB, T3B 3R7, CANADA. Tel: 403-297-8123, Ext 224. Fax: 403-297-3429. p. 2687

McManus, Molly, Assoc Librn, Coordr, Pub Serv, Millsaps College, 1701 N State St, Jackson, MS, 39210-0001. Tel: 601-974-1086. Fax: 601-974-1082. p. 1304

McManus, Regina, Head, Circ, Flagler County Public Library, 2500 Palm Coast Pkwy NW, Palm Coast, FL, 32137. Tel: 386-446-6763. Fax: 386-446-6773. p. 479

McManus, Suzanne, Librn, Smithtown Library, Kings Park Branch, One Church St, Kings Park, NY, 11754. Tel: 631-269-9191. Fax: 631-269-0807. p. 1744

McManus, Teresa, Chief Librn, Bronx Community College Library & Learning Center, 106 Meister Hall, 2115 University Ave, Bronx, NY, 10453. Tel: 718-289-5439, 718-289-5548. Fax: 718-289-6063. p. 1586

McMaster, Beverly A, Librn, United States Army, Martin Army Community Hospital Medical Library, Bldg 9200, Rm 010 MCXB-IL, 7950 Martin Loop, Fort Benning, GA, 31905-5637. Tel: 706-544-3533. Fax: 706-544-3215. p. 532

McMaster, Sarah D, Dir, Fairfield County Library, 300 W Washington St, Winnsboro, SC, 29180. Tel: 803-635-4971. Fax: 803-635-7715. p. 2207

McMeeking, Trixie L, Dir, Homer Public Library, 141 W Main St, Homer, MI, 49245. Tel: 517-568-3450. Fax: 517-568-4021. p. 1191

McMeen, Dawn, Librn, Scott County Library System, Princeton Branch, 328 River Dr, Princeton, IA, 52768. Tel: 563-289-4282. Fax: 563-289-4282. p. 814

McMillan, Alice, Actg Dir, Orange Public Library, 348 Main St, Orange, NJ, 07050-2794. Tel: 973-673-0153, Ext 10. Fax: 973-673-1847. p. 1516

McMillan, Betty, Asst Librn, The Center - Resources for Teaching & Learning Library, 2626 S Clearbrook Dr, Arlington Heights, IL, 60005-4626. Tel: 224-366-8500. Fax: 224-366-8514. p. 589

McMillan, Carolyn, Asst Librn, Southeast Regional Library, Carlyle Branch, 119 Souris W, Carlyle, SK, S0C 0R0, CANADA. Tel: 306-453-6120. Fax: 306-453-6120. p. 2929

McMillan, Carolyn, Librn, Southeast Regional Library, Kennedy Branch, 235 Scott St, Kennedy, SK, S0G 2R0, CANADA. Tel: 306-538-2020. p. 2930

McMillan, Gary, Dir, American Psychiatric Association, 1000 Wilson Blvd, Ste 1825, Arlington, VA, 22209-3901. Tel: 703-907-8648. Fax: 703-907-1084. p. 2448

McMillan, Glenda, Br Librn, Pope County Library System, Dover Branch, 80 Library Rd, Dover, AR, 72837. Tel: 479-331-2173. Fax: 479-331-4151. p. 114

McMillan, Judy, Ref Serv, Northwest Vista College, Redbud Hall, 3535 N Ellison Dr, San Antonio, TX, 78251. Tel: 210-486-4567. Fax: 210-486-9105. p. 2380

McMillan, Kate, Spec Coll Cat/Ref Librn, Indiana State University, 510 North 6 1/2 St, Terre Haute, IN, 47809. Tel: 812-237-8672. Fax: 812-237-3376. p. 781

McMillan, Lisa, ILL, Boise Public Library, 715 S Capitol Blvd, Boise, ID, 83702. Tel: 208-384-4076. p. 570

McMillan, Mary, Dir, Libr Serv, Marymount College Library, 30800 Palos Verdes Dr E, Rancho Palos Verdes, CA, 90275-6299. Tel: 310-377-5501, Ext 302. Fax: 310-377-6223. p. 213

McMillan, Mary Lou, Supvr, Elgin County Public Library, John Kenneth Galbraith Reference Library-Dutton Branch, 236 Shackleton St, Dutton, ON, N0L 1J0, CANADA. Tel: 519-762-2780. Fax: 519-762-0707. p. 2844

McMillan, Morgan T, Curator, Peter Wentz Farmstead Library, 2100 Schultz Rd, Worcester, PA, 19490. Tel: 610-584-5104. Fax: 610-584-6860. p. 2157

McMillan, Susan, Info Serv, York College of Pennsylvania, 441 Country Club Rd, York, PA, 17403-3651. Tel: 717-815-1480. Fax: 717-849-1608. p. 2160

McMillian, Morgan, Libr Dir, Lake Travis Community Library, 2300 Lohman's Spur, Ste 100, Austin, TX, 78734. Tel: 512-263-2885. Fax: 512-535-3044. p. 2281

McMillion, James, Assoc Dir, Southern Methodist University, Bridwell Library-Perkins School of Theology, 6005 Bishop Blvd, Dallas, TX, 75205. Tel: 214-768-3483. Fax: 214-768-4295. p. 2310

McMillion, Annie, Dir, West Virginia School of Osteopathic Medicine Library, 400 N Lee St, Lewisburg, WV, 24901. Tel: 304-647-6261. Fax: 304-645-4443. p. 2564

McMillon, Susan, Tech Serv Coordr, Davis & Elkins College, 100 Campus Dr, Elkins, WV, 26241. Tel: 304-637-1336. Fax: 304-637-1415. p. 2558

McMorran, Charles, Dep Dir, New Orleans Public Library, 219 Loyola Ave, New Orleans, LA, 70112-2044. Tel: 504-529-7323, 504-596-2570. Fax: 504-596-2609. p. 962

McMorrow, Kathleen, Librn, University of Toronto Libraries, Faculty of Music, Edward Johnson Bldg, 80 Queens Park Crescent, Toronto, ON, M5S 1A1, CANADA. Tel: 416-978-6920. Fax: 416-978-5571. p. 2866

McMullen, Anthony, Syst Librn, Edinboro University of Pennsylvania, 200 Tartan Ave, Edinboro, PA, 16444. Tel: 814-732-2779. Fax: 814-732-2883. p. 2053

McMullen, Cecelia, Head, Circ, Gonzaga University School of Law, 721 N Cincinnati St, Spokane, WA, 99202. Tel: 509-323-3728. Fax: 509-323-5733. p. 2536

McMullen, Cindy, Genealogy Librn, Kurth Memorial Library, 706 S Raguet, Lufkin, TX, 75904. Tel: 936-630-0560. Fax: 936-639-2487. p. 2358

McMullen, Dennis, Ref, Sandusky Library, 114 W Adams St, Sandusky, OH, 44870. Tel: 419-625-3834. Fax: 419-625-4574. p. 1934

McMullen, Heather, Mgr, Res, Instruction & Knowledge Serv, Harvard Library, John F Kennedy School of Government Library, 79 John F Kennedy St, Cambridge, MA, 02138. Tel: 617-495-1304. Fax: 617-495-1972. p. 1075

McMullen, Karen, Head, Access Serv, University of South Carolina, School of Medicine, 6311 Garners Ferry Rd, Columbia, SC, 29209. Tel: 803-733-3321. Fax: 803-733-1509. p. 2190

McMullen, Lois, Librn, Wissahickon Valley Public Library, Ambler Branch, 209 Race St, Ambler, PA, 19002. Tel: 215-646-1072. Fax: 215-654-0161. p. 2036

McMullen, Patsy, Librn, Lonoke Prairie County Regional Library Headquarters, Hazen Public, 121 US Hwy 70 E, Hazen, AR, 72064. Tel: 870-255-3576. Fax: 870-255-3576. p. 108

McMullen, Rosalie, Librn, Norton Public Library, One Washington Sq, Norton, KS, 67654-1615. Tel: 785-877-2481. p. 885

McMullen, Susan, Ref & Info Res Librn, Roger Williams University Library, One Old Ferry Rd, Bristol, RI, 02809. Tel: 401-254-3086. Fax: 401-254-3631. p. 2164

McMullin, Rachel, Info Literacy, West Chester University, 25 W Rosedale Ave, West Chester, PA, 19383. Tel: 610-738-0510. p. 2153

McMullin, William L, Dir, Northeast Regional Library, 1023 Fillmore St, Corinth, MS, 38834-4199. Tel: 662-287-7311. Fax: 662-286-8010. p. 1297

McMurray, Mark C, Archivist, Spec Coll Librn, St Lawrence University, 23 Romoda Dr, Canton, NY, 13617. Tel: 315-229-5476. Fax: 315-229-5729. p. 1602

McMurry, Nan, Bibliog Instr, Head, Coll Develop, University of Georgia Libraries, Athens, GA, 30602-1641. Tel: 706-542-8474. Fax: 706-542-4144. p. 510

McNabb, Brenda, Libr Serv Mgr, Saint Peter's Abbey & College Library, 100 College Dr, Muenster, SK, S0K 2Y0, CANADA. Tel: 306-682-7860. Fax: 306-682-4402. p. 2919

McNabb, Pat, Librn, Yoakum County Library, 205 W Fourth St, Denver City, TX, 79323. Tel: 806-592-2754. Fax: 806-592-2439. p. 2313

McNabb, Pat, Librn, Yoakum County Library, 901 Ave E, Plains, TX, 79355. Tel: 806-456-8725. Fax: 806-456-7056. p. 2370

McNabb-Graham, Mary, Lifelong Learning Mgr, Wake County Public Library System, Eva H Perry Regional Library, 2100 Shepherd's Vineyard Dr, Apex, NC, 27502. Tel: 919-387-4317. Fax: 919-387-4320. p. 1818

McNair, Alice, Dean, Red Deer College Library, 100 College Blvd, Red Deer, AB, T4N 5H5, CANADA. Tel: 403-342-3344. Fax: 403-346-8500. p. 2714

McNair, Clinton, Auromated Serv Adminr, Alachua County Library District, 401 E University Ave, Gainesville, FL, 32601-5453. Tel: 352-334-3995. Fax: 352-334-3918. p. 448

McNair, Irish, Libr Mgr, Charlotte Mecklenburg Library, Beatties Ford Road Branch, 2412 Beatties Ford Rd, Charlotte, NC, 28216. Tel: 704-416-3000. Fax: 704-416-3100. p. 1782

McNalley, Kathy, Ch, Youth Serv, Buchanan County Public Library, Rte 2, Poetown Rd, Grundy, VA, 24614-9613. Tel: 276-935-6581. Fax: 276-935-6292. p. 2467

McNally, Amy, Sr Librn, Hennepin County Library, Nokomis, 5100 34th Ave S, Minneapolis, MN, 55417-1545. Tel: 612-543-6803. Fax: 612-543-6802. p. 1264

McNally, Brian, Syst Librn, Mount Allison University Libraries & Archives, 49 York St, Sackville, NB, E4L 1C6, CANADA. Tel: 506-364-2237. Fax: 506-364-2617. p. 2766

McNally, Eileen, Br Mgr, Broward County Division of Libraries, Weston Branch, 4205 Bonaventure Blvd, Weston, FL, 33332. Tel: 954-389-2098, Ext 230. Fax: 954-389-2046. p. 442

McNally, Eileen, Asst Dir, Libby Memorial Library, 27 Staples St, Old Orchard Beach, ME, 04064. Tel: 207-934-4351. p. 994

McNally Lahey, Sharon, Libr Mgr, Fenwick & West LLP, Library, Silicon Valley Ctr, 801 California St, Mountain View, CA, 94041. Tel: 650-335-7249. Fax: 650-938-5200. p. 192

McNally, Nancy, Br Librn, Prince Edward Island Public Library Service, O'Leary Public, 18 Community St, O'Leary, PE, C0B 1V0, CANADA. Tel: 902-859-8788. p. 2876

McNally, Peter F, Prof, McGill University, 3661 Peel St, Montreal, QC, H3A 1X1, CANADA. Tel: 514-398-3367. Fax: 514-398-7193. p. 2979

McNally, Thomas F, Dean of Libr, University of South Carolina, 1322 Greene St, Columbia, SC, 29208-0103. Tel: 803-777-3142. p. 2189

McNamara, Antoinette, Sister, Acq of New Ser, Librn, IHM Library/Resource Center, 610 W Elm Ave, Monroe, MI, 48162-7909. Tel: 734-240-9713. Fax: 734-240-8347. p. 1209

McNamara, Cate, Librn, Glendale Community College, 6000 W Olive Ave, Glendale, AZ, 85302. Tel: 623-845-3122. Fax: 623-845-3102. p. 64

McNamara, Cate, Tech Librn, South Mountain Community College Library, 7050 S 24th St, Phoenix, AZ, 85042. Tel: 602-243-8192. Fax: 602-243-8180. p. 77

McNamara, Eileen, Br Mgr, Montgomery County-Norristown Public Library, Royersford Public, 200 S Fourth Ave, Royersford, PA, 19468. Tel: 610-948-7277. Fax: 610-948-7277. p. 2099

McNamara, Emily, Circ, Northport-East Northport Public Library, 151 Laurel Ave, Northport, NY, 11768. Tel: 631-261-6930. Fax: 631-261-6718. p. 1707

McNamara, Frances, Dir, Admin Desktop Syst & Integrated Libr Syst, University of Chicago Library, 1100 E 57th St, Chicago, IL, 60637-1502. Tel: 773-702-8465. Fax: 773-702-6623. p. 626

McNamara, Ingrid, Ref Librn, Hamilton Township Public Library, One Justice Samuel A Alito, Jr Way, Hamilton, NJ, 08619. Tel: 609-581-4060. Fax: 609-581-4067. p. 1490

McNamara, Laurence, Supv Libr Dir, Mercer County Library System, 2751 Brunswick Pike, Lawrenceville, NJ, 08648-4132. Tel: 609-989-6915. Fax: 609-538-9238. p. 1494

McNamara, Lisa, Sr Librn, Pierce County Library System, Sumner Branch, 1116 Fryar Ave, Sumner, WA, 98390. Tel: 253-548-3306. Fax: 253-863-0650. p. 2540

McNamee, Barbara, Dir, Monroe County Community College, 1555 S Raisinville Rd, Monroe, MI, 48161. Tel: 734-384-4244. Fax: 734-384-4160. p. 1209

McNamee, Gary, Info Res, Dow Chemical Library, Business Intelligence Ctr, B-1210, 2301 Brazosport Blvd, Freeport, TX, 77541. Tel: 979-238-4881. p. 2325

McNamer, Kristine, Librn, Blair-Preston Public Library, 122 S Urberg Ave, Blair, WI, 54616-0165. Tel: 608-989-2502. p. 2582

McNaney, Ariel, Commun Libr Mgr, Queens Borough Public Library, Arverne Community Library, 312 Beach 54th St, Arverne, NY, 11692. Tel: 718-634-4784. Fax: 718-318-2757. p. 1644

McNaught, Donna, Ch, Elk City Carnegie Library, 221 W Broadway, Elk City, OK, 73644. Tel: 580-225-0136. Fax: 580-225-1051. p. 1963

McNaughton, John, Dir, Ishpeming Carnegie Public Library, 317 N Main St, Ishpeming, MI, 49849-1994. Tel: 906-486-4381. Fax: 906-486-6226. p. 1194

McNaughton, Kim, Dir, Grace M Pickens Public Library, 209 E Ninth St, Holdenville, OK, 74848. Tel: 405-379-3245. Fax: 405-379-5725. p. 1965

McNeall, Carolyn, Asst Dir, Dulany Memorial Library, 501 S Broadway, Salisbury, MO, 65281. Tel: 660-388-5712. Fax: 660-388-5712. p. 1364

McNealy, Danielle, Children's Mgr, Pine Bluff & Jefferson County Library System, Main Library, 200 E Eighth Ave, Pine Bluff, AR, 71601. Tel: 870-534-4802. Fax: 870-534-8707. p. 112

McNealy, Terry A, Librn, Hunterdon County Historical Society, 114 Main St, Flemington, NJ, 08822. Tel: 908-782-1091. p. 1486

McNee, Laurie, Librn, Falmouth Public Library, North Falmouth Branch, Six Chester St, North Falmouth, MA, 02556-2408. Tel: 508-563-2922. p. 1089

McNeece, Judy, Dir, Dixie Regional Library System, 111 N Main St, Pontotoc, MS, 38863-2103. Tel: 662-489-3961. Fax: 662-489-7777. p. 1311

McNeely, Betty, Librn, Union County Library, Nance McNeely Public, 1177 B Springdale Ave, Myrtle, MS, 38650. Tel: 662-988-2895. Fax: 662-988-2895. p. 1310

McNeely, Bonnie, Dr, Exec Dir, University of Central Oklahoma, 100 N University Dr, Edmond, OK, 73034. Tel: 405-974-2883. Fax: 405-974-3806, 405-974-3874. p. 1962

McNeely, Cate V, Dep Dir, Richmond Public Library, 100-7700 Minoru Gate, Richmond, BC, V6Y 1R9, CANADA. Tel: 604-231-6420. Fax: 604-273-0459. p. 2736

McNeely, Gary, Librn, Kinchafoonee Regional Library System, Terrell County Library, 913 Forrester Dr SE, Dawson, GA, 39842-2106. Tel: 229-995-2902. Fax: 229-995-5989. p. 528

McNeer, Beth, Regional Dir, Allendale-Hampton-Jasper Regional Library, 158 McNair St, Allendale, SC, 29810-0280. Tel: 803-584-2371, 803-584-3513. Fax: 803-584-8134. p. 2180

McNeil, Alice, Dir, Educ Res, International Academy of Design & Technology, One N State St, Ste 526, Chicago, IL, 60602. Tel: 312-980-9241. Fax: 312-960-1499. p. 615

McNeil, Beth, Assoc Dean, Acad Affairs, Purdue University Libraries, 504 W State St, West Lafayette, IN, 47907-2058. Tel: 765-496-2261. Fax: 765-494-0156. p. 786

McNeil, Charles A, Head, Libr Syst, University of Massachusetts Dartmouth Library, 285 Old Westport Rd, North Dartmouth, MA, 02747-2300. Tel: 508-999-8678. Fax: 508-999-8987. p. 1112

McNeil, Cheryl, Ad, Orangeburg Library, 20 S Greenbush Rd, Orangeburg, NY, 10962-1311. Tel: 845-359-2244. Fax: 845-359-8692. p. 1711

McNeil, Eileen, Youth Serv Mgr, Grandview Heights Public Library, 1685 W First Ave, Columbus, OH, 43212. Tel: 614-486-2951. Fax: 614-481-7021. p. 1886

McNeil, Emily, Circ Supvr, Columbia University, Lehman Library, 420 W 118th St, New York, NY, 10027. Tel: 212-854-3794. Fax: 212-854-2495. p. 1675

McNeil, Genalyn, Circ Librn, Fuller Theological Seminary, 135 N Oakland Ave, Pasadena, CA, 91182. Tel: 626-584-5218. Fax: 626-584-5613. p. 206

McNeil, Heather, Ch, Youth Serv Coordr, Deschutes Public Library District, 507 NW Wall St, Bend, OR, 97701-2698. Tel: 541-617-7099. Fax: 541-617-7097. p. 1992

McNeil, Janet, Govt Doc Librn, New Brunswick Legislative Library, Legislative Bldg, 706 Queen St, Fredericton, NB, E3B 1C5, CANADA. Tel: 506-453-8348. Fax: 506-444-5889. p. 2763

McNeil, Julie, Libr Supvr-Ref, Jacksonville Public Library, 303 N Laura St, Jacksonville, FL, 32202-3505. Tel: 904-630-2665. Fax: 904-630-2431. p. 453

McNeil, Nancy, Libr Coordr, Campion College Library, University of Regina, 3737 Wascana Pkwy, Regina, SK, S4S 0A2, CANADA. Tel: 306-359-1202. Fax: 306-359-1200. p. 2922

McNeil, Ruth, Commun Relations Mgr, Upper Arlington Public Library, 2800 Tremont Rd, Columbus, OH, 43221. Tel: 614-486-9621. Fax: 614-486-4530. p. 1891

McNeil, Sybil B, Archivist, Dir, Wesleyan College, 4760 Forsyth Rd, Macon, GA, 31210-4462. Tel: 478-757-5201. Fax: 478-757-3898. p. 541

McNeil-Marshall, Susan, Libr Adminr, Woodridge Public Library, Three Plaza Dr, Woodridge, IL, 60517-5014. Tel: 630-964-7899. Fax: 630-964-0175. p. 721

McNeill, Andrea, Ch, C C Mellor Memorial Library, One Pennwood Ave, Edgewood, PA, 15218-1627. Tel: 412-731-0909. Fax: 412-731-8969. p. 2053

McNeill, Dale, Dir, Pub Libr Serv, Queens Borough Public Library, 89-11 Merrick Blvd, Jamaica, NY, 11432. Tel: 718-990-0802. p. 1643

McNeill, Dale, Asst Dir, Pub Serv, San Antonio Public Library, 600 Soledad, San Antonio, TX, 78205-2786. Tel: 210-207-2661. Fax: 210-207-2603. p. 2382

McNeill, John, Assoc Dir, Pace University, 78 N Broadway, White Plains, NY, 10603. Tel: 914-422-4414. Fax: 914-422-4139. p. 1769

McNeill, Joyce, Asst Dir, Adm Serv, Durham County Library, 300 N Roxboro St, Durham, NC, 27701. Tel: 919-560-0164. Fax: 919-560-0137. p. 1788

McNeilly, Kathy E, Dir, Oak Ridge Public Library, 1401 Oak Ridge Tpk, Oak Ridge, TN, 37830-6224. Tel: 865-425-3455. Fax: 865-425-3429. p. 2262

McNeley, Denise, Operations & Outreach Mgr, Boise Public Library, 715 S Capitol Blvd, Boise, ID, 83702. Tel: 208-472-1958. p. 570

McNellis, Marjorie, Librn, Shodair Hospital, 2755 Colonial Dr, Helena, MT, 59601-4926. Tel: 406-444-7518. Fax: 406-444-7536. p. 1383

McNichol, Megan, ILL, Eastern Maine Medical Center, 489 State St, Bangor, ME, 04402. Tel: 207-973-8228. Fax: 207-973-8233. p. 976

McNicholas, Jennifer, Libr Tech, Wisconsin Indianhead Technical College, 1900 College Dr, Rice Lake, WI, 54868. Tel: 715-234-7082, Ext 5424. Fax: 715-234-5172. p. 2634

McNicol, Nancy, Assoc Dir, Hamden Public Library, 2901 Dixwell Ave, Hamden, CT, 06518-3135. Tel: 203-287-2686. Fax: 203-287-2685. p. 343

McNiff, Karen, Genealogy Serv, Athol Public Library, 568 Main St, Athol, MA, 01331. Tel: 978-249-9515. Fax: 978-249-7636. p. 1050

McNitt, Virginia A, Mgr, Libr Serv, Finnegan, Henderson, Farabow, Garrett & Dunner, 901 New York Ave NW, Washington, DC, 20001-4413. Tel: 202-408-4372. Fax: 202-408-4400. p. 400

McNiven, Valerie, Mgr, Edmonton Public Library, Abbottsfield-Penny McKee Branch, 3410 118th Ave, Edmonton, AB, T5W 0Z4, CANADA. Tel: 780-496-7839. Fax: 780-496-8397. p. 2700

McNulty, Aimee, Youth Serv Librn, Orange County Library, Wilderness, 6421 Flat Run Rd, Locust Grove, VA, 22508. Tel: 540-854-5310, 540-972-1675. Fax: 540-854-5402. p. 2484

McNulty, Cheryl, Site Mgr, Geauga County Historical Society, 14653 E Park St, Burton, OH, 44021. Tel: 440-834-1492. Fax: 440-834-4012. p. 1862

McNulty, Diane R, Dir, Cary Area Public Library District, 1606 Three Oaks Rd, Cary, IL, 60013-1637. Tel: 847-639-4210, Ext 224. Fax: 847-639-8890. p. 601

McNulty, Emily, Br Mgr, Reading Public Library, Northwest, 901 Schuylkill Ave, Reading, PA, 19601. Tel: 610-655-6360. Fax: 610-655-6667. p. 2134

McNulty, Karen, Ch, Avon Free Public Library, 281 Country Club Rd, Avon, CT, 06001. Tel: 860-673-9712. Fax: 860-675-6364. p. 329

McNulty, Kathleen, Librn, Parkland Regional Library, Watson Branch, Main St, Watson, SK, S0K 4V0, CANADA. Tel: 306-287-3642. p. 2932

McNulty, Matthew, Librn, Everest College Library, 1815 Jet Wing Dr, Colorado Springs, CO, 80916. Tel: 719-638-6580. Fax: 719-638-6818. p. 295

McNulty, Phil, Dir, Newton Free Library, 330 Homer St, Newton Centre, MA, 02459-1429. Tel: 617-796-1360. Fax: 617-965-8457. p. 1110

McNutt, Barbara, Ch, Upper Dublin Public Library, 805 Loch Alsh Ave, Fort Washington, PA, 19034. Tel: 215-628-8744. p. 2058

McNutt, Karen, Dir, Richville Library, 743 Richville Rd, Standish, ME, 04084. Tel: 207-776-4698. p. 1002

McNutt, Theresa, Dir, Red Oak Public Library, 200 Lakeview Pkwy, Red Oak, TX, 75154. Tel: 469-218-1230. Fax: 469-218-1231. p. 2373

McPartland, Gail, Dep County Librn, Pub Serv, Contra Costa County Library, 1750 Oak Park Blvd, Pleasant Hill, CA, 94523-4497. Tel: 925-646-6434. Fax: 925-646-6461. p. 208

McPeak, Joseph, Assoc Dir, Free Library of Philadelphia, 1901 Vine St, Philadelphia, PA, 19103-1189. Tel: 215-686-5325. Fax: 215-563-3628. p. 2106

McPeters, Cindy, Br Mgr, El Paso Public Library, Jose Cisneros Cielo Vista, 1300 Hawkins, El Paso, TX, 79907-6803. Tel: 915-594-7680. p. 2316

McPhail, Bill, Librn, Royalton Public Library District, 305 South Dean St, Royalton, IL, 62983. Tel: 618-984-4463. Fax: 618-984-4463. p. 699

McPhail, Margo, Librn, Coronation Memorial Library, 5001 Royal St, Coronation, AB, T0C 1C0, CANADA. Tel: 403-578-3445. p. 2695

McPhaul, Adrienne, Ref Archivist/Librn, Hinds Community College, 505 E Main St, Raymond, MS, 39154. Tel: 601-857-3411. Fax: 601-857-3293. p. 1313

McPhaul-Moore, Libbie, Instr, Piedmont Community College, 1715 College Dr, Roxboro, NC, 27573. Tel: 336-599-1181, Ext 445. Fax: 336-599-9146. p. 1821

McPhearson, John, Asst Dir, Northwest Georgia Regional Library System, 310 Cappes St, Dalton, GA, 30720. Tel: 706-876-1360. Fax: 706-272-2977. p. 528

McPhearson, John, Mgr, Northwest Georgia Regional Library System, Catoosa County Library, Benton Place, 108 Catoosa Circle, Ringgold, GA, 30736. Tel: 706-965-3600. Fax: 706-965-3608. p. 528

McPhee, Casey, Dir, Largo Public Library, 120 Central Park Dr, Largo, FL, 33771. Tel: 727-587-6715, Ext 2511. Fax: 727-586-7353. p. 460

McPheeters, Karen, Admin Dir, Farmington Public Library, 2101 Farmington Ave, Farmington, NM, 87401. Tel: 505-599-1275. Fax: 505-599-1257. p. 1555

McPherson, Chandra, Librn, Appomattox Regional Library, Disputanta Branch, 10010 County Dr, Disputanta, VA, 23842. Tel: 804-991-2403. Fax: 804-991-2403. p. 2472

McPherson, Fiona A, Dir, Canada Department of Justice Library, EMB, Rm A-370, 284 Wellington St, Ottawa, ON, K1A 0H8, CANADA. Tel: 613-957-4611. p. 2828

McPherson, Janet, Librn, First District Court of Appeal Library, 2000 Drayton Dr, Tallahassee, FL, 32399. Tel: 850-487-1000. p. 492

McPherson, Julia, Ch, Dare County Library, 700 N Hwy 64-264, Manteo, NC, 27954. Tel: 252-473-2372. Fax: 252-473-6034. p. 1808

McPherson, Melissa, Dir, Libr Serv, Baker College of Jackson Library, 2800 Springport Rd, Jackson, MI, 49202-1255. Tel: 517-780-4572. Fax: 517-789-3058. p. 1195

McPherson, Nina, Cat, Media Spec, Ref Serv, Pellissippi State Technical Community College, 10915 Harding Valley Rd, Knoxville, TN, 37933. Tel: 865-539-7237. Fax: 865-694-6625. p. 2243

McPherson, Patricia, Ref, Stonehill College, 320 Washington St, Easton, MA, 02357-4015. Tel: 508-565-1844. Fax: 508-565-1424. p. 1087

McPherson, Ruth, Librn, First United Methodist Church Library, 500 E Colorado Blvd, Pasadena, CA, 91101. Tel: 626-796-0157. Fax: 626-568-1615. p. 206

McPhillips, Peggy, City Historian, Norfolk Public Library, 235 E Plume St, Norfolk, VA, 23510-1706. Tel: 757-664-7310. Fax: 757-441-5863. p. 2481

McQuade, Becky, Tech Serv Team Leader, Middletown Public Library, 125 S Broad St, Middletown, OH, 45044. Tel: 513-424-1251. Fax: 513-424-6585. p. 1917

McQuade, Jeanette, Br Mgr, Grand County Library District, Fraser Valley Branch, 241 Norgren Rd, Fraser, CO, 80442. Tel: 970-726-5689. Fax: 970-726-9226. p. 310

McQuaid, Mick, Asst Prof, University of Michigan, 304 West Hall, 1085 S University, Ann Arbor, MI, 48109-1107. Tel: 734-763-2285. Fax: 734-764-2475. p. 2967

McQuarrie, Laurie, Dir, Libr & Info Serv, Bangor Theological Seminary, Two College Circle, Bangor, ME, 04402-0411. Tel: 207-942-6781, Ext 203. Fax: 207-990-1267. p. 975

McQuarrie, Laurie, Dir, Libr & Info Serv, Bangor Theological Seminary, 159 State St, Portland, ME, 04101. Tel: 207-774-5212, Ext 201. Fax: 207-874-2214. p. 996

McQueen, Jim, Br Mgr, Charleston County Public Library, John's Island Regional, 3531 Maybank Hwy, John's Island, SC, 29455. Tel: 843-557-1945. Fax: 843-557-0080. p. 2183

McQueen, Mary, ILL & Distance Libr Serv Spec, Wichita Falls Public Library, 600 11th St, Wichita Falls, TX, 76301-4604. Tel: 940-767-0868. Fax: 940-720-6672. p. 2401

McQueeny, Nancy, Res, Kirkland & Ellis LLP Library, 300 N LaSalle St, 11th Flr, Chicago, IL, 60654. Tel: 312-862-2358. Fax: 312-862-2200. p. 616

McQuillan, Beth, Dir of Tech Serv, Lisle Library District, 777 Front St, Lisle, IL, 60532-3599. Tel: 630-971-1675. Fax: 630-971-1701. p. 666

McQuillan, Brenda M, Chief Librn, SSG Paul D Savanuck Memorial Library, Defense Information School, 6500 Mapes Rd, Rm 1161, Fort George G Meade, MD, 20755. Tel: 301-677-4694. Fax: 301-677-4697. p. 1028

McQuillen, Karen, Mgr, Educational Testing Service, Rosedale Rd, Princeton, NJ, 08541. Tel: 609-734-5667. Fax: 609-683-7186. p. 1522

McQuinn, Jamie, Mgr, Per, Dayton Metro Library, 215 E Third St, Dayton, OH, 45402-2103. Tel: 937-463-2665. Fax: 937-496-4300. p. 1892

McQuistan, Donna, Asst Dir, House Memorial Public Library, 220 Thurston Ave, Pender, NE, 68047. Tel: 402-385-2521. Fax: 402-385-2521. p. 1416

McQuiston, Kathleen, Asst Dir, Res Serv, Bucknell University, Library & Information Technology, 221 Ellen Clarke Bertrand Library, Lewisburg, PA, 17837. Tel: 570-577-3309. Fax: 570-577-3313. p. 2080

McRae, Kathryn, Libr Dir, Hawkins, Delafield & Wood, One Chase Manhattan Plaza, New York, NY, 10005. Tel: 212-820-9444. Fax: 212-344-6258. p. 1681

McRae, Sharon, Dir, Shaler North Hills Library, 1822 Mount Royal Blvd, Glenshaw, PA, 15116. Tel: 412-486-0211. Fax: 412-486-8286. p. 2061

McRary, LeeAnn, Librn, North Carolina Department of Correction, Foothills Correctional Institution Library, 5150 Western Ave, Morganton, NC, 28655. Tel: 828-438-5585. Fax: 828-438-6281. p. 1811

McRee, William, Extn Serv, Florence County Library System, 509 S Dargan St, Florence, SC, 29506. Tel: 843-662-8424. Fax: 843-661-7544. p. 2193

McReynolds, Mike, Cat, Shook, Hardy & Bacon, 2555 Grand Blvd, 3rd Flr, Kansas City, MO, 64108-2613. Tel: 816-474-6550. Fax: 816-421-5547. p. 1341

McRobinson, Mary, Univ Archivist, Willamette University, 900 State St, Salem, OR, 97301. Tel: 503-370-6764. Fax: 503-370-6141. p. 2019

McSall, Teresa, In Charge, Pennock Hospital, 1009 W Green St, Hastings, MI, 49058. Tel: 269-945-3451, Ext 199. Fax: 269-945-3035. p. 1189

McShane, Maria Kessler, Archivist, Spec Coll Librn, College of Saint Rose, 392-396 Western Ave, Albany, NY, 12203. Tel: 518-454-5190. Fax: 518-454-2897. p. 1568

McShane, Mark, Circ Supvr, Manchester Community College, 1066 Front St, Manchester, NH, 03102. Tel: 603-668-6706, Ext 239. Fax: 603-668-5354. p. 1456

McShane, Stephen, Archivist/Librn, Indiana University Northwest Library, 3400 Broadway, Gary, IN, 46408. Tel: 219-980-6628. Fax: 219-980-6558. p. 745

McShepard, Ester, Night Supvr, Fisk University, Fisk University, 1000 17th Ave N, Nashville, TN, 37208-3051. Tel: 615-329-8730. Fax: 615-329-8761. p. 2256

McSherry, Carolyn, Cat Spec, Northeastern Ohio Universities College of Medicine, 4209 State Rd 44, Rootstown, OH, 44272. Tel: 330-325-6600. Fax: 330-325-0522. p. 1932

McSwain, Connie, Dir, W G Rhea Public Library, 400 W Washington St, Paris, TN, 38242-3903. Tel: 731-642-1702. Fax: 731-642-1777. p. 2263

McSwain, Kathleen, Dir, Chicago Ridge Public Library, 10400 S Oxford Ave, Chicago Ridge, IL, 60415. Tel: 708-423-7753. Fax: 708-423-2758. p. 628

McSweeney, Carol, Bus Mgr, Tech Serv, Homer Township Public Library District, 14320 W 151st St, Homer Glen, IL, 60491. Tel: 708-301-7908. Fax: 708-301-4535. p. 657

McSweeney, Eamon, Circ Serv Supvr, Thousand Oaks Library, 1401 E Janss Rd, Thousand Oaks, CA, 91362-2199. Tel: 805-449-2660, Ext 7330. Fax: 805-373-6858. p. 275

McSweeney, J Emmett, Dir, Silas Bronson Library, 267 Grand St, Waterbury, CT, 06702-1981. Tel: 203-574-8221. Fax: 203-574-8055. p. 374

McSweeney, James, Regional Adminr, National Archives & Records Administration, 5780 Jonesboro Rd, Morrow, GA, 30260. Tel: 770-968-2100. Fax: 770-968-2457. p. 545

McSweeney, Jeanine, Coll Mgr, The Rockefeller University, 1222 York Ave, Welch Hall, New York, NY, 10065. Tel: 212-327-8980. Fax: 212-327-8802. p. 1698

McTaggart, Melinda, Librn, Worcester Free Library, 168 Main St, Ste 2, Worcester, NY, 12197. Tel: 607-397-7309. p. 1771

McTavish, Rebecca J, Dir, Du Bois Public Library, 31 S Brady St, Du Bois, PA, 15801. Tel: 814-371-5930. Fax: 814-371-2282. p. 2050

McTyre, Ellen, Ch, Mamaroneck Public Library District, 136 Prospect Ave, Mamaroneck, NY, 10543. Tel: 914-698-1250. Fax: 914-381-3088. p. 1657

McTyre, Ruthann Boles, Librn, University of Iowa Libraries, Rita Benton Music Library, 2006 Main Library, Iowa City, IA, 52242. Tel: 319-335-3086. p. 823

McVarish, Maureen, Br Mgr, Pickering Public Library, Claremont Branch, 4941 Old Brock Rd, Claremont, ON, L1Y 1B1, CANADA. Tel: 905-649-3341. Fax: 905-649-2065. p. 2836

McVarish, Maureen, Br Mgr, Pickering Public Library, Greenwood, 3540 Westney Rd, Greenwood, ON, L0H 1H0, CANADA. Tel: 905-683-8844. p. 2836

McVarish, Maureen, Br Mgr, Pickering Public Library, Petticoat Creek, 470 Kingston Rd, Pickering, ON, L1V 1A4, CANADA. Tel: 905-420-2254. Fax: 905-420-2860. p. 2836

McVarish, Maureen, Br Mgr, Pickering Public Library, Whitevale, 475 Whitevale Rd, Pickering, ON, L1X 2R5, CANADA. Tel: 905-294-0967. p. 2836

McVay-Gorrell, Patti, Media Libr Mgr, The College of Wooster Libraries, 1140 Beall Ave, Wooster, OH, 44691-2364. Tel: 330-263-2285. Fax: 330-263-2253. p. 1949

McVeigh, Jeanette, Coordr, Electronic Res, University of the Sciences in Philadelphia, 4200 Woodland Ave, Philadelphia, PA, 19104-4491. Tel: 215-895-1197. Fax: 215-596-8760. p. 2120

McVey, Kuniko, Librn, Harvard Library, Harvard-Yenching Library, Two Divinity Ave, Cambridge, MA, 02138. Tel: 617-495-2756. Fax: 617-496-6008. p. 1075

McVey, Susan, Dir, Oklahoma Department of Libraries, 200 NE 18th St, Oklahoma City, OK, 73105. Tel: 405-521-2502. Fax: 405-521-1077. p. 1974

McVicar-Keim, Mary, Ref, Rochester General Hospital, 1425 Portland Ave, Rochester, NY, 14621. Tel: 585-922-4723. Fax: 585-544-1504. p. 1731

McVoy, Cindy, Dir, Holland Patent Memorial Library, 9580 Main St, Holland Patent, NY, 13354-3819. Tel: 315-865-5034. Fax: 315-865-5034. p. 1637

McWhorter, Libby, Ch, Boyle County Public Library, 1857 S Danville Bypass, Danville, KY, 40422. Tel: 859-236-8466. Fax: 859-236-7692. p. 911

McWhorter, Susan, Med Librn, American Sports Medicine Institute, 2660 Tenth Ave S, Ste 505, Birmingham, AL, 35205. Tel: 205-918-2130. Fax: 205-918-2178. p. 6

McWilliams, Laura, Dir, Garrard County Public Library, 101 Lexington St, Lancaster, KY, 40444. Tel: 859-792-3424. Fax: 859-792-2366. p. 919

McWilliams, Leilani, Ch, Atlanta-Fulton Public Library System, Kirkwood, 11 Kirkwood Rd NE, Atlanta, GA, 30317. Tel: 404-377-6471. Fax: 404-373-5024. p. 512

McWilliams, Maria, ILL, Trinity University, One Trinity Pl, San Antonio, TX, 78212-7200. Tel: 210-999-8121. Fax: 210-999-8182. p. 2383

McWilliams, Patsy, Ref, Neshoba County Public Library, 230 Beacon St, Philadelphia, MS, 39350. Tel: 601-656-4911. Fax: 601-656-6894. p. 1311

McWilliams, Terry, Pub Relations, Midwest Old Settlers & Threshers Association, 405 E Threshers Rd, Mount Pleasant, IA, 52641. Tel: 319-385-8937. Fax: 319-385-0563. p. 833

McZorn, Bonita, Br Mgr, Atlanta-Fulton Public Library System, College Park Library, 3647 Main St, College Park, GA, 30337. Tel: 404-762-4061. Fax: 404-762-4062. p. 511

Meacham, Kathy, Head, Tech Serv, Arcadia Public Library, 20 W Duarte Rd, Arcadia, CA, 91006. Tel: 626-821-5574. Fax: 626-447-8050. p. 121

Meachum, Angie, Librn, East Central Arkansas Regional Library, Woodruff County, 201 Mulberry St, Augusta, AR, 72006. Tel: 870-347-5331. Fax: 870-347-5331. p. 117

Meachum, Maria, Dir, Wilmington Public Library District, 201 S Kankakee St, Wilmington, IL, 60481-1338. Tel: 815-476-2834. Fax: 815-476-7805. p. 720

Mead, Anne, Ref, Northwestern College, 101 Seventh St SW, Orange City, IA, 51041-1996. Tel: 712-707-7234. Fax: 712-707-7247. p. 836

Mead, Anne, Supvr, Brown County Library, Ashwaubenon Branch, 1060 Orlando Dr, Green Bay, WI, 54304. Tel: 920-492-4913. Fax: 920-492-4914. p. 2595

Mead, Jeanine, Librn, Neville Public Museum of Brown County Library, 210 Museum Pl, Green Bay, WI, 54303-2760. Tel: 920-448-7844. Fax: 920-448-4458. p. 2595

Mead, Marjorie L, Assoc Dir, Wheaton College, Marion E Wade Center, 351 E Lincoln, Wheaton, IL, 60187-4213. Tel: 630-752-5908. Fax: 630-752-5459. p. 718

Mead, Melissa, Spec Coll Librn, University of Rochester, River Campus Libraries, 755 Library Rd, Rochester, NY, 14627-0055. Tel: 585-275-4461. Fax: 585-273-5309. p. 1733

Mead, Sandi, Librn, Minnesota West Community & Technical College Libraries, 1450 College Way, Worthington, MN, 56187-3024. Tel: 507-372-3462. p. 1291

Mead, Wendy, Libr Tech, Inuvik Centennial Library, 100 Mackenzie Rd, Inuvik, NT, X0E 0T0, CANADA. Tel: 867-777-8620. Fax: 867-777-8621. p. 2775

Meade Husain, Brenda, Br Supvr, Coquitlam Public Library, City Centre, 3001 Burlington Dr, Coquitlam, BC, V3B 6X1, CANADA. Tel: 604-927-3566. Fax: 604-927-3570. p. 2727

Meade, Jennie C, Bibliographer, Rare Bks, George Washington University, Jacob Burns Law Library, 716 20th St NW, Washington, DC, 20052. Tel: 202-994-6857. Fax: 202-994-2874. p. 402

Meade, Jon, Librn, Arizona Department of Corrections - Adult Institutions, 10000 S Wilmot Rd, Tucson, AZ, 85734. Tel: 520-574-0024, Ext 37919. Fax: 520-574-7308. p. 85

Meade, Matthew T, Libr Assoc, Erikson Institute, 451 N LaSalle St, Ste 210, Chicago, IL, 60654. Tel: 312-893-7210. Fax: 312-893-7213. p. 613

Meador, Jean, Ch, Corpus Christi Public Libraries, Northwest Branch, 3202 McKinzie Rd, Corpus Christi, TX, 78410. Tel: 361-241-9329. p. 2302

Meador, Joanne, Tech Serv, Allen County Public Library, 106 W Main, Scottsville, KY, 42164. Tel: 270-237-3861. Fax: 270-237-4095. p. 934

Meador, John M, Jr, Dean of Libr, State University of New York at Binghamton, Vestal Pkwy E, Binghamton, NY, 13902. Tel: 607-777-2346. Fax: 607-777-4848. p. 1582

Meador, Malissia, Circ Supvr, Tyler Public Library, 201 S College Ave, Tyler, TX, 75702-7381. Tel: 903-593-7323. Fax: 903-531-1329. p. 2394

Meador, Roy, Dir, Spring Arbor University, 106 E Main St, Spring Arbor, MI, 49283. Tel: 800-968-9103, Ext 1444. Fax: 517-750-2108. p. 1229

Meadors, Greg, Dir, Whitley County Library, 285 S Third St, Williamsburg, KY, 40769. Tel: 606-549-0818. Fax: 606-539-9242. p. 937

Meadows, Brenda, Acq, ILL, United States Department of Defense, 2475 K St, Rm 315, Bldg 52, Wright-Patterson AFB, OH, 45433-8258. Tel: 937-255-3030. Fax: 937-255-8258. p. 1951

Meadows, Cynthia, Ref Serv, Carteret Community College Library, 201 College Circle, Morehead City, NC, 28557. Tel: 252-222-6213. Fax: 252-222-6219. p. 1810

Meadows, Deborah, Interim Dean, Libr Serv, Columbia Basin College Library, 2600 N 20th Ave, Pasco, WA, 99301. Tel: 509-547-0511. Fax: 509-546-0401. p. 2523

Meadows, Donna, Ref Librn, Austin Community College, Riverside Campus Library, 1020 Grove Blvd, Austin, TX, 78741. Tel: 512-223-6004. Fax: 512-223-6703. p. 2278

Meadows, Frances T, Br Mgr, Magee Public Library, 120 First St NW, Magee, MS, 39111. Tel: 601-849-3747. Fax: 601-849-6609. p. 1307

Meadows, Judith, Dir, State Law Library of Montana, 215 N Sanders, Helena, MT, 59601-4522. Tel: 406-444-3660. Fax: 406-444-3603. p. 1383

Meadows, Mavis, Asst Librn, John Mosser Public Library District, 106 W Meek St, Abingdon, IL, 61410-1451. Tel: 309-462-3129. Fax: 309-462-3129. p. 587

Meadows, Rosie, Br Mgr, Atlanta-Fulton Public Library System, West End Library, 525 Peeples St SW, Atlanta, GA, 30310. Tel: 404-752-8740. Fax: 404-752-8742. p. 513

Meadows, Susan, Librn, University of Missouri-Columbia, Library for Family & Community Medicine, M246 Medical Sciences Bldg, Columbia, MO, 65212. Tel: 573-882-6183. Fax: 573-882-9096. p. 1326

Meadows, Theresa, Dir, Waseca-Le Sueur Regional Library, 408 N State St, Waseca, MN, 56093. Tel: 507-835-2910. Fax: 507-835-3700. p. 1287

Meads, Charline, Tech Serv Librn, Pasquotank-Camden Library, 100 E Colonial Ave, Elizabeth City, NC, 27909. Tel: 252-335-2473, 252-335-7536. Fax: 252-331-7449. p. 1791

Meadwell, Grant, Exec Dir, Sir Sandford Fleming College, School of Environmental & Natural Resources, 200 Albert St S, Lindsay, ON, K9V 5E6, CANADA. Tel: 705-324-9144, Ext 3319. Fax: 705-878-9313. p. 2816

Meagher, Barbara, Ref, Central Connecticut State University, 1615 Stanley St, New Britain, CT, 06050. Tel: 860-832-2062. Fax: 860-832-3409. p. 353

Meagher, Betty, Cat, University of Denver, 2150 E Evans Ave, Denver, CO, 80208-2007. Tel: 303-871-3441. Fax: 303-871-2290. p. 303

Meagher, Caroline, Librn, Hancock Free Public Library, PO Box 159, Hancock, VT, 05748-0159. Tel: 802-767-4651. p. 2425

Meagher, Heather, Ref Librn, East Rockaway Public Library, 477 Atlantic Ave, East Rockaway, NY, 11518. Tel: 516-599-1664. Fax: 516-596-0154. p. 1617

Meagher, Rosann, Librn, Bryant & Stratton College Library, Richmond Campus, 8141 Hull Street Rd, Richmond, VA, 23235. Tel: 804-745-2444. Fax: 804-745-6884. p. 2498

Mealer, Margaret Catherine, Mgr, Rapides Parish Library, Boyce Branch, 500 A Ulster Ave, Boyce, LA, 71409. Tel: 318-793-2182. Fax: 318-793-2736. p. 940

Mealey, Nathan, Mgr, Libr Tech, Portland State University Library, 1875 SW Park Ave, Portland, OR, 97201-3220. Tel: 503-725-4515. Fax: 503-725-4524. p. 2014

Mealing, Cathleen, Dir, Bryant Library, Two Paper Mill Rd, Roslyn, NY, 11576-2193. Tel: 516-621-2240. Fax: 516-621-7211. p. 1735

Meaney, Elynne, Librn, Standardbred Canada Library, 2150 Meadowvale Blvd, Mississauga, ON, L5N 6R6, CANADA. Tel: 905-858-3060. Fax: 905-858-3111. p. 2823

Means, Joan, Br Mgr, Librn III, Montgomery City-County Public Library System, Governors Square Branch Library, 2885-B East South Blvd, Montgomery, AL, 36111. Tel: 334-284-7929. Fax: 334-240-4839. p. 29

Means, Judy, Support Serv Mgr, Avon Lake Public Library, 32649 Electric Blvd, Avon Lake, OH, 44012-1669. Tel: 440-933-8128. Fax: 440-933-5659. p. 1857

Means, Pat, Dir, Villisca Public Library, 204 S Third Ave, Villisca, IA, 50864. Tel: 712-826-2452. Fax: 712-826-2686. p. 848

Means, Robert, Humanities & Soc Sci Librn, Brigham Young University, Harold B Lee Library, 2060 HBLL, Provo, UT, 84602. Tel: 801-422-2927. Fax: 801-422-0466. p. 2411

Meany, Anne, Dir, Bernards Township Library, 32 S Maple Ave, Basking Ridge, NJ, 07920-1216. Tel: 908-204-3031. Fax: 908-766-1580. p. 1470

Meany, Brendon, Asst Dir, Raritan Public Library, 54 E Somerset St, Raritan, NJ, 08869. Tel: 908-725-0413. Fax: 908-725-1832. p. 1525

Mears, Frances, Asst Librn, Taylor Library, 49 E Derry Rd, East Derry, NH, 03041. Tel: 603-432-7186. Fax: 603-432-0985. p. 1446

Mears, Michelle R, Dir, Public Library of Enid & Garfield County, 120 W Maine, Enid, OK, 73701-5606. Tel: 580-234-6313. Fax: 580-249-9280. p. 1963

Mears, Sue, Ch, Gale Library, 16 S Main St, Newton, NH, 03858-3310. Tel: 603-382-4691. Fax: 603-382-2528. p. 1460

Mease, Carol, Librn, Clearfield County Law Library, Courthouse, 2nd Flr, Ste 228, 230 E Market St, Clearfield, PA, 16830. Tel: 814-765-2641. Fax: 814-765-7649. p. 2045

Meassick, Lisa, Contractor Librn, United States Air Force, AFRL/RVIL, 3550 Aberdeen Ave SE Bldg 570, Kirtland AFB, NM, 87117-5776. Tel: 505-846-4767. Fax: 505-846-4790. p. 1557

Mech, Jennifer, Youth Serv, Sidney Memorial Public Library, Eight River St, Sidney, NY, 13838. Tel: 607-563-1200, 607-563-8021. Fax: 607-563-7675. p. 1743

Mech, Terrence, Dr, Dir, King's College, 14 W Jackson St, Wilkes-Barre, PA, 18711-0850. Tel: 570-208-5943. Fax: 570-208-6022. p. 2155

Mechell, Barbara, Librn, Masonic Grand Lodge Library & Museum of Texas, 715 Columbus, Waco, TX, 76701-1349. Tel: 254-753-7395. Fax: 254-753-2944. p. 2397

Mecifi, Kelly, Tech Serv Librn, Robeson County Public Library, 101 N Chestnut St, Lumberton, NC, 28358-5639. Tel: 910-738-4859. Fax: 910-739-8321. p. 1808

Mecinski, Adam, Circ, Stevenson University Library, 1525 Greenspring Valley Rd, Stevenson, MD, 21153. Tel: 410-486-7000, 443-334-2233. Fax: 410-486-7329. p. 1043

Meck, Maureen A, Adminr, Ohio State University LIBRARIES, John A Prior Health Sciences Library, 376 W Tenth Ave, Columbus, OH, 43210-1240. Tel: 614-292-4853. Fax: 614-292-1920. p. 1889

Meck, Rene, Dir, Marfa Public Library, 115 E Oak St, Marfa, TX, 79843. Tel: 432-729-4631. Fax: 432-729-3424. p. 2359

Meck, Wanda, Pub Serv Librn, Carroll Community College, 1601 Washington Rd, Westminster, MD, 21157-6944. Tel: 410-386-8342. Fax: 410-386-8331. p. 1045

Meckle, Kim, Librn, Drake Public Library, 411 Main St, Drake, ND, 58736. Tel: 701-465-3732. Fax: 701-465-3634. p. 1840

Mecklenburg, Frank, Dr, Dir, Center for Jewish History, 15 W 16 St, New York, NY, 10011-6301. Tel: 212-744-6400. Fax: 212-988-1305. p. 1671

Meckley, Mary, Dir, W A Rankin Memorial Library, 502 Indiana St, Neodesha, KS, 66757-1532. Tel: 620-325-3275. Fax: 620-325-3275. p. 884

Mecks, Joi, Dir, Communications, District of Columbia Public Library, 901 G St NW, Washington, DC, 20001-4599. Tel: 202-727-1186. Fax: 202-727-1129. p. 398

Medal, Carole, Exec Dir, Gail Borden Public Library District, 270 N Grove Ave, Elgin, IL, 60120-5596. Tel: 847-429-4699. Fax: 847-742-0485. p. 640

Medallis, John, ILL, Linden Free Public Library, 31 E Henry St, Linden, NJ, 07036. Tel: 908-298-3830. Fax: 908-486-2636. p. 1495

Medaris, Connie, Bibliog Instr, Librn, Blue Ridge Community College, One College Lane, Weyers Cave, VA, 24486. Tel: 540-453-2247. Fax: 540-234-9598. p. 2502

Medaris, Linda, Chair, University of Central Missouri, 601 S Missouri, Warrensburg, MO, 64093. Tel: 660-543-8844. Fax: 660-543-4144. p. 1371

Meddaugh, Jim, ILL Librn, Piermont Public Library, 130 Rte 10, Piermont, NH, 03779-3205. Tel: 603-272-4967. Fax: 603-272-4947. p. 1462

Medders, Diane, Librn, Kinchafoonee Regional Library System, Webster County Library, 572 Washington St, Preston, GA, 31824-0316. Tel: 229-828-5740. Fax: 229-828-5740. p. 529

Medders, Mary Diane, Asst Dir, Kinchafoonee Regional Library System, 913 Forrester Dr SE, Dawson, GA, 39842-2106. Tel: 229-995-6331. Fax: 229-995-3383. p. 528

Meddings, Nancy, Dir, Allan Hancock College, 800 S College Dr, Santa Maria, CA, 93454. Tel: 805-922-6966, Ext 3475. Fax: 805-922-3763. p. 265

Medeiros, Denise, Dir, Wareham Free Library, 59 Marion Rd, Wareham, MA, 02571. Tel: 508-295-2343, Ext 1010. Fax: 508-295-2678. p. 1133

Medeiros, Helen, Circ Supvr, Taunton Public Library, 12 Pleasant St, Taunton, MA, 02780. Tel: 508-821-1410. Fax: 508-821-1414. p. 1130

Medeiros, Norm, Assoc Librn, Coordr, Coll Mgt & Metadata Serv, Haverford College, 370 Lancaster Ave, Haverford, PA, 19041-1392. Tel: 610-896-1173. Fax: 610-896-1102. p. 2067

Medeot, Catherine, Acad Tech Librn, Manhattanville College Library, 2900 Purchase St, Purchase, NY, 10577. Tel: 914-323-5424. Fax: 914-323-8139. p. 1724

Medina, Aida, Ref, Ser, Universidad del Turabo, PO Box 3030, Gurabo, PR, 00778-3030. Tel: 787-743-7979, Ext 4501. Fax: 787-743-7924. p. 2673

Medina, Alice, Commun Libr Mgr, County of Los Angeles Public Library, East Los Angeles Library, 4837 E Third St, Los Angeles, CA, 90022-1601. Tel: 323-264-0155. Fax: 323-264-5465. p. 141

Medina, Carolyn, Librn, Team Leader, Texas Department of State Health Services, 1100 W 49th St, Austin, TX, 78756-3199. Tel: 512-776-7559. Fax: 512-776-7474 (AV Library), 512-776-7683. p. 2282

Medina, Debbie, Br Mgr, San Bernardino County Library, Barstow Branch, 304 E Buena Vista, Barstow, CA, 92311. Tel: 760-256-4850. Fax: 760-256-4852. p. 228

Medina, Gary, Coll Serv Librn, Marymount College Library, 30800 Palos Verdes Dr E, Rancho Palos Verdes, CA, 90275-6299. Tel: 310-303-7375. Fax: 310-377-6223. p. 213

Medina, Joyce, Dir, Zia Enrichment Library, 162B Zia Blvd, San Ysidro, NM, 87053-6002. Tel: 505-867-3304, Ext 239. Fax: 505-867-3308. p. 1561

Medina, Nilsa, Librn, Avon Park Correctional Facility, State Rd 64 E, Avon Park, FL, 33825. Tel: 863-453-3174, Ext 404. Fax: 863-453-1531. p. 426

Medina Pascu, Isabel, Acq, St Thomas University Library, 16401 NW 37th Ave, Miami Gardens, FL, 33054. Tel: 305-628-6769. Fax: 305-628-6666. p. 469

Medina, Patricia, Circ, Notre Dame de Namur University Library, 1500 Ralston Ave, Belmont, CA, 94002-1908. Tel: 650-508-3748. Fax: 650-508-3697. p. 126

Medina, Rita Sue, Librn, Hatch Public Library, 530 E Hall, Hatch, NM, 87937. Tel: 575-267-5132. p. 1556

Medina, Tony, Tech Serv, Honeywell International, 101 Columbia Rd, Morristown, NJ, 07962-1021. Tel: 973-455-6290. Fax: 973-455-5295. p. 1504

Medina, Yesinia, Ref Asst, Lompoc Public Library, 501 E North Ave, Lompoc, CA, 93436-3498. Tel: 805-875-8775. Fax: 805-736-6440. p. 165

Medina, Yolanda, Circ, Reserves, Broward College, 3501 SW Davie Rd, Davie, FL, 33314. Tel: 954-201-6648. Fax: 954-201-6490. p. 435

Medina, Yolanda, Supvr, Tech Serv, Richardson Public Library, 900 Civic Center Dr, Richardson, TX, 75080. Tel: 972-744-4368. Fax: 972-744-5806. p. 2374

Medjo-Me-Zengue, Mary A, Dir, Addison Public Library, Four Friendship Plaza, Addison, IL, 60101. Tel: 630-458-3300. Fax: 630-543-6645. p. 587

Medkey, Pamela, Asst Dir, Fredonia Public Library, 807 Jefferson, Fredonia, KS, 66736. Tel: 620-378-2863. Fax: 620-378-2645. p. 868

Medland, Pam, Pub Serv Mgr, Okanagan Regional Library, 1430 KLO Rd, Kelowna, BC, V1W 3P6, CANADA. Tel: 250-860-4033. Fax: 250-861-8696. p. 2730

Medlar, Andrew, Asst Commissioner, Coll, Chicago Public Library, 400 S State St, Chicago, IL, 60605. Tel: 312-747-4300. Fax: 312-747-4968. p. 608

Medlin, Brenda, Acq, Mercer University, Jack Tarver Library, 1300 Edgewood Ave, Macon, GA, 31207. Tel: 478-301-2505. Fax: 478-301-2111. p. 540

Medlin, Cathy Lynn, Libr Dir, Lillian Tear Library, 501 N Commercial, Sedgwick, KS, 67135. Tel: 316-772-5727. p. 894

Medlock, Debbie, ILL, Marshall County Public Library System, 1003 Poplar St, Benton, KY, 42025. Tel: 270-527-9969. Fax: 270-527-0506. p. 907

Medows, Kevin, Head, Tech Serv, Warren-Newport Public Library District, 224 N O'Plaine Rd, Gurnee, IL, 60031. Tel: 847-244-3499. Fax: 847-244-5150. p. 653

Medrano, David, Dir, Pearsall Public Library, 200 E Trinity St, Pearsall, TX, 78061. Tel: 830-334-2496. Fax: 830-334-9194. p. 2369

Medvecky, Paulette, Dir, Wayne Public Library, 3737 S Wayne Rd, Wayne, MI, 48184. Tel: 734-721-7832. Fax: 734-721-0341. p. 1235

Medved, Jan D, Dir, Jackson County Law Library, Inc, 1125 Grand Blvd, Ste 1050, Kansas City, MO, 64106. Tel: 816-221-2221. Fax: 816-221-6607. p. 1337

Medved, Jenn, Campus Librn, Milwaukee Area Technical College, 6665 S Howell Ave, Oak Creek, WI, 53154. Tel: 414-571-4602. Fax: 414-571-4747. p. 2626

Medvedeff, Nicholas W, Librn, The King Library, 1065 Bristol Pike, Andalusia, PA, 19020. Tel: 215-637-6516. Fax: 209-370-9697. p. 2029

Medvedow, Jill, Dir, Institute of Contemporary Art Library, 955 Boylston St, Boston, MA, 02115. Tel: 617-266-5152. Fax: 617-266-4021. p. 1062

Medvetz, Wendy, Acq, Tech Serv, Capital University, Law School Library, 303 E Broad St, Columbus, OH, 43215. Tel: 614-236-6464. Fax: 614-236-6957. p. 1883

Medzie, Deena, Acq, Widener University, One University Pl, Chester, PA, 19013-5792. Tel: 610-499-4078. Fax: 610-499-4588. p. 2044

Meece, James H, Dep Librn, New York City Law Department, 100 Church St, Rm 6-310, New York, NY, 10007. Tel: 212-788-0858. Fax: 212-788-1239. p. 1688

Meece, Penny, Asst Dir, Maroa Public Library District, 305 E Garfield St, Maroa, IL, 61756. Tel: 217-794-5111. Fax: 217-794-3005. p. 670

Meeds, Donna, Digital Serv, Portland Community College Library, 12000 SW 49th AV, Portland, OR, 97219. Tel: 971-722-4460. Fax: 971-722-8397. p. 2013

Meehan, Beth, Tech Serv, Weston Public Library, 87 School St, Weston, MA, 02493. Tel: 781-893-3312. Fax: 781-529-0174. p. 1139

Meehan, Carole, Adult/Ref Serv, AV, Harrison Public Library, Bruce Ave, Harrison, NY, 10528. Tel: 914-835-0324. Fax: 914-835-1564. p. 1634

Meehan, Joseph M, Dir, Arizona Historical Society Library, 2340 N Fort Valley Rd, Flagstaff, AZ, 86001. Tel: 928-774-6272. Fax: 928-774-1596. p. 62

Meehan, Molly, Educ & Outreach Coordr, Accokeek Foundation Library, 3400 Bryan Point Rd, Accokeek, MD, 20607. Tel: 301-283-2113. Fax: 301-283-2049. p. 1009

Meehan, Tamiye Trejo, Dir, Indian Trails Public Library District, 355 S Schoenbeck Rd, Wheeling, IL, 60090. Tel: 847-459-4100. Fax: 847-459-4760. p. 719

Meehan, William, Dr, Asst Prof, Valdosta State University, Odum Library - MLIS, 1500 N Patterson St, Valdosta, GA, 31698-0144. Tel: 229-249-2726. Fax: 229-259-5055. p. 2964

Meek, Lyn, Dir, Cambria County Library System & District Center, 248 Main St, Johnstown, PA, 15901. Tel: 814-536-5131. Fax: 814-536-6905. p. 2073

Meeker, Robert, Ref Librn, Chicago State University, 9501 S Martin Luther King Jr Dr, LIB 440, Chicago, IL, 60628-1598. Tel: 773-995-2542. Fax: 773-995-3772. p. 610

Meeks, Diane, Mgr, Oconee Regional Library, Washington County, 314 S Harris St, Sandersville, GA, 31082-2669. Tel: 478-552-7466. Fax: 478-552-6064. p. 531

Meeks, Diane, Librn, Ducktown Community Library, 331 Main St, Ducktown, TN, 37326. Tel: 423-496-4004. p. 2233

Meeks, Elizabeth, Mgr, Redwood City Public Library, Fair Oaks, 2510 Middlefield Rd, Redwood City, CA, 94063-3402. Tel: 650-780-7261. Fax: 650-568-3371. p. 215

Meeks, Elizabeth, Mgr, Redwood City Public Library, Schaberg Branch, 2140 Euclid Ave, Redwood City, CA, 94061-1327. Tel: 650-780-7010. Fax: 650-568-1702. p. 215

Meeks, Karen, Br Mgr, Uncle Remus Regional Library System, Hancock County Library, 403 E Broad St, Sparta, GA, 31087. Tel: 706-444-5389. Fax: 706-444-6056. p. 542

Meeks, Stephen, Coordr, Cat, Georgia Northwestern Technical College, Bldg H, Rm 156, One Maurice Culberson Dr, Rome, GA, 30161. Tel: 706-295-6263. Fax: 706-295-6843. p. 548

Meeks, Trilby, Br Mgr, Charlotte Mecklenburg Library, Myers Park Branch, 1361 Queens Rd, Charlotte, NC, 28207. Tel: 704-416-5800. Fax: 704-416-5900. p. 1782

Meen, Donna, Dir, Libr Serv, Saint Joseph's College Library, University of Alberta, 11325 89th Ave, Edmonton, AB, T6G 2J5, CANADA. Tel: 780-492-7681, Ext 238. Fax: 780-492-8145. p. 2702

Meerians, Patti, Br Mgr, Hawaii State Public Library System, Kailua Public Library, 239 Kuulei Rd, Kailua, HI, 96734. Tel: 808-266-9911. Fax: 808-266-9915. p. 562

Meert, Deborah, Instrul Serv Librn, McGill University Libraries, Life Sciences Library, McIntyre Medical Science Bldg, 3655 Promenade Sir William Osler, Montreal, QC, H3G 1Y6, CANADA. Tel: 514-398-4475, Ext 09844. Fax: 514-398-3890. p. 2898

Meeske, Laurie, Internet Serv, Bergen County Cooperative Library System, 810 Main St, Hackensack, NJ, 07601. Tel: 201-489-1904. Fax: 201-489-4215. p. 2948

Meeske, Susan, Dir, Old Tappan Free Public Library, 56 Russell Ave, Old Tappan, NJ, 07675. Tel: 201-664-3499. Fax: 201-664-5999. p. 1516

Meetz, Marilyn, Br Mgr, Putnam County Library System, Interlachen Public Library, 133 N County Rd 315, Interlachen, FL, 32148. Tel: 386-684-1600. Fax: 386-684-1601. p. 478

Megarry, Susan, Librn, Butler County Law Library, Courthouse, 124 W Diamond St, Butler, PA, 16001. Fax: 724-284-5210. p. 2040

Megaw, Angela, Libr Dir, Gainesville State College, 1201 Bishop Farms Pkwy, Watkinsville, GA, 30677. Tel: 706-310-6305. Fax: 706-310-6237. p. 556

Meger, Andrew, Circ Mgr, Suffolk University, 73 Tremont St, Boston, MA, 02108. Tel: 617-573-8535. Fax: 617-573-8756. p. 1067

Meger, Jennifer, Asst Librn, Goulston & Storrs, PC, 400 Atlantic Ave, Boston, MA, 02110. Tel: 617-482-1776. p. 1061

Meghan, Cathey, ILL, Wofford College, 429 N Church St, Spartanburg, SC, 29303-3663. Tel: 864-597-4300. Fax: 864-597-4329. p. 2206

Megill, Jonathan, Ref Librn, Pennsylvania State University, 177 Vine Ave, Sharon, PA, 16146. Tel: 724-983-2883. Fax: 724-983-2881. p. 2139

Mehaffey, Angela, ILL Assoc, Irvine Sullivan Ingram Library, University of West Georgia, 1601 Maple St, Carrollton, GA, 30118. Tel: 678-839-6498. Fax: 678-839-6511. p. 523

Mehan, Kathi, Tech Serv Coordr, Nicholson Memorial Library System, 625 Austin St, Garland, TX, 75040-6365. Tel: 972-205-2500. Fax: 972-205-2523. p. 2327

Meheran, Laurie, Ch, Burlington Public Library, 34 Library Lane, Burlington, CT, 06013. Tel: 860-673-3331. Fax: 860-673-0897. p. 333

Mehigan, Jeff, Coordr, Lyman Library, Museum of Science, One Science Park, Boston, MA, 02114-1099. Tel: 617-589-0170. Fax: 617-589-0494. p. 1063

Mehl, Diane, Head, Circ & Tech Serv, Westland Public Library, 6123 Central City Pkwy, Westland, MI, 48185. Tel: 734-326-6123. Fax: 734-595-4612. p. 1236

Mehlin, Tracy, Info Tech, University of Washington Botanic Gardens, 3501 NE 41st St, Seattle, WA, 98105. Tel: 206-543-0415. Fax: 206-897-1435. p. 2533

Mehling, Beth, Br Mgr, North Madison County Public Library, Ralph E Hazelbaker Library, 1013 W Church St, Summitville, IN, 46070. Tel: 765-536-2335. Fax: 765-536-9050. p. 737

Mehling, Rebecca, Librn, Ohio State University LIBRARIES, Philip B Hardymon Medical Library, 1492 E Broad St, Columbus, OH, 43205. Tel: 614-257-3248. Fax: 614-257-3904. p. 1888

Mehmel, Angela, Br Head, Winnipeg Public Library, Transcona, 111 Victoria Ave W, Winnipeg, MB, R2C 1S6, CANADA. Tel: 204-986-3950. Fax: 204-986-3172. p. 2760

Mehnert, Patricia, Br Mgr, Jersey City Free Public Library, Pavonia, 326 Eighth St, Jersey City, NJ, 07302. Tel: 201-547-4808. Fax: 201-547-5222. p. 1492

Mehr, Linda Harris, Libr Dir, Academy of Motion Picture Arts & Sciences, 333 S La Cienega Blvd, Beverly Hills, CA, 90211. Tel: 310-247-3000, Ext 2201. Fax: 310-657-5193. p. 128

Mehra, Bharat, Asst Prof, University of Tennessee, Knoxville, 451 Communications Bldg, 1345 Circle Park Dr, Knoxville, TN, 37996-0341. Tel: 865-974-5917. Fax: 865-974-4967. p. 2974

Mehrens, Christopher, Dr, Head of Libr, Arizona State University Libraries, Music, Music Bldg, Tempe, AZ, 85287. Tel: 480-965-4267. Fax: 480-965-9598. p. 84

Mehrer, Jocelyn, Librn, Parkland Regional Library, Churchbridge Branch, 114 Rankin Rd, Churchbridge, SK, S0A 0M0, CANADA. Tel: 306-896-2322. p. 2931

Mehringer, Lynn, Dir, Lincoln Heritage Public Library, 105 Wallace St, Dale, IN, 47523-9267. Tel: 812-937-7170. Fax: 812-937-7102. p. 735

Mehta, Dipti, YA Serv, Stoughton Public Library, 84 Park St, Stoughton, MA, 02072-2974. Tel: 781-344-2711. Fax: 781-344-7340. p. 1129

Mehta, Mamta, Librn, Lakeview Public Library, 1120 Woodfield Rd, Rockville Centre, NY, 11570. Tel: 516-536-3071. Fax: 516-536-6260. p. 1734

Mehta, Sunil D, Head, Govt Doc, Johnson Free Public Library, 274 Main St, Hackensack, NJ, 07601-5797. Tel: 201-343-4169. Fax: 201-343-1395. p. 1489

Mehta, Usha, Dir, Morrison University Library, 10315 Professional Circle, Ste 201, Reno, NV, 89521. Tel: 775-850-0700. Fax: 775-850-0711. p. 1432

Mehu, Carole, Regional Libr Serv Dir, Norton Rose Canada LLP Library, One Place Ville Marie, Ste 2500, Montreal, QC, H3B 1R1, CANADA. Tel: 514-847-4701. Fax: 514-286-5474. p. 2900

Mei, James, Dir, Brescia University College Library, 1285 Western Rd, London, ON, N6G 1H2, CANADA. Tel: 519-432-8353, Ext 28250. Fax: 519-858-5137. p. 2816

Meier, Debbie, Dir, Westboro Public Library, W4941 Center St, Westboro, WI, 54490. Tel: 715-427-5864. Fax: 715-427-5354. p. 2648

Meier, Gayle, Dir, Libr Serv, Art Institute of Atlanta Library, 6600 Peachtree-Dunwoody Rd, 100 Embassy Row, Atlanta, GA, 30328-1635. Tel: 770-689-4887. Fax: 770-730-8767. p. 511

Meier, Janelle, Cat, Walla Walla Community College Library, 500 Tausick Way, Walla Walla, WA, 99362-9267. Tel: 509-527-4294. Fax: 509-527-4480. p. 2547

Meier, John J, Sci Librn, Pennsylvania State University Libraries, Physical & Mathematical Sciences, 201 Davey Lab, University Park, PA, 16802-6301. Tel: 814-867-1448. Fax: 814-865-2565. p. 2148

Meier, Mary, Libr Assoc, Madison Library, 1895 Village Rd, Madison, NH, 03849. Tel: 603-367-8545. Fax: 603-367-4479. p. 1455

Meiklejohn, Harriet, Tech Serv Librn, Santa Fe Community College Library, 6401 Richards Ave, Santa Fe, NM, 87508-4887. Tel: 505-428-1287. Fax: 505-428-1288. p. 1563

Meilaender, Marion, Coordr, Ser, Albion College, 602 E Cass St, Albion, MI, 49224-1879. Tel: 517-629-0285. Fax: 517-629-0504. p. 1148

Mein, Nardina, Dr, Dir, New Media & Info Tech, Wayne State University Libraries, Office of the Dean, 3100 Undergraduate Library, 5155 Gullen Mall, Detroit, MI, 48202. Tel: 313-577-6512. Fax: 313-577-7578. p. 1173

Meindl, Patricia, Librn, University of Toronto Libraries, A D Allen Chemistry Library, Lash Miller Laboratories, Rm 480, 80 St George St, Toronto, ON, M5S 3H6, CANADA. Tel: 416-978-3587. Fax: 416-946-8059. p. 2865

Meinen, Cindy, Circ, Mitchell Public Library, 221 N Duff St, Mitchell, SD, 57301-2596. Tel: 605-995-8480. Fax: 605-995-8482. p. 2215

Meinors, Mike, Dir, Pulitzer, Inc, 900 N Tucker Blvd, Saint Louis, MO, 63101. Tel: 314-340-8270. Fax: 314-340-3006. p. 1357

Meirose, Judy, Syst Librn, Florida Coastal School of Law, 8787 Baypine Rd, Jacksonville, FL, 32256. Tel: 904-680-7603. Fax: 904-680-7677. p. 452

Meisch, Lisa, Archivist, Curator, Texas State Library & Archives Commission, Sam Houston Regional Library & Research Center, 650 FM 1011, Liberty, TX, 77575. Tel: 936-336-8821. p. 2283

Meise, Michael, Asst Dir, Roanoke County Public Library, 3131 Electric Rd SW, Roanoke, VA, 24018-6496. Tel: 540-772-7507. Fax: 540-989-3129. p. 2494

Meisel, Gloria, User Educ Librn, SUNY Westchester Community College, 75 Grasslands Rd, Valhalla, NY, 10595-1693. Tel: 914-785-6968. Fax: 914-785-6513. p. 1760

Meisels, Sarah, Dir, Wheaton Public Library, 225 N Cross St, Wheaton, IL, 60187-5376. Tel: 630-868-7590. Fax: 630-668-8950. p. 719

Meisenheimer, Barbra, Commun Librn, Fort Vancouver Regional Library District, Vancouver Mall Community Library, 8700 NE Vancouver Mall Dr, Ste 285, Vancouver, WA, 98662. Tel: 360-892-8256. p. 2546

Meisenheimer, Mike, Libr Mgr, Tulsa Community College Learning Resources Center, Northeast Campus, 3727 E Apache St, Tulsa, OK, 74115-3150. Tel: 918-595-7501. Fax: 918-595-7504. p. 1983

Meisenheimer, Mike, LRC Supvr, Tulsa Community College Learning Resources Center, Southeast Campus, 10300 E 81st St, Tulsa, OK, 74133-4513. Tel: 918-595-7703. Fax: 918-595-7706. p. 1983

Meissner, Brandon, Coordr, Western Michigan University, Education Library, 2800 Sangren Hall, 1903 W Michigan Ave, Kalamazoo, MI, 49008. Tel: 269-387-5167. Fax: 268-387-5231. p. 1198

Meissner, Charlotte, Chief Exec Officer, Oakville Public Library, 120 Navy St, Oakville, ON, L6J 2Z4, CANADA. Tel: 905-815-2031. Fax: 905-815-2024. p. 2825

Meissner, Chris, Archivist, Librn, Lake Region State College, 1801 College Dr N, Devils Lake, ND, 58301. Tel: 701-662-1533. Fax: 701-662-1570. p. 1839

Meissner, Claire A, Librn, Barksdale Medical Library, Virginia Baptist Hospital, 3300 Rivermont Ave, Lynchburg, VA, 24503. Tel: 434-200-3147. p. 2475

Meissner, Claire A, Librn, Lynchburg General Hospital, 1901 Tate Springs Rd, Lynchburg, VA, 24501-1167. Tel: 434-200-3147. p. 2476

Meissner, Dennis, Coll Mgt, Minnesota Historical Society Library, 345 Kellogg Blvd W, Saint Paul, MN, 55102-1906. Tel: 651-259-3350. Fax: 651-297-7436. p. 1280

Meister, Barbara, Libr Dir, Ohio Christian University, 1476 Lancaster Pike, Circleville, OH, 43113. Tel: 740-477-7737, 740-477-7858. Fax: 740-477-7855. p. 1875

Meister, Christopher, Ref Serv, Ad, South Piedmont Community College, Cyber Center, 680 Hwy 74 W, Polkton, NC, 28135. Tel: 704-272-5389. Fax: 704-272-5384. p. 1814

Meister, Lynn, Asst Librn, Muscoda Public Library, 206 N Wisconsin Ave, Muscoda, WI, 53569. Tel: 608-739-3182. Fax: 608-739-3183. p. 2623

Meixell, Joan, Cat, Appalachian State University, Music Library, 813 Rivers St, Boone, NC, 28608-2097. Tel: 828-262-2388. Fax: 828-265-8642. p. 1777

Meixner, Judith, Ch, Plainville Public Library, 198 South St, Plainville, MA, 02762-1512. Tel: 508-695-1784. Fax: 508-695-6359. p. 1118

Meizner, Kathie, Mgr, Montgomery County Public Libraries, Kensington Park Library, 4201 Knowles Ave, Kensington, MD, 20895-2408. Tel: 240-773-9505. Fax: 301-897-2238. p. 1038

Meizner, Kathie, Mgr, Montgomery County Public Libraries, Noyes Children's Library, 10237 Carroll Pl, Kensington, MD, 20895-3361. Tel: 240-773-9575. Fax: 301-929-5470. p. 1039

Mejia, Rosi, Br Mgr, San Diego County Library, Crest, 105 Juanita Lane, El Cajon, CA, 92021-4399. Tel: 619-442-7083. Fax: 619-442-4972. p. 233

Mejias, Nelba, Actg Dir, Harrison Public Library, 415 Harrison Ave, Harrison, NJ, 07029. Tel: 973-483-2366. Fax: 973-483-1052. p. 1490

Melady, Grace, Head, Youth Serv, Harrison Memorial Library, Ocean Ave & Lincoln St, Carmel, CA, 93921. Tel: 831-624-4664. Fax: 831-624-0407. p. 132

Melady, Michele, Mgr, Canadian Broadcasting Corp, Reference & Image Research Libraries, 250 Front St W, Toronto, ON, M5V 3G5, CANADA. Tel: 416-205-8501. Fax: 416-205-3733. p. 2851

Melanson, Mark C, Sr Dir Gen, Corporate Resourcing Br & CFO, Library & Archives Canada, 550 De la Cité Blvd, Gatineau, QC, K1A 0N4, CANADA. Tel: 819-934-4627. Fax: 819-934-5262. p. 2883

Melanson, Pat, ILL, Agriculture & Agri-Food Canada, Canadian Agriculture Library, 32 Main St, Kentville, NS, B4N 1J5, CANADA. Tel: 902-679-5508. Fax: 902-679-5784. p. 2783

Melanson, Robert G, Dir, Winter Park Public Library, 460 E New England Ave, Winter Park, FL, 32789-4493. Tel: 407-623-3490. Fax: 407-623-3489. p. 505

Melby, Mary, Br Mgr, Maricopa County Library District, Northwest Regional, 16089 N Bullard, Surprise, AZ, 85374. Tel: 602-652-3401. Fax: 602-652-3420. p. 75

Melcher, Amanda, Acq of Monographs, University of Montevallo, Station 6100, Montevallo, AL, 35115-6100. Tel: 205-665-6104. Fax: 205-665-6112. p. 27

Melching, Lori, Adult Serv, Tech Serv, Portland Public Library, 301 Portland Blvd, Portland, TN, 37148-1229. Tel: 615-325-2279. Fax: 615-325-7061. p. 2263

Melchor, Lynn, ILL Coordr, Elon University, 308 N O'Kelly Ave, Elon, NC, 27244-0187. Tel: 336-278-6600. Fax: 336-278-6637. p. 1791

Meldau, Gayle, Mgr, Pub Serv, Mission Viejo Library, 100 Civic Ctr, Mission Viejo, CA, 92691. Tel: 949-830-7100, Ext 5132. Fax: 949-586-8447. p. 187

Meldrem, Joyce A, Dir, Loras College Library, 1450 Alta Vista St, Dubuque, IA, 52004-4327. Tel: 563-588-7189. Fax: 563-588-7147. p. 812

Melendez, Cynthia Cardona, Curator, Orange County Regional History Center, 65 E Central Blvd, Orlando, FL, 32801. Tel: 407-836-8587. Fax: 407-836-8550. p. 477

Meleski, Patricia, Librn, West Warren Library, 2370 Main St, West Warren, MA, 01092. Tel: 413-436-9892. Fax: 413-436-5086. p. 1138

Melewski, Carol, Circ Mgr, RCS Community Library, 15 Mountain Rd, Ravena, NY, 12143. Tel: 518-756-2053. Fax: 518-756-8595. p. 1726

Melgosa, Annette, Instrul Serv Librn & Coordr, Access Serv, Per, Walla Walla University Libraries, 104 S College Ave, College Place, WA, 99324-1159. Tel: 509-527-2684. Fax: 509-527-2001. p. 2513

Melgoza, Ezequiel, Librn, University of Texas at Brownsville & Texas Southmost College Library, 80 Fort Brown St, Brownsville, TX, 78521. Tel: 956-882-8221. Fax: 956-882-5495. p. 2292

Melhorn, Lorna, ILL, Palmyra Public Library, Borough Bldg, 325 S Railroad St, Palmyra, PA, 17078-2492. Tel: 717-838-1347. Fax: 717-838-1236. p. 2101

Melia, Marcy, Ch, Goodland Public Library, 812 Broadway, Goodland, KS, 67735. Tel: 785-899-5461. Fax: 785-899-5461. p. 869

Melia, Michele, Cat & Syst Librn, Champlain College Library, 163 S Willard St, Burlington, VT, 05401. Tel: 802-860-2717. p. 2420

Melian, Carlos, Assoc Univ Librn, Syst, Tech & Access Serv, Interim Dean, Libr & Learning Res, Northeastern Illinois University, 5500 N Saint Louis Ave, Chicago, IL, 60625-4699. Tel: 773-442-4450. Fax: 773-442-4531. p. 620

Melican, Eileen, In Charge, Worcester State Hospital Library, 305 Belmont St, Worcester, MA, 01604. Tel: 508-368-3300, Ext 83540. p. 1146

Melick, Cal, Pub Serv Librn, Washburn University, 1700 SW College Ave, Topeka, KS, 66621. Tel: 785-670-1276. Fax: 785-670-3223. p. 897

Melillo, Mike, Libr Assoc, McDonald Hopkins, LPA, 600 Superior Ave E, Ste 2100, Cleveland, OH, 44114. Tel: 216-348-5400. Fax: 216-348-5474. p. 1880

Melillo, Paolo, Br Mgr, Orange County Library District, Southeast, 5575 S Semoran Blvd, Orlando, FL, 32822. p. 476

Melin, Sue, Libr Assoc, Carlton Public Library, 310 Chestnut Ave, Carlton, MN, 55718. Tel: 218-384-3322. Fax: 218-384-4229. p. 1244

Melinda, McCrary, Curator, Richmond Museum of History, 400 Nevin Ave, Richmond, CA, 94801-3017. Tel: 510-235-7387. Fax: 510-235-4345. p. 216

Melinn, Carmen D, Ser & Archival Spec, Western Piedmont Community College, 1001 Burkemont Ave, Morganton, NC, 28655-4504. Tel: 828-448-6039. Fax: 828-448-6173. p. 1811

Melita, Lorraine, Coordr, Ref & Instrul Serv, SUNY Cortland, 81 Prospect Terrace, Cortland, NY, 13045. Tel: 607-753-2525. Fax: 607-753-5669. p. 1611

Melland, Ardell, Circ Mgr, Northern State University, 1200 S Jay St, Aberdeen, SD, 57401-7198. Tel: 605-626-2645. Fax: 605-626-2473. p. 2209

Mellby, Julie, Librn, Princeton University, Graphic Arts Collection, One Washington Rd, Princeton, NJ, 08544-2098. Tel: 609-258-3197. Fax: 609-258-2324. p. 1524

Mellett, Margaret, Asst Dir, Rutherford Public Library, 150 Park Ave, Rutherford, NJ, 07070. Tel: 201-939-8600. Fax: 201-939-4108. p. 1528

Mellick, Linda, Librn, Connecticut Judicial Branch Law Libraries, Danbury Law Library, Danbury Courthouse, 146 White St, Danbury, CT, 06810. Tel: 203-207-8625. Fax: 203-207-8627. p. 344

Mellin, Irene, Librn, Congregation Shaarey Zedek Library & Audio Visual Center, 27375 Bell Rd, Southfield, MI, 48034. Tel: 248-357-5544. Fax: 248-357-0227. p. 1228

Mellingen, Andrea, Librn, Montmorency County Public Libraries, 11901 Haymeadow Rd, Atlanta, MI, 49709. Tel: 989-785-3941. Fax: 989-785-3941. p. 1154

Mellis, John, In Charge, Queen's College Library, 210 Prince Philip Dr, Ste 3000, St. John's, NL, A1B 3R6, CANADA. Tel: 709-753-0116. Fax: 709-753-1214. p. 2773

Mello, David, Ch, Fall River Public Library, 104 N Main St, Fall River, MA, 02720. Tel: 508-324-2700. Fax: 508-324-2707. p. 1088

Mello, Diane, Br Head, Mariposa County Library, Bassett Memorial, 7971 Chilnualna Falls Rd, Wawona, CA, 95389. Tel: 209-375-6510. p. 184

Mello, Marjo, Dir, Brawley Public Library, 400 Main St, Brawley, CA, 92227-2491. Tel: 760-344-1891, Ext 10. Fax: 760-344-0212. p. 129

Mello, Peggy, Acq, Tech Serv, The William K Sanford Town Library, 629 Albany Shaker Rd, Loudonville, NY, 12211-1196. Tel: 518-458-9274. Fax: 518-438-0988. p. 1655

Mellon, Laura, Br Mgr, Wyoming County Public Library, Pineville Branch, Corner of Costle Rock & Bank St, Pineville, WV, 24874. Tel: 304-732-6228. Fax: 304-732-6899. p. 2570

Mellor, Beth Ann, Dir, Oakmont Carnegie Library, 700 Allegheny River Blvd, Oakmont, PA, 15139. Tel: 412-828-9532. Fax: 412-828-5979. p. 2100

Mellor, Bonnie, Br Mgr, Washington County Library System, New Harmony Valley Branch, 34 S 2900 East, New Harmony, UT, 84757. Tel: 435-867-0065. Fax: 435-867-0222. p. 2412

Mellor, Karen, Libr Prog Mgr, State of Rhode Island Office of Library & Information Services, One Capitol Hill, 4th Flr, Providence, RI, 02908. Tel: 401-574-9304. Fax: 401-574-9320. p. 2175

Mellor, Laura, Head, Youth Serv, Somerset County Library System, Hillsborough Public, Hillsborough Municipal Complex, 379 S Branch Rd, Hillsborough, NJ, 08844. Tel: 908-369-2200. Fax: 908-369-8242. p. 1475

Melnick, Deborah, Librn, Civil Court of the City of New York Library, 111 Centre St, Rm 1034, New York, NY, 10013. Tel: 646-386-5430. Fax: 212-748-5171. p. 1673

Melnick, Joni, Librn, Blairsville Public Library, 113 N Walnut St, Blairsville, PA, 15717-1348. Tel: 724-459-6077. Fax: 724-459-6097. p. 2035

Melnick, Ralph, Asst Dir, Westfield Athenaeum, Six Elm St, Westfield, MA, 01085-2997. Tel: 413-568-7833, Ext 82. Fax: 413-568-0988. p. 1138

Melnick, Todd, Assoc Librn, Pub Serv, Fordham University School of Law, 140 W 62nd St, New York, NY, 10023-7485. Tel: 212-636-7677. Fax: 212-930-8818. p. 1678

Melnicove, Annette, Libr Dir, A Max Brewer Memorial Law Library, Harry T & Harriette V Moore Justice Ctr, 2825 Judge Fran Jamieson Way, Viera, FL, 32940. Tel: 321-617-7295. Fax: 321-617-7303. p. 502

Melo, Olivia, Dir, Lakeville Public Library, Four Precinct St, Lakeville, MA, 02347. Tel: 508-947-9028. Fax: 508-923-9934. p. 1097

Melo, Olivia, Librn, Joseph H Plumb Memorial Library, 17 Constitution Way, Rochester, MA, 02770. Tel: 508-763-8600. Fax: 508-763-9593. p. 1120

Meloche, Joseph, Asst Prof, University at Buffalo, State University of New York, 534 Baldy Hall, Buffalo, NY, 14260. Tel: 716-645-2412. Fax: 716-645-3775. p. 2971

Melodie, Hoffman, Asst Librn, Emery County Library, Orangeville Branch, 125 S Main, Orangeville, UT, 84537. Tel: 435-748-2726. Fax: 435-748-2736. p. 2404

Melody, Coleman, Librn, West Chicago Public Library District, 118 W Washington St, West Chicago, IL, 60185. Tel: 630-231-1552. Fax: 630-231-1709. p. 717

Melone, Sue, Head, Circ, Poplar Creek Public Library District, 1405 S Park Ave, Streamwood, IL, 60107-2997. Tel: 630-837-6800. Fax: 630-837-6823. p. 708

Meloni, Alana, Ch, Cyrenius H Booth Library, 25 Main St, Newtown, CT, 06470. Tel: 203-426-3851. Fax: 203-270-4534. p. 361

Meloy, Tracie, Head, ILL, West Chester University, 25 W Rosedale Ave, West Chester, PA, 19383. Tel: 610-436-2747. p. 2153

Meloy, William, Coll Mgr for Ser/ Librn, California University of Pennsylvania, 250 University Ave, California, PA, 15419-1394. Tel: 724-938-4067. Fax: 724-938-5901. p. 2040

Melrose, Ann, Sr Librn, Hennepin County Library, Washburn, 5244 Lyndale Ave S, Minneapolis, MN, 55419-1222. Tel: 612-543-8378. Fax: 612-543-8377. p. 1265

Melroy, Virginia, Cat, University of Iowa Libraries, Law Library, 200 Boyd Law Bldg, Iowa City, IA, 52242-1166. Tel: 319-335-9077. Fax: 319-335-9039. p. 823

Melson, Margaret, Tech Serv, Lewes Public Library, 111 Adams Ave, Lewes, DE, 19958. Tel: 302-645-2733. Fax: 302-645-6235. p. 384

Melton, Carol, Ch, Emmet O'Neal Library, 50 Oak St, Mountain Brook, AL, 35213. Tel: 205-879-0459. Fax: 205-879-5388. p. 32

Melton, Donna, Circ Supvr, Salem College, 626 S Church St, Winston-Salem, NC, 27108. Tel: 336-917-5419. Fax: 336-917-5339. p. 1833

Melton, Eric, Asst Dir, Kirkendall Public Library, 1210 NW Prairie Ridge Dr, Ankeny, IA, 50021. Tel: 515-965-6460. Fax: 515-965-6474. p. 794

Melton, Greg, Dir, Remington College Library, 303 Rue Louis XIV, Lafayette, LA, 70508. Tel: 337-981-4010. Fax: 337-983-7130. p. 953

Melton, Janet, Br Mgr, Pamunkey Regional Library, Goochland Branch, 3075 River Rd W, Goochland, VA, 23063. Tel: 804-556-4774. Fax: 804-556-2941. p. 2469

Melton, Maureen, Dir, Museum of Fine Arts, Boston, 300 Massachusetts Ave, Boston, MA, 02115. Tel: 617-369-3385. Fax: 617-369-4257. p. 1064

Melton, Pamela, Assoc Dir, Libr Admin, University of South Carolina, Coleman Karesh Law Library, USC Law Ctr, 701 Main St, Columbia, SC, 29208. Tel: 803-777-5942. Fax: 803-777-9405. p. 2190

Melton, Terry, Circ Coordr, Montgomery County Memorial Library System, 104 I-45 N, Conroe, TX, 77301-2720. Tel: 936-788-8377, Ext 244. Fax: 936-788-8398. p. 2300

Melton, Vickie, Circ Supvr, California State University, 9001 Stockdale Hwy, Bakersfield, CA, 93311-1022. Tel: 661-654-3236. Fax: 661-654-3238. p. 123

Meltz, Elyse, Librn, Onondaga County Public Library, Paine, 113 Nichols Ave, Syracuse, NY, 13206. Tel: 315-435-5442. Fax: 315-435-3553. p. 1753

Meltzer, Leslie, Librn, West Stockbridge Public Library, Nine Main St, West Stockbridge, MA, 01266. Tel: 413-232-0308. p. 1137

Meltzer, Lois, Asst Dir, Ch, Cromwell Belden Public Library, 39 West St, Cromwell, CT, 06416. Tel: 860-632-3460. Fax: 860-632-3484. p. 334

Meluskey, Andrea, Dir, Shelter Rock Public Library, 165 Searingtown Rd, Albertson, NY, 11507. Tel: 516-248-7343. p. 1571

Melvie, Ann Marie, Librn, Saskatchewan Justice, Court of Appeal Library, Court House, 2425 Victoria Ave, Regina, SK, S4P 4W6, CANADA. Tel: 306-787-7399. Fax: 306-787-0505. p. 2924

Melville, Catherine, Coll Develop, Juneau Public Libraries, 292 Marine Way, Juneau, AK, 99801. Tel: 907-586-5324. Fax: 907-586-3419. p. 50

Melvin, Dena, Ref Librn, United States Army, Keith A Campbell Memorial Library, 2601 Harney Rd, Ste 29, Fort Sam Houston, TX, 78234-5029. Tel: 210-221-4387, 210-221-4702. Fax: 210-227-5921. p. 2320

Melvin, Maureen, Br Mgr, Saint Lucie County Library System, Port Saint Lucie Branch, 180 SW Prima Vista Blvd, Port Saint Lucie, FL, 34983. Tel: 772-871-5450. Fax: 772-871-5451. p. 447

Melvin, William, Mgr, Smith Peterson Law Library, 35 Main Pl, Ste 300, Council Bluffs, IA, 51503-0702. Tel: 712-328-1833. Fax: 712-328-8320. p. 805

Melyon, Ellen, Coll Develop, Kenosha Public Library, 812 56th St, Kenosha, WI, 53140-3735. Tel: 262-564-6327. Fax: 262-564-6370. p. 2601

Melz, Jill, Dir, Rake Public Library, 123 N Main St, Rake, IA, 50465. Tel: 641-566-3388. Fax: 641-566-3388. p. 840

Membiela, Clare, Assoc Dir, Thomas M Cooley Law School Libraries, 300 S Capitol Ave, Lansing, MI, 48901. Tel: 517-371-5140, Ext 3402. Fax: 517-334-5715, 517-334-5717. p. 1202

Memmott, H Kirk, Bus Librn, Brigham Young University, Harold B Lee Library, 2060 HBLL, Provo, UT, 84602. Tel: 801-422-2927. Fax: 801-422-0466. p. 2411

Men, Noreth, Syst Librn, El Camino College, 16007 S Crenshaw Blvd, Torrance, CA, 90506. Tel: 310-660-3525. Fax: 310-660-3513. p. 275

Menagh, Jacqueline, Prog & Vols Coordr,
Bereaved Families of Ontario Toronto Library,
80 Woodlawn Ave, Toronto, ON, M4T
1C1, CANADA. Tel: 416-440-0290. Fax:
416-440-0304. p. 2850

Menanteaux, Bob, Ref, Seattle University, School
of Law Library, Sullivan Hall, 901 12th Ave,
Seattle, WA, 98122-4411. Tel: 206-398-4221.
Fax: 206-398-4194. p. 2532

Menanteaux, Kathleen A, Dir of Libr Serv, Spoon
River College Library, 23235 N County Rd 22,
Canton, IL, 61520. Tel: 309-649-6222. Fax:
309-649-6235. p. 599

Menard, Barbara, Asst Circ Librn, Aldrich
Public Library, Six Washington St, Barre,
VT, 05641-4227. Tel: 802-476-7550. Fax:
802-479-0450 (Call before sending fax). p. 2418

Menard, Christine, Head, Ref & Res Serv,
Williams College, 55 Sawyer Library Dr,
Williamstown, MA, 01267. Tel: 413-597-2515.
Fax: 413-597-4106. p. 1140

Menard, Christy, Librn, Conant Public Library,
111 Main St, Winchester, NH, 03470. Tel:
603-239-4331. Fax: 603-239-4331. p. 1468

Menard, David, Br Mgr 1, Sno-Isle Libraries,
Camano Island Community Library, 848 N
Sunrise Blvd, Camano Island, WA, 98282. Tel:
360-387-5150. Fax: 360-387-5170. p. 2542

Menard, Elaine, Asst Prof, McGill University, 3661
Peel St, Montreal, QC, H3A 1X1, CANADA.
Tel: 514-398-3368. Fax: 514-398-7193. p. 2979

Menard, Francine, Libr Tech, Bibliotheque
Municipale de Saint Felicien, 1209 Blvd
Sacre-Coeur, Saint Felicien, QC, G8K
2R5, CANADA. Tel: 418-679-5334. Fax:
418-679-2178. p. 2908

Ménard, Françoise, Chef de Section, Bibliothèques
de Montrèal, La Petite-Patrie, 6707, avenue De
Lorimier, Montreal, QC, H2G 2P8, CANADA.
Tel: 514-872-4735. Fax: 514-872-0526. p. 2890

Ménard, Françoise, Chef de Section, Bibliothèques
de Montrèal, Rosemont, 3131, boulevard
Rosemont, Montreal, QC, H1Y 1M4, CANADA.
Tel: 514-872-4735. Fax: 514-872-0527. p. 2891

Menard, Margie, Dir, Kingston Library, 55 Franklin
St, Kingston, NY, 12401. Tel: 845-331-0507.
Fax: 845-331-7981. p. 1650

Menard, Michael, Curator, Librn, Museum of
Western Colorado, 462 Ute Ave, Grand Junction,
CO, 81501. Tel: 970-242-0971, Ext 209. Fax:
970-242-3960. p. 311

Menard, Nancy, Asst Dir, Wilbraham Public Library,
25 Crane Park Dr, Wilbraham, MA, 01095-1799.
Tel: 413-596-6141. Fax: 413-596-5090. p. 1140

Mencel, Dianne, Libr Tech, Wisconsin Indianhead
Technical College, 600 N 21st St, Superior, WI,
54880-5296. Tel: 715-394-6677, Ext 6276. Fax:
715-394-3771. p. 2641

Menchen, Margaret, Scholarly Res & Serv/Soc Sci
Librn, Colby College Libraries, 5100 Mayflower
Hill, Waterville, ME, 04901. Tel: 207-859-5144.
Fax: 207-859-5105. p. 1005

Mende, Barbara, Librn, Congregation Mishkan
Tefila, 300 Hammond Pond Pkwy, Chestnut
Hill, MA, 02167. Tel: 617-332-7770. Fax:
617-332-2871. p. 1081

Mende, Lynnette, Head, Acq, Prof, Erie Community
College-North, 6205 Main St, Williamsville,
NY, 14221-7095. Tel: 716-851-1271. Fax:
716-851-1277. p. 1769

Mendell, Rebecca, Librn, Folsom Lake College
Library, Ten College Pkwy, Folsom, CA, 95630.
Tel: 916-608-6708. Fax: 916-608-6533. p. 148

Mendelsohn, Jenny, Head, Ref, University of
Toronto Libraries, Robarts Library, 130 St
George St, Toronto, ON, M5S 1A5, CANADA.
Tel: 416 946-5519. Fax: 416-978-1608. p. 2867

Mendelsohn, Loren, Head of Libr, City College
of the City University of New York,
Science-Engineering, Marshak Bldg, Rm 29,
160 Convent Ave, New York, NY, 10031. Tel:
212-650-8244. Fax: 212-650-7626. p. 1673

Mendelson, Ruth, Librn, Bracewell & Giuliani LLP,
2000 K St NW, Ste 500, Washington, DC,
20006-1872. Tel: 202-828-5800, Ext 7660. Fax:
202-223-1225. p. 394

Mendenhall, Ann, Outreach Serv Librn, Pender
County Public Library, 103 S Cowan St,
Burgaw, NC, 28425. Tel: 910-259-1234. Fax:
910-259-0656. p. 1778

Mendenhall, John, Dir, Federal Trade Commission,
1111 Superior Ave, Ste 200, Cleveland, OH,
44114. Tel: 216-263-3455. Fax: 216-263-3426.
p. 1880

Mendes, Bonnie Davis, Libr Dir, Somerset Public
Library, 1464 County St, Somerset, MA, 02726.
Tel: 508-646-2829. Fax: 508-646-2831. p. 1124

Mendez, Deixter, In Charge, University of Puerto
Rico, Marine Science, PO Box 9022, Mayaguez,
PR, 00681-9022. Tel: 787-832-4040, Ext 2513.
p. 2674

Mendez, Jerry, Computer Lab/Per Supvr, Yuma
County Library District, 2951 S 21st Dr,
Yuma, AZ, 85364. Tel: 928-314-2456. Fax:
928-782-9420. p. 91

Mendieta, Toni, Librn, Yolo County Library, Winters
Branch, 708 Railroad Ave, Winters, CA, 95694.
Tel: 530-795-3177. Fax: 530-795-3132. p. 285

Mendina, Glenda, Mgr, Methodist Healthcare, 1265
Union Ave, Memphis, TN, 38104-3499. Tel:
901-726-7899. Fax: 901-726-8254. p. 2250

Mendive, Toni, Archivist, Northeastern Nevada
Museum Library, 1515 Idaho St, Elko, NV,
89801. Tel: 775-738-3418. Fax: 775-778-9318.
p. 1427

Mendola, James, Librn, DVA-WNY Healthcare
System, 3495 Bailey Ave, Buffalo, NY, 14215.
Tel: 716-862-8841. Fax: 716-862-8839. p. 1597

Mendonca, Liliana, In Charge, Klamath County
Library Services District, Chiloquin Branch,
140 First Ave, Chiloquin, OR, 97624. Tel:
541-783-3315. Fax: 541-783-3315. p. 2002

Mendoza, Ana, Assoc Dean, Admin Operations
& Budget, Florida International University,
11200 SW Eighth St, Miami, FL, 33199. Tel:
305-348-1900. Fax: 305-348-3408. p. 465

Mendoza, Anthanett, Diversity Spec, University of
Nebraska at Kearney, 2508 11th Ave, Kearney,
NE, 68849-2240. Tel: 308-865-8587. Fax:
308-865-8722. p. 1403

Mendoza, Aurora, Purchasing, San Bernardino
Public Library, 555 W Sixth St, San Bernardino,
CA, 92410-3001. Tel: 909-381-8215. Fax:
909-381-8229. p. 229

Mendoza, Candy, Br Mgr, Mid-Columbia Libraries,
Pasco Branch, 1320 W Hopkins, Pasco, WA,
99301. Tel: 509-545-1019. Fax: 509-547-5416.
p. 2518

Mendoza, Candy, Br Supvr, Mid-Columbia
Libraries, Keewaydin Park, 405 S Dayton,
Kennewick, WA, 99336. Tel: 509-586-3156.
p. 2518

Mendoza, Christine, Head, Coll Develop, Sunnyvale
Public Library, 665 W Olive Ave, Sunnyvale,
CA, 94086-7622. Tel: 408-730-7300. Fax:
408-735-8767. p. 273

Mendoza, Frank, Circ Mgr, Charlotte Mecklenburg
Library, ImaginOn: The Joe & Joan Martin
Center, 300 E Seventh St, Charlotte, NC, 28202.
Tel: 704-416-4600. Fax: 704-416-4700. p. 1782

Mendoza, Jo Ann, Br Mgr, Iberville Parish Library,
Bayou Sorrel, 33415 Hwy 75, Plaquemine, LA,
70764. Tel: 225-659-7055. Fax: 225-659-7055.
p. 966

Mendoza, Jose, Br Supvr, Walla Walla County Rural
Library District, Vista Hermosa Library, 76
Sarah Lynne Lane, Prescott, WA, 99348. Tel:
509-749-2099. Fax: 509-749-2099. p. 2547

Mendoza, Karina, Br Mgr, Stanislaus County Free
Library, Denair Branch, 4801 Kersey Rd, Denair,
CA, 95316-9350. Tel: 209-634-1283. Fax:
209-634-1283. p. 188

Mendoza, Mae, Circ, Ref, University of South
Carolina at Beaufort Library, One University
Blvd, Bluffton, SC, 29909-6085. Tel:
843-521-4126. Fax: 843-208-8296. p. 2182

Mendoza, Rebecca, In Charge, Imperial County Free
Library, Heber Branch, 1078 Dogwood Rd,
Heber, CA, 92257. Tel: 760-336-0737. Fax:
760-336-0748. p. 145

Menendez, Sandra, Circ Mgr, North Central
Regional Library, Omak Community, 30 S Ash,
Omak, WA, 98841. Tel: 509-826-1820. Fax:
509-826-5102. p. 2549

Menendez-Cuesta, Loanis, Ref Librn, YA
Librn, Delray Beach Public Library, 100 W
Atlantic Ave, Delray Beach, FL, 33444. Tel:
561-819-6299. Fax: 561-266-9757. p. 437

Meneo, Sue, Adult Serv, Southington Public Library
& Museum, 255 Main St, Southington, CT,
06489. Tel: 860-628-0947. Fax: 860-628-0488.
p. 368

Meneray, Wilbur E, Spec Coll Librn, Tulane
University, 7001 Freret St, New Orleans,
LA, 70118-5682. Tel: 504-247-1832. Fax:
504-865-6773. p. 963

Meng, Mark, Dr, Dir, Saint John's University,
Staten Island Campus, 300 Howard Ave, Staten
Island, NY, 10301. Tel: 718-390-4458. Fax:
718-390-4290. p. 1748

Meng, William, Dir, Saint Joseph's College, 222
Clinton Ave, Brooklyn, NY, 11205-3697. Tel:
718-940-5884. Fax: 718-636-7250. p. 1594

Mengel, Bea, Ch, YA Serv, Youth Serv, Clayton
County Library System, 865 Battlecreek Rd,
Jonesboro, GA, 30236. Tel: 770-473-3850. Fax:
770-473-3858. p. 536

Mengel, Elizabeth, Head, Coll Mgt, Johns Hopkins
University Libraries, The Sheridan Libraries,
3400 N Charles St, Baltimore, MD, 21218. Tel:
410-516-8325. Fax: 410-516-5080. p. 1014

Menish, M, Mrs, Ch, O'Neill Public Library,
601 E Douglas, O'Neill, NE, 68763. Tel:
402-336-3110. Fax: 402-336-3268. p. 1415

Menjiver, Rachel, Circ Supvr, ILL, Palestine
Public Library, 2000 S Loop 256, Ste 42,
Palestine, TX, 75801. Tel: 903-729-4121. Fax:
903-729-4062. p. 2368

Menke, Peggy, Librn, Tri-Valley School -
Community Library, Suntrana Rd, Healy, AK,
99743. Tel: 907-683-2507. Fax: 907-683-2517.
p. 49

Menke, Roberta, Librn, Newton Public Library &
Museum, 100 S Van Buren St, Newton, IL,
62448. Tel: 618-783-8141. Fax: 618-783-8149.
p. 680

Menken, Francine, Librn, Jewish Community
Center of Metropolitan Detroit, 6600 W Maple
Rd, West Bloomfield, MI, 48322-3022. Tel:
248-432-5546. Fax: 248-432-5552. p. 1236

Mennenga, Karen, Dir, Wellsburg Public Library,
515 N Adams, Wellsburg, IA, 50680. Tel:
641-869-5234. Fax: 641-869-5234. p. 851

Mennie, Carol C, Dir, Manasquan Public Library,
55 Broad St, Manasquan, NJ, 08736. Tel:
732-223-1503. Fax: 732-292-0336. p. 1499

Menninger, Margaret, Tech Serv, Redondo Beach
Public Library, 303 N Pacific Coast Hwy,
Redondo Beach, CA, 90277. Tel: 310-318-0675.
Fax: 310-318-3809. p. 215

Menon, Shirin, Librn, Dreyfus Corp Library, 200
Park Ave, 7th Flr, New York, NY, 10166. Tel:
212-922-6087. Fax: 212-922-7018. p. 1677

Menon, Vanaja, Dir, University of
Wisconsin-Parkside Library, 900 Wood Rd,
Kenosha, WI, 53141. Tel: 262-595-2356. Fax:
262-595-2545. p. 2601

Mentch, Fran, Librn, Cleveland State University,
University Library, Rhodes Tower, 2121
Euclid Ave, Cleveland, OH, 44115-2214. Tel:
216-687-2365. Fax: 216-687-9380. p. 1879

Mente, Anne, Tech Serv, Laredo Public Library,
1120 E Calton Rd, Laredo, TX, 78041. Tel:
956-795-2400. Fax: 956-795-2403. p. 2354

Mente, Jane, Chair, Mesa Community College
Library, 1833 W Southern Ave, Mesa, AZ,
85202. Tel: 480-461-7694. Fax: 480-461-7681.
p. 68

Mentore, Andra, Mgr, Vols Serv - S Region, Broward County Division of Libraries, 100 S Andrews Ave, Fort Lauderdale, FL, 33301. Tel: 954-201-8381. Fax: 954-357-5733. p. 440

Mentzer, Jennifer, Ch, Grafton Public Library, 35 Grafton Common, Grafton, MA, 01519. Tel: 508-839-4649. Fax: 508-839-7726. p. 1091

Menz, Leslie, Librn, Saint Francis Medical Center College of Nursing, 511 NE Greenleaf St, Peoria, IL, 61603. Tel: 309-655-2180. Fax: 309-655-3648. p. 690

Menz, Leslie, Chairperson, Heart of Illinois Library Consortium, 511 NE Greenleaf, Peoria, IL, 61603. p. 2942

Menzer, Karin A, Mgr, Ch Serv, Mead Public Library, 710 N Eighth St, Sheboygan, WI, 53081-4563. Tel: 920-459-3400, Ext 3433. Fax: 920-459-0204. p. 2637

Menzer, Shelly, Ch, Dwight Foster Public Library, 102 E Milwaukee Ave, Fort Atkinson, WI, 53538-2049. Tel: 920-563-7790. Fax: 920-563-7774. p. 2592

Menzics, Paula, Br Librn, Brooklyn Public Library, Cortelyou, 1305 Cortelyou Rd, Brooklyn, NY, 11226. Tel: 718-693-7763. Fax: 718-693-7874. p. 1591

Menzies, Xavier, Dir, Markham Public Library, 16640 S Kedzie Ave, Markham, IL, 60428. Tel: 708-331-0130. Fax: 708-331-0137. p. 670

Menzul, Faina, Dir, Becton, Dickinson & Co, One Becton Dr, Franklin Lakes, NJ, 07417-1884. Tel: 201-847-7230. Fax: 201-847-5377. p. 1486

Meola, Marc, Librn, The College of New Jersey Library, 2000 Pennington Rd, Ewing, NJ, 08628-0718. Tel: 609-771-2311, 609-771-2332. Fax: 609-637-5177. p. 1484

Merasty, Gerri, In Charge, Ayamicikiwikamik Public Library, PO Box 240, Sandy Bay, SK, S0P 0G0, CANADA. Tel: 306-754-2139. Fax: 306-754-2130. p. 2925

Merat, Carl, Dean, Liberty University Library, 1971 University Blvd, Lynchburg, VA, 24502. Tel: 434-592-3751. Fax: 434-582-2728. p. 2476

Mercadante, Jolene, Asst Dir, Agawam Public Library, 750 Cooper St, Agawam, MA, 01001. Tel: 413-789-1550. Fax: 413-789-1552. p. 1048

Mercante, Mary Ann, Asst Dean, Head, Tech Serv, Maryville University Library, 650 Maryville University Dr, Saint Louis, MO, 63141. Tel: 314-529-9650. Fax: 314-529-9941. p. 1356

Mercatante, Mike, Br Mgr, Saint Clair County Library System, Marysville Public, 1175 Delaware, Marysville, MI, 48040. Tel: 810-364-9493. Fax: 810-364-7491. p. 1219

Mercedes, Cobb, Br Serv Coordr, East Baton Rouge Parish Library, 7711 Goodwood Blvd, Baton Rouge, LA, 70806-7625. Tel: 225-231-3780. Fax: 225-231-3788. p. 942

Mercer, Beth, Dir, Ocoee River Regional Library, 718 George St NW, Athens, TN, 37303-2214. Tel: 423-745-5194. Fax: 423-745-8086. p. 2224

Mercer, Beth Allen, Regional Mgr, Tennessee State Library & Archives, 403 Seventh Ave N, Nashville, TN, 37243-0312. Tel: 800-624-1982. Fax: 615-532-2472, 615-741-6471. p. 2259

Mercer, Florence S, Dir, Libr Serv, Anna Jaques Hospital, 25 Highland Ave, Newburyport, MA, 01950. Tel: 978-463-1000, Ext 2480. Fax: 978-463-1286. p. 1109

Mercer, Gloritha, Dir, United States Army, Bldg 2109, Joint Base Lewis McChord, WA, 98433-9500. Tel: 253-966-1312. Fax: 253-967-3922. p. 2518

Mercer, Harriet, Librn, Law Society of Newfoundland Library, 196-198 Water St, St. John's, NL, A1C 1A9, CANADA. Tel: 709-753-7770. Fax: 709-753-0054. p. 2772

Mercer, Holly, Dir, East Central Arkansas Regional Library, 410 E Merriman Ave, Wynne, AR, 72396. Tel: 870-238-3850. Fax: 870-238-5434. p. 117

Mercer, Holly, Digital Serv & Scholarly Communications, Texas A&M University Libraries, 5000 TAMU, College Station, TX, 77843-5000. Tel: 979-862-2534. Fax: 979-845-6238. p. 2298

Mercer, Jeff, Librn, South Shore Public Libraries, 15442 Hwy Three, Hebbville, NS, B4V 6X6, CANADA. Tel: 902-543-2548. p. 2783

Mercer, Jimmy, Support Serv, Santa Fe Community College, 3000 NW 83rd St, Bldg Y-100, Gainesville, FL, 32606. Tel: 352-395-5406, Fax: 352-395-5102. p. 449

Mercer, John, Acq, Coll Develop Librn, Pfeiffer University, 48380 US Hwy 52 N, Misenheimer, NC, 28109. Tel: 704-463-3352. Fax: 704-463-3356. p. 1809

Mercer, Kent, Ref Serv, Olympic College, 1600 Chester Ave, Bremerton, WA, 98337. Tel: 360-475-7250. Fax: 360-475-7261. p. 2510

Mercer, Lynn, Mgr, Human Res, Muskingum County Library System, 220 N Fifth St, Zanesville, OH, 43701-3587. Tel: 740-453-0391, Ext 133. Fax: 740-455-6937. p. 1953

Mercer, Susan, Govt Doc, Per, Norfolk Public Library, 235 E Plume St, Norfolk, VA, 23510-1706. Tel: 757-664-7325. Fax: 757-441-5863. p. 2481

Merchant, Arthur, Tech Serv Librn, Clarence Dillon Public Library, 2336 Lamington Rd, Bedminster, NJ, 07921. Tel: 908-234-2325. Fax: 908-781-9402. p. 1471

Merchant, Diane, Dir, Marianne Beck Memorial Library, 112 W Central Ave, Howey in the Hills, FL, 34737. Tel: 352-324-0254. p. 451

Merchant, Tom, Libr Serv Mgr, Lake County Library System, 2401 Woodlea Rd, Tavares, FL, 32778. Tel: 352-253-6168. Fax: 352-253-6184. p. 499

Mercieca, Charles, Pres, International Association of Educators for World Peace, 2013 Orba Dr NE, Huntsville, AL, 35811-2414. Tel: 256-534-5501. Fax: 256-536-1018. p. 21

Mercier, Esther, Librn, Bibliotheque Municipale de Saint-Jacques De Leeds, 425 Principale St, Saint-Jacques de Leeds, QC, G0N 1J0, CANADA. Tel: 418-424-3181. Fax: 418-424-0126. p. 2911

Mercier, Jeanette, Circ Supvr, Richland Public Library, 955 Northgate Dr, Richland, WA, 99352-3539. Tel: 509-942-7456. Fax: 509-942-7442. p. 2526

Mercier, Mellanie, Automation Syst Coordr, Waukesha County Federated Library System, 831 N Grand Ave, Ste 220, Waukesha, WI, 53186-4822. Tel: 262-896-8080. Fax: 262-896-8086. p. 2645

Mercier, Pierre, Doc Delivery, Hopital Hotel-Dieu du CHUM, 3840 rue St-Urbain, Montreal, QC, H2W 1T8, CANADA. Tel: 514-890-8000, Ext 14355. p. 2896

Merckle, Cory, Circ, C W Clark Memorial Library, 160 N Main St, Oriskany Falls, NY, 13425. Tel: 315-821-7850. Fax: 315-821-7850. p. 1712

Mercuri, Joan, Dir, Frank Lloyd Wright Preservation Trust, 931 Chicago Ave, Oak Park, IL, 60302. Tel: 708-848-1976. Fax: 708-848-1248. p. 684

Meredith, Don, Librn, Harding University Graduate School of Religion, 1000 Cherry Rd, Memphis, TN, 38117. Tel: 901-761-1354. p. 2248

Meredith, Eva, Asst Librn, Bucklin Public Library, 201 N Main, Bucklin, KS, 67834. Tel: 620-826-3223. Fax: 620-826-3794. p. 858

Meredith, Gretchen, In Charge, Rochester Post-Bulletin Library, 18 First Ave SE, Rochester, MN, 55904-6118. Tel: 507-285-7737. Fax: 507-285-7772. p. 1272

Meredith, Julia, Dir, Independence Township Public Library, 6495 Clarkston Rd, Clarkston, MI, 48346-1501. Tel: 248-625-2212. Fax: 248-625-8852. p. 1163

Meredith, Larry, Dir, Gunnison Public Library of the Gunnison County Library District, 307 N Wisconsin, Gunnison, CO, 81230-2627. Tel: 970-641-3485. Fax: 970-641-4653. p. 312

Meredith, Mairi B, Tech Serv Librn, The University of Findlay, 1000 N Main St, Findlay, OH, 45840-3695. Tel: 419-434-4630. p. 1899

Meredith, Mary, Dir, Stephenville Public Library, 174 N Columbia, Stephenville, TX, 76401-3492. Tel: 254-918-1240. Fax: 254-918-1208. p. 2389

Meredith, Sharon, Tech Serv, Neosho/Newton County Library, 201 W Spring St, Neosho, MO, 64850. Tel: 417-451-4231. Fax: 417-451-6438. p. 1347

Merewether, Jamie, Librn, Crow Canyon Archaeological Center, 23390 County Rd K, Cortez, CO, 81321. Tel: 970-565-8975. Fax: 970-565-4859. p. 297

Merguerian, Gayane Karen, User Engagement & Assessment Librn, Northeastern University Libraries, Snell Library, 360 Huntington Ave, Boston, MA, 02115. Tel: 617-373-2747. p. 1065

Merick, Lori, Librn, Dolores County Public Library, Rico Public, Two N Commercial St, Rico, CO, 81332. Tel: 970-967-2103. Fax: 970-967-2103. p. 304

Mericle, Nancy, Dir, Delphos Public Library, 309 W Second St, Delphos, OH, 45833-1695. Tel: 419-695-4015. Fax: 419-695-4025. p. 1896

Meridith, Pamela, Dir, Libr Serv, Williams Baptist College, 91 W Fulbright, Walnut Ridge, AR, 72476. Tel: 870-759-4139. p. 116

Meridja, Saida, Chef de Section, Bibliothèques de Montrèal, L'Octogone, 1080, avenue Dollard, Montreal, QC, H8N 2T9, CANADA. Tel: 514-367-4384. Fax: 514-367-6604. p. 2890

Meringolo, Joe, Mgr, Libr Serv, Dickstein Shapiro LLP, Research Services, 1825 Eye St NW, Washington, DC, 20006. Tel: 202-420-4999. Fax: 202-420-2201. p. 398

Merka, Ludmila, In Charge, Value Line Publishing, Inc, 220 E 42nd St, 6th Flr, New York, NY, 10017. Tel: 212-907-1500. Fax: 212-818-9747. p. 1702

Merkel, Linda, ILL, Schaumburg Township District Library, 130 S Roselle Rd, Schaumburg, IL, 60193. Tel: 847-923-3341. Fax: 847-923-3342. p. 701

Merkey, Bonnie, Asst Librn, Ulysses Library Association, 401 N Main St, Ulysses, PA, 16948. Tel: 814-848-7226. Fax: 814-848-7226. p. 2147

Merkle, Janis, Asst Dir, New Glarus Public Library, 319 Second St, New Glarus, WI, 53574. Tel: 608-527-2003. Fax: 608-527-5126. p. 2625

Merkley, Cari, Access Serv, Mount Royal University Library, 4825 Mount Royal Gate SW, Calgary, AB, T3E 6K6, CANADA. Tel: 403-440-5068. Fax: 403-440-6758. p. 2692

Merkley, Wendy, Assoc Univ Librn, Info Syst & Tech Serv, University of Lethbridge Library, 4401 University Dr, Lethbridge, AB, T1K 3M4, CANADA. Tel: 403-329-2261, 403-329-2263. Fax: 403-329-2234. p. 2710

Merkowitz, Mary Jo, Dir, Dinsmore & Shohl Library, 255 E Fifth St, 1900 Chemed Ctr, Cincinnati, OH, 45202-3172. Tel: 513-977-8486. Fax: 513-977-8141. p. 1870

Merkt, Emily, Outreach Serv Librn, Medical College of Wisconsin Libraries, Health Research Ctr, 3rd Flr, 8701 Watertown Plank Rd, Milwaukee, WI, 53226-0509. Tel: 414-955-8427. Fax: 414-955-6532. p. 2619

Merlo, Loretta, Circ, Cornell University Library, The Samuel J Wood Library & The C V Starr Biomedical Information Center, 1300 York Ave, C115, Box 67, New York, NY, 10065-4896. Tel: 212-746-6050. Fax: 212-746-6494. p. 1642

Merly, Lisa, Circ Supvr, Louisville Public Library, 951 Spruce St, Louisville, CO, 80027. Tel: 303-335-4849. Fax: 303-335-4833. p. 317

Merolli, Barbara, Sci Librn, College of the Holy Cross, O'Callahan Science Library, Swords Bldg, Worcester, MA, 01610. Tel: 508-793-2643. p. 1144

Merrbach, Patricia, Br Mgr, Allegany County Library System, Frostburg Public, 65 E Main St, Frostburg, MD, 21532. Tel: 301-687-0790. Fax: 301-687-0791. p. 1026

Merrell, Rebecca, Per, Curtis Laws Wilson Library, 400 W 14th St, Rolla, MO, 65409-0060. Tel: 573-341-4013. Fax: 573-341-4233. p. 1351

Merriam, Nancy, Librn, New England Wireless & Steam Museum Inc Library, 1300 Frenchtown Rd, East Greenwich, RI, 02818. Tel: 401-885-0545. Fax: 401-884-0683. p. 2166

Merriam, Robert W, Dir, New England Wireless & Steam Museum Inc Library, 1300 Frenchtown Rd, East Greenwich, RI, 02818. Tel: 401-885-0545. Fax: 401-884-0683. p. 2166

Merrick, Andrea, Br Mgr, Mercer County Library System, Hopewell Branch, 245 Pennington-Titusville Rd, Pennington, NJ, 08534. Tel: 609-737-2610. Fax: 609-737-7419. p. 1494

Merrick, Deborha, Br Mgr, Thompson-Nicola Regional District Library System, Merritt Branch, 1691 Garcia St, Merritt, BC, V1K 1B8, CANADA. Tel: 250-378-4737. p. 2729

Merrick, Joanne, Head Librn, Carstairs Public Library, 1402 Scarlett Ranch Blvd, Carstairs, AB, T0M 0N0, CANADA. Tel: 403-337-3943. Fax: 403-337-3943. p. 2694

Merrick, Regina, Dir, Crittenden County Public Library, 204 W Carlisle St, Marion, KY, 42064-1727. Tel: 270-965-3354. Fax: 270-965-3354. p. 928

Merricks, Betsy, ILL, High Point University, 833 Montlieu Ave, High Point, NC, 27262-4221. Tel: 336-841-9170. Fax: 336-841-5123. p. 1802

Merrifield, Mark D, Dir, Nicolet Federated Library System, 515 Pine St, 3rd Flr, Green Bay, WI, 54301-5194. Tel: 920-448-4410. Fax: 920-448-4420. p. 2595

Merrill, Betsy, Librn, Northeastern Vermont Regional Hospital, 1315 Hospital Dr, Saint Johnsbury, VT, 05819. Tel: 802-748-7501. Fax: 802-748-7527. p. 2435

Merrill, Carol, Librn, Ghost Ranch Conference Center Library, HC 77, Box 11, Abiquiu, NM, 87510-9601. Tel: 505-685-4333. Fax: 505-685-4519. p. 1547

Merrill, Julie, Coll Develop, Regis College Library, 235 Wellesley St, Weston, MA, 02493. Tel: 781-768-7300. Fax: 781-768-7323. p. 1139

Merrill, Linda, Librn, Taylor Library, 49 E Derry Rd, East Derry, NH, 03041. Tel: 603-432-7186. Fax: 603-432-0985. p. 1446

Merrill, Treadwell, Ref Librn, Chicago State University, 9501 S Martin Luther King Jr Dr, LIB 440, Chicago, IL, 60628-1598. Tel: 773-995-2550. Fax: 773-995-3772. p. 610

Merrill, Yolanda, Humanities Librn, Washington & Lee University, University Library, 204 W Washington St, Lexington, VA, 24450-2116. Tel: 540-458-8662. Fax: 540-458-8964. p. 2475

Merriman, Dru-Ann, Pub Serv Librn/Interim Dir of Libr Serv, Texarkana College, 2500 N Robison Rd, Texarkana, TX, 75599. Tel: 903-832-5565, Ext 3215. Fax: 903-831-7429. p. 2391

Merriman, Kevin, Head, Coll Mgt, University Libraries, University of Memphis, 126 Ned R McWherter Library, Memphis, TN, 38152-3250. Tel: 901-678-8234. p. 2252

Merring, Lynn Connor, Librn, Stradling, Yocca, Carlson & Rauth, 660 Newport Ctr, Ste 1600, Newport Beach, CA, 92660. Tel: 949-725-4023. Fax: 949-725-4100. p. 194

Merritt, Chad, Asst Mgr, Cameron Parish Library, Johnson Bayou, 4586 Gulf Beach Hwy, Cameron, LA, 70631. Tel: 337-569-2892. Fax: 337-569-2905. p. 946

Merritt, Dawn Easton, Assoc Librn, Ref, Huron University College Library, 1349 Western Rd, London, ON, N6G 1H3, CANADA. Tel: 519-438-7224, Ext 209. Fax: 519-438-3938. p. 2817

Merritt, Dee Anne, Dir, Helen B Hoffman Plantation Library, 501 N Fig Tree Lane, Plantation, FL, 33317. Tel: 954-797-2140. Fax: 954-797-2767. p. 484

Merritt, Jackie, Br Mgr, Jackson District Library, Parma Branch, 102 Church St, Parma, MI, 49269. Tel: 517-531-4908. Fax: 517-531-5085. p. 1196

Merritt, Jackie, Br Mgr, Jackson District Library, Springport Branch, 110 Mechanic St, Springport, MI, 49284. Tel: 517-857-3833. Fax: 517-857-3833. p. 1196

Merritt, Jill, Br Librn, Washington State Library, Washington Correction Center Shelton Branch, PO Box 900, MS WS-01, Shelton, WA, 98584-0974. Tel: 360-432-1509. p. 2545

Merritt, Jill, Libr Assoc, Washington State Library, Washington State Penitentiary Branch Library-Main Institution, 1313 N 13th Ave, Walla Walla, WA, 99362-8817. Tel: 509-525-3610, 509-526-6408. Fax: 509-526-6469. p. 2545

Merritt, John, Tech Dir, Southern Baptist Theological Seminary, 2825 Lexington Rd, Louisville, KY, 40280-0294. Tel: 502-897-4127. p. 925

Merritt, Kelly, Mgr, Libr Media Serv, Ithaca College Library, 953 Danby Rd, Ithaca, NY, 14850-7060. Tel: 607-274-3880. Fax: 607-274-1539. p. 1643

Merritt, Maria, Admin Coordr, Medical University of South Carolina Library, 171 Ashley Ave, Ste 300, Charleston, SC, 29425-0001. Tel: 843-792-9211. Fax: 843-792-7947. p. 2184

Merritt, Roger, Circ, Motlow State Community College Libraries, Ledford Mill Rd, Tullahoma, TN, 37388. Fax: 931-393-1516. p. 2267

Merry, Allen, Head of Libr, Free Library of Philadelphia, Whitman Branch, 200 Snyder Ave, Philadelphia, PA, 19148-2620. Tel: 215-685-1754. Fax: 215-685-1753. p. 2109

Merry, Elizabeth, ILL, Antigo Public Library, 617 Clermont St, Antigo, WI, 54409-1894. Tel: 715-623-3724. Fax: 715-627-2317. p. 2578

Merry, Lois, Ref & Instruction Librn, Keene State College, 229 Main St, Keene, NH, 03435-3201. Tel: 603-358-2738. Fax: 603-358-2745. p. 1453

Mersch, Toni, Asst Librn, Monterey-Tippecanoe Township Public Library, 6260 E Main St, Monterey, IN, 46960. Tel: 574-542-2171. Fax: 574-542-2171. p. 765

Merseal, Christine, Genealogy Serv, Jefferson County Library, Northwest, 5680 State Rd PP, High Ridge, MO, 63049. Tel: 636-677-8186. Fax: 636-677-8243. p. 1331

Mershon, Peggy, Dep Dir, Laurel County Public Library District, 120 College Park Dr, London, KY, 40741. Tel: 606-864-5759. Fax: 606-862-8057. p. 922

Mersing-White, Pauletta, Circ, Elkins-Randolph County Public Library, 416 Davis Ave, Elkins, WV, 26241. Tel: 304-637-0287. Fax: 304-637-0288. p. 2558

Mersky, Roy M, Dir, University of Texas Libraries, Jamail Center for Legal Research, University of Texas School of Law, 727 E Dean Keeton St, Austin, TX, 78705-3224. Tel: 512-471-7726. Fax: 512-471-0243. p. 2284

Merten, Karen, Acq, Cincinnati State Technical & Community College, 3520 Central Pkwy, Cincinnati, OH, 45223-2612. Tel: 513-569-1607. Fax: 513-559-1527. p. 1869

Mertens, John F, Dir, Ozark Regional Library, 402 N Main St, Ironton, MO, 63650. Tel: 573-546-2615. Fax: 573-546-7225. p. 1333

Mertens, John F, Librn, Ozark Regional Library, Ironton Branch, 402 N Main St, Ironton, MO, 63650. Tel: 573-546-2615. p. 1333

Mertens, Marlys, Br Supvr, Scenic Regional Library of Franklin, Gasconade & Warren Counties, Warren County, 912 S Hwy 47, Warrenton, MO, 63383-2600. Tel: 636-456-3321. p. 1370

Mertz, Doris Ann, Dir, Custer County Library, 447 Crook St, Ste 4, Custer, SD, 57730-1509. Tel: 605-673-4803. Fax: 605-673-2385. p. 2211

Mertz, Paula, Dir, Socorro Public Library, 401 Park St, Socorro, NM, 87801-4544. Tel: 505-835-1114. Fax: 505-835-1182. p. 1565

Merwin, Edwin O, Jr, Assoc Prof, Librn, University of South Carolina, Peden McLeod Library, Walterboro, 807 Hampton St, Walterboro, SC, 29488. Tel: 843-549-6314. Fax: 843-549-4345. p. 2190

Merwin, Mark, Librn, Lockheed Martin Space Systems Co, 12257 S Wadsworth Blvd, Littleton, CO, 80125. Tel: 303-977-5532. Fax: 303-977-6412. p. 317

Merz, Bernice, Asst Librn, Warren Public Library, 15 Sackett Hill Rd, Warren, CT, 06754. Tel: 860-868-2195. p. 374

Merz, Lawrie, Pub Serv Coordr, Messiah College, One College Ave, Ste 3002, Mechanicsburg, PA, 17055. Tel: 717-691-6006, Ext 3880. Fax: 717-691-2356. p. 2087

Merz, Lynne, Tech Serv Supvr, Woodbridge Public Library, George Frederick Plaza, Woodbridge, NJ, 07095. Tel: 732-634-4450. p. 1545

Merz, Mildred, Info Literacy & Ref Librn, Oakland University Library, 2200 N Squirrel Rd, Rochester, MI, 48309-4402. Tel: 248-370-2457. Fax: 248-370-2474. p. 1221

Merz, Sylvia, Librn, Leland Township Public Library, 203 E Cedar, Leland, MI, 49654. Tel: 231-256-9152. Fax: 231-256-8847. p. 1203

Mesa, Tina, Dean, Learning Res, Palo Alto College, 1400 W Villaret St, San Antonio, TX, 78224-2499. Tel: 210-486-3901. Fax: 210-486-9184. p. 2380

Mescall, Beth, Dir, Davis, Graham & Stubbs LLP, 1550 17th St, Ste 500, Denver, CO, 80202. Tel: 303-892-7451. Fax: 303-893-1379. p. 300

Meshkov, Norma, Librn, Reform Congregation Keneseth Israel, 8339 Old York Rd, Elkins Park, PA, 19027. Tel: 215-887-8700. Fax: 215-887-1070. p. 2054

Mesina, Irene, Head Librn, Honolulu Community College Library, 874 Dillingham Blvd, Honolulu, HI, 96817-4598. Tel: 808-845-9199. Fax: 808-845-3618. p. 564

Mesmer, Renate, Head, Conserv, Folger Shakespeare Library, 201 E Capitol St SE, Washington, DC, 20003-1094. Tel: 202-544-4600. Fax: 202-544-4623. p. 400

Mesojednik, Suzi, ILL, Prairie Skies Public Library District, 125 W Editor St, Ashland, IL, 62612. Tel: 217-476-3417. Fax: 217-476-8076. p. 590

Messana, Valerie, Libr Dir, Mexico Free Public Library, 134 Main St, Mexico, ME, 04257. Tel: 207-364-3281. Fax: 207-364-5685. p. 992

Messely, Maryse, Dir, College Merici - Bibliotheque, 755 Grande Allée Ouest, Quebec, QC, G1S 1C1, CANADA. Tel: 418-683-2104, Ext 2213. Fax: 418-682-8938. p. 2904

Messenger, Cynthia, Dir, Hot Springs Public Library, 2005 Library Dr, Hot Springs, SD, 57747-2767. Tel: 605-745-3151. Fax: 605-745-6813. p. 2213

Messer, Joanne, Adminr, Alvan Bolster Ricker Memorial Library, 1211 Maine St, Poland, ME, 04274. Tel: 207-998-4390. Fax: 207-998-2120. p. 996

Messersmith, Diana, ILL, Pub Serv, Ref, Des Moines Area Community College Library, 2006 S Ankeny Blvd, Ankeny, IA, 50023. Tel: 515-964-6573. Fax: 515-965-7126. p. 793

Messick, Deborah, Bus Mgr, Fiscal Officer, Bristol Public Library, 1855 Greenville Rd, Bristolville, OH, 44402-9700. Tel: 330-889-3651. Fax: 330-889-9794. p. 1861

Messick, Diane, Circ, Garden Valley District Library, 342 Village Circle, Garden Valley, ID, 83622-8040. Tel: 208-462-3317. Fax: 208-462-3758. p. 574

Messick, Sandra, Dir, Woodruff Memorial Library, 522 Colorado Ave, La Junta, CO, 81050-2308. Tel: 719-384-4612. Fax: 719-383-2514. p. 314

Messick, Steve L, Dir, Iredell County Public Library, 201 N Tradd St, Statesville, NC, 28677. Tel: 704-878-3092. Fax: 704-878-5449. p. 1825

Messier, Cheryl, Asst Librn, Swanton Public Library, One First St, Swanton, VT, 05488. Tel: 802-868-7656. p. 2437

Messina, Elizabeth, Librn, Stewart B Lang Memorial Library, 2577 E Main St, Cato, NY, 13033. Tel: 315-626-2101. Fax: 315-626-3249. p. 1603

Messineo, Hedy, Librn, Chenango Memorial Hospital, 179 N Broad St, Norwich, NY, 13815. Tel: 607-337-4111, 607-337-4577. Fax: 607-334-2024. p. 1708

Messinger, Faye, Librn, Monterey History & Art Association, 155 Van Buren St, Monterey, CA, 93940. Tel: 831-372-1838. Fax: 831-624-9579. p. 189

Messinger, Luke, Exec Dir, Dawes Arboretum Library, 7770 Jacksontown Rd SE, Newark, OH, 43056-9380. Tel: 740-323-2355. Fax: 740-323-4058. p. 1921

Messler, Karen, Asst Librn, Des Moines Area Community College, 1125 Hancock Dr, Boone, IA, 50036-5326. Tel: 515-433-5041. Fax: 515-433-5044. p. 797

Messling, Deb, Ad, Phillipsburg Free Public Library, 200 Frost Ave, Phillipsburg, NJ, 08865. Tel: 908-454-3712. Fax: 908-859-4667. p. 1520

Messman-Mandicott, Lea, Dr, Assoc Dir, Frostburg State University, One Stadium Dr, Frostburg, MD, 21532. Tel: 301-687-4890. Fax: 301-687-7069. p. 1029

Messner, Tom, Dir of Libr Serv, Barry University, 11300 NE Second Ave, Miami, FL, 33161. Tel: 305-899-4062. Fax: 305-899-4792. p. 464

Messner, Tom, Dir, Northeastern State University, Broken Arrow Campus Library, Bldg E Library, 3100 E New Orleans St, Broken Arrow, OK, 74014. Tel: 918-449-6459. Fax: 918-449-6454. p. 1979

Messner, Wanda, Dir, Gaylord Public Library, 428 Main Ave, Gaylord, MN, 55334. Tel: 507-237-2280. Fax: 507-237-4177. p. 1252

Mestas, Marie, Dean, Libr & Learning Support Serv, San Bernardino Valley College Library, 701 S Mount Vernon Ave, San Bernardino, CA, 92410. Tel: 909-384-8576. p. 229

Mester, Ellen, County Librn, Madera County Library, 121 North G St, Madera, CA, 93637-3592. Tel: 559-675-7871. Fax: 559-675-7998. p. 181

Mestey, Jose, Fac Mgr, Park Ridge Public Library, 20 S Prospect, Park Ridge, IL, 60068-4188. Tel: 847-720-3210. Fax: 847-825-0001. p. 688

Mestre, Lori, Dr, Head of Libr, University of Illinois Library at Urbana-Champaign, Undergraduate, 1402 W Gregory Dr, Urbana, IL, 61801. Tel: 217-244-4171. Fax: 217-265-0936. p. 713

Meszaros, Rosemary, Govt Doc, Western Kentucky University Libraries, Helm-Cravens Library Complex, 1906 College Heights Blvd, No 11067, Bowling Green, KY, 42101-1067. Tel: 270-745-2905. Fax: 270-745-6422. p. 908

Metallo, Charmaine, Librn, United States Courts Library, US Courthouse, Rm 3625, 101 W Lombard St, Baltimore, MD, 21201. Tel: 410-962-0997. Fax: 410-962-9313. p. 1018

Metcalf, Craig, Dir, Stephen Leacock Memorial Library Museum, Old Brewery Bay, Orillia, ON, L3V 6K5, CANADA. Tel: 705-329-1908. Fax: 705-326-5578. p. 2826

Metcalf, Karen, Ch, Weare Public Library, Ten Paige Memorial Lane, Weare, NH, 03281. Tel: 603-529-2044. Fax: 603-529-7341. p. 1467

Metcalf, Mary, Librn, Greensboro Free Library, 53 Wilson St, Greensboro, VT, 05841. Tel: 802-533-2531. p. 2425

Metcalf, Patricia, Dir, Jerome Public Library, 100 First Ave E, Jerome, ID, 83338-2302. Tel: 208-324-5427. Fax: 208-324-6426. p. 576

Metcalf, Steve, Syst Mgr, Evergreen State College, Library Bldg, Rm 2300, 2700 Evergreen Pkwy NW, Olympia, WA, 98505-0002. Tel: 360-867-6260. Fax: 360-867-6790. p. 2522

Metcalf, Steven, Syst Adminr, Cooperating Libraries in Olympia, The Evergreen State College Library, L2300, Olympia, WA, 98505. Tel: 360-867-6260. Fax: 360-867-6790. p. 2957

Metcalf, Susan, Ref Librn/Soc Sci Liaison, Western Carolina University, 176 Central Dr, Cullowhee, NC, 28723. Tel: 828-227-3416. Fax: 828-227-7015. p. 1786

Metcalfe, William, Web Coordr, Chowan University, One University Pl, Murfreesboro, NC, 27855. Tel: 252-398-1194. Fax: 252-398-1301. p. 1811

Metheny, Heather, Dir, Chippewa Library Information Center, 2811 Darlington Rd, Beaver Falls, PA, 15010. Tel: 724-847-1450. Fax: 724-847-1449. p. 2031

Metoyer, Angela, Asst Ch, Natchitoches Parish Library, 450 Second St, Natchitoches, LA, 71457-4649. Tel: 318-357-3280. Fax: 318-357-7073. p. 958

Metoyer, Cheryl, Assoc Prof, University of Washington, Mary Gates Hall, Ste 370, Campus Box 352840, Seattle, WA, 98195-2840. Tel: 206-685-9937. Fax: 206-616-3152. p. 2976

Metro, Julie, Bibliog Instr, Pub Serv, Southern Arkansas University, 100 E University, Magnolia, AR, 71753-5000. Tel: 870-235-4174. Fax: 870-235-5018. p. 108

Metsack, Susan, Dir, Acworth Silsby Library, Five Lynn Hill Rd, Acworth, NH, 03601. Tel: 603-835-2150. p. 1437

Metter, Ellen, Coll Develop & Res Librn, Auraria Library, 1100 Lawrence St, Denver, CO, 80204-2095. Tel: 303-556-4516. Fax: 303-556-3528. p. 298

Metterville, Brenda, Dir, Merrick Public Library, Two Lincoln St, Brookfield, MA, 01506. Tel: 508-867-6339. Fax: 508-867-2981. p. 1071

Mettier, Donna, Sr Librn, Marin County Free Library, Novato Branch, 1720 Novato Blvd, Novato, CA, 94947. Tel: 415-898-4623. p. 257

Mettle, Doreen, Mgr, New Jersey Institute of Technology, University Heights, Newark, NJ, 07102-1982. Tel: 973-596-3206. Fax: 973-643-5601. p. 1511

Mettler, Linda, Librn, Hagerstown Jefferson Township Public Library, Ten W College St, Hagerstown, IN, 47346-1295. Tel: 765-489-5632. Fax: 765-489-5808. p. 747

Metts, Pamela Thomas, Dir, John L Street Library, 244 Main St, Cadiz, KY, 42211-9153. Tel: 270-522-6301. Fax: 270-522-1107. p. 909

Metz, Edward J, Head Librn, US Fire Administration, 16825 S Seton Ave, Emmitsburg, MD, 21727. Tel: 301-447-1030. Fax: 301-447-3217. p. 1028

Metz, John D, Dir, Archives, Rec & Coll, The Library of Virginia, 800 E Broad St, Richmond, VA, 23219-8000. Tel: 804-692-3607. Fax: 804-692-2277. p. 2489

Metz, Rosetta, Commun Outreach Coordr/Librn, Morton Grove Public Library, 6140 Lincoln Ave, Morton Grove, IL, 60053-2989. Tel: 847-929-5120. Fax: 847-965-7903. p. 676

Metz, Terrance J, Univ Librn, Washington & Lee University, University Library, 204 W Washington St, Lexington, VA, 24450-2116. Tel: 540-458-8640. Fax: 540-458-8964. p. 2475

Metzel, Nina, Librn, Collier County Public Library, Estates, 1266 Golden Gate Blvd W, Naples, FL, 34120. Tel: 239-455-8088. Fax: 239-455-8113. p. 471

Metzger, Elizabeth, Dir, Canastota Public Library, 102 W Center St, Canastota, NY, 13032. Tel: 315-697-7030. Fax: 315-697-8653. p. 1601

Metzger, Joy, Asst Dir, Whittemore Public Library, 405 Fourth St, Whittemore, IA, 50598. Tel: 515-884-2680. Fax: 515-884-2323. p. 853

Metzger, Melanie, Asst Dir, Ch, Lone Star College System, CyFair Library, 9191 Barker Cypress Rd, Cypress, TX, 77433. Tel: 281-290-3214, 281-290-3219. p. 2340

Metzger, Rebecca, Ref, Lafayette College, 710 Sullivan Rd, Easton, PA, 18042-1797. Tel: 610-330-5154. Fax: 610-252-0370. p. 2052

Metzger, Steve, Librn, Northern Lights College, 9471 Beattie Dr, Hudson's Hope, BC, V0C 1V0, CANADA. Tel: 250-783-5711. Fax: 250-783-5788. p. 2729

Metzler, Douglas, Assoc Prof, University of Pittsburgh, 135 N Bellefield Ave, Pittsburgh, PA, 15260. Tel: 412-624-5230. Fax: 412-624-5231. p. 2973

Metzler, Janet, Br Head, Los Angeles Public Library System, Chatsworth Branch, 21052 Devonshire St, Chatsworth, CA, 91311. Tel: 818-341-4276. Fax: 818-341-7905. p. 173

Metzler, Laura, Bus Librn, Cecil County Public Library, 301 Newark Ave, Elkton, MD, 21921-5441. Tel: 410-996-5600. Fax: 410-996-5604. p. 1027

Metzmeier, Kurt X, Prof, University of Louisville Libraries, Brandeis School of Law Library, 2301 S Third St, Louisville, KY, 40208. Tel: 502-852-6082. Fax: 502-852-8906. p. 926

Metzner, Nancy, Div Mgr, Reader Serv, High Point Public Library, 901 N Main St, High Point, NC, 27262. Tel: 336-883-3650. Fax: 336-883-3636. p. 1802

Meulemans, Connie, ILL, Todd Wehr Library, St Norbert College, 301 Third St, De Pere, WI, 54115. Tel: 920-403-3280. Fax: 920-403-4064. p. 2587

Meulemans, Yvonne N, Behav Sci & Nursing Librn, California State University, 333 S Twin Oaks Valley Rd, San Marcos, CA, 92096-0001. Tel: 760-750-4340. Fax: 760-750-3287. p. 254

Meunier, Judith, Tech Serv Librn, Plaistow Public Library, 85 Main St, Plaistow, NH, 03865. Tel: 603-382-6011. Fax: 603-382-0202. p. 1462

Meunier, Suzanne, Tech Serv, Harvard Library, Gordon McKay Library, School of Engineering & Applied Sciences, Pierce Hall, 29 Oxford St, Cambridge, MA, 02138. Tel: 617-495-2836. Fax: 617-495-9837. p. 1076

Meunier, William J, Coordr, Pub Serv, North Shore Community College Library, One Ferncroft Rd, Danvers, MA, 01923-4093. Tel: 978-739-5540. Fax: 978-739-5500. p. 1083

Meurer, Henrietta, Librn, West Public Library, 209 W Tokio Rd, West, TX, 76691. Tel: 254-826-3070. Fax: 254-826-4473. p. 2399

Meurer, Tamsie, Libr Dir, Charlestown-Clark County Public Library, 51 Clark Rd, Charlestown, IN, 47111. Tel: 812-256-3337. Fax: 812-256-3890. p. 731

Mevis, Susan Mary, Dir, Beaver Dam Community Library, 311 N Spring St, Beaver Dam, WI, 53916-2043. Tel: 920-887-4631, Ext 12. Fax: 920-887-4633. p. 2581

Mewborn, Ruth, Librn, Metropolitan Transition Center Library, 954 Forrest St, Baltimore, MD, 21202. Tel: 410-230-1472. Fax: 410-230-1472. p. 1016

Mewborn, Ruth, Librn, Patuxent Institution Library, 7555 Old Waterloo Rd, Jessup, MD, 20794. Tel: 410-799-3400, Ext 4226. Fax: 410-799-1137. p. 1033

Mewbourn, Andrea Y, Admin Serv, Orange Beach Public Library, 26267 Canal Rd, Orange Beach, AL, 36561-3917. Tel: 251-981-2923. Fax: 251-981-2920. p. 33

Meyer, Angela, Librn, Dodge Center Public Library, 13 First Ave NW, Dodge Center, MN, 55927. Tel: 507-374-2275. Fax: 507-374-2694. p. 1247

Meyer, Barbara, Asst Dir, Montgomery Free Library, 133 Clinton St, Montgomery, NY, 12549. Tel: 845-457-5616. Fax: 845-457-5616. p. 1662

Meyer, Beverly, Coordr, Educ Res Ctr, Chicago State University, 9501 S Martin Luther King Jr Dr, LIB 440, Chicago, IL, 60628-1598. Tel: 773-995-2587. Fax: 773-995-3772. p. 610

Meyer, Brad, Ref & Instruction Librn, Blinn College Library, 800 Blinn Blvd, Brenham, TX, 77833. Tel: 979-830-4250. Fax: 979-830-4222. p. 2291

Meyer, Callista M, Pub Serv, Elizabethtown Community & Technical College Library, 600 College Street Rd, Elizabethtown, KY, 42701. Tel: 270-706-8443. Fax: 270-769-1618. p. 912

Meyer, Carol, Br Mgr, Putnam County District Library, Fort Jennings Branch, 655 N Water St, Fort Jennings, OH, 45844-0218. Tel: 419-286-2351. p. 1926

Meyer, Christine, Libr Mgr, Department of Veterans Affairs, 325 New Castle Rd, Butler, PA, 16001. Tel: 724-285-2246. Fax: 724-477-5073. p. 2040

Meyer, Connie, Dir, Dwight Foster Public Library, 102 E Milwaukee Ave, Fort Atkinson, WI, 53538-2049. Tel: 920-563-7790. Fax: 920-563-7774. p. 2592

Meyer, Constance, Br Supvr, Cat, Ch, Crawford County Library System, 201 Plum St, Grayling, MI, 49738. Tel: 989-348-4067. Fax: 989-348-9294. p. 1186

Meyer, Constance A, Head of Libr, University of Maryland Libraries, Michelle Smith Performing Arts Library, 2511 Clarice Smith Performing Arts Library, College Park, MD, 20742-1630. Tel: 301-314-0535. Fax: 301-314-7170. p. 1025

Meyer, Currie, Mgr, Poudre River Public Library District, Council Tree Library, 2733 Council Tree Ave, Ste 200, Fort Collins, CO, 80525. Tel: 970-221-6740. p. 308

Meyer, Daphne, Asst Librn, Bethel-Tulpehocken Public Library, 8601 Lancaster Ave, Bethel, PA, 19507. Tel: 717-933-4060. Fax: 717-933-9655. p. 2033

Meyer, Darla, Asst Dir, Benedictine College Library, 1020 N Second St, Atchison, KS, 66002-1499. Tel: 913-360-7516. Fax: 913-360-7622. p. 856

Meyer, Deborah, Dir of Libr, Shorter College, 315 Shorter Ave, Rome, GA, 30165. Tel: 706-291-2121, Ext 7296. Fax: 706-236-1512. p. 549

Meyer, Deborah, Ch, Clyde Public Library, 222 W Buckeye St, Clyde, OH, 43410. Tel: 419-547-7174. Fax: 419-547-0480. p. 1882

Meyer, Elizabeth, Visual Res Librn, University of Cincinnati Libraries, Design, Architecture Art & Planning, 5480 Aronoff Ctr, Cincinnati, OH, 45221. Tel: 513-556-0279. Fax: 513-556-3006. p. 1874

Meyer, Florence, Head, Circ, Woodbury Public Library, 33 Delaware St, Woodbury, NJ, 08096. Tel: 856-845-2611. p. 1545

Meyer, Gail, Dir, Indian Temple Mound Museum Library, 139 Miracle Strip Pkwy SE, Fort Walton Beach, FL, 32548. Tel: 850-833-9595. Fax: 850-833-9675. p. 447

Meyer, Gerlene, Ch, YA Serv, Dordt College, 498 Fourth Ave NE, Sioux Center, IA, 51250. Tel: 712-722-6045. Fax: 712-722-1198. p. 843

Meyer, Harry, Evening Mgr, Hillsboro Public Library, 214 School St, Hillsboro, IL, 62049-1547. Tel: 217-532-3055. Fax: 217-532-6813. p. 656

Meyer, Holley C, Asst Dir/Ch, Bacon Free Library, 58 Eliot St, Natick, MA, 01760. Tel: 508-653-6730. p. 1107

Meyer, Holly, Br Mgr, Whitman County Rural Library District, Colton Branch, 760 Broadway Ave, Colton, WA, 99113. Tel: 509-229-3887. p. 2513

Meyer, Jane G, Librn, Ventura County Law Library, 800 S Victoria Ave, Ventura, CA, 93009-2020. Tel: 805-642-8982. Fax: 805-642-7177. p. 279

Meyer, Janet F, Librn, South Carolina Supreme Court Library, 1231 Gervais St, Columbia, SC, 29201-3206. Tel: 803-734-1080. Fax: 803-734-0519. p. 2189

Meyer, Jerry, Asst Dir, Davis County Library, 38 S 100 East, Farmington, UT, 84025. Tel: 801-451-2322. Fax: 801-451-9561. p. 2405

Meyer, Joanne A, Librn, Morton Memorial Library & Community House, 82 Kelly St, Rhinecliff, NY, 12574. Tel: 845-876-2903. Fax: 845-876-1584. p. 1727

Meyer, Julie, Instrul Design/Web Serv, Pennsylvania State University, 30 E Swedesford Rd, Malvern, PA, 19355. Tel: 610-648-3358. Fax: 610-725-5223. p. 2083

Meyer, Karla, In Charge, Perry-Lecompton Community Library, PO Box 700, Perry, KS, 66043. Tel: 785-597-5031. p. 889

Meyer, Kathy, Adminr, Bonaparte Public Library, 602 Second St, Bonaparte, IA, 52620. Tel: 319-592-3677. Fax: 319-592-3577. p. 797

Meyer, Kenton, Dr, Asst Dir, Milton L Rock Resource Center, 1720 Locust St, Philadelphia, PA, 19103. Tel: 215-893-5265. Fax: 215-717-3170. p. 2115

Meyer, Kristin, Br Mgr, Kent District Library, Englehardt Branch, 200 N Monroe St, Lowell, MI, 49331. Tel: 616-784-2007. Fax: 616-647-3924. p. 1165

Meyer, Kurt, Res, University of Maryland, Baltimore, Thurgood Marshall Law Library, 501 W Fayette St, Baltimore, MD, 21201-1768. Tel: 410-706-0735. Fax: 410-706-8354. p. 1019

Meyer, Lars, Sr Leader, Content Div, Emory University Libraries, Robert W Woodruff Library, 540 Asbury Circle, Atlanta, GA, 30322-2870. Tel: 404-727-2437. Fax: 404-727-1132. p. 514

Meyer, Laura, Ch, Evergreen Park Public Library, 9400 S Troy Ave, Evergreen Park, IL, 60805-2383. Tel: 708-422-8522. Fax: 708-422-8665. p. 645

Meyer, Lawrence R, Dir, San Bernardino County Law Library, 8401 N Haven Ave, Rancho Cucamonga, CA, 91730-3893. Tel: 909-885-3020, Ext 214. p. 213

Meyer, Lawrence R, Dir, Law Library for San Bernardino County, 402 North D St, San Bernardino, CA, 92401. Tel: 909-885-3020. p. 227

Meyer, Leslie, Dir, Libr & Archives, Petroleum Museum Library & Hall of Fame, 1500 Interstate 20 W, Midland, TX, 79701. Tel: 432-683-4403. Fax: 432-683-4509. p. 2363

Meyer, Linda, Libr Coordr, Per/Databases, Acq, San Jose City College Library, 2100 Moorpark Ave, San Jose, CA, 95128-2799. Tel: 408-298-2181, Ext 3944. Fax: 408-293-4728. p. 250

Meyer, Linda, Youth Serv Coordr, Liverpool Public Library, 310 Tulip St, Liverpool, NY, 13088-4997. Tel: 315-457-0310. Fax: 315-453-7867. p. 1653

Meyer, Linda S, Head, Circ, Sam Houston State University, 1830 Bobby K Marks Dr, Huntsville, TX, 77340. Tel: 936-294-3551. Fax: 936-294-3780. p. 2345

Meyer, Lindsey, Ref Serv, Edison Township Free Public Library, 340 Plainfield Ave, Edison, NJ, 08817. Tel: 732-287-2298. Fax: 732-819-9134. p. 1483

Meyer, Lynette, In Charge, First Presbyterian Church Library, 1340 Murchison St, El Paso, TX, 79902. Tel: 915-533-7551. Fax: 915-534-7167. p. 2317

Meyer, Marian L, Dir, Bellevue Public Library, 106 N Third St, Bellevue, IA, 52031. Tel: 563-872-4991. Fax: 563-872-4094. p. 796

Meyer, Mona, Govt Doc & Tech Serv Librn, University of Southern Indiana, 8600 University Blvd, Evansville, IN, 47712. Tel: 812-464-1920. Fax: 812-465-1693. p. 739

Meyer, Odessa, Ch, South Sioux City Public Library, 2121 Dakota Ave, South Sioux City, NE, 68776-3031. Tel: 402-494-7545. Fax: 402-494-7546. p. 1419

Meyer, Patti, Dir, Larsen Family Public Library, 7401 W Main St, Webster, WI, 54893-8209. Tel: 715-866-7697. Fax: 715-866-8842. p. 2647

Meyer, Paula, Circ, University of Manitoba Libraries, Donald W Craik Engineering Library, 351 Engineering Bldg, Winnipeg, MB, R3T 2N2, CANADA. Tel: 204-474-6360. Fax: 204-474-7520. p. 2758

Meyer, Renee, Adjunct Cat Librn, University of Miami, 1311 Miller Dr, Coral Gables, FL, 33146. Tel: 305-284-2251. Fax: 305-284-3554. p. 434

Meyer, Rick, Dir, Robey Memorial Library, 401 First Ave NW, Waukon, IA, 52172-1803. Tel: 563-568-4424. Fax: 563-568-5026. p. 850

Meyer, Ruth, Br Mgr, Williams County Public Library, West Unity Branch, 109 S High St, West Unity, OH, 43570. Tel: 419-924-5237. Fax: 419-924-5237. p. 1862

Meyer, Stan, Dr, Dir, Operations, Memphis Botanic Garden Foundation, Inc, 750 Cherry Rd, Memphis, TN, 38117. Tel: 901-576-4100. Fax: 901-682-1561. p. 2249

Meyer, Steve, Dir, Ray County Library, 215 E Lexington, Richmond, MO, 64085-1834. Tel: 816-776-5102, 816-776-5104. Fax: 816-776-5103. p. 1350

Meyer, Terry, Librn, Estrella Mountain Community College Library, 3000 N Dysart Rd, Avondale, AZ, 85323-1000. Tel: 623-935-8191. Fax: 623-935-8060. p. 57

Meyer, Theresa, Librn, Bethlehem Lutheran Church Library, 1145 N Fifth Ave, Saint Charles, IL, 60174-1230. Tel: 630-584-2199. Fax: 630-584-2674. p. 699

Meyer, Valerie R, Clinical Libr Spec, Drusch Professional Library, 11830 Westline Industrial Dr, Ste 106, Saint Louis, MO, 63146. Tel: 314-991-6213. Fax: 314-991-6284. p. 1354

Meyer-Ryerson, Sarah, Dir, Waverly Public Library, 1500 W Bremer Ave, Waverly, IA, 50677-2836. Tel: 319-352-1223. Fax: 319-352-0872. p. 851

Meyeraan, Joyce, Librn, Wellsburg Public Library, 515 N Adams, Wellsburg, IA, 50680. Tel: 641-869-5234. Fax: 641-869-5234. p. 851

Meyers, Angela, Ad, Matheson Memorial Library, 101 N Wisconsin, Elkhorn, WI, 53121. Tel: 262-723-2678. Fax: 262-723-2870. p. 2590

Meyers, Anita, Acq, City College of the City University of New York, North Academic Ctr, 160 Convent Ave, New York, NY, 10031. Tel: 212-650-7620. Fax: 212-650-7618. p. 1672

Meyers, Arthur S, Dir, Russell Library, 123 Broad St, Middletown, CT, 06457. Tel: 860-347-2528, Ext 141. p. 352

Meyers, Donna, Br Mgr, Cuyahoga County Public Library, Strongsville Branch, 18700 Westwood Dr, Strongsville, OH, 44136-3431. Tel: 440-238-5530. Fax: 440-572-8685. p. 1928

Meyers, Duane, Syst Adminr, SIAST-Saskatchewan Institute of Applied Science & Technology, 4500 Wascana Pkwy, Regina, SK, S4P 3S7, CANADA. Tel: 306-775-7403. Fax: 306-798-0560. p. 2924

Meyers, Eric, Asst Prof, University of British Columbia, The Irving K Barber Centre, 1961 E Mall, Ste 470, Vancouver, BC, V6T 1Z1, CANADA. Tel: 604-822-2404. Fax: 604-822-6006. p. 2977

Meyers, Heather, Asst Librn, Chinook Regional Library, Herbert Branch, 517 Herbert Ave, Herbert, SK, S0H 2A0, CANADA. Tel: 306-784-2484. p. 2928

Meyers, Louise, Dir, Stayton Public Library, 515 N First Ave, Stayton, OR, 97383-1703. Tel: 503-769-3313. Fax: 503-769-3218. p. 2020

Meyers, Mary, Librn, Savanna Public Library District, 326 Third St, Savanna, IL, 61074. Tel: 815-273-3714. Fax: 815-273-4634. p. 700

Meyers, Mary L, Circ Serv Supvr, Butt-Holdsworth Memorial Library, 505 Water St, Kerrville, TX, 78028. Tel: 830-257-8422. Fax: 830-792-5552. p. 2349

Meyers, Sally, Ch, Tom Green County Library System, 113 W Beauregard, San Angelo, TX, 76903. Tel: 915-655-7321. Fax: 915-659-4027. p. 2378

Meyerson, Valerie, Dir, Charlevoix Public Library, 220 W Clinton St, Charlevoix, MI, 49720. Tel: 231-237-7360. Fax: 231-547-0678. p. 1162

Meyman, Irina, Dir, Lutheran Medical Center, 150 55th St, Brooklyn, NY, 11220. Tel: 718-630-7200. Fax: 718-630-8918. p. 1593

Meyman, Irina, Pres, Brooklyn-Queens-Staten Island-Manhattan-Bronx Health Sciences Librarians, 150 55th St, Brooklyn, NY, 11220. Tel: 718-630-7200. Fax: 718-630-8918. p. 2949

Meyn, Marie, Dir, M Alice Frose Library, PO Box 150, Fawcett, AB, T0G 0Y0, CANADA. Tel: 780-954-3827. Fax: 780-954-3934. p. 2704

Meyor, Tom, Adult Serv, Lansdale Public Library, 301 Vine St, Lansdale, PA, 19446-3690. Tel: 215-855-3228. Fax: 215-855-6440. p. 2078

Meza, James, Dr, Dean, University of New Orleans, College of Education, Rm 342, New Orleans, LA, 70148. Tel: 504-280-6251, 504-280-6528. Fax: 504-280-1120. p. 2967

Mezynski, Andy, Bibliog Instruction/Ref, Los Angeles City College Library, 855 N Vermont Ave, Los Angeles, CA, 90029. Tel: 323-953-4000, Ext 2403. Fax: 323-953-4013. p. 171

Mi, Deborah, Br Mgr, Killgore Memorial Library, Britain Memorial, PO Box 180, Sunray, TX, 79086-0180. Tel: 806-948-5501. Fax: 806-948-5369. p. 2314

Mi, Jia, Electronic Res, The College of New Jersey Library, 2000 Pennington Rd, Ewing, NJ, 08628-0718. Tel: 609-771-2311, 609-771-2332. Fax: 609-637-5177. p. 1484

Mi, Misa, Librn, Children's Hospital of Michigan, Medical Library, 3901 Beaubien Blvd, 1st Flr, Detroit, MI, 48201. Tel: 313-745-0252, 313-745-5322. p. 1169

Mi, Misa, Med Librn, University of Toledo, Health Science Campus, Mail Stop 1061, 3000 Arlington Ave, Toledo, OH, 43614-5805. Tel: 419-383-4223. Fax: 419-383-6146. p. 1940

Miah, Abdul, Dr, Dir, J Sargeant Reynolds Community College Library, Parham Campus-Library & Information Services, 1651 E Parham Rd, Richmond, VA, 23228. Tel: 804-523-5323. Fax: 804-371-3086. p. 2489

Miah, Abdul J, Dr, Dir, J Sargeant Reynolds Community College Library, Downtown Campus-Library & Information Services, 700 E Jackson St, 2nd Flr, Richmond, VA, 23219-1543. Tel: 804-523-5211. Fax: 804-786-6200. p. 2488

Miah, Farid, Dr, Mgr, Libr Serv, Sunnybrook Health Sciences Centre, Dr R Ian MacDonald Library, 2075 Bayview Ave, Toronto, ON, M4N 3M5, CANADA. Tel: 416-480-6100, Ext 4562. Fax: 416-480-6848. p. 2859

Miah, Md Farid, Mgr, Libr Serv, Sunnybrook Health Sciences Centre - Library Services, 2075 Bayview Ave, Rm EG-29, Toronto, ON, M4N 3M5, CANADA. Tel: 416-480-6100, Ext 2560. Fax: 416-480-6848. p. 2859

Miano, Whitney, Mgr, Ser, Drury University, 900 N Benton Ave, Springfield, MO, 65802. Tel: 417-873-7340. Fax: 417-873-7432. p. 1366

Miao, Hong, Res & Instruction Librn, Marywood University Library, 2300 Adams Ave, Scranton, PA, 18509-1598. Tel: 570-961-4707. Fax: 570-961-4769. p. 2137

Mias, Jim, Libr Tech, Department of Veterans Affairs, 421 N Main St, Leeds, MA, 01053-9714. Tel: 413-584-4040, Ext 2432. Fax: 413-582-3039. p. 1098

Mibbs, Ellen R, Asst Dir, Youth Serv Librn, Havana Public Library District, 201 W Adams St, Havana, IL, 62644-1321. Tel: 309-543-4701. Fax: 309-543-2715. p. 654

Micalizzi, Paula, Ch, Free Public Library of Bayonne, 697 Avenue C, Bayonne, NJ, 07002. Tel: 201-858-6975. Fax: 201-437-6928. p. 1470

Micallef, Vince, Dir, Youngtown Public Library, 12035 Clubhouse Sq, Youngtown, AZ, 85363. Tel: 623-974-3401. p. 90

Micchelli, Thomas, AV, Cooper Union for Advancement of Science & Art Library, Seven E Seventh St, New York, NY, 10003. Tel: 212-353-4186. Fax: 212-353-4017. p. 1676

Miceli, Susan, Mgr, Ch Serv, Erie County Public Library, 160 E Front St, Erie, PA, 16507. Tel: 814-451-6928. Fax: 814-451-6907. p. 2055

Michael, Barbara, Med Librn, Department of Veterans Affairs, 800 Hospital Dr, Columbia, MO, 65201. Tel: 573-814-6000, Ext 52704. Fax: 573-814-6516. p. 1324

Michael, Bret, Adult Serv, Pinellas Park Public Library, 7770 52nd St, Pinellas Park, FL, 33781-3498. Tel: 727-541-0959. Fax: 727-541-0818. p. 483

Michael, Catherine, ILL, Louisiana State University Libraries, 295 Middleton Library, Baton Rouge, LA, 70803. Tel: 225-578-8560. Fax: 225-578-6992. p. 943

Michael, Cheryl, Dir, Wor-Wic Community College, 32000 Campus Dr, Salisbury, MD, 21804. Tel: 410-334-2883, 410-334-2884. Fax: 410-334-2956. p. 1041

Michael, Joshua, Libr Dir, Baptist Bible College, 730 E Kearney St, Springfield, MO, 65803. Tel: 417-268-6075. Fax: 417-268-6690. p. 1365

Michael, Joshua, Libr Dir, Baptist Bible College & Seminary, 538 Venard Rd, Clarks Summit, PA, 18411-1250. Tel: 570-585-9281. Fax: 570-585-9244. p. 2045

Michael, Karin, Youth Serv Librn, Chapel Hill Public Library, 100 Library Dr, Chapel Hill, NC, 27514. Tel: 919-969-2031. Fax: 919-968-2838. p. 1780

Michael, Nancy F, Mgr, Eli Lilly & Co, Lilly Corporate Ctr, Drop Code 0737, Indianapolis, IN, 46285. Tel: 317-651-2259. Fax: 317-276-4418. p. 751

Michael, Roxanne, Asst Dir, Akron Public Library, 350 Reed St, Akron, IA, 51001. Tel: 712-568-2601. Fax: 712-568-2601. p. 791

Michael, Sara, Mgr, Fairfield Bay Library, Inc, 369 Dave Creek Pkwy, Fairfield Bay, AR, 72088. Tel: 501-884-4930. p. 99

Michaelis, Kathryn Schneider, Dir, Wisconsin Library Services, 728 State St, Rm 464, Madison, WI, 53706-1494. Tel: 608-263-2773. Fax: 608-262-6067. p. 2958

Michaelis, Patricia, Dr, Div Head, Kansas State Historical Society, 6425 SW Sixth Ave, Topeka, KS, 66615-1099. Tel: 785-272-8681. Fax: 785-272-8682. p. 896

Michaels, Beverly, Br Mgr, Tredyffrin Public Library, Paoli Branch, 18 Darby Rd, Paoli, PA, 19301-1416. Tel: 610-296-7996. Fax: 610-296-9708. p. 2143

Michaels, Debbie, Pres, Elgin Public Library, PO Box 153, Elgin, ND, 58533-0153. Tel: 701-584-2181. p. 1840

Michaels, Jolene E, Dir, Mackinaw Area Public Library, 528 W Central Ave, Mackinaw City, MI, 49701-9681. Tel: 231-436-5451. Fax: 231-436-7344. p. 1205

Michaels, Lynne, Assoc Mgr, Washington County Library, Oakdale Branch, 1010 Heron Ave N, Oakdale, MN, 55128. Tel: 651-730-0504. Fax: 651-275-8591. p. 1290

Michaels, Lynne, Assoc Mgr, Washington County Library, Rosalie E Wahl Branch, 3479 Lake Elmo Ave N, Lake Elmo, MN, 55042. Tel: 651-777-7415. Fax: 651-777-7416. p. 1290

Michaels, Steve, Electronic Serv, Syst Librn, Western Theological Seminary, 101 E 13th St, Holland, MI, 49423. Tel: 616-392-8555, Ext 187. p. 1191

Michaelsen, Karen, Librn, Seattle Central Community College, 1701 Broadway, 2BE2101, Seattle, WA, 98122. Tel: 206-587-4098. Fax: 206-587-3878. p. 2530

Michalak, Rusty, Ref Librn, Goldey Beacom College, 4701 Limestone Rd, Wilmington, DE, 19808. Tel: 303-225-6227. Fax: 302-998-6189. p. 388

Michalak, Sarah, Univ Librn & Assoc Provost for Libr, University of North Carolina at Chapel Hill, Davis Library, 208 Raleigh St, Campus Box 3900, Chapel Hill, NC, 27514-8890. p. 1780

Michalek, Gabriella V, Head, Archives, Carnegie Mellon University, Hunt Library, 4909 Frew St, Pittsburgh, PA, 15213-3890. Tel: 412-268-2446. Fax: 412-268-2793. p. 2123

Michalek, Laura A, Mgr, Libr Syst & Support Serv, Waubonsee Community College, State Rte 47 at Waubonsee Dr, Sugar Grove, IL, 60554. Tel: 630-466-2405. Fax: 630-466-7799. p. 708

Michalowska, Magdalena, Chef de Div, Bibliothèques de Montrèal, Haut-Anjou, 7070, rue Jarry Est, Montreal, QC, H1J 1G4, CANADA. Tel: 514-493-8262. Fax: 514-493-8273. p. 2889

Michalowska, Magdalena, Chef de Div, Bibliothèques de Montrèal, Jean-Corbeil, 7500, avenue Goncourt, Montreal, QC, H1K 3X9, CANADA. Tel: 514-493-8262. Fax: 514-493-8273. p. 2890

Michalowskij, Patricia, Circuit Librn, United States Court of Appeals for the District of Columbia, US Court House, 333 Constitution Ave NW, Rm 5518, Washington, DC, 20001. Tel: 202-216-7400. p. 418

Michals, Mary, AV, Illinois Historic Preservation Agency, 112 N Sixth St, Springfield, IL, 62701. Tel: 217-785-7955. Fax: 217-785-6250. p. 705

Michalski, Chris, Dir, Irving Public Library, 801 W Irving Blvd, Irving, TX, 75015. Tel: 972-721-2606. Fax: 972-721-2463. p. 2346

Michalski, Sally, Tech Serv, Monroeville Public Library, 4000 Gateway Campus Blvd, Monroeville, PA, 15146-3381. Tel: 412-372-0500. Fax: 412-372-1168. p. 2091

Michaud, Alain, Head Librn, Bibliotheque Municipale de La Tuque, 575 rue St-Eugene, La Tuque, QC, G9X 2T5, CANADA. Tel: 819-523-3100. Fax: 819-523-4487. p. 2885

Michaud, Christine, Head, Ch, Durham Public Library, Seven Maple Ave, Durham, CT, 06422. Tel: 860-349-9544. Fax: 860-349-1897. p. 337

Michaud, Donatien, ILL, Hopital Maisonneuve-Rosemont, 5415 boul de l'Assomption, Montreal, QC, H1T 2M4, CANADA. Tel: 514-252-3462. Fax: 514-252-3574. p. 2896

Michaud, John, Ref & Instrul Serv Librn, Thomas M Cooley Law School Libraries, 300 S Capitol Ave, Lansing, MI, 48901. Tel: 517-371-5140, Ext 3308. Fax: 517-334-5715, 517-334-5717. p. 1202

Michaud, Lisa, Ch, Seabrook Library, 25 Liberty Lane, Seabrook, NH, 03874-4506. Tel: 603-474-2044. Fax: 603-474-1835. p. 1465

Michaud, Monique, In Charge, Planetary Association for Clean Energy Inc, 100 Bronson Ave, Ste 1001, Ottawa, ON, K1R 6G8, CANADA. Tel: 613-236-6265. Fax: 613-235-5876. p. 2832

Michaud, Susie, Libr Tech, West Nipissing Public Library, 225 rue Holditch, Ste 107, Sturgeon Falls, ON, P2B 1T1, CANADA. Tel: 705-753-2620. Fax: 705-753-2131. p. 2845

Michaud, Susie, Librn, West Nipissing Public Library, Cache Bay Branch, 55 Cache St, Cache Bay, ON, P0H 1G0, CANADA. Tel: 705-753-9393. Fax: 705-753-9393. p. 2846

Michaud, Sylvie, Chief Librn, Bibliotheque Municipale Francoise-Bedard, 67 rue du Rocher, Riviere-du-Loup, QC, G5R 1J8, CANADA. Tel: 418-867-6669. Fax: 418-862-3478. p. 2907

Michaud-Oystryk, Nicole, Head Librn, University of Manitoba Libraries, Elizabeth Dafoe Library, 25 Chancellor's Circle, Winnipeg, MB, R3T 2N2, CANADA. Tel: 204-474-9211. Fax: 204-474-7577. p. 2758

Michel, Lauren, ILL, Ref Serv, Cazenovia College, Lincklaen St, Cazenovia, NY, 13035. Tel: 315-655-7132. Fax: 315-655-8675. p. 1603

Michel, Margaret, Ref Serv, Liberty Municipal Library, 1710 Sam Houston Ave, Liberty, TX, 77575-4741. Tel: 936-336-8901. Fax: 936-336-2414. p. 2355

Michel, Peter, Dir, Spec Coll, University of Nevada, Las Vegas Libraries, 4505 Maryland Pkwy, Box 457001, Las Vegas, NV, 89154-7001. Tel: 702-895-2243. Fax: 702-895-2287. p. 1430

Michel, Stephanie, Ref, University of Portland, 5000 N Willamette Blvd, Portland, OR, 97203-5743. Tel: 503-943-7111. Fax: 503-943-7491. p. 2015

Michele-Ann, Goguen, Libr Mgr, Albert-Westmorland-Kent Regional Library, Bibliotheque Publique de Cap-Pele, 2638, Chemin Acadie, Cap-Pele, NB, E4N 1E3, CANADA. Tel: 506-577-2090. Fax: 506-577-2094. p. 2765

Michelin, Rosemary, Librn, Marquette Regional History Center, 145 W Spring St, Marquette, MI, 49855. Tel: 906-226-3571. Fax: 906-226-0919. p. 1206

Michelini, Angelina, Mgr, Network Serv, The Library Network, 41365 Vincenti Ct, Novi, MI, 48375. Tel: 248-536-3100. Fax: 248-536-3099. p. 2946

Michelle, Martin, Libr Serv Coordr, Burlington County College Library, 601 Pemberton-Browns Mills Rd, Pemberton, NJ, 08068. Fax: 609-894-4189. p. 1519

Michelman, Norma, Dir, Librn, Nancy Fawcett Memorial Library, 724 Oberfelder St, Lodgepole, NE, 69149-0318. Tel: 308-483-5714. p. 1407

Michels, David, Pub Serv Librn, Dalhousie University, Sir James Dunn Law Library, Weldon Law Bldg, 6061 University Ave, Halifax, NS, B3H 4H9, CANADA. Tel: 902-494-2640. Fax: 902-494-6669. p. 2780

Michels, Fredrick, Dean, Lake Superior State University, 906 Ryan Ave, Sault Sainte Marie, MI, 49783. Tel: 906-635-2815. Fax: 906-635-2193. p. 1226

Michels, Harold, VPres, Copper Development Association, 260 Madison Ave, 16th Flr, New York, NY, 10016. Tel: 212-251-7200. Fax: 212-251-7234. p. 1676

Michelson, Alan R, Head Librn, University of Washington Libraries, Architecture-Urban Planning, 334 Gould Hall, Box 355730, Seattle, WA, 98195-5730. Tel: 206-543-7091. p. 2533

Michelson, Craig, Curator, American Society of Military History Library, 1918 N Rosemead Blvd, South El Monte, CA, 91733. Tel: 626-442-1776. Fax: 626-443-1776. p. 270

Michetti, Giovanni, Asst Prof, University of British Columbia, The Irving K Barber Centre, 1961 E Mall, Ste 470, Vancouver, BC, V6T 1Z1, CANADA. Tel: 604-822-2404. Fax: 604-822-6006. p. 2977

Michie, Sharon, Br Mgr, Wayne County Public Library, Steele Memorial, 111 N Chestnut St, Mount Olive, NC, 28365. Tel: 919-705-1891. p. 1795

Michki, Kevin, Music Librn, State University of New York at Fredonia, 280 Central Ave, Fredonia, NY, 14063. Tel: 716-673-3117. Fax: 716-673-3185. p. 1624

Michlich, Sandra, Sr Librn, Neptune Public Library, 25 Neptune Blvd, Neptune, NJ, 07753-1125. Tel: 732-775-8241. Fax: 732-774-1132. p. 1507

Michniewicz, Daniel, Librn, Pub Serv, Seneca College of Applied Arts & Technology, Newnham Campus (Main), 1750 Finch Ave E, North York, ON, M2J 2X5, CANADA. Tel: 416-491-5050, Ext 22761. Fax: 416-492-7184. p. 2813

Micho, Lori, Dir, Johnson & Wales University, College of Business, 7150 Montview Blvd, Denver, CO, 80220. Tel: 303-256-9353. Fax: 303-256-9459. p. 302

Michrowski, Andrew, Dr, Pres, Planetary Association for Clean Energy Inc, 100 Bronson Ave, Ste 1001, Ottawa, ON, K1R 6G8, CANADA. Tel: 613-236-6265. Fax: 613-235-5876. p. 2832

Mick, Dawn, Head, Circ/ILL, Curtis Laws Wilson Library, 400 W 14th St, Rolla, MO, 65409-0060. Tel: 573-341-7832. Fax: 573-341-4233. p. 1351

Mickalow, Susan, Dep Chief Librn, Milton Public Library, 1010 Main St E, Milton, ON, L9T 6H7, CANADA. Tel: 905-875-2665 Ext 3260. Fax: 905-875-4324. p. 2822

Mickells, Greg, Dir, Madison Public Library, 201 W Mifflin St, Madison, WI, 53703. Tel: 608-266-6300. Fax: 608-266-4338. p. 2606

Mickie, Kenneth, Media Spec, Shenandoah University, 1460 University Dr, Winchester, VA, 22601. Tel: 540-665-5424. Fax: 540-665-4609. p. 2503

Mickles, Marsha, Librn, Bishop State Community College, Baker-Gaines Central Campus, 1365 Dr Martin Luther King Jr Ave, Mobile, AL, 36603-5362. Tel: 251-405-4424. Fax: 251-405-4423. p. 25

Mickowski, Barbara, YA Serv, Oceanside Library, 30 Davison Ave, Oceanside, NY, 11572-2299. Tel: 516-766-2360. Fax: 516-766-1895. p. 1709

Micucci, Kathleen, AV, Bryant Library, Two Paper Mill Rd, Roslyn, NY, 11576-2193. Tel: 516-621-2240. Fax: 516-621-7211. p. 1735

Middelton, Cheryl, Librn, Buncombe County Public Libraries, South Asheville Oakley, 749 Fairview Rd, Asheville, NC, 28803. Tel: 828-250-4754. p. 1774

Middleton, Ann, Dir, Bossier Parish Central Library, Bossier Parish Historical Center, 2206 Beckett St, Bossier City, LA, 71111. Tel: 318-746-7717. p. 946

Middleton, Anne G, Head, Tech Serv, United States Court of Appeals, 600 Camp St, Rm 106, New Orleans, LA, 70130. Tel: 504-310-7797. Fax: 504-310-7578. p. 964

Middleton, Cheryl, Assoc Univ Librn, Learning & Engagement, Oregon State University Libraries, 121 The Valley Library, Corvallis, OR, 97331-4501. Tel: 541-737-4667. Fax: 541-737-3453. p. 1994

Middleton, Dawn, Ch, Loveland Public Library, 300 N Adams Ave, Loveland, CO, 80537-5754. Tel: 970-962-2587. Fax: 970-962-2905. p. 317

Middleton, Gay G, Adminr, Woman's Hospital, Airline at Goodwood Blvd, 9050 Airline Hwy, Baton Rouge, LA, 70815. Tel: 225-924-8462. Fax: 225-924-8467. p. 945

Middleton, Glenda, Br Mgr, Kent District Library, Sand Lake/Nelson Township Branch, 88 Eighth St, Sand Lake, MI, 49343-9737. Tel: 616-784-2007. p. 1166

Middleton, Jeffrey, Dir, Central Arizona College, 8470 N Overfield Rd, Coolidge, AZ, 85128. Tel: 520-494-5286. Fax: 520-494-5284. p. 60

Middleton, Joseph, Head, Ref, Stonehill College, 320 Washington St, Easton, MA, 02357-4015. Tel: 508-565-1433. Fax: 508-565-1424. p. 1086

Middleton, Kathy, Sr Commun Libr Mgr, Contra Costa County Library, 1750 Oak Park Blvd, Pleasant Hill, CA, 94523-4497. Tel: 925-646-6434. Fax: 925-646-6461. p. 208

Middleton, Pam, Head, Pub Serv, Multnomah University, 8435 NE Glisan St, Portland, OR, 97220-5898. Tel: 503-251-5322. Fax: 503-254-1268. p. 2012

Middleton, Pat, Mgr, Robeson County Public Library, Gilbert Patterson Memorial, 210 N Florence St, Maxton, NC, 28364. Tel: 910-844-3884. Fax: 910-844-3884. p. 1808

Middleton, Sally, Head Librn, Bevill State Community College, 2631 Temple Ave N, Fayette, AL, 35555. Tel: 205-932-3221, Ext 5141. Fax: 205-932-8821. p. 17

Middleton, Sharla Ann, Librn, Abernathy Public Library, 811 Ave D, Abernathy, TX, 79311-3400. Tel: 806-298-4138. Fax: 806-298-2968. p. 2271

Middleton, Stephanie, Dir, Libr & Media Serv, Columbus Technical College Library, 928 Manchester Expressway, Columbus, GA, 31904-6577. Tel: 706-649-1852. Fax: 706-649-1885. p. 526

Midgette Spence, Juanita, Dr, Dir, Libr Serv, Elizabeth City State University, 1704 Weeksville Rd, Elizabeth City, NC, 27909. Tel: 252-335-3585. Fax: 252-335-3446. p. 1790

Midgley, Jennifer, Coordr, Pub Serv, Urbana University, 579 College Way, Urbana, OH, 43078-2091. Tel: 937-484-1435. Fax: 937-653-8551. p. 1942

Midkiff, Stephanie, Ref Librn, University of Oregon Libraries, John E Jaqua Law Library, William W Knight Law Ctr, 2nd Flr, 1515 Agate St, Eugene, OR, 97403-1221. Tel: 541-346-1661. Fax: 541-346-1669. p. 1997

Midlan, Phoebe, Dir, Hampton B Allen Library, 120 S Greene St, Wadesboro, NC, 28170. Tel: 704-694-5177. Fax: 704-694-5178. p. 1827

Midyette, David, Health Sci Librn, University of South Dakota, 414 E Clark St, Vermillion, SD, 57069. Tel: 605-677-5371. Fax: 605-677-6834. p. 2220

Mielczarek, Mary, Asst Dir, Oldham County Public Library, 308 Yager Ave, La Grange, KY, 40031. Tel: 502-222-9713. Fax: 502-222-1141. p. 919

Miele, Jennifer, Mgr, Pub Serv, Groton Public Library, 52 Newtown Rd, Groton, CT, 06340. Tel: 860-441-6750. Fax: 860-448-0363. p. 342

Mielish, Julia, Ref/Instruction Librn, Wake Technical Community College, Northern Wake Library, 6600 Louisburg Rd, Bldg B, Rm 239, Raleigh, NC, 27616. Tel: 919-532-5550. p. 1818

Mielke, Nancy, Bus/Educ/Humanities Librn, Tennessee Technological University, 1100 N Peachtree Ave, Cookeville, TN, 38505. Tel: 931-372-3326. Fax: 931-372-6112. p. 2231

Mielke, Ruth Anne, Youth Serv Mgr, Bartlett Public Library District, 800 S Bartlett Rd, Bartlett, IL, 60103. Tel: 630-837-2855. Fax: 630-837-2669. p. 592

Mieller, Carla, Librn, Morrin Municipal Library, 113 Main St, Morrin, AB, T0J 2B0, CANADA. Tel: 403-772-3922. Fax: 403-772-3922. p. 2712

Miemis, Michele, Circ, Levittown Public Library, One Bluegrass Lane, Levittown, NY, 11756-1292. Tel: 516-731-5728. Fax: 516-735-3168. p. 1652

Mier, Guadalupe J, Dir, Bellevue Public Library, 1003 Lincoln Rd, Bellevue, NE, 68005-3199. Tel: 402-293-3157. Fax: 402-293-3163. p. 1393

Mier, Karen, Dir, Plattsmouth Public Library, 401 Ave A, Plattsmouth, NE, 68048. Tel: 402-296-4154. Fax: 402-296-4712. p. 1417

Miesse, Catherine, Asst Dean, Tech Serv & Outreach, Loyola University Chicago Libraries, 1032 W Sheridan Rd, Chicago, IL, 60660. Tel: 773-508-2674. Fax: 773-508-2993. p. 617

Migaldi, Karen, Asst Dir, Crystal Lake Public Library, 126 Paddock St, Crystal Lake, IL, 60014. Tel: 815-459-1687. Fax: 815-459-9581. p. 632

Miglinas, Skirmante, Dir, Archives, Lithuanian Research & Studies Center, Inc, 5600 S Claremont Ave, Chicago, IL, 60636-1039. Tel: 773-434-4545. Fax: 773-434-9363. p. 617

Mignault, John, Syst Librn, The LuEsther T Mertz Library, The New York Botanical Garden, 2900 Southern Blvd, Bronx, NY, 10458-5126. Tel: 718-817-8536. Fax: 718-817-8956. p. 1587

Miguel-Stearns, Teresa, Assoc Librn, Admin, Yale University Library, Lillian Goldman Library Yale Law School, 127 Wall St, New Haven, CT, 06511. Tel: 203-432-8023. Fax: 203-432-2112. p. 358

Mihalcik, Trudy, Br Mgr, Calvert County Public Library, Southern Branch, 20 Appeal Lane, Lusby, MD, 20657. Tel: 410-326-5289. Fax: 410-326-8370. p. 1036

Mihalega, Anna, Ref & Instrul Serv, Instr Coordr, Point Park University Library, 414 Wood St, Pittsburgh, PA, 15222. Tel: 412-392-3166. Fax: 412-392-3168. p. 2127

Mihalic, Sue A, Asst Dir, Youth Serv Coordr, Saint Clair Shores Public Library, 22500 11 Mile Rd, Saint Clair Shores, MI, 48081-1399. Tel: 586-771-9020. Fax: 586-771-8935. p. 1224

Mihaly, David, Curator, Huntington Library, 1151 Oxford Rd, San Marino, CA, 91108. Tel: 626-405-3494. Fax: 626-449-5720. p. 255

Mihovich, Mary, Ref Librn, Loutit District Library, 407 Columbus Ave, Grand Haven, MI, 49417. Tel: 616-842-5560, Ext 221. Fax: 616-847-0570. p. 1183

Mijares, Mary, Br Serv Mgr, Sacramento Public Library, 828 I St, Sacramento, CA, 95814. Tel: 916-264-2770. Fax: 916-264-2755. p. 224

Mika, Stephanie, Bus Mgr, Sidney Public Library, 1112 12th Ave, Sidney, NE, 69162. Tel: 308-254-3110. Fax: 308-254-3710. p. 1419

Mikash, Debbi, Mgr, Pikes Peak Library District, Briargate Library, 9475 Briar Village Point, Colorado Springs, CO, 80920. Tel: 719-260-6882. p. 296

Mikeluk, Donna, Librn, Schreiber Township Public Library, 314 Scotia St, Schreiber, ON, P0T 2S0, CANADA. Tel: 807-824-2477. Fax: 807-824-2996. p. 2841

Mikesell, Brian, Dir, Bard College at Simon's Rock, 84 Alford Rd, Great Barrington, MA, 01230. Tel: 413-528-7274. Fax: 413-528-7380. p. 1092

Mikesell, Brian, Assoc Univ Librn, Syst, Saint John's University Library, 8000 Utopia Pkwy, Queens, NY, 11439. Tel: 718-990-6735. Fax: 718-380-0353. p. 1725

Mikesell, Sharon, Br Mgr, Laramie County Library System, Burns Branch, 112 Main St, Burns, WY, 82053. Tel: 307-547-2249. Fax: 307-547-9253. p. 2653

Mikesell, Sharon, Br Mgr, Laramie County Library System, Pine Bluffs Branch, 110 E Second St, Pine Bluffs, WY, 82082. Tel: 307-245-3646. Fax: 307-245-3029. p. 2653

Mikkelsen, Susan, Res Access & Instruction Librn, University of California, Merced Library, 5200 N Lake Rd, Merced, CA, 95343-5001. Tel: 209-228-4615. Fax: 209-228-4271. p. 186

Mikkelson, Sheila, Dir, Delaware City Public Library, 250 Fifth St, Delaware City, DE, 19706. Tel: 302-834-4148. p. 381

Mikolash, Jackie, Ref Supvr, University of Winnipeg Library, 515 Portage Ave, Winnipeg, MB, R3B 2E9, CANADA. Tel: 204-786-9871. Fax: 204-783-8910. p. 2759

Miksa, Francis L, Prof, University of Texas at Austin, One University Sta, D7000, Austin, TX, 78712-0390. Tel: 512-471-3821. Fax: 512-471-3971. p. 2975

Miksa, Shawne, Dr, Assoc Prof, University of North Texas, 1155 Union Circle, Denton, TX, 76203-5017. Tel: 940-565-2445. Fax: 940-565-3101. p. 2975

Miksicek, Barbara, Librn, Saint Louis Metropolitan Police Department, 315 S Tucker Blvd, Saint Louis, MO, 63102. Tel: 314-444-5581. Fax: 314-444-5689. p. 1359

Miksis, Kathleen, Promotional Serv Librn, Reading Public Library, 64 Middlesex Ave, Reading, MA, 01867-2550. Tel: 781-944-0840. Fax: 781-942-9106. p. 1120

Mikula, Susan, Youth Serv, Ventura County Library, Ray D Prueter Library, 510 Park Ave, Port Hueneme, CA, 93041. Tel: 805-486-5460. Fax: 805-487-9190. p. 280

Mikulich, Jo Anne, Librn, Coleraine Public Library, 203 Cole Ave, Coleraine, MN, 55722. Tel: 218-245-2315. Fax: 218-245-2315. p. 1246

Mikus, Debra, Br Mgr, Free Library of Philadelphia, Lawncrest Branch, 6098 Rising Sun Ave, Philadelphia, PA, 19111-6009. Tel: 215-685-0549. Fax: 215-685-0548. p. 2108

Mikytyshyn, Susan, Ch, Edmonton Public Library, Mill Woods, 601 Mill Woods Town Centre, 2331 66 St, Edmonton, AB, T6K 4B5, CANADA. Tel: 780-496-7276. Fax: 780-496-1450. p. 2700

Milam, Barbara, Asst Dir, Tech Serv, Kennesaw State University, 1000 Chastain Rd, Kennesaw, GA, 30144. Tel: 770-423-6259. Fax: 770-423-6727. p. 537

Milam, Beverly, Librn, Wilson Ihrig & Associates Library, 5776 Broadway, Oakland, CA, 94618. Tel: 510-658-6719. Fax: 510-652-4441. p. 196

Milan, Irene, Cleveland Satellite Librn, US Court of Appeals for the Sixth Circuit Library, 312 Potter Stewart US Courthouse, Cincinnati, OH, 45202. Tel: 216-357-7275. Fax: 513-564-7329. p. 1873

Milan, Sheila, Librn, Halifax County Library, W C "Billy" Jones Jr Memorial, 127 W South Main St, Littleton, NC, 27850. Tel: 252-586-3608. Fax: 252-586-3495. p. 1799

Milan, Thomas, Tech Coordr, H Leslie Perry Memorial Library, 205 Breckenridge St, Henderson, NC, 27536. Tel: 252-438-3316. Fax: 252-438-3744. p. 1800

Milanese, Erin, Sci Librn, Goshen College, Harold & Wilma Good Library, 1700 S Main, Goshen, IN, 46526-4794. Tel: 574-535-7426. Fax: 574-535-7438. p. 745

Milavec, Julie, Adminr, Plainfield Public Library District, 15025 S Illinois St, Plainfield, IL, 60544. Tel: 815-436-6639. Fax: 815-439-2878. p. 691

Milberg, Craig, Asst Dir, Discovery Syst, Davidson College, 209 Ridge Rd, Davidson, NC, 28035-0001. Tel: 704-894-2331. Fax: 704-894-2625. p. 1786

Milbourn, Teri, Br Mgr, Cass County Public Library, Northern Resource Center, 164 Cedar Tree Dr, Belton, MO, 64012. Tel: 816-331-0049. p. 1330

Milbrandt, Cheryl, Dir, Neshkoro Public Library, 132 S Main St, Neshkoro, WI, 54960. Tel: 920-293-4026. Fax: 920-293-4026. p. 2625

Milbrodt, Matthew S, Info Spec, US Bureau of the Census, 1211 N Eighth St, Kansas City, KS, 66101-2129. Tel: 913-551-6711. Fax: 913-551-6789. p. 875

Milburn, Berlene, Dir, Neighborhood Library, 1310 W Allen Ave, Fort Worth, TX, 76110. Tel: 817-921-5999. p. 2323

Milburn, Gina, Sr Mgr, Humanities Dept, Memphis Public Library & Information Center, 3030 Poplar Ave, Memphis, TN, 38111-3527. Tel: 901-415-2726. Fax: 901-323-7108. p. 2249

Milburn, Gina, Mgr, Memphis Public Library, Humanities, 3030 Poplar Ave, Memphis, TN, 38111. Tel: 901-415-2726. Fax: 901-323-7206. p. 2250

Milburn, Gina Gail, Dir, Barry-Lawrence Regional Library, 213 Sixth St, Monett, MO, 65708-2147. Tel: 417-235-6646. Fax: 417-235-6799. p. 1346

Milcarek, Doreen, Cent Libr Adminr, Onondaga County Public Library, The Galleries of Syracuse, 447 S Salina St, Syracuse, NY, 13202-2494. Fax: 315-435-8533. p. 1752

Milchman, Lisa, Asst Librn, Norwich Public Library, 368 Main St, Norwich, VT, 05055-9453. Tel: 802-649-1184. Fax: 802-649-3470. p. 2431

Milczarski, Vivian, Coll Develop/E-Res Librn, Mount Saint Mary College, 330 Powell Ave, Newburgh, NY, 12550-3494. Tel: 845-569-3523. Fax: 845-561-0999. p. 1704

Mildenberger, Noni, Br Head, Vancouver Public Library, Firehall, 1455 W Tenth Ave, Vancouver, BC, V6H 1J8, CANADA. Tel: 604-665-3970. Fax: 604-665-3401. p. 2744

Mildenstein, Lynne, Tech Serv Mgr, Deschutes Public Library District, 507 NW Wall St, Bend, OR, 97701-2698. Tel: 541-617-7061. Fax: 541-617-7059. p. 1992

Mileham, Trisha, Dir, Res Serv, Valparaiso University, 1410 Chapel Dr, Valparaiso, IN, 46383-6493. Tel: 219-464-5693. p. 783

Miles, Beverly, Br Mgr, Bossier Parish Central Library, East 80, 1050 Bellevue Rd, Haughton, LA, 71037. Tel: 318-949-1959, 318-949-2665. Fax: 318-949-2067. p. 946

Miles, Carol, Archives, Scituate Historical Society Library, 43 Cudworth Rd, Scituate, MA, 02066-3802. Tel: 781-545-1083. Fax: 781-544-1249. p. 1123

Miles, Corrie, Literacy Coordr, Oceanside Public Library, Oceanside READS Learning Center, 321 N Nevada St, Oceanside, CA, 92054-2811. Tel: 760-435-5682. Fax: 760-435-5681. p. 200

Miles, David, In Charge, Multnomah County Library, Kenton, 8226 N Denver Ave, Portland, OR, 97217. Tel: 503-988-5370. Fax: 503-988-5163. p. 2012

Miles, Dennis, Tech/Pub Serv Librn, Southeastern Oklahoma State University, 1405 N Fourth Ave, PMB 4105, Durant, OK, 74701-0609. Tel: 580-745-2396. Fax: 580-745-7463. p. 1961

Miles, George A, Curator, Western Americana Coll, Yale University Library, Beinecke Rare Book & Manuscript, 121 Wall St, New Haven, CT, 06520. Tel: 203-432-2958. Fax: 203-432-4047. p. 356

Miles, Harriet, Ch, Palmdale City Library, 700 E Palmdale Blvd, Palmdale, CA, 93550. Tel: 661-267-5600. Fax: 661-267-5606. p. 203

Miles, Jennifer, Dep Libr Dir, Boulder Public Library, 1001 Arapahoe Rd, Boulder, CO, 80302. Tel: 303-441-3100. Fax: 303-442-1808. p. 290

Miles, Jo Ann, In Charge, Siouxland Libraries, Hartford - West Central Branch, 705 E Second St, Hartford, SD, 57033. Tel: 605-528-3223. Fax: 605-528-3702. p. 2219

Miles, Kathleen, Dir, Iberia Parish Library, 445 E Main St, New Iberia, LA, 70560-3710. Tel: 337-364-7024, 337-364-7074. Fax: 337-364-7042. p. 959

Miles, Linda, Pub Serv Librn, Yeshiva University Libraries, Pollack Library-Landowne Bloom Library, Wilf Campus, 2520 Amsterdam Ave, New York, NY, 10033. Tel: 212-960-5378, 212-960-5379, 212-960-5380. Fax: 212-960-0066. p. 1704

Miles, Margaret, Br Mgr, Marin County Free Library, Fairfax Branch, 2097 Sir Francis Drake Blvd, Fairfax, CA, 94930-1198. Tel: 415-453-8092. p. 257

Miles, Margaret, Sr Librn, New Hanover County Public Library, 201 Chestnut St, Wilmington, NC, 28401. Tel: 910-798-6361. Fax: 910-798-6312. p. 1830

Miles, Michele, Librn, Fasken Martineau DuMoulin LLP, Bay Adelaide Centre, Box 20, 333 Bay St, Ste 2400, Toronto, ON, M5H 2T6, CANADA. Tel: 416-865-5143. Fax: 416-364-7813. p. 2853

Miles, Niger, AV Coordr, The Jewish Museum, 1109 Fifth Ave, New York, NY, 10128. Tel: 212-423-3234. Fax: 212-423-3232. p. 1683

Miles, Patricia, Dir, Comfort Public Library, 701 High St, Comfort, TX, 78013. Tel: 830-995-2398. Fax: 830-995-5574. p. 2299

Miles, Susan Ambrose, Tech Serv, Bruton Memorial Library, 302 W McLendon St, Plant City, FL, 33563. Tel: 813-757-9215. Fax: 813-757-9217. p. 484

Miles, Suzanne, Youth Serv, Cumberland County Public Library & Information Center, Cliffdale, 6882 Cliffdale Rd, Fayetteville, NC, 28314-1936. Tel: 910-864-3800. Fax: 910-487-9090. p. 1792

Miletic-Vejzovic, Laila, Head, Spec Coll & Archives, University of Central Florida Libraries, 4000 Central Florida Blvd, Bldg 2, Orlando, FL, 32816-2666. Tel: 407-823-2788. Fax: 407-823-2529. p. 477

Miley, Becky, Assoc Librn, Country Music Hall of Fame & Museum, 222 Fifth Ave S, Nashville, TN, 37203. Tel: 615-416-2036. Fax: 615-255-2245. p. 2255

Milford, Nancy, Ref Serv, Ad, Cuyahoga Falls Library, 2015 Third St, Cuyahoga Falls, OH, 44221-3294. Tel: 330-928-2117. Fax: 330-928-2535. p. 1892

Milford, Robin, Access Serv Asst, University of Western States, 2900 NE 132nd Ave, Portland, OR, 97230-3099. Tel: 503-251-5752. Fax: 503-251-5759. p. 2015

Milis, Susan, Ref, Normandale Community College Library, 9700 France Ave S, Bloomington, MN, 55431. Tel: 952-487-8290. Fax: 952-487-8101. p. 1242

Milite, William, Reserves, Fordham University Libraries, 441 E Fordham Rd, Bronx, NY, 10458-5151. Tel: 718-817-3570. Fax: 718-817-3582. p. 1586

Milius, Vivian, Children's & YA Librn, Madison Library District, 73 N Center, Rexburg, ID, 83440-1539. Tel: 208-356-3461. p. 582

Milius, Vivian, Ch, Springville Public Library, 50 S Main St, Springville, UT, 84663. Tel: 801-489-2720. Fax: 801-489-2709. p. 2416

Miljinovic, Susan, Librn, Baker & Hostetler LLP Library, 3200 National City Ctr, 1900 E Ninth St, Cleveland, OH, 44114-3485. Tel: 216-621-0200, 216-861-7101. Fax: 216-696-0740. p. 1875

Mill, David, Online Serv, Ref, Ursinus College Library, 601 E Main St, Collegeville, PA, 19426. Tel: 610-409-3000, Ext 2301. Fax: 610-489-0634. p. 2046

Millar, Carolyn, Libr Tech, Prince Edward Island Public Library Service, Tyne Valley Public, 19 Allen Rd, Tyne Valley, PE, C0B 2C0, CANADA. Tel: 902-831-2928. p. 2877

Millar, Ellen, Asst Archivist, Simcoe County Archives, 1149 Hwy 26, RR 2, Minesing, ON, L0L 1Y2, CANADA. Tel: 705-726-9300, Ext 1288. Fax: 705-725-5341. p. 2822

Millar, Janet, Librn, United States Army, Consumer Health Library, Eisenhower Army Medical Ctr, Rm 3-D-15, Fort Gordon, GA, 30905. Tel: 706-787-6765. Fax: 706-787-2327. p. 533

Millar, Janet, Librn, United States Army, Eisenhower Army Medical Center, Health Sciences Libr, DDEAMC, Fort Gordon, GA, 30905-5650. Tel: 706-787-6765. Fax: 706-787-2327. p. 533

Millar, Julia, Ref Librn, Norton Rose Canada LLP, Devon Tower, 400 Third Ave SW, Ste 3700, Calgary, AB, T2P 4H2, CANADA. Tel: 403-267-8384. Fax: 403-264-5973. p. 2692

Millard, Jane, Dir, Jefferson Public Library, 200 W Lincolnway, Jefferson, IA, 50129-2185. Tel: 515-386-2835. Fax: 515-386-8163. p. 824

Millard, John, Head, Digital Initiatives & Ctr for Digital Scholarship, Miami University Libraries, 225 King Library, Oxford, OH, 45056. Tel: 513-529-6789. Fax: 513-529-3110. p. 1926

Millard, Kate, Librn, Online Serv, Carolina Library Services, Inc, 147 Lake Ellen Dr, Chapel Hill, NC, 27514-1939. Tel: 919-929-4870. Fax: 919-933-1253. p. 1780

Millard, Kristine, Co-Dir, Lodi Woman's Club Public Library, 130 Lodi St, Lodi, WI, 53555-1217. Tel: 608-592-4130. Fax: 608-592-2327. p. 2605

Millard, Sandra, Assoc Univ Librn for Serv, Outreach & Assessment, University of Delaware Library, 181 S College Ave, Newark, DE, 19717-5267. Tel: 302-831-2231. Fax: 302-831-1046. p. 386

Millen, Barb, Chair, Department of Community Services, Government of Yukon, Watson Lake Community, Watson Lake Administration Bldg, 701 Adela Trail, Watson Lake, YT, Y0A 1C0, CANADA. Tel: 867-536-7517. Fax: 867-536-7515. p. 2933

Miller, Amy, Acq, Jacksonville Public Library, 200 Pelham Rd S, Jacksonville, AL, 36265. Tel: 256-435-6332. Fax: 256-435-4459. p. 22

Miller, Amy, Asst Librn, Buffalo History Museum Research Library, One Museum Ct, Buffalo, NY, 14216-3199. Tel: 716-873-9644. Fax: 716-873-8754. p. 1597

Miller, Andrea, Ref/Cat Librn, Detroit Baptist Theological Seminary Library, 4801 Allen Rd, Allen Park, MI, 48101. Tel: 313-381-0111. Fax: 313-381-0798. p. 1149

Miller, Andrea, Asst Prof, Missouri State University, Duane G Meyer Library, 901 S National Ave, Springfield, MO, 65897. Tel: 417-836-4525. Fax: 417-836-4764. p. 2968

Miller, Andy, Circ, Neumann College Library, One Neumann Dr, Aston, PA, 19014-1298. Tel: 610-558-5545. Fax: 610-459-1370. p. 2030

Miller, Ann, Br Mgr, Broward County Division of Libraries, Sunrise Dan Pearl Branch, 10500 W Oakland Park Blvd, Sunrise, FL, 33351. Tel: 954-749-2521. Fax: 954-749-2524. p. 442

Miller, Ann, Head, Metadata Serv, Digital Projects & Acq, University of Oregon Libraries, 1501 Kincaid St, Eugene, OR, 97403-1299. Tel: 541-346-3056. Fax: 541-346-3485. p. 1997

Miller, Anne, Pub Info Coordr, Belle W Baruch Institute for Marine & Coastal Sciences Library, University of South Carolina, Columbia, SC, 29208. Tel: 803-777-3927. Fax: 803-777-3935. p. 2186

Miller, Annette, Ch, Tomahawk Public Library, 300 W Lincoln Ave, Tomahawk, WI, 54487. Tel: 715-453-2455. Fax: 715-453-1630. p. 2642

Miller, April, Librn, Kanopolis Public Library, 221 N Kansas, Kanopolis, KS, 67454. Tel: 785-472-3053. p. 875

Miller, April, Librn, Southwestern Oklahoma State University, O H McMahan Library, 409 E Mississippi, Sayre, OK, 73662. Tel: 580-928-5533, Ext 2157, 580-928-5533, Ext 2185. Fax: 580-928-5533, Ext 2135. p. 1986

Miller, Arthur, Jr, Archivist, Spec Coll Librn, Lake Forest College, 555 N Sheridan, Lake Forest, IL, 60045. Tel: 847-735-5064. Fax: 847-735-6297. p. 663

Miller, Audrey, Asst Librn, Pinawa Public Library, Vanier Rd, Pinawa, MB, R0E 1L0, CANADA. Tel: 204-753-2496. Fax: 204-753-2770. p. 2750

Miller, Bambi, Librn, Tyler Memorial Library, Town Hall, 157 Main St, Charlemont, MA, 01339-9703. Tel: 413-339-0301. Fax: 413-339-0320. p. 1079

Miller, Barratt, Youth Serv Librn, Crook County Library, 175 NW Meadow Lakes Dr, Prineville, OR, 97754-1997. Tel: 541-447-7978, Ext 303. Fax: 541-447-1308. p. 2016

Miller, Barry, Dir, Communications & External Relations, University of North Carolina at Greensboro, 320 Spring Garden St, Greensboro, NC, 27402. Tel: 336-334-5880. Fax: 336-334-5399. p. 1797

Miller, Becky, Homebound & Vols Coordr, Alamogordo Public Library, 920 Oregon Ave, Alamogordo, NM, 88310. Tel: 575-439-4140. Fax: 575-439-4108. p. 1547

Miller, Ben, Dir, Slater Public Library, 105 N Tama St, Slater, IA, 50244. Tel: 515-228-3558. Fax: 515-228-3558. p. 844

Miller, Ben, Dir, Sauk City Public Library, 515 Water St, Sauk City, WI, 53583-1159. Tel: 608-643-8346. p. 2636

Miller, Beth, Mgr, Twin Lakes Library System, Lake Sinclair, 3061 N Columbia St, Ste A, Milledgeville, GA, 31061. Tel: 478-452-6522. Fax: 478-452-6524. p. 545

Miller, Beth, Librn, Monmouth County Library, Ocean Township, 701 Deal Rd, Ocean, NJ, 07712. Tel: 732-531-5092. Fax: 732-531-5262. p. 1499

Miller, Beverly, Librn, Nixon Peabody LLP, 401 Ninth St NW, Ste 900, Washington, DC, 20004. Tel: 202-585-8000, Ext 8320. Fax: 202-585-8080. p. 411

Miller, Bonnie, Mgr, United States Marine Corps, Bldg 633, Yuma, AZ, 85369. Tel: 928-269-2785. Fax: 928-344-5592. p. 91

Miller, Bonnie, ILL, Jenkintown Library, 460 Old York Rd, Jenkintown, PA, 19046-2829. Tel: 215-884-0593. Fax: 215-884-2243. p. 2072

Miller, Brenda, Ch, Currituck County Public Library, 4261 Caratoke Hwy, Barco, NC, 27917-9707. Tel: 252-453-8345. Fax: 252-453-8717. p. 1775

Miller, Brenda L, Librn, Thiele Kaolin, Co, 520 Kaolin Rd, Sandersville, GA, 31082. Tel: 478-552-3951. Fax: 478-552-4138. p. 549

Miller, Brian, Dir, Millington Public Library, 4858 Navy Rd, Millington, TN, 38053. Tel: 901-872-1585. Fax: 901-872-2554. p. 2253

Miller, Catherine, In Charge, New York State Supreme Court, Court House, 163 Arsenal St, Watertown, NY, 13601. Tel: 315-785-3064. Fax: 315-785-3330. p. 1763

Miller, Cathy, Libr Tech, Yakama Nation Library, Yakama Nation Cultural Ctr, Hwy 97 at Fort Rd, Toppenish, WA, 98948. Tel: 509-865-2800, Ext 6, 509-865-5121, Ext 4721, 509-865-5121, Ext 4747. Fax: 509-865-6101. p. 2541

Miller, Cathy, Librn, Hesseltine Public Library, 14 NW Division, Wilbur, WA, 99185. Tel: 509-647-5828. Fax: 509-647-2047. p. 2550

Miller, Charlie, Br Mgr, Laurens County Library, Clinton Public, 107 Jacobs Hwy, Ste A, Clinton, SC, 29325. Tel: 864-833-1853. Fax: 864-833-9666. p. 2199

Miller, Cheryl, Sr Mgr, Tech Serv, Autry National Center, Autry Library, 4700 Western Heritage Way, Los Angeles, CA, 90027-1462. Tel: 323-667-2000, Ext 349. Fax: 323-660-5721. p. 168

Miller, Chris, YA Serv, Coquitlam Public Library, 575 Poirier St, Coquitlam, BC, V3J 6A9, CANADA. Tel: 604-937-4140. Fax: 604-931-6739. p. 2727

Miller, Christina, Media Spec, York College Library, 94-20 Guy R Brewer Blvd, Jamaica, NY, 11451. Tel: 718-262-2475. Fax: 718-262-2027, 718-262-2997. p. 1646

Miller, Cindy, Librn, Griswold Public Library, 505 Main, Griswold, IA, 51535. Tel: 712-778-4130. Fax: 712-778-4140. p. 819

Miller, Cindy, Asst Librn, Gilman Public Library, 100 Main St, Alton, NH, 03809. Tel: 603-875-2550. Fax: 603-875-2550. p. 1437

Miller, Claudia, Tech Serv Dir, Homewood Public Library, 17917 Dixie Hwy, Homewood, IL, 60430-1703. Tel: 708-798-0121. Fax: 708-798-0662. p. 657

Miller, Colleen, Librn, Jasper Public Library, 98 18th St E, Jasper, AL, 35501. Tel: 205-221-8512. p. 23

Miller, Colleen, Ch, Maquoketa Public Library, 126 S Second St, Maquoketa, IA, 52060. Tel: 563-652-3874. p. 829

Miller, Conrad D, ILL, Ref, Maynard Public Library, 77 Nason St, Maynard, MA, 01754-2316. Tel: 978-897-1010. Fax: 978-897-9884. p. 1103

Miller, Cori, Media Librn, Molloy College, 1000 Hempstead Ave, Rockville Centre, NY, 11571. Tel: 516-678-5000, Ext 6159. Fax: 516-678-8908. p. 1734

Miller, Creighton, Res & Bibliog Instruction, Washburn University, School of Law Library, 1700 SW College Ave, Topeka, KS, 66621. Tel: 785-670-1041. Fax: 785-670-3194. p. 897

Miller, Cristina, Librn, University of Wisconsin-Milwaukee Libraries, American Geographical Society Library, Golda Meir Library, 2311 E Hartford Ave, Milwaukee, WI, 53211. Tel: 414-229-3984, 414-229-6282. Fax: 414-229-3624. p. 2622

Miller, Dave, Libr Mgr, Bartholomew County Public Library, Hope Branch, 635 Harrison St, Hope, IN, 47246. Tel: 812-546-5310. p. 733

Miller, Dave Timothy, Asst Dir, Western Plains Library System, 501 S 28th St, Clinton, OK, 73601-3996. Tel: 580-323-0974. Fax: 580-323-1190. p. 1960

Miller, David, Tech Serv, Curry College, 1071 Blue Hill Ave, Milton, MA, 02186-9984. Tel: 617-333-2101. Fax: 617-333-2164. p. 1106

Miller, David, Dir, Baker College of Clinton Township Library, 34950 Little Mack Ave, Clinton Township, MI, 48035-4701. Tel: 586-790-9584. Fax: 586-791-0967. p. 1163

Miller, David Robert, Libr Dir, Farmville Public Library, 4276 W Church St, Farmville, NC, 27828. Tel: 252-753-6713. Fax: 252-753-2855. p. 1792

Miller, Dawn, Adult Serv, Grayslake Area Public Library District, 100 Library Lane, Grayslake, IL, 60030-1684. Tel: 847-223-5313. Fax: 847-223-6482. p. 652

Miller, Deborah, Mgr, Department of Veterans Affairs, 4815 N Assembly St, Spokane, WA, 99205-2697. Tel: 509-434-7575. Fax: 509-434-7103. p. 2535

Miller, Deborah A, Librn, Winston & Strawn LLP, 1700 K St NW, Washington, DC, 20006. p. 423

Miller, Debra, Dean, Extn Serv, Carl Sandburg College, Carthage Branch Campus, 305 Sandburg Dr, Carthage, IL, 62321. Tel: 217-357-3129. Fax: 217-357-3512. p. 648

Miller, Denise, Adult Serv, Pottsville Free Public Library, 215 W Market St, Pottsville, PA, 17901-4304. Tel: 570-622-8105, 570-622-8880. Fax: 570-622-2157. p. 2131

Miller, Dennis, Ref, Abilene Public Library, 202 Cedar St, Abilene, TX, 79601-5793. Tel: 325-676-6026. p. 2271

Miller, Diane, Librn, Southeast Regional Library, Alameda Branch, 200-Fifth St, Alameda, SK, S0C 0A0, CANADA. Tel: 306-489-2066. p. 2929

Miller, Don, Mgr, The T Elmer Cox Library, 229 N Main St, Greeneville, TN, 37745. Tel: 423-638-9866. p. 2236

Miller, Donald J, Ref, University of Medicine & Dentistry of New Jersey, PO Box 19, New Brunswick, NJ, 08903. Tel: 732-235-7610. Fax: 732-235-7826. p. 1509

Miller, Donna, Libr Dir, Lucy Robbins Welles Library, 95 Cedar St, Newington, CT, 06111-2645. Fax: 860-667-1255. p. 361

Miller, Donna Lynn, Instruction & Ref Librn, Lebanon Valley College, 101 N College Ave, Annville, PA, 17003-1400. Tel: 717-867-6972. Fax: 717-867-6979. p. 2029

Miller, Donna S, Ref/Info Serv Librn, Troy University, 502 University Dr, Dothan, AL, 36304. Tel: 334-983-6556, Ext 1320. Fax: 334-983-6327. p. 15

Miller, Doreen, Ch Serv Librn, Rockwall County Library, 1215 E Yellowjacket Lane, Rockwall, TX, 75087. Tel: 972-204-7700. Fax: 972-204-7709. p. 2377

Miller, E Ethelbert, Dir, Howard University Libraries, Department of Afro-American Studies Resource Center, 500 Howard Pl NW, Rm 300, Washington, DC, 20059. Tel: 202-806-7242, 202-806-7686. Fax: 202-986-0538. p. 404

Miller, Ed, Spec Serv Mgr, Library System of Lancaster County, 1866 Colonial Village Lane, Ste 107, Lancaster, PA, 17601. Tel: 717-207-0500. Fax: 717-207-0504. p. 2077

Miller, Elaine, Curator, Washington State Historical Society Research Center, 315 N Stadium Way, Tacoma, WA, 98403. Tel: 253-798-5915. Fax: 253-597-4186. p. 2541

Miller, Elissa, Assoc Dir, Coll, District of Columbia Public Library, 901 G St NW, Washington, DC, 20001-4599. Tel: 202-727-3268. Fax: 202-727-1129. p. 398

Miller, Ellen, Ch, Shelter Rock Public Library, 165 Searingtown Rd, Albertson, NY, 11507. Tel: 516-248-7343. p. 1571

Miller, Ellen, Mgr, Br Serv, Spokane County Library District, Spokane Valley Library, 12004 E Main Ave, Spokane Valley, WA, 99206-5114. Tel: 509-893-8400. Fax: 509-893-8483. p. 2537

Miller, Elyse, Admin Coordr, Iowa City Public Library, 123 S Linn St, Iowa City, IA, 52240. Tel: 319-887-6003. Fax: 319-356-5494. p. 822

Miller, Erica, Mgr, Per, Willamette University, 900 State St, Salem, OR, 97301. Tel: 503-370-6739. Fax: 503-370-6141. p. 2019

Miller, Eugene, Pres, West Mississauga Jazz Muddies Library, 90 Prince George Dr, Toronto, ON, M9B 2X8, CANADA. Tel: 416-231-4055. Fax: 416-239-6284. p. 2867

Miller, Evelyn C, Head Librn, Flatonia Public Library, 208 N Main St, Flatonia, TX, 78941. Tel: 361-772-2088. p. 2319

Miller, Fran, Librn, Arkansas School for the Deaf Library, 2400 W Markham St, Little Rock, AR, 72205. Tel: 501-324-9515. Fax: 501-324-9553. p. 105

Miller, Frisk, Cataloger, Land O'Lakes Public Library, 4242 County Hwy B, Land O'Lakes, WI, 54540. Tel: 715-547-6006. Fax: 715-547-6004. p. 2605

Miller, Gail, Dir, Rahway Public Library, Two City Hall Plaza, Rahway, NJ, 07065. Tel: 732-340-1551. Fax: 732-340-0393. p. 1525

Miller, Gail Cross, Asst Librn, Missouri Supreme Court Library, Supreme Court Bldg, 207 W High St, Jefferson City, MO, 65101. Tel: 573-751-2636. Fax: 573-751-2573. p. 1335

Miller, Geoffrey, Media Spec, Richmond Public Library, 325 Civic Center Plaza, Richmond, CA, 94804-9991. Tel: 510-620-6555. Fax: 510-620-6850. p. 216

Miller, Glenn R, Exec Dir, Pennsylvania Library Association, 220 Cumberland Pkwy, Ste 10, Mechanicsburg, PA, 17055. Tel: 717-766-7663. Fax: 717-766-5440. p. 2954

Miller, Gloria, Team Leader, United States Army, Martin Rd, Bldg 4484, Redstone Arsenal, AL, 35898-5000. Fax: 256-842-7415. p. 34

Miller, Graydon, Head, Ref Serv, Pikes Peak Community College Library, 5675 S Academy Blvd, C7, Colorado Springs, CO, 80906-5498. Tel: 719-502-3389. p. 296

Miller, Harriet, ILL, Calvary Baptist Theological Seminary Library, 1380 S Valley Forge Rd, Lansdale, PA, 19446-4797. Tel: 215-368-7538, Ext 138. Fax: 215-368-1003. p. 2078

Miller, Heather, Teen Librn, Homewood Public Library, 1721 Oxmoor Rd, Homewood, AL, 35209-4085. Tel: 205-332-6621. Fax: 205-802-6424. p. 20

Miller, Heather, Assoc Dir, Tech Serv & Syst, University at Albany, State University of New York, 1400 Washington Ave, Albany, NY, 12222-0001. Tel: 518-442-3631. Fax: 518-442-3088. p. 1570

Miller, Henry, Dir, Historic Saint Mary's City, 18401 Rosecroft Rd, Saint Mary's City, MD, 20686. Tel: 240-895-4974. Fax: 240-895-4968. p. 1040

Miller, Ivy, Dir, Dixon Correctional Institute, PO Box 788, Jackson, LA, 70748. Tel: 225-634-1200, Ext 213. Fax: 225-634-4400. p. 951

Miller, Ivy, Upper Sch Librn, Wyoming Seminary, 201 N Sprague Ave, Kingston, PA, 18704-3593. Tel: 570-270-2168. Fax: 570-270-2178. p. 2074

Miller, Jackie, Br Mgr, South Mississippi Regional Library, 900 Broad St, Columbia, MS, 39429. Tel: 601-943-5420. Fax: 601-736-1379. p. 1296

Miller, Jacky, Ch, Rockingham County Public Library, 527 Boone Rd, Eden, NC, 27288. Tel: 336-627-1106. Fax: 336-623-1258. p. 1790

Miller, Jaclyn, Youth Serv, Rochester Hills Public Library, 500 Olde Towne Rd, Rochester, MI, 48307-2043. Tel: 248-650-7142. Fax: 248-650-7121. p. 1222

Miller, Jacqueline, Sister, Librn, Blessed Pope John XXIII National Seminary Library, 558 South Ave, Weston, MA, 02493. Tel: 781-899-5500, Ext 20. Fax: 781-899-9057. p. 1139

Miller, James, Adult Serv, Simsbury Public Library, 725 Hopmeadow St, Simsbury, CT, 06070. Tel: 860-658-7663. Fax: 860-658-6732. p. 367

Miller, James, Assoc Dean, University of New Orleans, College of Education, Rm 342, New Orleans, LA, 70148. Tel: 504-280-6251, 504-280-6528. Fax: 504-280-1120. p. 2967

Miller, Jamie, Ref Serv, Art Institute of Seattle Library, North Campus, 5th Flr, 2323 Elliott Ave, Seattle, WA, 98121. Tel: 206-239-2359. Fax: 206-441-3475. p. 2527

Miller, Jan, Br Mgr, Knox County Public Library System, Sequoyah Branch, 1140 Southgate Rd, Knoxville, TN, 37919-7646. Tel: 865-525-1541. Fax: 865-525-3148. p. 2242

Miller, Jane, Sr Librn, Pierce County Library System, Graham Branch, 9202 224th St E, Graham, WA, 98338. Tel: 253-548-3322. Fax: 253-846-5174. p. 2539

Miller, Jane, Tech Serv Mgr, Prescott Public Library, 800 Borner St N, Prescott, WI, 54021-1703. Tel: 715-262-5555. Fax: 715-262-4229. p. 2631

Miller, Janet, Ref Serv, Mims/Scottsmoor Public Library, 3615 Lionel Rd, Mims, FL, 32754. Tel: 321-264-5080. Fax: 321-264-5081. p. 470

Miller, Janice, Ch, Dir, Ackley Public Library, 401 State St, Ackley, IA, 50601. Tel: 641-847-2233. Fax: 641-847-2233. p. 791

Miller, Jenna, Ref Librn, Santa Fe Community College, 3000 NW 83rd St, Bldg Y-100, Gainesville, FL, 32606. Tel: 352-395-5329. Fax: 352-395-5102. p. 449

Miller, Jessica, Asst Dir, Flenniken Public Library, 102 E George St, Carmichaels, PA, 15320-1202. Tel: 724-966-5263. Fax: 724-966-9511. p. 2042

Miller, Jim, Ref, University of Maryland Libraries, Engineering & Physical Sciences Library, College Park, MD, 20742-7011. Tel: 301-405-9152. p. 1025

Miller, Jim, Br Mgr, Springfield-Greene County Library District, Midtown Carnegie Branch, 397 E Central, Springfield, MO, 65802-3834. Tel: 417-862-0135. Fax: 417-866-1259. p. 1368

Miller, Jindra, Head, Tech Serv, Harvard Library, History of Science Library - Cabot Science Library, Science Center, One Oxford St, Cambridge, MA, 02138. Tel: 617-495-5355. Fax: 617-495-5324. p. 1075

Miller, Joan, Circ, Kendallville Public Library, Limberlost Public, 164 Kelly St, Rome City, IN, 46784. Tel: 260-854-2775. Fax: 260-854-3382. p. 757

Miller, Jocelyn, Dir, Howard Whittemore Memorial Library, 243 Church St, Naugatuck, CT, 06770-4198. Tel: 203-729-4591. Fax: 203-723-1820. p. 353

Miller, Jodi, Circ, Leavenworth Public Library, 417 Spruce St, Leavenworth, KS, 66048. Tel: 913-682-5666. Fax: 913-682-1248. p. 879

Miller, John, Tech Librn, Traverse Des Sioux Library System, 1400 Madison Ave, Ste 622, Mankato, MN, 56001-5488. Tel: 507-625-6169. Fax: 507-625-4049. p. 1257

Miller, John, Libr Mgr, Dauphin County Library System, Kline Library, 530 S 29th St, Harrisburg, PA, 17104. Tel: 717-234-3934. Fax: 717-234-7713. p. 2064

Miller, John, Libr Mgr, Dauphin County Library System, William H & Marion C Alexander Family Library, 200 W Second St, Hummelstown, PA, 17036. Tel: 717-566-0949. Fax: 717-566-7178. p. 2064

Miller, John, Tech Serv Librn, Mansfield Public Library, 104 S Wisteria St, Mansfield, TX, 76063. Tel: 817-473-4391. Fax: 817-453-4975. p. 2359

Miller, John M, II, Librn, Snead State Community College, 220 N Walnut, Boaz, AL, 35957-1650. Tel: 256-840-4173. Fax: 256-593-3098. p. 10

Miller, Jolene, Asst Dir, University of Toledo, Health Science Campus, Mail Stop 1061, 3000 Arlington Ave, Toledo, OH, 43614-5805. Tel: 419-383-4223. Fax: 419-383-6146. p. 1940

Miller, Jonathan, Dir, Rollins College, 1000 Holt Ave, Campus Box 2744, Winter Park, FL, 32789-2744. Tel: 407-646-2676. Fax: 407-646-1515. p. 505

Miller, Joseph, Assoc Prof, University of Kentucky, 320 Little Library Bldg, Lexington, KY, 40506-0224. Tel: 859-257-8854. Fax: 859-257-4205. p. 2966

Miller, Joyce, Asst Librn, Mary E Bartlett Memorial Library, 22 Dalton Rd, Brentwood, NH, 03833. Tel: 603-642-3355. Fax: 603-642-3383. p. 1439

Miller, Joyce, Instrul Serv Librn, Ref, Adirondack Community College Library, Scoville Learning Center, 640 Bay Rd, Queensbury, NY, 12804. Tel: 518-743-2200, Ext 2485. Fax: 518-745-1442. p. 1725

Miller, Joyce Cortright, Librn, Anne Arundel Medical Center Library, 2001 Medical Pkwy, Annapolis, MD, 21401. Tel: 443-481-1000, Ext 4877. p. 1010

Miller, Judith, Spec Coll Librn, Valparaiso University, 1410 Chapel Dr, Valparaiso, IN, 46383-6493. Tel: 219-464-5808. p. 783

Miller, Judith L, Librn, Saegertown Area Library, 325 Broad St, Saegertown, PA, 16433. Tel: 814-763-5203. Fax: 814-763-4979. p. 2135

Miller, Judy, Mgr, Satilla Regional Library, Jeff Davis Public Library, 86 S Cromartie St, Hazlehurst, GA, 31539. Tel: 912-375-2386. Fax: 912-375-9507. p. 530

Miller, Julia E, Dir of Tech Serv, International Foundation of Employee Benefit Plans, 18700 W Bluemound Rd, Brookfield, WI, 53045-2936. Tel: 262-786-6710, Ext 5. Fax: 262-786-8780. p. 2583

Miller, Julie, Circ, Evangelical School of Theology, 121 S College St, Myerstown, PA, 17067. Tel: 717-866-5775. Fax: 717-866-4667. p. 2094

Miller, Julie L, Assoc Dean of Libr, Eastern Washington University, 816 F St, 100 LIB, Cheney, WA, 99004-2453. Tel: 509-359-4949. Fax: 509-359-6456. p. 2512

Miller, Karen, Mgr, Montgomery County Public Libraries, Damascus Library, 9701 Main St, Damascus, MD, 20872. Tel: 240-773-9440. p. 1038

Miller, Karen, Coordr, West Shore Medical Center Library, 1465 Parkdale Ave, Manistee, MI, 49660-9785. Tel: 231-398-1171. p. 1206

Miller, Karen, Assoc Dir, Main Libr Serv, Stark County District Library, 715 Market Ave N, Canton, OH, 44702-1018. Tel: 330-458-2833. Fax: 330-455-9596. p. 1864

Miller, Karen, Dir, Downingtown Library Co, 330 E Lancaster Ave, Downingtown, PA, 19335-2946. Tel: 610-269-2741. Fax: 610-269-3639. p. 2049

Miller, Karen S, Dep Dir, Bliss Memorial Public Library, 20 S Marion St, Bloomville, OH, 44818-9201. Tel: 419-983-4675. Fax: 419-983-4675. p. 1860

Miller, Kathleen, Dr, Dean of Libr Serv, Univ Librn, Florida Gulf Coast University Library, 10501 FGCU Blvd S, Fort Myers, FL, 33965-6501. Tel: 239-590-7605. p. 444

Miller, Kathleen M, Exec Dir, Rochester Regional Library Council, 390 Packetts Landing, Fairport, NY, 14450. Tel: 585-223-7570. Fax: 585-223-7712. p. 2950

Miller, Kathy, Br Mgr, Webster Parish Library, Springhill Branch, 217 N Main, Springhill, LA, 71075. Tel: 318-539-4117. Fax: 318-539-3718. p. 957

Miller, Kathy, Asst Librn, Hazel Mackin Community Library, 107 W Main St, Roberts, WI, 54023. Tel: 715-749-3849. p. 2635

Miller, Kelly, Head of Libr, University of California Los Angeles Library, College Library, Powell Library Bldg, Los Angeles, CA, 90095. Tel: 310-825-5756. Fax: 310-206-9312. p. 178

Miller, Kelly, Bus Librn, Springfield-Greene County Library District, 4653 S Campbell, Springfield, MO, 65810-1723. Tel: 417-882-0714. Fax: 417-883-9348. p. 1367

Miller, Kelly, Br Mgr, Springfield-Greene County Library District, Park Central Branch, 128 Park Central Sq, Springfield, MO, 65806-1311. Tel: 417-831-1342. p. 1368

Miller, Kenneth B, Jr, Dir, Bayliss Public Library, 541 Library Dr, Sault Sainte Marie, MI, 49783. Tel: 906-632-9331. Fax: 906-635-0210. p. 1226

Miller, Kent, Asst Dean, University of Kansas Libraries, 1425 Jayhawk Blvd, Lawrence, KS, 66045-7544. Tel: 785-864-3956. Fax: 785-864-5311. p. 878

Miller, Kim, Ref Librn, Killeen City Library System, 205 E Church Ave, Killeen, TX, 76541. Tel: 254-501-8949. Fax: 254-501-7704. p. 2350

Miller, Kris, Dir, Dowling Public Library, 1765 E Dowling Rd, Hastings, MI, 49058-9332. Tel: 269-721-3743. Fax: 269-721-3743. p. 1189

Miller, Kristin, Archivist, American Bible Society Library, 1865 Broadway, New York, NY, 10023-9980. Tel: 212-408-1203. Fax: 212-408-8724. p. 1667

Miller, Laura, Circ Serv Mgr, L E Phillips Memorial Public Library, 400 Eau Claire St, Eau Claire, WI, 54701. Tel: 715-839-5098. Fax: 715-839-5310. p. 2590

Miller, Laura O'Brien, Conservator, Yale University Library, Lewis Walpole Library, 154 Main St, Farmington, CT, 06032. Tel: 860-677-2140. Fax: 860-677-6369. p. 359

Miller, Lauren, Dir, Nelsonville Public Library, 95 W Washington, Nelsonville, OH, 45764-1177. Tel: 740-753-2118. Fax: 740-753-3543. p. 1920

Miller, Laurie B, Dir, Pierce County Law Library, County-City Bldg, 930 Tacoma Ave S, Rm 1A - 105, Tacoma, WA, 98402-2174. Tel: 253-798-2973. Fax: 253-798-2989. p. 2539

Miller, Lee, Tech Serv Mgr, Platte County Public Library, 904 Ninth St, Wheatland, WY, 82201-2699. Tel: 307-322-2689. Fax: 307-322-3540. p. 2661

Miller, Leo, ILL, York College, 1125 E Eighth St, York, NE, 68467-2699. Tel: 402-363-5703. Fax: 402-363-5685. p. 1424

Miller, Lesa, Br Mgr, Shreve Memorial Library, Belcher-Wyche Branch, 409 Charles St, Belcher, LA, 71004. Tel: 318-378-4567. Fax: 318-378-4567. p. 969

Miller, Lewis R, Dean of Libr, Butler University Libraries, 4600 Sunset Ave, Indianapolis, IN, 46208. Tel: 317-940-9227. Fax: 317-940-9711. p. 749

Miller, Lewis R, Dean of Libr, Butler University Libraries, Ruth Lilly Science Library, 740 W 46th St, Indianapolis, IN, 46208-3485. Tel: 317-940-9714. Fax: 317-940-9711. p. 749

Miller, Linda, Asst Librn, Fisher-Whiting Memorial Library, 609 Courtright St, Mapleton, IA, 51034. Tel: 712-881-1312. Fax: 712-881-1312. p. 829

Miller, Linda, Archivist, Roanoke College, 220 High St, Salem, VA, 24153. Tel: 540-375-2490. p. 2495

Miller, Linda, Assoc Dir, Pub Serv, Kanawha County Public Library, 123 Capitol St, Charleston, WV, 25301. Tel: 304-343-4646. Fax: 304-348-6530. p. 2556

Miller, Lindsey, Youth Serv Librn, Columbus-Lowndes Public Library, 314 N Seventh St, Columbus, MS, 39701. Tel: 662-329-5300. Fax: 662-329-5150. p. 1297

Miller, Lisa A, Asst Dir, Toledo Public Library, 173 NW Seventh St, Toledo, OR, 97391. Tel: 541-336-3132. Fax: 541-336-3428. p. 2021

Miller, Loftan, Col Librn, Rappahannock Community College Library, 12745 College Dr, Glenns, VA, 23149. Tel: 804-758-6710. Fax: 804-758-0213. p. 2467

Miller, Lois, In Charge, Schenectady County Public Library, Woodlawn, Two Sanford St, Schenectady, NY, 12304. Tel: 518-386-2248. Fax: 518-386-2248. p. 1741

Miller, Lydia, Asst Librn, Holderness Library, 866 US Rte 3, Holderness, NH, 03245. Tel: 603-968-7066. p. 1451

Miller, Lynda, Br Mgr, US Courts Library, Byron Rogers Courthouse, 1929 Stout St, Rm 430, Denver, CO, 80294. Tel: 303-844-3591. Fax: 303-844-5958. p. 303

Miller, Lynda, Ch, Fremont Public Library, Seven Jackie Bernier Dr, Fremont, NH, 03044. Tel: 603-895-9543. Fax: 603-895-0549. p. 1448

Miller, Lynda R, In Charge, United States Courts Library, B55 US Courthouse, 401 N Market St, Wichita, KS, 67202-2011. Tel: 316-269-6162. Fax: 316-269-6168. p. 900

Miller, Lynn, Ch, Reading Public Library, 100 S Fifth St, Reading, PA, 19602. Tel: 610-655-6350. p. 2133

Miller, Lynne, Br Mgr, Shaker Heights Public Library, 16500 Van Aken Blvd, Shaker Heights, OH, 44120-5318. Tel: 216-991-2030. Fax: 216-991-5951. p. 1934

Miller, Lynne, Br Mgr, Shaker Heights Public Library, Bertram Woods Branch, 20600 Fayette Rd, Shaker Heights, OH, 44122-2979. Tel: 216-991-2421. Fax: 216-991-3124. p. 1934

Miller, Marc, Archives & Spec Coll Librn, Client Serv Librn, Computer Instrul Serv Librn, AIDS Library, 1233 Locust St, 2nd Flr, Philadelphia, PA, 19107. Tel: 215-985-4851. Fax: 215-985-4492. p. 2102

Miller, Marcella, Admin Officer, McNeese State University, Curriculum Materials Center, PO Box 91380, Lake Charles, LA, 70609. Tel: 337-475-5410. Fax: 337-475-5398. p. 954

Miller, Marcia A, Librn, New York Presbyterian Hospital-Weill Cornell, 21 Bloomingdale Rd, White Plains, NY, 10605. Tel: 914-997-5897. Fax: 914-997-5861. p. 1768

Miller, Margaret, Instruction & Educ Res, Librn, University of South Dakota, 414 E Clark St, Vermillion, SD, 57069. Tel: 605-677-5371. Fax: 605-677-6834. p. 2220

Miller, Marie, Dir, East Lake Community Library, 4125 East Lake Rd, Palm Harbor, FL, 34685. Tel: 727-773-2665. Fax: 727-773-9583. p. 480

Miller, Marilyn, Ref, Oklahoma Department of Libraries, 200 NE 18th St, Oklahoma City, OK, 73105. Tel: 405-521-2502. Fax: 405-525-7804. p. 1974

Miller, Marilyn, Dir, Eastern Wyoming College Library, 3200 West C, Torrington, WY, 82240. Tel: 307-532-8210. Fax: 307-532-8225. p. 2661

Miller, Marjorie, Librn, Bovina Library Association, 33 Maple Ave, Bovina Center, NY, 13740. Tel: 607-832-4884. Fax: 607-832-4884. p. 1584

Miller, Mark, Librn, Montgomery College, School of Art & Design, 7600 Takoma Ave, Takoma Park, MD, 20912. Tel: 240-567-1538. Fax: 301-649-2940. p. 1037

Miller, Mark, Librn, Montgomery College, Takoma Park Campus Library, 7600 Takoma Ave, Takoma Park, MD, 20912. Tel: 240-567-1538. Fax: 240-567-5820. p. 1037

Miller, Marla, Acq Librn, University of Toronto Libraries, Scarborough Library, Scarborough College, 1265 Military Trail, Scarborough, ON, M1C 1A4, CANADA. Tel: 416-287-7497. Fax: 416-287-7507. p. 2867

Miller, Marsha, Ref/Instruction Librn, Indiana State University, 510 North 6 1/2 St, Terre Haute, IN, 47809. Tel: 812-237-2606. Fax: 812-237-3376. p. 781

Miller, Martin, Tech Serv Librn, Butler County Community College, College Dr, Oak Hills, Butler, PA, 16002. Tel: 724-284-8511. Fax: 724-285-6047. p. 2040

Miller, Marty, Ref Librn, Metropolitan Community College, Longview Campus Library, 500 SW Longview Rd, Lee's Summit, MO, 64081-2105. Tel: 816-604-2654. Fax: 816-604-2087. p. 1339

Miller, Mary, Librn, Winchester Hospital, 41 Highland Ave, Winchester, MA, 01890. Tel: 781-756-2165. Fax: 781-756-2059. p. 1141

Miller, Mary, Dir, Jonesville District Library, 310 Church St, Jonesville, MI, 49250-1087. Tel: 517-849-9701. Fax: 517-849-0009. p. 1196

Miller, Mary, Dir, Mississippi College, 151 E Griffith St, Jackson, MS, 39201-1391. Tel: 601-925-7120. Fax: 601-925-7112. p. 1304

Miller, Mary, Libr Dir, Lakewood Memorial Library, 12 W Summit St, Lakewood, NY, 14750. Tel: 716-763-6234. Fax: 716-763-3624. p. 1651

Miller, Mary, Br Mgr, Akron-Summit County Public Library, Green, 4046 Massillon Rd, Uniontown, OH, 44685-4046. Tel: 330-896-9074. Fax: 330-896-9412. p. 1852

Miller, Mary Ann, Head Librn, Suffolk County Community College, 121 Speonk Riverhead Rd, Riverhead, NY, 11901-9990. Tel: 631-548-2540. Fax: 631-369-2641. p. 1728

Miller, Mary Jane, Librn, Clarion County Historical Society, 17 S Fifth Ave, Clarion, PA, 16214-1501. Tel: 814-226-4450. Fax: 814-226-7106. p. 2045

Miller, Matt, Chief Tech Officer, Maricopa County Library District, 2700 N Central Ave, Ste 700, Phoenix, AZ, 85004. Tel: 602-652-3060. Fax: 602-652-3071. p. 74

Miller, Maureen, Librn, Deloitte & Touche Library, 555 12th St NW, Ste 500, Washington, DC, 20004. Tel: 202-220-2145. Fax: 202-661-1058. p. 397

Miller, Melissa, Librn, United States Court of Appeals, 110 E Court Ave, Ste 358, Des Moines, IA, 50309. Tel: 515-284-6228. Fax: 515-284-6296. p. 810

Miller, Melissa, Librn, Carney, Badley & Spellman Library, 701 Fifth Ave, Ste 3600, Seattle, WA, 98104-7010. Tel: 206-607-4149. Fax: 206-622-8983. p. 2527

Miller, Meredith R, Coordr, International Tennis Hall of Fame & Museum Library (IRC), 194 Bellevue Ave, Newport, RI, 02840-3515. Tel: 401-849-3990. Fax: 401-849-8780, 401-851-7920. p. 2169

Miller, Michael, Dir, Libr Serv, Appalachian Technical College, 125 Schoolhouse Rd, Epworth, GA, 30541. Tel: 706-492-4240. Fax: 706-492-4238. p. 532

Miller, Michael, Dir, Libr Serv, Appalachian Technical College, 100 Campus Dr, Jasper, GA, 30143. Tel: 706-253-4571. Fax: 706-253-4572. p. 536

Miller, Michael, Dir, Libr Serv, Appalachian Technical College, 8371 Main St, Woodstock, GA, 30188. Tel: 678-454-1800. Fax: 678-454-1899. p. 558

Miller, Michael, Ref Librn, Keosauqua Public Library, 608 First St, Keosauqua, IA, 52565. Tel: 319-293-3766. Fax: 319-293-3766. p. 825

Miller, Michael, Bibliographer, North Dakota State University Libraries, 1201 Albrecht Blvd, Fargo, ND, 58108. Tel: 701-231-8416. Fax: 701-231-6128. p. 1841

Miller, Michael, Ref Serv, Sherman Public Library, 421 N Travis, Sherman, TX, 75090-5975. Tel: 903-892-7240. Fax: 903-892-7101. p. 2387

Miller, Michael, Head, Archives & Spec Coll, Library of the Marine Corps, Gray Research Ctr, 2040 Broadway St, Quantico, VA, 22134-5107. Tel: 703-784-4834. Fax: 703-784-4665. p. 2486

Miller, Michael K, Appalachian Campus Librn, Chattahoochee Technical College Library, 980 S Cobb Dr SE, Marietta, GA, 30060-3300. Tel: 706-253-4571. Fax: 770-528-4454. p. 542

Miller, Michaela, Ch, Oak Ridge Public Library, 1401 Oak Ridge Tpk, Oak Ridge, TN, 37830-6224. Tel: 865-425-3455. Fax: 865-425-3429. p. 2262

Miller, Michelle, Dir, Jay C Byers Memorial Library, 215 E Wichita Ave, Cleveland, OK, 74020. Tel: 918-358-2676. Fax: 918-358-5606. p. 1960

Miller, Mike, Mgr, Austin Public Library, Austin History Center, 810 Guadalupe St, Austin, TX, 78701. Tel: 512-974-7436. Fax: 512-974-7483. p. 2278

Miller, Mitzi, Circ Serv Supvr, Mishawaka-Penn-Harris Public Library, Bittersweet, 602 Bittersweet Rd, Mishawaka, IN, 46544-4155. Tel: 574-259-0392, Ext 230. Fax: 574-259-0399. p. 765

Miller, Morgan, Br Mgr, Cecil County Public Library, Port Deposit Branch, 13 S Main St, Port Deposit, MD, 21904. Tel: 410-996-6055. Fax: 410-996-1047. p. 1027

Miller, Moriah, Ref, Franklin County Library System, 101 Ragged Edge Rd S, Chambersburg, PA, 17202. Tel: 717-709-0282. Fax: 717-263-2248. p. 2043

Miller, Nancy, Librn, McLean-Mercer Regional Library, Stanton Branch, 312 Harmon Ave, Stanton, ND, 58571. Tel: 701-745-3235. p. 1848

Miller, Nancy, Librn, North Central Regional Library, Coulee City Community, 405 W Main St, Coulee City, WA, 99115. Tel: 509-632-8751. p. 2548

Miller, Nancy Y, Dir, River Falls Public Library, 140 Union St, River Falls, WI, 54022. Tel: 715-425-0905, Ext 101. Fax: 715-425-0914. p. 2634

Miller, Nanette, Tech Serv, Hillsboro City Library, 118 S Waco St, Hillsboro, TX, 76645. Tel: 254-582-7385. Fax: 254-582-7765. p. 2333

Miller, Nannette, Dir, Boyne District Library, 201 E Main St, Boyne City, MI, 49712. Tel: 231-582-7861. Fax: 231-582-2998. p. 1159

Miller, Nannette D, Dir, Elk Rapids District Library, 300 Isle of Pines, Elk Rapids, MI, 49629. Tel: 231-264-9979. Fax: 231-264-9975. p. 1176

Miller, Nesial, Librn, Georgia Department of Corrections, Office of Library Services, 701 Prison Blvd, Sparta, GA, 31087. Tel: 706-444-1026. Fax: 706-444-1137. p. 552

Miller, Owen, Librn, Kaiser-Permanente Medical Center, 2425 Geary Blvd, Mezzanine M150, San Francisco, CA, 94115. Tel: 415-833-2000, 415-833-3837. Fax: 415-833-2200, 415-833-3257. p. 243

Miller, Pam, Tech Serv, Ottawa Library, 105 S Hickory St, Ottawa, KS, 66067-2306. Tel: 785-242-3080. Fax: 785-242-8789. p. 887

Miller, Pamela, Head, Circ, Crystal Lake Public Library, 126 Paddock St, Crystal Lake, IL, 60014. Tel: 815-459-1687. Fax: 815-459-9581. p. 632

Miller, Pamela, Librn, McGill University Libraries, Osler Library, McIntyre Medical Sciences Bldg, 3655 Promenade Sir William Osler, Montreal, QC, H3G 1Y6, CANADA. Tel: 514-398-4475, Ext 09873. Fax: 514-398-5747. p. 2899

Miller, Pat, Circ, Belleville Public Library, 121 E Washington St, Belleville, IL, 62220. Tel: 618-234-0441, Ext 15. Fax: 618-234-9474. p. 593

Miller, Patricia, Mgr, Henry County Public Library System, Cochran Public Library, 174 Burke St, Stockbridge, GA, 30281. Tel: 770-389-7896. Fax: 770-389-7921. p. 544

Miller, Patricia, Adult Serv Mgr, Daniel Boone Regional Library, 100 W Broadway, Columbia, MO, 65203. Tel: 573-443-3161. Fax: 573-443-3281. p. 1324

Miller, Patricia, Dir, Somers Library, 80 Primrose St, Rte 139 & Reis Park, Somers, NY, 10589. Tel: 914-232-5717. Fax: 914-232-1035. p. 1745

Miller, Patricia E, Librn, Scottdale Public Library, 235 Pittsburgh St, Scottdale, PA, 15683-1796. Tel: 724-887-6140. Fax: 724-887-6140. p. 2137

Miller, Patti A, Dir, Colon Township Library, 128 S Blackstone Ave, Colon, MI, 49040. Tel: 269-432-3958. Fax: 269-432-4554. p. 1165

Miller, Patty, Electronic Info Spec, Librn, Group Health Cooperative, Kathleen Hill Library, 320 Westlake Ave N, Ste 100, GHQ-E3S, Seattle, WA, 98109. Tel: 206-448-2542, 206-448-2771. Fax: 206-877-0687. p. 2528

Miller, Paul, Librn, American Jewish University, 15600 Mulholland Dr, Los Angeles, CA, 95311. Tel: 310-476-9777, Ext 238. Fax: 310-476-5423. p. 168

Miller, Paul, Librn, Santa Clara County Library District, Los Altos-Woodland Branch, 1975 Grant Rd, Los Altos, CA, 94022-6984. Tel: 650-969-6030. Fax: 650-969-4922. p. 181

Miller, Paula, Head Librn, Oregon County Library District, Koshkonong Public, 302 Diggins St, Koshkonong, MO, 65692. Tel: 417-867-5472. Fax: 417-867-5472. p. 1319

Miller, Paula J, Exec Dir, Pikes Peak Library District, 20 N Cascade Ave, Colorado Springs, CO, 80903. Tel: 719-531-6333. p. 296

Miller, Paulette, Asst Librn, Hutchinson Memorial Library, 228 N High St, Randolph, WI, 53956. Tel: 920-326-4640. Fax: 920-326-4642. p. 2632

Miller, Peggy, Circ, North Suburban Library District, 6340 N Second St, Loves Park, IL, 61111. Tel: 815-633-4247. Fax: 815-633-4249. p. 668

Miller, Penne, Librn, Scott County Library System, Princeton Branch, 328 River Dr, Princeton, IA, 52768. Tel: 563-289-4282. Fax: 563-289-4282. p. 814

Miller, Pennie V, Dir, Lena Community District Library, 300 W Mason St, Lena, IL, 61048. Tel: 815-369-3180. Fax: 815-369-3181. p. 665

Miller, Philip E, Dr, Librn, Hebrew Union College-Jewish Institute of Religion, One W Fourth St, New York, NY, 10012-1186. Tel: 212-674-5300. Fax: 212-388-1720. p. 1681

Miller, R Bruce, Univ Librn, University of California, Merced Library, 5200 N Lake Rd, Merced, CA, 95343-5001. Tel: 209-228-4237. Fax: 209-228-4271. p. 186

Miller, Rachelle, Dir, Troy-Miami County Public Library, 419 W Main St, Troy, OH, 45373. Tel: 937-339-0502. Fax: 937-335-4880. p. 1941

Miller, Ramona, Dir, Palmer Public Library, 520 Hanson Ave, Palmer, IA, 50571. Tel: 712-359-2296. p. 837

Miller, Randy L, Head, Ref & Instruction, Liberty University Library, 1971 University Blvd, Lynchburg, VA, 24502. Tel: 434-592-3096. Fax: 434-582-2728. p. 2476

Miller, Rebecca, Electronic Res, Head, Acq, Head, Ref, Trinity International University, 2065 Half Day Rd, Deerfield, IL, 60015-1241. Tel: 847-317-4013. Fax: 847-317-4012. p. 635

Miller, Renita, Res, Kirkland & Ellis LLP Library, 300 N LaSalle St, 11th Flr, Chicago, IL, 60654. Tel: 312-862-2358. Fax: 312-862-2200. p. 616

Miller, Richard, Dir, Libr Develop, Nebraska Library Commission, The Atrium, 1200 N St, Ste 120, Lincoln, NE, 68508-2023. Fax: 402-471-2083. p. 1406

Miller, Richard, Exec Dir, Osterhout Free Library, 71 S Franklin St, Wilkes-Barre, PA, 18701-1287. Tel: 570-823-0156. Fax: 570-823-5477. p. 2155

Miller, Rita, Asst Dir, Vermontville Township Library, 120 E First St, Vermontville, MI, 49096. Tel: 517-726-1362. Fax: 517-726-1362. p. 1233

Miller, Robert, Br Mgr, Mid-Continent Public Library, Blue Springs North Branch, 850 NW Hunter Dr, Blue Springs, MO, 64015-7721. Tel: 816-224-8772. Fax: 816-224-4723. p. 1332

Miller, Roberta, Librn, Lillooet Area Library Association, Bridge River Branch, Box 19, Shalaith, BC, V0N 3C0, CANADA. Tel: 250-259-8242. p. 2731

Miller, Robin, Ref Librn & Govt Publ, University of Wisconsin-Eau Claire, 105 Garfield Ave, Eau Claire, WI, 54702-4004. Tel: 715-836-3715. Fax: 715-836-2949. p. 2590

Miller, Robyn, Librn, Monmouth County Library, Marlboro Branch, One Library Ct, Marlboro, NJ, 07746-1102. Tel: 732-536-9406. Fax: 732-536-4708. p. 1499

Miller, Rod, Pub Serv Coordr, Arkansas Supreme Court Library, 625 Marshall St, Ste 1500, Little Rock, AR, 72201. Tel: 501-682-2147. Fax: 501-682-6877. p. 105

Miller, Ron, Dir, World Archaeological Society, 120 Lakewood Dr, Hollister, MO, 65672-9718. Tel: 417-334-2377. p. 1331

Miller, Ron, Syst Adminr, Southern Adventist University, 4851 Industrial Dr, Collegedale, TN, 37315. Tel: 423-236-2796. Fax: 423-236-1788. p. 2230

Miller, Rosalie V, Librn, Shepard-Pruden Memorial Library, 106 W Water St, Edenton, NC, 27932. Tel: 252-482-4112. Fax: 252-482-5451. p. 1790

Miller, Rosanne, Sr Librn, Children's & Br Serv, Orange Public Library & History Center, 407 E Chapman Ave, Orange, CA, 92866-1509. Tel: 714-288-2400. Fax: 714-771-6126. p. 201

Miller, Rosina, Dir, Great Lakes Colleges Association, 121 S Broad St, 7th Flr, Philadelphia, PA, 19107. Tel: 215-735-7300. Fax: 215-735-7373. p. 2110

Miller, Roxanne J, Dir, Knox Public Library, 620 S Main St, Knox, PA, 16232. Tel: 814-797-1054. Fax: 814-797-1054. p. 2075

Miller, Ruie, Br Mgr, Tacoma Public Library, Kobetich, 212 Brown's Point Blvd NE, Tacoma, WA, 98422. p. 2540

Miller, Ruie, Br Mgr, Tacoma Public Library, Swan Creek, 3828 Portland Ave, Tacoma, WA, 98404. p. 2540

Miller, Rush, Univ Librn, University of Pittsburgh, 3960 Forbes Ave, Pittsburgh, PA, 15260. Tel: 412-648-7710. Fax: 412-648-7887. p. 2128

Miller, Rush, Dir, University of Pittsburgh, Hillman Library, 271 Hillman Library, Pittsburgh, PA, 15260. Fax: 412-648-7887. p. 2129

Miller, Ruth, Dir, Harrisburg Public Library District, Two W Walnut St, Harrisburg, IL, 62946-1261. Tel: 618-253-7455. Fax: 618-252-1239. p. 653

Miller, Sara, YA Serv, Atlanta-Fulton Public Library System, Alpharetta Library, 238 Canton St, Alpharetta, GA, 30004. Tel: 770-740-2425. Fax: 770-740-2427. p. 511

Miller, Sarah, Librn, Canadian Environmental Law Association, 130 Spadina Ave, Ste 301, Toronto, ON, M5V 2L4, CANADA. Tel: 416-960-2284. Fax: 416-960-9392. p. 2851

Miller, Sharon, Dir, Mechanics' Institute Library, 57 Post St, San Francisco, CA, 94104-5003. Tel: 415-393-0101. Fax: 415-421-4192. p. 243

Miller, Sharon, Treas, Bay Area Library & Information Network, 1462 Cedar St, Berkeley, CA, 94702. Tel: 415-393-0113. p. 2938

Miller, Sheila, Librn, Muskegon Area District Library, Blind & Physically Handicapped Library, 4845 Airline Rd, Unit 5, Muskegon, MI, 49444. Tel: 231-737-6310. Fax: 231-737-6307. p. 1212

Miller, Sheri, Ch, Whitman County Rural Library District, 102 S Main St, Colfax, WA, 99111-1863. Tel: 509-397-4366. Fax: 509-397-6156. p. 2512

Miller, Sherree, Circ, Nova Scotia Agricultural College Library, 135 College Rd, Truro, NS, B2N 5E3, CANADA. Tel: 902-893-6669. Fax: 902-895-0934. p. 2786

Miller, Shirley, Dir, Vaughn Public Library, 502 W Main St, Ashland, WI, 54806. Tel: 715-682-7060, Ext 22. Fax: 715-682-7185. p. 2579

Miller, Stephen, Br Mgr, Great River Regional Library, Little Falls Public Library, 108 NE Third St, Little Falls, MN, 56345-2708. Tel: 320-632-9676. Fax: 320-632-1697. p. 1275

Miller, Stephen S, Dir, Landis Valley Museum, 2451 Kissel Hill Rd, Lancaster, PA, 17601. Tel: 717-569-0401. Fax: 717-560-2147. p. 2077

Miller, Steve, Ref Librn, Indiana University, Ruth Lilly Law Library, 530 W New York St, Indianapolis, IN, 46202-3225. Tel: 317-274-1929. Fax: 317-274-8825. p. 752

Miller, Steve, Dir, Wellman Scofield Public Library, 711 Fourth St, Wellman, IA, 52356. Tel: 319-646-6858. Fax: 319-646-6561. p. 851

Miller, Steve, Prof, University of Alabama, 514 Main Library, Tuscaloosa, AL, 35487. Tel: 205-348-4610. Fax: 205-348-3746. p. 2961

Miller, Sue, Librn, Putnam County Public Library District, Putnam County - Condit Branch, 105 N Center St, Putnam, IL, 60560. Tel: 815-437-2811. Fax: 815-437-2811. p. 655

Miller, Sue, Br Mgr, Prince George's County Memorial, Fairmount Heights Branch, 5904 Kolb St, Fairmount Heights, MD, 20743-6595. Tel: 301-883-2650. Fax: 301-925-7936. p. 1032

Miller, Susan, Librn, Saint Catherine Hospital, 4321 Fir St, East Chicago, IN, 46312. Tel: 219-392-7230. Fax: 219-392-7231. p. 736

Miller, Susan, Electronic Rec Archivist, Cleveland Museum of Art, 11150 East Blvd, Cleveland, OH, 44106-1797. Tel: 216-707-2530. Fax: 216-421-0921. p. 1877

Miller, Susan A, Dir, Bedford Public Library, 1323 K St, Bedford, IN, 47421. Tel: 812-275-4471. Fax: 812-278-5244. p. 726

Miller, Susanne, Youth Serv, Spokane Public Library, South Hill, 3324 S Perry Ave, Spokane, WA, 99203. Tel: 509-444-5388. Fax: 509-444-5371. p. 2538

Miller, Tatiana, Coll Mgt/Res Sharing, Medical College of Wisconsin Libraries, Health Research Ctr, 3rd Flr, 8701 Watertown Plank Rd, Milwaukee, WI, 53226-0509. Tel: 414-955-8140. Fax: 414-955-6532. p. 2619

Miller, Teri, Circ, Sierra Vista Public Library, 2600 E Tacoma, Sierra Vista, AZ, 85635-1399. Tel: 520-458-4225. Fax: 520-458-5377. p. 82

Miller, Teri, Outreach Serv Librn, Peoria Public Library, 107 NE Monroe St, Peoria, IL, 61602-1070. Tel: 309-497-2069. Fax: 309-497-2007. p. 690

Miller, Terry J, Mgr, Illinois Historic Preservation Agency, 307 Decatur St, Galena, IL, 61036. Tel: 815-777-3310. Fax: 815-777-3310. p. 647

Miller, Thurston D, Br Librn, Hesburgh Libraries, Chemistry-Physics, 231 Nieuwland Science Hall, Notre Dame, IN, 46556. Tel: 574-631-7203. Fax: 574-631-9661. p. 770

Miller, Thurston D, Br Librn, Hesburgh Libraries, Radiation Chemistry Data Center, Radiation Laboratory, Notre Dame, IN, 46556. Tel: 574-631-6527. p. 770

Miller, Tierney, Circ Mgr, Cherry Hill Public Library, 1100 Kings Hwy N, Cherry Hill, NJ, 08034-1911. Tel: 856-903-1245. Fax: 856-667-9503. p. 1478

Miller, Tina, Librn, John F Kennedy University, 100 Ellinwood Way, Pleasant Hill, CA, 94523-4817. Tel: 925-969-3120. p. 210

Miller, Tom, Head Librn, Rogue Community College, Riverside Campus Library, 205 S Central, Medford, OR, 97501. Tel: 541-245-7512. Fax: 541-774-1046. p. 1999

Miller, Tom, Dir, Miners' Museum Library, 17 Museum St, Glace Bay, NS, B1A 5T8, CANADA. Tel: 902-849-4522. Fax: 902-849-8022. p. 2780

Miller, Toni, Sr Librn, Hennepin County Library, Edina, 5280 Grandview Sq, Edina, MN, 55436. Tel: 612-543-6328. Fax: 612-543-6327. p. 1263

Miller, Toni, Sr Librn, Hennepin County Library, Linden Hills, 2900 W 43rd St, Minneapolis, MN, 55410-1515. Tel: 612-543-6328. Fax: 612-543-6827. p. 1263

Miller, Tracy, Br Mgr, Cecil County Public Library, Cecilton Branch, 215 E Main St, Cecilton, MD, 21913-1000. Tel: 410-275-1091. Fax: 410-275-1092. p. 1027

Miller, Tricia, Chief Librn, NASA, Kennedy Space Center, FL, 32899. Tel: 321-867-3600. Fax: 321-867-4534. p. 455

Miller, Trish, Br Mgr, Surrey Public Library, Semiahmoo Library, 1815-152 St, Surrey, BC, V4A 9Y9, CANADA. Tel: 604-592-6911. Fax: 604-502-5751. p. 2739

Miller, Valerie, Head, Circ, Farmingdale Public Library, 116 Merritts Rd, Farmingdale, NY, 11735. Tel: 516-249-9090, Ext 218. Fax: 516-694-9697. p. 1621

Miller, Vicki, Ch, Saint Mary's Public Library, 127 Center St, Saint Marys, PA, 15857. Tel: 814-834-6141. Fax: 814-834-9814. p. 2135

Miller, Vicki S, Coll Develop, Winston-Salem State University, 601 Martin Luther King Jr Dr, Winston-Salem, NC, 27110. Tel: 336-750-2986. Fax: 336-750-2459. p. 1834

Miller, Wayne L, Dir, Ogdensburg Public Library, 312 Washington St, Ogdensburg, NY, 13669-1518. Tel: 315-393-4325. Fax: 315-393-4344. p. 1709

Miller, William, Dean of Libr, Florida Atlantic University, 777 Glades Rd, Boca Raton, FL, 33431. Tel: 561-297-3717. Fax: 561-297-2189. p. 428

Miller, William, Librn, Florida Department of Corrections, Apalachee Correctional Institution-West Unit Library, 52 W Unit Dr, Sneads, FL, 32460. Tel: 850-718-0622. p. 491

Miller, William, Dir, What Cheer Public Library, 308 S Barnes St, What Cheer, IA, 50268-0008. Tel: 641-634-2859. Fax: 641-634-2007. p. 852

Miller, William, Dr, Dean, Univ Libr, Florida Atlantic University, 5353 Parkside Dr, Jupiter, FL, 33458. Tel: 561-297-3760. Fax: 561-799-8587. p. 455

Miller-Francisco, Emily, E-Res Syst & Web Coordr, Southern Oregon University, 1250 Siskiyou Blvd, Ashland, OR, 97520-5076. Tel: 541-552-6819. Fax: 541-552-6429. p. 1990

Miller-Pease, Kristi, Head, Youth Serv, Geneva Public Library District, 127 James St, Geneva, IL, 60134. Tel: 630-232-0780. Fax: 630-232-0881. p. 649

Miller-Ridlon, Ramona, Ref Librn, Santa Fe Community College, 3000 NW 83rd St, Bldg Y-100, Gainesville, FL, 32606. Tel: 352-381-3637. Fax: 352-395-5102. p. 449

Millette, Marjolaine, Coordr, College de Maisonneuve Centre des Medias, 3800 Est rue Sherbrooke E, Montreal, QC, H1X 2A2, CANADA. Tel: 514-254-7131, Ext 4239. Fax: 514-254-2517. p. 2893

Millette, Paul, Dir, Green Mountain College Library, One Brennan Circle, Poultney, VT, 05764-1078. Tel: 802-287-8224. Fax: 802-287-8222. p. 2432

Millhorn, James, Acq Analysis & Relations, Northern Illinois University Libraries, DeKalb, IL, 60115-2868. Tel: 815-753-1054. p. 635

Millhouse, Lisa, Br Mgr, Martins Ferry Public Library, Shadyside Branch, 4300 Central Ave, Shadyside, OH, 43947. Tel: 740-676-0506. Fax: 740-676-0123. p. 1915

Millican, Evans, Local Hist Librn, Flint River Regional Library, 800 Memorial Dr, Griffin, GA, 30223. Tel: 770-412-4770. p. 535

Millie-Koo, Felister, Dir, Midwestern Baptist College, 3400 Morgan Rd, Orion, MI, 48359-2042. Tel: 248-334-0961. Fax: 248-334-2185. p. 1215

Milligan, Aleina, Ch, Adair County Public Library, 307 Greensburg St, Columbia, KY, 42728-1488. Tel: 270-384-2472. Fax: 270-384-9446. p. 910

Milligan, Allison, Br Mgr, Mississippi County Library System, Leachville Public, 105 S Main St, Leachville, AR, 72438. Tel: 870-539-6485. Fax: 870-539-6485. p. 95

Milligan, G Michael, Computer Support Analyst 1, University of Washington Libraries, Media Center, Odegaard Undergraduate Library, Mezzanine Level, Box 353080, Seattle, WA, 98195-3080. Tel: 206-543-6051. Fax: 206-685-8485. p. 2534

Milligan, Jennifer, Dir, Sherrill-Kenwood Free Library, 543 Sherrill Rd, Sherrill, NY, 13461-1263. Tel: 315-363-5980. Fax: 315-363-4133. p. 1743

Milligan, Jessica, Computer Lab Librn/Circ, Benton County Public Library, 121 S Forrest Ave, Camden, TN, 38320-2055. Tel: 731-584-4772. Fax: 731-584-1098. p. 2226

Milligan, Lisa, Br Mgr, Brunswick County Library, Leland Branch, 487 Village Rd, Leland, NC, 28451. Tel: 910-371-9442. Fax: 910-371-1856. p. 1824

Milligan, Sarah, Oral Hist Adminr, Kentucky Historical Society, 100 W Broadway, Frankfort, KY, 40601. Tel: 502-564-1792. Fax: 502-564-4701. p. 913

Milligan, Sarah, Dir, Stillwater County Library, 27 N Fourth St, Columbus, MT, 59019. Tel: 406-322-5009. Fax: 406-322-5009. p. 1377

Milligen, Debra, Asst Librn, Weil, Gotshal & Manges LLP, 700 Louisiana St, Ste 1600, Houston, TX, 77002. Tel: 713-546-5131. Fax: 713-224-9511. p. 2345

Millikan, Karyn, Head, Ch, Tipton County Public Library, 127 E Madison St, Tipton, IN, 46072-1993. Tel: 765-675-8761. Fax: 765-675-4475. p. 782

Milliken, Dianne, Br Mgr, Columbus County Public Library, Chadbourn Community, 301 N Wilson St, Chadbourn, NC, 28431. Tel: 910-654-3322. Fax: 910-654-4392. p. 1829

Milliken, Janice K, Librn, Stanislaus County Law Library, 1101 13th St, Modesto, CA, 95354. Tel: 209-558-7759. Fax: 209-558-8284. p. 189

Milliken, Larry, Ref Librn, Drexel University Libraries, Hagerty Library, 33rd & Market Sts, Philadelphia, PA, 19104-2875. Tel: 215-895-2765. Fax: 215-895-2070. p. 2105

Milliman, Laura, Instruction/Ref Serv, Web Serv, Virginia Western Community College, 3095 Colonial Ave SW, Roanoke, VA, 24015-4705. Tel: 540-857-6509. Fax: 540-857-6058. p. 2495

Millington, Sherry, Tech Serv, Suwannee River Regional Library, 1848 Ohio Ave S, Dr Martin Luther King Jr Ave S, Live Oak, FL, 32064-4517. Tel: 386-364-3482. Fax: 386-364-6071. p. 461

Million, Tara, Librn, Lakeland Library Region, Meadow Lake Branch, SPMC Box 9000, 320 Centre St, Meadow Lake, SK, S9X 1V8, CANADA. Tel: 306-236-5396. Fax: 306-236-6282. p. 2920

Milliron DeBacker, Annette, Exec Dir, Mountain-Valley Library System, 55 E St, Santa Rosa, CA, 95404-4728. Tel: 707-544-0142. Fax: 707-544-8411. p. 267

Millis, Jonathan, Electronic Res Librn, Rochester Institute of Technology, National Technical Institute for the Deaf, Educational Technology Resource Room, 52 Lomb Memorial Dr, NTID at RIT, Rochester, NY, 14623. Tel: 585-475-7913. Fax: 585-475-7588. p. 1732

Miller, Nancy, Head Librn, Harvard Library, George David Birkhoff Mathematical Library, Science Ctr 337, One Oxford St, Cambridge, MA, 02138. Tel: 617-495-2147. p. 1074

Millman-Wilson, Doreen, Mgr, Toronto Rehab, 550 University Ave, Toronto, ON, M5G 2A2, CANADA. Tel: 416-597-3422, Ext 3750. Fax: 416-591-6515. p. 2864

Millott, Diane, Coordr, Acq, Lee County Library System, Processing Center, 881 Gunnery Rd N, Ste 2, Lehigh Acres, FL, 33971-1246. Tel: 239-461-7387. Fax: 239-461-7373. p. 446

Mills, Anice, Undergrad Serv Librn, Columbia University, Philip L Milstein Family College Library, 208 Butler Library, 535 W 114th St, New York, NY, 10027. Tel: 212-854-5327. Fax: 212-854-0089. p. 1675

Mills, Barry, Tech Serv Dir, Burlingame Public Library, 480 Primrose Rd, Burlingame, CA, 94010-4083. Tel: 650-558-7400. Fax: 650-342-1948. p. 130

Mills, Beth, Ref Serv, New Rochelle Public Library, One Library Plaza, New Rochelle, NY, 10801. Tel: 914-632-7878, Ext 1000. Fax: 914-632-0262. p. 1666

Mills, Bill, Assoc Librn, New York Law School Library, 185 W Broadway, New York, NY, 10013. Tel: 212-431-2380. Fax: 212-965-8839. p. 1689

Mills, Cantrelle, Electronic Res Librn, Texas A&M University at Galveston, 200 Seawolf Pkwy, Galveston, TX, 77553. Tel: 409-740-4560. Fax: 409-740-4702. p. 2326

Mills, Deana, Dir, Rector Public Library, 121 W Fourth St, Rector, AR, 72461. Tel: 870-595-2410. Fax: 870-595-2410. p. 113

Mills, Deborah, Cataloger, Art Gallery of Ontario, 317 Dundas St W, Toronto, ON, M5T 1G4, CANADA. Tel: 416-979-6642. Fax: 416-979-6602. p. 2850

Mills, Grace, Dir, Florida Agricultural & Mechanical University, 201 Beggs Ave, Orlando, FL, 32801. Tel: 407-254-3263. Fax: 407-254-3273. p. 475

Mills, Grace M, Dir, Hamline University, School of Law Library, 1536 Hewitt Ave, Saint Paul, MN, 55104-1237. Tel: 651-523-2119. Fax: 651-523-2863. p. 1278

Mills, Joyce W, Dr, Dir, Southern Polytechnic State University, 1100 S Marietta Pkwy, Marietta, GA, 30060-2896. Tel: 678-915-7306. Fax: 678-915-4944. p. 543

Mills, Kim, Librn, Piedmont Public Library, 106 N Main St, Piedmont, AL, 36272. Tel: 256-447-3369. Fax: 256-447-3383. p. 34

Mills, Larry, Sister, Asst Librn, Leanna Hicks Public Library, 2005 Inkster Rd, Inkster, MI, 48141. Tel: 313-563-2822. Fax: 313-274-5130. p. 1193

Mills, Laura, Univ Archivist, Roosevelt University, 430 S Michigan Ave, Chicago, IL, 60605. Tel: 312-341-2280, 341-1275. Fax: 312-341-2425. p. 623

Mills, Lynnette, Br Librn, Davis County Library, Kaysville Branch, 44 N Main St, Kaysville, UT, 84037. Tel: 801-544-2826. Fax: 801-544-5646. p. 2405

Mills, Maggie, Mgr, Salt Lake County Library Services, Park Branch, 4870 S 2700 West, Taylorsville, UT, 84118-2138. Tel: 801-944-7618. Fax: 801-965-3907. p. 2414

Mills, Margret, Pub Serv, Skagit Valley College, 2405 E College Way, Mount Vernon, WA, 98273-5899. Tel: 360-416-7760. Fax: 360-416-7698. p. 2521

Mills, Maryanne, Info Literacy, West Valley Community College Library, 14000 Fruitvale Ave, Saratoga, CA, 95070-5698. Tel: 408-741-4661. Fax: 408-741-2134. p. 268

Mills, Michon, In Charge, Carson-Tahoe Regional Medical Center, 1600 Medical Pkwy, Carson City, NV, 89703. Tel: 775-445-8788. Fax: 775-888-3203. p. 1425

Mills, Nancy, Librn, English Lutheran Church Library, 1509 King St, La Crosse, WI, 54601. Tel: 608-784-9335. Fax: 608-784-8936. p. 2603

Mills, Pat, Ch, Cedar City Public Library in the Park, 303 N 100 East, Cedar City, UT, 84720. Tel: 435-586-6661. Fax: 435-865-7280. p. 2404

Mills, Phyllis, Br Librn, Chesterfield County Library, Pageland Community Library, 109 W Blakeney St, Pageland, SC, 29728. Tel: 843-672-6930. Fax: 843-672-6670. p. 2186

Mills, Rose, Graphic & Visual Design Spec, Way Public Library, 101 E Indiana Ave, Perrysburg, OH, 43551. Tel: 419-874-3135, Ext 108. Fax: 419-874-6129. p. 1929

Mills, Susan, Asst Dir, Warren Public Library, 123 E Third St, Warren, IN, 46792. Tel: 260-375-3450. Fax: 260-375-3450. p. 785

Millsap, Gina, Exec Dir, Topeka & Shawnee County Public Library, 1515 SW Tenth Ave, Topeka, KS, 66604-1374. Tel: 785-580-4400. Fax: 785-580-4496. p. 897

Millsaps, Rita, Librn, Northeast Regional Library, Rienzi Public Library, School St, Rienzi, MS, 38865. Tel: 662-462-5015. p. 1297

Millson-Martula, Christopher, Dir, Libr Serv, Lynchburg College, 1501 Lakeside Dr, Lynchburg, VA, 24501-3199. Tel: 434-544-8399. Fax: 434-544-8499. p. 2476

Millton, Karen, Admin Serv, Asst Dir, Autauga-Prattville Public Library, 254 Doster St, Prattville, AL, 36067-3933. Tel: 334-365-3396. Fax: 334-365-3397. p. 34

Millward, Debbie L, Mgr, Pacific Newspaper Group Library, 200 Granville St, Vancouver, BC, V6C 3N3, CANADA. Tel: 604-605-2605. Fax: 604-605-2353. p. 2742

Millwood, Kent, Dir, Libr Serv, Anderson University Library, 316 Boulevard, Anderson, SC, 29621. Tel: 864-231-2049. Fax: 864-231-2191. p. 2181

Milman, Joeleen, Librn, Lakeland Library Region, Maymont Branch, PO Box 102, Maymont, SK, S0M 1T0, CANADA. Tel: 306-389-2006. p. 2920

Milnarich, Sarah, Dir, Joe Barnhart Bee County Public Library, 110 W Corpus Christi St, Beeville, TX, 78102-5604. Tel: 361-362-4901. Fax: 361-358-8694. p. 2288

Milnarich, Sarah, Dir, Coastal Bend College, 3800 Charco Rd, Beeville, TX, 78102-2110. Tel: 361-354-2741. Fax: 361-354-2719. p. 2288

Milne, Debbie, Librn, Cimarron City Library, Ingalls Branch, 220 S Main St, Ingalls, KS, 67853. Tel: 620-335-5580. p. 860

Milner, Alice, Librn, Virginia Department of Corrections, 1900 River Rd W, Crozier, VA, 23039. Tel: 804-784-6841. Fax: 804-784-6999. p. 2458

Milner, Devin, Coll Develop, San Diego Mesa College Library, 7250 Mesa College Dr, San Diego, CA, 92111-4998. Tel: 619-388-2547. Fax: 619-388-2922. p. 235

Milner, Kay, Dir, Karl Miles Lecompte Memorial Library, 110 S Franklin, Corydon, IA, 50060-1518. Tel: 641-872-1621. Fax: 641-872-1621. p. 804

Milner, Lesley, Assoc Dean, User Serv, Northeastern University Libraries, Snell Library, 360 Huntington Ave, Boston, MA, 02115. Tel: 617-373-4920. p. 1065

Milner, Linda, Asst Dir, Mid-Mississippi Regional Library System, 201 S Huntington St, Kosciusko, MS, 39090-9002. Tel: 662-289-5151. Fax: 662-289-5106. p. 1306

Milner, Renate, Dir, Lowndes County Historical Society & Museum, 305 W Central Ave, Valdosta, GA, 31601-5404. Tel: 229-247-4780. Fax: 229-247-2840. p. 555

Milnor, Barbara, Interim Dir, Basalt Regional Library District, 14 Midland Ave, Basalt, CO, 81621-8305. Tel: 970-927-4311. Fax: 970-927-1351. p. 289

Milo, Sue, Head, Tech Serv, Rockbridge Regional Library, 138 S Main St, Lexington, VA, 24450-2316. Tel: 540-463-4324. Fax: 540-464-4824. p. 2474

Milos, Courtney, Asst Librn, Southeast Regional Library, Fillmore Branch, 51 Main St, Fillmore, SK, S0G 1N0, CANADA. Tel: 306-722-3369. p. 2929

Milott, Alice, Librn, Pickaway County Law Library Association, 207 S Court St, Circleville, OH, 43113. Tel: 740-474-6026. Fax: 740-477-6334. p. 1875

Milrod, Leslie, Ch, Westhampton Free Library, Seven Library Ave, Westhampton Beach, NY, 11978-2697. Tel: 631-288-3335. Fax: 631-288-5715. p. 1768

Miltenberg, Anne, Ch, YA Serv, Hempstead Public Library, 115 Nichols Ct, Hempstead, NY, 11550-3199. Tel: 516-481-6990. Fax: 516-481-6719. p. 1634

Miltner, Susan, Ch, Lytton Public Library, 118 Main St, Lytton, IA, 50561. Tel: 712-466-2522. Fax: 712-466-2522. p. 828

Milton, Chris, Acq, Door County Library, 107 S Fourth Ave, Sturgeon Bay, WI, 54235. Tel: 920-746-2491. Fax: 920-743-6697. p. 2640

Milton, Denise, Dir, Jasper Public Library, 175 E Water St, Jasper, TX, 75951. Tel: 409-384-3791. Fax: 409-384-5881. p. 2348

Milunovich, Kent, Tech Serv, Seattle University, School of Law Library, 901 12th Ave, Seattle, WA, 98122-4411. Tel: 206-398-4221. Fax: 206-398-4194. p. 2532

Mimms, Mike, Media Serv Spec, University of Cincinnati, 2540 Clifton Ave, Cincinnati, OH, 45219. Tel: 513-556-0161. Fax: 513-556-6265. p. 1874

Mims, Gloria, Ref Librn, Atlanta-Fulton Public Library System, Auburn Avenue Research Library on African-American Culture & History, 101 Auburn Ave NE, Atlanta, GA, 30303. Tel: 404-730-4001, Ext 199. Fax: 404-730-5879. p. 511

Mims, Lisa M, Br Mgr, Dixie Regional Library System, Houston Carnegie Branch, 105 W Madison St, Houston, MS, 38851-2207. Tel: 662-456-3381. Fax: 662-456-3381. p. 1312

Mims, LuAnn, Col Archivist, Florida Southern College, 111 Lake Hollingsworth Dr, Lakeland, FL, 33801-5698. Tel: 863-680-4994. Fax: 863-680-4126. p. 459

Minars, Kelley, Web Serv Librn, University of Texas Health Science Center at San Antonio Libraries, 7703 Floyd Curl Dr, MSC 7940, San Antonio, TX, 78229-3900. Tel: 210-567-2400. Fax: 210-567-2490. p. 2383

Minasian, Charlotte, Librn, Addison Gilbert Hospital, 298 Washington St, Gloucester, MA, 01930. Tel: 978-283-4001, Ext 608. Fax: 978-281-1129. p. 1091

Minato, Lisa, Info Res, Belt Collins Hawaii LLC, 2153 N King St, Ste 200, Honolulu, HI, 96819-4570. Tel: 808-521-5361. Fax: 808-538-7819. p. 560

Mincey, Jennifer, Evening Librn, Wake Technical Community College, Northern Wake Library, 6600 Louisburg Rd, Bldg B, Rm 239, Raleigh, NC, 27616. Tel: 919-532-5550. p. 1818

Mincy, James, Librn, University of Arkansas-Pine Bluff, Music Lab, 1200 N University Dr, Pine Bluff, AR, 71601. Tel: 870-575-7036. p. 113

Mindeman, George A, Dir, Libr Serv, Covenant College, 14049 Scenic Hwy, Lookout Mountain, GA, 30750. Tel: 706-419-1430. Fax: 706-419-3480. p. 539

Minder, Jane, Ref Supvr, Kentucky Department for Libraries & Archives, 300 Coffee Tree Rd, Frankfort, KY, 40601. Tel: 502-564-8300. Fax: 502-564-5773. p. 913

Minei, Audrey, Tech Serv, East-West Center, 1601 East-West Rd, Honolulu, HI, 96848-1601. Tel: 808-944-7554. Fax: 808-944-7600. p. 560

Miner, Donna, Librn, Palliser Regional Library, Riverhurst Branch, 324 Teck St, Riverhurst, SK, S0H 3P0, CANADA. Tel: 306-353-2130. p. 2919

Miner, Glynis, Dir, Samuel H Wentworth Library, 35 Main St, Center Sandwich, NH, 03227. Tel: 603-284-6665. Fax: 603-284-6577. p. 1440

Miner, Jerry, Librn, Agriculture & Agri-Food Canada, Canadian Agriculture Library, 32 Main St, Kentville, NS, B4N 1J5, CANADA. Tel: 902-679-5508. Fax: 902-679-5784. p. 2783

Miner, Meg, Spec Coll Librn, Univ Archivist, Illinois Wesleyan University, One Ames Plaza, Bloomington, IL, 61701-7188. Tel: 556-309-1538. Fax: 309-556-3706. p. 595

Miner, Nancy, Asst Dir, Durham Public Library, Seven Mill Rd, Unit H, Durham, NH, 03824-0954. Tel: 603-868-6699. Fax: 603-868-9944. p. 1445

Miner, Tom, Dir, Elsie S Hogan Community Library, 100 N Curtis Ave, Willcox, AZ, 85643. Tel: 520-766-4250. Fax: 520-384-0126. p. 89

Miner, Vicki, Mat Mgr, Belhaven University, 1500 Peachtree St, Jackson, MS, 39202. Tel: 601-968-5945. Fax: 601-968-5968. p. 1303

Miners, Judy, Libr Dir, Alder Flats Public Library, PO Box 148, Alder Flats, AB, T0C 0A0, CANADA. Tel: 780-388-3881. Fax: 780-388-3887. p. 2683

Minerva, Tony, Electronic Res, Williams & Connolly Library, 725 12th St NW, Washington, DC, 20005. Tel: 202-434-5310. Fax: 202-434-5029. p. 423

Mines, Denise C, Syst Coordr, Law Library of Montgomery County, Court House, Swede & Airy Streets, Norristown, PA, 19404. Tel: 610-278-3806. Fax: 610-278-5998. p. 2098

Minges, Jim, Dir, Northeast Kansas Library System, 4317 W Sixth St, Lawrence, KS, 66049. Tel: 785-838-4090. Fax: 785-838-3989. p. 878

Minges, Shirley, Dir, Farnam Public Library, 313 Main St, Farnam, NE, 69029. Tel: 308-569-2318. p. 1398

Mingo, David, In Charge, Lafayette Public Library, Butler Memorial & Martin Luther King Center, 309 Cora St, Lafayette, LA, 70501. Tel: 337-234-0363. p. 952

Mingo, Verna, Head, Acq & Ser, Nova Scotia Agricultural College Library, 135 College Rd, Truro, NS, B2N 5E3, CANADA. Tel: 902-893-6669. Fax: 902-895-0934. p. 2786

Mingori, John, Libr Asst, Effingham Public Library, 30 Town House Rd, Effingham, NH, 03882. Tel: 603-539-1537. p. 1446

Minica, Kelley, Cat, Madison Area Technical College, 3550 Anderson St, Rm 230, Madison, WI, 53704. Tel: 608-243-4086. Fax: 608-246-6644. p. 2606

Minich, Irene, Librn, ENSCO, Inc, 5400 Port Royal Rd, Springfield, VA, 22151-2312. Tel: 703-321-4604. Fax: 703-321-4565. p. 2496

Minick, Evelyn, Dir, Libr Serv, Saint Joseph's University, Francis A Drexel Library, 5600 City Ave, Philadelphia, PA, 19131-1395. Tel: 610-660-1905. Fax: 610-660-1916. p. 2116

Minicozzi, Irene, Asst Librn, Yakima Valley Genealogical Society Library, 1901 S 12th Ave, Union Gap, WA, 98903. Tel: 509-248-1328. p. 2545

Miniel, Susan, Dir, Henry C Adams Memorial Library, 209 W Third St, Prophetstown, IL, 61277. Tel: 815-537-5462. Fax: 815-537-5462. p. 692

Minion, Robin, Dir, Olds College Library, 4500 50th St, Olds, AB, T4H 1R6, CANADA. Tel: 403-556-4600. Fax: 403-556-4705. p. 2713

Mink, Dorothy, Asst Librn, Potter County Free Public Library, 106 E Commercial Ave, Gettysburg, SD, 57442-1507. Tel: 605-765-9518. p. 2212

Minkel, Sean, Circ Librn, Tech Serv Librn, Rapid City Public Library, 610 Quincy St, Rapid City, SD, 57701-3630. Tel: 605-394-6139. Fax: 605-394-4064. p. 2217

Minkiewicz, Carol, Librn, Network Tech, Webmaster, Kellogg-Hubbard Library, 135 Main St, Montpelier, VT, 05602. Tel: 802-223-3338. Fax: 802-223-3338. p. 2429

Minkoff, Meredith, Ch, Mineola Memorial Library, 195 Marcellus Rd, Mineola, NY, 11501. Tel: 516-746-8488. Fax: 516-294-6459. p. 1661

Minks, Agnes, Librn, Wharton County Library, East Bernard Branch, 746 Clubside Dr, East Bernard, TX, 77435. Tel: 979-335-6142. p. 2400

Minks, Gina, Imaging & Presv Serv Mgr, Amigos Library Services, Inc, 14400 Midway Rd, Ste 200, Dallas, TX, 75244-3509. Tel: 972-340-2825. Fax: 972-991-6061. p. 2956

Minnehan, Shari, Dir, Churdan City Library, 414 Sand St, Churdan, IA, 50050. Tel: 515-389-3423. Fax: 515-389-3401. p. 802

Minnella, Rosemary, Br Supvr, Burlington Public Library, Brant Hills, 2255 Brant St, Burlington, ON, L7P 5C8, CANADA. Tel: 905-335-2209. p. 2798

Minnema, Tom, Circ Mgr, Goucher College Library, 1021 Dulaney Valley Rd, Baltimore, MD, 21204. Tel: 410-337-6356. Fax: 410-337-6419. p. 1014

Minner, Brook, Dir, Northeast Harbor Library, One Joy Rd, Northeast Harbor, ME, 04662. Tel: 207-276-3333. Fax: 207-276-3315. p. 994

Minnerly, Liz, Librn, Central Florida Community College, 3001 SW College Rd, Ocala, FL, 34474-4415. Tel: 352-237-2111, Ext 1344. Fax: 352-873-5818. p. 473

Minnich, Debbie, Asst Librn, West Virginia Junior College Library, 1000 Virginia St E, Charleston, WV, 25301. Tel: 304-345-2820, Ext 314. Fax: 304-345-1425. p. 2557

Minnick, Cindy, Br Supvr, Montgomery-Floyd Regional Library System, Meadowbrook Public, 267 Alleghany Springs Rd, Shawsville, VA, 24162. Tel: 540-268-1964. p. 2457

Minnick, Jo, Dir, Monon Town & Township Public Library, 427 N Market, Monon, IN, 47959. Tel: 219-253-6517. Fax: 219-253-8373. p. 765

Minnigh, Joel D, Dir, Wilkinsburg Public Library, 605 Ross Ave, Pittsburgh, PA, 15221-2195. Tel: 412-244-2941. Fax: 412-243-6943. p. 2130

Minnigh, Joel D, Dir, Wilkinsburg Public Library, Eastridge, 1900 Graham Blvd, Pittsburgh, PA, 15235. Tel: 412-342-0056. p. 2130

Minnis, Mary Lee, Asst Dir, Ch, Meadville Public Library, 848 N Main St, Meadville, PA, 16335-2689. Tel: 814-336-1773. Fax: 814-333-8173. p. 2086

Minnix, Linda, Media Spec, Ridge Career Center Library, 7700 State Rd 544, Winter Haven, FL, 33881. Tel: 863-419-3060, Ext 4133. Fax: 863-419-3062. p. 505

Minnix, Marsha, Circ, Chillicothe & Ross County Public Library, Richmond Dale Community Branch, 770 Main St, Richmond Dale, OH, 45673. Tel: 740-702-4190. Fax: 740-702-4191. p. 1867

Minor, Barb, Tech Spec, Faegre & Benson, LLP, 2200 Wells Fargo Ctr, 90 South Seventh St, Minneapolis, MN, 55402-3901. Tel: 612-766-7000. Fax: 612-766-1600. p. 1259

Minor, Eugenia, Cat, University of Mississippi, Three Grove Loop, University, MS, 38677. Tel: 662-915-6833. Fax: lweam@olemiss.edu. p. 1316

Minor, Jane, Librn, John F Kennedy University, 100 Ellinwood Way, Pleasant Hill, CA, 94523-4817. Tel: 925-969-3120. p. 210

Minor, Linda, Ref Serv, Ad, Forest Grove City Library, 2114 Pacific Ave, Forest Grove, OR, 97116-9019. Tel: 503-992-3280. Fax: 503-992-3333. p. 1998

Minor, Lynn Marie, Syst Coordr, Chesterfield Township Library, 50560 Patricia Ave, Chesterfield, MI, 48051-3804. Tel: 586-598-4900. Fax: 586-598-7900. p. 1163

Minor, Ronald L, Tech Info Spec, United States Department of Labor, 1301 Airport Rd, Beaver, WV, 25813-9426. Tel: 304-256-3229. Fax: 304-256-3372. p. 2553

Minorics, Sunny, Tech Librn, Free Public Library of Monroe Township, 713 Marsha Ave, Williamstown, NJ, 08094. Tel: 856-629-1212. Fax: 856-875-0191. p. 1544

Minshull, Janis, Youth Serv Librn, Conway Public Library, 15 Main St, Conway, NH, 03818. Tel: 603-447-5552. Fax: 603-447-6921. p. 1444

Minshull, Mary-Anne, Librn, Southwestern Manitoba Regional Library, Pierson Branch, 58 Railway Ave, Pierson, MB, R0M 1S0, CANADA. Tel: 204-634-2215. Fax: 204-634-2479. p. 2750

Minter, Nancy L, Pres, Interlibrary Users Association, c/o Urban Institute Library, 2100 M St NW, Washington, DC, 20037. Tel: 202-261-5534. Fax: 202-223-3043. p. 2940

Minton, Helena, Dir, Flint Memorial Library, 147 Park St, North Reading, MA, 01864. Tel: 978-664-4942. Fax: 978-664-0812. p. 1113

Minton, JoNell, Dir, Dunklin County Library, 209 N Main, Kennett, MO, 63857. Tel: 573-888-2261, 573-888-3561. Fax: 573-888-6393. p. 1341

Minton, Mandie, Librn, Research Planning Inc Library, 1121 Park St, Columbia, SC, 29201-3137. Tel: 803-256-7322. Fax: 803-254-6445. p. 2188

Minton, Renee, Ch, Milo Public Library, 123 Main St, Milo, IA, 50166. Tel: 641-942-6557. Fax: 641-942-6557. p. 832

Mintz, Annette, Circ, Gaston College, 201 Hwy 321 S, Dallas, NC, 28034-1499. Tel: 704-922-6359. Fax: 704-922-2342. p. 1786

Minutella, Ann, Assoc Dean, Libr for Pub & Admin Serv, Adelphi University Libraries, One South Ave, Garden City, NY, 11530. Tel: 516-877-3518. Fax: 516-877-3592. p. 1625

Minuti, Aurelia, Archivist, Head, Ref, Albert Einstein College of Medicine, 1300 Morris Park Ave, Bronx, NY, 10461. Tel: 718-430-3108. Fax: 718-430-8795. p. 1586

Miraflor, Angie, Actg Sr Librn, Prog & Youth Serv, San Jose Public Library, 150 E San Fernando St, San Jose, CA, 95112-3580. Tel: 408-808-2188. Fax: 408-808-2004. p. 250

Miranda, Ball, Dir, Lawrence County Public Library, 401 College St, Moulton, AL, 35650. Tel: 256-974-0883. Fax: 256-974-0890. p. 31

Miranda, Cecilia, Automation Syst Coordr, Tech Serv, Midland College, 3600 N Garfield, Midland, TX, 79705. Tel: 432-685-4560. Fax: 432-685-6710. p. 2363

Miranda, Joseph, Budget Analyst/Journal Ed, Northeastern University School of Law Library, 400 Huntington Ave, Boston, MA, 02115. Tel: 617-373-3552. Fax: 617-373-8705. p. 1066

Miranda, Salvatore, Head, Adult Serv, Tarpon Springs Public Library, 138 E Lemon St, Tarpon Springs, FL, 34689. Tel: 727-943-4922. Fax: 727-943-4926. p. 499

Mirando, Louis, Chief Librn, York University Libraries, Osgoode Hall Law School Library, One Scholar's Walk, York University, Toronto, ON, M3J 1P3, CANADA. Tel: 416-736-5646. Fax: 416-736-5298. p. 2868

Mirau, Dan, Dir, Concordia University College of Alberta, 7128 Ada Blvd, Edmonton, AB, T5B 4E4, CANADA. Tel: 780-479-9338. Fax: 780-471-6796. p. 2700

Mire, Ann, Acq, Ref Serv, Acadia Parish Library, 1125 N Parkerson Ave, Crowley, LA, 70526. Tel: 337-788-1880, 337-788-1881. Fax: 337-788-3759. p. 948

Mireles, Pura, Dir, Laguna Vista Public Library, 1300 Palm Blvd, Laguna Vista, TX, 78578. Tel: 956-943-7155. Fax: 956-943-2371. p. 2352

Miriello, Susan, Youth Serv Librn, Mifflin County Library, 123 N Wayne St, Lewistown, PA, 17044-1794. Tel: 717-242-2391. Fax: 717-242-2825. p. 2081

Mirkin, Sima, Cat, American University, 4801 Massachusetts Ave NW, Washington, DC, 20016-8182. Tel: 202-274-4344. Fax: 202-274-4365. p. 393

Mirmira, Uma, Head, ILL, Head, Info Serv, Addison Public Library, Four Friendship Plaza, Addison, IL, 60101. Tel: 630-458-3314. Fax: 630-543-6645. p. 587

Miro, Elizabeth, Libr Serv Supvr, Hialeah-John F Kennedy Library, 190 W 49th St, Hialeah, FL, 33012-3798. Tel: 305-821-2700. Fax: 305-818-9144. p. 450

Miros, Donna J, Cat, Mars Area Public Library, 107 Grand Ave, Mars, PA, 16046. Tel: 724-625-9048. Fax: 724-625-2871. p. 2084

Mirra, Teresa, Youth Serv, Lakeville Public Library, Four Precinct St, Lakeville, MA, 02347. Tel: 508-947-9028. Fax: 508-923-9934. p. 1097

Mirsky, Rosemary, Ad, Royal Oak Public Library, 222 E Eleven Mile Rd, Royal Oak, MI, 48067-2633. Tel: 248-246-3715. Fax: 248-246-3701. p. 1223

Mirvis, Diane, Univ Librn, University of Bridgeport, 126 Park Ave, Bridgeport, CT, 06604-5620. Tel: 203-576-4749. Fax: 203-576-4791. p. 332

Mirvis, Ronald, Head, Ref, Librn, Association of the Bar of the City of New York Library, 42 W 44th St, New York, NY, 10036. Tel: 212-382-6666. Fax: 212-382-6790. p. 1669

Mirwis, Allan, Reader Serv, Kingsborough Community College, 2001 Oriental Blvd, Brooklyn, NY, 11235. Tel: 718-368-5971. Fax: 718-368-5482. p. 1592

Mirza, Lora, Assoc Dir, Coll Develop, Georgia Perimeter College, Dunwoody Campus Library, 2101 Womack Rd, Dunwoody, GA, 30338-4497. Tel: 770-274-5091. Fax: 770-274-5090. p. 525

Mirzadeh, Azadeh, Per, Farmingdale State College of New York, 2350 Broadhollow Rd, Farmingdale, NY, 11735-1021. Tel: 631-420-2040. Fax: 631-420-2473. p. 1622

Mischak, Erin, Distance Educ Librn, University of Wisconsin Oshkosh, 801 Elmwood Ave, Oshkosh, WI, 54901. Tel: 920-424-1361. Fax: 920-424-7334. p. 2628

Mischke, Laura, Dept Chair, St Luke's College Library, 2620 Pierce St, Sioux City, IA, 51104. Tel: 712-279-3156. p. 844

Mischler, Susan, Dir, Boone-Madison Public Library, 375 Main St, Madison, WV, 25130-1295. Tel: 304-369-7842. Fax: 304-369-2950. p. 2564

Mischo, William, Librn, University of Illinois Library at Urbana-Champaign, Grainger Engineering Library Information Center, 1301 W Springfield, Urbana, IL, 61801. Tel: 217-333-3576. Fax: 217-244-7764. p. 712

Miser, Lisa, Librn, Proctor Free Library, Four Main St, Proctor, VT, 05765. Tel: 802-459-3539. Fax: 802-459-3539. p. 2432

Miser, Liz, Asst Dir, Hansford County Library, 122 Main St, Spearman, TX, 79081. Tel: 806-659-2231. Fax: 806-659-5042. p. 2388

Misfeldt, Rian, Mkt Librn, SIAST-Saskatchewan Institute of Applied Science & Technology, 4500 Wascana Pkwy, Regina, SK, S4P 3S7, CANADA. Tel: 306-775-7413. Fax: 306-798-0560. p. 2924

Misialek, Cheryl, Coordr, North Dakota Vision Services-School for the Blind, 500 Stanford Rd, Grand Forks, ND, 58203. Tel: 701-795-2700. Fax: 701-795-2727. p. 1842

Misko, Elaine J, Univ Librn, Carlow University, 3333 Fifth Ave, Pittsburgh, PA, 15213. Tel: 412-578-6139. Fax: 412-578-6242. p. 2122

Misner, Doug, Coll Mgr, Librn, Res, Utah State Historical Society, 300 Rio Grande, Salt Lake City, UT, 84101-1182. Tel: 801-533-3535. Fax: 801-533-3504. p. 2415

Misra, Jayasri, Ref Librn, Atlanta-Fulton Public Library System, Northeast-Spruill Oaks Regional Library, 9560 Spruill Rd, Alpharetta, GA, 30022. Tel: 770-360-8820. Fax: 770-360-8823. p. 512

Misra, Sue, Librn, Genesee District Library, Headquarters, G-4195 W Pasadena Ave, Flint, MI, 48504. Tel: 810-732-0110. Fax: 810-732-3146. p. 1180

Missall, Darlene, Asst Librn, Hutchinson Memorial Library, 228 N High St, Randolph, WI, 53956. Tel: 920-326-4640. Fax: 920-326-4642. p. 2632

Misselt, Barbara, Dir, East Central Regional Library, 244 S Birch, Cambridge, MN, 55008-1588. Tel: 763-689-7390. Fax: 763-689-7389. p. 1243

Misslin, Jane, Staff Librn, Concord Free Public Library, 129 Main St, Concord, MA, 01742-2494. Tel: 978-318-3300. Fax: 978-318-3344. p. 1082

Missner, Emily, Ref Librn, Drexel University Libraries, Hagerty Library, 33rd & Market Sts, Philadelphia, PA, 19104-2875. Tel: 215-895-6164. Fax: 215-895-2070. p. 2105

Missonis, George E, AV, Albright College, 13th & Exeter Sts, Reading, PA, 19604. Tel: 610-921-7203. Fax: 610-921-7509. p. 2132

Mitchell, Alecia, Br Mgr, Charlotte Mecklenburg Library, West Boulevard Branch, 2157 West Blvd, Charlotte, NC, 28208. Tel: 704-416-7400. Fax: 704-416-7500. p. 1782

Mitchell, Amanda, Electronic Res & Instruction Librn, State University of New York College of Technology, Bush Hall, Two Main St, Delhi, NY, 13753. Tel: 607-746-4635. Fax: 607-746-4327. p. 1613

Mitchell, Amy, Curator, Railroad & Heritage Museum Library, 315 West Ave B, Temple, TX, 76501. Tel: 254-298-5172. Fax: 254-298-5171. p. 2390

Mitchell, Amy, Dir, Health Info, Salt Lake Regional Medical Center, 1050 E South Temple, Salt Lake City, UT, 84102. Tel: 801-350-4060, 801-350-4111, 801-350-4631. Fax: 801-350-4390. p. 2414

Mitchell, Andrea L, Exec Dir, Substance Abuse Librarians & Information Specialists, PO Box 9513, Berkeley, CA, 94709-0513. Fax: 510-985-6459. p. 2939

Mitchell, Anne, Tech Serv, United States Army, Stimson Library, Medical Department Center & School, 3630 Stanley Rd, Bldg 2840, Ste 106, Fort Sam Houston, TX, 78234-6100. Tel: 210-221-6900. Fax: 210-221-8264. p. 2321

Mitchell, Betty, Librn, Pratt Memorial Library, 752 Main St, New Milford, PA, 18834. Tel: 570-465-3098. p. 2097

Mitchell, Beverly, Art & Dance Librn, Southern Methodist University, Hamon Arts Library, 6101 N Bishop Blvd, Dallas, TX, 75275. Tel: 214-768-1855. Fax: 214-768-1800. p. 2310

Mitchell, Bill, Asst Regional Dir, York Library Region, Four Carleton St, Fredericton, NB, E3B 5P4, CANADA. Tel: 506-457-7271. Fax: 506-457-4878. p. 2764

Mitchell, Bonnie, Dir, Framingham State College, 100 State St, Framingham, MA, 01701. Tel: 508-626-4651. Fax: 508-626-4649. p. 1090

Mitchell, Brenda, Dir, Roseland Community Hospital, 45 W 111th St, Chicago, IL, 60628. Tel: 773-995-3191. Fax: 773-995-5863. p. 623

Mitchell, Breon, Dir, Indiana University Bloomington, Lilly Library Rare Books & Manuscripts, 1200 E Seventh St, Bloomington, IN, 47405-5500. Tel: 812-855-2452. Fax: 812-855-3143. p. 728

Mitchell, Brian, Br Mgr, First Regional Library, Walls Public Library, 7181 Delta Bluff Pkwy, Walls, MS, 38680. Tel: 662-781-3664. Fax: 662-781-3427. p. 1302

Mitchell, Carol, Dir, Robertson County Public Library, 207 N Main St, Mount Olivet, KY, 41064. Tel: 606-724-5746. Fax: 606-724-5746. p. 930

Mitchell, Charlotte, In Charge, Fairmont First Baptist Church, 416 S Main, Fairmont, NC, 28340. Tel: 910-628-0626. Fax: 910-628-0627. p. 1792

Mitchell, Christopher, Dr, Dir, Wheaton College, Marion E Wade Center, 351 E Lincoln, Wheaton, IL, 60187-4213. Tel: 630-752-5908. Fax: 630-752-5459. p. 718

Mitchell, Cindy, Col Librn, Tippecanoe County-Ivy Tech Library, 3101 S Creasy Lane, Lafayette, IN, 47903. Tel: 765-269-5381. Fax: 765-269-5383. p. 759

Mitchell, Colleen, Dir, Sullivan City Public Library, Two W Water St, Sullivan, IL, 61951. Tel: 217-728-7221. Fax: 217-728-2215. p. 708

Mitchell, Cory, Coll Develop/Educ Mat Ctr/Instruction Librn, University of Wisconsin-Stout Library, 315 Tenth Ave, Menomonie, WI, 54751-0790. Tel: 715 232-2363. Fax: 715-232-1783. p. 2615

Mitchell, Debbie, Librn, Lovington Public Library, 115 Main St, Lovington, NM, 88260. Tel: 575-396-3144, 575-396-6900. Fax: 575-396-7189. p. 1559

Mitchell, Deborah, Dir, Warren County-Vicksburg Public Library, 700 Veto St, Vicksburg, MS, 39180-3595. Tel: 601-636-6411. Fax: 601-634-4809. p. 1317

Mitchell, Diane, Librn, Richland Public Library, 370 Scarbrough St, Richland, MS, 39218. Tel: 601-932-1846. Fax: 601-932-1688. p. 1313

Mitchell, Doris F, Assoc Dean, North Carolina Agricultural & Technical State University, 1601 E Market St, Greensboro, NC, 27411-0002. Tel: 336-334-7158, Ext 3204. Fax: 336-334-7783. p. 1797

Mitchell, Eileen, Asst Librn, Beach Haven Free Public Library, 247 N Beach Ave, Beach Haven, NJ, 08008-1865. Tel: 609-492-7081. Fax: 609-492-1048. p. 1471

Mitchell, Eleanor, Dir, Dickinson College, 333 W High St, Carlisle, PA, 17013-2896. Tel: 717-245-1142. Fax: 717-245-1439. p. 2041

Mitchell, Elizabeth, Librn, Princeton Public Library, 40 Main St, Princeton, ME, 04668. Tel: 207-796-5333. p. 998

Mitchell, Faye, Res, Sun Life Assurance Company of Canada, 150 King St W, 4th Flr, Toronto, ON, M5H 1J9, CANADA. Tel: 416-204-3835. Fax: 416-595-0346. p. 2858

Mitchell, Grace, Asst Dir, Prog Coordr, Dennis P McHugh Piermont Public Library, 25 Flywheel Park W, Piermont, NY, 10968. Tel: 845-359-4595. p. 1717

Mitchell, Gregory A, Dir, Texas A&M University-Commerce, 2600 S Neal St, Commerce, TX, 75429. Tel: 903-886-5716. Fax: 903-886-5434. p. 2300

Mitchell, Gretchen, Asst Dir, Support Serv, Jacksonville Public Library, 303 N Laura St, Jacksonville, FL, 32202-3505. Tel: 904-630-1666. Fax: 904-630-1435. p. 453

Mitchell, Heather, Exec Dir, New Hampshire Antiquarian Society Library, 300 Main St, Hopkinton, NH, 03229. Tel: 603-746-3825. p. 1452

Mitchell, James, Mgr, Cobb County Public Library System, East Marietta, 2051 Lower Roswell Rd, Marietta, GA, 30068. Tel: 770-509-2711. Fax: 770-509-2714. p. 543

Mitchell, Jana, Ref Mgr, Pine Bluff & Jefferson County Library System, Main Library, 200 E Eighth Ave, Pine Bluff, AR, 71601. Tel: 870-534-4802. Fax: 870-534-8707. p. 112

Mitchell, Jane, Adult Serv, St Pete Beach Public Library, 365 73rd Ave, Saint Pete Beach, FL, 33706-1996. Tel: 727-363-9238. Fax: 727-552-1760. p. 487

Mitchell, Janis, Acq, Doane College, 1014 Boswell Ave, Crete, NE, 68333-2421. Tel: 402-826-8565. Fax: 402-826-8199. p. 1396

Mitchell, Jennifer, Br Supvr, Licking County Library, Hervey Memorial, 15 N Main, Utica, OH, 43080. Tel: 740-892-2400. Fax: 740-892-2400. p. 1922

Mitchell, Jesse, Head, Tech Serv, Huntington Woods Public Library, 26415 Scotia, Huntington Woods, MI, 48070-1198. Tel: 248-543-9720. Fax: 248-543-2559. p. 1193

Mitchell, Jo Anne, Asst Dir, Richland Hills Public Library, 6724 Rena Dr, Richland Hills, TX, 76118-6297. Tel: 817-299-1860. Fax: 817-299-1863. p. 2374

Mitchell, John, Dir, Highwood Public Library, 102 Highwood Ave, Highwood, IL, 60040-1597. Tel: 847-432-5404. Fax: 847-432-5806. p. 656

Mitchell, John, Tech Serv, Poplar Creek Public Library District, 1405 S Park Ave, Streamwood, IL, 60107-2997. Tel: 630-837-6800. Fax: 630-837-6823. p. 708

Mitchell, John, Head, User Serv, Creighton University, Health Sciences Library-Learning Resource Center, 2770 Webster St, Omaha, NE, 68178-0210. Tel: 402-280-4127. Fax: 402-280-5134. p. 1412

Mitchell, Julie, Librn, Willow Public Library, 23557 W Willow Community Center Circle, Willow, AK, 99688. Tel: 907-495-7323. Fax: 907-495-5014. p. 55

Mitchell, Julie, Br Mgr, Siskiyou County Public Library, Dorris Branch, 800 Third St, Dorris, CA, 96023. Tel: 530-397-4932. Fax: 530-397-4932. p. 286

Mitchell, Julie, Ch, Siskiyou County Public Library, 719 Fourth St, Yreka, CA, 96097. Tel: 530-841-4178. Fax: 530-842-7001. p. 286

Mitchell, Kathleen, Dir, Clintonville Public Library, 75 Hemlock St, Clintonville, WI, 54929-1461. Tel: 715-823-4563. Fax: 715-823-7134. p. 2586

Mitchell, Kathryn, Youth Serv Dir, Homer Township Public Library District, 14320 W 151st St, Homer Glen, IL, 60491. Tel: 708-301-7908. Fax: 708-301-4535. p. 657

Mitchell, Kathy, Coll Develop, Beaufort County Library, 311 Scott St, Beaufort, SC, 29902. Tel: 843-255-6462. p. 2181

Mitchell, Kelly, Ref Librn, St Charles Community College, 4601 Mid Rivers Mall Dr, Cottleville, MO, 63376. Tel: 636-922-8798. Fax: 636-922-8433. p. 1326

Mitchell, Kimberly, Ref & Educ Librn, Albany College of Pharmacy & Health Sciences, 106 New Scotland Ave, Albany, NY, 12208. Tel: 518-694-7124. Fax: 518-694-7300. p. 1567

Mitchell, Larry, Interim Dir, Texas A&M University Libraries, Cushing Memorial Library & Archives, 5000 TAMU, College Station, TX, 77843-5000. Tel: 979-845-1951. Fax: 979-845-1441. p. 2299

Mitchell, Linda, Dir, Hoopeston Public Library, 110 N Fourth St, Hoopeston, IL, 60942-1422. Tel: 217-283-6711. Fax: 217-283-7077. p. 657

Mitchell, Linda, Govt Doc, Lakehead University Library, 955 Oliver Rd, Thunder Bay, ON, P7B 5E1, CANADA. Tel: 807-343-8072. Fax: 807-343-8007. p. 2848

Mitchell, Lisa, Cat Mgr, Hood College, 401 Rosemont Ave, Frederick, MD, 21701. Tel: 301-696-3874. Fax: 301-696-3796. p. 1029

Mitchell, Lise, Dir, Chippewa River District Library, 301 S University Ave, Mount Pleasant, MI, 48858-2597. Tel: 989-772-3488, Ext 12. Fax: 989-772-3280. p. 1211

Mitchell, Margaret, Dep Chief Exec Officer, Dir, London Public Library, 251 Dundas St, London, ON, N6A 6H9, CANADA. Tel: 519-661-5134. Fax: 519-663-9013. p. 2817

Mitchell, Margie, Adminr, Greater Egypt Regional Planning & Development Commission, 608 E College, Carbondale, IL, 62901. Tel: 618-549-3306. Fax: 618-549-3309. p. 600

Mitchell, Marlene, Youth Serv Mgr, Suwannee River Regional Library, 1848 Ohio Ave S, Dr Martin Luther King Jr Ave S, Live Oak, FL, 32064-4517. Tel: 386-364-3480. Fax: 386-364-6071. p. 461

Mitchell, Mary, Librn, Arlington Public Library, City Hall, 500 W First St, Arlington, OR, 97812. Tel: 541-454-2444. Fax: 541-454-2568. p. 1990

Mitchell, Mary, Assoc Librn, University of British Columbia Library, Law, 1822 East Mall, Vancouver, BC, V6T 1Z1, CANADA. Tel: 604-822-4203. Fax: 604-822-6864. p. 2743

Mitchell, Mary Kay, Coordr, Westminster Presbyterian Church Library, 2040 Washington Rd, Upper St Clair, PA, 15241. Tel: 412-835-6630. Fax: 412-835-5690. p. 2149

Mitchell, Michael, Tech Serv Librn, Brazosport College Library, 500 College Dr, Lake Jackson, TX, 77566. Tel: 979-230-3309. Fax: 979-230-3185. p. 2352

Mitchell, Michele, Head, Circ, Hillside Public Library, John F Kennedy Plaza, Hillside & Liberty Aves, Hillside, NJ, 07205-1893. Tel: 973-923-4413. p. 1491

Mitchell, Millie, Develop, University of Nevada-Reno, 1664 N Virginia St, Mailstop 0322, Reno, NV, 89557-0322. Tel: 775-682-5682. Fax: 775-784-4529. p. 1433

Mitchell, Monique, Dir, Roanoke-Chowan Community College, 109 Community College Rd, Ahoskie, NC, 27910. Tel: 252-862-1262. Fax: 252-862-1358. p. 1773

Mitchell, Nelson, Mkt/Pub Relations Coordr, Maricopa County Library District, 2700 N Central Ave, Ste 700, Phoenix, AZ, 85004. Tel: 602-652-3045. Fax: 602-652-3071. p. 74

Mitchell, Patricia, Br Mgr, Richland County Public Library, North Main, 5306 N Main St, Columbia, SC, 29203-6114. Tel: 803-754-7734. p. 2188

Mitchell, Perida, Ref, Thomas County Public Library System, 201 N Madison St, Thomasville, GA, 31792-5414. Tel: 229-225-5252. Fax: 229-225-5258. p. 553

Mitchell, Rachel, Electronic Res & Ref Librn, Mars Hill College, 124 Cascade St, Mars Hill, NC, 28754. Tel: 828-689-1244. p. 1809

Mitchell, Rebecca S, Dir, Alabama Public Library Service, 6030 Monticello Dr, Montgomery, AL, 36130. Tel: 334-213-3900. Fax: 334-213-3993. p. 27

Mitchell, Renee, Cataloger, Greene Public Library, 179 Hopkins Hollow Rd, Greene, RI, 02827. Tel: 401-397-3873. Fax: 401-385-9190. p. 2166

Mitchell, Rita, Info Literacy Librn, Cardinal Stritch University Library, 6801 N Yates Rd, Milwaukee, WI, 53207-3985. Tel: 414-410-4118. Fax: 414-410-4268. p. 2617

Mitchell, Robbie, Asst Libr Dir, Clayton Town & County Library, 45 N Midway St, Clayton, AL, 36016. Tel: 334-775-3506. Fax: 334-775-3538. p. 12

Mitchell, Samuel, Libr Dir, Hamilton North Public Library, 209 W Brinton, Cicero, IN, 46034. Tel: 317-984-5623. Fax: 317-984-7505. p. 732

Mitchell, Sandra, Librn Supvr, Lorain Public Library System, Columbia Branch, 13824 W River Rd N, Columbia Station, OH, 44028. Tel: 440-236-8751. Fax: 440-236-8956. p. 1911

Mitchell, Scott, In Charge, Stacks Rare Coin Company of NY, 123 W 57th St, New York, NY, 10019-2280. Tel: 212-582-2580. Fax: 212-245-5018. p. 1700

Mitchell, Selma, Cat, Watertown Regional Library, 160 Sixth St NE, Watertown, SD, 57201-2778. Tel: 605-882-6220. Fax: 605-882-6221. p. 2221

Mitchell, Serhania, ILL, Saint Martin Parish Library, 201 Porter St, Saint Martinville, LA, 70582. Tel: 337-394-2207, Ext 23. Fax: 337-394-2248. p. 967

Mitchell, Sharon, Circ, Plainsboro Free Public Library, 9 Van Doren St, Plainsboro, NJ, 08536. Tel: 609-275-2899. Fax: 609-799-5883. p. 1521

Mitchell, Stephen, In Charge, Harvard Library, Milman Parry Collection of Oral Literature, Widener, Rm C, Cambridge, MA, 02138. Tel: 617-496-2499. p. 1076

Mitchell, Susan, AV, Plymouth Public Library, 201 N Center St, Plymouth, IN, 46563. Tel: 574-936-2324. Fax: 574-936-7423. p. 773

Mitchell, Sylvia, Br Mgr, Hawaii State Public Library System, Liliha Public Library, 1515 Liliha St, Honolulu, HI, 96817-3526. Tel: 808-587-7577. Fax: 808-587-7579. p. 562

Mitchell, Tiffany, Operations Mgr, Institute of Noetic Sciences Library, 625 Second St, Ste 200, Petaluma, CA, 94952-9524. Tel: 707-775-3500. Fax: 707-781-7420. p. 207

Mitchell, Valencia, Adjunct Ref Librn, Cerritos College Library, 11110 Alondra Blvd, Norwalk, CA, 90650. Tel: 562-860-2451, Ext 2416. Fax: 562-467-5002. p. 195

Mitchell, Vicky, Head, Circ, Pearl River County Library System, Poplarville Public, 202 W Beers St, Poplarville, MS, 39470. Tel: 601-795-8411. Fax: 601-795-8411. p. 1311

Mitchell, Victoria, Head of Libr, University of Oregon Libraries, Mathematics, 210 Fenton Hall, University of Oregon, Eugene, OR, 97403. Tel: 541-346-3076. Fax: 541-346-3012. p. 1997

Mitchell, W Bede, Dr, Dean, Georgia Southern University, 1400 Southern Dr, Statesboro, GA, 30458. Tel: 912-478-5115. Fax: 912-478-0093. p. 552

Mitchell, Wendy, Dir, Clay Center Carnegie Library, 706 Sixth St, Clay Center, KS, 67432-2997. Tel: 785-632-3889. p. 861

Mitchell-Slezak, Gail L, Head, Circ, Greene Public Library, 179 Hopkins Hollow Rd, Greene, RI, 02827. Tel: 401-397-3873. Fax: 401-385-9190. p. 2166

Mitchem, Pam, Asst Prof, Spec Coll, Appalachian State University, William Leonard Eury Appalachian Collection, Belk Library, 4th Flr, 218 College St, Boone, NC, 28608. Tel: 828-262-7422. Fax: 828-262-2553. p. 1777

Mitgang, Gina, YA Serv, Ridgewood Public Library, 125 N Maple Ave, Ridgewood, NJ, 07450-3288. Tel: 201-670-5600. Fax: 201-670-0293. p. 1526

Mitnick, Eva, Ch, Los Angeles Public Library System, 630 W Fifth St, Los Angeles, CA, 90071-2097. Tel: 213-228-7480. Fax: 213-228-7485. p. 172

Mitrano, Diana, Cat Librn, Long Island University, One University Plaza, Brooklyn, NY, 11201-9926. Tel: 718-488-1081. Fax: 718-780-4057. p. 1593

Mitrowski, Marcia, Ref/YA, The Hampton Library, 2478 Main St, Bridgehampton, NY, 11932. Tel: 631-537-0015. Fax: 631-537-7229. p. 1585

Mitschke, Julia, Operations Mgr, Cedar Park Public Library, 550 Discovery Blvd, Cedar Park, TX, 78613. Tel: 512-401-5648. Fax: 512-259-5236. p. 2296

Mitsukawa, Michael I, Assoc Dir, Admin & Tech Serv, Boston College, 885 Centre St, Newton Centre, MA, 02459. Tel: 617-552-2355. Fax: 617-552-2889. p. 1110

Mittag, Carol, Access Serv, ILL, Ref Serv, Concordia University Wisconsin, 12800 N Lake Shore Dr, Mequon, WI, 53097-2402. Tel: 262-243-4330, 262-243-4403. Fax: 262-243-4424. p. 2615

Mittag, Erika, Head Librn, 3M Library & Information Services, Bldg 130-1-N, 6801 Riverplace Blvd, Austin, TX, 78726-9000. Tel: 512-984-2124. Fax: 512-984-3237. p. 2283

Mittenberg, Valerie, Coordr of Ref Serv, State University of New York College at New Paltz, 300 Hawk Dr, New Paltz, NY, 12561-2493. Tel: 845-257-3703. p. 1666

Mittge, Kevin, Ref Serv, Ad, Siuslaw Public Library District, 1460 Ninth St, Florence, OR, 97439-0022. Tel: 541-997-3132. Fax: 541-997-6473. p. 1998

Mittge, Kevin K, Br Mgr, Siuslaw Public Library District, Mapleton Branch, 88148 Riverview Ave, Mapleton, OR, 97453. Tel: 541-997-3132. Fax: 541-997-6473. p. 1998

Mittleman, Marilyn, Pub Serv, Saint Lucie County Library System, 101 Melody Lane, Fort Pierce, FL, 34950-4402. Tel: 772-462-1607. Fax: 772-462-2750. p. 447

Mittlestead, Carol, Assoc Librn, Coll, University of Ontario Institute of Technology Library, 2000 Simcoe St N, Oshawa, ON, L1H 7K4, CANADA. Tel: 905-721-8668, Ext 2214. Fax: 905-721-3029. p. 2827

Mittlieder, Dorothy, Acq, Metropolitan Community College Library, 30th & Fort Sts, Omaha, NE, 68103. Tel: 402-457-2762. Fax: 402-457-2655. p. 1413

Mittman, Lisa, Br Mgr, Harford County Public Library, Abingdon Branch, 2510 Tollgate Rd, Abingdon, MD, 21009. Tel: 410-638-3990. Fax: 410-638-3995. p. 1020

Mitton, Doris, Librn, Dalton Public Library, 741 Dalton Rd, Dalton, NH, 03598. Tel: 603-837-2751. Fax: 603-837-2273. p. 1444

Mitton, Lisa, Asst Librn, Attica Public Library, 305 S Perry St, Attica, IN, 47918. Tel: 765-764-4194. Fax: 765-764-0906. p. 725

Mitton, Pat, Br Mgr, Scott County Library System, Savage Public Library, 13090 Alabama Ave S, Savage, MN, 55378. Tel: 952-707-1770. Fax: 952-707-1775. p. 1284

Mitts, Hannah, Circ Supvr, Lindenwood University, 209 S Kingshighway, Saint Charles, MO, 63301. Tel: 636-949-4690. Fax: 636-949-4822. p. 1351

Mitts, Peggy, Librn, United States Court of Appeals, 600 Camp St, Rm 106, New Orleans, LA, 70130. Tel: 504-310-7797. Fax: 504-310-7578. p. 964

Mitus, Terri, Youth Serv, West Springfield Public Library, 200 Park St, West Springfield, MA, 01089. Tel: 413-736-4561, Ext 4. Fax: 413-736-6469. p. 1137

Mitzenmacher, Joe, Electronic Serv/Ref Librn, Loyola University Chicago Libraries, Law School Library, 25 E Pearson St, 3rd Flr, Chicago, IL, 60611. Tel: 312-915-6844. Fax: 312-915-6797. p. 617

Miwa, Marion, Chief Librn, The Bank of Nova Scotia Library, 44 King St W, Toronto, QC, M5H 1H1, CANADA. Tel: 416-866-4403. Fax: 416-866-4036. p. 2913

Mix, Joan, Cat, Mount Aloysius College Library, 7373 Admiral Peary Hwy, Cresson, PA, 16630-1999. Tel: 814-886-6445. Fax: 814-886-5767. p. 2048

Mix, Lisa, Archivist, Rare Bks, Spec Coll & Archives Librn, University of California San Francisco, 530 Parnassus Ave, San Francisco, CA, 94143-0840. Tel: 415-514-3706. p. 248

Mix, Lisa, Head, Archives, Cornell University Library, The Samuel J Wood Library & The C V Starr Biomedical Information Center, 1300 York Ave, C115, Box 67, New York, NY, 10065-4896. Tel: 212-746-6050. Fax: 212-746-6494. p. 1642

Mix, Nita, Br Mgr, Uncle Remus Regional Library System, Jasper County Library, 319 E Green St, Monticello, GA, 31064. Tel: 706-468-6292. Fax: 706-468-2060. p. 542

Mix, Peter, Sci, Fordham University Libraries, 441 E Fordham Rd, Bronx, NY, 10458-5151. Tel: 718-817-3570. Fax: 718-817-3582. p. 1586

Mix, Vickie, Govt Doc, South Dakota State University, 1300 N Campus Dr, Box 2115, Brookings, SD, 57007-1098. Tel: 605-688-5958. Fax: 605-688-6133. p. 2210

Mixdorf, David, Libr Dir, South Sioux City Public Library, 2121 Dakota Ave, South Sioux City, NE, 68776-3031. Tel: 402-494-7545. Fax: 402-494-7546. p. 1419

Mixon, Lynn, Librn, Carl & Mary Welhausen Library, 810 Front St, Yoakum, TX, 77995-3058. Tel: 361-293-5001. Fax: 361-293-7091. p. 2402

Mixon, Rhonda, Dir, H J Nugen Public Library, 103 E Main St, New London, IA, 52645. Tel: 319-367-7704. Fax: 319-367-7710. p. 835

Mixon, Shondra, Libr Asst II, Montgomery City-County Public Library System, 245 High St, Montgomery, AL, 36104. Tel: 334-240-4300. Fax: 334-240-4977. p. 29

Mixon, Winifred, Libr Serv Supvr/Sub Serv, Keene State College, 229 Main St, Keene, NH, 03435-3201. Tel: 603-358-2740. Fax: 603-358-2745. p. 1453

Mixson, Adrian, Libr Dir, Hall County Library System, 127 Main St NW, Gainesville, GA, 30501-3699. Tel: 770-532-3311, Ext 122. Fax: 770-532-4305. p. 534

Mixson, Jeanne, Br Coordr, East Baton Rouge Parish Library, Pride-Chaneyville Branch, 11360 Pride-Port Hudson Rd, Pride, LA, 70770. Tel: 225-658-1580. Fax: 225-658-1549. p. 943

Miyamoto, Shaun, Coordr, Heald College, 1500 Kapiolani Blvd, Honolulu, HI, 96814. Tel: 808-628-5525. Fax: 808-955-6964. p. 564

Miyaoka, Mayumi, Ref/Instruction/Archival Librn, Saint Joseph's College, 222 Clinton Ave, Brooklyn, NY, 11205-3697. Tel: 718-940-5884. Fax: 718-636-7250. p. 1594

Miyashiro, Debra, Head Librn, State of Hawaii Department of Business Economic Development & Tourism, 250 S Hotel St, 4th Flr, Honolulu, HI, 96813. Tel: 808-586-2424. Fax: 808-587-2790. p. 565

Mize, Robin, Tech Serv, Brenau University, 625 Academy St NE, Gainesville, GA, 30501-3343. Tel: 770-718-5303. Fax: 770-534-6254. p. 534

Mizener, David, Dr, Doc, The University of Texas-Pan American Library, 1201 W University Dr, Edinburg, TX, 78541-2999. Tel: 956-665-3306. Fax: 956-665-5396. p. 2315

Mizikar, Alisa, Ref Librn, Wittenberg University, 807 Woodlawn Ave, Springfield, OH, 45504. Tel: 937-327-7515. Fax: 937-327-6139. p. 1936

Mizrachi, Diane, Ref, University of California Los Angeles Library, College Library, Powell Library Bldg, Los Angeles, CA, 90095. Tel: 310-825-5756. Fax: 310-206-9312. p. 178

Mlinar, Courtney, Ref Librn, Nova Southeastern University, 3200 S University Dr, Fort Lauderdale, FL, 33328. Tel: 954-262-3106. Fax: 954-262-1821. p. 443

Mlsna, Kathryn, Circ Coordr, Milwaukee Public Library, 814 W Wisconsin Ave, Milwaukee, WI, 53233-2385. Tel: 414-286-3000. Fax: 414-286-2794. p. 2620

Mlynarski, Miriam, Coordr, Ref & Instrul Serv, Web Developer, Camden County College Library, College Dr, Blackwood, NJ, 08012. Tel: 856-227-7200, Ext 4615. Fax: 856-374-4897. p. 1473

Moak, Tom, Br Mgr, Mid-Columbia Libraries, Kennewick Branch, 1620 S Union, Kennewick, WA, 99338. Tel: 509-783-7878. Fax: 509-735-2063. p. 2518

Moats, Jean, Coll Mgt Librn, Johnson & Wales University, 801 W Trade St, Charlotte, NC, 28202. Tel: 980-598-1608. p. 1783

Moats, Linda, Circ Supvr, Perry Public Library, 3753 Main St, Perry, OH, 44081-9501. Tel: 440-259-3300. Fax: 440-259-3977. p. 1929

Moberg, Ester, Dir, Seaside Public Library, 60 N Roosevelt Dr, Seaside, OR, 97138. Tel: 503-738-6742. Fax: 503-738-6742. p. 2019

Moberg, Jane B, Dir, Info Serv, Michael Best & Friedrich LLP, 100 E Wisconsin Ave, Milwaukee, WI, 53202-4108. Tel: 414-271-6560. Fax: 414-277-0656. p. 2619

Moberg, Kristen, Dir, Ridgway Library District, 525 Clinton St, Ridgway, CO, 81432. Tel: 970-626-5252. Fax: 970-626-5252. p. 321

Moberly, Amy, Head, Cat & Innovative Syst Coordr, California Western School of Law Library, 290 Cedar St, San Diego, CA, 92101. Tel: 619-525-1421. Fax: 619-685-2918. p. 231

Moberly, Heather, Librn, Oklahoma State University Libraries, William E Brock Memorial Library at OSU Center for Veterinary Health Sciences, 102 McElroy Hall, Stillwater, OK, 74078-1071. Tel: 405-744-6655. Fax: 405-744-5609. p. 1978

Moberly, Heather K, Veterinary Med Librn, Oklahoma State University Libraries, Oklahoma State University, Athletic Ave, Stillwater, OK, 74078-1071. Tel: 405-744-6655. Fax: 405-744-5609. p. 1978

Mobley, Beth, Assoc Dir, Touro College, 225 Eastview Dr, Central Islip, NY, 11722-4539. Tel: 631-761-7000, 631-761-7150. Fax: 631-761-7159. p. 1605

Mobley, Chuck, Curator, San Francisco Camerawork, 657 Mission St, 2nd Flr, San Francisco, CA, 94105-4104. Tel: 415 512 2020. Fax: 415 512 7109. p. 245

Mobley, Dustin, Tech Coordr, Public Library of Johnston County & Smithfield, 305 E Market St, Smithfield, NC, 27577-3919. Tel: 919-934-8146. Fax: 919-934-8084. p. 1824

Mobley, Nancy, Br Mgr, Indianapolis-Marion County Public Library, Haughville, 2121 W Michigan St, Indianapolis, IN, 46222-3862. Tel: 317-275-4420. p. 754

Mobley, Ree, Librn, Museum of New Mexico/Museum of International Folk Art, 706 Camino Lejo, Santa Fe, NM, 87505. Tel: 505-476-1200. Fax: 505-476-1300. p. 1562

Mocerino, Susanne, Ch, Pocono Mountain Public Library, 5540 Memorial Blvd, Tobyhanna, PA, 18466. Tel: 570-894-8860. Fax: 570-894-8852. p. 2146

Mochetti, Helen, Ch, Westerly Public Library, 44 Broad St, Westerly, RI, 02891. Tel: 401-596-2877, Ext 317. Fax: 401-596-5600. p. 2178

Mochida, Paula, Interim Univ Librn, University of Hawaii at Manoa Library, 2550 McCarthy Mall, Honolulu, HI, 96822. Tel: 808-956-2477. Fax: 808-956-5968. p. 565

Mock, Donald L, Evening Supvr, Clarion University of Pennsylvania, 840 Wood St, Clarion, PA, 16214. Tel: 814-393-2484. Fax: 814-393-2344. p. 2045

Mock, Elizabeth, Archives & Spec Coll Librn, University of Massachusetts at Boston, 100 Morrissey Blvd, Boston, MA, 02125-3300. Tel: 617-287-5944. p. 1068

Mock, Jane, Dir, Gadsden County Public Library, 7325 Pat Thomas Pkwy, Quincy, FL, 32351. Tel: 850-627-7106. Fax: 850-627-7775. p. 485

Mock, Marci, Circ Librn, Sheridan County Public Library System, 335 W Alger St, Sheridan, WY, 82801-3899. Tel: 307-674-8585, Ext 5. p. 2660

Mock, Rosie, Info Tech, Minnesota State University, Mankato, ML3097, Mankato, MN, 56001. Tel: 507-389-5952. Fax: 507-389-5155. p. 1257

Mockovak, Holly E, Librn, Boston University Libraries, Music Library, 771 Commonwealth Ave, Boston, MA, 02215. Tel: 617-353-3705. Fax: 617-353-2084. p. 1058

Modak, Susan, Librn, Montgomery County Public Libraries, Noyes Children's Library, 10237 Carroll Pl, Kensington, MD, 20895-3361. Tel: 240-773-9575. Fax: 301-929-5470. p. 1039

Modder, Susan, Dir, Libr Develop, University of Wisconsin-Milwaukee Libraries, 2311 E Hartford Ave, Milwaukee, WI, 53211. Tel: 414-229-4785, 414-229-6202. Fax: 414-229-6766. p. 2622

Modig, Zeau, Dir, Riegelsville Public Library, 615 Easton Rd, Riegelsville, PA, 18077. Tel: 610-749-2357. p. 2134

Modschiedler, Christa, Bibliographer, University of Chicago Library, John Crerar Library, 5730 S Ellis Ave, Chicago, IL, 60637. Tel: 773-702-8759. p. 626

Moe, Jane, Dir, Constantine Township Library, 165 Canaris St, Constantine, MI, 49042-1015. Tel: 269-435-7957. Fax: 269-435-5800. p. 1166

Moe, Linda, Librn, Superior Public Library, Joan Salmen Memorial, Village Hall, 9240 E Main St, Solon Springs, WI, 54873-8051. Tel: 715-378-4452. p. 2641

Moe, Louise, Head, Ref Serv, Rochester Public Library, 101 Second St SE, Rochester, MN, 55904-3776. Tel: 507-328-2369. Fax: 507-328-2384. p. 1273

Moebs, Larissa, Pub Serv, Illinois Central College, One College Dr, East Peoria, IL, 61635-0001. Tel: 309-694-5461. Fax: 309-694-5473. p. 638

Moebus, Bonnie, Br Mgr, Wellington County Library, Elora Branch, 144 Geddes St, Elora, ON, N0B 1S0, CANADA. Tel: 519-846-0190. Fax: 519-846-0344. p. 2805

Moeckel, Lisa, Assoc Dean, Undergrad Educ, Syracuse University Library, 222 Waverly Ave, Syracuse, NY, 13244-2010. Tel: 315-443-2573. p. 1754

Moede, Christine, Dir, Brillion Public Library, 326 N Main St, Brillion, WI, 54110. Tel: 920-756-3215. Fax: 920-756-3874. p. 2583

Moeder, Jeanie, Admin Coordr, University of Kansas School of Medicine-Wichita, 1010 N Kansas, Wichita, KS, 67214-3199. Tel: 316-293-2629. Fax: 316-293-2608. p. 901

Moege, Paula, Asst Br Librn, Pottawatomie Wabaunsee Regional Library, Alma Branch, 115 W Third St, Alma, KS, 66401. Tel: 785-765-3647. Fax: 785-765-3647. p. 892

Moeller, Connie, Assoc Librn, University of Wisconsin-Superior, PO Box 2000, Belknap & Catlin, Superior, WI, 54880-2000. Tel: 715-394-8343. Fax: 715-394-8462. p. 2641

Moeller, Gerri, Automation Syst Coordr, Outagamie Waupaca Library System, 225 N Oneida, Appleton, WI, 54911-4780. Tel: 920-832-6190. Fax: 920-832-6422. p. 2578

Moeller, Jo, Br Mgr, San Diego County Library, Rancho Santa Fe Branch, 17040 Avenida de Acacias, Rancho Santa Fe, CA, 92067. Tel: 858-756-2512. Fax: 858-756-3485. p. 234

Moeller, Kathleen, Dir, University of Florida Health Science Center-Jacksonville, 653-1 W Eighth St, Jacksonville, FL, 32209-6511. Tel: 904-244-3240. Fax: 904-244-3191. p. 455

Moeller, Lindy, Ref Librn, Luther College, 700 College Dr, Decorah, IA, 52101. Tel: 563-387-1498. Fax: 563-387-1657. p. 807

Moeller, Mary, Dir, Libr Coll & Serv, Linda Hall Library, 5109 Cherry St, Kansas City, MO, 64110-2498. Tel: 816-926-8720. Fax: 816-926-8790. p. 1337

Moeller, Max, Curator, Hagley Museum & Library, 298 Buck Rd E, Wilmington, DE, 19807. Tel: 302-658-2400. Fax: 302-658-0568. p. 388

Moeller, Paul, Head, Ser & Digital Access Unit, University of Colorado Boulder, 1720 Pleasant St, 184 UCB, Boulder, CO, 80309-0184. Tel: 303-735-0492. Fax: 303-492-3340. p. 291

Moeller-Peiffer, Kathleen, Assoc State Librn, New Jersey State Library, 185 W State St, Trenton, NJ, 08618. Tel: 609-278-2640, Ext 152. Fax: 609-278-2652. p. 1536

Moeller-Peiffer, Kathleen, Assoc State Librn, Libr Develop, New Jersey Library Network, Library Development Bureau, 185 W State St, Trenton, NJ, 08608. Tel: 609-278-2640, Ext 152. Fax: 609-278-2650. p. 2949

Moellering, Katie, Adult Serv, Emmet O'Neal Library, 50 Oak St, Mountain Brook, AL, 35213. Tel: 205-879-0459. Fax: 205-879-5388. p. 32

Moen, William E, Dr, Assoc Dean, Res, Assoc Prof, Dir, Tex Ctr for Digital Knowledge, University of North Texas, 1155 Union Circle, Denton, TX, 76203-5017. Tel: 940-565-2445. Fax: 940-565-3101. p. 2975

Moennig, Nancy, Librn, South County Public Library District, Main St, Brussels, IL, 62013. Tel: 618-883-2522. p. 598

Moesch, Rick, Asst Librn, Hamburg Public Library, 102 Buffalo St, Hamburg, NY, 14075-5097. Tel: 716-649-4415. Fax: 716-649-4160. p. 1632

Moffat, Riley, Head, Ref, Brigham Young University-Hawaii, 55-220 Kulanui St, BYU-Hawaii, No 1966, Laie, HI, 96762-1294. Tel: 808-675-3884. Fax: 808-675-3877. p. 567

Moffet, Jame, Librn, Grosse Pointe Public Library, Woods, 20680 Mack Ave, Grosse Pointe Woods, MI, 48236. Tel: 313-343-2072. Fax: 313-343-2486. p. 1187

Moffitt, Jed, Assoc Dir-ITS, King County Library System, 960 Newport Way NW, Issaquah, WA, 98027. Tel: 425-369-3433. Fax: 425-369-3255. p. 2516

Mofford, Kari, Info Serv Librn, Sharon Public Library, 11 N Main St, Sharon, MA, 02067-1299. Tel: 781-784-1578. Fax: 781-784-4728. p. 1123

Mofidi, Faegheh, Br Mgr, Los Angeles Public Library System, Sylmar Branch, 11430 Polk St, Sylmar, CA, 91342-4055. Tel: 818-367-6102. Fax: 818-756-9290. p. 174

Mofield, Georgia, Br Supvr, Scenic Regional Library of Franklin, Gasconade & Warren Counties, Pacific Branch, 119 W Saint Louis St, Pacific, MO, 63069. Tel: 636-257-2712. p. 1369

Moga, Gabriel, Syst Adminr, University of Toronto Libraries, Faculty of Information Inforum, 140 Saint George St, 4th Flr, Toronto, ON, M5S 3G6, CANADA. Tel: 416-978-6122. Fax: 416-978-5769. p. 2866

Mogen, Pamela, Dir, Liberty Lake Municipal Library, 23123 E Mission Ave, Liberty Lake, WA, 99019-7613. Tel: 509-232-2510, 509-232-2511. Fax: 509-232-2512. p. 2520

Mogilewicz, Christine, Br Mgr, Hawaii State Public Library System, Waipahu Public Library, 94-275 Mokuola St, Waipahu, HI, 96797. Tel: 808-675-0358. Fax: 808-675-0360. p. 563

Moginot, Barbara J, Per, Malone University, 2600 Cleveland Ave NW, Canton, OH, 44709-3897. Tel: 330-471-8334. Fax: 330-454-6977. p. 1863

Mogle, Dawn, AV, Lake County Public Library, 1919 W 81st Ave, Merrillville, IN, 46410-5488. Tel: 219-769-3541. Fax: 219-756-9358. p. 763

Mogle, Dawn, Librn, Lake County Public Library, Talking Book Service, 1919 W 81st Ave, Merrillville, IN, 46410-5382. Tel: 219-769-3541, Ext 323. p. 764

Mogle, Kris, ILL, Drake University, 2725 University Ave, Des Moines, IA, 50311. Tel: 515-271-3993, Fax: 515-271-3933. p. 809

Mogren, Diane, Assoc Librn, Federal Reserve Bank of Cleveland, 1455 E Sixth St, Cleveland, OH, 44114. Tel: 216-579-2052, 216-579-2961. Fax: 216-579-3172. p. 1880

Moguel, Alicia, Br Mgr, Los Angeles Public Library System, Benjamin Franklin Branch, 2200 E First St, Los Angeles, CA, 91011. Tel: 323-263-6901. Fax: 323-526-3043. p. 173

Mohammad, Sandra, Br Mgr, Chicago Public Library, South Shore, 2505 E 73rd St, Chicago, IL, 60649. Tel: 312-747-5281. Fax: 312-747-3612. p. 609

Mohammadi, Jane, Syst Librn, United States Army, Casey Memorial Library, 72nd St & 761st Tank Battalion, Bldg 3202, Fort Hood, TX, 76544-5024. Tel: 254-287-0025. Fax: 254-288-4029. p. 2320

Mohanty, Suchi, Dir, University of North Carolina at Chapel Hill, Robert B House Undergraduate, 203 South Rd, CB No 3942, Chapel Hill, NC, 27514-8890. Tel: 919-962-1355. Fax: 919-962-2697. p. 1781

Moher, Brian, Dir, Fort Richardson Post Library, IMPA-FRA-HRE PL, Bldg 7, Chilkoot Ave, Fort Richardson, AK, 99505-0055. Tel: 907-384-1648. Fax: 907-384-7534. p. 48

Mohess, Neera, ILL, Ref & Instruction, Queensborough Community College, City University of New York, 222-05 56th Ave, Bayside, NY, 11364-1497. Tel: 718-631-6227. Fax: 718-281-5012. p. 1579

Mohl, Pam, Ch, Village Library of Morgantown, 207 N Walnut St, Morgantown, PA, 19543. Tel: 610-286-1022. Fax: 610-286-1024. p. 2092

Mohler, Joyce, Acq, Instrul Media, Ser, Ohio University-Lancaster Library, 1570 Granville Pike, Lancaster, OH, 43130-1097. Tel: 740-654-6711, Ext 621. Fax: 740-687-9497. p. 1909

Mohler, Melissa, Ref Serv, Bartow Public Library, 2150 S Broadway Ave, Bartow, FL, 33830. Tel: 863-534-0131. Fax: 863-534-0913. p. 426

Mohney, John, Dir, Paw Paw District Library, 609 W Michigan Ave, Paw Paw, MI, 49079-1072. Tel: 269-657-3800. Fax: 269-657-2603. p. 1217

Mohr, Deborah, Tech Serv, Monroe Community College, LeRoy V Good Library, 1000 E Henrietta Rd, Rochester, NY, 14692. Tel: 585-292-2316. p. 1730

Mohr, Rebecca, Circ, Alabama State University, 915 S Jackson St, Montgomery, AL, 36104. Tel: 334-229-4106, 334-229-6890. Fax: 334-229-4911, 334-229-4940. p. 28

Mohr, Vicki, Dir, Lowden Public Library, 605 Main St, Lowden, IA, 52255. Tel: 563-941-7629. p. 828

Mohr, Vicki, Head, Libr Develop, Oklahoma Department of Libraries, 200 NE 18th St, Oklahoma City, OK, 73105. Tel: 405-521-2502. Fax: 405-525-7804. p. 1974

Mohr-Tipton, Janis, Br Mgr, Jackson County Library Services, Central Point Branch, 116 S Third St, Central Point, OR, 97502. Tel: 541-664-3228. p. 2005

Mohr-Tipton, Janis, Br Mgr, Jackson County Library Services, Ruch Branch, 7919 Hwy 238, Ruch, OR, 97530-9728. Tel: 541-899-7438. p. 2005

Mohrer, Fruma, Archivist, YIVO Institute for Jewish Research, 15 W 16th St, New York, NY, 10011. Tel: 212-294-6143. Fax: 212-292-1892. p. 1704

Mohundro, Margaret, Dir, Sanibel Public Library District, 770 Dunlop Rd, Sanibel, FL, 33957. Tel: 239-472-2483. Fax: 239-472-9524. p. 489

Moir, Jean, Supvr, Middlesex County Library, Ilderton Branch, 40 Heritage Dr, Ilderton, ON, N0M 2A0, CANADA. Tel: 519-666-1599. Fax: 519-666-2107. p. 2845

Moir, Lindsay, Sr Librn, Glenbow Museum Library, 130 Ninth Ave SE, Calgary, AB, T2G 0P3, CANADA. Tel: 403-268-4198. Fax: 403-232-6569. p. 2691

Moir, Michael, Archivist, Spec Coll Librn, York University Libraries, 4700 Keele St, Toronto, ON, M3J 1P3, CANADA. Tel: 416-736-2100, Ext 22457. Fax: 416-736-5451. p. 2868

Moirano, Valerie, Commun Relations Librn, Cuyahoga Falls Library, 2015 Third St, Cuyahoga Falls, OH, 44221-3294. Tel: 330-928-2117, Ext 102. Fax: 330-928-2535. p. 1892

Moisan, Patty, Head, Ch, Harborfields Public Library, 31 Broadway, Greenlawn, NY, 11740-1382. Tel: 631-757-4200. Fax: 631-757-7216. p. 1631

Moisil, Ingrid, Res Librn, Bibliotheque Municipale de Gatineau, 144, boul de l'Hôpital, local 317, Gatineau, QC, J8T 7S7, CANADA. Tel: 819-243-2345, Ext 2567. Fax: 819-243-2306. p. 2882

Moitoso, Mary, Ser, Taunton Public Library, 12 Pleasant St, Taunton, MA, 02780. Tel: 508-821-1410. Fax: 508-821-1414. p. 1131

Mojock, Colleen, Librn, State Regional Correctional Facility Library, 801 Butler Pike, Mercer, PA, 16137. Tel: 724-662-1837, Ext 1126. Fax: 724-662-1940. p. 2088

Mokia, Rosemary N, Dr, Head, Acq & Ser, Grambling State University, 403 Main St, Grambling, LA, 71245. Tel: 318-274-2213. Fax: 318-274-3268. p. 950

Mokler, Alexis, Res, NYS Small Business Development Center Research Network, 22 Corporate Woods Blvd, 3rd Flr, Albany, NY, 12211. Tel: 518-641-0650. Fax: 518-443-5275. p. 1570

Mokrzycki, Karen, Bibliographer, Librn, University of California, 1156 High St, Santa Cruz, CA, 95064. Tel: 831-459-2021. Fax: 831-459-8206. p. 264

Mol, Barbara, Dep Dir, Seton Hall University, One Newark Ctr, Newark, NJ, 07102. Tel: 973-642-8765. p. 1513

Molander, Shane, Dep State Archivist, State Historical Society of North Dakota, North Dakota Heritage Ctr, 612 E Boulevard Ave, Bismarck, ND, 58505-0830. Tel: 701-328-3570. Fax: 701-328-2650. p. 1838

Molaro, Anthony, Assoc Dean, Libr & Instrul Tech, Prairie State College Library, 202 S Halsted St, Chicago Heights, IL, 60411-8200. Tel: 708-709-3551. Fax: 708-709-3940. p. 628

Moldovan, James, Cat, United States Courts for the Ninth Circuit Library, 95 Seventh St, San Francisco, CA, 94103. Tel: 415-556-9500. Fax: 415-556-9927. p. 247

Mole, Deborah, Ref & Instruction, University of Alaska Anchorage, Consortium Library, 3211 Providence Dr, Anchorage, AK, 99508-8176. Tel: 907-786-1871. Fax: 907-786-1834. p. 45

Molen, Janet, Sr Librn, Tampa-Hillsborough County Public Library System, Riverview Branch, 10509 Riverview Dr, Riverview, FL, 33569-4367. Fax: 813-671-7793. p. 498

Molendyke, Jay, Librn, Kent State University, 4314 Mahoning Ave NW, Warren, OH, 44483-1998. Tel: 330-675-8865, 330-847-0571. Fax: 330-675-8825. p. 1944

Molenkamp, Kathy, Dir, Grace Bible College, 1011 Aldon St SW, Grand Rapids, MI, 49509. Tel: 616-261-8575. Fax: 616-538-0599. p. 1184

Moles, Sandrah, Head, Ch, Lower Providence Community Library, 50 Parklane Dr, Eagleville, PA, 19403-1171. Tel: 610-666-6640. Fax: 610-666-5109. p. 2051

Molesco, Robert, Librn, California Court of Appeal, 750 B St, Ste 300, San Diego, CA, 92101-8173. Tel: 619-744-0760. Fax: 619-645-3009. p. 230

Molesworth, Bill, Chief Librn, Midland Public Library, 320 King St, Midland, ON, L4R 3M6, CANADA. Tel: 705-526-4216. Fax: 705-526-1474. p. 2821

Molina, Frank A, Dir, Cocopah Tribal Library, 14250 S Ave I County 15th & Ave G, Somerton, AZ, 85350. Tel: 928-627-8026. Fax: 928-627-2510. p. 82

Molina, Hilda, Dir, Elsa Public Library, 711 N Hidalgo St, Elsa, TX, 78543. Tel: 956-262-3061. Fax: 956-262-3066. p. 2318

Molina, Miguelina, Commun Relations Librn, Suffern Free Library, 210 Lafayette Ave, Suffern, NY, 10901. Tel: 845-357-1237. Fax: 845-357-3156. p. 1750

Molinaro, Mary, Assoc Dean, Libr Tech, University of Kentucky Libraries, I-85, 401 Hilltop Ave, Lexington, KY, 40506-0456. Tel: 859-257-0500, Ext 2029. p. 921

Molinaroli, Gloria, Ch, Saint Johnsbury Athenaeum, 1171 Main St, Saint Johnsbury, VT, 05819-2289. Tel: 802-748-8291. Fax: 802-748-8086. p. 2435

Molinas, Maryann, Librn, Tucumcari Public Library, 602 S Second, Tucumcari, NM, 88401-2899. Tel: 505-461-0295. Fax: 505-461-0297. p. 1566

Molineux, Mary S, Ref Librn, College of William & Mary in Virginia, Earl Gregg Swem Library, One Landrum Dr, Williamsburg, VA, 23187. Tel: 757-221-3076. Fax: 757-221-2635. p. 2502

Molitor, Sara, Br Mgr, Paulding County Carnegie Library, Payne Branch, 101 N Main St, Payne, OH, 45880. Tel: 419-263-3333. Fax: 419-263-3333. p. 1928

Moll, Ginny, Librn, Chester County Hospital Library, 701 E Marshall St, West Chester, PA, 19380. Tel: 610-431-5204. Fax: 610-696-8411. p. 2153

Moll, Kirk, Instruction Librn, Shippensburg University, 1871 Old Main Dr, Shippensburg, PA, 17257-2299. Tel: 717-477-1123, Ext 3305. Fax: 717-477-1389. p. 2140

Moll, Mary Ellen, Conmun Serv, Northport-East Northport Public Library, 151 Laurel Ave, Northport, NY, 11768. Tel: 631-261-6930. Fax: 631-261-6718. p. 1707

Mollard, Paul, Assoc Dir, Pub Computing, Kenyon College Library & Information Services, 103 College Dr, Gambier, OH, 43022-9624. Tel: 740-427-5186. Fax: 740-427-5272. p. 1901

Mollette, Nancy, Ref Serv, Jefferson Community & Technical College, 109 E Broadway, Louisville, KY, 40202. Tel: 502-213-2362. p. 924

Molleur, Elaine, Circ Librn, Weeks Public Library, 36 Post Rd, Greenland, NH, 03840-2312. Tel: 603-436-8548. Fax: 603-427-0913. p. 1449

Molleur, Geraldine, Coll Develop Librn, Palmer Public Library, 1455 N Main St, Palmer, MA, 01069. Tel: 413-283-3330. Fax: 413-283-9970. p. 1116

Mollner, Daniel, Govt Doc Librn, Gustavus Adolphus College, 800 W College Ave, Saint Peter, MN, 56082. Tel: 507-933-7569. Fax: 507-933-6292. p. 1283

Mollock, Sharon, Ser Librn, Morgan State University, 1700 E Cold Spring Lane, Baltimore, MD, 21251. Tel: 443-885-1712. p. 1016

Molloy, Carole A, Dir, Signal Hill Public Library, 1770 E Hill St, Signal Hill, CA, 90755. Tel: 562-989-7323. Fax: 562-989-7392. p. 269

Molloy, Peter, Dir, Hall of Flame, 6101 E Van Buren, Phoenix, AZ, 85008. Tel: 602-275-3473. Fax: 602-275-0896. p. 73

Moloney, Cathy, Libr Divisional Mgr, Florida Department of State, Division of Library & Information Services, R A Gray Bldg, 500 S Bronough St, Tallahassee, FL, 32399-0250. Tel: 850-245-6641. Fax: 850-245-6735. p. 493

Moloney, Cathy, Bur Chief, Florida Library Information Network, R A Gray Bldg, State Library & Archives of Florida, Tallahassee, FL, 32399-0250. Tel: 850-245-6687. Fax: 850-245-6744. p. 2940

Moloney, Joanne, Ch, Farmington Public Library, 117 Academy St, Farmington, ME, 04938. Tel: 207-778-4312. p. 985

Moloney, Patrick, Sr Librn, California Department of Corrections Library System, California Men's Colony-West, Hwy 1, San Luis Obispo, CA, 93409. Tel: 805-547-7900, Ext 7185. Fax: 805-547-7792. p. 221

Molony, Vallie, Librn, East Mississippi Regional Library System, Stonewall Public, 801 Erwin Rd, Stonewall, MS, 39363-9610. Tel: 601-659-3080. Fax: 601-659-3080. p. 1313

Molosky, Vince, Dir, PALnet, 1040 W Bristol Rd, Flint, MI, 48507. Tel: 810-766-4070. p. 2946

Mols, Frank, Dir, Lebanon Valley College, 101 N College Ave, Annville, PA, 17003-1400. Tel: 717-867-6977. Fax: 717-867-6979. p. 2029

Molter, Gina, Br Mgr, Beaufort County Library, Lobeco Branch, 1862 Trask Pkwy, Lobeco, SC, 29931. Tel: 843-255-6475. Fax: 843-255-9483. p. 2181

Moltz, Sandra, Head, Ref (Info Serv), Head, YA, Swampscott Public Library, 61 Burrill St, Swampscott, MA, 01907. Tel: 781-596-8867. Fax: 781-596-8826. p. 1130

Molyneaux, Luann, Libr Tech, Prince Edward Island Public Library Service, Crapaud Public, 20424 Trans Canada Hwy, Crapaud, PE, C0A 1J0, CANADA. Tel: 902-658-2297. p. 2876

Molzahn, Robert F, Pres, Water Resources Association of the Delaware River Basin Library, PO Box 867, Valley Forge, PA, 19482-0867. Tel: 610-917-0090. Fax: 610-917-0091. p. 2149

Moma, Nancy, Librn, Stonington Township Public Library, 500 E North St, Stonington, IL, 62567. Tel: 217-325-3512. Fax: 217-325-3750. p. 708

Moman, Orthella Polk, Coordr, Tech Serv, Tougaloo College, Tougaloo College, 500 W County Line Rd, Tougaloo, MS, 39174-9799. Tel: 601-977-7778. Fax: 601-977-7714. p. 1315

Momberg, Kristin, Ref, Tech Serv, Hunterdon County Library, 314 State Rte 12, Flemington, NJ, 08822. Tel: 908-788-1444. Fax: 908-806-4862. p. 1486

Momeni, Farzaneh, Commun Libr Mgr, Queens Borough Public Library, Mitchell-Linden Community Library, 29-42 Union St, Flushing, NY, 11354. Tel: 718-539-2330. p. 1645

Momon, Heath, In Charge, Argosy University, 1005 Atlantic Ave, Alameda, CA, 94501-1148. Tel: 510-217-4793. Fax: 510-215-0381. p. 119

Momon, Ritchie, Mgr, Kansas City Public Library, Trails West, 11401 E 23rd St, Independence, MO, 64052. Tel: 816-701-3583. Fax: 816-701-3493. p. 1338

Momosor, Stetson, Br Mgr, Anchorage Public Library, Muldoon Branch, 1251 Muldoon Rd, Ste 158, Anchorage, AK, 99504. Tel: 907-343-4223. Fax: 907-337-2122. p. 45

Momsen, Kay, Head, Tech Serv, Orland Park Public Library, 14921 Ravinia Ave, Orland Park, IL, 60462. Tel: 708-428-5100. Fax: 708-349-8322. p. 686

Monaco, Kathleen A, Head Librn, Bryant & Stratton College Library, 301 Centre Pointe Dr, Virginia Beach, VA, 23462. Tel: 757-499-7900. Fax: 757-499-9977. p. 2498

Monaco, Mary, ILL, Ref Serv, St Thomas University Library, 16401 NW 37th Ave, Miami Gardens, FL, 33054. Tel: 305-628-6671. Fax: 305-628-6666. p. 469

Monaco, Ralph, Chief Librn, New York Law Institute Library, 120 Broadway, Rm 932, New York, NY, 10271-0043. Tel: 212-732-8720. Fax: 212-406-1204. p. 1689

Monaco, Sheri, Br Mgr, Warren County Library, Franklin Branch, 1502 Rte 57, Washington, NJ, 07882. Tel: 908-689-7922. Fax: 908-689-8265. p. 1472

Monaghan, Debbie, Librn, Willow Grove Baptist Church Library, 1872 Kimball Ave, Willow Grove, PA, 19090. Tel: 215-659-4505. p. 2157

Monaghan, Mary, Asst Dir, Neighborhood Libr, Carnegie Library of Pittsburgh, 4400 Forbes Ave, Pittsburgh, PA, 15213-4080. Tel: 412-237-1891. Fax: 412-622-6278. p. 2122

Monahan, Agatha, Coll Develop, West Hartford Public Library, 20 S Main St, West Hartford, CT, 06107-2432. Tel: 860-561-6950. Fax: 860-561-6976. p. 376

Monahan, Diane, Adult Serv, Boyden Library, Ten Bird St, Foxborough, MA, 02035. Tel: 508-543-1245. Fax: 508-543-1193. p. 1089

Monahan, Michael, Ref Serv, Bosler Free Library, 158 W High St, Carlisle, PA, 17013-2988. Tel: 717-243-4642. Fax: 717-243-8281. p. 2041

Monajami, Sirous, AV Coordr, City College of San Francisco, 50 Phelan Ave, San Francisco, CA, 94112. Tel: 415-452-5469. Fax: 415-452-5588. p. 241

Monbarren, Denise, Spec Coll Librn, The College of Wooster Libraries, 1140 Beall Ave, Wooster, OH, 44691-2364. Tel: 330-263-2527. Fax: 330-263-2253. p. 1949

Moncrief, Charlotte, Syst Coordr, Library Management Network, Inc, 2132 Sixth Ave SE, Ste 106, Decatur, AL, 35601. Tel: 256-308-2529. Fax: 256-308-2533. p. 2937

Moncrief, Connie, Br Mgr, Pine Mountain Regional Library, Yatesville Public, 77 Childs Ave, Yatesville, GA, 31097-3661. Tel: 706-472-3048. Fax: 706-472-3049. p. 542

Moncrief, Erica, Dir, Capital Health Regional Medical Center, 750 Brunswick Ave, Trenton, NJ, 08638. Tel: 609-394-6065. Fax: 609-278-1882. p. 1535

Moncrief, Erica, Dir, Capital Health System at Mercer, 446 Bellevue Ave, Trenton, NJ, 08618. Tel: 609-394-4125. Fax: 609-394-4131. p. 1535

Monday, Laura, Head, Circ, Worth Public Library District, 6917 W 111th St, Worth, IL, 60482. Tel: 708-448-2855. Fax: 708-448-9174. p. 721

Mondello, Gail, Circ, Gloucester, Lyceum & Sawyer Free Library, Two Dale Ave, Gloucester, MA, 01930-5906. Tel: 978-281-9763. Fax: 978-281-9770. p. 1091

Mondowney, Jo Anne, Exec Dir, Detroit Public Library, 5201 Woodward Ave, Detroit, MI, 48202. Tel: 313-481-1300. Fax: 313-481-1477. p. 1170

Mondragon, Carla, Dir, Saguache County Public Library, 702 Pitkin Ave, Saguache, CO, 81149. Tel: 719-655-2551. Fax: 719-655-2579. p. 322

Mondt, Laura, Coordr, Instrul Serv, Richland Community College, One College Park, Decatur, IL, 62521. Tel: 217-875-7200, Ext 294. Fax: 217-875-6961. p. 634

Mones, James J, Dir, New York Times, Photo Library, 620 Eight Ave, 5th Flr, New York, NY, 10018. Tel: 212-556-1642. Fax: 646-428-6366. p. 1695

Monette, Alain, Librn, George G Croskery Memorial Library, 2490 Don Reid Dr, Ottawa, ON, K1H 1E1, CANADA. Tel: 613-232-1505, Ext 146. Fax: 613-232-1886. p. 2830

Monette, Sophie, Librn, Bibliotheque Municipale de Mont-Laurier, 385 rue du Pont, Mont-Laurier, QC, J9L 2R5, CANADA. Tel: 819-623-1833. Fax: 819-623-7079. p. 2887

Money, Cindy, Librn, Brumback Library, Convoy Branch, 116 E Tully St, Convoy, OH, 45832. Tel: 419-749-4000. p. 1943

Money, Cindy, Librn, Brumback Library, Wren Branch, 101 Washington St, Wren, OH, 45899. Tel: 419-495-4174. p. 1943

Money, Nancy, Adminr, Canadian Institute of Resources Law, University of Calgary, Murray Fraser Hall, Rm 3353, Calgary, AB, T2N 1N4, CANADA. Tel: 403-220-3200. Fax: 403-282-6182. p. 2691

Moneypenny, Lorraine, Head, Info Serv, Nexant Inc, 44 S Broadway, 4th Flr, White Plains, NY, 10601. Tel: 914-609-0375. Fax: 914-609-0399. p. 1768

Monfred, Edward, Libr Serv Dir, ITT Technical Institute, 13 Airline Dr, Albany, NY, 12205-1003. Tel: 518-452-9300, Ext 116. Fax: 518-452-9393. p. 1569

Monge, Robert, Instruction & Outreach, Western Oregon University, Wayne & Lynn Hamersly Library, 345 N Monmouth Ave, Monmouth, OR, 97361-1396. Tel: 803-838-8887. Fax: 503-838-8399. p. 2006

Mongeau, Deborah, Chair, Pub Serv, Robert L Carothers Library & Learning Commons, 15 Lippitt Rd, Kingston, RI, 02881. Tel: 401-874-4610. Fax: 401-874-4608. p. 2168

Monger, Leah, Head, Tech Serv, Ferris State University Library, 1010 Campus Dr, Big Rapids, MI, 49307-2279. Tel: 231-591-3500. Fax: 231-591-3724. p. 1158

Monhaut, Jennifer, Br Mgr, La Porte County Public Library, Rolling Prairie Branch, One E Michigan Ave, Rolling Prairie, IN, 46371. Tel: 219-778-2390. Fax: 219-778-2390. p. 759

Monica, Dixon, I, Access Serv, US Army Chaplain Center & School Library, 10100 Lee Rd, Fort Jackson, SC, 29207. Tel: 803-751-8871. Fax: 803-751-8393. p. 2194

Monie, Darren, Syst Coordr, Bonne Terre Memorial Library, Five SW Main St, Bonne Terre, MO, 63628. Tel: 573-358-2260. Fax: 573-358-5941. p. 1320

Monier, Susanne, Circ Librn, Newbury Town Library, 0 Lunt St, Byfield, MA, 01922-1232. Tel: 978-465-0539. Fax: 978-465-1071. p. 1072

Monigold, Sharon, Dir, Bethany Heritage Prog & Archivist, Bethany College, Mary Cutlip Center for Library & Information Technology, 300 Main St, Bethany, WV, 26032. Tel: 304-829-7321. Fax: 304-829-7333. p. 2554

Moning, Mandi, Archivist, Coordr, User Serv, Indiana University East Campus Library, 2325 Chester Blvd, Richmond, IN, 47374. Tel: 765-973-8204. Fax: 765-973-8315. p. 775

Monis, Christi, Ch, Mesquite Public Library, North Branch, 2600 Oates Dr, Mesquite, TX, 75150. Tel: 972-681-0465. Fax: 972-681-0467. p. 2362

Moniz, Janice, Supvr, Middlesex County Library, Glencoe Branch, 178 McKellar St, Glencoe, ON, N0L 1M0, CANADA. Tel: 519-287-2735. p. 2845

Moniz, Richard, Dir of Libr Serv, Johnson & Wales University, 801 W Trade St, Charlotte, NC, 28202. Tel: 980-598-1604. p. 1783

Monk, Patricia, Pub Serv Librn, Bernard E Witkin Alameda County Law Library, 12th & Oak St Bldg, 125 Twelfth St, Oakland, CA, 94607-4912. Tel: 510-272-6484. Fax: 510-208-4823. p. 199

Monner, Joanne, Librn, Milo Municipal Library, 116 Center St, Milo, AB, T0L 1L0, CANADA. Tel: 403-599-3850. Fax: 403-599-3850. p. 2711

Monnier, Cynthia, Dir, Indiana Chamber of Commerce, 115 W Washington St S, Ste 850, Indianapolis, IN, 46204-3497. Tel: 317-264-7511. Fax: 317-264-6855. p. 751

Monocchi, Kim, In Charge, Yale University Library, Astronomy, J W Gibbs Lab, Rm 217, 260 Whitney Ave, New Haven, CT, 06511-8903. Tel: 203-432-3033. Fax: 203-432-5048. p. 356

Monochello, Ashley, Youth Serv Librn, Pompton Lakes Public Library, 333 Wanaque Ave, Pompton Lakes, NJ, 07442. Tel: 973-835-0482. Fax: 973-835-4767. p. 1521

Monoco, John, Info Spec, Price Waterhouse Coopers LLP, 1900 St Antione St, Detroit, MI, 48226. Tel: 313-394-6000. Fax: 313-394-6010. p. 1171

Monroe, Kathleen L, Actg Dir, Livonia Public Library, Civic Center, 32777 Five Mile Rd, Livonia, MI, 48154-3045. Tel: 734-466-2480. Fax: 734-458-6011. p. 1203

Monroe, Kristen, Sr Librn, Denver Public Library, Athmar Park, 1055 S Tejon St, Denver, CO, 80223. Tel: 303-935-0721. Fax: 303-934-9388. p. 301

Monroe, Linda, Ch, Wagoner City Public Library, 302 N Main, Wagoner, OK, 74467-3834. Tel: 918-485-2126. Fax: 918-485-0179. p. 1985

Monroe, Marcia, Supvr, Access Serv, University of Washington Libraries, Tacoma Library, 1900 Commerce St, Box 358460, Tacoma, WA, 98402-3100. Tel: 253-692-4446. Fax: 253-692-4445. p. 2535

Monroe, Ruy W, Ref Serv, Ser, Universidad del Turabo, PO Box 3030, Gurabo, PR, 00778-3030. Tel: 787-743-7979, Ext 4501. Fax: 787-743-7924. p. 2673

Monroe, Shelby, Ad, Lithgow Public Library, 45 Winthrop St, Augusta, ME, 04330-5599. Tel: 207-626-2415. Fax: 207-626-2419. p. 974

Monroe, Susan, Librn, North Branch Area Library, 6355-379 St, North Branch, MN, 55056. Tel: 651-674-8443. Fax: 651-674-8443. p. 1268

Monroe, Will, Head, Instrul Tech, Louisiana State University Libraries, Paul M Hebert Law Center, One E Campus Dr, Baton Rouge, LA, 70803-1000. Tel: 225-578-7838. Fax: 225-578-5773. p. 944

Monsalve-Jones, Leslie Clarissa, Libr Dir, Southwestern College, 3960 San Felipe Rd, Santa Fe, NM, 87507. Tel: 505-467-6825. Fax: 505-467-6826. p. 1564

Monsen, Alda, Librn, New Castle County Law Library, 500 King St, Ste 2500, Wilmington, DE, 19801. Tel: 302-255-0847. Fax: 302-255-2223. p. 388

Monson, James, Govt Doc, Western Connecticut State University, 181 White St, Danbury, CT, 06810. Tel: 203-837-9112. Fax: 203-837-9108. p. 335

Monson, Michele, Dir, Two Harbors Public Library, 320 Waterfront Dr, Two Harbors, MN, 55616-3201. Tel: 218-834-3148. p. 1286

Monson, Rachel, Spec, Nunez Community College Library, 3710 Paris Rd, Chalmette, LA, 70043. Tel: 504-278-6230, 504-278-7498. Fax: 504-680-2584. p. 947

Monson, Sue, Br Head, Muskegon Area District Library, Dalton Township Branch, 3175 Fifth St, Twin Lake, MI, 49457-9501. Tel: 231-828-4188. Fax: 231 724-6675. p. 1213

Monsour, Jeanne, Librn, River Region Medical Center Library, 2100 Hwy 61 N, Vicksburg, MS, 39183. Tel: 601-883-5943, 601-883-6020. Fax: 601-883-5139. p. 1317

Monstad, Dorothy, Librn, KSH Solutions, One Pl Alexis Nihon, 3400 Maisonneuve West Bureau 1600, Montreal, QC, H3Z 3B8, CANADA. Tel: 514-932-4611. Fax: 514-932-9700. p. 2897

Montag, John, Dir, Nebraska Wesleyan University, 50th & St Paul, Lincoln, NE, 68504. Tel: 402-465-2400. Fax: 402-465-2189. p. 1406

Montague, Don, Dir, South American Explorers Library, 126 Indian Creek Rd, Ithaca, NY, 14850. Tel: 607-277-0488. Fax: 607-277-6122. p. 1643

Montague, Lynn, Youth Serv, Sun Prairie Public Library, 1350 Linnerud Dr, Sun Prairie, WI, 53590-2631. Tel: 608-825-7323. Fax: 608-825-3936. p. 2641

Montague, Rae-Anne, Asst Dean, University of Illinois at Urbana-Champaign, Library & Information Science Bldg, 501 E Daniel St, Champaign, IL, 61820-6211. Tel: 217-333-3280. Fax: 217-244-3302. p. 2965

Montague, Sharon, Spec Serv Dir, Rolling Meadows Library, 3110 Martin Lane, Rolling Meadows, IL, 60008. Tel: 847-259-6050. Fax: 847-259-5319. p. 698

Montague, Winnell Morris, Br Mgr, District of Columbia Public Library, Dorothy I Height/Benning Neighborhood Library, 3935 Benning Road NE, Washington, DC, 20019. Tel: 202-281-2586. Fax: 202-727-4076. p. 398

Montalto, Andrew, Law Librn, Middlesex Law Library at Cambridge, Superior Courthouse, 40 Thorndike St, Cambridge, MA, 02141. Tel: 617-494-4148. Fax: 617-225-0026. p. 1078

Montalvo, Cynthia, Ref, Baker & Botts LLP, One Shell Plaza, 910 Louisiana St, Houston, TX, 77002. Tel: 713-229-1643. Fax: 713-229-1522. p. 2334

Montalvo, Manuel, Dir, East Chicago Public Library, 2401 E Columbus Dr, East Chicago, IN, 46312-2998. Tel: 219-397-2453. Fax: 219-397-6715. p. 736

Montalvo, Manuel, Dir, East Chicago Public Library, Robert A Pastrick Branch, 1008 W Chicago Ave, East Chicago, IN, 46312. Tel: 219-397-2453. Fax: 219-397-6715. p. 736

Montambeault, Sharon, Asst Librn, Abbott Library, 542 Rte 11, Sunapee, NH, 03782. Tel: 603-763-5513. Fax: 603-763-8765. p. 1466

Montana, Vita, Libr Mgr, Dona Ana Community College Library, East Mesa Campus, 2800 N Sonoma Ranch Blvd, Las Cruces, NM, 88011. Tel: 575-528-7260. Fax: 575-528-7422. p. 1558

Montanez-Salas, Alida, Commun Libr Mgr, County of Los Angeles Public Library, Bell Library, 4411 E Gage Ave, Bell, CA, 90201-1216. Tel: 323-560-2149. Fax: 323-773-7557. p. 141

Montano, Kay, Dir, Lake View Public Library, 202 Main St, Lake View, IA, 51450. Tel: 712-657-2310. Fax: 712-657-2310. p. 826

Montanucci, Mary, Head, Circ, Anderson County Library, 300 N McDuffie St, Anderson, SC, 29621-5643. Tel: 864-260-4500. Fax: 864-260-4510. p. 2180

Monte, Catherine M, Dir, Fox Rothschild LLP, 2000 Market St, Philadelphia, PA, 19103-3291. Tel: 215-299-2732. Fax: 215-299-2150. p. 2106

Monte, Maura, Librn, Atlantic County Library System, Egg Harbor City Branch, 134 Philadelphia Ave, Egg Harbor City, NJ, 08215. Tel: 609-804-1063. Fax: 609-804-1082. p. 1500

Monteagudo, Merrie, Res, Union-Tribune Publishing Co Library, 350 Camino de la Reina, San Diego, CA, 92108. Tel: 619-299-3131. p. 238

Montei, Kay E, Dir, Columbia Township Library, 6456 Center St, Unionville, MI, 48767. Tel: 989-674-2651. Fax: 989-674-2138. p. 1232

Monteleon, Michelle, Learning Res Coordr, Hillsborough Community College, Plant City Campus Learning Resources Center, 1206 N Park Rd, Plant City, FL, 33563. Tel: 813-757-2163. Fax: 813-757-2167. p. 496

Montenora, Sandra, Circ, Franklin Square Public Library, 19 Lincoln Rd, Franklin Square, NY, 11010. Tel: 516-488-3444. Fax: 516-354-3368. p. 1624

Montet, Margaret, Info Literacy Librn, Bucks County Community College Library, 275 Swamp Rd, Newtown, PA, 18940-0999. Tel: 215-968-8373. Fax: 215-968-8142. p. 2097

Montgomerie, Paul, Mgr, Los Angeles Public Library System, East Valley Area, 5211 Tujunga Ave, Los Angeles, CA, 91601. Tel: 818-755-7666. Fax: 818-760-8924. p. 173

Montgomery, Adrienne, Dir, San Augustine Public Library, 413 E Columbia St, San Augustine, TX, 75972-2111. Tel: 936-275-5367. Fax: 936-275-5049. p. 2384

Montgomery, Bruce P, Dir, Archives & Spec Coll, Prof, University of Colorado Boulder, 1720 Pleasant St, 184 UCB, Boulder, CO, 80309-0184. Tel: 303-492-7242. Fax: 303-492-3960. p. 291

Montgomery, Bruce P, Prof & Fac Dir, Archives & Spec Coll, University of Colorado Boulder, Archives & Special Collections, 1720 Pleasant St, Boulder, CO, 80309-0184. Tel: 303-492-7394. Fax: 303-492-1881. p. 291

Montgomery, Chauncey, Dir, Community Library, 44 Burrer Dr, Sunbury, OH, 43074. Tel: 740-965-3901. Fax: 740-965-1258. p. 1937

Montgomery, Christine, AV, State Historical Society of Missouri Library, 1020 Lowry St, Columbia, MO, 65201-7298. Tel: 573-882-2476. Fax: 573-884-4950. p. 1324

Montgomery, Debbie, Assoc Dir, Tech Serv, University of Texas at Dallas, 800 W Campbell Rd, Richardson, TX, 75080. Tel: 972-883-2963. Fax: 972-883-2473. p. 2374

Montgomery, Diane, Adult Serv, Windsor-Severance Library, 720 Third St, Windsor, CO, 80550-5109. Tel: 970-686-5603, Ext 303. Fax: 970-686-2502. p. 326

Montgomery, Doug, Network Adminr, Preble County District Library, 450 S Barron St, Eaton, OH, 45320-2402. Tel: 937-456-4250. Fax: 937-456-6092. p. 1897

Montgomery, Elaine, Dir, Baxter Public Library, 202 E State St, Baxter, IA, 50028. Tel: 641-227-3934. Fax: 641-227-3217. p. 796

Montgomery, Frances, Actg Head, Maps, Data & Govt Info Ctr, Carleton University Library, 1125 Colonel By Dr, Ottawa, ON, K1S 5B6, CANADA. Tel: 613-520-2600, Ext 8196. Fax: 613-520-2750. p. 2830

Montgomery, Gwen, Asst Librn, Chrisman Public Library, 108 N Illinois St, Chrisman, IL, 61924. Tel: 217-269-3011. Fax: 217-269-3011. p. 629

Montgomery, Jack, Acq, Coll Develop, Western Kentucky University Libraries, Helm-Cravens Library Complex, 1906 College Heights Blvd, No 11067, Bowling Green, KY, 42101-1067. Tel: 270-745-2905. Fax: 270-745-6422. p. 908

Montgomery, James, Assoc Dir, Coll Serv, Smith College Libraries, Northampton, MA, 01063. Tel: 413-585-2921. Fax: 413-585-2904. p. 1113

Montgomery, Judith, Assoc Librn, Bowdoin College Library, 3000 College Sta, Brunswick, ME, 04011-8421. Tel: 207-725-3749. p. 979

Montgomery, Leigh, Librn, Christian Science Monitor Library, One Norway St, Boston, MA, 02115. Tel: 617-450-2688. Fax: 617-450-2689. p. 1059

Montgomery, Linda, Dir, Braille & Talking Bk Libr, Arizona State Library, Archives & Public Records, 1700 W Washington, Rm 200, Phoenix, AZ, 85007. Tel: 602-926-4035. Fax: 602-256-7983. p. 72

Montgomery, Linda, Head of Libr, Armour Public Library, 915 Main Ave, Armour, SD, 57313. Tel: 605-724-2743. p. 2210

Montgomery, Linda A, Dir, Arizona State Braille & Talking Book Library, 1030 N 32nd St, Phoenix, AZ, 85008. Tel: 602-255-5578. Fax: 602-286-0444. p. 72

Montgomery, Mark, Ref Librn, The Mary Baker Eddy Library, Lending & Reference Services, 200 Massachusetts Ave, P02-10, Boston, MA, 02115-3017. Tel: 617-450-7315. p. 1060

Montgomery, Mary, Dir, Bridge City Public Library, 101 Parkside Dr, Bridge City, TX, 77611. Tel: 409-735-4242. Fax: 409-738-2127. p. 2291

Montgomery, Mary, Librn, Historical Society of Seattle & King County, 2700 24th Ave E, Seattle, WA, 98112. Tel: 206-324-1126. Fax: 206-324-1346. p. 2528

Montgomery, Matthew, Tech Serv Librn, Mechanics' Institute Library, 57 Post St, San Francisco, CA, 94104-5003. Tel: 415-393-0115. Fax: 415-421-4192. p. 243

Montgomery, Melissa, Librn, Surgoinsville Public Library, 120 Old Stage Rd, Surgoinsville, TN, 37873-3145. Tel: 423-345-4805. Fax: 423-345-4825. p. 2266

Montgomery, Molly, Med Librn, Texas Health Presbyterian Hospital Library, 820 Walnut Hill Lane, Dallas, TX, 75231. Tel: 214-345-2310. Fax: 214-345-2350. p. 2311

Montgomery, Nicole, Librn, CoxHealth Libraries, Cox Medical Ctr N, 1423 N Jefferson Ave, J-200, Springfield, MO, 65802. Tel: 417-269-8018. Fax: 417-269-3492. p. 1366

Montgomery, Nicole, Librn, CoxHealth Libraries, David Miller Memorial Library, Cox Medical Ctr S, 3801 S National Ave, Springfield, MO, 65807. Tel: 417-269-3460. Fax: 417-269-3492. p. 1366

Montgomery, Nicole M, Librn, Eastern Kentucky University Libraries, Justice & Safety, Stratton Bldg, Richmond, KY, 40475. Tel: 859-622-1798. Fax: 859-622-8028. p. 934

Montgomery Reinert, Patti, Exec Dir, Michigan Maritime Museum, 91 Michigan Ave, South Haven, MI, 49090. Tel: 269-637-9156. Fax: 269-637-1594. p. 1227

Montgomery, Ruth Ann, Dir, Arrowhead Library System, 210 Dodge St, Janesville, WI, 53545-3809. Tel: 608-758-6693. Fax: 608-758-6689. p. 2599

Montgomery, Sandra, Ref, Sierra Joint Community College District, 5000 Rocklin Rd, Rocklin, CA, 95677. Tel: 916-660-7230. Fax: 916-630-4539. p. 219

Montgomery, Susan, Pub Serv Librn, Rollins College, 1000 Holt Ave, Campus Box 2744, Winter Park, FL, 32789-2744. Tel: 407-646-2295. Fax: 407-646-1515. p. 505

Montgomery, Susan, Librn, Potter County Law Library, 501 S Filmore, Ste 2B, Amarillo, TX, 79101. Tel: 806-379-2347. p. 2274

Montgomery, Teresa, E-Res Coll Develop Coordr, Southern Oregon University, 1250 Siskiyou Blvd, Ashland, OR, 97520-5076. Tel: 541-552-6837. Fax: 541-552-6429. p. 1990

Montoya, Cathy, Librn, Houston Community College - Southwest College, Alief Continuing Education Center, 13803 Bissonnet, Houston, TX, 77083. Tel: 713-718-5447. p. 2338

Montoya, Vanessa, Tech Serv, Pueblo of Pojoaque Public Library, 37 Camino del Rincon, Ste 2, Santa Fe, NM, 87506-9810. Tel: 505-455-7511. Fax: 505-455-0501. p. 1563

Montoya, Vivian, Librn, California Thoroughbred Breeders Association, 201 Colorado Pl, Arcadia, CA, 91007. Tel: 626-445-7800. Fax: 626-574-0852. p. 121

Montreuil, François, Dir, Bibliotheque et Archives nationales du Quebec, 475 de Maisonneuve E, Montreal, QC, H2L 5C4, CANADA. Tel: 514-873-1101, Ext 3287. Fax: 514-873-9312. p. 2888

Montri, Tracy, AV Mgr, Toledo-Lucas County Public Library, 325 N Michigan St, Toledo, OH, 43604-6614. Tel: 419-259-5285. Fax: 419-255-1334. p. 1939

Montrose, Alan, Sci Librn, NASA, 21000 Brookpark Rd, MS 60-3, Cleveland, OH, 44135. Fax: 216-433-5777. p. 1880

Monts-Rayfield, Nancy, Br Mgr, York County Library, Lake Wylie Public, 185 Blucher Circle, Lake Wylie, SC, 29710. Tel: 803-831-7774. Fax: 803-831-7943. p. 2203

Montserrat, Inglada, Ch, YA Librn, Whiting Public Library, 1735 Oliver St, Whiting, IN, 46394-1794. Tel: 219-473-4700, Ext 13. Fax: 219-659-5833. p. 788

Mony, Linda, Dir, McKay Library, 105 S Webster St, Augusta, MI, 49012-9601. Tel: 616-731-4000. Fax: 616-731-5323. p. 1154

Monypeny, David, Homebound Serv/Computer Access, Yuma County Library District, 2951 S 21st Dr, Yuma, AZ, 85364. Tel: 928-782-1871. Fax: 928-782-9420. p. 91

Monzon, Bobbie, Managing Librn, Mechanics' Institute Library, 57 Post St, San Francisco, CA, 94104-5003. Tel: 415-393-0107. Fax: 415-421-4192. p. 243

Monzon, Cesar, Info Spec, United States Department of Commerce Bureau of the Census, Four Copley Pl, Ste 301, Boston, MA, 02117. Tel: 617-424-4510. Fax: 617-424-0547. p. 1068

Mooar, Patricia, Ref Librn, Boynton Beach City Library, 208 S Seacrest Blvd, Boynton Beach, FL, 33435. Tel: 561-742-6390. Fax: 561-742-6381. p. 429

Moodie, Marlene, Br Mgr 1, Sno-Isle Libraries, Brier Community Library, 23303 Brier Rd, Brier, WA, 98036. Tel: 425-483-0888. Fax: 425-487-1880. p. 2542

Moody, Alvin, Librn, Mississippi Department of Corrections, Hwy 63 N, Leakesville, MS, 39451. Tel: 601-394-5600, Ext 1079. Fax: 601-394-5600, Ext 1182. p. 1307

Moody, Bill, Librn, Har Zion Temple, 1500 Hagys Ford Rd, Penn Valley, PA, 19072. Tel: 610-667-5000. Fax: 610-667-2032. p. 2102

Moody, Diane, Ref Serv, Albany Public Library, 1390 Waverly Dr SE, Albany, OR, 97322. Tel: 541-917-7580, Ext 4701. Fax: 541-917-7586. p. 1989

Moody, Donna, Librn, Brookside Congregational Church Library, 2013 Elm St, Manchester, NH, 03104. Tel: 603-669-2807. Fax: 603-668-9041. p. 1455

Moody, Donna, Dir, Claymont Public Library, 215 E Third St, Uhrichsville, OH, 44683. Tel: 740-922-3626. Fax: 740-922-3500. p. 1942

Moody, Hortense, Librn, Georgia Department of Corrections, Georgia State Prison, 300 First Ave S, Reidsville, GA, 30453. Tel: 912-557-7301. Fax: 912-557-7241. p. 547

Moody, Kathy, Mgr, Three Rivers Regional Library System, Brantley County Library, 133 E Cleveland St, Nahunta, GA, 31553-9470. Tel: 912-462-5454. Fax: 912-462-5329. p. 522

Moody, Kiya, Libr Asst, University of Chicago Library, Eckhart Library, 1118 E 58th St, Chicago, IL, 60637. Tel: 773-702-8778. Fax: 773-702-7535. p. 627

Moody, Marilyn, Dean, Boise State University, 1865 Cesar Chavez Lane, Boise, ID, 83725-1430. Tel: 208-426-4321. Fax: 208-334-2111. p. 570

Moody, Marilyn, Univ Librn, Portland State University Library, 1875 SW Park Ave, Portland, OR, 97201-3220. Tel: 503-725-4510. Fax: 503-725-4524. p. 2014

Moody, Renee, Br Mgr, Jersey City Free Public Library, Miller, 489 Bergen Ave, Jersey City, NJ, 07304. Tel: 201-547-4551. Fax: 201-434-1469. p. 1492

Moody, Sharon, Ch, Paul Pratt Memorial Library, 35 Ripley Rd, Cohasset, MA, 02025-2097. Tel: 781-383-1348. Fax: 781-383-1698. p. 1082

Moody, Susan, Libr Mgr, Kinuso Municipal Library, PO Box 60, Kinuso, AB, T0G 1K0, CANADA. Tel: 780-775-3694. Fax: 780-775-3560. p. 2708

Moog, Emily, Libr Dir, Carter, Ledyard & Milburn Library, Two Wall St, New York, NY, 10005. Tel: 212-238-8851. Fax: 212-732-3232. p. 1671

Moomau, Becky, Librn, The Koch Industries Invista, DuPont Co, 400 Du Pont Blvd, Waynesboro, VA, 22980. Tel: 540-949-2485. Fax: 540-949-2949. p. 2501

Moon, Barbara, Ch, Fremont County District Library, 925 Main, Ashton, ID, 83420. Tel: 208-652-7280. p. 569

Moon, Barbara, YA Serv, Suffolk Cooperative Library System, 627 N Sunrise Service Rd, Bellport, NY, 11713. Tel: 631-286-1600. Fax: 631-286-1647. p. 1580

Moon, Betsy, Cat Supvr, United States Senate Library, SRB-15 Senate Russell Bldg, Washington, DC, 20510-7112. Tel: 202-224-7106. Fax: 202-224-0879. p. 421

Moon, Carol Ann, Ref & Instrul Outreach Librn, Saint Leo University, 33701 State Rd 52, Saint Leo, FL, 33574. Tel: 352-588-8261. Fax: 352-588-8484. p. 487

Moon, Danelle, Dir, Spec Coll, San Jose State University, One Washington Sq, San Jose, CA, 95192-0028. Tel: 408-808-2061. Fax: 408-808-2141. p. 251

Moon, Fletcher, Head, Ref (Info Serv), Tennessee State University, 3500 John A Merritt Blvd, Nashville, TN, 37209. Tel: 615-963-5205. Fax: 615-963-5216. p. 2259

Moon, Lee, Operations Adminr, Three Rivers Regional Library System, 208 Gloucester St, Brunswick, GA, 31520-7007. Tel: 912-267-1212. Fax: 912-267-9597. p. 522

Moon, Melanie, Librn, Brown Mackie College-Cincinnati Library, 1011 Glendale-Milford Rd, Cincinnati, OH, 45215. Tel: 513-771-2424. Fax: 513-771-3413. p. 1868

Moon, Peter S, Mgr, Hartford Steam Boiler Inspection & Insurance Co, One State St, 9th Flr, Hartford, CT, 06102. Tel: 860-722-5486. Fax: 860-722-5530. p. 347

Moon, Richard G, Jr, Dir, North Adams Public Library, 74 Church St, North Adams, MA, 01247. Tel: 413-662-3133. Fax: 413-662-3039. p. 1111

Moon, Ruth, Librn, College of the Redwoods, 7351 Tompkins Hill Rd, Eureka, CA, 95501. Tel: 707-476-4260. Fax: 707-476-4432. p. 147

Moon, Sarah, Ref Librn, Finger Lakes Community College, 4355 Lakeshore Dr, Canandaigua, NY, 14424-8395. Tel: 585-394-3500, Ext 7371. Fax: 585-394-8708. p. 1601

Moon, Stephen, Asst Br Mgr, Duchesne Library, Roosevelt Branch, 70 W Lagoon 44-4, Roosevelt, UT, 84066-2841. Tel: 435-722-4441. Fax: 435-722-3386. p. 2404

Moon, Susan, Art Librn, University of California, Santa Barbara, Santa Barbara, CA, 93106-9010. Tel: 805-893-2478. Fax: 805-893-7010. p. 261

Moon, Susan, Head of Libr, University of California, Santa Barbara, Arts Library, UCSB Library, Santa Barbara, CA, 93106-9010. Tel: 805-893-3613. Fax: 805-893-5879. p. 262

Moon, Young, Head, Acq of New Ser/Per, Boston College Libraries, Thomas P O'Neill Jr Library (Central Library), 140 Commonwealth Ave, Chestnut Hill, MA, 02467. Tel: 617-552-3207. Fax: 617-552-0599. p. 1081

Moonan, Jeanne, AV, Normal Public Library, 206 W College Ave, Normal, IL, 61761. Tel: 309-452-1757. Fax: 309-452-5312. p. 681

Mooney, Barrie, Ref & Info Literacy Librn, Assumption College, 500 Salisbury St, Worcester, MA, 01609. Tel: 508-767-7036. Fax: 508-767-7374. p. 1143

Mooney, David, Librn, Community College of Allegheny County, 808 Ridge Ave, Pittsburgh, PA, 15212-6003. Tel: 412-237-2585. Fax: 412-237-6563. p. 2124

Mooney, Joan, Co-Dir, Waseca County Historical Society Library, 315 Second Ave NE, Waseca, MN, 56093. Tel: 507-835-7700. p. 1287

Mooney, Laura, ILL, Brookings Institution Library, 1775 Massachusetts Ave NW, Washington, DC, 20036. Tel: 202-797-6240. Fax: 202-797-2970. p. 394

Mooney, Linda, Paralegal Adminr/Law Librn, MMSD Law Library, 260 W Seeboth St, Milwaukee, WI, 53204. Tel: 414-225-2098. Fax: 414-225-0167. p. 2621

Mooney, Mary Margaret, Sister, Actg Librn, Presentation Center Library, 1101 32nd Ave S, Fargo, ND, 58103-6092. Tel: 701-237-4857. Fax: 701 237-9822. p. 1841

Mooney, Monica, Dir, Clarence Public Library, Three Town Pl, Clarence, NY, 14031. Tel: 716-741-2650. Fax: 716-741-1243. p. 1607

Mooney, Robin, Librn, Tahlequah Public Library, 120 S College Ave, Tahlequah, OK, 74464. Tel: 918-456-2581. Fax: 918-458-0590. p. 1980

Mooney, Sean, Web Librn, Mill Valley Public Library, 375 Throckmorton Ave, Mill Valley, CA, 94941-2698. Tel: 415-389-4292, Ext 107. Fax: 415-388-8929. p. 186

Mooney, Tom, Archivist, Cherokee National Historical Society, 21192 S Keeler Dr, Park Hill, OK, 74451. Tel: 918-456-6007. Fax: 918-456-6165. p. 1976

Mooneyhan, Laura, Ch, Rector Public Library, 121 W Fourth St, Rector, AR, 72461. Tel: 870-595-2410. Fax: 870-595-2410. p. 113

Moor, Ann, Dir, Bay City Public Library, 1100 Seventh St, Bay City, TX, 77414. Tel: 979-245-6931. Fax: 979-245-2614. p. 2286

Moore, Adam, Assoc Prof, University of Washington, Mary Gates Hall, Ste 370, Campus Box 352840, Seattle, WA, 98195-2840. Tel: 206-685-9937. Fax: 206-616-3152. p. 2976

Moore, Alice, Librn, Robert L Williams Public Library, 323 W Beech, Durant, OK, 74701. Tel: 580-924-3486. Fax: 580-924-8843. p. 1962

Moore, Alice Wiley, Head, Access Serv, Albion College, 602 E Cass St, Albion, MI, 49224-1879. Tel: 517-629-0285. Fax: 517-629-0504. p. 1148

Moore, Amber, Asst Librn, Albemarle Regional Library, Hertford County Library, 303 W Tryon St, Winton, NC, 27986. Tel: 252-358-7855. Fax: 252-358-0368. p. 1835

Moore, Andrea, Commun Relations Coordr, Carson City Library, 900 N Roop St, Carson City, NV, 89701. Tel: 775-887-2244. Fax: 775-887-2273. p. 1425

Moore, Andrew, Ref Librn, Wayland Free Public Library, Five Concord Rd, Wayland, MA, 01778. Tel: 508-358-2311. Fax: 508-358-5249. p. 1134

Moore, Angela, Librn, Carnegie-Schuyler Library, 303 E Second St, Pana, IL, 62557. Tel: 217-562-2326. Fax: 217-562-2343. p. 688

Moore, Anita W, Head Librn, Rust College, 150 E Rust Ave, Holly Springs, MS, 38635. Tel: 662-252-8000, Ext 4100. Fax: 662-252-8873. p. 1302

Moore, Ann, Dir, Charleston Public Library, 13 Atkinson Rd, Charleston, ME, 04422-3000. Tel: 207-285-3680. p. 982

Moore, Ann Marie, Head, Ref Serv, Manhasset Public Library, 30 Onderdonk Ave, Manhasset, NY, 11030. Tel: 516 627-2300, Ext 205. Fax: 516-627-4339. p. 1657

Moore, Ann S, ILL, Clarkson College Library, 101 S 42nd St, Omaha, NE, 68131-2739. Tel: 402-552-3387. Fax: 402-552-2899. p. 1411

Moore, Anna Mae, Archives, Coll, Tech Serv, Washington & Jefferson College Library, 60 S Lincoln St, Washington, PA, 15301. Tel: 724-223-6068. Fax: 724-223-5272. p. 2151

Moore, Anne, Dir, Garfield County Public Library System, 402 W Main, New Castle, CO, 81647. Tel: 970-984-2347. Fax: 970-984-2487. p. 319

Moore, Anne, Tech Serv Librn, Wheelock College Library, 132 The Riverway, Boston, MA, 02215-4815. Tel: 617-879-2221. Fax: 617-879-2408. p. 1068

Moore, Anne, Dir, Wegner Health Science Information Center, 1400 W 22nd St, Ste 100, Sioux Falls, SD, 57105. Tel: 605-357-1400. Fax: 605-357-1490. p. 2219

Moore, Barbara, Ref Serv Coordr, Shreve Memorial Library, 424 Texas St, Shreveport, LA, 71101. Tel: 318-226-5897. Fax: 318-226-4780. p. 969

Moore, Barbara, Youth Serv Mgr, Marion Public Library, 445 E Church St, Marion, OH, 43302-4290. Tel: 740-387-0992. Fax: 740-382-9954. p. 1914

Moore, Barbara, Dir, Driscoll Public Library, 202 E Hondo Ave, Devine, TX, 78016. Tel: 830-663-2993. Fax: 830-663-6380. p. 2313

Moore, Barbara N, Dir of Libr, Chattahoochee Technical College Library, 980 S Cobb Dr SE, Marietta, GA, 30060-3300. Tel: 770-528-4422. Fax: 770-528-4454. p. 542

Moore, Becky, Librn, Pima Community College, East, 8181 E Irvington Rd, Tucson, AZ, 85709-4000. Tel: 520-206-7693. Fax: 520-206-7690. p. 86

Moore, Ben, Ref Librn, Indiana Tech, 1600 E Washington Blvd, Fort Wayne, IN, 46803. Tel: 260-422-5561, Ext 2215. Fax: 260-422-3189. p. 741

Moore, Betty, Dir, Hampton Historical Society, 40 Park Ave, Hampton, NH, 03842. Tel: 603-929-0781. p. 1449

Moore, Betty Jo, Dir, White Pine Public Library, 1708 Main St, White Pine, TN, 37890. Tel: 865-674-6313. Fax: 865-674-8511. p. 2269

Moore, Bev, Spec Serv, Watertown Regional Library, 160 Sixth St NE, Watertown, SD, 57201-2778. Tel: 605-882-6220. Fax: 605-882-6221. p. 2221

Moore, Bonnie, Ser, Hennepin County Medical Center, Mail Code R2, 701 Park Ave, Minneapolis, MN, 55415. Tel: 612-873-2711. Fax: 612-904-4248. p. 1260

Moore, Bonnie, Dir, Ward County Library, 409 S Dwight, Monahans, TX, 79756. Tel: 432-943-3332. Fax: 432-943-3332. p. 2363

Moore, Brenda, Head Librn, Gary Public Library, John F Kennedy Branch, 3953 Broadway, Gary, IN, 46408-1799. Tel: 219-887-8112. Fax: 219-887-5967. p. 745

Moore, Bruce A, Cataloger, Siena Heights University Library, 1247 E Siena Heights Dr, Adrian, MI, 49221-1796. Tel: 517-264-7151. Fax: 517-264-7711. p. 1148

Moore, Carole, Chief Librn, University of Toronto Libraries, 130 St George St, Toronto, ON, M5S 1A5, CANADA. Tel: 416-978-2292. Fax: 416-978-1608. p. 2865

Moore, Carole, Chief Librn, University of Toronto Libraries, 252 Bloor St W, Toronto, ON, M5S 1V6, CANADA. Tel: 416-978-2292. Fax: 416-926-4737. p. 2867

Moore, Cassandra, Librn, Riverside Regional Medical Center, 500 J Clyde Morris Blvd, Newport News, VA, 23601. Tel: 757-240-2400. Fax: 757-240-2401. p. 2480

Moore, Cathy, Librn, Crittenden County Library, Gilmore Branch, 87 Front St, Gilmore, AR, 72339. Tel: 870-343-2697. Fax: 870-343-2601. p. 109

Moore, Cathy, Librn, Peninsula Regional Medical Center, 100 E Carroll St, Salisbury, MD, 21801. Tel: 410-543-7094. Fax: 410-543-7096. p. 1040

Moore, Charles, Librn, Mesa Community College Library, 1833 W Southern Ave, Mesa, AZ, 85202. Tel: 480-461-7686. Fax: 480-461-7681. p. 68

Moore, Charles, Pub Serv, East Chicago Public Library, 2401 E Columbus Dr, East Chicago, IN, 46312-2998. Tel: 219-397-2453. Fax: 219-397-6715. p. 736

Moore, Chas, Libr Dir, Mesa Community College, Paul A Elsner Library, 1833 W Southern Ave, Mesa, AZ, 85202. Tel: 480-461-7686. Fax: 480-461-7681. p. 2961

Moore, Cherrilynn, Tech Serv Mgr, Glendale Public Library, 5959 W Brown St, Glendale, AZ, 85302-1248. Tel: 623-930-3565. Fax: 623-842-4209. p. 64

Moore, Christa, In Charge, Klamath County Library Services District, Malin Branch, 2307 Front St, Malin, OR, 97632. Tel: 541-723-5210. Fax: 541-723-5930. p. 2002

Moore, Christa, In Charge, Klamath County Library Services District, Merrill Branch, 365 W Front, Merrill, OR, 97633. Tel: 541-798-5393. Fax: 541-798-5393. p. 2002

Moore, Christina, Librn, Worcester County Jail & House of Correction Library, Five Paul X Tivnan Dr, West Boylston, MA, 01583. Tel: 508-854-1800, Ext 2344. Fax: 508-852-8754. p. 1136

Moore, Christine, Librn, Glendale Community College, 6000 W Olive Ave, Glendale, AZ, 85302. Tel: 623-845-3425. Fax: 623-845-3102. p. 64

Moore, Cynthia A, Librn, La Plata Public Library, 103 E Moore, La Plata, MO, 63549. Tel: 660-332-4945. Fax: 660-332-4945. p. 1343

Moore, Daniel R, Automation Syst Coordr, Garnet A Wilson Public Library of Pike County, 207 N Market St, Waverly, OH, 45690-1176. Tel: 740-947-4921. Fax: 740-947-2918. p. 1945

Moore, David, Assoc Dir, University of Missouri, 23 Ellis Library, Columbia, MO, 65201-5149. Tel: 573-882-0191. Fax: 573-884-0345. p. 1325

Moore, David, Head, Tech Serv, Schenectady County Community College, 78 Washington Ave, Schenectady, NY, 12305. Tel: 518-381-1235. Fax: 518-381-1252. p. 1740

Moore, David Phillip, Interim Dir, University of Alabama in Huntsville, 301 Sparkman Dr NW, Huntsville, AL, 35899. Tel: 256-824-6285. Fax: 256-824-6083. p. 22

Moore, Dean, Mgr, Memphis Public Library, Frayser Branch, 3712 Argonne, Memphis, TN, 38127-4414. Tel: 901-357-4115. Fax: 901-358-0360. p. 2250

Moore, Deborah, Acq, Cat, Bristol Public Library, 701 Goode St, Bristol, VA, 24201-4199. Tel: 276-821-6195. Fax: 276-669-5593. p. 2452

Moore, Deborah, Ref Librn, Highline Community College Library, 2400 S 240th St, MS 25-4, Des Moines, WA, 98198. Tel: 206-878-3710, Ext 3518. Fax: 206-870-3776. p. 2514

Moore, Debra, Syst & Tech Serv Librn, Cerritos College Library, 11110 Alondra Blvd, Norwalk, CA, 90650. Tel: 562-860-2451, Ext 2418. Fax: 562-467-5002. p. 195

Moore, Deena, Bus & Human Res Mgr, Central Mississippi Regional Library System, 104 Office Park Dr, Brandon, MS, 39042-2404. Tel: 601-825-0100. Fax: 601-825-0199. p. 1294

Moore, Deirdre, Mgr, Libr Serv, Natural Resources Canada-Forestry, 1055 rue du PEPS, Quebec City, QC, G1V 4C7, CANADA. Tel: 418-648-4850. Fax: 418-648-3433. p. 2907

Moore, Diana, Govt Doc, Provincial Archives of New Brunswick, 23 Dineen Dr, Fredericton, NB, E3B 5A3, CANADA. Tel: 506-453-2122. Fax: 506-453-3288. p. 2763

Moore, Diane, Tech Serv, Lepper Public Library, 303 E Lincoln Way, Lisbon, OH, 44432-1400. Tel: 330-424-3117. Fax: 330-424-7343. p. 1910

Moore, Diane, Dr, Dean, Ventura College, 4667 Telegraph Rd, Ventura, CA, 93003-3889. Tel: 805-654-6468. Fax: 805-648-8900. p. 279

Moore, Dianne, Ref, Olympic College, 1600 Chester Ave, Bremerton, WA, 98337. Tel: 360-475-7250. Fax: 360-475-7261. p. 2510

Moore, DiAnne T, Libr Mgr, Weil, Gotshal & Manges LLP, 1300 Eye St NW, Ste 900, Washington, DC, 20005. Tel: 202-682-7117. Fax: 202-682-7297. p. 422

Moore, Dixie, ILL Librn, Mercer County Library, 601 Grant, Princeton, MO, 64673. Tel: 660-748-3725. Fax: 660-748-3723. p. 1350

Moore, Donna, Ref & Info Serv, Web Coordr, University of South Carolina at Beaufort Library, One University Blvd, Bluffton, SC, 29909-6085. Tel: 843-208-8024. Fax: 843-208-8296. p. 2182

Moore, Donna, Asst Dir, Sequatchie County Public Library, 227 Cherry St W, Dunlap, TN, 37327-5207. Tel: 423-949-2357. Fax: 423-949-6619. p. 2233

Moore, Dorothy, Head, Ref Serv, Oyster Bay-East Norwich Public Library, 89 E Main St, Oyster Bay, NY, 11771. Tel: 516-922-1212. Fax: 516-922-6453. p. 1714

Moore, Douglas, Info Spec, Concord University, 1000 Vermillion St, Athens, WV, 24712. Tel: 304-384-5372. Fax: 304-384-7955. p. 2553

Moore, Earlene J, Coll Develop, ILL, University of Tennessee at Martin, Ten Wayne Fisher Dr, Martin, TN, 38238. Tel: 731-881-7067. Fax: 731-881-7074. p. 2246

Moore, Elda, Librn, Tonkawa Public Library, 216 N Seventh, Tonkawa, OK, 74653. Tel: 580-628-3366. Fax: 580-628-3688. p. 1980

Moore, Elise, Libr Assoc, Anadarko Community Library, 215 W Broadway, Anadarko, OK, 73005-2841. Tel: 405-247-7351. Fax: 405-247-2024. p. 1956

Moore, Emily, Ch Prog, Pope County Library System, 116 E Third St, Russellville, AR, 72801. Tel: 479-968-4368. Fax: 479-968-3222. p. 114

Moore, Emily, Syst Coordr, United States Air Force, FL 2804, 100 Kindel Dr, Ste C212, Arnold AFB, TN, 37389-3212. Tel: 931-454-4430. Fax: 931-454-5421. p. 2223

Moore, Emily S, Libr Dir, University of Tennessee Space Institute Library, Library, MS-25, 411 B H Goethert Pkwy, Tullahoma, TN, 37388-9700. Fax: 931-393-7518. p. 2268

Moore, Francene, Ref Serv, North Carolina Agricultural & Technical State University, 1601 E Market St, Greensboro, NC, 27411-0002. Tel: 336-334-7159, Ext 3216. Fax: 336-334-7783. p. 1797

Moore, Gerald, Br Head, Charleston County Public Library, Dorchester Road Regional, 6325 Dorchester Rd, North Charleston, SC, 29418. Tel: 843-552-6466. Fax: 843-552-6775. p. 2183

Moore, Gloria, Dir, George H & Laura E Brown Library, 122 Van Norden St, Washington, NC, 27889. Tel: 252-946-4300. Fax: 252-975-2015. p. 1828

Moore, James, Librn, United States Army, 38 Screaming Eagle Blvd, Fort Campbell, KY, 42223-5342. Tel: 270-798-5729. Fax: 270-798-0369. p. 912

Moore, James, In Charge, Multnomah County Library, Fairview-Columbia Branch, 1520 NE Village St, Fairview, OR, 97024. Tel: 503-988-5655. Fax: 503-988-6111. p. 2012

Moore, Jan, Asst Librn, Grey Highlands Public Library, 101 Highland Dr, Flesherton, ON, N0C 1E0, CANADA. Tel: 519-924-2241. Fax: 519-924-2562. p. 2805

Moore, Janet A, Res, Drinker Biddle & Reath LLP, One Logan Sq, 18th & Cherry St, Philadelphia, PA, 19103. Tel: 215-988-2951. Fax: 215-564-1329, 215-988-2757. p. 2106

Moore, Janet L, Dir, Wernersville Public Library, 100 N Reber St, Wernersville, PA, 19565-1412. Tel: 610-678-8771. Fax: 610-678-3025. p. 2152

Moore, Jessica, Dir, Marlette District Library, 3116 Main St, Marlette, MI, 48453. Tel: 989-635-2838. Fax: 989-635-8005. p. 1206

Moore, Joan, Librn, Southwest Arkansas Regional Library, Horatio Branch, 108 Main St, Horatio, AR, 71842. Tel: 870-832-6882. Fax: 870-832-6882. p. 103

Moore, Jodie, Dir, Red Lodge Carnegie Library, Three W Eighth St, Red Lodge, MT, 59068. Tel: 406-446-1905. p. 1387

Moore, Johnetta, Ref & Instrul Serv Librn, Edmonds Community College Library, 20000 68th Ave W, Lynnwood, WA, 98036. Tel: 425-640-1529. p. 2520

Moore, Joi, Assoc Prof, University of Missouri-Columbia, 303 Townsend Hall, Columbia, MO, 65211. Tel: 573-882-4546. Fax: 573-884-2917. p. 2969

Moore, Joseph, Automation Syst Coordr, Thomas County Public Library System, 201 N Madison St, Thomasville, GA, 31792-5414. Tel: 229-225-5252. Fax: 229-225-5258. p. 553

Moore, Joy, Librn, Brumback Library, Ohio City Branch, 101 W Carmean St, Ohio City, OH, 45874. Tel: 419-965-2918. p. 1943

Moore, Joyce, Ch, Coordr, Teen Serv, Youth/Young Adult Librn, Vermillion Public Library, 18 Church St, Vermillion, SD, 57069-3093. Tel: 605-677-7060. Fax: 605-677-7160. p. 2221

Moore, Judi, Head of Libr, Free Library of Philadelphia, McPherson Square Branch, 601 E Indiana Ave, Philadelphia, PA, 19134-3042. Tel: 215-685-9994, 215-685-9995. Fax: 215-685-9984. p. 2108

Moore, Judy, Dir, Highland Community College Library, 2998 W Pearl City Rd, Freeport, IL, 61032-9341. Tel: 815-599-3539. Fax: 815-235-1366. p. 647

Moore, Julia, Pub Serv, Northwest Community College Library, 5331 McConnell Ave, Terrace, BC, V8G 4X2, CANADA. Tel: 250-638-5407. Fax: 250-635-1594. p. 2739

Moore, Julie, Dir, Sturgis Public Library, 1040 Second St, Sturgis, SD, 57785-1595. Tel: 605-347-2624. Fax: 605-720-7211. p. 2220

Moore, Julie L, Dir, Wildlife Information Service Library, 2001 Calle de Suenos, Las Cruces, NM, 88001-4311. Tel: 575-527-2547. p. 1558

Moore, Karen, Ch, Brentwood Public Library, 8765 Eulalie Ave, Brentwood, MO, 63144. Tel: 314-963-4675. Fax: 314-962-8675. p. 1320

Moore, Karen, Admin Librn, Wright County Library, 125 Court Sq, Hartville, MO, 65667-9998. Tel: 417-741-7595. Fax: 417-741-7927. p. 1330

Moore, Karen, Dir, Forest-Jackson Public Library, 102 W Lima St, Forest, OH, 45843-1128. Tel: 419-273-2400. Fax: 419-273-8007. p. 1900

Moore, Kate, Br Mgr, Maricopa County Library District, Litchfield Park Branch, 101 W Wigwam Blvd, Litchfield, AZ, 85340. Tel: 602-652-3451. Fax: 602-652-3470. p. 74

Moore, Kate, Br Mgr, Cabarrus County Public Library, Mt Pleasant Branch, 8556 Cook St, Mount Pleasant, NC, 28124. Tel: 704-436-2202. Fax: 704-436-8205. p. 1785

Moore, Kathryn, Librn, Canadian Agriculture Library, 6000 C&E Trail, Lacombe, AB, T4L 1W1, CANADA. Tel: 403-782-8136. Fax: 403-782-6120. p. 2708

Moore, Katie Bell, Dir, Charles A Ransom District Library, 180 S Sherwood Ave, Plainwell, MI, 49080-1896. Tel: 269-685-8024. Fax: 269-685-2266. p. 1218

Moore, Kay, Librn, Ramey & Flock, PC, 100 E Ferguson St, Ste 500, Tyler, TX, 75702. Tel: 903-597-3301. Fax: 903-597-2413. p. 2393

Moore, Kerri, Br Mgr, Sacramento Public Library, Arden-Dimick Community Library, 891 Watt Ave, Sacramento, CA, 95864. p. 224

Moore, Kevin, Br Librn, London Public Library, Pond Mills, 1166 Commissioners Rd E, London, ON, N5Z 4W8, CANADA. Tel: 519-685-1333. p. 2818

Moore, Kim Gordon, Media Spec, Miles College, 5500 Myron Massey Blvd, Fairfield, AL, 35064. Tel: 205-929-1708. Fax: 205-929-1635. p. 16

Moore, Laura, Dr, Circ, General Theological Seminary, 440 West 21st St, New York, NY, 10011. Tel: 646-717-9784. Fax: 212-924-6304. p. 1679

Moore, Lennis, Chief Exec Officer, Midwest Old Settlers & Threshers Association, 405 E Threshers Rd, Mount Pleasant, IA, 52641. Tel: 319-385-8937. Fax: 319-385-0563. p. 833

Moore, Linda, Dir, Millbrook Public Library, 3650 Grandview Rd, Millbrook, AL, 36054. Tel: 334-285-6688, Ext 22. Fax: 334-285-0152. p. 25

Moore, Linda, Libr Supvr, Marshalltown Community College, 3700 S Center St, Marshalltown, IA, 50158. Tel: 641-844-5690. Fax: 641-754-1442. p. 830

Moore, Linda, Archivist, Circ, Pub Serv Librn, Hillsdale College, 33 E College St, Hillsdale, MI, 49242. Tel: 517-607-2403. Fax: 517-607-2248. p. 1190

Moore, Linda, Librn, Bradford Public Library, 138 E Main St, Bradford, OH, 45308-1108. Tel: 937-448-2612. Fax: 937-448-2615. p. 1861

Moore, Lindy, Br Mgr, West Georgia Regional Library, Dog River Public Library, 6100 Georgia Hwy 5, Douglasville, GA, 30135. Tel: 770-577-5186. p. 524

Moore, Lou Ann, Cat, Wayne County Public Library, 1200 Oak St, Kenova, WV, 25530-1335. Tel: 304-453-2462. Fax: 304-453-2462. p. 2563

Moore, Lynn, Br Mgr, Dallas Public Library, Audelia Road, 10045 Audelia Rd, Dallas, TX, 75238-1999. Tel: 214-670-1350. Fax: 214-670-0790. p. 2306

Moore, Lynne, Br Mgr, Saint Tammany Parish Library, Folsom Branch, 82393 Railroad Ave, Folsom, LA, 70437. Tel: 985-796-9728. Fax: 985-796-9728. p. 948

Moore, Maralyn, Circ, Noxubee County Library System, 103 E King St, Macon, MS, 39341-2832. Tel: 662-726-5461. Fax: 662-726-4694. p. 1307

Moore, Marilyn, Head Librn, Northwestern Oklahoma State University, 709 Oklahoma Blvd, Alva, OK, 73717. Tel: 580-213-3111. Fax: 580-213-3140. p. 1956

Moore, Marilyn, Asst Dir & Syst Librn, Northwestern Oklahoma State University Libraries, 2929 E Randolph, Enid, OK, 73701. Tel: 580-213-3111. Fax: 580-213-3140. p. 1963

Moore, Martha, Dir, Associated Grant Makers, 55 Court St, Ste 520, Boston, MA, 02108. Tel: 617-426-2606, Ext 116. Fax: 617-426-2849. p. 1055

Moore, Martha, Dir, Lunenburg Public Library, 1023 Massachusetts Ave, Lunenburg, MA, 01462. Tel: 978-582-4140. Fax: 978-582-4141. p. 1101

Moore, Mary, Ref & Adult Serv Mgr, Huntsville-Madison Public Library, 915 Monroe St, Huntsville, AL, 35801. Tel: 256-532-5940. Fax: 256-532-5997. p. 21

Moore, Mary, Head, Tech Serv, Davis County Library, 38 S 100 East, Farmington, UT, 84025. Tel: 801-451-2322. Fax: 801-451-9561. p. 2405

Moore, Mary Alice, Curator, Mineral Point Public Library, 137 High St, Mineral Point, WI, 53565. Tel: 608-987-2447. Fax: 608-987-2447. p. 2622

Moore, Maxine R, Chairperson, Houston County Historical Commission Archives, Courthouse Annex, 401 E Goliad, Crockett, TX, 75835-4035. Tel: 936-544-3255, Ext 238. Fax: 936-544-8053. p. 2303

Moore, Melissa, Pub Serv Librn, Union University, 1050 Union University Dr, Jackson, TN, 38305-3697. Tel: 731-661-5408. Fax: 731-661-5175. p. 2238

Moore, Mern, Librn, Wallowa County Library, Imnaha Station, Imnaha Hwy, Imnaha, OR, 97842. Tel: 541-577-2308. p. 1996

Moore, Michelle, Dir, Librn, Missaukee District Library, 210 S Canal St, Lake City, MI, 49651. Tel: 231-839-2166. Fax: 231-839-3865. p. 1199

Moore, Mike, ILL/Tech Serv Librn, United States Geological Survey Library, 345 Middlefield Rd, Bldg 15 (MS-955), Menlo Park, CA, 94025-3591. Tel: 650-329-5009. Fax: 650-329-5132. p. 185

Moore, Millie, Coordr, Coll Mgt, Ser Librn, Tulane University, Rudolph Matas Library of the Health Sciences, Tulane Health Sciences Campus, 1430 Tulane Ave, SL-86, New Orleans, LA, 70112-2699. Tel: 504-988-2063. Fax: 504-988-7417. p. 963

Moore, Nancy, Br Supvr, Kern County Library, Wofford Heights Branch, 6400-B Wofford Blvd, Wofford Heights, CA, 93285. Tel: 760-376-6160. p. 125

Moore, Nancy, Ref Librn, Epstein, Becker & Green, 250 Park Ave, 12th Flr, New York, NY, 10177. Tel: 212-351-4695. Fax: 212-661-0989. p. 1677

Moore, Nancy, Dir, Five Rivers Public Library, 301 Walnut St, Parsons, WV, 26287. Tel: 304-478-3880. Fax: 304-478-3880. p. 2569

Moore, Nora, Br Librn, Bolivar County Library System, Thelma Rayner Memorial Library, 201 Front St, Merigold, MS, 38759. Tel: 662-748-2105. Fax: 662-748-2105. p. 1296

Moore, Pamela, Ch, Collier County Public Library, 2385 Orange Blossom Dr, Naples, FL, 34109. Tel: 239-593-0334. Fax: 239-254-8167. p. 471

Moore, Pamela, Br Mgr, Lebanon-Wilson County Library, Watertown Branch, 206 Public Sq, Watertown, TN, 37184-1422. Tel: 615-237-9700. Fax: 615-237-9700. p. 2245

Moore, Pat, Librn, Interlaken Public Library, 8390 Main St, Interlaken, NY, 14847. Tel: 607-532-4341. Fax: 607-532-4341. p. 1640

Moore, Pat, Assoc Univ Librn, Carleton University Library, 1125 Colonel By Dr, Ottawa, ON, K1S 5B6, CANADA. Tel: 613-520-2600, Ext 2745. Fax: 613-520-2750. p. 2830

Moore, Patricia, Mgr, Ch Serv, Logansport-Cass County Public Library, 616 E Broadway, Logansport, IN, 46947-3187. Tel: 574-753-6383. Fax: 574-722-5889. p. 761

Moore, Peggy, Head, Circ, Estes Park Public Library, 335 E Elkhorn Ave, Estes Park, CO, 80517. Tel: 970-586-8116. Fax: 970-586-0189. p. 306

Moore, Peter, Automation Syst Coordr, Mansfield-Richland County Public Library, 43 W Third St, Mansfield, OH, 44902-1295. Tel: 419-521-3105. Fax: 419-521-3126. p. 1912

Moore, Phyllis, Tech Serv, Beaver Island District Library, 26400 Donegal Bay Rd, Beaver Island, MI, 49782. Tel: 231-448-2701. Fax: 231-448-2801. p. 1156

Moore, Phyllis, Librn, Belle Center Free Public Library, 103 S Elizabeth St, Belle Center, OH, 43310. Tel: 937-464-3611. Fax: 937-464-3611. p. 1858

Moore, Rachel, Ref/Cat Librn, American Congregational Association, 14 Beacon St, 2nd Flr, Boston, MA, 02108-9999. Tel: 617-523-0470. Fax: 617-523-0491. p. 1054

Moore, Robert, Librn, Miami Correctional Facility, Phase I Library, 3038 W 850 S, Bunker Hill, IN, 46914. Tel: 765-689-8920, Ext 5344. Fax: 765-689-5964. p. 730

Moore, Ron, Br Mgr, Lake County Library System, Paisley County Library, 24954 County Rd 42, Paisley, FL, 32767. Tel: 352-669-1001. Fax: 352-669-2180. p. 500

Moore, Rosanne, Circ, Okefenokee Regional Library, 401 Lee Ave, Waycross, GA, 31501. Tel: 912-287-4978. Fax: 912-284-2533. p. 557

Moore, Rose, Circ & Ref, University Libraries, University of Memphis, Mathematics, 341 Dunn Hall, Memphis, TN, 38152. Tel: 901-678-2385. Fax: 901-678-2480. p. 2252

Moore, Roxann, Asst Dir, Ch, Corning Public Library, 603 Ninth St, Corning, IA, 50841-1304. Tel: 641-322-3866. Fax: 641-322-3491. p. 804

Moore, Roxanne, Librn, Arizona Department of Corrections - Adult Institutions, 26700 S Hwy 85, Buckeye, AZ, 85326. Tel: 623-386-6160, Ext 4908. Fax: 623-386-6160, Ext 4910. p. 58

Moore, Russell, Dir, Springfield Town Library, 43 Main St, Springfield, VT, 05156. Tel: 802-885-3108. Fax: 802-885-4906. p. 2436

Moore, Sarah, Dir, Richwood North Union Public Library, Four E Ottawa St, Richwood, OH, 43344-1296. Tel: 740-943-3054. Fax: 740-943-9211. p. 1931

Moore, Sharon, Dir of Libr Serv, Quinebaug Valley Community College Library, 742 Upper Maple St, Danielson, CT, 06239. Tel: 860-412-7272. Fax: 860-412-7277. p. 335

Moore, Sherri, Librn, Mount San Jacinto College, Menifee Valley, 28237 La Piedra, Menifee Valley, CA, 92584. Tel: 951-639-5455. Fax: 951-672-0874. p. 249

Moore, Susan, Dep Dir, San Diego County Library, 5560 Overland Ave, Ste 110, San Diego, CA, 92123. Tel: 858-694-2428. Fax: 858-495-5981. p. 233

Moore, Susan, Bibliographer, Cat, University of Northern Iowa Library, 1227 W 27th St, Cedar Falls, IA, 50613-3675. Tel: 319-273-3661. Fax: 319-273-2913. p. 799

Moore, Suzanne, Co-Mgr, Thomas County Public Library System, Boston Carnegie Public Library, 250 S Main St, Boston, GA, 31626-3674. Tel: 229-498-5101. Fax: 229-498-5101. p. 553

Moore, Suzanne, County Librn, Ashe County Public Library, 148 Library Dr, West Jefferson, NC, 28694. Tel: 336-846-2041. Fax: 336-846-7503. p. 1829

Moore, Suzanne, Libr Mgr, Bentley Municipal Library, 5014 - 49 Ave, Bentley, AB, T0C 0J0, CANADA. Tel: 403-748-4626. Fax: 403-748-4627. p. 2685

Moore, Sylvia, Coll Develop, Homebound Serv, Yuma County Library District, 2951 S 21st Dr, Yuma, AZ, 85364. Tel: 928-373-6488. Fax: 928-782-9420. p. 91

Moore, Tasmine Brown, Cataloger, Mississippi Delta Community College, 414 Hwy 3 South, Moorhead, MS, 38761. Tel: 662-246-6377. Fax: 662-246-8627. p. 1309

Moore, Thomas J, Dean of Libr, Central Michigan University, Park 407, Mount Pleasant, MI, 48859. Tel: 989-774-3500. Fax: 989-774-2179. p. 1211

Moore, Valerie, Circ, Washington County Library System, 341 Main St, Greenville, MS, 38701-4097. Tel: 662-335-2331. Fax: 662-390-4758. p. 1298

Moore, Virginia, Mgr, Park Center Inc, Library, Corporate Services, 909 E State Blvd, Fort Wayne, IN, 46805. Tel: 260-481-2700, Ext 2188. Fax: 260-481-2885. p. 742

Moore, Wayne, Asst State Archivist, Tennessee State Library & Archives, 403 Seventh Ave N, Nashville, TN, 37243-0312. Tel: 615-741-2561. Fax: 615-532-2472, 615-741-6471. p. 2259

Moore, Wendy, Acq Librn, University of Georgia, 225 Herty Dr, Athens, GA, 30602-6018. Tel: 706-542-5081. Fax: 706-542-5001. p. 510

Moore, Zebedee, Librn, Georgia Department of Corrections, Office of Library Services, PO Box 310, Valdosta, GA, 31603. Tel: 229-333-7900, 229-333-7991. Fax: 229-333-5387. p. 554

Moore-Asselin, Lise, Chief Exec Officer, Mattawa Public Library, 370 Pine St, Mattawa, ON, P0H 1V0, CANADA. Tel: 705-744-5550. Fax: 705-744-1714. p. 2821

Moore-Jansen, Cathy, Coordr, Coll Develop, Wichita State University Libraries, 1845 Fairmount, Wichita, KS, 67260-0068. Tel: 316-978-5080. Fax: 316-978-3048. p. 902

Moorehead, Grayce J, Asst Dir, Ref, Marian J Mohr Memorial Library, One Memorial Ave, Johnston, RI, 02919-3221. Tel: 401-231-4980. Fax: 401-231-4984. p. 2167

Moorehead, Penny V, Asst Dir, Mason City Public Library, 225 Second St SE, Mason City, IA, 50401. Tel: 641-421-3668. Fax: 641-423-2615. p. 830

Moorer, Candace, Ref Librn, Medical University of South Carolina Library, 171 Ashley Ave, Ste 300, Charleston, SC, 29425-0001. Tel: 843-792-9211. Fax: 843-792-7947. p. 2184

Moores, Paul, Coll Develop, Riverside Community College District, 4800 Magnolia Ave, Riverside, CA, 92506-1299. Tel: 951-222-8651. Fax: 951-328-3679. p. 217

Moores, Walter A, Librn, Oakland Public Library, 324 Holly St, Oakland, MS, 38948. Tel: 662-623-8651. Fax: 662-623-0089. p. 1310

Moorhead, Susan, Mgr, New Rochelle Public Library, Huguenot Children's Library, 794 North Ave, New Rochelle, NY, 10801. Tel: 914-632-8954. p. 1667

Moorleghen, Jean, Libr Dir, Law Library Association of Saint Louis, 1300 Civil Courts Bldg, Ten N Tucker Blvd, Saint Louis, MO, 63101. Tel: 314-622-4386. Fax: 314-241-0911. p. 1355

Moorman, Deborah, Br Mgr, Coastal Plain Regional Library, Irwin County, 310 S Beech St, Ocilla, GA, 31774. Tel: 229-468-2148. Fax: 229-468-2148. p. 554

Moorman, Jayne, Asst County Librn, Spartanburg County Public Libraries, 151 S Church St, Spartanburg, SC, 29306-3241. Tel: 864-596-3500. Fax: 864-596-3518. p. 2205

Moorman, John A, Dr, Dir, Williamsburg Regional Library, 7770 Croaker Rd, Williamsburg, VA, 23188-7064. Tel: 757-259-4040, 757-259-7770. Fax: 757-259-4079, 757-259-7798. p. 2503

Moorman, Paul, Librn, University of Southern California Libraries, Asa V Call Law Library, 699 Exposition Blvd, LAW 202, MC 0072, Los Angeles, CA, 90089-0072. Tel: 213-740-6482. Fax: 213-740-7179. p. 179

Moorman, Rebecca, Govt Doc Librn, Head, Tech Serv, University of Alaska Anchorage, Consortium Library, 3211 Providence Dr, Anchorage, AK, 99508-8176. Tel: 907-786-1974. Fax: 907-786-1834. p. 45

Moose, Lucinda W, Dir, Gaston County Public Library, 1555 E Garrison Blvd, Gastonia, NC, 28054. Tel: 704-868-2164. Fax: 704-853-6012. p. 1794

Moose, Lucinda W, Dir, Gaston-Lincoln Regional Library, 1555 E Garrison Blvd, Gastonia, NC, 28054. Tel: 704-868-2164, Ext 101. Fax: 704-853-6012. p. 1794

Moothart, Tom, Asst Dean, Res Delivery Serv, Colorado State University Libraries, Morgan Library, 1201 Center Avenue Mall, Fort Collins, CO, 80523-. Tel: 970-491-1838. Fax: 970-491-1195. p. 307

Moquin, Sherrie, Dir, Hammond Free Library, 17 N Main St, Hammond, NY, 13646. Tel: 315-324-5139. Fax: 315-324-6008. p. 1633

Mor, Tristan, Cat, Wakulla County Public Library, 4330 Crawfordville Hwy, Crawfordville, FL, 32327. Tel: 850-926-7415. Fax: 850-926-4513. p. 434

Mora, Izzy, Adminr, The Green House Cancer Resource Center, 10460 Vista del Sol, Ste 101, El Paso, TX, 79925. Tel: 915-562-7660. Fax: 915-562-7841. p. 2317

Mora, Josefina, Librn, NASA Goddard Institute for Space Studies Library, 2880 Broadway, Rm 710, New York, NY, 10025. Tel: 212-678-5613. Fax: 212-678-5552. p. 1687

Mora, Kathy, Dir, Great Falls Public Library, 301 Second Ave N, Great Falls, MT, 59401-2593. Tel: 406-453-0349, Ext 221. Fax: 406-453-0181. p. 1380

Mora-Ona, Sylvia, Asst Dir, Miami-Dade Public Library System, 101 W Flagler St, Miami, FL, 33130-1523. Tel: 305-375-5005. Fax: 305-375-3048. p. 466

Morais, Yasmin, Cat Librn, University of the District of Columbia, David A Clarke School of Law, Charles N & Hilda H M Mason Law Library, Bldg 39, Rm B-16, 4200 Connecticut Ave NW, Washington, DC, 20008. Tel: 202-274-7310. Fax: 202-274-7311. p. 421

Morales, Aixa, Coll Develop, University of Puerto Rico, 130 Ave Universidad, Arecibo, PR, 00612-3145. Tel: 787-815-0000, Ext 3151. Fax: 787-878-9363. p. 2671

Morales, Carlos, Sr Librn, California Department of Corrections Library System, Mule Creek State Prison, 4001 Hwy 104, Ione, CA, 95640. Tel: 209-274-4911, Ext 6510. Fax: 209-274-5904. p. 221

Morales, David, Circ Mgr, College of William & Mary in Virginia, Earl Gregg Swem Library, One Landrum Dr, Williamsburg, VA, 23187. Tel: 757-221-3050. Fax: 757-221-2635. p. 2502

Morales, Eileen K, Curator, Historical Society of Princeton, 158 Nassau St, Princeton, NJ, 08542. Tel: 609-921-6748. Fax: 609-921-6939. p. 1522

Morales, Fernando, Tech Serv, Banning Library District, 21 W Nicolet St, Banning, CA, 92220. Tel: 951-849-3192. p. 125

Morales, Gilberto, Info Res Spec, Baker Hughes-Houston Technology Center, 2001 Rankin Rd, Houston, TX, 77073. Tel: 713-625-6583. Fax: 713-625-5710. p. 2334

Morales, Irma, Br Head, Orange Public Library & History Center, El Modena Branch, 380 S Hewes St, Orange, CA, 92869-4060. Tel: 714-288-2450. Fax: 714-997-1041. p. 201

Morales, Johnette, Br Mgr, Las Vegas-Clark County Library District, Spring Valley Library, 4280 S Jones Blvd, Las Vegas, NV, 89103. Tel: 702-507-3820. Fax: 702-507-3838. p. 1430

Morales, Karen, Circ, Moreno Valley Public Library, 25480 Alessandro Blvd, Moreno Valley, CA, 92553. Tel: 951-413-3880. Fax: 951-413-3895. p. 191

Morales, Octavio, Computer Serv, Cornell University Library, The Samuel J Wood Library & The C V Starr Biomedical Information Center, 1300 York Ave, C115, Box 67, New York, NY, 10065-4896. Tel: 212-746-6050. Fax: 212-746-6494. p. 1642

Morales, Omero, Ref Serv, Ad, Dustin Michael Sekula Memorial Library, 1906 S Closner Blvd, Edinburg, TX, 78539. Tel: 956-383-6246. Fax: 956-318-3123. p. 2315

Morales Polataivao, Cheryl, Territorial Librn, Feleti Barstow Public Library, PO Box 997687, Pago Pago, AS, 96799. Tel: 684-633-5816. Fax: 684-633-5823. p. 2665

Morales, Theresa, Librn, Project Coordr, General Dynamics Corp, 75 Eastern Point Rd, Dept 455, Groton, CT, 06340. Tel: 860-433-3481. Fax: 860-433-0647. p. 342

Moralez, Kristine, Cultural Res Spec, Oceanside Public Library, 330 N Coast Hwy, Oceanside, CA, 92054-2824. Tel: 760-435-5571. Fax: 760-435-9614. p. 199

Moran, Alex, ILL, University of San Diego, Helen K & James S Copley Library, 5998 Alcala Park, San Diego, CA, 92110. Fax: 619-260-4617. p. 239

Moran, David, Tech Serv, Chickasaw Regional Library System, 601 Railway Express, Ardmore, OK, 73401. Tel: 580-223-3164. Fax: 580-223-3280. p. 1957

Moran, Dolores, ILL, Christiana Hospital Library, Christiana Hospital, 4755 Ogletown Stanton Rd, Newark, DE, 19718-0002. Tel: 302-733-1115. Fax: 302-733-1365. p. 385

Moran, Donna, Librn, Fresno County Public Library, Selma Branch, 2200 Selma St, Selma, CA, 93662-3151. Tel: 559-896-3393. p. 152

Moran, Frank J, Dean, Learning Serv, Blue Ridge Community College, One College Lane, Weyers Cave, VA, 24486. Tel: 540-453-2247. Fax: 540-234-9598. p. 2502

Moran, James, Ch, Upper Moreland Free Public Library, 109 Park Ave, Willow Grove, PA, 19090-3277. Tel: 215-659-0741. Fax: 215-830-1223. p. 2157

Moran, Jeri, Evening/Weekend Librn, Greenfield Community College Library, One College Dr, Greenfield, MA, 01301-9739. Tel: 413-775-1830. Fax: 413-775-1838. p. 1092

Moran, Kathleen, Br Mgr, Los Angeles Public Library System, Memorial, 4625 W Olympic Blvd, Los Angeles, CA, 90019-3810. Tel: 323-934-0855, 323-938-2732. Fax: 323-938-3378. p. 173

Moran, Kyle, Digital Librn, Free Methodist Church of North America, 770 N High School Rd, Indianapolis, IN, 46214. Tel: 317-244-3660. Fax: 317-244-1247. p. 751

Moran, Maggie, Pub Serv Librn, Ref Librn, Northwest Mississippi Community College, 4975 Hwy 51 N, Senatobia, MS, 38668-1701. Tel: 662-562-3278. Fax: 662-562-3280. p. 1315

Moran, Mary, Cat, Head, Acq, College of the Holy Cross, One College St, Worcester, MA, 01610. Tel: 508-793-2478. Fax: 508-793-2372. p. 1143

Moran, Mary Kay, Adult Serv, Loutit District Library, 407 Columbus Ave, Grand Haven, MI, 49417. Tel: 616-842-5560, Ext 220. Fax: 616-847-0570. p. 1183

Moran, Michael J, Dir, Libr & Info Serv, Bay Path College, 539 Longmeadow St, Longmeadow, MA, 01106. Tel: 413-565-1284. Fax: 413-567-8345. p. 1100

Moran, Pat, Archivist, Community College of Allegheny County, 808 Ridge Ave, Pittsburgh, PA, 15212-6003. Tel: 412-237-2585. Fax: 412-237-6563. p. 2124

Moran, Paulette, Asst Dir, Chesterfield Township Library, 50560 Patricia Ave, Chesterfield, MI, 48051-3804. Tel: 586-598-4900. Fax: 586-598-7900. p. 1163

Moran, Sheila, Ser, Massachusetts General Hospital, Treadwell Library, Bartlett Hall Ext - I, 55 Fruit St, Boston, MA, 02114-2696. Tel: 617-726-8600. Fax: 617-726-6784. p. 1063

Moran, Stacy, Asst Dir, Ottumwa Public Library, 102 W Fourth St, Ottumwa, IA, 52501. Tel: 641-682-7563. Fax: 641-682-4970. p. 837

Moran, Susy, Pres, Pittsburgh Toy Lending Library, c/o First United Methodist Church, 5401 Centre Ave, Rear, Pittsburgh, PA, 15232. Tel: 412-682-4430. p. 2127

Moran, Tom, Regional Br Operations Mgr, Austin Public Library, Little Walnut Creek, 835 W Rundberg Lane, Austin, TX, 78758. Tel: 512-974-9860. Fax: 512-974-9865. p. 2279

Moran, Tom J, Interim Dean, Shoreline Community College, 16101 Greenwood Ave N, Shoreline, WA, 98133-5696. Tel: 206-546-4774. Fax: 206-546-4604. p. 2535

Moran-Wallace, Kathleen, Head, Ch, Nevins Memorial Library, 305 Broadway, Methuen, MA, 01844-6898. Tel: 978-686-4080. Fax: 978-686-8669. p. 1105

Morasch, Caroline, Br Mgr, Whitman County Rural Library District, Endicott Branch, 324 E St, Endicott, WA, 99125. Tel: 509-657-3429. p. 2513

Morasch, Caroline, Br Mgr, Whitman County Rural Library District, LaCrosse Branch, 107 S Main, LaCrosse, WA, 99143. Tel: 509-549-3770. Fax: 509-549-3330. p. 2513

Morasch, James, Syst Coordr, Whitman County Rural Library District, 102 S Main St, Colfax, WA, 99111-1863. Tel: 509-397-4366. Fax: 509-397-6156. p. 2512

Morash, Meagan, Dir, Libr Serv, Booth University College, 300-290 Vaughan St, Winnipeg, MB, R3B 2L9, CANADA. Tel: 204-924-4857. Fax: 204-924-4873. p. 2754

Morberg, Mary, Librn, Northwest Regional Library, Godel Memorial Library, 314 E Johnson Ave, Warren, MN, 56762-1235. Tel: 218-745-5465. Fax: 218-745-8807. p. 1286

Morcerf, Nancy, Asst Libr Dir, Northport-East Northport Public Library, 151 Laurel Ave, Northport, NY, 11768. Tel: 631-261-6930. Fax: 631-261-6718. p. 1707

Morcerf, Nancy, Asst Libr Dir, Northport-East Northport Public Library, East Northport Public, 185 Larkfield Rd, East Northport, NY, 11731. Tel: 631-261-2313. Fax: 631-261-3523. p. 1707

Morchower, G, Librn, IGFA Fishing Hall of Fame & Museum, 300 Gulf Stream Way, Dania Beach, FL, 33004. Tel: 954-927-2628. Fax: 954-924-4299. p. 435

Morck, Melanie, Asst Librn, Edmonton Public Library, Capilano, 201 Capilano Mall, 5004-98 Ave, Edmonton, AB, T6A 0A1, CANADA. Tel: 780-496-1802. Fax: 780-496-7009. p. 2700

Morden, Jennifer, Br Mgr, Anderson County Library, Belton Branch, 91 Breazeale St, Belton, SC, 29627. Tel: 864-338-8330. Fax: 864-338-8696. p. 2180

More, Katherine, Prof, Seneca College of Applied Arts & Technology, 1750 Finch Ave E, Toronto, ON, M2J 2X5, CANADA. Tel: 416-491-5050, Ext 6706. Fax: 416-491-4606. p. 2978

More, Susan, Head, Tech Serv, Northeastern University School of Law Library, 400 Huntington Ave, Boston, MA, 02115. Tel: 617-373-3691. Fax: 617-373-8705. p. 1066

Morea, Michael, Electronic Res, Electronic Serv, Nassau Library System, 900 Jerusalem Ave, Uniondale, NY, 11553-3039. Tel: 516-292-8920, Ext 282. Fax: 516-565-0950. p. 1758

Moreau, Barbara, Ch, St Albert Public Library, Five Saint Anne St, St. Albert, AB, T8N 3Z9, CANADA. Tel: 780-459-1530. Fax: 780-458-5772. p. 2717

Moreau, Elizabeth, Br Mgr, Anchorage Public Library, Mountain View Branch, 120 Bragaw St, Anchorage, AK, 99508-1307. Tel: 907-343-2907. p. 45

Moreau, Karen, Youth Serv Librn, Darlington County Library, Society Hill Branch, 473 S Main St, Society Hill, SC, 29593. Tel: 843-378-0026. Fax: 843-378-0026. p. 2192

Moreau, Karen E, Ch, Darlington County Library, 204 N Main St, Darlington, SC, 29532. Tel: 843-398-4940. Fax: 843-398-4942. p. 2192

Morec, Marti, Coll Develop Librn, Berkeley Public Library, 2090 Kittredge St, Berkeley, CA, 94704. Tel: 510-981-6100. Fax: 510-981-6111. p. 126

Moree, Kathy, Acq, Cat, Tennessee Valley Authority, 1101 Market St, LP 4A-C, Chattanooga, TN, 37402. Tel: 423-751-4913. Fax: 423-751-4914. p. 2228

Morehart, Paul, Pres, Mount Sterling Public Library, 60 W Columbus St, Mount Sterling, OH, 43143. Tel: 740-869-2430. Fax: 740-869-3617. p. 1919

Morehead, Carolyn, Br Mgr, Bedford Public Library System, Big Island Library, 1111 Schooldays Rd, Big Island, VA, 24526. Tel: 434-299-5604. Fax: 434-299-6151. p. 2451

Morehead, Marilyn, Dir, Mary E Bartlett Memorial Library, 22 Dalton Rd, Brentwood, NH, 03833. Tel: 603-642-3355. Fax: 603-642-3383. p. 1439

Morehead, Sue, Ref Serv, Guernsey Memorial Library, Three Court St, Norwich, NY, 13815. Tel: 607-334-4034. Fax: 607-336-3901. p. 1708

Morehouse, Dorothy, Ch, Newark Public Library, 121 High St, Newark, NY, 14513-1492. Tel: 315-331-4370. Fax: 315-331-0552. p. 1704

Morehouse, Frank, Archivist, Diocesan Synod of Fredericton, c/o Provincial Archives of New Brunswick, PO Box 6000, Fredericton, NB, E3B 5H1, CANADA. Tel: 506-453-2122. Fax: 506-453-3288. p. 2763

Morehouse, John, In Charge, Salmagundi Club Library, 47 Fifth Ave, New York, NY, 10003. Tel: 212-255-7740. Fax: 212-229-0172. p. 1699

Morehouse, Judy, Tech Serv Coordr, Mooresville Public Library, 220 W Harrison St, Mooresville, IN, 46158-1633. Tel: 317-831-7323. Fax: 317-831-7383. p. 766

Morehouse, Lorraine, Cat, New Brunswick Public Library Service, 250 King St, Fredericton, NB, E3B 9M9, CANADA. Tel: 506-453-2354. Fax: 506-444-4064. p. 2763

Morehouse, Sarah, Info Res Coordr, Empire State College (Online Library), Three Union Ave, Saratoga Springs, NY, 12866. Tel: 518-587-2100. Fax: 518-581-9526. p. 1738

Morehouse, Val, Librn, Temple Isaiah, 3800 Mount Diablo Blvd, Lafayette, CA, 94549. Tel: 925-283-8575, Ext 322. Fax: 925-283-8355. p. 163

Moreland, Kathy, Librn, Tuscarawas County Law Library Association, 101 E High Ave, New Philadelphia, OH, 44663-2599. Tel: 330-365-3224. Fax: 330-343-5509. p. 1921

Moreland, Lisa, Dir, Caldwell Public Library, 120 S Main St, Caldwell, KS, 67022. Tel: 620-845-6879. p. 859

Moreland, Sharon, Tech Consult, Northeast Kansas Library System, 4317 W Sixth St, Lawrence, KS, 66049. Tel: 785-838-4090. Fax: 785-838-3989. p. 878

Moreland, Susan, Dep Dir, North Kingstown Free Library, 100 Boone St, North Kingstown, RI, 02852-5176. Tel: 401-294-3306. Fax: 401-294-1690. p. 2170

Moreland-Sender, Sharon, Dir, Huntingdon Valley Library, 625 Red Lion Rd, Huntingdon Valley, PA, 19006-6297. Tel: 215-947-5138. Fax: 215-938-5894. p. 2070

Morell, Melanie, Asst Librn, Fayette Community Library, 104 W State St, Fayette, IA, 52142. Tel: 563-425-3344. Fax: 563-425-3344. p. 816

Morelli, Marcia, Ref, Carlton Fields, 4221 W Boy Scout Blvd, Ste 1000, Tampa, FL, 33607. Tel: 813-223-7000. Fax: 813-229-4133. p. 496

Moren, Michele, Librn, Halliburton Energy Services, 2600 S Second St, Duncan, OK, 73536-0400. Tel: 580-251-3516. Fax: 580-251-2094. p. 1961

Morency, Carol, Mkt & Pub Relations Dir, Mount Prospect Public Library, Ten S Emerson St, Mount Prospect, IL, 60056. Tel: 847-253-5675. Fax: 847-253-0642. p. 677

Moreno, Israel, Libr Assoc, New York Public Library - Astor, Lenox & Tilden Foundations, 58th Street Branch, 127 E 58th St, (Between Park & Lexington Aves), New York, NY, 10022-1211. Tel: 212-759-7358. Fax: 212-758-6858. p. 1691

Moreno, Joe, Spec Coll Librn, Laredo Public Library, 1120 E Calton Rd, Laredo, TX, 78041. Tel: 956-795-2400. Fax: 956-795-2403. p. 2354

Moreno, Judi H, Pub Serv Librn, Central Maine Community College Library, 1250 Turner St, Auburn, ME, 04210-6498. Tel: 207-755-5265. Fax: 207-755-5494. p. 974

Moreno, Maria, Circ, Valencia Community College, East Campus, 701 N Econlockhatchee Trail, Orlando, FL, 32825. Tel: 407-582-2467. Fax: 407-582-8914. p. 478

Moreno, Pat, Br Librn, Sweetwater County Library System, Reliance Branch Library, 1329 Main St, Reliance, WY, 82943. Tel: 307-352-6670. Fax: 307-352-6670. p. 2655

Moreno, Pierrette, Acq, University of Texas Libraries, Jamail Center for Legal Research, University of Texas School of Law, 727 E Dean Keeton St, Austin, TX, 78705-3224. Tel: 512-471-7726. Fax: 512-471-0243. p. 2284

Moreno, Rafael, Br Supvr, Kern County Library, Arvin Branch, 201 Campus Dr, Arvin, CA, 93203. Tel: 661-854-5934. Fax: 661-584-3744. p. 124

Moreno, Rafael, Br Supvr, Kern County Library, Lamont Branch, 8304 Segrue Rd, Lamont, CA, 93241-2123. Tel: 661-845-3471. Fax: 661-845-7701. p. 124

Moreno, Shilo, Acq Asst, California State University Dominguez Hills, 1000 E Victoria St, Carson, CA, 90747. Tel: 310-243-2850. Fax: 310-516-4219. p. 132

Moreno, Shirley, Cat, St Louis College of Pharmacy, 4588 Parkview Pl, Saint Louis, MO, 63110. Tel: 314-446-8364. Fax: 314-446-8360. p. 1357

Moreno, Suzanne, Librn, Nace International Library, 1440 S Creek Dr, Houston, TX, 77084-4906. Tel: 281-228-6200. Fax: 281-228-6300. p. 2341

Moreno, Yolanda, Mgr, Libr Serv, Orange Public Library & History Center, 407 E Chapman Ave, Orange, CA, 92866-1509. Tel: 714-288-2400. Fax: 714-771-6126. p. 201

Moreno-Vega, Marta, Exec Dir, Caribbean Cultural Center Library, 408 W 58th St, New York, NY, 10019. Tel: 212-307-7420. Fax: 212-315-1086. p. 1671

Morey, Jill, Dir, Ypsilanti District Library, 5577 Whittaker Rd, Ypsilanti, MI, 48197. Tel: 734-482-4110. Fax: 734-482-0047. p. 1238

Morey, Marie, Dir, Gray Public Library, Five Hancock St, Gray, ME, 04039. Tel: 207-657-4110. Fax: 207-657-4138. p. 986

Morey, Sarah, IT Support, Tech Serv Mgr, Wayne Township Library, 80 N Sixth St, Richmond, IN, 47374-3079. Tel: 765-966-8291. Fax: 765-962-1318. p. 775

Morey, Tammy, Librn, Rochester Community Library, PO Box 309, Rochester, AB, T0G 1Z0, CANADA. Tel: 780-698-3970. Fax: 780-698-2290. p. 2715

Morgan, Alicia, Asst Dir, Human Res & Prog, Trails Regional Library, 432 N Holden St, Warrensburg, MO, 64093. Tel: 660-747-1699. Fax: 660-747-5774. p. 1371

Morgan, Alyssa, Ch, Morgan County Public Library, 110 S Jefferson St, Martinsville, IN, 46151. Tel: 765-342-3451. Fax: 765-342-9992. p. 763

Morgan, Anna Beth, Tech Serv, Missouri Southern State University, 3950 E Newman Rd, Joplin, MO, 64801-1595. Tel: 417-625-9386. Fax: 417-625-9734. p. 1336

Morgan, Anna Beth, Dir, Union University, 1050 Union University Dr, Jackson, TN, 38305-3697. Tel: 731-661-5410. Fax: 731-661-5175. p. 2238

Morgan, Anne, Librn, Institute of Historical Survey Foundation Library, 3035 S Main, Las Cruces, NM, 88005-3756. Tel: 575-525-3035. Fax: 575-525-0106. p. 1558

Morgan, Arlie Kay, Tech Serv Librn, Jackson County Public Library, 118 US Hwy, 421 N, McKee, KY, 40447. Tel: 606-287-8113. Fax: 606-287-7774. p. 928

Morgan, Benjamin, Syst & Web Develop Librn, University of North Carolina School of the Arts, 1533 S Main St, Winston-Salem, NC, 27127. Tel: 336-770-3270. Fax: 336-770-3271. p. 1833

Morgan, Beth, Librn, United States Navy, 1002 Balch Blvd, Bldg 1003, Stennis Space Center, MS, 39522-5001. Tel: 228-688-4398. Fax: 228-688-4191. p. 1315

Morgan, Betsy Susan, Librn, Glen Oaks Community College Library, 62249 Shimmel Rd, Centreville, MI, 49032-9719. Tel: 269-467-9945, Ext 202. Fax: 269-467-4114. p. 1162

Morgan, Bettie, Dir, Wilcox County Library, 100 Broad St, Camden, AL, 36726-1702. Tel: 334-682-4355. Fax: 334-682-5437. p. 11

Morgan, Bobbie, Dir, Cameron Parish Library, 501 Marshall St, Cameron, LA, 70631. Tel: 337-598-5950. Fax: 337-598-5949. p. 946

Morgan, Bonnie, Librn, College of the North Atlantic, Seal Cove Campus Learning Resource Centre, 1670 Conception Bay Hwy, Conception Bay South, NL, A0A 3T0, CANADA. Tel: 709-744-6829. Fax: 709-744-3929. p. 2771

Morgan, Brian, Bus Mgr, Somerset County Library System, One Vogt Dr, Bridgewater, NJ, 08807-2136. Tel: 908-526-4016, Ext 132. p. 1475

Morgan, Bronwyn, Dir, Libr Serv, Arkansas Northeastern College, 2501 S Division St, Blytheville, AR, 72315-5111. Tel: 870-762-3189. Fax: 870-762-5534. p. 95

Morgan, Carl, Acq, Orange Coast College Library, 2701 Fairview Rd, Costa Mesa, CA, 92628. Tel: 714-432-5885. Fax: 714-432-6850. p. 137

Morgan, Cathy, Dir, Correctional Institution for Women, PO Box 4004, Clinton, NJ, 08809-4004. Tel: 908-735-7111, Ext 3641. Fax: 908-735-0108. p. 1479

Morgan, Cherie, Coordr, Ref Serv-Adult, Sterling Municipal Library, Mary Elizabeth Wilbanks Ave, Baytown, TX, 77520. Tel: 281-427-7331. Fax: 281-420-5347. p. 2287

Morgan, Cheryl, Asst Dir, Info Tech, Forsyth County Public Library, 585 Dahlonega Rd, Cumming, GA, 30040-2109. Tel: 770-781-9840. Fax: 770-781-8089. p. 527

Morgan, Darlene, Dir, Pike-Amite-Walthall Library System, 1022 Virginia Ave, McComb, MS, 39648. Tel: 601-684-7034, Ext 11. Fax: 601-250-1213. p. 1307

Morgan, Denise, Br Mgr, Fairfax County Public Library, Sherwood Regional, 2501 Sherwood Hall Lane, Alexandria, VA, 22306-2799. Tel: 703-765-3645. p. 2461

Morgan, Donna, Dir, McDowell Public Library, 90 Howard St, Welch, WV, 24801. Tel: 304-436-3070. Fax: 304-436-8079. p. 2573

Morgan, Dorothy, Bus Mgr, Liverpool Public Library, 310 Tulip St, Liverpool, NY, 13088-4997. Tel: 315-457-0310. Fax: 315-453-7867. p. 1653

Morgan Echols, Lisa, Coll Develop Librn, Brenau University, 625 Academy St NE, Gainesville, GA, 30501-3343. Tel: 770-538-4723. Fax: 770-534-6254. p. 534

Morgan, Elizabeth, Doc Delivery, Librn, Harrisburg Hospital Library at PinnacleHealth System, Main Bldg, 2nd Flr, 111 S Front St, Harrisburg, PA, 17101-2099. Tel: 717-782-5511. Fax: 717-782-5512. p. 2065

Morgan, Ellen, Circ, Librn, Mill Memorial Library, 495 E Main St, Nanticoke, PA, 18634-1897. Tel: 570-735-3030. Fax: 570-735-0340. p. 2094

Morgan, Elois A, Mgr, Info Serv, Thomas Jefferson National Accelerator Facility Library, 12050 Jefferson Ave, ARC 126 (MS-1B), Newport News, VA, 23606. Tel: 757-269-7525. Fax: 757-269-7848. p. 2480

Morgan, Gail, Librn, Nute Library, 22 Elm St, Milton, NH, 03851. Tel: 603-652-7829. Fax: 603-652-4793. p. 1458

Morgan, Gary, Cat Librn, Doc Librn, State of Oregon Law Library, Supreme Court Bldg, 1163 State St, Salem, OR, 97301-2563. Tel: 503-986-5737. Fax: 503-986-5623. p. 2018

Morgan, J C, Libr Dir, Campbell County Public Library District, 3920 Alexandria Pike, Cold Spring, KY, 41076. Tel: 859-781-6166. Fax: 859-572-5032. p. 909

Morgan, Jack, Circ, Vanguard University of Southern California, 55 Fair Dr, Costa Mesa, CA, 92626. Tel: 714-556-3610, Ext 2400. Fax: 714-966-5478. p. 137

Morgan, James J, Dir, Educ Tech, Indiana University, Ruth Lilly Medical Library, 975 W Walnut St, IB 100, Indianapolis, IN, 46202-5121. Tel: 317-274-1408. Fax: 317-278-2349. p. 752

Morgan, Jamie, Dir, Roxana Public Library District, 200 N Central Ave, Roxana, IL, 62084-1102. Tel: 618-254-6713. Fax: 618-254-6904. p. 699

Morgan, Jenee, Cat Librn, Berklee College of Music Library, 150 Massachusetts Ave, Boston, MA, 02115. Tel: 617-747-8684. Fax: 617-747-2050. p. 1055

Morgan, Jennifer Bryan, Doc Librn, Indiana University, School of Law Library, Maurer School of Law, 211 S Indiana Ave, Bloomington, IN, 47405. Tel: 812-855-4611. Fax: 812-855-7099. p. 727

Morgan, Jo Anne, ILL, Taylor County Public Library, 403 N Washington St, Perry, FL, 32347-2791. Tel: 850-838-3512. Fax: 850-838-3514. p. 483

Morgan, Joan, Curator, Alaska Masonic Library & Museum, 518 E 14th St, Anchorage, AK, 99501-2213. Tel: 907-276-2665. p. 43

Morgan, JoAnn, Br Mgr, Los Angeles Public Library System, Exposition Park - Dr Mary McLeod Bethune Regional Branch, 3900 S Western Ave, Los Angeles, CA, 90062. Tel: 323-290-3113. Fax: 323-290-3153. p. 173

Morgan, Joy, Cat, Ref Serv, Kenai Community Library, 163 Main St Loop, Kenai, AK, 99611-7723. Tel: 907-283-4378. Fax: 907-283-2266. p. 50

Morgan, Joyce, Dir, Marengo County Public Library, 507 N Main St, Linden, AL, 36748. Tel: 334-295-2246. Fax: 334-295-2265. p. 23

Morgan, Judith, Dir, Oklahoma City University, Law Library, 2501 N Blackwelder, Oklahoma City, OK, 73106. Tel: 405-208-5271. Fax: 405-208-5172. p. 1974

Morgan, Karen, Archivist, Librn, University of Michigan-Dearborn, 4901 Evergreen Rd, Dearborn, MI, 48128-2406. Tel: 313-593-5618. Fax: 313-593-5478. p. 1168

Morgan, Kathie, Dir, Santa Barbara County Genealogical Society, 316 Castillo St, Santa Barbara, CA, 93101-3814. Tel: 805 682-4456. p. 260

Morgan, Kathy, Librn, Tok Community Library, Mile 1314 Alaska Hwy, Tok, AK, 99780. Tel: 907-883-5623. Fax: 907-883-5623. p. 54

Morgan, Kathy, Circ, Payson Public Library, 328 N McLane Rd, Payson, AZ, 85541. Tel: 928-474-9260. Fax: 928-474-2679. p. 70

Morgan, Kyle, Archivist, ONE Institute & Archives, 909 W Adams Blvd, Los Angeles, CA, 90007. Tel: 213-741-0094. p. 176

Morgan, Lee, Br Librn, Spartanburg County Public Libraries, Landrum Library, 111 Asbury Dr, Landrum, SC, 29356. Tel: 864-457-2218. p. 2205

Morgan, Lily, Dir, Independence Community College Library, 1057 W College Ave, Independence, KS, 67301. Tel: 620-331-4100. Fax: 620-331-6821. p. 873

Morgan, Linda, Br Mgr, Scott-Sebastian Regional Library, Hartford Library, 22 Broadway, Hartford, AR, 72938. p. 101

Morgan, Lisa, Br Mgr, Pasco County Library System, New River, 34043 State Rd 54, Zephyrhills, FL, 33543. Tel: 813-788-6375. Fax: 813-788-6977. p. 452

Morgan, Lisa, Circ, La Grange College, 601 Broad St, La Grange, GA, 30240-2999. Tel: 706-880-8012. Fax: 706-880-8040. p. 537

Morgan, Lisa Ann, Br Mgr, Pamunkey Regional Library, Hanover Branch, 7527 Library Dr, Hanover, VA, 23069. Tel: 804-365-6210. Fax: 804-365-6379. p. 2469

Morgan, Lori, Youth Serv, Jeffersonville Township Public Library, 211 E Court Ave, Jeffersonville, IN, 47130. Tel: 812-285-5636. Fax: 812-285-5639. p. 756

Morgan, Louis, Dr, Asst Dir, William G Squires Library, 260 11th St NE, Cleveland, TN, 37311. Tel: 423-614-8550. Fax: 423-614-8555. p. 2230

Morgan, Margaret, Head, Tech Serv, Freeport Public Library, 100 E Douglas St, Freeport, IL, 61032. Tel: 815-233-3000. Fax: 815-233-1099. p. 647

Morgan, Marianne, Librn, C G Jung Institute of San Francisco, 2040 Gough St, San Francisco, CA, 94109. Tel: 415-771-8055, Ext 207. Fax: 415-771-8926. p. 243

Morgan, Marsha, Librn, Stroud Public Library, 301 W Seventh St, Stroud, OK, 74079. Tel: 918-968-2567. Fax: 918-968-4700. p. 1979

Morgan, Mary, Librn, Southwest Arkansas Regional Library, Mineral Springs Branch, 310 E Runnels, Mineral Springs, AR, 71851. Tel: 870-287-7162. p. 103

Morgan, Mary, Librn, Luther Luckett Correctional Complex Library, 1612 Dawkins Rd, La Grange, KY, 40031. Tel: 502-222-0363. p. 919

Morgan, Maureen, Govt Doc, Ser Librn, Berry College, 2277 Martha Berry Hwy, Mount Berry, GA, 30149. Tel: 706-236-2221. p. 546

Morgan, Melissa S, Librn, Pima Council on Aging Library, 8467 E Broadway Blvd, Tucson, AZ, 85710-4009. Tel: 520-790-0504. Fax: 520-790-7577. p. 86

Morgan, Mia, Libr Dir, Marian Court College, 35 Little's Point Rd, Swampscott, MA, 01907-2896. Tel: 781-309-5219, 781-595-6768. Fax: 781-595-3560. p. 1130

Morgan, Michelle, Head, Circ, Marion Public Library, 600 S Washington St, Marion, IN, 46953-1992. Tel: 765-668-2900. Fax: 765-668-2911. p. 763

Morgan, Nancy, Acq of New Ser, Libr Tech, Tech Serv, Polk State College, 999 Ave H NE, Winter Haven, FL, 33881-4299. Tel: 863-297-1040. Fax: 863-297-1065. p. 504

Morgan, Natalie, Asst Libr Dir, Boerne Public Library, 451 N Main St, Bldg 100, Boerne, TX, 78006. Tel: 830-249-3053. Fax: 830-249-8410. p. 2290

Morgan, Nathan, Ref Librn/Instrul Serv, Creighton University, 2500 California Plaza, Omaha, NE, 68178-0209. Tel: 402-280-2927. Fax: 402-280-2435. p. 1412

Morgan, Pam, Coll Develop Officer, Old Dominion University Libraries, 4427 Hampton Blvd, Norfolk, VA, 23529-0256. Tel: 757-683-4148. Fax: 757-683-5767. p. 2482

Morgan, Pamela, Bibliographer, Vanderbilt University, Central Library, 419 21st Ave S, Nashville, TN, 37203-2427. Tel: 615-343-3081. Fax: 615-343-7451. p. 2260

Morgan Perry, Mona, Asst Dir, Cumberland County Historical Society Library, 981 Great St, Greenwich, NJ, 08323. Tel: 856-455-4055, 856-455-8580. p. 1488

Morgan, R Charles, Dep Dir, Mgr, United States Department of Energy, One Science.gov Way, Oak Ridge, TN, 37830. Tel: 865-576-1188. Fax: 865-576-3609. p. 2262

Morgan, Richard, ILL/Doc Delivery Supvr, Converse College, 580 E Main St, Spartanburg, SC, 29302. Tel: 864-596-9020, 864-596-9071. Fax: 864-596-9075. p. 2204

Morgan, Ronnie, IT Dept Head, Genesee District Library, G-4195 W Pasadena Ave, Flint, MI, 48504. Tel: 810-230-3341. Fax: 810-732-1161. p. 1179

Morgan, Saronda, Admin Serv, Transylvania County Library, 212 S Gaston, Brevard, NC, 28712. Tel: 828-884-3151. Fax: 828-877-4230. p. 1777

Morgan, Scott, Operations Dir, Cuyahoga County Public Library, 2111 Snow Rd, Parma, OH, 44134-2728. Tel: 216-398-1800. Fax: 216-398-1748. p. 1927

Morgan, Sonja, Librn, Mark & Emily Turner Memorial Library, 39 Second St, Presque Isle, ME, 04769. Tel: 207-764-2571. Fax: 207-768-5756. p. 998

Morgan, Stephanie, Br Mgr, Atlanta-Fulton Public Library System, Bankhead Courts Library, 1415 Maynard Rd NW, Atlanta, GA, 30331. Tel: 404-699-8959. Fax: 404-699-8961. p. 511

Morgan, Stephanie, YA Librn, Three Rivers Public Library, 920 W Michigan Ave, Three Rivers, MI, 49093-2137. Tel: 269-273-8666. Fax: 269-279-9654. p. 1230

Morgan, Stephanie, Ch, Kingston Library, 55 Franklin St, Kingston, NY, 12401. Tel: 845-331-0507. Fax: 845-331-7981. p. 1650

Morgan, Susan, Asst Dir, Onondaga Free Library, 4840 W Seneca Tpk, Syracuse, NY, 13215. Tel: 315-492-1727. Fax: 315-492-1323. p. 1753

Morgan, Susan, Circ Supvr, New Castle Public Library, 207 E North St, New Castle, PA, 16101-3691. Tel: 724-658-6659. Fax: 724-658-7209. p. 2096

Morgan, Tammie, Br Mgr, Knox County Public Library System, North Knoxville Branch, 2901 Ocoee Trail, Knoxville, TN, 37917-3233. Tel: 865-525-7036. Fax: 865-525-0796. p. 2242

Morgan, Terese, Ref Librn, Austin Community College, Riverside Campus Library, 1020 Grove Blvd, Austin, TX, 78741. Tel: 512-223-6181. Fax: 512-223-6703. p. 2278

Morgan, Tracy, Libr & Info Spec, Guelph General Hospital, 115 Delhi St, Guelph, ON, N1E 4J4, CANADA. Tel: 519-837-6440, Ext 2215. Fax: 519-837-6467. p. 2806

Morgan, Urla, Ch, Duncanville Public Library, 201 James Collins Blvd, Duncanville, TX, 75116. Tel: 972-780-5050. Fax: 972-780-4958. p. 2314

Morgan, William T, Adminr, Montgomery County Planning Commission Library, One Montgomery Plaza, 425 Swede St, Norristown, PA, 19401. Tel: 610-278-3732. Fax: 610-278-3941. p. 2098

Morgan-Lohr, Penelope, Mgr, Western Sullivan Public Library, 198 Bridge St, Narrowsburg, NY, 12764-6402. Tel: 845-252-3360. Fax: 845-252-3331. p. 1664

Morganstern, Betty I, Librn III/Info, Public Library Association of Annapolis & Anne Arundel County, Inc, Five Harry S Truman Pkwy, Annapolis, MD, 21401. Tel: 410-222-7371. Fax: 410-222-7188. p. 1010

Morganti, Deena J, Head Librn, Pennsylvania State University, Berks Campus, Tulpehocken Rd, Reading, PA, 19610. Tel: 610-396-6246. Fax: 610-396-6249. p. 2133

Morganti, Mary, Dir, Libr & Archives, California Historical Society, 678 Mission St, San Francisco, CA, 94105. Tel: 415-357-1848, Ext 20. Fax: 415-357-1850. p. 240

Morgen, Evelyn B, Dir, University of Connecticut Health Center, 263 Farmington Ave, Farmington, CT, 06034. Tel: 860-679-3808. Fax: 860-679-1230. p. 340

Morgenstern, Dan, Dir, Rutgers University Libraries, Institute of Jazz Studies, John Cotton Dana Library, 185 University Ave, 4th Flr, Newark, NJ, 07102. Tel: 973-353-5595. Fax: 973-353-5944. p. 1513

Morgenstern, Karen, Librn, Wilshire Boulevard Temple - Libraries, 3663 Wilshire Blvd, Los Angeles, CA, 90010-2798. Tel: 424-208-8945. Fax: 310-689-4569. p. 180

Morgeson, Amy, Dir, Marion County Public Library, 201 E Main St, Lebanon, KY, 40033-1133. Tel: 270-692-4698. Fax: 270-692-9555. p. 919

Morian, Juliane, Assoc Dir, Clinton-Macomb Public Library, 40900 Romeo Plank Rd, Clinton Township, MI, 48038-2955. Tel: 586-226-5091. Fax: 586-226-5008. p. 1164

Moriarty, George Marshall, Pres, Boston Athenaeum, 10 1/2 Beacon St, Boston, MA, 02108-3777. Tel: 617-227-0270. Fax: 617-227-5266. p. 1056

Moriconi, Cynthia, Librn, University of California, 1156 High St, Santa Cruz, CA, 95064. Tel: 831-459-3187. Fax: 831-459-4187. p. 264

Morihara, Chizu, Art Librn, University of California, Santa Barbara, Arts Library, UCSB Library, Santa Barbara, CA, 93106-9010. Tel: 805-893-2766. Fax: 805-893-5879. p. 262

Morin, Carolyn, In Charge, Schenectady County Public Library, Glenville, 20 Glenridge Rd, Scotia, NY, 12302. Tel: 518-386-2243. Fax: 518-386-2243. p. 1741

Morin, Chris, Br Mgr, Nashville Public Library, Donelson, 2315 Lebanon Rd, Nashville, TN, 37214-3410. Tel: 615-862-5859. Fax: 615-862-5799. p. 2257

Morin, Christine, Circ, Salem Public Library, 370 Essex St, Salem, MA, 01970-3298. Tel: 978-744-0860. Fax: 978-745-8616. p. 1122

Morin, Jodie, Coll Develop, Ref, Buena Vista University Library, 610 W Fourth St, Storm Lake, IA, 50588. Tel: 712-749-2097. Fax: 712-749-2059. p. 846

Morin, Kimberly, Ref, Bentley College, 175 Forest St, Waltham, MA, 02452-4705. Tel: 781-891-2168. Fax: 781-891-2830. p. 1132

Morin, Lisa, Dir, Lee Public Library, Seven Mast Rd, Lee, NH, 03824. Tel: 603-659-2626. Fax: 603-659-2986. p. 1454

Morin, Rebecca A, User Serv Librn, California Academy of Sciences Library, Golden Gate Park, 55 Music Concourse Dr, San Francisco, CA, 94118. Tel: 415-379-5495. Fax: 415-379-5729. p. 240

Morisak, Carol, Dir, Friench Simpson Memorial Library, 705 E Fourth St, Hallettsville, TX, 77964-2828. Tel: 361-798-3243. Fax: 361-798-5833. p. 2330

Morisse, Cheryl, ILL, Bonner Springs City Library, 200 E Third St, Bonner Springs, KS, 66012-1047. Tel: 913-441-2665. Fax: 913-441-2660. p. 858

Morissette, Brenda, Libr Tech, Northern College Library, 640 Latchford St, Haileybury, ON, P0J 1K0, CANADA. Tel: 705-672-3376, Ext 8806. Fax: 705-672-5404. p. 2807

Morisson-Colwell, Tess, Access Serv, Hood College, 401 Rosemont Ave, Frederick, MD, 21701. Tel: 301-696-3909. Fax: 301-696-3796. p. 1029

Morita, Kristina, Asst City Librn, Los Angeles Public Library System, 630 W Fifth St, Los Angeles, CA, 90071-2097. Tel: 213-228-7461. Fax: 213-228-7519. p. 172

Morita, Linda, Librn & Archivist, McMichael Canadian Art Collection, 10365 Islington Ave, Kleinburg, ON, L0J 1C0, CANADA. Tel: 905-893-1121, Ext 2255. Fax: 905-893-2588. p. 2815

Morita, Sharon, Cat, Everett Public Libraries, 410 Broadway, Everett, MA, 02149. Tel: 617-394-2307. Fax: 617-389-1230. p. 1087

Moritz, Traci Welch, Pub Serv Librn, Ohio Northern University, 525 S Main St, Ada, OH, 45810. Tel: 419-772-2181. Fax: 419-772-1927. p. 1851

Mork, Kendra, Librn, Goddard Public Library, 315 S Main St, Goddard, KS, 67052. Tel: 316-794-8771. p. 869

Morley, Debi, Dir, Sublette County Library, Big Piney Branch, 106 Fish St, Big Piney, WY, 83113. Tel: 307-276-3515. Fax: 307-276-3516. p. 2659

Morley, Gabriel, Dir, Lincoln Memorial University, Cumberland Gap Pkwy, Box 2012, Harrogate, TN, 37752. Tel: 423-869-7079. Fax: 423-869-6426. p. 2236

Morley, Jan, Librn, Columbiana County Law Library, 32 N Park Ave, Lisbon, OH, 44432. Tel: 330-420-3662. Fax: 330-424-7902. p. 1910

Morley, Juliana, Head, Ref & Instruction, Biola University Library, 13800 Biola Ave, La Mirada, CA, 90639. Tel: 562-944-0351, Ext 5620. Fax: 562-903-4840. p. 162

Morley, Susan, Mgr, CSA International, 178 Rexdale Blvd, Toronto, ON, M9W 1R3, CANADA. Tel: 416-747-4059. Fax: 416-747-4199. p. 2852

Morlock, Vickie, Adult Serv, ILL, Sidney Public Library, 1112 12th Ave, Sidney, NE, 69162. Tel: 308-254-3110. Fax: 308-254-3710. p. 1419

Mormon, Jill, Dir, Terrell State Hospital, 1200 E Brin Ave, Terrell, TX, 75160-2938. Tel: 972-551-8525, Ext 8525. Fax: 972-551-8371. p. 2391

Morningstar, Amanda J, Dir, Deckerville Public Library, 3542 N Main St, Deckerville, MI, 48427-9638. Tel: 810-376-8015. Fax: 810-376-8593. p. 1168

Moro, Nadia, Coll Tech, University of Toronto Libraries, Faculty of Information Inforum, 140 Saint George St, 4th Flr, Toronto, ON, M5S 3G6, CANADA. Tel: 416-978-5765. Fax: 416-978-5769. p. 2866

Moroney, Mary, Dir, Hulbert Community Library, 118 E Main St, Hulbert, OK, 74441. Tel: 918-772-3383. Fax: 918-772-3310. p. 1966

Moroney, Mary, Libr Dir, Bryant University, 1150 Douglas Pike, Smithfield, RI, 02917-1284. Tel: 401-232-6125. Fax: 401-232-6126. p. 2176

Moroney, Mary J, Exec Dir, Eastern Oklahoma District Library System, 814 W Okmulgee, Muskogee, OK, 74401-6839. Tel: 918-683-2846, Ext 239. Fax: 918-683-0436. p. 1969

Morong, Christine, Sr Librn, Ref, Skadden, Arps, Slate, Meagher & Flom LLP Library, 155 N Wacker Dr, Chicago, IL, 60606. Tel: 312-407-0941. Fax: 312-407-0411. p. 624

Morong, Michele, Librn, Albert F Totman Public Library, 28 Parker Head Rd, Phippsburg, ME, 04562-4576. Tel: 207-389-2309. Fax: 207-389-2309. p. 995

Moroni, Dana, In Charge, Merced County Library, Le Grand Branch, 12949 Le Grand Rd, Le Grand, CA, 95333. Tel: 209-389-4541. p. 186

Moroses, Louise, Ch, Bergenfield Public Library, 50 W Clinton Ave, Bergenfield, NJ, 07621-2799. Tel: 201-387-4040, Ext 896. Fax: 201-387-9004. p. 1472

Moroz, Judy, Cat, University of St Francis, 500 Wilcox St, Joliet, IL, 60435. Tel: 815-740-5041. Fax: 815-740-3364. p. 660

Morra, Sylvia T, Head, Coll Mgt, Elizabethtown College, One Alpha Dr, Elizabethtown, PA, 17022-2227. Tel: 717-361-1452. Fax: 717-361-1167. p. 2053

Morrell, Brian, Pres, Canal Society of New Jersey, Waterloo Village, Stanhope, NJ, 07874. Tel: 973-691-7448. Fax: 908-722-9556. p. 1532

Morrell, David, Adult Serv, Ref, West Springfield Public Library, 200 Park St, West Springfield, MA, 01089. Tel: 413-736-4561, Ext 3. Fax: 413-736-6469. p. 1137

Morrell, Harvey, Info Tech, University of Baltimore, Law Library, 1415 Maryland Ave, Baltimore, MD, 21201. Tel: 410-837-4554. Fax: 410-837-4570. p. 1018

Morren, Julie, Ch, Beresford Public Library, 115 S Third St, Beresford, SD, 57004-1798. Tel: 605-763-2782. Fax: 605-763-2403. p. 2210

Morrical, Beverly, ILL, Illinois Central College, One College Dr, East Peoria, IL, 61635-0001. Tel: 309-694-5461. Fax: 309-694-5473. p. 638

Morrill, Allen S, Dir, Thiel College, 75 College Ave, Greenville, PA, 16125-2183. Tel: 724-589-2124, 724-589-2205. Fax: 724-589-2122. p. 2063

Morrill, Linda, Dir, Lincoln Memorial Library, 21 W Broadway, Lincoln, ME, 04457. Tel: 207-794-2765. Fax: 207-794-2606. p. 990

Morrill, Mary Elizabeth, Tech Serv, Windsor Locks Public Library, 28 Main St, Windsor Locks, CT, 06096. Tel: 860-627-1495. Fax: 860-627-1496. p. 379

Morrill, Olga, Ch, Conway Public Library, 15 Main St, Conway, NH, 03818. Tel: 603-447-5552. Fax: 603-447-6921. p. 1444

Morrill, Richard, Librn, Clark Maxwell Jr Library, 1405 CR 526A, Sumterville, FL, 33585. Tel: 352-568-3074. Fax: 352-568-3376. p. 492

Morris, Aaron, ILL, Sturgis District Library, 255 North St, Sturgis, MI, 49091. Tel: 269-659-7224. Fax: 269-651-4534. p. 1229

Morris, Alicia, Head, Tech Serv, Tufts University, 35 Professors Row, Medford, MA, 02155-5816. Tel: 617-627-2399. Fax: 617-627-3002. p. 1104

Morris, Angela, Youth Serv Coordr, North Central Regional Library, 16 N Columbia St, Wenatchee, WA, 98801-8103. Tel: 509-663-1117, Ext 119. Fax: 509-662-8060. p. 2548

Morris, Angela G, Head, Pub Serv, Louisville Presbyterian Theological Seminary, 1044 Alta Vista Rd, Louisville, KY, 40205-1798. Tel: 502-895-3411. Fax: 502-895-1096. p. 925

Morris, Ann, Head Law Librn, Skadden, Arps, Slate, Meagher & Flom LLP Library, 155 N Wacker Dr, Chicago, IL, 60606. Tel: 312-407-0941. Fax: 312-407-0411. p. 624

Morris, Barry, Dir, J Robert Jamerson Memorial Library, 106 Main St, Appomattox, VA, 24522. Tel: 434-352-5340. Fax: 434-352-0933. p. 2448

Morris, Betsy, Asst Dir, Pioneer Library System, 2557 State Rte 21, Canandaigua, NY, 14424. Tel: 585-394-8260. Fax: 585-394-1935. p. 1601

Morris, Betty, Dr, Prog Chair, Jacksonville State University, 700 Pelham Rd N, Jacksonville, AL, 36265. Tel: 256-782-5011, 256-782-5096. Fax: 256-782-5321, 256-782-8136. p. 2961

Morris, Bonnie, Bibliog Instr, Ref Serv, North Georgia College & State University, 238 Georgia Circle, Dahlonega, GA, 30597-3001. Tel: 706-864-1521. p. 527

Morris, Bonnie, Librn, Valley Park Community Library, 320 Benton St, Valley Park, MO, 63088. Tel: 636-225-5608. Fax: 636-825-0079. p. 1370

Morris, Brenda, Asst Librn, Otsego District Public Library, 219 S Farmer St, Otsego, MI, 49078-1313. Tel: 269-694-9690. Fax: 269-694-9129. p. 1216

Morris, C Frances, Dir, United States Air Force, 744 Douhet Dr, Bldg 4244, Barksdale AFB, LA, 71110. Tel: 318-456-4182. Fax: 318-752-0509. p. 941

Morris, Candice, Ch, Lewis & Clark Library, 120 S Last Chance Gulch, Helena, MT, 59601. Tel: 406-447-1690, Ext 115. Fax: 406-447-1687. p. 1382

Morris, Carla, Mgr, Ch Serv, Provo City Library, 550 N University Ave, Provo, UT, 84601-1618. Tel: 801-852-6672. Fax: 801-852-6688. p. 2411

Morris, Chris, Dir, Cascade County Historical Society Archives, High Plains Heritage Ctr, 422 Second St S, Great Falls, MT, 59405. Tel: 406-727-7474. Fax: 406-761-3805. p. 1379

Morris, Clara, Dir, Bruneau District Library, 32073 Ruth St, Bruneau, ID, 83604. Tel: 208-845-2131. Fax: 208-845-2131. p. 572

Morris, Colleen, Asst Librn, West Tisbury Free Public Library, 1042 State Rd, West Tisbury, MA, 02575. Tel: 508-693-3366. Fax: 508-696-0130. p. 1138

Morris, Crystal, Cat, Gilpin County Public Library District, 15131 Hwy 119, Black Hawk, CO, 80422. Tel: 303-582-5777. Fax: 303-582-3938. p. 289

Morris, Darlene, Syst Coordr, University of Minnesota Duluth Library, 416 Library Dr, Duluth, MN, 55812. Tel: 218-726-8102. Fax: 218-726-8019. p. 1248

Morris, Deborah, Asst Music Librn, Roosevelt University, 430 S Michigan Ave, Chicago, IL, 60605. Tel: 312-341-2328. Fax: 312-341-2425. p. 623

Morris, Donna, Br Mgr, Chicago Public Library, Hall, 4801 S Michigan Ave, Chicago, IL, 60615. Tel: 312-747-2541. Fax: 312-747-1374. p. 608

Morris, Donna, Exec Dir, Metropolitan Library System in Oklahoma County, 300 Park Ave, Oklahoma City, OK, 73102. Tel: 405-606-3725. Fax: 405-606-3722. p. 1972

Morris, Donna Jones, State Librn, Utah State Library Division, 250 N 1950 West, Ste A, Salt Lake City, UT, 84116-7901. Tel: 801-715-6770. Fax: 801-715-6767. p. 2415

Morris, Fae, Librn, J T & E J Crumbaugh Memorial Public Church Library, 405 E Center St, Le Roy, IL, 61752-1723. Tel: 309-962-3911. p. 664

Morris, Irene, Dir, Polk County Law Library, Courthouse, Rm 3076, 255 N Broadway, Bartow, FL, 33830. Tel: 863-534-4013. Fax: 863-534-7443. p. 427

Morris, Jack V, II, Mgr, Weston Solutions Inc, 1400 Weston Way, West Chester, PA, 19380-0903. Tel: 610-701-3080. Fax: 610-701-3158. p. 2154

Morris, Jackie, Librn, Cave Springs Public Library, Midway Ave, Bentonville, AR, 72712. Tel: 479-248-7117. p. 95

Morris, Jane, Head Librn, Boston College Libraries, Social Work Library, McGuinn Hall 038, 140 Commonwealth Ave, Chestnut Hill, MA, 02467-3810. Tel: 617-552-3234. Fax: 617-552-3199. p. 1081

Morris, Janet, Educ Supvr, Federal Correctional Institution, 1100 River Rd, Hopewell, VA, 23860. Tel: 804-504-7800, Ext 1148. Fax: 804-863-1543. p. 2472

Morris, Jeffory, Curator, Arizona Museum for Youth Library, 35 N Robson St, Mesa, AZ, 85201. Tel: 480-644-5769. Fax: 480-644-2466. p. 68

Morris, Jennifer, Libr Tech, Buffalo History Museum Research Library, One Museum Ct, Buffalo, NY, 14216-3199. Tel: 716-873-9644. Fax: 716-873-8754. p. 1597

Morris, Jennifer, Outreach Serv Librn, Nioga Library System, 6575 Wheeler Rd, Lockport, NY, 14094. Tel: 716-434-6167. Fax: 716-434-8231. p. 1653

Morris, Jim, Exec Dir, Lake City Community College, 149 SE College Pl, Lake City, FL, 32025-2006. Tel: 386-754-4337. Fax: 386-754-4837. p. 457

Morris, Joan, ILL, Amarillo Public Library, 413 E Fourth Ave, Amarillo, TX, 79101. Tel: 806-378-3054. Fax: 806-378-9327. p. 2274

Morris, Julie, Ch, Benzie Shores District Library, 630 Main St, Frankfort, MI, 49635. Tel: 231-352-4671. Fax: 231-352-4671. p. 1181

Morris, Karen, Dir, Whiting Library, 117 Main St, Chester, VT, 05143. Tel: 802-875-2277. Fax: 802-875-2277. p. 2421

Morris, Karen T, Librn, Oklahoma State University Libraries, Mary L Williams Curriculum Materials Library, 001 Willard, Stillwater, OK, 74078-0001. Tel: 405-744-9769. Fax: 405-744-1726. p. 1978

Morris, Katherine Motika, Dir, Wayne County Public Library, Hwy 64 East, Waynesboro, TN, 38485. Tel: 931-722-5537. Fax: 931-722-5537. p. 2268

Morris, Kathy, Librn, Phinehas S Newton Library, On the Common, Royalston, MA, 01368. Tel: 978-249-3572. Fax: 978-249-3572. p. 1121

Morris, Kathy, Librn, Fairmount Community Library, 406 Chapel Dr, Syracuse, NY, 13219. Tel: 315-487-8933. Fax: 315-484-9475. p. 1751

Morris, Kimberli, Asst Law Librn, Ref, Pennsylvania State University - Dickinson School of Law (University Libraries), 1170 Harrisburg Pike, Carlisle, PA, 17013-1617. Tel: 814-863-0885. Fax: 717-240-5127. p. 2042

Morris, Lola, Dir, Crab Orchard Public Library District, 20012 Crab Orchard Rd, Marion, IL, 62959. Tel: 618-982-2141. Fax: 618-982-2141. p. 670

Morris, Lola, Dir, Crab Orchard Public Library District, Pittsburg Branch, 302 W Avery St, Pittsburg, IL, 62974-1009. Tel: 618-997-8111. Fax: 618-997-8111. p. 670

Morris, Louise, Asst Librn, Lago Vista Public Library, 5803 Thunderbird, Ste 40, Lago Vista, TX, 78645. Tel: 512-267-3868. Fax: 512-267-4855. p. 2352

Morris, Margaret, Dir, Manitou Springs Public Library, 701 Manitou Ave, Manitou Springs, CO, 80829-1887. Tel: 719-685-5206. Fax: 719-685-1169. p. 318

Morris, Marge, Mgr, American Association of Advertising Agencies, 405 Lexington Ave, 18th Flr, New York, NY, 10174. Tel: 212-682-2500. p. 1667

Morris, Margie Ann, Dir, Poestenkill Public Library, Nine Plank Rd, Poestenkill, NY, 12140. Tel: 518-283-3721. Fax: 518-283-5618. p. 1720

Morris, Marian, Dir, Baptist Medical Center Princeton, 701 Princeton Ave SW, Birmingham, AL, 35211. Tel: 205-783-3078. Fax: 205-783-7076. p. 6

Morris, Marie, Librn, The Fraser Institute Library, 1770 Burrard St, 4th Flr, Vancouver, BC, V6J 3G7, CANADA. Tel: 604-688-0221. Fax: 604-688-8539. p. 2741

Morris, Marjorie, Librn, Rowan University Library, Wilson Music Library, Main Campus, Rte 322, Glassboro, NJ, 08028. Tel: 856-256-4500, Ext 3542, 856-256-4799. Fax: 856-256-4924. p. 1488

Morris, Martin, Librn, Royal Victoria Hospital, Medical Library, 687 Pine Ave W, Rm H4-01, Montreal, QC, H3A 1A1, CANADA. Tel: 514-934-1934, Ext 35290. Fax: 514-843-1483. p. 2901

Morris, Miriam, Asst Dir, Br Serv, Dayton Metro Library, 215 E Third St, Dayton, OH, 45402-2103. Tel: 937-463-2665. Fax: 937-496-4300. p. 1892

Morris, Nancy, Coll Develop, Arizona State Braille & Talking Book Library, 1030 N 32nd St, Phoenix, AZ, 85008. Tel: 602-255-5578. Fax: 602-286-0444. p. 72

Morris, Nicole, Librn, Lincoln Public Library, 107 W Bean, Lincoln, AR, 72744. Tel: 479-824-3294. Fax: 479-824-4119. p. 105

Morris, Pat, Dir, Saint Edward Mercy Medical Center Library, 7301 Rogers Ave, Fort Smith, AR, 72917. Tel: 479-314-6520. Fax: 479-314-5646. p. 101

Morris, Peter, Syst Librn, Fairfield University, 1073 N Benson Rd, Fairfield, CT, 06430-5195. Tel: 203-254-4044. Fax: 203-254-4135. p. 339

Morris, Peter J, Syst Librn, Clarkson University Libraries, Andrew S Schuler Educational Resources Center, CU Box 5590, Eight Clarkson Ave, Potsdam, NY, 13699-5590. Tel: 315-268-4459. Fax: 315-268-7655. p. 1721

Morris, Petra, Supvr, Ch Serv, Arcadia Public Library, 20 W Duarte Rd, Arcadia, CA, 91006. Tel: 626-821-5568. Fax: 626-447-8050. p. 121

Morris, Rebecca, Dir, Sabine Parish Library, 705 Main St, Many, LA, 71449-3199. Tel: 318-256-4150. Fax: 318-256-4154. p. 956

Morris, Rebecca, Asst Prof, Simmons College, 300 The Fenway, Boston, MA, 02115. Tel: 617-521-2800. Fax: 617-521-3192. p. 2967

Morris, Rita, Ch, Lordsburg-Hidalgo Library, 208 E Third St, Lordsburg, NM, 88045. Tel: 575-542-9646. Fax: 575-542-9646. p. 1559

Morris, Robert, Sr Librn, California Department of Corrections Library System, Folsom State Prison, 300 Prison Rd, Represa, CA, 95671. Tel: 916-985-2561. Fax: 916-608-3130. p. 221

Morris, Rosemary, Ch & Youth Librn, Talbot County Free Library, 100 W Dover St, Easton, MD, 21601-2620. Tel: 410-822-1626. Fax: 410-820-8217. p. 1027

Morris, Sandra, Info Spec, Becton, Dickinson & Company, 21 Davis Dr, Research Triangle Park, NC, 27709. Tel: 919-597-6194. Fax: 919-597-6406. p. 1819

Morris, Sandra, Dir, Blake, Cassels & Graydon LLP, Commerce Ct W, 199 Bay St, Ste 4000, Toronto, ON, M5L 1A9, CANADA. Tel: 416-863-2650. Fax: 416-863-2653. p. 2850

Morris, Scott, Br Mgr, Saint Louis Public Library, Divoll, 4234 N Grand Blvd, Saint Louis, MO, 63107. Tel: 314-534-0313. Fax: 314-534-3353. p. 1360

Morris, Sharon, Dir, Libr Develop, Colorado State Library, 201 E Colfax Ave, Rm 309, Denver, CO, 80203-1799. Tel: 303-866-6730. Fax: 303-866-6940. p. 299

Morris, Sharon, Mgr, Johns Hopkins University Libraries, 1717 Massachusetts Ave, Washington, DC, 20036. Tel: 202-452-0714. p. 405

Morris, Sharon, Customer Serv Coordr, Broward County Division of Libraries, 100 S Andrews Ave, Fort Lauderdale, FL, 33301. Tel: 954-357-7511. Fax: 954-357-5733. p. 441

Morris, Sharon, Mgr, Johns Hopkins University Libraries, 9601 Medical Center Dr, Rockville, MD, 20850. Tel: 301-294-7033. Fax: 301-294-7032. p. 1037

Morris, Shelia, Co-Dir, Waseca County Historical Society Library, 315 Second Ave NE, Waseca, MN, 56093. Tel: 507-835-7700. p. 1287

Morris, Steven, Head, Digital Libr Initiatives, North Carolina State University Libraries, Two Broughton Dr, Raleigh, NC, 27695. Tel: 919-515-1361. Fax: 919-515-3628. p. 1816

Morris, Susan, Head, ILL, University of Georgia Libraries, Athens, GA, 30602-1641. Tel: 706-542-0642. Fax: 706-542-4144. p. 510

Morris, Susan, Libr Tech, Valley Forge Military Academy & College, 1001 Eagle Rd, Wayne, PA, 19087-3695. Tel: 610-989-1200, 610-989-1364. Fax: 610-975-9642. p. 2152

Morris, Tara, Head, Youth Serv, Haverstraw Kings Daughters Public Library, Ten W Ramapo Rd, Garnerville, NY, 10923. Tel: 845-786-3800. Fax: 845-786-3791. p. 1626

Morris, Teresa M, Ref & Instrul Serv Librn, College of San Mateo Library, Bldg 9, 1700 W Hillsdale Blvd, San Mateo, CA, 94402-3795. Tel: 650-574-6579. Fax: 650-574-6497. p. 255

Morris, Terry, Dir, Payson Public Library, 328 N McLane Rd, Payson, AZ, 85541. Tel: 928-474-9260. Fax: 928-474-2679. p. 70

Morris, Vanessa J, Asst Teaching Prof, Drexel University, Rush Bldg, Rm 306, 30 N 33rd St, Philadelphia, PA, 19104-2875. Tel: 215-895-2474. Fax: 215-895-2494. p. 2973

Morris, Vera, Librn, Garden State Youth Correctional Facility Library, PO Box 11401, Yardville, NJ, 08620-1401. Tel: 609-298-6300, Ext 2574. Fax: 609-298-8682. p. 1546

Morris, Vicki, Govt Doc, Henry Ford Community College, 5101 Evergreen Rd, Dearborn, MI, 48128-1495. Tel: 313-845-9761. Fax: 313-845-9795. p. 1167

Morris, Wanda, Exec Dir, Dying With Dignity Canada Library, 802-55 Eglinton Ave E, Toronto, ON, M4P 1G8, CANADA. Tel: 416-486-3998. Fax: 416-486-5562. p. 2853

Morris, Zenda, Libr Spec I, Okeechobee County Public Library, 206 SW 16th St, Okeechobee, FL, 34974. Tel: 863-763-3536. Fax: 863-763-5368. p. 474

Morris-Holmes, Karla A, Librn, Husch Blackwell Sanders LLP, 190 Carondelet Plaza, Ste 600, Saint Louis, MO, 63105. Tel: 314-480-1500. Fax: 314-480-1505. p. 1355

Morris-Horstman, Margaret, Asst Dir, First Church of Christ Congregational, 12 S Main St, West Hartford, CT, 06107. Tel: 860-232-3893. Fax: 860-232-8183. p. 376

Morrisey, Locke, Head, Res Serv & Coll, University of San Francisco, 2130 Fulton St, San Francisco, CA, 94117-1080. Tel: 412-422-5399. Fax: 415-422-5949. p. 248

Morrish, Jeanette F, Dir, Thomas E Fleschner Memorial Library, 11935 Silver Creek Dr, Birch Run, MI, 48415-9767. Tel: 989-624-9759. Fax: 989-624-0120. p. 1158

Morrison, Ann, Law Librn, Dalhousie University, Sir James Dunn Law Library, Weldon Law Bldg, 6061 University Ave, Halifax, NS, B3H 4H9, CANADA. Tel: 902-494-2640. Fax: 902-494-6669. p. 2780

Morrison, Barbara, Asst Dir, Tech, Chelmsford Public Library, 25 Boston Rd, Chelmsford, MA, 01824-3088. Tel: 978-256-5521. Fax: 978-256-8511. p. 1079

Morrison, Barbara, Libr Tech, United States Courts Library, 700 Stewart St, Rm 19105, Seattle, WA, 98101. Tel: 206-370-8975. Fax: 206-370-8976. p. 2533

Morrison, Bill, Tech Serv, Franklin County Library, 906 N Main St, Louisburg, NC, 27549-2199. Tel: 919-496-2111. Fax: 919-496-1339. p. 1807

Morrison, Carolyn, Circ, Mitchell Community College, 500 W Broad St, Statesville, NC, 28677. Tel: 704-878-3270. p. 1826

Morrison, Catherine, Ref Librn, Scarborough Public Library, 48 Gorham Rd, Scarborough, ME, 04074. Tel: 207-883-4723. Fax: 207-883-9728. p. 1000

Morrison, Daryl, Head, Spec Coll, University of California, Davis, 100 NW Quad, Davis, CA, 95616-5292. Tel: 530-752-6561. Fax: 530-752-3148. p. 139

Morrison, Donna, In Charge, Bureau of Land Management, 1300 Airport Lane, North Bend, OR, 97459-2000. Tel: 541-751-4285. Fax: 541-751-4303. p. 2008

Morrison, Gregory, Head, Ref, Wheaton College, 510 Irving Ave, Wheaton, IL, 60187-5593. Tel: 630-752-5847. Fax: 630-752-5855. p. 718

Morrison, Jane Gabovitch, Librn, Congregation Beth-El Zedeck, 600 W 70th St, Indianapolis, IN, 46260. Tel: 317-253-3441. Fax: 317-259-6849. p. 750

Morrison, Janet, Librn, Cavalier Public Library, 106 W Second Ave S, Cavalier, ND, 58220. Tel: 701-265-4746. p. 1839

Morrison, Jennifer, Dir, Cape Canaveral Public Library, 201 Polk Ave, Cape Canaveral, FL, 32920-3067. Tel: 321-868-1101. Fax: 321-868-1103. p. 431

Morrison, Jennifer, Dir, Palm Bay Public Library, 1520 Port Malabar Blvd NE, Palm Bay, FL, 32905. Tel: 321-952-4519. Fax: 321-952-4543. p. 479

Morrison, Jenny, Dir, Eau Gallie Public Library, 1521 Pineapple Ave, Melbourne, FL, 32935-6594. Tel: 321-255-4304. Fax: 321-255-4323. p. 463

Morrison, Kate, Supvr, Acq, Twin Falls Public Library, 201 Fourth Ave E, Twin Falls, ID, 83301-6397. Tel: 208-733-2964. Fax: 208-733-2965. p. 584

Morrison, Kim, Coordr, Libr Serv, Info Literacy, Chabot College Library, 25555 Hesperian Blvd, Hayward, CA, 94545. Tel: 510-723-6762. p. 157

Morrison, Kristie, Librn, Ashland Public Library, 224 Claremont Ave, Ashland, OH, 44805. Tel: 419-289-8188, Ext 15. Fax: 419-281-8552. p. 1855

Morrison, Larry, Electronic Res, Blue Ridge Regional Library, 310 E Church St, Martinsville, VA, 24112-2999. Tel: 276-403-5437. Fax: 276-632-1660. p. 2477

Morrison, Marcia, Dir, Libr Develop, California State University, Fresno, Henry Madden Library, 5200 N Barton Ave, Mail Stop ML-34, Fresno, CA, 93740-8014. Tel: 559-278-7177. Fax: 559-278-6952. p. 150

Morrison, Meris, Librn, Moore Free Library, 23 West St, Newfane, VT, 05345. Tel: 802-365-7948. Fax: 802-257-0725. p. 2430

Morrison, Michelle, Mgr, Human Res, Westerville Public Library, 126 S State St, Westerville, OH, 43081-2095. Tel: 614-882-7277, Ext 2197. Fax: 614-882-5369. p. 1947

Morrison, Nancy, Dir, Coll Serv, Bergen County Historical Society Library, 90 Center Ave, Westwood, NJ, 07675. Tel: 201-343-9492. p. 1543

Morrison, Patricia, Libr Supvr-Spec Coll, Jacksonville Public Library, 303 N Laura St, Jacksonville, FL, 32202-3505. Tel: 904-630-2960. Fax: 904-630-2431. p. 453

Morrison, Peggy, Pub Serv Librn/ILL, Access Serv/Govt Doc, Hendrix College, 1600 Washington Ave, Conway, AR, 72032. Tel: 501-450-1289. Fax: 501-450-3800. p. 97

Morrison, Randi, Br Mgr, Portsmouth Public Library, Wheelersburg Branch, 10745 Old Gallia Pike, Wheelersburg, OH, 45694. Tel: 740-574-6116. Fax: 740-574-8280. p. 1931

Morrison, Ray, Head, Circ, State University of New York at Oswego, SUNY Oswego, 7060 State Rte 104, Oswego, NY, 13126-3514. Tel: 315-312-3567. Fax: 315-312-3194. p. 1713

Morrison, Ray L, Dr, Dir of Libr, Mid-America Nazarene University, 2030 E College Way, Olathe, KS, 66062-1899. Tel: 913-971-3561. Fax: 913-971-3285. p. 886

Morrison, Rebecca, Asst Admin, Head, Ref (Info Serv), Wichita Falls Public Library, 600 11th St, Wichita Falls, TX, 76301-4604. Tel: 940-767-0868, Ext 233. Fax: 940-720-6672. p. 2401

Morrison, Reitha Z, Youth Serv, Iredell County Public Library, 201 N Tradd St, Statesville, NC, 28677. Tel: 704-928-2414. Fax: 704-878-5449. p. 1825

Morrison, Rob, Librn, National Louis University Library & Learning Support, 122 S Michigan Ave, Chicago, IL, 60603. Tel: 312-261-3372. Fax: 312-261-3372. p. 619

Morrison, Rosalind, In Charge, Colchester - East Hants Regional Library, Elmsdale Branch, 753 Hwy 2, Elmsdale, NS, B2S 1A8, CANADA. Tel: 902-883-9838. p. 2786

Morrison, Ruth, Sr Mgr, Bus/Sci Dept, Memphis Public Library & Information Center, 3030 Poplar Ave, Memphis, TN, 38111-3527. Tel: 901-415-2736. Fax: 901-323-7108. p. 2249

Morrison, Ruth W, Agency Mgr, Memphis Public Library, Science, Business, 3030 Poplar Ave, Memphis, TN, 38111. Tel: 901-415-2736. p. 2250

Morrison, Sara B, Dir, Briggs Public Library, 108 E Railroad St, Saint Johns, MI, 48879-1526. Tel: 989-224-4702. Fax: 989-224-1205. p. 1225

Morrison, Sara M, Cat, ILL, Erskine College & Theological Seminary, One Depot St, Due West, SC, 29639. Tel: 864-379-8898. Fax: 864-379-2900. p. 2193

Morrison, Sharon, Dir, Southeastern Oklahoma State University, 1405 N Fourth Ave, PMB 4105, Durant, OK, 74701-0609. Tel: 580-745-3172. Fax: 580-745-7463. p. 1961

Morrison, Susan, Cat Librn, Louisiana State University Libraries, Paul M Hebert Law Center, One E Campus Dr, Baton Rouge, LA, 70803-1000. Tel: 225-578-4048. Fax: 225-578-5773. p. 944

Morrison, Suzanne, Librn, US Courts Branch Library, 655 First Ave N, Ste 310, Fargo, ND, 58102. Tel: 701-297-7280. Fax: 701-297-7285. p. 1841

Morrisroe, Susan, Dir, Ref, Missouri State Library, James C Kirkpatrick State Information Ctr, 600 W Main St, Jefferson City, MO, 65101-1532. Tel: 573-751-2862. Fax: 573-751-3612. p. 1335

Morrissey, Christine A, Circ, Melrose Public Library, 69 W Emerson St, Melrose, MA, 02176. Tel: 781-665-2313. Fax: 781-662-4229. p. 1105

Morrissey, Claire, Librn, Iona College, Rockland Graduate Center, Two Blue Hill Plaza, Concourse Level, Pearl River, NY, 10965. Tel: 845-620-1350. Fax: 845-620-1260. p. 1666

Morrissey, Gail, Ref, La Grange Public Library, Ten W Cossitt Ave, La Grange, IL, 60525. Tel: 708-352-0576. p. 662

Morrissey, Leslie, Dir, Falmouth Public Library, 300 Main St, Falmouth, MA, 02540. Tel: 508-457-2555. Fax: 508-457-2559. p. 1088

Morrissey, Margaret, Dir, Jacob Edwards Library, 236 Main St, Southbridge, MA, 01550-2598. Tel: 508-764-5426. Fax: 508-764-5428. p. 1126

Morrissey, Renee, Librn, Alberta Innovates-Technology Futures, 250 Karl Clark Rd, Edmonton, AB, T6N 134, CANADA. Tel: 780-450-5229. Fax: 780-450-8996. p. 2698

Morrissey, William Patrick, Coll Develop Mgr, Barry University, 11300 NE Second Ave, Miami, FL, 33161. Tel: 305-899-3755. Fax: 305-899-4792. p. 464

Morrone, Melissa, Br Librn, Brooklyn Public Library, Flatlands, 2065 Flatbush Ave, Brooklyn, NY, 11234. Tel: 718-253-4409. Fax: 718-253-5018. p. 1591

Morrow, Abby, Youth Serv, Ellsworth Public Library, 20 State St, Ellsworth, ME, 04605. Tel: 207-667-6363. Fax: 207-667-4901. p. 984

Morrow, Allan, Dir, McCook Public Library District, 8419 W 50th St, McCook, IL, 60525-3186. Tel: 708-442-1242. Fax: 708-442-0148. p. 672

Morrow, Barbara R, Mgr, Plunkett & Cooney, 38585 Woodward Ave, Bloomfield Hills, MI, 48304. Tel: 248-901-4080. Fax: 248-901-4040. p. 1159

Morrow, Becky, Libr Asst, Indian Hills Community College, 721 N First St, Bldg CV06, Centerville, IA, 52544. Tel: 641-856-2143, Ext 2237. Fax: 641-856-5527. p. 801

Morrow, Craig, Librn, United States Army, Ireland Army Hospital Medical Library, Bldg 851, Ireland Ave, Fort Knox, KY, 40121-5520. Tel: 502-624-9550. Fax: 502-624-0280. p. 913

Morrow, Dana, Dir of Outreach, Metropolitan Library System in Oklahoma County, Outreach-Book Centers & Books by Mail, 300 NE 50th St, Oklahoma City, OK, 73105. Tel: 405-606-3835. Fax: 405-606-3815. p. 1973

Morrow, Diana, Dir, Gary Public Library, 220 W Fifth Ave, Gary, IN, 46402-1215. p. 744

Morrow, Diana, Head Librn, Gary Public Library, W E B Du Bois Branch, 1835 Broadway, Gary, IN, 46407-2298. Tel: 219-886-9120. Fax: 219-886-9319. p. 744

Morrow, Glenn, Head, Access Serv, Northwest Missouri State University, 800 University Dr, Maryville, MO, 64468-6001. Tel: 660-562-1192. Fax: 660-562-1049. p. 1344

Morrow, Glenn, ILL Coordr, Northwest Missouri State University, 800 University Dr, Maryville, MO, 64468-6001. Tel: 660-562-1192. Fax: 660-562-1049. p. 1344

Morrow, Hugh, Sr Consult, International Cadmium Association Library, 9222 Jeffery Rd, Great Falls, VA, 22066. Tel: 703-759-7400. Fax: 703-759-7003. p. 2467

Morrow, Jackie, Dir, Erick Community Library, 200 S Sheb Wooley, Erick, OK, 73645. Tel: 580-526-3425. p. 1963

Morrow, Jean, Head of Libr, New England Conservatory of Music, 33 Gainsborough St, Boston, MA, 02115. Tel: 617-585-1247. Fax: 617-585-1245. p. 1064

Morrow, Jean, Librn, New England Conservatory of Music, Idabelle Firestone Audio Library, 290 Huntington Ave, Boston, MA, 02115. Tel: 617-585-1255. Fax: 617-585-1245. p. 1064

Morrow, Jennifer, Archivist, Spec Coll Librn, Hiram College Library, 11694 Hayden St, Hiram, OH, 44234. Tel: 330-569-5361. Fax: 330-569-5491. p. 1905

Morrow, Katherine, Librn, East Central Regional Library, Mille Lacs Community Library, 285 2nd Ave S, Isle, MN, 56342-0147. Tel: 320-676-3929. Fax: 320-676-3929. p. 1244

Morrow, Kay, Dir, McCreary County Public Library District, Six N Main St, Whitley City, KY, 42653. Tel: 606-376-8738. Fax: 606-376-3631. p. 937

Morrow, Linda, Dir, Palomar College Library - Media Center, 1140 W Mission Rd, San Marcos, CA, 92069-1487. Tel: 760-744-1150, Ext 2848. Fax: 760-761-3500. p. 254

Morrow, Lory, Photog Archives Mgr, Montana Historical Society, 225 N Roberts St, Helena, MT, 59601-4514. Tel: 406-444-4714. Fax: 406-444-5297. p. 1382

Morrow, Patricia, Librn, Atlantic County Library System, Galloway Branch, 306 E Jimmie Leeds Rd, Galloway, NJ, 08205. Tel: 609-652-2352. Fax: 609-652-3613. p. 1500

Morrow, Paula, Libr Tech, Holy Cross College, 54515 State Rd 933 N, Box 308, Notre Dame, IN, 46556-0308. Tel: 574-239-8391. Fax: 574-239-8324. p. 771

Morrow Williams, Barbara, Commun Librn, Santa Clara County Library District, Saratoga Community Library, 13650 Saratoga Ave, Saratoga, CA, 95070-5099. Tel: 408-867-6129. Fax: 408-867-9806. p. 181

Morrow-Ruetten, Lydia, Acq, Ser, Governors State University Library, One University Pkwy, University Park, IL, 60466-0975. Tel: 708-534-4116. Fax: 708-534-4564. p. 711

Morse, Barbara, Head, Tech Serv, New Britain Public Library, 20 High St, New Britain, CT, 06051-4226. Tel: 860-224-3155. Fax: 860-223-6729. p. 354

Morse, Celia B, Dir, Berkley Public Library, 3155 Coolidge Hwy, Berkley, MI, 48072. Tel: 248-658-3440. Fax: 248-658-3441. p. 1157

Morse, Chelsea, Mgr, San Francisco Camerawork, 657 Mission St, 2nd Flr, San Francisco, CA, 94105-4104. Tel: 415 512 2020. Fax: 415 512 7109. p. 245

Morse, Karen Walton, Mgr, Libr & Archival Serv, Historic Hudson Valley Library, 639 Bedford Rd, Tarrytown, NY, 10591. Tel: 914-366-6901, 914-366-6902. Fax: 914-631-0089. p. 1754

Morse, Lois, Actg Br Mgr, Lincoln Library, Southeast, 2500 S Grand Ave E, Springfield, IL, 62703. Tel: 217-753-4980. Fax: 217-753-4982. p. 706

Morse, Lois, Actg Br Mgr, Lincoln Library, West, 1251 W Washington, Springfield, IL, 62702. Tel: 217-753-4985. Fax: 217-753-4984. p. 706

Morse, Lois, Circ, Lincoln Library, 326 S Seventh St, Springfield, IL, 62701. Tel: 217-753-4900. Fax: 217-753-5329. p. 706

Morse, Lori, Head Librn, Free Library of Philadelphia, General Information, 1901 Vine St, Philadelphia, PA, 19103-1189. Tel: 215-686-5322. p. 2107

Morse, Mary Beth, Acq, Christ the King Seminary Library, 711 Knox Rd, East Aurora, NY, 14052. Tel: 716-652-8959. Fax: 716-652-8903. p. 1616

Morse, Ruth, Commun Libr Mgr, County of Los Angeles Public Library, Gardena Mayme Dear Library, 1731 W Gardena Blvd, Gardena, CA, 90247-4726. Tel: 310-323-6363. Fax: 310-327-0992. p. 141

Morss, Robb, Dep Dir, Las Vegas-Clark County Library District, 7060 W Windmill Lane, Las Vegas, NV, 89113. Tel: 702-507-6290. p. 1429

Mort, Dori, IT Spec, Milton-Union Public Library, 560 S Main St, West Milton, OH, 45383. Tel: 937-698-5515. Fax: 937-698-3774. p. 1946

Mort, Rhonda, Ch, Willard Library of Evansville, 21 First Ave, Evansville, IN, 47710-1294. Tel: 812-425-4309. Fax: 812-421-9742. p. 739

Mortell, Jennifer, Circ, Clearwater Public Library System, Countryside, 2741 State Rd 580, Clearwater, FL, 33761. Tel: 727-562-4970. Fax: 727-669-1289. p. 432

Mortensen, Amy, Head, Adult Serv, ILL Supvr, Ref Librn, Twin Falls Public Library, 201 Fourth Ave E, Twin Falls, ID, 83301-6397. Tel: 208-733-2964. Fax: 208-733-2965. p. 584

Mortensen, Annabelle, Doc, Skokie Public Library, 5215 Oakton St, Skokie, IL, 60077-3680. Tel: 847-673-7774. Fax: 847-673-7797. p. 703

Mortensen, Belinda, Coll Develop Mgr, Westerville Public Library, 126 S State St, Westerville, OH, 43081-2095. Tel: 614-882-7277, Ext 2131. Fax: 614-882-4160. p. 1946

Mortensen, Heidi J, Med Librn, Sutter Roseville Medical Center Library, One Medical Plaza, Roseville, CA, 95661-3037. Tel: 916-781-1580. Fax: 916-781-1582. p. 220

Mortensen, Shelley, Asst Librn, Western Manitoba Regional Library, 710 Rosser Ave, Unit 1, Brandon, MB, R7A 0K9, CANADA. Tel: 204-727-6648. Fax: 204-727-4447. p. 2748

Mortenson, Wina, Youth Serv, Galesville Public Library, 16787 S Main St, Galesville, WI, 54630. Tel: 608-582-2552. p. 2593

Mortimer, Leslie, Ref & Coll Develop Librn, Patten Free Library, 33 Summer St, Bath, ME, 04530. Tel: 207-443-5141. Fax: 207-443-3514. p. 976

Morton, Andy, Head, Circ, Librn, Emerging Web Tech, University of Richmond, 28 Westhampton Way, Richmond, VA, 23173. Tel: 804-287-6047. Fax: 804-289-8757. p. 2491

Morton, Christine, Ref, Touro College, 225 Eastview Dr, Central Islip, NY, 11722-4539. Tel: 631-761-7000, 631-761-7150. Fax: 631-761-7159. p. 1605

Morton, Danny, Coordr, AV, Cleveland Community College, 137 S Post Rd, Shelby, NC, 28152. Tel: 704-484-4032. Fax: 704-484-4036. p. 1823

Morton, Denise, Dir, Omaha Correctional Center Library, 2323 East Ave J, Omaha, NE, 68111. Tel: 402-595-3964. Fax: 402-595-2227. p. 1413

Morton, Judy, Asst Br Librn, Pottawatomie Wabaunsee Regional Library, Eskridge Branch, 115 S Main St, Eskridge, KS, 66423. Tel: 785-449-2296. Fax: 785-449-2296. p. 893

Morton, Kathy, Librn, Clairmont Presbyterian Church Library, 1994 Clairmont Rd, Decatur, GA, 30033. Tel: 404-248-0187. Fax: 404-321-5057. p. 529

Morton, Kerry, Br Head, Toronto Public Library, Alderwood, 2 Orianna Dr, Toronto, ON, M8W 4Y1, CANADA. Tel: 416-394-5310. Fax: 416-394-5313. p. 2860

Morton, Lydia, Dir, Planned Parenthood of Indiana, 200 S Meridian St, Indianapolis, IN, 46206. Tel: 317-637-4377. Fax: 317-637-4378. p. 755

Morton, Muriel, Librn, York Library Region, Oromocto Branch, 54 Miramichi Rd, Oromocto, NB, E2V 1S2, CANADA. Tel: 506-357-3329. Fax: 506-357-5161. p. 2765

Morton, Russell, Dr, Pub Serv, Ashland Theological Seminary, 910 Center St, Ashland, OH, 44805. Tel: 419-289-5169. Fax: 419-289-5969. p. 1855

Morton, Sandra, Br Librn, Roane County Public Library, Geary Library-Health Care Facility, 98 Library Lane, Ste 1, Left Hand, WV, 25251-9744. Tel: 304-565-4608. Fax: 304-565-4608. p. 2572

Morton, Tracy, Br Head, Chatham-Kent Public Library, Merlin Branch, 13 Aberdeen St, Merlin, ON, N0P 1W0, CANADA. Tel: 519-689-4944. p. 2799

Morton, Valerie, Libr Dir, Vinalhaven Public Library, Six Carver St, Vinalhaven, ME, 04863. Tel: 207-863-4401. p. 1004

Morton, Vickie, Asst Dir, Gardendale Martha Moore Public Library, 995 Mt Olive Rd, Gardendale, AL, 35071. Tel: 205-631-6639. Fax: 205-631-0146. p. 18

Morton, Walter, Head, Cat, University of Mississippi Medical Center, 2500 N State St, Jackson, MS, 39216-4505. Tel: 601-984-1273. Fax: 601-984-1251. p. 1305

Morville, Susan, Librn, Washtenaw Community College, 4800 E Huron River Dr, Ann Arbor, MI, 48105-4800. Tel: 734-973-3313. Fax: 734-973-3446. p. 1153

Morwood, Melissa, Sr Librn, Palo Alto City Library, Mitchell Park, 3700 Middlefield Rd, Palo Alto, CA, 94303. Fax: 650-856-7925. p. 204

Moryl, John, Chief Librn, Yeshiva University Libraries, Pollack Library-Landowne Bloom Library, Wilf Campus, 2520 Amsterdam Ave, New York, NY, 10033. Tel: 212-960-5378, 212-960-5379, 212-960-5380. Fax: 212-960-0066. p. 1704

Mosburg, Dianna, Libr Tech, Southwestern Oklahoma State University, O H McMahan Library, 409 E Mississippi, Sayre, OK, 73662. Tel: 580-928-5533, Ext 2157, 580-928-5533, Ext 2185. Fax: 580-928-5533, Ext 2135. p. 1986

Mosby, Elizabeth, ILL, Ref, Oakwood College, 7000 Adventist Blvd, Huntsville, AL, 35896. Tel: 256-726-7246. Fax: 256-726-7538. p. 22

Moschberger, Grace, Br Mgr, Middletown Public Library, Navesink Branch, 149 Monmouth Ave, Navesink, NJ, 07752. Tel: 732-291-1120. p. 1502

Moscheni, Marinella, Librn, National Bureau of Economic Research, Inc Library, 365 Fifth Ave, 5th Flr, New York, NY, 10016-4309. Tel: 212-817-7955. Fax: 212-817-1597. p. 1687

Moscoso-Guzman, Nancy, In Charge, New Haven Free Public Library, Seymour Wilson Branch, 303 Washington St, New Haven, CT, 06511. Tel: 203-946-2226. Fax: 203-946-6540. p. 356

Moseley, Loretta, Adminr, National Park Service, Corner of Broadway & Ripley, PO Box 517, Mountainair, NM, 87036-0517. Tel: 505-847-2585. Fax: 505-847-2441. p. 1560

Moseley, Michelle, Educ Adminr, Mus Spec, Tampa Museum of Art, 120 W Gasparilla Plaza, Tampa, FL, 33602. Tel: 813-274-8130. Fax: 813-274-8732. p. 498

Moseley, Sandy, Br Mgr, Levy County Public Library System, Bronson Public, 600 Gilbert St, Bronson, FL, 32621. Tel: 352-486-2015. Fax: 352-486-2015. p. 430

Moseley, Sue, ILL Coordr, Hubbard Free Library, 115 Second St, Hallowell, ME, 04347. Tel: 207-622-6582. p. 987

Moser, Beth, ILL, Supvr, Tech Serv, Bard College at Simon's Rock, 84 Alford Rd, Great Barrington, MA, 01230. Tel: 413-528-7356. Fax: 413-528-7380. p. 1092

Moser, Kristen, Libr Spec, Umpqua Community College Library, 1140 Umpqua College Rd, Roseburg, OR, 97470. Tel: 541-440-7682. Fax: 541-440-4637. p. 2017

Moser, Mary Jean, Access Serv Mgr, Bucknell University, Circulation, Library & Information Technology, 130 Bertrand Library, Lewisburg, PA, 17837. Tel: 570-577-1882, 570-577-3287. p. 2080

Moser, Sarah, Info Serv, Newburyport Public Library, 94 State St, Newburyport, MA, 01950-6619. Tel: 978-465-4428. Fax: 978-463-0394. p. 1109

Moses, Colleen, Mgr, Cobb County Public Library System, Kemp Memorial, 4029 Due West Rd NW, Marietta, GA, 30064. Tel: 770-528-2527. Fax: 770-528-2592. p. 543

Moses, Deloris, Supv Librn, Western Region, Newark Public Library, Five Washington St, Newark, NJ, 07101. Tel: 973-733-7751. Fax: 973-733-5648. p. 1511

Moses, Deloris, Br Mgr, Newark Public Library, Weequahic, 355 Osborne Terrace, Newark, NJ, 07112. Tel: 973-733-7751. Fax: 973-733-7802. p. 1512

Moses, Fran, Asst Librn, Walpole Town Library, Bridge Memorial Library, 48 Main St, Walpole, NH, 03608. Tel: 603-756-9806. Fax: 603-756-3140. p. 1466

Moses, Ginny, Dir, Babcock Library, 25 Pompey Hollow Rd, Ashford, CT, 06278. Tel: 860-487-4420. Fax: 860-487-4438. p. 329

Moses, James, Regional Mgr, Saint Louis Public Library, Buder, 4401 Hampton Ave, Saint Louis, MO, 63109-2237. Tel: 314-352-2900. Fax: 314-352-5387. p. 1360

Moses, Sherod, Syst Analyst, Virginia State University, One Hayden Dr, Petersburg, VA, 23806-0001. Tel: 804-524-5942. Fax: 804-524-6959. p. 2484

Mosey, Anne, Cataloger, Wells Public Library, 1434 Post Rd, Wells, ME, 04090-4508. Tel: 207-646-8181, Ext. 207. Fax: 207-646-5636. p. 1006

Mosey-Bunch, Rosemary, Dir, Allan Shivers Library & Museum, 302 N Charlton St, Woodville, TX, 75979. Tel: 409-283-3709. Fax: 409-283-5258. p. 2401

Mosher, Beth, Cataloger, Clinton Public Library, 306 Eighth Ave S, Clinton, IA, 52732. Tel: 563-242-8441. Fax: 563-242-8162. p. 803

Mosher, Elaine C, Libr Coordr, The Women & Children's Hospital of Buffalo, 118 Hodge Ave, Buffalo, NY, 14222. Tel: 716-878-7304. Fax: 716-878-1987. p. 1600

Mosher, Ellen, Circ, Kettering College, 3737 Southern Blvd, Kettering, OH, 45429-1299. Tel: 937-395-8053, Ext 3. Fax: 937-395-8861. p. 1907

Mosher, Kathy, Libr Dir, Skaneateles Library Association, 49 E Genesee, Skaneateles, NY, 13152. Tel: 315-685-5135. p. 1744

Mosher, Laura, Ref Librn, United States Military Academy Library, Jefferson Hall Library & Learning Center, 758 Cullum Rd, West Point, NY, 10996. Tel: 845-938-3833. Fax: 845-938-4000. p. 1767

Moshfegh, Mahnaz, Acq/Ser Librn, Indiana University, Ruth Lilly Law Library, 530 W New York St, Indianapolis, IN, 46202-3225. Tel: 317-274-3884, 317-274-4028. Fax: 317-274-8825. p. 752

Moshier, Caleb, Ad, Plattsburgh Public Library, 19 Oak St, Plattsburgh, NY, 12901-2810. Tel: 518-563-0921. Fax: 518-563-1681. p. 1719

Moshiri, Farhad L, AV, University of the Incarnate Word, 4301 Broadway, UPO Box 297, San Antonio, TX, 78209-6397. Tel: 210-829-3842. Fax: 210-829-6041. p. 2384

Mosier, Cindy, Assoc Librn, Scott County Library System, Buffalo Branch, 329 Dodge St, Buffalo, IA, 52728. Tel: 563-381-1797. Fax: 563-381-1797. p. 813

Mosier, Eric M, Librn, San Diego Miramar College, 10440 Black Mountain Rd, San Diego, CA, 92126-2999. Tel: 619-388-7622. Fax: 619-388-7918. p. 235

Mosier, Kreg, Web Serv, Stephen F Austin State University, 1936 North St, Nacogdoches, TX, 75962. Tel: 936-468-2853. Fax: 936-468-7610. p. 2364

Mosier, Pearl, Circ, Sun Prairie Public Library, 1350 Linnerud Dr, Sun Prairie, WI, 53590-2631. Tel: 608-825-7323. Fax: 608-825-3936. p. 2641

Mosier, Shawna, Story Time Dir, Towanda Public Library, 620 Highland, Towanda, KS, 67144-9042. Tel: 316-536-2464. Fax: 316-536-2847. p. 898

Mosing, Steve, Automation Syst Mgr, Rochester Public Library, 101 Second St SE, Rochester, MN, 55904-3776. Tel: 507-328-2361. Fax: 507-328-2384. p. 1273

Moskal, Frederieke A, Head, Tech Serv, Lewis University Library, One University Pkwy, Unit 300, Romeoville, IL, 60446-2200. Tel: 815-836-5302. Fax: 815-838-9456. p. 698

Moskal, Robin, Assoc Dir, University of Maryland, Baltimore County, 1000 Hilltop Circle, Baltimore, MD, 21250. Tel: 410-455-2356. Fax: 410-455-1598. p. 1018

Moskala, Suzanne, Librn, United States Army, West Point Post Library, 622 Swift Rd, West Point, NY, 10996-1981. Tel: 845-938-2974. Fax: 845-938-3019. p. 1767

Moskovitz, Carolyn, Br Mgr, Alameda County Library, Castro Valley Branch, 3600 Norbridge Ave, Castro Valley, CA, 94546-5878. Tel: 510-667-7900. Fax: 510-537-5991. p. 149

Moskowitz Brown, Michelle, Operations Dir, Council of Archives & Research Libraries in Jewish Studies, 330 Seventh Ave, 21st Flr, New York, NY, 10001. Tel: 212-629-0500. Fax: 212-629-0508. p. 2950

Moskowitz, Nancy, Coll Develop Librn, New City Free Library, 220 N Main St, New City, NY, 10956. Tel: 845-634-4997. p. 1665

Moskowitz, Paula, Coordr, Info Literacy, Manhattanville College Library, 2900 Purchase St, Purchase, NY, 10577. Tel: 914-323-3159. Fax: 914-323-8139. p. 1724

Moskowitz, Rhoda, Librn, Metro West Medical Center, 67 Union St, Natick, MA, 01760. Tel: 508-650-7000, Ext 7255. Fax: 508-650-7669. p. 1107

Moskowitz, Vivian, Ref, Yeshiva University Libraries, Hedi Steinberg Library, 245 Lexington Ave, New York, NY, 10016. Tel: 212-340-7720. Fax: 212-340-7808. p. 1704

Mosler, J Rona, Dir, Hackettstown Free Public Library, 110 Church St, Hackettstown, NJ, 07840. Tel: 908-852-4936. Fax: 908-852-7850. p. 1489

Mosley, Christina, Asst Dir, Youth Serv Librn, Morristown-Hamblen Library, 417 W Main St, Morristown, TN, 37814-4686. Tel: 423-586-6410. Fax: 423-587-6226. p. 2253

Mosley, Melinda, Admin Serv Librn, United States Military Academy Library, Jefferson Hall Library & Learning Center, 758 Cullum Rd, West Point, NY, 10996. Tel: 845-938-3833. Fax: 845-938-4000. p. 1767

Mosley, Nancy, Cataloger, Mint Museum Library, 2730 Randolph Rd, Charlotte, NC, 28207. Tel: 704-337-2000, 704-337-2023. Fax: 704-337-2101. p. 1783

Mosley, Wanda, Asst Dir, Mississippi College, 101 W College St, Clinton, MS, 39058. Tel: 601-925-3729. Fax: 601-925-3435. p. 1296

Mospan, Jane, Librn, Pocahontas County Free Libraries, Green Bank Branch, Main St, Rte 28, Green Bank, WV, 24944. Tel: 304-456-4507. Fax: 304-456-4507. p. 2565

Mosquera, Clara, Res, Kirkland & Ellis LLP Library, 300 N LaSalle St, 11th Flr, Chicago, IL, 60654. Tel: 312-862-3189. Fax: 312-862-2200. p. 616

Moss, Alison, Head, Ref, Tippecanoe County Public Library, 627 South St, Lafayette, IN, 47901-1470. Tel: 765-429-0100. Fax: 765-429-0150. p. 759

Moss, Ann, Librn, Saint Martin's Episcopal Church, 717 Sage Rd, Houston, TX, 77056. Tel: 713-621-3040. Fax: 713-622-5701. p. 2342

Moss, Anna Leta, Circ, Lipscomb University, One University Park Dr, Nashville, TN, 37204-3951. Tel: 615-966-5717. Fax: 615-966-5874. p. 2257

Moss, Barbara, In Charge, Laws Railroad Museum & Historical Site Library, Library & Arts Bldg, Silver Canyon Rd, Bishop, CA, 93515. Tel: 760-873-5950. p. 129

Moss, Betty, Tech Serv, Chesterfield County Library, 119 W Main St, Chesterfield, SC, 29709-1512. Tel: 843-623-7489. Fax: 843-623-3295. p. 2186

Moss, Constance, Asst Dir, Nicholson Memorial Library System, 625 Austin St, Garland, TX, 75040-6365. Tel: 972-205-2500. Fax: 972-205-2523. p. 2327

Moss, Debbie, Asst Dir, Orange County Library District, 101 E Central Blvd, Orlando, FL, 32801. Tel: 407-835-7323. p. 476

Moss, Felicia L, Info Mgr/Libr Dir, United States Merit Systems Protection Board Library, 1615 M St NW, Washington, DC, 20036. Tel: 202-653-6772, Ext 1212. Fax: 202-653-6182. p. 420

Moss, Jane, Ch, Newbury Public Library, 933 Rte 103, Newbury, NH, 03255-5803. Tel: 603-763-5803. Fax: 603-763-5803. p. 1460

Moss, Janet, Head Law Librn, University of New Brunswick Libraries, Gerard V La Forest Law Library, Ludlow Hall, 2nd Flr, 41 Dineen Dr, Fredericton, NB, E3B 5A3, CANADA. Tel: 506-442-3266. Fax: 506-451-6948, 506-453-5186. p. 2764

Moss, Jocelyn, Librn, Marin History Museum Library, 1125 B St, San Rafael, CA, 94901. Tel: 415-454-8538. Fax: 415-454-6137. p. 257

Moss, Julie, Librn, Anshe Chesed Fairmount Temple, 23737 Fairmount Blvd, Beachwood, OH, 44122-2296. Tel: 216-464-1330, Ext 123. Fax: 216-464-3628. p. 1858

Moss, Kate, Circ, ILL, Ref, College of Saint Rose, 392-396 Western Ave, Albany, NY, 12203. Tel: 518-454-2154. Fax: 518-454-2897. p. 1568

Moss, Kristine, Asst Librn, Sheridan County Library, 801 Royal Ave, Hoxie, KS, 67740. Tel: 785-675-3102. p. 872

Moss, Laurel, Tech Serv, The Blue Mountains Public Library, 173 Bruce St S, Thornbury, ON, N0H 2P0, CANADA. Tel: 519-599-3681. Fax: 519-599-7951. p. 2847

Moss, Laurie A, Youth Serv Dir, Peru Public Library, 1409 11th St, Peru, IL, 61354. Tel: 815-223-0229. Fax: 815-223-1559. p. 691

Moss, Maria, Dir, Linwood Public Library, 301 Davis Ave, Linwood, NJ, 08221. Tel: 609-926-7991. Fax: 609-927-6147. p. 1495

Moss, Mary, Head, Coll Serv, Elmwood Park Public Library, One Conti Pkwy, Elmwood Park, IL, 60707. Tel: 708-395-1204. Fax: 708-453-4671. p. 643

Moss, Melba, Br Coordr, Saint Clair County Library System, 210 McMorran Blvd, Port Huron, MI, 48060-4098. Tel: 810-987-7323, Ext 136. Fax: 810-987-7874. p. 1219

Moss, Patricia, Br Supvr, Jackson/Hinds Library System, Lois A Flagg Library, 105 Williamson Ave, Edwards, MS, 39066-0140. Tel: 601-852-2230. Fax: 601-852-4539. p. 1303

Moss, Patsy G, Coordr, SCANA Corp/South Carolina Electric & Gas Co, Palmetto Ctr, 1426 Main St, Columbia, SC, 29201. Tel: 803-217-9942. Fax: 803-933-8067. p. 2188

Moss, Rick, Chief Curator, Oakland Public Library, 125 14th St, Oakland, CA, 94612. Tel: 510-637-0197. Fax: 510-637-0204. p. 197

Moss, Rick, Chief Curator, African Am Mus & Libr, Oakland Public Library, Main Library, 125 14th St, Oakland, CA, 94612. Tel: 510-238-3134. Fax: 510-238-2232. p. 198

Moss, Sonja, ILL, San Mateo Public Library, 1100 Park Ave, San Mateo, CA, 94403-7108. Tel: 650-522-7802. Fax: 650-522-7801. p. 256

Moss, Stuart, Dir, Nathan S Kline Institute for Psychiatric Research, 140 Old Orangeburg Rd, Bldg 35, Orangeburg, NY, 10962. Tel: 845-398-6576. Fax: 845-398-5551. p. 1711

Moss, Susan, Ref, Tech Serv, New Jersey Department of Law & Public Safety, 25 Market St, West Wing, 6th Flr, Trenton, NJ, 08625. Tel: 609-292-4958. Fax: 609-633-6555. p. 1535

Mossbeck, Thomas, Res Serv, National Model Railroad Association, 4121 Cromwell Rd, Chattanooga, TN, 37421-2119. Tel: 423-894-8144. Fax: 423-899-4869. p. 2228

Mosser, Janice, Dir, Portland District Library, 334 Kent St, Portland, MI, 48875-1735. Tel: 517-647-6981. Fax: 517-647-2738. p. 1220

Mosser, Shari, Head, Doc Delivery/ILL, North Dakota State Library, Library Memorial Bldg, 604 East Blvd Ave, Dept 250, Bismarck, ND, 58505-0800. Tel: 701-328-3252. Fax: 701-328-2040. p. 1838

Mossman, Katherine A, Asst Dir, Head, Adult Serv, Ref, Everett Public Library, 2702 Hoyt Ave, Everett, WA, 98201-3556. Tel: 425-257-8022. Fax: 425-257-8017. p. 2515

Mosson, Leslie, Librn, Allan Hancock College, 800 S College Dr, Santa Maria, CA, 93454. Tel: 805-922-6966, Ext 3758. Fax: 805-922-3763. p. 265

Most, Gregory, Image Coll, National Gallery of Art Library, Fourth St & Constitution Ave NW, Washington, DC, 20565. Tel: 202-842-6511. Fax: 202-789-3068. p. 409

Most, Linda, Asst Prof, Valdosta State University, Odum Library - MLIS, 1500 N Patterson St, Valdosta, GA, 31698-0144. Tel: 229-245-6534. Fax: 229-259-5055. p. 2964

Most, Marguerite, Ref Librn, Duke University Libraries, School of Law Library, 210 Science Dr, Durham, NC, 27708. Tel: 919-613-7120. Fax: 919-613-7237. p. 1788

Mostashari, Zary, PhD, Dean, Marymount University, 2807 N Glebe Rd, Arlington, VA, 22207-4299. Tel: 703-284-1533. Fax: 703-284-1685. p. 2449

Mostek, Susan, Dir of Develop, Interim Exec Dir, Phoenixville Public Library, 183 Second Ave, Phoenixville, PA, 19460-3420. Tel: 610-933-3013. Fax: 610-933-4338. p. 2120

Mosteller, Allen, Pub Serv, Ref Serv, Cleveland Community College, 137 S Post Rd, Shelby, NC, 28152. Tel: 704-484-4000. Fax: 704-484-4036. p. 1823

Mosura, Andrew, Head, Adult Serv, ILL, Ref Serv, Orland Park Public Library, 14921 Ravinia Ave, Orland Park, IL, 60462. Tel: 708-428-5100. Fax: 708-349-8322. p. 686

Mote, Terri, Ref, Bellaire City Library, 5111 Jessamine, Bellaire, TX, 77401-4498. Tel: 713-662-8160. Fax: 713-662-8169. p. 2288

Motiey, Haleh, Mgr, California State Library, 1600 Holloway Ave, San Francisco, CA, 94132. Tel: 415-469-6100. p. 241

Motley, Nobue, Head, Tech Serv, Notre Dame Seminary Library, 2901 S Carrollton Ave, New Orleans, LA, 70118-4391. Tel: 504-866-7426, Ext 3700. Fax: 504-866-6260. p. 962

Motlong, Alice, Librn, Sioux Narrows Public Library, PO Box 417, Sioux Narrows, ON, P0X 1N0, CANADA. Tel: 807-226-5204. Fax: 807-226-5712. p. 2842

Mott, Darlene, Pub Serv, Texas State Library & Archives Commission, Sam Houston Regional Library & Research Center, 650 FM 1011, Liberty, TX, 77575. Tel: 936-336-8821. p. 2283

Mott, Diane, Dir, Saint Dominic-Jackson Memorial Hospital, 969 Lakeland Dr, Jackson, MS, 39216. Tel: 601-200-6944. Fax: 601-200-8075. p. 1305

Mott, Judy, Libr Mgr, Seba Beach Public Library, 140 3rd St, Seba Beach, AB, T0E 2B0, CANADA. Tel: 780-797-3940. Fax: 780-797-3800. p. 2716

Motte, Flora, Librn, Emery County Library, Huntington Branch, 92 S Main, Huntington, UT, 84528. Tel: 435-687-9590. Fax: 435-687-9510. p. 2404

Motte, Kristin, Dir, Libr Serv, New England College of Optometry Library, 424 Beacon St, Boston, MA, 02115. Tel: 617-589-5658. Fax: 617-587-5573. p. 1064

Motte, Kristin, Asst Dir, Head, Info Serv, Wentworth Institute of Technology, 550 Huntington Ave, Boston, MA, 02115-5998. Tel: 617-989-4092. Fax: 617-989-4091. p. 1068

Motter, Laura, Asst Law Librn, Dauphin County Law Library, Dauphin County Courthouse, Front & Market Sts, 4th Flr, Harrisburg, PA, 17101. Tel: 717-780-6605. Fax: 717-780-6481. p. 2064

Mottinger, Rosemary Claire, Dir, Burlington Township Library, 135 Elm St, Burlington, MI, 49029. Tel: 517-765-2702. Fax: 517-765-2702. p. 1160

Motus, Arlene, Circ, Dormont Public Library, 2950 W Liberty Ave, Pittsburgh, PA, 15216-2594. Tel: 412-531-8754. Fax: 412-531-1601. p. 2125

Motuzick, Stasia, Librn, Harwinton Public Library, 80 Bentley Dr, Harwinton, CT, 06791. Tel: 860-485-9113. Fax: 860-485-2713. p. 348

Motz, Kristen, Libr Instruction, Ferris State University Library, 1010 Campus Dr, Big Rapids, MI, 49307-2279. Tel: 231-591-3500. Fax: 231-591-3724. p. 1158

Moudry, Mary Lou, Exec Dir, Crow Wing County Historical Society Archives Library, 320 Laurel St, Brainerd, MN, 56401-3523. Tel: 218-829-3268. Fax: 218-828-4434. p. 1242

Moukdad, Haidar, Dr, Assoc Prof, Dalhousie University, 6100 University Ave, Halifax, NS, B3H 3J5, CANADA. Tel: 902-494-3656. Fax: 902-494-2451. p. 2978

Moul, Rick, Exec Dir, Partnership Among South Carolina Academic Libraries, 1333 Main St, Ste 305, Columbia, SC, 29201. Tel: 803-734-0900. Fax: 803-734-0901. p. 2955

Moulaison, Heather Lea, Asst Prof, University of Missouri-Columbia, 303 Townsend Hall, Columbia, MO, 65211. Tel: 573-882-4546. Fax: 573-884-2917. p. 2969

Mouland, Tracy, Tech Serv, College of the North Atlantic, Bonavista Campus, PO Box 670, Bonavista, NL, A0C 1B0, CANADA. Tel: 709-468-1716. Fax: 709-468-2004. p. 2771

Mould, Louise, Librn, Holland College Library Services, 140 Weymouth St, Charlottetown, PE, C1A 4Z1, CANADA. Tel: 902-566-9558. Fax: 902-566-9522. p. 2875

Mould, Mary, Pub Relations, Teen Serv, Loudonville Public Library, 122 E Main St, Loudonville, OH, 44842-1267. Tel: 419-994-5531. Fax: 419-994-4321. p. 1911

Moulden, Carol, Librn, National Louis University Library & Learning Support, North Shore, 5202 Old Orchard Rd, Skokie, IL, 60077. Tel: 224-233-2235. Fax: 224-233-2288. p. 619

Moulding, Janet, Dir, Forbes Library, 20 West St, Northampton, MA, 01060-3798. Tel: 413-587-1011. Fax: 413-587-1015. p. 1113

Moulds, Loren, Digital Coll Librn, University of Virginia, Arthur J Morris Law Library, 580 Massie Rd, Charlottesville, VA, 22903-1789. Tel: 434-924-3877. Fax: 434-982-2232. p. 2455

Moulton, Candy, In Charge, Grand Encampment Museum, Inc Library, 807 Barnett Ave, Encampment, WY, 82325. Tel: 307-327-5308. p. 2654

Moulton, David, Dir, Strayer University, 1133 15th St NW, Washington, DC, 20005. Tel: 202-833-0542. Fax: 202-419-1463. p. 416

Moulton Janssen, Marlene, Dir, Anoka County Library, 707 County Rd 10 NE, Blaine, MN, 55434-2398. Tel: 763-785-3695. Fax: 763-717-3262. p. 1241

Moulton, Joan, Libr Dir, Blanche R Solomon Memorial Library, 17 Park St, Headland, AL, 36345. Tel: 334-693-2706. Fax: 334-693-5023. p. 20

Moulton, Maria, Dir, Ossipee Public Library, 74 Main St, Center Ossipee, NH, 03814. Tel: 603-539-6390. Fax: 603-539-5758. p. 1440

Moulton-Gertig, Suzanne, Dr, Head Music Librn, Prof, University of Denver, Music Library, 2344 E Iliff Ave, Denver, CO, 80208. Tel: 303-871-6421. Fax: 303-871-6886. p. 304

Mounce, Michael, Ref, Delta State University, Laflore Circle at Fifth Ave, Cleveland, MS, 38733-2599. Tel: 662-846-4440. Fax: 662-846-4443. p. 1296

Mounger, Roben, Asst Dir, Buffalo River Regional Library, 104 E Sixth St, Columbia, TN, 38401-3359. Tel: 931-388-9282. Fax: 931-388-1762. p. 2231

Mounier, Susan, Dir, Gloucester County Library System, Newfield Public, 115 Catawba Ave, Newfield, NJ, 08344-9511. Tel: 856-697-0415. Fax: 856-697-1544. p. 1507

Mount, Davina, Dir, Brantley Public Library, 9042 W Emmett Ave, Brantley, AL, 36009. Tel: 334-527-8624. Fax: 334-527-3216. p. 10

Mount, Joe, Acad Librn, Winona State University, 175 W Mark St, Winona, MN, 55987-5838. Tel: 507-457-5147. p. 1290

Mount, Lisa, Interim Dir, Clovis-Carver Public Library, 701 N Main, Clovis, NM, 88101. Tel: 505-769-7840. Fax: 505-769-7842. p. 1553

Mount, Patty, Mgr, Irving Public Library, Valley Ranch, 401 Cimmaron Trail, Irving, TX, 75063-4680. Tel: 972-721-4669. Fax: 972-831-0672. p. 2347

Mountain, Candace, Asst Dir, Richmond Free Public Library, 2821 State Rd, Richmond, MA, 01254-9472. Tel: 413-698-3834. p. 1120

Mountain, Mary, Exec Dir, Laramie Plains Museum Association Inc Library, 603 Ivinson Ave, Laramie, WY, 82070-3299. Tel: 307-742-4448. p. 2657

Mountain, Pam, Br Head, Toronto Public Library, Annette Street, 145 Annette St, Toronto, ON, M6P 1P3, CANADA. Tel: 416-393-7692. Fax: 416-393-7412. p. 2860

Mountain, Tim, Adult Serv, Ref, Fullerton Public Library, 353 W Commonwealth Ave, Fullerton, CA, 92832-1796. Tel: 714-738-6325. Fax: 714-447-3280. p. 154

Mountney, Sherry, Librn, Tamarack District Library, 832 S Lincoln Ave, Lakeview, MI, 48850. Tel: 989-352-6274. Fax: 989-352-7713. p. 1199

Mounts, Earl, Librn, Alcoa Technical Center Library, 100 Technical Dr, Alcoa Center, PA, 15069-0001. Tel: 724-337-2396, 724-337-5300. Fax: 724-337-2394. p. 2026

Mounts, Mark, Ref Librn, Dartmouth College Library, Feldberg Business Administration & Engineering Library, 6193 Murdough Ctr, Hanover, NH, 03755-3560. Tel: 603-646-2191. Fax: 603-646-2384. p. 1450

Mousseau, V Lynn, Cataloger, Ser Librn, Kansas City University of Medicine & Biosciences D'Angelo Library, 1750 Independence Ave, Kansas City, MO, 64106-1453. Tel: 816-654-7265. Fax: 816-654-7261. p. 1338

Moutenot, Anne, Tech Serv, North Indian River County Library, 1001 Sebastian Blvd, CR 512, Sebastian, FL, 32958. Tel: 772-589-1355. Fax: 772-388-3697. p. 491

Mouton, Kirsten, Br Mgr, San Bernardino County Library, Needles Branch, 1111 Bailey Rd, Needles, CA, 92363. Tel: 760-326-9255. Fax: 760-326-9238. p. 228

Moutseous, Margaret, Librn, Ivy Tech Community College, 3501 First Ave, Evansville, IN, 47710-3398. Tel: 812-429-1412. Fax: 812-429-9802. p. 739

Mouw, James, Assoc Univ Librn, Coll Serv, University of Chicago Library, 1100 E 57th St, Chicago, IL, 60637-1502. Tel: 773-702-8732. Fax: 773-702-6623. p. 626

Mowatt, Cheryle, Ref, Swan Library, Four N Main St, Albion, NY, 14411. Tel: 585-589-4246. Fax: 585-589-2473. p. 1571

Mowatt, Colleen, Br Head, Toronto Public Library, Oakwood Village Library & Arts Centre, 341 Oakwood Ave, Toronto, ON, M6E 2W1, CANADA. Tel: 416-394-1040. Fax: 416-394-1039. p. 2862

Mowdy, Brenda S, Librn, John B Curtis Free Public Library, 435 Main Rd, Bradford, ME, 04410. Tel: 207-327-2923. p. 978

Mowen, Mary Beth, Asst Librn, Keyser-Mineral County Public Library, 105 N Main St, Keyser, WV, 26726. Tel: 304-788-3222. Fax: 304-788-3222. p. 2563

Mower, Marion, Tech Serv Coordr, Meaford Public Library, 15 Trowbridge St W, Meaford, ON, N4L 1V4, CANADA. Tel: 519-538-1060, Ext 1123. Fax: 519-538-1808. p. 2821

Mowers, Susan, Dir, University of Ottawa Libraries, Map, Government Information & Data, Morisset Hall, 65 University, No 308, Ottawa, ON, K1N 9A5, CANADA. Tel: 613-562-5211. Fax: 613-562-5195. p. 2834

Mowery, Jack, Mobile Serv Mgr, Gallia County District Library, Seven Spruce St, Gallipolis, OH, 45631. Tel: 740-446-7323. Fax: 740-446-1701. p. 1901

Mowery, Mary, Access Serv, Shippensburg University, 1871 Old Main Dr, Shippensburg, PA, 17257-2299. Tel: 717-477-1461. Fax: 717-477-1389. p. 2140

Mowery, Rose, Librn, Brumback Library, Willshire Branch, 323 State St, Willshire, OH, 45898. Tel: 419-495-4138. p. 1943

Moxley, Clint, Br Mgr, Ohoopee Regional Library System, Ladson Genealogical Library, 125 Church St, Ste 104, Vidalia, GA, 30474. Tel: 912-537-8186. Fax: 912-537-8186. p. 556

Moxley, Melody A, Libr Serv Mgr, Rowan Public Library, 201 W Fisher St, Salisbury, NC, 28144-4935. Tel: 704-216-8230. Fax: 704-216-8237. p. 1822

Moxness, Mary J, Head Librn, Saint Mary's University of Minnesota, 700 Terrace Heights, No 26, Winona, MN, 55987-1399. Tel: 507-457-1561. Fax: 507-457-1565. p. 1289

Moxon, Jane, Librn, PricewaterhouseCoopers Library, 200-250 Howe St, Vancouver, BC, V6C 3S7, CANADA. Tel: 604-806-7087. Fax: 604-806-7806. p. 2742

Moxon, John, Tech Coordr, Rhinelander District Library, 106 N Stevens St, Rhinelander, WI, 54501-3193. Tel: 715-365-1070. Fax: 715-365-1076. p. 2633

Moxon, Kristine, Asst Librn, Nassau Free Library, 18 Church St, Nassau, NY, 12123-2704. Tel: 518-766-2715. Fax: 518-766-2715. p. 1664

Moy, Gene P, Govt Doc, Ref Librn, University of Detroit Mercy Library, Kresge Law Library, 651 E Jefferson, Detroit, MI, 48226. Tel: 313-596-0239. Fax: 313-596-0245. p. 1172

Moy, Naomi, Head, Ref Serv, California State University Dominguez Hills, 1000 E Victoria St, Carson, CA, 90747. Tel: 310-243-2086. Fax: 310-516-4219. p. 132

Moy, Sally, Syst Coordr, University of Detroit Mercy Library, Kresge Law Library, 651 E Jefferson, Detroit, MI, 48226. Tel: 313-596-0239. Fax: 313-596-0245. p. 1172

Moy, Walter, Online Serv, New York State Supreme Court, First Judicial District Criminal Law Library, 100 Centre St, 17th Flr, New York, NY, 10013. Tel: 646-386-3890, 646-386-3891. Fax: 212-748-7908. p. 1695

Moya, Jesus, Br Mgr, Saint Joseph County Public Library, Western Branch, 611 S Lombardy Dr, South Bend, IN, 46619. Tel: 574-282-4639. p. 779

Moye, Allen, Dir, DePaul University Libraries, Vincent G Rinn Law Library, 25 E Jackson Blvd, 5th Flr, Chicago, IL, 60604-2287. Tel: 312-362-6893. Fax: 312-362-6908. p. 612

Moye, Birdie B, Asst Librn, Pearisburg Public Library, 209 Fort Branch Rd, Pearisburg, VA, 24134. Tel: 540-921-2556. Fax: 540-921-1708. p. 2484

Moye, Stephanie, Ser Librn, Smithsonian Libraries, Smithsonian American Art Museum/National Portrait Gallery Library, Victor Bldg, Rm 2100, MRC 975, 750 Ninth St NW, Washington, DC, 20560. Tel: 202-633-8231. Fax: 202-633-8232. p. 415

Moye, Tanya, Mgr, Woodlawn Library, 2020 W Ninth St, Wilmington, DE, 19805. Tel: 302-571-7425. Fax: 302-571-7320. p. 389

Moyer, Alex, Head Librn, Montgomery College, Germantown Campus Library, 20200 Observation Dr, Germantown, MD, 20876. Tel: 301-353-7850. Fax: 301-353-7859. p. 1037

Moyer, Allison, Asst Dir, Pub Serv, Henry County Public Library System, 1001 Florence McGarity Blvd, McDonough, GA, 30252. Tel: 678-462-4346. Fax: 678-432-6153. p. 544

Moyer, Debora, Coordr, Jackson Community College, 2111 Emmons Rd, Jackson, MI, 49201-8399. Tel: 517-796-8621. Fax: 517-796-8623. p. 1195

Moyer, Eileen, Info Serv Librn, Tufts University, 145 Harrison Ave, Boston, MA, 02111-1843. Tel: 617-636-2466. Fax: 617-636-4039. p. 1068

Moyer, Hannah, Cat, United States Senate Library, SRB-15 Senate Russell Bldg, Washington, DC, 20510-7112. Tel: 202-224-7106. Fax: 202-224-0879. p. 421

Moyer, Harriet, Pub Serv, Montgomery House, 20 Church St, McEwensville, PA, 17749. Tel: 570-538-1381. Fax: 570-538-1381. p. 2085

Moyer, Jane S, Librn, Northampton County Historical & Genealogical Society, 342 Northampton St, Easton, PA, 18042. Tel: 610-253-1222. Fax: 610-253-4701. p. 2052

Moyer, Lisa, Circ, Penn State Erie, 4951 College Dr, Erie, PA, 16563-4115. Tel: 814-898-6106. Fax: 814-898-6350. p. 2056

Moyer, Sue, Librn, Scio Free Library, PO Box 77, Scio, NY, 14880-0075. Tel: 585-593-4816. Fax: 585-593-4816. p. 1741

Moyer, Susan, Dir, Dorothy Bramlage Public Library, 230 W Seventh, Junction City, KS, 66441-3097. Tel: 785-238-4311. Fax: 785-238-7873. p. 874

Moylan, Betsey, Dept Chair, Head, Ref Serv, University of Scranton, Monroe & Linden, Scranton, PA, 18510-4634. Tel: 570-941-4000, 570-941-4008. Fax: 570-941-7817. p. 2138

Moynihan, Gail, Ch, Deerfield Public Library, 12 W Nelson St, Deerfield, WI, 53531-9669. Tel: 608-764-8102. p. 2588

Moyo, Lesley, Dir of Libr Res & Instrul Serv, Virginia Polytechnic Institute & State University Libraries, Drill Field Dr, Blacksburg, VA, 24062-9001. Tel: 540-231-2708. Fax: 540-231-3946. p. 2451

Mozga, John, Asst Dir, Joliet Public Library, 150 N Ottawa St, Joliet, IL, 60432-4192. Tel: 815-740-2660. Fax: 815-740-6161. p. 660

Mozlack, Charmaine, Coordr, Coll Serv, Carnegie Library of Pittsburgh, 4400 Forbes Ave, Pittsburgh, PA, 15213-4080. Tel: 412-920-4522. Fax: 412-920-4531. p. 2122

Mrazik, Michele, Pub Serv, DeSales University, 2755 Station Ave, Center Valley, PA, 18034. Tel: 610-282-1100, Ext 1266. Fax: 610-282-2342. p. 2043

Mrkich, Francie, Dir, Access Serv, Columbia University, Access Services, Butler Library 207 C, 535 W 114th St, New York, NY, 10027. Tel: 212-854-2245. Fax: 212-854-0089. p. 1674

Mrowka, Timothy, Chairperson, Hartland Public Library, 61 Center St, West Hartland, CT, 06091. Tel: 860-379-0048. p. 376

Mrozowski, Patti, ILL, Penn State Erie, 4951 College Dr, Erie, PA, 16563-4115. Tel: 814-898-6106. Fax: 814-898-6350. p. 2056

Mubiru-Musoke, Margaret, Librn, Massachusetts Correctional Institution-Concord Library, 965 Elm St, Concord, MA, 01742-2119. Tel: 978-369-3220, Ext 292. Fax: 978-405-6108. p. 1083

Muccari, Cesare J, Dir, Greensburg Hempfield Area Library, 237 S Pennsylvania Ave, Greensburg, PA, 15601-3086. Tel: 724-837-5620. Fax: 724-836-0160. p. 2062

Muchow, Carolyn, Sr Librn, Hennepin County Library, Eden Prairie, 565 Prairie Center Dr, Eden Prairie, MN, 55344-5319. Tel: 612-543-6323. Fax: 612-543-6277. p. 1263

Muchow, Michael, Humanities Librn, University of Missouri-Columbia, Elmer Ellis Library, Ellis Library Bldg, Rm 104, Columbia, MO, 65201-5149. Tel: 573-882-6824. Fax: 573-882-8044. p. 1325

Muck, Donna, Librn, Gaylord City Library, 505 Main, Gaylord, KS, 67638-3884. Tel: 785-697-2650. p. 868

Muckerheide, Shayna, Tech Serv & Spec Projects Mgr, Bellevue Public Library, 224 E Main St, Bellevue, OH, 44811-1467. Tel: 419-483-4769. Fax: 419-483-0158. p. 1859

Muckleroy, Patrick, Pub Serv Librn, Western State College, 600 N Adams St, Gunnison, CO, 81231. Tel: 970-943-2054. Fax: 970-943-2042. p. 312

Mudge, James, Libr Tech, Goulston & Storrs, PC, 400 Atlantic Ave, Boston, MA, 02110. Tel: 617-482-1776. p. 1061

Mudgett, Shelly, Librn, Brevard Community College, 250 Community College Pkwy, Palm Bay, FL, 32909. Tel: 321-433-5262. Fax: 321-433-5309. p. 479

Mudie, Monique, Asst Librn, Beaver Valley Public Library, 1847 First St, Fruitvale, BC, V0G 1L0, CANADA. Tel: 250-367-7114. Fax: 250-367-7130. p. 2728

Mudrick, Kris, Per & Shared Res, Saint Joseph's University, Francis A Drexel Library, 5600 City Ave, Philadelphia, PA, 19131-1395. Tel: 610-660-3215. Fax: 610-660-1916. p. 2116

Mudry, Cathy, Circ Supvr, University of Manitoba Libraries, St John's College Library, 92 Dysart Rd, Winnipeg, MB, R3T 2M5, CANADA. Tel: 204-474-8542. Fax: 204-474-7614. p. 2759

Muehlbrad, Catherine, Head, Info Serv, Victoria Public Library, 302 N Main, Victoria, TX, 77901-6592. Tel: 361-485-3304. Fax: 361-485-3295. p. 2395

Muehlhauser, Martha, Libr Tech, Anoka-Ramsey Community College, 300 Spirit River Dr S, Cambridge, MN, 55008. Tel: 763-433-1875. p. 1243

Mueller, Ann, Acq, Monroe Public Library, 925 16th Ave, Monroe, WI, 53566-1497. Tel: 608-328-7010. Fax: 608-329-4657. p. 2623

Mueller, Brenda, Librn, Our Saviour's Lutheran Church Library, 300 Logan, Merrill, WI, 54452. Tel: 715-536-5813. Fax: 715-536-3658. p. 2616

Mueller, Carol, Asst Dir, Bloomfield Township Public Library, 1099 Lone Pine Rd, Bloomfield Township, MI, 48302-2410. Tel: 248-642-5800. Fax: 248-258-2555. p. 1159

Mueller, Debbie, Ref, Boonslick Regional Library, 219 W Third St, Sedalia, MO, 65301-4347. Tel: 660-827-7111. Fax: 660-827-4668. p. 1364

Mueller, Donna, In Charge, Sauk County Law Library, 515 Oak St, Baraboo, WI, 53913. Tel: 608-355-3287. Fax: 608-355-3480. p. 2580

Mueller, Jan, ILL, Kenton County Public Library, William E Durr Branch, 1992 Walton-Nicholson Rd, Independence, KY, 41051. Tel: 859-962-4030. Fax: 859-962-4037. p. 910

Mueller, Joan, Asst Dir, Oshkosh Public Library, 106 Washington Ave, Oshkosh, WI, 54901-4985. Tel: 920-236-5231. Fax: 920-236-5228. p. 2628

Mueller, Laura, Librn, Shriners' Hospital for Children, 2211 N Oak Park Ave, Chicago, IL, 60707. Tel: 773-385-5479. Fax: 773-385-5437. p. 624

Mueller, Libby, Ch, Edith Wheeler Memorial Library, 733 Monroe Tpk, Monroe, CT, 06468. Tel: 203-452-2850. Fax: 203-261-3359. p. 353

Mueller, Linda, Br Mgr, Great River Regional Library, Long Prairie Library, 42 Third St N, Ste 1, Long Prairie, MN, 56347. Tel: 320-732-2332. p. 1275

Mueller, Magda ("Maggi"), Archivist, Saint Paul School of Theology, 5123 E Truman Rd, Kansas City, MO, 64127. p. 1341

Mueller, Mark, Educ Librn, Tyndale University College & Seminary, 25 Ballyconnor Ct, Toronto, ON, M2M 4B3, CANADA. Tel: 416-226-6620, Ext 2227. Fax: 416-218-6765. p. 2864

Mueller, Melanie, Archivist, American Institute of Physics, One Physics Ellipse, College Park, MD, 20740-3843. Tel: 301-209-3177. Fax: 301-209-3144. p. 1024

Mueller, Mitzi, Ch, North Platte Public Library, 120 W Fourth St, North Platte, NE, 69101-3993. Tel: 308-535-8036. Fax: 308-535-8296. p. 1410

Mueller, Nathan, Librn, Northern Virginia Community College Libraries, Manassas Campus, Colgan Hall, Rm 129, 6901 Sudley Rd, Manassas, VA, 20109-2399. Tel: 703-257-6564. Fax: 703-368-1069. p. 2447

Mueller, Raymond, Chief Librn, Wisconsin Conservatory Music Library, 1584 N Prospect Ave, Milwaukee, WI, 53202. Tel: 414-276-5760. Fax: 414-276-6076. p. 2622

Mueller, Rebecca, Outreach Serv Librn, Salem County Library Commission, 900 Rte 45, Bldg 3, Pilesgrove, NJ, 08098. Tel: 856-769-1082. Fax: 856-769-2018. p. 1520

Mueller, Rebecca, Dir, Richmond Free Library, 201 Bridge St, Richmond, VT, 05477. Tel: 802-434-3036. Fax: 802-434-3223. p. 2434

Mueller, Sally W, Dir, Lake Alfred Public Library, 195 E Pomelo St, Lake Alfred, FL, 33850. Tel: 863-291-5378. Fax: 863-965-6386. p. 457

Mueller, Stacy, Ch, New London Public Library, 406 S Pearl St, New London, WI, 54961-1441. Tel: 920-982-8519. Fax: 920-982-8617. p. 2625

Mueller, Susan, Coordr, Coll Serv, University of Nebraska at Kearney, 2508 11th Ave, Kearney, NE, 68849-2240. Tel: 308-865-8853. Fax: 308-865-8722. p. 1403

Mueller, Veronica, Dir, Joseph Patch Library, 320 New Hampshire, Rte 25, Warren, NH, 03279-9716. Tel: 603-764-9072. p. 1467

Mueller-Alexander, Jeanette, Librn, Arizona State University Libraries, Library at the Polytechnic Campus, Academic Ctr, Bldg 20, 5988 S Backus Mall, Mesa, AZ, 85212. Tel: 480-965-3084. Fax: 480-727-1077. p. 84

Muench, Sarah, Ad, Cat Librn, Elm Grove Public Library, 13600 W Juneau Blvd, Elm Grove, WI, 53122-1679. Tel: 262-782-6717. Fax: 262-780-4827. p. 2591

Muether, Elizabeth, Asst Dir, Mercer County District Library, 303 N Main St, Celina, OH, 45822. Tel: 419-586-4442. Fax: 419-586-3222. p. 1866

Muether, John R, Dr, Dir, Libr Serv, Reformed Theological Seminary Library, 1231 Reformation Dr, Oviedo, FL, 32765. Tel: 407-366-9493, Ext 234. Fax: 407-366-9425. p. 478

Muffs, Lauren, Asst Dir, Poughkeepsie Public Library District, 93 Market St, Poughkeepsie, NY, 12601. Tel: 845-485-3445, Ext 3310. Fax: 845-485-3789. p. 1723

Muffs, Lauren, Asst Dir, Poughkeepsie Public Library District, Arlington, 504 Haight Ave, Poughkeepsie, NY, 12603. Tel: 845-485-3445, Ext 3310. Fax: 845-454-9308. p. 1723

Mugford, John, Regional Librn, New Mexico State Library, Library for the Blind & Physically Handicapped, 1209 Camino Carlos Rey, Santa Fe, NM, 87507-5166. Tel: 505-476-9772. Fax: 505-476-9776. p. 1563

Mugridge, Rebecca, Head, Cat, Pennsylvania State University Libraries, 510 Paterno Library, University Park, PA, 16802. Tel: 814-865-0401. Fax: 814-865-3665. p. 2148

MuGuffie, Raeshawn, Acq Librn, Elizabeth City State University, 1704 Weeksville Rd, Elizabeth City, NC, 27909. Tel: 252-335-3431. Fax: 252-335-3446. p. 1790

Muhammad, Brenda, AV, Houston Love Memorial Library, 212 W Burdeshaw St, Dothan, AL, 36303. Tel: 334-793-9767. Fax: 334-793-6645. p. 15

Muhammad, Fayrene, Asst Dir, Rockford Public Library, 215 N Wyman St, Rockford, IL, 61101-1023. Tel: 815-965-7606. Fax: 815-965-0866. p. 697

Muhammad, Khalil Gibran, Dr, Dir, New York Public Library - Astor, Lenox & Tilden Foundations, Schomburg Center for Research in Black Culture, 515 Malcolm X Blvd, New York, NY, 10037-1801. Tel: 212-491-2208. Fax: 212-491-6760. p. 1693

Muhlbach, Cindy, Dir, Brainerd Memorial Library, 920 Saybrook Rd, Haddam, CT, 06438. Tel: 860-345-2204. Fax: 860-345-7735. p. 343

Muhlhauser, Mike, Evening Circ Supvr, Santa Fe Community College, 3000 NW 83rd St, Bldg Y-100, Gainesville, FL, 32606. Tel: 352-395-5406. Fax: 352-395-5102. p. 449

Muhm, Kathy, Asst Dir, Westfield Memorial Library, 550 E Broad St, Westfield, NJ, 07090. Tel: 908-789-4090. Fax: 908-789-0921. p. 1543

Muhr, Charlene, Br Head, Half Hollow Hills Community Library, Melville Branch, 510 Sweet Hollow Rd, Melville, NY, 11747. Tel: 631-421-4535. Fax: 631-421-3715. p. 1615

Muhr, Heiko, Br Coordr, Indiana University Bloomington, Geography & Map Library, Student Bldg 015, 701 E Kirkwood Ave, Bloomington, IN, 47405. Tel: 812-855-1108. Fax: 812-855-4919. p. 727

Muhr, Peter, AV, Lindenhurst Memorial Library, One Lee Ave, Lindenhurst, NY, 11757-5399. Tel: 631-957-7755. Fax: 631-957-7114. p. 1652

Muilenburg, Lisa, Ref Librn, Del Mar College, Barth Learning Resource Center, 4101 Old Brownsville Rd, Corpus Christi, TX, 78405. Tel: 361-698-1742. Fax: 361-698-1795. p. 2302

Muir, Cecilia, Asst Dep Minister, Res Discovery Sector, Library & Archives Canada, 550 De la Cité Blvd, Gatineau, QC, K1A 0N4, CANADA. Tel: 613-992-7059. Fax: 613-992-5315. p. 2883

Muir, Dennis P, Interim Dir, Arizona State University Libraries, Library at the Polytechnic Campus, Academic Ctr, Bldg 20, 5988 S Backus Mall, Mesa, AZ, 85212. Tel: 480-727-1974. Fax: 480-727-1077. p. 84

Muir, Gordon, Assoc Librn, Coordr, Coll Develop & Mgt, State University of New York College at Plattsburgh, Two Draper Ave, Plattsburgh, NY, 12901-2697. Tel: 518-564-5304. Fax: 518-564-5209. p. 1719

Muir, Linda, Head Librn, Coastal Carolina Community College, 444 Western Blvd, Jacksonville, NC, 28546-6877. Tel: 910-455-1221, 910-938-6237. Fax: 910-455-7027. p. 1803

Muir, Mack, Web Coordr, Railway Mail Service Library, Inc, 117 E Main St, Boyce, VA, 22620-9639. Tel: 540-837-9090. p. 2452

Muir, Scott, Dir & Librn, Arizona State University Libraries, Downtown Phoenix Campus Library, UCENT Bldg, Ste L1-62, 411 N Central Ave, Phoenix, AZ, 85004-1213. Tel: 602-496-0311. Fax: 602-496-0312. p. 83

Muirhead, Leslie, Br Mgr, Hamilton Public Library, Dundas Branch, 18 Ogilvie St, Dundas, ON, L9H 2S2, CANADA. Tel: 905-627-3507, Ext 1404. p. 2809

Muirhead, Leslie, Br Mgr, Hamilton Public Library, Greensville, 59 Kirby Ave, Unit 5, Greensville, ON, L9H 4H6, CANADA. Tel: 905-546-3200, Ext 1404. p. 2809

Mujica, Mauro E, Chmn, US English, 1747 Pennsylvania Ave NW, Ste 1050, Washington, DC, 20006-2712. Tel: 202-833-0100. Fax: 202-833-0108. p. 421

Mukooza, Margaret N, Dir, Libr Serv, Morris College, 100 W College St, Sumter, SC, 29150-3599. Tel: 803-934-3230. Fax: 803-778-2923. p. 2206

Mulac, Carolyn, Div Chief, Chicago Public Library, General Information Services Division, 400 S State St, Chicago, IL, 60605. Tel: 312-747-4382. p. 608

Mulak, Lisa, Br Mgr, Cape Breton Regional Library, 50 Falmouth St, Sydney, NS, B1P 6X9, CANADA. Tel: 902-562-3161. Fax: 902-564-0765. p. 2785

Mulawka, Chet, Mgr, San Mateo County Library, San Carlos Library, 610 Elm St, San Carlos, CA, 94070. Tel: 650-591-0341. Fax: 650-591-1585. p. 256

Mulcahy, Julie, Cat, Tech Serv, New Castle Public Library, 207 E North St, New Castle, PA, 16101-3691. Tel: 724-658-6659. Fax: 724-658-7209. p. 2096

Mulcahy, Rita, Librn, Morris Public Library, 102 E Sixth St, Morris, MN, 56267-1211. Tel: 320-589-1634. Fax: 320-589-8892. p. 1267

Mulcrone, Mary Ellen, Asst Dir, Novi Public Library, 45245 W Ten Mile Rd, Novi, MI, 48375. Tel: 248-349-0720. Fax: 248-349-6520. p. 1214

Mulder, Glenda, Dir, Laurens Public Library, 273 N Third St, Laurens, IA, 50554. Tel: 712-841-4612. Fax: 712-841-4612. p. 827

Mulder, Ingrid, Ser, Dordt College, 498 Fourth Ave NE, Sioux Center, IA, 51250. Tel: 712-722-6048. Fax: 712-722-1198. p. 843

Mulder, James, Ref, Missouri Western State University, 4525 Downs Dr, Saint Joseph, MO, 64507-2294. Tel: 816-271-4368. Fax: 816-271-4574. p. 1352

Mulder, Jillian, Curator, Glens Falls-Queensbury Historical Association, 348 Glen St, Glens Falls, NY, 12801. Tel: 518-793-2826. Fax: 518-793-2831. p. 1629

Mulder, Linda, Dir, Flat Rock Public Library, 25200 Gibraltar Rd, Flat Rock, MI, 48134. Tel: 734-782-2430. Fax: 734-789-8265. p. 1178

Mulder, Nancy, Br Mgr, Kent District Library, Comstock Park Branch, 3943 West River Dr NE, Comstock Park, MI, 49321. Tel: 616-784-2007. Fax: 616-647-3864. p. 1165

Mule, Joseph J, Dir, Thayer Memorial Library, 717 Main St, Lancaster, MA, 01523-2248. Tel: 978-368-8928. Fax: 978-368-8929. p. 1097

Mulford, Mary Ann, Adult Serv, Lebanon Public Library, 101 S Broadway, Lebanon, OH, 45036. Tel: 513-932-2665. Fax: 513-932-7323. p. 1909

Mulhall-Briski, Colleen, Libr Assoc, DeVry University, 3880 Kilroy Airport Way, Long Beach, CA, 90806. Tel: 562-997-5351. Fax: 562-997-5389. p. 166

Mulhare, Suzanne, Librn III/Outreach Serv, Beverly Hills Public Library, 444 N Rexford Dr, Beverly Hills, CA, 90210-4877. Tel: 310-288-2220. Fax: 310-278-3387. p. 129

Mulhare, Suzanne, Ref Librn, Beverly Hills Public Library, 471 S Roxbury Dr, Beverly Hills, CA, 90212-4113. Tel: 310-288-2261, 310-550-4947. p. 129

Mulhern, Jean, PhD, Dir, Wilmington College, Pyle Ctr 1227, 1870 Quaker Way, Wilmington, OH, 45177-2473, Tel: 937-382-6661, Ext 346. Fax: 937-383-8571. p. 1949

Mulhern, John, Customer Serv Supvr, Huntington Public Library, 338 Main St, Huntington, NY, 11743. Tel: 631-427-5165. Fax: 631-421-7131. p. 1639

Mulhern, Yvonne, Ref/Outreach Librn, Tarleton State University Library, 201 Saint Felix, Stephenville, TX, 76401. Tel: 254-968-9934. Fax: 254-968-9467. p. 2389

Mulholland, Joan, Librn, Davis & Co, 666 Burrard St, Ste 2800, Vancouver, BC, V6C 2Z7, CANADA. Tel: 604-643-6425. Fax: 604-605-3598. p. 2740

Mulkey, Dorothy, Circ Supvr, Northwest University, 5520 108th Ave NE, Kirkland, WA, 98083-0579. Tel: 425-889-5266. Fax: 425-889-7801. p. 2519

Mulks, Gwendolyn, Head Librn, Ray Quinney & Nebeker PC, 36 S State St, Ste 1400, Salt Lake City, UT, 84111. Tel: 801-532-1500. Fax: 801-532-7543. p. 2413

Mull, Chris, Circ & Reserves Supvr, Miami University-Middletown, 4200 N University Blvd, Middletown, OH, 45042-3497. Tel: 513-727-3291. p. 1917

Mull, Terri, Br Mgr, Aiken-Bamberg-Barnwell-Edgefield Regional Library System, Blackville Branch, 19420 N Sol Blatt Ave, Blackville, SC, 29817. Tel: 803-284-2295. Fax: 803-284-2295. p. 2179

Mulla, Catherine, Tech Serv, Miller, Canfield, Paddock & Stone Library, 150 W Jefferson, Ste 2500, Detroit, MI, 48226. Tel: 313-963-6420. Fax: 313-496-8452. p. 1171

Mullaly-Quijas, Margaret, Dir, University of Missouri-Kansas City Libraries, Health Sciences Library, 2411 Holmes St, Kansas City, MO, 64108. Tel: 816-235-1871. Fax: 816-235-6570. p. 1341

Mullaly-Quijas, Peggy, Dr, Dir, Health Sciences Library Network of Kansas City, Inc, University of Missouri-Kansas City Health Sciences Library, 2411 Holmes St, Kansas City, MO, 64108-2792. Tel: 816-235-1880. Fax: 816-235-6570. p. 2947

Mullane, Muriel, Coll Develop, Ref Serv, Paradise Valley Community College Library, 18401 N 32nd St, Phoenix, AZ, 85032-1200. Tel: 602-787-7201. Fax: 602-787-7205. p. 75

Mullaney, B J, Info Serv, Cheyney University, 1837 University Circle, Cheyney, PA, 19319. Tel: 610-399-2203. Fax: 610-399-2491. p. 2044

Mullany, M St Michel, Sister, Archivist, Sisters, Servants of the Immaculate Heart of Mary Archives, Villa Maria House of Studies, 1140 King Rd, Immaculata, PA, 19345. Tel: 610-647-2160. Fax: 610-889-4874. p. 2071

Mullarkey, Andrea, Librn, Berkeley Public Library, 2090 Kittredge St, Berkeley, CA, 94704. Tel: 510-981-6100. Fax: 510-981-6111. p. 126

Mullarkey, Joseph, Coll Mgt Librn, Pub Serv, Moraine Valley Community College Library, 9000 W College Pkwy, Palos Hills, IL, 60465. Tel: 708-974-5293. Fax: 708-974-1184. p. 687

Mullen, Grace, Archivist, Asst Librn, Westminster Theological Seminary, 2960 W Church Rd, Glenside, PA, 19038. Tel: 215-572-3822. Fax: 215-887-3412. p. 2062

Mullen, Greg, City Librn, Santa Monica Public Library, 601 Santa Monica Blvd, Santa Monica, CA, 90401. Tel: 310-458-8611. Fax: 310-394-8951. p. 266

Mullen, Julie, Ref Librn, Chemung County Library District, 101 E Church St, Elmira, NY, 14901-2799. Tel: 607-733-9173. Fax: 607-733-9176. p. 1619

Mullen, Kara, Electronic Res Librn, Clayton State University, 2000 Clayton State Blvd, Morrow, GA, 30260. Tel: 678-466-4339. Fax: 678-466-4349. p. 545

Mullen, Kathy, Dir, Saint Mary's Health Center, 6420 Clayton Rd, Saint Louis, MO, 63117. Tel: 314-768-8112. Fax: 314-768-8974. p. 1361

Mullen, Kathy, Dir, Saint Mary's Health Center, Nancy Sue Claypool Health Information Center, 6420 Clayton Rd, Saint Louis, MO, 63117. Tel: 314-768-8636. Fax: 314-768-8974. p. 1361

Mullen, Kenzie, Br Mgr, Humboldt County Library, Trinidad Branch, Janis Ct, Trinidad, CA, 95570. Tel: 707-677-0227. p. 147

Mullen, Kris, Mgr, Massachusetts Taxpayers Foundation Library, 333 Washington St, Ste 853, Boston, MA, 02108. Tel: 617-720-1000. Fax: 617-720-0799. p. 1064

Mullen, Marilynn, Dir, Cranbury Public Library, 23 N Main St, Cranbury, NJ, 08512. Tel: 609-655-0555. Fax: 609-655-2858. p. 1480

Mullen, Mark, Actg Exec Dir, International Reading Association Library, 800 Barksdale Rd, Newark, DE, 19711. Tel: 302-731-1600, Ext 217. Fax: 302-731-1057. p. 385

Mullen, Mary, Outreach Serv Librn, Bethel Park Public Library, 5100 W Library Ave, Bethel Park, PA, 15102. Tel: 412-831-6800, Ext 262, 412-851-2465. Fax: 412-835-9360. p. 2033

Mullen, Michele, Librn, Cedarville Public Library, 639 Pirates Way, Cedarville, AR, 72932. Tel: 479-410-1853. Fax: 479-410-1853. p. 96

Mullen, Norma, Librn, Logan Public Library, 109 W Main St, Logan, KS, 67646. Tel: 785-689-4333. p. 880

Mullen, Susan, Librn, Annapolis Valley Regional Library, Port Williams Branch, Community Centre, 131 Main St, Port Williams, NS, B0P 1T0, CANADA. Tel: 902-542-3005. Fax: 902-542-3005. p. 2778

Mullen, Valerie E, Libr Assoc, Washington State Library, Clallam Bay Correction Center, 1830 Eagle Crest Way, Clallam Bay, WA, 98326-9775. Tel: 360-963-3216. Fax: 360-963-3293. p. 2544

Mullenax, Elisa S, Libr Tech, Tyler Junior College, 1327 S Baxter St, Tyler, TX, 75701. Tel: 903-510-2309. Fax: 903-510-2639. p. 2393

Muller, Cindy, Ref Serv, Legacy Emanuel Hospital & Health Center Library, 2801 N Gantenbein Ave, Portland, OR, 97227. Tel: 503-413-2558. Fax: 503-413-2544. p. 2011

Muller, Claudya, Dir, Chattahoochee Valley Libraries, 3000 Macon Rd, Columbus, GA, 31906-2201. Tel: 706-243-2669. Fax: 706-243-2710. p. 525

Muller, Janice Powell, Dir, Uniformed Services University of the Health Sciences, 4301 Jones Bridge Rd, Bethesda, MD, 20814-4799. Tel: 301-295-3350. Fax: 301-295-3795. p. 1022

Muller, Joy, Mgr, Seneca College of Applied Arts & Technology, Seneca @ York, 70 The Pond Rd, North York, ON, M3J 3M6, CANADA. Tel: 416-491-5050, Ext 30042. p. 2813

Muller, Julia C, Head, Res Serv, Savannah Morning News, 1375 Chatham Pkwy, Savannah, GA, 31405. Tel: 912-652-0319. Fax: 912-525-0795, 912-525-0796. p. 551

Muller, Karen, Dir, American Library Association Library, 50 E Huron St, Chicago, IL, 60611-2729. Tel: 312-280-2153. Fax: 312-280-3255. p. 605

Muller, Karen, Coll Develop Mgr, Tech Serv Coordr, Hillsboro Public Library, 2850 NE Brookwood Pkwy, Hillsboro, OR, 97124-5327. Tel: 503-615-6500. Fax: 503-615-6601. p. 2000

Muller, Kathy, Br Mgr, Saint Louis County Library, Rock Road Branch, 10267 St Charles Rock Rd, Saint Ann, MO, 63074. Tel: 314-429-5116. p. 1359

Muller, Kathy, Dir, Gardner Public Library, 114 W Third St, Wakefield, NE, 68784. Tel: 402-287-2334. Fax: 402-287-2334. p. 1422

Muller, Linda, Br Mgr, San Bernardino County Library, Twentynine Palms Branch, 6078 Adobe Rd, Twentynine Palms, CA, 92277. Tel: 760-367-9519. Fax: 760-361-0703. p. 229

Muller, Malinda, Dir, Prog & Partnerships, Los Angeles County Law Library, Mildred L Lillie Bldg, 301 W First St, Los Angeles, CA, 90012-3100. Tel: 213-785-2529. Fax: 213-613-1329. p. 172

Muller, Michelle, Head, Youth Serv, Goshen Free Public Library, 42 Main St, Goshen, MA, 01032-9608. Tel: 413-268-7033. p. 1091

Muller, Pamela, Librn, Bailey Cavalieri LLC, Ten W Broad St, Ste 2100, Columbus, OH, 43215-3422. Tel: 614-221-3155. Fax: 614-221-0479. p. 1883

Muller, Patricia O, Children's/Teen Coordr, Henrico County Public Library, 1001 N Laburnum Ave, Henrico, VA, 23223-2705. Tel: 804-290-9000. Fax: 804-222-5566. p. 2471

Muller, Ruth Anne, Dir, Olive Free Library Association, 4033 Rte 28A, West Shokan, NY, 12494. Tel: 845-657-2482. Fax: 845-657-2664. p. 1767

Muller, Sheri, Archivist, Res Serv Librn, Grand View University Library, 1350 Morton Ave, Des Moines, IA, 50316-1494. Tel: 515-263-6199. Fax: 515-263-2998. p. 809

Mullett, Carolyn, Librn, Wilder Memorial Library, 24 Lawrence Hill Rd, Weston, VT, 05161. Tel: 802-824-4307. p. 2439

Mullett, Mike, Info Tech Mgr, Daniel Boone Regional Library, 100 W Broadway, Columbia, MO, 65203. Tel: 573-443-3161. Fax: 573-443-3281. p. 1324

Mullie, Pierre, Syst/Electronic Res Librn, Canadian Police College Library, Canadian Police College, One Sandridge Rd, Bldg C, Ottawa, ON, K1G 3J2, CANADA. Tel: 613-993-3225. Fax: 613-993-2220. p. 2829

Mulligan, Anne-Marie, Coll Serv Librn, Episcopal Divinity School - Sherrill Library, 99 Brattle St, Cambridge, MA, 02138. Tel: 617-349-8824. Fax: 617-349-8849. p. 1073

Mulligan, Anne-Marie, Cat Librn, Lesley University, 89 Brattle St, Cambridge, MA, 02138-2790. Tel: 617-349-8840. Fax: 617-349-8849. p. 1077

Mulligan, Meredith, Tech Serv Librn, Weil, Gotshal & Manges Library, 767 Fifth Ave, New York, NY, 10153. Tel: 212-310-8626. Fax: 212-310-8007. p. 1702

Mulligan, Nina, Libr Tech, Clapp Memorial Library, 19 S Main St, Belchertown, MA, 01007-0627. Tel: 413-323-0417. Fax: 413-323-0453. p. 1052

Mullin, Dawn, Info Serv, South Carolina State Library, 1430-1500 Senate St, Columbia, SC, 29201. Tel: 803-737-3762. Fax: 803-734-8676. p. 2189

Mullin, John, Exec Dir, Collin College, 9700 Wade Blvd, Frisco, TX, 75035. Tel: 972-377-1560, 972-377-1577. Fax: 972-377-1511. p. 2325

Mullin, Linda, Tech Serv Supvr, Rice Lake Public Library, Two E Marshall St, Rice Lake, WI, 54868. Tel: 715-234-4861. Fax: 715-234-5026. p. 2633

Mullin, Mary, Pub Serv, Herkimer County Community College Library, 100 Reservoir Rd, Herkimer, NY, 13350. Tel: 315-866-0300, Ext 8270. Fax: 315-866-1806. p. 1635

Mullin, Michael C, Dir, Watertown Regional Library, 160 Sixth St NE, Watertown, SD, 57201-2778. Tel: 605-882-6220. Fax: 605-882-6221. p. 2221

Mullin, Rhonda, Mgr, Automation & Ser, Westchester Public Library, 200 W Indiana Ave, Chesterton, IN, 46304-3122. Tel: 219-926-7696. Fax: 219-926-6424. p. 732

Mullin, Timothy, Spec Coll Librn, Western Kentucky University Libraries, Helm-Cravens Library Complex, 1906 College Heights Blvd, No 11067, Bowling Green, KY, 42101-1067. Tel: 270-745-2905. Fax: 270-745-6422. p. 908

Mullin, Timothy J, Dept Head, Western Kentucky University Libraries, Kentucky Library & Museum, 1400 Kentucky St, Bowling Green, KY, 42101-3479. Tel: 270-745-2592. Fax: 270-745-6264. p. 908

Mullin, Viola, Ref Asst, Hartford Seminary Library, 77 Sherman St, Hartford, CT, 06105-2260. Tel: 860-509-9561. Fax: 860-509-9509. p. 346

Mullins, Beth, Ref Serv Librn, Tarrant County College, 828 Harwood Rd, Hurst, TX, 76054-3219. Tel: 817-515-6314. p. 2346

Mullins, Carol, Librn, Mercer County District Library, Mendon Branch, 105 W Market St, Mendon, OH, 45862. Tel: 419-795-6472. Fax: 419-795-6472. p. 1866

Mullins, Cecilia, Librn, Sharp County Library, 201 Church St, Hardy, AR, 72542. Tel: 870-856-3934. p. 102

Mullins, Cheryl, Head, Ref Serv, Canal Fulton Public Library, 154 Market St NE, Canal Fulton, OH, 44614-1196. Tel: 330-854-4148. Fax: 330-854-9520. p. 1863

Mullins, Christina, Ref, Outreach & Instruction Librn, University of Massachusetts at Boston, 100 Morrissey Blvd, Boston, MA, 02125-3300. Tel: 617-287-5933. p. 1068

Mullins, James L, Dr, Dean of Libr, Purdue University Libraries, 504 W State St, West Lafayette, IN, 47907-2058. Tel: 765-494-2900. Fax: 765-494-0156. p. 786

Mullins, Joy, Br Mgr, Iberville Parish Library, Bayou Pigeon, 36625 Hwy 75, Plaquemine, LA, 70764. Tel: 225-545-8567. Fax: 225-545-8567. p. 965

Mullins, Katie, YA Librn, Kendallville Public Library, 221 S Park Ave, Kendallville, IN, 46755-2248. Tel: 260-343-2010. Fax: 260-343-2011. p. 756

Mullins, Pamella, Dir, Anderson County Public Library, 114 N Main St, Lawrenceburg, KY, 40342. Tel: 502-839-6420. Fax: 502-839-7243. p. 919

Mullins, Ray, Br Mgr, Washington County Public Library, Mendota Branch, 2562 Mendota Rd, Mendota, VA, 24270-2018. Tel: 276-645-2374. Fax: 276-645-2330. p. 2443

Mullins, Terry, Tech Serv, Vienna Public Library, 2300 River Rd, Vienna, WV, 26105. Tel: 304-295-7771. Fax: 304-295-7776. p. 2573

Mullins, Tom, Rare Bks, Spec Coll Librn, Public Library of Anniston-Calhoun County, 108 E Tenth St, Anniston, AL, 36201. Tel: 256-237-8501, 256-237-8503. Fax: 256-238-0474. p. 4

Mulloy, Katherine, Ch, Lafayette Public Library, 301 W Congress, Lafayette, LA, 70501-6866. Tel: 337-261-5779. Fax: 337-261-5782. p. 952

Mulrenan, Mary, Mkt & Communications Mgr, Fairfax County Public Library, 12000 Government Center Pkwy, Ste 324, Fairfax, VA, 22035-0012. Tel: 703-324-3100. Fax: 703-324-8365. p. 2461

Mulroy, Kathy, Exec Dir, Radnor Memorial Library, 114 W Wayne Ave, Wayne, PA, 19087-4098. Tel: 610-687-1124. Fax: 610-687-1454. p. 2152

Mulroy, Kevin, Interim Head of Libr, University of California Los Angeles Library, The Arts Library, 1400 Public Policy Bldg, Los Angeles, CA, 90095. Tel: 310-825-3817. Fax: 310-825-1303. p. 178

Mulvany, Patrick, In Charge, Missouri Department of Natural Resources, 111 Fairgrounds Rd, Rolla, MO, 65401-2909. Tel: 573-368-2139. Fax: 573-368-2111. p. 1351

Mulvey, Sharon, Co-Dir, University of Wisconsin-Madison, Chemistry Library, 1101 University Ave, Madison, WI, 53706. Tel: 608-262-2942. Fax: 608-262-9002. p. 2608

Mulvey, Theodore, Info Literacy Librn, University of Wisconsin Oshkosh, 801 Elmwood Ave, Oshkosh, WI, 54901. Tel: 920-424-7329. Fax: 920-424-7338. p. 2628

Mulvihill, Rachel, Actg Head, Curric Mat Ctr, University of Central Florida Libraries, 4000 Central Florida Blvd, Bldg 2, Orlando, FL, 32816-2666. Tel: 407-823-2327. Fax: 407-823-3984. p. 477

Mulvihill, Tess, Asst Librn, Belmar Public Library, 517 Tenth Ave, Belmar, NJ, 07719. Tel: 732-681-0775. Fax: 732-681-8419. p. 1471

Mumbach, Mary K, Dr, Dir, Thomas More College of Liberal Arts, Six Manchester St, Merrimack, NH, 03054-4805. Tel: 603-880-0425. Fax: 603-880-9280. p. 1457

Mumbower, Kim, Tech Serv, Baldwin County Library Cooperative, Inc, 22251 Palmer St, Robertsdale, AL, 36567. Tel: 251-970-4010. Fax: 251-970-4011. p. 35

Mumford, John, Dir, Juniata College, 1815 Moore St, Huntingdon, PA, 16652-2120. Tel: 814-641-3450. Fax: 814-641-3435. p. 2070

Mumford, Scott, Adult Serv, Ref Serv, Franklin County Library, 906 N Main St, Louisburg, NC, 27549-2199. Tel: 919-496-2111. Fax: 919-496-1339. p. 1807

Muminovic, Meris, Acq, University of Dubuque Library, 2000 University Ave, Dubuque, IA, 52001. Tel: 563-589-3100. Fax: 563-589-3722. p. 812

Mumm, James A, Head, Acq, Head, Ser, Marquette University, Sensenbrenner Hall, 1103 W Wisconsin Ave, Milwaukee, WI, 53233-2313. Tel: 414-288-7092. Fax: 414-288-5914. p. 2618

Mumma, Polly, Adminr, Des Moines Area Community College Library, 1100 Seventh St, Des Moines, IA, 50314. Tel: 515-248-7210. Fax: 515-248-7534. p. 808

Mummert, Kelly, Assoc Librn, Libr Dir, Wheeling Jesuit University, 316 Washington Ave, Wheeling, WV, 26003-6295. Tel: 304-243-2226. Fax: 304-243-2466. p. 2575

Munch, Janet Butler, Dr, Spec Coll & Archives Librn, Lehman College, City University of New York, 250 Bedford Park Blvd W, Bronx, NY, 10468-1589. Tel: 718-960-8603. Fax: 718-960-8952. p. 1587

Munday, Elaine J, Dir, Taylor County Public Library, 205 N Columbia, Campbellsville, KY, 42718. Tel: 270-465-2562. Fax: 270-465-8026. p. 909

Munday, Mary, Head, Ref, Northbrook Public Library, 1201 Cedar Lane, Northbrook, IL, 60062-4581. Tel: 847-272-6224. Fax: 847-272-5362. p. 682

Munde, Gail, Dr, Asst Prof, East Carolina University, 101 Umstead Residence Hall, Greenville, NC, 27858-4353. Tel: 252-737-1151. Fax: 252-328-4368. p. 2971

Mundell, Nathan, Asst Circ Supvr, Cardinal Stritch University Library, 6801 N Yates Rd, Milwaukee, WI, 53207-3985. Tel: 414-410-4607. Fax: 414-410-4268. p. 2617

Mundle, Todd, Univ Librn, Kwantlen Polytechnic University Library, 12666 72 Ave., Surrey, BC, V3W 2M8, CANADA. Tel: 604-599-3400. Fax: 604-599-2106. p. 2738

Mundt, Madeleine, IT Mgr, Teton County Library, 125 Virginian Lane, Jackson, WY, 83001. Tel: 307-733-2164, Ext 143. Fax: 307-733-4568. p. 2656

Mundt, Patrick, Ref Librn, Milwaukee Area Technical College, 6665 S Howell Ave, Oak Creek, WI, 53154. Fax: 414-571-4747. p. 2626

Mundt, Virginia, Supvr, Pub Serv, Mesquite Public Library, 300 W Grubb Dr, Mesquite, TX, 75149. Tel: 972-216-6220. Fax: 972-216-6740. p. 2362

Mundwiler, Vicky, Librn, Peoria County Law Library, Peoria County Court House, 324 Main, Rm 211, Peoria, IL, 61602. Tel: 309-672-6084. p. 690

Mundy, Jim, Dir, Union League of Philadelphia Library, 140 S Broad St, Philadelphia, PA, 19102. Tel: 215-587-5594. Fax: 215-587-5598. p. 2118

Mundy, Mary Alice, Tech Serv, Laurens County Library, 1017 W Main St, Laurens, SC, 29360. Tel: 864-681-7323. Fax: 864-681-0598. p. 2199

Mundy, Sandra P, Dir, Jesse M Smith Memorial Library, 100 Tinkham Lane, Harrisville, RI, 02830. Tel: 401-710-7800. Fax: 401-710-7772. p. 2167

Munger, Lucinda, Dir, Orange County Public Library, 137 W Margaret Lane, Hillsborough, NC, 27278. Tel: 919-245-2528. Fax: 919-644-3003. p. 1802

Munger, Sandra, Head Librn, Canyon Area Library, 1501 Third Ave, Canyon, TX, 79015. Tel: 806-655-5015. Fax: 806-655-5032. p. 2294

Muniak, Rosellen, Librn, New Jersey Department of Corrections, 215 Burlington Rd S, Bridgeton, NJ, 08302. Tel: 856-459-8145. Fax: 856-459-8125. p. 1474

Muniz, Cris, Mgr, City of Commerce Public Library, Atlantic Branch, 2269 S Atlantic Blvd, Commerce, CA, 90040. Tel: 323-780-1176. Fax: 323-780-0308. p. 136

Muniz, Shelley, Tech Serv, Columbia College Library, 11600 Columbia College Dr, Sonora, CA, 95370-8581. Tel: 209-588-5238. Fax: 209-588-5121. p. 269

Munk, Beth, Ch, Kendallville Public Library, 221 S Park Ave, Kendallville, IN, 46755-2248. Tel: 260-343-2010. Fax: 260-343-2011. p. 756

Munk, Kindra, Librn, Rockland School Community Library, 321 E Center, Rockland, ID, 83271. Tel: 208-548-2222. Fax: 208-548-2224. p. 583

Munk, Stephen, Pres, Ash Stevens, Inc Library, 5861 John C Lodge Freeway, Detroit, MI, 48202. Tel: 313-872-6400. Fax: 313-872-6841. p. 1172

Munn, Lisa, Mgr, New Brunswick Emergency Measures Organization Library, Victoria Health Ctr, Ground Flr, 65 Brunswick St, Fredericton, NB, E3B 5H1, CANADA. Tel: 506-453-2133. Fax: 506-453-5513. p. 2763

Munn, Murray, Librn, Environment Canada, 91782 Alaska Hwy, Whitehorse, YT, Y1A 5B7, CANADA. Tel: 867-667-3407. Fax: 867-667-7962. p. 2934

Munnell, Barbra, Coll Develop, Dep Dir, Grove City College, 300 Campus Dr, Grove City, PA, 16127-2198. Tel: 724-458-3824. Fax: 724-458-2181. p. 2063

Munno, Nancy, Youth Serv, Brown Public Library, 93 S Main St, Northfield, VT, 05663. Tel: 802-485-4621. Fax: 802-485-4990. p. 2431

Munoff, Gerald, Univ Librn, University of California Library, Science, PO Box 19557, Irvine, CA, 92623-9557. Tel: 949-824-5212. Fax: 949-824-3114. p. 160

Munoz, Cindy, Info Spec, Driscoll Children's Hospital, 3533 S Alameda St, Corpus Christi, TX, 78411-1721. Tel: 361-694-5467. Fax: 361-808-2141. p. 2302

Munoz, Eeva, Assoc Univ Librn, Western University - Libraries, 1151 Richmond St, Ste 200, London, ON, N6A 3K7, CANADA. Tel: 519-661-2111, Ext 86897. Fax: 519-661-3493. p. 2819

Munoz, George, Conservator, The New York Society Library, 53 E 79th St, New York, NY, 10075. Tel: 212-288-6900 Ext 249. Fax: 212-744-5832. p. 1694

Munoz, Paula, Ref, Laramie County Community College Library, 1400 E College Dr, Cheyenne, WY, 82007-3204. Tel: 307-778-1378. Fax: 307-778-1399. p. 2652

Munoz, Solanyi, Dir, Ch Serv, Lawrence Public Library, 51 Lawrence St, Lawrence, MA, 01841. Tel: 978-620-3600. Fax: 978-688-3142. p. 1098

Munozospina, Carlos, Tech Serv, Jericho Public Library, One Merry Lane, Jericho, NY, 11753. Tel: 516-935-6790. Fax: 516-433-9581. p. 1647

Munro, Bill, Br Mgr, Atlanta-Fulton Public Library System, Ponce de Leon Library, 980 Ponce de Leon Ave NE, Atlanta, GA, 30306. Tel: 404-885-7820. Fax: 404-885-7822. p. 512

Munro, Carol, Librn, Palliser Regional Library, Assiniboia & District Public Library, 201 Third Ave W, Assiniboia, SK, S0H 0B0, CANADA. Tel: 306-642-3631. p. 2918

Munro, Catheryn, Br Mgr, Thompson-Nicola Regional District Library System, Clinton Branch, 1506 Tingley St, Clinton, BC, V0K 1K0, CANADA. Tel: 250-459-7752. Fax: 250-459-7752. p. 2729

Munro, Hilary, Head, Adult Serv, Medicine Hat Public Library, 414 First St SE, Medicine Hat, AB, T1A 0A8, CANADA. Tel: 403-502-8527. Fax: 403-502-8529. p. 2711

Munro, Pam M, Dir, Selbyville Public Library, 11 Main & McCabe Sts, Selbyville, DE, 19975. Tel: 302-436-8195. Fax: 302-436-1508. p. 386

Munro, Paul, Assoc Prof, University of Pittsburgh, 135 N Bellefield Ave, Pittsburgh, PA, 15260. Tel: 412-624-5230. Fax: 412-624-5231. p. 2973

Munsee, Jeanie, Dir, Edmonson County Public Library, 280 Ferguson St, Brownsville, KY, 42210. Tel: 270-597-2146. Fax: 270-597-3282. p. 908

Munson, Jeffrey, Dir, Franklin Grove Public Library, 112 S Elm St, Franklin Grove, IL, 61031. Tel: 815-456-2823. Fax: 815-456-2619. p. 647

Munson, Jim, Dir, Planning & Admin, University of California San Francisco, 530 Parnassus Ave, San Francisco, CA, 94143-0840. Tel: 415-476-8060. p. 248

Munson, Judith, Ch, South Kingstown Public Library, Kingston Free Branch, 2605 Kingstown Rd, Kingston, RI, 02881. Tel: 401-783-8254. Fax: 401-783-8254. p. 2171

Munson, Kathy, ILL, De Anza College, 21250 Stevens Creek Blvd, Cupertino, CA, 95014-5793. Tel: 408-864-8335. Fax: 408-864-8603. p. 138

Munson, Mary, ILL, US Census Bureau Library, Suitland Federal Center, Rm 1L1001, 4600 Silver Hill Rd, Suitland, MD, 20746. Tel: 301-763-2511. Fax: 301-763-4407. p. 1043

Munson, Robert, Coll Mgr, US National Park Service, 1800 Cabrillo Memorial Dr, San Diego, CA, 92106-3601. Tel: 619-523-4574. Fax: 619-226-6311. p. 238

Munson, Sally, Ref Librn, Dewey & LeBoeuf LLP Library, 1301 Avenue of the Americas, 22nd Flr, New York, NY, 10019. Tel: 212-259-8000. Fax: 212-259-6679. p. 1677

Munson, Stephanie, Vols Mgr, Hayner Public Library District, 326 Belle St, Alton, IL, 62002. Tel: 618-462-0677. Fax: 618-462-0665. p. 588

Munstedt, Peter, Librn, Massachusetts Institute of Technology Libraries, Lewis Music Library, Bldg 14E-109, 77 Massachusetts Ave, Cambridge, MA, 02139-4307. Tel: 617-253-5689. Fax: 617-253-3109. p. 1078

Munthali, Mwiza, Dir of Outreach, TransAfrica Forum, 1629 K St NW, Ste 1100, Washington, DC, 20006. Tel: 202-223-1960. Fax: 202-223-1966. p. 417

Muntz, Susan, Tech Serv, Ruth L Rockwood Memorial Library, Ten Robert Harp Dr, Livingston, NJ, 07039. Tel: 973-992-4600. Fax: 973-994-2346. p. 1496

Munz, Brenda, Librn, Cameron County Law Library, Court House, 20 E Fifth St, Emporium, PA, 15834. Tel: 814-486-2315. Fax: 814-486-0464. p. 2054

Murad, Hafsa, Info Literacy Librn, North Carolina Central University, 1801 Fayetteville St, Durham, NC, 27707-3129. Tel: 919-530-7315. Fax: 919-530-7612. p. 1789

Muralidharan, Mayu, Libr Tech, Southwest College of Naturopathic Medicine & Health Sciences Library, 2140 E Broadway Rd, Tempe, AZ, 85282-1751. Tel: 480-222-9247. Fax: 480-858-9116. p. 84

Muraski, Terri, Tech Librn, University of Wisconsin-Stevens Point, 900 Reserve St, Stevens Point, WI, 54481-1985. Tel: 715-346-3349. Fax: 715-346-3857. p. 2640

Murata, Susan, Dir, Kapiolani Community College Library, 4303 Diamond Head Rd, Honolulu, HI, 96816. Tel: 808-734-9267. Fax: 808-734-9453. p. 564

Murawski, Martina, Syst Mgr, Lois Wagner Memorial Library, 35200 Division Rd, Richmond, MI, 48062. Tel: 586-727-2665. Fax: 586-727-3774. p. 1221

Murchio, Christine, Dir, Woodbridge Public Library, George Frederick Plaza, Woodbridge, NJ, 07095. Tel: 732-634-4450. p. 1545

Murcray, Keri, Circ, California Baptist University, 8432 Magnolia Ave, Riverside, CA, 92504. Tel: 951-343-4228. p. 216

Murdoch, Robert, Asst Univ Librn, Coll Develop, Tech Serv, Brigham Young University, Harold B Lee Library, 2060 HBLL, Provo, UT, 84602. Tel: 801-422-2927. Fax: 801-422-0466. p. 2411

Murdock, Catherine, Asst Librn, Fremont Public Library, Seven Jackie Bernier Dr, Fremont, NH, 03044. Tel: 603-895-9543. Fax: 603-895-0549. p. 1448

Murdock, Colleen, Librn, Emery County Library, Ferron Branch, 55 N 200 West, Ferron, UT, 84523. Tel: 435-384-2637. Fax: 435-384-2876. p. 2404

Murdock, Hollie, Dir, Utah School for the Deaf & Blind, 742 Harrison Blvd, Ogden, UT, 84404. Tel: 801-629-4817. Fax: 801-629-4896. p. 2408

Murdock, Ronda, Libr Serv Coordr, French Institute-Alliance Francaise Library, 22 E 60th St, New York, NY, 10022-1077. Tel: 646-388-6636. Fax: 212-935-4119. p. 1679

Murdock, Stephanie, Librn, City of Wolfforth Library, 508 E Hwy 62-82, Wolfforth, TX, 79382-7001. Tel: 806-866-9280. Fax: 806-833-6932. p. 2401

Murdock, Tina, Music Librn, Dallas Public Library, 1515 Young St, Dallas, TX, 75201-5499. Tel: 214-670-1400. Fax: 214-670-7839. p. 2306

Murdock, William J, Univ Librn, Pace University, 861 Bedford Rd, Pleasantville, NY, 10570-2799. Tel: 914-773-3382. Fax: 914-773-3508. p. 1719

Muresan, Gheorghe, Asst Prof, Rutgers, The State University of New Jersey, Four Huntington St, New Brunswick, NJ, 08901-1071. Tel: 732-932-7500, Ext 8955. Fax: 732-932-2644. p. 2969

Murgai, Sarla, Ref Serv Librn, University of Tennessee at Chattanooga Library, 615 McCallie Ave, Dept 6456, Chattanooga, TN, 37403-2598. Tel: 423-425-4501. Fax: 423-425-4775. p. 2228

Murgas, Andy, Head, Computer Serv, Matteson Public Library, 801 S School St, Matteson, IL, 60443-1897. Tel: 708-748-4431. Fax: 708-748-0510. p. 671

Muri, Wendy, ILL, Chinook Regional Library, 1240 Chaplin St W, Swift Current, SK, S9H 0G8, CANADA. Tel: 306-773-3186. Fax: 306-773-0434. p. 2927

Murie, Judy, Dir, McKenzie County Public Library, 112 Second Ave NE, Watford City, ND, 58854. Tel: 701-444-3785. Fax: 701-444-3730. p. 1849

Murillo, Lisa, Sr Librn, Denver Public Library, Woodbury, 3265 Federal Blvd, Denver, CO, 80211-3211. Tel: 720-865-0930. Fax: 720-865-0933. p. 301

Murillo, Nancy, Libr Dir, Pittsburg-Camp County Public Library, 613 Quitman St, Pittsburg, TX, 75686-1035. Tel: 903-856-3302. Fax: 903-856-0591. p. 2370

Murphey, Dorothy, Librn, First Presbyterian Church, 5300 Main St, Houston, TX, 77004-6877. Tel: 713-620-6541. Fax: 713-620-6550. p. 2335

Murphree, Meredith, Br Mgr, Prince William Public Library System, Gainesville Neighborhood, 4603 James Madison Hwy, Haymarket, VA, 20169-2526. Tel: 703-792-5660. Fax: 703-754-2494. p. 2486

Murphree, Yvonne, Dir, Blountsville Public Library, 65 Chestnut St, Blountsville, AL, 35031. Tel: 205-429-3156. Fax: 205-429-4806. p. 10

Murphrey, Mary, Bus Mgr, Parmly Billings Library, 510 N Broadway, Billings, MT, 59101-1196. Tel: 406-657-8258. Fax: 406-657-8293. p. 1374

Murphy, Adam, Info Tech, Rossford Public Library, 720 Dixie Hwy, Rossford, OH, 43460-1289. Tel: 419-666-0924. Fax: 419-666-1989. p. 1932

Murphy, Anne, Dir, Bedford Park Public Library District, 7816 W 65th Pl, Bedford Park, IL, 60501. Tel: 708-458-6826. Fax: 708-458-9827. p. 593

Murphy, Anne, Head, Tech Serv, Bedford Public Library, Three Meetinghouse Rd, Bedford, NH, 03110-5406. Tel: 603-472-2300, 603-472-3023. Fax: 603-472-2978. p. 1438

Murphy, Anne, Mgr, Mississauga Library System, 301 Burnhamthorpe Rd W, Mississauga, ON, L5B 3Y3, CANADA. Tel: 905-615-3500. Fax: 905-615-3625. p. 2823

Murphy, Anne Marie, Sister, Asst Dir, IHM Library/Resource Center, 610 W Elm Ave, Monroe, MI, 48162-7909. Tel: 734-240-9713. Fax: 734-240-8347. p. 1209

Murphy, Annette, Dir, Menlo Public Library, Menlo Community Bldg, 504 Fifth St, Menlo, IA, 50164. Tel: 641-524-4201. Fax: 641-524-2682. p. 831

Murphy, Barbara, AV, Cat, Per, Lasalle Parish Library, 3108 N First St, Jena, LA, 71342. Tel: 318-992-5675. Fax: 318-992-7374, 318-992-7394. p. 951

Murphy, Betty, Librn, Kraft Food Ingredients Corp, 8000 Horizon Center Blvd, Memphis, TN, 38133. Tel: 901-381-6503. Fax: 901-381-6524, 901-381-6628. p. 2249

Murphy, Beverly, Asst Dir, Mkt & Publ, Duke University Libraries, Medical Center Library, DUMC Box 3702, Ten Bryan-Searle Dr, Durham, NC, 27710-0001. Tel: 919-660-1127. Fax: 919-681-7599. p. 1788

Murphy, Britt Anne, Actg Dir, Hendrix College, 1600 Washington Ave, Conway, AR, 72032. Tel: 501-450-1289. Fax: 501-450-3800. p. 97

Murphy, Britt Anne, Pub Serv Librn/Electronic Serv & Info Literacy, Hendrix College, 1600 Washington Ave, Conway, AR, 72032. Tel: 501-450-1288. Fax: 501-450-3800. p. 97

Murphy, Carol, YA Serv, West Deptford Public Library, 420 Crown Point Rd, West Deptford, NJ, 08086-9598. Tel: 856-845-5593. Fax: 856-848-3689. p. 1541

Murphy, Carolyn, Librn, Massachusetts Department of Corrections, 500 Colony Rd, Gardner, MA, 01440. Tel: 978-632-2000, Ext 325. Fax: 978-630-6044. p. 1090

Murphy, Carrie, Br Librn, Davis County Library, South Branch, 725 S Main St, Bountiful, UT, 84010. Tel: 801-295-8732. p. 2405

Murphy, Cathy, Chief Librn, Canadian Forces College, 215 Yonge Blvd, Toronto, ON, M5M 3H9, CANADA. Tel: 416-482-6800, Ext 6846. Fax: 416-480-9935. p. 2851

Murphy, Claire, Sr Libr Asst, Eatontown Library, 33 Broad St, Eatontown, NJ, 07724-1594. Tel: 732-389-2665. Fax: 732-389-7665. p. 1482

Murphy, Cynthia, Knowledge Mgr, Stewart McKelvey, 1959 Upper Water St, Ste 900, Halifax, NS, B3J 3N2, CANADA. Tel: 902-420-3200. Fax: 902-420-1417. p. 2781

Murphy, Darin, Dir, Libr Serv, Museum of Fine Arts, Boston, W Van Alan Clark Jr Library, 230 The Fenway, Boston, MA, 02115. Tel: 617-369-3650. p. 1064

Murphy, David, Ref Serv, Duxbury Free Library, 77 Alden St, Duxbury, MA, 02332. Tel: 781-934-2721, Ext 103. Fax: 781-934-0663. p. 1085

Murphy, Deborah, Bibliographer, Librn, University of California, 1156 High St, Santa Cruz, CA, 95064. Tel: 831-459-3253. Fax: 831-459-8206. p. 264

Murphy, Deborah, Dir, White Haven Area Community Library, PO Box 57, White Haven, PA, 18661. Tel: 570-443-8776. Fax: 570-443-8776. p. 2155

Murphy, Diane, ILL, Bibliotheque de Brossard, 7855 San Francisco Ave, Brossard, QC, J4X 2A4, CANADA. Tel: 450-923-6350, Ext 6286. Fax: 450-923-7042. p. 2880

Murphy, Ed, Sr Librn, NYS Supreme Court Library, Ninth Judicial District, 9th Flr, 111 Dr Martin Luther King Blvd, White Plains, NY, 10601. Tel: 914-824-5660. p. 1768

Murphy, Eileen, Tech Serv, Elwood Public Library, 1929 Jericho Tpk, East Northport, NY, 11731. Tel: 631-499-3722. Fax: 631-499-0057. p. 1617

Murphy, Elizabeth, Dir, Saint Augustine College Library, 1345 W Argyle, Chicago, IL, 60640. Tel: 773-878-3710. Fax: 773-878-0937. p. 623

Murphy, Elizabeth, Cat, Sampson-Clinton Public Library, 217 Graham St, Clinton, NC, 28328. Tel: 910-592-4153. Fax: 910-590-3504. p. 1784

Murphy, Emerson G, Dir, Northeast Georgia Regional Library System, 204 Ellison St, Ste F, Clarkesville, GA, 30523. Tel: 706-754-0416. Fax: 706-754-0420. p. 524

Murphy, Emily, Hist Coll Librn, Ref Serv, US National Park Service, 160 Derby St, Salem, MA, 01970. Tel: 978-740-1680. Fax: 978-740-1685. p. 1122

Murphy, Eva, Res, The State Library of Massachusetts, State House, Rm 341, 24 Beacon St, Boston, MA, 02133. Tel: 617-727-2590. Fax: 617-727-5819. p. 1067

Murphy, Eva, ILL, United States Army, Marquat Memorial Library, Bank Hall, Bldg D-3915, 3004 Ardennes St, Fort Bragg, NC, 28310-9610. Tel: 910-432-9222. Fax: 910-432-7788. p. 1794

Murphy, Hilary, Br Mgr, Markham Public Library, Cornell Branch, 6031 Hwy 7 E, Markham, ON, L6B 0T2, CANADA. Tel: 905-513-7977. p. 2820

Murphy, Jan, Outreach Librn, Cranbury Public Library, 23 N Main St, Cranbury, NJ, 08512. Tel: 609-655-0555. Fax: 609-655-2858. p. 1480

Murphy, Jan, Adminr, Ward County Public Library, 405 Third Ave SE, Minot, ND, 58701-4020. Tel: 701-852-5388. Fax: 701-837-4960. p. 1846

Murphy, Jan, Librn, Lake County Library District, Paisley Branch, 513 Mill St, Paisley, OR, 97636. Tel: 541-943-3911. Fax: 541-943-3911. p. 2003

Murphy, Janet, Ch, West Hartford Public Library, Bishop's Corner, 15 Starkel Rd, West Hartford, CT, 06117. Tel: 860-561-8210. p. 376

Murphy, Janice, Electronic Res Coordr, Ref Librn, Library of Michigan, 702 W Kalamazoo St, Lansing, MI, 48915. Tel: 517-373-1302. Fax: 517-373-5700. p. 1201

Murphy, Jean, Br Mgr, Colchester - East Hants Regional Library, Mount Uniacke Branch, 555 Hwy One, Mount Uniacke, NS, B0N 1Z0, CANADA. Tel: 902-866-0124. Fax: 902-866-0519. p. 2786

Murphy, Jeanne, Coordr, Pilgrim Psychiatric Center, Pilgrim Reading Room & Patients Library, Bldg 102, 998 Crooked Hill Rd, West Brentwood, NY, 11717-1087. Tel: 631-761-3813. Fax: 631-761-3103. p. 1765

Murphy, Jeffrey L, Librn, Murphy Public Library, Nine Blumenthal St, Murphy, NC, 28906. Tel: 828-837-2417. Fax: 828-837-6416. p. 1812

Murphy, Jennifer, Ch, Albany Public Library, 161 Washington Ave, Albany, NY, 12210. Tel: 518-427-4310. Fax: 518-449-3386. p. 1568

Murphy, Jennifer Lee, Librn, Wilkes County Public Library, 215 Tenth St, North Wilkesboro, NC, 28659. Tel: 336-838-2818. Fax: 336-667-2638. p. 1813

Murphy, JoAnn, Assoc Univ Librn, University of Northern British Columbia Library, 333 University Way, Prince George, BC, V2N 4Z9, CANADA. Tel: 250-960-6654. Fax: 250-960-6610. p. 2736

Murphy, JoAnna, Librn, Res Serv Spec, Stautzenberger College Library, 1796 Indian Wood Circle, Maumee, OH, 43537. Tel: 419-866-0261. p. 1915

Murphy, Josephine, Actg Chief Librn, Ref Serv, Kingsborough Community College, 2001 Oriental Blvd, Brooklyn, NY, 11235. Tel: 718-368-5584. Fax: 718-368-5482. p. 1592

Murphy, Judy, Dir, Helen Keller Public Library, 511 N Main St, Tuscumbia, AL, 35674. Tel: 256-383-7065. Fax: 256-389-9057. p. 39

Murphy, Judy, Ref, Riverdale Public Library District, 208 W 144th St, Riverdale, IL, 60827-2788. Tel: 708-841-3311. Fax: 708-841-1805. p. 695

Murphy, Julie, Mgr, Info Serv, Mgr, Libr Serv, Pacific Institute for Research & Evaluation, 1995 University Ave, Ste 450, Berkeley, CA, 94704. Tel: 510-486-1111, 510-883-5746. Fax: 510-644-0594. p. 127

Murphy, Karen, Br Mgr, Warren-Trumbull County Public Library, Cortland Branch, 212 N High St, Cortland, OH, 44410. Tel: 330-638-6335. p. 1944

Murphy, Kathleen, Head, Tech Serv, Elmhurst Public Library, 125 S Prospect, Elmhurst, IL, 60126-3298. Tel: 630-279-8696. Fax: 630-279-0636. p. 642

Murphy, Kathleen, Dir, Wilson College, 1015 Philadelphia Ave, Chambersburg, PA, 17201-1285. Tel: 717-264-4141, Ext 3344. Fax: 717-263-7194. p. 2043

Murphy, Kathy, Tech Serv, Wareham Free Library, 59 Marion Rd, Wareham, MA, 02571. Tel: 508-295-2343, Ext 1015. Fax: 508-295-2678. p. 1133

Murphy, Kevin, Dir, Southeast Kentucky Community & Technical College, 1300 Chichester Ave, Middlesboro, KY, 40965. Tel: 606-248-0469. Fax: 606-248-3233. p. 929

Murphy, Kim, Dir, Parrottsville Community Library, PO Box 147, Parrottsville, TN, 37843. Tel: 423-625-8990. Fax: 423-625-8990. p. 2263

Murphy, Kris, Dir, Chariton Free Public Library, 803 Braden Ave, Chariton, IA, 50049. Tel: 641-774-5514. Fax: 641-774-8695. p. 801

Murphy, Kristen, Dir, Med Libr, Maine General Medical Center Library, Six E Chestnut St, Augusta, ME, 04330. Tel: 207-626-1325. Fax: 207-626-1537. p. 974

Murphy, Lauren, Sr Librn, Pierce County Library System, Bonney Lake Branch, 18501 90th St E, Bonney Lake, WA, 98390. Tel: 253-548-3308. Fax: 253-863-6016. p. 2539

Murphy, Liam, Librn, Pub Info, United Nations Information Center, 1775 K St NW, Ste 400, Washington, DC, 20006. Tel: 202-454-2112. Fax: 202-331-9191. p. 417

Murphy, Linda, Librn, Montana State Prison Library, 600 Conley Lake Rd, Deer Lodge, MT, 59722. Tel: 406-846-1320, Ext 2410. Fax: 406-846-2951. p. 1377

Murphy, Linda, Adminr, Northeast Consortium of Colleges & Universities In Massachusetts, Merrimack College, 315 Turnpike St, North Andover, MA, 01845. Tel: 978-556-3400. Fax: 978-556-3738. p. 2945

Murphy, Lisa, Archivist, Kalamazoo College, 1200 Academy St, Kalamazoo, MI, 49006-3285. Tel: 269-337-7151. Fax: 269-337-7143. p. 1197

Murphy, Liz, Archivist, Curator, Westminster College, National Churchill Museum, 501 Westminster Ave, Fulton, MO, 65251-1299. Tel: 573-592-5626. Fax: 573-592-5222. p. 1328

Murphy, Loreen, Customer Serv Spec, State University of New York College of Technology, 34 Cornell Dr, Canton, NY, 13617-1098. Tel: 315-386-7228. Fax: 315-386-7931. p. 1602

Murphy, Louise, Dir, South Burlington Community Library, 540 Dorset St, South Burlington, VT, 05403. Tel: 802-652-7076. Fax: 802-652-7013. p. 2435

Murphy, Lynette, Ref, Graham Hospital Association, 210 W Walnut St, Canton, IL, 61520. Tel: 309-647-5240, Ext 2343. Fax: 309-649-5105. p. 599

Murphy, Lynne, Librn, Saint Francis Xavier University, West St, Antigonish, NS, B2G 2W5, CANADA. Tel: 902-867-2267. Fax: 902-867-5153. p. 2777

Murphy, Margaret, Dir, Farnsworth Public Library, 715 Main St, Oconto, WI, 54153-1795. Tel: 920-834-7730. p. 2626

Murphy, Margaret, Librn, Legislative Library of Nova Scotia, Province House, 2nd Flr, Halifax, NS, B3J 2P8, CANADA. Tel: 902-424-5932. Fax: 902-424-0220. p. 2781

Murphy, Maria, Mkt Mgr, Weston Hurd, LLP, The Tower at Erieview, Ste 1900, 1301 E Ninth St, Cleveland, OH, 44114-1862. Tel: 216-241-6602, Ext 3383. Fax: 216-621-8369. p. 1882

Murphy, Marilyn, Br Mgr, Garfield County Public Library System, Gordon Cooper Branch, 76 S Fourth St, Carbondale, CO, 81623-2014. Tel: 970-963-2889. Fax: 970-963-8573. p. 319

Murphy, Marilyn, Dir, Mount Mercy University, 1330 Elmhurst Dr NE, Cedar Rapids, IA, 52402-4797. Tel: 319-368-6465. Fax: 319-363-9060. p. 801

Murphy, Martha, Head Librn, Ontario Workplace Tribunals Library, 505 University Ave, 7th Flr, Toronto, ON, M5G 2P2, CANADA. Tel: 416-314-8957. Fax: 416-326-5164. p. 2857

Murphy, Mary, Dir, De Soto Public Library, 405 Walnut St, De Soto, IA, 50069. Tel: 515-834-2690. Fax: 515-834-2131, p. 807

Murphy, Mary, Tech Serv, Swansea Free Public Library, 69 Main St, Swansea, MA, 02777. Tel: 508-674-9609. Fax: 508-675-5444. p. 1130

Murphy, Mary, Asst Dir, Hackley Public Library, 316 W Webster Ave, Muskegon, MI, 49440. Tel: 231-722-7276, Ext 241. Fax: 231-726-5567. p. 1212

Murphy, Mary, Dir, Wauwatosa Public Library, 7635 W North Ave, Wauwatosa, WI, 53213-1718. Tel: 414-471-8484. Fax: 414-479-8984. p. 2647

Murphy, Maryanne, In Charge, Southeast State Correctional Facility Library, 546 State Farm Rd, Windsor, VT, 05089. Tel: 802-674-6717. Fax: 802-674-2249. p. 2440

Murphy, Maureen, Digital Assets Librn, Morton Arboretum, 4100 Illinois Rte 53, Lisle, IL, 60532-1293. Tel: 630-968-0074. Fax: 630-719-7950. p. 667

Murphy, Melissa, Ref Librn, Teen Serv, Meriden Public Library, 105 Miller St, Meriden, CT, 06450. Tel: 203-630-6347. Fax: 203-238-3647. p. 350

Murphy, Michael J, Mgr, Res, Toronto Real Estate Board Library, 1400 Don Mills Rd, Don Mills, ON, M3B 3N1, CANADA. Tel: 416-443-8152. Fax: 416-443-0797, 416-443-9703. p. 2802

Murphy, Miriam A, Assoc Dir, Indiana University, Ruth Lilly Law Library, 530 W New York St, Indianapolis, IN, 46202-3225. Tel: 317-274-3884, 317-274-4028. Fax: 317-274-8825. p. 752

Murphy, Nora, Archivist for Ref, Outreach & Instruction, Massachusetts Institute of Technology Libraries, Institute Archives & Special Collections, Bldg 14N-118, Hayden Library, 160 Memorial Dr, Cambridge, MA, 02139-4307. Tel: 617-253-8066. Fax: 617-258-7305. p. 1078

Murphy, Pamela, Br Mgr, Briggs Lawrence County Public Library, Chesapeake Branch, 11054-A County Rd 1, Chesapeake, OH, 45619. Tel: 740-867-3390. Fax: 740-867-4881. p. 1906

Murphy, Pamela, Dir, Clarksville-Montgomery County Public Library, 350 Pageant Lane, Ste 501, Clarksville, TN, 37040. Tel: 931-648-8826. Fax: 931-648-8831. p. 2229

Murphy, Pat, Dir, Motorcycle Industry Council, Two Jenner St, Ste 150, Irvine, CA, 92618-3806. Tel: 949-727-4211. Fax: 949-727-4217. p. 160

Murphy, Patricia, Dir, Ohio University, Shannon Hall, 1st Flr, 45425 National Rd, Saint Clairsville, OH, 43950-9724. Tel: 740-695-1720, 740-699-2519. Fax: 740-695-7075. p. 1933

Murphy, Peggy, Coll Serv Mgr, Los Angeles Public Library System, 630 W Fifth St, Los Angeles, CA, 90071-2097. Tel: 213-228-7191. Fax: 213-228-7189. p. 172

Murphy, Rebecca, Tech Serv, Albany Law School, 80 New Scotland Ave, Albany, NY, 12208. Tel: 518-445-2340. Fax: 518-472-5842. p. 1568

Murphy, Richard, Dir, Prince William Public Library System, 13083 Chinn Park Dr, Prince William, VA, 22192-5073. Tel: 703-792-6100. Fax: 703-792-4875. p. 2485

Murphy, Sandra, Mgr, Ref Serv, Ella M Everhard Public Library, 132 Broad St, Wadsworth, OH, 44281-1897. Tel: 330-334-5761. Fax: 330-334-6605. p. 1943

Murphy, Sarah A, Head of Libr, Ohio State University LIBRARIES, Veterinary Medicine, 225 Veterinary Medicine Academic Bldg, 1900 Coffey Rd, Columbus, OH, 43210. Tel: 614-292-6107. Fax: 614-292-7476. p. 1889

Murphy, Scott, Dir, Milton Public Library, 39 Bombadier Rd, Milton, VT, 05468. Tel: 802-893-4644. Fax: 802-893-1005. p. 2429

Murphy, Shari-Lynn, Actg Br Mgr, Hawaii State Public Library System, Ewa Beach Public & School Library, 91-950 North Rd, Ewa Beach, HI, 96706. Tel: 808-689-1204. Fax: 808-689-1349. p. 561

Murphy, Shelley, Syst Librn, Penticton Public Library, 785 Main St, Penticton, BC, V2A 5E3, CANADA. Tel: 250-770-7785. Fax: 250-770-7787. p. 2735

Murphy, Susan, Head Librn, University of Saskatchewan Libraries, Health Sciences, Health Sciences Bldg, Rm B-205, 107 Wiggins Rd, Saskatoon, SK, S7N 5E5, CANADA. Tel: 306-966-5991. Fax: 306-966-5918. p. 2927

Murphy, Tara, Br Mgr, Free Library of Philadelphia, Eastwick Branch, 2851 Island Ave, Philadelphia, PA, 19153-2314. Tel: 215-685-4170, 215-685-4171. Fax: 215-937-0412. p. 2107

Murphy, Theresa, Mgr, Baltimore County Public Library, Rosedale, 6105 Kenwood Ave, Baltimore, MD, 21237-2097. Tel: 410-887-0512. Fax: 410-866-4299. p. 1044

Murphy, Thomas, Dir, Episcopal Diocese of Western North Carolina, 900B Centre Park Dr, Asheville, NC, 28805. Tel: 828-225-6656. Fax: 828-225-6657. p. 1775

Murphy, Timothy H, Dir, Maurice M Pine Free Public Library, 10-01 Fair Lawn Ave, Fair Lawn, NJ, 07410. Tel: 201-796-3400. Fax: 201-794-6344. p. 1485

Murphy, Tinker, Asst Dir, The Farmington Library, Six Monteith Dr, Farmington, CT, 06032. Tel: 860-673-6791. Fax: 860-675-7148. p. 340

Murphy, Yvonne, Regional Br Mgr, Phoenix Public Library, Agave Library, 23550 N 36th Ave, Phoenix, AZ, 85310. Tel: 602-262-4636. p. 76

Murphy, Yvonne, Br Coordr, Scottsdale Public Library, Arabian Library, 10215 E McDowell Mountain Ranch Rd, Scottsdale, AZ, 85255-8601. Tel: 480-312-6225. p. 81

Murphy-Petersen, Devon, Asst Dir, Waukee Public Library, 950 Warrior Lane, Waukee, IA, 50263. Tel: 515-987-1280. Fax: 515-987-5262. p. 850

Murr, Betty, Dep Dir, Saint Charles City County Library District, 77 Boone Hills Dr, Saint Peters, MO, 63376-0529. Tel: 636-441-2300. Fax: 636-441-3132. p. 1363

Murra, Janeice, Dir, Dr Grace O Doane Alden Public Library, 1012 Water St, Alden, IA, 50006. Tel: 515-859-3820. Fax: 515-859-3919. p. 792

Murray, Adam, Dean, Murray State University, 205 Waterfield Library, Dean's Office, Murray, KY, 42071-3307. Tel: 270-809-2291. Fax: 270-809-5604. p. 930

Murray, Anne M, Dir, Southwick Public Library, 95 Feeding Hills Rd, Southwick, MA, 01077-9683. Tel: 413-569-1221. Fax: 413-569-0440. p. 1126

Murray, Bailey, YA Spec, Albany County Public Library, 310 S Eighth St, Laramie, WY, 82070-3969. Tel: 307-721-5459. Fax: 307-721-2584. p. 2657

Murray, Barbara J, Dir, Oxnard Public Library, 251 South A St, Oxnard, CA, 93030. Tel: 805-385-7522. Fax: 805-385-7526. p. 202

Murray, Betty-Kay, Head Librn, Peterborough Public Library, 345 Aylmer St N, Peterborough, ON, K9H 3V7, CANADA. Tel: 705-745-5382, Ext 2370. Fax: 705-745-8958. p. 2836

Murray, Bonnie, Coordr, The Library at Springfield Hospital Center, 6655 Sykesville Rd, Sykesville, MD, 21784. Tel: 410-970-7000, Ext 3481. Fax: 410-970-7197. p. 1043

Murray, Carolyn, Mkt, Fort McMurray Public Library, 151 MacDonald Dr, Fort McMurray, AB, T9H 5C5, CANADA. Tel: 780-743-7800. Fax: 780-743-7938. p. 2704

Murray, Carrie, Cat, Hoyt Library, 284 Wyoming Ave, Kingston, PA, 18704-3597. Tel: 570-287-2013. Fax: 570-283-2081. p. 2074

Murray, Catherine, Librn, Fox Harbour Public Library, PO Box 74, Fox Harbour, NL, A0B 1V0, CANADA. Tel: 709-227-2135. Fax: 709-227-2135. p. 2770

Murray, Chris, Circ Serv Supvr, Naperville Public Library, 95th Street, 3015 Cedar Glade Dr, Naperville, IL, 60564. Tel: 630-961-4100, Ext 4920. Fax: 630-637-4870. p. 679

Murray, Christopher, Dir, West Palm Beach Public Library, 411 Clematis St, West Palm Beach, FL, 33401. Tel: 561-868-7717. Fax: 561-868-7706. p. 504

Murray, Conor, Br Mgr, Fall River Public Library, East End, 1386 Pleasant St, Fall River, MA, 02723. Tel: 508-324-2709. Fax: 508-324-2709. p. 1088

Murray, Cynthia, Mgr, National Sea Grant Library, Ocean Science & Exploration Ctr, URI-Bay Campus, Narragansett, RI, 02882-1197. Tel: 401-874-6539. p. 2168

Murray, David, Exec Dir, Brookdale Community College, 765 Newman Springs Rd, Lincroft, NJ, 07738-1597. Tel: 732-224-2217. Fax: 732-224-2982. p. 1495

Murray, Debi, Chief Curator, Historical Society of Palm Beach County, 300 N Dixie Hwy, West Palm Beach, FL, 33401. Tel: 561-832-4164, Ext 105. Fax: 561-832-7965. p. 502

Murray, Donna L, Dir, Bayard Taylor Memorial Library, 216 E State St, Kennett Square, PA, 19348-3112. Tel: 610-444-2702. Fax: 610-444-1752. p. 2074

Murray, Ed, Br Mgr, Jacksonville Public Library, South Mandarin, 12125 San Jose Blvd, Jacksonville, FL, 32223-2636. Tel: 904-288-6385. Fax: 904-288-6399. p. 454

Murray, Elaine, Mgr, Halifax Public Libraries, J D Shatford Memorial, 10353 St Margaret Bay Rd, No 3 Hwy, Hubbards, NS, B0J 1T0, CANADA. Tel: 902-857-9176. Fax: 902-857-1397. p. 2779

Murray, Elaine D, Br Mgr, Halifax Public Libraries, Tantallon Public, 3646 Hammonds Plains Rd, Upper Tantallon, NS, B0J 3J0, CANADA. Tel: 902-826-3331. Fax: 902-826-3328. p. 2779

Murray, Elizabeth, Ch, Stillwater Public Library, 1107 S Duck St, Stillwater, OK, 74074. Tel: 405-372-3633, Ext 116. Fax: 405-624-0552. p. 1978

Murray, Elizabeth F, Librn, New York State Court of Appeals Library, 20 Eagle St, Albany, NY, 12207-1905. Tel: 518-455-7770. p. 1569

Murray, Eric, Librn, Herzing College Library, 3393 Peachtree Rd, Ste 1003, Atlanta, GA, 30326. Tel: 404-816-4533. Fax: 404-816-5576. p. 516

Murray, Frederic, Instrul Serv Librn, Southwestern Oklahoma State University, 100 Campus Dr, Weatherford, OK, 73096-3002. Tel: 580-774-7113. Fax: 580-774-3112. p. 1985

Murray, Harris, Libr Dir, Orangeburg-Calhoun Technical College, 3250 Saint Matthews Rd NE, Orangeburg, SC, 29118. Tel: 803-535-1262. Fax: 803-535-1240. p. 2201

Murray, James, Librn, Henry Lee Moon Library & Civil Rights Archives, 4805 Mount Hope Dr, Baltimore, MD, 21215-3297. Tel: 410-358-8900. Fax: 410-358-3386. p. 1016

Murray, Jane, Sr Librn, Tech Serv, Board of Governors of The Federal Reserve System, Research Library, 20th & C St NW, MS 102, Washington, DC, 20551. Tel: 202-452-3333. Fax: 202-530-6222. p. 394

Murray, Janice, Ref, Dr Martin Luther King Jr Library, 955 E University Blvd, Melbourne, FL, 32901. Tel: 321-952-4511. Fax: 321-952-4512. p. 463

Murray, Jennifer, Asst Dir, Superior Court Law Library, 101 W Jefferson, Phoenix, AZ, 85003. Tel: 602-506-3461. Fax: 602-506-2940. p. 77

Murray, John, Regional Dir, Wapiti Regional Library, 145 12th St E, Prince Albert, SK, S6V 1B7, CANADA. Tel: 306-764-0712. Fax: 306-922-1516. p. 2921

Murray, Juanita, Dir, Spec Coll, Vanderbilt University, Special Collections & University Archives, 419 21st Ave S, Nashville, TN, 37203-2427. Tel: 615-322-2807. p. 2261

Murray, Karen, Libr Tech, Hamilton Health Sciences, 286 Victoria Ave N, Hamilton, ON, L8L 5G4, CANADA. Tel: 905-527-4322, Ext 44247, 905-527-4322, Ext 44248. Fax: 905-577-1453. p. 2808

Murray, Kathleen, Head, Circ, Mount Prospect Public Library, Ten S Emerson St, Mount Prospect, IL, 60056. Tel: 847-253-5675. Fax: 847-253-0642. p. 677

Murray, Kathy, Head, Alaska Med Libr, University of Alaska Anchorage, Consortium Library, 3211 Providence Dr, Anchorage, AK, 99508-8176. Tel: 907-786-1870. Fax: 907-786-1834. p. 45

Murray, Kathy, Librn, Lewis & Clark Trail Heritage Foundation, Inc, PO Box 3434, Great Falls, MT, 59403-3434. Tel: 406-761-3950. p. 1380

Murray, Kelly, Asst Librn, Bibliothèque Allard Regional Library, 104086 PTH 11, Saint Georges, MB, R0E 1V0, CANADA. Tel: 204-367-8443. Fax: 204-367-1780. p. 2751

Murray, Kevin, Librn, Beaumont Juvenile Correctional Center, PO Box 8, Beaumont, VA, 23014-0008. Tel: 804-556-7221. Fax: 804-556-7238. p. 2450

Murray, Kim, In Charge, Spi Supplies Division of Structure Probe, Inc, 569 E Gay St, West Chester, PA, 19380. Tel: 610-436-5400. Fax: 610-436-5755. p. 2153

Murray, LaVonne, Librn, Scio Public Library, Town Hall, 38957 NW First Ave, Scio, OR, 97374. Tel: 503-394-3342. Fax: 503-394-2340. p. 2019

Murray, Lillian, Cat, Boston University Libraries, Music Library, 771 Commonwealth Ave, Boston, MA, 02215. Tel: 617-353-3705. Fax: 617-353-2084. p. 1058

Murray, Lisa, Dir, Cardington-Lincoln Public Library, 128 E Main St, Cardington, OH, 43315. Tel: 419-864-8181. Fax: 419-864-8184. p. 1865

Murray, Marc, Dir of Educ, Wire Association International Library, 1570 Boston Post Rd, Guilford, CT, 06437. Tel: 203-453-2777, Ext 121. Fax: 203-453-8384. p. 343

Murray, Marcia, Dir, Norwood Library, One Morton St, Norwood, NY, 13668-1100. Tel: 315-353-5692. Fax: 315-353-4688. p. 1708

Murray, Mary, Br Mgr, Harris County Public Library, Parker Williams Branch, 10851 Scarsdale Blvd, Ste 510, Houston, TX, 77089. Tel: 281-484-2036. Fax: 281-481-0729. p. 2336

Murray, Melanie, Dir, Lehigh Public Library, 241 Elm St, Lehigh, IA, 50557. Tel: 515-359-2967. Fax: 515-359-2973. p. 827

Murray, Michael, Asst Provost, Fuller Theological Seminary, 135 N Oakland Ave, Pasadena, CA, 91182. Tel: 626-584-5218. Fax: 626-584-5613. p. 206

Murray, P, Coll Develop, Fairleigh Dickinson University, 1000 River Rd, Teaneck, NJ, 07666-1914. Tel: 201-692-2285. Fax: 201-692-9815. p. 1532

Murray, Patricia, Libr Assoc, Desoto Parish Library, Logansport Branch, 203 Hwy 5, Logansport, LA, 71049. Tel: 318-697-2311. Fax: 318-697-4081. p. 955

Murray, Suzy, Br Mgr, Sacramento Public Library, North Natomas Library, 2500 New Market Dr, Sacramento, CA, 95835. p. 225

Murray, Tamara, Librn, Bethany Public Library, Eight Court St, Bethany, PA, 18431-9516. Tel: 570-253-4349. p. 2033

Murray, Tara, Libr Dir, American Philatelic Research Library, 100 Match Factory Pl, Bellefonte, PA, 16823. Tel: 814-933-3803. Fax: 814-933-6128. p. 2032

Murray, Terry, Mgr, Libr Operations, National Center for Atmospheric Research Library, 1850 Table Mesa Dr, Boulder, CO, 80305. Tel: 303-497-1178. Fax: 303-497-1170. p. 290

Murray, Timothy, Head, Spec Coll, University of Delaware Library, 181 S College Ave, Newark, DE, 19717-5267. Tel: 302-831-2231. Fax: 302-831-1046. p. 386

Murray, William, Head, Syst, United States Naval Academy, 589 McNair Rd, Annapolis, MD, 21402-5029. Tel: 410-293-6900. Fax: 410-293-6909. p. 1011

Murray-Rust, Catherine, Dean of Libr, Vice Provost, Learning Excellence, Georgia Institute of Technology Library, 704 Cherry St, Atlanta, GA, 30332-0900. Tel: 404-894-4501. Fax: 404-894-6084. p. 515

Murrell, Donna, Asst Librn, Casey County Public Library, 238 Middleburg St, Liberty, KY, 42539. Tel: 606-787-9381. Fax: 606-787-7720. p. 922

Murrell, Susan DeBrecht, Dir, Emmet O'Neal Library, 50 Oak St, Mountain Brook, AL, 35213. Tel: 205-879-0459. Fax: 205-879-5388. p. 32

Murrietta, Frances, Br Supvr, Yuma County Library District, Somerton Branch, 240 Canal St, Somerton, AZ, 85350. Tel: 928-373-6543. Fax: 928-627-8345. p. 92

Murrin, Nancy, Mgr, Greenville County Library System, Pelham Road (F W Symmes) Branch, 1508 Pelham Rd, Greenville, SC, 29615. Tel: 864-288-6688. Fax: 864-675-9149. p. 2196

Murry, Denise, Dir, Menard Public Library, 100 E Mission, Menard, TX, 76859. Tel: 325-396-2717. Fax: 325-396-2717. p. 2362

Murry, Mary Mahoney, Mgr, Rapides Parish Library, Georgie G Johnson Branch, 1610 Veterans Dr, Lecompte, LA, 71346. Tel: 318-776-5153. Fax: 318-776-6744. p. 940

Murtagh, Trevor, Media Spec, Pacific Union College, One Angwin Ave, Angwin, CA, 94508-9705. Tel: 707-965-7221. Fax: 707-965-6504. p. 121

Murtha, Carla, Ch, Peru Public Library, 102 E Main St, Peru, IN, 46970-2338. Tel: 765-473-3069. Fax: 765-473-3060. p. 772

Murtha, Leslie, Ref Serv, Atlantic Cape Community College, 5100 Black Horse Pike, Mays Landing, NJ, 08330. Tel: 609-343-4952. p. 1500

Murthy, Uma, Br Librn, Boston Public Library, Brighton Branch, 40 Academy Hill Rd, Brighton, MA, 02135-3316. Tel: 617-782-6032. Fax: 617-782-9883. p. 1057

Musacchio, Amanda, Access Serv Librn, Adler School of Professional Psychology, 17 N Dearborn St, Chicago, IL, 60602. Tel: 312-261-4070. Fax: 312-201-8756. p. 605

Musalem-Michelem, María, Ref Librn, Inter-American University of Puerto Rico, 104 Parque Industrial Turpeaux, Rd 1, Mercedita, PR, 00715-1602. Tel: 787-284-1912. Fax: 787-841-0103. p. 2674

Musante, Patricia, Dir, Potsdam Public Library, Civic Center, Ste 1, Two Park St, Potsdam, NY, 13676. Tel: 315-265-7230. Fax: 315-268-0306. p. 1722

Muscardin, Joann, Ch, Port Jefferson Free Library, 100 Thompson St, Port Jefferson, NY, 11777-1897. Tel: 631-473-0022. Fax: 631-473-4765. p. 1721

Muscarella, Mary, Dir, Town of North Collins Public Library, 2095 School St, North Collins, NY, 14111. Tel: 716-337-3211. Fax: 716-337-0647. p. 1706

Muse, Shirlee, Librn, Cuyahoga Community College, Western Campus Library, 11000 Pleasant Valley Rd, Parma, OH, 44130-5199. Tel: 216-987-5413. Fax: 216-987-5050. p. 1879

Musgrave, Delpha, Microfilm Presv Spec, State Historical Society of Iowa-Des Moines Library, 600 E Locust, Des Moines, IA, 50319-0290. Tel: 515-281-6200. Fax: 515-282-0502. p. 810

Musgrave, Sharon, Head, Coll Mgt Serv, Queen's University, 101 Union St, Kingston, ON, K7L 5C4, CANADA. Tel: 613-533-6000, Ext 7544. Fax: 613-533-6362. p. 2814

Musgrave, Sue, Librn, Wayne City Public Library, 102 S Main, Wayne City, IL, 62895. Tel: 618-895-2661. Fax: 618-895-2661. p. 716

Musgrove, Donna, Circ, Buckley Public Library, 408 Dewey Ave, Poteau, OK, 74953. Tel: 918-647-3833, 918-647-4444. Fax: 918-647-8910. p. 1976

Musgrove, Lisa, Br Mgr, Sonoma County Library, Sonoma Valley Regional, 755 W Napa St, Sonoma, CA, 95476. Tel: 707-996-5217. Fax: 707-996-5918. p. 268

Musgrove, Lisa, County Librn, Siskiyou County Public Library, 719 Fourth St, Yreka, CA, 96097. Tel: 530-841-4175. Fax: 530-842-7001. p. 286

Musick, Donna, Tech Serv, Concord University, 1000 Vermillion St, Athens, WV, 24712. Tel: 304-384-5369. Fax: 304-384-7955. p. 2553

Musick, Kathy, Br Mgr, Washington County Public Library, Hayters Gap, 7720 Hayters Gap Rd, Abingdon, VA, 24210-2823. Tel: 276-944-4442. Fax: 276-944-3011. p. 2443

Muska, Deborah, Ch, Stafford Library, Ten Levinthal Run, Stafford, CT, 06075. Tel: 860-684-2852. Fax: 860-684-2128. p. 369

Muskiewicz, Marion, Ref Librn, University of Massachusetts Lowell Libraries, Lydon Library, 84 University Ave, Lowell, MA, 01854-2896. Tel: 978-934-3209. Fax: 978-934-3014. p. 1101

Musmann, Klaus, Dr, Dir, Notre Dame de Namur University Library, 1500 Ralston Ave, Belmont, CA, 94002-1908. Tel: 650-508-3748. Fax: 650-508-3697. p. 126

Musnikow, Judy, Info Serv Librn, Tufts University, 145 Harrison Ave, Boston, MA, 02111-1843. Fax: 617-636-4039. p. 1068

Mussa, Haney, Br Head, Toronto Public Library, Albion, 1515 Albion Rd, Toronto, ON, M9V 1B2, CANADA. Tel: 416-394-5170. Fax: 416-394-5185. p. 2860

Mussehl, Denise, Ch, Belleville Public Library, 130 S Vine St, Belleville, WI, 53508-9102. Tel: 608-424-1812. Fax: 608-424-3545. p. 2581

Mussell, Amy M, Ref, University of Wisconsin Sheboygan, One University Dr, Sheboygan, WI, 53081-4789. Tel: 920-459-6625. Fax: 920-459-6602. p. 2637

Musselman, Carrie, Dir, Walker Public Library, 207 Fourth St, Walker, MN, 56484. Tel: 218-547-1019. Fax: 218-547-1019. p. 1287

Musselman, Jon, Head, Syst, University of Wisconsin - Platteville, One University Plaza, Platteville, WI, 53818. Tel: 608-342-1649. Fax: 608-342-1645. p. 2630

Musselman, Pam, Asst Librn, Claysburg Area Public Library, 957 Bedford St, Claysburg, PA, 16625. Tel: 814-239-8647. Fax: 814-239-2782. p. 2045

Musser, Deborah, Cat, Cabell County Public Library, 455 Ninth Street Plaza, Huntington, WV, 25701. Tel: 304-528-5700. Fax: 304-528-5701. p. 2561

Musser, Linda, Head of Libr, Pennsylvania State University Libraries, Fletcher L Byrom Earth & Mineral Sciences Library, 105 Deike Bldg, University Park, PA, 16802. Tel: 814-863-7073. Fax: 814-865-1379. p. 2148

Musser, Nancy, Adult Serv, Baldwin Borough Public Library, Wallace Bldg, 41 Macek Dr, Pittsburgh, PA, 15227-3638. Tel: 412-885-2255. Fax: 412-885-5255. p. 2121

Musser, Steven, Acq, Whittier College, Bonnie Bell Wardman Library, 7031 Founders Hill Rd, Whittier, CA, 90608-9984. Tel: 562-907-4247. Fax: 562-698-7168. p. 283

Mussett, Marianne, Toledo Satellite Librn, US Court of Appeals for the Sixth Circuit Library, 312 Potter Stewart US Courthouse, Cincinnati, OH, 45202. Tel: 419-259-7539. Fax: 513-564-7329. p. 1873

Mussett, Marianne C, Librn, United States Courts, 418 US Courthouse, 1716 Spielbusch Ave, Toledo, OH, 43604. Tel: 419-213-5655. Fax: 419-213-5660. p. 1940

Mussett, Steve, Cat Librn, University of Evansville, 1800 Lincoln Ave, Evansville, IN, 47722. Tel: 812-488-2464. Fax: 812-488-6996. p. 739

Must, Virginia, Librn, Pocahontas County Free Libraries, Hillsboro Public, Third St, Hillsboro, WV, 24946. Tel: 304-653-4936. Fax: 304-653-4936. p. 2565

Mustafa, Abdelwahid, Ref Librn, Atlanta-Fulton Public Library System, Auburn Avenue Research Library on African-American Culture & History, 101 Auburn Ave NE, Atlanta, GA, 30303. Tel: 404-730-4001, Ext 199. Fax: 404-730-5879. p. 511

Muszkiewicz, Rachael, Res Serv Librn, Valparaiso University, 1410 Chapel Dr, Valparaiso, IN, 46383-6493. Tel: 219-464-5464. p. 783

Mutale, Muritha, Mgr, ILL, Andrews University, 1400 Library Rd, Berrien Springs, MI, 49104-1400. Tel: 269-471-3264, 269-471-3275. Fax: 269-471-6166. p. 1157

Mutazz, Marquan, Librn, Kean University, 1000 Morris Ave, Union, NJ, 07083. Tel: 908-737-4600. Fax: 908-737-4620. p. 1537

Mutch, Kate, Pub Serv Librn, Natrona County Public Library, 307 E Second St, Casper, WY, 82601. Tel: 307-237-4935. Fax: 307-266-3734. p. 2652

Muterspaw, Kimberly, AV Spec, Mechanicsburg Public Library, 60 S Main St, Mechanicsburg, OH, 43044. Tel: 937-834-2004. Fax: 937-834-3396. p. 1916

Muth, Julianna, Ch, Stone Ridge Public Library, Rte 209, Stone Ridge, NY, 12484. Tel: 845-687-7023. Fax: 845-687-0094. p. 1749

Muth, Richard, Asst Dean, Indiana University of Pennsylvania, Northpointe Regional Campus Library, 167 Northpointe Blvd, Freeport, PA, 16229. Tel: 724-294-3306. Fax: 724-294-3307. p. 2071

Mutka, Martin E, Exec Dir, Library Consortium of Health Institutions in Buffalo, Abbott Hall, SUNY at Buffalo, 3435 Main St, Buffalo, NY, 14214. Tel: 716-829-3900, Ext 143. Fax: 716-829-2211. p. 2950

Mutschler, Susan, Mgr, Ref Serv, Citrus County Library System, Homosassa Public, 4100 S Grandmarch Ave, Homosassa, FL, 34446-1120. Tel: 352-628-5626. Fax: 352-628-3011. p. 427

Mutter, Valerie, Chief Librn, United States Air Force, 45th Space Wing Technical Library FL2513, Bldg 989, Rm A1-S3, 1030 S Hwy A1A, Patrick AFB, FL, 32925-3002. Tel: 321-494-6638, 321-494-7220. Fax: 321-494-6636. p. 481

Mutty, Stephanie S, Librn, United States Court of Appeals First Circuit Satellite Library, One Exchange Terrace, Rm 430, Providence, RI, 02903-1746. Tel: 401-752-7240. Fax: 401-752-7245. p. 2175

Mutz, Bertha, Tech Serv, National Society of the Daughters of the American Revolution, DAR Library, 1776 D St NW, Washington, DC, 20006-5303. Tel: 202-879-3229. Fax: 202-879-3227. p. 411

Mutz, Dixie, Dir, Falls City Public Library, 206 N Irvin, Falls City, TX, 78113. Tel: 830-254-3361. Fax: 830-254-3954. p. 2318

Mutz, Dixie, Dir, Karnes County Library System, Falls City Public Library, 206 N Irvin, Falls City, TX, 78113. Tel: 830-254-3361. Fax: 830-254-3954. p. 2319

Mutz, Janice, Info Literacy Librn, Lakehead University Library, 955 Oliver Rd, Thunder Bay, ON, P7B 5E1, CANADA. Tel: 807-343-8147. Fax: 807-343-8007. p. 2848

Mutzner, Marjorie F, Dir, J R Clarke Public Library, 102 E Spring St, Covington, OH, 45318. Tel: 937-473-2226. Fax: 937-473-8118. p. 1892

Muyumba, Valentine, Dept Chair, Cat, Interim Dept Chair, Acq, Indiana State University, 510 North 6 1/2 St, Terre Haute, IN, 47809. Tel: 812-237-2533. Fax: 812-237-3376. p. 781

Muzatko, Mindy, Head, Circ, Evergreen State College, Library Bldg, Rm 2300, 2700 Evergreen Pkwy NW, Olympia, WA, 98505-0002. Tel: 360-867-6581. Fax: 360-867-6790. p. 2522

Muzi, Lee, Librn, United States Army, 11 Hap Arnold Blvd, Tobyhanna, PA, 18466-5099. Tel: 570-615-7584, 570-895-8851. Fax: 570-895-7419. p. 2146

Muzzerall, Darla, Br Mgr, Halifax Public Libraries, Dartmouth North Branch, 134 Pinecrest Dr, Dartmouth, NS, B3A 2J9, CANADA. Tel: 902-490-5840. Fax: 902-490-5842. p. 2779

Muzzerall, Darla, Mgr, Halifax Public Libraries, Halifax North Memorial, 2285 Gottingen St, Halifax, NS, B3K 3B6, CANADA. Tel: 902-490-5723. Fax: 902-490-5737. p. 2779

Muzzy, Vicki, Coll Develop Mgr, Stark County District Library, 715 Market Ave N, Canton, OH, 44702-1018. Tel: 330-458-2643. Fax: 330-455-9596. p. 1864

Myall, Carolynne, Head, Coll Serv, Eastern Washington University, 816 F St, 100 LIB, Cheney, WA, 99004-2453. Tel: 509-359-6967. Fax: 509-359-2476. p. 2512

Myatt, Angela, Curric Liaison Librn, University of Texas Health Science Center at San Antonio Libraries, 7703 Floyd Curl Dr, MSC 7940, San Antonio, TX, 78229-3900. Tel: 210-567-2400. Fax: 210-567-2490. p. 2383

Myatt, Louise, In Charge, Napa City-County Library, Yountville Branch, 6548 Yount St, Yountville, CA, 94599-1271. Tel: 707-944-1888. p. 192

Myer, Gail K, Dir, Benson Memorial Library, 213 N Franklin St, Titusville, PA, 16354-1788. Tel: 814-827-2913. Fax: 814-827-9836. p. 2145

Myers, Ada, Br Supvr, Licking County Library, Buckeye Lake Branch, 41 First St, Buckeye Lake, OH, 43055. Tel: 740-928-0472. Fax: 740-928-0486. p. 1922

Myers, Amanda, Mgr, Baltimore County Public Library, Perry Hall, 9685 Honeygo Blvd, Baltimore, MD, 21128. Tel: 410-887-5195. Fax: 410-529-9430. p. 1044

Myers, Anne, Acq, Ser, Yale University Library, Lillian Goldman Library Yale Law School, 127 Wall St, New Haven, CT, 06511. Tel: 203-432-1600. Fax: 203-432-2112. p. 358

Myers, Ariel, Archivist, ILL, Lynchburg College, 1501 Lakeside Dr, Lynchburg, VA, 24501-3199. Tel: 434-544-8204. Fax: 434-544-8499. p. 2476

Myers, Cami, Circ Mgr, Chesapeake Public Library, Indian River, 2320 Old Greenbrier Rd, Chesapeake, VA, 23325-4916. Tel: 757-410-7010. Fax: 757-410-7014. p. 2456

Myers, Carla V, Ser, Tech Serv, Washington & Jefferson College Library, 60 S Lincoln St, Washington, PA, 15301. Tel: 724-223-6547. Fax: 724-223-5272. p. 2151

Myers, Carol, Asst Photo Archivist, Spec Coll Librn, San Diego Historical Society, Balboa Park, 1649 El Prado, Ste 3, San Diego, CA, 92101. Tel: 616-232-6203, Ext 127. Fax: 619-232-1059. p. 235

Myers, Carole, Head, Circ, Drew University Library, 36 Madison Ave, Madison, NJ, 07940. Tel: 973-408-3485. Fax: 973-408-3770. p. 1497

Myers, Charles J, Dir, University of the Sciences in Philadelphia, 4200 Woodland Ave, Philadelphia, PA, 19104-4491. Tel: 215-596-8790. Fax: 215-596-8760. p. 2120

Myers, Colette, Adult Serv, McHenry Public Library District, 809 N Front St, McHenry, IL, 60050. Tel: 815-385-0036. Fax: 815-385-7085. p. 672

Myers, Cynthia, Head, Tech Serv, George Mason University Libraries, School of Law, 3301 N Fairfax Dr, Arlington, VA, 22201-4426. Tel: 703-993-8120. Fax: 703-993-8113. p. 2462

Myers, Dayna, YA Serv, L E Phillips Memorial Public Library, 400 Eau Claire St, Eau Claire, WI, 54701. Tel: 715-839-2897. Fax: 715-839-5310. p. 2590

Myers, Douglas, Dir of Communications, Los Angeles County Law Library, Mildred L Lillie Bldg, 301 W First St, Los Angeles, CA, 90012-3100. Tel: 213-785-2529. Fax: 213-613-1329. p. 171

Myers, Eileen, Supvr, Access Serv, Wartburg College Library, 100 Wartburg Blvd, Waverly, IA, 50677-0903. Tel: 319-352-8464. Fax: 319-352-8312. p. 850

Myers, Elizabeth, Circ Serv Coordr, East Baton Rouge Parish Library, 7711 Goodwood Blvd, Baton Rouge, LA, 70806-7625. Tel: 225-231-3745. Fax: 225-231-3788. p. 942

Myers, Elizabeth, Dir, Wayne State University Libraries, Walter P Reuther Library of Labor & Urban Affairs, 5401 Cass Ave, Detroit, MI, 48202. Tel: 313-577-4024. Fax: 313-577-4300. p. 1173

Myers, Gene, Librn, Anoka County Law Library, 325 E Main St, Anoka, MN, 55303. Tel: 763-422-7487. Fax: 763-422-7453. p. 1239

Myers, Heather, Tech Serv & ILL Asst, Franklin College, 101 Branigin Blvd, Franklin, IN, 46131-2623. Tel: 317-738-8164. Fax: 317-738-8787. p. 743

Myers, Hope, ILL, Southern Illinois University Edwardsville, Campus Box 1063, 30 Hairpin Circle, Edwardsville, IL, 62026-1063. Tel: 618-650-2615, 618-650-2711. Fax: 618-650-2717. p. 639

Myers, Jacqueline, Libr Serv Rep, Coconino Community College, 2800 S Lone Tree Rd, Flagstaff, AZ, 86001-2701. Tel: 928-226-4205. Fax: 928-226-4103. p. 62

Myers, Janet, Br Mgr, Tacoma Public Library, Fern Hill, 765 S 84th St, Tacoma, WA, 98444. p. 2540

Myers, Janet, Br Mgr, Tacoma Public Library, South Tacoma, 3411 S 56th St, Tacoma, WA, 98409. p. 2540

Myers, Jennifer, Circ, Amarillo Public Library, 413 E Fourth Ave, Amarillo, TX, 79101. Tel: 806-378-3054. Fax: 806-378-9327. p. 2274

Myers, Jim, Ser Librn, William Carey University Libraries, 498 Tuscan Ave, Box 5, Hattiesburg, MS, 39401. Tel: 601-318-6169. Fax: 601-318-6171. p. 1301

Myers, Jonette, Children's Spec, Okeechobee County Public Library, 206 SW 16th St, Okeechobee, FL, 34974. Tel: 863-763-3536. Fax: 863-763-5368. p. 474

Myers, Joni, Circ Mgr, Minnesota State University, Mankato, ML3097, Mankato, MN, 56001. Tel: 507-389-5952. Fax: 507-389-5155. p. 1257

Myers, Joyce, Br Mgr, Manistee County Library, Wellston Branch, 1451 Seaman Rd, Wellston, MI, 49689-9510. Tel: 231-848-4013. p. 1206

Myers, Kathy, Dir, West Deer Library, Saxonburg Blvd, Gibsonia, PA, 15044. Tel: 724-443-5655. p. 2060

Myers, Kathy, Access Serv Librn, Carthage College, 2001 Alford Park Dr, Kenosha, WI, 53140-1900. Tel: 262-551-5900. Fax: 262-551-5904. p. 2601

Myers, Kenneth, Tech Serv, Palm Beach State College, 4200 Congress Ave, Mail Sta 17, Lake Worth, FL, 33461. Tel: 561-868-3800. Fax: 561-868-3708. p. 459

Myers, Kim, ILL, State University of New York College at Brockport, 350 New Campus Dr, Brockport, NY, 14420-2997. Tel: 585-395-2140. Fax: 585-395-5651. p. 1585

Myers, Larie, Assoc Dir, Ascension Parish Library, 500 Mississippi St, Donaldsonville, LA, 70346-2535. Tel: 225-647-8924. Fax: 225-473-9522. p. 949

Myers, Linda, Dir, Bloomfield Public Library, 200 Seneca St, Bloomfield, MO, 63825. Tel: 573-568-3626. Fax: 573-568-3626. p. 1319

Myers, Marilyn, Assoc Dean, Pub Serv, University of Houston, M D Anderson Library, 114 University Libraries, Houston, TX, 77204-2000. Tel: 713-743-9800. Fax: 713-743-9811. p. 2343

Myers, Mary, Dir, Highlands County Library System, 319 W Center Ave, Sebring, FL, 33870-3109. Tel: 863-402-6716. Fax: 863-385-2883. p. 491

Myers, Maurine, Asst Dir, Johnston Public Library, 6700 Merle Hay Rd, Johnston, IA, 50131-0327. Tel: 515-278-5233. Fax: 515-278-4975. p. 824

Myers, Melanie, Head, Libr Info Tech, Carnegie Mellon University, Hunt Library, 4909 Frew St, Pittsburgh, PA, 15213-3890. Tel: 412-268-2446. Fax: 412-268-2793. p. 2123

Myers, Nan, Dir, Pub Serv, Govt Doc, Wichita State University Libraries, 1845 Fairmount, Wichita, KS, 67260-0068. Tel: 316-978-5130. Fax: 316-978-3048. p. 902

Myers, Nanci, Ch, Haverhill Library Association, 67 Court St, Haverhill, NH, 03765. Tel: 603-989-5578. p. 1451

Myers, Nancy Turner, Soc Sci Librn, University of Missouri-Columbia, Elmer Ellis Library, Ellis Library Bldg, Rm 104, Columbia, MO, 65201-5149. Tel: 573-882-3342. Fax: 573-882-8044. p. 1325

Myers, Pamela, Dir, Pierceton & Washington Township Library, 101 Catholic St, Pierceton, IN, 46562. Tel: 574-594-5474. p. 773

Myers, Pamela A, Dir, Head, Ref, Georgetown Charter Township Library, 1525 Baldwin St, Jenison, MI, 49428. Tel: 616-457-9620. Fax: 616-457-3666. p. 1196

Myers, Patricia, Exec Dir, Campbell County Public Library System, 2101 S 4-J Rd, Gillette, WY, 82718-5205. Tel: 307-687-0009. Fax: 307-686-4009. p. 2655

Myers, Patti, Extn Serv Mgr, Kansas City, Kansas Public Library, 625 Minnesota Ave, Kansas City, KS, 66101. Tel: 913-551-3280. Fax: 913-279-2033. p. 875

Myers, Peggy, Circ, Twinsburg Public Library, 10050 Ravenna Rd, Twinsburg, OH, 44087-1796. Tel: 330-425-4268, Ext 141. Fax: 330-425-3622. p. 1941

Myers, Penelope, Head, Access Serv, Temple University Libraries, 1210 W Berks St, Philadelphia, PA, 19122-6088. Tel: 215-204-0749. Fax: 215-204-0769. p. 2117

Myers, Randall, Evening Circ Supvr, Georgetown College, 400 E College St, Georgetown, KY, 40324. Tel: 502-863-8406. Fax: 502-868-7740. p. 915

Myers, Ray, Asst Dir, Madison County Library System, 102 Priestley St, Canton, MS, 39046-4599. p. 1295

Myers, Rayleen, Admin Assoc, Arizona State University Libraries, Downtown Phoenix Campus Library, UCENT Bldg, Ste L1-62, 411 N Central Ave, Phoenix, AZ, 85004-1213. Tel: 602-496-0300. Fax: 602-496-0312. p. 83

Myers, Robert, Head, Ser Acq, Case Western Reserve University, School of Law Library, 11075 East Blvd, Cleveland, OH, 44106-7148. Tel: 216-368-8656. Fax: 216-368-1002. p. 1876

Myers, Robert C, Curator, Berrien County Historical Association Library, 313 N Cass St, Berrien Springs, MI, 49103-1038. Tel: 269-471-1202. Fax: 269-471-7412. p. 1157

Myers, Roger, Archivist, Librn, University of Arizona, Special Collections, 1510 E University, Tucson, AZ, 85721. Tel: 520-621-4345. Fax: 520-621-2709. p. 89

Myers, Roger, Ref & Instruction Librn, Maryville College, 502 E Lamar Alexander Pkwy, Maryville, TN, 37804-5907. Tel: 865-981-5259. Fax: 865-981-8267. p. 2247

Myers, Sandra, Admin Serv, Dixon Public Library, 230 N First St, Dixon, CA, 95620-3028. Tel: 707-678-2934. Fax: 707-678-3515. p. 140

Myers, Sara, Dir, Columbia Theological Seminary, 701 Columbia Dr, Decatur, GA, 30030. Tel: 404-687-4549. Fax: 404-687-4687. p. 529

Myers, Sarah, Libr Dir, Red Feather Lakes Community Library, 71 Firehouse Lane, Red Feather Lakes, CO, 80545. Tel: 970-881-2664. Fax: 970-881-2836. p. 321

Myers, Sheri, Syst Librn, Northern Kentucky University, University Dr, Highland Heights, KY, 41099. Tel: 859-572-5456. Fax: 859-572-5390. p. 917

Myers, Sidney, Tech Serv, Capilano College Library, 2055 Purcell Way, North Vancouver, BC, V7J 3H5, CANADA. Tel: 604-986-1911, Ext 2129. Fax: 604-984-1728. p. 2734

Myers, Susan, Ref, Everett Free Library, 137 E Main St, Everett, PA, 15537-1259. Tel: 814-652-5922. Fax: 814-652-5425. p. 2056

Myers, Tim, Sr Librn, National Endowment for Democracy Library, 1025 F St NW, Ste 800, Washington, DC, 20004. Tel: 202-378-9700. Fax: 202-378-9407. p. 409

Myers, Tracy, Mgr, District of Columbia Public Library, Southwest, 900 Wesley Pl SW, Washington, DC, 20024. Tel: 202-724-4752. p. 398

Myers, Troy, Chief Exec Officer, South Shore Public Libraries, 15442 Hwy Three, Hebbville, NS, B4V 6X6, CANADA. Tel: 902-543-2548. p. 2783

Myers, Yvonne O, Dir, Martins Ferry Public Library, 20 James Wright Pl, Martins Ferry, OH, 43935. Tel: 740-633-0314. Fax: 740-633-6242. p. 1914

Myers-Steele, Lori, Circ Serv Spec, Berea College, 100 Campus Dr, Berea, KY, 40404. Tel: 859-985-3285. Fax: 859-985-3912. p. 907

Myhre, Charlene, Ref & Instruction Librn, North Dakota State University Libraries, 1201 Albrecht Blvd, Fargo, ND, 58108. Tel: 701-231-9746. Fax: 701-231-6128. p. 1841

Myhre, Sarah, Libr Instruction, Ref Serv, Honolulu Community College Library, 874 Dillingham Blvd, Honolulu, HI, 96817-4598. Tel: 808-845-9194. Fax: 808-845-3618. p. 564

Myhres, Opal, Bibliog Instr, Yakima Valley Genealogical Society Library, 1901 S 12th Ave, Union Gap, WA, 98903. Tel: 509-248-1328. p. 2545

Myhrom-Kirtz, Kay, Ch, Chatfield Public Library, 314 S Main St, Chatfield, MN, 55923. Tel: 507-867-3480. Fax: 507-867-3480. p. 1245

Myitrai, Kathy, Librn, Alberta School for the Deaf Library, 6240 113 St, Edmonton, AB, T6H 3L2, CANADA. Tel: 780-436-0465. Fax: 780-436-0385. p. 2699

Mykytyshyn, Fred, Pres, Ukrainian National Home Association Library, 582 Burrows Ave, Winnipeg, MB, R2W 2A6, CANADA. Tel: 204-582-4528. p. 2757

Myles, Anthony, Tech Asst II, North Carolina School of Science & Mathematics Library, Library, Instructional Technologies & Communications, 1219 Broad St, Durham, NC, 27705. Tel: 919-416-2929. Fax: 919-416-2890. p. 1789

Myles, Barbara, Dir, Lincoln Public Library, Three Bedford Rd, Lincoln, MA, 01773. Tel: 781-259-8465. Fax: 781-259-1056. p. 1099

Myles, Beth, Br Mgr, Union County Public Library, Waxhaw Branch, 509 S Providence St, Waxhaw, NC, 28173. Tel: 704-843-3131. Fax: 704-843-5538. p. 1810

Mynatt, Lisa, Supvr, Circ, Laurel County Public Library District, 120 College Park Dr, London, KY, 40741. Tel: 606-864-5759. Fax: 606-862-8057. p. 922

Mynes, Jess, Cat, Mount Wachusett Community College Library, 444 Green St, Gardner, MA, 01440. Tel: 978-630-9125. Fax: 978-630-9556. p. 1090

Myrden, Sean, Tech Coordr, Riverhead Free Library, 330 Court St, Riverhead, NY, 11901-2885. Tel: 631-727-3228. Fax: 631-727-4762. p. 1728

Myrick, Amy, Programming Librn, Oneonta Public Library, 221 Second St S, Oneonta, AL, 35121. Tel: 205-274-7641. Fax: 205-274-7643. p. 32

Myrick, Tina, Dir, Robertson Memorial Library, 19 W 20th St, Higginsville, MO, 64037. Tel: 660-584-2880. Fax: 660-584-8181. p. 1330

Myroniuk, Theresa, Librn, Mannville Centenial Public Library, PO Box 186, Mannville, AB, T0B 2W0, CANADA. Tel: 780-763-3611. Fax: 780-763-3688. p. 2711

Naab, Michael, Dir, Tongass Historical Museum, 629 Dock St, Ketchikan, AK, 99901. Tel: 907-225-5600. Fax: 907-225-5602. p. 50

Nabors, Cecile, Govt Doc, Spec Coll & Archives Librn, University of North Alabama, One Harrison Plaza, Box 5028, Florence, AL, 35632-0001. Tel: 256-765-4468. Fax: 256-765-4438. p. 17

Nabozny, Carl, AV, Columbia-Greene Community College Library, 4400 Rte 23, Hudson, NY, 12534. Tel: 518-828-4181, Ext 3294. Fax: 518-828-4396. p. 1638

Nachand, Phyllis, Acq Asst, Indiana University Southeast Library, 4201 Grant Line Rd, New Albany, IN, 47150. Tel: 812-941-2262. Fax: 812-941-2656. p. 767

Nacheman, Elinor, Cat/Ref Librn, Rhode Island School of Design Library, 15 Westminster St, Providence, RI, 02903. Tel: 401-709-5943. Fax: 401-709-5932. p. 2174

Nachod, Katherine, Ref/Electronic Serv Librn, Law Library of Louisiana, Louisiana Supreme Court, 2nd Flr, 400 Royal St, New Orleans, LA, 70130-2104. Tel: 504-310-2400. Fax: 504-310-2419. p. 960

Nachreiner, Jackie, Circ, Rio Community Library, 324 W Lyons St, Rio, WI, 53960. Tel: 920-992-3206. Fax: 920-992-3983. p. 2634

Nadeau, Bertin, Mgr, Haut-Saint-Jean Regional Library, Monseigneur Plourde Public, 15 Bellevue St, Saint Francois, NB, E7A 1A4, CANADA. Tel: 506-992-6052. Fax: 506-992-6047. p. 2762

Nadeau, Carolanne, Chief Exec Officer, Otonabee-South Monaghan Township Public Library, 3252 CR 2, Keene, ON, K0L 2G0, CANADA. Tel: 705-295-6814. p. 2812

Nadeau, Carolanne, Chief Exec Officer, Otonabee-South Monaghan Township Public Library, Bailieboro Branch, 199 CR 28, Bailieboro, ON, K0L 1B0, CANADA. Tel: 705-939-6510. Fax: 705-939-6510. p. 2812

Nadeau, Carolanne, Chief Exec Officer, Otonabee-South Monaghan Township Public Library, Stewart Hall, 1490 Matchett Line, Peterborough, ON, K9J 6Y3, CANADA. Tel: 705-749-5642. p. 2812

Nadeau, Cheryl, Adult Serv, Southington Public Library & Museum, 255 Main St, Southington, CT, 06489. Tel: 860-628-0947. Fax: 860-628-0488. p. 368

Nadeau, Darlene, Officer, Canada School of Public Service Library, 241 Cité des jeunes Blvd, Gatineau, QC, K1N 6Z2, CANADA. Tel: 819-953-5295. Fax: 819-953-1702. p. 2882

Nadeau, Diane, Dir, Lisbon Falls Community Library, 28 Main St, Lisbon Falls, ME, 04252-0028. Tel: 207-353-6564. p. 990

Nadeau, Sharon, Dir, Fort Fairfield Public Library, 339 Main St, Fort Fairfield, ME, 04742-1199. Tel: 207-472-3880. p. 985

Nadler, Barbra, Dir, Sharon Public Library, 11 N Main St, Sharon, MA, 02067-1299. Tel: 781-784-1578. Fax: 781-784-4728. p. 1123

Nadler, Judith, Dir & Univ Librn, University of Chicago Library, 1100 E 57th St, Chicago, IL, 60637-1502. Tel: 773-702-8743. Fax: 773-702-6623. p. 626

Nadow, Elizabeth, Ch, Fiske Public Library, 110 Randall Rd, Wrentham, MA, 02093. Tel: 508-384-5440. Fax: 508-384-5443. p. 1146

Naff, Janet W, Librn, Nashville School of Law Library, 4013 Armory Oaks Dr, Nashville, TN, 37204. Tel: 615-256-3684. Fax: 615-244-2383. p. 2258

Naff, Kyle, Instrul Serv Librn, Ref Serv, University of Wisconsin-Whitewater Library, 800 W Main St, Whitewater, WI, 53190. Tel: 262-472-5519. Fax: 262-472-5727. p. 2649

Naftali, Timothy, Dir, Richard Nixon Library & Birthplace, 18001 Yorba Linda Blvd, Yorba Linda, CA, 92886. Tel: 714-993-5075. p. 285

Naftaly, Kathleen, Asst Dir, Crandall Public Library, 251 Glen St, Glens Falls, NY, 12801-3593. Tel: 518-792-6508. Fax: 518-792-5251. p. 1629

Naftzger, Jeannie, Librn, Chester County Law Library, Bar Association Bldg, 15 W Gay St, West Chester, PA, 19380-3014. Tel: 610-344-6166. Fax: 610-344-6994. p. 2153

Nafz, Kate, Ch, Maurice M Pine Free Public Library, 10-01 Fair Lawn Ave, Fair Lawn, NJ, 07410. Tel: 201-796-3400. Fax: 201-794-6344. p. 1485

Nafziger, Cassandra, Libr Tech, Copper Mountain College, 6162 Rotary Way, Joshua Tree, CA, 92252. Tel: 760-366-3794, Ext 5901. Fax: 760-366-5256. p. 161

Nagaruk, Jerri, Librn, Elim Community Library, 101 Hillside St, Elim, AK, 99739. Tel: 907-890-3501. Fax: 907-890-2363. p. 47

Nagata, Angela, Curric Coordr, Hawaii Center for the Deaf & Blind Library, 3440 Leahi Ave, Honolulu, HI, 96815. Tel: 808-733-4831. Fax: 808-733-4824. p. 560

Nagata, Judith, Electronic Serv Librn, Harrisburg Area Community College, 735 Cumberland St, Lebanon, PA, 17042. Tel: 717-780-2535. p. 2079

Nagel, Doreen, Br Mgr, Riverside County Library System, Anza Library, 57430 Mitchell Rd, Anza, CA, 92539. Tel: 951-763-4216. Fax: 951-763-0657. p. 217

Nagel, Mary, Ref Librn, Spokane Falls Community College, 3410 Ft George Wright Dr, MS 3020, Spokane, WA, 99224-5288. Tel: 509-533-3174. Fax: 509-533-3144. p. 2537

Nagel, Sarah C, Res Librn, Bryan Cave Law Library, 700 13th St NW, Ste 700, Washington, DC, 20005-3960. Tel: 202-508-6055. Fax: 202-508-6200. p. 395

Nagel, Sherry, Dir, Cobb Public Library, 109 Mifflin St, Cobb, WI, 53526. Tel: 608-623-2554. Fax: 608-623-2554. p. 2586

Nagle, Erin, Assessment & Mkt Librn, Clayton State University, 2000 Clayton State Blvd, Morrow, GA, 30260. Tel: 678-466-4330. Fax: 678-466-4349. p. 545

Nagle, Gail, Dir, Glendive Public Library, 200 S Kendrick, Glendive, MT, 59330. Tel: 406-377-3633. Fax: 406-377-4568. p. 1379

Nagler, Richard B, Dept Chair, Librn, Ref, Oakland Community College, 22322 Rutland Dr, Rm 230, Southfield, MI, 48075-4793. Tel: 248-233-2830. Fax: 248-233-2828. p. 1228

Nagra, Kanu, Electronic Res Librn, Borough of Manhattan Community College Library, 199 Chambers St, New York, NY, 10007. Tel: 212-220-8000, Ext 7487. Fax: 212-748-7466. p. 1671

Naguib, Sylvia, Curator, National Archives & Records Administration, 441 Freedom Pkwy, Atlanta, GA, 30307. Tel: 404-865-7123. Fax: 404-865-7102. p. 517

Nagy, Gregory, Curator, Harvard Library, Milman Parry Collection of Oral Literature, Widener, Rm C, Cambridge, MA, 02138. Tel: 617-496-2499. p. 1076

Nagy, James, Circ Serv Mgr, Massillon Public Library, 208 Lincoln Way E, Massillon, OH, 44646-8416. Tel: 330-832-9831, Ext 332. Fax: 330-830-2182. p. 1915

Nagy, Lisa, Coordr, Libr Serv, Wayne College Library, University of Akron-Wayne College, 1901 Smucker Rd, Orrville, OH, 44667-9758. Tel: 330-684-8789. Fax: 330-683-1381. p. 1925

Nagy, Rebecca, Libr Dir, Westfield Public Library, 147 Maple St, Westfield, PA, 16950-1616. Tel: 814-367-5411. Fax: 814-367-5411. p. 2155

Nagy, Suzanne, Head, Web Serv, Florida State University Libraries, Charlotte Edwards Maguire Medical Library, 1115 W Call St, Tallahassee, FL, 32304-3556. Tel: 850-644-7623. Fax: 850-644-9942. p. 495

Nagyova, Zdena, Ref Librn, Gowling Lafleur Henderson LLP, One First Canadian Pl, 100 King St W, Ste 1600, Toronto, ON, M5X 1G5, CANADA. Tel: 416-862-3633. Fax: 416-862-7661. p. 2854

Nahapetian, Stella, Br Mgr, Los Angeles Public Library System, Atwater, 3379 Glendale Blvd, Los Angeles, CA, 90039-1812. Tel: 323-664-1353. Fax: 323-913-4765. p. 173

Nahinsky, Beth, Asst Br Mgr, Louisville Free Public Library, Highlands-Shelby Park, Mid-City Mall, 1250 Bardstown Rd, Louisville, KY, 40204. Tel: 502-574-1672. Fax: 502-451-0548. p. 924

Nahl, Diane, Prof, University of Hawaii, 2550 The Mall, Honolulu, HI, 96822. Tel: 808-956-7321. Fax: 808-956-5835. p. 2964

Nahrwold, Carol, Reader Serv, Allen County Public Library, 900 Library Plaza, Fort Wayne, IN, 46802. Tel: 260-421-1236. Fax: 260-421-1386. p. 740

Naidoo, Jamie Campbell, Asst Prof, University of Alabama, 514 Main Library, Tuscaloosa, AL, 35487. Tel: 205-348-4610. Fax: 205-348-3746. p. 2961

Naidoo, Nesan, Dir, Drayton Valley Municipal Library, 5120 - 52 St, Drayton Valley, AB, T7A 1A1, CANADA. Tel: 780-514-2228. Fax: 780-514-2532. p. 2696

Nail, Ken, Jr, State Archivist, Alaska State Archives, 141 Willoughby Ave, Juneau, AK, 99801-1720. Tel: 907-465-2270. Fax: 907-465-2465. p. 49

Nail, Nancy, Ch, Clarion Public Library, 302 N Main St, Clarion, IA, 50525. Tel: 515-532-3673. Fax: 515-532-6322. p. 802

Naiman, Jean, Ch, Fairbury Public Library, 601 Seventh St, Fairbury, NE, 68352. Tel: 402-729-2843. Fax: 402-729-2880. p. 1398

Naimzadeh, Jennifer, Libr Mgr, Aiken-Bamberg-Barnwell-Edgefield Regional Library System, Bamberg County, 3156 Railroad Ave, Bamberg, SC, 29003-1017. Tel: 803-245-3022. Fax: 803-245-2422. p. 2179

Nair, Vijay, Ref Librn, Western Connecticut State University, 181 White St, Danbury, CT, 06810. Tel: 203-837-9116. Fax: 203-837-9108. p. 335

Naisbitt, Jane, Dir, Canadian War Museum, One Vimy Pl, Ottawa, ON, K1A 0M8, CANADA. Tel: 819-776-8652. Fax: 819-776-8623. p. 2830

Naismith, Rachael, Pub Serv, Ref & Info Serv, Springfield College, 263 Alden St, Springfield, MA, 01109-3797. Tel: 413-748-3505. Fax: 413-748-3631. p. 1128

Naizer, Holly, Librn, B J Hill Library, 402 W Travis St, Holland, TX, 76534-3015. Tel: 254-657-2884. Fax: 254-657-2845. p. 2333

Nakajima, Hiroshi, Dir of Tech Serv, Pima Community College, District Library Services, 4905B E Broadway Blvd, Tucson, AZ, 85709-1140. Tel: 520-206-4608. Fax: 520-206-4890. p. 86

Nakama, Marcia, Br Mgr, Hawaii State Public Library System, Kalihi-Palama Public Library, 1325 Kalihi St, Honolulu, HI, 96819. Tel: 808-832-3466. Fax: 808-832-3469. p. 562

Nakano, Kimberly, Dean, Libr & Media Serv, Green River Community College, 12401 SE 320th St, Auburn, WA, 98092-3699. Tel: 253-833-9111, Ext 3307. Fax: 253-288-3436, 253-288-3491. p. 2507

Nakashima, Cathy, Med Librn, Texas Health Presbyterian Hospital Library, 820 Walnut Hill Lane, Dallas, TX, 75231. Tel: 214-345-2310. Fax: 214-345-2350. p. 2311

Nalenko, Jason, Tech Spec, MacEwan Grant University Library, Center for the Arts & Communications Library, 10045 156th St, Edmonton, AB, T5P 2P7, CANADA. Tel: 780-497-4346. Fax: 780-497-4367. p. 2701

Nalepa, Angeline D, Librn, South Suburban College Library, 15800 S State St, Rm 1249, South Holland, IL, 60473-1200. Tel: 708-596-2000, Ext 2478. Fax: 708-210-5755. p. 704

Nall, Cynthia, Dir, Robertsdale Public Library, 18301 Pennsylvania St, Robertsdale, AL, 36567. Tel: 251-947-8960. Fax: 251-947-5521. p. 35

Nall, Shawna, ILL, Carnegie Public Library, 202 N Animas St, Trinidad, CO, 81082. Tel: 719-846-6841, 719-846-7517. Fax: 719-846-0885. p. 324

Nalwasky, Celeste, Librn, Saint Paul's Episcopal Church Library, 1066 Washington Rd, Pittsburgh, PA, 15228-2024. Tel: 412-531-7153. Fax: 412-531-9820. p. 2128

Nam, Wonki, Cat, Central State University, 1400 Brush Row Rd, Wilberforce, OH, 45384. Tel: 937-376-6520. Fax: 937-376-6132. p. 1948

Namiotka, David, Assoc State Librn, Libr Serv, State Library of Ohio, 274 E First Ave, Ste 100, Columbus, OH, 43201. Tel: 614-644-7061. Fax: 614-466-3584. p. 1890

Nance, David, Syst Programmer, Pittsburg State University, 1605 S Joplin St, Pittsburg, KS, 66762-5889. Tel: 620-235-4880. Fax: 620-235-4090. p. 890

Nance, James R, Syst Librn, University of Tennessee at Martin, Ten Wayne Fisher Dr, Martin, TN, 38238. Tel: 731-881-7093. Fax: 731-881-7074. p. 2246

Nance, Karolyn, Dir, Bartlett Public Library District, 800 S Bartlett Rd, Bartlett, IL, 60103. Tel: 630-837-2855. Fax: 630-837-2669. p. 592

Nance, Mildred, Mgr, Montgomery County Public Libraries, Chevy Chase Library, 8005 Connecticut Ave, Chevy Chase, MD, 20815-5997. Tel: 240-773-9590. p. 1038

Nance, Nadine, Coordr, Access Serv, Palm Beach Atlantic University, 300 Pembroke Pl, West Palm Beach, FL, 33401-6503. Tel: 561-803-2231. Fax: 561-803-2235. p. 503

Nancy, O'Neill, Librn, Hunters Community Library, 5014 Columbia River Rd, Bldg No 11, Hunters, WA, 99157. Tel: 509-722-3877. p. 2516

Nanez, Danny, Web Applications Developer, University of North Carolina at Greensboro, 320 Spring Garden St, Greensboro, NC, 27402. Tel: 336-256-1215. Fax: 336-334-5399. p. 1798

Nankin, Robert, Br Mgr, Rio Rancho Public Library, 755 Loma Colorado Dr NE, Rio Rancho, NM, 87124. Tel: 505-891-5013. Fax: 502-892-4782. p. 1561

Nankin, Robert, Br Mgr, Rio Rancho Public Library, Ester Bone Memorial Library, 950 Pinetree Rd SE, Rio Rancho, NM, 87124-7615. Tel: 505-891-5225. Fax: 505-891-1396. p. 1561

Nann, John, Ref, Yale University Library, Lillian Goldman Library Yale Law School, 127 Wall St, New Haven, CT, 06511. Tel: 203-432-1600. Fax: 203-432-2112. p. 358

Nanney, Cindy, Ad, Ref Librn, Polk County Public Library, 1289 W Mills St, Columbus, NC, 28722. Tel: 828-894-8721. Fax: 828-894-2761. p. 1785

Nansel, Lila, Asst Librn, Chouteau County Library, 1518 Main St, Fort Benton, MT, 59442. Tel: 406-622-5222. Fax: 406-622-5294. p. 1379

Naour, Joanne, Head, Circ, Ohio State University LIBRARIES, John A Prior Health Sciences Library, 376 W Tenth Ave, Columbus, OH, 43210-1240. Tel: 614-292-4861. Fax: 614-292-1920. p. 1889

Napier, Jane, Ch, Kellogg-Hubbard Library, 135 Main St, Montpelier, VT, 05602. Tel: 802-223-3338. Fax: 802-223-3338. p. 2429

Napier, Judy, Media Spec, Schaumburg Township District Library, 130 S Roselle Rd, Schaumburg, IL, 60193. Tel: 847-923-3180. Fax: 847-923-3188. p. 701

Napier, Kathy, Br Mgr, Scott County Public Library, Lexington Branch, 2781 Cherry St, Lexington, IN, 47138-8620. Tel: 812-889-3831. Fax: 812-889-3846. p. 777

Naples, Ann Marie, Teen Serv, West Hartford Public Library, 20 S Main St, West Hartford, CT, 06107-2432. Tel: 860-561-6950. Fax: 860-561-6976. p. 376

Napoka, Dora, Librn, Tuluksak School-Community Library, PO Box 115, Tuluksak, AK, 99679. Tel: 907-695-5636. Fax: 907-695-5645. p. 54

Napoli, Donald J, Dir, Saint Joseph County Public Library, 304 S Main, South Bend, IN, 46601-2125. Tel: 574-282-4646. Fax: 574-280-2763. p. 779

Nappi, Arno, Sr Law Librn, California Department of Corrections Library System, California State Prison, Sacramento Inmate Library, 100 Prison Rd, Represa, CA, 95671-0002. Tel: 916-985-8610, Ext 6571. Fax: 916-294-3128. p. 221

Nappi, Reta, YA Serv, South Portland Public Library, 482 Broadway, South Portland, ME, 04106. Tel: 207-767-7660. Fax: 207-767-7626. p. 1002

Napsha, Cheryl, Dir, Bethel Park Public Library, 5100 W Library Ave, Bethel Park, PA, 15102. Tel: 412-831-6800, Ext 262, 412-851-2465. Fax: 412-835-9360. p. 2033

Naputi, Erlinda, Ch, Joeten-Kiyu Public Library, Beach Rd, Susupe, Saipan, MP, 96950. Tel: 670-235-7322, 670-235-7324. Fax: 670-235-7550. p. 2669

Naranjilla, Carina, In Charge, Alberta Historical Resources Foundation Library, 8820 112th St, Edmonton, AB, T6G 2P8, CANADA. Tel: 780-431-2305. Fax: 780-427-5598. p. 2698

Naranjo, Becky, ILL, Midland County Public Library, 301 W Missouri, Midland, TX, 79701. Tel: 432-688-4320. Fax: 432-688-4939. p. 2363

Naranjo, Teresa, Dir, Santa Clara Pueblo Community Library, PO Box 580, Espanola, NM, 87532-0580. Tel: 505-753-7326. p. 1555

Narayan, Lakshmi, Head of Libr, Krotona Institute of Theosophy Library, Two Krotona Hill, Ojai, CA, 93023-3901. Tel: 805-646-2653. p. 200

Narayanan, Kamala, Librn, Dublin Public Library, 2249 E Cumberland, Dublin, IN, 47335. Tel: 765-478-6206. Fax: 765-478-6206. p. 736

Nardi, Chris, Coll Develop, USS Massachusetts Memorial Committee, Inc, Battleship Cove, Fall River, MA, 02721. Tel: 508-678-1100. Fax: 508-674-5597. p. 1088

Nardi, Marie, Commun Relations Coordr, Morse Institute Library, 14 E Central St, Natick, MA, 01760. Tel: 508-647-6524. Fax: 508-647-6527. p. 1107

Nardi, Wendy, Hist Coll Librn, Trenton Free Public Library, 120 Academy St, Trenton, NJ, 08608-1302. Tel: 609-392-7188. Fax: 609-396-7655. p. 1536

Nardini, Holly Grossetta, Yale University Library, Harvey Cushing/John Hay Whitney Medical Library, Sterling Hall of Medicine, 333 Cedar St, L110 SHM, New Haven, CT, 06520. Tel: 203-737-1537. Fax: 203-785-5636. p. 358

Nardone, Paul, Librn, Ruskin, Moscou & Faltischek PC, 1425 RXR Plaza, Uniondale, NY, 11556-0190. Tel: 516-663-6525. Fax: 516-663-6725. p. 1758

Nareau, Margaret, Libr Dir, Huntington Public Library, Seven E Main St, Huntington, MA, 01050. Tel: 413-667-3506. Fax: 413-667-0088. p. 1096

Naritomi, Brent, Info Res Mgr, Latham & Watkins, 600 W Broadway, Ste 1800, San Diego, CA, 92101. Tel: 619-236-2872. Fax: 619-696-7419. p. 231

Narosny, Judy, Tech Serv, Simmons College, 300 The Fenway, Boston, MA, 02115-5898. p. 1066

Narson, Marilyn, Circ, Saint John's University Library, 8000 Utopia Pkwy, Queens, NY, 11439. Tel: 718-990-6735. Fax: 718-380-0353. p. 1725

Nartker, Gail Ann, Dir, Sandusky District Library, 55 E Sanilac Ave, Sandusky, MI, 48471-1146. Tel: 810-648-2644. Fax: 810-648-1904. p. 1226

Narum, Dianne, Cat Librn, Bemidji State University, 1500 Birchmont Dr NE, Box 4, Bemidji, MN, 56601-2600. Tel: 218-755-3340. Fax: 218-755-2051. p. 1241

Narum, Jeanne, Circ/Tech, Minot Public Library, 516 Second Ave SW, Minot, ND, 58701-3792. Tel: 701-852-1045. Fax: 701-852-2595. p. 1846

Nary, Mildred, Librn, First Presbyterian Church, 11 Springfield Ave, Cranford, NJ, 07016. Tel: 908-276-8440. Fax: 908-276-2645. p. 1480

Nasby, Elizabeth, Mgr, Baltimore County Public Library, Parkville-Carney, 9509 Harford Rd, Baltimore, MD, 21234-3192. Tel: 410-887-5353. Fax: 410-668-3678. p. 1044

Naseman, Peggy, Pub Relations, Shelby County Libraries, 230 E North St, Sidney, OH, 45365-2785. Tel: 937-492-8354. Fax: 937-492-9229. p. 1934

Nash, Amanda, Head, Libr Instruction, Catawba College, 2300 W Innes St, Salisbury, NC, 28144-2488. Tel: 704-637-4739. Fax: 704-637-4304. p. 1822

Nash, Carolyn, Exec Dir, Genesee District Library, G-4195 W Pasadena Ave, Flint, MI, 48504. Tel: 810-230-3335. Fax: 810-732-1161. p. 1179

Nash, Crystal, Libr Dir, Lewis County Public Library, 15 Kyle Ave, Hohenwald, TN, 38462-1434. Tel: 931-796-5365. Fax: 931-796-7739. p. 2237

Nash, Hannah, Ch, Miles City Public Library, One S Tenth St, Miles City, MT, 59301-3398. Tel: 406-234-1496. Fax: 406-234-2095. p. 1386

Nash, Jacqueline, Librn, Cape Shore Public Library, General Delivery, St. Bride's, NL, A0B 2Z0, CANADA. Tel: 709-337-2360. Fax: 709-337-2360. p. 2771

Nash, Jeanette, Librn, Catlin Public Library District, 101 Mapleleaf Dr, Catlin, IL, 61817. Tel: 217-427-2550. Fax: 217-427-9830. p. 602

Nash, Jennifer, Ref Serv, Teen, Wallingford Public Library, 200 N Main St, Wallingford, CT, 06492-3791. Tel: 203-265-6754. Fax: 203-269-5698. p. 373

Nash, Joseph, Coll Develop, Outreach Serv Librn, The William K Sanford Town Library, 629 Albany Shaker Rd, Loudonville, NY, 12211-1196. Tel: 518-458-9274. Fax: 518-438-0988. p. 1655

Nash, Katie, Archivist & Spec Coll Librn, Elon University, 308 N O'Kelly Ave, Elon, NC, 27244-0187. Tel: 226-278-6681. Fax: 336-278-6637. p. 1791

Nash, Ken, Librn, College of New Rochelle, 125 Barclay, Rm 211, New York, NY, 10007. Tel: 212-815-1699. Fax: 212-815-7529. p. 1674

Nash, Mary, Head, Ref (Info Serv) Creighton University, 2500 California Plaza, Omaha, NE, 68178-0209. Tel: 402-280-2226. Fax: 402-280-2435. p. 1412

Nash, Michael, Dir, New York University, Tamiment Library/Robert F Wagner Labor Archives, Elmer Holmes Bobst Library, 70 Washington Sq S, 10th Flr, New York, NY, 10012. Tel: 212-998-2630. p. 1695

Nash, Robert, Coll Develop Librn, Spec Coll, University of Nebraska at Omaha, 6001 Dodge St, Omaha, NE, 68182-0237. Tel: 402-554-2884. Fax: 402-554-3215. p. 1414

Nash, Sally, Pub Serv Mgr, Timberland Regional Library, 415 Tumwater Blvd SW, Tumwater, WA, 98501-5799. Tel: 360-943-5001, Ext 2554. Fax: 360-586-6838. p. 2543

Nash, Tommy, Tech Serv, Faulkner-Van Buren Regional Library System, 1900 Tyler St, Conway, AR, 72032. Tel: 501-327-7482. Fax: 501-327-9098. p. 96

Naslund, Jo-Anne, Actg Head Librn, University of British Columbia Library, Education, 2125 Main Mall, Vancouver, BC, V6T 1Z4, CANADA. Tel: 604-822-0940. Fax: 604-822-5378. p. 2743

Nason, C M, Coordr, Algonquin College of Applied Arts & Technology, 1385 Woodroffe Ave, Ottawa, ON, K2G 1V8, CANADA. Tel: 613-727-4723, Ext 5066. Fax: 613-727-7759. p. 2978

Nason, Ella, Asst Dir, New Brunswick Public Library Service, 250 King St, Fredericton, NB, E3B 9M9, CANADA. Tel: 506-453-2354. Fax: 506-444-4064. p. 2763

Nass, Jan, Ser/Digital Librn, Martin Luther College Library, 1995 Luther Ct, New Ulm, MN, 56073-3965. Tel: 507-354-8221, Ext 327. Fax: 507-233-9107. p. 1268

Nasser, Brenda, Br Mgr, Calaveras County Library, Mokelumne Hill Branch, 8328 Main St, Mokelumne Hill, CA, 95245. Tel: 209-286-0507. p. 227

Nassim, Mohammad, Ref Librn, Venable LLP Library, 575 Seventh St, NW, Washington, DC, 20004-1601. Tel: 202-344-8552. Fax: 202-344-8300. p. 422

Nast, Jim, Computer Serv, Sedona Public Library, 3250 White Bear Rd, Sedona, AZ, 86336. Tel: 928-282-7714. Fax: 928-282-5789. p. 81

Nastaszewski, Kim, Librn, JFSA Holocaust Resource Center, 4794 S Eastern Ave, Ste A, Las Vegas, NV, 89119. Tel: 702-433-0005. p. 1429

Nasto, Ellen, Assoc Librn, Andrew W Mellon Foundation, 140 E 62nd St, New York, NY, 10065. Tel: 212-838-8400. Fax: 212-888-4172. p. 1685

Natal, Gerald, Health Sci Librn, University of Toledo, Health Science Campus, Mail Stop 1061, 3000 Arlington Ave, Toledo, OH, 43614-5805. Tel: 419-383-4223. Fax: 419-383-6146. p. 1940

Natarajan, Vani, Res & Instruction Librn, Barnard College, 3009 Broadway, New York, NY, 10027-6598. Tel: 212-854-8595. p. 1670

Nate, Lynette, Ch, Lincoln County Library, Cokeville Branch, 240 E Main St, Cokeville, WY, 83114. Tel: 307-279-3213. Fax: 307-279-3263. p. 2656

Nate, Mary, Dir, Bear Lake County Free Library, 138 N Sixth St, Montpelier, ID, 83254-1556. Tel: 208-847-1664. Fax: 208-847-1664. p. 579

Nathan, Carr, Info Tech, Newton Public Library, 720 N Oak, Newton, KS, 67114. Tel: 316-283-2890. Fax: 316-283-2916. p. 884

Nathan, Catherine, Dir, First Regional Library, 370 W Commerce St, Hernando, MS, 38632. Tel: 662-429-4439. Fax: 662-429-8853. p. 1301

Nathan, Lisa, Asst Prof, University of British Columbia, The Irving K Barber Centre, 1961 E Mall, Ste 470, Vancouver, BC, V6T 1Z1, CANADA. Tel: 604-822-2404. Fax: 604-822-6006. p. 2977

Nathan, Smith, Br Mgr, Jefferson Parish Library, Terrytown Branch, 680 Heritage Ave, Terrytown, LA, 70056. Tel: 504-364-2717. Fax: 504-364-2718. p. 957

Nation, William, Main Libr & Pub Serv Mgr, Boise Public Library, 715 S Capitol Blvd, Boise, ID, 83702. Tel: 208-384-4210. p. 570

Nations, Rebecca, Librn, Lincoln-Lawrence-Franklin Regional Library, 100 S Jackson St, Brookhaven, MS, 39601-3347. Tel: 601-833-3395, 601-833-5038. Fax: 601-833-3381. p. 1294

Natowitz, Allen, Dr, Dep Chief Librn, College of Staten Island Library, 2800 Victory Blvd, 1L, Staten Island, NY, 10314-6609. Tel: 718-982-4023. Fax: 718-982-4002. p. 1747

Natriello, Gary J, Dr, Interim Dir, Teachers College, Columbia University, 525 W 120th St, New York, NY, 10027-6696. Tel: 212-678-3087. p. 1701

Natzke, Teresa, Dir, Franklin Public Library, 32455 Franklin Rd, Franklin, MI, 48025. Tel: 248-851-2254. Fax: 248-851-5846. p. 1181

Naughton, Amy, Actg Dir, Pub Serv, Ref Serv, Minneapolis College of Art & Design Library, 2501 Stevens Ave, Minneapolis, MN, 55404-3593. Tel: 612-874-3752. Fax: 612-874-3704. p. 1260

Naughton, Leslie, Dir, Brielle Public Library, 610 South St, Brielle, NJ, 08730-1494. Tel: 732-528-9381. Fax: 732-223-0346. p. 1475

Naughton, Michael, Head, Tech, Boynton Beach City Library, 208 S Seacrest Blvd, Boynton Beach, FL, 33435. Tel: 561-742-6390. Fax: 561-742-6381. p. 429

Naughton, Sarah, Archivist, Edgewood College Library, 1000 Edgewood College Dr, Madison, WI, 53711-1997. Tel: 608-663-3300. Fax: 608-663-6778. p. 2606

Nault, Andre J, Head Librn, University of Minnesota Libraries-Twin Cities, Veterinary Medical, 450 Veterinary Science Bldg, 1971 Commonwealth Ave, Saint Paul, MN, 55108. Tel: 612-624-5376. Fax: 612-624-9782. p. 1262

Nault, Suzanne, Acq & Cat Librn, University of Massachusetts Lowell Libraries, 61 Wilder St, Lowell, MA, 01854-3098. Tel: 978-934-4592. Fax: 978-934-3015. p. 1100

Nauqti, Abhar, Info Serv, Tech Spec, Old Lyme, Two Library Lane, Old Lyme, CT, 06371. Tel: 860-434-1684. Fax: 860-434-9547. p. 363

Nauta, Laura R, Head, Cat, United States Naval Academy, 589 McNair Rd, Annapolis, MD, 21402-5029. Tel: 410-293-6900. Fax: 410-293-6909. p. 1011

Nauta, Tjalda, Dir, Rhode Island College, 600 Mt Pleasant Ave, Providence, RI, 02908-1924. Tel: 401-456-8126, Ext 8053. Fax: 401-456-9646. p. 2174

Nava, April, Librn, Moreno Valley Public Library, 25480 Alessandro Blvd, Moreno Valley, CA, 92553. Tel: 951-413-3880. Fax: 951-413-3895. p. 191

Navara, Marna, Dir, Stratford Public Library, 816 Shakespeare, Stratford, IA, 50249. Tel: 515-838-2131. Fax: 515-838-2131. p. 846

Navarre, Renee, Head, Circ, Matteson Public Library, 801 S School St, Matteson, IL, 60443-1897. Tel: 708-748-4431. Fax: 708-748-0510. p. 671

Navarro, Amalia, Asst Librn, Zapata County Public Library, 901 Kennedy St, Zapata, TX, 78076. Tel: 956-765-5351. Fax: 956-765-1578. p. 2402

Navarro, Amy, Tech Serv, Dustin Michael Sekula Memorial Library, 1906 S Closner Blvd, Edinburg, TX, 78539. Tel: 956-383-6246. Fax: 956-318-3123. p. 2315

Navarro, Cynthia Y, Coordr, Ser, Laredo Community College, West End Washington St, Laredo, TX, 78040. Tel: 956-721-5961. Fax: 956-721-5447. p. 2353

Navarro, Lisa, Circ, Everett Public Libraries, 410 Broadway, Everett, MA, 02149. Tel: 617-394-2300. Fax: 617-389-1230. p. 1087

Navarro, Mirna, Br Mgr, Nogales-Santa Cruz County Public Library, Sonoita Community Library, County Complex Bldg, 3147 State Rte 83, Sonoita, AZ, 85637. Tel: 520-455-5517. p. 69

Navarro, Mirna, Sr Libr Asst, Nogales-Santa Cruz County Public Library, 518 N Grand Ave, Nogales, AZ, 85621. Tel: 520-287-3343. Fax: 520-287-4823. p. 69

Navarro, Mirna, Br Mgr, Nogales-Santa Cruz County Public Library, Tubac Community Library, 50 Bridge Rd, Tubac, AZ, 85646. Tel: 520-398-9814. p. 70

Navarro, Rosendo, Br Mgr, Tulare County Library, Woodlake Branch, 400 W Whitney Ave, Woodlake, CA, 93286. Tel: 559-564-8424. Fax: 559-564-6725. p. 281

Navarro, Sharon, Librn, Moreno Valley Public Library, 25480 Alessandro Blvd, Moreno Valley, CA, 92553. Tel: 951-413-3880. Fax: 951-413-3895. p. 191

Nave, Rusty, Asst Librn, Martinsville Public Library District, 120 E Cumberland, Martinsville, IL, 62442-1000. Tel: 217-382-4113. Fax: 217-382-4113. p. 671

Navey, Dianne, Br Supvr, Gaston County Public Library, Stanley Branch, 205 N Peterson St, Stanley, NC, 28164. Tel: 704-263-4166. Fax: 704-263-4166. p. 1794

Navin, Krista, YA Librn, Palmer Public Library, 1455 N Main St, Palmer, MA, 01069. Tel: 413-283-3330. Fax: 413-283-9970. p. 1116

Navo, Glorieta, Commun Libr Mgr, County of Los Angeles Public Library, Lynwood Library, 11320 Bullis Rd, Lynwood, CA, 90262-3661. Tel: 310-635-7121. Fax: 310-635-4967. p. 142

Navratil, Constance, Circ, Normandale Community College Library, 9700 France Ave S, Bloomington, MN, 55431. Tel: 952-487-8290. Fax: 952-487-8101. p. 1242

Navratil, Heather, Ref & Instrul Serv Librn, Carroll College, 1601 N Benton Ave, Helena, MT, 59625. Tel: 406-447-4340. Fax: 406-447-4525. p. 1381

Nawalaniec, Theresa, Assoc Librn, Cleveland State University, University Library, Rhodes Tower, 2121 Euclid Ave, Cleveland, OH, 44115-2214. Tel: 216-687-3504. Fax: 216-687-9380. p. 1879

Nawrocki, Robert F, Chief Librn, Saint Augustine Historical Society, Six Artillery Lane, 2nd Flr, Saint Augustine, FL, 32084. Tel: 904-825-2333. p. 486

Naya, Denise, Sr Law Librn, Queens County Supreme Court Library, General Court House, 88-11 Sutphin Blvd, Jamaica, NY, 11435. Tel: 718-298-1206. Fax: 718-298-1189. p. 1646

Naylor, Dillon, Acq/Res Mgt Asst, Circ, Wilmington University Library, 320 DuPont Hwy, New Castle, DE, 19720. Tel: 302-328-9401. Fax: 302-328-0914. p. 385

Naylor, Eleanor R, Librn, Barium & Chemicals, Inc, 515 Kingsdale Rd, Steubenville, OH, 43952. Tel: 740-282-9776. Fax: 740-282-9161. p. 1936

Naylor, Jane, Asst Librn, Heavener Public Library, 203 E Ave C, Heavener, OK, 74937. Tel: 918-653-2870. Fax: 918-653-4805. p. 1965

Naylor, Janet, Librn, Pemberton & District Public Library, 7390 Cottonwood St, Pemberton, BC, V0N 2L0, CANADA. Tel: 604-894-6916. Fax: 604-894-6916. p. 2735

Naylor, Joan, Dir, Saint Charles Public Library, 210 N Cross St, Saint Charles, IA, 50240. Tel: 641-396-2945. p. 842

Naylor, Kim, Librn, Mohave Community College Library, North Mohave Campus, 480 S Central, Colorado City, AZ, 86021. Tel: 928-875-2799, Ext 2224. Fax: 928-875-2831. p. 66

Naylor, Patricia, Tech Serv, Morley Library, 184 Phelps St, Painesville, OH, 44077-3926. Tel: 440-352-3383, Ext 110. Fax: 440-352-2653. p. 1927

Naylor, Richard J, Dir, The William K Sanford Town Library, 629 Albany Shaker Rd, Loudonville, NY, 12211-1196. Tel: 518-458-9274. Fax: 518-438-0988. p. 1655

Naylor, Tom, Br Operations Supvr, Circ, Fac Serv, Mesa Public Library, 64 E First St, Mesa, AZ, 85201-6768. Tel: 480-644-4144. Fax: 480-644-2991. p. 69

Nayor/Farhar, Deborah, Res, Okeene Public Library, 215 N Main, Okeene, OK, 73763. Tel: 580-822-3306. Fax: 580-822-3309. p. 1971

Nazario, Kenia, Info Serv, Pontifical Catholic University Of Puerto Rico, Encarnacion Valdes Library, 2250 Avenida Las Americas, Ste 509, Ponce, PR, 00717-0777. Tel: 787-841-2000, Ext 1809. Fax: 787-284-0235. p. 2675

Nazario, Madeline, Bibliog Instr, ILL, Pontifical Catholic University Of Puerto Rico, Encarnacion Valdes Library, 2250 Avenida Las Americas, Ste

509, Ponce, PR, 00717-0777. Tel: 787-841-2000, Ext 1801, 787-841-2000, Ext 1802. Fax: 787-284-0235. p. 2674

Nazionale, Nina, Dir of Libr Operations, New York Historical Society Library, 170 Central Park W, New York, NY, 10024. Tel: 212-873-3400. Fax: 212-875-1591. p. 1689

Ndinyah, Josephine P M, Mgr, Libr Serv, Schlumberger-Doll Research, One Hampshire St, Cambridge, MA, 02139. Tel: 617-768-2110. Fax: 617-768-2380. p. 1078

Ndulute, Asteria, Govt Doc/Ref Librn, Tuskegee University, Hollis Burke Frissell Bldg, 1200 W Old Montgomery Rd, Tuskegee, AL, 36088. Tel: 334-727-8891. Fax: 334-727-9282. p. 39

Neace, Kristi, Adminr, First Baptist Church Library, 801 E Hwy 50, Union, MO, 63084. Tel: 636-583-2386. Fax: 636-583-4281. p. 1369

Neacsu, Dana, Ref Librn, Columbia University, Arthur W Diamond Law Library, 435 W 116th St, New York, NY, 10027. Tel: 212-854-3922. Fax: 212-854-3295. p. 1674

Nead, Marge, Dir, Colgate Rochester Crozer Divinity School, 1100 S Goodman St, Rochester, NY, 14620-2592. Tel: 585-340-9602. p. 1729

Neagle, Eric, Access Serv Librn, Illinois Institute of Technology, Chicago-Kent College of Law Library, 565 W Adams St, Chicago, IL, 60661. Tel: 312-906-5662. Fax: 312-906-5679. p. 615

Neal, Alan, Br Librn, Oxnard Public Library, South Oxnard, 4300 Saviers Rd, Oxnard, CA, 93033. Tel: 805-247-8951. Fax: 805-488-1336. p. 203

Neal, Anna, Head, Br Libr, Music Librn, University Libraries, University of Memphis, 126 Ned R McWherter Library, Memphis, TN, 38152-3250. Tel: 901-678-4412. p. 2252

Neal, Anna, Head, Br Libr, Music Librn, University Libraries, University of Memphis, Music, 115 Music Bldg, Memphis, TN, 38152. Tel: 901-678-4412. Fax: 901-678-3096. p. 2252

Neal, Diane, Assoc Prof, North Carolina Central University, 1801 Fayetteville St, Durham, NC, 27707. Tel: 919-530-6485. Fax: 919-530-6402. p. 2971

Neal, Donna B, Cat, Spec Coll & Archives Librn, South Dakota School of Mines & Technology, 501 E Saint Joseph St, Rapid City, SD, 57701-3995. Tel: 605-394-2418. Fax: 605-394-1256. p. 2217

Neal, Elaine, Coll Serv, Tech Serv, Val Verde County Library, 300 Spring St, Del Rio, TX, 78840. Tel: 830-774-7595. Fax: 830-774-7607. p. 2312

Neal, James G, Univ Librn, VPres for Info Serv, Columbia University, Butler Library, Rm 517, 535 W 114th St, New York, NY, 10027. Tel: 212-854-7309. Fax: 212-854-9099. p. 1674

Neal, Jan, Admin Librn, Salinas Public Library, 350 Lincoln Ave, Salinas, CA, 93901. Tel: 831-758-7454. Fax: 831-758-7336. p. 226

Neal, Joy C, Dir, La Conner Regional Library, 614 Morris St, La Conner, WA, 98257. Tel: 360-466-3352. Fax: 360-466-9178. p. 2519

Neal, Karen, Youth Serv Librn, Drake Community Library, 930 Park St, Grinnell, IA, 50112-2016. Tel: 641-236-2661. Fax: 641-236-2667. p. 819

Neal, Kathryn B, Librn, Media Spec, J F Drake State Technical College, 3421 Meridan St N, Huntsville, AL, 35811-1544. Tel: 256-539-8161, Ext 120, 256-551-3120. Fax: 256-551-3134. p. 22

Neal, Larry, Libr Dir, Clinton-Macomb Public Library, 40900 Romeo Plank Rd, Clinton Township, MI, 48038-2955. Tel: 586-226-5011. Fax: 586-226-5008. p. 1164

Neal, Laura A, Instruction Coordr, Shepherd University, 301 N King St, Shepherdstown, WV, 25443. Fax: 304-876-0731. p. 2571

Neal, Linette, Coordr, ILL, Ref Coordr, Fayetteville State University, 1200 Murchison Rd, Fayetteville, NC, 28301-4298. Tel: 910-672-1230. Fax: 910-672-1746. p. 1793

Neal, Lisa, Youth Serv, Davie County Public Library, 371 N Main St, Mocksville, NC, 27028-2115. Tel: 336-753-6030. Fax: 336-751-1370. p. 1810

Neal, Marilyn, Br Mgr, Tulsa City-County Library, Peggy V Helmerich Library, 5131 E 91st, Tulsa, OK, 74137. Tel: 918-596-2466. Fax: 918-596-2468. p. 1983

Neal, Michael, Coordr, Circ, Waterford Township Public Library, 5168 Civic Center Dr, Waterford, MI, 48329. Tel: 248-674-4831. Fax: 248-674-1910. p. 1235

Neal, Norma, Librn, Slocomb Public Library, 107 N Washington St, Slocomb, AL, 36375. Tel: 334-886-9009. Fax: 334-886-3729. p. 36

Neal, Pam, YA Librn, Bristol Public Library, 701 Goode St, Bristol, VA, 24201-4199. Tel: 276-821-6192. Fax: 276-669-5593. p. 2452

Neal, Patty, Ref, Wareham Free Library, 59 Marion Rd, Wareham, MA, 02571. Tel: 508-295-2343. Fax: 508-295-2678. p. 1133

Neal, Peggy, Client Serv Spec/Librn, Canada/Manitoba Business Service Centre Library, 240 Graham Ave, Ste 250, Winnipeg, MB, R3C 0J7, CANADA. Tel: 204-984-2272. Fax: 204-983-3852. p. 2754

Neal, Rosie, Pub Serv, Tougaloo College, Tougaloo College, 500 W County Line Rd, Tougaloo, MS, 39174-9799. Tel: 601-977-7706. Fax: 601-977-7714. p. 1315

Neal, Sally, Asst Dean, Pub Serv, Butler University Libraries, 4600 Sunset Ave, Indianapolis, IN, 46208. Tel: 317-940-9949. Fax: 317-940-9711. p. 749

Neal, Sharon, Libr Dir, Alvernia University, 400 St Bernardine St, Reading, PA, 19607-1737. Tel: 610-796-1465. Fax: 610-796-8347. p. 2132

Neal, Susan, Adult Serv, Euless Public Library, 201 N Ector Dr, Euless, TX, 76039-3595. Tel: 817-685-1484. Fax: 817-267-1979. p. 2318

Neal, Susan L, Adult Serv, Bedford Public Library, 2424 Forest Ridge Dr, Bedford, TX, 76021. Tel: 817-952-2335. Fax: 817-952-2396. p. 2288

Nealis, Karen, Librn, Monmouth County Library, Holmdel Branch, Four Crawfords Corner Rd, Holmdel, NJ, 07733. Tel: 732-946-4118. Fax: 732-946-2980. p. 1499

Neame, Simon, Dir, University of British Columbia Library, Irving K Barber Learning Centre, 1961 East Mall, Vancouver, BC, V6T 1Z1, CANADA. Tel: 604-822-3096. p. 2743

Neameyer, Jann, In Charge, North Dakota Veterans Home Library, 1400 Rose St, Lisbon, ND, 58054. Tel: 701-683-6534. Fax: 701-683-6550. p. 1845

Neapolitan, Alexis, Jr, Br Coordr, Hazleton Area Public Library, 55 N Church St, Hazleton, PA, 18201-5893. Tel: 570-454-2961. Fax: 570-454-0630. p. 2068

Near, Dee, Ref Librn, Merced College, 3600 M St, Merced, CA, 95348. Tel: 209-384-6086. Fax: 209-384-6084. p. 185

Near, Hollis P, Dir, Libr Serv, Cornish College of the Arts Library, 1000 Lenora St, Seattle, WA, 98121. Tel: 206-726-5041. Fax: 206-315-5811. p. 2527

Nearing, Jane, ILL Librn, Richardson Public Library, 900 Civic Center Dr, Richardson, TX, 75080. Tel: 972-744-4350. Fax: 972-744-5806. p. 2374

Neary, Coleen, Automated Syst & Serv Librn, Federal Reserve Bank of Richmond, 701 E Byrd St, Richmond, VA, 23219. Tel: 804-697-8125. Fax: 804-697-8134. p. 2488

Neary, Mary Ann, Assoc Law Librn, Educ & Ref, Boston College, 885 Centre St, Newton Centre, MA, 02459. Tel: 617-552-8612. Fax: 617-552-2889. p. 1110

Neary, Sandra, Dir, Bridgewater Library Association, 62 Main St S, Bridgewater, CT, 06752-9998. Tel: 860-354-6937. Fax: 860-354-4583. p. 332

Neas, Gisele, ILL, Cegep de L'Abitibi - Temiscamingue Bibliotheque, 425 Boul du College, Rouyn-Noranda, QC, J9X 5M5, CANADA. Tel: 819-762-0931, Ext 1216. Fax: 819-762-2071. p. 2908

Neath-Foster, Jacqueline, Interim Dir, Libr Serv, Tech Serv Librn, Atlantic Union College, 138 Main St, South Lancaster, MA, 01561. Tel: 978-368-2459. Fax: 978-368-2456. p. 1125

Neave, Jessica, Dir, Bay State College Library, 35 Commonwealth Ave, Boston, MA, 02116. Tel: 617-217-9296. Fax: 617-236-8023. p. 1055

Neavill, Gordon Barrick, Dr, Assoc Prof, Wayne State University, 106 Kresge Library, Detroit, MI, 48202. Tel: 313-577-1825. Fax: 313-577-7563. p. 2968

Nebeker, Birthe, Dir, Raritan Valley Community College, 118 Lamington Rd, Branchburg, Somerville, NJ, 08876. Tel: 908-218-8865. Fax: 908-526-2985. p. 1530

Neben, Mary, Transportation Res Librn, NDOR Transportation Resource Library, 1500 Nebraska Hwy 2, Lincoln, NE, 68502-5480. Tel: 402-479-4316. Fax: 402-479-3989. p. 1405

Neblock, Laurie, Librn, Underwood Memorial Hospital, 509 N Broad St, Woodbury, NJ, 08096. Tel: 856-845-0100, Ext 2901. Fax: 856-848-5752. p. 1545

Nebola, Delores, Librn, Telephone Museum of New Mexico Library, 110 Fourth St NW, Albuquerque, NM, 87102. Tel: 505-842-2937. Fax: 505-332-4088. p. 1550

Necakov-Avalos, Lillian, Br Head, Toronto Public Library, St Clair-Silverthorn, 1748 St Clair Ave W, Toronto, ON, M6N 1J3, CANADA. Tel: 416-393-7709. Fax: 416-393-7409. p. 2863

Necci, John, Dir, Temple University Libraries, Law Library, Charles Klein Law Bldg, 1719 N Broad St, Philadelphia, PA, 19124. Tel: 215-204-4538. Fax: 215-204-1785. p. 2117

Nedderman, Robert, Coll Develop, Dir, Hastings College, 705 E Seventh St, Hastings, NE, 68901-7620. Tel: 402-461-7330. Fax: 402-461-7480. p. 1401

Nedderman, Susan, Librn, First Presbyterian Church Library, 621 N Lincoln, Hastings, NE, 68901. Tel: 402-462-5147. Fax: 402-462-6818. p. 1401

Nededog, Lourdes, Tech Serv, University of Guam, Guam & Micronesia Collection, UOG Sta, Mangilao, GU, 96923. Tel: 671-735-2157, 671-735-2160. Fax: 671-734-7403. p. 2667

Nedell, Stephen, Ref, Syst Librn, Malden Public Library, 36 Salem St, Malden, MA, 02148-5291. Tel: 781-324-0218. Fax: 781-324-4467. p. 1102

Neder, Pamela K, Br Mgr, Allegany County Library System, LaVale Branch, 815 National Hwy, LaVale, MD, 21502. Tel: 301-729-0855. Fax: 301-729-3490. p. 1026

Nee, Louise, Asst Dir, Algonquin Area Public Library District, 2600 Harnish Dr, Algonquin, IL, 60102-5900. Tel: 847-458-6060, 847-658-4343. Fax: 847-458-9370. p. 588

Neeb, Louella, Asst Librn, Groves Public Library, 5600 W Washington St, Groves, TX, 77619. Tel: 409-962-6281. Fax: 409-962-3379. p. 2330

Needes, Hildegard, Circ/Bk Proc Librn, Benton County Public Library, 121 S Forrest Ave, Camden, TN, 38320-2055. Tel: 731-584-4772. Fax: 731-584-1098. p. 2226

Needham, Corrinne, Ch, Baldwinsville Public Library, 33 E Genesee St, Baldwinsville, NY, 13027-2575. Tel: 315-635-5631. Fax: 315-635-6760. p. 1577

Needham, Mickey, Br Mgr, Monroe County Public Library, Ellettsville Branch, 600 W Temperance St, Ellettsville, IN, 47429. Tel: 812-876-1272. Fax: 812-876-2515. p. 728

Needham, Tamara, Chief Exec Officer, Head Librn, Marathon Public Library, 22 Peninsula Rd, Marathon, ON, P0T 2E0, CANADA. Tel: 807-229-0740. Fax: 807-229-3336. p. 2820

Neef, Penny, Coordr, Youth Serv, West Bloomfield Township Public Library, 4600 Walnut Lake Rd, West Bloomfield, MI, 48323. Tel: 248-232-2252. Fax: 248-232-2291. p. 1236

Neel, Thomas Stephen, Dir, Ohio Genealogical Society Library, 611 State Rte 97 W, Bellville, OH, 44813-8813. Tel: 419-886-1903. Fax: 419-886-0092. p. 1859

Neels, Kattie, Supvr, Essex County Library, McGregor Branch, 9571 Walker Rd, McGregor, ON, N0R 1J0, CANADA. Tel: 226-946-1529, Ext 211. p. 2804

Neely, Alastair, Br Librn, London Public Library, Westmount, 3200 Wonderland Rd S, London, ON, N6L 1A6, CANADA. Tel: 519-473-4708. p. 2818

Neely, Benjamin K, Exec Dir, Adams County Historical Society Library, Lutheran Theological Seminary Campus, 368 Springs Ave, Gettysburg, PA, 17325. Tel: 717-334-4723. Fax: 717-334-0722. p. 2059

Neely, Colleen, Head of Acq/Cataloging, Carleton University Library, 1125 Colonel By Dr, Ottawa, ON, K1S 5B6, CANADA. Tel: 613-520-2600, Ext 8140. Fax: 613-520-2750. p. 2830

Neely, Eugene T, Univ Archivist, Adelphi University Libraries, One South Ave, Garden City, NY, 11530. Tel: 516-877-3543. Fax: 516-877-3675. p. 1625

Neely, Janie, Adult Serv, Asst Dir, Davie County Public Library, 371 N Main St, Mocksville, NC, 27028-2115. Tel: 336-753-6030. Fax: 336-751-1370. p. 1809

Neely, Janie, Asst Dir, Davie County Public Library, Cooleemee Branch, 7796 NC Hwy 801 S, Cooleemee, NC, 27014. Tel: 336-284-2805. Fax: 336-284-2805. p. 1810

Neely, Jason, Head, Ref (Info Serv), Russell Library, 123 Broad St, Middletown, CT, 06457. Tel: 860-347-2528, Ext 123. p. 352

Neely, Jennifer, Youth Serv, Dunellen Public Library, 100 New Market Rd, Dunellen, NJ, 08812. Tel: 732-968-4585. Fax: 732-424-1370. p. 1481

Neely, Karen, Outreach Mgr, Daniel Boone Regional Library, 100 W Broadway, Columbia, MO, 65203. Tel: 573-443-3161. Fax: 573-443-3281. p. 1324

Neely, Pamela, Head Librn, Coldspring Area Public Library, 14221 State Hwy 150 W, Coldspring, TX, 77331. Tel: 936-653-3104. Fax: 936-653-4628. p. 2298

Neer, Matt, Adult Serv Librn/Virtual Serv, Lake Forest Library, 360 E Deerpath Ave, Lake Forest, IL, 60045-2252. Tel: 847-810-4623. Fax: 847-234-1453. p. 663

Neer, Pat, Dir, Lacona Public Library, 107 E Main, Lacona, IA, 50139. Tel: 641-534-4400. p. 826

Neerman, Sandra M, Dir, Greensboro Public Library, 219 N Church St, Greensboro, NC, 27402-3178. Tel: 336-373-2699. Fax: 336-333-6781. p. 1796

Neeson, Alexis, Ref/Outreach Librn, Indian River State College, 3209 Virginia Ave, Fort Pierce, FL, 34981-5599. Tel: 772-462-7194. Fax: 772-462-4780. p. 446

Neff, B Robert, Tech Serv Librn, Guam Community College, One Sesame St, Mangilao, GU, 96921. Tel: 671-735-0228, 671-735-0229. p. 2667

Neff, Brett, Br Mgr, Stark County District Library, East Canton Branch, 224 N Wood St, East Canton, OH, 44730. Tel: 330-488-1501. Fax: 330-488-2509. p. 1864

Neff, Dee L, Dir, Annville Free Library, 216 E Main St, Annville, PA, 17003-1599. Tel: 717-867-1802. Fax: 717-867-5754. p. 2029

Neff, Gail, Tech Serv, Bluffton Public Library, 145 S Main St, Bluffton, OH, 45817. Tel: 419-358-5016. Fax: 419-358-9653. p. 1860

Neff, Judy, Asst Librn, Legislative Services Agency Library, State Capitol Bldg, Ground Flr, Des Moines, IA, 50319. Tel: 515-281-3569. Fax: 515-281-8027. p. 810

Neff, Paul, Ref, University of Alberta, 4901 46th Ave, Camrose, AB, T4V 2R3, CANADA. Tel: 780-679-1189. Fax: 780-679-1594. p. 2694

Negaard, Cara, Coll Develop, Head, Ref, Great Bend Public Library, 1409 Williams St, Great Bend, KS, 67530-4090. Tel: 620-792-2409. Fax: 620-792-5495, 620-793-7270. p. 869

Negip, Marilyn, Dir, Lasell College, 80 A Maple Ave, Newton, MA, 02466. Tel: 617-243-2243. Fax: 617-243-2458. p. 1109

Negray, Rose Ann, Cat, Streator Public Library, 130 S Park St, Streator, IL, 61364. Tel: 815-672-2729. Fax: 815-672-2729. p. 708

Negro, Sandra, Adjunct Fac Librn, HACC Central Pennsylvania's Community College, 731 Old Harrisburg Rd, Gettysburg, PA, 17325. Tel: 717-337-1644. Fax: 717-337-2329. p. 2060

Negron, David, Coordr, Tech Serv, University of Puerto Rico, Minillas Park, 170, 174 Rd, Bayamon, PR, 00959-1919. Tel: 787-993-0000, Ext 3222, 787-993-8857. Fax: 787-993-8914. p. 2672

Nehring, Fred, Dir, Whitehall Public Library, 36245 Park St, Whitehall, WI, 54773. Tel: 715-538-4107. Fax: 715-538-2301. p. 2648

Neibuhr, Melissa, Br Mgr, Brazoria County Library System, Manvel Branch, 20514B Hwy 6, Manvel, TX, 77578. Tel: 281-489-7596. Fax: 281-489-7596. p. 2275

Neiburger, Eli, Assoc Dir, IT & Product Develop, Ann Arbor District Library, 343 S Fifth Ave, Ann Arbor, MI, 48104. Tel: 734-327-4245. Fax: 734-327-8325. p. 1150

Neidert, Sarah, Webmaster, Brighton District Library, 100 Library Dr, Brighton, MI, 48116. Tel: 810-229-6571. Fax: 810-229-3161. p. 1159

Neidhamer, Brenda, Br Mgr, Tangipahoa Parish Library, Ponchatoula Branch, 380 N Fifth St, Ponchatoula, LA, 70454. Tel: 985-386-6554, 985-386-6593. Fax: 985-370-5019. p. 941

Neidmier, Virginia, Dir, Josephine-Louise Public Library, Five Scofield St, Walden, NY, 12586. Tel: 845-778-7621. Fax: 845-778-1946. p. 1762

Neihouse, Kris, Circ, Monroe County Public Library, 700 Fleming St, Key West, FL, 33040. Tel: 305-292-3595. Fax: 305-295-3626. p. 456

Neil, Barbara, Head, Circ, Lebanon Community Library, 125 N Seventh St, Lebanon, PA, 17046-5000. Tel: 717-273-7624. Fax: 717-273-2719. p. 2079

Neil, Erik H, Dir, Academy Art Museum, 106 South St, Easton, MD, 21601. Tel: 410-822-2787. Fax: 410-822-5997. p. 1027

Neil, Hattie, Br Mgr, Concordia Parish Library, Vidalia Branch, 408 Texas St, Vidalia, LA, 71373. Tel: 318-336-5043. Fax: 318-336-0904. p. 949

Neil, JoAnn, Supvr, Ser, Mississippi College, 151 E Griffith St, Jackson, MS, 39201-1391. Tel: 601-925-7120. Fax: 601-925-7112. p. 1304

Neil, Linda, Acq, Wilbur Wright College North, 4300 N Narragansett Ave, Chicago, IL, 60634-1500. Tel: 773-481-8684. Fax: 773-481-8407. p. 627

Neil, Pam, In Charge, US National Park Service, 170 Mile Creek Rd, Grand Portage, MN, 55605. Tel: 218-475-0123. Fax: 218-475-0174. p. 1253

Neill, Elizabeth, Ref Serv, Bellwood Public Library, 600 Bohland Ave, Bellwood, IL, 60104-1896. Tel: 708-547-7393. Fax: 708-547-9352. p. 593

Neill, Judy, Ref, College of Physicians & Surgeons of British Columbia, 100-1383 W Eighth Ave, Vancouver, BC, V6H 4C4, CANADA. Tel: 604-733-6671. Fax: 604-737-8582. p. 2740

Neill, Sharon, Access Serv, Bibliographer, University of Prince Edward Island, 550 University Ave, Charlottetown, PE, C1A 4P3, CANADA. Tel: 902-566-0343. Fax: 902-628-4305. p. 2876

Neill, Terri, Asst Librn, Ogunquit Memorial Library, 166 Shore Rd, Ogunquit, ME, 03907. Tel: 207-646-9024. p. 994

Neilsen, Kathrine, Librn, United States National Park Service, 13063 E Bonita Canyon Rd, Willcox, AZ, 85643-9737. Tel: 520-824-3560. Fax: 520-824-3421. p. 89

Neilson, Christine, Librn, University of Saskatchewan Libraries, Western College of Veterinary Medicine, WCVM Bldg, Rm 3110, 52 Campus Dr, Saskatoon, SK, S7N 5B4, CANADA. Tel: 306-966-7205. Fax: 306-966-7207. p. 2927

Neilson, Craig, Res Mgr, Utah State Library Division, 250 N 1950 West, Ste A, Salt Lake City, UT, 84116-7901. Tel: 801-715-6750. Fax: 801-715-6767. p. 2415

Neilson, Sue, Cat, American University Library, 4400 Massachusetts Ave NW, Washington, DC, 20016-8046. Tel: 202-885-3204. Fax: 202-885-3226. p. 393

Neilson, Susan, Lifelong Learning Mgr, Wake County Public Library System, Cameron Village Regional Library, 1930 Clark Ave, Raleigh, NC, 27605. Tel: 919-856-6718. Fax: 919-856-6722. p. 1817

Neiman, Kris, Head, Admin Serv, Kenosha Public Library, 812 56th St, Kenosha, WI, 53140-3735. Tel: 262-564-6325. Fax: 262-564-6370. p. 2601

Neiman, Miriam, YA Serv, Welles-Turner Memorial Library, 2407 Main St, Glastonbury, CT, 06033. Tel: 860-652-7719. Fax: 860-652-7721. p. 341

Neinstadt, Karen, Ref/Outreach Librn, Minnesota Department of Transportation Library, 395 John Ireland Blvd, MS 155, Saint Paul, MN, 55155. Tel: 651-366-3796. Fax: 651-366-3789. p. 1279

Neiport, Donna, Adult Serv Coordr, South Park Township Library, 2575 Brownsville Rd, South Park, PA, 15129-8527. Tel: 412-833-5585. Fax: 412-833-7368. p. 2142

Neis, Cathy, Br Mgr, Kent District Library, Gaines Township Branch, 421 68th St SE, Grand Rapids, MI, 49548. Tel: 616-784-2007. Fax: 616-647-3874. p. 1165

Neises, Sarah, Head, Pub Serv, University of Wisconsin Oshkosh, 801 Elmwood Ave, Oshkosh, WI, 54901. Tel: 920-424-0401. Fax: 920-424-7338. p. 2628

Neitling, Sally, Mgr, El Dorado County Library, South Lake Tahoe Branch, 1000 Rufus Allen Blvd, South Lake Tahoe, CA, 96150. Tel: 530-573-3185. Fax: 530-544-8954. p. 208

Neitzke, Cherie, Librn, Howe Memorial Library, 128 E Saginaw St, Breckenridge, MI, 48615. Tel: 989-842-3202. Fax: 989-842-3202. p. 1159

Neiweem, Jessica, Youth Serv Librn, Park County Public Library, 1500 Heart Mountain St, Cody, WY, 82414. Tel: 307-527-1880. Fax: 307-527-1888. p. 2653

Nell, Jill, Info Spec, Alverno College Library, 3401 S 39th St, Milwaukee, WI, 53215. Tel: 414-382-6052. Fax: 414-382-6354. p. 2617

Nellen, Katie, Ref Librn, Wyckoff Public Library, 200 Woodland Ave, Wyckoff, NJ, 07481. Tel: 201-891-4866. Fax: 201-891-3892. p. 1546

Nellis, Mary, Res, Nevada Power Co Library, 6226 W Sahara Ave, Las Vegas, NV, 89151. Tel: 702-367-5055. Fax: 702-227-2023. p. 1430

Nellis, Wade, Chair, Grande Prairie Public Library, 101-9839 103 Ave, Grande Prairie, AB, T8V 6M7, CANADA. Tel: 780-532-3580. Fax: 780-538-4983. p. 2705

Nellums, Olivia, Ref & Instruction Librn, Camden County College Library, College Dr, Blackwood, NJ, 08012. Tel: 856-227-7200, Ext 4405. Fax: 856-374-4897. p. 1473

Nelms, Rosemary, Dir, Commercial Appeal News Library, 495 Union Ave, Memphis, TN, 38103. Tel: 901-529-2781. Fax: 901-529-6460. p. 2248

Nelms, Willie E, Dir, Sheppard Memorial Library, 530 S Evans St, Greenville, NC, 27858-2308. Tel: 252-329-4585. Fax: 252-329-4587. p. 1799

Nelson, Adam, Libr Tech, Wisconsin Indianhead Technical College, 1019 S Knowles Ave, New Richmond, WI, 54017. Tel: 715-246-6561, Ext 4222. Fax: 715-246-2777. p. 2625

Nelson, Alicisa, Youth Serv Librn, Leesburg Public Library, 100 E Main St, Leesburg, FL, 34748. Tel: 352-728-9790. Fax: 352-728-9794. p. 461

Nelson, Amanda, Archivist, American Institute of Physics, One Physics Ellipse, College Park, MD, 20740-3843. Tel: 301-209-3177. Fax: 301-209-3144. p. 1024

Nelson, Amelia, Pub Serv Librn, Nelson-Atkins Museum of Art, 4525 Oak St, Kansas City, MO, 64111-1873. Tel: 816-751-1215. Fax: 816-751-0498. p. 1340

Nelson, Becky, Ch, Salida Regional Library, 405 E St, Salida, CO, 81201. Tel: 719-539-4826. p. 322

Nelson, Belle, Instruction/Info Lit Librn, Minnesota State University Moorhead, 1104 Seventh Ave S, Moorhead, MN, 56563. Tel: 218-477-5919. Fax: 218-477-5924. p. 1266

Nelson, Betty, Head, Circ, University of Detroit Mercy Library, 4001 W McNichols Rd, Detroit, MI, 48221-3038. Tel: 313-993-1071. Fax: 313-993-1780. p. 1172

Nelson, Bill, Dir, Natrona County Public Library, 307 E Second St, Casper, WY, 82601. Tel: 307-237-4935, Ext 115. Fax: 307-266-3734. p. 2652

Nelson, Bonnie Crotty, Mgr, RTI International, MCNC Campus Technical Library, 3021 Cornwallis Rd, Research Triangle Park, NC, 27709-3910. Tel: 919-248-1853. Fax: 919-248-1455. p. 1820

Nelson, Bonnie R, Assoc Librn, Info Syst, John Jay College of Criminal Justice, 899 Tenth Ave, New York, NY, 10019. Tel: 212-237-8267. Fax: 212-237-8221. p. 1683

Nelson, Brent, Ref Librn, University of Arkansas at Little Rock, 2801 S University Ave, Little Rock, AR, 72204. Tel: 501-569-8807. Fax: 501-569-3017. p. 107

Nelson, Bryce, Univ Librn, Seattle Pacific University Library, 3307 Third Ave W, Seattle, WA, 98119. Tel: 206-281-2414. Fax: 206-281-2936. p. 2530

Nelson, Carol, Ref, NHTI, Concord's Community College, 31 College Dr, Concord, NH, 03301-7425. Tel: 603-271-7186. Fax: 603-271-7189. p. 1443

Nelson, Carrie, Acq, Tech Serv, Flathead Valley Community College Library, 777 Grandview Dr, Kalispell, MT, 59901. Tel: 406-756-3855. Fax: 406-756-3854. p. 1384

Nelson, Carrie E, Syst Librn, Carlow University, 3333 Fifth Ave, Pittsburgh, PA, 15213. Tel: 412-578-6137. Fax: 412-578-6242. p. 2122

Nelson, Catherine, Head, Ser, University of California, Santa Barbara, Santa Barbara, CA, 93106-9010. Tel: 805-893-2444. Fax: 805-893-7010. p. 261

Nelson, Cathy, Asst Dir, Ch, Berlin-Peck Memorial Library, 234 Kensington Rd, Berlin, CT, 06037. Tel: 860-828-7125. Fax: 860-829-1848. p. 330

Nelson, Cheryl R, Mgr, Libr Serv, Kimberly-Clark Corp Library, 2100 Winchester Rd, Neenah, WI, 54957. Tel: 920-721-5262. Fax: 920-721-6394. p. 2624

Nelson, Cindy, Librn, Iowa Western Community College, 2700 College Rd, Council Bluffs, IA, 51503-7057. Tel: 712-325-3247. Fax: 712-325-3244. p. 805

Nelson, Cory, Sr Ref Librn/Sci & Tech, Cargill, Inc, 15407 McGinty Rd W, Wayzata, MN, 55391. Tel: 952-742-6498. Fax: 952-742-6062. p. 1287

Nelson, Cynthia, Curator, Kenosha County Historical Society, 220 51st Pl, Kenosha, WI, 53140. Tel: 262-654-5770. Fax: 262-654-1730. p. 2601

Nelson, Deanna, Ch, Lawrence County Public Library, 102 W Main & Jefferson, Louisa, KY, 41230. Tel: 606-638-0554, 606-638-4497. Fax: 606-638-1293. p. 923

Nelson, Debra, Circ, Elk Grove Village Public Library, 1001 Wellington Ave, Elk Grove Village, IL, 60007-3391. Tel: 847-439-0447. Fax: 847-439-0475. p. 641

Nelson, Denise, Bibliog Instr, Online Serv, Ref, Point Loma Nazarene University, 3900 Lomaland Dr, San Diego, CA, 92106-2899. Tel: 619-849-2355. Fax: 619-222-0711. p. 232

Nelson, Doreen, Librn, Stone Memorial Library, 1101 Main St, Conneautville, PA, 16406. Tel: 814-587-2142. Fax: 814-587-2142. p. 2047

Nelson, Edith, Dir, Canton Public Library, 225 N Broadway, Canton, SD, 57013-1715. Tel: 605-987-5831. Fax: 605-764-5831. p. 2211

Nelson, Elizabeth, Br Mgr, Knox County Public Library System, Fountain City Branch, 5300 Stanton Rd, Knoxville, TN, 37918. Tel: 865-689-2681. Fax: 865-689-3481. p. 2242

Nelson, Elizabeth N, Reader Serv, Johns Hopkins University-Peabody Conservatory of Music, 21 E Mount Vernon Pl, Baltimore, MD, 21202-2397. Tel: 410-659-8100, Ext 1159. Fax: 410-685-0657. p. 1015

Nelson, Eric, Exec Dir, Nordic Heritage Museum, Walter Johnson Memorial Library, 3014 NW 67th St, Seattle, WA, 98117. Tel: 206-789-5707, Ext 14. Fax: 206-789-3271. p. 2529

Nelson, Frank L, Dir, White City Public Library, 113 N Adolph, White City, KS, 66872. Tel: 785-349-5551. Fax: 785-349-5551. p. 900

Nelson, Gale L, Dir, Coleman Area Library, 111 First St, Coleman, MI, 48618. Tel: 989-465-6398. Fax: 989-465-1861. p. 1165

Nelson, Garet, Dir, Libr Serv, Lyndon State College, 1001 College Rd, Lyndonville, VT, 05851. Tel: 802-626-6446. Fax: 802-626-6331. p. 2427

Nelson, Gene, Dir, Provo City Library, 550 N University Ave, Provo, UT, 84601-1618. Tel: 801-852-6663. Fax: 801-852-6688. p. 2411

Nelson, Geraldine, Cat, Maple Springs Baptist Bible College & Seminary Library, 4130 Belt Rd, Capitol Heights, MD, 20743. Tel: 301-736-3631. Fax: 301-735-6507. p. 1023

Nelson, Gloria, Br Mgr, Cumberland County Public Library & Information Center, Spring Lake Branch, 101 Laketree Blvd, Spring Lake, NC, 28390-3189. Tel: 910-497-3650. Fax: 910-497-0523. p. 1793

Nelson, Holly, Info Spec, Brown, Rudnick, Berlack, Israels LLP, One Financial Ctr, Boston, MA, 02111. Tel: 617-856-8213. Fax: 617-856-8201. p. 1059

Nelson, Irving, Supvr, Office of Navajo Nation Library, Hwy 264, Post Office Loop Rd, Window Rock, AZ, 86515. Tel: 928-871-7303. Fax: 928-871-7304. p. 90

Nelson, Jamie, Spec Coll Librn, Augustana College Library, 3435 9 1/2 Ave, Rock Island, IL, 61201-2296. Tel: 309-794-7266. Fax: 309-794-7640. p. 696

Nelson, Jane Ann, Dir, Libr Serv, Augsburg College, 2211 Riverside Ave, Minneapolis, MN, 55454. Tel: 612-330-1603. Fax: 612-330-1436. p. 1259

Nelson, Janet, Dir, Community Hospital, 2021 N 12th St, Grand Junction, CO, 81501. Tel: 970-256-6209. Fax: 970-256-6526. p. 310

Nelson, Janet, Commun Serv, Winchester Public Library, 80 Washington St, Winchester, MA, 01890. Tel: 781-721-7171, Ext 24. Fax: 781-721-7170. p. 1142

Nelson, Jaye, Sr Dir, Info Serv, Los Angeles County Law Library, Mildred L Lillie Bldg, 301 W First St, Los Angeles, CA, 90012-3100. Tel: 213-785-2529. Fax: 213-613-1329. p. 171

Nelson, Jean, Dir, Redgranite Public Library, 135 W Bannerman Ave, Redgranite, WI, 54970. Tel: 920-566-0176. p. 2633

Nelson, Jennifer, Electronic Serv, Tech Serv Librn, Morningside College, 1601 Morningside Ave, Sioux City, IA, 51106. Tel: 712-274-5195. Fax: 712-274-5224. p. 844

Nelson, Jennifer K, Ref Librn, University of California, Berkeley, Law, 225 Boalt Hall, Berkeley, CA, 94720. Tel: 510-642-4044. Fax: 510-643-5039. p. 128

Nelson, Jeremy, Electronic Serv Librn, Western State College, 600 N Adams St, Gunnison, CO, 81231. Tel: 970-943-2022. Fax: 970-943-2042. p. 312

Nelson, Jessica, Ref/Instruction Librn, Northwestern College, 3003 Snelling Ave N, Saint Paul, MN, 55113. Tel: 651-631-5241. Fax: 651-631-5598. p. 1280

Nelson, Jill, Acq Mgr, Mars Hill College, 124 Cascade St, Mars Hill, NC, 28754. Tel: 828-689-1452. p. 1809

Nelson, Joyce, Br Mgr, Central Virginia Regional Library, Buckingham County Public, 1140 Main St, Dillwyn, VA, 23936-8413. Tel: 434-983-3848. Fax: 434-983-1587. p. 2463

Nelson, Judith, Ref Serv, Andrews University, 1400 Library Rd, Berrien Springs, MI, 49104-1400. Tel: 269-471-3639. Fax: 269-471-6166. p. 1157

Nelson, Judy, Dir, Kirkland Public Library, 513 W Main St, Kirkland, IL, 60146. Tel: 815-522-6260. Fax: 815-522-6260. p. 661

Nelson, Judy, Youth Serv Dir, Pierce County Library System, 3005 112th St E, Tacoma, WA, 98446-2215. Tel: 253-548-3412. Fax: 253-537-4600. p. 2539

Nelson, Juliet, Distance Educ Librn, SIAST-Saskatchewan Institute of Applied Science & Technology, 4500 Wascana Pkwy, Regina, SK, S4P 3S7, CANADA. Tel: 306-775-7408. Fax: 306-798-0560. p. 2924

Nelson, Karen, Ref, University of Mary Washington, 1801 College Ave, Fredericksburg, VA, 22401-4665. Tel: 540-654-1147. Fax: 540-654-1067. p. 2466

Nelson, Karin, Head, Automation, Tech Serv, Fox River Valley Public Library District, 555 Barrington Ave, Dundee, IL, 60118-1496. Tel: 847-428-3661. Fax: 847-428-0521. p. 637

Nelson, Kate, Adult Serv, Coll Develop, Mystic & Noank Library, Inc, 40 Library St, Mystic, CT, 06355. Tel: 860-536-7721. Fax: 860-536-2350. p. 353

Nelson, Kathie, Br Assoc, Modoc County Library, Adin Branch, Adin Community Hall, Hwy 299, Adin, CA, 96006. Tel: 530-299-3502. p. 120

Nelson, Kathy, Asst Librn, Stromsburg Public Library, 230 Central St, Stromsburg, NE, 68666. Tel: 402-764-7681. Fax: 402-764-7681. p. 1420

Nelson, Kevin, Coll Develop, Dir, Black & Veatch, 11401 Lamar, Overland Park, KS, 66211. Tel: 913-458-7884. Fax: 913-458-2934. p. 887

Nelson, Kim, Librn, Arkansas Methodist Hospital, 900 W Kings Hwy, Paragould, AR, 72450. Tel: 870-239-7101. Fax: 870-239-7400. p. 111

Nelson, Linda, Ref, Scott Community College Library, 500 Belmont Rd, Bettendorf, IA, 52722. Tel: 563-441-4151. Fax: 563-441-4154. p. 796

Nelson, Linda, Ch, Riverhead Free Library, 330 Court St, Riverhead, NY, 11901-2885. Tel: 631-727-3228. Fax: 631-727-4762. p. 1728

Nelson, Lindsay, Dir, Creighton Public Library, 701 State St, Creighton, NE, 68729-4000. Tel: 402-358-5115. Fax: 402-358-3767. p. 1396

Nelson, Lois, Asst Librn, Byron Public Library, 119 Kansas Ave, Byron, NE, 68325. Tel: 402-236-8752. p. 1395

Nelson, Lorrine, Dir, Howard Public Library, 3607 County Rte 70A, Hornell, NY, 14843. Tel: 607-566-2412. Fax: 607-566-3679. p. 1638

Nelson, Lyle, ILL, Maharishi University of Management Library, 1000 N Fourth St, Fairfield, IA, 52557. Tel: 641-472-1121. Fax: 641-472-1137. p. 815

Nelson, Mac, Cello Music Cataloger, University of North Carolina at Greensboro, 320 Spring Garden St, Greensboro, NC, 27402. Tel: 336-334-5781. Fax: 336-334-5399. p. 1798

Nelson, Marian, Dir, Wheaton Community Library, 901 First Ave N, Wheaton, MN, 56296. Tel: 320-563-8487. Fax: 320-563-8815. p. 1288

Nelson, Marie L, Chief Librn, United States Air Force, Air Force Flight Test Center Technical Research Library, 812 TSS/ENTL, 307 E Popson Ave, Bldg 1400, Rm 106, Edwards AFB, CA, 93524-6630. Tel: 661-277-3606. Fax: 661-277-6451. p. 144

Nelson, Marilyn, Asst Librn, Chinook Regional Library, Frontier Branch, First St W, Frontier, SK, S0N 0W0, CANADA. Tel: 306-296-4667. p. 2928

Nelson, Mark, Libr Syst & Serv Tech, Red River College Library, 2055 Notre Dame Ave, Winnipeg, MB, R3H 0J9, CANADA. Tel: 204-632-2417. Fax: 204-697-4791. p. 2757

Nelson, Marsha, Librn, Ryegate Corner Public Library, 18 S Bayley Hazen Rd, East Ryegate, VT, 05042. Tel: 802-584-3880. p. 2423

Nelson, Mary, Archivist, Racine Heritage Museum, 701 S Main St, Racine, WI, 53403-1211. Tel: 262-636-3926. Fax: 262-636-3940. p. 2632

Nelson, Mary Ann, Dir, University of Iowa Libraries, Law Library, 200 Boyd Law Bldg, Iowa City, IA, 52242-1166. Tel: 319-335-9002. Fax: 319-335-9039. p. 823

Nelson, Mary C, Archives, Coordr, Tech Serv, ILL, Massasoit Community College Library, One Massasoit Blvd, Brockton, MA, 02302. Tel: 508-588-9100, Ext 1943. Fax: 508-427-1265. p. 1071

Nelson, Melanie, Ref & Info Serv, Team Leader, University of Tulsa Libraries, Mabee Legal Information Center, 3120 E Fourth Pl, Tulsa, OK, 74104-3189. Tel: 918-631-2404. Fax: 918-631-3556. p. 1984

Nelson, Nancy, Head, Access Serv, University of Delaware Library, 181 S College Ave, Newark, DE, 19717-5267. Tel: 302-831-2231. Fax: 302-831-1046. p. 386

Nelson, Nancy, Dir, Veterans Affairs Medical Center, 1500 N Westwood, Poplar Bluff, MO, 63901-3318. Tel: 573-778-4120. Fax: 573-778-4239. p. 1350

Nelson, Nancy, Librn, Grassy Lake Public Library, PO Box 690, Grassy Lake, AB, T0K 0Z0, CANADA. Tel: 403-655-2232. Fax: 403-655-2259. p. 2706

Nelson, Pamela, Mgr, Libr Develop, Mount Prospect Public Library, Ten S Emerson St, Mount Prospect, IL, 60056. Tel: 847-253-5675. Fax: 847-253-0642. p. 677

Nelson, Pat, Librn, Vermont Public Library, 101 N Main St, Vermont, IL, 61484. Tel: 309-784-6291. Fax: 309-784-6291. p. 714

Nelson, Paula, Librn, Allen Public Library, 207 S Commerce, Allen, OK, 74825. Tel: 580-857-2933. Fax: 580-857-2933. p. 1955

Nelson, Paulette, Ch, Minot Public Library, 516 Second Ave SW, Minot, ND, 58701-3792. Tel: 701-838-0606. Fax: 701-852-2595. p. 1846

Nelson, Peter, Chief Librn, Mississippi Mills Libraries, 155 High St, Almonte, ON, K0A 1A0, CANADA. Tel: 613-256-1037. Fax: 613-256-4887. p. 2792

Nelson, Phyllis A, Asst Dir, Porter County Public Library System, 103 Jefferson St, Valparaiso, IN, 46383-4820. Tel: 219-462-0524, Ext 103. Fax: 219-477-4866. p. 783

Nelson, Rachelle, Cat, University of Pennsylvania Libraries, 3420 Walnut St, Philadelphia, PA, 19104-6206. Tel: 215-898-9048. Fax: 215-898-0559. p. 2118

Nelson, Randy, Ref, South Seattle Community College, 6000 16th Ave SW, Seattle, WA, 98106-1499. Tel: 206-768-6405. Fax: 206-763-5155. p. 2532

Nelson, Reed, Librn, Gibson, Dunn & Crutcher, 333 S Grand Ave, Los Angeles, CA, 90071-3197. Tel: 213-229-7000. Fax: 213-229-7520. p. 170

Nelson, Richard, Dir, North Shore Library, 6800 N Port Washington Rd, Glendale, WI, 53217. Tel: 414-351-3461. Fax: 414-351-3528. p. 2594

Nelson, Ronald C, Dir, Long Beach Museum of Art Library, 2300 E Ocean Blvd, Long Beach, CA, 90803. Tel: 562-439-2119, Ext 226. Fax: 562-439-3587. p. 166

Nelson, Roxanne M, Asst Dir, Pub Serv, Interim Dir, Mercer University, School of Medicine, Medical Library & LRC, 1550 College St, Macon, GA, 31207. Tel: 478-301-4057. Fax: 478-301-2051. p. 540

Nelson, Sandy, Cat, Tech Serv, Sidney Public Library, 1112 12th Ave, Sidney, NE, 69162. Tel: 308-254-3110. Fax: 308-254-3710. p. 1419

Nelson, Sandy, Genealogy Serv, Milton-Freewater Public Library, Eight SW Eighth Ave, Milton-Freewater, OR, 97862-1501. Tel: 541-938-8251. Fax: 541-938-8254. p. 2006

Nelson, Sean, Chief Financial Officer, Boston Public Library, 700 Boylston St, Boston, MA, 02117-0286. Tel: 617-536-5400. Fax: 617-236-4306. p. 1056

Nelson, Sharon, Assoc Dir, Tech Serv & Syst, Tech Serv Librn, Northern Illinois University Libraries, David C Shapiro Memorial Law Library, Normal Rd, DeKalb, IL, 60115-2890. Tel: 815-753-2021. Fax: 815-753-9499. p. 636

Nelson, Shelly, Dir, Gowrie Public Library, 1204 Market St, Gowrie, IA, 50543. Tel: 515-352-3315. Fax: 515-352-3713. p. 818

Nelson, Stephanie, Coordr, Electronic Res, Kapiolani Community College Library, 4303 Diamond Head Rd, Honolulu, HI, 96816. Tel: 808-734-9254. Fax: 808-734-9453. p. 564

Nelson, Stephen, Computer Serv, Tech Mgr, Marquette University, Sensenbrenner Hall, 1103 W Wisconsin Ave, Milwaukee, WI, 53233-2313. Tel: 414-288-7092. Fax: 414-288-5914. p. 2618

Nelson, Sue, Acq, Waseca-Le Sueur Regional Library, 408 N State St, Waseca, MN, 56093. Tel: 507-835-2910. Fax: 507-835-3700. p. 1287

Nelson, Terry, Sr Spec Coll & Commun Res Mgr, Denver Public Library, Blair-Caldwell African American Research Library, 2401 Welton St, Denver, CO, 80205-3015. Tel: 720-865-2401. Fax: 720-865-2418. p. 301

Nelson, Tiffany, Br Mgr, Fort Smith Public Library, 3201 Rogers Ave, Fort Smith, AR, 72903. Tel: 479-646-3945. Fax: 479-646-3965. p. 100

Nelson, Tiffany, Br Mgr, Fort Smith Public Library, Miller, 8701 S 28th St, Fort Smith, AR, 72908. Tel: 479-646-3945. Fax: 479-646-3965. p. 101

Nelson, Tina, Ch, Driftwood Public Library, 801 SW Hwy 101, Ste 201, Lincoln City, OR, 97367-2720. Tel: 541-996-2277. Fax: 541-996-1262. p. 2004

Nelson, Vesa J, Librn, Henry George School of Social Science, 121 E 30th St, New York, NY, 10016. Tel: 212-889-8020. Fax: 212-889-8953. p. 1680

Nelson, Wanda, Asst Librn, Belle Fourche Public Library, 905 Fifth Ave, Belle Fourche, SD, 57717-1795. Tel: 605-892-4407. p. 2210

Nelson, Wayne, Pres, Society for Academic Achievement Library, WCU Bldg, 510 Maine St, Quincy, IL, 62301. Tel: 217-224-0570. p. 693

Nelson, William, Genealogy Librn, West Florida Public Library, 200 W Gregory, Pensacola, FL, 32502. Tel: 850-494-7373. p. 482

Nemajovsky, Caryl, Syst Coordr, Darton College, 2400 Gillionville Rd, Albany, GA, 31707. Tel: 229-317-6765. Fax: 229-317-6652. p. 507

Nembhard, Merlene, Ref Librn, Barry University, 11300 NE Second Ave, Miami, FL, 33161. Tel: 305-899-4051. Fax: 305-899-4792. p. 464

Nemchek, Lee, Librn, Morrison & Foerster LLP Library, 555 W Fifth St, Ste 3500, Los Angeles, CA, 90013-1024. Tel: 213-892-5359. Fax: 213-892-5454. p. 175

Nemec, Ida, Dir, Plum Lake Public Library, 8789 Peterson St, Sayner, WI, 54560. Tel: 715-542-2020. Fax: 715-542-2627. p. 2636

Nemes, Paula, Outreach Librn, Marshall-Lyon County Library, 301 W Lyon St, Marshall, MN, 56258. Tel: 507-537-7003. p. 1258

Nemeth, Diane, Asst Dir, Helena Township Public Library, 8751 Helena Rd, Alden, MI, 49612. Tel: 231-331-4318. Fax: 231-331-4245. p. 1148

Nemetz, Marvia, Dir, Maple Rapids Public Library, 130 S Maple Ave, Maple Rapids, MI, 48853. Tel: 989-682-4464. Fax: 989-682-4149. p. 1206

Nemitz, Susan, Dir, Ramsey County Library, 4570 N Victoria St, Shoreview, MN, 55126. Tel: 651-486-2201. Fax: 651-486-2220. p. 1284

Nemota, Libby, ILL, Palm Beach County Library System, 3650 Summit Blvd, West Palm Beach, FL, 33406-4198. Tel: 561-233-2759. Fax: 561-233-2611. p. 503

Nemphos, Lou, Mgr, Ocean County Library, Whiting Reading Center, Whiting Commons Shopping Ctr, Rte 530, Whiting, NJ, 08759. Tel: 732-849-0391. Fax: 732-849-0283. p. 1535

Nenagh, Susan, Librn, Merced County Law Library, 670 W 22nd St, Merced, CA, 95340-3780. Tel: 209-385-7332. Fax: 209-385-7448. p. 185

Nenova, Milena, Dir, Peninsula Hospital Center, 51-15 Beach Channel Dr, Far Rockaway, NY, 11691-1074. Tel: 718-734-2887. Fax: 718-734-2234. p. 1621

Nenstiel, Susan, Librn, York County Library System, Kreutz Creek Valley, 66 Walnut Springs Rd, Hellam, PA, 17406. Tel: 717-252-4080. Fax: 717-252-0283. p. 2160

Nerbas, Marlies, Librn, Parkland Regional Library, Langenburg Branch, PO Box 549, Langenburg, SK, S0A 2A0, CANADA. Tel: 306-743-5394. p. 2932

Nerbonne, Elizabeth, Ref Serv, Rochester Public Library, 65 S Main St, Rochester, NH, 03867-2707. Tel: 603-332-1428. Fax: 603-335-7582. p. 1464

Nercessian, Y T, Asst Librn, Armenian Numismatic Society Research Library, 8511 Beverly Park Pl, Pico Rivera, CA, 90660-1920. Tel: 562-695-0380. p. 208

Nergelovic, Paul, Doc Librn, United States Military Academy Library, Jefferson Hall Library & Learning Center, 758 Cullum Rd, West Point, NY, 10996. Tel: 845-938-3833. Fax: 845-938-4000. p. 1767

Neri, Rita, Libr Mgr, Saint Francis Hospital, 100 Port Washington Blvd, Roslyn, NY, 11576. Tel: 516-562-6673. Fax: 516-562-6695. p. 1735

Nero, Kenneth, Chief Librn, National Labor Relations Board Library, 1099 14th St NW, Ste 8000, Washington, DC, 20570-0001. Tel: 202-273-3720. Fax: 202-273-2906. p. 410

Nero, Lut R, Dean, Cheyney University, 1837 University Circle, Cheyney, PA, 19319. Tel: 610-399-2203. Fax: 610-399-2491. p. 2044

Nero, Neil, Librn, Wellesley College, Science Library, Science Ctr, 106 Central St, Wellesley, MA, 02481. Tel: 781-283-3084. Fax: 781-283-3642. p. 1135

Neron, Aline, Prof, College Francois-Xavier-Garneau, 1660 blvd de l'Entente, Quebec, QC, G1S 4S3, CANADA. Tel: 418-688-8310, Ext 3504. Fax: 418-681-9384. p. 2978

Nersinger, Carol A, Dir, Albany Public Library, 161 Washington Ave, Albany, NY, 12210. Tel: 518-427-4379. Fax: 518-449-3386. p. 1568

Nerzak, Peter, Dir, Libr Serv, Pellissippi State Technical Community College, 10915 Harding Valley Rd, Knoxville, TN, 37933. Tel: 865-694-6517. Fax: 865-694-6625. p. 2243

Nesbit, Angus, Ref Librn, University of Oregon Libraries, John E Jaqua Law Library, William W Knight Law Ctr, 2nd Flr, 1515 Agate St, Eugene, OR, 97403-1221. Tel: 541-346-1673. Fax: 541-346-1669. p. 1997

Nesbit, Diane, Tech Serv Librn, Schoolcraft College, 18600 Haggerty Rd, Livonia, MI, 48152-2696. Tel: 734-462-4400, Ext 5319. Fax: 734-462-4495. p. 1204

Nesbitt, Cindy, Financial Mgr, Interim Dir, Giles County Public Library, 122 S Second St, Pulaski, TN, 38478-3285. Tel: 931-363-2720. Fax: 931-424-7032. p. 2263

Nesbitt, Jerry L, Dir, Ligonier Public Library, 300 S Main St, Ligonier, IN, 46767-1812. Tel: 260-894-4511. Fax: 260-894-4509. p. 761

Nesbitt, Marilynn, Dir, Lady Lake Public Library, 225 W Guava St, Lady Lake, FL, 32159. Tel: 352-753-2957. Fax: 352-753-3361. p. 457

Nesbitt, Teresa, Outreach Librn, Southern Crescent Technical College Library - Flint Campus, 1533 Hwy 19 S, Thomaston, GA, 30286. Tel: 706-646-6173, 706-646-6225. Fax: 706-646-6240. p. 553

Nesbitt, Wanda, Ref Serv, Dover Public Library, 45 S State St, Dover, DE, 19901. Tel: 302-736-7030. Fax: 302-736-5087. p. 382

Neseth, Pam, ILL, Metropolitan Community College Library, 30th & Fort Sts, Omaha, NE, 68103. Tel: 402-457-2760. Fax: 402-457-2655. p. 1413

Neslund, Joan, Internet Serv, Ref, Ellensburg Public Library, 209 N Ruby St, Ellensburg, WA, 98926-3397. Tel: 509-962-7250. Fax: 509-962-7295. p. 2514

Nesmith, E Deforest, Pub Serv, Union College Library, 3800 S 48th St, Lincoln, NE, 68506-4386. Tel: 402-486-2514. Fax: 402-486-2678. p. 1406

Nesmith, Stephanie, Head, Youth Serv, Hillside Public Library, John F Kennedy Plaza, Hillside & Liberty Aves, Hillside, NJ, 07205-1893. Tel: 973-923-4413. p. 1491

Nesmith, Wendy, ILL, University of Texas Libraries, Perry-Castaneda Library (Main Library), 101 E 21st St, Austin, TX, 78712-1266. Tel: 512-495-4350. p. 2284

Nesmith, Wendy, In Charge, University of Texas Libraries, Interlibrary Services Department, PO Box P, PCL1-343, S5463, Austin, TX, 78713-8916. Tel: 512-495-4134. Fax: 512-495-4283. p. 2284

Nespeco, Mary, ILL, Oceanside Library, 30 Davison Ave, Oceanside, NY, 11572-2299. Tel: 516-766-2360. Fax: 516-766-1895. p. 1709

Ness, Steve, Archivist, Librn, Lancaster Mennonite Historical Society Library, 2215 Millstream Rd, Lancaster, PA, 17602-1499. Tel: 717-393-9745. Fax: 717-393-8751. p. 2077

Nesselroad, Lara, Br Mgr, University of Oregon Libraries, Science, Onyx Bridge, Lower Level, University of Oregon, Eugene, OR, 97403. Tel: 541-346-2664. Fax: 541-346-3012. p. 1998

Nesselrode, Brian, Assoc Dir, Libr Serv, Flagler College, 44 Sevilla St, Saint Augustine, FL, 32084-4302. Tel: 904-819-6206. Fax: 904-823-8511. p. 486

Nesselrode, Doris, Media Spec, Ad, Northern Oklahoma College, 1220 E Grand Ave, Tonkawa, OK, 74653-4022. Tel: 580-628-6250. Fax: 580-628-6209. p. 1980

Nesset, Valerie, Asst Prof, University at Buffalo, State University of New York, 534 Baldy Hall, Buffalo, NY, 14260. Tel: 716-645-2412. Fax: 716-645-3775. p. 2971

Nessman, Cheryl, Coordr, Tech Serv, Manitowoc Public Library, 707 Quay St, Manitowoc, WI, 54220. Tel: 920-686-3000. p. 2612

Nesson, M Lou, Per, Massasoit Community College Library, One Massasoit Blvd, Brockton, MA, 02302. Tel: 508-588-9100, Ext 1932. Fax: 508-427-1265. p. 1071

Nesta, Angela, Librn, Cuyamaca College Library, 900 Rancho San Diego Pkwy, El Cajon, CA, 92019-4304. Tel: 619-660-4403. Fax: 619-660-4493. p. 145

Nestell, Clifford L, Mgr, Shawnee Mission Medical Center Library, 9100 W 74th St, Shawnee Mission, KS, 66204. Tel: 913-676-2101. Fax: 913-676-2106. p. 894

Nester, Annette, Head, Circ, Coventry Public Library, 1672 Flat River Rd, Coventry, RI, 02816. Tel: 401-822-6200. Fax: 401-822-9133. p. 2164

Nester, Susan, Head, Ref & Res Serv, Southern Maine Community College Library, Two Fort Rd, South Portland, ME, 04106. Tel: 207-741-5521. Fax: 207-741-5522. p. 1002

Nesting, Vicki, Asst Dir, Pub Serv, Saint Charles Parish Library, 160 W Campus Dr, Destrehan, LA, 70047. Tel: 985-764-2366. Fax: 985-764-0447. p. 948

Nestman, Lisa, Librn, Palliser Regional Library, Briercrest Branch, Community Ctr, Main St, Briercrest, SK, S0H 0K0, CANADA. Tel: 306-799-2137. p. 2918

Nestory, Michele, Librn, Fairleigh Dickinson University, Dickinson Hall, 140 University Plaza Dr, Hackensack, NJ, 07601. Tel: 201-692-2608. Fax: 201-692-7048. p. 1489

Neswick, Nadine, In Charge, Emanuel Medical Center Library, PO Box 819005, Turlock, CA, 95381-9005. Tel: 209-667-4200, Ext 5655. Fax: 209-664-5657. p. 277

Nett, Cara, Mgr, Computer Ctr & Cat Serv, Laramie County Library System, 2200 Pioneer Ave, Cheyenne, WY, 82001-3610. Tel: 307-773-7231. Fax: 307-634-2082. p. 2652

Nettles, Judy, Acq Librn, Mississippi College, 151 E Griffith St, Jackson, MS, 39201-1391. Tel: 601-925-7120. Fax: 601-925-7112. p. 1304

Nettleton, Tessa, Dir, Okotoks Public Library, 7 Riverside Dr, Okotoks, AB, T1S 1A6, CANADA. Tel: 403-938-2220. p. 2712

Netz, David, Dir, Sioux Center Public Library, 102 S Main Ave, Sioux Center, IA, 51250-1801. Tel: 712-722-2138. Fax: 712-722-1235. p. 843

Netzer-Wajda, Carrie, Ref Serv, Sarah Lawrence College, One Mead Way, Bronxville, NY, 10708. Tel: 914-395-2225. Fax: 914-395-2473. p. 1588

Neubauer, Michelle, Ch, Ref, New Berlin Public Library, 15105 Library Lane, New Berlin, WI, 53151. Tel: 262-785-4980. Fax: 262-785-4984. p. 2625

Neubauer, Susan, Tech Serv, Public Library of Arlington, 700 Massachusetts Ave, Arlington, MA, 02476. Tel: 781-316-3200, 781-316-3233. Fax: 781-316-3209. p. 1050

Neubert, Lori, Asst Librn, Cavalier County Library, 600 Fifth Ave, Langdon, ND, 58249. Tel: 701-256-5353. Fax: 701-256-5361. p. 1845

Neuburger, Evelyn, Mgr, Simpson, Gumpertz & Heger, Inc Library, 41 Seyon St, Bldg No 1, Ste 500, Waltham, MA, 02453. Tel: 781-907-9000. Fax: 781-907-9009. p. 1133

Neuerburg, Laurie, Cat, University of Houston, 2602 N Ben Jordan St, Victoria, TX, 77901-5699. Tel: 361-570-4177. Fax: 361-570-4155. p. 2395

Neufeld, Dee, Coordr, Potash Corporation of Saskatchewan Inc, 122 First Ave S, Ste 500, Saskatoon, SK, S7K 7G3, CANADA. Tel: 306-933-8501. p. 2926

Neufeld, Kenley, Dir, Santa Barbara City College, 721 Cliff Dr, Santa Barbara, CA, 93109-2394. Tel: 805-740-4435. Fax: 805-965-0771. p. 260

Neugebauer, Kyle, Dir, Algona Public Library, 210 N Phillips St, Algona, IA, 50511. Tel: 515-295-5476. Fax: 515-295-3307. p. 792

Neuhaus, Chris, Bibliographer, Instrul Serv Librn, Ref Serv, University of Northern Iowa Library, 1227 W 27th St, Cedar Falls, IA, 50613-3675. Tel: 319-273-3718. Fax: 319-273-2913. p. 799

Neuhaus, Ellen, Bibliographer, Distance Educ, Ref Serv, University of Northern Iowa Library, 1227 W 27th St, Cedar Falls, IA, 50613-3675. Tel: 319-273-3739. Fax: 319-273-2913. p. 799

Neuhaus, Paul, Assoc Librn, Santa Clara University, 500 El Camino Real, Santa Clara, CA, 95053-0500. Tel: 408-554-6830. Fax: 408-554-6827. p. 263

Neujahr, Joyce, Dir, Patron Serv, University of Nebraska at Omaha, 6001 Dodge St, Omaha, NE, 68182-0237. Tel: 402-554-3607. Fax: 402-554-3215. p. 1414

Neukam, Donna, Libr Asst, MedStar Franklin Square Medical Center, 9000 Franklin Square Dr, Baltimore, MD, 21237. Tel: 443-777-7363. Fax: 410-687-1742. p. 1016

Neukom, Samantha, Libr Tech, Atlantic Provinces Special Education Authority Library, 5940 South St, Halifax, NS, B3H 1S6, CANADA. Tel: 902-424-8525. Fax: 902-424-3808. p. 2780

Neuls, Anne, Librn, Southeast Regional Library, Grenfell Branch, 710 Desmond Ave, Grenfell, SK, S0G 2B0, CANADA. Tel: 306-697-2455. p. 2929

Neuman, Deborah, Head, Ref (Info Serv), Jericho Public Library, One Merry Lane, Jericho, NY, 11753. Tel: 516-935-6790. Fax: 516-433-9581. p. 1647

Neuman, Delia, PhD, Assoc Prof, Dir, Sch Libr Media Prog, Drexel University, Rush Bldg, Rm 306, 30 N 33rd St, Philadelphia, PA, 19104-2875. Tel: 215-895-2474. Fax: 215-895-2494. p. 2972

Neuman, Lisa, Ch, Menands Public Library, Four N Lyons Ave, Menands, NY, 12204. Tel: 518-463-4035. Fax: 518-449-3863. p. 1659

Neuman, Mary, Youth Serv, Asotin County Library, 417 Sycamore St, Clarkston, WA, 99403-2666. Tel: 509-758-5454. Fax: 509-751-1460. p. 2512

Neuman, Randy, Assoc Dir, Libr Serv, Huntington College, 2303 College Ave, Huntington, IN, 46750. Tel: 260-359-4063. Fax: 260-358-3698. p. 748

Neuman, Sheri, Librn, Smith Community Library, PO Box 134, Smith, AB, T0G 2B0, CANADA. Tel: 780-829-2389. Fax: 780-829-2389. p. 2717

Neumann-Wood, Vera, Spec Coll Librn, Selby Public Library, 1331 First St, Sarasota, FL, 34236-4899. Tel: 941-861-1100. Fax: 941-316-1188. p. 490

Neumayer, Alisa, Youth Serv, Roosevelt Public Library, Children's Room, 27 W Fulton Ave, Roosevelt, NY, 11575. Tel: 516-378-0222. Fax: 516-378-1011. p. 1735

Neumeyer, Robert, Pub Serv, Ser, Mercy Hospital of Pittsburgh, 1400 Locust St, Pittsburgh, PA, 15219. Tel: 412-232-7520. Fax: 412-232-8422. p. 2126

Neumiller, Marilyn, Assoc Dir, North Central Regional Library, 16 N Columbia St, Wenatchee, WA, 98801-8103. Tel: 509-663-1117, Ext 128. Fax: 509-662-8060. p. 2548

Neumyer, Jennifer, Outreach Librn, Spec Coll, University of Maryland-Eastern Shore, 11868 Academic Oval, Princess Anne, MD, 21853. Tel: 410-651-2200, 410-651-6621. Fax: 410-651-6269. p. 1036

Neunaber, Beth, Cat, Nampa Public Library, 101 11th Ave S, Nampa, ID, 83651. Tel: 208-468-5807. Fax: 208-318-0530. p. 580

Neurohr, Karen A, Assessment Librn, Oklahoma State University Libraries, Oklahoma State University, Athletic Ave, Stillwater, OK, 74078-1071. Tel: 405-744-2376. Fax: 405-744-5183. p. 1978

Neustaedter, Laurel, Curator, Sam Waller Museum Library, 306 Fischer Ave, The Pas, MB, R9A 1K4, CANADA. Tel: 204-623-3802. Fax: 204-623-5506. p. 2753

Nevens, Arlene, Dir, Sea Cliff Village Library, Sea Cliff & Central Ave, Sea Cliff, NY, 11579-0280. Tel: 516-671-4290. Fax: 516-759-6613. p. 1742

Neveu, Ruth, Pub Serv Librn, Lake Superior State University, 906 Ryan Ave, Sault Sainte Marie, MI, 49783. Tel: 906-635-2815. Fax: 906-635-2193. p. 1226

Neville, Anne, Shared Automation Syst Coordr, The Library Network, 41365 Vincenti Ct, Novi, MI, 48375. Tel: 248-536-3100. Fax: 248-536-3099. p. 2946

Neville, Gwenn, Librn, University Center Rochester, 851 30 Ave SE, Rochester, MN, 55904. Tel: 507-285-7233. Fax: 507-281-7772. p. 1273

Neville, Karen, Asst Dir, Worcester County Library, 307 N Washington St, Snow Hill, MD, 21863. Tel: 410-632-2600. Fax: 410-632-1159. p. 1042

Neville, Robert, Tech Serv, College of Charleston, 205 Calhoun St, Charleston, SC, 29401-3519. Tel: 843-953-5530. Fax: 843-953-6319. p. 2184

Neville, Teresa, Head Librn, Federal Deposit Insurance Corp Library, 550 17th St NW, Washington, DC, 20429-0002. Tel: 202-898-3631. Fax: 202-898-3984. p. 400

Neville, Tina, Head, Pub Serv, University of South Florida Saint Petersburg, 140 Seventh Ave S, POY118, Saint Petersburg, FL, 33701. Tel: 727-873-4081. Fax: 727-873-4196. p. 489

Nevins, Kate, Exec Dir, Lyrasis, 1438 W Peachtree St NW, Ste 200, Atlanta, GA, 30309-2955. Tel: 404-892-0943. Fax: 404-892-7879. p. 2941

Nevins, Tiffanie, Circ Supvr, University of Akron Libraries, School of Law Library, 150 University Ave, Akron, OH, 44325. Tel: 330-972-7330. Fax: 330-972-4948. p. 1853

Nevius, Deborah, Librn, Elk City Community Library, 100 School Rd, Elk City, ID, 83525. Tel: 208-842-2218. Fax: 208-842-2225. p. 574

New, Anne, Dir, Community Library of Castle Shannon, 3677 Myrtle Ave, Castle Shannon, PA, 15234-2198. Tel: 412-563-4552. Fax: 412-563-8228. p. 2042

New, Pat, ILL, Eastern Kentucky University Libraries, 521 Lancaster Ave, Richmond, KY, 40475-3102. Tel: 859-622-1778. Fax: 859-622-1174. p. 933

New, Robin, Law Librn, Murphy Oil Corp, 200 Peach St, El Dorado, AR, 71730. Tel: 870-864-6486. Fax: 870-864-6489. p. 98

New, Sarah, Digital Serv Librn, College of Southern Nevada, 6375 W Charleston Blvd, W10I, Las Vegas, NV, 89146. Tel: 702-651-7511. Fax: 702-651-5718. p. 1429

Newbegin, Gisela, Asst Dir, Head, Circ, DeForest Area Public Library, 203 Library St, DeForest, WI, 53532. Tel: 608-846-5482. Fax: 608-846-6875. p. 2588

Newberry, Brenda, Med Librn, Department of Veterans Affairs, 5500 Armstrong Rd, Battle Creek, MI, 49015. Tel: 269-966-5600, Ext 6495. Fax: 269-660-6031. p. 1155

Newberry, Jeff, Supvr, University of Texas Libraries, Collections Deposit Library, PO Box P, CDL, SS461, Austin, TX, 78713-8916. Tel: 512-495-4694. Fax: 512-495-4651. p. 2284

Newberry, Joan W, Spec Serv, Coastal Plain Regional Library, 2014 Chestnut Ave, Tifton, GA, 31794. Tel: 229-386-3400. Fax: 229-386-7007. p. 554

Newberry, Michele, Asst Dir, Libr Serv, Florida Center for Library Automation, 5830 NW 39th Ave, Gainesville, FL, 32606. Tel: 352-392-9020, Ext 349. Fax: 352-392-9185. p. 2940

Newbold, Elisabeth, Br Mgr, San Diego County Library, Alpine Branch, 2130 Arnold Way, Alpine, CA, 91901. Tel: 619-445-4221. Fax: 619-445-4856. p. 233

Newbury, Ann, Ch, Winterset Public Library, 123 N Second St, Winterset, IA, 50273-1508. Tel: 515-462-1731. Fax: 515-462-4196. p. 853

Newbury, Sally, Dir, Gilman-Danforth District Library, 715 N Maple St, Gilman, IL, 60938. Tel: 815-265-7522. Fax: 815-265-4599. p. 649

Newbury, Susan, Cat Mgr, John Carter Brown Library, Brown University, George & Brown Sts, Providence, RI, 02912. Tel: 401-863-2725. Fax: 401-863-3477. p. 2171

Newby, Katie, Mgr, Ad Serv, North Madison County Public Library System, 1600 Main St, Elwood, IN, 46036. Tel: 765-552-5001. Fax: 765-552-0955. p. 737

Newby, Lilith, Librn, College of New Rochelle, Brooklyn Campus, 1368 Fulton St, Brooklyn, NY, 11216. Tel: 718-638-2500. Fax: 914-654-5080. p. 1666

Newcom, Paula, Head, Youth Serv, Crown Point Community Library, 214 S Court St, Crown Point, IN, 46307. Tel: 219-663-0270, 219-663-0271. Fax: 219-663-0403. p. 734

Newcombe, Pat, Assoc Dir, Western New England University, 1215 Wilbraham Rd, Springfield, MA, 01119-2689. Tel: 413-782-1616. Fax: 413-782-1745. p. 1128

Newcombe, Rodd, Syst Librn, Florida Institute of Technology, 150 W University Blvd, Melbourne, FL, 32901-6988. Tel: 321-674-8021. Fax: 321-724-2559. p. 463

Newcomer, Carol, Dir, Waldron District Library, 107 N Main St, Waldron, MI, 49288-9811. Tel: 517-286-6511. Fax: 517-286-6511. p. 1233

Newcomer, Nara, Asst Music Librn, East Carolina University, Music Library, A J Fletcher Music Ctr, Rm A110, Greenville, NC, 27858. Tel: 252-328-1241. Fax: 252-328-1243. p. 1799

Newell, Bonnie, Curator, Burt County Museum, Inc Library, 319 N 13th St, Tekamah, NE, 68061. Tel: 402-374-1505. p. 1421

Newell, Brian, Librn, Logansport State Hospital, 1098 S State Rd 25, Logansport, IN, 46947-9699. Tel: 574-737-3712. Fax: 574-737-3909. p. 761

Newell, Cathy, Asst Librn, United States Army, Medical Library, Bldg 36000, Carl R Darnall Medical Ctr, Fort Hood, TX, 76544-5063. Tel: 254-288-8366. Fax: 254-288-8368. p. 2320

Newell, Crystal, Circ/Access Librn, Piedmont Virginia Community College, 501 College Dr, Charlottesville, VA, 22902. Tel: 434-961-5308. Fax: 434-977-6842. p. 2454

Newell, Katie, Dir, New Castle Public Library, 424 Delaware St, New Castle, DE, 19720-5099. Tel: 302-328-1995. Fax: 302-328-4412. p. 384

Newell, Laurie, Dir, Bloomfield Public Library, Nine Church St, Bloomfield, NY, 14469. Tel: 585-657-6264. Fax: 585-657-6038. p. 1583

Newell, Patrick, Head, Librn Info Tech, California State University, Fresno, Henry Madden Library, 5200 N Barton Ave, Mail Stop ML-34, Fresno, CA, 93740-8014. Tel: 559-278-6528. Fax: 559-278-6952. p. 150

Newell, Shelby, Librn, New Portland Community Library, 899 River Rd, New Portland, ME, 04961. Tel: 207-628-6561. Fax: 207-628-6561. p. 993

Newell, Wendy A, Ref, United States Army, 4300 Camp Hale Rd, Fort Drum, NY, 13602-5284. Tel: 315-772-6005. Fax: 315-772-8529. p. 1623

Newell, Zachary, Humanities Librn, Salem State University Library, 352 Lafayette St, Salem, MA, 01970-5353. Tel: 978-542-7406. Fax: 978-542-6596. p. 1122

Newfield, Harold, Cat, Queens University of Charlotte, 1900 Selwyn Ave, Charlotte, NC, 28274-0001. Tel: 704-337-2401. Fax: 704-337-2517. p. 1784

Newhall, Claudette, Librn, American Congregational Association, 14 Beacon St, 2nd Flr, Boston, MA, 02108-9999. Tel: 617-523-0470. Fax: 617-523-0491. p. 1054

Newhart, Colleen, Access Serv, College of Misericordia, 301 Lake St, Dallas, PA, 18612-1098. Tel: 570-674-6231. Fax: 570-674-6342. p. 2048

Newhouse, Gary, Dean, Librn & Media Serv, Oakton Community College Library, 1600 E Golf Rd, Rm 1410, Des Plaines, IL, 60016. Tel: 847-635-1642, 847-635-1644. Fax: 847-635-1987. p. 636

Newhouse, Julie, Adminr, National Archives & Records Administration, Denver Federal Ctr, Bldg 48, W Sixth Ave & Kipling St, Denver, CO, 80225-0307. Tel: 303-407-5740. Fax: 303-407-5707. p. 302

Newland, Alicia, Ch, W A Rankin Memorial Library, 502 Indiana St, Neodesha, KS, 66757-1532. Tel: 620-325-3275. Fax: 620-325-3275. p. 884

Newland, Candace Lynn, Asst Dir, Lima Public Library, 650 W Market St, Lima, OH, 45801. Tel: 419-228-5113. Fax: 419-224-2669. p. 1910

Newland, Cathy, Dir, Silver Lake Library, 203 Railroad St, Silver Lake, KS, 66539. Tel: 785-582-5141. Fax: 785-582-4282. p. 894

Newland, Sally, Librn, Amerind Foundation, Inc, 2100 N Amerind Rd, Dragoon, AZ, 85609. Tel: 520-586-3666. Fax: 520-586-4679. p. 61

Newlin, Harriet, Dir, American Falls District Library, 308 Roosevelt St, American Falls, ID, 83211-1219. Tel: 208-226-2335. Fax: 208-226-2303. p. 569

Newman, Ann E, Adminr, University of Nebraska Medical Center, 600 S 42nd St, Omaha, NE, 68198-6705. Tel: 402-559-7079. Fax: 402-559-5498. p. 1415

Newman, Anne, Librn, Paxton Carnegie Library, 254 S Market St, Paxton, IL, 60957-1499. Tel: 217-379-3431. Fax: 217-379-3431. p. 689

Newman, Carol, Coordr, Librn Serv, George H & Laura E Brown Library, 122 Van Norden St, Washington, NC, 27889. Tel: 252-946-4300. Fax: 252-975-2015. p. 1828

Newman, Cheryl, Librn, Tulsa City-County Library, Jenks Branch, 523 West B St, Jenks, OK, 74037. Tel: 918-746-5176. Fax: 918-746-5181. p. 1983

Newman, Dana, Br Mgr, Public Library Association of Annapolis & Anne Arundel County, Inc, Provinces, 2624 Annapolis Rd, Rte 175, Severn, MD, 21144. Tel: 410-222-6280. Fax: 410-222-6283. p. 1011

Newman, Diane, Librn Tech, North Island College, 1685 S Dogwood St, Campbell River, BC, V9W 8C1, CANADA. Tel: 250-923-9787. Fax: 250-923-9786. p. 2726

Newman Dinan, Pamela, Admin Dir, Interlibrary Delivery Service of Pennsylvania, c/o Bucks County IU, No 22, 705 N Shady Retreat Rd, Doylestown, PA, 18901. Tel: 215-348-2940, Ext 1620. Fax: 215-348-8315. p. 2954

Newman, Donnie, Dir, Media Serv, Carson-Newman College, 1634 Russell Ave, Jefferson City, TN, 37760. Tel: 865-471-3220. Fax: 865-471-3450. p. 2239

Newman, Emily, Ref, United States Courts for the Ninth Circuit Library, 95 Seventh St, San Francisco, CA, 94103. Tel: 415-556-9500. Fax: 415-556-9927. p. 247

Newman, Euthena, Head, Tech Serv, North Carolina Agricultural & Technical State University, 1601 E Market St, Greensboro, NC, 27411-0002. Tel: 336-334-7867, Ext 3225. Fax: 336-334-7783. p. 1797

Newman, Gary, Ref, Mount Vernon Public Library, 28 S First Ave, Mount Vernon, NY, 10550. Tel: 914-668-1840. Fax: 914-668-1018. p. 1664

Newman, Jeannette, Ch Serv Librn, Floral Park Public Library, 17 Caroline Pl, Floral Park, NY, 11001. Tel: 516-326-6330. Fax: 516-437-6959. p. 1622

Newman, Kay, Dir, Washington State Law Library, Temple of Justice, Olympia, WA, 98504. Tel: 360-357-2136. Fax: 360-357-2143. p. 2523

Newman, Ken, Br Mgr, Chippewa River District Library, Rolland Township, 324 Main St, Blanchard, MI, 49310. Tel: 989-561-2480. Fax: 989-561-2480. p. 1211

Newman, Marie S, Dir, Prof, Pace University, 78 N Broadway, White Plains, NY, 10603. Tel: 914-422-4169. Fax: 914-422-4139. p. 1769

Newman, Marjorie Kiefer, Adult Serv, Poplar Creek Public Library District, 1405 S Park Ave, Streamwood, IL, 60107-2997. Tel: 630-837-6800. Fax: 630-837-6823. p. 708

Newman, Mark W, Asst Prof, University of Michigan, 304 West Hall, 1085 S University, Ann Arbor, MI, 48109-1107. Tel: 734-763-2285. Fax: 734-764-2475. p. 2967

Newman, Mary, Librn, Frank Bertetti Benld Public Library, 308 E Central Ave, Benld, IL, 62009. Tel: 217-835-4045. Fax: 217-835-4045. p. 594

Newman, Mary, Dir, Blank Rome LLP Library, Chrysler Bldg, 15th Fl, 405 Lexington Ave, New York, NY, 10174. Tel: 212-885-5000. Fax: 212-885-5001. p. 1670

Newman, Mary, Dir, Mary E Tippitt Memorial Library, 120 Tiger Dr, Townsend, TN, 37882-4032. Tel: 865-448-1441. Fax: 865-448-1875. p. 2267

Newman, Mary Sheridan, Dir, Blank Rome LLP, One Logan Sq, 18th & Cherry Sts, Philadelphia, PA, 19103-6998. Tel: 215-569-5490. Fax: 215-832-5490. p. 2103

Newman, Maureen, Librn, Mgr, Freeborn & Peters Library, 311 S Wacker Dr, Ste 3000, Chicago, IL, 60606-6677. Tel: 312-360-6000. Fax: 312-360-6575. p. 613

Newman, Melinda, Br Head, East Baton Rouge Parish Library, Bluebonnet Regional, 9200 Bluebonnet Blvd, Baton Rouge, LA, 70810. Tel: 225-763-2240. Fax: 225-763-2253. p. 943

Newman, Michael, Bibliographer, Head Librn, Stanford University Libraries, Falconer Biology Library, Herrin Hall, 3rd Flr, Stanford, CA, 94305-5020. Tel: 650-723-1528. Fax: 650-725-7712. p. 271

Newman, Nola, Commun Librn, Fort Nelson Public Library, 5315-50th Ave S, Box 330, Fort Nelson, BC, V0C 1R0, CANADA. Tel: 250-774-6777. Fax: 250-774-6777. p. 2728

Newman, Peggy, Librn, Ardmore Free Library, 108 Ardmore Ave, Ardmore, PA, 19003-1399. Tel: 610-642-5187. Fax: 610-649-2618. p. 2029

Newman, Randy, Info Tech, Mississippi County Library System, Osceola Public, 320 West Hale Ave, Osceola, AR, 72370-2530. Tel: 870-563-2721. Fax: 870-563-6550. p. 96

Newman, Sharon, Asst Dir, Mary Lou Johnson Hardin County District Library, 325 E Columbus St, Kenton, OH, 43326-1546. Tel: 419-673-2278. Fax: 419-674-4321. p. 1907

Newman, Susan, Coordr, Ref (Info Serv), Mississippi College, 101 W College St, Clinton, MS, 39058. Tel: 601-925-3279. Fax: 601-925-3435. p. 1296

Newman, Susan, Dir, New Madrid County Library, 309 E Main St, Portageville, MO, 63873. Tel: 573-379-3583. Fax: 573-379-9220. p. 1350

Newman, Susan, Dir, New Madrid County Library, Rhodes Memorial, Main St, Gideon, MO, 63848. Tel: 573-379-3583. p. 1350

Newman, Tim, Syst Librn, University of Mary Washington, 1801 College Ave, Fredericksburg, VA, 22401-4665. Tel: 540-654-1147. Fax: 540-654-1067. p. 2466

Newman, Tracey, Circ Supvr, Capital University, Law School Library, 303 E Broad St, Columbus, OH, 43215. Tel: 614-236-6464. Fax: 614-236-6957. p. 1883

Newman, Valerie, In Charge, National Park Service, 190276 Old Oregon Trail, Gering, NE, 69341-8504. Tel: 308-436-9721. Fax: 308-436-7611. p. 1399

Newmark-Kruger, Barbara, Dir, Upper Saddle River Public Library, 245 Lake St, Upper Saddle River, NJ, 07458. Tel: 201-327-2583. Fax: 201-327-3966. p. 1537

Newnam, Amy, Asst Dir, Rockingham County Public Library, 527 Boone Rd, Eden, NC, 27288. Tel: 336-623-3168. Fax: 336-623-1171. p. 1790

Newnam, Barbara, Asst Dir, North Carolina School of Science & Mathematics Library, Library, Instructional Technologies & Communications, 1219 Broad St, Durham, NC, 27705. Tel: 919-416-2929. Fax: 919-416-2890. p. 1789

Newnam, Brenda, Mgr, Grove Public Library, 1140 Neo Loop, Grove, OK, 74344-8602. Tel: 918-786-2945. Fax: 918-786-5233. p. 1964

Newport, Cindy, Coordr, Circ, Pfeiffer University, 48380 US Hwy 52 N, Misenheimer, NC, 28109. Tel: 704-463-3363. Fax: 704-463-3356. p. 1809

Newsom, Elizabeth, Adjunct Lectr, University of Colorado Boulder, Archives & Special Collections, 1720 Pleasant St, Boulder, CO, 80309-0184. Tel: 303-492-6144, 303-492-7242. Fax: 303-492-1881. p. 291

Newsom, Kriston, Ch, Desoto Parish Library, Pelican Branch, 145 Jackson Ave, Pelican, LA, 71063-2803. Tel: 318-755-2353. Fax: 318-755-2031. p. 956

Newsome, James M, Head, Access Serv, Saint Catherine University, 2004 Randolph Ave, Mail F-10, Saint Paul, MN, 55105-1794. Tel: 651-690-6202. Fax: 651-690-8636. p. 1281

Newsome, Nancy, Librn, Calhoun County Public Library, Kinard Branch, 5416 SW State Rd 73, Kinard, FL, 32449. Tel: 850-639-5125. Fax: 850-639-5125. p. 427

Newsome, Nancy, Head, Ser, Western Carolina University, 176 Central Dr, Cullowhee, NC, 28723. Tel: 828-227-3489. Fax: 828-227-7015. p. 1786

Newsome, Romona, Automation Serv, Head, Tech Serv, Great Bend Public Library, 1409 Williams St, Great Bend, KS, 67530-4090. Tel: 620-792-2409. Fax: 620-792-5495, 620-793-7270. p. 869

Newson, Susan, Ref Serv, East Meadow Public Library, 1886 Front St, East Meadow, NY, 11554-1705. Tel: 516-794-2570. Fax: 516-794-1272. p. 1617

Newton, Allison, Librn, Southeast Regional Library, Oungre Branch, Lyndale School, Oungre, SK, S0C 1Z0, CANADA. Tel: 306-456-2662. p. 2930

Newton, Ashley, Librn, Lonoke Prairie County Regional Library Headquarters, Des Arc Public, 408 Curran St, Des Arc, AR, 72040. Tel: 870-256-3003. Fax: 870-256-3003. p. 108

Newton, Carmen, Admin Officer, Georgia State University Library, 100 Decatur St SE, Atlanta, GA, 30303-3202. Tel: 404-413-2713. Fax: 404-413-2701. p. 516

Newton, Darlene Marie, Children's Prog Coordr, Collins Public Library, 212 Main St, Collins, IA, 50055. Tel: 641-385-2464. Fax: 641-385-2205. p. 803

Newton, Frank, Tech Serv, Gardner-Webb University, 110 S Main St, Boiling Springs, NC, 28017. Tel: 704-406-4290. Fax: 704-406-4623. p. 1776

Newton, Karen, Asst Librn, Lucy Hill Patterson Memorial Library, 201 Ackerman St, Rockdale, TX, 76567. Tel: 512-446-3410. Fax: 512-446-5597. p. 2376

Newton, Margaret, Mgr, Bibliog Serv, Marigold Library System, 710-Second St, Strathmore, AB, T1P 1K4, CANADA. Tel: 403-934-5334, Ext 233. Fax: 403-934-5331. p. 2718

Newton, Matthew, Cat, Bureau of National Affairs, Inc Library, 1801 S Bell St, Rm 3200, Arlington, VA, 22202. Tel: 703-341-3308. Fax: 703-341-1636. p. 2449

Newton, Susan, Dir, Spaulding Memorial Library, 282 Sebago Rd, Sebago, ME, 04029-3732. Tel: 207-787-2321. p. 1000

Newton, Teresa, Dir, Lawrence County Public Library, 519 E Gaines St, Lawrenceburg, TN, 38464-3599. Tel: 931-762-4627. Fax: 931-766-1597. p. 2244

Newton, Teresa, Ch, Lincoln County Library, Star Valley, 261 Washington, Afton, WY, 83110. Tel: 307-885-3158. Fax: 307-885-9651. p. 2656

Newton, Verne, Libr Dir, Marist College, 3399 North Rd, Poughkeepsie, NY, 12601-1387. Tel: 845-575-3199. Fax: 845-575-3150. p. 1722

Newton, Victoria, Dir of Libr/Media Serv, Temple University Health System, 2301 E Allegheny Ave, Philadelphia, PA, 19134. Tel: 215-291-3168. Fax: 215-291-3159. p. 2117

Newton, Wanda, Dir, Devereux Foundation, 444 Devereux Dr, Villanova, PA, 19085. Tel: 610-542-3056. Fax: 610-542-3092. p. 2149

Newvine, Veronica, Dir, Hepburn Library of Hermon, 105 Main St, Hermon, NY, 13652-3100. Tel: 315-347-2285. Fax: 315-347-5058. p. 1635

Newyear, David, Adult Info Serv Mgr, Mentor Public Library, 8215 Mentor Ave, Mentor, OH, 44060. Tel: 440-255-8811. Fax: 440-255-0520. p. 1917

Newyear-Ramirez, Jo Anne, Assoc Univ Librn, Coll & Scholarly Communication, University of British Columbia Library, 1961 East Mall, Vancouver, BC, V6T 1Z1, CANADA. Tel: 604-822-2740. p. 2742

Newyear-Ramirez, JoAnne, Coordr, Electronic Health Library of British Columbia, c/o Bennett Library, 8888 University Dr, Burnaby, BC, V5A 1S6, CANADA. Tel: 778-782-5440. Fax: 778-782-3023. p. 2959

Ney, Mary-Margaret, In Charge, Southern Maine Library District, Five Monument Sq, Portland, ME, 04101-4072. Tel: 207-871-1766. p. 997

Ney, Nikki, Regional Br Mgr, Phoenix Public Library, Cesar Chavez Library, 3635 W Baseline Rd, Laveen, AZ, 85339. p. 76

Neyer, Linda, Database Coordr, Res Librn, Bloomsburg University of Pennsylvania, 400 E Second St, Bloomsburg, PA, 17815-1301. Tel: 570-389-4224. Fax: 570-389-3066. p. 2035

Nez, Ann, Coordr, Tech Serv, University of Washington Libraries, Marian Gould Gallagher Law Library, William H Gates Hall, Box 353025, Seattle, WA, 98195-3025. Tel: 206-543-6516. Fax: 206-685-2165. p. 2534

Nezarko, Sharon, Librn, Hines Creek Municipal Library, 212-10 St, Hines Creek, AB, T0H 2A0, CANADA. Tel: 780-494-3879. Fax: 780-494-3605. p. 2707

Ng, Ai Ling, Head of Libr, Free Library of Philadelphia, Walnut Street West Branch, 201 S 40th St, Philadelphia, PA, 19104-3609. Tel: 215-685-7671, 215-685-7672, 215-685-7678. Fax: 215-685-7679. p. 2109

Ng, Elise, Ref Librn, Kramer, Levin, Naftalis & Frankel LLP, 1177 Avenue of the Americas, New York, NY, 10036. Tel: 212-715-9321. Fax: 212-715-8000. p. 1684

Ng, Kwong Bor, Assoc Prof, Queens College of the City University of New York, Benjamin Rosenthal Library, Rm 254, 65-30 Kissena Blvd, Flushing, NY, 11367. Tel: 718-997-3790. Fax: 718-997-3797. p. 2970

Ng, Mimi, Acq, Info Tech, ILL, United States Army, RDECOM-ARDEC, Bldg 59, Phipps Rd, AMSRD-AAR-EMK, Picatinny Arsenal, NJ, 07806-5000. Tel: 973-724-4750. Fax: 973-724-3044. p. 1520

Ng, Rebecca, Tech Serv, Riverside Community College District, 4800 Magnolia Ave, Riverside, CA, 92506-1299. Tel: 951-222-8651. Fax: 951-328-3679. p. 217

Ng, Shannon, Br Mgr, Riverside County Library System, Idyllwild Library, 54401 Village Center Dr, Idyllwild, CA, 92549. Tel: 951-659-2300. Fax: 951-659-2453. p. 217

Ng, Suk Yin, Br Head, Toronto Public Library, Pape/Danforth, 701 Pape Ave, Toronto, ON, M4K 3S6, CANADA. Tel: 416-393-7727. Fax: 416-393-7503. p. 2862

Ng, Wendy, Automation Syst Coordr, United States Air Force, Air University - Muir S Fairchild Research Information Center, 600 Chennault Circle, Maxwell AFB, AL, 36112-6010. Tel: 334-953-6498. p. 24

Ng, Yvonne, Ref Serv, Ad, Arcadia Public Library, 20 W Duarte Rd, Arcadia, CA, 91006. Tel: 626-294-4808. Fax: 626-447-8050. p. 121

Ng-Chin, Eva, Tech Serv Librn, Merritt College Library, 12500 Campus Dr, Oakland, CA, 94619. Tel: 510-436-2461. Fax: 510-531-4960. p. 197

Nga, Pham, ILL, Fletcher Free Library, 235 College St, Burlington, VT, 05401. Tel: 802-863-3403. Fax: 802-865-7227. p. 2421

Ngai, Laura, Coordr, ILL & Doc Delivery Serv, University of Utah, S J Quinney Law Library, 332 S 1400 East, Salt Lake City, UT, 84112-0731. Tel: 801-581-3804. Fax: 801-585-3033. p. 2415

Ngo, Hang, Circ, Sidley Austin LLP, 1501 K St NW, Washington, DC, 20005. Tel: 202-736-8525. Fax: 202-736-8711. p. 414

Nguessan, Michel, Libr Tech, Governors State University Library, One University Pkwy, University Park, IL, 60466-0975. Tel: 708-235-2143. Fax: 708-534-4564. p. 711

Nguyen, Kim, Sr Librn, San Jose Public Library, Biblioteca Latinoamericana Branch, 921 S First St, San Jose, CA, 95110-2939. Tel: 408-294-1237. Fax: 408-297-4278. p. 251

Nguyen, Kim, Sr Librn, San Jose Public Library, East San Jose Carnegie, 1102 E Santa Clara St, San Jose, CA, 95116-2246. Tel: 408-808-3075. Fax: 408-288-9750. p. 251

Nguyen, Loan, Electronic Res Librn, University of Saint Thomas, 1100 W Main, Houston, TX, 77006. Tel: 713-525-2189. Fax: 713-525-3886. p. 2344

Nguyen, Lynn, Principal Librn, Tech & Support, Santa Ana Public Library, 26 Civic Center Plaza, Santa Ana, CA, 92701-4010. Tel: 714-647-5259. Fax: 714-647-5296. p. 259

Nguyen, Minh-Thu, Head, Tech Serv, Ecole Polytechnique de Montreal Bibliotheque, 2500, chemin de Polytechnique, Montreal, QC, H3T 1J4, CANADA. Tel: 514-340-4666. Fax: 514-340-4026. p. 2895

Nguyen, Nate, Tech Coordr, Grandview Heights Public Library, 1685 W First Ave, Columbus, OH, 43212. Tel: 614-486-2951. Fax: 614-481-7021. p. 1886

Nguyen, Thanh, Res Serv Librn, Georgetown University, Georgetown Law Library (John Wolff & Edward Bennett Williams Libraries), 111 G St NW, Washington, DC, 20001. Fax: 202-662-9168. p. 403

Nguyen, Tram, Tech Serv Coordr, South Central Kansas Library System, 321 N Main St, South Hutchinson, KS, 67505-1146. Tel: 620-663-3211. Fax: 620-663-9797. p. 895

Niang, Astou, Commun Serv Coordr, Centre de documentation sur l'education des adultes et la condition feminine, 110 rue Ste-Therese, Ste 101, Montreal, QC, H2Y 1E6, CANADA. Tel: 514-876-1180. Fax: 514-876-1325. p. 2892

Nianombeko-Ahmed, Nemoure, Br Mgr, Palm Beach County Library System, West Boynton Branch, 9451 Jog Rd, Boynton Beach, FL, 33437. Tel: 561-734-5556. Fax: 561-734-5392. p. 503

Niazov, Irene, Circ, De Anza College, 21250 Stevens Creek Blvd, Cupertino, CA, 95014-5793. Tel: 408-864-8763. Fax: 408-864-8603. p. 138

Nibaur, Marileen, Asst Librn, Elma Public Library, 710 Busti Ave, Elma, IA, 50628. Tel: 641-393-8100. Fax: 641-393-8100. p. 814

Niblett, Tammy, Br Mgr, Los Angeles Public Library System, Sherman Oaks Branch, 12511 Moorpark St, Sherman Oaks, CA, 91423. Tel: 818-205-9716. Fax: 818-205-9866. p. 174

Nicasio, Sandra, Circ Supvr, Yuma County Library District, 2951 S 21st Dr, Yuma, AZ, 85364. Tel: 928-373-6491. Fax: 928-782-9420. p. 91

Nicastro, Kathleen, Libr Asst, University of Rochester, Charlotte Whitney Allen Library, Memorial Art Gallery, 500 University Ave, Rochester, NY, 14607. Tel: 585-276-9001. Fax: 585-473-6266. p. 1733

Nice, Camille, Circ, Rocky River Public Library, 1600 Hampton Rd, Rocky River, OH, 44116-2699. Tel: 440-333-7610. Fax: 440-333-4184. p. 1932

Nicely, Consuelo, Human Res Adminr, Saint Joseph County Public Library, 304 S Main, South Bend, IN, 46601-2125. Tel: 574-282-4646. Fax: 574-280-2763. p. 779

Nicely, Marilyn, Tech Serv Librn, University of Oklahoma, Donald E Pray Law Library, 300 Timberdell Rd, Norman, OK, 73019. Tel: 405-325-4311. Fax: 405-325-6282. p. 1971

Nicely, Thelma, Librn, Saint Mary's Medical Center, 2900 First Ave, Huntington, WV, 25702-1271. Tel: 304-526-1814. Fax: 304-526-1314. p. 2562

Nichelini, Shari, Br Mgr, Sacramento Public Library, McKinley Neighborhood Library, 601 Alhambra Blvd, Sacramento, CA, 95816. p. 225

Nicholson, Suzanne, Ref, Beverly Public Library, 32 Essex St, Beverly, MA, 01915-4561. Tel: 978-921-6062. Fax: 978-922-8329. p. 1053

Nicholas Brodar, Maureen, Youth Serv Mgr, Shaker Heights Public Library, 16500 Van Aken Blvd, Shaker Heights, OH, 44120-5318. Tel: 216-991-2030. Fax: 216-991-5951. p. 1934

Nicholas, Jeffrey, Chief Librn, VA Hudson Valley Health Care System, PO Box 100, Montrose, NY, 10548-0100. Tel: 914-737-4400, Ext 2360. Fax: 914-737-4400, Ext 2754. p. 1663

Nicholas, Joan, Head, Adult Serv, Beloit Public Library, 605 Eclipse Blvd, Beloit, WI, 53511. Tel: 608-364-2909. Fax: 608-364-2907. p. 2581

Nicholas, Joyce, Tech Serv, Department of Veterans Affairs, 2101 N Elm St, Fargo, ND, 58102. Tel: 701-239-3755. Fax: 701-239-3775. p. 1840

Nicholas, Myra J, Mgr, Libr Serv, Pub Serv, Santa Barbara Public Library, 40 E Anapamu St, Santa Barbara, CA, 93101-2722. Tel: 805-564-5602. p. 261

Nicholls, David, Syst Coordr, Sarah Lawrence College, One Mead Way, Bronxville, NY, 10708. Tel: 914-395-2478. Fax: 914-395-2473. p. 1588

Nicholls Harrison, Tim, Adult & Commun Learning Serv Mgr, Owen Sound & North Grey Union Public Library, 824 First Ave W, Owen Sound, ON, N4K 4K4, CANADA. Tel: 519-376-6623. Fax: 519-376-7170. p. 2834

Nicholls, Melissa, ILL, Pepperdine University Libraries, 24255 Pacific Coast Hwy, Malibu, CA, 90263. Tel: 310-506-4252. Fax: 310-506-7225. p. 182

Nichols, Aaron, Access Serv, University of Wisconsin-Stevens Point, 900 Reserve St, Stevens Point, WI, 54481-1985. Tel: 715-346-3038. Fax: 715-346-3857. p. 2640

Nichols, Andrea, Outreach Serv Librn, Rockport Public Library, 17 School St, Rockport, MA, 01966. Tel: 978-546-6934. Fax: 978-546-1011. p. 1121

Nichols, Ann, Circ, Extn Serv, East Bonner County Free Library District, 1407 Cedar St, Sandpoint, ID, 83864-2052. Tel: 208-263-6930, Ext 257. Fax: 208-263-8320. p. 583

Nichols, Ann, Cat, Hopkinsville Community College Library, 720 North Dr, Hopkinsville, KY, 42240. Tel: 270-707-3760. Fax: 270-885-6048. p. 918

Nichols, Ann, Librn, King Public Library, 101 Pilot View Dr, King, NC, 27021-9180. Tel: 336-983-3868. Fax: 336-983-0769. p. 1804

Nichols, Anna L, Librn, Charles H Stone Memorial Library, 319 W Main St, Pilot Mountain, NC, 27041. Tel: 336-368-2370. Fax: 336-368-9587. p. 1814

Nichols, Barbara, Br Mgr, Rochester Public Library, Winton, 611 Winton Rd N, Rochester, NY, 14609. Tel: 585-428-8204. p. 1732

Nichols, Beatrice, Ref, Syst Librn, Eckerd College, 4200 54th Ave S, Saint Petersburg, FL, 33711. Tel: 727-864-8337. Fax: 727-864-8997. p. 488

Nichols, Beatrice, Librn, United States Army, Medical Library, Bldg 36000, Carl R Darnall Medical Ctr, Fort Hood, TX, 76544-5063. Tel: 254-288-8366. Fax: 254-288-8368. p. 2320

Nichols, Becky, Dir, Public Library of Selma & Dallas County, 1103 Selma Ave, Selma, AL, 36703-4445. Tel: 334-874-1725. Fax: 334-874-1729. p. 36

Nichols, Brenda, Dir, Libr Serv, Brattleboro Retreat, 75 Linden St, Brattleboro, VT, 05301. Tel: 802-258-3737, Ext 3221. Fax: 802-258-3796. p. 2419

Nichols, C Allen, Dir, Ella M Everhard Public Library, 132 Broad St, Wadsworth, OH, 44281-1897. Tel: 330-334-5761. Fax: 330-334-6605. p. 1943

Nichols, Catherine, Br Mgr, Oakland Public Library, Dimond, 3565 Fruitvale Ave, Oakland, CA, 94602. Tel: 510-482-7844. Fax: 510-482-7824. p. 198

Nichols, Cindy, Br Supvr, Tampa-Hillsborough County Public Library System, Seffner-Mango Branch, 410 North Kingsway Rd, Seffner, FL, 33584-3602. Tel: 813-273-3652. Fax: 813-276-2642. p. 498

Nichols, Debbie, Asst Dir, Tech Serv Librn, Maryville College, 502 E Lamar Alexander Pkwy, Maryville, TN, 37804-5907. Tel: 865-981-8255. Fax: 865-981-8267. p. 2247

Nichols, Dennis, Head, Adult Serv, Homewood Public Library, 1721 Oxmoor Rd, Homewood, AL, 35209-4085. Tel: 205-332-6620. Fax: 205-802-6424. p. 20

Nichols, Diane Pendleton, Assoc Dean of Libr, University of Louisville Libraries, 2215 S Third St, Louisville, KY, 40292. Tel: 502-852-8707. Fax: 502-852-7394. p. 926

Nichols, Diane Pendleton, Assoc Dean, Libr Operation & Dir, University of Louisville Libraries, William F Ekstrom Library, Belknap Campus, 2215 S Third St, Louisville, KY, 40292. Tel: 502-852-8707. Fax: 502-852-7397. p. 927

Nichols, Donna, Dir, Arthur Temple Sr Memorial Library, 106 Timberland Hwy, Pineland, TX, 75968. Tel: 409-584-2546. Fax: 409-584-3206. p. 2370

Nichols, Dwanna, Asst Librn, Crescent Heights Baptist Church Library, 1902 N Mockingbird Lane, Abilene, TX, 79603. Tel: 325-677-3749. p. 2272

Nichols, Faye, Librn, Gatesville Public Library, 111 N Eighth St, Gatesville, TX, 76528. Tel: 254-865-5367. Fax: 254-248-0986. p. 2327

Nichols, Ginni, YA Librn, Gardiner Public Library, 152 Water St, Gardiner, ME, 04345. Tel: 207-582-3312. Fax: 207-582-6104. p. 986

Nichols, Jim, Distance Educ Librn, State University of New York at Oswego, SUNY Oswego, 7060 State Rte 104, Oswego, NY, 13126-3514. Tel: 315-312-3549. Fax: 315-312-3194. p. 1713

Nichols, Karen, Coordr of Ref Serv, Lamar University, 211 Redbird Lane, Beaumont, TX, 77705. Tel: 409-880-8131. Fax: 409-880-2318. p. 2287

Nichols, Kathryn, Br Mgr, Sullivan County Public Library, Thomas Memorial Branch, 481 Cedar St, Bluff City, TN, 37618. Tel: 423-538-1980. Fax: 423-538-1980. p. 2225

Nichols, Kay, Ref Serv, Lockheed Martin Missiles & Fire Control, 1701 W Marshall Dr, Grand Prairie, TX, 75051. Tel: 972-603-7155. Fax: 972-603-0182. p. 2329

Nichols, Kelly, Dir, University Park Public Library District, 1100 Blackhawk Dr, University Park, IL, 60466. Tel: 708-534-2580. Fax: 708-534-2583. p. 711

Nichols, L Marie, Extn Spec, Metropolitan Library System in Oklahoma County, Wright Extension Library, 2101 Exchange Ave, Oklahoma City, OK, 73108-2625. Tel: 405-235-5035. Fax: 405-235-8938. p. 1973

Nichols, Lea-Ann, Asst Librn II, Mariposa County Law Library, 4978 10th St, Mariposa, CA, 95338. p. 183

Nichols, Leilania, Youth Serv, Wakulla County Public Library, 4330 Crawfordville Hwy, Crawfordville, FL, 32327. Tel: 850-926-7415. Fax: 850-926-4513. p. 434

Nichols, Lindsay, Sr Ref Librn, Suffolk University, 73 Tremont St, Boston, MA, 02108. Tel: 617-573-8535. Fax: 617-573-8756. p. 1067

Nichols, Lisa, Pub Serv Librn, Transylvania University Library, 300 N Broadway, Lexington, KY, 40508. Tel: 859-246-5003. Fax: 859-233-8779. p. 921

Nichols, Lou Ellen, Ch, Gardendale Martha Moore Public Library, 995 Mt Olive Rd, Gardendale, AL, 35071. Tel: 205-631-6639. Fax: 205-631-0146. p. 18

Nichols, Mary Anne, Instr, Kent State University, 314 Library, Kent, OH, 44242-0001. Tel: 330-672-2782. Fax: 330-672-7965. p. 2972

Nichols, Ozella, Br Mgr, Greenwood-Leflore Public Library System, Jodie Wilson Branch, 209 E Martin Luther King Jr Dr, Greenwood, MS, 38930-6625. Tel: 662-453-1761. p. 1299

Nichols, Pat, Dir, Quinerly Olschner Public Library, 451 Second St, Ayden, NC, 28513-7179. Tel: 252-746-7026. Fax: 252-746-7041. p. 1775

Nichols, Sandra L, Actg Librn, Continuing Educ Coordr, Adventist Health System, 701 W Plymouth Ave, DeLand, FL, 32720. Tel: 386-943-4863. Fax: 904-943-7141. p. 437

Nichols, Sarah, Head, Adult Serv, Carnegie Public Library, 127 S North St, Washington Court House, OH, 43160. Tel: 740-335-2540. Fax: 740-335-8409. p. 1945

Nichols, Sean, In Charge, Alberta Wilderness Association, 455 12th St NW, Calgary, AB, T2N 1Y9, CANADA. Tel: 403-283-2025. Fax: 403-270-2743. p. 2687

Nichols, Selena, In Charge, First Baptist Church, 700 N Highland Ave, Winston-Salem, NC, 27101. Tel: 336-722-5605. Fax: 336-722-6266. p. 1832

Nichols, Thayer, Br Supvr, Barry-Lawrence Regional Library, Mount Vernon Branch, 206 W Water, Mount Vernon, MO, 65712. Tel: 417-466-2921. Fax: 417-466-2936. p. 1346

Nichols-Brown, Kelley D, Libr Dir, Richton Park Public Library District, 4045 Sauk Trail, Richton Park, IL, 60471. Tel: 708-481-5333. Fax: 708-481-4343. p. 694

Nicholson, Beth, Dir, Clarksburg-Harrison Public Library, 404 W Pike St, Clarksburg, WV, 26301. Tel: 304-627-2236. Fax: 304-627-2239. p. 2557

Nicholson, Brenda, Dir, Hopkinton Town Library, Seven Church St, Hopkinton, NY, 12965. Tel: 315-328-4113. Fax: 315-328-4113. p. 1638

Nicholson, Caroline, Dir, Goodrich Memorial Library, 202 Main St, Newport, VT, 05855. Tel: 802-334-7902. Fax: 802-334-3890. p. 2430

Nicholson, Elizabeth, Info Serv Librn, Aurora University, 315 S Gladstone, Aurora, IL, 60506-4877. Tel: 630-844-5440. Fax: 630-844-3848. p. 591

Nicholson, Elizabeth, Asst Librn, Freshfields Bruckhaus Deringer US LLP, 520 Madison Ave, 34th Flr, New York, NY, 10022. Tel: 212-284-4933. Fax: 646-521-5733. p. 1679

Nicholson, Elizabeth, Librn, Tidioute Public Library, 197 Main St, Tidioute, PA, 16351. Tel: 814-484-3581. Fax: 814-484-3581. p. 2145

Nicholson, Heather, Librn, Coaldale Public Library, 2014 18th St, Coaldale, AB, T1M 1M1, CANADA. Tel: 403-345-1340. Fax: 403-345-1342. p. 2695

Nicholson, Jeffie, Mrs, Main Libr Coordr, Williamson County Public Library, 1314 Columbia Ave, Franklin, TN, 37064-3626. Tel: 615-595-1269. Fax: 615-595-1245. p. 2234

Nicholson, Jill, Chief Exec Officer, Lincoln Public Library, Moses F Rittenhouse Branch, 4080 John Charles Blvd, Vineland, ON, L0R 2C0, CANADA. Tel: 905-562-5711. Fax: 905-562-3454. p. 2794

Nicholson, Katie, Youth Serv Librn, Centre County Library & Historical Museum, 200 N Allegheny St, Bellefonte, PA, 16823-1601. Tel: 814-355-1516. Fax: 814-355-2700. p. 2032

Nicholson, Rebecca, ILL, Montana State University-Northern, 300 11th St W, Havre, MT, 59501. Tel: 406-265-3706. Fax: 406-265-3799. p. 1381

Nicholson, Shawn, Asst Dir, Digital Serv, Michigan State University Library, 100 Library, East Lansing, MI, 48824-1048. Tel: 517-884-6448. Fax: 517-432-4795. p. 1175

Nicholson, Shawn, Asst Dir, Digital Serv, Michigan State University Library, Digital Sources & Multimedia Center, W432 Library, East Lansing, MI, 48824. Tel: 517-884-6448. Fax: 517-432-4795. p. 1175

Nicholson, Shawn, Asst Dir, Digital Serv, Michigan State University Library, Voice Library, W 422 Library, East Lansing, MI, 48824. Tel: 517-884-6470. Fax: 517-432-4795. p. 1175

Nickel, Evelyn, Librn, Chinook Regional Library, Herbert Branch, 517 Herbert Ave, Herbert, SK, S0H 2A0, CANADA. Tel: 306-784-2484. p. 2928

Nickel, Karen, Libr Mgr, Three Hills Municipal Library, 160 Third Ave S, Three Hills, AB, T0M 2A0, CANADA. Tel: 403-443-2360. p. 2719

Nickell, Claudia, Asst Dir, Fort Morgan Public Library, 414 Main St, Fort Morgan, CO, 80701. Tel: 970-542-4000. Fax: 970-542-4013. p. 308

Nickell, Lynette, Ch, Ector County Library, 321 W Fifth St, Odessa, TX, 79761-5066. Tel: 432-332-0633, Ext 4013. Fax: 432-377-6502. p. 2366

Nickelson, Carol, Libr Asst, Graham County Public Library, 414 N West St, Hill City, KS, 67642-1646. Tel: 785-421-2722. Fax: 785-421-5583. p. 871

Nickerson, Brenda, Librn, Clymer-French Creek Free Library, 564 Clymer-Sherman Rd, Clymer, NY, 14724. Tel: 716-355-8823. Fax: 716-355-8824. p. 1608

Nickerson, Ellen J, Ch, Winthrop Public Library & Museum, Two Metcalf Sq, Winthrop, MA, 02152-3157. Tel: 617-846-1703. Fax: 617-846-7083. p. 1142

Nickerson, Matthew, Spec Projects Librn, Southern Utah University, 351 W University Blvd, Cedar City, UT, 84720. Tel: 435-586-1955. Fax: 435-865-8152. p. 2404

Nickisch Duggan, Heidi, Assoc Dir, Health Sci Libr, Northwestern University, Chicago, Galter Health Sciences Library, Montgomery Ward Bldg, 303 E Chicago Ave, Chicago, IL, 60611. Tel: 312-503-8133. Fax: 312-503-1204. p. 621

Nicklas, Tim, Dir, Grand County Historical Association Library, 110 E Byers Ave, Hot Sulphur Springs, CO, 80451. Tel: 970-725-3939. Fax: 970-725-0129. p. 313

Nickle, Elspeth, Librn, Southern Alberta Art Gallery Library, 601 Third Ave S, Lethbridge, AB, T1J 0H4, CANADA. Tel: 403-327-8770. Fax: 403-328-3913. p. 2710

Nickleberry-Brooks, Pam, Br Mgr, Memphis Public Library, South, 1929 S Third St, Memphis, TN, 38109. Tel: 901-946-8518. Fax: 901-946-1435. p. 2250

Nickles, Lon, Dir, Lumberton Public Library, 130 E Chance Rd, Lumberton, TX, 77657. Tel: 409-755-7400. p. 2358

Nickols, Jan, Adult Prog/Ref, Clearwater Public Library System, 100 N Osceola Ave, Clearwater, FL, 33755. Tel: 727-562-4970. Fax: 727-562-4977. p. 432

Nickolsen, Jill, Chief Exec Officer, Lincoln Public Library, 4996 Beam St, Beamsville, ON, L0R 1B0, CANADA. Tel: 905-563-7014. Fax: 905-563-1810. p. 2794

Nicks, Carol, Asst Librn, Canadian University College Library, 5410 Ramona Ave, Lacombe, AB, T4L 2B7, CANADA. Tel: 403-782-3381, Ext 4105. Fax: 403-782-3977. p. 2708

Nicks, Cynthia, Librn, Heartland Regional Medical Center, 5325 Faraon St, Saint Joseph, MO, 64506-3398. Tel: 816-271-6075. Fax: 816-271-6074. p. 1352

Nickum, Lisa, Govt Pub Librn, Colorado School of Mines, 1400 Illinois St, Golden, CO, 80401-1887. Tel: 303-273-3695. Fax: 303-273-3199. p. 309

Nicolas, Angel, Commun Libr Mgr, County of Los Angeles Public Library, Florence Library, 1610 E Florence Ave, Los Angeles, CA, 90001-2522. Tel: 323-581-8028. Fax: 323-587-3240. p. 141

Nicolazzi, Maureen, Librn III, North Babylon Public Library, 815 Deer Park Ave, North Babylon, NY, 11703-3812. Tel: 631-669-4020. Fax: 631-669-3432. p. 1706

Nicole, Guilbert, In Charge, Bibliotheque Municipale de Val-D'or, 600, 7e Rue, Val-d'Or, QC, J9P 3P3, CANADA. Tel: 819-874-7469, Ext 222. Fax: 819-825-3062. p. 2914

Nicoletti, Jeanette, Circ, Garden City Public Library, 60 Seventh St, Garden City, NY, 11530-2891. Tel: 516-742-8405. Fax: 516-742-2675. p. 1626

Nicoll, Victoria, Libr Tech, Stewart McKelvey, 1959 Upper Water St, Ste 900, Halifax, NS, B3J 3N2, CANADA. Tel: 902-420-3200, Ext 109. Fax: 902-420-1417. p. 2781

Nicula, Janet Gail, Dr, Dir, Joint Forces Staff College Library, 7800 Hampton Blvd, Norfolk, VA, 23511-1702. Tel: 757-443-6400. Fax: 757-443-6047. p. 2481

Nida, Christine, Circ, Newton Public Library, 100 N Third Ave W, Newton, IA, 50208. Tel: 641-792-4108. Fax: 641-791-0729. p. 835

Nie, Caroline, Head, Tech Serv, Concord Free Public Library, 129 Main St, Concord, MA, 01742-2494. Tel: 978-318-3368. Fax: 978-318-3344. p. 1082

Nie, Caroline, Tech Serv, Westwood Public Library, 668 High St, Westwood, MA, 02090. Tel: 781-320-1047. Fax: 781-326-5383. p. 1139

Niebuhr, Gary Warren, Dir, Greendale Public Library, 5647 Broad St, Greendale, WI, 53129-1887. Tel: 414-423-2136. Fax: 414-423-2139. p. 2596

Niebur, Kari, Ref Serv, Illinois Agricultural Association, 1701 N Towanda Ave, Bloomington, IL, 61701. Tel: 309-557-2552. Fax: 309-557-3185. p. 595

Niederjohn, Roberta, Mkt & Communications Spec, San Diego State University Library & Information Access, 5500 Campanile Dr, San Diego, CA, 92182-8050. Tel: 619-594-4991. Fax: 619-594-3270. p. 237

Niederklein, Jackie, Dir, Tobias Public Library, Main St, Tobias, NE, 68453. Tel: 402-243-2256. p. 1421

Niederkorn, Elizabeth, Librn, Toledo Zoological Society, 2700 Broadway, Toledo, OH, 43609. Tel: 419-385-5721, Ext 2043. Fax: 419-389-8670. p. 1940

Niedermeier, Bernadette, Children & Youth Serv Librn, West Haven Public Library, 300 Elm St, West Haven, CT, 06516-4692. Tel: 203-937-4233. p. 377

Niedringhaus, Kristina L, Assoc Prof of Law, Dir, Cleveland State University, Cleveland-Marshall Law Library, Cleveland-Marshall College of Law, 1801 Euclid Ave, Cleveland, OH, 44115-2223. Tel: 216-687-3547. Fax: 216-687-6881. p. 1878

Niedzolkowski, Tamara, Dir, Rollinsford Public Library, Three Front St, Ste B-2, Rollinsford, NH, 03869. Tel: 603-516-2665. p. 1464

Niehoff, Kate, Mgr, Ad Serv, Forest Park Public Library, 7555 Jackson Blvd, Forest Park, IL, 60130. Tel: 708-366-7171. Fax: 708-366-7293. p. 646

Nield, Kayla, In Charge, Mid-Columbia Libraries, West Richland Branch, 3803 W Van Giesen, West Richland, WA, 99353. Tel: 509-967-3191. Fax: 509-967-1224. p. 2518

Nielsen, Buzzy, Asst Dir, North Bend Public Library, 1800 Sherman Ave, North Bend, OR, 97459. Tel: 541-756-0400. Fax: 541-756-1073. p. 2008

Nielsen, Elizabeth A, Sr Archivist, Oregon State University Libraries, University Archives & Special Collections, 121 Valley Library, Corvallis, OR, 97331-4501. Tel: 541-737-0543. Fax: 541-737-3453. p. 1994

Nielsen, Jean, Hist Archivist, Miles City Public Library, One S Tenth St, Miles City, MT, 59301-3398. Tel: 406-234-1496. Fax: 406-234-2095. p. 1386

Nielsen, Jordan, Bus Librn, University of Arkansas Libraries, 365 N McIlroy Ave, Fayetteville, AR, 72701-4002. Tel: nielsen@uark.edu. Fax: 479-575-6656. p. 99

Nielsen, Margaret, Asst City Librn, Dike Public Library, 133 E Elder, Dike, IA, 50624-9612. Tel: 319-989-2608. Fax: 319-989-2984. p. 811

Nielsen, Patricia, Legis Ref Coordr, Oregon Legislative Library, 900 Court St NE, Rm 446, Salem, OR, 97301. Tel: 503-986-1668. Fax: 503-986-1005. p. 2017

Nielsen, Pauline, Librn, Ward County Public Library, Kenmare Branch, Five NE Third, Memorial Hall, Kenmare, ND, 58746. Tel: 701-385-4090. Fax: 701-385-4090. p. 1846

Nielsen, Robin, Librn, Intermountain Health Care, Eighth Ave & C St, Salt Lake City, UT, 84143-0001. Tel: 801-408-1054. Fax: 801-408-5287. p. 2412

Nielsen, Sara, Mgr, Commun Br & Adult Programming, Saint Charles City County Library District, 77 Boone Hills Dr, Saint Peters, MO, 63376-0529. Tel: 636-441-2300. Fax: 636-441-3132. p. 1363

Nielsen, Sara, Br Mgr, Saint Charles City County Library District, Boone's Trail Branch, Ten Fiddlecreek Plaza, New Melle, MO, 63365. Tel: 636-398-6200. Fax: 636-398-6200. p. 1364

Nielsen, Sara, Br Mgr, Saint Charles City County Library District, Library Express @ Discovery Village, 378 Shadow Pines Dr, Wentzville, MO, 63385-3745. Tel: 636-332-6476. Fax: 636-332-4165. p. 1364

Nielsen, Sara, Br Mgr, Saint Charles City County Library District, Library Express @ WingHaven, 7435 Village Center Dr, O'Fallon, MO, 63368-4768. Tel: 636-561-3385. Fax: 636-561-3819. p. 1364

Nielsen, Sara, Br Mgr, Saint Charles City County Library District, North County Branch, 1825 Commonfield Rd, Portage des Sioux, MO, 63373. Tel: 636-753-3070. Fax: 636-753-3070. p. 1364

Nielsen, Sara, Br Mgr, Saint Charles City County Library District, South County Branch, 198 Jackson St, Augusta, MO, 63332-1772. Tel: 636-228-4855. Fax: 636-228-4855. p. 1364

Nielsen, Steven, Dir, Bettendorf Public Library Information Center, 2950 Learning Campus Dr, Bettendorf, IA, 52722. Tel: 563-344-4175. Fax: 563-344-4185. p. 796

Nielsen, Tina, Chief Librn, Bowen Island Public Library, 430 Bowen Island Trunk Rd, Bowen Island, BC, V0N 1G0, CANADA. Tel: 604-947-9788. Fax: 604-947-9788. p. 2725

Nielson, Diane, Librn, ATK Launch Systems, PO Box 707, Brigham City, UT, 84302-0707. Tel: 435-863-2132. Fax: 435-863-6023. p. 2403

Nielson, Mariah, Art Librn, Oakland Museum of California Art Library, 1000 Oak St, Oakland, CA, 94607-4892. Tel: 510-238-3005. Fax: 510-238-6925. p. 197

Nielson, Wendy, Librn, Mount Carmel Lutheran Church Library, 8424 W Center St, Milwaukee, WI, 53222. Tel: 414-771-1270. Fax: 414-771-1616. p. 2621

Nielson, William, Chief Librn, Department of Veterans Affairs Medical Center, 3001 Green Bay Rd, North Chicago, IL, 60064. Tel: 847-688-1900, Ext 83757. Fax: 847-578-3819. p. 681

Nieman, Beth, Youth Serv Librn, Carlsbad Public Library, 101 S Halagueno St, Carlsbad, NM, 88220. Tel: 575-885-6776. Fax: 575-887-7706. p. 1552

Nieman, Dan, Asst Dir, South Sioux City Public Library, 2121 Dakota Ave, South Sioux City, NE, 68776-3031. Tel: 402-494-7545. Fax: 402-494-7546. p. 1419

Nieman, Erik J, Dir, Three Oaks Township Public Library, Three N Elm St, Three Oaks, MI, 49128-1303. Tel: 269-756-5621. Fax: 269-756-3004. p. 1230

Nieman, Ken, Assoc Dir, Finance/HR & Operations, Ann Arbor District Library, 343 S Fifth Ave, Ann Arbor, MI, 48104. Tel: 734-327-4517. Fax: 734-327-8324. p. 1150

Nieman, Vivian, Archivist, Anderson University, Robert A Nicholson Library, 1100 E Fifth St, Anderson, IN, 46012-3495. Tel: 765-641-4285. Fax: 765-641-3850. p. 724

Niemczyk, Anita J, Ref, Saint Ambrose University Library, 518 W Locust St, Davenport, IA, 52803. Tel: 563-333-5813. Fax: 563-333-6248. p. 807

Niemeier, Cheryl Lynn, Dir, Libr & Info Serv, Bose McKinney & Evans LLP, 111 Monument Circle, Ste 2700, Indianapolis, IN, 46204. Tel: 317-684-5166. Fax: 317-223-0166. p. 749

Niemeier, Julia, Pub Serv, Alpha Park Public Library District, 3527 S Airport Rd, Bartonville, IL, 61607-1799. Tel: 309-697-3822, Ext 17. Fax: 309-697-9681. p. 592

Niemeier, Martha, Assoc Dir, Coll Develop Librn, Interim Dir, University of Southern Indiana, 8600 University Blvd, Evansville, IN, 47712. Tel: 812-464-1834. Fax: 812-465-1693. p. 739

Niemeyer, Karen, Dir, Thorntown Public Library, 124 N Market St, Thorntown, IN, 46071-1144. Tel: 765-436-7348. Fax: 765-436-7011. p. 782

Niemezura, Lili-Ane, Ch, Central Islip Public Library, 33 Hawthorne Ave, Central Islip, NY, 11722. Tel: 631-234-9333. Fax: 631-234-9386. p. 1604

Niemla, Karen, Ref Librn, University of Louisiana at Monroe Library, 700 University Ave, Monroe, LA, 71209-0720. Tel: 318-342-3045. Fax: 318-342-1075. p. 958

Niemy, Molly, Educ Mgr, Larz Anderson Auto Museum Library & Archives, Larz Anderson Park, 15 Newton St, Brookline, MA, 02445. Tel: 617-522-6547. Fax: 617-524-0170. p. 1071

Nienke, Cheri, Acq, Asst Dir, Head, Cat, Andover Public Library, 1511 E Central Ave, Andover, KS, 67002. Tel: 316-558-3500. Fax: 316-558-3503. p. 856

Niepsuj, Bonnie, ILL, McHenry Public Library District, 809 N Front St, McHenry, IL, 60050. Tel: 815-385-0036. Fax: 815-385-7085. p. 672

Nieszczezewski, Evelyn, Acq, Nichols College, 124 Center Rd, Dudley, MA, 01571. Tel: 508-213-2220. Fax: 508-213-2323. p. 1085

Nieters, Laurie, Asst Librn, Mountain Iron Public Library, 5742 Mountain Ave, Mountain Iron, MN, 55768-9636. Tel: 218-735-8625. Fax: 218-735-8252. p. 1267

Nietfeld, Linda, Librn, Fort Recovery Public Library, 113 N Wayne St, Fort Recovery, OH, 45846. Tel: 419-375-2869. Fax: 419-375-2525. p. 1900

Niethammer, Leslee, Dir, Saline District Library, 555 N Maple Rd, Saline, MI, 48176. Tel: 734-429-2313. Fax: 734-944-0600. p. 1225

Nieto-Rodriguez, Elma, Br Mgr, San Antonio Public Library, Mission, 3134 Roosevelt Ave, San Antonio, TX, 78214. Tel: 210-207-2704. Fax: 210-207-2704. p. 2382

Nieuwkoop, Ann E, Assoc Dir, Western Theological Seminary, 101 E 13th St, Holland, MI, 49423. Tel: 616-392-8555, Ext 141. p. 1191

Nieves-Ortiz, Myrna I, Head Librn, University of Puerto Rico Library System, Social Sciences Reserve Room, Rio Piedras Campus, San Juan, PR, 00931. Tel: 787-764-0000, Ext 2483, 787-764-0000, Ext 5219. Fax: 787-772-1479. p. 2678

Niewenhous, Susan, Dir, Lewis-Clark State College Library, 500 Eighth Ave, Lewiston, ID, 83501. Tel: 208-792-2395. Fax: 208-792-2831. p. 578

Niewohner, Betty, Dir, Snyder Public Library, 203 Ash St, Snyder, NE, 68664. Tel: 402-568-2570. Fax: 402-568-2688. p. 1419

Niewyk, Ellen Buie, Curator, Spec Coll, Southern Methodist University, Hamon Arts Library, 6101 N Bishop Blvd, Dallas, TX, 75275. Tel: 214-768-1855. Fax: 214-768-1800. p. 2310

Niffin, Anette, Coll Develop, Britt Area Library, 841 Riverside Dr, Britt, ON, P0G 1A0, CANADA. Tel: 705-383-2292. Fax: 705-383-0077. p. 2797

Nigh, Susan, Circ, Melbourne Beach Public Library, 324 Ocean Ave, Melbourne Beach, FL, 32951. Tel: 321-956-5642. Fax: 321-953-6942. p. 464

Nightingale, Barbara, Commun Libr Mgr, County of Los Angeles Public Library, Artesia Library, 18722 S Clarkdale Ave, Artesia, CA, 90701-5817. Tel: 562-865-6614. Fax: 562-924-4644. p. 140

Nightingale, Eileen, Ch, YA Serv, Sidney Public Library, 1112 12th Ave, Sidney, NE, 69162. Tel: 308-254-3110. Fax: 308-254-3710. p. 1419

Niider, Kadri, Asst Librn, State University of New York, State College of Optometry, 33 W 42nd St, New York, NY, 10036-8003. Tel: 212-938-5690. Fax: 212-938-5696. p. 1700

Nikolai, Mary Fran, Dir, Garnavillo Public Library, 122 Main St, Garnavillo, IA, 52049. Tel: 563-964-2119. Fax: 563-964-2119. p. 817

Nikolis, Sally, Ch, South Huntington Public Library, 145 Pidgeon Hill Rd, Huntington Station, NY, 11746. Tel: 631-549-4411. Fax: 631-549-1266. p. 1639

Niland, Terri, Librn, Lawrence Memorial Hospital of Medford, 170 Governors Ave, Medford, MA, 02155-1698. Tel: 781-306-6606. Fax: 781-306-6655. p. 1104

Niles, Mary Ann, Dir, Middlesex Community College, Bldg 1-ARC, Springs Rd, Bedford, MA, 01730. Tel: 781-280-3703. Fax: 781-280-3771. p. 1052

Niles, Mary Ann, Dir, Middlesex Community College, Federal Bldg, E Merrimack St, Lowell, MA, 01852. Tel: 781-280-3703. Fax: 978-656-3031. p. 1100

Niles, Naomi, Assoc Librn, Metropolitan Museum of Art, Library & Teacher Resource Center in the Uris Center for Education, 1000 Fifth Ave, New York, NY, 10028-0198. Tel: 212-570-3788. p. 1686

Niles, Phyllis, Head, Per, Borough of Manhattan Community College Library, 199 Chambers St, New York, NY, 10007. Tel: 212-220-1450. Fax: 212-748-7466. p. 1671

Nilles, Judith, Sister, Libr Dir, Catholic Diocesan Archives, 1115 W Riverside Ave, Spokane, WA, 99201. Tel: 509-358-4293. p. 2535

Nilles, Virginia, Dir, Muncie Center Township Public Library, 2005 S High St, Muncie, IN, 47302. Tel: 765-747-8200. Fax: 765-747-8211. p. 767

Nilles, Virginia, Dir, Muncie Public Library, 2005 S High St, Muncie, IN, 47302. Tel: 765-747-8201. Fax: 765-747-8221. p. 767

Nilova, Olga, Outreach Librn, Spec Coll, The Rockefeller University, 1222 York Ave, Welch Hall, New York, NY, 10065. Tel: 212-327-8868. Fax: 212-327-8802. p. 1698

Nilsen, Ethel, Librn, Olive G Pettis Library, 36 Mill Village Rd, Goshen, NH, 03752. Tel: 603-863-6921. p. 1448

Nilsen, Judith, Asst Dir, Plainedge Public Library, 1060 Hicksville Rd, Massapequa, NY, 11758. Tel: 516-735-4133. Fax: 516-735-4192. p. 1658

Nilson, Wendy, Cat, Vermillion Public Library, 18 Church St, Vermillion, SD, 57069-3093. Tel: 605-677-7060. Fax: 605-677-7160. p. 2221

Nilsson, Frances, Head, Res Mgt, Merrimack College, 315 Turnpike St, North Andover, MA, 01845. Tel: 978-837-5215. Fax: 978-837-5434. p. 1111

Nilsson, Susan, Ch, Watsonville Public Library, 310 Union St, Watsonville, CA, 95076. Tel: 831-768-3400. Fax: 831-763-4015. p. 282

Nimersheim, Susan, Dir, Grant County Public Library District, 201 Barnes Rd, Williamstown, KY, 41097-9482. Tel: 859-824-2080. Fax: 859-824-2083. p. 937

Nimmer, David, Dir, W J Niederkorn Library, 316 W Grand Ave, Port Washington, WI, 53074-2293. Tel: 262-284-5031. Fax: 262-284-7680. p. 2631

Nimmo, Maureen, Dir, Lawrence Public Library, South Lawrence Branch, 135 Parker St, South Lawrence, MA, 01843. Tel: 978-682-1727. Fax: 978-688-3142. p. 1098

Nimmo, Maureen L, Dir, Lawrence Public Library, 51 Lawrence St, Lawrence, MA, 01841. Tel: 978-620-3600. Fax: 978-688-3142. p. 1098

Nims, Chris, Dir, Massachusetts Eye & Ear Infirmary Libraries, 243 Charles St, Boston, MA, 02114. Tel: 617-573-3196. Fax: 617-573-3370. p. 1063

Nims, Jenna, Librn, Maquoketa Public Library, 126 S Second St, Maquoketa, IA, 52060. Tel: 563-652-3874. p. 829

Nims, Kirk E, Librn, Environmental Protection Agency, 2000 Traverwood Dr, Ann Arbor, MI, 48105. Tel: 734-214-4434. Fax: 734-214-4525. p. 1151

Nimsakont, Emily, Cat Librn, Nebraska Library Commission, The Atrium, 1200 N St, Ste 120, Lincoln, NE, 68508-2023. Tel: 402-471-4031. Fax: 402-471-2083. p. 1406

Nimz, Karen, Librn, Milwaukee Secure Detention Facility Library, 1015 N Tenth St, Milwaukee, WI, 53233. Tel: 414-225-5685. Fax: 414-225-5681. p. 2621

Nimz, Tim, Dir, Edwin A Bemis Public Library, 6014 S Datura St, Littleton, CO, 80120-2636. Tel: 303-795-3961. Fax: 303-795-3996. p. 316

Nimz, Timothy, Dir, Littleton Historical Museum Research Center, 6028 S Gallup St, Littleton, CO, 80120. Tel: 303-795-3950. Fax: 303-730-9818. p. 317

Nine, Darla, Children's Prog Coordr, Covington-Veedersburg Public Library, Veedersburg Public, 408 N Main St, Veedersburg, IN, 47987. Tel: 765-294-2808. Fax: 765-294-4648. p. 734

Ninemire, David, Head Librn, Free Library of Philadelphia, Literature, 1901 Vine St, Philadelphia, PA, 19103-1189. Tel: 215-686-5402. p. 2108

Nino, Mary, Interim Assoc Dean, San Jose State University, One Washington Sq, San Jose, CA, 95192-0028. Tel: 408-808-2008. Fax: 408-808-2141. p. 251

Nino, Tylan, Circ, Hudson Valley Community College, 80 Vandenburgh Ave, Troy, NY, 12180. Tel: 518-629-7336. Fax: 518-629-7509. p. 1756

Nipper, Carter, Librn, Central Georgia Technical College Library, Milledgeville Campus, 54 Hwy 22 W, Milledgeville, GA, 31061. Tel: 478-445-2319. Fax: 478-445-2346. p. 540

Nipper, Elena, Purchasing, Vanguard University of Southern California, 55 Fair Dr, Costa Mesa, CA, 92626. Tel: 714-556-3610, Ext 2400. Fax: 714-966-5478. p. 137

Nippert, Jennifer, Dir, Owen County Public Library, 1370 Hwy 22 E, Owenton, KY, 40359. Tel: 502-484-3450. Fax: 502-484-3463. p. 931

Nisenson, Shari, Dir, Wilentz, Goldman & Spitzer, 90 Woodbridge Center Dr, Woodbridge, NJ, 07095. Tel: 732-855-6177. Fax: 732-726-6525. p. 1545

Nisly, Hope, Acq, Fresno Pacific University, 1717 S Chestnut Ave, Fresno, CA, 93702. Tel: 559-453-2223. Fax: 559-453-2124. p. 153

Nissen, Jill, Dir, St Louis College of Pharmacy, 4588 Parkview Pl, Saint Louis, MO, 63110. Tel: 314-446-8362. Fax: 314-446-8360. p. 1357

Nissenbaum, Robert J, Dir, Fordham University School of Law, 140 W 62nd St, New York, NY, 10023-7485. Tel: 212-636-7609. Fax: 212-930-8818. p. 1678

Nissler, Pam, Exec Dir, Jefferson County Public Library, 10200 W 20th Ave, Lakewood, CO, 80215. Tel: 303-232-7114. Fax: 303-275-2202. p. 315

Nisson, Theron, Br Mgr, Las Vegas-Clark County Library District, Las Vegas Library, 833 Las Vegas Blvd N, Las Vegas, NV, 89101. Tel: 702-507-3500. Fax: 702-507-3540. p. 1429

Nitch, Elizabeth, Principal Librn, Lee County Library System, South County Regional, 21100 Three Oaks Pkwy, Estero, FL, 33928-3020. Tel: 239-533-4402. Fax: 239-485-1130. p. 446

Nitecki, Danuta, Dean, Univ Libr, Drexel University Libraries, Hagerty Library, 33rd & Market Sts, Philadelphia, PA, 19104-2875. Tel: 215-895-2750. Fax: 215-895-2070. p. 2105

Nitsch, Lisa, Dept Chair, Los Angeles Trade Technical College Library, 400 W Washington Blvd, Los Angeles, CA, 90015. Tel: 213-763-3958. Fax: 213-763-5393. p. 175

Nitschke, Barbara, Asst Librn, Ashley Public Library, 113 First Ave NW, Ashley, ND, 58413-7037. Tel: 701-288-3510. p. 1837

Nitta, Steve, Bus & Human Res Mgr, Fresno County Public Library, 2420 Mariposa St, Fresno, CA, 93721-2285. Tel: 559-600-7323. p. 151

Nitz, Debby, Res Librn, Northfield Public Library, 210 Washington St, Northfield, MN, 55057. Tel: 507-645-1807. Fax: 507-645-1820. p. 1269

Nitz, Michael, Tech Serv, Appleton Public Library, 225 N Oneida St, Appleton, WI, 54911-4780. Tel: 920-832-6184. Fax: 920-832-6182. p. 2578

Nitzel, Heather, Youth Serv Librn, Robert L F Sikes Public Library, 1445 Commerce Dr, Crestview, FL, 32539. Tel: 850-682-4432. Fax: 850-689-4788. p. 434

Nitzsche, Sharon, Librn, Turon Community Library, 501 E Price, Turon, KS, 67583-9464. Tel: 620-497-6409. p. 898

Niu, Jinfang, Dr, Asst Prof, University of South Florida, 4202 Fowler Ave, CIS 1040, Tampa, FL, 33620-7800. Tel: 813-974-6837. Fax: 813-974-6840. p. 2964

Niven, R Garth, Chief Librn, Manitoba Law Library, Inc, Law Courts Bldg, Rm 331, 408 York Ave, Winnipeg, MB, R3C 0P9, CANADA. Tel: 204-945-1959. Fax: 204-948-2138. p. 2757

Niven, Ruth, Cat, Franklin Public Library, 310 Central St, Franklin, NH, 03235. Tel: 603-934-2911. Fax: 603-934-7413. p. 1447

Niven, Seiko, Br Mgr, Thompson-Nicola Regional District Library System, Logan Lake Branch, 70-150 Opal Dr, Logan Lake, BC, V0K 1W0, CANADA. Tel: 250-523-6745. Fax: 250-523-6745. p. 2729

Niwinski, Julie, Librn, Buncombe County Public Libraries, West Asheville, 942 Haywood Rd, Asheville, NC, 28806. Tel: 828-250-4750. p. 1774

Nix, Donna, Ref Librn, University of Saint Thomas, Charles J Keffer Library, 1000 LaSalle Ave, MOH 206, Minneapolis, MN, 55403. Tel: 651-962-4662. Fax: 651-962-4648. p. 1282

Nixdorff, John S, Dir of Libr, Venable LLP Library, 2049 Century Park, Ste 2100, Los Angeles, CA, 90067. Tel: 410-244-7492. Fax: 410-244-7742. p. 180

Nixdorff, John S, Dir, Venable LLP Library, 750 E Pratt St, 9th Flr, Baltimore, MD, 21202. Tel: 410-244-7502. Fax: 410-244-7742. p. 1019

Nixdorff, John S, Librn, Venable LLP Library, Towson Office, 210 Allegheny Ave, Towson, MD, 21204. Tel: 410-244-7492. Fax: 410-244-7742. p. 1019

Nixie, Kathy, Br Mgr, Bryan College Station Public Library System, Larry J Ringer Library, 1818 Harvey Mitchell Pkwy S, College Station, TX, 77840. Tel: 979-764-3625. Fax: 979-764-6379. p. 2292

Nixon, Gale, Mgr, Covington-Veedersburg Public Library, Veedersburg Public, 408 N Main St, Veedersburg, IN, 47987. Tel: 765-294-2808. Fax: 765-294-4648. p. 734

Nixon, Neal Dean, Dir, University of Louisville Libraries, Kornhauser Health Sciences Library, Health Sciences Ctr, 500 S Preston St, Louisville, KY, 40202. Tel: 502-852-8540. Fax: 502-852-1631. p. 927

Nixon, Paul, Pub Serv, Mount Vernon Nazarene University, 800 Martinsburg Rd, Mount Vernon, OH, 43050-9500. Tel: 740-397-9000, Ext 4240. Fax: 740-397-8847. p. 1919

Nizolek, Margaret, Asst Dir, SLIC, New Jersey State Library, 185 W State St, Trenton, NJ, 08618. Tel: 609-278-2640, Ext 148. Fax: 609-278-2652. p. 1536

Nkansah, Daniel Darkwa, Commun Libr Mgr, Queens Borough Public Library, North Hills Community Library, 57-04 Marathon Pkwy, Little Neck, NY, 11362. Tel: 718-225-3550. p. 1645

Nnacho, Igwe, Librn, Pickaway Correctional Institution Library, 11781 State Rte 762, Orient, OH, 43146. Tel: 614-877-4362. Fax: 614-877-0735. p. 1925

Noah, Wayne, Ref, Marlborough Public Library, 35 W Main St, Marlborough, MA, 01752-5510. Tel: 508-624-6900. Fax: 508-485-1494. p. 1103

Nobari, Nuchine, Head, Firmwide Libr Serv, Edwards Angell Palmer & Dodge LLP, 111 Huntington Ave, Boston, MA, 02199. Tel: 617-239-0104. Fax: 617-227-4420. p. 1060

Nobbs, Karen, Cat, Head, Coll Access, University of Iowa Libraries, Law Library, 200 Boyd Law Bldg, Iowa City, IA, 52242-1166. Tel: 319-335-9002. Fax: 319-335-9039. p. 823

Nobel, Steven, Commun Libr Mgr, Queens Borough Public Library, Middle Village Community Library, 72-31 Metropolitan Ave, Middle Village, NY, 11379. Tel: 718-326-1390. p. 1645

Noble, Ann A, Dir, Houston Baptist University, 7502 Fondren Rd, Houston, TX, 77074-3298. Tel: 281-649-3435. Fax: 281-649-3489. p. 2337

Noble, Barbara N, Dir, Harris-Stowe State University Library, 3026 Laclede Ave, Saint Louis, MO, 63103-2199. Tel: 314-340-3621. Fax: 314-340-3630. p. 1355

Noble, Carole, Outreach Serv Librn, Welles-Turner Memorial Library, 2407 Main St, Glastonbury, CT, 06033. Tel: 860-652-7718. Fax: 860-652-7721. p. 340

Noble, Catherine, Dir, Gutekunst Public Library, 309 Second St SE, State Center, IA, 50247-0550. Tel: 641-483-2741. Fax: 641-483-2131. p. 846

Noble, Clem, Librn, Baker & McKenzie, 1111 Brickell Ave, Ste 1700, Miami, FL, 33131. Tel: 305-789-8951. Fax: 305-789-8953. p. 464

Noble, Gordon, ILL, Bethlehem Public Library, 451 Delaware Ave, Delmar, NY, 12054-3042. Tel: 518-439-9314. Fax: 518-478-0901. p. 1614

Noble, Rebecca, Asst Librn, New Woodstock Free Library, 2106 Main St, New Woodstock, NY, 13122-8718. Tel: 315-662-3134. p. 1667

Noble, Terri, Libr Tech, Nova Scotia Community College, 372 Pleasant St, Yarmouth, NS, B5A 2L2, CANADA. Tel: 902-742-3416. Fax: 902-742-0519. p. 2786

Nobles, Steve, Acq, University of Tulsa Libraries, 2933 E Sixth St, Tulsa, OK, 74104-3123. Tel: 918-631-2869. Fax: 918-631-3791. p. 1984

Nobunaga, Wendy, Head, Cat, University of Southern California Libraries, Asa V Call Law Library, 699 Exposition Blvd, LAW 202, MC 0072, Los Angeles, CA, 90089-0072. Tel: 213-740-6482. Fax: 213-740-7179. p. 179

Nocek, Janet, Dir, Portland Library, 20 Freestone Ave, Portland, CT, 06480. Tel: 860-342-6770. Fax: 860-342-6778. p. 364

Nocito, Gabriela, Dir of Libr Serv, The National Hispanic University Library, 14271 Story Rd, San Jose, CA, 95127-3823. Tel: 408-273-2731. Fax: 408-254-1369. p. 250

Nock, Lori, Ch, Beaumont Public Library System, R C Miller Memorial, 1605 Dowlen Rd, Beaumont, TX, 77706. Tel: 409-866-9487. Fax: 409-866-3720. p. 2287

Noda, Keisuke, Dr, Dir, Unification Theological Seminary Library, 14 Seminary Dr, Barrytown, NY, 12507. Tel: 845-752-3000, Ext 232. Fax: 845-752-3021. p. 1578

Noda, Yoko, Circ Tech, Sofia University Library, 1069 E Meadow Circle, Palo Alto, CA, 94303. Tel: 650-493-4430, Ext 221. Fax: 650-852-9780. p. 205

Nodes, Jennifer, Rare Bks & Spec Coll Librn, Canizaro Library at Ave Maria University, 5251 Avila Ave, Ave Maria, FL, 34142. Tel: 239-348-4710. p. 426

Nodine, Polly S, AV Archivist/Librn, National Archives & Records Administration, 441 Freedom Pkwy, Atlanta, GA, 30307. Tel: 404-865-7125. Fax: 404-865-7102. p. 517

Nodine, Sara, Asst Librn, Head, Coll Develop, Spec Coll, Florida State University Libraries, Warren D Allen Music Library, Housewright Music Bldg, 122 N Copeland St, Tallahassee, FL, 32306-1180. Tel: 850-644-4698. Fax: 850-644-3982. p. 494

Nodler, Charles E, Archivist, Missouri Southern State University, 3950 E Newman Rd, Joplin, MO, 64801-1595. Tel: 417-625-9386. Fax: 417-625-9734. p. 1336

Noe, Amy, Ch, Vinton Public Library, 510 Second Ave, Vinton, IA, 52349. Tel: 319-472-4208. Fax: 319-472-2548. p. 849

Noe, Christopher, Asst Dir, University of Mississippi, Three Grove Loop, University, MS, 38677. Tel: 662-915-6850. Fax: 662-915-7731. p. 1316

Noe, David, Digital Serv Librn, Rollins College, 1000 Holt Ave, Campus Box 2744, Winter Park, FL, 32789-2744. Tel: 407-691-1127. Fax: 407-646-1515. p. 505

Noe, Janette, Coll Develop, Martin County Library System, 2351 SE Monterey Rd, Stuart, FL, 34996. Tel: 772-219-4968. Fax: 772-219-4959. p. 491

Noe, Marie, Customer Serv Mgr, Abilene Public Library, 202 Cedar St, Abilene, TX, 79601-5793. Tel: 325-437-4537. p. 2271

Noel, Caryn, Dir, SS Cyril & Methodius Seminary, 3535 Indian Trail, Orchard Lake, MI, 48324. Tel: 248-706-4211. Fax: 248-683-0526. p. 1215

Noel, Daniel, Chief Exec Officer, Clarence-Rockland Public Library, 1525 du Parc Ave, Unit 2, Rockland, ON, K4K 1C3, CANADA. Tel: 613-446-5680. Fax: 613-446-1518. p. 2839

Noel, Fred, Dir, Salish Kootenai College, PO Box 70, Pablo, MT, 59855. Tel: 406-275-4875. Fax: 406-275-4812. p. 1387

Noël, Jeanne-Mance, Libr Mgr, Chaleur Library Region, Lamèque Public Library, 46 du Pêcheur Nord St, Lameque, NB, E8T 1J3, CANADA. Tel: 506-344-3262. Fax: 506-344-3263. p. 2761

Noel, Kim, Circ Mgr, Springfield Technical Community College Library, One Armory Sq, Ste 1, Springfield, MA, 01105-1685. Tel: 413-755-4564. Fax: 413-755-6315. p. 1128

Noel, Michelle, Dir, Libr Serv, Truckee Meadows Community College, 7000 Dandini Blvd, Reno, NV, 89512-3999. Tel: 775-674-7610. Fax: 775-674-8231. p. 1432

Noel, Robert, Head of Libr, Indiana University Bloomington, Swain Hall Library, Swain Hall West 208, 727 E Third St, Bloomington, IN, 47405-7105. Tel: 812-855-2758. Fax: 812-855-5533. p. 728

Noerenberg, Sharon, Librn, Winsted Public Library, 180 Main Ave W, Winsted, MN, 55395. Tel: 320-485-3909. Fax: 320-485-3909. p. 1290

Noethlichs, Wolfgang, Dir, National Theatre School of Canada Library, 5030 Rue Saint Denis, Montreal, QC, H2J 2L8, CANADA. Tel: 514-842-7954, Ext 125. Fax: 514-842-5661. p. 2900

Noffke, Lynn, Dir, Limestone Township Library, 2701 W Tower Rd, Kankakee, IL, 60901. Tel: 815-939-1696. Fax: 815-939-1748. p. 661

Noffke, Nancy, Librn, Waseca-Le Sueur Regional Library, Montgomery Public, 104 Oak Ave SE, Montgomery, MN, 56069. Tel: 507-364-7615. p. 1287

Noffsinger, Martha, Circ Mgr, Carroll County Public Library, 136 Court St, Carrollton, KY, 41008. Tel: 502-732-7020. Fax: 502-732-7122. p. 909

Nofsinger, Christine, Librn, Marcellus Township-Wood Memorial Library, 205 E Main St, Marcellus, MI, 49067. Tel: 269-646-9654. Fax: 269-646-9603. p. 1206

Nofziger, Louise, Ch, Buhl Public Library, 215 Broadway N, Buhl, ID, 83316-1624. Tel: 208-543-6500. Fax: 208-543-2318. p. 572

Noga, Jennifer, Tech Serv, Guilford Technical Community College, 601 High Point Rd, Jamestown, NC, 27282. Tel: 336-334-4822, Ext 2232. Fax: 336-841-4350. p. 1803

Noga, Jennifer, Tech Serv Librn, Wake Forest University, Professional Center Library, Worrell Professional Ctr for Law & Management, 1834 Wake Forest Rd, Winston-Salem, NC, 27106. Tel: 336-758-5438. Fax: 336-758-6077. p. 1834

Noga, Michael, Coll Mgr, Massachusetts Institute of Technology Libraries, Science, Bldg 14S-134, 77 Massachusetts Ave, Cambridge, MA, 02139-4307. Tel: 617-253-1290. Fax: 617-253-6365. p. 1078

Nogami, Amy, Supvr, United States Army, Bldg 560, Schofield Barracks, HI, 96857-5000. Tel: 808-655-8002. Fax: 808-655-6375. p. 567

Noggle, Deborah L, Mgr, Allen County Public Library, Tecumseh, 1411 E State Blvd, Fort Wayne, IN, 46805. Tel: 260-421-1361. Fax: 260-482-5236. p. 741

Noguchi, Sachie, Coll Develop/Ref Librn, Columbia University, C V Starr East Asian Library, 300 Kent Hall, MC 3901, 1140 Amsterdam Ave, New York, NY, 10027. Tel: 212-854-4318. Fax: 212-662-6286. p. 1675

Nohrenberg, LaVena, Customer Experience Mgr, Eugene Public Library, 100 W Tenth Ave, Eugene, OR, 97401. Tel: 541-682-5450. Fax: 541-682-5898. p. 1996

Nokes, C Odessa, Ch, Salem Free Public Library, 112 W Broadway, Salem, NJ, 08079-1302. Tel: 856-935-0526. Fax: 856-935-5110. p. 1528

Nolan, Barbara J, Dir, Danville Public Library, 319 N Vermilion St, Danville, IL, 61832. Tel: 217-477-5223, Ext 113. Fax: 217-477-5230. p. 633

Nolan, Brandi, Librn, Kearney & Area Public Library, Eight Main St, Kearney, ON, P0A 1M0, CANADA. Tel: 705-636-5849. p. 2812

Nolan, Brian, Mgr, Precedent Res, Sullivan & Cromwell LLP, 125 Broad St, New York, NY, 10004. Tel: 212-558-3780. Fax: 212-558-3346. p. 1700

Nolan, Christina B, Dir, Ridgefield Library Association Inc, 472 Main St, Ridgefield, CT, 06877-4585. Tel: 203-438-2282. Fax: 203-438-4558. p. 365

Nolan, Christopher W, Asst Univ Librn, Pub Serv, Trinity University, One Trinity Pl, San Antonio, TX, 78212-7200. Tel: 210-999-8121. Fax: 210-999-8182. p. 2383

Nolan, Dan, Librn, Harrison Memorial Hospital, 2520 Cherry Ave, Bremerton, WA, 98310. Tel: 360-792-6500. Fax: 360-475-8566. p. 2510

Nolan, Danielle, Librn, Ninilchik Community Library, 15850 Sterling Hwy, Ninilchik, AK, 99639. Tel: 907-567-3333. p. 52

Nolan, Deborah A, Univ Librn, Towson University, 8000 York Rd, Towson, MD, 21252-0001. Tel: 410-704-2450. Fax: 410-704-3760. p. 1045

Nolan, Deirdre, Librn, Conde Nast Publications Library, Four Times Sq, New York, NY, 10036. Tel: 212-286-8245. Fax: 212-286-6763. p. 1675

Nolan, Ed, Media Spec, Naugatuck Valley Community College, 750 Chase Pkwy, Waterbury, CT, 06708. Tel: 203-575-8024. Fax: 203-575-8062. p. 375

Nolan, Edward W, Head, Spec Coll, Washington State Historical Society Research Center, 315 N Stadium Way, Tacoma, WA, 98403. Tel: 253-798-5914. Fax: 253-597-4186. p. 2541

Nolan, Irene, Coll Develop, Pub Serv, Hamden Public Library, 2901 Dixwell Ave, Hamden, CT, 06518-3135. Tel: 203-287-2686. Fax: 203-287-2685. p. 343

Nolan, Kim, Acq, ILL, Wells College, 170 Main St, Aurora, NY, 13026-0500. Tel: 315 364-3355. Fax: 315-364-3412. p. 1576

Nolan, Linda, Librn, Garnish Public Library, Sunset Dr, Garnish, NL, A0E 1T0, CANADA. Tel: 709-826-2371. p. 2770

Nolan, Liz, Head of Libr, Selby Public Library, 1331 First St, Sarasota, FL, 34236-4899. Tel: 941-861-1100. Fax: 941-316-1188. p. 490

Nolan, Margie, Dir, Seneca Public Library District, 210 N Main St, Seneca, IL, 61360. Tel: 815-357-6566. Fax: 815-357-6568. p. 701

Nolan, Marianne, Ref Coordr, Cleveland State University, University Library, Rhodes Tower, 2121 Euclid Ave, Cleveland, OH, 44115-2214. Tel: 216-687-2376. Fax: 216-687-9380. p. 1879

Nolan, Maureen, Actg Head Librn, University of Washington Libraries, Natural Sciences, Allen Library S, Ground & First Flrs, Box 352900, Seattle, WA, 98195-2900. Tel: 206-685-2126. Fax: 206-685-1665. p. 2534

Nolan, Maureen D, Actg Head Librn, University of Washington Libraries, Friday Harbor, 620 University Rd, Box 352900, Friday Harbor, WA, 98250-2900. Tel: 206-685-2126. Fax: 206-685-3892. p. 2534

Nolan, Michelle, Ch, Sullivan City Public Library, Two W Water St, Sullivan, IL, 61951. Tel: 217-728-7221. Fax: 217-728-2215. p. 708

Nolan, Stephen, Librn, College of the North Atlantic, Carbonear Campus Resource Center, Four Pikes Lane, Carbonear, NL, A1Y 1A7, CANADA. Tel: 709-596-6139, 709-596-8925. Fax: 709-596-2688. p. 2771

Nolan, Wendy, Libr Spec, Horry-Georgetown Technical College, 2050 Hwy 501 E, Conway, SC, 29526-9521. Tel: 843-349-7809. Fax: 843-347-0552. p. 2191

Noland, Abigail, Dir, Preble County District Library, 450 S Barron St, Eaton, OH, 45320-2402. Tel: 937-456-4250. Fax: 937-456-6092. p. 1897

Noland, Abigail, Dir, Preble County District Library, Library Administration & Resource Center, 450 S Barron St, Eaton, OH, 45320-2402. Tel: 937-456-4520. p. 1898

Noland, Jake, Librn, Reveille United Methodist Church Library, 4200 Cary Street Rd, Richmond, VA, 23221. Tel: 804-359-6041. Fax: 804-359-6090. p. 2489

Noland, Lanita, Tech Serv Dir, Lake Cities Library, 302 S Shady Shores Rd, Lake Dallas, TX, 75065-3609. Tel: 940-497-3566. Fax: 940-497-3567. p. 2352

Noland, Sharon, Cat, United States Air Force, 744 Douhet Dr, Bldg 4244, Barksdale AFB, LA, 71110. Tel: 318-456-4182. Fax: 318-752-0509. p. 941

Nolasco, Kristie, Br Mgr, Maricopa County Library District, Fairway, 10620 W Peoria Ave, Sun City, AZ, 85351-4144. Tel: 602-652-3000. p. 74

Nolasco, Kristine, Br Mgr, Maricopa County Library District, Sun City Branch Library, 16828 N 99th Ave, Sun City, AZ, 85351. Tel: 602-651-2001. Fax: 602-651-2015. p. 75

Nolen, Dan, Librn, Calhoun Correction Institution Library, 19562 SE Institution Dr, Unit 1, Blountstown, FL, 32424-5156. Tel: 850-237-6579. Fax: 850-237-6508. p. 427

Nolen, India, Asst Dir, J V Fletcher Library, 50 Main St, Westford, MA, 01886-2599. Tel: 978-399-2311. Fax: 978-692-4418. p. 1138

Nolen, Jennifer, Dir, Chaffee Public Library, 202 Wright Ave, Chaffee, MO, 63740. Tel: 573-887-3298. Fax: 573-887-3298. p. 1323

Nolen, Tina, Librn, Ashland City Public Library, 113 Second Ave N, Ashland, AL, 36251. Tel: 256-354-3427. Fax: 256-354-3427. p. 4

Nolen-Karras, Michele, Dir, Brewer Public Library, 325 N Central Ave, Richland Center, WI, 53581-1802. Tel: 608-647-6444. Fax: 608-647-6797. p. 2634

Nolette, Brenda, Youth Serv, Rye Public Library, 581 Washington Rd, Rye, NH, 03870. Tel: 603-964-8401. Fax: 603-964-7065. p. 1464

Nolfi, David, Health Sci Librn, Libr Assessment Coordr, Duquesne University, 600 Forbes Ave, Pittsburgh, PA, 15282. Tel: 412-396-4931. p. 2125

Nolfi, Josephine, Ch Mgr, Public Library of Youngstown & Mahoning County, 305 Wick Ave, Youngstown, OH, 44503-1079. Tel: 330-744-8636. Fax: 330-744-3355. p. 1952

Nolidis, Carla, Circ/Check-Out Supvr, Naperville Public Library, 200 W Jefferson Ave, Naperville, IL, 60540-5374. Tel: 630-961-4100, Ext 6321. Fax: 630-637-6389. p. 679

Nolin, Kelly, Spec Coll Librn, Univ Archivist, Norwich University, 23 Harmon Dr, Northfield, VT, 05663. Tel: 802-485-2722. Fax: 802-485-2173. p. 2431

Nolin, Linda, Circ Librn, Moultonborough Public Library, Four Holland St, Moultonborough, NH, 03254. Tel: 603-476-8895. p. 1458

Noll, Beth, Libr Mgr, Alachua County Library District, High Springs Branch, 135 NW First Ave, High Springs, FL, 32643-1001. Tel: 386-454-2515. Fax: 386-454-3439. p. 448

Noll, Charlene, Dir, Hillside Public Library, 155 Lakeville Rd, New Hyde Park, NY, 11040-3003. Tel: 516-355-7850. Fax: 516-355-7855. p. 1665

Nollenberger, Janice, Circ, Pemberville Public Library, 375 E Front St, Pemberville, OH, 43450. Tel: 419-287-4012. Fax: 419-287-4620. p. 1928

Noller, Denise, Librn, Sullivan & Cromwell LLP, 1701 Pennsylvania Ave NW, Washington, DC, 20006-5805. Tel: 202-956-7538. Fax: 202-293-6330. p. 416

Nollette, Patrice, Br Mgr, Mid-Continent Public Library, Riverside Branch, 2700 NW Vivion Rd, Riverside, MO, 64150-9432. Tel: 816-741-6288. Fax: 816-741-8596. p. 1333

Nollman, Toni, Asst Dir, Carnegie-Schuyler Library, 303 E Second St, Pana, IL, 62557. Tel: 217-562-2326. Fax: 217-562-2343. p. 688

Nolte, Dianne, Asst Librn, Ackley Public Library, 401 State St, Ackley, IA, 50601. Tel: 641-847-2233. Fax: 641-847-2233. p. 791

Nolte, Jim, Dir, Vermont College of Fine Arts Library, 36 College St, Montpelier, VT, 05602. Tel: 802-828-8512. Fax: 802-828-8514. p. 2429

Nolting, Dan, Head, Tech Serv, Chatham College, Woodland Rd, Pittsburgh, PA, 15232. Tel: 412-365-1243. Fax: 412-365-1465. p. 2124

Nolting, Diane, Mgr, Per, Saint Mary's College Library, 1928 Saint Mary's Rd, Moraga, CA, 94575. Tel: 925-631-4229. Fax: 925-376-6097. p. 191

Nombrano, Aurora, ILL, Tom Green County Library System, 113 W Beauregard, San Angelo, TX, 76903. Tel: 915-655-7321. Fax: 915-659-4027. p. 2378

Nomeland, Elana, Asst Librn, Minneota Public Library, 103 N Jefferson St, Minneota, MN, 56264-0217. Tel: 507-872-5473. Fax: 507-872-6144. p. 1263

Nonack, Stephen Z, Reader Serv, Boston Athenaeum, 10 1/2 Beacon St, Boston, MA, 02108-3777. Tel: 617-227-0270. Fax: 617-227-5266. p. 1056

Nonneman, Kathleen, Circ, Coll Develop, Ref Serv, Grand Island Public Library, 211 N Washington St, Grand Island, NE, 68801-5855. Tel: 308-385-5333. Fax: 308-385-5339. p. 1400

Nooble, Michele, Br Mgr, Public Library Association of Annapolis & Anne Arundel County, Inc, Eastport-Annapolis Neck, 269 Hillsmere Dr, Annapolis, MD, 21403. Tel: 410-222-1770. Fax: 410-222-1973. p. 1010

Noon, Sherry, Youth Serv Librn, Anderson County Public Library, 114 N Main St, Lawrenceburg, KY, 40342. Tel: 502-839-6420. Fax: 502-839-7243. p. 919

Noonan, Kathryn, Dir, Libr Serv, Lemuel Shattuck Hospital, 170 Morton St, Jamaica Plain, MA, 02130. Tel: 617-971-3225. Fax: 617-971-3850. p. 1097

Noonan, Marie, Res Sharing Spec, Capital District Library Council, 28 Essex St, Albany, NY, 12206. Tel: 518-438-2500. Fax: 518-438-2872. p. 2949

Noonan, Patricia K, Dir, Access & Tech Serv, Gail Borden Public Library District, 270 N Grove Ave, Elgin, IL, 60120-5596. Tel: 847-429-5983. Fax: 847-608-5201. p. 640

Noonan, Pattie, Assoc Dir, UBS Warburg Library, 299 Park Ave, New York, NY, 10171-0099. Tel: 212-821-3000. p. 1701

Noonan-Cifarelli, Yvonne, Curator, Oyster Bay Historical Society Library, 20 Summit St, Oyster Bay, NY, 11771. Tel: 516-922-5032. Fax: 516-922-6892. p. 1714

Noone, Fran, In Charge, Teck Cominco Metals Ltd, Cominco Research, Trail, BC, V1R 4S4, CANADA. Tel: 250-364-4432. Fax: 250-364-4456. p. 2739

Noorani, Jessica, Syst Adminr, Harrison County Public Library, 105 N Capitol Ave, Corydon, IN, 47112. Tel: 812-738-4110. Fax: 812-738-5408. p. 734

Norback, Carolyn, Asst Librn, Walpole Town Library, Bridge Memorial Library, 48 Main St, Walpole, NH, 03608. Tel: 603-756-9806. Fax: 603-756-3140. p. 1466

Norbeck, Kathy, Commun Br Supvr, Pierce County Library System, Buckley Branch, 123 S River Ave, Buckley, WA, 98321. Tel: 360-548-3710. Fax: 360-829-2874. p. 2539

Norberg, Lisa, Dean, Barnard College, 3009 Broadway, New York, NY, 10027-6598. Tel: 212-854-3953. p. 1670

Norbotten, Hans, Librn, Genesee District Library, Linden Area, 201 N Main, Linden, MI, 48451. Tel: 810-735-7700. Fax: 810-735-9163. p. 1180

Norcross, Mary, Ser, Dine College, PO Box 1000, Tsaile, AZ, 86556. Tel: 928-724-6758. p. 85

Nord, Karen, In Charge, Washburn County Law Library, Courthouse, Shell Lake, WI, 54871. Tel: 715-468-4688. Fax: 715-468-4678. p. 2638

Nord, Leslie, Mgr, Johnson County Library, De Soto Branch, 33145 W 83rd St, De Soto, KS, 66018. Tel: 913-495-7542. Fax: 913-583-1702. p. 888

Nord, Leslie, Mgr, Johnson County Library, Lackman, 15345 W 87th St Pkwy, Lenexa, KS, 66219. Tel: 913-495-7542. Fax: 913-495-7556. p. 888

Nord, Martin, ILL, Pub Serv Librn, Ref Serv, Hillsdale College, 33 E College St, Hillsdale, MI, 49242. Tel: 517-607-2606. Fax: 517-607-2248. p. 1190

Nordberg, Erik, Univ Archivist, Michigan Technological University, 1400 Townsend Dr, Houghton, MI, 49931-1295. Tel: 906-487-2505. p. 1191

Nordeng, Diane, Librn, Department of Veterans Affairs, 2101 N Elm St, Fargo, ND, 58102. Tel: 701-239-3755. Fax: 701-239-3775. p. 1840

Nordgren, Deb, Dir, University of Wisconsin-Superior, PO Box 2000, Belknap & Catlin, Superior, WI, 54880-2000. Tel: 715-394-8233. Fax: 715-394-8462. p. 2641

Nordgren, Debra, Assoc Prof, Chair, University of Wisconsin-Superior, Belknap & Catlin, PO Box 2000, Superior, WI, 54880. Tel: 715-394-8233. Fax: 715-394-8462. p. 2977

Nordgren, Layne, Dir, Digital Media Ctr, Pacific Lutheran University, 12180 Park Ave S, Tacoma, WA, 98447-0001. Tel: 253-535-7500. Fax: 253-535-7315. p. 2539

Nordgren, Peter, Asst Prof, University of Wisconsin-Superior, Belknap & Catlin, PO Box 2000, Superior, WI, 54880. Tel: 715-394-8528. Fax: 715-394-8462. p. 2977

Nordhaus, Kathy L, Principal Tech Librn, Raytheon Co, 13510 N Central Expressway, MS 211, Dallas, TX, 75243. Tel: 972-344-5036. Fax: 972-344-5042. p. 2309

Nordheden, Holly, Head, Tech Serv & Cat, Danville Area Community College Library, 2000 E Main St, Danville, IL, 61832-5199. Tel: 217-443-8852. Fax: 217-554-1623. p. 632

Nordheimer James, Carolyn, Chief Exec Officer, Whitchurch-Stouffville Public Library, 30 Burkholder St, Stouffville, ON, L4A 4K1, CANADA. Tel: 905-642-7323. Fax: 905-640-1384. p. 2845

Nordholm, Sarah, Asst Libr Dir, Summit County Library, 0037 Peak One Dr, Frisco, CO, 80443. Tel: 970-668-4131. Fax: 970-668-5556. p. 308

Nordin, Andy, Syst Coordr, East Central Regional Library, 244 S Birch, Cambridge, MN, 55008-1588. Tel: 763-689-7390. Fax: 763-689-7389. p. 1243

Nordin, Erin, Librn, Southeast Regional Library, Radville Branch, 420 Floren St, Radville, SK, S0C 2G0, CANADA. Tel: 306-869-2742. p. 2930

Nordin, Liz, Dir, Hesperia Community Library, 80 S Division St, Hesperia, MI, 49421-9004. Tel: 231-854-5125. Fax: 231-854-5125. p. 1189

Nordine, Ed, Asst Dean, Palm Beach Atlantic University, 300 Pembroke Pl, West Palm Beach, FL, 33401-6503. Tel: 561-803-2232. Fax: 561-803-2235. p. 503

Nordseth, Joan, Br Mgr, San Bernardino County Library, Trona Branch, 82805 Mountain View St, Trona, CA, 93562. Tel: 760-372-5847. Fax: 760-372-5847. p. 229

Nordstrom, Daniel, Cat/Metadata Librn, Multnomah University, 8435 NE Glisan St, Portland, OR, 97220-5898. Tel: 503-251-5322. Fax: 503-254-1268. p. 2012

Nordstrom, Lance, Librn, Workers' Compensation Board of British Columbia Library, 6951 Westminster Hwy, Richmond, BC, V7C 1C6, CANADA. Tel: 604-231-8450. Fax: 604-279-7608. p. 2737

Nordstrom, Sonja, Ser Librn, William J Campbell Library of the US Courts, 219 S Dearborn St, Rm 1637, Chicago, IL, 60604-1769. Tel: 312-435-5660. Fax: 312-408-5031. p. 607

Noreau, Patricia, Dir, University of Massachusetts Lowell Libraries, 61 Wilder St, Lowell, MA, 01854-3098. Tel: 978-934-4550, 978-934-4551. Fax: 978-934-3015. p. 1100

Norem, Jane, Govt Doc, Head Librn, Illinois Valley Community College, 815 N Orlando Smith Ave, Oglesby, IL, 61348-9692. Tel: 815-224-0387. Fax: 815-224-9147. p. 684

Norem, Monica, Ref Librn, Lone Star College System, CyFair Library, 9191 Barker Cypress Rd, Cypress, TX, 77433. Tel: 281-290-3214, 281-290-3219. p. 2340

Norgren, Dianne, Dir, Platteville Public Library, 504 Marion Ave, Platteville, CO, 80651. Tel: 970-785-2231. Fax: 970-785-0708. p. 320

Norheim, Gwen, In Charge, American Pharmacists Association Foundation Library, 1100 15th St NW, Ste 400, Washington, DC, 20005. Tel: 202-429-7524. Fax: 202-783-2351. p. 392

Nori, Uma, Head, Youth Serv, Thomas Ford Memorial Library, 800 Chestnut Ave, Western Springs, IL, 60558. Tel: 708-246-0520. Fax: 708-246-0403. p. 717

Noriega, Jose, Librn, South Texas College Library, 3201 W Pecan Blvd, McAllen, TX, 78501-6661. Tel: 956-872-8330. Fax: 956-872-7202. p. 2361

Norlin, Elaina, Regional Libr Mgr, Broward County Division of Libraries, African-American Research Library & Cultural Center, 2650 Sistrunk Blvd, Fort Lauderdale, FL, 33311. Tel: 954-357-6149. Fax: 954-357-6257. p. 441

Norlin, Jo Ann, AV, Park County Public Library, Powell Branch, 217 E Third, Powell, WY, 82435-1903. Tel: 307-754-8828. Fax: 307-754-8824. p. 2654

Norlin, Sandra K, Dir, Des Plaines Public Library, 1501 Ellinwood St, Des Plaines, IL, 60016-4553. Tel: 847-827-5551. Fax: 847-827-7974. p. 636

Norling, Jane, Dir, Beresford Public Library, 115 S Third St, Beresford, SD, 57004-1798. Tel: 605-763-2782. Fax: 605-763-2403. p. 2210

Norman, Amy, Ref & Instruction Librn, Tulsa Community College Learning Resources Center, Southeast Campus, 10300 E 81st St, Tulsa, OK, 74133-4513. Tel: 918-595-7702. Fax: 918-595-7706. p. 1983

Norman, Anne E, Dr, Dir, State of Delaware, 121 Duke of York St, Dover, DE, 19901. Tel: 302-739-4748. Fax: 302-739-6787. p. 382

Norman, Catherine, Youth Serv, Fairport Harbor Public Library, 335 Vine St, Fairport Harbor, OH, 44077-5799. Tel: 440-354-8191, Ext 23. Fax: 440-354-6059. p. 1899

Norman, Dawn, Commun Serv Supvr, Clark Memorial Library, 39 N Ninth St, Clarkdale, AZ, 86324. Tel: 928-639-2480. Fax: 928-639-2489. p. 60

Norman, Jeanie, Dir, Langley Public Library, 325 W Osage, Langley, OK, 74350. Tel: 918-782-4461. Fax: 918-782-1056. p. 1967

Norman, Kristy, Pub Support Serv Coordr, Derby Public Library, 1600 E Walnut Grove, Derby, KS, 67037. Tel: 316-788-0760. Fax: 316-788-7313. p. 863

Norman, Melorat J, Dir, Unity College, 90 Quaker Hill Rd, Unity, ME, 04988. Tel: 207-948-3131, Ext 265. Fax: 207-948-2795. p. 1004

Norman, Ola K, Br Mgr, Wilkes County Public Library, Traphill Branch, 6938 Traphill Rd, Traphill, NC, 28685. Tel: 336-957-2534. Fax: 336-957-2534. p. 1813

Norman, Robina, Librn, Beaufort, Hyde & Martin County Regional Library, Hazel W Guilford Memorial, 524 Main St, Aurora, NC, 27806. Tel: 252-322-5046. Fax: 252-322-7109. p. 1828

Norman, Sandra, Circ, John C Hart Memorial Library, 1130 Main St, Shrub Oak, NY, 10588. Tel: 914-245-5262. Fax: 914-245-2216. p. 1743

Norman, Steve, Libr Dir, Belfast Free Library, 106 High St, Belfast, ME, 04915. Tel: 207-338-3884. Fax: 207-338-3895. p. 977

Norman-Camp, Melody, Dir, Hubbard Free Library, 115 Second St, Hallowell, ME, 04347. Tel: 207-622-6582. p. 987

Normandeau, Louise, Libr Dir, Thorsby Municipal Library, 4901 - 48 Ave, Thorsby, AB, T0C 2P0, CANADA. Tel: 780-789-3808. Fax: 780-789-3805. p. 2719

Normore, Lorraine, Asst Prof, University of Tennessee, Knoxville, 451 Communications Bldg, 1345 Circle Park Dr, Knoxville, TN, 37996-0341. Tel: 865-974-2148. Fax: 865-974-4967. p. 2974

Norquist, Michelle, Assoc Dir, Kuyper College, 3333 E Beltline NE, Grand Rapids, MI, 49525. Tel: 616-222-3000. Fax: 616-222-3045, 616-988-3608. p. 1185

Norrell, Megan, Circ, Trumbull Library, 33 Quality St, Trumbull, CT, 06611. Tel: 203-452-5197. Fax: 203-452-5125. p. 373

Norris, Alice, Commun Libr Mgr, Queens Borough Public Library, Richmond Hill Community Library, 118-14 Hillside Ave, Richmond Hill, NY, 11418. Tel: 718-849-7150. Fax: 718-849-4717. p. 1645

Norris, Carolyn, Dir, Harnett County Public Library, Anderson Creek Public, 914 Anderson Creek School Rd, Bunn Level, NC, 28323. Tel: 910-814-4012. Fax: 910-814-0262. p. 1807

Norris, Darline, Acq, California State University, 9001 Stockdale Hwy, Bakersfield, CA, 93311-1022. Tel: 661-654-3262. Fax: 661-654-3238. p. 123

Norris, Denise, Dir, Learning Serv, Florida State College at Jacksonville, South Campus, 11901 Beach Blvd, Jacksonville, FL, 32246-6624. Tel: 904-646-2173. Fax: 904-646-2155. p. 453

Norris, Donna J, Dir, Rose Free Library, 4069 Main St, Rose, NY, 14542. Tel: 315-587-2335. Fax: 315-587-2335. p. 1735

Norris, Eric, Dir, Hays Public Library, 1205 Main, Hays, KS, 67601-3693. Tel: 785-625-9014. Fax: 785-625-8683. p. 871

Norris, Glada M, In Charge, Trinity Valley Community College Library, Health Occupational, 800 Ed Hall Dr, Kaufman, TX, 75142. Tel: 972-932-4309. Fax: 972-932-5010. p. 2277

Norris, Jennifer, Tech Serv, Antioch Public Library District, 757 Main St, Antioch, IL, 60002. Tel: 847-395-0874, Ext 235. Fax: 847-395-5399. p. 589

Norris, Jennifer, Asst Librn, Brookston - Prairie Township Public Library, 111 W Second St, Brookston, IN, 47923. Tel: 765-563-6511. Fax: 765-563-6833. p. 730

Norris, Jo, Librn II, Town of Vail Public Library, 292 W Meadow Dr, Vail, CO, 81657. Tel: 970-479-2195. Fax: 970-479-2192. p. 325

Norris, John, Syst Instruction Librn, Queens University of Charlotte, 1900 Selwyn Ave, Charlotte, NC, 28274-0001. Tel: 704-337-2278. Fax: 704-337-2517. p. 1784

Norris, Joyce Goering, Librn, Wichita Art Museum, 1400 W Museum Blvd, Wichita, KS, 67203-3296. Tel: 316-268-4918. Fax: 316-268-4980. p. 901

Norris, Kevin, Online Serv, University of Scranton, Monroe & Linden, Scranton, PA, 18510-4634. Tel: 570-941-4000, 570-941-4008. Fax: 570-941-7817. p. 2138

Norris, Kitty, Br Mgr, Central Rappahannock Regional Library, Cooper Branch, 20 Washington Ave, Colonial Beach, VA, 22443-2337. Tel: 804-224-0921. Fax: 804-224-1330. p. 2466

Norris, Laura, Access Serv, Doc Delivery, Vanderbilt University, Walker Management Library, Owen Graduate School of Management, 401 21st Ave S, Nashville, TN, 37203. Tel: 615-343-6036. Fax: 615-343-0061. p. 2261

Norris, Leslie, Commun Libr Mgr, Queens Borough Public Library, Hillcrest Community Library, 187-05 Union Tpk, Flushing, NY, 11366. Tel: 718-454-2786. Fax: 718-264-7567. p. 1644

Norris, Linda, Ch, Ligonier Valley Library Association, Inc, 120 W Main St, Ligonier, PA, 15658-1243. Tel: 724-238-6451. Fax: 724-238-6989. p. 2081

Norris, Marilyn, Extn Serv, Outreach Serv Librn, Collier County Public Library, Naples Regional Library, 650 Central Ave, Naples, FL, 34102. Tel: 239-261-8208. Fax: 239-649-1293. p. 471

Norris, Patricia, Assoc Dir, Grants & Prog, Illinois State Library, Gwendolyn Brooks Bldg, 300 S Second St, Springfield, IL, 62701-9713. Tel: 217-524-5867. Fax: 217-785-4326. p. 705

Norris, Peggy, Local Hist Librn, Ridgewood Public Library, 125 N Maple Ave, Ridgewood, NJ, 07450-3288. Tel: 201-670-5600. Fax: 201-670-0293. p. 1526

Norris, Rene, Head, Ch, Coal City Public Library District, 85 N Garfield St, Coal City, IL, 60416. Tel: 815-634-4552. Fax: 815-634-2950. p. 630

Norris, Robert, In Charge, Scottish Rite Masonic Library, 1895 Camino del Rio S, San Diego, CA, 92108. Tel: 619-293-4888. Fax: 619-297-2751. p. 238

Norris, Samuel, Dir, Mary Lou Johnson Hardin County District Library, 325 E Columbus St, Kenton, OH, 43326-1546. Tel: 419-673-2278. Fax: 419-674-4321. p. 1907

Norris, Sandy, Mgr, Swedish Medical Center Library, First Hill Campus, 747 Broadway, Seattle, WA, 98122-4307. Tel: 206-386-2484. Fax: 206-215-3081. p. 2532

Norris, Severa, ILL Supvr, Lamar University, 211 Redbird Lane, Beaumont, TX, 77705. Tel: 409-880-8118. Fax: 409-880-2318. p. 2287

Norris, Sherri, Circ Mgr, Milton Public Library, 1010 Main St E, Milton, ON, L9T 6H7, CANADA. Tel: 905-875-2665, Ext 3259. Fax: 905-875-4324. p. 2822

Norris, Tiffany, Pub Serv, Southwestern Baptist Theological Seminary Libraries, 2001 W Seminary Dr, Fort Worth, TX, 76115-2157. Tel: 817-923-1921, Ext 4000. Fax: 817-921-8765. p. 2323

North, Daniel L, Acq, University of West Florida, 11000 University Pkwy, Pensacola, FL, 32514-5750. Tel: 850-474-2449. Fax: 850-474-3338. p. 482

North, George, Dir, University of New Orleans, College of Education, Rm 342, New Orleans, LA, 70148. Tel: 504-280-6251, 504-280-6528. Fax: 504-280-1120. p. 2967

North, Kristin, Ch, Houston Love Memorial Library, 212 W Burdeshaw St, Dothan, AL, 36303. Tel: 334-793-9767. Fax: 334-793-6645. p. 15

North, Pam, Libr Serv Mgr, Sherwood Public Library, 22560 SW Pine St, Sherwood, OR, 97140-9019. Tel: 503-625-6688. Fax: 503-625-4254. p. 2019

Northam, Adam, Digital Coll Librn, Texas A&M University-Commerce, 2600 S Neal St, Commerce, TX, 75429. Tel: 903-468-8738. Fax: 903-886-5434. p. 2300

Northam, Linda, Librn, The Depot Public Library, 120 E Chestnut St, Throckmorton, TX, 76483-5901. Tel: 940-849-3076. Fax: 940-849-3076. p. 2393

Northam, Sarah, Head, Ref, Texas A&M University-Commerce, 2600 S Neal St, Commerce, TX, 75429. Tel: 903-886-5719. Fax: 903-886-5434. p. 2300

Northam, Sarah, Ref Serv, Texas A&M University-Commerce, 2600 S Neal St, Commerce, TX, 75429. Tel: 903-886-5714. Fax: 903-886-5434. p. 2300

Northcraft, Peggy, Dir, Marion County Sub-District Library, 212 S Main St, Palmyra, MO, 63461. Tel: 573-769-2830. Fax: 573-769-0405. p. 1348

Northcutt, Dena, Dir, Frederick Public Library, 200 E Grand, Frederick, OK, 73542. Tel: 580-335-3601. Fax: 580-335-3601. p. 1964

Northcutt, Lorie, Circ, Sampson-Clinton Public Library, 217 Graham St, Clinton, NC, 28328. Tel: 910-592-4153. Fax: 910-590-3504. p. 1784

Northington, Vickie, Supvr, Circ, University of Washington Libraries, Marian Gould Gallagher Law Library, William H Gates Hall, Box 353025, Seattle, WA, 98195-3025. Tel: 206-685-9459. Fax: 206-685-2165. p. 2534

Northrup, Kristen, Head, Tech Serv, North Dakota State Library, Library Memorial Bldg, 604 East Blvd Ave, Dept 250, Bismarck, ND, 58505-0800. Tel: 701-328-2491. Fax: 701-328-2040. p. 1838

Northrup, Lori, Assoc Dir, Chair, Coll Develop, Samford University Library, 800 Lakeshore Dr, Birmingham, AL, 35229. Tel: 205-726-2518. Fax: 205-726-4009. p. 9

Northrup, Mary, Ref, Metropolitan Community College, Maple Woods Community College Library, 2601 NE Barry Rd, Kansas City, MO, 64156. Tel: 816-604-3080. Fax: 816-437-3082. p. 1339

Norton, Betty, Acq, Emporia State University, 1200 Commercial St, Box 4051, Emporia, KS, 66801. Tel: 620-341-5084. Fax: 620-341-5997. p. 866

Norton, Brynne, Ref & ILL Serv Coordr, Philadelphia University, 4201 Henry Ave, Philadelphia, PA, 19144-5497. Tel: 215-951-2580. Fax: 215-951-2574. p. 2115

Norton, Carol, ILL, Ada Public Library, 124 S Rennie, Ada, OK, 74820. Tel: 580-436-8121. Fax: 580-436-0534. p. 1955

Norton, Cathy, Dir, Marine Biological Laboratory Woods Hole Oceanographic Institution Library, Seven MBL St, Woods Hole, MA, 02543. Tel: 508-289-7341. Fax: 508-289-7999. p. 1142

Norton, Donna, Dir, Elizabethtown Library Association, 8256 River St, Elizabethtown, NY, 12932. Tel: 518-873-2670. Fax: 518-873-2670. p. 1618

Norton, Eric, Head, Adult Serv, McMillan Memorial Library, 490 E Grand Ave, Wisconsin Rapids, WI, 54494-4898. Tel: 715-423-1040. Fax: 715-423-2665. p. 2650

Norton, Francis X, Ref Librn, Loyola University New Orleans, Loyola Law Library, School of Law, 7214 St Charles Ave, New Orleans, LA, 70118. Tel: 504-861-5539. Fax: 504-861-5895. p. 961

Norton, George, Curator, Spellman Museum of Stamps & Postal History Library, 235 Wellesley St, Weston, MA, 02493. Tel: 781-768-8367. p. 1139

Norton, Jennifer, Dir, Neligh Public Library, 710 Main St, Neligh, NE, 68756-1246. Tel: 402-887-5140. Fax: 402-887-4530. p. 1409

Norton, John, Bus Mgr, Woodridge Public Library, Three Plaza Dr, Woodridge, IL, 60517-5014. Tel: 630-964-7899. Fax: 630-964-0175. p. 721

Norton, Joyce, Librn, Nottoway County Public Libraries, Blackstone Branch, 415 S Main St, Blackstone, VA, 23824. Tel: 434-292-3587. Fax: 434-292-3587. p. 2458

Norton, Judith, Head, Access Serv, Spec Projects Librn, Oregon Health & Science University Library, 3181 SW Sam Jackson Park Rd, Portland, OR, 97239-3098. Tel: 503-494-3481. Fax: 503-494-3227. p. 2013

Norton, Julie, Instrul Serv/Ref Librn, Marquette University, Sensenbrenner Hall, 1103 W Wisconsin Ave, Milwaukee, WI, 53233-2313. Tel: 414-288-7092. Fax: 414-288-5914. p. 2618

Norton, Kathleen, Coll Develop, Mount Holyoke College Library, 50 College St, South Hadley, MA, 01075-1423. Tel: 413-538-2158. Fax: 413-538-2370. p. 1125

Norton, Linda, Dir, Washington County Library, 1444 Jackson Ave, Chipley, FL, 32428. Tel: 850-638-1314. Fax: 850-638-9499. p. 431

Norton, LuAnn, Tech Serv Librn, DeForest Area Public Library, 203 Library St, DeForest, WI, 53532. Tel: 608-846-5482. Fax: 608-846-6875. p. 2588

Norton, M Jay, Dr, Dir, The University of Southern Mississippi, 118 College Dr, No 5146, Hattiesburg, MS, 39406-0001. Tel: 601-266-4228. Fax: 601-266-5774. p. 2968

Norton, Maria, Dir, The Morristown & Morris Township Library, One Miller Rd, Morristown, NJ, 07960. Tel: 973-538-6161. Fax: 973-267-4064. p. 1505

Norton, Maria S, Dir, Morristown & Morris Township Library, North Jersey History & Genealogy Center, One Miller Rd, Morristown, NJ, 07960. Tel: 973-538-3473. Fax: 973-267-4064. p. 1505

Norton, Nan, Ref Librn, Loyola University Chicago Libraries, Law School Library, 25 E Pearson St, 3rd Flr, Chicago, IL, 60611. Tel: 312-915-8517. Fax: 312-915-6797. p. 617

Norton, Theresa, Automation Syst Coordr, University of North Dakota, School of Medicine and Health Sciences, 501 N Columbia Rd, Stop 9002, Grand Forks, ND, 58202-9002. Tel: 701-777-2946. Fax: 701-777-4790. p. 1842

Norvell, Alison A, Electronic Res Librn, Blue Ridge Community College Library, 180 W Campus Dr, Flat Rock, NC, 28731. Tel: 828-694-1636. Fax: 828-694-1692. p. 1793

Norvell, Belinda, Cat, Tech Serv, Hardin-Simmons University, 2341 Hickory St, Abilene, TX, 79698. Tel: 325-670-1236. Fax: 325-677-8351. p. 2272

Norvelle, Astrid, Cat, University of Arizona, James E Rogers College of Law Library, PO Box 210176, Tucson, AZ, 85721-0176. Tel: 520-621-1413. Fax: 520-621-3138. p. 89

Norwalk, Nancy, Dir, Philip Read Memorial Library, 1088 Rte 12A, Plainfield, NH, 03781. Tel: 603-675-6866. p. 1462

Norwood, Catherine, Circ, ILL, Ser, Flagler College, 44 Sevilla St, Saint Augustine, FL, 32084-4302. Tel: 904-819-6206. Fax: 904-823-8511. p. 486

Norwood, Cindy, Dir, Warren Free Public Library, 282 Main St, Warren, ME, 04864. Tel: 207-273-2900. p. 1004

Norwood, Deborah, Asst Dir, Pub Serv, George Washington University, Jacob Burns Law Library, 716 20th St NW, Washington, DC, 20052. Tel: 202-994-7338. Fax: 202-994-2874. p. 402

Norwood, Faith, Access Serv, Washington County Historical Association, 14th & Monroe Sts, Fort Calhoun, NE, 68023. Tel: 402-468-5740. Fax: 402-468-5741. p. 1398

Nosakhere, Akilah, Libr Syst Mgr, Ref Mgr, Atlanta-Fulton Public Library System, Auburn Avenue Research Library on African-American Culture & History, 101 Auburn Ave NE, Atlanta, GA, 30303. Tel: 404-730-4001, Ext 199. Fax: 404-730-5879. p. 511

Nosakhere, Akilah S, Libr Dir, New Mexico State University at Carlsbad, 1500 University Dr, Carlsbad, NM, 88220. Tel: 575-234-9330. p. 1553

Noseworthy, Keith, Electronic Serv Librn, Atlantic School of Theology Library, 624 Francklyn St, Halifax, NS, B3H 3B5, CANADA. Tel: 902-423-7986. Fax: 902-423-7941. p. 2780

Nossett, Denice, Br Mgr, Los Angeles Public Library System, Harbor City-Harbor Gateway, 24000 S Western Ave, Los Angeles, CA, 90710. Tel: 310-534-9520. Fax: 310-952-1932. p. 173

Notarmaso, Silvana, Rare Bk Cataloger, Rutgers University Libraries, Special Collections & University Archives, 169 College Ave, New Brunswick, NJ, 08901-1163. Tel: 848-932-6157. Fax: 732-932-7012. p. 1509

Notarstefano, Vincent, Mgr, Estee Lauder Cos, Inc, 125 Pinelawn Rd, Melville, NY, 11747. Tel: 631-531-1174. Fax: 631-531-1331. p. 1659

Notenboom, Leanne, Res, Blake, Cassels & Graydon LLP, Commerce Ct W, 199 Bay St, Ste 4000, Toronto, ON, M5L 1A9, CANADA. Tel: 416-863-2650. Fax: 416-863-2653. p. 2850

Notley, Sunya, Ref & Access Serv Librn, Nyack College Library, One South Blvd, Nyack, NY, 10960-3698. Tel: 845-353-0817. p. 1708

Noto, Frank, Coordr, Info Tech, Saint Charles City County Library District, 77 Boone Hills Dr, Saint Peters, MO, 63376-0529. Tel: 636-441-2300. Fax: 636-441-3132. p. 1363

Nott, Philip, Dir, Criswell College, 4010 Gaston Ave, Dallas, TX, 75246. Tel: 214-818-1378. Fax: 214-818-1310. p. 2305

Nottage, Eva, YA Serv, Watsonville Public Library, 310 Union St, Watsonville, CA, 95076. Tel: 831-768-3400. Fax: 831-763-4015. p. 282

Nottage, Judith, Librn, University of Maine at Augusta, 124 Eastport Hall, 128 Texas Ave, Bangor, ME, 04401. Tel: 207-262-7900. Fax: 207-262-7901. p. 976

Nottage, Mary Ellen Hennessey, Dir, Indiana Medical History Museum Collection, 3045 W Vermont St, Indianapolis, IN, 46222-4943. Tel: 317-635-7329. Fax: 317-635-7349. p. 752

Nottingham, Gail, Dir, Buena Vista Public Library, 131 Linderman Ave, Buena Vista, CO, 81211-9184. Tel: 719-395-8700. Fax: 719-395-6426. p. 293

Notzold, Gretchen Ann, Br Mgr, Teton County Library, Alta Branch, 50 Alta School Rd, Alta, WY, 83414. Tel: 307-353-2505. Fax: 307-353-2473. p. 2656

Nou, Anne, Info Serv Librn, Tufts University, 145 Harrison Ave, Boston, MA, 02111-1843. Fax: 617-636-4039. p. 1068

Nourse, Mary E, Librn, Department of Veterans Affairs Medical Center, 135 E 38th St, Erie, PA, 16504-1559. Tel: 814-868-8661. Fax: 814-860-2469. p. 2055

Noury, Lisette, In Charge, Bibliotheque Municipale, 16 rue Marechal, CP 370, Saint Jacques, QC, J0K 2R0, CANADA. Tel: 450-831-2296. Fax: 450-839-2387. p. 2908

Nova, Marla, Archivist, Museum of Art & History Library, 705 Front St, Santa Cruz, CA, 95060-4508. Tel: 831-429-1964, Ext 17. Fax: 831-429-1954. p. 264

Novak, Allen, Image Librn, Ringling College of Art & Design, 2700 N Tamiami Trail, Sarasota, FL, 34234. Tel: 941-359-7583. Fax: 941-359-7632. p. 490

Novak, Denise, Head of Acq Serv, Carnegie Mellon University, Hunt Library, 4909 Frew St, Pittsburgh, PA, 15213-3890. Tel: 412-268-2446. Fax: 412-268-2793. p. 2123

Novak, Frank R, Exec Dir, Rockford Public Library, 215 N Wyman St, Rockford, IL, 61101-1023. Tel: 815-965-7606. Fax: 815-965-0866. p. 697

Novak, Gail, Ref, New College of Florida University of South Florida Sarasota Manatee, 5800 Bay Shore Rd, Sarasota, FL, 34243-2109. Tel: 941-487-4406. Fax: 941-487-4307. p. 490

Novak, Gloria, Libr Mgr, Vancouver Island Regional Library, Nanaimo Wellington, 3032 Barons Rd, Nanaimo, BC, V9T 4B5, CANADA. Tel: 250-758-5544. Fax: 250-758-7513. p. 2733

Novak Gustainis, Emily R, Archivist, Librn, Historic New England, Library & Archives, 141 Cambridge St, Boston, MA, 02114. Tel: 617-227-3957. Fax: 617-973-9050. p. 1062

Novak, Liz, User Serv Librn, Loyola University Chicago Libraries, Health Sciences Library, Bldg 101, Rm 1717, 2160 S First Ave, Maywood, IL, 60153-5585. Tel: 708-216-4368. Fax: 708-216-8115. p. 617

Novak, Nichole, Br Librn, Illinois Institute of Technology, Louis W Biegler Library, 201 East Loop Rd, Wheaton, IL, 60187-8489. Tel: 630-682-6047. Fax: 630-682-6049. p. 615

Novak, Patty, Circ Librn, White Cloud Community Library, 1038 Wilcox Ave, White Cloud, MI, 49349. Tel: 231-689-6631. Fax: 231-689-6699. p. 1236

Novak, Roxie, Dir, Endeavor Public Library, 125 Park S, Endeavor, WI, 53930. Tel: 608-587-2902. Fax: 608-587-2902. p. 2591

Novak, Stephen, Head, Archives & Spec Coll, Columbia University, Augustus C Long Health Sciences Library, 701 W 168th St, Lobby Level, New York, NY, 10032. Tel: 212-305-3605. Fax: 212-234-0595. p. 1675

Novak, Vicki, Br Mgr, Maricopa County Library District, Fountain Hills Branch, 12901 N La Montana Dr, Fountain Hills, AZ, 85268. Tel: 602-652-3251. Fax: 602-652-3270. p. 74

Novak, Vickie L, Libr Dir, Glenview Public Library, 1930 Glenview Rd, Glenview, IL, 60025-2899. Tel: 847-729-7500. Fax: 847-729-7558. p. 650

Novakowski, Darlene, Asst Librn, East Bend Public Library, 332 W Main St, East Bend, NC, 27018. Tel: 336-699-3890. Fax: 336-699-2359. p. 1790

Novalis, Jenny, Tech Serv, Bedford Public Library System, 321 N Bridge St, Bedford, VA, 24523-1924. Tel: 540-586-8911, Ext 1114. Fax: 540-586-8875. p. 2450

Novara, Vincent J, Curator, University of Maryland Libraries, Michelle Smith Performing Arts Library, 2511 Clarice Smith Performing Arts Library, College Park, MD, 20742-1630. Tel: 301-405-9220. Fax: 301-314-7170. p. 1025

Novil, Rose, Br Librn, Oakton Community College Library, 1600 E Golf Rd, Rm 1410, Des Plaines, IL, 60016. Tel: 847-635-1474. Fax: 847-635-1987. p. 636

Novil, Rose, Head Librn, Oakton Community College Library, 7701 N Lincoln Ave, Rm A200, Skokie, IL, 60076-2895. Tel: 847-376-7632. Fax: 847-635-1449. p. 703

Novin, Dolores, Circ, McCowan Memorial Library, 15 Pitman Ave, Pitman, NJ, 08071. Tel: 856-589-1656. Fax: 856-582-4982. p. 1520

Novitt, Adam, Dir, Pelham Library, Two S Valley Rd, Pelham, MA, 01002. Tel: 413-253-0657. Fax: 413-253-0594. p. 1117

Novoa, Vincent, Head, Access Serv, University of California, Riverside Libraries, 900 University Ave, Riverside, CA, 92521. Tel: 951-827-7309. p. 218

Novosad, Jeanne, ILL, Syst Mgr, Palmer Public Library, 655 S Valley Way, Palmer, AK, 99645. Tel: 907-745-4690. Fax: 907-746-3570. p. 52

Novotny, Allana, Tech & Access Serv Librn, Nebraska Library Commission, The Atrium, 1200 N St, Ste 120, Lincoln, NE, 68508-2023. Tel: 402-471-6681. Fax: 402-471-2083. p. 1406

Novotny, Eric, Actg Head, Libr, Pennsylvania State University Libraries, George & Sherry Middlemas Arts & Humanities Library, Pennsylvania State University, W 202 Pattee Library, University Park, PA, 16802-1801. Tel: 814-865-1014. Fax: 814-863-7502. p. 2148

Novotny, Eric, Actg Head, Libr, Pennsylvania State University Libraries, News & Microforms Library, 21 Pattee Library, University Park, PA, 16802-1804. Tel: 814-863-0377. p. 2148

Novotny, Glenda, Circ, Arkansas State University, Palm & Iowa Sts, Beebe, AR, 72012. Tel: 501-882-8984. Fax: 501-882-8833. p. 94

Novotny, Linda, Asst Librn, Tech Support, Fort Nelson Public Library, 5315-50th Ave S, Box 330, Fort Nelson, BC, V0C 1R0, CANADA. Tel: 250-774-6777. Fax: 250-774-6777. p. 2728

Novy, Jim, Syst Serv, Lakeshores Library System, 725 Cornerstone Crossing, Ste C, Waterford, WI, 53185. Tel: 262-514-4500, Ext 65. Fax: 262-514-4544. p. 2644

Novy, Ron, AV Coordr, Head, Media Ctr, Florida Hospital College of Health Sciences, 671 Winyah Dr, Orlando, FL, 32803. Tel: 407-303-7747, Ext 9894. Fax: 407-303-9622. p. 475

Novy, Ron, Dir, Mississippi State University, Veterinary Medicine, PO Box 9825, Mississippi State, MS, 39762. Tel: 662-325-1240. Fax: 662-325-1144. p. 1309

Nowak, Bonnie, ILL, Huntington Beach Public Library System, 7111 Talbert Ave, Huntington Beach, CA, 92648. Tel: 714-842-4481. Fax: 714-375-5180. p. 158

Nowak, Christopher, Bus Mgr, Mastics-Moriches-Shirley Community Library, 407 William Floyd Pkwy, Shirley, NY, 11967. Tel: 631-399-1511. Fax: 631-281-4442. p. 1743

Nowak, Darlene, Supvr, ILL, San Diego State University Library & Information Access, 5500 Campanile Dr, San Diego, CA, 92182-8050. Tel: 619-594-6908. Fax: 619-594-3270. p. 237

Nowak, Karen, Distance Educ, Ref Serv, Concordia University Wisconsin, 12800 N Lake Shore Dr, Mequon, WI, 53097-2402. Tel: 262-243-4330, 262-243-4403. Fax: 262-243-4424. p. 2615

Nowak, Katheryn, Asst Librn, Young Men's Library Association, 37 Main St, Ware, MA, 01082-1317. Tel: 413-967-5491. Fax: 413-967-6060. p. 1133

Nowak, Nancy, Br Mgr, Elmont Public Library, Alden Manor, 799 Elmont Rd, Elmont, NY, 11003. Tel: 516-285-8000. Fax: 516-285-1219. p. 1620

Nowakowski, Jane, Cat, Rider University, Katharine Houk Talbott Library, Westminster Choir College, 101 Walnut Lane, Princeton, NJ, 08540-3899. Tel: 609-921-7100, Ext 8305. Fax: 609-497-0243. p. 1494

Nowell, Cathy, Adult Serv Mgr, Wake County Public Library System, East Regional Library, 946 Steeple Square Ct, Knightdale, NC, 27545. Tel: 919-217-5323. Fax: 919-217-5327. p. 1817

Nowels, Nieca, Mgr, Ad Serv, Westerville Public Library, 126 S State St, Westerville, OH, 43081-2095. Tel: 614-882-7277, Ext 2138. Fax: 614-882-4190. p. 1947

Nowesnick, Monica, Coordr, Libr Serv, St Margaret Mercy Healthcare Centers-South Campus, 24 Joliet St, Dyer, IN, 46311-1799. Tel: 219-865-2141, Ext 42133. Fax: 219-864-2146. p. 736

Nowesnick, Monica, Coordr, Saint Margaret Mercy-North Campus, 5454 Hohman Ave, Hammond, IN, 46320. Tel: 219-933-2133, Ext 32133. Fax: 219-933-2146. p. 748

Nowesnick, Monica A, Mgr, Saint Anthony Medical Center, 1201 S Main St, Crown Point, IN, 46307-8483. Tel: 219-757-6345. Fax: 219-757-6161. p. 734

Nowicki, Stacy, Dr, Dir, Kalamazoo College, 1200 Academy St, Kalamazoo, MI, 49006-3285. Tel: 269-337-5750. Fax: 269-337-7143. p. 1197

Nowinski, Barbara, Asst Dir, Traverse Area District Library, 610 Woodmere Ave, Traverse City, MI, 49686. Tel: 231-932-8500. Fax: 231-932-8578. p. 1231

Nowinski, Barbara, In Charge, Traverse Area District Library, East Bay Branch, 1989 Three Mile Rd N, Traverse City, MI, 49686. Tel: 231-922-2085. Fax: 231-922-2087. p. 1231

Nowlan, Gwendolyn, Dr, Prof, Southern Connecticut State University, 501 Crescent St, New Haven, CT, 06515. Tel: 203-392-5711. Fax: 203-392-5780. p. 2963

Nowlin, Bridget, Visual Image Curator, Cornish College of the Arts Library, 1000 Lenora St, Seattle, WA, 98121. Tel: 206-726-5041. Fax: 206-315-5811. p. 2527

Nowotny, Jerry, In Charge, San Antonio Scottish Rite Library, 308 Ave E, San Antonio, TX, 78298. Tel: 210-222-0133. Fax: 210-222-0136. p. 2382

Noyd, Ellen, Circ, Satellite Beach Public Library, 751 Jamaica Blvd, Satellite Beach, FL, 32937. Tel: 321-779-4004. Fax: 321-779-4036. p. 490

Noye, Kate, Outreach Serv Librn, Woodford County Library, 115 N Main St, Versailles, KY, 40383-1289. Tel: 859-873-5191. Fax: 859-873-1542. p. 936

Noyes, Esther, ILL, Anacortes Public Library, 1220 Tenth St, Anacortes, WA, 98221-1922. Tel: 360-293-1910, Ext 25. Fax: 360-293-1929. p. 2507

Noyes, Nicholas, Head, Libr Serv, Maine Historical Society, 489 Congress St, Portland, ME, 04101-3498. Tel: 207-774-1822. Fax: 207-775-4301. p. 996

Noyes, Roxanne, Asst County Dir, Emery County Library, 115 N 100 East, Castle Dale, UT, 84513. Tel: 435-381-2554. Fax: 435-381-2699. p. 2403

Nozero, Victoria, Dir, Res & Info Serv, University of Nevada, Las Vegas Libraries, 4505 Maryland Pkwy, Box 457001, Las Vegas, NV, 89154-7001. Tel: 702-895-2285. Fax: 702-895-2287. p. 1430

Nuber, Teresa, Dir, Lenawee County Library, 4459 W US Rte 223, Adrian, MI, 49221-1294. Tel: 517-263-1011. Fax: 517-263-7109. p. 1147

Nuckolls, Cindy, Br Mgr, Wyoming County Public Library, Mullens Area Public, 102 Fourth St, Mullens, WV, 25882. Tel: 304-294-6687. Fax: 304-294-6687. p. 2570

Nuckolls, Karen, Head, Tech Serv, University of Kentucky Libraries, Law Library, 620 S Limestone St, Lexington, KY, 40506-0048. Tel: 859-257-2437. Fax: 859-323-4906. p. 922

Nuding, Cathy, Youth Serv Librn, East Fishkill Public Library District, 348 Rte 376, Hopewell Junction, NY, 12533-6075. Tel: 845-221-9943, Ext 233. Fax: 845-226-1404. p. 1637

Nuebel, Rita, Co-Dir, Remsen Public Library, 211 Fulton, Remsen, IA, 51050. Tel: 712-786-2911. Fax: 712-786-3255. p. 840

Nuechterlein, Mary, Curator of Coll, Curator of Res Serv, Frankenmuth Historical Association, 613 S Main St, Frankenmuth, MI, 48734. Tel: 989-652-9701. Fax: 989-652-9390. p. 1181

Nuelle, Shannon, Ch, Cavalier County Library, 600 Fifth Ave, Langdon, ND, 58249. Tel: 701-256-5353. Fax: 701-256-5361. p. 1845

Nuernberger, Lois, Instrul Res Coordr, Wayne State College, 1111 Main St, Wayne, NE, 68787. Tel: 402-375-7568. Fax: 402-375-7538. p. 1423

Nuffer, Roy, Librn, Schoolcraft College, 18600 Haggerty Rd, Livonia, MI, 48152-2696. Tel: 734-462-4400, Ext 5315. Fax: 734-462-4495. p. 1204

Nugent, Beki, Outreach Coordr, Grant Parish Library, 300 Main St, Colfax, LA, 71417-1830. Tel: 318-627-9920. Fax: 318-627-9900. p. 947

Nugent, Chris, Dir, Warren Wilson College, 701 Warren Wilson Rd, Swannanoa, NC, 28778. Tel: 828-771-3061. Fax: 828-771-7085. p. 1826

Nugent, Georgia, Chmn, The Five Colleges of Ohio, 102 Allen House, Kenyon College, Gambier, OH, 43022. Tel: 740-427-5377. Fax: 740-427-5390. p. 2952

Nugent, Mike, Mgr, American Association of University Women, 900 Seventh St NW, Lobby Level, Washington, DC, 20001. Tel: 202-728-7700. Fax: 202-728-7664. p. 391

Nugent, Rebecca, Librn I/Gen Serv, North Olympic Library System, 2210 S Peabody St, Port Angeles, WA, 98362-6536. Tel: 360-417-8500. Fax: 360-457-3125. p. 2523

Nugent, Sara, Dir, Tappan Library, 93 Main St, Tappan, NY, 10983. Tel: 845-359-3877. p. 1754

Nugent, Sara, Pres, Library Association of Rockland County, PO Box 917, New City, NY, 10956-0917. Tel: 845-359-3877. p. 2950

Nuhn, Elaine, Libr Dir, Macon Public Library, 210 N Rutherford St, Macon, MO, 63552. Tel: 660-385-3314. Fax: 660-385-6610. p. 1344

Nullet, Joan G, Librn, Kettle Falls Public Library, 605 Meyers St, Kettle Falls, WA, 99141. Tel: 509-738-6817. Fax: 509-738-2787. p. 2519

Nunez, Annabelle, Info Serv Librn, University of Arizona, Arizona Health Sciences Library, 1501 N Campbell Ave, Tucson, AZ, 85724. Tel: 520-626-7172. Fax: 520-626-2922. p. 88

Nunez, Corie, Br Coordr, Cochise County Library District, Jimmie Libhart Library, 201 N Central, Bowie, AZ, 85605. Tel: 520-847-2522. Fax: 520-847-2522. p. 58

Nunez, Ivan, Info Tech Coordr, Cargill, Inc, 15407 McGinty Rd W, Wayzata, MN, 55391. Tel: 952-742-6498. Fax: 952-742-6062. p. 1287

Nunez, Jean, Libr Spec Supvr, Nunez Community College Library, 3710 Paris Rd, Chalmette, LA, 70043. Tel: 504-278-6230, 504-278-7498. Fax: 504-680-2584. p. 947

Nunez, Leida, Ch, Oceanside Public Library, Mission Branch, 3861 B Mission Ave, Oceanside, CA, 92058. Tel: 760-435-5592. Fax: 760-433-6850. p. 200

Nunez, Rosie, Cat, Wharton County Junior College, 911 Boling Hwy, Wharton, TX, 77488-3298. Tel: 979-532-6953. Fax: 979-532-6527. p. 2399

Nunez, Varrick, Ref, Lakeland Public Library, 100 Lake Morton Dr, Lakeland, FL, 33801-5375. Tel: 863-834-4265. Fax: 863-834-4293. p. 459

Nunley, Ann F, Librn, Altamont Public Library, Hwy 56, Altamont, TN, 37301. Tel: 931-692-2457. Fax: 931-692-2457. p. 2223

Nunley, Ben, Circ Supvr, Boyd County Public Library, 1740 Central Ave, Ashland, KY, 41101. Tel: 606-329-0090. Fax: 606-329-0578. p. 905

Nunley, Kellie, Tech Serv Supvr, Boyd County Public Library, 1740 Central Ave, Ashland, KY, 41101. Tel: 606-329-0090. Fax: 606-329-0578. p. 905

Nunley, Sandy, Asst Dir, Cat, Marion County Public Library, 201 E Main St, Lebanon, KY, 40033-1133. Tel: 270-692-4698. Fax: 270-692-9555. p. 920

Nunn, Dana, Acq & Cat, Ball Memorial Hospital, 2401 W University Ave, Muncie, IN, 47303-3499. Tel: 765-747-4470. Fax: 765-747-0137. p. 766

Nurse, Carol, Ref, Montclair State University, One Normal Ave, Montclair, NJ, 07043-1699. Tel: 973-655-7667. Fax: 973-655-7780. p. 1503

Nuss, Sandra, Asst Admin, Martin County Historical Society, Inc, 304 E Blue Earth Ave, Fairmont, MN, 56031. Tel: 507-235-5178. Fax: 507-235-5179. p. 1250

Nussbaumer, Kara, Libr Assoc II, Dickinson County Library, North Dickinson, W6588 M-69, Felch, MI, 49831. Tel: 906-542-7230. p. 1194

Nutbrown, Heather, Libr Mgr, Evansburg Public Library, 4707 46th Ave, Evansburg, AB, T0E 0T0, CANADA. Tel: 780-727-2030, 780-727-3925. Fax: 780-727-2060. p. 2703

Nutt, Julie, Youth Serv, Pekin Public Library, 301 S Fourth St, Pekin, IL, 61554-4284. Tel: 309-347-7111, Ext 224. Fax: 309-347-6587. p. 689

Nutt, Timothy G, Interim Head, Spec Coll, University of Arkansas Libraries, 365 N McIlroy Ave, Fayetteville, AR, 72701-4002. Tel: 479-575-8443. Fax: 479-575-6656. p. 99

Nuttall, Harry, Ref Librn, Jacksonville State University Library, 700 Pelham Rd N, Jacksonville, AL, 36265. Tel: 256-782-5255. Fax: 256-782-5872. p. 22

Nutter, Susan K, Vice Provost & Dir, North Carolina State University Libraries, Two Broughton Dr, Raleigh, NC, 27695. Tel: 919-515-7188. Fax: 919-515-3628. p. 1816

Nutty, David J, Dir, Univ Librn, University of Southern Maine, 314 Forest Ave, Portland, ME, 04104. Tel: 207-780-4276. Fax: 207-780-4042. p. 998

Nuvayestewa, Grace, Libr Spec, Institute of American Indian & Alaska Native Culture & Arts Development Library, 83 Avan Nu Po Rd, Santa Fe, NM, 87508. Tel: 505-424-5715. Fax: 505-424-3131. p. 1562

Nwaneri, Sebastine O, ILL, Alabama A&M University, 4900 Meridian St, Huntsville, AL, 35762. Tel: 256-372-4747. Fax: 256-372-5768. p. 21

Nwanze, Vanessa L, Ref Librn, Piedmont Community College, 1715 College Dr, Roxboro, NC, 27573. Tel: 336-599-1181, Ext 235. Fax: 336-599-9146. p. 1821

Nwoke, Barbara, Coll Develop, Head, Tech Serv, Hershey Public Library, 701 Cocoa Ave, Hershey, PA, 17033. Tel: 717-533-6555. Fax: 717-534-1666. p. 2069

Nyberg, Cheryl, Coordr of Ref Serv, University of Washington Libraries, Marian Gould Gallagher Law Library, William H Gates Hall, Box 353025, Seattle, WA, 98195-3025. Tel: 206-685-4924. Fax: 206-685-2165. p. 2534

Nyberg, Mary Jane, Librn, Polk Public Library, 180 N Main St, Polk, NE, 68654. Tel: 402-765-7266. Fax: 402-765-7266. p. 1417

Nyboer, Bob, Head, Adult Serv, Longmont Public Library, 409 Fourth Ave, Longmont, CO, 80501-6006. Tel: 303-651-8471. Fax: 303-651-8911. p. 317

Nyce, Dawn L, ILL, Eastern Mennonite University, 1200 Park Rd, Harrisonburg, VA, 22802-2462. Tel: 540-432-4175. Fax: 540-432-4977. p. 2470

Nyce, Lori, Syst/Electronic Serv Librn, Lebanon Valley College, 101 N College Ave, Annville, PA, 17003-1400. Tel: 717-867-6977. Fax: 717-867-6979. p. 2029

Nycum, Peter S, Dir, Lewis & Clark College, Paul L Boley Law Library, Lewis & Clark Law School, 10015 SW Terwilliger Blvd, Portland, OR, 97219. Tel: 503-768-6776. Fax: 503-768-6760. p. 2011

Nye, Valerie, Dir of Libr, Santa Fe University of Art & Design, 1600 St Michael's Dr, Santa Fe, NM, 87505-7634. Tel: 505-473-6575. Fax: 505-473-6593. p. 1564

Nyitray, Kristen, Spec Coll Librn, Stony Brook University, W-1502 Melville Library, John S Toll Rd, Stony Brook, NY, 11794-3300. Tel: 631-632-7100. Fax: 631-632-7116. p. 1749

Nykiforuk, Marilyn, Ch, Selby Public Library, 1331 First St, Sarasota, FL, 34236-4899. Tel: 941-861-1100. Fax: 941-316-1188. p. 490

Nyland, Nancy, Librn, Montgomery College, Germantown Campus Library, 20200 Observation Dr, Germantown, MD, 20876. Tel: 240-567-7854. Fax: 301-353-7859. p. 1037

Nylen, Robert, Curator, Nevada State Museum Library, 600 N Carson St, Carson City, NV, 89701-4004. Tel: 775-687-4810, Ext 239, 775-687-4810, Ext 240. Fax: 775-687-4168. p. 1426

Nyquist, Corinne, ILL Librn, State University of New York College at New Paltz, 300 Hawk Dr, New Paltz, NY, 12561-2493. Tel: 845-257-3681. p. 1666

Nystrom, Kathleen, Head, Tech Serv, Webster University, 101 Edgar Rd, Saint Louis, MO, 63119. Tel: 314-968-7151. Fax: 314-968-7113. p. 1363

Nystrom-Hilk, Nan, Sr Librn, Hennepin County Library, Long Lake, 1865 Wayzata Blvd W, Long Lake, MN, 55356-9587. Tel: 612-543-6153. Fax: 612-543-6427. p. 1264

Nystrom-Hilk, Nan, Sr Librn, Hennepin County Library, Wayzata, 620 Rice St, Wayzata, MN, 55391-1734. Tel: 612-543-6153. Fax: 612-543-6152. p. 1265

Nytes, Jackie, Chief Exec Officer, Indianapolis-Marion County Public Library, 2450 N Meridian St, Indianapolis, IN, 46208. Tel: 317-275-4001, Fax: 317-269-5300. p. 753

Nzurike, Lilian, Librn, The Geo Group Inc, 600 US Hwy 27 S, South Bay, FL, 33493. Tel: 561-992-9505, Ext 150. Fax: 561-992-9551. p. 491

O'Banion, Rona, Chief Exec Officer, Chief Librn, King Township Public Library, 1970 King Rd, King City, ON, L7B 1A6, CANADA. Tel: 905-833-5101. Fax: 905-833-0824. p. 2812

O'Bannon, Emma Lou, Ch, Brazoria County Library System, Angleton Branch, 401 E Cedar St, Angleton, TX, 77515-4652. Tel: 979-864-1519. Fax: 979-864-1518. p. 2275

O'Boyle, Richard, Electronic Res Librn, Info Access Librn, Calumet College of Saint Joseph, 2400 New York Ave, Whiting, IN, 46394. Tel: 219-473-4282. Fax: 219-473-4259. p. 787

O'Boyle, Robert, Acq, Archivist, Coll Develop, Onondaga Community College, 4585 W Seneca Tpk, Syracuse, NY, 13215-4585. Tel: 315-498-2334. Fax: 315-498-7213. p. 1752

O'Brennan, Robert, Chief Exec Officer, Fraser Valley Regional Library, 34589 Delair Rd, Abbotsford, BC, V2S 5Y1, CANADA. Tel: 604-859-7141. Fax: 604-859-5701. p. 2723

O'Brien, Allyson, Librn, Middlesex Community College, Federal Bldg, E Merrimack St, Lowell, MA, 01852. Tel: 978-937-5454. Fax: 978-656-3031. p. 1100

O'Brien, Allyson, Ref Librn, Henderson District Public Libraries, James I Gibson Library, 100 W Lake Mead Pkwy, Henderson, NV, 89015. Tel: 702-565-8402. Fax: 702-565-8832. p. 1428

O'Brien, Anita, Dir, Bacon Memorial District Library, 45 Vinewood, Wyandotte, MI, 48192-5221. Tel: 734-246-8357. Fax: 734-282-1540. p. 1237

O'Brien, Anita, Asst Librn, Little Silver Public Library, 484 Prospect Ave, Little Silver, NJ, 07739. Tel: 732-747-9649. p. 1496

O'Brien, Barbara, Col Archivist, McDaniel College, Two College Hill, Westminster, MD, 21157-4390. Tel: 410-857-2793. Fax: 410-857-2748. p. 1046

O'Brien, Chris, Circ, River Grove Public Library District, 8638 W Grand Ave, River Grove, IL, 60171. Tel: 708-453-4484. Fax: 708-453-4517. p. 694

O'Brien, Darby, Dir, Utica Public Library, 303 Genesee St, Utica, NY, 13501. Tel: 315-735-2279. Fax: 315-734-1034. p. 1760

O'Brien, David, Head, Access Serv, Hope College, Van Wylen Library, 53 Graves Pl, Holland, MI, 49422. Tel: 616-395-7791. Fax: 616-395-7965. p. 1190

O'Brien, Debora, Librn, New Marlborough Town Library, One Mill River Great Barrington Rd, Mill River, MA, 01244-0239. Tel: 413-229-6668. Fax: 413-229-6668. p. 1106

O'Brien, Diane R, Dir, Joint Free Public Library of the Chathams, 214 Main St, Chatham, NJ, 07928. Tel: 973-635-0603. Fax: 973-635-7827. p. 1478

O'Brien, Dinah L, Dir, Plymouth Public Library, 132 South St, Plymouth, MA, 02360-3309. Tel: 508-830-4250. Fax: 508-830-4258. p. 1118

O'Brien, Ellen, Dir, Tinton Falls Public Library, 664 Tinton Ave, Tinton Falls, NJ, 07724. Tel: 732-542-3110. Fax: 732-542-6755. p. 1533

O'Brien, Ellen, Ch, Warwick Public Library, 600 Sandy Lane, Warwick, RI, 02889-8298. Tel: 401-739-5440, Ext 213. Fax: 401-732-2055. p. 2177

O'Brien, Frances, Dean, West Virginia University Libraries, WVU Libraries, 1549 University Ave, Morgantown, WV, 26506. Tel: 304-293-4040. Fax: 304-293-6638. p. 2566

O'Brien, Glenda, Mgr, Libr Serv, Gowling Lafleur Henderson LLP, 160 Elgin St, Ottawa, ON, K1P 1C3, CANADA. Tel: 613-232-1781. Fax: 613-563-9869. p. 2831

O'Brien, Heather, Asst Prof, University of British Columbia, The Irving K Barber Centre, 1961 E Mall, Ste 470, Vancouver, BC, V6T 1Z1, CANADA. Tel: 604-822-2404. Fax: 604-822-6006. p. 2977

O'Brien, James, Pres, Chautauqua County Historical Society & Mcclurg Museum Library, Main & Portage St, Westfield, NY, 14787-0007. Tel: 716-326-2977. p. 1768

O'Brien, Jennifer, Ser Librn, Western Connecticut State University, 181 White St, Danbury, CT, 06810. Tel: 203-837-9100. Fax: 203-837-9108. p. 335

O'Brien, Jessica, Libr Spec for Tech & Learning Support, Lenoir-Rhyne University Library, 625 7th Ave NE, Hickory, NC, 28601. Tel: 828-328-7236. Fax: 828-328-7338. p. 1801

O'Brien, Julie, Dir, Scott County Library, 110 W Eighth, Scott City, KS, 67871-1599. Tel: 620-872-5341. Fax: 620-872-0248. p. 893

O'Brien, June, Ref Serv, AstraZeneca Pharmaceuticals, 1800 Concord Pike, Wilmington, DE, 19850-2902. Tel: 302-886-8232. Fax: 302-886-5369. p. 387

O'Brien, Lee, Assoc Dir, Cecil County Public Library, 301 Newark Ave, Elkton, MD, 21921-5441. Tel: 410-996-5600. Fax: 410-996-5604. p. 1027

O'Brien, Leslie, Dir, Tech Serv & Coll Mgt, Virginia Polytechnic Institute & State University Libraries, Drill Field Dr, Blacksburg, VA, 24062-9001. Tel: 540-231-4945. Fax: 540-231-3946. p. 2451

O'Brien, Lois A, Govt Doc, Libr Serv Coordr, Marquette University, Sensenbrenner Hall, 1103 W Wisconsin Ave, Milwaukee, WI, 53233-2313. Tel: 414-288-7092. Fax: 414-288-5914. p. 2618

O'Brien, Lynne, PhD, Dir, Acad Tech & Instrul Serv, Duke University Libraries, 411 Chapel Dr, Durham, NC, 27708. Tel: 919-660-5862. Fax: 919-660-5923. p. 1787

O'Brien, Margaret, ILL, Cortez Public Library, 202 N Park, Cortez, CO, 81321-3300. Tel: 970-565-8117. Fax: 970-565-8720. p. 297

O'Brien, Mary B, AV Librn, Quincy Public Library, 526 Jersey St, Quincy, IL, 62301-3996. Tel: 217-223-1309, Ext 205. Fax: 217-222-5672. p. 693

O'Brien, Mary C, Librn, US Environmental Protection Agency, 200 SW 35th St, Corvallis, OR, 97333. Tel: 541-754-4731. Fax: 541-754-4799. p. 1995

O'Brien, Mary Frances, Mgr, Libr Serv, Boston Public Library, 700 Boylston St, Boston, MA, 02117-0286. Tel: 617-536-5400. Fax: 617-236-4306. p. 1056

O'Brien, Mary Jane, Adult & Tech Serv Mgr, Bartlett Public Library District, 800 S Bartlett Rd, Bartlett, IL, 60103. Tel: 630-837-2855. Fax: 630-837-2669. p. 592

O'Brien, Mary Louise, Acq, Joint Forces Staff College Library, 7800 Hampton Blvd, Norfolk, VA, 23511-1702. Tel: 757-443-6404. Fax: 757-443-6044. p. 2481

O'Brien, Matavaine, Librn, American Samoa Office of Library Services, Matafao School Community Library, Fagaalu Village, AS, 96799. Tel: 684-633-2401. Fax: 684-633-2401. p. 2665

O'Brien, Michael, Syst Coordr, University of San Diego, Helen K & James S Copley Library, 5998 Alcala Park, San Diego, CA, 92110. Fax: 619-260-4617. p. 239

O'Brien, Nancy, Head Librn, University of Illinois Library at Urbana-Champaign, Social Sciences, Health & Education Library, 100 Main Library, MC-522, 1408 W Gregory Dr, Urbana, IL, 61801. Tel: 217-333-2408. Fax: 217-333-2214. p. 713

O'Brien, Nancy, Dir, Iowa Methodist Medical Center, 1200 Pleasant St, Des Moines, IA, 50309. Tel: 515-241-6490. Fax: 515-241-3383. p. 809

O'Brien, Patrick, Head, Tech Serv, Keene State College, 229 Main St, Keene, NH, 03435-3201. Tel: 603-358-2713. Fax: 603-358-2745. p. 1453

O'Brien, Sharon, Mem Serv Librn, Mohawk Valley Library System, 858 Duanesburg Rd, Schenectady, NY, 12306-1057. Tel: 518-355-2010. Fax: 518-355-0674. p. 1740

O'Brien, Sheila, Dir, Greenfield Public Library, 7215 W Coldspring, Greenfield, WI, 53220. Tel: 414-321-9595. Fax: 414-321-8595. p. 2596

O'Brien, Shelley L, Ref Librn, YA Serv, Melrose Public Library, 69 W Emerson St, Melrose, MA, 02176. Tel: 781-665-2313. Fax: 781-662-4229. p. 1105

O'Brien, Susan, Cat, Meriden Public Library, 105 Miller St, Meriden, CT, 06450. Tel: 203-238-2344, 203-238-2346. Fax: 203-238-3647. p. 350

O'Brien, Susan, Coordr, AV, Downers Grove Public Library, 1050 Curtiss St, Downers Grove, IL, 60515. Tel: 630-960-1200. Fax: 630-960-9374. p. 637

O'Brien, Suzanne, Dir, Sir Mortimer B Davis Jewish General Hospital, Hope & Cope Library, 3755 Cote Ste Catherine Rd, Montreal, QC, H3T 1E2, CANADA. Tel: 514-340-8255. Fax: 514-340-8605. p. 2901

O'Brien, Tara, Dir, Presv & Conserv, Historical Society of Pennsylvania, 1300 Locust St, Philadelphia, PA, 19107-5699. Tel: 215-732-6200, Ext 245. Fax: 215-732-2680. p. 2110

O'Brien, Wendy, Librn, Richmond Public Library, 19 Winchester Rd, Richmond, NH, 03470. Tel: 603-239-6164. Fax: 603-239-7332. p. 1463

O'Bryan, Charles R, Dir, State University of New York, College at Oneonta, 108 Ravine Pkwy, Oneonta, NY, 13820. Tel: 607-436-3702. Fax: 607-436-3081. p. 1711

O'Bryan, Katherine, Ser, Christian Theological Seminary Library, 1000 W 42nd St, Indianapolis, IN, 46208. Tel: 317-931-2364. Fax: 317-931-2363. p. 750

O'Byrne, Christopher, Res Librn, University of Notre Dame, 2345 Biolchini Hall of Law, Notre Dame, IN, 46556-4640. Tel: 574-631-5664. Fax: 574-631-6371. p. 771

O'Callaghan, Mary, Dir, Corporate Serv, Fraser Valley Regional Library, 34589 Delair Rd, Abbotsford, BC, V2S 5Y1, CANADA. Tel: 604-859-7141. Fax: 604-859-5701. p. 2723

O'Callaghan, Patricia, Librn, The Carmelite Province of the Most Pure Heart of Mary, Whitefriars Hall, 1600 Webster St NE, Washington, DC, 20017. Tel: 202-526-1221, Ext 204. p. 395

O'Connell, Betsy, Dir, Info Tech, Gail Borden Public Library District, 270 N Grove Ave, Elgin, IL, 60120-5596. Tel: 847-429-4689. Fax: 847-608-5029. p. 640

O'Connell, Carol, Ref Serv, Ch, Comsewogue Public Library, 170 Terryville Rd, Port Jefferson Station, NY, 11776. Tel: 631-928-1212. Fax: 631-928-6307. p. 1721

O'Connell, Dan, Circ, Wentworth Institute of Technology, 550 Huntington Ave, Boston, MA, 02115-5998. Tel: 617-989-4040. Fax: 617-989-4091. p. 1068

O'Connell, Eileen, Mgr, Albuquerque-Bernalillo County Library System, Special Collections, 423 Central Ave NE, Albuquerque, NM, 87102. Tel: 505-848-1376. Fax: 505-764-1574. p. 1548

O'Connell, Heath, Mgr, Fermi National Accelerator Laboratory Library, Kirk & Wilson Sts, Batavia, IL, 60510. Tel: 630-840-3401. Fax: 630-840-4636. p. 593

O'Connell, Jane, Dr, Dir, Hillview Free Library, 3717 Lake Shore Dr, Diamond Point, NY, 12824. Tel: 518-668-3012. Fax: 518-668-3012. p. 1614

O'Connell, John, Librn, Wayne Public Library, 3737 S Wayne Rd, Wayne, MI, 48184. Tel: 734-721-7832. Fax: 734-721-0341. p. 1235

O'Connell, Kathleen Mary, Asst Dir, Washington County Free Library, 100 S Potomac St, Hagerstown, MD, 21740. Tel: 301-739-3250. Fax: 301-739-7603. p. 1031

O'Connell, Marie, Learning Res Tech, Hillsborough Community College, Brandon Campus Learning Resources Center, 10414 E Columbus Dr, Tampa, FL, 33619-9640. Tel: 813-253-7803. p. 496

O'Connell, Mary, Ref Librn, Bridgewater Public Library, 15 South St, Bridgewater, MA, 02324-2593. Tel: 508-697-3331. Fax: 508-279-1467. p. 1070

O'Connell, Sandra, Br Mgr, Live Oak Public Libraries, Islands Branch, 125 Wilmington Island Rd, Savannah, GA, 31410. Tel: 912-897-6233. Fax: 912-897-1496. p. 550

O'Connell, Sean, Librn, Virginia Beach Public Library Department, Library Cataloging Services, 4100 Virginia Beach Blvd, Virginia Beach, VA, 23452. Tel: 757-385-0170. p. 2500

O'Connell, Shannon, ILL Librn, Res, Williams & Connolly Library, 725 12th St NW, Washington, DC, 20005. Tel: 202-434-5303. Fax: 202-434-5029. p. 423

O'Connell, Terence, Cat Librn, Northwestern University, Chicago, Pritzker Legal Research Center, 375 E Chicago Ave, Chicago, IL, 60611. Tel: 312-503-7364. Fax: 312-503-9230. p. 621

O'Connell-Cook, Melissa, Tech Serv, Hazleton Area Public Library, 55 N Church St, Hazleton, PA, 18201-5893. Tel: 570-454-2961. Fax: 570-454-0630. p. 2068

O'Connor, Alice, Doc Delivery, Bellevue University, 1000 Galvin Rd S, Bellevue, NE, 68005. Tel: 402-557-7311. Fax: 402-557-5427. p. 1393

O'Connor, Anne, Info & Tech Serv, E C Scranton Memorial Library, 801 Boston Post Rd, Madison, CT, 06443. Tel: 203-245-7365. Fax: 203-245-7821. p. 349

O'Connor, Anne, Head, Ref, University of New Haven, 300 Boston Post Rd, West Haven, CT, 06516. Tel: 203-932-7190. Fax: 203-932-1469. p. 377

O'Connor, Brian C, Dr, Prof, University of North Texas, 1155 Union Circle, Denton, TX, 76203-5017. Tel: 940-565-2445. Fax: 940-565-3101. p. 2975

O'Connor, Carin, Br Librn, Boston Public Library, Dudley Branch, 65 Warren St, Roxbury, MA, 02119. Tel: 617-442-6186. Fax: 617-427-9752. p. 1057

O'Connor, Carin, Librn, Boston Public Library, Honan-Allston Branch, 300 N Harvard St, Allston, MA, 02134. Tel: 617-787-6313. Fax: 617-859-2185. p. 1057

O'Connor, Cheryl, Exec Dir, LibraryLinkNJ, The New Jersey Library Cooperative, 44 Stelton Rd, Ste 330, Piscataway, NJ, 08854. Tel: 732-752-7720. Fax: 732-752-7785. p. 2949

O'Connor, Chris, Librn, Dillingham Public Library, 361 D St W, Dillingham, AK, 99576. Tel: 907-842-5610. Fax: 907-842-4237. p. 47

O'Connor, Daniel O, Assoc Prof, Rutgers, The State University of New Jersey, Four Huntington St, New Brunswick, NJ, 08901-1071. Tel: 732-932-7500, Ext 8955. Fax: 732-932-2644. p. 2969

O'Connor, Daragh, Dir, River Edge Free Public Library, 685 Elm Ave, River Edge, NJ, 07661. Tel: 201-261-1663. Fax: 201-986-0214. p. 1526

O'Connor, Deborah F, Dir, Geauga County Public Library, 12701 Ravenwood Dr, Chardon, OH, 44024-1336. Tel: 440-286-6811, Ext 101. Fax: 440-286-7419. p. 1866

O'Connor, Dennis, Circ, ILL, Naugatuck Valley Community College, 750 Chase Pkwy, Waterbury, CT, 06708. Tel: 203-575-8024. Fax: 203-575-8062. p. 375

O'Connor, Grace, Coll Develop, Ref, West Islip Public Library, Three Higbie Lane, West Islip, NY, 11795-3999. Tel: 631-661-7080. Fax: 631-661-7137. p. 1766

O'Connor, Helen, Info Syst, Palmer Public Library, 1455 N Main St, Palmer, MA, 01069. Tel: 413-283-3330. Fax: 413-283-9970. p. 1116

O'Connor, Jeanne, Ref & ILL Librn, Seton Hall University, One Newark Ctr, Newark, NJ, 07102. p. 1513

O'Connor, Kathleen, Asst Dean, Libr Serv, Gonzaga University, 502 E Boone Ave, Spokane, WA, 99258-0095. Tel: 509-313-6545. Fax: 509-323-5904. p. 2536

O'Connor, Kevin, Dr, Dean, Saddleback College, 28000 Marguerite Pkwy, Mission Viejo, CA, 92692. Tel: 949-582-4366. Fax: 949-364-0284. p. 187

O'Connor, Lisa, Br Mgr, Cumberland County Public Library & Information Center, Cumberland County Law Library, Courthouse, Rm 341, 117 Dick St, Fayetteville, NC, 28301. Tel: 910-321-6600. Fax: 910-485-5291. p. 1792

O'Connor, Lisa, Dr, Assoc Prof, University of Kentucky, 320 Little Library Bldg, Lexington, KY, 40506-0224. Tel: 859-257-5679. Fax: 859-257-4205. p. 2966

O'Connor, Michael, Asst Dir, Manchester-by-the-Sea Public Library, 15 Union St, Manchester-by-the-Sea, MA, 01944. Tel: 978-526-7711. Fax: 978-526-2018. p. 1102

O'Connor, Michael, Curator, Spec Coll, Hofstra University, 123 Hofstra University, Hempstead, NY, 11549. p. 1635

O'Connor, Michael, Curator, Hofstra University, Special Collections/Long Island Studies Institute, 032 Axinn Library, 123 Hofstra University, Hempstead, NY, 11549-1230. Tel: 516-463-6404, 516-463-6411. Fax: 516-463-6442. p. 1635

O'Connor, Patricia, Dir, Western State Law Library, 1111 N State College Blvd, Fullerton, CA, 92831-3014. Tel: 714-459-1175. Fax: 714-871-4806. p. 154

O'Connor, Patty, Adult Serv, Marysville Public Library, 231 S Plum St, Marysville, OH, 43040-1596. Tel: 937-642-1876. Fax: 937-642-3457. p. 1915

O'Connor, Phyllis G, Assoc Dean, Univ Libr, University of Akron Libraries, 315 Buchtel Mall, Akron, OH, 44325-1701. Tel: 330-972-6057. Fax: 330-972-5106. p. 1853

O'Connor, Rhonda, Libr Assoc, Missouri State University, Haseltine Library, Greenwood Laboratory School, 901 S National, Rm 3, Springfield, MO, 65897. Tel: 417-836-8563. p. 1367

O'Connor, Shannon, Dir, Edith B Ford Memorial Library, 7169 N Main St, Ovid, NY, 14521. Tel: 607-869-3031. Fax: 607-869-3031. p. 1713

O'Connor, Stephanie, Dir, Alliance Public Library, 1750 Sweetwater Ave, Ste 101, Alliance, NE, 69301-4438. Tel: 308-762-1387. Fax: 308-762-4148. p. 1391

O'Connor, Stephen, Syst Coordr, University of Rochester, River Campus Libraries, 755 Library Rd, Rochester, NY, 14627-0055. Tel: 585-275-4461. Fax: 585-273-5309. p. 1733

O'Connor, Thomas F, Brother, Pub Serv, Manhattan College, 4513 Manhattan College Pkwy, Riverdale, NY, 10471. Tel: 718-862-7166. Fax: 718-862-8028. p. 1728

O'Connor-Levy, Linda, Outreach Serv Librn, Manatee County Public Library System, 1301 Barcarrota Blvd W, Bradenton, FL, 34205. Tel: 941-748-5555. Fax: 941-749-7191. p. 429

O'Daniel, Clara, Dir, Rich Mountain Community College, 1100 College Dr, Mena, AR, 71953-2503. Tel: 501-394-7622, Ext 1370. Fax: 479-394-2828. p. 109

O'Dell, Frances, Sr, Ref Librn, Barry University, 11300 NE Second Ave, Miami, FL, 33161. Tel: 305-899-2977. Fax: 305-899-4792. p. 464

O'Dell, Kathleen, Commun Relations Mgr, Springfield-Greene County Library District, 4653 S Campbell, Springfield, MO, 65810-1723. Tel: 417-882-0714. Fax: 417-883-9348. p. 1367

O'Dell, Katie, Youth Serv Dir, Multnomah County Library, 205 NE Russell St, Portland, OR, 97212-3796. Tel: 503-988-5402. Fax: 503-988-5441. p. 2011

O'Dell, Lorraine, Dir, Bradley Beach Public Library, 511 Fourth Ave, Bradley Beach, NJ, 07720. Tel: 732-776-2995. Fax: 732-774-4591. p. 1474

O'Dell, Sue, Librn, Bowdoin College Library, Hatch Science Library, Hatch Science Bldg, 2nd Flr, 3100 College Sta, Brunswick, ME, 04011. Tel: 207-725-3004. Fax: 207-725-3095. p. 979

O'Doherty, Kathleen, Dir, Woburn Public Library, 45 Pleasant St, Woburn, MA, 01801. Tel: 781-933-0148. Fax: 781-938-7860. p. 1142

O'Donnel, Marj, Computer Tech, Lyon Township Public Library, 27005 S Milford Rd, South Lyon, MI, 48178. Tel: 248-437-8800. Fax: 248-437-4621. p. 1227

O'Donnell, Annette, Dir, Joice Public Library, 201 Main St, Joice, IA, 50446. Tel: 641-588-3330. Fax: 641-588-3330. p. 825

O'Donnell, Carol A, Dir, Rock Creek Public Library, 2988 High St, Rock Creek, OH, 44084-9703. Tel: 440-563-3340. Fax: 440-563-9566. p. 1932

O'Donnell, Courtney, Asst Librn, American Chemical Society Information Resource Center, 1155 16th St NW, Washington, DC, 20036. Tel: 202-872-4513. Fax: 202-872-6257. p. 392

O'Donnell, Ellen, Dir, Saint John Hospital & Medical Center Library, 22101 Moross Rd, Detroit, MI, 48236. Tel: 313-343-3733. Fax: 313-343-7598. p. 1172

O'Donnell, Frances, Archivist, Curator, Harvard Library, Andover-Harvard Theological Library, Divinity School, 45 Francis Ave, Cambridge, MA, 02138. Tel: 617-495-5788. Fax: 617-496-4111. p. 1074

O'Donnell, Jule, IT Mgr, Cambridge Public Library, 449 Broadway, Cambridge, MA, 02138. Tel: 617-349-4040. Fax: 617-349-4028. p. 1073

O'Donnell, Lorie, Ch, Jervis Public Library Association, Inc, 613 N Washington St, Rome, NY, 13440-4296. Tel: 315-336-4570. p. 1734

O'Donnell, Suzanna, Br Mgr, Wake County Public Library System, Zebulon Community Library, 1000 Dogwood Ave, Zebulon, NC, 27597. Tel: 919-404-3611. Fax: 919-404-3619. p. 1818

O'Donoghue, Laura, Asst State Librn, State Library of North Carolina, 109 E Jones St, Raleigh, NC, 27601. Tel: 919-807-7400. Fax: 919-733-8748. p. 1817

O'Donoghue, Rosemary, Archivist, Western New England University, 1215 Wilbraham Rd, Springfield, MA, 01119. Tel: 413-782-1495. Fax: 413-796-2011. p. 1128

O'Donovan, Doris, Acq, Rider University, 2083 Lawrenceville Rd, Lawrenceville, NJ, 08648-3099. Tel: 609-896-5111. Fax: 609-896-8029. p. 1494

O'Donovan, Patrice, Dir, Linfield College, Portland Campus, 2255 NW Northrup, Portland, OR, 97210. Tel: 503-413-7335. Fax: 503-413-8016. p. 2005

O'Dwyer, Joanne, Librn, Benewah County District Library, 46 Isaacson St, Fernwood, ID, 83830. Tel: 208-245-4883. Fax: 208-245-0129. p. 574

O'Gorman, James R, Ref Librn, Saint Ambrose University Library, 518 W Locust St, Davenport, IA, 52803. Tel: 563-333-6035. Fax: 563-333-6248. p. 807

O'Gorman, Kathryn C, Dir, Cincinnati State Technical & Community College, 3520 Central Pkwy, Cincinnati, OH, 45223-2612. Tel: 513-569-1695. Fax: 513-559-1527. p. 1869

O'Grady, Beth, Dir, Carson City Public Library, 102 W Main St, Carson City, MI, 48811-0699. Tel: 989-584-3680. Fax: 989-584-3680. p. 1161

O'Grady, Harold, Ref, Brooklyn Law School Library, 250 Joralemon St, Brooklyn, NY, 11201. Tel: 718-780-7981. Fax: 718-780-0369. p. 1590

O'Grady, Nancy, Ch, Woodbridge Public Library, George Frederick Plaza, Woodbridge, NJ, 07095. Tel: 732-634-4450. p. 1545

O'Grady, Susan, Chair, Savoy Hollow Library, Town Off Bldg, 720 Main St, Savoy, MA, 01256-9387. Tel: 413-743-4290. Fax: 413-743-4292. p. 1123

O'Grady, Tim, Archivist, City of Edmonton, Archives, 10440 - 108 Ave, 2nd Flr, Prince of Wales Armouries Heritage Centre, Edmonton, AB, T5H 3Z9, CANADA. Tel: 780-496-8711. Fax: 780-496-8732. p. 2699

O'Hanlon, Donna, Ch, Wanaque Public Library, 616 Ringwood Ave, Wanaque, NJ, 07465. Tel: 973-839-4434, Ext 103. Fax: 973-839-8904. p. 1539

O'Hanlon, Pat, Dir, Truth or Consequences Public Library, 325 Library Lane, Truth or Consequences, NM, 87901-2375. Tel: 505-894-3027. Fax: 505-894-2068. p. 1566

O'Hanlon, Pat, Dir, Truth or Consequences Public Library, Downtown, 401 N Foch St, Truth or Consequences, NM, 87901. Tel: 505-894-7821. p. 1566

O'Hanlon, Sean, Mgr, Info, Knowledge & Internal Serv, Deere & Co Library, One John Deere Pl, Moline, IL, 61265. Tel: 309-765-4733. Fax: 309-765-4088. p. 674

O'Hara, Christopher, Ch, New Providence Memorial Library, 377 Elkwood Ave, New Providence, NJ, 07974-1837. Tel: 908-665-0311. Fax: 908-665-2319. p. 1510

O'Hara, Ed, Dr, Dir, Western Connecticut State University, 181 White St, Danbury, CT, 06810. Tel: 203-837-9109. Fax: 203-837-9108. p. 335

O'Hara, Kelly, Circ Mgr, Jefferson Community & Technical College, Southwest Campus Library, 1000 Community College Dr, Louisville, KY, 40272. Tel: 502-213-7222. Fax: 502-935-8653. p. 924

O'Hara, Mary, ILL, Clarion Free Library, 644 Main St, Clarion, PA, 16214. Tel: 814-226-7172. Fax: 814-226-6750. p. 2045

O'Hara, Sean, Librn, Canadian Agriculture Library - Winnipeg, 195 Dafoe Rd, Winnipeg, MB, R3T 2M9, CANADA. Tel: 204-983-0721, 204-983-0755. Fax: 204-983-4604. p. 2754

O'Hara, Susan, In Charge, Ocean Medical Center, 425 Jack Martin Blvd, Brick, NJ, 08724. Tel: 732-836-4343. Fax: 732-206-8052. p. 1474

O'Hare, Earlene, Media Serv, Port Jefferson Free Library, 100 Thompson St, Port Jefferson, NY, 11777-1897. Tel: 631-473-0022. Fax: 631-473-4765. p. 1721

O'Hare, J, Asst Dir, North Shore Public Library, 250 Rte 25A, Shoreham, NY, 11786-9677. Tel: 631-929-4488. Fax: 631-929-4551. p. 1743

O'Hare, Liam, Syst Librn, Prince Edward Island Public Library Service, 89 Red Head Rd, Morell, PE, C0A 1S0, CANADA. Tel: 902-961-7323. Fax: 902-961-7322. p. 2876

O'Hare, Miriam, Govt Doc, Benedictine College Library, 1020 N Second St, Atchison, KS, 66002-1499. Tel: 913-360-7513. Fax: 913-360-7622. p. 856

O'Heir, Leslie, Librn, Wayne Presbyterian Church Library, 125 E Lancaster Ave, Wayne, PA, 19087. Tel: 610-688-8700. Fax: 610-688-8743. p. 2152

O'Herron, Virginia S, Univ Librn, Old Dominion University Libraries, 4427 Hampton Blvd, Norfolk, VA, 23529-0256. Tel: 757-683-4141. Fax: 757-683-5767. p. 2482

O'Kane, Peggy, Coordr, Ref & Res, Maine State Library, LMA Bldg, 230 State St, Augusta, ME, 04333. Tel: 207-287-5605. Fax: 207-287-5615. p. 974

O'Keefe, Margaret Rose, Ref Librn, William E Dermody Free Public Library, 420 Hackensack St, Carlstadt, NJ, 07072. Tel: 201-438-8866. Fax: 201-438-2733. p. 1477

O'Keefe, Terence, Tech Librn, Derby Public Library, 313 Elizabeth St, Derby, CT, 06418. Tel: 203-736-1482. Fax: 203-736-1419. p. 336

O'Keeffe, Maureen, Tech Serv, Dominican College Library, 480 Western Hwy, Blauvelt, NY, 10913-2000. Tel: 845-848-7505. Fax: 845-359-2525. p. 1583

O'Kennedy, Caro, Libr Mgr, Fraser Valley Regional Library, Maple Ridge Public Library, 130 - 22470 Dewdney Trunk Rd, Maple Ridge, BC, V2X 5Z6, CANADA. Tel: 604-467-7417. Fax: 604-467-7404. p. 2724

O'Kennedy, Caro, Libr Mgr, Fraser Valley Regional Library, Pitt Meadows Public Library, 12047 Harris Rd, Pitt Meadows, BC, V3Y 1Z2, CANADA. Tel: 604-465-4113. Fax: 604-465-9732. p. 2724

O'Laughlin, Mike, In Charge, Irish Genealogical Foundation Library, PO Box 7575, Kansas City, MO, 64116. Tel: 816-454-2410. Fax: 816-454-2410. p. 1337

O'Leary, Andrea, Asst Librn, Pennsylvania State Department of Health, 110 Pickering Way, Lionville, PA, 19353. Tel: 610-280-3464. Fax: 610-450-1932. p. 2082

O'Leary, Bridget, Ref Librn, Central New Mexico Community College Libraries, Montoya Campus Library, J Bldg, Rm 123, 4700 Morris NE, Albuquerque, NM, 87111. Tel: 505-224-5724. Fax: 505-224-5727. p. 1548

O'Leary, Kathleen, Br Mgr, Olathe Public Library, Indian Creek, 12990 S Black Bob Rd, Olathe, KS, 66062. Tel: 913-971-5240. Fax: 913-971-5239. p. 886

O'Leary, Maureen, Librn, St John's Medical Center, PO Box 428, Jackson, WY, 83001-0428. Tel: 307-739-7371. Fax: 307-739-7372. p. 2656

O'Leary, Michael, Mgr, Libr Serv, Concordia University, 4090 Geddes Rd, Ann Arbor, MI, 48105-2797. Tel: 734-995-7353. Fax: 734-995-7405. p. 1151

O'Leary, Mick, Exec Dir, Frederick Community College Library, 7932 Opossumtown Pike, Frederick, MD, 21702. Tel: 301-846-2444. Fax: 301-624-2877. p. 1028

O'Leary, Patrick K, Sr Dir, Admin Serv, Los Angeles County Law Library, Mildred L Lillie Bldg, 301 W First St, Los Angeles, CA, 90012-3100. Tel: 213-785-2529. Fax: 213-613-1329. p. 171

O'Leary, Theresa, Librn, Paul, Weiss, Rifkind, Wharton & Garrison Library, 1285 Avenue of the Americas, New York, NY, 10019-6064. Tel: 212-373-2401. Fax: 212-373-2268. p. 1697

O'Leary-Frick, Susan, Dir, Neuschafer Community Library, 317 Wolf River Dr, Fremont, WI, 54940-9054. Tel: 920-446-2474. Fax: 920-446-2480. p. 2593

O'Malley, Caris, Teen Serv Mgr, Maricopa County Library District, 2700 N Central Ave, Ste 700, Phoenix, AZ, 85004. Tel: 602-652-3056. Fax: 602-652-3071. p. 74

O'Malley, Della Hung, Ref Serv, Fairleigh Dickinson University, 1000 River Rd, Teaneck, NJ, 07666-1914. Tel: 201-692-2140. Fax: 201-692-9815. p. 1533

O'Malley, Elena, Asst Dir, Tech & Access Serv, Emerson College Library, 120 Boylston St, Boston, MA, 02116-4624. Tel: 617-824-8668. Fax: 617-824-7817. p. 1060

O'Malley, Karen, Ch, Parsippany-Troy Hills Free Public Library, Mount Tabor Branch, 31 Trinity Park, Mount Tabor, NJ, 07878. Tel: 973-627-9508. p. 1518

O'Malley, Michael, Archivist, Berry College, 2277 Martha Berry Hwy, Mount Berry, GA, 30149. Tel: 706-238-5886. Fax: 706-238-5917. p. 546

O'Malley, William T, Tech Serv, Robert L Carothers Library & Learning Commons, 15 Lippitt Rd, Kingston, RI, 02881. Tel: 401-874-4799. Fax: 401-874-4608. p. 2168

O'Mara, Joan, Librn, McGinnis, Lochridge & Kilgore, LLP, 600 Congress Ave, Ste 2100, Austin, TX, 78701. Tel: 512-495-6000. Fax: 512-495-6093. p. 2281

O'Mara, Timothy, Asst Librn, Mount Sinai Services-Queens Hospital Center Affiliation, 82-68 164th St, Jamaica, NY, 11432. Tel: 718-883-4021. Fax: 718-883-6125. p. 1643

O'Neal, Amy, Librn, Washington County Library, 201 E Third St, Plymouth, NC, 27962. Tel: 252-793-2113. Fax: 252-793-2818. p. 1814

O'Neal, Carole, In Charge, Dixon Correctional Center Library, 2600 N Brinton Ave, Dixon, IL, 61021-9524. Tel: 815-288-5561, Ext 3041. p. 637

O'Neal, Danny, Ref, University of South Florida, Hinks & Elaine Shimberg Health Sciences Library, 12901 Bruce B Downs Blvd, MDC Box 31, Tampa, FL, 33612-4799. Tel: 813-974-2399. Fax: 813-974-3605, 813-974-4930. p. 498

O'Neal, James, Librn, Middle Georgia Regional Library System, Library for the Blind & Physically Handicapped, Washington Memorial Library, 1180 Washington Ave, Macon, GA, 31201-1790. Tel: 478-744-0877. p. 541

O'Neal, Mary, Per, Webster University, 101 Edgar Rd, Saint Louis, MO, 63119. Tel: 314-968-6952. Fax: 314-968-7113. p. 1363

O'Neal, Michael L, Tech Serv, Valparaiso Community Library, 459 Valparaiso Pkwy, Valparaiso, FL, 32580. Tel: 850-729-5406. Fax: 850-729-1120. p. 501

O'Neal, Mike, Librn, Randolph Circuit Court, 100 S Main, Winchester, IN, 47394. Tel: 765-584-4128. Fax: 765-584-7186. p. 788

O'Neal, Nick, Circ Mgr, Kirkwood Public Library, 140 E Jefferson Ave, Kirkwood, MO, 63122. Tel: 314-821-5770, Ext 1027. Fax: 314-822-3755. p. 1342

O'Neal, Susan, Dir, Middletown Public Library, 55 New Monmouth Rd, Middletown, NJ, 07748. Tel: 732-671-3700, Ext 315. Fax: 732-671-5839. p. 1501

O'Neil, Gail, Librn, Warburg Public Library, 5212 50 Ave, Warburg, AB, T0C 2T0, CANADA. Tel: 780-848-2391. Fax: 780-848-2296. p. 2721

O'Neil, Genevieve, Circ/Reserves, Yukon College Library, 500 College Dr, Whitehorse, YT, Y1A 5K4, CANADA. Tel: 867-668-8870. Fax: 867-668-8808. p. 2934

O'Neil, Jennifer Ann, Dir, Florida Times Union, One Riverside Ave, Jacksonville, FL, 32202. Tel: 904-359-4111. Fax: 904-359-4090. p. 453

O'Neil, Katherine, Dir, Stockbridge Library Association, 46 Main St, Stockbridge, MA, 01262. Tel: 413-298-5501. Fax: 413-298-0218. p. 1129

O'Neil, Margaret, Librn, Penfield Public Library, 1985 Baird Rd, Penfield, NY, 14526. Tel: 585-340-8720. Fax: 585-340-8748. p. 1716

O'Neil, Mary Ann, Dir, Pima County Law Library, Superior Court Bldg, 110 W Congress, Rm 256, Tucson, AZ, 85701-1317. Tel: 520-724-8456. Fax: 520-724-9122. p. 86

O'Neill, Barbara, ILL, Ref, Washington County Cooperative Library Services, 111 NE Lincoln St, No 230-L MS58, Hillsboro, OR, 97124-3036. Tel: 503-846-3222. Fax: 503-846-3220. p. 2000

O'Neill, Bettijane, Chief Exec Officer, Chief Librn, Renfrew Public Library, 13 Railway Ave E, Renfrew, ON, K7V 3A9, CANADA. Tel: 613-432-8151. Fax: 613-432-7680. p. 2838

O'Neill, Camille, Ref, Arizona Western College & NAU Yuma Branch Campus, 2020 S Ave 8E, Yuma, AZ, 85366. Tel: 928-344-7777. Fax: 928-344-7751. p. 90

O'Neill, Cathy, Ref Serv, Southern New England School of Law Library, 333 Faunce Corner Rd, North Dartmouth, MA, 02747. Tel: 508-998-9888. p. 1112

O'Neill, Cheryl, Librn, Art Complex Museum, 189 Alden St, Duxbury, MA, 02331. Tel: 781-934-6634, Ext 35. Fax: 781-934-5117. p. 1085

O'Neill, Darren, Head, Media Serv, Morris County Library, 30 E Hanover Ave, Whippany, NJ, 07981. Tel: 973-285-6975. p. 1544

O'Neill, Francis, Sr Ref Librn, Maryland Historical Society Library, 201 W Monument St, Baltimore, MD, 21201. Tel: 410-685-3750. Fax: 410-385-0487. p. 1015

O'Neill, Gerard, Head Librn, Wilson Community College Library, 902 Herring Ave, Wilson, NC, 27893. Tel: 252-246-1235. Fax: 252-243-7148. p. 1831

O'Neill, Isabella, Curator, Spec Coll & Univ Archives, Bucknell University, Library & Information Technology, 221 Ellen Clarke Bertrand Library, Lewisburg, PA, 17837. Tel: 570-577-3230. Fax: 570-577-3313. p. 2080

O'Neill, John, Dr, Curator, Hispanic Society of America Library, 613 W 155th St, New York, NY, 10032. Tel: 212-926-2234, Ext 251. Tel: 212-690-0743. p. 1681

O'Neill, Lois, Ref Librn, Adelphi University Libraries, One South Ave, Garden City, NY, 11530. Tel: 516-877-3581. Fax: 516-877-3592. p. 1625

O'Neill, Louise, Assoc Dir, Libr Tech Serv, McGill University Libraries, 3459 McTavish St, Montreal, QC, H3A 1Y1, CANADA. Tel: 514-398-5898. Fax: 514-398-8919. p. 2898

O'Neill, Mary, Circ, Centralia Regional Library District, Sandoval Branch, 118 E Commercial, Sandoval, IL, 62882. Tel: 618-247-3873. p. 602

O'Neill, Mary, Ref Serv, University of the South, 735 University Ave, Sewanee, TN, 37383-1000. Tel: 931-598-1660. Fax: 931-598-1702. p. 2265

O'Neill, Megan, Web Serv & Emerging Tech Librn, Albion College, 602 E Cass St, Albion, MI, 49224-1879. Tel: 517-629-0270. Fax: 517-629-0504. p. 1148

O'Neill, Philip M, Sr Ref Librn, Barry University, 11300 NE Second Ave, Miami, FL, 33161. Tel: 305-899-3762. Fax: 305-899-4792. p. 464

O'Neill, Rhonda, Asst Dir, Alberta Law Libraries, Judicial, Calgary Courts Ctr, 2001-N, 601 - 5 St SW, Calgary, AB, T2P 5P7, CANADA. Tel: 403-297-3958. Fax: 403-297-2981. p. 2687

O'Neill, Rhonda, Asst Dir, Alberta Law Libraries, , Law Courts North, 5th Flr, 1A Sir Winston Churchill Sq, Edmonton, AB, T5J 0R2, CANADA. Tel: 780-427-3327. Fax: 780-427-0481. p. 2698

O'Neill, Rhonda, Asst Libr Dir, Alberta Law Libraries, Edmonton, Law Courts Bldg, 2nd Flr, 1A Sir Winston Churchill Sq, Edmonton, AB, T5J 0R2, CANADA. Tel: 403-297-3958. Fax: 780-427-0397. p. 2699

O'Neill, Robert K, Head Librn, Boston College Libraries, John J Burns Library of Rare Books & Special Collections, 140 Commonwealth Ave, Chestnut Hill, MA, 02467. Tel: 617-552-8297. Fax: 617-552-2465. p. 1080

O'Neill, Shannon, Archives, Barnard College, 3009 Broadway, New York, NY, 10027-6598. Tel: 212-854-4079. p. 1670

O'Niell, Renee, Librn, Illinois Auditor General Library, 740 E Ash St, Springfield, IL, 62703. Tel: 217-782-1055. Fax: 217-785-8222. p. 704

O'Pecko, Paul J, Dir of Libr, Mystic Seaport Museum, 75 Greenmanville Ave, Mystic, CT, 06355. Tel: 860-572-5367. Fax: 860-572-5394. p. 353

O'Quinn, Karen, Br Asst, Siskiyou County Public Library, Dunsmuir Branch, 5714 Dunsmuir Ave, Dunsmuir, CA, 96025. Tel: 530-235-2035. Fax: 530-235-0243. p. 286

O'Quinn, Ruby, Asst Librn, Saint Mary's Health Center, 6420 Clayton Rd, Saint Louis, MO, 63117. Tel: 314-768-8112. Fax: 314-768-8974. p. 1361

O'Rahilly, Andy, Supvr, Machine Lending, New Jersey State Library, Talking Book & Braille Center, 2300 Stuyvesant Ave, Trenton, NJ, 08618. Tel: 609-406-7179, Ext 819. Fax: 609-406-7181. p. 1536

O'Reilly, Kathleen, Cat, National Gallery of Canada Library, 380 Sussex Dr, Ottawa, ON, K1N 9N4, CANADA. Tel: 613-990-0592. Fax: 613-990-9818. p. 2832

O'Reilly, Kim, Mgr, Ch & Youth Serv, Oshawa Public Library, 65 Bagot St, Oshawa, ON, L1H 1N2, CANADA. Tel: 905-579-6111. Fax: 905-433-8107. p. 2827

O'Reilly, Margaret, Curator of Fine Arts, New Jersey State Museum, 205 West State St, Trenton, NJ, 08625. Tel: 609-292-5420. Fax: 609-292-7636. p. 1536

O'Reilly, Tara, Br Mgr, Santa Barbara Public Library, Carpinteria Branch, 5141 Carpinteria Ave, Carpinteria, CA, 93013. Tel: 805-684-4314. p. 261

O'Riley, Jane, Ref/Acq, Southern University at Shreveport, 3050 Martin Luther King Jr Dr, Shreveport, LA, 71107. Tel: 318-670-6482. Fax: 318-674-3403. p. 970

O'Riley, Margaret, Circ, John C Hart Memorial Library, 1130 Main St, Shrub Oak, NY, 10588. Tel: 914-245-5262. Fax: 914-245-2216. p. 1743

O'Rourke, Danny, Asst Dir, Murray Public Library, 166 E 5300 South, Murray, UT, 84107-6075. Tel: 801-264-2580. Fax: 801-264-2586. p. 2408

O'Rourke, Edward, Mgr, Baker Botts LLP, 1299 Pennsylvania Ave NW, Washington, DC, 20004-2400. Tel: 202-639-7967. Fax: 202-639-7890. p. 394

O'Rourke, Jan, District Consult Librn, Bucks County Free Library, 150 S Pine St, Doylestown, PA, 18901-4932. Tel: 215-348-0332, Ext 1131. Fax: 215-348-4760. p. 2050

O'Rourke, Jan, Asst Dir, Beaufort County Library, 311 Scott St, Beaufort, SC, 29902. Tel: 843-255-6464. p. 2181

O'Rourke, Joseph, Adult Serv Mgr, Delaware County District Library, 84 E Winter St, Delaware, OH, 43015. Tel: 740-362-3861. Fax: 740-369-0196. p. 1895

O'Rourke, Kerry, Dir, University of Medicine & Dentistry of New Jersey, PO Box 19, New Brunswick, NJ, 08903. Tel: 732-235-7606. Fax: 732-235-7826. p. 1509

O'Rourke, Penny, Dir, Byron Public Library District, 100 S Washington St, Byron, IL, 61010-1460. Tel: 815-234-5107. Fax: 815-234-5582. p. 598

O'Rourke, Ruth, Ad, Maquoketa Public Library, 126 S Second St, Maquoketa, IA, 52060. Tel: 563-652-3874. p. 829

O'Rourke, Steven, Dir, Erie Business Center South, 170 Cascade Galleria, New Castle, PA, 16101. Tel: 724-658-9066. Fax: 724-658-3083. p. 2095

O'Shea, Amy, Librn, Wisconsin Department of Veterans Affairs, 30 W Mifflin St, Ste 300, Madison, WI, 53703. Tel: 608-261-5408. Fax: 608-264-7615. p. 2610

O'Shea, Denise, Head, Access Serv Dept, Syst Librn, Montclair State University, One Normal Ave, Montclair, NJ, 07043-1699. Tel: 973-655-2098. Fax: 973-655-7780. p. 1503

O'Shea, John, Spec Coll Librn, Augusta State University, 2500 Walton Way, Augusta, GA, 30904-2200. Tel: 706-737-1745. Fax: 706-667-4415. p. 518

O'Shea, Julie, Coordr, Ser, Assumption College, 500 Salisbury St, Worcester, MA, 01609. Tel: 508-767-7137. Fax: 508-767-7374. p. 1143

O'Shea, Mary E, Dir, Planned Parenthood of Greater Cleveland, Inc Library, 3500 Lorain Ave, Ste 400, Cleveland, OH, 44113. Tel: 216-961-8804. Fax: 216-334-2211. p. 1881

O'Sullivan, Joseph, Sr Librn, Tampa-Hillsborough County Public Library System, Seminole Heights Branch, 4711 Central Ave, Tampa, FL, 33603-3934. Fax: 813-273-3670. p. 498

O'Sullivan, Nancy, Ref & Info Literacy Librn, Assumption College, 500 Salisbury St, Worcester, MA, 01609. Tel: 508-767-7135. Fax: 508-767-7374. p. 1143

O'Sullivan, Pamela, Head, Integrated Pub Serv, State University of New York College at Brockport, 350 New Campus Dr, Brockport, NY, 14420-2997. Tel: 585-395-5688. Fax: 585-395-5651. p. 1585

O'Tool, Joyce, Asst Librn, Sac City Public Library, 1001 W Main St, Sac City, IA, 50583. Tel: 712-662-7276. Fax: 712-662-7802. p. 841

O'Toole, Nancy, Librn, Readfield Community Library, 1151 Main St, Readfield, ME, 04355-3512. Tel: 207-685-4089. p. 999

O'Toole, Susan, Dir, Foley & Lardner, 777 E Wisconsin Ave, Milwaukee, WI, 53202-5306. Tel: 414-271-2400. Fax: 414-297-4900. p. 2618

O'Toole, Susan, Asst Br Supvr, Region of Waterloo Library, Bloomingdale Branch, 860 Sawmill Rd, Bloomingdale, ON, N0B 1K0, CANADA. Tel: 519-745-3151. p. 2793

Oakes, Bessie, Libr Prog Mgr, Utah State Library Division, 250 N 1950 West, Ste A, Salt Lake City, UT, 84116-7901. Tel: 801-715-6789. Fax: 801-715-6767. p. 2415

Oakes, Cheryl, Librn, Forest History Society Library, 701 William Vickers Ave, Durham, NC, 27701-3162. Tel: 919-682-9319. Fax: 919-682-2349. p. 1789

Oakes, Gloria, Asst Librn, River Valley Community College, One College Dr, Claremont, NH, 03743. Tel: 603-542-7744, Ext 465. Fax: 603-543-1844. p. 1442

Oakes, Marcia, Ref, Rhode Island State Law Library, Frank Licht Judicial Complex, 250 Benefit St, Providence, RI, 02903. Tel: 401-458-5274. Fax: 401-222-3865. p. 2175

Oakes, Rita, Chief of Br Serv, Ocean County Library, 101 Washington St, Toms River, NJ, 08753. Tel: 732-349-6200. p. 1534

Oakes, Sharyn, Head, Tech Serv, Coronado Public Library, 640 Orange Ave, Coronado, CA, 92118-1526. Tel: 619-522-2473. Fax: 619-435-4205. p. 137

Oakey, Alice, Br Supvr, Madison Public Library, Alicia Ashman Branch, 733 N High Point Rd, Madison, WI, 53717. Tel: 608-824-1785. Fax: 608-824-1790. p. 2607

Oakey, Alice, Br Supvr, Madison Public Library, Meadowridge, 5740 Raymond Rd, Madison, WI, 53711. Tel: 608-288-6160. Fax: 608-288-6162. p. 2607

Oakey, Kathleen, Ref & Instruction, Sheridan College Library, 1430 Trafalgar Rd, Oakville, ON, L6H 2L1, CANADA. Tel: 905-459-7533, Ext 5454. Fax: 905-815-4123. p. 2826

Oakland, Debbie, Dir, Dominy Memorial Library, 201 S Third St, Fairbury, IL, 61739. Tel: 815-692-3231. Fax: 815-692-3503. p. 645

Oakland, Jane, Circ Mgr, ILL, University of North Dakota, 215 Centennial Dr, Grand Forks, ND, 58202. Tel: 701-777-2204. Fax: 701-777-2217. p. 1843

Oakleaf, Barbara, Libr Mgr, Mgr, Ad Serv, Fremont County Library System, 451 N Second St, Lander, WY, 82520-2316. Tel: 307-332-5194. Fax: 307-332-1504, 307-332-3909. p. 2656

Oakleaf, Kathy, Mgr, Mississauga Library System, Churchill Meadows, 3801 Thomas St, Mississauga, ON, L5M 7G2, CANADA. Tel: 905-615-4735. p. 2823

Oakley, John, Br Mgr, Great River Regional Library, Bryant Library, 430 Main St, Sauk Centre, MN, 56378. Tel: 320-352-3016. Fax: 320-352-3016. p. 1274

Oakley, Mary, Tech Serv Coordr, West Plains Public Library, 750 W Broadway, West Plains, MO, 65775-2369. Tel: 417-256-4775. Fax: 417-256-8316. p. 1372

Oakley, Patti, Asst Librn, Electra Public Library, 401 N Waggoner, Electra, TX, 76360. Tel: 940-495-2208. Fax: 940-495-4143. p. 2317

Oakley, Valerie, Ref Librn, Fruitville Public Library, 100 Coburn Rd, Sarasota, FL, 34240. Tel: 941-861-2500. Fax: 941-861-2528. p. 489

Oaks, Deborah, Librn, Franklin Public Library, 421 12th St, Franklin, PA, 16323-0421. Tel: 814-432-5062. Fax: 814-432-8998. p. 2058

Oamil, Florida, Cataloger, Columbia International University, 7435 Monticello Rd, Columbia, SC, 29203-1599. Tel: 803-807-5107. Fax: 803-744-1391. p. 2187

Oandasan, Debra Anne, Librn, Cades Schutte, 1000 Bishop St, Ste 1200, Honolulu, HI, 96813-4212. Tel: 808-521-9200. Fax: 808-521-9210. p. 560

Oar, David, Librn, Bellevue College, 3000 Landerholm Circle SE, Bellevue, WA, 98007-6484. Tel: 425-564-3134. Fax: 425-564-6186. p. 2508

Oard, Douglas, Dr, Assoc Dean, Res, University of Maryland, 4105 Hornbake Bldg, College Park, MD, 20742-4345. Tel: 301-405-2033. Fax: 301-314-9145. p. 2967

Oates, Evangela, Instruction & Ref Librn, Mount Saint Mary College, 330 Powell Ave, Newburgh, NY, 12550-3494. Tel: 845-569-3546. Fax: 845-561-0999. p. 1704

Oates, Jennifer, Dr, Assoc Prof, Head Music Librn, Queens College, Aaron Copland School of Music Library, 65-30 Kissena Blvd, Flushing, NY, 11367. Tel: 718-997-3900. Fax: 718-997-3928. p. 1623

Oathout, Larry, Chief Operations Officer, Evansville Vanderburgh Public Library, 200 SE Martin Luther King Jr Blvd, Evansville, IN, 47713-1604. Tel: 812-428-8244. p. 738

Oathout, Larry, Dir, Tell City-Perry County Public Library, 2328 Tell St, Tell City, IN, 47586. Tel: 812-547-2661. Fax: 812-547-3038. p. 780

Oathout, Lesa, Ch, Marrowbone Public Library District, 216 W Main St, Bethany, IL, 61914. Tel: 217-665-3014. Fax: 217-665-3246. p. 595

Oatis, Vicki, Ch, Norwalk Public Library, One Belden Ave, Norwalk, CT, 06850. Tel: 203-899-2780. Fax: 203-857-4410. p. 362

Oatman, Linda, Dir, Hansen District Library, 120 Maple Ave W, Hansen, ID, 83334-4975. Tel: 208-423-4122. p. 575

Oatman, Linda, Sr Librn, Wisconsin Secure Program Facility Library, 1101 Morrison Dr, Boscobel, WI, 53805. Tel: 608-375-5656. Fax: 608-375-5434. p. 2583

Obarski, Ann Marie, Coll Develop, Tech Serv Mgr, Front Range Community College, 3705 W 112th Ave, Westminster, CO, 80031-2140. Tel: 303-404-5505. Fax: 303-404-5144. p. 326

Ober, Beverly, Librn, Woodland Public Library, 169 Main St, Baileyville, ME, 04694. Tel: 207-427-3235. Fax: 207-427-3673. p. 975

Ober, Kathleen S, Dir, Libr Serv, Art Institute of Pittsburgh Library, 420 Boulevard of the Allies, Pittsburgh, PA, 15219-1328. Tel: 412-291-6357. Fax: 412-263-3715, 412-291-6300. p. 2121

Ober, Michael J, Dir, Flathead Valley Community College Library, 777 Grandview Dr, Kalispell, MT, 59901. Tel: 406-756-3856. Fax: 406-756-3854. p. 1384

Ober, Nancy, Dir, Brownfield Community Library, 291 Banning Rd, Dawson, PA, 15428. Tel: 724-529-7680. Fax: 724-529-7680. p. 2049

Ober, Pam, Libr Assoc, New Hampshire State Library, Gallen State Office Park, Dolloff Bldg, 117 Pleasant St, Concord, NH, 03301-3852. Tel: 603-271-2417, 603-271-3429. Fax: 603-271-8370. p. 1443

Oberc, Susan, Chief Librn, NASA, 21000 Brookpark Rd, MS 60-3, Cleveland, OH, 44135. Tel: 216-433-5766. Fax: 216-433-5777. p. 1880

Oberg, Carl, Exec Dir, Foundation for Economic Education Library, 30 S Broadway, Irvington, NY, 10533. Tel: 914-591-7230. Fax: 914-591-8910. p. 1640

Oberg, Judy, Coll Develop, National Renewable Energy Laboratory Library, 15013 Denver West Pkwy, Golden, CO, 80401-3305. Tel: 303-275-4022. Fax: 303-275-4222. p. 310

Oberg, Judy, Mgr, Libr & Res Serv, Bishop & McKenzie LLP, Barristers & Solicitors Library, 10104 103rd Ave, Ste 2500, Edmonton, AB, T5J 1V3, CANADA. Tel: 780-426-5550. Fax: 780-426-1305. p. 2699

Oberhansli, Courtney, Dir, Mineral County Public Library, 110 First St, Hawthorne, NV, 89415. Tel: 775-945-2778. Fax: 775-945-0703. p. 1428

Oberhausen, Debra, Br Mgr, Louisville Free Public Library, Crescent Hill, 2762 Frankfort Ave, Louisville, KY, 40206. Tel: 502-574-1793. Fax: 502-894-8505. p. 924

Oberholtzer, Patrick, Instruction & Ref Librn, Gallaudet University Library, 800 Florida Ave NE, Washington, DC, 20002-3095. Tel: 202-651-5233. p. 401

Oberlander, Cyril, Assoc Libr Dir, State University of New York College at Geneseo, SUNY Geneseo, One College Circle, Geneseo, NY, 14454-1498. p. 1627

Oberle, George, Head of Libr, George Mason University Libraries, Johnson Center, 4400 University Dr, MSN 1A6, Fairfax, VA, 22030-4444. Tel: 703-993-9012. Fax: 703-993-9063. p. 2462

Oberle, Holly, Head, Music/Dance Libr, Ohio University Libraries, Music-Dance, Robert Gidden Hall, Fifth Flr, Athens, OH, 45701-2978. Tel: 740-593-4256. Fax: 740-593-9190. p. 1856

Oberlin, Melanie, Instrul Serv Librn, George Mason University Libraries, School of Law, 3301 N Fairfax Dr, Arlington, VA, 22201-4426. Tel: 703-993-8120. Fax: 703-993-8113. p. 2462

Obermaier, Jennifer, Asst Dir, Clearwater Public Library System, 100 N Osceola Ave, Clearwater, FL, 33755. Tel: 727-562-4973. Fax: 727-562-4977. p. 432

Oberman, Cerise G, Dean of Libr & Info Serv, State University of New York College at Plattsburgh, Two Draper Ave, Plattsburgh, NY, 12901-2697. Tel: 518-564-3180. Fax: 518-564-5209. p. 1719

Oberman, Tobi, Circ, Skokie Public Library, 5215 Oakton St, Skokie, IL, 60077-3680. Tel: 847-673-7774. Fax: 847-673-7797. p. 703

Oberstar, Kristina, Librn, Dunwoody College of Technology, 818 Dunwoody Blvd, Minneapolis, MN, 55403. Tel: 612-374-5800, Ext 2404. p. 1259

Oberweiser, Jodi, Dir, Drummond School & Community Library, 124 First St, Drummond, MT, 59832. Tel: 406-288-3700. p. 1378

Obien, Rodney, Univ Archivist, Worcester Polytechnic Institute, 100 Institute Rd, Worcester, MA, 01609-2280. Tel: 508-831-5410. Fax: 508-831-5829. p. 1145

Obien, Rodney, Archivist, Keene State College, 229 Main St, Keene, NH, 03435-3201. Tel: 603-358-2717. Fax: 603-358-2745. p. 1453

Objartel, Donna, Acq, Cat, Warren County Public Library District, 62 Public Sq, Monmouth, IL, 61462. Tel: 309-734-3166. Fax: 309-734-5955. p. 675

Obremski, Tracy, Circ Asst, Springfield Town Library, 43 Main St, Springfield, VT, 05156. Tel: 802-885-3108. Fax: 802-885-4906. p. 2436

Obrig, Kathe, Assoc Dir, Coll & Acces Serv, George Washington University, Paul Himmelfarb Health Sciences Library, 2300 I St NW, Washington, DC, 20037. Tel: 202-994-8906. Fax: 202-994-4343. p. 402

Obringer, David, Archivist & Spec Coll Librn, Edinboro University of Pennsylvania, 200 Tartan Ave, Edinboro, PA, 16444. Tel: 814-732-2779. Fax: 814-732-2883. p. 2053

OBrion, Catherine G, Archivist, Librn, Virginia State Law Library, Supreme Court Bldg, 2nd Flr, 100 N Ninth St, Richmond, VA, 23219-2335. Tel: 804-786-2075. Fax: 804-786-4542. p. 2493

Obrist, Krist, YA Serv, Monmouth Public Library, 168 S Ecols St, Monmouth, OR, 97361. Tel: 503-838-1932. Fax: 503-838-3899. p. 2006

Obst, Julie, E-Librn, Central Piedmont Community College Library, 1201 Elizabeth Ave, Charlotte, NC, 28235. Tel: 704-330-6498. Fax: 704-330-6887. p. 1781

Obst, Patricia, Ref Mgr, Summit Free Public Library, 75 Maple St, Summit, NJ, 07901-9984. Tel: 908-273-0350. Fax: 908-273-0031. p. 1532

Obuchan, Peter G, Dir, Libr Serv, Newbury College Library, 150 Fisher Ave, Brookline, MA, 02445-5796. Tel: 617-730-7070. Fax: 617-730-7239. p. 1071

Ocadiz, Jose, Br Mgr, San Diego County Library, Lincoln Acres, 2725 Granger Ave, National City, CA, 91950-0168. Tel: 619-475-9880. Fax: 619-475-4382. p. 234

Ocasek, Mary, Ref Librn, Benedictine University Library, 5700 College Rd, Lisle, IL, 60532-0900. Tel: 630-829-6050. Fax: 630-960-9451. p. 666

Ochoa, Rose, Acq, City University of New York, 365 Fifth Ave, New York, NY, 10016-4309. Tel: 212-817-7040. Fax: 212-817-2982. p. 1673

Ochs, Carey, Sr Librn, California Department of Corrections Library System, Ironwood State Prison Library Services-Central Library, 19005 Wiley's Well Rd, Blythe, CA, 92225. Tel: 760-921-3000, Ext 5623. Fax: 760-921-7526. p. 221

Ochs, Elna, Asst Librn, Greenup Township Public Library, 101 N Franklin St, Greenup, IL, 62428. Tel: 217-923-3616. Fax: 217-923-3616. p. 652

Ochs, Mary, Dir, Cornell University Library, Albert R Mann Library, Mann Library, Tower Rd, Ithaca, NY, 14853-4301. Tel: 607-255-5406. Fax: 607-255-0850. p. 1642

Ocken, Jillian, Commun Relations Coordr, Ames Public Library, 515 Douglas Ave, Ames, IA, 50010. Tel: 515-239-5634. Fax: 515-233-9001. p. 792

Ockochinski, Mary Anne, Librn, Parkland Regional Library, Springside Branch, 19 Main St, Springside, SK, S0A 3V0, CANADA. Tel: 306-792-4743. p. 2932

Ocon, Benjamin, City Librn, San Mateo Public Library, 1100 Park Ave, San Mateo, CA, 94403-7108. Tel: 650-522-7808. Fax: 650-522-7801. p. 256

Octobre, Marie, Librn, College of New Rochelle, Brooklyn Campus, 1368 Fulton St, Brooklyn, NY, 11216. Tel: 718-638-2500. Fax: 914-654-5080. p. 1666

Oda, James C, Dir, Flesh Public Library, 124 W Greene St, Piqua, OH, 45356-2399. Tel: 937-773-6753. Fax: 937-773-5981. p. 1930

Odahouski, Kris, Ch, Gadsden County Public Library, 7325 Pat Thomas Pkwy, Quincy, FL, 32351. Tel: 850-627-7106. Fax: 850-627-7775. p. 485

Odam, Teresa, Ser, Brigham Young University, Howard W Hunter Law Library, 256 JRCB, Provo, UT, 84602-8000. Tel: 801-422-3593. Fax: 801-422-0404. p. 2411

Ode, Dave, Actg Dir, South Dakota Department of Game, Fish & Parks Division of Wildlife, 523 E Capitol, Pierre, SD, 57501. Tel: 605-773-4345. Fax: 605-773-6245. p. 2216

Odeh, Hussein, Supv Librn, Jersey City Free Public Library, 472 Jersey Ave, Jersey City, NJ, 07302-3499. Tel: 201-547-4304. Fax: 201-946-7379. p. 1492

Odell, Paula, Adult Serv, Woodward Public Library, 1500 Main St, Woodward, OK, 73801. Tel: 580-254-8544, 580-254-8545. Fax: 580-254-8546. p. 1986

Odelvak, Janine, Pub Serv, Saint Clair County Community College, 323 Erie St, Port Huron, MI, 48060. Tel: 810-984-3881, 810-989-5640. Fax: 810-984-2852. p. 1219

Odems, Vanessa, Managing Librn, Milling, Benson, Woodward LLP, 909 Poydras St, Ste 2300, New Orleans, LA, 70112-1017. Tel: 504-569-7000, 504-569-7308. Fax: 504-569-7001. p. 961

Oden, Fred A, Pres, Fulton County Historical Society, Inc, 37 E 375 N, Rochester, IN, 46975-8384. Tel: 574-223-4436. Fax: 574-224-4436. p. 776

Odenwald, Hagen, Law Librn, Faegre & Benson, LLP, 2200 Wells Fargo Ctr, 90 South Seventh St, Minneapolis, MN, 55402-3901. Tel: 612-766-7000. Fax: 612-766-1600. p. 1259

Odewahn, Susan, Acq, Greenebaum, Doll & McDonald, 3500 National City Tower, Louisville, KY, 40202-3140. Tel: 502-589-4200. Fax: 502-587-3695. p. 923

Odhner, Carroll C, Dir, Bryn Athyn College, 2925 College Dr, Bryn Athyn, PA, 19009. Tel: 267-502-2547. Fax: 267-502-2637. p. 2038

Odland, Jake, Br Mgr, Olivia Public Library, 405 S Tenth St, Olivia, MN, 56277-1287. Tel: 320-523-1738. Fax: 320-523-1570. p. 1269

Odland, Jake, Head Librn, Renville City Library, 221 N Main, Renville, MN, 56284. Tel: 320-329-8193. p. 1272

Odo, Franklin, Div Chief, Library of Congress, Asian Division, Jefferson Bldg, Rm 149, Washington, DC, 20540-4810. Tel: 202-707-5919. Fax: 202-707-1724. p. 406

Odofin, Julie, Mgr, Policy & Strategic Planning, Oakland Public Library, 125 14th St, Oakland, CA, 94612. Tel: 510-238-6610. Fax: 510-238-2232. p. 197

Odom, Amee Huneycutt, Dir, Ref Serv, Wingate University, PO Box 219, Wingate, NC, 28174-1202. Tel: 704-233-8089. Fax: 704-233-8254. p. 1832

Odom, Dennis, Head, Acq, Texas Christian University, 2913 Lowden St, TCU Box 298400, Fort Worth, TX, 76129. Tel: 817-257-7106. Fax: 817-257-7282. p. 2323

Odom, Ed, Adult Ref, ILL, Mesquite Public Library, 300 W Grubb Dr, Mesquite, TX, 75149. Tel: 972-216-6220. Fax: 972-216-6740. p. 2362

Odom, Karen, Dir, Houston County Public Library System, 1201 Washington Ave, Perry, GA, 31069. Tel: 478-987-3050. Fax: 478-987-4572. p. 547

Odom, Karen, Head Librn, Houston County Public Library System, Centerville Branch, 310 E Church St, Centerville, GA, 31028. Tel: 478-953-4500. Fax: 478-953-7850. p. 547

Odom, Lauren, Ref Librn, Skadden, Arps, Slate, Meagher & Flom LLP Library, 155 N Wacker Dr, Chicago, IL, 60606. Tel: 312-407-0941. Fax: 312-407-0411. p. 624

Odom, Mac, Supvry Librn, United States Army, Bldg 465, Rm 113, White Sands Missile Range, NM, 88002-5039. Tel: 505-678-1556, 575-678-5820. Fax: 575-678-2270. p. 1566

Odom, Melanie, Ref Serv, Venice Public Library, 300 S Nokomis Ave, Venice, FL, 34285-2416. Tel: 941-861-1330. Fax: 941-486-2345. p. 501

Odsen, Beth, Tech Serv Librn, Alaska State Court Law Library, 303 K St, Anchorage, AK, 99501. Tel: 907-264-0585. Fax: 907-264-0733. p. 44

Odum, Donella L, Dir, Sallie Logan Public Library, 1808 Walnut St, Murphysboro, IL, 62966. Tel: 618-684-3271. Fax: 618-684-2392. p. 678

Odum, Mark X, Dir, National Rehabilitation Information Center, 8400 Corporate Dr, Ste 500, Landover, MD, 20785. Tel: 301-459-5900. Fax: 301-459-4263. p. 1034

Odvarko, Yarka, Librn, Littler Mendelson Library, 650 California St, 20th Flr, San Francisco, CA, 94108-2693. Tel: 415-399-8441. Fax: 415-399-8490. p. 243

Oechukwu, Susan, Ch, Englewood Public Library, 31 Engle St, Englewood, NJ, 07631. Tel: 201-568-2215. Fax: 201-568-6895. p. 1484

Oedekoven, Diana, Dir, Northern Wyoming Community College District - Gillette College, 300 W Sinclair, Gillette, WY, 82718. Tel: 307-686-0254, Ext 1453. Fax: 307-686-0339. p. 2655

Oeffner, Barbara, Dir, Seminole Tribe of Florida, Willie Frank Library, Big Cypress Reservation, HC 61, Box 46A, Clewiston, FL, 33440. Tel: 863-902-3200, Ext 13124. Fax: 863-902-3223. p. 474

Oehlerking, Rachel, Libr Mgr, Newbrook Public Library, PO Box 208, Newbrook, AB, T0A 2P0, CANADA. Tel: 780-576-3772. Fax: 780-576-3773. p. 2712

Oehlers, Joy, Ref Serv Librn, Kapiolani Community College Library, 4303 Diamond Head Rd, Honolulu, HI, 96816. Tel: 808-734-9268. Fax: 808-734-9453. p. 564

Oehlke, Vailey, Dir, Multnomah County Library, 205 NE Russell St, Portland, OR, 97212-3796. Tel: 503-988-5403. Fax: 503-988-5441. p. 2011

Oehrle, Kamie, Dir, Brown McCarroll, LLP Library, 111 Congress Ave, Ste 1400, Austin, TX, 78701-4043. Tel: 512-472-5456. Fax: 512-479-1101. p. 2279

Oelkrug, Paul, Spec Coll Librn, University of Texas at Dallas, 800 W Campbell Rd, Richardson, TX, 75080. Tel: 972-883-2553. Fax: 972-883-4590. p. 2374

Oellien, Maxine C, Librn, Napa County Law Library, Old Courthouse, Rm 132, 825 Brown St, Napa, CA, 94559. Tel: 707-299-1201. Fax: 707-253-4229. p. 193

Oels, Phil, Assoc Dir, Multimedia Serv, National University Library, 9393 Lightwave Ave, San Diego, CA, 92123-1447. Tel: 858-541-7942. Fax: 858-541-7994. p. 232

Oelschlegel, Sandy, Dir, University of Tennessee Graduate School of Medicine, 1924 Alcoa Hwy, Box U-111, Knoxville, TN, 37920. Tel: 865-305-6615. Fax: 865-305-9527. p. 2243

Oerichbauer, Edgar, Exec Dir, Koochiching County Historical Museum Library, 214 Sixth Ave, International Falls, MN, 56649. Tel: 218-283-4316. Fax: 218-283-8243. p. 1254

Oertli, David, Talking Bk/Braille Serv Dir, Nebraska Library Commission, The Atrium, 1200 N St, Ste 120, Lincoln, NE, 68508-2023. Fax: 402-471-2083. p. 1406

Oertli, David L, Dir, Nebraska Library Commission, 1200 N St, Ste 120, Lincoln, NE, 68508-2023. Tel: 402-471-4038. Fax: 402-471-2083. p. 1406

Oertli, Sandra, Librn, Montana Bible College Library, 20 Cornerstone Way, Bozeman, MT, 59718. Tel: 406-556-7215. Fax: 406-586-3585. p. 1375

Oesterle, Roger, Dir, Stamford Village Library, 117 Main St, Stamford, NY, 12167. Tel: 607-652-5001. Fax: 607-652-5001. p. 1747

Oestreich, Rebecca, Educ Curator, Elkhart County Historical Society, Inc, 304 W Vistula, Bristol, IN, 46507. Tel: 574-848-4322. Fax: 574-848-5703. p. 729

Oetken, Lois, Dir, Maranatha Baptist Bible College, 745 W Main St, Watertown, WI, 53094. Tel: 920-206-2375. Fax: 920-261-9109. p. 2644

Offenbecker, Linda, Dir, Bellaire Public Library, 111 S Bridge St, Bellaire, MI, 49615-9566. Tel: 231-533-8814. Fax: 231-533-5064. p. 1156

Offensend, David G, Chief Operating Officer, The New York Public Library - Astor, Lenox & Tilden Foundations, 476 Fifth Ave, (@ 42nd St), New York, NY, 10018-2788. Tel: 212-930-0600. Fax: 212-592-7440. p. 1690

Offerdahl, John, Ref Librn, Atlanta-Fulton Public Library System, Dr Robert E Fulton Regional at Ocee, 5090 Abbotts Bridge Rd, Alpharetta, GA, 30005-4601. Tel: 770-360-8897. Fax: 770-360-8892. p. 512

Offerman, Lauren, Asst Dir, Three Rivers Public Library District, 25207 W Channon Dr, Channahon, IL, 60410-5028. Tel: 815-467-6200. Fax: 815-467-4012. p. 603

Offineer, Linda, Pub Serv, Westminster College, Reeves Memorial Library, 501 Westminster Ave, Fulton, MO, 65251-1299. Tel: 573-592-5373. Fax: 573-642-6356. p. 1328

Offiong, Julia, Librn, The George Meany Memorial Archives Library, National Labor College, 10000 New Hampshire Ave, Silver Spring, MD, 20903. Tel: 301-431-5446. Fax: 301-628-0161. p. 1041

Offord, Jerome, Univ Librn, Lincoln University of Missouri, 712 Lee Dr, Jefferson City, MO, 65101. Tel: 573-681-5502. Fax: 573-681-5511. p. 1334

Offutt, Edie, Adult Serv, Bolivar-Harpers Ferry Public Library, 151 Polk St, Harpers Ferry, WV, 25425. Tel: 304-535-2301. Fax: 304-535-2301. p. 2560

Ofiara, David, Media Spec, Adirondack Community College Library, Scoville Learning Center, 640 Bay Rd, Queensbury, NY, 12804. Tel: 518-743-2200, Ext 2484. Fax: 518-745-1442. p. 1725

Oftelie, Jessica, Librn, Ironworld Discovery Center, 801 SW Hwy 169, Ste 1, Chisholm, MN, 55719. Tel: 218-254-1222, 218-254-7959. Fax: 218-254-7971. p. 1245

Ogale, Aruna, Exec Dir, Bereaved Families of Ontario Toronto Library, 80 Woodlawn Ave, Toronto, ON, M4T 1C1, CANADA. Tel: 416-440-0290. Fax: 416-440-0304. p. 2850

Ogbaa, Clara, Dr, Dir, Libr Serv, Gateway Community College, 20 Church St, New Haven, CT, 06510. Tel: 203-285-2058. Fax: 203-285-2055. p. 355

Ogburn, Joyce, Dean, University of Utah, Marriott Library, 295 S 1500 East, Salt Lake City, UT, 84112-0860. Tel: 801-581-8558. Fax: 801-585-7185. p. 2415

Ogden, Dorothy, Librn, Idaho School for the Deaf & Blind Library, 1450 Main St, Gooding, ID, 83330. Tel: 208-934-8751. Fax: 208-934-8352. p. 574

Ogden, James, III, Historian, National Park Service, 3370 Lafayette Rd, Fort Oglethorpe, GA, 30742. Tel: 706-866-9241. p. 533

Ogden, Kathy, ILL, Ref Serv, Seminole Community Library, 9200 113th St N, Seminole, FL, 33772. Tel: 727-394-6905. Fax: 727-398-3113. p. 491

Ogden, Kym, Tech Serv, La Porte County Public Library, 904 Indiana Ave, La Porte, IN, 46350-3435. Tel: 219-362-6156. Fax: 219-362-6158. p. 758

Ogden, Laura, ILL, Louisiana Tech University, Everett St at The Columns, Ruston, LA, 71272. Tel: 318-257-3555. Fax: 318-257-2579. p. 966

Ogden, Lennie, Evening Ref Librn, Southern New Hampshire University, 2500 N River Rd, Manchester, NH, 03106-1045. Tel: 603-645-9605. Fax: 603-645-9685. p. 1456

Ogden, Michelle, Br Mgr, Frankfort Community Public Library, Mulberry Community Library, 615 E Jackson St, Mulberry, IN, 46058-9539. Tel: 765-296-2604. Fax: 765-296-2604. p. 743

Ogden, Patti, Res Librn, University of Notre Dame, 2345 Biolchini Hall of Law, Notre Dame, IN, 46556-4640. Tel: 574-631-5996. Fax: 574-631-6371. p. 771

Ogden, Sherelyn, Conserv Librn, Minnesota Historical Society Library, 345 Kellogg Blvd W, Saint Paul, MN, 55102-1906. Tel: 651-259-3380. Fax: 651-297-7436. p. 1280

Ogea, Stacey, Librn, Public Libraries of Saginaw, Archer A Claytor Library, 1410 N 12th St, Saginaw, MI, 48601. Tel: 989-753-5591. Fax: 989-753-6850. p. 1224

Ogea, Stacey, Librn, Public Libraries of Saginaw, Ruth Brady Wickes Library, 1713 Hess, Saginaw, MI, 48601. Tel: 989-752-3821. Fax: 989-752-8685. p. 1224

Ogg, Mary-Jane, Dir, Harrison Community Library, 105 E Main St, Harrison, MI, 48625. Tel: 989-539-6711. Fax: 989-539-6301. p. 1188

Ogilvie, Connie, Ref Librn, Chemung County Library District, 101 E Church St, Elmira, NY, 14901-2799. Tel: 607-733-9173. Fax: 607-733-9176. p. 1619

Ogilvie, Heather, Br Supvr, Marion County Public Library System, Freedom Public Library, 5870 SW 95 St, Ocala, FL, 34476. Tel: 352-438-2580. Fax: 352-438-2582. p. 474

Ogilvie, Marilyn, Curator, University of Oklahoma, History of Science Collections, Rm 521 NW, Norman, OK, 73019. Tel: 405-325-2741. p. 1971

Ogle, Christophor M, Dean, VPres, Ripon College, 300 Seward St, Ripon, WI, 54971. Tel: 920-748-8175. Fax: 920-748-7243. p. 2634

Ogle, Joyce, Coordr, Methodist Hospital of Southern California, 300 W Huntington Dr, Arcadia, CA, 91007. Tel: 626-898-8000. Fax: 626-574-3712. p. 122

Oglesay, Malakia, Mgr, Info Sys, Asbury Park Public Library, 500 First Ave, Asbury Park, NJ, 07712. Tel: 732-774-4221. Fax: 732-988-6101. p. 1469

Oglesbee, Victoria, In Charge, Multnomah County Library, Holgate, 7905 SE Holgate Blvd, Portland, OR, 97206-3367. Tel: 503-988-5389. Fax: 503-988-5194. p. 2012

Ogoby, Cathryn, Asst Librn, Clive Public Library, 5115 50th St, Clive, AB, T0C 0Y0, CANADA. Tel: 403-784-3131. Fax: 403-784-3131. p. 2695

Ogora, Jane, Access Serv, Washington Adventist University, 7600 Flower Ave, Takoma Park, MD, 20912-7796. Tel: 301-891-4217. Fax: 301-891-4204. p. 1043

Ogrodowski, Jennifer, Ch, Saratoga Springs Public Library, 49 Henry St, Saratoga Springs, NY, 12866. Tel: 518-584-7860. Fax: 518-584-7866. p. 1738

Oguz, Fatih, Dr, Asst Prof, Valdosta State University, Odum Library - MLIS, 1500 N Patterson St, Valdosta, GA, 31698-0144. Tel: 229-245-3715. Fax: 229-259-5055. p. 2964

Ogyiri, Daniel, Adult Serv, New Rochelle Public Library, One Library Plaza, New Rochelle, NY, 10801. Tel: 914-632-7878, Ext 1000. Fax: 914-632-0262. p. 1666

Oh, Anna, Circ & Pub Serv Tech, University of Toronto Libraries, Faculty of Information Inforum, 140 Saint George St, 4th Flr, Toronto, ON, M5S 3G6, CANADA. Tel: 416-978-5767. Fax: 416-978-5769. p. 2866

Oh, Theresa, Doc, Battelle Energy Alliance, LLC, 1776 Science Center Dr, MS 2300, Idaho Falls, ID, 83415-2300. Tel: 208-526-1185. Fax: 208-526-0211. p. 576

Oh, Timothy, Librn, Mercy Hospital & Medical Center, 2525 S Michigan Ave, Chicago, IL, 60616-2477. Tel: 312-567-2363. Fax: 312-567-7086. p. 618

Ohannes, Elliott, Dir, Trinity Lutheran College, 2802 Wetmore Ave, Everett, WA, 98201. Tel: 425-392-0400, Ext 241. Fax: 425-392-0404. p. 2515

Ohland, Mary Jane, Dir, Winthrop Public Library, 305 N Main St, Winthrop, MN, 55396-9998. Tel: 507-647-5308. Fax: 507-647-3200. p. 1290

Ohler, Lila Angie, Acq, University of Maryland Libraries, Theodore R McKeldin Library, College Park, MD, 20742-7011. Tel: 301-405-9306. Fax: 301-314-9408. p. 1025

Ohles, Janet, Assoc Dir, Western Connecticut State University, 181 White St, Danbury, CT, 06810. Tel: 203-837-9122. Fax: 203-837-9108. p. 335

Ohlman, Nick, Archivist, Museum of Transportation, 3015 Barrett Station Rd, Saint Louis, MO, 63122. Tel: 314-615-8668, 314-965-8214. Fax: 314-965-0242. p. 1357

Ohlson-Martin, Terry, Co-Dir, New Hampshire Family Voices Library, Dept Health & Human Servs, Spec Med Servs, Thayer Bldg, 129 Pleasant St, Concord, NH, 03301. Tel: 603-271-4525. Fax: 603-271-4902. p. 1442

Ohm, Rebecca, Ref/Govt Doc Librn, Williams College, 55 Sawyer Library Dr, Williamstown, MA, 01267. Tel: 413-597-4321. Fax: 413-597-4106. p. 1141

Ohman, Elizabeth, Librn, Hogan & Hartson LLP Law Library, 875 Third Ave, 25th Flr, New York, NY, 10022. Tel: 212-918-3000, 212-918-6117. Fax: 212-918-3100. p. 1681

Ohrenberg, Laura, Adminr, The Ninety-Nines, Inc, 4300 Amelia Earhart Rd, Oklahoma City, OK, 73159-0040. Tel: 405-685-7969. Fax: 405-685-7985. p. 1973

Ohta, Hitoshi, Br Mgr, Los Angeles Public Library System, Little Tokyo, 203 S Los Angeles St, Los Angeles, CA, 90012. Tel: 213-612-0525. Fax: 213-612-0424. p. 173

Ohye, Judy S, Acq, Pasadena City College Library, 1570 E Colorado Blvd, Pasadena, CA, 91106-2003. Tel: 626-585-7329. Fax: 626-585-7913. p. 206

Oistad, Kay, Head, Ref, Res & Instruction, Florida Gulf Coast University Library, 10501 FGCU Blvd S, Fort Myers, FL, 33965-6501. Tel: 239-590-7604. p. 444

Oistad, Kay, Br Mgr, Collier County Public Library, Naples Regional Library, 650 Central Ave, Naples, FL, 34102. Tel: 239-262-4130. Fax: 239-649-1293. p. 471

Ojezua, Teresa I, Dir, Philander Smith College, 900 Daisy Bates Dr, Little Rock, AR, 72202. Tel: 501-370-5262. Fax: 501-370-5307. p. 107

Ojomo, Patience A, Br Mgr, Gary Public Library, Carter G Woodson Branch, 501 S Lake St, Gary, IN, 46403-2408. Tel: 219-938-3941. Fax: 219-938-8759. p. 745

Oka, Christine K, Libr Instruction, Northeastern University Libraries, Snell Library, 360 Huntington Ave, Boston, MA, 02115. Tel: 617-373-3316. p. 1065

Oka, Susan, Acq Librn, Academy of Motion Picture Arts & Sciences, 333 S La Cienega Blvd, Beverly Hills, CA, 90211. Tel: 310-247-3000, Ext 2216. Fax: 310-657-5193. p. 128

Okamura, Jill, Instruction Librn, Fullerton College, 321 E Chapman Ave, Fullerton, CA, 92832-2095. Tel: 714-992-7380. Fax: 714-992-9961. p. 153

Okaro, Anthony, Librn, Williams & Anderson, 111 Center, 22nd Flr, Little Rock, AR, 72201. Tel: 501-372-0800. Fax: 501-372-6453. p. 108

Okazaki, Gail, Head Librn, O'Melveny & Myers LLP, 400 S Hope St, Los Angeles, CA, 90071-2899. Tel: 213-430-6000. Fax: 213-430-6407. p. 176

Okazaki, Kiyo, Pub Serv Mgr, Sonoma County Library, 211 E St, Santa Rosa, CA, 95404. Tel: 707-545-0831. Fax: 707-575-0437. p. 267

OKeefe, Elizabeth, Dir of Coll, Dir, Info Syst, The Morgan Library, 225 Madison Ave, New York, NY, 10016. Tel: 212-685-0008. p. 1687

OKeefe, Laura, Head, Cat & Spec Coll, The New York Society Library, 53 E 79th St, New York, NY, 10075. Tel: 212-288-6900, Ext 240. Fax: 212-288-6870. p. 1694

Okezie, Amalaha, Archives Librn, Atlanta-Fulton Public Library System, Auburn Avenue Research Library on African-American Culture & History, 101 Auburn Ave NE, Atlanta, GA, 30303. Tel: 404-730-4001, Ext 199. Fax: 404-730-5879. p. 511

Oki, Laura, Asst Dir, Elko-Lander-Eureka County Library System, 720 Court St, Elko, NV, 89801. Tel: 775-738-3066. Fax: 775-738-8262. p. 1426

Okin, Avery Eli, Exec Dir, Brooklyn Bar Association Foundation Inc Library, 123 Remsen St, 2nd flr, Brooklyn, NY, 11201-4212. Tel: 718-624-0868. Fax: 718-797-1713. p. 1589

Okinaka, Massato, Conservator, Drew University Library, 36 Madison Ave, Madison, NJ, 07940. Tel: 973-408-3476. Fax: 973-408-3770. p. 1497

Okner, Sarah, Youth Serv Librn, Three Rivers Public Library District, 25207 W Channon Dr, Channahon, IL, 60410-5028. Tel: 815-467-6200. Fax: 815-467-4012. p. 603

Okobi, Elsie, Dr, Assoc Prof, Southern Connecticut State University, 501 Crescent St, New Haven, CT, 06515. Tel: 203-392-5709. Fax: 203-392-5780. p. 2963

Okolichany, Hedy, Circ, Albert Carlton-Cashiers Community Library, 249 Frank Allen Rd, Cashiers, NC, 28717-9561. Tel: 828-743-0215. Fax: 828-743-1638. p. 1780

Okonska, Maria, Head, Cat, Brooklyn Law School Library, 250 Joralemon St, Brooklyn, NY, 11201. Tel: 718-780-7977. Fax: 718-780-0369. p. 1590

Okoro, Daniel, Librn, Hocking Correctional Facility Library, 16759 Snake Hollow Rd, Nelsonville, OH, 45764-9658. Tel: 740-753-1917, Ext 213. Fax: 740-753-4277. p. 1920

Okpara, Ibiba, Br Mgr, Nashville Public Library, Mary & Charles W Pruitt Branch, 117 Charles E Davis Blvd, Nashville, TN, 37210-2745. Tel: 615-862-5985. Fax: 615-862-6745. p. 2258

Okrunlicova, Nicolette, Libr Asst, The Frontenac Law Association Library, Frontenac County Court House, Five Court St, Kingston, ON, K7L 2N4, CANADA. Tel: 613-542-0034. Fax: 613-531-9764. p. 2813

Okuhara, Keiko, Syst Librn, University of Hawaii, 2525 Dole St, Honolulu, HI, 96822-2328. Tel: 808-956-5581, 808-956-7583. Fax: 808-956-4615. p. 565

Okwei, Dorothea, In Charge, Ann Klein Forensic Center, Stuyvesant Ave, West Trenton, NJ, 08628. Tel: 609-633-0884. Fax: 609-633-2817. p. 1542

Ola, Alicia, Mgr, Brooklyn Public Library, Arlington, 203 Arlington Ave, Brooklyn, NY, 11207. Tel: 718-277-6105. Fax: 718-277-6177. p. 1590

Olafsson, Joey, Br Head, Winnipeg Public Library, West End, 999 Sargent Ave, Winnipeg, MB, R3E 3K6, CANADA. Tel: 204-986-4677. Fax: 204-986-7129. p. 2760

Olaworetan, Festus, Librn, Cook County Law Library, Maywood Branch, 1500 Maybrook Dr, Maywood, IL, 60153. Tel: 708-865-6020. Fax: 708-865-4938. p. 612

Olawski, Suzanne, Neighborhood Serv Mgr, Berkeley Public Library, 2090 Kittredge St, Berkeley, CA, 94704. Tel: 510-981-6100. Fax: 510-981-6111. p. 126

Olayiwola, Rekiat, Br Mgr, Cleveland Public Library, Fleet, 7224 Broadway Ave, Cleveland, OH, 44105. Tel: 216-623-6962. Fax: 216-623-6964. p. 1878

Olberding, Angie, Librn, Stuart Township Library, Second & Main St, Stuart, NE, 68780. Tel: 402-924-3242. Fax: 402-924-3242. p. 1420

Olczak, Lola, In Charge, EMS Technologies Canada, Ltd Library, 21025 Trans-Canada Hwy, Sainte-Anne-de-Bellevue, QC, H9X 3R2, CANADA. Tel: 514-457-2150, Ext 3259. Fax: 514-425-3048. p. 2909

Oldach, Linda R, Asst Dean, Mount Wachusett Community College Library, 444 Green St, Gardner, MA, 01440. Tel: 978-630-9126. Fax: 978-630-9556. p. 1090

Oldal, Maria, Head, Cat & Database Mgt, The Morgan Library, 225 Madison Ave, New York, NY, 10016. Tel: 212-685-0008. p. 1687

Oldenburg, Laura, Ch, Steger-South Chicago Heights Public Library District, 54 E 31st St, Steger, IL, 60475. Tel: 708-755-5040. Fax: 708-755-2504. p. 707

Olderr, Steven, Librn, Institute for Clinical Social Work Library, 200 N Michigan Ave, Ste 407, Chicago, IL, 60601. Tel: 312-726-8480. Fax: 312-726-7216. p. 615

Oldfield, Robert, Librn, California Department of Corrections Library System, Valley State Prison for Women, 21633 Ave 24, Chowchilla, CA, 93610. Tel: 559-665-6100, Ext 6066. p. 222

Oldham, Barbara, Ref Librn, Spokane Falls Community College, 3410 Ft George Wright Dr, MS 3020, Spokane, WA, 99224-5288. Tel: 509-533-3159. Fax: 509-533-3144. p. 2537

Oldham, Barbara, Librn, Wenatchee Valley College, 1300 Fifth St, Wenatchee, WA, 98801. Tel: 509-682-6714. Fax: 509-682-6711. p. 2549

Oldham, Bonnie, Coordr, Info Literacy, University of Scranton, Monroe & Linden, Scranton, PA, 18510-4634. Tel: 570-941-4000, 570-941-4008. Fax: 570-941-7817. p. 2138

Oldham, Crystal, Exec Dir, Hardwood Forest Foundation Library, 6830 Raleigh LaGrange Rd, Memphis, TN, 38134. Tel: 901-507-0312. Fax: 901-382-6419. p. 2248

Oldham, Doug, Librn, Mono County Free Library, 400 Sierra Park Blvd, Mammoth Lakes, CA, 93546. Tel: 760-934-8670. Fax: 760-934-6268. p. 182

Oldham, Linda, Ch, Greenwood Public Library, 310 S Meridian St, Greenwood, IN, 46143-3135. Tel: 317-883-4248. Fax: 317-881-1963. p. 747

Oldham, Lorraine, Librn, Tri-Valley Free Public Library, 633 E Main St, Hegins, PA, 17938-9303. Tel: 570-682-8922. Fax: 570-682-8922. p. 2068

Oldham, Nancy, Librn, Black River Falls Public Library, Childrens Room, 222 Fillmore St, Black River Falls, WI, 54615. Tel: 715-284-4112. Fax: 715-284-5369. p. 2582

Oldham, Nancy, Youth Serv, Black River Falls Public Library, 222 Fillmore St, Black River Falls, WI, 54615. Tel: 715-284-4112. Fax: 715-284-5369. p. 2582

Oldham, Peggy, Librn, Somervell County Library, 108 Allen Dr, Glen Rose, TX, 76043. Tel: 254-897-4582. Fax: 254-897-9882. p. 2328

Oldham, Vicki, Circ, Nampa Public Library, 101 11th Ave S, Nampa, ID, 83651. Tel: 208-468-5812. Fax: 208-318-0530. p. 580

Oldre, Bonnie K, Per, Ref, Century Public Library, 3300 N Century Ave, White Bear Lake, MN, 55110. Tel: 651-779-3968. Fax: 651-779-3963. p. 1288

Olds, Barbara, Head Acq/ILL Serv, Stephen F Austin State University, 1936 North St, Nacogdoches, TX, 75962. Tel: 936-468-1720. Fax: 936-468-7610. p. 2364

Olds, Carole, Dir of Libr, Pikes Peak Community College Library, 5675 S Academy Blvd, C7, Colorado Springs, CO, 80906-5498. Tel: 719-502-3249. p. 296

Olds, Kathleen, Assoc Dir, Northwood University, 2600 N Military Trail, West Palm Beach, FL, 33409-2911. Tel: 561-681-7998. Fax: 561-697-3138. p. 502

Olecheck, Sharon, Info Spec, International Foundation of Employee Benefit Plans, 18700 W Bluemound Rd, Brookfield, WI, 53045-2936. Tel: 262-786-6710, Ext 5. Fax: 262-786-8780. p. 2583

Oleisky, Marcia, Librn, Beth-El Synagogue, 5224 W 26th St, Saint Louis Park, MN, 55416. Tel: 952-920-3512. Fax: 952-920-8755. p. 1277

Olejnikova, Lucie, Electronic Serv Librn, Ref Librn, Pace University, 78 N Broadway, White Plains, NY, 10603. Tel: 914-422-4339. Fax: 914-422-4139. p. 1769

Olenik, Mose, Adminr, Mariposa Museum Library, 26 Main St, Peterborough, NH, 03458. Tel: 603-924-4555. Fax: 603-924-3212. p. 1461

Oles, Shirley, Libr Tech, VA Greater Los Angeles Health Care Center Sepulveda Campus, Bldg 22, 16111 Plummer St, Sepulveda, CA, 91343. Tel: 818-891-7711, Ext 9253. Fax: 818-895-9553. p. 268

Olesh, Elizabeth, Mgr, Outreach Serv, Nassau Library System, 900 Jerusalem Ave, Uniondale, NY, 11553-3039. Tel: 516-292-8920, Ext 237. Fax: 516-565-0950. p. 1758

Oleston, Jason, Dir, Libr Serv, Department of Veterans Affairs, 1660 S Columbian Way, Seattle, WA, 98108-1597. Tel: 206-764-2065. Fax: 206-764-2816. p. 2527

Oleston, Jason M, Chief, Libr Serv, VA Puget Sound Health Care System, American Lake Div, 9600 Veterans Dr SW, Bldg 71, Tacoma, WA, 98493-5000. Tel: 253-583-1510. Fax: 253-589-4029. p. 2541

Oleszkiewicz, Wanda, Head Librn, Husky Energy Corporate Library, 707 Eighth Ave SW, 19 Flr, Calgary, AB, T2P 3G7, CANADA. Tel: 403-298-6111. Fax: 403-298-6263. p. 2692

Olewine, Linda, Cat, University of Texas, M D Anderson Cancer Center Research Medical Library, 1400 Pressler St, Houston, TX, 77030-3722. Tel: 713-745-3086. Fax: 713-563-3650. p. 2344

Olewnik, Lauren, Instruction/Ref Serv, Castleton State College, 178 Alumni Dr, Castleton, VT, 05735. Tel: 802-468-1256. Fax: 802-468-1475. p. 2421

Olga, Yerbeek, Ref, Salve Regina University, 100 Ochre Point Ave, Newport, RI, 02840-4192. Tel: 401-341-2330. Fax: 401-341-2951. p. 2169

Olguin, Debbie, Youth Serv, Franklin Public Library, 9151 W Loomis Rd, Franklin, WI, 53132. Tel: 414-425-8214. Fax: 414-425-9498. p. 2593

Oligea, Yvonne, Dir, Brown County Public Library, Cordry Sweetwater, 8451 Nineveh Rd, Nineveh, IN, 46164. Tel: 812-988-2850. p. 767

Oliger, Yvonne C, Dir, Brown County Public Library, 205 Locust Lane, Nashville, IN, 47448. Tel: 812-988-1230. Fax: 812-988-8119. p. 767

Oligny, Cynthia, Dir, Middlefield Public Library, 188 Skyline Trail, Middlefield, MA, 01243. Tel: 413-623-6421. p. 1105

Olijnyk, Nicholas, Ref Librn, North Merrick Public Library, 1691 Meadowbrook Rd, North Merrick, NY, 11566. Tel: 516-378-7474. Fax: 516-378-0876. p. 1706

Olin, Billie, Sister, Archivist, Dominican Sisters-Congregation of The Holy Name Archives, 1520 Grand Ave, San Rafael, CA, 94901-2236. Tel: 415-257-4947. Fax: 415-453-8367. p. 256

Oling, Rebecca, Head, Instrul Serv, State University of New York, 735 Anderson Hill Rd, Purchase, NY, 10577-1400. Tel: 914-251-6417. Fax: 914-251-6437. p. 1724

Oliphant, Jo Ann, Head, Tech Serv, Victoria Public Library, 302 N Main, Victoria, TX, 77901-6592. Tel: 361-485-3304. Fax: 361-485-3295. p. 2395

Oliva, Victor, Coordr of Ref Serv, Adelphi University Libraries, One South Ave, Garden City, NY, 11530. Tel: 516-877-3587. Fax: 516-877-3592. p. 1625

Olivari, Karen, Teen Serv Librn, Bernards Township Library, 32 S Maple Ave, Basking Ridge, NJ, 07920-1216. Tel: 908-204-3031. Fax: 908-766-1580. p. 1470

Olivas, Antonia, Educ Librn, California State University, 333 S Twin Oaks Valley Rd, San Marcos, CA, 92096-0001. Tel: 760-750-4340. Fax: 760-750-3287. p. 254

Olive, Fred J, III, Head, User Serv/Circ, University of Alabama at Birmingham, Mervyn H Sterne Library, 917 13th St S, Birmingham, AL, 35205. Tel: 205-934-6364. p. 10

Olive, Joel D, Pub Serv, Williams Baptist College, 91 W Fulbright, Walnut Ridge, AR, 72476. Tel: 870-759-4139. p. 116

Oliveira, Michael, Archivist, ONE Institute & Archives, 909 W Adams Blvd, Los Angeles, CA, 90007. Tel: 213-741-0094. p. 176

Oliveira, Sue, Librn, Webb City Public Library, 101 S Liberty, Webb City, MO, 64870. Tel: 417-673-4326. Fax: 417-673-5703. p. 1372

Oliveira, Tony, Mgr, Knolls Atomic Power Laboratory Inc, Library, 35 Front St, Schenectady, NY, 12305. Tel: 518-395-4918. Fax: 518-395-7761. p. 1740

Oliver, Amie, Libr Assoc, Baylor University Libraries, Texas Collection, 1429 S Fifth St, Waco, TX, 76706. Tel: 254-710-1268. Fax: 254-710-1368. p. 2397

Oliver, Astrid, Libr Dir, Fort Lewis College Library, 1000 Rim Dr, Durango, CO, 81301-3999. Tel: 970-247-7250. Fax: 970-247-7149. p. 305

Oliver, Betty, Librn, Beaver City Public Library, 408 Tenth St, Beaver City, NE, 68926. Tel: 308-268-4115. p. 1393

Oliver, Dawn-Michelle, Ref, Alamance County Public Libraries, May Memorial Library, 342 S Spring St, Burlington, NC, 27215. Tel: 336-229-3588. Fax: 336-229-3592. p. 1779

Oliver, Denita, Librn, Central Alabama Community College, 1675 Cherokee Rd, Alexander City, AL, 35010. Tel: 256-215-4293. Fax: 256-234-0384. p. 3

Oliver, Diana, Librn, New Sharon Jim Ditzler Memorial Library, 37 Library Rd, New Sharon, ME, 04955. Tel: 207-779-1128. p. 993

Oliver, Doris, Asst Curator, Stevens Institute of Technology, Castle Point on Hudson, Hoboken, NJ, 07030. Tel: 201-216-5415. Fax: 201-216-8319. p. 1491

Oliver, Eileen, Dir, San Antonio College, 1001 Howard St, San Antonio, TX, 78212. Tel: 210-486-1577. p. 2381

Oliver, Felicia, Br Mgr, Calcasieu Parish Public Library, Epps Memorial, 1320 N Simmons St, Lake Charles, LA, 70601. Tel: 337-721-7090. Fax: 337-433-0033. p. 953

Oliver, Gary, Cat, Abilene Christian University, 221 Brown Library, ACU Box 29208, Abilene, TX, 79699-9208. Tel: 325-674-2344. Fax: 325-674-2202. p. 2271

Oliver, Janet, Librn, New Hanover County Public Library, 201 Chestnut St, Wilmington, NC, 28401. Tel: 910-798-6300. Fax: 910-798-6312. p. 1830

Oliver, Jeni, Br Librn, Community District Library, Morrice-Perry Township, 300 Main St, Morrice, MI, 48857. Tel: 517-625-7911. Fax: 517-625-7911. p. 1166

Oliver, Jim, Sr Librn/Youth Serv, Siouxland Libraries, 200 N Dakota Ave, Sioux Falls, SD, 57104. Tel: 605-367-8719. Fax: 605-367-4312. p. 2218

Oliver, Judy, Librn Asst, Genealogy & Local Hist, Gallatin County Public Library, 209 W Market St, Warsaw, KY, 41095. Tel: 859-567-2786. Fax: 859-567-4750. p. 936

Oliver, Kent L, Dir, Nashville Public Library, 615 Church St, Nashville, TN, 37219-2314. Tel: 615-862-5760. Fax: 615-862-5771. p. 2257

Oliver, Kurt, Mgr, Access Serv, Wentworth Institute of Technology, 550 Huntington Ave, Boston, MA, 02115-5998. Tel: 617-989-4040. Fax: 617-989-4091. p. 1068

Oliver, Lelon, Head, Circ, University of Alabama in Huntsville, 301 Sparkman Dr NW, Huntsville, AL, 35899. Tel: 256-824-6530. Fax: 256-824-6083. p. 22

Oliver, Patricia, Librn, Knolls Atomic Power Laboratory Inc, Library, 35 Front St, Schenectady, NY, 12305. Tel: 518-395-4918. Fax: 518-395-7761. p. 1740

Oliver, Peggy, Dir, Shubert Public Library, 313 Main St, Shubert, NE, 68437. Tel: 402-883-2593. p. 1419

Oliver, Phillip, Web Coordr, University of North Alabama, One Harrison Plaza, Box 5028, Florence, AL, 35632-0001. Tel: 256-765-4559. Fax: 256-765-4438. p. 17

Oliver, Rhonda, Br Mgr, Indianapolis-Marion County Public Library, Brightwood, 2435 N Sherman Dr, Indianapolis, IN, 46218-3852. Tel: 317-275-4310. p. 754

Oliver, Rick, Asst Dir, Assemblies of God Theological Seminary, 1435 N Glenstone Ave, Springfield, MO, 65802-2131. Tel: 417-268-1059. Fax: 417-268-1001. p. 1365

Oliver, Sandra, Br Mgr, Prince William Public Library System, Bull Run Regional, 8051 Ashton Ave, Manassas, VA, 20109-2892. Tel: 703-792-4500. Fax: 703-792-4520. p. 2486

Oliver, Valinda, Mgr, Cherokee Regional Library System, 305 S Duke St, LaFayette, GA, 30728-2936. Tel: 706-638-2992. Fax: 706-638-3979. p. 538

Oliver, Virginia, Librn, Grace Lutheran Church Library, 700 S 19th Ave, Show Low, AZ, 85901. Tel: 928-537-4817. p. 82

Oliver, Wendy, Librn, Akerman, Senterfitt & Eidson PA, 420 S Orange Ave, Ste 1200, Orlando, FL, 32801. Tel: 407-423-4000. Fax: 407-843-6610. p. 475

Oliver, William, Asst Librn, Grace Lutheran Church Library, 700 S 19th Ave, Show Low, AZ, 85901. Tel: 928-537-4817. p. 82

Oliver, Yvonne, Learning Res Ctr Adminr, Cove Library, 606 Main, Cove, OR, 97824. Tel: 541-568-4758, 541-568-5001. p. 1995

Olivero, Tara, Spec Coll & Archives Librn, Goucher College Library, 1021 Dulaney Valley Rd, Baltimore, MD, 21204. Tel: 410-337-6347. Fax: 410-337-6419. p. 1014

Olivier, Lyne, Bibliothecaire Responsable, Bibliothèques de Montréal, Mile End, 5434, avenue du Parc, Montreal, QC, H2V 4G7, CANADA. Tel: 514-872-6982. Fax: 514-872-0531. p. 2890

Olivier, Marie, Librn, College Stanislas Library, 780 Blvd Dollard, Outremont, QC, H2V 3G5, CANADA. Tel: 514-273-9521, Ext 244. Fax: 514-273-3409. p. 2902

Olivieri, Jody, Outreach Serv, Homer Township Public Library District, 14320 W 151st St, Homer Glen, IL, 60491. Tel: 708-301-7908. Fax: 708-301-4535. p. 657

Olivigni, Lisa, Dir, Crete Public Library, 305 E 13th St, Crete, NE, 68333. Tel: 402-826-3809. Fax: 402-826-4199. p. 1396

Oljace, Beth, Ind Rm Librn, Anderson City, Anderson, Stony Creek & Union Townships Public Library, 111 E 12th St, Anderson, IN, 46016-2701. Tel: 765-641-2442. Fax: 765-641-2197. p. 723

Olle-LaJoie, Maureen, Head, Circ, Head, Libr Syst, University of Wisconsin-River Falls, 410 S Third St, River Falls, WI, 54022. Tel: 715-425-3799. Fax: 715-425-0609. p. 2635

Olley, Lorraine H, Libr Dir, University of Saint Mary of the Lake - Mundelein Seminary, 1000 E Maple Ave, Mundelein, IL, 60060. Tel: 847-970-4820. Fax: 847-566-5229. p. 678

Olliff, Martin, Dr, Archivist, Troy University, 502 University Dr, Dothan, AL, 36304. Tel: 334-983-6556, Ext 1327. Fax: 334-983-6327. p. 15

Olliges, Rhonda, Br Mgr, Nelson County Public Library, Bloomfield Branch, 114 Fairfield Hill, Bloomfield, KY, 40008. Tel: 502-252-9129. Fax: 502-252-8255. p. 906

Ollis, Christie, Head, Media Serv, Arkansas State University, 322 University Loop West Circle, State University, AR, 72401. Tel: 870-972-3077. Fax: 870-972-3199. p. 115

Olmschenk, Monica, ILL, Saint Catherine University, Minneapolis Campus, 601 25th Ave S, Minneapolis, MN, 55454. Tel: 651-690-7782. p. 1281

Olmstead, Geri, Br Mgr, Saint Louis County Library, Thornhill Branch, 12863 Willowyck Dr, Saint Louis, MO, 63146-3771. Tel: 314-878-7730. p. 1359

Olmstead, Geri, Br Mgr, Springfield-Greene County Library District, Republic Branch, 921 N Lindsey Ave, Republic, MO, 65738-1248. Tel: 417-732-7284. Fax: 417-732-1256. p. 1368

Olmsted-Swanson, Dawn, Tech Serv Librn, Kettering University Library, 1700 W University Ave, Flint, MI, 48504-4898. Tel: 810-762-7817. Fax: 810-762-9744. p. 1180

Olney, James, Libr Dir, Northport-East Northport Public Library, 151 Laurel Ave, Northport, NY, 11768. Tel: 631-261-6930. Fax: 631-261-6718. p. 1707

Olney, Kyle, Access Serv Librn, Olivet Nazarene University, One University Ave, Bourbonnais, IL, 60914-2271. Tel: 815-928-5490. Fax: 815-939-5170. p. 596

Olsen, Amy, Librn, Lanpher Memorial Library, 141 Main St, Hyde Park, VT, 05655. Tel: 802-888-4628. p. 2426

Olsen, Barbara, Ref, Augusta County Library, 1759 Jefferson Hwy, Fishersville, VA, 22939. Tel: 540-885-3961, 540-949-6354. Fax: 540-943-5965. p. 2464

Olsen, Bev, Librn, Stavely Municipal Library, 4823 49th St, Stavely, AB, T0L 1Z0, CANADA. Tel: 403-549-2190. Fax: 403-549-2190. p. 2718

Olsen, Carolyn, Librn, Horton Free Public Library, 809 First Ave E, Horton, KS, 66439-1898. Tel: 785-486-3326. Fax: 785-486-2116. p. 872

Olsen, Colleen, Mgr, Twin Cities Biomedical Consortium, c/o Fairview University Medical Ctr, 2450 Riverside Ave, Minneapolis, MN, 55455. Tel: 612-273-6595. Fax: 612-273-2675. p. 2947

Olsen, Elaine, Cat, California State University, 9001 Stockdale Hwy, Bakersfield, CA, 93311-1022. Tel: 661-654-3257. Fax: 661-654-3238. p. 123

Olsen, Gail, Libr Tech, College of Saint Scholastica Library, 1200 Kenwood Ave, Duluth, MN, 55811-4199. Tel: 218-723-6295. Fax: 218-723-5948. p. 1247

Olsen, Jenny, Dir, Libr Serv, Cambridge Hospital-Cambridge Health Alliance, 1493 Cambridge St, Cambridge, MA, 02139. Tel: 617-665-1439. Fax: 617-665-1424. p. 1072

Olsen, Kathy, Coll Develop Mgr, Broward County Division of Libraries, 100 S Andrews Ave, Fort Lauderdale, FL, 33301. Tel: 954-357-5410. Fax: 954-357-5733. p. 440

Olsen, Kathy, Pub Serv, Haywood County Public Library, 678 S Haywood St, Waynesville, NC, 28786-4398. Tel: 828-452-5169, Ext 2507. Fax: 828-452-6746. p. 1828

Olsen, Kim, Assoc Librn, Scott County Library System, Durant Branch, 402 Sixth St, Durant, IA, 52747. Tel: 563-785-4725. Fax: 563-785-4725. p. 813

Olsen, Kolleen, Mgr, Libr Serv, University of Minnesota Medical Center - Fairview, Library, 2450 Riverside Ave, Minneapolis, MN, 55454. Tel: 612-273-6595. Fax: 612-273-2675. p. 1262

Olsen, Margaret E, Dir, Millington Arbela District Library, 8530 Depot St, Millington, MI, 48746. Tel: 989-871-2003. Fax: 989-871-5594. p. 1209

Olsen, Marilyn, Asst Librn, Emery County Library, Elmo Branch, 15 S 100 East, Elmo, UT, 84521. Tel: 435-653-2558. Fax: 435-653-2553. p. 2403

Olsen, Matthew, Dr, Head, Info Serv, Southeast Missouri State University, One University Plaza, Mail Stop 4600, Cape Girardeau, MO, 63701. Tel: 573-986-4967. Fax: 573-651-2666. p. 1322

Olsen, Michele, Libr Assoc, Western Illinois Correctional Center Library, 2500 Rt 99 S, Mount Sterling, IL, 62353. Tel: 217-773-4441, Ext 640. Fax: 217-773-3899. p. 677

Olsen, Pat, Dir, Centralia Public Library, 210 S Jefferson St, Centralia, MO, 65240. Tel: 573-682-2036. Fax: 573-682-5556. p. 1323

Olsen, Paula, Ref/Instruction Librn, Champlain College Library, 163 S Willard St, Burlington, VT, 05401. Tel: 802-865-6486. p. 2420

Olsen, Randy J, Univ Librn, Brigham Young University, Harold B Lee Library, 2060 HBLL, Provo, UT, 84602. Tel: 801-422-2927. Fax: 801-422-0466. p. 2411

Olsen, Sherrill, Mgr, Huntington Memorial Hospital, 100 W California Blvd, Pasadena, CA, 91105-3010. Tel: 626-397-5161. Fax: 626-397-2908. p. 206

Olsen, Shirley, Dir, Mackay District Library, 320 Capitol Ave, MacKay, ID, 83251. Tel: 208-588-3333. Fax: 208-588-3333. p. 578

Olsen, Sue, Acq, Cat, Hanson Public Library, 132 Maquan St, Hanson, MA, 02341. Tel: 781-293-2151. Fax: 781-293-6801. p. 1093

Olsen, Tom, Adminr, Las Vegas-Clark County Library District, City of Las Vegas Detention Facility, 3100 E Stewart Ave, Las Vegas, NV, 89101. Tel: 702-384-4887. Fax: 702-671-3971. p. 1429

Olsen, Tom, Librn, Las Vegas-Clark County Library District, Clark County Detention Facility, 330 S Casino Center Blvd, Las Vegas, NV, 89101. Tel: 702-384-4887. Fax: 702-671-3971. p. 1429

Olsen, Tom, Media Spec, University of Western States, 2900 NE 132nd Ave, Portland, OR, 97230-3099. Tel: 503-251-5755. Fax: 503-251-5759. p. 2015

Olsen-Lynch, Ellen, Info Serv Librn, Trent University, 1600 West Bank Dr, Peterborough, ON, K9J 7B8, CANADA. Tel: 705-748-1011, Ext 1324. Fax: 705-748-1126. p. 2836

Olshin, Josh, Adult Serv, Ref Serv, Stoughton Public Library, 84 Park St, Stoughton, MA, 02072-2974. Tel: 781-344-2711. Fax: 781-344-7340. p. 1129

Olson, Alexandra, Librn, Akerman, Senterfitt & Eidson PA, 420 S Orange Ave, Ste 1200, Orlando, FL, 32801. Tel: 407-423-4000. Fax: 407-843-6610. p. 475

Olson, Alice, Librn, Dr Shaw Memorial Library, 344 Pond Rd, Mount Vernon, ME, 04352. Tel: 207-293-2565. p. 992

Olson, Becky, Bus Mgr, Utah State University, 3000 Old Main Hill, Logan, UT, 84322-3000. Tel: 435-797-2631. Fax: 435-797-2880. p. 2407

Olson, Betty, Dir, De Soto Public Library, 712 S Main St, De Soto, MO, 63020. Tel: 636-586-3858. Fax: 636-586-1707. p. 1327

Olson, Beverly, Youth Serv, Sinte Gleska University Library, E Hwy 18, Mission, SD, 57555. Tel: 605-856-8100, 605-856-8112. Fax: 605-856-2011. p. 2215

Olson, Caralynn, Asst Librn, McKenzie County Public Library, 112 Second Ave NE, Watford City, ND, 58854. Tel: 701-444-3785. Fax: 701-444-3730. p. 1849

Olson, Carolyn, Ch, Willmar Public Library, 410 Fifth St SW, Willmar, MN, 56201-3298. Tel: 320-235-3162. Fax: 320-235-3169. p. 1289

Olson, Carolyn, Librn, Canadian Lutheran Bible Institute Library, 4837 52A St, Camrose, AB, T4V 1W5, CANADA. Tel: 780-672-4454. Fax: 780-672-4455. p. 2694

Olson, Chalermsee, Assoc Dean, Coll & Tech Serv, Northern Illinois University Libraries, DeKalb, IL, 60115-2868. Tel: 815-753-9805. p. 635

Olson, Charoltte, Head, ILL, University of Alabama in Huntsville, 301 Sparkman Dr NW, Huntsville, AL, 35899. Tel: 256-824-6522. Fax: 256-824-6862. p. 22

Olson, Chris D, Exec Dir, Metropolitan Library Service Agency, 1619 Dayton Ave, No 314, Saint Paul, MN, 55104-6206. Tel: 651-645-5731, Ext 105. Fax: 651-649-3169. p. 2947

Olson, Connie, Dir, Moundridge Public Library, 220 S Christian, Moundridge, KS, 67107. Tel: 620-345-6355. p. 884

Olson, David L, Dir, Wilton Free Public Library, Six Goodspeed St, Wilton, ME, 04294. Tel: 207-645-4831. Fax: 207-645-9417. p. 1007

Olson, Deb, Dir, Dows Community Library, 114 Ellsworth, Dows, IA, 50071. Tel: 515-852-4326. Fax: 515-852-4326. p. 811

Olson, Diane, Librn, Trinity Bible College, 50 Sixth Ave S, Ellendale, ND, 58436-7150. Tel: 701-349-5407. Fax: 701-349-5443. p. 1840

Olson, Doug, Sr Librn, California Department of Corrections Library System, California Correctional Center, 711-045 Center Rd, Susanville, CA, 96127. Tel: 530-257-2181, Ext 4198. Fax: 530-252-3020. p. 221

Olson, Doug, Sr Librn, California Department of Corrections Library System, High Desert State Prison, 475-750 Rice Canyon Rd, Susanville, CA, 96127. Tel: 530-251-5100, Ext 6449. Fax: 530-251-5036. p. 221

Olson, Elizabeth, Librn, Archer & Greiner Library, One Centennial Sq, Haddonfield, NJ, 08033-0968. Tel: 856-795-2121. Fax: 856-795-0574. p. 1489

Olson, Ellen, Br Mgr, Rockford Public Library, Rock River, 3128 11th St, Rockford, IL, 61109-2202. Tel: 815-965-7606, Ext 765. Fax: 815-963-8855. p. 698

Olson, Gary, Dir, Park Falls Public Library, 121 N Fourth Ave, Park Falls, WI, 54552. Tel: 715-762-3121. Fax: 715-762-2286. p. 2629

Olson, Gayle, Librn, Wapiti Regional Library, Smeaton Public Library, Main Street, Village Office, Smeaton, SK, S0J 2J0, CANADA. Tel: 306-426-2049. p. 2922

Olson, Ginger, Circ, Rochester Hills Public Library, 500 Olde Towne Rd, Rochester, MI, 48307-2043. Tel: 248-650-7162. Fax: 248-650-7121. p. 1222

Olson, Hope, Dr, Assoc Dean, Prof, University of Wisconsin-Milwaukee, 510 Bolton Hall, 3120 N Maryland Ave, Milwaukee, WI, 53211. Tel: 414-229-4707. Fax: 414-229-6699. p. 2976

Olson, Janice, Asst Librn, United States Courts Library, 700 Stewart St, Rm 19105, Seattle, WA, 98101. Tel: 206-370-8975. Fax: 206-370-8976. p. 2533

Olson, Jeffrey, PhD, Dir, Saint John's University, Saint Augustine Hall, Rm 408, 8000 Utopia Pkwy, Jamaica, NY, 11439. Tel: 718-990-5705. Fax: 718-990-2071. p. 2970

Olson, Jennifer, Tech Serv, University of Hartford Libraries, Mildred P Allen Memorial, 200 Bloomfield Ave, West Hartford, CT, 06117-0395. Tel: 860-768-4491. Fax: 860-768-5295. p. 376

Olson, Julie, Assoc Law Librn, Maine State Law & Legislative Reference Library, 43 State House Sta, Augusta, ME, 04333-0043. Tel: 207-287-1600. Fax: 207-287-6467. p. 974

Olson, Kathy, Exec Dir, Owensboro Area Museum of Science & History Library, 122 E Second St, Owensboro, KY, 42301. Tel: 270-687-2732. Fax: 270-687-2738. p. 931

Olson, Kelly, Access Serv, ILL, Supvr, Buena Vista University Library, 610 W Fourth St, Storm Lake, IA, 50588. Tel: 712-749-2098. Fax: 712-749-2059. p. 846

Olson, Kent, Head, Ref, Res & Instruction, University of Virginia, Arthur J Morris Law Library, 580 Massie Rd, Charlottesville, VA, 22903-1789. Tel: 434-924-4734. Fax: 434-982-2232. p. 2455

Olson, Kim, Asst Dir, Lake City Public Library, 110 E Washington St, Lake City, IA, 51449-1718. Tel: 712-464-3413. Fax: 712-464-3413. p. 826

Olson, Kyle, Actg Librn, Avon Park Correctional Facility, Work Camp, State Rd 64E, Avon Park, FL, 33825. p. 426

Olson, Laverne, Librn, Presho Public Library, 108 N Main St, Presho, SD, 57568. Tel: 605-895-2443. p. 2217

Olson, Linda M, Tech Serv, Superior Public Library, 1530 Tower Ave, Superior, WI, 54880-2532. Tel: 715-394-8860. Fax: 715-394-8870. p. 2641

Olson, Lynette, Adult Serv, Emporia Public Library, 110 E Sixth Ave, Emporia, KS, 66801-3960. Tel: 620-340-6451. Fax: 620-340-6444. p. 865

Olson, Marcia, Mgr, Gradient, 20 University Ave, Cambridge, MA, 02138. Tel: 617-395-5562. Fax: 617-395-5001. p. 1073

Olson, Marilyn, Head, Ch, Johnson Free Public Library, 274 Main St, Hackensack, NJ, 07601-5797. Tel: 201-343-4169. Fax: 201-343-1395. p. 1489

Olson, Maripat, Head, Tech Serv, Barrington Public Library District, 505 N Northwest Hwy, Barrington, IL, 60010. Tel: 847-382-1300. Fax: 847-382-1261. p. 592

Olson, Mary, Emerging Tech Librn, Iliff School of Theology, 2201 S University Blvd, Denver, CO, 80210. Tel: 303-765-3173. Fax: 303-777-0164. p. 302

Olson, Michael, Dean of Libr, Loyola University New Orleans, 6363 Saint Charles Ave, New Orleans, LA, 70118-6195. Tel: 504-864-7111. Fax: 504-864-7247. p. 961

Olson, Michael, Coll Develop, Clark University, 950 Main St, Worcester, MA, 01610-1477. Tel: 508-421-3804. Fax: 508-793-8871. p. 1143

Olson, Nancy, Circ, Bethel University Library, 3900 Bethel Dr, Saint Paul, MN, 55112. Tel: 651-638-6222. Fax: 651-638-6001. p. 1277

Olson, Nancy J, Dir, Lincoln Christian College & Seminary, 100 Campus View Dr, Lincoln, IL, 62656. Tel: 217-732-7788, Ext 2281. Fax: 217-732-3785. p. 665

Olson, Pamela Thoits, Librn, West Falmouth Library, 575 W Falmouth Hwy, West Falmouth, MA, 02574. Tel: 508-548-4709. Fax: 508-457-9534. p. 1137

Olson, Patricia, Dir, Balsam Lake Public Library, 404 Main St, Balsam Lake, WI, 54810-7261. Tel: 715-485-3215. Fax: 715-485-3215. p. 2580

Olson, Paula, Librn, Delnor Community Hospital, 300 Randall Rd, Geneva, IL, 60134. Tel: 630-208-4299. Fax: 630-208-3497. p. 648

Olson, Paula, Coordr, Fox Valley Health Science Library Consortium, c/o Delnor-Community Hospital, 300 Randall Rd, Geneva, IL, 60134. Tel: 630-208-4299. p. 2942

Olson, Penny R, Librn, East Central Regional Library, McGregor Public Library, Center Ave & Second St, McGregor, MN, 55760. Tel: 218-768-3305. Fax: 218-768-3305. p. 1244

Olson, Randy, Coordr, Cat, University of Wisconsin-Eau Claire, 105 Garfield Ave, Eau Claire, WI, 54702-4004. Tel: 715-836-4335. Fax: 715-836-2949. p. 2590

Olson, Ray, Libr Syst Mgr, Theological Consortium of Greater Columbus, Trinity Lutheran Seminary, 2199 E Main St, Columbus, OH, 43209-2334. Tel: 614-384-4646. Fax: 614-238-0263. p. 2953

Olson, Ray A, Dir, Trinity Lutheran Seminary, 2199 E Main St, Columbus, OH, 43209-2334. Tel: 614-384-4640. Fax: 614-238-0263. p. 1891

Olson, Robert, Librn, Centre for Suicide Prevention, 2005, 105 12 Ave SE, Ste 320, Calgary, AB, T2G 1A1, CANADA. Tel: 403-245-3900. Fax: 403-245-0299. p. 2691

Olson, Roberta, Dir, Church of Jesus Christ of Latter-Day Saints, 160 Washington Ave, Plainview, NY, 11803. Tel: 516-433-0122. p. 1718

Olson, Roberta M, Dir, Germantown Community Library, N112W16957 Mequon Rd, Germantown, WI, 53022. Tel: 262-253-7762. Fax: 262-253-7763. p. 2594

Olson, Roger, Tech Serv, San Diego Mesa College Library, 7250 Mesa College Dr, San Diego, CA, 92111-4998. Tel: 619-388-2548. Fax: 619-388-2922. p. 235

Olson, Roxie, Assoc Univ Librn, Digital Initiatives & Content Mgt, Assoc Univ Librn, Digital Initiatives & Open Access, Librn, Avera St Luke's Hospital, 305 S State St, Aberdeen, SD, 57401-4590. Tel: 605-622-5355. Fax: 605-622-5041. p. 2209

Olson, Scott, Librn, Minnesota Department of Corrections, 5329 Osgood Ave N, Stillwater, MN, 55082-1117. Tel: 651-779-1410. Fax: 651-779-1323. p. 1285

Olson, Sharon, Dept Supvr, Klamath County Library Services District, 126 S Third St, Klamath Falls, OR, 97601-6394. Tel: 541-882-8894. Fax: 541-882-6166. p. 2001

Olson, Stephanie, Librn, Rainy River Community College Library, 1501 Hwy 71, International Falls, MN, 56649. Tel: 218-285-2220. Fax: 218-285-2239. p. 1254

Olson, Stephanie Mallak, Dir, Iosco-Arenac District Library, 120 W Westover St, East Tawas, MI, 48730. Tel: 989-362-2651. Fax: 989-362-6056. p. 1175

Olson, Steven Kent, Br Mgr, Saint Joseph Public Library, East Hills Library, 502 N Woodbine Rd, Saint Joseph, MO, 64506. Tel: 816-236-2136. Fax: 816-236-1429. p. 1353

Olson, Susanne, Ref Serv, Webmaster, Groton Public Library, 99 Main St, Groton, MA, 01450. Tel: 978-448-8000. Fax: 978-448-1169. p. 1093

Olson, Teresa, ILL, Glen Ellyn Public Library, 400 Duane St, Glen Ellyn, IL, 60137-4508. Tel: 630-469-0879. Fax: 630-469-1086. p. 650

Olson, Teresa, Librn, Plankinton Community Library, PO Box 190, Plankinton, SD, 57368. Tel: 605-942-7600. Fax: 605-942-7453. p. 2217

Olson, Terrie, Circ, Tarpon Springs Public Library, 138 E Lemon St, Tarpon Springs, FL, 34689. Tel: 727-943-4922. Fax: 727-943-4926. p. 499

Olson, Terry, Dir, Hebron Secrest Library, 146 N Fourth St, Hebron, NE, 68370. Tel: 402-768-6701. Fax: 402-768-6701. p. 1402

Olson, Verna, Br Librn, Lake Agassiz Regional Library, Hawley Public Library, 421 Hartford St, Hawley, MN, 56549. Tel: 218-483-4549. Fax: 218-483-4549. p. 1266

Olson, William, Automation Syst Coordr, Sayville Library, 11 Collins Ave, Sayville, NY, 11782-3199. Tel: 631-589-4440. Fax: 631-589-6128. p. 1739

Olson-Kopp, Kim, Outreach Librn, Tech Coordr, Webmaster, Viterbo University, 900 Viterbo Dr, La Crosse, WI, 54601. Tel: 608-796-3263. Fax: 608-796-3275. p. 2603

Olstad, Jane, Acq, Ref, North Tonawanda Public Library, 505 Meadow Dr, North Tonawanda, NY, 14120-2888. Tel: 716-693-4132. Fax: 716-693-0719. p. 1707

Olszewski, Lawrence, Dir, OCLC Library, 6565 Kilgour Pl, Dublin, OH, 43017. Tel: 614-764-6000. Fax: 614-793-8707. p. 1896

Oltedale, Elsie, Dir, Louttit Library, 274 Victory Hwy, West Greenwich, RI, 02817. Tel: 401-397-3434. Fax: 401-397-3837. p. 2177

Olthoff, Kathy, Dir, Corwith Public Library, 110 NW Elm, Corwith, IA, 50430. Tel: 515-583-2536. Fax: 515-583-2536. p. 804

Olthoff, Kathy, Dir, Klemme Public Library, 204 E Main St, Klemme, IA, 50449. Tel: 641-587-2369. Fax: 641-587-2369. p. 825

Oltivero, Sulema, Asst Dir, Rhoads Memorial Library, 103 SW Second St, Dimmitt, TX, 79027. Tel: 806-647-3532. Fax: 806-647-1038. p. 2314

Oltman, Jeri, County Librn, Perquimans County Library, 110 W Academy St, Hertford, NC, 27944. Tel: 252-426-5319. Fax: 252-426-1556. p. 1801

Oltmann, Shannon M, Dr, Asst Prof, University of Kentucky, 320 Little Library Bldg, Lexington, KY, 40506-0224. Tel: 859-257-0788. Fax: 859-257-4205. p. 2966

Oltmanns, Gail, Assoc Univ Librn, Organizational Develop, Washington University Libraries, One Brookings Dr, Campus Box 1061, Saint Louis, MO, 63130-4862. Tel: 314-935-9334. Fax: 314-935-4045. p. 1362

Oltmanns, Judith, Tech Serv, Lied Scottsbluff Public Library, 1809 Third Ave, Scottsbluff, NE, 69361-2493. Tel: 308-630-6207. Fax: 308-630-6293. p. 1418

Oltremari, Patty, Acq, Automation Syst Coordr, Lamar State College, 317 Stilwell Blvd, Port Arthur, TX, 77640. Tel: 409-984-6225. Fax: 409-984-6008. p. 2371

Oltrop, Monique, Mgr, Point Pelee National Park Library, 407 Robson St, RR1, Leamington, ON, N8H 3V4, CANADA. Tel: 519-322-5700, Ext 21. Fax: 519-322-1277. p. 2816

Olver, Lynne, Dir, Libr Serv, Morris County Library, 30 E Hanover Ave, Whippany, NJ, 07981. Tel: 973-285-6930. p. 1544

Olvera, Joseph, Commun Libr Mgr, County of Los Angeles Public Library, Cudahy Library, 5218 Santa Ana St, Cudahy, CA, 90201-6098. Tel: 323-771-1345. Fax: 323-771-6973. p. 141

Olvera, Kristina, Asst Law Librn, Madera County Law Library, County Government Ctr, 209 W Yosemite Ave, Madera, CA, 93637-3596. Tel: 559-673-0378. Fax: 559-673-0378. p. 181

Oman, Ana, Dir, Wiggin & Dana LLP, 265 Church St, New Haven, CT, 06510. Tel: 203-498-4400. Fax: 203-782-2889. p. 356

Oman, Clara Irene, In Charge, Almena City Library, 415 Main, Almena, KS, 67622. Tel: 785-669-2336. p. 855

Omans, Cristy, Dir, Seville Township Public Library, 6734 N Lumberjack Rd, Riverdale, MI, 48877. Tel: 989-833-7776. Fax: 989-833-7776. p. 1221

Omer, Jessica, Circ, Bellevue University, 1000 Galvin Rd S, Bellevue, NE, 68005. Tel: 402-557-7308. Fax: 402-557-5427. p. 1393

Omlid, Judith, Asst Dir, McKenzie County Public Library, 112 Second Ave NE, Watford City, ND, 58854. Tel: 701-444-3785. Fax: 701-444-3730. p. 1849

Omoruyi, Joan, Res & Instruction Librn, Northeastern University Libraries, Snell Library, 360 Huntington Ave, Boston, MA, 02115. Tel: 617-373-2806. p. 1065

Omowale, Yusef, Dir, Southern California Library for Social Studies & Research, 6120 S Vermont Ave, Los Angeles, CA, 90044. Tel: 323-759-6063. Fax: 323-759-2252. p. 177

Ondricka, Deborah, Ref Serv, American River College Library, 4700 College Oak Dr, Sacramento, CA, 95841. Tel: 916-484-8455. Fax: 916-484-8018, 916-484-8657. p. 220

Ondrusek, Anita, Dr, Assoc Prof, Valdosta State University, Odum Library - MLIS, 1500 N Patterson St, Valdosta, GA, 31698-0144. Tel: 229-245-3742. Fax: 229-259-5055. p. 2964

Oneil, Julie, Learning Res Ctr Spec, Central Arizona College, 273 E Old West Hwy (US 60), Apache Junction, AZ, 85219-5231. Tel: 480-677-7747. Fax: 480-677-7738. p. 57

Oneil, Marie, Libr Tech, Government of Newfoundland & Labrador, PO Box 8700, St. John's, NL, A1B 4J6, CANADA. Tel: 709-729-0934. Fax: 709-729-2331. p. 2772

ONeill, Sheila, Head, Spec Coll & Archives, California State University, Sacramento Library, 2000 State University Dr E, Sacramento, CA, 95819-6039. Tel: 916-278-5679. Fax: 916-278-5917. p. 223

Onest, Trevor, Pub Serv Librn, Bethany College, Mary Cutlip Center for Library & Information Technology, 300 Main St, Bethany, WV, 26032. Tel: 304-829-7321. Fax: 304-829-7333. p. 2554

Ong, Belinda, Dr, Ref Librn, University of Alabama in Huntsville, 301 Sparkman Dr NW, Huntsville, AL, 35899. Tel: 256-824-6432. Fax: 256-824-6083. p. 22

Ongley, David, Dir, Tuzzy Consortium Library, 5421 North Star St, Barrow, AK, 99723. Tel: 907-852-4050. Fax: 907-852-4059. p. 46

Onianwa, Chukwuji, Br Mgr, Los Angeles Public Library System, Van Nuys Branch, 6250 Sylmar Ave Mall, Van Nuys, CA, 91401-2787. Tel: 818-756-8453. Fax: 818-756-9291. p. 174

Onieal, Marty, Regional Libr Mgr, Broward County Division of Libraries, North Regional-BC, 1100 Coconut Creek Blvd, Coconut Creek, FL, 33066. Tel: 954-201-2605. Fax: 954-201-2650. p. 442

Onieal, Marty, Regional Libr Mgr, Broward County Division of Libraries, Northwest Regional, 3151 University Dr, Coral Springs, FL, 33065. Tel: 954-341-3900, Ext 247. Fax: 954-341-3980. p. 442

Onion, Matthew, Dir, Ashland Community & Technical College, 1400 College Dr, Ashland, KY, 41101. Tel: 606-326-2113. Fax: 606-326-2186. p. 905

Onkst, Wayne, State Librn, Kentucky Department for Libraries & Archives, 300 Coffee Tree Rd, Frankfort, KY, 40601. Tel: 502-564-8300. Fax: 502-564-5773. p. 913

Onorati, Marilyn, Librn, Amelia County Historical Society Library, Jackson Bldg, 16501 Church St, Amelia, VA, 23002. Tel: 804-561-3180. p. 2447

Onsager, Lawrence, Dean of Libr, Andrews University, 1400 Library Rd, Berrien Springs, MI, 49104-1400. Tel: 269-471-3379. Fax: 269-471-6166. p. 1157

Onstad, David, Dir, United States Army, Bldg 2000, S 11th Ave, Fort McCoy, WI, 54656-5000. Tel: 608-388-2410. Fax: 608-388-2690. p. 2593

Ontell, Val, Instrul Serv Librn, San Diego Mesa College Library, 7250 Mesa College Dr, San Diego, CA, 92111-4998. Tel: 619-388-2549. Fax: 619-388-2922. p. 235

Ontko, Mike, Asst Dir, Coshocton Public Library, 655 Main St, Coshocton, OH, 43812-1697. Tel: 740-622-0956. Fax: 740-622-4331. p. 1891

Onufrak, Paul, Automation Libr, Eastern Shores Library System, 4632 S Taylor Dr, Sheboygan, WI, 53081-1107. Tel: 920-208-4900. Fax: 920-208-4901. p. 2637

Onukwufor, Gloria, Libr Serv Supvr, Central Piedmont Community College Library, 1201 Elizabeth Ave, Charlotte, NC, 28235. Tel: 704-330-3844. Fax: 704-330-6887. p. 1781

Ooton, Susan, Dir, Canon City Public Library, 516 Macon Ave, Canon City, CO, 81212-3380. Tel: 719-269-9020. Fax: 719-269-9031. p. 293

Opalko, Nancy, Ch, First Regional Library, Lafayette County-Oxford Public Library, 401 Bramlett Blvd, Oxford, MS, 38655. Tel: 662-234-5751. Fax: 662-234-3155. p. 1302

Oparanozie, Teri L, Head, Acq, Sam Houston State University, 1830 Bobby K Marks Dr, Huntsville, TX, 77340. Tel: 936-294-1623. Fax: 936-294-3780. p. 2345

Opasik, Scott, Head, Access Serv, Tech Serv, Indiana University South Bend, 1700 Mishawaka Ave, South Bend, IN, 46615. Tel: 574-520-4446. Fax: 574-520-4472. p. 778

Opatow, Dave, Dir, Freeport Memorial Library, 144 W Merrick Rd & S Ocean Ave, Freeport, NY, 11520. Tel: 516-379-3274. Fax: 516-868-9741. p. 1625

Opello, Olivia, Librn, Onondaga County Public Library, Hazard, 1620 W Genesee St, Syracuse, NY, 13204. Tel: 315-435-5326. p. 1752

Openo, Jason, Mgr, Edmonton Public Library, Whitemud Crossing, 145 Whitemud Crossing Shopping Ctr, 4211-106 St, Edmonton, AB, T6J 6L7, CANADA. Tel: 780-496-1822. Fax: 780-496-7007. p. 2700

Openo, Phuong, Tech Serv Librn, Dover Public Library, 73 Locust St, Dover, NH, 03820-3785. Tel: 603-516-6050. Fax: 603-516-6053. p. 1445

Openshaw, Jeri, Pub Relations, Utah State Library Division, 250 N 1950 West, Ste A, Salt Lake City, UT, 84116-7901. Tel: 801-715-6737. Fax: 801-715-6767. p. 2415

Opolski, Cheryl, Ch, Salem Public Library, 370 Essex St, Salem, MA, 01970-3298. Tel: 978-744-0860. Fax: 978-745-8616. p. 1122

Oppen, Pamela, Asst Dir, Haines Falls Free Library, 52 N Lake Rd, Haines Falls, NY, 12436. Tel: 518-589-5707. Fax: 518-589-0311. p. 1632

Oppenheim, Linda, Librn, Princeton University, Industrial Relations, Firestone Library, Social Science Reference Ctr, One Washington Rd, Princeton, NJ, 08544. Tel: 609-258-4043. Fax: 609-258-2907. p. 1524

Oppenheim, Michael, Coll & Donations of Libr Mat, University of California Los Angeles Library, Eugene & Maxine Rosenfeld Management Library, 110 Westwood Plaza, E-302, Los Angeles, CA, 90095. Tel: 310-825-0769. Fax: 310-825-6632. p. 179

Opper, Robert, Circ Mgr, Kent State University Libraries, 1125 Risman Dr, Kent, OH, 44242. Tel: 330-672-1671. Fax: 330-672-4811. p. 1907

Opstad, Stephanie, Librn, Anoka County Library, Johnsville, 12461 Oak Park Blvd, Blaine, MN, 55434. Tel: 763-767-3853. Fax: 763-767-3878. p. 1241

Opyoke, Oneita, Librn, Marion County Public Library, Fairview Public, 500 Main St, Fairview, WV, 26570. Tel: 304-449-1195. Fax: 304-449-1021. p. 2559

Oquendo, Grisel, Commun Libr Mgr, County of Los Angeles Public Library, Leland R Weaver Library, 4035 Tweedy Blvd, South Gate, CA, 90280-6199. Tel: 323-567-8853. Fax: 323-563-1046. p. 143

Oram, Richard W, Dr, Assoc Dir & Hobby Found Librn, University of Texas Libraries, Harry Ransom Center, 300 W 21st St, Austin, TX, 78712. Tel: 512-471-8944. p. 2284

Orange, Danelle, Digital Projects Librn, University of North Texas Health Science Center at Fort Worth, 3500 Camp Bowie Blvd, Fort Worth, TX, 76107-2699. Tel: 817-735-2070. Fax: 817-763-0325. p. 2324

Orange, Sue Ann, Youth Serv Coordr, FOR Sto-Rox Library, 500 Chartiers Ave, McKees Rocks, PA, 15136. Tel: 412-771-1222. Fax: 412-771-2340. p. 2085

Orange, Thomas, Libr Serv Coordr, Medaille College Library, 18 Agassiz Circle, Buffalo, NY, 14214. Tel: 716-880-2283. Fax: 716-884-9638. p. 1598

Orban, Liz, Circuit Librn, Community Health Network Library, 1500 N Ritter Ave, Indianapolis, IN, 46219. Tel: 765-298-2100. Fax: 317-351-7816. p. 750

Orblych, Teague, Bibliog Instr, Sr Assoc Librn, University of Michigan-Dearborn, 4901 Evergreen Rd, Dearborn, MI, 48128-2406. Tel: 313-593-5562. Fax: 313-593-5478. p. 1168

Orchard, Margaret, Librn, Stey-Nevant Public Library, 1000 Roemer Blvd, Farrell, PA, 16121-1899. Tel: 724-983-2714. Fax: 724-983-2710. p. 2057

Ordian, Svetlana, Librn, Bunker Hill Community College (BHCC), 250 New Rutherford Ave, Boston, MA, 02129-2991. Tel: 617-228-2211. Fax: 617-228-3288. p. 1059

Ordner, Craig, Archivist, Railroad & Heritage Museum Library, 315 West Ave B, Temple, TX, 76501. Tel: 254-298-5190. Fax: 254-298-5171. p. 2390

Ordonez-Mercado, Maria E, Head Librn, University of Puerto Rico Library System, Puerto Rican Collection, Rio Piedras Campus, Edif Jose M Lazaro, San Juan, PR, 00931. Tel: 787-764-0000, Ext 5160. Fax: 787-772-1479. p. 2678

Orebaugh, Melinda, Dir, Gundersen Lutheran Health System, 1900 South Ave, H01-011, La Crosse, WI, 54601-9980. Tel: 608-775-5410. Fax: 608-775-6343. p. 2603

Oregero, Jacqueline, Br Librn, Sussex County Library System, Dorothy E Henry Memorial, 66 Rte 94, Vernon, NJ, 07462. Tel: 973-827-8095. Fax: 973-827-8664. p. 1514

Orellana, Pedro, Br Asst, Los Angeles County Law Library, Long Beach, County Bldg, Rm 505, 415 W Ocean Blvd, Long Beach, CA, 90802. Tel: 562-983-7088. p. 172

Orengo, Yosenex, Libr Asst, Hunter College Libraries, Centro - Center for Puerto Rican Studies Library, 2180 Third Ave, Rm 121, New York, NY, 10035. Tel: 212-396-7874. Fax: 212-396-7707. p. 1682

Orenstein, David, Dir, Saint Peter's College, 99 Glenwood Ave, Jersey City, NJ, 07306. Tel: 201-761-6453. Fax: 201-432-4117. p. 1493

Oreste, Jimenez, Evening/Weekend Supvr, Drexel University Libraries, Hagerty Library, 33rd & Market Sts, Philadelphia, PA, 19104-2875. Tel: 215-895-2750. Fax: 215-895-2070. p. 2105

Orey, Michael, Dr, Assoc Prof, Learning, Design & Tech Prog Coordr, University of Georgia, College of Education, 224 River's Crossing, Athens, GA, 30602-7144. Tel: 706-542-4110. Fax: 706-542-4032. p. 2964

Orfirer, Lenore F, Librn, Santa Monica-UCLA Medical Center & Orthopaedic Hospital Library, 1250 16th St, Santa Monica, CA, 90404. Tel: 310-319-4000. Fax: 310-319-4328. p. 266

Orgeron, Elizabeth, Dean, State University of New York College of Agriculture & Technology, 142 Schenectady Ave, Cobleskill, NY, 12043. Tel: 518-234-5841. Fax: 518-255-5843. p. 1608

Orgeron, Elizabeth, Col Librn, Dir, Hartwick College, One Hartwick Dr, Oneonta, NY, 13820. Tel: 607-431-4440. Fax: 607-431-4457. p. 1710

Ori, David Alexander, Librn, Mount Vernon Public Library, 1220 Military Rd, Mount Vernon, AL, 36560. Tel: 251-829-9497. Fax: 251-829-5546. p. 31

Orick, Jan, Dir, Saint Jude Children's Research Hospital, 262 Danny Thomas Pl, Memphis, TN, 38105-3678. Tel: 901-595-3388. Fax: 901-595-3117. p. 2251

Orlandi, Robin, Dir, Hildebrand Memorial Library, 1033 Wisconsin Ave, Boscobel, WI, 53805-1597. Tel: 608-375-5723. Fax: 608-375-4750. p. 2582

Orlando, Jacqueline, Assoc Dir, Capital University, Law School Library, 303 E Broad St, Columbus, OH, 43215. Tel: 614-236-6464. Fax: 614-236-6957. p. 1883

Orlando, Lucia, Assoc Librn, Head, Res Serv, University of California, 1156 High St, Santa Cruz, CA, 95064. Tel: 831-459-1279. Fax: 831-459-8206. p. 264

Orlando, Michele, Circ, Elwood Public Library, 1929 Jericho Tpk, East Northport, NY, 11731. Tel: 631-499-3722. Fax: 631-499-0057. p. 1617

Orlando, Rosemary, Dir, Saint Clair Shores Public Library, 22500 11 Mile Rd, Saint Clair Shores, MI, 48081-1399. Tel: 586-771-9020. Fax: 586-771-8935. p. 1224

Orlando, Sharon, Youth Serv, Somerset County Library System, Watchung Public, 12 Stirling Rd, Watchung, NJ, 07069. Tel: 908-561-0117. Fax: 908-769-1145. p. 1475

Orlando, Susan, Dir, Forsyth Institute, 140 The Fenway, Boston, MA, 02115-3799. Tel: 617-892-8245. Fax: 617-892-8470. p. 1061

Orlando, Suzanne, Sr Librn, Adirondack Correctional Facility Library, PO Box 110, Ray Brook, NY, 12977-0110. Tel: 518-891-1343. Fax: 518-891-1343. p. 1726

Orlik, Mary, Asst Librn, Environment Canada Library, Burlington, 867 Lakeshore Rd, Burlington, ON, L7R 4A6, CANADA. Tel: 905-336-4982. Fax: 905-336-4428. p. 2798

Orlomoski, Amy E, Dir, Librn, Andover Public Library, 355 Rte 6, Andover, CT, 06232. Tel: 860-742-7428. Fax: 860-742-7428. p. 329

Orlomoski, Bobbi Ann, ILL, Canterbury Public Library, One Municipal Dr, Canterbury, CT, 06331-1453. Tel: 860-546-9022. Fax: 860-546-1142. p. 333

Orlov, Stanislav, Syst Librn, Mount Saint Vincent University Library, 166 Bedford Hwy, Halifax, NS, B3M 2J6, CANADA. Tel: 902-457-6250. Fax: 902-457-6445. p. 2781

Orlowski, Laura, Dir, Camden Township Public Library, 119 S Main St, Camden, MI, 49232. Tel: 517-368-5554. Fax: 517-368-5554. p. 1160

Orme, James, Dir, Libr & Info Serv, Great Lakes Christian College, 6211 W Willow Hwy, Lansing, MI, 48917. Tel: 517-321-0242 ext 251. Fax: 517-321-5902. p. 1201

Orme, William, Assoc Dean, Teaching, Learning & Res, Indiana University-Purdue University Indianapolis, 755 W Michigan St, Indianapolis, IN, 46202-5195. Tel: 317-274-0485. Fax: 317-278-0368. p. 753

Ormerod-Glynn, Barbara, Dep Dir, Greenwich Library, 101 W Putnam Ave, Greenwich, CT, 06830-5387. Tel: 203-622-7962. Fax: 203-622-7959. p. 341

Ormiston, Alice, Librn, Grapeland Public Library, 212 N Oak St, Grapeland, TX, 75844. Tel: 936-687-3425. Fax: 936-687-3461. p. 2329

Ormsbee, Lisette N, Dir, Roger & Peggy Madigan Library, 999 Hagan Way, Williamsport, PA, 17701. Tel: 570-327-4523. Fax: 570-327-4503. p. 2156

Ormsby, Cathy, Br Mgr, Maricopa County Library District, Perry Branch, 1965 E Queen Creek Rd, Gilbert, AZ, 85297. Tel: 602-652-3551. Fax: 602-651-3575. p. 75

Ormsby, Jennifer, Coordr, Los Angeles County Office of Education, 9300 Imperial Hwy, Downey, CA, 90242-2813. Tel: 562-922-6359. Fax: 562-940-1699. p. 144

Orn, Sothy, Adult Serv, Malden Public Library, 36 Salem St, Malden, MA, 02148-5291. Tel: 781-324-0108. Fax: 781-324-4467. p. 1102

Orndoff, Pat, Br Librn, Shenandoah County Library, Strasburg Community, 195 W King St, Strasburg, VA, 22657. Tel: 540-465-8464. Fax: 540-465-2739. p. 2460

Orndorff, Loretta F, Dir of Libr Serv, Cozen O'Connor, 1900 Market St, 3rd Flr, Philadelphia, PA, 19103. Tel: 215-665-2000. Fax: 215-665-2013. p. 2105

Orndorff-Tauber, Kathryn, Br Mgr, Adams Memorial Library, 1112 Ligonier St, Latrobe, PA, 15650. Tel: 724-539-1972. Fax: 724-537-0338. p. 2078

Orndorff-Tauber, Kathryn, Br Mgr, Adams Memorial Library, Unity, 156 Beatty County Rd, Latrobe, PA, 15650. Tel: 724-532-1840. Fax: 724-532-1841. p. 2079

Ornstein, Sarah, Librn, Davisville Free Library, 481 Davisville Rd, North Kingstown, RI, 02852. Tel: 401-884-5524. Fax: 401-884-9615. p. 2170

Oros, Susan, ILL Spec, University of Puget Sound, 1500 N Warner St, Campus Mail Box 1021, Tacoma, WA, 98416-1021. Tel: 253-879-2664. Fax: 253-879-3670. p. 2541

Orosco, Michelle, Librn, North Central Regional Library, Bridgeport Community, 1206 Columbia Ave, Bridgeport, WA, 98813. Tel: 509-686-7281. Fax: 509-686-7281. p. 2548

Orozco, Rachel, Dir, Rita & Truett Smith Public Library, 300 Country Club Rd, Bldg 300, Wylie, TX, 75098. Tel: 972-516-6250. p. 2401

Orr, Blanche, Br Mgr, Huntsville-Madison Public Library, Triana Youth Center Library, 640 Sixth St, Madison, AL, 35756. Tel: 256-772-3677. p. 21

Orr, Carol, Assoc Dir, Libr Serv, Upper Iowa University, 605 Washington St, Fayette, IA, 52142. Tel: 563-425-5270. Fax: 563-425-5271. p. 816

Orr, Cindy, Chairperson, Bow Island Municipal Library, 510 Centre St, Bow Island, AB, T0K 0G0, CANADA. Tel: 403-545-2828. Fax: 403-545-6642. p. 2686

Orr, Laura, Law Librn, Washington County Law Library, 111 NE Lincoln St, Hillsboro, OR, 97124. Tel: 503-846-8880. Fax: 503-846-3515. p. 2001

Orr, Linda, Tech Serv Librn, Transylvania University Library, 300 N Broadway, Lexington, KY, 40508. Tel: 859-246-5005. Fax: 859-233-8779. p. 921

Orr, Melissa, Libr Coordr, Scottsdale Public Library, Palomino Library, 12575 E Via Linda, Ste 102, Scottsdale, AZ, 85259-4310. Tel: 480-312-6110. p. 81

Orr, Michelle, Coll Develop, Digitization Librn, Johnson C Smith University, 100 Beatties Ford Rd, Charlotte, NC, 28216. Tel: 704-371-6740. Fax: 704-378-1191. p. 1783

Orr, Pam, Librn, Lapeer District Library, Metamora Branch, 4018 Oak St, Metamora, MI, 48455. Tel: 810-678-2991. Fax: 810-678-3253. p. 1202

Orr, Patricia L, Mgr, Libr Serv, Dykema Gossett PLLC, 39577 N Woodward Ave, Ste 300, Bloomfield Hills, MI, 48304-2820. Tel: 313-568-6716. Fax: 313-568-6735. p. 1159

Orr, Patricia L, Mgr, Libr Serv, Dykema Gossett PLLC, 400 Renaissance Ctr, 38th Flr, Detroit, MI, 48243. Tel: 313-568-6714. Fax: 313-568-6735. p. 1171

Orr, Pattie, Dean, Univ Libr, VPres, Info Tech, Baylor University Libraries, 1312 S Third St, Waco, TX, 76798. Tel: 254-710-3590. Fax: 254-710-3116. p. 2396

Orr, Philip, Distance Learning Librn, University of Southern Indiana, 8600 University Blvd, Evansville, IN, 47712. Tel: 812-461-5328. Fax: 812-465-1693. p. 739

Orr, Robin, Admin Librn, Indiana County Law Library, County Court House, 825 Philadelphia St, Indiana, PA, 15701. Tel: 724-465-3956. Fax: 724-465-3152. p. 2071

Orr, Sandy, Tech Serv Coordr, Spokane County Library District, 4322 N Argonne Rd, Spokane, WA, 99212-1868. Tel: 509-893-8200. Fax: 509-893-8472. p. 2536

Orr, Stacey, Adult Serv, Edward U Demmer Memorial Library, 6961 W School St, Three Lakes, WI, 54562. Tel: 715-546-3391. Fax: 715-546-2930. p. 2642

Orr, Stephanie, Br Mgr, Harris County Public Library, Jacinto City Branch, 921 Akron, Jacinto City, TX, 77029. Tel: 713-673-3237. Fax: 713-671-0458. p. 2336

Orrell, June, Mgr, Commun Libr, Vaughan Public Libraries, Maple Library, 10190 Keele St, Maple, ON, L6A 1G3, CANADA. Tel: 905-653-7323. Fax: 905-832-4971. p. 2848

Orrico, Jeff, Health Sci Librn, Sacred Heart University, 5151 Park Ave, Fairfield, CT, 06825-1000. Tel: 203-365-4841. Fax: 203-374-9968. p. 339

Orsborn, Mary F, Libr Tech, Texas Biomedical Research Institute, 7620 NW Loop 410, San Antonio, TX, 78227-5301. Tel: 210-258-9749. p. 2383

Orsini, Anthony, Dir, Tipp City Public Library, 11 E Main St, Tipp City, OH, 45371. Tel: 937-667-3826. Fax: 937-667-7968. p. 1938

Orsini, Sue Ann, Res, Fried, Frank, Harris, Shriver & Jacobson LLP, 1001 Pennsylvania Ave NW, Ste 800, Washington, DC, 20004. Tel: 202-639-7365. Fax: 202-639-7008. p. 401

Orsted, Linda R, Dir, Flenniken Public Library, 102 E George St, Carmichaels, PA, 15320-1202. Tel: 724-966-5263. Fax: 724-966-9511. p. 2042

Ortale, Monica, Ref Serv, South Texas College of Law, 1303 San Jacinto St, Houston, TX, 77002-7000. Tel: 713-646-1711. Fax: 713-659-2217. p. 2342

Ortega, Alma, Ref Serv, University of San Diego, Helen K & James S Copley Library, 5998 Alcala Park, San Diego, CA, 92110. Fax: 619-260-4617. p. 239

Ortega, Carmen, Dir, Inter-American University of Puerto Rico, 500 Carretera Dr, Bayamon, PR, 00957-6257. Tel: 787-257-7373, Ext 2501. Fax: 787-279-2205. p. 2671

Ortega, Carmen, Actg Dean, Universidad del Este Library, Calle 190, Esquina 220 Bo Sabana Abajo, Carolina, PR, 00984-2010. Tel: 787-257-7373, Ext 2501. Fax: 787-257-7373, Ext 2516. p. 2672

Ortega, Edna, Dir, Demarest Public Library, 90 Hardenburgh Ave, Demarest, NJ, 07627-2197. Tel: 201-768-8714. Fax: 201-767-8094. p. 1481

Ortega, Elizabeth, Libr Asst, Tohono O'odham Community College Library, Hwy 86 Milepost 115.5 N, Sells, AZ, 85634. Tel: 520-383-0032. Fax: 520-383-8403. p. 81

Ortega, John J, Head, Circ, United States Air Force Academy Libraries, 2354 Fairchild Dr, Ste 3A10, USAF Academy, CO, 80840-6214. Tel: 719-333-4406. Fax: 719-333-4754. p. 324

Ortega, Lina, Librn, University of Oklahoma, Chemistry-Mathematics, Physical Sciences Center, Chemistry & Mathematics, Rm 207, Norman, OK, 73019. Tel: 405-325-5628. Fax: 405-325-7650. p. 1971

Ortega, Lydia, Asst Librn, Ref, Pontificia Catholic University of Puerto Rico, Arecibo, PO Box 144045, Arecibo, PR, 00614-4045. Tel: 787-881-1212, Ext 6028. Fax: 787-881-0777. p. 2671

Ortega, Pamela, Ref Librn, Eastern Illinois University, 600 Lincoln Ave, Charleston, IL, 61920. Tel: 217-581-7548. p. 603

Ortega, Tina, Dir, Moriarty Community Library, 202 S Broadway, Moriarty, NM, 87035. Tel: 505-832-2513. Fax: 505-832-8296. p. 1560

Ortego, Cindy, Asst Dir, Coordr, Br Serv, Shreve Memorial Library, 424 Texas St, Shreveport, LA, 71101. Tel: 318-226-5881. Fax: 318-226-4780. p. 969

Ortego, Gilda, Univ Librn, Western New Mexico University, 1000 W College Ave, Silver City, NM, 88061. Tel: 575-538-6176. Fax: 505-538-6178. p. 1565

Orth, Joseph, Syst & Cat Librn, US Court of Appeals for the Sixth Circuit Library, 312 Potter Stewart US Courthouse, Cincinnati, OH, 45202. Tel: 513-564-7321. Fax: 513-564-7329. p. 1873

Ortiz, Augustina, Br Mgr, Tulare County Library, Orosi Branch, 12646 Ave 416, Orosi, CA, 93647. Tel: 559-519-5830. Fax: 559-528-9156. p. 281

Ortiz, Bailey, YA Serv, Lucy Robbins Welles Library, 95 Cedar St, Newington, CT, 06111-2645. Tel: 860-665-8704. Fax: 860-667-1255. p. 361

Ortiz, Daniel, Univ Librn, University of Massachusetts at Boston, 100 Morrissey Blvd, Boston, MA, 02125-3300. Tel: 617-287-5916. p. 1068

Ortiz, Ivelisse, Asst Commun Librn, Hartford Public Library, Dwight Branch, Seven New Park Ave, Hartford, CT, 06106. Tel: 860-695-7462. Fax: 860-722-6884. p. 346

Ortiz, Josefina, Head, Ser, University of Puerto Rico, Law School Library, Avenidas Ponce de Leon & Gandara, San Juan, PR, 00931. Tel: 787-999-9691. Fax: 787-999-9680. p. 2676

Ortiz-Hernandez, Evelyn N, Circ, Head, Pub Serv, Supreme Court Library of Puerto Rico, Munoz Rivera Ave, Puerta de Tierra, San Juan, PR, 00902. Tel: 787-289-0179, 787-723-3550. Fax: 787-724-5090. p. 2676

Ortman, Scott, Dir, Res, Crow Canyon Archaeological Center, 23390 County Rd K, Cortez, CO, 81321. Tel: 970-565-8975. Fax: 970-565-4859. p. 297

Orton, Laurie, Br Mgr, Henderson District Public Libraries, Lydia Malcolm Library, 2960 Sunridge Heights Pkwy, Ste 100, Henderson, NV, 89052. Tel: 702-263-7522, 702-263-7523. Fax: 702-263-7402. p. 1428

Ortyl, Sheila, Dir, Mary Esther Public Library, 100 Hollywood Blvd W, Mary Esther, FL, 32569-1957. Tel: 850-243-5731. Fax: 850-243-4931. p. 463

Orvedahl, Virginia, Dir, Halifax County Library, 33 S Granville St, Halifax, NC, 27839. Tel: 252-583-3631. Fax: 252-583-8661. p. 1799

Orvis, Julie, Asst Librn, University of Wisconsin-Rock County Library, 2909 Kellogg Ave, Janesville, WI, 53546-5606. Tel: 608-758-6531. Fax: 608-758-6560. p. 2600

Orvis, Kelly, Librn, Orleans Public Library, Sunrise Ave, La Fargeville, NY, 13656. Tel: 315-658-2703. Fax: 315-658-2513. p. 1650

Orwell, Mike, Head, Per, Ref Serv, Ad, New Castle Public Library, 207 E North St, New Castle, PA, 16101-3691. Tel: 724-658-6659. Fax: 724-658-7209. p. 2096

Oryall, Lyn, Dir, Santaquin City Library, 20 W 100 S, Santaquin, UT, 84655. Tel: 801-754-3030. Fax: 801-754-3030. p. 2416

Orzech, Mary Jo, Dir, State University of New York College at Brockport, 350 New Campus Dr, Brockport, NY, 14420-2997. Tel: 585-395-2140. Fax: 585-395-5651. p. 1585

Orzel, Linda, Asst Dir, Harris-Stowe State University Library, 3026 Laclede Ave, Saint Louis, MO, 63103-2199. Tel: 314-340-3621. Fax: 314-340-3630. p. 1355

Osbon, Ann, Asst Dir, Cranston Public Library, 140 Sockanosset Cross Rd, Cranston, RI, 02920-5539. Tel: 401-943-9080. Fax: 401-946-5079. p. 2164

Osborn, Barbara, Ch, Allegan District Library, 331 Hubbard St, Allegan, MI, 49010. Tel: 269-673-4625. Fax: 269-673-8661. p. 1148

Osborn, Beverly, Head, Automation, Union County Public Library, 316 E Windsor St, Monroe, NC, 28112. Tel: 704-283-8184. Fax: 704-282-0657. p. 1810

Osborn, Cassie, Dir, Earlham Public Library, 120 S Chestnut St, Earlham, IA, 50072. Tel: 515-758-2121. Fax: 515-758-2121. p. 813

Osborn, Cheryl, Br Head, Greater Victoria Public Library Board, Esquimalt, 1231 Esquimalt Rd, Victoria, BC, V9A 3P1, CANADA. Tel: 250-414-7198. Fax: 250-412-8542. p. 2745

Osborn, Dixie A, Dir, Nora E Larabee Memorial Library, 108 N Union St, Stafford, KS, 67578-1339. Tel: 620-234-5762. p. 895

Osborn, Edmond, Commun Libr Mgr, County of Los Angeles Public Library, Maywood Cesar Chavez Library, 4323 E Slauson Ave, Maywood, CA, 90270-2837. Tel: 323-771-8600. Fax: 323-560-0515. p. 142

Osborn, Lucie P, County Librn, Laramie County Library System, 2200 Pioneer Ave, Cheyenne, WY, 82001-3610. Tel: 307-773-7220. Fax: 307-634-2082. p. 2652

Osborn, Melissa, Acq, Ser, Penn State Erie, 4951 College Dr, Erie, PA, 16563-4115. Tel: 814-898-6106. Fax: 814-898-6350. p. 2056

Osborn, Pam, Asst Dir, White Lake Community Library, 3900 White Lake Dr, Whitehall, MI, 49461-9257. Tel: 231-894-9531. Fax: 231-893-8821. p. 1237

Osborn-Bensaada, Charlotte, Legis Librn, Thompson Coburn Library, 1909 K St NW, Ste 600, Washington, DC, 20006. Tel: 202-585-6900. Fax: 202-585-6969. p. 416

Osborne, Anne Reever, Asst Dir, Distance Learning, Webmaster, Tusculum College, Hwy 107, 60 Shiloh Rd, Greeneville, TN, 37743. Tel: 423-636-7320, Ext 5801. Fax: 423-787-8498. p. 2236

Osborne, Annette, Mgr, Okefenokee Regional Library, Appling County Public, 301 City Hall Dr, Baxley, GA, 31513. Tel: 912-367-8103. Fax: 912-367-8104. p. 557

Osborne, Becki, Circ, Thorntown Public Library, 124 N Market St, Thorntown, IN, 46071-1144. Tel: 765-436-7348. Fax: 765-436-7011. p. 782

Osborne, Caroline L, Libr Dir, Washington & Lee University, Wilbur C Hall Law Library, Lewis Hall, E Denny Circle, Lexington, VA, 24450. Tel: 540-458-8545. Fax: 540-458-8967. p. 2474

Osborne, Cindy, Br Mgr, High Plains Library District, Lincoln Park, 919 Seventh St, Ste 100, Greeley, CO, 80631. Tel: 970-506-8480. Fax: 970-506-8461. p. 312

Osborne, Crystal M, Dir, Elizabeth Jones Library, 1050 Fairfield Ave, Grenada, MS, 38901-3605. Tel: 662-226-2072. Fax: 662-226-8747. p. 1299

Osborne, Diane, Ser, Bellevue University, 1000 Galvin Rd S, Bellevue, NE, 68005. Tel: 402-557-7312. Fax: 402-557-5427. p. 1393

Osborne, Dianne, Libr Dir, Hancock County Public Library, 900 W McKenzie Rd, Greenfield, IN, 46140-1741. Tel: 317-467-6663. Fax: 317-462-5711. p. 746

Osborne, Donna, Dir, Berkeley County Library System, 1003 Hwy 52, Moncks Corner, SC, 29461. Tel: 843-719-4243. p. 2200

Osborne, Dot, Br Head, Charleston County Public Library, Folly Beach Branch, 45 Center St, Folly Beach, SC, 29439. Tel: 843-588-2001. p. 2183

Osborne, Jennifer, Teen Serv, Brighton District Library, 100 Library Dr, Brighton, MI, 48116. Tel: 810-229-6571, Ext 213. Fax: 810-229-3161. p. 1159

Osborne, Lori, Archivist, Evanston History Center Library & Archives, 225 Greenwood St, Evanston, IL, 60201. Tel: 847-475-3410. Fax: 847-475-3599. p. 643

Osborne, Mary, Med Librn, Providence Little Company of Mary San Pedro Hospital, 1300 W Seventh St, San Pedro, CA, 90732. Tel: 310-543-5911. p. 256

Osborne, Mary Ellen, Asst Librn, Ledyard Public Libraries, Gales Ferry Library, 18 Hurlbutt Rd, Gales Ferry, CT, 06335. Tel: 860-464-6943. p. 349

Osborne, Peter, III, Archives, Exec Dir, Minisink Valley Historical Society Library, 127 W Main St, Port Jervis, NY, 12771-1808. Tel: 845-856-2375. Fax: 845-856-1049. p. 1721

Osborne, Reed, Dir, Operations, Arapahoe Library District, 12855 E Adam Aircraft Circle, Englewood, CO, 80112. Tel: 303-542-7279. Fax: 303-798-2485. p. 305

Osborne, Vivian, Per, Texarkana College, 2500 N Robison Rd, Texarkana, TX, 75599. Tel: 903-832-5565, Ext 3231. Fax: 903-831-7429. p. 2391

Osburn, Charles, Prof, University of Alabama, 514 Main Library, Tuscaloosa, AL, 35487. Tel: 205-348-4610. Fax: 205-348-3746. p. 2961

Osburn, Gloria, Dir, Montpelier Public Library, 216 E Main St, Montpelier, OH, 43543-1199. Tel: 419-485-3287. Fax: 419-485-5671. p. 1918

Osburn, Pat, Ref Serv, Sullivan County Public Library, 100 S Crowder St, Sullivan, IN, 47882. Tel: 812-268-4957. Fax: 812-268-5370. p. 780

Osburn, Wade, Ref Serv, Freed-Hardeman University, 158 E Main St, Henderson, TN, 38340-2399. Tel: 731-989-6067. Fax: 731-989-6065. p. 2237

Osburne, Andrew, Res Ctr Mgr, Lake County Discovery Museum, 27277 Forest Preserve Dr, Wauconda, IL, 60084. Tel: 847-968-3381. Fax: 847-526-1545. p. 716

Osei-Sarfo, Olivia, Mgr, Chesapeake Public Library, Dr Clarence V Cuffee Library, 2726 Border Rd, Chesapeake, VA, 23324-3760. Tel: 757-410-7040. Fax: 757-410-7044. p. 2456

Osemota, Lucy, Evening/Weekend Librn, DeVry University, 2300 SW 145th Ave, Miramar, FL, 33027-4150. Tel: 954-499-9619. Fax: 954-499-9659. p. 470

Osen, Rick, Interim Dean of Libr, Western Washington University, 516 High St, MS 9103, Bellingham, WA, 98225. Tel: 360-650-3051. Fax: 360-650-3044. p. 2509

Osenenko, Natalie, Tech Serv, University of Medicine & Dentistry of New Jersey, 30 12th Ave, Newark, NJ, 07103-2706. Tel: 973-972-4580. p. 1513

Osenga, Annette, Dir, Life Chiropractic College-West Library, 25001 Industrial Blvd, Hayward, CA, 94545. Tel: 510-780-4507. Fax: 510-780-4590. p. 158

Osepchook, Felicity, Head Librn, New Brunswick Museum Archives & Research Library, 277 Douglas Ave, Saint John, NB, E2K 1E5, CANADA. Tel: 506-643-2324. Fax: 506-643-2360. p. 2767

Oser, Lynn, Dir, Wilmer, Cutler, Hale & Dorr Library, 1875 Pennsylvnia Ave NW, Washington, DC, 20006. Tel: 202-663-6771. Fax: 202-663-6363. p. 423

Oser, Lynn K, Mgr, Hale & Dorr Library, 60 State St, Boston, MA, 02109. Tel: 617-526-5900. Fax: 617-526-5000. p. 1061

Osgood, Alice, Ref Serv, North Castle Public Library, 19 Whippoorwill Rd E, Armonk, NY, 10504. Tel: 914-273-3887. Fax: 914-273-5572. p. 1575

OShea, Shannon, Prog Serv, United Nations Childrens Fund Library, Three UN Plaza, H-12C UNICEF House, New York, NY, 10017. Tel: 212-326-7064. Fax: 212-303-7989. p. 1702

Osif, Bonnie, Librn, Pennsylvania State University Libraries, Engineering, 325 Hammond Bldg, University Park, PA, 16802. Tel: 814-865-3697. Fax: 814-863-5989. p. 2148

Ositis, Kim, Ref, King County Law Library, W 621 King County Courthouse, 516 Third Ave, Seattle, WA, 98104. Tel: 206-296-0940. Fax: 206-205-0513. p. 2528

Oskey, Kelly, Circ Librn, Black Creek Village Library, 507 S Maple St, Black Creek, WI, 54106-9304. Tel: 920-984-3094. Fax: 920-984-3559. p. 2582

Oski, Judith, Ref, Gloucester, Lyceum & Sawyer Free Library, Two Dale Ave, Gloucester, MA, 01930-5906. Tel: 978-281-9763. Fax: 978-281-9770. p. 1091

Osland, Robin, Dir, Libr Serv, Redwood Falls Public Library, 509 S Lincoln St, Redwood Falls, MN, 56283. Tel: 507-627-8650. Fax: 507-627-5004. p. 1272

Osland, Sunny, Br Mgr, Jackson County Library, Heron Lake Branch, 401 Ninth St, Heron Lake, MN, 56137-1440. Tel: 507-793-2641. Fax: 507-793-2641. p. 1255

Oslund, Janet, Ch, Montrose Regional Library District, 320 S Second St, Montrose, CO, 81401-3909. Tel: 970-249-9656. Fax: 970-240-1901. p. 318

Oslund, Sandra, Dir, Bethel Seminary Library, 3949 Bethel Dr, Saint Paul, MN, 55112. Tel: 651-638-6184. Fax: 651-638-6006. p. 1277

Osmanski, Paul, Librn, Marist College Library, 815 Varnum St NE, Washington, DC, 20017-2199. Tel: 202-529-2821. p. 408

Osmanski, Paul S, Tech Serv, Woodstock Theological Center Library, Georgetown University, Lauinger Library, PO Box 571170, Washington, DC, 20057-1170. Tel: 202-687-7473. Fax: 202-687-7473. p. 423

Osmon, Lori, Youth Serv Librn, Washington Carnegie Public Library, 300 W Main St, Washington, IN, 47501-2698. Tel: 812-254-4586. Fax: 812-254-4585. p. 786

Osmond, Kathy, Pub Info Officer, Onondaga County Public Library, The Galleries of Syracuse, 447 S Salina St, Syracuse, NY, 13202-2494. Fax: 315-435-8533. p. 1752

Osmond, Shirley, Librn, Wapiti Regional Library, Cudworth Public Library, 426 Second Ave, Cudworth, SK, S0K 1B0, CANADA. Tel: 306-256-3530. p. 2921

Osmun, Curtis, Syst Librn, Art Institute of Chicago, 111 S Michigan Ave, Chicago, IL, 60603. Tel: 312-443-3671. Fax: 312-443-0849. p. 606

Osmun, Debbie, Br Mgr, Easton Area Public Library & District Center, Southside, 401 W Berwick St, Easton, PA, 18042. Tel: 610-258-3121. p. 2052

Osnes, Julie, Youth Serv Librn, Wayne Public Library, Robert B & Mary Y Benthack Library-Senior Ctr, 410 Pearl St, Wayne, NE, 68787. Tel: 402-375-3135. Fax: 402-375-5772. p. 1422

Osorio, Alba, Head, Puerto Rican Coll, University of Puerto Rico, Minillas Park, 170, 174 Rd, Bayamon, PR, 00959-1919. Tel: 787-993-0000, Ext 3222, 787-993-8857. Fax: 787-993-8914. p. 2672

Osorio, Audra, Ch, YA Serv, Mount Olive Public Library, 202 Flanders-Drakestown Rd, Flanders, NJ, 07836. Tel: 973-691-8686. Fax: 973-691-8542. p. 1485

Osorio, Nestor, Head, Ref & Res Serv, Northern Illinois University Libraries, DeKalb, IL, 60115-2868. Tel: 815-753-9837. p. 635

Osorio, Nestor, Ref Serv, Northern Illinois University Libraries, Faraday Library, Faraday Hall, Rm 212, DeKalb, IL, 60115. Tel: 815-753-9837. p. 635

Osorio, Sylvana, AV, Highland Park Public Library, 494 Laurel Ave, Highland Park, IL, 60035-2690. Tel: 847-432-0216. Fax: 847-432-9139. p. 655

Osowetski, Maureen, Libr Mgr, Brownvale Community Library, PO Box 407, Grimshaw, AB, T0H 0L0, CANADA. Tel: 780-597-2250. p. 2706

Osowski, June, Ch, Rutland Free Library, Ten Court St, Rutland, VT, 05701-4058. Tel: 802-773-1860. Fax: 802-773-1825. p. 2434

Osseni, Raimi, In Charge, Statistics Canada, 200-123 Main St, Winnipeg, MB, R3C 1A3, CANADA. Tel: 204-983-5883. Fax: 204-983-7543. p. 2757

Ossi, Kathy, Assoc Dir, Tech Serv, Williamson County Public Library, 1314 Columbia Ave, Franklin, TN, 37064-3626. Tel: 615-794-3105. Fax: 615-595-1245. p. 2234

Ost, Barbara, Assoc Librn, New York State Department of Correctional Services, State Campus, Bldg 2, Library Services, 1220 Washington Ave, Albany, NY, 12226-2050. Tel: 518-485-7109. Fax: 518-402-1742. p. 1569

Ost, Barbara A, Sr Librn, Coll Mgt, SIRSI Adminr, New York State Department of Law Library, The Capitol, Albany, NY, 12224. Tel: 518-474-3840. Fax: 518-473-1822. p. 1569

Ost, Evelyn, Dir, Rock County Public Library, 400 State St, Bassett, NE, 68714. Tel: 402-684-3800. Fax: 402-684-3930. p. 1392

Ostapchuk, Halyna, Librn, Saint Vladimir Institute Library, 620 Spadina Ave, Toronto, ON, M5S 2H4, CANADA. Tel: 416-923-3318. Fax: 416-923-8266. p. 2858

Ostaszewski, Ted, Tech Serv Coordr, Metropolitan Community College, Penn Valley Community College Library, 3201 SW Trafficway, Kansas City, MO, 64111-2764. Tel: 816-759-4095. p. 1339

Ostberg, Kathy, Adminr, Free Public Library of Audubon, 239 Oakland Ave, Audubon, NJ, 08106-1598. Tel: 856-547-8686. Fax: 856-547-0277. p. 1470

Ostby, Keri, Head, Tech Serv, Rochester Public Library, 101 Second St SE, Rochester, MN, 55904-3776. Tel: 507-328-2355. Fax: 507-328-2384. p. 1273

Ostby, Lloyd, Br Mgr, Norfolk Public Library, Lafayette, 1610 Cromwell Rd, Norfolk, VA, 23509. Tel: 757-441-2842. Fax: 757-441-1454. p. 2482

Osteen, Jerry, Info Tech Mgr, Greenville County Library System, 25 Heritage Green Pl, Greenville, SC, 29601-2034. Tel: 864-242-5000, Ext 4231. Fax: 864-235-8375. p. 2196

Ostendorf, Joellen, Dir, Troup-Harris Regional Library System, 115 Alford St, La Grange, GA, 30240-3041. Tel: 706-882-7784, Ext 12. Fax: 706-883-7342. p. 537

Ostendorp, Emma, Adult Literacy Coordr, Howard County Library System, Central Branch, 10375 Little Patuxent Pkwy, Columbia, MD, 21044-3499. Tel: 410-313-7900. Fax: 410-313-7864. p. 1026

Oster, Dianne, Archivist, Govt Doc Librn, Ser, Seton Hall University, One Newark Ctr, Newark, NJ, 07102. Tel: 973-642-8195. p. 1513

Osterbur, David, Access Serv, Harvard Library, Francis A Countway Library of Medicine, Boston Med Libr-Harvard Med Libr, Ten Shattuck St, Boston, MA, 02115. Tel: 617-432-4807. p. 1074

Ostercamp, Matt, Head, Syst, Head, Tech Serv, Trinity International University, 2065 Half Day Rd, Deerfield, IL, 60015-1241. Tel: 847-317-4005. Fax: 847-317-4012. p. 635

Osterhaus, Leah, Health Sci Librn, Mayo Clinic Health System - La Crosse, 700 West Ave S, La Crosse, WI, 54601. Tel: 608-785-0940, Ext 2685. Fax: 608-392-9495. p. 2603

Osterhoudt, Peter, Electronic Res, College of Saint Rose, 392-396 Western Ave, Albany, NY, 12203. Tel: 518-454-2026. Fax: 518-454-2897. p. 1568

Osterhout, Laura, Mem Serv Librn, Rochester Regional Library Council, 390 Packetts Landing, Fairport, NY, 14450. Tel: 585-223-7570. Fax: 585-223-7712. p. 2950

Osterreicher, Angela, Head, Libr & Info Serv, University of Manitoba Libraries, J W Crane Memorial Library, 2109 Portage Ave, Winnipeg, MB, R3J 0L3, CANADA. Tel: 204-831-2152. Fax: 204-888-1805. p. 2758

Ostertag, Karen, Coll Develop Librn, New City Free Library, 220 N Main St, New City, NY, 10956. Tel: 845-634-4997. p. 1665

Ostertag, Patricia, Circ, Mars Area Public Library, 107 Grand Ave, Mars, PA, 16046. Tel: 724-625-9048. Fax: 724-625-2871. p. 2084

Ostertag-Holtkamp, Barbara, Dir, Leach Library, 276 Mammoth Rd, Londonderry, NH, 03053. Tel: 603-432-1132. Fax: 603-437-6610. p. 1454

Osterud, Amelia, Access Serv, Carroll College, 100 N East Ave, Waukesha, WI, 53186. Tel: 262-650-4888. Fax: 262-524-7377. p. 2644

Osther, Jennifer, Librn, IBI Group Library, 230 Richmond St W, 5th Flr, Toronto, ON, M5V 1V6, CANADA. Tel: 416-596-1930, Ext 1250. Fax: 416-596-0644. p. 2854

Ostiguy, Christiane, Libr Tech, Institut de Recherche d'Hydro-Quebec Bibliotheque, 1800 Lionel-Boulet Blvd, CP 1000, Varennes, QC, J3X 1S1, CANADA. Tel: 450-652-8999. Fax: 450-652-8040. p. 2914

Ostiguy, Colleen, Computer Librn, Albany Law School, 80 New Scotland Ave, Albany, NY, 12208. Tel: 518-445-2340. Fax: 518-472-5842. p. 1568

Osting, Lori, Ref Librn, Greensburg-Decatur County Public Library, 1110 E Main St, Greensburg, IN, 47240. Tel: 812-663-2826. Fax: 812-663-5617. p. 746

Ostler, Jon, Dir of Libr, Snow College, 141 E Center St, Ephraim, UT, 84627. Tel: 435-283-7363. Fax: 435-283-7369. p. 2405

Ostness, Diana, Dir, Cumberland Public Library, 1305 Second Ave, Cumberland, WI, 54829. Tel: 715-822-2767. p. 2587

Ostovich, Karen, Access Serv Mgr, College of Saint Scholastica Library, 1200 Kenwood Ave, Duluth, MN, 55811-4199. Tel: 218-723-6140. Fax: 218-723-5948. p. 1247

Ostrander, Angela, Librn, Faith Public Library, 204 W Fifth St, Faith, SD, 57626. Tel: 605-967-2262. Fax: 605-967-2153. p. 2212

Ostroff, Christina, Digital Serv Librn, Manhattanville College Library, 2900 Purchase St, Purchase, NY, 10577. Tel: 914-323-5385. Fax: 914-323-8139. p. 1724

Ostrom, Vicky, Dir, J R Huffman Public Library, 375 Sabine St, Hemphill, TX, 75948. Tel: 409-787-4829. Fax: 409-787-2957. p. 2331

Ostrowski, Lawrence, Dir, White Lake Township Library, 7527 E Highland Rd, White Lake, MI, 48383-2938. Tel: 248-698-4942, Ext 7. Fax: 248-698-2550. p. 1236

Ostrowski, Marzenna, Coll Mgt Librn, Bucks County Community College Library, 275 Swamp Rd, Newtown, PA, 18940-0999. Tel: 215-504-8619. Fax: 215-968-8142. p. 2097

Ostrum, Catherine, Librn, Atlantic County Library System, Hammonton Branch, 451 Egg Harbor Rd, Hammonton, NJ, 08037. Tel: 609-561-2264. Fax: 609-561-1816. p. 1500

Osuch, Barbara Byrne, Dir, Park Forest Public Library, 400 Lakewood Blvd, Park Forest, IL, 60466. Tel: 708-748-3731. Fax: 708-748-8127. p. 688

Osuji, Cassandra, Circ Mgr, United States Army, Grant Library, 1637 Flint St, Fort Carson, CO, 80913-4105. Tel: 719-526-2350. Fax: 719-524-0070. p. 307

Osuna, Linda, Circ Mgr, Hillsboro Public Library, 2850 NE Brookwood Pkwy, Hillsboro, OR, 97124-5327. Tel: 503-615-6500. Fax: 503-615-6601. p. 2000

Oswald, Dawn, Circ Supvr, ILL, Penn State University York, 1031 Edgecomb Ave, York, PA, 17403-3398. Tel: 717-771-4020. Fax: 717-771-4022. p. 2159

Oswald, Debra, Ref Serv, Sinclair Community College Library, 444 W Third St, Dayton, OH, 45402-1460. Tel: 937-512-2855. Fax: 937-512-4564. p. 1894

Oswald, Diane, Ch, Decatur Public Library, 1700 Hwy 51 S, Decatur, TX, 76234-9292. Tel: 940-627-5512. Fax: 940-627-2905. p. 2311

Oswald, Leah, Ch, Iola Public Library, 218 E Madison Ave, Iola, KS, 66749. Tel: 620-365-3262. Fax: 620-365-5137. p. 874

Oswald, Patricia, Asst Librn, Alice M Farr Library, 1603 L St, Aurora, NE, 68818-2132. Tel: 402-694-2272. Fax: 402-694-2273. p. 1392

Oswell, Michelle, Librn, Rutgers University Libraries, Blanche & Irving Laurie Music Library, Eight Chapel Dr, New Brunswick, NJ, 08901-8527. Tel: 732-932-9783, Ext 36. Fax: 732-932-6777. p. 1509

Oszakiewski, Robert, Librn, Porter, Wright, Morris & Arthur, 1919 Pennsylvania Ave NW, Ste 500, Washington, DC, 20006-3434. Tel: 202-778-3044. Fax: 202-778-3063. p. 413

Ota, Sumie, Chief Librn, New York Public Library - Astor, Lenox & Tilden Foundations, Stephen A Schwarzman Building, Fifth Ave & 42nd St, New York, NY, 10018. Tel: 212-930-0716. p. 1693

Otaa-Gyamfi, Naana, Head Librn, DeVry University Library, 4800 Regent Blvd, Irving, TX, 75063-2440. Tel: 972-929-9336. Fax: 972-929-6778. p. 2346

Otak, Leah, Operations Dir, Nunavut Research Institute, PO Box 210, Igloolik, NU, X0A 0L0, CANADA. Tel: 867-934-2069. Fax: 867-934-2058. p. 2789

Otero, Maria M, Dir, University of Puerto Rico, Law School Library, Avenidas Ponce de Leon & Gandara, San Juan, PR, 00931. Tel: 787-999-9684, 787-999-9702. Fax: 787-999-9680. p. 2676

Oti, Felicia, Asst Dir, Franklin Public Library, 118 Main St, Franklin, MA, 02038. Tel: 508-520-4940. p. 1090

Otin, Gracie, Ref, Galveston College, 4015 Ave Q, Galveston, TX, 77550. Tel: 409-944-1240. Fax: 409-944-1521. p. 2326

Otis, Alexander, Dir, Libr Serv, Danville Public Library, Law, 511 Patton St, Danville, VA, 24541. Tel: 434-799-5195, Ext 7. Fax: 434-799-5118. p. 2459

Otis, Alexander, Dir, Libr Serv, Danville Public Library, Westover, 94 Clifton St, Danville, VA, 24541. Tel: 434-799-5195, Ext 7. p. 2460

Otis, Carroll, Per, St Luke's-Roosevelt Hospital Center, 1111 Amsterdam Ave, New York, NY, 10025. Tel: 212-523-4315. Fax: 212-523-4313. p. 1699

Otis, Linda, Tech Serv, Delray Beach Public Library, 100 W Atlantic Ave, Delray Beach, FL, 33444. Tel: 561-266-0194. Fax: 561-266-9757. p. 437

Otis, Maura Jean, Dir, Gays Mills Public Library, 205 Main St, Gays Mills, WI, 54631-8158. Tel: 608-735-4331. p. 2593

Otis, Sally, Librn, Hazard Library Association, 2487 Rte 34 B, Poplar Ridge, NY, 13139. Tel: 315-364-7975. Fax: 315-364-6704. p. 1720

Otsu, Kiyoshi, Media Librn, Indiana University, Ruth Lilly Law Library, 530 W New York St, Indianapolis, IN, 46202-3225. Tel: 317-274-3884, 317-274-4028. Fax: 317-274-8825. p. 752

Ott, Andrew, Libr Mgr, Blackburn College, 700 College Ave, Carlinville, IL, 62626. Tel: 217-854-3231, Ext 4220. Fax: 217-854-3231, 217-854-8564. p. 600

Ott, Arlene, Libr Dir, United States Air Force, 319 FSS/FSDL, 511 Holzapple St, Bldg 201, Grand Forks AFB, ND, 58205. Tel: 701-747-3046. Fax: 701-747-4584. p. 1843

Ott, Brian, Info Tech, Hampton Public Library, 4207 Victoria Blvd, Hampton, VA, 23669-4243. Tel: 757-727-1154. Fax: 757-727-1152. p. 2468

Ott, Carol, Circ, Mount Union College Library, 1972 Clark Ave, Alliance, OH, 44601-3993. Tel: 330-823-3844. Fax: 330-823-3963. p. 1854

Ott, Elaine, Dir, Marble Rock Public Library, 105 S Main St, Marble Rock, IA, 50653. Tel: 641-315-4480. Fax: 641-315-4480. p. 829

Ott, Elaine, Libr Asst, Aultman Hospital, Aultman Education Ctr, C2-230, 2600 Seventh St SW, Canton, OH, 44710-1799. Tel: 330-363-5000. Fax: 330-363-2604. p. 1863

Ott, Gail, Head of Libr, Jefferson-Madison Regional Library, Louisa County, 881 Davis Hwy, Mineral, VA, 23117. Tel: 540-894-5853. Fax: 540-894-9810. p. 2454

Ott, Katherine, Access & Info Serv Chair, Asst Dean, Clayton State University, 2000 Clayton State Blvd, Morrow, GA, 30260. Tel: 678-466-4325. Fax: 678-466-4349. p. 545

Ott, Lenie, Sr Dir, McCarthy Tétrault LLP, T-D Centre, Ste 5300, Toronto Dominion Bank Tower, Toronto, ON, M5K 1E6, CANADA. Tel: 416-601-8200, Ext 542737. Fax: 416-868-0673. p. 2855

Ott, Martha T, Dir, Kaplan University, 265 Western Ave, South Portland, ME, 04106. Tel: 207-774-6126, Ext 8745. Fax: 207-774-1715. p. 1001

Ott, Robin, In Charge, Huntington Beach Public Library System, Main Street Branch, 525 Main St, Huntington Beach, CA, 92648-5133. Tel: 714-375-5071. Fax: 714-375-5072. p. 159

Ott, Robin, Libr Spec, Huntington Beach Public Library System, Banning, 9281 Banning Ave, Huntington Beach, CA, 92646-8302. Tel: 714-375-5005. Fax: 714-375-5091. p. 159

Ott, Sandy, Dir, Elgin Public Library, 404 N Main St, Elgin, TX, 78621. Tel: 512-281-5678. Fax: 512-285-3015. p. 2318

Ott-Hamilton, Sandra, Dir, Alva Public Library, 504 Seventh St, Alva, OK, 73717. Tel: 580-327-1833. Fax: 580-327-5329. p. 1956

Ottaviano, Tom, Govt Doc, State University of New York College at Geneseo, SUNY Geneseo, One College Circle, Geneseo, NY, 14454-1498. p. 1627

Otte, Bobbi, Asst Dir, Rocky Mountain College, 1511 Poly Dr, Billings, MT, 59102-1796. Tel: 406-657-1086. Fax: 406-657-1085. p. 1374

Otte, Michelle, Dir, Kenyon Public Library, 709 Second St, Kenyon, MN, 55946-1339. Tel: 507-789-6821. Fax: 507-789-5604. p. 1255

Otte, Sue Prifogle, Dir, Rushville Public Library, 130 W Third St, Rushville, IN, 46173-1899. Tel: 765-932-3496. Fax: 765-932-4528. p. 776

Ottelien, Patricia, Asst Librn, Saint Joseph's Hospital, 611 Saint Joseph Ave, Marshfield, WI, 54449. Tel: 715-387-7374. Fax: 715-387-7107. p. 2613

Otten, Cheryl, Youth Serv, Neptune Public Library, 25 Neptune Blvd, Neptune, NJ, 07753-1125. Tel: 732-775-8241. Fax: 732-774-1132. p. 1507

Ottenhoff, Faith, Sr Res Librn, Finnegan, Henderson, Farabow, Garrett & Dunner, 901 New York Ave NW, Washington, DC, 20001-4413. Tel: 202-408-4364. Fax: 202-408-4400. p. 400

Otter, Saralyn, Supv Librn, Ch, Santa Clara County Library District, Morgan Hill Branch, 660 W Main Ave, Morgan Hill, CA, 95037-4128. Tel: 408-779-3196. Fax: 408-779-0883. p. 181

Otterson, Linda, Dir, Kindred Public Library, 330 Elm St, Kindred, ND, 58051. Tel: 701-428-3456, kindredpubliclibrary@gmail.com. p. 1845

Otterstrom-Cedar, Christina, Librn, Rycroft Municipal Library, 4732 50th St, Rycroft, AB, T0H 3A0, CANADA. Tel: 780-765-3973. Fax: 780-765-2002. p. 2715

Ottervik, Jennifer, Head Librn, Johns Hopkins University-Peabody Conservatory of Music, 21 E Mount Vernon Pl, Baltimore, MD, 21202-2397. Tel: 410-234-4594. Fax: 410-685-0657. p. 1015

Ottinger, Jeanne M, Ref Librn, Law Library of Montgomery County, Court House, Swede & Airy Streets, Norristown, PA, 19404. Tel: 610-278-3806. Fax: 610-278-5998. p. 2098

Ottman, Claire, Dir, Mgr, Cherry Valley Memorial Library, 61 Main St, Cherry Valley, NY, 13320. Tel: 607-264-8214. Fax: 607-264-8214. p. 1606

Ottman, June, Tech Serv, Ida Public Library, 320 N State St, Belvidere, IL, 61008-3299. Tel: 815-544-3838. Fax: 815-544-8909. p. 594

Otto, Carol, Pub Serv, Syst Adminr, California University of Pennsylvania, 250 University Ave, California, PA, 15419-1394. Tel: 724-938-4091. Fax: 724-938-5901. p. 2040

Otto, Julie, Ref Serv, New England Historic Genealogical Society Library, 99-101 Newbury St, Boston, MA, 02116-3007. Tel: 617-536-5740. Fax: 617-536-7307. p. 1065

Otto, Kathie, Head, Univ Archives & Area Res Ctr, University of Wisconsin-River Falls, 410 S Third St, River Falls, WI, 54022. Tel: 715-425-3567. Fax: 715-425-0609. p. 2635

Otto, Mary, Tech Serv, Helen Kate Furness Free Library, 100 N Providence Rd, Wallingford, PA, 19086. Tel: 610-566-9331. Fax: 610-566-9337. p. 2150

Otto, Molly, Mgr, Libr Serv, Colorado Joint Legislative Council, State Capitol Bldg, Rm 048, 200 E Colfax Ave, Denver, CO, 80203-1784. Tel: 303-866-4011. Fax: 303-866-2167. p. 299

Otto, Peter, Pub Serv, Mercer University Atlanta, 3001 Mercer University Dr, Atlanta, GA, 30341. Tel: 678-547-6256. Fax: 678-547-6270. p. 517

Otto, Theophil, Coll Develop, Eastern Washington University, 816 F St, 100 LIB, Cheney, WA, 99004-2453. Tel: 509-359-7895. Fax: 509-359-6456. p. 2512

Ottolenghi, Carol, Dir, Libr Serv, Ohio Attorney General, 30 E Broad St, 15th Flr, Columbus, OH, 43215. Tel: 614-466-2465, 614-466-4534. Fax: 614-752-9867. p. 1886

Ottosen, Charles, Librn, Regina Public Library, Glen Elm, 1601 Dewdney Ave E, Regina, SK, S4N 4N6, CANADA. Tel: 306-777-6080. Fax: 306-949-7268. p. 2923

Ottoson, Carolyn, Doc Librn, West Texas A&M University, University Dr & 26th St, Canyon, TX, 79016. Tel: 806-651-2204. Fax: 806-651-2213. p. 2294

Ottoson, Robin D, Libr Dir, Tabor College Library, 400 S Jefferson St, Hillsboro, KS, 67063. Tel: 620-947-3121, Ext 1202. Fax: 620-947-2607. p. 872

Otts, Martin, Info Spec, Hickory Public Library, 375 Third St NE, Hickory, NC, 28601-5126. Tel: 828-304-0500, Ext 7280. Fax: 828-304-0023. p. 1801

Ottum, Tamara, Syst Librn, Middlesex Community College, 100 Training Hill Rd, Middletown, CT, 06457-4889. Tel: 860-343-5835. Fax: 860-343-5874. p. 351

Ou, Carol, Syst Librn, Colorado College, 1021 N Cascade Ave, Colorado Springs, CO, 80903-3252. Tel: 719-389-6658. Fax: 719-389-6082. p. 294

Oubraham, Ourida, Actg Dir, Stevens Institute of Technology, Castle Point on Hudson, Hoboken, NJ, 07030. Tel: 201-216-5411. Fax: 201-216-8319. p. 1491

Oubre, Marcia, Librn, Fred Heutte Horticultural Library, c/o Norfolk Botanical Garden, 6700 Azalea Garden Rd, Norfolk, VA, 23518-5337. Tel: 757-441-5830, Ext 359, 757-441-5838. Fax: 757-441-5828. p. 2481

Ouellet, Annette, Ch, Somers Public Library, 51 Ninth District Rd, Somers, CT, 06071-0368. Tel: 860-763-3501. Fax: 860-763-1718. p. 367

Ouellet, Diane, Ref, Cegep Riviere du-Loup-Bibliotheque, 80 rue Frontenac, Riviere-du-Loup, QC, G5R 1R1, CANADA. Tel: 418-862-6903, Ext 2326. Fax: 418-862-4959. p. 2907

Ouellet, Gail, Libr Serv Mgr, Langley-Adams Library, 185 Main St, Groveland, MA, 01834-1314. Tel: 978-372-1732. Fax: 978-374-6590. p. 1093

Ouellet, Jacinthe, Tech Serv, Centre de Santé et de Services Sociaux de la Région de Thetford, 1717 rue Notre-Dame Est, Thetford Mines, QC, G6G 2V4, CANADA. Tel: 418-338-7777, Ext 4019. Fax: 418-338-7786. p. 2913

Ouellet, Marcel, Actg Librn, Hydro Quebec Bibliotheque, 800, De Maisonneuve E, blvd, 2nd Flr, Montreal, QC, H2L 4M8, CANADA. Tel: 514-840-3000, Ext 5939. Fax: 514-840-5044. p. 2896

Ouellet, Martine, In Charge, Hopital Riviere-Des-Prairies, 7070 boul Perras, Montreal, QC, H1E 1A4, CANADA. Tel: 514-323-7260, Ext 2316. Fax: 514-323-3512. p. 2896

Ouellet, Nathalie, Bibliog Instr, Ref, College de Maisonneuve Centre des Medias, 3800 Est rue Sherbrooke E, Montreal, QC, H1X 2A2, CANADA. Tel: 514-254-7131, Ext 4279. Fax: 514-254-2517. p. 2893

Ouellette, Amanda, Libr Asst, Maine State Law & Legislative Reference Library, 43 State House Sta, Augusta, ME, 04333-0043. Tel: 207-287-1600. Fax: 207-287-6467. p. 974

Ouellette, Cheryl Stern, Ch, Sherborn Library, Four Sanger St, Sherborn, MA, 01770-1499. Tel: 508-653-0770. Fax: 508-650-9243. p. 1123

Ouellette, George, Mgr, Digital Assets & Info Tech, Yale University Library, Lewis Walpole Library, 154 Main St, Farmington, CT, 06032. Tel: 860-677-2140. Fax: 860-677-6369. p. 359

Ouellette, Iris Jane, Libr Serv Mgr, Canada Department of National Defence, Nine Grove St, Dartmouth, NS, B3A 3C5, CANADA. Tel: 902-426-3100, Ext 135. Fax: 902-426-9654. p. 2779

Ouellette, Sheila, Dir, Saint Louis Community College, Instructional Resources, 5460 Highland Park Dr, Saint Louis, MO, 63110. Tel: 314-644-9557. p. 1358

Ouimet, Pamela, Communications Coordr, Regional Coordr, Northern New York Library Network, 6721 US Hwy 11, Potsdam, NY, 13676. Tel: 315-265-1119. Fax: 315-265-1881. p. 2950

Oulanov, Alexei, Access & Prog Dir, Medgar Evers College, 1650 Bedford Ave, Brooklyn, NY, 11225-2010. Tel: 718-270-4834. Fax: 718-270-5182. p. 1593

Ourada, Kari, Dir, Westbrook Public Library, 556 First Ave, Westbrook, MN, 56183. Tel: 507-274-6174. Fax: 507-274-6174. p. 1288

Ourom, Julie, Dir of Libr, Department of Community Services, Government of Yukon, Mayo Community, Mayo Administration Bldg, Mayo, YT, Y0B 1M0, CANADA. Tel: 867-996-2541. Fax: 867-996-2203. p. 2933

Ourom, Julie, Dir, Department of Community Services, Government of Yukon, 1171 First Ave, Whitehorse, YT, Y1A 0G9, CANADA. Tel: 867-667-5447. Fax: 867-393-6333. p. 2933

Ours, Michael, Electronic Res, Lynchburg College, 1501 Lakeside Dr, Lynchburg, VA, 24501-3199. Tel: 434-544-8204. Fax: 434-544-8499. p. 2476

Ouse, David, Libr Supvr, Pub Serv, Duluth Public Library, 520 W Superior St, Duluth, MN, 55802. Tel: 218-730-4208. Fax: 218-723-3815, 218-723-3822. p. 1247

Outen, Shirley, Acq, University of South Florida, Hinks & Elaine Shimberg Health Sciences Library, 12901 Bruce B Downs Blvd, MDC Box 31, Tampa, FL, 33612-4799. Tel: 813-974-2399. Fax: 813-974-3605, 813-974-4930. p. 498

Outlaw, Shirley Gray, Tech Serv, College of the Albemarle Library, 1208 N Road St, Elizabeth City, NC, 27906. Tel: 252-335-0821, Ext 2271. Fax: 252-335-0649. p. 1790

Outten, Kathy, ILL Coordr, Joe Barnhart Bee County Public Library, 110 W Corpus Christi St, Beeville, TX, 78102-5604. Tel: 361-362-4901. Fax: 361-358-8694. p. 2288

Outwater, Clay, Chair, Stroke Recovery Association, 80 Bradford St, Unit 239A, Barrie, ON, L4N 6S7, CANADA. Tel: 416-425-4209. Fax: 705-737-9982. p. 2794

Ouyang, Han, Asst Dir, Tech Serv, University of the District of Columbia, David A Clarke School of Law, Charles N & Hilda H M Mason Law Library, Bldg 39, Rm B-16, 4200 Connecticut Ave NW, Washington, DC, 20008. Tel: 202-274-7358. Fax: 202-274-7311. p. 421

Ouzts, Tracey, YA Librn, Greenwood County Library, 600 S Main St, Greenwood, SC, 29646. Tel: 864-941-4650. Fax: 864-941-4651. p. 2197

Ovadia, Steven, Webmaster/Ref Librn, Fiorello H LaGuardia Community College Library, 31-10 Thomson Ave, Long Island City, NY, 11101. Tel: 718-482-5421. Fax: 718-482-5444, 718-609-2011. p. 1654

Ovalle, Norma, Librn, Mathis Public Library, 103 Lamar St, Mathis, TX, 78368. Tel: 361-547-6201. Fax: 361-547-6201. p. 2360

Ovalles, Maria B, Syst & Network Librn, University of Guam, UOG Sta, Mangilao, GU, 96923. Tel: 671-735-2331, 671-735-2332. Fax: 671-734-6882. p. 2667

Overall, Alice D, Librn, Pike-Amite-Walthall Library System, Progress, 5071 Mt Herman Rd, McComb, MS, 39648-9767. Tel: 601-542-5501. p. 1308

Overall, Scott, Asst Curator, Asst Librn, University Club Library, One W 54th St, New York, NY, 10019. Tel: 212-572-3418. Fax: 212-572-3452. p. 1702

Overand, Ellen Rae, Librn, Chinook Regional Library, Shaunavon Branch, Grand Coteau Heritage & Cultural Ctr, 440 Centre St, Shaunavon, SK, S0N 2M0, CANADA. Tel: 306-297-3844. p. 2928

Overdorf, Ryan, Sr Electronic/Media Serv Librn, University of Toledo, LaValley Law Library, Mail Stop 508, 2801 W Bancroft St, Toledo, OH, 43606-3390. Tel: 419-530-2733. Fax: 419-530-5121. p. 1941

Overfield, Joan, Dir & Univ Librn, Fairfield University, 1073 N Benson Rd, Fairfield, CT, 06430-5195. Tel: 203-254-4044. Fax: 203-254-4133. p. 339

Overfield, Susan, Librn, Essex Free Library, Two Browns River Rd, Essex, VT, 05451. Tel: 802-879-0313. p. 2423

Overgaard, Lynn, Dir, Penn Yan Public Library, 214 Main St, Penn Yan, NY, 14527. Tel: 315-536-6114. Fax: 315-536-0131. p. 1716

Overland, Allen, Dir, National Endowment for Democracy Library, 1025 F St NW, Ste 800, Washington, DC, 20004. Tel: 202-378-9700. Fax: 202-378-9407. p. 409

Overley, Garon, Media Tech, Maysville Community & Technical College, 1755 US Hwy 68, Maysville, KY, 41056. Tel: 606-759-7141, Ext 66276. Fax: 606-759-7176. p. 928

Overman, Mark, Libr Tech, Department of Veterans Affairs, 4815 N Assembly St, Spokane, WA, 99205-2697. Tel: 509-434-7575. Fax: 509-434-7103. p. 2535

Overshiner, Barbara, Ref Serv, US Court of Appeals for the Sixth Circuit Library, 312 Potter Stewart US Courthouse, Cincinnati, OH, 45202. Tel: 513-564-7321. Fax: 513-564-7329. p. 1873

Overstreet, Alan, Dir, Provo College Library, 1450 W 820 N, Rm 111, Provo, UT, 84601. Tel: 801-818-8959. Fax: 801-375-9728. p. 2411

Overstreet, Leslie K, Curator, Natural Hist Rare Bks, Smithsonian Libraries, Joseph F Cullman 3rd, Library of Natural History, Nat Museum of Natural Hist, Rm CE-G15, MRC 154, Tenth St & Constitution Ave NW, Washington, DC, 20560. Tel: 202-633-1176. Fax: 202-633-0219. p. 414

Overstreet, Shirley, Librn, Petersburg Public Library, 1614 Main St, Petersburg, TX, 79250. Tel: 806-667-3657. p. 2369

Overton, Catherine, Asst Dir, Baldwin Public Library, 2385 Grand Ave, Baldwin, NY, 11510-3289. Tel: 516-223-6228. Fax: 516-623-7991. p. 1577

Overton, Linda, Head, Ch, Sachem Public Library, 150 Holbrook Rd, Holbrook, NY, 11741. Tel: 631-588-5024. Fax: 631-588-5064. p. 1637

Overton, Robert, Jr, Chief Operating Officer, Pensacola Historical Society, 110 E Church St, Pensacola, FL, 32502. Tel: 850-595-5985, Ext 106. Fax: 850-595-5989. p. 481

Overton, Tammy, Br Mgr, Desoto Parish Library, Stonewall Branch, 808 Hwy 171, Stonewall, LA, 71078. Tel: 318-925-9191. Fax: 318-925-3392. p. 956

Overturf, Jonathan, Interlibrary Serv Coordr, Hollins University, 7950 E Campus Dr, Roanoke, VA, 24020-1000. Tel: 540-362-6591, 540-362-7465. Fax: 540-362-6756. p. 2493

Ovesia, Steluta, Info Spec, Jardin Botanique de Montreal Bibliotheque, 4101 Sherbrooke St E, Montreal, QC, H1X 2B2, CANADA. Tel: 514-872-1440, 514-872-1824. Fax: 514-872-5167. p. 2897

Oviatt, Vinta, Instrul Serv Librn, Orange Coast College Library, 2701 Fairview Rd, Costa Mesa, CA, 92628. Tel: 714-432-5885. Fax: 714-432-6850. p. 137

Owad, Cynthia, Actg Dir, York Haven Community Library, Two N Front St, York Haven, PA, 17370. Tel: 717-266-4712. p. 2160

Owen, Ann, Tech Serv, Sacred Heart School of Theology, 7335 S Hwy 100, Franklin, WI, 53132. Tel: 414-425-8300, Ext 7278. Fax: 414-529-6992. p. 2593

Owen, Bonnie, Librn, Augusta Technical College, 3200 Augusta Tech Dr, Augusta, GA, 30906. Tel: 706-771-4165. Fax: 706-771-4169. p. 519

Owen, Brian, Assoc Univ Librn, Tech Serv & Spec Coll, Simon Fraser University Library, 8888 University Dr, Burnaby, BC, V5A 1S6, CANADA. Tel: 778-782-7095. Fax: 778-782-3023. p. 2725

Owen, Chadwick Brice, Assoc Prof, University of Louisville Libraries, University Archives & Records Center, Ekstrom Library, 2215 S Third St, Louisville, KY, 40208. Tel: 502-852-6674. Fax: 502-852-6673. p. 927

Owen, Christina, Dir, Anadarko Community Library, 215 W Broadway, Anadarko, OK, 73005-2841. Tel: 405-247-7351. Fax: 405-247-2024. p. 1956

Owen, Dana, Circ Asst, ILL, Longwood University, Redford & Race St, Farmville, VA, 23909. Tel: 434-395-2633. Fax: 434-395-2453. p. 2463

Owen, Dana L, Info Serv, Warsaw Community Public Library, 310 E Main St, Warsaw, IN, 46580-2882. Tel: 574-267-6011. Fax: 574-269-7739. p. 785

Owen, Frosty, Librn, Hunton & Williams, Riverfront Plaza, E Tower, 951 E Byrd St, Richmond, VA, 23219-4074. Tel: 804-344-8272. Fax: 804-788-8218. p. 2488

Owen, Hannah, Dep Dir, Youth Serv, Hickory Public Library, 375 Third St NE, Hickory, NC, 28601-5126. Tel: 828-305-0500, Ext 7264. Fax: 828-304-0023. p. 1801

Owen, Henry, III, Bus Librn, Northeastern Illinois University, 5500 N Saint Louis Ave, Chicago, IL, 60625-4699. Tel: 773-442-4420. Fax: 773-442-4531. p. 620

Owen, Jeffrey A, Exec Dir, Hayner Public Library District, 326 Belle St, Alton, IL, 62002. Tel: 618-462-0677. Fax: 618-462-0665. p. 588

Owen, Joseph, Ref, San Juan College Library, 4601 College Blvd, Farmington, NM, 87402. Tel: 505-566-3256. Fax: 505-566-3381. p. 1555

Owen, Keitha, Dir, Ocean Shores Public Library, 573 Point Brown Ave NW, Ocean Shores, WA, 98569. Tel: 360-289-3919. Fax: 360-289-4318. p. 2522

Owen, Matt, Syst Librn, San Diego Christian College, 2100 Greenfield Dr, El Cajon, CA, 92019-1161. Tel: 619-201-8747. Fax: 619-201-8799. p. 145

Owen, Melesha, Br Mgr, Hayward Public Library, Weekes Branch, 27300 Patrick Ave, Hayward, CA, 94544. Tel: 510-293-5239. Fax: 510-259-0429. p. 157

Owen, Richard, Librn, Baptist College of Health Sciences, 1003 Monroe, Memphis, TN, 38104. Tel: 901-572-2677. Fax: 901-572-2674. p. 2247

Owen, Sheila, Assoc Librn, Harding University Graduate School of Religion, 1000 Cherry Rd, Memphis, TN, 38117. Tel: 901-761-1354. p. 2248

Owen, Stephanie, Chairperson, Kennedy-King College, City Colleges of Chicago Library, 6403 S Halsted, Chicago, IL, 60621. Tel: 773-602-5449. Fax: 773-602-5450. p. 616

Owen, Steve, Librn, Northeast Medical Center, 920 Church St N, Concord, NC, 28025. Tel: 704-403-1798. Fax: 704-783-1776. p. 1785

Owen, Susan, Vis Librn, Gustavus Adolphus College, 800 W College Ave, Saint Peter, MN, 56082. Tel: 507-933-7556. Fax: 507-933-6292. p. 1283

Owen, Suzie, Dir, Melton Public Library, 8496 W College St, French Lick, IN, 47432-1026. Tel: 812-936-2177. Fax: 812-936-7524. p. 744

Owen, Theresa, Ch, Flagler County Public Library, 2500 Palm Coast Pkwy NW, Palm Coast, FL, 32137. Tel: 386-446-6763. Fax: 386-446-6773. p. 479

Owen, Thomas Louis, Dr, Assoc Archivist, Prof, University of Louisville Libraries, University Archives & Records Center, Ekstrom Library, 2215 S Third St, Louisville, KY, 40208. Tel: 502-852-8790. Fax: 502-852-6673. p. 927

Owen, Vicky, Bus Mgr, Chickasaw Regional Library System, 601 Railway Express, Ardmore, OK, 73401. Tel: 580-223-3164. Fax: 580-223-3280. p. 1957

Owen, Victoria, Head Librn, University of Toronto Libraries, Scarborough Library, Scarborough College, 1265 Military Trail, Scarborough, ON, M1C 1A4, CANADA. Tel: 416-287-7481. Fax: 416-287-7507. p. 2867

Owen, Walton, Curator, Fort Ward Museum, 4301 W Braddock Rd, Alexandria, VA, 22304-1008. Tel: 703-838-4848. Fax: 703-671-7350. p. 2445

Owen, Will, Assoc Univ Librn, Tech Serv & Syst, University of North Carolina at Chapel Hill, Davis Library, 208 Raleigh St, Campus Box 3900, Chapel Hill, NC, 27514-8890. p. 1780

Owen-Hazard, Nancy, Mgr, El Dorado County Library, Cameron Park Branch, 2500 Country Club Dr, Cameron Park, CA, 95682. Tel: 530-621-5500. Fax: 530-672-1346. p. 208

Owens, Amanda, Librn, Tulsa City-County Library, Pratt, 3219 S 113th West Ave, Sand Springs, OK, 74063. Tel: 918-591-4595. Fax: 918-591-4597. p. 1983

Owens, Audrey, Librn, Public Library of Steubenville & Jefferson County, Brilliant Branch, 103 Steuben St, Brilliant, OH, 43913. Tel: 740-598-4028. Fax: 740-598-4456. p. 1937

Owens, Barbara, Dir, Kinnelon Public Library, 132 Kinnelon Rd, Kinnelon, NJ, 07405-2393. Tel: 973-838-1321. Fax: 973-838-0741. p. 1493

Owens, Bernice, Mgr, Yakama Nation Library, Environmental Restoration Waste Management, 2808 Main St, Yakima, WA, 98903. Tel: 509-452-2502. Fax: 509-452-2503. p. 2541

Owens, Beth, Patron Serv Librn, Cleveland Institute of Art, 11141 East Blvd, Cleveland, OH, 44106. Tel: 216-421-7440, 216-421-7441. Fax: 216-421-7439. p. 1877

Owens, Bethia, Dir, Muldrow Public Library, 711 W Shanntel Smith Blvd, Muldrow, OK, 74948. Tel: 918-427-6703. Fax: 918-427-7315. p. 1969

Owens, Bethia, Librn, Stanley Tubbs Memorial Library, 101 E Cherokee, Sallisaw, OK, 74955. Tel: 918-775-4481. Fax: 918-775-4129. p. 1977

Owens, Brian, Archivist, University of Windsor, 401 Sunset Ave, Windsor, ON, N9B 3P4, CANADA. Tel: 519-253-3000, Ext 3851. p. 2871

Owens, Carla, Mgr, Libr Serv, Chicago Zoological Society, 3300 Golf Rd, Brookfield, IL, 60513. Tel: 708-688-8583. Fax: 708-688-7583. p. 598

Owens, Chris, Dir, Blanchester Public Library, 110 N Broadway, Blanchester, OH, 45107-1250. Tel: 937-783-3585. Fax: 937-783-2910. p. 1860

Owens, Dan, Dir, Walton County Public Library System, Three Circle Dr, De Funiak Springs, FL, 32435-2542. Tel: 850-892-3624. Fax: 850-892-4438. p. 437

Owens, David, Pub Serv Mgr, A T Still University of Health Sciences, Kirksville Campus, 800 W Jefferson St, Kirksville, MO, 63501. Tel: 660-626-2645. Fax: 660-626-2031, 660-626-2333. p. 1342

Owens, David, Head, Tech Serv, University of Missouri-Saint Louis Libraries, One University Blvd, Saint Louis, MO, 63121. Tel: 314-516-5060. Fax: 314-516-5853. p. 1362

Owens, Eleanor, Librn, Westwood First Presbyterian Church Library, 3011 Harrison Ave, Cincinnati, OH, 45211. Tel: 513-661-6846. Fax: 513-389-3683. p. 1874

Owens, Elena, Br Mgr, Wake County Public Library System, Holly Springs Community Library, 300 W Ballentine St, Holly Springs, NC, 27540. Tel: 919-577-1665. Fax: 919-577-1671. p. 1818

Owens, Ellen, Librn, Crouse Hospital Library, 736 Irving Ave, Syracuse, NY, 13210. Tel: 315-470-7380. Fax: 315-470-7443. p. 1751

Owens, Esther, Pub Serv Librn, Hinds Community College, Utica Campus Learning Resources/Library, Hwy 18 W, Utica, MS, 39175-9599. Tel: 601-885-7035. p. 1313

Owens, Evelyn, Librn, Lamson, Dugan & Murray LLP, 10306 Regency Pkwy Dr, Omaha, NE, 68114. Tel: 402-397-7300. Fax: 402-397-7824. p. 1413

Owens, Fonda, Dir, La Porte County Public Library, 904 Indiana Ave, La Porte, IN, 46350-3435. Tel: 219-362-6156. Fax: 219-362-6158. p. 758

Owens, Frances, Librn, Arizona Department of Corrections - Adult Institutions, 4374 Butte Ave, Florence, AZ, 85232. Tel: 520-868-0201, Ext 6207. Fax: 520-868-8556. p. 63

Owens, Genevieve S, Asst Dir, Williamsburg Regional Library, 7770 Croaker Rd, Williamsburg, VA, 23188-7064. Tel: 757-259-7740. Fax: 757-259-4079, 757-259-7798. p. 2503

Owens, Geoff, Access Serv, Mount Royal University Library, 4825 Mount Royal Gate SW, Calgary, AB, T3E 6K6, CANADA. Tel: 403-440-7737. Fax: 403-440-6758. p. 2692

Owens, Glenda, Br Librn, Nelson County Public Library, Bloomfield Branch, 114 Fairfield Hill, Bloomfield, KY, 40008. Tel: 502-252-9129. Fax: 502-252-8255. p. 906

Owens, Glenna, Assoc Dir, Appalachian School of Law Library, 1221 Edgewater Dr, Grundy, VA, 24614-7062. Tel: 276-935-6688, Ext 1303. Fax: 276-935-7138. p. 2467

Owens, Gwen, Dept Head, Georgetown University, Blommer Science Library, 302 Reiss Science Bldg, Box 571230, Washington, DC, 20057-1230. Tel: 202-687-5685. Fax: 202-687-5897. p. 402

Owens, Irene, Dean, North Carolina Central University, 1801 Fayetteville St, Durham, NC, 27707. Tel: 919-530-6485. Fax: 919-530-6402. p. 2971

Owens, Jacqulyn, Librn, Memphis Public Library, 303 S Eight St, Memphis, TX, 79245. Tel: 806-259-2062. Fax: 806-259-2062. p. 2362

Owens, Jennifer, Adult Serv Mgr, Fremont Public Library District, 1170 N Midlothian Rd, Mundelein, IL, 60060. Tel: 847-566-8702. Fax: 847-566-0204. p. 678

Owens, Jill, Dir, Columbus Public Library, 2504 14th St, Columbus, NE, 68601-4988. Tel: 402-564-7116. Fax: 402-563-3378. p. 1396

Owens, Jim, Exec Dir, Indiana Limestone Institute of America, Inc, Stone City Bank Bldg, Ste 400, Bedford, IN, 47421. Tel: 812-275-4426. Fax: 812-279-8682. p. 726

Owens, JoAnne, Asst Dir, Cleveland County Library System, 104 Howie Dr, Shelby, NC, 28150. Tel: 704-487-9069. Fax: 704-487-4856. p. 1823

Owens, Katherine, Ref & Instruction Librn, Flagler College, 44 Sevilla St, Saint Augustine, FL, 32084-4302. Tel: 904-819-6206. Fax: 904-823-8511. p. 486

Owens, Kris, Head Cataloger, Malone University, 2600 Cleveland Ave NW, Canton, OH, 44709-3897. Tel: 330-471-8557. Fax: 330-454-6977. p. 1863

Owens, Lynette, Dir, Viola Public Library, 137 S Main St, Viola, WI, 54664-7037. Tel: 608-627-1850. Fax: 608-627-1850. p. 2643

Owens, Martina, Cat, Lynn Haven Public Library, 901 Ohio Ave, Lynn Haven, FL, 32444. Tel: 850-265-2781. Fax: 850-265-7311. p. 461

Owens, Melissa, Librn, Barnsdall Public Library, 410 S Fifth St, Barnsdall, OK, 74002. Tel: 918-847-2118. Fax: 918-847-2118. p. 1957

Owens, Michael, Mgr, Metropolitan Library System in Oklahoma County, Ralph Ellison Library, 2000 NE 23rd St, Oklahoma City, OK, 73111-3402. Tel: 405-424-1437. Fax: 405-606-3460. p. 1972

Owens, Paige, Asst Dir, New Hanover County Public Library, 201 Chestnut St, Wilmington, NC, 28401. Tel: 910-798-6300. Fax: 910-798-6312. p. 1830

Owens, Patrick, Coll Develop, Central Washington University, 400 E University Way, Ellensburg, WA, 98926-7548. Tel: 509-963-1901. Fax: 509-963-3684. p. 2514

Owens, Rachel, Res Librn, Daytona Beach College Library, 1200 W International Speedway Blvd, Daytona Beach, FL, 32114. Tel: 386-506-3842. Fax: 386-506-3008. p. 435

Owens, Rita, Outreach Serv Librn, Polk County Public Library, 1289 W Mills St, Columbus, NC, 28722. Tel: 828-894-8721. Fax: 828-894-2761. p. 1785

Owens, Sharon, Libr Tech, Elizabeth City State University, 1704 Weeksville Rd, Elizabeth City, NC, 27909. Tel: 252-335-8515. Fax: 252-335-3446. p. 1791

Owens, Sheryl, Managing Librn, Columbus Metropolitan Library, Livingston Branch, 3434 E Livingston Ave, Columbus, OH, 43227. Tel: 614-645-2275. Fax: 614-479-4339. p. 1884

Owens, Stacey, Cat, Brewton Public Library, 206 W Jackson St, Brewton, AL, 36426. Tel: 251-867-4626. Fax: 251-809-1749. p. 10

Owens, Susan, YA Serv, Bryant Library, Two Paper Mill Rd, Roslyn, NY, 11576-2193. Tel: 516-621-2240. Fax: 516-621-7211. p. 1735

Owens, Sylvia, Ref Librn, Austin Community College, Round Rock Campus Library, 4400 College Park Dr, Round Rock, TX, 78665. Tel: 512-223-0118. Fax: 512-223-0903. p. 2278

Owens, Tammie, Asst Librn, Knott County Public Library, 238 Hwy 160 S, Hindman, KY, 41822. Tel: 606-785-5412. Fax: 606-785-4299. p. 918

Owens, Tonia, ILL, East Central Georgia Regional Library, 902 Greene St, Augusta, GA, 30901. Tel: 706-821-2600. Fax: 706-724-6762. p. 519

Owens, Walt, Dir, Wheeler Memorial Library, 49 E Main St, Orange, MA, 01364-1267. Tel: 978-544-2495, Ext 101. Fax: 978-544-1116. p. 1116

Owes, Jaunita M, Libr Dir, Montgomery City-County Public Library System, 245 High St, Montgomery, AL, 36104. Tel: 334-240-4989. Fax: 334-240-4977. p. 29

Owings, Connie, Tech Serv, Scott County Library System, 200 N Sixth Ave, Eldridge, IA, 52748. Tel: 563-285-4794. Fax: 563-285-4743. p. 813

Owiny, Sylvia A, Librn, Pennsylvania State University Libraries, Social Sciences, 201 Paterno Library, University Park, PA, 16802-1809. Tel: 814-865-8864. Fax: 814-865-1403. p. 2148

Owopetu, Ruth, Asst Dir, Tech Serv, Howard University Libraries, Law Library, 2929 Van Ness St NW, Washington, DC, 20008. Tel: 202-806-8036. Fax: 202-806-8400. p. 404

Owsu, Charles, Doc, Ref, Nassau Community College, One Education Dr, Garden City, NY, 11530-6793. Tel: 516-572-7400. Fax: 516-572-7846. p. 1626

Owusu-Ansah, Edward, Dr, Dean of Libr & Univ Coll, East Stroudsburg University, 216 Normal St, East Stroudsburg, PA, 18301-2999. Tel: 570-422-3467. Fax: 570-422-3151. p. 2051

Oxford, Amy, In Charge, Custer County Law Library, Courthouse, 431 S Tenth, Broken Bow, NE, 68822. Tel: 308-872-2121. Fax: 308-872-5826. p. 1394

Oxford, Mary-Catherine, Ad, Tulare Public Library, 475 North M St, Tulare, CA, 93274-4142. Tel: 559-685-4506. Fax: 559-685-2345. p. 276

Oxford, Ron Lynn, Librn, West Hills College Lemoore Library, 555 College Ave, Lemoore, CA, 93245. Tel: 559-925-3403. Fax: 559-924-1662. p. 164

Oxley, Martha, Ad, Ref Librn, Free Public Library of Monroe Township, 713 Marsha Ave, Williamstown, NJ, 08094. Tel: 856-629-1212. Fax: 856-875-0191. p. 1544

Oyarce, Guillermo, Dr, Assoc Prof, University of North Texas, 1155 Union Circle, Denton, TX, 76203-5017. Tel: 940-565-2445. Fax: 940-565-3101. p. 2975

Oyer, Kenny E, Sr, Librn, Alegent Health Bergan Mercy Medical Center, 7500 Mercy Rd, Omaha, NE, 68124-9832. Tel: 402-398-6092. Fax: 402-398-6923. p. 1411

Oyler, John, Ref & Instruction Librn, Saint Paul School of Theology, 5123 E Truman Rd, Kansas City, MO, 64127. p. 1341

Oyster, Linda, Dir, Waterloo Public Library, 23704 Cedar Dr, Waterloo, NE, 68069. Tel: 402-779-4171. Fax: 402-779-4369. p. 1422

Ozanich, Nicole E, Youth Serv Librn, Portage County Public Library, Charles M White Library Bldg, 1001 Main St, Stevens Point, WI, 54481-2860. Tel: 715-346-1544. Fax: 715-346-1239. p. 2640

Ozinga, Connie Jo, Dir, Elkhart Public Library, 300 S Second St, Elkhart, IN, 46516-3184. Tel: 574-522-3333. Fax: 574-293-9213, 574-522-2174. p. 737

Paananen, Lee Ann, Dir, Phoebe Apperson Hearst Library, 315 W Main, Lead, SD, 57754-1604. Tel: 605-584-2013. p. 2214

Paasch, Renee, Dir, Dickinson Area Public Library, 139 Third St W, Dickinson, ND, 58601. Tel: 701-456-7700. Fax: 701-456-7702. p. 1840

Paasch, Renee, Dir, Dickinson Area Public Library, Billings County Resource Center, PO Box 307, Medora, ND, 58645-0307. Tel: 701-623-4604. Fax: 701-623-4941. p. 1840

Pabarja, Julie, Res Serv Mgr, DLA Piper US LLP, 203 N LaSalle St, Ste 1900, Chicago, IL, 60601. Tel: 312-849-8639. Fax: 312-251-5845. p. 612

Pabellon, Wanda, Spec Coll & Archives Librn, University of Puerto Rico Library, Cayey Campus, 205 Ave Antonio R Barcelo, Cayey, PR, 00736. Tel: 787-738-2161, Ext 2026. Fax: 787-263-2108. p. 2672

Pablo, Carmella, Libr Asst, Tohono O'odham Community College Library, Hwy 86 Milepost 115.5 N, Sells, AZ, 85634. Tel: 520-383-0032. Fax: 520-383-8403. p. 81

Pace, Ansel, Interim Librn, Fruitland Baptist Bible Institute, 1455 Gillaim Rd, Hendersonville, NC, 28792. Tel: 828-685-8886. Fax: 828-685-8888. p. 1800

Pace, Carrie-Anne, Ch, Aaron Cutler Memorial Library, 269 Charles Bancroft Hwy, Litchfield, NH, 03052. Tel: 603-424-4044. Fax: 603-424-4044. p. 1454

Pace, Charles, Dir, Saint Louis County Library, 1640 S Lindbergh Blvd, Saint Louis, MO, 63131-3598. Tel: 314-994-3300, Ext 2150. Fax: 314-997-7602. p. 1358

Pace, Kathy, Bus Mgr, Skagit County Historical Museum, 501 S Fourth St, La Conner, WA, 98257. Tel: 360-466-3365. Fax: 360-466-1611. p. 2519

Pace, Pat, Extn Serv, Anderson County Library, 300 N McDuffie St, Anderson, SC, 29621-5643. Tel: 864-260-4500. Fax: 864-260-4510. p. 2180

Pace, Pat, Extn Serv, Supv Librn, Anderson County Library, West Side Community Center Branch Facility, 1100 W Franklin St, Anderson, SC, 29624. Tel: 864-260-4500, Ext 174. Fax: 864-260-4660. p. 2181

Pace, Rebecca, Librn, Peru Free Library, 3024 N Main St, Peru, NY, 12972. Tel: 518-643-8618. p. 1717

Pace-McGowan, Sarah, Ch, Marshall County Public Library System, 1003 Poplar St, Benton, KY, 42025. Tel: 270-527-9969. Fax: 270-527-0506. p. 907

Pacella, Veronica, Dir, Ellwood City Area Public Library, 510 Crescent Ave, Ellwood City, PA, 16117-1944. Tel: 724-758-6458. Fax: 724-758-0115. p. 2054

Pacenza, Joyce M, Dir, Tulsa County Law Library, 500 S Denver Ave, Tulsa, OK, 74103. Tel: 918-596-5404. Fax: 918-596-4509. p. 1984

Pacer, Matt, Computer Serv, Capital Area District Libraries, Downtown Lansing Library, 401 S Capitol Ave, Lansing, MI, 48933. Tel: 517-334-1532. Fax: 517-374-1068. p. 1200

Pacheco, Ana, Asst Librn, University of New Mexico, Taos Campus, 115 Civic Plaza Dr, Taos, NM, 87571. Tel: 575-737-6242. Fax: 575-737-6292. p. 1551

Pacheco, Nellie, Dir, Cochiti Pueblo Community Library, 245 Cochiti St, Cochiti, NM, 87072. Tel: 505-465-3118. Fax: 505-465-2203. p. 1553

Pacheco, Sarah, AV Coll, Syst Adminr, Fort Stockton Public Library, 500 N Water St, Fort Stockton, TX, 79735. Tel: 432-336-3374. Fax: 432-336-6648. p. 2321

Pacheco, Teresa, Electronic Res Librn, Gainesville State College, 3820 Mundy Mill Rd, Oakwood, GA, 30566. Tel: 678-717-3658. Fax: 770-718-3657. p. 547

Pachman, Frederic C, Dir, Monmouth Medical Center, 300 Second Ave, Long Branch, NJ, 07740. Tel: 732-923-6645. Fax: 732-222-3742. p. 1497

Pachman, Frederic C, V, Librn, New Jersey Scout Museum Library, 705 Ginesi Dr, 2nd Flr, Morganville, NJ, 07751. Tel: 732-862-1282. Fax: 732-536-2850. p. 1504

Pachnanda, Swadesh, Adult Serv, Tuckahoe Public Library, 71 Columbus Ave, Tuckahoe, NY, 10707. Tel: 914-961-2121. Fax: 914-961-3832. p. 1757

Pacholski, Sharon, Dir, Booth & Dimock Memorial Library, 1134 Main St, Coventry, CT, 06238. Tel: 860-742-7606. Fax: 860-742-7491. p. 334

Pacifici, Sabrina I, Sr Librn, United States Department of the Treasury, United States Department of the Treasury, 250 E St SW, Washington, DC, 20219. Tel: 202-874-4722. Fax: 202-874-5138. p. 419

Pacileo, Victoria, Asst Librn, Young Men's Institute Library, 847 Chapel St, New Haven, CT, 06510. Tel: 203-562-4045. p. 359

Pack, Jen, SW Ctr Librn, Fort Lewis College Library, 1000 Rim Dr, Durango, CO, 81301-3999. Tel: 970-247-7250. Fax: 970-247-7149. p. 305

Pack, Mary, Br Mgr, Sumter County Library, Wesmark Branch Library, 180 W Wesmark Blvd, Sumter, SC, 29150. Tel: 803-469-8110. Fax: 803-469-8347. p. 2206

Pack, Mary Margaret, Circ Librn, Wythe-Grayson Regional Library, Fries Public, 105 W Main St, Fries, VA, 24330. Tel: 276-744-3160. Fax: 276-744-3160. p. 2472

Pack, Tabitha, Libr Asst I, Montgomery City-County Public Library System, Governors Square Branch Library, 2885-B East South Blvd, Montgomery, AL, 36111. Tel: 334-284-7929. Fax: 334-240-4839. p. 29

Packard, Jerome, Asst Librn, New Mexico State Library, Library for the Blind & Physically Handicapped, 1209 Camino Carlos Rey, Santa Fe, NM, 87507-5166. Tel: 505-476-9771. Fax: 505-476-9776. p. 1563

Packard, Kathy, Cat, Normal Public Library, 206 W College Ave, Normal, IL, 61761. Tel: 309-452-1757. Fax: 309-452-5312. p. 681

Packard, Linda, Librn, Guilford Memorial Library, Four Library St, Guilford, ME, 04443. Tel: 207-876-4547. p. 987

Packard, Michael, Dir, Tredyffrin Public Library, 582 Upper Gulph Rd, Strafford, PA, 19087-2096. Tel: 610-688-7092. Fax: 610-688-2014. p. 2143

Packer, Becky, ILL, Fremont County Library System, 451 N Second St, Lander, WY, 82520-2316. Tel: 307-332-5194. Fax: 307-332-1504, 307-332-3909. p. 2656

Packer, Cheri, Librn, Emery County Library, Green River Branch, 85 S Long St, Green River, UT, 84525. Tel: 435-564-3349. Fax: 435-564-3399. p. 2404

Packer, Judy, Youth Serv Mgr, Wake County Public Library System, East Regional Library, 946 Steeple Square Ct, Knightdale, NC, 27545. Tel: 919-217-5316. Fax: 919-217-5327. p. 1817

Packer, Mary, ILL, North Suburban Library District, 6340 N Second St, Loves Park, IL, 61111. Tel: 815-633-4247. Fax: 815-633-4249. p. 668

Packman, Hedra L, Dir of Libr Serv, Free Library of Philadelphia, 1901 Vine St, Philadelphia, PA, 19103-1189. Tel: 215-686-5305. Fax: 215-563-3628. p. 2106

Paczelt, Anna E, Librn, Mahoning Law Library Association, Courthouse 4th Flr, 120 Market St, Youngstown, OH, 44503-1752. Tel: 330-740-2295. Fax: 330-744-1406. p. 1952

Paden, Joyce A, Dir, Martinsburg Community Library, 201 S Walnut St, Martinsburg, PA, 16662-1129. Tel: 814-793-3335. Fax: 814-793-9755. p. 2084

Paden, Patty, Asst Dir, Hillsboro Public Library, 214 School St, Hillsboro, IL, 62049-1547. Tel: 217-532-3055. Fax: 217-532-6813. p. 656

Paden, Spencer, Dir, Apache Junction Public Library, 1177 N Idaho Rd, Apache Junction, AZ, 85219. Tel: 480-474-8555. Fax: 480-983-4540. p. 57

Padgett, Doris, Dir, Sunnyvale Public Library, 402 Tower Pl, Sunnyvale, TX, 75182. Tel: 972-226-4491. Fax: 972-203-0310. p. 2389

Padgett, Judy, Dir, Madison Public Library, 1700 Fifth St, Madison, IL, 62060. Tel: 618-876-8448. Fax: 618-876-8316. p. 669

Padgett, Justin C, Dir, Cannon Falls Library, 306 W Mill St, Cannon Falls, MN, 55009-2045. Tel: 507-263-2804. p. 1244

Padgett, Katherine, Asst Br Mgr, Louisville Free Public Library, Jeffersontown Branch, 10635 Watterson Trail, Jeffersontown, KY, 40299. Tel: 502-267-5713. Fax: 502-266-6569. p. 924

Padgett, Kenan, Info Serv, ILL, Rhodes College, 2000 North Pkwy, Memphis, TN, 38112-1694. Tel: 901-843-3900. Fax: 901-843-3404. p. 2251

Padilla Bowen, Jessica, Commun Relations Coordr, Carlsbad City Library, 1775 Dove Lane, Carlsbad, CA, 92011-4048. Tel: 760-602-2012. Fax: 760-602-7942. p. 132

Padilla, Donald, Adult Serv, Socorro Public Library, 401 Park St, Socorro, NM, 87801-4544. Tel: 505-835-1114. Fax: 505-835-1182. p. 1565

Padilla, Irene, State Librn, Maryland State Department of Education, 200 W Baltimore St, Baltimore, MD, 21201-2595. Tel: 410-767-0435. Fax: 410-333-2507. p. 1015

Padilla, Kathy, Br Mgr, Placer County Library, Penryn Branch, 2215 Rippey Rd, Penryn, CA, 95663. Tel: 916-663-3621. Fax: 916-663-3621. p. 123

Padilla, Ruby, Libr Supvr-Popular Libr, Arizona Department of Corrections - Adult Institutions, 26700 S Hwy 85, Buckeye, AZ, 85326. Tel: 623-386-6160, Ext 4908. Fax: 623-386-6160, Ext 4910. p. 58

Padilla, Shelly, Circ Mgr, Natrona County Public Library, 307 E Second St, Casper, WY, 82601. Tel: 307-237-4935. Fax: 307-266-3734. p. 2652

Padilla, Sue, Dir, Newton Public Library, 100 N Third Ave W, Newton, IA, 50208. Tel: 641-792-4108. Fax: 641-791-0729. p. 835

Padilla, Virginia, Librn, Truchas Community Library, No 60 County Rd 75, Truchas, NM, 87578. Tel: 505-689-2683. Fax: 505-689-1155. p. 1566

Padnos, Mark, Coordr, Pub Serv, Bronx Community College Library & Learning Center, 106 Meister Hall, 2115 University Ave, Bronx, NY, 10453. Tel: 718-289-5440. Fax: 718-289-6063. p. 1586

Padua, Noelia, Dir, Pontifical Catholic University Of Puerto Rico, Monseignor Fremiot Torres Oliver Legal Information & Research Center, 2250 Avenida Las Americas, Ste 544, Ponce, PR, 00717-9997. Tel: 787-841-2000, Ext 1852. Fax: 787-841-5354. p. 2675

Padway, Janet, Coll Develop, Tech Serv, University of Wisconsin-Milwaukee Libraries, 2311 E Hartford Ave, Milwaukee, WI, 53211. Tel: 414-229-4785, 414-229-6202. Fax: 414-229-6766. p. 2622

Paeltz, Angela, Extn Spec, Metropolitan Library System in Oklahoma County, Luther Extension Library, 310 NE Third, Luther, OK, 73054-9999. Tel: 405-277-9967. Fax: 405-277-9238. p. 1973

Paese, Mary Jane, Dir, Raritan Public Library, 54 E Somerset St, Raritan, NJ, 08869. Tel: 908-725-0413. Fax: 908-725-1832. p. 1525

Paff, Ruth, Youth Serv, Kirchner-French Memorial Library, 101 Main St, Peterson, IA, 51047. Tel: 712-295-6705. Fax: 712-295-6705. p. 838

Pagan, Beryl, Bibliog Instr, Online Serv, Ref, Point Loma Nazarene University, 3900 Lomaland Dr, San Diego, CA, 92106-2899. Tel: 619-849-2355. Fax: 619-222-0711. p. 232

Pagan, Jose, Librn, University of Puerto Rico Library System, Documents & Maps Collection, Rio Piedras Campus, San Juan, PR, 00931. Tel: 787-764-0000, Ext 3514. Fax: 787-772-1479. p. 2677

Pagán, José, Asst Dir, Pub Serv, University of Puerto Rico Library System, University of Puerto Rico, Rio Piedras Campus, San Juan, PR, 00931. Tel: 787-764-0000, Ext 2789. Fax: 787-772-1479. p. 2677

Pagan, Maria G, Dir, Holyoke Public Library, 335 Maple St, Holyoke, MA, 01040-4999. Tel: 413-322-5640. Fax: 413-532-4230. p. 1095

Pagan-Falcon, Raul, Librn, Patent & Trademark, University of Puerto Rico, Minillas Park, 170, 174 Rd, Bayamon, PR, 00959-1919. Tel: 787-993-0000, Ext 3222, 787-993-8857. Fax: 787-993-8914. p. 2672

Paganelis, George, Curator, Tsakopoulos Hellenic Coll, California State University, Sacramento Library, 2000 State University Dr E, Sacramento, CA, 95819-6039. Tel: 916-278-4361. Fax: 916-278-5917. p. 223

Pagani, Melissa, Libr Asst/Youth Serv, John F Kennedy Memorial Library, 92 Hathaway St, Wallington, NJ, 07057. Tel: 973-471-1692. Fax: 973-471-1387. p. 1539

Pagano, James, Youth Serv Librn, Williston Park Public Library, 494 Willis Ave, Williston Park, NY, 11596. Tel: 516-742-1820. Fax: 516-294-5004. p. 1770

Page, Annie, Circ Supvr, Hopkins County-Madisonville Public Library, 31 S Main St, Madisonville, KY, 42431. Tel: 270-825-2680. Fax: 270-825-2777. p. 927

Page, Billie, Circ, Hoover Public Library, 200 Municipal Dr, Hoover, AL, 35216. Tel: 205-444-7810. Fax: 205-444-7878. p. 20

Page, Brian, Tech Coordr, Putnam County Library System, 50 E Broad St, Cookeville, TN, 38501. Tel: 931-526-2416. Fax: 931-372-8517. p. 2231

Page, Brittany, Prog Coordr, United States Air Force, 437 SVS/SVMG, 106 W McCaw St, Bldg 215, Charleston AFB, SC, 29404-4700. Tel: 843-963-3320. Fax: 843-963-3840. p. 2185

Page, Caprisha, Librn, East Central Arkansas Regional Library, Cross County, 410 E Merriman Ave, Wynne, AR, 72396. Tel: 870-238-3850. Fax: 870-238-5434. p. 117

Page, Catherine, Head, Circ, Haverhill Public Library, 99 Main St, Haverhill, MA, 01830-5092. Tel: 978-373-1586, Ext 602. Fax: 978-372-8508. p. 1094

Page, Catherine, Librn, Grand Rapids Public Library, Ottawa Hills, 1150 Giddings Ave SE, Grand Rapids, MI, 49506. Tel: 616-988-5412. Fax: 616-241-1460. p. 1185

Page, Daniel, Librn, East Arkansas Community College, 1700 Newcastle Rd, Forrest City, AR, 72335. Tel: 870-633-4480, Ext 322. Fax: 870-633-7222. p. 100

Page, Deborah, Librn, Cleveland County Library System, Spangler Library, 112 Piedmont Dr, Lawndale, NC, 28090. Tel: 704-538-7005. Fax: 704-538-0801. p. 1823

Page, Donna, Tech Serv, Elk Grove Village Public Library, 1001 Wellington Ave, Elk Grove Village, IL, 60007-3391. Tel: 847-439-0447. Fax: 847-439-0475. p. 641

Page, Donna, Asst Dir, User Serv, Rivier College, 420 S Main St, Nashua, NH, 03060-5086. Tel: 603-897-8536. Fax: 603-897-8889. p. 1459

Page, Dora, Tech Serv, Lyon County Library System, 20 Nevin Way, Yerington, NV, 89447. Tel: 775-463-6645. Fax: 775-463-6646. p. 1435

Page, Elaine Fetyko, Head, Tech Serv, Elmhurst College, 190 Prospect St, Elmhurst, IL, 60126. Tel: 630-617-3166. Fax: 630-617-3332. p. 642

Page, Eric, Archivist, Unity Library & Archives, 1901 NW Blue Pkwy, Unity Village, MO, 64065-0001. Tel: 816-524-3550, Ext 2021. p. 1370

Page, Jessica R, Librn, Ohio State University LIBRARIES, Food, Agricultural & Environmental Sciences, 045 Agriculture Administration Bldg, 2120 Fyffe Rd, Columbus, OH, 43210-1066. Tel: 614-688-8474. Fax: 614-292-0590. p. 1887

Page, John, Ref Librn, University of the District of Columbia, Learning Resources Division, 4200 Connecticut Ave NW, Washington, DC, 20008. Tel: 202-274-6370. Fax: 202-274-6012. p. 421

Page, Judy, Circ Librn, Peterborough Town Library, Two Concord St, Peterborough, NH, 03458. Tel: 603-924-8040. Fax: 603-924-8041. p. 1462

Page, Kacey, Asst Coll Mgr, Buffalo Museum of Science, 1020 Humboldt Pkwy, Buffalo, NY, 14211. Tel: 716-896-5200. Fax: 716-897-6723. p. 1597

Page, Karol, Adult Serv, Kesher Zion Synagogue Sisterhood Library, 1245 Perkiomen Ave, Reading, PA, 19602-1318. Tel: 610-374-1763. Fax: 610-375-1352. p. 2133

Page, Lanny, Tech Coordr, Fort Morgan Public Library, 414 Main St, Fort Morgan, CO, 80701. Tel: 970-542-4000. Fax: 970-542-4013. p. 308

Page, Leslie, Dir, Woonsocket Harris Public Library, 303 Clinton St, Woonsocket, RI, 02895. Tel: 401-769-9044. Fax: 401-767-4120. p. 2178

Page, Linda, Coll Develop, Tech Serv, Bibliotheque de Brossard, 7855 San Francisco Ave, Brossard, QC, J4X 2A4, CANADA. Tel: 450-923-6350, Ext 6278. Fax: 450-923-7042. p. 2880

Page, Mary, Asst Univ Librn, University of California, Davis, 100 NW Quad, Davis, CA, 95616-5292. Tel: 530-752-6561. Fax: 530-752-3148. p. 139

Page, Mary S, Assoc Dir, Coll & Tech Serv, Head, Cat, University of Central Florida Libraries, 4000 Central Florida Blvd, Bldg 2, Orlando, FL, 32816-2666. Tel: 407-823-2564. Fax: 407-823-6289. p. 477

Page, Michelle, Ch, Bristol Public Library, 701 Goode St, Bristol, VA, 24201-4199. Tel: 276-821-6193. Fax: 276-669-5593. p. 2452

Page, Patricia, Dir, Massapequa Public Library, 40 Harbor Lane, Massapequa Park, NY, 11762. Tel: 516-799-0770, Ext 306. Fax: 516-795-7528. p. 1658

Page, Patricia, Dir, Massapequa Public Library, Central Avenue, 523 Central Ave, Massapequa, NY, 11758. Tel: 516-799-0770, Ext 306. Fax: 516-798-2804. p. 1658

Page, Sally, Exec Dir, Davenport University, 6191 Kraft Ave SE, Grand Rapids, MI, 49512. Tel: 616-554-5612. Fax: 616-554-5226. p. 1184

Page, Yvette, Coordr, Libr Serv, The College of New Rochelle, 29 Castle Pl, New Rochelle, NY, 10805-2308. Tel: 914-654-5345. Fax: 914-654-5884. p. 1666

Page, Yvette, Librn, College of New Rochelle, Cardinal John O'Connor Campus, 332 E 149 St, Bronx, NY, 10451. Tel: 718-665-1310. Fax: 718-292-2906. p. 1666

Pagel, Scott B, Assoc Dean, Dir, George Washington University, Jacob Burns Law Library, 716 20th St NW, Washington, DC, 20052. Tel: 202-994-7337. Fax: 202-994-1430. p. 402

Pagenkopf, Mary, Head Librn, Alaska State Legislature, State Capitol, Juneau, AK, 99801-1182. Tel: 907-465-3808. Fax: 907-465-4844. p. 49

Paget, Amy, Asst County Librn, Tippecanoe County Public Library, 627 South St, Lafayette, IN, 47901-1470. Tel: 765-429-0100. Fax: 765-429-0150. p. 759

Paggi, Paula, Dir, Ref, Los Angeles Pierce College Library, 6201 Winnetka Ave, Woodland Hills, CA, 91371. Tel: 818-710-2843. Fax: 818-719-9058. p. 285

Pagles, Kathryn, Dir, Blount County Public Library, 508 N Cusick St, Maryville, TN, 37804-5714. Tel: 865-982-0981. Fax: 865-977-1142. p. 2246

Pagnucco, Lindsay, Librn, Vancouver Public Library, Riley Park Community, Little Mountain Neighbourhood House, 3981 Main St, Vancouver, BC, V5V 3P3, CANADA. Tel: 604-665-3964. Fax: 604-665-3553. p. 2744

Pagos, Hollin Elizabeth, Circ Mgr, Lynnfield Public Library, 18 Summer St, Lynnfield, MA, 01940-1837. Tel: 781-334-5411. Fax: 781-334-2164. p. 1101

Pahl, Jeanine, Librn, Oakes Public Library, 804 Main Ave, Oakes, ND, 58474. Tel: 701-742-3234. Fax: 701-742-2812. p. 1847

Pahls, Tracy, County Librn, Crittenden County Library, 100 N Currie St, Marion, AR, 72364. Tel: 870-739-3238. Fax: 870-739-4624. p. 109

Paick, Haewon, Br Mgr, Los Angeles Public Library System, Junipero Serra, 4607 S Main St, Los Angeles, CA, 90037-2641. Tel: 323-234-1685. Fax: 323-612-0432. p. 173

Paietta, Ann, Dir, Deep River Public Library, 150 Main St, Deep River, CT, 06417. Tel: 860-526-6039. Fax: 860-526-6040. p. 336

Paige, Kathy, Dir, Hepburn Library of Madrid, 11 Church St, Madrid, NY, 13660. Tel: 315-322-5673. Fax: 315-322-5673. p. 1656

Paige, LaVerne, Per, Sweet Briar College, 134 Chapel Rd, Sweet Briar, VA, 24595-1200. Tel: 434-381-6138. Fax: 434-381-6173. p. 2497

Paige, Patti, Head, Circ, Ela Area Public Library District, 275 Mohawk Trail, Lake Zurich, IL, 60047. Tel: 847-438-3433. Fax: 847-438-9290. p. 663

Paikowski, Gary, Dir, Grayson County College Library, 6101 Grayson Dr, Denison, TX, 75020-8299. Tel: 903-463-8637. Fax: 903-465-4123. p. 2312

Paille, Mario, Bibliog Instr, Ref, College de Maisonneuve Centre des Medias, 3800 Est rue Sherbrooke E, Montreal, QC, H1X 2A2, CANADA. Tel: 514-254-7131, Ext 4770. Fax: 514-254-2517. p. 2893

Painchaud, Sylvie A, In Charge, Centrale des Syndicats du Quebec, 320, rue St-Joseph Est, bur 100, Quebec, QC, G1K 9E7, CANADA. Tel: 418-649-8888. Fax: 418-649-8800. p. 2903

Paine, Laura, Supvr, Ventura County Library, Avenue Library, 606 N Ventura Ave, Ventura, CA, 93001. Tel: 805-643-6393. Fax: 805-648-3791. p. 279

Painter, Christine, Dir, Bud Werner Memorial Library, 1289 Lincoln Ave, Steamboat Springs, CO, 80487. Tel: 970-879-0240. Fax: 970-879-3476. p. 323

Painter, Jaime, Ref Librn, Indiana Wesleyan University, 4201 S Washington St, Marion, IN, 46953. Tel: 765-677-2445. Fax: 765-677-2676. p. 762

Painter, John C, Dir, Seaford District Library, 402 Porter St, Seaford, DE, 19973. Tel: 302-629-2524. Fax: 302-629-9181. p. 386

Painter, Maureen, Dir, Squamish Public Library, 37907 Second Ave, Squamish, BC, V8B 0A7, CANADA. Tel: 604-892-3110. Fax: 604-892-9376. p. 2738

Painter, Tina, Asst Dir, Bergenfield Public Library, 50 W Clinton Ave, Bergenfield, NJ, 07621-2799. Tel: 201-387-4040, Ext 845. Fax: 201-387-9004. p. 1472

Painter, Tina, Br Librn, Carson County Public Library, Groom Branch, 201 Broadway St, Groom, TX, 79039. Tel: 806-248-7353. Fax: 806-248-7353. p. 2368

Paisant, Joan, Circ Supvr, Saint John the Baptist Parish Library, 2920 New Hwy 51, LaPlace, LA, 70068. Tel: 985-652-2225, 985-652-6857. Fax: 985-652-8005. p. 954

Paisig, Joanne, Librn, Ministry of Highways & Infrastructure, 1855 Victoria Ave, Regina, SK, S4P 3T5, CANADA. Tel: 306-787-4800. Fax: 306-787-8700. p. 2922

Paisley, Danielle, Ref Serv, YA, Patchogue-Medford Library, 54-60 E Main St, Patchogue, NY, 11772. Tel: 631-654-4700, Ext 250. Fax: 631-289-3999. p. 1715

Paiva, Carla, Circ, Berkley Public Library, Three N Main St, Berkley, MA, 02779. Tel: 508-822-3329. Fax: 508-824-2471. p. 1053

Pajeau, Nancy, Head, Youth Serv, Stickney-Forest View Public Library District, 6800 W 43rd St, Stickney, IL, 60402. Tel: 708-749-1050. Fax: 708-749-1054. p. 707

Pajer, Kelly-Ann, Ch, Chappaqua Public Library, 195 S Greeley Ave, Chappaqua, NY, 10514. Tel: 914-238-4779. Fax: 914-238-3597. p. 1605

Pajewski, Amy L, Adjunct Fac Librn, Harrisburg Area Community College, 2010 Pennsylvania Ave, York, PA, 17404. Tel: 717-718-0328, Ext 3520. Fax: 717-718-8967. p. 2159

Pajor, Sue, Adult Serv Mgr, Asst Dir, Alsip-Merrionette Park Public Library District, 11960 S Pulaski Rd, Alsip, IL, 60803-1197. Tel: 708-371-5666. Fax: 708-371-5672. p. 588

Paju, Susan, Ref, Acton Memorial Library, 486 Main St, Acton, MA, 01720. Tel: 978-264-9641. Fax: 978-635-0073. p. 1047

Pakala, Denise Marchand, Assoc Librn, Tech Serv, Covenant Theological Seminary, 12330 Conway Rd, Saint Louis, MO, 63141. Tel: 314-392-4100, 314-434-4044. Fax: 314-392-4116, 314-434-4819. p. 1354

Pakala, James Cotton, Dir, Covenant Theological Seminary, 12330 Conway Rd, Saint Louis, MO, 63141. Tel: 314-392-4100, 314-434-4044. Fax: 314-392-4116, 314-434-4819. p. 1354

Pal, Surekha, Coordr, Circ, Aurora Public Library, One E Benton St, Aurora, IL, 60505-4299. Tel: 630-264-4100. Fax: 630-896-3209. p. 591

Paladines, Melissa, Libr Tech, Credit Valley Hospital, 2200 Eglinton Ave W, Mississauga, ON, L5M 2N1, CANADA. Tel: 905-813-1100, Ext 6871. Fax: 905-813-3969. p. 2822

Paladino, Paul H, Dir, Montrose Regional Library District, 320 S Second St, Montrose, CO, 81401-3909. Tel: 970-249-9656. Fax: 970-240-1901. p. 318

Palahniuk, Pat, Sr Librn, Hennepin County Library, Maple Grove, 8001 Main St N, Maple Grove, MN, 55369-4617. Tel: 612-543-6477. Fax: 612-543-6452. p. 1264

Palahniuk, Pat, Sr Librn, Hennepin County Library, Osseo, 415 Central Ave, Osseo, MN, 55369-1194. Tel: 612-543-6477. Fax: 612-543-5752. p. 1264

Palamar, Ann, Asst Librn, Britt Area Library, 841 Riverside Dr, Britt, ON, P0G 1A0, CANADA. Tel: 705-383-2292. Fax: 705-383-0077. p. 2797

Palan, Diane, Regional Br Operations Mgr, Austin Public Library, Yarborough, 2200 Hancock Dr, Austin, TX, 78756. Tel: 512-454-7208. Fax: 512-458-3047. p. 2279

Palanzo, Eddy, Mrs, Librn, The Washington Post, 1150 15th St NW, Washington, DC, 20071. Tel: 202-334-7341. Fax: 202-728-3130. p. 422

Palas, Bob, Ref Librn, North Chicago Public Library, 2100 Argonne Dr, North Chicago, IL, 60064. Tel: 847-689-0125. Fax: 847-689-9117. p. 682

Palascak, Helen, Dir, Upper St Clair Township Library, 1820 McLaughlin Run Rd, Upper St Clair, PA, 15241-2397. Tel: 412-835-5540. Fax: 412-835-6763. p. 2149

Palazzola, Benedette, Librn, University of Michigan, English Language Institute Library, 500 E Washington St, Ann Arbor, MI, 48104-2028. Tel: 734-647-0478. Fax: 734-763-0369. p. 1152

Palen, Jan, Sr Librn, Downey City Library, 11121 Brookshire Ave, Caller Box 7015, Downey, CA, 90241-7015. Tel: 562-904-7357. Fax: 562-923-3763. p. 144

Palermo, Jill C, Dir, Lewiston Public Library, 305 S Eighth St, Lewiston, NY, 14092. Tel: 716-754-4720. Fax: 716-754-7386. p. 1652

Palermo, Laura, Tech Serv, Brookhaven Free Library, 273 Beaver Dam Rd, Brookhaven, NY, 11719. Tel: 631-286-1923. Fax: 631-286-0120. p. 1589

Palguta, Debra, Br Mgr, Saint Joseph County Public Library, North Liberty Branch, 105 E Market, North Liberty, IN, 46554. Tel: 574-656-3664. p. 779

Paliatka, Jennifer, Ref & Instruction Librn, Elmhurst College, 190 Prospect St, Elmhurst, IL, 60126. Tel: 630-617-3158. Fax: 630-617-3332. p. 642

Palichuk, Carla, Mgr, Edmonton Public Library, Londonderry, 110 Londonderry Mall, 137th Ave & 66th St, Edmonton, AB, T5C 3C8, CANADA. Tel: 780-496-1814. Fax: 780-496-1452. p. 2700

Palin, Sally, Librn, Indiana Department of Environmental Management, 100 N Senate Ave, IGCN 1307, MC 60-01, Indianapolis, IN, 46204-2215. Tel: 317-233-3706. Fax: 317-233-5517. p. 751

Palko, Joanne, Head, Cat, Clark University, 950 Main St, Worcester, MA, 01610-1477. Tel: 508-793-7581. Fax: 508-793-8871. p. 1143

Palkovic, Mark, Head of Libr, University of Cincinnati Libraries, College-Conservatory of Music, 600 Blegen Library, Cincinnati, OH, 45221. Tel: 513-556-1964. Fax: 513-556-3777. p. 1874

Palladino, Richard L, Dir of Libr, Iona College, 715 North Ave, New Rochelle, NY, 10801-1890. Tel: 914-633-2351. Fax: 914-633-2136. p. 1666

Pallant, Joan, Head, Circ, Wittenberg University, 807 Woodlawn Ave, Springfield, OH, 45504. Tel: 937-327-7018. Fax: 937-327-6139. p. 1936

Pallas, Jean, Dir, Valatie Free Library, 3203 Church St, Valatie, NY, 12184-2301. Tel: 518-758-9321. Fax: 518-758-6497. p. 1760

Pallinger, Joyce, Mgr, MacNeal Hospital, 3249 S Oak Park Ave, Berwyn, IL, 60402. Tel: 708-783-3089. Fax: 708-783-3369. p. 594

Pallis, Joseph M, Dir, Saint Francis Hospital & Medical Center, 114 Woodland St, Hartford, CT, 06105. Tel: 860-714-4883. Fax: 860-714-8022. p. 347

Pallis, Mary Beth, Dir, Dunstable Free Public Library, 588 Main St, Dunstable, MA, 01827. Tel: 978-649-7830. Fax: 978-649-4215. p. 1085

Pallotti, Nicola, Chair, Southeastern Massachusetts Consortium of Health Science Libraries, Charlton Medical Library, 363 Highland Ave, Fall River, MA, 02720. Tel: 508-679-7196. Fax: 508-679-7458. p. 2945

Palluck, Trish, State Govt Info Coordr, Tech Serv Librn, Wyoming State Library, 2800 Central Ave, Cheyenne, WY, 82002. Tel: 307-777-5913. Fax: 307-777-6289. p. 2653

Pally, Barbara, Ch, Stoughton Public Library, 84 Park St, Stoughton, MA, 02072-2974. Tel: 781-344-2711. Fax: 781-344-7340. p. 1129

Palm, Susan, Br Mgr, Kern County Library, Boron Branch, 26967 20 Mule Team Rd, Boron, CA, 93516-1550. Tel: 760-762-5606. p. 124

Palm-Abramoff, Carolann, Mgr, North Port Public Library, 13800 S Tamiami Trail, North Port, FL, 34287-2030. Tel: 941-861-1300. Fax: 941-426-6564. p. 473

Palma, Kelly, Circ Mgr, New Carlisle Public Library, 111 E Lake Ave, New Carlisle, OH, 45344-1418. Tel: 937-845-3601. Fax: 937-845-0908. p. 1920

Palma, Maria, Librn, Farmers Insurance Group Library, 4680 Wilshire Blvd, Los Angeles, CA, 90010-3807. Tel: 323-932-3200. Fax: 323-932-3101. p. 170

Palmar, Shane, Libr Mgr, Rotary Club of Slave Lake Public Library, 101 Main St SE, Slave Lake, AB, T0G 2A0, CANADA. Tel: 780-849-5250. Fax: 780-849-3275. p. 2716

Palmateer, Judy, Dir, University of Wisconsin Center-Marathon County Library, 518 S Seventh Ave, Wausau, WI, 54401-5396. Tel: 715-261-6219. Fax: 715-261-6330. p. 2647

Palmatier, Roxanne B, Soc Sci & Govt Info Librn, Northeastern University Libraries, Snell Library, 360 Huntington Ave, Boston, MA, 02115. Tel: 617-373-4968. p. 1065

Palmer, Ann, Librn, National Multiple Sclerosis Society, 733 Third Ave, New York, NY, 10017. Tel: 212-986-3240. Fax: 212-986-7981. p. 1688

Palmer, Anne, Librn, Children's Mercy Hospital, 2401 Gillham Rd, Kansas City, MO, 64108. Tel: 816-234-3800. Fax: 816-234-3125. p. 1337

Palmer, Barbara, Br Head, Saskatoon Public Library, Carlyle King Branch, Cosmo Civic Centre, 3130 Laurier Dr, Saskatoon, SK, S7L 5J7, CANADA. Tel: 306-975-7595. Fax: 306-975-7588. p. 2926

Palmer, Carole, Prof, University of Illinois at Urbana-Champaign, Library & Information Science Bldg, 501 E Daniel St, Champaign, IL, 61820-6211. Tel: 217-333-3280. Fax: 217-244-3302. p. 2965

Palmer, Cathy, Bus Librn, Mokena Community Public Library District, 11327 W 195th St, Mokena, IL, 60448. Tel: 708-479-9663. Fax: 708-479-9684. p. 674

Palmer, Cheryl, Dir of Educ, Mint Museum Library, 2730 Randolph Rd, Charlotte, NC, 28207. Tel: 704-337-2031. Fax: 704-337-2101. p. 1783

Palmer, Christine, Outreach Librn, Springfield Township Library, 70 Powell Rd, Springfield, PA, 19064-2446. Tel: 610-543-2113. Fax: 610-543-1356. p. 2142

Palmer, Deidre, Librn, Pope Memorial Library, 121 Park St, Danville, VT, 05828. Tel: 802-684-2256. p. 2422

Palmer, Diana, Circ, Cedar Mill Community Library, 12505 NW Cornell Rd, Portland, OR, 97229. Tel: 503-644-0043. Fax: 503-644-3964. p. 2010

Palmer, Doris, Librn, Lillian Perdido Bay Library, 12634 Ickler Ave, Lillian, AL, 36549. Tel: 251-962-4700. Fax: 251-962-4700. p. 23

Palmer, Eileen, Exec Dir, Libraries of Middlesex Automation Consortium, 1030 Saint Georges Ave, Ste 203, Avenel, NJ, 07001. Tel: 732-750-2525. Fax: 732-750-9392. p. 2949

Palmer, Elizabeth, Ref, Tech Serv, Somerset County Library System, 11767 Beechwood St, Princess Anne, MD, 21853. Tel: 410-651-0852, Ext 11. Fax: 410-651-1388. p. 1036

Palmer, Eric, Dir, Baker College of Flint, 1050 W Bristol Rd, Flint, MI, 48507-5508. Tel: 810-766-4050. Fax: 810-766-2013. p. 1179

Palmer, Gehlen, Br Mgr, Lake County Library, Middletown Branch, Calistoga & Collayami Sts, Middletown, CA, 95461. Tel: 707-987-3674. Fax: 707-987-3674. p. 163

Palmer, Germaine, Info Literacy/Ref, Dillard University, 2601 Gentilly Blvd, New Orleans, LA, 70122-3097. Tel: 504-816-4254. Fax: 504-816-4787. p. 960

Palmer, Ginger, Ref Librn, Fletcher Memorial Library, 257 Main St, Hampton, CT, 06247. Tel: 860-455-1086. p. 344

Palmer, Ginger, Ref Librn, Fletcher Memorial Library, 88 Main St, Ludlow, VT, 05149. Tel: 802-228-3517, 802-228-8921. p. 2427

Palmer, Heather, Libr Coordr, Canadian Broadcasting Corp, Radio Archives, 205 Wellington St W, Toronto, ON, M5G 3G7, CANADA. Tel: 416-205-5880. Fax: 416-205-8602. p. 2850

Palmer, Helen, ILL, Pitkin County Library, 120 N Mill St, Aspen, CO, 81611. Tel: 970-925-4025. Fax: 970-925-3935. p. 288

Palmer, John, Asst Dir, Circ & Ref, ILL, Southwestern Assemblies of God University, 1200 Sycamore, Waxahachie, TX, 75165-2342. Tel: 972-825-4761. Fax: 972-923-0488. p. 2398

Palmer, Joseph C, Dir, Mansfield-Richland County Public Library, 43 W Third St, Mansfield, OH, 44902-1295. Tel: 419-521-3124. Fax: 419-521-3129. p. 1912

Palmer, Katherine, Dir, Planning, Policy & E-Serv Delivery, Toronto Public Library, 789 Yonge St, Toronto, ON, M4W 2G8, CANADA. Tel: 416-393-7131. Fax: 416-393-7229. p. 2860

Palmer, Katy, Dir, Western Yearly Meeting of Friends, 203 S East St, Plainfield, IN, 46168. Tel: 317-839-2789. Fax: 317-839-2616. p. 773

Palmer, Kent, Bus Librn, Naperville Public Library, 200 W Jefferson Ave, Naperville, IL, 60540-5374. Tel: 630-961-4100. Fax: 630-637-6389. p. 679

Palmer, Linda, Chief Librn, Burns Lake Public Library, 585 Government St, Burns Lake, BC, V0J 1E0, CANADA. Tel: 250-692-3192. Fax: 250-692-7488. p. 2726

Palmer, Lisa, Head, Youth Serv, Bloomingdale Public Library, 101 Fairfield Way, Bloomingdale, IL, 60108-1579. Tel: 630-529-3120. Fax: 630-529-3243. p. 595

Palmer, Lynne, Ref Serv, Bingham McCutchen, Three Embarcadero Ctr, San Francisco, CA, 94111. Tel: 415-393-2560. Fax: 415-393-2286. p. 240

Palmer, Lynne, Librn, Sappi Fine Paper North America, 300 Warren Ave, Westbrook, ME, 04092. Tel: 207-856-3538. Fax: 207-856-3770. p. 1006

Palmer, Martha, Cat, Taunton Public Library, 12 Pleasant St, Taunton, MA, 02780. Tel: 508-821-1410. Fax: 508-821-1414. p. 1131

Palmer, Maureen, Circ Supvr, Reedsburg Public Library, 370 Vine St, Reedsburg, WI, 53959-1917. Tel: 608-524-3316, 608-768-7323. Fax: 608-524-9024. p. 2633

Palmer, Michelle, Asst Librn, Ser, North Arkansas College Library, 1515 Pioneer Dr, Harrison, AR, 72601. Tel: 870-391-3356. Fax: 870-391-3245. p. 102

Palmer, Myra, Circ, Nobles County Library, 407 12th St, Worthington, MN, 56187. Tel: 507-372-2981. Fax: 507-372-2982. p. 1291

Palmer, Nancy, Div Mgr, Libr Operations, Hennepin County Library, 12601 Ridgedale Dr, Minnetonka, MN, 55305-1909. Tel: 612-919-8787. Fax: 612-543-8600. p. 1263

Palmer, Nanette, Librn, Lonoke Prairie County Regional Library Headquarters, William F Foster Public, 100 E Taylor St, England, AR, 72046-2181. Tel: 501-842-2051. Fax: 501-842-2051. p. 108

Palmer, Olia, Ref & Instruction Librn, Lone Star College System, North Harris College Library, 2700 W W Thorne Dr, Houston, TX, 77073. Tel: 281-618-5487. Fax: 281-618-5695. p. 2340

Palmer, Patricia, Access Serv Mgr, California Baptist University, 8432 Magnolia Ave, Riverside, CA, 92504. Tel: 951-343-4331. p. 216

Palmer, Patricia, Tech Serv Librn, Portsmouth Public Library, 175 Parrott Ave, Portsmouth, NH, 03801-4452. Tel: 603-766-1730. Fax: 603-433-0981. p. 1463

Palmer, Rhoda, Assoc Dir, Pub & Electronic Serv, Grace College & Grace Theological Seminary, 200 Seminary Dr, Winona Lake, IN, 46590. Tel: 574-372-5100, Ext 6294. Fax: 574-372-5176. p. 789

Palmer, Rose, Night Supvr, Loras College Library, 1450 Alta Vista St, Dubuque, IA, 52004-4327. Tel: 563-588-7009. Fax: 563-588-7147. p. 812

Palmer, Sara, Head of Libr, Free Library of Philadelphia, Greater Olney Branch, 5501 N Fifth St, Philadelphia, PA, 19120-2805. Tel: 215-685-2846. Fax: 215-548-2605. p. 2107

Palmer, Sonya, Librn, Integris Southwest Medical Center, 4401 S Western, Oklahoma City, OK, 73109-3607. Tel: 405-636-7437. Fax: 405-636-7660. p. 1972

Palmer, Susan, Exec Dir, The Five Colleges of Ohio, 102 Allen House, Kenyon College, Gambier, OH, 43022. Tel: 740-427-5377. Fax: 740-427-5390. p. 2952

Palmer, Suzy Szasz, Dean of Libr, Southside Virginia Library Network, Longwood University, 201 High St, Farmville, VA, 23909-1897. Tel: 434-395-2083. Fax: 434-395-2453. p. 2957

Palmiere, Kristen, Head, ILL, University of Texas at Dallas, 800 W Campbell Rd, Richardson, TX, 75080. Tel: 972-883-2950. Fax: 972-883-2473. p. 2374

Palmieri, Imma, Per, United States Merchant Marine Academy, 300 Steamboat Rd, Kings Point, NY, 11024-1699. Tel: 516-726-5746. Fax: 516-726-5900. p. 1649

Palmiero, Mary, Br Mgr, Hamilton North Public Library, Atlanta Branch, 100 S Walnut St, Atlanta, IN, 46031. Tel: 765-292-2521. Fax: 765-292-2249. p. 732

Palmini, Cathy, Ref Serv, University of Wisconsin-Stevens Point, 900 Reserve St, Stevens Point, WI, 54481-1985. Tel: 715-346-4725. Fax: 715-346-3857. p. 2640

Palmisano, Brenda, Circ, Hudson Public Library, Three Washington St at The Rotary, Hudson, MA, 01749-2499. Tel: 978-568-9644. Fax: 978-568-9646. p. 1096

Palmisano, Grace, Adult Ref, Franklin Square Public Library, 19 Lincoln Rd, Franklin Square, NY, 11010. Tel: 516-488-3444. Fax: 516-354-3368. p. 1624

Palmisano, Sharon, Librn, Anchorage Daily News Library, 1001 Northway Dr, Anchorage, AK, 99508. Tel: 907-257-4593. Fax: 907-258-2157. p. 44

Palmore, Cassandra, Supvr, Access Serv, University of Puget Sound, 1500 N Warner St, Campus Mail Box 1021, Tacoma, WA, 98416-1021. Tel: 253-879-3669. Fax: 253-879-3670. p. 2541

Palo, Eric, Dir, Renton Technical College, 3000 NE Fourth St, Renton, WA, 98056-4195. Tel: 425-235-2331. Fax: 425-235-7816. p. 2526

Palomba, Mary, Asst Dir, Enfield Public Library, 104 Middle Rd, Enfield, CT, 06082. Tel: 860-763-7510. Fax: 860-763-7514. p. 338

Palombi, Cathy, Access Serv Librn, University of Virginia, Arthur J Morris Law Library, 580 Massie Rd, Charlottesville, VA, 22903-1789. Tel: 434-924-3384. Fax: 434-982-2232. p. 2455

Palomino, Norma, Chief, Libr Serv, Inter-American Development Bank Library, 1300 New York Ave NW, Stop W-0102, Washington, DC, 20577. Tel: 202-623-3918. Fax: 202-623-3183. p. 405

Palomo, Florence, Librn, Conde Nast Publications Library, Four Times Sq, New York, NY, 10036. Tel: 212-286-8245. Fax: 212-286-6763. p. 1675

Pals, Nina, Librn, Sarah Bush Lincoln Health Center, 1000 Health Center Dr, Mattoon, IL, 61938. Tel: 217-258-2262, 217-348-2263. Fax: 217-258-2288. p. 672

Palser, Philip, In Charge, Chippewa Valley Technical College Library, 620 W Clairemont Ave, Eau Claire, WI, 54701-6162. Tel: 715-833-6364. Fax: 715-833-6470. p. 2589

Palsich, Dianne, Librn, Lakeland Library Region, Paradise Hill Branch, Second Ave, No 104, Paradise Hill, SK, S0M 2G0, CANADA. Tel: 306-344-4741. p. 2920

Palsmeier, Carol, Librn, Fall River Public Library, 314 Merchant Ave, Fall River, KS, 67047. Tel: 620-658-4973. p. 866

Paltzgraff, Robert L, Dr, Pres, Institute for Foreign Policy Analysis, Inc, 675 Massachusetts Ave, 10th flr, Cambridge, MA, 02139-3396. Tel: 617-492-2116. Fax: 617-492-8242. p. 1077

Paluck, Anne, Ref Serv, Middlesex Community College, 100 Training Hill Rd, Middletown, CT, 06457-4889. Tel: 860-343-5831. Fax: 860-343-5874. p. 351

Palumbo, Paulette, Tech Serv, Bryant Library, Two Paper Mill Rd, Roslyn, NY, 11576-2193. Tel: 516-621-2240. Fax: 516-621-7211. p. 1735

Paluskas, Paul, Media Spec, South Puget Sound Community College Library, 2011 Mottman Rd SW, Olympia, WA, 98512. Tel: 360-596-5271. Fax: 360-596-5714. p. 2522

Pamel, Diane, Dir, Southworth Library Association, 24 W Main St, Dryden, NY, 13053. Tel: 607-844-4782. Fax: 607-844-5310. p. 1615

Pamela, Ladner Ann, Dr, Asst Dean, Mississippi Gulf Coast Community College, 2300 Hwy 90, Gautier, MS, 39553. Tel: 228-497-7642. Fax: 228-497-7643. p. 1298

Pan, Deng M, Librn, Federal Reserve Bank of Kansas City, One Memorial Dr, Kansas City, MO, 64198. Tel: 816-881-2970. Fax: 816-881-2807. p. 1337

Pan, Denise, Assoc Dir, Tech Serv, Auraria Library, 1100 Lawrence St, Denver, CO, 80204-2095. Tel: 303-556-4762. Fax: 303-556-3528. p. 298

Pan, Patrick, Br Mgr, Markham Public Library, Unionville Branch, 15 Library Lane, Unionville, ON, L3R 5C4, CANADA. Tel: 905-513-7977, Ext 5551. Fax: 905-477-8608. p. 2820

Panado, Andy, Supvr, Access Serv, University of California San Francisco, Mission Bay FAMRI Library, William J Rutter Conference Ctr, Rm 150, 1675 Owens St, San Francisco, CA, 94143-2119. Tel: 415-514-4060. p. 248

Panagopoulos, Beata, Asst Dir, Head, Tech Serv, Suffolk University, 73 Tremont St, Boston, MA, 02108. Tel: 617-573-8535. Fax: 617-573-8756. p. 1067

Panak, Peggy L, Asst Dir, Zephyrhills Public Library, 5347 Eighth St, Zephyrhills, FL, 33542. Tel: 813-780-0064. Fax: 813-780-0066. p. 505

Panasik, Susan Marie, Legal Info Mgr, United States Department of Health & Human Services, Rm 4541, Cohen Bldg, 330 Independence Ave SW, Washington, DC, 20201. Tel: 202-619-0190. Fax: 202-619-3719. p. 419

Panasuk, Susan, AV, Herrick District Library, 300 S River Ave, Holland, MI, 49423-3290. Tel: 616-355-3100. p. 1190

Panbay, Sandra, In Charge, Watts, Griffis & McOuat Ltd Library, Eight King St E, Ste 400, Toronto, ON, M5C 1B5, CANADA. Tel: 416-364-6244. Fax: 416-864-1675. p. 2867

Pancerella-Willis, Gina, Librn, Anoka-Ramsey Community College, 11200 Mississippi Blvd NW, Coon Rapids, MN, 55433. Tel: 763-433-1197. p. 1246

Panciera, Benjamin, Dir, Linda Lear Ctr for Spec Coll & Archives, Connecticut College, 270 Mohegan Ave, New London, CT, 06320-4196. Tel: 860-439-2654. Fax: 860-439-2871. p. 359

Panciuk, Mircea, Exec Dir, Northern Lights Library System, 5650 48th St, Elk Point, AB, T0A 1A0, CANADA. Tel: 780-724-2596. p. 2703

Pancratz, Leslie, Librn, Norton Healthcare, 200 E Chestnut St, Louisville, KY, 40202. Tel: 502-629-8125. Fax: 502-629-8138. p. 925

Panda, Rosamond, Pub Serv, Ref Serv, Delaware State University, 1200 N Dupont Hwy, Dover, DE, 19901-2277. Tel: 302-857-6197. Fax: 302-857-6177. p. 382

Pando, Sarah, Asst Dir, Andrews County Library, 109 NW First St, Andrews, TX, 79714. Tel: 432-523-9819. Fax: 432-523-4570. p. 2275

Pandya, Niyati, Librn, Montgomery College, Rockville Campus Library, Macklin Tower, 51 Mannakee St, Rockville, MD, 20850. Tel: 240-567-4130. Fax: 240-567-7153. p. 1037

Pandya, Sonal, Res Librn, Linklaters, 1345 Sixth Ave, 19th Flr, New York, NY, 10105. Tel: 212-424-9000. Fax: 212-424-9100. p. 1685

Panek, Diane, Info Tech Mgr, United States Air Force, 55 FSS/FSDL, Bldg 73, 510 Custer Dr, Offutt AFB, NE, 68113-2150. Tel: 402-294-5543. Fax: 402-294-7124. p. 1411

Panella, Deborah, Dir, Libr Serv, Cravath, Swaine & Moore LLP, 825 Eighth Ave, New York, NY, 10019. Tel: 212-474-3500. Fax: 212-474-3556. p. 1676

Panella, Nancy, Dr, Librn, St Luke's-Roosevelt Hospital Center, 1111 Amsterdam Ave, New York, NY, 10025. Tel: 212-523-4315. Fax: 212-523-4313. p. 1699

Pang, June, Cat, Pace University, 861 Bedford Rd, Pleasantville, NY, 10570-2799. Tel: 914-773-3255. Fax: 914-773-3508. p. 1719

Pang, Xuan, ILL, University of Texas, School of Public Health Library, 1200 Herman Pressler Blvd, Houston, TX, 77030-3900. Tel: 713-500-9121. Fax: 713-500-9125. p. 2344

Pangallo, Karen, Dir, North Shore Community College Library, One Ferncroft Rd, Danvers, MA, 01923-4093. Tel: 978-762-4000. Fax: 978-739-5500. p. 1083

Panguelinan, Perry J, Ref Serv, University of Guam, Guam & Micronesia Collection, UOG Sta, Mangilao, GU, 96923. Tel: 671-735-2157, 671-735-2160. Fax: 671-734-7403. p. 2667

Paniccia, Vanessa, Ref & Instruction Librn, Daemen College Library, Research & Information Commons, 4380 Main St, Amherst, NY, 14226-3592. Tel: 716-839-8243. Fax: 716-839-8475. p. 1573

Panichella, Rosemary, Librn, Uniontown Hospital, 500 W Berkeley St, Uniontown, PA, 15401. Tel: 724-430-5178. Fax: 724-430-3349. p. 2147

Panik, Tina, Circ Mgr, Pub Serv Mgr, Avon Free Public Library, 281 Country Club Rd, Avon, CT, 06001. Tel: 860-673-9712. Fax: 860-675-6364. p. 329

Panitz, Zimra, Tech Serv, School of Visual Arts, 380 Second Ave, 2nd Flr, New York, NY, 10010-3994. Tel: 212-592-2660. Fax: 212-592-2655. p. 1699

Panke, Mary, Dir, Strategic Knowledge, Population Action International Library, 1300 19th St NW, Ste 200, Washington, DC, 20036-1624. Tel: 202-557-3400. Fax: 202-728-4177. p. 413

Pankey, Barbara, Ch, Circ Librn, Giles County Public Library, 122 S Second St, Pulaski, TN, 38478-3285. Tel: 931-363-2720. Fax: 931-424-7032. p. 2263

Pankey, William, Electronic Res, William Rainey Harper College Library, 1200 W Algonquin Rd, Palatine, IL, 60067. Tel: 847-925-6498. Fax: 847-925-6164. p. 687

Pankiewicz, Cynthia A, Cat, New England Institute of Technology Library, 1408 Division Rd, East Greenwich, RI, 02818-1205. Tel: 401-739-5000, Ext 3474. Fax: 401-886-0861. p. 2166

Pankow, David, Curator, Melbert B Cary Graphic Arts Coll & Mgr Cultural Coll, Rochester Institute of Technology, 90 Lomb Memorial Dr, Rochester, NY, 14623-5604. Tel: 585-475-2408. Fax: 585-475-7007. p. 1731

Pankowsky, Susan, Librn, West End Synagogue, 3810 W End Ave, Nashville, TN, 37205. Tel: 615-269-4592. Fax: 615-269-4695. p. 2261

Pankratz, Janice, Br Coordr, Marathon County Public Library, Stratford Branch, 400 N Fourth Ave, Stratford, WI, 54484. Tel: 715-687-4420. Fax: 715-687-4420. p. 2646

Pankratz, Lisa, Ref/Bibliog Instruction Librn, Clark State Community College Library, 570 E Leffel Lane, Springfield, OH, 45505. Tel: 937-328-6022. Fax: 937-328-6133. p. 1935

Pannabecker, Virginia, Health Sci Librn, Arizona State University Libraries, Downtown Phoenix Campus Library, UCENT Bldg, Ste L1-62, 411 N Central Ave, Phoenix, AZ, 85004-1213. Tel: 602-496-0683. Fax: 602-496-0312. p. 83

Pannell, Alan, Head, Ref, University of Colorado Boulder, The William A Wise Law Library, 2450 Kittredge Loop Dr, 402 UCB, Boulder, CO, 80309-0402. Tel: 303-735-1867. Fax: 303-492-2707. p. 292

Pannell, Krista, Ref Asst, Pepperdine University Libraries, Encino Graduate Campus Library, 16830 Ventura Blvd, Encino, CA, 91436. Tel: 818-501-1615. Fax: 815-501-1065. p. 182

Panneri, Theresa, Pres, Lakeview Area Public Library, 3271 S Main St, Sandy Lake, PA, 16145. Tel: 724-376-4217. p. 2136

Pannkuk, Jill, Dir, Liberal Memorial Library, 519 N Kansas, Liberal, KS, 67901-3345. Tel: 620-626-0180. Fax: 620-626-0182. p. 879

Pannkuk, Matthew, Dir, Seward County Community College Library, 1801 N Kansas, Liberal, KS, 67901. Tel: 620-417-1161. Fax: 620-629-2725. p. 879

Pannone, Jason A, Librn, Harvard Library, Robbins Library of Philosophy, Emerson Hall 211, Harvard University, Dept of Philosophy, 25 Quincy St, Cambridge, MA, 02138. Fax: 617-495-2192. p. 1076

Panoc, Maria, Librn, Lankenau Hospital, 100 Lancaster Ave, Wynnewood, PA, 19096. Tel: 610-645-2698. Fax: 610-645-3425. p. 2158

Panos, Peter, Col Librn, Caldwell College, 120 Bloomfield Ave, Caldwell, NJ, 07006-6195. Tel: 973-618-3312. Fax: 973-618-3360. p. 1476

Pansch, Detlev, Exec Dir, Barrington Public Library District, 505 N Northwest Hwy, Barrington, IL, 60010. Tel: 847-382-1300. Fax: 847-382-1261. p. 592

Pantalony, David, Curator of Instruments, The Bakken - A Library & Museum of Electricity in Life, 3537 Zenith Ave S, Minneapolis, MN, 55416. Tel: 612-926-3878, Ext 217. Fax: 612-927-7265. p. 1259

Pantell, Brenda E, Sr Librn, New York State Supreme Court Library, Brooklyn, Supreme Court Bldg, Rm 349, 360 Adams St, Brooklyn, NY, 11201-3782. Tel: 347-296-1144. Fax: 718-643-2412. p. 1594

Pantorno, Brandon, Dir, Comsewogue Public Library, 170 Terryville Rd, Port Jefferson Station, NY, 11776. Tel: 631-928-1212. Fax: 631-928-6307. p. 1721

Panza, Maria, Tech Serv, Norton Rose Canada LLP Library, One Place Ville Marie, Ste 2500, Montreal, QC, H3B 1R1, CANADA. Tel: 514-847-4701. Fax: 514-286-5474. p. 2900

Panzer, Michael, Mgr, Philadelphia Newspapers, Inc, 400 N Broad St, Philadelphia, PA, 19130-4099. Tel: 215-854-4753. Fax: 215-854-5697. p. 2114

Paolelli, Frank, Circ, University of Miami, Louis Calder Memorial Library, Miller School of Medicine, 1601 NW Tenth Ave, Miami, FL, 33136. Tel: 305-243-6403. Fax: 305-325-8853. p. 469

Paolillo, Pauline, Per, Cambria County Library System & District Center, 248 Main St, Johnstown, PA, 15901. Tel: 814-536-5131. Fax: 814-536-6905. p. 2073

Paolini, Francine, Co-Dir, Media Librn, Aquinas College, 1607 Robinson Rd SE, Grand Rapids, MI, 49506-1799. Tel: 616-632-2137. Fax: 616-732-4534. p. 1183

Paone, Kimberly, Dir, Matawan-Aberdeen Public Library, 165 Main St, Matawan, NJ, 07747. Tel: 732-583-9100. Fax: 732-583-9360. p. 1500

Paone, Richard O, Asst Law Librn, Cat, Pennsylvania State University - Dickinson School of Law (University Libraries), 1170 Harrisburg Pike, Carlisle, PA, 17013-1617. Tel: 717-240-5011. Fax: 717-240-5127. p. 2042

Papa, Carrie, Dir, Libr Serv, All Saints Healthcare, Saint Mary's Medical Center Library, 3801 Spring St, Racine, WI, 53405. Tel: 262-687-4011. Fax: 262-687-4175. p. 2632

Papa, Leo, Head, Info Tech, Canton Public Library, 1200 S Canton Center Rd, Canton, MI, 48188-1600. Tel: 734-397-0999. Fax: 734-397-1130. p. 1160

Papadopoulos, John, Chief Librn, University of Toronto Libraries, Bora Laskin Law Library, 78 Queen's Park, Toronto, ON, M5S 2C5, CANADA. Tel: 416-978-1073. Fax: 416-978-8396. p. 2866

Papandrea, Virginia, Dir, Red Bank Public Library, 84 W Front St, Red Bank, NJ, 07701. Tel: 732-842-0690. Fax: 732-842-4191. p. 1525

Papandreou, Jennifer, Mgr, GlaxoSmithKline, 7333 Mississauga Rd N, Mississauga, ON, L5N 6L4, CANADA. Tel: 905-819-3000, Ext 6023. Fax: 905-819-3096. p. 2822

Paparelli, Marita E, Librn, Lackawanna Bar Association, Courthouse, Ground Flr, 200 N Washington Ave, Scranton, PA, 18503. Tel: 570-963-6712. Fax: 570-344-2944. p. 2137

Papas, Philip R, Tech Serv, Touro College Libraries, 43 W 23rd St, Fifth Fl, New York, NY, 10010. Tel: 212-463-0400. Fax: 212-627-3696. p. 1701

Papcunik, Sandy, Librn, Cambria County Free Law Library, Court House, S Center St, Ebensburg, PA, 15931. Tel: 814-472-1501. Fax: 814-472-4799. p. 2052

Pape, Amanda, Coordr, Spec Serv, Tarleton State University Library, 201 Saint Felix, Stephenville, TX, 76401. Tel: 254-968-9251. Fax: 254-968-9467. p. 2389

Pape, Kathy, Dir, Conneaut Public Library, 304 Buffalo St, Conneaut, OH, 44030-2658. Tel: 440-593-1608. Fax: 440-593-4470. p. 1891

Pape, Sabrina L, Dir Gen, Publ Br, Vassar College Library, 124 Raymond Ave, Maildrop 20, Poughkeepsie, NY, 12604-0020. Tel: 845-437-5787. Fax: 845-437-5864. p. 1723

Pape, Wendy F, Dir, Princeton Public Library, Two Town Hall Dr, Princeton, MA, 01541. Tel: 978-464-2115. Fax: 978-464-2116. p. 1118

Papenfus, Esther, Mgr Fac, Foothills Art Center, 809 15th St, Golden, CO, 80401. Tel: 303-279-3922. Fax: 303-279-9470. p. 309

Papenfuss, Jerilyn, Dir, Iron Ridge Public Library, 205 Park St, Iron Ridge, WI, 53035. Tel: 920-387-3637. Fax: 920-387-3637. p. 2599

Papenfuss, Larry, Info Tech Dir, South Central Kansas Library System, 321 N Main St, South Hutchinson, KS, 67505-1146. Tel: 620-663-3211. Fax: 620-663-9797. p. 895

Papik, Barbara, Librn, Avera Sacred Heart Hospital, 501 Summit St, Yankton, SD, 57078-9967. Tel: 605-668-8384. Fax: 605-668-8488. p. 2222

Papke, Jackie, Librn, National Marine Fisheries Service, 3500 Delwood Beach Rd, Panama City, FL, 32408. Tel: 850-234-6541, Ext 227. Fax: 850-235-3559. p. 480

Papp, Lois, Head, Adult Serv, East Greenbush Community Library, Ten Community Way, East Greenbush, NY, 12061. Tel: 518-477-7476. Fax: 518-477-6692. p. 1616

Pappani, Laura, Br Mgr, Nevada County Library, Grass Valley Library - Royce Branch, 207 Mill St, Grass Valley, CA, 95945-6789. Tel: 530-273-4117. p. 193

Pappas, Carol, Coordr, Acq, Assumption College, 500 Salisbury St, Worcester, MA, 01609. Tel: 508-767-7076. Fax: 508-767-7374. p. 1143

Pappas, Dan, Head, Ref, NASA Ames Research Center, Technical Library, Bldg 202, Mail Stop 202-3, Moffett Field, CA, 94035-1000. Tel: 650-604-6325. Fax: 650-604-4988. p. 189

Pappas, Daniel, Tech Serv, Schulte Roth & Zabel LLP, 919 Third Ave, New York, NY, 10022. Tel: 212-756-2237. Fax: 212-593-5955. p. 1699

Pappas, David, Dir, Harrisburg Area Community College, One HACC Dr, Harrisburg, PA, 17110-2999. Tel: 717-780-2468. Fax: 717-780-2462. p. 2065

Pappas, E, Libr Coordr, Robert Morris University, 1000 Tower Lane, Bensenville, IL, 60106. Tel: 630-787-7879. Fax: 630-787-7802. p. 594

Pappathan, Matthew, Dir, Union Institute & University, 62 Ridge St, Ste 2, Montpelier, VT, 05602. Tel: 802-828-8746. Fax: 802-828-8748. p. 2429

Pappert, Joyce, Ch, Mars Area Public Library, 107 Grand Ave, Mars, PA, 16046. Tel: 724-625-9048. Fax: 724-625-2871. p. 2084

Pappius, Hanna M, Dir, The Polish Library, McGill University, 3479 Peel St, Montreal, QC, H3A 1W7, CANADA. Tel: 514-398-6978. p. 2900

Pappolla, Carol, Libr Serv Supvr, Purdue Pharma LP & Associated Companies, One Stamford Forum, 201 Tresser Blvd, Stamford, CT, 06901. Tel: 203-588-7265. Fax: 203-588-6212. p. 369

Paprocki, Rosemary, Asst Librn, University of Rochester, Rossell Hope Robbins Library, Rush Rhees Library, Rm 416, Rochester, NY, 14627. Tel: 585-275-0110. p. 1733

Paquet, Sonia, Dir, Canadian Music Centre, Quebec Region, 416 McGill St, Montreal, ON, H2Y 2G1, CANADA. Tel: 514-866-3477. Fax: 514-866-0456. p. 2851

Paquette, Andrian R, Curator, Old Slater Mill Association, 67 Roosevelt Ave, Pawtucket, RI, 02862. Tel: 401-725-8638. Fax: 401-722-3040. p. 2171

Paquette, Jocelyn, Libr Dir, Chaleur Library Region, Campbellton Centennial Library, 19 Aberdeen St, Ste 100, Campbellton, NB, E3N 2J4, CANADA. Tel: 506-753-5253. Fax: 506-753-3803. p. 2761

Paquette, Meg, Ch, South Burlington Community Library, 540 Dorset St, South Burlington, VT, 05403. Tel: 802-652-7080. Fax: 802-652-7013. p. 2435

Paquette, Michel, Head of Libr, Cegep de Baie-Comeau, 537 boul Blanche, Baie Comeau, QC, G5C 2B2, CANADA. Tel: 418-589-5707, Ext 325. Fax: 418-589-9842. p. 2879

Paquette-Lalonde, Lise, Librn, Greater Sudbury Public Library, Chelmsford Citizen Service Center Public Library, 3502 Errington St, Chelmsford, ON, P0M 1L0, CANADA. Tel: 705-688-3963, 705-855-2593. Fax: 705-855-4629. p. 2846

Paquin, Chantal, ILL & Distance Libr Serv Spec, Institut National de la Recherche Scientifique, Universite du Quebec, 490 de la Couronne, local 1401, Quebec, QC, G1K 9A9, CANADA. Tel: 418-654-3707. Fax: 418-654-2660. p. 2905

Paquin, Emilie, Head Librn, Bibliothèque Jean-Marc-Belzile, 378, rue Principale, Lachute, QC, J8H 1Y2, CANADA. Tel: 450-562-3781, Ext 255. Fax: 450-562-1431. p. 2885

Paquin, Johanne, Tech Serv, Centre d'acces a l'Information Juridique-Bibliotheque de Quebec, 300 Boul Jean-Lesage, Palais de Justice Ste 503, Quebec, QC, G1K 8K6, CANADA. Tel: 418-525-4208. p. 2904

Paradin, Joseph, Head of Libr, Free Library of Philadelphia, Philadelphia City Institute, 1905 Locust St, Philadelphia, PA, 19103-5730. Tel: 215-685-6621, 215-685-6623. Fax: 215-685-6622. p. 2109

Paradis, Betsy, Ref, Spec Coll, Belfast Free Library, 106 High St, Belfast, ME, 04915. Tel: 207-338-3884. Fax: 207-338-3895. p. 977

Paradis, Diane, Dir, College Saint-Alphonse Library, 97 Ave de la Montagne, Saint-Tite-Des Caps, QC, G0A 4J0, CANADA. Tel: 418-823-2759. Fax: 418-823-2838. p. 2911

Paradis, Monique, AV, Coll Develop, Cegep de Trois-Rivieres Bibliotheque, 3175 Laviolette, Trois-Rivieres, QC, G9A 5E6, CANADA. Tel: 819-376-1721, Ext 2609. Fax: 819-693-3844. p. 2914

Paradise, Andrew, Dir, Jackson Park Hospital Library, 7531 S Stony Island Ave, Chicago, IL, 60649. Tel: 773-947-7653. p. 616

Paradise, Andrew, Coordr, Chicago & South Consortium, Jackson Park Hospital & Medical Center, 7531 S Stony Island Ave, Chicago, IL, 60649-3993. Tel: 773-947-7653. p. 2942

Paradise, Carolyn, Dir, Casco Public Library, Five Leach Hill Rd, Casco, ME, 04015-3229. Tel: 207-627-4541. p. 981

Paradise, Nancy, Br Mgr, Long Beach Public Library, El Dorado, 2900 Studebaker Rd, Long Beach, CA, 90815. Tel: 562-570-3136. p. 167

Parady, Anne, Mgr, Youth Serv, Sweetwater County Library System, Rock Springs Library, 400 C St, Rock Springs, WY, 82901-6221. Tel: 307-352-6667, Ext 2300. Fax: 307-352-6657. p. 2655

Paraham, Greg, Info Serv Librn, Rhodes College, 2000 North Pkwy, Memphis, TN, 38112-1694. Tel: 901-843-3900. Fax: 901-843-3404. p. 2251

Parang, Elizabeth, Ser/Electronic Res Librn, Pepperdine University Libraries, 24255 Pacific Coast Hwy, Malibu, CA, 90263. Tel: 310-506-4252. Fax: 310-506-7225. p. 182

Parascandola, Jacqueline, Rare Bk Cataloger, Columbia University, Augustus C Long Health Sciences Library, 701 W 168th St, Lobby Level, New York, NY, 10032. Tel: 212-305-3605. Fax: 212-234-0595. p. 1675

Parascenzo-Brush, Marina, Librn, Stoel, Rives, Boley, Jones & Grey, One Union Sq, 600 University St, Ste 3600, Seattle, WA, 98101. Tel: 206-386-7502. Fax: 206-386-7500. p. 2532

Parbos, Jan, Asst Librn, Salem Township Library, 3007 142nd Ave, Burnips, MI, 49314. Tel: 616-896-8170. Fax: 616-896-8035. p. 1160

Parcell-Greene, Joyce, Br Supvr, Southside Regional Library, Butler Memorial, 515 Marshall St, Chase City, VA, 23924. Tel: 434-372-4286. Fax: 434-372-0303. p. 2452

Parchuck, Jill, Dir, Yale University Library, Social Science Libraries & Information Services, 140 Prospect St, New Haven, CT, 06511. Tel: 203-432-3300. Fax: 203-432-8979. p. 358

Pardi, Sarah, Ch, Free Public Library of the Borough of Fort Lee, 320 Main St, Fort Lee, NJ, 07024. Tel: 201-592-3620. Fax: 201-585-0375. p. 1486

Pardo, Leslie, Access Serv, Arizona State University, College of Law, 110 S McAllister Ave, Tempe, AZ, 85287-7806. Tel: 480-965-6141. Fax: 480-965-4283. p. 83

Pardue, David, Cat Supvr, McAllen Memorial Library, 601 N Main, McAllen, TX, 78501-4666. Tel: 956-688-3300. Fax: 956-688-3301. p. 2360

Pardue, Karen, Dept Chair, Head, Info Mgt, Colorado State University Pueblo Library, 2200 Bonforte Blvd, Pueblo, CO, 81001-4901. Tel: 719-549-2326. Fax: 719-549-2738. p. 320

Pare, Gilles, Librn, Le Devoir, 2050 rue de Bleury, 9th Flr, Montreal, QC, H3A 3M9, CANADA. Tel: 514-985-3333. Fax: 514-985-3360. p. 2897

Paredes, Manuel A, Dir, Cherry Hill Public Library, 1100 Kings Hwy N, Cherry Hill, NJ, 08034-1911. Tel: 856-667-0300. Fax: 856-667-9503. p. 1478

Paredes, Marguerite, Librn, Rhode Island Public Expenditure Council Library, 86 Weybosssett St, Providence, RI, 02903. Tel: 401-521-6320. Fax: 401-751-1915. p. 2174

Pareja, Jose Ignacio, Head, Wildman Sci Libr, Sci Tech Learning Spec, Earlham College, 801 National Rd W, Richmond, IN, 47374-4095. Tel: 765-983-1612. Fax: 765-983-1304. p. 774

Parent, Ingrid, Univ Librn, University of British Columbia Library, 1961 East Mall, Vancouver, BC, V6T 1Z1, CANADA. Tel: 604-827-3486. Fax: 604-822-3242. p. 2742

Parent, Jacinthe, Circ, Cegep de Granby Haute-Yamaska, 235 Saint Jacques St, Granby, QC, J2G 3N1, CANADA. Tel: 450-372-6614, Ext 1205. Fax: 450-372-6565. p. 2884

Parent, Kathy, Dir, Cattaraugus Free Library, 21 Main St, Cattaraugus, NY, 14719. Tel: 716-257-9500. Fax: 716-257-9500. p. 1603

Parent, Mariette, Pres, Societe de Genealogie de Quebec, 1210 av du Seminaire, CP 9066, Sainte-Foy, QC, G1V 4A8, CANADA. Tel: 418-651-9127. Fax: 418-651-2643. p. 2910

Parent, Mary, Supvr, Circ, North Seattle Community College, 9600 College Way N, Seattle, WA, 98103. Tel: 206-526-7714. Fax: 206-527-3614. p. 2529

Parent, Suzanne, Coll Develop, University of Maine School of Law, 246 Deering Ave, Portland, ME, 04102. Tel: 207-780-4829. Fax: 207-780-4913. p. 997

Parente, Sharon, Ref & Instruction Librn, Middle Tennessee State University, MTSU, PO Box 13, Murfreesboro, TN, 37132. Tel: 615-898-2549. p. 2254

Parenti, Pamela, YA Serv, Acton Memorial Library, 486 Main St, Acton, MA, 01720. Tel: 978-264-9641. Fax: 978-635-0073. p. 1047

Parette, Shanel, Circ & Stacks Supvr, Willamette University, 900 State St, Salem, OR, 97301. Tel: 503-370-6312. Fax: 503-370-6141. p. 2019

Parhad, Bronwyn, Head, Youth Serv, Winnetka-Northfield Public Library District, 768 Oak St, Winnetka, IL, 60093-2583. Tel: 847-446-7220. Fax: 847-446-5085. p. 720

Parham, Annette, Acq, Colonial Williamsburg Foundation, 313 First St, Williamsburg, VA, 23185-4306. Tel: 757-565-8532. Fax: 757-565-8508. p. 2502

Parham, Carolyn, Circ Serv Supvr, Santa Clara City Library, 2635 Homestead Rd, Santa Clara, CA, 95051. Tel: 408-615-2973. Fax: 408-247-9657. p. 262

Parham, Joy, Mgt Serv Officer, University of California, Merced Library, 5200 N Lake Rd, Merced, CA, 95343-5001. Tel: 209-228-4237. Fax: 209-228-4271. p. 186

Parham, Loretta, Dir, Atlanta University Center, 111 James P Brawley Dr SW, Atlanta, GA, 30314. Tel: 404-978-2061. Fax: 404-577-5158. p. 513

Parham, Lucretia, Dir, Acad Computing, Augusta Technical College, 3200 Augusta Tech Dr, Augusta, GA, 30906. Tel: 706-771-4165. Fax: 706-771-4169. p. 519

Parham, Marita, Ch, Roselle Free Public Library, 104 W Fourth Ave, Roselle, NJ, 07203. Tel: 908-245-5809. Fax: 908-298-8881. p. 1527

Parham, Marsha, Ch, Flint River Regional Library, 800 Memorial Dr, Griffin, GA, 30223. Tel: 770-412-4770. p. 535

Parham, R Bruce, Dir, National Archives & Records Administration, 654 W Third Ave, Anchorage, AK, 99501-2145. Tel: 907-261-7801. Fax: 907-261-7813. p. 45

Parham, Rita, Media Serv Librn, Louisiana State University Libraries, Paul M Hebert Law Center, One E Campus Dr, Baton Rouge, LA, 70803-1000. Tel: 225-578-4043. Fax: 225-578-5773. p. 944

Parham, Roberta, Patron Serv, Lawton Public Library, Branch Library, 1304 NW Kingswood, Lawton, OK, 73505-4076. Tel: 580-581-3457. p. 1967

Parham, Sandra, Dean, California State University Dominguez Hills, 1000 E Victoria St, Carson, CA, 90747. Tel: 310-243-2200. Fax: 310-516-4219. p. 132

Parham, Susan, Head, Scholarly Communication & Digital Curation, Georgia Institute of Technology Library, 704 Cherry St, Atlanta, GA, 30332-0900. Tel: 404-894-4501. Fax: 404-894-6084. p. 515

Parikh, Neel, Exec Dir, Pierce County Library System, 3005 112th St E, Tacoma, WA, 98446-2215. Tel: 253-548-3445. Fax: 253-537-4600. p. 2539

Parikh, Ramesh, Govt Doc, Ref Serv, Our Lady of Holy Cross College Library, 4123 Woodland Dr, New Orleans, LA, 70131. Tel: 504-398-2102. Fax: 504-391-2421. p. 962

Paringer, William, Librn, Kaiser-Permanente Medical Center, 10800 Magnolia Ave, Riverside, CA, 92505. Tel: 951-353-3659. Fax: 951-353-3262. p. 217

Paris, André, Chief Librn, Saint Paul University Library, 223 Main St, Ottawa, ON, K1S 1C4, CANADA. Tel: 613-236-1393, Ext 2220. Fax: 613-751-4031. p. 2833

Paris, Diana, Acq & Cat, Manchester Community College Library, Great Path, Manchester, CT, 06040. Tel: 860-512-2879. Fax: 860-512-2871. p. 350

Paris, Jennifer, Electronic Res, MiraCosta College Library, One Barnard Dr, Oceanside, CA, 92056-3899. Tel: 760-634-7814. Fax: 760-795-6723. p. 199

Paris, Lee Anne, Ref, Web Coordr, Oklahoma Christian University, 2501 E Memorial Rd, Edmond, OK, 73013. Tel: 405-425-5317. Fax: 405-425-5313. p. 1962

Paris, P, Adult Serv, Bellmore Memorial Library, 2288 Bedford Ave, Bellmore, NY, 11710. Tel: 516-785-2990. Fax: 516-783-8550. p. 1580

Paris, Terrence, Coll & Archives Librn, Mount Saint Vincent University Library, 166 Bedford Hwy, Halifax, NS, B3M 2J6, CANADA. Tel: 902-457-6526. Fax: 902-457-6445. p. 2781

Pariseau, Joanne, Dir, Jones Memorial Library, One Water St, Orleans, VT, 05860-1303. Tel: 802-754-6660. Fax: 802-754-6660. p. 2431

Parish, Betty, Librn, Simmons College of Kentucky Library, 1018 S Seventh St, Louisville, KY, 40203. Tel: 502-776-1443. Fax: 502-776-2227. p. 925

Parish, Cathryne, Dir, Illinois Central College, One College Dr, East Peoria, IL, 61635-0001. Tel: 309-694-8504. Fax: 309-694-5473. p. 638

Parish, Daniela, Librn, Warsaw Public Library, 1025 Webster St, Warsaw, IL, 62379-1454. Tel: 217-256-3417. Fax: 217-256-3154. p. 715

Parish, Elizabeth, User Serv Librn, Louisiana College, 1140 College Blvd, Pineville, LA, 71359. Tel: 318-487-7201. Fax: 318-487-7143. p. 965

Parish, Sharlene, Acq, Cat, Spooner Memorial Library, 421 High St, Spooner, WI, 54801-1431. Tel: 715-635-2792. Fax: 715-635-2147. p. 2639

Parisi, Lisa, Ref Librn, Florida Coastal School of Law, 8787 Baypine Rd, Jacksonville, FL, 32256. Tel: 904-680-7642. Fax: 904-680-7677. p. 452

Parisi, Mark, Ref Serv, Ad, Everett Public Libraries, 410 Broadway, Everett, MA, 02149. Tel: 617-394-2300. Fax: 617-389-1230. p. 1087

Parisi, Sara, Ch, Indian Valley Public Library, 100 E Church Ave, Telford, PA, 18969. Tel: 215-723-9109. Fax: 215-723-0583. p. 2145

Parizek, Michelle, Dir, Clutier Public Library, 404 Main St, Clutier, IA, 52217. Tel: 319-479-2171. Fax: 319-479-2903. p. 803

Park, Debra, Adult Coll Develop Librn, Spokane County Library District, 4322 N Argonne Rd, Spokane, WA, 99212-1868. Tel: 509-893-8200. Fax: 509-893-8472. p. 2536

Park, Eun, Assoc Prof, McGill University, 3661 Peel St, Montreal, QC, H3A 1X1, CANADA. Tel: 514-398-3364. Fax: 514-398-7193. p. 2979

Park, Gail, Br Head, Timberland Regional Library, Tumwater Branch, 7023 New Market St, Tumwater, WA, 98501-6563. Tel: 360-943-7790. Fax: 360-586-9028. p. 2544

Park, Gemma, Acq, University of the District of Columbia, Learning Resources Division, 4200 Connecticut Ave NW, Washington, DC, 20008. Tel: 202-274-6370. Fax: 202-274-6012. p. 421

Park, Janet, Br Mgr, Onondaga County Public Library, Mundy, 1204 S Geddes St, Syracuse, NY, 13204. Tel: 315-435-3797. Fax: 315-435-8557. p. 1752

Park, Joyce, Librn, Howe Community Library, 315 S Collins Freeway, Howe, TX, 75459. Tel: 903-532-3350. Fax: 903-532-3351. p. 2345

Park, Jung-ran, PhD, Asst Prof, Drexel University, Rush Bldg, Rm 306, 30 N 33rd St, Philadelphia, PA, 19104-2875. Tel: 215-895-2474. Fax: 215-895-2494. p. 2972

Park, Kathryn, Dir, Libr Instruction, Webmaster, College of the Mainland Library, 1200 Amburn Rd, Texas City, TX, 77591-2499. Tel: 409-938-1211, Ext 201. Fax: 409-938-8918. p. 2392

Park, Kwang-hee, Dr, Assoc Dir, South Baylo University Library, 1126 N Brookhurst St, Anaheim, CA, 92801-1704. Tel: 714-533-1495. Fax: 714-533-6040. p. 121

Park, Linda, Dir, Keuka College, 141 Central Ave, Keuka Park, NY, 14478-0038. Tel: 315-279-5208. Fax: 315-279-5334. p. 1649

Park, Rich, Dir, Human Res, Timberland Regional Library, 415 Tumwater Blvd SW, Tumwater, WA, 98501-5799. Tel: 360-943-5001, Ext 2513. Fax: 360-586-6838. p. 2543

Park, Sarah, PhD, Asst Prof, Saint Catherine University, 2004 Randolph Ave, Mailstop No 4125, Saint Paul, MN, 55105. Tel: 651-690-6802. Fax: 651-690-8724. p. 2968

Park, Sean, Network Adminr, Coos County Library Service District, Tioga Hall, 1988 Newmark Ave, Coos Bay, OR, 97420. Tel: 541-888-7459. Fax: 541-888-1529. p. 2953

Park, Taeyeol, Curric Support Spec, Georgetown University, Dahlgren Memorial Library, Preclinical Science Bldg GM-7, 3900 Reservoir Rd NW, Washington, DC, 20007. Tel: 202-687-5089. Fax: 202-687-1862. p. 402

Park, Young, Dr, Cat Librn, Naval History & Heritage, 805 Kidder-Breese St SE, Washington, DC, 20374-5060. Tel: 202-433-4132. Fax: 202-433-9553. p. 411

Parker, Ann, Dir, King Memorial Library, 9538 Rte 16, Machias, NY, 14101. Tel: 716-353-9915. Fax: 716-353-4774. p. 1656

Parker, Anne, Br Head, Greater Victoria Public Library Board, Emily Carr Branch, 3500 Blanshard St, Victoria, BC, V8X 1W3, CANADA. Tel: 250-475-6100. Fax: 250-475-6102. p. 2745

Parker, Ashley, Librn, Malvern-Hot Spring County Library, 202 E Third St, Malvern, AR, 72104. Tel: 501-332-5441. Fax: 501-332-6679. p. 108

Parker, Barbara, Mgr, Three Rivers Regional Library System, Charlton County Library, 701 Indian Trail, Folkston, GA, 31537. Tel: 912-496-2041. Fax: 912-496-1144. p. 522

Parker, Barry, Dr, Ser, California Baptist University, 8432 Magnolia Ave, Riverside, CA, 92504. Tel: 951-343-4228. p. 216

Parker, Beckye, Talking Bks, Southeast Kansas Library System, 218 E Madison Ave, Iola, KS, 66749. Tel: 620-365-5136. Fax: bparker@sekls.org. p. 874

Parker, Betty, Asst Dir, Ref Librn, Conway Public Library, 15 Main St, Conway, NH, 03818. Tel: 603-447-5552. Fax: 603-447-6921. p. 1444

Parker, Brenda, Ch, Lancaster County Library, 313 S White St, Lancaster, SC, 29720. Tel: 803-285-1502. Fax: 803-285-6004. p. 2198

Parker, Carmen, Tech Serv, Hillside Public Library, 405 N Hillside Ave, Hillside, IL, 60162-1295. Tel: 708-449-7510. Fax: 708-449-6119. p. 656

Parker, Carol, Tech Serv, Gulfport Public Library, 5501 28th Ave S, Gulfport, FL, 33707. Tel: 727-893-1076. Fax: 727-893-1072. p. 450

Parker, Carol, Dir, University of New Mexico, Law Library, 1117 Stanford Dr NE, Albuquerque, NM, 87131-1441. Tel: 505-277-6236. Fax: 505-277-0068. p. 1551

Parker, Carolyn, Coordr, Tech Serv, Tusculum College, Hwy 107, 60 Shiloh Rd, Greeneville, TN, 37743. Tel: 423-636-7320. Fax: 423-787-8498. p. 2236

Parker, Catherine, Outreach Serv, Rhinelander District Library, 106 N Stevens St, Rhinelander, WI, 54501-3193. Tel: 715-365-1070. Fax: 715-365-1076. p. 2633

Parker, Charlene, Br Mgr, High Plains Library District, Farr Regional Library, 1939 61st Ave, Greeley, CO, 80634. Tel: 970-506-8528. Fax: 970-506-8551. p. 312

Parker, Charlie, Exec Dir, Tampa Bay Library Consortium, Inc, 1202 Tech Blvd, Ste 202, Tampa, FL, 33619. Tel: 813-622-8252, 813-740-3963. Fax: 813-628-4425. p. 2941

Parker, Cheryl, Librn, Heartland Institute Library, 19 S LaSalle No 903, Chicago, IL, 60603. Tel: 312-377-4000. Fax: 312-377-5000. p. 614

Parker, Cindy, Dir, Friends Memorial Public Library, 230 Chase St, Kane, PA, 16735. Tel: 814-837-7010. Fax: 814-837-7010. p. 2074

Parker, Claire, Libr Asst, Gardiner Public Library, 152 Water St, Gardiner, ME, 04345. Tel: 207-582-3312. Fax: 207-582-6104. p. 986

Parker, Daniel R, Exec Dir, Clarion Free Library, 644 Main St, Clarion, PA, 16214. Tel: 814-226-7172. Fax: 814-226-6750. p. 2045

Parker, Denise, Dir, Br Serv, Lehigh Valley Hospital, Health Library & Learning Center, 17th & Chew, Allentown, PA, 18105. Tel: 610-402-2263. Fax: 610-402-2548. p. 2027

Parker, Dorothy, Br Mgr, Atlanta-Fulton Public Library System, Sandy Springs Regional Library, 395 Mount Vernon Hwy, Sandy Springs, GA, 30328. Tel: 404-303-6130. Fax: 404-303-6133. p. 512

Parker, Elizabeth, Librn, Buncombe County Public Libraries, Fairview Branch, One Taylor Rd, Fairview, NC, 28730. Tel: 828-250-6484. p. 1774

Parker, Ellen, Ref Serv, Atlantic Cape Community College, 5100 Black Horse Pike, Mays Landing, NJ, 08330. Tel: 609-343-4952. p. 1500

Parker, Eric C, Acq Librn, Northwestern University, Chicago, Pritzker Legal Research Center, 375 E Chicago Ave, Chicago, IL, 60611. Tel: 312-503-7920. Fax: 312-503-9230. p. 621

Parker, Gloria, Libr Mgr, Charles D Kelman Library, Wills Eye Hospital, 840 Walnut St, Philadelphia, PA, 19107. Tel: 215-928-3288. Fax: 215-928-7247. p. 2111

Parker, Gretchen, Asst Librn, King Public Library, 101 Pilot View Dr, King, NC, 27021-9180. Tel: 336-983-3868. Fax: 336-983-0769. p. 1804

Parker, Heather, Electronic Res Coordr, Alliant International University, 10455 Pomerado Rd, San Diego, CA, 92131-1799. Tel: 858-635-4693. Fax: 858-635-4599. p. 230

Parker, Holly, Br Librn, Lincoln County Library, Thayne Branch, 117 Peterson Pkwy, Thayne, WY, 83127. Tel: 307-883-7323. Fax: 307-883-7324. p. 2656

Parker, Janet, Librn, Ventura County Medical Center, 3291 Loma Vista Rd, Ventura, CA, 93003. Tel: 805-652-6030. Fax: 805-652-6158. p. 280

Parker, Jean, Asst Univ Librn, Tech Serv, Saint Louis University, 3650 Lindell Blvd, Saint Louis, MO, 63108-3302. Tel: 314-977-3098. Fax: 314-977-3108. p. 1360

Parker, Jeanette, Ser, Friends University, 2100 W University St, Wichita, KS, 67213-3397. Tel: 316-295-5887. Fax: 316-295-5080. p. 900

Parker, Jennifer, Br Mgr, Clay County Public Library System, Green Cove Springs Branch, 403 Ferris St, Green Cove Springs, FL, 32043. Tel: 904-269-6315, 904-284-6315. Fax: 904-284-4053. p. 475

Parker, Jennifer, Archit Librn, Hesburgh Libraries, Architecture, 117 Bond Hall, Notre Dame, IN, 46556-5652. Tel: 574-631-9401. Fax: 574-631-9662. p. 770

Parker, Jerry, Syst Adminr, Neosho/Newton County Library, 201 W Spring St, Neosho, MO, 64850. Tel: 417-451-4231. Fax: 417-451-6438. p. 1347

Parker, Joan, Dir, California State University, 8272 Moss Landing Rd, Moss Landing, CA, 95039. Tel: 831-771-4400. Fax: 831-632-4403. p. 192

Parker, Joan Elliott, Tech Serv, Ohio Township Public Library System, 4111 Lakeshore Dr, Newburgh, IN, 47630-2274. Tel: 812-853-5468. Fax: 812-853-0509. p. 768

Parker, Josie, Libr Dir, Ann Arbor District Library, 343 S Fifth Ave, Ann Arbor, MI, 48104. Tel: 734-327-4200. Fax: 734-327-8309. p. 1150

Parker, Josie, Libr Dir, Ann Arbor District Library, Malletts Creek Branch, 3090 E Eisenhower Pkwy, Ann Arbor, MI, 48108. Tel: 734-327-4263. Fax: 734-327-8309. p. 1150

Parker, Josie, Libr Dir, Ann Arbor District Library, Pittsfield Branch, 2359 Oak Valley Dr, Ann Arbor, MI, 48103. Tel: 743-327-4263. Fax: 743-327-8309. p. 1150

Parker, Josie, Libr Dir, Ann Arbor District Library, Traverwood, 3333 Traverwood Dr, Ann Arbor, MI, 48105. Tel: 734-327-4623. Fax: 734-327-8309. p. 1150

Parker, Josie, Libr Dir, Ann Arbor District Library, Washtenaw Library for the Blind & Physically Disabled, 343 S Fifth Ave, Ann Arbor, MI, 48104. Tel: 734-327-4263. Fax: 734-327-8309. p. 1150

Parker, Josie, Libr Dir, Ann Arbor District Library, West Branch, 2503 Jackson Rd, Ann Arbor, MI, 48103. Tel: 734-327-4263. Fax: 734-327-8309. p. 1151

Parker, June, Librn, Sheppard Memorial Library, East, 2000 Cedar Lane, Greenville, NC, 27858-4845. Tel: 252-329-4582. Fax: 252-329-4127. p. 1799

Parker, Karen, Ref & Acq Librn, Lone Star College System, North Harris College Library, 2700 W W Thorne Dr, Houston, TX, 77073. Tel: 281-618-5491. Fax: 281-618-5695. p. 2340

Parker, Kate, Ch, Lake Forest Library, 360 E Deerpath Ave, Lake Forest, IL, 60045-2252. Tel: 847-810-4631. Fax: 847-234-1453. p. 663

Parker, Kathleen, Dir, Libr, Media & Archives, Saint John's University, 2835 Abbey Plaza, Collegeville, MN, 56321. Tel: 320-363-2121. Fax: 320-363-2126. p. 1246

Parker, Kathleen, Dir, Libr, Media & Archives, College of Saint Benedict, 37 S College Ave, Saint Joseph, MN, 56374. Tel: 320-363-5195. Fax: 320-363-5197. p. 1277

Parker, Kathy, Dir, Libr Serv, United States Navy, Naval Medical Center, Library Bldg 5-2, Naval Medical Ctr, San Diego, CA, 92134-5200. Tel: 619-532-7950. Fax: 619-532-9293. p. 238

Parker, Kathy, Librn, Ford Heights Public Library District, 1537 Congress Lane, Ford Heights, IL, 60411. Tel: 708-757-0551. Fax: 708-757-0552. p. 646

Parker, Kathy, Dir, Glenwood-Lynwood Public Library District, 19901 Stony Island Ave, Glenwood, IL, 60411. Tel: 708-758-0090. Fax: 708-758-0106. p. 651

Parker, Kim, Circ, Mooresville Public Library, 304 S Main St, Mooresville, NC, 28115. Tel: 704-664-2927. Fax: 704-660-3292. p. 1810

Parker, Kimberly, Head, Electronic Acq, Yale University Library, Harvey Cushing/John Hay Whitney Medical Library, Sterling Hall of Medicine, 333 Cedar St, L110 SHM, New Haven, CT, 06520. Tel: 203-785-7116. Fax: 203-785-5636. p. 358

Parker, Kimberly, Educ Res Commons Supvr, Indiana University South Bend, 1700 Mishawaka Ave, South Bend, IN, 46615. Tel: 574-520-5548. Fax: 574-520-4472. p. 778

Parker, Laurel, Ch, Windham Public Library, 217 Windham Center Rd, Windham, ME, 04062. Tel: 207-892-1908. Fax: 207-892-1915. p. 1007

Parker, Lee, Libr Dir, Norton Public Library, 68 E Main St, Norton, MA, 02766. Tel: 508-285-0265. Fax: 508-285-0266. p. 1114

Parker, Lettice, Librn, Snohomish County Law Library, M/S 703, Rm 139, 3000 Rockefeller Ave, Everett, WA, 98201. Tel: 425-388-3010. Fax: 425-388-3020. p. 2515

Parker, Linda, Youth Serv Coordr, Coralville Public Library, 1401 Fifth St, Coralville, IA, 52241. Tel: 319-248-1850. Fax: 319-248-1890. p. 804

Parker, Lionell, Dir, Piedmont Community College, Caswell Learning Resources Center, 331 Piedmont Dr, Yanceyville, NC, 27379. Tel: 336-599-1181, Ext 248. Fax: 336-694-5893. p. 1821

Parker, Lois, Dir, Community Library of Western Perry County, Main St, Blain, PA, 17006. Tel: 717-536-3761. Fax: 717-536-3761. p. 2035

Parker, Lynette, Br Mgr, Shreve Memorial Library, North Caddo Branch, 615 N Pine St, Vivian, LA, 71082. Tel: 318-375-3975. Fax: 318-375-4597. p. 970

Parker, Margaret S, Libr Dir, Perry Public Library, 70 N Main St, Perry, NY, 14530-1299. Tel: 585-237-2243. Fax: 585-237-2008. p. 1716

Parker, Maria, Youth Serv, Wilkes County Public Library, 215 Tenth St, North Wilkesboro, NC, 28659. Tel: 336-838-2818. Fax: 336-667-2638. p. 1813

Parker, Marie, Libr Tech, Gadsden County Public Library, Chattahoochee Public Library, 300 Maple St, Chattahoochee, FL, 32324. Tel: 850-663-2707. Fax: 850-663-4598. p. 485

Parker, Mark R, Dir, Libr Serv, Placer County Library, 350 Nevada St, Auburn, CA, 95603-3789. Tel: 530-886-4500, 530-886-4550. Fax: 530-886-4555. p. 122

Parker, Martha, Librn in Residence, University of Arkansas Libraries, 365 N McIlroy Ave, Fayetteville, AR, 72701-4002. Tel: 479-575-2032. Fax: 479-575-6656. p. 99

Parker, Mary, Librn, Sloan Public Library, 311 Fourth St, Sloan, IA, 51055. Tel: 712-428-4200. p. 844

Parker, Mary, Librn, Grace Presbyterian Church, 444 Old York Rd, Jenkintown, PA, 19046. Tel: 215-887-6117. Fax: 215-887-5724. p. 2072

Parker, Mary Ellen D, Librn, Queen of the Holy Rosary College Library, 43326 Mission Blvd, Fremont, CA, 94539. Tel: 510-657-2468. p. 150

Parker, Melissa, Tech Coordr, Southeast Kansas Library System, 218 E Madison Ave, Iola, KS, 66749. Tel: 620-365-5136. Fax: 620-365-5137. p. 874

Parker, Michell, Mgr, Auglaize County Public District Library, New Bremen Public, 45 W Washington St, New Bremen, OH, 45869. Tel: 419-629-2158. Fax: 419-629-1351. p. 1944

Parker, Nina, Exec Dir, Black Heritage Library & Multicultural Center, 817 Harmon St, Findlay, OH, 45840. Tel: 419-423-4954. p. 1899

Parker, Pam, ILL, IWK Health Centre for Children, Women & Families, 5980 University Ave, Halifax, NS, B3H 4N1, CANADA. Tel: 902-470-7058. Fax: 902-470-7122. p. 2781

Parker, Pat, Asst Librn, Freedom Public Library, 38 Old Portland Rd, Freedom, NH, 03836. Tel: 603-539-5176. Fax: 603-539-1098. p. 1448

Parker, Reece, Libr Spec, Inyo County Free Library, Bishop Branch, 210 Academy Ave, Bishop, CA, 93514-2693. Tel: 760-873-5115. Fax: 760-873-5356. p. 159

Parker, Richard Leigh, Dir, Montcalm Community College Library, 2800 College Dr SW, Sidney, MI, 48885. Tel: 989-328-1291, Ext 291. Fax: 989-328-2950. p. 1227

Parker, Robert D, Dir, ACES Educational Center for the Arts, 55 Audubon St, New Haven, CT, 06510-1294. Tel: 203-777-5451. Fax: 203-782-3596. p. 355

Parker, Robert L, Fr, Dir, Bishop State Community College, Southwest Campus, 925 Dauphin Island Pkwy, Mobile, AL, 36605-3299. Tel: 251-665-4091. Fax: 251-479-7091. p. 25

Parker, Ron, Chief of Interpretation, National Park Service, Chickasaw Nat Recreation Area, 1054 NE Perimeter Rd, Sulphur, OK, 73086. Tel: 580-622-3165. Fax: 580-622-6931. p. 1979

Parker, Roxanna, Dir, Sutter County Free Library, 750 Forbes Ave, Yuba City, CA, 95991-3891. Tel: 530-822-7137. Fax: 530-671-6539. p. 286

Parker, Russell N, Head, Adult Serv, Elmwood Park Public Library, One Conti Pkwy, Elmwood Park, IL, 60707. Tel: 708-453-7645. Fax: 708-453-4671. p. 643

Parker, Shannon, Curator of Coll, Art Gallery of Nova Scotia Library, 1723 Hollis St, Halifax, NS, B3J 3C8, CANADA. Tel: 902-424-7542. Fax: 902-424-7359. p. 2780

Parker, Shawn, Circ Serv Dept Head, Hussey-Mayfield Memorial Public Library, 250 N Fifth St, Zionsville, IN, 46077-1324. Tel: 317-873-3149, Ext 11456. Fax: 317-873-8339. p. 789

Parker, Sheena, Dir, American Fork City Library, 64 S 100 East, American Fork, UT, 84003. Tel: 801-763-3070. Fax: 801-763-3073. p. 2403

Parker, Sheri, Libr Operations Coordr, Texas Wesleyan University, 1201 Wesleyan St, Fort Worth, TX, 76105. Tel: 817-531-4800. Fax: 817-531-4806. p. 2324

Parker, Sherie, Asst Br Mgr, Chesterfield County Public Library, Bon Air, 9103 Rattlesnake Rd, Richmond, VA, 23235. Tel: 804-320-2461. p. 2457

Parker, Shirley, Circ, Walters State Community College, 500 S Davy Crockett Pkwy, Morristown, TN, 37813-6899. Tel: 423-585-2600. Fax: 423-585-6959. p. 2253

Parker, Susan, Acq, Cerro Coso Community College Library, 3000 College Heights Blvd, Ridgecrest, CA, 93555-9571. Tel: 760-384-6135. Fax: 760-384-6139. p. 216

Parker, Susan, Head, Adult Serv, Marengo-Union Library District, 200 S State St, Marengo, IL, 60152. Tel: 815-568-8236. Fax: 815-568-5209. p. 670

Parker, Susy, Librn, Stella Hart Memorial Public Library, PO Box 88, Smiley, TX, 78159-0088. Tel: 830-587-6101. p. 2387

Parker, T, Outreach Librn, Union University, 1050 Union University Dr, Jackson, TN, 38305-3697. Tel: 731-661-5070. Fax: 731-661-5175. p. 2238

Parker, T R, Ref & Instruction Librn, Golden Gate Baptist Theological Seminary Library, 201 Seminary Dr, Mill Valley, CA, 94941. Tel: 415-380-1300. Fax: 415-380-1652. p. 186

Parker, Tammy, Br Mgr, Kanawha County Public Library, Clendenin, One Cardinal St, Clendenin, WV, 25045. Tel: 304-548-6370. Fax: 304-548-6395. p. 2556

Parker, Tara G, Dir, Eunice Public Library, 1003 Ave N, Eunice, NM, 88231. Tel: 575-394-2336, 575-394-2338. Fax: 575-394-0970. p. 1555

Parker, Toni, Br Mgr, Cleveland Public Library, Martin Luther King Jr Branch, 1962 Stokes Blvd, Cleveland, OH, 44106. Tel: 216-623-7018. Fax: 216-623-7020. p. 1878

Parker, Veronica, Libr Assoc II, Lorain Public Library System, South Lorain, 2121 Homewood Dr, Lorain, OH, 44055. Tel: 440-277-5672. Fax: 440-277-5727. p. 1911

Parker, Vicki J M, Ch Mgr, Westfield Washington Public Library, 333 W Hoover St, Westfield, IN, 46074-9283. Tel: 317-896-9391. Fax: 317-896-3702. p. 787

Parker, Wendy, Supvr, Info & Digital Serv, Federal Reserve Bank of Philadelphia, 100 N Sixth St, 4th Flr, Philadelphia, PA, 19106. Tel: 215-574-6540. Fax: 215-574-3847. p. 2106

Parker-Bellamy, Teresa A, Head, Bibliog Serv, Regent University, 1000 Regent University Dr, Virginia Beach, VA, 23464-9800. Tel: 757-352-4370. Fax: 757-352-4451. p. 2499

Parker-Gibson, Necia, Psychol, Sociol, Soc Work & Plant Sci Librn, University of Arkansas Libraries, 365 N McIlroy Ave, Fayetteville, AR, 72701-4002. Tel: 479-575-8421. Fax: 479-575-6656. p. 99

Parker-Muphy, Evelyn, Supvr, Pub Serv, Commodity Futures Trading Commission Library, 1155 21st St NW, Washington, DC, 20581. Tel: 202-418-5257. Fax: 202-418-5537. p. 396

Parker-O'Toole, Mare, Ad, Medfield Memorial Public Library, 468 Main St, Medfield, MA, 02052-2008. Tel: 508-359-4544. Fax: 508-359-8124. p. 1104

Parkhe, Smita, Cat/Electronic Coll Librn, Georgetown University, Georgetown Law Library (John Wolff & Edward Bennett Williams Libraries), 111 G St NW, Washington, DC, 20001. Fax: 202-662-9168. p. 403

Parkins, Susan, Outreach Serv Librn, Laramie County Library System, 2200 Pioneer Ave, Cheyenne, WY, 82001-3610. Tel: 307-773-7228. Fax: 307-634-2082. p. 2652

Parkinson, Carol, Librn, Ivy Tech Community College of Indiana, 200 Daniels Way, Bloomington, IN, 47404. Tel: 812-330-6236. Fax: 812-330-6082. p. 728

Parkinson, Jane, Archivist, Banff Centre, 107 Tunnel Mountain Dr, Banff, AB, T1L 1H5, CANADA. Tel: 403-762-6440. Fax: 403-762-6266. p. 2684

Parkinson, Scott, Tech Serv Librn, Cedar Crest College, 100 College Dr, Allentown, PA, 18104-6196. Tel: 610-606-4666, Ext 3387. Fax: 610-740-3769. p. 2026

Parkinson, Stephanie, Librn, Rossburn Regional Library, 57 High St, Rossburn, MB, R0J 1V0, CANADA. Tel: 204-859-2687. Fax: 204-859-2687. p. 2751

Parkinson, Thomas, Automation Syst Coordr, Upper Merion Township Library, 175 W Valley Forge Rd, King of Prussia, PA, 19406-2399. Tel: 610-265-1196. Fax: 610-265-3398. p. 2074

Parkison, Peg, Circ, Per, Northern Wyoming Community College District, 3059 Coffeen Ave, Sheridan, WY, 82801-1500. Tel: 307-674-6446. Fax: 307-674-3350. p. 2660

Parkoff, Cara, Assoc Col Librn, Fisher College Library, 118 Beacon St, Boston, MA, 02116. Tel: 617-236-8875. Fax: 617-670-4426. p. 1061

Parks, Ann, Librn, Madison County Public Library, Mars Hill Branch, 25 Dogwood St, Mars Hill, NC, 28754-9783. Tel: 828-689-5183. Fax: 828-689-5183. p. 1809

Parks, Becky, Libr Tech, Jackson-Madison County General Hospital, 620 Skyline Dr, Jackson, TN, 38301. Tel: 731-541-4140. Fax: 731-541-6983. p. 2238

Parks, Bonnie, Cat/Syst Librn, University of Portland, 5000 N Willamette Blvd, Portland, OR, 97203-5743. Tel: 503-943-7111. Fax: 503-943-7491. p. 2015

Parks, Farah, Librn, North Carolina Department of Correction, 527 Commerce Dr, Caller No 5005, Elizabeth City, NC, 27906-5005. Tel: 252-331-4881. Fax: 252-331-4867. p. 1791

Parks, Harriette, Br Mgr, Cleveland Public Library, Harvard-Lee, 16918 Harvard Ave, Cleveland, OH, 44128. Tel: 216-623-6990. Fax: 216-623-6992. p. 1878

Parks, Joan, Head, Ref, Southwestern University, 1100 E University Ave, Georgetown, TX, 78626. Tel: 512-863-1561. Fax: 512-863-8198. p. 2327

Parks, Julie, In Charge, Elko-Lander-Eureka County Library System, Tuscarora Branch, 55 Weed St, Tuscarora, NV, 89834. Tel: 775-756-6597. p. 1427

Parks, Margie, Asst Librn, Richland Parish Library, 1410 Louisa St, Rayville, LA, 71269-3299. Tel: 318-728-4806. Fax: 318-728-6108. p. 966

Parks, Mary Beth, Br Mgr, Carnegie Library of Pittsburgh, Woods Run, 1201 Woods Run Ave, Pittsburgh, PA, 15212-2335. Tel: 412-761-3729. p. 2123

Parks, Michele, Librn, Regional West Medical Center Library, 4021 Ave B, Scottsbluff, NE, 69361. Tel: 308-630-1368. Fax: 308-630-1721. p. 1418

Parks, Patty, Commun Serv Mgr, Richmond Public Library, 101 E Franklin St, Richmond, VA, 23219-2193. Tel: 804-646-5177. Fax: 804-646-7685. p. 2489

Parks, Stuart, Archivist, North Carolina Office of Archives & History, One Festival Park Blvd, Manteo, NC, 27954. Tel: 252-473-2655. Fax: 252-473-1483. p. 1808

Parks, Sue, Asst Dean, Spec Libr, University of North Texas Libraries, PO Box 305190, Denton, TX, 76203-5190. Tel: 940-369-7249. Fax: 940-369-8760. p. 2313

Parkzes, Monica, Librn, Army Times Publishing Co Library, 6883 Commercial Dr, Springfield, VA, 22159. Tel: 703-658-8488. Fax: 703-750-8622. p. 2496

Parmele, Alicia, Youth Serv, Algonquin Area Public Library District, 2600 Harnish Dr, Algonquin, IL, 60102-5900. Tel: 847-458-6060, 847-658-4343. Fax: 847-458-9370. p. 588

Parmenter, Julie, Ref, Shook, Hardy & Bacon, 2555 Grand Blvd, 3rd Flr, Kansas City, MO, 64108-2613. Tel: 816-474-6550. Fax: 816-421-5547. p. 1341

Parmesar, Taj, Assoc, Info Res, National Economic Research Associates, Inc, 360 Hamilton Ave, 10th Flr, White Plains, NY, 10601. Tel: 914-448-4064. Fax: 914-448-4040. p. 1768

Parnell, Jerry, Spec Coll Librn, William Madison Randall Library, 601 S College Rd, Wilmington, NC, 28403-5616. Tel: 910-962-3000. Fax: 910-962-3078. p. 1831

Parnell, Joan, Pres, Halstead Public Library, 264 Main St, Halstead, KS, 67056-0285. Tel: 316-835-2170. Fax: 316-835-2170. p. 870

Parnes, Carole D, Mgr, CBS News Reference Library, 524 W 57th St, Ste 533/2, New York, NY, 10019. Tel: 212-975-2877. Fax: 212-975-3940. p. 1671

Parnes, Daria, Br Mgr, Fairfax County Public Library, Chantilly Regional, 4000 Stringfellow Rd, Chantilly, VA, 20151-2628. Tel: 703-502-3883. p. 2461

Parnprome, Tetima, Pub Serv/Instruction Librn, Cochise College Library, Andrea Cracchiolo Library, 901 N Colombo Ave, Sierra Vista, AZ, 85635. Tel: 520-515-5383. Fax: 520-515-5464. p. 61

Paro, Lauren, Ch, Hinsdale Public Library, 58 Maple St, Hinsdale, MA, 01235. Tel: 413-655-2303. Fax: 413-655-2303. p. 1095

Parodi, Susan, YA Librn, Old Lyme, Two Library Lane, Old Lyme, CT, 06371. Tel: 860-434-1684. Fax: 860-434-9547. p. 363

Paroline Vernon, Kathleen, Mgr, New Bedford Free Public Library, Howland Green, Three Rodney French Blvd, New Bedford, MA, 02744. Tel: 508-991-6213. Fax: 508-979-1774. p. 1108

Parpart, Paulette, Cat Librn, Missoula Public Library, 301 E Main, Missoula, MT, 59802-4799. Tel: 406-721-2665. Fax: 406-728-5900. p. 1386

Parr, Bonnie, Hist Doc Conservator, Illinois Historic Preservation Agency, 112 N Sixth St, Springfield, IL, 62701. Tel: 217-785-7934. Fax: 217-785-6250. p. 705

Parr, Caroline, Youth Serv Coordr, Central Rappahannock Regional Library, 1201 Caroline St, Fredericksburg, VA, 22401-3761. Tel: 540-372-1144. Fax: 540-373-9411. p. 2465

Parr, Kimberly, Dir, Macomb County Historical Society, 15 Union St, Mount Clemens, MI, 48043. Tel: 586-465-2488. p. 1210

Parr, Marilyn, Asst Librn, Crystal City Public Library, 736 Mississippi Ave, Crystal City, MO, 63019-1646. Tel: 636-937-7166. Fax: 636-937-3193. p. 1327

Parr, Mary E, Librn, Union Springs Public Library, 103 N Prairie, Union Springs, AL, 36089. Tel: 334-738-2760. Fax: 334-738-2760. p. 39

Parr, Tari, Ch, Illiopolis-Niantic Public Library District, Sixth & Mary Sts, Illiopolis, IL, 62539. Tel: 217-486-5561. Fax: 217-486-7811. p. 658

parra, Joanne, Sr Ref Librn, Moorestown Public Library, 111 W Second St, Moorestown, NJ, 08057-2481. Tel: 856-234-0333. Fax: 856-778-9536. p. 1504

Parra, Mariela, Coop Librn, Devon Canada Corp, 2000, 400 - Third Ave SW, Calgary, AB, T2P 4H2, CANADA. Tel: 403-232-5581. p. 2691

Parrella, Francis, Per, Suffolk County Community College, 1001 Crooked Hill Rd, Brentwood, NY, 11717. Tel: 631-851-6740. Fax: 631-851-6509. p. 1584

Parrilla, Nilca, Tech Serv Dir, University of Puerto Rico, Conrado F Asenjo Library (Medical Sciences Campus), Medical Sciences Campus, Main Bldg, Unit C, San Juan, PR, 00935. Tel: 787-758-2525, Ext 1346. Fax: 787-759-6713, 282-6438. p. 2676

Parrillo, Cathy, Circ, Onondaga County Public Library, The Galleries of Syracuse, 447 S Salina St, Syracuse, NY, 13202-2494. Fax: 315-435-8533. p. 1752

Parrillo, Whitney, Dir, Astoria Public Library District, 220 W Broadway, Astoria, IL, 61501-9630. Tel: 309-329-2423. Fax: 309-329-2842. p. 590

Parris, Annissa, Dir, Locust Grove Public Library, 715 Harold Andrews Blvd, Locust Grove, OK, 74352. Tel: 918-479-6585. Fax: 918-479-6582. p. 1967

Parris, Brenda P, Cat, Ref Serv, Tech Serv, Calhoun Community College, Hwy 31 N, Decatur, AL, 35609. Tel: 256-306-2778. Fax: 256-306-2780. p. 14

Parris, John, AV, Media Serv, Alpena Community College, The Center Bldg, Rm 111, 665 Johnson St, Alpena, MI, 49707. Tel: 989-358-7244. Fax: 989-358-7556. p. 1150

Parrish, Jenni, Dir, University of California, 200 McAllister St, San Francisco, CA, 94102-4978. Tel: 415-565-4757. Fax: 415-581-8849. p. 248

Parrish, Lila, Pub Serv, Austin Presbyterian Theological Seminary, 100 E 27th St, Austin, TX, 78705-5797. Tel: 512-472-6736. Fax: 512-322-0901. p. 2278

Parrish, Patty, Libr Dir, Burgettstown Community Library, Two Kerr St, Burgettstown, PA, 15021-1127. Tel: 724-947-9780. Fax: 724-947-5116. p. 2039

Parrish, Phyllis, Librn, Oostburg Public Library, 213 N Eighth St, Oostburg, WI, 53070. Tel: 920-564-2934. p. 2627

Parrish, Sandra, Coll Develop, Campbell River Museum & Archives, 470 Island Hwy, Campbell River, BC, V9W 4Z9, CANADA. Tel: 250-287-3103. Fax: 250-286-0109. p. 2726

Parrish, Susan, Commun Relations Librn, Cumberland County Public Library & Information Center, 300 Maiden Lane, Fayetteville, NC, 28301-5000. Tel: 910-483-7727. Fax: 910-486-5372. p. 1792

Parrott, Becky, Br Mgr, Stanislaus County Free Library, Riverbank Branch, 3442 Santa Fe Ave, Riverbank, CA, 95367-2319. Tel: 209-869-7008. Fax: 209-869-7008. p. 188

Parrott, Denise, Mgr, Syst & Coll Access, Nova Scotia Provincial Library, 2021 Brunswick St, 2nd Flr, Halifax, NS, B3K 2Y5, CANADA. Tel: 902-424-2458. Fax: 902-424-0633. p. 2782

Parrott, James Steve, Br Librn, Kershaw County Library, Elgin Branch, 2652 Main St, Elgin, SC, 29045. Tel: 803-438-7881. Fax: 803-438-4428. p. 2182

Parrott, Karen, Librn, Delaware State Law Library in Kent County, Thomas Collins Bldg, 540 S DuPont Hwy, Ste 3, Dover, DE, 19901-3615. Tel: 302-739-5467. Fax: 302-739-6721. p. 382

Parrott, Linda, Librn, Augusta Township Public Library, 4500 County Rd 15, RR 2, Brockville, ON, K6V 5T2, CANADA. Tel: 613-926-2449. Fax: 613-702-0441. p. 2797

Parrott, Neva, Asst Librn, Missouri State University-West Plains, 304 W Trish Knight St, West Plains, MO, 65775. Tel: 417-255-7947. Fax: 417-255-7944. p. 1372

Parrott, Steve, Pub Serv Mgr, Kershaw County Library, 1304 Broad St, Camden, SC, 29020-3595. Tel: 803-425-1508. Fax: 803-425-7180. p. 2182

Parrott, Tammy, Br Mgr, Mid-Continent Public Library, Edgerton Branch, 404 Frank St, Edgerton, MO, 64444-9221. Tel: 816-790-3569. Fax: 816-790-3569. p. 1332

Parry, Daria A, Assoc Dir, Harford County Public Library, 1221-A Brass Mill Rd, Belcamp, MD, 21017-1209. Tel: 410-273-5600, Ext 2246. Fax: 410-273-5606. p. 1020

Parry, Jennifer, Dir, Libr Serv, Port Colborne Public Library, 310 King St, Port Colborne, ON, L3K 4H1, CANADA. Tel: 905-834-6512. Fax: 905-835-5775. p. 2837

Parry, Karen, Info Serv, East Brunswick Public Library, Two Jean Walling Civic Center, East Brunswick, NJ, 08816-3599. Tel: 732-390-6950. Fax: 732-390-6796. p. 1481

Parry, Linda, Outreach Serv Librn, Wicomico Public Library, 122 S Division St, Salisbury, MD, 21801. Tel: 410-749-3612, Ext 140. Fax: 410-548-2968. p. 1040

Parry, Linda, Outreach Librn, Wicomico Public Library, Bivalve Station, 21109 Bivalve Lodge Rd, Bivalve, MD, 21109. Tel: 410-873-2472. p. 1041

Parry, Linda, Outreach Librn, Wicomico Public Library, Pittsville Branch, 34372 Old Ocean City Rd, Pittsville, MD, 21850-2008. Tel: 410-835-2353. p. 1041

Parry, Linda, Outreach Serv Librn, Wicomico Public Library, Centre Branch, N Salisbury Blvd, Salisbury, MD, 21801. Tel: 410-546-5397. p. 1041

Parry, Michelle, ILL, State University of New York at Oswego, SUNY Oswego, 7060 State Rte 104, Oswego, NY, 13126-3514. Tel: 315-312-4232. Fax: 315-312-3194. p. 1713

Parry, Norm, Dir, New Woodstock Free Library, 2106 Main St, New Woodstock, NY, 13122-8718. Tel: 315-662-3134. p. 1667

Parry, Susan, Dir, Orange County Community College Library, 115 South St, Middletown, NY, 10940. Tel: 845-341-4251. Fax: 845-341-4250. p. 1660

Parry, Todd, Webmaster, Indian River County Library System, 1600 21st St, Vero Beach, FL, 32960. Tel: 772-770-5060. Fax: 772-770-5066. p. 501

Parry, Valerie M, Dean of Libr, Gardner-Webb University, 110 S Main St, Boiling Springs, NC, 28017. Tel: 704-406-4293. Fax: 704-406-4623. p. 1776

Parsells, Ian, Head Librn, Derby Neck Library, 307 Hawthorne Ave, Derby, CT, 06418-1199. Tel: 203-734-1492. Fax: 203-732-2913. p. 336

Parsels, Ian, Teen Librn, Glen Rock Public Library, 315 Rock Rd, Glen Rock, NJ, 07452-1795. Tel: 201-670-3970. Fax: 201-445-0872. p. 1488

Parson, Karen, Dir, Fox Valley Technical College, 1825 N Bluemound Dr, Appleton, WI, 54914. Tel: 920-735-4762. Fax: 920-735-4870. p. 2578

Parson, Karen, Mgr, Libr Serv, Fox Valley Technical College, 150 N Campbell Rd, Oshkosh, WI, 54903. Tel: 920-735-4762. Fax: 920-236-6160. p. 2627

Parsons, Alice, Dir, Northwood University, 4000 Whiting Dr, Midland, MI, 48640-2398. Tel: 989-837-4339. Fax: 989-832-5031. p. 1208

Parsons, Amy, Cat, Ref, Otterbein University, 138 W Main St, Westerville, OH, 43081. Tel: 614-823-1026. Fax: 614-823-1921. p. 1946

Parsons, Ann Marie, Ref Serv Coordr, United States Trademark Office Law Library, 600 Dulany St, MDE 4B65, Alexandria, VA, 22314-5791. Tel: 571-272-9694. Fax: 571-273-9694. p. 2446

Parsons, Carolyn, Spec Coll Librn, University of Mary Washington, 1801 College Ave, Fredericksburg, VA, 22401-4665. Tel: 540-654-1752. Fax: 540-654-1067. p. 2466

Parsons, Charlotte L, Dir, Washington County Public Library, 205 Oak Hill St, Abingdon, VA, 24210. Tel: 276-676-6222. Fax: 276-676-6235. p. 2443

Parsons, Deborah, Dir, Marple Public Library, 2599 Sproul Rd, Broomall, PA, 19008-2399. Tel: 610-356-1510. Fax: 610-356-3589. p. 2038

Parsons, Duncan A, Dean, Northeast State Community College, 2425 Hwy 75, Blountville, TN, 37617-6350. Tel: 423-354-2429. Fax: 423-323-0254. p. 2224

Parsons, Edith, Mgr, Edmonton Public Library, Castle Downs, 106 Lakeside Landing, 15379 Castle Downs Rd, Edmonton, AB, T5X 3Y7, CANADA. Tel: 780-496-2708. Fax: 780-496-7005. p. 2700

Parsons, Edith, Mgr, Edmonton Public Library, Jasper Place, 9010 156th St, Edmonton, AB, T5R 5X7, CANADA. Tel: 780-496-2708. Fax: 780-496-7005. p. 2700

Parsons, Jeff, Dir, Midfield Public Library, 400 Breland Dr, Midfield, AL, 35228-2732. Tel: 205-923-1027. Fax: 205-923-1027. p. 25

Parsons, Jim, Assoc Dir, Ref, Res & Instruction, Saint John's University, 2835 Abbey Plaza, Collegeville, MN, 56321. Tel: 320-363-5907. Fax: 320-363-2126. p. 1246

Parsons, Jim, Assoc Dir, Ref, Res & Instruction, College of Saint Benedict, 37 S College Ave, Saint Joseph, MN, 56374. Tel: 320-363-5907. Fax: 320-363-5197. p. 1277

Parsons, Karen, Pub Serv, Ref Librn, Spring Arbor University, 106 E Main St, Spring Arbor, MI, 49283. Tel: 800-968-9103, Ext 1436. Fax: 517-750-2108. p. 1229

Parsons, Karen, Dir, Addison Public Library, Six South St, Addison, NY, 14801. Tel: 607-359-3888. Fax: 607-359-3611. p. 1567

Parsons, Kathy A, Stacks & Media, Iowa State University Library, 302 Parks Library, Ames, IA, 50011-2140. Tel: 515-294-1442, 515-294-1443. Fax: 515-294-5525. p. 793

Parsons, Martha, ILL, Washington State University Extension, 905 Plum St SE, Olympia, WA, 98501-1529. Tel: 360-956-2076. Fax: 360-236-2076. p. 2523

Parsons, Mary, ILL Coordr, Russell Public Library, 126 E Sixth St, Russell, KS, 67665-2041. Tel: 785-483-2742. Fax: 785-483-6254. p. 892

Parsons, Matthew, Librn, University of Washington Libraries, Map Collection & Cartographic Information Services, Suzzallo/Allen Library, Basement, Universtiy of Washington, Box 352900, Seattle, WA, 98195-2900. Tel: 206-543-9392. Fax: 206-685-8049. p. 2534

Parsons, Stephanie, Ref Serv, High Point University, 833 Montlieu Ave, High Point, NC, 27262-4221. Tel: 336-841-9102. Fax: 336-841-5123. p. 1802

Parsons, Stu, Ch, Sandwich Public Library, 142 Main St, Sandwich, MA, 02563. Tel: 508-888-0625. Fax: 508-833-1076. p. 1122

Parsons, Sue, Info Res, Canadian Institute of Resources Law, University of Calgary, Murray Fraser Hall, Rm 3353, Calgary, AB, T2N 1N4, CANADA. Tel: 403-220-3200. Fax: 403-282-6182. p. 2691

Partanen, Kimberly, Dir, Fort St John Public Library Association, 10015-100th Ave, Fort Saint John, BC, V1J 1Y7, CANADA. Tel: 250-785-3731. Fax: 250-785-7982. p. 2728

Partdo, Patricia, Adjunct Ref Librn, University of Miami, 1311 Miller Dr, Coral Gables, FL, 33146. Tel: 305-284-2251. Fax: 305-284-3554. p. 434

Partello, Patricia L, Assoc Librn, Ref, New York State Department of Law Library, The Capitol, Albany, NY, 12224. Tel: 518-474-3840. Fax: 518-473-1822. p. 1569

Parten, Carol, In Charge, Multnomah County Library, Midland, 805 SE 122nd Ave, Portland, OR, 97233-1107. Tel: 503-988-5392. Fax: 503-988-5189. p. 2012

Parthasarathi, Hema, Adult Serv, AV, Fairport Public Library, One Fairport Village Landing, Fairport, NY, 14450. Tel: 585-223-9091. Fax: 585-223-3998. p. 1621

Partin, Christina, Ref Librn, Middlesborough-Bell County Public Library, 126 S 20th St, Middlesboro, KY, 40965-1212. Tel: 606-248-4812. Fax: 606-248-8766. p. 929

Partin, Gail, Assoc Dir, Law Librn, Pennsylvania State University - Dickinson School of Law (University Libraries), 1170 Harrisburg Pike, Carlisle, PA, 17013-1617. Tel: 717-240-5294. Fax: 717-240-5127. p. 2042

Partin, Madge, Br Mgr, Beaufort, Hyde & Martin County Regional Library, Robersonville Public, 119 S Main St, Robersonville, NC, 27871. Tel: 252-508-0342. Fax: 252-795-3359. p. 1828

Partin, Margaret, Librn, Robersonville Public Library, 119 S Main St, Robersonville, NC, 27871. Tel: 252-795-3591. Fax: 252-795-3359. p. 1820

Partington, Judith, Head Librn, Filson Historical Society Library, 1310 S Third St, Louisville, KY, 40208. Tel: 502-635-5083. Fax: 502-635-5086. p. 923

Partington, Linda, Sr Librn, Canadian Broadcasting Corp, Radio Archives, 205 Wellington St W, Toronto, ON, M5G 3G7, CANADA. Tel: 416-205-5880. Fax: 416-205-8602. p. 2850

Parton, Bill, Dir, Arkansas Tech University, 305 West Q St, Russellville, AR, 72801-2222. Tel: 479-968-0417. Fax: 479-964-0559. p. 113

Parton, Pam, Br Librn, Daviess County Library, Jamesport Branch, 101 E Main, Jamesport, MO, 64648. Tel: 660-684-6120. p. 1329

Partovi, Pat, Dir, Spokane Public Library, 906 W Main Ave, Spokane, WA, 99201-0976. Tel: 509-444-5300. Fax: 509-444-5365. p. 2537

Partrick, Cindy, Dir, Central Square Library, 637 S Main St, Central Square, NY, 13036. Tel: 315-668-6104. Fax: 315-668-6104. p. 1605

Partridge, Bede, Tech Serv, Mount Angel Abbey Library, One Abbey Dr, Saint Benedict, OR, 97373. Tel: 503-845-3303, 503-845-3317. Fax: 503-845-3500. p. 2017

Partridge, Leslie, Br Mgr, Lee County Public Library, Redbone, 104 Thundering Springs Rd, Leesburg, GA, 31763. Tel: 229-903-8871. Fax: 229-903-8872. p. 539

Partridge, Tracie, Br Mgr, Wichita Public Library, Orchard Park, 4808 W Ninth St, Wichita, KS, 67212. Tel: 316-337-9084. p. 901

Partridge, Tracie, Br Mgr, Wichita Public Library, Westlink Branch, 8515 Bekemeyer St, Wichita, KS, 67212. Tel: 316-337-9456. p. 901

Parus, Dale, Dir, Harper Woods Public Library, 19601 Harper, Harper Woods, MI, 48225-2001. Tel: 313-343-2575. Fax: 313-343-2127. p. 1188

Parvas, Shahana, Circ Serv Mgr, Alexandria Library, Ellen Coolidge Burke Branch, 4701 Seminary Rd, Alexandria, VA, 22304. Tel: 703-746-1704. Fax: 703-746-1775. p. 2444

Parveen, Nasim, Head Librn, Boston University Libraries, Stone Science Library, 771 Commonwealth Ave, Boston, MA, 02215. Tel: 617-353-5679. Fax: 617-353-5358. p. 1059

Parvin, Kendi, In Charge, Wisconsin Medical Society Library, 330 E Lakeside St, Madison, WI, 53715-2074. Tel: 608-442-3800. Fax: 608-442-3802. p. 2611

Parvin, Morteza, Tech Serv, John Marshall Law School, 1422 W Peachtree St NW, Atlanta, GA, 30309. Tel: 404-872-3593, Ext 167. Fax: 404-873-3802. p. 516

Pascale, Christee, Coordr, Tech Serv, Ref, Utica College, 1600 Burrstone Rd, Utica, NY, 13502-4892. Tel: 315-792-3217. Fax: 315-792-3361. p. 1760

Pascasio, Christian R, Res Librn, Federal Reserve Bank of Richmond, 701 E Byrd St, Richmond, VA, 23219. Tel: 804-697-8125. Fax: 804-697-8134. p. 2488

Paschal, Dawn, Asst Dean, Digital Libr & ePublishing Serv, Colorado State University Libraries, Morgan Library, 1201 Center Avenue Mall, Fort Collins, CO, 80523-. Tel: 970-491-1838. Fax: 970-491-1195. p. 307

Paschal, Janetta, Head, Tech Serv, Angelo State University Library, 2025 S Johnson, San Angelo, TX, 76904-5079. Tel: 325-486-6530. Fax: 325-942-2198. p. 2378

Paschall, Charlene, Circ, Ozark-Dale County Public Library, Inc, 416 James St, Ozark, AL, 36360. Tel: 334-774-2399, 334-774-5480. p. 33

Paschen, Ken, Head, Circ, ILL, Ellensburg Public Library, 209 N Ruby St, Ellensburg, WA, 98926-3397. Tel: 509-962-7250. Fax: 509-962-7295. p. 2514

Paschild, Cristine, Head, Spec Coll, Univ Archivist, Portland State University Library, 1875 SW Park Ave, Portland, OR, 97201-3220. Tel: 503-725-9883. Fax: 503-725-4524. p. 2014

Paschold, Steve, Ref Librn, John Brown University Library, 2000 W University, Siloam Springs, AR, 72761. Tel: 479-524-7202. Fax: 479-524-7335. p. 115

Pasco, Rebecca, Dr, Coordr, University of Nebraska at Omaha, College of Education, Roskens 308, Omaha, NE, 68182-0163. Tel: 402-554-2119. Fax: 402-554-2125. p. 2969

Pasco, Robert, Dir, Shenandoah County Library, Basye-Orkney Springs Community, Airport Rd, Basye, VA, 22810. Tel: 540-984-8200, Ext 206. Fax: 540-856-2148. p. 2460

Pasco, Robert, Dir, Shenandoah County Library, Fort Valley Community, 6190 Woodstock Tower Rd, Fort Valley, VA, 22652. Tel: 540-984-8200, Ext 206. Fax: 540-933-6013. p. 2460

Pasco, Robert, Dir, Shenandoah County Library, Mt Jackson Community, 5901 Main St, Mount Jackson, VA, 22842. Tel: 540-984-8200, Ext 206. Fax: 540-477-2294. p. 2460

Pascoe, Andrea, YA Serv, Lizard Butte Public Library, 429 Main St, Ste 105, Marsing, ID, 83639. Tel: 208-896-4690. Fax: 208-896-4472. p. 578

Pascolo, Rita, Tech Serv, Transportation Safety Board of Canada Library, Place du Centre, 200 Promenade du Portage, 4th Flr, Gatineau, QC, K1A 1K8, CANADA. Tel: 819-953-1574. Fax: 819-997-2229. p. 2884

Pascual, Candice, Librn, Everest University, 1199 E Bay Dr, Largo, FL, 33770. Tel: 727-725-2688. Fax: 727-796-3722. p. 460

Pascual, Jean D, Dir, Hebron Public Library, 606 Lincoln Ave, Hebron, ND, 58638-7050. Tel: 701-878-4110. p. 1844

Pascuzzi, Kathleen, Asst Help Desk Mgr/Circ Supvr, Iona College, 715 North Ave, New Rochelle, NY, 10801-1890. Tel: 914-633-2351. Fax: 914-633-2136. p. 1666

Pash, Anthony, Acad Librn, Acadia University, 50 Acadia St, Wolfville, NS, B4P 2R6, CANADA. Tel: 902-585-1249. Fax: 902-585-1748. p. 2786

Pashaie, Billy, Instruction & Outreach, Cypress College Library, 9200 Valley View St, Cypress, CA, 90630-5897. Tel: 714-484-7418. Fax: 714-826-6723. p. 138

Pashkova-Balkenhol, Tatiana, Asst Instrul Design Librn, Longwood University, Redford & Race St, Farmville, VA, 23909. Tel: 434-395-2442. Fax: 434-395-2453. p. 2463

Pasicznyuk, Robert, Libr Dir, Cedar Rapids Public Library West, 2600 Edgewood Rd SW, Ste 330, Cedar Rapids, IA, 52404. Tel: 319-398-5123. Fax: 319-398-0476. p. 800

Pasini, Nicole, Mgr, San Mateo County Library, Portola Valley Library, 765 Portola Rd, Portola Valley, CA, 94028. Tel: 650-851-0560. Fax: 650-851-8365. p. 256

Pasini, Nicole, Mgr, San Mateo County Library, Woodside Library, 3140 Woodside Rd, Woodside, CA, 94062. Tel: 650-851-0147. Fax: 650-851-2695. p. 256

Paskett, Malayna, Cataloger, Tech Serv Supvr, Davis County Library, 38 S 100 East, Farmington, UT, 84025. Tel: 801-451-2322. Fax: 801-451-9561. p. 2405

Paskoff, Beth, Dr, Dir, Louisiana State University, 267 Coates Hall, Baton Rouge, LA, 70803. Tel: 225-578-3158. Fax: 225-578-4581. p. 2966

Pasley, Cherry, Librn, Missouri Department of Corrections, Women's Eastern Reception & Diagnostic Correctional Center, 1101 E Hwy 54, Vandalia, MO, 63382-2905. Tel: 573-594-6686. Fax: 573-594-6789. p. 1335

Pasnick, Ann, Tech Serv, Niles Public Library District, 6960 Oakton St, Niles, IL, 60714. Tel: 847-663-1234. Fax: 847-663-1350. p. 680

Pasoff, Bryna, Librn, Temple Am Echad, One Saperstein Plaza, Lynbrook, NY, 11563. Tel: 516-593-4004. Fax: 516-593-2739. p. 1655

Pason, Phyllis, Librn, Hunterdon County Law Library, 65 Park Ave, Flemington, NJ, 08822. Tel: 908-237-5936. Fax: 908-237-5937. p. 1486

Pason, Phyllis, Dir, Somerset County Law Library, 20 N Bridge St, Somerville, NJ, 08876. Tel: 908-231-7612. Fax: 908-253-8590. p. 1530

Pasour, Christine, Ref Librn, Belmont Abbey College, 100 Belmont-Mt Holly Rd, Belmont, NC, 28012. Tel: 704-461-6748. Fax: 704-461-6743. p. 1776

Pasqua, Barbara, Asst Law Librn, Fayette County Law Library, Court House, 61 E Main St, Ste D, Uniontown, PA, 15401-3514. Tel: 724-430-1228. Fax: 724-430-4886. p. 2147

Pasqual, Patricia E, Dir, Foundation Center-Washington, DC Library, 1627 K St NW, 3rd Flr, Washington, DC, 20006. Tel: 202-331-1400, Ext 4022. Fax: 202-331-1739. p. 401

Pass, Amy, Info Literacy Librn, The Sage Colleges, 140 New Scotland Ave, Albany, NY, 12208. Tel: 518-292-1701. Fax: 518-292-1904. p. 1570

Pass, Amy, Info Literacy Librn, The Sage Colleges, 45 Ferry St, Troy, NY, 12180. Tel: 518-292-1701. Fax: 518-244-2400. p. 1756

Pass, Gregory, PhD, Asst Univ Librn, Spec Coll, Saint Louis University, 3650 Lindell Blvd, Saint Louis, MO, 63108-3302. Tel: 314-977-3196. Fax: 314-977-3108. p. 1360

Passage, Mary, Adult Serv, Southern Tier Library System, 9424 Scott Rd, Painted Post, NY, 14870-9598. Tel: 607-962-3141. Fax: 607-962-5356. p. 1714

Passalacqua, Debbie, Head of Libr, Broward College, North Campus Library LRC, 1100 Coconut Creek Blvd, Coconut Creek, FL, 33066. Tel: 954-201-2600. Fax: 954-201-2650. p. 435

Passalacqua, Julie, Asst City Librn, Santa Clara City Library, 2635 Homestead Rd, Santa Clara, CA, 95051. Tel: 408-615-2900. Fax: 408-247-9657. p. 262

Passanese, Lillian, Ref & Instrul Serv, Instr Coordr, Niagara County Community College, 3111 Saunders Settlement Rd, Sanborn, NY, 14132. Tel: 716-614-6790. Fax: 716-614-6816, 716-614-6828. p. 1737

Passardi, Roberta S, Dir, Mary D Edwards Public Library, c/o Hall Memorial School, 111 River Rd, Rte 32, Willington, CT, 06279. Tel: 860-429-3854. Fax: 860-429-2136. p. 378

Passaretti, Cathy, Supvr, Haliburton County Public Library, Cardiff Branch, 2778 Monck Rd, Cardiff, ON, K0L 1M0, CANADA. Tel: 613-339-2712. p. 2807

Passaro, Patricia L, In Charge, United States Army, Kimbrough Ambulatory Care Center Medical Library, 2480 Llewellyn Ave, Ste 5800, Fort George G Meade, MD, 20755-5800. Tel: 301-677-8228. Fax: 301-677-8108. p. 1028

Passaur, Rebecca, Mgr, Tech Serv, Independence Public Library, 220 E Maple, Independence, KS, 67301-3899. Tel: 620-331-3030. Fax: 620-331-4093. p. 873

Passehl, Erin, Archives & Exhibits, Western Oregon University, Wayne & Lynn Hamersly Library, 345 N Monmouth Ave, Monmouth, OR, 97361-1396. Tel: 503-838-8893. Fax: 503-838-8399. p. 2006

Passey, Samuel J, Dir, Uintah County Library, 204 E 100 N, Vernal, UT, 84078-2695. Tel: 435-789-0091. Fax: 435-789-6822. p. 2416

Passmore, Kyle, Dep Law Librn, University of Akron Libraries, School of Law Library, 150 University Ave, Akron, OH, 44325. Tel: 330-972-7330. Fax: 330-972-4948. p. 1853

Paster, Amy, Head Librn, Pennsylvania State University Libraries, Life Sciences, 401 Paterno Library, University Park, PA, 16802-1811. Tel: 814-865-3708. p. 2148

Pasternack, Louise, Librn Dir, DeVry University, 6600 Dumbarton Circle, Fremont, CA, 94555. Tel: 510-574-1221. p. 149

Pastore, Laurie, Dir, Commack Public Library, 18 Hauppauge Rd, Commack, NY, 11725-4498. Tel: 631-499-0888. Fax: 631-499-0591. p. 1609

Pastorello, Maryalyce, Cat, Medford Public Library, 111 High St, Medford, MA, 02155. Tel: 781-395-7950. Fax: 781-391-2261. p. 1104

Pastrana, Jill Pinkney, Dr, Assoc Prof, University of Wisconsin-Eau Claire, 105 Garfield Ave, Eau Claire, WI, 54702. Tel: 715-836-2635. Fax: 715-836-5099. p. 2976

Pastucha, Joy, Acq, Warren Wilson College, 701 Warren Wilson Rd, Swannanoa, NC, 28778. Tel: 828-771-3063. Fax: 828-771-7085. p. 1826

Pastula, Matthew, Dir, Northern Marianas College, Fina Sisu Lane, Bldg O, Saipan, MP, 96950. Tel: 670-234-3690, Ext 1122. Fax: 670-234-0759. p. 2669

Paszamant, Carol, Librn, New Jersey Department of Transportation, 1035 Parkway Ave, Trenton, NJ, 08618-2309. Tel: 609-530-5289. Fax: 609-530-2052. p. 1535

Paszkowski, Diane, Librn, Crowley, Haughey, Hanson, Toole & Dietrich Library, 490 N 31st St, Ste 500, Billings, MT, 59101-1288. Tel: 406-252-3441. p. 1374

Pata, Elizabete, Libr Mgr, New York Public Library - Astor, Lenox & Tilden Foundations, South Beach Branch, 21-25 Robin Rd, (@ Ocean Ave & Father Capodanno Blvd), Staten Island, NY, 10305. Tel: 718-816-5834. Fax: 718-816-5936. p. 1693

Patadal, Elissa, Cat, Mid-America Christian University, 3500 SW 119th St, Oklahoma City, OK, 73170-9797. Tel: 405-691-3800. Fax: 405-692-3165. p. 1973

Patak, James, Curator, American Theatre Organ Society, Inc, Five E Van Buren St, Ste 210, Joliet, IL, 60432-4223. Tel: 708-562-8538. p. 659

Patak, Trudie, Ch, Perry Carnegie Library, 302 N Seventh St, Perry, OK, 73077. Tel: 580-336-4721. Fax: 580-336-5497. p. 1976

Patane, John, Dir, Pennsauken Free Public Library, 5605 Crescent Blvd, Pennsauken, NJ, 08110. Tel: 856-665-5959. Fax: 856-486-0142. p. 1519

Patanella, Virginia, Br Mgr, Tangipahoa Parish Library, Independence Branch, 290 S Pine St, Independence, LA, 70443. Tel: 985-878-2970. Fax: 985-878-1996. p. 941

Patashnick, Arnold, Co-Chair, First Unitarian Universalist Society of Albany, 405 Washington Ave, Albany, NY, 12206. Tel: 518-463-7135. Fax: 518-463-1429. p. 1569

Patch, Yvonne, Br Mgr, Hamilton Public Library, Sherwood, 467 Upper Ottawa St, Hamilton, ON, L8T 3T3, CANADA. Tel: 905-546-3200, Ext 3436. p. 2809

Patch, Yvonne, Br Mgr, Hamilton Public Library, Valley Park, 970 Paramount Dr, Hamilton, ON, L8J 1Y2, CANADA. Tel: 905-546-3200, Ext 3436. p. 2809

Patchett, Sidney A, Dir, Lantana Public Library, 205 W Ocean Ave, Lantana, FL, 33462. Tel: 561-540-5740. Fax: 561-540-5742. p. 460

Pate, Brandi, Circ Supvr, Southeastern Oklahoma State University, 1405 N Fourth Ave, PMB 4105, Durant, OK, 74701-0609. Tel: 580-745-2702. Fax: 580-745-7463. p. 1961

Pate, Davin, Asst Mgr, Dallas Public Library, 1515 Young St, Dallas, TX, 75201-5499. Tel: 214-670-1608. Fax: 214-670-1647. p. 2306

Pate, Eunice, Librn, Central Presbyterian Church Library, 125 N Seventh St, Terre Haute, IN, 47807-3195. Tel: 812-232-5049. p. 781

Pate, Jessie, Ad, Lincoln County Public Libraries, 220 W Sixth St, Libby, MT, 59923-1898. Tel: 406-293-2778. Fax: 406-293-4235. p. 1385

Pate, Lisa, Info Spec, University of New Mexico, Valencia Campus, 280 La Entrada, Los Lunas, NM, 87031. Tel: 505-925-8992. Fax: 505-925-8994. p. 1551

Pate, Michael, Adult Serv, Highlands County Library System, 319 W Center Ave, Sebring, FL, 33870-3109. Tel: 863-402-6716. Fax: 863-385-2883. p. 491

Patel, Kiran B, Supv Librn, Ref & Tech Serv, Nutley Free Public Library, 93 Booth Dr, Nutley, NJ, 07110-2782. Tel: 973-667-0405. p. 1515

Paterick, Rick, Coordr, Ref, Lehigh Carbon Community College Library, 4525 Education Park Dr, Schnecksville, PA, 18078-9372. Tel: 610-799-1196. Fax: 610-779-1159. p. 2136

Paterno, Amelia, Librn, Susquehanna County Historical Society & Free Library Association, Susquehanna Branch, 83 Erie Blvd, Ste C, Susquehanna, PA, 18847. Tel: 570-853-4106. Fax: 570-853-3265. p. 2092

Pateros, Susan, Tech Serv, Sonnenschein, Nath & Rosenthal, 8000 Sears Tower, 233 S Wacker Dr, Ste 7800, Chicago, IL, 60606-6404. Tel: 312-876-8000. Fax: 312-876-7934. p. 625

Paterra, Alice, Librn, Worcester County Library, Berlin Branch, 220 N Main St, Berlin, MD, 21811. Tel: 410-641-0650. Fax: 410-641-9566. p. 1042

Paterson, Seale, Librn, New Orleans Public Library, Cita Dennis Hubbell Branch, 725 Pelican Ave, New Orleans, LA, 70114. Tel: 504-596-2640. Fax: 504-596-2666. p. 962

Pathak, Susanna, Assoc Dir, University of Wisconsin-Milwaukee Libraries, 2311 E Hartford Ave, Milwaukee, WI, 53211. Tel: 414-229-4785, 414-229-6202. Fax: 414-229-6766. p. 2622

Patillo, David, Info Tech, Springfield-Greene County Library District, 4653 S Campbell, Springfield, MO, 65810-1723. Tel: 417-882-0714. Fax: 417-883-9348. p. 1367

Patillo, Ericka, Dir, University of Houston, Music Library, 220 Moores School of Music Bldg, Houston, TX, 77204-4017. Tel: 713-743-3770. Fax: 713-743-9918. p. 2343

Patkau, Lynn, Chief Librn, Township of Springwater Public Library, 12 Finlay Mill Rd, Midhurst, ON, L0L 1X0, CANADA. Tel: 705-737-5650. Fax: 705-737-3594. p. 2821

Patkau, Lynn, Chief Librn, Township of Springwater Public Library, Elmvale Branch, 50 Queen St W, Elmvale, ON, L0L 1P0, CANADA. Tel: 705-322-1482. Fax: 705-322-0173. p. 2821

Patkau, Lynn, Chief Librn, Township of Springwater Public Library, Minesing Branch, Minesing Community Ctr, 2347 Ronald Rd, Minesing, ON, L0L 1Y0, CANADA. Tel: 705-737-5650. Fax: 705-737-3594. p. 2821

Patkus, Ronald, Asst Dir, Spec Coll, Outreach Prog, Vassar College Library, 124 Raymond Ave, Maildrop 20, Poughkeepsie, NY, 12604-0020. Tel: 845-437-5760. Fax: 845-437-5864. p. 1723

Paton, Jennie, Librn, United States Air Force, Air Force Flight Test Center Technical Research Library, 812 TSS/ENTL, 307 E Popson Ave, Bldg 1400, Rm 106, Edwards AFB, CA, 93524-6630. Tel: 661-275-5516. Fax: 661-275-6070. p. 144

Patout, Gerald, Dir, Louisiana State University, 2048 Johnson Hwy, Eunice, LA, 70535. Tel: 337-550-1380. Fax: 337-550-1455. p. 949

Patricia, Uttaro, Dir, Rochester Public Library, 115 South Ave, Rochester, NY, 14604-1896. Tel: 585-428-8045. Fax: 585-428-8353. p. 1732

Patrick, Ann, Res & Instrul Serv, Keystone College, One College Green, La Plume, PA, 18440-0200. Tel: 570-945-8332. Fax: 570-945-8969. p. 2075

Patrick, Anna, Libr Tech, Media Serv, Tech Serv, Grays Harbor College, 1620 Edward P Smith Dr, Aberdeen, WA, 98520-7599. Tel: 360-538-4050. Fax: 360-538-4294. p. 2507

Patrick, Brent, Night/Weekend Serv Coordr, University of California, Merced Library, 5200 N Lake Rd, Merced, CA, 95343-5001. Tel: 209-406-9688. Fax: 209-228-4271. p. 186

Patrick, Diane, Dir of Educ, New Jersey State Prison, PO Box 861, Trenton, NJ, 08625. Tel: 609-292-9700, Ext 4285. Fax: 609-777-1885. p. 1536

Patrick, Elaine, Pub Serv, Duncanville Public Library, 201 James Collins Blvd, Duncanville, TX, 75116. Tel: 972-780-5050. Fax: 972-780-4958. p. 2314

Patrick, James, Librn, Yuma County Library District, 2951 S 21st Dr, Yuma, AZ, 85364. Tel: 928-373-6484. Fax: 928-782-9420. p. 91

Patrick, Jeffrey, Mgr, National Park Service, Wilson's Creek National Battlefield, 6424 W Farm Rd 182, Republic, MO, 65738-9514. Tel: 417-732-2662. Fax: 417-732-1167. p. 1350

Patrick, Jill, Dir, Libr Serv, Ontario College of Art & Design, 100 McCaul St, Toronto, ON, M5T 1W1, CANADA. Tel: 416-977-6000, Ext 255. Fax: 416-977-6006. p. 2856

Patrick, Kasie, Per, Troy University, 502 University Dr, Dothan, AL, 36304. Tel: 334-983-6556, Ext 1322. Fax: 334-983-6327. p. 15

Patrick, Lorraine, Ref Serv, Bellevue University, 1000 Galvin Rd S, Bellevue, NE, 68005. Tel: 402-557-7316. Fax: 402-557-5427. p. 1393

Patrick, Lydia, Internet Serv, Fairfax County Public Library, 12000 Government Center Pkwy, Ste 324, Fairfax, VA, 22035-0012. Tel: 703-324-3100. Fax: 703-324-8365. p. 2461

Patrick, M, Database Mgr, Syst Coordr, Parkland Regional Library, Hwy 52 W, Yorkton, SK, S3N 3Z4, CANADA. Tel: 306-783-7022. Fax: 306-782-2844. p. 2931

Patrick, Sandy, Coordr, Circ, Wells Public Library, 1434 Post Rd, Wells, ME, 04090-4508. Tel: 207-646-8181, Ext. 203. Fax: 207-646-5636. p. 1006

Patrick, Sue, Br Head, Toronto Public Library, Eatonville, 430 Burnhamthorpe Rd, Toronto, ON, M9B 2B1, CANADA. Tel: 416-394-5270. Fax: 416-394-5276. p. 2861

Patridge, Ann, Head Librn, Vermont Public Library, 101 N Main St, Vermont, IL, 61484. Tel: 309-784-6291. Fax: 309-784-6291. p. 714

Patridge, Norm, Circ Serv Supvr, Saint Mary's College Library, 1928 Saint Mary's Rd, Moraga, CA, 94575. Tel: 925-631-4229. Fax: 925-376-6097. p. 191

Patrimonia, Richard, Asst Librn, Maimonides Medical Center, Administration, 4802 Tenth Ave, Fifth Fl, Brooklyn, NY, 11219. Tel: 718-283-7406. Fax: 718-283-7063. p. 1593

Patriquin, Charlotte Slocum, Chief Info Officer, Mount Holyoke College Library, 50 College St, South Hadley, MA, 01075-1423. Tel: 413-538-2225. Fax: 413-538-2370. p. 1125

Patry, Claudine, Pub Serv Mgr, Bibliotheque Municipale de Gatineau, Édifice Pierre Papin, CP 1970 Succ. Hull, Gatineau, QC, J8X 3Y9, CANADA. p. 2882

Patt, Dottie, Libr Dir, Wolcott Civic Free Library, 5890 New Hartford St, Wolcott, NY, 14590. Tel: 315-594-2265. Fax: 315-594-2681. p. 1770

Pattan, Shirley, In Charge, Mid-Columbia Libraries, Basin City Branch, 50-A N Canal Blvd, Basin City, WA, 99343. Tel: 509-269-4201. Fax: 509-269-4201. p. 2518

Pattantyus, Christine, Head, Ch, Grinnell Library Association, 2642 E Main St, Wappingers Falls, NY, 12590. Tel: 845-297-3428. Fax: 845-297-1506. p. 1762

Pattee, Amy, Asst Prof, Simmons College, 300 The Fenway, Boston, MA, 02115. Tel: 617-521-2800. Fax: 617-521-3192. p. 2967

Pattee, Sherrill, Br Assoc, Las Vegas-Clark County Library District, Indian Springs Library, 715 Gretta Lane, Indian Springs, NV, 89018. Tel: 702-879-3845. Fax: 702-879-5227. p. 1429

Patten, Christine, Libr Serv Mgr, Seminole County Public Library System, 215 N Oxford Rd, Casselberry, FL, 32707. Tel: 407-665-1501. Fax: 407-665-1510. p. 431

Patten, Peter, Ref Librn, Fordham University Libraries, 441 E Fordham Rd, Bronx, NY, 10458-5151. Tel: 718-817-3570. Fax: 718-817-3582. p. 1586

Patterson, Ann, Adult Serv, Greece Public Library, Two Vince Tofany Blvd, Greece, WI, 14612. Tel: 585-225-8951. Fax: 585-225-2777. p. 1630

Patterson, Beth, PhD, Govt Doc, Drew University Library, 36 Madison Ave, Madison, NJ, 07940. Tel: 973-408-3480. Fax: 973-408-3770. p. 1497

Patterson, Bonnie Duprey, Ch, Cross' Mills Public Library, 4417 Old Post Rd, Charlestown, RI, 02813. Tel: 401-364-6211. Fax: 401-364-0609. p. 2164

Patterson, Brenda, Ad, Lakeland Public Library, 100 Lake Morton Dr, Lakeland, FL, 33801-5375. Tel: 863-834-4280. Fax: 863-834-4293. p. 459

Patterson, Brenda, Asst Librn, Friona Public Library, 109 W Seventh St, Friona, TX, 79035-2548. Tel: 806-250-3200. Fax: 806-250-2185. p. 2325

Patterson, Carolyn, Acq, Ser, Queens University of Charlotte, 1900 Selwyn Ave, Charlotte, NC, 28274-0001. Tel: 704-337-2401. Fax: 704-337-2517. p. 1784

Patterson, Carolyn Sue, Acq Librn, Mercer County Public Library, 109 W Lexington St, Harrodsburg, KY, 40330-1542. Tel: 859-734-3680. Fax: 859-734-7524. p. 916

Patterson, Cynthia, Supvr, Circ, Lawrence University, 113 S Lawe St, Appleton, WI, 54911-5683. Fax: 920-832-6967. p. 2578

Patterson, Dan, Head, ILL, Chicago School of Professional Psychology Library, 325 N Wells St, 6th Flr, Chicago, IL, 60610. Tel: 312-410-8956. Fax: 312-644-6075. p. 610

Patterson, Dave, Librn, Canada College Library, Bldg 9, 3rd Flr, 4200 Farm Hill Blvd, Redwood City, CA, 94061-1099. Tel: 650-306-3383. Fax: 650-306-3434. p. 215

Patterson, Deborah, Librn, Volusia County Law Library, Courthouse Annex, Rm 208, 125 E Orange Ave, Daytona Beach, FL, 32114. Tel: 386-257-6041. Fax: 386-257-6052. p. 436

Patterson, Erin, Acad Librn, Acadia University, 50 Acadia St, Wolfville, NS, B4P 2R6, CANADA. Tel: 902-585-1249. Fax: 902-585-1748. p. 2786

Patterson, Gail, Children & Teen Librn, South Haven Memorial Library, 314 Broadway St, South Haven, MI, 49090. Tel: 269-637-2403. Fax: 269-639-1685. p. 1227

Patterson, Gail, Librn, United States Army, Bldg T-530, Solomons Rd, Fort Story, VA, 23459-5067. Tel: 757-422-7548. Fax: 757-422-7773. p. 2465

Patterson, Greg, Head, Knowledge Mgt, United States Navy, Naval Hospital Library, HP01 One Boone Rd, Bremerton, WA, 98312-1898. Tel: 360-475-4316. Fax: 360-475-4324. p. 2511

Patterson, Heidi O, Librn, Western Pennsylvania Hospital, 4800 Friendship Ave, Pittsburgh, PA, 15224. Tel: 412-578-5556. Fax: 412-578-7317. p. 2129

Patterson, Hope, Cat, ILL, Mendocino College Library, 1000 Hensley Creek Rd, Ukiah, CA, 95482-7821. Tel: 707-468-3053. Fax: 707-468-3056. p. 277

Patterson, James, Dir, Libr Serv, Northwestern Connecticut Community College Library, Park Pl E, Winsted, CT, 06098. Tel: 860-738-6480. Fax: 860-379-4995. p. 379

Patterson, Jane, Mgr, BCA Research Group Library, 1002 Sherbrooke St W, Ste 1600, Montreal, QC, H3A 3L6, CANADA. Tel: 514-499-9550. Fax: 514-843-1763. p. 2888

Patterson, Jean, Circ Mgr, Mamie Doud Eisenhower Public Library, Three Community Park Rd, Broomfield, CO, 80020-3781. Tel: 720-887-2306. Fax: 720-887-1384. p. 292

Patterson, Kelly, Adminr, Crew Public Library, 109 S Main St, Salem, IA, 52649. Tel: 319-258-9007. Fax: 319-258-9007. p. 842

Patterson, Kim, Dir, Southeast Arkansas Regional Library, 107 E Jackson St, Monticello, AR, 71655. Tel: 870-367-8584. Fax: 870-367-5166. p. 109

Patterson, Marilyn, Br Mgr, Great River Regional Library, Al Ringsmuth Library, 253 N Fifth Ave, Waite Park, MN, 56387-0395. Tel: 320-253-9359. Fax: 320-253-9359. p. 1275

Patterson, Marsha L, Dir, Bremen Public Library, 304 N Jackson St, Bremen, IN, 46506. Tel: 574-546-2849. Fax: 574-546-4938. p. 729

Patterson, Mary, Tech Serv Librn, Hamilton Public Library, 861 Broadway St, Hamilton, IL, 62341. Tel: 217-847-2219. Fax: 217-847-3014. p. 653

Patterson, Mary Kay, Circ, Hamilton East Public Library, One Library Plaza, Cumberland Rd, Noblesville, IN, 46060-5639. Tel: 317-770-3226. Fax: 317-776-6936. p. 769

Patterson, Michele, Ref, Beech Grove Public Library, 1102 Main St, Beech Grove, IN, 46107. Tel: 317-788-4203. Fax: 317-788-0489. p. 726

Patterson, Myra, Info Tech, Iredell County Public Library, 201 N Tradd St, Statesville, NC, 28677. Tel: 704-878-3148. Fax: 704-878-5449. p. 1825

Patterson, Nick, Music Librn, Columbia University, The Gabe M Wiener Music & Arts Library, 701 Dodge Hall, 2960 Broadway, New York, NY, 10027. Tel: 212-854-4711. Fax: 212-854-4748. p. 1675

Patterson, Noreen, Dir, Phoenix Public Library, 34 Elm St, Phoenix, NY, 13135. Tel: 315-695-4355. Fax: 315-695-4355. p. 1717

Patterson, Patricia R, Assoc Libr Dir, United States Naval Academy, 589 McNair Rd, Annapolis, MD, 21402-5029. Tel: 410-293-6900. Fax: 410-293-6909. p. 1011

Patterson, Renee, Circ Serv Sr Libr Mgr, Alachua County Library District, 401 E University Ave, Gainesville, FL, 32601-5453. Tel: 352-334-1258. Fax: 352-334-3918. p. 448

Patterson, Rita, Commun Relations Librn, Olathe Public Library, 201 E Park St, Olathe, KS, 66061. Tel: 913-971-6879. Fax: 913-971-6809. p. 886

Patterson, Sandy, Dir, Wetmore Public Library, 333 Second St, Wetmore, KS, 66550. Tel: 785-866-2250. Fax: 785-866-2250. p. 899

Patterson, Shelly, Librn, Cecil County Circuit Court Library, Courthouse, 2nd Flr, 129 E Main St, Elkton, MD, 21921. Tel: 410-996-5325. Fax: 410-996-5120. p. 1027

Patterson, Stephanie, Dir, Maryville Public Library, 509 N Main, Maryville, MO, 64468. Tel: 660-582-5281. Fax: 660-582-2411. p. 1344

Patterson, Steve, Libr Asst, University of Western Ontario, North Campus Bldg, Rm 280, London, ON, N6A 5B7, CANADA. Tel: 519-661-2111, Ext 88489. Fax: 519-661-3848. p. 2819

Patterson, Thomas, Coordr, Doc Delivery, Walden University Library, 100 Washington Ave S, Ste 900, Minneapolis, MN, 55401. p. 1262

Patterson, Vicki, AV, Librn for the Handicapped, Northwest Regional Library System, 898 W 11 St, Panama City, FL, 32401. Tel: 850-522-2100. Fax: 850-522-2138. p. 480

Patterson, Wanda, Asst Dir, Sweetwater Public Library, 210 Mayes Ave, Sweetwater, TN, 37874. Tel: 423-337-5274. Fax: 423-337-0552. p. 2266

Patterson, Zelda, Circ, Muskingum University Library, 163 Stormont St, New Concord, OH, 43762-1199. Tel: 740-826-8156. Fax: 740-826-8404. p. 1920

Patteson, Rita, Dir, Librn/Curator of Ms, Baylor University Libraries, Armstrong Browning Library, 710 Speight Ave, Waco, TX, 76798-7152. Tel: 254-710-4967. Fax: 254-710-3552. p. 2396

Patti, Angela, Librn, New York Supreme Court, 77 W Eagle St, Buffalo, NY, 14202. Tel: 716-845-9400. Fax: 716-852-3454. p. 1598

Pattison, Elizabeth, Libr Tech, Regional Mental Health Care London, 850 Highbury Ave N, London, ON, N6A 4H1, CANADA, Tel: 519-455-5110, Ext 47543. Fax: 519-455-3620. p. 2818

Pattison, Laura, Librn, Boston Public Library, Orient Heights, 18 Barnes Ave, East Boston, MA, 02128-1234. Tel: 617-567-2516. Fax: 617-561-0288. p. 1057

Patton, Amy, Circ, Tech Serv, Lake County Library, 1425 N High St, Lakeport, CA, 95453-3800. Tel: 707-263-8816. Fax: 707-263-6796. p. 163

Patton, Carla, Librn, Avondale Public Library, 495 E Western Ave, Avondale, AZ, 85323. Tel: 623-478-3100. Fax: 623-478-3809. p. 57

Patton, David, Dir, Marion Carnegie Library, 206 S Market St, Marion, IL, 62959-2519. Tel: 618-993-5935. Fax: 618-997-6485. p. 670

Patton, Gayle, Dep Dir, Mansfield-Richland County Public Library, 43 W Third St, Mansfield, OH, 44902-1295. Tel: 419-521-3100. Fax: 419-525-4750. p. 1912

Patton, Gwendolyn M, Archivist, H Councill Trenholm State Technical College Library, 3086 Mobile Hwy, Montgomery, AL, 36108. Tel: 334-420-4475. Fax: 334-420-4476. p. 28

Patton, Ida, Pub Serv, Washington County Public Library, 205 Oak Hill St, Abingdon, VA, 24210. Tel: 276-676-6390. Fax: 276-676-6235. p. 2443

Patton, Janet, Asst Librn, Streeter Centennial Library, 5280 50th Ave SE, Streeter, ND, 58483. Tel: 701-424-3602. p. 1848

Patton, Josie, Mgr, ILL, Tulane University, Rudolph Matas Library of the Health Sciences, Tulane Health Sciences Campus, 1430 Tulane Ave, SL-86, New Orleans, LA, 70112-2699. Tel: 504-988-2413. Fax: 504-988-7417. p. 963

Patton, Julia, Pub Serv, Valley Forge Christian College, 1401 Charlestown Rd, Phoenixville, PA, 19460. Tel: 610-917-2004. Fax: 610-917-2008. p. 2120

Patton, L K, Dr, Exec Dir, Kentucky Covered Bridge Association Library, 62 Miami Pkwy, Fort Thomas, KY, 41075-1137. Tel: 859-441-7000. p. 913

Patton, Philip, Libr & Instrul Tech Adminr, Cochise College Library, Andrea Cracchiolo Library, 901 N Colombo Ave, Sierra Vista, AZ, 85635. Tel: 520-515-5390. Fax: 520-515-5464. p. 61

Patton, Rebecca, Continuing Educ Supvr, Arrowhead Library System, 5528 Emerald Ave, Mountain Iron, MN, 55768-2069. Tel: 218-741-3840. Fax: 218-748-2171. p. 1267

Patton, Stephen, Electronic Serv Librn, Delta State University, Laflore Circle at Fifth Ave, Cleveland, MS, 38733-2599. Tel: 662-846-4440. Fax: 662-846-4443. p. 1296

Patton, Susan, Dir, Madill City County Library, 500 W Overton St, Madill, OK, 73446. Tel: 580-795-2749. Fax: 580-795-2749. p. 1967

Pattwell, Paul D, Supv Librn, Staff Develop, Outreach & Admin Initiatives, Newark Public Library, Five Washington St, Newark, NJ, 07101. Tel: 973-733-7735. Fax: 973-733-5648. p. 1511

Paty, Morgan, Ref, YA Librn, Public Library of Johnston County & Smithfield, 305 E Market St, Smithfield, NC, 27577-3919. Tel: 919-934-8146. Fax: 919-934-8084. p. 1824

Patzer, Renee, Cat, Topeka & Shawnee County Public Library, 1515 SW Tenth Ave, Topeka, KS, 66604-1374. Tel: 785-580-4400. Fax: 785-580-4496. p. 897

Patzold, Karen, Col Librn, College of the North Atlantic, Gander Campus, One Magee Rd, Gander, NL, A1V 1W8, CANADA. Tel: 709-651-4815. Fax: 709-651-4854. p. 2771

Paul, Angela, Ref Librn, Wichita State University Libraries, 1845 Fairmount, Wichita, KS, 67260-0068. Tel: 316-978-5084. Fax: 316-978-3048. p. 902

Paul, Beth, Tech Serv Spec, Federal Reserve Bank of Philadelphia, 100 N Sixth St, 4th Flr, Philadelphia, PA, 19106. Tel: 215-574-6540. Fax: 215-574-3847. p. 2106

Paul, Betsy, Head, Ch, Andover Public Library, 142 W Main St, Andover, OH, 44003-9318. Tel: 440-293-6792. Fax: 440-293-5720. p. 1854

Paul, Carolyn, Access Serv, Massachusetts General Hospital, Treadwell Library, Bartlett Hall Ext - I, 55 Fruit St, Boston, MA, 02114-2696. Tel: 617-726-8600. Fax: 617-726-6784. p. 1063

Paul, David J, Head, Info Serv, Southern Maryland Regional Library Association, Inc, 37600 New Market Rd, Charlotte Hall, MD, 20622-3041. Tel: 301-843-3634, 301-884-0436, 301-934-9442. Fax: 301-884-0438. p. 1023

Paul, Eddie, Head Biblio & Info Serv, Bibliotheque Publique Juive, One carré Cummings, 5151 ch de la Cote Ste Catherine, Montreal, QC, H3W 1M6, CANADA. Tel: 514-345-2627, Ext 3004. Fax: 514-342-6477. p. 2888

Paul, Eli, Mgr, Mo Valley Spec Coll, The Kansas City Public Library, 14 W Tenth St, Kansas City, MO, 64105. Tel: 816-701-3527. Fax: 816-701-3401. p. 1338

Paul, Helen Marie, Sister, Tech Serv Mgr, Silver Lake College, 2406 S Alverno Rd, Manitowoc, WI, 54220. Tel: 920-686-6171. Fax: 920-684-7082. p. 2612

Paul, Isabel, Mgr, Henrico County Public Library, Municipal Government & Law Library, County of Henrico Government Ctr, 4301 E Parham Rd, Henrico, VA, 23228. Tel: 804-501-4780, 804-501-5155. Fax: 804-672-1948. p. 2471

Paul, Lesley, Dir, Frank J Basloe Library of Herkimer New York, 245 N Main St, Herkimer, NY, 13350-1918. Tel: 315-866-1733. Fax: 315-866-1733. p. 1635

Paul, Linda, Cataloger/Ref Librn, Indiana Tech, 1600 E Washington Blvd, Fort Wayne, IN, 46803. Tel: 260-422-5561, Ext 2215. Fax: 260-422-3189. p. 741

Paul, Paula, Librn, Steep Falls Public Library, 1128 Pequawket Trail, Steep Falls, ME, 04085. Tel: 207-675-3132. p. 1002

Paul, Susan, Ref & Access Serv Librn, Lorain County Community College, 1005 Abbe Rd N, North Elyria, OH, 44035-1691. Tel: 440-366-7422. Fax: 440-366-4127. p. 1924

Paule, Jean, Archivist, Occidental College Library, 1600 Campus Rd, Los Angeles, CA, 90041. Tel: 323-259-1413. Fax: 323-341-4991. p. 176

Pauley, Joy, Coordr, Tech Serv, Southern Nazarene University, 4115 N College, Bethany, OK, 73008. Tel: 405-491-6350. Fax: 405-491-6355. p. 1958

Pauley, Lynn, Dir, Jackson County Library, Ravenswood Branch, 323 Virginia St, Ravenswood, WV, 26164. Tel: 304-273-5343. Fax: 304-273-5395. p. 2570

Paulhus, Richard, Chef de Div, Bibliothèques de Montrèal, Hochelaga, 1870, rue Davidson, Montreal, QC, H1W 2Y6, CANADA. Tel: 514-872-6629. Fax: 514-872-4617. p. 2890

Paulhus, Richard, Chef de Div, Bibliothèques de Montrèal, Langelier, 6473, rue Sherbrooke Est, Montreal, QC, H1N 1C5, CANADA. Tel: 514-872-6629. Fax: 514-872-4617. p. 2890

Paulhus, Richard, Chef de Div, Bibliothèques de Montrèal, Mercier, 8105, rue Hochelaga, Montreal, QC, H1L 2K9, CANADA. Tel: 514-872-6629. Fax: 514-872-4617. p. 2890

Paulic, Mary Ann, Commun Librn, Congress Public Library, 26750 Santa Fe Rd, Congress, AZ, 85332. Tel: 928-427-3945. Fax: 928-427-3945. p. 60

Paulichuk, Cheryl, Libr Mgr, Alice Melnyk Public Library, 5009 50th Ave, Two Hills, AB, T0B 4K0, CANADA. Tel: 780-657-3553. Fax: 780-657-3553. p. 2720

Paulik, Laurie, Librn, United States Department of Agriculture, USDA/APHIS/WS, 4101 LaPorte Ave, Fort Collins, CO, 80521-2154. Tel: 970-266-6016. Fax: 970-266-6010. p. 308

Paulini, Diane, Libr Asst, Elmhurst Memorial Healthcare, 155 E Brush Hill Rd, Elmhurst, IL, 60126. Tel: 331-221-1000, Ext 14130. Fax: 331-221-3788. p. 642

Paulins, Ruth, Circ, Oak Hill Public Library, 226 S Front St, Oak Hill, OH, 45656. Tel: 740-682-6457. Fax: 740-682-3522. p. 1924

Paulk, Christie, Youth Serv, South Georgia Regional Library System, 300 Woodrow Wilson Dr, Valdosta, GA, 31602-2592. Tel: 229-333-0086. Fax: 229-333-7669. p. 555

Paulk, J Sara, Asst Dir, Fitzgerald-Ben Hill County Library, 123 N Main St, Fitzgerald, GA, 31750-2591. Tel: 229-426-5080. Fax: 229-426-5084. p. 532

Paulk, J Sara, Dir, Wythe-Grayson Regional Library, 147 S Independence Ave, Independence, VA, 24348-2800. Tel: 276-773-2761. Fax: 276-773-3289. p. 2472

Paulls, Linda, Assoc Librn, Saint Vincent's Hospital & Medical Center, 170 W 12th St, New York, NY, 10011. Tel: 212-604-7811. Fax: 212-604-7888. p. 1699

Paulo, Lisa, Dir, Franklin Square Public Library, 19 Lincoln Rd, Franklin Square, NY, 11010. Tel: 516-488-3444. Fax: 516-354-3368. p. 1624

Paulos, Afeworki, Soc Sci Librn, Carnegie Mellon University, Hunt Library, 4909 Frew St, Pittsburgh, PA, 15213-3890. Tel: 412-268-2446. Fax: 412-268-2793. p. 2123

Pauls, Stuart, Libr Mgr, Vermilion Public Library, 5001 49th Ave, Vermilion, AB, T9X 1B8, CANADA. Tel: 780-853-4288. Fax: 780-853-1783. p. 2720

Paulsen, Cathy, Ref Librn, Chappaqua Public Library, 195 S Greeley Ave, Chappaqua, NY, 10514. Tel: 914-238-4779. Fax: 914-238-3597. p. 1605

Paulsen, Yvonne, Circ, Tech Serv, Mayville Public Library, 111 N Main St, Mayville, WI, 53050. Tel: 920-387-7910. Fax: 920-387-7917. p. 2613

Paulson, Anita, Dir of Libr Serv, Marion County Library, 308 Old Main, Yellville, AR, 72687. Tel: 870-449-6015. Fax: 870-449-6015. p. 117

Paulson, Carl, Sr Librn, New York State Department of Corrections & Community Supervision, 555 Devils Den Rd, Altona, NY, 12910. Tel: 518-236-7841, Ext 4560. p. 1573

Paulson, Deborah J, Dir, Columbia County Public Library, 308 NW Columbia Ave, Lake City, FL, 32055. Tel: 386-758-2101. Fax: 386-758-2135. p. 457

Paulsrud, Theresa, Head, Acq, Chapman University, One University Dr, Orange, CA, 92866-1099. Tel: 714-532-7756. Fax: 714-532-7743. p. 200

Paulus, Kristine, Chief Librn, Monroe College, 2468 Jerome Ave, Bronx, NY, 10468. Tel: 718-933-6700. Fax: 718-584-4242. p. 1588

Pauly, Regina, Head, Instrul Mat Lab, University of Wisconsin - Platteville, One University Plaza, Platteville, WI, 53818. Tel: 608-342-1099. Fax: 608-342-1645. p. 2630

Paunicka, Merribeth, Children's Mgr, Westchester Public Library, 200 W Indiana Ave, Chesterton, IN, 46304-3122. Tel: 219-926-7696. Fax: 219-926-6424. p. 732

Paus, Shelly, Br Mgr, Brooklyn Public Library, Leonard, 81 Devoe St, Brooklyn, NY, 11211. Tel: 718-486-3365. Fax: 718-486-3370. p. 1591

Paus, Stephanie, Librn, Parkland Regional Library, Balcarres Branch, 209 Main St, Balcarres, SK, S0G 0C0, CANADA. Tel: 306-334-2966. p. 2931

Pause, Tracey, Dir, Hurley Library District, 44 Main St, Hurley, NY, 12443-5106. Tel: 845-338-2092. Fax: 845-338-2092. p. 1639

Paustenbaugh, Jennifer Ford, Dr, Assoc Dean, Libr for Planning & Assessment, Oklahoma State University Libraries, Oklahoma State University, Athletic Ave, Stillwater, OK, 74078-1071. Tel: 405-744-9778. Fax: 405-744-7579. p. 1978

Paustenbaugh, Richard T, Assoc Dean, Libr for Res & Instruction Serv, Oklahoma State University Libraries, Oklahoma State University, Athletic Ave, Stillwater, OK, 74078-1071. Tel: 405-744-5271. Fax: 405-744-5183. p. 1978

Pauwels, Colleen K, Dir, Indiana University, School of Law Library, Maurer School of Law, 211 S Indiana Ave, Bloomington, IN, 47405. Tel: 812-855-9666. Fax: 812-855-7099. p. 727

Pava, Joseph, Coll Develop, South Windsor Public Library, 1550 Sullivan Ave, South Windsor, CT, 06074. Tel: 860-644-1541. Fax: 860-644-7645. p. 368

Pavel, Frank, Asst Dir, Goldwater Memorial Hospital, 900 Main, Roosevelt Island, New York, NY, 10001. Tel: 212-318-4800. Fax: 212-318-4628. p. 1680

Pavey, Patricia, Librn, Jewish Community Center Saskatoon, Congregation Agudas Israel, 715 McKinnon Ave, Saskatoon, SK, S7H 2G2, CANADA. Tel: 306-343-7023. Fax: 306-343-1244. p. 2925

Pavlik, Janice, Librn, Howe Memorial Library, 128 E Saginaw St, Breckenridge, MI, 48615. Tel: 989-842-3202. Fax: 989-842-3202. p. 1159

Pavlis, Natalie, Customer Serv Coordr, Lethbridge Public Library, 810 Fifth Ave S, Lethbridge, AB, T1J 4C4, CANADA. Tel: 403-380-7343. Fax: 403-329-1478. p. 2709

Pavlovic, Gordana, Mgr, Xerox Research Centre of Canada Library, 2660 Speakman Dr, Mississauga, ON, L5K 2L1, CANADA. Tel: 905-823-7091. Fax: 905-822-7022. p. 2823

Pavlovsky, Taras, Dean of Libr, The College of New Jersey Library, 2000 Pennington Rd, Ewing, NJ, 08628-0718. Tel: 609-771-2311, 609-771-2332. Fax: 609-637-5177. p. 1484

Pavluk, Linda, Circ, Wilmington Memorial Library, 175 Middlesex Ave, Wilmington, MA, 01887-2779. Tel: 978-658-2967. Fax: 978-658-9699. p. 1141

Pavoldi, Terry, Librn, Middleburgh Library Association, 323 Main St, Middleburgh, NY, 12122. Tel: 518-827-5142. Fax: 518-827-5148. p. 1660

Pavon, Gemma, Electronic Reserves Librn, Saint Mary's College Library, 1928 Saint Mary's Rd, Moraga, CA, 94575. Tel: 925-631-4229. Fax: 925-376-6097. p. 191

Pavy, Jeanne, Humanities Librn, University of New Orleans, 2000 Lakeshore Dr, New Orleans, LA, 70148. Tel: 504-280-6547. Fax: 504-280-7277. p. 964

Pawlek, Cynthia, Assoc Librn, Dartmouth College Library, 6025 Baker Berry Library, Rm 115, Hanover, NH, 03755-3525. Tel: 603-646-2236. Fax: 603-646-3702. p. 1450

Pawlek, Cynthia, Dep Librn, Dartmouth College Library, Baker-Berry Library, 6025 Baker-Berry Library, Hanover, NH, 03755-3525. Tel: 603-646-2560. Fax: 603-646-2167. p. 1450

Pawlek, Sarah, Mgr, Info Desks, Babson College, 231 Forest St, Babson Park, MA, 02457-0310. Tel: 781-239-5604. Fax: 781-239-5226. p. 1051

Pawloski, Lynn, Ch, Southington Public Library & Museum, 255 Main St, Southington, CT, 06489. Tel: 860-628-0947. Fax: 860-628-0488. p. 368

Pawlowicz, Esther, Tech Serv Mgr, Johnson City Public Library, 100 W Millard St, Johnson City, TN, 37604. Tel: 423-434-4343. Fax: 423-434-4469. p. 2240

Pawlowski, Dorothy, Adult Serv, Ridgefield Library Association Inc, 472 Main St, Ridgefield, CT, 06877-4585. Tel: 203-438-2282. Fax: 203-438-4558. p. 365

Pawlowski, Jack, Head, Circ, Warrenville Public Library District, 28 W 751 Stafford Pl, Warrenville, IL, 60555. Tel: 630-393-1171. Fax: 630-393-1688. p. 715

Paxson, Holly, Br Mgr, Maricopa County Library District, Queen Creek Branch, 21802 S Ellsworth Rd, Queen Creek, AZ, 85242. Tel: 602-652-3351. Fax: 602-652-3360. p. 75

Paxton, Jennie, Human Res Mgr, Shreve Memorial Library, 424 Texas St, Shreveport, LA, 71101. Tel: 318-226-4789. Fax: 318-226-4780. p. 969

Payen, Carole, Secy Gen, Bibliotheque et Archives nationales du Quebec, 475 de Maisonneuve E, Montreal, QC, H2L 5C4, CANADA. Tel: 514-873-1101, Ext 3255. Fax: 514-873-9312. p. 2888

Payette, Pat, Tech Serv, Free Public Library of Bayonne, 697 Avenue C, Bayonne, NJ, 07002. Tel: 201-858-6970. Fax: 201-437-6928. p. 1470

Payette, Suzanne, Dir, Bibliotheque de Brossard, 7855 San Francisco Ave, Brossard, QC, J4X 2A4, CANADA. Tel: 450-923-6350, Ext 6291. Fax: 450-923-7042. p. 2880

Payette, Wendy, Dir, East Brookfield Public Library, Memorial Town Complex, 122 Connie Mack Dr, East Brookfield, MA, 01515. Tel: 508-867-7928. Fax: 508-867-4181. p. 1085

Payeur, Suzanne, Tech Serv, Centre Jeunesse de Montreal - Institut universitaire, 1001 boul de Maisonneuve est, 5ieme etage, Montreal, QC, H2L 4R5, CANADA. Tel: 514-896-3396. Fax: 514-896-3483. p. 2893

Payne, Ann, Circ Mgr, Chesapeake Public Library, Greenbrier, 1214 Volvo Pkwy, Chesapeake, VA, 23320-7600. Tel: 757-410-7070. Fax: 757-410-7071. p. 2456

Payne, Arnette, Cat, Creighton University, 2500 California Plaza, Omaha, NE, 68178-0209. Tel: 402-280-1806. Fax: 402-280-2435. p. 1412

Payne, Cindy, Circ Supvr, Centralia Regional Library District, 515 E Broadway, Centralia, IL, 62801. Tel: 618-532-5222. Fax: 618-532-8578. p. 602

Payne, Clay, Br Mgr, Atlanta-Fulton Public Library System, South Fulton Regional Library, 4055 Flatshoals Rd SW, Union City, GA, 30291. Tel: 770-306-3092. Fax: 770-306-3127. p. 512

Payne, Daniel, Head, Instrul Serv, Ontario College of Art & Design, 100 McCaul St, Toronto, ON, M5T 1W1, CANADA. Tel: 416-977-6000, Ext 217. Fax: 416-977-6006. p. 2856

Payne, Danielle A, Dir, Oxford Public Library, 201 E Smith, Oxford, IN, 47971. Tel: 765-385-2177. Fax: 765-385-2313. p. 772

Payne, David, Head of Libr, Free Library of Philadelphia, Tacony Branch, 6742 Torresdale Ave, Philadelphia, PA, 19135-2416. Tel: 215-685-8755, 215-685-8758. Fax: 215-685-8718. p. 2109

Payne, Erlene, Librn, Trident Technical College, Palmer Campus Learning Resources Center, LR-P, PO Box 118067, Charleston, SC, 29423-8067. Tel: 843-722-5539. Fax: 843-720-5614. p. 2185

Payne, Jeane, Head, Circ, Floyd Memorial Library, 539 First St, Greenport, NY, 11944-1399. Tel: 631-477-0660. Fax: 631-477-2647. p. 1631

Payne, Jeanine, Br Coordr, Washington County Public Library, 14102 Saint Stephens Ave, Chatom, AL, 36518. Tel: 251-847-2097. Fax: 251-847-2098. p. 12

Payne, John K, Dir, Libr & Info Serv, Saint Michael's College, One Winooski Park, Box L, Colchester, VT, 05439-2525. Tel: 802-654-2401. Fax: 802-654-2630. p. 2422

Payne, Kate, Acq, Ithaca College Library, 953 Danby Rd, Ithaca, NY, 14850-7060. Tel: 607-274-3206. Fax: 607-274-1539. p. 1643

Payne, Kathy, Head, Ref, Weber State University, 2901 University Circle, Ogden, UT, 84408-2901. Tel: 801-626-6511. Fax: 801-626-7045. p. 2409

Payne, Kenna, Ch, National City Public Library, 1401 National City Blvd, National City, CA, 91950-4401. Tel: 619-336-4350. Fax: 619-336-4368. p. 193

Payne, Kevin, Br Mgr, Cuyahoga County Public Library, Brook Park Branch, 6155 Engle Rd, Brook Park, OH, 44142-2105. Tel: 216-267-5250. Fax: 216-267-3776. p. 1927

Payne, Kevin, Br Mgr, Cuyahoga County Public Library, Parma Heights Branch, 6206 Pearl Rd, Parma Heights, OH, 44130-3045. Tel: 440-884-2313. Fax: 440-884-2713. p. 1927

Payne, Lillian, ILL, Holmes County Public Library, 303 N J Harvey Etheridge, Bonifay, FL, 32425. Tel: 850-547-3573. Fax: 850-547-2801. p. 429

Payne, Margot, Dir, Commun Relations, Putnam County Public Library, 103 E Poplar St, Greencastle, IN, 46135-1655. Tel: 765-653-2755. Fax: 765-653-2756. p. 746

Payne, Pamela, ILL, Huntsville-Madison Public Library, 915 Monroe St, Huntsville, AL, 35801. Tel: 256-532-5940. Fax: 256-532-5997. p. 21

Payne, Patricia, Dir, Lesley University, 89 Brattle St, Cambridge, MA, 02138-2790. Tel: 617-349-8840. Fax: 617-349-8849. p. 1077

Payne, Rene M, Image Archivist, Denver Museum of Nature & Science, 2001 Colorado Blvd, Denver, CO, 80205-5798. Tel: 303-370-8250. Fax: 303-331-6492. p. 300

Payne, Renee, Libr Supvr, Thomas Branigan Memorial Library, 200 E Picacho Ave, Las Cruces, NM, 88001-3499. Tel: 575-528-4017. Fax: 575-528-4030. p. 1557

Payne, Robert, Asst Tech Serv Librn, Beth Israel Medical Center, 317 E 17th, New York, NY, 10003. Tel: 212-420-2855. Fax: 212-420-4640. p. 1670

Payne, William, Ref Librn, San Diego State University, 720 Heber Ave, Calexico, CA, 92231-0550. Tel: 760-768-5626. Fax: 760-768-5525. p. 131

Payne, Yadira, Govt Info Librn, Augusta State University, 2500 Walton Way, Augusta, GA, 30904-2200. Tel: 706-737-1745. Fax: 706-667-4415. p. 518

Payne-Goodridge, Henrietta, Ref Librn, Atlanta-Fulton Public Library System, Auburn Avenue Research Library on African-American Culture & History, 101 Auburn Ave NE, Atlanta, GA, 30303. Tel: 404-730-4001, Ext 199. Fax: 404-730-5879. p. 511

Paynter, Marion, Mgr, Charlotte Observer Newsroom Library, 600 S Tryon, Charlotte, NC, 28202. Tel: 704-358-5212. Fax: 704-358-5203. p. 1782

Payonk, Karen, Asst Dir, Ch, Lititz Public Library, 651 Kissel Hill Rd, Lititz, PA, 17543. Tel: 717-626-2255. Fax: 717-627-4191. p. 2082

Payson, Tiina, Mgr, Edmonton Public Library, Woodcroft, 13420 114th Ave, Edmonton, AB, T5M 2Y5, CANADA. Tel: 780-496-6894. Fax: 780-496-7089. p. 2700

Payton, Anne M, Dr, Dir, Fort Valley State University, 1005 State University Dr, Fort Valley, GA, 31030-4313. Tel: 478-825-6343. Fax: 478-825-6663, 478-825-6916. p. 533

Payton, Erin, Sr Librn, Central Piedmont Community College Library, 1201 Elizabeth Ave, Charlotte, NC, 28235. Tel: 704-330-6814. Fax: 704-330-6887. p. 1781

Payton, Evelyn, Ref, Bracebridge Public Library, 94 Manitoba St, Bracebridge, ON, P1L 2B5, CANADA. Tel: 705-645-4171. Fax: 705-645-6551. p. 2796

Payton, Glenn, Librn, Aero Systems Engineering Inc Library, 358 E Fillmore Ave, Saint Paul, MN, 55107. Tel: 651-220-1209. Fax: 651-227-0519. p. 1277

Payton, Mary, Dir, Maquon Public Library District, 210 Main St, Maquon, IL, 61458-0230. Tel: 309-875-3573. Fax: 309-875-3573. p. 670

Payton, Renee, Librn, Missouri Department of Corrections, Missouri Eastern Correctional Center, 18701 US Hwy 66, Pacific, MO, 63069-3525. Tel: 636-257-3322, Ext 219. Fax: 636-257-5296. p. 1334

Paz, Susan, Asst Dean, Finance & Admin, University of North Texas Libraries, PO Box 305190, Denton, TX, 76203-5190. Tel: 940-369-8165. Fax: 940-369-8760. p. 2313

Pazienza, Lois, Asst Librn, Metascience Foundation Library, PO Box 32, Kingston, RI, 02881-0032. Tel: 401-294-2414. Fax: 401-294-8429. p. 2167

Pazour, Kevin Matthew, Exec Dir, Historical Society of Porter County, 153 S Franklin St, Valparaiso, IN, 46383. Tel: 219-465-3595. Fax: 219-462-2640. p. 783

Peabody, Linda, Archivist, Pub Serv, San Joaquin Delta College, 5151 Pacific Ave, Stockton, CA, 95207-6370. Tel: 209-954-5147. Fax: 209-954-5691. p. 272

Peach, Amanda, Instrul Serv Librn, Berea College, 100 Campus Dr, Berea, KY, 40404. Tel: 859-985-3279. Fax: 859-985-3912. p. 907

Peach, Brenda, Tech Serv, College of the North Atlantic, Carbonear Campus Resource Center, Four Pikes Lane, Carbonear, NL, A1Y 1A7, CANADA. Tel: 709-596-8940. Fax: 709-596-2688. p. 2771

Peach, Cindy, Circ Mgr, Fowlerville District Library, 131 Mill St, Fowlerville, MI, 48836. Tel: 517-223-9089. Fax: 517-223-0781. p. 1181

Peach, Larry, Dr, Dean, Tennessee Technological University, College of Education - Dept of Curriculum & Instruction, PO Box 5042, Cookeville, TN, 38505. Tel: 931-372-3181. Fax: 931-372-6270. p. 2974

Peacock, Cathy, Asst Librn, Kenora Public Library, 24 Main St S, Kenora, ON, P9N 1S7, CANADA. Tel: 807-467-2081. Fax: 807-467-2085. p. 2812

Peacock, Diane, Supvr, Haliburton County Public Library, Minden Branch, 176 Bobcaygeon Rd, Minden, ON, K0M 2K0, CANADA. Tel: 705-286-2491. p. 2808

Peacock, Gary, Ref Librn, Luzerne County Community College Library, 1333 S Prospect St, Nanticoke, PA, 18634-3899. Tel: 800-377-5222, Ext 7424. Fax: 570-735-6130. p. 2094

Peacock, Hannah, Ch, Head, Youth Serv, Burnham Memorial Library, 898 Main St, Colchester, VT, 05446. Tel: 802-879-7576. Fax: 802-879-5079. p. 2422

Peacock, Joyce, Ref Librn, Cypress College Library, 9200 Valley View St, Cypress, CA, 90630-5897. Tel: 714-484-7068. Fax: 714-826-6723. p. 138

Peacock, Roberta, Dir, C E Weldon Public Library, 100 Main St, Martin, TN, 38237-2445. Tel: 731-587-3148. Fax: 731-587-4674. p. 2246

Peacock, Sharon, Librn, Trafford Community Public Library, 416 Brinton Ave, Trafford, PA, 15085. Tel: 412-372-5115. Fax: 412-372-0993. p. 2146

Peak, Caroline, Br Mgr, Cleveland Public Library, Collinwood, 856 E 152nd St, Cleveland, OH, 44110. Tel: 216-623-6934. Fax: 216-623-6936. p. 1878

Peak, Denise, Libr Tech, Providence Saint Joseph Medical Center, 501 S Buena Vista St, Burbank, CA, 91505-4866. Tel: 818-847-3822. Fax: 818-847-3823. p. 130

Peak, Tina M, Dir, Lake Wales Public Library, 290 Cypress Garden Lane, Lake Wales, FL, 33853. Tel: 863-678-4004. Fax: 863-678-4051. p. 458

Peake, Beryle, Librn, Wapiti Regional Library, Leask Public Library, First Ave RM Office Complex, Leask, SK, S0J 1M0, CANADA. Tel: 306-466-4577. p. 2921

Peake, Connie, Libm, Wapiti Regional Library, Leask Public Library, First Ave RM Office Complex, Leask, SK, S0J 1M0, CANADA. Tel: 306-466-4577. p. 2921

Peake, Erica, Syst Mgr, Kershaw County Library, 1304 Broad St, Camden, SC, 29020-3595. Tel: 803-425-1508. Fax: 803-425-7180. p. 2182

Peake, Kim, Dir, Youth Serv, Grande Prairie Public Library District, 3479 W 183rd St, Hazel Crest, IL, 60429. Tel: 708-798-5563. Fax: 708-798-5874. p. 654

Pealer, Carla, Cataloger, Syst Librn, Oregon Health & Science University Library, 3181 SW Sam Jackson Park Rd, Portland, OR, 97239-3098. Tel: 503-494-5114. Fax: 503-494-3227. p. 2013

Pearce, Ann, Librn, North Central Kansas Libraries System, Subregional Talking Books, Manhattan Public Library, 629 Poyntz Ave, Manhattan, KS, 66502-6131. Tel: 785-776-4741, Ext 143. Fax: 785-776-1545. p. 882

Pearce, Ann, Libr Serv Mgr, McMaster University Library, Innis Business Library, Kenneth Taylor Hall, 1280 Main St W, Rm 108, Hamilton, ON, L8S 4M4, CANADA. Tel: 905-525-9140, Ext 22081. Fax: 905-524-0816. p. 2810

Pearce, Charlie, State Librn, State of Mississippi Judiciary, Carroll Gartin Justice Bldg, 450 High St, Jackson, MS, 39201. Tel: 601-359-3672. Fax: 601-359-2912. p. 1305

Pearce, Deborah, Librn, Lakeland Library Region, Meota Branch, Box 214, Meota, SK, S0M 1X0, CANADA. Tel: 306-892-2004. Fax: 306-892-2004. p. 2920

Pearce, Eileen, Adult Serv, Windsor Locks Public Library, 28 Main St, Windsor Locks, CT, 06096. Tel: 860-627-1495. Fax: 860-627-1496. p. 379

Pearce, Kate, Br Mgr, Granville County Library System, South, 1547 S Campus Dr, Creedmoor, NC, 27522-7381. Tel: 919-528-1752. Fax: 919-528-1752. p. 1814

Pearce, Tim, Dir, Campus Serv & Libr Res Ctr, Lambton College, 1457 London Rd, Sarnia, ON, N7S 6K4, CANADA. Tel: 519-541-2441. Fax: 519-541-2426. p. 2839

Pearl, Glenn, Head, Ser, Ref Librn, Southeastern University, 1000 Longfellow Blvd, Lakeland, FL, 33801. Tel: 863-667-5089. Fax: 863-669-4160. p. 460

Pearlman, Eden, Dir, Evanston History Center Library & Archives, 225 Greenwood St, Evanston, IL, 60201. Tel: 847-475-3410. Fax: 847-475-3599. p. 643

Pearlman, Nancy, Exec Dir, Educational Communications, Inc, PO Box 351419, Los Angeles, CA, 90035-9119. Tel: 213-705-4992. Fax: 310-559-9160. p. 170

Pearlman, Stefanie, Ref, University of Nebraska-Lincoln, Marvin & Virginia Schmid Law Library, 40 Fair St, Lincoln, NE, 68583. Tel: 402-472-3547. Fax: 402-472-8260. p. 1407

Pearman, Freda, Circ, Dundee Public Library, 202 E Main St, Dundee, FL, 33838. Tel: 863-439-9424. Fax: 863-439-9426. p. 438

Pearsall, Patrice, Tech Serv, Algonquin Area Public Library District, 2600 Harnish Dr, Algonquin, IL, 60102-5900. Tel: 847-458-6060, 847-658-4343. Fax: 847-458-9370. p. 588

Pearson, Andrew, Dir, Bridgewater College, 402 E College St, Bridgewater, VA, 22812. Tel: 540-828-5410. Fax: 540-828-5482. p. 2452

Pearson, Anna, ILL, A K Smiley Public Library, 125 W Vine St, Redlands, CA, 92373. Tel: 909-798-7565. Fax: 909-798-7566. p. 215

Pearson, Barbara, Dir, Altadena Library District, 600 E Mariposa St, Altadena, CA, 91001. Tel: 626-798-0833. Fax: 626-798-5351. p. 120

Pearson, Cathy, Pub Serv, Marlboro County Library, 200 John Corry Rd, Bennettsville, SC, 29512. Tel: 843-479-5630. Fax: 843-479-5645. p. 2182

Pearson, Charla, Tech Serv, Maud Preston Palenske Memorial Library, 500 Market St, Saint Joseph, MI, 49085. Tel: 269-983-7167. Fax: 269-983-5804. p. 1225

Pearson, Cheryl, Dir, Kettleson Memorial Library, 320 Harbor Dr, Sitka, AK, 99835-7553. Tel: 907-747-8708. Fax: 907-747-8755. p. 53

Pearson, David, Curator, Columbia River Maritime Museum Library, 1792 Marine Dr, Astoria, OR, 97103. Tel: 503-325-2323. Fax: 503-325-2331. p. 1990

Pearson, Debra, Circ, ILL, University of Nebraska-Lincoln, 1248 R St, Lincoln, NE, 68588-4100. Tel: 402-472-2526. p. 1407

Pearson, Drew, Br Mgr, Public Library of Cincinnati & Hamilton County, Bond Hill, 1740 Langdon Farm Rd at Jordan Crossing, Cincinnati, OH, 45237. Tel: 513-369-4445. Fax: 513-369-4532. p. 1871

Pearson, Elizabeth, Ch Mgr, Miami-Dade Public Library System, 101 W Flagler St, Miami, FL, 33130-1523. Tel: 305-375-5021. Fax: 305-375-3048. p. 466

Pearson, Elizabeth, Asst Dir, Marian College, 3200 Cold Spring Rd, Indianapolis, IN, 46222. Tel: 317-955-6223. Fax: 317-955-6418. p. 755

Pearson, Elizabeth, Dir, Montreat College, 310 Gaither Circle, Montreat, NC, 28757. Tel: 828-669-8012, Ext 3502. Fax: 828-350-2083. p. 1810

Pearson, Frederic, Dep Librn, Cook County Law Library, 2900 Richard J Daley Ctr, 50 W Washington, Chicago, IL, 60602. Tel: 312-603-2416. Fax: 312-603-4716. p. 611

Pearson, George, Ref Librn, Florida International University, 3000 NE 151st St, North Miami, FL, 33181-3600. Tel: 305-919-5272. Fax: 305-919-5914. p. 472

Pearson, James A, Info Syst Mgr, Chesapeake Public Library, 298 Cedar Rd, Chesapeake, VA, 23322-5512. Tel: 757-410-7101, 757-410-7104. Fax: 757-410-7175. p. 2456

Pearson, Jeffrey, Head of Libr, University of Michigan, Askwith Media Library, Shapiro Library, Rm 2002, 919 S University Ave, Ann Arbor, MI, 48109-1185. Tel: 734-763-3758. Fax: 734-764-7087. p. 1153

Pearson, Jo, Asst Dir, Marion Public Library, 1095 Sixth Ave, Marion, IA, 52302. Tel: 319-377-3412. Fax: 319-377-0113. p. 830

Pearson, Joanne, Ch, Berkshire Athenaeum, One Wendell Ave, Pittsfield, MA, 01201-6385. Tel: 413-499-9480. Fax: 413-499-9489. p. 1117

Pearson, John, Librn, Darby Free Library, 1001 Main St, Darby, PA, 19023-0169. Tel: 610-586-7310. Fax: 610-586-2781. p. 2049

Pearson, Joyce, Dir, University of Kansas Libraries, Wheat Law Library, Green Hall, Rm 200, 1535 W 15th St, Lawrence, KS, 66045-7608. Tel: 785-864-3025. Fax: 785-864-3680. p. 878

Pearson, Judy, Dir, Grantsburg Public Library, 415 S Robert St, Grantsburg, WI, 54840-7423. Tel: 715-463-2244. Fax: 715-463-5555. p. 2595

Pearson, Julie, Cat Librn, Carlsbad Public Library, 101 S Halagueno St, Carlsbad, NM, 88220. Tel: 575-885-6776. Fax: 575-887-7706. p. 1552

Pearson, Lisa E, Interim Libr Supvr, Harvard Library, Arnold Arboretum Horticultural Library, 125 Arborway, Jamaica Plain, MA, 02130. Tel: 617-522-1086. Fax: 617-524-1418. p. 1074

Pearson, Lynnanne, Reader Serv, Skokie Public Library, 5215 Oakton St, Skokie, IL, 60077-3680. Tel: 847-673-7774. Fax: 847-673-7797. p. 703

Pearson, Peggy, Librn, Northwest Regional Library, Hallock Public Library, 163 Third St S, Hallock, MN, 56728. Tel: 218-843-2401. Fax: 218-843-2401. p. 1286

Pearson, Peggy, Librn, Northwest Regional Library, Karlstad Satellite, 104 - 1st South, Ste 4, Karlstad, MN, 56732. Tel: 218-436-7323. p. 1286

Pearson, Robbie, In Charge, Cobre Valley Community Hospital, 5880 S Hospital Dr, Globe, AZ, 85501. Tel: 928-425-3261, Ext 1195. Fax: 928-425-7903. p. 64

Pearson, Shamika, Libr Assoc/Teen Serv, Coweta Public Library System, 85 Literary Lane, Newnan, GA, 30265. Tel: 770-683-2052. Fax: 770-683-0065. p. 546

Pearson, Stacy, Media Spec, Allen County Public Library, 900 Library Plaza, Fort Wayne, IN, 46802. Tel: 260-421-1211. Fax: 260-421-1386. p. 740

Pearson, Tracey, Dir, Libr Serv, Methodist College, 5400 Ramsey St, Fayetteville, NC, 28311. Tel: 910-630-7587. Fax: 910-630-7119. p. 1793

Pearson, Wanda L, Dir, Brownsburg Public Library, 450 S Jefferson St, Brownsburg, IN, 46112-1310. Tel: 317-852-3167. Fax: 317-858-2382. p. 730

Pearson, Warren, Fac Mgr, Cambridge Public Library, 449 Broadway, Cambridge, MA, 02138. Tel: 617-349-4040. Fax: 617-349-4028. p. 1073

Peart, G, Dr, Dir, Livingstone College, 701 W Monroe St, Salisbury, NC, 28144. Tel: 704-216-6029. Fax: 704-216-6798. p. 1822

Pease, Janet, Librn, Syracuse University Library, Carnegie Library, Carnegie Bldg, Syracuse, NY, 13244-2010. Tel: 315-443-9768. Fax: 315-443-5549. p. 1754

Pease, Karen, Br Head, Muskegon Area District Library, Muskegon Heights Branch, 2808 Sanford St, Muskegon Heights, MI, 49444-2010. Tel: 231-739-6075. Fax: 231-737-6307. p. 1213

Pease, Kenneth, Adult Serv, Malden Public Library, 36 Salem St, Malden, MA, 02148-5291. Tel: 781-324-0218. Fax: 781-324-4467. p. 1102

Pease, Mina, Librn, Library of the Legal Aid Society of Westchester County, One N Broadway, Ste 910, White Plains, NY, 10601-2352. Tel: 914-286-3400. Fax: 914-682-4112. p. 1768

Pease, Renee, Ch, Welles-Turner Memorial Library, 2407 Main St, Glastonbury, CT, 06033. Tel: 860-652-7725. Fax: 860-652-7721. p. 340

Pease, Sallie, Ch, Waterloo-Grant Township Public Library, 300 S Wayne St, Waterloo, IN, 46793-0707. Tel: 260-837-4491. Fax: 260-837-9148. p. 786

Peaster, Carol, Curator, Mississippi Museum of Art, 201 E Pascagoula, Jackson, MS, 39201. Tel: 601-960-1515. Fax: 601-960-1505. p. 1305

Peaster, Max C, Dir, Erie County Law Library, Court House, Rm 01, 140 W Sixth St, Erie, PA, 16501. Tel: 814-451-6319. Fax: 814-451-6320. p. 2055

Peavy, Kristina, Pub Serv Librn, Wesleyan College, 4760 Forsyth Rd, Macon, GA, 31210-4462. Tel: 478-757-5204. Fax: 478-757-3898. p. 541

Peavy, Shirley, In Charge, URS Corporation, 1375 Euclid Ave, Ste 600, Cleveland, OH, 44115-1808. Tel: 216-622-2400. Fax: 216-622-2428. p. 1881

Peay, Wayne J, Dir, University of Utah, Spencer S Eccles Health Sciences Library, Bldg 589, 10 N 1900 E, Salt Lake City, UT, 84112-5890. Tel: 801-581-8771. Fax: 801-581-3632. p. 2415

Peay, Wayne J, Dir, National Network of Libraries of Medicine Midcontinental Region, Univ Utah, Spencer S Eccles Health Sci Libr, Bldg 589, Ten N 1900 E, Salt Lake City, UT, 84112-5890. Tel: 801-587-3412. Fax: 801-581-3632. p. 2956

Pec, Steve, Librn, Greene County Historical Society, 90 County Rd 42, Coxsackie, NY, 12051-3022. Tel: 518-731-1033, 518-731-6822. p. 1612

Pecho, Isaias, Librn, Commonwealth of Puerto Rico, 254 Tetuan & Cruz Sts, San Juan, PR, 00902. Tel: 787-725-9420, Ext 2139. Fax: 787-721-8329. p. 2675

Pecht, Forrest, Librn, US Architectural & Transportation Barriers Compliance Board, 1331 F St NW, Ste 1000, Washington, DC, 20004-1111. Tel: 202-272-0080. Fax: 202-272-0081. p. 421

Pecht, Lee, Head, Spec Coll & Archives, Rice University, 6100 Main, MS-44, Houston, TX, 77005. Tel: 713-348-2120. Fax: 713-348-5258. p. 2341

Peck, Benjamin, Access Serv Librn, Connecticut College, 270 Mohegan Ave, New London, CT, 06320-4196. Tel: 860-439-2650. Fax: 860-439-2871. p. 359

Peck, Brian M, Tech Librn & Indexer, North Carolina Legislative Library, 500 Legislative Office Bldg, 300 N Salisbury St, Raleigh, NC, 27603-5925. Tel: 919-733-9390. Fax: 919-715-5460. p. 1815

Peck, Christina, Mgr, Access Serv, Arizona State University Libraries, Fletcher Library, 4701 W Thunderbird Rd, Glendale, AZ, 85306. Tel: 602-543-5718. Fax: 602-543-8540. p. 83

Peck, Christine, Libr Mgr, Timberland Regional Library, Aberdeen Branch, 121 E Market St, Aberdeen, WA, 98520-5292. Tel: 360-533-2360. Fax: 360-533-9771. p. 2543

Peck, Cynthia, Asst Librn, ILL, Sam Fore Jr Wilson County Public Library, One Library Lane, Floresville, TX, 78114. Tel: 830-393-7361. Fax: 830-393-7337. p. 2319

Peck, Jane, Asst Dir, Framingham Public Library, 49 Lexington St, Framingham, MA, 01702-8278. Tel: 508-532-5570. Fax: 508-820-7210. p. 1090

Peck, Jane, Br Mgr, Framingham Public Library, Christa Corrigan McAuliffe Branch, Ten Nicholas Rd, Framingham, MA, 01701-3469. Tel: 508-532-5636. Fax: 508-788-1930. p. 1090

Peck, Judi, Human Res Mgr, Maricopa County Library District, 2700 N Central Ave, Ste 700, Phoenix, AZ, 85004. Tel: 602-652-3033. Fax: 602-652-3078. p. 74

Peck, Mona, Asst Librn, Lane County Library, 144 South Lane, Dighton, KS, 67839. Tel: 620-397-2808. Fax: 620-397-5937. p. 863

Peck, Parkie, Br Mgr, Saint Louis County Library, Natural Bridge Branch, 7606 Natural Bridge Rd, Saint Louis, MO, 63121. Tel: 314-382-3116. p. 1359

Peckar, Rissa, Libr Dir, Cadwalader, Wickersham & Taft Library, One World Financial Ctr, New York, NY, 10281. Tel: 212-504-6767. Fax: 212-993-3351. p. 1671

Peckham, Courtney Ellis, Archivist, Coll Develop, Curator, Essex Historical Society & Shipbuilding Museum, Inc, 28 Main St, Essex, MA, 01929. Tel: 978-768-3866. Fax: 978-768-2541. p. 1087

Peconie, Ann, Dir, Walter Elwood Museum Library, 366 W Main St, Amsterdam, NY, 12010-2228. Tel: 518-843-5151. Fax: 518-843-6098. p. 1574

Pecora, James, Chief Tech Officer, Free Library of Philadelphia, 1901 Vine St, Philadelphia, PA, 19103-1189. Tel: 215-686-5322. Fax: 215-563-3628. p. 2106

Pecoraro, John, Asst Dir, Manhattan Public Library, 629 Poyntz Ave, Manhattan, KS, 66502-6086. Tel: 785-776-4741. Fax: 785-776-1545. p. 881

Pecoraro, John, Coordr, Big Country Library System, 202 Cedar St, Abilene, TX, 79601-5793. Tel: 325-676-6021. Fax: 325-676-6028. p. 2272

Pecoskie, Jennifer, Dr, Asst Prof, Wayne State University, 106 Kresge Library, Detroit, MI, 48202. Tel: 313-577-1825. Fax: 313-577-7563. p. 2968

Pecquet, Christian, Planning & Develop Librn, Syst Analyst, Bibliothèques de Montrèal, 801, rue Brennan, 5e Etage, Bureau 5206, Montreal, QC, H3C 0G4, CANADA. Tel: 514-872-2741. Fax: 514-872-0530. p. 2889

Peda, Erma Rose, Dir, Sweet Home Public Library, 1101 13th Ave, Sweet Home, OR, 97386-2197. Tel: 541-367-5007. Fax: 541-367-3754. p. 2020

Peddle, Patricia, Librn, Burin Public Library, Rte 220, Burin Bay Arm, NL, A0E 1G0, CANADA. Tel: 709-891-1924. Fax: 709-891-1924. p. 2769

Peden, Brenda, ILL, Normal Public Library, 206 W College Ave, Normal, IL, 61761. Tel: 309-452-1757. Fax: 309-452-5312. p. 681

Pedersen, Barbara, Youth Serv Coordr, Ericson Public Library, 702 Greene St, Boone, IA, 50036. Tel: 515-432-3727. Fax: 515-432-1103. p. 797

Pedersen, Emily, Br Librn, Grand County Library District, Kremmling Branch, 300 S Eighth St, Kremmling, CO, 80459. Tel: 970-724-9228. Fax: 970-724-3419. p. 310

Pedersen, Krista, Ch, Bay County Library System, 500 Center Ave, Bay City, MI, 48708. Tel: 989-894-2837. Fax: 989-894-2021. p. 1155

Pedersen, Lila, Dir, University of North Dakota, School of Medicine and Health Sciences, 501 N Columbia Rd, Stop 9002, Grand Forks, ND, 58202-9002. Tel: 701-777-3993. Fax: 701-777-4790. p. 1842

Pedersen, Sue, Dir, Alta Community Library, 1009 Main St, Alta, IA, 51002. Tel: 712-200-1250. p. 792

Pedersen, Wayne, Acq, Doc Delivery, ILL, Iowa State University Library, 302 Parks Library, Ames, IA, 50011-2140. Tel: 515-294-1442, 515-294-1443. Fax: 515-294-5525. p. 793

Pedersen-Faria, Sarah, Children's Prog Dir, Cumston Public Library, 796 Main St, Monmouth, ME, 04259. Tel: 207-933-4788. Fax: 207-933-3413. p. 992

Pederson, Ann, Dir, Altru Health System, 1200 S Columbia Rd, Grand Forks, ND, 58201. Tel: 701-780-5186. Fax: 701-780-5772. p. 1842

Pederson, Jane, Asst City Librn, Beresford Public Library, 115 S Third St, Beresford, SD, 57004-1798. Tel: 605-763-2782. Fax: 605-763-2403. p. 2210

Pederson, Martha, Asst Librn, North Conway Public Library, 2719 White Mountain Hwy, North Conway, NH, 03860. Tel: 603-356-2961. p. 1460

Pederson, Randy, Head, Syst, University of North Dakota, 3051 University Ave, Stop 9000, Grand Forks, ND, 58202-9000. Tel: 701-777-4643. Fax: 701-777-3319. p. 1843

Pedi, Mario, Fr, Librn, Marmion Academy Library, 1000 Butterfield Rd, Aurora, IL, 60504-9742. Tel: 630-897-6936. Fax: 630-897-7086. p. 592

Pedraza, Ellen, Ref Serv, Gateway Technical College, 3520 30th Ave, Kenosha, WI, 53144-1690. Tel: 262-564-2786. Fax: 262-564-2787. p. 2601

Pedri, Lynne, Dir, Hurley Public Library, 405 Fifth Ave N, Hurley, WI, 54534-1170. Tel: 715-561-5707. Fax: 715-561-3222. p. 2599

Pedroja, Virginia, Dir, Madison Public Library, 110 S First St, Madison, KS, 66860. Tel: 620-437-2634. Fax: 620-437-2631. p. 881

Pedrosian, Annette, Music Librn, Occidental College Library, 1600 Campus Rd, Los Angeles, CA, 90041. Tel: 323-259-2942. Fax: 323-341-4991. p. 176

Pedroza, Edward, Br Supvr, Colton Public Library, Luque Branch, 294 East O St, Colton, CA, 92324. Tel: 909-370-5189. Fax: 909-370-5182. p. 135

Pedroza, Edward, Libr Dir, Colton Public Library, 656 N Ninth St, Colton, CA, 92324. Tel: 909-370-5189. p. 135

Pedzich, Joan, Dir, Libr Serv, Harris, Beach PLLC, 99 Garnsey Rd, Pittsford, NY, 14534. Tel: 585-419-8800, Ext 8917. Fax: 585-419-8814. p. 1718

Peebles, Margaret, Dir, Br Serv, Gail Borden Public Library District, 270 N Grove Ave, Elgin, IL, 60120-5596. Tel: 847-931-2091. Fax: 847-531-7367. p. 640

Peek, Robin, Assoc Prof, Simmons College, 300 The Fenway, Boston, MA, 02115. Tel: 617-521-2800. Fax: 617-521-3192. p. 2967

Peel, Carol, Children's Prog, Luther Area Public Library, 115 State St, Luther, MI, 49656. Tel: 231-797-8006. Fax: 231-797-8010. p. 1204

Peel, Nan, Dir, Center Moriches Free Public Library, 235 Main St, Center Moriches, NY, 11934. Tel: 631-878-0940. p. 1604

Peeler, Dana, Asst Dir, Ohoopee Regional Library System, 610 Jackson St, Vidalia, GA, 30474-2835. Tel: 912-537-9283. Fax: 912-537-3735. p. 555

Peeling, Mary Alice, Tech Serv, Widener University, School of Law Library, 4601 Concord Pike, Wilmington, DE, 19803. Tel: 302-477-2115. Fax: 302-477-2240. p. 389

Peeling, Paul, Mgr, Info Tech & Media Serv, Towson University, 8000 York Rd, Towson, MD, 21252-0001. Tel: 410-704-4895. Fax: 410-704-5246. p. 1045

Peelle-Haddeman, Linda, Br Coordr, Willows Public Library, Bayliss, 7830 Rd 39, Glenn, CA, 95943. Tel: 530-934-2287. p. 284

Peeples, David, Librn & Coordr, Echols & Lanier County Libr, South Georgia Regional Library System, Lakeland Branch, 18 S Valdosta Rd, Lakeland, GA, 31635. Tel: 229-482-2904. Fax: 229-482-1177. p. 555

Peeples, David, Managing Librn, South Georgia Regional Library System, 300 Woodrow Wilson Dr, Valdosta, GA, 31602-2592. Tel: 229-333-0086. Fax: 229-333-7669. p. 555

Peeples, Jacqueline, Libr Spec, Hobbs Public Library, 509 N Shipp, Hobbs, NM, 88240. Tel: 575-397-9328. Fax: 575-397-1508. p. 1556

Peeples, Pam, Libr Mgr, Saint Dominic-Jackson Memorial Hospital, 969 Lakeland Dr, Jackson, MS, 39216. Tel: 601-200-6944. Fax: 601-200-8075. p. 1305

Peeples, Stacey C, Archivist, Pennsylvania Hospital, Historic Library, Three Pine Ctr, 800 Spruce St, Philadelphia, PA, 19107-6192. Tel: 215-829-5434. Fax: 215-829-7155. p. 2113

Peer, Jeanne T, Head, Tech Serv, Westfield Athenaeum, Six Elm St, Westfield, MA, 01085-2997. Tel: 413-568-7833, Ext 7. Fax: 413-568-0988. p. 1138

Peercy, Lisa, Dir, Human Res, Akron-Summit County Public Library, 60 S High St, Akron, OH, 44326. Tel: 330-643-9106. Fax: 330-643-9160. p. 1852

Peers, Kevin, Ref Librn, Bellarmine University, 2001 Newburg Rd, Louisville, KY, 40205-0671. Tel: 502-272-8315. Fax: 502-272-8038. p. 923

Peery, Ian, Automation & Tech Serv Mgr, Glenside Public Library District, 25 E Fullerton Ave, Glendale Heights, IL, 60139-2697. Tel: 630-260-1550. Fax: 630-260-1433. p. 650

Peevyhouse, Janice, Dir, Newbern City Library, 220 E Main St, Newbern, TN, 38059-1528. Tel: 731-627-3153. Fax: 731-627-3129. p. 2261

Pegg, Chris, Digital Learning Libr Serv, Augsburg College, 2211 Riverside Ave, Minneapolis, MN, 55454. Tel: 612-330-1604. Fax: 612-330-1436. p. 1259

Pegg, Paris, Dir, Wayne Township Library, 80 N Sixth St, Richmond, IN, 47374-3079. Tel: 765-966-8291. Fax: 765-962-1318. p. 775

Pegg, Paris, Dir, Wayne Township Library, Wayne County Contractual Library, 80 N Sixth St, Richmond, IN, 47374. Tel: 765-966-8291. Fax: 765-962-1318. p. 775

Pegues, Wanda, Librn, Northwest Mississippi Community College, 5197 WE Ross Pkwy, Southaven, MS, 38671. Tel: 662-280-6164. Fax: 662-280-6161. p. 1315

Pehrson, Heather, Br Mgr, Saint Louis County Library, Mid-County Branch, 7821 Maryland Ave, Saint Louis, MO, 63105. Tel: 314-721-3008. p. 1359

Pei, Jingru, Commun Libr Mgr, Queens Borough Public Library, Woodside Community Library, 54-22 Skillman Ave, Woodside, NY, 11377. Tel: 718-429-4700. p. 1646

Pei, Marianne, Ref, Mamaroneck Public Library District, 136 Prospect Ave, Mamaroneck, NY, 10543. Tel: 914-698-1250. Fax: 914-381-3088. p. 1657

Peifer, Pamela, Asst Dir, Admin, Harvard Library, Harvard Law School Library, Langdell Hall, 1545 Massachusetts Ave, Cambridge, MA, 02138. Tel: 617-495-3170. Fax: 617-495-4449. p. 1075

Peiffer, Joan, Dir, Grove Family Library, 101 Ragged Edge Rd S, Chambersburg, PA, 17201. Tel: 717-264-9663. Fax: 717-264-6055. p. 2043

Peihl, Mark, Archivist, Historical & Cultural Society of Clay County, 202 First Ave N, Moorhead, MN, 56560-1985. Tel: 218-299-5511, Ext 6734. Fax: 218-299-5510. p. 1265

Peine, Kim, Info Tech, ILL, Ref & Instrul Serv Librn, Dorothy Alling Memorial Library, 21 Library Lane, Williston, VT, 05495. Tel: 802-878-4918. Fax: 802-878-3964. p. 2440

Peirce-Roalsen, Bonnie, Head, Ch, Dover Town Library, 56 Dedham St, Dover, MA, 02030-2214. Tel: 508-785-8113. Fax: 508-785-0138. p. 1085

Pekala, Greg, Dir, MacCormac College Library, 29 E Madison, 2nd Flr, Chicago, IL, 60602-4405. Tel: 312-922-1884, Ext 215. Fax: 312-377-7572. p. 618

Pekar, Paula Sue, Dir, Shiner Public Library, 115 E Wolters/Second St, Shiner, TX, 77984-0308. Tel: 361-594-3044. Fax: 361-594-4249. p. 2387

Peker, Amy, Dir, Castleton Public Library, 85 S Main St, Castleton-on-Hudson, NY, 12033. Tel: 518-732-0879. Fax: 518-732-0835. p. 1603

Peker, Svetlana, Ref Librn, West Orange Free Public Library, 46 Mount Pleasant Ave, West Orange, NJ, 07052-4903. Tel: 973-736-0198. Fax: 973-736-1655. p. 1541

Peladeau, Ginette, Librn, Plantagenet Village Library System, Alfred Branch, 330 Saint-Philippe St, Alfred, ON, K0B 1A0, CANADA. Tel: 613-679-2663. Fax: 613-679-2663. p. 2836

Pelak, Patricia, Dir, Little Falls Public Library, Eight Warren St, Little Falls, NJ, 07424. Tel: 973-256-2784. Fax: 973-256-6312. p. 1495

Pelavin, Susan, Youth Serv Librn, Oradell Free Public Library, 375 Kinderkamack Rd, Oradell, NJ, 07649-2122. Tel: 201-262-2613. Fax: 201-262-9112. p. 1516

Pelchat, Pat, Librn, Wapiti Regional Library, Shell Lake Public Library, Main St, Village Office, Shell Lake, SK, S0J 2G0, CANADA. Tel: 306-427-2272. p. 2922

Pelczynski, Tony, Circ, University of California, 200 McAllister St, San Francisco, CA, 94102-4978. Tel: 415-565-4757. Fax: 415-581-8849. p. 248

Pelepchuk, Anna, Head, Circ, Bloomfield Township Public Library, 1099 Lone Pine Rd, Bloomfield Township, MI, 48302-2410. Tel: 248-642-5800. Fax: 248-258-2555. p. 1159

Pelerin, Judith, Dir, Bibliotheque Municipale, 681 Commercial, Notre-Dame Du Lac, QC, G0L 1X0, CANADA. Tel: 418-899-6004. p. 2902

Peletich, Darcy, Librn, Kino Institute Diocesan Library, 400 E Monroe St, Phoenix, AZ, 85004-2336. Tel: 602-354-2311. p. 73

Pelfrey, Barbara, Dir, Harriman Public Library, 601 Walden St, Harriman, TN, 37748-2506. Tel: 865-882-3195. Fax: 865-882-3188. p. 2236

Pelfrey, Debbie, Dir, Graysville Public Library, 151 Mill St, Graysville, TN, 37338-5044. Tel: 423-775-0966. Fax: 423-775-6952. p. 2235

Pelham, Margy, Acq, Grangeville Centennial Library, 215 W North, Grangeville, ID, 83530-1729. Tel: 208-983-0951. Fax: 208-983-2336. p. 575

Pelish, Nora, Acq, Irondequoit Public Library, 45 Cooper Rd, Rochester, NY, 14617. Tel: 585-336-6062. Fax: 585-336-6066. p. 1729

Pelkey, Charley, Libr Tech, G Robert Cotton Regional Correctional Facility Library, 3500 N Elm Rd, Jackson, MI, 49201. Tel: 517-780-5172. Fax: 517-780-5100. p. 1195

Pelkey, Frank, Outreach Serv Librn, Crandall Public Library, 251 Glen St, Glens Falls, NY, 12801-3593. Tel: 518-792-6508. Fax: 518-792-5251. p. 1629

Pelkey, Lori, Br Mgr, Corvallis-Benton County Public Library, Monroe Community Library, 668 Commercial St, Monroe, OR, 97456. Tel: 541-847-5174. Fax: 541-847-5174. p. 1994

Pelky, Kymberley, Ch, Oneida Community Library, 201 Elm St, Oneida, WI, 54155. Tel: 920-869-2210. Fax: 920-869-1299. p. 2627

Pellack, Lorraine, Sci, Iowa State University Library, 302 Parks Library, Ames, IA, 50011-2140. Tel: 515-294-1442, 515-294-1443. Fax: 515-294-5525. p. 793

Pelle, Beth, Assoc Dir, Frederick County Public Libraries, 110 E Patrick St, Frederick, MD, 21701. Tel: 301-600-1613. Fax: 301-600-3789. p. 1028

Pellegrene, Tom, Mgr, News Tech, Journal Gazette Library, 600 W Main St, Fort Wayne, IN, 46802. Tel: 260-461-8377. Fax: 260-461-8648. p. 742

Pellegrini, Sally, Head, Commun Relations & Lovcal Hist, New City Free Library, 220 N Main St, New City, NY, 10956. Tel: 845-634-4997. p. 1664

Pellegrino, Catherine, Bibliog Instruction Coordr, Ref Librn, Saint Mary's College, Notre Dame, IN, 46556-5001. Tel: 574-284-5286. Fax: 574-284-4791. p. 771

Pellegrino, Jane, Dept Head, United States Navy, Bldg 1, 4th Flr, 620 John Paul Jones Circle, Portsmouth, VA, 23708-2197. Tel: 757-953-5530. Fax: 757-953-7533. p. 2485

Pellegrino, Roberto, ILL, Alberta Innovates-Technology Futures, 250 Karl Clark Rd, Edmonton, AB, T6N 134, CANADA. Tel: 780-450-5057. Fax: 780-450-8996. p. 2698

Pellegrino, Sue, Circ Supvr, North Carolina Wesleyan College, 3400 N Wesleyan Blvd, Rocky Mount, NC, 27804. Tel: 252-985-5350. Fax: 252-985-5235. p. 1821

Pellen, Rita, Assoc Dean, Florida Atlantic University, 777 Glades Rd, Boca Raton, FL, 33431. Tel: 561-297-3781. Fax: 561-297-2189. p. 428

Pellerin, Guylaine, Dir, Saint Lambert Municipal Library, 490 Mercille Ave, Saint Lambert, QC, J4P 2L5, CANADA. Tel: 450-466-3910. Fax: 450-923-6512. p. 2909

Pellerin, Guylaine, Dir, Saint Lambert Municipal Library, Preville, 120 de Poitou, Saint Lambert, QC, J4S 1E1, CANADA. Tel: 450-923-6510. p. 2909

Pellerin, Isabelle, Head Librn, Bibliothèques de Montrèal, Père-Ambroise, 2093, rue de la Visitation, Montreal, QC, H2L 3C9, CANADA. Tel: 514-872-9541. Fax: 514-872-1626. p. 2891

Pellerin, Marie-Claude, Acq of Monographs, Ser, Ministere des Ressources naturelles et de la Faune, 5700 4e Ave Ouest, B-201, Quebec, QC, G1H 6R1, CANADA. Tel: 418-627-8686, Ext 3545. Fax: 418-644-1124. p. 2906

Pelletier, Brenda, Ser, University of Maine at Fort Kent, 23 University Dr, Fort Kent, ME, 04743. Tel: 207-834-7523. Fax: 207-834-7518. p. 986

Pelletier, Carolee, Assoc Librn, North Shore Medical Center, Salem Hospital, 81 Highland Ave, Salem, MA, 01970. Tel: 978-354-4950. Fax: 978-744-9110. p. 1121

Pelletier, Colleen, Tech Serv, Plattsburgh Public Library, 19 Oak St, Plattsburgh, NY, 12901-2810. Tel: 518-563-0921. Fax: 518-563-1681. p. 1719

Pelletier, Daniel J, Dir, Kramer, Levin, Naftalis & Frankel LLP, 1177 Avenue of the Americas, New York, NY, 10036. Tel: 212-715-9321. Fax: 212-715-8000. p. 1684

Pelletier, Francine, Librn, Centre d'acces a l'Information Juridique-Bibliotheque de Quebec, 300 Boul Jean-Lesage, Palais de Justice Ste 503, Quebec, QC, G1K 8K6, CANADA. Tel: 418-525-0057. Fax: 418-525-4208. p. 2904

Pelletier, Francine, Librn, Cegep de Sherbrooke, 475 rue du Cegep, Sherbrooke, QC, J1E 4K1, CANADA. Tel: 819-564-6350, Ext 5231, 819-564-6350, Ext 5233. Fax: 819-564-4025. p. 2912

Pelletier, Gary, Libr Tech, Department of Veterans Affairs, Togus VA Medical Ctr, One VA Center, Augusta, ME, 04330. Tel: 207-623-5773. Fax: 207-623-5766. p. 974

Pelletier, Josee, Coordr, Access Serv, Coordr, Coll Develop, Coordr, Ref (Info Serv), Universite du Quebec a Rimouski - Bibliotheque, 300 Allee des Ursulines, Rimouski, QC, G5L 3A1, CANADA. Tel: 418-723-1986, Ext 1479. Fax: 418-724-1621. p. 2907

Pelletier, Lucie, Actg Adminr, Institut de Readaption Gingras-Lindsay-de-Montreal, 6300 Darlington Ave, Montreal, QC, H3S 2J4, CANADA. Tel: 514-340-2085, Ext 2270. Fax: 514-340-2716. p. 2896

Pelletier, Marie, Librn, Seminaire de Nicolet Library, 900 Blvd Louis Frechette, Bureau 110, Nicolet, QC, J3T 1V5, CANADA. Tel: 819-293-4838. Fax: 819-293-4543. p. 2902

Pelletier, Mary, Head, Ref, Somerset Public Library, 1464 County St, Somerset, MA, 02726. Tel: 508-646-2829. Fax: 508-646-2831. p. 1124

Pelletier, Michaela, Circ, Amesbury Public Library, 149 Main St, Amesbury, MA, 01913. Tel: 978-388-8148. p. 1048

Pelletier, Odette, Tech Serv, Bibliotheques de Trois-Rivieres, 1425 Place de l'Hotel de Ville, CP 1713, Trois-Rivieres, QC, G9A 5L9, CANADA. Tel: 819-372-4645. Fax: 819-693-1892. p. 2913

Pelletier, Paul, Govt Doc Librn, Worcester Public Library, Three Salem Sq, Worcester, MA, 01608. Tel: 508-799-1655. Fax: 508-799-1652. p. 1145

Pelletier, Sheryl, Libr Mgr, Sexsmith Shannon Municipal Library, 9917 99th Ave, Sexsmith, AB, T0H 3C0, CANADA. Tel: 780-568-4333. Fax: 780-568-7249. p. 2716

Pelletier, Sylvie, Dir, Bibliotheque Louis-Ange-Santerre, 500, ave Jolliet, Sept Iles, QC, G4R 2B4, CANADA. Tel: 418-964-3355. Fax: 418-964-3353. p. 2911

Pelletier, Wendy L, Librn, Moosilauke Public Library, 165 Lost River Rd, North Woodstock, NH, 03262. Tel: 603-745-9971. p. 1461

Pelley, Janet, Regional Dir, Colchester - East Hants Regional Library, 754 Prince St, Truro, NS, B2N 1G9, CANADA. Tel: 902-895-0235, 902-895-1625, 902-895-4183. Fax: 902-895-7149. p. 2785

Pellington, Mary Ellen, Dir, Octavia Fellin Public Library, 115 W Hill Ave, Gallup, NM, 87301. Tel: 505-863-1291. Fax: 505-722-5090. p. 1556

Pellman, Adam, Acq & Cat Librn, Seton Hill University, One Seton Hill Dr, Greensburg, PA, 15601. Tel: 724-838-2438. Fax: 724-838-4203. p. 2062

Pelloth, Patricia, Librn, West Woodstock Library, Five Bungay Hill Connector, Woodstock, CT, 06281. Tel: 860-974-0376. p. 380

Pells, Catherine, Br Mgr, Montgomery County Memorial Library System, South Branch, 2101 Lake Robbins Dr, The Woodlands, TX, 77380. Tel: 936-442-7727. Fax: 936-788-8372. p. 2301

Pelofsky, Barry, Libr Distribution Mgr, JBI International, 110 E 30th St, New York, NY, 10016. Tel: 212-889-2525. Fax: 212-689-3692. p. 1683

Peloquin, Margaret, Head Librn, Austin Community College, Eastview Campus Library, 3401 Webberville Rd, Austin, TX, 78702. Tel: 512-223-5117. Fax: 512-223-5111. p. 2278

Peltier, Janet, Circ Librn, Lincoln Public Library, 22 Church St, Lincoln, NH, 03251. Tel: 603-745-8159. Fax: 603-745-2037. p. 1454

Peltier, Nancy, Admin Mgr, Wilfrid Laurier University Library, 75 University Ave W, Waterloo, ON, N2L 3C5, CANADA. Tel: 519-884-0710, Ext 3642. Fax: 519-884-3209. p. 2869

Pelton, Barbara, In Charge, Saint Peter Regional Treatment Center Libraries, MSH Education Dept Library, 2100 Sheppard Dr, Saint Peter, MN, 56082. Tel: 507-985-2320. p. 1283

Peltz, Jessie, Librn, Public Library of Steubenville & Jefferson County, Adena Branch, 167 Hanna Ave, Adena, OH, 43901-7953. Tel: 740-546-3782. Fax: 740-546-3382. p. 1937

Peluso, Nancy, Govt Doc, Connecticut State Library, 231 Capitol Ave, Hartford, CT, 06106. Tel: 860-757-6599. Fax: 860-757-6503. p. 345

Pelyhes, Marlene, Info Tech Mgr, Mentor Public Library, 8215 Mentor Ave, Mentor, OH, 44060. Tel: 440-255-8811. Fax: 440-255-0520. p. 1917

Pelzmann, Lisa, In Charge, Northwest Atlantic Fisheries Organization Library, Two Morris Dr, Ste 100, Dartmouth, NS, B3B 1K8, CANADA. Tel: 902-468-5590. Fax: 902-468-5538. p. 2779

Pemberton, Becky, Librn, Minnesota Department of Corrections, 1000 Lake Shore Dr, Moose Lake, MN, 55767. Tel: 218-485-5000, Ext 5202. Fax: 218-485-5113. p. 1266

Pemberton, J Michael, Prof, University of Tennessee, Knoxville, 451 Communications Bldg, 1345 Circle Park Dr, Knoxville, TN, 37996-0341. Tel: 865-974-2148. Fax: 865-974-4967. p. 2974

Pemberton, Patrick, Supvr, Access Serv, National University Library, 9393 Lightwave Ave, San Diego, CA, 92123-1447. Tel: 858-541-7900. Fax: 858-541-7994. p. 232

Pemberton, Sara, Coordr, Ch Serv, Downers Grove Public Library, 1050 Curtiss St, Downers Grove, IL, 60515. Tel: 630-960-1200. Fax: 630-960-9374. p. 637

Pembroke, Judy, Tech Serv, Bennington Free Library, 101 Silver St, Bennington, VT, 05201. Tel: 802-442-9051. p. 2418

Pen, Emma F C, Dir, American Samoa Community College Library, Malaeimi Village, Malaeimi Rd, Mapusaga, AS, 96799. Tel: 684-699-5728. Fax: 684-699-5732. p. 2665

Pena, David, Dir, Palm Beach State College, 3160 PGA Blvd, Palm Beach Gardens, FL, 33410-2893. Tel: 561-207-5810. Fax: 561-207-5805. p. 479

Pena, Fernando, Librn, Grolier Club of New York Library, 47 E 60th St, New York, NY, 10022. Tel: 212-838-6690. Fax: 212-838-2445. p. 1680

Pena, Paula, Head, Circ, Warren-Newport Public Library District, 224 N O'Plaine Rd, Gurnee, IL, 60031. Tel: 847-244-5150, Ext 3024. Fax: 847-244-3499. p. 653

Pena, Sylvia, Dir, Kenedy Public Library, 303 W Main St, Kenedy, TX, 78119. Tel: 830-583-3313. Fax: 830-583-3270. p. 2349

Pence, Cheryl, Spec Coll Librn, Illinois Historic Preservation Agency, 112 N Sixth St, Springfield, IL, 62701. Tel: 217-785-7956. Fax: 217-785-6250. p. 705

Pencek, Elaine, Media Librn, Lackawanna College, 501 Vine St, Scranton, PA, 18509. Tel: 570-961-7875. Fax: 570-961-7817. p. 2137

Penco, Rita, Dir, Client Serv, Fraser Valley Regional Library, 34589 Delair Rd, Abbotsford, BC, V2S 5Y1, CANADA. Tel: 604-859-7141. Fax: 604-859-5701. p. 2723

Pendell, Kimberly, Soc Work & Soc Sci Librn, Portland State University Library, 1875 SW Park Ave, Portland, OR, 97201-3220. Tel: 503-725-4501. Fax: 503-725-4524. p. 2014

Pender, Constance, Mgr, University of South Carolina Sumter, 200 Miller Rd, Sumter, SC, 29150-2498. Tel: 803-775-8727. Fax: 803-938-3811. p. 2206

Pendergraft, Kim, Cat, Eastern Oklahoma State College Library, 1301 W Main St, Wilburton, OK, 74578. Tel: 918-465-1779. Fax: 918-465-0112. p. 1986

Pendergraft, Latoyah, Librn, Latimer County Public Library, 301 W Ada Ave, Wilburton, OK, 74578. Tel: 918-465-3751. Fax: 918-465-4287. p. 1986

Pendergraft, Maria, Librn, Prairie Grove Public Library, 123 S Neal St, Prairie Grove, AR, 72753. Tel: 479-846-3782. Fax: 479-846-3428. p. 113

Pendergrass, Andrew, Br Mgr, Fairfax County Public Library, Reston Regional, 11925 Bowman Towne Dr, Reston, VA, 20190-3311. Tel: 703-689-2700. p. 2461

Pendergrass, Darrell, Dir, Washburn Public Library, 307 Washington Ave, Washburn, WI, 54891-1165. Tel: 715-373-6172. Fax: 715-373-6186. p. 2644

Pendergrass, Linda, Sr Librn, Bloomfield Public Library, 90 Broad St, Bloomfield, NJ, 07003. Tel: 973-566-6200, Ext 225. Fax: 973-566-6217. p. 1473

Pendleton, Debbie, Asst Dir, Pub Serv, Alabama Department of Archives & History Research Room, 624 Washington Ave, Montgomery, AL, 36130-0100. Tel: 334-242-4435. Fax: 334-240-3433. p. 27

Pendleton, Jo, Ref Librn, McLennan Community College Library, 1400 College Dr, Waco, TX, 76708-1498. Tel: 254-299-8000. Fax: 254-299-8026. p. 2397

Pendleton, Kevin, Asst Dir, Weber County Library System, 2464 Jefferson Ave, Ogden, UT, 84401-2464. Tel: 801-337-2617. Fax: 801-337-2615. p. 2408

Pendleton, Kim, Electronic Serv, Per, Oceanside Public Library, 330 N Coast Hwy, Oceanside, CA, 92054-2824. Tel: 760-435-5583. Fax: 760-435-9614. p. 199

Pendleton, Laura, Circ Supvr, Oceanside Public Library, Mission Branch, 3861 B Mission Ave, Oceanside, CA, 92058. Tel: 760-435-5578. Fax: 760-433-6850. p. 200

Pendleton, Lynn P, Librn, Princeton Community Hospital Library, 122 12th St, Princeton, WV, 24740-2352. Tel: 304-487-7000, 304-487-7714. Fax: 304-487-7524. p. 2570

Pendleton, Mark, Adult Progs & Promotions Mgr, Thomas Branigan Memorial Library, 200 E Picacho Ave, Las Cruces, NM, 88001-3499. Tel: 575-528-4001. Fax: 575-528-4030. p. 1557

Pendleton, Nancy, Pub Serv, Cedar Park Public Library, 550 Discovery Blvd, Cedar Park, TX, 78613. Tel: 512-401-5640. Fax: 512-259-5236. p. 2296

Penegor, Barbara, Br Mgr, Kentucky Regional Library for the Blind & Physically Handicapped, 300 Coffee Tree Rd, Frankfort, KY, 40601. Tel: 502-564-8300, Ext 282. Fax: 502-564-5773. p. 914

Penfold, Anne, Circ Mgr, St Catharines Public Library, 54 Church St, St. Catharines, ON, L2R 7K2, CANADA. Tel: 905-688-6103, Ext 244. Fax: 905-688-6292. p. 2843

Penford Ferry, Barbara, Dir, National Geographic Society Library, Image Collection, 1145 17th St NW, Washington, DC, 20036. Tel: 202-857-7493. Fax: 202-429-5776. p. 410

Penhorwood, Jan, Pub Serv Librn, Kwantlen Polytechnic University Library, 12666 72 Ave., Surrey, BC, V3W 2M8, CANADA. Tel: 604-599-3236. Fax: 604-599-2106. p. 2738

Penick, Hal, Syst Coordr, Iowa City Public Library, 123 S Linn St, Iowa City, IA, 52240. Tel: 319-887-6035. Fax: 319-356-5494. p. 823

Penick, Patti, Youth Serv, Goffstown Public Library, Two High St, Goffstown, NH, 03045-1910. Tel: 603-497-2102. Fax: 603-497-8437. p. 1448

Peniston, William A, Librn, Newark Museum Library, 49 Washington St, Newark, NJ, 07102-3176. Tel: 973-596-6625. Fax: 973-642-0459. p. 1511

Penka, Stoyanova, Treas, Toronto Health Libraries Association, 3409 Yonge St, Toronto, ON, M4N 2L0, CANADA. Tel: 416-485-0377. Fax: 416-485-6877. p. 2960

Penke, Ann, Dir, Lakeland College, W3718 South Dr, Plymouth, WI, 53073. Tel: 920-565-1242. Fax: 920-565-1206. p. 2630

Penkova, Snejanka, Dir, University of Puerto Rico Library System, University of Puerto Rico, Rio Piedras Campus, San Juan, PR, 00931. Tel: 787-764-0000, Ext 5085. Fax: 787-772-1479. p. 2676

Penkova, Snejanka, Dir, University of Puerto Rico Library System, Gerardo Selles Sola Library (Education Libray), Eugenio Maria de Hostos Bldg, Rio Piedras Campus, San Juan, PR, 00931. Tel: 787-764-0000, Ext 4149. p. 2678

Penland, Tammy, Support Serv Mgr, Wichita Public Library, 223 S Main St, Wichita, KS, 67202. Tel: 316-261-8534. Fax: 316-858-7321. p. 901

Penley, Nicole, Outreach Serv Spec, South Central Kansas Library System, 321 N Main St, South Hutchinson, KS, 67505-1146. Tel: 620-663-3211. Fax: 620-663-9797. p. 895

Penn, Don, Librn, Kinney Public Library, 400 Main St, Kinney, MN, 55758. Tel: 218-258-2232. p. 1255

Penn, Maureen, Dir, Libr Serv, Lac La Biche County Library Board, 8702 91st Ave, Lac La Biche, AB, T0A 2C0, CANADA. Tel: 780-623-7467. Fax: 780-623-7497. p. 2708

Penn, Maureen, Dir, Libr Serv, Lac La Biche County Library Board, Plamondon Municipal Library, Ecole Plamondon, Plamondon, AB, T0A 2T0, CANADA. Tel: 780-623-7467. p. 2708

Pennavaria, Katherine, Librn, Western Kentucky University Libraries, Glasgow Library, 500 Hilltopper Way, Glasgow, KY, 42141. Tel: 270-659-6911. Fax: 270-659-6990. p. 908

Penne, Bryan, Ch, Librn, Tuscola Public Library, 112 E Sale St, Tuscola, IL, 61953. Tel: 217-253-3812. Fax: 217-253-4599. p. 710

Pennebecker, Kristi, Dir, Lettie W Jensen Public Library, 278 N Main St, Amherst, WI, 54406-9101. Tel: 715-824-5510. p. 2578

Pennebecker, Kristi E, Dir, Weyauwega Public Library, 301 S Mill St, Weyauwega, WI, 54983. Tel: 920-867-3742. Fax: 920-867-3741. p. 2648

Pennell, Kathy, Dir, North Las Vegas Library District, 2300 Civic Center Dr, North Las Vegas, NV, 89030-5839. Tel: 702-633-1070. Fax: 702-649-2576. p. 1432

Pennell, Kathy, Dir, North Las Vegas Library District, Aliante Library, 2400 Deer Springs Way, North Las Vegas, NV, 89084. Tel: 702-839-2980. Fax: 702-839-5707. p. 1432

Pennell, Kelly-Ann, Br Mgr, Ocean County Library, Little Egg Harbor Branch, 290 Mathistown Rd, Little Egg Harbor, NJ, 08087. Tel: 609-294-1197. Fax: 609-294-1302. p. 1534

Pennell, Yodona, Syst Programmer, Syst Coordr, Gila County Library District, 1400 E Ash St, Globe, AZ, 85501-1414. Tel: 928-402-8769. Fax: 928-425-3462. p. 65

Pennella, Kara, Mgr, Pub Serv, Tipp City Public Library, 11 E Main St, Tipp City, OH, 45371. Tel: 937-667-3826. Fax: 937-667-7968. p. 1938

Penner, Bradley, Libr Div Mgr/Pub Serv, Oceanside Public Library, 330 N Coast Hwy, Oceanside, CA, 92054-2824. Tel: 760-435-5575. Fax: 760-435-9614. p. 199

Penner, Mary Anne, Dir, Cold Lake Public Library, 5513-B 48th Ave, Cold Lake, AB, T9M 1X9, CANADA. Tel: 780-594-5101. Fax: 780-594-7787. p. 2695

Penner, Mary Anne, Dir, Cold Lake Public Library, Harbor View, 1301 Eighth Ave, Cold Lake, AB, T9M 1J7, CANADA. Tel: 780-639-3967. Fax: 780-639-3963. p. 2695

Penner, Wanda, Librn, Peace River Bible Institute Library, 9601 100th St, Sexsmith, AB, T0H 3C0, CANADA. Tel: 780-568-3962, Ext 240. Fax: 780-568-4431. p. 2716

Pennese, Kristine, Ch, Upper Merion Township Library, 175 W Valley Forge Rd, King of Prussia, PA, 19406-2399. Tel: 610-265-1196. Fax: 610-265-3398. p. 2074

Penney, Jamie, Head, Tech Serv, Reading Public Library, 64 Middlesex Ave, Reading, MA, 01867-2550. Tel: 781-944-0840. Fax: 781-942-6704. p. 1120

Penney, Jeanne, Librn, Campbell Public Library, 721 Broad St, Campbell, NE, 68932. Tel: 402-756-8121. p. 1395

Penney, Linda, Cat Librn, Willow Branch Township Library, 330 N Eldon, Cisco, IL, 61830. Tel: 217-669-2312. Fax: 217-669-2312. p. 629

Penniman, Chris, Dir, Instrul Tech, Connecticut College, 270 Mohegan Ave, New London, CT, 06320-4196. Tel: 860-439-2381. Fax: 860-439-2871. p. 359

Penniman, Sarah, ILL, Delaware Valley College of Science & Agriculture, 700 E Butler Ave, Doylestown, PA, 18901-2699. Tel: 215-489-2254. Fax: 215-230-2967. p. 2050

Penninger, Monica, Dir, Santa Fe Springs City Library, Betty Wilson Center Library Station, 11641 Florence Ave, Santa Fe Springs, CA, 90670. Tel: 562-929-7431. p. 265

Penninger, Monica, Dir, Santa Fe Springs City Library, Nieto Branch Library Station, 9255 Pioneer Blvd, Santa Fe Springs, CA, 90670. Tel: 562-692-0261. p. 265

Pennington, Aimee, Br Mgr, Public Library of Cincinnati & Hamilton County, Wyoming Branch, 500 Springfield Pike, Wyoming, OH, 45215. Tel: 513-369-6014. Fax: 513-369-6052. p. 1873

Pennington, Buddy, Jr, Dir, Coll & Access Mgt, University of Missouri-Kansas City Libraries, 800 E 51st St, Kansas City, MO, 64110. Tel: 816-235-1548. Fax: 816-333-5584. p. 1341

Pennington, Esther, Br Mgr, Calcasieu Parish Public Library, Maplewood, 91 Center Circle, Sulphur, LA, 70663. Tel: 337-721-7104. Fax: 337-625-5692. p. 954

Pennington, Esther, Br Mgr, Calcasieu Parish Public Library, Sulphur Regional, 1160 Cypress St, Sulphur, LA, 70663. Tel: 337-721-7141. Fax: 337-527-7200. p. 954

Pennington, Lisa, Head Librn, Jesse Wakefield Memorial Library, 207 Spruce Dr, Port Lions, AK, 99550. Tel: 907-454-2288. Fax: 907-454-2420. p. 52

Pennington, Teresa, Dir, Paris Carnegie Public Library, 207 S Main St, Paris, IL, 61944. Tel: 217-463-3950. Fax: 217-463-1155. p. 688

Pennington, Theresa, Dir, Martelle Public Library, 202 South St, Martelle, IA, 52305. Tel: 319-482-4121. Fax: 319-482-4121. p. 830

Pennino, John, Archivist, Metropolitan Opera Archives, Lincoln Center Plaza, New York, NY, 10023. Tel: 212-799-3100, Ext 2525. Fax: 212-870-7657. p. 1687

Penny, Keely, Tech Serv, Plainville Public Library, 198 South St, Plainville, MA, 02762-1512. Tel: 508-695-1784. Fax: 508-695-6359. p. 1118

Pennycuff, Tim, Archivist, University of Alabama at Birmingham, Lister Hill Library of the Health Sciences, 1700 University Blvd, Birmingham, AL, 35294-0013. Tel: 205-934-5460. Fax: 205-934-3545. p. 10

Penovich, Linda, Finance Mgr, Kitsap Regional Library, 1301 Sylvan Way, Bremerton, WA, 98310-3498. Tel: 360-415-6729. Fax: 360-405-9128. p. 2510

Penrod, Karen, Ref Librn, New England College, 28 Bridge St, Henniker, NH, 03242-3298. Tel: 603-428-2344. Fax: 603-428-4273. p. 1451

Penrod, Michael, Dir, Wood County District Public Library, 251 N Main St, Bowling Green, OH, 43402-2477. Tel: 419-352-5104. Fax: 419-354-0405. p. 1861

Penrose, Wendy, Head, Tech Serv, Oxnard Public Library, 251 South A St, Oxnard, CA, 93030. Tel: 805-385-7523. Fax: 805-385-7526. p. 202

Penry, Amy M, Asst Dir, Rock Island Public Library, 401 19th St, Rock Island, IL, 61201. Tel: 309-732-7302. Fax: 309-732-7309. p. 696

Pensiero, Ben, Coll Develop, New Braunfels Public Library, 700 E Common St, New Braunfels, TX, 78130-5689. Tel: 830-221-4325. Fax: 830-608-2151. p. 2365

Penteliuk, David, Br Mgr, Mississauga Library System, Burnhamthorpe, 3650 Dixie Rd, Mississauga, ON, L4Y 3V9, CANADA. Tel: 905-615-4635. p. 2823

Pentlin, Floyd, Instr, University of Central Missouri, Dept of Educational Leadership & Human Development, Lovinger 4101, Warrensburg, MO, 64093. Tel: 660-543-4910. Fax: 660-543-4164. p. 2968

Penwarden, Ann P, Asst Dir, Monroe Community College, LeRoy V Good Library, 1000 E Henrietta Rd, Rochester, NY, 14692. Tel: 585-292-2322. p. 1730

Penwell, Laurel, Br Mgr, Durango Public Library, Fort Lewis Mesa, 11274 Hwy 140, Hesperus, CO, 81326. Tel: 970-588-3331. p. 304

Peo, Florentine, Librn, American Samoa Office of Library Services, Leone Midkiff Branch, Leone Village, AS, 96799. Tel: 684-688-7458. Fax: 684-633-4240. p. 2665

Peoples, Deborah, Sci Librn, Ohio Wesleyan University, 43 Rowland, Delaware, OH, 43015-2370. Tel: 740-368-3241. Fax: 740-368-3222. p. 1896

Peoples, Jean, Librn, Settlement Music School, 416 Queen St, Philadelphia, PA, 19147-3094. Tel: 215-320-2604. Fax: 215-551-0483. p. 2117

Peoples, Lee, Assoc Dir, Oklahoma City University, Law Library, 2501 N Blackwelder, Oklahoma City, OK, 73106. Tel: 405-208-5271. Fax: 405-208-5172. p. 1974

Pepa, Gail, Dir, Deer Park Public Library, 44 Lake Ave, Deer Park, NY, 11729-6047. Tel: 631-586-3000. Fax: 631-586-3006. p. 1613

Pepich, Bruce W, Curator of Coll, Exec Dir, Racine Art Museum Library, 441 Main St, Racine, WI, 53403. Tel: 262-638-8300, Ext 106. Fax: 262-898-1045. p. 2632

Pepin, Veronique, Librn, Tecsult, Inc, 85 W Saint Catherine, Montreal, QC, H2X 3P4, CANADA. Tel: 514-287-8500, Ext 8546. Fax: 514-287-8531. p. 2902

Pepo, Kelly, Br Mgr, Orange County Library District, Edgewater, 5049 Edgewater Dr, Orlando, FL, 32810-4743. p. 476

Peppard, Dorothy, Ch, Haddonfield Public Library, 60 Haddon Ave, Haddonfield, NJ, 08033-2422. Tel: 856-429-1304. Fax: 856-429-3760. p. 1489

Pepper, Dawn, Acq, Cat, Libr Tech, Minneapolis Community & Technical College Library, Wheelock Whitney Hall, 1501 Hennepin Ave, Minneapolis, MN, 55403. Tel: 612-659-6289. Fax: 612-659-6295. p. 1261

Pepper, Janice E, Cat Librn, Library of the Marine Corps, Gray Research Ctr, 2040 Broadway St, Quantico, VA, 22134-5107. Tel: 703-784-1839. Fax: 703-784-4306. p. 2486

Pepper, Jerold, Librn, Adirondack Museum Library, Rte 28N & 30, Blue Mountain Lake, NY, 12812. Tel: 518-352-7311. Fax: 518-352-7653. p. 1583

Pepper-Rotness, Barbara, Tech Support, Montana Historical Society, 225 N Roberts St, Helena, MT, 59601-4514. Tel: 406-444-9526. Fax: 406-444-5297. p. 1382

Pepperman, Nancy, Br Mgr, Hancock County Library System, Waveland Public Library, 345 Coleman Ave, Waveland, MS, 39576. Tel: 228-467-9240. Fax: 228-467-1336. p. 1294

Peppers, Alison, Head, Pub Serv, Mary Baldwin College, 109 E Frederick St, Staunton, VA, 24401. Tel: 540-887-7299. Fax: 540-887-7137. p. 2496

Peppers, Marla, Assoc Univ Librn, California State University, Los Angeles, 5151 State University Dr, Los Angeles, CA, 90032-8300. Tel: 323-343-3950. Fax: 323-343-3935. p. 169

Peppiatt, Linda, Dep Dir, Newmarket Public Library, 438 Park Ave, Newmarket, ON, L3Y 1W1, CANADA. Tel: 905-953-5110. Fax: 905-953-5104. p. 2824

Pepple, Judith, Dir, Apache County Library District, 30 S Second W, Saint Johns, AZ, 85936. Tel: 928-337-4923. Fax: 928-337-3960. p. 79

Pequeno, Samie, Librn, Department of Veterans Affairs, 300 Veterans Blvd, Big Spring, TX, 79720. Tel: 432-263-7361. Fax: 432-268-5064. p. 2289

Perales, Rebecca, Pub Serv Librn, El Paso Community College Library, Rio Grande Campus Library, 1111 N Oregon, El Paso, TX, 79902. Tel: 915-831-4019. p. 2316

Peralez, Ricardo, Assoc Libr Dir, The University of Texas-Pan American Library, 1201 W University Dr, Edinburg, TX, 78541-2999. Tel: 956-665-2758. Fax: 956-665-5396. p. 2315

Peralta, Lorna, Librn, Mesa Community College Library, 1833 W Southern Ave, Mesa, AZ, 85202. Tel: 480-654-7743. Fax: 480-461-7681. p. 68

Peralta, Lorna, Librn, Mesa Community College Library, Red Mountain, 7110 E McKellips Rd, Mesa, AZ, 85207. Tel: 480-654-7743. Fax: 480-654-7401. p. 69

Perault, Maureen, Librn, Washtenaw Community College, 4800 E Huron River Dr, Ann Arbor, MI, 48105-4800. Tel: 734-973-3407. Fax: 734-973-3446. p. 1153

Perbohner, Ann, Phys Sci Librn, Dartmouth College Library, Kresge Physical Sciences Library, 6115 Fairchild Hall, Hanover, NH, 03755-3571. Tel: 603-646-3563. Fax: 603-646-3681. p. 1450

Percelli, Irene, Dir, Millville Public Library, 210 Buck St, Millville, NJ, 08332. Tel: 856-825-7087. Fax: 856-327-8572. p. 1502

Perch, Ted, Dir, Willimantic Public Library, 905 Main St, Willimantic, CT, 06226. Tel: 860-465-3080. Fax: 860-465-3083. p. 378

Percic, Melissa A W, Dir, Carnegie Public Library, 219 E Fourth St, East Liverpool, OH, 43920-3143. Tel: 330-385-2048. Fax: 330-385-7600. p. 1897

Percival, Allison, Ch, Brazoria County Library System, Brazoria Branch, 620 S Brooks, Brazoria, TX, 77422-9022. Tel: 979-798-2372. Fax: 979-798-4013. p. 2275

Percival, Bonnie, Head, Spec Coll, Ref Serv, Dixie State College of Utah, 225 S 700 E, Saint George, UT, 84770. Tel: 435-652-7718. Fax: 435-656-4169. p. 2411

Percy, Elsie, Librn, Brigus Public Library, General Delivery, Brigus, NL, A0A 1K0, CANADA. Tel: 709-528-3156. p. 2769

Percy, Kumar, Head, Res Serv, University of Texas Libraries, Jamail Center for Legal Research, University of Texas School of Law, 727 E Dean Keeton St, Austin, TX, 78705-3224. Tel: 512-471-7726. Fax: 512-471-0243. p. 2284

Percy, Theresa Rini, Dir, Port Townsend Public Library, 1220 Lawrence St, Port Townsend, WA, 98368-6527. Tel: 360-385-3181. Fax: 360-385-5805. p. 2524

Perdew, Rhett, Librn, Lackawanna College, 501 Vine St, Scranton, PA, 18509. Tel: 570-961-7831. Fax: 570-961-7817. p. 2137

Perdue, Derek, Br Mgr, Arlington Public Library System, Southwest, 3111 SW Green Oaks Blvd, Arlington, TX, 76017. Tel: 817-459-6386. p. 2277

Perehudoff, Pearl, Br Head, Vancouver Public Library, West Point Grey, 4480 W Tenth Ave, Vancouver, BC, V6R 2H9, CANADA. Tel: 604-665-3982. Fax: 604-665-3551. p. 2744

Pereira, Cornelius A, Acq & Cat, Southern Illinois University Carbondale, Law Library, Lesar Law Bldg, 1150 Douglas Dr, Carbondale, IL, 62901. Tel: 618-453-8781. Fax: 618-453-8728. p. 600

Pereira, Heather, Br Mgr, Santa Cruz City-County Library System Headquarters, Capitola Branch, 2005 Wharf Rd, Capitola, CA, 95010-2002. Tel: 831-427-7706, Ext 7721. Fax: 831-427-7725. p. 264

Pereira, Heather, Br Mgr, Santa Cruz City-County Library System Headquarters, La Selva Beach Branch, 316 Estrella, La Selva Beach, CA, 95076. Tel: 831-427-7706, Ext 7721. p. 264

Pereira, Karen, Tech Serv, Taunton Public Library, 12 Pleasant St, Taunton, MA, 02780. Tel: 508-821-1410. Fax: 508-821-1414. p. 1131

Pereira, Laura, Librn, Old Dartmouth Historical Society, 791 Purchase St, New Bedford, MA, 02740-6398. Tel: 508-997-0046. Fax: 508-207-1064. p. 1109

Pereira, Paula, Circ Mgr, Dallas County Community College District, 1402 Corinth St, Dallas, TX, 75215. Tel: 214-860-5779. p. 2305

Perekrestov, Michael, Librn, Holy Trinity Orthodox Seminary Library, 1407 Robinson Rd, Jordanville, NY, 13361-0036. Tel: 315-858-3116. Fax: 315-858-0945. p. 1648

Perella, Margaret, Dir, Pequea Valley Public Library, 31 Center St, Intercourse, PA, 17534. Tel: 717-768-3160. Fax: 717-768-3888. p. 2072

Perelman, Rimma, Chief, Libr Serv, Saint Vincent's Hospital & Medical Center, 170 W 12th St, New York, NY, 10011. Tel: 212-604-7812. Fax: 212-604-7888. p. 1699

Perera, Michelle, Asst Libr Dir, Rancho Cucamonga Public Library, 7368 Archibald Ave, Rancho Cucamonga, CA, 91730. Tel: 909-477-2720, Ext 5055. Fax: 909-477-2721. p. 213

Peres, Andre, Librn, Mount Sinai Medical Center, 4300 Alton Rd, Miami Beach, FL, 33140. Tel: 305-674-2840. Fax: 305-674-2843. p. 469

Peret, Robert, Circ, Ref, Southwestern College, 100 College St, Winfield, KS, 67156-2498. Tel: 620-229-6225. Fax: 620-229-6382. p. 902

Peretich, Jamie, Access Serv, Chatham College, Woodland Rd, Pittsburgh, PA, 15232. Tel: 412-365-1619. Fax: 412-365-1465. p. 2124

Perez, Andrea, Homebound Delivery Coordr, Westland Public Library, 6123 Central City Pkwy, Westland, MI, 48185. Tel: 734-326-6123. Fax: 734-595-4612. p. 1236

Perez, Carla, Cat, Tech Serv, Sweetwater County Library System, 300 N First East, Green River, WY, 82935. Tel: 307-875-3615. Fax: 307-872-3203. p. 2655

Perez, Carlos, Media Spec, University of the Sacred Heart, Rosales St, PO Box 12383, Santurce, PR, 00914-0383. Tel: 787-728-1515, Ext 4353. Fax: 787-268-8868. p. 2678

Perez, Celia, Acq of New Ser, Harold Washington College Library, City Colleges of Chicago, 30 E Lake St, 5th Flr, Chicago, IL, 60601-9996. Tel: 312-553-5635. Fax: 312-553-5783. p. 614

Perez, Clementine, ILL, State University of New York, State College of Optometry, 33 W 42nd St, New York, NY, 10036-8003. Tel: 212-938-5690. Fax: 212-938-5696. p. 1700

Perez, Doris, ILL, Wilford Hall Medical Center Library, 59MDW/SGN, Lackland AFB, TX, 78236-5300. Tel: 210-292-5777. Fax: 210-292-7030. p. 2352

Perez, Heather Halpin, Archivist, Atlantic City Free Public Library, One N Tennessee Ave, Atlantic City, NJ, 08401. Tel: 609-345-2269. Fax: 609-345-5570. p. 1470

Perez, Heidrun, Info Res Tech, Latham & Watkins, 600 W Broadway, Ste 1800, San Diego, CA, 92101. Tel: 619-238-2834. Fax: 619-696-7419. p. 231

Perez, Jorge, Head Librn, Saint Petersburg College, Tarpon Springs Campus Library, 600 Klosterman Rd, Tarpon Springs, FL, 34689. Tel: 727-712-5728. Fax: 727-712-5706. p. 483

Perez, Jose Eddie, Automated Syst Coordr, Laredo Community College, West End Washington St, Laredo, TX, 78040. Tel: 956-721-5282. Fax: 956-721-5447. p. 2353

Perez, Josh, Automation Syst Coordr, Indian River County Library System, 1600 21st St, Vero Beach, FL, 32960. Tel: 772-770-5060. Fax: 772-770-5066. p. 501

Perez, Juanita, Coordr, Acq, Laredo Community College, West End Washington St, Laredo, TX, 78040. Tel: 956-721-5961. Fax: 956-721-5447. p. 2353

Perez Lopez, Myrna E, Dir, Evangelical Seminary of Puerto Rico, 776 Ponce de Leon Ave, San Juan, PR, 00925-9907. Tel: 787-763-6700, Ext 231. Fax: 787-751-0847. p. 2676

Perez, Magda, Dir, Info Literacy, University of Puerto Rico Library, Cayey Campus, 205 Ave Antonio R Barcelo, Cayey, PR, 00736. Tel: 787-738-2161, Ext 2453. Fax: 787-263-2108. p. 2672

Perez, Maria N, Librn, Woodhull Medical & Mental Health Center, 760 Broadway, Rm 3A160, Brooklyn, NY, 11206. Tel: 718-963-8275, 718-963-8397. Fax: 718-963-8888. p. 1595

Perez, Marina, Librn IV, San Diego Public Library, 820 E St, San Diego, CA, 92101-6478. Tel: 619-236-5838. Fax: 619-238-6639. p. 235

Perez, Melissa, Ch, Grand Prairie Public Library System, 901 Conover Dr, Grand Prairie, TX, 75051. Tel: 972-237-5700. Fax: 972-237-5750. p. 2329

Perez, Melissa, Libr Mgr, Plano Public Library System, L E R Schimelpfenig Library, 5024 Custer Rd, Plano, TX, 75023. Tel: 972-769-4200. Fax: 972-769-4210. p. 2371

Perez, Michelle, Ch, Stanton County Library, 103 E Sherman, Johnson, KS, 67855. Tel: 620-492-2302. Fax: 620-492-2203. p. 874

Perez, Miriam, Br Mgr, Riverside Public Library, Eastside Library & Cybrary, 4033-C Chicago Ave, Riverside, CA, 92507. Tel: 951-369-8120. p. 218

Perez, Naomi, Acq, Saint Thomas University Library, Law Library, 16401 NW 37th Ave, Miami Gardens, FL, 33054. Tel: 305-623-2365. Fax: 305-623-2337. p. 469

Perez, Patricia, Dir, Lake Placid Public Library, 2471 Main St, Lake Placid, NY, 12946. Tel: 518-523-3200. Fax: 518-523-3200. p. 1650

Perez, Ramon, Sr Col Lab Tech/Media Serv, Queensborough Community College, City University of New York, 222-05 56th Ave, Bayside, NY, 11364-1497. Tel: 718-281-5407. Fax: 718-281-5012. p. 1579

Perez, Rochelle, Instruction & Outreach, Pub Serv, Cosumnes River College Library, 8401 Center Pkwy, Sacramento, CA, 95823. Tel: 916-691-7629. Fax: 916-691-7349. p. 223

Perez, Wendi, Exec Dir, American Rhinologic Society Library, PO Box 495, Warwick, NY, 10990-0495. Tel: 845-988-1631. Fax: 845-986-1527. p. 1762

Perez-Gilbe, Hector, Head Librn/Prog Dir, Saint Petersburg College, Health Education Center, 7200 66th St N, Pinellas Park, FL, 33781. Tel: 727-341-3657. Fax: 727-341-3658. p. 483

Perez-Gomez, Analiza, Per/Circ Librn, Laredo Community College, West End Washington St, Laredo, TX, 78040. Tel: 956-721-5842. Fax: 956-721-5447. p. 2353

Perez-Stable, Maria A, Head, Cent Ref Serv, Western Michigan University, Arcadia at Vande Giessen St, Kalamazoo, MI, 49008-5353. Tel: 269-387-5322. Fax: 269-387-5077. p. 1198

Pergander, Mary, Dir, Deerfield Public Library, 920 Waukegan Rd, Deerfield, IL, 60015. Tel: 847-945-3311. Fax: 847-945-3402. p. 634

Peri, Janet, Asst Libr Dir, University of Texas, Health Science Center at Houston, Dental Branch Library, 6516 M D Anderson Blvd, Rm 133, Houston, TX, 77030. Tel: 713-500-4204. Fax: 713-500-4100. p. 2344

Perille, Gina, Communications Mgr, Boston Public Library, 700 Boylston St, Boston, MA, 02117-0286. Tel: 617-536-5400. Fax: 617-236-4306. p. 1056

Perini, Mike, Dir, Port St John Public Library, 6500 Carole Ave, Cocoa, FL, 32927. Tel: 321-633-1867. Fax: 321-633-1869. p. 433

Perisho, Stephen, Info Spec, Seattle Pacific University Library, 3307 Third Ave W, Seattle, WA, 98119. Tel: 206-281-2417. Fax: 206-281-2936. p. 2530

Perito, Patricia, Dir, Town of Pelham Public Library, 530 Colonial Ave, Pelham, NY, 10803. Tel: 914-738-1234. Fax: 914-738-0809. p. 1716

Perkins, Barbara, Head, ILL, Pierce College Library, 9401 Farwest Dr SW, Lakewood, WA, 98498. Tel: 253-964-6547. Fax: 253-964-6713. p. 2519

Perkins, Beth, Head, Circ, University of Mary Washington, 1801 College Ave, Fredericksburg, VA, 22401-4665. Tel: 540-654-1147. Fax: 540-654-1067. p. 2466

Perkins, Carol, ILL, Stevens Institute of Technology, Castle Point on Hudson, Hoboken, NJ, 07030. Tel: 201-216-5200. Fax: 201-216-8319. p. 1491

Perkins, Catherine, Archives Supvr, Instrul Serv Librn, Wagner College, One Campus Rd, Staten Island, NY, 10301-4495. Tel: 718-390-3401. Fax: 718-420-4218. p. 1748

Perkins, Cathy, Cat, Tech Serv, Waterville Public Library, 73 Elm St, Waterville, ME, 04901-6078. Tel: 207-872-5433. Fax: 207-873-4779. p. 1006

Perkins, Christine, Asst Dir, Bellingham Public Library, 210 Central Ave, CS-9710, Bellingham, WA, 98227-9710. Tel: 360-778-7206. p. 2508

Perkins, Christine, Asst Dir, Bellingham Public Library, Barkley, 3111 Newmarket St, Ste 102, Bellingham, WA, 98226. Tel: 360-778-7206. p. 2508

Perkins, Cindy, Med Librn, Children's Hospital Central California, 9300 Valley Children's Pl, Madera, CA, 93638-8762. Tel: 559-353-6170. Fax: 559-353-6176. p. 181

Perkins, Cindy, Librn, Motion Picture & Television Fund, 23388 Mulholland Dr, Woodland Hills, CA, 91364. Tel: 818-876-1888, Ext 2449. Fax: 818-225-1359. p. 285

Perkins, David, Curator, Sheridan County Historical Society, Inc, Hwy 20 & Nelson Ave, Rushville, NE, 69360. Tel: 308-638-7643. p. 1418

Perkins, Elaine, Commun Libr Supvr, Yakima Valley Libraries, Moxee Library, 255 W Seattle, Moxee, WA, 98936. Tel: 509-575-8854. Fax: 509-575-8854. p. 2550

Perkins, Eva, Librn, Northridge Hospital, 18300 Roscoe Blvd, Northridge, CA, 91328. Tel: 818-885-8500, Ext 4608. Fax: 818-885-0372. p. 195

Perkins, Fatima, Adult Serv Mgr, Cuyahoga County Public Library, 2111 Snow Rd, Parma, OH, 44134-2728. Tel: 216-398-1800. Fax: 216-398-1748. p. 1927

Perkins, Hoke, Assoc Univ Librn, Philanthropy & Dir of the Harrison Institute, University of Virginia, PO Box 400114, Charlottesville, VA, 22904-4114. Tel: 434-924-3021. Fax: 434-924-1431. p. 2454

Perkins, Jody, Br Mgr, Madison County Library System, Madison Public Library, 994 Madison Ave, Madison, MS, 39110. Tel: 601-856-2749. Fax: 601-856-2681. p. 1295

Perkins, John M, Ref, Mercer University, Walter F George School of Law, Furman Smith Law Library, 1021 Georgia Ave, Macon, GA, 31201-1001. Tel: 478-301-2667. Fax: 478-301-2284. p. 540

Perkins, Kay, Dir, Geary Public Library, 106 W Main, Geary, OK, 73040. Tel: 405-884-2372. Fax: 405-884-2372. p. 1964

Perkins, Kelley, Br Mgr, Prince George's County Memorial, New Carrollton Branch, 7414 Riverdale Rd, New Carrollton, MD, 20784-3799. Tel: 301-459-6900. p. 1032

Perkins, Kelli, Ref, Herrick District Library, 300 S River Ave, Holland, MI, 49423-3290. Tel: 616-355-3100. p. 1190

Perkins, Lee, Dir, Rice Public Library, Eight Wentworth St, Kittery, ME, 03904. Tel: 207-439-1553. Fax: 207-439-1765. p. 989

Perkins, Leon, Tech Serv, Temple Public Library, 100 W Adams Ave, Temple, TX, 76501-7641. Tel: 254-298-5560. Fax: 254-298-5328. p. 2391

Perkins, Lisa, Librn, Seymour Community Library, 123 N Fifth, Seymour, IA, 52590. Tel: 641-898-2966. Fax: 641-898-2305. p. 842

Perkins, Lorelei, Libr Dir, City of Melissa Public Library, 3411 Barker Ave, Melissa, TX, 75454. Tel: 972-837-4540. Fax: 972-837-2006. p. 2361

Perkins, Margaret, Ref Librn, Tech Coordr, Holliston Public Library, 752 Washington St, Holliston, MA, 01746. Tel: 508-429-0617. Fax: 508-429-0625. p. 1095

Perkins, Margaret Y, Actg Dir, Medway Public Library, 26 High St, Medway, MA, 02053. Tel: 508-533-3217. Fax: 508-533-3219. p. 1104

Perkins, Mark, Acq, Cat, Madison Area Technical College, 3550 Anderson St, Rm 230, Madison, WI, 53704. Tel: 608-246-6923. Fax: 608-246-6644. p. 2606

Perkins, Mary, Pub Relations, Hancock County Library System, 312 Hwy 90, Bay Saint Louis, MS, 39520-3595. Tel: 228-467-5282. Fax: 228-467-5503. p. 1293

Perkins, Priscilla L, Dir, Western New England University, 1215 Wilbraham Rd, Springfield, MA, 01119. Tel: 413-782-1535. Fax: 413-796-2011. p. 1128

Perkins, Rebecca, Ref Librn, Greensburg-Decatur County Public Library, 1110 E Main St, Greensburg, IN, 47240. Tel: 812-663-2826. Fax: 812-663-5617. p. 746

Perkins, Rick, Br Adminr, Siskiyou County Public Library, Etna Branch, 121 Collier Way, Etna, CA, 96027-0130. Tel: 530-467-3661. p. 286

Perkins, Roseanne, Youth Serv Librn, Louisa Gonser Community Library, 70 Bieber Alley, Kutztown, PA, 19530-1113. Tel: 610-683-5820. Fax: 610-683-8155. p. 2075

Perkins, Roseanne, Instr, Kutztown University, Kutztown, PA, 19530. Tel: 610-683-4300. Fax: 610-683-1326. p. 2973

Perkins, Ruth, Info Literacy, Ref, Kutztown University, 15200 Kutztown Rd, Bldg 5, Kutztown, PA, 19530-0735. Tel: 610-683-4484. Fax: 610-683-4747. p. 2075

Perkins, Sheila D, Librn, Saint Clairsville Public Library, 108 W Main St, Saint Clairsville, OH, 43950-1225. Tel: 740-695-2062. Fax: 740-695-6420. p. 1933

Perkins, Susan R, Dir, Herkimer County Historical Society Library, Eckler Bldg, 406 N Main St, Herkimer, NY, 13350. Tel: 315-866-6413. p. 1635

Perkins, Suzanne, Dir, Cape Porpoise Library, Atlantic Hall, Cape Porpoise, ME, 04014. Tel: 207-967-5668. Fax: 207-967-5668. p. 981

Perkins, Tammy, Ch, Marlboro County Library, 200 John Corry Rd, Bennettsville, SC, 29512. Tel: 843-479-5630. Fax: 843-479-5645. p. 2182

Perkins, William, Res Librn, Federal Reserve Bank of Richmond, 701 E Byrd St, Richmond, VA, 23219. Tel: 804-697-8125. Fax: 804-697-8134. p. 2488

Perkinson, Beth, Human Res, Warren County Memorial Library, 119 South Front St, Warrenton, NC, 27589. Tel: 252-257-4990. Fax: 252-257-4089. p. 1828

Perkner, Stanislav, Dr, Librn, Humphreys College Library, 6650 Inglewood Ave, Stockton, CA, 95207. Tel: 209-235-2933. Fax: 209-478-8721. p. 272

Perkoski, Robert, Lecturer, University of Pittsburgh, 135 N Bellefield Ave, Pittsburgh, PA, 15260. Tel: 412-624-5230. Fax: 412-624-5231. p. 2973

Perks, Jenn, Ch, The Blue Mountains Public Library, 173 Bruce St S, Thornbury, ON, N0H 2P0, CANADA. Tel: 519-599-3681. Fax: 519-599-7951. p. 2847

Perky, Rachel, Circ Supvr, Union Theological Seminary & Presbyterian School of Christian Education, 3401 Brook Rd, Richmond, VA, 23227. Tel: 804-278-4310. Fax: 804-278-4375. p. 2490

Perlin, Daniel, Ref Librn, York University Libraries, Osgoode Hall Law School Library, One Scholar's Walk, York University, Toronto, ON, M3J 1P3, CANADA. Tel: 416-736-5380. Fax: 416-736-5298. p. 2868

Perlin, Marjorie, Head, Circ, Chappaqua Public Library, 195 S Greeley Ave, Chappaqua, NY, 10514. Tel: 914-238-4779, Ext 101. Fax: 914-238-3597. p. 1605

Perlman, Steven, Librn, Department of Veterans Affairs, 508 Fulton St, Durham, NC, 27705. Tel: 919-286-6929, Ext 6656. Fax: 919-286-6859. p. 1787

Perlmutter, Mary Jeanne, Supv Librn & Law Libr Coordr, New York State Department of Correctional Services, State Campus, Bldg 2, Library Services, 1220 Washington Ave, Albany, NY, 12226-2050. Tel: 518-485-7109. Fax: 518-402-1742. p. 1569

Perloff, Deborah, Ch, Pease Public Library, One Russell St, Plymouth, NH, 03264-1414. Tel: 603-536-2616. Fax: 603-536-2369. p. 1462

Permenter, Alice, Librn, Mississippi Delta Community College, GHEC Library, 2900A Hwy 1 S, Greenville, MS, 38701. Tel: 662-332-8467. Fax: 662-332-8931. p. 1309

Perna, Gicele, Ch, Saint Lucie County Library System, 101 Melody Lane, Fort Pierce, FL, 34950-4402. Tel: 772-462-2812. Fax: 772-462-2750. p. 447

Pernell, Rebecca, Mgr, Access Serv, Thomas Jefferson University, 1020 Walnut St, Philadelphia, PA, 19107. Tel: 215-503-2828. Fax: 215-923-3203. p. 2118

Pernetti, Guy, Pres, Portage County Historical Society Museum & Library, 6549 N Chestnut St, Ravenna, OH, 44266. Tel: 330-296-3523. p. 1931

Perona, Linda, Head Librn, Blue Mound Memorial Library District, 213 S St Marie St, Blue Mound, IL, 62513-9733. Tel: 217-692-2774. Fax: 217-692-2191. p. 596

Perone, Colleen, Adult Serv, Southington Public Library & Museum, 255 Main St, Southington, CT, 06489. Tel: 860-628-0947. Fax: 860-628-0488. p. 368

Perone, Jan, Newspaper Librn, Illinois Historic Preservation Agency, 112 N Sixth St, Springfield, IL, 62701. Tel: 217-558-8856. Fax: 217-785-6250. p. 705

Perone, Karen, Syst Coordr, Rodman Public Library, 215 E Broadway St, Alliance, OH, 44601-2694. Tel: 330-821-2665. Fax: 330-821-5053. p. 1854

Perone, Robert, Dir, Bradford County Public Library, 456 W Pratt St, Starke, FL, 32091-3396. Tel: 904-368-3920. Fax: 904-964-2164. p. 491

Perot, Jessica, Asst Librn, Mose Hudson Tapia Public Library, 13885 S Wintzell Ave, Bayou La Batre, AL, 36509. Tel: 251-824-4213. Fax: 251-824-3196. p. 6

Perrance, Rene, Librn, Minnesota Braille & Talking Book Library, 388 SE Sixth Ave, Faribault, MN, 55021-6340. Tel: 507-384-6870. Fax: 507-333-4832. p. 1251

Perrault, Anna, Prof Emeritus, University of South Florida, 4202 Fowler Ave, CIS 1040, Tampa, FL, 33620-7800. Tel: 813-974-3520. Fax: 813-974-6840. p. 2964

Perrault, Anne, Asst Prof, University at Buffalo, State University of New York, 534 Baldy Hall, Buffalo, NY, 14260. Tel: 716-645-2412. Fax: 716-645-3775. p. 2971

Perrault, Anne, Asst Prof, University of South Carolina, 1501 Greene St, Columbia, SC, 29208. Tel: 803-777-3858. Fax: 803-777-7938. p. 2973

Perrault, Claudine, Dir, Estes Park Public Library, 335 E Elkhorn Ave, Estes Park, CO, 80517. Tel: 970-586-8116. Fax: 970-586-0189. p. 306

Perreault, Denis, Cat, Ministere de la Sante et des Services Sociaux, 1075, Chemin Ste-Foy, 5e etage, Quebec, QC, G1S 2M1, CANADA. Tel: 418-266-7015. Fax: 418-266-7024. p. 2905

Perreault, Kathy, Librn, Ojibway & Cree Cultural Centre, 273 Third Ave, Ste 204, Timmins, ON, P4N 1E2, CANADA. Tel: 705-267-7911. Fax: 705-267-4988. p. 2849

Perreault, Micheline, Dir, Societe Genealogique Canadienne-Francaise, 3440 Davidson St., Montreal, QC, H1W 2Z5, CANADA. Tel: 514-527-1010. Fax: 514-527-0265. p. 2901

Perrella, Filomena, YA Serv, Peninsula Public Library, 280 Central Ave, Lawrence, NY, 11559. Tel: 516-239-3262. Fax: 516-239-8425. p. 1651

Perrenod, William, Libr Dir, Concordia College, 171 White Plains Rd, Bronxville, NY, 10708. Tel: 914-337-9300, Ext 2202. Fax: 914-395-4893. p. 1588

Perrera, Anne, Ref Serv, Web Serv, National Library of Medicine, Bldg 38, Rm 2E-17B, 8600 Rockville Pike, Bethesda, MD, 20894. Tel: 301-496-6308. Fax: 301-496-4450. p. 1022

Perrett, Solveig, Librn, Saint Johns Episcopal Church Library, 372 N Main St, Valentine, NE, 69201. Tel: 402-376-1723, 402-376-4929. p. 1422

Perretta, Susan R, Dir, Judge Francis J Catania Law Library, Court House, 201 W Front St, Media, PA, 19063. Tel: 610-891-4462. Fax: 610-891-4480. p. 2087

Perricone, Lillian, Mgr, Bienes Mus of the Modern Bk, Broward County Division of Libraries, 100 S Andrews Ave, Fort Lauderdale, FL, 33301. Tel: 954-357-8243. Fax: 954-357-5733. p. 440

Perrie, Vicki, Dir, Superior Public Library, 449 N Kansas, Superior, NE, 68978-1852. Tel: 402-879-4200. p. 1420

Perrigo, Ann, Dir, Allegan District Library, 331 Hubbard St, Allegan, MI, 49010. Tel: 269-673-4625. Fax: 269-673-8661. p. 1148

Perrin, Dianne, Librn, Wapiti Regional Library, Duck Lake Public Library, 410 Victoria Ave, Duck Lake, SK, S0K 1J0, CANADA. Tel: 306-467-2016. p. 2921

Perrin, Karen, Dir, Illinois Department of Transportation, 320 Harry Hanley Bldg, 2300 S Dirksen Pkwy, Springfield, IL, 62764-0001. Tel: 217-782-6680. Fax: 217-524-3834. p. 704

Perrin-Mohr, Maryalice, Archivist, New England Conservatory of Music, 33 Gainsborough St, Boston, MA, 02115. Tel: 617-585-1252. Fax: 617-585-1245. p. 1064

Perritt, Patsy, Dr, Librn, University Baptist Church Library, 5775 Highland Rd, Baton Rouge, LA, 70808. Tel: 225-766-9474. Fax: 225-766-9101. p. 945

Perron, Sandra, Librn, Silsby Free Public Library, 226 Main St, Charlestown, NH, 03603. Tel: 603-826-7793. Fax: 603-826-7793. p. 1441

Perrone, Fernanda H, Dr, Head, Exhibitions Prog Curator/William E Griffis Coll, Rutgers University Libraries, Special Collections & University Archives, 169 College Ave, New Brunswick, NJ, 08901-1163. Tel: 848-932-6154. Fax: 732-932-7012. p. 1509

Perroni, Mary Booker, Dir, Friendswood Public Library, 416 S Friendswood Dr, Friendswood, TX, 77546-3897. Tel: 281-482-7135. Fax: 281-482-2685. p. 2325

Perros, Fran, Info Serv, United States Department of State, 2201 C St NW, Rm 3239, Washington, DC, 20520-2442. Tel: 202-647-0451. Fax: 202-647-2971. p. 419

Perrotta, Lorraine, Tech Serv, Huntington Library, 1151 Oxford Rd, San Marino, CA, 91108. Tel: 626-405-2184. Fax: 626-449-5720. p. 255

Perrotti, Janet, Head, Circ, Hamden Public Library, 2901 Dixwell Ave, Hamden, CT, 06518-3135. Tel: 203-287-2686. Fax: 203-287-2685. p. 343

Perry, Allison, Librn, Bond, Schoeneck & King, PLLC, One Lincoln Ctr, Syracuse, NY, 13202-1355. Tel: 315-218-8000. Fax: 315-218-8100. p. 1751

Perry, Amanda, Dir, Libr Serv, Winooski Memorial Library, Champlain Mill, Level 2, One Main St, Winooski, VT, 05404. Tel: 802-655-6424. Fax: 802-655-6431. p. 2440

Perry, Angela, Librn, United States Army, United States Disciplinary Barracks Library, 1301 N Warehouse Rd, Fort Leavenworth, KS, 66027-2304. Tel: 913-758-3864. Fax: 913-758-3927. p. 867

Perry, Annette, Asst Librn, Albemarle Regional Library, Ahoskie Public Library, 210 E Church St, Ahoskie, NC, 27910. Tel: 252-332-5500. Fax: 252-332-6435. p. 1835

Perry, Barbara, Br Mgr, Hall County Library System, Blackshear Place, 2927 Atlanta Hwy, Gainesville, GA, 30507. Tel: 770-532-3311, Ext 151. Fax: 770-287-3653. p. 534

Perry, Beth, Pub Serv, Mercer University Atlanta, 3001 Mercer University Dr, Atlanta, GA, 30341. Tel: 678-547-6435. Fax: 678-547-6270. p. 517

Perry, Candace, Curator, Schwenkfelder Library & Heritage Center, 105 Seminary St, Pennsburg, PA, 18073. Tel: 215-679-3103, Ext 12. Fax: 215-679-8175. p. 2102

Perry, Cathie, Instrul Serv Librn, Vancouver Community College, 250 W Pender St, Vancouver, BC, V6B 1S9, CANADA. Tel: 604-443-8349. Fax: 604-443-8588. p. 2743

Perry, Claudia, Assoc Prof, Queens College of the City University of New York, Benjamin Rosenthal Library, Rm 254, 65-30 Kissena Blvd, Flushing, NY, 11367. Tel: 718-997-3790. Fax: 718-997-3797. p. 2970

Perry, Danica, Br Mgr, Mansfield-Richland County Public Library, Crestview Branch, 1575 State Rte 96 E, Ashland, OH, 44805-9262. Tel: 419-895-0010. Fax: 419-895-0010. p. 1913

Perry, Deborah, Outreach Librn, Anderson County Public Library, 114 N Main St, Lawrenceburg, KY, 40342. Tel: 502-839-6420. Fax: 502-839-7243. p. 919

Perry, Debra, Assoc Librn, Youth Serv, Hartford Public Library, 500 Main St, Hartford, CT, 06103-3075. Tel: 860-695-6333. Fax: 860-722-6897. p. 346

Perry, Debra, Librn, Atlanta-Fulton Public Library System, Dogwood Library, 1838 Donald L Hollowell Pkwy NW, Atlanta, GA, 30318. Tel: 404-792-4961. Fax: 404-792-4963. p. 512

Perry, Dorothy, Campus Librn, Coll Develop, Ref Librn, Pensacola State College, 1000 College Blvd, Pensacola, FL, 32504-8998. Tel: 850-484-2252. Fax: 850-484-2355. p. 482

Perry, Dorothy, Campus Ref & Instrul Serv Librn, Pensacola State College, Warrington Campus, 5555 West Hwy 98, Pensacola, FL, 32507-1097. Tel: 850-484-2252. Fax: 850-484-2355. p. 482

Perry, Emma Bradford, Dean of Libr, Southern University, 167 Roosevelt Steptoe Ave, Baton Rouge, LA, 70813-0001. Tel: 225-771-4991. Fax: 225-771-4113. p. 944

Perry, Fran J, Librn, Harrison County Law Library, 1801 23rd Ave, Gulfport, MS, 39501. Tel: 228-865-4068. Fax: 228-865-4067. p. 1299

Perry, Gail, Librn, Valhalla Public Library, PO Box 68, Valhalla Centre, AB, T0H 3M0, CANADA. Tel: 780-356-3834. Fax: 780-356-3834. p. 2720

Perry, Glenda L, Librn, Metropolitan Nashville General Hospital, 1818 Albion St, Nashville, TN, 37208. Tel: 615-341-4100. Fax: 615-341-4501. p. 2257

Perry, Heather, ILL, Ref Serv, Stonehill College, 320 Washington St, Easton, MA, 02357-4015. Tel: 508-565-1313. Fax: 508-565-1424. p. 1086

Perry, Heather, Youth Serv Librn, Little Elm Public Library, 100 W Eldorado Pkwy, Little Elm, TX, 75068. Tel: 214-975-0430. Fax: 972-377-5546. p. 2356

Perry, Janet, Br Mgr, Jefferson Parish Library, Harahan Branch, 219 Soniat Ave, Harahan, LA, 70123. Tel: 504-736-8745. Fax: 504-736-8746. p. 956

Perry, Jennifer M, Mgr, Elsie Quirk Public Library of Englewood, 100 W Dearborn St, Englewood, FL, 34223-3309. Tel: 941-861-1200. p. 439

Perry, Jerry, Dir, University of Colorado Denver, 12950 E Montview Blvd, Aurora, CO, 80045. Tel: 303-724-2152. Fax: 303-724-2166. p. 289

Perry, Joan, Ser, Brown, Rudnick, Berlack, Israels LLP, One Financial Ctr, Boston, MA, 02111. Tel: 617-856-8213. Fax: 617-856-8201. p. 1059

Perry, Jody, Dir, Info Res & Serv, Marshall University Libraries, One John Marshall Dr, Huntington, WV, 25755-2060. Tel: 304-696-3226. Fax: 304-696-5858. p. 2561

Perry, Jone, Asst Librn, Daviess County Library, 306 W Grand, Gallatin, MO, 64640-1132. Tel: 660-663-3222. Fax: 660-663-3250. p. 1329

Perry, Judy M, Acq, Supvr, McAllen Memorial Library, 601 N Main, McAllen, TX, 78501-4666. Tel: 956-688-3300. Fax: 956-688-3301. p. 2360

Perry, Katherine, Dir, Virtual Library of Virginia, George Mason University, Fenwick B222, Fairfax, VA, 22030. Tel: 703-993-4652. Fax: 703-993-4662. p. 2957

Perry, Kay, Libr Assoc, Anadarko Community Library, 215 W Broadway, Anadarko, OK, 73005-2841. Tel: 405-247-7351. Fax: 405-247-2024. p. 1956

Perry, Kim, ILL, Dickstein Shapiro LLP, Research Services, 1825 Eye St NW, Washington, DC, 20006. Tel: 202-420-4999. Fax: 202-420-2201. p. 398

Perry, Kim, Circ Mgr, Bradford-West Gwillimbury Public Library, 425 Holland St W, Bradford, ON, L3Z 0J2, CANADA. Tel: 905-775-3328. Fax: 905-775-1236. p. 2796

Perry, Lathornia, Librn, Evening Post Publishing Co, 134 Columbus St, Charleston, SC, 29403. Tel: 843-937-5698. Fax: 843-937-5696. p. 2184

Perry, Lewis, Network Adminr, University of the District of Columbia, David A Clarke School of Law, Charles N & Hilda H M Mason Law Library, Bldg 39, Rm B-16, 4200 Connecticut Ave NW, Washington, DC, 20008. Tel: 202-274-7310. Fax: 202-274-7311. p. 421

Perry, Lora R, Dir, Walter J Hanna Memorial Library, 4615 Gary Ave, Fairfield, AL, 35064. Tel: 205-783-6007. Fax: 205-783-6041. p. 16

Perry, Louise, Mgr, Henrico County Public Library, North Park Branch Library, 8508 Franconia Rd, Henrico, VA, 23227-1213. Tel: 804-290-9700. Fax: 804-264-7035. p. 2471

Perry, Marita, Circ, Chillicothe & Ross County Public Library, South Salem Branch, Buckskin Elementary School, 4297 Broadway St, South Salem, OH, 45681. Tel: 937-981-2400. Fax: 937-981-3194. p. 1867

Perry, Mary, Libr Assoc, Georgia Highlands College Libraries, 3175 Cedartown Hwy SE, Rome, GA, 30161. Tel: 706-295-6318. Fax: 706-295-6365. p. 548

Perry, Mary Jean, Dir, Toponas Public Library, 33650 Hwy 134, Toponas, CO, 80479. Tel: 970-638-4436. p. 324

Perry, Mary Jean, Librn, Yampa Public Library, 310 Main St, Yampa, CO, 80483. Tel: 970-638-4654. Fax: 970-638-4654. p. 326

Perry, Maureen, Ref Serv, University of Southern Maine, 51 Westminster St, Lewiston, ME, 04240. Tel: 207-753-6540. Fax: 207-753-6543. p. 990

Perry, Michelle, Librn, Colonial Penn Life Insurance Co, 399 Market St, 5th Flr, Philadelphia, PA, 19106. Tel: 215-928-8000. Fax: 215-928-6035. p. 2104

Perry, Nancy, Ch, Norwell Public Library, 64 South St, Norwell, MA, 02061-2433. Tel: 781-659-2015. Fax: 781-659-6755. p. 1115

Perry, Nichelle, Assoc Dir, Ref & Instruction, North Carolina Central University, School of Law Library, 1512 S Alston Ave, Durham, NC, 27707. Tel: 919-530-5255. Fax: 919-530-7926. p. 1789

Perry, Pam, Asst Br Mgr, Shreve Memorial Library, Hollywood/Union Avenue, 2105 Hollywood Ave, Shreveport, LA, 71108. Tel: 318-636-5520. p. 969

Perry, Pamela, Bibliog Instr, Saddleback College, 28000 Marguerite Pkwy, Mission Viejo, CA, 92692. Tel: 949-582-4966. Fax: 949-364-0284. p. 187

Perry, Pamela, Online Serv Librn, MiraCosta College Library, One Barnard Dr, Oceanside, CA, 92056-3899. Tel: 760-795-6719. Fax: 760-795-6723. p. 199

Perry, Patrick, Dir, Bovey Public Library, 402 Second St, Bovey, MN, 55709. Tel: 218-245-3691. Fax: 218-245-3691. p. 1242

Perry, Rebecca, Tech Serv, Hampton Public Library, 4207 Victoria Blvd, Hampton, VA, 23669-4243. Tel: 757-727-1218. Fax: 757-727-1151. p. 2468

Perry, Rhonda, Youth Serv Coordr, Cobourg Public Library, 200 Ontario St, Cobourg, ON, K9A 5P4, CANADA. Tel: 905-372-9271. Fax: 905-372-4538. p. 2800

Perry, Robin, Asst Librn, Massachusetts Trial Court Law Libraries, Superior Courthouse, 186 S Main St, Fall River, MA, 02721. Tel: 508-491-3475. Fax: 508-491-3482. p. 1088

Perry, Ron, Head, Ref, Nashville Public Library, 615 Church St, Nashville, TN, 37219-2314. Tel: 615-862-5760. Fax: 615-862-5771. p. 2257

Perry, Sally, Librn, First Baptist Church Library, 612 N Duke St, Lancaster, PA, 17602. Tel: 717-392-8818. Fax: 717-392-2182. p. 2076

Perry, Sally, Librn, Reeves County Library, 505 S Park St, Pecos, TX, 79772-3735. Tel: 432-445-5340. Fax: 432-445-1028. p. 2369

Perry, Sharon, Spec Coll Librn, Paulina June & George Pollak Library, 800 N State College Blvd, Fullerton, CA, 92834. Tel: 714-278-2714. Fax: 714-278-2439. p. 154

Perry, Shelley, Libr Dir, Illiopolis-Niantic Public Library District, Sixth & Mary Sts, Illiopolis, IL, 62539. Tel: 217-486-5561. Fax: 217-486-7811. p. 658

Perry, Steve, Dir, Texas State Technical College Library, 300 Homer K Taylor Dr, Sweetwater, TX, 79556. Tel: 325-235-7406. Fax: 325-235-7462. p. 2390

Perry, Susan, Ser Librn, State University of New York College at Brockport, 350 New Campus Dr, Brockport, NY, 14420-2997. Tel: 585-395-5811. Fax: 585-395-5651. p. 1585

Perry, Susan, Br Mgr, Nashville Public Library, Green Hills, 3701 Benham Ave, Nashville, TN, 37215-2121. Tel: 615-862-5863. Fax: 615-862-5881. p. 2257

Perry, Teresa, Librn, Mason County Library System, Hannan, 6760 Ashton-Upland Rd, Ashton, WV, 25503. Tel: 304-743-6200. Fax: 304-743-6200. p. 2570

Perry, Tessa, Assoc Librn, Tech Serv, Virginia State University, One Hayden Dr, Petersburg, VA, 23806-0001. Tel: 804-524-5580. Fax: 804-524-6959. p. 2484

Perry, Valerie, Head of Libr, University of Kentucky Libraries, Agricultural Information Center, N24 Agricultural Sciences Ctr N, Lexington, KY, 40546-0091. Tel: 859-257-2758. Fax: 859-323-4719. p. 922

Perry-Ollila, Craig, Media Serv, Bellingham Technical College Library, 3028 Lindbergh Ave, Bellingham, WA, 98225-1599. Tel: 360-752-8383. Fax: 360-752-8384. p. 2508

Perryman, Wayne, Chair, Access Serv, Humboldt State University Library, One Harpst St, Arcata, CA, 95521-8299. Tel: 707-826-5598. Fax: 707-826-3440. p. 122

Persak, Virginia, Librn, Washington State Library, Washington State Reformatory, PO Box 777, MS-NM-83, Monroe, WA, 98272-0777. Tel: 360-794-2673, 360-794-2872. Fax: 360-794-2648. p. 2545

Persaud, Nicole, Info Tech, The William K Sanford Town Library, 629 Albany Shaker Rd, Loudonville, NY, 12211-1196. Tel: 518-458-9274. Fax: 518-438-0988. p. 1655

Perschbacher, Virginia, Dean, Southeast Arkansas College Library, 1900 Hazel St, Pine Bluff, AR, 71613-3900. Tel: 870-543-5936, 870-543-5988. Fax: 870-543-5937. p. 112

Persello, Karen, Head, Youth Serv, Chelsea District Library, 221 S Main St, Chelsea, MI, 48118-1267. Tel: 734-475-8732. Fax: 734-475-6190. p. 1163

Pershing, Gwendolyn, Head of Libr, Indiana University Bloomington, Education Library, Wright Education 1160, 201 N Rose St, Bloomington, IN, 47405-1006. Tel: 812-856-8590. Fax: 812-856-8593. p. 727

Pershing, Joan E, Dir, Wauseon Public Library, 117 E Elm St, Wauseon, OH, 43567. Tel: 419-335-6626. Fax: 419-335-0642. p. 1945

Persic, Peter, Dir, Pub Relations, Los Angeles Public Library System, 630 W Fifth St, Los Angeles, CA, 90071-2097. Tel: 213-228-7555. Fax: 213-228-7569. p. 172

Persick, Jenna, Acq, Coll Develop, Chester County Library System, 450 Exton Square Pkwy, Exton, PA, 19341-2496. Tel: 610-280-2600. Fax: 610-280-2688. p. 2056

Persick, Mike, Head, Acq & Ser, Haverford College, 370 Lancaster Ave, Haverford, PA, 19041-1392. Tel: 610-896-1175. Fax: 610-896-1102. p. 2067

Persily, Gail, Dir, Educ & Pub Serv, University of California San Francisco, 530 Parnassus Ave, San Francisco, CA, 94143-0840. Tel: 415-476-3766. p. 248

Persing, Robert, Ser, University of Pennsylvania Libraries, 3420 Walnut St, Philadelphia, PA, 19104-6206. Tel: 215-898-2815. Fax: 215-898-0559. p. 2118

Person, Craig, Head, Access Serv, Northern Kentucky University, University Dr, Highland Heights, KY, 41099. Tel: 859-572-6167. Fax: 859-572-5390. p. 917

Person, Debora, Admin Librn, University Of Wyoming, Dept 3035, 1000 E University Ave, Laramie, WY, 82071. Tel: 307-766-2210. Fax: 307-766-4044. p. 2657

Person, Kimberly, Libr Supvr-Popular Libr, Eastern Connecticut Health Network, 71 Haynes St, Manchester, CT, 06040-4188. Tel: 860-647-6853. Fax: 860-647-6443. p. 349

Personeus, Jackie, Br Mgr 1, Sno-Isle Libraries, Sultan Community Library, 319 Main St, Ste 100, Sultan, WA, 98294. Tel: 360-793-1695. Fax: 360-793-9634. p. 2542

Persons, Nancy, Dept Chair, Librn, Santa Rosa Junior College, 1501 Mendocino Ave, Santa Rosa, CA, 95401. Tel: 707-521-6902. Fax: 707-527-4545. p. 267

Persons, Sharon, Head, Res & Instruction, Northeastern University School of Law Library, 400 Huntington Ave, Boston, MA, 02115. Tel: 617-373-3883. Fax: 617-373-8705. p. 1066

Persson, Brittany, Ref/Acq, Seton Hall University, One Newark Ctr, Newark, NJ, 07102. Tel: 973-642-8767. p. 1513

Perugino, Patricia, Dir, Bloomingdale Free Public Library, Municipal Bldg, 101 Hamburg Tpk, Bloomingdale, NJ, 07403-1297. Tel: 973-838-0077, Fax: 973-838-2482. p. 1473

Perzeski, Donna, Mgr, Libr Serv, Ohio College of Podiatric Medicine Library, 6000 Rockside Woods Blvd, Independence, OH, 44131. Tel: 216-231-3300, Ext 7506. Fax: 216-447-0626. p. 1906

Pesale, Robert, Info Tech Coordr, West Bloomfield Township Public Library, 4600 Walnut Lake Rd, West Bloomfield, MI, 48323. Tel: 248-232-2315. Fax: 248-232-2291. p. 1236

Pesch, Christine, Ser & Presv Librn, Yale University Library, Divinity School Library, 409 Prospect St, New Haven, CT, 06511-2108. Tel: 203-432-5295. Fax: 203-432-3906. p. 357

Pesch, Nancy, Asst Librn, Shelbyville Free Public Library, 154 N Broadway St, Shelbyville, IL, 62565-1698. Tel: 217-774-4432. Fax: 217-774-2634. p. 702

Pesch, Wendy, Librn, Baton Rouge General Medical Center, 3600 Florida Blvd, Baton Rouge, LA, 70806. Tel: 225-387-7012. Fax: 225-381-6116. p. 942

Peschel, Susan, Photog Curator/Photographic Serv Adminr, University of Wisconsin-Milwaukee Libraries, American Geographical Society Library, Golda Meir Library, 2311 E Hartford Ave, Milwaukee, WI, 53211. Tel: 414-229-3984, 414-229-6282. Fax: 414-229-3624. p. 2622

Peschell, Gary, Librn, College of the North Atlantic, Raymond J Condon Memorial Library, Labrador West Campus, One Campbell Dr, Labrador City, NL, A2V 2Y1, CANADA. Tel: 709-944-6862. Fax: 709-944-6581. p. 2771

Pescoe, Susan, Cat Librn, Glen Rock Public Library, 315 Rock Rd, Glen Rock, NJ, 07452-1795. Tel: 201-670-3970. Fax: 201-445-0872. p. 1488

Pesheck, Susan, Ch, River Falls Public Library, 140 Union St, River Falls, WI, 54022. Tel: 715-425-0905, Ext 105. Fax: 715-425-0914. p. 2634

Pesik, Lori, Cat, Saint Mary's University of Minnesota, 700 Terrace Heights, No 26, Winona, MN, 55987-1399. Tel: 507-457-6665. Fax: 507-457-1565. p. 1289

Pesnell, Tedy, Tech Serv, Bossier Parish Central Library, 2206 Beckett St, Bossier City, LA, 71111. Tel: 318-746-1693. Fax: 318-746-7768. p. 945

Pessier, Johanne, Dir, College Lionel-Groulx, 100, rue Duquet, Sainte-Therese, QC, J7E 3G6, CANADA. Tel: 450-430-3120, Ext 407. Fax: 450-971-7883. p. 2979

Pestka, Joanna M, VPres, Capital Planning & Fac Operations, The New York Public Library - Astor, Lenox & Tilden Foundations, 476 Fifth Ave, (@ 42nd St), New York, NY, 10018-2788. Tel: 212-930-0071. Fax: 212-592-7440. p. 1690

Pet, Judith Ann, Dir, Manhattan-Elwood Public Library District, 240 Whitson St, Manhattan, IL, 60442. Tel: 815-478-3987. Fax: 815-478-3988. p. 669

Peter, David M, Dean, Vincennes University, Shake Learning Resources Center, 1002 N First St, Vincennes, IN, 47591. Tel: 812-888-5815. Fax: 812-888-5471. p. 784

Peter, Karen, Br Mgr, Hamilton Public Library, Terryberry, 100 Mohawk Rd W, Hamilton, ON, L9C 1W1, CANADA. Tel: 905-546-3200, Ext 7065. p. 2809

Peter, Phylis, Youth Serv Librn, Newton Public Library, 100 N Third Ave W, Newton, IA, 50208. Tel: 641-792-4108. Fax: 641-791-0729. p. 835

Peter-Cherneff, Brigitte, Head of Libr, British Columbia Institute of Technology Library, 3700 Willingdon Ave, SE14, Burnaby, BC, V5G 3H2, CANADA. Tel: 604-432-8360. Fax: 604-430-5443. p. 2725

Peter-Cherneff, Brigitte, Chief Librn, Salt Spring Island Public Library, 129 McPhillips Ave, Salt Spring Island, BC, V8K 2T6, CANADA. Tel: 250-537-4666. Fax: 250-537-4666. p. 2737

Peterangelo, Sally, Dir, Mountain Iron Public Library, 5742 Mountain Ave, Mountain Iron, MN, 55768-9636. Tel: 218-735-8625. Fax: 218-735-8252. p. 1267

Peterman, Ginger, Br Mgr, Chesterfield County Public Library, LaPrade, 9000 Hull St Rd, Richmond, VA, 23236. Tel: 804-276-7755. p. 2457

Peterman, Kevin, AV, Suffolk County Community College, 1001 Crooked Hill Rd, Brentwood, NY, 11717. Tel: 631-851-6740. Fax: 631-851-6509. p. 1584

Peters, Andy, Assoc Dir, Tech, Pioneer Library System, 225 N Webster Ave, Norman, OK, 73069-7133. Tel: 405-701-2690. Fax: 405-701-2649. p. 1970

Peters, Cathy, Br Mgr, Richmond Hill Public Library, Oak Ridges Moraine Library, 13085 Yonge St, Unit 12, Richmond Hill, ON, L4E 3L2, CANADA. Tel: 905-773-5533. Fax: 905-773-8107. p. 2839

Peters, Christina, Pub Serv Librn, Outreach, Northeast State Community College, 2425 Hwy 75, Blountville, TN, 37617-6350. Tel: 423-354-2429. Fax: 423-323-0254. p. 2224

Peters, Dawn, Dir, Orchard Park Public Library, S-4570 S Buffalo St, Orchard Park, NY, 14127. Tel: 716-662-9851. Fax: 716-667-3098. p. 1712

Peters, Deann, ILL, West Florida Public Library, 200 W Gregory St, Pensacola, FL, 32502. Tel: 850-436-5060. p. 482

Peters, Elaine, Libr Tech, Alberta Human Services, 855 Eighth Ave SW, 5th Flr, Calgary, AB, T2P 3P1, CANADA. Tel: 403-297-6344. Fax: 403-297-6235. p. 2687

Peters, Ellen, Br Mgr, Great River Regional Library, Eagle Bend Library, 127 E Main, Eagle Bend, MN, 56446. Tel: 218-738-4590. Fax: 218-738-4590. p. 1275

Peters, Ellen, Br Mgr, Great River Regional Library, Staples Public Library, 122 6th St NE, Staples, MN, 56479. Tel: 218-894-1401. Fax: 218-894-1401. p. 1276

Peters, Gail, Asst Librn, Bevill State Community College, 1411 Indiana Ave, Jasper, AL, 35501-4967. Tel: 205-387-0511, Ext 5718. Fax: 205-387-5190. p. 23

Peters, Ginnie, Asst Dir, Perry Public Library, 1101 Willis Ave, Perry, IA, 50220-1649. Tel: 515-465-3569. Fax: 515-465-9881. p. 838

Peters, Gretchen, ILL Coordr, Olivet College Library, 333 S Main St, Olivet, MI, 49076-9730. Tel: 269-749-6658. Fax: 269-749-7121. p. 1215

Peters, Janet, Tech Serv, Shook, Hardy & Bacon, 2555 Grand Blvd, 3rd Flr, Kansas City, MO, 64108-2613. Tel: 816-474-6550. Fax: 816-421-5547. p. 1341

Peters, Jennifer, Head, Tech Serv, Rockhurst University, 1100 Rockhurst Rd, Kansas City, MO, 64110-2561. Tel: 816-501-4134. Fax: 816-501-4666. p. 1340

Peters, Jennifer, Metadata Librn/Spec, Seneca College of Applied Arts & Technology, Newnham Campus (Main), 1750 Finch Ave E, North York, ON, M2J 2X5, CANADA. Tel: 416-491-5050, Ext 22070. Fax: 416-491-3349. p. 2813

Peters, Lisa, Access Serv, Case Western Reserve University, School of Law Library, 11075 East Blvd, Cleveland, OH, 44106-7148. Tel: 216-368-2793. Fax: 216-368-1002. p. 1876

Peters, Magnolia, Br Mgr, Cleveland Public Library, Addison, 6901 Superior Ave, Cleveland, OH, 44103. Tel: 216-623-6906. Fax: 216-623-6909. p. 1878

Peters, Margaret, Ref Serv, Wright Memorial Public Library, 1776 Far Hills Ave, Oakwood, OH, 45419-2598. Tel: 937-294-7171. Fax: 937-294-8578. p. 1924

Peters, Marjorie, Ref, College of DuPage Library, 425 Fawell Blvd, Glen Ellyn, IL, 60137-6599. Tel: 630-942-2337. Fax: 630-858-8757. p. 649

Peters, Mark, Mgr, Florida State College at Jacksonville, Downtown Campus, 101 W State St, Jacksonville, FL, 32202-3056. Tel: 904-633-8368. Fax: 904-633-8328. p. 453

Peters, Marlow E, Dir, Sharon Public Library, 133 E Main St, Sharon, TN, 38255. Tel: 731-456-2707. Fax: 731-456-2707. p. 2265

Peters, Mary Nelson, Libr Serv Mgr, Texas Scottish Rite Hospital, 2222 Welborn St, Dallas, TX, 75219-3993. Tel: 214-559-5000, 214-559-7875. Fax: 214-559-7835. p. 2311

Peters, MaryJane, Head, Circ, McHenry Nunda Public Library District, 813 W Rte 120, McHenry, IL, 60051. Tel: 815-385-6303. p. 672

Peters, Mata, Librn, American Samoa Office of Library Services, Faga'itua Branch, Faga'itua Village, AS, 96799. Tel: 684-622-7504. Fax: 684-633-4240. p. 2665

Peters, Melissa, Br Mgr, Jackson District Library, Carnegie, 244 W Michigan Ave, Jackson, MI, 49201. Tel: 517-788-4099, Ext 236. Fax: 517-782-8635. p. 1195

Peters, Melissa, Cent Serv Coordr, Jackson District Library, 290 W Michigan Ave, Jackson, MI, 49201. Tel: 517-788-4087, Ext 1333. Fax: 517-782-8635. p. 1195

Peters, Michael, Div Chief, Chicago Public Library, Humanities, 400 S State St, Chicago, IL, 60605. Tel: 312-747-4811. p. 609

Peters, Mindy L, Librn, Carpenter Technology Corp, 1600 Centre Ave, Reading, PA, 19601. Tel: 610-208-2807. p. 2133

Peters, Nevin, Libr Tech, Ser, Harrington College of Design Library, 200 W Madison St, Chicago, IL, 60606. Tel: 312-697-8019. Fax: 312-697-8115. p. 614

Peters, Pamela J, Dir, State University of New York College of Technology, Bush Hall, Two Main St, Delhi, NY, 13753. Tel: 607-746-4635. Fax: 607-746-4327. p. 1613

Peters, Patricia, Youth Serv Supvr, Lewisville Public Library System, 1197 W Main at Civic Circle, Lewisville, TX, 75067. Tel: 972-219-3691. Fax: 972-219-5094. p. 2355

Peters, Rebecca, Cat, University of Wisconsin-Stout Library, 315 Tenth Ave, Menomonie, WI, 54751-0790. Tel: 715-232-2094. Fax: 715-232-1783. p. 2615

Peters, Sally, Reader Serv, Ref Serv, Palo Alto Research Center (PARC), 3333 Coyote Hill Rd, Palo Alto, CA, 94304-1314. Tel: 650-812-4042. p. 204

Peters, Sharon, Dir, Mid-State Technical College, 933 Michigan Ave, Stevens Point, WI, 54481. Tel: 715-342-3129, 715-344-3063. Fax: 715-342-3134. p. 2639

Peters, Sharon, Archivist, The Mohawk Council of Akwesasne, Angus Mitchell Memorial Bldg, Saint-Regis, QC, N0M 1A0, CANADA. Tel: 613-575-1500, 613-575-2222. Fax: 613-575-1726. p. 2911

Peters, Stephen, Cat, Northern Michigan University, 1401 Presque Isle, Marquette, MI, 49855. Tel: 906-227-2123. Fax: 906-227-1333. p. 1207

Peters, Thomas, Dean of Libr Serv, Missouri State University, 850 S John Q Hammons Pkwy, Springfield, MO, 65807. Tel: 417-836-4525. Fax: 417-836-4764. p. 1366

Peters, Timothy, Dir, Info Serv, Central Michigan University, Park 407, Mount Pleasant, MI, 48859. Tel: 989-774-3720. Fax: 989-774-2179. p. 1211

Peters, Timothy, Off-Campus Libr Serv, Central Michigan University, Park 407, Mount Pleasant, MI, 48859. Tel: 989-774-3720. Fax: 989-774-2179. p. 1211

Peters, Todd C, Computer Serv, Texas State University-San Marcos, Wood & Talbot St, San Marcos, TX, 78666-4604. Tel: 512-245-2133. Fax: 512-245-3002. p. 2385

Peters, Victoria, Coordr, Acq, Minnesota State University, Mankato, ML3097, Mankato, MN, 56001. Tel: 507-389-5952. Fax: 507-389-5155. p. 1257

Peters, William, Dir, Settlement Music School, Kardon-Northeast - Sol Schoenbach Library, 3745 Clarendon Ave, Philadelphia, PA, 19114. Tel: 215-320-2622. Fax: 215-637-8716. p. 2117

Petersen, Bonnie, Dir of Tech Serv, Kirkwood Public Library, 140 E Jefferson Ave, Kirkwood, MO, 63122. Tel: 314-821-5770, Ext 1014. Fax: 314-822-3755. p. 1342

Petersen, Carolyn, Dir, Odessa College, 201 W University Blvd, Odessa, TX, 79764. Tel: 432-335-6640. Fax: 432-335-6610. p. 2366

Petersen, Casey, Consumer Health Librn, St Mary's Hospital Medical Center, 700 S Park St, Madison, WI, 53715. Tel: 608-512-4000. Fax: 608-258-6119. p. 2607

Petersen, Chris, Res Asst, Oregon State University Libraries, University Archives & Special Collections, 121 Valley Library, Corvallis, OR, 97331-4501. Tel: 541-737-2810. Fax: 541-737-3453. p. 1995

Petersen, Drake, Librn, University of King's College Library, 6350 Coburg Rd, Halifax, NS, B3H 2A1, CANADA. Tel: 902-422-1271. Fax: 902-423-3357. p. 2783

Petersen, Helen, Dir, Ch Serv, Clarence Dillon Public Library, 2336 Lamington Rd, Bedminster, NJ, 07921. Tel: 908-234-2325. Fax: 908-781-9402. p. 1471

Petersen, Julie, Librn, McLean-Mercer Regional Library, Washburn Branch, 705 Main St, Washburn, ND, 58577. Tel: 701-462-8180. Fax: 701-462-8180. p. 1848

Petersen, Karen, Librn, Santa Rosa Junior College, 1501 Mendocino Ave, Santa Rosa, CA, 95401. Tel: 707-778-3972. Fax: 707-527-4545. p. 267

Petersen, Kristi, Cat, Southwest Minnesota State University Library, 1501 State St, Marshall, MN, 56258. Tel: 507-537-6162. Fax: 507-537-6200. p. 1258

Petersen, Loralee, Dir, Withee Public Library, 511 Division St, Withee, WI, 54498. Tel: 715-229-2010. Fax: 715-229-2010. p. 2650

Petersen, Lori, Tech Serv Adminr, Waterloo Public Library, 415 Commercial St, Waterloo, IA, 50701-1385. Tel: 319-291-4521. Fax: 319-291-6736. p. 850

Petersen, Mary, Mgr, Brookhaven National Laboratory, Research Library, Bldg 477, Upton, NY, 11973-5000. Tel: 631-344-3489. Fax: 631-344-2090. p. 1758

Petersen, Nancy, Mgr, Coll Develop, Knox County Public Library System, 500 W Church Ave, Knoxville, TN, 37902-2505. Tel: 865-215-8750. Fax: 865-215-8742. p. 2241

Petersen, Rebecca, Dir, Manitowoc-Calumet Library System, 4519 Lincoln Ave, Two Rivers, WI, 54241. Tel: 920-553-6257. Fax: 920-553-6259. p. 2643

Petersen, Sheila, Librn, Battle Creek Public Library, 115 Main St, Battle Creek, IA, 51006. Tel: 712-365-4912. Fax: 712-365-4912. p. 796

Petersen, Shirley, Tech Serv, Des Moines Area Community College Library, 2006 S Ankeny Blvd, Ankeny, IA, 50023. Tel: 515-964-6634. Fax: 515-965-7126. p. 793

Peterson, Adrian, Learning Commons Supvr, Snow College, 141 E Center St, Ephraim, UT, 84627. Tel: 435-283-7363. Fax: 435-283-7369. p. 2405

Peterson, Adrianne, Mgr, Jefferson County Public Library, Conifer Public, 10441 Hwy 73, Conifer, CO, 80433. Tel: 303-982-5310. p. 315

Peterson, Adrianne, Mgr, Jefferson County Public Library, Edgewater Branch, 5843 W 25th Ave, Edgewater, CO, 80214. p. 315

Peterson, Adrianne, Mgr, Jefferson County Public Library, Wheat Ridge Library, 5475 W 32nd Ave, Wheat Ridge, CO, 80212. p. 315

Peterson, Al, Head, Pub Serv, North Dakota State Library, Library Memorial Bldg, 604 East Blvd Ave, Dept 250, Bismarck, ND, 58505-0800. Tel: 701-328-4021. Fax: 701-328-2040. p. 1838

Peterson, Andrea, Actg Asst Dean, Coll & Tech, Head, Info Tech, Western Washington University, 516 High St, MS 9103, Bellingham, WA, 98225. Tel: 360-650-3894. Fax: 360-650-3954. p. 2509

Peterson, Andrea, Dir, Lake Geneva Public Library, 918 W Main St, Lake Geneva, WI, 53147-1890. Tel: 262-249-5299. Fax: 262-249-5284. p. 2604

Peterson, Angela, Librn, Northwest Regional Library, Greenbush Public Library, 242 Main St N, Greenbush, MN, 56726-0009. Tel: 218-782-2218. Fax: 218-782-2218. p. 1286

Peterson, Anne, Curator, Southern Methodist University, DeGolyer Library of Special Collections, 6404 Robert S Hyer Lane, Dallas, TX, 75275. Tel: 214-768-2661. Fax: 214-768-1565. p. 2310

Peterson, Ardith, Circ, Brownsburg Public Library, 450 S Jefferson St, Brownsburg, IN, 46112-1310. Tel: 317-852-3167. Fax: 317-852-7734. p. 730

Peterson, Ashley, Access Serv Librn, Wheelock College Library, 132 The Riverway, Boston, MA, 02215-4815. Tel: 617-879-2398. Fax: 617-879-2408. p. 1068

Peterson, Barbara, Dir, Prospect Public Library, 17 Center St, Prospect, CT, 06712. Tel: 203-758-3001. Fax: 203-758-0080. p. 365

Peterson, Barbara, Dir, Council Bluffs Public Library, 400 Willow Ave, Council Bluffs, IA, 51503-4269. Tel: 712-323-7553, Ext 123. Fax: 712-323-1269. p. 805

Peterson, Becky, Ref, Alamance County Public Libraries, May Memorial Library, 342 S Spring St, Burlington, NC, 27215. Tel: 336-229-3588. Fax: 336-229-3592. p. 1779

Peterson, Ben, Tech Spec, Brandon Township Public Library, 304 South St, Ortonville, MI, 48462. Tel: 248-627-1460. Fax: 248-627-9880. p. 1215

Peterson, Bernice J, In Charge, Bayliss Public Library, Brevort Township Community, 4009 N Church St, Moran, MI, 49760. Tel: 906-643-8098. Fax: 906-643-6525. p. 1226

Peterson, Betsy Bahr, Dir, Mashantucket Pequot Museum & Research Center, 110 Pequot Trail, Mashantucket, CT, 06338. Tel: 860-396-6858. Fax: 860-396-6874. p. 350

Peterson, Carl, Spec Coll Librn, Colgate University, 13 Oak Dr, Hamilton, NY, 13346-1398. Tel: 315-228-7300. Fax: 315-228-7934. p. 1633

Peterson, Carla, Asst Dir, Yuma County Library District, 2951 S 21st Dr, Yuma, AZ, 85364. Tel: 928-373-6461. Fax: 928-782-9420. p. 91

Peterson, Carla, Asst Dir, Yuma Public Library, 114 W Third Ave, Yuma, CO, 80759-2402. Tel: 970-848-2368. Fax: 970-848-0423. p. 326

Peterson, Carol, Archivist, San Mateo County History Museum & Archives, 2200 Broadway, Redwood City, CA, 94063. Tel: 650-299-0104. Fax: 650-299-0141. p. 215

Peterson, Carolyn, Dir of Libr Serv, Shaw University, 118 E South St, Raleigh, NC, 27601. Tel: 919-546-8407. Fax: 919-831-1161. p. 1817

Peterson, Cathy, ILL Coordr, George Fox University, 416 N Meridian St, Newberg, OR, 97132. Tel: 503-554-2410. Fax: 503-554-3599. p. 2007

Peterson, Cathy W, Dir, Tomah Public Library, 716 Superior Ave, Tomah, WI, 54660-2098. Tel: 608-374-7470. Fax: 608-374-7471. p. 2642

Peterson, Christina, Coordr, Info Literacy & Distance Educ, San Jose State University, One Washington Sq, San Jose, CA, 95192-0028. Tel: 408-808-2099. Fax: 408-808-2141. p. 251

Peterson, Christine, Librn, Community College of Rhode Island, One John H Chafee Blvd, Newport, RI, 02840. Tel: 401-825-1000. p. 2169

Peterson, Cindy, Tech Serv, Melbourne Public Library, 540 E Fee Ave, Melbourne, FL, 32901. Tel: 321-952-4514. Fax: 321-952-4518. p. 463

Peterson, Cynthia L, Dir, Libr Serv, East Texas Baptist University, 1209 N Grove St, Marshall, TX, 75670-1498. Tel: 903-923-2256. Fax: 903-935-3447. p. 2359

Peterson, Dave, Libr Syst Adminr, Snow College, 141 E Center St, Ephraim, UT, 84627. Tel: 435-283-7360. Fax: 435-283-7369. p. 2405

Peterson, Debra D, Librn, Sedro-Woolley Public Library, 802 Ball Ave, Sedro-Woolley, WA, 98284-2008. Tel: 360-855-1166. p. 2535

Peterson, Dee, Pub Serv Librn, Ref, Ohio Wesleyan University, 43 Rowland, Delaware, OH, 43015-2370. Tel: 740-368-3240. Fax: 740-368-3222. p. 1896

Peterson, Dennis, Sr Dir for Libr Serv, Palmer College of Chiropractic-Davenport Campus, 1000 Brady St, Davenport, IA, 52803-5287. Tel: 563-884-5442. Fax: 563-884-5897. p. 806

Peterson, Diana, Archivist, Haverford College, 370 Lancaster Ave, Haverford, PA, 19041-1392. Tel: 610-896-1284. Fax: 610-896-1102. p. 2067

Peterson, Elizabeth, Dir, Library of Congress, American Folklife Center, Library of Congress Thomas Jefferson Bldg, G53, 101 Independence Ave SE, Washington, DC, 20540-4610. Tel: 202-707-5510. Fax: 202-707-2076. p. 406

Peterson, Ellen, Pub Serv, University of Hawaii, 310 Kaahumanu Ave, Kahului, HI, 96732. Tel: 808-984-3582. Fax: 808-244-9644. p. 566

Peterson, Ellen, Circ Supvr, Davis County Library, Central Branch, 155 N Wasatch Dr, Layton, UT, 84041. Tel: 801-547-0729. p. 2405

Peterson, Gabe, Assoc Prof, North Carolina Central University, 1801 Fayetteville St, Durham, NC, 27707. Tel: 919-530-6485. Fax: 919-530-6402. p. 2971

Peterson, Gail, Br Serv Coordr, Palm Beach County Library System, 3650 Summit Blvd, West Palm Beach, FL, 33406-4198. Tel: 561-233-2712. Fax: 561-233-2622. p. 503

Peterson, Gerry L, Archivist, Bibliographer, Spec Coll Librn, University of Northern Iowa Library, 1227 W 27th St, Cedar Falls, IA, 50613-3675. Tel: 319-273-6307. Fax: 319-273-2913. p. 799

Peterson, Holly, Dir, Friends of Historic Boonville, 614 E Morgan, Boonville, MO, 65233. Tel: 660-882-7977. Fax: 660-882-9194. p. 1320

Peterson, Jacque, Libr Coordr, Alaska State Library, Library Development, 344 W Third Ave, Ste 125, Anchorage, AK, 99501. Tel: 907-269-6571. Fax: 907-269-6580. p. 44

Peterson, Jane, Libr Serv Mgr, Oro Valley Public Library, 1305 W Naranja Dr, Oro Valley, AZ, 85737-9762. Tel: 520-229-5300. Fax: 520-229-5319. p. 70

Peterson, Janet, Reserves Supvr, University of Wisconsin-Eau Claire, 105 Garfield Ave, Eau Claire, WI, 54702-4004. Tel: 715-836-3715. Fax: 715-836-2949. p. 2590

Peterson, Jill, Dir, Sheffield Public Library, 123 S Third St, Sheffield, IA, 50475. Tel: 641-892-4717. Fax: 641-892-4248. p. 842

Peterson, Jim, Tech Coordr, Goodnight Memorial Library, 203 S Main St, Franklin, KY, 42134. Tel: 270-586-8397. Fax: 270-586-8397. p. 914

Peterson, John, Archivist, Lutheran Theological Seminary, 7301 Germantown Ave, Philadelphia, PA, 19119-1794. Tel: 215-248-6383. Fax: 215-248-6327. p. 2112

Peterson, Jolene, Cat, Libr Tech, Ridgewater College Library, 2101 15th Ave NW, Willmar, MN, 56201. Tel: 320-222-7537. Fax: 320-222-7539. p. 1289

Peterson, Jonna, Educ Coordr, Ref Librn, Library of Rush University Medical Center, Armour Academic Ctr, 600 S Paulina St, 5th Flr, Chicago, IL, 60612-3874. Tel: 312-942-2274. Fax: 312-942-3143. p. 617

Peterson, Julie, Curator, Walker Memorial Library, 800 Main St, Westbrook, ME, 04092. Tel: 207-854-0630. Fax: 207-854-0629. p. 1006

Peterson, Karen, Ch, Nottawa Township Library, 685 E Main St, Centreville, MI, 49032-9603. Tel: 269-467-6289. Fax: 269-467-4422. p. 1162

Peterson, Karen, Archivist, Oregon Health & Science University Library, 3181 SW Sam Jackson Park Rd, Portland, OR, 97239-3098. Tel: 503-494-3460. Fax: 503-494-3227. p. 2013

Peterson, Katewin, Br Mgr, La Crosse County Library, Onalaska Public, 741 Oak Ave S, Onalaska, WI, 54650. Tel: 608-781-9568. Fax: 608-781-9594. p. 2598

Peterson, Kaye, Asst Dir, St Catharine College Library, 2735 Bardstown Rd, Saint Catharine, KY, 40061. Tel: 859-336-5082, Ext 1260. Fax: 859-336-5031. p. 934

Peterson, Kelly, Digital Projects Librn, Instrul Serv Librn, Oregon Institute of Technology Library, 3201 Campus Dr, Klamath Falls, OR, 97601-8801. Tel: 541-885-1783. Fax: 541-885-1777. p. 2002

Peterson, Kenneth, ILS Adminr, Regional Adminr, Boston Public Library, 700 Boylston St, Boston, MA, 02117-0286. Tel: 617-536-5400. Fax: 617-236-4306. p. 1056

Peterson, Kim, Dir of Tech Serv, Saint Louis Public Library, 1415 Olive St, Saint Louis, MO, 63103-2315. Tel: 314-539-0300. Fax: 314-241-3840. p. 1359

Peterson, Kris, Prog Dir, Springmier Community Library, 311 W Marengo Rd, Tiffin, IA, 52340-9308. Tel: 319-545-2960. Fax: 319-545-2863. p. 847

Peterson, Leslie M, Asst Dean, Minnesota State University, Mankato, ML3097, Mankato, MN, 56001. Tel: 507-389-2290. Fax: 507-389-5155. p. 1257

Peterson, Lillie, Tech Serv, The Library of Hattiesburg, Petal, Forrest County, 329 Hardy St, Hattiesburg, MS, 39401-3496. Tel: 601-582-4461. Fax: 601-582-5338. p. 1300

Peterson, Linda, Ch, Leominster Public Library, 30 West St, Leominster, MA, 01453. Tel: 978-534-7522. Fax: 978-840-3357. p. 1098

Peterson, Lorna, Assoc Prof, University at Buffalo, State University of New York, 534 Baldy Hall, Buffalo, NY, 14260. Tel: 716-645-2412. Fax: 716-645-3775. p. 2971

Peterson, Maria X, Unit Mgr, Chicago Public Library, Thomas Hughes Children's Library, 400 S State St, Chicago, IL, 60605. Tel: 312-747-4614. Fax: 312-747-4223. p. 609

Peterson, Mark, Exec Dir, Winona County Historical Society, 160 Johnson St, Winona, MN, 55987. Tel: 507-454-2723. Fax: 507-454-0006. p. 1290

Peterson, Mary, Instrul Serv Librn, Simpson College, 508 North C St, Indianola, IA, 50125-1216. Tel: 515-961-1663. Fax: 515-961-1363. p. 822

Peterson, Melissa, Chair, Erie Community College-South Campus, 4041 Southwestern Blvd, Orchard Park, NY, 14127. Tel: 716-851-1772. Fax: 716-851-1778. p. 1712

Peterson, Merlin, Dir, Pope County Historical Society, 809 S Lake Shore Dr, Glenwood, MN, 56334. Tel: 320-634-3293. p. 1252

Peterson, Myrene, Librn, Enderlin Municipal Library, 303 Railway St, Enderlin, ND, 58027. Tel: 701-437-2953. Fax: 701-437-2104. p. 1840

Peterson, Nancy, Librn, Health One Presbyterian-Saint Luke's Medical Center, 1719 E 19th Ave, Denver, CO, 80218-1281. Tel: 303-839-6670. Fax: 303-869-1643. p. 302

Peterson, Nedra, Dir, Woodbury University Library, 7500 Glenoaks Blvd, Burbank, CA, 91510-1099. Tel: 818-252-5200. Fax: 818-767-4534. p. 130

Peterson, Oona, ILL, Faegre & Benson, LLP, 2200 Wells Fargo Ctr, 90 South Seventh St, Minneapolis, MN, 55402-3901. Tel: 612-766-7000. Fax: 612-766-1600. p. 1259

Peterson, Pamela, Tech Serv, Saint Petersburg Public Library, 3745 Ninth Ave N, Saint Petersburg, FL, 33713. Tel: 727-893-7724. Fax: 727-892-5432. p. 488

Peterson, Pat, Circ, Maud Preston Palenske Memorial Library, 500 Market St, Saint Joseph, MI, 49085. Tel: 269-983-7167. Fax: 269-983-5804. p. 1225

Peterson, Pat, Ref & ILL Librn, Spec, Southeast Community College-Lincoln Campus, 8800 O St, Lincoln, NE, 68520. Tel: 402-437-2585. Fax: 402-437-2404. p. 1406

Peterson, Patricia, Br Mgr, Public Library of Cincinnati & Hamilton County, Saint Bernard, 4803 Tower Ave, Cincinnati, OH, 45217. Tel: 513-369-4462. Fax: 513-369-4463. p. 1873

Peterson, Paula, Asst Dir, Boylston Public Library, 695 Main St, Boylston, MA, 01505-1399. Tel: 508-869-2371. Fax: 508-869-6195. p. 1069

Peterson, Rachel, Pub Serv, Chowan University, One University Pl, Murfreesboro, NC, 27855. Tel: 252-398-6202. Fax: 252-398-1301. p. 1811

Peterson, Rick, Dep Dir, Duke University Libraries, Medical Center Library, DUMC Box 3702, Ten Bryan-Searle Dr, Durham, NC, 27710-0001. Tel: 919-660-1100. Fax: 919-681-7599. p. 1788

Peterson, Rick, Mgr, Access Serv, Lewis & Clark College, Aubrey R Watzek Library, 0615 SW Palatine Hill Rd, Portland, OR, 97219-7899. Tel: 503-768-7274. Fax: 503-768-7282. p. 2011

Peterson, Rose, Mgr, Coll Mgt, Mgr, Info Tech, Rockford Public Library, 215 N Wyman St, Rockford, IL, 61101-1023. Tel: 815-965-7606. Fax: 815-965-0866. p. 697

Peterson, Ruth, Dir, Blair Public Library, 210 S 17th St, Blair, NE, 68008. Tel: 402-426-3617. p. 1394

Peterson, Sandra K, Govt Doc, Yale University Library, Government Documents & Information Center, 38 Mansfield St, New Haven, CT, 06511. Tel: 203-432-3212. Fax: 203-432-3214. p. 358

Peterson, Sherrie, Libr Dir, Newell Public Library, 205 E Second, Newell, IA, 50568. Tel: 712-272-4334. Fax: 712-272-4334. p. 835

Peterson, Sue, Ref Librn, Benedictine University Library, 5700 College Rd, Lisle, IL, 60532-0900. Tel: 630-829-6590. Fax: 630-960-9451. p. 666

Peterson, Susan M, Dir, East Longmeadow Public Library, 60 Center Sq, East Longmeadow, MA, 01028-2459. Tel: 413-525-5400. Fax: 413-525-0344. p. 1086

Peterson, Toby, Head, Access Serv, Hood College, 401 Rosemont Ave, Frederick, MD, 21701. Tel: 301-696-3924. Fax: 301-696-3796. p. 1029

Peterson, Victoria, Tech Mgr, Mancos Public Library, 211 W First St, Mancos, CO, 81328. Tel: 970-533-7600. Fax: 970-533-7289. p. 318

Peterson, Willene, Librn, First Baptist Church, 395 Marion St NE, Salem, OR, 97301. Tel: 503-364-2285. Fax: 503-391-9272. p. 2017

Peterson, Yvonne, Asst Librn, Leroy Community Library, 104 W Gilbert, Le Roy, MI, 49655. Tel: 231-768-4493. Fax: 231-768-5024. p. 1203

Peterson-Winter, Barbara, Circ Librn, Dover Public Library, 73 Locust St, Dover, NH, 03820-3785. Tel: 603-516-6050. Fax: 603-516-6053. p. 1445

Peth, Sara, Libr Mgr, Department of Veterans Affairs, 2215 Fuller Rd, Ann Arbor, MI, 48105. Tel: 734-845-5408. Fax: 734-845-3110. p. 1151

Pethe, Marlyn, Dir, University of Tampa, 401 W Kennedy Blvd, Tampa, FL, 33606-1490. Tel: 813-253-6231. Fax: 813-258-7426. p. 499

Petino, Taya, Br Mgr, Ocean County Library, Point Pleasant Beach Branch, 710 McLean Ave, Point Pleasant Beach, NJ, 08742-2522. Tel: 732-892-4575. Fax: 732-701-1941. p. 1534

Petit, Darlene, Librn, Wisewood Library, PO Box 309, Buffalo Narrows, SK, S0M 0J0, CANADA. Tel: 306-235-4240. Fax: 306-235-4511. p. 2917

Petit, Joan, Humanities & Soc Sci Librn, Soc Media Coordr, Portland State University Library, 1875 SW Park Ave, Portland, OR, 97201-3220. Tel: 503-725-2397. Fax: 503-725-4524. p. 2014

Petit, Michael, Cat, American University, 4801 Massachusetts Ave NW, Washington, DC, 20016-8182. Tel: 202-274-4345. Fax: 202-274-4365. p. 393

Petite, Trisha, Librn, Gardere, Wynne & Sewell Library, 1000 Louisiana, Ste 3400, Houston, TX, 77002. Tel: 713-276-5500. Fax: 713-276-6736. p. 2335

Petitti, Adrianne, Info Spec, Towers Perrin Information Centre, South Tower, Ste 1501, 175 Bloor St E, Toronto, ON, M4W 3T6, CANADA. Tel: 416-960-2836. Fax: 416-960-2819. p. 2864

Petkoff, Alec, Dep Dir, American Legion National Headquarters, 1608 K St NW, Washington, DC, 20006. Tel: 202-263-2988. Fax: 202-861-2728. p. 392

Petkus, Norma, Dir, Bradford Public Library, 138 E Main St, Bradford, OH, 45308-1108. Tel: 937-448-2612. Fax: 937-448-2615. p. 1861

Petosa, Francine, Dir, Bristol Public Library, Five High St, Bristol, CT, 06010. Tel: 860-584-7787. Fax: 860-584-7696. p. 332

Petraits, Ellen, Res & Instruction Librn, Rhode Island School of Design Library, 15 Westminster St, Providence, RI, 02903. Tel: 401-709-5905. Fax: 401-709-5932. p. 2174

Petrak, Janet C, Librn, Excela Health, 532 W Pittsburgh St, Greensburg, PA, 15601-2282. Tel: 724-832-4088. Fax: 724-832-4661. p. 2062

Petrak, Janet C, Librn, Frick Hospital, 508 S Church St, Mount Pleasant, PA, 15666. Tel: 724-547-1352. Fax: 724-547-1693. p. 2093

Petrash, Antonia, Dir, Glen Cove Public Library, Four Glen Cove Ave, Glen Cove, NY, 11542-2885. Tel: 516-676-2130. Fax: 516-676-2788. p. 1628

Petri, Laurie, Assoc Librn, University of Wisconsin, 2000 W Fifth St, Marshfield, WI, 54449-3310. Tel: 715-389-6512, 715-389-6531. Fax: 715-389-6539. p. 2613

Petri, N, Bus Officer, Queen's University, 101 Union St, Kingston, ON, K7L 5C4, CANADA. Tel: 613-533-2518. Fax: 613-533-6362. p. 2814

Petric, Doug, Librn, Groveland Correctional Facility Library, 7000 Rte 36, Sonyea Rd, Sonyea, NY, 14556-0001. Tel: 585-658-2871. p. 1745

Petrich, Kurt, Head, Automation, Stinson Memorial Public Library District, 409 S Main St, Anna, IL, 62906. Tel: 618-833-2521. Fax: 618-833-3560. p. 589

Petrick, Joseph, Tech Serv, State University of New York, College of Technology, Upper Colleg Dr, Alfred, NY, 14802. Tel: 607-587-4313. Fax: 607-587-4351. p. 1572

Petricka, David, Librn, Antique Stove Association Library, 823 Lincoln Ave SW, Faribault, MN, 55021-6636. Tel: 507-210-4304. p. 1250

Petrie, Angela, Youth Serv, Stillwater Public Library, 224 N Third St, Stillwater, MN, 55082. Tel: 651-275-4338. Fax: 651-275-4342. p. 1285

Petrie, Linda, Govt Doc Mgr, Wabash College, PO Box 352, Crawfordsville, IN, 47933. Tel: 765-361-6361. Fax: 765-361-6295. p. 734

Petrie, Sandy, Dir, Noble County Public Library, 813 E Main St, Albion, IN, 46701. Tel: 260-636-7197. Fax: 260-636-3321. p. 723

Petrikas, Susan, Ad, Seabrook Library, 25 Liberty Lane, Seabrook, NH, 03874-4506. Tel: 603-474-2044. Fax: 603-474-1835. p. 1465

Petrikas, Susan, YA Librn, Seabrook Library, 25 Liberty Lane, Seabrook, NH, 03874-4506. Tel: 603-474-2044. Fax: 603-474-1835. p. 1465

Petrillo, Susi, Mgr, Libr Serv, Sierra Nevada Memorial Hospital, 155 Glasson Way, Grass Valley, CA, 95945-5723. Tel: 530-274-6064. Fax: 530-274-6214. p. 156

Petrisor, Christina, Head Librn, Lacombe Public Library, 101-5214 50 Ave, Lacombe, AB, T4L 0B6, CANADA. Tel: 403-782-3433. Fax: 403-782-3329. p. 2709

Petro, Mary, Dir, North Suburban Library District, 6340 N Second St, Loves Park, IL, 61111. Tel: 815-633-4247. Fax: 815-633-4249. p. 668

Petroccione, Patricia, Dir, Walter T McCarthy Law Library, Court House, 1425 N Courthouse Rd, Ste 1700, Arlington, VA, 22201. Tel: 703-228-7005. Fax: 703-228-7360. p. 2449

Petrocelli, Nino, Sr, Pres, Bridgeville Public Library, 505 McMillen St, Bridgeville, PA, 15017. Tel: 412-221-3737. Fax: 412-220-8124. p. 2037

Petrongolo, Robin, Asst Librn, Runnemede Free Public Library, Broadway & Black Horse Pike, Runnemede, NJ, 08078. Tel: 856-939-4688. Fax: 856-939-6371. p. 1528

Petrosillo, Judith, Libr Mgr, Berne Public Library, 1656 Helderberg Trail, Berne, NY, 12023-0209. Tel: 518-872-1246. Fax: 518-872-9024. p. 1581

Petroski, Barb, Librn, Portage County Historical Society Museum & Library, 6549 N Chestnut St, Ravenna, OH, 44266. Tel: 330-296-3523. p. 1931

Petrov, Kate, Pub Relations Mgr, Greenwich Library, 101 W Putnam Ave, Greenwich, CT, 06830-5387. Tel: 203-625-6550. Fax: 203-622-7959. p. 341

Petrowski, Carol, Ref Librn, La Crosse County Library, Onalaska Public, 741 Oak Ave S, Onalaska, WI, 54650. Tel: 608-781-9568. Fax: 608-781-9594. p. 2598

Petrucelli, Mary Ellen, Admin Coordr, Lady Lake Public Library, 225 W Guava St, Lady Lake, FL, 32159. Tel: 352-753-2957. Fax: 352-753-3361. p. 457

Petruga, Patricia, Clinical Libr Tech, Bridgepoint Health Clinical Library, 14 St Matthews Rd, Toronto, ON, M4M 2B5, CANADA. Tel: 416-461-8252, Ext 2436. Fax: 416-470-6721. p. 2850

Petrus, Janice, Dir, Albion Area Public Library, 111 E Pearl St, Albion, PA, 16401-1202. Tel: 814-756-5400. Fax: 814-756-5400. p. 2026

Petrus, Patricia, Asst Librn, Chester Public Library, 21 W Main St, Chester, CT, 06412. Tel: 860-526-0018. p. 334

Petrus, Robin, Dir, Broome Community College, 907 Front St, Binghamton, NY, 13905-1328. Tel: 607-778-5201. Fax: 607-778-5108. p. 1581

Petruzzelli, Barbara, Dir, Mount Saint Mary College, 330 Powell Ave, Newburgh, NY, 12550-3494. Tel: 845-569-3601. Fax: 845-561-0999. p. 1704

Petruzzi, Anthony, Mgr, Literacy Serv, Morley Library, 184 Phelps St, Painesville, OH, 44077-3926. Tel: 440-352-3383, Ext 408. Fax: 440-352-2653. p. 1927

Petruzzi, Mary, Admin Officer, University of Connecticut Health Center, 263 Farmington Ave, Farmington, CT, 06034. Tel: 860-679-3808. Fax: 860-679-1230. p. 340

Petry, Bonnie, Ref Librn, California State University, San Bernardino, 5500 University Pkwy, San Bernardino, CA, 92407-2318. Tel: 909-537-5114. Fax: 909-537-7048. p. 227

Petry, Maureen, Ch, North Castle Public Library, 19 Whippoorwill Rd E, Armonk, NY, 10504. Tel: 914-273-3887. Fax: 914-273-5572. p. 1575

Petry, Maureen, Dir, Warner Library, 121 N Broadway, Tarrytown, NY, 10591. Tel: 914-631-7734. Fax: 914-631-2324. p. 1754

Petry, Traci, Dir, Divide County Public Library, 204 First St NE, Crosby, ND, 58730. Tel: 701-965-6305. p. 1839

Petryk, Gail, Membership Serv Supvr, Edmonton Public Library, Mill Woods, 601 Mill Woods Town Centre, 2331 66 St, Edmonton, AB, T6K 4B5, CANADA. Tel: 780-496-1821. Fax: 780-496-1450. p. 2700

Petsch, Janalee, Dir, Southeast Community College, 600 State St, Milford, NE, 68405. Tel: 402-761-2131, Ext 8245. Fax: 402-761-2324. p. 1408

Pettegrew, Linda, Per, The Master's Seminary Library, 13248 Roscoe Blvd, Sun Valley, CA, 91352. Tel: 818-909-5634. Fax: 818-909-5680. p. 273

Pettegrew, Martha, Br Supvr, Barry-Lawrence Regional Library, Aurora Branch, 202 Jefferson, Aurora, MO, 65605. Tel: 417-678-2036. Fax: 417-678-2041. p. 1346

Petter, Chris, Spec Coll Librn, University of Victoria Libraries, McPherson Library, PO Box 1800, Victoria, BC, V8W 3H5, CANADA. Tel: 250-721-8211. Fax: 250-721-8215. p. 2746

Petterchak, Lou, Sr Librn, Denver Public Library, Ross-Barnum Branch, 3570 W First Ave, Denver, CO, 80219-1346. Tel: 303-935-1891. Fax: 303-934-9324. p. 301

Pettey, Kara, Ch, Madison-Jefferson County Public Library, 420 W Main St, Madison, IN, 47250-3796. Tel: 812-265-2744. Fax: 812-265-2217. p. 762

Pettijohn, Barbara, Head, Ref, Manchester Public Library, 586 Main St, Manchester, CT, 06040. Tel: 860-643-2471. Fax: 860-643-9453. p. 350

Pettijohn, Patricia, Head, Coll & Tech Serv, University of South Florida Saint Petersburg, 140 Seventh Ave S, POY118, Saint Petersburg, FL, 33701. Tel: 727-873-4401. Fax: 727-873-4196. p. 489

Pettijohn, Patricia C, Coll Develop, University of South Florida, Louis de la Parte Florida Mental Health Institute Research Library, 13301 Bruce B Downs Blvd, Tampa, FL, 33612-3899. Tel: 813-974-4471. Fax: 813-974-7242. p. 498

Pettinato, Tammy, Ref Librn, University of California Los Angeles Library, Hugh & Hazel Darling Law Library, 112 Law Bldg, Box 951458, 385 Charles E Young Dr E, Los Angeles, CA, 90095-1458. Tel: 310-825-7826. Fax: 310-825-1372. p. 178

Pettine, Maryellen, Coordr, Acq, Bristol Community College, 777 Elsbree St, Fall River, MA, 02720. Tel: 508-678-2811, Ext 2281. Fax: 508-730-3270. p. 1088

Pettinger, Gloria, Mgr, Diocese of Boise, 303 Federal Way, Boise, ID, 83705. Tel: 208-342-1311. Fax: 208-342-0224. p. 571

Pettis, Tami, Dir, Sheffield Public Library, 136 E Cook St, Sheffield, IL, 61361. Tel: 815-454-2628. Fax: 815-454-2628. p. 702

Pettit, Doris, Mgr, Dayton Metro Library, Vandalia Branch, 500 S Dixie Dr, Vandalia, OH, 45377. Tel: 937-496-8960. Fax: 937-496-4360. p. 1893

Pettit, Elsie, Librn, University of Tennessee College of Social Work Library at Nashville, 193-E Polk Ave, Ste 292, Nashville, TN, 37210. Tel: 615-251-1774. Fax: 615-742-1085. p. 2260

Pettit, Jody, Dir, Priest Lake Public Library, 28769 N Hwy 57, Priest Lake, ID, 83856. Tel: 208-443-2454. Fax: 208-443-2454. p. 582

Pettit, Michele, Dir, McGregor Public Library, 334 Main St, McGregor, IA, 52157. Tel: 563-873-3318. Fax: 563-873-3318. p. 831

Pettit, Nancy, Libr Tech II, Colorado Department of Corrections, Four Mile Correctional Center Library, CMC - FMCC, PO Box 300, Canon City, CO, 81215. Tel: 719-269-5601, Ext 3339. Fax: 719-269-5364. p. 293

Pettitt, Heidi, Tech Serv Librn, Loras College Library, 1450 Alta Vista St, Dubuque, IA, 52004-4327. Tel: 563-588-7873. Fax: 563-588-7147. p. 812

Pettus, Chris L, Acq, Mineral Area College, 5270 Flat River Rd, Park Hills, MO, 63601. Tel: 573-518-2236. Fax: 573-518-2162. p. 1349

Pettway Vann, Charlcie, Ref & Instruction Librn, Jacksonville State University Library, 700 Pelham Rd N, Jacksonville, AL, 36265. Tel: 256-782-5255. Fax: 256-782-5872. p. 22

Petty, Ellen, Dir, Garner Public Library, 416 State St, Garner, IA, 50438. Tel: 641-923-2850. Fax: 641-923-2339. p. 817

Petty, Janet, Assoc Librn, Miami Valley Hospital, One Wyoming St, Dayton, OH, 45409. Tel: 937-208-2624. Fax: 937-208-2569. p. 1893

Petty, Nancy, Br Librn, Marshall County Public Library System, Calvert City, 23 Park Rd, Calvert City, KY, 42029. Tel: 270-395-5745. Fax: 270-395-8398. p. 907

Petty, Sue, Head, Tech Serv, Lima Public Library, MediaMobile, 650 W Market St, Lima, OH, 45801. Tel: 419-228-5113, Ext 126. Fax: 419-224-2669. p. 1910

Petty, Sue Wright, Head, Tech, Lima Public Library, 650 W Market St, Lima, OH, 45801. Tel: 419-228-5113. Fax: 419-224-2669. p. 1910

Peucker, Paul M, Dr, Archivist, Moravian Archives, 41 W Locust St, Bethlehem, PA, 18018-2757. Tel: 610-866-3255. Fax: 610-866-9210. p. 2034

Pevahouse, Dorothy, Dir, Perry County Public Library, Rte 10, Linden, TN, 37096-9802. Tel: 931-589-5011. Fax: 931-589-6210. p. 2245

Pevar, Susan, Asst Prof, Spec Coll Librn, Lincoln University, 1570 Old Baltimore Pike, Lincoln University, PA, 19352. Tel: 484-365-7266. Fax: 610-932-1206. p. 2082

Peverada, Mary, Ch, YA Serv, Portland Public Library, Five Monument Sq, Portland, ME, 04101. Tel: 207-871-1700, Ext 707. Fax: 207-871-1703. p. 997

Peverill, Kathleen, Mgr, Halifax Public Libraries, Sackville Branch, 636 Sackville Dr, Lower Sackville, NS, B4C 2S4, CANADA. Tel: 902-865-8653. Fax: 902-865-2370. p. 2779

Pevler, Austin, Librn, Sinclair Community College Library, 444 W Third St, Dayton, OH, 45402-1460. Tel: 937-512-3925. Fax: 937-512-4564. p. 1894

Pew, Stephen C, Cat Librn, Salem State University Library, 352 Lafayette St, Salem, MA, 01970-5353. Tel: 978-542-6769. Fax: 978-542-6596. p. 1122

Peyton, Allison, Br Mgr, Kings County Library, Corcoran Branch, 1001-A Chittenden, Corcoran, CA, 93212. Tel: 559-992-3314. Fax: 559-992-3364. p. 156

Peyton, Allison, Br Mgr, Kings County Library, Stratford Branch, 20300 Main St, Stratford, CA, 93266. Tel: 559-947-3003. p. 156

Peyton, Janice Lucas, PhD, Dir, Lone Star College System, Montgomery College Library, 3200 College Park Dr, Conroe, TX, 77384. Tel: 936-273-7388, 936-273-7392. Fax: 936-273-7395. p. 2340

Peyton, Miranda, Librn, Mundare Municipal Library, 5128 50th St, Mundare, AB, T0B 3H0, CANADA. Tel: 780-764-3929. Fax: 780-764-2003. p. 2712

Peyton, William Preston, Librn, Sirote & Permutt, PC, 2311 Highland Ave S, Birmingham, AL, 35205-2792. Tel: 205-930-5233. Fax: 205-930-5101. p. 9

Pfaff, Caryl, Head Librn, Lac Courte Oreilles Ojibwa Community College Library, 13466 W Trepania Rd, Hayward, WI, 54843-2181. Tel: 715-634-4790, Ext 108. Fax: 715-634-5049. p. 2597

Pfaff, Karla D, Dir, Grimes Public Library, 200 N James, Grimes, IA, 50111. Tel: 515-986-3551. Fax: 515-986-9553. p. 819

Pfaff, Larry, Head, Reader Serv, Art Gallery of Ontario, 317 Dundas St W, Toronto, ON, M5T 1G4, CANADA. Tel: 416-979-6642. Fax: 416-979-6602. p. 2850

Pfander, Jeanne, Br Head, University of Arizona, Science-Engineering, 744 N Highland, Bldg 54, Tucson, AZ, 85721. Tel: 520-621-6394. Fax: 520-621-3655. p. 89

Pfannenstiel, Cynthia, Pub Serv, Pittsburg State University, 1605 S Joplin St, Pittsburg, KS, 66762-5889. Tel: 620-235-4880. Fax: 620-235-4090. p. 890

Pfannkuch, Renee, Dir, Manning Public Library, 310 Main St, Manning, IA, 51455. Tel: 712-655-2260. Fax: 712-655-2260. p. 829

Pfarner, Jane, Coll Serv Div Mgr, Kenton County Public Library, 502 Scott Blvd, Covington, KY, 41011. Tel: 859-962-4208. Fax: 859-962-4096. p. 910

Pfeifer, Judith, Librn, Evans City Public Library, 204 S Jackson St, Evans City, PA, 16033-1138. Tel: 724-538-8695. Fax: 724-538-5630. p. 2056

Pfeifer, Virginia, Circ Serv Coordr, Sachem Public Library, 150 Holbrook Rd, Holbrook, NY, 11741. Tel: 631-588-5024. Fax: 631-588-5064. p. 1637

Pfeiffer, Bob, Dir, South Milwaukee Public Library, 1907 Tenth Ave, South Milwaukee, WI, 53172. Tel: 414-768-8195. Fax: 414-768-8072. p. 2639

Pfeiffer, Donna, Librn, Pulaski County Public Library, Science Hill Branch, 215 Main St, Science Hill, KY, 42553. Tel: 606-423-4221. Fax: 606-423-4221. p. 935

Pfeiffer, Julie, Librn, Hooker County Library, 102 N Cleveland Ave, Mullen, NE, 69152. Tel: 308-546-2240. Fax: 308-546-2240. p. 1409

Pfeiffer, Lisa, Cat, Rawlins Municipal Library, 1000 E Church St, Pierre, SD, 57501. Tel: 605-773-7421. Fax: 605-773-7423. p. 2216

Pfeiffer, Mary, Librn, National Institute on Drug Abuse, 5500 Nathan Shock Dr, Baltimore, MD, 21224-6823. Tel: 410-550-1488. Fax: 410-550-1438. p. 1016

Pfeiffer, Molly, Ref Librn, Jefferson County Library, Northwest, 5680 State Rd PP, High Ridge, MO, 63049. Tel: 636-677-8186. Fax: 636-677-8243. p. 1331

Pfeifle, Barbara E, Dir, Info Tech, Libr Dir, Lexington Theological Seminary, 631 S Limestone, Lexington, KY, 40508. Tel: 859-280-1229. Fax: 859-281-6042. p. 921

Pfeil, Pam, Librn, Jackson County Law Library, Justice Bldg, 100 S Oakdale, Medford, OR, 97501. Tel: 541-774-6436. Fax: 541-774-6767. p. 2005

Pfeuffer, Debbie, Ch, Oakland Public Library, Two Municipal Plaza, Oakland, NJ, 07436. Tel: 201-337-3742. Fax: 201-337-0261. p. 1515

Pfister, Jude, Curator, National Park Service, 30 Washington Pl, Morristown, NJ, 07960-4299. Tel: 973-539-2313, Ext 204. Fax: 973-451-9212. p. 1505

Pfister, Michelle, Dir, Yorkville Public Municipal Library, 902 Game Farm Rd, Yorkville, IL, 60560. Tel: 630-553-4354. Fax: 630-553-0823. p. 722

Pfister, Susan, Cat, Quinnipiac University, 275 Mount Carmel Ave, Hamden, CT, 06518. Tel: 203-582-8918. Fax: 203-582-3451. p. 343

Pfistperer, Matt, Librn, Grinnell Library Association, 2642 E Main St, Wappingers Falls, NY, 12590. Tel: 845-297-3428. Fax: 845-297-1506. p. 1762

Pfledderer, Cynthia, Pub Serv Librn, Southlake Public Library, 1400 Main St, Ste 130, Southlake, TX, 76092-7640. Tel: 817-748-8243. p. 2388

Pflug, Oliver, Coll Mgt Librn, University of Great Falls Library, 1301 20th St S, Great Falls, MT, 59405-4948. Tel: 406-791-5311. Fax: 406-791-5395. p. 1380

Pflug, Pat, Ch, Evans City Public Library, 204 S Jackson St, Evans City, PA, 16033-1138. Tel: 724-538-8695. Fax: 724-538-5630. p. 2056

Pfohl, Daniel, Syst Coordr, William Madison Randall Library, 601 S College Rd, Wilmington, NC, 28403-5616. Tel: 910-962-3000. Fax: 910-962-3078. p. 1831

Pfotenhauer, Sue, Coll Mgt Librn, St Charles Public Library District, One S Sixth Ave, Saint Charles, IL, 60174-2105. Tel: 630-584-0076, Ext 220. Fax: 630-584-3448. p. 699

Pfrehm, Barb, AV Coordr, Rose State College, 6420 SE 15th St, Midwest City, OK, 73110. Tel: 405-733-7914. Fax: 405-736-0260. p. 1968

Pfundt, Alex, Librn, Talbot Research Library, 333 Cottman Ave, 3rd Flr, Philadelphia, PA, 19111-2497. Tel: 215-728-2711. Fax: 215-728-3655. p. 2117

Phair, Arden, Curator, St Catharines Museum, 1932 Welland Canals Pkwy, RR 6, St. Catharines, ON, L2R 7K6, CANADA. Tel: 905-984-8880, Ext 231. Fax: 905-984-6910. p. 2843

Pham, John, Br Mgr, Los Angeles Public Library System, Wilmington, 1300 N Avalon Blvd, Los Angeles, CA, 90744. Tel: 310-834-1082. Fax: 310-548-7418. p. 174

Pham, Sylvia, Ref Librn, Kutztown University, 15200 Kutztown Rd, Bldg 5, Kutztown, PA, 19530-0735. Tel: 610-683-4484. Fax: 610-683-4747. p. 2075

Pham, Vannie, Circ, Saddleback College, 28000 Marguerite Pkwy, Mission Viejo, CA, 92692. Tel: 949-582-2523. Fax: 949-364-0284. p. 187

Phares, Carol, Asst Dir, Ch, Pearl River County Library System, 900 Goodyear Blvd, Picayune, MS, 39466. Tel: 601-798-5081. Fax: 601-798-5082. p. 1311

Phares, Karen, Ch Serv Librn, Ref, Orange Public Library, 220 N Fifth St, Orange, TX, 77630. Tel: 409-883-1086. Fax: 409-883-1057. p. 2367

Pharis, Judy, Librn, Amity Township Public Library, 604 E Main St, Cornell, IL, 61319. Tel: 815-358-2231. Fax: 815-358-2217. p. 631

Pharis, Lee, Mgr, Exponent, 149 Commonwealth Dr, Menlo Park, CA, 94025. Tel: 650-688-7141. Fax: 650-329-9526. p. 185

Pharo, Sam, Dir, Boonton Holmes Public Library, 621 Main St, Boonton, NJ, 07005. Tel: 973-334-2980. Fax: 973-334-3917. p. 1473

Phelan, Jenifer, Info Spec, Seattle Pacific University Library, 3307 Third Ave W, Seattle, WA, 98119. Tel: 206-281-2074. Fax: 206-281-2936. p. 2530

Phelan, Molly, Br Librn, Brooklyn Public Library, Cypress Hills, 1197 Sutter Ave, Brooklyn, NY, 11208. Tel: 718-277-6004. Fax: 718-277-6009. p. 1591

Phelan, Paul, Dir, W Walworth Harrison Public Library, One Lou Finney Lane, Greenville, TX, 75401-5988. Tel: 903-457-2992. Fax: 903-457-2961. p. 2329

Phelps, Alison, Librn, Kansas Community Memorial Library, 107 N Front St, Kansas, IL, 61933. Tel: 217-948-5484. Fax: 217-948-5484. p. 661

Phelps, Ann, Head Librn, Beaufort, Hyde & Martin County Regional Library, Martin Memorial, 200 N Smithwick St, Williamston, NC, 27892. Tel: 252-792-7476. Fax: 252-792-8964. p. 1828

Phelps, Ann, Librn, Martin Memorial Library, 200 N Smithwick St, Williamston, NC, 27892. Tel: 252-792-7476. Fax: 252-792-8964. p. 1830

Phelps, Lena, Chair, Libr Serv, South Florida State College Library, 600 W College Dr, Avon Park, FL, 33825-9356. Tel: 863-784-7303. Fax: 863-452-6042. p. 426

Phelps, Sue, Cat, Orem Public Library, 58 N State St, Orem, UT, 84057-5596. Tel: 801-229-7050. Fax: 801-229-7130. p. 2409

Phelps, Sue, Ref Librn, Washington State University Libraries, 14204 NE Salmon Creek Ave, Vancouver, WA, 98686. Tel: 360-546-9178. Fax: 360-546-9039. p. 2546

Phenix, Shelia, Br Mgr, Webster Parish Library, Minden Main, 521 East & West St, Minden, LA, 71055. Tel: 318-371-3080. Fax: 318-371-3081. p. 957

Phetterplace, Peggy, Circ, Edison State College, 8099 College Pkwy SW, Bldg J, Fort Myers, FL, 33919. Tel: 239-489-9299. Fax: 239-489-9095. p. 444

Phifer, Aleathia L, Libr Tech, Bishop State Community College, Carver Campus, 414 Stanton St, Mobile, AL, 36617-2399. Tel: 251-662-5391. Fax: 251-479-9071. p. 25

Phifer, Jan, Circ, Harlan Community Library, 718 Court St, Harlan, IA, 51537. Tel: 712-755-5934. Fax: 712-755-3952. p. 820

Phifer, Wanda, Librn, Greensboro Public Library, Vance H Chavis Lifelong Learning Branch, 900 S Benbow Rd, Greensboro, NC, 27406. Tel: 336-373-5841. Fax: 336-412-5960. p. 1796

Philbert, Medaline, Asst Univ Librn, Pace University, 861 Bedford Rd, Pleasantville, NY, 10570-2799. Tel: 914-773-3945. Fax: 914-773-3508. p. 1719

Philbin, Paul, Head, Access & Tech Serv, University of Vermont Libraries, 538 Main St, Burlington, VT, 05405-0036. Tel: 802-656-1369. Fax: 802-656-4038. p. 2421

Philbin, Timothy, ILL, William Rainey Harper College Library, 1200 W Algonquin Rd, Palatine, IL, 60067. Tel: 847-925-6584. Fax: 847-925-6164. p. 687

Philbrick, Harry, Dir, Aldrich Museum of Contemporary Arts Library, 258 Main St, Ridgefield, CT, 06877. Tel: 203-438-4519. Fax: 203-438-0198. p. 365

Philip, Brenda, Coll Mgt, Green River Community College, 12401 SE 320th St, Auburn, WA, 98092-3699. Tel: 253-833-9111, Ext 2100. Fax: 253-288-3436, 253-288-3491. p. 2507

Philippi, Sue, Tech Mgr, C C Mellor Memorial Library, One Pennwood Ave, Edgewood, PA, 15218-1627. Tel: 412-731-0909. Fax: 412-731-8969. p. 2053

Philipps, Jane, Coord, Coll Develop, Queen's University, 101 Union St, Kingston, ON, K7L 5C4, CANADA. Tel: 613-533-3040. Fax: 613-533-6362. p. 2814

Philips, Christine, Law Librn, Lane County Law Library, Public Service Bldg, 125 E Eighth Ave, Eugene, OR, 97401. Tel: 541-682-4337. Fax: 541-682-4315. p. 1997

Philips, Norma, Dir, Merrill Public Library, 321 Fourth St, Merrill, IA, 51038. Tel: 712-938-2503. Fax: 712-938-2503. p. 832

Philips, Sarah M, Head, Ref, University of North Florida, Bldg 12-Library, One UNF Dr, Jacksonville, FL, 32224-2645. Tel: 904-620-1530. Fax: 904-620-2719. p. 455

Philips, Warren, In Charge, Validata Computer & Research Corp Library, 428 S Perry St, Montgomery, AL, 36104-4236. Tel: 334-834-2324. Fax: 334-262-5648. p. 31

Phillabaum, Winona, Commun Libr Mgr, County of Los Angeles Public Library, Lloyd Taber-Marina del Rey Library, 4533 Admiralty Way, Marina del Rey, CA, 90292-5416. Tel: 310-821-3415. Fax: 310-306-3372. p. 143

Phillibert, Margaret, Librn, Boston Public Library, Lower Mills, 27 Richmond St, Dorchester, MA, 02124-5610. Tel: 617-298-7841. Fax: 617-296-2086. p. 1057

Phillip, Jenny, Circ, Todd Wehr Library, St Norbert College, 301 Third St, De Pere, WI, 54115. Tel: 920-403-3280. Fax: 920-403-4064. p. 2587

Phillip, Zelantha A, Div Mgr, Queens Borough Public Library, Information Services Division, 89-11 Merrick Blvd, Jamaica, NY, 11432. Tel: 718-990-0700. Fax: 718-658-8342. p. 1644

Phillipo, Zeta, Ch Serv Librn, County of Brant Public Library, 12 William St, Paris, ON, N3L 1K7, CANADA. Tel: 519-442-2433. Fax: 519-442-7582. p. 2835

Phillipo, Zeta, Ch, County of Brant Public Library, Burford Branch, 24 Park Ave, Burford, ON, N0E 1A0, CANADA. Tel: 519-449-5371. Fax: 519-449-5371. p. 2835

Phillips, Amy, Librn, Colorado Technical University Library, 4435 N Chestnut, Colorado Springs, CO, 80907. Tel: 719-590-6708. Fax: 719-590-6818. p. 295

Phillips, Ann, Coll Develop, Huntsville-Madison Public Library, 915 Monroe St, Huntsville, AL, 35801. Tel: 256-532-5993. Fax: 256-532-5997. p. 21

Phillips, Audrey, Dir, Goodnight Memorial Library, 203 S Main St, Franklin, KY, 42134. Tel: 270-586-8397. Fax: 270-586-8397. p. 914

Phillips, Barbara, Ref, Saint Francis Xavier University, West St, Antigonish, NS, B2G 2W5, CANADA. Tel: 902-867-2267. Fax: 902-867-5153. p. 2777

Phillips, Betty, Librn, Res Coordr, Wilbur Smith Associates Corporate Library, 1301 Gervais St, Columbia, SC, 29201-3326. Tel: 803-251-2055. Fax: 803-251-2064. p. 2188

Phillips, Beverly R, Head, Info Serv, University of Wisconsin-Madison, Steenbock Memorial Agricultural Library, 550 Babcock Dr, Madison, WI, 53706. Tel: 608-263-2411. Fax: 608-263-3221. p. 2610

Phillips, Carl D, Dir, The California Maritime Academy Library, 200 Maritime Academy Dr, Vallejo, CA, 94590. Tel: 707-654-1090. Fax: 707-654-1094. p. 278

Phillips, Carol, Youth Serv, East Brunswick Public Library, Two Jean Walling Civic Center, East Brunswick, NJ, 08816-3599. Tel: 732-390-6789. Fax: 732-390-6796. p. 1481

Phillips, Carrie, Archives & Spec Coll Librn, Bluffton University, One University Dr, Bluffton, OH, 45817-2104. Tel: 419-358-3275. Fax: 419-358-3384. p. 1860

Phillips, Cathy, Tech Serv, Lawrence Technological University Library, 21000 W Ten Mile Rd, Southfield, MI, 48075-1058. Tel: 248-204-3000. Fax: 248-204-3005. p. 1228

Phillips, Chris, Br Coordr, Indiana University Bloomington, Life Sciences Library, Jordan Hall A304, 1001 E Third St, Bloomington, IN, 47405-7005. Tel: 812-855-8947. p. 727

Phillips, Cindy, Actg Dir, Libr Serv, Jefferson County Public Library, 10200 W 20th Ave, Lakewood, CO, 80215. Tel: 303-232-7114. Fax: 303-275-2202. p. 315

Phillips, Connie, Asst Dir, North Baltimore Public Library, 230 N Main St, North Baltimore, OH, 45872-1125. Tel: 419-257-3621. Fax: 419-257-3859. p. 1923

Phillips, Dave, Head, Youth Serv, Goshen Public Library & Historical Society, 203 Main St, Goshen, NY, 10924. Tel: 845-294-6606. Fax: 845-294-7158. p. 1629

Phillips, Deborah, Br Mgr, Mountain Regional Library System, Towns County Public Library, 99 S Berrong St, Hiawassee, GA, 30546. Tel: 706-896-6169. Fax: 706-896-2309. p. 558

Phillips, Denise, Acq, Santa Ana College, 1530 W 17th St, Santa Ana, CA, 92706-3398. Tel: 714-564-6700. Fax: 714-564-6729. p. 259

Phillips, Denise, ILL, Hershey Public Library, 701 Cocoa Ave, Hershey, PA, 17033. Tel: 717-533-6555. Fax: 717-534-1666. p. 2069

Phillips, Dennis J, Dir, Pennsylvania State Lehigh Valley Library, 8380 Mohr Lane, Fogelsville, PA, 18051-9999. Tel: 610-285-5027. Fax: 610-285-5158. p. 2057

Phillips, Diana A, Circ Mgr, Belen Public Library, 333 Becker Ave, Belen, NM, 87002. Tel: 505-864-7522. p. 1552

Phillips, Diane, Ref Serv, Southwest Virginia Community College Library, Russell Hall, 599 Community College Rd, Cedar Bluff, VA, 24609. Tel: 276-964-7265. Fax: 276-964-7259. p. 2453

Phillips, Donna, Head Librn, Mercy Medical Center, 801 Fifth St, Sioux City, IA, 51101. Tel: 712-279-2310. p. 843

Phillips, Donna, Asst Dir, Wayne County Public Library, 1001 E Ash St, Goldsboro, NC, 27530. Tel: 919-735-1824. Fax: 919-731-2889. p. 1795

Phillips, Donna, Asst Librn, Jefferson City Public Library, 1427 Russell Ave, Jefferson City, TN, 37760. Tel: 865-475-9094. Fax: 865-475-1253. p. 2239

Phillips, Edie, Tech Serv Mgr, Park County Public Library, 1500 Heart Mountain St, Cody, WY, 82414. Tel: 307-527-1880. Fax: 307-527-1888. p. 2653

Phillips, Edith, Adminr, Winneconne Public Library, 31 S Second St, Winneconne, WI, 54986. Tel: 920-582-7091. Fax: 920-582-9426. p. 2649

Phillips, Ellen, Ch, Enfield Public Library, 104 Middle Rd, Enfield, CT, 06082. Tel: 860-763-7510. Fax: 860-763-7514. p. 338

Phillips, Emily, Bus Mgr, Willard Library of Evansville, 21 First Ave, Evansville, IN, 47710-1294. Tel: 812-425-4309. Fax: 812-421-9742. p. 739

Phillips, Evelyn, Asst Librn, Summers County Public Library, 201 Temple St, Hinton, WV, 25951. Tel: 304-466-4490. Fax: 304-466-5260. p. 2560

Phillips, Gail Baldon, Exec Dir, Oil Information Library of Wichita Falls, 718 Lamar St, Wichita Falls, TX, 76301-6877. Tel: 940-322-4241. Fax: 940-322-8695. p. 2401

Phillips, Gregory, Ref Serv, W T Bland Public Library, 1995 N Donnelly St, Mount Dora, FL, 32757. Tel: 352-735-7180. Fax: 352-735-0074. p. 471

Phillips, Holly, Dir, Moultrie-Colquitt County Library, 204 Fifth St SE, Moultrie, GA, 31768. Tel: 229-985-6540. Fax: 229-985-0936. p. 545

Phillips, Holly, ILL, Toronto Rehab, 550 University Ave, Toronto, ON, M5G 2A2, CANADA. Tel: 416-597-3422, Ext 3050. Fax: 416-591-6515. p. 2864

Phillips, Ideta, Librn, Illinois Criminal Justice Information Authority Library, 300 W Adams, Ste 700, Chicago, IL, 60606-3997. Tel: 312-793-8550. Fax: 312-793-8422. p. 614

Phillips, Janet, Asst Librn, Jemez Springs Public Library, 30 Jemez Plaza, Jemez Springs, NM, 87025. Tel: 505-829-9155. Fax: 505-829-3339. p. 1557

Phillips, Jean M, Librn, University of Wisconsin-Madison, Space Science & Engineering Center - Schwerdtfeger Library, 1225 W Dayton St, Madison, WI, 53706. Tel: 608-262-8164. Fax: 608-262-5974. p. 2610

Phillips, John B, Head Librn, Oklahoma State University Libraries, Documents Department, Edmon Low Library, 5th Flr, Stillwater, OK, 74078-1071. Tel: 405-744-6546. Fax: 405-744-5183. p. 1978

Phillips, John B, Head, Govt Doc, Oklahoma State University Libraries, Oklahoma State University, Athletic Ave, Stillwater, OK, 74078-1071. Tel: 405-744-9729. Fax: 405-744-5183. p. 1978

Phillips, Joi, Asst Dir, Delta State University, Laflore Circle at Fifth Ave, Cleveland, MS, 38733-2599. Tel: 662-846-4447. Fax: 662-846-4443. p. 1296

Phillips, Joshua, Ref Librn, Loyola Law School, 919 S Albany St, Los Angeles, CA, 90015-1211. Tel: 213-736-1413. Fax: 213-487-2204. p. 175

Phillips, Julie, Mgr, Greenville County Library System, Fountain Inn (Kerry Ann Younts Culp) Branch, 311 N Main St, Fountain Inn, SC, 29644. Tel: 864-862-2576. Fax: 864-862-6376. p. 2196

Phillips, Kara, Coll Develop, Seattle University, School of Law Library, Sullivan Hall, 901 12th Ave, Seattle, WA, 98122-4411. Tel: 206-398-4221. Fax: 206-398-4194. p. 2532

Phillips, Kathleen, Ch, Seymour Library, 161 East Ave, Brockport, NY, 14420-1987. Tel: 585-637-1050. Fax: 585-637-1051. p. 1585

Phillips, Kathleen, Dir, Madison County Public Library, 1335 N Main St, Marshall, NC, 28753-6901. Tel: 828-649-3741. Fax: 828-649-3504. p. 1809

Phillips, Kathryn, Librn, Smithsonian Libraries, Freer Gallery of Art & Arthur M Sackler Gallery Library, Arthur M Sackler Gallery, Rm 2057, MRC 707, 12th St & Jefferson Dr SW, Washington, DC, 20560. Tel: 202-633-0478. Fax: 202-786-2936. p. 414

Phillips, Kathy, Coordr, Northeast Alabama Regional Medical Center, 400 E Tenth St, Anniston, AL, 36207. Tel: 256-235-5224, 256-235-5800. p. 4

Phillips, Kathy, Librn, Mid Florida Research & Education Center Library, 2725 S Binion Rd, Apopka, FL, 32703-8504. Tel: 407-884-2034, Ext 140. Fax: 407-814-6186. p. 425

Phillips, Kathy, Asst Librn, Five Rivers Public Library, 301 Walnut St, Parsons, WV, 26287. Tel: 304-478-3880. Fax: 304-478-3880. p. 2569

Phillips, Kerry, Libr Commun Serv Mgr, Richmond Public Library, Ginter Park, 1200 Westbrook Ave, Richmond, VA, 23227. Tel: 804-646-1236. Fax: 804-646-3865. p. 2490

Phillips, Kerry Q, Dir, Thomasville Public Library, 1401 Mosley Dr, Thomasville, AL, 36784. Tel: 334-636-5343. Fax: 334-636-5343. p. 37

Phillips, Kirsten, Admin Serv, Consortium of College & University Media Centers, Indiana University, Franklin Hall 0009, 601 E Kirkwood Ave, Bloomington, IN, 47405-1223. Tel: 812-855-6049. Fax: 812-855-2103. p. 2943

Phillips, Lauren, Head, Coll Mgt, New Canaan Library, 151 Main St, New Canaan, CT, 06840. Tel: 203-594-5000. Fax: 203-594-5026. p. 354

Phillips, Laurie, Assoc Dean, Tech Serv, Loyola University New Orleans, 6363 Saint Charles Ave, New Orleans, LA, 70118-6195. Tel: 504-864-7111. Fax: 504-864-7247. p. 961

Phillips, Linda, Coll Mgt Librn, University of Tennessee, Knoxville, 1015 Volunteer Blvd, Knoxville, TN, 37996-1000. Tel: 865-974-4702. Fax: 865-974-4259. p. 2243

Phillips, Lindsey, Admin Officer, Castillo de San Marcos & Fort Matanzas National Monuments, One S Castillo Dr, Saint Augustine, FL, 32084-3699. Tel: 904-829-6506, Ext 223. Fax: 904-823-9388. p. 486

Phillips, Lori, Tech Serv, Croton Free Library, 171 Cleveland Dr, Croton-on-Hudson, NY, 10520. Tel: 914-271-6612. Fax: 914-271-0931. p. 1612

Phillips, Lori, Assoc Dean, University of Wyoming Libraries, 13th & Ivinson, Laramie, WY, 82071. Tel: 307-766-3859. Fax: 307-766-2510. p. 2658

Phillips, Lynne, Coll Mgr, Chesapeake Bay Maritime Museum Library, 213 N Talbot St, Saint Michaels, MD, 21663. Tel: 410-745-4972. Fax: 410-745-6088. p. 1040

Phillips, Mabel Gaye, Dir, Christian County Library, 1005 N Fourth Ave, Ozark, MO, 65721. Tel: 417-581-2432. Fax: 417-581-8855. p. 1348

Phillips, Margaret, Instruction & Learning Librn, Michigan Technological University, 1400 Townsend Dr, Houghton, MI, 49931-1295. Tel: 906-487-1443. p. 1191

Phillips, Marilyn, Head, Youth Serv, University City Public Library, 6701 Delmar Blvd, University City, MO, 63130. Tel: 314-727-3150. Fax: 314-727-6005. p. 1370

Phillips, Marilyn Sue, Acad Res Librn, Mountain State University Library, 609 S Kanawha St, Beckley, WV, 25801. Tel: 304-929-1534. Fax: 304-929-1665. p. 2553

Phillips, Mark, Asst Dean, Digital Libr, University of North Texas Libraries, PO Box 305190, Denton, TX, 76203-5190. Tel: 940-565-2415. Fax: 940-369-8760. p. 2313

Phillips, Marlena, Circ Librn, Wythe-Grayson Regional Library, Whitetop Public, 16309 Highlands Pkwy, Whitetop, VA, 24292. Tel: 276-388-2873. Fax: 276-388-2873. p. 2472

Phillips, Mary, Librn, Elton B Stephens Library, 17 School St, Clio, AL, 36017-9298. Tel: 334-397-2911. Fax: 334-397-2910. p. 12

Phillips, Mary, Teen Serv Librn, New City Free Library, 220 N Main St, New City, NY, 10956. Tel: 845-634-4997. p. 1665

Phillips, Matthew, Circ Asst, St John's College Library, 60 College Ave, Annapolis, MD, 21401. Tel: 410-972-4117. Fax: 410-295-6936. p. 1011

Phillips, Melissa, Interim Dir, Pub Serv Librn, Maitland Public Library, 501 S Maitland Ave, Maitland, FL, 32751-5672. Tel: 407-647-7700. p. 462

Phillips, Merrilyn, Librn, Rupert J Smith Law Library of Saint Lucie County, 218 S Second St, Courthouse Addition, Rm 102, Fort Pierce, FL, 34950. Tel: 772-462-2370. Fax: 772-462-2145. p. 447

Phillips, Michael, ILL, College of Charleston, 205 Calhoun St, Charleston, SC, 29401-3519. Tel: 843-953-5530. Fax: 843-953-6319. p. 2184

Phillips, Michele C, Dir, Ellenburg Sarah A Munsil Free Library, 5139 Rte 11, Ellenburg Depot, NY, 12935. Tel: 518-594-7314. p. 1619

Phillips, Nancy Kim, Customer Serv Mgr, Arlington Heights Memorial Library, 500 N Dunton Ave, Arlington Heights, IL, 60004-5966. Tel: 847-506-2668. Fax: 847-506-2650. p. 589

Phillips, Pamela, Coordr, Baptist Medical Center Library, 2105 E South Blvd, Montgomery, AL, 36116-2001. Tel: 334-286-2718. Fax: 334-286-5691. p. 28

Phillips, Patricia L, Dean, Learning Res, Eastern Shore Community College, 29300 Lankford Hwy, Melfa, VA, 23410. Tel: 757-789-1721. Fax: 757-789-1739. p. 2478

Phillips, Robert L, Dr, Assoc Dean, Ref Serv, Southwestern Baptist Theological Seminary Libraries, 2001 W Seminary Dr, Fort Worth, TX, 76115-2157. Tel: 817-923-1921, Ext 4000. Fax: 817-921-8765. p. 2323

Phillips, Samuel D, Circ, Media Serv, Ser, J Sargeant Reynolds Community College Library, Downtown Campus-Library & Information Services, 700 E Jackson St, 2nd Flr, Richmond, VA, 23219-1543. Tel: 804-523-5211. Fax: 804-786-6200. p. 2488

Phillips, Sandra, Circ, Missouri Western State University, 4525 Downs Dr, Saint Joseph, MO, 64507-2294. Tel: 816-271-4368. Fax: 816-271-4574. p. 1352

Phillips, Sandra P, Asst Librn, Charles H Stone Memorial Library, 319 W Main St, Pilot Mountain, NC, 27041. Tel: 336-368-2370. Fax: 336-368-9587. p. 1814

Phillips, Sharon, Librn II, Ref Librn, Montgomery City-County Public Library System, Juliette Hampton Morgan Memorial Library (Main Library), 245 High St, Montgomery, AL, 36104. Tel: 334-240-4999. Fax: 334-240-4980. p. 30

Phillips, Sharon, Dir, Pub Serv & Organizational Develop, Wayne State University Libraries, Office of the Dean, 3100 Undergraduate Library, 5155 Gullen Mall, Detroit, MI, 48202. Tel: 313-577-4238. Fax: 313-577-5525. p. 1173

Phillips, Sharon, Dir, New York State Library, 222 Madison Ave, Cultural Education Ctr, Albany, NY, 12230-0001. Tel: 518-474-5935. Fax: 518-486-1957. p. 1570

Phillips, Shawn, Coll Develop, Theosophical Society Library, 809 Mason St, San Francisco, CA, 94108-2210. Tel: 415-771-8777. p. 247

Phillips, Sherlane, Coll Mgt, Outreach Serv Librn, Lloydminster Public Library, 5010 49th St, Lloydminster, AB, T9V 0K2, CANADA. Tel: 780-875-0850. Fax: 780-875-6523. p. 2710

Phillips, Sherry, Librn, Blandinsville-Hire District Library, 130 S Main St, Blandinsville, IL, 61420. Tel: 309-652-3166. Fax: 309-652-3166. p. 595

Phillips, Susan J, Dir, Hall Memorial Library, 93 Main St, Ellington, CT, 06029. Tel: 860-870-3160. Fax: 860-870-3163. p. 338

Phillips, Tracy, Mgr, Dayton Metro Library, Fort McKinley, 3735 Salem Ave, Dayton, OH, 45406. Tel: 937-496-8932. Fax: 937-496-4332. p. 1893

Phillips, Vicki, Head, Sci & Eng, Oklahoma State University Libraries, Oklahoma State University, Athletic Ave, Stillwater, OK, 74078-1071. Tel: 405-744-9729. Fax: 405-744-5183. p. 1978

Phillips, Vicki W, Head Librn, Oklahoma State University Libraries, Science & Engineering Division, Edmon Low Library, 3rd Flr, Stillwater, OK, 74078-1071. Tel: 405-744-6309. Fax: 405-744-5183. p. 1978

Phillips, Wanda, Ref Serv, Peoria Public Library, 107 NE Monroe St, Peoria, IL, 61602-1070. Tel: 309-497-2160. Fax: 309-497-2007. p. 690

Phillips, Wendy A, Dir, Carmel Clay Public Library, 55 Fourth Ave SE, Carmel, IN, 46032-2278. Tel: 317-814-3900. Fax: 317-571-4285. p. 731

Phillips, Yvonne, Web Coordr, Red Deer College Library, 100 College Blvd, Red Deer, AB, T4N 5H5, CANADA. Tel: 403-342-3344. Fax: 403-346-8500. p. 2714

Phillis, Susan, Chief, Brooklyn Public Library, Business, 280 Cadman Plaza W, Brooklyn, NY, 11201. Tel: 718-623-7100. Fax: 718-222-5651. p. 1591

Philo, Thomas, Archivist, Cataloger, California State University Dominguez Hills, 1000 E Victoria St, Carson, CA, 90747. Tel: 310-243-3361. Fax: 310-516-4219. p. 132

Philos, John, Librn, State of Delaware, Delaware Library Access Services, 43 S Dupont Hwy, Dover, DE, 19901-7430. Tel: 302-739-4748, Ext 125. Fax: 302-739-6787. p. 382

Philpot, Shirley, Librn, Southwest Arkansas Regional Library, Polk County Library, 410 Eighth St, Mena, AR, 71953. Tel: 479-394-2314. Fax: 479-394-2314. p. 103

Philpott, Ann, Circ, Sidney Memorial Public Library, Eight River St, Sidney, NY, 13838. Tel: 607-563-1200, 607-563-8021. Fax: 607-563-7675. p. 1743

Phinney, Jessica, Curator, Antique Boat Museum, 750 Mary St, Clayton, NY, 13624. Tel: 315-686-4104. Fax: 315-686-2775. p. 1607

Phinney, John, Librn, Southern Methodist University, Institute for Study of Earth & Man Reading Room, N L Heroy Science Hall, Rm 129, 3225 Daniels Ave, Dallas, TX, 75275. Tel: 214-768-2430. Fax: 214-768-4289. p. 2310

Phinsee-Clack, Faye, ILL, California State University Dominguez Hills, 1000 E Victoria St, Carson, CA, 90747. Tel: 310-243-3758. Fax: 310-516-4219. p. 132

Phippin, Stephanie, ILL, Goodnight Memorial Library, 203 S Main St, Franklin, KY, 42134. Tel: 270-586-8397. Fax: 270-586-8397. p. 914

Phipps, Breyanna, Asst Dir, Robinson Public Library District, 606 N Jefferson St, Robinson, IL, 62454-2665. Tel: 618-544-2917. Fax: 618-544-7172. p. 695

Phipps, Debbie, Media Serv, Central College, Campus Box 6500, 812 University St, Pella, IA, 50219-1999. Tel: 641-628-5218. Fax: 641-628-5327. p. 838

Phipps, Elizabeth, Head, Cat, University of Southern Maine, 314 Forest Ave, Portland, ME, 04104. Tel: 207-780-4990. Fax: 207-780-4042. p. 998

Phipps, Jean, Librn, Elroy Community Library, 13512 Fm 812, Del Valle, TX, 78617. Tel: 512-243-1981. p. 2312

Phipps, Shannon, Adult Serv, Distance Educ, Switzerland County Public Library, 205 Ferry St, Vevay, IN, 47043. Tel: 812-427-3363. Fax: 812-427-3654. p. 784

Phipps, Sheila, Br Mgr, Lonesome Pine Regional Library, Jonnie B Deel Memorial, 198 Chase St, Clintwood, VA, 24228. Tel: 276-926-6617. Fax: 276-926-6795. p. 2504

Phlegar, Barbara, Access Serv, ILL Spec, Pub Serv, Charlotte Community Library, 226 S Bostwick St, Charlotte, MI, 48813-1801. Tel: 517-543-8859. Fax: 517-543-8868. p. 1162

Phoenix, Jack, Support Serv, London Public Library, 20 E First St, London, OH, 43140. Tel: 740-852-9543. Fax: 740-852-3691. p. 1911

Phyillaier, Cynthia, Librn, Holy Cross Hospital of Silver Spring, 1500 Forest Glen Rd, Silver Spring, MD, 20910. Tel: 301-754-7245. Fax: 301-754-7247. p. 1041

Piacenti, Sue, Librn, Hazleton Area Public Library, McAdoo, Southside Branch, 15 Kelayres Rd, McAdoo, PA, 18237. Tel: 570-929-1120. p. 2068

Piacentini, Lynne, Ref Serv, Saint Joseph College, 1678 Asylum Ave, West Hartford, CT, 06117-2791. Tel: 860-231-5751. Fax: 860-523-4356. p. 376

Piana, Kristine, Head, Ch, Locust Valley Library, 170 Buckram Rd, Locust Valley, NY, 11560-1999. Tel: 516-671-1837. Fax: 516-676-8164. p. 1654

Pianosi, Amy, Librn, Correctional Service of Canada, Hwy 33, Bath, ON, K0H 1G0, CANADA. Tel: 613-351-8000. Fax: 613-351-8136. p. 2794

Piantigini, Cathy, Ch, Somerville Public Library, 79 Highland Ave, Somerville, MA, 02143. Tel: 617-623-5000, Ext 2950. Fax: 617-628-4052. p. 1124

Piasecki, Patricia S, Asst Satellite Librn, Library of the US Courts, Robert A Grant Courthouse, 204 S Main St, Rm 316, South Bend, IN, 46601. Tel: 574-246-8050. Fax: 574-246-8002. p. 779

Piasecki, Sara, Photo Archivist, Anchorage Museum, 625 C St, Anchorage, AK, 99501. Tel: 907-929-9235. Fax: 907-929-9233. p. 44

Piasecki, Sara, Head, Archives, Head, Historical Coll, Oregon Health & Science University Library, 3181 SW Sam Jackson Park Rd, Portland, OR, 97239-3098. Tel: 503-418-2287. Fax: 503-494-3227. p. 2013

Piastuch-Temmen, Lisa, Coordr, Institute for American Indian Studies, 38 Curtis Rd, Washington, CT, 06793-0260. Tel: 860-868-0518. Fax: 860-868-1649. p. 374

Piattelli, Christine, Ch, John C Hart Memorial Library, 1130 Main St, Shrub Oak, NY, 10588. Tel: 914-245-5262. Fax: 914-245-2216. p. 1743

Piattelli, Richard, Adult Serv, Nanuet Public Library, 149 Church St, Nanuet, NY, 10954. Tel: 845-623-4281. Fax: 845-623-2415. p. 1664

Picard, Amy, Head Librn, Norman Regional Hospital, 901 N Porter, Norman, OK, 73070. Tel: 405-307-1425. Fax: 405-307-1428. p. 1970

Picard, Brittany, ILL, Ref Serv, Iberia Parish Library, 445 E Main St, New Iberia, LA, 70560-3710. Tel: 337-364-7024, 337-364-7074. Fax: 337-364-7042. p. 959

Picard, Dennis D, Dir, Storrowton Village Museum Library, 1305 Memorial Ave, West Springfield, MA, 01089. Tel: 413-205-5051. Fax: 413-205-5054. p. 1137

Picard, Genevieve, Asst Dir, Ipswich Public Library, 25 N Main St, Ipswich, MA, 01938-2217. Tel: 978-356-6648. Fax: 978-356-6647. p. 1097

Picard, Isabelle, In Charge, Bibliotheque Gabrielle-Roy, Jean-Baptiste-Duberger, 2475 Central Blvd, Quebec, QC, G1P 4S1, CANADA. Tel: 418-641-6799. p. 2903

Picard, Isabelle, In Charge, Bibliotheque Gabrielle-Roy, Les Saules, 2035 Blvd Masson, Quebec, QC, G1P 1J3, CANADA. Tel: 418-641-6796. p. 2903

Picardo, Kathryn, Cat, Philadelphia College of Osteopathic Medicine, 4170 City Ave, Philadelphia, PA, 19131-1694. Tel: 215-871-6470. Fax: 215-871-6478. p. 2114

Picary-Lecours, Charlotte, Dir, Bibliotheque Municipale de Shawinigan, 550 Av de Hotel de Ville, CP 400, Shawinigan, QC, G9N 6V3, CANADA. Tel: 819-536-7218. Fax: 819-536-0808. p. 2912

Picca, David, Librn, Miami Dade College, Kendall Campus Library, 11011 SW 104th St, Miami, FL, 33176-3393. Tel: 305-237-0996, 305-237-2015, 305-237-2291. Fax: 305-237-2923. p. 466

Piccininni, James, Dean of Libr, University of Saint Thomas, 1100 W Main, Houston, TX, 77006. Tel: 713-525-2192. Fax: 713-525-3886. p. 2344

Piccinino, Rocco, Head Librn, Smith College Libraries, Anita O'K & Robert R Young Science Library, Clark Science Center, Bass Hall, Northampton, MA, 01063. Tel: 413-585-2951. Fax: 413-585-4480. p. 1114

Piccoli, Roberta, Mgr, Res, Consumer Reports, 101 Truman Ave, Yonkers, NY, 10703-1057. Tel: 914-378-2000. Fax: 914-378-2913. p. 1771

Piccolotti, Laurie, Sr Librn, Patton State Hospital, Staff Library, 3102 E Highland Ave, Patton, CA, 92369. Tel: 909-425-7484. Fax: 909-425-6053. p. 207

Pichardo, Dorothy, Mgr, Washington County Library, Sam Mitchell Public Library, 3731 Roche Ave, Vernon, FL, 32462. Tel: 850-535-1208. Fax: 850-535-1208. p. 431

Piché, Jean-Stéphen, Asst Dep Minister, Acq Sector, Library & Archives Canada, 550 De la Cité Blvd, Gatineau, QC, K1A 0N4, CANADA. Tel: 819-934-5790. Fax: 819-934-4422. p. 2883

Pichler, Susanne, Librn, Andrew W Mellon Foundation, 140 E 62nd St, New York, NY, 10065. Tel: 212-838-8400. Fax: 212-888-4172. p. 1685

Pichnarcik, Jake, Head, ILL, Texas A&M University-Commerce, 2600 S Neal St, Commerce, TX, 75429. Tel: 903-886-5717. Fax: 903-886-5434. p. 2300

Pickar, Sue, Syst Adminr, Cass District Library, 319 M-62 N, Cassopolis, MI, 49031-1099. Tel: 269-445-3400, Ext 33. Fax: 269-445-8795. p. 1161

Pickard, Mary Ann, Archivist, Huntingdon College, 1500 E Fairview Ave, Montgomery, AL, 36106. Tel: 334-833-4413. Fax: 334-263-4465. p. 29

Pickard, Sue, Res Librn, Zotos International Library, 100 Tokeneke Rd, Darien, CT, 06820-1005. Tel: 203-656-7700, 203-656-7805. Fax: 203-656-7963. p. 336

Pickard-Four, Karen, Br Mgr, Los Angeles Public Library System, Studio City Branch, 4400 Babcock Ave, Studio City, CA, 91604-1399. Tel: 818-755-7873. Fax: 818-755-7873. p. 174

Pickavet, Chris, Tech Serv Supvr, Carlsbad City Library, 1775 Dove Lane, Carlsbad, CA, 92011-4048. Tel: 760-602-2029. Fax: 760-602-7942. p. 132

Pickell, Barbara, Dir, Clearwater Public Library System, 100 N Osceola Ave, Clearwater, FL, 33755. Tel: 727-562-4971. Fax: 727-562-4977. p. 432

Picken, Beverly, Br Mgr, Wellington County Library, Erin Branch, 14 Boland Dr, Erin, ON, N0B 1T0, CANADA. Tel: 519-833-9762. p. 2805

Pickens, Matthew, Ref Librn, Curtis Laws Wilson Library, 400 W 14th St, Rolla, MO, 65409-0060. Tel: 573-341-7839. Fax: 573-341-4233. p. 1351

Pickeral, Elaine, Br Mgr, Prince George's County Memorial, Mount Rainier Branch, 3409 Rhode Island Ave, Mount Rainier, MD, 20712-2073. Tel: 301-864-8937. Fax: 301-779-6207. p. 1032

Pickering, Anna-Marie, Libr Asst II, Marshall-Lyon County Library, 301 W Lyon St, Marshall, MN, 56258. Tel: 507-537-7003. p. 1258

Pickering, Gerianne, Cat, Grand Island Public Library, 211 N Washington St, Grand Island, NE, 68801-5855. Tel: 308-385-5333, Ext 124. Fax: 308-385-5339. p. 1400

Pickering, Lenore, In Charge, Beauregard Parish Library, Fields Branch, 13287 Hwy 389, Fields, LA, 70653. Tel: 337-463-6217. Fax: 337-462-5434. p. 948

Pickering, Nancy, Dir, Van Horne Public Library, 114 Main St, Van Horne, IA, 52346. Tel: 319-228-8744. Fax: 319-228-8744. p. 848

Pickering, Robert B, Sr Curator, Thomas Gilcrease Institute of American History & Art Library, 1400 Gilcrease Museum Rd, Tulsa, OK, 74127-2100. Tel: 918-596-2700. Fax: 918-596-2770. p. 1981

Pickett, Carmelita, Coll Develop & Acq, Texas A&M University Libraries, 5000 TAMU, College Station, TX, 77843-5000. Tel: 979-862-1033. Fax: 979-845-6238. p. 2298

Pickett, Jennifer, Ref Librn, Brooks Free Library, 739 Main St, Harwich, MA, 02645. Tel: 508-430-7562. Fax: 508-430-7564. p. 1094

Pickett, John, Dir, Johnson County Law Library, Courthouse, Rm 101, 100 N Kansas Ave, Olathe, KS, 66061. Tel: 913-715-4154. Fax: 913-715-4152. p. 886

Pickett, Julie, Ch, Stowe Free Library, 90 Pond St, Stowe, VT, 05672. Tel: 802-253-6145. Fax: 802-253-4808. p. 2436

Pickett, Kate, YA Serv, Johnson County Library, 9875 W 87th St, Overland Park, KS, 66212. Tel: 913-261-2332. Fax: 913-495-2460. p. 888

Pickett, Keith, Ref & Educ Librn, Tulane University, Rudolph Matas Library of the Health Sciences, Tulane Health Sciences Campus, 1430 Tulane Ave, SL-86, New Orleans, LA, 70112-2699. Tel: 504-988-2406. Fax: 504-988-7417. p. 963

Pickett, Kelly, Asst Librn, Ohio Legislative Service Commission Library, 77 S High St, 9th Flr, Columbus, OH, 43215-6136. Tel: 614-466-2242. Fax: 614-644-1721. p. 1887

Pickett, Lisa, Dir, Columbia County Library, Public Library of Camden & Ouachita County, 120 Harrison Ave SW, Camden, AR, 71701. Tel: 870-836-5083. Fax: 870-836-0163. p. 108

Pickett, Olivia K, Dir, Libr Serv, Georgetown University, Maternal & Child Health Library, 2115 Wisconsin Ave NW, Ste 601, Washington, DC, 20007. Tel: 202-784-9770. Fax: 202-784-9777. p. 403

Pickney, Mary Beth, Br Mgr, Saint Lucie County Library System, Morningside Branch, 2410 Morningside Blvd, Port Saint Lucie, FL, 34952. Tel: 772-337-5632. Fax: 772-337-5631. p. 447

Pickrel, Teri, Dir, Burkburnett Library, 215 E Fourth St, Burkburnett, TX, 76354-3446. Tel: 940-569-2991. Fax: 940-569-1620. p. 2293

Picone, Deborah, Librn, American Academy of Dramatic Arts Library, 120 Madison Ave, New York, NY, 10016. Tel: 212-686-9244, Ext 337. Fax: 212-545-7934. p. 1667

Picos-Lee, Mayra, Bibliog Instr, Palmer Theological Seminary, Six Lancaster Ave, Wynnewood, PA, 19096. Tel: 610-645-9332. p. 2158

Picquet, D Cheryn, Assoc Dir, Head, Tech Serv, University of Tennessee, Taylor Law Center, 1505 W Cumberland Ave, Knoxville, TN, 37996-1800. Tel: 865-974-6729. Fax: 865-974-6571, 865-974-6595. p. 2243

Pictras, Angela, Adult Serv, Circ, Saint Petersburg Public Library, 3745 Ninth Ave N, Saint Petersburg, FL, 33713. Tel: 727-893-7724. Fax: 727-892-5432. p. 488

Pidde, Paul, Br Mgr, Converse County Library, Glenrock Branch, 518 S Fourth St, Glenrock, WY, 82637. Tel: 307-436-2573. Fax: 307-436-8525. p. 2654

Piddle, Janette, Librn, Comfrey Public Library, 306 Brown St W, Comfrey, MN, 56019-1167. Tel: 507-877-6600. Fax: 507-877-3492. p. 1246

Pidgeon, Alice, Head, Tech Serv, Pace University, 78 N Broadway, White Plains, NY, 10603. Tel: 914-422-4280. Fax: 914-422-4139. p. 1769

Pidzarko, Eugene, Dir, Lowell Public Library, 1505 E Commercial Ave, Lowell, IN, 46356-1899. Tel: 219-696-7704. Fax: 219-696-5280. p. 762

Pidzarko, Eugene B, Vis Asst Prof, Libr Sci, Purdue University, 2200 169th St, Hammond, IN, 46323-2094. Tel: 219-989-2903. Fax: 219-989-2070. p. 747

Piechnik, Katrina, Libr Syst Mgr, Jenkins Law Library, 833 Chestnut St, Ste 1220, Philadelphia, PA, 19107-4429. Tel: 215-574-7907. Fax: 215-574-7920. p. 2111

Piechowski, Bernice, Dir, Browns Valley Public Library, 15 S Third St, Browns Valley, MN, 56219. Tel: 320-695-2318. Fax: 320-695-2125. p. 1243

Piedalue, Helene, Acq, Cegep St Jean Sur Richelieu Bibliotheque, 30 boul du Seminaire, CP 1018, Saint-Jean-Sur-Richelieu, QC, J3B 7B1, CANADA. Tel: 450-347-5301, Ext 2333. Fax: 450-347-3329, 450-358-9350. p. 2911

Piehl, Ann, Ch, Whitefish Bay Public Library, 5420 N Marlborough Dr, Whitefish Bay, WI, 53217. Tel: 414-964-4380. Fax: 414-964-5733. p. 2648

Piehl, Kathy, Instrul Serv Librn, Ref Librn, Minnesota State University, Mankato, ML3097, Mankato, MN, 56001. Tel: 507-389-5952. Fax: 507-389-5155. p. 1257

Piehler, Heide, Ch, Shorewood Public Library, 3920 N Murray Ave, Shorewood, WI, 53211-2385. Tel: 414-847-2670. p. 2638

Piel, Susan, Ad, Woodbury Public Library, 269 Main St S, Woodbury, CT, 06798. Tel: 203-263-3502. Fax: 203-263-0571. p. 380

Piel, Suzanne, Ch, Clive Public Library, 1900 NW 114th St, Clive, IA, 50325. Tel: 515-453-2221. Fax: 515-453-2246. p. 803

Pieniaszek, Nadine, Med Librn, Kent General Hospital, 640 S State St, Dover, DE, 19901. Tel: 302-744-7421. Fax: 302-744-7460. p. 382

Pienkos, Kenneth, Dir, Oxford Public Library, 48 S Second St, Oxford, PA, 19363-1377. Tel: 610-932-9618. Fax: 610-932-9251. p. 2101

Pienkowski, Kathy, Circ Serv Mgr, Citizens Library, 55 S College St, Washington, PA, 15301. Tel: 724-222-2400. Fax: 724-222-2606. p. 2151

Pieper, Susan, Dir, Paulding County Carnegie Library, 205 S Main St, Paulding, OH, 45879-1492. Tel: 419-399-2032. Fax: 419-399-2114. p. 1928

Pierard, Cynthia, Head, Ref & Res Serv, New Mexico State University Library, 2911 McFie Circle, Las Cruces, NM, 88003. Tel: 575-646-7010. Fax: 575-646-6940. p. 1558

Pierce, Alison, Circ Librn, Brownell Library, Six Lincoln St, Essex Junction, VT, 05452-3154. Tel: 802-878-6955. Fax: 802-878-6946. p. 2423

Pierce, Anna, Circ, SUNY Westchester Community College, 75 Grasslands Rd, Valhalla, NY, 10595-1693. Tel: 914-606-7847. Fax: 914-785-6513. p. 1760

Pierce, B J, Br Mgr, Baker County Public Library, Richland Branch, 45794 Hwy 86, Richland, OR, 97870. Tel: 541-893-6088. p. 1991

Pierce, Brenda, Asst Dean, Oakland University Library, 2200 N Squirrel Rd, Rochester, MI, 48309-4402. Tel: 248-370-2488. Fax: 248-370-2474. p. 1221

Pierce, Cathy, Br Mgr, Kanawha County Public Library, Glasgow Branch, 129 Fourth Ave, Glasgow, WV, 25086. Tel: 304-595-3131. Fax: 304-595-3148. p. 2556

Pierce, Cathy, Br Mgr, Kanawha County Public Library, Marmet Branch, 9303 Oregon Ave, Marmet, WV, 25315. Tel: 304-949-6628. Fax: 304-949-6639. p. 2556

Pierce, Cathy, Br Mgr, Kanawha County Public Library, Riverside, One Warrior Way, Belle, WV, 25015. Tel: 304-949-2400. Fax: 304-949-2509. p. 2556

Pierce, Diana, Co-Dir, Brown, Rudnick, Berlack, Israels LLP, One Financial Ctr, Boston, MA, 02111. Tel: 617-856-8213. Fax: 617-856-8201. p. 1059

Pierce, Donna, Dir, Krum Public Library, 803 E McCart St, Krum, TX, 76249-6823. Tel: 940-482-3455. Fax: 940-482-0088. p. 2351

Pierce, Glen, Archivist, Messiah College, One College Ave, Ste 3002, Mechanicsburg, PA, 17055. Tel: 717-691-6006, Ext 6048. Fax: 717-691-2356. p. 2087

Pierce, Glen A, Dir, Messiah College, Brethren in Christ Historical Library & Archives, One College Ave, Grantham, PA, 17027-9795. Tel: 717-691-6048. Fax: 717-691-6042. p. 2087

Pierce, Janell, Info Literacy Librn, Mesa Community College Library, 1833 W Southern Ave, Mesa, AZ, 85202. Tel: 480-461-7266. Fax: 480-461-7681. p. 68

Pierce, Janet, Head, Content & Delivery Serv, Teachers College, Columbia University, 525 W 120th St, New York, NY, 10027-6696. Tel: 212-678-3458. p. 1701

Pierce, Jennifer, Dr, Asst Prof, University of Iowa, 3087 Main Library, Iowa City, IA, 52242-1420. Tel: 319-335-5707. Fax: 319-335-5374. p. 2965

Pierce, Jenny, Pub Serv, University of Medicine & Dentistry of New Jersey, Academic Ctr, One Medical Center Dr, Stratford, NJ, 08084. Tel: 856-566-6800. Fax: 856-566-6380. p. 1532

Pierce, Jo Ann, Youth Serv, Lawrence Library, 15 Main St, Pepperell, MA, 01463. Tel: 978-433-0330. Fax: 978-433-0317. p. 1117

Pierce, Karen, Librn, Slippery Rock Community Library, 316 N Main St, Slippery Rock, PA, 16057. Tel: 724-738-9179. p. 2140

Pierce, Karen, Dir, Carroll County Library, 625 High St, Ste 102, Huntingdon, TN, 38344-3903. Tel: 731-986-1919. Fax: 731-986-1335. p. 2237

Pierce, Linda, Coll Develop Librn, Head, Pub Serv, Gonzaga University, 502 E Boone Ave, Spokane, WA, 99258-0095. Tel: 509-323-3834. Fax: 509-323-5806. p. 2536

Pierce, Mary, Ref Librn, Rogue Community College, Wiseman Ctr, 3345 Redwood Hwy, Grants Pass, OR, 97527. Tel: 541-956-7151. Fax: 541-471-3588. p. 1999

Pierce, Melissa, Circ, Libr Tech, Reserves, Clarion University of Pennsylvania, 840 Wood St, Clarion, PA, 16214. Tel: 814-393-2304. Fax: 814-393-2344. p. 2045

Pierce, Nancy, Dir, Nottoway County Public Libraries, 414 Tyler St, Crewe, VA, 23930. Tel: 434-645-9310. Fax: 434-645-8513. p. 2458

Pierce, Pat, Head, Ch, Lucy Robbins Welles Library, 95 Cedar St, Newington, CT, 06111-2645. Tel: 860-665-8783. Fax: 860-667-1255. p. 361

Pierce, Sally K, Librn, Jackson Public Library, 100 N Missouri St, Jackson, MO, 63755-1888. Tel: 573-243-5150. Fax: 573-243-8292. p. 1334

Pierce, Sandra, Ch, Northwest Regional Library System, 898 W 11 St, Panama City, FL, 32401. Tel: 850-522-2100. Fax: 850-522-2138. p. 480

Pierce, Shawn, Tech Serv, Arkansas Supreme Court Library, 625 Marshall St, Ste 1500, Little Rock, AR, 72201. Tel: 501-682-6878. Fax: 501-682-6877. p. 105

Pierce, Shawn, Syst Dir, Pope County Library System, 116 E Third St, Russellville, AR, 72801. Tel: 479-968-4368. Fax: 479-968-3222. p. 114

Pierce, Shawnna, Libr Tech, University of the Fraser Valley, Heritage Park (Mission) Campus, 33700 Prentis Ave, Mission, BC, V2V 7B1, CANADA. Tel: 604-820-6009. p. 2724

Pierce, Sonja, Librn, Mid-America College of Funeral Service Library, 3111 Hamburg Pike, Jeffersonville, IN, 47130. Tel: 812-288-8878. Fax: 812-288-5942. p. 756

Pierce, Stephanie, Reader Serv, Library for the Blind & Physically Handicapped, 900 W Capitol Ave, Ste 100, Little Rock, AR, 72201-3108. Tel: 501-682-1155. Fax: 501-682-2856. p. 106

Pierce, Susan, ILL Librn, Brownell Library, Six Lincoln St, Essex Junction, VT, 05452-3154. Tel: 802-878-6955. Fax: 802-878-6946. p. 2423

Pierce, Sydney, Dr, Assoc Dean, Catholic University of America, Marist Hall, 228, 620 Michigan Ave NE, Washington, DC, 20064. Tel: 202-319-5877. Fax: 202-319-5574. p. 2963

Pierce, Timatha, Exec Dir, Historical Society of Carroll County Library, 210 E Main St, Westminster, MD, 21157. Tel: 410-848-6494. Fax: 410-848-3596. p. 1046

Pierce, Valerie, Br Mgr, Norfolk Public Library, Park Place, 620 W 29th St, Norfolk, VA, 23508. Tel: 757-664-7330. Fax: 757-664-7331. p. 2482

Pierce, Vicky, Librn, Van Buren District Library, Bloomingdale Branch, 109 E Kalamazoo Ave, Bloomingdale, MI, 49026. Tel: 269-521-7601. Fax: 269-521-7601. p. 1168

Pierce, Yvette, Media Spec, Florence-Darlington Technical College Libraries, Segars Library Health Sciences Campus, 320 W Cheves St, Florence, SC, 29501. Tel: 843-676-8575. p. 2194

Pierceall, Tracy, Librn, Illinois Environmental Protection Agency Library, 1021 N Grand Ave E, Springfield, IL, 62702-4072. Tel: 217-782-9691. Fax: 217-524-4916. p. 704

Piercy, Earlene, Br Mgr, Chickasaw Regional Library System, Davis Public Library, 209 E Benton, Davis, OK, 73030. Tel: 580-369-2468. Fax: 580-369-3290. p. 1957

Piercy, Nancy, Acq, University of Puget Sound, 1500 N Warner St, Campus Mail Box 1021, Tacoma, WA, 98416-1021. Tel: 253-879-3258. Fax: 253-879-3670. p. 2541

Pieri, Charles, Assoc Dir, Elkhart Public Library, Osolo, 3429 E Bristol St, Elkhart, IN, 46514. Tel: 574-264-7234. Fax: 574-264-7343. p. 737

Pierini, Rosalyn, Librn, San Luis Obispo County Library, Arroyo Grande Branch, 800 W Branch St, Arroyo Grande, CA, 93420. Tel: 805-473-7161. Fax: 805-473-7173. p. 254

Pierobon, Nancy, Ref Serv, Humber College, 205 Humber College Blvd, Toronto, ON, M9W 5L7, CANADA. Tel: 416-675-5079. Fax: 416-675-7439. p. 2854

Pieron, Andriette, Dir, Palouse Area Library Information Services, c/o Neill Public Library, 210 N Grand Ave, Pullman, WA, 99163. Tel: 509-338-3269. Fax: 509-334-6051. p. 2957

Pierotti, Alice, Br Mgr, First Regional Library, Emily Jones Pointer Public Library, 104 Main St, Como, MS, 38619-0128. Tel: 662-526-5283. Fax: 662-526-5283. p. 1302

Pierre Giraud, Jean, Dir, College Marie de France Library, 4635 chemin Queen Mary, Montreal, QC, H3W 1W3, CANADA. Tel: 514-737-1177. Fax: 514-737-0789. p. 2894

Pierre, Gwendolyn, Br Mgr, Beaumont Public Library System, Theodore R Johns Sr Branch Library, 4255 Fannett Rd, Beaumont, TX, 77705. Tel: 409-842-5233. Fax: 409-842-5422. p. 2287

Pierre, Jennifer, Br Supvr, Saint John the Baptist Parish Library, West, 2979 Hwy 18, Edgard, LA, 70049. Tel: 985-497-3453. Fax: 985-497-3453. p. 955

Pierre, Vivica, Dir, Libr & Info Serv, Bunker Hill Community College (BHCC), 250 New Rutherford Ave, Boston, MA, 02129-2991. Tel: 617-228-3240. Fax: 617-228-3288. p. 1059

Pierschalla, Linda A, Dir, Oscar Grady Public Library, 151 S Main St, Saukville, WI, 53080-1930. Tel: 262-284-6022. Fax: 262-284-1933. p. 2636

Pierson, Conita, Head of Libr, Free Library of Philadelphia, Overbrook Park, 7422 Haverford Ave, Philadelphia, PA, 19151-2995. Tel: 215-685-0182. Fax: 215-685-0183. p. 2108

Pierson, Kate, Dir, Youth Serv, Glen Ellyn Public Library, 400 Duane St, Glen Ellyn, IL, 60137-4508. Tel: 630-469-0879. Fax: 630-469-1086. p. 650

Pierson, Leif, Re/Ser Librn, Tyler Junior College, 1327 S Baxter St, Tyler, TX, 75701. Tel: 903-510-2502, 903-510-2503. Fax: 903-510-2639. p. 2393

Pierson, Margo, Access Serv, Asst Libr Dir, Syst Tech, Southern Arkansas University, 100 E University, Magnolia, AR, 71753-5000. Tel: 870-235-4177. Fax: 870-235-5018. p. 108

Pierson, Seline, Br Mgr, Jackson County Library Services, Rogue River Branch, 412 E Main St, Rogue River, OR, 97537. Tel: 541-864-8850. Fax: 541-864-8871. p. 2005

Pierson, Steve, Mgr, Salt Lake County Library Services, Holladay, 2150 E Murray-Holladay Rd, Salt Lake City, UT, 84117-5241. Tel: 801-944-7524. Fax: 801-278-8947. p. 2414

Piertsma, Eleanor, Br Support, Stormont, Dundas & Glengarry County Library, Iroquois Branch, One Dundas St & Elizabeth St, Iroquois, ON, K0E 1K0, CANADA. Tel: 613-652-4377. p. 2801

Piesner, Stacey, Res Spec, PricewaterhouseCoopers, National Tax Research Services, Royal Trust Tower, 77 King St W, Ste 3000, Toronto, ON, M5K 1G8, CANADA. Tel: 416-815-5103. Fax: 416-814-3200. p. 2857

Pieszak, Anne, Ch, Prescott Valley Public Library, 7401 E Civic Circle, Prescott Valley, AZ, 86314. Tel: 928-759-3040. Fax: 928-759-3121. p. 79

Pietlicki, Beverly, Dir, Paul Memorial Library, 76 Main St, Newfields, NH, 03856-8312. Tel: 603-778-8169. Fax: 603-772-9004. p. 1460

Pietrafesa, Nina, Asst Dir, Jordanville Public Library, 189 Main St, Jordanville, NY, 13361-2729. Tel: 315-858-2874. Fax: 315-858-2874. p. 1648

Pietraszewski, Barbara, Asst Bus Librn, Hesburgh Libraries, Thomas J Mahaffey Jr Business Information Center, L001 Mendoza College of Business, Notre Dame, IN, 46556. Tel: 574-631-9099. Fax: 574-631-6367. p. 770

Pietrobono, Judy, Head, Circ, South Brunswick Public Library, 110 Kingston Lane, Monmouth Junction, NJ, 08852. Tel: 732-329-4000, Ext 7280. Fax: 732-329-0573. p. 1502

Pifer, Jill, Dir, Fairview Heights Public Library, 10017 Bunkum Rd, Fairview Heights, IL, 62208-1703. Tel: 618-489-2070. Fax: 618-489-2079. p. 645

Pifer, Richard, Pub Serv, Ref Serv, Wisconsin Historical Society Library, 816 State St, Madison, WI, 53706. Tel: 608-264-6534. Fax: 608-264-6520. p. 2610

Piffl, Kathryn, Librn, Leigh Yawkey Woodson Art Museum Library, 700 N 12th St, Wausau, WI, 54403-5007. Tel: 715-845-7010. Fax: 715-845-7103. p. 2647

Pifher, Karen, Br Dir, Somerset County Library System, Peapack & Gladstone Public, School St, Peapack, NJ, 07977. Tel: 908-234-0598. Fax: 908-719-2236. p. 1475

Pigford, Samuel, Res Coordr, York Technical College Library, 452 S Anderson Rd, Rock Hill, SC, 29730. Tel: 803-981-7247. Fax: 803-327-4535. p. 2203

Pigg, Sarah, Librn, Planned Parenthood of Southern New England, 345 Whitney Ave, New Haven, CT, 06511-2384. Tel: 203-865-5158. Fax: 203-752-2914. p. 356

Pike, Dorothy, Br Mgr, Wellington County Library, Harriston Branch, 88 Mill St, Harriston, ON, N0G 1Z0, CANADA. Tel: 519-338-2396. p. 2805

Pike, Elyse, Librn, Grey Bruce Health Services, 1800 Eighth St E, Owen Sound, ON, N4K 6M9, CANADA. Tel: 519-376-2121, Ext 2043. Fax: 519-372-3947. p. 2834

Pike, George, Dir, University of Pittsburgh, Law Bldg, 3900 Forbes Ave, 4th Flr, Pittsburgh, PA, 15260. Tel: 412-648-1322. Fax: 412-648-1352. p. 2129

Pike, Jeffrey, Cat, Tech & Ref, Groton Public Library, 99 Main St, Groton, MA, 01450. Tel: 978-448-8000. Fax: 978-448-1169. p. 1093

Pike, Jordan, Librn, Eastern Health, St Claire's Mercy Hospital Library, 154 Le Marchant Rd, St. John's, NL, A1C 5B8, CANADA. Tel: 709-777-5414. Fax: 709-777-5812. p. 2772

Pike, June, Br Mgr, Galax-Carroll Regional Library, Carroll County Public, 101 Beaver Dam Rd, Hillsville, VA, 24343. Tel: 276-728-2228, 276-728-3334. Fax: 276-728-3830. p. 2466

Pike, Mark, Asst Dean, Admin Serv, Kent State University Libraries, 1125 Risman Dr, Kent, OH, 44242. Tel: 330-672-1841. Fax: 330-672-4811. p. 1907

Pike, Roberta A, Cat, Per, Tech Serv, Kingsborough Community College, 2001 Oriental Blvd, Brooklyn, NY, 11235. Tel: 718-368-5639. Fax: 718-368-5482. p. 1592

Pikowski, Krystyna, Acq, Centenary College, 400 Jefferson St, Hackettstown, NJ, 07840. Tel: 908-852-1400, Ext 2345. Fax: 908-850-9528. p. 1489

Pikramenos, Tony, Librn, Reading Public Library, 717 Vermont Rte 106, Reading, VT, 05062. Tel: 802-484-5588. p. 2433

Pikula, Katie, Youth Serv Librn, Lewis Egerton Smoot Memorial Library, 8562 Dahlgren Rd, King George, VA, 22485-3503. Tel: 540-775-7951. Fax: 540-775-5292. p. 2472

Pikula, Linda, Regional Librn, National Oceanic & Atmospheric Administration, 4301 Rickenbacker Causeway, Miami, FL, 33149. Tel: 305-361-4429. Fax: 305-361-4448. p. 468

Pikula, Linda, Regional Dir, United States National Oceanic & Atmospheric, National Hurricane Center/Tropical Prediction Center Library, 11691 SW 17 St, Miami, FL, 33165-2149. Tel: 305-229-4406. Fax: 305-553-9879. p. 468

Pikula, Linda L, Regional Dir, United States National Oceanic & Atmospheric Administration, 4301 Rickenbacker Causeway, Miami, FL, 33149-1097. Tel: 305-361-4428, 305-361-4429. Fax: 305-361-4448. p. 468

Pilachowski, David M, Dir, Williams College, 55 Sawyer Library Dr, Williamstown, MA, 01267. Tel: 413-597-2502. Fax: 413-597-4106. p. 1140

Pilaroscia, Margaret, Adult Serv, Programming, Fairport Public Library, One Fairport Village Landing, Fairport, NY, 14450. Tel: 585-223-9091. Fax: 585-223-3998. p. 1621

Pilcher, Heather, Ref Librn, University of Louisiana at Monroe Library, 700 University Ave, Monroe, LA, 71209-0720. Tel: 318-342-1060. Fax: 318-342-1075. p. 958

Pilek, Barbara, Chief, Br & Reading, Library of Parliament, Confederation Building Branch, Confederation Bldg, Rm G-48, Ottawa, ON, K1A 0A9, CANADA. Tel: 613-943-7051. Fax: 613-996-0862. p. 2831

Pilek, Barbara, Chief, Br & Reading, Library of Parliament, Main Library, Centre Block, 111 Wellington, Ottawa, ON, K1A 0A9, CANADA. Tel: 613-943-7051. Fax: 613-941-4087. p. 2831

Pilek, Barbara, Chief, Library of Parliament, Branches & Information Service, Centre Block, Parliament Bldgs, Ottawa, ON, K1A 0A9, CANADA. Tel: 613-943-7051. Fax: 613-992-1273. p. 2831

Pilette, Roberta, Head, Presv, Yale University Library, Sterling Memorial Library, 120 High St, New Haven, CT, 06520. Tel: 203-432-1714. Fax: 203-432-9900. p. 359

Pilger, Barbara, Br Mgr, Starke County Public Library System, Hamlet Branch, Six N Starke St, Hamlet, IN, 46532. Tel: 574-867-6033. p. 757

Pilgram, Carolyn, Librn, Mid-Mississippi Regional Library System, Attala County, 201 S Huntington St, Kosciusko, MS, 39090-9002. Tel: 662-289-5141. Fax: 662-289-9983. p. 1306

Pilgrim, Juanita, Br Mgr, Enoch Pratt Free Library, Clifton, 2001 N Wolfe St, Baltimore, MD, 21213-1477. Tel: 410-396-0984. Fax: 410-396-0985. p. 1013

Pilikowski, Carlee, Communications & Info, Marigold Library System, 710-Second St, Strathmore, AB, T1P 1K4, CANADA. Tel: 403-934-5334, Ext 237. Fax: 403-934-5331. p. 2718

Pilkington, Angie, Youth Serv Mgr, Burlington Public Library, 210 Court St, Burlington, IA, 52601. Tel: 319-753-1647. Fax: 319-753-0789. p. 797

Pilkington-Smyth, Joan, Asst Dir, Attleboro Public Library, 74 N Main St, Attleboro, MA, 02703. Tel: 508-222-0157, 508-222-0159. Fax: 508-226-3326. p. 1050

Pillar, Jeane, Circ, Fort Smith Public Library, 3201 Rogers Ave, Fort Smith, AR, 72903. Tel: 479-783-0229. Fax: 479-782-8571. p. 100

Pillatzki, Kathy, Asst Dir, Coll Serv, Henry County Public Library System, 1001 Florence McGarity Blvd, McDonough, GA, 30252. Tel: 678-432-5154. Fax: 678-432-6153. p. 544

Pilling, Ann, Coord Librn, Fac/Staff/Circ/Mat Handling & Libr Mgt, Magrath Public Library, Six N First St W, Magrath, AB, T0K 1J0, CANADA. Tel: 403-758-6498. Fax: 403-758-6442. p. 2710

Pillow, Lisa, Coll Develop Librn, University of Wisconsin-River Falls, 410 S Third St, River Falls, WI, 54022. Tel: 715-425-3360. Fax: 715-425-0609. p. 2635

Pillow, Susan Hall, Dir, George M Jones Library Association, 2311 Memorial Ave, Lynchburg, VA, 24501. Tel: 434-846-0501. Fax: 434-846-1572. p. 2475

Pillsbury, Penelope D, Dir, Brownell Library, Six Lincoln St, Essex Junction, VT, 05452-3154. Tel: 802-878-6955. Fax: 802-878-6946. p. 2423

Pilmanis, Aldona, Head, Ch, The Nyack Library, 59 S Broadway, Nyack, NY, 10960. Tel: 845-358-3370, Ext 28. p. 1708

Piloiu, Rares, Info Literacy Librn, Otterbein University, 138 W Main St, Westerville, OH, 43081. Tel: 614-823-1314. Fax: 614-823-1921. p. 1946

Pilon, Isabelle, Dir, Libr Network, Bibliotheque du CAIJ Montreal, One Notre-Dame East, 17th Flr, Rm 17.50, Montreal, QC, H2Y 1B6, CANADA. Tel: 514-866-2057. Fax: 514-879-8592. p. 2888

Pilon, Steven, Ref Serv, Christendom College, 263 St Johns Way, Front Royal, VA, 22630. Tel: 540-636-2900, Ext 132. Fax: 540-636-6569. p. 2466

Pilote, Lynda, Acq, Tech Serv, Racine Louise Documentation Center, 500 Sherbrooke W, Montreal, QC, H3A 3G6, CANADA. Tel: 514-499-5188. Fax: 514-873-4900. p. 2897

Pilotte, Alime, Librn, Jolys Regional Library, Saint Malo, PO Box 593, Saint Malo, MB, R0A 1T0, CANADA. Tel: 204-347-5606. p. 2751

Pim, Cornelia, Librn, Travis Avenue Baptist Church Library, 800 W Berry St, Fort Worth, TX, 76110. Tel: 817-924-4266. Fax: 817-921-9620. p. 2324

Pimentel, Adele, Asst Ch, San Juan Bautista City Library, 801 Second St, San Juan Bautista, CA, 95045. Tel: 831-623-4687. Fax: 831-623-4701. p. 252

Pimentel, Graziela, Br Head, Toronto Public Library, Maria A Shchuka Branch, 1745 Eglinton Ave W, Toronto, ON, M6E 2H4, CANADA. Tel: 416-394-1000. Fax: 416-394-1034. p. 2863

Pimentel, Rosa M, Dir, Inter-American University of Puerto Rico, Information Access Center, Carr PR 1, Esq Calle Francisco Sein, Hato Rey, PR, 00919. Tel: 787-250-1912, Ext 2160, 787-250-1912, Ext 2514. Fax: 787-751-3915. p. 2673

Pinamont, Joan, Librn, Colorado Department of Transportation Library, Shumate Bldg, 4201 E Arkansas Ave, Denver, CO, 80222. Tel: 303-757-9972. p. 299

Pindar, Maia, Ref Serv, Webmaster, Palo Alto Research Center (PARC), 3333 Coyote Hill Rd, Palo Alto, CA, 94304-1314. Tel: 650-812-4042. p. 204

Pinder, Jo Ann, Asst Dir, Support Serv, Baltimore County Public Library, 320 York Rd, Towson, MD, 21204-5179. Tel: 410-887-6100. Fax: 410-887-6103. p. 1044

Pine, Sallie, Br Mgr, Alameda County Library, 2450 Stevenson Blvd, Fremont, CA, 94538-2326. Tel: 510-745-1500. Fax: 510-793-2987. p. 149

Pine, Sallie, Br Mgr, Alameda County Library, Centerville, 3801 Nicolet Ave, Fremont, CA, 94536-3493. Tel: 510-795-2629. Fax: 510-790-5734. p. 149

Pine, Sallie, Br Mgr, Alameda County Library, Fremont Library, 2400 Stevenson Blvd, Fremont, CA, 94538-2325. Tel: 510-745-1400. Fax: 510-797-6557. p. 149

Pine, Sallie, Br Mgr, Alameda County Library, Irvington, 41825 Greenpark Dr, Fremont, CA, 94538-4084. Tel: 510-795-2631. Fax: 510-490-5622. p. 149

Pine, Sallie, Br Mgr, Alameda County Library, Niles, 150 I St, Fremont, CA, 94536-2998. Tel: 510-795-2626. p. 149

Pineau, Priscilla, Ch, Jay-Niles Memorial Library, 983 Main St, North Jay, ME, 04262. Tel: 207-645-4062. p. 994

Pineda, Marika, Interim Dir, Lane Community College Library, 4000 E 30th Ave, Eugene, OR, 97405-0640. Tel: 541-463-5220. Fax: 541-463-4150. p. 1996

Pinella, Barbara, In Charge, Saint Vincent's Hospital & Medical Center of New York-Westchester, 275 North St, Harrison, NY, 10528. Tel: 914-967-6500, Ext 5310. Fax: 914-925-5158. p. 1634

Pinet, Celine, Dean of Instruction, West Valley Community College Library, 14000 Fruitvale Ave, Saratoga, CA, 95070-5698. Tel: 408-741-2140. Fax: 408-741-2134. p. 268

Pingle, Peggy, Br Mgr, Perry County District Library, Corning Branch, 113 11th Hill St, Corning, OH, 43730. Tel: 740-347-4763. Fax: 740-347-9219. p. 1921

Pinilla, Lynn, Br Mgr, Clay County Public Library System, 1895 Town Center Blvd, Orange Park, FL, 32003. Tel: 904-278-3720. Fax: 904-278-6220. p. 475

Pinion, April, Dir, Elgin Community Library, 8183 State Hwy 17, Elgin, OK, 73538. Tel: 580-492-6650. Fax: 580-492-5787. p. 1963

Pinkerman, Loren L, Dir, La Grange College, 601 Broad St, La Grange, GA, 30240-2999. Tel: 706-880-8234. Fax: 706-880-8040. p. 537

Pinkey, Susan, Circ, Gettysburg College, 300 N Washington St, Gettysburg, PA, 17325. Tel: 717-337-7005. Fax: 717-337-7001. p. 2059

Pinkham, Jeffrey, Ref, Ashland University Library, 509 College Ave, Ashland, OH, 44805-3796. Tel: 419-289-5400. Fax: 419-289-5422. p. 1855

Pinkham, Mary, Ch, Boothbay Harbor Memorial Library, Four Oak St, Boothbay Harbor, ME, 04538. Tel: 207-633-3112. p: 978

Pinkner, Kerry, Ch, Pauline Haass Public Library, N64 W23820 Main St, Sussex, WI, 53089-3120. Tel: 262-246-5182. Fax: 262-246-5236. p. 2642

Pinkner, Kerry, Ch Mgr, Waukesha Public Library, 321 Wisconsin Ave, Waukesha, WI, 53186-4786. Tel: 262-524-3695. Fax: 262-524-3677. p. 2645

Pinkney, Rhonda, Mgr, Charlotte Mecklenburg Library, Steele Creek, 13620 Steele Creek Rd, Charlotte, NC, 28273. Tel: 704-416-6800. Fax: 704-416-6900. p. 1782

Pinkos, Elaine, Tech Serv, College of Our Lady of the Elms, 291 Springfield St, Chicopee, MA, 01013-2839. Tel: 413-265-2280, Ext 2285. Fax: 413-594-7418. p. 1082

Pinkowski, Patricia E, Dir, Alzheimer's Association, 225 N Michigan Ave, 17th Flr, Chicago, IL, 60601. Tel: 312-335-5730. Fax: 866-244-1631. p. 605

Pinkston, Alexandra, Br Mgr, Davidson County Public Library System, North Davidson Public, 559 Critcher Dr, Welcome, NC, 27374. Tel: 336-242-2050. Fax: 336-731-3719. p. 1806

Pinkston, Ione, Ch, Washington County Public Library, 210 E Main St, Springfield, KY, 40069. Tel: 859-336-7655. Fax: 859-336-0256. p. 935

Pinkston, Jerry, Info Tech Dir, New Orleans Public Library, 219 Loyola Ave, New Orleans, LA, 70112-2044. Tel: 504-529-7323, 504-596-2570. Fax: 504-596-2609. p. 962

Pinnel, Frances B, Librn, Saint Christopher's Hospital for Children, 3601 A St, Philadelphia, PA, 19134-1095. Tel: 215-427-5374. Fax: 215-427-6872. p. 2116

Pinnell, Julie, Dir, Doane College, 1014 Boswell Ave, Crete, NE, 68333-2421. Tel: 402-826-8565. Fax: 402-826-8199. p. 1396

Pinnell, Julie, Info Serv Librn, Nebraska Library Commission, The Atrium, 1200 N St, Ste 120, Lincoln, NE, 68508-2023. Tel: 402-471-3249. Fax: 402-471-2083. p. 1406

Pinnell, Richard, Mgr, Univ Map Libr & Br Libr Serv, University of Waterloo Library, University Map Library, 200 University Ave W, Waterloo, ON, N2L 3G1, CANADA. Tel: 519-888-4567, Ext 33412. p. 2870

Pinney, Dianne, Librn, Waseca-Le Sueur Regional Library, Le Sueur Public, 118 E Ferry St, Le Sueur, MN, 56058. Tel: 507-665-2662. p. 1287

Pinnick, Denise J, Dir, Oakland City University, 605 W Columbia St, Oakland City, IN, 47660. Tel: 812-749-1267. Fax: 812-749-1414. p. 771

Pinnix-Broome, Tina, Librn, United States Air Force, 1050 W Perimeter Rd, Bldg 1053, Andrews AFB, MD, 20762-6601. Tel: 240-857-2354. Fax: 240-857-8608. p. 1009

Pino, Joseph, Libr Spec II, Coconino Community College, 2800 S Lone Tree Rd, Flagstaff, AZ, 86001-2701. Tel: 928-226-4296. Fax: 928-226-4103. p. 62

Pino, Lucy, Dir, Magdalena Public Library, 108 N Main St, Magdalena, NM, 87825. Tel: 505-854-2361. p. 1560

Pino, Ricardo, Br Mgr, Passaic Public Library, Reid Memorial Branch, 80 Third St, Passaic, NJ, 07055. Tel: 973-777-6044. p. 1518

Pino, Ricardo, Ref Librn, Passaic Public Library, 195 Gregory Ave, Passaic, NJ, 07055. Tel: 973-779-0474. Fax: 973-779-0889. p. 1518

Pinochet, Loreto, Photo Archivist, Montana Historical Society, 225 N Roberts St, Helena, MT, 59601-4514. Tel: 406-444-2681. Fax: 406-444-5297. p. 1382

Pinsonat, Rhonda, Bus Mgr, East Baton Rouge Parish Library, 7711 Goodwood Blvd, Baton Rouge, LA, 70806-7625. Tel: 225-231-3705. Fax: 225-231-3788. p. 942

Pinta, Marilyn, Dir, Manly Public Library, 127 S Grant, Manly, IA, 50456. Tel: 641-454-2982. Fax: 641-454-2252. p. 829

Pintado, Vanessa, Asst Librn, Hispanic Society of America Library, 613 W 155th St, New York, NY, 10032. Tel: 212-926-2234, Ext 251. Fax: 212-690-0743. p. 1681

Pinter, Aniko, Librn, American Hungarian Library & Historical Society, 215 E 82nd St, New York, NY, 10028. Tel: 212-744-5298. p. 1668

Pinter, Sherry, Ref Serv, West Bridgewater Public Library, 80 Howard St, West Bridgewater, MA, 02379-1710. Tel: 508-894-1255. Fax: 508-894-1258. p. 1137

Pinto, Caro, Soc Sci & Emerging Tech Librn, Hampshire College Library, 893 West St, Amherst, MA, 01002-5001. Tel: 413-559-5704. Fax: 413-559-5419. p. 1048

Pinto, David, Dir, Richard Stockton College of New Jersey Library, 101 Vera King Farris Dr, Galloway, NJ, 08205-9441. Tel: 609-652-4343. Fax: 609-652-4964. p. 1487

Pinto, Holly, Dir, Holland & Hart, 555 17th St, Ste 3200, Denver, CO, 80201-3950. Tel: 303-295-8091. Fax: 303-295-8261. p. 302

Pinto, Mark, Dir, Adult Serv, Head, Ref, Phoenixville Public Library, 183 Second Ave, Phoenixville, PA, 19460-3420. Tel: 610-933-3013, Ext 32. Fax: 610-933-4338. p. 2120

Pinto, Rosa, Br Head, Toronto Public Library, Agincourt District, 155 Bonis Ave, Toronto, ON, M1T 3W6, CANADA. Tel: 416-396-8943. Fax: 416-396-8956. p. 2860

Pinto, Usha, Commun Libr Mgr, Queens Borough Public Library, Maspeth Community Library, 69-70 Grand Ave, Maspeth, NY, 11378. Tel: 718-639-5228. p. 1645

Pinzger, Marilyn, Access Serv Librn, University of Wisconsin-Parkside Library, 900 Wood Rd, Kenosha, WI, 53141. Tel: 262-595-2166. Fax: 262-595-2545. p. 2601

Pinzino, Jane, Acad Outreach/Sem Librn, Earlham College, 801 National Rd W, Richmond, IN, 47374-4095. Tel: 765-983-1290. Fax: 765-983-1304. p. 774

Piorun, Mary, Assoc Dir, Tech Initiatives & Res Mgt, University of Massachusetts Medical School, 55 Lake Ave N, Worcester, MA, 01655-2397. Tel: 508-856-2206. Fax: 508-856-5039. p. 1145

Piorunski, Michael, Librn, Friedenwald-Romano Library, Johns Hopkins Hospital, Woods Res Bldg, 600 N Wolfe St, Rm 3B-50, Baltimore, MD, 21287-9105. Tel: 410-955-3127. Fax: 410-955-0046. p. 1013

Piotrowicz, Lynn, Dir, Tucker Free Library, 31 Western Ave, Henniker, NH, 03242. Tel: 603-428-3471. Fax: 603-428-7106. p. 1451

Piotrowski, Ann, Acad Media Serv Mgr, Saint Catherine University, 2004 Randolph Ave, Mail F-10, Saint Paul, MN, 55105-1794. Tel: 651-690-6658. Fax: 651-690-8636. p. 1281

Piotrowski, Debra, In Charge, Sheehan Phinney Bass & Green PA Library, 1000 Elm St, No 1800, Manchester, NH, 03105. Tel: 603-668-0300. Fax: 603-627-8121. p. 1456

Piotter, Rose, Librn, Lenawee County Library, Deerfield Branch, 170 Raisin St, Deerfield, MI, 49238-9717. Tel: 517-447-3400. Fax: 517-447-3400. p. 1147

Piper, Carol, Circ Librn, Sullivan City Public Library, Two W Water St, Sullivan, IL, 61951. Tel: 217-728-7221. Fax: 217-728-2215. p. 708

Piper, Dave, Digital Res Librn, University of Arizona, Arizona Health Sciences Library, 1501 N Campbell Ave, Tucson, AZ, 85724. Tel: 520-626-2529. Fax: 520-626-2922. p. 88

Piper, Denise, Br Head, Toronto Public Library, York Woods, 1785 Finch Ave W, Toronto, ON, M3N 1M6, CANADA. Tel: 416-395-5980. Fax: 416-395-5991. p. 2863

Piper, Jessica, Br Mgr, Nashville Public Library, Z Alexander Looby Branch, 2301 Rosa L Parks Blvd, Nashville, TN, 37228-1221. Tel: 615-862-5867. Fax: 615-862-5797. p. 2257

Piper, Matthew, Circ Mgr, Clinton-Macomb Public Library, South, 35891 S Gratiot Ave, Clinton Township, MI, 48035. Tel: 586-226-5074. Fax: 586-226-5078. p. 1164

Piper, Michael, Dir of Libr Serv, Art Institute of Indianapolis Library, 3500 Depauw Blvd, Indianapolis, IN, 46268. Tel: 317-613-4800, 317-613-4803. Fax: 317-613-4808. p. 749

Piper, Paul, Ref Librn, Western Washington University, 516 High St, MS 9103, Bellingham, WA, 98225. Tel: 360-650-3097. Fax: 360-650-3044. p. 2509

Piperno-Jones, Carla, Dir, Springport Free Library, 171 Cayuga St, Union Springs, NY, 13160. Tel: 315-889-7766. Fax: 315-889-7766. p. 1757

Pipes, Richard, Acq, Coll Develop, Ref Serv, Wingate University, PO Box 219, Wingate, NC, 28174-1202. Tel: 704-233-8089. Fax: 704-233-8254. p. 1832

Pipes, Robert, Tech Serv Coordr, Mount San Jacinto College, 1499 N State St, San Jacinto, CA, 92583-2399. Tel: 951-487-6752, Ext 1584. Fax: 951-654-8387. p. 249

Pipia, Lisa, Law Librn, Harter, Secrest & Emery LLP, 1600 Bausch & Lomb Pl, Rochester, NY, 14604. Tel: 585-231-1228. Fax: 585-232-2152. p. 1729

Pipkin, Pamela, Dir, Rusk County Library, 106 E Main St, Henderson, TX, 75652. Tel: 903-657-8557. Fax: 903-657-7637. p. 2332

Pipon, Sharon, Mgr, Pfizer Canada, Inc, 17300 Trans-Canada Hwy, Pointe-Claire, QC, H9J 2M5, CANADA. Tel: 514-426-7060. Fax: 514-426-7558. p. 2903

Pippin, Alan, Ref Librn, Rockwall County Library, 1215 E Yellowjacket Lane, Rockwall, TX, 75087. Tel: 972-204-7700. Fax: 972-204-7709. p. 2377

Pippitt, Amanda, Archivist, Coordr, Access Serv, Millikin University, 1184 W Main, Decatur, IL, 62522. Tel: 217-424-6214. Fax: 217-424-3992. p. 634

Piprell, Rhian, Dep Dir, Coquitlam Public Library, 575 Poirier St, Coquitlam, BC, V3J 6A9, CANADA. Tel: 604-937-4132. Fax: 604-931-6739. p. 2727

Piprell, Rhian, Dir, Coquitlam Public Library, City Centre, 3001 Burlington Dr, Coquitlam, BC, V3B 6X1, CANADA. Tel: 604-937-4132. Fax: 604-927-3570. p. 2727

Piquet, Jeanette Moore, Libr Dir, Richmond Heights Memorial Library, 8001 Dale Ave, Richmond Heights, MO, 63117. Tel: 314-645-6202. Fax: 314-781-3434. p. 1350

Piqune, Karen Gail, Coll Develop, Geoscience Librn, American Association of Petroleum Geologists Foundation, 1444 S Boulder, Tulsa, OK, 74101-3604. Tel: 918-560-2620. Fax: 918-560-2642. p. 1980

Pirie, Joan, Assoc Dir, Tech Serv, Vassar College Library, 124 Raymond Ave, Maildrop 20, Poughkeepsie, NY, 12604-0020. Tel: 845-437-5760. Fax: 845-437-5864. p. 1723

Pirillo, Joseph, ILL, Lakeland College, W3718 South Dr, Plymouth, WI, 53073. Tel: 920-565-1238. Fax: 920-565-1206. p. 2630

Pirkle, Rachel, Ch, Aiken-Bamberg-Barnwell-Edgefield Regional Library System, 314 Chesterfield St SW, Aiken, SC, 29801-7171. Tel: 803-642-7575. Fax: 803-642-7597. p. 2179

Piro, Stephanie, Adult Prog Coordr, Ad, Goodwin Library, 422 Main St, Farmington, NH, 03835-1519. Tel: 603-755-2944. Fax: 603-755-2944. p. 1447

Pirog, Stan, Librn, GateWay Community College Library, 108 N 40th St, Phoenix, AZ, 85034-1704. Tel: 602-286-8456. Fax: 602-286-8459. p. 73

Piroli, Vivienne, Dep Dir, Simmons College, 300 The Fenway, Boston, MA, 02115-5898. p. 1066

Pirone, Marcia, Doc, Tech Spec, Dartmouth College Library, Kresge Physical Sciences Library, 6115 Fairchild Hall, Hanover, NH, 03755-3571. Tel: 603-646-3563. Fax: 603-646-3681. p. 1450

Pirtle, Brenda, Dir, Lee Ola Roberts Public Library, 140 W Main St, Whiteville, TN, 38075. Tel: 731-254-8834. Fax: 731-254-8805. p. 2269

Pisani-Kristl, Heather, Coll Develop, Librn III, San Diego County Library, 5560 Overland Ave, Ste 110, San Diego, CA, 92123. Tel: 858-694-2674. Fax: 858-495-5981. p. 233

Pisani-Kristl, Heather, Assoc Dir, Norfolk Public Library, 139 Main St, Norfolk, MA, 02056. Tel: 508-528-3380. Fax: 508-528-6417. p. 1111

Pisano, Anna, Circ, Ch, Everett Public Libraries, 410 Broadway, Everett, MA, 02149. Tel: 617-394-2306. Fax: 617-389-1230. p. 1087

Pisano, Concetta, Coll Develop, Carroll County Public Library, 115 Airport Dr, Westminster, MD, 21157. Tel: 410-386-4500, Ext 142. Fax: 410-386-4509. p. 1045

Pisano, Sandy, Assoc Dir, Libr Operations, Capitol College, 11301 Springfield Rd, Laurel, MD, 20708. Tel: 301-369-2800. Fax: 301-369-2552. p. 1034

Pisapia, Bart, Br Mgr, Collins LeRoy Leon County Public Library System, Lake Jackson, Huntington Oaks Plaza, 3840-302 N Monroe, Tallahassee, FL, 32303. Tel: 850-606-2850. Fax: 850-606-2851. p. 492

Pisaretz, Liz, Coordr, Circ, Norwalk Community College, 188 Richards Ave, Norwalk, CT, 06854-1655. Tel: 203-857-7200. Fax: 203-857-7380. p. 362

Piscadlo, Bruce S, Dir, Law Library of Montgomery County, Court House, Swede & Airy Streets, Norristown, PA, 19404. Tel: 610-278-3805. Fax: 610-278-5998. p. 2098

Pisciotta, Henry, Head Librn, Pennsylvania State University Libraries, Architecture & Landscape Architecture, 111 Stuckeman Family Bldg, University Park, PA, 16802-1912. Tel: 814-865-3665. Fax: 814-865-5073. p. 2148

Pisciotta, Henry, Librn, Pennsylvania State University Libraries, George & Sherry Middlemas Arts & Humanities Library, Pennsylvania State University, W 202 Pattee Library, University Park, PA, 16802-1801. Tel: 814-865-6778. Fax: 814-863-7502. p. 2148

Pisciotta, Robert A, Assoc Libr Dir, Tech Serv Supvr, University of Kansas Medical Center, 2100 W 39th Ave, Kansas City, KS, 66160-7180. Tel: 913-588-7311. Fax: 913-588-7304. p. 876

Piscitelli, Felicia, Rare Bk Cataloger, Texas A&M University Libraries, Cushing Memorial Library & Archives, 5000 TAMU, College Station, TX, 77843-5000. Tel: 979-845-1951. Fax: 979-845-1441. p. 2299

Piscitelli, Rosalie, Head, Syst, Weil, Gotshal & Manges Library, 767 Fifth Ave, New York, NY, 10153. Tel: 212-310-8626. Fax: 212-310-8007. p. 1702

Piscitello, Christina, Regional Libr Supvr, Wake County Public Library System, Eva H Perry Regional Library, 2100 Shepherd's Vineyard Dr, Apex, NC, 27502. Tel: 919-387-4305. Fax: 919-387-4320. p. 1818

Piskorik, Elizabeth, Per, Ref, Linden Free Public Library, 31 E Henry St, Linden, NJ, 07036. Tel: 908-298-3830. Fax: 908-486-2636. p. 1495

Pistilli, Susan, Mgr, Libr Serv, International Council of Shopping Centers, 1221 Avenue of the Americas, 41st Flr, New York, NY, 10020-1099. Tel: 646-728-3670. Fax: 732-694-1714. p. 1683

Pitawanakwat, Lee Ann, Chief Librn, Magnetawan First Nation Public Library, Ten Regional Rd & Hwy 529, Britt, ON, P0G 1A0, CANADA. Tel: 705-383-2477. Fax: 705-383-2566. p. 2797

Pitcher, Betty, Librn, Winterton Public Library, Main St, Winterton, NL, A0B 3M0, CANADA. Tel: 709-583-2119. Fax: 709-583-2119. p. 2773

Pitcher, Ellen, Ref Serv, Starke County Public Library System, 152 W Culver Rd, Knox, IN, 46534-2220. Tel: 574-772-7323. p. 757

Pitcher, Karen, Ref Librn, Broome Community College, 907 Front St, Binghamton, NY, 13905-1328. Tel: 607-778-5468. Fax: 607-778-5108. p. 1581

Pitcher, Kate, Coll Develop Librn, State University of New York College at Geneseo, SUNY Geneseo, One College Circle, Geneseo, NY, 14454-1498. Tel: 585-245-5064. p. 1627

Pitcher, Sara, Archives, Coe College, 1220 First Ave NE, Cedar Rapids, IA, 52402-5092. Tel: 319-399-8787. Fax: 319-399-8019. p. 800

Pitchford, Amanda, Coll Develop, North Island College, 2300 Ryan Rd, Courtenay, BC, V9N 8N6, CANADA. Tel: 250-334-5097. Fax: 250-334-5291. p. 2727

Pitchford, Martha, Asst Dir, Lakeland Library Cooperative, 4138 Three Mile Rd NW, Grand Rapids, MI, 49534-1134. Tel: 616-559-5253, Ext 202. Fax: 616-559-4329. p. 2946

Pitchon, Cindy A, Asst Dir, HSLC/Access PA, 3600 Market St, Ste 550, Philadelphia, PA, 19104-2646. Tel: 215-222-1532. Fax: 215-222-0416. p. 2954

Pitkin, Lisa, Tech Serv, Guilderland Public Library, 2228 Western Ave, Guilderland, NY, 12084-9701. Tel: 518-456-2400. Fax: 518-456-0923. p. 1632

Pitman, Alicia, Asst Dir, Ch, Pendleton Community Library, 595 E Water St, Pendleton, IN, 46064-1070. Tel: 765-778-7527, Ext 105. Fax: 765-778-7529. p. 772

Pitman, Marilyn, Dir, Bristol Hospital & Health Care Group, 41 Brewster Rd, Bristol, CT, 06011. Tel: 860-585-3239. p. 332

Pitschel, Barbara M, Head Librn, San Francisco Botanical Garden Society at Strybing Arboretum, 1199 Ninth Ave, (Ninth Ave at Lincoln Way), San Francisco, CA, 94122-2384. Tel: 415-661-1316, Ext 303. Fax: 415-661-3539. p. 244

Pitschmann, Louis A, Dr, Dean of Libr, University of Alabama, University Libraries, University of Alabama Campus, Capstone Dr, Tuscaloosa, AL, 35487. Tel: 205-348-7561. Fax: 205-348-8833. p. 38

Pitstick, Carla, Librn, Fonda Public Library, 104 W Second & Main, Fonda, IA, 50540. Tel: 712-288-4466. Fax: 712-288-6633. p. 816

Pitt, Elizabeth, Acq Librn, Asst Prof, Lincoln University, 1570 Old Baltimore Pike, Lincoln University, PA, 19352. Tel: 484-365-7357. Fax: 610-932-1206. p. 2082

Pittam, Joyce, Dir, Woolworth Community Library, 100 E Utah Ave, Jal, NM, 88252. Tel: 505-395-3268. Fax: 505-395-2138. p. 1557

Pittari, S, Coll Develop, Library of the Legal Aid Society of Westchester County, One N Broadway, Ste 910, White Plains, NY, 10601-2352. Tel: 914-286-3400. Fax: 914-682-4112. p. 1768

Pittenger, Beck, Asst Dir, Ch, Yankton Community Library, 515 Walnut, Yankton, SD, 57078-4042. Tel: 605-668-5275. Fax: 605-668-5277. p. 2222

Pittman, Alex, Dir, Br Serv, Wright State University, 7600 State Rte 703 E, Celina, OH, 45822-2952. Tel: 937-775-8360. Fax: 419-586-8334. p. 1866

Pittman, Betsy, Univ Archivist, University of Connecticut Library, 369 Fairfield Rd, Storrs, CT, 06269-1005. Tel: 860-486-2219. Fax: 860-486-0584. p. 370

Pittman, Donna, Develop Dir, Champaign Public Library, 200 W Green St, Champaign, IL, 61820-5193. Tel: 217-403-2050. Fax: 217-403-2053. p. 602

Pittman, Gena, Dir, Grace Medical Center, 2412 50th St, Lubbock, TX, 79412. Tel: 806-788-4026. Fax: 806-788-4284. p. 2357

Pittman, Hilary, Librn, Tulsa World, 315 S Boulder Ave, Tulsa, OK, 74103-3401. Tel: 918-582-0921. Fax: 918-581-8425. p. 1984

Pittman, Karan Berryman, Coll Develop, Dir, Libr Serv, Andrew College, 501 College St, Cuthbert, GA, 39840. Tel: 229-732-5944. Fax: 229-732-5957. p. 527

Pittman, Kitty, ILL, Pub Serv, Oklahoma Department of Libraries, 200 NE 18th St, Oklahoma City, OK, 73105. Tel: 405-521-2502. Fax: 405-525-7804. p. 1974

Pittman, Lydia, Tech Serv, Lasell College, 80 A Maple Ave, Newton, MA, 02466. Tel: 617-243-2207. Fax: 617-243-2458. p. 1109

Pittman, Mary Jane, Regional Librn, Nova Scotia Community College, 75 High St, Bridgewater, NS, B4V 1V8, CANADA. Tel: 902-543-0690. Fax: 902-543-0652. p. 2778

Pittman, Melody, Dir, Germantown Community Library, 1925 Exeter Rd, Germantown, TN, 38138-2815. Tel: 901-757-7323, Ext 7480. Fax: 901-756-9940. p. 2235

Pittman, Melody, Dir, Wolf River Library Consortium, c/o Germantown Community Library, 1925 Exeter Rd, Germantown, TN, 38138-2815. Tel: 901-757-7323. Fax: 901-756-9940. p. 2955

Pittman, Mignon, Circ, Interim Dir, Calloway County Public Library, 710 Main St, Murray, KY, 42071. Tel: 270-753-2288. Fax: 270-753-8263. p. 930

Pittman, Penny, Asst Librn, Warner Memorial Library, PO Box 270, Warner, AB, T0K 2L0, CANADA. Tel: 403-642-3988. p. 2721

Pittman, Susan Heckler, Dir, St Marys Community Public Library, 140 S Chestnut St, Saint Marys, OH, 45885-2307. Tel: 419-394-7471. Fax: 419-394-7291. p. 1933

Pitts, Angie, Media Spec, Greenwood County Library, Ware Shoals Community Library, 54 S Greenwood Ave, Ware Shoals, SC, 29692. Tel: 864-456-2813. Fax: 864-456-2813. p. 2197

Pitts, Ashley, Generalist Librn, University of Saint Thomas, Cardinal Beran Library at Saint Mary's Seminary, 9845 Memorial Dr, Houston, TX, 77024-3498. Tel: 713-686-4345, Ext 248, 713-686-4345, Ext 265. Fax: 713-681-7550. p. 2344

Pitts, Chrisler, Librn, Kean University, 1000 Morris Ave, Union, NJ, 07083. Tel: 908-737-4600. Fax: 908-737-4620. p. 1537

Pitts, Gloria, Archives Mgr, North Carolina Agricultural & Technical State University, 1601 E Market St, Greensboro, NC, 27411-0002. Tel: 336-334-7159, Ext 3235. Fax: 336-334-7783. p. 1797

Pitts, Karen, Ms, Rare Bks, National Library of Medicine, Bldg 38, Rm 2E-17B, 8600 Rockville Pike, Bethesda, MD, 20894. Tel: 301-496-6308. Fax: 301-496-4450. p. 1022

Pitts, Lesley, Pres, The Mary Baker Eddy Library, Lending & Reference Services, 200 Massachusetts Ave, P02-10, Boston, MA, 02115-3017. Tel: 617-450-7325. p. 1060

Pitts, Linda, Circ Serv Librn, Southwest Public Libraries, Westland Area Library, 4740 W Broad St, Columbus, OH, 43228. Tel: 614-878-1301. Fax: 614-878-3454. p. 1903

Pitts, Martha, Asst Librn, Bay Correctional Facility Library, 5400 Bay Line Dr, Panama City, FL, 32404. Tel: 850-769-1455, Ext 243. Fax: 850-769-1942. p. 480

Pitts, Mary Margaret, Librn, Boston Public Library, Hyde Park Branch, 35 Harvard Ave, Hyde Park, MA, 02136-2862. Tel: 617-361-2524. Fax: 617-361-6791. p. 1057

Pitts, Pam, Tech Serv, Crown College, 8700 College View Dr, Saint Bonifacius, MN, 55375-9002. Tel: 952-446-4415. Fax: 952-446-4149. p. 1274

Pitts, Rob, Syst Adminr, Starke County Public Library System, 152 W Culver Rd, Knox, IN, 46534-2220. Tel: 574-772-7323. p. 757

Pitts, Susie, Ref Librn, Pamunkey Regional Library, 7527 Library Dr, Hanover, VA, 23069. Tel: 804-537-6211. Fax: 804-537-6389. p. 2469

Pitts, Terence, Exec Dir, Cedar Rapids Museum of Art, 410 Third Ave SE, Cedar Rapids, IA, 52401. Tel: 319-366-7503. Fax: 319-366-4111. p. 800

Pittson, Cynthia, Head, Ref, Pace University, 78 N Broadway, White Plains, NY, 10603. Tel: 914-422-4482. Fax: 914-422-4139. p. 1769

Pituch, Rosalee, Librn, Rebecca M Arthurs Memorial Library, 223 Valley St, Brookville, PA, 15825-0223. Tel: 814-849-5512. Fax: 814-849-6211. p. 2038

Pityk, Melissa A, Youth Serv Librn, Lexington County Public Library System, Irmo Branch, 6251 St Andrews Rd, Columbia, SC, 29212-3152. Tel: 803-798-7880. Fax: 803-798-8570. p. 2199

Pitz, Lauren, Br Librn, Saint Charles Parish Library, 160 W Campus Dr, Destrehan, LA, 70047. Tel: 985-764-2366. Fax: 985-764-0447. p. 948

Piush, Evelyn, Br Head, Winnipeg Public Library, West Kildonan, 365 Jefferson Ave, Winnipeg, MB, R2V 0N3, CANADA. Tel: 204-986-4384. Fax: 204-986-3373. p. 2760

Pixley, Bill, Libr Dir, C E Brehm Memorial Public Library District, 101 S Seventh St, Mount Vernon, IL, 62864. Tel: 618-242-6322. Fax: 618-242-0810. p. 677

Pixley, Karen, Dir, Auburndale Public Library, 100 W Bridgers Ave, Auburndale, FL, 33823. Tel: 863-965-5548. Fax: 863-965-5554. p. 425

Pixley, Peggy, Ref, Oral Roberts University Library, 7777 South Lewis Ave, Tulsa, OK, 74171. Tel: 918-495-6732. Fax: 918-495-6893. p. 1981

Pizarro, Luz, Ref Serv, Inter-American University of Puerto Rico, School of Law Library, PO Box 70351, Hato Rey, PR, 00936. Tel: 787-751-1912. Fax: 787-753-6851. p. 2673

Pizzamiglio, Nadia, In Charge, Bibliotheque Gabrielle-Roy, Canardiere, 1601, Chemin De La Canardiere, Quebec, QC, G1J 2E1, CANADA. Tel: 418-641-6793. p. 2903

Pizzamiglio, Nadia, In Charge, Bibliotheque Gabrielle-Roy, Saint-Albert, Five rue des Ormes, Quebec, QC, G1L 1M5, CANADA. Tel: 418-641-6793. p. 2903

Pizzamiglio, Nadia, In Charge, Bibliotheque Gabrielle-Roy, Saint-Charles, 400 Fourth Ave, Quebec, QC, G1J 2Z9, CANADA. Tel: 418-641-6795. p. 2903

Pizzo, Diane, Coll Mgt, Connecticut State Library, 231 Capitol Ave, Hartford, CT, 06106. Tel: 860-757-6500. Fax: 860-757-6503. p. 345

Pizzoli, Dora, Circ Supvr, Finkelstein Memorial Library, 24 Chestnut St, Spring Valley, NY, 10977-5594. Tel: 845-352-5700. Fax: 845-352-2319. p. 1746

Plaat, Jennifer P, Dir, Saint John's Mercy Medical Center, Tower B, 621 S New Ballas Rd, Ste 1000, Saint Louis, MO, 63141. Tel: 314-251-6340. Fax: 314-251-4299. p. 1357

Place, Lindsay, Librn for Blind & Physically Handicapped, Parkersburg & Wood County Public Library, Services for the Blind & Physically Handicapped, 3100 Emerson Ave, Parkersburg, WV, 26104. Tel: 304-420-4587, Ext 13. Fax: 304-420-4589. p. 2568

Place, Lynn, Dir, Germantown Library, 31 Palatine Park Rd, Germantown, NY, 12526-5309. Tel: 518-537-5800. Fax: 518-537-5928. p. 1628

Placek, Dorothy, Librn, Williston Community Library, Tioga Community Library, 321 N Benson St, Tioga, ND, 58852. Tel: 701-664-3627. p. 1849

Placer, Chandra, Br Librn, Spartanburg County Public Libraries, Westside Library, 525 Oak Grove Rd, Spartanburg, SC, 29301. Tel: 864-574-6815. p. 2205

Placke, Jessica, Dir, Ivy Technical Community College, 50 W Fall Creek Pkwy N Dr, Indianapolis, IN, 46208-5752. Tel: 317-921-4782. Fax: 317-921-4355. p. 755

Placke, Margaret, Assoc State Librn, State Library of Louisiana, 701 N Fourth St, Baton Rouge, LA, 70802-5232. Tel: 225-342-4951. Fax: 225-219-4804. p. 945

Placzek, Sandy, Pub Serv, University of Nebraska-Lincoln, Marvin & Virginia Schmid Law Library, 40 Fair St, Lincoln, NE, 68583. Tel: 402-472-3547. Fax: 402-472-8260. p. 1407

Plageman, Kathy, Supvr, Circ, South Burlington Community Library, 540 Dorset St, South Burlington, VT, 05403. Tel: 802-652-7080. Fax: 802-652-7013. p. 2435

Plagman, Karen, Dir, Lied Irwin Public Library, 509 Ann St, Irwin, IA, 51446. Tel: 712-782-3335. Fax: 712-782-3335. p. 824

Plaisance, Annette, Br Mgr, Lafourche Parish Public Library, Golden Meadow Branch, 1403 N Bayou Dr, Golden Meadow, LA, 70357-2513. Tel: 985-475-5660. Fax: 985-475-5660. p. 971

Plaisted, Cathie, Coordr, Serv to the Aged in Genesee County, Richmond Memorial Library, 19 Ross St, Batavia, NY, 14020. Tel: 585-343-9550. Fax: 585-344-4651. p. 1578

Plambeck, Hans J, Dir, New Hartford Public Library, Two Library Lane, New Hartford, NY, 13413-2815. Tel: 315-733-1535. Fax: 315-733-0795. p. 1665

Planas, Dorothy, Head, Ref, University of Mary Hardin-Baylor, 900 College St, UMHB Sta, Box 8016, Belton, TX, 76513-2599. Tel: 254-295-4637. Fax: 254-295-4642. p. 2289

Planck, Judith, Br Mgr, Crooked Tree District Library, Boyne Falls Branch, 3008 Railroad St, Boyne Falls, MI, 49713. Tel: 231-549-2277. p. 1234

Planco, Terri, ILL, Lucy Robbins Welles Library, 95 Cedar St, Newington, CT, 06111-2645. Tel: 860-665-8718. Fax: 860-667-1255. p. 361

Planeuf, Janine, Librn, Wapiti Regional Library, St Louis Public Library, 205 Second St, St. Louis, SK, S0J 2C0, CANADA. Tel: 306-422-8511. p. 2922

Planiczka, Mary Caryl, Asst Libr Dir, Ch, South Park Township Library, 2575 Brownsville Rd, South Park, PA, 15129-8527. Tel: 412-833-5585. Fax: 412-833-7368. p. 2142

Plank, Elissa, Head, Circ, Louisiana State University Libraries, 295 Middleton Library, Baton Rouge, LA, 70803. Tel: 225-578-3216. Fax: 225-578-9432. p. 943

Plank, Jim, Circ, Cheyney University, 1837 University Circle, Cheyney, PA, 19319. Tel: 610-399-2203. Fax: 610-399-2491. p. 2044

Plankinton-Murphy, Helen, Tech Serv & Automation, Beck Bookman Library, 420 W Fourth St, Holton, KS, 66436-1572. Tel: 785-364-3532. Fax: 785-364-5402. p. 872

Plant, Betty J, Dir, Runge Public Library, 311 N Helena, Runge, TX, 78151. Tel: 830-239-4192. Fax: 830-239-4629. p. 2377

Plant, Rachel A, Youth Serv Librn, Bixby Memorial Free Library, 258 Main St, Vergennes, VT, 05491. Tel: 802-877-2211. Fax: 802-877-2411. p. 2437

Plant, Randy, Br Head, Winnipeg Public Library, Munroe, 489 London St, Winnipeg, MB, R2K 2Z4, CANADA. Tel: 204-986-3736. Fax: 204-986-7125. p. 2760

Plante, Christine, Br Mgr, San Diego County Library, Spring Valley Branch, 836 Kempton St, Spring Valley, CA, 91977. Tel: 619-463-3006. Fax: 619-463-8917. p. 234

Plante, Raymond, Ref Librn, United States Postal Service Library, 475 L'Enfant Plaza SW, Rm 11800, Washington, DC, 20260-1540. Tel: 202-268-2906. Fax: 202-268-4423. p. 421

Plante, Suzanne, In Charge, Commission d'Acces A L'Information, 575, Rue St-Amable No. 1.10, Quebec, QC, G1R 2G4, CANADA. Tel: 418-528-1355. Fax: 418-529-3102. p. 2904

Plante, Suzelle, Librn, Bibliotheque Municipale, PO Box 730, Temiscaming, QC, J0Z 3R0, CANADA. Tel: 819-627-9778. Fax: 819-627-3019. p. 2913

Plaskon, Denise, Librn, New Bedford Free Public Library, Francis J Lawler Branch, 745 Rockdale Ave, New Bedford, MA, 02740. Tel: 508-991-6216. Fax: 508-961-3077. p. 1108

Plaso, Kathy, Asst Syst Adminr, Somerset County Federated Library System, 6022 Glades Pike, Ste 120, Somerset, PA, 15501-0043. Tel: 814-445-2556. Fax: 814-443-0650. p. 2141

Plasterer, Mark, Dir, Multimedia Serv, Central Texas College, Bld 102, 6200 W Central Texas Expressway, Killeen, TX, 76549. Tel: 254-526-1537. Fax: 254-526-1878. p. 2350

Plasterer, Rick, In Charge, Presbyterian Church of the Atonement Library, 10613 Georgia Ave, Silver Spring, MD, 20902. Tel: 301-649-4131. Fax: 301-649-9633. p. 1042

Plaston, Kristine, Chair, Red Deer College Library, 100 College Blvd, Red Deer, AB, T4N 5H5, CANADA. Tel: 403-342-3578. Fax: 403-346-8500. p. 2714

Plata, Francisco, Per, Pontifical Catholic University Of Puerto Rico, Encarnacion Valdes Library, 2250 Avenida Las Americas, Ste 509, Ponce, PR, 00717-0777. Tel: 787-841-2000, Ext 1809. Fax: 787-284-0235. p. 2675

Plate, Kathy, Dir, Prattsburgh Library, 26 Main St, Prattsburgh, NY, 14873. Tel: 607-522-3490. Fax: 607-522-3490. p. 1724

Plater, Cassandra, Ref Librn, North Carolina Agricultural & Technical State University, 1601 E Market St, Greensboro, NC, 27411-0002. Tel: 336-334-7159, Ext 3205. Fax: 336-334-7783. p. 1797

Platkowski, Melissa, Electronic Res Mgt Librn, University of Wisconsin-Green Bay, 2420 Nicolet Dr, Green Bay, WI, 54311-7001. Tel: 920-465-2764. Fax: 920-465-2136. p. 2596

Platt, Carolyn, Head, Tech Serv, Jones Library, Inc, 43 Amity St, Amherst, MA, 01002-2285. Tel: 413-259-3214. Fax: 413-256-4096. p. 1048

Platt, Ellen J, Dir, Pub Serv, Santa Clara University, Heafey Law Library, School of Law, 500 El Camino Real, Santa Clara, CA, 95053-0430. Tel: 408-554-5139. Fax: 408-554-5318. p. 263

Platt, Kathie, Coll Develop, Dir, Bern Community Library, 401 Main St, Bern, KS, 66408. Tel: 785-336-3000. Fax: 785-336-3000. p. 858

Platt, Kathy, Libr Dir, Sac & Fox National Public Library, 920883 S Hwy 99, Stroud, OK, 74079-5178. Tel: 918-968-0706. Fax: 918-968-4837. p. 1979

Platt, Mary, Asst Dir, Virtual Res, Kennesaw State University, 1000 Chastain Rd, Kennesaw, GA, 30144. Tel: 770-423-6197. Fax: 770-423-6185. p. 537

Platt, Mary, Cat Librn, Union University, 1050 Union University Dr, Jackson, TN, 38305-3697. Tel: 731-661-5414. Fax: 731-661-5175. p. 2238

Platt, Stephen, Ref Librn, Henderson District Public Libraries, 280 S Green Valley Pkwy, Henderson, NV, 89012. Tel: 702-492-7252. Fax: 702-492-1711. p. 1428

Platt, Susan, Info & Res Mgr, Alberta Law Libraries, Judicial, Calgary Courts Ctr, 2001-N, 601 - 5 St SW, Calgary, AB, T2P 5P7, CANADA. Tel: 403-297-7355. Fax: 403-297-2981. p. 2687

Platt, Virginia D, Dir, DeWitt Public Library, 205 W Maxwell, DeWitt, AR, 72042. Tel: 870-946-1151. Fax: 870-946-1151. p. 97

Platt-Brown, Jane, Librn, Cadwalader, Wickersham & Taft, 700 Sixth St NW, Suite 300, Washington, DC, 20001. Tel: 202-862-2217. Fax: 202-862-2400. p. 395

Platte, Amy, Libr Tech, Michigan Department of Corrections, Carson City Correctional Facility Library, PO Box 5000, Carson City, MI, 48811-5000. Tel: 989-548-3941, Ext 6331. Fax: 989-584-6535. p. 1161

Platte, Kelly, Dir, Denver Public Library, 100 Washington St, Denver, IA, 50622. Tel: 319-984-5140. Fax: 319-984-5140. p. 808

Platte, Mike, Asst Dir, Saranac Public Library, 61 Bridge St, Saranac, MI, 48881. Tel: 616-642-9146. Fax: 616-642-6430. p. 1226

Platteter, Steven, Automation Serv, Mid-Wisconsin Federated Library System, 112 Clinton St, Horicon, WI, 53032. Tel: 920-485-0833. Fax: 920-485-0899. p. 2598

Platts, Barbara, Mgr, Libr Serv, Munson Healthcare, Department of Library Services, 1105 Sixth St, Traverse City, MI, 49684. Tel: 231-935-6544. Fax: 231-935-7124. p. 1231

Platts, Daphne, Dir, Sublette County Library, 155 S Tyler Ave, Pinedale, WY, 82941. Tel: 307-367-4115. Fax: 307-367-6722. p. 2658

Plaut, Daphne, Dir, Kaiser Permanente, 3800 N Interstate Ave, Portland, OR, 97227-1098. Tel: 503-335-6744. p. 2011

Player, Deloris, Brother, Head, Circ & Reserve, Tuskegee University, Hollis Burke Frissell Bldg, 1200 W Old Montgomery Rd, Tuskegee, AL, 36088. Tel: 334-727-8900. Fax: 334-727-9282. p. 39

Player, Elouise, Librn, Broward County Division of Libraries, Books by Mail, 100 S Andrews Ave, 6th Flr, Fort Lauderdale, FL, 33301. Tel: 954-765-4356. p. 441

Pleasant, Zach, Info Serv Mgr, Institute of Transportation Engineers, 1099 14th St NW, Ste 300W, Washington, DC, 20005-3438. Tel: 202-289-0222, Ext 120. Fax: 202-289-7722. p. 405

Plessl, Anne, Libr Develop, McMaster University Library, 1280 Main St W, Hamilton, ON, L8S 4L6, CANADA. Tel: 905-525-9140, Ext 24865. Fax: 905-524-9850. p. 2810

Pletcher, Sandra, Corrections Librn, State Correctional Institution, Laurel Highlands Library, 5706 Glades Pike, Somerset, PA, 15501. Tel: 814-445-6501. Fax: 814-443-0208. p. 2141

Pletka, Scott, Asst Dir, Logansport-Cass County Public Library, 616 E Broadway, Logansport, IN, 46947-3187. Tel: 574-753-6383. Fax: 574-722-5889. p. 761

Plett, Claudia E, Dir, Libr & Archives, Dir, Libr & Info Serv, Librn, Inola Public Library, 15 North Broadway, Inola, OK, 74036. Tel: 918-543-8862. Fax: 918-543-3999. p. 1966

Plett, Katherine, Dir, College of New Caledonia Library, 3330 22nd Ave, Prince George, BC, V2N 1P8, CANADA. Tel: 250-562-2131, Ext 298. Fax: 250-561-5845. p. 2736

Plett, Rachel, Librn, Evergreen Regional Library, Arborg Branch, Box 4053, Arborg, MB, R0C 0A0, CANADA. Tel: 204-376-5388. p. 2749

Plett, Vanessa, Libr Mgr, Rosemary Community Library, 622 Dahlia St, Rosemary, AB, T0J 2W0, CANADA. Tel: 403-378-4493, Ext 150. Fax: 403-378-4388. p. 2715

Pletz, James, Dir, The Library Network, 41345 Vincenti Ct, Novi, MI, 48375. Tel: 248-536-3100. Fax: 248-536-3099. p. 2946

Plew, Joey, Dir, Grandview Public Library, 112 S Third St, Grandview, TX, 76050. Tel: 817-866-3995. Fax: 817-866-2037. p. 2329

Plimpton, Becky, Dir, Joshua Hyde Public Library, 306 Main St, Sturbridge, MA, 01566-1242. Tel: 508-347-2512. Fax: 508-347-2872. p. 1129

Plimpton, Susan, Ch, Southwest Harbor Public Library, 338 Main St, Southwest Harbor, ME, 04679. Tel: 207-244-7065. Fax: 207-244-7065. p. 1002

Plizga, Brenda, Br Mgr, West Bloomfield Township Public Library, 4600 Walnut Lake Rd, West Bloomfield, MI, 48323. Tel: 248-232-2293. Fax: 248-232-2291. p. 1236

Plocher, Carol, Br Mgr, Great River Regional Library, Delano Library, 160 Railroad Ave E, Delano, MN, 55328. Tel: 763-972-3467. Fax: 763-972-3467. p. 1275

Plodowski, Katherin, Circ Supvr, Indiana University South Bend, 1700 Mishawaka Ave, South Bend, IN, 46615. Tel: 574-520-4380. Fax: 574-520-4472. p. 778

Plohr, Jennifer, Head, Ref, Ela Area Public Library District, 275 Mohawk Trail, Lake Zurich, IL, 60047. Tel: 847-438-3433. Fax: 847-438-9290. p. 663

Plomske, Maureen, Librn, Kitchener Public Library, Pioneer Park, 150 Pioneer Dr, Kitchener, ON, N2H 2H1, CANADA. Tel: 519-748-2740. Fax: 519-748-2740. p. 2815

Ploof, Charmaine, Librn, Iosco-Arenac District Library, Omer Branch, 205 E Center St, Omer, MI, 48749. Tel: 989-653-2230. Fax: 989-653-2230. p. 1176

Ploszaj, Stan, Sr Librn, Tech Serv, Bloomfield Public Library, 90 Broad St, Bloomfield, NJ, 07003. Tel: 973-566-6200, Ext 222. Fax: 973-566-6217. p. 1473

Plotin, Stephanie, Ref Librn, University of California Los Angeles Library, Hugh & Hazel Darling Law Library, 112 Law Bldg, Box 951458, 385 Charles E Young Dr E, Los Angeles, CA, 90095-1458. Tel: 310-825-7826. Fax: 310-825-1372. p. 178

Plotkin, Elaine, Adult Serv Spec, Harris County Public Library, 8080 El Rio, Houston, TX, 77054. Tel: 713-749-9030. Fax: 713-749-9090. p. 2335

Plotkin, Mark, Librn, Akerman, Senterfitt & Eidson PA, 420 S Orange Ave, Ste 1200, Orlando, FL, 32801. Tel: 305-374-5600. Fax: 407-843-6610. p. 475

Plotkin, Stephen, Archivist, National Archives & Records Administration, Columbia Point, Boston, MA, 02125. Tel: 617-514-1600. Fax: 617-514-1593. p. 1064

Plouffe, Martine, Ref Serv Librn, Bibliotheque Municipale de Gatineau, 144, boul de l'Hôpital, local 317, Gatineau, QC, J8T 7S7, CANADA. Tel: 819-243-2345, Ext 2513. Fax: 819-243-2569. p. 2882

Plouffe, Martine, Ref Serv Mgr, Bibliotheque Municipale de Gatineau, Édifice Pierre Papin, CP 1970 Succ. Hull, Gatineau, QC, J8X 3Y9, CANADA. p. 2882

Plourde, Ruby, Ref Mgr, Westchester Public Library, 200 W Indiana Ave, Chesterton, IN, 46304-3122. Tel: 219-926-7696. Fax: 219-926-6424. p. 732

Plowman, Catherine, Mgr, Idaho National Laboratory, 1765 N Yellowstone Hwy, Idaho Falls, ID, 83415-2300. Tel: 208-526-4828. Fax: 208-526-1697. p. 576

Plowman, Robert, Dir, National Archives & Records Administration, 14700 Townsend Rd, Philadelphia, PA, 19154-1096. Tel: 215-597-9752. Fax: 215-671-0273. p. 2112

Plowman, Stephanie, Spec Coll Librn, Gonzaga University, 502 E Boone Ave, Spokane, WA, 99258-0095. Tel: 509-323-3847. Fax: 509-323-5904. p. 2536

Plozaj, Stan, Head, Tech Serv, Saint Thomas Aquinas College, 125 Rte 340, Sparkill, NY, 10976. Tel: 845-398-4222. Fax: 845-359-9537. p. 1746

Plude, Victoria, Dir, Fort Edward Free Library, 23 East St, Fort Edward, NY, 12828. Tel: 518-747-6743. Fax: 518-747-6743. p. 1624

Plumb, Erick, Pub Serv Librn, Monona Public Library, 1000 Nichols Rd, Monona, WI, 53716-2531. Tel: 608-222-6127. Fax: 608-222-8590. p. 2623

Plumb, Pat, Acq Librn, Western State Law Library, 1111 N State College Blvd, Fullerton, CA, 92831-3014. Tel: 714-459-1113. Fax: 714-871-4806. p. 154

Plumb, Tawnya, Electronic Serv, University Of Wyoming, Dept 3035, 1000 E University Ave, Laramie, WY, 82071. Tel: 307-766-2210. Fax: 307-766-4044. p. 2657

Plumley, Jeff, Circ Mgr, Librn, Crowell Public Library, 1890 Huntington Dr, San Marino, CA, 91108-2595. Tel: 626-300-0777, Ext 534. Fax: 626-284-0766. p. 254

Plumley, Thad, Dir, National Ground Water Association, 601 Dempsey Rd, Westerville, OH, 43081-8978. Tel: 614-898-7791. p. 1946

Plummer, Deanna, Cataloger, Harrison County Library System, 2600 24th Ave, No 6, Gulfport, MS, 39501-2081. Tel: 228-868-1383. Fax: 228-863-7433. p. 1299

Plummer, Madeleine, Principal Librn, Lee County Library System, Fort Myers-Lee County Public, 2050 Central Ave, Fort Myers, FL, 33901-3917. Tel: 941-479-4632. Fax: 239-479-4634. p. 445

Plummer, Pamela, Dir, Harriette Person Memorial Library, 606 Main St, Port Gibson, MS, 39150-2330. Tel: 601-437-5202. Fax: 601-437-5787. p. 1312

Plummer, Rona, Mgr, AV Serv, Saint Joseph County Public Library, 304 S Main, South Bend, IN, 46601-2125. Tel: 574-282-4646. Fax: 574-280-2763. p. 779

Plunket, Linda, Assoc Univ Librn, Grad & Res Serv, Boston University Libraries, Mugar Memorial Library, 771 Commonwealth Ave, Boston, MA, 02215. Tel: 617-353-3710. Fax: 617-353-2084. p. 1058

Plunket, Linda, Librn, Boston University Libraries, Pickering Educational Resources Library, Two Sherborn St, Boston, MA, 02215. Tel: 617-353-3735. Fax: 617-353-6105. p. 1058

Plunkett, Becki, Spec Coll & Archives Librn, State Historical Society of Iowa-Des Moines Library, 600 E Locust, Des Moines, IA, 50319-0290. Tel: 515-281-6200. Fax: 515-282-0502. p. 810

Plunkett, David, Circ, Jefferson-Madison Regional Library, 201 E Market St, Charlottesville, VA, 22902-5287. Tel: 434-979-7151, Ext 206, 434-979-7151, Ext 207. Fax: 434-971-7035. p. 2453

Plunkett, Genine, Mgr, Ref Serv, Denver Public Library, Ten W 14th Ave Pkwy, Denver, CO, 80204-2731. Tel: 720-865-1345. Fax: 720-865-1481. p. 300

Plunkett, Judy, Tech Serv, Robinson Public Library District, Oblong Branch, 110 E Main St, Oblong, IL, 62449. Tel: 618-592-3001. Fax: 618-592-3001. p. 695

Plunkett, Kathryn, Digital Serv Librn, Info Literacy Librn, Southeastern Oklahoma State University, 1405 N Fourth Ave, PMB 4105, Durant, OK, 74701-0609. Tel: 580-745-2702. Fax: 580-745-7463. p. 1961

Plunkett, Michelle, Adult & Children's Ref, New Berlin Public Library, 15105 Library Lane, New Berlin, WI, 53151. Tel: 262-785-4980. Fax: 262-785-4984. p. 2625

Plunkett, Nora, Res, Prudential Financial, Business Library, 16 Prudential Plaza, 751 Broad St, Newark, NJ, 07102-3714. Tel: 973-802-6749. Fax: 973-367-8149. p. 1512

Pluskal, Pat, Librn, Concord Free Public Library, Fowler Memorial, 1322 Main St, Concord, MA, 01742. Tel: 978-318-3350. Fax: 978-318-0906. p. 1082

Pluss, Deborah, Database Mgr, William Paterson University of New Jersey, 300 Pompton Rd, Wayne, NJ, 07470. Tel: 973-720-3143. Fax: 973-720-3171. p. 1540

Plutchak, T Scott, Dir, University of Alabama at Birmingham, Lister Hill Library of the Health Sciences, 1700 University Blvd, Birmingham, AL, 35294-0013. Tel: 205-934-5460. Fax: 205-934-3545. p. 10

Plutt, Kim, Br Librn, Park County Public Library, Lake George Branch, 37900 Hwy 24, Lake George, CO, 80827. Tel: 719-748-3812. Fax: 719-748-3812. p. 289

Plybon, Amanda, Educ & Pub Prog Coordr, Westminster College, National Churchill Museum, 501 Westminster Ave, Fulton, MO, 65251-1299. Tel: 573-592-6242. Fax: 573-592-5222. p. 1328

Plyler, Anne, AV Coll, Spec Projects, James Prendergast Library Association, 509 Cherry St, Jamestown, NY, 14701. Tel: 716-484-7135. Fax: 716-487-1148. p. 1647

Plym, Glynis, Coordr, Ser, Bradley University, 1501 W Bradley Ave, Peoria, IL, 61625. Tel: 309-677-2850. Fax: 309-677-2558. p. 690

Plymire, Carrie, Head, Tech Proc, Washington County Free Library, 100 S Potomac St, Hagerstown, MD, 21740. Tel: 301-739-3250. Fax: 301-739-7603. p. 1031

Plymire, Sandi, Dir, Muskingum County Library System, 220 N Fifth St, Zanesville, OH, 43701-3587. Tel: 740-453-0391, Ext 129. Fax: 740-455-6937. p. 1953

Poage, Joanne, Head, Ref, Bedford Free Public Library, Seven Mudge Way, Bedford, MA, 01730-2168. Tel: 781-275-9440. Fax: 781-275-3590. p. 1052

Pober, Stacy, Electronic Res, Manhattan College, 4513 Manhattan College Pkwy, Riverdale, NY, 10471. Tel: 718-862-7166. Fax: 718-862-8028. p. 1728

Pober, Susan, Info Serv, Millburn Free Public Library, 200 Glen Ave, Millburn, NJ, 07041. Tel: 973-376-1006, Ext 17. Fax: 973-376-0104. p. 1502

Pocatko, Mona, Supvr, Public Library of Youngstown & Mahoning County, Special Delivery, Main Library, 305 Wick Ave, Youngstown, OH, 44503. Tel: 330-744-8636. p. 1953

Pocchiari, Louis, Doc, Ref, Cambria County Library System & District Center, 248 Main St, Johnstown, PA, 15901. Tel: 814-536-5131. Fax: 814-536-6905. p. 2073

Poch, Cheryl, Dir, Fowlerville District Library, 131 Mill St, Fowlerville, MI, 48836. Tel: 517-223-9089. Fax: 517-223-0781. p. 1181

Pochert, Marjorie, Librn, Memorial Presbyterian Church, 1310 Ashman St, Midland, MI, 48640. Tel: 989-835-6759. p. 1208

Pochini, Diane, Pub Serv, Harvard Library, Blue Hill Meteorological Observatory Library, Pierce Hall, 29 Oxford St, Cambridge, MA, 02138. Tel: 617-495-2836. Fax: 617-495-9837. p. 1074

Podbielski, Mary Ann, Ch, Dundee Public Library, 202 E Main St, Dundee, FL, 33838. Tel: 863-439-9424. Fax: 863-439-9426. p. 438

Podboy, Alvin M, Dir, Baker & Hostetler LLP Library, 3200 National City Ctr, 1900 E Ninth St, Cleveland, OH, 44114-3485. Tel: 216-621-0200, 216-861-7101. Fax: 216-696-0740. p. 1875

Podgajny, Stephen J, Exec Dir, Portland Public Library, Five Monument Sq, Portland, ME, 04101. Tel: 207-871-1700. Fax: 207-871-1703. p. 997

Podhradsky, Anne, Librn, Wagner Public Library, 106 Sheridan Ave SE, Wagner, SD, 57380-9701. Tel: 605-384-5248. Fax: 605-384-5248. p. 2221

Podles, Lina, Dir, Hoboken Public Library, 500 Park Ave, Hoboken, NJ, 07030. Tel: 201-420-2346. Fax: 201-420-2299. p. 1491

Podlubny, Don, Chairperson, Hinton Municipal Library, 803 Switzer Dr, Hinton, AB, T7V 1V1, CANADA. Tel: 780-865-2363. Fax: 780-865-4292. p. 2707

Podolski, Debbie, Dir, Farmingdale Public Library, 116 Merritts Rd, Farmingdale, NY, 11735. Tel: 516-249-9090. Fax: 516-694-9697. p. 1621

Podrygula, Susan, Coll Develop, Ser, Minot State University, 500 University Ave W, Minot, ND, 58707. Tel: 701-858-3200. Fax: 701-858-3581. p. 1846

Podvia, Mark W, Archivist, Assoc Law Librn, Ref, Pennsylvania State University - Dickinson School of Law (University Libraries), 1170 Harrisburg Pike, Carlisle, PA, 17013-1617. Tel: 717-240-5015. Fax: 717-240-5127. p. 2042

Podzamsky, Karen, Librn, Filger Public Library, 261 E Fifth St, Minonk, IL, 61760. Tel: 309-432-2929. Fax: 309-432-2929. p. 674

Poe, Becky, Asst Dir, Mound City Public Library, 207 E Sixth St, Mound City, MO, 64470. Tel: 660-442-5700. Fax: 660-442-3149. p. 1347

Poe, Carol, Libr Tech, Northwest Nazarene University, 623 University Blvd, Nampa, ID, 83686. Tel: 208-467-8616. Fax: 208-467-8610. p. 580

Poe, Jodi, Head, Tech Serv, Jacksonville State University Library, 700 Pelham Rd N, Jacksonville, AL, 36265. Tel: 256-782-5255. Fax: 256-782-5872. p. 22

Poe, Judy, Head, Tech Serv, Pine River Public Library District, 395 Bayfield Center Dr, Bayfield, CO, 81122. Tel: 970-884-2222. Fax: 970-884-7155. p. 289

Poe, Karen, Dir, Southwestern Virginia Training Center, 160 Training Center Rd, Hillsville, VA, 24343. Tel: 276-728-3121. Fax: 276-728-3127. p. 2472

Poe, Patricia, Librn, Saint Clair County Public Library, Ragland Branch, 738 Main St, Ragland, AL, 35131. Tel: 205-472-2007. Fax: 205-472-2007. p. 5

Poe, Trea, Librn, Genesee County Circuit Court, County Court House, Ste 204, 900 S Saginaw St, Flint, MI, 48502. Tel: 810-257-3253. Fax: 810-239-9280. p. 1179

Poehler, M J, Dir, Kansas City Art Institute Library, 4538 Warwick Blvd, Kansas City, MO, 64111. Tel: 816-802-3390. Fax: 816-802-3338. p. 1338

Poell, Nate, Tech Serv, Baker University, 518 Eighth St, Baldwin City, KS, 66006-0065. Tel: 785-594-4582. Fax: 785-594-6721. p. 857

Poelman, Kathryn, Tech Spec, Veterans Administration Center, 3687 Veterans Dr, Fort Harrison, MT, 59636. Tel: 406-447-7366. Fax: 406-447-7992. p. 1379

Poenisch, Joyce, Librn, Marfa Public Library, 115 E Oak St, Marfa, TX, 79843. Tel: 432-729-4631. Fax: 432-729-3424. p. 2359

Poet, Patricia, Instrul Media, York College of Pennsylvania, 441 Country Club Rd, York, PA, 17403-3651. Tel: 717-815-1458. Fax: 717-849-1608. p. 2160

Poeton, John Thomas, Librn, Aldrich Public Library, East Barre Branch, 134 Mill St, East Barre, VT, 05649. Tel: 802-476-5118. p. 2418

Poetter, Shellie, In Charge, Faribault County Library Service, Frost Public, 345 Dewey St, Blue Earth, MN, 56033. Tel: 507-878-3102. Fax: 507-878-3102. p. 1242

Poggi, Chris, Ch, YA Librn, Bennington Free Library, 101 Silver St, Bennington, VT, 05201. Tel: 802-442-9051. p. 2418

Pogosyan, Nina, Br Mgr, San Francisco Public Library, Ingleside Branch Library, 1298 Ocean Ave, San Francisco, CA, 94112-1717. Tel: 415-355-2898. Fax: 415-469-7390. p. 246

Pogue, Andi Adkins, Pub Serv Librn, Cosumnes River College Library, 8401 Center Pkwy, Sacramento, CA, 95823. Tel: 916-691-7904. Fax: 916-691-7349. p. 223

Pogue, Shaen L, Youth Serv, Ozark Regional Library, 402 N Main St, Ironton, MO, 63650. Tel: 573-546-2615. Fax: 573-546-7225. p. 1333

Pogue, Sissy, Mgr, Wayne County Public Library, Clifton Branch, 300 E Water St, Clifton, TN, 38425-0501. Tel: 931-676-3678. Fax: 931-676-3678. p. 2268

Pohjola, Kate, Dir, Lapeer District Library, Clifford, 9530 Main St, Clifford, MI, 48727. Tel: 989-761-7393. Fax: 989-761-7541. p. 1202

Pohjola, Kate A, Dir, Lapeer District Library, 201 Village West Dr S, Lapeer, MI, 48446-1699. Tel: 810-664-9521. Fax: 810-664-8527. p. 1202

Pohl, Denise, Dir, Rockwell City Public Library, 424 Main St, Rockwell City, IA, 50579-1415. Tel: 712-297-8422. Fax: 712-297-8422. p. 841

Pohl, Elizabeth L, Dir, Lithgow Public Library, 45 Winthrop St, Augusta, ME, 04330-5599. Tel: 207-626-2415. Fax: 207-626-2419. p. 974

Pohl, Jennifer, Youth Serv Librn, Long Beach Public Library, 111 W Park Ave, Long Beach, NY, 11561-3326. Tel: 516-432-7201. Fax: 516-889-4641. p. 1654

Pohlman, Audra, Pub Serv Asst, Methodist Theological School in Ohio Library, 3081 Columbus Pike, Delaware, OH, 43015. Tel: 740-362-3439. Fax: 740-362-3456. p. 1895

Pohlman, Joy, ILL Librn, Wisconsin Library Services, 728 State St, Rm 464, Madison, WI, 53706-1494. Tel: 608-265-4167. Fax: 608-262-6067. p. 2958

Pohlman, Julie, Mgr, Libr & Res Serv, Wisconsin Legislative Reference Bureau, One E Main St, Madison, WI, 53703-3373. Fax: 608-266-5648. p. 2611

Pohnl, Donald, Librn, Saint Luke's Hospital, 1026 A Ave NE, Cedar Rapids, IA, 52402. Tel: 319-369-7358. Fax: 319-369-8036. p. 801

Poillon, Deborah, Dir, Cape May County Library, 30 Mechanic St, Cape May Court House, NJ, 08210. Tel: 609-463-6350. Fax: 609-465-3895. p. 1477

Poindexter, Jennifer, Br Mgr, Memphis Public Library, Hollywood, 1530 N Hollywood, Memphis, TN, 38108. Tel: 901-323-6201. Fax: 901-323-5610. p. 2250

Poindexter, Marilyn, Librn, Perkins School for the Blind, 175 N Beacon St, Watertown, MA, 02472. Tel: 617-972-7240. Fax: 617-972-7363. p. 1133

Poinsett, Judy, Librn, Sally Stretch Keen Memorial Library, 94 Main St, Vincentown, NJ, 08088. Tel: 609-859-3598. Fax: 609-859-4029. p. 1537

Pointer, Kristine, Br Mgr, Timberland Regional Library, Ilwaco Branch, 158 First Ave N, Ilwaco, WA, 98624. Tel: 360-642-3908. Fax: 360-642-8417. p. 2543

Pointon, Sandra, Dir, Lemont Public Library District, 50 E Wend St, Lemont, IL, 60439-6439. Tel: 630-257-6541. Fax: 630-257-7737. p. 664

Pointon, Scott, Dir, White Oak Library District, 121 E Eighth St, Lockport, IL, 60441. Tel: 815-838-0755. p. 667

Poirier, Eve, Head Librn, NorQuest College, 10215-108th St, 5th Flr, Edmonton, AB, T5J 1L6, CANADA. Tel: 708-644-6070. Fax: 780-644-6082. p. 2701

Poirier, Gilberte, Librn, Centre Hospitalier Universitaire du Sherbrooke Bibliotheque, Hotel-Dieu, 580 rue Bowen S, Sherbrooke, QC, J1G 2E8, CANADA. Tel: 819-346-1110, Ext 2-1126. Fax: 819-822-6745. p. 2912

Poirier, Steve, Coordr, Hockey Hall of Fame, 400 Kipling Ave, Toronto, ON, M8V 3L1, CANADA. Tel: 416-360-7735. Fax: 416-251-5770. p. 2854

Poitinger, Leigh, Dir, San Jose Mercury News Library, 750 Ridder Park Dr, San Jose, CA, 95190. Tel: 408-920-5346. Fax: 408-271-3799. p. 250

Poitras, Gilles, Head, Access Serv, Golden Gate University, 536 Mission St, San Francisco, CA, 94105-2967. Tel: 415-442-7242. Fax: 415-543-6779. p. 242

Poitras, Lise, Mgr, Haut-Saint-Jean Regional Library, Dr Lorne J Violette Public Library, 180 Rue St-Jean, Saint Leonard, NB, E7E 2B9, CANADA. Tel: 506-423-3025. Fax: 506-423-3026. p. 2762

Pojman, Paul, Librn, Bedford Historical Society Library, 30 S Park St, Bedford, OH, 44146-3635. Tel: 440-232-0796. p. 1858

Pokaski, Ann Marie, Youth Serv, Hanson Public Library, 132 Maquan St, Hanson, MA, 02341. Tel: 781-293-2151. Fax: 781-293-6801. p. 1093

Pokol, Albert, Archives Librn, Spec Coll, California University of Pennsylvania, 250 University Ave, California, PA, 15419-1394. Tel: 724-938-5773. Fax: 724-938-5901. p. 2040

Pokorny, Renee, Head of Libr, Free Library of Philadelphia, Fumo Family Branch, 2437 S Broad St, Philadelphia, PA, 19148-3508. Tel: 215-685-1758. Fax: 215-685-1757. p. 2107

Polakowski, Betsy J, Tech Serv, University of Saint Thomas, Archbishop Ireland Memorial Library, 2260 Summit Ave, Mail No IRL, Saint Paul, MN, 55105. Tel: 651-962-5452. Fax: 651-962-5460. p. 1282

Poland, Mary, Mgr, ILL, North Georgia College & State University, 238 Georgia Circle, Dahlonega, GA, 30597-3001. p. 527

Poland, Matt, Chief Exec Officer, Hartford Public Library, 500 Main St, Hartford, CT, 06103-3075. Tel: 860-695-6300. Fax: 860-722-6900. p. 345

Poland, Patricia, Hist Coll Librn, Union County Public Library, 316 E Windsor St, Monroe, NC, 28112. Tel: 704-283-8184. Fax: 704-282-0657. p. 1810

Poland, Renee, Br Mgr, Tuscarawas County Public Library, Tuscarawas Branch, 209 S Main St, Tuscarawas, OH, 44682. Tel: 740-922-2748. Fax: 740-922-2748. p. 1921

Polanka, Sue, Head, Ref (Info Serv), Wright State University Libraries, 126 Dunbar Library, 3640 Colonel Glenn Hwy, Dayton, OH, 45435-0001. Tel: 937-775-3142. Fax: 937-775-4109. p. 1895

Polansky, Judith, Commun Libr Mgr, County of Los Angeles Public Library, Anthony Quinn Library, 3965 Cesar E Chavez Ave, Los Angeles, CA, 90063. Tel: 323-264-7715. Fax: 323-262-7121. p. 143

Polard, Sharna, Libr Mgr, Misericordia Community Hospital - Caritas Health Group, 16940 87th Ave, Edmonton, AB, T5R 4H5, CANADA. Tel: 780-735-7251. Fax: 780-735-2509. p. 2701

Polardino, Linda S, Librn, Department of Veterans Affairs, 5500 Armstrong Rd, Battle Creek, MI, 49015. Tel: 269-966-5600, Ext 6490. Fax: 269-660-6031. p. 1155

Polaski, Beverly, Ref Serv, Franklin Public Library, 9151 W Loomis Rd, Franklin, WI, 53132. Tel: 414-425-8214. Fax: 414-425-9498. p. 2593

Polczynski, John Michael, Network Adminr, Peoples Library, 880 Barnes St, New Kensington, PA, 15068. Tel: 724-339-1021, Ext 17. Fax: 724-339-2027. p. 2097

Poldberg, Rose Anne, Dir, Kimballton Public Library, 118 Main St, Kimballton, IA, 51543. Tel: 712-773-3002. p. 825

Poldek, Leslie Dianne, Dir, Streator Public Library, 130 S Park St, Streator, IL, 61364. Tel: 815-672-2729. Fax: 815-672-2729. p. 708

Polege, Judy, Circ, ILL, University of Wisconsin, 2000 W Fifth St, Marshfield, WI, 54449-3310. Tel: 715-389-6512, 715-389-6531. Fax: 715-389-6539. p. 2613

Polen, Tami, Br Mgr, Tuscarawas County Public Library, Sugarcreek Branch, 120 S Broadway, Sugarcreek, OH, 44681. Tel: 330-852-2813. Fax: 330-852-2813. p. 1921

Polette, Loretta, Tech Serv Librn, Bonne Terre Memorial Library, Five SW Main St, Bonne Terre, MO, 63628. Tel: 573-358-2260. Fax: 573-358-5941. p. 1320

Poletti, Edward, Chief Librn, Central Arkansas Veterans Healthcare System, 4300 W Seventh St, Little Rock, AR, 72205-5484. Tel: 501-257-5620. Fax: 501-257-5626. p. 106

Poley, Darren, Prog Coordr, Villanova University, 800 Lancaster Ave, Villanova, PA, 19085. Tel: 610-519-6371. Fax: 610-519-5018. p. 2149

Poliakevitch, Tatyana, Librn, Red Deer Public Library, Dawe, 56 Holt St, Red Deer, AB, T4N 6A6, CANADA. Tel: 403-341-3822. Fax: 403-343-2120. p. 2714

Policano, Bonnie, Head, Circ, Reed Memorial Library, 167 E Main St, Ravenna, OH, 44266-3197. Tel: 330-296-2827. Fax: 330-296-3780. p. 1931

Policastri, Joan, Foreign Comparative & Intl Law Librn, University of Denver, Westminster Law Library, 2255 E Evans Ave, Denver, CO, 80208. Tel: 303-871-6188. Fax: 303-871-6999. p. 304

Polich, Deborah, Dir, Oceanside Public Library, 330 N Coast Hwy, Oceanside, CA, 92054-2824. Tel: 760-435-5560. Fax: 760-435-9614. p. 199

Polikoff, Susan, Head, Coll & Tech Serv, Poughkeepsie Public Library District, 93 Market St, Poughkeepsie, NY, 12601. Tel: 845-485-3445, Ext 3305. Fax: 845-485-3789. p. 1723

Poling, Eleanor, Dir, Pleasants County Public Library, 101 Lafayette St, Saint Marys, WV, 26170-1025. Tel: 304-684-7494. Fax: 304-684-7495. p. 2571

Poling, Lynda, Br Mgr, Long Beach Public Library, Brewitt, 4036 E Anaheim St, Long Beach, CA, 90804. Tel: 562-570-1040. p. 167

Polirer, Sarah, Mgr, Cigna Co Library, 900 Cottage Grove Rd, Bloomfield, CT, 06002. Tel: 860-226-3257. Fax: 860-226-5128. p. 330

Polishchuk, Slava, Conservator, Brooklyn College Library, 2900 Bedford Ave, Brooklyn, NY, 11210-2889. Tel: 718-951-5336. Fax: 718-951-4540. p. 1589

Politano, Maria, Br Mgr, Mississauga Library System, Malton Branch, 3540 Morningstar Dr, Malton, ON, L4T 1Y2, CANADA. Tel: 905-615-4640. p. 2823

Polites, Bente, Spec Coll Librn, Villanova University, 800 Lancaster Ave, Villanova, PA, 19085. Tel: 610-519-5182. Fax: 610-519-5018. p. 2149

Polizzi, Barbara, Dir, Mineral Point Public Library, 137 High St, Mineral Point, WI, 53565. Tel: 608-987-2447. Fax: 608-987-2447. p. 2622

Polizzi, Leticia, Commun Libr Mgr, County of Los Angeles Public Library, Sorensen Library, 6934 Broadway Ave, Whittier, CA, 90606-1994. Tel: 562-695-3979. Fax: 562-695-8925. p. 143

Polk, Eileen, Librn, Temple Beth El, 7400 Telegraph Rd, Bloomfield Hills, MI, 48301-3876. Tel: 248-851-1100, Ext 3138. Fax: 248-851-1187. p. 1159

Polk, Karen, Asst Librn, Miller & Chevalier, 655 15th St NW, Ste 900, Washington, DC, 20005-5701. Tel: 202-626-6094. Fax: 202-626-5801. p. 408

Polk, Ruth, Librn, Temple Sinai Library, 3100 Military Rd NW, Washington, DC, 20015. Tel: 202-363-6394. Fax: 202-363-6396. p. 416

Polk, Sylvia, Br Mgr, Fort Worth Library, Wedgwood, 3816 Kimberly Lane, Fort Worth, TX, 76133. Tel: 817-292-3368. Fax: 817-346-1862. p. 2322

Polkinghorne, Denise, Librn, Lakeland Library Region, Marsden Branch, 104 Centre St, Marsden, SK, S0M 1P0, CANADA. Tel: 306-826-5666. p. 2920

Poll, Laura M, Archivist, Librn, Monmouth County Historical Association Library & Archives, 70 Court St, Freehold, NJ, 07728. Tel: 732-462-1466. Fax: 732-462-8346. p. 1487

Pollack, Andre, Info Spec, Educational Testing Service, Rosedale Rd, Princeton, NJ, 08541. Tel: 609-734-1722. Fax: 609-683-7186. p. 1522

Pollack, Carrie, Res, Kirkland & Ellis LLP Library, 300 N LaSalle St, 11th Flr, Chicago, IL, 60654. Tel: 312-862-2305. Fax: 312-862-2200. p. 616

Pollack, Martha E, Dean, Prof, University of Michigan, 304 West Hall, 1085 S University, Ann Arbor, MI, 48109-1107. Tel: 734-763-2285. Fax: 734-764-2475. p. 2967

Pollack, Neil, Br Mgr, Broward County Division of Libraries, Davie-Cooper City Branch, 4600 SW 82nd Ave, Davie, FL, 33328. Tel: 954-680-0050. Fax: 954-680-0052. p. 441

Pollack, Sandy, Res, Florida Diagnostic & Learning Resource System, Main Library, 4th Flr, 100 S Andrews Ave, Fort Lauderdale, FL, 33301. Tel: 954-357-7177. Fax: 954-357-7507. p. 443

Pollack, Ted, Sr Law Librn, New York State Supreme Court, First Judicial District Criminal Law Library, 100 Centre St, 17th Flr, New York, NY, 10013. Tel: 646-386-3890, 646-386-3891. Fax: 212-748-7908. p. 1695

Pollak, Elaine, Ch, Hamilton Township Public Library, One Justice Samuel A Alito, Jr Way, Hamilton, NJ, 08619. Tel: 609-581-4060. Fax: 609-581-4067. p. 1490

Pollak, Lorraine, Librn, International Stamp Collectors Society Library, PO Box 854, Van Nuys, CA, 91408-0854. Tel: 818-997-6496. p. 279

Pollak, Marsha, Head, Cat, Sunnyvale Public Library, 665 W Olive Ave, Sunnyvale, CA, 94086-7622. Tel: 408-730-7300. Fax: 408-735-8767. p. 273

Pollakoff, Stan, Dir, Sussex County Library System, 125 Morris Tpk, Newton, NJ, 07860-0076. Tel: 973-948-3660. Fax: 973-948-2071. p. 1514

Pollard, Barbara, Librn, North Central Regional Library, Oroville Community, 1276 Main St, Oroville, WA, 98844. Tel: 509-476-2662. Fax: 509-476-2662. p. 2549

Pollard, Betsy L, Librn, Harnett County Public Library, Erwin Public, 110 West F St, Erwin, NC, 28339. Tel: 910-897-5780. Fax: 910-897-4474. p. 1807

Pollard, Cindy D, Dir, Ardmore Higher Education Center Library, 611 Veterans Blvd, Ardmore, OK, 73401. Tel: 580-220-2856. Fax: 580-223-5611. p. 1956

Pollard, Frances, Pub Serv, Virginia Historical Society Library, 428 North Blvd, Richmond, VA, 23220. Tel: 804-358-4901. Fax: 804-355-2399. p. 2492

Pollard, Joan, Librn, Southside Regional Medical Center, 200 Medical Park Blvd, Petersburg, VA, 23805. Tel: 804-765-5663. Fax: 804-765-5664. p. 2484

Pollard, Libby, Dir, Jeffersonville Township Public Library, 211 E Court Ave, Jeffersonville, IN, 47130. Tel: 812-285-5633. Fax: 812-285-5639. p. 756

Pollard, Lisa, Youth Serv Coordr, Scott County Library System, 13090 Alabama Ave S, Savage, MN, 55378-1479. Tel: 952-707-1760. Fax: 952-707-1775. p. 1283

Pollard, Melody, Librn, Izard County Library, 915 E Main St, Melbourne, AR, 72556. Tel: 870-368-7467. p. 109

Pollard, Richard C, Librn, Paulina June & George Pollak Library, 800 N State College Blvd, Fullerton, CA, 92834. Tel: 714-278-2714. Fax: 714-278-2439. p. 154

Pollard, Russell O, Coll Mgt, Harvard Library, Andover-Harvard Theological Library, Divinity School, 45 Francis Ave, Cambridge, MA, 02138. Tel: 617-495-5788. Fax: 617-496-4111. p. 1074

Pollard, Sandy, Dir, Stuart Public Library, 111 NE Front St, Stuart, IA, 50250. Tel: 515-523-2152. Fax: 515-523-2152. p. 846

Pollard, Tom, Jr, Syst Adminr, Highline Community College Library, 2400 S 240th St, MS 25-4, Des Moines, WA, 98198. Tel: 206-878-3710, Ext 3236. Fax: 206-870-3776. p. 2514

Pollard, William, Archivist, Mary Baldwin College, 109 E Frederick St, Staunton, VA, 24401. Tel: 540-887-7239. Fax: 540-887-7137. p. 2496

Pollard, Zennie, Head Librn, Izard County Library, 915 E Main St, Melbourne, AR, 72556. Tel: 870-368-7467. p. 109

Pollari, Cathy, Res Librn, Penobscot Marine Museum, Nine Church St, Searsport, ME, 04974. Tel: 207-548-2529, Ext 212. Fax: 207-548-2520. p. 1000

Pollchik, Allan, Dr, Dir, Ohio University Chillicothe Campus, 101 University Dr, Chillicothe, OH, 45601-0629. Tel: 740-774-7201. Fax: 740-774-7268. p. 1867

Pollender, Wilfred Lawrence, Ref, Edwards Angell Palmer & Dodge LLP, 111 Huntington Ave, Boston, MA, 02199. Tel: 617-239-0610. Fax: 617-227-4420. p. 1060

Polley, Deborah, Mgr, ILL, Wabash College, PO Box 352, Crawfordsville, IN, 47933. Tel: 765-361-6161. Fax: 765-361-6295. p. 734

Polley, Grant, AV, Harcum College Library, 750 Montgomery Ave, Bryn Mawr, PA, 19010-3476. Tel: 610-526-6085. Fax: 610-526-6086. p. 2039

Polley, Virginia, Instrul Serv Librn, Stevenson University Library, 1525 Greenspring Valley Rd, Stevenson, MD, 21153. Tel: 443-334-2688. Fax: 410-486-7329. p. 1043

Pollino, Rebecca, Librn, Portage Public Library, 704 Main St, Portage, PA, 15946-1715. Tel: 814-736-4340. Fax: 814-736-4413. p. 2131

Pollis, Eileen, Adult Serv, Long Beach Public Library, 111 W Park Ave, Long Beach, NY, 11561-3326. Tel: 516-432-7201. Fax: 516-889-4641. p. 1654

Pollitt, Traci, Br Supvr, Gaston County Public Library, Dallas Branch, 105 S Holland St, Dallas, NC, 28034. Tel: 704-922-3621. Fax: 704-922-3621. p. 1794

Pollitz, John, Dir of Libr, University of Wisconsin-Eau Claire, 105 Garfield Ave, Eau Claire, WI, 54702-4004. Tel: pollitjh@uwec.edu. Fax: 715-836-2949. p. 2590

Pollock, Adele, Ch, Tremont District Public Library, 215 S Sampson St, Tremont, IL, 61568. Tel: 309-925-5432, 309-925-5597. Fax: 309-925-9953. p. 710

Pollock, Alexa, Circ Mgr, Snow College, 141 E Center St, Ephraim, UT, 84627. Tel: 435-283-7363. Fax: 435-283-7369. p. 2405

Pollock, Chad, Tech Serv Supvr, Rogers Public Library, 711 S Dixieland Rd, Rogers, AR, 72758. Tel: 479-621-1152, Ext 12. Fax: 479-621-1165. p. 113

Pollock, Diane, Coordr, University Center Rochester, 851 30 Ave SE, Rochester, MN, 55904. Tel: 507-285-7229. Fax: 507-281-7772. p. 1273

Pollock, Janine, Head Librn, Free Library of Philadelphia, Rare Book, 1901 Vine St, Philadelphia, PA, 19103-1189. Tel: 215-686-5416. p. 2109

Pollock, Jennifer, Head of Libr, University of Cincinnati Libraries, Design, Architecture Art & Planning, 5480 Aronoff Ctr, Cincinnati, OH, 45221. Tel: 513-556-1319. Fax: 513-556-3006. p. 1874

Pollock, Ludmila, Dir, Cold Spring Harbor Laboratory, One Bungtown Rd, Cold Spring Harbor, NY, 11724-2203. Tel: 516-367-6872. Fax: 516-367-6843. p. 1609

Pollock, Maureen, Sr Librn, Lee County Library System, Bonita Springs Public, 26876 Pine Ave, Bonita Springs, FL, 34135-5009. Tel: 239-533-4860. p. 445

Pollock, Peggy, Br Support, Stormont, Dundas & Glengarry County Library, Finch Branch, 17A George St, Finch, ON, K0C 1K0, CANADA. Tel: 613-984-2807. p. 2801

Pollock, Peggy, Br Support, Stormont, Dundas & Glengarry County Library, Winchester Branch, 547 St Lawrence St, Winchester, ON, K0C 2K0, CANADA. Tel: 613-774-2612. Fax: 613-774-5866. p. 2802

Pollock, Sally, Librn, Township Library of Lower Southampton, 1983 Bridgetown Pike, Feasterville, PA, 19053-4493. Tel: 215-355-1183. Fax: 215-364-5735. p. 2057

Polly, Jean, Dir, Liverpool Public Library, 310 Tulip St, Liverpool, NY, 13088-4997. Tel: 315-457-0310. Fax: 315-453-7867. p. 1653

Polly, Margaret A, Dir, Whiting Public Library, 407 Whittier St, Whiting, IA, 51063. Tel: 712-455-2612. Fax: 712-455-2612. p. 852

Polmatier, Karen, Cat, West Hartford Public Library, 20 S Main St, West Hartford, CT, 06107-2432. Tel: 860-561-6950. Fax: 860-561-6976. p. 376

Polo, Janethe, Educ Coordr, Librn, Norwegian American Hospital, 1044 N Francisco Ave, Chicago, IL, 60622. Tel: 773-292-8200, Ext 4670. Fax: 773-292-5954. p. 621

Polodna, David, Dir, Winding Rivers Library System, 800 Main St, La Crosse, WI, 54601-4122. Tel: 608-789-7151. Fax: 608-789-7106. p. 2604

Polott, E Leslie, Dir, Hudson Library & Historical Society, 96 Library St, Hudson, OH, 44236-5122. Tel: 330-653-6658. Fax: 330-650-3373. p. 1905

Polowy, Barbara, Head Librn, Smith College Libraries, Hillyer Art Library, Brown Fine Arts Ctr, Smith College, Northampton, MA, 01063. Tel: 413-585-2941. Fax: 413-585-6975. p. 1114

Polsgrove-Roberts, Jacqueline, Br Mgr, Cass County Public Library, Genealogy, 400 E Mechanic, Harrisonville, MO, 64701. Tel: 816-884-6285. p. 1330

Polsom, Leslie, Dir, Ref, Saskatchewan Legislative Library, 234-2405 Legislative Dr, Regina, SK, S4S 0B3, CANADA. Tel: 306-787-1825. Fax: 306-787-5856. p. 2924

Polson, Jerilyn, Br Mgr, Fairfax County Public Library, Oakton Library, 10304 Lynnhaven Pl, Oakton, VA, 22124-1785. Tel: 703-242-4020. p. 2461

Polson, Natalie, Circ Serv Coordr, University of Utah, Marriott Library, 295 S 1500 East, Salt Lake City, UT, 84112-0860. Tel: 801-581-8558. Fax: 801-585-7185. p. 2415

Polumsky, Susan, Dir, Wallowa County Library, 207 NW Logan, Enterprise, OR, 97828-0186. Tel: 541-426-3969. Fax: 541-426-3969. p. 1996

Polyak, Toni, Br Mgr, Gaines County Library, Seagraves Branch, 311 Hill St, Seagraves, TX, 79359. Tel: 806-546-2480. Fax: 806-546-3053. p. 2386

Polymenakos, Maria, Head, Adult Serv, Upper Darby Township & Sellers Memorial Free Public Library, 76 S State Rd, Upper Darby, PA, 19082. Tel: 610-789-4440. p. 2149

Polzer, Jessica, Instrul Serv Librn, Ref Serv, University of Wisconsin-Stout Library, 315 Tenth Ave, Menomonie, WI, 54751-0790. Tel: 715-232-2141. Fax: 715-232-1783. p. 2615

Poma, Mike, Ref Serv, Creighton University, 2500 California Plaza, Omaha, NE, 68178-0209. Tel: 402-280-2298. Fax: 402-280-2435. p. 1412

Pomerantz, Gloria, Prog Coordr, Peninsula Public Library, 280 Central Ave, Lawrence, NY, 11559. Tel: 516-239-3262. Fax: 516-239-8425. p. 1651

Pomerantz, Sarah, Acq Librn, Adelphi University Libraries, One South Ave, Garden City, NY, 11530. Tel: 516-877-3525. Fax: 516-877-3592. p. 1625

Pomeroy, Amanda, Mgr, Danbury Hospital, 24 Hospital Ave, Danbury, CT, 06810. Tel: 203-797-7419. Fax: 203-731-8662. p. 335

Pomeroy, Brenna, Asst Dir, Ref Serv, Oxford Free Library, 339 Main St, Oxford, MA, 01540. Tel: 508-987-6003. Fax: 508-987-3896. p. 1116

Pomeroy, Dan, Librn, Tennessee State Museum Library, Polk Cultural Ctr, 505 Deaderick St, Nashville, TN, 37243-1120. Tel: 615-741-2692. Fax: 615-741-7231. p. 2259

Pomeroy, Karin, Asst Dir, Fowlerville District Library, 131 Mill St, Fowlerville, MI, 48836. Tel: 517-223-9089. Fax: 517-223-0781. p. 1181

Pomeroy, Peggy, Cat, Libr Assoc, West Virginia University Institute of Technology, 405 Fayette Pike, Montgomery, WV, 25136-2436. Tel: 304-442-3082. Fax: 304-442-3091. p. 2565

Pomes, Stephen V, Libr Dir, US Department of the Interior, 1201 Elmwood Park Blvd, MS-5031, New Orleans, LA, 70123-2394. Tel: 504-736-0057, 504-736-2521. Fax: 504-736-2525. p. 964

Pompelia, Mark, Visual Res Librn, Rhode Island School of Design Library, 15 Westminster St, Providence, RI, 02903. Tel: 401-709-5935. Fax: 401-709-5932. p. 2174

Pon, Gary, Info Spec, Canadian Pacific Railway, 401 Ninth Ave SW, 7th Flr, Calgary, AB, T2P 4Z4, CANADA. Tel: 403-319-3794. Fax: 403-319-6257. p. 2691

Ponce, Becky, Libr Tech, Dona Ana Community College Library, 3400 S Espina, Rm 260, Las Cruces, NM, 88003. Tel: 575-527-7555. Fax: 575-527-7636. p. 1558

Ponce de Leon, Cecily, Ch, Plano Public Library System, Maribelle M Davis Library, 7501-B Independence Pkwy, Plano, TX, 75025. Tel: 972-208-8000. Fax: 972-208-8037. p. 2370

Ponce-Wolfe, Jana Christine, Dir, Libr Serv, Parker Public Library, 1001 S Navajo Ave, Parker, AZ, 85344. Tel: 928-669-2622. Fax: 928-669-8668. p. 70

Pond, Arthur, Br Mgr, Los Angeles Public Library System, Frances Howard Goldwyn-Hollywood Regional Branch, 1623 N Ivar Ave, Los Angeles, CA, 90028-6305. Tel: 323-467-1821. Fax: 323-467-5707. p. 173

Pond, Melissa, Librn, Leech Lake Tribal College Library, 6945 Littlewolf Rd NW, Cass Lake, MN, 56633. Tel: 218-335-4240. Fax: 218-335-4282. p. 1244

Pond, Pat, Br Mgr, Wayne County Public Library, Doylestown Branch, 169 N Portage St, Doylestown, OH, 44230. Tel: 330-658-4677. Fax: 330-658-4671. p. 1950

Ponder, Marilyn, Ch, Port Isabel Public Library, 213 Yturria St, Port Isabel, TX, 78578. Tel: 956-943-1822. Fax: 956-943-4638. p. 2371

Ponder, Peppa, Asst Librn, Pine Forest Regional Library, R E Blackwell Memorial, 403 S Fir Ave, Collins, MS, 39428. Tel: 601-765-8582. Fax: 601-765-8582. p. 1314

Ponder, Sue, Dir, Prairie City Public Library, 100 E Fifth, Prairie City, IA, 50228. Tel: 515-994-2308. p. 839

Ponella, Philip, Dir, Indiana University Bloomington, William & Gayle Cook Music Library, Simon Music Library & Recital Ctr M160, 200 S Jordan Ave, Bloomington, IN, 47405. Tel: 812-855-2970. Fax: 812-855-3843. p. 727

Pong, Connie, Spec Coll Librn, New Orleans Baptist Theological Seminary, 4110 Seminary Pl, New Orleans, LA, 70126. Tel: 504-282-4455, Ext 8454. Fax: 504-816-8429. p. 961

Ponikvar, Laura M, Image & Instrul Serv Librn, Cleveland Institute of Art, 11141 East Blvd, Cleveland, OH, 44106. Tel: 216-421-7442. Fax: 216-421-7439. p. 1877

Ponischil, Susan, Tech Serv, Aquinas College, 1607 Robinson Rd SE, Grand Rapids, MI, 49506-1799. Tel: 616-632-2134. Fax: 616-732-4534. p. 1183

Ponnappa, Biddanda, Dir, Tri-Cities Area Health Sciences Libraries Consortium, East Tenn State Univ, James H Quillen Col of Med, Medical Library, Johnson City, TN, 37614. Tel: 423-439-6252. Fax: 423-439-7025. p. 2955

Ponnappa, Biddanda (Suresh) P, Dir, East Tennessee State University, James H Quillen College of Medicine Library, Maple St, Bldg 4, Johnson City, TN, 37614. Tel: 423-439-6355. Fax: 423-439-7025. p. 2239

Ponshock, Lore, Dir, Lester Public Library of Rome, 1157 Rome Center Dr, Nekoosa, WI, 54457. Tel: 715-325-8990. Fax: 715-325-8993. p. 2624

Ponstein, Beth, Librn, Long Island Community Library, Main St, Long Island, KS, 67647-0195. Tel: 785-854-7474. p. 880

Pont, Janet, Exec Dir, Congregation Shaarey Zedek Library & Audio Visual Center, 27375 Bell Rd, Southfield, MI, 48034. Tel: 248-357-5544. Fax: 248-357-0227. p. 1228

Pontbriand, France, Librn, Centre de Santé et Services Sociaux de Laval - Cite de la Sante, 1755 boul Rene-Laennec, Laval, QC, H7M 3L9, CANADA. Tel: 450-668-1010, Ext 23215. Fax: 450-975-5572. p. 2886

Pontius, Marilyn, Librn, Washington County Free Library, Hancock War Memorial, Park Rd, Hancock, MD, 21750. Tel: 301-678-5300. p. 1031

Pontius, William, Asst Librn, Lake Andes Carnegie Public Library, Fifth & Main St, Lake Andes, SD, 57356. Tel: 605-487-7524. p. 2214

Pontoriero, Catherine, Asst Prof, Ref Librn, Ocean County College Library, College Dr, Toms River, NJ, 08754. Tel: 732-255-0400, Ext 2254. Fax: 732-255-0421. p. 1533

Ponville, Myra, Staff Develop Coordr, Fort Bend County Libraries, 1001 Golfview Dr, Richmond, TX, 77469-5199. Tel: 281-341-2622. Fax: 281-341-2688. p. 2374

Ponzini, Suzanne, YA Serv, Port Washington Public Library, One Library Dr, Port Washington, NY, 11050. Tel: 516-883-4400. Fax: 516-883-7927. p. 1721

Ponzio, Renee, Mgr, Ref Serv, L E Phillips Memorial Public Library, 400 Eau Claire St, Eau Claire, WI, 54701. Tel: 715-839-1683. Fax: 715-839-5310. p. 2590

Pool, Clancy, Br Coordr, Whitman County Rural Library District, 102 S Main St, Colfax, WA, 99111-1863. Tel: 509-397-4366. Fax: 509-397-6156. p. 2513

Pool, Clancy, Br Mgr, Whitman County Rural Library District, St John Branch, One E Front St, Saint John, WA, 99171. Tel: 509-648-3319. p. 2513

Pool, Jacquie, Dir, Plum City Public Library, 611 Main St, Plum City, WI, 54761-9044. Tel: 715-647-2373. Fax: 715-647-2373. p. 2630

Pool, James, Circ, Arlington Public Library System, 101 E Abram St, MS 10-0100, Arlington, TX, 76010-1183. Tel: 817-459-6910. Fax: 817-459-6936. p. 2276

Pool, Jesse, Librn, First Regional Library, M R Dye Public Library, 2885 Goodman Rd, Horn Lake, MS, 38637. Tel: 662-393-5654. Fax: 662-342-9468. p. 1301

Pool, Kristen, Asst Dir, Kent Free Library, 312 W Main, Kent, OH, 44240-2493. Tel: 330-673-4414. Fax: 330-673-0226. p. 1906

Pool, Marji, Adminr, Lockwood, Andrews & Newnam, Inc, 2925 Briarpark Dr, Ste 400, Houston, TX, 77042. Tel: 713-266-6900. Fax: 713-266-2089. p. 2340

Pool, Rebecca, Dir, Deer Park Public Library, 3009 Center St, Deer Park, TX, 77536-5099. Tel: 281-478-7208. Fax: 281-478-7212. p. 2311

Poole, Christopher, Ault Prog Librn/Acq, Giles County Public Library, 122 S Second St, Pulaski, TN, 38478-3285. Tel: 931-363-2720. Fax: 931-424-7032. p. 2263

Poole, Connie, Dir, Southern Illinois University School of Medicine Library, 801 N Rutledge, Springfield, IL, 62702. Tel: 217-545-2658. Fax: 217-545-0988. p. 706

Poole, Deborah, Assoc Dean, Pub Serv, Loyola University New Orleans, 6363 Saint Charles Ave, New Orleans, LA, 70118-6195. Tel: 504-864-7111. Fax: 504-864-7247. p. 961

Poole, Eva D, Dir, Denton Public Library, 502 Oakland St, Denton, TX, 76201. Tel: 940-349-8750. Fax: 940-349-8101. p. 2312

Poole, Francis, Head, Flm & Video Coll, University of Delaware Library, 181 S College Ave, Newark, DE, 19717-5267. Tel: 302-831-2231. Fax: 302-831-1046. p. 386

Poole, Jason, Ch, Webster Public Library, Webster Plaza, 980 Ridge Rd, Webster, NY, 14580. Tel: 585-872-7075. p. 1765

Poole, Jocelyn, Head, Info Serv, Georgia Southern University, 1400 Southern Dr, Statesboro, GA, 30458. Tel: 912-478-5115. Fax: 912-478-0093. p. 552

Poole, Joy, Dep State Librn, New Mexico State Library, 1209 Camino Carlos Rey, Santa Fe, NM, 87507. Tel: 505-476-9763. Fax: 505-476-9761. p. 1563

Poole, Kathy, Supvr (Weekend), University of Redlands, 1200 E Colton Ave, Redlands, CA, 92374-3758. Tel: 909-748-8022. Fax: 909-335-5392. p. 215

Poole, Kelly, Br Mgr, Lexington County Public Library System, Cayce-West Columbia Branch, 1500 Augusta Rd W, Columbia, SC, 29169. Tel: 803-794-6791. Fax: 803-926-5383. p. 2199

Poole, Lakysha, Librn, Florida Department of Corrections, 11120 NW Gainesville Rd, Ocala, FL, 34482. Tel: 352-401-5312. Fax: 352-732-5331. p. 473

Poole, Mary, Ref Librn, North Greenville University, 7801 N Tigerville Rd, Tigerville, SC, 29688. Tel: 864-977-7091. Fax: 864-977-2126. p. 2206

Poole, Mary G, Dir, Caldwell Parish Library, 211 Jackson, Columbia, LA, 71418. Tel: 318-649-2259. Fax: 318-649-7768. p. 947

Poole, Rebecca, Circ Supvr, Converse College, 580 E Main St, Spartanburg, SC, 29302. Tel: 864-596-9020, 864-596-9071. Fax: 864-596-9075. p. 2204

Poole-Naranjo, Loraine, Dr, Dir, Libr Res Ctr, Berean Institute Library, 1901 W Girard Ave, Philadelphia, PA, 19130. Tel: 215-763-4833, Ext 117. Fax: 215-236-6011. p. 2103

Poon, Cindy, Pub Serv Mgr, Ajax Public Library, 55 Harwood Ave S, Ajax, ON, L1S 2H8, CANADA. Tel: 905-683-4000, Ext 8801. Fax: 905-683-6960. p. 2791

Poon, Wei Chi, Mrs, Asian Am Studies Librn, University of California, Berkeley, Ethnic Studies, 30 Stephens Hall, MC 2360, Berkeley, CA, 94720-2360. Tel: 510-642-2220. Fax: 510-643-8433. p. 128

Poonja, Azmin, Mgr, Vols Serv, Calgary Public Library, W R Castell Central Library, 616 Macleod Trail SE, Calgary, AB, T2G 2M2, CANADA. Tel: 403-260-2600. Fax: 403-237-5393. p. 2689

Poor, Michelle, Head, Tech Serv, Brockton Public Library System, 304 Main St, Brockton, MA, 02301-5390. Tel: 508-580-7890. Fax: 508-580-7898. p. 1070

Poorbaugh, Susan, Archivist, Art Librn, Museum of New Mexico, Museum of Fine Arts Library, 107 W Palace Ave, Santa Fe, NM, 87501. Tel: 505-476-5061. Fax: 505-476-5076. p. 1562

Poore, Erin, Head, Info Serv, Bethlehem Area Public Library, 11 W Church St, Bethlehem, PA, 18018. Tel: 610-867-3761, Ext 219. Fax: 610-867-2767. p. 2034

Poore, Sami, Supvr, Leath Thomas Memorial Library, Kemp-Sugg Memorial, 279 Second St, Ellerbe, NC, 28338-9001. Tel: 910-652-6130. Fax: 910-652-6130. p. 1820

Poortenga, Linda, Managing Librn, Jasper County Public Library, 208 W Susan St, Rensselaer, IN, 47978. Tel: 219-866-5881. Fax: 219-866-7378. p. 774

Popa, Radu D, Asst Dean, Libr Serv, Dir, Law Libr, New York University School of Law, 40 Washington Sq S, New York, NY, 10012-1099. Tel: 212-998-6300. Fax: 212-995-4559. p. 1695

Popadak, John, Acq Librn, Youngstown State University, One University Plaza, Youngstown, OH, 44555-0001. Tel: 330-941-3679. Fax: 330-941-3734. p. 1953

Poparad, Christa, Curric Mat Librn, Head, Ref, Pub Serv Librn, Lynchburg College, 1501 Lakeside Dr, Lynchburg, VA, 24501-3199. Tel: 434-544-8204. Fax: 434-544-8499. p. 2476

Pope, Angela, YA Serv, Atlanta-Fulton Public Library System, Adams Park Library, 2231 Campbellton Rd SW, Atlanta, GA, 30311. Tel: 404-752-8763. Fax: 404-752-8765. p. 511

Pope, Angie, Circ, Community College of Beaver County Library, One Campus Dr, Monaca, PA, 15061-2588. Tel: 724-775-8561. Fax: 724-728-8024. p. 2090

Pope, Barbara, Per, Pittsburg State University, 1605 S Joplin St, Pittsburg, KS, 66762-5889. Tel: 620-235-4884. Fax: 620-235-4090. p. 890

Pope, Betty B, Librn, Public Library of Johnston County & Smithfield, Kenly Public, 205 Edgerton St, Kenly, NC, 27542. Tel: 919-284-4217. p. 1824

Pope, Beverly, Librn, Florida Department of Agriculture & Consumer Services, 1911 SW 34th St, Gainesville, FL, 32608. Tel: 352-395-4720. Fax: 352-395-4614. p. 449

Pope, Cristina, Dir, SUNY Upstate Medical University, 766 Irving Ave, Syracuse, NY, 13210-1602. Tel: 315-464-4582. Fax: 315-464-4584. p. 1753

Pope, Jennifer, ILL, Mgr, Access Serv, Whitman College, 345 Boyer Ave, Walla Walla, WA, 99362. Tel: 509-527-5191. Fax: 509-527-5900. p. 2547

Pope, Kitty, Chief Exec Officer, Guelph Public Library, 100 Norfolk St, Guelph, ON, N1H 4J6, CANADA. Tel: 519-824-6220. Fax: 519-824-8342. p. 2807

Pope, Michele, Ser/Doc Librn, Loyola University New Orleans, Loyola Law Library, School of Law, 7214 St Charles Ave, New Orleans, LA, 70118. Tel: 504-861-5539. Fax: 504-861-5895. p. 961

Pope, Nolan, Automation Syst Coordr, University of Wisconsin-Madison, 728 State St, Madison, WI, 53706. Tel: 608-262-3193. Fax: 608-265-2754. p. 2608

Pope Robbins, Laura, ILL, Web Coordr, Dowling College Library, 150 Idle Hour Blvd, Oakdale, NY, 11769-1999. Tel: 631-244-5023. Fax: 631-244-3374. p. 1709

Pope, Susan, Adult Serv, Scituate Town Library, 85 Branch St, Scituate, MA, 02066. Tel: 781-545-8727. Fax: 781-545-8728. p. 1123

Popejoy, Faith, Asst Librn, Jonesville District Library, 310 Church St, Jonesville, MI, 49250-1087. Tel: 517-849-9701. Fax: 517-849-0009. p. 1196

Popejoy, Mona, Syst Adminr, Chickasaw Regional Library System, 601 Railway Express, Ardmore, OK, 73401. Tel: 580-223-3164. Fax: 580-223-3280. p. 1957

Popejoy, Tammy, In Charge, American Institute of Baking, 1213 Bakers Way, Manhattan, KS, 66502. Tel: 785-537-4750, Ext 125. Fax: 785-537-1493. p. 881

Popescu, Adriana, Librn, Princeton University, Engineering, Williams St, Princeton, NJ, 08544. Tel: 609-258-6567. Fax: 609-258-7366. p. 1523

Popesu, Adriana, Head Librn, Princeton University, Harold P Furth Library, James Forrestal Campus, C-Site, Rm A108, Princeton, NJ, 08543-0451. Tel: 609-243-3565. Fax: 609-243-2299. p. 1523

Popko, John, Univ Librn, Seattle University, A A Lemieux Library, 901 12th Ave, Seattle, WA, 98122-4411. Tel: 206-296-6201. Fax: 206-296-2572. p. 2532

Popkoff, Robert, Br Librn, Brooklyn Public Library, Clarendon, 2035 Nostrand Ave, Brooklyn, NY, 11210. Tel: 718-421-1159. Fax: 718-421-1244. p. 1591

Poplau, Janice J, Cat Librn, Birmingham-Southern College, 900 Arkadelphia Rd, Birmingham, AL, 35254. Tel: 205-226-4740. Fax: 205-226-4743. p. 8

Poplawska, Paulina, Asst Dir, ILL, Liberal Memorial Library, 519 N Kansas, Liberal, KS, 67901-3345. Tel: 620-626-0180. Fax: 620-626-0182. p. 879

Poplees, Julie A, Ch, Pleasant Valley Free Library, 1584 Main St, Pleasant Valley, NY, 12569. Tel: 845-635-8460. Fax: 845-635-9556. p. 1719

Popma, Paula, Head, Pub Serv, California State University, Fresno, Henry Madden Library, 5200 N Barton Ave, Mail Stop ML-34, Fresno, CA, 93740-8014. Tel: 559-278-5794. Fax: 559-278-6952. p. 150

Popoli, Chris, Human Res Mgr, Cook Memorial Public Library District, 413 N Milwaukee Ave, Libertyville, IL, 60048-2280. Tel: 847-362-2330. Fax: 847-362-2354. p. 665

Popovich, Emily, Mgr, Timberland Regional Library, Raymond Branch, 507 Duryea St, Raymond, WA, 98577-1829. Tel: 360-942-2408. Fax: 360-942-5670. p. 2544

Popovitch-Krekic, Rozha, Ref, Mount Saint Mary's College, 12001 Chalon Rd, Los Angeles, CA, 90049-1599. Tel: 310-954-4370. Fax: 310-954-4379. p. 175

Popowich, Emma, Ref Serv, University of Manitoba Libraries, Elizabeth Dafoe Library, 25 Chancellor's Circle, Winnipeg, MB, R3T 2N2, CANADA. Tel: 204-474-9544. Fax: 204-474-7577. p. 2758

Popowich, Fred, Dep Chief Librn, Pictou - Antigonish Regional Library, 182 Dalhousie, New Glasgow, NS, B2H 5E3, CANADA. Tel: 902-755-6031. Fax: 902-755-6775. p. 2784

Popp, Bill, Archivist, Saint Charles County Historical Society Archives, 101 S Main St, Saint Charles, MO, 63301-2802. Tel: 636-946-9828. p. 1352

Poppe, Ardith, Dir, Shoshone-Bannock Library, Pima & Bannock Dr, Fort Hall, ID, 83203. Tel: 208-478-3882. p. 574

Poppel, Ruth, In Charge, Wilkin County Museum Library, 704 Nebraska Ave, Breckenridge, MN, 56520. Tel: 218-643-1303, 218-643-1703. p. 1243

Poppeliers, Natalia Taylor, Coll Coordr, University of South Carolina Aiken, 471 University Pkwy, Aiken, SC, 29801. Tel: 803-641-3492. Fax: 803-641-3302. p. 2180

Poppen, Eva, Ref Coordr, Scott County Library System, 13090 Alabama Ave S, Savage, MN, 55378-1479. Tel: 952-707-1760. Fax: 952-707-1775. p. 1283

Poppendeck, Caroline, Youth Serv, Chemung County Library District, 101 E Church St, Elmira, NY, 14901-2799. Tel: 607-733-8604. Fax: 607-733-9176. p. 1619

Poppino, Stephen, Ref, College of Southern Idaho Library, 315 Falls Ave, Twin Falls, ID, 83301-3367. Tel: 208-732-6500. Fax: 208-736-3087. p. 584

Poquet, Ginette, Librn, Bibliotheque Municipale, 260 Pettigrew, Saint-Leonard de Portneuf, QC, G0A 4A0, CANADA. Tel: 418-337-6741. Fax: 418-337-6742. p. 2911

Poquette, Cindy Lou, Dir, Indian River Area Library, 3546 S Straits Hwy, Indian River, MI, 49749. Tel: 231-238-8581. Fax: 231-238-9494. p. 1193

Poquette, Frank, Libr Tech, Minnesota Department of Corrections, 7600 - 525th St, Rush City, MN, 55069. Tel: 320-358-0400, Ext 373. Fax: 763-689-7555. p. 1273

Poquette, Judy, Librn, North Hero Public Library, 1395 US Rte Two, North Hero, VT, 05474. Tel: 802-372-5458. p. 2430

Poquette, Tammy, Circ Mgr, Champlain College Library, 163 S Willard St, Burlington, VT, 05401. Tel: 802-865-6489. p. 2420

Porath, Sue, ILL & Children's Coll Develop Librn, Shawano City-County Library, 128 S Sawyer St, Shawano, WI, 54166-2496. Tel: 715-526-3829. Fax: 715-526-6772. p. 2636

Porcari, George, Acq, Art Center College of Design, 1700 Lida St, Pasadena, CA, 91103. Tel: 626-396-2231. Fax: 626-568-0428. p. 205

Porcaro, Patricia, Head, Reader Serv, College of the Holy Cross, One College St, Worcester, MA, 01610. Tel: 508-793-3372. Fax: 508-793-2372. p. 1143

Porcella, Karen, Dir, Peninsula Public Library, 280 Central Ave, Lawrence, NY, 11559. Tel: 516-239-3262. Fax: 516-239-8425. p. 1651

Porcella, Luisa, Tech Serv, Millburn Free Public Library, 200 Glen Ave, Millburn, NJ, 07041. Tel: 973-376-1006, Ext 21. Fax: 973-376-0104. p. 1502

Porcello, Lorraine, Librn, Highland Hospital Library, Highland Hospital, 1000 South Ave, Rochester, NY, 14620. Tel: 585-341-0378. p. 1729

Porfiri, Lois, Sr Librn, Hennepin County Library, Northeast, 2200 Central Ave NE, Minneapolis, MN, 55418-3708. Tel: 612-543-6778. Fax: 612-543-6777. p. 1264

Porfirio-Milton, Dawn, Br Mgr, Phoenix Public Library, Desert Sage Library, 7602 W Encanto Blvd, Phoenix, AZ, 85035. p. 76

Porobic, Amra, Mgr, Libr Serv, Insurance Bureau of Canada Library, 777 Bay St, Ste 2400, Toronto, ON, M5G 2C8, CANADA. Tel: 416-362-2031, Ext 4350. Fax: 416-361-5952. p. 2855

Porpiglia, Johanna, Dir, Miami-Dade County Law Library, County Courthouse, Rm 321A, 73 W Flagler St, Miami, FL, 33130. Tel: 305-349-7548. Fax: 305-349-7552. p. 466

Porreca, Ann, Asst Librn, Jeannette Public Library Association, 500 Magee Ave, Jeannette, PA, 15644-3416. Tel: 724-523-5702. Fax: 724-523-2357. p. 2072

Portalupi, Elaine, Head, Ch, Head, Youth Serv, Hudson Library & Historical Society, 96 Library St, Hudson, OH, 44236-5122. Tel: 330-653-6658. Fax: 330-650-3373. p. 1905

Porte, Shannon, Head, Pub Serv, University of St Francis, 500 Wilcox St, Joliet, IL, 60435. Tel: 815-740-5061. Fax: 815-740-3364. p. 660

Portelance, Julie, Asst Librn, Hearst Public Library, 801 George St, Hearst, ON, P0L 1N0, CANADA. Tel: 705-372-2843. Fax: 705-372-2833. p. 2811

Porter, Alle, Mgr, ILL, Saint Mary's College Library, 1928 Saint Mary's Rd, Moraga, CA, 94575. Tel: 925-631-4229. Fax: 925-376-6097. p. 191

Porter, Ann, Communications Coordr, Scottsdale Public Library, 3839 N Drinkwater Blvd, Scottsdale, AZ, 85251-4467. Tel: 480-312-7323. Fax: 480-312-7993. p. 81

Porter, Beth, Dir, Heyworth Public Library District, 119 E Main St, Heyworth, IL, 61745. Tel: 309-473-2313. Fax: 309-473-9253. p. 655

Porter, Betty, Asst Dir, Educ Serv, Xavier University, 3800 Victory Pkwy, Cincinnati, OH, 45207-5211. Tel: 513-745-4830. Fax: 513-745-1932. p. 1875

Porter, Billie, Dir, Waurika Library, 98 Meridian St, Waurika, OK, 73573. Tel: 580-228-3274. Fax: 580-228-3274. p. 1985

Porter, Brandi, Libr Dir, Mount Aloysius College Library, 7373 Admiral Peary Hwy, Cresson, PA, 16630-1999. Tel: 814-886-6445. Fax: 814-886-5767. p. 2048

Porter, Christine A, Dir, Middletown Public Library, 20 N Catherine St, Middletown, PA, 17057-1401. Tel: 717-944-6412. Fax: 717-930-0510. p. 2089

Porter, Daisy, Dir of Serv, Arlington Heights Memorial Library, 500 N Dunton Ave, Arlington Heights, IL, 60004-5966. Tel: 847-506-2668. Fax: 847-506-2650. p. 589

Porter, Danalene, Br Mgr, Van Buren Public Library, 111 N 12th St, Van Buren, AR, 72956. Tel: 479-474-6045. Fax: 479-471-3227. p. 116

Porter, Gail, Spec Format Cataloger, Chicago State University, 9501 S Martin Luther King Jr Dr, LIB 440, Chicago, IL, 60628-1598. Tel: 773-995-2551. Fax: 773-995-3772. p. 610

Porter, George, Librn, California Institute of Technology, Earthquake Engineering Research, Sherman Fairchild Library, 200 E California Blvd, M/C 1-43, Pasadena, CA, 91125. Tel: 626-395-3409. Fax: 626-568-2719. p. 205

Porter, George, Eng Librn, California Institute of Technology, Sherman Fairchild Library of Engineering & Applied Science, Fairchild Library I-43, Pasadena, CA, 91125. Tel: 626-395-3404. Fax: 626-431-2681. p. 206

Porter, Gordon, Dir, Church of Jesus Christ of Latter-Day Saints, 41 S Hobson, Mesa, AZ, 85204. Tel: 480-964-1200. Fax: 480-964-7137. p. 68

Porter, Jana, Ref Librn, Elgin Community College, 1700 Spartan Dr, Elgin, IL, 60123. Tel: 847-214-7337. p. 641

Porter, Jared, Mgr, Info Tech, Asbury Theological Seminary, 204 N Lexington Ave, Wilmore, KY, 40390-1199. Tel: 859-858-2233. Fax: 859-858-2330. p. 938

Porter, Jean, Circ Serv, ILL, Spring Green Community Library, 230 E Monroe St, Spring Green, WI, 53588-8035. Tel: 608-588-2276. p. 2639

Porter, Jennifer, Circ Supvr, Valley City State University Library, 101 College St SW, Valley City, ND, 58072-4098. Tel: 701-845-7276. Fax: 701-845-7437. p. 1848

Porter, Julia, Ref Librn, St Charles Community College, 4601 Mid Rivers Mall Dr, Cottleville, MO, 63376. Tel: 636-922-8450. Fax: 636-922-8433. p. 1326

Porter, Kate, Asst Dir, Upper Arlington Public Library, 2800 Tremont Rd, Columbus, OH, 43221. Tel: 614-486-9621. Fax: 614-486-4530. p. 1891

Porter, Kimberly, Dir of Educ, High Street Christian Church, 131 S High St, Akron, OH, 44308-1497. Tel: 330-434-1039. Fax: 330-434-7271. p. 1853

Porter, Kitty, Ref Librn, Vanderbilt University, Science & Engineering, 3200 Stevenson Ctr, 419 21st Ave S, Nashville, TN, 37240-0007. Tel: 615-343-7106. Fax: 615-343-7249. p. 2261

Porter, Lawrence, Fr, Dir, Monsignor James C Turro Seminary Library, Seton Hall University, 400 S Orange Ave, South Orange, NJ, 07079. Tel: 973-761-9198, 973-761-9336, 973-761-9584. Fax: 973-275-2074. p. 1530

Porter, Linda, Coll Develop, Marion County Public Library System, 2720 E Silver Springs Blvd, Ocala, FL, 34470. Tel: 352-671-8551. Fax: 352-368-4545. p. 474

Porter, Linda, Tech Serv, Thorntown Public Library, 124 N Market St, Thorntown, IN, 46071-1144. Tel: 765-436-7348. Fax: 765-436-7011. p. 782

Porter, Marguerite, Librn, Regina Public Library, Sherwood Village, 6121 Rochdale Blvd, Regina, SK, S4X 2R1, CANADA. Tel: 306-777-6088. Fax: 306-949-7270. p. 2923

Porter, Marjorie, Dir, Benzonia Public Library, 891 Michigan Ave, Benzonia, MI, 49616-9784. Tel: 231-882-4111. Fax: 231-882-4111. p. 1157

Porter, Marlene, Dir, University of Toledo, Health Science Campus, Mail Stop 1061, 3000 Arlington Ave, Toledo, OH, 43614-5805. Tel: 419-383-4223. Fax: 419-383-6146. p. 1940

Porter, Mary, Tech Serv, Indian Valley Public Library, 100 E Church Ave, Telford, PA, 18969. Tel: 215-723-9109. Fax: 215-723-0583. p. 2145

Porter, Patricia, Librn, Amberton University, 1700 Eastgate Dr, Garland, TX, 75041. Tel: 972-279-6511, Ext 138. Fax: 972-686-5567. p. 2327

Porter, Ray, Tech Serv, Catawba College, 2300 W Innes St, Salisbury, NC, 28144-2488. Tel: 704-637-4215. Fax: 704-637-4304. p. 1822

Porter, Sandra L, Dir, Eaton Rapids Public Library, 220 S Main St, Eaton Rapids, MI, 48827-1256. Tel: 517-663-8118, Ext 4. Fax: 517-663-1940. p. 1176

Porter Smith, Sally, Br Experience Dir, Pierce County Library System, 3005 112th St E, Tacoma, WA, 98446-2215. Tel: 253-548-3422. Fax: 253-537-4600. p. 2539

Porter, Stephanie, Libr Asst, Conemaugh Memorial Medical Center, 1086 Franklin St, Johnstown, PA, 15905-4398. Tel: 814-534-5960, 814-534-9111. Fax: 814-534-3244. p. 2073

Porter, Suzanne, Curator, Duke University Libraries, Medical Center Library, DUMC Box 3702, Ten Bryan-Searle Dr, Durham, NC, 27710-0001. Tel: 919-660-1143. Fax: 919-681-7599. p. 1788

Porter, Tana M, Dr, Librn, Res, Orange County Regional History Center, 65 E Central Blvd, Orlando, FL, 32801. Tel: 407-836-8541. Fax: 407-836-8550. p. 477

Porter, Tobe, Dir, Port Orford Public Library District, 1421 Oregon St, Port Orford, OR, 97465. Tel: 541-332-5622. Fax: 541-332-2140. p. 2009

Porter, Travis, Assoc Dir, Br Mgr, Ada Community Library, 10664 W Victory Rd, Boise, ID, 83709. Tel: 208-362-0181, Ext 24. Fax: 208-362-0303. p. 570

Porter, William, Dir, Roxbury Township Public Library, 103 Main St, Succasunna, NJ, 07876. Tel: 973-584-2400. Fax: 973-584-5484. p. 1532

Porter-Lanski, Dani L, Develop Dir, University of Arkansas Libraries, 365 N McIlroy Ave, Fayetteville, AR, 72701-4002. Tel: 479-575-4444. Fax: 479-575-6656. p. 99

Porter-McBride, Rhonda, Dir, Illinois Veteran's Home Library, One Veterans Dr, Manteno, IL, 60950-9466. Tel: 815-468-6581, Ext 272. Fax: 815-468-0570. p. 670

Portera, Linda, Dir, Neighborhood Libr, Brooklyn Public Library, Grand Army Plaza, Brooklyn, NY, 11238-5698. Tel: 718-230-2095. Fax: 718-230-2784. p. 1590

Porterfield, David, Head, Adult Serv, Martinsburg-Berkeley County Public Library, 101 W King St, Martinsburg, WV, 25401. Tel: 304-267-8933. Fax: 304-267-9720. p. 2565

Porterfield, David L, Libr Dir, California Area Public Library, 100 Wood St, California, PA, 15419. Tel: 724-938-2907. Fax: 724-938-9119. p. 2040

Porterfield, Diane, Libr Dir, Central Pennsylvania College Library, 600 Valley Rd, Summerdale, PA, 17093. Tel: 717-728-2227. Fax: 717-728-2300. p. 2144

Porterfield, Lori, Asst Librn, Pearisburg Public Library, 209 Fort Branch Rd, Pearisburg, VA, 24134. Tel: 540-921-2556. Fax: 540-921-1708. p. 2484

Porterfield, Paul, Head, Media Serv, University of Richmond, 28 Westhampton Way, Richmond, VA, 23173. Tel: 804-289-8453. Fax: 804-289-8757. p. 2491

Porteur, Stanley, Acq, Per, Bloomfield College Library, Liberty St & Oakland Ave, Bloomfield, NJ, 07003. Tel: 973-748-9000, Ext 335. Fax: 973-743-3998. p. 1473

Porteus, Andrew, Online Serv, Ref, Niagara Falls Public Library, 4848 Victoria Ave, Niagara Falls, ON, L2E 4C5, CANADA. Tel: 905-356-8080. Fax: 905-356-7004. p. 2824

Portis, Maggie, Asst Librn, New York School of Interior Design Library, 170 E 70th St, New York, NY, 10021. Tel: 212-472-1500, Ext 214. Fax: 212-472-8175. p. 1694

Portley, Mary Beth, Adult Serv-Fiction, Jervis Public Library Association, Inc, 613 N Washington St, Rome, NY, 13440-4296. Tel: 315-336-4570. p. 1734

Portman, Julie, Tech Serv Librn, Fontbonne University, 6800 Wydown Blvd, Saint Louis, MO, 63105. Tel: 314-889-4569. Fax: 314-719-8040. p. 1354

Portman, Sally, Librn, North Central Regional Library, Winthrop Community, 49 Hwy 20, Winthrop, WA, 98862. Tel: 509-996-2685. p. 2549

Portner, Cassandra, Ch, Stayton Public Library, 515 N First Ave, Stayton, OR, 97383-1703. Tel: 503-769-3313. Fax: 503-769-3218. p. 2020

Portnowitz, Patricia A, Dir, Franklin T Degroodt Library, 6475 Minton Rd SW, Palm Bay, FL, 32908. Tel: 321-952-6317. Fax: 321-952-6320. p. 479

Portolese, Donna Renee, Libr Asst, Neuse Regional Library, Maysville Public Library, 605 Seventh St, Maysville, NC, 28555. Tel: 910-743-3796. Fax: 910-743-3796. p. 1805

Portugal, Rhoda, Ref Librn, Rutherford Public Library, 150 Park Ave, Rutherford, NJ, 07070. Tel: 201-939-8600. Fax: 201-939-4108. p. 1528

Posada, Luz, Tech Serv, Paterson Free Public Library, 250 Broadway, Paterson, NJ, 07501. Tel: 973-321-1223, Ext 2320. Fax: 973-321-1205. p. 1518

Posas, Liza, Ref Librn, Autry National Center, Braun Research Library, 234 Museum Dr, Los Angeles, CA, 90065. Tel: 323-221-2164, Ext 256. Fax: 322-221-8223. p. 168

Posega, Anne, Head, Spec Coll, Washington University Libraries, One Brookings Dr, Campus Box 1061, Saint Louis, MO, 63130-4862. Tel: 314-935-5495. Fax: 314-935-4045. p. 1362

Posey, Betty, Librn, American Donkey & Mule Society Library, 1346 Morningside Ave, Lewisville, TX, 75057. Tel: 972-219-0781. Fax: 972-219-0781. p. 2355

Posey, Christina, Librn, United States Navy, Naval Surface Warfare Ctr, Bldg 1194, 6090 Jenkins Rd, Ste 209, Dahlgren, VA, 22448-5000. Tel: 540-653-7474. Fax: 540-653-0260. p. 2459

Posey, Donna, Br Mgr, Harrison County Library System, Woolmarket Library, 8455 Woolmarket Rd, Biloxi, MS, 39532. Tel: 228-354-9464. Fax: 228-354-9466. p. 1300

Posey, George M, Pres, Newport Aeronautical Sales Corp Library, 1542 Monrovia Ave, Newport Beach, CA, 92663-2807. Tel: 949-574-4100. Fax: 949-574-4106. p. 194

Posey, Maria, Br Mgr, La Porte County Public Library, Kingsford Heights Branch, 436 Evanston, Kingsford Heights, IN, 46346. Tel: 219-393-3280. Fax: 219-393-3280. p. 759

Posey, Stephanie, Dir of Educ, Thomas Memorial Hospital Library, 4605 MacCorkle Ave SW, South Charleston, WV, 25309. Tel: 304-766-5377. Fax: 304-766-5925. p. 2572

Posey, Susann, Tech Serv Librn, Lutheran Theological Seminary, 66 Seminary Ridge, Gettysburg, PA, 17325. Tel: 717-338-3032. Fax: 717-337-1611. p. 2060

Poshek, Joseph, Dean, Orange Coast College Library, 2701 Fairview Rd, Costa Mesa, CA, 92628. Tel: 714-432-5885. Fax: 714-432-6850. p. 137

Posmantur, Craig, Librn, Temple Beth Tzedek, 621 Getzville Rd, Amherst, NY, 14226. Tel: 716-838-3232. Fax: 716-835-6154. p. 1573

Posner, Beth, ILL, City University of New York, 365 Fifth Ave, New York, NY, 10016-4309. Tel: 212-817-7051. Fax: 212-817-2982. p. 1673

Posner, Marion, Libr Dir, Chocorua Public Library, 125 Deer Hill Rd, Chocorua, NH, 03817. Tel: 603-323-8610. p. 1441

Post, Anne, Chief Librn, United States Fish & Wildlife Service, 698 Conservation Way, Shepherdstown, WV, 25443. Tel: 304-876-7304. Fax: 304-876-7213. p. 2571

Post, Barbara, Mgr, Info Serv, Transportation Research Board, 500 Fifth St NW, Washington, DC, 20001. Tel: 202-334-2990. Fax: 202-334-2527. p. 2940

Post, Bill, Vice Provost & CIO, Info Res, California State University, Chico, 400 W First St, Chico, CA, 95929-0295. Tel: 530-898-6212. Fax: 530-898-4443. p. 133

Post, Bradley, Acq Mgr, State University of New York College of Technology, Bush Hall, Two Main St, Delhi, NY, 13753. Tel: 607-746-4635. Fax: 607-746-4327. p. 1613

Post, Diana, Dr, Pres, Rachel Carson Council, Inc Library, PO Box 10779, Silver Spring, MD, 20914-0779. Tel: 301-593-7507. Fax: 301-593-7508. p. 1041

Post, Diane, Asst Librn, Mount Ida College, Wadsworth Library, 777 Dedham St, Newton, MA, 02459. Tel: 617-928-4552. Fax: 617-928-4038. p. 1110

Post, Jennifer, Dr, Ref, Mansfield University, Mansfield, PA, 16933. Tel: 570-662-4686. Fax: 570-662-4993. p. 2084

Post, Joy, Librn, Springboro Public Library, 110 S Main St, Springboro, PA, 16435-1108. Tel: 814-587-3901. Fax: 814-587-3901. p. 2142

Post, Lynne, Regional Librn, Canada Department of Fisheries & Oceans, 343 Ave Universite, Moncton, NB, E1C 9B6, CANADA. Tel: 506-851-6264. Fax: 506-851-2766. p. 2765

Post, Patricia A, Dir, Central Minnesota Libraries Exchange, Miller Ctr, Rm 130-D, Saint Cloud State University, Saint Cloud, MN, 56301-4498. Tel: 320-308-2950. Fax: 320-654-5131. p. 2946

Post, Phyllis, Tech Serv, Capital University, Law School Library, 303 E Broad St, Columbus, OH, 43215. Tel: 614-236-6464. Fax: 614-236-6957. p. 1883

Postar, Adeen, Dep Dir, American University, 4801 Massachusetts Ave NW, Washington, DC, 20016-8182. Tel: 202-274-4377. Fax: 202-274-4365. p. 393

Postelnek, Rosie, Ref Serv, Beaumont Public Library System, R C Miller Memorial, 1605 Dowlen Rd, Beaumont, TX, 77706. Tel: 409-866-9487. Fax: 409-866-3720. p. 2287

Postema, Beth E, Dep Dir, Fargo Public Library, 102 N Third St, Fargo, ND, 58102. Tel: 701-241-8198. Fax: 701-241-8581. p. 1841

Postema, Susan, Asst Librn, Thornapple Kellogg School & Community Library, 3885 Bender Rd, Middleville, MI, 49333-9273. Tel: 269-795-5434. Fax: 269-795-8997. p. 1208

Posteraro, Catherine, Pharm Librn, Saint Joseph College, 1678 Asylum Ave, West Hartford, CT, 06117-2791. Tel: 860-231-5484. Fax: 860-523-4356. p. 376

Posthumus, Sueann, Youth Serv, Allendale Township Library, 6175 Library Ln, Allendale, MI, 49401. Tel: 616-895-4178, Ext 13. Fax: 616-895-5178. p. 1149

Postlethwaite, Bonnie, Assoc Dean of Libr, University of Missouri-Kansas City Libraries, 800 E 51st St, Kansas City, MO, 64110. Tel: 816-235-1558. Fax: 816-333-5584. p. 1341

Postlewait, Cheryl, Dir, Kansas City Kansas Community College Library, 7250 State Ave, Kansas City, KS, 66112-3098. Tel: 913-288-7230. Fax: 913-288-7606. p. 875

Postlewait, Fred, Tech Coordr, Leavenworth Public Library, 417 Spruce St, Leavenworth, KS, 66048. Tel: 913-682-5666. Fax: 913-682-1248. p. 879

Postma, Jill Hamrin, Res Librn, Adler Planetarium & Astronomy Museum, 1300 S Lake Shore Dr, Chicago, IL, 60605-2489. Tel: 312-322-0594, 312-542-2206. Fax: 312-341-9935. p. 604

Poston, Bonnie, Coll Develop, Wake Forest University, Coy C Carpenter School of Medicine Library, Medical Center Blvd, Winston-Salem, NC, 27157-1069. Tel: 336-716-4691. Fax: 336-716-2186. p. 1834

Poston, Cathy, VPres, Buchanan County Genealogical Society Library, 103 Fourth Ave SE, Independence, IA, 50644. Tel: 319-334-9333. p. 822

Poston, Ed, Instrul Serv Librn, Berea College, 100 Campus Dr, Berea, KY, 40404. Tel: 859-985-3172. Fax: 859-985-3912. p. 907

Poston, Janice, Instrul Serv Librn, Ref Serv, Spalding University Library, 853 Library Lane, Louisville, KY, 40203-9986. Tel: 502-585-7130. Fax: 502-585-7156. p. 925

Poston, Linda, Dean, Libr Serv, Nyack College Library, One South Blvd, Nyack, NY, 10960-3698. Fax: 845-353-0817. p. 1708

Poswencyk, Douglas, Br Dir, Somerset County Library System, Watchung Public, 12 Stirling Rd, Watchung, NJ, 07069. Tel: 908-561-0117. Fax: 908-769-1145. p. 1475

Potap, Olga, Acq Librn, Boston University Libraries, School of Theology Library, 745 Commonwealth Ave, 2nd Flr, Boston, MA, 02215. Tel: 617-353-3034. Fax: 617-358-0699. p. 1058

Pothier, Geraldine, Head, Tech Serv, Winchester Public Library, 80 Washington St, Winchester, MA, 01890. Tel: 781-721-7171, Ext 27. Fax: 781-721-7170. p. 1142

Pothier-Comeau, Cecile, Ref Librn, Universite Sainte-Anne, 1695, Rte 1, Church Point, NS, B0W 1M0, CANADA. Tel: 902-769-2114, Ext 161. Fax: 902-769-0137. p. 2778

Potratz, Lois, Dir, Spillman Library, 719 Wisconsin Ave, North Fond du Lac, WI, 54937-1335. Tel: 920-929-3771. Fax: 920-929-3669. p. 2625

Potrykus, Lorraine, Librn, Montgomery Watson Harza Library, 175 W Jackson Blvd, Chicago, IL, 60604. Tel: 312-831-3397. Fax: 312-831-3999. p. 619

Pott, Kenneth R, Exec Dir, The Heritage Museum & Cultural Center, Priscilla U Byrns Heritage Ctr, 708 Market St, Saint Joseph, MI, 49085. Tel: 269-983-1191. Fax: 269-983-1274. p. 1225

Potter, Angie, Ch, Porter Memorial Library, 92 Court St, Machias, ME, 04654-2102. Tel: 207-255-3933. p. 991

Potter, Belinda, Circ, Montana State University-Northern, 300 11th St W, Havre, MT, 59501. Tel: 406-265-3706. Fax: 406-265-3799. p. 1381

Potter, Brenda, Govt Doc, Saint Mary's University, 5429 Inglis St, Halifax, NS, B3H 3C3, CANADA. Tel: 902-420-5548. Fax: 902-420-5561. p. 2782

Potter, Cindy, Univ Librn, Texas Wesleyan University, 1201 Wesleyan St, Fort Worth, TX, 76105. Tel: 817-531-4800. Fax: 817-531-4806. p. 2324

Potter, Dorothy F, Tech Serv, Pasadena City College Library, 1570 E Colorado Blvd, Pasadena, CA, 91106-2003. Tel: 626-585-7846. Fax: 626-585-7913. p. 206

Potter, Doug, Cat, Mid-Mississippi Regional Library System, 201 S Huntington St, Kosciusko, MS, 39090-9002. Tel: 662-289-5151. Fax: 662-289-5106. p. 1306

Potter, Jill, In Charge, City of Kawartha Lakes Public Library, Downeyville Branch, Saint Luke's School, 335 Saint Luke's Rd (Downeyville) RR 5, Lindsay, ON, K9V 4R5, CANADA. Tel: 705-799-5265. p. 2816

Potter, Jill, In Charge, City of Kawartha Lakes Public Library, Dunsford Branch, 26 Community Center Rd, Dunsford, ON, K0M 1L0, CANADA. Tel: 705-793-3037. Fax: 705-793-2380. p. 2816

Potter, Jo-Ann, Libr Tech, Nova Scotia Community College, One Main St, Springhill, NS, B0M 1X0, CANADA. Tel: 902-597-4109. Fax: 902-597-8548. p. 2784

Potter, John, Librn, ITT Technical Institute Library, 4020 Sparks Dr SE, Grand Rapids, MI, 49546-6192. Tel: 616-956-1060. Fax: 616-956-5606. p. 1185

Potter, Julie, Dir, Barton County Library, 300 W Tenth St, Lamar, MO, 64759. Tel: 417-682-5355. Fax: 417-682-3206. p. 1343

Potter, Katherine, Admin Librn, Delaware Division of Substance Abuse & Mental Health, 1901 N Dupont Hwy, New Castle, DE, 19720. Tel: 302-255-2789. Fax: 302-255-4458. p. 384

Potter, Kelley, Mgr, Lending Serv, Caledon Public Library, 150 Queen St S, Bolton, ON, L7E 1E3, CANADA. Tel: 905-857-1400. Fax: 905-857-8280. p. 2795

Potter, Kim, Circ, Liberal Memorial Library, 519 N Kansas, Liberal, KS, 67901-3345. Tel: 620-626-0180. Fax: 620-626-0182. p. 879

Potter, Michelle, Dir, Stanwood Public Library, 202 E Broadway, Stanwood, IA, 52337-0234. Tel: 563-942-3531. Fax: 563-942-3531. p. 845

Potter, Shannon D, Br Supvr, Gaston County Public Library, Belmont Branch, 125 Central Ave, Belmont, NC, 28012. Tel: 704-825-5426. Fax: 704-825-5426. p. 1794

Potter, Steven, Dir, Mid-Continent Public Library, 15616 E US Hwy 24, Independence, MO, 64050-2098. Tel: 816-836-5200. Fax: 816-521-7253. p. 1332

Potter, Ted, Head, Pub Serv, University of Iowa Libraries, Law Library, 200 Boyd Law Bldg, Iowa City, IA, 52242-1166. Tel: 319-335-9002. Fax: 319-335-9039. p. 823

Potter, Theodore, Assoc Dir, Marquette University, Sensenbrenner Hall, 1103 W Wisconsin Ave, Milwaukee, WI, 53233-2313. Tel: 414-288-7092. Fax: 414-288-5914. p. 2618

Potter, William Gray, Assoc Provost, Univ Librn, University of Georgia Libraries, Athens, GA, 30602-1641. Tel: 706-542-0621. Fax: 706-542-4144. p. 510

Potter-Henderson, Leslie, Ser, Shoreline Community College, 16101 Greenwood Ave N, Shoreline, WA, 98133-5696. Tel: 206-546-4554. Fax: 206-546-4604. p. 2535

Potters, Bonnie, Coll Develop, Clearwater Public Library System, 100 N Osceola Ave, Clearwater, FL, 33755. Tel: 727-562-4970. Fax: 727-562-4977. p. 432

Potterton, Bruce, Head Librn, Turtle Bay Music School Library, 244 E 52nd St, New York, NY, 10022-6201. Tel: 212-753-8811, Ext 13. Fax: 212-752-6228. p. 1701

Potthoff, Renita, Dir, Monterey-Tippecanoe Township Public Library, 6260 E Main St, Monterey, IN, 46960. Tel: 574-542-2171. Fax: 574-542-2171. p. 765

Pottier, Anne, Assoc Univ Librn, McMaster University Library, 1280 Main St W, Hamilton, ON, L8S 4L6, CANADA. Tel: 905-524-9140, Ext 22410. Fax: 905-524-9850. p. 2810

Pottier, Anne, Assoc Univ Librn, McMaster University Library, H G Thode Library of Science & Engineering, 1280 Main St W, Hamilton, ON, L8S 4P5, CANADA. Tel: 905-524-9140, Ext 22410. Fax: 905-777-1110. p. 2810

Pottle, Connie, Youth Serv Mgr, Delaware County District Library, 84 E Winter St, Delaware, OH, 43015. Tel: 740-362-3861. Fax: 740-369-0196. p. 1895

Potts, Barbara, Reserves Mgr/Circ, Kent State University, 6000 Frank Ave NW, North Canton, OH, 44720-7548. Tel: 330-244-3324. Fax: 330-494-6212. p. 1923

Potts, Elizabeth, Dir, Maury County Public Library, 211 W Eighth St, Columbia, TN, 38401. Tel: 931-375-6501. Fax: 931-375-6519. p. 2231

Potts, Kenneth, Coll Develop Librn, California State University, Stanislaus, One University Circle, Turlock, CA, 95382. Tel: 209-667-3332. p. 277

Potts, Linda, Librn, Idabel Public Library, Two SE Ave D, Idabel, OK, 74745. Tel: 580-286-1074, 580-286-6406. Fax: 580-286-3708. p. 1966

Potts, Mary Ann, Librn, Motley County Library, 1105 Main St, Matador, TX, 79244. Tel: 806-347-2717. p. 2360

Potts, Renee, Libr Spec, Saint Louis Community College, Forest Park Campus Library, 5600 Oakland Ave, Saint Louis, MO, 63110-1316. Tel: 314-644-9681. Fax: 314-644-9240. p. 1357

Potvin, Christiane, Tech Serv, Defence R&D Canada-Valcartier Library, 2459 Pie-XI Blvd N, Val-Belair, QC, G3J 1X5, CANADA. Tel: 418-844-4000, Ext 4262. Fax: 418-844-4624. p. 2914

Potvin, Parisse, Ref, Tele-Universite, 455 rue du Parvis, Quebec, QC, G1K 9H6, CANADA. Tel: 418-657-2747. Fax: 418-657-2094. p. 2906

Potvin, Robert, Chef de Div, Bibliothèques de Montrèal, L'Île-Bizard, 500, montée de l'Église, Montreal, QC, H9C 1G9, CANADA. Tel: 514-620-6199. Fax: 514-620-0707. p. 2890

Potvin, Terrence, Circ Mgr, Henry Ford Community College, 5101 Evergreen Rd, Dearborn, MI, 48128-1495. Tel: 313-845-9760. Fax: 313-845-9795. p. 1167

Poulain Romard, Judith, Librn, Fortress of Louisbourg Library, 259 Park Service Rd, Louisbourg, NS, B1C 2L2, CANADA. Tel: 902-733-3534. Fax: 902-733-2423. p. 2783

Pouletsos, Debbie, Head, Circ, Sayville Library, 11 Collins Ave, Sayville, NY, 11782-3199. Tel: 631-589-4440. Fax: 631-589-6128. p. 1739

Poulin, Angela, Librn, New Hampshire Department of Corrections, 138 E Milan Rd, Berlin, NH, 03570. Tel: 603-752-0460. Fax: 603-752-0405. p. 1439

Poulin, Eric, Coordr, Libr Serv, Greenfield Community College Library, One College Dr, Greenfield, MA, 01301-9739. Tel: 413-775-1834. Fax: 413-775-1838. p. 1092

Poulin, Priscilla, Librn, Andover Public Library, 11 School St, Andover, NH, 03216. Tel: 603-735-5333. Fax: 603-735-6975. p. 1437

Poulin, Sonia, Dir, Alberta Law Libraries, Calgary Branch, Calgary Court Centre, 601 Fifth St SW, Calgary, AB, T2P 5P7, CANADA. Tel: 4780-422-1011. Fax: 403-297-5171. p. 2687

Poulin, Sonia, Dir, Alberta Law Libraries, , Law Courts North, 5th Flr, 1A Sir Winston Churchill Sq, Edmonton, AB, T5J 0R2, CANADA. Tel: 780-427-3327. Fax: 780-427-0481. p. 2698

Poulin, Sonia, Libr Dir, Alberta Law Libraries, Edmonton, Law Courts Bldg, 2nd Flr, 1A Sir Winston Churchill Sq, Edmonton, AB, T5J 0R2, CANADA. Tel: 780-422-1011. Fax: 780-427-0397. p. 2699

Poulos, Paul, Dr, Dir, Mendocino County Historical Society, 603 W Perkins St, Ukiah, CA, 95482-4726. Tel: 707-462-6969. p. 277

Poulson, Michael, Assoc Librn, New Mexico Supreme Court, 237 Don Gaspar, Santa Fe, NM, 87501. Tel: 505-827-4850. Fax: 505-827-4852. p. 1563

Poulter, Anne, Asst Dir, Coll Res, William Mitchell College of Law, 871 Summit Ave, Saint Paul, MN, 55105. Tel: 651-290-6303. Fax: 651-290-6318. p. 1283

Poultney, Judy, Cat, Ch, Normal Public Library, 206 W College Ave, Normal, IL, 61761. Tel: 309-452-1757. Fax: 309-452-5312. p. 681

Poulton, Linda, Curator, Muncy Historical Society & Museum of History, 40 N Main St, Muncy, PA, 17756-1004. Tel: 570-546-5917. p. 2093

Pound, Sarah, ILL, Emporia Public Library, 110 E Sixth Ave, Emporia, KS, 66801-3960. Tel: 620-340-6462. Fax: 620-340-6444. p. 865

Poundstone, Kathie, Ref, Porterville Public Library, 41 W Thurman, Porterville, CA, 93257-3652. Tel: 559-784-0177. Fax: 559-781-4396. p. 212

Pountney, Norma, Br Mgr, Omaha Public Library, South Omaha, 2808 Q St, Omaha, NE, 68107. Tel: 402-444-4850. Fax: 402-444-6644. p. 1414

Poursaba, Corby, Asst Librn, Mabel C Fry Public Library, 1200 Lakeshore Dr, Yukon, OK, 73099. Tel: 405-354-8232. Fax: 405-350-7928. p. 1987

Povilaitis, Bonnie, Dir, Pathfinder Community Library, 812 Michigan Ave, Baldwin, MI, 49304. Tel: 231-745-4010. Fax: 231-745-7681. p. 1155

Pow, Virginia, Librn, University of Alberta, William C Wonders Map Collection, 1-55 Cameron Library, Edmonton, AB, T6G 2J8, CANADA. Tel: 780-492-7919. Fax: 780-492-2721. p. 2703

Powell, Anette, Dir, United States Air Force, Andrews Air Force Base Library FL4425, 89 SVS/SVMG, Brookley & D St, Bldg 1642, Andrews AFB, DC, 20762. Tel: 301-981-1637. Fax: 301-981-4231. p. 417

Powell, Anne Elizabeth, Cat, Syst Coordr, Point Loma Nazarene University, 3900 Lomaland Dr, San Diego, CA, 92106-2899. Tel: 619-849-2355. Fax: 619-222-0711. p. 232

Powell, Antoinette, Music Librn, Ref Librn, Lawrence University, 113 S Lawe St, Appleton, WI, 54911-5683. Tel: 920-832-6995. Fax: 920-832-6967. p. 2578

Powell, Barbara, Cat Supvr, Blackwater Regional Library, 22511 Main St, Courtland, VA, 23837. Tel: 757-653-2821. Fax: 757-653-9374. p. 2458

Powell, Barry W, Sr, Libr Tech, Department of Veterans Affairs-Memphis, 1030 Jefferson Ave, Memphis, TN, 38104-2193. Tel: 901-523-8990, Ext 5883. Fax: 901-577-7338. p. 2248

Powell, Becky, Dir, New Waverly Public Library, 9372 State Hwy 75 S, New Waverly, TX, 77358. Tel: 936-344-2198. Fax: 936-344-2198. p. 2365

Powell, Bobbie, ILL, Battelle Memorial Institute, 505 King Ave, Columbus, OH, 43201. Tel: 614-424-6302. Fax: 614-458-6302. p. 1883

Powell, Brad, Br Mgr, Saint Johns County Public Library System, Hastings Branch, 6195 S Main St, Hastings, FL, 32145. Tel: 904-827-6971. Fax: 904-692-1255. p. 487

Powell, Candace, Tech Serv, Angelina College Library, 3500 S First St, Lufkin, TX, 75904. Tel: 936-633-5219. Fax: 936-633-5442. p. 2358

Powell, Cheryl, Br Mgr, Brooklyn Public Library, Carroll Gardens, 396 Clinton St, Brooklyn, NY, 11231. Tel: 718-596-6972. Fax: 718-596-0370. p. 1591

Powell, Cindy, Ch, Coffeyville Public Library, 311 W Tenth, Coffeyville, KS, 67337-5816. Tel: 620-251-1370. Fax: 620-251-1512. p. 861

Powell, Connie, Tech Serv, Christian County Library, 1005 N Fourth Ave, Ozark, MO, 65721. Tel: 417-581-2432. Fax: 417-581-8855. p. 1348

Powell, David, Circ Mgr, Jessamine County Public Library, 600 S Main St, Nicholasville, KY, 40356-1839. Tel: 859-885-3523. Fax: 859-885-5164. p. 931

Powell, David, Asst Librn, Ref, Methodist Theological School in Ohio Library, 3081 Columbus Pike, Delaware, OH, 43015. Tel: 740-362-3438. Fax: 740-362-3456. p. 1895

Powell, Dianne, Mgr, United States Department of the Interior, Denver Fed Ctr, Sixth Ave & Kipling St, Bldg 67, Denver, CO, 80225. Tel: 303-445-2072. Fax: 303-445-6303. p. 303

Powell, Doris, Ch, YA Serv, Lee County Library, 107 Hawkins Ave, Sanford, NC, 27331-4399. Tel: 919-718-4665. Fax: 919-775-1832. p. 1823

Powell, Edgar, Web Coordr, Jackson State University, 1325 J R Lynch St, Jackson, MS, 39217. Tel: 601-979-2123. Fax: 601-979-2239. p. 1303

Powell, Erica, Tech Serv, University of Miami, Louis Calder Memorial Library, Miller School of Medicine, 1601 NW Tenth Ave, Miami, FL, 33136. Tel: 305-243-6931. Fax: 305-325-8853. p. 469

Powell, Hannah, Asst Mgr, Kingsport Public Library & Archives, 400 Broad St, Kingsport, TN, 37660-4292. Tel: 423-224-2539. Fax: 423-224-2558. p. 2240

Powell, Helen, Asst Librn, Ref Serv, Dalhousie University, Sexton Design & Technology Library, 1360 Barrington St, Halifax, NS, B3J 2X4, CANADA. Tel: 902-494-3240. Fax: 902-494-6089. p. 2781

Powell, Jade, Pub Serv, Public Library of Enid & Garfield County, 120 W Maine, Enid, OK, 73701-5606. Tel: 580-234-6313. Fax: 580-249-9280. p. 1963

Powell, Jean, Electronic & Ad, Wasilla Meta-Rose Public Library, 391 N Main St, Wasilla, AK, 99654-7085. Tel: 907-864-9177. Fax: 907-376-2347. p. 55

Powell, Jennifer, Librn, Summit Christian College Library, 2025 21st St, Gering, NE, 69341. Tel: 308-632-6933. Fax: 308-632-8599. p. 1399

Powell, Jill, Eng Librn, Cornell University Library, Engineering, Virtual Library, Carpenter Hall, Ithaca, NY, 14853-2201. Tel: 607-254-6261. p. 1641

Powell, JoAnne, Head, Ch, Peabody Institute Library of Danvers, 15 Sylvan St, Danvers, MA, 01923-2735. Tel: 978-774-0554. Fax: 978-762-0251. p. 1083

Powell, Jody, Ch, Logan Public Library, 121 E Sixth St, Logan, IA, 51546. Tel: 712-644-2551. Fax: 712-644-2551. p. 828

Powell, John, Access Serv, Ref Serv, Peirce College Library, 1420 Pine St, Philadelphia, PA, 19102-4699. Tel: 215-670-9269. Fax: 215-670-9338. p. 2113

Powell, Karen, Dir, New York City Correctional Institution for Men Library, 10-10 Hazen St, East Elmhurst, NY, 11370. Tel: 718-546-7359. Fax: 718-546-7357. p. 1616

Powell, Kathy, Br Mgr, Live Oak Public Libraries, Ola Wyeth Branch, Four E Bay St, Savannah, GA, 31401. Tel: 912-232-5488. Fax: 912-232-5488. p. 550

Powell, Laura, Br Mgr, Sacramento Public Library, Southgate Community Library, 6132 66th Ave, Sacramento, CA, 95823. p. 225

Powell, Linda, Dir, Orena Humphrey Public Library, 900 Main St, Ste 1, Whitwell, TN, 37397-5249. Tel: 423-658-6134. Fax: 423-658-7726. p. 2269

Powell, Margaret K, Exec Dir, Librn, Yale University Library, Lewis Walpole Library, 154 Main St, Farmington, CT, 06032. Tel: 860-284-5025. Fax: 860-677-6369. p. 359

Powell, Marilyn, Circ, Media Serv, New Albany-Floyd County Public Library, 180 W Spring St, New Albany, IN, 47150-3692. Tel: 812-944-8464. Fax: 812-949-3532. p. 768

Powell, Martha C, Dir of Tech Serv, Southern Baptist Theological Seminary, 2825 Lexington Rd, Louisville, KY, 40280-0294. p. 925

Powell, Mary, Fiscal Officer, Tiffin-Seneca Public Library, 77 Jefferson St, Tiffin, OH, 44883. Tel: 419-447-3751. Fax: 419-447-3045. p. 1938

Powell, Mary Jo, ILL/Doc Delivery Serv Libr Ref Dept Asst, Mohave Community College Library, Lake Havasu City Campus, 1977 W Acoma Blvd, Lake Havasu City, AZ, 86403-2999. Tel: 928-453-5809. Fax: 928-453-8335. p. 66

Powell, Michael, Libr Asst, Fisk University, Fisk University, 1000 17th Ave N, Nashville, TN, 37208-3051. Tel: 615-329-8734. Fax: 615-329-8761. p. 2256

Powell, Monique, Dir, Vance-Granville Community College, State Rd 1126, Poplar Creek Rd, Exit 209, Henderson, NC, 27536. Tel: 252-492-2061. Fax: 252-738-3372. p. 1800

Powell, Niki, Br Mgr, Chickasaw Regional Library System, Love County, 500 S Hwy 77, Marietta, OK, 73448. Tel: 580-276-3783. Fax: 580-276-1483. p. 1957

Powell, Nikita, Supvr, Access Serv, Regent University, 1000 Regent University Dr, Virginia Beach, VA, 23464-9800. Tel: 757-352-4465. Fax: 757-352-4451. p. 2499

Powell, Pamela C, Archivist, Chester County Historical Society Library, 225 N High St, West Chester, PA, 19380. Tel: 610-692-4800. Fax: 610-692-4357. p. 2153

Powell, Patricia, Libr Asst, Shaw University, 118 E South St, Raleigh, NC, 27601. Tel: 919-546-8324. Fax: 919-831-1161. p. 1817

Powell, Patricia, Tech Serv, Roanoke College, 220 High St, Salem, VA, 24153. Tel: 540-375-2292. p. 2495

Powell, Reese, Cir & Acq Librn, William Carey University Libraries, 498 Tuscan Ave, Box 5, Hattiesburg, MS, 39401. Tel: 601-318-6169. Fax: 601-318-6171. p. 1301

Powell, Richard J, Librn, Scolaro, Shulman, Cohen, Fetter & Burstein, PC, 507 Plum St, Ste 300, Syracuse, NY, 13204. Tel: 315-471-8111, Ext 238. Fax: 315-425-3638. p. 1753

Powell, Rob, Network Adminr, Jefferson County Library, 5678 State Rd PP, High Ridge, MO, 63049-2216. Tel: 636-677-8689. Fax: 636-677-1769. p. 1331

Powell, Rose M, Cataloger, Syst Adminr, Southern University at Shreveport, 3050 Martin Luther King Jr Dr, Shreveport, LA, 71107. Tel: 318-670-6392. Fax: 318-674-3403. p. 970

Powell, Sara, Dir, Montezuma Township Library, 309 N Aztec, Montezuma, KS, 67867. Tel: 620-846-7032. Fax: 620-846-7032. p. 884

Powell, Shanise, Student Serv Librn, Bibliothèque Allard Regional Library, 104086 PTH 11, Saint Georges, MB, R0E 1V0, CANADA. Tel: 204-367-8443. Fax: 204-367-1780. p. 2751

Powell, Stacie, Youth Serv Librn, Oconee County Public Library, 501 W South Broad St, Walhalla, SC, 29691. Tel: 864-638-4133. Fax: 864-638-4132. p. 2207

Powell, Steve, Br Mgr, Cobb County Public Library System, West Cobb Regional, 1750 Dennis Kemp Lane, Kennesaw, GA, 30152. Tel: 770-528-4699. Fax: 770-528-4619. p. 543

Powell, Tracy, Per, Emory University Libraries, Pitts Theology Library, Candler School of Theology, 505 S Kilgo Circle NE, Atlanta, GA, 30322-2810. Tel: 404-727-4166. Fax: 404-727-1219. p. 514

Powelson, Susan, Dir, Health Sci Libr, University of Calgary Library, Health Sciences Library, Health Sci Ctr, 3330 Hospital Dr NW, Calgary, AB, T2N 4N1, CANADA. Tel: 403-220-6858. Fax: 403-210-9847. p. 2693

Power, Becky, Acq, Texas A&M University-Texarkana, 7101 University Ave, Texarkana, TX, 75503. Tel: 903-223-3089. Fax: 903-334-6695. p. 2392

Power, Jean, Asst Librn, Stamford Village Library, 117 Main St, Stamford, NY, 12167. Tel: 607-652-5001. Fax: 607-652-5001. p. 1747

Power, June, Access Serv Librn, University of North Carolina at Pembroke, Faculty Row, Pembroke, NC, 28372. Tel: 910-521-6516. Fax: 910-521-6547. p. 1814

Power, Marlene, Pub Serv Librn, Redeemer College Library, 777 Garner Rd E, Ancaster, ON, L9K 1J4, CANADA. Tel: 905-648-2131. Fax: 905-648-2134. p. 2792

Power, Mary Alice, Ref Librn, Lawrence Technological University Library, 21000 W Ten Mile Rd, Southfield, MI, 48075-1058. Tel: 248-204-3000. Fax: 248-204-3005. p. 1228

Power, Michael, Libr Tech II, College of the North Atlantic, Baie Verte Campus, One Terranova Rd, Baie Verte, NL, A0K 1B0, CANADA. Tel: 709-532-8066. Fax: 709-532-4624. p. 2771

Power, P Paul, Mgr, Lockheed Martin Corp, 700 N Frederick Ave, Gaithersburg, MD, 20879. Tel: 301-240-5500. Fax: 301-240-6855. p. 1030

Power Taylor, Anita, Libr Tech, Department of Justice, East Block, Confederation Bldg, 5th Flr, 100 Prince Philip Dr, St. John's, NL, A1B 4J6, CANADA. Tel: 709-729-2912. Fax: 709-729-1370. p. 2772

Power, William R, Pres, Peabody Historical Society & Museum, 35 Washington St, Peabody, MA, 01960-5520. Tel: 978-531-0805. Fax: 978-531-7292. p. 1116

Powers, Andi, Dir, City of Wolfforth Library, 508 E Hwy 62-82, Wolfforth, TX, 79382-7001. Tel: 806-866-9280. Fax: 806-833-6932. p. 2401

Powers, Angela, Dir, Webster-Addison Public Library, 331 S Main St, Webster Springs, WV, 26288. Tel: 304-847-5764. Fax: 304-847-5764. p. 2573

Powers, Ann M, Dir, Reeseville Public Library, 216 S Main St, Reeseville, WI, 53579. Tel: 920-927-7390. Fax: 920-927-7390. p. 2633

Powers, Anne, Ref, Santa Monica College Library, 1900 Pico Blvd, Santa Monica, CA, 90405-1628. Tel: 310-434-4334, 310-434-4692. Fax: 310-434-4387. p. 266

Powers, Anne, Tech Coordr, Volusia County Public Library, 1290 Indian Lake Rd, Daytona Beach, FL, 32124. Tel: 386-248-1745. Fax: 386-248-1746. p. 436

Powers, Anne, Info & Educ Serv Librn/Pub Serv, Duke University Libraries, Medical Center Library, DUMC Box 3702, Ten Bryan-Searle Dr, Durham, NC, 27710-0001. Tel: 919-660-1128. Fax: 919-681-7599. p. 1788

Powers, Anthony E, Br Mgr, Chicago Public Library, Austin-Irving, 6100 W Irving Park Rd, Chicago, IL, 60634. Tel: 312-744-6222. Fax: 312-744-0059. p. 608

Powers, Carla, Libr Mgr, Duluth Public Library, 520 W Superior St, Duluth, MN, 55802. Tel: 218-730-4225. Fax: 218-723-3815, 218-723-3822. p. 1247

Powers, Carolyn T, Dir, Falmouth Historical Society, Palmer Ave at the Village Green, Falmouth, MA, 02541. Tel: 508-548-4857. Fax: 508-540-0968. p. 1088

Powers, Catherine, Head of Libr, Kuskokwim Consortium Library, 420 State Hwy, Bethel, AK, 99559. Tel: 907-543-4516. Fax: 907-543-4503. p. 46

Powers, Charles V, Jr, Dir, Queen Anne's County Free Library, 121 S Commerce St, Centreville, MD, 21617. Tel: 410-758-0980. Fax: 410-758-0614. p. 1023

Powers, Christine, Dir, Naples Public Library, 940 Roosevelt Trail, Naples, ME, 04055. Tel: 207-693-6841. Fax: 207-693-7098. p. 992

Powers, Clair, Electronic Res & Instruction Librn, Phillips Theological Seminary Library, 901 N Mingo Rd, Tulsa, OK, 74116. Tel: 918-270-6431. Fax: 918-270-6490. p. 1982

Powers, Donna, Dir, Fair Haven Library, 748 River Rd, Fair Haven, NJ, 07704. Tel: 732-747-5031, Ext 220. Fax: 732-747-6962. p. 1485

Powers, Geraldine, Dir, Burkley Library & Resource Center, 208 E Fillmore St, Dewitt, NE, 68341. Tel: 402-683-2145. Fax: 402-683-2145. p. 1397

Powers, Heidi, Supvr, Deschutes Public Library District, Sunriver Area Branch, 56855 Venture Lane, Sunriver, OR, 97707. Tel: 541-312-1080. Fax: 541-593-9286. p. 1992

Powers, Karen Mohr, Chief Financial Officer, Rockford Public Library, 215 N Wyman St, Rockford, IL, 61101-1023. Tel: 815-965-7606. Fax: 815-965-0866. p. 697

Powers, Kathleen, Asst Dir, Wayland Free Public Library, Five Concord Rd, Wayland, MA, 01778. Tel: 508-358-2311. Fax: 508-358-5249. p. 1134

Powers, Laurel, Br Mgr, Live Oak Public Libraries, Tybee Island Branch, 403 Butler Ave, Tybee Island, GA, 31328. Tel: 912-786-7733. Fax: 912-786-7734. p. 550

Powers, Lindsey, Asst Librn, Phoenix Art Museum Library, 1625 N Central Ave, Phoenix, AZ, 85004-1685. Tel: 602-257-2136. Fax: 602-253-8662. p. 75

Powers, Martha, Pub Serv, Ohoopee Regional Library System, 610 Jackson St, Vidalia, GA, 30474-2835. Tel: 912-537-9283. Fax: 912-537-3735. p. 555

Powers, Mary Janice, Librn, Moraine Park Technical College Library, 700 Gould St, Beaver Dam, WI, 53916-1994. Tel: 920-887-4406. Fax: 920-887-4473. p. 2581

Powers, Nancy, Br Mgr, Atlanta-Fulton Public Library System, Buckhead Library, 269 Buckhead Ave NE, Atlanta, GA, 30305. Tel: 404-814-3500. Fax: 404-814-3503. p. 511

Powers, Priscilla, Mgr, Libr Syst & Serv, Dowling College Library, 150 Idle Hour Blvd, Oakdale, NY, 11769-1999. Tel: 631-244-3280. Fax: 631-244-3374. p. 1709

Powers, Robert, Mgr, Libr & Archives, California Institute of Technology, 4800 Oak Grove Dr, MS 111-113, Pasadena, CA, 91109-8099. Tel: 818-354-9263. Fax: 818-393-6752. p. 206

Powers, Rosanne, In Charge, Florida Department of Corrections, 16415 Spring Hill Dr, Brooksville, FL, 34604-8167. Tel: 352-754-6715, Ext 169. Fax: 352-544-2307. p. 430

Powers, Rosanne, Libr Tech, Florida Department of Corrections, 9544 CR 476B, Bushnell, FL, 33513. Tel: 352-793-2525, Ext 6161. Fax: 352-793-3542. p. 431

Powers, Sheran, ILL, Fort Hays State University, 600 Park St, Hays, KS, 67601-4099. Tel: 785-628-4431. Fax: 785-628-4096. p. 871

Powers, Sylvia, Br Mgr, Harris County Public Library, Maud Smith Marks Branch, 1815 Westgreen Blvd, Katy, TX, 77450. Tel: 281-492-8592. Fax: 281-492-3420. p. 2336

Powers, Theresa, Dir, Lincoln Park Public Library, 1381 Southfield Rd, Lincoln Park, MI, 48146. Tel: 313-381-0374. Fax: 313-381-2205. p. 1203

Powers, Theresa, Dir, Taylor Community Library, 12303 Pardee Rd, Taylor, MI, 48180-4219. Tel: 734-287-4840. Fax: 734-287-4141. p. 1230

Powers, Vicki L, Librn, Eula & David Wintermann Library, 101 N Walnut Ave, Eagle Lake, TX, 77434. Tel: 979-234-5411. Fax: 979-234-5442. p. 2314

Powers-Nosal, Martha, Libr Tech, Colorado Department of Corrections, Colorado Women's Correctional Facility Library, 3800 Grandview Ave, Canon City, CO, 81212. Tel: 719-269-4707, Ext 3818. Fax: 719-269-4716. p. 293

Powers-Schaub, Gail, Libr Dir, Baker College of Muskegon Library, 1903 Marquette Ave, Muskegon, MI, 49442-3404. Tel: 231-777-5331. Fax: 231-777-5334. p. 1212

Powis, Katherine, Librn, Horticultural Society of New York, Inc Library, 148 W 37th St, 13th Flr, New York, NY, 10018. Tel: 212-757-0915, Ext 109. Fax: 212-246-1207. p. 1681

Poworoznek, Emily L, Librn, University of New Hampshire Library, Engineering, Mathematics & Computer Science, Kingsbury Hall, 33 Academic Way, Durham, NH, 03824. Tel: 603-862-4168. Fax: 603-862-4112. p. 1446

Poworoznek, Emily LeViness, Librn, University of New Hampshire Library, Chemistry, Parsons Hall, 23 College Rd, Durham, NH, 03824-3598. Tel: 603-862-4168. Fax: 603-862-4278. p. 1446

Poworoznek, Emily LeViness, Librn, University of New Hampshire Library, David G Clark Memorial Physics Library, DeMeritt Hall, Nine Library Way, Durham, NH, 03824-3568. Tel: 603-862-2348. Fax: 603-862-2998. p. 1446

Poyer, Bob, Asst Dir, Pub Serv, Educ Serv, Medical University of South Carolina Library, 171 Ashley Ave, Ste 300, Charleston, SC, 29425-0001. Tel: 843-792-9211. Fax: 843-792-7947. p. 2184

Poyer, Helen, Dir, Cobb County Public Library System, 266 Roswell St, Marietta, GA, 30060-2004. Tel: 770-528-2324. Fax: 770-528-2349. p. 542

Poyer, Jill, Libr Dir, McMinnville Public Library, 225 NW Adams St, McMinnville, OR, 97128-5425. Tel: 503-435-5562. Fax: 503-435-5560. p. 2005

Poynor, Lauryn, Coll Develop Mgr, Mobile Public Library, 700 Government St, Mobile, AL, 36602. Tel: 251-208-7106. Fax: 251-208-5865. p. 25

Poyser, Linda, Librn, Vankleek Hill Public Library, 94 Main St E, VanKleek Hill, ON, K0B 1R0, CANADA. Tel: 613-678-2216. Fax: 613-678-2216. p. 2868

Pozdol, Joseph, Info Spec, University of Southern California Libraries, Norris Medical Library, 2003 Zonal Ave, Los Angeles, CA, 90089-9130. Tel: 323-442-1121. Fax: 323-221-1235. p. 179

Pozyck, Alan, Ch, Stanly County Public Library, 133 E Main St, Albemarle, NC, 28001. Tel: 704-986-3759. Fax: 704-983-6713. p. 1773

Pozzebon, Mary Ellen, Electronic Res Librn, Middle Tennessee State University, MTSU, PO Box 13, Murfreesboro, TN, 37132. Tel: 615-898-2526. p. 2254

Prabhakar, Padmini, YA Serv, Cerritos Library, 18025 Bloomfield Ave, Cerritos, CA, 90703. Tel: 562-916-1350. Fax: 562-916-1375. p. 133

Pradhan, Pramod, Asst Commun Librn, Hartford Public Library, Mark Twain Branch, 256 Farmington Ave, Hartford, CT, 06105. Tel: 860-695-7540. Fax: 860-722-6877. p. 346

Prado, Candi, Mgr, Heald College, 1450 N Main St, Salinas, CA, 93906. Tel: 831-443-1700. Fax: 831-444-4601. p. 226

Prado, Ralph, Librn, Reed Smith LLP, Law Library, 355 S Grand Ave, Ste 2900, Los Angeles, CA, 90017. Tel: 213-457-8000. Fax: 213-457-8080. p. 199

Prado-Guyer, Cynthia, Librn, University of Southern California Libraries, Asa V Call Law Library, 699 Exposition Blvd, LAW 202, MC 0072, Los Angeles, CA, 90089-0072. Tel: 213-740-6482. Fax: 213-740-7179. p. 179

Prager, Stephen, Br Mgr, Mobile Public Library, Moorer Spring Hill, Four McGregor Ave, Mobile, AL, 36608. Tel: 251-470-7770. Fax: 251-470-7774. p. 25

Prague, Janet, Ch, Needham Free Public Library, 1139 Highland Ave, Needham, MA, 02494-3298. Tel: 781-455-7559, Fax: 781-455-7591. p. 1108

Prasad, Wendy, Sr Librn, Tampa-Hillsborough County Public Library System, West Tampa Branch, 2312 W Union St, Tampa, FL, 33607-3423. Fax: 813-276-8264. p. 498

Prasher, Janet, Assoc Dir, Fairfax County Public Library, 12000 Government Center Pkwy, Ste 324, Fairfax, VA, 22035-0012. Tel: 703-324-3100. Fax: 703-324-8365. p. 2461

Prasifka, Jeanette, Med Librn, Texas Health Presbyterian Hospital Library, 820 Walnut Hill Lane, Dallas, TX, 75231. Tel: 214-345-2310. Fax: 214-345-2350. p. 2311

Prasse, Karen, Ref Librn, Burlington Public Library, 820 E Washington, Burlington, WA, 98233. Tel: 360-755-0760. Fax: 360-755-0717. p. 2511

Prather, Beth, Librn, Coke County Library, 706 Austin St, Robert Lee, TX, 76945. Tel: 325-453-2495. p. 2376

Prather, Cindy, Tech Serv, Conneaut Public Library, 304 Buffalo St, Conneaut, OH, 44030-2658. Tel: 440-593-1608. Fax: 440-593-4470. p. 1891

Prather, David, Ch, Lee County Library, 219 N Madison St, Tupelo, MS, 38804-3899. Tel: 662-841-9027. Fax: 662-840-7615. p. 1316

Prather, Emily, Tech Serv Coordr, North Central College, 320 E School St, Naperville, IL, 60540. Tel: 630-637-5709. Fax: 630-637-5716. p. 679

Prather, Terry B, Br Mgr, Cabarrus County Public Library, Kannapolis Branch, 850 Mountain St, Kannapolis, NC, 28081. Tel: 704-920-1180. Fax: 704-938-3512. p. 1785

Pratt, Carolyn A, Librn, Mitchell Silberberg & Knupp LLP, 11377 W Olympic Blvd, Los Angeles, CA, 90064-1683. Tel: 310-312-2000. Fax: 310-312-3100. p. 175

Pratt, Estina, Ref Serv, Compton Community College Library, 1111 E Artesia Blvd, Compton, CA, 90221. Tel: 310-900-1600, Ext 2175. Fax: 310-900-1693. p. 136

Pratt, Greg, Sr Info Spec, University of Texas, M D Anderson Cancer Center Research Medical Library, 1400 Pressler St, Houston, TX, 77030-3722. Tel: 713-745-5156. Fax: 713-563-3650. p. 2344

Pratt, Hal, Dir, Bloomsburg Public Library, 225 Market St, Bloomsburg, PA, 17815-1726. Tel: 570-784-0883. Fax: 570-784-8541. p. 2035

Pratt, Heather, Libr Coordr, Alberta Law Libraries - High Prairie, Courthouse, 4911-53 Ave, High Prairie, AB, T0G 1E0, CANADA. Tel: 780-523-6600. Fax: 780-523-6643. p. 2706

Pratt, Jennifer, Libr Develop Section Chief, State Library of North Carolina, 109 E Jones St, Raleigh, NC, 27601. Tel: 919-807-7415. Fax: 919-733-8748. p. 1817

Pratt, Jere, Circ, Lewis-Clark State College Library, 500 Eighth Ave, Lewiston, ID, 83501. Tel: 208-792-2833. Fax: 208-792-2831. p. 578

Pratt, Jill, Ch, Greensburg-Decatur County Public Library, 1110 E Main St, Greensburg, IN, 47240. Tel: 812-663-2826. Fax: 812-663-5617. p. 746

Pratt, Kathleen, Ref, Cotuit Library, 871 Main St, Cotuit, MA, 02635. Tel: 508-428-8141. Fax: 508-428-4636. p. 1083

Pratt, Mary Lou, Ref, Cabell County Public Library, 455 Ninth Street Plaza, Huntington, WV, 25701. Tel: 304-528-5700. Fax: 304-528-5701. p. 2561

Pratt, Michele, Dir, Baker College of Auburn Hills Library, 1500 University Dr, Auburn Hills, MI, 48326-2642. Tel: 248-276-8223. Fax: 248-340-0607. p. 1154

Pratt, Sandy, Dep Dir, Ref Serv, Tech Serv, Coeur d'Alene Public Library, 702 E Front Ave, Coeur d'Alene, ID, 83814-2373. Tel: 208-769-2315. Fax: 208-769-2381. p. 573

Pratt, Stephenie, Librn, Southwestern Illinois Metropolitan & Regional Planning Commission, 2511 Vandalia St, Collinsville, IL, 62234. Tel: 618-344-4250, Ext 119. Fax: 618-344-4253. p. 631

Pratt, Susan, Dir, Milford Memorial Library, 1009 Ninth St, Ste 5, Milford, IA, 51351. Tel: 712-338-4643. Fax: 712-338-4859. p. 832

Pratt, Tracey, Ser, Springfield Town Library, 43 Main St, Springfield, VT, 05156. Tel: 802-885-3108. Fax: 802-885-4906. p. 2436

Pratt, Wanda, Assoc Prof, University of Washington, Mary Gates Hall, Ste 370, Campus Box 352840, Seattle, WA, 98195-2840. Tel: 206-685-9937. Fax: 206-616-3152. p. 2976

Pravata, Richard, Ref, Baker & Botts LLP, One Shell Plaza, 910 Louisiana St, Houston, TX, 77002. Tel: 713-229-1643, Fax: 713-229-1522. p. 2334

Pray, Lou, Dir, Lopez Island Library, 2265 Fisherman Bay Rd, Lopez Island, WA, 98261. Tel: 360-468-2265. Fax: 360-468-3850. p. 2520

Prazak, Catherine, Librn, Castroville Public Library, 802 London St, Castroville, TX, 78009. Tel: 830-931-4095. Fax: 830-931-9050. p. 2295

Prchal, Laurel, Br Mgr, Jackson County Library Services, Talent Branch, 101 Home St, Talent, OR, 97540. Tel: 541-535-4163. Fax: 541-535-4163. p. 2005

Prechel, Amelia, Electronic Serv Librn, Illinois College of Optometry Library, 3241 S Michigan Ave, Chicago, IL, 60616-3878. Tel: 312-949-7160. Fax: 312-949-7337. p. 614

Prechtel, Karyn, Dep Dir, Pima County Public Library, 101 N Stone Ave, Tucson, AZ, 85701. Tel: 520-564-5600. Fax: 520-594-5621. p. 86

Preece, Barbara T, Dean of Libr, California State University, 333 S Twin Oaks Valley Rd, San Marcos, CA, 92096-0001. Tel: 760-750-4350. Fax: 760-750-3287. p. 254

Preece, Jennifer, Dr, Dean, University of Maryland, 4105 Hornbake Bldg, College Park, MD, 20742-4345. Tel: 301-405-2033. Fax: 301-314-9145. p. 2967

Preece, Kerry, Head, Youth Serv, McMillan Memorial Library, 490 E Grand Ave, Wisconsin Rapids, WI, 54494-4898. Tel: 715-423-1040. Fax: 715-423-2665. p. 2650

Preece, Susan M, Dir, Topsham Public Library, 25 Foreside Rd, Topsham, ME, 04086. Tel: 207-725-1727. Fax: 207-725-1735. p. 1003

Prefontaine, Gabrielle, Archivist, University of Winnipeg Library, 515 Portage Ave, Winnipeg, MB, R3B 2E9, CANADA. Tel: 204-786-9914. Fax: 204-783-8910. p. 2759

Préfontaine, Marie-Jeanne, Dir, Coll Develop, Universite du Quebec a Montreal Bibliotheque, CP 8889 Succ Centre-Ville, Montreal, QC, H3C 3P3, CANADA. Tel: 514-987-3824. Fax: 514-987-3542. p. 2902

Preilis, Wendy, Adult Learning Ctr Spec, Johnson County Public Library, 401 State St, Franklin, IN, 46131-2545. Tel: 317-738-4677. Fax: 317-738-9635. p. 744

Prein, Tom, Coll Develop Librn, Mesa Community College Library, 1833 W Southern Ave, Mesa, AZ, 85202. Tel: 480-461-7675. Fax: 480-461-7681. p. 68

Preiss, Kathleen, Dir, Ontonagon Township Library, Rockland Township, 40 National Ave, Rockland, MI, 49960. Tel: 906-886-2821. Fax: 906-886-2821. p. 1215

Preiss, Margaret, Coordr, Children's Res & Mkt, Saint Charles City County Library District, 77 Boone Hills Dr, Saint Peters, MO, 63376-0529. Tel: 636-441-2300. Fax: 636-441-3132. p. 1363

Prellwitz, Andrew R, Asst Librn, Chair, Libr Serv, User Serv, Ripon College, 300 Seward St, Ripon, WI, 54971. Tel: 920-748-8175. Fax: 920-748-7243. p. 2634

Prendergast, Faye, Br Mgr, Saint Tammany Parish Library, Causeway Branch, 3457 Hwy 190, Mandeville, LA, 70471. Tel: 985-626-9779. Fax: 985-626-9783. p. 948

Prendergast, Kerry, Dir, Wildlife Conservation Society Library, 2300 Southern Blvd, Bronx, NY, 10460. Tel: 718-220-6874. p. 1588

Prendergast, Kevin, ILL, Ref, Montclair State University, One Normal Ave, Montclair, NJ, 07043-1699. Tel: 973-655-7143. Fax: 973-655-7780. p. 1503

Prendergast, Neville, Dir, Tulane University, Rudolph Matas Library of the Health Sciences, Tulane Health Sciences Campus, 1430 Tulane Ave, SL-86, New Orleans, LA, 70112-2699. Tel: 504-988-2060. Fax: 504-988-7417. p. 963

Prendergast, Neville, Assoc Dir, Health Info Res, Washington University Libraries, Bernard Becker Medical Library, 660 S Euclid Ave, Campus Box 8132, Saint Louis, MO, 63110. Tel: 314-362-2782. Fax: 314-454-6606. p. 1362

Prenger, Becky, Mgr, Auglaize County Public District Library, Francis J Stallo Memorial, 196 E Fourth St, Minster, OH, 45865. Tel: 419-628-2925. Fax: 419-628-4556. p. 1944

Prenger, Marianne, Librn, Saint Joseph Medical Center, 7601 Osler Dr, Towson, MD, 21204. Tel: 410-337-1210. Fax: 410-337-1116. p. 1045

Prennace, Jenny, In Charge, US Geological Survey Library, 2255 N Gemini Dr, Flagstaff, AZ, 86001. Tel: 928-556-7272. Fax: 928-556-7237. p. 63

Prenovost, David, Media Spec, Green River Community College, 12401 SE 320th St, Auburn, WA, 98092-3699. Tel: 253-833-9111, Ext 2109. Fax: 253-288-3436, 253-288-3491. p. 2507

Prentice, Katie, Head, Educ & Info Serv, University of Texas Health Science Center at San Antonio Libraries, 7703 Floyd Curl Dr, MSC 7940, San Antonio, TX, 78229-3900. Tel: 210-567-2400. Fax: 210-567-2490. p. 2383

Prescott, Barbara, Chairperson, Edson Public Library, 4726-8 Avenue, Edson, AB, T7E 1S8, CANADA. Tel: 780-723-6691. Fax: 780-723-9728. p. 2703

Prescott, Joan C, Dir, Rogers Free Library, 525 Hope St, Bristol, RI, 02809. Tel: 401-253-6948. Fax: 401-253-5270. p. 2164

Prescott, Martha, Librn, Berkshire Medical Center, 725 North St, Pittsfield, MA, 01201. Tel: 413-447-2734. p. 1117

Prescott, Patricia M, Dir, Webb Institute, 298 Crescent Beach Rd, Glen Cove, NY, 11542-1398. Tel: 516-671-0439. Fax: 516-674-9838. p. 1628

Prescott, Valerie, Tech Serv, Herkimer County Community College Library, 100 Reservoir Rd, Herkimer, NY, 13350. Tel: 315-866-0300, Ext 8270. Fax: 315-866-1806. p. 1635

Preslar, Gail, Info Spec, Eastman Chemical Co, Business Library, Bldg 280, Lincoln St, Kingsport, TN, 37662-5280. Tel: 423-229-6117. Fax: 423-224-0111. p. 2240

Preslar, Gail, Librn, Eastman Chemical Co, Bldg 150B, PO Box 1972, Kingsport, TN, 37662-5150. Tel: 423-229-1845. Fax: 423-229-6114. p. 2240

Presler, Renita, Br Mgr, Martin County Library System, Indiantown Branch, 15200 SW Adams Ave, Indiantown, FL, 34956. Tel: 772-597-4200. Fax: 772-597-3637. p. 492

Presley, Beverly, Librn, Clark University, 950 Main St, Worcester, MA, 01610-1477. Tel: 508-793-7706. Fax: 508-793-8871. p. 1143

Presley, Beverly, Librn, Clark University, Guy H Burnham Map & Aerial Photography Library, 950 Main St, Worcester, MA, 01610-1477. Tel: 508-793-7706. Fax: 508-793-8881. p. 1143

Presley, Michele, Dir, Addison Township Public Library, 1440 Rochester Rd, Leonard, MI, 48367-3555. Tel: 248-628-7180. Fax: 248-628-6109. p. 1203

Preslock, Karen, Paulding Campus Librn, Chattahoochee Technical College Library, 980 S Cobb Dr SE, Marietta, GA, 30060-3300. Tel: 770-443-3630. Fax: 770-528-4454. p. 542

Presnell, Laura, Librn, Haywood County Public Library, Fines Creek, Fines Creek Community Bldg, 190 Fines Creek Rd, Clyde, NC, 28721. Tel: 828-627-0146. p. 1829

Pressey, Kathy, Asst Librn, Pittsfield Public Library, 205 N Memorial, Pittsfield, IL, 62363-1406. Tel: 217-285-2200. Fax: 217-285-9423. p. 691

Pressley, Gary James, Br Librn, Graham County Public Library, 80 Knight St, Robbinsville, NC, 28771. Tel: 828-479-8796. Fax: 828-479-3156. p. 1820

Pressley, Marla, Access Serv Asst, ILL, Wingate University, PO Box 219, Wingate, NC, 28174-1202. Tel: 704-233-8089. Fax: 704-233-8254. p. 1832

Pressman Levy, Nancy, Head of Libr, Princeton University, Donald E Stokes Library - Public & International Affairs & Population Research, Wallace Hall, Princeton, NJ, 08544. Tel: 609-258-4782. Fax: 609-258-6844. p. 1524

Presswood, Charlotte, Assoc Librn, Lees-McRae College, 191 Main St W, Banner Elk, NC, 28604-9238. Tel: 828-898-8727. Fax: 828-898-8710. p. 1775

Prest, Loring, Chairperson, Electronic Res Librn, Webmaster, California University of Pennsylvania, 250 University Ave, California, PA, 15419-1394. Tel: 724-938-5769. Fax: 724-938-5901. p. 2040

Prest, Stacy, Libr Supvr-Popular Libr, Walla Walla Community College Library, 500 Tausick Way, Walla Walla, WA, 99362-9267. Tel: 509-527-4294. Fax: 509-527-4480. p. 2547

Prestamo, Anne M, Dr, Assoc Dean, Libr for Coll & Tech Serv, Oklahoma State University Libraries, Oklahoma State University, Athletic Ave, Stillwater, OK, 74078-1071. Tel: 405-744-9755. Fax: 405-744-5183. p. 1978

Prestia, Laura, YA Spec, Albany County Public Library, 310 S Eighth St, Laramie, WY, 82070-3969. Tel: 307-721-2580. Fax: 307-721-2584. p. 2657

Prestinary, Patricia, Librn, Smith Group, Inc, 301 Battery St, San Francisco, CA, 94111-3203. Tel: 415-227-0100. Fax: 415-495-5091. p. 247

Preston, Deana, In Charge, New York State Office of Parks Recreation & Historic Preservation, 312 Fair St, Kingston, NY, 12401-3836. Tel: 845-338-2786. Fax: 845-334-8173. p. 1650

Preston, Elizabeth, Librn, Christ Episcopal Church Library, 1412 Providence Rd, Charlotte, NC, 28207. Tel: 704-333-0378. Fax: 704-333-8420. p. 1783

Preston, Jim, Dir, Moody Bible Institute, 820 N La Salle Blvd, Chicago, IL, 60610-3284. Tel: 312-329-4136. Fax: 312-329-8959. p. 619

Preston, Karen, Electronic Res Librn, Life University, 1269 Barclay Circle, Marietta, GA, 30060. Tel: 770-426-2690. Fax: 770-426-2745. p. 543

Preston, Leslie, Head, Acq, Fashion Institute of Technology-SUNY, Seventh Ave at 27th St, New York, NY, 10001-5992. Tel: 212-217-4346. Fax: 212-217-4371. p. 1678

Preston, Margaret, Ref Librn, New Hartford Public Library, Two Library Lane, New Hartford, NY, 13413-2815. Tel: 315-733-1535. Fax: 315-733-0795. p. 1665

Preston, Marie, Libr Tech, North Carolina Central University, School of Library & Information Sciences, James E Shepard Memorial Library, 3rd Flr, 1801 Fayetteville St, Durham, NC, 27707. Tel: 919-530-6400. Fax: 919-530-6402. p. 1789

Preston, Michelle, Dir, Canmore Public Library, 950 Eighth Ave, Canmore, AB, T1W 2T1, CANADA. Tel: 403-678-2468. Fax: 403-678-2165. p. 2694

Preston, Norma, Librn Supvr, Lorain Public Library System, South Lorain, 2121 Homewood Dr, Lorain, OH, 44055. Tel: 440-277-5672. Fax: 440-277-5727. p. 1911

Preston, Patrick, Human Res Mgr, Sonoma County Library, 211 E St, Santa Rosa, CA, 95404. Tel: 707-545-0831. Fax: 707-575-0437. p. 267

Preston, Pauline, Br Head, Vancouver Public Library, Outreach Services, 345 Robson St, Ste 302, Vancouver, BC, V6B 6B3, CANADA. Tel: 604-331-4100. Fax: 604-331-4101. p. 2744

Preston, Steve, Dir, Amherst County Public Library, 382 S Main St, Amherst, VA, 24521. Tel: 434-946-9488. Fax: 434-946-9348. p. 2447

Preston, Steve, Dir, Amherst County Public Library, Madison Heights Branch, 200 River James Shopping Ctr, Madison Heights, VA, 24572. Tel: 434-846-8171. Fax: 434-846-3102. p. 2447

Preston, Tatum, Adminr, Birmingham Museum of Art, 2000 Eighth Ave N, Birmingham, AL, 35203-2278. Tel: 205-254-2982. Fax: 205-254-2710. p. 7

Presutti, Robert, Archivist, Emory University Libraries, Pitts Theology Library, Candler School of Theology, 505 S Kilgo Circle NE, Atlanta, GA, 30322-2810. Tel: 404-727-4166. Fax: 404-727-1219. p. 514

Preswood, Donese, Cat, Ref Serv, Lees-McRae College, 191 Main St W, Banner Elk, NC, 28604-9238. Tel: 828-898-8727. Fax: 828-898-8710. p. 1775

Prete, Mark R, Dr, VPres, Charlotte Hungerford Hospital, 540 Litchfield, Torrington, CT, 06790. Tel: 860-496-6434. p. 372

Pretlow, Cassi, Coll Develop, Aurora Public Library, 14949 E Alameda Pkwy, Aurora, CO, 80012. Tel: 303-739-6622. Fax: 303-739-6579. p. 288

Pretlow, Delores, Dr, Libr Dir, Virginia Union University, 1500 N Lombardy St, Richmond, VA, 23220. Tel: 804-257-5821. Fax: 804-257-5818. p. 2493

Pretorius, Fred, Dir, Info Serv, Mintz, Levin, Cohn, Ferris, Glovsky & Popeo, One Financial Ctr, Boston, MA, 02111. Tel: 617-542-6000, Ext 4852. Fax: 617-542-2241. p. 1064

Pretty, Darlene, Ch, Woodstock Public Library, 445 Hunter St, Woodstock, ON, N4S 4G7, CANADA. Tel: 519-539-4801. Fax: 519-539-5246. p. 2872

Pretz, Katy, Teen Serv, Citizens Library, 55 S College St, Washington, PA, 15301. Tel: 724-222-2400. Fax: 724-222-2606. p. 2151

Pretzer, Nannette, Dir, Saint Charles District Library, 104 W Spruce St, Saint Charles, MI, 48655-1238. Tel: 989-865-9371. Fax: 989-865-6666. p. 1224

Preudhomme, Gene, Librn, Supreme Court, Appellate Division, 27 Madison Ave, New York, NY, 10010. Tel: 212-340-0478. p. 1700

Preuit, Theresa, Assoc Dir, Coll Mgt, Assoc Dir, Pub Serv, Mercer University, Jack Tarver Library, 1300 Edgewood Ave, Macon, GA, 31207. Tel: 478-301-2960. Fax: 478-301-2111. p. 540

Preusz, Jan, Dir, New Castle-Henry County Public Library, 376 S 15th St, New Castle, IN, 47362-3205. Tel: 765-529-0362, Ext 301. Fax: 765-521-3581. p. 768

Prevedel, Amy, Literacy Prog Coordr, Oakland Public Library, Main Library, 125 14th St, Oakland, CA, 94612. Tel: 510-238-3134. Fax: 510-238-2232. p. 198

Previte, Colleen, Archivist, Spec Coll Librn, Framingham State College, 100 State St, Framingham, MA, 01701. Tel: 508-626-4648. Fax: 508-626-4649. p. 1090

Prevost, Gloria, Ch, Pawtucket Public Library, 13 Summer St, Pawtucket, RI, 02860. Tel: 401-725-3714. Fax: 401-728-2170. p. 2171

Prevost, S, Br Mgr, New Orleans Public Library, Central City Branch, 2405 Jackson Ave, Bldg C, Rm 235, New Orleans, LA, 70113. Tel: 504-596-3112. p. 962

Prew, Pauline, Librn, Diocesan Resource Center, 34 Fenner St, Providence, RI, 02903. Tel: 401-278-4646. Fax: 401-278-4645. p. 2172

Prewitt, Rickley, ILL, Arizona Western College & NAU Yuma Branch Campus, 2020 S Ave 8E, Yuma, AZ, 85366. Tel: 928-344-7777. Fax: 928-344-7751. p. 90

Prezeau, Helene, Tech Serv, Hospital Santa Cabrini, 5655 est Saint Zotique, Montreal, QC, H1T 1P7, CANADA. Tel: 514-252-6488. Fax: 514-252-6432. p. 2896

Preziosa, Theresa, Ch, Burlington County Library, Pemberton Community Library, 16 Broadway, Browns Mills, NJ, 08015. Tel: 609-893-8262. Fax: 609-893-7547. p. 1543

Pribbenow, Jon, Asst Dir, Rio Community Library, 324 W Lyons St, Rio, WI, 53960. Tel: 920-992-3206. Fax: 920-992-3983. p. 2634

Pribe, Liz, Librn, Rideau Lakes Public Library, Delta Branch, 18 King St, Unit 2, Delta, ON, K0E 1G0, CANADA. Tel: 613-928-2991. Fax: 613-928-2991. p. 2803

Pribyl, David, Head, Tech Serv, Roosevelt University, 430 S Michigan Ave, Chicago, IL, 60605. Tel: 312-341-3647. Fax: 312-341-2425. p. 623

Pribyl, David, Head, Tech Serv, Roosevelt University, Robert R McCormick Tribune Foundation Library, 1400 N Roosevelt Blvd, Schaumburg, IL, 60173. Tel: 847-619-7980. Fax: 847-619-7983. p. 623

Price, Anne, Head, Pub Serv, University of Mary Hardin-Baylor, 900 College St, UMHB Sta, Box 8016, Belton, TX, 76513-2599. Tel: 254-295-4639. Fax: 254-295-4642. p. 2289

Price, Arlisa, Dir, Forrest City Public Library, 421 S Washington, Forrest City, AR, 72335-3839. Tel: 870-633-5646. Fax: 870-633-5647. p. 100

Price, Barbara, Libr Coordr, Gloucester County Historical Society Library, 17 Hunter St, Woodbury, NJ, 08096-4605. Tel: 856-845-4771. Fax: 856-845-0131. p. 1545

Price, Carolyn, Br Mgr, Forsyth County Public Library, Clemmons Branch, 3554 Clemmons Rd, Old Hwy 158, Clemmons, NC, 27012. Tel: 336-703-2920. Fax: 336-712-4452. p. 1832

Price, Carolyn, Outreach Serv Librn, Washington County Public Library, 615 Fifth St, Marietta, OH, 45750-1973. Tel: 740-373-1057, Ext 230. p. 1913

Price, Celia, Syst Librn, University of Saint Francis, 201 Pope John Paul II Ctr, 2701 Spring St, Fort Wayne, IN, 46808. Tel: 260-399-7700, Ext 6066. Fax: 260-399-8166. p. 742

Price, Darlene, Dir, East Central Georgia Regional Library, 902 Greene St, Augusta, GA, 30901. Tel: 706-821-2600. Fax: 706-724-6762. p. 519

Price, Ellen, Cat, Sullivan County Public Library, 1655 Blountville Blvd, Blountville, TN, 37617. Tel: 423-279-2714. Fax: 423-279-2836. p. 2224

Price, Erin, Br Mgr, Winn Parish Library, Calvin Branch, 255 Second St, Calvin, LA, 71410. Tel: 318-727-9644. p. 972

Price, Jamie, Ref Serv, Jefferson College of Health Sciences, 920 S Jefferson St, Roanoke, VA, 24016. Tel: 540-985-4636. Fax: 540-224-4404. p. 2494

Price, Jan, Libr & Info Res Coordr, Metropolitan Council Library, 390 Robert St N, Saint Paul, MN, 55101. Tel: 651-602-1412. Fax: 651-602-1496. p. 1279

Price, Janet, Asst Dir, Head, Ref, Anderson County Library, 300 N McDuffie St, Anderson, SC, 29621-5643. Tel: 864-260-4500. Fax: 864-260-4510. p. 2180

Price, Janet, Dir, United States Air Force, FL 4803, 400 Shaw Dr, Shaw AFB, SC, 29152. Tel: 803-895-4518. Fax: 803-895-3961. p. 2204

Price, Jason, Head, Bibliog Access Serv, Claremont Colleges Library, 800 Dartmouth Ave, Claremont, CA, 91711. Tel: 909-621-8014. p. 134

Price, Jason, Libr Dir, Frank Phillips College, 1301 Roosevelt St, Borger, TX, 79008. Tel: 806-457-4200, Ext 787. Fax: 806-457-4230. p. 2290

Price, Jeanne Frazier, Dir, University of Nevada, Las Vegas Libraries, Wiener-Rogers Law Library, William S Boyd School of Law, 4505 Maryland Pkwy, Las Vegas, NV, 89154-1080. Tel: 702-895-2404. Fax: 702-895-2410. p. 1431

Price, Judith A, Mgr, Public Service Enterprise Group, 80 Park Plaza, Mailcode P3C, Newark, NJ, 07101. Tel: 973-430-7332, Ext 5633. Fax: 973-802-1054. p. 1512

Price, Kathy, Ch, Olean Public Library, 134 N Second St, Olean, NY, 14760-2583. Tel: 716-372-0200. Fax: 716-372-8651. p. 1710

Price, Kay, Circ Mgr, ILL, Phoenixville Public Library, 183 Second Ave, Phoenixville, PA, 19460-3420. Tel: 610-933-3013, Ext 22. Fax: 610-933-4338. p. 2120

Price, Larry, Br Adminr, Nashville Public Library, 615 Church St, Nashville, TN, 37219-2314. Tel: 615-862-5760. Fax: 615-862-5771. p. 2257

Price, Leah, Br Mgr, Oconee County Public Library, Westminster Branch, 112 W North Ave, Westminster, SC, 29693. Tel: 864-647-3215. Fax: 864-647-3233. p. 2207

Price, Leslie, Librn, Cold Lake Public Library, 5513-B 48th Ave, Cold Lake, AB, T9M 1X9, CANADA. Tel: 780-594-5101. Fax: 780-594-7787. p. 2695

Price, M Loretta, Acq, University of Tennessee, Taylor Law Center, 1505 W Cumberland Ave, Knoxville, TN, 37996-1800. Tel: 865-974-9746. Fax: 865-974-6571, 865-974-6595. p. 2243

Price, Marcy, Dir, South Bannock Library District, 18 N Main St, Downey, ID, 83234. Tel: 208-897-5270. Fax: 208-897-5270. p. 573

Price, Marcy, Dir, South Bannock Library District, Lava Hot Springs Branch, 33 E Main St, Lava Hot Springs, ID, 83246-9999. Tel: 208-776-5301. Fax: 208-776-5301. p. 573

Price, Margo, Info Res, Talisman Energy Inc, 2000, 888 Third St SW, Calgary, AB, T2P 5C5, CANADA. Tel: 403-237-1429. Fax: 403-231-2823. p. 2693

Price, Marjorie, Librn, United States Courts Library, US Court House, 300 Virginia St E, Rm 7400, Charleston, WV, 25301. Tel: 304-347-3420. Fax: 304-347-3423. p. 2556

Price, Mary, Circ Mgr, Oklahoma Baptist University, 500 W University, OBU Box 61310, Shawnee, OK, 74804-2504. Tel: 405-878-2264. Fax: 405-878-2256. p. 1977

Price, MaryJo, Spec Coll Librn, Frostburg State University, One Stadium Dr, Frostburg, MD, 21532. Tel: 301-687-4889. Fax: 301-687-7069. p. 1029

Price, Michael, Dir, Peterborough Town Library, Two Concord St, Peterborough, NH, 03458. Tel: 603-924-8040. Fax: 603-924-8041. p. 1462

Price, Michelle, Outreach & Spec Coll Librn, Saint John Fisher College, 3690 East Ave, Rochester, NY, 14618-3599. Tel: 585-899-3743. Fax: 585-385-8445. p. 1732

Price, Nancy, Mgr, Brunswick County Library, 109 W Moore St, Southport, NC, 28461. Tel: 910-457-6237. p. 1824

Price, Nikol, Div Chair, Estrella Mountain Community College Library, 3000 N Dysart Rd, Avondale, AZ, 85323-1000. Tel: 623-935-8191. Fax: 623-935-8060. p. 57

Price, Pam, Syst Adminr, Albemarle Regional Library, 303 W Tryon St, Winton, NC, 27986. Tel: 252-358-7864. Fax: 252-358-7868. p. 1835

Price, Pamela A, Dir, Libr Serv, Mercer County Community College Library, 1200 Old Trenton Rd, West Windsor, NJ, 08550. Tel: 609-570-3562. Fax: 609-570-3845. p. 1542

Price, Randy, Circ, Marshall University Libraries, Joan C Edwards School of Medicine Health Science Libraries, 1600 Medical Center Dr, Ste 2400, Huntington, WV, 25701-3655. Tel: 304-691-1750. Fax: 304-691-1766. p. 2562

Price, Rebecca, Librn, University of Michigan, Art, Architecture & Engineering Library, Duderstadt Ctr, 2281 Bonnisteel Blvd, Ann Arbor, MI, 48109-2094. Tel: 734-647-5747. Fax: 734-764-4487. p. 1152

Price, Sandra, Libr Asst, Davis College, 4747 Monroe St, Toledo, OH, 43623. Tel: 419-473-2700. Fax: 419-473-2472. p. 1939

Price, Saondra, Dir, Library at Cedar Creek Lake, 410 E Cedar Creek Pkwy, Seven Points, TX, 75143-8397. Tel: 903-432-4185. Fax: 903-432-4108. p. 2386

Price, Sharon, Tech Serv Mgr, L E Phillips Memorial Public Library, 400 Eau Claire St, Eau Claire, WI, 54701. Tel: 715-839-1647. Fax: 715-839-5310. p. 2590

Price, Sheryl, Chief Exec Officer, Librn, Marmora & Lake Public Library, 37 Forsyth St, Marmora, ON, K0K 2M0, CANADA. Tel: 613-472-3122. p. 2820

Price, Shirley, Asst Librn, Southwest Arkansas Regional Library, Delight Branch, 420 Antioch St, Delight, AR, 71940. Tel: 870-379-2456. p. 103

Price, Stan, Web Adminr, University of South Carolina Aiken, 471 University Pkwy, Aiken, SC, 29801. Tel: 803-641-3510. Fax: 803-641-3302. p. 2180

Price, Susan, Br Librn, London Public Library, Masonville, 30 North Centre Rd, London, ON, N5X 3W1, CANADA. Tel: 519-660-4646. p. 2818

Price, Tabitha, Circ Supvr, Bluefield College, 3000 College Dr, Bluefield, VA, 24605. Tel: 276-326-4238. Fax: 276-326-4288. p. 2451

Price, Terry, Dir, Chelsea Public Library, 618 Pine St, Chelsea, OK, 74016-0064. Tel: 918-789-3364. Fax: 918-789-4219. p. 1959

Price, Tippi, Access Serv Librn, Trinity Christian College, 6601 W College Dr, Palos Heights, IL, 60463. Tel: 708-597-3000, Ext 4795. Fax: 708-385-5665. p. 687

Price, Violet, Head, Tech Serv, State University of New York Downstate Medical Center, 395 Lenox Rd, Brooklyn, NY, 11203. Tel: 718-270-7400. Fax: 718-270-7413, 718-270-7468. p. 1595

Price, Winnifred, Asst Dir, New Castle-Henry County Public Library, 376 S 15th St, New Castle, IN, 47362-3205. Tel: 765-529-0362, Ext 302. Fax: 765-521-3581. p. 768

Pricer, Wayne, Ref & ILL Librn, Schoolcraft College, 18600 Haggerty Rd, Livonia, MI, 48152-2696. Tel: 734-462-4400, Ext 5317. Fax: 734-462-4495. p. 1204

Prichard, Lisa, Access Serv Librn, Jefferson College Library, 1000 Viking Dr, Hillsboro, MO, 63050. Tel: 636-797-3000, 636-942-3000. Fax: 636-789-3954. p. 1331

Prichard, Nancy, Head, Coll Mgt, Mount Prospect Public Library, Ten S Emerson St, Mount Prospect, IL, 60056. Tel: 847-253-5675. Fax: 847-253-0642. p. 677

Prichard, Reda, Libr Asst, Belle Plaine Community Library, 904 12th St, Belle Plaine, IA, 52208-1711. Tel: 319-444-2902. Fax: 319-444-2902. p. 796

Prichard, Tammy, Adminr, Medina Memorial Hospital, 200 Ohio St, Medina, NY, 14103. Tel: 585-798-8148. p. 1659

Pricone, Kathy, Circ, Niles Public Library District, 6960 Oakton St, Niles, IL, 60714. Tel: 847-663-1234. Fax: 847-663-1350. p. 680

Priddis, Marissa, Dir, Alexandrian Public Library, 115 W Fifth St, Mount Vernon, IN, 47620. Tel: 812-838-3286. Fax: 812-838-9639. p. 766

Priddle, Charlotte, Librn, New York University, Fales Library & Special Collections, 70 Washington Sq S, New York, NY, 10012. Tel: 212-998-2596. Fax: 212-995-3835. p. 1695

Pride, Linda, Adult Prog Coordr, Adult Ref Librn, Redford Township District Library, 25320 W Six Mile, Redford, MI, 48240. Tel: 313-531-5960. Fax: 313-531-1721. p. 1220

Pride, Lula, Br Mgr, East Baton Rouge Parish Library, Zachary Branch, 1900 Church St, Zachary, LA, 70791. Tel: 225-658-1880. Fax: 225-658-1844. p. 943

Pride, Marseille, Head, Pub Serv & Outreach, Liberty University Library, 1971 University Blvd, Lynchburg, VA, 24502. Tel: 434-592-4012. Fax: 434-582-2728. p. 2476

Pride, Ruthie L, Asst Librn, Phillips Community College of the University of Arkansas, 1000 Campus Dr, Helena, AR, 72342. Tel: 870-338-6474. Fax: 870-338-2783. p. 103

Prideaux, Jan, Mgr, Libr Serv, Tucson Electric Power Co Library, 3950 E Irvington, Tucson, AZ, 85714-2114. Tel: 520-745-3318. Fax: 520-571-4019. p. 88

Pridgen, Blake, Ref & Instruction Librn, Flagler College, 44 Sevilla St, Saint Augustine, FL, 32084-4302. Tel: 904-819-6206. Fax: 904-823-8511. p. 486

Pridgen, Morris D, Jr, Dir, Libr Serv, Columbus County Public Library, 407 N Powell Blvd, Whiteville, NC, 28472. Tel: 910-642-3116. Fax: 910-642-7271. p. 1829

Pridgen, Pamela J, Dir, Library of Hattiesburg, Petal, Forrest County, Petal Branch, 714 S Main St, Petal, MS, 39465. Tel: 601-584-7610. p. 1300

Pridgen, Pamela J, Dir, The Library of Hattiesburg, Petal, Forrest County, 329 Hardy St, Hattiesburg, MS, 39401-3496. Tel: 601-584-3162. Fax: 601-582-5338. p. 1300

Priebe, Lori, Dir, Danvers Township Library, 117 E Exchange St, Danvers, IL, 61732-9347. Tel: 309-963-4269. Fax: 309-963-4269. p. 632

Prien, Sharon, ILL, Alaska Resources Library & Information Services, Library Bldg, 3211 Providence Dr, Ste 111, Anchorage, AK, 99508-4614. Tel: 907-786-7677. Fax: 907-786-7652. p. 43

Priepke, Steven K, Exec Dir, Sigma Alpha Epsilon Fraternity & Foundation, 1856 Sheridan Rd, Evanston, IL, 60201-3837. Tel: 847-475-1856. Fax: 847-475-2250. p. 644

Pries, Joan, Chief Librn, University of Toronto Libraries, Caven Library, Knox College, 59 Saint George St, Toronto, ON, M5S 2E6, CANADA. Tel: 416-978-6090. Fax: 416-971-2133. p. 2865

Priest, Kim, Dir, Mary Cotton Public Library, 915 Virginia, Sabetha, KS, 66534-1950. Tel: 785-284-3160. Fax: 785-284-3605. p. 892

Priest, Marilyn, Coll Spec, Dartmouth College Library, Feldberg Business Administration & Engineering Library, 6193 Murdough Ctr, Hanover, NH, 03755-3560. Tel: 603-646-2191. Fax: 603-646-2384. p. 1450

Priester, Lynne, Asst Librn, Brandywine Community Library, 60 Tower Dr, Topton, PA, 19562-1301. Tel: 610-682-7115. Fax: 610-682-7385. p. 2146

Priestley, Holly, Br Mgr, Ouachita Parish Public Library, Sterlington Memorial Branch, 305 Keystone Rd, Monroe, LA, 71203. Tel: 318-327-1382. Fax: 318-665-9476. p. 958

Priestman, Ann, Ref & Info Literacy Librn, Arapahoe Community College, 5900 S Santa Fe Dr, Littleton, CO, 80160. Tel: 303-797-5731. Fax: 303-798-4173. p. 316

Prieth, Geraldine, Dir, Melbourne Public Library, 540 E Fee Ave, Melbourne, FL, 32901. Tel: 321-952-4514. Fax: 321-952-4518. p. 463

Prieur, Linda, Br Support, Stormont, Dundas & Glengarry County Library, Ingleside Branch, Ten Memorial Sq, Ingleside, ON, K0C 1M0, CANADA. Tel: 613-537-2592. p. 2801

Priewe, Matthew, Librn, College of Marin Library, 835 College Ave, Kentfield, CA, 94904. Tel: 415-457-8811, 415-485-9656. Fax: 415-457-5395. p. 161

Prike, Elizabeth, Mgr, Libr Serv, Cox Smith Matthews Inc, 112 E Pecan, Ste 1800, San Antonio, TX, 78205-1521. Tel: 210-554-5500. Fax: 210-226-8395. p. 2379

Prime, Jacqueline, Dir, Phillips Free Public Library, 25 Templeton Rd, Phillipston, MA, 01331-9704. Tel: 978-249-1734. Fax: 978-249-3356. p. 1117

Prime, Jacqueline, Dir, Boynton Public Library, 27 Boynton Rd, Templeton, MA, 01468-1412. Tel: 978-939-5582. Fax: 978-939-8755. p. 1131

Primeaux, Beckie, Br Mgr, Cameron Parish Library, Grand Chenier Branch, 2867 Grand Chenier Hwy, Grand Chenier, LA, 70643. Tel: 337-538-2214. Fax: 337-538-2216. p. 946

Primer, Ben, Archivist, Assoc Univ Librn, Spec Coll Librn, Princeton University, One Washington Rd, Princeton, NJ, 08544-2098. Tel: 609-258-3184. Fax: 609-258-0441. p. 1523

Primich, Tracy, Dir, Vanderbilt University, Science & Engineering, 3200 Stevenson Ctr, 419 21st Ave S, Nashville, TN, 37240-0007. Tel: 615-343-6043. Fax: 615-343-7249. p. 2261

Primus, Joanna, Head, Instruction & Libr Access Serv, Chicago School of Professional Psychology Library, 325 N Wells St, 6th Flr, Chicago, IL, 60610. Tel: 312-329-6632. Fax: 312-644-6075. p. 610

Prince, Barbara, Dir, Hanover Town Library, 130 Etna Rd, Etna, NH, 03750. Tel: 603-643-3116. Fax: 603-643-3116. p. 1447

Prince, Barbara, Coordr, Librarians of the Upper Valley Coop, c/o Hanover Town Library, 130 Etna Rd, Etna, NH, 03750. Tel: 603-643-3116. p. 2948

Prince, Denise, Librn, Conservatoire de Musique de Montreal Bibliotheque, 4750 Ave Henri-Julien, Montreal, QC, H2T 2C8, CANADA. Tel: 514 873-3485. Fax: 514-873-3346. p. 2895

Prince, Frances, Br Mgr, Horry County Memorial Library, Loris Branch, 4316 Main St, Loris, SC, 29569. Tel: 843-756-8101. Fax: 843-756-1988. p. 2191

Prince, Francis, In Charge, Winn Correctional Center Library, PO Box 1260, Winnfield, LA, 71483-1260. Tel: 318-628-3971. p. 971

Prince, Kathy, Librn, Wright County Library, Mountain Grove Branch, 206 Green St, Mountain Grove, MO, 65711. Tel: 417-926-4453. Fax: 417-926-6240. p. 1330

Prince, Katrina, Mgr, Metropolitan Library System in Oklahoma County, Bethany Library, 3510 N Mueller Ave, Bethany, OK, 73008-3971. Tel: 405-789-8363. Fax: 405-606-3239. p. 1972

Prince, Lisa C, Curator of Hist, Sacramento Archives & Museum Collection Center, 551 Sequoia Pacific Blvd, Sacramento, CA, 95814-0229. Tel: 916-264-7072. Fax: 916-264-7582. p. 224

Prince, Mary Miles, Assoc Dir, Vanderbilt University, Alyne Queener Massey Law Library, 131 21st Ave S, Nashville, TN, 37203. Tel: 615-322-0021. Fax: 615-343-1265. p. 2261

Prince, Monique, Mgr, Access Serv, Baruch College-CUNY, 151 E 25 St, Box H-0520, New York, NY, 10010-2313. Tel: 646-312-1670. p. 1670

Prince, Zack, Supvr, Ser, Dallas Baptist University, 3000 Mountain Creek Pkwy, Dallas, TX, 75211-9299. Tel: 214-333-5298. Fax: 214-333-5323. p. 2305

Princz, Marina, Librn, VanDusen Botanical Gardens Association, 5251 Oak St, Vancouver, BC, V6M 4H1, CANADA. Tel: 604-257-8668. Fax: 604-266-4236. p. 2744

Prindiville, Sue, Libr Mgr, Naperville Public Library, 200 W Jefferson Ave, Naperville, IL, 60540-5374. Tel: 630-961-4100, Ext 6307. Fax: 630-637-6389. p. 679

Prine, Cynthia, Br Mgr, Prince George's County Memorial, Oxon Hill Branch, 6200 Oxon Hill Rd, Oxon Hill, MD, 20745-3091. Tel: 301-839-2400. p. 1033

Pring, Johnathan, ILL, Sheridan College Library, 1430 Trafalgar Rd, Oakville, ON, L6H 2L1, CANADA. Tel: 905-459-7533, Ext 5280. Fax: 905-815-4123. p. 2826

Pring, Johnathan, Ref, Sheridan College Library, Davis Campus, 7899 McLaughlin Rd, Brampton, ON, L6V 1G6, CANADA. Tel: 905-459-7533. Fax: 905-874-4345. p. 2826

Pringle, Bill, Chair, Department of Community Services, Government of Yukon, Isabelle Pringle Community, PO Box 93, Carcross, YT, Y0B 1B0, CANADA. Tel: 867-821-3801. Fax: 867-821-3801. p. 2933

Pringle, Charlotte, Br Mgr, East Baton Rouge Parish Library, Delmont Gardens, 3351 Lorraine St, Baton Rouge, LA, 70805. Tel: 225-354-7080. Fax: 225-354-7049. p. 943

Pringle, Dawn, Dir, Jordan Valley District Library, One Library Lane, East Jordan, MI, 49727. Tel: 231-536-7131. Fax: 231-536-3646. p. 1174

Pringle, Jeanine, Cat, Cheltenham Township Library System, 215 S Keswick Ave, Glenside, PA, 19038-4420. Tel: 215-885-0457. Fax: 215-885-1239. p. 2061

Pringle, Jonathan, Archivist, Museum of Northern Arizona-Harold S Colton Memorial Library, 3101 N Fort Valley Rd, Flagstaff, AZ, 86001. Tel: 928-774-5211, Ext 256. Fax: 928-779-1527. p. 62

Pringle, Julie, Coordr, Coll Mgt, Fairfax County Public Library, 12000 Government Center Pkwy, Ste 324, Fairfax, VA, 22035-0012. Tel: 703-324-3100. Fax: 703-324-8365. p. 2461

Pringle, LaJuan, Br Mgr, Charlotte Mecklenburg Library, Independence Regional, 6000 Conference Dr, Charlotte, NC, 28212. Tel: 704-416-4800. p. 1782

Pringle, Robert, Treas, Inland NorthWest Health Sciences Libraries, PO Box 10283, Spokane, WA, 99209-0283. Tel: 509-368-6973. Fax: 509-358-7928. p. 2957

Pringle, Robert M, Jr, Dir, Libr Serv, Washington State University, 600 N Riverpoint Blvd, Spokane, WA, 99202. Tel: 509-358-7930. Fax: 509-358-7928. p. 2538

Pringle, Sherri, Libr Tech, Georgian College-Owen Sound Campus, Main Bldg, 1st Flr, Rm 206, 1450 Eighth St, Owen Sound, ON, N4K 5R4, CANADA. Tel: 519-376-0840, Ext 2034. Fax: 519-376-5395. p. 2834

Prins, Jennifer, Acq, Ser, Ottawa Office of the Auditor General, West Tower, 240 Sparks St, 11th Flr, Ottawa, ON, K1A 0G6, CANADA. Tel: 613-995-3708. Fax: 613-952-5131. p. 2832

Prinsen, Charlene, Br Mgr, Jackson County Library Services, Eagle Point Branch, 239 W Main St, Eagle Point, OR, 97524. Tel: 541-826-3313. Fax: 541-826-2993. p. 2005

Printz, Lisa, Br Librn, Park County Public Library, Powell Branch, 217 E Third, Powell, WY, 82435-1903. Tel: 307-754-8828. Fax: 307-754-8824. p. 2654

Prior, Barbara, Librn, Oberlin College Library, Clarence Ward Art Library, Allen Art Bldg, 83 N Main St, Oberlin, OH, 44074-1193. Tel: 440-775-8635. Fax: 440-775-5145. p. 1925

Prior, Elizabeth, Asst Dir, Broward County Division of Libraries, 100 S Andrews Ave, Fort Lauderdale, FL, 33301. Tel: 954-357-7379. Fax: 954-357-5733. p. 440

Prior, Susan, Librn, College of the North Atlantic, Anna Templeton Campus, 278 Duckworth St, St. John's, NL, A1C 1H3, CANADA. Tel: 709-758-7448. Fax: 709-758-7231. p. 2771

Prior, Susan, Librn, College of the North Atlantic, One Prince Philip Dr, St. John's, NL, A1C 5P7, CANADA. Tel: 709-758-7448. Fax: 709-758-7231. p. 2771

Priore, Charles, Sci Librn, Saint Olaf College, Rolvaag Memorial Library, Glasoe Science Library, Halvorson Music Library, 1510 Saint Olaf Ave, Northfield, MN, 55057-1097. Tel: 507-786-3099. Fax: 507-786-3734. p. 1269

Priore, Greg, Mgr & Archivist, William R Oliver Spec Coll, Carnegie Library of Pittsburgh, 4400 Forbes Ave, Pittsburgh, PA, 15213-4080. Tel: 412-622-1932. Fax: 412-622-6278. p. 2122

Priscilla, Coatney, Dir, William Leonard Public Library District, 13820 Central Park Ave, Robbins, IL, 60472-1999. Tel: 708-597-2760. Fax: 708-597-2778. p. 695

Pritchard, Alicia, Br Mgr, Brooklyn Public Library, Brower Park, 725 Saint Marks Ave, Brooklyn, NY, 11216. Tel: 718-773-7208. Fax: 718-773-7838. p. 1591

Pritchard, Cheryl, Head, Tech Serv, Gonzaga University School of Law, 721 N Cincinnati St, Spokane, WA, 99202. Tel: 509-323-3761. Fax: 509-323-3761. p. 2536

Pritchard, Colleen, Div Dir, Tech Serv, United States Department of Health & Human Services, Food & Drug Administration Biosciences Library, WO2, 3rd Flr, 10903 New Hampshire Ave, Silver Spring, MD, 20993. Tel: 301-796-2373. p. 1039

Pritchard, Dan, Assoc Dir, Info Gateway, United States Military Academy Library, Jefferson Hall Library & Learning Center, 758 Cullum Rd, West Point, NY, 10996. Tel: 845-938-3833. Fax: 845-938-4000. p. 1767

Pritchard, Holly, Head, Circ, J V Fletcher Library, 50 Main St, Westford, MA, 01886-2599. Tel: 978-399-2313. Fax: 978-692-4418. p. 1138

Pritchard, John, Dir, Mooresville Public Library, 304 S Main St, Mooresville, NC, 28115. Tel: 704-664-2927. Fax: 704-660-3292. p. 1810

Pritchard, Karen, Dir, Centerburg Public Library, 49 E Main St, Centerburg, OH, 43011. Tel: 740-625-6538. Fax: 740-625-7311. p. 1866

Pritchard, Kathleen C, AV, West Hempstead Public Library, 500 Hempstead Ave, West Hempstead, NY, 11552. Tel: 516-481-6591. Fax: 516-481-2608. p. 1766

Pritchard, Laura, Dir, Dannemora Free Library, Village Community Ctr, 40 Emmons St, Dannemora, NY, 12929. Tel: 518-492-7005. Fax: 518-492-7005. p. 1613

Pritchard, Patricia, Br Mgr, Peoria Public Library, McClure, 315 W McClure Ave, Peoria, IL, 61604-3556. Tel: 309-497-2701. Fax: 309-497-2711. p. 690

Pritchard, Phil, Curator, VPres, Hockey Hall of Fame, 400 Kipling Ave, Toronto, ON, M8V 3L1, CANADA. Tel: 416-360-7735. Fax: 416-251-5770. p. 2854

Pritchard, Sarah M, Univ Librn, Northwestern University Library, 1970 Campus Dr, Evanston, IL, 60208-2300. Tel: 847-491-7658. p. 644

Pritchard, Tamar, ILL, Ref, New Jersey Department of Law & Public Safety, 25 Market St, West Wing, 6th Flr, Trenton, NJ, 08625. Tel: 609-292-4958. Fax: 609-633-6555. p. 1535

Pritchard, Trisha, Commun Libr Mgr, County of Los Angeles Public Library, Littlerock Library, 35119 80th St E, Littlerock, CA, 93543. Tel: 661-944-4138. Fax: 661-944-4150. p. 142

Pritcher, Barbara, Librn, First Baptist Church, 301 S Center St, Ste 500, Arlington, TX, 76010. Tel: 817-277-6353. Fax: 817-276-6499. p. 2277

Pritchett, Carla, Govt Doc/Micro Ref Librn, Tulane University, Law Library, 6329 Freret St, New Orleans, LA, 70118-6231. Tel: 504-865-5994. Fax: 504-865-5917. p. 963

Pritchett, John C, Dir, Columbia College, 1301 Columbia College Dr, Columbia, SC, 29203-9987. Tel: 803-786-3716. Fax: 803-786-3700. p. 2187

Pritsky, Richard, Asst Dir, Carpenter-Carse Library, 69 Ballards Corner Rd, Hinesburg, VT, 05461. Tel: 802-482-2878. p. 2425

Pritt, Andrea, Info Res & Serv Support Spec, Pennsylvania State University, One Campus Dr, Mont Alto, PA, 17237-9703. Tel: 717-749-6040. Fax: 717-749-6059. p. 2091

Prive, Monique, Coordr, Acq, Per, Lyndon State College, 1001 College Rd, Lyndonville, VT, 05851. Tel: 802-626-6366. Fax: 802-626-6331. p. 2427

Prizio, Lisa, Librn, Chichester Town Library, 161 Main St, Chichester, NH, 03258. Tel: 603-798-5613. Fax: 603-798-5439. p. 1441

Probeyahn, Carol, Dir, East Meadow Public Library, 1886 Front St, East Meadow, NY, 11554-1705. Tel: 516-794-2570. Fax: 516-794-1272. p. 1617

Probst, Karen, ILL, Appleton Public Library, 225 N Oneida St, Appleton, WI, 54911-4780. Tel: 920-832-6175. Fax: 920-832-6182. p. 2578

Probst, Laura, Dean, Univ Libr, Florida International University, 11200 SW Eighth St, Miami, FL, 33199. Tel: 305-348-2461. Fax: 305-348-3408. p. 465

Probst, Laura, Dean of Libr, Florida International University, 3000 NE 151st St, North Miami, FL, 33181-3600. Tel: 305-919-5714. Fax: 305-919-5914. p. 472

Probst, Margo, Circ Mgr, Helen Matthes Library, 100 E Market Ave, Effingham, IL, 62401-3499. Tel: 217-342-2464, Ext 2. Fax: 217-342-2413. p. 639

Probst, Sandy, Coordr, Media Serv, Lock Haven University of Pennsylvania, 401 N Fairview Ave, Lock Haven, PA, 17745-2390. Tel: 570-484-2228. Fax: 570-484-2506. p. 2082

Probst, Steven, Educ Serv Librn, Valparaiso University, School of Law Library, 656 S Greenwich St, Valparaiso, IN, 46383. Tel: 219-465-7827. Fax: 219-465-7917. p. 784

Procarione, Norma Rae, Librn, Price City Library, 159 E Main St, Price, UT, 84501-3046. Tel: 435-636-3188. Fax: 435-637-2905. p. 2410

Procell, James, Asst Dir, University of Louisville Libraries, Dwight Anderson Music Library, 105 W Brandeis Ave, Louisville, KY, 40208. Tel: 502-852-0528. Fax: 502-852-7701. p. 926

Proces, Paul, New Media Librn, Bucks County Community College Library, 275 Swamp Rd, Newtown, PA, 18940-0999. Tel: 215-497-8711. Fax: 215-968-8142. p. 2097

Proces, Stephen Lewis, Dir, Neenah Public Library, 240 E Wisconsin Ave, Neenah, WI, 54956-3010. Tel: 920-886-6315. Fax: 920-886-6324. p. 2624

Prochaska, Holly, Head of Libr, University of Cincinnati Libraries, Geology-Mathematics-Physics, 240 Braunstein Hall, Cincinnati, OH, 45221. Tel: 513-556-1389. Fax: 513-556-1930. p. 1874

Prochaska, Misty, Dir, Libr Serv, Hamilton College Library, 1821 K St, Lincoln, NE, 68508. Tel: 402-474-5315. Fax: 402-474-5302. p. 1404

Prochniak, Mary, Head Librn, University of Wisconsin-Madison, L & S Learning Support Services, Van Hise Hall, 1220 Linden Dr, Madison, WI, 53706. Tel: 608-262-1408. Fax: 608-262-7579. p. 2609

Prochnik, Bernie, Librn, Bath Public Library, Four W Branch Rd, Bath, NH, 03740. Tel: 603-747-3372. Fax: 603-747-3372. p. 1438

Procious, Jean Marie, Dir, Salem Athenaeum, 337 Essex St, Salem, MA, 01970. Tel: 978-744-2540. Fax: 978-744-7536. p. 1122

Prock, Jana, Dir, Keller Public Library, 640 Johnson Rd, Keller, TX, 76248. Tel: 817-743-4800. Fax: 817-743-4890. p. 2349

Prock, Krista, Info Literacy, Ref Librn, Kutztown University, 15200 Kutztown Rd, Bldg 5, Kutztown, PA, 19530-0735. Tel: 610-683-4484. Fax: 610-683-4747. p. 2075

Procko, Claudia, Circ, Leesburg Public Library, 100 E Main St, Leesburg, FL, 34748. Tel: 352-728-9790. Fax: 352-728-9794. p. 461

Procter, Coral, Br Mgr, Sacramento Public Library, Orangevale Neighborhood Library, 8820 Greenback Lane, No L, Orangevale, CA, 95662. p. 225

Proctor, Angie, Librn, Public Library of Johnston County & Smithfield, Princeton Public, 101 Dr Donnie Jones Blvd, Princeton, NC, 27569. Tel: 919-936-9996. Fax: 919-936-2962. p. 1824

Proctor, David, Dir, Ballard, Spahr LLP Library, 1735 Market St, 51st Flr, Philadelphia, PA, 19103-7599. Tel: 215-864-8150. Fax: 215-864-8999. p. 2103

Proctor, Drew, Cat, Columbia Basin College Library, 2600 N 20th Ave, Pasco, WA, 99301. Tel: 509-542-4479. Fax: 509-546-0401. p. 2523

Proctor, Esther, Archivist, Manchester Historical Museum, Ten Union St, Manchester-by-the-Sea, MA, 01944. Tel: 978-526-7230. Fax: 978-526-6060. p. 1102

Proctor, Lynne, Libr Mgr, Pikes Peak Library District, Cheyenne Mountain Library, 1785 S Eighth St, Colorado Springs, CO, 80905. Tel: 719-633-6278. p. 296

Proctor, Lynne, Libr Mgr, Pikes Peak Library District, Rockrimmon Library, 832 Village Center Dr, Colorado Springs, CO, 80919. Tel: 719-593-8000. p. 296

Proctor, Nancy, Ref Librn, Tennessee Valley Authority, TVA Research Library-Knoxville, WT CC - K, 400 W Summit Hill Dr, Knoxville, TN, 37902. Tel: 865-632-7865. Fax: 865-632-4475. p. 2243

Proctor, Sandra J, Librn, Morris James LLP, 500 Delaware Ave, Ste 1500, Wilmington, DE, 19801-1494. Tel: 302-888-6863. Fax: 302-571-1750. p. 388

Proehl, Andrea, Ref Librn, Santa Rosa Junior College, 1501 Mendocino Ave, Santa Rosa, CA, 95401. Tel: 707-527-4904. Fax: 707-527-4545. p. 267

Profeta, Patricia C, Dr, Assoc Dean, Learning Res, Indian River State College, 3209 Virginia Ave, Fort Pierce, FL, 34981-5599. Tel: 772-462-7600. Fax: 772-462-4780. p. 446

Proffer, Kristi, Circ, Lasalle Parish Library, 3108 N First St, Jena, LA, 71342. Tel: 318-992-5675. Fax: 318-992-7374, 318-992-7394. p. 951

Proffer, Kristie, Br Mgr, Lasalle Parish Library, Olla Branch, 1449 Blake St, Olla, LA, 71465. Tel: 318-495-5570. Fax: 318-495-5593. p. 952

Proffitt, Judy E, Dir, Noxubee County Library System, 103 E King St, Macon, MS, 39341-2832. Tel: 662-726-5461. Fax: 662-726-4694. p. 1307

Prohl, Pat, Head, Circ, La Grange Public Library, Ten W Cossitt Ave, La Grange, IL, 60525. Tel: 708-352-0576, Ext 12. p. 662

Prokopeak, Susan, Librn, Joliet Junior College, J-Bldg, 3rd Flr, 1215 Houbolt Rd, Joliet, IL, 60431-8938. Tel: 815-729-9020, Ext 2215. Fax: 815-744-2465. p. 659

Prokosch, Wendy, Librn, Mora Public Library, 200 W Maple Ave, Mora, MN, 55051-1330. Tel: 320-679-2642. p. 1267

Proksa, Amber, Br Mgr, Chicago Public Library, Legler, 115 S Pulaski Rd, Chicago, IL, 60624. Tel: 312-746-7730. Fax: 312-746-7750. p. 609

Prolman, Lisa, Asst Libr Dir, Greenfield Public Library, 402 Main St, Greenfield, MA, 01301. Tel: 413-772-1544. Fax: 413-772-1589. p. 1092

Proper, Joann, Circ, Colonial Williamsburg Foundation, 313 First St, Williamsburg, VA, 23185-4306. Tel: 757-565-8500. Fax: 757-565-8508. p. 2502

Propes, Kara, YA Serv, Faulkner-Van Buren Regional Library System, 1900 Tyler St, Conway, AR, 72032. Tel: 501-327-7482. Fax: 501-327-9098. p. 96

Prophet, Mary Webb, Interim Dir, Denison University Libraries, 400 W Loop, Granville, OH, 43023. Tel: 740-587-6215. Fax: 740-587-6285. p. 1902

Propp, Dale, Dir, Texas State Law Library, Tom C Clark Bldg, 205 W 14th St, Austin, TX, 78701-1614. Tel: 512-463-1722. Fax: 512-463-1728. p. 2282

Propp, Ruth, Cat Librn, Rosebud County Library, 201 N Ninth Ave, Forsyth, MT, 59327. Tel: 406-346-7561. Fax: 406-346-7685. p. 1378

Prorak, Diane, Ref & Instrul Serv, Instr Coordr, University of Idaho Library, Rayburn St, Moscow, ID, 83844. Tel: 208-885-2508. Fax: 208-885-6817. p. 579

Pross, Trevor, Chief Exec Officer, Belleville Public Library, 254 Pinnacle St, Belleville, ON, K8N 3B1, CANADA. Tel: 613-968-6731. Fax: 613-968-6841. p. 2795

Prosser, Deborah, Dir, Gainesville State College, 3820 Mundy Mill Rd, Oakwood, GA, 30566. Tel: 678-717-3466. Fax: 770-718-3657. p. 547

Prostang, Ellen, Br Head, Toronto Public Library, Fairview, 35 Fairview Mall Dr, Toronto, ON, M2J 4S4, CANADA. Tel: 416-395-5750. Fax: 416-395-5756. p. 2861

Prothe, Linda, Circ, Paola Free Library, 101 E Peoria, Paola, KS, 66071-1798. Tel: 913-259-3655. Fax: 913-259-3656. p. 889

Prothero-Brooks, Clive, Curator, Royal Canadian Artillery Museum Library, CFB Shilo, Shilo, MB, R0K 2A0, CANADA. Tel: 204-765-3000, Ext 4066. Fax: 204-765-5289. p. 2751

Prothro, Jaime, Customer Serv Mgr, Wichita Public Library, 223 S Main St, Wichita, KS, 67202. Tel: 316-261-8530. Fax: 316-262-4540. p. 901

Protka, Jacqueline, Digital Assets & Media Librn, Corcoran Gallery of Art/College of Art & Design Library, 500 17th St NW, Washington, DC, 20006. Tel: 202-478-1544. Fax: 202-628-7908. p. 396

Protter, Christina, Ref Serv, Oconee Regional Library, 801 Bellevue Ave, Dublin, GA, 31021. Tel: 478-272-5710. Fax: 478-275-5381. p. 531

Protzko, Shandra, Libr Serv Dir, National Jewish Health, 1400 Jackson St, Denver, CO, 80206-2762. Tel: 303-398-1483. Fax: 303-270-2149. p. 302

Proudfoot, Bill, Automation Librn, Web Coordr, West Valley Community College Library, 14000 Fruitvale Ave, Saratoga, CA, 95070-5698. Tel: 408-741-2559. Fax: 408-741-2134. p. 268

Proudfoot, Mary, Ch, Commun Serv, The Brookfield Library, 182 Whisconier Rd, Brookfield, CT, 06804. Tel: 203-775-6241. Fax: 203-740-7723. p. 332

Proulx, Krista, ILL, Ser, UMC Library, 2900 University Ave, Crookston, MN, 56716-0801. Tel: 218-281-8399. Fax: 218-281-8080. p. 1246

Proulx, Madeleine, Info Serv, Ecole Polytechnique de Montreal Bibliotheque, 2500, chemin de Polytechnique, Montreal, QC, H3T 1J4, CANADA. Tel: 514-340-4666. Fax: 514-340-4026. p. 2895

Prouse, Margaret R, Dr, Dir, Libr Serv, Delaware Technical & Community College, Terry Bldg, 1st Flr, 100 Campus Dr, Dover, DE, 19904-1383. Tel: 302-857-1060. Fax: 302-857-1099. p. 382

Prout, Edith, Acq, Jenkintown Library, 460 Old York Rd, Jenkintown, PA, 19046-2829. Tel: 215-884-0593. Fax: 215-884-2243. p. 2072

Prout, Eva, Br Head, Toronto Public Library, Jane/Sheppard, 1906 Sheppard Ave W, Toronto, ON, M3L 1Y7, CANADA. Tel: 416-395-5966. Fax: 416-395-5427. p. 2862

Prout, Wil, Libr Dir, Hilbert College, 5200 S Park Ave, Hamburg, NY, 14075. Tel: 716-649-7900, Ext 238. Fax: 716-648-6530. p. 1632

Prouty, Howard, Acq Archivist, Academy of Motion Picture Arts & Sciences, 333 S La Cienega Blvd, Beverly Hills, CA, 90211. Tel: 310-247-3000, Ext 2225. Fax: 310-657-5193. p. 129

Prouty, Jill, Br Supvr, Flint River Regional Library, Peachtree City Library, 201 Willowbend Rd, Peachtree City, GA, 30269. Tel: 770-631-2520. p. 535

Prouty, Scott, Photo Librn, American Institute of Physics, One Physics Ellipse, College Park, MD, 20740-3843. Tel: 301-209-3177. Fax: 301-209-3144. p. 1024

Provencher, James, Ref Librn, Riverhead Free Library, 330 Court St, Riverhead, NY, 11901-2885. Tel: 631-727-3228. Fax: 631-727-4762. p. 1728

Provencher, Patrick, Asst Regional Dir, Haut-Saint-Jean Regional Library, 15, rue de l'Église St, Ste 102, Edmundston, NB, E3V 1J3, CANADA. Tel: 506-735-2074. Fax: 506-735-2193. p. 2762

Provenzano, Deborah, Coll Develop, Suffolk County Community College, 533 College Rd, Selden, NY, 11784-2899. Tel: 631-451-4800. Fax: 631-451-4697. p. 1742

Provenzano, Elaine, Admin & Outreach Coordr, Manhattanville College Library, 2900 Purchase St, Purchase, NY, 10577. Tel: 914-323-5207. Fax: 914-323-8139. p. 1724

Provenzano, Sandra Parker, Head Cataloger, Harvard Library, Dumbarton Oaks Research Library, 1703 32nd St NW, Washington, MA, 20007. Tel: 202-339-6400. Fax: 202-625-0279. p. 1074

Providence, Bert, Br Head, Toronto Public Library, Northern Elms, 123B Rexdale Blvd, Unit 5, Toronto, ON, M9W 1P1, CANADA. Tel: 416-394-5230. Fax: 416-394-5235. p. 2862

Providenti, Michael, Librn, Web Coordr, Northern Kentucky University, University Dr, Highland Heights, KY, 41099. Tel: 859-572-5936. Fax: 859-572-5390. p. 917

Provine, Rick, Dir, DePauw University, 11 E Larrabee St, Greencastle, IN, 46135. Tel: 765-658-4420. Fax: 765-658-4017. p. 746

Provorse, Kathy, Dir, Dolgeville-Manheim Public Library, 24 N Main St, Dolgeville, NY, 13329. Tel: 315-429-3421. Fax: 315-429-3421. p. 1615

Provost, Darylyne, Asst Dir, Syst, Web & Emerging Tech, Colby College Libraries, 5100 Mayflower Hill, Waterville, ME, 04901. Tel: 207-859-5117. Fax: 207-859-5105. p. 1005

Provost, Karen, Libr Mgr, Proskauer Rose LLP Library, 1585 Broadway, Concourse Level, New York, NY, 10036. Tel: 212-969-5001. Fax: 212-969-2931. p. 1698

Provost, Roland, Dir, Societe d'Histoire et d'Archeologie des Monts, Inc, 675 Blvd Saint Anne Ouest, Sainte-Anne-des-Monts, QC, G4V 1T9, CANADA. Tel: 418-763-7871. p. 2910

Provost, Sylvie, Dir, Bibliotheque Montarville-Boucher de la Bruere, 501 Chemin Du Lac, Boucherville, QC, J4B 6V6, CANADA. Tel: 450-463-7120. Fax: 450-449-6865. p. 2880

Prozzo, Deborah, Br Supvr, Bristol Public Library, Manross Memorial, 260 Central St, Forestville, CT, 06010. Tel: 860-584-7790. p. 332

Prucha, Christina, Archivist, Cat Librn, Logan University/College of Chiropractic Library, 1851 Schoettler Rd, Chesterfield, MO, 63006. Tel: 636-227-2100. Fax: 636-207-2448. p. 1323

Prucha, Cris, Info Serv, University of Wisconsin-La Crosse, 1631 Pine St, La Crosse, WI, 54601-3748. Tel: 608-785-8637. Fax: 608-785-8639. p. 2603

Prud'homme, Johanne, Bibliothecaire Responsable, Bibliothèques de Montrèal, Frontenac, 2550, rue Ontario Est, Montreal, QC, H2K 1W7, CANADA. Tel: 514-872-7889. Fax: 514-872-7893. p. 2889

Prudholme-Wardor, Linda, Libr Mgr, Peace River Municipal Library, 9807 97th Ave, Peace River, AB, T8S 1H6, CANADA. Tel: 780-624-4076. Fax: 780-624-4086. p. 2713

Pruett, Catherine J, Youth Serv, Marion County Library, 101 E Court St, Marion, SC, 29571-3699. Tel: 843-423-8300. Fax: 843-423-8302. p. 2200

Pruett, Cathy, Youth Serv Librn, Marion County Public Library, Mannington Public, 109 Clarksburg St, Mannington, WV, 26582. Tel: 304-986-2803. Fax: 304-986-3425. p. 2559

Pruett, Gretchen, Dir, New Braunfels Public Library, 700 E Common St, New Braunfels, TX, 78130-5689. Tel: 830-221-4300. Fax: 830-608-2151. p. 2365

Pruett, Mary B, Dir, Hickman County Public Library, 120 W Swan St, Centerville, TN, 37033. Tel: 931-729-5130. Fax: 931-729-6950. p. 2226

Pruett, Mary Beth, Dir, Hickman County Public Library, East Hickman Public Library, 5009 Hwy 100, Lyles, TN, 37098. Tel: 931-670-5767. Fax: 931-670-1933. p. 2226

Pruett, Ronald, Ref Asst, Belmont Abbey College, 100 Belmont-Mt Holly Rd, Belmont, NC, 28012. Tel: 704-461-6748. Fax: 704-461-6743. p. 1776

Pruett, Sarah, Librn, Spencer Public Library, 300 Fourth St, Spencer, NC, 28159. Tel: 704-636-9072. p. 1825

Prugno, Tavi, Asst Dir, Snow Library, 67 Main St, Orleans, MA, 02653-2413. Tel: 508-240-3760. Fax: 508-255-5701. p. 1116

Pruitt, Betty, Librn, Birmingham Public Library, Ensley Branch, 1201 25th St, Ensley, AL, 35218. Tel: 205-785-2625. Fax: 205-785-6625. p. 7

Pruitt, John, Jr, Pres, Frances L N Waller Research Library, 8956 Courthouse Rd, Spotsylvania, VA, 22553. Tel: 540-507-7112. p. 2496

Pruitt, Johnetta, Outreach Serv Librn, Fauquier County Public Library, John Marshall Branch, 4133 Rectortown Rd, Marshall, VA, 20115. Tel: 540-364-4910. Fax: 540-364-4911. p. 2501

Pruitt, Linda, Ch, Kellogg-Hubbard Library, 135 Main St, Montpelier, VT, 05602. Tel: 802-223-3338. Fax: 802-223-3338. p. 2429

Pruitt, Paul, Coll Develop, University of Alabama, School of Law Library, 101 Paul Bryant Dr, Tuscaloosa, AL, 35487. Tel: 205-348-5925. Fax: 205-348-1112. p. 38

Pruitt, Shelley, Dir, Green County Public Library, 112 W Court St, Greensburg, KY, 42743. Tel: 270-932-7081. Fax: 270-932-7081. p. 915

Prunty, Susan, In Charge, Davis Brown Law Firm, 215 Tenth St, Ste 1300, Des Moines, IA, 50309. Tel: 515-288-2500. Fax: 515-243-0654. p. 808

Prunty, Thresa, Asst Dir, Ritchie County Public Library, 608 E Main St, Harrisville, WV, 26362. Tel: 304-643-2717. Fax: 304-643-4019. p. 2560

Prusacki, Dana, Archivist, Belleville Public Library, 121 E Washington St, Belleville, IL, 62220. Tel: 618-234-0441, Ext 22. Fax: 618-234-9474. p. 593

Prushiek, Jill, Dr, Assoc Prof, University of Wisconsin-Eau Claire, 105 Garfield Ave, Eau Claire, WI, 54702. Tel: 715-836-2635. Fax: 715-836-5099. p. 2976

Pruter, Robert, Ref/Govt Doc Librn, Lewis University Library, One University Pkwy, Unit 300, Romeoville, IL, 60446-2200. Tel: 815-836-5664. Fax: 815-838-9456. p. 698

Pryce, Laura, Youth Serv Librn, Bartlesville Public Library, 600 S Johnstone, Bartlesville, OK, 74003. Tel: 918-338-4170. Fax: 918-337-5338. p. 1957

Pryer, Jonathan, Ref, Sayville Library, 11 Collins Ave, Sayville, NY, 11782-3199. Tel: 631-589-4440. Fax: 631-589-6128. p. 1739

Prykucki, Debbie, Head, Circ, Clinton-Macomb Public Library, 40900 Romeo Plank Rd, Clinton Township, MI, 48038-2955. Tel: 586-226-5021. Fax: 586-226-5008. p. 1164

Pryma, Katharine, Br Mgr, Mississauga Library System, Sheridan, 2225 Erin Mills Pkwy, Mississauga, ON, L5K 1T9, CANADA. Tel: 905-615-4815. Fax: 905-615-4816. p. 2823

Pryor, Charles, Dr, Dept Head, Prof, University of Louisiana at Monroe, 306 Strauss Hall, 700 University Ave, Monroe, LA, 71209. Tel: 318-342-1246. Fax: 318-342-1213. p. 2966

Pryor, Chris, Ref, Saint Louis County Library, 1640 S Lindbergh Blvd, Saint Louis, MO, 63131-3598. Tel: 314-997-3300, Ext 2052. Fax: 314-997-7602. p. 1358

Prysiazny, Laurel, County Librn, Fresno County Public Library, 2420 Mariposa St, Fresno, CA, 93721-2285. Tel: 559-600-7323. p. 151

Pryszlak, Lydia, Br Mgr, Cleveland Public Library, Rockport, 4421 W 140th St, Cleveland, OH, 44135. Tel: 216-623-7053. Fax: 216-623-7055. p. 1878

Prytz, Gladys, Libr Tech, Wisconsin Indianhead Technical College, 1900 College Dr, Rice Lake, WI, 54868. Tel: 715-234-7082, Ext 5424. Fax: 715-234-5172. p. 2634

Przybylowicz, Linda, Youth Serv Librn, Wayne County Library, 221 Burke St, River Rouge, MI, 48218. Tel: 313-843-2040. Fax: 313-842-4716. p. 1221

Psarras, Terry, Mgr, Libr Serv, Carlton Fields, 4221 W Boy Scout Blvd, Ste 1000, Tampa, FL, 33607. Tel: 813-223-7000. Fax: 813-229-4133. p. 496

Ptacek, Bill, Dir, King County Library System, 960 Newport Way NW, Issaquah, WA, 98027. Tel: 425-369-3232. Fax: 425-369-3255. p. 2516

Ptacek, Cheryl A, Head Librn, Lang Memorial Library, 2405 Ave F, Wilson, KS, 67490. Tel: 785-658-3648. p. 902

Ptak, Elena, Librn, North Central Regional Library, East Wenatchee Community, 271 Ninth St NE, East Wenatchee, WA, 98802-4438. Tel: 509-886-7404. Fax: 509-886-7404. p. 2548

Ptasik, Bogdan, Br Mgr, Chicago Public Library, Scottsdale, 4101 W 79th St, Chicago, IL, 60652. Tel: 312-747-0193. Fax: 312-747-0144. p. 609

Ptasik, Elzbieta, Br Mgr, Chicago Public Library, Archer Heights, 5055 S Archer Ave, Chicago, IL, 60632. Tel: 312-747-9241. Fax: 312-747-5861. p. 608

Puccetti, Robin, Dir, Independence Public Library, 175 Monmouth St, Independence, OR, 97351-2423. Tel: 503-838-1811. Fax: 503-838-4486. p. 2001

Pucci, Eileen, In Charge, New York State Department of Correctional Services, 594 Rte 216, Stormville, NY, 12582. Tel: 845-221-2711, Ext 4562. p. 1750

Puccio, Carol, Tech Coordr, Cherry Hill Public Library, 1100 Kings Hwy N, Cherry Hill, NJ, 08034-1911. Tel: 856-903-1242. Fax: 856-667-9503. p. 1478

Puccio, Sandy, Br Mgr, San Diego County Library, Valley Center Branch, 29200 Cole Grade Rd, Valley Center, CA, 92082-5880. Tel: 760-749-1305. Fax: 760-749-1764. p. 234

Puccio, Todd, Dir of Tech Serv, Nova Southeastern University, 3200 S University Dr, Fort Lauderdale, FL, 33328. Tel: 954-262-3106. Fax: 954-262-1821. p. 443

Puchalski, Irene, Librn, University of Toronto Libraries, John H Daniels Faculty of Architecture, Landscape & Design, Shore + Moffat Library, 230 College St, 2nd Flr, Toronto, ON, M5T 1R2, CANADA. Tel: 416-978-6787. Fax: 416-971-2094. p. 2865

Puchino, Janet, Head of Libr, Free Library of Philadelphia, Charles Santore Branch, 932 S Seventh St, Philadelphia, PA, 19147-2932. Tel: 215-686-1766. Fax: 215-686-1765. p. 2109

Puckett, Janet L, Librn, Saint Mary's Regional Medical Center, 305 S Fifth, Enid, OK, 73701. Tel: 580-249-3092. Fax: 580-249-3091. p. 1963

Puckett, John, AV Tech Spec, Florida State University Libraries, College of Nursing, Learning Resource Center, 102 College of Nursing, Tallahassee, FL, 32306-4310. Tel: 850-644-1291. Fax: 850-644-7660. p. 494

Puckett, Jonathan, Circ, Ivy Tech Community College of Indiana, Northeast, 3800 N Anthony Blvd, Fort Wayne, IN, 46805-1430. Tel: 260-480-4246. Fax: 260-480-4121. p. 742

Puckett, Michele Morante, Dir, Consumers Energy, Corporate Library, One Energy Plaza, EP1-244, Jackson, MI, 49201. Tel: 517-788-0541. Fax: 517-768-3804. p. 1195

Puckett, Robert A, Dir, Wichita-Sedgwick County Historical Museum Library, 204 S Main St, Wichita, KS, 67202. Tel: 316-265-9314. Fax: 316-265-9319. p. 901

Pudden, Judith, Archivist, Royal Ontario Museum, 100 Queen's Park, Toronto, ON, M5S 2C6, CANADA. Tel: 416-586-5595. Fax: 416-586-5519. p. 2858

Pudenz, Nancy, Ch, Carroll Public Library, 118 E Fifth St, Carroll, IA, 51401. Tel: 712-792-3432. Fax: 712-792-0141. p. 798

Puderak, Danylo, Exec Dir, Ukrainian Canadian Congress - Saskatchewan Provincial Council Inc, 4-2345 Avenue C N, Saskatoon, SK, S7L 5Z5, CANADA. Tel: 306-652-5850. Fax: 306-665-2127. p. 2927

Puderbaugh, Dena, Librn, Prairie-River Library District, Kooskia Community, 026 S Main St, Kooskia, ID, 83539. Tel: 208-926-4539. Fax: 208-926-4539. p. 577

Puetz, Barbara, Asst Librn, Wilhoit Public Library, 9325 Donegal Dr, Ste B, Wilhoit, AZ, 86332. Tel: 928-442-3611. Fax: 928-442-3611. p. 89

Puff, Charlotte, Ch, Brandywine Community Library, 60 Tower Dr, Topton, PA, 19562-1301. Tel: 610-682-7115. Fax: 610-682-7385. p. 2146

Pugh, Adria, YA Serv, Way Public Library, 101 E Indiana Ave, Perrysburg, OH, 43551. Tel: 419-874-3135, Ext 109. Fax: 419-874-6129. p. 1929

Pugh, Daniela, Asst Librn, ILL, Weil, Gotshal & Manges Library, 767 Fifth Ave, New York, NY, 10153. Tel: 212-310-8626. Fax: 212-310-8007. p. 1702

Pugh, Michauna, Asst Librn, Gadsden County Public Library, Havana Public, 203 E Fifth Ave, Havana, FL, 32333. Tel: 850-539-2844. p. 485

Pugh, Nicole, Adult Serv, Asst Dir, YA Serv, Putnam County Library System, 50 E Broad St, Cookeville, TN, 38501. Tel: 931-526-2416. Fax: 931-372-8517. p. 2231

Pugh, Penny, Head, Ref, West Virginia University Libraries, WVU Libraries, 1549 University Ave, Morgantown, WV, 26506. Tel: 304-293-4040. Fax: 304-293-6638. p. 2566

Pugh, Ronnie, Br Mgr, Nashville Public Library, Old Hickory Branch, 1010 Jones St, Old Hickory, TN, 37138-2915. Tel: 615-862-5869. Fax: 615-862-5896. p. 2258

Pugh, Rosanne, Librn, Slatington Library, 650 Main St, Slatington, PA, 18080. Tel: 610-767-6461. Fax: 610-767-6461. p. 2140

Pugh, Shirley Faye, Librn, Evelyn Thornton-Warrior Public Library, Ten First St, Warrior, AL, 35180-1501. Tel: 205-647-3006. Fax: 205-647-9280. p. 40

Pugh, Susan, Asst Librn, Breathitt County Public Library, 1024 College Ave, Jackson, KY, 41339. Tel: 606-666-5541. Fax: 606-666-8166. p. 919

Pughsley, Frances, Librn, Alston & Bird Law Library, One Atlantic Ctr, 1201 W Peachtree St, Atlanta, GA, 30309-3424. Tel: 404-881-7120. Fax: 404-881-7777. p. 510

Puglisi, Patricia, Librn, Lockheed Martin Corp, 5600 Sand Lake Rd, MP 30, Orlando, FL, 32819-8907. Tel: 407-356-2051. Fax: 407-356-3665. p. 476

Pujadas, Ivette, Head, Circ, Free Public Library of Hasbrouck Heights, 320 Boulevard, Hasbrouck Heights, NJ, 07604. Tel: 201-288-0484, 201-288-0488. Fax: 201-288-5467. p. 1490

Pukkila, Marilyn R, Scholarly Res & Serv/Soc Sci & Humanities Librn, Colby College Libraries, 5100 Mayflower Hill, Waterville, ME, 04901. Tel: 207-859-5145. Fax: 207-859-5105. p. 1005

Pukl, Joseph, Acq, University of South Carolina, 1322 Greene St, Columbia, SC, 29208-0103. Tel: 803-777-3142. p. 2189

Puko, Dennis G, Librn, Mercer County Regional Planning Commission Library, 2491 Highland Rd, Hermitage, PA, 16148. Tel: 724-981-2412. Fax: 724-981-7677. p. 2068

Pukteris, Marek, Librn, Sir Mortimer B Davis Jewish General Hospital, Lady Davis Institute for Medical Research, 3755 Cote Ste Catherine Rd, Montreal, QC, H3T1E2, CANADA. Tel: 514-340-8260, Ext 3795. Fax: 514-340-7502. p. 2901

Pukteris, Marek, Head, Pub Serv, John Abbott College, 21,275 Lakeshore Rd, Sainte-Anne-de-Bellevue, QC, H9X 3L9, CANADA. Tel: 514-457-6610, Ext 5335. p. 2910

Pula, Cheryl, Ref, Dunham Public Library, 76 Main St, Whitesboro, NY, 13492. Tel: 315-736-9734. Fax: 315-736-3265. p. 1769

Pulatova, Irina, Med Librn, Calvary Hospital, 1740 Eastchester Rd, Bronx, NY, 10461. Tel: 718-518-2229. Fax: 718-518-2686. p. 1586

Puleo, Edna, Dir, Rockaway Borough Free Public Library, 82 E Main St, Rockaway, NJ, 07866. Tel: 973-627-5709. Fax: 973-627-5796. p. 1527

Puleo, Mary, Asst Dir, Everett Public Libraries, 410 Broadway, Everett, MA, 02149. Tel: 617-394-2304. Fax: 617-389-1230. p. 1087

Pulera, Linda M, Librn, Gateway Technical College, 1001 S Main St, Racine, WI, 53403-1582. Tel: 262-619-6220. Fax: 262-619-6221. p. 2632

Puletasi, Evelini, Librn, American Samoa Office of Library Services, Olosega School Library, Pago Pago, AS, 96799. Tel: 684-655-1206. Fax: 684-633-4240. p. 2665

Puley, Ken, Sr Librn, Canadian Broadcasting Corp, Radio Archives, 205 Wellington St W, Toronto, ON, M5G 3G7, CANADA. Tel: 416-205-5880. Fax: 416-205-8602. p. 2850

Pulfrey, Anne K, Archivist, City & County of Honolulu, Department of Customer Services, City Hall Annex, 558 S King St, Honolulu, HI, 96813-3006. Tel: 808-523-4044. Fax: 808-768-3769. p. 560

Pulice, Daniela L, Dir, Pleasant Valley Free Library, 1584 Main St, Pleasant Valley, NY, 12569. Tel: 845-635-8460. Fax: 845-635-9556. p. 1719

Pulis, Melissa, Librn, Foundation Center-Cleveland Library, 1422 Euclid Ave, Ste 1600, Cleveland, OH, 44115-2001. Tel: 216-861-1934. Fax: 216-861-1936. p. 1880

Pullattayil, Abdul, Health Sci Librn, Humber River Regional Hospital, 2111 Finch Ave W, Downsview, ON, M3N 1N1, CANADA. Tel: 416-744-2500, Ext 2583. Fax: 416-747-3819. p. 2802

Pullen, Craig, Computer Serv Librn, Lindenhurst Memorial Library, One Lee Ave, Lindenhurst, NY, 11757-5399. Tel: 631-957-7755. Fax: 631-957-7114. p. 1652

Pullen, Kim, Ref Librn, Bossier Parish Community College Library, 6220 E Texas St, Bossier City, LA, 71111. Tel: 318-678-6423. Fax: 318-678-6400. p. 946

Pullen, Virginia, Librn, Wyoming Women's Center Library, 1000 W Griffith, Lusk, WY, 82225. Tel: 307-334-3693, Ext 244. Fax: 307-334-2254. p. 2658

Pulley, Natalie, Ch, East Central Georgia Regional Library, Columbia County Public Library, 7022 Evans Town Center Blvd, Evans, GA, 30809. Tel: 706-447-7664. Fax: 706-868-3351. p. 519

Pulley, Natalie, Chief Librn, Aiken-Bamberg-Barnwell-Edgefield Regional Library System, Edgefield County, 105 Courthouse Sq, Edgefield, SC, 29824. Tel: 803-637-4025. Fax: 803-637-4026. p. 2179

Pulley, Susie, Librn, Van Zandt County Library, 317 First Monday Lane, Canton, TX, 75103. Tel: 903-567-4276. Fax: 903-567-6981. p. 2294

Pulley, Tracy, Tech Serv, Albany County Public Library, 310 S Eighth St, Laramie, WY, 82070-3969. Tel: 307-721-2580. Fax: 307-721-2584. p. 2657

Pulleyblank, Marcia, Librn, George Brown College of Applied Arts & Technology, 200 King St E, Toronto, ON, M5A 3W8, CANADA. Tel: 416-415-5000, Ext 2173. Fax: 416-415-2698. p. 2853

Pulliam, Beatrice, Access Serv, Providence College, One Cunningham Sq, Providence, RI, 02918-0001. Tel: 401 865-1622. Fax: 401-865-2823. p. 2173

Pulliam, Linda, Lending Serv Librn, Florida Library Information Network, R A Gray Bldg, State Library & Archives of Florida, Tallahassee, FL, 32399-0250. Tel: 850-245-6672. Fax: 850-245-6744. p. 2940

Pulliam, Lori, Br Serv Mgr, Oak Park Public Library, 834 Lake St, Oak Park, IL, 60301. Tel: 708-383-8200. Fax: 708-697-6900. p. 684

Pulliam, Lori, Br Serv Mgr, Oak Park Public Library, Dole Branch, 255 Augusta St, Oak Park, IL, 60302. Tel: 708-386-9032. Fax: 708-445-2385. p. 684

Pulliam, Lori, Mgr, Oak Park Public Library, Maze Branch, 845 S Gunderson Ave, Oak Park, IL, 60304. Tel: 708-386-4751. Fax: 708-386-0023. p. 684

Pullin, Mary, Asst Dir, Public Library of Youngstown & Mahoning County, 305 Wick Ave, Youngstown, OH, 44503-1079. Tel: 330-744-8636. Fax: 330-744-3355. p. 1952

Pullin, Mike, Syst Librn, University of North Texas Health Science Center at Fort Worth, 3500 Camp Bowie Blvd, Fort Worth, TX, 76107-2699. Tel: 817-735-2070. Fax: 817-763-0325. p. 2324

Pullins, Leslie, Dir, Fentress County Public Library, 306 S Main St, Jamestown, TN, 38556-3845. Tel: 931-879-7512. Fax: 931-879-6984. p. 2239

Pullman, Ethan, Ref Librn, Carnegie Mellon University, Hunt Library, 4909 Frew St, Pittsburgh, PA, 15213-3890. Tel: 412-268-2446. Fax: 412-268-2793. p. 2123

Pullman, ShienDee, Dir, Gibbs Memorial Library, 305 E Rusk St, Mexia, TX, 76667-2398. Tel: 254-562-3231. Fax: 254-472-0140. p. 2362

Puls, Grace, Librn, Grace Lutheran Church Library, 200 N Catherine Ave, La Grange, IL, 60525-1826. Tel: 708-352-0730. Fax: 708-352-0737. p. 662

Pulsford, Cindy, Head Librn, Johnston City Public Library, 506 Washington Ave, Johnston City, IL, 62951-1697. Tel: 618-983-6359. Fax: 618-983-6359. p. 659

Pulsifer, Thelma, In Charge, Western Counties Regional Library, Isaiah W Wilson Memorial, 84 Warwick St, Digby, NS, B0V 1A0, CANADA. Tel: 902-245-2163. p. 2787

Pulver, A Issac, Dir, Saratoga Springs Public Library, 49 Henry St, Saratoga Springs, NY, 12866. Tel: 518-584-7860. Fax: 518-584-7866. p. 1738

Pulver, Emilie, Spec Projects Librn, Lutheran School of Theology at Chicago & McCormick Theological Seminary, 1100 E 55th St, Chicago, IL, 60615-5199. Tel: 773-256-0730. Fax: 773-256-0737. p. 618

Pulver, Tom, Dir, Fairfax Public Law Library, 4110 Chain Bridge Rd, Rm 115, Fairfax, VA, 22030. Tel: 703-246-2170. Fax: 703-591-0310. p. 2461

Pummill, Cathy, Libr Asst II, Chillicothe Correctional Institution Library, 15802 State Rte 104 N, Chillicothe, OH, 45601. Tel: 740-774-7080, Ext 2381. Fax: 740-774-7082. p. 1867

Pumphrey, Mark, Dep Dir of Libr - Main Libr, El Paso Public Library, 501 N Oregon St, El Paso, TX, 79901. Tel: 915-543-5401. Fax: 915-543-5410. p. 2316

Pumphrey, Mark E, Dir, Polk County Public Library, 1289 W Mills St, Columbus, NC, 28722. Tel: 828-894-8721. Fax: 828-894-2761. p. 1785

Pumputiene, Irena, Librn, Balzekas Museum of Lithuanian Culture, 6500 S Pulaski Rd, Chicago, IL, 60629. Tel: 773-582-6500. Fax: 773-582-5133. p. 606

Pumroy, Eric, Dir, Libr Coll, Head, Spec Coll, Bryn Mawr College, 101 N Merion Ave, Bryn Mawr, PA, 19010-2899. Tel: 610-526-5272. Fax: 610-526-7480. p. 2039

Punch, Walter T, Dir, Wentworth Institute of Technology, 550 Huntington Ave, Boston, MA, 02115-5998. Tel: 617-989-4097. Fax: 617-989-4091. p. 1068

Pundsack, Karen, Coordr, Patron Serv, Great River Regional Library, 1300 W St Germain St, Saint Cloud, MN, 56301-3667. Tel: 320-650-2516. Fax: 320-650-2501. p. 1274

Puniello, Francoise, Assoc Univ Librn, Fac Planning & Mgt, Rutgers University Libraries, 169 College Ave, New Brunswick, NJ, 08901-1163. Tel: 732-932-7505. Fax: 732-932-7637. p. 1508

Puniello, Francoise, Assoc Univ Librn, Rutgers University Libraries, Kilmer Library, 75 Ave E, Piscataway, NJ, 08854-8040. Tel: 732-932-7129. Fax: 732-445-3472. p. 1509

Puniello, Francoise, Assoc Univ Librn, Rutgers University Libraries, Library of Science & Medicine, 165 Bevier Rd, Piscataway, NJ, 08854-8009. Tel: 732-445-3854. Fax: 732-445-5703. p. 1509

Punneo, Jackie, Librn, Chattanooga Times Free Press Library, 400 E 11th St, Chattanooga, TN, 37403. Tel: 423-757-6238. Fax: 423-668-5067. p. 2227

Puntney, Rhonda, Youth Serv, Lakeshores Library System, 725 Cornerstone Crossing, Ste C, Waterford, WI, 53185. Tel: 262-514-4500, Ext 67. Fax: 262-514-4544. p. 2644

Pupino, Kaaren, Acq, Head, Tech Serv, Ser, University of North Dakota, 215 Centennial Dr, Grand Forks, ND, 58202. Tel: 701-777-2204. Fax: 701-777-2217. p. 1843

Purce, Mame, Coll Develop, Ref Librn, West Chester University, 25 W Rosedale Ave, West Chester, PA, 19383. Tel: 610-738-0467. p. 2153

Purcell, Aaron, Dir, Spec Coll, Virginia Polytechnic Institute & State University Libraries, Drill Field Dr, Blacksburg, VA, 24062-9001. Tel: 540-231-9672. Fax: 540-231-3946. p. 2451

Purcell, Chris, Web Developer, Drake University, 2725 University Ave, Des Moines, IA, 50311. Tel: 515-271-2975. Fax: 515-271-3933. p. 809

Purcell, Elsie, Circ Mgr, Mustang Public Library, 1201 N Mustang Rd, Mustang, OK, 73064. Tel: 405-376-2226. Fax: 405-376-9925. p. 1969

Purcell, Kathleen V, Librn V/Human Res, Public Library Association of Annapolis & Anne Arundel County, Inc, Five Harry S Truman Pkwy, Annapolis, MD, 21401. Tel: 410-222-7107. Fax: 410-222-7188. p. 1010

Purcell, Sandra, Asst Librn, Casey Township Library, 307 E Main St, Casey, IL, 62420. Tel: 217-932-2105. Fax: 217-932-2105. p. 602

Purchase, Daphne, Ch, Avondale Public Library, 495 E Western Ave, Avondale, AZ, 85323. Tel: 623-478-3100. Fax: 623-478-3809. p. 57

Purdue, Jeff, Coll Develop Librn, Western Washington University, 516 High St, MS 9103, Bellingham, WA, 98225. Tel: 360-650-3079. Fax: 360-650-3044. p. 2509

Purdy, Charlanne, Sr Librn, Tampa-Hillsborough County Public Library System, Ruskin Branch, One Dickman Dr SE, Ruskin, FL, 33570-4314. Fax: 813-671-7698. p. 498

Purdy, Dan, Head of Libr, Lincoln County Law Library, Lincoln County Courthouse, 32 High St, Wiscasset, ME, 04578. Tel: 207-882-7517. p. 1008

Purdy, David J, Learning Res Ctr Coordr, Colorado Mountain College, Timberline Campus Learning Resources Center, 901 S Hwy 24, Leadville, CO, 80461. Tel: 719-486-4249. Fax: 719-486-4221. p. 316

Purdy, Deborah, Webmaster, YA Serv, Haverford Township Free Library, 1601 Darby Rd, Havertown, PA, 19083-3798. Tel: 610-446-3082, Ext 207. Fax: 610-853-3090. p. 2067

Purdy, Kris, Acq, Ohio State University LIBRARIES, Agricultural Technical Institute Library, Halterman Hall, 1328 Dover Rd, Wooster, OH, 44691-4000. Tel: 330-287-1225. Fax: 330-287-1333. p. 1887

Purdy, Mary, Acq, Slippery Rock University of Pennsylvania, Slippery Rock, PA, 16057-9989. Tel: 724-738-2058. Fax: 724-738-2661. p. 2140

Purdy, Rebecca, Mgr, Youth Serv, Central Rappahannock Regional Library, 1201 Caroline St, Fredericksburg, VA, 22401-3761. Tel: 540-372-1144. Fax: 540-373-9411. p. 2465

Pure, Jo-Ann, Ref Serv, Haddonfield Public Library, 60 Haddon Ave, Haddonfield, NJ, 08033-2422. Tel: 856-429-1304. Fax: 856-429-3760. p. 1489

Purewal, Armajot, Cat Librn, Mississippi Valley State University, 14000 Hwy 82 W, Itta Bena, MS, 38941. Tel: 662-254-3494. Fax: 662-254-3499. p. 1302

Purifoy, Marian, ILL, Putnam County Library System, 601 College Rd, Palatka, FL, 32177-3873. Tel: 386-329-0126. Fax: 386-329-1240. p. 478

Purington, Donald, Asst Librn, Heath Public Library, One E Main St, Heath, MA, 01346. Tel: 413-337-4934. Fax: 413-337-8542. p. 1095

Purintun, Mary, Dir, Hazel L Meyer Memorial Library, 114 First St, De Smet, SD, 57231. Tel: 605-854-3842. Fax: 605-854-3842. p. 2211

Purintun, Nancy, Dir, Overton Community Library, 407 Hwy 30, Overton, NE, 68863. Tel: 308-987-2543. p. 1416

Puritz, Mary Lou, Librn, Roanoke Public Libraries, Williamson Road, 3837 Williamson Rd NW, Roanoke, VA, 24012. Tel: 540-853-2340. Fax: 540-853-1065. p. 2494

Purkis, Trish, Asst Archivist, Sir Alexander Galt Museum & Archives, West End of Fifth Ave S, Lethbridge, AB, T1J 0P6, CANADA. Tel: 403-329-7302. Fax: 403-329-4958. p. 2710

Purkiss Oleson, Marissa, Br Mgr, San Bernardino County Library, Bloomington Branch, 10145 Orchard St, Bloomington, CA, 92316. Tel: 909-877-1453. Fax: 909-820-0533. p. 228

Puro, Alice, ILL, University of Dallas, 1845 E Northgate Dr, Irving, TX, 75062-4736. Tel: 972-721-5328. Fax: 972-721-4010. p. 2347

Purpera, Donna, Librn, Georgia Gulf Corp Library, 26100 Hwy 405, Plaquemine, LA, 70764. Tel: 225-298-2785. Fax: 225-687-8630. p. 965

Purpora, Samantha, Info Spec, Medaille College Library, 18 Agassiz Circle, Buffalo, NY, 14214. Tel: 716-880-2283. Fax: 716-884-9638. p. 1598

Purrington, Win, Tech Serv, Canton Public Library, 40 Dyer Ave, Canton, CT, 06019. Tel: 860-693-5800. Fax: 860-693-5804. p. 333

Purschke, Pat, Chairperson, Lamont Public Library, 4811 50 Ave, Lamont, AB, T0B 2R0, CANADA. Tel: 780-895-2299. Fax: 780-895-2600. p. 2709

Purser, Cynthia, Assoc Dir, Scott County Library System, 13090 Alabama Ave S, Savage, MN, 55378-1479. Tel: 952-707-1765. Fax: 952-707-1775. p. 1283

Purtee, Beth, Tech Serv Librn, Trevecca Nazarene University, 73 Lester Ave, Nashville, TN, 37210-4227. Tel: 615-248-1455. Fax: 615-248-1452. p. 2259

Purtee, Beth, Coordr, Christian Library Consortium, c/o ACL, PO Box 4, Cedarville, OH, 45314. Tel: 937-766-2255. Fax: 937-766-5499. p. 2951

Purtee, Sharon Ann, Mgr, Cat & Coll Serv, University of Cincinnati Libraries, Donald C Harrison Health Sciences Library, PO Box 670574, Cincinnati, OH, 45267-0574. Tel: 513-558-1019. Fax: 513-558-2682. p. 1874

Purtell, Joe, Libr Serv Mgr, Anaheim Public Library, Sunkist, 901 S Sunkist St, Anaheim, CA, 92806-4739. Tel: 714-765-3576. Fax: 714-765-3574. p. 121

Purves, Dennis Patrick, Jr, Dir, Linden Free Public Library, 31 E Henry St, Linden, NJ, 07036. Tel: 908-298-3830. Fax: 908-486-2636. p. 1495

Purvis, Dot, Br Mgr, Morton Public Library, 16 E Fourth Ave, Morton, MS, 39117. Tel: 601-732-6288. Fax: 601-732-6288. p. 1309

Purvis, Lola H, Chief, Libr Serv, Department of Veterans Affairs, VA Medical Center, 2495 Shreveport Hwy 71 N, Alexandria, LA, 71360. Tel: 318-473-0010, Ext 2548. Fax: 318-473-9491. p. 939

Purvis, Miranda, Asst Dir, Ricks Memorial Library (Yazoo Library Association), 310 N Main St, Yazoo City, MS, 39194-4253. Tel: 662-746-5557. Fax: 662-746-7309. p. 1318

Puryer, Sinda M, Circ, ILL, Flathead Valley Community College Library, 777 Grandview Dr, Kalispell, MT, 59901. Tel: 406-756-3856. Fax: 406-756-3854. p. 1384

Pusateri, Rachel, Pub Serv Librn, Green Mountain College Library, One Brennan Circle, Poultney, VT, 05764-1078. Tel: 802-287-8225. Fax: 802-287-8222. p. 2432

Pusey, Ann, Br Mgr, Orange County Public Library, Carrboro Cybrary Branch, Carrboro Century Ctr, 100 N Greensboro St, Carrboro, NC, 27510. Tel: 919-918-7387. Fax: 919-918-3960. p. 1803

Pusey, Anne, Br Mgr, Orange County Public Library, Carrboro Branch, McDougle Middle School, 900 Old Fayetteville Rd, Chapel Hill, NC, 27516. Tel: 919-969-3006. Fax: 919-969-3008. p. 1802

Pushkar, J, Asst Librn, Congregation B'Nai Israel, 4401 Indian School Rd NE, Albuquerque, NM, 87110-3914. Tel: 505-266-0155. Fax: 505-268-6136. p. 1549

Pushkina, Natalya, Librn, Massachusetts Department of Corrections, Institutional Library at Massachusetts Treatment Center, One Administration Rd, Bridgewater, MA, 02324. Tel: 508-279-8100, Ext 8443. p. 1070

Puska, Martha, Libr Tech, Finlandia University, 601 Quincy St, Hancock, MI, 49930-1882. Tel: 906-487-7252. Fax: 906-487-7297. p. 1187

Pustejovsky, Cynthia, Br Librn, Butte County Library, Biggs Branch, 464A B St, Biggs, CA, 95917-9796. Tel: 530-868-5724. p. 202

Pustejovsky, Cynthia, Br Librn, Butte County Library, Durham Branch, 2545 Durham-Dayton Hwy, Durham, CA, 95938-9615. Tel: 530-879-3835. p. 202

Pustejovsky, Cynthia, Br Librn, Butte County Library, Gridley Branch, 299 Spruce St, Gridley, CA, 95948-0397. Tel: 530-846-3323. p. 202

Pustz, Jennifer, Historian, Historic New England, Library & Archives, 141 Cambridge St, Boston, MA, 02114. Tel: 617-227-3957, Ext 251. Fax: 617-973-9050. p. 1062

Puterbaugh, Mark, Info Serv, Eastern University, 1300 Eagle Rd, Saint Davids, PA, 19087. Tel: 610-341-1461. Fax: 610-341-1375. p. 2135

Puterbaugh, Travis, Archivist, Asst Curator, Tampa Bay History Center, 801 Old Water St, Tampa, FL, 33602. Tel: 813-228-0097. Fax: 813-223-7021. p. 497

Puterko, Susan, Br Mgr, Chicago Public Library, Hegewisch, 3048 E 130th St, Chicago, IL, 60633. Tel: 312-747-0046. Fax: 312-747-8862. p. 608

Puthoff, Marian, In Charge, Siouxland Libraries, Humboldt Branch, 201 S Main St, Humboldt, SD, 57035-0166. Tel: 605-363-3361. Fax: 605-363-3361. p. 2219

Putnam, Cheryl, Mgr, Synergy Medical Education Alliance, Covenant Houghton Bldg, 2nd Flr, 1000 Houghton Ave, Ste 2000, Saginaw, MI, 48602-5398. Tel: 989-583-6846. Fax: 989-583-6898. p. 1224

Putnam, Laurie, Pub Serv, New Milford Public Library, 24 Main St, New Milford, CT, 06776. Tel: 860-355-1191, Ext 203. Fax: 860-350-9579. p. 360

Putnam, Linda, Ref, Portland Public Library, Five Monument Sq, Portland, ME, 04101. Tel: 207-871-1725. Fax: 207-871-1703. p. 997

Putnam, Lucy, Archivist, Home Missioners of America, PO Box 465618, Cincinnati, OH, 45246-5618. Tel: 513-881-7439. Fax: 513-874-1690. p. 1870

Putnam, Lydia, Coordr, Ser, Biblical Theological Seminary Library, 200 N Main St, Hatfield, PA, 19440-2499. Tel: 215-368-5000, Ext 123. Fax: 215-368-6906. p. 2067

Putnam, Sarah, Librn, Orford Social Library, 573 NH Rte 10, Orford, NH, 03777. Tel: 603-353-9756. p. 1461

Putnam, Sumner, Dir, Clarence Dillon Public Library, 2336 Lamington Rd, Bedminster, NJ, 07921. Tel: 908-234-2325. Fax: 908-781-9402. p. 1471

Putnam, Thomas, Dir, National Archives & Records Administration, Columbia Point, Boston, MA, 02125. Tel: 617-514-1600. Fax: 617-514-1593. p. 1064

Putt, Steven, Electronic Serv, Calvin College & Calvin Theological Seminary, 1855 Knollcrest Circle SE, Grand Rapids, MI, 49546-4402. Tel: 616-526-6311. Fax: 616-526-6470. p. 1184

Puttaiah, Prema, Libr Assoc, Circ & Reserves, West Virginia University Institute of Technology, 405 Fayette Pike, Montgomery, WV, 25136-2436. Tel: 304-442-3230. Fax: 304-442-3091. p. 2565

Putz, Heidi, Ref, Shook, Hardy & Bacon, 2555 Grand Blvd, 3rd Flr, Kansas City, MO, 64108-2613. Tel: 816-474-6550. Fax: 816-421-5547. p. 1341

Putz, Ro, Br Coordr, Sweet Briar College, 134 Chapel Rd, Sweet Briar, VA, 24595-1200. Tel: 434-381-6138. Fax: 434-381-6173. p. 2497

Puwalski, Stan, Evening Supvr, DeVry University Library, 1350 Alum Creek Dr, Columbus, OH, 43209. Tel: 614-257-4625. Fax: 614-252-4108. p. 1885

Puxley, Katie, Doc Delivery, Mount Saint Vincent University Library, 166 Bedford Hwy, Halifax, NS, B3M 2J6, CANADA. Tel: 902-457-6435. Fax: 902-457-6445. p. 2781

Pyatt, Sherman, Br Mgr, Charleston County Public Library, Cooper River Memorial, 3503 Rivers Ave, Charleston Heights, SC, 29405. Tel: 843-572-4094. Fax: 843-747-6904. p. 2183

Pyatt, Tim, Univ Archivist & Assoc Dir of RBMSCL, Duke University Libraries, 411 Chapel Dr, Durham, NC, 27708. Tel: 919-684-8929. Fax: 919-660-5923. p. 1787

Pyatt, Timothy D, Head & Dorothy Foehr Huck Chair, Pennsylvania State University Libraries, Eberly Family Special Collections Library, 104 Paterno Library, University Park, PA, 16802-1808. Tel: 814-865-1793, 814-865-7931. Fax: 814-863-5318. p. 2148

Pye, Beth, Ref & Instrul Serv Librn, Gordon College Library, 419 College Dr, Barnesville, GA, 30204. Tel: 770-358-5078. Fax: 770-358-5240. p. 521

Pye, Linda, Tech Serv Librn, Southwestern Oklahoma State University, 100 Campus Dr, Weatherford, OK, 73096-3002. Tel: 580-774-7021. Fax: 580-774-3112. p. 1985

Pye, Nicole, Archivist, Ref Librn, Mid-Continent Public Library, Midwest Genealogy Center, 3440 S Lee's Summit Rd, Independence, MO, 64055-1923. Tel: 816-252-7228. Fax: 816-254-7146. p. 1333

Pyeatt, Fran, Cat, Sullivan County Public Library, 1655 Blountville Blvd, Blountville, TN, 37617. Tel: 423-279-2714. Fax: 423-279-2836. p. 2224

Pyko, Marie, Pub Serv Mgr, Topeka & Shawnee County Public Library, 1515 SW Tenth Ave, Topeka, KS, 66604-1374. Tel: 785-580-4400. Fax: 785-580-4496. p. 897

Pyle, Albert, Exec Dir, Mercantile Library Association, 414 Walnut St, Cincinnati, OH, 45202. Tel: 513-621-0717. Fax: 513-621-2023. p. 1871

Pyle, Cathy, Supvr, Ser, Barry University, 11300 NE Second Ave, Miami, FL, 33161. Tel: 305-899-3760. Fax: 305-899-4792. p. 464

Pyle, Delores, Mgr, Cabell County Public Library, West Huntington, 901 W 14th St, Huntington, WV, 25704. Tel: 304-528-5697. Fax: 304-528-5697. p. 2561

Pyle, Erica, Libr Dir, Columbia Public Library, 106 N Metter, Columbia, IL, 62236-2299. Tel: 618-281-4237. Fax: 618-281-6977. p. 631

Pyle, James W, Librn, Licking County Law Library Association, 65 E Main St, Newark, OH, 43055. Tel: 740-349-6561. Fax: 740-349-6561. p. 1922

Pyle, Nancy, Educ Serv Supvr, Marion General Hospital, 441 N Wabash Ave, Marion, IN, 46952. Tel: 765-662-4760. Fax: 765-662-4523. p. 763

Pyles, Kathy, ILL, Andover Public Library, 1511 E Central Ave, Andover, KS, 67002. Tel: 316-558-3500. Fax: 316-558-3503. p. 856

Pyne, Ruth, Dir, Libr Serv, Anna Maria College, 50 Sunset Lane, Paxton, MA, 01612-1198. Tel: 508-849-3406. Fax: 508-849-3408. p. 1116

Pyne, Shirley, Tech Serv, Milton Public Library, 476 Canton Ave, Milton, MA, 02186-3299. Tel: 617-698-5757. Fax: 617-698-0441. p. 1106

Pype, Paul, Syst Librn, Alberta Legislature Library, 216 Legislature Bldg, 10800-97 Ave, Edmonton, AB, T5K 2B6, CANADA. Tel: 780-644-5015. Fax: 780-427-6016. p. 2699

Pyper, Cathy, Br Head, Toronto Public Library, Eglinton Square, Eglinton Square Mall, One Eglinton Sq, Unit 126, Toronto, ON, M1L 2K1, CANADA. Tel: 416-396-8920. Fax: 416-396-3557. p. 2861

Pyper, Jane, City Librn, Toronto Public Library, 789 Yonge St, Toronto, ON, M4W 2G8, CANADA. Tel: 416-393-7131. Fax: 416-393-7229. p. 2860

Pyrzynski, Mary Ann, Mgr, Patron Serv, Tinley Park Public Library, 7851 Timber Dr, Tinley Park, IL, 60477-3398. Tel: 708-532-0160, Ext 3. Fax: 708-532-2981. p. 709

Pyzinski, Susan, Assoc Librn, Tech Serv, Harvard Library, Houghton Library-Rare Books & Manuscripts, Houghton Library, Cambridge, MA, 02138. Tel: 617-495-2441. Fax: 617-495-1376. p. 1075

Qi, Lily, Tech Serv, Cheyney University, 1837 University Circle, Cheyney, PA, 19319. Tel: 610-399-2203. Fax: 610-399-2491. p. 2044

Qian, Jin, Dir, Libr & Info Serv, Wilson Elser Moskowitz Edelman & Dicker LLP, 150 E 42nd St, New York, NY, 10017. Tel: 212-490-3000. Fax: 212-490-3038. p. 1703

Qian, Shu, Sci Ref Instruction Librn, University of Maryland, Baltimore County, 1000 Hilltop Circle, Baltimore, MD, 21250. Tel: 410-455-2356. p. 1018

Qin, Liping, Head, Cat, The John Marshall Law School, 315 S Plymouth Ct, Chicago, IL, 60604. Tel: 312-427-2737. Fax: 312-427-8307. p. 618

Qiu, Sandy, Sr Librn, Ref, Skadden, Arps, Slate, Meagher & Flom LLP Library, 155 N Wacker Dr, Chicago, IL, 60606. Tel: 312-407-0941. Fax: 312-407-0411. p. 624

Qiu, Shu, Dir, Dalton Community Library, 113 E Main St, Dalton, PA, 18414. Tel: 570-563-2014. Fax: 570-563-2512. p. 2048

Qu, Yan, Br Mgr, Cambridge Public Library, O'Connell Branch, 48 Sixth St, Cambridge, MA, 02141. Tel: 617-349-4019. Fax: 617-349-4420. p. 1073

Quackenbush, Pam, Tech Serv, Lyon Township Public Library, 27005 S Milford Rd, South Lyon, MI, 48178. Tel: 248-437-8800. Fax: 248-437-4621. p. 1227

Quadri, Kulsum, Dir, Maywood Public Library, 459 Maywood Ave, Maywood, NJ, 07607-1909. Tel: 201-845-2915. Fax: 201-845-7387. p. 1500

Qualey, Debbie, Asst Dir, ILL Librn, Ingalls Memorial Library, 203 Main St, Rindge, NH, 03461. Tel: 603-899-3303. Fax: 603-899-5797. p. 1463

Quam, Allison, Pub Serv Coordr, Winona State University, 175 W Mark St, Winona, MN, 55987-5838. Tel: 507-457-2644. p. 1290

Quan, Kathryn, Br Head, Toronto Public Library, Sanderson, 327 Bathurst St, Toronto, ON, M5T 1J1, CANADA. Tel: 416-393-7653. Fax: 416-393-7702. p. 2863

Quan, Shirley N, Coll Develop Mgr, OC Public Libraries, 1501 E St Andrew Pl, Santa Ana, CA, 92705-4048. Tel: 714-566-3000. Fax: 714-566-3042. p. 258

Quance, Marilyn, Head, Tech Serv, Wayne State College, 1111 Main St, Wayne, NE, 68787. Tel: 402-375-7474. Fax: 402-375-7538. p. 1423

Quarders, Mandy, Br Mgr, Campbell County Public Library System, Wright Branch, 305 Wright Blvd, Wright, WY, 82732. Tel: 307-464-0500. Fax: 307-464-0502. p. 2655

Quarles, Brandon, Dir, Baylor University Libraries, Sheridan & John Eddie Williams Legal Research & Technology Center, 1114 S University Parks Dr, One Bear Pl, No 97128, Waco, TX, 76798-7128. Tel: 254-710-2168. Fax: 254-710-2294. p. 2397

Quarles, Melissa, Ch, Monroe Free Library, 44 Millpond Pkwy, Monroe, NY, 10950. Tel: 845-783-4411. Fax: 845-782-4707. p. 1662

Quarles, Robert, Libr Dir, Atlanta Metropolitan State College Library, 1630 Metropolitan Pkwy SW, Atlanta, GA, 30310. Tel: 404-756-4010. Fax: 404-756-5613. p. 513

Quarstein, John V, Dir, Virginia War Museum, Major George B Collings Memorial Library, 9285 Warwick Blvd, Newport News, VA, 23607. Tel: 757-247-8523. Fax: 757-247-8627. p. 2480

Quarton, Barbara, Coordr, Instruction, California State University, San Bernardino, 5500 University Pkwy, San Bernardino, CA, 92407-2318. Tel: 909-537-7553. Fax: 909-537-7048. p. 227

Quashnick, Amanda, Librn, United States Navy, Command Library, Puget Sound Naval Shipyard & Intermediate Maintenance Facility, 1400 Farragut Ave, Bremerton, WA, 98314-5001. Tel: 360-476-2767. Fax: 360-476-1730. p. 2511

Quast, Debra M, Dir, Westmont College, 955 La Paz Rd, Santa Barbara, CA, 93108-1099. Tel: 805-565-6000, 805-565-6147. Fax: 805-565-6220. p. 262

Quataro, Harry, Registrar, Saint Lucie County Historical Museum, 414 Seaway Dr, Fort Pierce, FL, 34949. Tel: 772-462-1795. Fax: 772-462-1877. p. 447

Quattrocchi, Karen, Online Serv, Nicolet Area Technical College, 5364 College Dr, Rhinelander, WI, 54501. Tel: 715-365-4409. Fax: 715-365-4404. p. 2633

Queen, Leota, Librn, Lockwood Public Library, 721 Main St, Lockwood, MO, 65682. Tel: 417-232-4204. p. 1343

Queener, Frank, Dir, Finger Lakes Community College, 4355 Lakeshore Dr, Canandaigua, NY, 14424-8395. Tel: 585-394-3500, Ext 7371. Fax: 585-394-8708. p. 1601

Queler, Reva, ILL, John C Hart Memorial Library, 1130 Main St, Shrub Oak, NY, 10588. Tel: 914-245-5262. Fax: 914-245-2216. p. 1743

Quelland, Nancy, Dir, Palmdale City Library, 700 E Palmdale Blvd, Palmdale, CA, 93550. Tel: 661-267-5600. Fax: 661-267-5606. p. 203

Query, Lance, Dean of Libr, Tulane University, 7001 Freret St, New Orleans, LA, 70118-5682. Tel: 504-865-5131. Fax: 504-865-6773. p. 963

Quesada, Debbie, Br Mgr, Florence County Library System, Lake City Public Library, 221 E Main St, Lake City, SC, 29560-2113. Tel: 843-394-8071. Fax: 843-394-1033. p. 2193

Quesenberry, Gina, Commun Libr Mgr, County of Los Angeles Public Library, El Monte Library, 3224 Tyler Ave, El Monte, CA, 91731-3356. Tel: 626-444-9506. Fax: 626-443-5864. p. 141

Quesnel, Helene, Br Head, Ch, Township of Russell Public Library, 1053 Concession St, Box 280, Russell, ON, K4R 1E1, CANADA. Tel: 613-445-5331. Fax: 613-445-8014. p. 2839

Quezada, Shelley, Ref Serv, Middlesex Community College, Bldg 1-ARC, Springs Rd, Bedford, MA, 01730. Tel: 781-280-3708. Fax: 781-280-3771. p. 1052

Quick, Angela Myatt, Dir, Maryville College, 502 E Lamar Alexander Pkwy, Maryville, TN, 37804-5907. Tel: 865-981-8038. Fax: 865-981-8267. p. 2247

Quick, Anne, Librn I, Youth Serv, Dobbs Ferry Public Library, 55 Main St, Dobbs Ferry, NY, 10522. Tel: 914-693-6614. Fax: 914-693-4671. p. 1615

Quick, Brenda, Circ Supvr, Sandhills Community College, 3395 Airport Rd, Pinehurst, NC, 28374. Tel: 910-695-3969. Fax: 910-695-3947. p. 1814

Quick, Larry, Computer Serv, Easton Area Public Library & District Center, 515 Church St, Easton, PA, 18042-3587. Tel: 610-258-2917. Fax: 610-253-2231. p. 2052

Quick, Margaret, Dir, NorthEast-Millerton Library, 75 Main St, Millerton, NY, 12546-5172. Tel: 518-789-3340. Fax: 518-789-6802. p. 1661

Quick, Spring, Adult Serv, Silver Falls Library District, 410 S Water St, Silverton, OR, 97381-2137. Tel: 503-873-5173. Fax: 503-873-6227. p. 2020

Quigel, James, Head, Hist Coll & Labor Archives, Pennsylvania State University Libraries, Eberly Family Special Collections Library, 104 Paterno Library, University Park, PA, 16802-1808. Tel: 814-863-3181. Fax: 814-863-5318. p. 2148

Quigley, Anne, Dir, Valentine Public Library, 324 N Main St, Valentine, NE, 69201. Tel: 402-376-3160. Fax: 402-376-3160. p. 1422

Quigley, Brian, Interim Head of Libr, University of California, Berkeley, Earth Sciences & Maps, 50 McCone Hall, Berkeley, CA, 94720-6000. Tel: 510-642-2997. Fax: 510-643-6576. p. 127

Quigley, Brian, Head Librn, University of California, Berkeley, Mathematics-Statistics, 100 Evans Hall, Berkeley, CA, 94720-6000. Tel: 510-642-3381. Fax: 510-642-8257. p. 128

Quigley, Brian, Assoc Dir, University of Texas Libraries, Jamail Center for Legal Research, University of Texas School of Law, 727 E Dean Keeton St, Austin, TX, 78705-3224. Tel: 512-471-7726. Fax: 512-471-0243. p. 2284

Quigley, Jane, Head of Libr, Dartmouth College Library, Kresge Physical Sciences Library, 6115 Fairchild Hall, Hanover, NH, 03755-3571. Tel: 603-646-3563. Fax: 603-646-3681. p. 1450

Quigley, Kristin, Cataloger, Head, Tech Serv, Idaho State Law Library, 322 E Front St, Ste 560, Boise, ID, 83702. Tel: 208-364-4557. Fax: 208-334-2467. p. 571

Quigley, Megan, Ch, Saxton B Little Free Library, Inc, 319 Rte 87, Columbia, CT, 06237-1143. Tel: 860-228-0350. Fax: 860-228-1569. p. 334

Quigley, Shelagh, Dir, Human Res, Kingston Frontenac Public Library, 130 Johnson St, Kingston, ON, K7L 1X8, CANADA. Tel: 613-549-8888, Ext 1515. Fax: 613-549-8476. p. 2813

Quigley, Thomas, Br Head, Vancouver Public Library, Joe Fortes Branch, 870 Denman St, Vancouver, BC, V6G 2L8, CANADA. Tel: 604-665-3972. Fax: 604-665-3524. p. 2744

Quijano, Andrea, Electronic Res Librn, The Rockefeller University, 1222 York Ave, Welch Hall, New York, NY, 10065. Tel: 212-327-8944. Fax: 212-327-8802. p. 1698

Quiles, Esther, Librn, Anderson, Kill & Olick, 1251 Avenue of the Americas, New York, NY, 10020-1182. Tel: 212-278-1069. Fax: 212-278-1733. p. 1669

Quiles-Miranda, Zulma, Coordr, Info Serv, University of Puerto Rico Library, Rio Piedras Campus, San Juan, PR, 00931. Tel: 787-764-0000, Ext 2359. Fax: 787-764-2890. p. 2676

Quillen, C L, Adult Serv, Info Serv, Old Bridge Public Library, One Old Bridge Plaza, Old Bridge, NJ, 08857-2498. Tel: 732-607-7921, 732-721-5600, Ext 5010. Fax: 732-679-0556. p. 1516

Quillen, Chris, ILL, Emmanuel School of Religion Library, One Walker Dr, Johnson City, TN, 37601-9438. Tel: 423-926-1186. Fax: 423-926-6198. p. 2239

Quillen, Evelyn, Libr Serv Supvr, White & Williams, LLP, 1800 One Liberty Pl, Philadelphia, PA, 19103-7395. Tel: 215-864-7000. Fax: 215-864-7123. p. 2120

Quillen, Steven, Coll Develop, National Oceanic & Atmospheric Administration, 1315 East West Hwy, 2nd Flr, Silver Spring, MD, 20910. Tel: 301-713-2600, Ext 157. Fax: 301-713-4598. p. 1042

Quilliam, Patricia, Asst Librn, Swanton Public Library, One First St, Swanton, VT, 05488. Tel: 802-868-7656. p. 2437

Quimby, Sean M, Sr Dir, Spec Coll, Syracuse University Library, 222 Waverly Ave, Syracuse, NY, 13244-2010. Tel: 315-443-2573. p. 1754

Quiner, Theresa, Circ Supvr, Orange County Public Library, 137 W Margaret Lane, Hillsborough, NC, 27278. Tel: 919-245-2525. Fax: 919-644-3003. p. 1802

Quinlan, Elizabeth, Sr Info Spec, John D & Catherine T MacArthur Foundation Library, 140 S Dearborn St, Ste 1200, Chicago, IL, 60603-5285. Tel: 312-726-8000. Fax: 312-920-6259. p. 618

Quinlan, Jennifer, Fac Librn, Mount Hood Community College Library, 26000 SE Stark St, Gresham, OR, 97030. Tel: 503-491-7161. Fax: 503-491-7389. p. 1999

Quinlan, Kathy, Asst Dir, Cary Memorial Library, 1874 Massachusetts Ave, Lexington, MA, 02420. Tel: 781-862-6288, Ext 314. Fax: 781-862-7355. p. 1099

Quinlan, Maureen P, Govt Doc Law Librn, Ref Serv, University of Maine School of Law, 246 Deering Ave, Portland, ME, 04102. Tel: 207-780-4829. Fax: 207-780-4913. p. 997

Quinlan, Nora, Head, Ref, Nova Southeastern University Libraries, 3100 Ray Ferrero Jr Blvd, Fort Lauderdale, FL, 33314. Tel: 954-262-4637. Fax: 954-262-3805. p. 444

Quinn, Ann, Head, Ch, Carnegie Public Library, 127 S North St, Washington Court House, OH, 43160. Tel: 740-335-2540. Fax: 740-335-8409. p. 1945

Quinn, Arthur G, Dir, Libr Serv, St Vincent de Paul Regional Seminary Library, 10701 S Military Trail, Boynton Beach, FL, 33436-4811. Tel: 561-732-4424, Ext 174. Fax: 561-737-2205. p. 429

Quinn, Ashley, Coordr, Access Serv, University of Dayton Libraries, 300 College Park Dr, Dayton, OH, 45469-1360. Tel: 937-229-4221. Fax: 937-229-4215. p. 1894

Quinn, Chris, Acq, Ser, Saint John's College, 1160 Camino Cruz Blanca, Santa Fe, NM, 87505. Tel: 505-984-6043. Fax: 505-984-6004. p. 1563

Quinn, David J, Dr, Head of Libr, Suffolk County Community College, 1001 Crooked Hill Rd, Brentwood, NY, 11717. Tel: 631-851-6740. Fax: 631-851-6509. p. 1584

Quinn, Donna M, Coordr, Pennsylvania Hospital, Medical Library, Three Pine Ctr, 800 Spruce St, Philadelphia, PA, 19107-6192. Tel: 215-829-3370. Fax: 215-829-7155. p. 2113

Quinn, Doreen, Librn, Harbour Grace Public Library, Harvey St, Harbour Grace, NL, A0A 2M0, CANADA. Tel: 709-596-3894. p. 2770

Quinn, Elizabeth, Tech Serv Supvr, Cherry Hill Public Library, 1100 Kings Hwy N, Cherry Hill, NJ, 08034-1911. Tel: 856-903-1250. Fax: 856-667-9503. p. 1478

Quinn, Frank, Dir, Point Loma Nazarene University, 3900 Lomaland Dr, San Diego, CA, 92106-2899. Tel: 619-849-2355. Fax: 619-222-0711. p. 232

Quinn, Frank, Pres, Association of Christian Librarians, PO Box 4, Cedarville, OH, 45314. Tel: 937-766-2255. Fax: 937-766-5499. p. 2951

Quinn, Glenna, Coll Develop, Saint Francis Xavier University, West St, Antigonish, NS, B2G 2W5, CANADA. Tel: 902-867-2168. Fax: 902-867-5153. p. 2777

Quinn, Jackie, Head Librn, Hinds Community College, Jackson Academic & Technical Center Learning Resources/Library, 3925 Sunset Dr, Jackson, MS, 39213-5899. Tel: 601-987-8123. Fax: 601-982-5804. p. 1313

Quinn, Jackie, Dir, Wibaux Public Library, 115 S Wibaux, Wibaux, MT, 59353. Tel: 406-796-2452. Fax: 406-796-2452. p. 1390

Quinn, James, Head Librn, Free Library of Philadelphia, Newspaper & Microfilm Center, 1901 Vine St, Philadelphia, PA, 19103-1189. Tel: 215-686-5431. Fax: 215-567-0398. p. 2108

Quinn, Joan M, Head, Libr Database, Elizabethtown College, One Alpha Dr, Elizabethtown, PA, 17022-2227. Tel: 717-361-1457. Fax: 717-361-1167. p. 2053

Quinn, Judy, Acq, Cat, Gateway Technical College, 3520 30th Ave, Kenosha, WI, 53144-1690. Tel: 262-564-2604, 564-2654. Fax: 262-564-2787. p. 2601

Quinn, Karen, Ch, Dir, Corbit-Calloway Memorial Library, 115 High St, Odessa, DE, 19730. Tel: 302-378-8838. Fax: 302-378-7803. p. 386

Quinn, Karen, Librn, Rhode Island State Law Library, Frank Licht Judicial Complex, 250 Benefit St, Providence, RI, 02903. Tel: 401-222-3275. Fax: 401-222-3865. p. 2175

Quinn, Kateri, Dir, Spring Lake Public Library, 1501 Third Ave, Spring Lake, NJ, 07762. Tel: 732-449-6654. p. 1532

Quinn, Kathryn, Librn, North Haven Library, 33 Main St, North Haven, ME, 04853. Tel: 207-867-9797. Fax: 207-867-9797. p. 994

Quinn, Lisa, Asst Librn, Canton Public Library, 786 Washington St, Canton, MA, 02021-3029. Tel: 781-821-5027. Fax: 781-821-5029. p. 1079

Quinn, Lisa, Ref Librn, Massapequa Public Library, 40 Harbor Lane, Massapequa Park, NY, 11762. Tel: 516-799-0770, Ext 302. Fax: 516-795-7528. p. 1658

Quinn, Lori, Actg Dir, Glen Rock Public Library, 315 Rock Rd, Glen Rock, NJ, 07452-1795. Tel: 201-670-3970. Fax: 201-445-0872. p. 1488

Quinn, Marilyn, Cat, Rider University, 2083 Lawrenceville Rd, Lawrenceville, NJ, 08648-3099. Tel: 609-895-5727. Fax: 609-896-8029. p. 1494

Quinn, Mary, Br Mgr, Jersey City Free Public Library, Glenn D Cunningham Branch Library & Community Center, 275 Martin Luther King Jr Dr, Jersey City, NJ, 07305. Tel: 201-547-4555. Fax: 201-547-5880. p. 1492

Quinn, Mary Anne, Adult Serv, Warwick Public Library, 600 Sandy Lane, Warwick, RI, 02889-8298. Tel: 401-739-5440, Ext 128. Fax: 401-732-2055. p. 2177

Quinn, Mary Rose, Dir, Stevens Memorial Library, 345 Main St, North Andover, MA, 01845. Tel: 978-688-9505. Fax: 978-688-9507. p. 1112

Quinn, Patricia, Assoc Dir, Rye Public Library, 581 Washington Rd, Rye, NH, 03870. Tel: 603-964-8401. Fax: 603-964-7065. p. 1464

Quinn, Paul, Mgr, Three Rivers Regional Library System, Camden County Library, 1410 Hwy 40 E, Kingsland, GA, 31548-9380. Tel: 912-729-2040, 912-729-3741. Fax: 912-729-2039. p. 522

Quinn, Robin, Dir, Hastings Memorial Library, 505 Central Ave, Grant, NE, 69140-3017. Tel: 308-352-4894. Fax: 308-352-2358. p. 1400

Quinn, Susan, Ch, River Forest Public Library, 735 Lathrop Ave, River Forest, IL, 60305-1883. Tel: 708-366-5205, Ext 315. Fax: 708-366-8699. p. 694

Quinn, Susan, Dir, Ocean County Library, 101 Washington St, Toms River, NJ, 08753. Tel: 732-349-6200. p. 1534

Quinn, Susan, Dir, East Williston Public Library, Two Prospect St, East Williston, NY, 11596. Tel: 516-741-1213. Fax: 516-746-3130. p. 1617

Racine, Richard, Dir, Haute-Yamaska, 135-1 Principale, Granby, QC, J2G 2V1, CANADA. Tel: 450-372-4500. Fax: 450-372-9904. p. 2884

Rackauskas, John A, Dr, Pres, Lithuanian Research & Studies Center, Inc, 5600 S Claremont Ave, Chicago, IL, 60636-1039. Tel: 773-434-4545. Fax: 773-434-9363. p. 617

Rackemann, Adelaide C, Librn, Cylburn Arboretum Association Library, 4915 Greenspring Ave, Baltimore, MD, 21209. Tel: 410-367-2217. Fax: 410-367-8039. p. 1012

Racki, David K, Access Serv Librn, Fresno City College Library, 1101 E University Ave, Fresno, CA, 93741. Tel: 559-442-8204. Fax: 559-265-5758. p. 151

Rackley, Nora, Govt Doc, Lake-Sumter Community College Library, 9501 US Hwy 441, Leesburg, FL, 34788-8751. Tel: 352-365-3586. Fax: 352-365-3590. p. 461

Racz, Adrienne, Libr Serv Rep, Franklin Medical Center, 164 High St, Greenfield, MA, 01301. Tel: 413-773-2211. Fax: 413-773-2094. p. 1092

Radcliff, Sharon, Ref & Instruction Librn, Saint Mary's College Library, 1928 Saint Mary's Rd, Moraga, CA, 94575. Tel: 925-631-4229. Fax: 925-376-6097. p. 191

Radcliffe, Katharina, Dir, Delanco Public Library, M Joan Pearson School, 1303 Burlington Ave, Delanco, NJ, 08075. Tel: 856-461-6850. Fax: 856-461-6850. p. 1481

Rade, Karen A, Dir, Montauk Library, 871 Montauk Hwy, Montauk, NY, 11954. Tel: 631-668-3377. Fax: 631-668-3468. p. 1662

Radebaugh, Jacqueline, Electronic Res & Syst Librn, Columbus State University Libraries, 4225 University Ave, Columbus, GA, 31907. Tel: 706-565-3555. Fax: 706-568-2084. p. 526

Rader, Conrad, Head, Adult Serv, Niles District Library, 620 E Main St, Niles, MI, 49120. Tel: 269-683-8545, Ext 113. Fax: 269-683-0075. p. 1214

Rader, Kay, Libr Mgr, San Luis Obispo County Library, Atascadero Branch, 6850 Morro Rd, Atascadero, CA, 93422. Tel: 805-461-6161. Fax: 805-461-6045. p. 254

Rader, Kay, Ref Serv Mgr, Springfield-Greene County Library District, 4653 S Campbell, Springfield, MO, 65810-1723. Tel: 417-882-0714. Fax: 417-883-9348. p. 1367

Rader, Robin, Libr Dir, Salvation Army School for Officer Training, 201 Lafayette Ave, Suffern, NY, 10901. Tel: 845-368-7228. Fax: 845-357-6644. p. 1750

Radermacher, Sharon, Tech Serv, Public Library of Mount Vernon & Knox County, 201 N Mulberry St, Mount Vernon, OH, 43050-2413. Tel: 740-392-2665. Fax: 740-397-3866. p. 1919

Radev, Dragomir, Assoc Prof, University of Michigan, 304 West Hall, 1085 S University, Ann Arbor, MI, 48109-1107. Tel: 734-763-2285. Fax: 734-764-2475. p. 2967

Radford, Lois, Coordr, Tidewater Community College, 1428 Cedar Rd, Chesapeake, VA, 23322. Fax: 757-822-5173. p. 2456

Radford, Suzette, Head, Circ, Northwestern University Library, 1970 Campus Dr, Evanston, IL, 60208-2300. Tel: 847-491-7658. p. 644

Radginski, Martha, Br Mgr, Saint Charles City County Library District, Middendorf-Kredell Branch, 2750 Hwy K, O'Fallon, MO, 63368-7859. Tel: 636-272-4999, 636-978-7926. Fax: 636-978-7998. p. 1364

Radick, Caryn, Digital Archivist, Rutgers University Libraries, Special Collections & University Archives, 169 College Ave, New Brunswick, NJ, 08901-1163. Tel: 848-932-6152. Fax: 732-932-7012. p. 1509

Radigan, Barbara, Dir, Pulteney Free Library, 9226 Rte 74, Pulteney, NY, 14874. Tel: 607-868-3652. Fax: 607-868-3652. p. 1724

Radin, Saul, Curator of Coll, Eastchester Historical Society, 390 California Rd, Eastchester, NY, 10709. Tel: 914-793-1900. p. 1618

Radioli, Jo Ann, Mgr, Brooklyn Public Library, Service to the Aging, 1743 86th St, Brooklyn, NY, 11214. Tel: 718-236-1760. Fax: 718-234-2680. p. 1592

Radisauskas, Christina, Info Literacy, Aquinas College, 1607 Robinson Rd SE, Grand Rapids, MI, 49506-1799. Tel: 616-632-2124. Fax: 616-732-4534. p. 1183

Radke, Jamie, Chief, Circ Br, United States Naval War College Library, 686 Cushing Rd, Newport, RI, 02841-1207. Tel: 401-841-2641. Fax: 401-841-6491. p. 2169

Radmam, Louise, Librn, Commission Scolaire de la Capitale, Louis-Jolliet, 1201 De Le Pointe-Aux-Lievres, Quebec, QC, G1N 4M1, CANADA. Tel: 418-525-8230. Fax: 418-525-8772. p. 2904

Radman, Carrie, Youth Serv Mgr, Columbiana Public Library, 332 N Middle St, Columbiana, OH, 44408. Tel: 330-482-5509. Fax: 330-482-9669. p. 1883

Radman, Ljiljana, Info Spec, Hatch Research & InfoCentres, 2800 Speakman Dr, Mississauga, ON, L5K 2R7, CANADA. Tel: 905-403-4196. Fax: 905-855-8270. p. 2822

Radniecki, Tara, Emerging Tech Librn, Ref & Instruction, Loyola Marymount University, One LMU Dr, MS 8200, Los Angeles, CA, 90045-2659. Tel: 310-337-7686. Fax: 310-338-4366. p. 175

Radnor, Mary, Res Sharing Librn, Florida International University, 3000 NE 151st St, North Miami, FL, 33181-3600. Tel: 305-919-5764. Fax: 305-919-5914. p. 472

Radonovich, Nancy, Cataloger, Head, Tech Serv, Louisiana State University at Alexandria, 8100 Hwy 71 S, Alexandria, LA, 71302. Tel: 318-473-6509. Fax: 318-473-6556. p. 939

Radoopersad, Guyatri Sharon, Law Librn, Lee County Law Library, Lee County Justice Ctr, 1700 Monroe St, Fort Myers, FL, 33901. Tel: 239-533-9195. Fax: 239-485-2598. p. 445

Radosevich, Debra, Dir, Thomaston Public Library, 248 Main St, Thomaston, CT, 06787. Tel: 860-283-4339. Fax: 860-283-4330. p. 372

Radosh, Sondra M, Head, Youth Serv, Jones Library, Inc, 43 Amity St, Amherst, MA, 01002-2285. Tel: 413-259-3219. Fax: 413-256-4096. p. 1049

Radovic, Sara, Br Mgr, Jacksonville Public Library, Bradham-Brooks Northwest Branch, 1755 Edgewood Ave W, Jacksonville, FL, 32208-7206. Tel: 904-765-5402. Fax: 904-768-7609. p. 453

Radovsky, Jennie, Br Mgr, Norfolk Public Library, Janaf, 124 Janaf Shopping Ctr, Norfolk, VA, 23502. Tel: 757-441-5660. Fax: 757-441-5715. p. 2482

Radtke, Nancy, Librn, Clinton Township Public Library, 110 S Elm St, Waterman, IL, 60556. Tel: 815-264-3339. Fax: 815-264-3814. p. 715

Radtke, Steven, Coll Mgr, Curator, Tri-Cities Historical Society Museum, 200 Washington Ave, Grand Haven, MI, 49417. Tel: 616-842-0700. Fax: 616-842-3698. p. 1183

Radujko, Gabriella, Dir, Bronxville Public Library, 201 Pondfield Rd, Bronxville, NY, 10708. Tel: 914-337-7680. Fax: 914-337-0332. p. 1588

Radzibon, Kathy, Librn, Presque Isle District Library, Onaway Branch, 20774 State St, Onaway, MI, 49765. Tel: 989-733-6621. Fax: 989-733-7842. p. 1222

Radziewicz, Mary Ellen, Youth Serv, Woods Memorial Library, 19 Pleasant St, Barre, MA, 01005. Tel: 978-355-2533. Fax: 978-355-2511. p. 1051

Rae, Deborah, Head, Metadata Serv, University of Delaware Library, 181 S College Ave, Newark, DE, 19717-5267. Tel: 302-831-2231. Fax: 302-831-1046. p. 386

Rae, Jana, Br Mgr, Aiken-Bamberg-Barnwell-Edgefield Regional Library System, Mobley Library/Johnston Branch, 407 Calhoun St, Johnston, SC, 29832. Tel: 803-275-5157. Fax: 803-275-2754. p. 2179

Raeber, Rochelle, Br Head, Saskatoon Public Library, Rusty MacDonald Branch, 225 Primrose Dr, Saskatoon, SK, S7K 5E4, CANADA. Tel: 306-975-7605. Fax: 306-975-7603. p. 2926

Raeford, Rosalyn, Dept Head, Cat, Duke University Libraries, 411 Chapel Dr, Durham, NC, 27708. Tel: 919-660-5892. Fax: 919-660-5923. p. 1787

Rael, Sylvia, Head, Pub Serv, Colorado Mesa University, 1200 College Pl, Grand Junction, CO, 81501. Tel: 970-248-1029. Fax: 970-248-1930. p. 310

Raeske-Grinch, Rebecca, Res Sharing Spec, Otterbein University, 138 W Main St, Westerville, OH, 43081. Tel: 614-823-1215. Fax: 614-823-1921. p. 1946

Raetzman, Amanda, Ref, Willmar Public Library, 410 Fifth St SW, Willmar, MN, 56201-3298. Tel: 320-235-3162. Fax: 320-235-3169. p. 1289

Rafael, Lucy, Librn, Center for Early Education Library, 563 N Alfred St, West Hollywood, CA, 90048-2512. Tel: 323-651-0707. Fax: 323-651-0860. p. 283

Rafael, Santos, Libr Tech, Universidad Central Del Caribe, Avenida Laurel, Santa Juanita, Bayamon, PR, 00956. Tel: 787-798-3001, Ext 2308. Fax: 787-785-3425. p. 2672

Rafal, Jane, VPres, OLI Systems, Inc Library, 108 American Rd, Morris Plains, NJ, 07950. Tel: 973-539-4996. Fax: 973-539-5922. p. 1504

Rafal, Marian, Head, Youth Serv, Bloomfield Township Public Library, 1099 Lone Pine Rd, Bloomfield Township, MI, 48302-2410. Tel: 248-642-5800. Fax: 248-258-2555. p. 1159

Rafal, Marshall, Pres, OLI Systems, Inc Library, 108 American Rd, Morris Plains, NJ, 07950. Tel: 973-539-4996, Ext 21. Fax: 973-539-5922. p. 1504

Raff, Amy, Asst Dir, Woodstock Library, Five Library Lane, Woodstock, NY, 12498-1299. Tel: 845-679-2213. Fax: 845-679-7149. p. 1771

Raffensperger, Thomas, Libr Dir, Westfield State University, 577 Western Ave, Westfield, MA, 01085-2580. Tel: 413-572-5251. Fax: 413-572-5520. p. 1138

Rafferty, Carol, Librn, Lemmon Public Library, 303 First Ave W, Lemmon, SD, 57638. Tel: 605-374-5611. p. 2214

Rafferty, Emily, Archivist, Assoc Librn, Baltimore Museum of Art, Ten Art Museum Dr, Baltimore, MD, 21218-3898. Tel: 443-573-1780. Fax: 443-573-1781. p. 1012

Rafferty, Jackie, Libr Dir, Paul Pratt Memorial Library, 35 Ripley Rd, Cohasset, MA, 02025-2097. Tel: 781-383-1348. Fax: 781-383-1698. p. 1082

Rafferty, John, Pres, Canadian National Institute for the Blind, 1929 Bayview Ave, Toronto, ON, M4G 3E8, CANADA. Fax: 416-480-7700. p. 2852

Rafferty, Rusty P, Chief Doc Librn, United States Army, Combined Arms Research Library, US Army Command & General Staff College, Eisenhower Hall, 250 Gibbon Ave, Fort Leavenworth, KS, 66027-2314. Tel: 913-758-3128. Fax: 913-758-3014. p. 867

Rafferty, Sharon, Tech Serv Librn, Seabrook Library, 25 Liberty Lane, Seabrook, NH, 03874-4506. Tel: 603-474-2044. Fax: 603-474-1835. p. 1465

Rafter, William, Head, Cat, Head, Per, Interim Head, Libr Syst, West Virginia University Libraries, WVU Libraries, 1549 University Ave, Morgantown, WV, 26506. Tel: 304-293-4040. Fax: 304-293-6638. p. 2566

Raftery, Susan R, Dean, Metropolitan Community College Library, 30th & Fort Sts, Omaha, NE, 68103. Tel: 402-457-2368. Fax: 402-457-2655. p. 1413

Rafuse, Rachael, Br Mgr, Mid-Continent Public Library, Platte City Branch, 2702 Prairie View Rd, Platte City, MO, 64079-7604. Tel: 816-858-2322. Fax: 816-858-3084. p. 1333

Ragains, Bonnie, Head, Ser, University of Nevada-Reno, Savitt Medical Library & IT Department, Pennington Medical Education

Bldg, 1664 N Virginia St, Mail Stop 306, Reno, NV, 89557. Tel: 775-784-4625. Fax: 775-784-4489. p. 1433

Ragan, Debra, Asst Librn, Wilford Hall Medical Center Library, 59MDW/SGN, Lackland AFB, TX, 78236-5300. Tel: 210-292-5770. Fax: 210-292-7030. p. 2352

Rager, Janie L, Assoc Dean, Libr Serv, Info & Instruction Librn, Saint Francis University, 106 Franciscan Way, Loretto, PA, 15940. Tel: 814-472-3011. Fax: 814-472-3154. p. 2083

Ragheb, Mohamed, Tech Mgr, Ella M Everhard Public Library, 132 Broad St, Wadsworth, OH, 44281-1897. Tel: 330-334-5761. Fax: 330-334-6605. p. 1943

Raglin, Mary Grace, Br Head, Librn, Letcher County Public Libraries, Blackey Branch, 295 Main Street Loop, Blackey, KY, 41804. Tel: 606-633-4013. Fax: 606-633-9808. p. 937

Ragnow, Marguerite, Curator, University of Minnesota Libraries-Twin Cities, James Ford Bell Library, 472 Wilson Library, 309 19th Ave S, Minneapolis, MN, 55455. Tel: 612-624-1528. Fax: 612-626-9353. p. 1262

Ragona, Denise, Bus Mgr, Helen M Plum Memorial Public Library District, 110 W Maple St, Lombard, IL, 60148-2594. Tel: 630-627-0316. Fax: 630-627-0336. p. 667

Ragsdale, Logan, Div Mgr, Queens Borough Public Library, Social Sciences Division, 89-11 Merrick Blvd, Jamaica, NY, 11432. Tel: 718-990-0761, 718-990-0762. p. 1645

Ragsdale, Pam, Librn, KPMG LLP Library, 303 E Wacker Dr, Chicago, IL, 60601. Tel: 312-665-5386. Fax: 312-665-6000. p. 616

Ragucci, Matthew, Librn, Monmouth County Library, Colts Neck Branch, One Winthrop Dr, Colts Neck, NJ, 07722. Tel: 732-431-5656. Fax: 732-462-0327. p. 1499

Ragus, Margaret, Circ, North Richland Hills Public Library, 9015 Grand Ave, North Richland Hills, TX, 76180. Tel: 817-427-6800. Fax: 817-427-6808. p. 2366

Rahkonen, Carl, Dr, Librn, Indiana University of Pennsylvania, Harold S Orendorff Library, 101 Cogswell Hall, 422 S 11th St, Indiana, PA, 15705-1071. Tel: 724-357-5644. Fax: 724-357-4891. p. 2071

Rahman, Katie, ILL Spec, Laramie County Library System, 2200 Pioneer Ave, Cheyenne, WY, 82001-3610. Tel: 307-773-7233. Fax: 307-634-2082. p. 2652

Rahn, Darlene J, Libr Spec, Centralia College, 600 Centralia College Blvd, Centralia, WA, 98531. Tel: 360-736-9391, Ext 350. Fax: 360-330-7502. p. 2511

Rahn, Eleane, YA Librn, Marion County Public Library, 201 E Main St, Lebanon, KY, 40033-1133. Tel: 270-692-4698. Fax: 270-692-9555. p. 920

Rahn, Katrina, Libr Dir, Sofia University Library, 1069 E Meadow Circle, Palo Alto, CA, 94303. Tel: 650-493-4430, Ext 221. Fax: 650-852-9780. p. 205

Rahn, Suzanne, Cat, Capital District Library Council, 28 Essex St, Albany, NY, 12206. Tel: 518-438-2500. Fax: 518-438-2872. p. 2949

Raible, Sarah A P, Dir, Meherrin Regional Library, 133 W Hicks St, Lawrenceville, VA, 23868. Tel: 434-848-2418. Fax: 434-848-4786. p. 2473

Raiche, Kristin, Ch, Windsor Locks Public Library, 28 Main St, Windsor Locks, CT, 06096. Tel: 860-627-1495. Fax: 860-627-1496. p. 379

Raider, Joanne, Librn, Western Connecticut State University, Robert S Young Business Library, 181 White St, Danbury, CT, 06810-6885. Tel: 203-837-9139. Fax: 203-837-9135. p. 335

Raiford, Charlene, Evening Ref Librn, North Carolina Central University, School of Law Library, 1512 S Alston Ave, Durham, NC, 27707. Tel: 919-530-7179. Fax: 919-530-7926. p. 1789

Railey, Valerie A, Librn, United States Courts Library, 940 Front St, Rm 3185, San Diego, CA, 92101-8920. Tel: 619-557-5066. Fax: 619-557-5077. p. 238

Railsback, Beth, Dir, Carnegie City-County Library, 2810 Wilbarger St, Vernon, TX, 76384. Tel: 940-552-2462. Fax: 940-552-6206. p. 2395

Raine, Kristy, Archives, Ref Serv, Mount Mercy University, 1330 Elmhurst Dr NE, Cedar Rapids, IA, 52402-4797. Tel: 319-368-6465. Fax: 319-363-9060. p. 801

Raine, Melinda, Assoc Univ Librn, Pub Serv, Pepperdine University Libraries, 24255 Pacific Coast Hwy, Malibu, CA, 90263. Tel: 310-506-4252. Fax: 310-506-7225. p. 182

Raines, Anna, Librn, Swaney Memorial Library, 100 Court St, New Cumberland, WV, 26047. Tel: 304-564-3471. Fax: 304-564-3471. p. 2567

Raines, Annis, Librn, Florence County Library System, Olanta Public Library, PO Box 263, Olanta, SC, 29114-0263. Tel: 843-396-4287. Fax: 843-396-9317. p. 2193

Raines, Jack, Chief, Department of Veterans Affairs North Texas Health Care System, 4500 S Lancaster Rd, Dallas, TX, 75216. Tel: 214-857-1250. p. 2307

Raines, M Diane, Ser, Tech Serv, Westminster College, 1840 S 1300 East, Salt Lake City, UT, 84105-3697. Tel: 801-832-2250. Fax: 801-832-3109. p. 2415

Rainey, Barbara, Br Mgr, Seminole County Public Library System, East Branch, 310 Division St, Oviedo, FL, 32765. Tel: 407-665-1561. Fax: 407-665-1585. p. 431

Rainey, Barbara, Br Mgr, Seminole County Public Library System, North Branch, 150 N Palmetto Ave, Sanford, FL, 32771. Tel: 407-665-1621. Fax: 407-665-1615. p. 431

Rainey, Betty, Br Mgr, Middle Georgia Regional Library System, Ideal Public Library, 605 Tom Watson Ave, Ideal, GA, 31041. Tel: 478-949-2720. Fax: 478-949-2720. p. 541

Rainey, Erica, Tech Serv, North Greenville University, 7801 N Tigerville Rd, Tigerville, SC, 29688. Tel: 864-977-7091. Fax: 864-977-2126. p. 2206

Rainey, Jesse, Ch, The American Humane Association, 63 Inverness Dr E, Englewood, CO, 80112-5117. Tel: 303-792-9900. Fax: 303-792-5333. p. 305

Rainey, Kay, Circ, Mississippi County Library System, Osceola Public, 320 West Hale Ave, Osceola, AR, 72370-2530. Tel: 870-563-2721. Fax: 870-563-6550. p. 96

Rainey, Sarah, Dir, Otterbein Public Library, 23 E First St, Otterbein, IN, 47970. Tel: 765-583-2107. Fax: 765-583-2337. p. 772

Rainson, Thomas, Head, Info Tech, Macomb County Library, 16480 Hall Rd, Clinton Township, MI, 48038-1132. Tel: 586-412-5983. Fax: 586-412-5958. p. 1164

Rainville, Ellen Downey, Dir, J V Fletcher Library, 50 Main St, Westford, MA, 01886-2599. Tel: 978-399-2312. Fax: 978-692-4418. p. 1138

Rainwater, Holli, Outreach Serv Librn, Coshocton Public Library, 655 Main St, Coshocton, OH, 43812-1697. Tel: 740-622-0956. Fax: 740-622-4331. p. 1891

Rainwater, Patsy, Dir, Reynolds County Library District, 2306 Pine St, Centerville, MO, 63633. Tel: 573-648-2471. Fax: 573-648-2471. p. 1323

Rainwater, Roger, Spec Coll Librn, Texas Christian University, 2913 Lowden St, TCU Box 298400, Fort Worth, TX, 76129. Tel: 817-257-7106. Fax: 817-257-7282. p. 2323

Rairdon, Nancy, Ch, Peach Public Libraries, 315 Martin Luther King Jr Dr, Fort Valley, GA, 31030-4196. Tel: 478-825-1640. Fax: 478-825-2061. p. 533

Rais, Shirley, Per, Loma Linda University, 11072 Anderson St, Loma Linda, CA, 92350-0001. Tel: 909-558-4581. Fax: 909-558-4121. p. 165

Raisch, Marylin, Assoc Law Librn, Intl & Foreign Law, Georgetown University, Georgetown Law Library (John Wolff & Edward Bennett Williams Libraries), 111 G St NW, Washington, DC, 20001. Fax: 202-662-9168. p. 403

Raisch, Patti, Supv Librn, Charlotte County Library System, Mid-County Regional Library, 2050 Forrest Nelson Blvd, Port Charlotte, FL, 33952. Tel: 941-613-3171. Fax: 941-613-3177. p. 484

Raiteri, Steve, AV, Greene County Public Library, 76 E Market St, Xenia, OH, 45385-3100. Tel: 937-352-4000, Ext 1233. Fax: 937-372-4673. p. 1951

Raitz, Brian E, Dir, Parkersburg & Wood County Public Library, 3100 Emerson Ave, Parkersburg, WV, 26104-2414. Tel: 304-420-4587. Fax: 304-420-4589. p. 2568

Rajagopal, Karpagam, Circ, Tech Serv, Front Range Community College, 3705 W 112th Ave, Westminster, CO, 80031-2140. Tel: 303-404-5555. Fax: 303-404-5144. p. 326

Rajaii, Mohammad, Br Coordr, Indiana University Bloomington, Swain Hall Library, Swain Hall West 208, 727 E Third St, Bloomington, IN, 47405-7105. Tel: 812-855-2758. Fax: 812-855-5533. p. 728

Rajamani, Karthi, Children & Teen Librn, Pembroke Public Library, 237 Victoria St, Pembroke, ON, K8A 4K5, CANADA. Tel: 613-732-8844. Fax: 613-732-1116. p. 2835

Rajcevic, Peter, Chief Tech Officer, Fac Mgr, Plainfield Public Library, 800 Park Ave, Plainfield, NJ, 07060-2594. Tel: 908-757-1111, Ext 130. Fax: 908-754-0063. p. 1521

Rajewska, Dorota, Br Head, Toronto Public Library, Long Branch, 3500 Lakeshore Blvd W, Toronto, ON, M8W 1N6, CANADA. Tel: 416-394-5320. Fax: 416-394-5326. p. 2862

Rajguru, Nalini, Mgr, Libr Serv, Caplin & Drysdale Library, One Thomas Circle, NW, Ste 1100, Washington, DC, 20005. Tel: 202-862-5073. Fax: 202-429-3301. p. 395

Rajner, Christine, Librn, Theresa Free Library, 301 Main St, Theresa, NY, 13691. Tel: 315-628-5972. Fax: 315-628-4839. p. 1755

Rajotte, Betsy, Ch, Monson Free Library, Two High St, Monson, MA, 01057-1095. Tel: 413-267-3866. Fax: 413-267-5496. p. 1106

Rajpar, Shamim, Info Literacy Librn, Mount Aloysius College Library, 7373 Admiral Peary Hwy, Cresson, PA, 16630-1999. Tel: 814-886-6445. Fax: 814-886-5767. p. 2048

Rajput, Toby, Librn, National Louis University Library & Learning Support, North Shore, 5202 Old Orchard Rd, Skokie, IL, 60077. Tel: 224-233-2515. Fax: 224-233-2515. p. 619

Rakas, Laurel, Ch, Pemberville Public Library, 375 E Front St, Pemberville, OH, 43450. Tel: 419-287-4012. Fax: 419-287-4620. p. 1928

Rakhshani, Diane, Mgr, Pine Mountain Regional Library, Manchester Public, 218 Perry St, Manchester, GA, 31816-0709. Tel: 706-846-3851. Fax: 706-846-9632. p. 542

Rakowitz, Beverly, Librn, United States Army, Brooke Army Medical Center Library, Medical Library MCHE-EDL, 3551 Roger Brooke Dr, Bldg 3600, Rm 371-17, Fort Sam Houston, TX, 78234-6200. Tel: 210-916-1119. Fax: 210-916-5709. p. 2320

Raleigh, Denise, Dir, Mkt, Develop & Communications, Gail Borden Public Library District, 270 N Grove Ave, Elgin, IL, 60120-5596. Tel: 847-429-5981. Fax: 847-742-0485. p. 640

Raley, Bill, Br Mgr, Nicholson Memorial Library System, South Garland Branch Library, 4845 Broadway Blvd, Garland, TX, 75043. Tel: 972-205-3920. p. 2327

Raley, Marianne, Ref Librn, Youth Serv Coordr, Natchez Adams Wilkinson Library Service, 220 S Commerce St, Natchez, MS, 39120-3502. Tel: 601-445-8862. Fax: 601-446-7795. p. 1309

Raley, Tavia, Asst Librn, Pima Public Library, 50 S 200 West, Pima, AZ, 85543. Tel: 928-485-2822. Fax: 928-485-0701. p. 77

Rallis, Evan, Spec Coll Librn, New York State Historical Association, 5798 State Hwy 80, Cooperstown, NY, 13326. Tel: 607-547-1473. Fax: 607-547-1405. p. 1610

Ralls, Marilyn, Dir, Gibson Memorial Library, 200 W Howard, Creston, IA, 50801-2339. Tel: 641-782-2277. Fax: 641-782-4604. p. 805

Ralph, Lynette, Asst Dir, Southeastern Louisiana University, SLU Box 10896, 1211 SGA Dr, Hammond, LA, 70402. Tel: 985-549-3860. Fax: 985-549-3995. p. 950

Ralph, Susan, Dir, Bainbridge College Library, 2500 E Shotwell St, Bainbridge, GA, 39818. Tel: 229-248-2590. Fax: 229-248-2589. p. 521

Ralston, Carl, Dir, Libr Serv, Argosy University, 1515 Central Pkwy, Eagan, MN, 55121. Tel: 651-846-3351. Fax: 651-994-0105. p. 1249

Ralston, Carol, Head Librn, Seymour Public Library, 46 Church St, Seymour, CT, 06483. Tel: 203-888-3903. Fax: 203-888-4099. p. 366

Ralston, Jennifer, Mat Mgt Adminr, Harford County Public Library, 1221-A Brass Mill Rd, Belcamp, MD, 21017-1209. Tel: 410-273-5600, Ext 2273. Fax: 410-273-5606. p. 1020

Ralston, Jill, Pub Relations Coordr, Avon Lake Public Library, 32649 Electric Blvd, Avon Lake, OH, 44012-1669. Tel: 440-933-8128. Fax: 440-933-5659. p. 1857

Ralston, Nancy M, Dir, Clarkson College Library, 101 S 42nd St, Omaha, NE, 68131-2739. Tel: 402-552-2557. Fax: 402-552-2899. p. 1411

Ralston, Rick, Asst Dir, Libr Operations, Indiana University, Ruth Lilly Medical Library, 975 W Walnut St, IB 100, Indianapolis, IN, 46202-5121. Tel: 317-274-1409. Fax: 317-278-2349. p. 752

Ralston, Tracy, Dir, Post University, 800 Country Club Rd, Waterbury, CT, 06723-2540. Tel: 203-596-4564. Fax: 203-575-9691. p. 375

Ram, Rose, Outreach Serv Librn, Brigham Young University-Hawaii, 55-220 Kulanui St, BYU-Hawaii, No 1966, Laie, HI, 96762-1294. Tel: 808-675-3882. Fax: 808-675-3877. p. 567

Ramachandran, Hema, Access Serv Librn, Pasadena City College Library, 1570 E Colorado Blvd, Pasadena, CA, 91106-2003. Tel: 626-585-3309. Fax: 626-585-7913. p. 206

Ramachandran, Shantha, Libr Assoc/Copy Cataloger, Mercer County Community College Library, 1200 Old Trenton Rd, West Windsor, NJ, 08550. Tel: 609-570-3555. Fax: 609-570-3845. p. 1542

Ramage, Gregory, Mgr, Info Tech, Upper Arlington Public Library, 2800 Tremont Rd, Columbus, OH, 43221. Tel: 614-486-9621. Fax: 614-486-4530. p. 1891

Ramage, Janet, Chief Exec Officer, White River Public Library, 123 Superior St, White River, ON, P0M 3G0, CANADA. Tel: 807-822-1113. Fax: 807-822-1113. p. 2871

Ramage, Lisa, Ch, Mid-Mississippi Regional Library System, 201 S Huntington St, Kosciusko, MS, 39090-9002. Tel: 662-289-5151. Fax: 662-289-5106. p. 1306

Ramanjulu, Jay, Pub Serv, Oklahoma City Community College, 7777 S May Ave, Oklahoma City, OK, 73159. Tel: 405-682-1611, Ext 7202. Fax: 405-682-7585. p. 1973

Rambo, Neil, Actg Assoc Dean, Actg Dir, University of Washington Libraries, Health Sciences Library, T-334 Health Sciences Bldg, Box 357155, 1959 NE Pacific St, Seattle, WA, 98195-7155. Tel: 206-543-5531. Fax: 206-543-3389. p. 2534

Rambow, Judi, Lead Librn, Kalamazoo Public Library, Alma Powell Branch, 1000 W Paterson St, Kalamazoo, MI, 49007. Tel: 269-553-7961. Fax: 269-344-0782. p. 1197

Ramdial, Opal, Treas, Lakeview Public Library, 1120 Woodfield Rd, Rockville Centre, NY, 11570. Tel: 516-536-3071. Fax: 516-536-6260. p. 1734

Ramer, Donna, Cat, Tech Serv, University of Mobile, 5735 College Pkwy, Mobile, ALL, 36613-2842. Tel: 251-442-2478. Fax: 251-442-2515. p. 26

Ramey, Cindy, Librn, Northeast Regional Library, Marietta Public Library, Seven County Rd 4060, Marietta, MS, 38856. Tel: 662-728-9320. p. 1297

Ramey, Marsha, Br Mgr, Saint Louis County Library, Samuel C Sachs Branch, 16400 Burkhardt Pl, Chesterfield, MO, 63017. Tel: 636-728-0001. p. 1359

Ramezani, Sara, Coordr, Popular Serv, Cabell County Public Library, 455 Ninth Street Plaza, Huntington, WV, 25701. Tel: 304-528-5700. Fax: 304-528-5701. p. 2561

Ramie, Crystal, Human Res Mgr, Oakland Public Library, 125 14th St, Oakland, CA, 94612. Tel: 510-238-6716. Fax: 510-238-2232. p. 197

Ramie, Crystal, Human Res Mgr, Oakland Public Library, Main Library, 125 14th St, Oakland, CA, 94612. Tel: 510-238-3134. Fax: 510-238-2232. p. 198

Ramirez, Al, IT Mgr, Bartlett Public Library District, 800 S Bartlett Rd, Bartlett, IL, 60103. Tel: 630-837-2855. Fax: 630-837-2669. p. 592

Ramirez, Antonio, Ref Librn, Saint John's University Library, Rittenberg Law Library, 8000 Utopia Pkwy, Queens, NY, 11439. Tel: 718-990-6651, 718-990-6659. Fax: 718-990-6649. p. 1725

Ramirez, Cristina, Commun Serv Mgr, Richmond Public Library, Broad Rock, 4820 Warwick Rd, Richmond, VA, 23224. Tel: 804-646-0527. Fax: 804-646-7014. p. 2490

Ramirez, Edna Amalia, Automation Syst Coordr, Pontifical Catholic University Of Puerto Rico, Encarnacion Valdes Library, 2250 Avenida Las Americas, Ste 509, Ponce, PR, 00717-0777. Tel: 787-841-2000, Ext 1813. Fax: 787-284-0235. p. 2674

Ramirez, Elizabeth, Doc, Nevada Power Co Library, 6226 W Sahara Ave, Las Vegas, NV, 89151. Tel: 702-367-5055. Fax: 702-227-2023. p. 1430

Ramirez, Jennifer, Libr Dir, Elvis Maxine Gilliam Memorial Public Library, 205 E Beltline Rd, Wilmer, TX, 75172. Tel: 972-441-3713. Fax: 972-525-3914. p. 2401

Ramirez, Laura Lucio, Br Mgr, Nova Southeastern University Libraries, North Miami Campus, FGSEHS Tech Bldg, 1750 NE 167th St, North Miami Beach, FL, 33162-3017. Tel: 954-262-8423. Fax: 954-262-3219. p. 444

Ramirez, Maria, Libr Tech, Kaiser-Permanente Medical Center, 10800 Magnolia Ave, Riverside, CA, 92505. Tel: 951-353-3659. Fax: 951-353-3262. p. 217

Ramirez, Martha, Bibliographer, Librn, University of California, 1156 High St, Santa Cruz, CA, 95064. Tel: 831-459-2536. Fax: 831-459-8206. p. 264

Ramirez, Marvin, Actg Librn, Airline Pilots Association International, 535 Herndon Pkwy, Herndon, VA, 20172-5226. Tel: 703-689-4204. Fax: 703-464-2104. p. 2471

Ramirez, Nola, In Charge, Merced County Library, Gustine Branch, 205 Sixth St, Gustine, CA, 95322-1112. Tel: 209-854-3013. p. 185

Ramirez, Olivia, Youth Serv, Onslow County Public Library, 58 Doris Ave E, Jacksonville, NC, 28540. Tel: 910-455-7350, Ext 240. Fax: 910-455-1661. p. 1803

Ramirez, Rosa, Asst Librn, Reagan County Library, 300 Courthouse Sq, Big Lake, TX, 76932. Tel: 325-884-2854. p. 2289

Ramirez, Rue, Assoc Univ Librn, Libr Syst & Info Tech, University of British Columbia Library, 1961 East Mall, Vancouver, BC, V6T 1Z1, CANADA. Tel: 604-822-5241. p. 2742

Ramirez, Teresa, Dir, Crystal City Memorial Library, 101 E Dimmit St, Crystal City, TX, 78839-3505. Tel: 830-374-0036. Fax: 830-374-2123. p. 2304

Ramirez-Rivera, Lourdes, Head Librn, University of Puerto Rico Library System, Planning Library, Rio Piedras Campus, Plaza Universitaria, San Juan, PR, 00931. Tel: 787-764-0000, Ext 85524. Fax: 787-772-1479. p. 2678

Ramkey, Carol E, Dir, Library of the Marine Corps, Gray Research Ctr, 2040 Broadway St, Quantico, VA, 22134-5107. Tel: 703-784-4764. Fax: 703-784-4306. p. 2486

Ramler, Joe, Sr Res Economist, Montana Department of Commerce, 301 S Park, Helena, MT, 59620. Tel: 406-841-2719. Fax: 406-841-2731. p. 1382

Ramlow, Edith, Mgr, College of Central Florida Citrus Campus Learning Resources Center, 3800 S Lecanto Hwy, C2-202, Lecanto, FL, 34461. Tel: 352-249-1205. Fax: 352-249-1212. p. 460

Ramon, Dinorah, Cat Spec, Laredo Community College, West End Washington St, Laredo, TX, 78040. Tel: 956-721-5272. Fax: 956-721-5447. p. 2353

Ramona, Rose, Head Archivist, University of Northern British Columbia Library, 333 University Way, Prince George, BC, V2N 4Z9, CANADA. Tel: 250-960-6603. Fax: 250-960-6610. p. 2736

Ramonas, Paul, Res, Jenner & Block Library, 353 N Clark St, Ste 4300, Chicago, IL, 60654. Tel: 312-222-9350. Fax: 312-527-0484. p. 616

Ramos, Daniel, Circ Mgr, Info Serv Librn, Val Verde County Library, 300 Spring St, Del Rio, TX, 78840. Tel: 830-774-7595. Fax: 830-774-7607. p. 2312

Ramos, Edwin, Head Librn, Pontifical Catholic University of Puerto Rico, Ramon Emeterio Betances St 482, Mayaguez, PR, 00680. Tel: 787-834-5151, Ext 5008. Fax: 787-831-7155. p. 2673

Ramos, Mario, Info Tech, Randolph Community College, 629 Industrial Park Ave, Asheboro, NC, 27205-7333. Tel: 336-633-0204. Fax: 336-629-4695. p. 1773

Ramos, Mario, Supvr, Computer Serv & Ref (Info Serv), High Point Public Library, 901 N Main St, High Point, NC, 27262. Tel: 336-883-3633. Fax: 336-883-3636. p. 1802

Ramos, Migdalia, Music & Media Librn, Pontifical Catholic University Of Puerto Rico, Encarnacion Valdes Library, 2250 Avenida Las Americas, Ste 509, Ponce, PR, 00717-0777. Tel: 787-841-2000, Ext 1807. Fax: 787-284-0235. p. 2674

Ramos-Ankrum, Angeles, Tech Serv Librn, Louisville Presbyterian Theological Seminary, 1044 Alta Vista Rd, Louisville, KY, 40205-1798. Tel: 502-895-3411, Ext 397. Fax: 502-895-1096. p. 925

Ramos-Vance, Ellisa, Br Mgr, Jackson County Library Services, White City Branch, 3143 Ave C, White City, OR, 97503. Tel: 541-864-8880. Fax: 541-864-8880. p. 2006

Ramoy, Tina, Librn, Hughes, Hubbard & Reed LLP Library, 1775 I St NW, Ste 600, Washington, DC, 20006-2401. Tel: 202-721-4600. Fax: 202-721-4646. p. 404

Ramp, Barbara, Coordr, Youth Serv, Lethbridge Public Library, 810 Fifth Ave S, Lethbridge, AB, T1J 4C4, CANADA. Tel: 403-380-7312. Fax: 403-329-1478. p. 2709

Rampp, Carrie, Dir, Libr Serv & Instrul Tech, Bucknell University, Library & Information Technology, 221 Ellen Clarke Bertrand Library, Lewisburg, PA, 17837. Tel: 570-577-1557. Fax: 570-577-3313. p. 2080

Ramsay, Diane, Dir, Auburn Public Library, 369 Southbridge St, Auburn, MA, 01501. Tel: 508-832-7790. Fax: 508-832-7792. p. 1051

Ramsay, Diane, Youth Serv Coordr, Chicopee Public Library, 449 Front St, Chicopee, MA, 01013. Tel: 413-594-1800, Ext 120. Fax: 413-594-1819. p. 1081

Ramsay, Gary, Ref, Confederation Centre Public Library, Queen & Richmond St, Charlottetown, PE, C1A 8G8, CANADA. Tel: 902-368-4642. Fax: 902-368-4652. p. 2875

Ramsay, Janelle, Young Reader's Serv, Beaumont Library District, 125 E Eighth St, Beaumont, CA, 92223-2194. Tel: 951-845-1357. Fax: 951-845-6217. p. 125

Ramsay, John, Asst Dir, Springfield City Library, 220 State St, Springfield, MA, 01103. Tel: 413-263-6828, Ext 293. Fax: 413-263-6825. p. 1127

Ramsay, Linda, Librn, Lafleur & Brown Library, One Place Ville Marie, 37th Flr, Montreal, QC, H3B 3P4, CANADA. Tel: 514-392-9538. Fax: 514-878-1450. p. 2897

Ramsay, LIsa, Ref Supvr, Linebaugh Public Library System of Rutherford County, 105 W Vine St, Murfreesboro, TN, 37130-3673. Tel: 615-893-4131. Fax: 615-848-5038. p. 2254

Ramsdell, Edward L, Librn, The New England Electric Railway Historical Society, 195 Log Cabin Rd, Kennebunkport, ME, 04046. Tel: 207-967-2712. Fax: 207-967-0867. p. 989

Ramsdell, Kristin, Ref Librn, California State University, East Bay Library, 25800 Carlos Bee Blvd, Hayward, CA, 94542-3052. Tel: 510-885-4814. Fax: 510-885-2049. p. 157

Ramsden, Ann, Dir, Musee Heritage Museum, Five Saint Anne St, St. Albert, AB, T8N 3Z9, CANADA. Tel: 780-459-1528. Fax: 780-459-1232. p. 2717

Ramsell, Michelle, Dir, Tuscarawas County Public Library, 121 Fair Ave NW, New Philadelphia, OH, 44663-2600. Tel: 330-364-4474. Fax: 330-364-8217. p. 1921

Ramseur, Monisa, Librn, East Cleveland Public Library, North Branch Library & Technology Center, 1425 Hayden Ave, East Cleveland, OH, 44112. Tel: 216-268-6283. Fax: 216-268-6297. p. 1897

Ramseur, Wendy, Pub Serv Librn, Durham Technical Community College, 1637 Lawson St, Durham, NC, 27703. Tel: 919-536-7211. Fax: 919-686-3471. p. 1788

Ramsey, Anne-Marie, Br Mgr, Prince George's County Memorial, Accokeek Branch, 15773 Livingston Rd, Accokeek, MD, 20607-2249. Tel: 301-292-0984, 301-292-2880. Fax: 301-292-0984. p. 1032

Ramsey, Beccy, Ch, Ridgemont Public Library, 124 E Taylor St, Mount Victory, OH, 43340-8811. Tel: 937-354-4445. Fax: 937-354-4445. p. 1919

Ramsey, Christiane, Humanities & Soc Sci Librn, Brigham Young University, Harold B Lee Library, 2060 HBLL, Provo, UT, 84602. Tel: 801-422-2927. Fax: 801-422-0466. p. 2411

Ramsey, Debbie, Librn, Keephills Public Library, 51515 Range Rd 32A, Duffield, AB, T0E 0N0, CANADA. Tel: 780-731-0000, 780-731-3965. Fax: 780-731-2433. p. 2697

Ramsey, Donna, Librn, United States Army, Van Noy Library, 5966 12th St, Bldg 1024, Fort Belvoir, VA, 22060-5554. Tel: 703-806-3238. p. 2464

Ramsey, Elizabeth, Ref Librn, Montana Tech Library, 1300 W Park St, Butte, MT, 59701-8997. Tel: 406-496-4839. Fax: 406-496-4133. p. 1376

Ramsey, Glenda, Librn, Catawba County Library, Southwest, West Over Plaza, 2944 Hwy 127 S, Hickory, NC, 28602. Tel: 828-294-2343. Fax: 828-294-2477. p. 1813

Ramsey, Jim, Adult Serv, Middleton Public Library, 7425 Hubbard Ave, Middleton, WI, 53562-3117. Tel: 608-827-7423. Fax: 608-836-5724. p. 2616

Ramsey, Melanie, Ch, Holidaysburg Area Public Library, 405 Clark St, Hollidaysburg, PA, 16648-2100. Tel: 814-695-5961. Fax: 814-695-6824. p. 2069

Ramsey, Mike, Info Scientist, Eastman Chemical Co, Research Library, Bldg 150B, Kingsport, TN, 37662. Tel: 423-229-4290. Fax: 423-224-0519. p. 2240

Ramsey, Rebecca, Dir, Lamoni Public Library, 301 W Main St, Lamoni, IA, 50140. Tel: 641-784-6686. Fax: 641-784-6693. p. 826

Ranadive, Mary, Asst Univ Librn, Pub Serv, Towson University, 8000 York Rd, Towson, MD, 21252-0001. Tel: 410-704-2618. Fax: 410-704-3760. p. 1045

Rance, Donald, Ref Librn, Art Gallery of Ontario, 317 Dundas St W, Toronto, ON, M5T 1G4, CANADA. Tel: 416-979-6642. Fax: 416-979-6602. p. 2850

Rancier, Wendy, Ch, Roanoke County Public Library, 3131 Electric Rd SW, Roanoke, VA, 24018-6496. Tel: 540-772-7507. Fax: 540-989-3129. p. 2494

Ranck, Jennifer, Dir, Somerset County Library System, 11767 Beechwood St, Princess Anne, MD, 21853. Tel: 410-651-0852, Ext 11. Fax: 410-651-1388. p. 1036

Ranck, Mary Lou, Ref Librn, Caplin & Drysdale Library, One Thomas Circle, NW, Ste 1100, Washington, DC, 20005. Tel: 202-862-7835. Fax: 202-429-3301. p. 395

Rancourt, Jay, Librn, Cook Memorial Library, 93 Main St, Tamworth, NH, 03886. Tel: 603-323-8510. Fax: 603-323-2077. p. 1466

Rand, Charles E, Dir, National Cowboy & Western Heritage Museum, 1700 NE 63rd St, Oklahoma City, OK, 73111. Tel: 405-478-2250, Ext 273. Fax: 405-478-6421. p. 1973

Rand, Charles Edwin, Librn & Archivist, Shaker Library, 707 Shaker Rd, New Gloucester, ME, 04260. Tel: 207-926-4597. p. 993

Randall, Barbara Nichols, Dir, Guilderland Public Library, 2228 Western Ave, Guilderland, NY, 12084-9701. Tel: 518-456-2400. Fax: 518-456-0923. p. 1632

Randall, Bill, Dr, Assoc VPres, Learning Tech Syst, North Carolina Community College System, 200 W Jones St, Raleigh, NC, 27603-1379. Tel: 919-807-7100. Fax: 919-807-7164, 919-807-7175. p. 2951

Randall, Cara J, Librn, California State Railroad Museum Library, 113 I St, Sacramento, CA, 95814. Tel: 916-445-3492. Fax: 916-327-5655. p. 223

Randall, Chris, Bus Mgr, Bellwood Public Library, 600 Bohland Ave, Bellwood, IL, 60104-1896. Tel: 708-547-7393. Fax: 708-547-9352. p. 593

Randall, Elizabeth, Dir, Libr Serv, Holmes Public Library, 470 Plymouth St, Halifax, MA, 02338. Tel: 781-293-2271. Fax: 781-294-8515. p. 1093

Randall, Jessy, Spec Coll Librn, Colorado College, 1021 N Cascade Ave, Colorado Springs, CO, 80903-3252. Tel: 719-389-6658. Fax: 719-389-6082. p. 294

Randall, Leslie, Dir, Glenwood Public Library, 108 SE First Ave, Glenwood, MN, 56334-1622. Tel: 320-634-3375. Fax: 320-634-5099. p. 1252

Randall, Melissa, Cataloger/Ref Librn, University of Dallas, 1845 E Northgate Dr, Irving, TX, 75062-4736. Tel: 972-721-5397. Fax: 972-721-4010. p. 2347

Randall, Sherri, Br Mgr, Weston County Public Library, Upton Branch, 722 Fourth St, Upton, WY, 82730. Tel: 307-468-2324. Fax: 307-468-2324. p. 2658

Randall, Shirley, Librn, Fowler Public Library, 510 Main St, Fowler, KS, 67844-0135. Tel: 620-646-5550. p. 867

Randall, Todd, Librn, Penfield Public Library, 1985 Baird Rd, Penfield, NY, 14526. Tel: 585-340-8720. Fax: 585-340-8748. p. 1716

Randall-Dill, Ann, Tech Coordr, Erie County Public Library, 160 E Front St, Erie, PA, 16507. Tel: 814-451-6900. Fax: 814-451-6907. p. 2055

Randazzo, Jennifer, In Charge, St John Macomb Hospital Center Library, 11800 E 12 Mile Rd, Warren, MI, 48093. Tel: 586-573-5117. Fax: 586-573-5042. p. 1234

Randelia, Gool, Commun Outreach Librn, Ivy Tech Community College, 8204 Hwy 311, Sellersburg, IN, 47172-1897. Tel: 812-246-3301, Ext 4225. Fax: 812-246-9905. p. 777

Randell, Kent, Archivist, Findlandia University, Finnish American Heritage Center & Historical Archive, 435 Quincy St, Hancock, MI, 49930-1845. Tel: 906-487-7347. Fax: 906-487-7557. p. 1188

Randeree, Ebrahim, Asst Dean, Florida State University, College of Communication & Information, 142 Collegiate Loop, Tallahassee, FL, 32306-2100. Tel: 850-645-5674. Fax: 850-644-9763. p. 2963

Randleman, Anna, Dir, Granger Public Library, 2216 Broadway, Granger, IA, 50109. Tel: 515-999-2088. Fax: 515-999-9156. p. 818

Randleman, Sue, Dir, North Logan City Library, 475 E 2500 North, North Logan, UT, 84341-1523. Tel: 435-755-7091. Fax: 435-227-0032. p. 2408

Rando, Ruth, Dir, Librn, Closter Public Library, 280 High St, Closter, NJ, 07624-1898. Tel: 201-768-4197. Fax: 201-768-4220. p. 1479

Randolph, Alpha, Circ, Dominican Theological Library, 487 Michigan Ave NE, Washington, DC, 20017-1585. Tel: 202-495-3821. Fax: 202-495-3873. p. 399

Randolph, Elizabeth, Br Mgr, Anderson William E Library Penn Hills, Lincoln Park Satellite, 7300 Ridgeview Ave, Pittsburgh, PA, 15235. Tel: 412-362-7729. Fax: 412-362-7729. p. 2121

Randolph, Jonathan, ILL, Abbot Public Library, 235 Pleasant St, Marblehead, MA, 01945. Tel: 781-631-1481. Fax: 781-639-0558. p. 1102

Randolph, Ramona, Librn, California State Department of Food & Agriculture, 3294 Meadowview Rd, Sacramento, CA, 95832-1448. Tel: 916-262-1157. Fax: 916-262-1191. p. 222

Randolph, Sundra L, Dir, South Plainfield Free Public Library, 2484 Plainfield Ave, South Plainfield, NJ, 07080. Tel: 908-754-7885. Fax: 908-753-3846. p. 1531

Randolph, Susan, Circ Mgr, Gallia County District Library, Seven Spruce St, Gallipolis, OH, 45631. Tel: 740-446-7323. Fax: 740-446-1701. p. 1901

Randolph, Terri, Tech Serv, Riegelsville Public Library, 615 Easton Rd, Riegelsville, PA, 18077. Tel: 610-749-2357. p. 2134

Randy, Bossarte, Librn, United States National Oceanic & Atmospheric Administration, 4301 Rickenbacker Causeway, Miami, FL, 33149-1097. Tel: 305-361-4428, 305-361-4429. Fax: 305-361-4448. p. 468

Randy, Wayland, Mgr, Metropolitan Library System in Oklahoma County, Southern Oaks Library, 6900 S Walker, Oklahoma City, OK, 73139-7203. Tel: 405-631-4468. Fax: 405-606-3484. p. 1973

Rane, Joel, Assoc Librn, Inglewood Public Library, 101 W Manchester Blvd, Inglewood, CA, 90301-1771. Tel: 310-412-5397. Fax: 310-412-8848. p. 159

Raney, Janey, Br Mgr, Mesa County Public Library District, Gateway Branch, 42700 Hwy No 141, Gateway, CO, 81522. Tel: 970-931-2428. Fax: 970-931-2428. p. 311

Ranf, Sherry, Librn, Humboldt County Library, Denio Branch, PO Box 230, Denio, NV, 89404-0230. Tel: 775-941-0330. Fax: 775-941-0330. p. 1435

Ranganathan, Savi, Ref Serv, Meharry Medical College Library, 1005 Dr D B Todd Jr Blvd, Nashville, TN, 37208. Tel: 615-327-6728. Fax: 615-327-6448. p. 2257

Rangarajan, Latha, Acq Librn, University of Detroit Mercy Library, Kresge Law Library, 651 E Jefferson, Detroit, MI, 48226. Tel: 313-596-0239. Fax: 313-596-0245. p. 1172

Rangel, Danielle, Cat, Pleasanton Public Library, 321 N Main, Pleasanton, TX, 78064. Tel: 830-569-3622. Fax: 830-569-6082. p. 2371

Ranger, Joshua, Archivist & Communications Librn, University of Wisconsin Oshkosh, 801 Elmwood Ave, Oshkosh, WI, 54901. Tel: 920-424-0828. Fax: 920-424-7338. p. 2628

Ranger, Patricia, Libr Coordr, DeVry Calgary Library, 2700, 3rd Ave SE, Calgary, AB, T2A 7W4, CANADA. Tel: 403-207-3100. Fax: 403-207-6226. p. 2691

Ranieri, Ann, Dir of Libr Serv, Harcum College Library, 750 Montgomery Ave, Bryn Mawr, PA, 19010-3476. Tel: 610-526-6085. Fax: 610-526-6086. p. 2039

Ranieri, Ann E, Head, Tech Serv, Arcadia University, 450 S Easton Rd, Glenside, PA, 19038-3295. Tel: 215-572-2136. Fax: 215-572-0240. p. 2061

Ranisate, Allison, ILL, University of North Dakota, School of Medicine and Health Sciences, 501 N Columbia Rd, Stop 9002, Grand Forks, ND, 58202-9002. Tel: 701-777-3993. Fax: 701-777-4790. p. 1842

Ranjit, Kathryn, Librn, Peter Lougheed Ctr Knowledge Ctr, University of Calgary Library, Health Sciences Library, Health Sci Ctr, 3330 Hospital Dr NW, Calgary, AB, T2N 4N1, CANADA. Tel: 403-943-4736. Fax: 403-210-9847. p. 2693

Rank, Robin, Ref & Instruction Librn, Kalamazoo College, 1200 Academy St, Kalamazoo, MI, 49006-3285. Tel: 269-337-7153. Fax: 269-337-7143. p. 1197

Rankel, Kaye, Librn, Gillett Public Library, 200 E Main St, Gillett, WI, 54124-9386. Tel: 920-855-6224. Fax: 920-855-6533. p. 2594

Rankin, Ammie, Librn, Longton Library, 512A Kansas Ave, Longton, KS, 67352. Tel: 620-642-6012. Fax: 620-642-6012. p. 880

Rankin, Bonnie, Ch, Chelmsford Public Library, MacKay, 43 Newfield St, North Chelmsford, MA, 01863-1799. Tel: 978-251-3212. Fax: 978-251-8782. p. 1080

Rankin, Cindy, Br Mgr, Mendenhall Public Library, 1630 Simpson Hwy 149, Mendenhall, MS, 39114. Tel: 601-847-2181. Fax: 601-847-2188. p. 1308

Rankin, Danee, Dir, Wasco City/Community Library, 1017 Clarke St, Wasco, OR, 97065. Tel: 541-442-8505. Fax: 541-442-5001. p. 2022

Rankin, Darcy, Electronic Serv, Langston University, PO Box 1600, Langston, OK, 73050-1600. Tel: 405-466-3293. Fax: 405-466-3459. p. 1967

Rankin, Jeanne, Br Mgr, Los Angeles Public Library System, North Hollywood Regional, 5211 Tujunga Ave, North Hollywood, CA, 91601-3179. Tel: 818-766-7185. Fax: 818-756-9135. p. 174

Rankin, Jocelyn, Dr, Br Mgr, Centers for Disease Control & Prevention, MS C-04, 1600 Clifton Rd NE, Atlanta, GA, 30333. Tel: 404-639-1761. Fax: 404-639-1160. p. 514

Rankin, Joy L, Dir, Roosevelt Public Library, 27 W Fulton Ave, Roosevelt, NY, 11575. Tel: 516-378-0222. Fax: 516-378-1011. p. 1735

Rankin, Louise, ILL, Chickasaw Regional Library System, 601 Railway Express, Ardmore, OK, 73401. Tel: 580-223-3164. Fax: 580-223-3280. p. 1957

Rankin, Mary, Dir, Dallas County Law Library, George Allen Courts Bldg, 600 Commerce St, Ste 292, Dallas, TX, 75202-4606. Tel: 214-653-7481. Fax: 214-653-6103. p. 2305

Rankin, Teri, Youth Serv, O'Fallon Public Library, 120 Civic Plaza, O'Fallon, IL, 62269-2692. Tel: 618-632-3783. Fax: 618-632-3759. p. 684

Rankin, Zandi, Ch, Hemphill County Library, 500 Main St, Canadian, TX, 79014. Tel: 806-323-5282. Fax: 806-323-6102. p. 2294

Rankins, Deborah, Asst Dir, Alabama Southern Community College, 2800 S Alabama Ave, Monroeville, AL, 36460. Tel: 334-637-3146. Fax: 251-575-5116. p. 26

Rankins, Deborah, Asst Dir, Alabama Southern Community College, Thomasville Campus-Kathryn Tucker Windham Museum Library, 30755 Hwy 43, Thomasville, AL, 36784-2519. Tel: 334-637-3146. Fax: 334-636-1478. p. 27

Rankow, Valerie, Dir, Brookhaven Memorial Hospital Medical Library, 101 Hospital Rd, Patchogue, NY, 11772-4897. Tel: 631-654-7774. Fax: 631-447-3723. p. 1715

Ranney, Diane M, Asst Dir, Jonathan Bourne Public Library, 19 Sandwich Rd, Bourne, MA, 02532-3699. Tel: 508-759-0644, Ext 103. Fax: 508-759-0647. p. 1069

Ransom, Barbara, Dir, Serv Develop, Planning & Support, Richmond Hill Public Library, One Atkinson St, Richmond Hill, ON, L4C 0H5, CANADA. Tel: 905-884-9288. Fax: 905-770-0312, 905-884-6544. p. 2839

Ransom, Christina, Librn, Champlain Valley Physicians Hospital Medical Center Library, 75 Beekman St, Plattsburgh, NY, 12901. Tel: 518-562-7325. Fax: 518-562-7129. p. 1718

Ransom, Jennifer, Ref, The College of New Rochelle, 29 Castle Pl, New Rochelle, NY, 10805-2308. Tel: 914-654-5345. Fax: 914-654-5884. p. 1666

Ransom, John, Libr Tech, Rutherford B Hayes Presidential Center Library, Spiegel Grove, Fremont, OH, 43420-2796. Tel: 419-332-2081, Ext 232. Fax: 419-332-4952. p. 1900

Ransom, Marcia, Dir, Springdale Public Library, 405 S Pleasant St, Springdale, AR, 72764. Tel: 479-750-8180. Fax: 479-750-8182. p. 115

Ransom, Stanley, Dir, Plattsburgh Public Library, 19 Oak St, Plattsburgh, NY, 12901-2810. Tel: 518-563-0921. Fax: 518-563-1681. p. 1719

Ransome, Deborah, Asst Dir, Natchitoches Parish Library, 450 Second St, Natchitoches, LA, 71457-4649. Tel: 318-357-3280. Fax: 318-357-7073. p. 958

Ranson, Peggy, Mgr, Queen Anne's County Free Library, Kent Island Branch, 200 Library Circle, Stevensville, MD, 21666-4026. Tel: 410-643-8161. Fax: 410-643-7098. p. 1023

Rantin, Dene, Media Spec, Greenforest Community Baptist Church-Christian Academic Center Library, 3250 Rainbow Dr, Decatur, GA, 30034. Tel: 404-486-6744. Fax: 404-486-1127. p. 530

Ranum, Mark, Admin Dir, Plum Creek Library System, 290 S Lake St, Worthington, MN, 56187. Tel: 507-376-5803. Fax: 507-376-9244. p. 1291

Ranzan, David, Univ Archivist, Salisbury University, 1101 Camden Ave, Salisbury, MD, 21801-6863. Tel: 410-543-6130. Fax: 410-543-6203. p. 1040

Rao, Dittakavi, Assoc Dir, Duquesne University, Center for Legal Information, 900 Locust St, Pittsburgh, PA, 15282. Tel: 412-396-5014. Fax: 412-396-6294. p. 2125

Rao, Kathleen, Tech Serv, Sherborn Library, Four Sanger St, Sherborn, MA, 01770-1499. Tel: 508-653-0770. Fax: 508-650-9243. p. 1123

Rao, Sai, Dir, North Bergen Free Public Library, 8411 Bergenline Ave, North Bergen, NJ, 07047-5097. Tel: 201-869-4715. Fax: 201-868-0968. p. 1514

Rao, Srivalli, Librn, Mercy College Libraries, White Plains Campus, 277 Martine Ave & S Broadway, White Plains, NY, 10601. Tel: 914-948-3666, Ext 3329. Fax: 914-686-1858. p. 1615

Rapacki, Sean, YA Serv, Ella M Everhard Public Library, 132 Broad St, Wadsworth, OH, 44281-1897. Tel: 330-334-5761. Fax: 330-334-6605. p. 1943

Rapalee, Elizabeth, Dir, Wadhams Free Library, 763 NYS Rte 22, Wadhams, NY, 12993. Tel: 518-962-8717. p. 1762

Rapatano, Enza, Ser, Bentley College, 175 Forest St, Waltham, MA, 02452-4705. Tel: 781-891-2168. Fax: 781-891-2830. p. 1132

Rape-Ott, Cheryl, Librn, Pike-Amite-Walthall Library System, Liberty Branch, 196 Clinic Dr, Liberty, MS, 39654. Tel: 601-657-8781. Fax: 601-657-8781. p. 1308

Rapecis, Richard, Dir, Bayville Free Library, 34 School St, Bayville, NY, 11709. Tel: 516-628-2765. Fax: 516-628-2738. p. 1579

Raper, Bennie, Dir, Englewood Public Library, 35 Carroll, Englewood, TN, 37329. Tel: 423-887-7152. p. 2234

Raphael, Brian, Asst Dir, University of Southern California Libraries, Asa V Call Law Library, 699 Exposition Blvd, LAW 202, MC 0072, Los Angeles, CA, 90089-0072. Tel: 213-740-6482. Fax: 213-740-7179. p. 179

Raphael, Honora, Music, Brooklyn College Library, 2900 Bedford Ave, Brooklyn, NY, 11210-2889. Tel: 718-951-5845. Fax: 718-951-4540. p. 1589

Raphael, Honora, Librn, Brooklyn College Library, Walter W Gerboth Music Library, 2900 Bedford Ave, Brooklyn, NY, 11210-2889. Tel: 718-951-5845. p. 1590

Rapier, Jennifer, Librn, Moreno Valley Public Library, 25480 Alessandro Blvd, Moreno Valley, CA, 92553. Tel: 951-413-3880. Fax: 951-413-3895. p. 191

Rapp, Andrea, Librn, Isaac M Wise Temple Library, 8329 Ridge Rd, Cincinnati, OH, 45236. Tel: 513-793-2556, Ext 123. Fax: 513-793-3322. p. 1875

Rapp, Robert, Info Tech Mgr, Menomonee Falls Public Library, W156 N8436 Pilgrim Rd, Menomonee Falls, WI, 53051. Tel: 262-532-8900. Fax: 262-532-8939. p. 2614

Rapp Weiss, Melanie, Br Mgr, Cuyahoga County Public Library, Garfield Heights Branch, 5400 Transportation Blvd, Garfield Heights, OH, 44125-3203. Tel: 216-475-8178. Fax: 216-475-1015. p. 1927

Rappaport, Karen, Librn, Wells Memorial Library, 12230 NYS Rte 9N, Box 57, Upper Jay, NY, 12987-0057. Tel: 518-946-2644. Fax: 518-946-2644. p. 1758

Rappaport, Sharon, Head, YA, Manhasset Public Library, 30 Onderdonk Ave, Manhasset, NY, 11030. Tel: 516 627-2300, Ext 209. Fax: 516-627-4339. p. 1657

Raptis, Toni, Per, Patchogue-Medford Library, 54-60 E Main St, Patchogue, NY, 11772. Tel: 631-654-4700, Ext 228. Fax: 631-289-3999. p. 1715

Rapuano, Jennifer, Ser, Vineyard Haven Public Library, 200 Main St, Vineyard Haven, MA, 02568-9710. Tel: 508-696-4211, Ext 12. Fax: 508-696-7495. p. 1132

Rarden, Donna, Dir, Sayre Public Library, 113 E Poplar, Sayre, OK, 73662. Tel: 580-928-2641. Fax: 580-928-1189. p. 1977

Rardin, Barbara A, Dir, Ericson Public Library, 702 Greene St, Boone, IA, 50036. Tel: 515-432-3727. Fax: 515-432-1103. p. 797

Rasch, Kathryn M, Cat, North Suburban Library District, 6340 N Second St, Loves Park, IL, 61111. Tel: 815-633-4247. Fax: 815-633-4249. p. 668

Rasche, Donna, Dir, Brewer Public Library, 100 S Main St, Brewer, ME, 04412. Tel: 207-989-7943. Fax: 207-989-8426. p. 978

Raschke, Diane, Ch, Clintonville Public Library, 75 Hemlock St, Clintonville, WI, 54929-1461. Tel: 715-823-4563. Fax: 715-823-7134. p. 2586

Raschke, Gregory, Assoc Dir, Coll & Scholarly Communication, North Carolina State University Libraries, Two Broughton Dr, Raleigh, NC, 27695. Tel: 919-515-7188. Fax: 919-515-3628. p. 1816

Raschke, Vera, Librn, Legislative Library of the Northwest Territories, Legislative Assembly Bldg, 4570 - 48th St, Yellowknife, NT, X1A 2L9, CANADA. Tel: 867-669-2202. Fax: 867-873-0207. p. 2775

Raschkow, Elenka, Dir, Libr Serv, Lansing Community College Library, 200 Technology & Learning Ctr, 419 N Capitol Ave, Lansing, MI, 48933. Tel: 517-483-1639. Fax: 517-483-5300. p. 1201

Rascoe, Paul, Doc, University of Texas Libraries, Perry-Castaneda Library (Main Library), 101 E 21st St, Austin, TX, 78712-1266. Tel: 512-495-4350. p. 2284

Rascoe, Zoe, Ref Serv, Motlow State Community College Libraries, Ledford Mill Rd, Tullahoma, TN, 37388. Fax: 931-393-1516. p. 2267

Rash, David, Pub Serv, Everett Community College, 2000 Tower St, Everett, WA, 98201-1352. Tel: 425-388-9494. Fax: 425-388-9144. p. 2515

Rash, Elaine, Head, Youth Serv, Osterhout Free Library, 71 S Franklin St, Wilkes-Barre, PA, 18701-1287. Tel: 570-823-0156. Fax: 570-823-5477. p. 2155

Rash, Ivy, Br Librn, Pottawatomie Wabaunsee Regional Library, Onaga Branch, 313 Leonard St, Onaga, KS, 66521. Tel: 785-889-4531. Fax: 785-889-4531. p. 893

Rashid, Marcine, Librn, Ira C Reed Public Library, 302 Commercial St, Lafayette, IL, 61449. Tel: 309-995-3042. Fax: 309-995-3042. p. 663

Rasimowicz, Michael, Dir, Info Tech, New Jersey State Library, 185 W State St, Trenton, NJ, 08618. Tel: 609-278-2640, Ext 199. Fax: 609-278-2650. p. 1536

Raska-engelson, Marilyn, Dir, Radcliffe Public Library, 210 Isabella, Radcliffe, IA, 50230. Tel: 515-899-7914. Fax: 515-899-7914. p. 839

Raske, Rick, Mgr, Baxter International, 25212 W Illinois Rte 120, RLT 22, Round Lake, IL, 60073. Tel: 847-270-5360. Fax: 847-270-5381. p. 699

Raskie, Ruth, Ch, Carnegie-Evans Public Library, 203 Benton Ave E, Albia, IA, 52531-2036. Tel: 641-932-2469. Fax: 641-932-2469. p. 791

Rasmus, Francesca Lane, Dir, Libr & Info Serv, Pacific Lutheran University, 12180 Park Ave S, Tacoma, WA, 98447-0001. Tel: 253-535-7500. Fax: 253-535-7315. p. 2539

Rasmus, Sherri, Dir, Saranac Public Library, 61 Bridge St, Saranac, MI, 48881. Tel: 616-642-9146. Fax: 616-642-6430. p. 1226

Rasmuson, Lori, Asst Librn, Swaledale Public Library, 504 Main St, Swaledale, IA, 50477. Tel: 641-995-2352. Fax: 641-995-2352. p. 847

Rasmussen, Andrea, Librn, Ropes & Gray LLP Library, Prudential Tower, 800 Boylston St, Boston, MA, 02199. Tel: 617-951-7855. Fax: 617-951-7050. p. 1066

Rasmussen, Cathy, Librn, Nampa Municipal Library, 10203 99th Ave, Nampa, AB, T0H 2R0, CANADA. Tel: 780-322-3805. Fax: 780-322-3955. p. 2712

Rasmussen, Claire, Ref Serv, Madison Area Technical College, 3550 Anderson St, Rm 230, Madison, WI, 53704. Tel: 608-246-6085. Fax: 608-246-6644. p. 2606

Rasmussen, Danielle, Asst Librn, Garland Public Library, 86 W Factory St, Garland, UT, 84312. Tel: 435-257-3117. Fax: 435-257-1217. p. 2406

Rasmussen, Debi, Librn, Lapeer District Library, Hadley Branch, 3556 Hadley Rd, Hadley, MI, 48440. Tel: 810-797-4101. Fax: 810-797-2912. p. 1202

Rasmussen, Debi, Librn, Lapeer District Library, Metamora Branch, 4018 Oak St, Metamora, MI, 48455. Tel: 810-678-2991. Fax: 810-678-3253. p. 1202

Rasmussen, Edie, Prof, University of British Columbia, The Irving K Barber Centre, 1961 E Mall, Ste 470, Vancouver, BC, V6T 1Z1, CANADA. Tel: 604-822-2404. Fax: 604-822-6006. p. 2977

Rasmussen, Frances, ILL, Linfield College, 900 S Baker St, McMinnville, OR, 97128. Tel: 503-883-2517. Fax: 503-883-2566. p. 2005

Rasmussen, Linda, Dir, Libr & Info Serv, Grace District Library, 204 S Main, Grace, ID, 83241. Tel: 208-425-3695. Fax: 208-425-3695. p. 575

Rasmussen, Linda, Chair, Library Consortium of Eastern Idaho, 113 S Garfield, Pocatello, ID, 83204-3235. Tel: 208-425-3695. p. 2941

Rasmussen, Marsha, Assoc Librn, Electronic Res & Tech Serv, Southwestern Adventist University, 101 W Magnolia St, Keene, TX, 76059. Tel: 817-202-6603. Fax: 817-556-4722. p. 2349

Rasmussen, Mary, Librn, Nebraska Legislative Council, 1201 State Capitol Bldg, 1445 K St, Lincoln, NE, 68508. Tel: 402-471-0075. Fax: 402-479-0967. p. 1405

Rasmussen, Pam, Mgr, Washoe County Library System, Incline Village Library, 845 Alder Ave, Incline Village, NV, 89451. Tel: 775-832-4132. Fax: 775-832-4180. p. 1434

Rasmussen, Pamela, Asst Dir, Whiting Public Library, 407 Whittier St, Whiting, IA, 51063. Tel: 712-455-2612. Fax: 712-455-2612. p. 852

Rasmussen, Rosemary, Ch, White Plains Public Library, 100 Martine Ave, White Plains, NY, 10601-2599. Tel: 914-422-1400. Fax: 914-422-1462. p. 1769

Rasor, Michael, Adult Serv, Peru Public Library, 102 E Main St, Peru, IN, 46970-2338. Tel: 765-473-3069. Fax: 765-473-3060. p. 772

Rastogi, Sonal, Asst Dir, Pub Serv, Norfolk Public Library, 235 E Plume St, Norfolk, VA, 23510-1706. Tel: 757-664-7327. Fax: 757-441-5863. p. 2481

Rastorfer, Renee, Head, Res Serv, Western New England University, 1215 Wilbraham Rd, Springfield, MA, 01119-2689. Tel: 413-782-1459. Fax: 413-782-1745. p. 1128

Rasymas, Antanas, ILL, American Dental Association Department of Library Services, 211 E Chicago Ave, 6th Flr, Chicago, IL, 60611-2678. Tel: 312-440-2653. Fax: 312-440-2774. p. 605

Ratajcrak, Amanda, Asst Librn, Rick Warren Memorial Public Library District, 114 S Fourth St, Elkville, IL, 62932-1097. Tel: 618-568-1843. Fax: 618-568-1843. p. 642

Ratchenski, Rebecca, Ch, Cavalier Public Library, 106 W Second Ave S, Cavalier, ND, 58220. Tel: 701-265-4016. p. 1839

Ratchford, Amy, Librn, Chadbourne & Parke LLP, 1200 New Hampshire Ave NW, Ste 300, Washington, DC, 20036. Tel: 202-974-5695. Fax: 202-974-5602. p. 396

Ratcliff, Catherine, Dir, Kingman Public Library, 123 W State St, Kingman, IN, 47952. Tel: 765-397-3138. Fax: 765-397-3566. p. 757

Ratcliff, Marcia, Head, Ref, Oceanside Library, 30 Davison Ave, Oceanside, NY, 11572-2299. Tel: 516-766-2360. Fax: 516-766-1895. p. 1709

Ratcliffe, Sam, Head, Spec Coll, Southern Methodist University, Hamon Arts Library, 6101 N Bishop Blvd, Dallas, TX, 75275. Tel: 214-768-1855. Fax: 214-768-1800. p. 2310

Rath, Linda, Grad Serv Librn, Baruch College-CUNY, 151 E 25 St, Box H-0520, New York, NY, 10010-2313. Tel: 646-312-1622. p. 1670

Rath, Logan, Emerging Tech Librn, State University of New York College at Brockport, 350 New Campus Dr, Brockport, NY, 14420-2997. Tel: 585-395-2568. Fax: 585-395-5651. p. 1585

Rath, Susan, Acq, California State University, East Bay Library, 25800 Carlos Bee Blvd, Hayward, CA, 94542-3052. Tel: 510-885-3627. Fax: 510-885-2049. p. 157

Rath, Zoe, Ref Librn, Berklee College of Music Library, 150 Massachusetts Ave, Boston, MA, 02115. Tel: 617-747-8143. Fax: 617-747-2050. p. 1055

Rathbone, Cathy, Br Mgr, Yakima Valley Libraries, Richard E Ostrander West Valley Community Library, 223 S 72nd Ave, Yakima, WA, 98908. Tel: 509-966-7070. Fax: 509-966-7070. p. 2550

Rathbone, Marjorie, Assoc Dir, Res Mgt, Saint Joseph's University, Francis A Drexel Library, 5600 City Ave, Philadelphia, PA, 19131-1395. Tel: 610-660-1912. Fax: 610-660-1916. p. 2116

Rathbun, James, Pub Serv Librn, Baxter Memorial Library, 71 South St, Gorham, ME, 04038. Tel: 207-222-1190. Fax: 207-839-7749. p. 986

Rathbun, Merrilyn, Res Supvr, Fort Lauderdale Historical Society, 219 SW Second Ave, Fort Lauderdale, FL, 33301. Tel: 954-463-4431. Fax: 954-523-6228. p. 443

Rathe, Joy, Dir, Willow Branch Township Library, 330 N Eldon, Cisco, IL, 61830. Tel: 217-669-2312. Fax: 217-669-2312. p. 629

Rathemacher, Andree J, Head, Acq, Ser, Web Coordr, Robert L Carothers Library & Learning Commons, 15 Lippitt Rd, Kingston, RI, 02881. Tel: 401-874-5096. Fax: 401-874-4608. p. 2168

Rathgeb, Mary Elizabeth, Sister, ILL, Saint Joseph's Seminary, 201 Seminary Ave, Yonkers, NY, 10704. Tel: 914-367-8262. Fax: 914-968-8787. p. 1771

Rathi, Dinesh, Dr, Asst Prof, University of Alberta, 3-20 Rutherford S, Edmonton, AB, T6G 2J4, CANADA. Tel: 780-492-4578. Fax: 780-492-2430. p. 2977

Rathjens, Wendy, Ch, Baldwin Public Library, 2385 Grand Ave, Baldwin, NY, 11510-3289. Tel: 516-223-6228. Fax: 516-623-7991. p. 1577

Rathke, Karen, Dir, George P & Susan Platt Cady Library, 42 E River St, Nichols, NY, 13812. Tel: 607-699-3835. Fax: 607-699-3835. p. 1705

Ratkin, Annette, Dir, Jewish Federation Libraries, Archives of the Jewish Federation of Nashville & Middle Tennessee, 801 Percy Warner Blvd, Nashville, TN, 37205. Tel: 615-356-3242, Ext 255. Fax: 615-352-0056. p. 2256

Ratliff, Cosette, Supvr, Ad Serv, Alameda Free Library, 1550 Oak St, Alameda, CA, 94501-2932. Tel: 510-747-7716. p. 119

Ratliff, Cosette, Br Mgr, Dallas Public Library, Polk-Wisdom, 7151 Library Lane, Dallas, TX, 75232-3899. Tel: 214-670-1947. Fax: 214-670-0589. p. 2307

Ratliff, Dave, In Charge, Multnomah County Library, Central, 801 SW Tenth Ave, Portland, OR, 97205-2597. Tel: 503-988-5231. Fax: 503-988-5226. p. 2012

Ratliff, Jacob, Archivist, Taxonomy Librn, National Fire Protection Association, One Batterymarch Park, Quincy, MA, 02169-7471. Tel: 617 984 7447. Fax: 617-984-7060. p. 1119

Ratliff, Jaime, Classified Libr Librn, United States Navy, 1002 Balch Blvd, Bldg 1003, Stennis Space Center, MS, 39522-5001. Tel: 228-688-4496. Fax: 228-688-4191. p. 1315

Ratliff, Jim, Librn, Arcadia Commons Campus, Kalamazoo Valley Community College Libraries, 6767 West O Ave, Kalamazoo, MI, 49003. Tel: 269-488-4328, 269-488-4380. Fax: 269-488-4488. p. 1197

Ratliff, Ramona, Asst Dir, York College, 1125 E Eighth St, York, NE, 68467-2699. Tel: 402-363-5703. Fax: 402-363-5685. p. 1424

Ratliff, Ron, Ref Librn, Manhattan Christian College Library, 1415 Anderson Ave, Manhattan, KS, 66502-4081. Tel: 785-539-3571, Ext 110. Fax: 785-539-0832. p. 881

Ratliff, Rosanna, Assoc Dir, Baylor Health Sciences Library, 3302 Gaston Ave, Dallas, TX, 75246. Tel: 214-828-8151. Fax: 214-820-2095. p. 2304

Ratt, Lucy, Librn, Keethanow Public Library, PO Box 70, Stanley Mission, SK, S0J 2P0, CANADA. Tel: 306-635-2104. Fax: 306-635-2050. p. 2927

Ratterman, Eleanor, Libr Mgr, Jamestown Public Library, 200 W Main St, Jamestown, NC, 27282. Tel: 336-454-4815. Fax: 336-454-0630. p. 1803

Rattliff, Jimmie, Dir, Hominy Public Library, 121 W Main, Hominy, OK, 74035. Tel: 918-885-4486. Fax: 918-885-2837. p. 1965

Rattray, Russell, Tech Serv, New England College, 28 Bridge St, Henniker, NH, 03242-3298. Tel: 603-428-2344. Fax: 603-428-4273. p. 1451

Rau, Cheryl, Br Asst, Huron County Library, Kirkton Branch, 70497 Perth Rd 164, Kirkton, ON, N0K 1K0, CANADA. Tel: 519-229-8854. p. 2800

Rau, Erik, Dir of Libr Serv, Hagley Museum & Library, 298 Buck Rd E, Wilmington, DE, 19807. Tel: 302-658-2400. Fax: 302-658-0568. p. 388

Rau, Patti, Asst Dir, ILL Librn, Cook Memorial Library, 93 Main St, Tamworth, NH, 03886. Tel: 603-323-8510. Fax: 603-323-2077. p. 1466

Rau, Rebecca, Youth Serv Librn, Lincoln Heritage Public Library, 105 Wallace St, Dale, IN, 47523-9267. Tel: 812-937-7170. Fax: 812-937-7102. p. 735

Rauch, Cindy, Dir, Homewood Public Library, 17917 Dixie Hwy, Homewood, IL, 60430-1703. Tel: 708-798-0121. Fax: 708-798-0662. p. 657

Rauch, Clare, Family Res Ctr Librn, SUNY Upstate Medical University, 766 Irving Ave, Syracuse, NY, 13210-1602. Tel: 315-464-7204. Fax: 315-464-4584. p. 1753

Rauch, Steve, Circ Supvr, Beaverton City Library, 12375 SW Fifth St, Beaverton, OR, 97005-2883. Tel: 503-526-2598. Fax: 503-526-2636. p. 1991

Rauchwerger, Diane, Librn, Congregation Beth Am Library, 26790 Arastradero Rd, Los Altos Hills, CA, 94022. Tel: 650-493-4661. Fax: 650-494-8248. p. 167

Rauenswinter, Judy, ILL, Edinboro University of Pennsylvania, 200 Tartan Ave, Edinboro, PA, 16444. Tel: 814-732-2779. Fax: 814-732-2883. p. 2053

Rauh, Anne, Librn, Syracuse University Library, Carnegie Library, Carnegie Bldg, Syracuse, NY, 13244-2010. Tel: 315-443-2160. Fax: 315-443-5549. p. 1754

Rauh, Anne, Info Serv Librn, University of Wisconsin-Madison, Kurt Wendt Engineering Library, 215 N Randall Ave, Madison, WI, 53706. Tel: 608-262-3493. Fax: 608-262-4739, 608-265-8751. p. 2610

Rauh, Jill, Doc, Ref, Benton Harbor Public Library, 213 E Wall St, Benton Harbor, MI, 49022-4499. Tel: 269-926-6139. Fax: 269-926-1674. p. 1156

Raulerson, Spring, Coordr, Florida Diagnostic & Learning Resource System, Main Library, 4th Flr, 100 S Andrews Ave, Fort Lauderdale, FL, 33301. Tel: 754-321-1700. Fax: 954-357-7507. p. 443

Rauls, Karen, Circ Supvr, Apache Junction Public Library, 1177 N Idaho Rd, Apache Junction, AZ, 85219. Tel: 480-474-8555. Fax: 480-983-4540. p. 57

Raum, Hans, Assoc Librn, Ref Serv, Middlebury College Library, 110 Storrs Ave, Middlebury, VT, 05753-6007. Tel: 802-443-5493. Fax: 802-443-2074, 802-443-5698. p. 2428

Raum, Tamar, Sr Librn, New York City Law Department, 100 Church St, Rm 6-310, New York, NY, 10007. Tel: 212-788-1608. Fax: 212-788-1239. p. 1688

Raupach, Melinda, Libr Assoc, University of New Hampshire at Manchester Library, 400 Commercial St, Manchester, NH, 03101. Tel: 603-641-4330. Fax: 603-641-4124. p. 1456

Rausch, Mary, Head, Cat, West Texas A&M University, University Dr & 26th St, Canyon, TX, 79016. Tel: 806-651-2219. Fax: 806-651-2213. p. 2294

Rauschenberger, Mike, Pub Serv, Northwest Community College Library, 5331 McConnell Ave, Terrace, BC, V8G 4X2, CANADA. Tel: 250-638-5407. Fax: 250-635-1594. p. 2739

Rautenkranz, Frank, Librn, Mgr, Canadian Nuclear Safety Commission Library, 280 Slater St, Ottawa, ON, K1P 1C2, CANADA. Tel: 613-995-2060. Fax: 613-995-5086. p. 2829

Rautenstrauch, Denine, Librn, Enterprise Public Library, 101 NE First St, Enterprise, OR, 97828-1173. Tel: 541-426-3906. p. 1996

Rauth, Eileen, Br Mgr, Burlington County Library, Cinnaminson Branch, 1619 Riverton Rd, Cinnaminson, NJ, 08077. Tel: 856-829-9340. Fax: 856-829-2243. p. 1543

Raven, Janna, Br Mgr, Fort Bend County Libraries, First Colony, 2121 Austin Pkwy, Sugar Land, TX, 77479-1219. Tel: 281-265-0969. Fax: 281-265-4440. p. 2375

Raven, Meg, Coordr, Pub Serv, Librn, Mount Saint Vincent University Library, 166 Bedford Hwy, Halifax, NS, B3M 2J6, CANADA. Tel: 902-457-6403. Fax: 902-457-6445. p. 2781

Raven, Rebecca, Dir, Pub Serv, Hamilton Public Library, 55 York Blvd, Hamilton, ON, L8R 3K1, CANADA. Tel: 905-546-3200, Ext 3455. Fax: 905-546-3202. p. 2808

Ravenell, Alma, Dir, Wiley College, 711 Wiley Ave, Marshall, TX, 75670-5151. Tel: 903-927-3275. Fax: 903-934-9333. p. 2360

Raver, Scott, Res, Gray, Plant, Mooty, 500 IDS Ctr, 800 S Eighth, Minneapolis, MN, 55402. Tel: 612-632-3000, 612-632-3122. p. 1260

Ravera, Laura, Dir, Minoa Library, 242 N Main St, Minoa, NY, 13116. Tel: 315-656-7401. Fax: 315-656-7033. p. 1662

Ravetto, Jessica, Librn, American Academy of Ophthalmology Library, 655 Beach St, San Francisco, CA, 94109. Tel: 415-561-8500. Fax: 415-561-8533. p. 240

Rawe, Rosanne, Acq, Ser, Northern Kentucky University, University Dr, Highland Heights, KY, 41099. Tel: 859-572-5456. Fax: 859-572-5390. p. 917

Rawles-Heiser, Carolyn, Dir, Corvallis-Benton County Public Library, 645 NW Monroe Ave, Corvallis, OR, 97330. Tel: 541-766-6910. p. 1994

Rawlings, Gail, Mgr, Libr, Info Mgt Syst & Standards, Supreme Court of Canada Library, 301 Wellington St, Ottawa, ON, K1A 0J1, CANADA. Tel: 613-996-8183. Fax: 613-952-2832. p. 2833

Rawlings, Margaret L, Librn, Barry Public Library, 880 Bainbridge St, Barry, IL, 62312. Tel: 217-335-2149. Fax: 217-335-2149. p. 592

Rawlings, Shari, Ch, Hope Welty Public Library District, 100 S Madison St, Cerro Gordo, IL, 61818. Tel: 217-763-5001. Fax: 217-763-5391. p. 602

Rawlins, Ben, Electronic Res Librn, Georgetown College, 400 E College St, Georgetown, KY, 40324. Tel: 502-863-8403. Fax: 502-868-7740. p. 915

Rawlins, Carol Ann, Asst Librn, Lago Vista Public Library, 5803 Thunderbird, Ste 40, Lago Vista, TX, 78645. Tel: 512-267-3868. Fax: 512-267-4855. p. 2352

Rawlins, Kathleen L, Asst Dir, Cambridge Historical Commission Archive, 831 Massachusetts Ave, 2nd Flr, Cambridge, MA, 02139. Tel: 617-349-4683. Fax: 617-349-3116. p. 1072

Rawlins, Lynn, Br Mgr, Wellington County Library, Arthur Branch, 183 George St, Arthur, ON, N0G 1A0, CANADA. Tel: 519-848-3999. p. 2805

Rawls, Ginny, YA Serv, Alexandria Library, Charles E Beatley Jr Central (Hqtrs), 5005 Duke St, Alexandria, VA, 22304-2903. Tel: 703-746-1767. p. 2444

Rawoof, Jane, Cat, ILL, Broome Community College, 907 Front St, Binghamton, NY, 13905-1328. Tel: 607-778-5020. Fax: 607-778-5108. p. 1581

Rawson, Sandra, Br Mgr, Thompson-Nicola Regional District Library System, Savona Branch, 60 Savona St, Savona, BC, V0K 2J0, CANADA. Tel: 250-373-2666. p. 2730

Rawson, William, Librn, Hartnell College, 411 Central Ave, Salinas, CA, 93901. Tel: 831-755-6700. Fax: 831-759-6084. p. 2962

Ray, Amanda, Adult Serv, Libr Asst, Barry-Lawrence Regional Library, Cassville Branch, 301 W 17th St, Cassville, MO, 65625-1044. Tel: 417-847-2121. Fax: 417-847-4679. p. 1346

Ray, Anna, Librn, Cumberland County Public Library & Information Center, Hope Mills Branch, 3411 Golfview Rd, Hope Mills, NC, 28348-2266. Tel: 910-425-8455. Fax: 910-423-0997. p. 1792

Ray, Carol Atkins, Asst City Librn, Pretty Prairie Public Library, 119 W Main St, Pretty Prairie, KS, 67570. Tel: 620-459-6392. Fax: 620-459-7354. p. 891

Ray, Dian, Dir, Llano County Library System, 102 E Haynie, Llano, TX, 78643. Tel: 325-247-5248. Fax: 325-247-1778. p. 2356

Ray, Donald, Coll Develop, Mercy College Libraries, 555 Broadway, Dobbs Ferry, NY, 10522. Tel: 914-674-7429. Fax: 914-674-7581. p. 1615

Ray, Emily, Monographs Tech Serv Librn, Vassar College Library, 124 Raymond Ave, Maildrop 20, Poughkeepsie, NY, 12604-0020. Tel: 845-437-5760. Fax: 845-437-5864. p. 1723

Ray, Ginny, Dir, Neosho/Newton County Library, 201 W Spring St, Neosho, MO, 64850. Tel: 417-451-4231. Fax: 417-451-6438. p. 1347

Ray, Glenn, Asst Prof, University of Pittsburgh, 135 N Bellefield Ave, Pittsburgh, PA, 15260. Tel: 412-624-5230. Fax: 412-624-5231. p. 2973

Ray, Gloria, Coll Develop, Info Serv, Ref Serv, East Bonner County Free Library District, 1407 Cedar St, Sandpoint, ID, 83864-2052. Tel: 208-263-6930, Ext 204. Fax: 208-263-8320. p. 583

Ray, Jack G, Assoc Dir, Loyola-Notre Dame Library, Inc, 200 Winston Ave, Baltimore, MD, 21212. Tel: 410-617-6800. Fax: 410-617-6895. p. 1015

Ray, Jennifer, Dir, Cass District Library, 319 M-62 N, Cassopolis, MI, 49031-1099. Tel: 269-445-3400, Ext 25. Fax: 269-445-8795. p. 1161

Ray, June, Librn, Henry A Malley Memorial Library, 101 S Lincoln, Broadus, MT, 59317. Tel: 406-436-2812. p. 1375

Ray, Kathlin, Sr Dir, Libr, University of Nevada-Reno, 1664 N Virginia St, Mailstop 0322, Reno, NV, 89557-0322. Tel: 775-682-5677. Fax: 775-784-4529. p. 1433

Ray, Kathy, Asst Dir, Locust Valley Library, 170 Buckram Rd, Locust Valley, NY, 11560-1999. Tel: 516-671-1837. Fax: 516-676-8164. p. 1654

Ray, Kelly, Youth Serv Librn, Flat Rock Public Library, 25200 Gibraltar Rd, Flat Rock, MI, 48134. Tel: 734-782-2430. Fax: 734-789-8265. p. 1178

Ray, Kelly, Youth Librn, Bacon Memorial District Library, 45 Vinewood, Wyandotte, MI, 48192-5221. Tel: 734-246-8357. Fax: 734-282-1540. p. 1237

Ray, Krickett, Asst Librn, Lost Rivers District Library, 126 S Front St, Arco, ID, 83213. Tel: 208-527-8511. p. 569

Ray, LaDonna, Dir, Mickey Reily Public Library, 604 S Mathews St, Corrigan, TX, 75939. Tel: 936-398-4156. Fax: 936-398-5113. p. 2302

Ray, Laura, Educ Prog Librn, Cleveland State University, Cleveland-Marshall Law Library, Cleveland-Marshall College of Law, 1801 Euclid Ave, Cleveland, OH, 44115-2223. Tel: 216-687-6880. Fax: 216-687-6881. p. 1878

Ray, Linda, ILL, Bellevue Public Library, 1003 Lincoln Rd, Bellevue, NE, 68005-3199. Tel: 402-293-3157. Fax: 402-293-3163. p. 1393

Ray, Nancy, Dir, Darlington County Library, 204 N Main St, Darlington, SC, 29532. Tel: 843-398-4940. Fax: 843-398-4942. p. 2192

Ray, Patsy, Br Head, Choctaw County Public Library, 124 N Academy Ave, Butler, AL, 36904. Tel: 251-542-9379. p. 11

Ray, Patsy, Br Mgr, Choctaw County Public Library, Silas Branch, 130 Indian Way, Silas, AL, 36919. Tel: 251-542-9379. p. 11

Ray, Phyllis, Br Mgr, Fairfax County Public Library, Thomas Jefferson Branch, 7415 Arlington Blvd, Falls Church, VA, 22042-7499. Tel: 703-573-1060. p. 2461

Ray, Rebekah, Head of Libr, Free Library of Philadelphia, Haddington Branch, 446 N 65th St, Philadelphia, PA, 19151-4003. Tel: 215-685-1970. Fax: 215-685-1971. p. 2108

Ray, Regina, Ch, Houston County Public Library System, 1201 Washington Ave, Perry, GA, 31069. Tel: 478-987-3050. Fax: 478-987-4572. p. 547

Ray, Rob, Spec Coll & Univ Archives, San Diego State University Library & Information Access, 5500 Campanile Dr, San Diego, CA, 92182-8050. Tel: 619-594-4303. Fax: 619-594-0466. p. 237

Ray, Steven, Info Tech Dir, Crandall Public Library, 251 Glen St, Glens Falls, NY, 12801-3593. Tel: 518-792-6508. Fax: 518-792-5251. p. 1629

Ray, Susan, Ref, Simsbury Public Library, 725 Hopmeadow St, Simsbury, CT, 06070. Tel: 860-658-7663. Fax: 860-658-6732. p. 367

Ray, Susan, Dir, Catskill Public Library, One Franklin St, Catskill, NY, 12414-1407. Tel: 518-943-4230. Fax: 518-943-1439. p. 1603

Ray, Tammyann, Librn, Oswayo Valley Memorial Library, 103 N Pleasant St, Shinglehouse, PA, 16748. Tel: 814-697-6691. Fax: 814-697-6691. p. 2140

Rayburn, Kellee, Ch, Lake County Public Library, 1919 W 81st Ave, Merrillville, IN, 46410-5488. Tel: 219-769-3541. Fax: 219-756-9358. p. 763

Rayburn, Martha, Librn, First Regional Library, Sam Lapidus Memorial Public Library, 108 Missouri St, Crenshaw, MS, 38621-5450. Tel: 662-382-7479. Fax: 662-382-7479. p. 1302

Rayburn, Renee, Ch, Long Beach Public Library, 209 Jeff Davis Ave, Long Beach, MS, 39560. Tel: 228-863-0711. Fax: 228-863-8511. p. 1307

Rayburn, Richard, Archivist, National Archives & Records Administration, 5780 Jonesboro Rd, Morrow, GA, 30260. Tel: 770-968-2100. Fax: 770-968-2457. p. 545

Rayfield, Patricia, Head Librn, Belmont Hills Public Library, 120 Mary Watersford Rd, Bala Cynwyd, PA, 19004. Tel: 610-664-1063. Fax: 610-664-8427. p. 2030

Rayford, Jocelyn, Ref Serv, Ozark-Dale County Public Library, Inc, 416 James St, Ozark, AL, 36360. Tel: 334-774-2399, 334-774-5480. p. 33

Rayhill, Gladys, Libr Dir, Belt Public Library, 404 Millard St, Belt, MT, 59412. Tel: 406-277-3136. Fax: 406-277-3136. p. 1373

Rayme, Mary, Dir, Pioneer Memorial Library, PO Drawer 13, Rte 33E, Harman, WV, 26270-0013, Tel: 304-227-4788. Fax: 304-227-4788. p. 2560

Rayment, Cathy, Prov Libr Leader, BC Cancer Agency, 675 W Tenth Ave, Vancouver, BC, V5Z 1L3, CANADA. Tel: 604-675-8004. Fax: 604-675-8009. p. 2740

Rayment, Peter, Dir, Toledo Public Library, 173 NW Seventh St, Toledo, OR, 97391. Tel: 541-336-3132. Fax: 541-336-3428. p. 2021

Raymond, Anthony, Assoc Librn, Santa Clara University, 500 El Camino Real, Santa Clara, CA, 95053-0500. Tel: 408-554-5430. Fax: 408-554-6827. p. 263

Raymond, Brigitte, Tech Serv Mgr, Bibliothèques de Montrèal, 801, rue Brennan, 5e Etage, Bureau 5206, Montreal, QC, H3C 0G4, CANADA. Tel: 514-872-1542. Fax: 514-872-0530. p. 2889

Raymond, Chadwick, Dir, Northbrook Public Library, 1201 Cedar Lane, Northbrook, IL, 60062-4581. Tel: 847-272-6224. Fax: 847-272-5362. p. 682

Raymond, Denise, Circ Supvr, Iberia Parish Library, 445 E Main St, New Iberia, LA, 70560-3710. Tel: 337-364-7024, 337-364-7074. Fax: 337-364-7042. p. 959

Raymond, Joyce, Mgr, Pavillion Public Library, 203 N Main, Pavillion, WY, 82523. Tel: 307-856-0151; 307-857-7440. Fax: 307-857-7440. p. 2658

Raymond, Kathleen, Dir of Circ, Putnam Public Library, 225 Kennedy Dr, Putnam, CT, 06260-1691. Tel: 860-963-6826. Fax: 860-963-6828. p. 365

Raymond, Kathleen, Ref Serv, Germantown Community Library, 1925 Exeter Rd, Germantown, TN, 38138-2815. Tel: 901-757-7323, Ext 7478. Fax: 901-756-9940. p. 2235

Raymond, Kelly, Asst Librn, Southeast Regional Library, Bengough Branch, 301 Main St, Bengough, SK, S0C 0K0, CANADA. Tel: 306-268-2022. p. 2929

Raymond, Lisa, Assoc Libr Dir, Marine Biological Laboratory Woods Hole Oceanographic Institution Library, WHOI Data Library & Archives, McLean MS 8, 360 Woods Hole Rd, Woods Hole, MA, 02543-1539. Tel: 508-289-2269. Fax: 508-457-2156. p. 1142

Raymond, Lisa, Coordr of Ref Serv, Walden University Library, 100 Washington Ave S, Ste 900, Minneapolis, MN, 55401. p. 1262

Raymond, Marie, Early Literacy Coordr, Scottsdale Public Library, 3839 N Drinkwater Blvd, Scottsdale, AZ, 85251-4467. Tel: 480-312-7323. Fax: 480-312-7993. p. 81

Raymond, Marilyn, Dir, Bridgewater Town Library, 955 River Rd, Plymouth, NH, 03264. Tel: 603-968-7911. Fax: 603-968-3506. p. 1462

Raymond, Michelle, Head of Libr, Fort Kent Public Library, One Monument Sq, Fort Kent, ME, 04743. Tel: 207-834-3048. Fax: 207-834-2630. p. 985

Raymond, Pamela, Librn, Mount McGregor Correctional Facility Library, 1000 Mount McGregor Rd, Wilton, NY, 12831-1223. Tel: 518-587-3960. Fax: 518-587-3960. p. 1770

Raymond, Sandra, Ref Librn, Wayland Free Public Library, Five Concord Rd, Wayland, MA, 01778. Tel: 508-358-2311. Fax: 508-358-5249. p. 1134

Raymond, Susan, Evening Supvr, Atlantic Union College, 138 Main St, South Lancaster, MA, 01561. Tel: 978-368-2450. Fax: 978-368-2456. p. 1125

Raymond, Terri, Youth Serv Coordr, Norfolk Public Library, 235 E Plume St, Norfolk, VA, 23510-1706. Tel: 757-664-7328, Ext 347. Fax: 757-441-5863. p. 2481

Raynard, Melissa, Librn, University of Manitoba Libraries, Concordia Hospital Library, 1095 Concordia Ave, Winnipeg, MB, R2K 3S8, CANADA. Tel: 204-661-7440. Fax: 204-661-7282. p. 2758

Rayner, Ashley, Ref Librn, Northwestern College, 4811 N Milwaukee Ave, Chicago, IL, 60630. Tel: 773-777-4220. Fax: 773-205-2126. p. 621

Raynes, Lu, Actg Mgr, Putnam County Library, Buffalo Branch, 3530 Buffalo Rd, Buffalo, WV, 25033-9434. Tel: 304-937-3538. Fax: 304-937-3538. p. 2562

Raynor, John, Ref, High Point Public Library, 901 N Main St, High Point, NC, 27262. Tel: 336-883-3670. Fax: 336-883-3636. p. 1802

Raynor, Julie, Supvr, AV & Media Serv, High Point Public Library, 901 N Main St, High Point, NC, 27262. Tel: 336-883-3093. Fax: 336-883-3636. p. 1802

Razer, Lee, ILL, Central Arkansas Library System, 100 Rock St, Little Rock, AR, 72201-4698. Tel: 501-918-3000. p. 106

Raznick, Barbara, Libr Dir, Saul Brodsky Jewish Community Library, 12 Millstone Campus Dr, Saint Louis, MO, 63146-5776. Tel: 314-442-3720. Fax: 314-432-1277. p. 1353

Razo, Virginia, Coordr, Acq, Argonne National Laboratory, 9700 S Cass Ave, Bldg 240, Argonne, IL, 60439-4801. Tel: 630-252-4270. Fax: 630-252-5024. p. 589

Razumny, Aja, Pub Libr & Continuing Educ Coordr, Alaska State Library, Library Development, 344 W Third Ave, Ste 125, Anchorage, AK, 99501. Tel: 907-465-2458. Fax: 907-269-6580. p. 44

Razzaghi, Farzaneh, Dr, Dean of Libr, The University of Texas-Pan American Library, 1201 W University Dr, Edinburg, TX, 78541-2999. Tel: 956-665-2755. Fax: 956-665-5396. p. 2315

Razzo, Marilyn, Asst Librn, Fernie Heritage Library, 492 Third Ave, Fernie, BC, V0B 1M0, CANADA. Tel: 250-423-4458. Fax: 250-423-7906. p. 2728

Rea, Allison, Ref Librn, University of California, Berkeley, Jean Gray Hargrove Music Library, Hargrove Music Library, Berkeley, CA, 94720-6000. Tel: 510-643-6197. Fax: 510-642-8237. p. 128

Rea, Ann, Librn, Beal College Library, 99 Farm Rd, Bangor, ME, 04401-6831. Tel: 207-947-4591. Fax: 207-947-0208. p. 975

Rea, Nancy, Dep Dir, Libr Serv, Hyde Park Historical Society Archives, 35 Harvard Ave, Hyde Park, MA, 02136. Tel: 617-361-4398. Fax: 617-361-4398. p. 1097

Rea, Nancy, Ch, Waltham Public Library, 735 Main St, Waltham, MA, 02451. Tel: 781-314-3425. Fax: 781-314-3426. p. 1133

Read, Allison, Ref Librn, Greenwood County Library, 600 S Main St, Greenwood, SC, 29646. Tel: 864-941-4650. Fax: 864-941-4651. p. 2197

Read, Barbara, Dir, Rolling Hills Consolidated Library, 1904 N Belt Hwy, Saint Joseph, MO, 64506-2201. Tel: 816-232-5479, Ext 2401. Fax: 816-236-2133. p. 1352

Read, Barbara, Dir, Rolling Hills Consolidated Library, Savannah, 514 W Main St, Savannah, MO, 64485-1670. Tel: 816-324-4569. Fax: 816-324-3562. p. 1352

Read, Christina, Human Res, Whatcom County Library System, 5205 Northwest Dr, Bellingham, WA, 98226-9050. Tel: 360-384-3150. Fax: 360-384-4947. p. 2509

Read, Kim, Ref Librn (Info Serv), Clark College, Mail Stop LIB 112, 1933 Fort Vancouver Way, Vancouver, WA, 98663-3598. Tel: 360-992-2826. Fax: 360-992-2869. p. 2545

Read, Steven D, Dir, McPherson Public Library, 214 W Marlin, McPherson, KS, 67460-4299. Tel: 620-245-2570. Fax: 620-245-2567. p. 883

Read, Vicki, Head, Patron Serv, Utah State University, 3000 Old Main Hill, Logan, UT, 84322-3000. Tel: 435-797-2914. Fax: 435-797-2880. p. 2407

Reade, Elisabeth K, Chief, Libr Serv, Reade International Corp, 850 Waterman Ave, East Providence, RI, 02914. Tel: 401-433-7000. Fax: 401-433-7001. p. 2166

Reader, Jean, Circ Supvr, Wake Forest University, Professional Center Library, Worrell Professional Ctr for Law & Management, 1834 Wake Forest Rd, Winston-Salem, NC, 27106. Tel: 336-758-5438. Fax: 336-758-6077. p. 1834

Reading, Barbara, Dir, Libr Develop, Missouri State Library, James C Kirkpatrick State Information Ctr, 600 W Main St, Jefferson City, MO, 65101-1532. Tel: 573-751-2679. Fax: 573-751-3612. p. 1335

Ready, Judy, Asst Librn, La Crescent Public Library, 321 Main St, La Crescent, MN, 55947. Tel: 507-895-4047. Fax: 507-895-7153. p. 1255

Reagan, Jan, Libr Serv Section Chief, State Library of North Carolina, 109 E Jones St, Raleigh, NC, 27601. Tel: 919-807-7443. Fax: 919-733-8748. p. 1817

Reagan, Katherine, Curator, Cornell University Library, Division of Rare & Manuscript Collections, 2B Carl A Kroch Library, Ithaca, NY, 14853. Tel: 607-255-3530. Fax: 607-255-9524. p. 1641

Reagan, Martha, Ref Serv, Boston Herald, One Herald Sq, Boston, MA, 02118. Tel: 617-619-6680. Fax: 617-619-6450. p. 1056

Reakes, Patrick, Head, Allen H Neuharth Journalism & Communications Libr, University of Florida Libraries, 535 Library W, Gainesville, FL, 32611-7000. Tel: 352-273-2770. Fax: 352-392-5809. p. 450

Real, Nana, Dir, Dundy County Library, 126 Seventh Ave E, Benkelman, NE, 69021. Tel: 308-423-2333. p. 1394

Reale, Sue Ann, Head, Ch, Syosset Public Library, 225 S Oyster Bay Rd, Syosset, NY, 11791-5897. Tel: 516-921-7161. Fax: 516-921-8771. p. 1751

Ream, Dan, Dir, Richard Bland College Library, 11301 Johnson Rd, Petersburg, VA, 23805. Tel: 804-862-6226. Fax: 804-862-6125. p. 2484

Ream, Daniel, Dir, Distance Educ, Outreach Serv Librn, Virginia Commonwealth University Libraries, James Cabell Branch Library, Monroe Park Campus, 901 Park Ave, Richmond, VA, 23284-2033. Tel: 804-828-6545. Fax: 804-828-0151. p. 2492

Ream, Kathy, Head, Cat, Boone-Madison Public Library, 375 Main St, Madison, WV, 25130-1295. Tel: 304-369-7842. Fax: 304-369-2950. p. 2564

Reamer, Joan, ILL, Caldwell College, 120 Bloomfield Ave, Caldwell, NJ, 07006-6195. Tel: 973-618-3312. Fax: 973-618-3360. p. 1476

Reames, John, Coll Mgt, Santa Fe Community College, 3000 NW 83rd St, Bldg Y-100, Gainesville, FL, 32606. Tel: 352-395-5406. Fax: 352-395-5102. p. 449

Reams, Don, Supv Librn, NASA, 21000 Brookpark Rd, MS 60-3, Cleveland, OH, 44135. Fax: 216-433-5777. p. 1880

Reams, Donald, Instrul Serv Librn, Ref Serv, Ohio State University LIBRARIES, Louis Bromfield Library - Mansfield Campus, 1660 University Dr, Mansfield, OH, 44906-1599. Tel: 419-755-4350. Fax: 419-755-4327. p. 1887

Reardon, Deanna, Librn, Saint Edward Public Library, 302 Beaver, Saint Edward, NE, 68660. Tel: 402-678-2204. Fax: 402-678-2204. p. 1418

Reardon, Emily, Ref Serv, Belmont Public Library, 336 Concord Ave, Belmont, MA, 02478-0904. Tel: 617-489-2000, 617-993-2850. Fax: 617-993-2893. p. 1052

Reardon, John, ILL, Brockton Public Library System, 304 Main St, Brockton, MA, 02301-5390. Tel: 508-580-7890. Fax: 508-580-7898. p. 1070

Reardon, Siobhan, Pres & Dir, Free Library of Philadelphia, 1901 Vine St, Philadelphia, PA, 19103-1189. Tel: 215-686-5300. Fax: 215-686-5368. p. 2106

Rearick, Daisy, Per, Truman State University, 100 E Normal, Kirksville, MO, 63501-4211. Tel: 660-785-4048. p. 1342

Reason, Judy, Librn, Fulton Public Library, Hickman Public, 902 Moscow Ave, Hickman, KY, 42050. Tel: 270-236-2464. Fax: 270-236-1442. p. 914

Reason, Marjorie C, Circ, Darlington County Library, 204 N Main St, Darlington, SC, 29532. Tel: 843-398-4940. Fax: 843-398-4942. p. 2192

Reason, Sudie, Mrs, Librn, Martin Community College Library, 1161 Kehukee Park Rd, Williamston, NC, 27892-4425. Tel: 252-792-1521, Ext 280. Fax: 252-792-4425. p. 1830

Reasoner, Mary Beth, Ch, Tecumseh District Library, 215 N Ottawa St, Tecumseh, MI, 49286-1564. Tel: 517-423-2238. Fax: 517-423-5519. p. 1230

Reaume, Renee, Head, Health Info Network, University of Calgary Library, Health Sciences Library, Health Sci Ctr, 3330 Hospital Dr NW, Calgary, AB, T2N 4N1, CANADA. Tel: 403-220-5573. Fax: 403-210-9847. p. 2693

Reaux, Gladys, Br Supvr, Jackson/Hinds Library System, Ella Bess Austin Library, 420 W Cunningham Ave, Terry, MS, 39170. Tel: 601-878-5336. Fax: 601-878-0609. p. 1303

Reaveley, Melanie, Libr Mgr, Vancouver Island Regional Library, Cowichan, 2687 James St, Duncan, BC, V9L 2X5, CANADA. Tel: 250-746-7661. Fax: 250-746-5595. p. 2732

Reaves, James E, Dir, United Methodist Historical Society, 2200 St Paul St, Baltimore, MD, 21218-5897. Tel: 410-889-4458. Fax: 410-889-1501. p. 1018

Reaves, Jennifer, Sr Librn, Cat & Tech Serv, Denton Public Library, 502 Oakland St, Denton, TX, 76201. Tel: 940-349-8752. Fax: 940-349-8101. p. 2312

Reaves, Paula, Asst Librn, Head, Tech Serv, Ref Serv, University of Arkansas-Monticello Library, 514 University Dr, Monticello, AR, 71656. Tel: 870-460-1080. Fax: 870-460-1980. p. 110

Reavie, Keir, Head, Biological & Agr Sci, University of California, Davis, 100 NW Quad, Davis, CA, 95616-5292. Tel: 530-752-6561. Fax: 530-752-3148. p. 139

Reavis, Dorla, Asst Librn, Divernon Township Library, 221 S Second St, Divernon, IL, 62530. Tel: 217-628-3813. Fax: 217-628-3813. p. 636

Reavis, Paul, Librn, Hopkins & Carley Library, PO Box 1469, San Jose, CA, 95109-1469. Tel: 408-286-9800. Fax: 408-998-4790. p. 249

Rebar, Diane, Info Serv, Hoyt Library, 284 Wyoming Ave, Kingston, PA, 18704-3597. Tel: 570-287-2013. Fax: 570-283-2081. p. 2074

Rebholz, Maureen, Dir of Educ, Illinois Valley Community Hospital, 925 West St, Peru, IL, 61354. Tel: 815-780-3485. Fax: 815-224-1747. p. 691

Rebori, Lisa, VPres, Coll, Houston Museum of Natural Science Library, One Hermann Circle Dr, Houston, TX, 77030-1799. Tel: 713-639-4600, 713-639-4670. Fax: 713-639-4767. p. 2338

Rebovich, Nadine, ILL, Lincoln Public Library, Three Bedford Rd, Lincoln, MA, 01773. Tel: 781-259-8465. Fax: 781-259-1056. p. 1099

Rech, Nikki, Info Serv Librn, Rhodes College, 2000 North Pkwy, Memphis, TN, 38112-1694. Tel: 901-843-3900. Fax: 901-843-3404. p. 2251

Rechel, Michael, Cat, Abington Township Public Library, 1030 Old York Rd, Abington, PA, 19001-4594. Tel: 215-885-5180. Fax: 215-885-9242. p. 2025

Rechsteiner, Kelly, YA Serv, North Merrick Public Library, 1691 Meadowbrook Rd, North Merrick, NY, 11566. Tel: 516-378-7474. Fax: 516-378-0876. p. 1706

Recht, Paul, Ref/Circ Supvr, Allegheny County Law Library, 921 City-County Bldg, 414 Grant St, Pittsburgh, PA, 15219-2543. Tel: 412-350-5353. Fax: 412-350-5889. p. 2121

Recker, Anne, Librn, Saint Thomas Aquinas Church, 2210 Lincoln Way, Ames, IA, 50014. Tel: 515-292-3810. Fax: 515-292-3841. p. 793

Recker, Mimi, Dept Head, Prof, Utah State University, 2830 Old Main Hill, Education, Bldg 215, Logan, UT, 84322. Tel: 435-797-2692. Fax: 435-797-2693. p. 2975

Reckhow, Susan, Dir, Onondaga Free Library, 4840 W Seneca Tpk, Syracuse, NY, 13215. Tel: 315-492-1727. Fax: 315-492-1323. p. 1753

Record, Patricia, Ref, Logan Library, 255 N Main, Logan, UT, 84321-3914. Tel: 435-716-9123. Fax: 435-716-9145. p. 2407

Records, Janet, Asst Br Mgr, Chesterfield County Public Library, Chester Branch, 11800 Centre St, Chester, VA, 23831. Tel: 804-748-6314. p. 2457

Recore-Migirditch, Peter, Asst Dir, Finance/Admin, University at Albany, State University of New York, 1400 Washington Ave, Albany, NY, 12222-0001. Tel: 518-442-3563. Fax: 518-442-3663. p. 1570

Rector, Amy, Circ Supvr, Harrison Memorial Library, Ocean Ave & Lincoln St, Carmel, CA, 93921. Tel: 831-624-4629. Fax: 831-624-0407. p. 132

Rector, Lucy Holman, Dean of Libr & Instrul Serv, Harford Community College Library, 401 Thomas Run Rd, Bel Air, MD, 21015. Tel: 410-836-4144. Fax: 410-836-4481. p. 1019

Rector, Peggy, Tech Serv, McCreary County Public Library District, Six N Main St, Whitley City, KY, 42653. Tel: 606-376-8738. Fax: 606-376-3631. p. 937

Red Ear Horse, Donna, Dir, Oglala Lakota College, Oglala/White Clay College Center, PO Box 19, Oglala, SD, 57764. Tel: 605-867-5780. Fax: 605-867-1243. p. 2214

Red Owl, Phinet, Dir, Oglala Lakota College, East Wakpamni College Center, PO Box 612, Batesland, SD, 57716. Tel: 605-288-1834, 605-862-2032. Fax: 605-288-1828. p. 2213

Reda, Sheryl A, Assoc Librn, Meadville-Lombard Theological School Library, 5701 S Woodlawn Ave, Chicago, IL, 60637. Tel: 773-256-3000, Ext 225. Fax: 773-256-3007. p. 618

Redalen, Susan J, Librn, Briggs & Morgan, 2200 IDS Ctr, 80 S Elg, Minneapolis, MN, 55402. Tel: 612-977-8400. p. 1259

Redburn, Maria, Dir, Bedford Public Library, 2424 Forest Ridge Dr, Bedford, TX, 76021. Tel: 817-952-2335. Fax: 817-952-2396. p. 2287

Redcay, Sheila, Dir, Matthews Public Library, 102 W Main St, Fredericksburg, PA, 17026. Tel: 717-865-5523. Fax: 717-865-5523. p. 2059

Redd, Kathryn, Librn, Nucla Public Library, 544 Main St, Nucla, CO, 81424. Tel: 970-864-2166. p. 319

Redd, Kay, Br Mgr, Saint Tammany Parish Library, Abita Springs Branch, 71683 Leveson St, Abita Springs, LA, 70420. Tel: 985-893-6285. Fax: 985-893-6285. p. 948

Redd, Rea Andrew, Interim Dir, Waynesburg College, 93 Locust Ave, Waynesburg, PA, 15370-1242. Tel: 724-852-3254. Fax: 724-627-4188. p. 2152

Redden, Carla, Libr Coordr, Maysville Community & Technical College, 1755 US Hwy 68, Maysville, KY, 41056. Tel: 606-759-7141, Ext 66190. Fax: 606-759-7176. p. 928

Redden, Melanie, Librn & Info Dir, Robertson County Library, Franklin Carnegie Library, 315 E Decherd St, Franklin, TX, 77856. Tel: 979-828-4331. p. 2324

Redden, Sarah, Head, Circ, Michigan City Public Library, 100 E Fourth St, Michigan City, IN, 46360-3393. Tel: 219-873-3063. Fax: 219-873-3068. p. 764

Redden, Teresa, Dir, Hudson Public Library, 555 Main St, Hudson, CO, 80642. Tel: 303-536-4550. Fax: 303-536-4404. p. 313

Reddick, Freda, Asst Dir, W G Rhea Public Library, 400 W Washington St, Paris, TN, 38242-3903. Tel: 731-642-1702. Fax: 731-642-1777. p. 2263

Reddick, Mary, Head, User Serv, California State University, Sacramento Library, 2000 State University Dr E, Sacramento, CA, 95819-6039. Tel: 916-278-5679. Fax: 916-278-5917. p. 223

Reddick, Sharon, Regional Mgr, North Central Regional Library, Omak Community, 30 S Ash, Omak, WA, 98841. Tel: 509-826-1820. Fax: 509-826-5102. p. 2549

Reddigan, Linda, Libr Tech, College of the North Atlantic, Placentia Campus, PO Box 190, Placentia, NL, A0B 2Y0, CANADA. Tel: 709-227-6264. Fax: 709-227-7185. p. 2771

Redding, Lorna I, Acq, Normandale Community College Library, 9700 France Ave S, Bloomington, MN, 55431. Tel: 952-487-8292. Fax: 952-487-8101. p. 1242

Reddish, Cheryl, Dir, Warren County Memorial Library, 119 South Front St, Warrenton, NC, 27589. Tel: 252-257-4990. Fax: 252-257-4089. p. 1828

Reddy, Joan, Asst Dir, Admin, Siouxland Libraries, 200 N Dakota Ave, Sioux Falls, SD, 57104. Tel: 605-367-8721. Fax: 605-367-4312. p. 2218

Reddy, Michael, Dir, Libr Serv, Lewis & Roca Library, Renaisance Tower, No 2, 40 N Central Ave, Ste 1900, Phoenix, AZ, 85004-4429. Tel: 602-262-5303. Fax: 602-734-3739. p. 74

Reddy, Umashanie, Mgr, Diversity Serv, Calgary Public Library, W R Castell Central Library, 616 Macleod Trail SE, Calgary, AB, T2G 2M2, CANADA. Tel: 403-260-2702. Fax: 403-260-2737. p. 2689

Redeker, Kathy, Circ, Emporia State University, 1200 Commercial St, Box 4051, Emporia, KS, 66801. Tel: 620-341-5207. Fax: 620-341-5997. p. 866

Redemer, Blaine, Govt Doc Mgr, Illinois State Library, Gwendolyn Brooks Bldg, 300 S Second St, Springfield, IL, 62701-9713. Tel: 217-782-5432. Fax: 217-785-4326. p. 705

Redfearn, Caroline, Dir, West Memphis Public Library, 213 N Avalon, West Memphis, AR, 72301. Tel: 870-732-7590. Fax: 870-732-7636. p. 117

Redfearn, E Patricia, Dir, George Hail Free Library, 530 Main St, Warren, RI, 02885. Tel: 401-245-7686. Fax: 401-245-7470. p. 2177

Redfearn, Kathleen, Ch, Dartmouth Public Libraries, 732 Dartmouth St, Dartmouth, MA, 02748. Tel: 508-999-0726. Fax: 508-992-9914. p. 1084

Redfield, Dale, East Region & Adult Serv Mgr, Ventura County Library, 5600 Everglades St, Ste A, Ventura, CA, 93003. Tel: 805-677-7158. Fax: 805-677-7173. p. 279

Redfield, David, Assoc VPres, Instruction & Learning Res, American River College Library, 4700 College Oak Dr, Sacramento, CA, 95841. Tel: 916-484-8455. Fax: 916-484-8018, 916-484-8657. p. 220

Redfield, Eileen, Circ Mgr, Cape Cod Community College, 2240 Iyannough Rd, West Barnstable, MA, 02668-1599. Tel: 508-362-2131. Fax: 508-375-4020. p. 1136

Redford, John, Music & Media Librn, Biola University Library, 13800 Biola Ave, La Mirada, CA, 90639. Tel: 562-944-0351, Ext 5613. Fax: 562-903-4840. p. 162

Redhage, Nell, Dir, Washington Public Library, 410 Lafayette St, Washington, MO, 63090. Tel: 636-390-1071. Fax: 636-239-1744. p. 1371

Redigan, Mary, Librn, Saint Clair County Library System, Library for the Blind & Physically Handicapped, 210 McMorran Blvd, Port Huron, MI, 48060. Tel: 810-982-3600. Fax: 810-987-7327. p. 1219

Redin, Alison P, Info Res, X L Global Services Corporate Library, 70 Seaview Ave, Stamford, CT, 06902-6036. Tel: 203-964-5218. Fax: 203-964-0763. p. 370

Reding, Sue, Dir, Arcade Free Library, 365 W Main St, Arcade, NY, 14009. Tel: 585-492-1297. Fax: 585-492-3305. p. 1574

Redinger, Gloria, Tech Serv Mgr, Illinois Wesleyan University, One Ames Plaza, Bloomington, IL, 61701-7188. Tel: 309-556-3526. Fax: 309-556-3706. p. 595

Redington, Cara, Youth Serv, Cape Canaveral Public Library, 201 Polk Ave, Cape Canaveral, FL, 32920-3067. Tel: 321-868-1101. Fax: 321-868-1103. p. 431

Redington, Daniel L, Dir, Mary Meuser Memorial Library, 1803 Northampton St, Easton, PA, 18042-3183. Tel: 610-258-3040. p. 2052

Redington, Deirdre, Tech Serv Librn, Bradley University, 1501 W Bradley Ave, Peoria, IL, 61625. Tel: 309-677-2850. Fax: 309-677-2558. p. 690

Redker, Amanda, Ch, Thomas County Public Library System, 201 N Madison St, Thomasville, GA, 31792-5414. Tel: 229-225-5252. Fax: 229-225-5258. p. 553

Redman, Dee Ann, Asst Dir, Parmly Billings Library, 510 N Broadway, Billings, MT, 59101-1196. Tel: 406-657-8295. Fax: 406-657-8293. p. 1374

Redman, Ronda, Cat, Central College, Campus Box 6500, 812 University St, Pella, IA, 50219-1999. Tel: 641-628-5177. Fax: 641-628-5327. p. 838

Redmon, Michael E, Dir, Res, Santa Barbara Historical Museum, 136 E De La Guerra St, Santa Barbara, CA, 93101. Tel: 805-966-1601. Fax: 805-966-1603. p. 260

Redmon, Sherrill, Dir, Smith College Libraries, Sophia Smith Collection, Seven Neilson Dr, Northampton, MA, 01063. Tel: 413-585-2978. Fax: 413-585-2886. p. 1114

Redmond, Glenda, Librn, Mississippi Gulf Coast Community College, PO Box 548, Perkinston, MS, 39573-0011. Tel: 601-928-6259. Fax: 601-928-6359. p. 1311

Redmond, Jennie M, Dep Dir, Dorchester County Library, 506 N Parler Ave, Saint George, SC, 29477-2297. Tel: 843-563-9189. Fax: 843-563-7823. p. 2204

Redmond, Lois, Asst Dir, Dandridge Memorial Library, 1235 Circle Dr, Dandridge, TN, 37725-4750. Tel: 865-397-9758. Fax: 865-397-0950. p. 2232

Redmond, Lucy, Mgr, Ref Serv, Sullivan & Cromwell LLP, 125 Broad St, New York, NY, 10004. Tel: 212-558-3780. Fax: 212-558-3346. p. 1700

Redmond, Shauna, Actg Librn, Pasadena Public Library, Hill Avenue, 55 S Hill Ave, Pasadena, CA, 91106. Tel: 626-744-7264. Fax: 626-440-0183. p. 207

Redwing, DeAnn, Circ Serv, Gaston-Lincoln Regional Library, 1555 E Garrison Blvd, Gastonia, NC, 28054. Tel: 704-868-2164. Fax: 704-853-6012. p. 1794

Reeb, Brenda, Librn, University of Rochester, Business & Government Information Library, Rush Rhees Library, Rochester, NY, 14627. Tel: 585-275-4482. Fax: 585-273-5316. p. 1733

Reeb, Richard, Tech Serv, University of Wisconsin-Madison, 728 State St, Madison, WI, 53706. Tel: 608-262-3193. Fax: 608-265-2754. p. 2608

Reece, Anne, Acq, Cat, Hellenic College-Holy Cross Greek Orthodox School of Theology, 50 Goddard Ave, Brookline, MA, 02445-7496. Tel: 617-850-1367. Fax: 617-850-1470. p. 1071

Reece, Dee, In Charge, Honey Creek Church Preservation Library, 31031 PP Ave, New Providence, IA, 50206-8008. Tel: 641-497-5499. p. 835

Reecy, Agnes, Asst Librn, Edgemont Public Library, 412 Second Ave, Edgemont, SD, 57735. Tel: 605-662-7712. Fax: 605-662-7922. p. 2212

Reed, Alice, Assoc Librn, Blue Mound Memorial Library District, 213 S St Marie St, Blue Mound, IL, 62513-9733. Tel: 217-692-2774. Fax: 217-692-2191. p. 596

Reed, Alice B, Cat, First Reformed Church of Schenectady, Eight N Church St, Schenectady, NY, 12305-1699. Tel: 518-377-2201. Fax: 518-374-4098. p. 1740

Reed, Allison, Asst Librn, Polson City Library, Two First Ave E, Polson, MT, 59860. Tel: 406-883-8225. Fax: 406-883-8239. p. 1387

Reed, Amber, Commun Librn, Monroe County Library System, L S Navarre Branch, 1135 E Second St, Monroe, MI, 48161-1920. Tel: 734-241-5577. Fax: 734-241-5577. p. 1210

Reed, Ann Cober, Ref Librn, University of Maryland-Eastern Shore, 11868 Academic Oval, Princess Anne, MD, 21853. Tel: 410-651-2200, 410-651-6621. Fax: 410-651-6269. p. 1036

Reed, Anna, Mgr, Access Serv, State University of New York College of Technology, Bush Hall, Two Main St, Delhi, NY, 13753. Tel: 607-746-4635. Fax: 607-746-4327. p. 1613

Reed, Anne, Ref Serv, Public Library of Brookline, 361 Washington St, Brookline, MA, 02445. Tel: 617-730-2370. Fax: 617-730-2160. p. 1071

Reed, Barbara, Br Mgr, Allendale-Hampton-Jasper Regional Library, Allendale Branch, 158 McNair St, Allendale, SC, 29810-2804. Tel: 803-584-2371. Fax: 803-584-8134. p. 2180

Reed, Betty, Head, Circ, University Park Public Library District, 1100 Blackhawk Dr, University Park, IL, 60466. Tel: 708-534-2580. Fax: 708-534-2583. p. 711

Reed, Bonnie, Ref Librn, Kalkaska County Library, 247 S Cedar St, Kalkaska, MI, 49646. Tel: 231-258-9411. p. 1198

Reed, Brenda, Libr Dir, Palo Verde Valley Library District, 125 W Chanslorway, Blythe, CA, 92225-1293. Tel: 760-922-5371. Fax: 760-922-5334. p. 129

Reed, C Anthony, Archivist, Wentworth Institute of Technology, 550 Huntington Ave, Boston, MA, 02115-5998. Tel: 617-989-4040. Fax: 617-989-4091. p. 1068

Reed, Carol, Ch, Jamestown Public Library, 200 W Main St, Jamestown, NC, 27282. Tel: 336-454-4815. Fax: 336-454-0630. p. 1803

Reed, Carol, Ref, United States Air Force, Air Force Research Laboratory, Wright Research Site Technical Library, Det 1 AFRL/WSC, Bldg 642, Rm 1300, 2950 Hobson Way, Wright-Patterson AFB, OH, 45433-7765. Tel: 937-255-5511, Ext 4271. Fax: 937-656-7746. p. 1951

Reed, Caroline, Ref, New College of Florida University of South Florida Sarasota Manatee, 5800 Bay Shore Rd, Sarasota, FL, 34243-2109. Tel: 941-487-4568. Fax: 941-487-4307. p. 490

Reed, Carolyn Ryan, Dir, East Orange Public Library, 21 S Arlington Ave, East Orange, NJ, 07018-3892. Tel: 973-266-5600. Fax: 973-675-6128. p. 1482

Reed, Catherine, Dir of Coll, College of William & Mary in Virginia, Earl Gregg Swem Library, One Landrum Dr, Williamsburg, VA, 23187. Tel: 757-221-7615. Fax: 757-221-2635. p. 2502

Reed, Christy, Mgr, Brown County Public Library, Mt Orab Branch, 613 S High St, Mount Orab, OH, 45154. Tel: 937-444-1414. Fax: 937-444-6502. p. 1919

Reed, Cindy, Coll Develop, Head, Ref, ILL, Harrison Regional Library System, 50 Lester St, Columbiana, AL, 35051. Tel: 205-669-3910. Fax: 205-669-3940. p. 13

Reed, Claudia, Dir, Mount Saint Mary's College, 12001 Chalon Rd, Los Angeles, CA, 90049-1599. Tel: 310-954-4370. Fax: 310-954-4379. p. 175

Reed, Danley, Dept Head, University of South Carolina, Math, LeConte College, 3rd Flr, Columbia, SC, 29208. Tel: 803-777-4741. p. 2190

Reed, Deborah, Dir, Norma Anders Public Library, 320 Main St, Dysart, IA, 52224. Tel: 319-476-5210. Fax: 319-476-2671. p. 812

Reed, Denise, Br Mgr, Llano County Library System, Kingsland Branch, 125 W Polk, Kingsland, TX, 78639. Tel: 325-388-3170. p. 2356

Reed, Donna L, Dir, Portland Community College Library, 12000 SW 49th AV, Portland, OR, 97219. Tel: 971-722-4497. Fax: 971-722-8397. p. 2013

Reed, Earline, Librn, Benton County Library System, Hickory Flat Public Library, 1067 Spruce St, Hickory Flat, MS, 38633. Tel: 662-333-7663. Fax: 662-333-7663. p. 1293

Reed, Elizabeth, Dir, Lacon Public Library District, 205 Sixth St, Lacon, IL, 61540. Tel: 309-246-2855. Fax: 309-246-4047. p. 662

Reed, Elizabeth, Br Mgr, Akron-Summit County Public Library, Richfield Branch, 3761 S Grant St, Richfield, OH, 44286-9603. Tel: 330-659-4343. Fax: 330-659-6205. p. 1852

Reed, Erika, Dir, Marion County Public Library, 321 Monroe St, Fairmont, WV, 26554-2952. Tel: 304-366-1210. Fax: 304-366-4831. p. 2559

Reed, Erika, Dir, Marion County Public Library, Fairview Public, 500 Main St, Fairview, WV, 26570. Tel: 304-366-1210. Fax: 304-449-1021. p. 2559

Reed, Fred, Coordr, Tech Support, Xavier University of Louisiana, One Drexel Dr, New Orleans, LA, 70125-1098. Tel: 504-520-7663. Fax: 504-520-7940. p. 964

Reed, Gabrielle, Access Serv, Visual Res, Massachusetts College of Art & Design, 621 Huntington Ave, Boston, MA, 02115-5882. Tel: 617-879-7199. Fax: 617-879-7110. p. 1063

Reed, Heidi, Dir, Young Men's Library Association, 37 Main St, Ware, MA, 01082-1317. Tel: 413-967-5491. Fax: 413-967-6060. p. 1133

Reed, Helen, Dean, University of Northern Colorado Libraries, 501 20th St, Greeley, CO, 80639. Tel: 970-351-2601. Fax: 970-351-2963. p. 312

Reed, Helen S, Librn, William H Miller Law Library, 207 City-County Courts Bldg, 825 Sycamore, Evansville, IN, 47708-1849. Tel: 812-435-5175. Fax: 812-435-5438. p. 739

Reed, Jacqueline, Br Mgr, Mid-Continent Public Library, Blue Springs South Branch, 2220 South Hwy 7, Blue Springs, MO, 64014-3957. Tel: 816-229-3571. Fax: 816-224-2078. p. 1332

Reed, James, Curator, Archives & Libr, History San Jose, 1650 Senter Rd, San Jose, CA, 95112. Tel: 408-521-5026. Fax: 408-287-2291. p. 249

Reed, Jane, Assoc Dir, University Club Library, One W 54th St, New York, NY, 10019. Tel: 212-572-3418. Fax: 212-572-3452. p. 1702

Reed, Jason T, Ch Mgr, Dorchester County Library, Summerville Branch, 76 Old Trolley Rd, Summerville, SC, 29485. Tel: 843-871-5075. Fax: 843-875-4811. p. 2204

Reed, Joyce K, Computer Tech, Barry-Lawrence Regional Library, 213 Sixth St, Monett, MO, 65708-2147. Tel: 417-235-6646. Fax: 417-235-6799. p. 1346

Reed, Katharine, Cat, Nelson-Atkins Museum of Art, 4525 Oak St, Kansas City, MO, 64111-1873. Tel: 816-751-0409. Fax: 816-751-0498. p. 1340

Reed, Kathleen, Coordr, Virginia Aquarium & Marine Science Center, 717 General Booth Blvd, Virginia Beach, VA, 23451. Tel: 757-385-3474, 757-385-7777. Fax: 757-437-6055. p. 2500

Reed, Kathryn, Ch, Russell Adelia McConnell Library, Mamie's Place Children's Library & Learning Center, 284 Church St, Alexander City, AL, 35010. Tel: 256-234-4644. p. 4

Reed, Kelly, Ch, Richland Public Library, 955 Northgate Dr, Richland, WA, 99352-3539. Tel: 509-942-7452. Fax: 509-942-7442. p. 2526

Reed, Kerry, Head, Youth Serv, Lake Villa District Library, 1001 E Grand Ave, Lake Villa, IL, 60046. Tel: 847-356-7711, Ext 246. Fax: 847-265-9595. p. 663

Reed, Kristine, Asst Dean, Libr, Texas Woman's University Libraries, 304 Administration Dr, Denton, TX, 76204. Tel: 940-898-3767. Fax: 940-898-3809. p. 2312

Reed, Liz, Dir, Baldwin County Library Cooperative, Inc, 22251 Palmer St, Robertsdale, AL, 36567. Tel: 251-970-4010. Fax: 251-970-4011. p. 35

Reed, Lynne, Pub Serv, Catawba County Library, 115 West C St, Newton, NC, 28658. Tel: 828-465-8664. Fax: 828-465-8983. p. 1813

Reed, Marci, Br Mgr, Louisville Free Public Library, Fairdale Branch, 10616 W Manslick Rd, Fairdale, KY, 40118. Tel: 502-375-2051. Fax: 502-375-2016. p. 924

Reed, Marcia, Head, Coll Develop, Getty Research Institute, 1200 Getty Center Dr, Ste 1100, Los Angeles, CA, 90049-1688. Tel: 310-440-7390. Fax: 310-440-7780. p. 170

Reed, Margaret, Periodicals Librn, Ouachita Baptist University, 410 Ouachita, OBU Box 3742, Arkadelphia, AR, 71998-0001. Tel: 870-245-5117. Fax: 870-245-5245. p. 93

Reed, Margaret, Asst Dir, Youth Serv, Argie Cooper Public Library, 100 S Main St, Shelbyville, TN, 37160-3984. Tel: 931-684-7323. Fax: 931-685-4848. p. 2265

Reed, Margaret, Librn, Nova Scotia Department of Transportation & Public Works, 107 Parent Dr, Halifax, NS, B2T 1J6, CANADA. Tel: 902-860-2999. p. 2782

Reed, Marie, Br Assoc, Las Vegas-Clark County Library District, Goodsprings Library, 365 W San Pedro Ave, Goodsprings, NV, 89019. Tel: 702-874-1366. Fax: 702-874-1335. p. 1429

Reed, Mary, Dir, Latah County Historical Society Library, 327 E Second St, Moscow, ID, 83843. Tel: 208-882-1004. Fax: 208-882-0759. p. 579

Reed, Mary, Adminr, Jackson County Public Library, 303 W Second St, Seymour, IN, 47274-2147. Tel: 812-522-3412, Ext 233, Fax: 812-522-5456. p. 777

Reed, Mary Griffith, Ch, Georgetown Charter Township Library, 1525 Baldwin St, Jenison, MI, 49428. Tel: 616-457-9620. Fax: 616-457-3666. p. 1196

Reed, Maryruth, Dir, Mitchell Public Library, 1449 Center Ave, Mitchell, NE, 69357. Tel: 308-623-2222. Fax: 308-623-2222. p. 1409

Reed, Melanie, Libr Tech, Shippensburg University, 1871 Old Main Dr, Shippensburg, PA, 17257-2299. Tel: 717-477-1325. Fax: 717-477-1389. p. 2140

Reed, Nancy, Librn, Western Plains Library System, Minnie R Slief Memorial Library, 201 S Cearlock St, Cheyenne, OK, 73628. Tel: 580-497-3777. Fax: 580-497-3777. p. 1961

Reed, Nathanael, Ref, Samuels Public Library, 538 Villa Ave, Front Royal, VA, 22630. Tel: 540-635-3153. Fax: 540-635-7229. p. 2466

Reed, Randa, Circ Supvr, Ozark Christian College, 1111 N Main, Joplin, MO, 64801-4804. Tel: 417-626-1234, Ext 2700. Fax: 417-624-0090. p. 1336

Reed, Renee, Coordr Librn, Adult Learning/Literacy & Libr Mgt, Hennepin County Library, Augsburg Park, 7100 Nicollet Ave S, Richfield, MN, 55423-3117. Tel: 612-543-8758. Fax: 612-543-6202. p. 1263

Reed, Renee, Coordr Librn, Adult Learning/Literacy & Libr Mgt, Hennepin County Library, Excelsior, 343 Third St, Excelsior, MN, 55331-1878. Tel: 612-543-8758. Fax: 612-543-6352. p. 1263

Reed, Renee, Coordr Librn, Adult Learning/Literacy & Libr Mgt, Hennepin County Library, Franklin, 1314 E Franklin Ave, Minneapolis, MN, 55404-2924. Tel: 612-543-8758. Fax: 612-543-6927. p. 1263

Reed, Renee, Coordr Librn, Adult Learning/Literacy & Libr Mgt, Hennepin County Library, Hosmer, 347 E 36th St, Minneapolis, MN, 55408-4567. Tel: 612-543-8758. Fax: 612-543-6902. p. 1263

Reed, Renee, Coordr Librn, Adult Learning/Literacy & Libr Mgt, Hennepin County Library, Minnetonka, 17524 Excelsior Blvd, Minnetonka, MN, 55345-1099. Tel: 612-543-8758. Fax: 612-543-5727. p. 1264

Reed, Renee, Coordr Librn, Adult Learning/Literacy & Libr Mgt, Hennepin County Library, North Regional, 1315 Lowry Ave N, Minneapolis, MN, 55411. Tel: 612-543-8758. Fax: 612-543-8452. p. 1264

Reed, Renee, Coordr Librn, Adult Learning/Literacy & Libr Mgt, Hennepin County Library, Sumner, 611 Van White Memorial Blvd, Minneapolis, MN, 55411-4196. Tel: 612-543-8758. Fax: 612-543-6877. p. 1265

Reed, Robyn, Biomedical Info & Emerging Technologies, Pennsylvania State University, College of Medicine, Penn State Hershey, Harrell Health Sciences Library, 500 University Dr, Hershey, PA, 17033. Tel: 717-531-6137. Fax: 717-531-8635. p. 2069

Reed, Sandra, Ch, Val Verde County Library, 300 Spring St, Del Rio, TX, 78840. Tel: 830-774-7595. Fax: 830-774-7607. p. 2312

Reed, Sharon Kay, Dir, Huntsville Public Library, 314 Court House Sq, Huntsville, TN, 37756. Tel: 423-663-9230. p. 2237

Reed, Shelly A, Head Librn, Sutton Memorial Library, 201 S Saunders, Sutton, NE, 68979. Tel: 402-773-5259. Fax: 402-773-5259. p. 1420

Reed, Susan L, Dir, Pawtucket Public Library, 13 Summer St, Pawtucket, RI, 02860. Tel: 401-725-3714. Fax: 401-728-2170. p. 2171

Reed, Terry, Fac Mgr, Montgomery City-County Public Library System, 245 High St, Montgomery, AL, 36104. Tel: 334-240-4995. Fax: 334-240-4977. p. 29

Reed, Todd, Dir, Sturgis District Library, 255 North St, Sturgis, MI, 49091. Tel: 269-659-7225. Fax: 269-651-4534. p. 1229

Reed, Tracey, Br Mgr, Clearwater Public Library System, Countryside, 2741 State Rd 580, Clearwater, FL, 33761. Tel: 727-562-4970. Fax: 727-669-1289. p. 432

Reed, Trina, Dir, Uniondale Public Library, 400 Uniondale Ave, Uniondale, NY, 11553-1995. Tel: 516-489-2220. Fax: 516-489-4005. p. 1758

Reed, Troy, Br Mgr, Maricopa County Library District, Southeast Regional, 775 N Greenfield Rd, Gilbert, AZ, 85234. Tel: 602-652-3237. Fax: 602-652-3240. p. 75

Reed, William, Librn, Cleveland Public Library, 17121 Lake Shore Blvd, Cleveland, OH, 44110-4006. Tel: 216-623-2911. Fax: 216-623-7036. p. 1878

Reed-Armbrister, Tracey, Supvr, Youth Serv, Smyth-Bland Regional Library, 118 S Sheffey St, Marion, VA, 24354. Tel: 276-783-2323, Ext 223. Fax: 276-783-5279. p. 2477

Reed-Gorski, Alice, Librn, Exeter Hospital Inc, Five Alumni Dr, Exeter, NH, 03833-2160. Tel: 603-580-6226. Fax: 603-580-7928. p. 1447

Reeder, Christine, Librn, Pasadena Public Library, Lamanda Park, 140 S Altadena Dr, Pasadena, CA, 91107. Tel: 626-744-7266. p. 207

Reeder, Jean, Librn, Dr W B Konkle Memorial Library, 384 Broad St, Montoursville, PA, 17754-2206. Tel: 570-368-1840. Fax: 570-368-7416. p. 2092

Reeder, Jeremy, Dep Dir, Maricopa County Library District, 2700 N Central Ave, Ste 700, Phoenix, AZ, 85004. Tel: 602-652-3000. Fax: 602-652-3071. p. 74

Reeder, Lanell, Teen Serv, Orem Public Library, 58 N State St, Orem, UT, 84057-5596. Tel: 801-229-7050. Fax: 801-229-7130. p. 2409

Reeder, Mary, Br Mgr, Mid-Continent Public Library, Grain Valley Branch, 110 Front St, Grain Valley, MO, 64029-9308. Tel: 816-228-4020. Fax: 816-228-4007. p. 1332

Reeder, Pamela K, Dir, Murrell Memorial Library, Missouri Valley College, Tech Center Bldg, 500 E College St, Marshall, MO, 65340. Tel: 660-831-4180, 660-831-4181. Fax: 660-831-4068. p. 1344

Reeder, Vern, Asst Prof, Missouri State University, Duane G Meyer Library, 901 S National Ave, Springfield, MO, 65897. Tel: 417-836-4525. Fax: 417-836-4764. p. 2968

Reeder, Wilma, Mgr, Ser, Lycoming College, 700 College Pl, Williamsport, PA, 17701-5192. Tel: 570-321-4053. Fax: 570-321-4090. p. 2156

Reedy, Brian, Curator, National Park Service, Department of Interior, One Washington Pkwy, Farmington, PA, 15437. Tel: 724-329-5811. Fax: 724-329-8682. p. 2057

Reedy, Conrad, Librn, Kettle Moraine Correctional Institution Library, W9071 Forest Dr, Plymouth, WI, 53073. Tel: 920-526-3244, Ext 309. Fax: 920-526-3989. p. 2630

Reedy, Melody, Dir, North Central University Library, 915 E 14th St, Minneapolis, MN, 55404. Tel: 612-343-4491. Fax: 612-343-8069. p. 1261

Reedy, Vicki, Acq Mgr, Montgomery-Floyd Regional Library System, 125 Sheltman St, Christiansburg, VA, 24073. Tel: 540-382-6965. Fax: 540-382-6964. p. 2457

Reef, Frank, Dir, Kent Public Library, 17 Sybil's Crossing, Kent Lakes, NY, 10512. Tel: 845-225-8585. Fax: 845-225-8549. p. 1649

Reeg-Steidinger, Jana, Ref Serv, University of Wisconsin-Stout Library, 315 Tenth Ave, Menomonie, WI, 54751-0790. Tel: 715-232-1553. Fax: 715-232-1783. p. 2615

Reel, Brad, Ref & ILL Librn, University of Southern Indiana, 8600 University Blvd, Evansville, IN, 47712. Tel: 812-464-1824, 812-464-8600. Fax: 812-465-1693. p. 739

Reel, Christina L, Head Librn, Homer Community Library, 500 E Second St, Homer, IL, 61849. Tel: 217-896-2121. Fax: 217-896-2121. p. 657

Rees, Joshua, Cat, Daly City Public Library, 40 Wembley Dr, Daly City, CA, 94015-4399. Tel: 650-991-8023. Fax: 650-991-5726. p. 138

Rees, Larry, Dir, Jefferson Community & Technical College, Southwest Campus Library, 1000 Community College Dr, Louisville, KY, 40272. Tel: 502-213-7210. Fax: 502-935-8653. p. 924

Rees, Linda, Librn, Reagan County Library, 300 Courthouse Sq, Big Lake, TX, 76932. Tel: 325-884-2854. p. 2289

Rees, Lois, Circ Supvr, Freeport Public Library, 100 E Douglas St, Freeport, IL, 61032. Tel: 815-233-3000. Fax: 815-233-1099. p. 647

Rees, Marilyn, Head, Circ, Louis Bay 2nd Library, 345 Lafayette Ave, Hawthorne, NJ, 07506-2599. Tel: 973-427-5745, Ext 16. Fax: 973-427-5269. p. 1490

Rees, Pam, Dir, Grand View University Library, 1350 Morton Ave, Des Moines, IA, 50316-1494. Tel: 515-263-2877. Fax: 515-263-2998. p. 809

Rees, Warren, Res Librn, University of Notre Dame, 2345 Biolchini Hall of Law, Notre Dame, IN, 46556-4640. Tel: 574-631-4436. Fax: 574-631-6371. p. 771

Reese, Amy, Chair of Instruction, Ref Librn, Baton Rouge Community College, 201 Community College Dr, Baton Rouge, LA, 70806. Tel: 225-216-8621. Fax: 225-216-8712. p. 942

Reese, Barry, Dir, Twin Lakes Library System, 151 S Jefferson St SE, Milledgeville, GA, 31061-3419. Tel: 478-452-0677. Fax: 478-452-0680. p. 545

Reese, Diana, Institutional Libr Serv Coordr, Buena Vista Correctional Complex Library, 15125 Hwys 24 & 285, Buena Vista, CO, 81211. Tel: 719-395-7254. Fax: 719-395-7214. p. 293

Reese, Diana, Tech Serv, Colorado Department of Corrections, Centennial Correctional Facility Library, PO Box 600, Canon City, CO, 81215-0600. Tel: 719-269-5546. Fax: 719-269-5545. p. 293

Reese, E Gail, Assoc Dir, Coll & Personnel, Case Western Reserve University, 11055 Euclid Ave, Cleveland, OH, 44106. Tel: 216-368-5291. Fax: 216-368-6950. p. 1876

Reese, Garth, Dr, Head, Spec Coll & Archives, University of Idaho Library, Rayburn St, Moscow, ID, 83844. Tel: 208-885-5813. Fax: 208-885-6817. p. 579

Reese, Joel, Local Hist Librn, Iredell County Public Library, 201 N Tradd St, Statesville, NC, 28677. Tel: 704-878-3093. Fax: 704-878-5449. p. 1825

Reese, Noreen, Asst Dir, Warren-Newport Public Library District, 224 N O'Plaine Rd, Gurnee, IL, 60031. Tel: 847-244-5150, Ext 3026. Fax: 847-244-3499. p. 653

Reese, Sean, Librn, Maynard, Cooper & Gale, Amsouth Harbert Plaza, Ste 2400, 1901 Sixth Ave N, Birmingham, AL, 35203-2602. Tel: 205-254-1000, 205-488-3570. Fax: 205-254-1999. p. 9

Reese, Vali, Circ Supvr, Mount San Jacinto College, 1499 N State St, San Jacinto, CA, 92583-2399. Tel: 951-487-6752, Ext 1580. Fax: 951-654-8387. p. 249

Reese, Virginia, Head of Libr, Jefferson-Madison Regional Library, Greene County, 222 Main St, Standardsville, VA, 22973. Tel: 434-985-5227. Fax: 434-985-3315. p. 2454

Reese, Yvonne, Librn, University of Florida, 200 Ninth St SE, Vero Beach, FL, 32962. Tel: 772-778-7200. Fax: 772-778-7205. p. 502

Reeve, Carole, Br Head, Winnipeg Public Library, Osborne, 625 Osborne St S, Winnipeg, MB, R3L 2B3, CANADA. Tel: 204-986-4775. Fax: 204-986-7124. p. 2760

Reeve, Katherine, Dept Head, Arizona Historical Society, 949 E Second St, Tucson, AZ, 85719. Tel: 520-617-1151. Fax: 520-629-8966. p. 85

Reeve, Walter, Circ Supvr, Johnson State College Library, 337 College Hill, Johnson, VT, 05656. Tel: 802-635-1273. Fax: 802-635-1294. p. 2427

Reeve, Wendy, Ref Supvr, Supvr, Network Serv, Cutchogue-New Suffolk Free Library, 27550 Main Rd, Cutchogue, NY, 11935. Tel: 631-734-6360. Fax: 631-734-7010. p. 1613

Reeves, Alice, Pres, Fayette County Historical Society, Inc Library, 195 Lee St, Fayetteville, GA, 30214-2081. Tel: 770-716-6020. Fax: 770-716-9203. p. 532

Reeves, Allison, Assoc Dir, Carroll College, 100 N East Ave, Waukesha, WI, 53186. Tel: 262-524-7180. Fax: 262-524-7377. p. 2644

Reeves, Ann, Assoc Dir, Eureka Public Library District, 202 S Main St, Eureka, IL, 61530. Tel: 309-467-2922. Fax: 309-467-3527. p. 643

Reeves, Anne, Ch, Iberville Parish Library, 24605 J Gerald Berret Blvd, Plaquemine, LA, 70764. Tel: 225-687-2520, 225-687-4397. Fax: 225-687-9719. p. 965

Reeves, Babette, Ch, Alamosa Public Library, 300 Hunt Ave, Alamosa, CO, 81101. Tel: 719-589-6592, Ext 2550. Fax: 719-589-3786. p. 287

Reeves, Betty, Asst Librn, Carnegie-Evans Public Library, 203 Benton Ave E, Albia, IA, 52531-2036. Tel: 641-932-2469. Fax: 641-932-2469. p. 791

Reeves, Bobby, Coordr, Ser, American University Library, 4400 Massachusetts Ave NW, Washington, DC, 20016-8046. Tel: 202-885-3167. Fax: 202-885-3226. p. 393

Reeves, Bonnie, Ch, Township Library of Lower Southampton, 1983 Bridgetown Pike, Feasterville, PA, 19053-4493. Tel: 215-355-1183. Fax: 215-364-5735. p. 2057

Reeves, Cathy, Dir, Dodge City Public Library, 1001 N Second Ave, Dodge City, KS, 67801-4484. Tel: 620-225-0248. Fax: 620-225-2761. p. 863

Reeves, Cathy L, Dir, Dodge City Community College, 2501 N 14th, Dodge City, KS, 67801. Tel: 620-225-1321, Ext 287, 620-227-9287. Fax: 620-225-0918. p. 863

Reeves, Charles, Archives Dir, National Archives & Records Administration, 5780 Jonesboro Rd, Morrow, GA, 30260. Tel: 770-968-2100. Fax: 770-968-2457. p. 545

Reeves, Donald, Curator, Westerners International Library, 1700 NE 63rd St, Oklahoma City, OK, 73111. Tel: 405-478-8408. p. 1975

Reeves, Gloria, Asst Dir, Ouachita Parish Public Library, 1800 Stubbs Ave, Monroe, LA, 71201. Tel: 318-327-1490. Fax: 318-327-1373. p. 957

Reeves, Greg, Head Librn, Boone Daniel Regional Library, Callaway County Public Library, 710 Court St, Fulton, MO, 65251. Tel: 573-642-7261. Fax: 573-642-4439. p. 1324

Reeves, Julie, Acq, Pequannock Township Public Library, 477 Newark Pompton Tpk, Pompton Plains, NJ, 07444. Tel: 973-835-7460. Fax: 973-835-1928. p. 1521

Reeves, Kim, Librn, Walsh College, 41500 Gardenbrook Rd, Novi, MI, 48375-1313. Tel: 248-679-1410. Fax: 248-349-7616. p. 1215

Reeves, Kimberly, Br Coordr, Walsh College, 3838 Livernois Rd, Troy, MI, 48083-5066. Tel: 248-679-1410. Fax: 248-349-7616. p. 1232

Reeves, Larry, Assoc Dean, Vanderbilt University, 419 21st Ave S, Nashville, TN, 37203-2427. Tel: 615-322-7100. Fax: 615-343-8279. p. 2260

Reeves, Larry, Assoc Dir, George Mason University Libraries, 4400 University Dr, MSN 2FL, Fairfax, VA, 22030-4444. Tel: 703-993-2250. Fax: 703-993-2200. p. 2462

Reeves, Larry, Assoc Dir, George Mason University Libraries, School of Law, 3301 N Fairfax Dr, Arlington, VA, 22201-4426. Tel: 703-993-8120. Fax: 703-993-8113. p. 2462

Reeves, Linda, Ref Serv, Northwest Vista College, Redbud Hall, 3535 N Ellison Dr, San Antonio, TX, 78251. Tel: 210-486-4569. Fax: 210-486-9105. p. 2380

Reeves, Lynn, Dep Librn, Third Judicial Circuit Court, Wayne County, Two Woodward Ave, Ste 780, Detroit, MI, 48226-3461. Tel: 313-224-5265. Fax: 313-967-3562. p. 1172

Reeves, Melanie, Br Mgr, Norfolk Public Library, Little Creek, 7853 Tarpon Pl, Norfolk, VA, 23518. Tel: 757-441-1751. Fax: 757-441-1747. p. 2482

Reeves, Ronald, Ref, Barrington Public Library, 281 County Rd, Barrington, RI, 02806. Tel: 401-247-1920. Fax: 401-247-3763. p. 2163

Reeves, Ruth, Adult Serv, Normal Public Library, 206 W College Ave, Normal, IL, 61761. Tel: 309-452-1757. Fax: 309-452-5312. p. 681

Reeves, Sharon Stewart, Mgr, Union-Tribune Publishing Co Library, 350 Camino de la Reina, San Diego, CA, 92108. Tel: 619-299-3131. p. 238

Reeves, Tolley, Librn, Houston Community College Northeast College, Pinemont Campus Library, 1265 Pinemont, Houston, TX, 77018-1303. Tel: 713-718-8443. Fax: 713-718-8438. p. 2338

Reeves, Victoria, Circ, Zephyrhills Public Library, 5347 Eighth St, Zephyrhills, FL, 33542. Tel: 813-780-0064. Fax: 813-780-0066. p. 505

Reff, Yvonne, Ref Librn, Roswell P Flower Memorial Library, 229 Washington St, Watertown, NY, 13601-3388. Tel: 315-785-7705. Fax: 315-788-2584. p. 1763

Refior, Debra, Head, Youth Serv, Orion Township Public Library, 825 Joslyn Rd, Lake Orion, MI, 48362. Tel: 248-693-3000, Ext 341. Fax: 248-693-3009. p. 1199

Regalado, Mariana, Assoc Librn, Info Serv, Brooklyn College Library, 2900 Bedford Ave, Brooklyn, NY, 11210-2889. Tel: 718-951-5336. Fax: 718-951-4540. p. 1589

Regan, Anita, Libr Asst, Prescott & Russell Law Association Library, 59 Court St, L'Orignal, ON, K0B 1K0, CANADA. Tel: 613-675-2424. Fax: 613-675-1003. p. 2819

Regan, Brenda, Librn, Concord Public Library, 374 Main St, Concord, VT, 05824. Tel: 802-695-2220. p. 2422

Regan, M Lee, Ref Librn, Plymouth Public Library, 132 South St, Plymouth, MA, 02360-3309. Tel: 508-830-4250. Fax: 508-830-4258. p. 1118

Regazzi, John, Dr, Prof, Long Island University, C W Post Campus, 720 Northern Blvd, Brookville, NY, 11548-1300. Tel: 516-299-3322. Fax: 516-299-4168. p. 2970

Rege, Karen, Dr, Dir, Delaware County Community College Library, 901 S Media Line Rd, Media, PA, 19063-1094. Tel: 610-359-5149, 610-359-5326. Fax: 610-359-5272. p. 2087

Regenberg, Pat, Coordr, Basic Health Sciences Library Network, Overlook Hospital Health Science Library, 99 Beauvoir Ave, Summit, NJ, 07902. Tel: 908-522-2886. Fax: 908-522-2274. p. 2948

Regenberg, Patricia, Mgr, Overlook Hospital, 99 Beauvoir Ave, Summit, NJ, 07902-0220. Tel: 908-522-2119. Fax: 908-522-2274. p. 1532

Regenberg, Patricia, Libr Mgr, New Jersey Health Sciences Library Network, Overlook Hospital Library, 99 Beauvoir Ave, Summit, NJ, 07902. Tel: 908-522-2886. Fax: 908-522-2274. p. 2949

Regensburg, Brooke, Tech Asst, Washtenaw Community College, 4800 E Huron River Dr, Ann Arbor, MI, 48105-4800. Tel: 734-973-3426. Fax: 734-973-3446. p. 1153

Regensburger, Jeff, Managing Librn, Columbus Metropolitan Library, Northwest, 2280 Hard Rd, Columbus, OH, 43235. Tel: 614-807-2659. Fax: 614-807-2659. p. 1885

Regensburger, Jeff, Libr Mgr, Worthington Libraries, Northwest Library, 2280 Hard Rd, Columbus, OH, 43235. Tel: 614-807-2652. Fax: 614-807-2659. p. 1951

Regester, Anita, Dir, Spring City Free Public Library, 245 Broad St, Spring City, PA, 19475-1702. Tel: 610-948-4130. Fax: 610-948-9478. p. 2142

Regester, Charlotte, Dir, Red Waller Community Library, 109 Mitcham St, Malakoff, TX, 75148. Tel: 903-489-1818. Fax: 903-489-2517. p. 2359

Reghi, Janis M, Dir, Lois Wagner Memorial Library, 35200 Division Rd, Richmond, MI, 48062. Tel: 586-727-2665. Fax: 586-727-3774. p. 1221

Regier, Elaine, Librn, Federal Aviation Administration, Mike Monroney Aeronautical Center Library, Academy Bldg 14, Rm 114, 6500 S MacArthur Blvd, Oklahoma City, OK, 73169. Tel: 405-954-2665. Fax: 405-954-4742. p. 1972

Regier, Katherine, Libr Dir, Haven Public Library, 121 N Kansas St, Haven, KS, 67543. Tel: 620-465-3524. Fax: 620-465-3524. p. 870

Regina, Kristen, Head Librn, Hillwood Estate, Museum & Gardens, 4155 Linnean Ave NW, Washington, DC, 20008. Tel: 202-243-3953. Fax: 202-966-7846. p. 403

Regis, June, Librn, Saint Francis Hospital, 3237 S 16th St, Milwaukee, WI, 53215. Tel: 414-647-5156. Fax: 414-647-5195. p. 2621

Register, Janet, Librn, South Georgia Regional Library System, Hahira Branch, 220 E Main St, Hahira, GA, 31632. Tel: 229-794-3063. p. 555

Reglar, Carl, Ref Serv, Sarah Lawrence College, One Mead Way, Bronxville, NY, 10708. Tel: 914-395-2225. Fax: 914-395-2473. p. 1588

Regnani, Donna, Librn, Trinity County Law Library, Courthouse, 11 Court St, Weaverville, CA, 96093. Tel: 530-623-1369. p. 282

Regnier, Rex, Media Spec, Clovis Community College Library, 417 Schepps Blvd, Clovis, NM, 88101. Tel: 575-769-4080. Fax: 575-769-4190. p. 1553

Regnier, Silvia, Librn, Nutana Collegiate Institute, 411 11th St E, Saskatoon, SK, S7N 0E9, CANADA. Tel: 306-683-7583. Fax: 306-683-7587. p. 2925

Reha, Jodie, Cat Librn, Chesapeake Public Library, 298 Cedar Rd, Chesapeake, VA, 23322-5512. Tel: 757-926-5740. Fax: 757-410-7112. p. 2456

Rehak, Judy, Actg State Librn, Minnesota State Law Library, Minnesota Judicial Ctr, Rm G25, 25 Rev Dr Martin Luther King Jr Blvd, Saint Paul, MN, 55155. Tel: 651-296-2775. Fax: 651-296-6740. p. 1280

Rehkopf, Sue, Archivist, The Episcopal Diocese of Missouri Archives, 1210 Locust St, Saint Louis, MO, 63103-2322. Tel: 314-231-1220. Fax: 314-231-3373. p. 1354

Rehm, Karen G, In Charge, National Park Service, PO Box 210, Yorktown, VA, 23690-0210. Tel: 757-898-2416. Fax: 757-898-6346. p. 2505

Rehnborg, Ruthann, Tech Serv, US Courts Library, Byron Rogers Courthouse, 1929 Stout St, Rm 430, Denver, CO, 80294. Tel: 303-844-3591. Fax: 303-844-5958. p. 303

Rehor, Anne, Youth Serv Librn, Ontario Public Library, 1850 Ridge Rd, Ontario, NY, 14519. Tel: 315-524-8381. Fax: 315-524-5838. p. 1711

Rehwaldt-Hays, Sue, In Charge, Clarinda Treatment Complex, Professional Library, 1800 N 16th St, Clarinda, IA, 51632-1174. Tel: 712-542-2161. Fax: 712-542-6113. p. 802

Rehwaldt-Hays, Sue, In Charge, Clarinda Treatment Complex, Resident's Library, 1800 N 16th St, Clarinda, IA, 51632-1174. Tel: 712-542-2161. Fax: 712-542-6113. p. 802

Reibach, Lois, Cat, Athenaeum of Philadelphia, 219 S Sixth St, East Washington Square, Philadelphia, PA, 19106-3794. Tel: 215-925-2688. Fax: 215-925-3755. p. 2103

Reich, Barbara S, Dir, Hackensack University Medical Center, 30 Prospect Ave, Hackensack, NJ, 07601. Tel: 201-996-2326. Fax: 201-996-2467. p. 1489

Reich, Carol, Reader Serv Mgr, Hillsboro Public Library, 2850 NE Brookwood Pkwy, Hillsboro, OR, 97124-5327. Tel: 503-615-6500. Fax: 503-615-6601. p. 2000

Reich, Christopher J, Dir, Putnam Museum of History & Natural Science, 1717 W 12th St, Davenport, IA, 52804. Tel: 563-324-1933, Ext 216. Fax: 563-324-6638. p. 806

Reich, Debra, Br Mgr, Gunnison Public Library of the Gunnison County Library District, Crested Butte Library, 507 Maroon Ave, Crested Butte, CO, 81224. Tel: 970-349-6535. Fax: 970-641-4653. p. 312

Reich, Linda, Bus Mgr, Tombigbee Regional Library System, Amory Municipal Library, 401 Second Ave N at Fourth St, Amory, MS, 38821. Tel: 662-256-5261. Fax: 662-256-6321. p. 1318

Reich, Patricia, Dir, Jean M Thomsen Memorial Library, 105 N Gershwin St, Stetsonville, WI, 54480. Tel: 715-678-2892. Fax: 715-678-2892. p. 2639

Reich, Steve, Managing Librn, Austin Public Library, Carver, 1161 Angelina St, Austin, TX, 78702. Tel: 512-974-1020. Fax: 512-974-1021. p. 2279

Reichard, Krista, Ref & Instruction Librn, Concordia University Library, 2811 NE Holman St, Portland, OR, 97211-6067. Tel: 503-493-6246. Fax: 503-280-8697. p. 2010

Reichardt, Carol, Ref/Instruction Librn, Eastern Connecticut State University, 83 Windham St, Willimantic, CT, 06226-2295. Tel: 860-465-5566. Fax: 860-465-5521. p. 378

Reichardt, Karen, Asst Dir, Tech, Asst Dir, Tech Serv, Live Oak Public Libraries, 2002 Bull St, Savannah, GA, 31401. Tel: 912-652-3694. Fax: 912-652-3638. p. 550

Reichel, Debby, Curric Media/Mats, Columbia International University, 7435 Monticello Rd, Columbia, SC, 29203-1599. Tel: 803-807-5159. Fax: 803-744-1391. p. 2187

Reichel, Mary, Dir, Appalachian State University, 218 College St, Boone, NC, 28608. Tel: 828-262-6725. Fax: 828-262-3001. p. 1776

Reicheneder, Elysse, Libr Mgr, Irricana Library, Curling Rink, West Side, 302-3 St, Irricana, AB, T0M 1B0, CANADA. Tel: 403-935-4818. Fax: 403-935-4818. p. 2707

Reichert, Allen, Electronic Serv, ILL, Otterbein University, 138 W Main St, Westerville, OH, 43081. Tel: 614-823-1215. Fax: 614-823-1921. p. 1946

Reichert, Andrea, Curator, Manitoba Crafts Museum & Library, 1B-183 Kennedy St, Winnipeg, MB, R3C 1S6, CANADA. Tel: 204-487-6117. Fax: 204-487-6117. p. 2756

Reichert, Darlene, Pub Serv, Dordt College, 498 Fourth Ave NE, Sioux Center, IA, 51250. Tel: 712-722-6040. Fax: 712-722-1198. p. 843

Reichert, Jen, Patron Serv, Dorothy Alling Memorial Library, 21 Library Lane, Williston, VT, 05495. Tel: 802-878-4918. Fax: 802-878-3964. p. 2440

Reichert, Joyce, Librn, Shawano City-County Library, Mattoon-Hutchins Community Library, 311 Slate Ave, Mattoon, WI, 54450-0266. Tel: 715-489-3333. p. 2637

Reichert, Liz, Acq, Carlton Fields, 4221 W Boy Scout Blvd, Ste 1000, Tampa, FL, 33607. Tel: 813-223-7000. Fax: 813-229-4133. p. 496

Reichert, Patricia, Sr Legis Librn, Wisconsin Legislative Reference Bureau, One E Main St, Madison, WI, 53703-3373. Fax: 608-266-5648. p. 2611

Reichling, Sue, Supvr, Missouri State University, Music Library, Ellis Hall, Rm 209, 901 S National, Springfield, MO, 65804-0095. Tel: 417-836-5434. p. 1367

Reichmann, Doug, Govt Doc Tech, Southwestern Oklahoma State University, 100 Campus Dr, Weatherford, OK, 73096-3002. Tel: 580-774-7069. Fax: 580-774-3112. p. 1985

Reick, Kathy, Dir, University of Montana, 25 Basin Creek Rd, Butte, MT, 59701. Tel: 406-496-3737. Fax: 406-496-3710. p. 1376

Reid, Aldric M, Librn, New York State Division of Housing & Community Renewal, 25 Beaver St, 7th Flr, New York, NY, 10004. Tel: 212-480-7424. Fax: 212-480-7416. p. 1694

Reid, Annie, Ref & Instruction Librn, Univ Archivist, Dominican University of California, 50 Acacia Ave, San Rafael, CA, 94901-2298. Tel: 415-257-0169. Fax: 415-459-2309. p. 256

Reid, Becky, Dir, Nicholas County Public Library, 223 N Broadway, Carlisle, KY, 40311. Tel: 859-289-5595. Fax: 859-289-4340. p. 909

Reid, Benjamin, Dir, Rose Memorial Library, 79 E Main St, Stony Point, NY, 10980-1699. Tel: 845-786-2100. Fax: 845-786-6042. p. 1750

Reid, Bonnie, Info Serv Coordr, Ref Serv Coordr, Downers Grove Public Library, 1050 Curtiss St, Downers Grove, IL, 60515. Tel: 630-960-1200. Fax: 630-960-9374. p. 637

Reid, Bruce D, Head Librn, Pennsylvania State University, Wilkes-Barre Commonwealth College, PO Box PSU, Lehman, PA, 18627-0217. Tel: 570-675-9212. Fax: 570-675-7436. p. 2080

Reid, Camilla B, Dir, Augusta State University, 2500 Walton Way, Augusta, GA, 30904-2200. Tel: 706-737-1745. Fax: 706-667-4415. p. 518

Reid, Carol, Librn, Heartland Community College Library, 1500 W Raab Rd, Normal, IL, 61761. Tel: 309-268-8279. Fax: 309-268-7989. p. 681

Reid, Carol Ketteman, Librn, Free Will Baptist Bible College, 3630 W End Ave, Nashville, TN, 37205. Tel: 615-844-5274. Fax: 615-269-6028. p. 2256

Reid, Catherine, Librn, York Library Region, Newcastle Branch, 100 Fountain Head Lane, Miramichi, NB, E1V 4A1, CANADA. Tel: 506-623-2450. Fax: 506-623-2335. p. 2765

Reid, Chris, Res, Pinal County Historical Society, Inc Library, 715 S Main St, Florence, AZ, 85132. Tel: 520-868-4382. p. 63

Reid, Denise, Acq, College of Eastern Utah Library, 451 E & 400 N, Price, UT, 84501. Tel: 435-613-5278. Fax: 435-613-5863. p. 2410

Reid, Diana, Librn, Vermontville Township Library, 120 E First St, Vermontville, MI, 49096. Tel: 517-726-1362. Fax: 517-726-1362. p. 1233

Reid, Eileen, Circ, Fordham University Westchester Library, 400 Westchester Ave, West Harrison, NY, 10604. Tel: 914-367-3426. p. 1766

Reid, Fran, Head, Ref, Satellite Beach Public Library, 751 Jamaica Blvd, Satellite Beach, FL, 32937. Tel: 321-779-4004. Fax: 321-779-4036. p. 490

Reid, Gloria, Br Mgr, Prairie-River Library District, Craigmont Community, 112 W Main St, Craigmont, ID, 83523-9700. Tel: 208-924-5510. Fax: 208-924-5510. p. 577

Reid, Gloria, Circ, Acton Memorial Library, 486 Main St, Acton, MA, 01720. Tel: 978-264-9641. Fax: 978-635-0073. p. 1047

Reid, Gwen, Librn, Pima County Juvenile Court Center Library, 2225 E Ajo Way, Tucson, AZ, 85713-6295. Tel: 520-740-2082. Fax: 520-740-4570. p. 86

Reid, Holly, Cat, Libr Tech, Moody Bible Institute, 820 N La Salle Blvd, Chicago, IL, 60610-3284. Tel: 312-329-4136. Fax: 312-329-8959. p. 619

Reid, Janine, Exec Dir, High Plains Library District, 2650 W 29th St, Greeley, CO, 80631. Tel: 970-506-8563. Fax: 970-506-8551. p. 311

Reid, Jeanne, Pub Info, Warner Library, 121 N Broadway, Tarrytown, NY, 10591. Tel: 914-631-7734. Fax: 914-631-2324. p. 1754

Reid, John, Dir, West Bend Community Memorial Library, 630 Poplar St, West Bend, WI, 53095-3380. Tel: 262-335-5151, Ext 125. Fax: 262-335-5150. p. 2648

Reid, Jolene, ILL, Nova Scotia Agricultural College Library, 135 College Rd, Truro, NS, B2N 5E3, CANADA. Tel: 902-893-6669. Fax: 902-895-0934. p. 2786

Reid, Judi, Circ Supvr, Johnson County Public Library, 401 State St, Franklin, IN, 46131-2545. Tel: 317-738-2833. Fax: 317-738-9635. p. 744

Reid, Kendall, Librn, Tacoma Community College Library, 6501 S 19th St, Tacoma, WA, 98466-6100. Tel: 253-566-5102. Fax: 253-566-5398. p. 2540

Reid, Kevin, Asst Librn, Henderson Community College, 2660 S Green St, Henderson, KY, 42420. Tel: 270-831-9760. Fax: 270-831-9765. p. 917

Reid, Lynda, Dir of Libr Serv, Collingwood Public Library, 55 St Marie St, Collingwood, ON, L9Y 0W6, CANADA. Tel: 705-445-1571, Ext 6223. Fax: 705-445-3704. p. 2800

Reid, Marg, Asst Head Librn, Carstairs Public Library, 1402 Scarlett Ranch Blvd, Carstairs, AB, T0M 0N0, CANADA. Tel: 403-337-3943. Fax: 403-337-3943. p. 2694

Reid, Margaret E, Librn, Nova Scotia Department of Transportation & Public Works, PO Box 186, Halifax, NS, B3J 2N2, CANADA. Tel: 902-424-6720. Fax: 902-425-3994. p. 2782

Reid, Marianne, Cat, Brandon University, 270 18th St, Brandon, MB, R7A 6A9, CANADA. Tel: 204-727-7384. Fax: 204-727-1072. p. 2747

Reid, Martha, State Librn, State of Vermont Department of Libraries, 109 State St, Montpelier, VT, 05609-0601. Tel: 802-828-3265. Fax: 802-828-2199. p. 2429

Reid, Maureen, Librn, Wapiti Regional Library, Saskatchewan Penitentiary, Box 160, Prince Albert, SK, S6V 5R6, CANADA. Tel: 306-765-8000, Ext 5643. p. 2922

Reid, Michele, Dean of Libr, North Dakota State University Libraries, 1201 Albrecht Blvd, Fargo, ND, 58108. Tel: 701-231-8888. Fax: 701-231-6128. p. 1841

Reid, Mike, Asst Librn, Lincoln Christian College & Seminary, 100 Campus View Dr, Lincoln, IL, 62656. Tel: 217-732-7788, Ext 2283. Fax: 217-732-3785. p. 665

Reid, Neal, Dean, Christian Union Bible College Library, 905 Ethel Ave, Heath, OH, 43056-1605. Tel: 937-981-2897. Fax: 937-981-2897. p. 1904

Reid, Nelda M, Dir, Southwestern Community College Library, 447 College Dr, Sylva, NC, 28779. Tel: 828-586-4091, Ext 268. Fax: 828-586-3129. p. 1826

Reid, Pat, Tech Serv Assoc, Corcoran Gallery of Art/College of Art & Design Library, 500 17th St NW, Washington, DC, 20006. Tel: 202-478-1545. Fax: 202-628-7908. p. 396

Reid, Paul, Circ, ILL, Hennepin County Medical Center, Mail Code R2, 701 Park Ave, Minneapolis, MN, 55415. Tel: 612-873-2710. Fax: 612-904-4248. p. 1260

Reid, Robert A, Sr Lecturer, University of Wisconsin-Eau Claire, 105 Garfield Ave, Eau Claire, WI, 54702. Tel: 715-836-2635. Fax: 715-836-5099. p. 2976

Reid, Ron, Sr Mgr, LINC, Memphis Public Library & Information Center, 3030 Poplar Ave, Memphis, TN, 38111-3527. Tel: 901-415-2716. Fax: 901-323-7108. p. 2249

Reid, Rose, Librn, Bighorn Library, Two Heart Mountain Dr, Exshaw, AB, T0L 2C0, CANADA. Tel: 403-673-3571. Fax: 403-673-3571. p. 2703

Reid, Ruth, Br Mgr, Massanutten Regional Library, Shenandoah Community, 418 S Third St, Shenandoah, VA, 22849. Tel: 540-652-2665. Fax: 540-652-6245. p. 2470

Reid, Sandy, Admin Librn, Website Mgr, Christian Union Bible College Library, 905 Ethel Ave, Heath, OH, 43056-1605. Tel: 937-981-2897. Fax: 937-981-2897. p. 1904

Reid, Sara Ellen, Br Mgr, Memphis Public Library, Cherokee, 3300 Sharpe, Memphis, TN, 38111. Tel: 901-743-3655. Fax: 901-743-9030. p. 2249

Reid, Sara Ellen, Br Mgr, Memphis Public Library, Parkway Village, 4655 Knight Arnold Rd, Memphis, TN, 38118-3234. Tel: 901-363-8923. Fax: 901-794-2344. p. 2250

Reid, Sarah, Youth Serv, Broome County Public Library, 185 Court St, Binghamton, NY, 13901-3503. Tel: 607-778-6456. Fax: 607-778-6429. p. 1582

Reid, Sheila Pickering, Ch, Wister Public Library, 101 Caston, Wister, OK, 74966. Tel: 918-655-7654. Fax: 918-655-3267. p. 1986

Reid, Shirley, Circ, Sweet Briar College, 134 Chapel Rd, Sweet Briar, VA, 24595-1200. Tel: 434-381-6138. Fax: 434-381-6173. p. 2497

Reid, Thomas, Dir, Reformed Presbyterian Theological Seminary Library, 7418 Penn Ave, Pittsburgh, PA, 15208-2594. Tel: 412-731-8690. Fax: 412-731-4834. p. 2128

Reid, Wood, Asst Dir, Schulte Roth & Zabel LLP, 919 Third Ave, New York, NY, 10022. Tel: 212-756-2305. Fax: 212-593-5955. p. 1699

Reidelbach, John, Electronic Res Coordr, University of Nebraska at Omaha, 6001 Dodge St, Omaha, NE, 68182-0237. Tel: 402-554-2846. Fax: 402-554-3215. p. 1414

Reidelbach, Marie A, Assoc Dir, University of Nebraska Medical Center, 600 S 42nd St, Omaha, NE, 68198-6705. Tel: 402-559-7087. Fax: 402-559-5498. p. 1415

Reider, Sandra, Lead Libr Tech, Olympic College, Johnson Library, 937 W Alpine Way, Shelton, WA, 98584-1200. Tel: 360-432-5461. Fax: 360-432-5468. p. 2510

Reidner, Nancy, Ch, Rusk County Community Library, 418 Corbett Ave, Ladysmith, WI, 54848-1396. Tel: 715-532-2604. Fax: 715-532-2658. p. 2604

Reidt, Sharon, Tech Serv Spec, Marlboro College, 64 Dalrymple Rd, Marlboro, VT, 05344-0300. Tel: 802-258-9221. Fax: 802-451-7550. p. 2428

Reidy, Geri, Circ Supvr, Clark Public Library, 303 Westfield Ave, Clark, NJ, 07066. Tel: 732-388-5999. Fax: 732-388-7866. p. 1479

Reidy, Karen, Librn, Sacred Heart Academy, c/o Sacred Heart Academy, 265 Benham St, Hamden, CT, 06514. Tel: 203-288-2309. Fax: 203-230-9680. p. 343

Reidy, Robin, Librn, Pasadena Public Library, Linda Vista, 1281 Bryant St, Pasadena, CA, 91103. Tel: 626-744-7278. p. 207

Reidy, Stephanie, Dir, Libr Serv, Baltimore City Community College, 2901 Liberty Heights Ave, Baltimore, MD, 21215. Tel: 410-462-8400. Fax: 410-462-8233. p. 1011

Reierson, Deborah, Sr Librn, Hennepin County Library, East Lake, 2727 E Lake St, Minneapolis, MN, 55406. Tel: 612-543-8428. Fax: 612-543-8427. p. 1263

Reif, Eric, Music Librn, Hampton University, Music, 130 E Tyler St, Hampton, VA, 23668. Tel: 757-727-5411. p. 2468

Reif, Kathleen, Dir, Saint Mary's County Memorial Library, 23250 Hollywood Rd, Leonardtown, MD, 20650. Tel: 301-475-2846. Fax: 301-884-4415. p. 1035

Reiff, Melissa, Dir, Hazel Green Public Library, 1610 Fairplay, Hazel Green, WI, 53811. Tel: 608-854-2952. Fax: 608-854-2417. p. 2598

Reighard, Neda, Circ Supvr, Central Bible College, 3000 N Grant Ave, Springfield, MO, 65803. Tel: 417-833-2551, Ext 1198. Fax: 417-833-5478. p. 1366

Reigle, Cathy, Coordr, Pueblo Grande Museum and Archaeological Park, 4619 E Washington St, Phoenix, AZ, 85034-1909. Tel: 602-495-0901. Fax: 602-495-5645. p. 77

Reike, Sheila, Br Mgr, Great River Regional Library, Cokato Library, 175 Fourth St W, Cokato, MN, 55321. Tel: 320-286-5760. Fax: 320-286-5760. p. 1275

Reilender, Catherine L, Dir of Libr Serv, Midway College, 512 E Stephens St, Midway, KY, 40347-1120. Tel: 859-846-5315. Fax: 859-846-5333. p. 929

Reill, Peter, Dir, University of California Los Angeles Library, William Andrews Clark Memorial Library, 2520 Cimarron St, Los Angeles, CA, 90018. Tel: 323-731-8529. Fax: 323-731-8617. p. 178

Reilly, Anne, Tech Serv Mgr, Worthington Libraries, 820 High St, Worthington, OH, 43085. Tel: 614-807-2631. Fax: 614-807-2642. p. 1950

Reilly, Barbara, ILL, Louisiana State University Health Sciences Center, 1501 Kings Hwy, Shreveport, LA, 71130. Tel: 318-675-5452. Fax: 318-675-5442. p. 968

Reilly, Bernard F, Pres, Center for Research Libraries, 6050 S Kenwood, Chicago, IL, 60637-2804. Tel: 773-955-4545, Ext 334. Fax: 773-955-4339. p. 2942

Reilly, Dina M, Dir of Libr, Lincoln Township Public Library, 2099 W John Beers Rd, Stevensville, MI, 49127. Tel: 269-429-9575. Fax: 269-429-3500. p. 1229

Reilly, Elizabeth, Curator, University of Louisville Libraries, Special Collections/Photographic Archives, Belknap Campus, 2215 S Third St, Louisville, KY, 40208. Tel: 502-852-8730. Fax: 502-852-8734. p. 927

Reilly, Felicia, Archivist, American Society of Anesthesiologists, 520 N Northwest Hwy, Park Ridge, IL, 60068-2573. Tel: 847-825-5586. Fax: 847-825-1692. p. 688

Reilly, Karen J, Assoc Dir, Libr Serv, College of the Holy Cross, One College St, Worcester, MA, 01610. Tel: 508-793-2520. Fax: 508-793-2372. p. 1143

Reilly, Margaret, Tech Serv, West Hempstead Public Library, 500 Hempstead Ave, West Hempstead, NY, 11552. Tel: 516-481-6591. Fax: 516-481-2608. p. 1766

Reilly, Michael J, Librn, Hourigan, Kluger & Quinn, 600 Third Ave, Kingston, PA, 18704-5815. Tel: 570-287-3000. Fax: 570-287-8005. p. 2074

Reilly, Susan, Dir, Moundsville-Marshall County Public Library, 700 Fifth St, Moundsville, WV, 26041-1993. Tel: 304-845-6911. Fax: 304-845-6912. p. 2567

Reilly, Tori, Asst Dir, Tech Serv & Automation, Fairport Public Library, One Fairport Village Landing, Fairport, NY, 14450. Tel: 585-223-9091. Fax: 585-223-3998. p. 1621

Reim, Christine, Youth Serv Librn, Palmer Public Library, 1455 N Main St, Palmer, MA, 01069. Tel: 413-283-3330. Fax: 413-283-9970. p. 1116

Reiman, Anne M, Librn, Verrill Dana Library, One Portland Sq, Portland, ME, 04112. Tel: 207-253-4856. Fax: 207-774-7499. p. 998

Reiman, Lorraine, Libr Dir, McLeod Health, 144 N Ravenel St, Florence, SC, 29506. Tel: 843-777-2275. Fax: 843-777-2274. p. 2194

Reimann, Cindy, Curator, Dir, Cloud County Historical Society Museum Library, 635 Broadway, Concordia, KS, 66901. Tel: 785-243-2866. p. 862

Reimann, Kristin, ILL, Cornell College, 620 Third St SW, Mount Vernon, IA, 52314-1012. Tel: 319-895-4260, 895-4271. Fax: 319-895-5936. p. 834

Reimer, Lucille, Dir, Limon Memorial Public Library, 205 E Ave, Limon, CO, 80828. Tel: 719-775-2163. Fax: 719-775-8808. p. 316

Reimers, Molly, Children's Mgr, Security Public Library, 715 Aspen Dr, Security, CO, 80911-1807. Tel: 719-391-3191. Fax: 719-392-7641. p. 322

Reimold, Pauline, Librn, United States Navy, 1481 D St, Bldg 3016, Norfolk, VA, 23521. Tel: 757-462-7691. Fax: 757-462-4950. p. 2483

Rein, Laura, Dean of Libr, Webster University, 101 Edgar Rd, Saint Louis, MO, 63119. Tel: 314-968-7152. Fax: 314-968-7113. p. 1363

Rein, Meg, Mgr, ILL, Carroll College, 100 N East Ave, Waukesha, WI, 53186. Tel: 262-650-4889. Fax: 262-524-7377. p. 2644

Rein, Sally, Ref Serv, Ad, Patchogue-Medford Library, 54-60 E Main St, Patchogue, NY, 11772. Tel: 631-654-4700, Ext 235. Fax: 631-289-3999. p. 1715

Reinauer, Olivia, Libr, Humanities & Soc Sci, University of Richmond, 28 Westhampton Way, Richmond, VA, 23173. Tel: 804-289-8977. Fax: 804-289-8757. p. 2491

Reinbold, Jan, Dir, Southern Nazarene University, 4115 N College, Bethany, OK, 73008. Tel: 405-491-6350. Fax: 405-491-6355. p. 1958

Reinboldt, Valerie, Librn, Chinook Regional Library, Fox Valley Branch, 85 Centre St E, Fox Valley, SK, S0N 0V0, CANADA. Tel: 306-666-2045. p. 2928

Reinecke, Ann M, Sr Mgr/Cir, Adult Serv, Tech Serv, Caroline County Public Library, 100 Market St, Denton, MD, 21629. Tel: 410-479-1343. Fax: 410-479-1443. p. 1027

Reiner, MaryAnn, Head, Circ, Monroe Township Public Library, Four Municipal Plaza, Monroe Township, NJ, 08831-1900. Tel: 732-521-5000, Ext 101. Fax: 732-521-4766. p. 1503

Reinert, Ruth Ann, Coll Develop, Public Libraries of Saginaw, 505 Janes Ave, Saginaw, MI, 48607. Tel: 989-755-0904. Fax: 989-755-9829. p. 1223

Reines, Aaron, Circ Supvr, Saint Leo University, 33701 State Rd 52, Saint Leo, FL, 33574. Tel: 352-588-8648. Fax: 352-588-8484. p. 487

Reinfeld-Bruno, Judith, Outreach Serv Librn, Scarsdale Public Library, 54 Olmsted Rd, Scarsdale, NY, 10583. Tel: 914-722-1300. Fax: 914-722-1305. p. 1739

Reinhardt, Anne, Spec Projects, American Philosophical Society Library, 105 S Fifth St, Philadelphia, PA, 19106-3386. Tel: 215-440-3400. Fax: 215-440-3423. p. 2103

Reinhardt, Vicki, Dir, Lyons Township District Library, 309 Bridge St, Lyons, MI, 48851. Tel: 989-855-3414. Fax: 989-855-2069. p. 1204

Reinhart, Lore, Ch, Randolph Township Free Public Library, 28 Calais Rd, Randolph, NJ, 07869. Tel: 973-895-3556. Fax: 973-895-4946. p. 1525

Reinhart, Marjorie, Human Res Mgr, Albany Public Library, 161 Washington Ave, Albany, NY, 12210. Tel: 518-427-4336. Fax: 518-449-3386. p. 1568

Reinhart, Scott, Asst Dir, Operations, Carroll County Public Library, 115 Airport Dr, Westminster, MD, 21157. Tel: 410-386-4500, Ext 137. Fax: 410-386-4509. p. 1045

Reinhart, Sean, Dir, Libr & Commun Serv, Hayward Public Library, 835 C St, Hayward, CA, 94541-5120. Tel: 510-881-7956. p. 157

Reinhart, Tricia, Circ Supvr, Northeastern University Libraries, Snell Library, 360 Huntington Ave, Boston, MA, 02115. Tel: 617-373-4970. p. 1065

Reinhold, Amy, Cat, Bethel University Library, 3900 Bethel Dr, Saint Paul, MN, 55112. Tel: 651-638-6222. Fax: 651-638-6001. p. 1277

Reinholt, Susie, Dir, Plymouth Public Library, 201 N Center St, Plymouth, IN, 46563. Tel: 574-936-2324. Fax: 574-936-7423. p. 773

Reining, Larry, Ref Librn, Spalding University Library, 853 Library Lane, Louisville, KY, 40203-9986. Tel: 502-585-7130. Fax: 502-585-7156. p. 925

Reinke, Fern, Librn, Bawlf Public Library, 203 Hanson St, Bawlf, AB, T0B 0J0, CANADA. Tel: 780-373-3882. Fax: 780-373-3882. p. 2684

Reinl, Cynthia, Librn, Bellin Hospital, 744 S Webster Ave, Green Bay, WI, 54301-3581. Tel: 920-433-3693. Fax: 920-433-7498. p. 2595

Reinmann, Kris, Libr Tech, Department of Veterans Affairs, Lyons Campus Patient's Library, 151 Knollcroft Rd, Lyons, NJ, 07939. Tel: 908-647-0180, Ext 6421, 973-676-1000. Fax: 908-604-5837. p. 1497

Reinmiller, Jim, Dir, Hazleton Area Public Library, 55 N Church St, Hazleton, PA, 18201-5893. Tel: 570-454-2961. Fax: 570-454-0630. p. 2068

Reinsfelder, Tom, Ref Librn, Pennsylvania State University, One Campus Dr, Mont Alto, PA, 17237-9703. Tel: 717-749-6040. Fax: 717-749-6059. p. 2091

Reinstrom, Lorel, Dir, Desoto County Library, 125 N Hillsborough Ave, Arcadia, FL, 34266. Tel: 863-993-4851. Fax: 863-491-4095. p. 425

Reinumagi, Linda, Librn, Niagara Falls Public Library, 1425 Main St, Niagara Falls, NY, 14305. Tel: 716-286-4881. Fax: 716-286-4912. p. 1705

Reis, Nanette, Dir, Oceanic Free Library, 109 Avenue of Two Rivers, Rumson, NJ, 07760. Tel: 732-842-2692. Fax: 732-842-5713. p. 1528

Reis, Tovah, Mrs, Librn, Temple Emanu-El Library, 99 Taft Ave, Providence, RI, 02906. Tel: 401-331-1616. Fax: 401-421-9279. p. 2175

Reis-Bradley, Vanessa, Librn, St Luke's Hospital-Allentown Campus, 1736 Hamilton St, Allentown, PA, 18104. Tel: 610-770-8355. Fax: 610-770-8736. p. 2027

Reis-Bradley, Vanessa, Librn, St Luke's Hospital & Health Network, 801 Ostrum St, Bethlehem, PA, 18015. Tel: 610-770-8355. Fax: 610-770-8736. p. 2035

Reise, Elaine, Ref, Montville Township Public Library, 90 Horseneck Rd, Montville, NJ, 07045-9626. Tel: 973-402-0900. Fax: 973-402-0592. p. 1504

Reiser, Bill, Libr Mgr, Monroe County Library System, Ellis Reference & Information Center, 3700 S Custer Rd, Monroe, MI, 48161-9716. Tel: 734-241-5277. Fax: 734-242-9037. p. 1210

Reish, Joseph, Dean, Western Michigan University, Arcadia at Vande Giessen St, Kalamazoo, MI, 49008-5353. Tel: 269-387-5059. Fax: 269-387-5077. p. 1198

Reiskind, Alix, Visual Res Librn, Harvard Library, Frances Loeb Library, Harvard Graduate School of Design, 48 Quincy St, Gund Hall, Cambridge, MA, 02138. Tel: 617-495-9163. p. 1076

Reisler, Reina, Dir, Community Medical Center, 99 Hwy 37 W, Toms River, NJ, 08755. Tel: 732-557-8117. Fax: 732-557-8354. p. 1533

Reisler, Reina, Librn, Monmouth-Ocean Biomedical Information Consortium, Community Medical Ctr, 99 Hwy 37 W, Toms River, NJ, 08755. Tel: 732-557-8117. Fax: 732-557-8354. p. 2949

Reisman, Elizabeth, Automation Librn, Ref Librn, United States Army, RDECOM-ARDEC, Bldg 59, Phipps Rd, AMSRD-AAR-EMK, Picatinny Arsenal, NJ, 07806-5000. Tel: 973-724-5350. Fax: 973-724-3044. p. 1520

Reisman, Myra, Chief Librn, Touro College Libraries, 43 W 23rd St, Fifth Fl, New York, NY, 10010. Tel: 212-463-0400, Ext 5321. Fax: 212-627-3696. p. 1701

Reiss, Joe, Dir, Post Falls Public Library, 821 N Spokane St, Post Falls, ID, 83854-9315. Tel: 208-773-1506. Fax: 208-773-1507. p. 582

Reiss, Laurel M, Dir, Head Librn, Erie Public Library District, 802 Eighth Ave, Erie, IL, 61250. Tel: 309-659-2707. Fax: 309-659-2707. p. 643

Reiss, Susan, Head Music Librn, Bennington College, Jennings Music Library, One College Dr, Jennings Music Bldg, Bennington, VT, 05201. Tel: 802-440-4512. Fax: 802-440-4511. p. 2418

Reissig, Anne, Cat, Patchogue-Medford Library, 54-60 E Main St, Patchogue, NY, 11772. Tel: 631-654-4700, Ext 288. Fax: 631-289-3999. p. 1715

Reist, Aynne, Children's Serv Supvr, Naperville Public Library, Naper Boulevard, 2035 S Naper Blvd, Naperville, IL, 60565-3353. Tel: 630-961-4100, Ext 2235. Fax: 630-961-4119. p. 679

Reist, Inge, Coll Develop, The Frick Collection, Ten E 71st St, New York, NY, 10021. Tel: 212-288-8700. Fax: 212-879-2091. p. 1679

Reist, Marie, Adult Serv, Pryor Public Library, 505 E Graham, Pryor, OK, 74361. Tel: 918-825-0777. Fax: 918-825-0856. p. 1976

Reister, Stephanie, Ch, Germantown Community Library, N112W16957 Mequon Rd, Germantown, WI, 53022. Tel: 262-253-7760. Fax: 262-253-7763. p. 2594

Reister, Willa, ILL, Knox County Public Library System, 500 W Church Ave, Knoxville, TN, 37902-2505. Tel: 865-215-8750. Fax: 865-215-8742. p. 2241

Reiswig, Jenny, Asst Dir, University of California, San Diego, Biomedical Library, 9500 Gilman Dr, 0699, La Jolla, CA, 92093-0699. Tel: 858-534-3418. Fax: 858-822-2219. p. 162

Reitan, Beth, Dir, Bottineau County Public Library, 314 W Fifth St, Bottineau, ND, 58318-9600. Tel: 701-228-2967. Fax: 701-228-2171. p. 1838

Reiter, Betty Anne, Dir of Libr Serv, Groton Public Library, 52 Newtown Rd, Groton, CT, 06340. Tel: 860-441-6750. Fax: 860-448-0363. p. 342

Reiter, Nancy, Br Mgr, Riverside County Library System, El Cerrito Library, 7581 Rudell Rd, Corona, CA, 92881. Tel: 951-270-5012. p. 217

Reiter, Sue, Cat, ILL, University of Dubuque Library, 2000 University Ave, Dubuque, IA, 52001. Tel: 563-589-3100. Fax: 563-589-3722. p. 812

Reiterman, Sue, Br Mgr, Burlingame Public Library, Easton Drive Branch, 1800 Easton Dr, Burlingame, CA, 94010. Tel: 650-340-6180. Fax: 650-340-6184. p. 131

Reiterman, Susan, Ch, Burlingame Public Library, 480 Primrose Rd, Burlingame, CA, 94010-4083. Tel: 650-558-7440. Fax: 650-342-1948. p. 130

Reitman, Jo, Dir, Butler Public Library, 12621 W Hampton Ave, Butler, WI, 53007-1705. Tel: 262-783-2535. Fax: 262-783-9900. p. 2584

Reitsma, Alvina, Dir, Sanborn Public Library, 407 Main St, Sanborn, IA, 51248. Tel: 712-930-3215. Fax: 712-930-3170. p. 842

Reitsma, Denise, Head, Youth Serv, Howe Library, 13 South St, Hanover, NH, 03755. Tel: 603-643-4120. Fax: 603-643-0725. p. 1450

Reitsma, Helen, Cat & Ref, Redeemer College Library, 777 Garner Rd E, Ancaster, ON, L9K 1J4, CANADA. Tel: 905-648-2131. Fax: 905-648-2134. p. 2792

Reitz, Joan, Instruction Librn, Western Connecticut State University, 181 White St, Danbury, CT, 06810. Tel: 203-837-8308. Fax: 203-837-9108. p. 335

Reitz, Karen, Sr Librn, Ref, Redondo Beach Public Library, 303 N Pacific Coast Hwy, Redondo Beach, CA, 90277. Tel: 310-318-0675. Fax: 310-318-3809. p. 215

Rekart, Sue, Pub Serv Coordr, Wicomico Public Library, 122 S Division St, Salisbury, MD, 21801. Tel: 410-749-3612, Ext 148. Fax: 410-548-2968. p. 1040

Rekedal, Char, Librn, Marshall-Lyon County Library, Cottonwood Community, 86 W Main St, Cottonwood, MN, 56229. Tel: 507-423-6488. Fax: 507-423-5368. p. 1258

Rekowski, Lois, Dir, Libr Serv, Jefferson Community College Library, 4000 Sunset Blvd, Steubenville, OH, 43952-3598. Tel: 740-264-5591, Ext 154. Fax: 740-264-1338. p. 1936

Rekowski, Richard G, Dir, Mary H Weir Public Library, 3442 Main St, Weirton, WV, 26062. Tel: 304-797-8510. Fax: 304-797-8526. p. 2573

Rekrut, Ala, Archivist, Archives of Manitoba, 130-200 Vaughan St, Winnipeg, MB, R3C 1T5, CANADA. Tel: 204-945-3971. Fax: 204-948-2008. p. 2754

Rekuc, Bob, Ref Serv, Indian Valley Public Library, 100 E Church Ave, Telford, PA, 18969. Tel: 215-723-9109. Fax: 215-723-0583. p. 2145

Rele, Shilpa, Digital Projects Librn, Loyola Marymount University, One LMU Dr, MS 8200, Los Angeles, CA, 90045-2659. Tel: 310-338-2792. Fax: 310-338-4366. p. 175

Remack, Barbara, Tech Serv, Lexington County Public Library System, 5440 Augusta Rd, Lexington, SC, 29072. Tel: 803-785-2624. Fax: 803-785-2601. p. 2199

Remak-Honnef, Elizabeth, Bibliographer, Librn, University of California, 1156 High St, Santa Cruz, CA, 95064. Tel: 831-459-2459. Fax: 831-459-8206. p. 264

Remaly, Dania, Librn, Purdue University Libraries, Aviation Technology, Terminal Bldg 163, West Lafayette, IN, 47907-2058. Tel: 765-494-7640. Fax: 765-494-0156. p. 786

Rematore, Andrea, Circ, National Semiconductor Corp, 2900 Semiconductor Dr, MS-DT-05, Santa Clara, CA, 95052-8090. Tel: 408-721-3810. Fax: 408-721-7060. p. 262

Rembish, Judy, Libr Coordr, Alberta Law Libraries - Leduc, Courthouse, 4612-50th St, Leduc, AB, T9E 6L1, CANADA. Tel: 780-980-7592. Fax: 780-986-0345. p. 2709

Rembish, Judy, Libr Coordr, Alberta Law Libraries - Sherwood Park, Courthouse, 190 Chippewa Rd, Sherwood Park, AB, T8A 4H5, CANADA. Tel: 780-416-4087. Fax: 780-449-1490. p. 2716

Remelts, Glenn A, Dir, Calvin College & Calvin Theological Seminary, 1855 Knollcrest Circle SE, Grand Rapids, MI, 49546-4402. Tel: 616-526-7197. Fax: 616-526-6470. p. 1184

Remhof, Tamara, Head, Tech Serv, Texas A&M University-Commerce, 2600 S Neal St, Commerce, TX, 75429. Tel: 903-886-5717. Fax: 903-886-5434. p. 2300

Remilien, Suzie, Ref Librn, Long Island University, One University Plaza, Brooklyn, NY, 11201-9926. Tel: 718-488-1081. Fax: 718-780-4057. p. 1593

Remillard, Jeannie, Libr Assoc, Washington State Library, Stafford Creek Correctional Center Branch Library, 191 Constantine Way, MS WA-39, Aberdeen, WA, 98520. Tel: 360-537-2258. Fax: 360-537-2501. p. 2545

Remillard, Kathleen, Adult Serv, Ref Librn, Brewster Ladies' Library Association, 1822 Main St, Brewster, MA, 02631. Tel: 508-896-3913. Fax: 508-896-9372. p. 1069

Remillard, Stephanie, Dir, Campbellsport Public Library, 220 N Helena St, Campbellsport, WI, 53010-0405. Tel: 920-533-8534. Fax: 920-533-8712. p. 2584

Remington, Kerry J, Dir, Rutland Free Public Library, 280 Main St, Rutland, MA, 01543. Tel: 508-886-4108. Fax: 508-886-4141. p. 1121

Reminick, Gerald, Reader Serv, Ref, Suffolk County Community College, 1001 Crooked Hill Rd, Brentwood, NY, 11717. Tel: 631-851-6740. Fax: 631-851-6509. p. 1584

Remnek, Miranda Beaven, Head of Libr, University of Illinois Library at Urbana-Champaign, Slavic & East European, 225 Main Library, 1408 W Gregory Dr, Urbana, IL, 61801. Tel: 217-333-1340. Fax: 217-244-8976. p. 713

Remoaldo, Susan C, Br Mgr, Hawaii State Public Library System, Waimea Public Library, 9750 Kaumualii Hwy, Waimea, HI, 96796. Tel: 808-338-6848. Fax: 808-338-6847. p. 563

Rempe, Angela, Asst Librn, Wellsburg Public Library, 515 N Adams, Wellsburg, IA, 50680. Tel: 641-869-5234. Fax: 641-869-5234. p. 851

Remy, Barbara, Librn, Lake County Library District, Christmas Valley Branch, Christmas Tree Lane, Christmas Valley, OR, 97641. Tel: 541-576-2336. Fax: 541-576-2336. p. 2003

Remy, Charles, Electronic Res, University of Tennessee at Chattanooga Library, 615 McCallie Ave, Dept 6456, Chattanooga, TN, 37403-2598. Tel: 423-425-4501. Fax: 423-425-4775. p. 2228

Remy, Richard J, Mgr, Online Serv, Southern Research Institute, 2000 Ninth Ave S, Birmingham, AL, 35205. Tel: 205-581-2000, Ext 2272. Fax: 205-581-2008. p. 9

Ren, Jie, Br Mgr, Los Angeles Public Library System, Cahuenga, 4591 Santa Monica Blvd, Los Angeles, CA, 90029-1827. Tel: 323-664-6418. Fax: 323-664-6200. p. 173

Ren, Rena, Pub Serv Mgr, Laredo Public Library, 1120 E Calton Rd, Laredo, TX, 78041. Tel: 956-795-2400. Fax: 956-795-2403. p. 2353

Renaldi, Shirley, Admin Supvr, German-Masontown Public Library, Nine S Washington St, Masontown, PA, 15461-2025. Tel: 724-583-7030. Fax: 724-583-0979. p. 2085

Renaud, John, Dir, Coll Develop & Scholarly Communication, University of Miami Libraries, 1300 Memorial Dr, Coral Gables, FL, 33146. Tel: 305-284-3233. Fax: 305-284-4027. p. 434

Rence, Linda, Br Mgr, Rupp Ida Public Library, Erie Islands, 281 Concord Ave, Put-In-Bay, OH, 43456. Tel: 419-285-4004. Fax: 419-285-4004. p. 1930

Rench, Marge, Asst Librn, Frackville Free Public Library, 56 N Lehigh Ave, Frackville, PA, 17931-1424. Tel: 570-874-3382. Fax: 570-874-3382. p. 2058

Rencher, Natalie, Dir, Kings County Library, 401 N Douty St, Hanford, CA, 93230. Tel: 559-582-0261. Fax: 559-583-6163. p. 156

Rencic, Mary, Dir, Marie Fleche Memorial Library, 49 S White Horse Pike, Berlin, NJ, 08009. Tel: 856-767-2448. Fax: 856-768-7421. p. 1472

Rencsko, Carly, Assoc Librn, Youth Serv, James Blackstone Memorial Library, 758 Main St, Branford, CT, 06405-3697. Tel: 203-488-1441. Fax: 203-481-6077. p. 331

Rendall, Cathy, Libr Mgr, Three Hills Municipal Library, 160 Third Ave S, Three Hills, AB, T0M 2A0, CANADA. Tel: 403-443-2360. p. 2719

Rendell, Douglas W, Dir, Peabody Institute Library of Danvers, 15 Sylvan St, Danvers, MA, 01923-2735. Tel: 978-774-0554. Fax: 978-762-0251. p. 1083

Rendfeld, Connie, Digital Initiatives Librn, Indiana State Library, 315 W Ohio St, Indianapolis, IN, 46202. Tel: 317-232-3694. Fax: 317-232-0002. p. 752

Rendle, Hugh, Dir, Tyndale University College & Seminary, 25 Ballyconnor Ct, Toronto, ON, M2M 4B3, CANADA. Tel: 416-226-6620, Ext 6716. Fax: 416-218-6765. p. 2864

Rendon, Holanda, Ref, University of the Sacred Heart, Rosales St, PO Box 12383, Santurce, PR, 00914-0383. Tel: 787-728-1515, Ext 4353. Fax: 787-268-8868. p. 2678

Rendon, Noelia, Acq, Inter-American University of Puerto Rico, School of Law Library, PO Box 70351, Hato Rey, PR, 00936. Tel: 787-751-1912. Fax: 787-753-6851. p. 2673

Rendon, Ruben, Dir, Harlingen Public Library, 410 76 Dr, Harlingen, TX, 78550. Tel: 956-216-5800. Fax: 956-430-6654. p. 2331

Rendulic, Fran, Asst Dir, Rostraver Public Library, 700 Plaza Dr, Belle Vernon, PA, 15012. Tel: 724-379-5511. Fax: 724-379-6090. p. 2032

Rene, Jean, Asst Div Mgr, Queens Borough Public Library, Literature & Languages Division, 89-11 Merrick Blvd, Jamaica, NY, 1432. Tel: 718-990-8622. Fax: 718-658-8342. p. 1645

Rene, Nicole, Prof, College de Maisonneuve, 3800, rue Sherbrooke Est, Montreal, QC, H1X 2A2, CANADA. Tel: 514-254-7131. Fax: 514-251-9741. p. 2978

Renear, Allen, Interim Dean, Prof, University of Illinois at Urbana-Champaign, Library & Information Science Bldg, 501 E Daniel St, Champaign, IL, 61820-6211. Tel: 217-333-3280. Fax: 217-244-3302. p. 2965

Renel-Faledas, Laurie, Asst Dir, Crandon Public Library, 110 W Polk St, Crandon, WI, 54520-1458. Tel: 715-478-3784. Fax: 715-478-3784. p. 2587

Renfro, Nancy, Dir, Holston River Regional Library, 2700 S Roan St, Ste 435, Johnson City, TN, 37601-7587. Tel: 423-926-2951. Fax: 423-926-2956. p. 2239

Renfro, Pam, Librn, Cimarron City Library, Ensign Branch, 108 Aubrey, Ensign, KS, 67841. Tel: 620-865-2199. p. 860

Renfro, Patricia E, Dep Univ Librn, Columbia University, Butler Library, Rm 517, 535 W 114th St, New York, NY, 10027. Tel: 212-854-7309. Fax: 212-854-9099. p. 1674

Renfroe-Warren, April, Cat Librn, Macon State College Library, 100 College Station Dr, Macon, GA, 31206-5144. Tel: 478-471-2008. Fax: 478-471-2869. p. 540

Reng, Jodi, Exec Dir, Timberland Regional Library, 415 Tumwater Blvd SW, Tumwater, WA, 98501-5799. Tel: 360-943-5001, Ext 2501. Fax: 360-586-6838. p. 2543

Renga, Alan, Archivist, San Diego Aero-Space Museum, Inc, 2001 Pan American Plaza, Balboa Park, San Diego, CA, 92101-1636. Tel: 619-234-8291, Ext 25. Fax: 619-233-4526. p. 232

Renick, Katherine, Librn, Marin General Hospital, 250 Bon Air Rd, Greenbrae, CA, 94904. Tel: 415-925-7393. Fax: 415-925-7396. p. 156

Renick, Martha, Librn, Marion County Law Library, 555 Court St, Salem, OR, 97309. Tel: 503-588-5090. Fax: 503-373-4386. p. 2017

Renick, Tim, Dir, United States Army, US Army Logistics University, Bldg 12420, 562 Quarters Rd, Fort Lee, VA, 23801-1705. Tel: 804-765-4722. Fax: 804-765-4660. p. 2465

Renison, Susan, Res Librn, Watsonville Public Library, 310 Union St, Watsonville, CA, 95076. Tel: 831-768-3400. Fax: 831-763-4015. p. 282

Renken, Ellen, Librn, Crawford Public Library, 601 Second St, Crawford, NE, 69339. Tel: 308-665-1780. Fax: 308-665-1780. p. 1396

Renner, Barbara, Librn, St Mary's Correctional Center Library, 2880 N Pleasants Hwy, Saint Mary's, WV, 26170. Tel: 304-684-5500. Fax: 304-684-4000. p. 2571

Renner, Eric, Dir, Pinhole Resource Library, Star Rte 15, San Lorenzo, NM, 88041. Tel: 505-536-9942. p. 1561

Renner, Kathy, Coordr, Ser & Electronic Res, Westminster College, Reeves Memorial Library, 501 Westminster Ave, Fulton, MO, 65251-1299. Tel: 573-592-5248. Fax: 573-642-6356. p. 1328

Renners, Tim, Dir, Ivy Tech Community College, 590 Ivy Tech Dr, Madison, IN, 47250. Tel: 800-403-2190, Ext 4106. Fax: 812-265-4028. p. 762

Rennie, Elizabeth, Instruction Librn, Outreach Librn, Thompson Rivers University, 900 McGill Rd, Kamloops, BC, V2C 5N3, CANADA. Tel: 250-828-5300. Fax: 250-828-5313. p. 2730

Rennie, Elizabeth, Librn, Thompson Rivers University, 1250 Western Ave, Williams Lake, BC, V2G 1H7, CANADA. Tel: 250-392-8030. Fax: 250-392-4984. p. 2746

Rennie, Mary, Br Coordr, Erie County Public Library, 160 E Front St, Erie, PA, 16507. Tel: 814-451-6910. Fax: 814-451-6907. p. 2055

Rennie, Mary, Br Coordr, Erie County Public Library, Edinboro Branch, 413 W Plum St, Edinboro, PA, 16412-2508. Tel: 814-451-6910. p. 2055

Rennie, Mary, Br Coordr, Erie County Public Library, Iroquois Avenue, 4212 Iroquois Ave, Erie, PA, 16511-2198. Tel: 814-451-6910. Fax: 814-451-6969. p. 2055

Rennie, Mary, Br Coordr, Erie County Public Library, Lincoln Community Center, 1255 Manchester Rd, Erie, PA, 16505-2614. Tel: 814-451-6910. Fax: 814-451-6969. p. 2055

Rennie, Mary, Br Coordr, Erie County Public Library, Millcreek, 2088 Interchange Rd, Ste 280, Erie, PA, 16565-0601. Tel: 814-451-6910. Fax: 814-451-6969. p. 2055

Reno, Lindsey, Acq Librn, Occidental College Library, 1600 Campus Rd, Los Angeles, CA, 90041. Tel: 323-259-2965. Fax: 323-341-4991. p. 176

Reno, Michael, Mgr, Network Serv, Worcester Public Library, Three Salem Sq, Worcester, MA, 01608. Tel: 508-799-1655. Fax: 508-799-1652. p. 1145

Reno, Tamara, Dir, Legal Res, Moore & Van Allen PLLC, Bank of America Corporate Ctr, 100 N Tryon, Ste 4700, Charlotte, NC, 28202. Tel: 704-331-1000. Fax: 704-339-5946. p. 1783

Renschler, Catherine, In Charge, Adams County Historical Society Archives, 1330 N Burlington Ave, Hastings, NE, 68902. Tel: 402-463-5838. p. 1401

Rensler, Jenny, Ref Serv, University of Maryland, Baltimore, Thurgood Marshall Law Library, 501 W Fayette St, Baltimore, MD, 21201-1768. Tel: 410-706-2466. Fax: 410-706-8354. p. 1019

Renteria, Phil, Librn, California Department of Corrections Library System, Central California Women's Facility, 23370 Rd 22, Chowchilla, CA, 93610. Tel: 559-665-5531. Fax: 559-665-6037. p. 221

Rentof, Beryl, Ref, Fashion Institute of Technology-SUNY, Seventh Ave at 27th St, New York, NY, 10001-5992. Tel: 212-217-4401. Fax: 212-217-4371. p. 1678

Rentz, Jacky, Asst Librn, McMillan Memorial Library, 205 E Second Ave, Red Springs, NC, 28377. Tel: 910-843-4205. p. 1819

Rentz, Paivi, Acq, Texas State University-San Marcos, Wood & Talbot St, San Marcos, TX, 78666-4604. Tel: 512-245-2133. Fax: 512-245-3002. p. 2385

Reny, Isabelle, Head of Libr, Federation des Travailleurs et Travailleuses du Quebec, 565 Cremazie Blvd E, Ste 12100, Montreal, QC, H2M 2W3, CANADA. Tel: 514-383-8025. Fax: 514-383-0502. p. 2895

Renz, Lisa, Youth Serv, Utica Public Library, 303 Genesee St, Utica, NY, 13501. Tel: 315-735-2279. Fax: 315-734-1034. p. 1760

Renze, Patricia, Mgr, Libr Serv, Kelley Drye & Warren, 101 Park Ave, New York, NY, 10178. Tel: 212-808-7800. Fax: 212-808-7897. p. 1684

Repass, Dara, Head Librn, Jonestown Community Library, 18649 FM1431, Ste 10A, Jonestown, TX, 78645. Tel: 512-267-7511. Fax: 512-267-4572. p. 2348

Repenning, Thomas, Dir, College of Southern Maryland Library, 8730 Mitchell Rd, La Plata, MD, 20646. Tel: 301-934-7630. Fax: 301-934-7699. p. 1034

Repetti, Roberta, Acq, Christiana Hospital Library, Christiana Hospital, 4755 Ogletown Stanton Rd, Newark, DE, 19718-0002. Tel: 302-733-1118. Fax: 302-733-1365. p. 385

Repetto, Ann, Librn, Washington University Libraries, Bernard Becker Medical Library, 660 S Euclid Ave, Campus Box 8132, Saint Louis, MO, 63110. Tel: 314-362-7080. Fax: 314-454-6606. p. 1362

Repinski, Sara, Acq, Widener University, School of Law Library, 4601 Concord Pike, Wilmington, DE, 19803. Tel: 302-477-2036. Fax: 302-477-2240. p. 389

Repka-Peters, Margie, Dir, Upper Moreland Free Public Library, 109 Park Ave, Willow Grove, PA, 19090-3277. Tel: 215-659-0741. Fax: 215-830-1223. p. 2157

Repman, Denise, Head, Cat, Delgado Community College, Bldg 10, Rm 116, 615 City Park Ave, New Orleans, LA, 70119. Tel: 504-671-5330. p. 959

Repp, Amber, Asst Dir, Akron Law Library, 209 S High St, 4th Flr, Akron, OH, 44308-1675. Tel: 330-643-2804. Fax: 330-535-0077. p. 1851

Repp, Kevin, Curator, Modern Bks & Ms, Yale University Library, Beinecke Rare Book & Manuscript, 121 Wall St, New Haven, CT, 06520. Tel: 203-432-2967. Fax: 203-432-4047. p. 356

Repp, Laurie, Asst Dir, Cat & Ref, Heidelberg University, 10 Greenfield St, Tiffin, OH, 44883-2420. Tel: 419-448-2104. Fax: 419-448-2578. p. 1938

Repp, Margaret, Dir, Bushnell Public Library, 455 N Dean, Bushnell, IL, 61422-1299. Tel: 309-772-2060. Fax: 309-772-9038. p. 598

Repplinger, John, Sci, Willamette University, 900 State St, Salem, OR, 97301. Tel: 503-370-6525. Fax: 503-370-6141. p. 2019

Resch, Tyler, Librn, Bennington Museum, 75 Main St, Bennington, VT, 05201. Tel: 802-447-1571. Fax: 802-442-8305. p. 2418

Reschenthaler, Jan, Dir, Tech Coordr, Jefferson Hills Library, 925 Old Clairton Rd, Jefferson Hills, PA, 15025-3158. Tel: 412-655-7741. Fax: 412-655-4003. p. 2072

Resco, Carol S, Dir, Libr Serv, Oregon Health & Science University, OGI School of Science & Engineering, 20000 NW Walker Rd, Beaverton, OR, 97006-8921. Tel: 503-748-1060. Fax: 503-748-1029. p. 1991

Reseigh, Melanie, Br Mgr, Knox County Public Library System, Carter Branch, 9036 Asheville Hwy, Knoxville, TN, 37924. Tel: 865-933-5438. Fax: 865-932-1221. p. 2242

Resendez, Brandi, Libr Mgr, Sequoyah Regional Library System, Gilmer County Public, 268 Calvin Jackson Dr, Ellijay, GA, 30540. Tel: 706-635-4528. Fax: 706-635-3528. p. 523

Resetar, Donna R R, Assoc Dean, Libr Serv, Valparaiso University, 1410 Chapel Dr, Valparaiso, IN, 46383-6493. Tel: 219-464-6183. p. 783

Resnick, Paul, Prof, University of Michigan, 304 West Hall, 1085 S University, Ann Arbor, MI, 48109-1107. Tel: 734-763-2285. Fax: 734-764-2475. p. 2967

Resnick, Rachel R, Res Librn, Madlyn & Leonard Abramson Center for Jewish Life, 1425 Horsham Rd, North Wales, PA, 19454-1320. Tel: 215-371-1333. Fax: 215-371-3015. p. 2099

Resnik, Rachel, Tech Serv, Massachusetts College of Art & Design, 621 Huntington Ave, Boston, MA, 02115-5882. Tel: 617-879-7115. Fax: 617-879-7110. p. 1063

Resnik, Robert, Dir, Fletcher Free Library, 235 College St, Burlington, VT, 05401. Tel: 802-865-7222. Fax: 802-865-7227. p. 2420

Ressel, Maggie, Dir, Info Serv, University of Nevada, Las Vegas Libraries, 4505 Maryland Pkwy, Box 457001, Las Vegas, NV, 89154-7001. Tel: 702-895-2286. Fax: 702-895-2287. p. 1430

Ressel, Maggie, Pub Serv, University of Nevada-Reno, 1664 N Virginia St, Mailstop 0322, Reno, NV, 89557-0322. Tel: 775-682-5653. Fax: 775-784-4529. p. 1433

Ressler, Cindy, Asst Librn, Chinook Regional Library, Burstall Branch, Martin St & Hamilton Ave, Burstall, SK, S0N 0H0, CANADA. Tel: 306-679-2177. p. 2928

Ressler, Marlene, Outreach Serv Librn, Preble County District Library, 450 S Barron St, Eaton, OH, 45320-2402. Tel: 937-456-4250. Fax: 937-456-6092. p. 1897

Ressmeyer, Ellen, Archivist, West Virginia State University, Campus Box L17, Institute, WV, 25112. Tel: 304-766-3116. Fax: 304-766-4103. p. 2562

Resti, Justin, Ref Serv, K&L Gates LLP, 1601 K St NW, L-3, Washington, DC, 20006. Tel: 202-778-9169. Fax: 202-778-9100. p. 406

Resto, Jeri, Librn, Cuyamaca College Library, 900 Rancho San Diego Pkwy, El Cajon, CA, 92019-4304. Tel: 619-660-4423. Fax: 619-660-4493. p. 145

Restuccia, Magdalene, ILL, University of Scranton, Monroe & Linden, Scranton, PA, 18510-4634. Tel: 570-941-4000, 570-941-4008. Fax: 570-941-7817. p. 2138

Retelle, Julie A, Asst Col Librn for Access Serv, Bates College, 48 Campus Ave, Lewiston, ME, 04240. Tel: 207-786-6265. Fax: 207-786-6055. p. 989

Reter, Jude, Managing Dir, ipIQ/The Patent Board Research Library, 222 Haddon Ave, 3rd Flr, Westmont, NJ, 08108. Tel: 856-671-6800. Fax: 856-671-6801. p. 1543

Rethard, Ann, Asst Libr Dir, Cat, Haltom City Public Library, 4809 Haltom Rd, Haltom City, TX, 76117-3622. Tel: 817-222-7792. Fax: 817-834-1446. p. 2330

Rethlefsen, Melissa, Librn, Mayo Foundation, 200 First St SW, Rochester, MN, 55905. Tel: 507-284-3893. Fax: 507-266-4065. p. 1272

Rethman, Mary Lou, Head, Ref, Indian River County Library System, 1600 21st St, Vero Beach, FL, 32960. Tel: 772-770-5060. Fax: 772-770-5066. p. 501

Retkwa, Jean, Adult Serv, Woodbridge Public Library, George Frederick Plaza, Woodbridge, NJ, 07095. Tel: 732-634-4450. p. 1545

Retseck, Chris, Librn, Lake County Public Library, Munster Branch, 8701 Calumet Ave, Munster, IN, 46321-2526. Tel: 219-836-8450. Fax: 219-836-5694. p. 764

Rettig, Chris, Librn, Lake County Public Library, Black Oak, 5921 W 25th Ave, Gary, IN, 46406-3024. Tel: 219-844-8809. Fax: 219-844-5824. p. 763

Rettig, Chris, Br Mgr, Lake County Public Library, Griffith Branch, 940 N Broad St, Griffith, IN, 46319-1528. Tel: 219-838-2825. p. 764

Rettig, James, Dir & Assoc Dean for Info Serv, United States Naval Academy, 589 McNair Rd, Annapolis, MD, 21402-5029. Tel: 410-293-6900. Fax: 410-293-6909. p. 1011

Rettig, Jeanne, Br Mgr, Public Library of Cincinnati & Hamilton County, Oakley, 4033 Gilmore Ave, Cincinnati, OH, 45209. Tel: 513-369-6038. Fax: 513-369-6055. p. 1872

Rettinger, Elise, Librn, Mercer Human Resource Consulting, 1981 McGill College Ave, Ste 800, Montreal, QC, H3A 3T5, CANADA. Tel: 514-285-1802. Fax: 514-285-8831. p. 2899

Rettinger, Karin, Photo Archivist, Res Spec, Marshall County Historical Society Library, 123 N Michigan St, Plymouth, IN, 46563. Tel: 574-936-2306. Fax: 574-936-9306. p. 773

Retzlaff, Karen, Librn, Carnegie Regional Library, Aneta Public, 11995 19th St NE, Aneta, ND, 58212. Tel: 701-326-4235. p. 1842

Retzlaff, Marci, ILL, Youth Serv, Norfolk Public Library, 308 Prospect Ave, Norfolk, NE, 68701-4138. Tel: 402-844-2109. Fax: 402-844-2102. p. 1410

Retzlaff, Vickie, Librn, Grant County Library, Harrison & Grant St, Hyannis, NE, 69350. Tel: 308-458-2218. Fax: 308-458-2485. p. 1402

Reuben, Julie, ILL Coordr, California State University, Stanislaus, One University Circle, Turlock, CA, 95382. p. 277

Reucroft, Margaret, Adult Serv, Westwood Public Library, 668 High St, Westwood, MA, 02090. Tel: 781-326-7562. Fax: 781-326-5383. p. 1139

Reuland, Mary, Dir, Snow Library, 67 Main St, Orleans, MA, 02653-2413. Tel: 508-240-3760. Fax: 508-255-5701. p. 1116

Reusing, Patricia, Dir, St Barnabas Medical Center, 94 Old Short Hills Rd, Livingston, NJ, 07039. Tel: 973-322-5050. Fax: 973-322-5279. p. 1496

Reuter, Pat, Curator, Canadian County Historical Museum Library, 300 S Grand Ave, El Reno, OK, 73036. Tel: 405-262-5121. p. 1962

Reutty, Michele, Dir, Rockaway Township Free Public Library, 61 Mount Hope Rd, Rockaway, NJ, 07866. Tel: 973-627-2344. Fax: 973-627-7658. p. 1527

Revell, Donna, Br Mgr, Wellington County Library, Hillsburgh Branch, 98B Main St, Hillsburgh, ON, N0B 1Z0, CANADA. Tel: 519-855-4010. Fax: 519-855-4873. p. 2805

Revels, Chris, In Charge, Kings Mountain National Military Park Library, 2625 Park Rd, Blacksburg, SC, 29702. Tel: 864-936-7921. Fax: 864-936-9897. p. 2182

Revels, Mary Beth, Dir, St Joseph Public Library, 927 Felix St, Saint Joseph, MO, 64501-2799. Tel: 816-232-7729. Fax: 816-279-3372. p. 1352

Revennaugh, Tanna, Ref Librn, Atlanta-Fulton Public Library System, Northeast-Spruill Oaks Regional Library, 9560 Spruill Rd, Alpharetta, GA, 30022. Tel: 770-360-8820. Fax: 770-360-8823. p. 512

Revere, Judy, Asst Librn, Keyport Free Public Library, 109 Broad St, Keyport, NJ, 07735. Tel: 732-264-0543. Fax: 732-264-0875. p. 1493

Revie, Gretchen, Ref Librn, Lawrence University, 113 S Lawe St, Appleton, WI, 54911-5683. Fax: 920-832-6967. p. 2578

Revilla, Vicente, Ref & Instruction, Borough of Manhattan Community College Library, 199 Chambers St, New York, NY, 10007. Tel: 212-220-1498. Fax: 212-748-7466. p. 1671

Rexford, Victoria, Br Mgr, Timberland Regional Library, North Mason, 23081 NE State Rte 3, Belfair, WA, 98528-9334. Tel: 360-275-3232. Fax: 360-275-6999. p. 2543

Rexin, Betty, Tech Serv, Davis & Co, 666 Burrard St, Ste 2800, Vancouver, BC, V6C 2Z7, CANADA. Tel: 604-643-6425. Fax: 604-605-3598. p. 2740

Rexon, Deborah, Librn, Pennco Tech Library, 3815 Otter St, Bristol, PA, 19007. Tel: 215-824-3200. Fax: 215-785-1945. p. 2037

Rexwinkle, Eva, Librn, Edna Public Library, 105 N Delaware, Edna, KS, 67342. Tel: 620-922-3470. p. 864

Reyes, Christine, Asst Librn, Saint Joseph's Medical Center Library, 1800 N California St, Stockton, CA, 95213. Tel: 209-467-6332. Fax: 209-461-5098. p. 272

Reyes, Dawn, Ch, Arlington Public Library System, Lake Arlington, 4000 W Green Oaks Blvd, Arlington, TX, 76016-4442. Tel: 817-478-3762. Fax: 817-561-9823. p. 2276

Reyes, Estella, ILL, Alhambra Public Library, 101 S First St, Alhambra, CA, 91801-3432. Tel: 626-570-5008. Fax: 626-457-1104. p. 120

Reyes, Gisel, Info Spec, USDA Forest Service, Jardin Botanico Sur, 1201 Calle Ceiba, San Juan, PR, 00926-1119. Tel: 787-766-5335, Ext 350. Fax: 787-766-6302. p. 2678

Reyes, Misty, Bus & Human Res Mgr, Cherokee Regional Library System, 305 S Duke St, LaFayette, GA, 30728-2936. Tel: 706-638-2992. Fax: 706-638-3979. p. 538

Reyes, Patty, Operations Dir, Fort Vancouver Regional Library District, 1007 E Mill Plain Blvd, Vancouver, WA, 98663. Tel: 360-695-1561. Fax: 360-693-2681. p. 2546

Reyes, Rachel, Librn, Abiquiu Public Library, 29 Abiquiu Pueblo, County Rd 187, Abiquiu, NM, 87510. Tel: 505-685-4884. Fax: 505-685-0754. p. 1547

Reyes, Rachel, Acq, McAllen Memorial Library, 601 N Main, McAllen, TX, 78501-4666. Tel: 956-688-3300. Fax: 956-688-3301. p. 2360

Reyes, Roger, Bus Mgr, Suffolk Cooperative Library System, 627 N Sunrise Service Rd, Bellport, NY, 11713. Tel: 631-286-1600. Fax: 631-286-1647. p. 1580

Reyes-Gavilan, Richard, Dir & Chief Librn, Brooklyn Public Library, Grand Army Plaza, Brooklyn, NY, 11238-5698. Tel: 718-230-2100. Fax: 718-398-3947. p. 1590

Reylek, Melina, Commun Librn, Black Canyon City Community Library, 34701 S Old Black Canyon Hwy, Black Canyon City, AZ, 85324. Tel: 623-374-5866. Fax: 623-374-0465. p. 58

Reyna, Greysi, Asst Dir, Ramirez Libr, University of Texas Health Science Center at San Antonio Libraries, 7703 Floyd Curl Dr, MSC 7940, San Antonio, TX, 78229-3900. Tel: 210-567-2400. Fax: 210-567-2490. p. 2383

Reynard, Colleen, Librn, Southeast Regional Library, Indian Head Branch, 419 Grand Ave, Indian Head, SK, S0G 2K0, CANADA. Tel: 306-695-3922. p. 2930

Reynertson, Donna, Head, Circ, Itasca Community Library, 500 W Irving Park Rd, Itasca, IL, 60143. Tel: 630-773-1699. Fax: 630-773-1707. p. 658

Reynold, Lisa, Outreach Serv Librn, Lee College Library, 150 Lee Dr, Baytown, TX, 77520. Tel: 281-425-6379. Fax: 281-425-6557. p. 2286

Reynolds, Angela, Libr Supvr-Popular Libr, Allegheny Wesleyan College Library, 2161 Woodsdale Rd, Salem, OH, 44460. Tel: 330-337-6403. Fax: 330-337-6255. p. 1933

Reynolds, Annie, Librn, Kaslo & District Public Library, 413 Fourth St, Kaslo, BC, V0G 1M0, CANADA. Tel: 250-353-2942. p. 2730

Reynolds, Barbara, Head, Circ, Patchogue-Medford Library, 54-60 E Main St, Patchogue, NY, 11772. Tel: 631-654-4700, Ext 215. Fax: 631-289-3999. p. 1715

Reynolds, Barry, Coordr, Patrick Henry Community College, 645 Patriot Ave, Martinsville, VA, 24115. Tel: 276-656-0276. Fax: 276-656-0327. p. 2478

Reynolds, Beth, Ch, Norwich Public Library, 368 Main St, Norwich, VT, 05055-9453. Tel: 802-649-1184. Fax: 802-649-3470. p. 2431

Reynolds, Bonnie, Ch, Midland Public Library, 320 King St, Midland, ON, L4R 3M6, CANADA. Tel: 705-526-4216. Fax: 705-526-1474. p. 2821

Reynolds, Brian, Asst Br Mgr, Louisville Free Public Library, Shawnee, 3912 W Broadway, Louisville, KY, 40211. Tel: 502-574-1722. Fax: 502-776-9983. p. 924

Reynolds, Brian A, Dir, San Luis Obispo County Library, 995 Palm St, San Luis Obispo, CA, 93401. Tel: 805-781-5774. Fax: 805-781-1320. p. 253

Reynolds, Carol, Librn, Marian & Ralph Feffer Library, 10460 N 56th St, Scottsdale, AZ, 85253. Tel: 480-951-0323. Fax: 480-951-7150. p. 80

Reynolds, Celia, Coordr, ILL, Coordr, Ref (Info Serv), University of North Alabama, One Harrison Plaza, Box 5028, Florence, AL, 35632-0001. Tel: 256-765-4625. Fax: 256-765-4438. p. 17

Reynolds, Charles, Head of Libr, University of Michigan, Music Library, School of Music, 3239 Moore Bldg, Ann Arbor, MI, 48109-2085. Tel: 734-764-2512. Fax: 734-764-5097. p. 1153

Reynolds, Cheryl, Circ Serv, Lock Haven University of Pennsylvania, 401 N Fairview Ave, Lock Haven, PA, 17745-2390. Tel: 570-484-2365. Fax: 570-484-2506. p. 2082

Reynolds, Christy, Br Mgr, Cecil County Public Library, Chesapeake City Branch, 2527 Augustine Herman Hwy, Chesapeake City, MD, 21915. Tel: 410-996-1134. p. 1027

Reynolds, Claudia, Ref Librn, Rumford Public Library, 56 Rumford Ave, Rumford, ME, 04276-1919. Tel: 207-364-3661. Fax: 207-364-7296. p. 999

Reynolds, Cynthia, Librn, Rasmussen College, 6000 E State St, 4th Flr, Rockford, IL, 61108. Tel: 815-316-4800, Ext 4841. Fax: 815-316-4801. p. 697

Reynolds, Danielle, Ref Librn, Neligh Public Library, 710 Main St, Neligh, NE, 68756-1246. Tel: 402-887-5140. Fax: 402-887-4530. p. 1409

Reynolds, Debbie A, Dir, Lamar Public Library, 102 E Parmenter St, Lamar, CO, 81052-3239. Tel: 719-336-4632. Fax: 719-336-1294. p. 316

Reynolds, Ellen, Pub & Outreach Serv Librn, Pioneer Library System, 2557 State Rte 21, Canandaigua, NY, 14424. Tel: 585-394-8260. Fax: 585-394-1935. p. 1601

Reynolds, Geoffrey D, Dir, Hope College, The Joint Archives of Holland, Theil Research Ctr, Nine E Tenth St, Holland, MI, 49423-3513. Tel: 616-395-7798. Fax: 616-395-7197. p. 1190

Reynolds, Heather, Youth Serv, Park City Library, 1255 Park Ave, Park City, UT, 84060. Tel: 435-615-5603. Fax: 435-615-4903. p. 2410

Reynolds, Jamie, Dir, Edison College, 26300 Airport Rd, Punta Gorda, FL, 33950. Tel: 941-637-5644. Fax: 941-637-3501. p. 485

Reynolds, Jane, Dir of Libr Serv, Dallas Christian College, 2700 Christian Pkwy, Dallas, TX, 75234. Tel: 972-241-3371. Fax: 972-241-8021. p. 2305

Reynolds, Janet, Asst Librn, Ch, Tech Serv, Linn County Library District No 2, 209 N Broadway, La Cygne, KS, 66040. Tel: 913-757-2151. Fax: 913-757-2405. p. 877

Reynolds, Jeffrey, Dir, Waterville Public Library, 206 White St, Waterville, NY, 13480. Tel: 315-841-4651. Fax: 315-841-4258. p. 1764

Reynolds, Jonathan, Talking Bks Libr Mgr, Jacksonville Public Library, Talking Books/Special Needs Library, 303 N Laura St, Conference Level, Jacksonville, FL, 32202. Tel: 904-630-1999. p. 454

Reynolds, Judith K, Dir, Meigs County - Decatur Public Library, 120 E Memorial Dr, Decatur, TN, 37322. Tel: 423-334-3332. Fax: 423-334-1816. p. 2232

Reynolds, Karen, Adult Ref Librn, Atlanta-Fulton Public Library System, Sandy Springs Regional Library, 395 Mount Vernon Hwy, Sandy Springs, GA, 30328. Tel: 404-303-6130. Fax: 404-303-6133. p. 512

Reynolds, Kathy, Dir, Southern Union State Community College, Valley Campus, 321 Fob James Dr, Valley, AL, 36854. Tel: 334-756-4151. Fax: 334-756-5183. p. 40

Reynolds, Kathy E, Dir, Southern Union State Community College, 750 Robert St, Wadley, AL, 36276. Tel: 256-395-2211, Ext 5130. Fax: 256-395-2215. p. 40

Reynolds, Kathy E, Dir, Southern Union State Community College, Opelika Campus, 1701 Lafayette Pkwy, Opelika, AL, 36801. Tel: 334-745-6437. Fax: 334-749-5505. p. 40

Reynolds, Keri, Asst Librn, Stanstead College, 450 Dufferin St, Stanstead, QC, J0B 3E0, CANADA. Tel: 819-876-7891, Ext 278. Fax: 819-876-5891. p. 2913

Reynolds, Kevin, Asst Univ Librn, Pub Serv, University of the South, 735 University Ave, Sewanee, TN, 37383-1000. Tel: 931-598-1366. Fax: 931-598-1702. p. 2265

Reynolds, Kevin, Head, Ref, University of the South, 735 University Ave, Sewanee, TN, 37383-1000. Tel: 931-598-1366. Fax: 931-598-1702. p. 2265

Reynolds, Leslie, Dir, Texas A&M University Libraries, West Campus Library, Olsen Blvd, Bldg 1511, College Station, TX, 77843-5001. Tel: 979-458-0138. Fax: 979-862-2977. p. 2299

Reynolds, Leslie J, Dir, Texas A&M University Libraries, Policy Sciences & Economics, 1016 Annenberg Presidential Conference Ctr, College Station, TX, 77843-5002. Tel: 979-862-3544. Fax: 979-862-3791. p. 2299

Reynolds, Linda, Asst Dir, Dir, E Tex Res Ctr, Spec Coll & Archives Librn, Stephen F Austin State University, 1936 North St, Nacogdoches, TX, 75962. Tel: 936-468-1562. Fax: 936-468-7610. p. 2364

Reynolds, Lynda, Dir, Stillwater Public Library, 1107 S Duck St, Stillwater, OK, 74074. Tel: 405-372-3633, Ext 101. Fax: 405-624-0552. p. 1978

Reynolds, Margaret, Exec Dir, Association of Book Publishers of British Columbia Library, 107-100 W Pender St, Vancouver, BC, V6B 1R8, CANADA. Tel: 604-684-0228. Fax: 604-684-5788. p. 2740

Reynolds, Martha, Instrul Serv Librn, Pub Serv, Berry College, 2277 Martha Berry Hwy, Mount Berry, GA, 30149. Tel: 706-236-1705. p. 546

Reynolds, Mary, Cat, Ref Librn, Regis College Library, 100 Wellesley St W, Toronto, ON, M5S 2Z5, CANADA. Tel: 416-922-5474, Ext 233. Fax: 416-922-2898. p. 2857

Reynolds, Melissa, Regional Librn, Volusia County Public Library, Deltona Regional, 2150 Eustace Ave, Deltona, FL, 32725. Tel: 386-789-7207. Fax: 386-789-7211. p. 436

Reynolds, Patricia, Circ, East Lyme Public Library, Inc, 39 Society Rd, Niantic, CT, 06357-1100. Tel: 860-739-6926. Fax: 860-691-0020. p. 361

Reynolds, Penny, Circ/Interlibr Serv Librn, University of Texas at Tyler Library, 3900 University Blvd, Tyler, TX, 75799. Tel: 903-566-7342. Fax: 903-566-2513. p. 2394

Reynolds, Peter, Mgr, Info Serv, American Booksellers Association, 200 White Plains Rd, Tarrytown, NY, 10591. Tel: 914-591-2665. Fax: 914-591-2720. p. 1754

Reynolds, Renee, Dir, Searcy Hospital Patient Library, 325 E Coy S Hwy, Mount Vernon, AL, 36560. Tel: 251-662-6700, 251-662-6842. Fax: 251-829-9075. p. 32

Reynolds, Robert, Dr, Exec Dir, Pennsylvania German Heritage Library, 22 Luckenbill Rd, Kutztown, PA, 19530. Tel: 484-646-4165. Fax: 610-683-4638. p. 2075

Reynolds, Sharon, Librn, Decatur Herald & Review Library, 601 E William St, Decatur, IL, 62525-1190. Tel: 217-421-6979. Fax: 217-421-7965. p. 633

Reynolds, Stephanie D, Dr, Asst Prof, University of Kentucky, 320 Little Library Bldg, Lexington, KY, 40506-0224. Tel: 859-257-5894. Fax: 859-257-4205. p. 2966

Reynolds, Teresa W, Br Mgr, Kinchafoonee Regional Library System, Clay County Library, 208 S Hancock St, Fort Gaines, GA, 39851-9506. Tel: 229-768-2248. Fax: 229-768-2248. p. 528

Reynolds, Todd S, Dir, Coyle Free Library, 102 N Main St, Chambersburg, PA, 17201-1676. Tel: 717-263-1054, Ext 204. Fax: 717-709-0288. p. 2043

Reynolds, Toni, Br Mgr, Cass District Library, Howard, 2341 Yankee St, Niles, MI, 49120. Tel: 269-684-1680. Fax: 269-684-1680. p. 1161

Reynolds, Trent, Dir, United States Marine Corps, Bldg AS-201, Jacksonville, NC, 28540. Tel: 910-449-6715. Fax: 910-449-6037. p. 1803

Reynolds, Veronica, Coll Develop Librn, New City Free Library, 220 N Main St, New City, NY, 10956. Tel: 845-634-4997. p. 1665

Reynolds, Wendy, Client Serv Mgr, Ontario Legislative Library, Legislative Bldg, Queen's Park, Toronto, ON, M7A 1A9, CANADA. Tel: 416-325-2145. Fax: 416-325-3925. p. 2856

Reynolds-Pope, Tonia, Ref Serv, NASA, Library, Bldg 21, Code 272, Greenbelt, MD, 20771. Tel: 301-286-4746. Fax: 301-286-1755. p. 1030

Reynoso, Pedro, Instruction & Outreach, Chabot College Library, 25555 Hesperian Blvd, Hayward, CA, 94545. Tel: 510-723-6767. p. 157

Rezabek, Charlene, Tech Serv, Monroe Community College, LeRoy V Good Library, 1000 E Henrietta Rd, Rochester, NY, 14692. Tel: 585-292-2330. p. 1730

Rezai-Atrie, Mariam, Librn, Saint Augustine's Seminary Library, 2661 Kingston Rd, Scarborough, ON, M1M 1M3, CANADA. Tel: 416-261-7207, Ext 271. Fax: 416-261-2529. p. 2841

Rezak, Sheila A, Educ Librn, Purdue University, 2200 169th St, Hammond, IN, 46323-2094. Tel: 219-989-2677. Fax: 219-989-2070. p. 747

Rezeau, Michelle, Acq, Ser, BCC-UCF Joint Use Library, 1519 Clearlake Rd, Cocoa, FL, 32922. Tel: 321-433-7189. Fax: 321-433-7678. p. 433

Rezek, Yvonne, Chair, Ref & Res Serv, Grant MacEwan University Library, 10700 104th Ave, Edmonton, AB, T5J 4S2, CANADA. Tel: 780-497-5850. Fax: 780-497-5895. p. 2701

Rezendes, Karin, Supvr, Coll Develop, Lancaster Public Library, 125 N Duke St, Lancaster, PA, 17602-2883. Tel: 717-394-2651. Fax: 717-394-3083. p. 2077

Rezendes, Robert, Access Serv Librn, Bristol Community College, 777 Elsbree St, Fall River, MA, 02720. Tel: 508-678-2811. Fax: 508-730-3270. p. 1088

Reznicek, Amy, Librn, North Bend Public Library, 140 E Eighth St, North Bend, NE, 68649. Tel: 402-652-8356. Fax: 402-652-8356. p. 1410

Reznick, Carolyn, Dir, Ruth Keeler Memorial Library, 276 Titicus Rd, North Salem, NY, 10560-1708. Tel: 914-669-5161. Fax: 914-669-5173. p. 1707

Reznik, Olive, Librn, Legal Aid Society, 199 Water St, New York, NY, 10038. Tel: 212-298-5258; 212-577-3300. Fax: 212-693-1149. p. 1685

Rhan, Cathy, Supvr, Central Kansas Library System, Subregional Library for the Blind & Physically Handicapped, 1409 Williams St, Great Bend, KS, 67530-4020. Tel: 620-792-4865. Fax: 620-792-5495. p. 869

Rhea, Ada, Dir, Bean Station Public Library, 895 Broadway Dr, Bean Station, TN, 37708. Tel: 865-993-3068. Fax: 865-993-3068. p. 2224

Rheault, Ghyslaine, Info Spec, Banque Nationale du Canada, 600 rue de la Gauchetiere ouest, Montreal, QC, H3B 4L2, CANADA. Tel: 514-394-5000, Ext 5470. Fax: 514-394-4167. p. 2888

Rheault, Rejeanne, Dir, Bibliotheque Paul-O-Trepanier, 11 rue Dufferin, Granby, QC, J2G 4W5, CANADA. Tel: 450-776-8310. Fax: 450-776-8313. p. 2884

Rhees, David, Dir, The Bakken - A Library & Museum of Electricity in Life, 3537 Zenith Ave S, Minneapolis, MN, 55416. Tel: 612-926-3878, Ext 213. Fax: 612-927-7265. p. 1259

Rheiner, Cheryl, Ref, West Deptford Public Library, 420 Crown Point Rd, West Deptford, NJ, 08086-9598. Tel: 856-845-5593. Fax: 856-848-3689. p. 1541

Rheinheimer, Teresa, Libr Dir, Middlebury Community Public Library, 101 E Winslow St, Middlebury, IN, 46540. Tel: 574-825-5601. Fax: 574-825-5150. p. 764

Rheins, Susan Miller, Dir, Colorado Agency for Jewish Education Library, 300 S Dahlia St, Ste 101, Denver, CO, 80246. Tel: 303-321-3191, Ext 220. Fax: 303-321-5436. p. 299

Rhim, Choonhee, Chairperson, East Los Angeles College, 1301 Avenida Cesar Chaves, Monterey Park, CA, 91754. Tel: 323-265-8758. Fax: 323-267-3714. p. 190

Rhine, Stephanie, Libr Assoc, Lima Public Library, Elida Branch, 200 W Main St, Elida, OH, 45807. Tel: 419-339-6097. Fax: 419-339-6554. p. 1910

Rho, Jinja, Supvr, Govt Docs, Dallas Baptist University, 3000 Mountain Creek Pkwy, Dallas, TX, 75211-9299. Tel: 214-333-5214. Fax: 214-333-5323. p. 2305

Rhoades, Carol, Coordr, Acq, Bradley University, 1501 W Bradley Ave, Peoria, IL, 61625. Tel: 309-677-2850. Fax: 309-677-2558. p. 690

Rhoades, Jennifer, Br Mgr, Western Sullivan Public Library, 19 Center St, Jeffersonville, NY, 12748. Tel: 845-482-4350. Fax: 845-482-3092. p. 1647

Rhoades, Teresa, Tech Serv, Bartholomew County Public Library, 536 Fifth St, Columbus, IN, 47201-6225. Tel: 812-379-1255. Fax: 812-379-1275. p. 733

Rhoads, Bertha, Librn, Udall Public Library, 109 E First St, Udall, KS, 67146. Tel: 620-782-3435. p. 898

Rhoads, Carol, Librn, Missouri Department of Corrections, Tipton Correctional Center, 619 N Osage Ave, Tipton, MO, 65081-8038. Tel: 660-433-2031, Ext 2325. Fax: 660-433-2804. p. 1335

Rhoads, Kirsen, Commun Relations Coordr, Milanof-Schock Library, 1184 Anderson Ferry Rd, Mount Joy, PA, 17552. Tel: 717-653-1510. Fax: 717-653-6590. p. 2093

Rhoads, Mary, Asst Dir, Ch, Johnson County Library, 171 N Adams Ave, Buffalo, WY, 82834. Tel: 307-684-5546. Fax: 307-684-7888. p. 2651

Rhoda, Christopher, VPres for Info Serv, Thomas College Library, 180 W River Rd, Waterville, ME, 04901. Tel: 207-859-1204. p. 1005

Rhode, Kathee, Dir, Lower Macungie Library, 3450 Brookside Rd, Macungie, PA, 18062. Tel: 610-966-6864. Fax: 610-965-0384. p. 2083

Rhode, Shirley, Dir, Lowell Public Library, 105 N River St, Lowell, WI, 53557. Tel: 920-927-5700. Fax: 920-927-5700. p. 2605

Rhoden, Brian, Br Librn, London Public Library, R E Crouch Branch, 550 Hamilton Rd, London, ON, N5Z 1S4, CANADA. Tel: 519-673-0111. p. 2818

Rhodes, Angela, Asst Librn, Electronic Res & Syst Librn, State University of New York, PO Box 902, Morrisville, NY, 13408-0902. Tel: 315-684-6055. Fax: 315-684-6115. p. 1663

Rhodes, Barbara, Dir, Collinsville Memorial Public Library District, 408 W Main St, Collinsville, IL, 62234. Tel: 618-344-1112. Fax: 618-345-6401. p. 630

Rhodes, Chris, Circ, United States Air Force, 744 Douhet Dr, Bldg 4244, Barksdale AFB, LA, 71110. Tel: 318-456-4182. Fax: 318-752-0509. p. 941

Rhodes, Christen, Br Mgr, Mid-Continent Public Library, Boardwalk Branch, 8656 N Ambassador Dr, Kansas City, MO, 64154-2558. Tel: 816-741-9011. Fax: 816-741-4793. p. 1332

Rhodes, D, Br Mgr, New Orleans Public Library, Rosa Keller Branch, 4300 S Broad, New Orleans, LA, 70125. Tel: 504-596-2660. Fax: 504-596-2678. p. 962

Rhodes, Don, Tech Serv, Holmes County Public Library, 303 N J Harvey Etheridge, Bonifay, FL, 32425. Tel: 850-547-3573. Fax: 850-547-2801. p. 429

Rhodes, Eileen, Dir, Libr & Info Serv, Lincoln College Library, 1760 Mapleton Ave, Suffield, CT, 06078-1463. Tel: 860-668-3515. Fax: 860-668-7369. p. 372

Rhodes, Gloria L, Outreach Librn, San Diego State University Library & Information Access, 5500 Campanile Dr, San Diego, CA, 92182-8050. Tel: 619-594-1169. Fax: 619-594-3270. p. 237

Rhodes, Helen, Librn, Jennings City Library, Kansas Ave, Jennings, KS, 67643. Tel: 785-678-2666. Fax: 785-678-2666. p. 874

Rhodes, Jerome, Youth Serv Librn, Dolton Public Library District, 14037 Lincoln, Dolton, IL, 60419-1091. Tel: 708-849-2385. Fax: 708-841-2725. p. 637

Rhodes, Jessica, YA Librn, Franklin Township Free Public Library, 485 DeMott Lane, Somerset, NJ, 08873. Tel: 732-873-8700. Fax: 732-873-0746. p. 1529

Rhodes, Joan, Dir, Vespasian Warner Public Library District, 310 N Quincy, Clinton, IL, 61727. Tel: 217-935-5174. Fax: 217-935-4425. p. 630

Rhodes, Linda, Dir, Seminole Public Library, 424 N Main, Seminole, OK, 74868. Tel: 405-382-4221. Fax: 405-382-0050. p. 1977

Rhodes, Lois, Br Mgr, Abbeville County Library System, Calhoun Falls Branch, 409 N Tugaloo St, Calhoun Falls, SC, 29628. Tel: 864-418-8724. Fax: 864-418-8724. p. 2179

Rhodes, Naomi, Ref Serv, Dare County Library, Kill Devil Hills Branch, 400 Mustian St, Kill Devil Hills, NC, 27948. Tel: 252-441-4331. Fax: 252-441-0608. p. 1808

Rhodes, Nina, Cat, Tech Serv, West New York Public Library, 425 60th St, West New York, NJ, 07093-2211. Tel: 201-295-5135. Fax: 201-662-1473. p. 1541

Rhodes, Pam, Circ, Oak Hill Public Library, 226 S Front St, Oak Hill, OH, 45656. Tel: 740-682-6457. Fax: 740-682-3522. p. 1924

Rhodes, Pamela, Br Mgr, Los Angeles Public Library System, Granada Hills Branch, 10640 Petit Ave, Granada Hills, CA, 91344-6305. Tel: 818-368-5687. Fax: 818-756-9286. p. 173

Rhodes, Teresa, Mkt, Outreach Coordr, Salem Public Library, 821 E State St, Salem, OH, 44460-2298. Tel: 330-332-0042. Fax: 330-332-4488. p. 1934

Rholes, Julia M, Dean of Libr, University of Mississippi, One Library Loop, University, MS, 38677. Tel: 662-915-5672. Fax: 662-915-5734. p. 1316

Rhue, Monika, Dir of Libr Serv, Johnson C Smith University, 100 Beatties Ford Rd, Charlotte, NC, 28216. Tel: 704-371-6730. Fax: 704-378-1191. p. 1783

Rhutasel, Neal, Res Project Mgr, Group Technology Library & Information Services, 150 W Warrenville Rd, MC F1, Naperville, IL, 60563. Tel: 630-420-5784. Fax: 630-420-3697. p. 678

Rhyins, Lorna, Adult & Teen Serv, Edith Wheeler Memorial Library, 733 Monroe Tpk, Monroe, CT, 06468. Tel: 203-452-2850. Fax: 203-261-3359. p. 353

Rhymer, Elizabeth, Dir, Freedom Public Library, 38 Old Portland Rd, Freedom, NH, 03836. Tel: 603-539-5176. Fax: 603-539-1098. p. 1448

Rhynard, Kathy, Govt Doc Spec, Valparaiso University, 1410 Chapel Dr, Valparaiso, IN, 46383-6493. Tel: 219-464-6121. p. 783

Rhys, Lynne, Pub Serv, John Marshall Law School, 1422 W Peachtree St NW, Atlanta, GA, 30309. Tel: 404-872-3593. Fax: 404-873-3802. p. 516

Rhys, Will, Librn, Goodspeed Musicals, 20 Norwich Rd, East Haddam, CT, 06423-1344. Tel: 860-873-8664, Ext 373. Fax: 860-873-2329. p. 337

Rials, Mattie J, Ch, Pike-Amite-Walthall Library System, 1022 Virginia Ave, McComb, MS, 39648. Tel: 601-684-2661, Ext 12. Fax: 601-250-1213. p. 1308

Rian, Jennifer, Innovative Serv Librn, Luther College, 700 College Dr, Decorah, IA, 52101. Tel: 563-387-1790. Fax: 563-387-1657. p. 807

Rian, Jennifer, Educ Coordr, Ironworld Discovery Center, 801 SW Hwy 169, Ste 1, Chisholm, MN, 55719. Tel: 218-254-1236. Fax: 218-254-7971. p. 1245

Ribant Payne, Kathryn, Programming Spec, Sterling Heights Public Library, 40255 Dodge Park Rd, Sterling Heights, MI, 48313-4140. Tel: 586-446-2640. Fax: 586-276-4067. p. 1229

Ribas, Mel, Mgr, Albuquerque-Bernalillo County Library System, South Valley, 3904 Isleta Blvd SW, Albuquerque, NM, 87105. Tel: 505-877-5170. Fax: 505-877-6639. p. 1548

Rible, Jim, Syst Coordr, Southern Oregon University, 1250 Siskiyou Blvd, Ashland, OR, 97520-5076. Tel: 541-552-6821. Fax: 541-552-6429. p. 1990

Riboldi, Ellen, Dir, Ventress Memorial Library, 15 Library Plaza, Marshfield, MA, 02050. Tel: 781-834-5535. Fax: 781-837-8362. p. 1103

Ricard, Theresa, Br Mgr, Martin County Library, Truman Branch, 101 E Ciro St, Truman, MN, 56088-2017. Tel: 507-776-2717. p. 1250

Ricci, Ann, Br Mgr, Warwick Public Library, Conimicut, 55 Beach Ave, Warwick, RI, 02889. Tel: 401-737-6546. p. 2177

Ricci, Charle, ILL, Eastern Shore Public Library, 23610 Front St, Accomac, VA, 23301. Tel: 757-678-7800, 757-787-3400, 757-824-5151. Fax: 757-787-2241. p. 2443

Ricci, Lee J, Dir, Community Library, 110 Union St, Cobleskill, NY, 12043-3830. Tel: 518-234-7897. Fax: 518-234-1163. p. 1608

Ricci, Shelby, Tech Serv, Palatine Public Library District, 700 N North Ct, Palatine, IL, 60067-8159. Tel: 847-358-5881. p. 686

Riccio, Darsie, Dept Adminr, Dartmouth College Library, Sanborn English Library, HB 6032 Sanborn House, Hanover, NH, 03755-3525. Tel: 603-646-3993. Fax: 603-646-2159. p. 1450

Ricciuti, Heather, The Mary Cutlip Dir of Libr & Learning Res, Bethany College, Mary Cutlip Center for Library & Information Technology, 300 Main St, Bethany, WV, 26032. Tel: 304-829-7321. Fax: 304-829-7333. p. 2554

Rice, Amy, Instruction/Cat Librn, Mount Vernon Nazarene University, 800 Martinsburg Rd, Mount Vernon, OH, 43050-9500. Tel: 740-397-9000, Ext 4240. Fax: 740-397-8847. p. 1919

Rice, Amy C, Coordr, Tech Syst & Serv, Whitworth University, 300 W Hawthorne Rd, Spokane, WA, 99251-0001. Tel: 509-777-4480. Fax: 509-777-3231. p. 2538

Rice, Ann-Margaret, Head, Adult/Teen Serv, Head, Circ, Goshen Public Library, 601 S Fifth St, Goshen, IN, 46526-3994. Tel: 574-533-9531. Fax: 574-533-5211. p. 746

Rice, Anna, Media Serv, Allan Hancock College, 800 S College Dr, Santa Maria, CA, 93454. Tel: 805-922-6966, Ext 3224. Fax: 805-922-3763. p. 265

Rice, Anne Layton, Libr Adminr, Monroe County Public Library, 700 Fleming St, Key West, FL, 33040. Tel: 305-292-3594. Fax: 305-295-3626. p. 456

Rice, Barbara, Br Mgr, Fairfax County Public Library, Martha Washington Branch, 6614 Fort Hunt Rd, Alexandria, VA, 22307-1799. Tel: 703-768-6700. p. 2461

Rice, Bennie, Br Mgr, Pointe Coupee Parish Library, Innis Branch, 4306 Nichols Ave, Innis, LA, 70747. Tel: 225-492-2632. Fax: 225-492-2632. p. 964

Rice, Beverly, Circ Librn, Ingalls Memorial Library, 203 Main St, Rindge, NH, 03461. Tel: 603-899-3303. Fax: 603-899-5797. p. 1463

Rice, Brenda, Bibliographer, University of Chicago Library, John Crerar Library, 5730 S Ellis Ave, Chicago, IL, 60637. Tel: 773-702-8774. p. 626

Rice, Brittany, Co-Pres, Maryland Association of Health Science Librarians, VA Medical HealthCare System, Medical Library, Ten N Greene St, Baltimore, MD, 21201. Tel: 301-896-3199. p. 2944

Rice, Christine P, Librn, Coraopolis Memorial Library, 601 School St, Coraopolis, PA, 15108-1196. Tel: 412-264-3502. Fax: 412-269-8982. p. 2047

Rice, Connie, Doc Delivery & Mail Serv Mgr, Roger & Peggy Madigan Library, 999 Hagan Way, Williamsport, PA, 17701. Tel: 570-327-4523. Fax: 570-327-4503. p. 2156

Rice, Curt, Ref Librn, Indiana Wesleyan University, 4201 S Washington St, Marion, IN, 46953. Tel: 219-769-5173. Fax: 765-677-2676. p. 762

Rice, Debbie, Librn, Central Christian Church Library, 205 E Short St, Lexington, KY, 40507. Tel: 859-233-1551. Fax: 859-252-9287. p. 920

Rice, Forrest, Librn, Community United Methodist Church Library, 20 N Center St, Naperville, IL, 60540-4611. Tel: 630-355-1483. Fax: 630-778-2011. p. 678

Rice, Fran, Dir, Info Syst & Digital Access, University of Dayton Libraries, 300 College Park Dr, Dayton, OH, 45469-1360. Tel: 937-229-4221. Fax: 937-229-4215. p. 1894

Rice, Gitta, Res Librn, Ontario Ministry of Finance, 95 Grosvenor St, 1st Flr, Toronto, ON, M7A 1Y8, CANADA. Tel: 416-325-1254. Fax: 416-325-1212. p. 2856

Rice, Jamie Kingman, Res Librn, Maine Historical Society, 489 Congress St, Portland, ME, 04101-3498. Tel: 207-774-1822. Fax: 207-775-4301. p. 996

Rice, Jane, Asst Librn, Moultonborough Public Library, Four Holland St, Moultonborough, NH, 03254. Tel: 603-476-8895. p. 1458

Rice, Janet, Youth Serv Librn, Grimes Public Library, 200 N James, Grimes, IA, 50111. Tel: 515-986-3551. Fax: 515-986-9553. p. 819

Rice, Jeanne, Dir, Norwalk Public Library, 101 Railroad St, Norwalk, WI, 54648. Tel: 608-823-7473. p. 2626

Rice, Jeff, Br Mgr, Palm Beach County Library System, Tequesta Branch, 461 Old Dixie Hwy N, Tequesta, FL, 33469. Tel: 561-746-5970. Fax: 561-744-7251. p. 503

Rice, Jim, Ref & Pub Serv Librn, Walla Walla Community College Library, 500 Tausick Way, Walla Walla, WA, 99362-9267. Tel: 509-527-4294. Fax: 509-527-4480. p. 2547

Rice, Joseph, Dir, Brown Deer Public Library, 5600 W Bradley Rd, Brown Deer, WI, 53223-3510. Tel: 414-357-0106. Fax: 414-354-8081. p. 2583

Rice, Judy, Libr Mgr, Metropolitan Community College, Longview Campus Library, 500 SW Longview Rd, Lee's Summit, MO, 64081-2105. Tel: 816-604-2278. Fax: 816-604-2087. p. 1339

Rice, Linda, Dir, Crockett Memorial Library, 258 E Church St, Alamo, TN, 38001-1108. Tel: 731-696-4220. Fax: 731-696-5107. p. 2223

Rice, Linda K, Dir, Bosler Free Library, 158 W High St, Carlisle, PA, 17013-2988. Tel: 717-243-4642. Fax: 717-243-8281. p. 2041

Rice, Lisa, Librn, Annapolis Valley Regional Library, Wolfville Branch, 21 Elm Ave, Wolfville, NS, B4P 2A1, CANADA. Tel: 902-542-5760. Fax: 902-542-5780. p. 2778

Rice, Lisa R, Dir, Warren County Public Library, 1225 State St, Bowling Green, KY, 42101. Tel: 270-781-4882. Fax: 270-781-7323. p. 907

Rice, M, Dir, Mayville Public Library, 52 Center Ave N, Mayville, ND, 58257. Tel: 701-788-3388. p. 1846

Rice, Marilyn, Tech Serv Librn, Fairfield Public Library, 1080 Old Post Rd, Fairfield, CT, 06824. Tel: 203-256-3155. p. 339

Rice, Mary, Librn, Charles County Circuit Court, 200 Charles St, La Plata, MD, 20646. Tel: 301-932-3322. Fax: 301-932-3324. p. 1033

Rice, Mary Lou, Librn, Blood Center of Wisconsin, 638 N 18th St, Milwaukee, WI, 53233-2121. Tel: 414-937-6112. Fax: 414-937-6332. p. 2617

Rice, Michael, Electronic Res Coordr, Messiah College, One College Ave, Ste 3002, Mechanicsburg, PA, 17055. Tel: 717-691-6006, Ext 7069. Fax: 717-691-2356. p. 2087

Rice, Molly, Dir, Beardstown Houston Memorial Library, 13 Boulevard Rd, Beardstown, IL, 62618-8119. Tel: 217-323-4204. Fax: 217-323-4217. p. 593

Rice, Rosemarie, Asst Dir, Tompkins County Public Library, 101 E Green St, Ithaca, NY, 14850-5613. Tel: 607-272-4557, Ext 233. Fax: 607-272-8111. p. 1643

Rice, Rosemary, Libr Asst, East Mississippi Community College, Golden Triangle Campus Library, 8731 S Frontage Rd, Mayhew, MS, 39753. Tel: 662-243-1914. Fax: 662-243-1952. p. 1314

Rice, Ruchie, Coordr, Info Tech & Tech Serv, Fairfield County District Library, 219 N Broad St, Lancaster, OH, 43130-3098. Tel: 740-653-2745. Fax: 740-653-4199. p. 1908

Rice, Sherwin, Dir, Libr Serv, Bladen Community College Library, 7418 NC HWY 41 W, Dublin, NC, 28332. Tel: 910-879-5641. Fax: 910-879-5642. p. 1787

Rice, Susan, Libr Coordr, Montrose Regional Library District, Naturita Branch, Naturita, CO, 81422. Tel: 970-865-2848. Fax: 970-865-2157. p. 319

Rice, Susan, Br Mgr, Akron-Summit County Public Library, Portage Lakes, 4261 Manchester Rd, Akron, OH, 44319-2659. Tel: 330-644-7050. Fax: 330-644-7050. p. 1852

Rice, Suzanne S, Asst Dean, Pub Serv, Ball State University Libraries, 2000 W University Ave, Muncie, IN, 47306-1099. Tel: 765-285-1307. Fax: 765-285-2644. p. 766

Rice, Tammy, Dir, Sheldon Public Library District, 125 N Fifth, Sheldon, IL, 60966. Tel: 815-429-3521. Fax: 815-429-3804. p. 702

Rice, Ted, Ch, Atlanta-Fulton Public Library System, Northeast-Spruill Oaks Regional Library, 9560 Spruill Rd, Alpharetta, GA, 30022. Tel: 770-360-8820. Fax: 770-360-8823. p. 512

Rice-Gutierrez, Rosemary D, Dir, Bridgeport Public Library, 3399 Williamson Rd, Bridgeport, MI, 48601. Tel: 989-777-6030. Fax: 989-777-6880. p. 1159

Rice-Lively, Mary Lynn, Assoc Dean, University of Texas at Austin, One University Sta, D7000, Austin, TX, 78712-0390. Tel: 512-471-3821. Fax: 512-471-3971. p. 2975

Rich, Allison, Cat, John Carter Brown Library, Brown University, George & Brown Sts, Providence, RI, 02912. Tel: 401-863-2725. Fax: 401-863-3477. p. 2171

Rich, Barbara A, Dir, Earle A Rainwater Memorial Library, 124 Ninth Ave SW, Childersburg, AL, 35044. Tel: 256-378-7239. Fax: 256-378-7287. p. 12

Rich, Barrett, Ch, Weston County Public Library, 23 W Main St, Newcastle, WY, 82701. Tel: 307-746-2206. Fax: 307-746-2218. p. 2658

Rich, Becka, Dep Dir, Nova Southeastern University Libraries, Shepard Broad Law Center Library, 3305 College Ave, Fort Lauderdale, FL, 33314. Tel: 954-262-6100. p. 444

Rich, Carol, Head, Tech Serv, Ellensburg Public Library, 209 N Ruby St, Ellensburg, WA, 98926-3397. Tel: 509-962-7258. Fax: 509-962-7295. p. 2514

Rich, Chris, Br Mgr, Clermont County Public Library, Goshen Branch, 6678 State Rte 132, Goshen, OH, 45122. Tel: 513-722-1221. Fax: 513-722-2158. p. 1858

Rich, Deborah, Syst Librn, Thomas Crane Public Library, 40 Washington St, Quincy, MA, 02269-9164. Tel: 617-376-1300. Fax: 617-376-1313. p. 1119

Rich, Hallie, Mkt Dir, Cuyahoga County Public Library, 2111 Snow Rd, Parma, OH, 44134-2728. Tel: 216-398-1800. Fax: 216-398-1748. p. 1927

Rich, Leslie, Assoc Dir, Tech, New York University School of Law, 40 Washington Sq S, New York, NY, 10012-1099. Tel: 212-998-6300. Fax: 212-995-4559. p. 1695

Rich, Linda, Chair, Libr Teaching & Learning, Coordr of Ref Serv, Bowling Green State University Libraries, 204 Wm T Jerome Library, Bowling Green, OH, 43403-0170. p. 1861

Rich, Marcia, Dir, Acton Memorial Library, 486 Main St, Acton, MA, 01720. Tel: 978-264-9641. Fax: 978-635-0073. p. 1047

Rich, Margie, Librn, Waynesville Township Library, 303 E Second St, Waynesville, IL, 61778. Tel: 217-949-5111. Fax: 217-949-5111. p. 716

Rich, Robert, Asst Librn, Ref, Vanderbilt University, Anne Potter Wilson Music Library, Blair School of Music, 2400 Blakemore Ave, Nashville, TN, 37212. Tel: 615-322-7171. Fax: 615-343-0050. p. 2261

Rich, Suzanne, Dir, Underwood Memorial Library, 2006 Main St, Fayette, ME, 04349. Tel: 207-685-3778. p. 985

Rich, Suzy, Head Librn, Tri-Area Library, Two W Main St, Jamestown, IN, 46147. Tel: 765-676-6190. p. 756

Richard, Bonnie, Br Mgr, Vermilion Parish Library, Delcambre Branch, 206 W Main St, Delcambre, LA, 70528-2918. Tel: 337-685-2388. Fax: 337-685-2388. p. 939

Richard, Bonnie, Br Mgr, Iberia Parish Library, Delcambre Branch, 206 W Main St, Delcambre, LA, 70528-2918. Tel: 337-685-2388. Fax: 337-685-2388. p. 959

Richard, Cynthia, In Charge, Hospital Center of Val D'or, 725 Sixth St, Val-d'Or, QC, J9P 3Y1, CANADA. Tel: 819-825-5858. Fax: 819-825-7919. p. 2914

Richard, Debbi, Dir, Distance Educ, Dallas Baptist University, 3000 Mountain Creek Pkwy, Dallas, TX, 75211-9299. Tel: 214-333-5225. Fax: 214-333-5323. p. 2305

Richard, Gisele, Asst Librn, Canada Department of Fisheries & Oceans, 343 Ave Universite, Moncton, NB, E1C 9B6, CANADA. Tel: 506-851-6254. Fax: 506-851-2766. p. 2765

Richard, Gwendolyn, Chairperson, Houston Community College Northeast College, Codwell Campus Library, 555 Community College Dr, Houston, TX, 77013-6127. Tel: 713-718-8354. Fax: 713-718-8330. p. 2337

Richard, Gwendolyn, Chairperson, Houston Community College Northeast College, North Forest Campus Library, 7525 Tidwell Rd, Houston, TX, 77016-4413. Tel: 713-635-0427. p. 2338

Richard, Gwendolyn, Dir, Libr Serv, Houston Community College Northeast College, Northline Library, 8001 Fulton St, Houston, TX, 77022. Tel: 713-718-8045. Fax: 713-718-8063. p. 2338

Richard, Gwendolyn, NE Dir of Libr Serv, Houston Community College Northeast College, Pinemont Campus Library, 1265 Pinemont, Houston, TX, 77018-1303. Tel: 713-718-8443. Fax: 713-718-8438. p. 2338

Richard, Jack, Dir, Almond Tea Gallery Library, 2250 Front St, Cuyahoga Falls, OH, 44221. Tel: 330-929-1575. Fax: 330-929-2285. p. 1892

Richard, Jane, Project Mgr, Wisconsin Public Library Consortium, c/o South Central Library System, 5250 E Terrace Dr, Madison, WI, 53718. p. 2958

Richard, Jennifer, Head, Res Serv, Acadia University, 50 Acadia St, Wolfville, NS, B4P 2R6, CANADA. Tel: 902-585-1249. Fax: 902-585-1748. p. 2786

Richard, Leslie, Circ, Calhoun Community College, Hwy 31 N, Decatur, AL, 35609. Tel: 256-306-2769. Fax: 256-306-2780. p. 14

Richard, Nathalie, Ref Librn, Universite de Moncton, 415 Ave de l'Universite, Moncton, NB, E1A 3E9, CANADA. Tel: 506-858-4012. Fax: 506-858-4086. p. 2766

Richard, Nicole, Libr Mgr, Chaleur Library Region, Atholville Public Library, 275 rue Notre-Dame, Atholville, NB, E3N 4T1, CANADA. Tel: 506-789-2914. Fax: 506-789-2056. p. 2761

Richard, Pat, Librn, Sandisfield Free Public Library, 23 Sandisfield Rd, Sandisfield, MA, 01255. Tel: 413-258-4966. p. 1122

Richard, Patricia, Br Mgr, Oakland Public Library, Elmhurst, 1427 88th Ave, Oakland, CA, 94621. Tel: 510-615-5727. Fax: 510-615-5869. p. 198

Richard, Patricia, Supvr, Circ, Lee Library Association, 100 Main St, Lee, MA, 01238-1688. Tel: 413-243-0385. Fax: 413-243-0381. p. 1098

Richard, Sarah, Libr Mgr, York Library Region, Stanley Community Library, 28 Bridge St, Unit 2, Stanley, NB, E6B 1B2, CANADA. Tel: 506-367-2492. Fax: 506-367-2764. p. 2765

Richard, Stacey, Librn, Kaw City Public Library, 900 Morgan Sq E, Kaw City, OK, 74641. Tel: 580-269-1317. Fax: 580-269-2957. p. 1966

Richard, Susan M, Head, Ref, University of Louisiana at Lafayette, PO Box 40199, Lafayette, LA, 70504-0199. Tel: 337-482-1169. Fax: 337-482-6399. p. 953

Richards, Anne, Circ Serv Mgr, Grandview Heights Public Library, 1685 W First Ave, Columbus, OH, 43212. Tel: 614-486-2951. Fax: 614-481-7021. p. 1886

Richards, Anne, Media Spec, Sweet Briar College, 134 Chapel Rd, Sweet Briar, VA, 24595-1200. Tel: 434-381-6138. Fax: 434-381-6173. p. 2497

Richards, Barbara, Head, Circ, Stow-Munroe Falls Public Library, 3512 Darrow Rd, Stow, OH, 44224. Tel: 330-688-3295. p. 1937

Richards, Charlene, Human Res Mgr, King County Library System, 960 Newport Way NW, Issaquah, WA, 98027. Tel: 425-369-3207. Fax: 425-369-3255. p. 2516

Richards, Charri, Librn, New Mexico State Library, 356-D E Ninth St, Cimarron, NM, 87714. Tel: 575-376-2474. Fax: 575-376-2433. p. 1553

Richards, Cynthia, Pub Serv, University of the Virgin Islands, Two John Brewers Bay, Saint Thomas, VI, 00802-9990. Tel: 340-693-1369. Fax: 340-693-1365. p. 2679

Richards, David, Assoc Prof, Missouri State University, Duane G Meyer Library, 901 S National Ave, Springfield, MO, 65897. Tel: 417-836-4525. Fax: 417-836-4764. p. 2968

Richards, David E, Head, Spec Coll, Missouri State University, 850 S John Q Hammons Pkwy, Springfield, MO, 65807. Tel: 417-836-4299. Fax: 417-836-4764. p. 1367

Richards, David L, PhD, Dr, Dir, University of Maine, 56 Norridgewock Ave, Skowhegan, ME, 04976. Tel: 207-474-7133. Fax: 207-474-8878. p. 1001

Richards, Diane, Coll Develop, Minnesota State University, Mankato, ML3097, Mankato, MN, 56001. Tel: 507-389-5952. Fax: 507-389-5155. p. 1257

Richards, Hoy A, Librn, Richards & Associates Library, 4723 Stonebriar Circle, College Station, TX, 77842. Tel: 979-985-5990. Fax: 979-690-6196. p. 2298

Richards, Ian, Sr Commun Libr Mgr, Contra Costa County Library, El Sobrante Branch, 4191 Appian Way, El Sobrante, CA, 94803-2298. Tel: 510-374-3991. Fax: 510-222-4137. p. 209

Richards, Ian, Sr Commun Libr Mgr, Contra Costa County Library, Pinole Library, 2935 Pinole Valley Rd, Pinole, CA, 94564-1494. Tel: 510-758-2741. Fax: 510-758-2745. p. 209

Richards, James, Br Mgr, Southeast Regional Library, 49 Bison Ave, Weyburn, SK, S4H 0H9, CANADA. Tel: 306-848-3102. Fax: 306-842-2665. p. 2929

Richards, Jamie, Tech Coordr, Huntington Woods Public Library, 26415 Scotia, Huntington Woods, MI, 48070-1198. Tel: 248-543-9720. Fax: 248-543-2559. p. 1193

Richards, Janice, Dir, Oglala Lakota College, Pahin Sinte College Center, PO Box 220, Porcupine, SD, 57772. Tel: 605-867-5404. Fax: 605-867-1242. p. 2214

Richards, Jean A, Librn, Saratoga Hospital, 211 Church St, Saratoga Springs, NY, 12866. Tel: 518-583-8301. Fax: 518-580-4285. p. 1738

Richards, Joan, Hist Coll Librn, Lancaster Historical Commission, Town Hall, 695 Main St, Lancaster, MA, 01523-2245. Tel: 978-368-1162. Fax: 978-368-4005. p. 1097

Richards, Kelly, Br Operations Mgr, Genesee District Library, G-4195 W Pasadena Ave, Flint, MI, 48504. Tel: 810-230-3330, 230-3331. Fax: 810-732-1161. p. 1179

Richards, Kimberly, Archivist, Dir, Historical Society of Berks County, 940 Centre Ave, Reading, PA, 19601. Tel: 610-375-4375. Fax: 610-375-4376. p. 2133

Richards, Larry, Head Librn, Free Library of Philadelphia, Interlibrary Loan, 1901 Vine St, Philadelphia, PA, 19103-1189. Tel: 215-686-5360. Fax: 215-563-3628. p. 2108

Richards, Louise M, Head Librn, University of Washington Libraries, Fisheries-Oceanography, 151 Oceanography Teaching Bldg, Box 357952, Seattle, WA, 98195-7952. Tel: 206-543-4279. Fax: 206-543-4909. p. 2534

Richards, Marion, Mgr, The World Bank Group Library, 1818 H St NW, MSN MC-C3-220, Washington, DC, 20433. Tel: 202-473-2000, 202-473-8670. Fax: 202-522-1160. p. 423

Richards, Nancy, Head, Circ, Head, Tech Serv, Memorial Hall Library, Two N Main St, Andover, MA, 01810. Tel: 978-623-8401. Fax: 978-623-8407. p. 1049

Richards, Patricia, Ch, Kenton County Public Library, 502 Scott Blvd, Covington, KY, 41011. Tel: 859-962-4060. Fax: 859-962-4096. p. 910

Richards, Roberta, Fac Librn-Rock Creek Campus, Portland Community College Library, 12000 SW 49th AV, Portland, OR, 97219. Tel: 971-722-7374. Fax: 971-722-8397. p. 2013

Richards, Roberta, Coordr, Portland Area Library System, Port Community College, SYLIB202, Portland, OR, 97219. Tel: 503-977-4571. Fax: 503-977-4977. p. 2953

Richards, Rosemary, Librn, Transportation Safety Board of Canada Library, Place du Centre, 200 Promenade du Portage, 4th Flr, Gatineau, QC, K1A 1K8, CANADA. Tel: 819-994-8020. Fax: 819-997-2239. p. 2884

Richards, Samuel, Librn, United States Air Force, 72nd FSS/FSDL, Bldg 5702, 6120 Arnold St, Tinker AFB, OK, 73145-8101. Tel: 405-734-2626. Fax: 405-734-9511. p. 1980

Richards, Serenity, Br Mgr, Librn, Albert Carlton-Cashiers Community Library, 249 Frank Allen Rd, Cashiers, NC, 28717-9561. Tel: 828-743-0215. Fax: 828-743-1638. p. 1780

Richards, Stacy, Head Librn, Westside Public Library, 5151 Walnut Grove Rd, Walnut Grove, AL, 35990. Tel: 205-589-6699. Fax: 205-589-6699. p. 40

Richards, Susan, Dir, Northwest College, 231 W Sixth St, Powell, WY, 82435. Tel: 307-754-6207. Fax: 307-754-6010. p. 2659

Richards, William, Coll Develop Librn, Georgia College & State University, 320 N Wayne St, Milledgeville, GA, 31061-3397. Tel: 478-445-4047. Fax: 478-445-6847. p. 544

Richards-Jones, Jane, Asst Librn, Frost Free Library, 28 Jaffrey Rd, Marlborough, NH, 03455. Tel: 603-876-4479. Fax: 603-876-4479. p. 1457

Richardson, Angela, Circ, ILL, Illinois Mathematics & Science Academy, 1500 W Sullivan Rd, Aurora, IL, 60506-1000. Tel: 630-907-5920. Fax: 630-907-5004. p. 591

Richardson, Athena, Teen Serv, Goodnight Memorial Library, 203 S Main St, Franklin, KY, 42134. Tel: 270-586-8397. Fax: 270-586-8397. p. 914

Richardson, Beth, Libr Mgr, Alix Public Library, PO Box 69, Alix, AB, T0C 0B0, CANADA. Tel: 403-747-3233. p. 2683

Richardson, Carlotta, Libr Mgr, Walla Walla County Rural Library District, Touchet Community Library, 161 Hanson Rd, Touchet, WA, 99360. Tel: 509-394-2329. Fax: 509-394-2329. p. 2547

Richardson, Carol, Dir, Bridgman Public Library, 4460 Lake St, Bridgman, MI, 49106-9510. Tel: 269-465-3663. Fax: 269-465-3249. p. 1159

Richardson, Carolyn, Librn, Oldham County Public Library, 914 Main St, Vega, TX, 79092. Tel: 806-267-2635. Fax: 806-267-2635. p. 2395

Richardson, Cheryl, Librn, Yavapai County Free Library District, 172 E Merritt St, Ste E, Prescott, AZ, 86301. Tel: 928-771-3191. Fax: 928-771-3113. p. 79

Richardson, Christopher, Dir, Libr Serv, Southern Virginia University, One University Hill Dr, Buena Vista, VA, 24416. Tel: 540-261-8440. Fax: 540-261-8496. p. 2453

Richardson, Darlene, Dir, Leon Public Library, 200 W First St, Leon, IA, 50144. Tel: 641-446-3746, 641-446-6332. Fax: 641-446-3746. p. 827

Richardson, David, Mgr, Libr Serv, Whitehead Institute for Biomedical Research, Nine Cambridge Ctr, Cambridge, MA, 02142. Tel: 617-258-5132. Fax: 617-324-0266. p. 1079

Richardson, Dawn, Ch, Tombigbee Regional Library System, 338 Commerce, West Point, MS, 39773. Tel: 662-494-4872. Fax: 662-494-0300. p. 1317

Richardson, Donald, Asst Dir, Syst & Tech, Worcester Polytechnic Institute, 100 Institute Rd, Worcester, MA, 01609-2280. Tel: 508-831-5410. Fax: 508-831-5829. p. 1145

Richardson, Donna, Chief Librn, Dalhousie University, Sexton Design & Technology Library, 1360 Barrington St, Halifax, NS, B3J 2X4, CANADA. Tel: 902-494-3979. Fax: 902-494-6089. p. 2780

Richardson, Eliana, Asst Librn, Kemper-Newton Regional Library System, Union Public, 101 Peachtree, Union, MS, 39365-2617. Tel: 601-774-5096. Fax: 601-774-5096. p. 1316

Richardson, Elizabeth, ILL, Kent State University Libraries, 1125 Risman Dr, Kent, OH, 44242. Tel: 330-672-2177. Fax: 330-672-4811. p. 1907

Richardson, Elizabeth J, Info Serv Librn, Tufts University, 145 Harrison Ave, Boston, MA, 02111-1843. Tel: 617-636-4039. p. 1068

Richardson, Ellen, Ref Librn, University of South Carolina, Coleman Karesh Law Library, USC Law Ctr, 701 Main St, Columbia, SC, 29208. Tel: 803-777-5942. Fax: 803-777-9405. p. 2190

Richardson, Estella, Head, Access Serv, Georgia Institute of Technology Library, 704 Cherry St, Atlanta, GA, 30332-0900. Tel: 404-894-4501. Fax: 404-894-6084. p. 515

Richardson, Evallou, Tech Serv, Sheffield Public Library, 316 N Montgomery Ave, Sheffield, AL, 35660. Tel: 256-386-5633. Fax: 256-386-5608. p. 36

Richardson, Evelyn, Genealogy Librn, Logan County Public Library, 201 W Sixth St, Russellville, KY, 42276. Tel: 270-726-6129. Fax: 270-726-6127. p. 934

Richardson, Faye, Librn, Columbus-Lowndes Public Library, Crawford Public, Main St, Crawford, MS, 39743. Tel: 662-272-5144. p. 1297

Richardson, Gail P, Dir, Audubon Public Library, 401 N Park Pl, Audubon, IA, 50025-1258. Tel: 712-563-3301. Fax: 712-563-2580. p. 795

Richardson, Heidi, Br Mgr, Harford County Public Library, Whiteford Branch, 2407 Whiteford Rd, Whiteford, MD, 21160-1218. Tel: 410-452-8831. Fax: 410-638-3610. p. 1020

Richardson, Helena, Youth Serv Librn, Fauquier County Public Library, Bealeton Branch, 10877 Willow Dr N, Bealeton, VA, 22712. Tel: 540-439-9728. Fax: 540-439-9731. p. 2501

Richardson, Helene, Cat, Murray Public Library, 166 E 5300 South, Murray, UT, 84107-6075. Tel: 801-264-2580. Fax: 801-264-2586. p. 2408

Richardson, Jackie, Br Mgr, Uncle Remus Regional Library System, Greene County Library, 610 S Main St, Greensboro, GA, 30642. Tel: 706-453-7276. Fax: 706-453-0500. p. 542

Richardson, Janice, Head Librn, Oregon County Library District, 20 Court Sq, Alton, MO, 65606. Tel: 417-778-6414. Fax: 417-778-6414. p. 1319

Richardson, Jeanne, Chief Officer, Coll Serv, Scholarly Communications Officer, Arizona State University Libraries, Collections & Scholarly Communication, PO Box 871006, Tempe, AZ, 85287-1006. Tel: 480-965-5250. Fax: 480-965-9127. p. 83

Richardson, Jeanne, Coll & Scholarly Communications, Arizona State University Libraries, 300 E Orange Mall Dr, Tempe, AZ, 85287-1006. Tel: 480-965-5345. Fax: 480-965-9169. p. 83

Richardson, Kathleen, Tech Serv Librn, Bluegrass Community & Technical College, Oswald Bldg, 470 Cooper Dr, Lexington, KY, 40506-0235. Tel: 859-246-6386. Fax: 859-246-4675. p. 920

Richardson, Kelley, Youth Serv, Hancock County Public Library, 240 Court Sq, Hawesville, KY, 42348. Tel: 270-927-6760. Fax: 270-927-6847. p. 916

Richardson, Lakishia, Spec Coll, Tuskegee University, Hollis Burke Frissell Bldg, 1200 W Old Montgomery Rd, Tuskegee, AL, 36088. Tel: 334-727-8890. Fax: 334-727-9282. p. 39

Richardson, Larry, Dir, Operations, National Museum of American Jewish Military History Library, 1811 R St NW, Washington, DC, 20009. Tel: 202-265-6280. Fax: 202-234-5662. p. 410

Richardson, Laura, Genealogy & Outreach Librn, Ogden Farmers' Library, 269 Ogden Center Rd, Spencerport, NY, 14559. Tel: 585-617-6181. Fax: 585-352-3406. p. 1746

Richardson, Laurie, Tech Serv, United States Army, Aviation Center Library, Bldg 212,Fifth Ave & Novosal, Fort Rucker, AL, 36362-5000. Tel: 334-255-3695. Fax: 334-255-1567. p. 18

Richardson, Lillian, Mgr, Albuquerque-Bernalillo County Library System, Taylor Ranch, 5700 Bogart NW, Albuquerque, NM, 87120. Tel: 505-897-8816. Fax: 505-897-8813. p. 1548

Richardson, Lori, Head, Youth Serv, Michigan City Public Library, 100 E Fourth St, Michigan City, IN, 46360-3393. Tel: 219-873-3045. Fax: 219-873-3068. p. 764

Richardson, Lynn, Tech Serv, Allerton Public Library District, 201 N State St, Monticello, IL, 61856. Tel: 217-762-4676. Fax: 217-762-2021. p. 675

Richardson, Martha, Affiliate Serv/Develop Librn, Northeast Georgia Regional Library System, 204 Ellison St, Ste F, Clarkesville, GA, 30523. Tel: 706-754-0416. Fax: 706-754-0420. p. 524

Richardson, Mary, Coll Develop, Librn, Sausalito Public Library, 420 Litho St, Sausalito, CA, 94965-1933. Tel: 415-289-4121. Fax: 415-331-7943. p. 268

Richardson, Mary, Librn, Warren County Public Library District, Alexis Branch, 102 W Broadway, Alexis, IL, 61412. Tel: 309-482-6109. p. 675

Richardson, Mary Ellen, Asst Dir, Corning Public Library, 613 Pine St, Corning, AR, 72422. Tel: 870-857-3453. Fax: 870-857-3453. p. 97

Richardson, Mike, Dr, Chair, Southeastern Louisiana University, PO Box 10549, Hammond, LA, 70402. Tel: 985-549-5713. Fax: 985-549-5712. p. 2966

Richardson, Miriam, Asst Librn, Eldorado Memorial Public Library District, 1001 Grant St, Eldorado, IL, 62930-1714. Tel: 618-273-7922. Fax: 618-273-4402. p. 640

Richardson, Pam, Circ Asst, Rivier College, 420 S Main St, Nashua, NH, 03060-5086. Tel: 603-897-8256. Fax: 603-897-8889. p. 1459

Richardson, Rick, Librn, San Juan County Library, 80 N Main St, Monticello, UT, 84535. Tel: 435-587-2281. Fax: 435-587-2281. p. 2408

Richardson, Samuel, Ref, Walters State Community College, 500 S Davy Crockett Pkwy, Morristown, TN, 37813-6899. Tel: 423-585-2600. Fax: 423-585-6959. p. 2253

Richardson, Samuel S, Head, Circ, University of Tennessee at Martin, Ten Wayne Fisher Dr, Martin, TN, 38238. Tel: 731-881-7061. Fax: 731-881-7074. p. 2246

Richardson, Shirley A, Circ, Latt Maxcy Memorial Library, 15 N Magnolia Ave, Frostproof, FL, 33843. Tel: 863-635-7857. Fax: 863-635-8502. p. 447

Richardson, Stacey, Ch, Hudson Library & Historical Society, 96 Library St, Hudson, OH, 44236-5122. Tel: 330-653-6658. Fax: 330-650-3373. p. 1905

Richardson, Steve, Ref, Furman University Libraries, 3300 Poinsett Hwy, Greenville, SC, 29613-4100. Tel: 864-294-3227. Fax: 864-294-3004. p. 2195

Richardson, Sylvia, Mgr, Ad Serv, Palos Verdes Library District, 701 Silver Spur Rd, Rolling Hills Estates, CA, 90274. Tel: 310-377-9584, Ext 210. Fax: 310-541-6807. p. 219

Richardson, Tami, Adult Serv Mgr, Rice Lake Public Library, Two E Marshall St, Rice Lake, WI, 54868. Tel: 715-234-4861. Fax: 715-234-5026. p. 2633

Richardson, Theodora, Librn, G Werber Bryan Psychiatric Hospital Library, 220 Faison Dr, Columbia, SC, 29203. Tel: 803-935-5395. Fax: 803-935-7110. p. 2187

Richardson, Theodore, Librn, United States Department of the Interior, 801 N Quincy St, Arlington, VA, 22203. Tel: 703-235-3804. Fax: 703-235-9014. p. 2450

Richardson, Valerie, Libr Found Dir, Springfield-Greene County Library District, 4653 S Campbell, Springfield, MO, 65810-1723. Tel: 417-882-0714. Fax: 417-883-9348. p. 1367

Richardson, Virginia, Asst Librn, William D Weeks Memorial Library, 128 Main St, Lancaster, NH, 03584-3031. Tel: 603-788-3352. Fax: 603-788-3203. p. 1453

Richardson, Yunhwa, ILL/Circ Supvr, United States Army, Fort Wainwright Post Library, Santiago Ave, Bldg 3700, Fort Wainwright, AK, 99703-6600. Tel: 907-353-2642. Fax: 907-353-2609. p. 48

Richardson-Rogers, Karen, Managing Librn, Columbus Metropolitan Library, Linden Branch, 2223 Cleveland Ave, Columbus, OH, 43211. Tel: 614-645-2275. Fax: 614-479-4239. p. 1884

Richbourg, Elizabeth, Librn, Baptist Hospital, 1000 W Moreno St, Pensacola, FL, 32501. Tel: 850-434-4877. p. 481

Richel, Lynee, Bibliog Instruction Coordr, County College of Morris, 214 Center Grove Rd, Randolph, NJ, 07869-2086. p. 1525

Richer, Claudine, Dir, Bibliotheque Marie-Antoinette-Foucher, 185 rue Du Palais, Saint Jerome, QC, J7Z 1X6, CANADA. Tel: 450-432-1226. Fax: 450-436-1211. p. 2908

Richer, Linda S, Mgr, W E Upjohn Institute for Employment Research, 300 S Westnedge Ave, Kalamazoo, MI, 49007-4686. Tel: 269-343-5541, Ext 418. Fax: 269-343-3308. p. 1198

Richert, Christina, Supvr, Essex County Library, Amherstburg Branch, 232 Sandwich St S, Amherstburg, ON, N9V 2A4, CANADA. Tel: 226-946-1549, Ext 240. p. 2804

Richert, Paul, Dir, University of Akron Libraries, School of Law Library, 150 University Ave, Akron, OH, 44325. Tel: 330-972-7330. Fax: 330-972-4948. p. 1853

Riches, Jonathan S, Librn, Reformed Episcopal Seminary, 826 Second Ave, Blue Bell, PA, 19422. Tel: 610-292-9852. Fax: 610-292-9853. p. 2036

Richey, Cynthia K, Dir, Mt Lebanon Public Library, 16 Castle Shannon Blvd, Pittsburgh, PA, 15228-2252. Tel: 412-531-1912. Fax: 412-531-1161. p. 2126

Richey, Judith, In Charge, Indiana Women's Prison Library, 401 N Randolph St, Indianapolis, IN, 46201. Tel: 317-639-2671, Ext 248. Fax: 317-684-9643. p. 753

Richey, Robin, Ch, Eureka Public Library District, 202 S Main St, Eureka, IL, 61530. Tel: 309-467-2922. Fax: 309-467-3527. p. 643

Richey, Sandi, Circ Supvr, ILL, University of Redlands, 1200 E Colton Ave, Redlands, CA, 92374-3758. Tel: 909-748-8022. Fax: 909-335-5392. p. 215

Richi, Edward, Curator, Printed Mat, Delaware Historical Society Research Library, 505 N Market St, Wilmington, DE, 19801. Tel: 302-295-2387. Fax: 302-655-7844. p. 387

Richie, Richard P, Curator, Yale University Library, Sterling Memorial Library, 120 High St, New Haven, CT, 06520. Tel: 203-432-1858. Fax: 203-432-1294. p. 359

Richie, Shannon G, Ref, Pennsylvania State University, 76 University Dr, Hazleton, PA, 18202-8025. Tel: 570-450-3562. Fax: 570-450-3128. p. 2068

Richins, Karen, Librn, Palo Alto City Library, Mitchell Park, 3700 Middlefield Rd, Palo Alto, CA, 94303. Fax: 650-856-7925. p. 204

Richlan, Robert, Ref, Fairleigh Dickinson University, 285 Madison Ave, M-LAO-03, Madison, NJ, 07940. Tel: 973-443-8515. Fax: 973-443-8525. p. 1497

Richland, Lisa, Dir, Floyd Memorial Library, 539 First St, Greenport, NY, 11944-1399. Tel: 631-477-0660. Fax: 631-477-2647. p. 1631

Richman, Jana Stevens, Dir, Polytechnic Institute of NYU, Five MetroTech Ctr, Brooklyn, NY, 11201-3840. Tel: 718-260-3530. Fax: 718-260-3756. p. 1594

Richmire, Beverley, Br Support, Stormont, Dundas & Glengarry County Library, Morrisburg Branch, 28 Ottawa St (Arena SE), Morrisburg, ON, K0C 1X0, CANADA. Tel: 613-543-3384. Fax: 613-543-2427. p. 2802

Richmire, Beverley, Br Support, Stormont, Dundas & Glengarry County Library, Williamsburg Branch, 4296 Main St (Hwy 31), Williamsburg, ON, K0C 2H0, CANADA. Tel: 613-535-2185. p. 2802

Richmond, Andrew, Dir, Rye Public Library, 581 Washington Rd, Rye, NH, 03870. Tel: 603-964-8401. Fax: 603-964-7065. p. 1464

Richmond, Camille, Asst Librn, Madisonville Community College, 2000 College Dr, Madisonville, KY, 42431. Tel: 270-824-1721. Fax: 270-825-8553. p. 928

Richmond, David, Dep Dir, Mgt Serv, Phoenix Public Library, 1221 N Central Ave, Phoenix, AZ, 85004-1820. Tel: 602-262-4636. Fax: 602-261-8836. p. 76

Richmond, Ginny, Dir, Hibbing Public Library, 2020 E Fifth Ave, Hibbing, MN, 55746-1702. Tel: 218-362-5959. Fax: 218-312-9779. p. 1254

Richmond, Jeanette, Librn, Washington Metropolitan Area Transit Authority, 600 Fifth St NW, Washington, DC, 20001. Tel: 202-962-1012. Fax: 202-962-2550. p. 422

Richmond, John D, Dir, Alpha Park Public Library District, 3527 S Airport Rd, Bartonville, IL, 61607-1799. Tel: 309-697-3822. Fax: 309-697-9681. p. 592

Richmond, Larry, Br Mgr, Public Library of Cincinnati & Hamilton County, Mount Washington, 2049 Beechmont Ave, Cincinnati, OH, 45230. Tel: 513-369-6033. Fax: 513-369-6044. p. 1872

Richmond, Lisa, Dir, Wheaton College, 510 Irving Ave, Wheaton, IL, 60187-5593. Tel: 630-752-5102. Fax: 630-752-5855. p. 718

Richmond, Marsha, Dir, Oregon Trail Library District, 200 South Main St, Boardman, OR, 97818. Tel: 541-481-3365. Fax: 541-481-2668. p. 1992

Richmond, Mary, Asst Librn, Fayette County Historical Society Library, 100 N Walnut St, West Union, IA, 52175-1347. Tel: 563-422-5797. p. 852

Richmond, Patricia, Cat, Pepperdine University Libraries, 24255 Pacific Coast Hwy, Malibu, CA, 90263. Tel: 310-506-4252. Fax: 310-506-7225. p. 182

Richmond, Ron, Dir, Libr & Info Serv, Info Spec, Richmond State Hospital, 498 NW 18th St, Richmond, IN, 47374. Tel: 765-966-0511. Fax: 765-966-6993. p. 775

Richmond, Sandra, Librn I, Louisville Public Library, 951 Spruce St, Louisville, CO, 80027. Tel: 303-335-4849. Fax: 303-335-4833. p. 317

Richmond, Vernette R, Head, Circ, Oak Brook Public Library, 600 Oak Brook Rd, Oak Brook, IL, 60523. Tel: 630-368-7712. Fax: 630-368-7704, 630-990-4509. p. 683

Richner, Mary Lee, Info Spec, PPG Industries, Inc, Technical Information Center, 4325 Rosanna Dr, Allison Park, PA, 15101. Tel: 412-492-5268. Fax: 412-492-5509. p. 2128

Richter, Ingrid, Head, Syst, The New York Society Library, 53 E 79th St, New York, NY, 10075. Tel: 212-288-6900, Ext 241. Fax: 212-744-5832. p. 1694

Richter, Linda L, Libr Dir, Trenton Public Library, 118 E Indiana, Trenton, IL, 62293. Tel: 618-224-7662. Fax: 618-224-7671. p. 710

Richter, Mary, Dir, Bancroft Public Library, 208 E Ramsey St, Bancroft, IA, 50517. Tel: 515-885-2753. Fax: 515-885-2753. p. 795

Richter, Robert, Sr Librn, New York State Department of Correctional Services, 354 Hunter St, Ossining, NY, 10562. Tel: 914-941-0108. Fax: 914-941-6583. p. 1712

Richter, Shirley, Ser, Starkville-Oktibbeha County Public Library System, 326 University Dr, Starkville, MS, 39759. Tel: 662-323-2766, 662-323-2783. Fax: 662-323-9140. p. 1315

Richter, Stephanie, Libr Spec, Humboldt County Law Library, Courthouse, 825 Fourth St, RM 812, Eureka, CA, 95501. Tel: 707-476-2356. Fax: 707-445-6297. p. 147

Richter, Tedra, Ref & Libr Instruction, University of Indianapolis, 1400 E Hanna Ave, Indianapolis, IN, 46227-3697. Tel: 317-788-3268. Fax: 317-788-3275. p. 755

Richter, Wendy, Dr, Dir, Arkansas History Commission Library, One Capitol Mall, 2nd Flr, Little Rock, AR, 72201. Tel: 501-682-6901. Fax: 501-682-6916. p. 105

Richter, Will, Ref Librn, Grand Rapids Area Library, 140 NE Second St, Grand Rapids, MN, 55744-2601. Tel: 218-326-7640. Fax: 218-326-7644. p. 1253

Richtmyer, David, Sr Cat Librn, Boston College Libraries, John J Burns Library of Rare Books & Special Collections, 140 Commonwealth Ave, Chestnut Hill, MA, 02467. Tel: 617-552-0543. Fax: 617-552-2465. p. 1080

Ricigliano, Lori, Assoc Dir, Info & Access Serv, University of Puget Sound, 1500 N Warner St, Campus Mail Box 1021, Tacoma, WA, 98416-1021. Tel: 253-879-3229. Fax: 253-879-3670. p. 2541

Rickabaugh, Donna, Dir, Walled Lake City Library, 1499 E West Maple Rd, Walled Lake, MI, 48390. Tel: 248-624-3772. Fax: 248-624-0041. p. 1233

Rickard, Jennifer, Tech Serv, Carleton A Friday Memorial Library, 155 E First St, New Richmond, WI, 54017. Tel: 715-243-0431. Fax: 715-246-2691. p. 2625

Rickard, Lynne, Circ Mgr, Bloomington Public Library, 205 E Olive St, Bloomington, IL, 61701. Tel: 309-828-6091. Fax: 309-828-7312. p. 595

Rickard, Phyllis J, Dir, North Adams Community Memorial Library, 110 E Main St, North Adams, MI, 49262. Tel: 517-287-4426. p. 1214

Rickel, Becky, Libr Dir, Shiocton Public Library, W7740 Pine St, Shiocton, WI, 54170. Tel: 920-986-3933. Fax: 920-986-3743. p. 2638

Rickelman, Mary, Cataloger/Ref Librn, Coordr, Instruction, Florida Hospital College of Health Sciences, 671 Winyah Dr, Orlando, FL, 32803. Tel: 407-303-7747, Ext 6046. Fax: 407-303-9622. p. 475

Ricker, Alison Scott, Sci Librn, Oberlin College Library, Science, Science Center N174, 119 Woodland St, Oberlin, OH, 44074-1083. Tel: 440-775-8310. p. 1925

Ricker, Bev, Supvr, Extn Serv, Putnam County District Library, The Educational Service Ctr, 124 Putnam Pkwy, Ottawa, OH, 45875-1471. Tel: 419-523-3747. Fax: 419-523-6477. p. 1926

Ricker, Chris, Managing Librn, Monterey County Free Libraries, 188 Seaside Ctr, Marina, CA, 93933-2500. Tel: 831-883-7567. Fax: 831-883-7574. p. 182

Rickers, Roberta, Br Supvr, Southside Regional Library, Ripberger Public, 117 S Broad St, Kenbridge, VA, 23944. Tel: 434-676-3456. Fax: 434-676-3211. p. 2452

Rickerson, Carla T, Head, Spec Coll, University of Washington Libraries, Allen Library, 4th Flr, Rm 482, Box 352900, Seattle, WA, 98195-2900. Tel: 206-685-4480. Fax: 206-543-1931. p. 2533

Rickerson, Jim, Head, Tech Serv, Statesboro Regional Public Libraries, 124 S Main St, Statesboro, GA, 30458. Tel: 912-764-1333. Fax: 912-764-1348. p. 552

Rickert, Herb, Jr, Webmaster, Emerson Process Management, RA Engel Technical Ctr, 1700 12th Ave, Marshalltown, IA, 50158. Tel: 641-754-2161. Fax: 641-754-3159. p. 830

Ricketts, Amadee, Lead Librn, Youth Serv, Prescott Public Library, 215 E Goodwin St, Prescott, AZ, 86303. Tel: 928-777-1506. Fax: 928-771-5829. p. 78

Rickey, Violet, ILL/Doc Delivery Serv, Mountain Area Health Education Center, 121 Hendersonville Rd, Asheville, NC, 28803. Tel: 828-257-4446. Fax: 828-257-4712. p. 1775

Rickling, Iraida B, Univ Librn, Florida Solar Energy Center, 1679 Clearlake Rd, Cocoa, FL, 32922-5703. Tel: 321-638-1460. Fax: 321-638-1010, 321-638-1463. p. 433

Rickman, Melissa, Ref & Libr Instruction, University of Science & Arts of Oklahoma, 1901 S 17th St, Chickasha, OK, 73018. Tel: 405-574-1341. Fax: 405-574-1220. p. 1960

Rickord, Laura, Head, Circ, Gladwin County District Library, 402 James Robertson Dr, Gladwin, MI, 48624. Tel: 989-426-8221. Fax: 989-426-6958. p. 1183

Ricks, Suzanne, Librn, Eastern Idaho Technical College, 1600 S 25th E, Idaho Falls, ID, 83404. Tel: 208-524-3000, Ext 3312. Fax: 208-524-3007. p. 576

Ricotta, Denise, Ref Librn, Tech Librn, Windsor Public Library, 323 Broad St, Windsor, CT, 06095. Tel: 860-285-1922. Fax: 860-285-1889. p. 379

Riczker, Renee, Dir, West Orange Free Public Library, 46 Mount Pleasant Ave, West Orange, NJ, 07052-4903. Tel: 973-736-0198. Fax: 973-736-1655. p. 1541

Riddle, Carolyn, Cat, Big Bend Community College Library, 7662 Chanute St, Moses Lake, WA, 98837. Tel: 509-793-2350. Fax: 509-762-2402. p. 2521

Riddle, John, Head of Libr, Pennsylvania State University, One University Dr, Uniontown, PA, 15401. Tel: 724-430-4156. Fax: 724-430-4152. p. 2147

Riddle, Kathy, Libr Spec, Maysville Community & Technical College Library, Rowan Campus Library, 609 Viking Dr, Morehead, KY, 40351. Tel: 606-783-1538, Ext 66366. p. 928

Riddle, Laura, Librn, Southwest Mississippi Community College, Lakeside Dr, Summit, MS, 39666. Tel: 601-276-2004. Fax: 601-276-3748. p. 1315

Riddle, Norma, Archivist, Dir, Rec Mgt, Appalachian State University, William Leonard Eury Appalachian Collection, Belk Library, 4th Flr, 218 College St, Boone, NC, 28608. Tel: 828-262-4041. Fax: 828-262-2553. p. 1777

Riddoch, Heidi, Librn, North Bingham County District Library, 197 W Locust St, Shelley, ID, 83274-1139. Tel: 208-357-7801. Fax: 208-357-2272. p. 584

Riddoch, Heidi, Treas, Library Consortium of Eastern Idaho, 113 S Garfield, Pocatello, ID, 83204-3235. Tel: 208-357-7801. p. 2941

Ridener, Ruth, Librn, First Baptist Church of West Terre Haute Library, 205 S Fifth, West Terre Haute, IN, 47885. Tel: 812-533-2016. p. 787

Ridenour, Anthony, Exec Dir, San Diego Model Railroad Museum, 1649 El Prado, San Diego, CA, 92101. Tel: 619-696-0199. Fax: 619-696-0239. p. 235

Ridenour, Lois, Librn, Southern Illinois University Edwardsville, Campus Box 1111, 2800 College Ave, Alton, IL, 62002. Tel: 618-650-3830. Fax: 618-650-2717. p. 588

Rider, Deborah, ILL, Oil City Library, Two Central Ave, Oil City, PA, 16301-2795. Tel: 814-678-3072. Fax: 814-676-8028. p. 2100

Rider, Jimi, Supv Librn, New Hanover County Public Library, Northeast Regional Library, 1241 Military Cutoff Rd, Wilmington, NC, 28403. Tel: 910-798-6370. Fax: 910-256-1238. p. 1830

Rider, Kass, Librn, Arendtsville Library, One Chestnut St, Arendtsville, PA, 17303. Tel: 717-677-0444. Fax: 717-677-0445. p. 2029

Rider, Robin, Spec Coll Librn, University of Wisconsin-Madison, 728 State St, Madison, WI, 53706. Tel: 608-262-3193. Fax: 608-265-2754. p. 2608

Rider, Sheila, Youth Serv Coordr, Cumberland County Public Library & Information Center, 300 Maiden Lane, Fayetteville, NC, 28301-5000. Tel: 910-483-7727. Fax: 910-486-5372. p. 1792

Rider, Van, Academy Librn, Northern Marianas College, Fina Sisu Lane, Bldg O, Saipan, MP, 96950. Tel: 670-234-3690, Ext 1122. Fax: 670-234-0759. p. 2669

Ridge, Gloria, In Charge, Elko-Lander-Eureka County Library System, Jackpot Branch, 2301 Progressive Rd, Jackpot, NV, 89825. Tel: 775-755-2356. p. 1427

Ridge, Marian, Regional Dir, Kitchigami Regional Library, 310 Second St N, Pine River, MN, 56474. Tel: 218-587-2171. Fax: 218-587-4855. p. 1270

Ridgeway, Beth, Dir, Sheffield Public Library, 316 N Montgomery Ave, Sheffield, AL, 35660. Tel: 256-386-5633. Fax: 256-386-5608. p. 36

Ridgeway, Dianne, ILL, Dover Public Library, 45 S State St, Dover, DE, 19901. Tel: 302-736-7030. Fax: 302-736-5087. p. 382

Ridgeway, Jeff, Head, Ch, Washington County Free Library, 100 S Potomac St, Hagerstown, MD, 21740. Tel: 301-739-3250. Fax: 301-739-7603. p. 1031

Ridgeway, Laurie, YA Serv, Rogers Memorial Library, 91 Coopers Farm Rd, Southampton, NY, 11968. Tel: 631-283-0774. Fax: 631-287-6539. p. 1746

Ridgeway, Trish, Dir, Handley Regional Library, 100 W Piccadilly St, Winchester, VA, 22601. Tel: 540-662-9041, Ext 14. Fax: 540-662-9053. p. 2503

Ridgway, Richard, Acq Librn, Neumann College Library, One Neumann Dr, Aston, PA, 19014-1298. Tel: 610-361-5316. Fax: 610-459-1370. p. 2030

Ridinger, Robert, Bibliographer, Northern Illinois University Libraries, DeKalb, IL, 60115-2868. Tel: 815-753-1367. p. 635

Ridings, Ginger, Br Librn, Spartanburg County Public Libraries, Inman Library, 50 Mill St, Inman, SC, 29349. Tel: 864-472-8363. p. 2205

Ridlen, Peggy, Ref & Instrul Serv Librn, Fontbonne University, 6800 Wydown Blvd, Saint Louis, MO, 63105. Tel: 314-889-4616. Fax: 314-719-8040. p. 1354

Ridler, Penny, Br Mgr, Caledon Public Library, Caledon East Branch, 6500 Old Church Rd, Caledon East, ON, L0N 1E0, CANADA. Tel: 905-584-1456. p. 2795

Ridley, Michael, Chief Librn, University of Guelph, 50 Stone Rd E, Guelph, ON, N1G 2W1, CANADA. Tel: 519-824-4120, Ext 52075, 519-824-4120, Ext 52181. Fax: 519-824-6931. p. 2807

Ridnour, Sue, Mgr, Ch Serv, Flower Mound Public Library, 3030 Broadmoor Lane, Flower Mound, TX, 75022. Tel: 972-874-6153. Fax: 972-874-6466. p. 2319

Ridout, Shelley, Librn, Horry County Memorial Library, North Myrtle Beach Branch, 910 First Ave S, North Myrtle Beach, SC, 29582. Tel: 843-915-5281. Fax: 843-915-6280. p. 2191

Ridout, Theresa, Bus Mgr, Neshoba County Public Library, 230 Beacon St, Philadelphia, MS, 39350. Tel: 601-656-4911. Fax: 601-656-6894. p. 1311

Ridzy, Suzanne, Circ Supvr, Somerset County Library System, Mary Jacobs Memorial, 64 Washington St, Rocky Hill, NJ, 08553. Tel: 609-924-7073. Fax: 609-924-7668. p. 1475

Rieber, Jessica, Clinical Librn, Virtual Ref, Northwest Hospital & Medical Center, 1550 N 115th St, D-110, Seattle, WA, 98133. Tel: 206-368-1850. Fax: 206-368-1949. p. 2529

Rieber, Lloyd, PhD, Prog Head/Prof, University of Georgia, College of Education, 224 River's Crossing, Athens, GA, 30602-7144. Tel: 706-542-4110. Fax: 706-542-4032. p. 2964

Riechers, Kurt, Tech Coordr, Appleton Public Library, 225 N Oneida St, Appleton, WI, 54911-4780. Tel: 920-832-6170. Fax: 920-832-6182. p. 2578

Ried, Patty, Circ, Surrey Township Public Library, 105 E Michigan, Farwell, MI, 48622. Tel: 989-588-9782. Fax: 989-588-4488. p. 1178

Riedel, Heidi, Info Spec, American Water Works Association, 6666 W Quincy Ave, Denver, CO, 80235. Tel: 303-347-6292. Fax: 303-795-7603. p. 298

Riedel, Tom, Distance Educ, Regis University, 3333 Regis Blvd, Denver, CO, 80221-1099. Tel: 303-458-4030. Fax: 303-964-5497. p. 303

Rieder, Sarah, Pub Serv, Pocono Mountain Public Library, 5540 Memorial Blvd, Tobyhanna, PA, 18466. Tel: 570-894-8860. Fax: 570-894-8852. p. 2146

Riedesel, Beth, Libr Dir, Yorktown Public Library, 103 W Main, Yorktown, TX, 78164-5000. Tel: 361-564-3232. Fax: 361-564-3232. p. 2402

Riedesel, Laureen, Dir, Beatrice Public Library, 100 N 16th St, Beatrice, NE, 68310-4100. Tel: 402-223-3584. Fax: 402-223-3913. p. 1393

Riedlinger, Jean E, Ref Serv, American College of Obstetricians & Gynecologists, 409 12th St SW, Washington, DC, 20024-2188. Tel: 202-863-2518. Fax: 202-484-1595. p. 392

Riedy, Laurie, Br Coordr, Menominee County Library, Hermansville Branch, W5480 First St, Hermansville, MI, 49847. Tel: 906-498-2253. p. 1229

Riegel, Donna, Dr, Admin Supvr, Jacksonville Public Library, 303 N Laura St, Jacksonville, FL, 32202-3505. Tel: 904-630-2023. Fax: 904-630-2431. p. 453

Rieger, Kathy, Dir, James Blackstone Memorial Library, 758 Main St, Branford, CT, 06405-3697. Tel: 203-488-1441. Fax: 203-481-6077. p. 331

Rieger, Oya, Assoc Univ Librn, Cornell University Library, 201 Olin Library, Ithaca, NY, 14853-5301. Tel: 607-254-5160. Fax: 607-255-6788. p. 1641

Riegert, Maria, Mgr, Stony Brook University, Marine & Atmospheric Sciences Information Center, 165 Challenger Hall, Stony Brook, NY, 11794-5000. Tel: 631-632-8679. Fax: 631-632-2364. p. 1750

Riegle-Coursey, Ann, Dir, New Madison Public Library, 142 S Main St, New Madison, OH, 45346. Tel: 937-996-1741. Fax: 937-996-1473. p. 1921

Riegler, Sue, Dir, Helena Township Public Library, 8751 Helena Rd, Alden, MI, 49612. Tel: 231-331-4318. Fax: 231-331-4245. p. 1148

Rieh, Soo Young, Assoc Prof, University of Michigan, 304 West Hall, 1085 S University, Ann Arbor, MI, 48109-1107. Tel: 734-763-2285. Fax: 734-764-2475. p. 2967

Riehl, Donna, Youth Serv Mgr, Strathcona County Library, 401 Festival Lane, Sherwood Park, AB, T8A 5P7, CANADA. Tel: 780-410-8600. Fax: 780-467-6861. p. 2716

Riehl, Susan, Pub Serv, Tech Serv, Carroll College, 100 N East Ave, Waukesha, WI, 53186. Tel: 262-650-4832. Fax: 262-524-7377. p. 2644

Riehl, Teddie, Libr Dir, Espanola Public Library, 313 N Paseo de Onate, Espanola, NM, 87532. Tel: 505-747-6087. Fax: 505-753-5543. p. 1555

Riehle, Tina, Br Mgr, Public Library of Cincinnati & Hamilton County, Sharonville, 10980 Thornview Dr, Cincinnati, OH, 45241. Tel: 513-369-6049. Fax: 513-369-4504. p. 1873

Riehman-Murphy, Christina, Ref Librn, Cheltenham Township Library System, Glenside Free Library, 215 S Keswick Ave, Glenside, PA, 19038-4420. Tel: 215-885-0455. Fax: 215-885-1019. p. 2061

Rieker, Michael, Librn, Fresno County Public Library, Orange Cove Branch, 915 Park Blvd, Orange Cove, CA, 93646. Tel: 559-600-9292. p. 152

Riemann, Frederick A, Chief Librn, Chevron Law Library, 1400 Smith St, 7th Flr, Houston, TX, 77002. Tel: 713-372-9116. Fax: 713-372-9282. p. 2334

Riemer, Marilene, Librn, Tampa Campus, Keiser University Library System, 1500 NW 49th St, Fort Lauderdale, FL, 33309. Tel: 954-351-4035. Fax: 954-351-4051. p. 443

Rienzo, Theresa, Assoc Librn, Access Serv/Grad Studies, Molloy College, 1000 Hempstead Ave, Rockville Centre, NY, 11571. Tel: 516-678-5000, Ext 6967. Fax: 516-678-8908. p. 1734

Ries-Taggart, Jennifer, Exec Dir, Brighton Memorial Library, 2300 Elmwood Ave, Rochester, NY, 14618. Tel: 585-784-5300. Fax: 585-784-5333. p. 1728

Riesenberg, Lisa, Ch, West Bend Public Library, 316 S Broadway, West Bend, IA, 50597. Tel: 515-887-6411. Fax: 515-887-6412. p. 851

Riesgaard, Serena, Dir, Avoca Public Library, 213 N Elm St, Avoca, IA, 51521. Tel: 712-343-6358. Fax: 712-343-6358. p. 795

Riesgraf, Nancy, Acq, Cat, Ref, Hibbing Public Library, 2020 E Fifth Ave, Hibbing, MN, 55746-1702. Tel: 218-362-5959. Fax: 218-312-9779. p. 1254

Riesterer, Becky, Head, Circ, Walsh College, 3838 Livernois Rd, Troy, MI, 48083-5066. Tel: 248-823-1339. Fax: 248-689-9066. p. 1232

Riesterer, Mary, Asst Librn, Chilton Public Library, 221 Park St, Chilton, WI, 53014. Tel: 920-849-4414. Fax: 920-849-2370. p. 2585

Riesterer, Wolfgang, Media Spec, St Thomas University Library, 16401 NW 37th Ave, Miami Gardens, FL, 33054. Tel: 305-628-6733. Fax: 305-628-6666. p. 469

Rieth, Dianne, Librn, Monmouth County Library, Howell Branch, 318 Old Tavern Rd, Howell, NJ, 07731. Tel: 732-938-2300. Fax: 732-938-4739. p. 1499

Riether, Debbie, Ref, Margaret E Heggan Free Public Library of the Township of Washington, 606 Delsea Dr, Sewell, NJ, 08080. Tel: 856-589-3334. Fax: 856-582-2042. p. 1529

Rife, Bridget D, Circ, Info Spec, Buchanan County Public Library, Rte 2, Poetown Rd, Grundy, VA, 24614-9613. Tel: 276-935-6582. Fax: 276-935-6292. p. 2467

Rife, Cheryl, Mgr, Libr Serv, Flagstaff City-Coconino County Public Library System, Forest Lakes Community Library, 417 Old Rim Rd, Forest Lakes, AZ, 85931. Tel: 928-535-9125. Fax: 928-535-4729. p. 62

Riffe, Linda, Head, Ref, Putnam County Library, 4219 State Rte 34, Hurricane, WV, 25526. Tel: 304-757-7308. Fax: 304-757-7384. p. 2562

Riffe, Noreen, Spec Coll Supvr, Pueblo City-County Library District, 100 E Abriendo Ave, Pueblo, CO, 81004-4290. Tel: 719-562-5626. Fax: 719-562-5619. p. 320

Riffle, Linda, Mgr, GrafTech International Holdings, Inc, 12900 Snow Rd, Cleveland, OH, 44130. Tel: 216-676-2000. p. 1880

Riffle, Vera, Br Mgr, Warren-Trumbull County Public Library, Lordstown Branch, 1471 Salt Springs Rd SW, Warren, OH, 44481. Tel: 330-824-2094. p. 1945

Rifkin, Laura, Head, Ch, Librn, Closter Public Library, 280 High St, Closter, NJ, 07624-1898. Tel: 201-768-4197. Fax: 201-768-4220. p. 1479

Rigby, Erin, Circ Librn, Poplar Bluff Public Library, 318 N Main St, Poplar Bluff, MO, 63901. Tel: 573-686-8639. Fax: 573-785-6876. p. 1349

Rigby, Sarah, Dir, Newton Town Library, 51 South Center St, Newton, UT, 84327. Tel: 435-563-9283. p. 2408

Rigby, Virginia, Doc, Ref Librn, Lone Star College System, North Harris College Library, 2700 W W Thorne Dr, Houston, TX, 77073. Tel: 281-618-5490. Fax: 281-618-5695. p. 2340

Rigda, Christine, Libr Syst Coordr, University of Toledo, 2801 W Bancroft St, Mail Stop 509, Toledo, OH, 43606-3390. Tel: 419-530-2333. Fax: 419-530-2726. p. 1941

Rigdon, Helen, Dir, Missouri River Regional Library, 214 Adams St, Jefferson City, MO, 65101-3244. Tel: 573-634-6034, Ext 234. p. 1335

Rigg, Darlene, Head, Ref, Lowell Public Library, 1505 E Commercial Ave, Lowell, IN, 46356-1899. Tel: 219-696-7704. Fax: 219-696-5280. p. 762

Riggall, Alan, Librn, State Correctional Institution, Box A, Bellefonte, PA, 16823-0820. Tel: 814-355-4874. p. 2032

Riggi, Wendy, Cataloger/Ref Librn, Grove City Community Library, 125 W Main St, Grove City, PA, 16127-1569. Tel: 724-458-7320. Fax: 724-458-7332. p. 2063

Riggle, Sharlotte, Ref, Chickasaw Regional Library System, 601 Railway Express, Ardmore, OK, 73401. Tel: 580-223-3164. Fax: 580-223-3280. p. 1957

Riggs, Janet M, Chair, Central Pennsylvania Consortium, Dickinson College, 249 W Louther St, Carlisle, PA, 17013. Tel: 717-245-1984. Fax: 717-245-1807. p. 2953

Riggs, Krista, Librn, Fresno County Public Library, Woodward Park Regional, 944 E Perrin Ave, Fresno, CA, 93720. Tel: 559-600-3135. Fax: 559-600-1348. p. 153

Riggs, LaVeda, Ch, Linn County Library District No 2, 209 N Broadway, La Cygne, KS, 66040. Tel: 913-757-2151. Fax: 913-757-2405. p. 877

Riggs, Michelle, Archives & Spec Coll Librn, Louisiana State University at Alexandria, 8100 Hwy 71 S, Alexandria, LA, 71302. Tel: 318-619-2960. Fax: 318-473-6556. p. 939

Riggs, Shannon, Circ, Neuse Regional Library, 510 N Queen St, Kinston, NC, 28501. Tel: 252-527-7066. Fax: 252-527-8220. p. 1805

Riggs, Sue, Asst Dir, Clermont County Public Library, 326 Broadway St, Batavia, OH, 45103. Tel: 513-732-2736. Fax: 513-732-3177. p. 1857

Righter, Loretta, Head, Ref, Montgomery County-Norristown Public Library, 1001 Powell St, Norristown, PA, 19401-3817. Tel: 610-278-5100. p. 2098

Rigley, Susan, Commun Br Supvr, Pierce County Library System, Orting Branch, 202 Washington Ave S, Orting, WA, 98360. Tel: 253-548-3312. Fax: 360-893-4149. p. 2539

Rigney, Margaret, Dir, Connors State College, 1000 College Rd, Warner, OK, 74469-9700. Tel: 918-463-6210. Fax: 918-463-6314. p. 1985

Rigney, Margaret, Dir, Connors State College, Muskogee Campus Library, 201 Court St, Muskogee, OK, 74401. Tel: 918-684-5408. Fax: 918-684-0404. p. 1985

Rigsby, Judith, Head, Acq & Coll Develop, Oral Roberts University Library, 7777 South Lewis Ave, Tulsa, OK, 74171. Tel: 918-495-6895. Fax: 918-495-6895. p. 1981

Rigsby, Lisa, Dir, De Soto Trail Regional Library, 145 E Broad St, Camilla, GA, 31730-1842. Tel: 229-336-8372. Fax: 229-336-9353. p. 522

Rigual, Michelle, Assoc Dir, University of New Mexico, Law Library, 1117 Stanford Dr NE, Albuquerque, NM, 87131-1441. Tel: 505-277-6236. Fax: 505-277-0068. p. 1551

Riibe, Cam, Acq, Per, Northwestern College, 101 Seventh St SW, Orange City, IA, 51041-1996. Tel: 712-707-7234. Fax: 712-707-7247. p. 836

Riis, Marvene, Librn, South Dakota State Historical Society, 900 Governors Dr, Pierre, SD, 57501-2217. Tel: 605-773-4233. Fax: 605-773-6041. p. 2216

Rike, Becky, Dir, Corning Public Library, 603 Ninth St, Corning, IA, 50841-1304. Tel: 641-322-3866. Fax: 641-322-3491. p. 804

Riker, Ross, Automation Mgr, Goshen Public Library, 601 S Fifth St, Goshen, IN, 46526-3994. Tel: 574-533-9531. Fax: 574-533-5211. p. 746

Riker, Tom, Coll Mgt Librn, Bronx Community College Library & Learning Center, 106 Meister Hall, 2115 University Ave, Bronx, NY, 10453. Tel: 718-289-5439, 718-289-5548. Fax: 718-289-6063. p. 1586

Riles, Zetta, Br Mgr, Amarillo Public Library, North Branch, 1500 NE 24th St, Amarillo, TX, 79107. Tel: 806-381-7931. Fax: 806-381-7929. p. 2274

Riley, A, Br Mgr, New Orleans Public Library, Norman Mayer Branch, 3001 Gentilly Blvd, New Orleans, LA, 70122. Tel: 504-596-3100. p. 962

Riley, Ann, Asst Dir, Tech Serv, University of Missouri-Columbia, Elmer Ellis Library, Ellis Library Bldg, Rm 104, Columbia, MO, 65201-5149. Tel: 573-882-1685. Fax: 573-882-8044. p. 1325

Riley, Betty, Br Mgr, Burke County Public Library, C B Hildebrand Public, 201 S Center St, Hildebran, NC, 28637. Tel: 828-397-3600. Fax: 828-397-3600. p. 1811

Riley, Betty, Br Mgr, Burke County Public Library, Valdese Branch, 213 St Germain Ave SE, Valdese, NC, 28690-2846. Tel: 828-874-2421. Fax: 828-874-1211. p. 1811

Riley, Camille, Dir, West Virginia University Libraries, George R Farmer, Jr College of Law Library, One Law Center Dr, Morgantown, WV, 26506. Tel: 304-293-7641. Fax: 304-293-6020. p. 2566

Riley, Camille M, Libr Dir, Mid-Atlantic Law Library Cooperative, College of Law Library, West Virginia University, Morgantown, WV, 26506-6135. Tel: 304-293-7641. Fax: 304-293-6020. p. 2958

Riley, Carol, Dir, Lincoln Public Library, 22 Church St, Lincoln, NH, 03251. Tel: 603-745-8159. Fax: 603-745-2037. p. 1454

Riley, Carol, Head, Circ, Pennsylvania State University, 30 E Swedesford Rd, Malvern, PA, 19355. Tel: 610-648-3205. Fax: 610-725-5223. p. 2083

Riley, David W, Pres, Extrusion Engineers Library, 858 Princeton Ct, Branchburg, NJ, 08853-4101. Tel: 908-369-7260. p. 1474

Riley, Dean, Syst Coordr, Houston Baptist University, 7502 Fondren Rd, Houston, TX, 77074-3298. Tel: 281-649-3435. Fax: 281-649-3489. p. 2337

Riley, Debbie, In Charge, Tillamook County Library, Bay City, 1716 Third St, Tillamook, OR, 97141. Tel: 503-377-0231. Fax: 503-815-1911. p. 2021

Riley, Diane, Dir of Tech Serv, Nazareth College of Rochester Library, 4245 East Ave, Rochester, NY, 14618-3790. Tel: 585-389-2152. Fax: 585-389-2145. p. 1730

Riley, Dixie, Librn, Chappell Memorial Library & Art Gallery, 289 Babcock Ave, Chappell, NE, 69129. Tel: 308-874-2626. Fax: 308-874-2626. p. 1395

Riley, Eric S, Sr Librn, District of Columbia Public Library, Watha T Daniel Shaw Interim Library, 945 Rhode Island Ave NW, Washington, DC, 20001. Tel: 202-671-0265. p. 398

Riley, J, Librn, Northeast Fisheries Science Center, 166 Water St, Woods Hole, MA, 02543-1097. Tel: 508-495-2260. Fax: 508-495-2258. p. 1142

Riley, Jacquelene, Head of Libr, University of Cincinnati Libraries, Classics, 417 Blegen Library, Cincinnati, OH, 45221. Tel: 513-556-1316. Fax: 513-556-6244. p. 1874

Riley, James, Librn, Department of Correctional Education, 1954 State Farm Rd, State Farm, VA, 23160-9998. Tel: 804-784-3551, Ext 2259. Fax: 804-784-2480. p. 2496

Riley, Jane, Libr Asst, Des Moines Area Community College Library, 906 N Grant Rd, Carroll, IA, 51401. Tel: 712-792-1755, 712-792-8316. Fax: 712-792-8500. p. 798

Riley, Jennifer, Ch, Milton-Freewater Public Library, Eight SW Eighth Ave, Milton-Freewater, OR, 97862-1501. Tel: 541-938-8248. Fax: 541-938-8254. p. 2006

Riley, Jim, Archivist, Idaho State Historical Society, Idaho History Ctr, 2205 Old Penitentiary Rd, Boise, ID, 83712. Tel: 208-334-3356. Fax: 208-334-3198. p. 571

Riley, Joanne, Assoc Univ Librn, University of Massachusetts at Boston, 100 Morrissey Blvd, Boston, MA, 02125-3300. Tel: 617-287-5927. p. 1068

Riley, Kasey, Communications Mgr, Johnson County Library, 9875 W 87th St, Overland Park, KS, 66212. Tel: 913-495-2345. Fax: 913-495-2460. p. 888

Riley, Kate, Head, YA, Bayport-Blue Point Public Library, 203 Blue Point Ave, Blue Point, NY, 11715-1217. Tel: 631-363-6133. Fax: 631-363-6133. p. 1583

Riley, Kim, Asst Dir, Sheridan Public Library, 103 W First St, Sheridan, IN, 46069. Tel: 317-758-5201. Fax: 317-758-0045. p. 778

Riley, Laura, Head, Ch, Ridgefield Park Free Public Library, 107 Cedar St, Ridgefield Park, NJ, 07660. Tel: 201-641-0689. Fax: 201-440-1058. p. 1526

Riley, LeeAnn, Co-Dir, Erwin Library & Institute, 104 Schuyler St, Boonville, NY, 13309. Tel: 315-942-4834. Fax: 315-942-5629. p. 1584

Riley, Leslie S W, Pub Serv Consult & Outreach Coordr, Ramapo Catskill Library System, 619 Rte 17M, Middletown, NY, 10940-4395. Tel: 845-343-1131, Ext 239. Fax: 845-343-1205. p. 1660

Riley, Lynne, Access Serv Librn, Worcester Polytechnic Institute, 100 Institute Rd, Worcester, MA, 01609-2280. Tel: 508-831-5410. Fax: 508-831-5829. p. 1145

Riley, Lynne, Br Mgr, Perry County District Library, Junction City Branch, Main St, Junction City, OH, 43748. Tel: 740-987-7646. Fax: 740-987-2238. p. 1921

Riley, Matthew, Ref & Info Serv, Web Coordr, Friendswood Public Library, 416 S Friendswood Dr, Friendswood, TX, 77546-3897. Tel: 281-482-7135. Fax: 281-482-2685. p. 2325

Riley, Oliva, Librn, DeVry University Library, 1350 Alum Creek Dr, Columbus, OH, 43209. Tel: 614-253-7291, Ext 1365. Fax: 614-252-4108. p. 1885

Riley, Pat, Mgr, Jasper-Dubois County Contractual Public Library, Dubois County Branch, 4153 South St, Rd 162, Huntingburg, IN, 47542. Tel: 812-482-6241. Fax: 812-482-6737. p. 756

Riley, Randy, Coordr, Library of Michigan, 702 W Kalamazoo St, Lansing, MI, 48915. Tel: 517-373-5860. Fax: 517-373-5700. p. 1201

Riley, Raymond, Asst Dir, Winchester Public Library, 203 Fourth St, Winchester, KS, 66097. Tel: 913-774-4967. Fax: 913-774-4967. p. 902

Riley, Ruth, Dir, Libr Serv, University of South Carolina, School of Medicine, 6311 Garners Ferry Rd, Columbia, SC, 29209. Tel: 803-733-3344. Fax: 803-733-1509. p. 2190

Riley, Ruth, Dir, Columbia Area Medical Librarians' Association, University of South Carolina, School of Medicine Library, 6311 Garner's Ferry Rd, Columbia, SC, 29209. Tel: 803-733-3361. Fax: 803-733-1509. p. 2955

Riley, Sabrina, Dir, Ser, Spec Coll & Archives Librn, Union College Library, 3800 S 48th St, Lincoln, NE, 68506-4386. Tel: 402-486-2514. Fax: 402-486-2678. p. 1406

Riley, Stephanie, Dir, McGregor-McKinney Public Library, 101 E Fulton St, Hartford, AL, 36344. Tel: 334-588-2384. Fax: 334-588-2384. p. 20

Riley, Susan, Dir, Mamaroneck Public Library District, 136 Prospect Ave, Mamaroneck, NY, 10543. Tel: 914-698-1250. Fax: 914-381-3088. p. 1657

Riley, Thom, Info Tech Dir, Lakeland Library Cooperative, 4138 Three Mile Rd NW, Grand Rapids, MI, 49534-1134. Tel: 616-559-5253. Fax: 616-559-4329. p. 2946

Riley, Trevor, Ref & Instruction Librn, United States Coast Guard Academy Library, 35 Mohegan Ave, New London, CT, 06320-4195. Tel: 860-444-8510. Fax: 860-444-8516. p. 360

Riley, Valerie, Librn, Poinsett County Public Library, Weiner Branch, 203 W Second, Weiner, AR, 72479. Tel: 870-684-2235. Fax: 870-684-7635. p. 102

Riley, Vicki, Mgr, Youth Serv, Sweetwater County Library System, White Mountain Library, 2935 Sweetwater Dr, Rock Springs, WY, 82901-4331. Tel: 307-362-2665, Ext 3310. Fax: 307-352-6655. p. 2656

Riley-Bensley, Judi Y, Youth Serv, Los Lunas Public Library, 460 Main St NE, Los Lunas, NM, 87031. Tel: 505-839-3850. Fax: 505-352-3582. p. 1559

Rillero, Anne, Pub Serv, Pacific Whale Foundation Library, 300 Maalaea Rd, Ste 211, Wailuku, HI, 96793. Tel: 808-249-8811 (Maui line), 808-879-8860. Fax: 808-243-9021, 808-879-2615. p. 568

Rima, Linda, Acq Librn, Harris County Public Library, 8080 El Rio, Houston, TX, 77054. Tel: 713-749-9041. Fax: 713-749-9090. p. 2335

Rimes, Courtney, Bibliog Instr, Ref, Delgado Community College, Bldg 10, Rm 116, 615 City Park Ave, New Orleans, LA, 70119. Tel: 504-671-5315. p. 959

Rimland, Emily, Info Literacy Librn, Pennsylvania State University Libraries, Library Learning Services, 305 Pattee Library, Tower, University Park, PA, 16802-1803. Tel: 814-863-7355. Fax: 814-865-3665. p. 2148

Rimmer, Anne, Assoc Dir, Western State Law Library, 1111 N State College Blvd, Fullerton, CA, 92831-3014. Tel: 714-459-1113. Fax: 714-871-4806. p. 154

Rimmer, Doug, Asst Dep Minister, Coll Mgt Sector, Library & Archives Canada, 550 De la Cité Blvd, Gatineau, QC, K1A 0N4, CANADA. Tel: 819-934-4618. Fax: 819-934-5262. p. 2883

Rimonte, Jimmy, Dir, Libr Serv, University of West Los Angeles, 9920 S LaCienega Blvd, Inglewood, CA, 90301-4423. Tel: 310-342-5206. Fax: 310-342-5298. p. 160

Rimpau, Ina, Br Mgr, Newark Public Library, Vailsburg, 75 Alexander St, Newark, NJ, 07106. Tel: 973-733-7755. p. 1512

Rimpley, Darlene, Librn, Finch Memorial Public Library, 205 N Walnut, Arnold, NE, 69120. Tel: 308-848-2219. Fax: 308-848-4729. p. 1392

Rinaldi, Kim, Dir, Margaret E Heggan Free Public Library of the Township of Washington, 606 Delsea Dr, Sewell, NJ, 08080. Tel: 856-589-3334. Fax: 856-582-2042. p. 1529

Rinck, Jared, Librn, Metropolitan Community College, Blue River Library, 20301 E 78 Hwy, Independence, MO, 64057. Tel: 816-220-6740. Fax: 816-220-6751. p. 1339

Rincon, Cecilia, Br Mgr, San Diego County Library, Fallbrook Branch, 113 S Main Ave, Fallbrook, CA, 92028. Tel: 760-728-2373. Fax: 760-728-4731. p. 233

Rind, Debbie, Circ Media, Canada/Manitoba Business Service Centre Library, 240 Graham Ave, Ste 250, Winnipeg, MB, R3C 0J7, CANADA. Tel: 204-984-2272. Fax: 204-983-3852. p. 2754

Rinderknecht, Deborah, Dir, University of Pittsburgh, Johnstown Campus, 450 Schoolhouse Rd, Johnstown, PA, 15904. Tel: 814-269-7288. Fax: 814-269-7286. p. 2073

Rindsleisch, Mary, Asst Dir, Ridgefield Library Association Inc, 472 Main St, Ridgefield, CT, 06877-4585. Tel: 203-438-2282. Fax: 203-438-4558. p. 365

Rine, Nancy, Dir, Fried, Frank, Harris, Shriver & Jacobson Library, One New York Plaza, New York, NY, 10004. Tel: 212-859-4886. Fax: 212-859-8000. p. 1679

Rinehart, Elizabeth, Head, Tech Serv, Goshen Public Library, 601 S Fifth St, Goshen, IN, 46526-3994. Tel: 574-533-9531. Fax: 574-533-5211. p. 746

Rineholt, Pamela, Libr Dir, Collins College Libraries, 1140 S Priest Dr, Tempe, AZ, 85281. Tel: 480-446-1185. Fax: 480-902-0663. p. 84

Rines, Allen, Asst Dir, Foley & Hoag LLP Library, 155 Seaport Blvd, Boston, MA, 02210. Tel: 617-832-7070. Fax: 617-832-7000. p. 1061

Rines, Julie M, Ch, Thomas Crane Public Library, 40 Washington St, Quincy, MA, 02269-9164. Tel: 617-376-1332. Fax: 617-376-1313. p. 1119

Riney, Judith N, Sister, Dir, Libr & Info Serv, Brescia University, 717 Frederica St, Owensboro, KY, 42301. Tel: 270-686-4288. Fax: 270-686-4266. p. 931

Ring, Amy, Br Mgr, Saint Johns County Public Library System, Ponte Vedra Beach Branch, 101 Library Blvd, Ponte Vedra Beach, FL, 32082. Tel: 904-827-6951. Fax: 904-827-6955. p. 487

Ring, Brenna, Br Mgr, San Diego County Library, Rancho San Diego, 11555 Via Rancho San Diego, El Cajon, CA, 92019. Tel: 619-660-5370. Fax: 619-660-6327. p. 234

Ring, Daniel, Info Literacy & Ref Librn, Oakland University Library, 2200 N Squirrel Rd, Rochester, MI, 48309-4402. Tel: 248-370-2498. Fax: 248-370-2474. p. 1221

Ring, Judith A, State Librn, Florida Department of State, Division of Library & Information Services, R A Gray Bldg, 500 S Bronough St, Tallahassee, FL, 32399-0250. Tel: 850-245-6600. Fax: 850-245-6735. p. 493

Ring, Sheila, Dir, Bristol Bay Borough Libraries, 101 Main St, Naknek, AK, 99633. Tel: 907-246-4465. p. 51

Ring, Sue, Br Supvr, Davenport Public Library, Fairmount Street, 3000 N Fairmount St, Davenport, IA, 52804-1160. Tel: 563-888-3390. Fax: 563-326-7806. p. 806

Ringdahl, Kerstin, Spec Coll, Univ Archivist, Pacific Lutheran University, 12180 Park Ave S, Tacoma, WA, 98447-0001. Tel: 253-535-7500. Fax: 253-535-7315. p. 2539

Ringenberg, Kathleen, Br Mgr, Timberland Regional Library, Westport Branch, 101 E Harms Ave, Westport, WA, 98595. Tel: 360-268-0521. Fax: 360-268-0558. p. 2544

Ringer, LaDonna, Asst Librn, Terra Alta Public Library, 701-B E State Ave, Terra Alta, WV, 26764-1204. Tel: 304-789-2724. Fax: 304-789-2724. p. 2572

Ringer, Margot A, Asst Librn, Guernsey County Law Library, Guernsey County Court House, 801 Wheeling Ave, Rm D 301, Cambridge, OH, 43725. Tel: 740-432-9258. p. 1863

Ringgenberg, Judy, Librn, North Dakota Department of Corrections, 701 16 Ave SW, Mandan, ND, 58554-5800. Tel: 701-667-1479. Fax: 701-667-1414. p. 1845

Ringler, Kim, Dir, Avon Grove Library, 117 Rosehill Ave, West Grove, PA, 19390-1214. Tel: 610-869-2004. Fax: 610-869-2957. p. 2154

Ringwald, Edna M, Asst Librn, Bucklin Public Library, 201 N Main, Bucklin, KS, 67834. Tel: 620-826-3223. Fax: 620-826-3794. p. 858

Ringwald, Mary, Dir, Loogootee Public Library, 106 N Line St, Loogootee, IN, 47553-1263. Tel: 812-295-3713. Fax: 812-295-3713. p. 762

Rink, Tom, Instruction Librn, Northeastern State University, Broken Arrow Campus Library, Bldg E Library, 3100 E New Orleans St, Broken Arrow, OK, 74014. Tel: 918-449-6457. Fax: 918-449-6454. p. 1979

Rinker, Cindy, Libr Asst, Youth Serv, Barry-Lawrence Regional Library, Mount Vernon Branch, 206 W Water, Mount Vernon, MO, 65712. Tel: 417-466-2921. Fax: 417-466-2936. p. 1346

Rinkin, Robert, Br Mgr, Fort Worth Library, Summerglen, 4205 Basswood Blvd, Fort Worth, TX, 76137-1402. Tel: 817-232-0478. Fax: 817-232-1065. p. 2322

Rinn, Martha, Librn, Texas Lutheran University, 1000 W Court St, Seguin, TX, 78155-5978. Tel: 830-372-8100. Fax: 830-372-8156. p. 2386

Rintelman, Dona L, Asst Dir, Watertown Library Association, 470 Main St, Watertown, CT, 06795. Tel: 860-945-5360. Fax: 860-945-5367. p. 375

Rintelman, Joan K, Dir, Watertown Library Association, 470 Main St, Watertown, CT, 06795. Tel: 860-945-5360. Fax: 860-945-5367. p. 375

Rinz, Beth Maher, Librn, Sherwin-Williams Automotive Finishes Corp Library, 4440 Warrensville Center Rd, Cleveland, OH, 44128. Tel: 216-332-8427. Fax: 216-332-8800. p. 1881

Rinzel, Dennis, AV, University of Wisconsin-Madison, L & S Learning Support Services, Van Hise Hall, 1220 Linden Dr, Madison, WI, 53706. Tel: 608-262-1408. Fax: 608-262-7579. p. 2609

Riordan, Dale, Sci Librn, Franklin & Marshall College, Martin Library of the Sciences, PO Box 3003, Lancaster, PA, 17604-3003. Tel: 717-291-3843. Fax: 717-291-4088. p. 2076

Riordan, Ellen, Coordr, Ch Serv, Enoch Pratt Free Library, 400 Cathedral St, Baltimore, MD, 21201-4484. Tel: 410-396-5430. Fax: 410-396-1441. p. 1012

Riordan, Jennifer, Ch, Kings County Library, 401 N Douty St, Hanford, CA, 93230. Tel: 559-582-0261. Fax: 559-583-6163. p. 156

Riordan, Mary, Info Serv Librn, University of Arizona, Arizona Health Sciences Library, 1501 N Campbell Ave, Tucson, AZ, 85724. Tel: 520-626-3510. Fax: 520-626-2922. p. 88

Rios, David, Asst Univ Librn, Admin Serv, University of California, Riverside Libraries, 900 University Ave, Riverside, CA, 92521. Tel: 951-827-3234. p. 218

Rios, DeDe, Dir, Baptist Health System, 8400 Datapoint Dr, San Antonio, TX, 78229. Tel: 210-297-7639. Fax: 210-297-0716. p. 2379

Rios, Elodia, Asst Dir, Donna Public Library, 301 S Main St, Donna, TX, 78537. Tel: 956-464-2221. Fax: 956-464-2172. p. 2314

Rios, Iraida, Cataloger, University of Puerto Rico, Minillas Park, 170, 174 Rd, Bayamon, PR, 00959-1919. Tel: 787-993-0000, Ext 3222, 787-993-8857. Fax: 787-993-8914. p. 2672

Rios, Isabel, Circ Supvr, Baker College of Muskegon Library, 1903 Marquette Ave, Muskegon, MI, 49442-3404. Tel: 231-777-5330. Fax: 231-777-5334. p. 1212

Rios Kravitz, Rhonda, Dr, Dean, Sacramento City College, 3835 Freeport Blvd, Sacramento, CA, 95822. Tel: 916-558-2253. Fax: 916-558-2114. p. 224

Rios, Leslie, Librn, Lincoln Land Community College Library, 5250 Shepherd Rd, Springfield, IL, 62794. Tel: 217-786-2354. Fax: 217-786-2251. p. 705

Rios, Luis, Ref, University of Puerto Rico, 130 Ave Universidad, Arecibo, PR, 00612-3145. Tel: 787-815-0000, Ext 3151. Fax: 787-878-9363. p. 2671

Rios, Rosa H, Circ Asst, Laredo Community College, West End Washington St, Laredo, TX, 78040. Tel: 956-721-5275. Fax: 956-721-5447. p. 2353

Rios, Senele, Br Mgr, Los Angeles Public Library System, Mark Twain Branch, 9621 S Figueroa St, Los Angeles, CA, 90003. Tel: 323-755-4088. Fax: 323-612-0437. p. 174

Rioux, Kevin, PhD, Assoc Prof, Saint John's University, Saint Augustine Hall, Rm 408, 8000 Utopia Pkwy, Jamaica, NY, 11439. Tel: 718-990-1458. Fax: 718-990-2071. p. 2970

Rioux, Marie-Line, Libr Tech, Douglas Mental Health University Institute, 6875 LaSalle Blvd, Perry Pavilion, Rm E4501, Montreal, QC, H4H 1R3, CANADA. Tel: 514-762-3029. Fax: 514-762-3039. p. 2895

Rioux, Mary, In Charge, Hillsborough County Law Library, 300 Chestnut St, Manchester, NH, 03101. Tel: 603-627-5605. p. 1455

Ripley, Cynthia, Librn, Allen County Law Library Association, Inc, Courthouse, Rm 105, 715 S Calhoun St, Fort Wayne, IN, 46802. Tel: 260-449-7638. Fax: 260-422-0791. p. 740

Ripley, Gord, Syst Librn, Trent University, 1600 West Bank Dr, Peterborough, ON, K9J 7B8, CANADA. Tel: 705-748-1011, Ext 1324. Fax: 705-748-1126. p. 2836

Ripley, Gord, Actg Syst Librn, University of Prince Edward Island, 550 University Ave, Charlottetown, PE, C1A 4P3, CANADA. Tel: 902-566-0343. Fax: 902-628-4305. p. 2876

Ripoll, Jeannie, Dir, Long Beach Public Library, 209 Jeff Davis Ave, Long Beach, MS, 39560. Tel: 228-863-0711. Fax: 228-863-8511. p. 1307

Ripp, Donna, Co-Dir, Erwin Library & Institute, 104 Schuyler St, Boonville, NY, 13309. Tel: 315-942-4834. Fax: 315-942-5629. p. 1584

Rippel, Kathleen, Supvr, Tech Serv & ILL, Central Kansas Library System, 1409 Williams St, Great Bend, KS, 67530-4020. Tel: 620-792-4865. Fax: 620-792-5495. p. 869

Rippins, Gina, ILL, BCC-UCF Joint Use Library, 1519 Clearlake Rd, Cocoa, FL, 32922. Tel: 321-433-7804. Fax: 321-433-7678. p. 433

Ripplinger, Lillian, Librn, Southeast Regional Library, Montmartre Branch, 136 Central Ave, Montmartre, SK, S0G 3M0, CANADA. Tel: 306-424-2029. p. 2930

Ripplinger, Marlene, Librn, Harvey Public Library, 119 E Tenth St, Harvey, ND, 58341. Tel: 701-324-2156. Fax: 701-324-2156. p. 1844

Rippstein, Kathy, Circ Supvr, Concordia University, 800 N Columbia Ave, Seward, NE, 68434-1595. Tel: 402-643-7254. Fax: 402-643-4218. p. 1419

Rippy, Linda, Exec Dir, Marshall County Historical Society Library, 123 N Michigan St, Plymouth, IN, 46563. Tel: 574-936-2306. Fax: 574-936-9306. p. 773

Risa, Terry, Librn, Opheim Community Library, 100 Rock St, Opheim, MT, 59250. Tel: 406-762-3213. Fax: 406-762-3348. p. 1387

Risacher, Jody A, Dir, Cumberland County Public Library & Information Center, 300 Maiden Lane, Fayetteville, NC, 28301-5000. Tel: 910-483-7727. Fax: 910-486-5372. p. 1792

Risch, Cathy, Asst Librn, Howells Public Library, 130 N Third St, Howells, NE, 68641. Tel: 402-986-1210. Fax: 402-986-1210. p. 1402

Risch, Elaine, Coll Develop, Ramapo College of New Jersey, 505 Ramapo Valley Rd, Mahwah, NJ, 07430-1623. Tel: 201-684-7570. p. 1498

Risch, Joan, Librn, College of Marin Library, 835 College Ave, Kentfield, CA, 94904. Tel: 415-457-8811, 415-485-9656. Fax: 415-457-5395. p. 161

Risch, Mary Jo, In Charge, Huron County Law Library, 250 E Huron Ave, 2nd Flr, Bad Axe, MI, 48413. Tel: 989-269-7112. Fax: 989-269-0005. p. 1155

Risell, Rosette, Acq, Naval Research Laboratory, 4555 Overlook Ave SW, Code 5596, Washington, DC, 20375-5334. Tel: 202-767-2357. Fax: 202-767-3352. p. 411

Rish, Jane, Librn, VA Pittsburgh Healthcare System, 7180 Highland Dr, Pittsburgh, PA, 15206. Tel: 412-365-5515. Fax: 412-365-5510. p. 2129

Rish, Jane, Librn, VA Pittsburgh Healthcare System, Medical Library University Drive Division, University Dr, Pittsburgh, PA, 15240. Tel: 412-688-6000, Ext 814718. Fax: 412-688-6586. p. 2129

Rish, Jennifer G, Dir, Info Res, Sullivan & Cromwell LLP, 125 Broad St, New York, NY, 10004. Tel: 212-558-3715. Fax: 212-558-3346. p. 1700

Rishar, Rebecca, Tech Serv Librn, Alvernia University, 400 St Bernardine St, Reading, PA, 19607-1737. Tel: 610-796-8395. Fax: 610-796-8347. p. 2132

Rishling, Linda, Circ, Mitchell Public Library, 221 N Duff St, Mitchell, SD, 57301-2596. Tel: 605-995-8480. Fax: 605-995-8482. p. 2215

Risinger, Linda, Librn, Orchard Public Library, 232 Windom, Orchard, NE, 68764. Tel: 402-893-4606. Fax: 402-893-4606. p. 1415

Risinger, Lorry, Youth Serv, Lynchburg Public Library, 2315 Memorial Ave, Lynchburg, VA, 24501. Tel: 434-455-6300. p. 2476

Riskedahl, Laura, AV, Coe College, 1220 First Ave NE, Cedar Rapids, IA, 52402-5092. Tel: 319-399-8211. Fax: 319-399-8019. p. 800

Riskind, Mary, Dir, Bergenfield Public Library, 50 W Clinton Ave, Bergenfield, NJ, 07621-2799. Tel: 201-387-4040, Ext 829. Fax: 201-387-9004. p. 1472

Risley, Carine, Mgr, San Mateo County Library, Atherton Library, Two Dinkelspiel Station Lane, Atherton, CA, 94027. Tel: 650-328-2422. Fax: 650-328-4138. p. 255

Risley, Carine, Mgr, San Mateo County Library, Brisbane Library, 250 Visitacion Ave, Brisbane, CA, 94005. Tel: 415-467-2060. Fax: 415-467-4824. p. 255

Risley, Suzanne M, Info Tech, VPres, Libr Serv, Mitchell College Library, 437 Pequot Ave, New London, CT, 06320-4498. Tel: 860-701-5155. Fax: 860-701-5099. p. 360

Risner, Kim, Dir, Pryor Public Library, 505 E Graham, Pryor, OK, 74361. Tel: 918-825-0777. Fax: 918-825-0856. p. 1976

Risse, Sherri, Br Mgr, Evansville Vanderburgh Public Library, McCollough Branch, 5115 Washington Ave, Evansville, IN, 47715. Tel: 812-426-9791. Fax: 812-473-0877. p. 738

Rissinger, Michael, Cat, Pew Charitable Trusts Library, One Commerce Sq, 2005 Market St, Ste 1700, Philadelphia, PA, 19103-7017. Tel: 215-575-9050. Fax: 215-575-4939. p. 2114

Rist, Kelly, Asst Dir, Brumback Library, 215 W Main St, Van Wert, OH, 45891-1695. Tel: 419-238-2168. Fax: 419-238-3180. p. 1943

Rister, Amram S, Librn, Touro College Libraries, 43 W 23rd St, Fifth Fl, New York, NY, 10010. Tel: 212-463-0400, Ext 5321. Fax: 212-627-3696. p. 1701

Ristic, Jovanka, Ref Serv, University of Wisconsin-Milwaukee Libraries, American Geographical Society Library, Golda Meir Library, 2311 E Hartford Ave, Milwaukee, WI, 53211. Tel: 414-229-3984, 414-229-6282. Fax: 414-229-3624. p. 2622

Ritchey, Alice, Circ, Shelby County Public Library, 309 Eighth St, Shelbyville, KY, 40065. Tel: 502-633-3803. Fax: 502-633-4025. p. 935

Ritchey, Sandi, ILL, Mount Angel Abbey Library, One Abbey Dr, Saint Benedict, OR, 97373. Tel: 503-845-3303, 503-845-3317. Fax: 503-845-3500. p. 2017

Ritchhart, Tandy, In Charge, Southwest Kansas Library System, Talking Books, 100 Military Ave, Ste 210, Dodge City, KS, 67801-4484. Tel: 620-225-1231. Fax: 620-225-0252. p. 864

Ritchie, Dave, Automation Syst Coordr, SUNY Cortland, 81 Prospect Terrace, Cortland, NY, 13045. Tel: 607-753-2525. Fax: 607-753-5669. p. 1611

Ritchie, Jessica, Libr Spec, Old Dominion University Libraries, Elise N Hofheimer Art Library, Diehn Fine & Performing Arts Ctr, Rm 109, Norfolk, VA, 23529. Tel: 757-683-4059. p. 2483

Ritchie, Susan, Librn, Shepherd of the Valley Lutheran Church Library, 1500 W Maryland Ave, Phoenix, AZ, 85015. Tel: 602-249-1936. Fax: 602-249-1983. p. 77

Ritchie, Vanessa, Librn, Mississippi Gulf Coast Community College, PO Box 548, Perkinston, MS, 39573-0011. Tel: 601-928-6242. Fax: 601-928-6359. p. 1311

Riter, Cindy, Tech Serv, Williams County Public Library, 107 E High St, Bryan, OH, 43506-1702. Tel: 419-636-6734. Fax: 419-636-3970. p. 1862

Riter, Robert, Asst Prof, University of Alabama, 514 Main Library, Tuscaloosa, AL, 35487. Tel: 205-348-4610. Fax: 205-348-3746. p. 2961

Ritten, Karla, Coll Develop, Lewis & Clark Library, 120 S Last Chance Gulch, Helena, MT, 59601. Tel: 406-447-1690, Ext 133. Fax: 406-447-1687. p. 1382

Rittenberger, Alexis D, Metadata Librn, Washington & Jefferson College Library, 60 S Lincoln St, Washington, PA, 15301. Tel: 724-503-1001, Ext 3039. Fax: 724-223-5272. p. 2151

Rittenburg, Mary, Dir, Valparaiso Public Library, 300 W Second St, Valparaiso, NE, 68065. Tel: 402-784-6141. Fax: 402-784-6141. p. 1422

Rittenhouse, Elaine, Tech Serv Librn, Nesmith Library, Eight Fellows Rd, Windham, NH, 03087. Tel: 603-432-7154. Fax: 603-537-0097. p. 1468

Ritter, Anne, Br Mgr, Librn, Acadia Parish Library, Iota Branch, 119 Duson, Iota, LA, 70543. Tel: 337-779-2770. Fax: 337-779-2770. p. 948

Ritter, Chris, Dir, Bethel-Tulpehocken Public Library, 8601 Lancaster Ave, Bethel, PA, 19507. Tel: 717-933-4060. Fax: 717-933-9655. p. 2033

Ritter, Chris M, Head Librn, Antique Automobile Club of America, 501 W Governor Rd, Hershey, PA, 17033-2219. Tel: 717-534-2082. Fax: 717-534-9101. p. 2068

Ritter, Diana, Outreach Coordr, Ritchie County Public Library, 608 E Main St, Harrisville, WV, 26362. Tel: 304-643-2717. Fax: 304-643-4019. p. 2560

Ritter, Marian, Head Music Libr, Western Washington University, 516 High St, MS 9103, Bellingham, WA, 98225. Tel: 630-650-3696. Fax: 360-650-3044. p. 2509

Ritter, MaryJane, Librn, Berkeley County Library System, Hanahan Branch, 1274 Yeamans Hall Rd, Hanahan, SC, 29406-2627. Tel: 843-747-5400. Fax: 843-747-5400. p. 2200

Ritter, Maureen, Supv Librn, Support Serv, Newark Public Library, Five Washington St, Newark, NJ, 07101. Tel: 973-733-7794. Fax: 973-733-5648. p. 1511

Ritter-Vicich, Kathryn, Cat Librn, Pocono Mountain Public Library, 5540 Memorial Blvd, Tobyhanna, PA, 18466. Tel: 570-894-8860. Fax: 570-894-8852. p. 2146

Ritterbush, Jon, Electronic Res/Ser Librn, University of Nebraska at Kearney, 2508 11th Ave, Kearney, NE, 68849-2240. Tel: 308-865-8585. Fax: 308-865-8722. p. 1403

Ritterhouse, Kathy, Dir, Grand Prairie Public Library System, 901 Conover Dr, Grand Prairie, TX, 75051. Tel: 972-237-5700. Fax: 972-237-5750. p. 2329

Rittner, Stephen, Librn, Rittners School of Floral Design Library, 345 Marlborough St, Boston, MA, 02115. Tel: 617-267-3824. Fax: 617-267-3824. p. 1066

Rittscher, Carol, Youth Serv, Liberal Memorial Library, 519 N Kansas, Liberal, KS, 67901-3345. Tel: 620-626-0180. Fax: 620-626-0182. p. 879

Rivard, Bernadette D, Dir, Bellingham Public Library, 100 Blackstone St, Bellingham, MA, 02019. Tel: 508-966-1660. Fax: 508-966-3189. p. 1052

Rivard, Timothy, Dir, Learning Serv, MassBay Community College, 50 Oakland St, Wellesley, MA, 02481. Tel: 781-239-2631. Fax: 781-239-3621. p. 1134

Rivenburgh, Edwin, Dir, State University of New York College at Geneseo, SUNY Geneseo, One College Circle, Geneseo, NY, 14454-1498. p. 1627

Rivens, Julia, Tech Asst, Horry-Georgetown Technical College, Georgetown Campus, 4003 S Fraser St, Georgetown, SC, 29440. Tel: 843-520-1407. Fax: 843-520-1462. p. 2192

Rivera, Alexis, Libr Tech, Pontifical Catholic University Of Puerto Rico, Encarnacion Valdes Library, 2250 Avenida Las Americas, Ste 509, Ponce, PR, 00717-0777. Tel: 787-841-2000, Ext 1809. Fax: 787-284-0235. p. 2675

Rivera, Angel, Ref/Outreach Librn, University of Texas at Tyler Library, 3900 University Blvd, Tyler, TX, 75799. Tel: 903-566-7165. Fax: 903-566-2513. p. 2394

Rivera, Christina, Pres, Medical & Scientific Libraries of Long Island, c/o Palmer Sch of Libr & Info Sci, C W Post Campus, Long Island Univ, Brookville, NY, 11548. Tel: 516-299-2866. Fax: 516-299-4168. p. 2950

Rivera, Ed, Instrul Serv Librn, Ref Librn, Berkeley College, White Plains Campus, 99 Church St, White Plains, NJ, 10601. Tel: 914-694-1122, Ext 3371. p. 1545

Rivera, Felix A, Ref & Flm Librn, Hunter College Libraries, Centro - Center for Puerto Rican Studies Library, 2180 Third Ave, Rm 121, New York, NY, 10035. Tel: 212-772-5704. Fax: 212-396-7707. p. 1682

Rivera, George, Exec Dir, Triton Museum of Art Library, 1505 Warburton Ave, Santa Clara, CA, 95050. Tel: 408-247-3754, Ext 11. Fax: 408-247-3796. p. 263

Rivera, Lisa, Ch, Speer Memorial Library, 801 E 12th St, Mission, TX, 78572. Tel: 956-580-8750. Fax: 956-580-8756. p. 2363

Rivera, Liza, Dir, Boricua College, 186 N Sixth St, Brooklyn, NY, 11211. Tel: 718-782-2200. Fax: 718-782-2050. p. 1589

Rivera, Liza, Dir, Boricua College, 3755 Broadway, New York, NY, 10032. Tel: 212-694-1000, Ext 666 or 667. Fax: 212-694-1015. p. 1671

Rivera, Maria de los Angeles, Acq, Pontifical Catholic University Of Puerto Rico, Encarnacion Valdes Library, 2250 Avenida Las Americas, Ste 509, Ponce, PR, 00717-0777. Tel: 787-841-2000, Ext 1817. Fax: 787-284-0235. p. 2674

Rivera, Melissa, Per, Manchester Community College Library, Great Path, Manchester, CT, 06040. Tel: 860-512-2884. Fax: 860-512-2871. p. 350

Rivera, Melva, Cat, Universidad del Turabo, PO Box 3030, Gurabo, PR, 00778-3030. Tel: 787-743-7979, Ext 4501. Fax: 787-743-7924. p. 2673

Rivera, Michelle, Dir, Ref & Libr Info Serv, University of Puerto Rico Library, Cayey Campus, 205 Ave Antonio R Barcelo, Cayey, PR, 00736. Tel: 787-738-2161, Ext 2021, 787-738-5651. Fax: 787-263-2108. p. 2672

Rivera, Mildred I, Dir, Med Libr, Universidad Central Del Caribe, Avenida Laurel, Santa Juanita, Bayamon, PR, 00956. Tel: 787-798-3001, Ext 2305. Fax: 787-785-3425. p. 2672

Rivera, Pedro L, Cat, Pontifical Catholic University Of Puerto Rico, Encarnacion Valdes Library, 2250 Avenida Las Americas, Ste 509, Ponce, PR, 00717-0777. Tel: 787-841-2000, Ext 1801, 787-841-2000, Ext 1802. Fax: 787-284-0235. p. 2675

Rivera, Rita, Tech Serv, Cedar Mill Community Library, 12505 NW Cornell Rd, Portland, OR, 97229. Tel: 503-644-0043. Fax: 503-644-3964. p. 2010

Rivera, Sarah, Libr Tech, Beckman Coulter, Inc, 11800 SW 147th Ave, M/C 21-BO1, Miami, FL, 33196-2500. Tel: 305-380-4205. Fax: 305-380-4344. p. 464

Rivera, Simonette, In Charge, US Geological Survey Water Resources Division, Bldg 4 2045 Rte 112, Coram, NY, 11727. Tel: 631-736-0783. Fax: 631-736-4283. p. 1610

Rivera-Marrero, Doris E, Head Librn, University of Puerto Rico Library System, Music Library, Agustin Stahl Bldg, Rio Piedras Campus, San Juan, PR, 00931. Tel: 787-764-0000, Ext 5202. Fax: 787-772-1479. p. 2678

Rivera-Said, Miildred, Commun Libr Mgr, Queens Borough Public Library, South Ozone Park Community Library, 128-16 Rockaway Blvd, South Ozone Park, NY, 11420. Tel: 718-529-1660. p. 1645

Rivera-Sierra, Ismael, Dir, Libr Serv, Saint John's University Library, Kathryn & Shelby Cullom Davis Library, 101 Murray St, 3rd Flr, New York, NY, 10007. Tel: 212-277-5135. Fax: 212-277-5140. p. 1725

Rivero, Brenda S, Dir, Mississippi Gulf Coast Community College, PO Box 548, Perkinston, MS, 39573-0011. Tel: 601-928-6380. Fax: 601-928-6359. p. 1311

Rivers, Claire, Interim Dir, Libr Serv, Pacific Northwest College of Art, 1241 NW Johnson St, Portland, OR, 97209. Tel: 503-821-8970. p. 2013

Rivers, Claudia, Spec Coll & Archives Librn, University of Texas at El Paso Library, 500 W University Ave, El Paso, TX, 79968-0582. Tel: 915-747-6725. Fax: 915-747-5345. p. 2317

Rivers, David, Dir of Outreach, Dir, Pub Serv, Medical University of South Carolina Library, 171 Ashley Ave, Ste 300, Charleston, SC, 29425-0001. Tel: 843-792-9211. Fax: 843-792-7947. p. 2184

Rivers, Julie, Res Analyst, The Parrott Centre, 376 Wallbridge-Loyalist Rd, Belleville, ON, K8N 5B9, CANADA. Tel: 613-969-1913, Ext 2363. Fax: 613-969-5183. p. 2795

Rivers, Mildred, Ch, Finkelstein Memorial Library, 24 Chestnut St, Spring Valley, NY, 10977-5594. Tel: 845-352-5700. Fax: 845-352-2319. p. 1746

Rivers, Rene, In Charge, House Research Institute, 2100 W Third St, 4th Flr, Los Angeles, CA, 90057-1922. Tel: 213-483-4431. Fax: 213-413-8789. p. 171

Rivers-Moore, Agnes, Librn, West Grey Public Library, Normanby Township Public, 574 Louisa St, Ayton, ON, N0G 1C0, CANADA. Tel: 519-665-7784. p. 2803

Rivers-Moore, Agnes, Chief Exec Officer, Chief Librn, Hanover Public Library, 451 Tenth Ave, Hanover, ON, N4N 2P1, CANADA. Tel: 519-364-1420. Fax: 519-364-1747. p. 2811

Rivest, John, Evening Librn, Georgia Northwestern Technical College, Bldg H, Rm 156, One Maurice Culberson Dr, Rome, GA, 30161. Tel: 706-295-6845. Fax: 706-295-6843. p. 548

Rivest, John, Music, Shorter College, 315 Shorter Ave, Rome, GA, 30165. Tel: 706-291-2121, Ext 7296. Fax: 706-236-1512. p. 549

Riviere, Mary Martha, Circ, Columbia Theological Seminary, 701 Columbia Dr, Decatur, GA, 30030. Tel: 404-687-4549. Fax: 404-687-4687. p. 529

Rivin, Nancy, Dir, Temple Emanu-El, 8500 Hillcrest Rd, Dallas, TX, 75225. Tel: 214-706-0000. Fax: 214-706-0025. p. 2310

Rivin, Nancy, Dir, Temple Emanu-El, William P Budner Youth Library, 8500 Hillcrest Rd, Dallas, TX, 75225. Tel: 214-706-0000, Ext 155. p. 2311

Rix, Wright, Principal Librn, Ref, Santa Monica Public Library, 601 Santa Monica Blvd, Santa Monica, CA, 90401. Tel: 310-458-8271. Fax: 310-394-8951. p. 266

Rixen, Mary, Dir, Murray State College Library, One Murray Campus St LS 101, Tishomingo, OK, 73460. Tel: 580-371-2371. Fax: 580-371-9844. p. 1980

Rizer, Sally, Dir, Clark County Public Library, 201 S Fountain Ave, Springfield, OH, 45506. Tel: 937-323-9751. Fax: 937-328-6908. p. 1935

Rizio, Ron, Prog Coordr, Ref Serv, Montville Township Public Library, 90 Horseneck Rd, Montville, NJ, 07045-9626. Tel: 973-402-0900. Fax: 973-402-0592. p. 1504

Rizvi, Ahtasham, Coll Liaison, Sheridan College Library, 1430 Trafalgar Rd, Oakville, ON, L6H 2L1, CANADA. Tel: 905-845-9430, Ext 2495. Fax: 905-815-4123. p. 2826

Rizvl, Yasmin Saira, Head, Access/Tech Serv, Columbia University, Thomas J Watson Library of Business & Economics, 130 Uris Hall, 3022 Broadway, MC 9163, New York, NY, 10027. Tel: 212-854-7804. Fax: 212-854-5723. p. 1675

Rizzo, Carl, Cat, Rider University, 2083 Lawrenceville Rd, Lawrenceville, NJ, 08648-3099. Tel: 609-896-5111. Fax: 609-896-8029. p. 1494

Rizzo, Gaye, Dir, Windsor Public Library, 323 Broad St, Windsor, CT, 06095. Tel: 860-285-1912. Fax: 860-285-1889. p. 379

Rizzuti, LeeAnn, Pub Serv Spec, Walla Walla Public Library, 238 E Alder, Walla Walla, WA, 99362. Tel: 509-524-4435. Fax: 509-524-7950. p. 2547

Roach, Brenda, Libr Supvr-Popular Libr, Lindenwold Public Library, 310 E Linden Ave, Lindenwold, NJ, 08021. Tel: 856-784-5602. Fax: 856-566-1413. p. 1495

Roach, Deneen, Dir, Mather Memorial Library, 23866 Rte 220, Ulster, PA, 18850. Tel: 570-358-3595. Fax: 570-358-3595. p. 2147

Roach, Eileen, Asst Librn, Cushman Library, 28 Church St, Bernardston, MA, 01337. Tel: 413-648-5402. Fax: 413-648-0168. p. 1053

Roach, Julie, Ch, Cambridge Public Library, 449 Broadway, Cambridge, MA, 02138. Tel: 617-349-4040. Fax: 617-349-4028. p. 1073

Roach, Justine, Librn, New Hanover County Public Library, 201 Chestnut St, Wilmington, NC, 28401. Tel: 910-798-6300. Fax: 910-798-6312. p. 1830

Roach, Justine, Librn, New Hanover County Public Library, Law Library, 201 Chestnut St, Wilmington, NC, 28401. Tel: 910-798-6306. p. 1830

Roach, Linda, Librn, Hoyle, Fickler, Herschel & Mathes LLP, One S Broad St, Ste 1500, Philadelphia, PA, 19107. Tel: 215-981-5852. Fax: 215-981-5959. p. 2111

Roach, Mary, Asst Dean, University of Kansas Libraries, 1425 Jayhawk Blvd, Lawrence, KS, 66045-7544. Tel: 785-864-3956. Fax: 785-864-5311. p. 878

Roache, James, Pres, Canton Historical Society Library, 1400 Washington St, Canton, MA, 02021. Tel: 781-828-8537. p. 1079

Roachell, Maxine, Asst Librn, Kemper-Newton Regional Library System, J Elliott McMullan Library, 300 W Church St, Newton, MS, 39345-2208. Tel: 601-683-3367. Fax: 601-683-3367. p. 1316

Roan, Jim, Ref Librn, Smithsonian Libraries, National Museum of American History Library, NMAH Rm 5016, MRC 630, 14th & Constitution Ave NW, Washington, DC, 20560. Tel: 202-633-3860. Fax: 202-357-4256. p. 415

Roan, Joan, Circ Supvr, Ames Free Library, 53 Main St, North Easton, MA, 02356. Tel: 508-238-2000. Fax: 508-238-2980. p. 1112

Roane, Teresa, Mgr, Museum of the Confederacy, 1201 E Clay St, Richmond, VA, 23219. Tel: 804-649-1861. Fax: 804-644-7150. p. 2489

Roark, Barbara, Dir, Franklin Public Library, 9151 W Loomis Rd, Franklin, WI, 53132. Tel: 414-425-8214. Fax: 414-425-9498. p. 2593

Roark, Brent, Media Spec, Putnamville Correctional Facility, 1946 W US 40, Greencastle, IN, 46135-9275. Tel: 765-653-8441. Fax: 765-653-4157. p. 746

Roark, Carol, Spec Coll & Archives Librn, Dallas Public Library, 1515 Young St, Dallas, TX, 75201-5499. Tel: 214-670-1400. Fax: 214-670-7839. p. 2306

Roark, Jackie, Mgr, Catahoula Parish Library, 300 Bushley St, Harrisonburg, LA, 71340. Tel: 318-744-5271. Fax: 318-744-5251. p. 950

Roark, Joan, Cat, Rainbow City Public Library, 3702 Rainbow Dr, Rainbow City, AL, 35906. Tel: 256-442-8477. Fax: 256-442-4128. p. 34

Roark, Nancy, Regional Mgr, Tennessee State Library & Archives, 403 Seventh Ave N, Nashville, TN, 37243-0312. Tel: 615-741-2764. Fax: 615-532-2472, 615-741-6471. p. 2259

Rob, MacKenzie, Libr Tech, Capital Health/Nova Scotia Hospital, Hugh Bell Bldg, Rm 200, 300 Pleasant St, Dartmouth, NS, B2Y 3Z9, CANADA. Tel: 902-464-3255. Fax: 902-464-4804. p. 2779

Robak, Margaret, Librn, Frisbie Memorial Hospital, 11 Whitehall Rd, Rochester, NH, 03867. Tel: 603-335-8419. Fax: 603-330-8946. p. 1464

Robar, Randy, Dir of Educ, Essex Historical Society & Shipbuilding Museum, Inc, 28 Main St, Essex, MA, 01929. Tel: 978-768-3866. Fax: 978-768-2541. p. 1087

Robards, Paul, Dir, Middle Georgia College, 1100 Second St SE, Cochran, GA, 31014-1599. Tel: 478-934-3074. Fax: 478-934-3378. p. 525

Robare, Andrea, Ref Serv, Southern Vermont College Library, 982 Mansion Dr, Bennington, VT, 05201-6002. Tel: 802-447-6311. Fax: 802-447-4695. p. 2419

Robarts, Barbara R, Dir, William D Weeks Memorial Library, 128 Main St, Lancaster, NH, 03584-3031. Tel: 603-788-3352. Fax: 603-788-3203. p. 1453

Robarts, Phyllis, Librn, Temple Judea, 5500 Granada Blvd, Coral Gables, FL, 33146. Tel: 305-667-5657. Fax: 305-665-5834. p. 434

Robb, Beth, Mgr, Libr Serv, Our Lady of the Resurrection Medical Center Library, 5645 W Addison, Chicago, IL, 60634-4455. Tel: 773-282-7000, Ext 4332. p. 622

Robb, Carol Ann, Head, Adult Serv, Pittsburg Public Library, 308 N Walnut, Pittsburg, KS, 66762-4732. Tel: 620-231-8110. Fax: 620-232-2258. p. 890

Robb, Carrie, Head, Syst Admin, Alexandrian Public Library, 115 W Fifth St, Mount Vernon, IN, 47620. Tel: 812-838-3286. Fax: 812-838-9639. p. 766

Robb, Gaylord, Ref, Salisbury University, 1101 Camden Ave, Salisbury, MD, 21801-6863. Tel: 410-543-6130. Fax: 410-543-6203. p. 1040

Robb, Jenny E, Curator, Ohio State University LIBRARIES, Billy Ireland Cartoon Library & Museum, 27 W 17th Ave Mall, Columbus, OH, 43210-1393. Tel: 614-292-0538. Fax: 614-292-9101. p. 1888

Robb, Jim, Dir, North Arkansas College Library, 1515 Pioneer Dr, Harrison, AR, 72601. Tel: 870-391-3359. Fax: 870-391-3245. p. 102

Robb, Jim, Dir, North Arkansas College Library, North Campus, 1320 Spring Rd, Harrison, AR, 72601. Tel: 870-391-3359. Fax: 870-391-3341. p. 102

Robb, Joan, Coll Develop, Govt Doc Coordr, University of Wisconsin-Green Bay, 2420 Nicolet Dr, Green Bay, WI, 54311-7001. Tel: 920-465-2384. Fax: 920-465-2136. p. 2596

Robb, Liz, Tech Support, CPI Canada, Inc, 45 River Dr, Georgetown, ON, L7G 2J4, CANADA. Tel: 905-877-0161. Fax: 905-877-5327. p. 2806

Robb, Mary Denise, Asst Librn, Akron Department of Planning & Urban Development Library, 403 Municipal Bldg, 166 S High St, Akron, OH, 44308. Tel: 330-375-2084. Fax: 330-375-2387. p. 1851

Robb, Samantha, Librn, Elliott Lasater Maysville Public Library, 508 Williams St, Maysville, OK, 73057. Tel: 405-867-4748. Fax: 405-867-4748. p. 1968

Robb, Suzanne, Librn, CH2M Hill, 2300 NW Walnut Blvd, Corvallis, OR, 97330-3596. Tel: 208-345-5310, Ext 26222. Fax: 541-752-0276. p. 1994

Robben, Kimberly, Mgr, Libr Operations, Wilsonville Public Library, 8200 SW Wilsonville Rd, Wilsonville, OR, 97070. Tel: 503-570-1597. Fax: 503-682-8685. p. 2023

Robbins, Ann, Circ, Northwest Regional Library System, 898 W 11 St, Panama City, FL, 32401. Tel: 850-522-2100. Fax: 850-522-2138. p. 480

Robbins, Carla, Br Mgr, Irondequoit Public Library, 45 Cooper Rd, Rochester, NY, 14617. Tel: 585-336-6062. Fax: 585-336-6066. p. 1729

Robbins, Eric, Asst Dir, Northbrook Public Library, 1201 Cedar Lane, Northbrook, IL, 60062-4581. Tel: 847-272-6224. Fax: 847-272-5362. p. 682

Robbins, Joan, Circ Supvr, New Bern-Craven County Public Library, 400 Johnson St, New Bern, NC, 28560-4098. Tel: 252-638-7800. Fax: 252-638-7817. p. 1812

Robbins, Kathy, Librn, Quatrefoil Library, 1619 Dayton Ave, Ste 105, Saint Paul, MN, 55104-6206. Tel: 651-641-0969. p. 1280

Robbins, Lee, Librn, University of Toronto Libraries, Astronomy & Astrophysics, 60 Saint George St, Rm 1306, Toronto, ON, M5S 1A7, CANADA. Tel: 416-978-4268. Fax: 416-946-7287. p. 2865

Robbins, Linda Miller, Exec Dir, Jefferson County Public Law Library, Old Jail Bldg, Ste 240, 514 W Liberty St, Louisville, KY, 40202-2806. Tel: 502-574-5943. Fax: 502-574-3483. p. 924

Robbins, Louise S, Dir, Prof, University of Wisconsin-Madison, 4217 H C White Hall, 600 N Park St, Madison, WI, 53706. Tel: 608-263-2908. Fax: 608-263-4849. p. 2976

Robbins, Mary, Dir, The W H & Edgar Magness Community House & Library, 118 W Main St, McMinnville, TN, 37110. Tel: 931-473-2428. Fax: 931-473-6778. p. 2247

Robbins, Molly, Asst Dir, Ossining Public Library, 53 Croton Ave, Ossining, NY, 10562-4903. Tel: 914-941-2416. Fax: 914-941-7464. p. 1712

Robbins, Molly, Head, Adult Serv, Ossining Public Library, 53 Croton Ave, Ossining, NY, 10562-4903. Tel: 914-941-2416. Fax: 914-941-7464. p. 1712

Robbins, Paul, Librn, Maine Department of Corrections, 1202 Dover Rd, Charleston, ME, 04422. Tel: 207-285-0876. Fax: 207-285-0815. p. 982

Robbins, Richard G, Dr, Chief Librn, US Department of Defense Armed Forces Pest Management Board, Walter Reed Army Medical Ctr, Forest Glen Section, Washington, DC, 20307-5001. Tel: 301-295-8309. Fax: 301-295-7473. p. 418

Robbins, Roger, Ref Serv, Tech Serv Librn, Lebanon Public Library, Nine E Park St, Lebanon, NH, 03766. Tel: 603-448-2459. p. 1454

Robbins, Steve, Assoc Dir, Tech Serv, Grace College & Grace Theological Seminary, 200 Seminary Dr, Winona Lake, IN, 46590. Tel: 574-372-5100, Ext 6292. Fax: 574-372-5176. p. 789

Robbins, Tiffany R, Dir, Sayre Public Library, Inc, 122 S Elmer Ave, Sayre, PA, 18840. Tel: 570-888-2256. Fax: 570-888-3355. p. 2136

Roberge, Alain, Chief Librn, Universite de Moncton, 415 Ave de l'Universite, Moncton, NB, E1A 3E9, CANADA. Tel: 506-858-4012. Fax: 506-858-4086. p. 2766

Roberson, Allen, Dir, South Carolina Confederate Relic Room & Military Museum Library, 301 Gervais St, Columbia, SC, 29201-3027. Tel: 803-737-8095. Fax: 803-737-8099. p. 2189

Roberson, Beth, Asst Librn, Park County Public Library, Meeteetse Branch, 2107 Idaho, Meeteetse, WY, 82433. Tel: 307-868-2248. Fax: 307-868-2248. p. 2654

Roberson, Gloria Grant, Ref Librn, Adelphi University Libraries, One South Ave, Garden City, NY, 11530. Tel: 516-877-3578. Fax: 516-877-3592. p. 1625

Roberson, Janis, Dir, Grapevine Public Library, 1201 Municipal Way, Grapevine, TX, 76051. Tel: 817-410-3410. Fax: 817-410-3084. p. 2329

Roberson, Julie A, Dir, King College, 1350 King College Rd, Bristol, TN, 37620. Tel: 423-652-6301. Fax: 423-652-4871. p. 2225

Roberson, Kip, Dir, Pierson Library, 5376 Shelburne Rd, Shelburne, VT, 05482. Tel: 802-985-5124. Fax: 802-985-5129. p. 2435

Roberson, Marla, Dir, Tri-County Technical College Library, 7900 Hwy 76, Pendleton, SC, 29670. Tel: 864-646-1750. Fax: 864-646-1543. p. 2202

Roberson, Mary, Librn, Kansas City Public Library, Westport, 118 Westport Rd, Kansas City, MO, 64111. Tel: 816-701-3588. Fax: 816-701-3498. p. 1338

Roberson, Mary, Coordr, ILL & Doc Delivery Serv, Southwestern Oklahoma State University, 100 Campus Dr, Weatherford, OK, 73096-3002. Tel: 580-774-7023. Fax: 580-774-3112. p. 1985

Roberson, Meredith, Mgr, Johnson County Library, Cedar Roe, 5120 Cedar, Roeland Park, KS, 66205. Tel: 913-384-8595. Fax: 913-384-8597. p. 888

Roberson, William, Dir, Long Island University, 100 Second Ave, Brentwood, NY, 11717. Tel: 631-273-5112. Fax: 631-273-5198. p. 1584

Robert, Lena, ILL Asst, Rivier College, 420 S Main St, Nashua, NH, 03060-5086. Tel: 603-897-8587. Fax: 603-897-8889. p. 1459

Robert, Liss, Supvr, East Jersey State Prison Library, Law, Lock Bag R, Woodbridge Ave, Rahway, NJ, 07065. Tel: 732-499-5010. p. 1524

Robert, Mario, Actg Librn, Montreal City Hall, 275 Notre Dame St E, R-113, Montreal, QC, H2Y 1C6, CANADA. Tel: 514-872-9092. Fax: 514-872-3475. p. 2899

Roberta, Depp, Dir, Mamie Doud Eisenhower Public Library, Three Community Park Rd, Broomfield, CO, 80020-3781. Tel: 720-887-2355. Fax: 720-887-1384. p. 292

Robertelli, Darlene, Ref, Jersey Shore University Medical Center, 1945 Rte 33, Neptune, NJ, 07754-0397. Tel: 732-776-4265. Fax: 732-776-4530. p. 1507

Roberton, Sheila, Librn, Southeast Regional Library, Kipling Branch, 207 Sixth Ave, Kipling, SK, S0G 2S0, CANADA. Tel: 306-736-2911. p. 2930

Roberts, Allison, Libr Supvr-Popular Libr, University of Tennessee, Knoxville, Agriculture-Veterinary Medicine, A-113 Veterinary Teaching Hospital, 2407 Joe Johnson Dr, Knoxville, TN, 37996-4541. Tel: 865-974-0356. Fax: 865-974-4732. p. 2244

Roberts, Anna Ray, Dir, Wytheville Community College Library, 1000 E Main St, Wytheville, VA, 24382. Tel: 276-223-4742. Fax: 276-223-4745. p. 2505

Roberts, Barbara, Dir, Harrison Regional Library System, 50 Lester St, Columbiana, AL, 35051. Tel: 205-669-3893. Fax: 205-669-3940. p. 13

Roberts, Barbara, Dir, Pelham Public Library, 3160 Pelham Pkwy, Pelham, AL, 35124. Tel: 205-620-6418. Fax: 205-620-6469. p. 33

Roberts, Barbara, Asst Dir, Miami Dade College, Wolfson Campus Library, 300 NE Second Ave, Miami, FL, 33132. Tel: 305-237-3144. Fax: 305-237-3707. p. 466

Roberts, Barbara L, City Librn, Dir of Libr Serv, Palm Springs Public Library, 300 S Sunrise Way, Palm Springs, CA, 92262-7699. Tel: 760-323-7323. Fax: 760-327-5744. p. 203

Roberts, Belinda, Circ Librn, Wythe-Grayson Regional Library, Rural Retreat Public, 119 N Greever St, Rural Retreat, VA, 24368-2450. Tel: 276-686-8337. Fax: 276-686-8337. p. 2472

Roberts, Bianca, Asst Dir, Tangipahoa Parish Library, Administration Office, 200 E Mulberry St, Amite, LA, 70422. Tel: 985-748-7559. Fax: 985-748-2812. p. 941

Roberts, Bobby, Dr, Dir, Central Arkansas Library System, 100 Rock St, Little Rock, AR, 72201-4698. Tel: 501-918-3037. p. 106

Roberts, Brent S, Dir, Montana State University, 1500 University Dr, Billings, MT, 59101-0298. Tel: 406-657-1655. Fax: 406-657-2037. p. 1374

Roberts, Bridget, Circ Serv, Spring Green Community Library, 230 E Monroe St, Spring Green, WI, 53588-8035. Tel: 608-588-2276. p. 2639

Roberts, Carla, Head, Popular Libr, Licking County Library, 101 W Main St, Newark, OH, 43055-5054. Tel: 740-349-5550. Fax: 740-349-5535. p. 1922

Roberts, Carol, Dir, Presv Serv, Tennessee State Library & Archives, 403 Seventh Ave N, Nashville, TN, 37243-0312. Tel: 615-741-2997. Fax: 615-532-2472, 615-741-6471. p. 2259

Roberts, Carol R, Dir, Wilton Public & Gregg Free Library, Seven Forest Rd, Wilton, NH, 03086. Tel: 603-654-2581. Fax: 603-654-3674. p. 1468

Roberts, Carolyn, Circ, Tidewater Community College Learning Resources Center, 300 Granby St, Norfolk, VA, 23510. Tel: 757-822-1100. Fax: 757-822-1106. p. 2483

Roberts, Cecilia, Info Serv Dir/Ref, Regis College Library, 235 Wellesley St, Weston, MA, 02493. Tel: 781-768-7300. Fax: 781-768-7323. p. 1139

Roberts, Celia, Ref, Simsbury Public Library, 725 Hopmeadow St, Simsbury, CT, 06070. Tel: 860-658-7663. Fax: 860-658-6732. p. 367

Roberts, Christine, Dir, Johnston Community College Library, Learning Resource Ctr, 245 College Rd, Smithfield, NC, 27577. Tel: 919-464-2252. p. 1824

Roberts, Connie, Dir of Tech Serv, Hamilton College, 198 College Hill Rd, Clinton, NY, 13323-1299. Tel: 315-859-4490. Fax: 315-859-4578. p. 1607

Roberts, Cynthia, Dir of Libr Serv, Community College of Baltimore County, Y Bldg, 800 S Rolling Rd, Catonsville, MD, 21228. Tel: 443-840-4589. Fax: 410-455-6436. p. 1023

Roberts, Cynthia, Dir, Libr Serv, Community College of Baltimore County, Dundalk Library, K Bldg, 7200 Sollers Point Rd, Baltimore, MD, 21222. Fax: 443-840-3559. p. 1023

Roberts, Dan, Ref, Ozark Regional Library, 402 N Main St, Ironton, MO, 63650. Tel: 573-546-2615. Fax: 573-546-7225. p. 1333

Roberts, David, Dir, Wissahickon Valley Public Library, Ambler Branch, 209 Race St, Ambler, PA, 19002. Tel: 215-646-1072. Fax: 215-654-0161. p. 2036

Roberts, David J, Dir, Wissahickon Valley Public Library, 650 Skippack Pike, Blue Bell, PA, 19422. Tel: 215-643-1320, Ext 11. Fax: 215-643-6611. p. 2036

Roberts, Dianne, Ch, Longwood Public Library, 800 Middle Country Rd, Middle Island, NY, 11953. Tel: 631-924-6400. Fax: 631-924-7538. p. 1660

Roberts, Doreen, Librn, St Luke's Hospital, 915 E First St, Duluth, MN, 55805. Tel: 218-249-5320. Fax: 218-249-5926. p. 1248

Roberts, Doreen, Circ Supvr, Chinook Regional Library, 1240 Chaplin St W, Swift Current, SK, S9H 0G8, CANADA. Tel: 306-773-3186. Fax: 306-773-0434. p. 2927

Roberts, Elaine, Librn, Victor Public Library, 710 Second St, Victor, IA, 52347. Tel: 319-647-3646. Fax: 319-647-3646. p. 848

Roberts, Ellen, Br Mgr, Robinson Public Library District, Susie Wesley Memorial, 105 S Main, Flat Rock, IL, 62427. Tel: 618-584-3636. Fax: 618-584-3636. p. 695

Roberts, Frances, Dir, Grant County Library, 215 E Grant Ave, Ulysses, KS, 67880-2958. Tel: 620-356-1433. Fax: 620-356-1344. p. 898

Roberts, Frank, Br Mgr, Saint Lucie County Library System, Zora Neale Hurston Branch, 3008 Avenue D, Fort Pierce, FL, 34947. Tel: 772-462-2154. Fax: 772-462-2844. p. 447

Roberts, Franklin D, Dir, University of Maine at Farmington, 116 South St, Farmington, ME, 04938-1990. Tel: 207-778-7215. Fax: 207-778-7223. p. 985

Roberts, Gail, Tech Serv, Cheshire Public Library, 104 Main St, Cheshire, CT, 06410-2499. Tel: 203-272-2245. Fax: 203-272-7714. p. 333

Roberts, Gail, Dir, Libr & Media Serv, Southwest Georgia Technical College Library, 15689 US Hwy 19 N, Thomasville, GA, 31792. Tel: 229-225-3958. Fax: 229-225-3959. p. 553

Roberts, Gail, Youth Serv, New Bedford Free Public Library, 613 Pleasant St, New Bedford, MA, 02740-6203. Tel: 508-991-6275. Fax: 508-991-6368. p. 1108

Roberts, Gail, Br Mgr, Cass County Public Library, Archie Branch, 315 S Main, Archie, MO, 64725. Tel: 816-293-5579. p. 1330

Roberts, Geri, Asst Admin, Beaumont Public Library System, 801 Pearl St, Beaumont, TX, 77701. Tel: 409-981-5911. Fax: 409-838-6838. p. 2287

Roberts, Geri, Asst Admin, Beaumont Public Library System, Beaumont Public, 801 Pearl St, Beaumont, TX, 77701. Tel: 409-833-7308. p. 2287

Roberts, Gregg, Librn, Branchville Correctional Facility Library, 21390 Old State Rd 37, Branchville, IN, 47514. Tel: 812-843-5921, Ext 4328. Fax: 812-843-4262. p. 729

Roberts, Helen, ILL, Paola Free Library, 101 E Peoria, Paola, KS, 66071-1798. Tel: 913-259-3655. Fax: 913-259-3656. p. 889

Roberts, Jackie, Libr Mgr, Metropolitan Community College, Penn Valley Community College Library, 3201 SW Trafficway, Kansas City, MO, 64111-2764. Tel: 816-604-4088. p. 1339

Roberts, James, Chief Info Officer, National Film Board of Canada, 3155 Cote-de-Liesse Rd, Saint Laurent, QC, H4N 2N4, CANADA. Tel: 514-496-1044. Fax: 514-283-9811. p. 2909

Roberts, Janet, Dir, Wymore Public Library, 116 W F St, Wymore, NE, 68466. Tel: 402-645-3787. Fax: 402-645-3787. p. 1424

Roberts, Jennifer K, Tech Serv, Garnet A Wilson Public Library of Pike County, 207 N Market St, Waverly, OH, 45690-1176. Tel: 740-947-4921. Fax: 740-947-2918. p. 1945

Roberts, Jenny, Circ, Chillicothe & Ross County Public Library, Kingston Branch, 17 Main St, Kingston, OH, 45644. Tel: 740-702-4180. Fax: 740-702-4181. p. 1867

Roberts, Jo Dee, Br Mgr, Cameron Parish Library, Grand Lake, 961 Hwy 384, Lake Charles, LA, 70607. Tel: 337-598-5950. p. 946

Roberts, Joni R, Assoc Univ Librn, Pub Serv & Coll, Willamette University, 900 State St, Salem, OR, 97301. Tel: 503-370-6741. Fax: 503-370-6141. p. 2018

Roberts, Joshua, Digital Initiatives & Syst Librn, University of the Arts University Libraries, Anderson Hall, 1st Flr, 333 S Broad St, Philadelphia, PA, 19102. Tel: 215-717-6244. Fax: 215-717-6287. p. 2119

Roberts, Juanita M, Dir, Libr Serv - Univ Archives & Mus, Tuskegee University, Hollis Burke Frissell Bldg, 1200 W Old Montgomery Rd, Tuskegee, AL, 36088. Tel: 334-727-8892, 334-727-8894. Fax: 334-727-9282. p. 39

Roberts, June, Librn, Warren Hospital, 185 Roseberry St, Phillipsburg, NJ, 08865. Tel: 908-859-6700, Ext 2012. Fax: 908-213-6698. p. 1520

Roberts, Kelly, Coordr, Ch Serv, New Woodstock Free Library, 2106 Main St, New Woodstock, NY, 13122-8718. Tel: 315-662-3134. p. 1667

Roberts, Kelsey, Librn, Polsinelli Shughart PC, 700 W 47th St, Ste 1000, Kansas City, MO, 64112. Tel: 816-753-1000. Fax: 816-753-1536. p. 1340

Roberts, Kim, Dir, Philadelphia Public Library, 714 Thompson St, Philadelphia, TN, 37846. Tel: 865-458-9493. Fax: 865-458-9493. p. 2263

Roberts, Laurie S, Dir, Tazewell County Public Library, 310 E Main St, Tazewell, VA, 24651. Tel: 276-988-2541. Fax: 276-988-5980. p. 2497

Roberts, Lisa, Dir, Principia College, One Maybeck Pl, Elsah, IL, 62028-9703. Tel: 618-374-5235. Fax: 618-374-5107. p. 643

Roberts, Lizz, Commun Relations Coordr, Whatcom County Library System, 5205 Northwest Dr, Bellingham, WA, 98226-9050. Tel: 360-384-3150. Fax: 360-384-4947. p. 2509

Roberts, Lois, Head, Pub Serv, Statesboro Regional Public Libraries, 124 S Main St, Statesboro, GA, 30458. Tel: 912-764-1336. Fax: 912-764-1348. p. 552

Roberts, Lois, Syst Librn, Northwest Nazarene University, 623 University Blvd, Nampa, ID, 83686. Tel: 208-467-8608. Fax: 208-467-8610. p. 580

Roberts, Lynda, Mgr, Libr Serv, Bull, Housser & Tupper Library, 3000 Royal Centre, 1055 W Georgia St, Vancouver, BC, V6E 3R3, CANADA. Tel: 604-641-4878. Fax: 604-646-2535. p. 2740

Roberts, Lynn, Acq, McMurry University, Sayles Blvd & S 14th, Abilene, TX, 79605. Tel: 325-793-4692. Fax: 325-793-4930. p. 2272

Roberts, Lynn, Media Spec, Parkersburg & Wood County Public Library, 3100 Emerson Ave, Parkersburg, WV, 26104-2414. Tel: 304-420-4587, Ext 18. Fax: 304-420-4589. p. 2568

Roberts, Malinda, Dir, Spencer Public Library, 21 E Third St, Spencer, IA, 51301-4188. Tel: 712-580-7290. Fax: 712-580-7468. p. 845

Roberts, Margaret Arianne, Librn, Sistersville Public Library, 518 Wells St, Sistersville, WV, 26175. Tel: 304-652-6701. Fax: 304-652-6701. p. 2572

Roberts, Marilyn, Circ, Ch, Delaware County Library, 429 S Ninth St, Jay, OK, 74346. Tel: 918-253-8521. Fax: 918-253-8726. p. 1966

Roberts, Marisol, Librn, Hopping, Green & Sams, PO Box 6526, Tallahassee, FL, 32314-6526. Tel: 850-222-7500. Fax: 850-224-8551. p. 495

Roberts, Mark E, Dr, Dir, Holy Spirit Res Ctr, Oral Roberts University Library, Holy Spirit Research Center, 7777 S Lewis Ave, Tulsa, OK, 74171. Tel: 918-495-6868. Fax: 918-495-6662. p. 1982

Roberts, Martha, Librn, VA Medical Center, 940 Belmont St, Brockton, MA, 02301. Tel: 774-826-1142. Fax: 774-826-1537. p. 1071

Roberts, Mary, Libr Serv Mgr, Mohave County Library District, Bullhead City Branch, 1170 E Hancock Rd, Bullhead City, AZ, 86442. Tel: 928-758-0714, Ext 2041. Fax: 928-758-0720. p. 66

Roberts, Mary, Libr Mgr, Peoria Public Library, 8463 W Monroe St, Peoria, AZ, 85345. Tel: 623-773-7557. Fax: 623-773-7567. p. 71

Roberts, Melissa, Cataloger, Nashua Community College, 505 Amherst St, Nashua, NH, 03063-1026. Tel: 603-882-6923, Ext 1532. Fax: 603-882-8690. p. 1458

Roberts, Park, Dir, Libr & Mus Serv, The Morgan Library, 225 Madison Ave, New York, NY, 10016. Tel: 212-685-0008. p. 1687

Roberts, Patti, Tech Serv, Kalsec, Inc, 3713 W Main St, Kalamazoo, MI, 49006. Tel: 269-349-9711. Fax: 269-382-3060. p. 1197

Roberts, Paul, Interim Archivist, University of Wisconsin-Stout Library, 315 Tenth Ave, Menomonie, WI, 54751-0790. Tel: 715-232-2300. Fax: 715-232-1783. p. 2615

Roberts, Paul A, Librn, Southeastern Bible College Library, 2545 Valleydale Rd, Birmingham, AL, 35244. Tel: 205-970-9233. Fax: 205-970-9207. p. 9

Roberts, Pauline, Br Mgr, Gadsden Public Library, Hoyt Warsham, 2700 W Meighan Blvd, Gadsden, AL, 35904. Tel: 256-549-4688. p. 18

Roberts, Rebecca K, Info Literacy & Assessment Mgr, Youngstown State University, One University Plaza, Youngstown, OH, 44555-0001. Tel: 330-941-1720. Fax: 330-941-3734. p. 1953

Roberts, Rita, Librn, Michael Donovan Library, 655 Topsail Rd, St. John's, NL, A1E 2E3, CANADA. Tel: 709-737-2621. Fax: 709-737-2621. p. 2772

Roberts, Rob, Head, Fac & Security, University of Florida Libraries, 535 Library W, Gainesville, FL, 32611-7000. Tel: 352-273-2575. Fax: 352-392-4507. p. 450

Roberts, Roberta, In Charge, Pulp & Paper Research Institute of Canada, 570 Saint Jean Blvd, Pointe-Claire, QC, H9R 3J9, CANADA. Tel: 514-630-4100. Fax: 514-630-4134. p. 2903

Roberts, Ryan, Librn, Lincoln Land Community College Library, 5250 Shepherd Rd, Springfield, IL, 62794. Tel: 217-786-2771. Fax: 217-786-2251. p. 705

Roberts, Sandra, Libr Coordr, Jefferson Community & Technical College, Carrollton Campus, 324 Main St, Carrollton, KY, 41008. Tel: 502-213-5520. p. 924

Roberts, Sharon, Circ, Elmont Public Library, 700 Hempstead Tpk, Elmont, NY, 11003-1896. Tel: 516-354-5280. Fax: 516-354-3276. p. 1620

Roberts, Sharon A, Asst Dean, Coll Res Mgt, Ball State University Libraries, 2000 W University Ave, Muncie, IN, 47306-1099. Tel: 765-285-1305. Fax: 765-285-2008. p. 766

Roberts, Sherryl, Dir, Coffee County-Manchester Library, 1005 Hillsboro Hwy, Manchester, TN, 37355-2099. Tel: 931-723-5143. Fax: 931-723-0713. p. 2246

Roberts, Shirley J, Outreach Serv Librn, Eastern Oregon University, One University Blvd, La Grande, OR, 97850. Tel: 541-962-3540. Fax: 541-962-3335. p. 2003

Roberts, Susan, Bur Chief, Bureau of Braille & Talking Book Library Services, 420 Platt St, Daytona Beach, FL, 32114-2804. Tel: 386-239-6000. Fax: 386-239-6069. p. 435

Roberts, Susan, Coordr, Ch Serv, Coordr, Extn Serv, Mansfield-Richland County Public Library, 43 W Third St, Mansfield, OH, 44902-1295. Tel: 419-521-3127. Fax: 419-525-4750. p. 1912

Roberts, Susan, Br Mgr, Carnegie Public Library, Jeffersonville Branch, Eight N Main St, Jeffersonville, OH, 43128-1063. Tel: 740-426-9292. Fax: 740-426-9284. p. 1945

Roberts, Susan, Br Mgr, Colleton County Memorial Library, Edisto Beach Branch, 71 Station Ct, Edisto Beach, SC, 29438. Tel: 843-869-2499. p. 2207

Roberts, Thea, Librn, Heartland Regional Library System, 304 N St Louis St, Iberia, MO, 65486. Tel: 573-793-6746. Fax: 573-793-6037. p. 1331

Roberts, Tim, Librn, Hospital for Special Surgery, 535 E 70th St, New York, NY, 10021. Tel: 212-606-1000, 212-606-1210. Fax: 212-774-2779. p. 1681

Roberts, Toni, Dir, Rippey Public Library, 224 Main St, Rippey, IA, 50235. Tel: 515-436-7714. Fax: 515-436-7485. p. 840

Roberts, Valerie C, Librn, Saint Francis Hospital, 241 North Rd, Poughkeepsie, NY, 12601. Tel: 845-431-8132. Fax: 845-485-2964. p. 1723

Roberts, Wendy, Dir, Laurel Public Library, 101 E Fourth St, Laurel, DE, 19956-1567. Tel: 302-875-3184. p. 384

Roberts, Wes, Librn, Corporation of the City of Burlington, 426 Brant St, Burlington, ON, L7R 3Z6, CANADA. Tel: 905-335-7777. Fax: 905-335-7881. p. 2798

Roberts, Wesley, Sr Librn, Job & Career Educ Ctr, Carnegie Library of Pittsburgh, 4400 Forbes Ave, Pittsburgh, PA, 15213-4080. Tel: 412-578-2521. Fax: 412-622-3136. p. 2122

Robertson, Anne Murray, Br Mgr, Dakota County Library System, Galaxie, 14955 Galaxie Ave, Apple Valley, MN, 55124. Tel: 952-891-7054. Fax: 952-891-7048. p. 1249

Robertson, Anthony, Br Mgr, Brooklyn Public Library, Crown Heights, 560 New York Ave, Brooklyn, NY, 11225. Tel: 718-773-1180. Fax: 718-773-0144. p. 1591

Robertson, Bev, Dir, Libr Serv, Mars Hill College, 124 Cascade St, Mars Hill, NC, 28754. Tel: 828-689-1561. p. 1809

Robertson, Brenda, Librn, University of North Texas Libraries, Dallas Campus Library, 7400 University Hills Blvd, Dallas, TX, 75241. Tel: 972-780-3625, Ext 1617. Fax: 972-780-3676. p. 2313

Robertson, Clay, Dir, West Carroll Parish Library, 101 Marietta St, Oak Grove, LA, 71263. Tel: 318-428-4100. Fax: 318-428-9887. p. 965

Robertson, Cyndy, Asst Dean of Libr, Coordr, Spec Coll, University of Louisiana at Monroe Library, 700 University Ave, Monroe, LA, 71209-0720. Tel: 318-342-1054. Fax: 318-342-1075. p. 958

Robertson, Cyndy, Coordr, Spec Coll & Libr Develop, University of Louisiana at Monroe Library, 700 University Ave, Monroe, LA, 71209-0720. Tel: 318-342-1054. Fax: 318-342-1075. p. 958

Robertson, Debbie, Asst Librn, Chinook Regional Library, Kincaid Branch, Village Office, Kincaid, SK, S0H 2J0, CANADA. Tel: 306-264-3910. p. 2928

Robertson, Debora, Dir, Briar Cliff University, 3303 Rebecca St, Sioux City, IA, 51104-2324. Tel: 712-279-1771. Fax: 712-279-1723. p. 843

Robertson, Delight, Librn, Sisseton Wahpeton College Library, Agency Village, PO Box 689, Sisseton, SD, 57262-0698. Tel: 605-698-3966, Ext 1320. Fax: 605-698-3132. p. 2219

Robertson, Eliza S, Dir, National Humanities Center Library, Seven Alexander Dr, Research Triangle Park, NC, 27709. Tel: 919-549-0661. Fax: 919-990-8535. p. 1819

Robertson, Ginni, Librn, Independent Presbyterian Church, 3100 Highland Ave S, Birmingham, AL, 35205-1400. Tel: 205-933-1830. Fax: 205-933-1836. p. 8

Robertson, Grant, Br Supvr, Bruce County Public Library, Lucknow Branch, 526 Campbell St, Lucknow, ON, N0G 2H0, CANADA. Tel: 519-528-3011. p. 2837

Robertson, Grant, Br Supvr, Bruce County Public Library, Ripley Branch, 23 Jessie St, Ripley, ON, N0G 2R0, CANADA. Tel: 519-395-5919. p. 2837

Robertson, Jack, Found Librn, Thomas Jefferson Foundation Inc, 1329 Kenwood Farm Lane, Charlottesville, VA, 22902. Tel: 434-984-7545. Fax: 434-984-7546. p. 2454

Robertson, Jane, Dir, Anne West Lindsey District Library, 600 N Division St, Carterville, IL, 62918. Tel: 618-985-3298. Fax: 618-985-9474. p. 601

Robertson, Jean Burritt, Dir, Rhode Island Economic Development Corp, One W Exchange St, Providence, RI, 02903. Tel: 401-222-2601, Ext 132. Fax: 401-222-2102. p. 2174

Robertson, Jo, Dr, Chair, Murray State University, 3201 Alexander Hall, Murray, KY, 42071-3309. Tel: 270-809-2500. Fax: 270-809-3799. p. 2966

Robertson, Justin, Asst Dir, Pub Serv, University of South Alabama, Biomedical Library, Biomedical Library Bldg, 5791 USA Dr N, Mobile, AL, 36688-0002. Tel: 251-460-7043. Fax: 251-460-6958. p. 26

Robertson, Katherine, Librn, Olmsted Public Library, 160 N Front St, Olmsted, IL, 62970. Tel: 618-742-8296. Fax: 618-742-8296. p. 685

Robertson, Kathleen M, Libr Dir, Union Free Public Library, 979 Buckley Hwy, Union, CT, 06076. Tel: 860-684-4913. Fax: 860-684-4913. p. 373

Robertson, Kaye, Exec Dir, Nova Southeastern University, 3200 S University Dr, Fort Lauderdale, FL, 33328. Tel: 954-262-3106. Fax: 954-262-1821. p. 443

Robertson, Kevin, ILL Librn, Rosalind Franklin University of Medicine & Science, 3333 Green Bay Rd, North Chicago, IL, 60064. Tel: 847-578-3243. Fax: 847-578-3401. p. 682

Robertson, Linda, AV, Louisburg College, 501 N Main St, Louisburg, NC, 27549-7704. Tel: 919-497-3253. Fax: 919-496-5444. p. 1807

Robertson, Lynette, Br Mgr, Dallas Public Library, Pleasant Grove, 7310 Lake June Rd, Dallas, TX, 75217. Tel: 214-670-0965. p. 2307

Robertson, Marlene, Librn, Nexen Inc Library, 801 Seventh Ave SW, Calgary, AB, T2P 3P7, CANADA. Tel: 403-699-5425. Fax: 403-232-1826. p. 2692

Robertson, Mary L, Curator, Huntington Library, 1151 Oxford Rd, San Marino, CA, 91108. Tel: 626-405-2204. Fax: 626-449-5720. p. 255

Robertson, Meg, Br Mgr, Ramsey County Library, New Brighton Branch, 400 Tenth St NW, New Brighton, MN, 55112-6806. Tel: 651-724-6002. p. 1284

Robertson, Michelle, Automation Librn, Anne Arundel Community College, 101 College Pkwy, Arnold, MD, 21012-1895. Tel: 410-777-2211. Fax: 410-777-2652. p. 1011

Robertson, Nancy, State Librn, Library of Michigan, 702 W Kalamazoo St, Lansing, MI, 48915. Tel: 517-373-9464. Fax: 517-373-5700. p. 1201

Robertson, Nathan, Dir, Info Policy & Mgt, University of Maryland, Baltimore, Thurgood Marshall Law Library, 501 W Fayette St, Baltimore, MD, 21201-1768. Tel: 410-706-1213. Fax: 410-706-8354. p. 1019

Robertson, Nicole, Ref Serv, Vance-Granville Community College, State Rd 1126, Poplar Creek Rd, Exit 209, Henderson, NC, 27536. Tel: 252-492-2061. Fax: 252-738-3372. p. 1800

Robertson, Paris, Dep Fiscal Officer, Tech Coordr, Upper Sandusky Community Library, 301 N Sandusky Ave, Upper Sandusky, OH, 43351-1139. Tel: 419-294-1345. Fax: 419-294-4499. p. 1942

Robertson, Pat, Br Supvr, Flint River Regional Library, J Joel Edwards Public Library, 7077 Hwy 19 S, Zebulon, GA, 30295. Tel: 770-567-2014. p. 535

Robertson, Pat, Asst Librn, Shelbyville Free Public Library, 154 N Broadway St, Shelbyville, IL, 62565-1698. Tel: 217-774-4432. Fax: 217-774-2634. p. 702

Robertson, Patrice, Br Mgr, Campbell County Public Library, Staunton River Memorial, 500 Washington St, Altavista, VA, 24517. Tel: 434-369-5140. Fax: 434-369-1723. p. 2495

Robertson, Sally, Cat, Ref Serv, Ser, Nashville State Technical Community College, 120 White Bridge Rd, Nashville, TN, 37209-4515. Tel: 615-353-3270. Fax: 615-353-3558. p. 2258

Robertson, Sandra, ILL, Chickasha Public Library, 527 W Iowa Ave, Chickasha, OK, 73018. Tel: 405-222-6075. Fax: 405-222-6072. p. 1959

Robertson, Sarah, Adult Serv, Three Rivers Public Library District, 25207 W Channon Dr, Channahon, IL, 60410-5028. Tel: 815-467-6200. Fax: 815-467-4012. p. 603

Robertson, Steve, Sr Librn, California Department of Corrections Library System, California Men's Colony-East, Hwy 1 Drawer B, San Luis Obispo, CA, 93409. Tel: 805-547-7900, Ext 4197. p. 221

Robertson, Susan, Coll Develop, Evanston Public Library, 1703 Orrington, Evanston, IL, 60201. Tel: 847-448-8619. Fax: 847-866-0313. p. 643

Robertson, Susan, Dir, Gore Place Society, Inc Library, 52 Gore St, Waltham, MA, 02453. Tel: 781-894-2798. Fax: 781-894-5745. p. 1133

Robertson, Terry, Sem Coll Librn, Andrews University, 1400 Library Rd, Berrien Springs, MI, 49104-1400. Tel: 269-471-3269. Fax: 269-471-6166. p. 1157

Robertson-Henry, Karen, Librn, Michigan Jewish Institute Library, 25401 Coolidge Hwy, Oak Park, MI, 48237. Tel: 248-414-6900, Ext 105. Fax: 248-414-6907. p. 1215

Robeson, Mary Anne, Mgr, Hudson Yablonski Community Library, 208 Illinois St, Hudson, WY, 82515. Tel: 307-332-3605. Fax: 307-332-3625. p. 2656

Robichaud, Jeremy J, Circ, Maynard Public Library, 77 Nason St, Maynard, MA, 01754-2316. Tel: 978-897-1010. Fax: 978-897-9884. p. 1103

Robichaud, Louise, Chef de Section, Bibliothèques de Montrèal, Georges-Vanier, 2450, rue Workman, Montreal, QC, H3J 1L8, CANADA. Tel: 514-872-3763. Fax: 514-872-0511. p. 2889

Robichaud, Louise, Chef de Section, Bibliothèques de Montrèal, Saint-Charles, 2333, rue Mullins (adultes), 1050, rue Hibernia (jeunes), Montreal, QC, H3K 3E3, CANADA. Tel: 514-872-3763. p. 2891

Robichaud, Marie-Josée, Pub Serv, Universite de Moncton, Centre de Ressources Pédagogiques, 68, rue Notre-Dame-du-Sacré-Coeur, Pavillon Jeanne-de-Valois, local B-010, Moncton, NB, E1A 3E9, CANADA. Tel: 506-858-4356. Fax: 506-858-4317. p. 2766

Robichaud, Pierre, Libr Asst, Public Service Labour Relations Board Library, West Tower, 6th Flr, 240 Sparks St, Ottawa, ON, K1P 5V2, CANADA. Tel: 613-990-1800. Fax: 613-990-1849. p. 2833

Robichaud, Steve, Tech Serv, Southern New Hampshire University, 2500 N River Rd, Manchester, NH, 03106-1045. Tel: 603-645-9605. Fax: 603-645-9685. p. 1456

Robicheaux, Patty, Br Mgr, Saint Mary Parish Library, 206 Iberia St, Franklin, LA, 70538-4906. Tel: 337-828-1624. Fax: 337-828-2329. p. 949

Robillard, Diane, Syst Librn, Chicopee Public Library, 449 Front St, Chicopee, MA, 01013. Tel: 413-594-1800. Fax: 413-594-1819. p. 1081

Robillard, Lise, In Charge, Agriculture & Agri-Food Canada, Plant Research Library, Wm Saunders Bldg No 49, CEF, 960 Carling Ave, Ottawa, ON, K1A 0C6, CANADA. Tel: 613-759-1368. Fax: 613-759-1599. p. 2827

Robillard, Tanya, Circ, Saint Joseph College, 1678 Asylum Ave, West Hartford, CT, 06117-2791. Tel: 860-232-4571. Fax: 860-523-4356. p. 376

Robin, Annabeth, Dir, Phillips 66 Research Library, 122 PLB PRC, Bartlesville, OK, 74003-6670. Tel: 918-661-3433. Fax: 918-662-2171. p. 1958

Robinett, Carol, Webmaster, South Macon Public Library District, 451 W Glenn St, Macon, IL, 62544. Tel: 217-764-3356. Fax: 217-764-5490. p. 669

Robinette, Christine, Libr Dir, Ignacio Community Library District, 470 Goddard Ave, Ignacio, CO, 81137. Tel: 970-563-9287. Fax: 970-563-9296. p. 313

Robins, David, Dr, Asst Prof, Kent State University, 314 Library, Kent, OH, 44242-0001. Tel: 330-672-2782. Fax: 330-672-7965. p. 2972

Robins, Jennifer, Dr, Assoc Prof, University of Central Missouri, Dept of Educational Leadership & Human Development, Lovinger 4101, Warrensburg, MO, 64093. Tel: 660-543-8879. Fax: 660-543-4164. p. 2968

Robins, Jill, Dir, Lewis, Brisbois, Bisgaard & Smith, 221 N Figueroa St, Ste 1300, Los Angeles, CA, 90012. Tel: 213-580-7908. Fax: 213-250-7900. p. 171

Robins, Judith, Coll Supvr, American Society of Anesthesiologists, 520 N Northwest Hwy, Park Ridge, IL, 60068-2573. Tel: 847-825-5586. Fax: 847-825-1692. p. 688

Robins, Kathy, Syst Adminr, Parmly Billings Library, 510 N Broadway, Billings, MT, 59101-1196. Tel: 406-657-8258. Fax: 406-657-8293. p. 1374

Robins, Sharani, Ref Librn, Dartmouth Public Libraries, 732 Dartmouth St, Dartmouth, MA, 02748. Tel: 508-999-0726. Fax: 508-992-9914. p. 1084

Robinson, Aeisia, Mgr, Queens Borough Public Library, Central Circulation Services Division, 89-11 Merrick Blvd, Jamaica, NY, 11432. Tel: 718-990-0771. Fax: 718-658-8342. p. 1644

Robinson, Albert, Librn, St Vincent Hospital Library, 455 St Michael's Dr, Santa Fe, NM, 87505. Tel: 505-820-5218. Fax: 505-989-6478. p. 1563

Robinson, Albert, Chair, New Mexico Consortium of Biomedical & Hospital Libraries, c/o St Vincent Hospital, 455 St Michaels Dr, Santa Fe, NM, 87505. Tel: 505-820-5218. Fax: 505-989-6478. p. 2949

Robinson, Alexandra, Adult Serv, Aaron Cutler Memorial Library, 269 Charles Bancroft Hwy, Litchfield, NH, 03052. Tel: 603-424-4044. Fax: 603-424-4044. p. 1454

Robinson, Alfenette, Br Supvr, Jackson/Hinds Library System, Annie Thompson Jeffers Library, 111 Madison St, Bolton, MS, 39041. Tel: 601-866-4247. Fax: 601-866-4653. p. 1303

Robinson, Amanda, Access Serv, Brockville Public Library, 23 Buell St, Brockville, ON, K6V 5T7, CANADA. Tel: 613-342-3936. Fax: 613-342-9598. p. 2797

Robinson, Ann, ILL, Ref Librn, Sci Librn, Harvard Library, History of Science Library - Cabot Science Library, Science Center, One Oxford St, Cambridge, MA, 02138. Tel: 617-495-5355. Fax: 617-495-5324. p. 1075

Robinson, Ann, Dir, Seabrook Library, 25 Liberty Lane, Seabrook, NH, 03874-4506. Tel: 603-474-2044. Fax: 603-474-1835. p. 1465

Robinson, Anna, Head, Ch, Stinson Memorial Public Library District, 409 S Main St, Anna, IL, 62906. Tel: 618-833-2521. Fax: 618-833-3560. p. 589

Robinson, Arthur, Dr, Ref, La Grange College, 601 Broad St, La Grange, GA, 30240-2999. Tel: 706-880-8289. Fax: 706-880-8040. p. 537

Robinson, Bonnie, Louisville Satellite Librn, US Court of Appeals for the Sixth Circuit Library, 312 Potter Stewart US Courthouse, Cincinnati, OH, 45202. Tel: 502-625-3850. Fax: 513-564-7329. p. 1873

Robinson, Caitlin, Head, Coll Serv, University of Iowa Libraries, Law Library, 200 Boyd Law Bldg, Iowa City, IA, 52242-1166. Tel: 319-335-9049. Fax: 319-335-9039. p. 823

Robinson, Carla, Librn, Florida Atlantic University, 500 NW California Blvd, Port Saint Lucie, FL, 34986. Tel: 772-462-3311. Fax: 772-873-3409. p. 485

Robinson, Carla Ruth, Assoc Univ Librn, Florida Atlantic University, 5600 US 1 N, Fort Pierce, FL, 34946. Tel: 772-242-2201. Fax: 772-242-2348. p. 446

Robinson, Carol, Libr Asst, Baxter Memorial Library, 71 South St, Gorham, ME, 04038. Tel: 207-222-1190. Fax: 207-839-7749. p. 986

Robinson, Carol, Coll Mgr, Massachusetts Institute of Technology Libraries, Barker Engineering, Bldg 10-500, 77 Massachusetts Ave, Cambridge, MA, 02139-4307. Tel: 617-253-7749. Fax: 617-258-5623. p. 1077

Robinson, Carolyn, Dr, Dir, Staff Develop, Central Virginia Training Center, PO Box 1098, Lynchburg, VA, 24505. Tel: 434-947-6171, 434-947-6871. Fax: 434-947-2395. p. 2475

Robinson, Cathy, Circ, Polk County Public Library, 1289 W Mills St, Columbus, NC, 28722. Tel: 828-894-8721. Fax: 828-894-2761. p. 1785

Robinson, Chantal, Librn, Quebec Office quebecois de la Langue Francaise Bibliotheque, 125 W Sherbrooke, Montreal, QC, H2X 1X4, CANADA. Tel: 514-873-2996, 514-873-2997. Fax: 514-873-2868. p. 2900

Robinson, Cherie, Dir, Jackson County Memorial Library, 411 N Wells St, Rm 121, Edna, TX, 77957-2734. Tel: 361-782-2162. Fax: 361-782-6708. p. 2315

Robinson, Cynthia, Assoc Dir, Knowledge & Content Mgt, Babson College, 231 Forest St, Babson Park, MA, 02457-0310. Tel: 781-239-5257. Fax: 781-239-5226. p. 1051

Robinson, Cynthia, Dir, Pennsylvania State University, College of Medicine, Penn State Hershey, Harrell Health Sciences Library, 500 University Dr, Hershey, PA, 17033. Tel: 717-531-8628. Fax: 717-531-8636. p. 2069

Robinson, David, Dir, Oklahoma State University-Oklahoma City Library, 900 N Portland, Oklahoma City, OK, 73107-6195. Tel: 405-945-3241. Fax: 405-945-3289. p. 1975

Robinson, David, Syst Librn, Middle Tennessee State University, MTSU, PO Box 13, Murfreesboro, TN, 37132. Tel: 615-898-2572. p. 2254

Robinson, David, Ad, Shenandoah County Library, 514 Stoney Creek Blvd, Edinburg, VA, 22824. Tel: 540-984-8200. Fax: 540-984-8207. p. 2460

Robinson, DeBarbara, Br Mgr, Richland County Public Library, Eastover Branch, 608 Main St, Eastover, SC, 29044. Tel: 803-353-8584. p. 2188

Robinson, Denise, Asst Dir, Brownsburg Public Library, 450 S Jefferson St, Brownsburg, IN, 46112-1310. Tel: 317-852-3167, Ext 101. Fax: 317-852-7734. p. 730

Robinson, Denise, Interim Libr Mgr, Central Carolina Technical College Library, 506 N Guignard Dr, Sumter, SC, 29150. Tel: 803-778-6647. Fax: 803-778-7889. p. 2206

Robinson, Diana, Librn, New York State Department of State-Office of Fire Prevention & Control, 600 College Ave, Montour Falls, NY, 14865. Tel: 607-535-7136, Ext 605. Fax: 607-535-4841. p. 1663

Robinson, Dicki, Dir, Kanab City Library, 374 N Main St, Kanab, UT, 84741-3259. Tel: 435-644-2394, 435-644-3518. Fax: 435-644-2822. p. 2406

Robinson, Elizabeth A, Librn, Invermere Public Library, 201 Seventh Ave, Invermere, BC, V0A 1K0, CANADA. Tel: 250-342-6416. Fax: 250-342-6416. p. 2729

Robinson, Emily, Instrul Serv Librn, Northern Virginia Community College Libraries, Medical Education Campus, 6699 Springfield Center Dr, Rm 341, Springfield, VA, 22150. Tel: 703-822-9052. Fax: 703-822-6612. p. 2447

Robinson, Eric, Coordr, ILL, Wisconsin Library Services, 728 State St, Rm 464, Madison, WI, 53706-1494. Tel: 608-265-4167. Fax: 608-262-6067. p. 2958

Robinson, Erik, Tech Coordr, West Warwick Public Library, 1043 Main St, West Warwick, RI, 02893. Tel: 401-828-3750. Fax: 401-828-8493. p. 2178

Robinson, Erin, Dir, Cordelia A Greene Library, 11 S Main St, Castile, NY, 14427. Tel: 585-493-5466. Fax: 585-493-5782. p. 1603

Robinson, Erskine, Pub Serv, Miles College, 5500 Myron Massey Blvd, Fairfield, AL, 35064. Tel: 205-929-1000. Fax: 205-929-1635. p. 16

Robinson, Fran, Br Mgr, Washington County Library System, Leland Library, 107 N Broad St, Leland, MS, 38756-2797. Tel: 601-686-7353. Fax: 601-686-7353. p. 1299

Robinson, Gail S, Dir, Bridgeton Free Public Library, 150 E Commerce St, Bridgeton, NJ, 08302-2684. Tel: 856-451-2620. p. 1474

Robinson, Georgia, Ref, City of Kawartha Lakes Public Library, Lindsay Branch, 190 Kent St W, Lindsay, ON, K9V 2Y6, CANADA. Tel: 705-324-5632. Fax: 705-324-7140. p. 2816

Robinson, Gleneice A, Dr, Dir, Fort Worth Library, 500 W Third St, Fort Worth, TX, 76102. Tel: 817-871-7706. Fax: 817-871-7734. p. 2321

Robinson, Gregory, Head, Pub Serv, Head, Res Serv, Eastern Connecticut State University, 83 Windham St, Willimantic, CT, 06226-2295. Tel: 860-465-5553. Fax: 860-465-5521. p. 378

Robinson, Gregory, Dir, Nevada State College, 1125 Nevada State Dr, Henderson, NV, 89002. Tel: 702-992-2032. Fax: 702-992-2801. p. 1428

Robinson, Heather, Head, Ch, St Thomas Public Library, 153 Curtis St, St. Thomas, ON, N5P 3Z7, CANADA. Tel: 519-631-6050. Fax: 519-631-1987. p. 2844

Robinson, Howard, Dr, Archives, Spec Coll, Alabama State University, 915 S Jackson St, Montgomery, AL, 36104. Tel: 334-229-4106, 334-229-6890. Fax: 334-229-4911, 334-229-4940. p. 28

Robinson, J Carmen, Interim Dir, Lower Columbia College, 1600 Maple St, Longview, WA, 98632-3907. Tel: 360-442-2660. Fax: 360-442-2669. p. 2520

Robinson, James, Supvr of Educ, Federal Correctional Institution - Morgantown Library, PO Box 1000, Morgantown, WV, 26507-1000. Tel: 304-296-4416, Ext 351. Fax: 304-284-3622, 304-296-7549. p. 2566

Robinson, Jane, Head, Ref, Southern University, 167 Roosevelt Steptoe Ave, Baton Rouge, LA, 70813-0001. Tel: 225-771-2875. Fax: 225-771-4113. p. 944

Robinson, Janet, Ref Serv, Aiken-Bamberg-Barnwell-Edgefield Regional Library System, Aiken County, 314 Chesterfield St SW, Aiken, SC, 29801. Tel: 803-642-2020. Fax: 803-642-7570. p. 2179

Robinson, Jeana, Ch, Okmulgee Public Library, 218 S Okmulgee Ave, Okmulgee, OK, 74447. Tel: 918-756-1448. Fax: 918-758-1148. p. 1975

Robinson, Jeannette, Librn, Rockbridge Regional Library, Bath County Public, 96 Courthouse Hill Rd, Warm Springs, VA, 24484. Tel: 540-839-7286. Fax: 540-839-3058. p. 2474

Robinson, Jennifer, Tech Serv Librn, Averett University Library, 344 W Main St, Danville, VA, 24541-2849. Tel: 434-791-5693. Fax: 434-791-5637. p. 2459

Robinson, JoAnn, Librn, Uniontown Public Library, PO Box 637, Uniontown, AL, 36786-0637. Tel: 334-628-6681. Fax: 334-628-6681. p. 39

Robinson, Joanne, Ch, Peters Township Public Library, 616 E McMurray Rd, McMurray, PA, 15317-3495. Tel: 724-941-9430. Fax: 724-941-9438. p. 2086

Robinson, Jontyule, Dr, Curator, Tuskegee University, Hollis Burke Frissell Bldg, 1200 W Old Montgomery Rd, Tuskegee, AL, 36088. Tel: 334-727-8888. Fax: 334-725-2400. p. 39

Robinson, Judith, Prof, University at Buffalo, State University of New York, 534 Baldy Hall, Buffalo, NY, 14260. Tel: 716-645-2412. Fax: 716-645-3775. p. 2971

Robinson, Julia, Coll Develop, Libr Instruction, Ref Librn, Ohio University-Lancaster Library, 1570 Granville Pike, Lancaster, OH, 43130-1097. Tel: 740-654-6711, Ext 222. Fax: 740-687-9497. p. 1909

Robinson, Julie, Circ, Bruton Memorial Library, 302 W McLendon St, Plant City, FL, 33563. Tel: 813-757-9215. Fax: 813-757-9217. p. 484

Robinson, Julie, Res & Instruction Librn, Murray State University, 205 Waterfield Library, Dean's Office, Murray, KY, 42071-3307. Tel: 270-809-2846. Fax: 270-809-3736. p. 930

Robinson, Julie, Br Mgr, Kansas City Public Library, Irene H Ruiz Biblioteca de las Americas, 2017 W Pennway, Kansas City, MO, 64108. Tel: 816-701-3487. Fax: 816-701-3497. p. 1338

Robinson, Julie Anne, Ref Librn, Marshall University Libraries, One John Marshall Dr, Huntington, WV, 25755-2060. Tel: 304-691-1766. Fax: 304-691-1766. p. 2561

Robinson, Kara, Head, Ref Serv, Kent State University Libraries, 1125 Risman Dr, Kent, OH, 44242. Tel: 330-672-1664. Fax: 330-672-4811. p. 1907

Robinson, Karen, Asst Librn, Swarthmore Public Library, Borough Hall, 121 Park Ave, Swarthmore, PA, 19081-1536. Tel: 610-543-0436, 610-543-3171. Fax: 610-328-6699. p. 2145

Robinson, Karen, Asst Teaching Prof, St Louis, University of Missouri-Columbia, 303 Townsend Hall, Columbia, MO, 65211. Tel: 573-882-4546. Fax: 573-884-2917. p. 2969

Robinson, Kathryn, Head, Ch, Russell Library, 123 Broad St, Middletown, CT, 06457. Tel: 860-347-2528, Ext 147. p. 352

Robinson, Kathryn, Dir, Crafton Public Library, 140 Bradford Ave, Pittsburgh, PA, 15205. Tel: 412-922-6877. Fax: 412-922-7637. p. 2124

Robinson, Kristen, Librn, Parowan Public Library, 16 S Main St, Parowan, UT, 84761. Tel: 435-477-3491. Fax: 435-477-8671. p. 2410

Robinson, Lakesha, Coordr, Charles Bass Correctional Complex Library, 7177 Cockrill Bend Industrial Rd, Nashville, TN, 37243-0470. Tel: 615-350-3361, Ext 1195. Fax: 615-350-3319. p. 2255

Robinson, Lakesha, In Charge, Bass Charles Correctional Complex Library, MTCX Annex-Site No 2, 7466 Centennial Blvd-Extended, Nashville, TN, 32243-0466. Tel: 615-350-3361, Ext 2201. Fax: 615-350-3395. p. 2255

Robinson, Lauren, Ref, Sandwich Public Library, 142 Main St, Sandwich, MA, 02563. Tel: 508-888-0625. Fax: 508-833-1076. p. 1122

Robinson, Leanne, Supvr, Middlesex County Library, Lucan Branch, 261 Main St, Lucan, ON, N0M 2J0, CANADA. Tel: 519-227-4682. p. 2845

Robinson, Linda, Head, Circ, Chelmsford Public Library, 25 Boston Rd, Chelmsford, MA, 01824-3088. Tel: 978-256-5521. Fax: 978-256-8511. p. 1079

Robinson, Linda, Circ Supvr, Wegner Health Science Information Center, 1400 W 22nd St, Ste 100, Sioux Falls, SD, 57105. Tel: 605-357-1400. Fax: 605-357-1490. p. 2219

Robinson, Lorri, Principal Librn, Tampa-Hillsborough County Public Library System, Brandon Regional Library, 619 Vonderburg Dr, Brandon, FL, 33511-5972. Fax: 813-273-5632. p. 497

Robinson, Lucy, Info Spec, Webber International University, 1201 State Rd 17, Babson Park, FL, 33827. Tel: 863-638-2937. Fax: 863-638-2778. p. 426

Robinson, Lynn, Cat, Bellingham Technical College Library, 3028 Lindbergh Ave, Bellingham, WA, 98225-1599. Tel: 360-752-8383. Fax: 360-752-8384. p. 2508

Robinson, Margaret, Head, Instrul Serv, University Libraries, University of Memphis, 126 Ned R McWherter Library, Memphis, TN, 38152-3250. Tel: 901-678-8206. p. 2252

Robinson, Marilyn, Interim Dir, Fayette County Public Library, 828 N Grand Ave, Connersville, IN, 47331. Tel: 765-827-0883. Fax: 765-825-4592. p. 733

Robinson, Marline C, Libr Coordr, Josey Health Sciences Library, Palmetto Health Richland, Five Richland Medical Park, Columbia, SC, 29203. Tel: 803-434-6312. Fax: 803-434-2651. p. 2187

Robinson, Marlyn, Ref Serv, University of Texas Libraries, Jamail Center for Legal Research, University of Texas School of Law, 727 E Dean Keeton St, Austin, TX, 78705-3224. Tel: 512-471-7726. Fax: 512-471-0243. p. 2284

Robinson, Mary Ann, Dr, Assoc Prof, University of South Alabama, 3800 UCOM-University Commons, Mobile, AL, 36688. Tel: 251-380-2861. Fax: 251-380-2713. p. 2961

Robinson, Mary M, Librn, Buffalo Bill Historical Center, 720 Sheridan Ave, Cody, WY, 82414. Tel: 307-578-4059. Fax: 307-527-6042. p. 2653

Robinson, Melissa, Ch, Bloomington Public Library, 205 E Olive St, Bloomington, IL, 61701. Tel: 309-828-6091. Fax: 309-828-7312. p. 595

Robinson Mercer, Judith G, Asst Dean, Libr & Learning Res, Eastern Virginia Medical School, 740 W Olney Rd, Norfolk, VA, 23501. Tel: 757-446-5841. Fax: 757-446-5134. p. 2481

Robinson, Michael, Br Mgr, Burlington County Library, Riverton Free Branch, 306 Main St, Riverton, NJ, 08077. Tel: 856-829-2476. p. 1543

Robinson, Michael, Dir, North Dakota State University Libraries, 1201 Albrecht Blvd, Fargo, ND, 58108. Tel: 701-231-1017. Fax: 701-231-6128. p. 1841

Robinson, Michaele, Mgr, Scripps Mercy Hospital Medical Library, 4077 Fifth Ave, MER-36, San Diego, CA, 92103-2180. Tel: 619-260-7024. Fax: 619-260-7262. p. 238

Robinson, Michelle, Br Mgr, Arlington County Department of Libraries, Plaza Library, 2100 Clarendon Blvd, Lobby, Arlington, VA, 22201. Tel: 703-228-3708. Fax: 703-228-3354. p. 2448

Robinson, Mike, Head, Libr Syst, University of Alaska Anchorage, Consortium Library, 3211 Providence Dr, Anchorage, AK, 99508-8176. Tel: 907-786-1001. Fax: 907-786-1834. p. 45

Robinson, Mike, ILL Librn, US Department of Commerce, Radio Bldg, Rm 1202, 325 Broadway MC5, Boulder, CO, 80305-3328. Tel: 303-497-3271. Fax: 303-497-3890. p. 291

Robinson, Nancy, Ch, North Kansas City Public Library, 2251 Howell St, North Kansas City, MO, 64116. Tel: 816-221-3360. Fax: 816-221-8298. p. 1348

Robinson, Nancy, Asst Dir, Spring City Free Public Library, 245 Broad St, Spring City, PA, 19475-1702. Tel: 610-948-4130. Fax: 610-948-9478. p. 2142

Robinson, Neva, Coll Develop, Escondido Public Library, 239 S Kalmia St, Escondido, CA, 92025. Tel: 760-839-4214. Fax: 760-741-4255. p. 146

Robinson, Nick, Dir, Libr Serv, University of California-Berkeley, 109 Moses Hall, IGS-UC Berkeley, Berkeley, CA, 94720. Tel: 510-642-1472. Fax: 510-643-0866. p. 127

Robinson, Nick, Dir, University of California, Berkeley, Institute of Governmental Studies, 109 Moses Hall, Ground flr, 94720-2370, Berkeley, CA, 94720-2370. Tel: 510-642-1472. Fax: 510-643-0866. p. 128

Robinson, Nicole, Ref Serv, Muskingum University Library, 163 Stormont St, New Concord, OH, 43762-1199. Tel: 740-826-8154. Fax: 740-826-8404. p. 1920

Robinson, Paul, Br Head, Toronto Public Library, Fairview, 35 Fairview Mall Dr, Toronto, ON, M2J 4S4, CANADA. Tel: 416-395-5750. Fax: 416-395-5756. p. 2861

Robinson, Paula, Ref, Duke University Libraries, Ford Library, One Towerview Rd, Durham, NC, 27708. Tel: 919-660-7942. Fax: 919-660-7950. p. 1787

Robinson, Regan, Pub Serv Mgr, Whatcom County Library System, 5205 Northwest Dr, Bellingham, WA, 98226-9050. Tel: 360-384-3150. Fax: 360-384-4947. p. 2509

Robinson, Rick, Ref Serv Coordr, Sonoma State University Library, 1801 E Cotati Ave, Rohnert Park, CA, 94928-3609. Tel: 707-664-4196. Fax: 707-664-2090. p. 219

Robinson, Scottie, Ch, Lee Public Library, Seven Mast Rd, Lee, NH, 03824. Tel: 603-659-2626. Fax: 603-659-2986. p. 1454

Robinson, Sean, Mgr, Bibliog & Info Tech Serv, Allen County Public Library, 900 Library Plaza, Fort Wayne, IN, 46802. Tel: 260-421-1288. Fax: 260-421-1386. p. 740

Robinson, Shannon, Fine Arts Liaison Librn, Denison University Libraries, 400 W Loop, Granville, OH, 43023. Tel: 740-587-6688. Fax: 740-587-6285. p. 1902

Robinson, Shannon Marie, Access Serv Librn, University of the Arts University Libraries, Anderson Hall, 1st Flr, 333 S Broad St, Philadelphia, PA, 19102. Tel: 215-717-6290. Fax: 215-717-6287. p. 2119

Robinson, Sharon, Prog Mgr, Atlanta-Fulton Public Library System, Auburn Avenue Research Library on African-American Culture & History, 101 Auburn Ave NE, Atlanta, GA, 30303. Tel: 404-730-4001, Ext 199. Fax: 404-730-5879. p. 511

Robinson, Shawn, Patron Serv, Lyme Academy College of Fine Arts, 84 Lyme St, Old Lyme, CT, 06371-2333. Tel: 860-434-5232, Ext 130. Fax: 860-434-2095. p. 363

Robinson, Sue, Ch, Anderson City, Anderson, Stony Creek & Union Townships Public Library, 111 E 12th St, Anderson, IN, 46016-2701. Tel: 765-241-2448. Fax: 765-641-2197. p. 723

Robinson, Sue, Dir, Galien Township Public Library, 302 N Main St, Galien, MI, 49113. Tel: 269-545-8281. Fax: 269-545-8281. p. 1182

Robinson, Suzanne, Dir, Washington Township Public Library, 107 N Main St, Lynn, IN, 47355. Tel: 765-874-1488. Fax: 765-874-1427. p. 762

Robinson, Suzanne, Br Mgr, Nashville Public Library, Inglewood, 4312 Gallatin Rd, Nashville, TN, 37216-2192. Tel: 615-862-5866. Fax: 615-862-5888. p. 2257

Robinson, T Kim, Head of Libr, Free Library of Philadelphia, Nicetown-Tioga Branch, 3720 N Broad St, Philadelphia, PA, 19140-3608. Tel: 215-685-9789, 215-685-9790. Fax: 215-685-9788. p. 2108

Robinson, Tami Echavarria, Coordr, Instrul Serv, Whitworth University, 300 W Hawthorne Rd, Spokane, WA, 99251-0001. Tel: 509-777-4483. Fax: 509-777-3221. p. 2538

Robinson, Tammy, Br Head, Oshawa Public Library, Northview, 250 Beatrice St E, Oshawa, ON, L1G 7T6, CANADA. Tel: 905-576-6040. p. 2827

Robinson, Tonya, Librn, Brunswick Community College Library, 50 College Rd, Supply, NC, 28462. Tel: 910-755-7331. Fax: 910-754-7805. p. 1826

Robinson, Tracey, Head, Info Serv, Harvard Library, 1341 Massachusetts Ave, Wadsworth House, Cambridge, MA, 02138. Tel: 617-495-3650. Fax: 617-495-0370. p. 1073

Robinson, Trina, Head, Acq, George Washington University, Jacob Burns Law Library, 716 20th St NW, Washington, DC, 20052. Tel: 202-994-8550. Fax: 202-994-2874. p. 402

Robinson-El, Edward, Mgr, District of Columbia Public Library, West End, 1101 24th St NW, Washington, DC, 20037. Tel: 202-724-8707. p. 399

Robinson-Paquette, Mindy, Online Serv, Ref, Sanofi Aventis, Nine Great Valley Pkwy, Malvern, PA, 19355. Tel: 610-889-8655. Fax: 610-889-8988. p. 2083

Robishaw, Susan, Asst Dir, Geisinger Health System, 100 N Academy Ave, Danville, PA, 17822-2101. Tel: 570-271-8198. Fax: 570-271-5738. p. 2049

Robison, Barbara, Pres, Greenwood County Historical Society Library, 120 W Fourth, Eureka, KS, 67045-1445. Tel: 316-583-6682. p. 866

Robison, C Brad, Ref/Spec Projects Librn, Rose State College, 6420 SE 15th St, Midwest City, OK, 73110. Tel: 405-733-7402. Fax: 405-736-0260. p. 1968

Robison, Cooper, Ch, Poplar Bluff Public Library, 318 N Main St, Poplar Bluff, MO, 63901. Tel: 573-686-8639. Fax: 573-785-6876. p. 1349

Robison, Mary, Archives, Ref & Info Serv, General Theological Seminary, 440 West 21st St, New York, NY, 10011. Tel: 212-243-5150. Fax: 212-924-6304. p. 1679

Robison, Sharon, Ch, Thelma Dingus Bryant Library, 409 W Main St, Wallace, NC, 28466. Tel: 910-285-3796. Fax: 910-285-8224. p. 1827

Robitaille, Anne, Tech Serv, Institut National de la Recherche Scientifique, Universite du Quebec, 490 de la Couronne, local 1401, Quebec, QC, G1K 9A9, CANADA. Tel: 418-654-2588. Fax: 418-654-2660. p. 2905

Robitaille, Bob, Admin Officer, Pennsylvania Office of Attorney General, 1525 Strawberry Sq, Harrisburg, PA, 17120. Tel: 717-787-3176. Fax: 717-772-4526. p. 2066

Robitaille, Carole, Prof, College Francois-Xavier-Garneau, 1660 blvd de l'Entente, Quebec, QC, G1S 4S3, CANADA. Tel: 418-688-8310, Ext 3504. Fax: 418-681-9384. p. 2978

Robitaille, Liz, Librn, Englehart Public Library, 71 Fourth Ave, Englehart, ON, P0J 1H0, CANADA. Tel: 705-544-2100. Fax: 705-544-2238. p. 2804

Robitallie, Elise, Librn, Visidyne, Inc Library, Ten Corporate Pl, Ste 10, 99 S Bedford St, Burlington, MA, 01803-5168. Tel: 781-273-2820. Fax: 781-272-1068. p. 1072

Robl, Greg, Libr Tech III, University of Colorado Boulder, Archives & Special Collections, 1720 Pleasant St, Boulder, CO, 80309-0184. Tel: 303-492-3907. Fax: 303-492-1881. p. 291

Robles, Andrea, Tech Serv, Blanchard-Santa Paula Public Library District, 119 N Eighth St, Santa Paula, CA, 93060-2709. Tel: 805-525-3615. Fax: 805-933-2324. p. 266

Robles, Daniel O, District Librn, Blanchard-Santa Paula Public Library District, 119 N Eighth St, Santa Paula, CA, 93060-2709. Tel: 805-525-3615. Fax: 805-933-2324. p. 266

Roblin, Beryl C, Br Mgr, Blackwater Regional Library, Ruth Camp Campbell Memorial, 280 N College Dr, Franklin, VA, 23851. Tel: 757-562-4801. Fax: 757-562-0162. p. 2458

Robnett, Bill, Dir, California State University-Monterey Bay, 100 Campus Ctr, Seaside, CA, 93955-8001. Tel: 831-582-4448. Fax: 831-582-3875. p. 268

Robotewskyj, Lydia, Circ Supvr, Franklin Public Library, 9151 W Loomis Rd, Franklin, WI, 53132. Tel: 414-425-8214. Fax: 414-425-9498. p. 2593

Robrock, Janice, Ref, United States Air Force, Bldg 219, 7424 N Homer Dr, 56 SVS/SVMG FL 4887, Luke AFB, AZ, 85309-1220. Tel: 623-856-7191. Fax: 623-935-2023. p. 68

Robson, Timothy D, Dep Dir, Case Western Reserve University, 11055 Euclid Ave, Cleveland, OH, 44106. Tel: 216-368-6508. Fax: 216-368-6950. p. 1876

Roby, Errin, Assoc Librn, Baltimore County Circuit Court Library, 401 Bosley Ave, Towson, MD, 21204. Tel: 410-887-3086. Fax: 410-887-4807. p. 1044

Roby, Mary, Assoc Dean, Gardner-Webb University, 110 S Main St, Boiling Springs, NC, 28017. Tel: 704-406-4298. Fax: 704-406-4623. p. 1776

Roca, Joan, Dean, Minnesota State University, Mankato, ML3097, Mankato, MN, 56001. Tel: 507-389-5953. Fax: 507-389-5155. p. 1257

Rocap, Ruth Elaine, Head, Tech Serv, Troup-Harris Regional Library System, 115 Alford St, La Grange, GA, 30240-3041. Tel: 706-882-7784, Ext 17. Fax: 706-883-7342. p. 537

Roccaforte, Clare, Pub Relations, Northwestern University Library, 1970 Campus Dr, Evanston, IL, 60208-2300. Tel: 847-491-7658. p. 644

Rocci, Keith, First Year Experience Librn, Washburn University, 1700 SW College Ave, Topeka, KS, 66621. Tel: 785-670-1490. Fax: 785-670-3223. p. 897

Rocco, Brian, Tech Serv, Marymount Manhattan College, 221 E 71st St, New York, NY, 10021. Tel: 212-774-4802. Fax: 212-458-8207. p. 1685

Rocha, Fernanda, Licensing & Copyright Ed, The Miami Herald, One Herald Plaza, Miami, FL, 33132. Tel: 305-376-3737. Fax: 305-376-4424, 305-995-8183. p. 467

Rocha, Maria, Asst Librn, Fayette Public Library, 855 S Jefferson, La Grange, TX, 78945. Tel: 979-968-3765. Fax: 979-968-5357. p. 2351

Rocha, Mayra, Libr Dir, Speer Memorial Library, 801 E 12th St, Mission, TX, 78572. Tel: 956-580-8750. Fax: 956-580-8756. p. 2363

Rochat, Julie, Dir, Hamline University, Bush Memorial Library, 1536 Hewitt, Saint Paul, MN, 55104. Tel: 651-523-2375. Fax: 651-523-2199. p. 1278

Roche, Ann R, Asst Librn, Southport Memorial Library, 1032 Hendricks Hill Rd, Southport, ME, 04576-3309. Tel: 207-633-2741. p. 1002

Roche, Bernadette, Dir, United States Air Force, Maxwell Gunter Community Library System, MSD/MSEL, 481 Williamson St, Bldg 1110 Gunter Annex, Maxwell AFB, AL, 36114. Tel: 334-416-3179. Fax: 334-416-2949. p. 25

Roche, Catherine, Dir, Moore County Library, 101 Saunders St, Carthage, NC, 28327. Tel: 910-947-5335. Fax: 910-947-3660. p. 1779

Roche, Joan, ILL, Whittier Public Library, 7344 S Washington Ave, Whittier, CA, 90602. Tel: 562-567-9900. Fax: 562-567-2880. p. 283

Roche, Mary Beth, Dir, Libr Serv, Lackawanna College, 501 Vine St, Scranton, PA, 18509. Tel: 570-504-1589. Fax: 570-961-7817. p. 2137

Roche, Michael, Tech Serv, Rockingham County Public Library, 527 Boone Rd, Eden, NC, 27288. Tel: 336-623-1017. Fax: 336-623-4835. p. 1790

Roche, Michael, Regional Librn, Northeast Regional Library, Vermont Department of Libraries, 23 Tilton Rd, Saint Johnsbury, VT, 05819. Tel: 802-748-3428. p. 2435

Roche, Philip, Instruction Librn, Southern Utah University, 351 W University Blvd, Cedar City, UT, 84720. Tel: 435-865-8734. Fax: 435-865-8152. p. 2404

Roche, Richard, Head, Adult Serv, Thomas Ford Memorial Library, 800 Chestnut Ave, Western Springs, IL, 60558. Tel: 708-246-0520. Fax: 708-246-0403. p. 717

Rochefort, Jacqueline, Tech Spec, Hopital Louis-H Lafontaine, 7401 Hochelaga, Montreal, QC, H1N 3M5, CANADA. Tel: 514-251-4000, Ext 2965. Fax: 514-251-0270. p. 2896

Rocher, Claire, Communications Coordr, Bibliothèques de Montrèal, 801, rue Brennan, 5e Etage, Bureau 5206, Montreal, QC, H3C 0G4, CANADA. Tel: 514-872-9080. Fax: 514-872-1155. p. 2889

Rochesort, Suzanne, Dir, Bibliotheque Municipale, 959, rue de l'Hotel de ville, Saint-Jean-Chrysostome, QC, G6Z 2N8, CANADA. Tel: 418-839-5242. Fax: 418-834-4719. p. 2911

Rock, Eleanor, Adult Serv Coordr, Hopewell Public Library, 13 E Broad St, Hopewell, NJ, 08525. Tel: 609-466-1625. Fax: 609-466-1996. p. 1491

Rock, Leslie, Dir, Bedford County Library, 240 S Wood St, Bedford, PA, 15522. Tel: 814-623-5010. p. 2031

Rockefeller, Elsworth, Adult & Teen Serv Mgr, Oak Park Public Library, 834 Lake St, Oak Park, IL, 60301. Tel: 708-383-8200. Fax: 708-697-6900. p. 684

Rockefeller, Julie, YA Librn, Bedford Free Library, On the Village Green, Bedford, NY, 10506. Tel: 914-234-3570. Fax: 914-234-0546. p. 1579

Rockey, Steven W, Dir, Cornell University Library, Mathematics, 420 Malott Hall, Ithaca, NY, 14853-4201. Tel: 607-255-5268. Fax: 607-254-5023. p. 1642

Rockliff, Cory, Tech Serv Librn, Bard Graduate Center Library, 38 W 86th St, New York, NY, 10024. Tel: 212-501-3037. Fax: 212-501-3098. p. 1669

Rockmuller, Ellen, Dir, East Rockaway Public Library, 477 Atlantic Ave, East Rockaway, NY, 11518. Tel: 516-599-1664. Fax: 516-596-0154. p. 1617

Rockwell, Jasmine, Coordr, Ch & Youth Serv, South Dakota State Library, 800 Governors Dr, Pierre, SD, 57501-2294. Tel: 605-773-3131. p. 2216

Rockwell, Jenny, Br Mgr, Oakland Public Library, Golden Gate, 5606 San Pablo Ave, Oakland, CA, 94608. Tel: 510-597-5023. Fax: 510-597-5030. p. 198

Rockwell, Judy, Head, Ref, Burlington Public Library, 166 E Jefferson St, Burlington, WI, 53105. Tel: 262-763-7623. Fax: 262-763-1938. p. 2584

Rockwell-Kincannon, Janeanne, Pub Serv, Western Oregon University, Wayne & Lynn Hamersly Library, 345 N Monmouth Ave, Monmouth, OR, 97361-1396. Tel: 503-838-9493. Fax: 503-838-8399. p. 2006

Rockwood, D Stephen, Dean, Libr Serv, Mount Saint Mary's University, 16300 Old Emmitsburg Rd, Emmitsburg, MD, 21727-7799. Tel: 301-447-5244. Fax: 301-447-5099. p. 1027

Rod, Catherine M, Archivist, Spec Coll Librn, Grinnell College Libraries, 1111 Sixth Ave, Grinnell, IA, 50112-1770. Tel: 641-269-3364. Fax: 641-269-4283. p. 819

Rod, Janice, Cat/Metadata Librn, Saint John's University, 2835 Abbey Plaza, Collegeville, MN, 56321. Tel: 320-363-2617. Fax: 320-363-2126. p. 1246

Rod, Janice, Cat/Metadata Librn, College of Saint Benedict, 37 S College Ave, Saint Joseph, MN, 56374. Tel: 320-363-2617. Fax: 320-363-5197. p. 1277

Rod-Welch, Leila, Outreach Serv Librn, University of Northern Iowa Library, 1227 W 27th St, Cedar Falls, IA, 50613-3675. Tel: 319-273-3730. Fax: 319-273-2913. p. 799

Rodarte, Antonio, Access Serv, University of Texas at El Paso Library, 500 W University Ave, El Paso, TX, 79968-0582. Tel: 915-747-6700. Fax: 915-747-5345. p. 2317

Rodarte, Isabel, Dir, Northern New Mexico College, 921 Paseo de Onate, Espanola, NM, 87532. Tel: 505-747-2241. Fax: 505-747-2245. p. 1555

Rodas, Christine, Br Mgr, Ocean County Library, Stafford Branch, 129 N Main St, Manahawkin, NJ, 08050-2933. Tel: 609-597-3381. Fax: 609-978-0770. p. 1534

Rodd, Leslie, Mgr, Grants & Develop, Oakland Public Library, 125 14th St, Oakland, CA, 94612. Tel: 510-238-6932. Fax: 510-238-2232. p. 197

Roddam, Barbara, Per & Binding Tech, Southwestern Oklahoma State University, 100 Campus Dr, Weatherford, OK, 73096-3002. Tel: 580-774-7022. Fax: 580-774-3112. p. 1985

Rodden, Ruth, Circ Mgr, Topeka & Shawnee County Public Library, 1515 SW Tenth Ave, Topeka, KS, 66604-1374. Tel: 785-580-4400. Fax: 785-580-4496. p. 897

Roddy, Kevin, Info Literacy, Kapiolani Community College Library, 4303 Diamond Head Rd, Honolulu, HI, 96816. Tel: 808-734-9268. Fax: 808-734-9453. p. 564

Roddy, Maria, Br Mgr, Salinas Public Library, Cesar Chavez Library, 615 Williams Rd, Salinas, CA, 93905. Tel: 831-758-7346. Fax: 831-758-9172. p. 226

Roddy, Nansu, Ad, Bitterroot Public Library, 306 State St, Hamilton, MT, 59840-2759. Tel: 406-363-1670. Fax: 406-363-1678. p. 1380

Rodefeld, Rolf, Periodicals Librn, University of Wisconsin-Madison, Kurt Wendt Engineering Library, 215 N Randall Ave, Madison, WI, 53706. Tel: 608-262-3493. Fax: 608-262-4739, 608-265-8751. p. 2610

Rodeffer, Stephanie, Prog Dir, National Park Service, 255 N Commerce Park Loop, Tucson, AZ, 85745. Tel: 520-791-6401. Fax: 520-791-6465. p. 86

Rodegerdts, Alexis, Pub Serv Spec, Walla Walla Public Library, 238 E Alder, Walla Walla, WA, 99362. Tel: 509-524-4609. Fax: 509-524-7950. p. 2547

Roderer, Debbie, Asst Dir, Dorothy Alling Memorial Library, 21 Library Lane, Williston, VT, 05495. Tel: 802-878-4918. Fax: 802-878-3964. p. 2440

Rodes, Virginia, Libr Dir, Calumet College of Saint Joseph, 2400 New York Ave, Whiting, IN, 46394. Tel: 219-473-7372. Fax: 219-473-4259. p. 787

Rodgers, Bonnie, Librn, St Paul Public Library, 145 Fifth St, Saint Paul, AR, 72760. Tel: 479-677-2907. p. 114

Rodgers, Brenda, ILL, Saint Mary's College of Maryland Library, 18952 E Fisher Rd, Saint Mary's City, MD, 20686-3001. Tel: 240-895-4256. Fax: 240-895-4914. p. 1040

Rodgers, Carol, Br Mgr, Roanoke County Public Library, Mount Pleasant, 2918 JAE Valley Rd, Roanoke, VA, 24014. Tel: 540-427-3130. Fax: 540-427-3130. p. 2494

Rodgers, Charles R, Dir of Libr, Pasco-Hernando Community College-East Campus, 36727 Blanton Rd, Dade City, FL, 33523-7599. Tel: 352-518-1307. Fax: 352-518-1350. p. 435

Rodgers, Cynthia A, Br Mgr, Chicago Public Library, John Merlo Branch, 644 W Belmont Ave, Chicago, IL, 60657. Tel: 312-744-1139. Fax: 312-744-0716. p. 609

Rodgers, Dee, ILL, Washington State University, 600 N Riverpoint Blvd, Spokane, WA, 99202. Tel: 509-358-7930. Fax: 509-358-7928. p. 2538

Rodgers, Jo Ann, Br Mgr, Charlotte Mecklenburg Library, North County Regional, 16500 Holly Crest Lane, Huntersville, NC, 28078. Tel: 704-416-6000. Fax: 704-416-6100. p. 1782

Rodgers, Linda, Dir, Skene Memorial Library, 1017 Main St, Fleischmanns, NY, 12430. Tel: 845-254-4581. Fax: 845-254-4581. p. 1622

Rodgers, Marilyn, Assoc Dean of Libr, University of Missouri-Saint Louis Libraries, One University Blvd, Saint Louis, MO, 63121. Tel: 314-516-5060. Fax: 314-516-5853. p. 1362

Rodgers, Molly, Dir, Wayne County Public Library, 1406 N Main St, Honesdale, PA, 18431-2006. Tel: 570-253-1220. Fax: 570-253-1240. p. 2069

Rodgers, Sara, Adult/Ref Serv, Librn II, Dobbs Ferry Public Library, 55 Main St, Dobbs Ferry, NY, 10522. Tel: 914-231-3057. Fax: 914-693-4671. p. 1615

Rodgers, Susan, Librn, Palo Alto City Library, Children's, 1276 Harriet St, Palo Alto, CA, 94301. Fax: 650-463-4964. p. 204

Rodgers, William, Div Mgr, Info & Coll Serv, Hennepin County Library, 12601 Ridgedale Dr, Minnetonka, MN, 55305-1909. Tel: 612-543-8508. Fax: 612-543-8600. p. 1263

Rodic, Vera, Info Spec, Teck Metals Ltd Product Technology Group, PTC, Sheridan Science & Technology Park, 2380 Speakman Dr, Mississauga, ON, L5K 1B4, CANADA. Tel: 905-287-2276. Fax: 905-822-2882. p. 2823

Rodio, Joseph, Dir, South Hadley Public Library, 27 Bardwell St, South Hadley, MA, 01075. Tel: 413-538-5045. Fax: 413-539-9250. p. 1125

Rodio, Lorna, Ref Librn, Massasoit Community College Library, One Massasoit Blvd, Brockton, MA, 02302. Tel: 508-588-9100, Ext 1941. Fax: 508-427-1265. p. 1071

Rodkey, Ashley, Asst Dir, Pelham Library, Two S Valley Rd, Pelham, MA, 01002. Tel: 413-253-0657. Fax: 413-253-0594. p. 1117

Rodney, Cathryn, Chief Librn, Bracebridge Public Library, 94 Manitoba St, Bracebridge, ON, P1L 2B5, CANADA. Tel: 705-645-4171. Fax: 705-645-6551. p. 2796

Rodney, Mae L, Dir, Winston-Salem State University, 601 Martin Luther King Jr Dr, Winston-Salem, NC, 27110. Tel: 336-750-2440. Fax: 336-750-2459. p. 1834

Rodney, Marcia, Res Analyst, Ball Aerospace & Technologies Corp, 1600 Commerce St, Boulder, CO, 80301-2734. Tel: 303-939-5755. Fax: 303-939-4142. p. 289

Rodney-Hill, Cyanna, Info Serv, Norfolk State University Library, 700 Park Ave, Norfolk, VA, 23504-8010. Tel: 757-823-8517. Fax: 757-823-2431. p. 2482

Rodrick, Jennifer, Youth Serv Mgr, West Palm Beach Public Library, 411 Clematis St, West Palm Beach, FL, 33401. Tel: 561-868-7722. Fax: 561-868-7706. p. 504

Rodrigues, Denyse, E-Learning Librn, Mount Saint Vincent University Library, 166 Bedford Hwy, Halifax, NS, B3M 2J6, CANADA. Tel: 902-457-6200. Fax: 902-457-6445. p. 2781

Rodriguez, Ana Milagros, Librn, United States Court of Appeals, Federal Bldg, Rm 121, 150 Chardon Ave, Hato Rey, PR, 00918. Tel: 787-772-3096. Fax: 787-766-5747. p. 2673

Rodriguez, Anna M, Circ Supvr, ILL, Palo Alto College, 1400 W Villaret St, San Antonio, TX, 78224-2499. Tel: 210-486-3901. Fax: 210-486-9184. p. 2380

Rodriguez, Blanca, Ch, A K Smiley Public Library, 125 W Vine St, Redlands, CA, 92373. Tel: 909-798-7565. Fax: 909-798-7566. p. 215

Rodriguez, Carlos, Assoc Dean, Tech & Info Res, Grand Valley State University Libraries, One Campus Dr, Allendale, MI, 49401-9403. Tel: 616-331-2628. p. 1149

Rodriguez, Carol, Dir, Beekman Library, 11 Town Center Blvd, Hopewell Junction, NY, 12533. Tel: 845-724-3414. Fax: 845-724-3941. p. 1637

Rodriguez, Catalina, Dir, Human Res, Stanford University Libraries, 557 Escondido Mall, Stanford, CA, 94305-6004. Tel: 650-725-1064. p. 270

Rodriguez, Cesar, Curator, Yale University Library, Sterling Memorial Library, 120 High St, New Haven, CT, 06520. Tel: 203-432-1835. Fax: 203-432-1294. p. 359

Rodriguez, Christine, Supv Librn, Burbank Public Library, Buena Vista, 300 N Buena Vista St, Burbank, CA, 91505-3208. Tel: 818-238-5620. Fax: 818-238-5623. p. 130

Rodriguez, David M, Chairperson, Glendale Community College, 6000 W Olive Ave, Glendale, AZ, 85302. Tel: 623-845-3125. Fax: 623-845-3102. p. 64

Rodriguez, Derek, Project Librn, Triangle Research Libraries Network, Wilson Library, CB No 3940, Chapel Hill, NC, 27514-8890. Tel: 919-962-8022. Fax: 919-962-4452. p. 2951

Rodriguez, Diane, Librn, Hassard Bonnington, Two Embarcadero Ctr, Ste 1800, San Francisco, CA, 94111. Tel: 415-288-9800. Fax: 415-288-9801. p. 242

Rodriguez, Elisa, Head, Youth Serv, Lyons Public Library, 4209 Joliet Ave, Lyons, IL, 60534-1597. Tel: 708-447-3577. Fax: 708-447-3589. p. 668

Rodriguez, Gladys, Circ, Universidad Adventista de las Antillas, Carr 106 Km 2 Interior, Bo La Quinta, Mayaguez, PR, 00680. Tel: 787-834-9595, Ext 2313. Fax: 787-834-6015. p. 2674

Rodriguez, Harmony, Assoc Librn, Ventura College, 4667 Telegraph Rd, Ventura, CA, 93003-3889. Tel: 805-654-6400, Ext 3257. Fax: 805-648-8900. p. 279

Rodriguez, Jesus, Syst Adminr, United States Air Force, 305 W F St, Bldg 278, Eglin AFB, FL, 32542-6842. Tel: 850-882-5016. Fax: 850-882-2621. p. 439

Rodriguez, Jill, Dir, Bensenville Community Public Library, 200 S Church Rd, Bensenville, IL, 60106. Tel: 630-766-4642, Ext 426. Fax: 630-766-0788. p. 594

Rodriguez, Joshua, Ch, Bethlehem Area Public Library, South Side, 400 Webster St, Bethlehem, PA, 18015. Tel: 610-867-7852. Fax: 610-867-9821. p. 2034

Rodriguez, Julia, Info Literacy & Educ Tech Librn, Oakland University Library, 2200 N Squirrel Rd, Rochester, MI, 48309-4402. Tel: 248-370-2490. Fax: 248-370-2474. p. 1221

Rodriguez, Kathryn G, Libr Asst, Stearns, Weaver, Miller, Weissler, Alhadeff & Sitterson, 2200 Museum Tower, 150 W Flagler St, Miami, FL, 33130. Tel: 305-789-3225. Fax: 305-789-3395. p. 468

Rodriguez, Kelly, Fine Arts Dept Mgr, Miami-Dade Public Library System, 101 W Flagler St, Miami, FL, 33130-1523. Tel: 305-375-5015. Fax: 305-375-3048. p. 466

Rodriguez, Kim, Div Dir, Human Res, Gwinnett County Public Library, 1001 Lawrenceville Hwy NW, Lawrenceville, GA, 30046-4707. Tel: 770-822-5331. p. 538

Rodriguez, Linda, Syst Coordr, University of Tampa, 401 W Kennedy Blvd, Tampa, FL, 33606-1490. Tel: 813-253-6231. Fax: 813-258-7426. p. 499

Rodriguez, Luis, Univ Librn, Kean University, 1000 Morris Ave, Union, NJ, 07083. Tel: 908-737-4600. Fax: 908-737-4620. p. 1537

Rodriguez, Maria, Dir, Saint John Vianney College, 2900 SW 87th Ave, Miami, FL, 33165. Tel: 305-223-4561. Fax: 305-223-0650. p. 468

Rodriguez, Mariya, Br Mgr, San Antonio Public Library, Molly Pruitt Library, 5110 Walzem Rd, San Antonio, TX, 78218. Tel: 210-650-1122. Fax: 210-650-1291. p. 2382

Rodriguez, Mark, Br Mgr, Stockton-San Joaquin County Public Library, Thornton Branch, 26341 N Thornton Rd, Thornton, CA, 95686. p. 273

Rodriguez, Miriam, Asst Dir, Pub Serv, Dallas Public Library, 1515 Young St, Dallas, TX, 75201-5499. Tel: 214-670-1400. Fax: 214-670-7839. p. 2306

Rodriguez, Obed, Libr Mgr, Everman Public Library, 100 N Race St, Everman, TX, 76140. Tel: 817-551-0726. Fax: 817-551-1999. p. 2318

Rodriguez, Rebecca, Librn, Ft Lauderdale Campus, Keiser University Library System, 1500 NW 49th St, Fort Lauderdale, FL, 33309. Tel: 954-351-4035. Fax: 954-351-4051. p. 443

Rodriguez, Robert, Dir, Robert J Kleberg Public Library, 220 N Fourth St, Kingsville, TX, 78363. Tel: 361-592-6381. p. 2350

Rodriguez, Tomasa, Tech Serv, Port Chester-Rye Brook Public Library, One Haseco Ave, Port Chester, NY, 10573. Tel: 914-939-6710, Ext 107. Fax: 914-939-4735. p. 1720

Rodriguez, Victor, Head Librn, Universidad del Este Library, Calle 190, Esquina 220 Bo Sabana Abajo, Carolina, PR, 00984-2010. Tel: 787-257-7373, Ext 2504. Fax: 787-257-7373, Ext 2516. p. 2672

Rodriguez, Vidalina, Spec Coll & Archives Librn, Pontifical Catholic University Of Puerto Rico, Encarnacion Valdes Library, 2250 Avenida Las Americas, Ste 509, Ponce, PR, 00717-0777. Tel: 787-841-2000, Ext 1808. Fax: 787-284-0235. p. 2675

Rodriguez-Gonzalez, Elsa E, Librn, University of Puerto Rico Library System, Monserrate Santana de Pales Library, Rio Piedras Campus, Facultad de Ciencias Sociales, San Juan, PR, 00931. Tel: 787-764-0000, Ext 4262, 787-764-0000, Ext 5635. Fax: 787-772-1479. p. 2677

Rodriguez-Parrilla, Iris D, Head Librn, University of Puerto Rico Library System, Arts Collection, Recinto de Rio Piedras, San Juan, PR, 00931. Tel: 787-764-0000, Ext 5156. Fax: 787-763-5685. p. 2677

Rodriquez, Alicia, Outreach & Partnerships Coordr, Hunter College Libraries, Centro - Center for Puerto Rican Studies Library, 2180 Third Ave, Rm 121, New York, NY, 10035. Tel: 212-396-7874. Fax: 212-396-7707. p. 1682

Rodvik, Ruth A, Dir, Sheldon Public Library, 925 Fourth Ave, Sheldon, IA, 51201-1517. Tel: 712-324-2442. Fax: 712-324-2442. p. 842

Roe, Brent, Assoc Univ Librn, Info Serv, York University Libraries, 4700 Keele St, Toronto, ON, M3J 1P3, CANADA. Tel: 416-736-5601. Fax: 416-736-5451. p. 2868

Roe, Brent, Exec Dir, Canadian Association of Research Libraries, 350 Albert St, Ste 600, Ottawa, ON, K1R 1B1, CANADA. Tel: 613-562-5800, Ext 3652. Fax: 613-562-5297. p. 2959

Roe, Debbie, Head, Ch, Windsor Public Library, 323 Broad St, Windsor, CT, 06095. Tel: 860-285-1910. Fax: 860-285-1889. p. 379

Roe, Linda L, Dep Dir, Des Moines Public Library, 1000 Grand Ave, Des Moines, IA, 50309. Tel: 515-283-4102. Fax: 515-237-1654. p. 808

Roe, Lisa, Br Mgr, Chicago Public Library, Bucktown-Wicker Park, 1701 N Milwaukee Ave, Chicago, IL, 60647. Tel: 312-744-6022. Fax: 312-744-5521. p. 608

Roe, Lynn A, Dir, Dixon Public Library, 221 S Hennepin Ave, Dixon, IL, 61021-3093. Tel: 815-284-7261. Fax: 815-288-7323. p. 637

Roe, Marilyn J, Dir, MedCentral Health System, 335 Glessner Ave, Mansfield, OH, 44903-2265. Tel: 419-526-8515. Fax: 419-526-8124. p. 1913

Roe, Ruth E, Librn, Orange County Museum of Art Library, 850 San Clemente Dr, Newport Beach, CA, 92660. Tel: 949-759-1122. Fax: 949-759-5623. p. 194

Roeder, Catherine G, Head, Bibliog Control, Southeast Missouri State University, One University Plaza, Mail Stop 4600, Cape Girardeau, MO, 63701. Tel: 573-651-2745. Fax: 573-651-2666. p. 1322

Roegge, Kathy, Head, Circ, Winnetka-Northfield Public Library District, 768 Oak St, Winnetka, IL, 60093-2583. Tel: 847-446-7220. Fax: 847-446-5085. p. 720

Roehling, Steve, Br Mgr, El Paso Public Library, Richard Burges Regional, 9600 Dyer, El Paso, TX, 79924. Tel: 915-759-2400. Fax: 915-759-2424. p. 2316

Roehrs, Jean, Dir, Med Libr, Indian Health Services, 4212 N 16th St, Phoenix, AZ, 85016. Tel: 602-263-1676. Fax: 602-263-1577. p. 73

Roeleveld, Denise, Info Tech, PricewaterhouseCoopers, National Tax Research Services, Royal Trust Tower, 77 King St W, Ste 3000, Toronto, ON, M5K 1G8, CANADA. Tel: 416-815-5103. Fax: 416-814-3200. p. 2857

Roemer, Marilyn, Chairperson, RCMP Centennial Library, 264 24th St, Fort Macleod, AB, T0L 0Z0, CANADA. Tel: 403-553-3880. p. 2704

Roeper, Susan, Chief Librn, Sterling & Francine Clark Art Institute Library, 225 South St, Williamstown, MA, 01267. Tel: 413-458-0550. Fax: 413-458-9542. p. 1140

Roepke, Rebecca, Dir, Libr Serv, Cudahy Family Library, 3500 Library Dr, Cudahy, WI, 53110. Tel: 414-769-2246. Fax: 414-769-2252. p. 2587

Roesch, Gay, Librn, Colorado Joint Legislative Council, State Capitol Bldg, Rm 048, 200 E Colfax Ave, Denver, CO, 80203-1784. Tel: 303-866-4799. Fax: 303-866-2167. p. 299

Roesler, Karen, Dir, Meriden Public Library, 105 Miller St, Meriden, CT, 06450. Tel: 203-238-2344, 203-238-2346. Fax: 203-238-3647. p. 350

Roethemeyer, Robert V, Dir, Libr Serv, Concordia Theological Seminary, 6600 N Clinton St, Fort Wayne, IN, 46825. Tel: 260-452-2145. Fax: 260-452-2126. p. 741

Roether, Diane, Dir of Libr Serv, North Central Texas College Library, 1525 W California St, Gainesville, TX, 76240-0815. Tel: 940-668-4283. p. 2326

Roets, Veda, Librn, Altoona Public Library, 713 Main St, Altoona, KS, 66710. Tel: 620-568-6681. p. 855

Roever, Margaret, Asst Librn, Ashaway Free Library, 15 Knight St, Ashaway, RI, 02804-1410. Tel: 401-377-2770. Fax: 401-377-2770. p. 2163

Roewe, Patrick, Br Serv Mgr, Spokane County Library District, 4322 N Argonne Rd, Spokane, WA, 99212-1868. Tel: 509-893-8200. Fax: 509-893-8472. p. 2536

Roewe, Patrick, Mgr, Br Serv, Spokane County Library District, North Spokane Library, 44 E Hawthorne Rd, Spokane, WA, 99218-1597. Tel: 509-893-8350. Fax: 509-893-8481. p. 2537

Roff, Jill Robin, Librn, Hinckley, Allen & Snyder LLP, 50 Kennedy Plaza, Providence, RI, 02903. Tel: 617-345-9000. Fax: 617-345-9600. p. 2172

Roff, Sandra, Archivist, Baruch College-CUNY, 151 E 25 St, Box H-0520, New York, NY, 10010-2313. Tel: 646-312-1623. p. 1670

Roffo, Maureen, Libr Asst, Central Square Library, 637 S Main St, Central Square, NY, 13036. Tel: 315-668-6104. Fax: 315-668-6104. p. 1605

Rofini, Diane P, Librn, Chester County Historical Society Library, 225 N High St, West Chester, PA, 19380. Tel: 610-692-4800. Fax: 610-692-4357. p. 2153

Rofini, Laurie A, Dir, Chester County Archives & Records Services Library, 601 Westtown Rd, Ste 080, West Chester, PA, 19382-4958. Tel: 610-344-6760. Fax: 610-344-5616. p. 2153

Rogal, Margaret, Ref, Augustana College Library, 3435 9 1/2 Ave, Rock Island, IL, 61201-2296. Tel: 309-794-7266. Fax: 309-794-7640. p. 696

Rogalski, Josh, Computer Tech, Seymour Public Library District, 176-178 Genesee St, Auburn, NY, 13021. Tel: 315-252-2571. Fax: 315-252-7985. p. 1576

Rogalski, Mary E, Dir, Libr Serv, Choate, Hall & Stewart LLP Library, Two International Pl, Boston, MA, 02110. Tel: 617-248-5202. Fax: 617-248-4000. p. 1059

Rogan, Mary Ellen, Asst Dir, Plainfield Public Library, 800 Park Ave, Plainfield, NJ, 07060-2594. Tel: 908-757-1111, Ext 132. Fax: 908-754-0063. p. 1521

Rogan, Michael, Music Librn, Tufts University, 35 Professors Row, Medford, MA, 02155-5816. Tel: 617-627-2846. Fax: 617-627-3002. p. 1104

Rogan, Michael, Music Librn, Tufts University, Lilly Music Library, Granoff Music Ctr, Rm M030 Lower Level, 20 Talbot Ave, Medford, MA, 02155. Tel: 617-627-2846. Fax: 617-627-3002. p. 1104

Rogan, Phyllis, Ref Librn, Chemung County Library District, 101 E Church St, Elmira, NY, 14901-2799. Tel: 607-733-9173. Fax: 607-733-9176. p. 1619

Rogan, Rebecca, Ref Librn, Chappaqua Public Library, 195 S Greeley Ave, Chappaqua, NY, 10514. Tel: 914-238-4779. Fax: 914-238-3597. p. 1605

Roger, Tensae, Assoc Dir, Br Serv, Johnson County Library, 9875 W 87th St, Overland Park, KS, 66212. Tel: 913-495-2549. Fax: 913-495-2460. p. 888

Rogers, Andrea, Librn, Beaumont Hospital, 468 Cadieux Rd, Grosse Pointe, MI, 48230. Tel: 313-343-1000, 313-343-1620. Fax: 313-343-1947. p. 1187

Rogers, Ann G, Libr Spec, Ser, Florida Southern College, 111 Lake Hollingsworth Dr, Lakeland, FL, 33801-5698. Tel: 863-680-4496. Fax: 863-680-4126. p. 459

Rogers, Anne, Dir, Sci Knowledge Serv, Cargill, Inc, 15407 McGinty Rd W, Wayzata, MN, 55391. Tel: 952-742-6498. Fax: 952-742-6062. p. 1287

Rogers, Anthony, Electronic Res Librn, Pittsburgh Theological Seminary, 616 N Highland Ave, Pittsburgh, PA, 15206-2596. Tel: 412-924-1352. Fax: 412-362-2329. p. 2127

Rogers, Arline, Libr Spec, Inyo County Free Library, Big Pine Branch, 500 S Main St, Big Pine, CA, 93513. Tel: 760-938-2420. p. 159

Rogers, Becky, Libr Mgr, Peterborough Public Library, 345 Aylmer St N, Peterborough, ON, K9H 3V7, CANADA. Tel: 705-745-5382. Fax: 705-745-8958. p. 2836

Rogers, Ben, Dir, Baylor University Libraries, W R Poage Legislative Library, Baylor Collections of Political Materials, 201 Baylor Ave, Waco, TX, 76706. Tel: 254-710-3540. Fax: 254-710-3059. p. 2396

Rogers, Bonnie, Asst Librn, Goodwater Public Library, 36 Weogufka St, Goodwater, AL, 35072. Tel: 256-839-5741. Fax: 256-839-5741. p. 18

Rogers, Carton, Vice Provost & Dir, University of Pennsylvania Libraries, 3420 Walnut St, Philadelphia, PA, 19104-6206. Tel: 215-898-7091. Fax: 215-898-0559. p. 2118

Rogers, Cheryl M, Admin Senior Librn, Uncle Remus Regional Library System, 1121 East Ave, Madison, GA, 30650. Tel: 706-342-4974, Ext 21. Fax: 706-342-4510. p. 541

Rogers, Chris, Br Librn, Spartanburg County Public Libraries, Pacolet Library, 390 W Main St, Pacolet, SC, 29372. Tel: 864-474-0421. p. 2205

Rogers, Curtis R, Dir, Communications, South Carolina State Library, 1430-1500 Senate St, Columbia, SC, 29201. Tel: 803-734-8666. Fax: 803-734-8676. p. 2189

Rogers, Denise, Librn, Sundridge-Strong Union Public Library, 110 Main St, Sundridge, ON, P0A 1Z0, CANADA. Tel: 705-384-7311. Fax: 705-384-7311. p. 2847

Rogers, Diana, Asst Librn, Mayo Clinic Scottsdale Libraries, 13400 E Shea Blvd, Scottsdale, AZ, 85259. Tel: 480-301-8443. Fax: 480-301-7005. p. 80

Rogers, Dora, Br Mgr, Shreve Memorial Library, Atkins Branch, 3704 Greenwood Rd, Shreveport, LA, 71109. Tel: 318-635-6222. Fax: 318-635-6912. p. 969

Rogers, Elizabeth S, Head, Tech Serv & ILL, Clinton-Essex-Franklin Library System, 33 Oak St, Plattsburgh, NY, 12901-2810. Tel: 518-563-5190, Ext 14. Fax: 518-563-0421. p. 1718

Rogers, Emily, Coordr, Pub Serv, University of Wisconsin-Green Bay, 2420 Nicolet Dr, Green Bay, WI, 54311-7001. Tel: 920-465-2304. Fax: 920-465-2136. p. 2596

Rogers, Estaline, Pub Serv, Palm Beach State College, 4200 Congress Ave, Mail Sta 17, Lake Worth, FL, 33461. Tel: 561-868-3800. Fax: 561-868-3708. p. 459

Rogers, Flossie Benton, Dir, Libr Serv, Citrus County Library System, 425 W Roosevelt Blvd, Beverly Hills, FL, 34465-4281. Tel: 352-746-9077. Fax: 352-746-9493. p. 427

Rogers, Ginger, Dir, Bicknell-Vigo Township Public Library, 201 W Second St, Bicknell, IN, 47512. Tel: 812-735-2317. Fax: 812-735-2018. p. 726

Rogers, Hyacinth, Nursing Educator, Jack C Montgomery VA Medical Center, 1011 Honor Heights Dr, Muskogee, OK, 74401. Tel: 918-680-3753. Fax: 918-680-3752. p. 1969

Rogers, James, Govt Doc, Salem International University Benedum Library, KD Hurley Blvd, Salem, WV, 26426. Tel: 304-326-1390. Fax: 304-326-1240. p. 2571

Rogers, Jennifer, Br Mgr, Josephine Community Libraries, Inc, Illinois Valley, 209 W Palmer St, Cave Junction, OR, 97523-0190. Tel: 541-592-4778. p. 1999

Rogers, Jillian, Youth Spec, Greenwood-Leflore Public Library System, 405 W Washington St, Greenwood, MS, 38930-4297. Tel: 662-453-3634. Fax: 662-453-0683. p. 1299

Rogers, Jim, Br Librn, Phillips-Lee-Monroe Regional Library, Monroe County Library, 270 Madison St, Clarendon, AR, 72029-2792. Tel: 870-747-5593. Fax: 870-747-5593. p. 103

Rogers, Jim, Pres, Wolfeboro Historical Society Library, 233 S Main St, Wolfeboro, NH, 03894-4412. Tel: 603-569-1683. p. 1468

Rogers, Joan, Dir, Waterford Township Public Library, Leggett, 3621 Pontiac Lake Rd, Waterford, MI, 48328. Tel: 248-618-7691. Fax: 248-673-1082. p. 1235

Rogers, Joan M, Coordr, Libr Serv, Dir, Waterford Township Public Library, 5168 Civic Center Dr, Waterford, MI, 48329. Tel: 248-618-7691. Fax: 248-674-1910. p. 1235

Rogers, Joanne, Librn, Orr's Island Library, 1699 Harpswell Islands Rd, Orr's Island, ME, 04066. Tel: 207-833-7811. p. 995

Rogers, Jonice, ILL, University of Missouri-Kansas City Libraries, Health Sciences Library, 2411 Holmes St, Kansas City, MO, 64108. Tel: 816-235-1878. Fax: 816-235-6570. p. 1341

Rogers, Judith, Librn, Weld Free Public Library, 25 Church St, Weld, ME, 04285. Tel: 207-585-2439. Fax: 207-585-2439. p. 1006

Rogers, Judith, ILL, State Law Library of Montana, 215 N Sanders, Helena, MT, 59601-4522. Tel: 406-444-3660. Fax: 406-444-3603. p. 1383

Rogers, Judith V, Adminr, Ref & Info Serv, Team Leader, University of the Virgin Islands, RR 2, Box 10000, Kingshill, VI, 00850-9781. Tel: 340-692-4132. Fax: 340-692-4135. p. 2679

Rogers, Justin, Port St Lucie Campus Libr Dir, Keiser University Library System, 1500 NW 49th St, Fort Lauderdale, FL, 33309. Tel: 954-351-4035. Fax: 954-351-4051. p. 443

Rogers, Keith, Tech Serv, Friendswood Public Library, 416 S Friendswood Dr, Friendswood, TX, 77546-3897. Tel: 281-482-7135. Fax: 281-482-2685. p. 2325

Rogers Kroll, Dawn, ILL, Sidney Memorial Public Library, Eight River St, Sidney, NY, 13838. Tel: 607-563-1200, 607-563-8021. Fax: 607-563-7675. p. 1743

Rogers, Lala, Br Mgr, Chicago Public Library, Sherman Park, 5440 S Racine Ave, Chicago, IL, 60609. Tel: 312-747-0477. Fax: 312-747-1474. p. 609

Rogers, Liam, Dir, Fallsburg Library Inc, 12 Railroad Plaza, South Fallsburg, NY, 12779. Tel: 845-436-6067. Fax: 845-434-1254. p. 1745

Rogers, Liisa, Dir, Healthwise Inc, 2601 N Bogus Basin Rd, Boise, ID, 83702. Tel: 208-331-6957. Fax: 208-345-1897. p. 571

Rogers, Linda, Dir, Powell County Public Library, 725 Breckenridge St, Stanton, KY, 40380. Tel: 606-663-4511. Fax: 606-663-4346. p. 936

Rogers, Linda, Coordr, Mercer County Correction Center Library, PO Box 8068, Trenton, NJ, 08650-0068. Tel: 609-989-6901, Ext 2282. Fax: 609-397-4589. p. 1535

Rogers, Linda, Coll Develop Librn, Kwantlen Polytechnic University Library, 12666 72 Ave., Surrey, BC, V3W 2M8, CANADA. Tel: 604-599-2942. Fax: 604-599-2106. p. 2738

Rogers, Linda, Br Librn, South Interlake Regional Library, Teulon Branch, 19 Beach Rd E, Teulon, MB, R0C 3B0, CANADA. Tel: 204-886-3648. Fax: 204-886-3661. p. 2752

Rogers, Lisa, Coordr, Distance Learning, Ref & Instrul Serv, Instr Coordr, Utica College, 1600 Burrstone Rd, Utica, NY, 13502-4892. Tel: 315-792-3342. Fax: 315-792-3361. p. 1759

Rogers, Margaret N, Dir, Libr Serv, Northwest Mississippi Community College, 4975 Hwy 51 N, Senatobia, MS, 38668-1701. Tel: 662-562-3278. Fax: 662-562-3280. p. 1315

Rogers, Marilyn, Head, Ser, University of Arkansas Libraries, 365 N McIlroy Ave, Fayetteville, AR, 72701-4002. Tel: 479-575-4101. Fax: 479-575-6656. p. 99

Rogers, Marsha, Librn, Selden Public Library, 109 S Kansas Ave, Selden, KS, 67757. Tel: 785-386-4321. p. 894

Rogers, Mary, Assoc Dir, Info Syst, Trumbull Library, 33 Quality St, Trumbull, CT, 06611. Tel: 203-452-5197. Fax: 203-452-5125. p. 373

Rogers, Melissa, Dir, Resurrection Metropolitan Community Church, 2025 W 11th St, Houston, TX, 77008. Tel: 713-861-9149. Fax: 713-861-2520. p. 2341

Rogers, Michelle, Br Librn, Laurel-Jones County Library System, Inc, Ellisville Public, 201 Poplar St, Ellisville, MS, 39437. Tel: 601-477-9271. Fax: 601-477-3004. p. 1307

Rogers, Michelle, Librn, Polsinelli Shughart PC, 700 W 47th St, Ste 1000, Kansas City, MO, 64112. Tel: 816-753-1000. Fax: 816-753-1536. p. 1340

Rogers, Michelle L, PhD, Asst Prof, Drexel University, Rush Bldg, Rm 306, 30 N 33rd St, Philadelphia, PA, 19104-2875. Tel: 215-895-2474. Fax: 215-895-2494. p. 2972

Rogers, Mike E, Dir, Northeast Arkansas Regional Library System, 120 N 12th St, Paragould, AR, 72450. Tel: 870-236-8711. Fax: 870-236-1442. p. 111

Rogers, Mindy, Admin Serv Mgr, Arkansas State Library, 900 W Capitol, Ste 100, Little Rock, AR, 72201-3108. Tel: 501-682-2053. Fax: 501-682-1529. p. 105

Rogers, Mona, Librn, Ilsley Public Library, Sarah Partridge Community, 431 E Main St, East Middlebury, VT, 05740. Tel: 802-388-7588. p. 2428

Rogers, Nancy, Dir, Millbrook Free Library, Three Friendly Lane, Millbrook, NY, 12545. Tel: 845-677-3611. Fax: 845-677-5127. p. 1661

Rogers, Pat, Lifelong Learning Mgr, Wake County Public Library System, Southeast Regional Library, 908 Seventh Ave, Garner, NC, 27529. Tel: 919-662-2264. Fax: 919-662-2270. p. 1818

Rogers, Patricia, Circ Supvr, Palm Springs Public Library, 217 Cypress Lane, Palm Springs, FL, 33461-1698. Tel: 561-965-2204. Fax: 561-964-2803. p. 480

Rogers, Patricia J, Dir, Abbot Public Library, 235 Pleasant St, Marblehead, MA, 01945. Tel: 781-631-1481. Fax: 781-639-0558. p. 1102

Rogers, Peggy, Govt Doc, Per, Southern Arkansas University, 100 E University, Magnolia, AR, 71753-5000. Tel: 870-235-5066. Fax: 870-235-5018. p. 108

Rogers, Rebecca, Sr Libr Tech, Whitman Public Library, 100 Webster St, Whitman, MA, 02382. Tel: 781-447-7613. Fax: 781-447-7678. p. 1140

Rogers, Roma, Librn, Oshkosh Public Library, 307 W First St, Oshkosh, NE, 69154. Tel: 308-772-4554. Fax: 308-772-4492. p. 1415

Rogers, Ruth, Spec Coll Librn, Wellesley College, 106 Central St, Wellesley, MA, 02481-8275. Tel: 781-283-2166. Fax: 781-283-3690. p. 1135

Rogers, Samantha, Mgr, Sanford-Brown College, 1101 EastPort Plaza Dr, Collinsville, IL, 62234. Tel: 618-344-5668. Fax: 314-421-5256. p. 631

Rogers, Sandra, Dir, Greene County Public Library, 120 N 12th St, Paragould, AR, 72450. Tel: 870-236-8711. Fax: 870-236-1442. p. 111

Rogers, Shelby, II, Circ Supvr, ILL, Palo Alto College, 1400 W Villaret St, San Antonio, TX, 78224-2499. Tel: 210-486-3901. Fax: 210-486-9184. p. 2380

Rogers, Shelley, Sr Cataloger, Irvine Sullivan Ingram Library, University of West Georgia, 1601 Maple St, Carrollton, GA, 30118. Tel: 678-839-6498. Fax: 678-839-6511. p. 523

Rogers, Shelley, Tech Serv Supvr, Arrowhead Library System, 5528 Emerald Ave, Mountain Iron, MN, 55768-2069. Tel: 218-741-3840. Fax: 218-748-2171. p. 1267

Rogers, Stacey, Dir, Justin Community Library, 408 Pafford St, Justin, TX, 76247-9442. Tel: 940-648-3649. Fax: 940-648-8423. p. 2348

Rogers, Susan, Dir, The Gunnery, 99 Green Hill Rd, Washington, CT, 06793. Tel: 860-868-7334, Ext 224. Fax: 860-868-0859. p. 374

Rogers, Susan, Asst Librn, Nakusp Public Library Association, 92 W Sixth Ave, Nakusp, BC, V0G 1R0, CANADA. Tel: 250-265-3363. Fax: 250-265-3363. p. 2732

Rogers, Terri, Asst Dir, Centralia Regional Library District, 515 E Broadway, Centralia, IL, 62801. Tel: 618-532-5222. Fax: 618-532-8578. p. 602

Rogers, Tomi Jill, Dir, Medford Public Library, 123 S Main St, Medford, OK, 73759. Tel: 580-395-2801. Fax: 580-395-2342. p. 1968

Rogers, Will, Jr, Ref Serv, Youth Serv, Destin Library, 150 Sibert Ave, Destin, FL, 32541-1523. Tel: 850-837-8572. Fax: 850-837-5248. p. 438

Rogers-Urbanek, Jenica P, Dir of Libr Serv, State University of New York College at Potsdam, 44 Pierrepont Ave, Potsdam, NY, 13676-2294. Tel: 315-267-3328. Fax: 315-267-2744. p. 1722

Rogers-Willis, Jane, Librn, Hare Bay-Dover Public Library, Jane Collins Academy, 12 Anstey's Rd, Hare Bay, NL, A0G 2P0, CANADA. Tel: 709-537-2391. Fax: 709-537-2374. p. 2770

Rogerson, Holly, Ref, Vineland Public Library, 1058 E Landis Ave, Vineland, NJ, 08360. Tel: 856-794-4244. Fax: 856-691-0366. p. 1538

Rogge, Stephen L, Dir, Rapides Parish Library, 411 Washington St, Alexandria, LA, 71301-8338. Tel: 318-445-6436, Ext 1001. Fax: 318-445-6478. p. 940

Roggenstein, Carol, Br Mgr, Palm Beach County Library System, Gardens, 11303 Campus Dr, Palm Beach Gardens, FL, 33410. Tel: 561-626-6133. Fax: 561-626-9864. p. 503

Rogler, Hilary, Circ, ILL, Per, Hellenic College-Holy Cross Greek Orthodox School of Theology, 50 Goddard Ave, Brookline, MA, 02445-7496. Tel: 617-850-1244. Fax: 617-850-1470. p. 1071

Rognlie, Jane, Fac Librn-Sylvania Campus, Portland Community College Library, 12000 SW 49th AV, Portland, OR, 97219. Tel: 971-722-4590. Fax: 971-722-8397. p. 2013

Rogoschewsky, Tanya, Librn, Regina Public Library, Connaught, 3435 13th Ave, Regina, SK, S4T 1P8, CANADA. Tel: 306-777-6078. p. 2923

Rogoz, Jessica, Head, Tech Serv, Hamden Public Library, 2901 Dixwell Ave, Hamden, CT, 06518-3135. Tel: 203-287-2686. Fax: 203-287-2685. p. 343

Rohan, Pat, Ref Mgr, Kirkwood Public Library, 140 E Jefferson Ave, Kirkwood, MO, 63122. Tel: 314-821-5770, Ext 1025. Fax: 314-822-3755. p. 1342

Rohde, Jen L, Managing Archivist, National Archives of The Christian & Missionary Alliance, 8595 Explorer Dr, Colorado Springs, CO, 80920-1012. Tel: 719-265-2105. Fax: 719-599-8234. p. 295

Rohlfing, Cindy, Librn, International Business College Library, 5699 Coventry Ln, Fort Wayne, IN, 46804-7145. Tel: 260-459-4500. Fax: 260-436-1896. p. 742

Rohlfs, Emily, Dir, Keokuk Public Library, 210 N Fifth St, Keokuk, IA, 52632. Tel: 319-524-1483. Fax: 319-524-2320. p. 825

Rohling, Sarah, Librn, Metcalf & Eddy Inc, PO Box 4071, Wakefield, MA, 01880-5371. Tel: 781-246-5200. Fax: 781-245-6293. p. 1132

Rohmiller, Thomas, In Charge, United States Air Force, National Air & Space Intelligence Center Research Center, NASIC/GXKA, 4180 Watson Way, Wright-Patterson AFB, OH, 45433-5648. Tel: 937-257-3531. Fax: 937-257-0122. p. 1951

Rohner, Susan, Librn, Johns Hopkins University Libraries, William H Welch Medical Library, 1900 E Monument St, Baltimore, MD, 21205. Tel: 410-955-3028. Fax: 410-955-0200. p. 1015

Roholt, Lori, Programming Serv, New Ulm Public Library, 17 N Broadway, New Ulm, MN, 56073-1786. Tel: 507-359-8331. Fax: 507-354-3255. p. 1268

Rohr, Rebecca, Head, Tech Serv, Lucius Beebe Memorial Library, 345 Main St, Wakefield, MA, 01880-5093. Tel: 781-246-6334. Fax: 781-246-6385. p. 1132

Rohrbach, Kenneth J, Libr Dir, Scenic Regional Library of Franklin, Gasconade & Warren Counties, 308 Hawthorne Dr, Union, MO, 63084. Tel: 636-583-3224. p. 1369

Rohrbaugh, Ann, Dir, Kalamazoo Public Library, 315 S Rose St, Kalamazoo, MI, 49007-5264. Tel: 269-553-7828. Fax: 269-553-7999. p. 1197

Rohrbaugh, Barbara, Libr Asst, Hubbard Free Library, 115 Second St, Hallowell, ME, 04347. Tel: 207-622-6582. p. 987

Rohrbaugh, Dennis E, Archivist, Librn, American Federation of Jews from Central Europe, Inc, 15 W 16th St, 4th Flr, New York, NY, 10011. Tel: 212-921-3871. Fax: 212-921-3860. p. 1668

Rohrer, Aaron, Ch, Kingman Carnegie Public Library, 455 N Main St, Kingman, KS, 67068-1395. Tel: 620-532-3061. Fax: 620-532-2528. p. 876

Rohrer, Cassidy, Archivist, Tribune Publishing Co, 101 N Fourth St, Columbia, MO, 65201-4416. Tel: 573-815-1703. Fax: 573-815-1701. p. 1325

Rohrer, Lorie, Head, Ch, Lake Forest Library, 360 E Deerpath Ave, Lake Forest, IL, 60045-2252. Tel: 847-810-4632. Fax: 847-234-1453. p. 663

Rohrer, Susan, Mgr, Washington State Historical Society, 211 21st Ave SW, Olympia, WA, 98501. Tel: 360-753-2580. Fax: 360-586-8322. p. 2523

Rohrer, Thomas, Librn, Genesee District Library, Library for the Blind & Physically Handicapped, G-4195 W Pasadena Ave, Flint, MI, 48504. Tel: 810-732-1120. Fax: 810-732-1715. p. 1180

Rohrer, Tom, Ref, Genesee District Library, Headquarters Reference, G-4195 W Pasadena Ave, Flint, MI, 48504. Tel: 810-732-0110. Fax: 810-732-3146. p. 1180

Rohrer, Tom, Sr Librn, Genesee District Library, Headquarters, G-4195 W Pasadena Ave, Flint, MI, 48504. Tel: 810-732-0110. Fax: 810-732-3146. p. 1180

Roiger, Betty, Cat, New Ulm Public Library, 17 N Broadway, New Ulm, MN, 56073-1786. Tel: 507-359-8330. Fax: 507-354-3255. p. 1268

Roiger, Linda, Dir, Springfield Public Library, 120 N Cass Ave, Springfield, MN, 56087-1506. Tel: 507-723-3510. Fax: 507-723-6422. p. 1285

Roinick, Carol, Dir, Sullivan County Library, 216 Center St, Dushore, PA, 18614. Tel: 570-928-9352. Fax: 570-928-8820. p. 2051

Rojas, Alexandra, Ref Coordr, Fiorello H LaGuardia Community College Library, 31-10 Thomson Ave, Long Island City, NY, 11101. Tel: 718-482-5421. Fax: 718-482-5444, 718-609-2011. p. 1654

Rojas, Carmen, Librn, Grand Rapids Public Library, West Leonard Branch, 1017 Leonard NW, Grand Rapids, MI, 49504. Tel: 616-988-5416. Fax: 616-301-9438. p. 1185

Rojas, Rosemary, Mgr, Crittenton Hospital Medical Center, 1101 W University Dr, Rochester, MI, 48307-1831. Tel: 248-601-6138. Fax: 248-652-5001. p. 1221

Rokos, Sue Z, Asst Dir, Ch, Mohawk Valley Library System, 858 Duanesburg Rd, Schenectady, NY, 12306-1057. Tel: 518-355-2010. Fax: 518-355-0674. p. 1740

Roksandic, Stevo, Dir, Mount Carmel, 793 W State St, Columbus, OH, 43222-1560. Tel: 614-234-1644. Fax: 614-234-1257. p. 1886

Roksandic, Stevo, Dir, Central Ohio Hospital Library Consortium, 127 S Davis Ave, Columbus, OH, 43222. Tel: 614-234-1644. Fax: 614-234-1257. p. 2951

Roland, Daniel, Asst Prof, Kent State University, 314 Library, Kent, OH, 44242-0001. Tel: 330-672-2782. Fax: 330-672-7965. p. 2972

Roland, David, Asst Regional Adminr, National Archives & Records Administration, 900 Market St, Philadelphia, PA, 19107-4292. Tel: 215-305-2003. Fax: 215-606-0116. p. 2113

Roland, Debbie, Dir, Calhoun County Museum & Cultural Center, 313 Butler St, Saint Matthews, SC, 29135. Tel: 803-874-3964. Fax: 803-874-4790. p. 2204

Roland, Elizabeth, Ref Librn, Endicott College Library, 376 Hale St, Beverly, MA, 01915. Tel: 978-232-2275. Fax: 978-232-2700. p. 1054

Rolen, Rhonda, Ser & Electronic Res Librn, Grambling State University, 403 Main St, Grambling, LA, 71245. Tel: 318-274-2757. Fax: 318-274-3268. p. 950

Roles, Eryn, Res & Instruction Librn, Marshall University Libraries, One John Marshall Dr, Huntington, WV, 25755-2060. Tel: 304-696-2336. Fax: 304-696-5858. p. 2562

Roley, Kris, Cat, ILL Spec, Oregon Health & Science University Library, 3181 SW Sam Jackson Park Rd, Portland, OR, 97239-3098. Tel: 503-494-3460. Fax: 503-494-3227. p. 2013

Rolfe, Alexander, Tech Serv & Syst Librn, George Fox University, 416 N Meridian St, Newberg, OR, 97132. Tel: 503-554-2410. Fax: 503-554-3599. p. 2007

Rolfe, Jorry, Chair, Linn-Benton Community College Library, 6500 SW Pacific Blvd, Albany, OR, 97321-3799. Tel: 541-917-4649. Fax: 541-917-4659. p. 1989

Roll, Barbara, Bus Mgr, Wayne Township Library, 80 N Sixth St, Richmond, IN, 47374-3079. Tel: 765-966-8291. Fax: 765-962-1318. p. 775

Roll, Colleen, Circ Asst, Montana State University-Northern, 300 11th St W, Havre, MT, 59501. Tel: 406-265-3706. Fax: 406-265-3799. p. 1381

Roll, Cris, Circ Supvr, Lake Superior State University, 906 Ryan Ave, Sault Sainte Marie, MI, 49783. Tel: 906-635-2815. Fax: 906-635-2193. p. 1226

Roll, Harriet, Dir, Harvard Diggins Public Library, 900 E McKinley St, Harvard, IL, 60033. Tel: 815-943-4671. Fax: 815-943-2312. p. 654

Roll, Jarrod, Dir, Monroe County Local History Room & Library, 200 W Main St, Sparta, WI, 54656-2141. Tel: 608-269-8680. Fax: 608-269-8921. p. 2639

Roll, Todd, Ref, University of Wisconsin Center-Marathon County Library, 518 S Seventh Ave, Wausau, WI, 54401-5396. Tel: 715-261-6220. Fax: 715-261-6330. p. 2647

Rolle, Janice, Br Mgr, Broward County Division of Libraries, Pompano Beach Branch, 1213 E Atlantic Blvd, Pompano Beach, FL, 33060. Tel: 954-786-2181. Fax: 954-786-2134. p. 442

Roller, Georgia, Curator, Fort Steele Heritage Town Library, 9851 Hwy 93-95, Fort Steele, BC, V0B 1N0, CANADA. Tel: 250-417-6000, Ext 108. Fax: 250-489-2624. p. 2728

Rollie, Trinita, Cat, Southwestern Christian College, Hogan Steward Learning Ctr, 200 Bowser St, Terrell, TX, 75160-3400. Tel: 972-524-3341, Ext 109. Fax: 972-563-7133. p. 2391

Rollings, Jantha, Libr Dir, Arcola Public Library District, 407 E Main St, Arcola, IL, 61910-1513. Tel: 217-268-4477. Fax: 217-268-4478. p. 589

Rollins, Deborah, Coll Serv, University of Maine, 5729 Fogler Library, Orono, ME, 04469-5729. Fax: 207-581-1653. p. 994

Rollins, Debra, Instrul Serv Librn & Coordr, Info Literacy & Outreach, Louisiana State University at Alexandria, 8100 Hwy 71 S, Alexandria, LA, 71302. Tel: 318-473-6443. Fax: 318-473-6556. p. 940

Rollins, Gene, Asst Dir, Technology & Tech Serv, Harris County Public Library, 8080 El Rio, Houston, TX, 77054. Tel: 713-749-9020. Fax: 713-749-9090. p. 2335

Rollins, Kim, Ref, Utah Valley University Library, 800 W University Pkwy, Orem, UT, 84058-5999. Tel: 801-863-7326. Fax: 801-863-7065. p. 2409

Rollins, Kimberly, Exec Secy, Utah Academic Library Consortium, University of Utah, 295 S 1500 E, Salt Lake City, UT, 84112-0860. Tel: 801-581-3852, 801-581-7701. Fax: 801-585-7185. p. 2956

Rollins, Mary, Ch, Enterprise Public Library, 101 E Grubbs St, Enterprise, AL, 36330. Tel: 334-347-2636. Fax: 334-393-6477. p. 15

Rollins, Peggy, Ch, Yolo County Library, Admin Off, 226 Buckeye St, Woodland, CA, 95695-2600. Tel: 530-757-5597. Fax: 530-757-5590. p. 284

Rollins, Peggy, Ch, Yolo County Library, Davis Branch, 315 E 14th St, Davis, CA, 95616. Tel: 530-757-5593. Fax: 530-757-5590. p. 284

Rollins, Rod, Supvr, California Department of Corrections Library System, California Substance Abuse Treatment Facility & State Prison, 900 Quebec Ave, Corcoran, CA, 93212. Tel: 559-992-7100. Fax: 559-992-7182. p. 221

Rollins, Stephen, Dean of Libr, University of Alaska Anchorage, Consortium Library, 3211 Providence Dr, Anchorage, AK, 99508-8176. Tel: 907-786-1825. Fax: 907-786-1834. p. 45

Rollinson, M Elizabeth, Asst Dir, Pomfret Public Library, 449 Pomfret St, Pomfret, CT, 06258. Tel: 860-928-3475. p. 364

Rollison, Jeff, Dir, Immaculata University, 1145 King Rd, Immaculata, PA, 19345-0705. Tel: 610-647-4400, Ext 3841. Fax: 610-640-5828. p. 2071

Rollo, Rebecca, Circ, Otterbein University, 138 W Main St, Westerville, OH, 43081. Tel: 614-823-1799. Fax: 614-823-1921. p. 1946

Roloff, Ronald, AV, Ector County Library, 321 W Fifth St, Odessa, TX, 79761-5066. Tel: 432-332-0633, Ext 4017. Fax: 432-377-6502. p. 2366

Rolon, Edwin Xavier, Asst Curator, Hispanic Society of America Library, 613 W 155th St, New York, NY, 10032. Tel: 212-926-2234, Ext 262. Fax: 212-690-0743. p. 1681

Rolph, Daniel N, Dr, Head, Ref Serv, Historian, Historical Society of Pennsylvania, 1300 Locust St, Philadelphia, PA, 19107-5699. Tel: 215-732-6200, Ext 203. Fax: 215-732-2680. p. 2110

Rom, Cristine C, Dir, Libr Serv, Cleveland Institute of Art, 11141 East Blvd, Cleveland, OH, 44106. Tel: 216-421-7440, 216-421-7441. Fax: 216-421-7439. p. 1877

Roma, Mark, Mgr, Dayton Metro Library, Belmont, 1041 Watervliet Ave, Dayton, OH, 45420. Tel: 937-496-8920. p. 1893

Romalis, Carl, Librn, Arthurkill Correctional Facility Library, 2911 Arthurkill Rd, Staten Island, NY, 10309. Tel: 718-356-7333, Ext 4600. Fax: 718-356-7333, Ext 2099. p. 1747

Roman, Ann, Regional Librn, Nova Scotia Community College, 80 Mawiomi Pl, Dartmouth, NS, B2Y 0A5, CANADA. Tel: 902-491-1035. Fax: 902-491-1037. p. 2780

Roman, Anne, Interim Dir, Springfield Free Public Library, 66 Mountain Ave, Springfield, NJ, 07081-1786. Tel: 973-376-4930. Fax: 973-376-1334. p. 1532

Roman, Carolee, Head, Coll Serv, Pennsylvania State University-Harrisburg Library, 351 Olmsted Dr, Middletown, PA, 17057-4850. Tel: 917-948-6359. Fax: 717-948-6757. p. 2089

Roman, Cynthia, Curator, Yale University Library, Lewis Walpole Library, 154 Main St, Farmington, CT, 06032. Tel: 860-677-2140. Fax: 860-677-6369. p. 359

Roman, Karen, Dir, Farmington Public Library, 108 W Harrison St, Farmington, MO, 63640. Tel: 573-756-5779. Fax: 573-756-0614. p. 1327

Roman, Marcia, Librn, State Correctional Institution, Somerset Library, 1590 Walters Mill Rd, Somerset, PA, 15510-0001. Tel: 814-443-8100. Fax: 814-443-8157. p. 2142

Roman, Susan, Dean, Prof, Dominican University, 7900 W Division St, River Forest, IL, 60305. Tel: 708-524-6845. Fax: 708-524-6657. p. 2965

Romanace, Giselle, Computer Syst Librn, Wilkes University, 187 S Franklin St, Wilkes-Barre, PA, 18766-0998. Tel: 570-408-4250. Fax: 570-408-7823. p. 2156

Romanelli, Peg, Librn, Rock Falls Public Library District, 1007 Seventh Ave, Rock Falls, IL, 61071. Tel: 815-626-3958. Fax: 815-626-8750. p. 696

Romanello, Nancy, Access Serv, University of Connecticut at Stamford, One University Pl, Stamford, CT, 06901-2315. Tel: 203-251-8518. Fax: 203-251-8501. p. 370

Romaniuk, Elena, Coordr, Ser, University of Victoria Libraries, McPherson Library, PO Box 1800, Victoria, BC, V8W 3H5, CANADA. Tel: 250-721-8211. Fax: 250-721-8215. p. 2746

Romanko, Patti, Instrul Serv Librn, Douglas College Library, 700 Royal Ave, New Westminster, BC, V3M 5Z5, CANADA. Tel: 604-527-5183. Fax: 604-527-5193. p. 2733

Romano, Anne Marie, Dir, Silver Hill Hospital, 208 Valley Rd, New Canaan, CT, 06840. Tel: 203-966-3561, Ext 2270. Fax: 203-801-2388. p. 354

Romano, Pia, Info Serv, Wentworth Institute of Technology, 550 Huntington Ave, Boston, MA, 02115-5998. Tel: 617-989-4040. Fax: 617-989-4091. p. 1068

Romano, Rena, Bus Off Mgr, Millis Public Library, 25 Auburn Rd, Millis, MA, 02054-1203. Tel: 508-376-8282. Fax: 508-376-1278. p. 1106

Romano, Stephanie, Circ Supvr, Old Lyme, Two Library Lane, Old Lyme, CT, 06371. Tel: 860-434-1684. Fax: 860-434-9547. p. 363

Romano, T Wayne, Ch, Danville Public Library, 511 Patton St, Danville, VA, 24541. Tel: 434-799-5195. Fax: 434-792-5172. p. 2459

Romanowski, Tom, Coordr, Lancaster County Prison Library, Law, 625 E King St, Lancaster, PA, 17602-3199. Tel: 717-299-7814. p. 2077

Romans, Anne Francis, Dir, Witherle Memorial Library, 41 School St, Castine, ME, 04421. Tel: 207-326-4375. p. 981

Romans, Larry, Head, Govt Docs & Media Serv, Vanderbilt University, Central Library, 419 21st Ave S, Nashville, TN, 37203-2427. Tel: 615-322-2838. Fax: 615-343-7451. p. 2260

Romansky, Moira, Mgr, NASA, 12600 NASA Rd, Las Cruces, NM, 88012. Tel: 575-524-5683. p. 1558

Rombouth, Tracy, Libr Mgr, Alliance Public Library, PO Box 185, Alliance, AB, T0B 0A0, CANADA. Tel: 780-879-3733. p. 2683

Rome, Alan K, Librn, Saint Mary Seminary, 28700 Euclid Ave, Wickliffe, OH, 44092-2585. Tel: 440-943-7665. Fax: 440-585-3528. p. 1947

Romelczyk, Carolyn, Dir, Pontiac Free Library, 101 Greenwich Ave, Warwick, RI, 02886. Tel: 401-737-3292. Fax: 401-737-3292. p. 2177

Romelczyk, Jerry, Dir, Walpole Public Library, 65 Common St, Walpole, MA, 02081. Tel: 508-660-7334. Fax: 508-660-2714. p. 1132

Romeo, Cara, Commun Serv, Alexander Mitchell Public Library, 519 S Kline St, Aberdeen, SD, 57401-4495. Tel: 605-626-7097. Fax: 605-626-3506. p. 2209

Romeo, Donna M, Dir, Lyndhurst Free Public Library, 355 Valley Brook Ave, Lyndhurst, NJ, 07071. Tel: 201-804-2486. Fax: 201-939-7677. p. 1497

Romeo, Elena, Dir, Palm Springs Public Library, 217 Cypress Lane, Palm Springs, FL, 33461-1698. Tel: 561-965-2204. Fax: 561-964-2803. p. 480

Romer, Anne, Libr Dir, Charlotte E Hobbs Memorial Library, 227 Main St, Lovell, ME, 04051. Tel: 207-925-3177. Fax: 207-925-3177. p. 991

Romer, Greg, Dir, Newcomerstown Public Library, 123 E Main St, Newcomerstown, OH, 43832-1093. Tel: 740-498-8228. Fax: 740-498-8221. p. 1922

Romer, Ward, Librn, Cayuga Medical Center at Ithaca, 101 Dates Dr, Ithaca, NY, 14850. Tel: 607-274-4407. Fax: 607-274-4214. p. 1641

Romero, Adela, Mgr, Coll Develop, Supreme Court of Canada Library, 301 Wellington St, Ottawa, ON, K1A 0J1, CANADA. Tel: 613-996-0166. Fax: 613-952-2832. p. 2833

Romero, Cindy, Mgr, Youth Serv, Sr Librn, Glendora Public Library & Cultural Center, 140 S Glendora Ave, Glendora, CA, 91741. Tel: 626-852-4813. Fax: 626-852-4899. p. 156

Romero, Effie, Circ, Pueblo Community College Library, 900 W Orman Ave, Pueblo, CO, 81004-1430. Tel: 719-549-3308. Fax: 719-549-3309. p. 321

Romero, Georg, Dir, Cabrillo College, 6500 Soquel Dr, Aptos, CA, 95003-3198. Tel: 831-479-6537. Fax: 831-479-6500. p. 121

Romero, Hazel, Cat, Museum of New Mexico, Palace of the Governors-Fray Angelico Chavez History Library, 120 Washington Ave, Santa Fe, NM, 87501. Tel: 505-476-5025. Fax: 505-476-5053. p. 1562

Romero, Helen, Librn, Marin County Free Library, South Novato Branch, Six Hamilton Landing, Ste 140A, Novato, CA, 94949. Tel: 415-506-3164. p. 257

Romero, Lisa, Librn, University of Illinois Library at Urbana-Champaign, Communications, 122 Gregory Hall, Urbana, IL, 61801. Tel: 217-333-6348. p. 712

Romero, Liz, ILL, Ventura County Library, 5600 Everglades St, Ste A, Ventura, CA, 93003. Tel: 805-677-7150. Fax: 805-677-7173. p. 279

Romero, Lori, Dir, White Pine County Library, 950 Campton, Ely, NV, 89301-1965. Tel: 775-289-3737. Fax: 775-289-1555. p. 1427

Romero, Michelle, Asst Archivist, Northeastern University Libraries, Snell Library, 360 Huntington Ave, Boston, MA, 02115. Tel: 617-373-7656. p. 1065

Romero, Ramona, Bibliographer, Vanderbilt University, Central Library, 419 21st Ave S, Nashville, TN, 37203-2427. Tel: 615-343-4236. Fax: 615-343-7451. p. 2260

Romero, Regina, Assoc Dir, Finance, Yale University Library, Beinecke Rare Book & Manuscript, 121 Wall St, New Haven, CT, 06520. Tel: 203-432-2955. Fax: 203-432-4047. p. 356

Romero, Rosaura, Per, Pontifical Catholic University Of Puerto Rico, Encarnacion Valdes Library, 2250 Avenida Las Americas, Ste 509, Ponce, PR, 00717-0777. Tel: 787-841-2000, Ext 1809. Fax: 787-284-0235. p. 2675

Romic, Bob, Librn, United States Army, Clock Tower Bldg, Rock Island, IL, 61204. Tel: 309-794-5884. Fax: 309-794-5807. p. 696

Romick, Cynthia, Children's Mgr, Findlay-Hancock County District Public Library, 206 Broadway, Findlay, OH, 45840-3382. Tel: 419-422-1712. Fax: 419-422-0638. p. 1899

Romig, Margaret, Res, Nevada Power Co Library, 6226 W Sahara Ave, Las Vegas, NV, 89151. Tel: 702-367-5055. Fax: 702-227-2023. p. 1430

Romine, Charles, Circ Mgr, Dayton Metro Library, 215 E Third St, Dayton, OH, 45402-2103. Tel: 937-463-2665. Fax: 937-496-4300. p. 1892

Romine, Janet, Head, Pub Serv, Truman State University, 100 E Normal, Kirksville, MO, 63501-4211. Tel: 660-785-7418. p. 1342

Rominger, Denise, ILL, Northland Pioneer College Libraries, PO Box 610, Holbrook, AZ, 86025. Tel: 928-532-6122. p. 65

Rominski, Barbara C, Head, Res Libr, Archives & Rec Mgt, San Francisco Museum of Modern Art, 151 Third St, San Francisco, CA, 94103-3107. Tel: 415-357-4121. Fax: 415-357-4038. p. 245

Romito, David, Librn, University of North Carolina at Chapel Hill, Couch Biology (Zoology Section), 213 Wilson Hall, CB No 3280, Chapel Hill, NC, 27599. Tel: 919-962-2264. Fax: 919-843-8393. p. 1780

Romito, David, Librn, University of North Carolina at Chapel Hill, Kenan (Chemistry), Wilson Library, 2nd Level, CB No 3290, Chapel Hill, NC, 27599. Tel: 919-962-1188. Fax: 919-962-2388. p. 1781

Romkens, Mathias, Dr, Dir, USDA-ARS, 598 McElroy Dr, Oxford, MS, 38655-2117. Tel: 662-232-2996. Fax: 662-232-2920. p. 1310

Romyak, Nicole, Acad Prog Librn, Horry-Georgetown Technical College, 2050 Hwy 501 E, Conway, SC, 29526-9521. Tel: 843-349-5397. Fax: 843-347-0552. p. 2191

Ronald, Karen, Town Librn, Fairfield Public Library, 1080 Old Post Rd, Fairfield, CT, 06824. Tel: 203-256-3158. p. 339

Ronalter, Patricia, Ref Serv, Manchester Community College Library, Great Path, Manchester, CT, 06040. Tel: 860-512-2876. Fax: 860-512-2871. p. 350

Ronan, Catherine, Br Mgr, Santa Monica Public Library, Fairview, 2101 Ocean Park Blvd, Santa Monica, CA, 90405-5013. Tel: 310-450-0443. Fax: 310-450-5749. p. 266

Ronan, Linda, Asst Dir, Pub Serv, Library of Rush University Medical Center, Armour Academic Ctr, 600 S Paulina St, 5th Flr, Chicago, IL, 60612-3874. Tel: 312-942-2280. Fax: 312-942-3143. p. 617

Roncevich, Patricia, Acq, Ser Librn, University of Pittsburgh, Law Bldg, 3900 Forbes Ave, 4th Flr, Pittsburgh, PA, 15260. Tel: 412-648-1321. Fax: 412-648-1352. p. 2129

Rondeau, Christiane, Libr Tech, Centre de Santé et de Services Sociaux du Nord de Lanaudière Bibliothèque, 1000 Blvd Ste-Anne, Saint Charles Borromee, QC, J6E 6J2, CANADA. Tel: 450-759-8222. Fax: 450-759-7343. p. 2908

Rondeau, Vicki, Br Mgr, Sacramento Public Library, South Natomas Community Library, 2901 Truxel Rd, Sacramento, CA, 95833. p. 225

Rondinaro, Luke, Dir, Montour Falls Memorial Library, 406 Main St, Montour Falls, NY, 14865. Tel: 607-535-7489. Fax: 607-535-7489. p. 1662

Roney, Sharon, Librn, Ohio Bureau of Worker's Compensation, 30 W Spring St, 3rd Flr, Columbus, OH, 43215-2256. Tel: 614-466-7388. Fax: 614-644-9634. p. 1886

Rongitsch, Janet L, Librn, Zelle, Hofmann, Voelbel, Mason & Gette, 500 Washington Ave S, Ste 4000, Minneapolis, MN, 55415. Tel: 612-336-9129. Fax: 612-336-9100. p. 1263

Ronk, Sue Ellen, Cat, Ashland University Library, 509 College Ave, Ashland, OH, 44805-3796. Tel: 419-289-5400. Fax: 419-289-5422. p. 1855

Ronkartz, Trudy, Librn, Acadia Parish Library, Rayne Branch, 109 W Perrodin, Rayne, LA, 70578. Tel: 337-334-3188. Fax: 337-334-1181. p. 948

Ronn, Micheol, Assoc Dir of Libr, Touro College Libraries, 43 W 23rd St, Fifth Fl, New York, NY, 10010. Tel: 212-463-0400, Ext 224. Fax: 212-627-9144. p. 1701

Ronnander, Doris, Librn, Spring Valley Public Library, E 121 S Second St, Spring Valley, WI, 54767. Tel: 715-778-4590. Fax: 715-778-4590. p. 2639

Ronning, Kim, Tech Serv, Yeshiva University Libraries, Dr Lillian & Dr Rebecca Chutick Law Library, Benjamin N Cardozo School of Law, 55 Fifth Ave, New York, NY, 10003-4301. Tel: 212-790-0223. Fax: 212-790-0236. p. 1703

Ronning, Teresa, Chair, Dir, Adirondack Community College Library, Scoville Learning Center, 640 Bay Rd, Queensbury, NY, 12804. Tel: 518-743-2200, Ext 2261. Fax: 518-745-1442. p. 1725

Ronsen, Jennifer, Automation Syst Coordr, Texas State Library & Archives Commission, 1201 Brazos, Austin, TX, 78711. Tel: 512-463-5458. Fax: 512-936-0685. p. 2283

Roode, Adrienne, Librn, Brescia University College Library, 1285 Western Rd, London, ON, N6G 1H2, CANADA. Tel: 519-432-8353, Ext 28140. Fax: 519-858-5137. p. 2816

Roof, Deb K, Circ Supvr, Messiah College, One College Ave, Ste 3002, Mechanicsburg, PA, 17055. Tel: 717-691-6006, Ext 7293. Fax: 717-691-2356. p. 2087

Rook, Colleen, Librn, Worsley & District Public Library, PO Box 246, Worsley, AB, T0H 3W0, CANADA. Tel: 780-685-3842. Fax: 780-685-3766. p. 2722

Rook, Diane, Librn, Goodmans LLP Library, Bay Adelaide Ctr, 333 Bay St, Ste 3400, Toronto, ON, M5H 2S7, CANADA. Tel: 416-979-2211, Ext 6070. Fax: 416-979-1234. p. 2854

Rook-Schilf, Suzanne, Head, Ref Serv, Clemson University Libraries, Box 343001, Clemson, SC, 29634-3001. Tel: 864-656-6834. Fax: 864-656-0758. p. 2186

Rooker, Hazel, Tech Serv, Jefferson Public Library, 321 S Main St, Jefferson, WI, 53549-1772. Tel: 920-674-7733. Fax: 920-674-7735. p. 2600

Rooker, Jill, Dr, Prof, University of Central Oklahoma, 100 N University Dr, Edmond, OK, 73034. Tel: 405-974-5437. Fax: 405-974-3857. p. 2972

Rooks, Amy, Ch, Oconee Regional Library, 801 Bellevue Ave, Dublin, GA, 31021. Tel: 478-272-5710. Fax: 478-275-5381. p. 531

Rooks, Dana, Dean of Libr, University of Houston, M D Anderson Library, 114 University Libraries, Houston, TX, 77204-2000. Tel: 713-743-9800. Fax: 713-743-9811. p. 2343

Rooks, Dana, Pres, Houston Area Research Library Consortium, c/o University of Houston Libraries, 114 University Libraries, Houston, TX, 77204-2000. Tel: 713-743-9807. Fax: 713-743-9811. p. 2956

Rooks, Georgia, Dir, Oglala Lakota College, Eagle Nest College Center, PO Box 350, Wanblee, SD, 57577. Tel: 605-462-6274. Fax: 605-462-6105. p. 2213

Rooks, Gina, Librn, White County Regional Library System, Rose Bud Public, 548 Hwy 5 S, Rose Bud, AR, 71237. Tel: 501-556-4447. Fax: 501-556-4447. p. 115

Room, Teri, Coll Develop, Skokie Public Library, 5215 Oakton St, Skokie, IL, 60077-3680. Tel: 847-673-7774. Fax: 847-673-7797. p. 703

Roome, Dee Ann, Circ & ILL Mgr, MacMurray College, 447 E College Ave, Jacksonville, IL, 62650-2510. Tel: 217-479-7111. Fax: 217-245-5214. p. 659

Rooney, Gloria, Cat Librn, Boynton Beach City Library, 208 S Seacrest Blvd, Boynton Beach, FL, 33435. Tel: 561-742-6390. Fax: 561-742-6381. p. 429

Rooney, Pete, Librn, San Joaquin College of Law Library, 901 Fifth St, Clovis, CA, 93612. Tel: 559-323-2100, Ext 121. Fax: 559-323-5566. p. 135

Roork, Betty J, Librn, Fulton County Library, 131 Pickren St, Salem, AR, 72576. Tel: 870-895-2014. Fax: 870-895-2014. p. 114

Roos, Barbara, Head, YA, East Baton Rouge Parish Library, 7711 Goodwood Blvd, Baton Rouge, LA, 70806-7625. Tel: 225-231-3770. Fax: 225-231-3788. p. 942

Roos, Bonnie, Libr Dir, United States Air Force, 366 FSS/FSDL, 480 Fifth Ave, Ste 100, Mountain Home AFB, ID, 83648. Tel: 208-828-2326. Fax: 208-832-9840. p. 580

Roos, Jay, Tech Coordr, Great River Regional Library, 1300 W St Germain St, Saint Cloud, MN, 56301-3667. Tel: 320-650-2534. Fax: 320-650-2501. p. 1274

Roos, Matthew, Circ, Lynn University Library, 3601 N Military Trail, Boca Raton, FL, 33431-5598. Tel: 561-237-7066. Fax: 561-237-7074. p. 428

Roos, Shirley, Librn, Holly Township Library, 1116 N Saginaw St, Holly, MI, 48442-1395. Tel: 248-634-1754. Fax: 248-634-8088. p. 1191

Roosa, Mark, Dean of Libr, Pepperdine University Libraries, 24255 Pacific Coast Hwy, Malibu, CA, 90263. Tel: 310-506-4252. Fax: 310-506-7225. p. 182

Roose, Dan, Asst Dean, Tech Serv, Butler University Libraries, 4600 Sunset Ave, Indianapolis, IN, 46208. Tel: 317-940-9236. Fax: 317-940-9711. p. 749

Roose, Rob, Support Serv Mgr, Spokane Public Library, 906 W Main Ave, Spokane, WA, 99201-0976. Tel: 509-444-5320. Fax: 509-444-5365. p. 2537

Roose, Tereasa, Br Mgr, Ref Serv, Clearwater Public Library System, East, 2251 Drew St, Clearwater, FL, 33765. Tel: 727-562-4970. p. 432

Root, Clyde R, Dr, Dir of Libr, Bethel College, 1001 W McKinley Ave, Mishawaka, IN, 46545. Tel: 574-257-3347. Fax: 574-257-3499. p. 765

Root, Mark, Head, Ref, Bethel College, 1001 W McKinley Ave, Mishawaka, IN, 46545. Tel: 574-257-3347. Fax: 574-257-3499. p. 765

Root, Patricia, Head, Ref Serv, Bronxville Public Library, 201 Pondfield Rd, Bronxville, NY, 10708. Tel: 914-337-7680. Fax: 914-337-0332. p. 1588

Root, Vicki, Dir, Libr Serv, Thompson Home Public Library, 125 W Center St, Ithaca, MI, 48847. Tel: 989-875-4184. Fax: 989-875-3374. p. 1194

Rootes, Mary Jane, Instrul Serv Librn, Irvine Sullivan Ingram Library, University of West Georgia, 1601 Maple St, Carrollton, GA, 30118. Tel: 678-839-6498. Fax: 678-839-6511. p. 523

Rooth, Ron, Librn, Cape Breton University Library, 1250 Grand Lake Rd, Sydney, NS, B1P 6L2, CANADA. Tel: 902-563-1421. Fax: 902-563-1826. p. 2785

Roovaart, Carol, Ch, Altoona Public Library, 700 Eighth St SW, Altoona, IA, 50009. Tel: 515-967-3881. Fax: 515-967-6934. p. 792

Roper, Dee, Cat, Gadsden Public Library, 254 College St, Gadsden, AL, 35901. Tel: 256-549-4699. p. 18

Roper, John, Res Librn, University of Virginia, Arthur J Morris Law Library, 580 Massie Rd, Charlottesville, VA, 22903-1789. Tel: 434-924-4327. Fax: 434-982-2232. p. 2455

Roper, Linda, Dir, Olton Area Library, 701 Main St, Olton, TX, 79064. Tel: 806-285-7772. Fax: 806-285-7790. p. 2367

Roper, Paula, Soc Sci Librn, University of Missouri-Columbia, Elmer Ellis Library, Ellis Library Bldg, Rm 104, Columbia, MO, 65201-5149. Tel: 573-882-3326. Fax: 573-882-8044. p. 1325

Ropson, Kim, Head, Ch, Marshfield Public Library, 211 E Second St, Marshfield, WI, 54449. Tel: 715-387-8494, Ext 218. Fax: 715-387-6909. p. 2613

Roque, Rita, Librn, Union City Public Library, Summit Branch, 1800 Summit Ave, Union City, NJ, 07087-4320. Tel: 201-866-7503. Fax: 201-348-2635. p. 1537

Rorissa, Abebe, Dr, Assoc Prof, University at Albany, State University of New York, Draper 116, 135 Western Ave, Albany, NY, 12222. Tel: 518-442-5123. Fax: 518-442-5367. p. 2970

Rork, Claire, Circ Coordr, New England College of Optometry Library, 424 Beacon St, Boston, MA, 02115. Tel: 617-587-5657. Fax: 617-587-5573. p. 1064

Rortvedt, Colleen T, Asst Dir, Appleton Public Library, 225 N Oneida St, Appleton, WI, 54911-4780. Tel: 920-832-6168. Fax: 920-832-6182. p. 2578

Rorvik, Erica, Commun Librn, Moody County Resource Center, 610 W Community Dr, Flandreau, SD, 57028. Tel: 605-997-3326. Fax: 605-997-2457. p. 2212

Rosa, Gloria, Dir, Brodhead Memorial Public Library, 902 W Second Ave, Brodhead, WI, 53520-1308. Tel: 608-897-4070. p. 2583

Rosa, Lucille M, Head, Tech Serv Div, United States Naval War College Library, 686 Cushing Rd, Newport, RI, 02841-1207. Tel: 401-841-2641. Fax: 401-841-6491. p. 2169

Rosacker, Caroline, Ch, Guttenberg Public Library, 603 S Second St, Guttenberg, IA, 52052. Tel: 563-252-3108. p. 820

Rosado, Sandy, Head, Tech Serv, Eastern Connecticut State University, 83 Windham St, Willimantic, CT, 06226-2295. Tel: 860-465-4464. Fax: 860-465-5523. p. 378

Rosales, Aurelia, Br Mgr, Tulare County Library, Dinuba Branch, 150 South I St, Dinuba, CA, 93618. Tel: 559-591-5828. Fax: 559-591-5886. p. 280

Rosalia, Kerri, Dir, Mastics-Moriches-Shirley Community Library, 407 William Floyd Pkwy, Shirley, NY, 11967. Tel: 631-399-1511. Fax: 631-281-4442. p. 1743

Rosapepe, Diana, Dir, Roanoke County Public Library, 3131 Electric Rd SW, Roanoke, VA, 24018-6496. Tel: 540-772-7507. Fax: 540-989-3129. p. 2494

Rosario, Carmen, In Charge, National Astronomy & Ionosphere Center, Carretera 625 Final, Arecibo, PR, 00612. Tel: 787-878-2612, Ext 215. Fax: 787-878-1861. p. 2671

Rosario, Linda, Head, Tech Serv, Scotch Plains Public Library, 1927 Bartle Ave, Scotch Plains, NJ, 07076-1212. Tel: 908-322-5007. Fax: lindar@scotlib.org. p. 1528

Rosario, Luz, Librn, Lebanon County Law Library, 400 S Eighth St, Rm 305, Lebanon, PA, 17042. Tel: 717-274-2801, Ext 2280. Fax: 717-273-7490. p. 2080

Rosario, Rosa, Ref Serv, City of Tavares Public Library, 314 N New Hampshire Ave, Tavares, FL, 32778. Tel: 352-742-6204. Fax: 352-742-6472. p. 499

Rosario, Sonia, Libr Tech, Department of Veterans Affairs, Library Service 142D, Ten Calle Casia, San Juan, PR, 00921-3201. Tel: 787-641-7582, Ext 12165, 787-641-7582, Ext 12226. Fax: 787-641-4550. p. 2676

Rosario, Yolanda, Dir, Carlos Albizu Miranda Library, San Francisco Corner, 151 Tanca St, San Juan, PR, 00902. Tel: 787-725-6500, Ext 1567, 787-725-6500, Ext 1568. p. 2675

Rosas, Barbara, Tech Serv, Gloucester County Library System, 389 Wolfert Station Rd, Mullica Hill, NJ, 08062. Tel: 856-223-6000. Fax: 856-223-6039. p. 1507

Rosato, Lynn M, Dir, Bethel Public Library, 189 Greenwood Ave, Bethel, CT, 06801-2598. Tel: 203-794-8756. Fax: 203-794-8761. p. 330

Rosauer, Greg, Weekend Per Supvr, Northwestern College, 3003 Snelling Ave N, Saint Paul, MN, 55113. Tel: 651-631-5241. Fax: 651-631-5598. p. 1280

Rosburg, Elaine, Librn, Aurora Public Library, 401 Woodruff St, Aurora, IA, 50607. Tel: 319-634-3660. Fax: 319-634-3960. p. 795

Roscello, Annemarie, Ref, Bergen Community College, 400 Paramus Rd, Paramus, NJ, 07652-1595. Tel: 201-447-7131. Fax: 201-493-8167. p. 1517

Rosch, Victoria, Assoc State Librn, New Jersey State Library, 185 W State St, Trenton, NJ, 08618. Tel: 609-278-2640, Ext 157. Fax: 609-278-2652. p. 1536

Roscoe, Linda, Head, Access Serv, Lesley University, 89 Brattle St, Cambridge, MA, 02138-2790. Tel: 617-349-8840. Fax: 617-349-8849. p. 1077

Rose, Becky, Info Tech, Lynn University Library, 3601 N Military Trail, Boca Raton, FL, 33431-5598. Tel: 561-237-7060. Fax: 561-237-7074. p. 428

Rose, Camille, Head, Youth Serv, Kankakee Public Library, 201 E Merchant St, Kankakee, IL, 60901. Tel: 815-939-4564. Fax: 815-939-9057. p. 661

Rose, Carrie, Librn, Connecticut Legislative Library, Legislative Office Bldg, Rm 5400, 300 Capitol Ave, Hartford, CT, 06106-1591. Tel: 860-240-8888. Fax: 860-240-8881. p. 344

Rose, Claire, Dep Dir, Peter White Public Library, 217 N Front St, Marquette, MI, 49855. Tel: 906-226-4305. Fax: 906-226-1783. p. 1207

Rose, Coleen, Cat Librn, Southwest Baptist University Libraries, 1600 University Ave, Bolivar, MO, 65613. Tel: 417-328-1631. Fax: 417-328-1652. p. 1320

Rose, Dianne E, Adminr, GE Betz, 4636 Somerton Rd, Trevose, PA, 19053-6783. Tel: 215-953-2546. p. 2146

Rose, Donna, Head, Cat, University of Arkansas at Little Rock, 2801 S University Ave, Little Rock, AR, 72204. Tel: 501-569-8817. Fax: 501-569-3017. p. 107

Rose, Elizabeth, Tech Serv, Goodnow Library, 21 Concord Rd, Sudbury, MA, 01776-2383. Tel: 978-443-1035. Fax: 978-443-1047. p. 1129

Rose, Elizabeth, Dr, Libr Dir, Fairfield Museum & History Center, 370 Beach Rd, Fairfield, CT, 06824. Tel: 203-259-1598, Ext 106. Fax: 203-255-2716. p. 339

Rose, Ellen R, Libr Asst III, Kansas Department of Corrections, 1607 State St, Ellsworth, KS, 67439. Tel: 785-472-5501, Ext 250; 785-472-6250. Fax: 785-472-4032. p. 865

Rose, Eloise, Ch, Hickory Public Library, Ridgeview, 706 First St SW, Hickory, NC, 28602. Tel: 828-345-6037. Fax: 828-267-0485. p. 1801

Rose, Jacqueline, Mgr, Lake Oswego Public Library, 706 Fourth St, Lake Oswego, OR, 97034-2399. Tel: 503-675-2539. Fax: 503-635-4171. p. 2003

Rose, Janet, Youth Serv, Saint Clair County Library System, 210 McMorran Blvd, Port Huron, MI, 48060-4098. Tel: 810-987-7323, Ext 132. Fax: 810-987-7874. p. 1219

Rose, Janine, Librn, Garfield County Public Library System, Silt Branch, PO Box 10, Silt, CO, 81652-0010. Tel: 970-876-5500. Fax: 970-876-5921. p. 319

Rose, Jean, Tech Serv Mgr, St Charles Community College, 4601 Mid Rivers Mall Dr, Cottleville, MO, 63376. Tel: 636-922-8439. Fax: 636-922-8433. p. 1326

Rose, John S, Libr Dir, American Indian College, 10020 N 15th Ave, Phoenix, AZ, 85021-2199. Tel: 602-944-3335, Ext 251. p. 71

Rose, Kathleen W, Dir, Pearl River Public Library, 80 Franklin Ave, Pearl River, NY, 10965. Tel: 845-735-4084. Fax: 845-735-4041. p. 1716

Rose, Ken, Syst Mgr, Carnegie Mellon University, Hunt Library, 4909 Frew St, Pittsburgh, PA, 15213-3890. Tel: 412-268-2446. Fax: 412-268-2793. p. 2123

Rose, LaVera, Dir, Oglala Lakota College, Three Mile Creek Rd, Kyle, SD, 57752. Tel: 605-455-6064. Fax: 605-455-6070. p. 2213

Rose, Lee C, Acq, Hollins University, 7950 E Campus Dr, Roanoke, VA, 24020-1000. Tel: 540-362-6240. Fax: 540-362-6756. p. 2493

Rose, Lin, Librn, American Geological Institute Library, 4220 King St, Alexandria, VA, 22302-1502. Tel: 703-379-2480, Ext 239. Fax: 703-379-7563. p. 2445

Rose, Linda, Mgr, Shoalwater Bay Tribal Community Library, 2373 Old Tokeland Rd, Tokeland, WA, 98590. Tel: 360-267-8190. Fax: 360-267-6778. p. 2541

Rose, Lora, Asst Libr Dir, Massanutten Regional Library, 174 S Main St, Harrisonburg, VA, 22801. Tel: 540-434-4475. Fax: 540-434-4382. p. 2470

Rose, Margaret, Spec Coll Librn, Corpus Christi Public Libraries, 805 Comanche, Corpus Christi, TX, 78401. Tel: 361-826-7000. Fax: 361-826-7046. p. 2301

Rose, Mark, Dir, Nampa Public Library, 101 11th Ave S, Nampa, ID, 83651. Tel: 208-468-5805. Fax: 208-318-0530. p. 580

Rose, Mark Phillip, Info Serv Mgr, Intergovernmental Committee on Urban & Regional Research, 40 Wynford Dr, Ste 210, Toronto, ON, M3C 1J5, CANADA. Tel: 416-952-1437. p. 2855

Rose, Matthew, Br Mgr, Sonoma County Library, Sebastopol Regional, 7140 Bodega Ave, Sebastopol, CA, 95472. Tel: 707-823-7691. Fax: 707-823-7172. p. 268

Rose, Michael, Pub Serv Librn, Rockingham Community College, 315 Wrenn Memorial Rd, Wentworth, NC, 27375. Tel: 336-342-4261, Ext 2271. Fax: 336-342-1203. p. 1829

Rose, Pam, Commun Outreach Mgr, Mentor Public Library, 8215 Mentor Ave, Mentor, OH, 44060. Tel: 440-255-8811. Fax: 440-255-0520. p. 1917

Rose, Patricia, Librn, Julia Adams Morse Memorial Library, 105 Main St, Greene, ME, 04236. Tel: 207-946-5544. p. 986

Rose, Patricia A, Librn, Knoxville Public Library, 200 E Main St, Knoxville, IL, 61448-1351. Tel: 309-289-2113. Fax: 309-289-8063. p. 661

Rose, Patsy, Ch, Orange Beach Public Library, 26267 Canal Rd, Orange Beach, AL, 36561-3917. Tel: 251-981-2923. Fax: 251-981-2920. p. 33

Rose, Rebecca, Acq, Riley County Kansas Genealogical Society Library, 2005 Claflin, Manhattan, KS, 66502-3415. Tel: 785-565-6495. p. 882

Rose, Roxann, Acq, Circ, Utah State Library Division, 250 N 1950 West, Ste A, Salt Lake City, UT, 84116-7901. Tel: 801-715-6777. Fax: 801-715-6767. p. 2415

Rose, Sara, Human Res Mgr, Pueblo City-County Library District, 100 E Abriendo Ave, Pueblo, CO, 81004-4290. Tel: 719-562-5632. Fax: 719-562-5619. p. 320

Rose, Susan S, Dir, Libr Serv, Fayetteville Technical Community College, 2201 Hull Rd, Fayetteville, NC, 28303. Tel: 910-678-8382. Fax: 910-678-8401. p. 1793

Rose, Tina, Librn, Oakridge Public Library, 48318 E First St, Oakridge, OR, 97463. Tel: 541-782-2258. Fax: 541-782-1081. p. 2008

Rose, Toni, Dir, Sheridan Public Library, 142 NW Yamhill, Sheridan, OR, 97378-1843. Tel: 503-843-3420. Fax: 503-843-2561. p. 2019

Roseberry, Ann, Dir, Richland Public Library, 955 Northgate Dr, Richland, WA, 99352-3539. Tel: 509-942-7454. Fax: 509-942-7442. p. 2526

Roseberry, Susan, Sr Libr Assoc, Lee County Library System, Outreach Services, 21100 Three Oaks Pkwy, Estero, FL, 33928. Tel: 239-390-3231. Fax: 239-498-6424. p. 446

Roseboro, Clevell S, II, Interim Dir, Libr Serv, Saint Augustine's College, 1315 Oakwood Ave, Raleigh, NC, 27610-2298. Tel: 919-516-4145. Fax: 919-516-4758. p. 1817

Roseborough, Dewitt, Archivist, The Naval Institute, 291 Wood Rd, Annapolis, MD, 21402-5035. Tel: 410-295-1024. Fax: 410-269-7940. p. 1010

Rosebrock, Anne, Librn, Orlando Health, Clifford E Graese Community Health Library, 1414 Kuhl Ave, MP 28, Orlando, FL, 32806. Tel: 321-841-4636. p. 477

Rosedale, Jeff, Actg Dir, Manhattanville College Library, 2900 Purchase St, Purchase, NY, 10577. Tel: 914-323-5277. Fax: 914-323-8139. p. 1724

Rosekrans, Rick, Controller, The Library Network, 41365 Vincenti Ct, Novi, MI, 48375. Tel: 248-536-3100. Fax: 248-536-3099. p. 2946

Roselle, Ann, Librn, Phoenix College, 1202 W Thomas Rd, Phoenix, AZ, 85013. Tel: 602-285-7457. Fax: 602-285-7368. p. 76

Roselle, Carla, Libr Dir, W H Walters Free Public Library, 1001 East Blvd, Alpha, NJ, 08865. Tel: 908-454-1445. p. 1469

Roseman, Shelley, Dir, University of Connecticut, 99 E Main St, Waterbury, CT, 06702-2311. Tel: 203-236-9900. Fax: 203-236-9905. p. 375

Rosen, Ann G, Br Mgr, Beaufort County Library, Bluffton Branch Library, 120 Palmetto Way, Bluffton, SC, 29910. Tel: 843-255-6506. Fax: 843-255-9509. p. 2181

Rosen, Claude Martin, Dir, Libr Serv, Indiana University Southeast Library, 4201 Grant Line Rd, New Albany, IN, 47150. Tel: 812-941-2631. Fax: 812-941-2656. p. 767

Rosen, Debbie, Head, Circ Serv, Lake Villa District Library, 1001 E Grand Ave, Lake Villa, IL, 60046. Tel: 847-356-7711, Ext 221. Fax: 847-265-9595. p. 663

Rosen, Fran, Acq, Coll Develop, Ferris State University Library, 1010 Campus Dr, Big Rapids, MI, 49307-2279. Tel: 231-591-3500. Fax: 231-591-3724. p. 1158

Rosen, Janice, Librn for Deaf, DC Regional Library for the Blind & Physically Handicapped, Adaptive Services Division, Rm 215, 901 G St NW, Washington, DC, 20001. Tel: 202-559-5368 (videophone), 202-727-2142. Fax: 202-727-0322. p. 397

Rosen, Janice, Archivist, Canadian Jewish Congress Charities Committee, 1590 Docteur Penfield Ave, Montreal, QC, H3G 1C5, CANADA. Tel: 514-931-7531. Fax: 514-931-0548. p. 2892

Rosen, Leila, Librn, Aesthetic Realism Foundation, Eli Siegel Collection, 141 Greene St, New York, NY, 10012-3201. Tel: 212-777-4490. Fax: 212-777-4426. p. 1667

Rosen, Martha, Librn, Smithsonian Libraries, National Museum of Natural History Library, Nat Museum of Natural Hist, Rm 51, MRC 154, Tenth St & Constitution Ave NW, Washington, DC, 20013-0712. Tel: 202-633-1674. Fax: 202-357-1896. p. 415

Rosen, Meeghan, Head, Tech Serv, Chapel Hill Public Library, 100 Library Dr, Chapel Hill, NC, 27514. Tel: 919-969-2046. Fax: 919-968-2838. p. 1780

Rosen, Ralph, Media Ctr Mgr, Berklee College of Music Library, 150 Massachusetts Ave, Boston, MA, 02115. Tel: 617-747-8338. Fax: 617-747-2050. p. 1055

Rosen, Rhonda, Head, Media & Access Serv, Loyola Marymount University, One LMU Dr, MS 8200, Los Angeles, CA, 90045-2659. Tel: 310-338-4584. Fax: 310-338-4366. p. 175

Rosen, Vicki, Ref Serv, University of San Francisco, 2130 Fulton St, San Francisco, CA, 94117-1080. Tel: 415-422-5387. Fax: 415-422-5949. p. 248

Rosen, Wendy L, Ref Librn, New Bern-Craven County Public Library, 400 Johnson St, New Bern, NC, 28560-4098. Tel: 252-638-7800. Fax: 252-638-7817. p. 1812

Rosenbalm, Sandy, Dir, Claiborne County Public Library, 1304 Old Knoxville Rd, Tazewell, TN, 37879. Tel: 423-626-5414. Fax: 423-626-9481. p. 2266

Rosenbaum, Harold, Asst Dir, Martin Methodist College, 433 W Madison St, Pulaski, TN, 38478-2799. Tel: 931-363-9843. Fax: 931-363-9844. p. 2264

Rosenbaum, Marion, Archivist, Gwynedd-Mercy College, 1325 Sumneytown Pike, Gwynedd Valley, PA, 19437. Tel: 215-646-7300, Ext 493. Fax: 215-641-5596. p. 2063

Rosenbaum, Myra, Asst Dir, Treat Memorial Library, 56 Main St, Livermore Falls, ME, 04254. Tel: 207-897-3631. p. 990

Rosenberg, Elizabeth, Dir, Haworth Municipal Library, 300 Haworth Ave, Haworth, NJ, 07641. Tel: 201-384-1020. Fax: 201-385-7750. p. 1490

Rosenberg, Gary R, Res Librn, Douglas County Historical Society, 5730 N 30th St, No 11A, Omaha, NE, 68111. Tel: 402-451-1013. Fax: 402-453-9448. p. 1412

Rosenberg, Janice Z, Sr Librn, Foundation Center-Washington, DC Library, 1627 K St NW, 3rd Flr, Washington, DC, 20006. Tel: 202-331-1400, Ext 4027. Fax: 202-331-1739. p. 401

Rosenberg, Laurie, Circ Supvr, Shaker Heights Public Library, Bertram Woods Branch, 20600 Fayette Rd, Shaker Heights, OH, 44122-2979. Tel: 216-991-2421. Fax: 216-991-3124. p. 1934

Rosenberg, Rachel A, Dir of Communications, University of Chicago Library, 1100 E 57th St, Chicago, IL, 60637-1502. Tel: 773-834-1519. Fax: 773-702-6623. p. 626

Rosenberg, Robyn, Instruction Librn, Sci Librn, University of Texas Libraries, McKinney Engineering Library, One University Sta S5435, ECJ 1.300, Austin, TX, 78712. Tel: 512-495-4511. Fax: 512-495-4507. p. 2284

Rosenberg, Sherry, Exec Dir, Thompson Institute, 5650 Derry St, Harrisburg, PA, 17111. Tel: 717-564-4112, 717-901-5867. Fax: 717-558-1344. p. 2066

Rosenberg, Steve, Br Mgr, Brooklyn Public Library, Midwood, 975 E 16th St, Brooklyn, NY, 11230. Tel: 718-252-0967. Fax: 718-252-1263. p. 1591

Rosenberg, Victor, Assoc Prof, University of Michigan, 304 West Hall, 1085 S University, Ann Arbor, MI, 48109-1107. Tel: 734-763-2285. Fax: 734-764-2475. p. 2967

Rosenberg-Justman, Gayle, Tech Serv, Wilmette Public Library District, 1242 Wilmette Ave, Wilmette, IL, 60091-2558. Tel: 847-256-6920. Fax: 847-256-6944. p. 720

Rosenberger, Diane, Tech Serv, Federal Reserve Bank of San Francisco, 101 Market St, San Francisco, CA, 94105-1579. Tel: 415-974-3216. Fax: 415-974-3429. p. 242

Rosenberger, Luke, Dir, Libr Tech & Hist Coll, University of Texas Health Science Center at San Antonio Libraries, 7703 Floyd Curl Dr, MSC 7940, San Antonio, TX, 78229-3900. Tel: 210-567-2400. Fax: 210-567-2490. p. 2383

Rosenberger, Stephen, Ref Fac, Fashion Institute of Technology-SUNY, Seventh Ave at 27th St, New York, NY, 10001-5992. Tel: 212-217-4396. Fax: 212-217-4371. p. 1678

Rosenblum, Lisa, Dir, Sunnyvale Public Library, 665 W Olive Ave, Sunnyvale, CA, 94086-7622. Tel: 408-730-7300. Fax: 408-735-8767. p. 273

Rosenblum, Sarah, Dir, Marshalltown Public Library, 105 W Boone St, Marshalltown, IA, 50158-4911. Tel: 641-754-5738. Fax: 641-754-5708. p. 830

Rosenbohm, Janice S, Dir, Atchison County Library, 200 S Main St, Rock Port, MO, 64482-1532. Tel: 660-744-5404. Fax: 660-744-2861. p. 1351

Rosenbrook, Margaret B, Dir, Falmouth Area Library, 219 E Prosper Rd, Falmouth, MI, 49632-0602. Tel: 231-826-3738. p. 1177

Rosenburgh, Amy, Br Mgr, Walla Walla County Rural Library District, Prescott Library, 103 South D St, Prescott, WA, 99348. Tel: 509-849-2411. Fax: 509-849-2411. p. 2547

Rosendahl, Matthew D, Dir, Wisconsin Indianhead Technical College, 600 N 21st St, Superior, WI, 54880-5296. Tel: 715-394-6677, Ext 6276. Fax: 715-394-3771. p. 2641

Rosendale, Nadine, Br Mgr, Carroll County Public Library, Eldersburg Branch, 6400 W Hemlock Dr, Eldersburg, MD, 21784-6538. Tel: 410-386-4460. Fax: 410-386-4466. p. 1046

Rosene, Richard, Head of Libr, Brown Mackie College Library, 309 Buttermilk Pike, Fort Mitchell, KY, 41017. Tel: 859-341-5627. Fax: 859-341-6483. p. 913

Rosenfeld, Alice, Br Head, Mariposa County Library, Yosemite National Park Branch, Girls Club Bldg, 58 Cedar Ct, Yosemite National Park, CA, 95389. Tel: 209-372-4552. p. 184

Rosenfeld, Elena, Assoc Dir, Pub Serv, High Plains Library District, 2650 W 29th St, Greeley, CO, 80631. Tel: 970-506-8567. Fax: 970-506-8551. p. 311

Rosenfeld, Jenny, Syst Librn, Woodbury University Library, 7500 Glenoaks Blvd, Burbank, CA, 91510-1099. Tel: 818-252-5200. Fax: 818-767-4534. p. 130

Rosenfeld, Wendy, Head, Outreach Serv, Palm Beach County Library System, Palm Beach County Library Annex, 4639 Lake Worth Rd, Greenacres, FL, 33463-3451. Tel: 561-649-5500. Fax: 561-649-5402. p. 503

Rosenfeld, Wendy, Outreach Librn, Palm Beach County Library System, 3650 Summit Blvd, West Palm Beach, FL, 33406-4198. Tel: 561-649-5500. Fax: 561-233-2692. p. 503

Rosenheim, Nancy, Head, Acq, Boise State University, 1865 Cesar Chavez Lane, Boise, ID, 83725-1430. Tel: 208-426-1660. Fax: 208-334-2111. p. 570

Rosenkrans, Korin, Head, Customer & Info Serv, Parsippany-Troy Hills Free Public Library, 449 Halsey Rd, Parsippany, NJ, 07054. Tel: 973-887-5150. Fax: 973-887-0062. p. 1517

Rosenquest, Carolyn, Ch, Crafton Public Library, 140 Bradford Ave, Pittsburgh, PA, 15205. Tel: 412-922-6877. Fax: 412-922-7637. p. 2124

Rosensteel, Sandy, Libr Coordr, Dunbar Community Library, 60 Connellsville St, Dunbar, PA, 15431. Tel: 724-322-6109. Fax: 724-277-4775. p. 2051

Rosensweig, Jesama, Librn, Real Estate Commission Library, 633 N Fourth St, Boise, ID, 83702-4510. Tel: 208-334-3285, Ext 106. Fax: 208-334-2050. p. 571

Rosenthal, Danielle, Web Develop Librn, Florida Gulf Coast University Library, 10501 FGCU Blvd S, Fort Myers, FL, 33965-6501. Tel: 239-590-7633. p. 445

Rosenthal, Florence, Coordr, Albert Einstein Healthcare Network, 5501 Old York Rd, Philadelphia, PA, 19141. Tel: 215-456-6345. Fax: 215-456-8267. p. 2106

Rosenthal, Freda, Ref Serv, Ad, Onslow County Public Library, 58 Doris Ave E, Jacksonville, NC, 28540. Tel: 910-455-7350, Ext 225. Fax: 910-455-1661. p. 1803

Rosenthal, Judy, Librn, Staunton Public Library, 306 W Main St, Staunton, IL, 62088. Tel: 618-635-3852. Fax: 618-635-2246. p. 707

Rosenthal, Nan, Br Mgr, Camden County Library System, William G Rohrer Memorial Library - Haddon Township, 15 MacArthur Blvd, Westmont, NJ, 08108. Tel: 856-854-2752. Fax: 856-854-8825. p. 1538

Rosenthal, Nina, Ref Librn, Sullivan & Cromwell LLP, 125 Broad St, New York, NY, 10004. Tel: 212-558-3780. Fax: 212-558-3346. p. 1700

Rosenthal, Richard, Sr Librn, California Department of Corrections Library System, California State Prison, Corcoran, 4001 King Ave, Corcoran, CA, 93212. Tel: 559-992-8800, Ext 5560. Fax: 559-992-7354. p. 221

Rosenthal, Roger C, Exec Dir, Migrant Legal Action Program Library, 1001 Connecticut Ave NW, Ste 915, Washington, DC, 20036. Tel: 202-775-7780. Fax: 202-775-7784. p. 408

Rosenthal, Sheila, Mgr, Libr Serv, Carnegie Mellon University, Software Engineering Institute Library, 4500 Fifth Ave, Pittsburgh, PA, 15213-2612. Tel: 412-268-7733. Fax: 412-268-1340. p. 2124

Rosenthal, Sheryl, Dir, United States Securities & Exchange Commission Library, 100 F St NE, Rm 1500, Washington, DC, 20549-0002. Tel: 202-551-5450. Fax: 202-772-9326. p. 421

Rosenzweig, James, Educ Librn, Northeastern Illinois University, 5500 N Saint Louis Ave, Chicago, IL, 60625-4699. Tel: 773-442-4454. Fax: 773-442-4531. p. 620

Rosenzweig, Louise, Mgr, Libr Serv, University of Texas at Austin, 1616 Guadalupe St, Ste 4.202, Austin, TX, 78701. Tel: 512-232-3138. Fax: 512-232-3088. p. 2283

Rosenzweig, Sheri L, Ref Librn, Visual Res, Boston Architectural College, 320 Newbury St, Boston, MA, 02115. Tel: 617-585-0257. Fax: 617-585-0151. p. 1055

Rosewicz, LeeAnn, Libr Asst, Youth Serv, Barry-Lawrence Regional Library, Monett Branch, 213 Sixth St, Monett, MO, 65708. Tel: 417-235-6646. Fax: 417-235-6799. p. 1346

Rosga, Kathleen, Asst Dir & Br Mgr, Jeffersonville Township Public Library, 211 E Court Ave, Jeffersonville, IN, 47130. Tel: 812-285-5647. Fax: 812-285-5642. p. 756

Rosga, Kathleen, Asst Dir & Br Mgr, Jeffersonville Township Public Library, Clarksville Branch, 1312 Eastern Blvd, Clarksville, IN, 47129-1704. Tel: 812-285-5640. Fax: 812-285-5642. p. 756

Rosin, Andrea, Librn, Parkland Regional Library, Bredenbury Branch, TD Bank Bldg, Bredenbury, SK, S0A 0H0, CANADA. Tel: 306-898-4683. p. 2931

Rosine, Diane, Librn, Cubic Defense Applications, Inc, 9333 Balboa Ave, San Diego, CA, 92123. Tel: 858-505-2280. Fax: 858-505-1542. p. 231

Roske, Peggy, Archivist, Saint John's University, 2835 Abbey Plaza, Collegeville, MN, 56321. Tel: 320-363-2129. Fax: 320-363-2126. p. 1246

Roske, Peggy, Archivist, College of Saint Benedict, 37 S College Ave, Saint Joseph, MN, 56374. Tel: 320-363-5019. Fax: 320-363-5197. p. 1277

Roskelley, Georgia, Libr Asst, Youth Serv, Barry-Lawrence Regional Library, Pierce City Branch, 101 N Walnut St, Pierce City, MO, 65723. Tel: 417-476-5110. Fax: 417-476-5110. p. 1347

Rosko, Tom, Archivist, Head of Libr, Massachusetts Institute of Technology Libraries, Institute Archives & Special Collections, Bldg 14N-118, Hayden Library, 160 Memorial Dr, Cambridge, MA, 02139-4307. Tel: 617-253-5688. Fax: 617-258-7305. p. 1078

Rosman, Barbara, Mgr, Memorial Hospital, 3073 White Mountain Hwy, North Conway, NH, 03860. Tel: 603-356-5461, Ext 157. Fax: 603-356-8135. p. 1460

Rosner, Debra, Circ, Margaret E Heggan Free Public Library of the Township of Washington, 606 Delsea Dr, Sewell, NJ, 08080. Tel: 856-589-3334. Fax: 856-582-2042. p. 1529

Ross, Alexandra, Bus Librn, Humber College, Lakeshore Campus Library, 3199 Lakeshore Blvd W, Toronto, ON, M8V 1K8, CANADA. Tel: 416-675-6622, Ext 3250. Fax: 416-252-0918. p. 2854

Ross, Alison, Cat Librn, Eastern Shores Library System, 4632 S Taylor Dr, Sheboygan, WI, 53081-1107. Tel: 920-208-4900. Fax: 920-208-4901. p. 2637

Ross, Andrea, Br Mgr, Washington County Library System, Torrey Wood Memorial, 302 East Ave N, Hollandale, MS, 38748-3714. Tel: 662-827-2335. Fax: 662-827-2335. p. 1299

Ross, Anne, Tech Serv Mgr, Kitsap Regional Library, 1301 Sylvan Way, Bremerton, WA, 98310-3498. Tel: 360-405-9122. Fax: 360-405-9128. p. 2510

Ross, Bernadette, Ref Librn, Fayetteville State University, 1200 Murchison Rd, Fayetteville, NC, 28301-4298. Tel: 910-672-1231. Fax: 910-672-1746. p. 1793

Ross, Bernadette, Ref Librn, United States Army, John L Throckmorton Library, IMSE-BRG-MWR-L Bldg 1-3346, Randolph St, Fort Bragg, NC, 28310-5000. Tel: 910-396-2665. Fax: 910-907-2274. p. 1794

Ross, Bonnie, Dir, Anna Field Fernald Library, 35 S Main St, Detroit, ME, 04929-3252. Tel: 207-257-4488. Fax: 207-257-2434. p. 983

Ross, Bonnie, Br Mgr, Johnson County Library, Kaycee Branch, 231 Ritter Ave, Kaycee, WY, 82639. Tel: 307-738-2473. Fax: 307-738-2473. p. 2651

Ross, Carla, Librn, Holmes Community College, 1180 W Monroe St, Grenada, MS, 38901. Tel: 662-227-2313. Fax: 662-227-2290. p. 1299

Ross, Cathy, Supvr, Talisman Energy Inc, 2000, 888 Third St SW, Calgary, AB, T2P 5C5, CANADA. Tel: 403-237-1429. Fax: 403-231-2823. p. 2693

Ross, Celia, Instrul Serv Librn, Ref Serv, DePaul University Libraries, O'Hare, 3166 S River Rd, Des Plaines, IL, 60018. Tel: 312-476-3600, 312-476-3611. Fax: 847-296-4381. p. 612

Ross, Celia, Fac Res Serv/Ref Serv Librn, University of Michigan, Kresge Business Administration Library, Stephen M Ross School of Business, 701 Tappan St, K3330, Ann Arbor, MI, 48109-1234. Tel: 734-763-5452. Fax: 734-764-3839. p. 1152

Ross, Celyne, Librn, Bibliotheque de Repentigny, One Place d'Evry, Repentigny, QC, J6A 8H7, CANADA. Tel: 450-470-3001, Ext 3427. Fax: 450-470-3079. p. 2907

Ross, Chy, Managing Librn I, Sno-Isle Libraries, Lake Stevens Community Library, 1804 Main St, Lake Stevens, WA, 98258-7712. Tel: 425-334-1900. Fax: 425-334-9487. p. 2542

Ross, Constance, Dir, Madeline Island Public Library, One Library St, La Pointe, WI, 54850. Tel: 715-747-3662. Fax: 715-747-3661. p. 2604

Ross, David, Commun Librn, Monroe County Library System, Carleton Branch, 1444 Kent St, Carleton, MI, 48117. Tel: 734-654-2180. Fax: 734-654-8767. p. 1210

Ross, David E, Commun Librn, Monroe County Library System, Newport Branch, 8120 N Dixie Hwy, Newport, MI, 48166. Tel: 734-586-2117. Fax: 734-586-1116. p. 1210

Ross, David E, Commun Librn, Monroe County Library System, South Rockwood Branch, 12776 Dixie Hwy, South Rockwood, MI, 48179. Tel: 734-379-3333. Fax: 734-379-3333. p. 1210

Ross, Deborah, Govt Doc, Tech Support, Thiel College, 75 College Ave, Greenville, PA, 16125-2183. Tel: 724-589-2127. Fax: 724-589-2122. p. 2063

Ross, Doris, Circ, Mgr, Desoto Parish Library, 109 Crosby St, Mansfield, LA, 71052. Tel: 318-872-6100. Fax: 318-872-6120. p. 955

Ross, Faith, Univ Librn, Midwestern University Library, 555 31st St, Downers Grove, IL, 60515. Tel: 630-515-6185. Fax: 630-515-7144. p. 637

Ross, Gail, Mgr, Baltimore County Public Library, Arbutus, 855 Sulphur Spring Rd, Baltimore, MD, 21227-2598. Tel: 410-887-1451. Fax: 410-536-0328. p. 1044

Ross, Gail, Libr Mgr, York Library Region, Upper Miramichi Community Library, Central New Brunswick Academy Bldg, 7263 Rte 8, New Bandon, NB, E9C 2A7, CANADA. Tel: 506-369-2022. Fax: 506-369-2023. p. 2765

Ross, Glenn, Dir, Libr Serv, Holland & Knight LLP, 100 N Tampa St, Ste 4100, Tampa, FL, 33602. Tel: 813-227-6629. Fax: 813-223-9240. p. 496

Ross, Henry A, Dir, Gardenview Horticultural Park Library, 16711 Pearl Rd, Strongsville, OH, 44136-6048. Tel: 440-238-6653. p. 1937

Ross, Ian, Dir, Whitby Public Library, 405 Dundas St W, Whitby, ON, L1N 6A1, CANADA. Tel: 905-668-6531. Fax: 905-668-7445. p. 2870

Ross, James, Admin Dir, Washington County Historical Society Library, 49 E Maiden St, Washington, PA, 15301. Tel: 724-225-6740. Fax: 724-225-8495. p. 2151

Ross, Jeffrey, Ref Librn, Columbia University, Avery Architectural & Fine Arts Library, 1172 Amsterdam Ave, MC 0301, New York, NY, 10027. Tel: 212-854-6199. Fax: 212-854-8904. p. 1674

Ross, Jessica, Dir, Washington County Public Library, 14102 Saint Stephens Ave, Chatom, AL, 36518. Tel: 251-847-2097. Fax: 251-847-2098. p. 12

Ross, John, Dir, Fort Hays State University, 600 Park St, Hays, KS, 67601-4099. Tel: 785-628-4431. Fax: 785-628-4096. p. 871

Ross, Julie, Ch, Bourbonnais Public Library District, 250 W John Casey Rd, Bourbonnais, IL, 60914. Tel: 815-933-1727. Fax: 815-933-1961. p. 596

Ross, Kate, Acq Librn, Head, Tech Serv, Saint John Fisher College, 3690 East Ave, Rochester, NY, 14618-3599. Tel: 585-385-8136. Fax: 585-385-8445. p. 1732

Ross, Kevin, Assoc Dean, Chapman University, One University Dr, Orange, CA, 92866-1099. Tel: 714-532-7756. Fax: 714-532-7743. p. 200

Ross, Kim, Librn, Cedar Valley College Library, 3030 N Dallas Ave, Lancaster, TX, 75134-3799. Tel: 972-860-8150. Fax: 972-860-8221. p. 2353

Ross, Krista, Dir, Spec Needs, Southwest Wisconsin Library System, 1775 Fourth St, Fennimore, WI, 53809-1137. Tel: 608-822-3393. Fax: 608-822-6251. p. 2591

Ross, Larry, Head, Info Serv, George Washington University, Jacob Burns Law Library, 716 20th St NW, Washington, DC, 20052. Tel: 202-994-0057. Fax: 202-994-2874. p. 402

Ross, Leslie, Ref, Saint Ambrose University Library, 518 W Locust St, Davenport, IA, 52803. Tel: 563-333-6472. Fax: 563-333-6248. p. 807

Ross, MacKenzie, Head Librn, Bixby Memorial Free Library, 258 Main St, Vergennes, VT, 05491. Tel: 802-877-2211. Fax: 802-877-2411. p. 2437

Ross, Margaret J, Dir, Info Serv, McNess, Wallace & Nurick LLC, 100 Pine St, Harrisburg, PA, 17108. Tel: 717-237-5205. Fax: 717-237-5300. p. 2065

Ross, Matthew, Ref, Putnam County District Library, The Educational Service Ctr, 124 Putnam Pkwy, Ottawa, OH, 45875-1471. Tel: 419-523-3747. Fax: 419-523-6477. p. 1926

Ross, Michelle, Music, Oral Roberts University Library, 7777 South Lewis Ave, Tulsa, OK, 74171. Tel: 918-495-7519. Fax: 918-495-6893. p. 1981

Ross, Nancy, Tech Serv, Huntington City Township Public Library, 200 W Market St, Huntington, IN, 46750-2655. Tel: 260-356-0824. Fax: 260-356-3073. p. 748

Ross, Nancy, Br Mgr, Bryan College Station Public Library System, Carnegie History Center, 111 S Main St, Bryan, TX, 77803. Tel: 979-209-5631. p. 2292

Ross, Pam, Exec Dir, Snyder County Libraries, Community Bldg, One N High St, Selinsgrove, PA, 17870-1599. Tel: 570-374-7163. Fax: 570-374-2120. p. 2138

Ross, Pat, Dir, Bassett Historical Center, 3964 Fairystone Park Hwy, Bassett, VA, 24055. Tel: 276-629-9191. Fax: 276-629-9840. p. 2450

Ross, Patty Ayala, Br Mgr, Timberland Regional Library, William G Reed Library, 710 W Alder St, Shelton, WA, 98584-2571. Tel: 360-426-1362. Fax: 360-427-2025. p. 2544

Ross, Philip, Sr Librn, Torrance Public Library, Walteria, 3815 W 242nd St, Torrance, CA, 90505-6410. Tel: 310-375-8418. Fax: 310-375-8325. p. 276

Ross, Rebecca, In Charge, US Department of Interior, National Park Service, Two Mark Bird Lane, Elverson, PA, 19520. Tel: 610-582-8773, Ext 240. Fax: 610-582-2768. p. 2054

Ross, Richard S, Col Librn, Trinity College Library, 300 Summit St, Hartford, CT, 06106. Tel: 860-297-2258. Fax: 860-297-2251. p. 347

Ross, Ruth M, Dean of Libr, Olympic College, 1600 Chester Ave, Bremerton, WA, 98337. Tel: 360-475-7250. Fax: 360-475-7261. p. 2510

Ross, Saundra, Librn, Birmingham Public Library, North Avondale, 501 43rd St N, Birmingham, AL, 35222. Tel: 205-592-2082. Fax: 205-595-9871. p. 7

Ross, Seamus, Dean, University of Toronto, 140 St George St, Toronto, ON, M5S 3G6, CANADA. Tel: 416-978-3234. Fax: 416-978-5762. p. 2978

Ross, Shelley, Chief Librn, Medicine Hat Public Library, 414 First St SE, Medicine Hat, AB, T1A 0A8, CANADA. Tel: 403-502-8528. Fax: 403-502-8529. p. 2711

Ross, Sheri, PhD, Asst Prof, Saint Catherine University, 2004 Randolph Ave, Mailstop No 4125, Saint Paul, MN, 55105. Tel: 651-690-6802. Fax: 651-690-8724. p. 2968

Ross, Stephanie, Asst Dir, Green Tree Public Library, Ten W Manilla Ave, 1st Flr, Pittsburgh, PA, 15220-3310. Tel: 412-921-9292. Fax: 412-921-4004. p. 2125

Ross, Steve, Pres, World Research Foundation Library, 41 Bell Rock Plaza, Sedona, AZ, 86351. Tel: 928-284-3300. Fax: 928-284-3530. p. 81

Ross, Susan, Head, Circ, Midlothian Public Library, 14701 S Kenton Ave, Midlothian, IL, 60445-4122. Tel: 708-535-2027. Fax: 708-535-2053. p. 674

Ross, Susan, Head, Client Serv, Ottawa Office of the Auditor General, West Tower, 240 Sparks St, 11th Flr, Ottawa, ON, K1A 0G6, CANADA. Tel: 613-995-3708. Fax: 613-952-5131. p. 2832

Ross, Terri, Librn, Indiana Supreme Court Law Library, 316 State House, 200 W Washington St, Indianapolis, IN, 46204-2788. Tel: 317-232-2557. Fax: 317-233-8693. p. 752

Ross, Terry, Outreach Serv Librn, Ser, Madison Area Technical College, 3550 Anderson St, Rm 230, Madison, WI, 53704. Tel: 608-246-6635. Fax: 608-246-6644. p. 2606

Ross, Trudie, Librn, Dying With Dignity Canada Library, 802-55 Eglinton Ave E, Toronto, ON, M4P 1G8, CANADA. Tel: 416-486-3998. Fax: 416-486-5562. p. 2853

Ross, Vickie, Circ Librn, Lee County Library, 219 N Madison St, Tupelo, MS, 38804-3899. Tel: 662-841-9027. Fax: 662-840-7615. p. 1316

Ross, William E, Dr, Spec Coll Librn, University of New Hampshire Library, 18 Library Way, Durham, NH, 03824. Tel: 603-862-0346. Fax: 603-862-2956. p. 1445

Rossbottom, Misty, In Charge, Faith Presbyterian Church Library, 5400 Loch Raven Blvd, Baltimore, MD, 21239. Tel: 410-435-4330. Fax: 410-435-8449. p. 1013

Rosseel, Trish, Interim Head Librn, University of British Columbia Library, Humanities & Social Sciences, Koerner Library, 1958 Main Mall, Vancouver, BC, V6T 1Z2, CANADA. Tel: 604-822-8667. Fax: 604-822-9122. p. 2743

Rosselet, Stuart, Circ, Govt Doc, Bemidji State University, 1500 Birchmont Dr NE, Box 4, Bemidji, MN, 56601-2600. Tel: 218-755-4233. Fax: 218-755-2051. p. 1241

Rosselli, Nicholas, Syst Coordr, Web Coordr, Indiana University Northwest Library, 3400 Broadway, Gary, IN, 46408. Tel: 219-980-6929. Fax: 219-980-6558. p. 745

Rosser, Chris, Theological Librn, Oklahoma Christian University, 2501 E Memorial Rd, Edmond, OK, 73013. Tel: 405-425-5323. Fax: 405-425-5313. p. 1962

Rosser-Hogben, Debra, Exec Dir, Milanof-Schock Library, 1184 Anderson Ferry Rd, Mount Joy, PA, 17552. Tel: 717-653-1510. Fax: 717-653-6590. p. 2093

Rosset, Marie, Chief Exec Officer, Powassan & District Union Public Library, 324 Clark St, Powassan, ON, P0H 1Z0, CANADA. Tel: 705-724-3618. Fax: 705-724-5525. p. 2838

Rossetti, Margaret, Ch, Boyden Library, Ten Bird St, Foxborough, MA, 02035. Tel: 508-543-1245. Fax: 508-543-1193. p. 1089

Rossetto, Gail, Dir, Northumberland Public Library, 31 State St, Groveton, NH, 03582. Tel: 603-636-2066. Fax: 603-636-2066. p. 1449

Rossi, Gladys, Br Mgr, Akron-Summit County Public Library, Northwest Akron, 1720 Shatto Ave, Akron, OH, 44313. Tel: 330-836-1081. Fax: 330-836-1574. p. 1852

Rossi, Jenna, Br Mgr, McDonald County Library, Noel Library, 626 Johnson Dr, Noel, MO, 64854. Tel: 417-475-3223. Fax: 417-475-3223. p. 1349

Rossi, Karen, Mgr, Carnegie Library of Pittsburgh, Downtown & Business, 612 Smithfield St, Pittsburgh, PA, 15222-2506. Tel: 412-281-5945. p. 2122

Rossi, Peter, Cat, Benedict College Library, 1600 Harden St, Columbia, SC, 29204. Tel: 803-705-4364. Fax: 803-748-7539. p. 2186

Rossignol, Lucien R, Head Librn, Smithsonian Libraries, National Museum of American History Library, NMAH Rm 5016, MRC 630, 14th & Constitution Ave NW, Washington, DC, 20560. Tel: 202-633-2067. Fax: 202-357-4256. p. 415

Rossini, Adriana, Registrar & Dir, Student Serv, University of Toronto, 140 St George St, Toronto, ON, M5S 3G6, CANADA. Tel: 416-978-8589. Fax: 416-978-5762. p. 2978

Rossiter, Debra, Dir, Camp Point Public Library Distict, 206 E State St, Camp Point, IL, 62320. Tel: 217-593-7021. Fax: 217-593-6121. p. 599

Rossiter, Shannon, Dir, Mohave County Historical Society, 400 W Beale St, Kingman, AZ, 86401. Tel: 928-753-3195. Fax: 928-718-1562. p. 66

Rossman, Deborah, Dir, Ida Rupp Public Library, 310 Madison St, Port Clinton, OH, 43452. Tel: 419-732-3212. Fax: 419-734-9867. p. 1930

Rossman, Jae, Asst Dir, Spec Coll, Yale University Library, Robert B Haas Family Arts Library, Loria Ctr, 180 York St, New Haven, CT, 06520. Tel: 203-432-1712. Fax: 203-432-0549. p. 358

Rossman, Jae J, Spec Coll Librn, Arts of the Bk, Yale University Library, Sterling Memorial Library, 120 High St, New Haven, CT, 06520. Tel: 203-432-1712. Fax: 203-432-1294. p. 359

Rossman, Janet N, Youth Serv Librn, Perry Public Library, 70 N Main St, Perry, NY, 14530-1299. Tel: 585-237-2243. Fax: 585-237-2008. p. 1716

Rossman, Michelle, Chairperson, Ref, Lakeland Community College Library, 7700 Clocktower Dr, Kirtland, OH, 44094-5198. Tel: 440-525-7067. Fax: 440-525-7602. p. 1908

Rossman, Rhonda, YA Serv, Pittsford Community Library, 24 State St, Pittsford, NY, 14534. Tel: 585-248-6275. Fax: 585-248-6259. p. 1718

Rossmann, Brian, Assoc Dean of Libr, Montana State University Libraries, Centennial Mall, Bozeman, MT, 59717. Tel: 406-994-5298. Fax: 406-994-2851. p. 1375

Rossnagel, Elizabeth, Chief Exec Officer, Sault Sainte Marie Public Library, Churchill, 301 Lake St, Sault Ste. Marie, ON, P6A 4B5, CANADA. Tel: 705-759-5246. p. 2840

Rossnagel, Elizabeth, Chief Exec Officer, Sault Sainte Marie Public Library, Korah, 496 Second Line W, Sault Ste. Marie, ON, P6C 2K4, CANADA. Tel: 705-759-5246. p. 2840

Rossnagel, Elizabeth, Chief Exec Officer, Sault Ste Marie Public Library, 50 East St, Sault Ste. Marie, ON, P6A 3C3, CANADA. Tel: 705-759-5246. Fax: 705-759-8752. p. 2840

Rosson, Loren, Circ Librn, Nashua Public Library, Two Court St, Nashua, NH, 03060. Tel: 603-589-4617. Fax: 603-594-3457. p. 1458

Rosswurm, Kevin M, Dir, Cuyahoga Falls Library, 2015 Third St, Cuyahoga Falls, OH, 44221-3294. Tel: 330-928-2117. Fax: 330-928-2535. p. 1892

Rostomian, Patricia, Br Mgr, Los Angeles Public Library System, Canoga Park Branch, 20939 Sherman Way, Canoga Park, CA, 91303. Tel: 818-887-0320. Fax: 818-346-1074. p. 173

Roszel, Karen, Ch, Bloomsburg Public Library, 225 Market St, Bloomsburg, PA, 17815-1726. Tel: 570-784-0883. Fax: 570-784-8541. p. 2035

Roszman, Debby, Commun Relations Coordr, Tiffin-Seneca Public Library, 77 Jefferson St, Tiffin, OH, 44883. Tel: 419-447-3751. Fax: 419-447-3045. p. 1938

Rotella, William, Syst Coordr, US Army War College Library, 122 Forbes Ave, Carlisle, PA, 17013-5220. Tel: 717-245-4704. Fax: 717-245-3323. p. 2042

Roth, Amy, Pres, Longboat Library, Inc, 555 Bay Isles Rd, Longboat Key, FL, 34228-3102. Tel: 941-387-0504. p. 461

Roth, Emma, Librn, Clay Springs Public Library, 2106 Granite Rd, Clay Springs, AZ, 85923. Tel: 928-739-4848. Fax: 928-739-4848. p. 60

Roth, Jane, Br Mgr, Mississippi County Library System, Manila Public, 103 N Dewey St, Manila, AR, 72442. Tel: 870-561-3525. Fax: 870-561-3525. p. 96

Roth, Jeffrey, VPres, Strategic Planning, The New York Public Library - Astor, Lenox & Tilden Foundations, 476 Fifth Ave, (@ 42nd St), New York, NY, 10018-2788. Tel: 212-592-7501. Fax: 212-592-7440. p. 1690

Roth, John D, Dr, Dir, Goshen College, Mennonite Historical Library, 1700 S Main, Goshen, IN, 46526. Tel: 574-535-7418. Fax: 574-535-7438. p. 746

Roth, Karen L, Mgr, Libr Serv, Morton Plant Mease Health Care, 300 Pinellas St, Clearwater, FL, 33756. Tel: 727-462-7889. Fax: 727-461-8755. p. 432

Roth, Laura, Dir, Heginbotham Library, 539 S Baxter St, Holyoke, CO, 80734-1497. Tel: 970-854-2597. Fax: 970-854-2636. p. 313

Roth, Noah, Head, Ref, Tech Coordr, Parkland Community Library, 4422 Walbert Ave, Allentown, PA, 18104-1619. Tel: 610-398-1361. Fax: 610-398-3538. p. 2027

Roth, Renee, Ref & Instruction Librn, Roosevelt University, Robert R McCormick Tribune Foundation Library, 1400 N Roosevelt Blvd, Schaumburg, IL, 60173. Tel: 847-619-7980. Fax: 847-619-7983. p. 623

Roth, Rhonda, Info Serv Librn, Mkt, Seneca College of Applied Arts & Technology, Newnham Campus (Main), 1750 Finch Ave E, North York, ON, M2J 2X5, CANADA. Tel: 416-491-5050, Ext 22093. Fax: 416-492-7184. p. 2813

Roth, Sheila, Asst Librn, Blue Ridge Township Public Library, 116 E Oliver St, Mansfield, IL, 61854. Tel: 217-489-9033. Fax: 217-489-9320. p. 670

Roth, Suzie, Res & Instruction Librn, Embry-Riddle Aeronautical University, 3700 Willow Creek Rd, Prescott, AZ, 86301-3720. Tel: 928-777-3858. p. 78

Roth, Tom, Cat, Coll Develop, ILL, State Library of Kansas, State Capitol Bldg, Topeka, KS, 66612. Tel: 785-296-3296. Fax: 785-296-6650. p. 896

Rothenberg, Lisa, Cataloger, Lincoln Public Library, Three Bedford Rd, Lincoln, MA, 01773. Tel: 781-259-8465. Fax: 781-259-1056. p. 1099

Rothenberg, Peter, Curator, Museum of Early Trades & Crafts Library, Nine Main St, Madison, NJ, 07940. Tel: 973-377-2982, Ext 13. Fax: 973-377-7358. p. 1498

Rothenberg, Sandra, Ref Serv, Framingham State College, 100 State St, Framingham, MA, 01701. Tel: 508-626-4653. Fax: 508-626-4649. p. 1090

Rothenfluh, Julie, Dep Dir, Naperville Public Library, 200 W Jefferson Ave, Naperville, IL, 60540-5374. Tel: 630-961-4100, Ext 6144. Fax: 630-637-6389. p. 679

Rotherham, Robin, Dir, Hellertown Area Library, 409 Constitution Ave, Hellertown, PA, 18055-1928. Tel: 610-838-8381. Fax: 610-838-8466. p. 2068

Rothers, Karen, Librn, Clara City Public Library, 126 N Main St, Clara City, MN, 56222. Tel: 320-847-3535. Fax: 320-847-3535. p. 1245

Rothhaar, Jan, Tech Serv, Broward College, 3501 SW Davie Rd, Davie, FL, 33314. Tel: 954-201-6648. Fax: 954-201-6490. p. 435

Rothlein, Barbara, Br Mgr, Ocean County Library, Jackson Branch, Two Jackson Dr, Jackson, NJ, 08527-3601. Tel: 732-928-4400. Fax: 732-833-0615. p. 1534

Rothman, David, Info Serv Spec, Community-General Hospital of Greater Syracuse, 4900 Broad Rd, Syracuse, NY, 13215-2299. Tel: 315-492-5471. Fax: 315-492-5221. p. 1751

Rothman, John, Archives, City University of New York, 365 Fifth Ave, New York, NY, 10016-4309. Tel: 212-817-7040. Fax: 212-817-2982. p. 1673

Rothman, Kara, Commun Relations Coordr, Henrico County Public Library, 1001 N Laburnum Ave, Henrico, VA, 23223-2705. Tel: 804-290-9000. Fax: 804-222-5566. p. 2471

Rothman, Karen, Head, Ref, Way Public Library, 101 E Indiana Ave, Perrysburg, OH, 43551. Tel: 419-874-3135, Ext 134. Fax: 419-874-6129. p. 1929

Rothrock, Donna, Librn, Salem College, Lorraine F Rudolph Fine Arts Center Library, 601 S Church St, Winston-Salem, NC, 27101. Tel: 336-917-5475. Fax: 336-721-2683. p. 1833

Rothschild, Evelyn, Dir, Oceanside Library, 30 Davison Ave, Oceanside, NY, 11572-2299. Tel: 516-766-2360. Fax: 516-766-1895. p. 1709

Rothstein, Kathleen, Br Mgr, Pasco County Library System, Land O' Lakes Branch, 2818 Collier Pkwy, Land O' Lakes, FL, 34639. Tel: 813-929-1214. Fax: 813-929-1235. p. 452

Rothstein, Linda, Librn I, Pasco County Library System, Centennial Park, 5740 Moog Rd, Holiday, FL, 34690. Tel: 727-834-3204. Fax: 727-834-3225. p. 451

Rothstein, Sarah, Pub Serv, Salem College, 626 S Church St, Winston-Salem, NC, 27108. Tel: 336-721-2649. Fax: 336-917-5339. p. 1833

Rothweiler, Jeffrey A, Dir/Fiscal Officer, Pataskala Public Library, 101 S Vine St, Pataskala, OH, 43062. Tel: 740-927-9986. Fax: 740-964-6204. p. 1928

Rothwell, Barbara, Law Librn, Foster Pepper PLLC, 1111 Third Ave, Ste 3400, Seattle, WA, 98101. Tel: 206-447-2811. Fax: 206-749-2049. p. 2529

Rothwell, Brian, Chief Librn, Charlie Norwood VA Medical Center Library, One Freedom Way, Augusta, GA, 30904-6285. Tel: 706-733-0188, Ext 7501. Fax: 706-823-3920. p. 520

Rothwell, Roberta B, Dir, Sutton Free Public Library, Four Uxbridge Rd, Sutton, MA, 01590. Tel: 508-865-8752. Fax: 508-865-8751. p. 1130

Rotman, Sara, Circ, Allendale Township Library, 6175 Library Ln, Allendale, MI, 49401. Tel: 616-895-4178. Fax: 616-895-5178. p. 1149

Rotroff, Kristi, Dir, Northwest State Community College Library, 22600 State Rte 34, Archbold, OH, 43502-9517. Tel: 419-267-1272. Fax: 419-267-5657. p. 1854

Rott, Janice, Librn, Ashley Public Library, 113 First Ave NW, Ashley, ND, 58413-7037. Tel: 701-288-3510. p. 1837

Rottler, Monica, Libr Asst, Oaklyn Memorial Library, 602 Newton Ave, Oaklyn, NJ, 08107. Tel: 856-858-8226. p. 1515

Rottmann, Anne G, Librn, Committee on Legislative Research, State Capitol Bldg, 117A, Jefferson City, MO, 65101. Tel: 573-751-4633. Fax: 573-751-0130. p. 1334

Rottmund, Kelly, Mgr, Teen Dept, Carnegie Library of Pittsburgh, 4400 Forbes Ave, Pittsburgh, PA, 15213-4080. Tel: 412-578-2600. Fax: 412-622-6278. p. 2122

Rottmund, Maura, Dir, Hawley Library, 103 Main Ave, Hawley, PA, 18428-1325. Tel: 570-226-4620. Fax: 570-226-8233. p. 2068

Rotz, Barbara, Coll Mgt, Coordr, Tech Serv, Shippensburg University, 1871 Old Main Dr, Shippensburg, PA, 17257-2299. Tel: 717-477-1027. Fax: 717-477-1389. p. 2140

Rouch, Selena, Br Librn, Fulton County Public Library, Fulton Branch, 514 State Rd 25, Fulton, IN, 46931. Tel: 574-857-3895. Fax: 574-857-2215. p. 776

Roudebush, LaWanda, Dir, Davenport Public Library, Richardson-Sloane Special Collections Center, Scott County Genealogical Society, 321 Main St, Davenport, IA, 52801-1409. Tel: 563-326-7902. Fax: 563-326-7901. p. 806

Rouff, Lyn, Asst Librn, Berwick Public Library, 103 Old Pine Hill Rd, Berwick, ME, 03901. Tel: 207-698-5737. Fax: 207-698-5737. p. 977

Roughen, Jane, Br Supvr, Madison Public Library, Sequoya Branch, 4340 Tokay Blvd, Madison, WI, 53711. Tel: 608-266-6385. Fax: 608-266-7353. p. 2607

Rouhana, Lauren, Coll Mgr, Hernando County Public Library System, 238 Howell Ave, Brooksville, FL, 34601. Tel: 352-754-4043. Fax: 352-754-4044. p. 430

Roukens, Joanne, Asst Dir, LibraryLinkNJ, The New Jersey Library Cooperative, 44 Stelton Rd, Ste 330, Piscataway, NJ, 08854. Tel: 732-752-7720. Fax: 732-752-7785. p. 2949

Roulier, Jean-François, Coll Develop Coordr, Coordr, Cat & Acq, Prog Coordr, Bibliothèques de Laval, 1535 boul Chomedey, Laval, QC, H7V 3Z4, CANADA. Tel: 450-978-6888, Ext 5649. Fax: 450-978-5833. p. 2886

Roullard, Jo, Br Mgr, Stanislaus County Free Library, Patterson Branch, 46 N Salado, Patterson, CA, 95363-2587. Tel: 209-892-6473. Fax: 209-892-5100. p. 188

Roullard, Josephine, Br Mgr, Stanislaus County Free Library, David F Bush Library (Oakdale Branch), 151 S First Ave, Oakdale, CA, 95361-3902. Tel: 209-847-4204. Fax: 209-847-4205. p. 188

Roullard, June, Librn, Department of Veterans Affairs, Togus VA Medical Ctr, One VA Center, Augusta, ME, 04330. Tel: 207-623-5773. Fax: 207-623-5766. p. 974

Roun, Claudia, Dir, Moores Memorial Library, Nine W Slokom Ave, Christiana, PA, 17509-1202. Tel: 610-593-6683. Fax: 610-593-7044. p. 2044

Rounce, Cathie, Sr Asst Librn, Haldimand County Public Library, Jarvis Branch, Two Monson St, Jarvis, ON, N0A 1J0, CANADA. Tel: 519-587-4746. Fax: 519-587-3470. p. 2803

Rounds, Andrea, Dir, Whitman Public Library, 100 Webster St, Whitman, MA, 02382. Tel: 781-447-7613. Fax: 781-447-7678. p. 1140

Rounds, Laura, Tech Serv Librn, University of Tampa, 401 W Kennedy Blvd, Tampa, FL, 33606-1490. Tel: 813-253-6231. Fax: 813-258-7426. p. 499

Rounds, Leslie L, Exec Dir, Dyer Library, 371 Main St, Saco, ME, 04072. Tel: 207-283-3861. Fax: 207-283-0754. p. 999

Rounds, Marvella, Cat, University of Maryland-Eastern Shore, 11868 Academic Oval, Princess Anne, MD, 21853. Tel: 410-651-2200, 410-651-6621. Fax: 410-651-6269. p. 1036

Rounds, Mary, Librn, Corvallis-Benton County Public Library, Alsea Community Library, 19192 Alsea Hwy, Alsea, OR, 97324. Tel: 541-487-5061. Fax: 541-487-5061. p. 1994

Roundtree, Koven, Human Res Sr Adminr, Prince George's County Memorial Library System, 6532 Adelphi Rd, Hyattsville, MD, 20782-2098. Tel: 301-699-3500. Fax: 301-927-6516. p. 1032

Roundtree, Lorilie, Librn, Folsom Lake College Library, Ten College Pkwy, Folsom, CA, 95630. Tel: 916-608-6818. Fax: 916-608-6533. p. 148

Rounsville, Lorine, Dir, Hamlin Memorial Library, 123 S Mechanic St, Smethport, PA, 16749-1270. Tel: 814-887-9262. Fax: 814-887-9234. p. 2141

Rountree, Brian, Instr, Red River College, W210B-160 Princess St, Winnipeg, MB, R3B 1K9, CANADA. Tel: 204-949-8476. Fax: 204-949-0032. p. 2978

Rountree, Brian, Brother, Librn, Grand Lodge of Manitoba, Grand Lodge of Manitoba, 420 Corydon Ave, Winnipeg, MB, R3L 0N8, CANADA. Tel: 204-453-7410. Fax: 204-284-3527. p. 2755

Rountree, Christi, Info Spec, Air Force Research Laboratory, Technical Library, 203 W Eglin Blvd, Ste 300, Eglin AFB, FL, 32542-6843. Tel: 850-882-3212, 850-882-5586. Fax: 850-882-3214. p. 439

Rountree, Jo-Ann, Dir, Jackson County Public Library System, 2929 Green St, Marianna, FL, 32446. Tel: 850-482-9631. Fax: 850-482-9632. p. 462

Rountree, Linda, Circ, Helen Lehmann Memorial Library, 17435 Fifth St, Montverde, FL, 34756. Tel: 407-469-3838. Fax: 407-469-2773. p. 470

Roupe, Cindy, Dir, Pub Serv, Ref, State Library of Kansas, State Capitol Bldg, Topeka, KS, 66612. Tel: 785-296-3296. Fax: 785-296-6650. p. 896

Rourke, Cindy, Dean, Saint Clair County Community College, 323 Erie St, Port Huron, MI, 48060. Tel: 810-984-3881, 810-989-5640. Fax: 810-984-2852. p. 1219

Rourke, Diane, Dir, Doctor's Hospital, Baptist Health, 5000 University Dr, Coral Gables, FL, 33146. Tel: 305-669-2360. Fax: 305-669-2456. p. 434

Rourke, Diane, Dir, Baptist Hospital of Miami, 8900 N Kendall Dr, Miami, FL, 33176. Tel: 786-596-6506. Fax: 786-596-5910. p. 464

Rourke, Diane, Dir, South Miami Hospital, 6200 SW 73rd St, Miami, FL, 33143. Tel: 786-662-8219. Fax: 786-662-5124. p. 468

Rourke, Jill, Commun Libr Dir, Fort Vancouver Regional Library District, 1007 E Mill Plain Blvd, Vancouver, WA, 98663. Tel: 360-695-1561. Fax: 360-693-2681. p. 2546

Rourke, Jill, Dir, Fremont County Library System, 451 N Second St, Lander, WY, 82520-2316. Tel: 307-332-5194. Fax: 307-332-1504, 307-332-3909. p. 2656

Rourke, Lorna, Univ Librn, Saint Jerome's University Library, 290 Westmount Rd N, Waterloo, ON, N2L 3G3, CANADA. Tel: 519-884-8111, Ext 28271. Fax: 519-884-5759. p. 2869

Rouse, Karolyn, Asst Librn, Edna Zybell Memorial Library, 309 Sixth Ave, Box P, Clarence, IA, 52216. Tel: 563-452-3734. Fax: 563-452-3520. p. 802

Rouse, Lenore, Curator, Catholic University of America, Rare Books Special Collections, 214 Mullen Library, 620 Michigan Ave NE, Washington, DC, 20064. Tel: 202-319-5091. Fax: 202-319-4735. p. 396

Rouse, Michael, Br Mgr, Jacksonville Public Library, University Park, 3435 University Blvd N, Jacksonville, FL, 32277-2464. Tel: 904-630-1265. Fax: 904-744-6892. p. 454

Rouse, Zachary, Supvr, Access Serv, Columbia University, Avery Architectural & Fine Arts Library, 1172 Amsterdam Ave, MC 0301, New York, NY, 10027. Tel: 212-854-6199. Fax: 212-854-8904. p. 1674

Rouse, Zachary, Asst Librn, Oldham County Public Library, 914 Main St, Vega, TX, 79092. Tel: 806-267-2635. Fax: 806-267-2635. p. 2395

Roush, Adrienne, Librn, Grays Harbor College, 1620 Edward P Smith Dr, Aberdeen, WA, 98520-7599. Tel: 360-538-4050. Fax: 360-538-4294. p. 2507

Roush, Barbara, Ser, University of California, 200 McAllister St, San Francisco, CA, 94102-4978. Tel: 415-565-4757. Fax: 415-581-8849. p. 248

Rousseau, Carmen, Coll Develop Librn, Ref Librn, Universite du Quebec en Outaouais, 283, Blvd Alexandre-Tache, Case postale 1250, succ Hull, Gatineau, QC, J8X 3X7, CANADA. Tel: 819-595-3900, Ext 1860. Fax: 819-773-1669. p. 2884

Rousseau, Lina, In Charge, Bibliotheque de Charlesbourg, 7950 First Ave, Charlesbourg, QC, G1H 2Y4, CANADA. Tel: 418-641-6287. Fax: 418-624-7886. p. 2880

Rousseau, Linda P, Asst Dir, Head, Circ, Charleston Southern University, 9200 University Blvd, Charleston, SC, 29406. Tel: 843-863-7941. Fax: 843-863-7947. p. 2183

Rousseau, Susan N, Ref/YA, Portsmouth Free Public Library, 2658 E Main Rd, Portsmouth, RI, 02871. Tel: 401-683-9457. Fax: 401-683-5013. p. 2171

Rousseau, Thais, Head Librn, Capital Area District Libraries, Dansville Library, 1379 E Mason St, Dansville, MI, 48819. Tel: 517-623-6511. Fax: 517-623-0520. p. 1200

Rousseau, Tyler, Ref, Monroe Township Public Library, Four Municipal Plaza, Monroe Township, NJ, 08831-1900. Tel: 732-521-5000, Ext 123. Fax: 732-521-4766. p. 1503

Rousseau, Tyler, YA Serv, Trenton Free Public Library, 120 Academy St, Trenton, NJ, 08608-1302. Tel: 609-392-7188. Fax: 609-396-7655. p. 1536

Rousseaux, Kim, Asst Librn, Chinook Regional Library, Vanguard Branch, Library/Musem Bldg, Dominion St, Vanguard, SK, S0N 2V0, CANADA. Tel: 306-582-2244. p. 2929

Roussel, Chris, Dir, Lawton Public Library, 125 S Main St, Lawton, MI, 49065. Tel: 269-624-5481. Fax: 269-624-1909. p. 1203

Roussel, Denis, Br Mgr, Government of Canada, Federal Courts & Tax Court of Canada, Courts Administration Service-Library Services, 90 Sparks St, Ottawa, ON, K1A 0H9, CANADA. Tel: 613-992-1704. Fax: 613-943-8449. p. 2831

Roussel, Denis, Librn, Government of Canada, Courts Administration Service, Tax Library, 200 Kent St, Ottawa, ON, K1A 0M1, CANADA. Tel: 613-992-1704. Fax: 613-943-8449. p. 2831

Roussel, Helene, Dir, Bibliotheque et Archives nationales du Quebec, 475 de Maisonneuve E, Montreal, QC, H2L 5C4, CANADA. Tel: 514-873-1101, Ext 3245. Fax: 514-873-9312. p. 2888

Roussin, Erin, Head Librn, Kenora Public Library, 24 Main St S, Kenora, ON, P9N 1S7, CANADA. Tel: 807-467-2081. Fax: 807-467-2085. p. 2812

Roussin, Erin, Head Librn, Kenora Public Library, Keewatin Branch, 221 Main St, Keewatin, ON, P0X 1C0, CANADA. Tel: 807-547-2145. Fax: 807-547-3145. p. 2812

Routliffe, Susan, Assoc Univ Librn, Info Res & Serv, University of Waterloo Library, 200 University Ave W, Waterloo, ON, N2L 3G1, CANADA. Tel: 519-888-4567, Ext 33312. Fax: 519-888-4320. p. 2869

Routon, ViAnne, Librn, Summerfield Public Library, 300 Main, Summerfield, KS, 66541. Tel: 785-244-6531. p. 895

Routsong, Scott, Youth Serv, Coastal Plain Regional Library, 2014 Chestnut Ave, Tifton, GA, 31794. Tel: 229-386-3400. Fax: 229-386-7007. p. 554

Roux, Johanne, Libr Tech, Ontario Ministry of Northern Development, Mines & Forestry Library, 933 Ramsey Lake Rd, Level A-3, Sudbury, ON, P3E 6B5, CANADA. Tel: 705-670-5614. Fax: 705-670-5770. p. 2847

Roux, Yvonne, Ref Serv, Ch, William Paterson University of New Jersey, 300 Pompton Rd, Wayne, NJ, 07470. Tel: 973-720-3184. Fax: 973-720-3171. p. 1540

Roux, Yvonne, Prof, William Paterson University, College of Education, 1600 Valley Rd, Wayne, NJ, 07470. Tel: 973-720-2331, 973-720-2980. Fax: 973-720-2585. p. 2969

Rouzer, Steve, Tech Serv, Stevenson University Library, 1525 Greenspring Valley Rd, Stevenson, MD, 21153. Tel: 410-486-7000, 443-334-2233. Fax: 410-486-7329. p. 1043

Roveland-Brenton, Blythe, Archivist, Saint John's University Library, 8000 Utopia Pkwy, Queens, NY, 11439. Tel: 718-990-6735. Fax: 718-380-0353. p. 1725

Roveland-Brenton, Blythe, Assoc Univ Librn, Coll & Access, Rare Bk Librn, Univ Archivist, Saint John's University Library, 8000 Utopia Pkwy, Queens, NY, 11439. Tel: 718-990-6735. Fax: 718-380-0353. p. 1725

Rovero, Marie, Acq, Hartford Seminary Library, 77 Sherman St, Hartford, CT, 06105-2260. Tel: 860-509-9562. Fax: 860-509-9509. p. 346

Rovida, Daniela, Libr Mgr, Apache County Library District, Concho Public, 18 County Rd 5101, Concho, AZ, 85924. Tel: 928-337-2167. Fax: 928-337-2167. p. 80

Rovner, Abigail, Librn, Central Piedmont Community College Library, 1201 Elizabeth Ave, Charlotte, NC, 28235. Tel: 704-330-4103. Fax: 704-330-6887. p. 1781

Rowden, Andrew, Dir, Scott County Public Library, 108 S Main St, Scottsburg, IN, 47170. Tel: 812-752-2751. Fax: 812-752-2878. p. 777

Rowden, Andy, Dir, Tyson Library, 325 W Tyson St, Versailles, IN, 47042. Tel: 812-689-5894. Fax: 812-689-7401. p. 784

Rowden, Bess, Asst Librn, Milton Free Public Library, 13 Main St, Milton Mills, NH, 03852. Tel: 603-473-8535. p. 1458

Rowe, Adelaide, YA Serv, Elk Grove Village Public Library, 1001 Wellington Ave, Elk Grove Village, IL, 60007-3391. Tel: 847-439-0447. Fax: 847-439-0475. p. 641

Rowe, Barbara, Youth Serv, Sturgis District Library, 255 North St, Sturgis, MI, 49091. Tel: 269-659-7224. Fax: 269-651-4534. p. 1230

Rowe, Dora, Dir, James L Hamner Public Library, 16351 Dunn St, Amelia, VA, 23002. Tel: 804-561-4559. Fax: 804-561-3174. p. 2447

Rowe, Linda, Sr Librn, California Department of Corrections Library System, California State Prison, Los Angeles County, 44750 60th St W, Lancaster, CA, 93536-7620. Tel: 661-729-2000, Ext 5610. Fax: 661-729-6993. p. 221

Rowe, Marcy, Dir, Boise Basin Library District, 123 Montgomery St, Idaho City, ID, 83631. Tel: 208-392-4558. Fax: 208-392-4920. p. 576

Rowe, Monk, Dir, Jazz Archives, Hamilton College, 198 College Hill Rd, Clinton, NY, 13323-1299. Tel: 315-859-4071. Fax: 315-859-4578. p. 1607

Rowe, Rhonda, Asst Mgr, Edmonton Public Library, Londonderry, 110 Londonderry Mall, 137th Ave & 66th St, Edmonton, AB, T5C 3C8, CANADA. Tel: 780-496-1814. Fax: 780-496-1452. p. 2700

Rowe, Ruth, Dir, West Winfield Library, 179 South St, West Winfield, NY, 13491-2826. Tel: 315-822-6394. Fax: 315-822-6394. p. 1767

Rowe, Sara, Ref Serv, Presbyterian College, 211 E Maple St, Clinton, SC, 29325. Tel: 864-833-8299. Fax: 864-833-8315. p. 2186

Rowe, Sharon, Dir, Statesboro Regional Public Libraries, 124 S Main St, Statesboro, GA, 30458. Tel: 912-764-1328. Fax: 912-764-1348. p. 552

Rowe, Sharon Clontz, Dir, Marlboro County Library, 200 John Corry Rd, Bennettsville, SC, 29512. Tel: 843-479-5630. Fax: 843-479-5645. p. 2182

Rowe, Stephanie, Head of Libr, Free Library of Philadelphia, Falls of Schuylkill Branch, 3501 Midvale Ave, Philadelphia, PA, 19129-1633. Tel: 215-685-2093. Fax: 215-685-2092. p. 2107

Rowe, Susan, Dir, Gilbertsville Free Library, 17 Commercial St, Gilbertsville, NY, 13776-0332. Tel: 607-783-2832. Fax: 607-783-2832. p. 1628

Rowe, Violet F, Dir, Glenshaw Public Library, 1504 Butler Plank Rd, Glenshaw, PA, 15116-2397. Tel: 412-487-2121. p. 2061

Rowe, Wayne J, Chief, Ref Br, United States Naval War College Library, 686 Cushing Rd, Newport, RI, 02841-1207. Tel: 401-841-6500. Fax: 401-841-6491. p. 2169

Rowe, Wendy, Ch, Barrington Public Library, 105 Ramsdell Lane, Barrington, NH, 03825. Tel: 603-664-9715. Fax: 603-664-5219. p. 1438

Rowe-Jackson, Valerie, Dep Dir, Richland County Public Library, 1431 Assembly St, Columbia, SC, 29201-3101. Tel: 803-799-9084. Fax: 803-929-3448. p. 2188

Rowe-Rawlinson, Liz, Dir, Info Tech, Rocky River Public Library, 1600 Hampton Rd, Rocky River, OH, 44116-2699. Tel: 440-333-7610. Fax: 440-333-4184. p. 1932

Rowell, Barbara, Dir, Jacksonville Public Library, 200 Pelham Rd S, Jacksonville, AL, 36265. Tel: 256-435-6332. Fax: 256-435-4459. p. 22

Rowell, Charlotte, Ref Librn, Seymour Public Library, 46 Church St, Seymour, CT, 06483. Tel: 203-888-3903. Fax: 203-888-4099. p. 366

Rowell, Christine, Librn, Hydrosource Associates Library, 26 Winter St, Ashland, NH, 03217. Tel: 603-968-3733. Fax: 603-968-7605. p. 1438

Rowell, Greg, Librn, Riverview Hospital, 2601 Lougheed Hwy, Coquitlam, BC, V3C 4J2, CANADA. Tel: 604-524-7000, 604-524-7386. Fax: 604-524-7021. p. 2727

Rowell, Lisa, Dir, Albertville Public Library, 200 Jackson St, Albertville, AL, 35950. Tel: 256-891-8290. Fax: 256-891-8295. p. 3

Rowell, Maralie, ILL, Emmaus Public Library, 11 E Main St, Emmaus, PA, 18049. Tel: 610-965-9284. Fax: 610-965-6446. p. 2054

Rowell, Randy, Tech Serv, Gardendale Martha Moore Public Library, 995 Mt Olive Rd, Gardendale, AL, 35071. Tel: 205-631-6639. Fax: 205-631-0146. p. 18

Rowell, Regina Ann, Info Spec, United States Air Force, David Grant USAF Medical Center Learning Resource Center, 101 Bodin Circle, Travis AFB, CA, 94535-1800. Tel: 707-423-5344. Fax: 707-423-7965. p. 276

Rowell, Sarah, Sr Circ & Reserves Coordr, Milwaukee School of Engineering, 500 E Kilbourn Ave, Milwaukee, WI, 53202. Tel: 414-277-7180. Fax: 414-277-7186. p. 2620

Rowhani, Shahla, Librn, Bellevue College, 3000 Landerholm Circle SE, Bellevue, WA, 98007-6484. Tel: 425-564-2260. Fax: 425-564-6186. p. 2508

Rowland, Alexandra, Librn, Arizona Department of Corrections - Adult Institutions, Arizona State Prison Phoenix-West, 3402 W Cocopah St, Phoenix, AZ, 85009. Tel: 602-352-0350, Ext 109. Fax: 602-352-0357. p. 71

Rowland, Annie, ILL, South Country Library, 22 Station Rd, Bellport, NY, 11713. Tel: 631-286-0818. Fax: 631-286-4873. p. 1580

Rowland, Lucy, Res, Sci, University of Georgia Libraries, Athens, GA, 30602-1641. Tel: 706-542-6643. Fax: 706-542-4144. p. 510

Rowland, Sandra M, Asst Dir, Westfield Washington Public Library, 333 W Hoover St, Westfield, IN, 46074-9283. Tel: 317-896-9391. Fax: 317-896-3702. p. 787

Rowland, Saresta, Librn, Beth David Congregation, 2625 SW Third Ave, Miami, FL, 33129. Tel: 305-854-3911. Fax: 305-285-5841. p. 464

Rowland, Sharon, Circ, Midland County Public Library, 301 W Missouri, Midland, TX, 79701. Tel: 432-688-4320. Fax: 432-688-4939. p. 2363

Rowlands, Anne, Develop Dir, Wilton Library Association, 137 Old Ridgefield Rd, Wilton, CT, 06897-3019. Tel: 203-762-3950. Fax: 203-834-1166. p. 378

Rowlands, Rebecca, Head, Adult Serv, Topsfield Town Library, One S Common St, Topsfield, MA, 01983-1496. Tel: 978-887-1528. Fax: 978-887-0185. p. 1131

Rowlands, Wendy, Librn, Colorado Department of Corrections, Colorado State Penitentiary Library, PO Box 777, Canon City, CO, 81215-0777. Tel: 719-269-5268. Fax: 719-269-5125. p. 293

Rowles-Channell, Jamie, Br Mgr, Roanoke County Public Library, Vinton Branch, 800 E Washington Ave, Vinton, VA, 24179. Tel: 540-857-5043. Fax: 540-344-3285. p. 2494

Rowley, Keith, Tech Serv, Utah Valley University Library, 800 W University Pkwy, Orem, UT, 84058-5999. Tel: 801-863-8780. Fax: 801-863-7065. p. 2409

Rowley, Tim, Asst Dir, Syst & Tech Serv, Utah Valley University Library, 800 W University Pkwy, Orem, UT, 84058-5999. Tel: 801-863-8107. Fax: 801-863-7065. p. 2409

Rowlison de Ortiz, Lisa, Head, Cat & Ser, University of California, Berkeley, Technical Services, 250 Moffit Library, Berkeley, CA, 94720-6000. Tel: 510-643-8239. Fax: 510-642-8331. p. 128

Rowold, Roberta, Adult Ref Librn, Leesburg Public Library, 100 E Main St, Leesburg, FL, 34748. Tel: 352-728-9790. Fax: 352-728-9794. p. 461

Rowse, Melissa, Dir, Montgomery House, 20 Church St, McEwensville, PA, 17749. Tel: 570-538-1381. Fax: 570-538-1381. p. 2085

Rowshon, Parveen, Br Mgr, Brooklyn Public Library, Windsor Terrace, 160 E Fifth St, Brooklyn, NY, 11218. Tel: 718-686-9707. Fax: 718-686-0162. p. 1592

Roy, Anjana, Mgr, Good Samaritan Medical Center, 1309 N Flagler Dr, West Palm Beach, FL, 33401. Tel: 561-650-6315. Fax: 561-671-7428. p. 502

Roy, Annette, Tech Serv, Bibliotheque H J Hemens, 339 Chemin Grande-Cote, Rosemere, QC, J7A 1K2, CANADA. Tel: 450-621-6132. Fax: 450-621-6131. p. 2907

Roy, Bertrand, Dir, Foreign Missions Society of Quebec Library, 180 Place Juge Desnoyers, Laval, QC, H7G 1A4, CANADA. Tel: 450-667-4190. Fax: 450-667-4194. p. 2886

Roy, Carolynn Sarah, Pub Serv Librn, Tennessee Wesleyan College, 23 Coach Farmer Dr, Athens, TN, 37303. Tel: 423-252-1103. Fax: 423-746-5272. p. 2224

Roy, Cathy, Ref Serv, Niagara Falls Public Library, 4848 Victoria Ave, Niagara Falls, ON, L2E 4C5, CANADA. Tel: 905-356-8080. Fax: 905-356-7004. p. 2824

Roy, Chris, Per, Southern New Hampshire University, 2500 N River Rd, Manchester, NH, 03106-1045. Tel: 603-645-9605. Fax: 603-645-9685. p. 1456

Roy, Crystal, Coordr, North Dakota Vision Services-School for the Blind, 500 Stanford Rd, Grand Forks, ND, 58203. Tel: 701-795-2700. Fax: 701-795-2727. p. 1842

Roy, David A, Info Res Spec, Workplace Safety & Insurance Board, 200 Front St W, 17th Flr, Toronto, ON, M5V 3J1, CANADA. Tel: 416-344-4962. Fax: 416-344-4050. p. 2868

Roy, Debra J, Dir, Hazen Memorial Library, Three Keady Way, Shirley, MA, 01464. Tel: 978-425-2620. Fax: 978-425-2621. p. 1124

Roy, Gail, Asst Dean, Northern Maine Community College Library, 33 Edgemont Dr, Presque Isle, ME, 04769-2016. Tel: 207-768-2734. Fax: 207-768-2823. p. 998

Roy, Harriet, Asst Dir, Pahkisimon Nuye?ah Library System, 118 Avro Pl, Air Ronge, CANADA. Tel: 306-425-4525. Fax: 306-425-4572. p. 2917

Roy, Jeanne, Info Tech, University of Maine at Farmington, 116 South St, Farmington, ME, 04938-1990. Tel: 207-778-7210. Fax: 207-778-7223. p. 985

Roy, Jeanne, Adult Serv, Moses Greeley Parker Memorial Library, 28 Arlington St, Dracut, MA, 01826. Tel: 978-454-5474. Fax: 978-454-9120. p. 1085

Roy, Joseph, Sr, Dir, Southern Poverty Law Center, 400 Washington Ave, Montgomery, AL, 36104. Tel: 334-956-8200. Fax: 334-956-8483. p. 31

Roy, Loriene, Prof, University of Texas at Austin, One University Sta, D7000, Austin, TX, 78712-0390. Tel: 512-471-3821. Fax: 512-471-3971. p. 2975

Roy, Marlene, Res & Learning Resources Mgr, International Institute for Sustainable Development, 161 Portage Ave E 6th flr, Winnipeg, MB, R3B 0Y4, CANADA. Tel: 204-958-7724. Fax: 204-958-7710. p. 2756

Roy, Michael D, Dean, Middlebury College Library, 110 Storrs Ave, Middlebury, VT, 05753-6007. Tel: 802-443-5490. Fax: 802-443-2074, 802-443-5698. p. 2428

Roy, Ryan, Pub Serv Librn, Millsaps College, 1701 N State St, Jackson, MS, 39210-0001. Tel: 601-974-1072. Fax: 601-974-1082. p. 1304

Roy, Theresa, Regional Libr Mgr, Lafayette Public Library, Southside, 5417 Johnston St, Lafayette, LA, 70503. Tel: 337-981-1028. p. 953

Royal, Texana, Librn, Georgia Department of Corrections, Office of Library Services, 1412 Plunkett Rd, Unadilla, GA, 31091. Tel: 478-627-2000, www.dcor.state.ga.us. Fax: 478-627-2140. p. 554

Royalty, Mary, Acq, Hanover College, 121 Scenic Dr, Hanover, IN, 47243. Tel: 812-866-7161. Fax: 812-866-7172. p. 748

Royan, Nancy, Dir, Wedsworth Memorial Library, 13 Front St N, Cascade, MT, 59421. Tel: 406-468-2257. Fax: 406-468-2740. p. 1376

Royer, Barbara, Dir, Yavapai-Prescott Tribal Library, 530 E Merritt, Prescott, AZ, 86301-2038. Tel: 928-515-7321. Fax: 928-442-1450. p. 79

Royer, Debra, Dir, Portland Art Museum, 1219 SW Park Ave, Portland, OR, 97205-2486. Tel: 503-276-4526. p. 2013

Royer, Janet, Circ, Syst Coordr, Burlington Public Library, 820 E Washington, Burlington, WA, 98233. Tel: 360-755-0760. Fax: 360-755-0717. p. 2511

Royer, Susan B, Dep Dir, Huntsville-Madison Public Library, 915 Monroe St, Huntsville, AL, 35801. Tel: 256-532-5952. Fax: 256-532-5997. p. 21

Royka, Margaret A, Dir, Truro Public Library, Five Library Lane, North Truro, MA, 02652. Tel: 508-487-1125. Fax: 508-487-3571. p. 1113

Royster, Donna, Cat, North Carolina Agricultural & Technical State University, 1601 E Market St, Greensboro, NC, 27411-0002. Tel: 336-334-7159. Fax: 336-334-7783. p. 1797

Royster, Josaine, Ref Serv, Union County College Libraries, 1033 Springfield Ave, Cranford, NJ, 07016. Tel: 908-709-7623. Fax: 908-709-7589. p. 1480

Royston, Tricia, Librn, New London County Historical Society Library, 11 Blinman St, New London, CT, 06320. Tel: 860-443-1209. Fax: 860-443-1209. p. 360

Roz, Conner, Dir, Sidney Memorial Public Library, Eight River St, Sidney, NY, 13838. Tel: 607-563-1200, 607-563-8021. Fax: 607-563-7675. p. 1743

Rozelle, Liz, Dir, Yorktown-Mount Pleasant Township Public Library, 8920 W Adaline St, Yorktown, IN, 47396. Tel: 765-759-9723. Fax: 765-759-7260. p. 789

Rozen, Celia, Coll Develop Coordr, Alaska Resources Library & Information Services, Library Bldg, 3211 Providence Dr, Ste 111, Anchorage, AK, 99508-4614. Tel: 907-786-7676. Fax: 907-786-7652. p. 43

Rozene, Janette M, Head, Cat, Fashion Institute of Technology-SUNY, Seventh Ave at 27th St, New York, NY, 10001-5992. Tel: 212-217-4358. Fax: 212-217-4371. p. 1678

Rozewicz, B L, Dir, Gilman Museum Library, At the Cave, 726 Durham St, Hellertown, PA, 18055-1926. Tel: 610-838-8767. Fax: 610-838-2961. p. 2068

Rozgonyi, Tim, Res Editor, Times Publishing Co, 490 First Ave S, Saint Petersburg, FL, 33701-4223. Tel: 727-893-8111. Fax: 727-893-8107. p. 488

Rozier, Eddie, Librn, David D Acker Library & Knowledge Repository, 9820 Belvoir Rd, Fort Belvoir, VA, 22060. Tel: 703-805-5143. Fax: 703-805-3443. p. 2464

Rozier, Gina, Mgr, Mkt & Develop, Durham County Library, 300 N Roxboro St, Durham, NC, 27701. Tel: 919-560-0151. Fax: 919-560-0137. p. 1788

Rozmarynowski, Mark L, Dir, University of Wisconsin Baraboo-Sauk County, 1006 Connie Rd, Baraboo, WI, 53913. Tel: 608-355-5249. Fax: 608-355-5291. p. 2580

Roznoy, Cynthia, Curator, Mattatuck Historical Society Library, 144 W Main St, Waterbury, CT, 06702. Tel: 203-753-0381, Ext 15. Fax: 203-756-6283. p. 374

Rozum, Betty, Assoc Dean, Tech Serv, Utah State University, 3000 Old Main Hill, Logan, UT, 84322-3000. Tel: 435-797-2632. Fax: 435-797-2880. p. 2407

Ruark, Jean M, Communications Coordr, Mansfield-Richland County Public Library, 43 W Third St, Mansfield, OH, 44902-1295. Tel: 419-521-3101. Fax: 419-522-5375. p. 1912

Ruban, John, Info Tech Serv, Ocean City Free Public Library, 1735 Simpson Ave, Ste 4, Ocean City, NJ, 08226. Tel: 609-399-2434. Fax: 609-398-0751. p. 1516

Rubens, Charlotte, ILL, University of California, Berkeley, 255 Doe Library, Berkeley, CA, 94720-6000. Tel: 510-642-3773. Fax: 510-643-8179. p. 127

Rubenstein, Ellen, PhD, Dr, Asst Prof, University of Oklahoma, Bizzell Memorial Library, 401 W Brooks, Rm 120, Norman, OK, 73019-6032. Tel: 405-325-3921. Fax: 405-325-7648. p. 2972

Rubenstein, Kristin, Libr Assoc/Ch, Coweta Public Library System, 85 Literary Lane, Newnan, GA, 30265. Tel: 770-683-2052. Fax: 770-683-0065. p. 546

Rubenstein, Nancy F, Dir, Heidelberg University, 10 Greenfield St, Tiffin, OH, 44883-2420. Tel: 419-448-2104. Fax: 419-448-2578. p. 1938

Rubey, Daniel, Dr, Dean of Libr & Info Serv, Hofstra University, 123 Hofstra University, Hempstead, NY, 11549. p. 1635

Rubin, Catherine, Librn, United Nations Information Center, 1775 K St NW, Ste 400, Washington, DC, 20006. Tel: 202-454-2112. Fax: 202-331-9191. p. 417

Rubin, Catherine, Asst Regional Librn, North Carolina Regional Library for the Blind & Physically Handicapped, 1841 Capital Blvd, Raleigh, NC, 27635. Tel: 919-733-4376. Fax: 919-733-6910. p. 1815

Rubin, Deborah, Asst Mgr, Dallas Public Library, Skillman Southwestern, 5707 Skillman St, Dallas, TX, 75206. Tel: 214-670-6078. Fax: 214-670-6184. p. 2307

Rubin, Faith B, Educ Dir, Temple Sinai, 1401 N Limekiln Pike, Dresher, PA, 19025. Tel: 215-643-6510, Ext 110. Fax: 215-643-9441. p. 2050

Rubin, Grail, Librn, Gibbons Municipal Library, 4807 50th Ave, Gibbons, AB, T0A 1N0, CANADA. Tel: 780-923-2004. Fax: 780-923-2015. p. 2705

Rubin, Hillary, Br Mgr, Kenyon & Kenyon LLP, One Broadway, 10th Flr, New York, NY, 10004-1007. Tel: 212-425-7200. Fax: 212-908-6113. p. 1684

Rubin, J Adam, Ref Librn, John A Logan College, 700 Logan College Rd, Carterville, IL, 62918. Tel: 618-985-3741, Ext 8279. Fax: 618-985-3899. p. 601

Rubin, Katharine, Acq, Cat, Coll Develop, Our Lady of Holy Cross College Library, 4123 Woodland Dr, New Orleans, LA, 70131. Tel: 504-398-2119. Fax: 504-391-2421. p. 962

Rubin, Linda, Mgr, Saint Mary Medical Center, 1050 Linden Ave, Long Beach, CA, 90813. Tel: 562-491-9295. Fax: 562-491-9293. p. 167

Rubin, Rachel, Dir, Bexley Public Library, 2411 E Main St, Bexley, OH, 43209. Tel: 614-231-9709. p. 1860

Rubin, Richard, Dr, Dir, Kent State University, 314 Library, Kent, OH, 44242-0001. Tel: 330-672-2782. Fax: 330-672-7965. p. 2971

Rubin, William, Br Mgr, Cuyahoga County Public Library, Mayfield Branch, 6080 Wilson Mills Rd, Mayfield Village, OH, 44143-2103. Tel: 440-473-0350. Fax: 440-473-0774. p. 1927

Rubin, William, Br Mgr, Cuyahoga County Public Library, Richmond Heights Branch, 5235 Wilson Mills Rd, Richmond Heights, OH, 44143-3016. Tel: 440-449-2666. Fax: 440-473-3264. p. 1928

Rubino, Cynthia, Dir, Lewisboro Library, 15 Main St, South Salem, NY, 10590-1413. Tel: 914-763-3857. Fax: 914-763-2193. p. 1745

Rubino, Kit, Youth Serv, Roselle Park, 404 Chestnut St, Roselle Park, NJ, 07204-1506. Tel: 908-245-2456. Fax: 908-245-9204. p. 1528

Rubinstein, Ernie, PhD, Theological Librn, Drew University Library, 36 Madison Ave, Madison, NJ, 07940. Tel: 973-408-3472. Fax: 973-408-3770. p. 1497

Rubinstein, Roslyn, Dir, Waterford Public Library, 49 Rope Ferry Rd, Waterford, CT, 06385. Tel: 860-444-5805. Fax: 860-437-1685. p. 375

Ruboyianes, Victor, Librn, Arizona Department of Corrections - Adult Institutions, 4374 Butte Ave, Florence, AZ, 85232. Tel: 520-868-0201, Ext 5022. Fax: 520-868-8556. p. 63

Ruby, Carolyn, Librn, Idaho State Historical Society, Idaho History Ctr, 2205 Old Penitentiary Rd, Boise, ID, 83712. Tel: 208-334-3356. Fax: 208-334-3198. p. 571

Ruby, Penny, Librn, Clallam County Law Library, County Courthouse, 223 E Fourth St, Ste 17, Port Angeles, WA, 98362-3015. Tel: 360-417-2287. p. 2523

Ruch, Jean, Ref, North Brunswick Free Public Library, 880 Hermann Rd, North Brunswick, NJ, 08902. Tel: 732-246-3545. Fax: 732-246-1341. p. 1514

Rucinski, Paula Jean, Mgr, Richard T Liddicoat Gemological Library & Information Center, 5345 Armada Dr, Carlsbad, CA, 92008. Tel: 760-603-4174. Fax: 760-603-4256. p. 132

Rucinski, Taryn, Ref Librn, Pace University, 78 N Broadway, White Plains, NY, 10603. Tel: 914 422-4358. Fax: 914-422-4139. p. 1769

Ruck, Deborah, Info Res, Medical College of Wisconsin Libraries, Health Research Ctr, 3rd Flr, 8701 Watertown Plank Rd, Milwaukee, WI, 53226-0509. Tel: 414-955-8522. Fax: 414-955-6532. p. 2619

Rucker, Alena Jewel, Cataloger, Interim Dir, West Virginia University Institute of Technology, 405 Fayette Pike, Montgomery, WV, 25136-2436. Tel: 304-442-3230. Fax: 304-442-3091. p. 2565

Rucker, Banny, Head, Ref, South San Francisco Public Library, 840 W Orange Ave, South San Francisco, CA, 94080-3125. Tel: 650-829-3867. Fax: 650-829-3866. p. 270

Rucker, JoAnn, Br Mgr, Timberland Regional Library, South Bend Branch, First & Pacific, South Bend, WA, 98586. Tel: 360-875-5532. Fax: 360-875-6563. p. 2544

Rucker, John, Asst Dir, Coordr, Info Tech, Branch District Library, Ten E Chicago St, Coldwater, MI, 49036-1615. Tel: 517-278-2341, Ext 15. Fax: 517-279-7134. p. 1164

Rucker, Melissa, Cat Librn, University of the Incarnate Word, 4301 Broadway, UPO Box 297, San Antonio, TX, 78209-6397. Tel: 210-829-6097. Fax: 210-829-6041. p. 2384

Rucker, Michael R, Supv Librn, United States Navy, Naval Consolidated Brig Library, Bldg 3107, 1050 Remount Rd, Charleston, SC, 29406-3515. Tel: 843-743-0306, Ext 3059. Fax: 843-743-0339, 843-743-0364. p. 2185

Rucker, Rob, Head, Res & Info Serv, North Carolina State University Libraries, Two Broughton Dr, Raleigh, NC, 27695. Tel: 919-515-7188. Fax: 919-515-3628. p. 1816

Rucker-Shamu, Marian, Assoc Dean, Bowie State University, 14000 Jericho Park Rd, Bowie, MD, 20715. Tel: 301-860-3850. Fax: 301-860-3848. p. 1022

Ruda, Sharon, Assoc Dir, Talking Bks & Braille Serv, Illinois State Library, Gwendolyn Brooks Bldg, 300 S Second St, Springfield, IL, 62701-9713. Tel: 217-782-9435. Fax: 217-785-4326. p. 705

Ruda, Sharon, Assoc Dir, Illinois State Library, Talking Book & Braille Service, Gwendolyn Brooks Bldg, 300 S Second St, Springfield, IL, 62701-1796. Tel: 217-782-9435. Fax: 217-558-4723. p. 705

Rudasill, Tom, Dir, Vespasian Warner Public Library District, 310 N Quincy, Clinton, IL, 61727. Tel: 217-935-5174. Fax: 217-935-4425. p. 630

Rudavsky, Arnona, Sr Assoc Librn for Pub Serv, Hebrew Union College-Jewish Institute of Religion, HUC-JIR, 3101 Clifton Ave, Cincinnati, OH, 45220-2488. Tel: 513-221-1875. Fax: 513-221-0519. p. 1870

Rudd, Kathryn, Acq, Normandale Community College Library, 9700 France Ave S, Bloomington, MN, 55431. Tel: 952-487-8290. Fax: 952-487-8101. p. 1242

Rudd, Lynda, Tech Serv, Alexandria Library, 5005 Duke St, Alexandria, VA, 22304. Tel: 703-746-1764. Fax: 703-746-1747. p. 2444

Rudd, Lynda, Br Mgr, Alexandria Library, Technical Services, 5005 Duke St, Alexandria, VA, 22304-2903. Tel: 703-746-1764. Fax: 703-746-1747. p. 2445

Rudd, Patrick, Coordr, Access Serv, Elon University, 308 N O'Kelly Ave, Elon, NC, 27244-0187. Tel: 336-278-6600. Fax: 336-278-6637. p. 1791

Rudd, Peggy D, Dir, State Librn, Texas State Library & Archives Commission, 1201 Brazos St, Austin, TX, 78701. Tel: 512-463-5460. p. 2282

Rudd, Shawn, Dir, Crescent Community Library, 205 N Grand, Crescent, OK, 73028. Tel: 405-969-3779. Fax: 405-969-3779. p. 1961

Ruddell, Teresa C, Librn, Regional Medical Center, 900 Hospital Dr, Madisonville, KY, 42431-1694. Tel: 270-825-5252. Fax: 270-825-3411. p. 928

Rudder, Leah, Children's Mgr, Laurel County Public Library District, 120 College Park Dr, London, KY, 40741. Tel: 606-864-5759. Fax: 606-862-8057. p. 922

Rudder-Kilkenny, Lorna, Dir, Cent Libr, Queens Borough Public Library, 89-11 Merrick Blvd, Jamaica, NY, 11432. Tel: 718-990-0753. p. 1643

Ruddock, Rebecca, Assoc Dir, Texas Tech University Health Sciences, Delia Montes-Gallo Library of the Health Sciences, 4800 Alberta Ave, El Paso, TX, 79905. Tel: 915-545-6650. Fax: 915-545-6656. p. 2358

Ruddy, Janet, Instrul & Ref Serv Coordr, King's College, 14 W Jackson St, Wilkes-Barre, PA, 18711-0850. Tel: 570-208-5840. Fax: 570-208-6022. p. 2155

Ruddy, Mary, Ref, Jenner & Block Library, 353 N Clark St, Ste 4300, Chicago, IL, 60654. Tel: 312-222-9350. Fax: 312-527-0484. p. 616

Ruddy, Thomas, Circ Supvr, King's College, 14 W Jackson St, Wilkes-Barre, PA, 18711-0850. Tel: 570-208-5840. Fax: 570-208-6022. p. 2155

Rudecoff, Christine, Dir of Libr, State University of New York, PO Box 902, Morrisville, NY, 13408-0902. Tel: 315-684-6055. Fax: 315-684-6115. p. 1663

Rudeen, Marlys, Dep State Librn, Washington State Library, 6880 Capitol Blvd S, Tumwater, WA, 98501-5513. Tel: 360-704-7132. Fax: 360-586-7575. p. 2544

Rudelich, Catherine, Div Mgr, Cumberland County Public Library & Information Center, 300 Maiden Lane, Fayetteville, NC, 28301-5000. Tel: 910-483-7727. Fax: 910-486-5372. p. 1792

Ruder, Clarice, Principal Librn, Tampa-Hillsborough County Public Library System, Jan Kaminis Platt Regional Library, 3910 S Manhattan Ave, Tampa, FL, 33611-1214. Fax: 813-272-6071. p. 498

Ruder, Susan, Dir, Pittsford Public Library, 9268 E Hudson Rd, Pittsford, MI, 49271. Tel: 517-523-2565. Fax: 517-523-2565. p. 1218

Rudi, Marilynn, Archivist, Librn, Canada Department of Fisheries & Oceans, One Challenger Dr, Dartmouth, NS, B2Y 4A2, CANADA. Tel: 902-426-3683. Fax: 902-496-1544. p. 2778

Rudisill, Judi, Head, Info Tech, Orion Township Public Library, 825 Joslyn Rd, Lake Orion, MI, 48362. Tel: 248-693-3000, Ext 322. Fax: 248-693-3009. p. 1199

Rudkin, Pam, Br Mgr, Central Arkansas Library System, Maumelle Branch, Ten Lake Point Dr, Maumelle, AR, 72113-6230. Tel: 501-851-2551. p. 106

Rudmik, Norma, Per, Ser, Brevard Community College, Philip F Nohrr Learning Resource Ctr, 3865 N Wickham Rd, Melbourne, FL, 32935-2399. Tel: 321-433-5575. Fax: 321-433-5619. p. 463

Rudner, Andrea, Med Librn, Richmond University Medical Center, 355 Bard Ave, Staten Island, NY, 10310-1664. Tel: 718-818-3117. Fax: 718-727-2456. p. 1748

Rudnick, Tracey, Librn, University of Connecticut Library, Music & Dramatic Arts Library, 1295 Storrs Rd, Unit 1153, Storrs, CT, 06269-1153. Tel: 860-486-0519, Fax: 860-486-5551. p. 371

Rudnicky, Susan, Coll Develop, Dir, Swan Library, Four N Main St, Albion, NY, 14411. Tel: 585-589-4246. Fax: 585-589-2473. p. 1571

Rudokas, Judy, Dir, Middletown Regional Hospital, 105 McKnight Dr, Middletown, OH, 45044-8787. Tel: 513-420-5164. p. 1918

Rudolf, Kenneth, Dir, University of La Verne, 320 E D St, Ontario, CA, 91764. Tel: 909-460-2065. Fax: 909-460-2083. p. 200

Rudolph, Arwen, Rural Br Supvr, Palliser Regional Library, 366 Coteau St W, Moose Jaw, SK, S6H 5C9, CANADA. Tel: 306-693-3669. Fax: 306-692-5657. p. 2918

Rudolph, Carlethia, Mgr, Georgetown County Library, Waccamaw, 24 Commerce Lane, Pawleys Island, SC, 29585. Tel: 843-545-3623. Fax: 843-545-3624. p. 2195

Rudolph, Cathy, Ref Asst, Lompoc Public Library, 501 E North Ave, Lompoc, CA, 93436-3498. Tel: 805-875-8775. Fax: 805-736-6440. p. 165

Rudolph, Jennifer, Coordr, Pub Serv & Instruction, Massasoit Community College Library, One Massasoit Blvd, Brockton, MA, 02302. Tel: 508-588-9100, Ext 1946. Fax: 508-427-1265. p. 1071

Rudolph, Leah, Dir, Abington Community Library, 1200 W Grove St, Clarks Summit, PA, 18411-9501. Tel: 570-587-3440. p. 2045

Rudolph, Marilyn, Librn, Worcester Public Library, Great Brook Valley, 89 Tacoma St, Worcester, MA, 01605-3518. Tel: 508-799-1729. p. 1145

Rudolph, Roy, Libr Dir, Longy School of Music, One Follen St, Cambridge, MA, 02138. Tel: 617-876-0956, Ext 540. Fax: 617-354-8841. p. 1077

Rudowsky, Catherine, Bus Serv, Soc Sci Librn, Slippery Rock University of Pennsylvania, Slippery Rock, PA, 16057-9989. Tel: 724-738-2657. Fax: 724-738-2661. p. 2140

Rudshteyn, Alex, Network Serv, Brooklyn College Library, 2900 Bedford Ave, Brooklyn, NY, 11210-2889. Tel: 718-951-5336. Fax: 718-951-4540. p. 1589

Rudy, Clint, Syst Adminr, Portsmouth Public Library, Churchland, 4934 High St W, Portsmouth, VA, 23703. Tel: 757-686-2538. p. 2485

Rudy, Joel, III, Ref & Instrul Serv Librn, Virginia Highlands Community College Library, 100 VHCC Dr, Abingdon, VA, 24210. Tel: 276-739-2542. Fax: 276-739-2593. p. 2443

Rudy, Lana, Librn, Rochester General Hospital, 1425 Portland Ave, Rochester, NY, 14621. Tel: 585-922-4743. Fax: 585-544-1504. p. 1731

Rudzevicius, Diane, Dir, Industry Canada, 235 Queen St, Ottawa, ON, K1A 0H5, CANADA. Tel: 613-954-2728. Fax: 613-954-0548. p. 2831

Rudzinski, Diana, Asst Dir, Burlington Public Library, 34 Library Lane, Burlington, CT, 06013. Tel: 860-673-3331. Fax: 860-673-0897. p. 333

Rue, Charlene, Dir, Coll Develop, Brooklyn Public Library, Grand Army Plaza, Brooklyn, NY, 11238-5698. Tel: 718-230-2102. Fax: 718-230-2097. p. 1590

Rueckert, Michelle, In Charge, Wisconsin Center for the Blind & Visually Impaired, 1700 W State St, Janesville, WI, 53546. Tel: 608-758-6118. Fax: 608-758-6161. p. 2600

Ruef, Sally, Ref, Welles-Turner Memorial Library, 2407 Main St, Glastonbury, CT, 06033. Tel: 860-652-7719. Fax: 860-652-7721. p. 341

Rueff, Mary, Dir, Pub & Tech Serv, Hussey-Mayfield Memorial Public Library, 250 N Fifth St, Zionsville, IN, 46077-1324. Tel: 317-873-3149, Ext 13002. Fax: 317-873-8339. p. 789

Rueger, Jackie, Acq Mgr, Marion County Public Library, 321 Monroe St, Fairmont, WV, 26554-2952. Tel: 304-366-1210. Fax: 304-366-4831. p. 2559

Ruegg, Lillie, MLIS Ref, Info Literacy Librn, Greenville Technical College Library, 620 S Pleasantburg Dr, Greenville, SC, 29607. Tel: 864-250-8319. Fax: 864-250-8506. p. 2197

Ruelle, Joan, Dean & Univ Librn, Elon University, 308 N O'Kelly Ave, Elon, NC, 27244-0187. Tel: 336-278-6572. Fax: 336-278-6637. p. 1791

Ruess, Diane, Outreach Serv Librn, University of Alaska Fairbanks, 310 Tanana Dr, Fairbanks, AK, 99775. Tel: 907-474-6349. Fax: 907-474-6841. p. 48

Ruf, Walter, Dir, Libr Serv, Argosy University, 1550 Wilson Blvd, Ste 600, Arlington, VA, 22209. Fax: 703-243-5682. p. 2448

Rufe, Laurie, Dir, Roswell Museum & Art Center Library, 100 W 11th St, Roswell, NM, 88201. Tel: 575-624-6744, Ext 25. Fax: 575-624-6765. p. 1561

Rufe, Mary, Librn, American Public Power Association Library, 2301 M St NW, Washington, DC, 20037-1484. Tel: 202-467-2957. Fax: 202-467-2910. p. 392

Ruff, Collette, Dir, Oglala Lakota College, Pass Creek College Center, PO Box 630, Allen, SD, 57714. Tel: 605-455-2757. Fax: 605-455-2428. p. 2214

Ruff, David C, Exec Dir, Rolling Meadows Library, 3110 Martin Lane, Rolling Meadows, IL, 60008. Tel: 847-259-6050. Fax: 847-259-5319. p. 698

Ruff, June, Dir, Brownell Public Library, PO Box 135, Brownell, KS, 67521-0135. Tel: 785-481-2345. p. 858

Ruff, Rosalie, Head, Info Serv, Hammond Public Library, 564 State St, Hammond, IN, 46320-1532. Tel: 219-931-5100, Ext 327. Fax: 219-931-3474. p. 747

Ruff, Ruth, Asst Dir, Upper Peninsula Library for the Blind & Physically Handicapped, 1615 Presque Isle Ave, Marquette, MI, 49855. Tel: 906-228-7697. Fax: 906-228-5627. p. 1207

Ruffcorn, Katie, Commun Libr Supvr, Yakima Valley Libraries, Terrace Heights Library, 4011 Commonwealth Dr, Yakima, WA, 98901. Tel: 509-457-5319. Fax: 509-457-5319. p. 2551

Ruffin, Angela, Dir, National Network of Libraries of Medicine, Nat Libr of Med, 8600 Rockville Pike, Rm B1E03, Bethesda, MD, 20894. Tel: 301-496-4777. Fax: 301-480-1467. p. 2944

Ruffin, Cynthia, Asst Librn, Pub Serv, North Carolina Central University, School of Law Library, 1512 S Alston Ave, Durham, NC, 27707. Tel: 919-530-6333. Fax: 919-530-7926. p. 1789

Rufty, Sandra, Libr Assoc, Northwestern State University Libraries, 1800 Line Ave, Shreveport, LA, 71101. Tel: 318-677-3007. Fax: 318-676-7087. p. 968

Ruggeri, Barbara, Clinical Serv Librn, Medical College of Wisconsin Libraries, Children's Hospital of Wisconsin Library, 9000 W Wisconsin Ave, Milwaukee, WI, 53226. Tel: 414-266-2340. p. 2619

Ruggeri, Cindy, Br Mgr, Fort Bend County Libraries, Sugar Land Branch, 550 Eldridge Rd, Sugar Land, TX, 77478. Tel: 281-277-8943. Fax: 281-277-8945. p. 2375

Ruggeri, Kathleen, Head, Tech Serv, Bedford Free Public Library, Seven Mudge Way, Bedford, MA, 01730-2168. Tel: 781-275-9440. Fax: 781-275-3590. p. 1052

Ruggeri, Patricia M, Tech Coordr, Manlius Library, One Arkie Albanese Ave, Manlius, NY, 13104. Tel: 315-682-6400. Fax: 315-682-4490. p. 1657

Ruggeri, Sylvia, Ref & Instruction Librn, Pennsylvania State University Libraries, William & Joan Schreyer Business Library, 301 Paterno Library, University Park, PA, 16802-1810. Tel: 814-867-3717. Fax: 814-863-6370. p. 2148

Ruggieri, Melanie, Electronic Res, Lincoln Public Library, 145 Old River Rd, Lincoln, RI, 02865. Tel: 401-333-2422. Fax: 401-333-4154. p. 2168

Ruggles, Tim, Cat, Dalhousie University, W K Kellogg Health Sciences Library, Tupper Medical Bldg, 5850 College St, Halifax, NS, B3H 1X5, CANADA. p. 2780

Ruhl, Taylor, Dean, Imperial Valley College, 380 E Ira Aten Rd, Imperial, CA, 92251. Tel: 760-355-6378. Fax: 760-355-1090. p. 159

Ruhland, Liz, Commun Libr Mgr, Contra Costa County Library, El Cerrito Library, 6510 Stockton Ave, El Cerrito, CA, 94530-3189. Tel: 510-526-7512. Fax: 510-526-6375. p. 209

Ruhnke, Charm N, Libr Dir, Peru Public Library, 1409 11th St, Peru, IL, 61354. Tel: 815-223-0229. Fax: 815-223-1559. p. 691

Ruhs, Anna, YA Librn, Starkville-Oktibbeha County Public Library System, 326 University Dr, Starkville, MS, 39759. Tel: 662-323-2766, 662-323-2783. Fax: 662-323-9140. p. 1315

Ruiz, Deborah, Pub Serv Librn, Monterey Peninsula College Library, 980 Fremont Blvd, Monterey, CA, 93940-4704. Tel: 831-646-3097. Fax: 831-645-1308. p. 190

Ruiz, John Martin, Fr, Librn, Dominican Theological Library, 487 Michigan Ave NE, Washington, DC, 20017-1585. Tel: 202-495-3821. Fax: 202-495-3873. p. 399

Ruiz, Leticia, Circ, El Progreso Memorial Library, 301 W Main St, Uvalde, TX, 78801. Tel: 830-278-2017. Fax: 830-278-4940. p. 2394

Ruiz, Lynn, Circ, North Palm Beach Public Library, 303 Anchorage Dr, North Palm Beach, FL, 33408. Tel: 561-841-3383. Fax: 561-848-2874. p. 473

Ruiz, Miriam, Coordr, ILL, Miami Children's Hospital Medical Library, 3100 SW 62nd Ave, Miami, FL, 33155-3009. Tel: 305-666-6511, Ext 4470. Fax: 305-284-1145. p. 466

Ruiz, Sara, Coordr, Pub Serv Librn III, University of Puerto Rico, Alfonso Valdes Ave, No 259 N, Mayaguez, PR, 00681. Tel: 787-265-3810, 787-832-4040. Fax: 787-265-5483. p. 2674

Ruiz-Hearne, Norma Jean, Dir, Edwards Public Library, 210 W Gilbert St, Henrietta, TX, 76365-2816. Tel: 940-538-4791. Fax: 940-538-5861. p. 2332

Rule, Judy K, Dir, Cabell County Public Library, 455 Ninth Street Plaza, Huntington, WV, 25701. Tel: 304-528-5700. Fax: 304-528-5701. p. 2561

Rule, Margaret, Sr VPres & Chief Financial Officer, Ontario Library Consortium, Owen Sound & North Grey Union Public Library, 824 First Ave W, Owen Sound, ON, N4K 4K4, CANADA. p. 2960

Ruleman, Alice, Asst Librn, Crichton College, 255 N Highland St, Memphis, TN, 38111. Tel: 901-320-9770. Fax: 901-320-9785. p. 2248

Ruley, Karyn, Tech Support, Crawford County Library System, 201 Plum St, Grayling, MI, 49738. Tel: 989-348-9214. Fax: 989-348-9294. p. 1186

Rulli, Donna-Lee, Head Librn, State Education Resource Center Library, 25 Industrial Park Rd, Middletown, CT, 06457-1516. Tel: 860-632-1485, Ext 219. Fax: 860-632-0438. p. 352

Rumball, Heather, Dir of Develop, Pres, Toronto Pub Libr Found, Toronto Public Library, 789 Yonge St, Toronto, ON, M4W 2G8, CANADA. Tel: 416-393-7131. Fax: 416-393-7229. p. 2860

Rumbaugh, Christopher, Adult Serv Mgr, Salem Public Library, 585 Liberty St SE, Salem, OR, 97301. Tel: 503-588-6449. Fax: 503-588-6055. p. 2018

Rumery, Beth, Librn, University of Connecticut at Avery Point Library, 1084 Shennecossett Rd, Groton, CT, 06340-6097. Tel: 860-405-9148. Fax: 860-405-9150. p. 342

Rumery, Beth, Info Serv, Lyme Academy College of Fine Arts, 84 Lyme St, Old Lyme, CT, 06371-2333. Tel: 860-434-5232, Ext 130. Fax: 860-434-2095. p. 363

Rumery, Joyce, Dean of Libr, University of Maine, 5729 Fogler Library, Orono, ME, 04469-5729. Fax: 207-581-1653. p. 994

Rumery, Nancy, Dir, Haskell Free Library, Inc, 93 Caswell Ave, Derby Line, VT, 05830. Tel: 802-873-3022. Fax: 802-873-3022. p. 2423

Ruminson, Kevin, Act Asst Univ Librn, Admin Serv, University of California Library, PO Box 19557, Irvine, CA, 92623-9557. Tel: 949-824-4440. p. 160

Rumler, Mary, Acq, Ser, Library of Michigan, 702 W Kalamazoo St, Lansing, MI, 48915. Tel: 517-373-1580. Fax: 517-373-8936. p. 1201

Rummer, Bob, Project Leader, United States Forest Service, George W Andrews Forestry Sciences Lab, 521 Devall Dr, Auburn, AL, 36849-5418. Tel: 334-826-8700. Fax: 334-821-0037. p. 6

Rumph, Virginia, Ser, Butler University Libraries, 4600 Sunset Ave, Indianapolis, IN, 46208. Tel: 317-940-6491. Fax: 317-940-9711. p. 749

Rumrill, Alan, Dir, Historical Society of Cheshire County, 246 Main St, Keene, NH, 03431. Tel: 603-352-1895. Fax: 603-352-9226. p. 1452

Rumschlag, Denise H, Mgr, Libr Serv, St Vincent Hospital & Health Services, 2001 W 86th St, Indianapolis, IN, 46260. Tel: 317-338-3757. Fax: 317-338-6516. p. 755

Rumsey, Carla, Dir, Vermontville Township Library, 120 E First St, Vermontville, MI, 49096. Tel: 517-726-1362. Fax: 517-726-1362. p. 1233

Rundall, Becky, Libr Tech, Saint Francis Medical Center College of Nursing, 511 NE Greenleaf St, Peoria, IL, 61603. Tel: 309-655-2180. Fax: 309-655-3648. p. 690

Rundel, Judi, Br Mgr, Collins LeRoy Leon County Public Library System, Parkway, Cross Creek Sq, 1210 Capital Circle SE, Tallahassee, FL, 32301. Tel: 850-606-2750. Fax: 850-606-2751. p. 492

Rundell, Sherry, Cat, John & Mable Ringling Museum of Art Library, 5401 Bayshore Rd, Sarasota, FL, 34243. Tel: 941-359-5700, Ext 2701. Fax: 941-360-7370. p. 490

Rundgren, Jean, Asst Librn, Waterboro Public Library, 187 Main St, East Waterboro, ME, 04030. Tel: 207-247-3363. Fax: 207-247-3363. p. 984

Rundquist, Christy, Dir, Pepin Public Library, 510 Second St, Pepin, WI, 54759. Tel: 715-442-4932. p. 2629

Rundquist, Jenny, Tech Support Analyst, Frances L Simek Memorial Library-Medford, 400 N Main, Medford, WI, 54451. Tel: 715-748-2505. Fax: 715-748-4160. p. 2614

Runge, Donna, Dir, Wessington Public Library, 240 Wessington St, Wessington, SD, 57381. Tel: 605-458-2596. p. 2222

Runge, Franklin, Fac Serv Librn, University of Kentucky Libraries, Law Library, 620 S Limestone St, Lexington, KY, 40506-0048. Tel: 859-257-1081. Fax: 859-323-4906. p. 922

Runge, Lavone, Br Coordr, Marathon County Public Library, Marathon City Branch, 515 Washington St, Marathon, WI, 54448. Tel: 715-443-2775. Fax: 715-443-2775. p. 2646

Rungren, Lawrence, Exec Dir, Merrimack Valley Library Consortium, 1600 Osgood St, North Andover, MA, 01845. Tel: 978-557-5409. Fax: 978-557-8101. p. 2945

Runion, Susan, Asst Dir, Mohawk Community Library, 200 S Sycamore Ave, Sycamore, OH, 44882. Tel: 419-927-2407. Fax: 419-927-2958. p. 1937

Runion-Slear, Ruth, ILL, Pennsylvania State University-Harrisburg Library, 351 Olmsted Dr, Middletown, PA, 17057-4850. Tel: 717-948-6070. Fax: 717-948-6757. p. 2089

Runis, Alice, Tech Serv, Iliff School of Theology, 2201 S University Blvd, Denver, CO, 80210. Tel: 303-765-3173. Fax: 303-777-0164. p. 302

Runnells, Frances, Head, Ch, Head, Youth Serv, Brandon Township Public Library, 304 South St, Ortonville, MI, 48462. Tel: 248-627-1473. Fax: 248-627-9880. p. 1215

Runnells, Rory, Coordr, Manitoba Association of Playwrights Library, 100 Arthur St, Ste 503, Winnipeg, MB, R3B 1H3, CANADA. Tel: 204-942-8941. Fax: 204-942-1555. p. 2756

Runnels, Cindy, Dir, Kaiser-Permanente Medical Center, 9400 E Rosecrans Ave, Bellflower, CA, 90706. Tel: 562-461-4247. Fax: 562-461-4948. p. 125

Runnels, Marquenez, Circ Supvr, DeSoto Public Library, 211 E Pleasant Run Rd, Ste C, DeSoto, TX, 75115-3939. Tel: 972-230-9656. Fax: 972-230-5797. p. 2313

Running Hawk, Sharon, Asst Dir, Oglala Lakota College, Three Mile Creek Rd, Kyle, SD, 57752. Tel: 605-455-6069. Fax: 605-455-6070. p. 2213

Runowski, Cris, Learning Res Ctr Asst, Holy Family University Library, 9801 Frankford Ave, Philadelphia, PA, 19114. Tel: 267-341-3315, 267-341-3316. Fax: 215-632-8067. p. 2111

Runyan, Donna, Librn, Bethesda United Methodist Church Library, 8300 Old Georgetown Rd, Bethesda, MD, 20814. Tel: 301-652-2990. Fax: 301-652-1965. p. 1021

Runyan, Linda, Mgr, Carbon County Library System, Elk Mountain Branch, 105 Bridge St, Elk Mountain, WY, 82324. Tel: 307-348-7421. Fax: 307-348-7421. p. 2659

Runyan, Linda, Mgr, Carbon County Library System, Hanna Branch, 303 Third St, Hanna, WY, 82327. Tel: 307-325-9357. Fax: 307-325-9357. p. 2659

Runyan, Theresa, Br Mgr, Jackson District Library, Summit, 104 Bird Ave, Jackson, MI, 49203. Tel: 517-783-4030. Fax: 517-783-1788. p. 1196

Runyon, Bev, Dir, Stockport Public Library, 113 E Beswick St, Stockport, IA, 52651. Tel: 319-796-4681. Fax: 319-796-4681. p. 846

Runyon, David, Univ Librn, Harrisburg University of Science & Technology, 326 Market St, Harrisburg, PA, 17101. Tel: 717-901-5188. p. 2065

Runyon, Joanna, Libr Dir, Smith Center Public Library, 117 W Court St, Smith Center, KS, 66967-2601. Tel: 785-282-3361. Fax: 785-282-6740. p. 894

Ruoff, Sandra, Dir, Guilford Free Library, 67 Park St, Guilford, CT, 06437. Tel: 203-453-8282. Fax: 203-453-8288. p. 342

Rupa, M, Pub Serv, International North American Library, 90 Nolan Ct, No 21, Markham, ON, L3R 4L9, CANADA. Tel: 905-946-9588. Fax: 905-946-9590. p. 2820

Rupe, Roxanne, Br Mgr, Nelsonville Public Library, Coolville Public, 26401 Main St, Coolville, OH, 45723-9059. Tel: 740-667-3354. Fax: 740-667-3354. p. 1920

Rupel, Rosalinda, Tech Serv, Clifford Chance LLP Library, 31 W 52nd St, New York, NY, 10019. Tel: 212-878-3238. Fax: 212-878-3474. p. 1673

Rupert, Elizabeth, Ch, Manatee County Public Library System, 1301 Barcarrota Blvd W, Bradenton, FL, 34205. Tel: 941-748-5555. Fax: 941-749-7191. p. 429

Rupkalvis, Cari, Dir, Tarpon Springs Public Library, 138 E Lemon St, Tarpon Springs, FL, 34689. Tel: 727-943-4922. Fax: 727-943-4926. p. 499

Rupp, Jackie, Asst Librn, Belle Plaine Community Library, 904 12th St, Belle Plaine, IA, 52208-1711. Tel: 319-444-2902. Fax: 319-444-2902. p. 796

Rupp-Serrano, Karen, Coll Develop, University of Oklahoma, 401 W Brooks, Norman, OK, 73019. Tel: 405-325-9142. Fax: 405-325-7550. p. 1971

Rupp-Serrano, Karen, Dir, Coll Develop & Scholarly Communication, University of Oklahoma, 401 W Brooks, Norman, OK, 73019. Tel: 405-325-2611. Fax: 405-325-7550. p. 1971

Ruppel, Katherine, Learning Res Ctr Coordr, Holy Family University Library, 9801 Frankford Ave, Philadelphia, PA, 19114. Tel: 267-341-4010. Fax: 215-504-2050. p. 2111

Ruppert, Mary Jo, Dir, Cherokee Public Library, 215 S Second St, Cherokee, IA, 51012. Tel: 712-225-3498. Fax: 712-225-4964. p. 801

Rusch, Chris, Librn, Tiller Community Library, 27812 Tiller Trail Hwy, Tiller, OR, 97484. Tel: 541-825-3837. p. 2021

Rusch, Evan, Govt Doc, Minnesota State University, Mankato, ML3097, Mankato, MN, 56001. Tel: 507-389-5952. Fax: 507-389-5155. p. 1257

Rusch, Stacy, Conservator, Virginia Historical Society Library, 428 North Blvd, Richmond, VA, 23220. Tel: 804-358-4901. Fax: 804-355-2399. p. 2492

Ruschak, Iren, Tech Serv, New Brunswick Free Public Library, 60 Livingston Ave, New Brunswick, NJ, 08901-2597. Tel: 732-745-5108. Fax: 732-846-0226. p. 1508

Ruschau, Marjorie, Cataloger, Essex Library Association, Inc, 33 West Ave, Essex, CT, 06426-1196. Tel: 860-767-1560. Fax: 860-767-2500. p. 338

Rush, Abigail, Coordr, Electronic Serv & Syst, Presbyterian College, 211 E Maple St, Clinton, SC, 29325. Tel: 864-833-7026. Fax: 864-833-8315. p. 2186

Rush, John, Dir, Emmaus Bible College Library, 2570 Asbury Rd, Dubuque, IA, 52001-3096. Tel: 563-588-8000, Ext 1003. Fax: 563-588-1216. p. 811

Rush, Katherine, Circ & Tech Serv Coordr, Northfield Public Library, 210 Washington St, Northfield, MN, 55057. Tel: 507-645-1800. Fax: 507-645-1820. p. 1269

Rush, Kathy, Tech Serv Mgr, Carson City Library, 900 N Roop St, Carson City, NV, 89701. Tel: 775-887-2244. Fax: 775-887-2273. p. 1425

Rush, Leslie, Automation Serv, Montgomery County-Norristown Public Library, 1001 Powell St, Norristown, PA, 19401-3817. Tel: 610-278-5100, Ext 125. p. 2098

Rush, Martha, Access Serv, College of William & Mary in Virginia, The Wolf Law Library, 613 S Henry St, Williamsburg, VA, 23187. Tel: 757-221-3255. Fax: 757-221-3051. p. 2502

Rush, Pamela K, Asst Librn, Somerset Community College Library, Harold B Strunk Learning Resource Ctr, 808 Monticello St, Somerset, KY, 42501. Tel: 606-451-6715. Fax: 606-679-5139. p. 935

Rusheen, Patricia, Dir, Libr Serv, Seltzer, Caplan, McMahon, Vitek, 750 B St, Ste 2100, San Diego, CA, 92101. Tel: 619-685-3009. Fax: 619-615-0315. p. 238

Rushford, Nicole, Librn, Wyoming Public Library, 109 Main St, Wyoming, IA, 52362. Tel: 563-488-3975. Fax: 563-488-3975. p. 854

Rushing, Dale, Br Mgr, Madera County Library, Oakhurst Branch, 49044 Civic Circle, Oakhurst, CA, 93644-0484. Tel: 559-683-4838. Fax: 559-642-4591. p. 182

Rushing, Jenny, Coordr of Ref Serv, Belmont University, 1900 Belmont Blvd, Nashville, TN, 37212-3757. Tel: 615-460-6782. Fax: 615-460-5641. p. 2255

Rushing, Mark, Dir, Sampson Community College Library, 1801 Sunset Ave, Hwy 24 W, Clinton, NC, 28328. Tel: 910-592-8081, Ext 5002. Fax: 910-592-8048. p. 1785

Rushing, Mary, Ch, Fleming County Public Library, 202 Bypass Blvd, Flemingsburg, KY, 41041-7934. Tel: 606-845-7851. Fax: 606-845-7045. p. 912

Rushing, Trina, Acq Librn, Henderson County Public Library, 301 N Washington St, Hendersonville, NC, 28739. Tel: 828-697-4725. Fax: 828-692-8449, 828-697-4700. p. 1801

Rushton, Christine, Tech Serv, Springfield Township Library, 70 Powell Rd, Springfield, PA, 19064-2446. Tel: 610-543-2113. Fax: 610-543-1356. p. 2142

Rusiewski, Charles, Librn, Kaskaskia College Library, 27210 College Rd, Centralia, IL, 62801. Tel: 618-545-3130. Fax: 618-532-9241. p. 602

Rusin, Deborah, Ref Serv, Latham & Watkins, Sears Tower, 233 S Wacker Dr, Ste 5800, Chicago, IL, 60606. Tel: 312-876-7700. Fax: 312-993-9767. p. 616

Rusin, Deborah L, Dir, Libr & Res Serv, Katten, Muchin, Rosenman LLP Library, 525 W Monroe St, Ste 1900, Chicago, IL, 60661-3693. Tel: 312-902-5675. p. 616

Rusin, Nancy, Librn, Detroit Health Department Library, 1151 Taylor St, Rm 243-B, Detroit, MI, 48202. Tel: 313-876-4096. Fax: 313-871-9437. p. 1169

Rusinak, Maryanne, Ch, Concordia University, 7400 Augusta St, River Forest, IL, 60305-1499. Tel: 708-209-3587. Fax: 708-209-3175. p. 694

Rusk, Carol, Benjamin & Irma Weiss Librn, Whitney Museum of American Art, 945 Madison Ave, New York, NY, 10021. Tel: 215-570-3649. p. 1702

Rusk, Cherie, Br Mgr, Timberland Regional Library, Salkum Branch, 2480 US Hwy 12, Salkum, WA, 98582. Tel: 360-985-2148. Fax: 360-985-7704. p. 2544

Rusk, Donna, Tech Serv, Converse County Library, 300 Walnut St, Douglas, WY, 82633. Tel: 307-358-3644. Fax: 307-358-6743. p. 2654

Rusk, Judi, Dir, Libr Serv, Winters Public Library, 120 N Main, Winters, TX, 79567. Tel: 325-754-4251. p. 2401

Rusk, Michael David, Dean, Tulsa Community College Learning Resources Center, Metro Campus, 909 S Boston Ave, Tulsa, OK, 74119-2011. Tel: 918-595-7728. Fax: 918-595-7179. p. 1983

Ruskin, Suzy, Dir, Green Tree Public Library, Ten W Manilla Ave, 1st Flr, Pittsburgh, PA, 15220-3310. Tel: 412-921-9292. Fax: 412-921-4004. p. 2125

Rusnak, Gloria, Circ, Fanwood Memorial Library, 14 Tillotson Rd, Fanwood, NJ, 07023-1399. Tel: 908-322-6400. Fax: 908-322-5590. p. 1485

Rusnak, Helen, Cluster Coordr, Hartford Public Library, Goodwin Branch, 460 New Britain Ave, Hartford, CT, 06106. Tel: 860-695-7480. Fax: 860-722-6887. p. 346

Russ, Cathy, Dir, Troy Public Library, 510 W Big Beaver Rd, Troy, MI, 48084-5289. Tel: 248-524-3538. Fax: 248-524-0112. p. 1232

Russ, Jodi, Commun Librn, Monroe County Library System, Bedford Branch Library, 8575 Jackman Rd, Temperance, MI, 48182. Tel: 734-847-6747. Fax: 734-847-6591. p. 1210

Russ, Karen, Doc Librn, Ref, University of Arkansas at Little Rock, 2801 S University Ave, Little Rock, AR, 72204. Tel: 501-569-8444. Fax: 501-569-3017. p. 107

Russ, Ronald S, Instrul & Electronic Res Librn, Arkansas State University, Palm & Iowa Sts, Beebe, AR, 72012. Tel: 501-882-8959. Fax: 501-882-8833. p. 94

Russel, Donald, Dir, Providence College, One Cunningham Sq, Providence, RI, 02918-0001. Tel: 401-865-1188. Fax: 401-865-2823. p. 2173

Russell, Alfreda, Sr Law Librn, Northeastern University School of Law Library, 400 Huntington Ave, Boston, MA, 02115. Tel: 617-373-3589. Fax: 617-373-8705. p. 1066

Russell, Allison, Librn, Oregon Public Library, 103 S Washington St, Oregon, MO, 64473. Tel: 660-446-3586. Fax: 660-446-3586. p. 1348

Russell, Ann, Tech Librn, Gardiner Public Library, 152 Water St, Gardiner, ME, 04345. Tel: 207-582-3312. Fax: 207-582-6104. p. 986

Russell, Ann, Sr Dir, Michener Institute for Applied Health Sciences Library, 222 Saint Patrick St, 2nd Flr, Toronto, ON, M5T 1V4, CANADA. Tel: 416-596-3123. Fax: 416-596-3137. p. 2855

Russell, Arthur James, III, Libr Tech, VA Puget Sound Health Care System, American Lake Div, 9600 Veterans Dr SW, Bldg 71, Tacoma, WA, 98493-5000. Tel: 253-583-1513. Fax: 253-589-4029. p. 2541

Russell, Barbara, Br Mgr, Washington County Library, 1444 Jackson Ave, Chipley, FL, 32428. Tel: 850-638-1314. Fax: 850-638-9499. p. 431

Russell, Barbara, Dir, Portland Public Library, 301 Portland Blvd, Portland, TN, 37148-1229. Tel: 615-325-2279. Fax: 615-325-7061. p. 2263

Russell, Becky, Sr Librn, Denver Public Library, Hampden, 9755 E Girard Ave, Denver, CO, 80231-5003. Tel: 303-750-3885. Fax: 303-751-4878. p. 301

Russell, Brenda C, Dir, TLL Temple Memorial Library, 300 Park St, Diboll, TX, 75941. Tel: 936-829-5497. Fax: 936-829-5465. p. 2313

Russell, Cara, Dir, Dripping Springs Community Library, 501 Sportsplex Dr, Dripping Springs, TX, 78620. Tel: 512-858-7825. Fax: 512-858-2639. p. 2314

Russell, Carolyn, Asst Dir, Laurel-Jones County Library System, Inc, 530 Commerce St, Laurel, MS, 39440. Tel: 601-428-4313. Fax: 601-428-0597. p. 1306

Russell, Celisa, Br Mgr, Dixie Regional Library System, Sherman Public, 20 W Lamar St, Sherman, MS, 38869. Tel: 662-840-2513. Fax: 662-840-2513. p. 1312

Russell, Cheryl, Br Mgr, Eagle Valley Library District, 600 Broadway, Eagle, CO, 81631. Tel: 970-328-8800. Fax: 970-328-6901. p. 305

Russell, Chris, Tech Asst, Mountain Area Health Education Center, 121 Hendersonville Rd, Asheville, NC, 28803. Tel: 828-257-4445. Fax: 828-257-4712. p. 1775

Russell, Chriss, Circ, Marion County Public Library, 321 Monroe St, Fairmont, WV, 26554-2952. Tel: 304-366-1210. Fax: 304-366-4831. p. 2559

Russell, Christina, Asst Librn, Lyons Township District Library, 309 Bridge St, Lyons, MI, 48851. Tel: 989-855-3414. Fax: 989-855-2069. p. 1204

Russell, Christine, Dir, Louisiana State University Libraries, LSU School of Veterinary Medicine Library, Skip Bertman Dr, Baton Rouge, LA, 70803-8414. Tel: 225-578-9800. Fax: 225-578-9798. p. 944

Russell, Clara, Libr Dir, Fort Bend County Libraries, 1001 Golfview Dr, Richmond, TX, 77469-5199. Tel: 281-341-2618. Fax: 281-341-2688. p. 2374

Russell, Claudette, Children & Youth Serv Librn, Chesterfield Public Library, 524 Rte 63, Chesterfield, NH, 03443-0158. Tel: 603-363-4621. Fax: 603-363-4958. p. 1441

Russell, Cora, Supvr, Acq, California University of Pennsylvania, 250 University Ave, California, PA, 15419-1394. Tel: 724-938-5702. Fax: 724-938-5901. p. 2040

Russell, Dana, Head, Youth Serv, New Lenox Public Library District, 120 Veterans Pkwy, New Lenox, IL, 60451. Tel: 815-485-2605. Fax: 815-485-2548. p. 680

Russell, Deborah, Info Serv, Kentucky Wesleyan College, 3000 Frederica St, Owensboro, KY, 42301. Tel: 270-852-3259. Fax: 270-926-3196. p. 931

Russell, Dianne, Librn, The Evangelical & Reformed Historical Society, 555 W James St, Lancaster, PA, 17603. Tel: 717-290-8711. Fax: 717-735-8157. p. 2076

Russell, Donna, Circ Supvr, Citrus County Library System, Coastal Region, 8619 W Crystal St, Crystal River, FL, 34428-4468. Tel: 352-795-3716. Fax: 352-795-3103. p. 427

Russell, Dorothy, Ref, Emmaus Public Library, 11 E Main St, Emmaus, PA, 18049. Tel: 610-965-9284. Fax: 610-965-6446. p. 2054

Russell, Elinor, Dir, Libr & Info Serv, Dow, Lohnes PLLC, 1200 New Hampshire NW, Ste 800, Washington, DC, 20036-6802. Tel: 202-776-2653. Fax: 202-776-2222. p. 399

Russell, Elizabeth, Archivist, Michigan Technological University, 1400 Townsend Dr, Houghton, MI, 49931-1295. Tel: 906-487-2505. p. 1191

Russell, Elizabeth, Med Librn, Regional Mental Health Care London, 850 Highbury Ave N, London, ON, N6A 4H1, CANADA. Tel: 519-455-5110, Ext 49685. Fax: 519-455-3620. p. 2818

Russell, Elizabeth, Librn, Regional Mental Health Care St Thomas, 467 Sunset Dr, St. Thomas, ON, N5P 3V9, CANADA. Tel: 519-631-8510, Ext 49685. Fax: 519-631-9691. p. 2844

Russell, Elizabeth, Med Librn, Regional Mental Health Care Saint Thomas, Patient Library, 467 Sunset Dr, St. Thomas, ON, N5P 3V9, CANADA. Tel: 519-631-8510, Ext 49685. Fax: 519-631-9691. p. 2844

Russell, Elizabeth, Pres, Southwestern Ontario Health Libraries & Information Network, St Joseph's Health Care London - Regional Mental Health Staff Libraries, 467 Sunset Dr, St. Thomas, ON, N5P 3V9, CANADA. Tel: 519-631-8510, Ext 49685. p. 2960

Russell, Gail, Br Mgr, Spencer County Public Library, Marylee Vogel Branch, PO Box 155, Richland, IN, 47634-0155. Tel: 812-359-4146. Fax: 812-359-4223. p. 776

Russell, Hilary, Libr Mgr, Fraser Valley Regional Library, Clearbrook Library, 32320 George Ferguson Way, Abbotsford, BC, V2T 6N4, CANADA. Tel: 604-859-7814. Fax: 604-859-7329. p. 2723

Russell, Hillary, Libr Mgr, Fraser Valley Regional Library, Mount Lehman Library, 5875 Mount Lehman Rd, Abbotsford, BC, V4X 1VS, CANADA. Tel: 604-856-4988. Fax: 604-856-4908. p. 2724

Russell, Hillary, Libr Mgr, Fraser Valley Regional Library, MSA Centennial Library, 33660 S Fraser Way, Abbotsford, BC, V2S 2B9, CANADA. Tel: 604-853-1753. Fax: 604-853-7861. p. 2724

Russell, Janet, Cat Librn, Boston University Libraries, School of Theology Library, 745 Commonwealth Ave, 2nd Flr, Boston, MA, 02215. Tel: 617-353-1353. Fax: 617-358-0699. p. 1058

Russell, Janice, Asst Librn, Niagara Health System, 142 Queenston St, St. Catharines, ON, L2R 7C6, CANADA. Tel: 905-378-4647, Ext 44354. Fax: 905-704-4767. p. 2843

Russell, Jennifer, Asst Dir, Southeast Steuben County Library, 300 Civic Center Plaza, Ste 101, Corning, NY, 14830. Tel: 607-936-3713, Ext 208. Fax: 607-936-1714. p. 1611

Russell, Jennifer, Teen & Adult Librn, Rose Memorial Library, 79 E Main St, Stony Point, NY, 10980-1699. Tel: 845-786-2100. Fax: 845-786-6042. p. 1750

Russell, Joann, In Charge, Newfoundland & Labrador Teachers' Association Library, Three Kenmount Rd, St. John's, NL, A1B 1W1, CANADA. Tel: 709-726-3223. Fax: 709-726-4302. p. 2773

Russell, John, Ref/Archives (Info Serv), Johnson County Community College, 12345 College Blvd, Box 21, Overland Park, KS, 66210. Tel: 913-469-8500, Ext 3284. Fax: 913-469-3816. p. 888

Russell, Judith C, Dean, Univ Libr, University of Florida Libraries, 535 Library W, Gainesville, FL, 32611-7000. Tel: 352-273-2505. Fax: 352-392-7251. p. 449

Russell, Julia, Reader Serv, YA Serv, High Point Public Library, 901 N Main St, High Point, NC, 27262. Tel: 336-883-3073. Fax: 336-883-3636. p. 1802

Russell, Julie, Asst Dir, Southwest Harbor Public Library, 338 Main St, Southwest Harbor, ME, 04679. Tel: 207-244-7065. Fax: 207-244-7065. p. 1002

Russell, Julie, In Charge, Stanly County Public Library, Norwood Branch, 207 Pee Dee Ave, Norwood, NC, 28128. Tel: 704-474-3625. p. 1773

Russell, Katherine, Electronic Info Librn, Rivier College, 420 S Main St, Nashua, NH, 03060-5086. Tel: 603-897-8683. Fax: 603-897-8889. p. 1459

Russell, Kathie, Cat, San Diego Christian College, 2100 Greenfield Dr, El Cajon, CA, 92019-1161. Tel: 619-201-8747. Fax: 619-201-8799. p. 145

Russell, Kathy, ILL, Curry College, 1071 Blue Hill Ave, Milton, MA, 02186-9984. Tel: 617-333-2100. Fax: 617-333-2164. p. 1106

Russell, Kirk, Tech Serv, Bakersfield College, 1801 Panorama Dr, Bakersfield, CA, 93305-1298. Tel: 661-395-4461. Fax: 661-395-4397. p. 123

Russell, Kristine, Dir, Frankfort Free Library, 123 Frankfort St, Frankfort, NY, 13340. Tel: 315-894-9611. Fax: 315-894-9611. p. 1624

Russell, Linda A, Circ, Saint Mary's College of Maryland Library, 18952 E Fisher Rd, Saint Mary's City, MD, 20686-3001. Tel: 240-895-4256. Fax: 240-895-4914. p. 1040

Russell, Lisa, ILL Supvr, McDaniel College, Two College Hill, Westminster, MD, 21157-4390. Tel: 410-857-2788. Fax: 410-857-2748. p. 1046

Russell, Lisa, Law Librn, Seneca County Law Library, Seneca County Courthouse Annex, 117 E Market St, Ste 4303, Tiffin, OH, 44883. Tel: 567-230-0204. p. 1938

Russell, Lorrie, Asst Dir, High Point Public Library, 901 N Main St, High Point, NC, 27262. Tel: 336-883-3644. Fax: 336-883-3636. p. 1802

Russell, Lourie, Librn, Katten Muchin Rosenman LLP, 2900 K St NW, Ste 200, Washington, DC, 20007. Tel: 202-625-3500. Fax: 202-298-7570. p. 406

Russell, Marilyn L, Dr, Libr Dir, Haskell Indian Nations University, 155 Indian Ave, Lawrence, KS, 66046. Tel: 785-832-6661. Fax: 785-749-8473. p. 877

Russell, Martha, Dir, Deaf Smith County Library, 211 E Fourth St, Hereford, TX, 79045. Tel: 806-364-1206. Fax: 806-363-7063. p. 2332

Russell, Mary, Supvr, NHAIS Serv, New Hampshire State Library, 20 Park St, Concord, NH, 03301-6314. Tel: 603-271-2866. Fax: 603-271-2205, 603-271-6826. p. 1443

Russell, Mary Jo, Mgr, Libr Serv, Vassar Brothers Medical Center, 45 Reade Pl, Poughkeepsie, NY, 12601. Tel: 845-437-3121. Fax: 845-437-3002. p. 1723

Russell, Michael, Digital Serv, Newmarket Public Library, 438 Park Ave, Newmarket, ON, L3Y 1W1, CANADA. Tel: 905-953-5110. Fax: 905-953-5104. p. 2824

Russell, Nancy, Ch, Tappan Library, 93 Main St, Tappan, NY, 10983. Tel: 845-359-3877. p. 1754

Russell, Pat, Circ, University of Winnipeg Library, 515 Portage Ave, Winnipeg, MB, R3B 2E9, CANADA. Tel: 204-786-9801. Fax: 204-783-8910. p. 2759

Russell, Patricia, Asst Pub Serv Librn, Maitland Public Library, 501 S Maitland Ave, Maitland, FL, 32751-5672. Tel: 407-647-7700. p. 462

Russell, Patti, Acq, Cat, Marylhurst University, 17600 Pacific Hwy (Hwy 43), Marylhurst, OR, 97036-7036. Tel: 503-699-6261, Ext 3373. Fax: 503-636-1957. p. 2004

Russell, R Scott, Ref, Shook, Hardy & Bacon, 2555 Grand Blvd, 3rd Flr, Kansas City, MO, 64108-2613. Tel: 816-474-6550. Fax: 816-421-5547. p. 1341

Russell, Reva E, ILL/Circ Supvr, Virginia Highlands Community College Library, 100 VHCC Dr, Abingdon, VA, 24210. Tel: 276-739-2542. Fax: 276-739-2593. p. 2443

Russell, Robert, Dir, Northern State University, 1200 S Jay St, Aberdeen, SD, 57401-7198. Tel: 605-626-7770. Fax: 605-626-2473. p. 2209

Russell, Roger G, Asst Dir, User Serv, East Carolina University, William E Laupus Health Sciences Library, 600 Moye Blvd, Health Sciences Bldg, Greenville, NC, 27834. Tel: 252-744-3215. Fax: 252-744-3512. p. 1799

Russell, Sarah, Librn, Hamilton Medical Center, 1200 Memorial Dr, Dalton, GA, 30720-2529. Tel: 706-272-6056. Fax: 706-272-6094. p. 528

Russell, Scott, Mkt & Commun Relations Mgr, Salt Lake County Library Services, 2197 E Fort Union Blvd, Salt Lake City, UT, 84121-3139. Tel: 801-943-4636. Fax: 801-942-6323. p. 2413

Russell, Sharon, Tech Serv, Woodstock Theological Center Library, Georgetown University, Lauinger Library, PO Box 571170, Washington, DC, 20057-1170. Tel: 202-687-7473. p. 423

Russell, Sherry, Libr Dir, West Plains Public Library, 750 W Broadway, West Plains, MO, 65775-2369. Tel: 417-256-4775. Fax: 417-256-8316. p. 1372

Russell, Stacey, Fiscal Officer, Muskingum County Library System, 220 N Fifth St, Zanesville, OH, 43701-3587. Tel: 740-453-0391, Ext 130. Fax: 740-455-6937. p. 1953

Russell, Tad, Circ, Libr Asst, Greenwood-Leflore Public Library System, 405 W Washington St, Greenwood, MS, 38930-4297. Tel: 662-453-3634. Fax: 662-453-0683. p. 1299

Russin, Deborah, Head, Tech Serv, East Islip Public Library, 381 E Main St, East Islip, NY, 11730-2896. Tel: 631-581-9200. Fax: 631-581-2245. p. 1617

Russin, Sharon, Acq, Nassau Community College, One Education Dr, Garden City, NY, 11530-6793. Tel: 516-572-7400. Fax: 516-572-7846. p. 1626

Russnak, Linda, Librn, Chauvin Municipal Library, 5200 Fourth Ave N, Chauvin, AB, T0B 0V0, CANADA. Tel: 780-858-3746. Fax: 780-858-2392. p. 2695

Russo, Alysha, Circ Supvr, Lycoming College, 700 College Pl, Williamsport, PA, 17701-5192. Tel: 570-321-4053. Fax: 570-321-4090. p. 2156

Russo, Ann, Ch Serv Librn, Medfield Memorial Public Library, 468 Main St, Medfield, MA, 02052-2008. Tel: 508-359-4544. Fax: 508-359-8124. p. 1104

Russo, Audrey, Librn, Manatee County Law Library, Manatee County Judicial Ctr, Rm 1101, 1051 Manatee Ave W, Bradenton, FL, 34205. Tel: 941-741-4090. Fax: 941-741-4085. p. 429

Russo, Barbara, Campus Librn, Golden Gate Baptist Theological Seminary Library, 7393 S Alton Way, Centennial, CO, 80112-2302. Tel: 303-779-6431. Fax: 303-779-6432. p. 294

Russo, Carol, Br Mgr, Broward County Division of Libraries, Hollywood Branch, 2600 Hollywood Blvd, Hollywood, FL, 33020. Tel: 954-926-2430. Fax: 954-926-2433. p. 441

Russo, Concetta, Sister, Librn, Monsignor James C Turro Seminary Library, Seton Hall University, 400 S Orange Ave, South Orange, NJ, 07079. Tel: 973-761-9198, 973-761-9336, 973-761-9584. Fax: 973-275-2074. p. 1530

Russo, Holly, Adult Serv Mgr, Johnson City Public Library, 100 W Millard St, Johnson City, TN, 37604. Tel: 423-434-4354. Fax: 423-434-4469. p. 2240

Russo, Mary Anne, Youth Serv, Hubbard Public Library, 436 W Liberty St, Hubbard, OH, 44425. Tel: 330-534-3512. Fax: 330-534-7836. p. 1905

Russo, Mike, Instruction Coordr, Louisiana State University Libraries, 295 Middleton Library, Baton Rouge, LA, 70803. Tel: 225-578-6823. Fax: 225-578-9432. p. 943

Russo, Roseanne, Info Serv, Marion County Public Library System, 2720 E Silver Springs Blvd, Ocala, FL, 34470. Tel: 352-671-8551. Fax: 352-368-4545. p. 474

Russo, RoseMary, Librn, United States Department of Justice, 700 Army Navy Dr, Arlington, VA, 22202. Tel: 202-307-8932. Fax: 202-307-8939. p. 2450

Russo, Tina L, Principal Librn, Tampa-Hillsborough County Public Library System, Jimmie B Keel Regional Library, 2902 W Bearss Ave, Tampa, FL, 33618-1828. Fax: 813-264-3834. p. 497

Russo, Trudy, Coll Develop/Ref Librn, Lakehead University Library, 955 Oliver Rd, Thunder Bay, ON, P7B 5E1, CANADA. Tel: 807-343-8728. Fax: 807-343-8007. p. 2848

Russomano, Harriet, Librn, Historical Society of Ocean Grove, 50 Pitman Ave, Ocean Grove, NJ, 07756. Tel: 732-774-1869. Fax: 732-774-1685. p. 1516

Russov, Olga, Librn/ Head, Ser & Acq, Kennesaw State University, 1000 Chastain Rd, Kennesaw, GA, 30144. Tel: 770-423-6189. Fax: 770-423-6185. p. 537

Rust, Amanda, Asst Head, Res & Instruction, Arts & Humanities, Northeastern University Libraries, Snell Library, 360 Huntington Ave, Boston, MA, 02115. Tel: 617-373-8548. p. 1065

Rust, Debbie, Children's Coordr, Buffalo Public Library, Hwy 79, Buffalo, TX, 75831. Tel: 903-322-4146. Fax: 903-322-3253. p. 2293

Rust, Denice, Circ, University of Montana Western, 710 S Atlantic St, Dillon, MT, 59725. Tel: 406-683-7541. Fax: 406-683-7493. p. 1378

Rust, Linda, Ser Librn, Northwestern College, 3003 Snelling Ave N, Saint Paul, MN, 55113. Tel: 651-631-5241. Fax: 651-631-5598. p. 1280

Rustad, Julie, Distance Educ Librn, College of Saint Scholastica Library, 1200 Kenwood Ave, Duluth, MN, 55811-4199. Tel: 218-723-6140. Fax: 218-723-5948. p. 1247

Rustemeyer, Patricia, Commun Serv, Prospect Heights Public Library District, 12 N Elm St, Prospect Heights, IL, 60070-1450. Tel: 847-259-3500. Fax: 847-259-4602. p. 692

Rustic, Amy, Ref Librn, Pennsylvania State University, New Kensington, 3550 Seventh St Rd, Rte 780, Upper Burrell, PA, 15068-1798. Tel: 724-334-6072. Fax: 724-334-6113. p. 2149

Rustin, Jane, Dir, Wayne County Public Library, 1001 E Ash St, Goldsboro, NC, 27530. Tel: 919-735-1824. Fax: 919-731-2889. p. 1795

Ruston, Gregg, Info Serv Supvr, Viterbo University, 900 Viterbo Dr, La Crosse, WI, 54601. Tel: 608-796-3277. Fax: 608-796-3275. p. 2603

Ruter, Jeanna, Dir, Avon Free Library, 143 Genesee St, Avon, NY, 14414. Tel: 585-226-8461. Fax: 585-226-6615. p. 1577

Rutger, William, Dir, Milan-Berlin Township Public Library, 19 E Church St, Milan, OH, 44846. Tel: 419-499-4117. Fax: 419-499-4697. p. 1918

Ruth, Michele D, Coll Develop Librn, Georgetown College, 400 E College St, Georgetown, KY, 40324. Tel: 502-863-8412. Fax: 502-868-7740. p. 915

Rutherford, Ann, Librn, Miles Community College Library, 2715 Dickinson, Miles City, MT, 59301. Tel: 406-874-6105. Fax: 406-874-6282. p. 1386

Rutherford, Brenda, ILL/Doc Delivery Serv, Ser/ILL, Gordon College Library, 419 College Dr, Barnesville, GA, 30204. Tel: 770-358-5078. Fax: 770-358-5240. p. 521

Rutherford, Charlean, Librn, Lena Cagle Public Library, 401 Alabama Ave, Bridgeport, AL, 35740. Tel: 256-495-2259. Fax: 256-495-2119. p. 11

Rutherford, Linda, Coordr, Circ & Tech Serv, Mott Community College, 1401 E Court St, Flint, MI, 48503. Tel: 810-762-0402. Fax: 810-762-0407. p. 1180

Rutherford, Noel, Coll Develop, Nashville Public Library, 615 Church St, Nashville, TN, 37219-2314. Tel: 615-862-5760. Fax: 615-862-5771. p. 2257

Rutherford, Robert, Dr, Exec Dir, Arizona State University, Farmer Bldg 434, Tempe, AZ, 85287. Tel: 480-965-4602. Fax: 480-965-1863. p. 2961

Rutherford, Sally, Librn, Maryland General Hospital, 827 Linden Ave, Baltimore, MD, 21201. Tel: 410-225-8383. Fax: 410-225-8119. p. 1015

Ruthrauff, Lynn, Head of Libr, Free Library of Philadelphia, Lovett Memorial Branch, 6945 Germantown Ave, Philadelphia, PA, 19119-2189. Tel: 215-685-2095. Fax: 215-685-2094. p. 2108

Ruthruff, Linda, Dir, Grangeville Centennial Library, 215 W North, Grangeville, ID, 83530-1729. Tel: 208-983-0951. Fax: 208-983-2336. p. 575

Ruthven, Kerri-Ann, Br Mgr, Wake County Public Library System, Athens Drive Community Library, 1420 Athens Dr, Raleigh, NC, 27606. Tel: 919-233-4000. Fax: 919-233-4082. p. 1817

Rutkair, Jennifer, Archivist, Whyte Museum of the Canadian Rockies, 111 Bear St, Banff, AB, T1L 1A3, CANADA. Tel: 403-762-2291, Ext 335. Fax: 403-762-2339. p. 2684

Rutkowkski, Patricia, Dir, New Britain Public Library, 20 High St, New Britain, CT, 06051-4226. Tel: 860-224-3155, Ext 113. Fax: 860-223-6729. p. 354

Rutkowski, Ed, Asst Dir, Brighton District Library, 100 Library Dr, Brighton, MI, 48116. Tel: 810-229-6571, Ext 222. Fax: 810-229-3161. p. 1159

Rutkowski, Helena, Per, Workers' Compensation Board of British Columbia Library, 6951 Westminster Hwy, Richmond, BC, V7C 1C6, CANADA. Tel: 604-231-8450. Fax: 604-279-7608. p. 2737

Rutkowski, Joanette, Sister, Archivist, Hilbert College, 5200 S Park Ave, Hamburg, NY, 14075. Tel: 716-649-7900, Ext 361. Fax: 716-648-6530. p. 1632

Rutkowski, Katherine, Sr Res Librn, Consumer Electronics Association, 1919 S Eads St, Arlington, VA, 22202. Tel: 703-907-7763. p. 2449

Rutkowski, Sandra, Sister, Dir, Lourdes University, 6832 Convent Blvd, Sylvania, OH, 43560. Tel: 419-824-3762. Fax: 419-824-3511. p. 1938

Rutland, Jessie, Circ, Ref Asst, Flagler College, 44 Sevilla St, Saint Augustine, FL, 32084-4302. Tel: 904-819-6206. Fax: 904-823-8511. p. 486

Rutledge, Ann, Br Mgr, Eastern Shore Public Library, Northampton Memorial Library, 500 Tazewell Ave, Cape Charles, VA, 23310. Tel: 757-331-1300. p. 2443

Rutledge, Diane, Dir, Silsbee Public Library, Santa Fe Park, Silsbee, TX, 77656. Tel: 409-385-4831. Fax: 409-385-7382. p. 2387

Rutledge, Lisa, Acq, Mississippi College, 101 W College St, Clinton, MS, 39058. Tel: 601-925-3232. Fax: 601-925-3435. p. 1296

Rutledge, Maria, Head of Librn, Kern County Library, Beale Memorial, 701 Truxtun Ave, Bakersfield, CA, 93301-4816. Tel: 661-868-0701. Fax: 661-868-0831. p. 124

Rutledge, Sue, Pres, Literacy Project, Saint Clair County Literacy System, Literacy Project, 210 McMorran Blvd, Port Huron, MI, 48060. Tel: 810-987-7323, Ext 156. Fax: 810-987-7327. p. 1219

Ruttenber, Susan J, Dir, Montvale Free Public Library, 12 Mercedes Dr, Ste 100, Montvale, NJ, 07645. Tel: 201-391-5090. Fax: 201-307-5647. p. 1503

Rutter, Deborah, Coll Develop, Dep Dir, Cheshire Public Library, 104 Main St, Cheshire, CT, 06410-2499. Tel: 203-272-2245. Fax: 203-272-7714. p. 333

Ruttman, Margaret, Dir, Hansford County Library, 122 Main St, Spearman, TX, 79081. Tel: 806-659-2231. Fax: 806-659-5042. p. 2388

Ruttum Senturia, Laura, Dir, History Colorado, 1200 Broadway, Denver, CO, 80203-2109. Tel: 303-866-2305. Fax: 303-866-2796. p. 302

Rutty, Linda, Head of Librn, Volusia County Public Library, Oak Hill Public, 125 E Halifax Ave, Oak Hill, FL, 32759. Tel: 386-345-5510. Fax: 386-345-5510. p. 436

Rutz, Linda, Coordr, Tech Serv, Way Public Library, 101 E Indiana Ave, Perrysburg, OH, 43551. Tel: 419-874-3135, Ext 114. Fax: 419-874-6129. p. 1929

Ruwell, Mary Elizabeth, Dr, Archivist, Curator, Spec Coll, United States Air Force Academy Libraries, 2354 Fairchild Dr, Ste 3A10, USAF Academy, CO, 80840-6214. Tel: 719-333-6919. Fax: 719-333-4754. p. 324

Rux, Alicia, Asst Librn, Crowheart Public Library, 33 Old Yellowstone Hwy, Crowheart, WY, 82512. Tel: 307-486-2280. p. 2654

Rux, Erika, Computer & Web Serv Librn, Concordia College, 901 S Eighth St, Moorhead, MN, 56562. Tel: 218-299-4640. Fax: 218-299-4253. p. 1265

Ruzicka, Joyce, Librn, North Bend Public Library, 140 E Eighth St, North Bend, NE, 68649. Tel: 402-652-8356. Fax: 402-652-8356. p. 1410

Ruzicka, Kristen, Ref Serv Coordr, Flesh Public Library, 124 W Greene St, Piqua, OH, 45356-2399. Tel: 937-773-6753. Fax: 937-773-5981. p. 1930

Ruzicka, Virginia, Dir, Rockford Public Library, 202 W Main Ave, Rockford, IA, 50468-1212. Tel: 641-756-3725. Fax: 641-756-3725. p. 841

Ryall, Heather, Br Supvr, Caledon Public Library, Margaret Dunn Branch, 20 Snellcrest Dr, Mayfield, ON, L7C 1B5, CANADA. Tel: 905-843-0457. p. 2795

Ryall, Judy, Librn, Canada-Newfoundland Offshore Petroleum Board Library, TD Pl, 3rd Flr, 140 Water St, St. John's, NL, A1C 6H6, CANADA. Tel: 709-778-1449. Fax: 709-778-1473. p. 2771

Ryals, Robert, Ref, Archives & Doc Librn, Winthrop University, 824 Oakland Ave, Rock Hill, SC, 29733. Tel: 803-323-2257. Fax: 803-323-2215. p. 2203

Ryan, Allan, Asst Dir, Tech Serv, Saint John's University Library, Rittenberg Law Library, 8000 Utopia Pkwy, Queens, NY, 11439. Tel: 718-990-6651, 718-990-6659. Fax: 718-990-6649. p. 1725

Ryan, Amy, Pres, Boston Public Library, 700 Boylston St, Boston, MA, 02117-0286. Tel: 617-536-5400. Fax: 617-236-4306. p. 1056

Ryan, Amy, Dir, Vineyard Haven Public Library, 200 Main St, Vineyard Haven, MA, 02568-9710. Tel: 508-696-4211, Ext 11. Fax: 508-696-7495. p. 1132

Ryan, Amy, Dir, German-Masontown Public Library, Nine S Washington St, Masontown, PA, 15461-2025. Tel: 724-583-7030. Fax: 724-583-0979. p. 2085

Ryan, Angela, Trades & Electronic Res Librn, Kwantlen Polytechnic University Library, 12666 72 Ave., Surrey, BC, V3W 2M8, CANADA. Tel: 604-598-6040. Fax: 604-598-6035. p. 2738

Ryan, Anna, Youth Serv, Muscle Shoals Public Library, 1918 E Avalon, Muscle Shoals, AL, 35661. Tel: 256-386-9212. Fax: 256-386-9211. p. 32

Ryan, Anne, Ref Serv, Ser, Minneapolis Community & Technical College Library, Wheelock Whitney Hall, 1501 Hennepin Ave, Minneapolis, MN, 55403. Tel: 612-659-6291. Fax: 612-659-6295. p. 1261

Ryan, Ashley, Ref, Trinity University, 125 Michigan Ave NE, Washington, DC, 20017. Tel: 202-884-9350. Fax: 202-884-9241. p. 417

Ryan, Beth-Ann, Dep Dir, State of Delaware, 121 Duke of York St, Dover, DE, 19901. Tel: 302-739-4748. Fax: 302-739-6787. p. 382

Ryan, Charlotte, Head, Ch, Head, Youth Serv, Upper Darby Township & Sellers Memorial Free Public Library, 76 S State Rd, Upper Darby, PA, 19082. Tel: 610-789-4440. p. 2149

Ryan, Christina, ILL Supvr, Smith College Libraries, Northampton, MA, 01063. Tel: 413-585-2910. Fax: 413-585-2904. p. 1113

Ryan, Christine, Librn, Vermont Law School, 68 North Windsor, South Royalton, VT, 05068. Tel: 802-831-1448. Fax: 802-763-7159. p. 2436

Ryan, Christy, Interim Dir, Phoenix School of Law, 4041 N Central Ave, Ste 150, Phoenix, AZ, 85012. Tel: 602-682-6898. Fax: 602-682-6996. p. 76

Ryan, Diana, Dir, Coll Develop, Thomas Jefferson University, 1020 Walnut St, Philadelphia, PA, 19107. Tel: 215-503-2829. Fax: 215-923-3203. p. 2118

Ryan, Frances, ILL, Ser, Castleton State College, 178 Alumni Dr, Castleton, VT, 05735. Tel: 802-468-1256. Fax: 802-468-1475. p. 2421

Ryan, Georgia, Circ, Delaware Technical & Community College, PO Box 630, Sea Shore Hwy, Georgetown, DE, 19947-0630. Tel: 302-856-9033. Fax: 302-858-5462. p. 383

Ryan, Janet, Head, Prog & Outreach, Jones Library, Inc, 43 Amity St, Amherst, MA, 01002-2285. Tel: 413-259-3223. Fax: 413-256-4096. p. 1048

Ryan, Jeanette L, Dep Dir, University of Arizona, Arizona Health Sciences Library, 1501 N Campbell Ave, Tucson, AZ, 85724. Tel: 520-626-6143. Fax: 520-626-2922. p. 88

Ryan, Jeanine, Ch, Umatilla Public Library, 412 Hatfield Dr, Umatilla, FL, 32784-8913. Tel: 352-669-3284. Fax: 352-669-2927. p. 501

Ryan, Jeanne, Interim Dir, Roselle Free Public Library, 104 W Fourth Ave, Roselle, NJ, 07203. Tel: 908-245-5809. Fax: 908-298-8881. p. 1527

Ryan, Joyce, AV, Outreach Serv Librn, Santa Fe Springs City Library, 11700 E Telegraph Rd, Santa Fe Springs, CA, 90670-3600. Tel: 562-868-7738. Fax: 562-929-3680. p. 265

Ryan, Julie, Libr Tech Spec, College of Lake County, 19351 W Washington St, Grayslake, IL, 60030. Tel: 847-543-2734. Fax: 847-223-7690. p. 652

Ryan, Lauren, Br Dir, Somerset County Library System, North Plainfield Library, Six Rockview Ave, North Plainfield, NJ, 07060. Tel: 908-755-7909. Fax: 908-755-8177. p. 1475

Ryan, Lee, Ref, University of San Francisco, Zief Law Library, 2101 Fulton St, San Francisco, CA, 94117-1004. Tel: 415-422-6679. Fax: 415-422-2345. p. 249

Ryan, Linda, Dir, Long Island University, C W Post Campus, 720 Northern Blvd, Brookville, NY, 11548-1300. Tel: 516-299-4109. Fax: 516-299-4168. p. 2969

Ryan, Lisa, Head, Adult Serv, Dexter District Library, 3255 Alpine St, Dexter, MI, 48130. Tel: 734-426-4477. Fax: 734-426-1217. p. 1174

Ryan, Lisa, Ref Librn, LIM College Library, 216 E 45th St, 2nd Flr, New York, NY, 10017. Tel: 646-218-4126. Fax: 212-750-3453. p. 1685

Ryan, Marianne, Assoc Univ Librn, Pub Serv, Northwestern University Library, 1970 Campus Dr, Evanston, IL, 60208-2300. Tel: 847-491-7658. p. 644

Ryan, Mary, Dir, University of Arkansas for Medical Sciences Library, 4301 W Markham St, SLOT 586, Little Rock, AR, 72205-7186. Tel: 501-686-6730. Fax: 501-296-1423. p. 107

Ryan, Mary, Head, Coll Serv, Curry College, 1071 Blue Hill Ave, Milton, MA, 02186-9984. Tel: 617-333-2937. Fax: 617-333-2164. p. 1106

Ryan, Mary, Head, Ref, University of Missouri-Columbia, Elmer Ellis Library, Ellis Library Bldg, Rm 104, Columbia, MO, 65201-5149. Tel: 573-882-9165. Fax: 573-882-8044. p. 1325

Ryan, Mary Ann, Acq Librn, Fishkill Historical Society, 504 Rte 9, Fishkill, NY, 12524-2248. Tel: 845-896-9560. p. 1622

Ryan, Mary Jo, Communications Coordr, Nebraska Library Commission, The Atrium, 1200 N St, Ste 120, Lincoln, NE, 68508-2023. Tel: 402-471-4343. Fax: 402-471-2083. p. 1406

Ryan, Michael T, Dir, Columbia University, Rare Book & Manuscript, Butler Library, 6th Flr E, 535 W 114th St, New York, NY, 10027. Tel: 212-854-2232. Fax: 212-854-1365. p. 1675

Ryan, Michelle, Head, Ref, Department of Canadian Heritage, 15 Eddy St, 2nd Flr, Gatineau, QC, K1A 0M5, CANADA. Tel: 819-953-0527. Fax: 819-953-7988. p. 2883

Ryan, Nancy, Br Mgr, Fairfax County Public Library, Herndon Fortnightly Branch, 768 Center St, Herndon, VA, 20170-4640. Tel: 703-437-8855. p. 2461

Ryan, Nancy D, Dir, Lynnfield Public Library, 18 Summer St, Lynnfield, MA, 01940-1837. Tel: 781-334-5411. Fax: 781-334-2164. p. 1101

Ryan, Nanette, Ch, West Bridgewater Public Library, 80 Howard St, West Bridgewater, MA, 02379-1710. Tel: 508-894-1255. Fax: 508-894-1258. p. 1137

Ryan, Pam, Librn, California State Department of Water Resources, 1416 Ninth St, Rm 1118-13, Sacramento, CA, 95814. Tel: 916-651-0822. Fax: 916-653-0952. p. 223

Ryan, Sarah, Ref, Yale University Library, Lillian Goldman Library Yale Law School, 127 Wall St, New Haven, CT, 06511. Tel: 203-432-1600. Fax: 203-432-2112. p. 358

Ryan, Shamus, Libr Tech, Group Health Cooperative, 201 16th Ave E, Seattle, WA, 98112. Tel: 206-326-3393. Fax: 206-326-2629. p. 2527

Ryan, Susan, In Charge, Napa City-County Library, American Canyon Branch, 3421 Broadway-Hwy 29, Ste E-3, American Canyon, CA, 94503. Tel: 707-644-1136. p. 192

Ryan, Susan, Librn, Seyfarth Shaw, 975 F St NW, Washington, DC, 20004. Tel: 202-828-3559, 202-828-5345. Fax: 202-828-5393. p. 413

Ryan, Susan M, Actg Dir, Assoc Dir, Stetson University, 421 N Woodland Blvd, Unit 8418, DeLand, FL, 32723. Tel: 386-822-7181. p. 437

Ryan, Sylvia, Librn, Department of Veterans Affairs Medical Center, 3001 Green Bay Rd, North Chicago, IL, 60064. Tel: 847-688-1900, Ext 83757. Fax: 847-578-3819. p. 681

Ryan, Tari, Libr Asst, Cape May County Library, Stone Harbor Branch, 9508 Second Ave, Stone Harbor, NJ, 08247. Tel: 609-368-6809. p. 1477

Ryan, Tom, Automation & Networking Mgr, Council Bluffs Public Library, 400 Willow Ave, Council Bluffs, IA, 51503-4269. Tel: 712-323-7553. Fax: 712-323-1269. p. 805

Ryan, William, Assoc Librn, Foreign & Intl Law, American University, 4801 Massachusetts Ave NW, Washington, DC, 20016-8182. Tel: 202-274-4331. Fax: 202-274-4365. p. 393

Ryant, Romana, Asst Librn, Spillville Public Library, 201 Oak St, Spillville, IA, 52168. Tel: 563-562-4373. Fax: 563-562-4373. p. 845

Rybarczyk, Nathan, ILL, Baraboo Public Library, 230 Fourth Ave, Baraboo, WI, 53913. Tel: 608-356-6166. Fax: 608-355-2779. p. 2580

Ryberg, Susan G, Ref, Mount Olive College, 634 Henderson St, Mount Olive, NC, 28365-1699. Tel: 919-658-7869, Ext 1411. Fax: 919-658-8934. p. 1811

Rybicki, Steve, Pub Serv Librn, Macomb Community College Libraries, Center Campus, C-Bldg, 44575 Garfield Rd, Clinton Township, MI, 48038-1139. Tel: 586-286-2026. Fax: 586-286-2002. p. 1234

Rybicki-Judkins, Gene, Librn, Varnum Memorial Library, 194 Main St, Jeffersonville, VT, 05464. Tel: 802-644-2117. p. 2426

Rybnikar, Ron, Archivist, Babson College, 231 Forest St, Babson Park, MA, 02457-0310. Tel: 781-239-4570. Fax: 781-239-5226. p. 1051

Ryburn, Patty, Ref, Canton Public Library, 786 Washington St, Canton, MA, 02021-3029. Tel: 781-821-5027. Fax: 781-821-5029. p. 1079

Rychlik, Marjorie, Dir, Sheridan Memorial Library, 5805 Logan Park Dr, Sheridan, TX, 77475. Tel: 979-234-5154. Fax: 979-234-5154. p. 2386

Ryckbosch, Bart, Archivist, Art Institute of Chicago, 111 S Michigan Ave, Chicago, IL, 60603. Tel: 312-443-3671. Fax: 312-443-0849. p. 606

Ryckman, Linda, Libr Adminr, Ile a la Crosse Public Library, PO Box 540, Ile a la Crosse, SK, S0M 1C0, CANADA. Tel: 306-833-3027. Fax: 306-833-2189. p. 2917

Ryckman, Nancy, Asst Head, Ref & Instrul Serv, University of North Carolina at Greensboro, 320 Spring Garden St, Greensboro, NC, 27402. Tel: 336-256-0345. Fax: 336-334-5399. p. 1798

Ryckman, Pat, Br Mgr, Alexandria Library, James M Duncan Jr Branch, 2501 Commonwealth Ave, Alexandria, VA, 22301. Tel: 703-746-1705. Fax: 703-746-1785. p. 2444

Ryczek, Marianne, Ch, Northlake Public Library District, 231 N Wolf Rd, Northlake, IL, 60164. Tel: 708-562-2301. Fax: 708-562-8120. p. 683

Ryden, Patricia, Asst Dir, Wiggin Memorial Library, Ten Bunker Hill Ave, Stratham, NH, 03885. Tel: 603-772-4346. p. 1465

Ryder, Jill, Librn, Southern Adirondack Library System, 22 Whitney Pl, Saratoga Springs, NY, 12866-4596. Tel: 518-584-7300. Fax: 518-587-5589. p. 1739

Ryder, Suzanne, Chief Librn, Naval Research Laboratory, 4555 Overlook Ave SW, Code 5596, Washington, DC, 20375-5334. Tel: 202-767-2357. Fax: 202-767-3352. p. 411

Ryder, Vanessa, Circ, Sunderland Public Library, 20 School St, Sunderland, MA, 01375. Tel: 413-665-2642. Fax: 413-665-1435. p. 1130

Ryder-Cunningham, Nancey, Ser, University of Medicine & Dentistry of New Jersey, 30 12th Ave, Newark, NJ, 07103-2706. Tel: 973-972-4580. p. 1513

Rydin, Roger, Archivist, Oral Roberts University Library, 7777 South Lewis Ave, Tulsa, OK, 74171. Tel: 918-495-6750. Fax: 918-495-6751. p. 1981

Rydin, Roger, Archivist, Oral Roberts University Library, Holy Spirit Research Center, 7777 S Lewis Ave, Tulsa, OK, 74171. Tel: 918-495-6750. Fax: 918-495-6662. p. 1982

Ryen, Maria, Bus Mgr, Rye Free Reading Room, 1061 Boston Post Rd, Rye, NY, 10580. Tel: 914-967-0480. Fax: 914-967-5522. p. 1736

Ryer, Jeanne, Ad, Norwell Public Library, 64 South St, Norwell, MA, 02061-2433. Tel: 781-659-2015. Fax: 781-659-6755. p. 1115

Ryer, Nina, ILL, Tech Serv, W J Niederkorn Library, 316 W Grand Ave, Port Washington, WI, 53074-2293. Tel: 262-284-5031. Fax: 262-284-7680. p. 2631

Ryken, Barbara, Dir, Samuel Merritt College, 400 Hawthorne Ave, Oakland, CA, 94609. Tel: 510-869-8692. Fax: 510-869-6633. p. 199

Rymer, Cheryl, Asst Librn, Fairport Harbor Public Library, 335 Vine St, Fairport Harbor, OH, 44077-5799. Tel: 440-354-8191. Fax: 440-354-6059. p. 1899

Rymsza-Pawlowska, Elzbieta, Dir, Res Mgt & Digital Serv, Catholic University of America, 620 Michigan Ave NE, 315 Mullen Library, Washington, DC, 20064. Tel: 202-319-5554. Fax: 202-319-4735. p. 395

Ryner, Eugenia B, Dir, United States Department of Justice, MCB No 4, Quantico, VA, 22135. Tel: 702-632-3215. Fax: 703-632-3214. p. 2487

Ryner, Katherine H, Assoc Dir, Head, Coll Support Serv, Saint Mary's College of Maryland Library, 18952 E Fisher Rd, Saint Mary's City, MD, 20686-3001. Tel: 240-895-4260. Fax: 240-895-4914. p. 1040

Rynkiewicz, Robert, Asst Dir, Atlantic City Free Public Library, One N Tennessee Ave, Atlantic City, NJ, 08401. Tel: 609-345-2269, Ext 3024. Fax: 609-345-5570. p. 1470

Rynkowski, Kristen, Librn, Clinton Correctional Facility Library, PO Box 2000, Dannemora, NY, 12929-2000. Tel: 518-492-2511. Fax: 518-492-2099. p. 1613

Rynning, Connie, Br Mgr, Riverside County Library System, Woodcrest Library, 16625 Krameria, Riverside, CA, 92504. Tel: 951-789-7324. Fax: 951-789-7321. p. 218

Ryther, Sherry, Ch, Park Falls Public Library, 121 N Fourth Ave, Park Falls, WI, 54552. Tel: 715-762-3121. Fax: 715-762-2286. p. 2629

Rytter, Kirsten, Tech Spec, Transport Canada, 344 Edmonton St, 2nd Flr, Winnipeg, MB, R3C 0P6, CANADA. Tel: 204-984-1886. Fax: 204-984-4874. p. 2757

Ryzner, Vanessa, Circ Coordr, Upper St Clair Township Library, 1820 McLaughlin Run Rd, Upper St Clair, PA, 15241-2397. Tel: 412-835-5540. Fax: 412-835-6763. p. 2149

Rzasa, Kay, Br Mgr, Fairfax County Public Library, George Mason Regional, 7001 Little River Tpk, Annandale, VA, 22003-5975. Tel: 703-256-3800. p. 2461

Rzepczynski, Mary, Asst Dir, Delta Township District Library, 5130 Davenport Dr, Lansing, MI, 48917-2040. Tel: 517-321-4014. Fax: 517-321-2080. p. 1200

Rzetelny, Sheryl, Head, Bus Serv, Canton Public Library, 1200 S Canton Center Rd, Canton, MI, 48188-1600. Tel: 734-397-0999. Fax: 734-397-1130. p. 1160

Saab, Lila, Br Mgr, Oakville Public Library, Glen Abbey, 1415 Third Line, Oakville, ON, L6M 3G2, CANADA. Tel: 905-815-2039, Ext 3596. Fax: 905-815-5978. p. 2825

Saad, Sandra, Mkt & Develop, Beaufort County Library, 311 Scott St, Beaufort, SC, 29902. Tel: 843-255-6467. p. 2181

Saadaoui, Leila, Librn - Fr Serv, Laurentian University, 935 Ramsey Lake Rd, Sudbury, ON, P3E 2C6, CANADA. Tel: 705-675-151, Ext 3319. Fax: 705-675-4877. p. 2846

Saage, Wallace, Curator, The Heritage Society Library, 1100 Bagby, Houston, TX, 77002. Tel: 713-655-1912. Fax: 713-655-9249. p. 2336

Saalseld, Kim, Br Mgr, Eagle Valley Library District, Avon Public, 200 Benchmark Rd, Avon, CO, 81620. Tel: 970-949-6797. Fax: 970-949-0233. p. 305

Saathoff, Dorothy, Dir, Hondo Public Library, 1011 19th St, Hondo, TX, 78861-2431. Tel: 830-426-5333. Fax: 830-426-7089. p. 2333

Saba, Beatrice, Br Mgr, Live Oak Public Libraries, Rincon Branch, 17th St & Hwy 21, Rincon, GA, 31326. Tel: 912-826-2222. Fax: 912-826-6304. p. 550

Sabados, Laura, Librn, Southeast Regional Library, Stoughton Branch, 232 Main St, Stoughton, SK, S0G 4T0, CANADA. Tel: 306-457-2484. p. 2931

Sabanos, Jacqueline, Head, Acq, University of San Diego, Helen K & James S Copley Library, 5998 Alcala Park, San Diego, CA, 92110. Fax: 619-260-4617. p. 239

Sabatino, Susan, Govt Doc, Ref, William Paterson University of New Jersey, 300 Pompton Rd, Wayne, NJ, 07470. Tel: 973-720-3127. Fax: 973-720-3171. p. 1540

Sabatka, Paula, Br Mgr, Head Librn, Fremont County Library System, Dubois Branch, 202 N First, Dubois, WY, 82513. Tel: 307-455-2992. Fax: 307-455-2032. p. 2657

Sabbagh, Lia, Coordr, Englewood Hospital & Medical Center, 350 Engle St, Englewood, NJ, 07631. Tel: 201-894-3069. Fax: 201-894-9049. p. 1484

Sabbagh, Lia, Coordr, Bergen Passaic Health Sciences Library Consortium, c/o Englewood Hospital & Medical Ctr, Health Sciences Library, 350 Engle St, Englewood, NJ, 07631. Tel: 201-894-3069. Fax: 201-894-9049. p. 2948

Sabbar, Carol, Dir of Computer Ctr, Carthage College, 2001 Alford Park Dr, Kenosha, WI, 53140-1900. Tel: 262-551-5900. Fax: 262-551-5904. p. 2601

Sabbe, Nancy, Dir, Madison Public Library, 209 E Center St, Madison, SD, 57042-2998. Tel: 605-256-7525. Fax: 605-256-7526. p. 2214

Sabel, Myra, Electronic Serv Librn, Alabama Supreme Court & State Law Library, Heflin-Torbert Judicial Bldg, 300 Dexter Ave, Montgomery, AL, 36104. Tel: 334-229-0580. Fax: 334-229-0543. p. 28

Sabetta, Anne, Libr Coordr, Jefferson Community & Technical College, Shelby County Campus, 1361 Frankfort Rd, Shelbyville, KY, 40065. Tel: 502-213-3618. p. 924

Sabin, Marion, Libr Tech, South Piedmont Community College, Carpenter Library, Technical Education Bldg, 4209 Old Charlotte Hwy, Monroe, NC, 28110. Tel: 704-290-5851. Fax: 704-290-5880. p. 1815

Sabine, Mandy, Treas, Southeast Regional Library System, 252 W 13th St, Wellston, OH, 45692. Tel: 740-384-2103. Fax: 740-384-2106. p. 2952

Sabine, Virnna, Libr Asst, Kingswood University, 26 Western St, Sussex, NB, E4E 1E6, CANADA. Tel: 506-432-4400. Fax: 506-432-4425. p. 2767

Sabine-Kildiss, Luisa, Dir, Chatham Public Library, 11 Woodbridge Ave, Chatham, NY, 12037-1399. Tel: 518-392-3666. Fax: 518-392-1546. p. 1605

Sabini, Tricia, Ch, Ossining Public Library, 53 Croton Ave, Ossining, NY, 10562-4903. Tel: 914-941-2416. Fax: 914-941-7464. p. 1712

Sablan, Greg, Tech Serv, Northern Marianas College, Fina Sisu Lane, Bldg O, Saipan, MP, 96950. Tel: 670-234-3690, Ext 1122. Fax: 670-234-0759. p. 2669

Sabo, Barbara L, Coordr, Circ, California University of Pennsylvania, 250 University Ave, California, PA, 15419-1394. Tel: 724-938-4092. Fax: 724-938-5901. p. 2040

Sabo, Lelani, Dir, Martin Curtis Hendersonville Public Library, 140 Saundersville Rd, Hendersonville, TN, 37075-3525. Tel: 615-824-0656. Fax: 615-824-3112. p. 2237

Sabo, Patti, Asst Librn, Chilton Public Library, 221 Park St, Chilton, WI, 53014. Tel: 920-849-4414. Fax: 920-849-2370, p. 2585

Sabol, Dee, Commun Engagement & Outreach Officer, Pikes Peak Library District, 20 N Cascade Ave, Colorado Springs, CO, 80903. Tel: 719-531-6333. p. 296

Sabol, Elaine, Librn, Indian River State College, 500 NW California Blvd, Port Saint Lucie, FL, 34986. Tel: 772-336-6380. Fax: 772-873-3409. p. 485

Sabolcik, Cara, Pub Serv Librn, St John's College Library, 60 College Ave, Annapolis, MD, 21401. Tel: 410-295-6927. Fax: 410-295-6936. p. 1011

Sabourin, Janice, Asst Mgr, Edmonton Public Library, Strathcona, 8331 104th St, Edmonton, AB, T6E 4E9, CANADA. Tel: 780-496-1828. Fax: 780-496-1451. p. 2700

Sabourin, Julie, Librn, Providence Community Library, Fox Point Library, 90 Ives St, Providence, RI, 02906. Tel: 401-331-0390. p. 2173

Sabraw, Karen, Librn, Lakeland Library Region, North Battleford Public Library, 1392 101st St, North Battleford, SK, S9A 1A2, CANADA. Tel: 306-445-3206. Fax: 306-445-6454. p. 2920

Sacchetti, Jim, Ref Librn, Massasoit Community College Library, One Massasoit Blvd, Brockton, MA, 02302. Tel: 508-588-9100, Ext 1941. Fax: 508-427-1265. p. 1071

Sacco, Gail Alter, Dir, Voorheesville Public Library, 51 School Rd, Voorheesville, NY, 12186. Tel: 518-765-2791. Fax: 518-765-3007. p. 1761

Sacco, Karen, ILL, Ridley Township Public Library, 100 E MacDade Blvd, Folsom, PA, 19033-2592. Tel: 610-583-0593. Fax: 610-583-9505. p. 2057

Sacco, Kathleen, Syst Adminr, State University of New York at Fredonia, 280 Central Ave, Fredonia, NY, 14063. Tel: 716-673-3181. Fax: 716-673-3185. p. 1624

Sacco, Patricia, Br Mgr, Brooklyn Public Library, Bushwick, 340 Bushwick Ave, Brooklyn, NY, 11206. Tel: 718-602-1348. Fax: 718-602-1352. p. 1591

Sachar, Steven, Commun Librn Mgr, Queens Borough Public Library, Poppenhusen Community Library, 121-23 14th Ave, College Point, NY, 11356. Tel: 718-359-1102. Fax: 718-353-8894. p. 1645

Sachdeva, Marion, Head, Tech Serv, University of New Haven, 300 Boston Post Rd, West Haven, CT, 06516. Tel: 203-932-7193. Fax: 203-932-1469. p. 377

Sacho, Gail D, Br Mgr, Fort Loudon Community Library, 210 Mullen St, Fort Loudon, PA, 17224. Tel: 717-369-4704. Fax: 717-369-4757. p. 2058

Sachon, Mark, Head, Ser, Carnegie Library of Pittsburgh, 4400 Forbes Ave, Pittsburgh, PA, 15213-4080. Tel: 412-622-3156. Fax: 412-622-6278. p. 2122

Sachs, Martha, Curator, Alice Marshall Women's Hist Coll, Pennsylvania State University-Harrisburg Library, 351 Olmsted Dr, Middletown, PA, 17057-4850. Tel: 717-948-6280. Fax: 717-948-6757. p. 2089

Sachse, Renate, Cat, Franklin & Marshall College, 450 College Ave, Lancaster, PA, 17603-3318. Tel: 717-399-4435. Fax: 717-291-4160. p. 2076

Sachse, Sharon, Circ Tech, United States Geological Survey Library, 345 Middlefield Rd, Bldg 15 (MS-955), Menlo Park, CA, 94025-3591. Tel: 650-329-5027. Fax: 650-329-5132. p. 185

Sack, Beth, ILL, Supvr, Access Serv, Bard College at Simon's Rock, 84 Alford Rd, Great Barrington, MA, 01230. Tel: 413-528-7361. Fax: 413-528-7380. p. 1092

Sack, John, Dir of Highwire Press, Stanford University Libraries, 557 Escondido Mall, Stanford, CA, 94305-6004. Tel: 650-725-1064. p. 270

Sackash, Ruth, Librn, Sykesville Public Library, 21 E Main St, Sykesville, PA, 15865-0021. Tel: 814-894-5243. Fax: 814-894-5243. p. 2145

Sackett, Carol, Circ Supvr, Keuka College, 141 Central Ave, Keuka Park, NY, 14478-0038. Tel: 315-279-5224, 315-279-5632. Fax: 315-279-5334. p. 1649

Sackett, Jennifer, Dir, Lincoln County Public Library, 306 W Main St, Lincolnton, NC, 28092. Tel: 704-735-8044. Fax: 704-732-9042. p. 1807

Sackett, Judy, Dir, Human Res, University of Kentucky Libraries, I-85, 401 Hilltop Ave, Lexington, KY, 40506-0456. Tel: 859-257-0500, Ext 2088. p. 921

Sackett, Mary, Head, Conserv & Presv, Getty Research Institute, 1200 Getty Center Dr, Ste 1100, Los Angeles, CA, 90049-1688. Tel: 310-440-7390. Fax: 310-440-7780. p. 170

Sackett, Nancy, Outreach Serv Librn, Lewistown Public Library, 701 W Main St, Lewistown, MT, 59457. Tel: 406-538-5212. Fax: 406-538-3920. p. 1384

Sackinger, Stefani, Librn, Good Samaritan Regional Medical Center, 3600 NW Samaritan Dr, Corvallis, OR, 97330. Tel: 541-768-6200. Fax: 541-768-5087. p. 1994

Sacks, Barbara, Mgr, Libr Syst, Long Island Jewish Medical Center, 270-05 76th Ave, New Hyde Park, NY, 11040. Tel: 718-470-7070. Fax: 718-470-6150. p. 1665

Sacolic, Brian, Ref, Wilkes University, 187 S Franklin St, Wilkes-Barre, PA, 18766-0998. Tel: 570-408-4250. Fax: 570-408-7823. p. 2156

Sacra, Veronica, Govt Doc, Mgt Prog Analyst, United States Department of Justice, MCB No 4, Quantico, VA, 22135. Tel: 703-632-3213. Fax: 703-632-3214. p. 2487

Saczkowski, Inge, Ch, Niagara Falls Public Library, 4848 Victoria Ave, Niagara Falls, ON, L2E 4C5, CANADA. Tel: 905-356-8080. Fax: 905-356-7004. p. 2824

Saddler, Nancy, Adult Serv, ILL, Pioneer Memorial Library, 375 W Fourth St, Colby, KS, 67701-2197. Tel: 785-460-4470. Fax: 785-460-4472. p. 861

Sade, Marianne, Ref, Maryland Institute College of Art, 1401 Mount Royal Ave, Baltimore, MD, 21217. Tel: 410-225-2304, 410-225-2311. Fax: 410-225-2316. p. 1015

Sadeghi Pari, Akram, Cat Librn, University of Cincinnati, 2540 Clifton Ave, Cincinnati, OH, 45219. Tel: 513-556-0154. Fax: 513-556-6265. p. 1874

Sadkin, Amy, Dir, Newbury Town Library, 0 Lunt St, Byfield, MA, 01922-1232. Tel: 978-465-0539. Fax: 978-465-1071. p. 1072

Sadler, Cathy, Outreach Serv Librn, Taylor County Public Library, 403 N Washington St, Perry, FL, 32347-2791. Tel: 850-838-3512. Fax: 850-838-3514. p. 483

Sadler, Christopher A, Br Mgr, Jackson District Library, Hanover Branch, 118 W Main St, Hanover, MI, 49241. Tel: 517-905-1399. Fax: 517-563-8346. p. 1196

Sadler, Diane, Dir, Bradford County Library System, 16093 Rte 6, Troy, PA, 16947. Tel: 570-297-2436. Fax: 570-297-4197. p. 2146

Sadler, John, Dir, Western University - Libraries, John & Dotsa Bitove Family Law Library, Josephine Spencer Niblett Law Bldg, London, ON, N6A 3K7, CANADA. Tel: 519-661-3171. Fax: 519-661-2012. p. 2819

Sadler, Lori, Ref Asst, Lady Lake Public Library, 225 W Guava St, Lady Lake, FL, 32159. Tel: 352-753-2957. Fax: 352-753-3361. p. 457

Sadler, Molly, Ch, Flagstaff City-Coconino County Public Library System, 300 W Aspen, Flagstaff, AZ, 86001. Tel: 928-213-2331. Fax: 928-774-9573. p. 62

Sadler, Shawna, Assoc Librn, Info Tech Serv, University of Calgary Library, 2500 University Dr NW, Calgary, AB, T2N 1N4, CANADA. Tel: 403-220-3739. Fax: 403-282-1218. p. 2693

Sadler, Stephen, Librn, Grandview Hospital, 405 Grand Ave, Dayton, OH, 45405. Tel: 937-226-3379. Fax: 937-226-3609. p. 1893

Sadlik, Jeanne, Head, User Serv, Interim Dir, Loyola University Chicago Libraries, Health Sciences Library, Bldg 101, Rm 1717, 2160 S First Ave, Maywood, IL, 60153-5585. Tel: 708-216-5304. Fax: 708-216-8115. p. 617

Sadowitz, Daniel, Libr Dir, United States Army, Van Noy Library, 5966 12th St, Bldg 1024, Fort Belvoir, VA, 22060-5554. Tel: 703-806-3323. p. 2464

Sadowski, Ed, Ref & Info Literacy Librn, Arapahoe Community College, 5900 S Santa Fe Dr, Littleton, CO, 80160. Tel: 303-797-5729. Fax: 303-798-4173. p. 316

Sadusky, Lynda, ILL Coordr, Drexel University Health Sciences Libraries, 245 N 15th St MS 449, Philadelphia, PA, 19102-1192. Fax: 215-762-8180. p. 2105

Sady, Amber, Youth Serv Librn, Carson City Library, 900 N Roop St, Carson City, NV, 89701. Tel: 775-887-2244. Fax: 775-887-2273. p. 1425

Saecker, Tasha, Dir, Menasha Public Library, 440 First St, Menasha, WI, 54952-3191. Tel: 920-967-3661. Fax: 920-967-5159. p. 2614

Saed, Christine, Br Mgr, Oakland Public Library, West Oakland, 1801 Adeline St, Oakland, CA, 94607. Tel: 510-238-7352. Fax: 510-238-7551. p. 198

Saeedpour, Vera Beaudin, Dir, The Kurdish Library, 144 Underhill Ave, Brooklyn, NY, 11238. Tel: 718-783-7930. p. 1593

Saeger, Lynnette, Dir, Librn, Southern Lehigh Public Library, 3200 Preston Lane, Center Valley, PA, 18034. Tel: 610-282-8825. Fax: 610-282-8828. p. 2043

Saeli, Marie, Dir, Franklin Park Public Library District, 10311 Grand Ave, Franklin Park, IL, 60131. Tel: 847-455-6016. Fax: 847-455-6416. p. 647

Saenger, Paul, Coll Develop, Curator, Rare Bks, Newberry Library, 60 W Walton St, Chicago, IL, 60610-3305. Tel: 312-255-3533. p. 620

Saenz, Andrea, First Dep Commissioner, Chicago Public Library, 400 S State St, Chicago, IL, 60605. Tel: 312-747-4018. Fax: 312-745-1590. p. 608

Saenz, Janie, Br Mgr, Duval County-San Diego Public Library, Benavides Branch, 131 Mesquite St, Benavides, TX, 78341. Tel: 361-256-4646. Fax: 361-256-4646. p. 2384

Saffady, William, Dr, Prof, Long Island University, C W Post Campus, 720 Northern Blvd, Brookville, NY, 11548-1300. Tel: 516-299-2179. Fax: 516-299-4168. p. 2970

Saffari, Abbas, Libr Mgr, Vancouver Island Regional Library, Comox Branch, 1729 Comox Ave, Comox, BC, V9M 3M2, CANADA. Tel: 250-339-2971. Fax: 250-339-2940. p. 2732

Saffell, Kathleen, Librn, San Luis Obispo County Library, Creston Branch, 6290 Adams, Creston, CA, 93432. Tel: 805-237-3010. p. 254

Saffioti-Hughes, Carollee, Dir, Wabeno Public Library, 4556 N Branch St, Wabeno, WI, 54566. Tel: 715-473-4131. Fax: 715-473-4131. p. 2643

Safley, Ellen Derey, Dir of Libr, University of Texas at Dallas, 800 W Campbell Rd, Richardson, TX, 75080. Tel: 972-883-2916. Fax: 972-883-2473. p. 2374

Safran, Lois, Librn, Temple Emanuel Library, 225 N Country Club Rd, Tucson, AZ, 85716. Tel: 520-327-4501. Fax: 520-327-4504. p. 88

Safratowich, Michael, Cat, University of North Dakota, School of Medicine and Health Sciences, 501 N Columbia Rd, Stop 9002, Grand Forks, ND, 58202-9002. Tel: 701-777-2602. Fax: 701-777-4790. p. 1842

Saft, Roger, Asst Dir, Prescott Public Library, 215 E Goodwin St, Prescott, AZ, 86303. Tel: 928-777-1523. Fax: 928-771-5829. p. 78

Sagaas, Christopher, Ref Serv, Ad, Albany Public Library, 161 Washington Ave, Albany, NY, 12210. Tel: 518-427-4323. Fax: 518-449-3386. p. 1568

Sagan, Belinda, Tech Info Spec, United States Navy, Philadelphia Naval Surface Warfare Center-Carderock Div, Bldg 77L, 1000 Kittyhawk Ave, Philadelphia, PA, 19112. Tel: 215-897-7078. Fax: 215-897-8380. p. 2118

Sagan, Kim, Circ Supvr, Brookfield Public Library, 1900 N Calhoun Rd, Brookfield, WI, 53005. Tel: 262-782-4140. Fax: 262-796-6670. p. 2583

Sagar, Henrietta, Tech Serv, Sturgis District Library, 255 North St, Sturgis, MI, 49091. Tel: 269-659-7224. Fax: 269-651-4534. p. 1229

Sagar, Mary, Admin Librn, Chandler Public Library, 22 S Delaware, Chandler, AZ, 85225. Tel: 480-782-2820. Fax: 480-782-2823. p. 59

Sage, Donelda, Dir, Burlingame Community Library, 122 W Sante Fe Ave, Burlingame, KS, 66413. Tel: 785-654-3400. Fax: 785-654-3411. p. 859

Sage, Pamela R, Head, Ref & Info Serv, Librn III, Montgomery City-County Public Library System, Juliette Hampton Morgan Memorial Library (Main Library), 245 High St, Montgomery, AL, 36104. Tel: 334-240-4999. Fax: 334-240-4980. p. 30

Sage, Tim, Librn, Grand Rapids Public Library, West Side, 713 Bridge St NW, Grand Rapids, MI, 49504. Tel: 616-988-5414. Fax: 616-458-0103. p. 1185

Sager, Natalie, Ref, United States Senate Library, SRB-15 Senate Russell Bldg, Washington, DC, 20510-7112. Tel: 202-224-7106. Fax: 202-224-0879. p. 421

Sager, Norma, Libr Assoc, Beacon College Library, 101 W Main St, Leesburg, FL, 34748. Tel: 352-787-0735. Fax: 352-787-7924. p. 460

Sager, Ruth, Libr Asst, Deseronto Public Library, 358 Main St W, Deseronto, ON, K0K 1X0, CANADA. Tel: 613-396-2744. Fax: 613-396-3466. p. 2802

Sagevick, Cathy, Ref Serv, Mineola Memorial Library, 195 Marcellus Rd, Mineola, NY, 11501. Tel: 516-746-8488. Fax: 516-294-6459. p. 1661

Sagi, Helen, Acq Mgr, Wilfrid Laurier University Library, 75 University Ave W, Waterloo, ON, N2L 3C5, CANADA. Tel: 519-884-0710, Ext 2475. Fax: 519-884-3209. p. 2869

Sagissor, Kathie, Librn, Plainview Public Library, 345 First Ave NW, Plainview, MN, 55964-1295. Tel: 507-534-3425. p. 1271

Sagmoen, Sarah, Instrul Serv, University of Illinois at Springfield, One University Plaza, MS BRK-140, Springfield, IL, 62703-5407. Tel: 217-206-6618. Fax: 217-206-6354. p. 707

Sago, Roberta, Spec Coll Librn, Black Hills State University, 1200 University St, Unit 9676, Spearfish, SD, 57799-9676. Tel: 605-642-6361. Fax: 605-642-6298. p. 2220

Sago, Roberta, Archives, Spec Coll, Black Hills State University, E Y Berry Library Learning Ctr, 1200 University St, Unit 9676, Spearfish, SD, 57799-9676. Tel: 605-642-6361. Fax: 605-642-6298. p. 2973

Sagraves, Barb, Head, Presv, Dartmouth College Library, Baker-Berry Library, 6025 Baker-Berry Library, Hanover, NH, 03755-3525. Tel: 603-646-2560. Fax: 603-646-2167. p. 1450

Saha, Virginia, Dir, Cleveland Health Sciences Library, School of Medicine, Robbins Bldg, 2109 Adelbert Rd, Cleveland, OH, 44106-4914. Tel: 216-368-4540. Fax: 216-368-3008, 216-368-6421. p. 1876

Sahak, Judy Harvey, Librn, Claremont Colleges Library, Ella Strong Denison Library, Scripps College, 1030 N Columbia Ave, Claremont, CA, 91711. Tel: 909-621-8973. Fax: 909-607-1548. p. 134

Sahanatien, Shirley, Librn, Wahta Mohawks, 2664 Meskoa Rd 38, Bala, ON, P0C 1A0, CANADA. Tel: 705-756-2354. Fax: 705-756-2376. p. 2793

Sahey, Kevin, Ad, Casa Grande Public Library, 449 N Dry Lake, Casa Grande, AZ, 85222. Tel: 520-421-8710, Ext 5160. Fax: 520-421-8701. p. 59

Sahl, Silke, Coordr, Northeast Foreign Law Libraries Cooperative Group, Columbia University Library, 435 W 116th St, New York, NY, 10027. Tel: 212-854-1411. Fax: 212-854-3295. p. 2950

Sahlem, James R, Dir, New York Supreme Court, 77 W Eagle St, Buffalo, NY, 14202. Tel: 716-845-9400. Fax: 716-852-3454. p. 1598

Sahlin, Gunnar, Ref, Norwalk Community College, 188 Richards Ave, Norwalk, CT, 06854-1655. Tel: 203-857-7200. Fax: 203-857-7380. p. 362

Sahm, Tatiana, Librn, Onondaga County Public Library, Northeast Community Center, 716 Hawley Ave, Syracuse, NY, 13203. Tel: 315-472-6343, Ext 208. p. 1753

Sahr, Patricia, Dir, Nassau Free Library, 18 Church St, Nassau, NY, 12123-2704. Tel: 518-766-2715. Fax: 518-766-2715. p. 1664

Sahraie, Arlene, Dir, Libr Serv, Bergen County Cooperative Library System, 810 Main St, Hackensack, NJ, 07601. Tel: 201-489-1904. Fax: 201-489-4215. p. 2948

Saia, Denise, Dir, Franklin Township Public Library, 1584 Coles Mill Rd, Franklinville, NJ, 08322. Tel: 856-694-2833. Fax: 856-694-1708. p. 1487

Said, Ismail, In Charge, Northern Illinois University Libraries, Rockford Education Center, NIU REC, 8500 E State St, Rockford, IL, 61108. Tel: 815-753-8760. Fax: 815-753-8769. p. 636

Sailor, Emily, Prog Coordr, Warren County Historical Society, 210 Fourth Ave, Warren, PA, 16365. Tel: 814-723-1795. Fax: 814-723-1795. p. 2150

Sailors, Lori, Fed Doc Librn, Nebraska Library Commission, The Atrium, 1200 N St, Ste 120, Lincoln, NE, 68508-2023. Tel: 402-471-7741. Fax: 402-471-2083. p. 1406

Sain, Annette, Dir, College of the Ozarks, Brownell Research Center Library, Ralph Foster Museum, One Cultural Ct, Point Lookout, MO, 65726. Tel: 417-690-3407. Fax: 417-690-2606. p. 1349

Sain, Lorraine, Dir, McMillan Township Library, 200 Cedar St, Ewen, MI, 49925. Tel: 906-988-2515. Fax: 906-988-2255. p. 1177

Saini, Sanjeev, Librn, Independent Institute Library, 100 Swan Way, Oakland, CA, 94621-1428. Tel: 510-632-1366, Ext 143. Fax: 510-568-6040. p. 196

Saint, Barbara, Librn, University of British Columbia Library, Saint Paul's Hospital Library, 1081 Burrard St, Vancouver, BC, V6Z 1Y6, CANADA. Tel: 604-682-2344, Ext 62090. Fax: 604-806-8013. p. 2743

Saint John, Nancy, Br Mgr, San Diego County Library, El Cajon Branch, 201 E Douglas, El Cajon, CA, 92020. Tel: 619-588-3708. Fax: 619-588-3701. p. 233

Saint-Arnaud, Marcelle, Mgr, Coll Develop, Canada Department of Justice Library, EMB, Rm A-370, 284 Wellington St, Ottawa, ON, K1A 0H8, CANADA. Tel: 613-957-4606. p. 2828

Saint-Gelais, Marie Paule, Head of Libr, Federation des Medecins Omnipraticiens Du Quebec, Two Place Alexis Nihon, 20e étage, 2000-3500 boul de Maisonneuve Ouest, Westmount, QC, H3Z 3C1, CANADA. Tel: 514-878-1911, Ext 258. Fax: 514-878-4455. p. 2915

Sajdak, Bruce, Coordr, Info Literacy, Smith College Libraries, Northampton, MA, 01063. Tel: 413-585-2967. Fax: 413-585-2904. p. 1113

Sakai, Diane, President-Elect, Hawaii Library Consortium, c/o Hawaii Business Research Library, 590 Lipoa Pkwy, No 136, Kihei, HI, 96753. Tel: 808-455-0378. p. 2941

Sakai, Diane H, Librn, Leeward Community College Library, 96-045 Ala Ike, Pearl City, HI, 96782-3393. Tel: 808-455-0378. Fax: 808-453-6729. p. 567

Sakarya, Mustafa, Media Spec, Mercy College Libraries, 555 Broadway, Dobbs Ferry, NY, 10522. Tel: 914-674-7799. Fax: 914-674-7581. p. 1615

Sakellarios, Mary Helen, Ch, Palm Springs Public Library, 217 Cypress Lane, Palm Springs, FL, 33461-1698. Tel: 561-965-2204. Fax: 561-964-2803. p. 480

Sakowski, Donna, Outreach Serv Librn, Saint Clair Shores Public Library, 22500 11 Mile Rd, Saint Clair Shores, MI, 48081-1399. Tel: 586-771-9020. Fax: 586-771-8935. p. 1224

Saksa, Connie, Br Mgr, San Diego County Library, Fletcher Hills, 576 Garfield Ave, El Cajon, CA, 92020-2792. Tel: 619-466-1132. Fax: 619-466-4682. p. 233

Salaba, Athena, Dr, Asst Prof, Kent State University, 314 Library, Kent, OH, 44242-0001. Tel: 330-672-2782. Fax: 330-672-7965. p. 2972

Salahuddin, Bilal, Br Mgr, Harris County Public Library, High Meadows, 4500 Aldine Mail Rte, Houston, TX, 77039. Tel: 281-590-1456. Fax: 281-987-3560. p. 2336

Salame, Salvadore, Br Mgr, Brooklyn Public Library, Pacific, 25 Fourth Ave, Brooklyn, NY, 11217. Tel: 718-638-1531. Fax: 718-638-1580. p. 1592

Salami, Lola, Law Librn, Alberta Law Libraries, Judicial, Calgary Courts Ctr, 2001-N, 601 - 5 St SW, Calgary, AB, T2P 5P7, CANADA. Tel: 403-297-3231. Fax: 403-297-2981. p. 2687

Salamon, Anaïs, Head Librn, McGill University Libraries, Islamic Studies, Morrice Hall, 3485 McTavish St, Montreal, QC, H3A 1Y1, CANADA. Tel: 514-398-4688. Fax: 514-398-8189. p. 2898

Salamone, Sue, Ch Serv Librn, Johnson County Public Library, Clark Pleasant Library, 530 Tracy Rd, Ste 250, New Whiteland, IN, 46184-9699. Tel: 317-535-6206. Fax: 317-535-6018. p. 744

Salas, Jan, ILL, University of New Hampshire Library, 18 Library Way, Durham, NH, 03824. Tel: 603-862-1173. Fax: 603-862-0247. p. 1445

Salas, Jennifer, Youth Serv Coordr, Martin County Library System, 2351 SE Monterey Rd, Stuart, FL, 34996. Tel: 772-221-1405. Fax: 772-219-4959. p. 491

Salas, Sam, Ad, Bulverde Area Rural Library District, 131 Bulverde Crossing, Bulverde, TX, 78163. Tel: 830-438-4864. Fax: 830-980-3362. p. 2293

Salas, Victor, Evening Ref Librn, The John Marshall Law School, 315 S Plymouth Ct, Chicago, IL, 60604. Tel: 312-427-2737. Fax: 312-427-8307. p. 618

Salaun, Jean-Michel, Dir, Universite de Montreal, 3150, rue Jean-Brillant, bur C-2004, Montreal, QC, H3T 1N8, CANADA. Tel: 514-343-6044. Fax: 514-343-5753. p. 2979

Salazar, Anibal, Head, Ref, North Merrick Public Library, 1691 Meadowbrook Rd, North Merrick, NY, 11566. Tel: 516-378-7474. Fax: 516-378-0876. p. 1706

Salazar, Carrie, Visual Res Curator, Lesley University, 700 Beacon St, Boston, MA, 02215-2598. Tel: 617-585-6673. Fax: 617-585-6655. p. 1062

Salazar, Gerardo, Libr Dir, San Benito Public Library, 101 W Rose St, San Benito, TX, 78586-5169. Tel: 956-361-3860. Fax: 956-361-3867. p. 2384

Salazar, Janet, Br Mgr, Charles County Public Library, Waldorf West Branch, 10405 O'Donnell Pl, Waldorf, MD, 301-645-1395. Tel: 301-645-1395. p. 1034

Salazar, Lisa, Dir, East Granby Public Library, 24 Center St, East Granby, CT, 06026. Tel: 860-653-3002. Fax: 860-653-3936. p. 337

Salazar, Ramiro S, Dir, San Antonio Public Library, 600 Soledad, San Antonio, TX, 78205-2786. Tel: 210-207-2500. Fax: 210-207-2603. p. 2382

Salazar-Mallorquin, Jenny, Ser Librn, Inter-American University of Puerto Rico, San German Campus, Ave Inter-American University, Rd 102, K 30 6, San German, PR, 00683-9801. Tel: 787-264-1912, Ext 7537. Fax: 787-264-2544. p. 2675

Salber, Cecilia, Acq, Kingsborough Community College, 2001 Oriental Blvd, Brooklyn, NY, 11235. Tel: 718-368-5430. Fax: 718-368-5482. p. 1592

Salber, Peter, Coordr, User Serv, Long Island University, One University Plaza, Brooklyn, NY, 11201-9926. Tel: 718-780-4180. Fax: 718-780-4057. p. 1593

Salcedo, Dianne, Br Librn, Tech Serv, Wheeler Memorial Library, 49 E Main St, Orange, MA, 01364-1267. Tel: 978-544-2495. Fax: 978-544-1116. p. 1116

Salcedo, Marina, Tech Serv, University of Florida Health Science Center-Jacksonville, 653-1 W Eighth St, Jacksonville, FL, 32209-6511. Tel: 904-244-3240. Fax: 904-244-3191. p. 455

Saldana, Lupe, Circ, Loveland Public Library, 300 N Adams Ave, Loveland, CO, 80537-5754. Tel: 970-962-2591. Fax: 970-962-2905. p. 317

Saldanha, Guy, ILL Supvr, Bowdoin College Library, 3000 College Sta, Brunswick, ME, 04011-8421. p. 979

Saldivar, Tanya, Librn, Collier County Public Library, Immokalee Branch, 417 N First St, Immokalee, FL, 34142. Tel: 239-657-2882. Fax: 239-657-4901. p. 471

Sale, Betsy, Chmn, Harrodsburg Historical Society, 220 S Chiles St, Harrodsburg, KY, 40330-1631. Tel: 859-734-5985. p. 916

Sale, Cheryl J, Dir, Hillsboro Public Library, 214 School St, Hillsboro, IL, 62049-1547. Tel: 217-532-3055. Fax: 217-532-6813. p. 656

Sale, Kathy, Ref, North Florida Community College Library, 325 NW Turner Davis Dr, Madison, FL, 32340-1699. Tel: 850-973-9452. p. 462

Saleh, Dahlia, Librn, Allstate Insurance Co, 2775 Sanders Rd, A5, Northbrook, IL, 60062-6127. Tel: 847-402-8735. Fax: 847-326-7320. p. 682

Salela, Pamela, Instrul Serv Librn, University of Illinois at Springfield, One University Plaza, MS BRK-140, Springfield, IL, 62703-5407. Tel: 217-206-6783. Fax: 217-206-6354. p. 707

Salem, Linda, Head, Ref Serv, San Diego State University Library & Information Access, 5500 Campanile Dr, San Diego, CA, 92182-8050. Tel: 619-594-5148. Fax: 619-594-3270. p. 237

Salemme, Kevin, Dir, Media Instrul Serv, Merrimack College, 315 Turnpike St, North Andover, MA, 01845. Tel: 978-837-5215. Fax: 978-837-5434. p. 1111

Salenikas, Marina, Ch, Stevens Memorial Library, 345 Main St, North Andover, MA, 01845. Tel: 978-688-9505. Fax: 978-688-9507. p. 1112

Salerno, Cheryl, Circ, Oklahoma Wesleyan University Library, 2201 Silver Lake Rd, Bartlesville, OK, 74006-6299. Tel: 918-335-6285. Fax: 918-335-6220. p. 1958

Sales, Robin, Libr Dir, Kellogg-Hubbard Library, 135 Main St, Montpelier, VT, 05602. Tel: 802-223-3338. Fax: 802-223-3338. p. 2429

Saleta, Kathy, Circ, Hillside Public Library, 405 N Hillside Ave, Hillside, IL, 60162-1295. Tel: 708-449-7510. Fax: 708-449-6119. p. 656

Salfer, Myla, ILL Spec, Traverse Des Sioux Library System, 1400 Madison Ave, Ste 622, Mankato, MN, 56001-5488. Tel: 507-625-6169. Fax: 507-625-4049. p. 1257

Salgado, Jose, Ref, San Diego City College, 1313 Park Blvd, San Diego, CA, 92101-4712. Tel: 619-388-3421. Fax: 619-388-3410. p. 232

Salgado, Kathy, Ref, Kettering College, 3737 Southern Blvd, Kettering, OH, 45429-1299. Tel: 937-395-8053, Ext 6. Fax: 937-395-8861. p. 1907

Salhany, Stephen R, Cat Librn, Ser, University of Maine School of Law, 246 Deering Ave, Portland, ME, 04102. Tel: 207-780-4829. Fax: 207-780-4913. p. 997

Saliba, Elizabeth, Dir, Phoenix College, 1202 W Thomas Rd, Phoenix, AZ, 85013. Tel: 602-285-7457. Fax: 602-285-7368. p. 76

Salinas, Andrew, Ref Archivist, Amistad Research Center, Tulane University, Tilton Hall, 6823 St Charles Ave, New Orleans, LA, 70118. Tel: 504-862-3228. Fax: 504-862-8961. p. 959

Salinas, Rovina, Mgr, Instrul Tech, Contra Costa County Office of Education, 77 Santa Barbara Rd, Pleasant Hill, CA, 94523. Tel: 925-942-5332. Fax: 925-942-5398. p. 210

Salinero, David, Doc, Ref, Delta State University, Laflore Circle at Fifth Ave, Cleveland, MS, 38733-2599. Tel: 662-846-4440. Fax: 662-846-4443. p. 1296

Salisbury, Kim, Asst Librn, Maple Rapids Public Library, 130 S Maple Ave, Maple Rapids, MI, 48853. Tel: 989-682-4464. Fax: 989-682-4149. p. 1206

Salisbury, Lutishoor, Head of Libr, University of Arkansas Libraries, Chemistry & Biochemistry, University of Arkansas, 225 CHEM, Fayetteville, AR, 72701-4002. Tel: 479-575-2557. Fax: 479-575-6656. p. 100

Salkowitz, Lauren, Br Co-Mgr, Iberia Parish Library, Lydia Branch, 4800 Freyou Rd, New Iberia, LA, 70560. Tel: 337-364-7808. Fax: 337-364-7808. p. 959

Sall, Janice, Asst Libr Dir, Allendale Township Library, 6175 Library Ln, Allendale, MI, 49401. Tel: 616-895-4178, Ext 14. Fax: 616-895-5178. p. 1149

Sallade, Kelley, Dir, Rock Hill Public Library, 9811 Manchester Rd, Rock Hill, MO, 63119. Tel: 314-962-4723. Fax: 314-962-3932. p. 1351

Sallee, Donna, Librn, Inman Public Library, 100 N Main, Inman, KS, 67546. Tel: 620-585-2474. p. 873

Sallee, Patricia, Tech Serv Mgr, McCracken County Public Library, 555 Washington St, Paducah, KY, 42003-1735. Tel: 270-442-2510, Ext 13. Fax: 270-443-9322. p. 932

Sallforf, Paula, Dir, Saginaw Public Library, 355 W McLeroy Blvd, Saginaw, TX, 76179. Tel: 817-232-0300. Fax: 817-232-9134. p. 2378

Salloom, Clara, Bibliographer, Ref Librn, Harcum College Library, 750 Montgomery Ave, Bryn Mawr, PA, 19010-3476. Tel: 610-526-6085. Fax: 610-526-6086. p. 2039

Salls, Timothy, Archivist, New England Historic Genealogical Society Library, 99-101 Newbury St, Boston, MA, 02116-3007. Tel: 617-536-5740, Ext 232. Fax: 617-536-7307. p. 1065

Sally, Dana, Dean, Western Carolina University, 176 Central Dr, Cullowhee, NC, 28723. Tel: 828-227-7307. Fax: 828-227-7015. p. 1786

Sally, Fredella, Librn, Caritas Holy Family Hospital & Medical Center, 70 East St, Methuen, MA, 01844-4597. Tel: 978-687-0151, Ext 2392. Fax: 978-688-7689. p. 1105

Salm, Judy, Ref Serv, Fort Hays State University, 600 Park St, Hays, KS, 67601-4099. Tel: 785-628-4537. Fax: 785-628-4096. p. 871

Salm, Kay, Sr Res Spec, Northrop Grumman Corp, Integrated Systems Western Region Library, One Hornet Way, TS20/W7, El Segundo, CA, 90245. Tel: 310-331-7105. Fax: 310-332-5562. p. 176

Salmans, Janice, Head Librn, Stratton Public Library, 331 New York Ave, Stratton, CO, 80836-1128. Tel: 719-348-5922. Fax: 719-348-5922. p. 323

Salmans, Karen S, Dir, Hanston City Library, 105 N Logan, Hanston, KS, 67849-9409. Tel: 620-623-2798. p. 870

Salmon, Angela, Pub Serv Asst, College of Coastal Georgia, Camden Center Learning Resources Center, 8001 Lakes Blvd, Kingsland, GA, 31548. Tel: 912-510-3331. p. 521

Salmon, Helen, Info Res, University of Guelph, 50 Stone Rd E, Guelph, ON, N1G 2W1, CANADA. Tel: 519-824-4120, Ext 52121. Fax: 519-824-6931. p. 2807

Salmon, Jane, Mgr, Ch Serv, Barrie Public Library, 60 Worsley St, Barrie, ON, L4M 1L6, CANADA. Tel: 705-728-1010, Ext 7017. Fax: 705-728-4322. p. 2793

Salmon, Linda, Pub Serv, Pocono Mountain Public Library, 5540 Memorial Blvd, Tobyhanna, PA, 18466. Tel: 570-894-8860. Fax: 570-894-8852. p. 2146

Salmon, Michael W, AV Coordr, Cat, Ref, LA84 Foundation, 2141 W Adams Blvd, Los Angeles, CA, 90018. Tel: 323-730-4646. Fax: 323-730-0546. p. 171

Salmon, Patricia, Curator of Hist, Staten Island Institute of Arts & Sciences, Snug Harbor Cultural Center, 1000 Richmond Terrace, Bldg H, Staten Island, NY, 10301. Tel: 718-727-1135. Fax: 718-273-5683. p. 1748

Salmon, Robin, Curator, Brookgreen Gardens Library, 1931 Brookgreen Dr, Murrells Inlet, SC, 29576. Tel: 843-235-6000. Fax: 843-235-6003. p. 2201

Salmon, Rosemarie, Librn, The Church of Jesus Christ of Latter-Day Saints, 76 Saint Paul Dr, Ventura, CA, 93003. Tel: 805-643-5607. p. 279

Salmon, Virginia, Pub Serv Librn, Per, Northeast State Community College, 2425 Hwy 75, Blountville, TN, 37617-6350. Tel: 423-354-2429. Fax: 423-323-0254. p. 2224

Salmons, Nadine, Tech Serv Mgr, United States Army, Grant Library, 1637 Flint St, Fort Carson, CO, 80913-4105. Tel: 719-526-8140. Fax: 719-524-0070. p. 307

Salmons, Richard, Dir, Fort McMurray Public Library, 151 MacDonald Dr, Fort McMurray, AB, T9H 5C5, CANADA. Tel: 780-743-7800. Fax: 780-743-7938. p. 2704

Salnave, Melissa, Librn, Fort Bend County Libraries, Fort Bend County Law Library, 401 Jackson, Richmond, TX, 77469. Tel: 281-341-3718. Fax: 281-342-0734. p. 2375

Salner, David, Access Serv, Hood College, 401 Rosemont Ave, Frederick, MD, 21701. Tel: 301-696-3909. Fax: 301-696-3796. p. 1029

Salo, Pam, Dir, Buchanan District Library, 128 E Front St, Buchanan, MI, 49107. Tel: 269-695-3681. Fax: 269-695-0004. p. 1160

Salomon, Carol, Archivist, Sci, Cooper Union for Advancement of Science & Art Library, Seven E Seventh St, New York, NY, 10003. Tel: 212-353-4187. Fax: 212-353-4017. p. 1676

Salomon, Kathleen, Asst Dir, Getty Research Institute, 1200 Getty Center Dr, Ste 1100, Los Angeles, CA, 90049-1688. Tel: 310-440-7390. Fax: 310-440-7780. p. 170

Salonen, Ethel M, Dept Head, Mitre Corp, 202 Burlington Rd, Bedford, MA, 01730-1420. Tel: 781-271-7667. Fax: 781-271-2452. p. 1052

Salonen, Ethel M, Dept Head, Info Serv, The MITRE Corporation, 202 Burlington Rd, MS C222, Bedford, MA, 01730. Tel: 781-271-4570. Fax: 781-271-2185. p. 1052

Salonen, Michelle, Librn, Mattice-Val Cote Public Library, Hwy 11, Mattice, ON, P0L 1T0, CANADA. Tel: 705-364-5301. Fax: 705-364-6431. p. 2821

Salony, Timothy, Syst Coordr, Altoona Area Public Library, 1600 Fifth Ave, Altoona, PA, 16602-3693. Tel: 814-946-0417, Ext 132. Fax: 814-946-3230. p. 2028

Salony, Timothy Joseph, Syst Adminr, Blair County Library System, 1600 Fifth Ave, Altoona, PA, 16602-3621. Tel: 814-946-0417. Fax: 814-946-3230. p. 2028

Salpeter, Michael, Asst Br Mgr, Atlanta-Fulton Public Library System, Northeast-Spruill Oaks Regional Library, 9560 Spruill Rd, Alpharetta, GA, 30022. Tel: 770-360-8820. Fax: 770-360-8823. p. 512

Salrin, Melissa M, Archivist & Spec Coll Librn, Whitman College, 345 Boyer Ave, Walla Walla, WA, 99362. Tel: 509-526-4731. Fax: 509-527-5900. p. 2547

Salsbury, Kathleen, Bibliog Instr, Circ, Ref Serv, Munson-Williams-Proctor Arts Institute Library, 310 Genesee St, Utica, NY, 13502. Tel: 315-797-0000, Ext 2123. Fax: 315-797-5608. p. 1759

Salt, Elizabeth, Cat, Otterbein University, 138 W Main St, Westerville, OH, 43081. Tel: 614-823-1939. Fax: 614-823-1921. p. 1946

Salter, Anne, Dir, Oglethorpe University, 4484 Peachtree Rd NE, Atlanta, GA, 30319. Tel: 404-364-8511. Fax: 404-364-8517. p. 517

Salter, Elaine, Cat, Wellington County Library, 552 Wellington Rd 18, RR1, Fergus, ON, N1M 2W3, CANADA. Tel: 519-846-0918, Ext 223. Fax: 519-846-2066. p. 2805

Saltkill, Jeannie, Asst Dir, Polk County Library, 1690 W Broadway St, Bolivar, MO, 65613. Tel: 417-326-4531. Fax: 417-326-4366. p. 1320

Saltman, Judith, Prof, University of British Columbia, The Irving K Barber Centre, 1961 E Mall, Ste 470, Vancouver, BC, V6T 1Z1, CANADA. Tel: 604-822-2404. Fax: 604-822-6006. p. 2977

Saltsman, Joyce, Circ, Indiana University-Purdue University Fort Wayne, 2101 E Coliseum Blvd, Fort Wayne, IN, 46805-1499. Tel: 260-481-4137. Fax: 260-481-6509. p. 741

Saltxmann, Mona, Dir, Bristol Public Library, 1855 Greenville Rd, Bristolville, OH, 44402-9700. Tel: 330-889-3651. Fax: 330-889-9794. p. 1861

Saltz, Ryan, Circ Librn, Florida Coastal School of Law, 8787 Baypine Rd, Jacksonville, FL, 32256. Tel: 904-680-7663. Fax: 904-680-7677. p. 452

Saltzman, Jane, Coordr, Evansville Area Library Consortium, 3700 Washington Ave, Evansville, IN, 47750. Tel: 812-485-4151. Fax: 812-485-7564. p. 2943

Saltzman, Maureen, Ref Librn, Stoneham Public Library, 431 Main St, Stoneham, MA, 02180. Tel: 781-438-1324. Fax: 781-279-3836. p. 1129

Saltzman, Sherri, Ser & Electronic Res Librn, Loyola University Chicago Libraries, Elizabeth M Cudahy Memorial Library, 6525 N Sheridan Rd, Chicago, IL, 60626. p. 617

Salvado, Lucy, Mgr, Ch Serv, Yorba Linda Public Library, 18181 Imperial Hwy, Yorba Linda, CA, 92886-3437. Tel: 714-777-2873. Fax: 714-777-0640. p. 285

Salvadori, T R, Coll Develop, Margaret E Heggan Free Public Library of the Township of Washington, 606 Delsea Dr, Sewell, NJ, 08080. Tel: 856-589-3334. Fax: 856-582-2042. p. 1529

Salvarrey, Gustavo, Music & Media Librn, Per, University of Puerto Rico Library, Cayey Campus, 205 Ave Antonio R Barcelo, Cayey, PR, 00736. Tel: 787-738-2161, Ext 2138. Fax: 787-263-2108. p. 2672

Salvatore, Russo, Asst Dir, Pub Serv, Touro College Libraries, 43 W 23rd St, Fifth Fl, New York, NY, 10010. Tel: 212-463-0400, Ext 222. Fax: 212-627-3696. p. 1701

Salvetti, M Eva, Libr Tech, Pension Benefit Guaranty Corporation, 1200 K St NW, Ste 360, Washington, DC, 20005-4026. Tel: 202-326-4000, Ext 3242. Fax: 202-326-4011. p. 412

Salvo, Angelo, Archivist, Bethune-Cookman College, 640 Mary McLeod Bethune Blvd, Daytona Beach, FL, 32114. Tel: 386-481-2186. Fax: 386-481-2182. p. 435

Salyards, Jackie, Dir, Randolph County Library, 111 W Everett St, Pocahontas, AR, 72455. Tel: 870-892-5617. Fax: 870-892-1142. p. 113

Salyer, Anna, Head, Commun Outreach, University of Washington Libraries, Tacoma Library, 1900 Commerce St, Box 358460, Tacoma, WA, 98402-3100. Tel: 253-692-4448. Fax: 253-692-4445. p. 2535

Salyers, Catherine, Dir, Saint Joseph's College, Hwy 231 S, Rensselaer, IN, 47978. Tel: 219-866-6212. Fax: 219-866-6135. p. 774

Salyers, Lisa, Br Mgr, Public Library of Cincinnati & Hamilton County, Blue Ash Branch, 4911 Cooper Rd, Blue Ash, OH, 45242. Tel: 513-369-6051. Fax: 513-369-4464. p. 1871

Salzberg, Anne, Librn, Reed Smith, LLP, 3110 Fairview Park Dr, Ste 1400, Falls Church, VA, 22042. Tel: 703-641-4200, 703-641-4367. Fax: 703-641-4340. p. 2463

Salzer, Adele, Br Mgr, Saint Tammany Parish Library, Pearl River Branch, 64580 Hwy 41, Pearl River, LA, 70452. Tel: 985-863-5518. Fax: 985-863-5518. p. 948

Salzer, Margaret, Dir, Dewey County Library, 212 Main, Timber Lake, SD, 57656. Tel: 605-865-3541. p. 2220

Salzman, Sandra, Tech Serv, Hartland Public Library, 110 E Park Ave, Hartland, WI, 53029. Tel: 262-367-3350. Fax: 262-369-2251. p. 2597

Salzman, Scott, Syst Librn, Furman University Libraries, 3300 Poinsett Hwy, Greenville, SC, 29613-4100. Tel: 864-294-3204. Fax: 864-294-3004. p. 2195

Salzmann, Rana Hutchinson, Librn, American Planning Association, 122 S Michigan Ave, Ste 1600, Chicago, IL, 60603-6107. Tel: 312-431-9100, Ext 6353. Fax: 312-431-9985. p. 606

Samad, Evelyn, Librn, Tippecanoe County-Ivy Tech Library, 3101 S Creasy Lane, Lafayette, IN, 47903. Tel: 765-269-5382. Fax: 765-269-5383. p. 759

Samadi, Mehry, Cat, University of San Francisco, Zief Law Library, 2101 Fulton St, San Francisco, CA, 94117-1004. Tel: 415-422-6679. Fax: 415-422-2345. p. 249

Samaras, Julie, Librn, Waverly Public Library, 291 N Pearl St, Waverly, IL, 62692. Tel: 217-435-2051. Fax: 217-435-2051. p. 716

Sambets, Nancy, Librn, Museum of York County, 4621 Mount Gallant Rd, Rock Hill, SC, 29732-9905. Tel: 803-329-2121. Fax: 803-329-5249. p. 2202

Samdahl, Don, Head Librn, Virginia Military Institute, Letcher Ave, Lexington, VA, 24450. Tel: 540-464-7228. Fax: 540-464-7279. p. 2474

Samek, Toni, Dr, Prof, University of Alberta, 3-20 Rutherford S, Edmonton, AB, T6G 2J4, CANADA. Tel: 780-492-4578. Fax: 780-492-2430. p. 2977

Samet O'Leary, Jan, Acq of Monographs & Journals, Coll Develop, Dir, Hood College, 401 Rosemont Ave, Frederick, MD, 21701. Tel: 301-696-3934. Fax: 301-696-3796. p. 1029

Sami, Rahul, Asst Prof, University of Michigan, 304 West Hall, 1085 S University, Ann Arbor, MI, 48109-1107. Tel: 734-763-2285. Fax: 734-764-2475. p. 2967

Samitt, Mindy, Sr Info Spec, GE Asset Management, 3003 Summer St, Stamford, CT, 06905. Tel: 203-921-2003. p. 369

Samko, Patrice, Coordr, Ref (Info Serv), Burbank Public Library, 110 N Glenoaks Blvd, Burbank, CA, 91502-1203. Tel: 818-238-5600. Fax: 818-238-5553. p. 130

Samland, Amanda, Librn, Johnson & Wales University, College of Business, 7150 Montview Blvd, Denver, CO, 80220. Tel: 303-256-9378. Fax: 303-256-9459. p. 302

Samland, Amanda, Asst Librn, American Institute of Baking, 1213 Bakers Way, Manhattan, KS, 66502. Tel: 785-537-4750, Ext 125. Fax: 785-537-1493. p. 881

Sammet, Lisa, Libr Dir, Jeudevine Memorial Library, 93 N Main St, Hardwick, VT, 05843. Tel: 802-586-7533. Fax: 802-472-3793. p. 2425

Sammis, Betty, Dir, North Palm Beach Public Library, 303 Anchorage Dr, North Palm Beach, FL, 33408. Tel: 561-841-3383. Fax: 561-848-2874. p. 473

Sammon, Christine E, Dir, Alberta College of Art & Design, 1407 14th Ave NW, Calgary, AB, T2N 4R3, CANADA. Tel: 403-284-7630. Fax: 403-289-6682. p. 2687

Sammons, Christa A, Curator, Coll of German Lit, Yale University Library, Beinecke Rare Book & Manuscript, 121 Wall St, New Haven, CT, 06520. Tel: 203-432-2964. Fax: 203-432-4047. p. 356

Samokishyn, Marta, Coll Develop Librn, Saint Paul University Library, 223 Main St, Ottawa, ON, K1S 1C4, CANADA. Tel: 613-236-1393, Ext 2313. Fax: 613-751-4031. p. 2833

Samora, Tara-jean, ILL Coordr, Lyndon State College, 1001 College Rd, Lyndonville, VT, 05851. Tel: 802-626-6366. Fax: 802-626-6331. p. 2427

Samowitz, Len, Chief, Ref Serv, Federal Deposit Insurance Corp Library, 550 17th St NW, Washington, DC, 20429-0002. Tel: 202-898-3631. Fax: 202-898-3984. p. 400

Sampey, Betty, Br Mgr, Lafourche Parish Public Library, Gheens Branch, 153 N Leon Dr, Gheens, LA, 70355. Tel: 985-532-2288. Fax: 985-532-2288. p. 971

Sampietro, Susan, Ref Librn, Westwood Free Public Library, 49 Park Ave, Westwood, NJ, 07675. Tel: 201-664-0583. Fax: 201-664-6088. p. 1543

Sample, Deb, Br Librn, Holmes Community College, Ridgeland Campus, 412 W Ridgeland Ave, Ridgeland, MS, 39158-1410. Tel: 601-605-3303. Fax: 601-605-3410. p. 1314

Sample, Holbrook, Mgr, Libr Serv, Public Library of Cincinnati & Hamilton County, 800 Vine St, Cincinnati, OH, 45202-2009. Tel: 513-369-4408. Fax: 513-369-6993. p. 1871

Sample, Johnathon, ILL Spec, Southeastern Oklahoma State University, 1405 N Fourth Ave, PMB 4105, Durant, OK, 74701-0609. Tel: 580-745-2931. Fax: 580-745-7463. p. 1961

Sample, Judith, Ref, Amarillo Public Library, 413 E Fourth Ave, Amarillo, TX, 79101. Tel: 806-378-3054. Fax: 806-378-9327. p. 2274

Sample, Mark, Dir, Media Serv, Stanly Community College, Snyder Bldg, Albemarle, NC, 28001. Tel: 704-991-0259. Fax: 704-991-0112. p. 1773

Sample, Rick A, Dir, Libr Serv, Capitol College, 11301 Springfield Rd, Laurel, MD, 20708. Tel: 301-369-2800. Fax: 301-369-2552. p. 1034

Sample, Sharon, Access & Ser Librn, Quincy University, 1800 College Ave, Quincy, IL, 62301-2699. Tel: 217-228-5432, Ext 3801. Fax: 217-228-5354. p. 693

Sampley, Lisa, Mgr, Coll Serv, Springfield-Greene County Library District, 4653 S Campbell, Springfield, MO, 65810-1723. Tel: 417-882-0714. Fax: 417-883-9348. p. 1367

Sampsel, Laurie, Head Music Libr, Prof, University of Colorado Boulder, 1720 Pleasant St, 184 UCB, Boulder, CO, 80309-0184. Tel: 303-492-3929. Fax: 303-492-3340. p. 291

Sampsel, Laurie, Fac Dir, University of Colorado Boulder, Howard B Waltz Music Library, Imig Music Bldg, N250, 1720 Pleasant St, 184 UCB, Boulder, CO, 80309-0184. Tel: 303-492-3929. Fax: 303-735-0100. p. 292

Sampson, Ann, Librn, North Central Missouri College Library, Geyer Hall, Rm 103, 1301 Main St, Trenton, MO, 64683. Tel: 660-359-3948, Ext 1322, 660-359-3948, Ext 1325, 660-359-3948, Ext 1335, 660-359-3948, Ext 322. Fax: 660-359-2211. p. 1369

Sampson, Debra, Dir, Academy of Art University Library, 180 New Montogomery, 6th Flr, San Francisco, CA, 94105. Tel: 415-618-3899. Fax: 415-618-3981. p. 240

Sampson, Dennis, Librn, Library of the Friends of Boerner Botanical Gardens, 9400 Boerner Dr, Hales Corners, WI, 53130. Tel: 414-525-5637. p. 2597

Sampson, Dennis, Dir, New Berlin Public Library, 15105 Library Lane, New Berlin, WI, 53151. Tel: 262-785-4980. Fax: 262-785-4984. p. 2625

Sampson, Linda, Asst Librn, Abington Public Library, 600 Gliniewicz Way, Abington, MA, 02351. Tel: 781-982-2139. Fax: 781-878-7361. p. 1047

Sampson, Lynda, Adjunct Ref Librn, Cerritos College Library, 11110 Alondra Blvd, Norwalk, CA, 90650. Tel: 562-860-2451, Ext 2430. Fax: 562-467-5002. p. 195

Sampson, Margaret, Librn, Jackson County Library, Interior Branch, PO Box 24, Interior, SD, 57750. p. 2213

Sampson, Margaret, Mgr, Libr Serv, Children's Hospital of Eastern Ontario, 401 Smyth Rd, Ottawa, ON, K1H 8L1, CANADA. Tel: 613-737-7600, Ext 2206. Fax: 613-738-4806. p. 2830

Sampson, Michelle, Dir, Wadleigh Memorial Library, 49 Nashua St, Milford, NH, 03055-3753. Tel: 603-673-2408. Fax: 603-672-6064. p. 1457

Sampson, Sara, Dep Dir, University of North Carolina at Chapel Hill, Kathrine R Everett Law Library, UNC Law Library, 160 Ridge Rd, CB No 3385, Chapel Hill, NC, 27599-3385. Tel: 919-962-6202. p. 1781

Sampson, Sherry, Dir, Moffat County Libraries, 570 Green St, Craig, CO, 81625-3027. Tel: 970-824-5116. Fax: 970-824-2867. p. 297

Sampson, Vince L, Mgr, Illinois Agricultural Association, 1701 N Towanda Ave, Bloomington, IL, 61701. Tel: 309-557-2552. Fax: 309-557-3185. p. 595

Sampson, Zora, Dir, University of Wisconsin - Platteville, One University Plaza, Platteville, WI, 53818. Tel: 608-342-1645. p. 2630

Sampson, Zora J, Dir, University of Wisconsin, 1800 College Dr, Rice Lake, WI, 54868-2497. Tel: 715-234-8369. Fax: 715-234-1975. p. 2634

Samra, Gurpreet, Dir, Ecorse Public Library, 4184 W Jefferson Ave, Ecorse, MI, 48229. Tel: 313-389-2030. Fax: 313-389-2032. p. 1176

Samra, Gurpreet, Dir, Wayne County Library, 221 Burke St, River Rouge, MI, 48218. Tel: 313-843-2040. Fax: 313-842-4716. p. 1221

Sams, Annanaomi, Dir, Pacific Northwest National Laboratory, 2770 University Dr, Richland, WA, 99354. Tel: 509-372-7448. Fax: 509-372-7426. p. 2526

Sams, Annanaomi, Dir, Washington State University Tri-Cities, 2770 University Dr, Richland, WA, 99354. Tel: 509-372-7448. Fax: 509-372-7281. p. 2526

Sams, Jennifer, Instruction & Learning Librn, Michigan Technological University, 1400 Townsend Dr, Houghton, MI, 49931-1295. Tel: 906-487-2698. p. 1191

Sams, Melinda, Coordr, Georgia Northwestern Technical College, Gordon County Campus Library, 1151 Hwy 53 Spur SW, Calhoun, GA, 30701. Tel: 706-624-1122. Fax: 706-624-1107. p. 548

Samsa, Heather, Media Serv, Toccoa Falls College, PO Box 800749, Toccoa Falls, GA, 30598. Tel: 706-886-6831, Ext 5300. Fax: 706-282-6010. p. 554

Samson, Lisa, Librn, Moretown Memorial Library, 897 Rte 100-B, Moretown, VT, 05660-9120. Tel: 802-496-9728. p. 2429

Samson, Sarah, Circ, ILL & Distance Libr Serv Spec, Reserves, Universite Laval Bibliotheque, Bibliotheque des Sciences Humaines et Sociales, Pavillon Jean-Charles-Bonenfant, 2345, allée des Bibliothèques, Quebec, QC, G1V 0A6, CANADA. Fax: 418-656-3048. p. 2906

Samsundar, Devica, Online Serv, Baptist Hospital of Miami, 8900 N Kendall Dr, Miami, FL, 33176. Tel: 786-596-6506. Fax: 786-596-5910. p. 464

Samsundar, Devica, Online Serv, South Miami Hospital, 6200 SW 73rd St, Miami, FL, 33143. Tel: 786-662-8219. Fax: 786-662-5124. p. 468

Samuel, Eunice G, Head, Ref Serv, Tuskegee University, Hollis Burke Frissell Bldg, 1200 W Old Montgomery Rd, Tuskegee, AL, 36088. Tel: 334-727-8892, 334-727-8894. Fax: 334-727-9282. p. 39

Samuel, Judith, Librn, Los Angeles Trade Technical College Library, 400 W Washington Blvd, Los Angeles, CA, 90015. Tel: 213-763-3958. Fax: 213-763-5393. p. 175

Samuel, T Huang, Assoc Dean, Advan & Develop, University of Florida Libraries, 535 Library W, Gainesville, FL, 32611-7000. Tel: 352-273-2505. Fax: 352-392-7251. p. 449

Samuels, Alix, Adult Serv, New Braunfels Public Library, 700 E Common St, New Braunfels, TX, 78130-5689. Tel: 830-221-4316. Fax: 830-608-2151. p. 2365

Samuels, Deborra, Libr Mgr, United States Environmental Protection Agency, 75 Hawthorne St, 13th Flr, San Francisco, CA, 94105. Tel: 415-972-3655. Fax: 415-947-3553. p. 248

Samuels, Kay, Managing Librn, WeirFoulds Library, The Exchange Tower, Ste1600, 130 King St W, Toronto, ON, M5X 1J5, CANADA. Tel: 416-947-5057. Fax: 416-365-1876. p. 2867

Samuels, Merrily, Asst Dir, Hampstead Public Library, Nine Mary E Clark Dr, Hampstead, NH, 03841. Tel: 603-329-6411. Fax: 603-329-6036. p. 1449

Samuels, Tara, Ref Serv, Ad, Otis Library, Two Cliff St, Norwich, CT, 06360. Tel: 860-889-2365, Ext 13. Fax: 860-886-4744. p. 362

Samuelson, Claire, Dir, Casemate Museum Library, 20 Bernard Rd, Fort Monroe, VA, 23651-1004. Tel: 757-788-3391. Fax: 757-788-3886. p. 2465

Samuelson, Ryan, Doc, Midwestern State University, 3410 Taft Ave, Wichita Falls, TX, 76308-2099. Tel: 940-397-4177. Fax: 940-397-4689. p. 2400

Samuelson, Todd, Curator, Texas A&M University Libraries, Cushing Memorial Library & Archives, 5000 TAMU, College Station, TX, 77843-5000. Tel: 979-845-1951. Fax: 979-845-1441. p. 2299

Samul, Tara, Head, Adult Serv, Head, Ref, New London Public Library, 63 Huntington St, New London, CT, 06320. Tel: 860-447-1411. Fax: 860-443-2083. p. 360

Samwald, Elaine, Coll Develop Librn, Kwantlen Polytechnic University Library, 12666 72 Ave., Surrey, BC, V3W 2M8, CANADA. Tel: 604-599-3066. Fax: 604-599-2106. p. 2738

San Ramon, Maria Rapada, Tech Serv, North Chicago Public Library, 2100 Argonne Dr, North Chicago, IL, 60064. Tel: 847-689-0125, Ext 105. Fax: 847-689-9117. p. 682

Sanabria, Diane, YA Serv, Leominster Public Library, 30 West St, Leominster, MA, 01453. Tel: 978-534-7522. Fax: 978-840-3357. p. 1098

Sanada, Joy, Librn, Douglas County Library System, Myrtle Creek Branch, 231 Division, Myrtle Creek, OR, 97457. Tel: 541-863-5945. Fax: 541-863-5945. p. 2016

Sanak, Francene, Dir, Trenton Veterans Memorial Library, 2790 Westfield Rd, Trenton, MI, 48183-2482. Tel: 734-676-9777. Fax: 734-676-9895. p. 1232

Sanborn, Carol, Youth Serv Librn, Hampton Falls Free Public Library, Seven Drinkwater Rd, Hampton Falls, NH, 03844-2116. Tel: 603-926-3682. Fax: 603-926-0170. p. 1449

Sanborn, Colin, Circ Librn, Fiske Free Library, 108 Broad St, Claremont, NH, 03743-2673. Tel: 603-542-7017. Fax: 603-542-7029. p. 1441

Sanborn, George, Ref, State Transportation Library, Ten Park Plaza, Boston, MA, 02116. Tel: 617-973-8000. Fax: 617-973-7153. p. 1067

Sanborn, Karen, Media Spec, Castleton State College, 178 Alumni Dr, Castleton, VT, 05735. Tel: 802-468-1256. Fax: 802-468-1475. p. 2421

Sanborn, Michael, Dir, General Phineas Banning Residence Museum Library, 401 East M St, Wilmington, CA, 90744. Tel: 310-548-7777. Fax: 310-548-2644. p. 284

Sanchez, Ana, Ref Librn, Palestine Public Library, 2000 S Loop 256, Ste 42, Palestine, TX, 75801. Tel: 903-729-4121. Fax: 903-729-4062. p. 2368

Sanchez, Aurelia, Asst Librn, Rivkin Radler LLP, 926 RexCorp Plaza, Uniondale, NY, 11556-0926. Tel: 516-357-3453, 516-357-3454, 516-357-3455. Fax: 516-357-3333. p. 1758

Sanchez, Cynthia, Lead Access Serv Librn, Palo Alto College, 1400 W Villaret St, San Antonio, TX, 78224-2499. Tel: 210-486-3579. Fax: 210-486-9184. p. 2380

Sanchez, Diana A, Financial Serv Adminr, Alachua County Library District, 401 E University Ave, Gainesville, FL, 32601-5453. Tel: 352-334-3913. Fax: 352-334-3918. p. 448

Sanchez, Edward, Head, Libr Info Tech, Marquette University Libraries, 1355 W Wisconsin Ave, Milwaukee, WI, 53233. Tel: 414-288-6043. Fax: 414-288-7813. p. 2618

Sanchez, Elaine, Cat, Texas State University-San Marcos, Wood & Talbot St, San Marcos, TX, 78666-4604. Tel: 512-245-2133. Fax: 512-245-3002. p. 2385

Sanchez, Erica, Head, Tech Serv, Forest Park Public Library, 7555 Jackson Blvd, Forest Park, IL, 60130. Tel: 708-366-7171. Fax: 708-366-7293. p. 646

Sanchez, G Kristin, Pub Serv Librn, El Paso Community College Library, Rio Grande Campus Library, 1111 N Oregon, El Paso, TX, 79902. Tel: 915-831-4019. p. 2316

Sanchez, Heidi, Dir, Five Towns College Library, 305 N Service Rd, Dix Hills, NY, 11746. Tel: 631-656-2138. Fax: 631-656-2171. p. 1614

Sanchez, Iris, Dir, Aransas County Public Library, 701 E Mimosa, Rockport, TX, 78382-4150. Tel: 361-790-0153. Fax: 361-790-0150. p. 2376

Sanchez, Jessica, Digital Tech/Ref Librn, Kettering University Library, 1700 W University Ave, Flint, MI, 48504-4898. Tel: 810-762-7815. Fax: 810-762-9744. p. 1180

Sanchez, Joseph, Dir of Libr Serv, Red Rocks Community College, 13300 W Sixth Ave, Lakewood, CO, 80228-1255. Tel: 303-914-6743. Fax: 303-914-6741. p. 315

Sanchez, Kristin, Coordr, Del Norte Biosciences Library Consortium, El Paso Community Coll, El Paso, TX, 79998. Tel: 915-831-4458. Fax: 915-831-4639. p. 2956

Sanchez, Leo, Librn, California Department of Corrections Library System, California Medical Facility, 1600 California Dr, Vacaville, CA, 95696. Tel: 707-448-6841, Ext 2603. Fax: 707-449-6541. p. 221

Sanchez, Liliana, Librn, University of Texas at Brownsville & Texas Southmost College Library, 80 Fort Brown St, Brownsville, TX, 78521. Tel: 956-882-6576. Fax: 956-882-5495. p. 2292

Sanchez, Lora, Ch, Lincoln County Library, 519 Emerald, Kemmerer, WY, 83101. Tel: 307-877-6961. Fax: 307-877-4147. p. 2656

Sanchez, Lynn, Librn, El Paso County Law Library, 500 E San Antonio St, Rm 1202, El Paso, TX, 79901. Tel: 915-546-2245. Fax: 915-542-0440. p. 2316

Sanchez, Mary, Managing Librn, Pima County Public Library, Eckstrom-Columbus, 4350 E 22nd St, Tucson, AZ, 85711. Tel: 520-594-5285. Fax: 520-594-5286. p. 87

Sanchez, Mary G., Info Spec, International Foundation of Employee Benefit Plans, 18700 W Bluemound Rd, Brookfield, WI, 53045-2936. Tel: 262-786-6710, Ext 5. Fax: 262-786-8780. p. 2583

Sanchez, Monica, Sr Librn, Englewood Public Library, 31 Engle St, Englewood, NJ, 07631. Tel: 201-568-2215. Fax: 201-568-6895. p. 1484

Sanchez, Rosa, Libr Tech, Universidad Central Del Caribe, Avenida Laurel, Santa Juanita, Bayamon, PR, 00956. Tel: 787-798-3001, Ext 2308. Fax: 787-785-3425. p. 2672

Sanchez, Ruben, Dir, Inter-American University of Puerto Rico, School of Law Library, PO Box 70351, Hato Rey, PR, 00936. Tel: 787-751-1912. Fax: 787-753-6851. p. 2673

Sanchez, Sandra, Tech Serv, A K Smiley Public Library, 125 W Vine St, Redlands, CA, 92373. Tel: 909-798-7676. Fax: 909-798-7566. p. 215

Sanchez, Tommy, Outreach Prog/IT Support, Belen Public Library, 333 Becker Ave, Belen, NM, 87002. Tel: 505-864-7522. p. 1552

Sanchez, Victor, Head, Tech Serv, River Parishes Community College Library, 7384 John LeBlanc Blvd (Hwy 22), Sorrento, LA, 70778. Tel: 225-675-0218, 225-675-0231. Fax: 225-675-8595. p. 970

Sanchez-Lugo, Jose A, Asst Prof, University of Puerto Rico, Rio Piedras Campus, PO Box 21906, San Juan, PR, 00931-1906. Tel: 787-764-0000, Ext 1286, 787-764-0000, Ext 5028. Fax: 787-764-2311. p. 2677

Sanciprian, Jorge, In Charge, Hialeah-John F Kennedy Library, Wilde-e-Library, 5400 W 18th Ave, Hialeah, FL, 33012. Tel: 305-818-9766. p. 451

Sancken, Renata, Teen Librn, New Albany-Floyd County Public Library, 180 W Spring St, New Albany, IN, 47150-3692. Tel: 812-944-8464. Fax: 812-949-3532. p. 768

Sand, Jeff, Automation Serv Coordr, Villa Park Public Library, 305 S Ardmore Ave, Villa Park, IL, 60181-2698. Tel: 630-834-1164. Fax: 630-834-0489. p. 714

Sandak, Catherine, Info Tech Mgr, Leonia Public Library, 227 Fort Lee Rd, Leonia, NJ, 07605. Tel: 201-592-5770. Fax: 201-592-5775. p. 1495

Sandberg, Elaine, Doc, South Carolina State Library, 1430-1500 Senate St, Columbia, SC, 29201. Tel: 803-734-8625. Fax: 803-734-8676. p. 2189

Sandberg, Louise, Spec Coll Librn, Lawrence Public Library, 51 Lawrence St, Lawrence, MA, 01841. Tel: 978-620-3600. Fax: 978-688-3142. p. 1098

Sandberg, Patricia, Br Mgr, Carroll County Public Library, Mount Airy Branch, 705 Ridge Ave, Mount Airy, MD, 21771-3911. Tel: 410-386-4470. Fax: 410-386-4477. p. 1046

Sandberg, Scott, Vis Librn, Indiana University Northwest Library, 3400 Broadway, Gary, IN, 46408. Tel: 219-980-6580. Fax: 219-980-6558. p. 745

Sandberg, Tami, Librn, NREL Nat Wind Tech Ctr, National Renewable Energy Laboratory Library, 15013 Denver West Pkwy, Golden, CO, 80401-3305. Tel: 303-384-6963. Fax: 303-275-4222. p. 310

Sandefur, Shannon, Pub Serv, Youth Serv, Daviess County Public Library, 2020 Frederica St, Owensboro, KY, 42301. Tel: 270-684-0211. Fax: 270-684-0218. p. 931

Sandell, Ami, Dir, Monroe County Public Library, 500 W Fourth St, Tompkinsville, KY, 42167. Tel: 270-487-5301. Fax: 270-487-5309. p. 936

Sander, Christine D, Dir, Stockton Public Library, 124 N Cedar, Stockton, KS, 67669-1636. Tel: 785-425-6372. Fax: 785-425-6372. p. 895

Sander, Sandra, Dir, Libr Serv, Northampton Community College, 3835 Green Pond Rd, Bethlehem, PA, 18020-7599. Tel: 610-861-5360. Fax: 610-861-5373. p. 2034

Sander, Sandra L, Dir, Libr Serv, Northampton Community College, 3835 Green Pond Rd, Bethlehem, PA, 18020. Tel: 610-861-5358. Fax: 610-861-5373. p. 2973

Sandercock, Pat, Gen Mgr, Health Knowledge Network, University of Calgary Library, Health Sciences Library, Health Sci Ctr, 3330 Hospital Dr NW, Calgary, AB, T2N 4N1, CANADA. Tel: 403-220-8250. Fax: 403-210-9847. p. 2693

Sanderling, Marija, Ref Librn, Lane Memorial Library, Two Academy Ave, Hampton, NH, 03842. Tel: 603-926-3368. Fax: 603-926-1348. p. 1449

Sanders, A Carolyn, Media Spec, Central State University, 1400 Brush Row Rd, Wilberforce, OH, 45384. Tel: 937-376-6213. Fax: 937-376-6132. p. 1948

Sanders, Alice, Asst Librn, Florida Department of Agriculture & Consumer Services, 1911 SW 34th St, Gainesville, FL, 32608. Tel: 352-395-4720. Fax: 352-395-4614. p. 449

Sanders, Anne, Actg Br Supvr, Jackson/Hinds Library System, Charles Tisdale, 807 E Northside Dr, Jackson, MS, 39206-5537. Tel: 601-366-0021. Fax: 601-366-9364. p. 1303

Sanders, Beverly, Mgr, South Georgia Regional Library System, Mae Wisenbaker McMullen Memorial Southside Library, 527 Griffin Ave, Valdosta, GA, 31601-6343. Tel: 229-253-8313. p. 555

Sanders, Blanche, Archivist, Alcorn State University, 1000 ASU Dr, Alcorn State, MS, 39096-7500. Tel: 601-877-2359. Fax: 601-877-3885. p. 1293

Sanders, Bruce, Cat, DePauw University, 11 E Larrabee St, Greencastle, IN, 46135. Tel: 765-658-4420. Fax: 765-658-4017. p. 746

Sanders, Catherine, Archivist, Database Mgr, Ser, Carroll College, 100 N East Ave, Waukesha, WI, 53186. Tel: 262-951-3016. Fax: 262-524-7377. p. 2644

Sanders, Chinell, Br Librn, Suffolk Public Library System, Chuckatuck Branch, 5881 Godwin Blvd, Suffolk, VA, 23432. Tel: 757-514-7310. p. 2497

Sanders, Courtney, Res Analyst, Republican National Committee Library, 310 First St SE, Washington, DC, 20003. Tel: 202-863-8815. Fax: 202-863-8744. p. 413

Sanders, Dawn, Cat, Nelson-Atkins Museum of Art, 4525 Oak St, Kansas City, MO, 64111-1873. Tel: 816-751-0400. Fax: 816-751-0498. p. 1340

Sanders, Dede, Asst Dir, Cameron Parish Library, 501 Marshall St, Cameron, LA, 70631. Tel: 337-775-5421. Fax: 337-775-5346. p. 946

Sanders, Ellen, Librn, Insurance Institute for Highway Safety Library, 1005 N Glebe Rd, Ste 800, Arlington, VA, 22201. Tel: 703-247-1554. Fax: 703-247-1678. p. 2449

Sanders, Emily, Coordr, Ch Serv, Meigs County District Public Library, 216 W Main, Pomeroy, OH, 45769-1032. Tel: 740-992-5813. Fax: 740-992-6140. p. 1930

Sanders, Gayle, Cat, San Juan College Library, 4601 College Blvd, Farmington, NM, 87402. Tel: 505-566-3289. Fax: 505-566-3381. p. 1555

Sanders, Jan, Dir, Info Serv, Pasadena Public Library, 285 E Walnut St, Pasadena, CA, 91101. Tel: 626 744-3867. Fax: 626-585-8396. p. 207

Sanders, Jesse, Br Mgr, Cuyahoga County Public Library, Warrensville Heights Branch, 4415 Northfield Rd, Warrensville Heights, OH, 44128-4603. Tel: 216-464-5280. Fax: 216-464-6475. p. 1928

Sanders, Jill, Dir, Elkader Public Library, 130 N Main St, Elkader, IA, 52043. Tel: 563-245-1446. Fax: 563-245-1446. p. 814

Sanders, Lori, Librn, Baker, Manock & Jensen Library, 5260 N Palm Ave, Ste 421, Fresno, CA, 93704. Tel: 559-436-2086. p. 150

Sanders, Mark, Asst Dir, Pub Serv, East Carolina University, J Y Joyner Library, E Fifth St, Greenville, NC, 27858-4353. Tel: 242-328-2900. Fax: 252-328-6892. p. 1798

Sanders, Martha, Ch, Buda Public Library, 303 Main St, Buda, TX, 78610. Tel: 512-295-5899. Fax: 512-295-6525. p. 2293

Sanders, Patrick, Tech Serv, Pike-Amite-Walthall Library System, 1022 Virginia Ave, McComb, MS, 39648. Tel: 601-684-2661, Ext 14. Fax: 601-250-1213. p. 1308

Sanders, Paul, Asst Dir, Tell City-Perry County Public Library, 2328 Tell St, Tell City, IN, 47586. Tel: 812-547-2661. Fax: 812-547-3038. p. 780

Sanders, Paula, Assoc Librn, Iowa Wesleyan College, 107 W Broad St, Mount Pleasant, IA, 52641. Tel: 319-385-6316. Fax: 319-385-6324. p. 833

Sanders, Richard, Dir, Hart County Library, 150 Benson St, Hartwell, GA, 30643. Tel: 706-376-4655. Fax: 706-376-1157. p. 536

Sanders, Robert, Dr, Prof, Appalachian State University, RCOE, Dept of LES, 311 Edwin Duncan Hall, Boone, NC, 28608. Tel: 828-262-7236. Fax: 828-262-6035. p. 2971

Sanders, Sandra, Dir, Madison County Library System, 102 Priestley St, Canton, MS, 39046-4599. p. 1295

Sanders, Sandra G, Prof, Middle Tennessee State University, PO Box 91, Murfreesboro, TN, 37132. Tel: 615-898-2804. Fax: 615-898-2859. p. 2974

Sanders, Scott, Archivist, Antioch College, One Morgan Pl, Yellow Springs, OH, 45387-1694. Tel: 973-286-5534. Fax: 937-769-1239. p. 1952

Sanders, Sharon K, Librn, Southeast Missourian Newspaper Library, 301 Broadway, Cape Girardeau, MO, 63701-7330. Tel: 573-335-6611, Ext 136. p. 1322

Sanders, Stephen, Dir, Wisconsin Department of Public Instruction, Instructional Media & Technology Team, 125 S Webster St, Madison, WI, 53707. Tel: 608-266-3856. Fax: 608-267-1052. p. 2610

Sanders, Susan, Librn, Shippensburg Public Library, 73 W King St, Shippensburg, PA, 17257-1299. Tel: 717-532-4508. Fax: 717-532-2454. p. 2140

Sanders, Tammy, Head Librn, Bevill State Community College, PO Box 9, Hamilton, AL, 35570-0009. Tel: 205-921-3177, Ext 5356. Fax: 205-952-9617. p. 19

Sanders, Tina, In Charge, Georgia Department of Corrections, Office of Library Services, 2971 Old Bethel Rd, Chester, GA, 31012. Tel: 478-358-7200. Fax: 478-358-7303. p. 524

Sanders, Tom, Head Librn, Westminster Presbyterian Church Library, 2040 Washington Rd, Upper St Clair, PA, 15241. Tel: 412-835-6630. Fax: 412-835-5690. p. 2149

Sanderson, Barbara, Circ, George H & Ella M Rodgers Memorial Library, 194 Derry Rd, Hudson, NH, 03051. Tel: 603-886-6030, Ext 4516. Fax: 603-816-4501. p. 1452

Sanderson, Cherie, Dir, Boulder Junction Public Library, 5386 Park St, Boulder Junction, WI, 54512-9605. Tel: 715-385-2050. p. 2583

Sanderson, Denise, Br Mgr, San Francisco Public Library, Glen Park Branch Library, 2825 Diamond St, San Francisco, CA, 94131-3033. Tel: 415-355-2858. Fax: 415-469-8557. p. 246

Sanderson, Diana, Archivist, Warren Wilson College, 701 Warren Wilson Rd, Swannanoa, NC, 28778. Tel: 828-771-3055. Fax: 828-771-7085. p. 1826

Sanderson, Fredda, Librn, Northeast Regional Library, Iuka Public Library, 204 N Main St, Iuka, MS, 38852-2331. Tel: 662-423-6300. Fax: 662-423-6300. p. 1297

Sanderson, James W, ILL, Sr Librn, YA Serv, Newport News Public Library System, West Avenue, 30th & West Ave, Newport News, VA, 23607. Tel: 757-247-8505. Fax: 757-247-2344. p. 2480

Sanderson, Kim, Cat/Metadata Librn, Davidson College, 209 Ridge Rd, Davidson, NC, 28035-0001. Tel: 704-894-2331. Fax: 704-894-2625. p. 1786

Sanderson, Linda, Adult Serv, Pub Serv, Suwannee River Regional Library, 1848 Ohio Ave S, Dr Martin Luther King Jr Ave S, Live Oak, FL, 32064-4517. Tel: 386-362-2317. Fax: 386-364-6071. p. 461

Sanderson, Patricia, Libr Tech, New Mexico Junior College, One Thunderbird Circle, Hobbs, NM, 88240. Tel: 575-492-2870. Fax: 575-492-2883. p. 1557

Sanderson, Suzanne, Librn, Plymouth Congregational Church, 1217 Sixth Ave, Seattle, WA, 98101-3199. Tel: 206-622-4865. Fax: 206-622-8726. p. 2529

Sandford, Betsy, Tech Serv Librn, West Valley Community College Library, 14000 Fruitvale Ave, Saratoga, CA, 95070-5698. Tel: 408-741-2478. Fax: 408-741-2134. p. 268

Sandford, Deborah, Head, Youth Serv, Springfield Free Public Library, 66 Mountain Ave, Springfield, NJ, 07081-1786. Tel: 973-376-4930, Ext 232. Fax: 973-376-1334. p. 1532

Sandford, Diane, Dir, Fried, Frank, Harris, Shriver & Jacobson LLP, 1001 Pennsylvania Ave NW, Ste 800, Washington, DC, 20004. Tel: 202-639-7102. Fax: 202-639-7004. p. 401

Sandford, Ellen, Librn, Jefferson Health System, Paoli Memorial Hospital, 255 W Lancaster Ave, Paoli, PA, 19301. Tel: 610-648-1570. Fax: 610-648-1551. p. 2101

Sandford, India K, Br Mgr, Ohoopee Regional Library System, Tattnall County Public, 129 Tattnall St, Reidsville, GA, 30453-0338. Tel: 912-557-6247. Fax: 912-557-6247. p. 556

Sandford, Mark, Cat Librn, William Paterson University of New Jersey, 300 Pompton Rd, Wayne, NJ, 07470. Tel: 973-720-2437. Fax: 973-720-3171. p. 1540

Sandford, Wendy, Librn, Wayne Public Library, Preakness, Wayne Civic Ctr, 1006 Hamburg Tpk, Wayne, NJ, 07470. Tel: 973-694-7110. Fax: 973-694-8415. p. 1540

Sandfort, Josef, Dir, Ledding Library of Milwaukie, 10660 SE 21st Ave, Milwaukie, OR, 97222. Tel: 503-786-7580. Fax: 503-659-9497. p. 2006

Sandgathe, Trevor, Libr Tech, Oregon State University Libraries, University Archives & Special Collections, 121 Valley Library, Corvallis, OR, 97331-4501. Tel: 541-737-2075. Fax: 541-737-3453. p. 1995

Sandhu, Evgheni, Network Serv, Fordham University Libraries, 441 E Fordham Rd, Bronx, NY, 10458-5151. Tel: 718-817-3570. Fax: 718-817-3582. p. 1586

Sandia, Tamara, Librn, Jemez Pueblo Community Library, 20 Mission Rd, Jemez Pueblo, NM, 87024. Tel: 575-834-9171. Fax: 575-834-9173. p. 1557

Sandifer, Cecelia Y, Br Mgr, Pearl Public Library, 2416 Old Brandon Rd, Pearl, MS, 39208-4601. Tel: 601-932-2562. Fax: 601-932-3535. p. 1311

Sandifer, Kevin, In Charge, First Baptist Church of Blanchard, 201 Attaway St, Blanchard, LA, 71009. Tel: 318-929-2346. Fax: 318-929-4680. p. 945

Sandino, Margarita, Educ Curator, Dixon Gallery & Gardens Library, 4339 Park Ave, Memphis, TN, 38117. Tel: 901-761-5250. Fax: 901-682-0943. p. 2248

Sandland, Anissa, Ad, Tech Serv Librn, Saint Peter Public Library, 601 S Washington Ave, Saint Peter, MN, 56082-1447. Tel: 507-934-7420. Fax: 507-934-1204. p. 1283

Sandler, Carol, Dir, The Strong Museum Library, One Manhattan Sq, Rochester, NY, 14607. Tel: 585-263-2700. Fax: 585-263-2493. p. 1732

Sandler, William S, Pres, Valve Manufacturers Association of America, 1050 17th St NW, Ste 280, Washington, DC, 20036. Tel: 202-331-8105. Fax: 202-296-0378. p. 421

Sandlin, Linda, Dir, Clay County Public Library, 211 Bridge St, Manchester, KY, 40962. Tel: 606-598-2617. Fax: 606-598-4671. p. 928

Sandner, Arlene, Ch, New City Free Library, 220 N Main St, New City, NY, 10956. Tel: 845-634-4997. p. 1665

Sandner, Fred, Circ, Media Spec, Finkelstein Memorial Library, 24 Chestnut St, Spring Valley, NY, 10977-5594. Tel: 845-352-5700. Fax: 845-352-2319. p. 1746

Sandness, Susan, Libr Mgr, North Miami Beach Public Library, 1601 NE 164th St, North Miami Beach, FL, 33162-4099. Tel: 305-948-2970. Fax: 305-787-6007. p. 473

Sando, Kimberley, Syst Librn, DeSales University, 2755 Station Ave, Center Valley, PA, 18034. Tel: kim.sando@desales.edu. Fax: 610-282-2342. p. 2043

Sandor, Carole, Tech Support, Brunswick Community College Library, 50 College Rd, Supply, NC, 28462. Tel: 910-755-7331. Fax: 910-754-7805. p. 1826

Sandor, Jill, Librn, American Bar Association Library, 740 15th St NW, 9th Flr, Washington, DC, 20005. Tel: 202-662-1015. Fax: 202-662-1032. p. 391

Sandor, Manette, Circ Librn, Argosy University of Chicago Library, 225 N Michigan Ave, Chicago, IL, 60601. Tel: 312-777-7653. Fax: 312-777-7749. p. 606

Sandoro, Mary Ann, Librn, Collector Car Appraisers Association Library, 24 Myrtle Ave, Buffalo, NY, 14204. Tel: 716-855-1931. p. 1597

Sandoval, Bertha, Librn, Montgomery & Andrews, 325 Paseo de Peralta, Santa Fe, NM, 87501. Tel: 505-982-3873. Fax: 505-982-4289. p. 1562

Sandoval, Lucy, Cat, El Progreso Memorial Library, 301 W Main St, Uvalde, TX, 78801. Tel: 830-278-2017. Fax: 830-278-4940. p. 2394

Sandoval, Rachel, Instruction & Outreach, West Valley Community College Library, 14000 Fruitvale Ave, Saratoga, CA, 95070-5698. Tel: 408-741-2479. Fax: 408-741-2134. p. 268

Sandoval, Victor, Librn, New Mexico Behavioral Health Institute at Las Vegas, 3695 Hot Springs Blvd, Las Vegas, NM, 87701. Tel: 505-454-2108. Fax: 505-454-2136. p. 1558

Sandquist, Michelle, Asst Librn, Earlham Public Library, 120 S Chestnut St, Earlham, IA, 50072. Tel: 515-758-2121. Fax: 515-758-2121. p. 813

Sands, Bryan, Info Tech Dir, Pasadena Public Library, 285 E Walnut St, Pasadena, CA, 91101. Tel: 626-744-4066. Fax: 626-585-8396. p. 207

Sands, Fay, Circ Supvr, Lamar University, 211 Redbird Lane, Beaumont, TX, 77705. Tel: 409-880-8133. Fax: 409-880-2318. p. 2287

Sands, Joyce, Dep Dir, Lancaster Public Library, 125 N Duke St, Lancaster, PA, 17602-2883. Tel: 717-396-9313, Ext 110. Fax: 717-606-4599. p. 2077

Sands, Judith, Dir, Rochelle Park Library, 151 W Passaic St, Rochelle Park, NJ, 07662. Tel: 201-587-7730, Ext 602. Fax: 201-587-9855. p. 1527

Sands, Kathleen, Ch, East Hampton Public Library, 105 Main St, East Hampton, CT, 06424. Tel: 860-267-6621. Fax: 860-267-4427. p. 337

Sands, Marlene, Librn, Cave Springs Public Library, Midway Ave, Bentonville, AR, 72712. Tel: 479-248-7117. p. 95

Sands, Tonya, Br Mgr, Athens Regional Library System, East Athens Community Resource Center, 400 McKinley Dr, Athens, GA, 30601. Tel: 706-613-3657. Fax: 706-613-3657. p. 508

Sandstedt, Phyllis, Ch, First Congregational Church Library, 2101 16th St, Greeley, CO, 80631. Tel: 970-353-0828. Fax: 970-353-8447. p. 311

Sandstrom, Lorraine, Br Mgr, Springfield-Greene County Library District, The Library Center, 4653 S Campbell, Springfield, MO, 65810-1723. Tel: 417-882-0714. Fax: 417-883-9348. p. 1368

Sandstrom, Pamela, Dir, Libr Prog & Develop, Indiana University-Purdue University Fort Wayne, 2101 E Coliseum Blvd, Fort Wayne, IN, 46805-1499. Tel: 260-481-5404. Fax: 260-481-6509. p. 741

Sandt, Judy, Ref Serv, Pennsylvania State Lehigh Valley Library, 8380 Mohr Lane, Fogelsville, PA, 18051-9999. Tel: 610-285-5028. Fax: 610-285-5158. p. 2057

Sandusky, Robert, Asst Univ Librn, Info Tech, University of Illinois at Chicago, MC 234, 801 S Morgan St, Chicago, IL, 60607. Tel: 312-996-2716. Fax: 312-413-0424. p. 627

Sandusky, Timothy, Head, Access Serv, Ohio Dominican University Library, 1216 Sunbury Rd, Columbus, OH, 43219. Tel: 614-251-4676. Fax: 614-252-2650. p. 1886

Sandwell-Weiss, Leah, Ref, University of Arizona, James E Rogers College of Law Library, PO Box 210176, Tucson, AZ, 85721-0176. Tel: 520-621-1413. Fax: 520-621-3138. p. 89

Sandy, Amy, Librn, Parkersburg & Wood County Public Library, Waverly, 450 Virginia St, Waverly, WV, 26184. Tel: 304-464-5668. Fax: 304-464-5668. p. 2568

Sandy, Katherine, Ch, La Crosse County Library, Administration Ctr, 103 State St, Holmen, WI, 54636. Tel: 608-526-9600. Fax: 608-526-3299. p. 2598

Saner, Eileen K, Dir, Associated Mennonite Biblical Seminary Library, 3003 Benham Ave, Elkhart, IN, 46517. Tel: 574-296-6233. Fax: 574-295-0092. p. 737

Sanfilippo, Sarah, Dir, Southern Vermont College Library, 982 Mansion Dr, Bennington, VT, 05201-6002. Tel: 802-447-6311. Fax: 802-447-4695. p. 2419

Sanford, Ann, Cat, Nevada State Library & Archives, 100 N Stewart St, Carson City, NV, 89701-4285. Tel: 775-684-3308. Fax: 775-684-3330. p. 1426

Sanford, Carolyn, Instrul Serv Librn, Res, Carleton College, One N College St, Northfield, MN, 55057-4097. Tel: 507-222-4266. Fax: 507-222-4087. p. 1269

Sanford, Cathy, Dep County Librn, Support Serv, Contra Costa County Library, 1750 Oak Park Blvd, Pleasant Hill, CA, 94523-4497. Tel: 925-646-6434. Fax: 925-646-6461. p. 208

Sanford, Chris, Dir, Davis County Library, 38 S 100 East, Farmington, UT, 84025. Tel: 801-451-2322. Fax: 801-451-9561. p. 2405

Sanford, Daniel, Librn, Ivy Tech Community College, 220 Dean Johnson Blvd, South Bend, IN, 46601. Tel: 574-289-7001, Ext 1125. Fax: 574-236-7165. p. 778

Sanford, Eva, Ad, Willard Library of Evansville, 21 First Ave, Evansville, IN, 47710-1294. Tel: 812-425-4309. Fax: 812-421-9742. p. 739

Sanford, Nancy, Dir, Florence-Lauderdale Public Library, 350 N Wood Ave, Florence, AL, 35630. Tel: 256-764-6564. Fax: 256-764-6629. p. 17

Sanford, Robin, Tech Serv & Syst Librn, Lithgow Public Library, 45 Winthrop St, Augusta, ME, 04330-5599. Tel: 207-626-2415. Fax: 207-626-2419. p. 974

Sanford, Robin, Cat, University of New England Libraries, Josephine S Abplanalp Library, Portland Campus, 716 Stevens Ave, Portland, ME, 04103. Tel: 207-221-4328. Fax: 207-221-4893. p. 978

Sanford, Shirley, Librn, Logan County Libraries, DeGraff Branch, One S Main St, DeGraff, OH, 43318. Tel: 937-585-5010. p. 1859

Sanger, Lois, Mgr, Libr Serv, Memorial Hospital, 219 S Washington St, Easton, MD, 21601. Tel: 410-822-1000, Ext 5776. Fax: 410-820-4020. p. 1027

SanGiovanni, Anne M, Court Adminr, Allegany County Circuit Court Law Library, Allegany County Circuit Courthouse, 30 Washington St, Cumberland, MD, 21502. Tel: 301-777-5925. Fax: 301-777-2055. p. 1026

Sanguinet, Bonnie, Sr Mgr, Campus Libr & Instrul Res, Saint Louis Community College, Meramec Campus Library, 11333 Big Bend Rd, Saint Louis, MO, 63122-5720. Tel: 314-984-7624. Fax: 314-984-7225. p. 1358

Sankar, S, In Charge, Erico, Inc, 34600 Solon Rd, Solon, OH, 44139. Tel: 440-248-0100. Fax: 440-248-0723. p. 1935

Sanker, Mary, Br Mgr, Public Library of Cincinnati & Hamilton County, Mariemont Branch, 3810 Pocahontas Ave, Mariemont, OH, 45227. Tel: 513-369-4467. Fax: 513-369-4468. p. 1872

Sankner, Gail M, Tech Serv, Old Bridge Public Library, One Old Bridge Plaza, Old Bridge, NJ, 08857-2498. Tel: 732-607-7921, 732-721-5600, Ext 5010. Fax: 732-679-0556. p. 1516

Sankowski, Andrew, Coll Develop, Info Res, Saint John's University Library, 8000 Utopia Pkwy, Queens, NY, 11439. Tel: 718-990-6735. Fax: 718-380-0353. p. 1725

Sankowski, Andrew, Dir of Coll, Dir, Info Mgt, Saint John's University Library, Rittenberg Law Library, 8000 Utopia Pkwy, Queens, NY, 11439. Tel: 718-990-6651, 718-990-6659. Fax: 718-990-6649. p. 1725

Sann, Fern, Ref, David & Joyce Milne Public Library, 1095 Main St, Williamstown, MA, 01267-2627. Tel: 413-458-5369. Fax: 413-458-3085. p. 1140

Sanner, Abby, Dir, Oakland Public Library, Two Municipal Plaza, Oakland, NJ, 07436. Tel: 201-337-3742. Fax: 201-337-0261. p. 1515

Sannini, Mary, Circ, ILL, Cheltenham Township Library System, Elkins Park Free Library, 563 E Church Rd, Elkins Park, PA, 19027-2499. Tel: 215-635-5000. Fax: 215-635-5844. p. 2061

Sansalone, Joseph, Mgr, Ad Serv, Oshawa Public Library, 65 Bagot St, Oshawa, ON, L1H 1N2, CANADA. Tel: 905-579-6111. Fax: 905-433-8107. p. 2827

Sansbury, Joan K, Curator, Librn, Scottish Rite Library, 1733 16th St NW, Washington, DC, 20009-3103. Tel: 202-777-3139. Fax: 202-464-0487. p. 413

Sansing, Jocelyne, Libr Mgr, Pikes Peak Library District, Old Colorado City Library, 2418 W Pikes Peak Ave, Colorado Springs, CO, 80904. Tel: 719-634-1698. p. 296

Sansing, Jocelyne, Libr Mgr, Pikes Peak Library District, Ute Pass Library, 8010 Severy, Cascade, CO, 80809. Tel: 719-684-9342. p. 296

Sansolo, Mara, Pub Serv Librn, University of South Florida Saint Petersburg, 140 Seventh Ave S, POY118, Saint Petersburg, FL, 33701. Tel: 727-873-4401. Fax: 727-873-4196. p. 489

Sansone, Laurie, Dir, Union Township Public Library, Vaux Hall Branch, 123 Hilton Ave, Vaux Hall, NJ, 07088. Tel: 908-851-5451. Fax: 908-810-7072. p. 1537

Sansone, Laurie D, Dir, Union Township Public Library, 1980 Morris Ave, Union, NJ, 07083-3578. Tel: 908-851-5453. Fax: 908-851-4671. p. 1537

Sansone-Beiser, Antoinette, Librn, Lowell Observatory Library, 1400 W Mars Hill Rd, Flagstaff, AZ, 86001. Tel: 928-233-3216. Fax: 928-774-6296. p. 62

SanSoucie, Susan A, Dir, Montague Public Libraries, 201 Ave A, Turners Falls, MA, 01376-1989. Tel: 413-863-3214. Fax: 413-863-3227. p. 1131

Sant, Delilah, Ch, Hyrum Library, 50 W Main, Hyrum, UT, 84319. Tel: 435-245-6411. Fax: 435-245-0180. p. 2406

Santa Cruz, Norma, Libr Tech, California Department of Justice Library, 110 West A St, Ste 1311, San Diego, CA, 92101. p. 230

Santa Lucia, Carol, Dir, Libr Serv, Windham Free Library Association, On the Green, Windham, CT, 06280. Tel: 860-423-0636. Fax: 860-423-0636. p. 379

Santagati, Richard, Pres, Northeast Consortium of Colleges & Universities In Massachusetts, Merrimack College, 315 Turnpike St, North Andover, MA, 01845. Tel: 978-556-3400. Fax: 978-556-3738. p. 2945

Santaliz, Lorraine, Youth Serv, Whitehall Township Public Library, 3700 Mechanicsville Rd, Whitehall, PA, 18052-3399. Tel: 610-432-4339. Fax: 610-432-9387. p. 2155

Santamaria, Angela, Mgr, Washington State University Extension, 905 Plum St SE, Olympia, WA, 98501-1529. Tel: 360-956-2076. Fax: 360-236-2076. p. 2523

Santana, Gilda, Head, Archit Info Res & Serv, University of Miami Libraries, Paul Buisson School of Architecture Reference Library, 1223 Dickison Dr, Bldg 48, Coral Gables, FL, 33146. Tel: 305-284-5282. Fax: 305-284-1894. p. 434

Santana, Victoria, Ref Librn, Oklahoma City University, Law Library, 2501 N Blackwelder, Oklahoma City, OK, 73106. Tel: 405-208-5271. Fax: 405-208-5172. p. 1974

Santanella, Carolyn, Asst Librn, Smith Moore, LLP, 300 N Greene St, Greensboro, NC, 27401. Tel: 336-378-5272. Fax: 336-433-7566. p. 1797

Santanella, Colleen, Br Coordr, Enfield Public Library, Pearl Street, 159 Pearl St, Enfield, CT, 06082. Tel: 860-253-6433. Fax: 860-253-6433. p. 338

Santella, Terri, Dep Circuit Librn, United States Court of Appeals for the District of Columbia, US Court House, 333 Constitution Ave NW, Rm 5518, Washington, DC, 20001. Tel: 202-216-7400. p. 418

Santer, Susan, Dir, Oregon Public Library, 256 Brook St, Oregon, WI, 53575. Tel: 608-835-3656. Fax: 608-835-2856. p. 2627

Santes, Heather, Assoc Mgr, Edmonton Public Library, Mill Woods, 601 Mill Woods Town Centre, 2331 66 St, Edmonton, AB, T6K 4B5, CANADA. Tel: 780-496-7842. Fax: 780-496-1450. p. 2700

Santiago, Jay, Ref Serv, United States Trademark Office Law Library, 600 Dulany St, MDE 4B65, Alexandria, VA, 22314-5791. Tel: 571-272-9699. Fax: 571-273-9699. p. 2446

Santiago, Jose, Asst Commun Librn, Hartford Public Library, Barbour, 281 Barbour St, Hartford, CT, 06120. Tel: 860-695-7400. Fax: 860-722-6881. p. 346

Santiago, Lillian E, Spec Coll Librn, Inter-American University of Puerto Rico, School of Law Library, PO Box 70351, Hato Rey, PR, 00936. Tel: 787-751-1912. Fax: 787-753-6851. p. 2673

Santiago, Marlyn, Circ, Pontifical Catholic University Of Puerto Rico, Encarnacion Valdes Library, 2250 Avenida Las Americas, Ste 509, Ponce, PR, 00717-0777. Tel: 787-841-2000, Ext 1801, 787-841-2000, Ext 1802. Fax: 787-284-0235. p. 2675

Santiago, Myrna Rosario, Librn, Inter-American University of Puerto Rico, Call Box 10004, Guayama, PR, 00785-0004. Tel: 787-864-2222. Fax: 787-864-8232. p. 2673

Santiago, Nivia, Asst Librn, University of Puerto Rico, Rio Piedras Campus, San Juan, PR, 00931. Tel: 787-764-0000, Ext 2359. Fax: 787-764-2890. p. 2676

Santiago, Raymond, Dir, Miami-Dade Public Library System, 101 W Flagler St, Miami, FL, 33130-1523. Tel: 305-375-5026. Fax: 305-375-3048. p. 466

Santiago, Roshni, Asst Librn, White & Case LLP, 701 13th St NW, Washington, DC, 20005-3807. Tel: 202-626-6475. Fax: 202-639-9355. p. 422

Santiago, Tina, Acq, Columbia-Greene Community College Library, 4400 Rte 23, Hudson, NY, 12534. Tel: 518-828-4181, Ext 3284. Fax: 518-828-4396. p. 1638

Santiapillai, Terry, Brother, Ref/Archives Librn, Quincy University, 1800 College Ave, Quincy, IL, 62301-2699. Tel: 217-228-5432, Ext 3801. Fax: 217-228-5354. p. 693

Santillan, Roman A, Mgr, District of Columbia Public Library, Mount Pleasant, 3160 16th St NW, Washington, DC, 20010. Tel: 202-671-0199, 202-671-0200. Fax: 202-673-2184. p. 398

Santillo, C Alfred, Asst Librn, Sharon Springs Free Library, Main St, Rte 10, Sharon Springs, NY, 13459. Tel: 518-284-2625. Fax: 518-284-3126. p. 1742

Santillo, Carol, Tech Info Spec, Massapequa Public Library, 40 Harbor Lane, Massapequa Park, NY, 11762. Tel: 516-799-0770, Ext 338. Fax: 516-795-7528. p. 1658

Santillo, Morgan, Ref/IT Librn, Edison Township Free Public Library, 340 Plainfield Ave, Edison, NJ, 08817. Tel: 732-287-2298. Fax: 732-819-9134. p. 1483

Santino, Joanne, Libr Mgr, Nixon Peabody LLP, 100 Summer St, Boston, MA, 02110-1832. Tel: 617-345-1360. Fax: 617-345-1300. p. 1065

Santo, Jennifer, Ref, Locust Valley Library, 170 Buckram Rd, Locust Valley, NY, 11560-1999. Tel: 516-671-1837. Fax: 516-676-8164. p. 1654

Santora, Deirdre, Assoc Librn, Access Serv, James Blackstone Memorial Library, 758 Main St, Branford, CT, 06405-3697. Tel: 203-488-1441. Fax: 203-481-6077. p. 331

Santora, John, Fiscal Serv Mgr, Baltimore County Public Library, 320 York Rd, Towson, MD, 21204-5179. Tel: 410-887-6170. Fax: 410-887-6103. p. 1044

Santorio, Joanne, Libr Tech, United States Department of Justice, 3150 Horton Rd, Fort Worth, TX, 76119. Tel: 817-534-8400, Ext 3214. Fax: 817-413-3376. p. 2324

Santoro, Claire, Teen Librn, Free Public Library of Hasbrouck Heights, 320 Boulevard, Hasbrouck Heights, NJ, 07604. Tel: 201-288-0484, 201-288-0488. Fax: 201-288-5467. p. 1490

Santoro, Mary Catherine, Librn, Virginia Museum of Natural History Library, 21 Starling Ave, Martinsville, VA, 24112. Tel: 276-634-4172. Fax: 276-634-4199. p. 2478

Santos, Ana, Asst Dir, Lawrence Public Library, 51 Lawrence St, Lawrence, MA, 01841. Tel: 978-620-3600. Fax: 978-688-3142. p. 1098

Santos, Bonnie, Librn, Lorain County Printing & Publishing Co, 225 East Ave, Elyria, OH, 44035. Tel: 440-329-7000. Fax: 440-329-7282. p. 1898

Santos, Carmen, Spec Coll Librn, University of Puerto Rico, Conrado F Asenjo Library (Medical Sciences Campus), Medical Sciences Campus, Main Bldg, Unit C, San Juan, PR, 00935. Tel: 787-758-2525, Ext 1224. Fax: 787-759-6713, 282-6438. p. 2676

Santos, Eileen, Asst Dir, Pub Serv, Howard University Libraries, Law Library, 2929 Van Ness St NW, Washington, DC, 20008. Tel: 202-806-8301. Fax: 202-806-8590. p. 404

Santos, Jose, Ref Serv, Pontifical Catholic University Of Puerto Rico, Encarnacion Valdes Library, 2250 Avenida Las Americas, Ste 509, Ponce, PR, 00717-0777. Tel: 787-841-2000, Ext 1801, 787-841-2000, Ext 1802. Fax: 787-284-0235. p. 2675

Santos, Kathryn, Archivist, California State Railroad Museum Library, 113 I St, Sacramento, CA, 95814. Tel: 916-322-0375. Fax: 916-327-5655. p. 223

Santos, Linda, Asst Dir, Mason Library, 231 Main St, Great Barrington, MA, 01230. Tel: 413-528-2403. p. 1092

Santos, Lionel, II, Coordr, Heald College, 1500 Kapiolani Blvd, Honolulu, HI, 96814. Tel: 808-628-5525. Fax: 808-955-6964. p. 564

Santos, Mary Jane, Dir, Delaware County District Library, 84 E Winter St, Delaware, OH, 43015. Tel: 740-362-3861. Fax: 740-369-0196. p. 1895

Santos, Rodner, AV Tech Equip Mgr, Dona Ana Community College Library, 3400 S Espina, Rm 260, Las Cruces, NM, 88003. Tel: 575-527-7555. Fax: 575-527-7636. p. 1558

Santoso, Dee, Dep Libr Dir, Manchester City Library, 405 Pine St, Manchester, NH, 03104-6199. Tel: 603-624-6550. Fax: 603-624-6559. p. 1455

Santry, Rebecca, Ch, Cranberry Public Library, 2525 Rochester Rd, Ste 300, Cranberry Township, PA, 16066-6423. Tel: 724-776-9100, Ext 1124. Fax: 724-776-2490. p. 2048

Santucci, Lisa, Asst Dean, Instruction & Emerging Tech, Miami University Libraries, 225 King Library, Oxford, OH, 45056. Tel: 513-529-1747. Fax: 513-529-3110. p. 1926

Santulli, Joan, Admin Serv, Chemung County Library District, 101 E Church St, Elmira, NY, 14901-2799. Tel: 607-733-9173. Fax: 607-733-9176. p. 1619

Santy, Gail, Supvr, Ref & Outreach Serv, Central Kansas Library System, 1409 Williams St, Great Bend, KS, 67530-4020. Tel: 620-792-4865. Fax: 620-792-5495. p. 869

Sanudo, Manuel, Ref, Queens College, Benjamin S Rosenthal Library, 65-30 Kissena Blvd, Flushing, NY, 11367-0904. Tel: 718-997-3700. Fax: 718-997-3753. p. 1623

Sanute, Lynee, Instruction & Ref Librn, Adams State University, 208 Edgemont Ave, Alamosa, CO, 81101-2373. Tel: 719-587-7781. Fax: 719-587-7590. p. 287

Sanz, Timothy L, Cat Chief, United States Army, Combined Arms Research Library, US Army Command & General Staff College, Eisenhower Hall, 250 Gibbon Ave, Fort Leavenworth, KS, 66027-2314. Tel: 913-758-3024. Fax: 913-758-3014. p. 867

Sapida, Kayatta, Librn, United States Army, Aliamanu Military Reservation, 1782 Bougainvillea Loop, Honolulu, HI, 96789. Tel: 808-833-4851. Fax: 808-833-3714. p. 565

Sapiie, Jacquelyn, Mgr, Libr Serv, Ref Librn, American Bible Society Library, 1865 Broadway, New York, NY, 10023-9980. Tel: 212-408-1203. Fax: 212-408-8724. p. 1667

Sapir, Jeanne, Br Mgr, Cuyahoga County Public Library, Southeast Branch, 70 Columbus Rd, Bedford, OH, 44146-2836. Tel: 440-439-4997. Fax: 440-439-5846. p. 1928

Sapp, Gregg, Dean, Libr & Media Serv, Evergreen State College, Library Bldg, Rm 2300, 2700 Evergreen Pkwy NW, Olympia, WA, 98505-0002. Tel: 360-867-6607. Fax: 360-867-6790. p. 2522

Sapp, Jan, Syst Adminr, Carrollton Public Library, 1700 Keller Springs Rd, Carrollton, TX, 75006. Tel: 972-466-3591. Fax: 972-466-4265. p. 2295

Sapp, Lauren B, Dr, Dir, Florida Agricultural & Mechanical University Libraries, 1500 S Martin Luther King Blvd, Tallahassee, FL, 32307-4700. Tel: 850-599-3370. Fax: 850-561-2293. p. 492

Sappenfield, Carlin, Ref Librn, Vanderbilt University, Science & Engineering, 3200 Stevenson Ctr, 419 21st Ave S, Nashville, TN, 37240-0007. Tel: 615-343-7107. Fax: 615-343-7249. p. 2261

Sappington, Brenda, Librn, Northeast Regional Library, Tishomingo Library, Hwy 25, Main St, Tishomingo, MS, 38873. Tel: 662-438-7640. Fax: 662-438-7640. p. 1298

Sappington, Jayne, Cat, Texas Tech University Libraries, 18th & Boston Ave, Lubbock, TX, 79409-0002. Tel: 806-742-2261. Fax: 806-742-0737. p. 2358

Sappington, Kay, Dir, Union County Library, 219 King St, New Albany, MS, 38652. Tel: 662-534-1991. Fax: 662-534-1937. p. 1310

Saracevic, Tefko, Prof, Rutgers, The State University of New Jersey, Four Huntington St, New Brunswick, NJ, 08901-1071. Tel: 732-932-7500, Ext 8955. Fax: 732-932-2644. p. 2969

Sarajean, Petite, Govt Doc, Case Western Reserve University, School of Law Library, 11075 East Blvd, Cleveland, OH, 44106-7148. Tel: 216-368-6356. Fax: 216-368-1002. p. 1876

Saramak, Mary, Dir, Sound Shore Health System of Westchester, 16 Guion Pl, New Rochelle, NY, 10802. Tel: 914-365-3566. Fax: 914-576-4028. p. 1667

Saratora, Mary, Head, Circ, Peabody Institute Library of Danvers, 15 Sylvan St, Danvers, MA, 01923-2735. Tel: 978-774-0554. Fax: 978-762-0251. p. 1083

Saravo, Joseph, Curator, Isabella Stewart Gardner Museum Library, 280 The Fenway, Boston, MA, 02115-5897. Tel: 617-278-5121. Fax: 617-278-5177. p. 1061

Sarazin, Stephen, Dir, Aston Public Library, 3270 Concord Rd, Aston, PA, 19014. Tel: 610-494-5877. Fax: 610-494-1314. p. 2030

Sarcia, Eleanor, Librn, Mental Health Legal Advisors Committee, 24 School St, 8th Flr, Boston, MA, 02108. Tel: 617-338-2345. Fax: 617-338-2347. p. 1064

Sarette, Catherine, Youth Serv Coordr, Whatcom County Library System, 5205 Northwest Dr, Bellingham, WA, 98226-9050. Tel: 360-384-3150. Fax: 360-384-4947. p. 2509

Sarff, JoEllen, Br Mgr, Prince George's County Memorial, Largo-Kettering, 9601 Capital Lane, Largo, MD, 20774. Tel: 301-336-4044. Fax: 301-333-8857. p. 1032

Sargeant, Brad, Tech Spec, Springfield Public Library, 225 Fifth St, Springfield, OR, 97477-4697. Tel: 541-726-3766. Fax: 541-726-3747. p. 2020

Sargent, Edward, Asst Dean, Lake Washington Technical College, 11605 132nd Ave NE, Kirkland, WA, 98034-8505. Tel: 425-739-8100, Ext 492. Fax: 425-739-8198. p. 2519

Sargent, Joanne, Librn, Third District Court of Appeals, 2001 SW 117th Ave, Miami, FL, 33175. Tel: 305-229-3200. p. 468

Sargent, Judith, Br Assoc, Las Vegas-Clark County Library District, Mesquite Library, 121 W First North St, Mesquite, NV, 89027-4759. Tel: 702-507-4312. Fax: 702-346-5224, 702-346-5788. p. 1429

Sargent, Liz, Lea Archivist, Mgr, Houston Public Library, Houston Metropolitan Research Center, Archives & Local History, Julia Ideson Bldg, 500 McKinney, Houston, TX, 77002. Tel: 832-393-1658, 832-393-1659. p. 2339

Sargent, Robert, Dir, Franklin Public Library, 310 Central St, Franklin, NH, 03235. Tel: 603-934-2911. Fax: 603-934-7413. p. 1447

Sargent, William, Bus Mgr, Spokane County Library District, 4322 N Argonne Rd, Spokane, WA, 99212-1868. Tel: 509-893-8200. Fax: 509-893-8471. p. 2536

Sarich, Adrianne, Coordr, Access Serv, Huron University College Library, 1349 Western Rd, London, ON, N6G 1H3, CANADA. Tel: 519-438-7224, Ext 209. Fax: 519-438-3938. p. 2817

Sarick, Richard A, ILL, Cameron County Public Library, 27 W Fourth St, Emporium, PA, 15834. Tel: 814-486-8011. Fax: 814-486-3725. p. 2054

Sarin, Lindsay, Electronic Ref Librn, University of the District of Columbia, Learning Resources Division, 4200 Connecticut Ave NW, Washington, DC, 20008. Tel: 202-274-6370. Fax: 202-274-6012. p. 421

Sarjeant, Bruce, Govt Doc, Northern Michigan University, 1401 Presque Isle, Marquette, MI, 49855. Tel: 906-227-1580. Fax: 906-227-1333. p. 1207

Sark, Stephanie, Librn, Wabash Valley Correctional Facility, Level Three Library, 6908 S Old US Hwy 41, Carlisle, IN, 47838. Tel: 812-398-5050, Ext 3271. Fax: 812-398-2125. p. 731

Sarkissian, Alex, AV Mgr, Wayne Township Library, 80 N Sixth St, Richmond, IN, 47374-3079. Tel: 765-966-8291. Fax: 765-962-1318. p. 775

Sarkodie-Mensah, Kwasi, Instrul Serv Librn, Boston College Libraries, Thomas P O'Neill Jr Library (Central Library), 140 Commonwealth Ave, Chestnut Hill, MA, 02467. Tel: 617-552-4465. Fax: 617-552-0599. p. 1081

Sarles, Christie V, Co-Dir, Tuftonboro Free Library, 221 Middle Rd, Center Tuftonboro, NH, 03816. Tel: 603-569-4256. Fax: 603-569-5885. p. 1441

Sarli, Cathy, Librn, Washington University Libraries, Bernard Becker Medical Library, 660 S Euclid Ave, Campus Box 8132, Saint Louis, MO, 63110. Tel: 314-362-7865. Fax: 314-454-6606. p. 1362

Sarlo, Susie, Dir, Koshare Indian Museum Library, 115 W 18th St, La Junta, CO, 81050. Tel: 719-384-4411. Fax: 719-384-8836. p. 314

Sarmiento, Beatriz, Dir of Libr Serv, City of Commerce Public Library, 5655 Jillson St, Commerce, CA, 90040-1485. Tel: 323-722-6660. Fax: 323-724-1978. p. 136

Sarmiento, Roberto A, Head Librn, Northwestern University Library, Transportation Library, 1970 Campus Dr, Evanston, IL, 60208. Tel: 847-491-2913. Fax: 847-491-8601. p. 644

Sarnese, Jeanne, Dir, Prospect Community Library, 357 Main St, Prospect, PA, 16052. Tel: 724-865-9718. Fax: 724-865-9718. p. 2132

Sarno, Deborah, Circ, John C Hart Memorial Library, 1130 Main St, Shrub Oak, NY, 10588. Tel: 914-245-5262. Fax: 914-245-2216. p. 1743

Sarnoff, Stephanie, Dir, Schaumburg Township District Library, 130 S Roselle Rd, Schaumburg, IL, 60193. Tel: 847-923-3200. Fax: 847-923-3131. p. 701

Sarquhar, Pamela, Librn, Southwest Arkansas Regional Library, Ben Lomond Branch, 448 Wilson Creek Rd, Ben Lomond, AR, 71823. Tel: 870-287-4374. Fax: 870-287-4374. p. 103

Sarr, Debra, Circ Librn, West Orange Free Public Library, 46 Mount Pleasant Ave, West Orange, NJ, 07052-4903. Tel: 973-736-0198. Fax: 973-736-1655. p. 1541

Sarra, Amanda, Dir of Libr Serv, Everglades University, 5002 T-REX Ave, Ste 100, Boca Raton, FL, 33431. Tel: 561-912-1211. Fax: 561-912-1191. p. 428

Sarratt, Susan, Ch, Cherokee County Public Library, 300 E Rutledge Ave, Gaffney, SC, 29340-2227. Tel: 864-487-2711. Fax: 864-487-2752. p. 2194

Sartain, Donna, Dir, Pleasant Grove Public Library, 501 Park Rd, Pleasant Grove, AL, 35127. Tel: 205-744-1731. Fax: 205-744-5479. p. 34

Sartain, Dorthea, Curator, The Explorers Club, 46 E 70th St, New York, NY, 10021. Tel: 212-628-8383. Fax: 212-288-4449. p. 1677

Sartin, Margie, Ref, San Juan College Library, 4601 College Blvd, Farmington, NM, 87402. Tel: 505-566-3249. Fax: 505-566-3381. p. 1555

Sartori, Donna, Circ, Mgr, ILL, University of Guelph, 50 Stone Rd E, Guelph, ON, N1G 2W1, CANADA. Tel: 519-824-4120, Ext 52075, 519-824-4120, Ext 52181. Fax: 519-824-6931. p. 2807

Sartori, Michael, Asst Prof, Syst Librn, McNeese State University, 4205 Ryan St, Lake Charles, LA, 70609. Tel: 337-475-5720. Fax: 337-475-5719, 337-475-5727. p. 954

Sarvey, Roy, Circ, C W Clark Memorial Library, 160 N Main St, Oriskany Falls, NY, 13425. Tel: 315-821-7850. Fax: 315-821-7850. p. 1712

Sasaki, Stefanie, Libr Instruction, Ref Serv, Honolulu Community College Library, 874 Dillingham Blvd, Honolulu, HI, 96817-4598. Tel: 808-845-9463. Fax: 808-845-3618. p. 564

Sasbender, Kathy, Coordr, Department of Veteran Affairs, 500 E Veterans St, Tomah, WI, 54660. Tel: 608-372-1270. Fax: 608-372-1670. p. 2642

Sass, Rivkah K, Dir, Sacramento Public Library, 828 I St, Sacramento, CA, 95814. Tel: 916-264-2770. Fax: 916-264-2755. p. 224

Sassa, Reiko, Dir, Japan Society, 333 E 47th St, New York, NY, 10017. Tel: 212-715-1273. Fax: 212-715-1279. p. 1683

Sasser, Lisa, Ch, Thomas-Wilhite Memorial Library, 101 E Thomas, Perkins, OK, 74059. Tel: 405-547-5185. Fax: 405-547-1040. p. 1976

Sasseville, Pierre, Coordr, Cegep de Saint-Laurent Bibliotheque, 625 Boul Ste-Croix, Saint Laurent, QC, H4L 3X7, CANADA. Tel: 514-747-6521. Fax: 514-748-1249, 514-855-1942. p. 2909

Sassman, Cheryl, Head, Circ, Texas Christian University, 2913 Lowden St, TCU Box 298400, Fort Worth, TX, 76129. Tel: 817-257-7106. Fax: 817-257-7282. p. 2323

Sasso, Carol, Mgr, Off of the Dean of Libr & Info Serv, Hofstra University, 123 Hofstra University, Hempstead, NY, 11549. Tel: 516-463-5943. p. 1635

Sasso, Maureen Diana, Dir, Info Serv, Duquesne University, 600 Forbes Ave, Pittsburgh, PA, 15282. Tel: 412-396-5680. p. 2125

Satchell, James E, III, Coordr, Access Serv, Norfolk State University Library, 700 Park Ave, Norfolk, VA, 23504-8010. Tel: 757-823-8796. Fax: 757-823-2431. p. 2482

Satchell, Michelle, Mgr, Bayliss Public Library, Pickford Community Library, 230 E Main St, Pickford, MI, 49774. Tel: 906-647-1288. Fax: 906-647-1288. p. 1226

Satersmoen, Carol, Bibliog Instr, Pub Serv, Aims Community College, College Ctr, 5401 W 20th St, 750.1, Greeley, CO, 80634-3002. Tel: 970-339-6589. Fax: 970-506-6937. p. 311

Sathan, Eleanor, Ref, Memorial Hall Library, Two N Main St, Andover, MA, 01810. Tel: 978-623-8401. Fax: 978-623-8407. p. 1049

Sathaye, Tuki, Head, Adult Serv, Itasca Community Library, 500 W Irving Park Rd, Itasca, IL, 60143. Tel: 630-773-1699. Fax: 630-773-1707. p. 658

Sathe, Nila, Assoc Dir, Res, Vanderbilt University, Annette & Irwin Eskind Biomedical Library, 2209 Garland Ave, Nashville, TN, 37232-8340. Tel: 615-936-5790. Fax: 615-936-1384. p. 2260

Sather, Andrew, Interim Asst Dir, Tech Serv, Jenkins Law Library, 833 Chestnut St, Ste 1220, Philadelphia, PA, 19107-4429. Tel: 215-574-7903. Fax: 215-574-7920. p. 2111

Sather, Ellen, Pres, Frances O'Brien Memorial Library, 51790 McKenzie St, Blue River, OR, 97413. Tel: 541-822-3249. p. 1992

Sathrum, Robert, Chair, Ref Serv, Humboldt State University Library, One Harpst St, Arcata, CA, 95521-8299. Tel: 707-826-5617. Fax: 707-826-3440. p. 122

Satkalmi, Aru, Sr Res Librn, Saint John's University Library, Rittenberg Law Library, 8000 Utopia Pkwy, Queens, NY, 11439. Tel: 718-990-6769. Fax: 718-990-6649. p. 1725

Satriano, Christine, Sr Librn, Denver Public Library, Ross-University Hills, 4310 E Amherst Ave, Denver, CO, 80222-6703. Tel: 303-757-2714. Fax: 303-692-5606. p. 301

Satterfield, Barbara, Cat, Marion County Public Library, 321 Monroe St, Fairmont, WV, 26554-2952. Tel: 304-366-1210. Fax: 304-366-4831. p. 2559

Satterfield, Jay, Spec Coll Librn, Dartmouth College Library, Rauner Special Collections Library, 6065 Webster Hall, Hanover, NH, 03755-3519. Tel: 603-646-0538. Fax: 603-646-0447. p. 1450

Satterfield, Susanne, Outreach Coordr, Person County Public Library, 319 S Main St, Roxboro, NC, 27573. Tel: 336-597-7881. Fax: 336-597-5081. p. 1821

Satterthwaite, Mimi, Ref, Abington Township Public Library, 1030 Old York Rd, Abington, PA, 19001-4594. Tel: 215-885-5180. Fax: 215-885-9242. p. 2025

Satterwhite, Melissa, Dir, Teague Public Library, 400 Main St, Teague, TX, 75860. Tel: 254-739-3311. Fax: 254-739-3118. p. 2390

Saturley, Jacqueline, Dir, Hopkinsville-Christian County Public Library, 1101 Bethel St, Hopkinsville, KY, 42240. Tel: 270-887-4262. Fax: 270-887-4264. p. 918

Saturley, Jacquelyn, Ad, Archivist, Roseville Public Library, 29777 Gratiot Ave, Roseville, MI, 48066. Tel: 586-445-5407. Fax: 586-445-5499. p. 1223

Satushek, Barbara, Acq, Bellingham Technical College Library, 3028 Lindbergh Ave, Bellingham, WA, 98225-1599. Tel: 360-752-8383. Fax: 360-752-8384. p. 2508

Satyendra, Gita, Bibliog Instr, Distance Educ, Saddleback College, 28000 Marguerite Pkwy, Mission Viejo, CA, 92692. Tel: 949-582-4654. Fax: 949-364-0284. p. 187

Sauceda, Eduardo, Circ Serv Dept Head, California State University, Sacramento Library, 2000 State University Dr E, Sacramento, CA, 95819-6039. Tel: 916-278-5679. Fax: 916-278-5917. p. 223

Sauceda, Nicole, Circ Asst, Sam Fore Jr Wilson County Public Library, One Library Lane, Floresville, TX, 78114. Tel: 830-393-7361. Fax: 830-393-7337. p. 2319

Saucier, Marci, Ch, Saint Charles Parish Library, 160 W Campus Dr, Destrehan, LA, 70047. Tel: 985-764-2366. Fax: 985-764-0447. p. 948

Saudargas, Thomas, Dir of Tech Serv, Maricopa County Community College District, 2411 W 14th St, Tempe, AZ, 85281-6942. Tel: 480-731-8774. Fax: 480-731-8787. p. 2937

Sauder, Molly, Archivist, Librn, The Old Jail Art Center, 201 S Second St, Albany, TX, 76430. Tel: 325-762-2269. Fax: 325-762-2260. p. 2272

Sauer, Anne, Univ Archivist, Tufts University, 35 Professors Row, Medford, MA, 02155-5816. Tel: 617-627-2696. Fax: 617-627-3002. p. 1104

Sauer, Greg, Assoc Dir, Gen Libr Serv, Norwich University, 23 Harmon Dr, Northfield, VT, 05663. Tel: 802-485-2175. Fax: 802-485-2173. p. 2431

Sauer, James, Ref Librn, Pennsylvania State University, 30 E Swedesford Rd, Malvern, PA, 19355. Tel: 610-648-3354. Fax: 610-725-5223. p. 2083

Sauer, James L, Dir, Eastern University, 1300 Eagle Rd, Saint Davids, PA, 19087. Tel: 610-341-5981. Fax: 610-341-1375. p. 2135

Sauer, Joan Casson, Asst Dir, Bryant Library, Two Paper Mill Rd, Roslyn, NY, 11576-2193. Tel: 516-621-2240. Fax: 516-621-7211. p. 1735

Sauer, Julie, Br Librn, Riverside Regional Library, Perryville Branch, 800 City Park Dr, Ste A, Perryville, MO, 63775. Tel: 573-547-6508. Fax: 573-547-3715. p. 1334

Sauer, Laurie, Info Tech Librn, Knox College, Two E South St, Galesburg, IL, 61401. Tel: 309-341-7788. Fax: 309-341-7799. p. 648

Sauers, Michael, Tech Innovation Librn, Nebraska Library Commission, The Atrium, 1200 N St, Ste 120, Lincoln, NE, 68508-2023. Tel: 402-471-3106. Fax: 402-471-2083. p. 1406

Saul, Nancy, Ref, Simon Wiesenthal Center & Museum of Tolerance, 1399 S Roxbury Dr, Los Angeles, CA, 90035-4709. Tel: 310-772-7605. Fax: 310-277-6568. p. 177

Saule, Mara, Dean of Libr & Info Serv, University of Vermont Libraries, 538 Main St, Burlington, VT, 05405-0036. Tel: 802-656-2003. Fax: 802-656-4038. p. 2421

Saulig, Mary, Dir, Libr Serv, Goodmans LLP Library, Bay Adelaide Ctr, 333 Bay St, Ste 3400, Toronto, ON, M5H 2S7, CANADA. Tel: 416-979-2211, Ext 6070. Fax: 416-979-1234. p. 2854

Saulmon, Sharon, Dean, Rose State College, 6420 SE 15th St, Midwest City, OK, 73110. Tel: 405-736-0259. Fax: 405-736-0260. p. 1968

Saulo, Consuelo, Coordr, ILL, Florida Hospital College of Health Sciences, 671 Winyah Dr, Orlando, FL, 32803. Tel: 407-303-7747, Ext 9875. Fax: 407-303-9622. p. 476

Saulsberry, Mildred, Circ, Memphis Theological Seminary Library, 168 E Parkway S, Memphis, TN, 38104. Tel: 901-334-5813. Fax: 901-452-4051. p. 2250

Saulsbury, Patricia, Learning Res Coordr, Sierra College Library, 250 Sierra College Dr, Grass Valley, CA, 95945. Tel: 530-274-5304. Fax: 530-274-5333. p. 156

Saumell, Kathy, Libr Asst, Fermi National Accelerator Laboratory Library, Kirk & Wilson Sts, Batavia, IL, 60510. Tel: 630-840-3401. Fax: 630-840-4636. p. 593

Saunders, Aimee, Ms & Archives Librn, Redwood Library & Athenaeum, 50 Bellevue Ave, Newport, RI, 02840-3292. Tel: 401-847-0292. Fax: 401-847-0192. p. 2169

Saunders, Carol, Br Mgr, Kern County Library, Clara M Jackson Branch Branch, 500 W Kern Ave, McFarland, CA, 93250-1355. Tel: 661-792-2318. Fax: 661-792-6588. p. 124

Saunders, Carol, Br Mgr, Kern County Library, Delano Branch, 925 Tenth Ave, Delano, CA, 93215-2229. Tel: 661-725-1078. p. 124

Saunders, Carol J, Interim Dir, Ref Librn, Hyannis Public Library Association, 401 Main St, Hyannis, MA, 02601-3019. Tel: 508-775-2280. Fax: 508-790-0087. p. 1096

Saunders, Charles D, Librn, Richmond Newspapers, Inc Library, 300 E Franklin St, Richmond, VA, 23219. Tel: 804-649-6224, 804-649-6286. Fax: 804-649-6935. p. 2489

Saunders, Cindy, In Charge, Department of Natural Resources, Government of Newfoundland & Labrador, 50 Elizabeth Ave, St. John's, NL, A1B 1W5, CANADA. Tel: 709-729-3159. Fax: 709-729-4491. p. 2772

Saunders, Connie, Cat, ILL, Fleming County Public Library, 202 Bypass Blvd, Flemingsburg, KY, 41041-7934. Tel: 606-845-7851. Fax: 606-845-7045. p. 912

Saunders, Dawn, Librn, Reiss-Davis Child Study Center, 3200 Motor Ave, Los Angeles, CA, 90034-3710. Tel: 310-204-1666, Ext 359. Fax: 310-838-4637. p. 177

Saunders, Deborah, Dir, Gallia County District Library, Seven Spruce St, Gallipolis, OH, 45631. Tel: 740-446-7323. Fax: 740-446-1701. p. 1901

Saunders, Dianne, Br Mgr, Montgomery County Public Library, Allen Library-Biscoe Branch, 307 Page St, Biscoe, NC, 27209-0518. Tel: 910-428-2551. Fax: 910-428-2551. p. 1827

Saunders, Jesse, Head, Syst & Web Mgt, Southwestern University, 1100 E University Ave, Georgetown, TX, 78626. Tel: 512-863-1561. Fax: 512-863-8198. p. 2327

Saunders, Laura, Asst Prof, Simmons College, 300 The Fenway, Boston, MA, 02115. Tel: 617-521-2800. Fax: 617-521-3192. p. 2967

Saunders, Laverna, Dr, Univ Librn, Duquesne University, 600 Forbes Ave, Pittsburgh, PA, 15282. Tel: 412-396-6130. p. 2125

Saunders, Marc, Pub Serv Mgr, Prince George Public Library, 887 Dominion St, Prince George, BC, V2L 5L1, CANADA. Tel: 250-563-9251. Fax: 250-563-0892. p. 2736

Saunders, Megan, Evening Circ, University of Washington Libraries, Tacoma Library, 1900 Commerce St, Box 358460, Tacoma, WA, 98402-3100. Tel: 253-692-4657. Fax: 253-692-4445. p. 2535

Saunders, Michael, Archivist, Washington State Office of Secretary of State, 1129 Washington St SE, Olympia, WA, 98504-2283. Tel: 425-564-3950. Fax: 425-564-3945. p. 2523

Saunders, Mike, Ser, National Gallery of Canada Library, 380 Sussex Dr, Ottawa, ON, K1N 9N4, CANADA. Tel: 613-991-5058. Fax: 613-990-9818. p. 2832

Saunders, Pamela, Librn, Atlantic County Library System, Pleasantville Branch, 33 Martin L King Jr Ave, Pleasantville, NJ, 08232. Tel: 609-641-1778. Fax: 609-641-0771. p. 1500

Saunders, Perri, Dir, White Pigeon Township Library, 102 N Kalamazoo St, White Pigeon, MI, 49099-9726. Tel: 269-483-7409. Fax: 269-483-9923. p. 1237

Saunders, Phyllis, Admin Librn, Chandler Public Library, Hamilton, 3700 S Arizona Ave, Chandler, AZ, 85248-4500. Tel: 480-782-2831. Fax: 480-782-2833. p. 60

Saunders, Rebecca, Genealogy Serv, Northwest Regional Library System, 898 W 11 St, Panama City, FL, 32401. Tel: 850-522-2100. Fax: 850-522-2138. p. 480

Saunders, Richard L, Archivist, Curator, University of Tennessee at Martin, Ten Wayne Fisher Dr, Martin, TN, 38238. Tel: 731-881-7094. Fax: 731-881-7074. p. 2246

Saunders, Sara, Supvry Archivist, National Archives & Records Administration, 441 Freedom Pkwy, Atlanta, GA, 30307. Tel: 404-865-7155. Fax: 404-865-7102. p. 517

Saunders, Sharon K, Syst & Cat Librn, Bates College, 48 Campus Ave, Lewiston, ME, 04240. Tel: 207-786-8327. Fax: 207-786-6055. p. 989

Saunders, Stewart, Librn, Purdue University Libraries, Mathematical Sciences, Mathematical Sciences Bldg 311, 105 N University St, West Lafayette, IN, 47907-2058. Tel: 765-494-2855. Fax: 765-494-0548. p. 787

Saunders, Suzanne, Librn, Lovington Public Library District, 110 W State St, Lovington, IL, 61937. Tel: 217-873-4468. Fax: 217-873-6068. p. 668

Saunders, Teresa, Tech Serv, Western Connecticut State University, 181 White St, Danbury, CT, 06810. Tel: 203-837-9106. Fax: 203-837-9108. p. 335

Saunders, Wesley, Asst Dir, Support Serv, Rapides Parish Library, 411 Washington St, Alexandria, LA, 71301-8338. Tel: 318-445-241, Ext 1044. Fax: 318-445-6478. p. 940

Saurman, Louis, Pub Relations, Newtown Library Co, 114 Centre Ave, Newtown, PA, 18940. Tel: 215-968-7659. p. 2098

Sauro, Christine, Head Librn, McAlester Public Library, 401 N Second St, McAlester, OK, 74501. Tel: 918-426-0930. Fax: 918-423-5731. p. 1968

Sauser, Kathleen, Asst Dir, Hamann Memorial Library, 311 E Main, Anthon, IA, 51004. Tel: 712-373-5275. Fax: 712-373-5275. p. 794

Sautter, Betty, Tech Serv, Southwest Wisconsin Library System, 1775 Fourth St, Fennimore, WI, 53809-1137. Tel: 608-822-3393. Fax: 608-822-6251. p. 2591

Sauvageau, Philippe, Dir, Assemblee Nationale du Quebec Bibliotheque, 1035 Rue des Parlementaires, Edifice Pamphile-Lemay, Quebec, QC, G1A 1A3, CANADA. Tel: 418-643-2708. Fax: 418-646-3207. p. 2903

Sauve, Diane, Librn, INRS - Institut Armand-Frappier - Bibliotheque, 531 blvd des Prairies, Laval, QC, H7V 1B7, CANADA. Tel: 450-687-5010, Ext 4340. Fax: 450-686-5501. p. 2886

Sauve, Greg, Head, ILL, Rochester Public Library, 101 Second St SE, Rochester, MN, 55904-3776. Tel: 507-328-2368. Fax: 507-328-2384. p. 1273

Sauve, Hanne, Librn, Spanish Public Library, Eight Trunk Rd, Spanish, ON, P0P 2A0, CANADA. Tel: 705-844-2555. Fax: 705-844-2555. p. 2842

Sauve, Jennifer, Pub Serv, College of New Caledonia Library, 3330 22nd Ave, Prince George, BC, V2N 1P8, CANADA. Tel: 250-562-2131, Ext 298. Fax: 250-561-5845. p. 2736

Sauvey, Gretchen, Knowledge Mgt Spec, United States Institute of Peace, 2301 Constitution Ave NW, Washington, DC, 20037. Tel: 202-429-4742, 202-457-1700. p. 420

Sauvola, Irma, Librn, Health Sciences North, 41 Ramsey Lake Rd, Sudbury, ON, P3E 5J1, CANADA. Tel: 705-523-7100, Ext 3375. Fax: 705-523-7317. p. 2846

Sauvola, Michael, Network Adminr, Northern Waters Library Service, 3200 E Lakeshore Dr, Ashland, WI, 54806-2510. Tel: 715-682-2365. Fax: 715-685-2704. p. 2579

Sauwen, Merla, Librn, Woodruff Community Library, 6414 W First St, Woodruff, AZ, 85942. Tel: 928-524-3885. Fax: 928-524-3885. p. 90

Sauzer, Jennifer, Circ Mgr, Columbia College Chicago Library, 624 S Michigan Ave, Chicago, IL, 60605-1996. Tel: 312-369-8540. Fax: 312-344-8062. p. 611

Savage, Andrea, Ch, Bay City Public Library, 1100 Seventh St, Bay City, TX, 77414. Tel: 979-245-6931. Fax: 979-245-2614. p. 2286

Savage, Caitlin, Head, Circ, Morton Grove Public Library, 6140 Lincoln Ave, Morton Grove, IL, 60053-2989. Tel: 847-929-5125. Fax: 847-965-7903. p. 676

Savage, Carolyn, Ref Librn, Chapin Memorial Library, 400 14th Ave N, Myrtle Beach, SC, 29577-3612. Tel: 843-918-1275. Fax: 843-918-1288. p. 2201

Savage, Donna D, Univ Librn, Tarleton State University Library, 201 Saint Felix, Stephenville, TX, 76401. Tel: 254-968-9246. Fax: 254-968-9467. p. 2389

Savage, Elaine, Dir, Palos Heights Public Library, 12501 S 71st Ave, Palos Heights, IL, 60463. Tel: 708-448-1473. Fax: 708-448-8950. p. 687

Savage, Norm, Libr Mgr, Killam Municipal Library, PO Box 329, Killam, AB, T0B 2L0, CANADA. Tel: 780-385-3032. p. 2708

Savage, Stephen, Head, Monographs, San Diego State University Library & Information Access, 5500 Campanile Dr, San Diego, CA, 92182-8050. Tel: 619-594-5895. Fax: 619-594-3270. p. 237

Savage, Tammy, Tech Serv, Garrett Public Library, 107 W Houston St, Garrett, IN, 46738. Tel: 260-357-5485. Fax: 260-357-5170. p. 744

Savakinus-Moran, Mary Ann, Exec Dir, Lackawanna Historical Society Library, 232 Monroe Ave, Scranton, PA, 18510. Tel: 570-344-3841. Fax: 570-344-3815. p. 2137

Savard, Gerry, Pres, American-Canadian Genealogical Society Library, Four Elm St, Manchester, NH, 03103-7242. Tel: 603-622-1554. p. 1455

Savard, Nicolas, Mgr, Ref & Res Support Serv, Canada Department of Justice Library, EMB, Rm A-370, 284 Wellington St, Ottawa, ON, K1A 0H8, CANADA. Tel: 613-957-4606. p. 2828

Savard, Rejean, Prof, Universite de Montreal, 3150, rue Jean-Brillant, bur C-2004, Montreal, QC, H3T 1N8, CANADA. Tel: 514-343-6044. Fax: 514-343-5753. p. 2979

Savaria, Jean-Francois, Librn, Prince Edward Island Public Library Service, Summerside Rotary Library, 192 Water St, Summerside, PE, C1N 1B1, CANADA. Tel: 902-436-7323, 902-888-8370. Fax: 902-888-8055. p. 2876

Savaria, Kristen, Tech Serv, East Longmeadow Public Library, 60 Center Sq, East Longmeadow, MA, 01028-2459. Tel: 413-525-5400. Fax: 413-525-0344. p. 1086

Savary, Karine, Archivist, La Societe d'Histoire de Sherbrooke, 275, rue Dufferin, Sherbrooke, QC, J1H 4M5, CANADA. Tel: 819-821-5406. Fax: 819-821-5417. p. 2912

Savas, Nancy, Mgr, Montgomery County Public Libraries, Aspen Hill Library, 4407 Aspen Hill Rd, Rockville, MD, 20853-2899. Tel: 240-773-9401. Fax: 301-871-0443. p. 1038

Savas, Nancy, Mgr, Montgomery County Public Libraries, Germantown Library, 19840 Century Blvd, Germantown, MD, 20874. Tel: 240-773-0126. Fax: 240-777-0129. p. 1038

Savedow, Paul, Head Librn, Free Library of Philadelphia, Education, Philosophy & Religion, 1901 Vine St, Philadelphia, PA, 19103-1189. Tel: 215-686-5392. p. 2107

Savery, Wendy, Dir, Gilbert Hart Library, 14 S Main, Wallingford, VT, 05773. Tel: 802-446-2685. Fax: 802-446-2685. p. 2438

Savilla, Tretha, Br Mgr, Putnam County Library, Eleanor Branch, 203 Eleanor Circle, Eleanor, WV, 25070. Tel: 304-586-4295. Fax: 304-586-4295. p. 2562

Saville, Carole, Librn, St Luke's Hospital Library, 4201 Belfort Rd, Jacksonville, FL, 32216. Tel: 904-296-3735. Fax: 904-296-4644. p. 454

Savin, Danielle, Tech Serv, Plymouth Public Library, 132 South St, Plymouth, MA, 02360-3309. Tel: 508-830-4250. Fax: 508-830-4258. p. 1118

Savini, Thomas M, Dir, Chancellor Robert R Livingston Masonic Library of Grand Lodge, 71 W 23rd St, 14th Flr, New York, NY, 10010-4171. Tel: 212-337-6619. Fax: 212-633-2639. p. 1672

Savitsky, Tanya, Librn, Ringtown Area Library, 132 W Main St, Ringtown, PA, 17967-9538. Tel: 570-889-5503. p. 2135

Savitts, Patricia, Circ, University of Scranton, Monroe & Linden, Scranton, PA, 18510-4634. Tel: 570-941-7526. Fax: 570-941-7817. p. 2138

Savitz, Renee, Br Librn, Duplin County Library, Rose Hill Community Memorial Library, 113 S Walnut St, Rose Hill, NC, 28458. Tel: 910-289-2490. Fax: 910-289-2186. p. 1804

Savoie, Denise M, Head, ILL, Universite de Moncton, 415 Ave de l'Universite, Moncton, NB, E1A 3E9, CANADA. Tel: 506-858-4012. Fax: 506-858-4086. p. 2766

Savoie, Marina, Circ & ILL Coordr, Bradley University, 1501 W Bradley Ave, Peoria, IL, 61625. Tel: 309-677-2850. Fax: 309-677-2558. p. 690

Savoie, Terttu, Tech Serv, Eastern Nazarene College, 23 E Elm Ave, Quincy, MA, 02170. Tel: 617-745-3850. Fax: 617-745-3913. p. 1119

Savolainen, Mary, Coordr, Circ, Wheaton College Library, 26 E Main St, Norton, MA, 02766-2322. Tel: 508-286-3708. p. 1115

Savolis, Mark, Head, Archives & Spec Coll, College of the Holy Cross, One College St, Worcester, MA, 01610. Tel: 508-793-2506. Fax: 508-793-2372. p. 1143

Savopol, Florin, Mgr, Natural Resources Canada, National Air Photo Library, 615 Booth St, Rm 180, Ottawa, ON, K1A 0E9, CANADA. Tel: 613-943-0234. Fax: 613-995-4568. p. 2832

Savoy, Margaret, Ch, Elyria Public Library System, 320 Washington Ave, Elyria, OH, 44035-5199. Tel: 440-323-5747. Fax: 440-323-5788. p. 1898

Savoy, Patrola, Br Mgr, Evangeline Parish Library, Chataignier Branch, 6215 Charles Armand Jr St, Chataignier, LA, 70524. Tel: 337-885-2028. Fax: 337-885-2028. p. 971

Savoy, Stephanie, Asst Br Mgr, Pointe Coupee Parish Library, Morganza Branch, 221 S Louisiana, Hwy 1, Morganza, LA, 70759. Tel: 225-694-2428. Fax: 225-694-2428. p. 964

Sawall, Pam, Cat, Head, Tech Serv, Monmouth County Library, 125 Symmes Dr, Manalapan, NJ, 07726. Tel: 732-431-7220. Fax: 732-308-2955. p. 1498

Sawallis, Pam, Ref Serv Coordr, Birmingham-Southern College, 900 Arkadelphia Rd, Birmingham, AL, 35254. Tel: 205-226-4749. Fax: 205-226-4743. p. 8

Sawatzky, Denice, Interlibrary Serv Coordr, University of California, Merced Library, 5200 N Lake Rd, Merced, CA, 95343-5001. Tel: 209-228-2963. Fax: 209-228-4271. p. 186

Sawchuk, Natalka, Asst Dir, Libr for Pub Serv & Syst, Iona College, 715 North Ave, New Rochelle, NY, 10801-1890. Tel: 914-633-2220. Fax: 914-633-2136. p. 1666

Sawczyn, Luba, Head, Ref, Chapel Hill Public Library, 100 Library Dr, Chapel Hill, NC, 27514. Tel: 919-969-2032. Fax: 919-968-2838. p. 1780

Sawina, Jodie, Digital Serv, Tech Serv Mgr, Chula Vista Public Library, 365 F St, Chula Vista, CA, 91910-2697. Tel: 619-691-5138. Fax: 619-427-4246. p. 134

Sawka, Kristin, Head of Libr, Free Library of Philadelphia, Bustleton Avenue Branch, 10199 Bustleton Ave, Philadelphia, PA, 19116-3718. Tel: 215-685-0472. Fax: 215-698-8892. p. 2107

Sawka, Michelle, In Charge, Canadian Urban Transit Association Library, 55 York St, Ste 1401, Toronto, ON, M5J 1R7, CANADA. Tel: 416-365-9800, Ext 113. Fax: 416-365-1295. p. 2852

Sawkiw, Michael, Pres, Ukrainian Congress Committee of America Library, 311 Massachusetts Ave NE, Washington, DC, 20002. Tel: 202-547-0018. Fax: 202-543-5502. p. 417

Sawtelle, Julie, Dir, Cumston Public Library, 796 Main St, Monmouth, ME, 04259. Tel: 207-933-4788. Fax: 207-933-3413. p. 992

Sawusch, Ann Mina, Librn, University of Buffalo Research Institute on Addictions, 1021 Main St, Buffalo, NY, 14203-1016. Tel: 716-887-2511. Fax: 716-887-2490. p. 1599

Sawyer, Barbara, Librn, Frenchman's Bay Library, 1776 US Hwy, No 1, Sullivan, ME, 04664. Tel: 207-422-2307. p. 1003

Sawyer, Becky, Head, Cat, New Providence Memorial Library, 377 Elkwood Ave, New Providence, NJ, 07974-1837. Tel: 908-665-0311. Fax: 908-665-2319. p. 1510

Sawyer, Cara Elizabeth, Head Librn, Cherryfield Free Public Library, 35 Main St, Cherryfield, ME, 04622. Tel: 207-546-4228. Fax: 207-546-4228. p. 982

Sawyer, Dennis, Libr Tech, Hotel Dieu Shaver Health & Rehabilitation Centre, 541 Glenridge Ave, Saint Catharines, ON, L2T 4C2, CANADA. Tel: 905-685-1381, Ext 85266. Fax: 905-687-3228. p. 2839

Sawyer, Ginger, Ch, York County Library, 138 E Black St, Rock Hill, SC, 29731. Tel: 803-981-5888. Fax: 803-981-5866. p. 2203

Sawyer, Jack, Ref Librn, College of Southern Nevada, Cheyenne Campus, 3200 E Cheyenne Ave, C2A, North Las Vegas, NV, 89030. Tel: 702-651-4444. Fax: 702-643-4812. p. 1429

Sawyer, Michael, Dir, Pine Bluff & Jefferson County Library System, Main Library, 200 E Eighth Ave, Pine Bluff, AR, 71601. Tel: 870-534-4615. Fax: 870-534-8707. p. 112

Sawyer, Michael, Dir, Calcasieu Parish Public Library, 301 W Claude St, Lake Charles, LA, 70605-3457. Tel: 337-721-7147. Fax: 337-475-8806. p. 953

Sawyer, Nancy, Br Mgr, Timberland Regional Library, Mountain View, 210 Silverbrook Rd, Randle, WA, 98377. Tel: 360-497-2665. Fax: 360-497-7080. p. 2543

Sawyer, Nora, Ref Librn, Littler Mendelson Library, 650 California St, 20th Flr, San Francisco, CA, 94108-2693. Tel: 415-399-8441. Fax: 415-399-8490. p. 243

Sawyer, Patricia, Dir, Friendship Free Library, 40 W Main St, Friendship, NY, 14739-8701. Tel: 585-973-7724. Fax: 585-973-7724. p. 1625

Sawyer, Suzanne, Br Mgr, East Bonner County Free Library District, Clark Fork Branch, 601 Main St, Clark Fork, ID, 83811. Tel: 208-266-1321. Fax: 208-266-1663. p. 584

Sawyer, Suzanne, Electronic Res Librn, Lansing Community College Library, 200 Technology & Learning Ctr, 419 N Capitol Ave, Lansing, MI, 48933. Tel: 517-483-9717. Fax: 517-483-5300. p. 1201

Sawyer, Sylvia, Acq, Carson-Newman College, 1634 Russell Ave, Jefferson City, TN, 37760. Tel: 865-471-3335. Fax: 865-471-3450. p. 2239

Sawyer-Ratliff, Suzanne, Dir, Libr Serv, University of Colorado Boulder, Equity Diversity & Education Library, School of Education, Campus Box 249, Rm 344, Boulder, CO, 80309-0249. Tel: 303-492-3359. Fax: 303-492-7090. p. 291

Sawyerr, Clifton, Ref Librn, North Carolina Agricultural & Technical State University, 1601 E Market St, Greensboro, NC, 27411-0002. Tel: 336-334-7159, Ext 3217. Fax: 336-334-7783. p. 1797

Saxe, Coleen, Librn, Good Samaritan Regional Health Center, 605 N 12th St, Mount Vernon, IL, 62864. Tel: 618-241-2062. Fax: 618-241-3817. p. 678

Saxenian, Annalee, Dean, University of California at Berkeley, 102 South Hall, Berkeley, CA, 94720-4600. Tel: 510-642-1464. Fax: 510-642-5814. p. 2962

Saxon, Sean, Head, Tech Serv, University of Nevada, Las Vegas Libraries, Wiener-Rogers Law Library, William S Boyd School of Law, 4505 Maryland Pkwy, Las Vegas, NV, 89154-1080. Tel: 702-895-2400. Fax: 702-895-2410. p. 1431

Saxton, Amy, Pub Serv Librn, University of Hawaii at Hilo Library, 200 W Kawili St, Hilo, HI, 96720-4091. Tel: 808-974-7759. Fax: 808-974-7329. p. 559

Saxton, Jane D, Dir, Libr Serv, Bastyr University Library, 14500 Juanita Dr NE, Kenmore, WA, 98028. Tel: 425-602-3024. Fax: 425-602-3188. p. 2518

Saxton, Jennifer, Librn, Miami Dade College, Kendall Campus Library, 11011 SW 104th St, Miami, FL, 33176-3393. Tel: 305-237-0996, 305-237-2015, 305-237-2291. Fax: 305-237-2923. p. 466

Saxton, Matthew, Assoc Dean, Academics, University of Washington, Mary Gates Hall, Ste 370, Campus Box 352840, Seattle, WA, 98195-2840. Tel: 206-685-9937. Fax: 206-616-3152. p. 2976

Saxton, Sara, Youth Serv Librn, Wasilla Meta-Rose Public Library, 391 N Main St, Wasilla, AK, 99654-7085. Tel: 907-864-9173. Fax: 907-376-2347. p. 55

Saye, Sharon R, Dir, Bridgeport Public Library, 1200 Johnson Ave, Bridgeport, WV, 26330. Tel: 304-842-8248. Fax: 304-842-4018. p. 2555

Sayer, Katherine, Govt Doc, US Courts Library, Byron Rogers Courthouse, 1929 Stout St, Rm 430, Denver, CO, 80294. Tel: 303-844-3591. Fax: 303-844-5958. p. 303

Sayers, John E, Dir, Kewanee Public Library District, 102 S Tremont St, Kewanee, IL, 61443. Tel: 309-852-4505. Fax: 309-852-4466. p. 661

Sayers, June, Bus Mgr, Montgomery-Floyd Regional Library System, 125 Sheltman St, Christiansburg, VA, 24073. Tel: 540-382-6965. Fax: 540-382-6964. p. 2457

Sayers, Teresa, Br Mgr, Boone County Public Library, Chapin Memorial, 6517 Market St, Petersburg, KY, 41080. p. 909

Sayles, Julie, Govt Doc, Ser, Lee College Library, 150 Lee Dr, Baytown, TX, 77520. Tel: 281-425-6379. Fax: 281-425-6557. p. 2286

Saylor, Elke, Reader Serv, Whitefish Bay Public Library, 5420 N Marlborough Dr, Whitefish Bay, WI, 53217. Tel: 414-964-4380. Fax: 414-964-5733. p. 2648

Saylor, Gerard, Dir, L D Fargo Public Library, 120 E Madison St, Lake Mills, WI, 53551-1644. Tel: 920-648-2166. Fax: 920-648-5561. p. 2604

Saylor, John, Assoc Univ Librn, Cornell University Library, 201 Olin Library, Ithaca, NY, 14853-5301. Tel: 607-255-4134. Fax: 607-255-6788. p. 1641

Saylor, Maurice, Head Librn, Catholic University of America, Music, 101 Ward Hall, 620 Michigan St, Washington, DC, 20064. Tel: 202-319-5424. Fax: 202-319-6280. p. 396

Saylor, Nicole, Head, Archives, Library of Congress, American Folklife Center, Library of Congress Thomas Jefferson Bldg, G53, 101 Independence Ave SE, Washington, DC, 20540-4610. Tel: 202-707-5510. Fax: 202-707-2076. p. 406

Saylor, Susan, Spec Projects, Tech Serv, Gates Public Library, 902 Elmgrove Rd, Rochester, NY, 14624. Tel: 585-247-6446. Fax: 585-426-5733. p. 1729

Sayre, Janet, Cat, Tech Serv, Houston County Public Library System, 1201 Washington Ave, Perry, GA, 31069. Tel: 478-987-3050. Fax: 478-987-4572. p. 547

Sayre, John Richard, Dir, Monmouth College, 700 E Broadway, Monmouth, IL, 61462-1963. Tel: 309-457-2192. Fax: 309-457-2226. p. 675

Sayre McCoy, Patricia, Head, Cat & Ser, University of Chicago Library, D'Angelo Law Library, 1121 E 60th St, Chicago, IL, 60637-2786. Tel: 773-702-9620. Fax: 773-702-2889. p. 626

Sayres-McGrath, Penny, Librn, Adams Center Free Library, 18267 State Rte 177, Adams Center, NY, 13606. Tel: 315-583-5501. Fax: 315-583-6247. p. 1567

Sayward, Jacob, Ser Librn, Fordham University School of Law, 140 W 62nd St, New York, NY, 10023-7485. Tel: 646-312-8882. Fax: 212-930-8818. p. 1678

Saz, Wendy, Head of Libr, Jefferson-Madison Regional Library, Crozet Branch, The Old C&O Sta, PO Box 430, Crozet, VA, 22932-0430. Tel: 434-823-4050. Fax: 434-823-8399. p. 2453

Sbar, Shelley, Librn, Jack Balaban Memorial Library of Temple Sinai, 2101 New Albany Rd, Cinnaminson, NJ, 08077-3536. Tel: 856-829-0658. Fax: 856-829-0310. p. 1479

Sbardellati, Judy, Br Mgr, San Bernardino County Library, Running Springs Branch, 2677 Whispering Pines Dr, Running Springs, CA, 92382. Tel: 909-867-3604. p. 229

Sbaschnik, Werner, Sr Asst Librn, Cat/Syst, State University of New York, 223 Store Hill Rd, Old Westbury, NY, 11568. Tel: 516-876-3154. Fax: 516-876-3325. p. 1710

Sbisa, Joseph, Dir, Washington Parish Library System, 825 Free St, Franklinton, LA, 70438. Tel: 985-839-7806. Fax: 985-839-7808. p. 950

Scaggs, Deirdre, Assoc Dean, Spec Coll, University of Kentucky Libraries, I-85, 401 Hilltop Ave, Lexington, KY, 40506-0456. Tel: 859-257-3653. p. 921

Scaggs, Deirdre, Assoc Dean, Spec Coll, University of Kentucky Libraries, Special Collections, King Bldg, Lexington, KY, 40506-0039. Tel: 859-257-3653. Fax: 859-257-6311. p. 922

Scaggs, Martha, Br Mgr, Wayne County Public Library, Rittman Branch, 49 W Ohio Ave, Rittman, OH, 44270. Tel: 330-925-2761. Fax: 330-925-6217. p. 1950

Scala, Barbara, Tech Serv Librn, Spartanburg Community College Library, 800 Brisack Rd, Spartanburg, SC, 29305. Tel: 864-592-4615. Fax: 864-592-4762. p. 2205

Scales, Aileen, Exec Dir, Consortium of College & University Media Centers, Indiana University, Franklin Hall 0009, 601 E Kirkwood Ave, Bloomington, IN, 47405-1223. Tel: 812-855-6049. Fax: 812-855-2103. p. 2943

Scalese, Gisela, Librn, Lakehead University Library, Education Library, Lakehead University, Bora Laskin Bldg, Thunder Bay, ON, P7B 5E1, CANADA. Tel: 807-343-8719. Fax: 807-346-7996. p. 2848

Scalessa, Nicole H, Info Tech Mgr, Library Company of Philadelphia, 1314 Locust St, Philadelphia, PA, 19107-5698. Tel: 215-546-3181. Fax: 215-546-5167. p. 2112

Scalia, Liz, Librn, American Institutes for Research Library, 10720 Columbia Pike, Ste 500, Silver Spring, MD, 20901. Tel: 301-592-3347. Fax: 301-592-8602. p. 1041

Scalise, Barbara, Dir, Blount Library, Inc, Five N Main St, Franklinville, NY, 14737. Tel: 716-676-5715. Fax: 716-676-5715. p. 1624

Scalise, Rachael, Br Mgr, Monmouth County Library, West Long Branch, 95 Poplar Ave, West Long Branch, NJ, 07764. Tel: 732-222-5993. Fax: 732-229-5138. p. 1499

Scamman, Carol, Ref Serv, Stephen F Austin State University, 1936 North St, Nacogdoches, TX, 75962. Tel: 936-468-1710. Fax: 936-468-7610. p. 2364

Scammell, Janice, Head, Ref Serv, Carleton University Library, 1125 Colonel By Dr, Ottawa, ON, K1S 5B6, CANADA. Tel: 613-520-2600, Ext 2017. Fax: 613-520-2750. p. 2830

Scanga, Lynn, Mgr, Continued Educ, Ohio Valley General Hospital Library, 25 Heckel Rd, McKees Rocks, PA, 15136. Tel: 412-777-6159. Fax: 412-777-6866. p. 2085

Scanlan, Molly, Dir, O'Fallon Public Library, 120 Civic Plaza, O'Fallon, IL, 62269-2692. Tel: 618-632-3783. Fax: 618-632-3759. p. 684

Scanlan, Patrick J, Dr, Dir, Baldwin Wallace University, 57 E Bagley Rd, Berea, OH, 44017. Tel: 440-826-2204. Fax: 440-826-8558. p. 1859

Scanlon, Bridget, Coordr, Staten Island University Hospital, 475 Seaview Ave, Staten Island, NY, 10305. Tel: 718-226-9545. Fax: 718-226-8582. p. 1748

Scanlon, Linda, Info Serv Librn, Stevens Institute of Technology, Castle Point on Hudson, Hoboken, NJ, 07030. Tel: 201-216-5200. Fax: 201-216-8319. p. 1491

Scanlon, Seamus, Librn, City College of the City University of New York, Center for Worker Education Library, 25 Broadway, 7th Flr, New York, NY, 10004. Tel: 212-925-6625, Ext 228. Fax: 212-925-0963. p. 1673

Scanlon, Violet, Adult Serv, Norwood Public Library, 198 Summit St, Norwood, NJ, 07648-1835. Tel: 201-768-9555. Fax: 201-767-2176. p. 1515

Scannell, Kathryn Geoffrion, Dir, Merrimack College, 315 Turnpike St, North Andover, MA, 01845. Tel: 978-837-5215. Fax: 978-837-5434. p. 1111

Scannell, Kerri, Tech Serv, University of Kentucky Libraries, Lucille Little Fine Arts Library & Learning Center, 160 Patterson Dr, Lexington, KY, 40506-0224. Tel: 859-257-4630. Fax: 859-257-4662. p. 922

Scannell, Kim, Librn, The Center - Resources for Teaching & Learning Library, 2626 S Clearbrook Dr, Arlington Heights, IL, 6005-4626. Tel: 224-366-8500. Fax: 224-366-8514. p. 589

Scannell, Kristine, Librn, Lebanon VA Medical Center Library, 1700 S Lincoln Ave, Lebanon, PA, 17042-7597. Tel: 717-272-6621, Ext 4746. Fax: 717-228-6069. p. 2080

Scantlebury, Jane, Mgr, Berkeley Information Network, Berkeley Public Library, 2090 Kittredge St, Berkeley, CA, 94704. Tel: 510-981-6150, 510-981-6166. Fax: 510-981-6246. p. 2938

Scappaticci, Dominic, Br Mgr, San Francisco Public Library, Eureka Valley-Harvey Milk Memorial Branch Library, One Jose Sarria Ct, San Francisco, CA, 94114-1621. Tel: 415-355-5616. Fax: 415-552-2584. p. 246

Scarborough, Debra G, Spec Coll Librn, American College of Obstetricians & Gynecologists, 409 12th St SW, Washington, DC, 20024-2188. Tel: 202-863-2518. Fax: 202-484-1595. p. 392

Scarborough, Debra G, Treas, District of Columbia Area Health Science Libraries, Washington. Tel: 202-863-2518. p. 2940

Scarborough, James, Media Spec, Orem Public Library, 58 N State St, Orem, UT, 84057-5596. Tel: 801-229-7050. Fax: 801-229-7130. p. 2409

Scarborough, Linda, Br Mgr, Lonesome Pine Regional Library, Wise County Public, 124 Library Rd SW, Wise, VA, 24293. Tel: 276-328-8061. Fax: 276-328-1739. p. 2504

Scarbrough, Jill, Dir, Brazil Public Library, 204 N Walnut St, Brazil, IN, 47834. Tel: 812-448-1981. Fax: 812-446-3215. p. 729

Scarcelle, Ed, Dir, New School, Harry Scherman Library, 150 W 85th St, New York, NY, 10024-4499. Tel: 212-580-0210, Ext 4828. Fax: 212-580-1738. p. 1688

Scardellato, Kathy, Exec Dir, Ontario Council of University Libraries, 130 Saint George St, Toronto, ON, M5S 1A5, CANADA. Tel: 416-946-0578. Fax: 416-978-6755. p. 2960

Scarlet, Rose, Actg Head Librn, Garnett Public Library, 125 W Fourth St, Garnett, KS, 66032-1350. Tel: 785-448-3388. Fax: 785-448-3936. p. 868

Scarlet, Rose, Ref/Cat Librn, Missouri State University-West Plains, 304 W Trish Knight St, West Plains, MO, 65775. Tel: 417-255-7948. Fax: 417-255-7944. p. 1372

Scarlett, Angela, Dir, Wolfe City Public Library, 203 E Williams St, Wolfe City, TX, 75496. Tel: 903-496-7311. Fax: 903-496-7311. p. 2401

Scarletto, Edith, Head of Libr, Kent State University Libraries, Map, 410 McGilvery Hall, Kent, OH, 44242-0001. Tel: 330-672-2017. p. 1907

Scarola, Raymond, Libr Asst, Everest University, 9200 Southpark Center Loop, Orlando, FL, 32819. Tel: 407-851-2525, Ext 204. Fax: 407-345-8671. p. 475

Scarpitti, Michelle, Financial Dir, Akron-Summit County Public Library, 60 S High St, Akron, OH, 44326. Tel: 330-643-9000. Fax: 330-643-9160. p. 1852

Scarr, Carrie, Asst Dir, West Fargo Public Library, 109 Third St E, West Fargo, ND, 58078. Tel: 701-433-5460. Fax: 701-433-5479. p. 1849

Scarth, Beth K, Dir, Sandy Public Library, 38980 Proctor Blvd, Sandy, OR, 97055-8040. Tel: 503-668-5537. Fax: 503-668-3153. p. 2019

Schaade, Rebecca, Coordr, Pub Serv, Fairfield County District Library, 219 N Broad St, Lancaster, OH, 43130-3098. Tel: 740-653-2745. Fax: 740-653-4199. p. 1908

Schaadt, Mike, Dir, Virginia Reid Moore Marine Research Library, 3720 Stephen White Dr, San Pedro, CA, 90731. Tel: 310-548-7562, Ext 230. Fax: 310-548-2649. p. 256

Schaaf, Bethany, Librn, Waterford Public Library, 24 S Park Row, Waterford, PA, 16441. Tel: 814-796-4729. Fax: 814-796-4729. p. 2151

Schaaf, Dan, Tech Spec, Michigan City Public Library, 100 E Fourth St, Michigan City, IN, 46360-3393. Tel: 219-873-3044. Fax: 219-873-3068. p. 764

Schaaf, Molly, Sr Librn, Hennepin County Library, Champlin, 12154 Ensign Ave N, Champlin, MN, 55316-9998. Tel: 612-543-6253. Fax: 612-543-6252. p. 1263

Schaaf, Molly, Sr Librn, Hennepin County Library, Rogers, 21300 John Milless Dr, Rogers, MN, 55374-9998. Tel: 612-543-6253. Fax: 612-543-6052. p. 1264

Schaafsma, Freda, Librn, Township of Athens Public Library, Five Central St, Athens, ON, K0E 1B0, CANADA. Tel: 613-924-2048. p. 2792

Schaafsma, Roberta, Dir & J S Bridwell Endowed Librn, Southern Methodist University, Bridwell Library-Perkins School of Theology, 6005 Bishop Blvd, Dallas, TX, 75205. Tel: 214-768-3483. Fax: 214-768-4295. p. 2310

Schaal, Kate, Librn, Quechee Public Library Association, 1957 Quechee Main St, Quechee, VT, 05059. Tel: 802-295-1232. Fax: 802-295-1232. p. 2433

Schaal, Vivian, Librn, Flagler Community Library, 311 Main Ave, Flagler, CO, 80815-9237. Tel: 719-765-4310. Fax: 719-765-4498. p. 306

Schaale, Janet Moyer, Br Mgr, Blackwater Regional Library, Claremont Public, 91 Mancha Ave, Claremont, VA, 23899. Tel: 757-866-8627. Fax: 757-866-8628. p. 2458

Schaap, Ann, Librn, Norton Healthcare, 200 E Chestnut St, Louisville, KY, 40202. Tel: 502-629-8125. Fax: 502-629-8138. p. 925

Schaarschmidt, Erin, YA Serv, Port Jefferson Free Library, 100 Thompson St, Port Jefferson, NY, 11777-1897. Tel: 631-473-0022. Fax: 631-473-4765. p. 1721

Schabowski, Annette B, Curator, American Sokol Educational & Physical Culture Organization, 9126 Ogden Ave, Brookfield, IL, 60513. Tel: 708-255-5397. Fax: 708-255-5398. p. 598

Schacht, Chuck, Ch, Romeo District Library, 65821 Van Dyke, Washington, MI, 48095. Tel: 586-752-0603. Fax: 586-752-8416. p. 1235

Schacht, Katherine, Asst Dir, Youth Serv Librn, Mansfield Public Library, 255 Hope St, Mansfield, MA, 02048-2353. Tel: 508-261-7380. Fax: 508-261-7422. p. 1102

Schachter, Ruth, Dir, Art Institute of Philadelphia Library, 1622 Chestnut St, Philadelphia, PA, 19103. Tel: 215-405-6378. p. 2103

Schack, Shana, Outreach Librn, Shelby County Public Library, 309 Eighth St, Shelbyville, KY, 40065. Tel: 502-633-3803. Fax: 502-633-4025. p. 935

Schade, Angel, Circ, Saint Paul's College, 115 College Dr, Lawrenceville, VA, 23868-1299. Tel: 434-848-1836. Fax: 434-848-1861. p. 2473

Schader, Barbara, Asst Univ Librn, Coll & Scholarly Communications, University of California, Riverside Libraries, 900 University Ave, Riverside, CA, 92521. Tel: 951-827-4614. p. 218

Schadlich, Tom, Tech Serv, Norwalk Public Library, One Belden Ave, Norwalk, CT, 06850. Tel: 203-899-2780. Fax: 203-857-4410. p. 362

Schadt, Audrey, Cat, Salisbury University, 1101 Camden Ave, Salisbury, MD, 21801-6863. Tel: 410-543-6130. Fax: 410-543-6203. p. 1040

Schaeberle, Ruth, ILL, Martin Memorial Library, 159 E Market St, York, PA, 17401-1269. Tel: 717-846-5300. Fax: 717-848-2330. p. 2159

Schaebler, Alice, Sister, ILL, Immaculata University, 1145 King Rd, Immaculata, PA, 19345-0705. Tel: 610-647-4400, Ext 3838. Fax: 610-640-5828. p. 2071

Schaedler, Lois, Br Librn, Lake Agassiz Regional Library, Mahnomen Public Library, 203 S Main St, Mahnomen, MN, 56557-4709. Tel: 218-935-2843. Fax: 218-935-2574. p. 1266

Schaefer, Carol, Head Librn, Blackburn College, 700 College Ave, Carlinville, IL, 62626. Tel: 217-854-3231, Ext 4220. Fax: 217-854-3231, 217-854-8564. p. 600

Schaefer, Edell, Dir, Brookfield Public Library, 1900 N Calhoun Rd, Brookfield, WI, 53005. Tel: 262-782-4140. Fax: 262-796-6670. p. 2583

Schaefer, Heather, Ref Serv, Ad, Sussex County Library System, 125 Morris Tpk, Newton, NJ, 07860-0076. Tel: 973-948-3660. Fax: 973-948-2071. p. 1514

Schaefer, Julie, Dep Dir, Dearborn Public Library, 16301 Michigan Ave, Dearborn, MI, 48126. Tel: 313-943-2330. Fax: 313-943-2853. p. 1167

Schaefer, Karl, Ref & Instrul Serv, Instr Coordr, Drake University, 2725 University Ave, Des Moines, IA, 50311. Tel: 515-271-2924. Fax: 515-271-3933. p. 809

Schaefer, Karma, Librn, First United Methodist Church, 411 Turner St, Clearwater, FL, 33756. Tel: 727-446-5955. Fax: 727-447-1308. p. 432

Schaefer, Kay, Head, Circ, Stinson Memorial Public Library District, 409 S Main St, Anna, IL, 62906. Tel: 618-833-2521. Fax: 618-833-3560. p. 589

Schaefer, Patricia M, Res, New London County Historical Society Library, 11 Blinman St, New London, CT, 06320. Tel: 860-443-1209. Fax: 860-443-1209. p. 360

Schaefer, Steve, Interim Dir, Uncle Remus Regional Library System, 1121 East Ave, Madison, GA, 30650. Tel: 706-342-4974. Fax: 706-342-4510. p. 541

Schaeffer, Amy, Asst Librn, Arlington Baptist College, 3001 W Division, Arlington, TX, 76012-3425. Tel: 817-461-8741, Ext 127. Fax: 817-274-1138. p. 2276

Schaeffer, Darla, Info Spec, Minot Public Library, 516 Second Ave SW, Minot, ND, 58701-3792. Tel: 701-852-0333. Fax: 701-852-2595. p. 1846

Schaeffer, Stuart, Head, Ref, Farmingdale Public Library, 116 Merritts Rd, Farmingdale, NY, 11735. Tel: 516-249-9090, Ext 203. Fax: 516-694-9697. p. 1621

Schaefgen, Susan M, Mgr, Libr Serv, Porter, Wright, Morris & Arthur, LLP, Huntington Ctr, 41 S High St, Columbus, OH, 43215-6194. Tel: 614-227-2152. Fax: 614-227-2100. p. 1890

Schafer, Allison, Circ Asst, Bellevue University, 1000 Galvin Rd S, Bellevue, NE, 68005. Tel: 402-557-7314. Fax: 402-557-5427. p. 1393

Schafer, Christine, Libr Dir, Wartburg College Library, 100 Wartburg Blvd, Waverly, IA, 50677-0903. Tel: 319-352-8500. Fax: 319-352-8312. p. 850

Schafer, Jacki, Asst Dir, Belvedere-Tiburon Library, 1501 Tiburon Blvd, Tiburon, CA, 94920. Tel: 415-789-2665. Fax: 415-789-2650. p. 275

Schafer, Janice, Asst Librn, Wellsburg Public Library, 15 N Adams, Wellsburg, IA, 50680. Tel: 641-869-5234. Fax: 641-869-5234. p. 851

Schafer, Jason, Librn, Cleveland Metroparks Zoo Library, 3900 Wildlife Way, Cleveland, OH, 44109. Tel: 216-635-3333. Fax: 216-661-3312. p. 1877

Schafer, Jay, Dir, University of Massachusetts Amherst, 154 Hicks Way, Amherst, MA, 01003-9275. Tel: 413-545-0284. Fax: 413-545-6873. p. 1049

Schafer, Johnny, Ref, Howard County Library, 500 Main St, Big Spring, TX, 79720-2532. Tel: 432-264-2260. Fax: 432-264-2263. p. 2289

Schafer, Kathy, Br Coordr, Shelby County Libraries, A J Wise Fort Loramie Branch, 300 E Park St, Fort Loramie, OH, 45845. Tel: 937-295-3155. Fax: 937-295-3155. p. 1935

Schafer, Laura, Automation Librn, Ref, Kansas Supreme Court, Kansas Judicial Ctr, 301 SW Tenth St, Topeka, KS, 66612-1502. Tel: 785-296-3258. Fax: 785-296-1863. p. 896

Schafer, Nancy, Head, Ref & Res Serv, Old Dominion University Libraries, 4427 Hampton Blvd, Norfolk, VA, 23529-0256. Tel: 757-683-4183. Fax: 757-683-5767. p. 2482

Schafer, Nicholas, Coordr, Develop & Communication, Saint Joseph County Public Library, 304 S Main, South Bend, IN, 46601-2125. Tel: 574-282-4646. Fax: 574-280-2763. p. 779

Schafer, Ron, In Charge, Nevada Department of Corrections, Ely State Prison Library, 4569 N State Rte 490, Ely, NV, 89301. Tel: 775-289-8800, Ext 2244. Fax: 775-289-1273. p. 1427

Schafer, Steve, Dir, Libr Serv, Athabasca University Library, One University Dr, Athabasca, AB, T9S 3A3, CANADA. Tel: 780-675-6259. Fax: 780-675-6478. p. 2684

Schafer, Tony, Popular Librn/Teen Mgr, Toledo-Lucas County Public Library, 325 N Michigan St, Toledo, OH, 43604-6614. Tel: 419-259-5297. Fax: 419-255-1334. p. 1939

Schafer, Verlene, Libr Media Prog Dir, Southern Utah University, 351 W University Blvd, Cedar City, UT, 84720. Tel: 435-865-8031. Fax: 435-865-8152. p. 2404

Schafer, Verlene, Dir, Libr Media Prog, Southern Utah University Sherratt Library, 351 W University Blvd, Cedar City, UT, 84720. Tel: 435-865-8031, 435-865-8172. Fax: 435-865-8152. p. 2975

Schaff, Curt, Librn, Hatton School & Public Library, 503 Fourth St, Hatton, ND, 58240. Tel: 701-543-3456. Fax: 701-543-3459. p. 1844

Schaffer, Karen S, Librn, Pratt & Whitney, 600 Metcalf Rd, San Jose, CA, 95138-9602. Tel: 408-776-4957. Fax: 408-776-5995. p. 250

Schaffer, Marysue, Assoc Dir, Coll Mgt, Washington University Libraries, Bernard Becker Medical Library, 660 S Euclid Ave, Campus Box 8132, Saint Louis, MO, 63110. Tel: 314-362-0997. Fax: 314-454-6606. p. 1362

Schaffer, Paul L, Interim Dir, Massena Public Library, 122 Main, Massena, IA, 50853. Tel: 712-779-3726. p. 831

Schaffler, David, Ser Librn, United States Department of State, 2201 C St NW, Rm 3239, Washington, DC, 20520-2442. Tel: 202-647-1099. Fax: 202-647-2971. p. 419

Schaffner, Ellen, Libr Dir, Pike County Public Library, 201 Broad St, Milford, PA, 18337-1398. Tel: 570-296-8211. Fax: 570-296-8987. p. 2090

Schaffner, Jane, Dir, McComb Public Library, 113 S Todd St, McComb, OH, 45858. Tel: 419-293-2425. Fax: 419-293-2748. p. 1916

Schaffner, Pam, Dep Circuit Librn, US Court of Appeals for the Sixth Circuit Library, 312 Potter Stewart US Courthouse, Cincinnati, OH, 45202. Tel: 513-564-7321. Fax: 513-564-7329. p. 1873

Schaffner, Paula, Youth Serv Mgr, Saline District Library, 555 N Maple Rd, Saline, MI, 48176. Tel: 734-429-5450. Fax: 734-944-0600. p. 1225

Schaffter, David A, Head, Acq, United States Air Force Academy Libraries, 2354 Fairchild Dr, Ste 3A10, USAF Academy, CO, 80840-6214. Tel: 719-333-4654. Fax: 719-333-4754. p. 324

Schaible, Fran, Tech Serv Mgr, Cherry Valley Public Library District, 755 E State St, Cherry Valley, IL, 61016-9699. Tel: 815-332-5161, Ext 32. Fax: 815-332-2441. p. 604

Schaible, Josephine, Libr Assoc/Circ, Mercer County Community College Library, 1200 Old Trenton Rd, West Windsor, NJ, 08550. Tel: 609-570-3554, 609-570-3560. Fax: 609-570-3845. p. 1542

Schalk-Greene, Kathy, Dir, Mount Laurel Library, 100 Walt Whitman Ave, Mount Laurel, NJ, 08054. Tel: 856-234-7319, Ext 304. Fax: 856-234-6916. p. 1506

Schall, Elaine, Head, Circ, Osterhout Free Library, 71 S Franklin St, Wilkes-Barre, PA, 18701-1287. Tel: 570-823-0156. Fax: 570-823-5477. p. 2155

Schall, Jane, Dir, Menomonee Falls Public Library, W156 N8436 Pilgrim Rd, Menomonee Falls, WI, 53051. Tel: 262-532-8900. Fax: 262-532-8939. p. 2614

Schall, Richard, Computer Serv Mgr, Carnegie Mellon University, Hunt Library, 4909 Frew St, Pittsburgh, PA, 15213-3890. Tel: 412-268-2446. Fax: 412-268-2793. p. 2123

Schaller, Anne, Curator, Natick Historical Society, 58 Eliot St, Natick, MA, 01760. Tel: 508-647-4841. p. 1108

Schaller, Jeff, Actg Sr Librn, California Department of Corrections Library System, Calipatria State Prison, 7018 Blair Rd, Calipatria, CA, 92233. Tel: 760-348-7000, Ext 7612. Fax: 760-348-6041. p. 221

Schamber, Linda, Dr, Assoc Dean, Academics, Assoc Dir, PhD Prog, University of North Texas, 1155 Union Circle, Denton, TX, 76203-5017. Tel: 940-565-2445. Fax: 940-565-3101. p. 2975

Schambow, Betty, Dir, Allen Dietzman Library, 220 W Barber Ave, Livingston, WI, 53554. Tel: 608-943-6801. Fax: 608-943-6800. p. 2605

Schandorff, LaRita, Instrul Serv Librn, Northwest Nazarene University, 623 University Blvd, Nampa, ID, 83686. Tel: 208-467-8606. Fax: 208-467-8610. p. 580

Schanot, John, Tech Serv Dir, Collin College, 2800 E Spring Creek Pkwy, Plano, TX, 75074. Tel: 972-881-5628. Fax: 972-881-5610. p. 2370

Schantz, Michael, Dr, Dir, Edward M David Research Library, Woodmere Art Museum, 9201 Germantown Ave, Philadelphia, PA, 19118. Tel: 215-247-0948. Fax: 215-247-2387. p. 2105

Schapiro, Benjamin Hall, Dir, Morton Grove Public Library, 6140 Lincoln Ave, Morton Grove, IL, 60053-2989. Tel: 847-965-4220. Fax: 847-965-4234. p. 676

Schapiro, Carol, Librn, Touro College Libraries, 43 W 23rd St, Fifth Fl, New York, NY, 10010. Tel: 212-463-0400, Ext 5321. Fax: 212-627-3696. p. 1701

Schapiro, Moshe, Ref, Yeshiva University Libraries, Mendel Gottesman Library of Hebraica-Judaica, 2520 Amsterdam Ave, New York, NY, 10033. Tel: 212-960-5382. Fax: 212-960-0066. p. 1704

Schappert, Catherine H, Exec Dir, Northeastern Pennsylvania Library Network, c/o Marywood University Library, 2300 Adams Ave, Scranton, PA, 18509-1598. Tel: 570-348-6260. Fax: 570-961-4769. p. 2954

Scharbach, Wilf, Tech Serv, Manitoba Law Library, Inc, Law Courts Bldg, Rm 331, 408 York Ave, Winnipeg, MB, R3C 0P9, CANADA. Tel: 204-945-1958. Fax: 204-948-2138. p. 2757

Schard, Robin, Assoc Dir, University of Miami, 1311 Miller Dr, Coral Gables, FL, 33146. Tel: 305-284-2251. Fax: 305-284-3554. p. 434

Schardt, Connie, Assoc Dir, Educ Serv/Pub Serv, Duke University Libraries, Medical Center Library, DUMC Box 3702, Ten Bryan-Searle Dr, Durham, NC, 27710-0001. Tel: 919-660-1124. Fax: 919-681-7599. p. 1788

Schardt, Jan, Acq, Circ, Tech Serv, Napa Valley College Library, 1700 Bldg, 2277 Napa-Vallejo Hwy, Napa, CA, 94558. Tel: 707-256-7412. Fax: 707-253-3015. p. 193

Scharf, Colin, Libr Serv Supvr, Bethany Lutheran College Memorial Library, 700 Luther Dr, Mankato, MN, 56001-4490. Tel: 507-344-7000. Fax: 507-344-7376. p. 1257

Scharf, Davida, Dir, Ref & Libr Info Serv, New Jersey Institute of Technology, University Heights, Newark, NJ, 07102-1982. Tel: 973-596-3206. Fax: 973-643-5601. p. 1511

Scharf, Irene F, Lead Ref Librn, Palo Alto College, 1400 W Villaret St, San Antonio, TX, 78224-2499. Tel: 210-486-3574. Fax: 210-486-9184. p. 2380

Scharf, Margaret K, Assoc Dir, Communications, Assessment & Pub Relations, University of Central Florida Libraries, 4000 Central Florida Blvd, Bldg 2, Orlando, FL, 32816-2666. Tel: 407-823-6193. Fax: 407-823-2529. p. 477

Scharn, Tracy, Adjunct Instruction, Western Oregon University, Wayne & Lynn Hamersly Library, 345 N Monmouth Ave, Monmouth, OR, 97361-1396. Tel: 503-838-8892. Fax: 503-838-8399. p. 2006

Scharnhorst, Lisa, Br Mgr, Seattle Public Library, Broadview, 12755 Greenwood Ave N, Seattle, WA, 98133. Tel: 206-684-7519. p. 2531

Schatten, Nicole, ILL, Mathematica Policy Research Inc Library, 600 Alexander Park, Princeton, NJ, 08543. Tel: 609-275-2334. Fax: 609-799-1654. p. 1522

Schattle, Erica, Coordr, Outreach Serv, Ref Librn, Emerson College Library, 120 Boylston St, Boston, MA, 02116-4624. Tel: 617-824-8340. Fax: 617-824-7817. p. 1060

Schatz, Martha, Dir, Rutherford County Library, 255 Callahan Koon Rd, Spindale, NC, 28160. Tel: 828-287-6117. Fax: 828-287-6119. p. 1825

Schatzle, Chad, Ref Librn, University of Nevada, Las Vegas Libraries, Wiener-Rogers Law Library, William S Boyd School of Law, 4505 Maryland Pkwy, Las Vegas, NV, 89154-1080. Tel: 702-895-2400. Fax: 702-895-2410. p. 1431

Schaub, Denis, Acq, Per, Sr Librn, Ref, Wagner College, One Campus Rd, Staten Island, NY, 10301-4495. Tel: 718-390-3401. Fax: 718-420-4218. p. 1748

Schaub, Jacob, Music Cataloger, Vanderbilt University, Anne Potter Wilson Music Library, Blair School of Music, 2400 Blakemore Ave, Nashville, TN, 37212. Tel: 615-322-3022. Fax: 615-343-0050. p. 2261

Schaub, Mary Elizabeth, Head, Coll Serv, Manhattanville College Library, 2900 Purchase St, Purchase, NY, 10577. Tel: 914-323-5207. Fax: 914-323-8139. p. 1724

Schaubhut, Diana, Coll Develop, ILL, Ser, Our Lady of Holy Cross College Library, 4123 Woodland Dr, New Orleans, LA, 70131. Tel: 504-394-7744. Fax: 504-391-2421. p. 962

Schauer, Bruce, Assoc Dir, Pub Serv, King County Library System, 960 Newport Way NW, Issaquah, WA, 98027. Tel: 425-450-1771. Fax: 425-369-3255. p. 2516

Schauf, Suzanne, Dir, Pavilion Public Library, Five Woodrow Dr, Pavilion, NY, 14525. Tel: 585-584-8843. Fax: 585-584-8801. p. 1715

Schaufler, Elizabeth A, Spec Coll Librn, Princeton University, Chemistry, Frick Laboratory, One Washington Rd, Princeton, NJ, 08544. Tel: 609-258-8601. p. 1523

Schauls, Lynne M, Dir, Centuria Public Library, 409 Fourth St, Centuria, WI, 54824-7468. Tel: 715-646-2630. Fax: 715-646-2630. p. 2585

Schaumberg, Barb, Circ, ILL, Phillips Public Library, 286 Cherry St, Phillips, WI, 54555-1240. Tel: 715-339-2868. p. 2629

Schaus, Margaret, Bibliographer, Lead Ref Librn, Haverford College, 370 Lancaster Ave, Haverford, PA, 19041-1392. Tel: 610-896-1166. Fax: 610-896-1102. p. 2067

Schawang, Hope, Dir, The Falls City Library & Arts Center, 1400 Stone St, Falls City, NE, 68355. Tel: 402-245-2913. Fax: 402-245-3031. p. 1398

Sche, Josephine, Dr, Chairperson, Prof, Southern Connecticut State University, 501 Crescent St, New Haven, CT, 06515. Tel: 203-392-5710. Fax: 203-392-5780. p. 2963

Scheaffer, Kathleen, Outreach & Instrul Coordr, University of Toronto Libraries, Faculty of Information Inforum, 140 Saint George St, 4th Flr, Toronto, ON, M5S 3G6, CANADA. Tel: 416-978-5770. Fax: 416-978-5769. p. 2865

Schear, Elyse, Ref & Teen Serv, West Milford Township Library, 1490 Union Valley Rd, West Milford, NJ, 07480. Tel: 973-728-2820. Fax: 973-728-2106. p. 1541

Schechter, Carol, Librn, Anaheim Regional Medical Center, 1111 W La Palma Ave, Anaheim, CA, 92801. Tel: 714-999-6020. Fax: 714-999-3907. p. 121

Schechter, Carol, Librn, Saint Jude Medical Center, 101 E Valencia Mesa Dr, Fullerton, CA, 92835. Tel: 714-871-3280. Fax: 714-447-6481. p. 154

Schechter, Carol, Med Librn, Long Beach Memorial/Miller Children's Hospital Long Beach, 2801 Atlantic Ave, Long Beach, CA, 90806-1737. Tel: 562-933-3841. Fax: 562-933-3847. p. 166

Schechter, Roberta, Ref Serv, Edison Township Free Public Library, 340 Plainfield Ave, Edison, NJ, 08817. Tel: 732-287-2298. Fax: 732-819-9134. p. 1483

Schechter, Steven, Dir, Govt & Commun Affairs, Brooklyn Public Library, Grand Army Plaza, Brooklyn, NY, 11238-5698. Tel: 718-230-2091. Fax: 718-230-2751. p. 1590

Schecter, Jack, Librn, Agudath Israel Congregation, 1400 Coldrey Ave, Ottawa, ON, K1Z 7P9, CANADA. Tel: 613-728-3501, Ext 232. Fax: 613-728-4468. p. 2827

Schecter, Jack, Librn, Greenberg Families Library, 21 Nadolny Sachs PR, Ottawa, ON, K2A 1R9, CANADA. Tel: 613-798-9818. Fax: 613-798-9839. p. 2831

Schecter, Karen, Chief Librn, Smiths Falls Public Library, 81 Beckwith St N, Smiths Falls, ON, K7A 2B9, CANADA. Tel: 613-283-2911. Fax: 613-283-9834. p. 2842

Schedlich, Katie, ILL, Huron County Library, Administration Office, 77722B London Rd, Clinton, ON, N0M 1L0, CANADA. Tel: 519-482-5457. Fax: 519-482-7820. p. 2799

Scheer, Carolyn, Ref Librn, Scenic Regional Library of Franklin, Gasconade & Warren Counties, 308 Hawthorne Dr, Union, MO, 63084. Tel: 636-583-3224. p. 1369

Scheer, Frank R, Dr, Curator, Pres, Railway Mail Service Library, Inc, 117 E Main St, Boyce, VA, 22620-9639. Tel: 540-837-9090. p. 2452

Scheer, John, Tech Serv Librn, Willard Library of Evansville, 21 First Ave, Evansville, IN, 47710-1294. Tel: 812-425-4309. Fax: 812-421-9742. p. 739

Scheeser, Gary, Dir, Res & Develop, Neville Chemical Co, 2800 Neville Rd, Pittsburgh, PA, 15225-1496. Tel: 412-331-4200. Fax: 412-771-0226. p. 2126

Scheetz, Anita A, Dir, Fort Peck Community College Library, 605 Indian St, Poplar, MT, 59255. Tel: 406-768-6340. Fax: 406-768-6301. p. 1387

Scheetz, George H, Dir, Batavia Public Library District, Ten S Batavia Ave, Batavia, IL, 60510-2793. Tel: 630-879-1393. Fax: 630-879-9118. p. 592

Scheetz, Jennifer, Archivist, Librn, Charleston Museum Library, 360 Meeting St, Charleston, SC, 29403. Tel: 843-722-2996, Ext 243. Fax: 843-722-1784. p. 2183

Schefler, Elizabeth A, Libr Serv Mgr, Chicago Bridge & Iron Co, 1515 Broad St, Bloomfield, NJ, 07003. Tel: 973-893-2251. Fax: 973-893-2119. p. 1473

Schefris, Sandra R, Dir, American Medical Association, 515 N State St, 9th Flr, Chicago, IL, 60654. Tel: 312-464-4860. Fax: 312-464-5226. p. 606

Schehl, Linda, Head, Adult Serv, Helen M Plum Memorial Public Library District, 110 W Maple St, Lombard, IL, 60148-2594. Tel: 630-627-0316. Fax: 630-627-0336. p. 667

Scheibel, Kathleen, Dir, Brookhaven Free Library, 273 Beaver Dam Rd, Brookhaven, NY, 11719. Tel: 631-286-1923. Fax: 631-286-0120. p. 1589

Scheiberg, Susan, Assoc Dir, RAND Corporation Library, 1776 Main St, M1LIB, Santa Monica, CA, 90407. Tel: 310-393-0411, Ext 7788. Fax: 310-451-7029. p. 266

Scheiblberg, Nicole, Youth Serv Dir, Basalt Regional Library District, 14 Midland Ave, Basalt, CO, 81621-8305. Tel: 970-927-4311. Fax: 970-927-1351. p. 289

Scheible, Patrick, Lead Libr Tech, University of Washington Libraries, Drama, Hutchinson Hall, Rm 145, Box 353950, Seattle, WA, 98195-3950. Tel: 206-685-3693. Fax: 206-543-8512. p. 2533

Scheick, Amy, Dr, Coordr, University of Central Florida, College of Education, PO Box 161250, Orlando, FL, 32816. Tel: 407-823-0228. Fax: 407-823-4880. p. 2963

Scheid, Ann, Archivist, Greene & Greene Archives, The Huntington Library, 1151 Oxford Rd, San Marino, CA, 91108. Tel: 626-405-2232. Fax: 626-796-6498. p. 255

Scheid, Kristofer, Ref, Hamline University, Bush Memorial Library, 1536 Hewitt, Saint Paul, MN, 55104. Tel: 651-523-2375. Fax: 651-523-2199. p. 1278

Scheide, Mary, Br Mgr, Dakota County Library System, Farmington Branch, 508 Third St, Farmington, MN, 55024-1357. Tel: 651-438-0254. Fax: 651-463-7979. p. 1249

Scheidler, Ann, Dir, Pro-Life Action League Library, 6160 N Cicero Ave, Ste 600, Chicago, IL, 60646. Tel: 773-777-2900. Fax: 773-777-3061. p. 622

Scheier, Robert, Electronic Res, College of the Holy Cross, One College St, Worcester, MA, 01610. Tel: 508-793-3495. Fax: 508-793-2372. p. 1143

Scheimann, Linda, Res, Star Tribune, 425 Portland Ave, Minneapolis, MN, 55488. Tel: 612-673-4375. Fax: 612-673-4459. p. 1261

Schein, Cindi, Asst Librn, Galesville Public Library, 16787 S Main St, Galesville, WI, 54630. Tel: 608-582-2552. p. 2593

Scheinbuks, Julian, Dr, Dir, Distance Learning, Chicago State University, 9501 S Martin Luther King Jr Dr, LIB 440, Chicago, IL, 60628-1598. Tel: 773-995-2983. Fax: 773-995-3772. p. 610

Scheirer, Judith, Librn, Tremont District Public Library, 215 S Sampson St, Tremont, IL, 61568. Tel: 309-925-5432, 309-925-5597. Fax: 309-925-9953. p. 710

Schell, Jessica, Circ Serv Coordr, Fowlerville District Library, 131 Mill St, Fowlerville, MI, 48836. Tel: 517-223-9089. Fax: 517-223-0781. p. 1181

Schell, Michael, Syst Adminr, Fort Erie Public Library, 136 Gilmore Rd, Fort Erie, ON, L2A 2M1, CANADA. Tel: 905-871-2546. Fax: 905-871-2191. p. 2806

Schell, Rhonda, ILL, Daviess County Public Library, 2020 Frederica St, Owensboro, KY, 42301. Tel: 270-684-0211. Fax: 270-684-0218. p. 931

Schell, Terri, Human Res Sr Adminr, Harford County Public Library, 1221-A Brass Mill Rd, Belcamp, MD, 21017-1209. Tel: 410-273-5600, Ext 2223. Fax: 410-273-5606. p. 1020

Schell, William, Exec Dir, Martin Memorial Library, 159 E Market St, York, PA, 17401-1269. Tel: 717-846-5300. Fax: 717-848-2330. p. 2159

Schellberg, Abigail, Div Mgr, Pub Serv, Corona Public Library, 650 S Main St, Corona, CA, 92882. Tel: 951-736-2381. Fax: 951-736-2499. p. 136

Schellenberg, Chris, Commun Serv & Mkt Coordr, Vigo County Public Library, One Library Sq, Terre Haute, IN, 47807. Tel: 812-232-1113, Ext 2281. Fax: 812-232-3208. p. 782

Schelleng, Jessica, Ref Librn, Pamunkey Regional Library, 7527 Library Dr, Hanover, VA, 23069. Tel: 804-537-6211. Fax: 804-537-6389. p. 2469

Schelleng, Jessica, Ref, Pamunkey Regional Library, Mechanicsville Branch, 7179 Stonewall Pkwy, Mechanicsville, VA, 23111. Tel: 804-746-9615. Fax: 804-730-4292. p. 2469

Schellenger, Sarah, Br Mgr, Public Library of Cincinnati & Hamilton County, Northside, 4219 Hamilton Ave, Cincinnati, OH, 45223. Tel: 513-369-4449. Fax: 513-369-4533. p. 1872

Scheller, Candy, Asst Librn, Green Forest Public Library, 206 E Main St, Green Forest, AR, 72638-2627. Tel: 870-438-6700. Fax: 870-438-4586. p. 101

Scheller, Helen, Librn, Parkland Regional Library, Sturgis Branch, 222 Main St, Sturgis, SK, S0A 4A0, CANADA. Tel: 306-548-2824. p. 2932

Schelling, Lisa, Digital Spacial Data Librn, University of Wisconsin-Milwaukee Libraries, American Geographical Society Library, Golda Meir Library, 2311 E Hartford Ave, Milwaukee, WI, 53211. Tel: 414-229-3984, 414-229-6282. Fax: 414-229-3624. p. 2622

Schelp, Alan, Head, Electronic Serv, Sachem Public Library, 150 Holbrook Rd, Holbrook, NY, 11741. Tel: 631-588-5024. Fax: 631-588-5064. p. 1637

Schemm, Karyn, Bus & Finance Mgr, Fac Dir, Tech Coordr, Andover Public Library, 1511 E Central Ave, Andover, KS, 67002. Tel: 316-558-3500. Fax: 316-558-3503. p. 856

Schempp, Sharon, Librn, Lakeland Library Region, Neilburg Branch, Box 174, Neilburg, SK, S0M 2C0, CANADA. Tel: 306-823-4234. p. 2920

Schenck, Cathy, Librn, Keeneland Association, Keeneland Race Course, 4201 Verailles Rd, Lexington, KY, 40588. Tel: 859-254-3412, Ext 223. Fax: 859-288-4191. p. 920

Schenck, Robert, Dir, College of the Albemarle Library, 1208 N Road St, Elizabeth City, NC, 27906. Tel: 252-335-0821, Ext 2270. Fax: 252-335-0649. p. 1790

Schenk, Joseph, Dir, Texas A&M University-Corpus Christi, Art Museum of South Texas Library, 1902 N Shoreline, Corpus Christi, TX, 78401-1164. Tel: 361-825-3500. Fax: 361-825-3520. p. 2302

Schenk-Webster, Theresa, Head, Ad Ref Serv, Ashland Public Library, 224 Claremont Ave, Ashland, OH, 44805. Tel: 419-289-8188. Fax: 419-281-8552. p. 1855

Schenkel, Hunt, Archivist, Schwenkfelder Library & Heritage Center, 105 Seminary St, Pennsburg, PA, 18073. Tel: 215-679-3103, Ext 13. Fax: 215-679-8175. p. 2102

Schenkel, Nick, Dir, West Lafayette Public Library, 208 W Columbia St, West Lafayette, IN, 47906. Tel: 765-743-2261. Fax: 765-743-0540. p. 787

Schenstorm, Judi, Librn, Brownfield Public Library, 216 Main St, Brownfield, ME, 04010. Tel: 207-935-3003. p. 979

Scheper, Carol, Commun Libr Mgr, Queens Borough Public Library, Broad Channel Community Library, 16-26 Cross Bay Blvd, Broad Channel, NY, 11693. Tel: 718-318-4943. p. 1644

Schepis, Sandy, Virtual Serv Coordr, SUNY Westchester Community College, 75 Grasslands Rd, Valhalla, NY, 10595-1693. Tel: 914-606-6629. Fax: 914-785-6513. p. 1760

Scheps, Susan, Head, Ch, Shaker Heights Public Library, 16500 Van Aken Blvd, Shaker Heights, OH, 44120-5318. Tel: 216-991-2030. Fax: 216-991-5951. p. 1934

Scherber, Marla, Br Mgr, Great River Regional Library, St Michael Public Library, 11800 Town Center Dr NE, Ste 100, Saint Michael, MN, 55376-0309. Tel: 763-497-1998. Fax: 763-497-1998. p. 1275

Scherer, Carol, Libr Dir, Churubusco Public Library, 116 N Mulberry St, Churubusco, IN, 46723. Tel: 260-693-6466. Fax: 260-693-6466. p. 732

Scherer, Helga, Head, Tech Serv, Morton Grove Public Library, 6140 Lincoln Ave, Morton Grove, IL, 60053-2989. Tel: 847-929-5111. Fax: 847-965-7903. p. 676

Scherer, Irene, Head, Info Serv, Community Library, 24615 89th St, Salem, WI, 53168. Tel: 262-843-3348. Fax: 262-843-3144. p. 2636

Scherer, Janet, Asst Dir, South Huntington Public Library, 145 Pidgeon Hill Rd, Huntington Station, NY, 11746. Tel: 631-549-4411. Fax: 631-549-1266. p. 1639

Scherer, Kristi, Dir, Creston-Dement Library District, 107 S Main St, Creston, IL, 60113-0056. Tel: 815-384-3111. Fax: 815-384-3111. p. 631

Scherer, Leslie, Dir, Wallingford Public Library, 200 N Main St, Wallingford, CT, 06492-3791. Tel: 203-265-6754. Fax: 203-269-5698. p. 373

Scherer, Leslie, Dir, Wallingford Public Library, Yalesville Branch, 400 Church St, Yalesville, CT, 06492. Tel: 203-269-3688. p. 374

Scherer, Nicole, Teen Librn, Fairfield Public Library, 1080 Old Post Rd, Fairfield, CT, 06824. Tel: 203-256-3155. p. 339

Scherf, Kim, Dir, Farmersburg Public Library, 208 S Main St, Farmersburg, IA, 52047. Tel: 563-536-2229. Fax: 563-536-2229. p. 815

Scherfen, Marilyn C, Dir, Atlantic Highlands Public Library Association, 48 Ave C, Atlantic Highlands, NJ, 07716. Tel: 732-291-1956. Fax: 732-291-9725. p. 1470

Scherma, Jay, Dir, Thomas Memorial Library, Six Scott Dyer Rd, Cape Elizabeth, ME, 04107. Tel: 207-799-1720. p. 980

Schermerhorn, Steve, Automation Librn, Tech Serv, San Joaquin Delta College, 5151 Pacific Ave, Stockton, CA, 95207-6370. Tel: 209-954-5152. Fax: 209-954-5691. p. 272

Scherrer, Emily, Youth Serv Mgr, Yuma County Library District, 2951 S 21st Dr, Yuma, AZ, 85364. Tel: 928-373-6494. Fax: 928-782-9420. p. 91

Scherzinger, Christine, Dir, Libr & Res Serv, Duane Morris LLP Library, 30 S 17th St, Philadelphia, PA, 19103-4196. Tel: 215-979-1720. Fax: 215-979-1020. p. 2106

Schetroma, Beth, Ref, James V Brown Library of Williamsport & Lycoming County, 19 E Fourth St, Williamsport, PA, 17701-6390. Tel: 570-326-0536. Fax: 570-326-1671. p. 2156

Scheuering, J, Ch, Bryant Library, Two Paper Mill Rd, Roslyn, NY, 11576-2193. Tel: 516-621-2240. Fax: 516-621-7211. p. 1735

Scheuerman, Elaine, Dep Dir, Finney County Public Library, 605 E Walnut St, Garden City, KS, 67846. Tel: 620-272-3680. Fax: 620-272-3682. p. 868

Scheuermann, Pamela, Librn, United States Army Medical Research Institute of Chemical Defense, 3100 Ricketts Point Rd, Aberdeen Proving Ground, MD, 21010-5400. Tel: 410-436-4135. Fax: 410-436-3176. p. 1009

Schewe, Judy, Dir, Bristol Library, 6750 County Rd 32, Canandaigua, NY, 14424. Tel: 585-229-5862. Fax: 585-229-2787. p. 1601

Schiavo, Frank, Librn, Simon, Peragine, Smith & Redfearn LLP, Energy Ctr, 1100 Poydras St, 30th Flr, New Orleans, LA, 70163. Tel: 504-569-2030. Fax: 504-569-2999. p. 963

Schiavo, Julie, Ref, Louisiana State University Health Sciences Center, 433 Bolivar St, Box B3-1, New Orleans, LA, 70112-2223. Tel: 504-619-8550. Fax: 504-619-8723. p. 961

Schiavo, Julie, Ref, Louisiana State University Health Sciences Center, School of Dentistry Library, 1100 Florida Ave, New Orleans, LA, 70119-2799. Tel: 504-941-8158. Fax: 504-941-8161. p. 961

Schiavone, Nancy, Ref Serv, Missouri Southern State University, 3950 E Newman Rd, Joplin, MO, 64801-1595. Tel: 417-625-9386. Fax: 417-625-9734. p. 1336

Schichtel, Nan, Ref & Instruction Librn, Grand Rapids Community College, 140 Ransom NE Ave, Grand Rapids, MI, 49503. Tel: 616-234-3082. Fax: 616-234-3878. p. 1185

Schicitano, Elaine, Acq, Wellesley Free Library, 530 Washington St, Wellesley, MA, 02482. Tel: 781-235-1610. Fax: 781-235-0495. p. 1135

Schick, Joan, Librn, First United Methodist Church Library, 1421 Spruce, Boulder, CO, 80302. Tel: 303-442-3770. Fax: 303-442-4752. p. 290

Schick, Joan, Librn, Lake Linden-Hubbell Public & School Library, 601 Calumet St, Lake Linden, MI, 49945. Tel: 906-296-6211. Fax: 906-296-9332. p. 1199

Schick, Leslie, Assoc Dean, Libr Serv, Dir, Health Sci Libr, University of Cincinnati Libraries, PO Box 210033, Cincinnati, OH, 45221-0033. Tel: 513-558-4321. Fax: 513-558-2682. p. 1874

Schick, Leslie, Assoc Dean, Dir, University of Cincinnati Libraries, Donald C Harrison Health Sciences Library, PO Box 670574, Cincinnati, OH, 45267-0574. Tel: 513-558-0127. Fax: 513-558-2682. p. 1874

Schide, Debbie, Librn, Palo Alto Medical Foundation, Ames Bldg, 795 El Camino Real, Palo Alto, CA, 94301-2302. Tel: 650-326-8120, Ext 4831. Fax: 650-853-2909. p. 204

Schiebelbein, Ann, Web Serv Librn, Alberta Government Library, Capital Blvd, 11th Flr, 10044 - 108 St, Edmonton, AB, T5J 5E6, CANADA. Tel: 780-427-2985. Fax: 780-427-5927. p. 2698

Schiefelbein, Dan, Dir, Iowa Central Community College, 330 Ave M, Fort Dodge, IA, 50501. Tel: 515-576-7201, Ext 2618. Fax: 515-576-0099, Ext 2631. p. 817

Schiefelbein, Dan, Dir, Iowa Central Community College, Webster City Center, 1725 Beach St, Webster City, IA, 50595. Tel: 515-832-1632, Ext 2821. Fax: 515-576-0099, Ext 2820. p. 817

Schiefelbein, Dan, ILL, Iowa Central Community College, Eagle Grove, 316 NW Third St, Eagle Grove, IA, 50533. Tel: 515-448-4723. Fax: 515-448-2800. p. 817

Schiefer, Jo Anne, Senior Citizen Outreach, Tiffin-Seneca Public Library, 77 Jefferson St, Tiffin, OH, 44883. Tel: 419-447-3751. Fax: 419-447-3045. p. 1938

Schieman, Pat, Coord, Ad Serv, Lethbridge Public Library, 810 Fifth Ave S, Lethbridge, AB, T1J 4C4, CANADA. Tel: 403-380-7325. Fax: 403-329-1478. p. 2709

Schienle, David, Coordr, Res Serv, Catholic Diocese of Fairbanks, Chancery Bldg, 1316 Peger Rd, Fairbanks, AK, 99709-5199. Tel: 907-374-9500. Fax: 907-374-9580. p. 47

Schierhorst, Gisele Ira, Head Librn, Stony Brook University, Music, Melville Library, Rm W1530, Stony Brook, NY, 11794-3333. Tel: 631-632-7097. Fax: 631-632-7116. p. 1750

Schierts, Judith A, Librn, Wabasha Public Library, 168 Alleghany Ave, Wabasha, MN, 55981-1286. Tel: 651-565-3927. Fax: 651-565-3927. p. 1287

Schiesser, Paul, Actg Supv Librn, Br, Oakland Public Library, Main Library, 125 14th St, Oakland, CA, 94612. Tel: 510-238-3134. Fax: 510-238-2232. p. 198

Schiesser, Rita, Dir, Algoma Public Library, 406 Fremont St, Algoma, WI, 54201. Tel: 920-487-2295. Fax: 920-487-3941. p. 2577

Schiff, Howard, Exec Dir, Maryland Pharmacists Association Library, Kelly Memorial Bldg, 650 W Lombard St, Baltimore, MD, 21201-1572. Tel: 410-727-0746. Fax: 410-727-2253. p. 1015

Schiff, Susan, Libr Asst, George F Johnson Memorial Library, 1001 Park St, Endicott, NY, 13760. Tel: 607-757-5350. Fax: 607-757-2491. p. 1620

Schiffenbauer, Zelda, Head Librn, Economists Inc Library, 1200 New Hampshire Ave NW, Ste 400, Washington, DC, 20036-6809. Tel: 202-223-4700. Fax: 202-296-7138. p. 399

Schiffer, Frank, AV, Bethel University Library, 3900 Bethel Dr, Saint Paul, MN, 55112. Tel: 651-638-6222. Fax: 651-638-6001. p. 1277

Schiffer, Michael, Assoc Dir, Computing Serv, DePaul University Libraries, Vincent G Rinn Law Library, 25 E Jackson Blvd, 5th Flr, Chicago, IL, 60604-2287. Tel: 312-362-6311. Fax: 312-362-6908. p. 612

Schiffgen, Marion, Commun Librn, Ash Fork Public Library, 518 Lewis Ave, Ash Fork, AZ, 86320. Tel: 928-637-2442. Fax: 928-637-2442. p. 57

Schiffgens, Erika, Pub Serv Librn, Wilson College, 1015 Philadelphia Ave, Chambersburg, PA, 17201-1285. Tel: 717-264-4141, Ext 3294. Fax: 717-263-7194. p. 2043

Schiffhauer, Mary, Librn, Buffalo & Erie County Public Library System, Crane, 633 Elmwood, Buffalo, NY, 14222-1801. Tel: 716-883-6651. Fax: 716-883-6651. p. 1596

Schildknecht, Marge, Pub Serv Librn, Elgin Community College, 1700 Spartan Dr, Elgin, IL, 60123. Tel: 847-241-7174. p. 641

Schill, Caroline, Head, Youth Serv, La Grange Public Library, Ten W Cossitt Ave, La Grange, IL, 60525. Tel: 708-352-0576, Ext 22. p. 662

Schiller, Dan, Prof, University of Illinois at Urbana-Champaign, Library & Information Science Bldg, 501 E Daniel St, Champaign, IL, 61820-6211. Tel: 217-333-3280. Fax: 217-244-3302. p. 2965

Schiller, Jeff, Info Spec, Alcohol Research Group Library, 6475 Christie Ave, Ste 400, Emeryville, CA, 94608-1010. Tel: 510-597-3440. Fax: 510-985-6459. p. 146

Schiller, Nicholas, Syst Instruction Librn, Washington State University Libraries, 14204 NE Salmon Creek Ave, Vancouver, WA, 98686. Tel: 360-546-9171. Fax: 360-546-9039. p. 2546

Schillig, Jennifer E, Ch, Free Public Library of Monroe Township, 713 Marsha Ave, Williamstown, NJ, 08094. Tel: 856-629-1212. Fax: 856-875-0191. p. 1544

Schilling, Cindy, Dir, Wells Public Library, 1434 Post Rd, Wells, ME, 04090-4508. Tel: 207-646-8181, Ext 206. Fax: 207-646-5636. p. 1006

Schilling, Henrietta, In Charge, Lafayette Public Library, Milton Branch, Cedar Village Shopping Ctr, Hwy 92, Milton, LA, 70558. Tel: 337-856-5261. p. 952

Schilling, Liz, Sr Librn, American Health Care Association, 1201 L St NW, Washington, DC, 20005. Tel: 202-898-2842. Fax: 202-842-3860. p. 392

Schilling, Ralph, Media Serv, Western Nevada Community College, 2201 W College Pkwy, Carson City, NV, 89703. Tel: 775-445-3229. Fax: 775-445-3363. p. 1426

Schilling, Yvonne, Tech Serv, Highlands County Library System, 319 W Center Ave, Sebring, FL, 33870-3109. Tel: 863-402-6716. Fax: 863-385-2883. p. 491

Schillo, Deborah, Librn, Southern Highland Craft Guild, Blue Ridge Pkwy, Milepost 382, 370 Riceville Rd, Asheville, NC, 28805. Tel: 828-298-7928. Fax: 828-298-7962. p. 1775

Schilt, Margaret, Fac Serv Librn, University of Chicago Library, D'Angelo Law Library, 1121 E 60th St, Chicago, IL, 60637-2786. Tel: 773-702-6716. Fax: 773-702-2889. p. 626

Schimdt, Bart, Digital Projects Librn, Drake University, 2725 University Ave, Des Moines, IA, 50311. Tel: 515-271-2940. Fax: 515-271-3933. p. 809

Schimelman, Ashley, Ch, San Marcos Public Library, 625 E Hopkins, San Marcos, TX, 78666. Tel: 512-393-8200. p. 2384

Schimelpfenig, Robert, Archive Spec, Washington State University Libraries, 14204 NE Salmon Creek Ave, Vancouver, WA, 98686. Tel: 360-546-9249. Fax: 360-546-9039. p. 2546

Schimizzi, Tony, Cataloger, University of Alabama at Birmingham, Mervyn H Sterne Library, 917 13th St S, Birmingham, AL, 35205. Tel: 205-934-6364. p. 10

Schimka, Jane, ILL, Rusk County Community Library, 418 Corbett Ave, Ladysmith, WI, 54848-1396. Tel: 715-532-2604. Fax: 715-532-2658. p. 2604

Schimmel, Sandra, ILL, Osterhout Free Library, 71 S Franklin St, Wilkes-Barre, PA, 18701-1287. Tel: 570-823-0156. Fax: 570-823-5477. p. 2155

Schimmelmann, Jeanne R, Ch, Wickliffe Public Library, 1713 Lincoln Rd, Wickliffe, OH, 44092. Tel: 440-944-6010. Fax: 440-944-7264. p. 1947

Schimmelpfeng, Richard H, Librn, Mansfield Historical Society, 954 Storrs Rd, Storrs, CT, 06268. Tel: 860-429-6575. p. 370

Schindele-Cupples, Carrie, Ref Librn, Springfield Public Library, 225 Fifth St, Springfield, OR, 97477-4697. Tel: 541-726-3766. Fax: 541-726-3747. p. 2020

Schink, Christy, Ch, Scenic Regional Library of Franklin, Gasconade & Warren Counties, 308 Hawthorne Dr, Union, MO, 63084. Tel: 636-583-3224. p. 1369

Schinker, Rose, Dir, La Vista Public Library, 9110 Giles Rd, La Vista, NE, 68128. Tel: 402-537-3900. Fax: 402-537-3902. p. 1403

Schinker, Rose, Coll Develop, University of Nebraska Medical Center, 600 S 42nd St, Omaha, NE, 68198-6705. Tel: 402-559-5418. Fax: 402-559-5498. p. 1415

Schinn, Michael, Mgr, Info Tech, Ridgewood Public Library, 125 N Maple Ave, Ridgewood, NJ, 07450-3288. Tel: 201-670-5600. Fax: 201-670-0293. p. 1526

Schinner, Maureen, Webmaster/Ref Librn, Alverno College Library, 3401 S 39th St, Milwaukee, WI, 53215. Tel: 414-382-6058. Fax: 414-382-6354. p. 2617

Schipp, John, Mgr, Old Cathedral Library, 205 Church St, Vincennes, IN, 47591-1133. Tel: 812-882-5638. Fax: 812-882-4042. p. 784

Schipper, Chris, Dir, Libr Serv, San Juan College Library, 4601 College Blvd, Farmington, NM, 87402. Tel: 505-566-3449. Fax: 505-566-3381. p. 1555

Schipper, Christopher, Ref, San Juan College Library, 4601 College Blvd, Farmington, NM, 87402. Tel: 505-566-3097. Fax: 505-566-3381. p. 1555

Schipper, Joan, Head Librn, Munger, Tolles & Olson LLP, 355 S Grand Ave, 35th Flr, Los Angeles, CA, 90071-1560. Tel: 213-683-9100. Fax: 213-683-5173. p. 176

Schipper, Rachel A, Assoc Dean, Tech & Support Serv, University of Florida Libraries, 535 Library W, Gainesville, FL, 32611-7000. Tel: 352-273-2505. Fax: 352-392-7251. p. 449

Schira, Rainer, Electronic Res, Ref, Brandon University, 270 18th St, Brandon, MB, R7A 6A9, CANADA. Tel: 204-727-7463. Fax: 204-727-1072. p. 2747

Schiraldi, Hilary, Interim Head Librn, University of California, Berkeley, Thomas J Long Business & Economics Library, Haas School of Business, Rm S352, Berkeley, CA, 94720-6000. Tel: 510-642-0370. Fax: 510-643-5277. p. 128

Schirer-Suter, Myron, Dr, Dir of Libr Serv, Gordon College, 255 Grapevine Rd, Wenham, MA, 01984-1899. Tel: 978-867-4083. Fax: 978-867-4660. p. 1136

Schirmer, Robert W, Univ Archivist, The University of Findlay, 1000 N Main St, Findlay, OH, 45840-3695. Tel: 419-434-4767. p. 1899

Schirmer, Sheryl D, Dir, Bluffton Public Library, 145 S Main St, Bluffton, OH, 45817. Tel: 419-358-5016. Fax: 419-358-9653. p. 1860

Schirota, Erin, Head, Youth Serv, Bronxville Public Library, 201 Pondfield Rd, Bronxville, NY, 10708. Tel: 914-337-7680. Fax: 914-337-0332. p. 1588

Schirra, Margareta, Libr Tech, Nova Scotia Community College, 75 High St, Bridgewater, NS, B4V 1V8, CANADA. Tel: 902-543-0684. Fax: 902-543-0652. p. 2778

Schisler, Cheri, Dir, Mulberry Public Library, 103 E Canal St, Mulberry, FL, 33860. Tel: 863-425-3246. Fax: 863-425-8818. p. 471

Schjott, Monica, Librn, Durham Region Law Association, 150 Bond St E, Oshawa, ON, L1G 0A2, CANADA. Tel: 905-579-9554. Fax: 905-579-1801. p. 2826

Schlabach, Mary Beth, Head, Ref & Instruction, Goshen College, Harold & Wilma Good Library, 1700 S Main, Goshen, IN, 46526-4794. Tel: 574-535-7428. Fax: 574-535-7438. p. 745

Schlachter, Virginia, ILL, Mount Prospect Public Library, Ten S Emerson St, Mount Prospect, IL, 60056. Tel: 847-253-5675. Fax: 847-253-0642. p. 677

Schlaeger, Susan, Commun Libr Mgr, County of Los Angeles Public Library, Temple City Library, 5939 Golden West Ave, Temple City, CA, 91780-2292. Tel: 626-285-2136. Fax: 626-285-2314. p. 143

Schlaht, Lynne, Asst Dir, Adel Public Library, 303 S Tenth St, Adel, IA, 50003-1797. Tel: 515-993-3512. Fax: 515-993-3191. p. 791

Schlake, Carol, Br Mgr, Indianapolis-Marion County Public Library, Pike, 6525 Zionsville Rd, Indianapolis, IN, 46268-2352. Tel: 317-275-4480. p. 754

Schlanger, Seth, Actg Librn, Temple Beth Torah Library, Rte 9 W, 330 N Highland Ave, Upper Nyack, NY, 10960. Tel: 845-358-2248. Fax: 845-358-3450. p. 1758

Schlapkohl, Ann, Dir, Manson Public Library, 1312 10th Ave, Manson, IA, 50563. Tel: 712-469-3986. Fax: 712-469-3076. p. 829

Schlappi, Janis, Ch, Johnson Public Library, 131 E Catherine St, Darlington, WI, 53530. Tel: 608-776-4171. p. 2587

Schlatter, Mel, Computer Serv, Oral Roberts University Library, 7777 South Lewis Ave, Tulsa, OK, 74171. Tel: 918-495-7189. Fax: 918-495-6893. p. 1981

Schlaudroff, Richard, Tech Serv, The Art Institute of Dallas, Two North Park E, 8080 Park Lane, Ste 100, Dallas, TX, 75231-5993. Tel: 469-587-1244. Fax: 214-692-8106. p. 2304

Schlechte, Todd, Dir, Gretna Public Library, 736 South St, Gretna, NE, 68028. Tel: 402-332-4480. Fax: 402-332-2506. p. 1400

Schlee, Kathryn, Librn, Syngenta Crop Protection Library, 410 Swing Rd, Greensboro, NC, 27409. Tel: 336-632-5696. Fax: 336-299-8318. p. 1797

Schlegel, Carolyn K, Librn, Virgil Biegert Public Library, 214 N Market, Shickley, NE, 68436. Tel: 402-627-3365. Fax: 402-627-3365. p. 1419

Schlegel, Jean, Dir, Ness City Public Library, 113 S Iowa Ave, Ness City, KS, 67560-1992. Tel: 785-798-3415. Fax: 785-798-2313. p. 884

Schleicher, Becky, Circ Supvr, Northwestern College, 3003 Snelling Ave N, Saint Paul, MN, 55113. Tel: 651-631-5241. Fax: 651-631-5598. p. 1280

Schleicher, Carin, Br Librn, Siouxland Libraries, Caille Branch, 4100 Carnegie Circle, Sioux Falls, SD, 57106-2320. Tel: 605-367-8714. Fax: 605-362-2816. p. 2219

Schleif, Tom, Exec Dir, Kenosha County Historical Society, 220 51st Pl, Kenosha, WI, 53140. Tel: 262-654-5770. Fax: 262-654-1730. p. 2601

Schleigh-Hayes, Amy, Electronic Res Librn, College of Saint Elizabeth, Two Convent Rd, Morristown, NJ, 07960-6989. Tel: 973-290-4237. Fax: 973-290-4226. p. 1504

Schlekau, Linda, Br Mgr, Fairfax County Public Library, Burke Centre Library, 5935 Freds Oak Rd, Burke, VA, 22015-2599. Tel: 703-249-1520. p. 2461

Schlembach, Mary, Librn, University of Illinois Library at Urbana-Champaign, Physics-Astronomy, 204 Loomis Lab, 110 W Green St, Urbana, IL, 61801. Tel: 217-333-3158. p. 712

Schlenk, Jamie, Youth Serv Dept Head, Hussey-Mayfield Memorial Public Library, 250 N Fifth St, Zionsville, IN, 46077-1324. Tel: 317-873-3149, Ext 11650. Fax: 317-873-8339. p. 789

Schleper, Susan, Librn, Saint Cloud Hospital, 1406 Sixth Ave N, Saint Cloud, MN, 56303. Tel: 320-251-2700, Ext 54686. Fax: 320-656-7039. p. 1276

Schlesinger, Frances, Ref Librn, University of Massachusetts at Boston, 100 Morrissey Blvd, Boston, MA, 02125-3300. Tel: 617-287-5943. p. 1068

Schlesinger, Michael, In Charge, Julien & Schlesinger, PC, One Whitehall St, New York, NY, 10004. Tel: 212-962-8020. p. 1684

Schlessinger, Burd, Accessioning Archivist, Smith College Libraries, Sophia Smith Collection, Seven Neilson Dr, Northampton, MA, 01063. Tel: 413-585-4884. Fax: 413-585-2886. p. 1114

Schlessinger, Kenneth, Chief Librn, Lehman College, City University of New York, 250 Bedford Park Blvd W, Bronx, NY, 10468-1589. Tel: 718-960-7776. Fax: 718-960-8952. p. 1587

Schlichter, Marcus, Acq Librn, Archivist, Wayne State College, 1111 Main St, Wayne, NE, 68787. Tel: 402-375-7266. Fax: 402-375-7538. p. 1423

Schlichting, Eunice, Curator, Putnam Museum of History & Natural Science, 1717 W 12th St, Davenport, IA, 52804. Tel: 563-324-1933, Ext 216. Fax: 563-324-6638. p. 806

Schlimgen, Joan B, Asst Dir for Res, University of Arizona, Arizona Health Sciences Library, 1501 N Campbell Ave, Tucson, AZ, 85724. Tel: 520-626-6140. Fax: 520-626-2922. p. 88

Schlimm, Chrysostom V, Fr, Spec Coll Librn, Saint Vincent College & Seminary Library, 300 Fraser Purchase Rd, Latrobe, PA, 15650-2690. Tel: 724-805-2966. Fax: 724-805-2905. p. 2079

Schlimme, Bill, Ref Librn, Pamunkey Regional Library, 7527 Library Dr, Hanover, VA, 23069. Tel: 804-537-6211. Fax: 804-537-6389. p. 2469

Schlimpert, Kathleen, Br Librn, Riverside Regional Library, Altenburg Branch, 66 Poplar St, Altenburg, MO, 63732. Tel: 573-824-5267. Fax: 573-824-5267. p. 1334

Schlindwein, Ann Marie, Mgr, Ad Serv, Erie County Public Library, 160 E Front St, Erie, PA, 16507. Tel: 814-451-6900. Fax: 814-451-6907. p. 2055

Schlinke, John, Archit/Art Librn, Roger Williams University Library, Architecture, One Old Ferry Rd, Bristol, RI, 02809-2921. Tel: 401-254-3833. p. 2164

Schlinke, John, Archit/Art Librn, Roger Williams University Library, One Old Ferry Rd, Bristol, RI, 02809. Tel: 401-254-3833. Fax: 401-254-3631. p. 2164

Schlissel, Judith T, Dir, Blume, Goldfaden, Berkowitz, Donnelly, Fried & Forte, PC, One Main St, Chatham, NJ, 07928. Tel: 973-635-5400, Ext 149. Fax: 973-635-9339. p. 1478

Schlosser, John, Coordr, Info Tech, Santa Clara City Library, 2635 Homestead Rd, Santa Clara, CA, 95051. Tel: 408-615-2948. Fax: 408-247-9657. p. 262

Schlottman, Andrea, Br Mgr, Worcester County Library, Ocean City Branch, 10003 Coastal Hwy, Ocean City, MD, 21842. Tel: 410-524-1818. Fax: 410-289-5577. p. 1042

Schlotzhauer, Vernon, Librn, Pennsylvania State University Libraries, Social Sciences, 201 Paterno Library, University Park, PA, 16802-1809. Tel: 814-863-4644. Fax: 814-865-1403. p. 2148

Schlueter, Laura, Digital Content Librn, SUNY Upstate Medical University, 766 Irving Ave, Syracuse, NY, 13210-1602. Tel: 315-464-7195. Fax: 315-464-4584. p. 1753

Schlumpf-Manion, Amy, Info Serv Librn, Aurora University, 315 S Gladstone, Aurora, IL, 60506-4877. Tel: 630-844-5442. Fax: 630-844-3848. p. 591

Schlundt, Sherry, Ch, Teen Librn, Kirkendall Public Library, 1210 NW Prairie Ridge Dr, Ankeny, IA, 50021. Tel: 515-965-6460. Fax: 515-965-6474. p. 794

Schluterbusch, LaDonna, Librn, Hoesch Memorial Public Library, City Park W Second, Alma, NE, 68920. Tel: 308-928-2600. Fax: 308-928-2662. p. 1391

Schmacher, Janice, Asst Librn, Jewell Public Library, 216 Delaware, Jewell, KS, 66949. Tel: 785-428-3630. Fax: 785-428-3630. p. 874

Schmalenberg, Mojgan, Info Tech, Caledon Public Library, 150 Queen St S, Bolton, ON, L7E 1E3, CANADA. Tel: 905-857-1400. Fax: 905-857-8280. p. 2795

Schmaltz, Betty, Dir, Bussey Community Public Library, 401 Merrill St, Bussey, IA, 50044. Tel: 641-944-5994. p. 798

Schmaltz, Mary Jane, Asst Dir, Bismarck Veterans Memorial Public Library, 515 N Fifth St, Bismarck, ND, 58503-4081. Tel: 701-355-1483. Fax: 701-221-3729. p. 1837

Schmand, Kathleen L, Coordr, Commun Affairs, Grants & Develop, Northern Arizona University, Bldg 028, Knoles Dr, Flagstaff, AZ, 86011. Tel: 928-523-0341. Fax: 928-523-3770. p. 62

Schmandt, Erin N, Dir, River Rapids District Library, 227 E Broad St, Chesaning, MI, 48616. Tel: 989-845-3211. Fax: 989-845-2166. p. 1163

Schmehl, Charlie, Librn, Urban Research & Development Corp Library, 28 W Broad St, Bethlehem, PA, 18018. Tel: 610-865-0701. Fax: 610-868-7613. p. 2035

Schmelz, Lynne, Librn, Harvard Library, History of Science Library - Cabot Science Library, Science Center, One Oxford St, Cambridge, MA, 02138. Tel: 617-495-5355. Fax: 617-495-5324. p. 1075

Schmelz, Lynne M, Librn, Harvard Library, Godfrey Lowell Cabot Science Library, Science Center, One Oxford St, Cambridge, MA, 02138. Tel: 617-495-5351. Fax: 617-495-5324. p. 1074

Schmetzke, Axel, Dr, Bibliog Instr, Media Spec, University of Wisconsin-Stevens Point, 900 Reserve St, Stevens Point, WI, 54481-1985. Tel: 715-346-4658. Fax: 715-346-3857. p. 2640

Schmezer, Mary, Ref Serv, Ad, Morgantown Public Library System, 373 Spruce St, Morgantown, WV, 26505. Tel: 304-291-7425. Fax: 304-291-7427. p. 2566

Schmid, Jena, Main Libr Adminr, Nashville Public Library, 615 Church St, Nashville, TN, 37219-2314. Tel: 615-862-5806. Fax: 615-862-5771. p. 2257

Schmid, Kay, Dir, Roman L & Victoria E Hruska Memorial Public Library, 399 N Fifth St, David City, NE, 68632. Tel: 402-367-3100. Fax: 402-367-3105. p. 1397

Schmid, Patti, Head, Libr Serv, Cumberland County College Library, 3322 College Dr, Vineland, NJ, 08360. Tel: 856-691-8600, Ext 261. Fax: 856-691-1969. p. 1538

Schmid, Peter F, Visual Res Archivist, Web Coordr, Providence Archives, 4800 37th Ave SW, Seattle, WA, 98126. Tel: 206-923-4012. Fax: 206-923-4001. p. 2530

Schmid, Taryn, Pub Serv, Okanagan College Library, 1000 KLO Rd, Kelowna, BC, V1Y 4X8, CANADA. p. 2730

Schmid-Perry, Cynthia, Dir, Ohio County Public Library, 100 N High St, Rising Sun, IN, 47040-1022. Tel: 812-438-2257. Fax: 812-438-2257. p. 775

Schmida, Linda, Youth Serv, Summit County Library, 6505 N Landmark Dr, Ste 100, Park City, UT, 84098-6009. Tel: 435-615-3903. Fax: 435-615-3905. p. 2410

Schmidlen, Roberta, Adult Serv, Saint Albans Free Library, 11 Maiden Lane, Saint Albans, VT, 05478. Tel: 802-524-1507. Fax: 802-524-1514. p. 2434

Schmidt, Adam, Ch, Newark Public Library, Vailsburg, 75 Alexander St, Newark, NJ, 07106. Tel: 973-733-7755. p. 1512

Schmidt, Beth, Chair, Memorial Presbyterian Church, 1310 Ashman St, Midland, MI, 48640. Tel: 989-835-6759. p. 1208

Schmidt, C Evlyn, Acq Mgr, Dir, Oklahoma Panhandle State University, 409 W Sewell, Goodwell, OK, 73939. Tel: 580-349-1542. Fax: 580-349-1541. p. 1964

Schmidt, Catherine, Dir, Elmendaro Township Library, 224 Commercial St, Hartford, KS, 66854. Tel: 620-392-5518. p. 870

Schmidt, Claudia, Librn, Valley Regional Library, 141 Main St S, South Morris, MB, R0G 1K0, CANADA. Tel: 204-746-2136. Fax: 204-746-6953. p. 2752

Schmidt, Craig F, Chairperson, Orland Hills Public Library District, 16033 94th Ave, Orland Hills, IL, 60477-4623. Tel: 708-349-6666. Fax: 708-349-1358. p. 686

Schmidt, Dale, Exec Dir, Clearwater Marine Aquarium Library, 249 Windward Passage, Clearwater, FL, 33767. Tel: 727-441-1790, Ext 222. Fax: 727-442-9466. p. 432

Schmidt, Dara, Br Mgr, Anythink Libraries, Anythink Brighton, 327 E Bridge St, Brighton, CO, 80601. Tel: 303-405-3230. p. 323

Schmidt, Darlene, Librn, Atchison County Library, 200 S Main St, Rock Port, MO, 64482-1532. Tel: 660-744-5404. Fax: 660-744-2861. p. 1351

Schmidt, Dawn Marie, Sr Librn, Ch Serv, Peoria Public Library, 8463 W Monroe St, Peoria, AZ, 85345. Tel: 623-773-7562. Fax: 623-773-7567. p. 71

Schmidt, Debbie, Ch, Glenwood Public Library, 109 N Vine St, Glenwood, IA, 51534-1516. Tel: 712-527-5252. Fax: 712-527-3619. p. 818

Schmidt, Diane, Librn, University of Illinois Library at Urbana-Champaign, Biology, 101 Burrill Hall, 407 S Goodwin Ave, Urbana, IL, 61801. Tel: 217-333-0281. Fax: 217-333-3662. p. 712

Schmidt, Diane, Interim Veterinary Med Librn, University of Illinois Library at Urbana-Champaign, Veterinary Medicine, 1257 Veterinary Med Basic Science Bldg, 2001 S Lincoln Ave, Urbana, IL, 61802. Tel: 217-333-8778. Fax: 217-333-2286. p. 713

Schmidt, Dianne, ILL, Minnesota State University Moorhead, 1104 Seventh Ave S, Moorhead, MN, 56563. Tel: 218-477-2922. Fax: 218-477-5924. p. 1266

Schmidt, Doreen, Librn, Prairie-River Library District, Peck Community, 217 N Main St, Peck, ID, 83545. Tel: 208-486-6161. Fax: 208-486-6161. p. 577

Schmidt, Erika, Cataloger, Ref Librn, Mechanics' Institute Library, 57 Post St, San Francisco, CA, 94104-5003. Tel: 415-393-0115. Fax: 415-421-4192. p. 243

Schmidt, Erin, Librn/Irvine Location, Alliant International University, 10455 Pomerado Rd, San Diego, CA, 92131-1799. Tel: 949-812-7454. Fax: 858-635-4599. p. 230

Schmidt, Evelyn, Cat, Orem Public Library, 58 N State St, Orem, UT, 84057-5596. Tel: 801-229-7050. Fax: 801-229-7130. p. 2409

Schmidt, Ford, Head, Ref, Willamette University, 900 State St, Salem, OR, 97301. Tel: 503-375-5407. Fax: 503-370-6141. p. 2019

Schmidt, Gary, Automation Serv, Instr, Ref Librn, Ocean County College Library, College Dr, Toms River, NJ, 08754. Tel: 732-255-0400, Ext 2248. Fax: 732-255-0421. p. 1533

Schmidt, Gretchen, Br Mgr, San Diego County Library, Del Mar Branch, 1309 Camino del Mar, Del Mar, CA, 92014-2693. Tel: 858-755-1666. Fax: 858-755-8734. p. 233

Schmidt, Gwen, Coordr, Outreach Serv, Saskatoon Public Library, 311-23rd St E, Saskatoon, SK, S7K 0J6, CANADA. Tel: 306-975-7606. Fax: 306-975-7542. p. 2926

Schmidt, Helen, ILL, Pub Serv, Ref Serv, Polk State College, 999 Ave H NE, Winter Haven, FL, 33881-4299. Tel: 863-297-1040. Fax: 863-297-1065. p. 504

Schmidt, Helen, Librn, Polk State College, Lakeland Campus Library, 3425 Winter Lake Rd, Sta 62, Lakeland, FL, 33803. Tel: 863-297-1042. Fax: 863-297-1064. p. 505

Schmidt, Helen, Ref, Polk State College, Lakeland Campus Library, 3425 Winter Lake Rd, Sta 62, Lakeland, FL, 33803. Tel: 863-297-1042. Fax: 863-297-1064. p. 505

Schmidt, Janine, Dir, McGill University Libraries, 3459 McTavish St, Montreal, QC, H3A 1Y1, CANADA. Tel: 514-398-1840. Fax: 514-398-3561. p. 2898

Schmidt, Jennifer, Instrul Serv Librn, Southeastern Wisconsin Information Technology Exchange, Inc, 6801 N Yates Rd, Milwaukee, WI, 53217-3985. Tel: 414-351-2423. Fax: 414-228-4146. p. 2958

Schmidt, Jim, Assoc Dir, Springfield-Greene County Library District, 4653 S Campbell, Springfield, MO, 65810-1723. Tel: 417-882-0714. Fax: 417-883-9348. p. 1367

Schmidt, Joyce, Librn, Deshler Public Library, 310 E Pearl St, Deshler, NE, 68340. Tel: 402-365-4107. Fax: 402-365-4107. p. 1397

Schmidt, June, Assoc Dean, Tech Serv, Mississippi State University, 395 Hardy Rd, Mississippi State, MS, 39762. Tel: 662-325-7668. Fax: 662-325-9344. p. 1309

Schmidt, Karen, Univ Librn, Illinois Wesleyan University, One Ames Plaza, Bloomington, IL, 61701-7188. Tel: 309-556-3350. Fax: 309-556-3706. p. 595

Schmidt, Kari, Electronic Res, American University Library, 4400 Massachusetts Ave NW, Washington, DC, 20016-8046. Tel: 202-885-3203. Fax: 202-885-3226. p. 393

Schmidt, Karyn, Librn, Ettrick Public Library, 15570 School St, Ettrick, WI, 54627. Tel: 608-525-3408. p. 2591

Schmidt, Karyn, Dir, Taylor Memorial Library, 402 Second St, Taylor, WI, 54659. Tel: 715-662-2310. Fax: 715-662-2034. p. 2642

Schmidt, Kathy, Asst Dir, Tech Serv & Automation, Fountaindale Public Library District, 300 W Briarcliff Rd, Bolingbrook, IL, 60440-2844. Tel: 630-759-2102, Ext 4154. Fax: 630-759-9519. p. 596

Schmidt, Kathy, Librn, Phillips, McFall, McCaffrey, McVay & Murrah PC, Corporate Tower, 13th Flr, 101 N Robinson, Oklahoma City, OK, 73102. Tel: 405-235-4100. Fax: 405-235-4133. p. 1975

Schmidt, Krista, Ref Librn/Sci Liaison, Western Carolina University, 176 Central Dr, Cullowhee, NC, 28723. Tel: 828-227-2215. Fax: 828-227-7015. p. 1786

Schmidt, Larry, Interim Head of Libr, University of Wyoming Libraries, Brinkerhoff Earth Resources Information Center, 1000 E University Ave, Laramie, WY, 82071. Tel: 307-766-2844. Fax: 307-766-6679. p. 2658

Schmidt, Laura, Archivist, Wheaton College, Marion E Wade Center, 351 E Lincoln, Wheaton, IL, 60187-4213. Tel: 630-752-5908. Fax: 630-752-5459. p. 718

Schmidt, Lili, Cat, Milton-Freewater Public Library, Eight SW Eighth Ave, Milton-Freewater, OR, 97862-1501. Tel: 541-938-8249. Fax: 541-938-8254. p. 2006

Schmidt, Linda, ILL, Pub Serv, Ref Serv, College of the Ozarks, Lyons Memorial Library, One Opportunity Ave, Point Lookout, MO, 65726. Tel: 417-690-3411. Fax: 417-334-3085. p. 1349

Schmidt, Mari, Asst Dir/Bus Mgr, Menomonee Falls Public Library, W156 N8436 Pilgrim Rd, Menomonee Falls, WI, 53051. Tel: 262-532-8900. Fax: 262-532-8939. p. 2614

Schmidt, Marnie, Adult Ref, New Berlin Public Library, 15105 Library Lane, New Berlin, WI, 53151. Tel: 262-785-4980. Fax: 262-785-4984. p. 2625

Schmidt, Martin, Ref, Maharishi University of Management Library, 1000 N Fourth St, Fairfield, IA, 52557. Tel: 641-472-1148. Fax: 641-472-1137. p. 815

Schmidt, Mary, Ref Asst, Synergy Medical Education Alliance, Covenant Houghton Bldg, 2nd Flr, 1000 Houghton Ave, Ste 2000, Saginaw, MI, 48602-5398. Tel: 989-583-6846. Fax: 989-583-6898. p. 1224

Schmidt, Mary, Dir, Gorham-Macbane Public Library, 405 White St, Springfield, TN, 37172-2340. Tel: 615-384-5123. Fax: 615-384-0106. p. 2266

Schmidt, MaryAnn, Sister, Cataloger, Alverno College Library, 3401 S 39th St, Milwaukee, WI, 53215. Tel: 414-382-6063. Fax: 414-382-6354. p. 2617

Schmidt, Maxine, Head Librn, University of Massachusetts Amherst, Science & Engineering Library, A273 Lederle Graduate Research Ctr Lowrise, Amherst, MA, 01003. Tel: 413-545-1370. Fax: 413-577-1534. p. 1049

Schmidt, Maxine, Head, Sci Libr, University of Massachusetts Amherst, 154 Hicks Way, Amherst, MA, 01003-9275. Tel: 413-545-6739. Fax: 413-545-6873. p. 1049

Schmidt, Nancy L, Libr Dir, Laurel Public Library, 720 W Third St, Laurel, MT, 59044. Tel: 406-628-4961. Fax: 406-628-4961. p. 1384

Schmidt, Norma A, Coll Develop Librn, Prince George's Community College Library, 301 Largo Rd, Largo, MD, 20774-2199. Tel: 301-322-0471. Fax: 301-808-8847. p. 1034

Schmidt, Rebecca, Librn, Montana Department of Corrections, Four North Haynes, Miles City, MT, 59301-1058. Tel: 406-233-2216. Fax: 406-233-2204. p. 1386

Schmidt, Rhonda, Librn, Western Plains Library System, Cordell Public Library, 208 S College, Cordell, OK, 73632-5210. Tel: 580-832-3530. Fax: 580-832-3530. p. 1960

Schmidt, Rich, Doc Delivery, Libr Serv Coordr, Willamette University, 900 State St, Salem, OR, 97301. Tel: 503-370-6312. Fax: 503-370-6141. p. 2019

Schmidt, Rita, Asst Dir, Fort Dodge Public Library, 424 Central Ave, Fort Dodge, IA, 50501. Tel: 515-573-8167, Ext 229. Fax: 515-573-5422. p. 817

Schmidt, Robert, Archivist, Miami University Libraries, 225 King Library, Oxford, OH, 45056. Tel: 513-529-6720. Fax: 513-529-3110. p. 1926

Schmidt, Robert, Archivist, Miami University Libraries, University Archives, Withrow Hall, Oxford, OH, 45056. Tel: 513-529-6720. p. 1926

Schmidt, Rosa, Librn, Oakland Public Library, 110 E Third St, Oakland, NE, 68045-1356. Tel: 402-685-5113. Fax: 402-685-5113. p. 1411

Schmidt, Sara, Spec Coll Librn, Schreiner University, 2100 Memorial Blvd, Kerrville, TX, 78028-5697. Tel: 830-792-7337. Fax: 830-792-7448. p. 2350

Schmidt, Sarah, Govt Info/Ref Librn, Angelo State University Library, 2025 W Johnson, San Angelo, TX, 76904-5079. Tel: 325-486-6527. Fax: 325-942-2198. p. 2378

Schmidt, Sherrie, Univ Librn, Arizona State University Libraries, 300 E Orange Mall Dr, Tempe, AZ, 85287-1006. Tel: 480-965-3417. Fax: 480-965-9169. p. 83

Schmidt, Steven J, Supvr, Libr Develop, Indiana State Library, 315 W Ohio St, Indianapolis, IN, 46202. Tel: 317-232-3715. Fax: 317-232-0002. p. 752

Schmidt, Susan, Dir, Town of Johnsburg Library, 219 Main St, North Creek, NY, 12853. Tel: 518-251-4343. Fax: 518-251-9991. p. 1706

Schmidt, Susan K, Librn IV/Mats Mgt, Public Library Association of Annapolis & Anne Arundel County, Inc, Five Harry S Truman Pkwy, Annapolis, MD, 21401. Tel: 410-222-7075. Fax: 410-222-7188. p. 1010

Schmidt, Tessa Michaelson, Asst Dir, Ruby M Sisson Memorial Library, 811 San Juan St, Pagosa Springs, CO, 81147. Tel: 970-264-2209. Fax: 970-264-4764. p. 319

Schmidt, Theresa, Librn, Albert Lea Public Library, 211 E Clark St, Albert Lea, MN, 56007. Tel: 507-377-4350. Fax: 507-377-4339. p. 1239

Schmidt, Tom, Librn, United States Army, Bldg 2000, S 11th Ave, Fort McCoy, WI, 54656-5000. Tel: 608-388-2410. Fax: 608-388-2690. p. 2593

Schmidt, Valerie, Librn, Huntington Beach Public Library System, Banning, 9281 Banning Ave, Huntington Beach, CA, 92646-8302. Tel: 714-375-5005. Fax: 714-375-5091. p. 159

Schmidt-Ramsey, Karen, Asst Dir, Prog Coordr, North Versailles Public Library, 1401 Greensburg Ave, North Versailles, PA, 15137. Tel: 412-823-2222. Fax: 412-823-2012. p. 2099

Schmidtgall, Kathleen, Librn, Weston Public Library, 108 E Main St, Weston, OR, 97886. Tel: 541-566-2378. Fax: 541-566-2378. p. 2022

Schmit, Karla M, Asst Dir, Pa Ctr for the Bk, Educ & Behav Sci Librn, Pennsylvania State University Libraries, Education & Behavioral Sciences, 501 Paterno Library, University Park, PA, 16802-1812. Tel: 814-863-5521. p. 2148

Schmit, Lynn, Dir, Mahomet Public Library District, 1702 E Oak Street Mahomet, Mahomet, IL, 61853-7427. Tel: 217-586-2611. Fax: 217-586-5710. p. 669

Schmitt, Diana, Ad, James Kennedy Public Library, 320 First Ave E, Dyersville, IA, 52040. Tel: 563-875-8912. Fax: 563-875-6162. p. 812

Schmitt, Diane, Pub Serv Mgr, Mount Hood Community College Library, 26000 SE Stark St, Gresham, OR, 97030. Tel: 503-491-7652. Fax: 503-491-7389. p. 1999

Schmitt, John, Ref Serv, Regis University, 3333 Regis Blvd, Denver, CO, 80221-1099. Tel: 303-458-4030. Fax: 303-964-5497. p. 303

Schmitt, Lavon, In Charge, Siouxland Libraries, Valley Springs Branch, 401 Broadway Ave, Valley Springs, SD, 57068. Tel: 605-757-6264. Fax: 605-757-6730. p. 2219

Schmitt, Linda, Ch, Lynn Haven Public Library, 901 Ohio Ave, Lynn Haven, FL, 32444. Tel: 850-265-2781. Fax: 850-265-7311. p. 461

Schmitt, Lynn, Librn, First Presbyterian Church Library, 145 Main St, Phoenixville, PA, 19460. Tel: 610-933-8816. Fax: 610-933-8060. p. 2120

Schmitt, Marcia, Librn, Wilhoit Public Library, 9325 Donegal Dr, Ste B, Wilhoit, AZ, 86332. Tel: 928-442-3611. Fax: 928-442-3611. p. 89

Schmitt, Molly, Ch, Jefferson County Library, Northwest, 5680 State Rd PP, High Ridge, MO, 63049. Tel: 636-677-8186. Fax: 636-677-8243. p. 1331

Schmitz, Bonnie, Acq, Jamestown College, 6070 College Lane, Jamestown, ND, 58405-0001. Tel: 701-252-3467, Ext 2432. Fax: 701-253-4446. p. 1844

Schmitz, Caroline, Head, Circ, Lawrence Technological University Library, 21000 W Ten Mile Rd, Southfield, MI, 48075-1058. Tel: 248-204-3000. Fax: 248-204-3005. p. 1228

Schmitz du Moulin, Beatrice, Acq, Huron University College Library, 1349 Western Rd, London, ON, N6G 1H3, CANADA. Tel: 519-438-7224, Ext 209. Fax: 519-438-3938. p. 2817

Schmitz, Kris, Mgr, Montana State Library, 1515 E Sixth Ave, Helena, MT, 59620-1800. Tel: 406-444-3117. Fax: 406-444-0266. p. 1383

Schmitz, Laura, Tech Serv Supvr, Putnam County District Library, The Educational Service Ctr, 124 Putnam Pkwy, Ottawa, OH, 45875-1471. Tel: 419-523-3747. Fax: 419-523-6477. p. 1926

Schmitz, Marianne, Head Librn, German Historical Institute Library, 1607 New Hampshire Ave NW, Washington, DC, 20009-2562. Tel: 202-552-8929. Fax: 202-483-3430. p. 403

Schmitz, Sandy, Tech Serv Mgr, Ventura County Library, 5600 Everglades St, Ste A, Ventura, CA, 93003. Tel: 805-677-7170. Fax: 805-677-7173. p. 279

Schmitz, Tom, Librn, Lincoln Regional Center, Medical Library, W Prospector Pl & Folsom St, Lincoln, NE, 68509. Tel: 402-471-5475. Fax: 402-479-5460. p. 1405

Schmitz, Tom, Librn, Lincoln Regional Center, Patients' Library, W Prospector Pl & Folsom St, Lincoln, NE, 68922. Tel: 402-479-5475. Fax: 402-479-5460. p. 1405

Schmitz-Garrett, Susan, Libr Dir, Security Public Library, 715 Aspen Dr, Security, CO, 80911-1807. Tel: 710-390-2814. Fax: 719-392-7641. p. 322

Schmitzer, Frank, Managing Librn, Austin Public Library, University Hills, 4721 Loyola Lane, Austin, TX, 78723. Tel: 512-974-9940. Fax: 512-974-9944. p. 2279

Schmuckal, Christine, Librn, United States Geological Survey, Great Lakes Science Center, 1451 Green Rd, Ann Arbor, MI, 48105-2807. Tel: 734-214-7210. Fax: 734-994-8780. p. 1151

Schmudde, Jan, Dir, Northlake Public Library District, 231 N Wolf Rd, Northlake, IL, 60164. Tel: 708-562-2301. Fax: 708-562-8120. p. 683

Schmuland, Arlene, Head, Archives & Spec Coll, University of Alaska Anchorage, Consortium Library, 3211 Providence Dr, Anchorage, AK, 99508-8176. Tel: 907-786-1849. Fax: 907-786-1834. p. 45

Schmuldt, Michael, Media Serv Tech, Provena Saint Joseph Medical Center, 333 N Madison St, Joliet, IL, 60435. Tel: 815-725-7133, Ext 3530. Fax: 815-773-7755. p. 660

Schnackenberg, Bill, Dr, Educ Mgr, Wyoming State Penitentiary Library, 2900 S Higley Blvd, Rawlins, WY, 82301. Tel: 307-328-1441. Fax: 307-328-7471. p. 2659

Schnake, Mary, Asst Librn, Nashville Public Library, 219 E Elm St, Nashville, IL, 62263-1711. Tel: 618-327-3827. Fax: 618-327-4820. p. 679

Schnall, Linda, Ch, Bethpage Public Library, 47 Powell Ave, Bethpage, NY, 11714-3197. Tel: 516-931-3907. Fax: 516-931-3926. p. 1581

Schnarr, Chris, Librn, Kitchener Public Library, Grand River Stanley Park, 175 Indian Rd, Kitchener, ON, N2B 2S7, CANADA. Tel: 519-896-1736. Fax: 519-896-1736. p. 2815

Schnarre, Virginia Ann, Instrul Serv Librn, Warner University, 13895 Hwy 27, Lake Wales, FL, 33859. Tel: 863-638-7620. Fax: 863-638-7675. p. 458

Schnebly, Susan, Librn, Washington County Free Library, Williamsport Memorial, 104 E Potomac St, Williamsport, MD, 21795. Tel: 301-223-7027. p. 1031

Schneck, Susan, Circ Asst, Citizens Library, 55 S College St, Washington, PA, 15301. Tel: 724-222-2400. Fax: 724-222-2606. p. 2151

Schneider, Austin R, Dir, Mercer County District Library, 303 N Main St, Celina, OH, 45822. Tel: 419-586-4442. Fax: 419-586-3222. p. 1866

Schneider, Barbara D, Head Librn, Massachusetts Trial Court, Court House, 76 East St, Pittsfield, MA, 01201. Tel: 413-442-5059. Fax: 413-448-2474. p. 1118

Schneider, Cary, Dir, Los Angeles Times, 202 W First St, Los Angeles, CA, 90012-0267. Tel: 213-237-7181. p. 174

Schneider, David, Librn, Nationwide Library, One Nationwide Plaza 1-01-05, Columbus, OH, 43215. Tel: 614-249-6414. Fax: 614-249-2218. p. 1886

Schneider, Diana Trang, Asst Dir, Auglaize County Public District Library, 203 S Perry St, Wapakoneta, OH, 45895-1999. Tel: 419-738-2921. Fax: 419-738-5168. p. 1944

Schneider, Edward, Dr, Asst Prof, University of South Florida, 4202 Fowler Ave, CIS 1040, Tampa, FL, 33620-7800. Tel: 813-974-7540. Fax: 813-974-6840. p. 2964

Schneider, Elizabeth, Dir, Massachusetts General Hospital, Treadwell Library, Bartlett Hall Ext - I, 55 Fruit St, Boston, MA, 02114-2696. Tel: 617-726-8600. Fax: 617-726-6784. p. 1063

Schneider, Hope, Tech Serv, Greenfield Community College Library, One College Dr, Greenfield, MA, 01301-9739. Tel: 413-775-1833. Fax: 413-775-1838. p. 1092

Schneider, Janet, Mgr, Arapahoe Library District, Smoky Hill Public Library, 5430 S Biscay Circle, Centennial, CO, 80015. Fax: 303-690-4572. p. 306

Schneider, Janet, Chief Librn, United States Department of Veterans Affairs, Library Service (142D), 13000 Bruce B Downs Blvd, Tampa, FL, 33612. Tel: 813-972-7531. Fax: 813-978-5917. p. 498

Schneider, Janet, Acq, Henry Ford Community College, 5101 Evergreen Rd, Dearborn, MI, 48128-1495. Tel: 313-845-9764. Fax: 313-845-9795. p. 1167

Schneider, Joanne, Univ Librn, Colgate University, 13 Oak Dr, Hamilton, NY, 13346-1398. Tel: 315-228-7300. Fax: 315-228-7934. p. 1633

Schneider, Joyce, Dep Dir, Human Res Mgr, Properties Mgr, Washington County Library, 8595 Central Park Pl, Woodbury, MN, 55125-9453. Tel: 651-275-8500. Fax: 651-275-8509. p. 1290

Schneider, Julia, Dir, Missouri Western State University, 4525 Downs Dr, Saint Joseph, MO, 64507-2294. Tel: 816-271-4368. Fax: 816-271-4574. p. 1352

Schneider, Julie, Dir, University of Wisconsin-Madison, Ebling Library, 750 Highland Ave, Madison, WI, 53705. Tel: 608-263-5755. Fax: 608-262-4732. p. 2609

Schneider, June, Br Mgr, Ocean County Library, Upper Shores Branch, 112 Jersey City Ave, Lavallette, NJ, 08735. Tel: 732-793-3996. Fax: 732-793-4942. p. 1535

Schneider, Karen, Dir, Holy Names College, 3500 Mountain Blvd, Oakland, CA, 94619. Tel: 510-436-1160. Fax: 510-436-1260. p. 196

Schneider, Karen, Librn, The Phillips Collection Library, 1600 21st St NW, Washington, DC, 20009-1090. Tel: 202-387-2151, Ext 212. Fax: 202-387-2436. p. 413

Schneider, Karin, Asst Dir, Licia & Mason Beekley Community Library, Ten Central Ave, New Hartford, CT, 06057. Tel: 860-379-7235. Fax: 860-379-5806. p. 355

Schneider, Kim, Libr Mgr, Gravette Public Library, 407 Charlotte St SE, Gravette, AR, 72736-9363. Tel: 479-787-6955. Fax: 479-787-9780. p. 101

Schneider, Linda, Dir, Conestoga College Institute of Technology & Advanced Learning, 299 Doon Valley Dr, Kitchener, ON, N2G 4M4, CANADA. Tel: 519-748-5220, Ext 3361. Fax: 519-748-3538. p. 2815

Schneider, Linda-Jean, Dir, Drinker Biddle & Reath LLP, One Logan Sq, 18th & Cherry St, Philadelphia, PA, 19103. Tel: 215-988-2951. Fax: 215-564-1329, 215-988-2757. p. 2106

Schneider, Lorraine, Dir, Greenfield Public Library, 202 S First St, Greenfield, IA, 50849-1470. Tel: 641-743-6120. p. 819

Schneider, Lynne, Asst Dir, Sewickley Public Library, Inc, 500 Thorn St, Sewickley, PA, 15143-1333. Tel: 412-741-6920. Fax: 412-741-6099. p. 2139

Schneider, Madlyn, Commun Libr Mgr, Queens Borough Public Library, Queens Village Community Library, 94-11 217th St, Queens Village, NY, 11428. Tel: 718-776-6800. Fax: 718-479-4609. p. 1645

Schneider, Melissa, Asst Dir, Ch, New Berlin Public Library, 15105 Library Lane, New Berlin, WI, 53151. Tel: 262-785-4980. Fax: 262-785-4984. p. 2625

Schneider, Michael, Acq Librn, South College Library, 3904 Lonas Dr, Knoxville, TN, 37909. Tel: 865-251-1750, 865-251-1832. p. 2243

Schneider, Renee, Asst Dir, Blue Earth County Library System, 100 E Main St, Mankato, MN, 56001. Tel: 507-304-4016. Fax: 507-304-4009. p. 1257

Schneider, Richard, Asst Dir, Pub Serv, Muskegon Area District Library, 4845 Airline Rd, Unit 5, Muskegon, MI, 49444-4503. Tel: 231-737-6248. Fax: 231-737-6307. p. 1212

Schneider, Sheri, Electronic Res, Info & Instrul Serv Librn, Cedar Crest College, 100 College Dr, Allentown, PA, 18104-6196. Tel: 610-606-4666, Ext 3387. Fax: 610-740-3769. p. 2026

Schneider, Tina, Ref & Instrul Serv, Instr Coordr, Ohio State University LIBRARIES, Lima Campus Library, 4240 Campus Dr, Lima, OH, 45804. Tel: 419-995-8401. Fax: 419-995-8138. p. 1888

Schneider, Valetta, Dir, Western Nebraska Community College Library, 1601 E 27th NE, Scottsbluff, NE, 69361-1899. Tel: 308-635-6040. Fax: 308-635-6086. p. 1418

Schneider, Wendy, Co-Dir, Harris County Public Library, Tomball Branch, 30555 Tomball Pkwy, Tomball, TX, 77375. Tel: 832-559-4200. Fax: 832-559-4248. p. 2336

Schneider, William, Curator, Oral Hist, University of Alaska Fairbanks, 310 Tanana Dr, Fairbanks, AK, 99775. Tel: 907-474-5355. Fax: 907-474-6841. p. 48

Schneiderman, Karen, Emerging Tech Librn, Ref, Brooklyn Law School Library, 250 Joralemon St, Brooklyn, NY, 11201. Tel: 718-780-7980. Fax: 718-780-0369. p. 1590

Schneiderman, Victoria, Ref, Medford Public Library, 111 High St, Medford, MA, 02155. Tel: 781-395-7950. Fax: 781-391-2261. p. 1104

Schneidermann, Lynn, ILL, Creighton University, 2500 California Plaza, Omaha, NE, 68178-0209. Tel: 402-280-2260. Fax: 402-280-2435. p. 1412

Schnelbach, Leah, Dir, General Society of Mechanics & Tradesmen Library, The New York Center for Independent Publishing, 20 W 44th St, New York, NY, 10036. Tel: 212-764-7021. p. 1679

Schnelker, Renata, Acq Asst, Kalamazoo College, 1200 Academy St, Kalamazoo, MI, 49006-3285. Tel: 269-337-7150. Fax: 269-337-7143. p. 1197

Schnell, Eric H, Info Tech, Ohio State University LIBRARIES, John A Prior Health Sciences Library, 376 W Tenth Ave, Columbus, OH, 43210-1240. Tel: 614-292-4870. Fax: 614-292-1920. p. 1889

Schnell, Lin, Human Res Dir, The Seattle Public Library, 1000 Fourth Ave, Seattle, WA, 98104-1109. Tel: 206-733-9922. p. 2531

Schnell, Marilyn, Circ, Eagle Grove Memorial Library, 101 S Cadwell, Eagle Grove, IA, 50533. Tel: 515-448-4115. Fax: 515-448-5279. p. 813

Schnell, Robert, Commun Libr Mgr, Queens Borough Public Library, Astoria Community Library, 14-01 Astoria Blvd, Long Island City, NY, 11102. Tel: 718-278-2220. p. 1644

Schnell, Tamara, Assoc Dean, Lincoln Land Community College Library, 5250 Shepherd Rd, Springfield, IL, 62794. Tel: 217-786-2354. Fax: 217-786-2251. p. 705

Schnell, Willow, Libr Mgr, New Sarepta Public Library, 5150 Centre St, New Sarepta, AB, T0B 3M0, CANADA. Tel: 780-975-7513. Fax: 780-941-2224. p. 2712

Schnelle, Rebekah, Dir, Terril Community Library, 115 N State St, Terril, IA, 51364. Tel: 712-853-6224. Fax: 712-853-6599. p. 847

Schneller, Laurie, In Charge, Massena Memorial Hospital Library, One Hospital Dr, Massena, NY, 13662. Tel: 315-764-1711. Fax: 315-769-4780. p. 1658

Schneller, Vicky, Mgr, Libr Serv, Ball Aerospace & Technologies Corp, 1600 Commerce St, Boulder, CO, 80301-2734. Tel: 303-939-5755. Fax: 303-939-4142. p. 289

Schneller, William, Dir, Berkley Public Library, Three N Main St, Berkley, MA, 02779. Tel: 508-822-3329. Fax: 508-824-2471. p. 1053

Schnepp, Travis, Exec Dir, Maui Historical Society, 2375 A Main St, Wailuku, HI, 96793. Tel: 808-244-3326. p. 567

Schnirring, Cheryl, Curator of Manuscripts, Illinois Historic Preservation Agency, 112 N Sixth St, Springfield, IL, 62701. Tel: 217-785-7942. Fax: 217-785-6250. p. 705

Schnupp, Christopher, Adult Ref Librn, Gold Coast Public Library, 50 Railroad Ave, Glen Head, NY, 11545. Tel: 516-759-8300. Fax: 516-759-8308. p. 1628

Schnupp, Joy, Ch, Burlington Public Library, 166 E Jefferson St, Burlington, WI, 53105. Tel: 262-763-7623. Fax: 262-763-1938. p. 2584

Schnur, Wendy, Ref Serv Coordr, Mystic Seaport Museum, 75 Greenmanville Ave, Mystic, CT, 06355. Tel: 860-572-5367. Fax: 860-572-5394. p. 353

Schnurer, Daphne, Librn, Elk Point Public Library, 5123 - 50 Ave, Elk Point, AB, T0A 1A0, CANADA. Tel: 780-724-3737. Fax: 780-724-3739. p. 2703

Schobernd, Beth, Assoc Dean, Tech Serv, Illinois State University, 201 N School St, Normal, IL, 61790-8900. Tel: 309-438-3451. Fax: 309-438-3676. p. 681

Schock, Cathy, Librn, First Baptist Church Library, 1401 S Covell Ave, Sioux Falls, SD, 57105. Tel: 605-336-0966. Fax: 605-336-3294. p. 2218

Schock, Shirley L, Dir, Camden-Jackson Township Public Library, 258 Main St, Camden, IN, 46917. Tel: 574-686-2120. Fax: 574-686-2120. p. 731

Schoeck, Natalia, Librn, Degenkolb Engineers Library, 235 Montgomery St, Ste 500, San Francisco, CA, 94104-2908. Tel: 415-392-6952. Fax: 415-981-3157. p. 241

Schoen, David, Dir, Niagara University Library, 5795 Lewiston Rd, Niagara University, NY, 14109. Tel: 716-286-8001. Fax: 716-286-8030. p. 1705

Schoen, Jane, Admin Dir, Cicero Public Library, 5225 W Cermak Rd, Cicero, IL, 60804. Tel: 708-652-8084. Fax: 708-652-8095. p. 629

Schoen, Jane, Dir, Cicero Public Library, South, 5444 W 34th St, Cicero, IL, 60804. Tel: 708-863-8440. Fax: 708-863-8455. p. 629

Schoen, Janis A, Dir, Locust Valley Library, 170 Buckram Rd, Locust Valley, NY, 11560-1999. Tel: 516-671-1837. Fax: 516-676-8164. p. 1654

Schoenborn, Mary, Coordr, Ref (Info Serv), University of Minnesota Libraries-Twin Cities, Reference Services (Wilson Library), 309 19th Ave S, Minneapolis, MN, 55455. Tel: 612-626-7308. Fax: 612-626-9353. p. 1262

Schoenhaar, Cheryl, Media/IT Mgr, University of Wisconsin Colleges, 1500 University Dr, Waukesha, WI, 53188. Tel: 262-521-5473. Fax: 262-521-5116. p. 2645

Schoenhals, Mandi, Asst Dir, Alva Public Library, 504 Seventh St, Alva, OK, 73717. Tel: 580-327-1833. Fax: 580-327-5329. p. 1956

Schoening, Paul, Dir, Washington University Libraries, Bernard Becker Medical Library, 660 S Euclid Ave, Campus Box 8132, Saint Louis, MO, 63110. Tel: 314-362-3119. Fax: 314-747-4416. p. 1362

Schoening, Taj, Bus Mgr, Milwaukee Public Library, 814 W Wisconsin Ave, Milwaukee, WI, 53233-2385. Tel: 414-286-3000. Fax: 414-286-2794. p. 2620

Schoenrock, Ellen, ILL, Abilene Christian University, 221 Brown Library, ACU Box 29208, Abilene, TX, 79699-9208. Tel: 325-674-2344. Fax: 325-674-2202. p. 2271

Schoettgen, Thea, Libr Tech, Alpine County Library, Bear Valley Branch, 367 Creekside Dr, Bear Valley, CA, 95223. Tel: 209-753-6219. Fax: 209-753-2219. p. 184

Schofield, Amy, Dir, Kershaw County Library, 1304 Broad St, Camden, SC, 29020-3595. Tel: 803-425-1508. Fax: 803-425-7180. p. 2182

Schofield, Darla, Librn, Douglas County Library System, Riddle Branch, 637 First Ave, Riddle, OR, 97469. Tel: 541-874-2070. Fax: 541-874-2070. p. 2016

Schofield, Donna, Asst Librn, Pinawa Public Library, Vanier Rd, Pinawa, MB, R0E 1L0, CANADA. Tel: 204-753-2496. Fax: 204-753-2770. p. 2750

Schofield, Dorothy, Curator, The Sandwich Glass Museum Library, 129 Main St, Sandwich, MA, 02563-2233. Tel: 508-888-0251. Fax: 508-888-4941. p. 1122

Schofield, Pamela, Res, The State Library of Massachusetts, State House, Rm 341, 24 Beacon St, Boston, MA, 02133. Tel: 617-727-2590. Fax: 617-727-5819. p. 1067

Schofield-Bodt, Cindy, Tech Serv, Southern Connecticut State University, 501 Crescent St, New Haven, CT, 06515. Tel: 203-392-5778. Fax: 203-392-5775. p. 356

Schofield-Dahl, Lynn, Dir, Boulder City Library, 701 Adams Blvd, Boulder City, NV, 89005-2697. Tel: 702-293-1281. Fax: 702-293-0239. p. 1425

Scholes, Debora, Head, Tech Serv, Brigham Young University-Idaho, 525 S Center St, Rexburg, ID, 83460-0405. Tel: 208-496-9522. Fax: 208-496-9503. p. 582

Scholey, Janet, Ch, Villisca Public Library, 204 S Third Ave, Villisca, IA, 50864. Tel: 712-826-2452. Fax: 712-826-2686. p. 848

Scholfield, Yvonne, AV, Coordr, Philadelphia College of Osteopathic Medicine, 4170 City Ave, Philadelphia, PA, 19131-1694. Tel: 215-871-6470. Fax: 215-871-6478. p. 2114

Scholl, Jane, Dir, Wyoming Public Library District, 119 N Seventh St, Wyoming, IL, 61491. Tel: 309-695-2241. Fax: 309-695-2241. p. 722

Scholl, Jochen, Assoc Prof, University of Washington, Mary Gates Hall, Ste 370, Campus Box 352840, Seattle, WA, 98195-2840. Tel: 206-685-9937. Fax: 206-616-3152. p. 2976

Scholl, Patty, Mgr, Saint Joseph Mercy Oakland Hospital Library, 44405 Woodward Ave, Pontiac, MI, 48341-2985. Tel: 248-858-3496. Fax: 248-858-6496. p. 1219

Scholl, Phillip, AV, Media Spec, Panola College, 1109 W Panola St, Carthage, TX, 75633. Tel: 903-693-1146. Fax: 903-693-1115. p. 2295

Scholtens, Anita, Head, Circ, Hinsdale Public Library, 20 E Maple St, Hinsdale, IL, 60521. Tel: 630-986-1976. Fax: 630-986-9654. p. 656

Scholtz, James C, Exec Dir, McHenry Public Library District, 809 N Front St, McHenry, IL, 60050. Tel: 815-385-0036. Fax: 815-385-7085. p. 672

Scholtz, Mary, Dir, Suntree/Viera Public Library, 902 Jordan Blass Dr, Melbourne, FL, 32940. Tel: 321-255-4404. Fax: 321-255-4406. p. 463

Scholz, Donna, Dir of Circ, Grande Prairie Public Library District, 3479 W 183rd St, Hazel Crest, IL, 60429. Tel: 708-798-5563. Fax: 708-798-5874. p. 654

Scholz, Ursula, Head, Access Serv, Loyola University Chicago Libraries, Elizabeth M Cudahy Memorial Library, 6525 N Sheridan Rd, Chicago, IL, 60626. Tel: 773-508-2636. p. 617

Schomber, Jeni, Head, Youth Serv, Beloit Public Library, 605 Eclipse Blvd, Beloit, WI, 53511. Tel: 608-364-5754. Fax: 608-364-2907. p. 2581

Schomberg, Jessica, Cat Librn, Minnesota State University, Mankato, ML3097, Mankato, MN, 56001. Tel: 507-389-5952. Fax: 507-389-5155. p. 1257

Schomer, Mary, Ch, Edward F Owen Memorial Library, 1120 Willow Dr, Carter Lake, IA, 51510-1332. Tel: 712-347-5492. Fax: 712-347-5013. p. 799

Schonhart, Christine, Br Serv Mgr, Boston Public Library, 700 Boylston St, Boston, MA, 02117-0286. Tel: 617-536-5400. Fax: 617-236-4306. p. 1056

Schontag, Dawn, Libr Asst, Bacon Free Library, 58 Eliot St, Natick, MA, 01760. Tel: 508-653-6730. p. 1107

Schoo, Julie, Dir, National Press Club, 529 14th St NW, 13th Flr, Washington, DC, 20045. Tel: 202-662-7507. Fax: 202-879-6725. p. 411

Schoolcraft, Cindy, Res Sharing Librn, Westminster College, Reeves Memorial Library, 501 Westminster Ave, Fulton, MO, 65251-1299. Tel: 573-592-5245. Fax: 573-642-6356. p. 1328

Schoon, Beverly, Ad, Lowell Public Library, 1505 E Commercial Ave, Lowell, IN, 46356-1899. Tel: 219-696-7704. Fax: 219-696-5280. p. 762

Schoonover, Claudia, Asst Dir, Pub Serv, Missouri River Regional Library, 214 Adams St, Jefferson City, MO, 65101-3244. Tel: 573-634-6064, Ext 245. p. 1335

Schoonover, Erin, Sr Librn, Redondo Beach Public Library, 303 N Pacific Coast Hwy, Redondo Beach, CA, 90277. Tel: 310-318-0675. Fax: 310-318-3809. p. 215

Schorlemer, Beth, Mgr, San Antonio Public Library, Brook Hollow, 530 Heimer Rd, San Antonio, TX, 78232. Tel: 210-496-6315. p. 2382

Schorr, Andrea, Cat & Acq, University of Texas Health Science Center at San Antonio Libraries, 7703 Floyd Curl Dr, MSC 7940, San Antonio, TX, 78229-3900. Tel: 210-567-2400. Fax: 210-567-2490. p. 2383

Schory, Nancy, Ch, North Canton Public Library, 185 N Main St, North Canton, OH, 44720-2595. Tel: 330-499-4712. Fax: 330-499-7356. p. 1923

Schott, Barbara, Tech Coordr, Floyd Memorial Library, 539 First St, Greenport, NY, 11944-1399. Tel: 631-477-0660. Fax: 631-477-2647. p. 1631

Schott, Jane, Librn, Pocahontas Public Library, 14 Second Ave NW, Pocahontas, IA, 50574. Tel: 712-335-4471. Fax: 712-335-4471. p. 839

Schott, Lynn, Ref, Bergen Community College, 400 Paramus Rd, Paramus, NJ, 07652-1595. Tel: 201-447-8889. Fax: 201-493-8167. p. 1517

Schottlaender, Brian E C, Univ Librn, University of California, San Diego, 9500 Gilman Dr, Mail Code 0175G, La Jolla, CA, 92093-0175. Tel: 858-534-3060. Fax: 858-534-4970. p. 162

Schouest, Todd J, Dir, Plaquemines Parish Library, 8442 Hwy 23, Belle Chasse, LA, 70037. Tel: 504-398-7302. Fax: 504-398-4580. p. 945

Schouten, Janice, Librn, Porzio, Bromberg & Newman Library, 100 Southgate Pkwy, Morristown, NJ, 07962-1997. Tel: 973-889-4368. Fax: 973-538-5146. p. 1505

Schow, Elizabeth, Adult Serv, Brigham City Library, 26 E Forest, Brigham City, UT, 84302-2198. Tel: 435-723-5850. Fax: 435-723-2813. p. 2403

Schow, Elizabeth, Circ, Brigham City Library, 26 E Forest, Brigham City, UT, 84302-2198. Tel: 435-723-5850. Fax: 435-723-2813. p. 2403

Schow, Leslie, Mgr, Salt Lake County Library Services, Herriman Branch, 13011 S Pioneer St, Herriman, UT, 84065-8904. Tel: 801-944-7682. Fax: 801-446-5348. p. 2414

Schrader, Paula, Outreach & Instructional Serv Librn, Northwest Florida State College, 100 College Blvd, Niceville, FL, 32578. Tel: 850-729-5392. Fax: 850-729-5295. p. 472

Schraeder, Jill, Asst Dir, Glenn A Jones Memorial Library, 400 S Parish Ave, Johnstown, CO, 80534. Tel: 970-587-2459. Fax: 970-587-2352. p. 314

Schrager, Carole, Co-Chair, Temple Am Echad, One Saperstein Plaza, Lynbrook, NY, 11563. Tel: 516-593-4004. Fax: 516-593-2739. p. 1655

Schram, Diane, Cat, Metropolitan Community College Library, 30th & Fort Sts, Omaha, NE, 68103. Tel: 402-457-2761. Fax: 402-457-2655. p. 1413

Schram, Kathleen, Asst Dir, Bonner Springs City Library, 200 E Third St, Bonner Springs, KS, 66012-1047. Tel: 913-441-2665. Fax: 913-441-2660. p. 858

Schram, Nancy, Dep Libr Serv Dir, Thousand Oaks Library, 1401 E Janss Rd, Thousand Oaks, CA, 91362-2199. Tel: 805-449-2660, Ext 7351. Fax: 805-373-6858. p. 275

Schramm, JoAnne, Librn, Zion Lutheran Church, 3644 Bolivar Ave, North Highlands, CA, 95660. Tel: 916-332-4001. Fax: 916-332-4030. p. 194

Schrammel, Debra S, Chief Librn, Peirce College Library, 1420 Pine St, Philadelphia, PA, 19102-4699. Tel: 215-670-9269, Ext 9270. Fax: 215-670-9338. p. 2113

Schramski, Suzanne, Tech Serv, Grand Ledge Area District Library, 131 E Jefferson St, Grand Ledge, MI, 48837-1534. Tel: 517-627-7014. Fax: 517-627-6276. p. 1183

Schranz, Stefanie, Librn, Graham Community Library, Ralston Community Centre, R35 Dugway Dr, Ralston, AB, T0J 2N0, CANADA. Tel: 403-544-3670. Fax: 403-544-3814. p. 2714

Schraut, Debbie, Cat Librn, Missouri History Museum, 225 S Skinker Blvd, Saint Louis, MO, 63105. Tel: 314-746-4500. Fax: 314-746-4548. p. 1356

Schrauth, Christine, Br Mgr, Pittsylvania County Public Library, Mt Hermon Branch Library, 2725 Franklin Tpk, Ste J, Danville, VA, 24540. Tel: 434-835-0326. Fax: 434-835-0321. p. 2456

Schrecker, Diane, Instrul Serv Librn, Ashland University Library, 509 College Ave, Ashland, OH, 44805-3796. Tel: 419-289-5400. Fax: 419-289-5422. p. 1855

Schreffler, Ann, Br Mgr, Martin County Library System, Robert Morgade Library, Indian River Community College, Chastain Campus, 5851 SE Community Dr, Stuart, FL, 34997. Tel: 772-463-3245. Fax: 772-463-3246. p. 492

Schreiber, Emma, Asst Br Librn, Pottawatomie Wabaunsee Regional Library, Onaga Branch, 313 Leonard St, Onaga, KS, 66521. Tel: 785-889-4531. Fax: 785-889-4531. p. 893

Schreiber, Judy, Coordr, Pennsylvania Board of Probation & Parole Library, 1101 S Front St, Ste 5600, Harrisburg, PA, 17104-2552. Tel: 717-787-6151. Fax: 717-772-4185. p. 2065

Schreiber, Kathleen, Librn, Harlowton Public Library, 17 S Central Ave, Harlowton, MT, 59036. Tel: 406-632-5584. p. 1381

Schreiber, Linda, Asst Librn, Bertolet Memorial Library District, 705 S Main St, Leaf River, IL, 61047. Tel: 815-738-2742. Fax: 815-738-2742. p. 664

Schreiber, Michael H, Curator, The Shore Line Trolley Museum Library, 17 River St, East Haven, CT, 06512. Tel: 203-467-6927. Fax: 203-467-7635. p. 337

Schreiber, Robin Mills, Assoc Dean, Emory University School of Law, 1301 Clifton Rd, Atlanta, GA, 30322. Tel: 404-727-6983. Fax: 404-727-2202. p. 514

Schreiber, Tim, Info Serv, Lake Land College Library, 5001 Lake Land Blvd, Mattoon, IL, 61938. Tel: 217-234-5540. Fax: 217-234-5533. p. 671

Schreibstein, Florence, Asst Dir, Albert Einstein College of Medicine, 1300 Morris Park Ave, Bronx, NY, 10461. Tel: 718-430-3110. Fax: 718-430-8795. p. 1586

Schrein, Catherine, Mgr, Somerset County Park Commission, 190 Lord Stirling Rd, Basking Ridge, NJ, 07920. Tel: 908-766-2489, Ext 324. Fax: 908-766-2687. p. 1470

Schreiner, Anne Marie, Sister, Info Spec, Saint Vincent's Hospital, 810 St Vincent's Dr, Birmingham, AL, 35205-1695. Tel: 205-939-7832. Fax: 205-930-2182. p. 9

Schreiner, Erin, Spec Coll Librn, The New York Society Library, 53 E 79th St, New York, NY, 10075. Tel: 212-288-6900 Ext 242. Fax: 212-744-5832. p. 1694

Schreiner, Leo, Br Mgr, Tillamook County Library, 1716 Third St, Tillamook, OR, 97141. Tel: 503-842-4792. Fax: 503-815-8194. p. 2021

Schreiner, Martin, Interim Librn, Harvard Library, Lamont Library-Undergraduate, Harvard Yard, Harvard University, Cambridge, MA, 02138. Tel: 617-495-2450. Fax: 617-496-3692. p. 1076

Schreiner, Rebecca, Libr Dir, McKendree University, 701 College Rd, Lebanon, IL, 62254-1299. Tel: 618-537-6950. Fax: 618-537-8411. p. 664

Schrey, Carol, Dir, Ella Johnson Memorial Public Library District, 109 S State St, Hampshire, IL, 60140. Tel: 847-683-4490. Fax: 847-683-4493. p. 653

Schreyer, Alice D, Asst Univ Librn, Humanities, Soc Sci & Spec Coll, University of Chicago Library, 1100 E 57th St, Chicago, IL, 60637-1502. Tel: 773-702-0095. Fax: 773-702-3728. p. 626

Schriar, Suzanne, Assoc Dir, Libr Automation & Tech, Illinois State Library, Gwendolyn Brooks Bldg, 300 S Second St, Springfield, IL, 62701-9713. Tel: 217-785-1533. Fax: 217-785-4326. p. 705

Schriber, Cynthia, Librn, Thomson Reuters Westlaw, 610 Opperman Dr, Eagan, MN, 55123. Tel: 651-848-2760. Fax: 651-848-2627. p. 1249

Schriek, Robert, Ref, Joint Free Public Library of the Chathams, 214 Main St, Chatham, NJ, 07928. Tel: 973-635-0603. Fax: 973-635-7827. p. 1478

Schrill, Beth, Asst Librn, Jim Lucas Checotah Public Library, 626 W Gentry, Checotah, OK, 74426-2218. Tel: 918-473-6715. Fax: 918-473-6603. p. 1959

Schrimpf, Catherine, Asst Dir, Libr Serv, Hayner Public Library District, 326 Belle St, Alton, IL, 62002. Tel: 618-462-0677. Fax: 618-462-0665. p. 588

Schrimsher, Robert, Librn, Samford University Library, Global Drug Information Center McWhorter School of Pharmacy, Ingalls Bldg, 800 Lakeshore Dr, Birmingham, AL, 35229. Tel: 205-726-2161, 205-726-2891. Fax: 205-726-4012. p. 9

Schriver, Beverly, Ref Serv, Sacred Heart Medical Center at RiverBend, 3333 RiverBend Dr, Springfield, OR, 97477. Tel: 541-222-2280. p. 2020

Schriver, Christine, Br Coordr, County of Brant Public Library, 12 William St, Paris, ON, N3L 1K7, CANADA. Tel: 519-442-2433. Fax: 519-442-7582. p. 2835

Schroader, Patricia, Ch, Warsaw Community Public Library, 310 E Main St, Warsaw, IN, 46580-2882. Tel: 574-267-6011. Fax: 574-269-7739. p. 785

Schrock, Amy, Asst Dir, New Carlisle & Olive Township Public Library, 408 S Bray St, New Carlisle, IN, 46552. Tel: 574-654-3046. Fax: 574-654-8260. p. 768

Schrock, Lee Ann, Asst Librn, Mary S Biesecker Public Library, 230 S Rosina Ave, Somerset, PA, 15501. Tel: 814-445-4011. Fax: 814-443-0725. p. 2141

Schroder, Ann, Ref, Inver Hills Community College Library, 2500 80th St E, Inver Grove Heights, MN, 55076-3209. Tel: 651-450-8623. Fax: 651-450-3679. p. 1254

Schroder, Simone, ILL Librn, John Brown University Library, 2000 W University, Siloam Springs, AR, 72761. Tel: 479-524-7202. Fax: 479-524-7335. p. 115

Schroeder, Ann, Pub Serv, Vermont Technical College, Main St, Randolph Center, VT, 05061. Tel: 802-728-1237. Fax: 802-728-1506. p. 2433

Schroeder, Barbara, Dir, Elma Public Library, 710 Busti Ave, Elma, IA, 50628. Tel: 641-393-8100. Fax: 641-393-8100. p. 814

Schroeder, Betsy, Br Mgr, Cecil County Public Library, North East Branch, 106 W Cecil Ave, North East, MD, 21901. Tel: 410-996-6269. Fax: 410-996-6268. p. 1027

Schroeder, Carol, Ref, Metropolitan Community College, Maple Woods Community College Library, 2601 NE Barry Rd, Kansas City, MO, 64156. Tel: 816-604-3080. Fax: 816-437-3082. p. 1339

Schroeder, Cherie, Dir, Hanson-McCook County Regional Library, 306 Main St, Spencer, SD, 57374. Tel: 605-246-2740. p. 2220

Schroeder, David E, Dir, Kenton County Public Library, 502 Scott Blvd, Covington, KY, 41011. Tel: 859-962-4080. Fax: 859-962-4096. p. 910

Schroeder, Edwin, Assoc Univ Librn, Yale University Library, Beinecke Rare Book & Manuscript, 121 Wall St, New Haven, CT, 06520. Tel: 203-432-2959. Fax: 203-432-4047. p. 356

Schroeder, Eileen, Dr, Assoc Prof, University of Wisconsin-Whitewater, 800 W Main St, Whitewater, WI, 53190. Tel: 262-472-1380. Fax: 262-472-2841. p. 2977

Schroeder, Eileen E, Dr, Co-Dir, University of Wisconsin System School Library Education Consortium, Grad & Continuing Educ, Univ Wisconsin-Whitewater, 800 W Main St, Whitewater, WI, 53190. Tel: 262-472-1463. Fax: 262-472-5210. p. 2958

Schroeder, Elizabeth, Cat Librn, Metadata Librn, Cardinal Stritch University Library, 6801 N Yates Rd, Milwaukee, WI, 53207-3985. Tel: 414-410-4258. Fax: 414-410-4268. p. 2617

Schroeder, Eunice, Music Librn, University of California, Santa Barbara, Arts Library, UCSB Library, Santa Barbara, CA, 93106-9010. Tel: 805-893-3612. Fax: 805-893-5879. p. 262

Schroeder, Eunice M, Dir, Stevens County Library, 500 Monroe, Hugoton, KS, 67951-2639. Tel: 620-544-2301. Fax: 620-544-2322. p. 872

Schroeder, Grace, Librn, Maryland House of Correction Library, Rte 175, Box 534, Jessup, MD, 20794. Tel: 410-799-0100, Ext 1446. Fax: 410-799-3013. p. 1033

Schroeder, Jennifer, Dir, Cloud County Community College Library, 2221 Campus Dr, Concordia, KS, 66901-5305. Tel: 785-243-1435, Ext 224. Fax: 785-243-1043. p. 862

Schroeder, Judy, Circ Supvr, Putnam County District Library, The Educational Service Ctr, 124 Putnam Pkwy, Ottawa, OH, 45875-1471. Tel: 419-523-3747. Fax: 419-523-6477. p. 1926

Schroeder, Kathleen A, Ref, National Reference Center for Bioethics Literature, Georgetown University, 37th & O St NW, Washington, DC, 20057. Tel: 202-687-3885. Fax: 202-687-6770. p. 411

Schroeder, Lauren, Ref Serv, University of Houston, The O'Quinn Law Library, 12 Law Library, Houston, TX, 77204-6054. Tel: 713-743-2300. Fax: 713-743-2296. p. 2343

Schroeder, Patrick A, In Charge, National Park Service, PO Box 218, Appomattox, VA, 24522-0218. Tel: 434-352-8987. Fax: 434-352-8330. p. 2448

Schroeder, Randall, Head, Pub Serv, Ferris State University Library, 1010 Campus Dr, Big Rapids, MI, 49307-2279. Tel: 231-591-3500. Fax: 231-591-3724. p. 1158

Schroeder, Robert, Educ Librn, Portland State University Library, 1875 SW Park Ave, Portland, OR, 97201-3220. Tel: 503-725-4519. Fax: 503-725-4524. p. 2014

Schroeder, Sandy, Circ, Riverdale Public Library District, 208 W 144th St, Riverdale, IL, 60827-2788. Tel: 708-841-3311. Fax: 708-841-1805. p. 695

Schroeder, Sharon, Archivist, Librn, Goodhue County Historical Society Library, 1166 Oak St, Red Wing, MN, 55066-2447. Tel: 651-388-6024. Fax: 651-388-3577. p. 1271

Schroeder, Susan, Dir, Bridge Academy Public Library, 44 Middle Rd, Dresden, ME, 04342. Tel: 207-737-8810. Fax: 207-737-8810. p. 984

Schroeder, Susan, Coll Develop, Willard Library, Seven W Van Buren St, Battle Creek, MI, 49017-3009. Tel: 269-968-8166. Fax: 269-968-3284. p. 1155

Schroeder, Suzanna, Head, Electronic & Media Serv, Ursuline College, 2550 Lander Rd, Pepper Pike, OH, 44124-4398. Tel: 440-646-8178. Fax: 440-449-3180. p. 1929

Schroeder, Theresa, Br Mgr, Anoka County Library, Mississippi, 410 Mississippi St NE, Fridley, MN, 55432-4416. Tel: 763-571-1934. Fax: 763-574-8026. p. 1241

Schroer, Craig, Librn, University of Texas Libraries, Nettie Lee Benson Latin American Collection, Sid Richardson Hall 1-108, Austin, TX, 78713-8916. Tel: 512-495-4520. Fax: 512-495-4568. p. 2283

Schroer, Muffet, Cat, Head, Tech Serv, Glenview Public Library, 1930 Glenview Rd, Glenview, IL, 60025-2899. Tel: 847-729-7500. Fax: 847-729-7558. p. 650

Schroer, Tara, Libr Coordr, Colby Community College, 1255 S Range Ave, Colby, KS, 67701. Tel: 785-462-3984, Ext 5487. Fax: 785-460-4600. p. 861

Schroth, Kristin, Br Librn, United States Court of Appeals, One J F Gerry Plaza, Fourth & Cooper, Camden, NJ, 08101. Tel: 856-968-4859. Fax: 856-968-4871. p. 1477

Schrupp, Robin M, Dir, Grant County Public Library, 207 E Park Ave, Milbank, SD, 57252-2497. Tel: 605-432-6543. Fax: 605-432-4635. p. 2215

Schryba, William, Tech Serv & Automation, Union County College Libraries, 1033 Springfield Ave, Cranford, NJ, 07016. Tel: 908-709-7623. Fax: 908-709-7589. p. 1480

Schryver, Ryan, Reserves & Info Serv Librn, University of Wisconsin-Madison, Kurt Wendt Engineering Library, 215 N Randall Ave, Madison, WI, 53706. Tel: 608-262-3493. Fax: 608-262-4739, 608-265-8751. p. 2610

Schual, Nora, Dir, Amityville Public Library, Oak & John Sts, Amityville, NY, 11701. Tel: 631-264-0567. Fax: 631-264-2006. p. 1573

Schubart, Mary, Dir, Islip Public Library, 71 Monell Ave, Islip, NY, 11751-3999. Tel: 631-581-5933. Fax: 631-277-8429. p. 1641

Schubert, Blythe, Dir, Kate Love Simpson Morgan County Library, 358 E Main St, McConnelsville, OH, 43756-1130. Tel: 740-962-2533. Fax: 740-962-3316. p. 1916

Schubert, Marge, Librn, Dunklin County Library, Holcomb Branch, W Main St, Holcomb, MO, 63852. Tel: 573-792-3268. p. 1342

Schubert, Patricia, Talking Bks, Manatee County Public Library System, 1301 Barcarrota Blvd W, Bradenton, FL, 34205. Tel: 941-748-5555. Fax: 941-749-7191. p. 429

Schuchard, Constance C, Librn, Cumberland County Historical Society Library, 981 Great St, Greenwich, NJ, 08323. Tel: 856-455-4055, 856-455-8580. p. 1488

Schuchardt, Maria, Data Mgr, University of Arizona, Space Imagery Center, 1629 E University Blvd, Tucson, AZ, 85721-0092. Tel: 520-621-4861. Fax: 520-621-4933. p. 89

Schuck, Andy, Libr Prog, Adult Serv, Westland Public Library, 6123 Central City Pkwy, Westland, MI, 48185. Tel: 734-326-6123. Fax: 734-595-4612. p. 1236

Schuck, Beth, Assoc Univ Librn, Northern Arizona University, Bldg 028, Knoles Dr, Flagstaff, AZ, 86011. Tel: 928-523-6779. Fax: 928-523-3770. p. 62

Schuele, Jane, ILL, Benedictine College Library, 1020 N Second St, Atchison, KS, 66002-1499. Tel: 913-360-7609. Fax: 913-360-7622. p. 856

Schuele, Marilyn Jo, Dir, Cedar Rapids Public Library, 423 W Main St, Cedar Rapids, NE, 68627. Tel: 308-358-0603. Fax: 308-358-0117. p. 1395

Schueler, Dolores, Librn, Boston Public Library, Kirstein Business, 20 City Hall Ave, Boston, MA, 02108. Tel: 617-523-0860. Fax: 617-523-3153. p. 1057

Schueneman, Bruce, Prof & Assoc Dir of Syst & Tech Serv, Texas A&M University-Kingsville, 700 University Blvd, MSC 197, Kingsville, TX, 78363-8202. Tel: 361-593-4082. Fax: 361-593-4093. p. 2351

Schuette, Kay, Ch, Louis Latzer Memorial Public Library, 1001 Ninth St, Highland, IL, 62249. Tel: 618-654-5066. Fax: 618-654-1324. p. 655

Schuetz, Robert, Assoc Dir, American InterContinental University, Buckhead Campus Library, 3330 Peachtree Rd NE, Atlanta, GA, 30326. Tel: 404-965-6571. Fax: 404-965-5705. p. 510

Schuetz, Ronald L, Dir, Franklin College, 101 Branigin Blvd, Franklin, IN, 46131-2623. Tel: 317-738-8164. Fax: 317-738-8787. p. 743

Schuh, Laurie, ILL, Tech Serv, Oostburg Public Library, 213 N Eighth St, Oostburg, WI, 53070. Tel: 920-564-2934. p. 2627

Schuit, Barb, Asst Dir, Johnson Free Public Library, 274 Main St, Hackensack, NJ, 07601-5797. Tel: 201-343-4169. Fax: 201-343-1395. p. 1489

Schuit, Barbara, Librn, Lilian S Besore Memorial Library, 305 E Baltimore St, Greencastle, PA, 17225-1004. Tel: 717-597-7920. Fax: 717-597-5320. p. 2062

Schuitema, Joan, Tech Serv Coordr, Northeastern Illinois University, 5500 N Saint Louis Ave, Chicago, IL, 60625-4699. Tel: 773-442-4446. Fax: 773-442-4531. p. 621

Schule, Diane, Dir, Marshall County Library System, 109 E Gholson Ave, Holly Springs, MS, 38635. Tel: 662-252-3823. Fax: 662-252-3066. p. 1302

Schulenburg, Sandra, Circ Supvr, Brighton District Library, 100 Library Dr, Brighton, MI, 48116. Tel: 810-229-6571, Ext 231. Fax: 810-229-3161. p. 1159

Schuler, Amy C, Mgr, Info Serv, Cary Institute of Ecosystem Studies Library, Plant Science Bldg, 2801 Sharon Turnpike, Millbrook, NY, 12545. Tel: 845-677-7600, Ext 164. Fax: 845-677-5976. p. 1661

Schuler, C, Tech Serv, Bellmore Memorial Library, 2288 Bedford Ave, Bellmore, NY, 11710. Tel: 516-785-2990. Fax: 516-783-8550. p. 1580

Schuler, Peggy, Ch, Camp Verde Community Library, 130 Black Bridge Loop Rd, Camp Verde, AZ, 86322. Tel: 928-567-3414. Fax: 928-567-9583. p. 59

Schulhauser, Karin, Br Mgr, Whatcom County Library System, Sumas Branch, 451 Second St, Sumas, WA, 98295. Tel: 360-988-2501. Fax: 360-988-2501. p. 2510

Schuller, Cindy, Cat/Metadata Librn, Creighton University, 2500 California Plaza, Omaha, NE, 68178-0209. Tel: 402-280-2220. Fax: 402-280-2435. p. 1412

Schuller, Linda, Librn, Simmons College, Graduate School of Management Library, 300 The Fenway, Boston, MA, 02215. Tel: 617-521-2767. p. 1067

Schulman, Donna L, Libr Dir, Rutgers University Libraries, School of Management & Labor Relations, SMLR Labor Educ Ctr, 50 Labor Center Way, New Brunswick, NJ, 08901-8553. Tel: 732-932-9608. Fax: 732-932-8677. p. 1509

Schult, Julia, Adult Prog Librn, Baldwinsville Public Library, 33 E Genesee St, Baldwinsville, NY, 13027-2575. Tel: 315-635-5631. Fax: 315-635-6760. p. 1577

Schulte, Amy, ILL, Musser Public Library, 304 Iowa Ave, Muscatine, IA, 52761-3875. Tel: 563-263-3065. Fax: 563-264-1033. p. 834

Schulte, Jessi, YA Serv, Skokie Public Library, 5215 Oakton St, Skokie, IL, 60077-3680. Tel: 847-673-7774. Fax: 847-673-7797. p. 703

Schulte, Shirley, Librn, Bird Island Public Library, 260 S Main, Bird Island, MN, 55310-1226. Tel: 320-365-4640. Fax: 320-365-4640. p. 1241

Schulte, Stephanie, Ref Serv, Indiana University-Purdue University Fort Wayne, 2101 E Coliseum Blvd, Fort Wayne, IN, 46805-1499. Tel: 260-481-6512. Fax: 260-481-6509. p. 741

Schulte, Stephanie, Assoc Dir, Customer Serv, Davenport Public Library, 321 Main St, Davenport, IA, 52801-1490. Tel: 563-328-6838. Fax: 563-326-7809. p. 806

Schulteis, Ramie, Librn, Sylvan Grove Public Library, 122 S Main St, Sylvan Grove, KS, 67481. Tel: 785-526-7188. Fax: 785-526-7189. p. 895

Schulten, Jane, Admin Dir, Crete Public Library District, 1177 N Main St, Crete, IL, 60417. Tel: 708-672-8017. Fax: 708-672-3529. p. 632

Schultis, Ann, Dir, Libr Syst, Park University Library, 8700 NW River Park Dr, Parkville, MO, 64152. Tel: 816-584-6285. Fax: 816-741-4911. p. 1349

Schultis, Catherine, Br Mgr, Cuyahoga County Public Library, Brecksville Branch, 9089 Brecksville Rd, Brecksville, OH, 44141-2313. Tel: 440-526-1102. Fax: 440-526-8793. p. 1927

Schultz, Abigail, Access Serv, University of Texas Libraries, Jamail Center for Legal Research, University of Texas School of Law, 727 E Dean Keeton St, Austin, TX, 78705-3224. Tel: 512-471-7726. Fax: 512-471-0243. p. 2284

Schultz, Diane, Dir, Human Res, Arlington Heights Memorial Library, 500 N Dunton Ave, Arlington Heights, IL, 60004-5966. Tel: 847-506-2648. Fax: 847-506-2650. p. 589

Schultz, Edna, Asst Dir, Lexington Public Library, 907 N Washington, Lexington, NE, 68850. Tel: 308-324-2151. Fax: 308-324-2140. p. 1404

Schultz, George, Tech Info Spec, United States Army, Aviation Applied Technology Directorate, Technical Library, Bldg 401, Rm 100C, Fort Eustis, VA, 23604-5577. Tel: 757-878-0083. Fax: 757-878-0008. p. 2464

Schultz, Geralyn, Youth Serv Librn, Rockland Memorial Library, 20 Belmont St, Rockland, MA, 02370-2232. Tel: 781-878-1236. Fax: 781-878-4013. p. 1120

Schultz, Iris, Libr Asst, Canton Public Library, 225 N Broadway, Canton, SD, 57013-1715. Tel: 605-987-5831. Fax: 605-764-5831. p. 2211

Schultz, Janice, Br Mgr, Mid-Continent Public Library, Midwest Genealogy Center, 3440 S Lee's Summit Rd, Independence, MO, 64055-1923. Tel: 816-478-7664. Fax: 816-254-7146. p. 1333

Schultz, Jennifer, Youth Serv Librn, Fauquier County Public Library, 11 Winchester St, Warrenton, VA, 20186-2825. Tel: 540-349-1128. Fax: 540-349-3278. p. 2500

Schultz, Joan, Dir, Upham Memorial Library, 138 W Main St, Fredericksburg, IA, 50630. Tel: 563-237-6498. Fax: 563-237-6218. p. 817

Schultz, Johnna, Operations Dir, Helen Matthes Library, 100 E Market Ave, Effingham, IL, 62401-3499. Tel: 217-342-2464, Ext 7. Fax: 217-342-2413. p. 639

Schultz, Karen, Librn, Dodge Memorial Public Library, 22440 Railroad St, Olive Branch, IL, 62969. Tel: 618-776-5115. Fax: 618-776-5115. p. 685

Schultz, Karen, Br Mgr, Saint Joseph Public Library, Washington Park, 1821 N Third St, Saint Joseph, MO, 64505-2533. Tel: 816-232-2052. Fax: 816-236-2151. p. 1353

Schultz, Kathy, Ch, Hastings Public Library, 517 W Fourth St, Hastings, NE, 68901-7560. Tel: 402-461-2346. Fax: 402-461-2359. p. 1401

Schultz, Kristin, Adult Serv, Bellwood Public Library, 600 Bohland Ave, Bellwood, IL, 60104-1896. Tel: 708-547-7393. Fax: 708-547-9352. p. 593

Schultz, Linda, Asst Dir, Klamath Community College, 7390 S Sixth St, Klamath Falls, OR, 97603. Tel: 541-880-2253. Fax: 541-885-7758. p. 2001

Schultz, Lisa, Ref Librn, Loyola Law School, 919 S Albany St, Los Angeles, CA, 90015-1211. Tel: 213-736-8132. Fax: 213-487-2204. p. 175

Schultz, Lois, Head, Tech Serv, Librn, Northern Kentucky University, University Dr, Highland Heights, KY, 41099. Tel: 859-572-5275. Fax: 859-572-5390. p. 917

Schultz, Marian, Dr, Dean of Libr, Shippensburg University, 1871 Old Main Dr, Shippensburg, PA, 17257-2299. Tel: 717-477-1463. Fax: 717-477-1389. p. 2140

Schultz, Marie, Info Res, Hollister Incorporated, 2000 Hollister Dr, Libertyville, IL, 60048. Tel: 847-680-1000. Fax: 847-918-3453. p. 665

Schultz, Mary, Fiscal Officer, Massillon Public Library, 208 Lincoln Way E, Massillon, OH, 44646-8416. Tel: 330-832-9831, Ext 315. Fax: 330-830-2182. p. 1915

Schultz, Monica, Dir, Info Tech, Peninsula Libraries Automated Network, 2471 Flores St, San Mateo, CA, 94403-4000. Tel: 650-349-5538. Fax: 650-349-5089. p. 2938

Schultz, Patricia, Tech Serv Librn, Bryant University, 1150 Douglas Pike, Smithfield, RI, 02917-1284. Tel: 401-232-6296. Fax: 401-232-6126. p. 2176

Schultz, R, Br Mgr, New Orleans Public Library, Lakeview Branch, 6317 Argonne Blvd (@ Harrison Ave), New Orleans, LA, 70124. Tel: 504-596-2638. p. 962

Schultz, Richard, Coordr, Finance & Support Serv, Saint Charles City County Library District, 77 Boone Hills Dr, Saint Peters, MO, 63376-0529. Tel: 636-441-2300. Fax: 636-441-3132. p. 1363

Schultz, Rob, Circ, Marshfield Public Library, 211 E Second St, Marshfield, WI, 54449. Tel: 715-387-8494, Ext 230. Fax: 715-387-6909. p. 2613

Schultz, Ronald, Librn, Sutter Medical Center of Santa Rosa, 3325 Chanate Rd, Santa Rosa, CA, 95404-1794. Tel: 707-576-4675. Fax: 707-576-4321. p. 268

Schultz, Ruth, Pub Serv Mgr, American Dental Association Department of Library Services, 211 E Chicago Ave, 6th Flr, Chicago, IL, 60611-2678. Tel: 312-440-2653. Fax: 312-440-2774. p. 605

Schultz, Sandy, Dir, Liberty Hill Public Library, 355 Loop 332, Liberty Hill, TX, 78642. Tel: 512-778-6400. Fax: 512-778-5822. p. 2355

Schultz, Shannon M, Dir, Portage Public Library, 253 W Edgewater St, Portage, WI, 53901. Tel: 608-742-4959. Fax: 608-742-3819. p. 2631

Schultz, Tom, Tech Serv, William Woods University, One University Ave, Fulton, MO, 65251. Tel: 573-592-4291. Fax: 573-592-1159. p. 1329

Schultz, Vivienne, Librn, Harrington Public Library, S 11 Third St, Harrington, WA, 99134. Tel: 509-253-4345. Fax: 509-253-4370. p. 2516

Schultz-Jones, Barbara, Asst Prof, University of North Texas, 1155 Union Circle, Denton, TX, 76203-5017. Tel: 940-565-2445. Fax: 940-565-3101. p. 2975

Schultz-Nielsen, Sarah C, Asst Dir, Youth Serv Librn, Lithgow Public Library, 45 Winthrop St, Augusta, ME, 04330-5599. Tel: 207-626-2415. Fax: 207-626-2419. p. 974

Schultze, Phyllis, Librn, Rutgers University Libraries, Don M Gottfredson Library of Criminal Justice, 123 Washington St, Ste 350, Newark, NJ, 07102-3094. Tel: 973-353-3118. Fax: 973-353-1275. p. 1513

Schulz, Carol, Pres, Kenilworth Historical Society, 415 Kenilworth Ave, Kenilworth, IL, 60043-1134. Tel: 847-251-2565. Fax: 847-251-2565. p. 661

Schulz, Megan, Ref Librn, State Library of Kansas, State Capitol Bldg, Topeka, KS, 66612. Tel: 785-296-3296. Fax: 785-296-6650. p. 896

Schulz, Michael, Dir, University of Montana Western, 710 S Atlantic St, Dillon, MT, 59725. Tel: 406-683-7492. Fax: 406-683-7493. p. 1378

Schulz, Richard, Assoc Univ Librn, Tech Serv, Princeton University, One Washington Rd, Princeton, NJ, 08544-2098. Tel: 609-258-5297. Fax: 609-258-0441. p. 1523

Schulz, Suzanne, Librn, Reardan Memorial Library, 120 S Oak, Reardan, WA, 99029. Tel: 509-994-9997. p. 2525

Schulz, Travis, Librn, Medcenter One, 622 Ave A East, Bismarck, ND, 58501. Tel: 701-323-5391. Fax: 701-323-6967. p. 1838

Schulze, Jennifer, Adult Serv, Ref, Westfield Memorial Library, 550 E Broad St, Westfield, NJ, 07090. Tel: 908-789-4090. Fax: 908-789-0921. p. 1543

Schulze, Kara, Asst Librn, Chester College of New England, 40 Chester St, Chester, NH, 03036-4301. Tel: 603-887-7425. Fax: 603-887-1777. p. 1441

Schulze, Theodora, Dir, American Conservatory of Music, 252 Wildwood Rd, Hammond, IN, 46324. Tel: 219-931-6000. Fax: 219-931-6089. p. 747

Schumacher, Beth, Dir, Moore Public Library, 7239 Huron Ave, Lexington, MI, 48450. Tel: 810-359-8267. Fax: 810-359-2986. p. 1203

Schumacher, Claudia, Ref Librn, Fiske Public Library, 110 Randall Rd, Wrentham, MA, 02093. Tel: 508-384-5440. Fax: 508-384-5443. p. 1146

Schumacher, Heather Isbell, Curator of Images, Delaware Historical Society Research Library, 505 N Market St, Wilmington, DE, 19801. Tel: 302-295-2386. Fax: 302-655-7844. p. 387

Schumacher, John, Coordr, Electronic Res, SUNYConnect, Office of Library & Information Services, SUNY Plaza, Albany, NY, 12246. Tel: 518-443-5577. Fax: 518-443-5358. p. 2950

Schumacher, Mark, Ref Librn, University of North Carolina at Greensboro, 320 Spring Garden St, Greensboro, NC, 27402. Tel: 336-334-3215. Fax: 336-334-5399. p. 1798

Schumacher, Sara, Tech Serv Librn, University of the Cumberlands/Cumberland College, 821 Walnut St, Williamsburg, KY, 40769. Tel: 606-539-4464. Fax: 606-539-4317. p. 937

Schumacher, Susan, Youth Serv Coordr, Duluth Public Library, 520 W Superior St, Duluth, MN, 55802. Tel: 218-730-4219. Fax: 218-723-3815, 218-723-3822. p. 1247

Schumacher, Zoe, Supvr, Deschutes Public Library District, Sisters Branch, 110 N Cedar St, Sisters, OR, 97759. Tel: 541-312-1070. Fax: 541-549-9620. p. 1992

Schumann, Amy, YA Serv, Bethel Public Library, 189 Greenwood Ave, Bethel, CT, 06801-2598. Tel: 203-794-8756. Fax: 203-794-8761. p. 330

Schumann, Michele, Ch, Brigham City Library, 26 E Forest, Brigham City, UT, 84302-2198. Tel: 435-723-5850. Fax: 435-723-2813. p. 2403

Schumm, Aimee, Supvr, Pub Serv, Louisville Public Library, 951 Spruce St, Louisville, CO, 80027. Tel: 303-335-4849. Fax: 303-335-4833. p. 317

Schummer, Nancy, AV, YA Serv, Roswell Public Library, 301 N Pennsylvania Ave, Roswell, NM, 88201. Tel: 575-622-7101. Fax: 575-622-7107. p. 1561

Schumway, Jean, Media Librn, Ref Librn, Butler County Community College, College Dr, Oak Hills, Butler, PA, 16002. Tel: 724-284-8511. Fax: 724-285-6047. p. 2040

Schurdevin, Lynette, Adminr, Thomas Branigan Memorial Library, 200 E Picacho Ave, Las Cruces, NM, 88001-3499. Tel: 575-528-4000. Fax: 575-528-4030. p. 1557

Schureman, Tiffany, Archivist, Res Librn, Fort Worth Museum of Science & History Library, 1600 Gendy St, Fort Worth, TX, 76107. Tel: 817-255-9305. Fax: 817-255-9595. p. 2322

Schuricht, Robert, Per, Lakeland College, W3718 South Dr, Plymouth, WI, 53073. Tel: 920-565-1238. Fax: 920-565-1206. p. 2630

Schurk, William, Sound Rec Archivist, Bowling Green State University Libraries, Music Library & Sound Recordings Archives, Jerome Library, 3rd Flr, Bowling Green, OH, 43403. Tel: 419-372-2308. Fax: 419-372-2499. p. 1861

Schurkamp, Trish, Dir, Wyandotte County Museum, 631 N 126th St, Bonner Springs, KS, 66012. Tel: 913-721-1078. Fax: 913-721-1394. p. 858

Schurr, Andrea, Web Serv, University of Tennessee at Chattanooga Library, 615 McCallie Ave, Dept 6456, Chattanooga, TN, 37403-2598. Tel: 423-425-4501. Fax: 423-425-4775. p. 2228

Schurr, KaeLi, Archivist, Curator, Site Mgr, North Carolina Office of Archives & History, One Festival Park Blvd, Manteo, NC, 27954. Tel: 252-473-2655. Fax: 252-473-1483. p. 1808

Schuster, Connie, Co-Dir, Ocheyedan Public Library, 874 Main St, Ocheyedan, IA, 51354. Tel: 712-758-3352. Fax: 712-758-3352. p. 836

Schuster, David, Dir, Libr Info Tech & Technical Support, Texas Woman's University Libraries, 304 Administration Dr, Denton, TX, 76204. Tel: 940-898-3909. Fax: 940-898-3764. p. 2312

Schuster, Janice, Ref Serv, Providence College, One Cunningham Sq, Providence, RI, 02918-0001. Tel: 401 865-2631. Fax: 401-865-2823. p. 2173

Schuster, Linda, Dir, Price James Memorial Library, 104 E Morgan, Tipton, MO, 65081. Tel: 660-433-5622. p. 1368

Schuster, Linda, Head, Youth Serv, T B Scott Library, 106 W First St, Merrill, WI, 54452-2398. Tel: 715-536-7191. Fax: 715-536-1705. p. 2616

Schuster, Melissa, Dir, Scotland County Memorial Library, 306 W Madison, Memphis, MO, 63555. Tel: 660-465-7042. Fax: 660-465-7334. p. 1345

Schusterich, Jo Ann, Dir, Mkt, Hinsdale Public Library, 20 E Maple St, Hinsdale, IL, 60521. Tel: 630-986-1976. Fax: 630-986-9654. p. 656

Schut, Alan, Sr Librn, Dominican University of California, 50 Acacia Ave, San Rafael, CA, 94901-2298. Tel: 415-458-3703. Fax: 415-459-2309. p. 256

Schutt, Melissa, Coll Develop Mgr, Richmond Public Library, 101 E Franklin St, Richmond, VA, 23219-2193. Tel: 804-646-4807. Fax: 804-646-4757. p. 2489

Schuttringer, Fu Yuan, Coll Develop, Sr Assoc Librn, University of Michigan-Dearborn, 4901 Evergreen Rd, Dearborn, MI, 48128-2406. Tel: 313-583-6324. Fax: 313-593-5478. p. 1168

Schutz, Christine, Dir, The College of Idaho, 2112 Cleveland Blvd, Caldwell, ID, 83605-4432. Tel: 208-459-5506. Fax: 208-459-5299. p. 572

Schutz, Irene, ILL, Blauvelt Free Library, 541 Western Hwy, Blauvelt, NY, 10913. Tel: 845-359-2811. Fax: 845-398-0017. p. 1583

Schuyler, Carol, Dir, Support Serv Div, Kitsap Regional Library, 1301 Sylvan Way, Bremerton, WA, 98310-3498. Tel: 360-405-9127. Fax: 360-405-9128. p. 2510

Schuyler, Michael, Acq, Asst Librn, Cat, Munson-Williams-Proctor Arts Institute Library, 310 Genesee St, Utica, NY, 13502. Tel: 315-797-0000, Ext 2229. Fax: 315-797-5608. p. 1759

Schwab, Ann, Sr Librn, Denver Public Library, Westwood, 1000 S Lowell Blvd, Denver, CO, 80219-3339. Tel: 303-936-8808. Fax: 303-937-4454. p. 301

Schwab, Janie, Exec Dir, Dudley Observatory Library, 107 Nott Terrace, Ste 201, Schenectady, NY, 12308. Tel: 518-382-7583. Fax: 518-382-7584. p. 1740

Schwabenbauer, Lori A, Dir of Libr Serv, Holy Family University Library, 9801 Frankford Ave, Philadelphia, PA, 19114. Tel: 267-341-3315, 267-341-3316. Fax: 215-632-8067. p. 2111

Schwandt-Lehner, Leann, Ref Serv, Jefferson Public Library, 321 S Main St, Jefferson, WI, 53549-1772. Tel: 920-674-7733. Fax: 920-674-7735. p. 2600

Schwanger, Amy, Br Mgr, Willard Memorial Library, North Fairfield Public Library, Five E Main St, North Fairfield, OH, 44855. Tel: 419-744-2285. Fax: 419-744-2115. p. 1948

Schwanz, Bonnie, Asst Dir, Westchester Public Library, 10700 Canterbury St, Westchester, IL, 60154. Tel: 708-562-3573. Fax: 708-562-1298. p. 717

Schwarten., Mary Anne, Librn, Emerson Public Library, 110 Main St, Emerson, NE, 68733. Tel: 402-695-2449. Fax: 402-695-2449. p. 1398

Schwarting, Paulette, Tech Serv, Virginia Historical Society Library, 428 North Blvd, Richmond, VA, 23220. Tel: 804-358-4901. Fax: 804-355-2399. p. 2492

Schwartz, April, Dir, Touro College, 225 Eastview Dr, Central Islip, NY, 11722-4539. Tel: 631-761-7000, 631-761-7150. Fax: 631-761-7159. p. 1605

Schwartz, Betsy, Syst Librn, Brookhaven National Laboratory, Research Library, Bldg 477, Upton, NY, 11973-5000. Tel: 631-344-2758. Fax: 631-344-2090. p. 1758

Schwartz, Bonnie Fox, Head, Res Serv, Weil, Gotshal & Manges Library, 767 Fifth Ave, New York, NY, 10153. Tel: 212-310-8626. Fax: 212-310-8007. p. 1702

Schwartz, Brandon, Media Serv, Syst Tech, Southwestern Oklahoma State University, 100 Campus Dr, Weatherford, OK, 73096-3002. Tel: 580-774-7061. Fax: 580-774-3112. p. 1985

Schwartz, Carolyn, Head, Access Serv, Westfield State University, 577 Western Ave, Westfield, MA, 01085-2580. Tel: 413-572-5327. Fax: 413-572-5520. p. 1138

Schwartz, Carolyn S, Prof, Simmons College, 300 The Fenway, Boston, MA, 02115. Tel: 617-521-2800. Fax: 617-521-3192. p. 2967

Schwartz, Cathy, Dir, West Point Public Library, 317 Fifth St, West Point, IA, 52656. Tel: 319-837-6315. Fax: 319-837-6250. p. 852

Schwartz, Daniel, Libr Dir, Butt-Holdsworth Memorial Library, 505 Water St, Kerrville, TX, 78028. Tel: 830-257-8422. Fax: 830-792-5552. p. 2349

Schwartz, Diane, Dir of Libr, Buffalo General Health System, 100 High St, Buffalo, NY, 14203. Tel: 716-859-2878. Fax: 716-859-1527. p. 1597

Schwartz, Dorothy, Librn, New York Methodist Hospital, 506 Sixth St, Brooklyn, NY, 11215. Tel: 718-780-5197. p. 1594

Schwartz, Eleanor, Circ Coordr, Syst Adminr, T B Scott Library, 106 W First St, Merrill, WI, 54452-2398. Tel: 715-536-7191. Fax: 715-536-1705. p. 2616

Schwartz, Gina, Asst Librn, Mount Olive Public Library, 100 N Plum St, Mount Olive, IL, 62069-1755. Tel: 217-999-7311. Fax: 217-999-7360. p. 677

Schwartz, Jay, Media Serv, Suffolk County Community College, 121 Speonk Riverhead Rd, Riverhead, NY, 11901-9990. Tel: 631-548-2544. Fax: 631-369-2641. p. 1728

Schwartz, Jennifer, Circ Supvr, Westborough Public Library, 55 W Main St, Westborough, MA, 01581. Tel: 508-366-3050. Fax: 508-366-3049. p. 1138

Schwartz, Judith K, Dir, Trocaire College Library, 360 Choate Ave, Buffalo, NY, 14220-2094. Tel: 716-827-2434. Fax: 716-828-6102, 716-828-6107. p. 1599

Schwartz, Kara, Assoc Librn, Circ & Tech Serv, Eastern Maine Community College Library, Katahdin Hall, 354 Hogan Rd, Bangor, ME, 04401-4280. Tel: 207-974-4640. Fax: 207-974-4641. p. 975

Schwartz, Katherine, Commun Libr Mgr, County of Los Angeles Public Library, Malibu Library, 23555 W Civic Center Way, Malibu, CA, 90265-4804. Tel: 310-456-6438. Fax: 310-456-8681. p. 142

Schwartz, Kathryn, Dir, Flint Public Library, 1026 E Kearsley St, Flint, MI, 48502-1994. Tel: 810-232-7111. Fax: 810-249-2635. p. 1179

Schwartz, Kim, Dir, Agency Public Library, 104 E Main St, Agency, IA, 52530. Tel: 641-937-6002. Fax: 641-937-5241. p. 791

Schwartz, Kris, IT & Network Syst, St Croix Falls Public Library, 230 S Washington St, Saint Croix Falls, WI, 54024. Tel: 715-483-1777. Fax: 715-483-1777. p. 2635

Schwartz, Krista, Libr Asst, Milltown Public Library, 61 W Main St, Milltown, WI, 54858. Tel: 715-825-2313. Fax: 715-825-4422. p. 2616

Schwartz, Larry, Coll Develop, Minnesota State University Moorhead, 1104 Seventh Ave S, Moorhead, MN, 56563. Tel: 218-477-2922. Fax: 218-477-5924. p. 1266

Schwartz, Laura, Librn, University of Texas Libraries, Fine Arts, Doty Fine Arts Bldg 3-200, 23rd & Trinity, Austin, TX, 78713. Tel: 512-495-4476. Fax: 512-495-4490. p. 2284

Schwartz, Lee, Br Supvr, Marion County Public Library System, Belleview Public Library, 13145 SE Hwy 484, Belleview, FL, 34420. Tel: 352-438-2500. Fax: 352-438-2502. p. 474

Schwartz, Linda, Mgr, Enoch Pratt Free Library, Brooklyn, 300 E Patapsco Ave, Baltimore, MD, 21225-1828. Tel: 410-396-1120. Fax: 410-396-1698. p. 1013

Schwartz, Lisa, Tech Serv, Unilever Bestfoods Information Center, 800 Sylvan Ave, Englewood Cliffs, NJ, 07632-3201. Tel: 201-894-7568. Fax: 201-871-8265. p. 1484

Schwartz, Louise, Asst Librn, Bethel-Tulpehocken Public Library, 8601 Lancaster Ave, Bethel, PA, 19507. Tel: 717-933-4060. Fax: 717-933-9655. p. 2033

Schwartz, Mark, Communications Officer I, Alexandria Library, 5005 Duke St, Alexandria, VA, 22304. Tel: 703-746-1770. p. 2444

Schwartz, Martin, Librn, United States Courts Library, 2500 Tulare St, Ste 2401, Fresno, CA, 93721. Tel: 559-499-5615. p. 153

Schwartz, Mary, Sr Librn, Center for Creative Leadership Library, One Leadership Pl, Greensboro, NC, 27410. Tel: 336-286-4083. Fax: 336-286-4087. p. 1795

Schwartz, Mary, Asst Librn, H F Brigham Free Public Library, 104 Main St, Bakersfield, VT, 05441. Tel: 802-827-4414. p. 2417

Schwartz, Nathan, Syst Librn, Anderson University, Robert A Nicholson Library, 1100 E Fifth St, Anderson, IN, 46012-3495. Tel: 765-641-4275. Fax: 765-641-3850. p. 724

Schwartz, Ray, Info Tech, William Paterson University of New Jersey, 300 Pompton Rd, Wayne, NJ, 07470. Tel: 973-720-3192. Fax: 973-720-3171. p. 1540

Schwartz, Rhonda, Dir, University of North Dakota, 215 Centennial Dr, Grand Forks, ND, 58202. Tel: 701-777-2204. Fax: 701-777-2217. p. 1843

Schwartz, Rhonda, Interim Dir, Mid-America Law Library Consortium, Univ of North Dakota School of Law, Thormodsgard Library, Grand Forks, ND, 58202. Tel: 701-777-2204. Fax: 701-777-4956. p. 2951

Schwartz, Roberta, Tech Serv Mgr, Bowdoin College Library, 3000 College Sta, Brunswick, ME, 04011-8421. Tel: 207-725-3134. p. 979

Schwartz, Ruth Ann, Ref, Saint Mary's University of Minnesota, 700 Terrace Heights, No 26, Winona, MN, 55987-1399. Tel: 507-457-6664. Fax: 507-457-1565. p. 1289

Schwartz, Thomas, Dr, Dir, Res Serv, Illinois Historic Preservation Agency, 112 N Sixth St, Springfield, IL, 62701. Tel: 217-782-2118. Fax: 217-785-6250. p. 705

Schwartzkopf, Becky, Ref Librn, Ser, Minnesota State University, Mankato, ML3097, Mankato, MN, 56001. Tel: 507-389-5952. Fax: 507-389-5155. p. 1257

Schwarz, Debra, Mgr, Pillsbury Winthrop LLP, 50 Fremont St, San Francisco, CA, 94105. Tel: 415-983-1130. Fax: 415-983-1200. p. 244

Schwarz, Gregory C, In Charge, Saint-Gaudens National Historic Site Library, National Park Service, 139 Saint-Gaudens Rd, Cornish, NH, 03745-4232. Tel: 603-675-2175. Fax: 603-675-2701. p. 1444

Schwarz, Joy, ILL, Winnefox Library System, 106 Washington Ave, Oshkosh, WI, 54901-4985. Tel: 920-236-5220. Fax: 920-236-5228. p. 2628

Schwarz, Joy, Pres, Fox Valley Library Council, c/o OWLS, 225 N Oneida St, Appleton, WI, 54911. Tel: 920-832-6190. Fax: 920-832-6422. p. 2958

Schwarz, Lu Anne W, Librn, Atlanta Botanical Garden, 1345 Piedmont Ave NE, Atlanta, GA, 30309-3366. Tel: 404-591-1546, 404-591-1725. Fax: 404-876-7472. p. 511

Schwarzbard, Jerry, Spec Coll Librn, Jewish Theological Seminary Library, 3080 Broadway, New York, NY, 10027. Tel: 212-678-8973. Fax: 212-678-8891, 212-678-8998. p. 1683

Schwarzer, Rich, Chief Exec Officer, Orangeville Public Library, One Mill St, Orangeville, ON, L9W 2M2, CANADA. Tel: 519-941-0440, Ext 2243. Fax: 519-941-4698. p. 2826

Schwarzwalder, Robert, Dr, Assoc Univ Librn, Eng & Sci, Stanford University Libraries, 557 Escondido Mall, Stanford, CA, 94305-6004. Tel: 650-725-1064. p. 270

Schweda, Joyce, Dir of Tech Serv, Rolling Meadows Library, 3110 Martin Lane, Rolling Meadows, IL, 60008. Tel: 847-259-6050. Fax: 847-259-5319. p. 698

Schwedt, Rachel, Curric Librn, Liberty University Library, 1971 University Blvd, Lynchburg, VA, 24502. Tel: 434-592-3357. Fax: 434-582-2728. p. 2476

Schwegel, Richard, Head, Access Serv, North Park University, Brandel Library, 5114 N Christiana Ave, Chicago, IL, 60625. Tel: 773-244-5580, 773-244-6200. Fax: 773-244-4891. p. 620

Schwegel, Richard C, Dir, Roosevelt University, Performing Arts Library, 430 S Michigan Ave, Rm 1111, Chicago, IL, 60605. Tel: 312-341-3648. Fax: 312-341-6394. p. 623

Schweid, Jean, Ref Librn, Groton Public Library, 52 Newtown Rd, Groton, CT, 06340. Tel: 860-441-6750. Fax: 860-448-0363. p. 342

Schweigert, Robbi, Librn, Five Towns College Library, 305 N Service Rd, Dix Hills, NY, 11746. Tel: 631-656-2138. Fax: 631-656-2171. p. 1614

Schweikert, C, Access Serv Librn, Cat Librn, Lenoir-Rhyne University Library, 625 7th Ave NE, Hickory, NC, 28601. Tel: 828-328-7236. Fax: 828-328-7338. p. 1801

Schweiner, Deneen, Libr Assoc, Brown County Library, Denmark Branch, 450 N Wall St, Denmark, WI, 54208. Tel: 920-863-6613. Fax: 920-863-3001. p. 2595

Schweinfest, Cindy, Br Mgr, Charleston County Public Library, Mount Pleasant Regional, 1133 Mathis Ferry Rd, Mount Pleasant, SC, 29464. Tel: 843-849-6161. Fax: 843-849-6166. p. 2183

Schweinsberg, Catherine, Dir, Libr Serv, Brevard County Library System, 308 Forrest Ave, 2nd Flr, Cocoa, FL, 32922-7781. Tel: 321-633-1801. Fax: 321-633-1798. p. 433

Schweinsberg, Catherine, Dir, Central Brevard Library & Reference Center, 308 Forrest Ave, Cocoa, FL, 32922. Tel: 321-633-1792. Fax: 321-633-1806. p. 433

Schweinsburg, Jane, Asst Libr Dir, Coventry Public Library, 1672 Flat River Rd, Coventry, RI, 02816. Tel: 401-822-9104. Fax: 401-822-9133. p. 2164

Schweiss, Joe, Librn, Henry County Library, 172 Eminence Terrace, Eminence, KY, 40019-1146. Tel: 502-845-5682. Fax: 502-845-4807. p. 912

Schweitzberger, Kathleen, Head, Cat & Metadata Serv, University of Missouri-Kansas City Libraries, 800 E 51st St, Kansas City, MO, 64110. Tel: 816-235-2227. Fax: 816-333-5584. p. 1341

Schweitzer, Aileen, Dir, Thomas Nelson Community College Library, Wythe Hall 228, 99 Thomas Nelson Dr, Hampton, VA, 23666. Tel: 757-825-2871. Fax: 757-825-2870. p. 2468

Schweitzer, Andrea, Br Mgr, Coshocton Public Library, 655 Main St, Coshocton, OH, 43812-1697. Tel: 740-622-0956. Fax: 740-622-4331. p. 1891

Schweitzer, Andrea, Br Mgr, Coshocton Public Library, West Lafayette Branch, 601 E Main St, West Lafayette, OH, 43845. Tel: 740-545-6672. Fax: 740-545-6418. p. 1892

Schweizer, Elizabeth, Librn, Presbyterian Church of Chatham Township Library, 240 Southern Blvd, Chatham, NJ, 07928. Tel: 973-635-2340. Fax: 973-635-2447. p. 1478

Schweizer, Linda, Ref Librn, United States Department of State, 2201 C St NW, Rm 3239, Washington, DC, 20520-2442. Tel: 202-647-1099. Fax: 202-647-2971. p. 419

Schwelm, Anne, Asst Libr Dir, Cabrini College Library, 610 King of Prussia Rd, Radnor, PA, 19087-3698. Tel: 610-902-8536. Fax: 610-902-8539. p. 2132

Schwenker, Arleen, Tech Serv, North Babylon Public Library, 815 Deer Park Ave, North Babylon, NY, 11703-3812. Tel: 631-669-4020. Fax: 631-669-3432. p. 1706

Schweppe, Janet, In Charge, Hayner Public Library District, Alton Square, 132 Alton Sq, Alton, IL, 62002-6115. Fax: 618-463-1277. p. 588

Schwesig, William, Bibliographer, University of Chicago Library, D'Angelo Law Library, 1121 E 60th St, Chicago, IL, 60637-2786. Tel: 773-702-3731. Fax: 773-702-2889. p. 626

Schweyer, Kathlyn, Dir, Knowledge & Res Serv, Lowenstein Sandler PC Library, 65 Livingston Ave, Roseland, NJ, 07068. Tel: 973-422-2942. Fax: 973-597-6123. p. 1527

Schwichtenberg, Suzanne, Adult Serv, Lewis & Clark Library, 120 S Last Chance Gulch, Helena, MT, 59601. Tel: 406-447-1690, Ext 130. Fax: 406-447-1687. p. 1382

Schwickerath, Dana, Ch, Charles City Public Library, 106 Milwaukee Mall, Charles City, IA, 50616-2281. Tel: 641-257-6319. Fax: 641-257-6325. p. 801

Schwiderski, Jill, Br Mgr, Commun Relations Librn, Hector Public Library, 126 S Main, Hector, MN, 55342. Tel: 320-848-2841. Fax: 320-848-2841. p. 1254

Schwieterman, Rick J, Chief Financial Officer, Treas, OCLC Online Computer Library Center, Inc, 6565 Kilgour Pl, Dublin, OH, 43017-3395. Tel: 614-764-6000. Fax: 614-718-1017. p. 2952

Schwind, Teresa, Adult Serv, Huntington Public Library, 338 Main St, Huntington, NY, 11743. Tel: 631-427-5165. Fax: 631-421-7131. p. 1639

Schwindt, Joanne, Librn, Tescott Public Library, PO Box 53, Tescott, KS, 67484-0053. Tel: 785-283-4437. Fax: 785-283-4435. p. 896

Schwing, Laurie J, Mgr, Libr Serv, Harrisburg Hospital Library at PinnacleHealth System, Main Bldg, 2nd Flr, 111 S Front St, Harrisburg, PA, 17101-2099. Tel: 717-782-5534. Fax: 717-782-5512. p. 2065

Schwisow, Barbara J, Dir, Struckman-Baatz Public Library, 104 SW Ave, Western, NE, 68464. Tel: 402-433-2177. Fax: 402-433-2177. p. 1423

Schwoch, Arlie J, Dir, Hauge Memorial Library, 50655 Charles St, Osseo, WI, 54758. Tel: 715-597-3444. p. 2628

Schwoebel, Kristina, Ref Librn, Loyola University Chicago Libraries, Elizabeth M Cudahy Memorial Library, 6525 N Sheridan Rd, Chicago, IL, 60626. p. 617

Schwotzer, Pam, Ref Librn, Amesbury Public Library, 149 Main St, Amesbury, MA, 01913. Tel: 978-388-8148. p. 1048

Sciacca, Vickie, Sr Commun Libr Mgr, Contra Costa County Library, Lafayette Library, 3491 Mount Diablo Blvd, Lafayette, CA, 94549-4594. Tel: 925-385-2280. p. 209

Sciammarella, Susan, Coordr, Pub Serv & Info Literacy, Queensborough Community College, City University of New York, 222-05 56th Ave, Bayside, NY, 11364-1497. Tel: 718-631-6601. Fax: 718-281-5012. p. 1579

Scibelli, Jaime, Sci Librn, NASA, 21000 Brookpark Rd, MS 60-3, Cleveland, OH, 44135. Fax: 216-433-5777. p. 1880

Scidmore, Eileen, Br Head, Toronto Public Library, Dawes Road, 416 Dawes Rd, Toronto, ON, M4B 2E8, CANADA. Tel: 416-396-3820. Fax: 416-396-3825. p. 2861

Scigliano, Marisia, Tech Serv Librn, Trent University, 1600 West Bank Dr, Peterborough, ON, K9J 7B8, CANADA. Tel: 705-748-1011, Ext 1390. Fax: 705-748-1126. p. 2836

Scinta, Diane, Ch, Cold Spring Harbor Library, 95 Harbor Rd, Cold Spring Harbor, NY, 11724. Tel: 631-692-6820. Fax: 631-692-6827. p. 1609

Sciochetti, Melanie, Mgr, Pew Charitable Trusts Library, One Commerce Sq, 2005 Market St, Ste 1700, Philadelphia, PA, 19103-7017. Tel: 215-575-4920. Fax: 215-575-4939. p. 2114

Scircle, Kathy, Br Librn, Frankfort Community Public Library, Rossville Community Library, 400 W Main St, Rossville, IN, 46065-9446. Tel: 765-379-2246. Fax: 765-379-2246. p. 743

Sciurba, Roseann, In Charge, Klamath County Library Services District, Bly Branch, Gearhart School, 61100 Metler St, Bly, OR, 97622. Tel: 541-353-2299. Fax: 541-353-2299. p. 2002

Scleuher, Joe, Libr Mgr, General Motors Corp, Information Research, GM Technical Ctr, MC 480-106-314, 30500 Mound Rd, Warren, MI, 48090-9055. Tel: 586-986-2000. Fax: 586-986-2009. p. 1234

Scofield, Constance V, Dir, University of Wisconsin, 750 W Bay Shore, Marinette, WI, 54143-1299. Tel: 715-735-4306. Fax: 715-735-4307. p. 2612

Scoggin, Etheldra, Ref Librn, Loyola University New Orleans, Loyola Law Library, School of Law, 7214 St Charles Ave, New Orleans, LA, 70118. Tel: 504-861-5539. Fax: 504-861-5895. p. 961

Scoggins, Brenda, Ref Serv, Mooresville Public Library, 304 S Main St, Mooresville, NC, 28115. Tel: 704-664-2927. Fax: 704-660-3292. p. 1810

Scoggins, Slade, ILL Coordr, Cleveland State Community College Library, 3535 Adkisson Dr, Cleveland, TN, 37312-2813. Tel: 423-478-6209. Fax: 423-478-6255. p. 2229

Scoles, Clyde, Dir, Toledo-Lucas County Public Library, 325 N Michigan St, Toledo, OH, 43604-6614. Tel: 419-259-5207. Fax: 419-255-1334. p. 1939

Sconce, Judy A, Librn, Brown Mackie College, 325 E US Hwy 20, Michigan City, IN, 46360-7362. Tel: 219-877-3100. Fax: 219-877-3110. p. 764

Sconyers, Judy, Acq, Garrett College, 687 Mosser Rd, McHenry, MD, 21541. Tel: 301-387-3022. Fax: 301-387-3055. p. 1035

Scoones, Lori, Dir, Lockheed Martin Corp, Bldg 6, 497 Electronics Pkwy, E7-G92, Syracuse, NY, 13221. Tel: 315-456-2269. Fax: 315-456-0099. p. 1752

Scorza, Joseph C, Exec Dir, HSLC/Access PA, 3600 Market St, Ste 550, Philadelphia, PA, 19104-2646. Tel: 215-222-1532. Fax: 215-222-0416. p. 2954

Scot, Diane, Librn, Daytona Beach Campus, Keiser University Library System, 1500 NW 49th St, Fort Lauderdale, FL, 33309. Tel: 954-351-4035. Fax: 954-351-4051. p. 443

Scott, Alba, Regional Librn, US Department of the Interior, Bureau of Reclamation, 2800 Cottage Way, Rm W-1825, Sacramento, CA, 95825-1898. Tel: 916-978-5593. Fax: 916-978-5599. p. 225

Scott, Anais, Ch, Dixon Homestead Library, 180 Washington Ave, Dumont, NJ, 07628. Tel: 201-384-2030. Fax: 201-384-5878. p. 1481

Scott, Anais, Ch, Trenton Free Public Library, 120 Academy St, Trenton, NJ, 08608-1302. Tel: 609-392-7188. Fax: 609-396-7655. p. 1536

Scott, Andy, Ref Serv, Franklin Public Library, 9151 W Loomis Rd, Franklin, WI, 53132. Tel: 414-425-8214. Fax: 414-425-9498. p. 2593

Scott, Angela, Cat, Jefferson County Public Library, 375 S Water St, Monticello, FL, 32344. Tel: 850-342-0205. Fax: 850-342-0207. p. 470

Scott, Angie, Librn, Breckinridge County Public Library, Irvington Branch, 212 E First St, Irvington, KY, 40146. Tel: 270-547-7404. Fax: 270-547-7420. p. 916

Scott, Ann, Outreach Serv Librn, New Port Richey Public Library, 5939 Main St, New Port Richey, FL, 34652. Tel: 727-853-1279. Fax: 727-853-1280. p. 472

Scott, Anne, In Charge, Napa City-County Library, Calistoga Branch, 1108 Myrtle, Calistoga, CA, 94515-1730. Tel: 707-942-4833. Fax: 707-942-0941. p. 192

Scott, Anne, Ref Serv, Columbia State Community College, 1665 Hampshire Pike, Columbia, TN, 38401. Tel: 931-540-2851. Fax: 931-540-2565. p. 2231

Scott, Anne, Tech Serv, Dawson College Library, 3040 Sherbrooke St W, Westmount, QC, H3Z 1A4, CANADA. Tel: 514-931-8731, Ext 1796. Fax: 514-931-3567. p. 2915

Scott, Barbara, Br Mgr, Tacoma Public Library, Swasey Branch, 7001 Sixth Ave, Tacoma, WA, 98406. p. 2540

Scott, Benjamin, III, YA Serv, Atlanta-Fulton Public Library System, Northeast-Spruill Oaks Regional Library, 9560 Spruill Rd, Alpharetta, GA, 30022. Tel: 770-360-8820. Fax: 770-360-8823. p. 512

Scott, Beth Ann, Dir, Janesville Public Library, 227 Main St, Janesville, IA, 50647. Tel: 319-987-2925. Fax: 319-987-2925. p. 824

Scott, Brad, Librn, Baker College of Flint, 1050 W Bristol Rd, Flint, MI, 48507-5508. Tel: 810-766-2016. Fax: 810-766-2013. p. 1179

Scott, Brillie, ILL, Per, United Theological Seminary Library, 4501 Denlinger Rd, Trotwood, OH, 45426. Tel: 937-529-2201, Ext 3400. Fax: 937-529-2292. p. 1941

Scott, Candice, Dr, Dir, Schreiner University, 2100 Memorial Blvd, Kerrville, TX, 78028-5697. Tel: 830-792-7318. Fax: 830-792-7448. p. 2350

Scott, Carol, Head, Circ, Frankfort Community Public Library, 208 W Clinton St, Frankfort, IN, 46041. Tel: 765-654-8746. Fax: 765-654-8747. p. 743

Scott, Carol, Librn, Fair Haven Free Library, 107 Main St, Fair Haven, VT, 05743. Tel: 802-265-8011. p. 2424

Scott, Carole, Libr Mgr, Tewksbury Township Public Library, 31 Main St, Oldwick, NJ, 08858. Tel: 908-439-3761. Fax: 908-439-2326. p. 1516

Scott, Carolyn, Librn, Young, Moore, Henderson, PA Library, 3101 Glenwood Ave, Raleigh, NC, 27622. Tel: 919-782-6860. Fax: 919-782-6753. p. 1819

Scott, Carrie, Commun Outreach Supvr-Literacy, Carlsbad City Library, Library Learning Center, 3368 Eureka Pl, Carlsbad, CA, 92008. Tel: 760-931-4515. Fax: 760-729-8335. p. 132

Scott, Catherine, Coll Asst, Baltimore Museum of Industry, 1415 Key Hwy, Baltimore, MD, 21230. Tel: 410-727-4808, Ext 110. Fax: 410-727-4869. p. 1012

Scott, Cathleen O, Ref Librn, Le Moyne College, 1419 Salt Springs Rd, Syracuse, NY, 13214-1301. Tel: 315-445-4627. Fax: 315-445-4642. p. 1751

Scott, Christi, Libr Spec, Horry-Georgetown Technical College, 2050 Hwy 501 E, Conway, SC, 29526-9521. Tel: 843-349-7596. Fax: 843-347-0552. p. 2191

Scott, Christy, Ref & ILL Librn, Walla Walla University Libraries, 104 S College Ave, College Place, WA, 99324-1159. Tel: 509-527-2134. Fax: 509-527-2192. p. 2513

Scott, Cinda, Ch, Bradford Public Library District, 111 S Peoria St, Bradford, IL, 61421. Tel: 309-897-8400. Fax: 309-897-8314. p. 597

Scott, Cindy, Br Mgr, Stanislaus County Free Library, Nora Ballard Library (Waterford Branch), 324 E St, Waterford, CA, 95386-9005. Tel: 209-874-2191. Fax: 209-874-2191. p. 188

Scott, Claudia, Assoc Dir, Electronic Res Librn, Westmont College, 955 La Paz Rd, Santa Barbara, CA, 93108-1099. Tel: 805-565-6000, 805-565-6147. Fax: 805-565-6220. p. 262

Scott, Connie, Libr Dir, Indiana Tech, 1600 E Washington Blvd, Fort Wayne, IN, 46803. Tel: 260-422-5561, Ext 2224. Fax: 260-422-3189. p. 741

Scott, Cynthia, Dir, Middleton Community Library, 110 Bolton Ave, Middleton, TN, 38052-3403. Tel: 731-376-0680. Fax: 731-376-0680. p. 2253

Scott, Cynthia, Circ, ILL, Per, Texas A&M University Central Texas, 1901 S Clear Creek Rd, Killeen, TX, 76549. Tel: 254-526-1618. Fax: 254-526-1589, 254-526-1993. p. 2350

Scott, Cynthia L, Dir, Wolfeboro Public Library, 259 S Main St, Wolfeboro, NH, 03894. Tel: 603-569-2428. Fax: 603-569-8180. p. 1468

Scott, Dan, Syst Librn, Laurentian University, 935 Ramsey Lake Rd, Sudbury, ON, P3E 2C6, CANADA. Tel: 705-675-1151, Ext 3315. Fax: 705-675-4877. p. 2846

Scott, Darwin, Librn, Princeton University, Mendel Music Library, Woolworth Center for Musical Studies, Princeton, NJ, 08544. Tel: 609-258-4251. Fax: 609-258-6793. p. 1524

Scott, David, Br Mgr, Palm Beach County Library System, Greenacres Branch, 3750 Jog Rd, Greenacres City, FL, 33467. Tel: 561-641-9100. Fax: 561-642-0823. p. 503

Scott, David, Doc Delivery, ILL, Ferris State University Library, 1010 Campus Dr, Big Rapids, MI, 49307-2279. Tel: 231-591-3500. Fax: 231-591-3724. p. 1158

Scott, Deborah Emont, Dir, Taft Museum of Art Library, 316 Pike St, Cincinnati, OH, 45202-4293. Tel: 513-684-4525. Fax: 513-241-7762. p. 1873

Scott, Diane, Circ Mgr, Xavier University of Louisiana, One Drexel Dr, New Orleans, LA, 70125-1098. Tel: 504-520-7305. Fax: 504-520-7940. p. 964

Scott, Edward A, Dr, Libr Dir, United States Air Force Academy Libraries, 2354 Fairchild Dr, Ste 3A10, USAF Academy, CO, 80840-6214. Tel: 719-333-4406. Fax: 719-333-4754. p. 324

Scott, Elainea, Prog Mgr, Tulare County Office of Education, 7000 Doe Ave, Ste A, Visalia, CA, 93291. Tel: 559-651-3042. Fax: 559-651-1012. p. 281

Scott, Elijah, Dir of Libr, Georgia Highlands College Libraries, 3175 Cedartown Hwy SE, Rome, GA, 30161. Tel: 706-295-6318. Fax: 706-295-6365. p. 548

Scott, Elizabeth, Archivist, Saint Michael's College, One Winooski Park, Box L, Colchester, VT, 05439-2525. Tel: 802-654-2540. Fax: 802-654-2630. p. 2422

Scott, Elizabeth M, Archivist, Rec Mgt Librn, Pittsburgh Theological Seminary, 616 N Highland Ave, Pittsburgh, PA, 15206-2596. Tel: 412-924-1353. Fax: 412-362-2329. p. 2127

Scott, Eric, Dir, Admin Serv, Head, Access Serv, University of California, Merced Library, 5200 N Lake Rd, Merced, CA, 95343-5001. Tel: 209-675-8040. Fax: 209-228-4271. p. 186

Scott, Fran, Mgr, Archit Libr/Ref & Instrul Serv, Rensselaer Libraries, Rensselaer Polytechnic Inst, 110 Eighth St, Troy, NY, 12180-3590. Tel: 518-276-8300. Fax: 518-276-2044. p. 1756

Scott, Gail, Ch, Crete Public Library District, 1177 N Main St, Crete, IL, 60417. Tel: 708-672-8017. Fax: 708-672-3529. p. 632

Scott, Gertie, Br Mgr, Librn III, Montgomery City-County Public Library System, Coliseum Boulevard Branch Library, 840 Coliseum Blvd, Montgomery, AL, 36109. Tel: 334-271-7005. Fax: 334-244-5754. p. 29

Scott, Glenda, Br Librn, Dunklin County Library, Hornersville Branch, 502 School St, Hornersville, MO, 63855. Tel: 573-737-2728. p. 1342

Scott, Hal, Br Mgr, Albemarle Regional Library, Hertford County Library, 303 W Tryon St, Winton, NC, 27986. Tel: 252-358-7855. Fax: 252-358-0368. p. 1835

Scott, Jamie, Dir, North Madison County Public Library System, 1600 Main St, Elwood, IN, 46036. Tel: 765-552-5001. Fax: 765-552-0955. p. 737

Scott, Jane, Pub Serv Librn, George Fox University, 416 N Meridian St, Newberg, OR, 97132. Tel: 503-554-2410. Fax: 503-554-3599. p. 2007

Scott, Janet, Ref Serv, McHenry County College Library, 8900 US Hwy 14, Crystal Lake, IL, 60012-2738. Tel: 815-455-8533. Fax: 815-455-3999. p. 632

Scott, Janet L, Librn, Sweet Springs Public Library, 217 Turner St, Sweet Springs, MO, 65351. Tel: 660-335-4314. p. 1368

Scott, Janice, Librn, Kansas Heritage Center Library, 1000 N Second Ave, Dodge City, KS, 67801-4415. Tel: 620-227-1616. Fax: 620-227-1701. p. 863

Scott, Jeff, Dep County Librn, Tulare County Library, 200 W Oak Ave, Visalia, CA, 93291-4993. Tel: 559-733-6954, Ext 222. Fax: 559-730-2524. p. 280

Scott, Jeff, Dep County Librn, Tulare County Library, Visalia Headquarters Branch, 200 W Oak Ave, Visalia, CA, 93291. Tel: 559-713-2721. Fax: 559-737-4586. p. 281

Scott, JoAnne, Libr Tech, Dow Chemical Library, Business Intelligence Ctr, B-1210, 2301 Brazosport Blvd, Freeport, TX, 77541. Tel: 979-238-2011, 979-238-4854. p. 2325

Scott, Judy, Br Mgr, Rampart Public Library District, Florissant Public Library, 334 Circle Dr, Florissant, CO, 80816. Tel: 719-748-3939. Fax: 719-748-3939. p. 326

Scott, Judy, Br Mgr, Grant Parish Library, Georgetown Branch, 4570 Hwy 500, Georgetown, LA, 71432. Tel: 318-827-9427. Fax: 318-827-9427. p. 947

Scott, Judy Ann, Adult Serv, Weston County Public Library, 23 W Main St, Newcastle, WY, 82701. Tel: 307-746-2206. Fax: 307-746-2218. p. 2658

Scott, Julie, Exec Dir, Rosicrucian Order, AMORC, Rosicrucian Park, 1342 Naglee Ave, San Jose, CA, 95191. Tel: 408-947-3600. Fax: 408-947-3677. p. 250

Scott, K, Circ, Woodstock Public Library, 445 Hunter St, Woodstock, ON, N4S 4G7, CANADA. Tel: 519-539-4801. Fax: 519-539-5246. p. 2872

Scott, Karen, Br Coordr, Lennox & Addington County Public Library, Bath Branch, 197 Davey St, Bath, ON, K0H 1G0, CANADA. Tel: 613-352-5600. p. 2824

Scott, Karen, Br Coordr, Lennox & Addington County Public Library, South Fredericksburgh, 2478 County Rd 8, Bath, ON, K0H 1G0, CANADA. Tel: 613-354-4114. p. 2824

Scott, Karen, Br Coordr, Lennox & Addington County Public Library, Stella Branch, 5555 Front Rd, Stella, ON, K0H 2S0, CANADA. Tel: 613-389-9371. p. 2824

Scott, Kathleen, Librn, Washtenaw Community College, 4800 E Huron River Dr, Ann Arbor, MI, 48105-4800. Tel: 734-973-3430. Fax: 734-973-3446. p. 1153

Scott, Kathleen, Librn, West Grey Public Library, Neustadt Public, 511 Mill St, Neustadt, ON, N0G 2M0, CANADA. Tel: 519-799-5830. Fax: 519-799-5830. p. 2803

Scott, Kenneth, Head Librn, Community Library, Ten John St, Lyman, ME, 04002-7312. Tel: 207-499-7114. p. 991

Scott, Kerry, Head, Coll Develop, Librn, University of California, 1156 High St, Santa Cruz, CA, 95064. Tel: 831-459-2802. Fax: 831-459-8206. p. 264

Scott, Kifflie, Pub Serv Mgr, Teen Librn, Menomonee Falls Public Library, W156 N8436 Pilgrim Rd, Menomonee Falls, WI, 53051. Tel: 262-532-8900. Fax: 262-532-8939. p. 2614

Scott, Kim, Br Mgr, Albuquerque-Bernalillo County Library System, San Pedro Branch, 5600 Trumbull Ave SE, Albuquerque, NM, 87108. Tel: 505-256-2067. Fax: 505-256-2064. p. 1548

Scott, Kim, Mgr, Albuquerque-Bernalillo County Library System, Ernie Pyle Branch, 900 Girard Blvd SE, Albuquerque, NM, 87106. Tel: 505-256-2065. Fax: 505-256-2069. p. 1548

Scott, Kim Allen, Spec Coll & Archives Librn, Montana State University Libraries, Centennial Mall, Bozeman, MT, 59717. Tel: 406-984-5297. Fax: 406-994-2851. p. 1375

Scott, Kinney, Libr Dir, Sweetwater County Library System, 300 N First East, Green River, WY, 82935. Tel: 307-875-3615, Ext 5130. Fax: 307-872-3203. p. 2655

Scott, Kristy, Libr Tech II, Colorado Department of Corrections, LaVista Correctional Facility Library, 1401 W 17th St, Pueblo, CO, 81003. Tel: 719-544-4800, Ext 3721. Fax: 719-583-5909. p. 320

Scott, L, Librn, Robert Morris University, 3101 Montvale Dr, Springfield, IL, 62704-4260. Tel: 217-726-1675, 217-726-1676. Fax: 217-726-1684. p. 706

Scott, Laura, Supvr, Virginia Beach Public Library Department, Subregional Library for the Blind & Handicapped, Bayside Special Library Services, 936 Independence Blvd, Virginia Beach, VA, 23455. Tel: 757-385-2680. p. 2500

Scott, Laurie, Assoc Univ Librn, Queen's University, 101 Union St, Kingston, ON, K7L 5C4, CANADA. Tel: 613-533-6000, Ext 77694. Fax: 613-533-6362. p. 2814

Scott, Lee, Tech Consult, South Central Kansas Library System, 321 N Main St, South Hutchinson, KS, 67505-1146. Tel: 620-663-3211. Fax: 620-663-9797. p. 895

Scott, Linda, Tech Serv Mgr, Mount Union College Library, 1972 Clark Ave, Alliance, OH, 44601-3993. Tel: 330-823-3844. Fax: 330-823-3963. p. 1854

Scott, Lisa, Bibliog Instr, Bentley College, 175 Forest St, Waltham, MA, 02452-4705. Tel: 781-891-2168. Fax: 781-891-2830. p. 1132

Scott, Lisette, Ch, Programming Librn, Dunbar Free Library, 401 Rte 10 S, Grantham, NH, 03753. Tel: 603-863-2172. Fax: 603-863-2172. p. 1448

Scott, Lloyd, Info Serv, Cincinnati Christian University, 2700 Glenway Ave, Cincinnati, OH, 45204-3200. Tel: 513-244-8680. Fax: 513-244-8434. p. 1869

Scott, Lucinda, Librn, Northwest Florida Water Management District, 81 Water Management Dr, Havana, FL, 32333. Tel: 850-539-5999. Fax: 850-539-2777. p. 450

Scott, Lydia, Mgr, Carnegie Library of Pittsburgh, South Side, 2205 E Carson St, Pittsburgh, PA, 15203. Tel: 412-431-0505. p. 2123

Scott, Marguerite, Br Coordr, Birmingham Public Library, 2100 Park Pl, Birmingham, AL, 35203. Tel: 205-226-4025. Fax: 205-250-0725. p. 7

Scott, Marguerite, Librn, Birmingham Public Library, North Birmingham, 2501 N 31st Ave, Birmingham, AL, 35207. Tel: 205-226-4025. Fax: 205-250-0725. p. 7

Scott, Mary, Br Mgr, Lincoln County Public Library, Florence Soule Shanklin Memorial, 7837 Fairfield Forest Rd, Denver, NC, 28037. Tel: 704-483-3589. Fax: 704-483-8317. p. 1807

Scott, Mary Ann, Head, Adult Serv, Brighton District Library, 100 Library Dr, Brighton, MI, 48116. Tel: 810-229-6571, Ext 225. Fax: 810-229-3161. p. 1159

Scott, Mary Woods, Librn, Ohio State University LIBRARIES, Orton Memorial Library of Geology, 180 Orton Hall, 155 S Oval Mall, Columbus, OH, 43210. Tel: 614-292-6152. p. 1889

Scott, Melanie, Dir, Desert Research Institute, 755 E Flamingo Rd, Las Vegas, NV, 89119-7363. Tel: 775-674-7083. Fax: 702-862-5542. p. 1429

Scott, Melanie, Dir, Libr Serv, Desert Research Institute, 2215 Raggio Pkwy, Reno, NV, 89512-1095. Tel: 775-674-7083. Fax: 775-674-7183. p. 1432

Scott, Melissa, Tech Coordr, Fayette County Public Library, 828 N Grand Ave, Connersville, IN, 47331. Tel: 765-827-0883. Fax: 765-825-4592. p. 733

Scott, Melody, Head, Youth Serv, Hammond Public Library, 564 State St, Hammond, IN, 46320-1532. Tel: 219-931-5100, Ext 330. Fax: 219-931-3474. p. 747

Scott, Michael, Asst Dir, Southeastern Libraries Cooperating, 2600 19th St NW, Rochester, MN, 55901-0767. Tel: 507-288-5513. Fax: 507-288-8697. p. 2947

Scott, Michelle, Head Librn, Boissevain & Morton Regional Library, 436 S Railway, Boissevain, MB, R0K 0E0, CANADA. Tel: 204-534-6478. Fax: 204-534-3710. p. 2747

Scott, Miranda, Info Spec, Colgate-Palmolive Co, 909 River Rd, Piscataway, NJ, 08855. Tel: 732-878-7574. Fax: 732-878-7128. p. 1520

Scott, Mitchell, Ref Librn, Spalding University Library, 853 Library Lane, Louisville, KY, 40203-9986. Tel: 502-585-7130. Fax: 502-585-7156. p. 925

Scott, Mona, Bus Mgr, Metropolitan Library Service Agency, 1619 Dayton Ave, No 314, Saint Paul, MN, 55104-6206. Tel: 651-645-5731. Fax: 651-649-3169. p. 2947

Scott, Nancy H, Dir, Eureka Public Library District, 202 S Main St, Eureka, IL, 61530. Tel: 309-467-2922. Fax: 309-467-3527. p. 643

Scott, Neil, Circ/Reserves, Middle Tennessee State University, MTSU, PO Box 13, Murfreesboro, TN, 37132. Tel: 615-898-2539. p. 2254

Scott, Norma, Dir, Somerset Public Library, 208 Hud St, Somerset, WI, 54025. Tel: 715-247-5228. Fax: 715-247-5141. p. 2638

Scott, Patricia, Asst Dir, Res & Educ, Loyola University Chicago Libraries, Law School Library, 25 E Pearson St, 3rd Flr, Chicago, IL, 60611. Tel: 312-915-8515. Fax: 312-915-6797. p. 617

Scott, Patricia, Librn, Archives & Coll Develop, Roger & Peggy Madigan Library, 999 Hagan Way, Williamsport, PA, 17701. Tel: 570-327-4523. Fax: 570-327-4503. p. 2156

Scott, Patty, Dir, Neptune City Library, 106 W Sylvania Ave, Neptune City, NJ, 07753. Tel: 732-988-8866. p. 1507

Scott, Paula, Dr, Librn, Driscoll Children's Hospital, 3533 S Alameda St, Corpus Christi, TX, 78411-1721. Tel: 361-694-5467. Fax: 361-808-2141. p. 2302

Scott, Peggy, Dir, Benson Public Library, 300 S Huachuca, Benson, AZ, 85602-6650. Tel: 520-586-9535. Fax: 520-586-3224. p. 58

Scott, Penny, Ref Serv, University of San Francisco, 2130 Fulton St, San Francisco, CA, 94117-1080. Tel: 415-422-5389. Fax: 415-422-5949. p. 248

Scott, Rachel, Ref Librn, Belmont University, 1900 Belmont Blvd, Nashville, TN, 37212-3757. Tel: 615-460-6782. Fax: 615-460-5641. p. 2255

Scott, Rebecca, Dean, Libr & Learning Res, Napa Valley College Library, 1700 Bldg, 2277 Napa-Vallejo Hwy, Napa, CA, 94558. Tel: 707-256-7438. Fax: 707-253-3015. p. 193

Scott, Rejeanor H, Dir of Libr Serv, Edgecombe Community College, 2009 W Wilson St, Tarboro, NC, 27886. Tel: 252-823-5166. Fax: 252-823-6817. p. 1826

Scott, Rejeanor H, Dir of Libr Serv, Edgecombe Community College, Rocky Mount Campus, 225 Tarboro St, Rocky Mount, NC, 27801. Tel: 252-446-0436. Fax: 252-985-2212. p. 1826

Scott, Richard W, Electronic Res & Per Librn, Walla Walla University Libraries, 104 S College Ave, College Place, WA, 99324-1159. Tel: 509-527-2684. Fax: 509-527-2001. p. 2513

Scott, Rose, Exec Dir, Josephine County Historical Society, 512 SW Fifth St, Grants Pass, OR, 97526. Tel: 541-479-7827. p. 1999

Scott, RyAnne, Libr Dir, American Numismatic Association Library, 818 N Cascade Ave, Colorado Springs, CO, 80903-3279. Tel: 719-482-9867. Fax: 719-634-4085. p. 294

Scott, Sammi, Borrower Serv Librn, Delaware County Library, 429 S Ninth St, Jay, OK, 74346. Tel: 918-253-8521. Fax: 918-253-8726. p. 1966

Scott, Sandy, Librn, Public Library of Steubenville & Jefferson County, Dillonvale-Mt Pleasant Branch, 192 Cole St, Dillonvale, OH, 43917. Tel: 740-769-2090. Fax: 740-769-2771. p. 1937

Scott, Sharon, Head, Electronic Res & Continuation, University of California, Riverside Libraries, 900 University Ave, Riverside, CA, 92521. Tel: 951-827-2813. p. 218

Scott, Sharon, Librn, Northeastern Illinois University, Carruthers Center for Inner City Studies, 700 E Oakwood Blvd, Chicago, IL, 60653. Tel: 773-256-2134, 773-268-7500, Ext 163. Fax: 773-442-4531. p. 621

Scott, Sharon, Tech Serv Coordr, Cumberland County Library System, 19 S West St, Carlisle, PA, 17013-2839. Tel: 717-240-7872. p. 2041

Scott, Sharon, Circ, South Interlake Regional Library, 419 Main St, Stonewall, MB, R0C 2Z0, CANADA. Tel: 204-467-8415. Fax: 204-467-9809. p. 2752

Scott, Sharon Faith, Librn, United States Navy, NAS Dr, Corpus Christi, TX, 78419. Tel: 361-961-3574. p. 2302

Scott, Sheila G, Librn, Boston Public Library, West Roxbury Branch, 1961 Centre St, West Roxbury, MA, 02132-2595. Tel: 617-325-3147. Fax: 617-325-1972. p. 1057

Scott, Shelley Ann, Dir, M Alice Chapin Memorial Library, 120 E Main St, Marion, MI, 49665. Tel: 231-743-2421. Fax: 231-743-2421. p. 1206

Scott, Susan, Dir, Gale Free Library, 23 Highland St, Holden, MA, 01520-2599. Tel: 508-210-5566. Fax: 508-829-0232. p. 1095

Scott, Susan, Dir, Ohio State University LIBRARIES, Newark Campus Library, Warner Library & Student Center, 1179 University Dr, Newark, OH, 43055-1797. Tel: 740-366-9307. Fax: 740-366-9264. p. 1889

Scott, Susan M, Dir, Western Sullivan Public Library, 19 Center St, Jeffersonville, NY, 12748. Tel: 845-482-4350. Fax: 845-482-3092. p. 1647

Scott, Tara, Ref Librn, Westland Public Library, 6123 Central City Pkwy, Westland, MI, 48185. Tel: 734-326-6123. Fax: 734-595-4612. p. 1236

Scott, Teretha, Br Mgr, Collins LeRoy Leon County Public Library System, Fort Braden, 16327 Blountstown Hwy, Tallahassee, FL, 32310. Tel: 850-606-2900. Fax: 850-606-2901. p. 492

Scott, Thomas L, Dir, Kentucky Christian University, 100 Academic Pkwy, Grayson, KY, 41143-2205. Tel: 606-474-3275. Fax: 606-474-3123. p. 915

Scott, Timothy, Adminr, Saint Joseph's Abbey, 167 N Spencer Rd, Spencer, MA, 01562-1233. Tel: 508-885-8700, Ext 524. Fax: 508-885-8701. p. 1126

Scott, Tina, Asst Dir, Chautauqua-Cattaraugus Library System, 106 W Fifth St, Jamestown, NY, 14701. Tel: 716-484-7136. p. 1646

Scott, Tina, Asst Dir, James Prendergast Library Association, 509 Cherry St, Jamestown, NY, 14701. Tel: 716-484-7135. Fax: 716-487-1148. p. 1647

Scott, Torie, Fac Librn-Cascade Campus, Portland Community College Library, 12000 SW 49th AV, Portland, OR, 97219. Tel: 971-722-5433. Fax: 971-722-8397. p. 2013

Scott, Ursula, Ref Serv, Uniformed Services University of the Health Sciences, 4301 Jones Bridge Rd, Bethesda, MD, 20814-4799. Tel: 301-295-3399. Fax: 301-295-3795. p. 1022

Scott Weber, Chela, Dir, Libr & Archives, Brooklyn Historical Society Othmer Library, 128 Pierrepont St, Brooklyn, NY, 11201-2711. Tel: 718-222-4111. Fax: 718-222-3794. p. 1590

Scott, Wendy, Exec Dir, DeWitt Community Library, Shoppingtown Mall, 3649 Erie Blvd E, DeWitt, NY, 13214. Tel: 315-446-3578. Fax: 315-446-1955. p. 1614

Scott, Wilbertine, Ref, Cleveland Bradley County Public Library, 795 Church St NE, Cleveland, TN, 37311-5295. Tel: 423-472-2163. Fax: 423-339-9791. p. 2229

Scott-Branch, Jamillah, Media & Tech Serv Librn, Elizabeth City State University, 1704 Weeksville Rd, Elizabeth City, NC, 27909. Tel: 252-335-8516. Fax: 252-335-3446. p. 1790

Scott-Peterman, Dana, Head, Access Serv, Yale University Library, Seeley G Mudd Library, 38 Mansfield St, New Haven, CT, 06511. Tel: 203-432-3203. Fax: 203-432-3214. p. 358

Scott-Smith, Christine Ku, Dir, University of Guam, UOG Sta, Mangilao, GU, 96923. Tel: 671-735-2333. Fax: 671-734-6882. p. 2667

Scott-Smith, Sandra, Operations Mgr, Consortium for Open Learning, 333 Sunrise Ave, No 229, Roseville, CA, 95661-3480. Tel: 916-788-0660. Fax: 916-788-0696. p. 2938

Scotto, Cara, Asst Prof, Info Literacy & Outreach Librn, Felician College Library, 262 S Main St, Lodi, NJ, 07644-2198. Tel: 201-559-6133. Fax: 201-559-6148. p. 1496

Scoville, Marilyn, Ref & Instrul Serv, Instr Coordr, Saint Michael's College, One Winooski Park, Box L, Colchester, VT, 05439-2525. Tel: 802-654-2410. Fax: 802-654-2630. p. 2422

Scretchen, Denise, Br Mgr, Public Library of Cincinnati & Hamilton County, Forest Park Branch, 655 Waycross Rd, Forest Park, OH, 45240. Tel: 513-369-4478. Fax: 513-369-4480. p. 1871

Scrimgeour, Andrew D, Dr, Dean of Libr, Drew University Library, 36 Madison Ave, Madison, NJ, 07940. Tel: 973-408-3322. Fax: 973-408-3770. p. 1497

Scritchfield, Larry, Syst Adminr, Cochise County Library District, Old High School, 2nd Flr, 100 Clawson, Bisbee, AZ, 85603. Tel: 520-432-8930. Fax: 520-432-7339. p. 58

Scritchfield, Teresa, Librn, White County Regional Library System, Lyda Miller Library, 2609 Hwy 367 N, Bald Knob, AR, 72010. Tel: 501-724-5452. p. 115

Scriven, Gayle, Dir, Florence Public Library, 324 Main St, Florence, KS, 66851. Tel: 620-878-4649. p. 866

Scrivener, Chris, Br Coordr, County of Brant Public Library, Burford Branch, 24 Park Ave, Burford, ON, N0E 1A0, CANADA. Tel: 519-449-5371. Fax: 519-449-5371. p. 2835

Scrivner, Kristie, ILL, Winchester Public Library, 203 Fourth St, Winchester, KS, 66097. Tel: 913-774-4967. Fax: 913-774-4967. p. 902

Scro, Suzanne, Br Mgr, Ocean County Library, Manchester Branch, 21 Colonial Dr, Lakehurst, NJ, 08733-3801. Tel: 732-657-7600. Fax: 732-323-9246. p. 1534

Scroggins, Cindy, Dir, Baylor Health Sciences Library, 3302 Gaston Ave, Dallas, TX, 75246. Tel: 214-828-8930. Fax: 214-820-2095. p. 2304

Scroggins, Lisa, Dir, Claud H Gilmer Memorial Library, 206 N Hwy 377, Rocksprings, TX, 78880. Tel: 830-683-8130. Fax: 830-683-8131. p. 2376

Scruggs, Melissa, Dir, Beersheba Springs Public Library, Hwy 56, Beersheba Springs, TN, 37305. Tel: 931-692-3029. Fax: 931-692-3029. p. 2224

Scruggs, Sarah Isabelle, Chief Librn, G V (Sonny) Montgomery VA Medical Center Library, 1500 E Woodrow Wilson Dr, Jackson, MS, 39216. Tel: 601-364-1273. Fax: 601-364-1316. p. 1305

Scucces, Adrianne, Youth Serv Librn, Aldrich Public Library, Six Washington St, Barre, VT, 05641-4227. Tel: 802-476-7550. Fax: 802-479-0450 (Call before sending fax). p. 2418

Scudder, Beth A, Dir, McKinney Memorial Public Library, 101 E Hunt St, McKinney, TX, 75069. Tel: 972-547-7323. Fax: 972-542-0868. p. 2361

Scull, Barbara, Librn, Middletown Public Library, 20 N Catherine St, Middletown, PA, 17057-1401. Tel: 717-944-6412. Fax: 717-930-0510. p. 2089

Scully, Jean M, Dir, Redondo Beach Public Library, 303 N Pacific Coast Hwy, Redondo Beach, CA, 90277. Tel: 310-318-0675. Fax: 310-318-3809. p. 215

Scully, Mike, Libr Syst Coordr, Swedish Medical Center Library, First Hill Campus, 747 Broadway, Seattle, WA, 98122-4307. Tel: 206-386-2484. Fax: 206-215-3081. p. 2532

Scurry, Paulette, Br Mgr, East Central Georgia Regional Library, Wallace Branch, 1237 Laney-Walker Blvd, Augusta, GA, 30901. Tel: 706-722-6275. Fax: 706-724-0715. p. 520

Scussel, Adreana, Tech Serv Librn, Stafford Library, Ten Levinthal Run, Stafford, CT, 06075. Tel: 860-684-2852. Fax: 860-684-2128. p. 369

Seabold, Tracy Carr, Dir, Info Serv, Mississippi Library Commission, 3881 Eastwood Dr, Jackson, MS, 39211. Tel: 601-432-4450. Fax: 601-432-4480. p. 1304

Seabolt, Denise Ash, Libr Admin Serv Dir, West Virginia Library Commission, State Capitol Complex, 1900 Kanawha Blvd E, Charleston, WV, 25305-0620. Tel: 304-558-2041, Ext 2087. Fax: 304-558-2044. p. 2557

Seabolt, Pamela, Head, Tech/Extn Serv, Frankfort Community Public Library, 208 W Clinton St, Frankfort, IN, 46041. Tel: 765-654-8746. Fax: 765-654-8747. p. 743

Seabright, Alice, Circ, Lord Fairfax Community College, 173 Skirmisher Lane, Middletown, VA, 22645-1745. Tel: 540-868-7156. Fax: 540-868-7171. p. 2479

Seaders, Cheryl, Circ, Linn-Benton Community College Library, 6500 SW Pacific Blvd, Albany, OR, 97321-3799. Tel: 541-917-4638. Fax: 541-917-4659. p. 1989

Seager, Sandy, Dir, Avoca Free Library, 18 N Main St, Avoca, NY, 14809-0519. Tel: 607-566-9279. Fax: 607-566-9279. p. 1576

Seagle, Mary, ILL, University of Montevallo, Station 6100, Montevallo, AL, 35115-6100. Tel: 205-665-6100. Fax: 205-665-6112. p. 27

Seago, Brenda L, PhD, Dir of Libr, Prof, Georgia Health Sciences University, 1459 Laney-Walker Blvd, Augusta, GA, 30912-4400. Tel: 706-721-2856. Fax: 706-721-2018. p. 520

Seagrave, Gerald, Librn, Connecticut Police Academy, 285 Preston Ave, Meriden, CT, 06450. Tel: 203-238-6531. Fax: 203-238-6643. p. 350

Seaholm, Jill, Head, Genealogical Serv, Swenson Swedish Immigration Research Center, Augustana College, 3520 Seventh Ave, Rock Island, IL, 61201. Tel: 309-794-7204. Fax: 309-794-7443. p. 696

Seal, Afton Elizabeth, Dir, Guilford Smith Memorial Library, 17 Main St, South Windham, CT, 06266-1121. Tel: 860-423-5159. Fax: 860-423-5159. p. 368

Seal, Diana, Cat, YA Serv, Meade County Public Library, 400 Library Pl, Brandenburg, KY, 40108-1045. Tel: 270-422-2094. Fax: 270-422-3133. p. 908

Seal, Jean, Br Mgr, Catahoula Parish Library, Sicily Island Branch, PO Box 266, Sicily Island, LA, 71368. Tel: 318-389-5804. Fax: 318-389-5804. p. 951

Seal, Robert, Dean of Libr, Loyola University Chicago Libraries, 1032 W Sheridan Rd, Chicago, IL, 60660. Tel: 773-508-2641. Fax: 773-508-2993. p. 617

Seal, Robert, Dean of Libr, Loyola University Chicago Libraries, Elizabeth M Cudahy Memorial Library, 6525 N Sheridan Rd, Chicago, IL, 60626. p. 617

Sealand, Evans, Dr, Archivist, United Church of Christ, 125 Sherman St, Hartford, CT, 06105. Tel: 860-233-5564. Fax: 860-231-8111. p. 347

Sealine, Holly, Libr Dir, Norwalk Easter Public Library, 1051 North Ave, Norwalk, IA, 50211. Tel: 515-981-0217. Fax: 515-981-4346. p. 836

Seally, Joan, Mgr, Borden Ladner Gervais LLP Library, Centennial Place, East Tower, 1900, 530-Third Ave SW, Calgary, AB, T2P 0R3, CANADA. Tel: 403-232-9500. Fax: 403-266-1395. p. 2688

Seals, Nova, Archives & Spec Coll Librn, Connecticut College, 270 Mohegan Ave, New London, CT, 06320-4196. Tel: 860-439-2686. Fax: 860-439-2871. p. 359

Sealy, Irene, Dir, Cochran County Love Memorial Library, 318 S Main, Morton, TX, 79346-3006. Tel: 806-266-5051. Fax: 806-266-8057. p. 2363

Seaman, David, Assoc Librn, Dartmouth College Library, 6025 Baker Berry Library, Rm 115, Hanover, NH, 03755-3525. Tel: 603-646-2236. Fax: 603-646-3702. p. 1450

Seaman, David, Assoc Librn, Dartmouth College Library, Baker-Berry Library, 6025 Baker-Berry Library, Hanover, NH, 03755-3525. Tel: 603-646-2560. Fax: 603-646-2167. p. 1450

Seaman, Paula, ILL, Lewis & Clark Community College, 5800 Godfrey Rd, Godfrey, IL, 62035. Tel: 618-466-3411, Ext 4304. Fax: 618-468-4301. p. 651

Seaman, Priscilla, Ref & Libr Instruction, University of Tennessee at Chattanooga Library, 615 McCallie Ave, Dept 6456, Chattanooga, TN, 37403-2598. Tel: 423-425-4501. Fax: 423-425-4775. p. 2228

Seaman, Sally, Cat, Lynn University Library, 3601 N Military Trail, Boca Raton, FL, 33431-5598. Tel: 561-237-7073. Fax: 561-237-7074. p. 428

Seaman, Sara, Dir, National Park Community College Library, 101 College Dr, Hot Springs, AR, 71913. Tel: 501-760-4101, 501-760-4110. Fax: 501-760-4106. p. 104

Seaman, Scott, Dean of Libr, Ohio University Libraries, 30 Park Pl, Athens, OH, 45701-2978. Tel: 740-593-2705. Fax: 740-593-2708. p. 1856

Seaman, Sheila, Pub Serv, College of Charleston, 205 Calhoun St, Charleston, SC, 29401-3519. Tel: 843-953-5530. Fax: 843-953-6319. p. 2184

Seaman, Terri, Librn, Project Mgr, United States Army, Fort Riley Post Library, Bldg 5306, Hood Dr, Fort Riley, KS, 66442-6416. Tel: 785-239-5305. Fax: 785-239-4422. p. 867

Seamands, Nancy, Librn, A Herr Smith & E E Smith Library, 105 E Adams St, Loda, IL, 60948. Tel: 217-386-2783. Fax: 217-386-2223. p. 667

Seamans, James, Librn, Sullivan University Library, Spencerian College Lexington Campus, 1575 Winchester Rd, Lexington, KY, 40505-4520. Tel: 859-977-5465. Fax: 859-224-7744. p. 926

Seamans, Nancy H, Dr, Dean of Libr, Georgia State University Library, 100 Decatur St SE, Atlanta, GA, 30303-3202. Tel: 404-413-2700. Fax: 404-413-2701. p. 516

Seamans, Sally, Image Librn, Montserrat College of Art, 23 Essex St, Beverly, MA, 01915. Tel: 978-921-4242, Ext 1210. Fax: 978-922-4268. p. 1054

Seamans, Sue, Librn, Falconer Public Library, 101 W Main St, Falconer, NY, 14733. Tel: 716-665-3504. Fax: 716-665-9203. p. 1621

Seamon, George, Jr, Dir, Libr Develop Consult, Northwest Kansas Library System, Two Washington Sq, Norton, KS, 67654-1615. Tel: 785-877-5148. Fax: 785-877-5697. p. 885

Seamster, Gale, Br Mgr, Campbell County Public Library, Patrick Henry Memorial, 204 Lynchburg Ave, Brookneal, VA, 24528. Tel: 434-376-3363. Fax: 434-376-1111. p. 2495

Searer, Kim, Librn, Motorola Technical & Business Library, 8000 W Sunrise Blvd, Fort Lauderdale, FL, 33322. Tel: 954-723-5049. Fax: 954-723-4466. p. 443

Seargeant, Windell, Librn, Southeast Regional Library, Redvers Branch, 23B Railway Ave, Redvers, SK, S0C 2H0, CANADA. Tel: 306-452-3255. p. 2930

Searing, Susan E, Librn, University of Illinois Library at Urbana-Champaign, Library & Information Science Virtual Library, 310 Main Library, 1408 W Gregory Dr, Urbana, IL, 61801. Tel: 217-333-3804, 217-333-4456. p. 712

Searles, Kathleen, Dir, Libr & Media, Oregon Coast Community College Library, 332 SW Coast Hwy, Newport, OR, 97365-4928. Tel: 541-574-7126. Fax: 541-265-3820. p. 2008

Searles, Mary S, Dir, Law Librn, New Hampshire Law Library, Supreme Court Bldg, One Charles Doe Dr, Concord, NH, 03301-6160. Tel: 603-271-3777. Fax: 603-513-5450. p. 1443

Searles, Melissa, Asst Dir, GEP Dodge Library, Two Main St, Bennington, NH, 03442-4109. Tel: 603-588-6585. Fax: 603-588-6585. p. 1439

Sears, Amy, Ch, Teaneck Public Library, 840 Teaneck Rd, Teaneck, NJ, 07666. Tel: 201-837-4171. Fax: 201-837-0410. p. 1533

Sears, Carlton A, Dir, Public Library of Youngstown & Mahoning County, 305 Wick Ave, Youngstown, OH, 44503-1079. Tel: 330-744-8636. Fax: 330-744-3355. p. 1952

Sears, Carolyn, Libr Serv Adminr, Commun Serv, Chesterfield County Public Library, 9501 Lori Rd, Chesterfield, VA, 23832. Tel: 804-748-1761. Fax: 804-751-4679. p. 2457

Sears, Deborah, Ref Serv Coordr, Jackson District Library, 290 W Michigan Ave, Jackson, MI, 49201. Tel: 517-788-4087, Ext 1344. Fax: 517-782-8635. p. 1195

Sears, Debra, Extn Serv Mgr, LeRoy Collins Leon County Public Library System, 200 W Park Ave, Tallahassee, FL, 32301-7720. Tel: 850-606-2665. Fax: 850-606-2601. p. 492

Sears, Dennis, Ref, Brigham Young University, Howard W Hunter Law Library, 256 JRCB, Provo, UT, 84602-8000. Tel: 801-422-3593. Fax: 801-422-0404. p. 2411

Sears Ilnicki, Wendy, Asst Dir, Mgr, Bibliog Serv, Yellowhead Regional Library, 433 King St, Spruce Grove, AB, T7X 2Y1, CANADA. Tel: 780-962-2003, Ext 225. Fax: 780-962-2770. p. 2717

Sears, Jan, Dir, Kimball Public Library, 208 S Walnut St, Kimball, NE, 69145. Tel: 308-235-4523. Fax: 308-235-2971. p. 1403

Sears, Jill, Br Mgr, Broward County Division of Libraries, Imperial Point, 5985 N Federal Hwy, Fort Lauderdale, FL, 33308. Tel: 954-492-1881. Fax: 954-492-1804. p. 441

Sears, JoAnn, Coll Coordr, University of Michigan, Shapiro Science Library, 3175 Shapiro Library, 919 S University Ave, Ann Arbor, MI, 48109-1185. Tel: 734-936-2341. Fax: 734-763-9813. p. 1153

Sears, Patsy, Ref, University of Montevallo, Station 6100, Montevallo, AL, 35115-6100. Tel: 205-665-6100. Fax: 205-665-6112. p. 27

Sears, Robert E, Dir, Libr Serv, Southern Wesleyan University, 916 Wesleyan Dr, Central, SC, 29630-9748. Tel: 864-644-5064. Fax: 864-644-5904. p. 2183

Sears, Russell, Librn, Glendale Community College, 6000 W Olive Ave, Glendale, AZ, 85302. Tel: 623-845-3110. Fax: 623-845-3102. p. 64

Sears, Sandra, Dir, Perry Memorial Library, 22 SE Fifth Ave, Perryton, TX, 79070. Tel: 806-435-5801. Fax: 806-435-4266. p. 2369

Sears, Stephen A, Electronic Res, Johns Hopkins University School of Advanced International Studies, 1740 Massachusetts Ave NW, Washington, DC, 20036. Tel: 202-663-5907. Fax: 202-663-5916. p. 405

Sears, Suzanne, Asst Dean, Pub Serv, University of North Texas Libraries, PO Box 305190, Denton, TX, 76203-5190. Tel: 940-565-2868. Fax: 940-369-8760. p. 2313

Seary, Cathy, Ref Librn, YA Serv, George F Johnson Memorial Library, 1001 Park St, Endicott, NY, 13760. Tel: 607-757-5350. Fax: 607-757-2491. p. 1620

Seaton, Cindy, Librn, Fayette County Law Library, 110 E Court House, Washington Court House, OH, 43160-1355. Tel: 740-335-3608. Fax: 740-335-3608. p. 1945

Seaton, Jennifer, Libr Dir, Carthage Public Library, 612 S Garrison Ave, Carthage, MO, 64836. Tel: 417-237-7040. Fax: 417-237-7041. p. 1322

Seavey, Joan, Mgr, Canton Free Library, Morley Branch, 7230 County Rte 27, Canton, NY, 13617. Tel: 315-379-0066. p. 1602

Seavey, Patricia, Libr Mgr, Santa Fe Public Library, Southside Branch Library, 6599 Jaguar Dr, Santa Fe, NM, 85707. Tel: 505-955-2811. p. 1564

Seay, Cynthia, Br Mgr, Pamunkey Regional Library, Lois Wickham Jones - Montpelier Branch, 17205 Sycamore Tavern Lane, Montpelier, VA, 23192. Tel: 804-883-7116. Fax: 804-883-5165. p. 2469

Seay, Cynthia, Br Mgr, Norfolk Public Library, Mary D Pretlow Anchor Branch Library, 111 W Ocean View Ave, Norfolk, VA, 23503-1608. Tel: 757-441-1750. Fax: 757-441-1748. p. 2482

Sebald-Kinder, Shirley, Dir, Miami Valley Hospital, One Wyoming St, Dayton, OH, 45409. Tel: 937-208-6236. Fax: 937-208-2569. p. 1893

Sebastian, Marion, Ser, New York Institute of Technology, 1855 Broadway, New York, NY, 10023. Tel: 212-261-1526. Fax: 212-261-1681. p. 1689

Sebastian, Rose, Circ Mgr, Palo Alto City Library, College Terrace, 2300 Wellesley St, Palo Alto, CA, 94306. Tel: 650-329-2478. p. 204

Sebastian, Rose, Circ Mgr, Palo Alto City Library, Downtown, 270 Forest Ave, Palo Alto, CA, 94301. Tel: 650-329-2478. Fax: 650-327-7568. p. 204

Sebastian, Rose, Mgr, Circ Serv, Palo Alto City Library, 1213 Newell Rd, Palo Alto, CA, 94303-2907. Tel: 650-329-2478. Fax: 650-327-2033. p. 204

Sebastian, Terry, Ref, College of Lake County, 19351 W Washington St, Grayslake, IL, 60030. Tel: 847-543-2469. Fax: 847-223-7690. p. 652

Sebbas, Sandra, Br Mgr, Anythink Libraries, Anythink Huron Street, 9417 Huron St, Thornton, CO, 80260. Tel: 303-452-7534. Fax: 303-450-2578. p. 324

Sebela, Mary, Dir of Circ, Rolling Meadows Library, 3110 Martin Lane, Rolling Meadows, IL, 60008. Tel: 847-259-6050. Fax: 847-259-5319. p. 698

Sebright, Terence F, PhD, Admin Librn, Southern Crescent Technical College Library - Flint Campus, 1533 Hwy 19 S, Thomaston, GA, 30286. Tel: 706-646-6173, 706-646-6225. Fax: 706-646-6240. p. 553

Seckelson, Linda, Reader Serv, Metropolitan Museum of Art, Thomas J Watson Library, 1000 Fifth Ave, New York, NY, 10028-0198. Tel: 212-570-3759. Fax: 212-570-3847. p. 1686

Seckman, David, Librn, Timberland Regional Library, Elma Branch, 118 N First, Elma, WA, 98541-0547. Tel: 360-482-3737. Fax: 360-482-3047. p. 2543

Secord, Anne Marie, Dir, Libr Serv, National University Library, 9393 Lightwave Ave, San Diego, CA, 92123-1447. Tel: 858-541-7913. Fax: 858-541-7994. p. 232

Secrist, Diane, Actg Librn, Phillips State Prison, 2989 W Rock Quarry Rd, Buford, GA, 30519-4198. Tel: 770-932-4500, Ext 4676. Fax: 770-932-4676. p. 522

Secter, Ann, Ch, Computer Serv, Bryant Library, Two Paper Mill Rd, Roslyn, NY, 11576-2193. Tel: 516-621-2240. Fax: 516-621-7211. p. 1735

Sedberry, Patti, Librn, Stonewall County Library, 516 S Washington St, Aspermont, TX, 79502. Tel: 940-989-2730. Fax: 940-989-2730. p. 2277

Sedestrom, Dave, Financial Mgr, Allen County Public Library, 900 Library Plaza, Fort Wayne, IN, 46802. Tel: 260-421-1270. Fax: 260-421-1388. p. 740

Sedey, Joe, Br Mgr, Saint Louis Public Library, Kingshighway, 2260 S Vandeventer Ave, Saint Louis, MO, 63110. Tel: 314-771-5450. Fax: 314-771-9877. p. 1360

Sedgwick, Mary, Tech Serv, Mount Saint Mary's College, 12001 Chalon Rd, Los Angeles, CA, 90049-1599. Tel: 310-954-4370. Fax: 310-954-4379. p. 175

Sedivy, Carol, Librn, Spencer Township Library, 110 Main St, Spencer, NE, 68777. Tel: 402-589-1131. p. 1420

Sedjro, Agnes, Librn, College Marie de France Library, 4635 chemin Queen Mary, Montreal, QC, H3W 1W3, CANADA. Tel: 514-737-1177. Fax: 514-737-0789. p. 2894

Sedlacek, Beverly, Dir, Nebraska Methodist College, 720 N 87th St, Omaha, NE, 68114. Tel: 402-354-7249. Fax: 402-354-7250. p. 1413

Sedlak, Belinda, Tech Serv, Westmoreland County Community College, 400 Armbrust Rd, Youngwood, PA, 15697-1895. Tel: 724-925-4096. Fax: 724-925-1150. p. 2160

Sedlak, Karen, Librn, Harry Benge Crozier Memorial Library, 184 W Moss St, Paint Rock, TX, 76866. Tel: 325-456-1420. p. 2367

Sedlock, Barbara, Assoc Librn, Defiance College, 201 College Pl, Defiance, OH, 43512-1667. Tel: 419-783-2487. Fax: 419-783-2594. p. 1895

Sedmak, Scott A, Chief Financial Officer, Public Library Association of Annapolis & Anne Arundel County, Inc, Five Harry S Truman Pkwy, Annapolis, MD, 21401. Tel: 410-222-7236. Fax: 410-222-7188. p. 1010

See, Carol, Librn, Hardy County Public Library, 102 N Main St, Moorefield, WV, 26836. Tel: 304-538-6560. Fax: 304-538-2639. p. 2566

Seeber, Kevin, Instruction Coordr, Colorado State University Pueblo Library, 2200 Bonforte Blvd, Pueblo, CO, 81001-4901. Tel: 719-549-2363. Fax: 719-549-2738. p. 320

Seeber, Lynette C, Dir, Briceville Public Library, 921 Andy's Ridge Rd, Briceville, TN, 37710. Tel: 865-426-6220. Fax: 865-426-6220. p. 2225

Seebruch, Carol, Librn, Jacobs Canada Inc, 205 Quarry Park Blvd SE, Calgary, AB, T2C 3E7, CANADA. Tel: 403-258-6411. Fax: 403-255-1421. p. 2692

Seedorff, Jane A, Librn, Lamont Public Library, 616 Bush St, Lamont, IA, 50650. Tel: 563-924-3203. Fax: 563-924-3203. p. 827

Seeger, Dawn, Cat, Phillips Public Library, 286 Cherry St, Phillips, WI, 54555-1240. Tel: 715-339-2868. p. 2629

Seeger, Evelyn, Sr Ref Librn, Sullivan & Cromwell LLP, 125 Broad St, New York, NY, 10004. Tel: 212-558-3780. Fax: 212-558-3346. p. 1700

Seeger, Leinaala, Dir, University of Hawaii, 2525 Dole St, Honolulu, HI, 96822-2328. Tel: 808-956-5577. Fax: 808-956-4615. p. 565

Seegert, Lynda C, Head, Cat, Six Mile Regional Library District, 2001 Delmar St, Granite City, IL, 62040-4590. Tel: 618-452-6238. Fax: 618-876-6317. p. 651

Seegmiller, Janet B, Spec Coll Librn, Southern Utah University, 351 W University Blvd, Cedar City, UT, 84720. Tel: 435-586-7945. Fax: 435-865-8152. p. 2404

Seegraber, Lori, Ch, Librn, Crane Thomas Public Library, Adams Shore Branch, 519 Sea St, Quincy, MA, 02169. Tel: 617-376-1325, 617-376-1326. Fax: 617-376-1437. p. 1119

Seegraber, Rita, Acq, Thomas Crane Public Library, 40 Washington St, Quincy, MA, 02269-9164. Tel: 617-376-1306. Fax: 617-376-1438. p. 1119

Seelau, Paul H, Dir, Scott County Library System, 200 N Sixth Ave, Eldridge, IA, 52748. Tel: 563-285-4794. Fax: 563-285-4743. p. 813

Seele, Carl A, Sr Librn, Napa State Hospital, 2100 Napa-Vallejo Hwy, Napa, CA, 94558. Tel: 707-253-5477. Fax: 707-253-5873. p. 193

Seeley, Jody, Children's Serv Coordr, Youth Serv Coordr, Meaford Public Library, 15 Trowbridge St W, Meaford, ON, N4L 1V4, CANADA. Tel: 519-538-1060, Ext 1123. Fax: 519-538-1808. p. 2821

Seeley, Lois, Asst Librn, Palliser Regional Library, Assiniboia & District Public Library, 201 Third Ave W, Assiniboia, SK, S0H 0B0, CANADA. Tel: 306-642-3631. p. 2918

Seeley, Maxine, Librn, Law Society of Saskatchewan Libraries, Court House, 2425 Victoria Ave, Regina, SK, S4P 3M3, CANADA. Tel: 306-569-8020. Fax: 306-569-0155. p. 2922

Seelick, Beth, Outreach/Educ, SUNY Westchester Community College, 75 Grasslands Rd, Valhalla, NY, 10595-1693. Tel: 914-785-6960. Fax: 914-785-6513. p. 1760

Seelig, Cindy, Br Mgr, Warren County Library, Northeast Branch, 40 US Hwy 46, Hackettstown, NJ, 07840. Tel: 908-813-3858. Fax: 908-813-3813. p. 1472

Seelig, Katharine, Asst Dir, Network Adminr, Lisle Library District, 777 Front St, Lisle, IL, 60532-3599. Tel: 630-971-1675. Fax: 630-971-1701. p. 666

Seelman, Gary, Librn, Vernon Public Library, 4441 Peterboro St, Vernon, NY, 13476-3643. Tel: 315-829-2463. p. 1761

Seelman, Robert, Asst Librn, Vernon Public Library, 4441 Peterboro St, Vernon, NY, 13476-3643. Tel: 315-829-2463. p. 1761

Seely, Kristi, Dir, Lehi City Library, 120 N Center St, Lehi, UT, 84043. Tel: 801-768-7150. Fax: 801-766-8856. p. 2406

Seeman, Corey, Dir, University of Michigan, Kresge Business Administration Library, Stephen M Ross School of Business, 701 Tappan St, K3330, Ann Arbor, MI, 48109-1234. Tel: 734-764-9969. Fax: 734-764-3839. p. 1152

Seer, Gitelle, Dir, Libr Serv, Dewey & LeBoeuf LLP Library, 1301 Avenue of the Americas, 22nd Flr, New York, NY, 10019. Tel: 212-259-6610. Fax: 212-259-6679. p. 1677

Seese, Emilee, Dir, Ritchie County Public Library, 608 E Main St, Harrisville, WV, 26362. Tel: 304-643-2717. Fax: 304-643-4019. p. 2560

Seesengood, Phyllis, Tech Serv Librn, Joplin Public Library, 300 S Main, Joplin, MO, 64801. Tel: 417-623-7953. Fax: 417-625-4728. p. 1335

Seewald, Joel, Sci Librn, Sr Assoc Librn, Web Coordr, University of Michigan-Dearborn, 4901 Evergreen Rd, Dearborn, MI, 48128-2406. Tel: 313-583-6326. Fax: 313-593-5478. p. 1168

Sefa-Boakye, Yaa, Commun Libr Mgr, County of Los Angeles Public Library, Sunkist Library, 840 N Puente Ave, La Puente, CA, 91746-1316. Tel: 626-960-2707. Fax: 626-338-5141. p. 143

Sefton, Candy, Circ, Cincinnati State Technical & Community College, 3520 Central Pkwy, Cincinnati, OH, 45223-2612. Tel: 513-569-1606. Fax: 513-559-1527. p. 1869

Sefton, Julia, Children's Serv Coordr, Riegelsville Public Library, 615 Easton Rd, Riegelsville, PA, 18077. Tel: 610-749-2357. p. 2134

Segal, Joan, Actg Dir, US Department of Commerce, Radio Bldg, Rm 1202, 325 Broadway MC5, Boulder, CO, 80305-3328. Tel: 303-497-5565. Fax: 303-497-3890. p. 291

Segall, B K, Circ, Warren Wilson College, 701 Warren Wilson Rd, Swannanoa, NC, 28778. Tel: 828-771-3064. Fax: 828-771-7085. p. 1826

Segars, Glenda, Dr, Dir, Itawamba Community College, 602 W Hill St, Fulton, MS, 38843. Tel: 662-862-8383. Fax: 662-862-8410. p. 1298

Segars, Glenda, Dr, Dir, Itawamba Community College, 2176 S Eason Blvd, Tupelo, MS, 38804. Tel: 662-620-5090. Fax: 662-620-5095. p. 1316

Seger, Cindy, Ch, Old Town Public Library, 46 Middle St, Old Town, ME, 04468. Tel: 207-827-3972. Fax: 207-827-3978. p. 994

Seger, Peg, Head, Outreach Serv, University of Texas Health Science Center at San Antonio Libraries, 7703 Floyd Curl Dr, MSC 7940, San Antonio, TX, 78229-3900. Tel: 210-567-2400. Fax: 210-567-2490. p. 2383

Seggeling, Sue, Ch, Prospect Heights Public Library District, 12 N Elm St, Prospect Heights, IL, 60070-1450. Tel: 847-259-3500. Fax: 847-259-4602. p. 692

Seggelink, Mary, Dir, Florence County Library, 400 Olive Ave, Florence, WI, 54121. Tel: 715-528-3094. Fax: 715-528-5338. p. 2592

Segina, Beverly, Coll Develop Librn, Harrisburg Area Community College, One HACC Dr, Harrisburg, PA, 17110-2999. Tel: 717-780-2466. Fax: 717-780-2462. p. 2065

Segroves, Doris, Tech Serv, Argie Cooper Public Library, 100 S Main St, Shelbyville, TN, 37160-3984. Tel: 931-684-7323. Fax: 931-685-4848. p. 2265

Seguin, Benoit, Dir, Universite du Quebec a Trois-Rivieres - Service de la bibliotheque, Pavillon Albert-Tessier, 3351 Blvd des Forges, Trois-Rivieres, QC, G9A 5H7, CANADA. Tel: 819-376-5011, Ext 2265. Fax: 819-376-5144. p. 2914

Seguin, Brian, Librn/Ref & Res, Acq, Cat, Alliant International University, One Beach St, Ste 100, San Francisco, CA, 94133. Tel: 415-955-2131. Fax: 415-955-2180. p. 240

Seguin, Diane, Tech Serv, Hospital Santa Cabrini, 5655 est Saint Zotique, Montreal, QC, H1T 1P7, CANADA. Tel: 514-252-6488. Fax: 514-252-6432. p. 2896

Seguin, Francois, Librn, Bibliothèques de Montrèal, Maisonneuve, 4120 rue Ontario Est, Montreal, QC, H1V 1J9, CANADA. Tel: 514-872-6976. Fax: 514-872-0522. p. 2890

Seguin, Lise, Circ Supvr, Laurentian University, 935 Ramsey Lake Rd, Sudbury, ON, P3E 2C6, CANADA. Tel: 705-675-1151, Ext 3336. Fax: 705-675-4877. p. 2846

Séguin, Lucie, Librn, Universite du Quebec, CP 8889, Succ Centre-Ville, 1255 Rue St Denis, Locale-A-1200, Montreal, QC, H3C 3P3, CANADA. Tel: 514-987-6134. Fax: 514-987-0262. p. 2902

Segur, Judith Ann, Asst Dir, Flint Memorial Library, 147 Park St, North Reading, MA, 01864. Tel: 978-664-4942. Fax: 978-664-0812. p. 1113

Segura, Jean, Br Mgr, Iberia Parish Library, Coteau Branch, 6308 Coteau Rd, New Iberia, LA, 70560. Tel: 337-364-7430. Fax: 337-364-7430. p. 959

Segura, Stella, ESL Coordr, Plainfield Public Library, 800 Park Ave, Plainfield, NJ, 07060-2594. Tel: 908-757-1111, Ext 121. Fax: 908-754-0063. p. 1521

Seguro, Leo, Br Mgr, Las Vegas-Clark County Library District, West Las Vegas Library, 951 W Lake Mead Blvd, Las Vegas, NV, 89106. Tel: 702-507-3980. Fax: 702-507-3996. p. 1430

Sehgal, Gurmeet, Ref, Loma Linda University, 11072 Anderson St, Loma Linda, CA, 92350-0001. Tel: 909-558-4581. Fax: 909-558-4121. p. 165

Sehgal, Vandana, Circ, Lincolnwood Public Library District, 4000 W Pratt Ave, Lincolnwood, IL, 60712. Tel: 847-677-5277. Fax: 847-677-1937. p. 666

Sehring, Hope, Dir, Jeannette Public Library Association, 500 Magee Ave, Jeannette, PA, 15644-3416. Tel: 724-523-5702. Fax: 724-523-2357. p. 2072

Seibel, Bev, Asst Librn, Chinook Regional Library, Hodgeville Branch, Main St, Hodgeville, SK, S0H 2B0, CANADA. Tel: 306-677-2223. p. 2928

Seibel, Jolene, Librn, Northwest Regional Library, Red Lake Falls Public Library, 105 Champagne Ave, Red Lake Falls, MN, 56750-4001. Tel: 218-253-2992. Fax: 218-253-2992. p. 1286

Seibel, Rebecca, Librn, Morrill Memorial & Harris Library, 220 Justin Morrill Memorial Hwy, Strafford, VT, 05072-9730. Tel: 802-765-4037. p. 2437

Seibert, Debbie, Syst Adminr, Tell City-Perry County Public Library, 2328 Tell St, Tell City, IN, 47586. Tel: 812-547-2661. Fax: 812-547-3038. p. 780

Seibert, Jutta, Acad Integration, Res Serv, Villanova University, 800 Lancaster Ave, Villanova, PA, 19085. Tel: 610-519-7876. Fax: 610-519-5018. p. 2149

Seibert, Matthew, Emerging Tech Librn, Bucks County Community College Library, 275 Swamp Rd, Newtown, PA, 18940-0999. Tel: 215-968-8304. Fax: 215-968-8142. p. 2097

Seid, Ruth, Mgr, Los Angeles Public Library System, Hollywood Area, 694 S Oxford St, Los Angeles, CA, 90005. Tel: 213-368-7683. Fax: 213-639-1654. p. 173

Seidel, Angela, Instr, Cambria-Rowe Business College, 221 Central Ave, Johnstown, PA, 15902. Tel: 814-536-5168. Fax: 814-536-5160. p. 2073

Seidel, Charlynn, Br Mgr, Chattahoochee Valley Libraries, Marion County Public Library, 123 E Fifth Ave, Buena Vista, GA, 31803-2113. Tel: 229-649-6385. Fax: 229-649-6385. p. 526

Seidel, Ellen, Head, Coll & Tech Serv, Michigan Technological University, 1400 Townsend Dr, Houghton, MI, 49931-1295. Tel: 906-487-3064. p. 1191

Seidel, Kathryn, Ref Librn, Baton Rouge Community College, 201 Community College Dr, Baton Rouge, LA, 70806. Tel: 225-216-8553. Fax: 225-216-8712. p. 942

Seidel, Shelma, Circ, Havre Hill County Library, 402 Third St, Havre, MT, 59501. Tel: 406-265-2123. Fax: 406-262-1091. p. 1381

Seiden, Peggy, Col Librn, Swarthmore College, 500 College Ave, Swarthmore, PA, 19081-1081. Tel: 610-328-8489. Fax: 610-328-7329. p. 2145

Seidenberg, Edward, Asst State Librn, Texas State Library & Archives Commission, 1201 Brazos St, Austin, TX, 78701. Tel: 512-463-5460. p. 2282

Seidenfrau, Gail, Head, Circ, New City Free Library, 220 N Main St, New City, NY, 10956. Tel: 845-634-4997. p. 1664

Seidensticker, Trisha, YA Librn, Alexandrian Public Library, 115 W Fifth St, Mount Vernon, IN, 47620. Tel: 812-838-3286. Fax: 812-838-9639. p. 766

Seidl, Donna, Ref, Nassau Community College, One Education Dr, Garden City, NY, 11530-6793. Tel: 516-572-7400. Fax: 516-572-7846. p. 1626

Seidl, Faye, Dir, Coon Rapids Public Library, 123 Third Ave, Coon Rapids, IA, 50058-1601. Tel: 712-999-5410. Fax: 712-999-5410. p. 804

Seidl, James C, Dir, Woodlands Library Cooperative, 415 S Superior, Ste A, Albion, MI, 49224-2174. Tel: 517-629-9469. Fax: 517-629-3812. p. 1148

Seidl, Jomichele, Asst Chief Librn, Powell River Public Library, 4411 Michigan Ave, Powell River, BC, V8A 2S3, CANADA. Tel: 604-485-8664. Fax: 604-485-5320. p. 2735

Seidl, Nicolette, Dir, Evergreen Park Public Library, 9400 S Troy Ave, Evergreen Park, IL, 60805-2383. Tel: 708-422-8522. Fax: 708-422-8665. p. 645

Seier, Staci, Circ, Pankhurst Memorial Library, Three S Jefferson Ave, Amboy, IL, 61310-1400. Tel: 815-857-3925. Fax: 815-857-3065. p. 588

Seifer, Marc, Librn, Metascience Foundation Library, PO Box 32, Kingston, RI, 02881-0032. Tel: 401-294-2414. Fax: 401-294-8429. p. 2167

Seifert, Marge, Bibliog Instr, Pub Serv, Southern Adventist University, 4851 Industrial Dr, Collegedale, TN, 37315. Tel: 423-236-2788. Fax: 423-236-1788. p. 2230

Seifert, Sally, Ch, Youth Serv Librn, Charlotte Community Library, 226 S Bostwick St, Charlotte, MI, 48813-1801. Tel: 517-543-8859. Fax: 517-543-8868. p. 1162

Seiferth, I Jeremy, Digital Librn, University of Massachusetts at Boston, 100 Morrissey Blvd, Boston, MA, 02125-3300. Tel: 617-287-5938. p. 1068

Seiffert, Deb, Coordr, Dubuque (Iowa) Area Library Information Consortium, c/o NE Iowa Community College, Burton Payne Library, 10250 Sundown Rd, Peosta, IA, 52068. Tel: 563-556-5110, Ext 269. Fax: 563-557-0340. p. 2943

Seiffert, Deborah, Dir, Northeast Iowa Community College, 10250 Sundown Rd, Peosta, IA, 52068. Tel: 563-556-5110, Ext 224. Fax: 563-557-0340. p. 838

Seifrid, Andi, Acq Mgr, Aurora University, 315 S Gladstone, Aurora, IL, 60506-4877. Tel: 630-844-5444. Fax: 630-844-3848. p. 591

Seifrig, Mary Ellen, Acq, ILL, Saint Meinrad Archabbey & School of Theology, 200 Hill Dr, Saint Meinrad, IN, 47577. Tel: 812-357-6401. Fax: 812-357-6398. p. 777

Seigler, Michael E, Dir, Smyrna Public Library, 100 Village Green Circle, Smyrna, GA, 30080-3478. Tel: 770-431-2860. Fax: 770-431-2862. p. 551

Seiler, Dian, Dir, Roxbury Library Association, 53742 State Hwy 30, Roxbury, NY, 12474. Tel: 607-326-7901. Fax: 607-326-7901. p. 1736

Seiler, Susi, Head, Tech Serv, Nova Southeastern University Libraries, 3100 Ray Ferrero Jr Blvd, Fort Lauderdale, FL, 33314. Tel: 954-262-4665. Fax: 954-262-3805. p. 444

Seim, Cindy, Circ, The William K Sanford Town Library, 629 Albany Shaker Rd, Loudonville, NY, 12211-1196. Tel: 518-458-9274. Fax: 518-438-0988. p. 1655

Seisser, Colleen, Teen Librn, Mount Prospect Public Library, Ten S Emerson St, Mount Prospect, IL, 60056. Tel: 847-253-5675. Fax: 847-253-0642. p. 677

Seitz, Dorothy, Dir, Bliss Memorial Public Library, 20 S Marion St, Bloomville, OH, 44818-9201. Tel: 419-983-4675. Fax: 419-983-4675. p. 1860

Seitz, Lola, Dir, Pawnee City Public Library, 735 Eighth St, Pawnee City, NE, 68420. Tel: 402-852-2118. Fax: 402-852-3134. p. 1416

Seitz, Nancy, Circ Mgr, George F Johnson Memorial Library, 1001 Park St, Endicott, NY, 13760. Tel: 607-757-5350. Fax: 607-757-2491. p. 1621

Seitz, Richard, Cat, Eastern Illinois University, 600 Lincoln Ave, Charleston, IL, 61920. Tel: 217-581-7559. p. 603

Seitz, Ryan, Tech Coordr, Herbert Wescoat Memorial Library, 120 N Market St, McArthur, OH, 45651-1218. Tel: 740-596-5691. Fax: 740-596-2477. p. 1916

Seivers, Jessica, Supvr, Preble County District Library, Preble County Room, 450 S Barron St, Eaton, OH, 45320-2402. Tel: 937-456-4970. p. 1898

Sekula, Jennifer, Ref Serv, College of William & Mary in Virginia, The Wolf Law Library, 613 S Henry St, Williamsburg, VA, 23187. Tel: 757-221-3255. Fax: 757-221-3051. p. 2502

Sekula, Toni, Adult Serv, Speedway Public Library, 5633 W 25th St, Speedway, IN, 46224-3899. Tel: 317-243-8959. Fax: 317-243-9373. p. 780

Selak, Maria F, Ch, Girard Free Library, 105 E Prospect St, Girard, OH, 44420-1899. Tel: 330-545-2508. Fax: 330-545-8213. p. 1902

Selakovich, Tabitha, Dir, John C Fremont Library District, 130 Church Ave, Florence, CO, 81226. Tel: 719-784-4649. Fax: 719-784-4937. p. 307

Selander, Vicki, City Librn, Dir, Castle Rock Public Library, 137 Cowlitz St W, Castle Rock, WA, 98611-8998. Tel: 360-274-6961. Fax: 360-274-4876. p. 2511

Selberg, Janice, Dir, Ave Maria School of Law Library, 1025 Commons Circle, Naples, FL, 34119. Tel: 239-687-5504. p. 471

Selby, Courtney, Coll Develop Mgr, University of Tulsa Libraries, Mabee Legal Information Center, 3120 E Fourth Pl, Tulsa, OK, 74104-3189. Tel: 918-631-2404. Fax: 918-631-3556. p. 1984

Selby, Gay Kozak, Chief Librn, County of Brant Public Library, Burford Branch, 24 Park Ave, Burford, ON, N0E 1A0, CANADA. Tel: 519-449-5371. Fax: 519-449-5371. p. 2835

Selby, Nancy, Librn, Somerset County Circuit Court Library, Courthouse, 30512 Prince William St, Princess Anne, MD, 21853. Tel: 410-621-7581. Fax: 410-621-7595. p. 1036

Seldeen, Jacque V, Br Mgr, Martinsburg-Berkeley County Public Library, Naylor Memorial Public Library, 105 Potato Hill St, Hedgesville, WV, 25427. Tel: 304-754-3949. p. 2565

Selden, David, Librn, National Indian Law Library, 1522 Broadway, Boulder, CO, 80302-6217. Tel: 303-447-8760. Fax: 303-443-7776. p. 291

Selden, Karen, Cat Librn, University of Colorado Boulder, The William A Wise Law Library, 2450 Kittredge Loop Dr, 402 UCB, Boulder, CO, 80309-0402. Tel: 303-492-7535. Fax: 303-492-2707. p. 292

Seldin, Sian, Sr Res Librn, Board of Governors of The Federal Reserve System, Research Library, 20th & C St NW, MS 102, Washington, DC, 20551. Tel: 202-452-3333. Fax: 202-530-6222. p. 394

Selecky, Helenmary, Tech Serv Librn, Wilkes University, 187 S Franklin St, Wilkes-Barre, PA, 18766-0998. Tel: 570-408-4258. Fax: 570-408-7823. p. 2156

Self, Michelle, Dir, Shelton Township Library, 313 C St, Shelton, NE, 68876. Tel: 308-647-5182. p. 1419

Self, Phyllis, Dean of Libr, Western Illinois University Libraries, One University Circle, Macomb, IL, 61455. Tel: 309-298-2762. Fax: 309-298-2791. p. 668

Self, Steve, Ref Librn, Austin Community College, Eastview Campus Library, 3401 Webberville Rd, Austin, TX, 78702. Tel: 512-223-5134. Fax: 512-223-5111. p. 2278

Self, William, Dir, Lenox Hill Hospital, 100 E 77th St, New York, NY, 10075. Tel: 212-434-2077. Fax: 212-434-4829. p. 1685

Selfridge, Anna B, Curator, Allen County Historical Society, 620 W Market St, Lima, OH, 45801-4604. Tel: 419-222-9426. Fax: 419-222-0649. p. 1909

Selin, Helaine, Bibliog Instr, Ref, Hampshire College Library, 893 West St, Amherst, MA, 01002-5001. Tel: 413-559-5440. Fax: 413-559-5419. p. 1048

Selius, Rima, Adult Serv, Shenango Valley Community Library, 11 N Sharpsville Ave, Sharon, PA, 16146. Tel: 724-981-4360. Fax: 724-981-5208. p. 2139

Selje, Lisa, Dir, Matheson Memorial Library, 101 N Wisconsin, Elkhorn, WI, 53121. Tel: 262-723-2678. Fax: 262-723-2870. p. 2590

Sell, Joyce, Asst Librn, Chilton Public Library, 221 Park St, Chilton, WI, 53014. Tel: 920-849-4414. Fax: 920-849-2370. p. 2585

Sell, Kathy D, Illinois Libr Loan & Adult Acq, Chillicothe Public Library District, 430 N Bradley Ave, Chillicothe, IL, 61523-1920. Tel: 309-274-2719. Fax: 309-274-3000. p. 628

Sell, Linda, Circ, Manatee County Public Library System, 1301 Barcarrota Blvd W, Bradenton, FL, 34205. Tel: 941-748-5555. Fax: 941-749-7191. p. 429

Sell, Mary, Dir, William Adams Bachelder Library, 12 Chase Hill Rd, East Andover, NH, 03231. Tel: 603-735-5333. p. 1446

Sellar, Melanie, Educ Serv Librn, Marymount College Library, 30800 Palos Verdes Dr E, Rancho Palos Verdes, CA, 90275-6299. Tel: 310-303-7303. Fax: 310-377-6223. p. 213

Sellards, Valerie Ann, Tech Serv Librn, Mountain State University Library, 609 S Kanawha St, Beckley, WV, 25801. Tel: 304-929-1469. Fax: 304-929-1665. p. 2553

Sellars, Vanessa, Bus Mgr, Duke University Libraries, Medical Center Library, DUMC Box 3702, Ten Bryan-Searle Dr, Durham, NC, 27710-0001. Tel: 919-660-1149. Fax: 919-681-7599. p. 1788

Sellberg, Roxanne, Assoc Univ Librn, Admin Serv, Northwestern University Library, 1970 Campus Dr, Evanston, IL, 60208-2300. Tel: 847-491-7658. p. 644

Selle, Rose, Youth Serv Librn, Kaukauna Public Library, 111 Main Ave, Kaukauna, WI, 54130-2436. Tel: 920-766-6340. Fax: 920-766-6343. p. 2600

Selle, Shelley, Dir, McFarland Public Library, 5920 Milwaukee St, McFarland, WI, 53558-8962. Tel: 608-838-4590. p. 2614

Sellen, Mary, Univ Librn, Christopher Newport University, One Avenue of the Arts, Newport News, VA, 23606. Tel: 757-594-7130. Fax: 757-594-7717. p. 2479

Sellens, Sharri, Asst Librn, Beck Bookman Library, 420 W Fourth St, Holton, KS, 66436-1572. Tel: 785-364-3532. Fax: 785-364-5402. p. 872

Sellers, Brenda, Librn, Moultrie Technical College Library, Tifton Campus, 52 Tech Dr, Tifton, GA, 31794. Tel: 229-391-2623. Fax: 229-391-2626. p. 546

Sellers, Charlotte, Info Serv, Jackson County Public Library, 303 W Second St, Seymour, IN, 47274-2147. Tel: 812-522-3412, Ext 224. Fax: 812-522-5456. p. 777

Sellers, Cheri, Asst Librn, Via Christi Libraries, East Harry Street, 3600 E Harry St, Wichita, KS, 67218. Tel: 316-689-5376. Fax: 316-691-6721. p. 901

Sellers, Claire, YA Serv, Lafayette Public Library, 301 W Congress, Lafayette, LA, 70501-6866. Tel: 337-261-5775. Fax: 337-261-5782. p. 952

Sellers, Connie, Sr Ref Librn, Suffolk University, 73 Tremont St, Boston, MA, 02108. Tel: 617-573-8535. Fax: 617-573-8756. p. 1067

Sellers, Connie, Weekend Ref Librn, Boston College, 885 Centre St, Newton Centre, MA, 02459. Tel: 617-552-4434. Fax: 617-552-2889. p. 1110

Sellers, John, In Charge, Harrisonburg-Rockingham Historical Society Library, 382 High St, Dayton, VA, 22821. Tel: 540-879-2616. Fax: 540-879-2616. p. 2460

Sellers, Minna, Info Serv Librn, Fort Lewis College Library, 1000 Rim Dr, Durango, CO, 81301-3999. Tel: 970-247-7250. Fax: 970-247-7149. p. 305

Sellers, Norma L, Dir, United States Army, Stimson Library, Medical Department Center & School, 3630 Stanley Rd, Bldg 2840, Ste 106, Fort Sam Houston, TX, 78234-6100. Tel: 210-221-6900. Fax: 210-221-8264. p. 2321

Sellers, Sherri, Librn, Snyder County Libraries, Beavertown Community Library, 111 W Walnut St, Beavertown, PA, 17813-9730. Tel: 570-658-3437. Fax: 570-658-3437. p. 2138

Sellers, Vicki, Youth Serv, Sequoyah Regional Library System, 116 Brown Industrial Pkwy, Canton, GA, 30114-2899. Tel: 770-479-3090, Ext 221. Fax: 770-479-3069. p. 523

Sellers, Vionnette Dover, Info Syst Coordr, Academy of Motion Picture Arts & Sciences, 333 S La Cienega Blvd, Beverly Hills, CA, 90211. Tel: 310-247-3000, Ext 2299. Fax: 310-657-5193. p. 129

Selletti, Barbara, ILL, Reserves, Neumann College Library, One Neumann Dr, Aston, PA, 19014-1298. Tel: 610-558-5545. Fax: 610-459-1370. p. 2030

Sellie, Alycia, Librn, Brooklyn College Library, 2900 Bedford Ave, Brooklyn, NY, 11210-2889. Tel: 718-951-5336. Fax: 718-951-4540. p. 1589

Sellman, Christine, Libr Asst, Calaveras County Library, Murphys Branch, 480 Park Lane, Murphys, CA, 95247. Tel: 209-728-3036. p. 227

Sellman, Norma, Librn, Hampton University, Architecture, 130 E Tyler St, Hampton, VA, 23668. Tel: 757-727-5443. p. 2468

Sells, Malinda S, Librn, Yadkin County Public Library, 233 E Main St, Yadkinville, NC, 27055. Tel: 336-679-8792. Fax: 336-679-4625. p. 1835

Sells, Vicki, Librn, University of the South, 735 University Ave, Sewanee, TN, 37383-1000. Tel: 931-598-1364. Fax: 931-598-1702. p. 2265

Selmeister, Annette, Head Librn, Hometown Public Library, 4331 Southwest Hwy, Hometown, IL, 60456-1161. Tel: 708-636-0997. Fax: 708-636-8127. p. 657

Selmer-Larsen, Denise, YA Serv, Annie Halenbake Ross Library, 232 W Main St, Lock Haven, PA, 17745-1241. Tel: 570-748-3321. Fax: 570-748-1050. p. 2082

Selness, Sushila Shah, Tech Serv Librn, University of San Diego, Katherine M & George M Pardee Jr Legal Research Center, 5998 Alcala Park, San Diego, CA, 92110-2492. Tel: 619-260-6813. Fax: 619-260-4616. p. 239

Selph, Melissa, Emerging Tech Librn, Pinal County Library District, 92 W Butte Ave, Florence, AZ, 85132. Tel: 520-855-6024. Fax: 520-866-6533. p. 63

Selter, Angela, Cataloger, Marion County Public Library, 201 E Main St, Lebanon, KY, 40033-1133. Tel: 270-692-4698. Fax: 270-692-9555. p. 920

Seltzer, Miriam, Assoc Librn, Tufts University, Edwin Ginn Library, Mugar Bldg, 1st Flr, 160 Packard St, Medford, MA, 02155-7082. Tel: 617-627-2974. Fax: 617-627-3736. p. 1104

Selzer, Ellen, Dir, Coldwater-Wilmore Regional Library, 221 E Main, Coldwater, KS, 67029. Tel: 620-582-2333. Fax: 620-582-2333. p. 861

Selzer, Karon, Librn, Palliser Regional Library, Moose Jaw Public Library, 461 Langdon Crescent, Moose Jaw, SK, S6H 0X6, CANADA. Tel: 306-692-2787. Fax: 306-692-3368. p. 2919

Sembler, Kristina, Ch, South Country Library, 22 Station Rd, Bellport, NY, 11713. Tel: 631-286-0818. Fax: 631-286-4873. p. 1580

Semenza, Jenny, Interim Assoc Univ Librn, Pub Serv, Idaho State University, Idaho State University, 850 S Ninth Ave, Pocatello, ID, 83209-8089. Tel: 208-282-2581. Fax: 208-282-5847. p. 581

Semeroz, Gloria, Librn, Everest University, 2401 N Harbor City Blvd, Melbourne, FL, 32935. Tel: 321-253-2929, Ext 176. Fax: 321-255-2017. p. 463

Semifero, Angela, Dep Dir, Marshall District Library, 124 W Green St, Marshall, MI, 49068. Tel: 269-781-7821. Fax: 269-781-7090. p. 1207

Semko, Barb, Librn, Parkland Regional Library, Lintlaw Branch, PO Box 157, Lintlaw, SK, S0A 2H0, CANADA. Tel: 306-325-2166. p. 2932

Semmerling, Lee, Distance Educ, Moraine Valley Community College Library, 9000 W College Pkwy, Palos Hills, IL, 60465. Tel: 708-608-4009. Fax: 708-974-1184. p. 687

Semones, Helen, Circ, Bridgewater College, 402 E College St, Bridgewater, VA, 22812. Tel: 540-515-3782. Fax: 540-828-5482. p. 2452

Semprebon, Galen, Pres, Connecticut Electric Railway Association, Inc, 58 North Rd, East Windsor, CT, 06088-0360. Tel: 860-627-6540. Fax: 860-627-6510. p. 337

Semrinec, Vickie, Circ & Ref Asst, Lake Michigan College, 2755 E Napier Ave, Benton Harbor, MI, 49022. Tel: 269-927-8605. Fax: 269-927-6656. p. 1156

Semtner, Anita, Dir, Saint Gregory's University, 1900 W MacArthur St, Shawnee, OK, 74804. Tel: 405-878-5111, 405-878-5295. Fax: 405-878-5198. p. 1977

Sen, Kristin, Mgr, Libr Serv, Via Christi Libraries, North Saint Francis Street, 929 N Saint Francis St, Wichita, KS, 67214-1315. Tel: 316-268-5515. Fax: 316-268-8694. p. 901

Sena, MaryAnn, Per, Fairleigh Dickinson University, 1000 River Rd, Teaneck, NJ, 07666-1914. Tel: 201-692-2279, Ext 2276. Fax: 201-692-9815. p. 1532

Sena-Gutierrez, Josephine, Govt Doc, Per, New Mexico Highlands University, Ninth & National Ave, Las Vegas, NM, 87701. Tel: 505-454-3411. Fax: 505-454-0026. p. 1559

Senack, Julie, Head Ref Librn, Atlantic City Free Public Library, One N Tennessee Ave, Atlantic City, NJ, 08401. Tel: 609-345-2269, Ext 3063. Fax: 609-345-5570. p. 1470

Senatore, Carol, Tech Serv, Northport-East Northport Public Library, 151 Laurel Ave, Northport, NY, 11768. Tel: 631-261-6930. Fax: 631-261-6718. p. 1707

Senatro, Mary Ann, Dir, Bedford Public Library, Three Meetinghouse Rd, Bedford, NH, 03110-5406. Tel: 603-472-2300, 603-472-3023. Fax: 603-472-2978. p. 1438

Sendelbach, Judy, Librn, Toledo Hospital, 2142 N Cove Blvd, Toledo, OH, 43606. Tel: 419-291-3641. Fax: 419-479-6953. p. 1939

Sendze, Monique, Assoc Dir, Info Tech, Douglas County Libraries, 100 S Wilcox, Castle Rock, CO, 80104. Tel: 303-688-7617. Fax: 303-688-7655. p. 294

Seneca, Jennifer, Youth Serv Librn, Ascension Parish Library, 500 Mississippi St, Donaldsonville, LA, 70346-2535. Tel: 225-473-8052. Fax: 225-473-9522. p. 949

Seneca, Jennifer, Asst Dir, Livingston Parish Library, 13986 Florida Blvd, Livingston, LA, 70754-6340. Tel: 225-686-2436. Fax: 225-686-3888. p. 955

Seneca, Michael, Archivist, Athenaeum of Philadelphia, 219 S Sixth St, East Washington Square, Philadelphia, PA, 19106-3794. Tel: 215-925-2688. Fax: 215-925-3755. p. 2103

Senecal, Mary, Libr Tech, Clapp Memorial Library, 19 S Main St, Belchertown, MA, 01007-0627. Tel: 413-323-0417. Fax: 413-323-0453. p. 1052

Senechal, Rachael, Coordr of Develop, Prog Coordr, Kellogg-Hubbard Library, 135 Main St, Montpelier, VT, 05602. Tel: 802-223-3338. Fax: 802-223-3338. p. 2429

Senechal, Yvonne, Librn, Vues & Voix, 1055 boul Rene-Levesque E bur 501, Montreal, QC, H2L 4S5, CANADA. Tel: 514-282-1999. Fax: 514-282-1676. p. 2902

Senesicy, Marilyn, ILL, Rockaway Borough Free Public Library, 82 E Main St, Rockaway, NJ, 07866. Tel: 973-627-5709. Fax: 973-627-5796. p. 1527

Senevisai, Barbara, Sr Librn, Hennepin County Library, North Regional, 1315 Lowry Ave N, Minneapolis, MN, 55411. Tel: 612-543-8453. Fax: 612-543-8452. p. 1264

Senezak, Christina, Mgr, Libr Serv, Patterson, Belknap, Webb & Tyler LLP Library, 1133 Avenue of the Americas, New York, NY, 10036. Tel: 212-336-2930. Fax: 212-336-2955. p. 1697

Senft-Paras, Kim Ann, Libr Dir, Washington-Centerville Public Library, 111 W Spring Valley Rd, Centerville, OH, 45458. Tel: 937-610-4420. Fax: 937-433-1366. p. 1866

Sengupta, Kankana, Info Spec, Conference Board, Inc, 845 Third Ave, New York, NY, 10022. Tel: 212-759-0900. Fax: 212-836-9750. p. 1676

Sengupta, Mimi, Head, Circ Serv, Scotch Plains Public Library, 1927 Bartle Ave, Scotch Plains, NJ, 07076-1212. Tel: 908-322-5007. Fax: 908-322-0490. p. 1528

Senig, Scott, Syst Adminr, South Huntington Public Library, 145 Pidgeon Hill Rd, Huntington Station, NY, 11746. Tel: 631-549-4411. Fax: 631-549-1266. p. 1639

Senior, Heidi, Ref, University of Portland, 5000 N Willamette Blvd, Portland, OR, 97203-5743. Tel: 503-943-7111. Fax: 503-943-7491. p. 2015

Seniuk, Peggy, Librn, Davis College, 4747 Monroe St, Toledo, OH, 43623. Tel: 419-473-2700. Fax: 419-473-2472. p. 1939

Senkow, Barb, Coordr, Prairie Farm Rehabilitation Administration, 408-1800 Hamilton St, Regina, SK, S4P 4L2, CANADA. Tel: 306-780-8408. Fax: 306-780-5018. p. 2923

Senkus, Linda, Dir, Beardsley & Memorial Library, 40 Munro Pl, Winsted, CT, 06098. Tel: 860-379-6043. Fax: 860-379-3621. p. 379

Sennett, Terry, Dir, Clinton Community Library, 1215 Centre Rd, Rhinebeck, NY, 12572. Tel: 845-266-5530. Fax: 845-266-5748. p. 1727

Sennyey, Pongracz, Assoc Dir, Furman University Libraries, 3300 Poinsett Hwy, Greenville, SC, 29613-4100. Tel: 864-294-2190. Fax: 864-294-3004. p. 2195

Sennyey, Pongracz, Dir, Saint Edwards University, 3001 S Congress Ave, Austin, TX, 78704-6489. Tel: 512-448-8470. Fax: 512-448-8737. p. 2281

Sens, Jean-Mark, Head, Coll Develop, Nicholls State University, 906 E First St, Thibodaux, LA, 70310. Tel: 985-448-4646, 985-448-4660. Fax: 985-448-4925. p. 971

Sensabaugh, Elizabeth, Br Supvr, Montgomery-Floyd Regional Library System, Blacksburg Area Branch, 200 Miller St, Blacksburg, VA, 24060. Tel: 540-552-8246. Fax: 540-552-8265. p. 2457

Sensel, Nancy, ILL, University of Denver, Westminster Law Library, 2255 E Evans Ave, Denver, CO, 80208. Tel: 303-871-6188. Fax: 303-871-6999. p. 304

Sensenig, Brenda, Ch, Archbold Community Library, 205 Stryker St, Archbold, OH, 43502-1142. Tel: 419-446-2783. Fax: 419-446-2142. p. 1854

Senzel, Howard, Pub Serv, Southern New England School of Law Library, 333 Faunce Corner Rd, North Dartmouth, MA, 02747. Tel: 508-998-9888. p. 1112

Seo, Hilary, Presv Librn, Iowa State University Library, 302 Parks Library, Ames, IA, 50011-2140. Tel: 515-294-1442, 515-294-1443. Fax: 515-294-5525. p. 793

Seow, Khuan, Tech Mgr, Barrie Public Library, 60 Worsley St, Barrie, ON, L4M 1L6, CANADA. Tel: 705-728-1010, Ext 7010. Fax: 705-728-4322. p. 2793

Sepa, Lisa, Head Librn, Tech Serv, Webmaster, University of Hawaii, 310 Kaahumanu Ave, Kahului, HI, 96732. Tel: 808-984-3577. Fax: 808-244-9644. p. 566

Sepesky, Carol, Prog Training Coordr, Monessen Public Library & District Center, 326 Donner Ave, Monessen, PA, 15062-1182. Tel: 724-684-4750. Fax: 724-684-7077. p. 2091

Sepnafski, Marla, Dir, Wisconsin Valley Library Service, 300 N First St, Wausau, WI, 54403. Tel: 715-261-7250. Fax: 715-261-7259. p. 2647

Sepnafski, Marla Rae, Dir, Wisconsin Valley Library Service, 300 N First St, Wausau, WI, 54403. Tel: 715-261-7251. Fax: 715-261-7259. p. 2958

Serafini, Laura, Head, Access Serv, Occidental College Library, 1600 Campus Rd, Los Angeles, CA, 90041. Tel: 323-259-2594. Fax: 323-341-4991. p. 176

Serafini, Patricia, Distance Educ Coordr, University of Toronto Libraries, 252 Bloor St W, Toronto, ON, M5S 1V6, CANADA. Tel: 416-978-1903. Fax: 416-926-4737. p. 2867

Seratt, Mary, Coordr, Youth Serv, Memphis Public Library & Information Center, 3030 Poplar Ave, Memphis, TN, 38111-3527. Tel: 901-415-2839. Fax: 901-323-7108. p. 2249

Seratt, Mary M, Coordr, Youth Serv, Memphis Public Library, Children's Department, 3030 Poplar Ave, Memphis, TN, 38111-3527. Tel: 901-415-2739. Fax: 901-323-7108. p. 2249

Serdyuk, Yana V, Dir, Concordia University, 7400 Augusta St, River Forest, IL, 60305-1499. Tel: 708-209-3053. Fax: 708-209-3175. p. 694

Serebrin, Raymond, Dir, Jefferson County Rural Library District, 620 Cedar Ave, Port Hadlock, WA, 98339-9514. Tel: 360-385-6544. Fax: 360-385-7921. p. 2524

Sereda, Sofie, Sr Libr Asst & Cataloguer, College of Physicians of Philadelphia, 19 S 22nd St, Philadelphia, PA, 19103-3097. Tel: 215-399-2305. Fax: 215-561-6477. p. 2104

Seredynska, Katherine, Mgr, Pub Serv, Region of Waterloo Library, 2017 Nafziger Rd, Baden, ON, N3A 3H4, CANADA. Tel: 519-575-4590. Fax: 519-634-5371. p. 2793

Seredynska, Katherine, Mgr, Pub Serv, Region of Waterloo Library, Baden Branch, 115 Snyder's Rd E, Baden, ON, N3A 2V4, CANADA. Tel: 519-634-8933. p. 2793

Serfass, Melissa, Electronic Res, Ref Serv, University of Arkansas at Little Rock, Pulaski County Law Library, 1203 McMath Ave, Little Rock, AR, 72202-5142. Tel: 501-324-9444. Fax: 501-324-9447. p. 107

Sergeeva, Lada, Librn, IBM Canada Ltd-Toronto Lab, 8200 Warden Ave, Dept Z3, Markham, ON, L6G 1C7, CANADA. Tel: 905-413-3555. p. 2820

Sergis, Carol K, Dir, Libr Serv, Schulte Roth & Zabel LLP, 919 Third Ave, New York, NY, 10022. Tel: 212-756-2302. Fax: 212-593-5955. p. 1699

Sergiy, Panko, Bibliographer, Librn, Shevchenko Scientific Society Inc, 63 Fourth Ave, New York, NY, 10003. Tel: 212-254-5130. Fax: 212-254-5239. p. 1699

Serico, Susan, Dir, North Haledon Free Public Library, 129 Overlook Ave, North Haledon, NJ, 07508-2533. Tel: 973-427-6213. Fax: 973-427-1826. p. 1514

Serindag, Yuksel, Acq, Trinity College Library, 300 Summit St, Hartford, CT, 06106. Tel: 860-297-2249. Fax: 860-297-2251. p. 347

Serling, Kitty, Med Librn, Research Medical Center, 2316 E Meyer Blvd, Kansas City, MO, 64132-1199. Tel: 816-276-4309. Fax: 816-276-3106. p. 1340

Serlis-McPhillips, Sophia, Asst Dir, Commun Relations, Middle Country Public Library, 101 Eastwood Blvd, Centereach, NY, 11720. Tel: 631-585-9393, Ext 219. Fax: 631-585-5035. p. 1604

Sermons, Penny, Dir, Libr Res Ctr, Beaufort County Community College Library, Hwy 264 E, Washington, NC, 27889. Tel: 252-940-6243. Fax: 252-946-9575. p. 1828

Serna, Kim, Regional Mgr, Libr Serv, Jones Day, 2727 N Harwood St, Dallas, TX, 75201-1515. Tel: 214-969-4823. Fax: 214-969-5100. p. 2308

Serna, Kimberly, Librn, Jones Day, 717 Texas St, Ste 3300, Houston, TX, 77002. Tel: 832-239-3939. Fax: 832-239-3600. p. 2340

Serna, Lupe, Dir, Kendrick Memorial Library, 301 W Tate, Brownfield, TX, 79316-4387. Tel: 806-637-3848. p. 2292

Serna, Nellie, Br Mgr, Madera County Library, Chowchilla Branch, 300 Kings Ave, Chowchilla, CA, 93610-2059. Tel: 559-665-2630. Fax: 559-665-4216. p. 182

Serra, Danielle, YA Serv, Cliffside Park Free Public Library, 505 Palisade Ave, Cliffside Park, NJ, 07010. Tel: 201-945-2867. Fax: 201-945-1016. p. 1479

Serra, Lynn, Asst Dir, Head, Tech Serv, Woodbridge Town Library, Ten Newton Rd, Woodbridge, CT, 06525. Tel: 203-389-3438. Fax: 203-389-3457. p. 380

Serrano, Samuel, Head, Circ, University of Puerto Rico, Law School Library, Avenidas Ponce de Leon & Gandara, San Juan, PR, 00931. Tel: 787-999-9898. Fax: 787-999-9680. p. 2676

Serrano, Stacey M, Dir, Rice Avenue Community Public Library, 705 Rice Ave, Girard, PA, 16417-1122. Tel: 814-774-4982. p. 2060

Serrato, Jesus, Tech Serv Librn, University of Saint Thomas, 1100 W Main, Houston, TX, 77006. Tel: 713-525-2192. Fax: 713-525-3886. p. 2344

Servaes, Brita, Undergrad Serv Librn, New School, Raymond Fogelman Library, 55 W 13th St, New York, NY, 10011. Tel: 212-229-5307, Ext 3163. Fax: 212-229-5306. p. 1688

Servant, Lise, Curator, Jardin Botanique de Montreal Bibliotheque, 4101 Sherbrooke St E, Montreal, QC, H1X 2B2, CANADA. Tel: 514-872-1440, 514-872-1824. Fax: 514-872-5167. p. 2897

Servello-Cammack, Angie, Policy Publ & Info Res Coordr, Workplace Safety & Insurance Board, 200 Front St W, 17th Flr, Toronto, ON, M5V 3J1, CANADA. Tel: 416-344-6384. Fax: 416-344-4050. p. 2868

Server, Jennifer, Dir of Educ, Cedarhurst Center for the Arts, 2600 Richview Rd, Mount Vernon, IL, 62864. Tel: 618-242-1236. Fax: 618-242-9530. p. 677

Servey, Patsy, ILL Librn, Waupaca Area Public Library, 107 S Main St, Waupaca, WI, 54981-1521. Tel: 715-258-4414. p. 2645

Service, Frances, In Charge, Mohawk Valley Psychiatric Center, 1400 Noyes St at York, Utica, NY, 13502-3852. Tel: 315-738-4033. p. 1759

Session, Kathleen, Librn, Humphreys County Library System, Isola Public, 203 Julia St, Isola, MS, 38754. Tel: 662-962-3606. p. 1294

Sessions, Denise, Librn, Shaw Memorial Library, 312 Main St, Plainfield, MA, 01070-9709. Tel: 413-634-5406. Fax: 413-634-5683. p. 1118

Sessions, Katy, Regional Mgr, North Central Regional Library, Wenatchee Public (Headquarters), 310 Douglas St, Wenatchee, WA, 98801-2864. Tel: 509-662-5021, Ext 28. Fax: 509-663-9731. p. 2549

Sestak, Ivan, Sr IT Adminr, University of Toronto Libraries, Faculty of Information Inforum, 140 Saint George St, 4th Flr, Toronto, ON, M5S 3G6, CANADA. Tel: 416-978-6121. Fax: 416-978-5769. p. 2866

Sestokas, Frank, Children's Serv Supvr, Mkt Coordr, Worcester Public Library, Three Salem Sq, Worcester, MA, 01608. Tel: 508-799-1655. Fax: 508-799-1652. p. 1145

Sestrick, Timothy, Head, Music & Media Serv, Gettysburg College, 300 N Washington St, Gettysburg, PA, 17325. Tel: 717-337-7045. Fax: 717-337-7001. p. 2059

Setford, David, Exec Dir, Hyde Collection Library, 161 Warren St, Glens Falls, NY, 12801. Tel: 518-792-1761. Fax: 518-792-9197. p. 1629

Seth, Ervin, Children's Mgr, Charlotte Mecklenburg Library, ImaginOn: The Joe & Joan Martin Center, 300 E Seventh St, Charlotte, NC, 28202. Tel: 704-416-4600. Fax: 704-416-4700. p. 1782

Sethi, Bali, Acq, International North American Library, 90 Nolan Ct, No 21, Markham, ON, L3R 4L9, CANADA. Tel: 905-946-9588. Fax: 905-946-9590. p. 2820

Sethuraman, Ramachandran, Dr, Br Coordr, Long Beach City College, 4901 E Carson St, Long Beach, CA, 90808. Tel: 562-938-3115. Fax: 562-938-3062, 562-938-4777. p. 166

Setnosky, Julie, Coll Develop, Ref Serv, Minneapolis Community & Technical College Library, Wheelock Whitney Hall, 1501 Hennepin Ave, Minneapolis, MN, 55403. Tel: 612-659-6292. Fax: 612-659-6295. p. 1261

Setser, Laurel, Dir, Avon-Washington Township Public Library, 498 N State Rd 267, Avon, IN, 46123. Tel: 317-272-4818. Fax: 317-272-7302. p. 725

Sette, Lynn, Ref Librn, Yale University Library, Harvey Cushing/John Hay Whitney Medical Library, Sterling Hall of Medicine, 333 Cedar St, L110 SHM, New Haven, CT, 06520. Tel: 203-785-5352. Fax: 203-785-5636. p. 358

Settoon, Paula, Exec Dir, Northeastern State University, 711 N Grand Ave, Tahlequah, OK, 74464-2333. Tel: 918-456-5511, Ext 3200. Fax: 918-458-2197. p. 1979

Setzer, Jason, Librn, Davidson County Community College, 297 DCCC Rd, Lexington, NC, 27295. Tel: 336-249-8186, Ext 271. Fax: 336-248-8531. p. 1806

Setzer, Tina J, Dir, Schiller Park Public Library, 4200 Old River Rd, Schiller Park, IL, 60176-1699. Tel: 847-678-0433. Fax: 847-678-0567. p. 701

Setzler Simensen, Kristen, Dir, Calhoun County Library, 900 FR Huff Dr, Saint Matthews, SC, 29135-1261. Tel: 803-874-3389. Fax: 803-874-4154. p. 2204

Seufer, Beth, Syst Librn, ECPI University, 7802 Airport Center Dr, Greensboro, NC, 27409. Tel: 336-665-1400. Fax: 336-664-0801. p. 1796

Seveneant, Lori, Circ, Franklin Square Public Library, 19 Lincoln Rd, Franklin Square, NY, 11010. Tel: 516-488-3444. Fax: 516-354-3368. p. 1624

Sevenski, Pam, Dir, West Frankfort Public Library, 402 E Poplar St, West Frankfort, IL, 62896. Tel: 618-932-3313. Fax: 618-932-3313. p. 717

Severance, Yvette, Librn, Sheldon Public Library, 1640 Main St, Sheldon, VT, 05483. Tel: 802-933-7323. p. 2435

Severens, Charles, Librn, Caritas Carney Hospital, 2100 Dorchester Ave, Dorchester, MA, 02124-5666. Tel: 617-296-4000, Ext 2050. Fax: 617-474-3861. p. 1084

Severino, Christine, Librn, State of New Jersey - Department of Banking & Insurance Library, 20 W State St, Trenton, NJ, 08608-1206. Tel: 609-777-0558, Ext 50274. Fax: 609-633-8213. p. 1536

Severns, Tara, Pub Serv, Windward Community College Library, 45-720 Keaahala Rd, Kaneohe, HI, 96744. Tel: 808-235-7440. Fax: 808-235-7344. p. 566

Severson, Eileen, Treas, Northwestern Wisconsin Health Science Library Consortium, c/o Gundersen Lutheran Medical Center, 1900 South Ave, Mail Stop H01-011, Lacrosse, WI, 54601. Tel: 608-775-5410. Fax: 608-775-6343. p. 2958

Severson, JoAnn, Br Mgr, Sacramento Public Library, E K McClatchy Neighborhood Library, 2112 22nd St, Sacramento, CA, 95818. p. 225

Severson, Matthew, Photographic Serv Adminr, Academy of Motion Picture Arts & Sciences, 333 S La Cienega Blvd, Beverly Hills, CA, 90211. Tel: 310-247-3000, Ext 2227. Fax: 310-657-5193. p. 129

Severson, Rick, Head Librn, National College of Naturopathic Medicine Library, 049 SW Porter, Portland, OR, 97201. Tel: 503-552-1542. Fax: 503-219-9709. p. 2012

Severy, Marion, Pub Serv Librn, Ref, California Institute of Integral Studies, 1453 Mission St, 2nd Flr, San Francisco, CA, 94103. Tel: 415-575-6183. Fax: 415-575-1264. p. 241

Severy, Robin, Asst Librn, Platt Memorial Library, 279 Main St, Shoreham, VT, 05770-9759. Tel: 802-897-2647. p. 2435

Sevier, Jennifer, Br Mgr, Peoria Public Library, Lakeview, 1137 W Lake, Peoria, IL, 61614-5935. Tel: 309-497-2204. Fax: 309-497-2211. p. 690

Sevilla-Marzona, Judy, Librn, Rio Hondo Community College Library, 3600 Workman Mill Rd, Whittier, CA, 90601. Tel: 562-908-3417. Fax: 562-463-4642. p. 283

Seward, Baiba, Ref Serv, Dykema Gossett PLLC, 39577 N Woodward Ave, Ste 300, Bloomfield Hills, MI, 48304-2820. Tel: 313-568-6714. Fax: 248-203-0763. p. 1159

Seward, Baiba, Ref, Dykema Gossett PLLC, 400 Renaissance Ctr, 38th Flr, Detroit, MI, 48243. Tel: 313-568-6714. Fax: 313-568-6735. p. 1171

Seward, Ellen, Libr Asst/Tech Serv Spec, Mechanicsburg Public Library, 60 S Main St, Mechanicsburg, OH, 43044. Tel: 937-834-2004. Fax: 937-834-3396. p. 1916

Seward, Helena, Libr Asst Supvr, Montgomery College, Takoma Park Campus Library, 7600 Takoma Ave, Takoma Park, MD, 20912. Tel: 240-567-1539. Fax: 240-567-5820. p. 1037

Sewell, Jeff, Mgr, Shook, Hardy & Bacon, 2555 Grand Blvd, 3rd Flr, Kansas City, MO, 64108-2613. Tel: 816-474-6550. Fax: 816-421-5547. p. 1341

Sewell, Justin, Tech Serv Librn, Arapahoe Community College, 5900 S Santa Fe Dr, Littleton, CO, 80160. Tel: 303-797-5730. Fax: 303-798-4173. p. 316

Sewell, Lisa, Librn, NASA Ames Research Center, Life Sciences Library, Mail Stop 239-13, Moffett Field, CA, 94035-1000. Tel: 650-604-5387. Fax: 650-604-7741. p. 189

Sewell, Stan, Br Mgr, San Bernardino County Library, Loma Linda Branch, 25581 Barton Rd, Loma Linda, CA, 92354. Tel: 909-796-8621. Fax: 909-796-4221. p. 228

Sewerin, Cristina, Librn, University of Toronto Libraries, Engineering & Computer Science Library, Sandford Fleming Bldg, Rm 2402, Ten King's College Rd, Toronto, ON, M5S 1A5, CANADA. Tel: 416-978-6494. Fax: 416-971-2091. p. 2865

Sexton, Adelaide, Ref, Chelsea Public Library, 569 Broadway, Chelsea, MA, 02150-2991. Tel: 617-466-4350. Fax: 617-466-4359. p. 1080

Sexton, Carol, Ch, Pulaski County Public Library, 304 S Main St, Somerset, KY, 42501-1402. Tel: 606-679-8401. Fax: 606-679-1779. p. 935

Sexton, Ellen, Info Literacy, John Jay College of Criminal Justice, 899 Tenth Ave, New York, NY, 10019. Tel: 212-237-8258. Fax: 212-237-8221. p. 1684

Sexton, Jean, Coordr, Cat, University of North Carolina at Pembroke, Faculty Row, Pembroke, NC, 28372. Tel: 910-521-6516. Fax: 910-521-6547. p. 1814

Sexton, Jennifer, Librn, Crittenden County Library, Crawfordsville Branch, 5444 Main St, Crawfordsville, AR, 72327. Tel: 870-823-5204. p. 109

Sexton, Jennifer, Librn, Crittenden County Library, Horseshoe Branch, 3181 Horseshoe Circle, Hughes, AR, 72348. Tel: 870-339-3862. p. 109

Sexton, Marcia, Tech Serv, Ramapo College of New Jersey, 505 Ramapo Valley Rd, Mahwah, NJ, 07430-1623. Tel: 201-684-6749. p. 1498

Sexton, Mark, Mgr, Info Sys, University of Nevada-Reno, Savitt Medical Library & IT Department, Pennington Medical Education Bldg, 1664 N Virginia St, Mail Stop 306, Reno, NV, 89557. Tel: 775-784-4625. Fax: 775-784-4489. p. 1433

Sexton, Mary, Librn, Fort Worth Library, Diamond Hill/Jarvis Branch, 1300 NE 35th St, Fort Worth, TX, 76106. Tel: 817-624-7331. Fax: 817-625-4029. p. 2322

Sexton, Molly, Develop Officer/Grants, Redwood Library & Athenaeum, 50 Bellevue Ave, Newport, RI, 02840-3292. Tel: 401-847-0292. Fax: 401-847-0192. p. 2169

Sexton, Nancy D, Acq, Cat, Emmet O'Neal Library, 50 Oak St, Mountain Brook, AL, 35213. Tel: 205-879-0459. Fax: 205-879-5388. p. 32

Sexton, Pat, Coll Develop Spec, Wake Technical Community College, 9101 Fayetteville Rd, Raleigh, NC, 27603-5696. Tel: 919-866-5650. Fax: 919-662-3575. p. 1818

Sexton, Sue, Librn, East Mississippi Regional Library System, Pachuta Public, Hwy 11N, Pachuta, MS, 39347. Tel: 601-776-3131. p. 1313

Sexton, Sue, Librn, East Mississippi Regional Library System, Quitman Public Library, 116 Water St, Quitman, MS, 39355. Tel: 601-776-2492. Fax: 601-776-6599. p. 1313

Sexton, Susan, ILL, Environmental Protection Agency - R S Kerr Environmental Research Center, 919 Kerr Lab Research Dr, Ada, OK, 74820. Tel: 580-436-8800. Fax: 580-436-8503. p. 1955

Seymour, Anne, Assoc Dir, University of Pennsylvania Libraries, Biomedical Library, Johnson Pavilion, 3610 Hamilton Walk, Philadelphia, PA, 19104-6060. Tel: 215-898-4115. Fax: 215-573-4143. p. 2119

Seymour, Bonnie G, Dir, Public Library of Anniston-Calhoun County, 108 E Tenth St, Anniston, AL, 36201. Tel: 256-237-8501, 256-237-8503. Fax: 256-238-0474. p. 4

Seymour, Celene, Assoc Dean, Marshall University Libraries, Graduate College Library, 100 Angus E Peyton Dr, South Charleston, WV, 25303-1600. Tel: 304-746-8900. Fax: 304-746-8905. p. 2562

Seymour, Charles, Grad Ref Librn, Grand Canyon University, 3300 W Camelback Rd, Phoenix, AZ, 85017-3030. Tel: 602-639-6641. Fax: 602-639-7835. p. 73

Seymour, Jill R, Librn, South Mountain Community College Library, 7050 S 24th St, Phoenix, AZ, 85042. Tel: 602-243-8164. Fax: 602-243-8180. p. 77

Seymour, Kathy, Br Mgr, Central Arkansas Library System, Esther Nixon Branch, 308 W Main St, Jacksonville, AR, 72076-4507. Tel: 501-982-5533. p. 106

Seymour, Linda, Dir, Barnard Library, 521 Elm, La Crosse, KS, 67548. Tel: 785-222-2826. Fax: 785-222-2826. p. 876

Seymour, Monika, Chief Librn, Niagara Falls Public Library, 4848 Victoria Ave, Niagara Falls, ON, L2E 4C5, CANADA. Tel: 905-356-8080. Fax: 905-356-7004. p. 2824

Seymour, Nancy S, Libr Serv Mgr, Jones Day, 325 John H McConnell Blvd, Ste 600, Columbus, OH, 43215-2673. Tel: 614-469-3939. Fax: 614-461-4198. p. 1886

Seymour, Nancy S, Libr Serv Mgr, Jones Day, 500 Grant St, 31st Flr, Pittsburgh, PA, 15219. Tel: 412-394-7226. Fax: 412-394-7959. p. 2126

Seymour-Ford, Jan, Librn, Perkins School for the Blind, Samuel P Hayes Research Library, 175 N Beacon St, Watertown, MA, 02472. Tel: 617-972-7250. Fax: 617-923-8076. p. 1134

Seymoure, Rene, Asst Librn, White Hall Township Library, 119 E Sherman St, White Hall, IL, 62092. Tel: 217-374-6014. Fax: 217-374-6554. p. 719

Sezzi, Peter H, Assoc Librn, Ventura College, 4667 Telegraph Rd, Ventura, CA, 93003-3899. Tel: 805-654-6400, Ext 3258. Fax: 805-648-8900. p. 279

Sforza, Marianne A, Dir, Western Allegheny Community Library, 8042 Steubenville Pike, Oakdale, PA, 15071-9375. Tel: 724-695-8150. Fax: 724-695-2860. p. 2100

Sgarro, Bonnie S, Cat, Syst Librn, Bard College, One Library Rd, Annandale-on-Hudson, NY, 12504. Tel: 845-758-7619. Fax: 845-758-5801. p. 1574

Sgro, Holly, Asst Dir, Ch, Highland Public Library, 30 Church St, Highland, NY, 12528. Tel: 845-691-2275. Fax: 845-691-6302. p. 1636

Shackelford, Lucy, Dir, The Washington Post, 1150 15th St NW, Washington, DC, 20071. Tel: 202-334-7341. Fax: 202-728-3130. p. 422

Shacklett, Rita, Dir, Linebaugh Public Library System of Rutherford County, 105 W Vine St, Murfreesboro, TN, 37130-3673. Tel: 615-893-4131, Ext 112. Fax: 615-848-5038. p. 2254

Shadburne, Marilyn, Circ, Silver Falls Library District, 410 S Water St, Silverton, OR, 97381-2137. Tel: 503-873-5173. Fax: 503-873-6227. p. 2020

Shaddi, Robert, Dean, Wilkes University, 187 S Franklin St, Wilkes-Barre, PA, 18766-0998. Tel: 570-408-4250. Fax: 570-408-7823. p. 2156

Shaddy, Robert, Chief Librn, Queens College, Benjamin S Rosenthal Library, 65-30 Kissena Blvd, Flushing, NY, 11367-0904. Tel: 718-997-3700. Fax: 718-997-3753. p. 1623

Shaddy, Robert, Chief Librn, Queens College of the City University of New York, Benjamin Rosenthal Library, Rm 254, 65-30 Kissena Blvd, Flushing, NY, 11367. Tel: 718-997-3790. Fax: 718-997-3797. p. 2970

Shaddy, Rose Kuei-Hsiang, Librn, State of Ohio Department of Corrections, 2001 E Central Ave, Toledo, OH, 43608. Tel: 419-726-7977, Ext 7233. Fax: 419-726-7158. p. 1939

Shadix, Michael D, Librn, Roosevelt Warm Springs Institute for Rehabilitation, 6391 Roosevelt Hwy, Warm Springs, GA, 31830. Tel: 706-655-5616. Fax: 706-655-5630. p. 556

Shadle, Paula, Mgr, Ch Serv, Avon Lake Public Library, 32649 Electric Blvd, Avon Lake, OH, 44012-1669. Tel: 440-933-8128. Fax: 440-933-5659. p. 1856

Shadowens, Paulina, Ch, Lane Memorial Library, Two Academy Ave, Hampton, NH, 03842. Tel: 603-926-4729. Fax: 603-926-1348. p. 1449

Shadrix, Pam, ILL, Life University, 1269 Barclay Circle, Marietta, GA, 30060. Tel: 770-426-2688. Fax: 770-426-2745. p. 543

Shafer, Connie, Librn, Shubert Public Library, 313 Main St, Shubert, NE, 68437. Tel: 402-883-2593. p. 1419

Shafer, Daryl, Acq, A T Still University of Health Sciences, Kirksville Campus, 800 W Jefferson St, Kirksville, MO, 63501. Tel: 660-626-2124. Fax: 660-626-2031, 660-626-2333. p. 1342

Shafer, John, Ref, University of San Francisco, Zief Law Library, 2101 Fulton St, San Francisco, CA, 94117-1004. Tel: 415-422-6679. Fax: 415-422-2345. p. 249

Shafer, Karla, Dir, Hooper Public Library, 126 N Main, Hooper, NE, 68031. Tel: 402-654-3833. p. 1402

Shafer, Leesa, Dir, Spearville Township Library, 414 N Main St, Spearville, KS, 67876. Tel: 620-385-2501. Fax: 620-385-2508. p. 895

Shafer, Lori, Ref, Briggs Lawrence County Public Library, 321 S Fourth St, Ironton, OH, 45638. Tel: 740-532-1124. Fax: 740-532-4948. p. 1906

Shafer, Pam, Dir, Lone Star College System, Tomball College Library, 30555 Tomball Pkwy, Tomball, TX, 77375-4036. Tel: 832-559-4217. Fax: 832-559-4248. p. 2340

Shafer, Sheri L, Chief Financial Officer, New Jersey State Library, 185 W State St, Trenton, NJ, 08618. Tel: 609-278-2640, Ext 137. Fax: 609-278-2649. p. 1536

Shaffer, Barbara, Dir, State University of New York at Oswego, SUNY Oswego, 7060 State Rte 104, Oswego, NY, 13126-3514. Tel: 315-312-3557. Fax: 315-312-3194. p. 1713

Shaffer, Carol, Librn, Sheboygan County Historical Research Center Library, 518 Water St, Sheboygan Falls, WI, 53085. Tel: 920-467-4667. Fax: 920-467-1395. p. 2638

Shaffer, Carolyn, Libr Dir, Black Earth Public Library, 1210 Mills St, Black Earth, WI, 53515. Tel: 608-767-2400, Ext 3. Fax: 608-767-2064. p. 2582

Shaffer, Chris, Libr Dir, Univ Librn, Oregon Health & Science University Library, 3181 SW Sam Jackson Park Rd, Portland, OR, 97239-3098. Tel: 503-494-6057. Fax: 503-494-3227. p. 2013

Shaffer, Christopher, Libr Dir, Troy University, 502 University Dr, Dothan, AL, 36304. Tel: 334-983-6556, Ext 1320. Fax: 334-983-6327. p. 15

Shaffer, Cyndie, Librn, Marinette County Library System, Crivitz Public Library, 606 Louisa St, Crivitz, WI, 54114. Tel: 715-854-7562. Fax: 715-854-7562. p. 2612

Shaffer, David, Dir, Rappahannock County Library, Four Library Rd, Washington, VA, 22747. Tel: 540-675-3780. Fax: 540-675-1290. p. 2501

Shaffer, Duane, Coll Develop, Sanibel Public Library District, 770 Dunlop Rd, Sanibel, FL, 33957. Tel: 239-472-2483. Fax: 239-472-9524. p. 489

Shaffer, E, Archivist, Vancouver Holocaust Education Centre Library & Archives, 50-950 W 41st Ave, Vancouver, BC, V5Z 2N7, CANADA. Tel: 604-264-0499. Fax: 604-264-0497. p. 2743

Shaffer, Gary, Chief Exec Officer, Tulsa City-County Library, 400 Civic Ctr, Tulsa, OK, 74103. Tel: 918-596-7923. Fax: 918-596-7964. p. 1982

Shaffer, Jaimie, Circ, University of Dubuque Library, 2000 University Ave, Dubuque, IA, 52001. Tel: 563-589-3100. Fax: 563-589-3722. p. 812

Shaffer, Janna C, Dir, Samuel W Smith Memorial Public Library, 201 E Maple St, Port Allegany, PA, 16743. Tel: 814-642-9210. Fax: 814-642-7555. p. 2131

Shaffer, John, In Charge, Williams County Law Library Association, One Courthouse Sq, Bryan, OH, 43506. Tel: 419-636-4600. Fax: 419-636-9886. p. 1862

Shaffer, Lisa, Ref & Educ Librn, Albany College of Pharmacy & Health Sciences, 106 New Scotland Ave, Albany, NY, 12208. Tel: 518-694-7342. Fax: 518-694-7300. p. 1567

Shaffer, Peggy, Libr Develop Coordr, Lakeshores Library System, 725 Cornerstone Crossing, Ste C, Waterford, WI, 53185. Tel: 262-514-4500, Ext 68. Fax: 262-514-4544. p. 2644

Shaffer, Roberta I, Assoc Librn, Libr Serv, Library of Congress, 101 Independence Ave at First St SE, Washington, DC, 20540. Tel: 202-707-5000. Fax: 202-707-1925. p. 406

Shaffer, Roberta I, Exec Dir, Fedlink, c/o Federal Library & Information Center Committee, 101 Independence Ave SE, Adams Bldg, Rm 217, Washington, DC, 20540-4935. Tel: 202-707-4800. Fax: 202-707-4818. p. 2940

Shaffer, Theresa, ILL, Ref, Saint Bonaventure University, 3261 W State Rd, Saint Bonaventure, NY, 14778. Tel: 716-375-2323. Fax: 716-375-2389. p. 1737

Shaffer-Duong, Amy, Ch, Palmyra Public Library, Borough Bldg, 325 S Railroad St, Palmyra, PA, 17078-2492. Tel: 717-838-1347. Fax: 717-838-1236. p. 2101

Shaffett, John, Dir, The Baptist College of Florida, 5400 College Dr, Graceville, FL, 32440-1833. Tel: 850-263-3261, Ext 424. Fax: 850-263-5704. p. 450

Shah, Arti, Div Chief, United States Patent & Trademark Office, 400 Dulany St, Rm 1D58, Alexandria, VA, 22314. Tel: 571-272-3547. Fax: 571-273-0048. p. 2446

Shah, Karen, Coll Develop, Northland Public Library, 300 Cumberland Rd, Pittsburgh, PA, 15237-5455. Tel: 412-3366-8100, Ext 111. Fax: 412-366-2064. p. 2126

Shah, Stacey, Distance Learning Librn, Elgin Community College, 1700 Spartan Dr, Elgin, IL, 60123. Tel: 847-214-7337. p. 641

Shahbodaghi, Kathy, Head, Youth Serv, Columbus Metropolitan Library, 96 S Grant Ave, Columbus, OH, 43215-4781. Tel: 614-645-2275. Fax: 614-849-1157. p. 1884

Shaheen, Carol, Dir, Newfoundland Area Public Library, Main St, Newfoundland, PA, 18445. Tel: 570-676-4518. Fax: 570-676-4518. p. 2097

Shaheen, Min, Govt Doc Librn, Miami-Dade Public Library System, 101 W Flagler St, Miami, FL, 33130-1523. Tel: 305-375-5575. Fax: 305-375-3048. p. 466

Shahen, Greg, Mgr, KTA-Tator Inc Library, 115 Technology Dr, Pittsburgh, PA, 15275-1085. Tel: 412-788-1300. Fax: 412-788-1306. p. 2126

Shaia, Lisa, Ch, Oliver Wolcott Library, 160 South St, Litchfield, CT, 06759-0187. Tel: 860-567-8030. Fax: 860-567-4784. p. 349

Shaikh, Farida, Libr Coordr, Vaughan Public Libraries, Ansley Grove Library, 350 Ansley Grove Rd, Woodbridge, ON, L4L 5C9, CANADA. Tel: 905-653-7323. Fax: 905-856-6151. p. 2848

Shakal, Andrea, Circ, Destin Library, 150 Sibert Ave, Destin, FL, 32541-1523. Tel: 850-837-8572. Fax: 850-837-5248. p. 438

Shaklee, Kate, Librn, El Reno Carnegie Library, 215 E Wade, El Reno, OK, 73036-2753. Tel: 405-262-2409. Fax: 405-422-2136. p. 1962

Shaklee, Mary, Tech Serv, Public Library of Enid & Garfield County, 120 W Maine, Enid, OK, 73701-5606. Tel: 580-234-6313. Fax: 580-249-9280. p. 1963

Shalala, Bonnie, Br Mgr, Drinker Biddle & Reath LLP, One Logan Sq, 18th & Cherry St, Philadelphia, PA, 19103. Tel: 215-988-2951. Fax: 215-564-1329, 215-988-2757. p. 2106

Shalette, Alan, Dir, Maxwell Museum of Anthropology, University of New Mexico, Albuquerque, NM, 87131. Tel: 505-277-4405, 505-277-8675. p. 1549

Shalley, Doris, Bibliog Instr, Librn, Online Serv, GlaxoSmithKline Pharmaceuticals, Marketing Library, One Franklin Plaza, Philadelphia, PA, 19101. Tel: 215-751-5576. Fax: 215-751-5509. p. 2110

Shallow, Sandra, Libr Tech, College of the North Atlantic, Burin Campus, PO Box 370, Burin Bay Arm, NL, A0E 1G0, CANADA. Tel: 709-891-5622. Fax: 709-891-2256. p. 2771

Shaloiko, John L, Exec Dir, Southeastern New York Library Resources Council, 21 S Elting Corners Rd, Highland, NY, 12528-2805. Tel: 845-883-9065. Fax: 845-883-9483. p. 2950

Shalongo, Joette, Pub Serv, Thomas Beaver Free Library, 205 Ferry St, Danville, PA, 17821-1939. Tel: 570-275-4180. Fax: 570-275-8480. p. 2049

Shama, Carol R, Exec Dir, Wood Library Association of Canandaigua, 134 N Main St, Canandaigua, NY, 14424-1295. Tel: 585-394-1381. Fax: 585-394-2954. p. 1601

Shaman, William, Archivist, Instrul Serv Librn, Spec Coll Librn, Bemidji State University, 1500 Birchmont Dr NE, Box 4, Bemidji, MN, 56601-2600. Tel: 218-755-3342. Fax: 218-755-2051. p. 1241

Shamansky, Mairlyne, Archivist, Simpson University, 2211 College View Dr, Redding, CA, 96003-8606. Tel: 530-226-4115. Fax: 530-226-4858. p. 214

Shamash, Leann, Librn, Temple Sinai Library, 50 Sewall Ave, Brookline, MA, 02446. Tel: 617-277-5888. Fax: 617-277-5842. p. 1072

Shamchuk, Lisa, Ref Librn, Grant MacEwan University Library, 10700 104th Ave, Edmonton, AB, T5J 4S2, CANADA. Tel: 780-497-5850. Fax: 780-497-5895. p. 2701

Shammo, Naomi, Librn, Birchard Public Library of Sandusky County, Gibsonburg Branch, 100 N Webster St, Gibsonburg, OH, 43431. Tel: 419-637-2173. p. 1900

Shan, Feng, Head, Electronic Res, Indiana University South Bend, 1700 Mishawaka Ave, South Bend, IN, 46615. Tel: 574-520-4189. Fax: 574-520-4472. p. 778

Shanafelt, Nancy, Ch, Eccles-Lesher Memorial Library, 673 Main St, Rimersburg, PA, 16248-4817. Tel: 814-473-3800. Fax: 814-473-8200. p. 2134

Shanafelt, Nancy F, Cat, McMurry University, Sayles Blvd & S 14th, Abilene, TX, 79605. Tel: 325-793-4692. Fax: 325-793-4930. p. 2272

Shanck, Winter, Archivist, Educational Broadcasting Corp, 450 W 33rd St, New York, NY, 10001. Tel: 212-560-3067. Fax: 212-560-3199. p. 1677

Shanda, Subia, Dir, Lampasas Public Library, 201 S Main, Lampasas, TX, 76550-2843. Tel: 512-556-3251. Fax: 512-556-4065. p. 2353

Shandor, Karen M, Libr Tech, Library of the US Courts, Robert A Grant Courthouse, 204 S Main St, Rm 316, South Bend, IN, 46601. Tel: 574-246-8050. Fax: 574-246-8002. p. 779

Shane, Clasina, Librn, Monterey Institute for Research & Astronomy, 200 Eighth St, Marina, CA, 93933. Tel: 831-883-1000. Fax: 831-883-1031. p. 183

Shane, Jordana, Coordr, Info Literacy, Philadelphia University, 4201 Henry Ave, Philadelphia, PA, 19144-5497. Tel: 215-951-2629. Fax: 215-951-2574. p. 2115

Shane, Margaret, Archivist, Info & Rec Mgr, Alberta Teachers' Association Library, 11010 142 St, Edmonton, AB, T5N 2R1, CANADA. Tel: 780-447-9429. Fax: 780-455-6481. p. 2699

Shane, Marjorie, Librn, Groton Free Public Library, 1304 Scott Hwy, Groton, VT, 05046. Tel: 802-584-3358. p. 2425

Shanefield, Irene D, Librn, Jewish Rehabilitation Hospital Medical Library, 3205 Pl Alton Goldbloom, Laval, QC, H7V 1R2, CANADA. Tel: 450-688-9550, Ext 226. Fax: 450-688-3673. p. 2886

Shaner, Sally A, Librn, Opp Public Library, 1604 N Main St, Opp, AL, 36467. Tel: 334-493-6423. Fax: 334-493-6423. p. 32

Shaner, Susan E, State Archivist, Hawaii State Archives, Iolani Palace Grounds, 364 S King St, Honolulu, HI, 96813. Tel: 808-586-0329. Fax: 808-586-0330. p. 561

Shanfield, Joy, Info Res, Toronto Rehab, 550 University Ave, Toronto, ON, M5G 2A2, CANADA. Tel: 416-597-3422, Ext 3050. Fax: 416-591-6515. p. 2864

Shanholtz, Cindy, Br Mgr, Keyser-Mineral County Public Library, Fort Ashby Public, PO Box 74, Fort Ashby, WV, 26719-0064. Tel: 304-298-4493. Fax: 304-298-4014. p. 2563

Shank, Beverly, Asst Dir, Watertown Free Public Library, 123 Main St, Watertown, MA, 02472. Tel: 617-972-6438. Fax: 617-926-4375. p. 1134

Shank, Diane, Head, Cat, Head, Tech Serv, Oklahoma Baptist University, 500 W University, OBU Box 61310, Shawnee, OK, 74804-2504. Tel: 405-878-2257. Fax: 405-878-2270. p. 1977

Shank, Gail, Reader Serv, Curry College, 1071 Blue Hill Ave, Milton, MA, 02186-9984. Tel: 617-333-2170. Fax: 617-333-2164. p. 1106

Shank, Karin, Res, North Carolina Biotechnology Center Library, 15 Alexander Dr, Research Triangle Park, NC, 27709. Tel: 919-541-9366. Fax: 919-990-9521. p. 1820

Shankle, Beth, Res Librn, National Press Club, 529 14th St NW, 13th Flr, Washington, DC, 20045. Tel: 202-662-7509. Fax: 202-879-6725. p. 411

Shanks, Barbara, Librn for Blind & Physically Handicapped, Evansville Vanderburgh Public Library, Talking Books Service, 200 SE Martin Luther King Jr Blvd, Evansville, IN, 47713-1604. Tel: 812-428-8235. p. 738

Shanks, Barry, Ref Librn, University of New Hampshire School of Law, Two White St, Concord, NH, 03301. Tel: 603-228-1541, Ext 1130. Fax: 603-228-0388. p. 1443

Shanks, Lynn, Dir of Develop, Crandall Public Library, 251 Glen St, Glens Falls, NY, 12801-3593. Tel: 518-792-6508. Fax: 518-792-5251. p. 1629

Shanks, Sharon, Dir, Nelson County Public Library, 201 Cathedral Manor, Bardstown, KY, 40004-1515. Tel: 502-348-3714. Fax: 502-348-5578. p. 906

Shanley, Caitlin, Instrul Design Librn, University of Tennessee at Chattanooga Library, 615 McCallie Ave, Dept 6456, Chattanooga, TN, 37403-2598. Tel: 423-425-4501. Fax: 423-425-4775. p. 2228

Shanley, Catherine M, Asst Dir, Manhattan College, 4513 Manhattan College Pkwy, Riverdale, NY, 10471. Tel: 718-862-7166. Fax: 718-862-8028. p. 1728

Shanman, Roberta, Head, Ref, RAND Corporation Library, 1776 Main St, M1LIB, Santa Monica, CA, 90407. Tel: 310-393-0411, Ext 7788. Fax: 310-451-7029. p. 266

Shannahan, Eileen, Tech Serv, Seminole Community Library, 9200 113th St N, Seminole, FL, 33772. Tel: 727-394-6905. Fax: 727-398-3113. p. 491

Shannahan, Tom, Dir, Adams Memorial Library, 205 Central St, Central Falls, RI, 02863. Tel: 401-727-7440. Fax: 401-727-7442. p. 2164

Shannon, Carol, Dir, East Rochester Public Library, 57 Main St, East Rochester, NH, 03868. Tel: 603-332-8013. p. 1446

Shannon, Cherill, Cat, Canmore Public Library, 950 Eighth Ave, Canmore, AB, T1W 2T1, CANADA. Tel: 403-678-2468. Fax: 403-678-2165. p. 2694

Shannon, Colleen, Info Spec, Hershey Foods Corp, 1025 Reese Ave, Hershey, PA, 17033-2272. Tel: 717-534-5106. Fax: 717-534-5069. p. 2069

Shannon, Don, Coordr, USS Massachusetts Memorial Committee, Inc, Battleship Cove, Fall River, MA, 02721. Tel: 508-678-1100. Fax: 508-674-5597. p. 1088

Shannon, Don, Coordr, PT Boats, Inc, 1384 Cordova Cove, Ste 2, Memphis, TN, 38138-2200. Tel: 508-678-1100. p. 2250

Shannon, Donna M, Assoc Prof, University of South Carolina, 1501 Greene St, Columbia, SC, 29208. Tel: 803-777-3858. Fax: 803-777-7938. p. 2973

Shannon, Janene, Dir, Lost Nation Public Library, 410 Main St, Lost Nation, IA, 52254. Tel: 563-678-2114. Fax: 563-678-2368. p. 828

Shannon, Kathy, Exec Dir, Petroleum Museum Library & Hall of Fame, 1500 Interstate 20 W, Midland, TX, 79701. Tel: 432-683-4403. Fax: 432-683-4509. p. 2363

Shannon, Lucia, Ref, Brockton Public Library System, 304 Main St, Brockton, MA, 02301-5390. Tel: 508-580-7890. Fax: 508-580-7898. p. 1070

Shannon, Meaghan, Copyright Officer, Fanshawe College, 1001 Fanshawe College Blvd, London, ON, N5Y 5R6, CANADA. Tel: 519-452-4240. Fax: 519-452-4473. p. 2817

Shanton, Kristina, Music, Ithaca College Library, 953 Danby Rd, Ithaca, NY, 14850-7060. Tel: 607-274-3206. Fax: 607-274-1539. p. 1643

Shao, Dongfang, Dir, Stanford University Libraries, East Asia Library, 560 Escondido Mall, Stanford, CA, 94305-6004. Tel: 650-725-3435. Fax: 650-724-2028. p. 271

Shapansky, Lori, Librn, Norman Wells Community Library, PO Box 97, Norman Wells, NT, X0E 0V0, CANADA. Tel: 867-587-3714. Fax: 867-587-3714. p. 2775

Shapiola, Annemarie, Ch, Dwight D Eisenhower Public Library, 537 Totowa Rd, Totowa, NJ, 07512-1699. Tel: 973-790-3265, Ext 11. Fax: 973-790-0306. p. 1535

Shapiro, Deborah, Dir, Middlesex County Historical Society Library, 151 Main St, Middletown, CT, 06457-3423. Tel: 860-346-0746. Fax: 860-346-0746. p. 352

Shapiro, Fred, Coll Librn, Yale University Library, Lillian Goldman Library Yale Law School, 127 Wall St, New Haven, CT, 06511. Tel: 203-432-1600. Fax: 203-432-2112. p. 358

Shapiro, Harriet, Head, Exhibitions, The New York Society Library, 53 E 79th St, New York, NY, 10075. Tel: 212-288-6000 Ext 221. Fax: 212-744-5832. p. 1694

Shapiro, June, Br Mgr, Clayton County Library System, Morrow Branch, 6225 Maddox Rd, Morrow, GA, 30260. Tel: 404-366-7749. Fax: 404-363-4569. p. 537

Shapiro, Lee, Ref Librn, NASA Headquarters Library, 300 E St SW, Rm 1J20, Washington, DC, 20546. Tel: 202-358-0171. Fax: 202-358-3251. p. 409

Shapiro, Marian, Coordr, Tech Serv, Harris-Stowe State University Library, 3026 Laclede Ave, Saint Louis, MO, 63103-2199. Tel: 314-340-3621. Fax: 314-340-3630. p. 1355

Shapiro, Martin, Coll Develop, American University Library, 4400 Massachusetts Ave NW, Washington, DC, 20016-8046. Tel: 202-885-3854. Fax: 202-885-3226. p. 393

Shapiro, Robin, Fac Librn-Rock Creek Campus, Portland Community College Library, 12000 SW 49th AV, Portland, OR, 97219. Tel: 971-722-7126. Fax: 971-722-8397. p. 2013

Shapiro, Steven, Electronic Res Librn, Montclair State University, One Normal Ave, Montclair, NJ, 07043-1699. Tel: 973-655-4428. Fax: 973-655-7780. p. 1503

Shapiro, Susan, Access Serv, Mount Saint Mary's College, 12001 Chalon Rd, Los Angeles, CA, 90049-1599. Tel: 310-954-4370. Fax: 310-954-4379. p. 175

Shapka, Leanne, Librn, Lakeland Library Region, Macklin Branch, Box 652, Macklin, SK, S0L 2C0, CANADA. Tel: 306-753-2933. Fax: 306-753-3234. p. 2920

Shapoval, Sandy, Libr Dir, Phillips Theological Seminary Library, 901 N Mingo Rd, Tulsa, OK, 74116. Tel: 918-270-6437. Fax: 918-270-6490. p. 1982

Sharbaugh, Lisa, Libr Support Spec, South Central Kansas Library System, 321 N Main St, South Hutchinson, KS, 67505-1146. Tel: 620-663-3211. Fax: 620-663-9797. p. 895

Sharbaugh, Thomas L, Dir, Salamanca Public Library, 155 Wildwood Ave, Salamanca, NY, 14779. Tel: 716-945-1890. Fax: 716-945-2741. p. 1737

Share, Ellen, Librn, Washington Hebrew Congregation Libraries, 3935 Macomb St NW, Washington, DC, 20016-3741. Tel: 301-354-3212. Fax: 301-354-3200. p. 422

Shari, Ferda, Br Mgr, Martins Ferry Public Library, Victoria Read Flushing Branch, 300 High St, Flushing, OH, 43977. Tel: 740-968-3891. Fax: 740-968-0648. p. 1915

Sharkey, Anne, Info Res, Standards Council of Canada, 270 Albert St, Ste 200, Ottawa, ON, K1P 6N7, CANADA. Tel: 613-238-3222, Ext 460. Fax: 613-569-7808. p. 2833

Sharkey, Leslie Ann, Head Librn, Fox Creek Municipal Library, 501 Eighth St, Fox Creek, AB, T0H 1P0, CANADA. Tel: 780-622-2343. Fax: 780-622-4160. p. 2705

Sharkey, Lisa, Librn, Planned Parenthood of Minnesota & South Dakota, 1200 Lagoon Ave S, Minneapolis, MN, 55408. Tel: 612-823-6568. Fax: 612-825-3522. p. 1261

Sharkey, Stephanie, Libr Spec, Northern Virginia Community College Libraries, Woodbridge Library, 15200 Neabsco Mills Rd, Seefeldt 427, Woodbridge, VA, 22191. Tel: 703-878-5727. Fax: 703-670-8433. p. 2448

Sharkey, Wendy, Cat Librn, Bennington Free Library, 101 Silver St, Bennington, VT, 05201. Tel: 802-442-9051. p. 2418

Sharkoski, Nicholas, Librn, Albert C Wagner Youth Correctional Facility Library, 500 Ward Ave, Bordentown, NJ, 08505-2928. Tel: 609-298-0500. Fax: 609-298-3639. p. 1474

Sharma, Ravindra, Dr, Dean, Monmouth University, 400 Cedar Ave, West Long Branch, NJ, 07764. Tel: 732-571-3450. Fax: 732-263-5124. p. 1541

Sharma, Ritu, Asst Librn, Capital Health System at Mercer, 446 Bellevue Ave, Trenton, NJ, 08618. Tel: 609-394-4282. Fax: 609-394-4131. p. 1535

Sharon, Stephanie, Multimedia, Chester County Library System, 450 Exton Square Pkwy, Exton, PA, 19341-2496. Tel: 610-280-2600. Fax: 610-280-2688. p. 2056

Sharon, Yearwood, Ch, C E Brehm Memorial Public Library District, 101 S Seventh St, Mount Vernon, IL, 62864. Tel: 618-242-6322. Fax: 618-242-0810. p. 677

Sharp, Andrew, Dir, Jones County Junior College, 900 S Court St, Ellisville, MS, 39437. Tel: 601-477-4055. Fax: 601-477-2600. p. 1298

Sharp, Avery, Outreach Librn, Baylor University Libraries, Armstrong Browning Library, 710 Speight Ave, Waco, TX, 76798-7152. Tel: 254-710-4964. Fax: 254-710-3552. p. 2396

Sharp, Carla, Head, Youth Serv, Brighton District Library, 100 Library Dr, Brighton, MI, 48116. Tel: 810-229-6571, Ext 209. Fax: 810-229-3161. p. 1159

Sharp, Chris, Govt Doc Librn, Kennesaw State University, 1000 Chastain Rd, Kennesaw, GA, 30144. Tel: 770-423-6191. Fax: 770-423-6185. p. 537

Sharp, David, Head, Coll, E-Res & Ser, Carleton University Library, 1125 Colonel By Dr, Ottawa, ON, K1S 5B6, CANADA. Tel: 613-520-2600, Ext 8372. Fax: 613-520-2750. p. 2830

Sharp, Gary, Dir, North Bend Public Library, 1800 Sherman Ave, North Bend, OR, 97459. Tel: 541-756-0400. Fax: 541-756-1073. p. 2008

Sharp, Janice, Dir, Edna Buschow Memorial Library, 321 W First St, Valley Center, KS, 67147. Tel: 316-755-7350. Fax: 316-755-7351. p. 898

Sharp, Jody, Coordr, Tech Serv, Baltimore County Public Library, 320 York Rd, Towson, MD, 21204-5179. Tel: 410-887-8630. Fax: 410-887-6103. p. 1044

Sharp, Joy, Coordr, Ch Serv, Polk County Public Library, 1289 W Mills St, Columbus, NC, 28722. Tel: 828-894-8721. Fax: 828-894-2761. p. 1785

Sharp, Laurel, Ch, Altadena Library District, 600 E Mariposa St, Altadena, CA, 91001. Tel: 626-798-0833. Fax: 626-798-5351. p. 120

Sharp, Ron, Ref Serv, Sr Info Spec, Indiana State Library, 315 W Ohio St, Indianapolis, IN, 46202. Tel: 317-232-3727. Fax: 317-232-0002. p. 752

Sharp, Ross, Coordr, Libr Serv, Newton-Wellesley Hospital, 2014 Washington St, Newton Lower Falls, MA, 02462-1699. Tel: 617-243-6279. Fax: 617-243-6595. p. 1111

Sharp, Susie, Librn, New Rockford Public Library, 10 Eight St N, New Rockford, ND, 58356. Tel: 701-947-5540. Fax: 701-947-5540. p. 1847

Sharp, Tammie, Human Res Mgr, Kansas City, Kansas Public Library, 625 Minnesota Ave, Kansas City, KS, 66101. Tel: 913-279-2256. Fax: 913-279-2033. p. 875

Sharpe, Amy, Asst Librn, Sharp HealthCare, 7901 Frost St, San Diego, CA, 92123. Tel: 858-939-3242. Fax: 858-939-3248. p. 238

Sharpe, Annette, Dir, Hollis Public Library, PO Box 5, Hollis, AK, 99950. Tel: 907-530-7112. p. 49

Sharpe, Barbara, Br Mgr, Aiken-Bamberg-Barnwell-Edgefield Regional Library System, Midland Valley, Nine Hillside Rd, Langley, SC, 29834. Tel: 803-593-7379. Fax: 803-593-5253. p. 2179

Sharpe, Deb, Librn, Bracken Memorial Library, 57 Academy Rd, Woodstock, CT, 06281. Tel: 860-928-0046. Fax: 860-928-2117. p. 380

Sharpe, Heather, Commun Relations Mgr, Lancaster Public Library, 125 N Duke St, Lancaster, PA, 17602-2883. Tel: 717-394-2651, Ext 119. Fax: 717-394-3083. p. 2077

Sharpe, Patti, Librn, Patterson Palmer Library, PO Box 1068, Truro, NS, B2N 5B9, CANADA. Tel: 902-897-2000. Fax: 902-893-3071. p. 2786

Sharpe, Rod, Music Librn, Western Illinois University Libraries, One University Circle, Macomb, IL, 61455. Tel: 309-298-2039. Fax: 309-298-2791. p. 669

Sharpe, Tania, Mgr, Pub Serv, Chatham-Kent Public Library, 120 Queen St, Chatham, ON, N7M 2G6, CANADA. Tel: 519-354-2940. Fax: 519-354-7366. p. 2799

Sharples, Mary Beth, Dir, Midlothian Public Library, 14701 S Kenton Ave, Midlothian, IL, 60445-4122. Tel: 708-535-2027. Fax: 708-535-2053. p. 674

Sharpley, Suzan B, Dir, Marin County Law Library, 20 N San Pedro Rd, Ste 2015, San Rafael, CA, 94903. Tel: 415-499-6357. Fax: 415-499-6837. p. 257

Sharps, Andrea, Mgr, Coll Serv, Spokane County Library District, 4322 N Argonne Rd, Spokane, WA, 99212-1868. Tel: 509-893-8200. Fax: 509-893-8472. p. 2536

Sharron, David, Head, Spec Coll, Univ Archivist, Brock University, 500 Glenridge Ave, St. Catharines, ON, L2S 3A1, CANADA. Tel: 905-688-5550, Ext 3264. Fax: 905-988-5490. p. 2842

Sharrow, Shirley A, Librn, Naval Air Warfare Center, 22560 Epic Dr, Ste 100, California, MD, 20619. Tel: 301-862-0337. Fax: 301-862-5499. p. 1022

Sharry, Sharon A, Dir, Jones Library, Inc, 43 Amity St, Amherst, MA, 01002-2285. Tel: 413-259-3090. Fax: 413-256-4096. p. 1048

Shatara, Barbara, Adult Serv, Outreach Serv Librn, Fletcher Free Library, 235 College St, Burlington, VT, 05401. Tel: 802-865-7211. Fax: 802-865-7227. p. 2420

Shatara, Halimeh, Libr Tech, Palm Beach State College, 1977 College Dr, Belle Glade, FL, 33430. Tel: 561-993-1155. Fax: 561-993-1157. p. 427

Shatarevyan, Suzanna, Ref/Digital Mgt Librn, Loyola Law School, 919 S Albany St, Los Angeles, CA, 90015-1211. Tel: 213-736-1147. Fax: 213-487-2204. p. 175

Shattuck, Beverly A, Dir, University of South Florida, Hinks & Elaine Shimberg Health Sciences Library, 12901 Bruce B Downs Blvd, MDC Box 31, Tampa, FL, 33612-4799. Tel: 813-974-2399. Fax: 813-974-3605, 813-974-4930. p. 498

Shattuck, Jennifer, Br Mgr, Great River Regional Library, Grey Eagle Community Library, 118 State St E, Grey Eagle, MN, 56336. Tel: 320-285-2505. Fax: 320-285-2505. p. 1275

Shatzer, Jennifer, Mgr, Tech Serv, Wayne County Public Library, 220 W Liberty St, Wooster, OH, 44691-3593. Tel: 330-804-4679. Fax: 330-262-1352. p. 1950

Shaughnessy, Amy, Youth Serv Librn, Saint Clair Shores Public Library, 22500 11 Mile Rd, Saint Clair Shores, MI, 48081-1399. Tel: 586-771-9020. Fax: 586-771-8935. p. 1224

Shaughnessy, Amy, Syst Librn, Suburban Library Cooperative, 44750 Delco Blvd, Sterling Heights, MI, 48313. Tel: 586-685-5750. Fax: 586-685-3010. p. 2946

Shaughnessy, Belinda, Asst Librn, Moses Taylor Hospital Medical Library, 700 Quincy Ave, Scranton, PA, 18510. Tel: 570-340-2125. Fax: 570-963-8994. p. 2137

Shaughnessy, Jean, Ch, Athol Public Library, 568 Main St, Athol, MA, 01331. Tel: 978-249-9515. Fax: 978-249-7636. p. 1050

Shaughnessy, Joe, Dir, Hill College Library, 112 Lamar Dr, Hillsboro, TX, 76645. Tel: 254-659-7831. Fax: 254-582-7591. p. 2333

Shaughnessy, Rita, Librn, University of Toronto Libraries, Family & Community Medicine Library, 500 University Ave, Toronto, ON, M5G 1V7, CANADA. Tel: 416-978-5606. Fax: 416-978-3912. p. 2866

Shave, Diane, Libr Dir, Breton Municipal Library, 4916-50 Ave, Breton, AB, T0C 0P0, CANADA. Tel: 780-696-3740. Fax: 780-696-3590. p. 2686

Shave, Tina, Dir, Fort Hunter Free Library, 351 Main St, Fort Hunter, NY, 12069. Tel: 518-829-7248. Fax: 518-829-7248. p. 1624

Shaver, Carolyn, Adult Serv, Pryor Public Library, 505 E Graham, Pryor, OK, 74361. Tel: 918-825-0777. Fax: 918-825-0856. p. 1976

Shaver, Denise, Ch, Belmont Public Library, 336 Concord Ave, Belmont, MA, 02478-0904. Tel: 617-489-2000, 617-993-2850. Fax: 617-993-2893. p. 1052

Shaver, Paul, Circ Supvr, Englewood Public Library, 31 Engle St, Englewood, NJ, 07631. Tel: 201-568-2215. Fax: 201-568-6895. p. 1484

Shaw, Amy, Syst Librn, Saint Catherine University, 2004 Randolph Ave, Mail F-10, Saint Paul, MN, 55105-1794. Tel: 651-690-6423. Fax: 651-690-8636. p. 1281

Shaw, Bob, ILL Librn, Wisconsin Library Services, 728 State St, Rm 464, Madison, WI, 53706-1494. Tel: 608-265-4167. Fax: 608-262-6067. p. 2958

Shaw, Bobbi, Circ, Park University Library, 8700 NW River Park Dr, Parkville, MO, 64152. Tel: 816-584-6285. Fax: 816-741-4911. p. 1349

Shaw, Brenda, Librn, Jersey City Medical Center Library, 355 Grand St, Jersey City, NJ, 07302. Tel: 201-915-2009. Fax: 201-915-2911. p. 1492

Shaw, Cathy, Dir, Edgewood Public Library, 203 W Union St, Edgewood, IA, 52042. Tel: 563-928-6242. Fax: 563-928-6242. p. 813

Shaw, Conni L, Tech Serv, Grove City College, 300 Campus Dr, Grove City, PA, 16127-2198. Tel: 724-458-3842. Fax: 724-458-2181. p. 2063

Shaw, Courtney, Librn, Smithsonian Libraries, National Museum of Natural History Library, Nat Museum of Natural Hist, Rm 51, MRC 154, Tenth St & Constitution Ave NW, Washington, DC, 20013-0712. Tel: 202-633-1675. Fax: 202-357-1896. p. 415

Shaw, Deb, Dir, Moose Lake Public Library, 313 Elm Ave, Moose Lake, MN, 55767. Tel: 218-485-4424. Fax: 218-485-4424. p. 1266

Shaw, Debora, Dr, Dean, Indiana University, Wells Library 001, 1320 E Tenth St, Bloomington, IN, 47405-3907. Tel: 812-855-2018. Fax: 812-855-6166. p. 2965

Shaw, Debra, Adult Serv, Plainfield-Guilford Township Public Library, 1120 Stafford Rd, Plainfield, IN, 46168-2230. Tel: 317-839-6602. Fax: 317-838-3805. p. 773

Shaw, Diane W, Spec Coll Librn, Lafayette College, 710 Sullivan Rd, Easton, PA, 18042-1797. Tel: 610-330-5401. Fax: 610-252-0370. p. 2052

Shaw, Eileen, Br Mgr, Whatcom County Library System, Everson McBeath Community, 104 Kirsch Dr, Everson, WA, 98247. Tel: 360-966-5100. Fax: 360-966-5100. p. 2509

Shaw, Frankie, Br Mgr, Wellington County Library, Puslinch Township, 29 Wellington Rd 46S, RR3, Guelph, ON, N1H 6H9, CANADA. Tel: 519-763-8026. Fax: 519-763-4122. p. 2805

Shaw, Holly, Ch, Silsby Free Public Library, 226 Main St, Charlestown, NH, 03603. Tel: 603-826-7793. Fax: 603-826-7793. p. 1441

Shaw, Jackie, Dir, Sylvester Memorial Wellston Public Library, 135 E Second St, Wellston, OH, 45692. Tel: 740-384-6660. Fax: 740-384-5001. p. 1946

Shaw, James, Dir of Coll, University of Nebraska at Omaha, 6001 Dodge St, Omaha, NE, 68182-0237. Tel: 402-554-2225. Fax: 402-554-3215. p. 1414

Shaw, Janet, Librn, Missouri Department of Corrections, Women's Eastern Reception & Diagnostic Correctional Center, 1101 E Hwy 54, Vandalia, MO, 63382-2905. Tel: 573-594-6686. Fax: 573-594-6789. p. 1335

Shaw, Jean, Ch, Caribou Public Library, 30 High St, Caribou, ME, 04736. Tel: 207-493-4214. Fax: 207-493-4654. p. 981

Shaw, Jean, AV, Mercer County District Library, 303 N Main St, Celina, OH, 45822. Tel: 419-586-4442. Fax: 419-586-3222. p. 1866

Shaw, Jean, Librn, Lillooet Area Library Association, Gold Bridge Branch, General Delivery, Gold Bridge, BC, V0K 1P0, CANADA. Tel: 250-238-2521. Fax: 250-238-2521. p. 2731

Shaw, Jocelyn, Ref Serv, Ad, Website Mgr, Hackley Public Library, 316 W Webster Ave, Muskegon, MI, 49440. Tel: 231-722-7276, Ext 272. Fax: 231-726-5567. p. 1212

Shaw, Joyce M, Head Librn & Assoc Prof, Gulf Coast Research Laboratory, 703 E Beach Dr, Ocean Springs, MS, 39564. Tel: 228-872-4213, 228-872-4253. Fax: 228-872-4264. p. 1310

Shaw, Kerrie, Dir, Libr Serv, Eastern Virginia Medical School, 740 W Olney Rd, Norfolk, VA, 23501. Tel: 757-446-5840. Fax: 757-446-5134. p. 2481

Shaw, Linda, Ref, Hamilton East Public Library, One Library Plaza, Cumberland Rd, Noblesville, IN, 46060-5639. Tel: 317-770-3207. Fax: 317-776-6936. p. 769

Shaw, Linda, Librn, Celina Public Library, 142 N Ohio St, Celina, TX, 75009. Tel: 972-382-8655. Fax: 972-382-3736. p. 2296

Shaw, Linda, In Charge, Prosper Community Library, 700 N Coleman Rd, Prosper, TX, 75078. Tel: 469-219-2499. Fax: 972-346-9115. p. 2372

Shaw, Lindsay, Ch, Providence Athenaeum, 251 Benefit St, Providence, RI, 02903-2799. Tel: 401-421-6970. Fax: 401-421-2860. p. 2173

Shaw, Louis, Bus Mgr, Carrier Mills-Stonefort Public Library District, 109 W Oak St, Carrier Mills, IL, 62917. Tel: 618-994-2011. Fax: 618-994-2303. p. 601

Shaw, Lucy, Libr Asst II, Yuma County Library District, Dateland Branch, Ave 64E & Interstate 8, Dateland, AZ, 85333. Tel: 928-454-2242. Fax: 928-454-2217. p. 91

Shaw, Lucy, Libr Asst II, Yuma County Library District, Roll Branch, 5151 S Ave 39E, Roll, AZ, 85347. Tel: 928-785-9575. Fax: 928-785-3701. p. 92

Shaw, Mabel, Asst Intl & Foreign Law Librn, Georgetown University, Georgetown Law Library (John Wolff & Edward Bennett Williams Libraries), 111 G St NW, Washington, DC, 20001. Fax: 202-662-9168. p. 403

Shaw, Mark, Dir, Southwest Public Libraries, Westland Area Library, 4740 W Broad St, Columbus, OH, 43228. Tel: 614-878-1301. Fax: 614-878-3454. p. 1903

Shaw, Mark M, Dir, Southwest Public Libraries, SPL Admin, 3359 Park St, Groye City, OH, 43123. Tel: 614-875-6716, Ext 119. Fax: 614-875-2219. p. 1903

Shaw, Meg, Head of Libr, University of Kentucky Libraries, Lucille Little Fine Arts Library & Learning Center, 160 Patterson Dr, Lexington, KY, 40506-0224. Tel: 859-257-4908. Fax: 859-257-4662. p. 922

Shaw, Megan, Ch, La Crosse County Library, Administration Ctr, 103 State St, Holmen, WI, 54636. Tel: 608-526-9600. Fax: 608-526-3299. p. 2598

Shaw, Michael, Br Mgr, Norfolk Public Library, Barron F Black Branch, 6700 E Tanners Creek Rd, Norfolk, VA, 23513. Tel: 757-441-5806. Fax: 757-441-5891. p. 2481

Shaw, Sam, Dir, Nebraska Department of Corrections, PO Box 2500, Sta B, Lincoln, NE, 68502. Tel: 402-471-3161, Ext 3267. Fax: 402-479-5819. p. 1405

Shaw, Sandra, Dir, Community Free Library, 86 Public Sq, Holley, NY, 14470. Tel: 585-638-6987. Fax: 585-638-7436. p. 1637

Shaw, Sara, Coordr, Salt Lake County Library Services, Alta Reading Room, Alta Community Ctr, Sandy, UT, 84092-6001. Tel: 801-742-2068. p. 2414

Shaw, Sherill, Cat, College of Eastern Utah Library, 451 E & 400 N, Price, UT, 84501. Tel: 435-613-5208. Fax: 435-613-5863. p. 2410

Shaw, Shileen, Ch, Newark Public Library, Weequahic, 355 Osborne Terrace, Newark, NJ, 07112. Tel: 973-733-7751. Fax: 973-733-7802. p. 1512

Shaw, Susan, Dir, Thompson Public Library, 142 Jackson St N, Thompson, IA, 50478. Tel: 641-584-2829. p. 847

Shaw, Susan, Acq, Moundsville-Marshall County Public Library, 700 Fifth St, Moundsville, WV, 26041-1993. Tel: 304-845-6911. Fax: 304-845-6912. p. 2567

Shaw, Tamara, Ref Serv, University of San Diego, Helen K & James S Copley Library, 5998 Alcala Park, San Diego, CA, 92110. Fax: 619-260-4617. p. 239

Shaw, Theresa, Br Mgr, Phoenix Public Library, Saguaro Library, 2808 N 46th St, Phoenix, AZ, 85008-1504. p. 76

Shaw, Tom, Librn, Outreach Serv Librn, Wilkinsburg Public Library, 605 Ross Ave, Pittsburgh, PA, 15221-2195. Tel: 412-244-4378. Fax: 412-243-6943. p. 2130

Shaw Widman, Karen, Media Serv, East Meadow Public Library, 1886 Front St, East Meadow, NY, 11554-1705. Tel: 516-794-2570. Fax: 516-794-1272. p. 1617

Shaw-Daigle, Christine, Librn, University of Manitoba Libraries, Carolyn Sifton-Helene Fuld Library, St Boniface Hospital, 409 Tache Ave, Winnipeg, MB, R2H 2A6, CANADA. Tel: 204-237-2808. Fax: 204-235-3339. p. 2759

Shawcross, Maggie, Librn, North Colorado Medical Center, Wellspring Community Health Library, 1801 16th St, Greeley, CO, 80631. Tel: 970-350-6074. Fax: 970-392-2450. p. 312

Shawcross, Nancy, Curator of Manuscripts, University of Pennsylvania Libraries, Rare Book & Manuscript Library, 3420 Walnut St, Philadelphia, PA, 19104. Tel: 215-898-2055. p. 2119

Shawver, Vincent, Fed Libr Mgr, US Environmental Protection Agency, 901 N Fifth St, Kansas City, KS, 66101-2907. Tel: 913-551-7979. Fax: 913-551-8762. p. 876

Shay, Esti, Law Librn, El Paso County Bar Association Law Library, Penrose Library, 20 N Cascade Ave, Colorado Springs, CO, 80903. Tel: 719-531-6333. p. 295

Shay, Lynn, Head, Ser, University of West Florida, 11000 University Pkwy, Pensacola, FL, 32514-5750. Tel: 850-474-2460. Fax: 850-474-3338. p. 482

Shay, Patty, Coordr, ILL, University of Kansas School of Medicine-Wichita, 1010 N Kansas, Wichita, KS, 67214-3199. Tel: 316-293-2629. Fax: 316-293-2608. p. 900

Shaykett, Jessica, Librn, American Craft Council Library, 1224 Marshall St NE, Ste 200, Minneapolis, MN, 55413. Tel: 612-206-3118. Fax: 612-355-2330. p. 1258

Shcerzay, Ali, Sr Librn, Peoria Public Library, 8463 W Monroe St, Peoria, AZ, 85345. Tel: 623-773-7540. Fax: 623-773-7567. p. 71

Shea, Alison, Ref Librn, Fordham University School of Law, 140 W 62nd St, New York, NY, 10023-7485. Tel: 212-636-6751. Fax: 212-930-8818. p. 1678

Shea, Ellen, Pub Serv, Harvard Library, Arthur & Elizabeth Schlesinger Library on the History of Women in America, Three James St, Cambridge, MA, 02138-3766. Tel: 617-495-8549. Fax: 617-496-8340. p. 1076

Shea, Gerard, Asst Prof, Pub Serv Librn, Felician College Library, 262 S Main St, Lodi, NJ, 07644-2198. Tel: 201-559-3514. Fax: 201-559-3328. p. 1496

Shea, Jack, Dir, Teton Science School Library, One Ditch Creek Rd, Kelly, WY, 83011. Tel: 307-733-4765. Fax: 307-739-9388. p. 2656

Shea, Jaymee, Libr Mgr, Water Valley Public Library, PO Box 250, Water Valley, AB, T0M 2E0, CANADA. Tel: 403-637-3899. p. 2721

Shea, Jonathan D, Archivist, Dir, Polish Genealogical Society of Connecticut Inc, Eight Lyle Rd, New Britain, CT, 06053-2104. Tel: 860-223-5596. p. 354

Shea, Karen, Dir of Libr Serv, Librn, The Hastings Center, 21 Malcolm Gordon Dr, Garrison, NY, 10524-5555. Tel: 845-424-4040, Ext 226. Fax: 845-424-4545. p. 1627

Shea, Karen, Access Serv Librn, United States Military Academy Library, Jefferson Hall Library & Learning Center, 758 Cullum Rd, West Point, NY, 10996. Tel: 845-938-3833. Fax: 845-938-4000. p. 1767

Shea, Kathleen, Mgr, Rim Community Library, 3404 Mustang Ave, Heber, AZ, 85928. Tel: 928-535-5749. Fax: 928-535-6409. p. 65

Shea, Linda, Ch, Sidney Memorial Public Library, Eight River St, Sidney, NY, 13838. Tel: 607-563-1200, 607-563-8021. Fax: 607-563-7675. p. 1743

Shea, Louise, VPres, Staff Serv, The New York Public Library - Astor, Lenox & Tilden Foundations, 476 Fifth Ave, (@ 42nd St), New York, NY, 10018-2788. Tel: 212-592-7302. Fax: 212-592-7440. p. 1690

Shea, Maire, Circ, Swansea Free Public Library, 69 Main St, Swansea, MA, 02777. Tel: 508-674-9609. Fax: 508-675-5444. p. 1130

Shea, Marsha J, Head, Tech Serv, SI Group, Inc, 2750 Balltown Rd, Schenectady, NY, 12309-1094. Tel: 518-347-4401. Fax: 518-347-6401. p. 1741

Shea, Maxine, Dir, Marcus Public Library, 106 N Locust St, Marcus, IA, 51035. Tel: 712-376-2328. Fax: 712-376-4628. p. 829

Shea, Richard, Melbourne Campus Libr Dir, Keiser University Library System, 1500 NW 49th St, Fort Lauderdale, FL, 33309. Tel: 954-351-4035. Fax: 954-351-4051. p. 443

Shea-Clark, Laura, Libr Serv Mgr, Mountain View Public Library, 585 Franklin St, Mountain View, CA, 94041-1998. Tel: 650-903-6335. Fax: 650-962-0438. p. 192

Shead, Susan, Dir, Eastford Public Library, 179 Eastford Rd, Eastford, CT, 06242. Tel: 860-974-0125. Fax: 860-974-0125. p. 338

Sheads, Scott S, Head Archivist, Fort McHenry National Monument & Historic Shrine Library, 2400 E Fort Ave, Baltimore, MD, 21230-5393. Tel: 410-962-4290, Ext 244. Fax: 410-962-2500. p. 1013

Sheaffer, Ellen, Cat, Garrett College, 687 Mosser Rd, McHenry, MD, 21541. Tel: 301-387-3002. Fax: 301-387-3055. p. 1035

Sheaffer, Gavin, YA Serv, Rosenberg Library, 2310 Sealy Ave, Galveston, TX, 77550. Tel: 409-763-8854, Ext 116. Fax: 409-763-0275. p. 2326

Sheaffer, Karalee, ILL, Per, Tech Serv, Sanofi Aventis, Nine Great Valley Pkwy, Malvern, PA, 19355. Tel: 610-889-8655. Fax: 610-889-8988. p. 2083

Sheagley, Sue, Children's & AV Cataloger, Kokomo-Howard County Public Library, 220 N Union St, Kokomo, IN, 46901-4614. Tel: 765-457-3242. Fax: 765-457-3683. p. 758

Sheahan, Lynell, Librn, Randall Public Library, 107 Main St, Randall, KS, 66963. Tel: 785-739-2331. p. 891

Shear, Joan A, Legal Info Librn, Boston College, 885 Centre St, Newton Centre, MA, 02459. Tel: 617-552-2895. Fax: 617-552-2889. p. 1110

Shear, Laurie, County Librn, Potter-Tioga Library System, 502 Park Ave, Coudersport, PA, 16915-1672. Tel: 814-274-7422. Fax: 814-274-9137. p. 2047

Sheard, Latina, Br Mgr, Central Arkansas Library System, Sue Cowan Williams Branch, 1800 S Chester St, Little Rock, AR, 72206-1010. Tel: 501-376-4282. p. 106

Shearer, Barbara, Dir, Florida State University Libraries, Charlotte Edwards Maguire Medical Library, 1115 W Call St, Tallahassee, FL, 32304-3556. Tel: 850-644-8970. Fax: 850-644-9942. p. 495

Shearer, Barbara, Chair, Consortium of Southern Biomedical Libraries, Meharry Medical College, 1005 Dr D B Todd Blvd, Nashville, TN, 37208. Tel: 615-327-6728. Fax: 615-327-6448. p. 2955

Shearer, Donna, Dir, Geneva Public Library, 1043 G St, Geneva, NE, 68361. Tel: 402-759-3416. Fax: 402-759-3416. p. 1399

Shearer, Gail, Asst Dir, Southern Lehigh Public Library, 3200 Preston Lane, Center Valley, PA, 18034. Tel: 610-282-8825. Fax: 610-282-8828. p. 2043

Shearer, Gary, Archivist, Spec Coll Librn, Pacific Union College, One Angwin Ave, Angwin, CA, 94508-9705. Tel: 707-965-6675. Fax: 707-965-6504. p. 121

Shearer, Jocelyn, VPres, National Geographic Society Library, National Geographic Digital Motion, 1145 17th St NW, Washington, DC, 20036. Tel: 202-857-7000, 202-857-7695. Fax: 202-429-5755. p. 410

Shearer, Kim, ILL, Suburban Library Cooperative, 44750 Delco Blvd, Sterling Heights, MI, 48313. Tel: 586-685-5750. Fax: 586-685-3010. p. 2946

Shearer, Laurie, Br Mgr, San Bernardino County Library, Big Bear Lake Branch, 41930 Garstin Dr, Big Bear Lake, CA, 92315. Tel: 909-866-5571. Fax: 909-866-4382. p. 228

Shearer, Peggy, Librn, Avonmore Public Library, 619 Allegheny Ave, Avonmore, PA, 15618. Tel: 724-697-4828. Fax: 724-697-1322. p. 2030

Shearrer, Cindy, Assoc Law Librn, University of Missouri-Columbia, Law Library, 203 Hulston Hall, Columbia, MO, 65211-4190. Tel: 573-882-1125. Fax: 573-882-9676. p. 1326

Shearwood, Debbie, Asst Librn, Palliser Regional Library, Davidson Branch, 314 Washington Ave, Davidson, SK, S0G 1A0, CANADA. Tel: 306-567-2022. Fax: 306-567-2081. p. 2918

Sheary, Edward J, Dir, Buncombe County Public Libraries, 67 Haywood St, Asheville, NC, 28801. Tel: 828-250-4700. Fax: 828-250-4746. p. 1774

Sheble, Mary Ann, Dean, Oakland Community College, Library Systems, 2900 Featherstone Rd, MTEC A210, Auburn Hills, MI, 48326. Tel: 248-341-2053. Fax: 248-232-4089. p. 1154

Sheckells, Diane, Asst Librn, East Kingston Public Library, 47 Maplevale Rd, East Kingston, NH, 03827. Tel: 603-642-8333. p. 1446

Shecter, Gary, Ref, Peirce College Library, 1420 Pine St, Philadelphia, PA, 19102-4699. Tel: 215-670-9269. Fax: 215-670-9338. p. 2113

Shedd, Carol, Ref Librn, George Hail Free Library, 530 Main St, Warren, RI, 02885. Tel: 401-245-7686. Fax: 401-245-7470. p. 2177

Shedd, Debbie, Br Head, Cullman County Public Library System, Fairview Public, 7525 Alabama Hwy, 69 North, Cullman, AL, 35058. Tel: 256-796-5424. Fax: 256-796-5424. p. 13

Shedd, Shirley, Archivist, Evangel University, 1111 N Glenstone Ave, Springfield, MO, 65802. Tel: 417-865-2815, Ext 7268. p. 1366

Shedden, David, Dir, Poynter Institute for Media Studies, 801 Third St S, Saint Petersburg, FL, 33701. Tel: 727-821-9494, Ext 252. Fax: 727-898-9201. p. 488

Shedlock, James, Dir, Northwestern University, Chicago, Galter Health Sciences Library, Montgomery Ward Bldg, 303 E Chicago Ave, Chicago, IL, 60611. Tel: 312-503-8133. Fax: 312-503-1204. p. 621

Shedloski, Denise, Dir of Libr, Alexandria Public Library, Ten Maple Dr, Alexandria, OH, 43001. Tel: 740-924-3561. Fax: 740-924-3007. p. 1853

Sheedy, Linda K, Librn, Kitchell Memorial Library, 300 SE Fifth St, Morrisonville, IL, 62546. Tel: 217-526-4553. Fax: 217-526-3695. p. 676

Sheedy, Sally, Syst Instruction Librn, Whatcom Community College Library, 237 W Kellogg Rd, Bellingham, WA, 98226. Tel: 360-383-3300. p. 2509

Sheehan, Amy, Ref, Hamline University, Bush Memorial Library, 1536 Hewitt, Saint Paul, MN, 55104. Tel: 651-523-2375. Fax: 651-523-2199. p. 1278

Sheehan, Beth, Librn, University of Illinois Library at Urbana-Champaign, Social Sciences, Health & Education Library, 100 Main Library, MC-522, 1408 W Gregory Dr, Urbana, IL, 61801. Tel: 217-244-1866. Fax: 217-333-2214. p. 713

Sheehan, Carla, Ch, Southington Public Library & Museum, 255 Main St, Southington, CT, 06489. Tel: 860-628-0947. Fax: 860-628-0488. p. 368

Sheehan, Cheryl, Br Serv Coordr, San Antonio Public Library, 600 Soledad, San Antonio, TX, 78205-2786. Tel: 210-207-2587. Fax: 210-207-2603. p. 2382

Sheehan, Constance, Ref, St Francis Public Library, 4230 S Nicholson Ave, Saint Francis, WI, 53235. Tel: 414-481-7323. Fax: 414-481-8949. p. 2635

Sheehan, Deborah, Circ, Indian Prairie Public Library District, 401 Plainfield Rd, Darien, IL, 60561-4207. Tel: 630-887-8760. Fax: 630-887-8801. p. 633

Sheehan, Ellen, Dir, Libr Serv, Saint Mary's Hospital, 56 Franklin St, Waterbury, CT, 06706. Tel: 203-709-6408. Fax: 203-709-7738. p. 375

Sheehan, Geri, Per, Stonehill College, 320 Washington St, Easton, MA, 02357-4015. Tel: 508-565-1293. Fax: 508-565-1424. p. 1087

Sheehan, Jack, ILL Coordr, Mid-Michigan Library League, 210 1/2 N Mitchell, Cadillac, MI, 49601-1835. Tel: 231-775-3037. Fax: 231-775-1749. p. 2946

Sheehan, Kevin, Circ Supvr, Massachusetts Institute of Technology Libraries, Rotch Library-Architecture & Planning, Bldg 7-238, 77 Massachusetts Ave, Cambridge, MA, 02139-4307. Tel: 617-253-1837. Fax: 617-253-9331. p. 1078

Sheehan, Kevin, Dr, Coll Mgr, Maritime Museum of San Diego, 1492 N Harbor Dr, San Diego, CA, 92101. Tel: 619-234-9153, Ext 118. Fax: 619-234-8345. p. 232

Sheehan, Lynn, Dir, University of Charleston, 2300 MacCorkle Ave SE, Charleston, WV, 25304-1099. Tel: 304-357-4918. Fax: 304-357-4715. p. 2556

Sheehan, Marion, Libr Dir, Canterbury Public Library, One Municipal Dr, Canterbury, CT, 06331-1453. Tel: 860-546-9022. Fax: 860-546-1142. p. 333

Sheehan, Michael, Asst Dir, Northern Waters Library Service, 3200 E Lakeshore Dr, Ashland, WI, 54806-2510. Tel: 715-682-2365, Ext 12. Fax: 715-685-2704. p. 2579

Sheehan, Nancy, Youth Serv, Lucius Beebe Memorial Library, 345 Main St, Wakefield, MA, 01880-5093. Tel: 781-246-6334. Fax: 781-246-6385. p. 1132

Sheehan, Tim, Dir, Chester Public Library, Three Chester St, Jct 121 & 102, Chester, NH, 03036. Tel: 603-887-3404. Fax: 603-887-2701. p. 1441

Sheehy, Carolyn A, Dir, Libr Serv, North Central College, 320 E School St, Naperville, IL, 60540. Tel: 630-637-5701. Fax: 630-637-5716. p. 679

Sheehy, Christian, Mgr, Public Library of Cincinnati & Hamilton County, TechCenter, South Bldg, 2nd Flr, 800 Vine St, Cincinnati, OH, 45202-2009. Tel: 513-369-3125. Fax: 513-369-3123. p. 1873

Sheehy, Helen M, Head of Libr, Pennsylvania State University Libraries, Social Sciences, 201 Paterno Library, University Park, PA, 16802-1809. Tel: 814-863-1347. Fax: 814-865-1403. p. 2148

Sheehy, Louise, Asst Dir, Trumbull Library, 33 Quality St, Trumbull, CT, 06611. Tel: 203-452-5197. Fax: 203-452-5125. p. 373

Sheehy, Lynn, County Librn, Plumas County Library, 445 Jackson St, Quincy, CA, 95971-9410. Tel: 530-283-6310. Fax: 530-283-3242. p. 212

Sheehy, Sandra, Cataloger, Ch, Rossford Public Library, 720 Dixie Hwy, Rossford, OH, 43460-1289. Tel: 419-666-0924. Fax: 419-666-1989. p. 1932

Sheehy, Timothy, Librn, United States Courts Library, 700 Stewart St, Rm 19105, Seattle, WA, 98101. Tel: 206-370-8975. Fax: 206-370-8976. p. 2533

Sheely, Phyllis, Asst Librn, Earlham Public Library, 120 S Chestnut St, Earlham, IA, 50072. Tel: 515-758-2121. Fax: 515-758-2121. p. 813

Sheets, Audrey, Br Mgr, Saint Joseph Public Library, Carnegie Public, 316 Massachusetts St, Saint Joseph, MO, 64504-1449. Tel: 816-238-0526. Fax: 816-238-9438. p. 1353

Sheets, Clara J, Managing Librn, Jenkins, Fenstermaker, PLLC, PO Box 2688, Huntington, WV, 25726-2688. Tel: 304-523-2100. Fax: 304-523-2347. p. 2561

Sheets, Deborah, Adult & YA Cataloger, Kokomo-Howard County Public Library, 220 N Union St, Kokomo, IN, 46901-4614. Tel: 765-457-3242. Fax: 765-457-3683. p. 758

Sheets, Kris, Br Supvr, Smyth-Bland Regional Library, Saltville Public, 111 Palmer Ave, Saltville, VA, 24370. Tel: 276-496-5514. Fax: 276-496-4249. p. 2477

Sheets, Lucy, Exec Dir, Indiana Christian University Library, 10511 Greenfield Ave, Noblesville, IN, 46060. Tel: 317-773-3909. Fax: 317-773-1403. p. 769

Sheets, Michael, Head, Tech Serv, Crown Point Community Library, 214 S Court St, Crown Point, IN, 46307. Tel: 219-663-0270, 219-663-0271. Fax: 219-663-0403. p. 734

Sheets, Sandy, Supvr, Saint Luke's Hospital, 5901 Monclova Rd, Maumee, OH, 43537-1855. Tel: 419-897-8421. Fax: 419-897-8381. p. 1915

Sheets, Sarah, Tech Serv Coordr, University of California, Merced Library, 5200 N Lake Rd, Merced, CA, 95343-5001. Tel: 209-228-4422. Fax: 209-228-4271. p. 186

Sheetz, Christine, Instrul Serv/Ref Librn, Lorain County Community College, 1005 Abbe Rd N, North Elyria, OH, 44035-1691. Tel: 440-366-7288. Fax: 440-366-4127. p. 1924

Sheffer, Beth, Coll Mgr, National Museum of Racing & Hall of Fame, 191 Union Ave, Saratoga Springs, NY, 12866. Tel: 518-584-0400, Ext 141. Fax: 518-584-4574. p. 1738

Sheffer, Karen, Supvry Librn, Environmental Protection Agency, West Bldg, Rm 3340, 1301 Constitution Ave NW, Washington, DC, 20004. Tel: 202-566-9982. Fax: 202-566-0574. p. 399

Sheffer, Polly, Librn, Ossipee Public Library, 74 Main St, Center Ossipee, NH, 03814. Tel: 603-539-6390. Fax: 603-539-5758. p. 1440

Sheffield, Barbara, Circ, Mansfield Public Library, 255 Hope St, Mansfield, MA, 02048-2353. Tel: 508-261-7380. Fax: 508-261-7422. p. 1102

Sheffield, Blinn, Ch, Independence Public Library, 220 E Maple, Independence, KS, 67301-3899. Tel: 620-331-3030. Fax: 620-331-4093. p. 873

Sheffield, Brenda, Acq, Trinity University, One Trinity Pl, San Antonio, TX, 78212-7200. Tel: 210-999-8173. Fax: 210-999-8120. p. 2383

Sheffield, Josh, Info Tech, Ocmulgee Regional Library System, 535 Second Ave, Eastman, GA, 31023. Tel: 478-374-4711. Fax: 478-374-5646. p. 531

Sheffield, Lisa, Adult Serv Coordr, Transylvania County Library, 212 S Gaston, Brevard, NC, 28712. Tel: 828-884-3151, Ext 226. Fax: 828-877-4230. p. 1777

Sheffield, Rebecca Susanne, Head of Acq Serv, Ball State University Libraries, 2000 W University Ave, Muncie, IN, 47306-1099. Tel: 765-285-8031. Fax: 765-285-2008. p. 766

Sheffield-Warman, Nancy, Head, Tech Serv, Palm Harbor Library, 2330 Nebraska Ave, Palm Harbor, FL, 34683. Tel: 727-784-3332. Fax: 727-785-6534. p. 480

Sheffler, Victoria, Archivist, Northeastern State University, 711 N Grand Ave, Tahlequah, OK, 74464-2333. Tel: 918-456-5511, Ext 3200. Fax: 918-458-2197. p. 1979

Sheidlower, Scott, Head, Info Literacy, York College Library, 94-20 Guy R Brewer Blvd, Jamaica, NY, 11451. Tel: 718-262-2017. Fax: 718-262-2027, 718-262-2997. p. 1646

Sheilds, Allison, Head, Circ, Monmouth University, 400 Cedar Ave, West Long Branch, NJ, 07764. Tel: 732-571-3450, Ext 4413. Fax: 732-263-5124. p. 1541

Sheinbaum, Ken, Dir, Monmouth County Library, 125 Symmes Dr, Manalapan, NJ, 07726. Tel: 732-431-7220. Fax: 732-308-2955. p. 1498

Sheinwald, Fran, Sr Librn, New York State Department of Law Library, 120 Broadway, 25th Flr, New York, NY, 10271. Tel: 212-416-8012. Fax: 212-416-6130. p. 1694

Sheinwald, Franette, Sr Librn, NYC Libr, New York State Department of Law Library, The Capitol, Albany, NY, 12224. Tel: 212-416-8012. Fax: 212-416-6130. p. 1569

Shelar, James W, Librn, Arnold & Porter Library, 555 12th St NW, Washington, DC, 20004-1206. Tel: 202-942-5000. Fax: 202-942-5999. p. 393

Shelburne, Pam, Br Mgr, Morgan County Public Library, Brooklyn Branch, Six E Mill St, Brooklyn, IN, 46111. Tel: 317-834-2003. p. 763

Shelden, Louise, Dir, Union Carnegie Public Library, 182 N Main St, Union, OR, 97883. Tel: 541-562-5811. Fax: 541-562-5811. p. 2022

Sheldon, Brooke E, Prof, University of Texas at Austin, One University Sta, D7000, Austin, TX, 78712-0390. Tel: 512-471-3821. Fax: 512-471-3971. p. 2975

Sheldon, Chris, Ref/Syst Librn, New York Chiropractic College Library, 2360 State Rte 89, Seneca Falls, NY, 13148-9460. Tel: 315-568-3244. Fax: 315-568-3119. p. 1742

Sheldon, Doris, Commun Librn, Monroe County Library System, Summerfield-Petersburg Branch, 60 E Center St, Petersburg, MI, 49270. Tel: 734-279-1025. Fax: 734-279-2328. p. 1210

Sheldon, Gail A, Dir, Oneonta Public Library, 221 Second St S, Oneonta, AL, 35121. Tel: 205-274-7641. Fax: 205-274-7643. p. 32

Sheldon-Hess, Coral, Web Librn, University of Alaska Anchorage, Consortium Library, 3211 Providence Dr, Anchorage, AK, 99508-8176. Tel: 907-786-1871. Fax: 907-786-1834. p. 45

Sheley, Christina, Dept Head, Indiana University Bloomington, Business/SPEA Information Commons, SPEA 150, 1315 E Tenth St, Bloomington, IN, 47405. Tel: 812-855-1957. Fax: 812-855-3398. p. 727

Shelfer, Katherine, PhD, Assoc Prof, Saint John's University, Saint Augustine Hall, Rm 408, 8000 Utopia Pkwy, Jamaica, NY, 11439. Tel: 718-990-6200. Fax: 718-990-2071. p. 2970

Shelford, Holly A, Youth Serv Librn, Knoxville Public Library, 213 E Montgomery St, Knoxville, IA, 50138-2296. Tel: 641-828-0585. Fax: 641-828-0513. p. 825

Shell, Sandra, Br Mgr, Blue Ridge Regional Library, Collinsville Branch, 2540 Virginia Ave, Collinsville, VA, 24078. Tel: 276-647-1112. Fax: 276-647-4574. p. 2478

Shell, Suzanne L, Dir, United States Marine Corps, Bldg 298, Marine Corps Air Station, Cherry Point, NC, 28533-0009. Tel: 252-466-3552. Fax: 252-466-5402. p. 1784

Shellabarger, Sheila, Assoc Univ Librn, Pub Serv, Wright State University Libraries, 126 Dunbar Library, 3640 Colonel Glenn Hwy, Dayton, OH, 45435-0001. Tel: 937-775-2685. Fax: 937-775-4109. p. 1895

Shellehamer, Denise, Cat, New Cumberland Public Library, One Benjamin Plaza, New Cumberland, PA, 17070-1597. Tel: 717-774-7820. Fax: 717-774-7824. p. 2096

Shellenberger, Dawn, Ref, United States Environmental Protection Agency Region 3, 1650 Arch St, 3PM52, Philadelphia, PA, 19103. Tel: 215-814-5364. Fax: 215-814-5253. p. 2118

Shelley, Anne, Contract Librn, Minnesota Department of Transportation Library, 395 John Ireland Blvd, MS 155, Saint Paul, MN, 55155. Tel: 651-366-3797. Fax: 651-366-3789. p. 1279

Shelley, Kim, Br Supvr, Lincoln City Libraries, Bethany Branch, 1810 N Cotner Blvd, Lincoln, NE, 68505. Tel: 402-441-8550. Fax: 402-441-8552. p. 1405

Shelley, Kim, Br Supvr, Lincoln City Libraries, Victor E Anderson Branch, 3635 Touzalin Ave, Lincoln, NE, 68507-1698. Tel: 402-441-8542. Fax: 402-441-8543. p. 1405

Shelley, Kristin, Dir, East Lansing Public Library, 950 Abbott Rd, East Lansing, MI, 48823-3105. Tel: 517-319-6913. Fax: 517-351-9536. p. 1175

Shelley, Lanny, Librn, Colorado Department of Corrections, Limon Correctional Facility-Law Library, 49030 State Hwy 71, Limon, CO, 80826. Tel: 719-775-9221, Ext 3238. p. 316

Shelley, Lugene, Librn, Williamsburg Public Library, 511 W Second St, Williamsburg, PA, 16693. Tel: 814-832-3367. Fax: 814-832-3845. p. 2156

Shelley, Rose, Br Mgr, Pamunkey Regional Library, Upper King William Branch, Sharon Office Park, 694-J Sharon Rd, King William, VA, 23086. Tel: 804-769-3731. Fax: 804-769-1176. p. 2470

Shelley, Werts, Head of Libr, Los Angeles Southwest College, Cox Bldg, 1600 W Imperial Hwy, Los Angeles, CA, 90047-4899. Tel: 323-241-5235. Fax: 323-241-5221. p. 174

Shelley, Zhang, Cat, Cobb County Public Library System, 266 Roswell St, Marietta, GA, 30060-2004. Tel: 770-528-2354. Fax: 770-528-2349. p. 542

Shellhase, Jeremy, Syst Coordr, Humboldt State University Library, One Harpst St, Arcata, CA, 95521-8299. Tel: 707-826-3144. Fax: 707-826-3440. p. 122

Shellhouse, Emily, Ref & Teen Librn, Granville Public Library, 217 E Broadway, Granville, OH, 43023-1398. Tel: 740-587-0196. Fax: 740-587-0197. p. 1903

Shelly, Diane, Exec Dir, Art Center Manatee, 209 Ninth St W, Bradenton, FL, 34205. Tel: 941-746-2862. Fax: 941-746-2319. p. 429

Shelly, Leo, Ref Librn, Millersville University, Nine N George St, Millersville, PA, 17551. Tel: 717-872-3610. Fax: 717-872-3854. p. 2090

Shelly, Marjorie, Dir, Pittsford Community Library, 24 State St, Pittsford, NY, 14534. Tel: 585-248-6275. Fax: 585-248-6259. p. 1718

Shelly, Melvin R, Dir, Blanche K Werner Public Library, 203 Prospect Dr, Trinity, TX, 75862. Tel: 936-594-2087. Fax: 936-594-9513. p. 2393

Shelp, Lorrie, Chairperson, Kinuso Municipal Library, PO Box 60, Kinuso, AB, T0G 1K0, CANADA. Tel: 780-775-3694. Fax: 780-775-3560. p. 2708

Shelsy, Sue, Cat, Reader Serv, Hinsdale Public Library, 58 Maple St, Hinsdale, MA, 01235. Tel: 413-655-2303. Fax: 413-655-2303. p. 1095

Shelton, Barbara C, Dir, Jefferson City Public Library, 1427 Russell Ave, Jefferson City, TN, 37760. Tel: 865-475-9094. Fax: 865-475-1253. p. 2239

Shelton, Brenda, Asst Dir, Rector Public Library, 121 W Fourth St, Rector, AR, 72461. Tel: 870-595-2410. Fax: 870-595-2410. p. 113

Shelton, Brett, Asst Dir, Riverdale Public Library District, 208 W 144th St, Riverdale, IL, 60827-2788. Tel: 708-841-3311. Fax: 708-841-1805. p. 695

Shelton, Deborah, Head, Ch, Morley Library, 184 Phelps St, Painesville, OH, 44077-3926. Tel: 440-352-3383, Ext 207. Fax: 440-352-2653. p. 1927

Shelton, Diane, Dir, Libr Serv, Graceland University, One University Pl, Lamoni, IA, 50140. Tel: 641-784-5301. Fax: 641-784-5497. p. 826

Shelton, Iris, Br Librn, McDowell Public Library, Bradshaw Branch, City Hall Bldg, Main St, Bradshaw, WV, 24817. Tel: 304-967-5140. Fax: 304-967-5140. p. 2573

Shelton, Lois, Supvr, El Centro Public Library, 1140 N Imperial Ave, El Centro, CA, 92243. Tel: 760-337-4565. Fax: 760-352-1384. p. 145

Shelton, Michelle, Ch, McAllen Memorial Library, 601 N Main, McAllen, TX, 78501-4666. Tel: 956-688-3300. Fax: 956-688-3301. p. 2360

Shelton, Nancy, Asst Br Mgr, Sullivan County Public Library, Sullivan Gardens Branch, 104 Bluegrass Dr, Kingsport, TN, 37660. Tel: 423-349-5990. Fax: 423-349-5990. p. 2225

Shelton, Pamela, Dir, United States Army, Casey Memorial Library, 72nd St & 761st Tank Battalion, Bldg 3202, Fort Hood, TX, 76544-5024. Tel: 254-287-0025. Fax: 254-288-4029. p. 2320

Shelton, Ronald, ILL, Pub Serv Librn, Virginia Union University, 1500 N Lombardy St, Richmond, VA, 23220. Tel: 804-278-5721. Fax: 804-257-5818. p. 2493

Shelton, Sally Jo, Libr Info/Fac Facilitator, Oral Roberts University Library, 7777 South Lewis Ave, Tulsa, OK, 74171. Tel: 918-495-6902. Fax: 918-495-6893. p. 1981

Shelton, Sara, Br Mgr, San Diego County Library, Descanso Branch, 9545 River Dr, Descanso, CA, 91916. Tel: 619-445-5279. Fax: 619-445-4891. p. 233

Shelton, Susan Theriault, Dir, Leominster Public Library, 30 West St, Leominster, MA, 01453. Tel: 978-534-7522. Fax: 978-840-3357. p. 1098

Shelton-Council, Tanya, Cent Libr Mgr, Cecil County Public Library, 301 Newark Ave, Elkton, MD, 21921-5441. Tel: 410-996-5600. Fax: 410-996-5604. p. 1027

Shelver, Elizabeth, Librn, Central Lutheran Church Library, 333 12th St S, Minneapolis, MN, 55404. Tel: 612-870-4416. Fax: 612-870-0417. p. 1259

Shen, Jean, Sr Librn, New York Public Library - Astor, Lenox & Tilden Foundations, 58th Street Branch, 127 E 58th St, (Between Park & Lexington Aves), New York, NY, 10022-1211. Tel: 212-759-7358. Fax: 212-758-6858. p. 1691

Shen, Lan, Humanities Librn, Purdue University, 2200 169th St, Hammond, IN, 46323-2094. Tel: 219-989-2678. Fax: 219-989-2070. p. 747

Shen, May, Ch, Dallas Public Library, Arcadia Park, 1302 N Justin Ave, Dallas, TX, 75211-1142. Tel: 214-670-6446. Fax: 214-670-7502. p. 2306

Shen, Phil, Info Tech, Albert Einstein College of Medicine, 1300 Morris Park Ave, Bronx, NY, 10461. Tel: 718-430-3108. Fax: 718-430-8795. p. 1586

Shen, Vivian, Conserv Librn, Presv Librn, Fordham University Libraries, 441 E Fordham Rd, Bronx, NY, 10458-5151. Tel: 718-817-3570. Fax: 718-817-3582. p. 1586

Shen, Zhijia, Dir, University of Washington Libraries, East Asia, 322 Gowen Hall, 3rd Flr, Box 353527, Seattle, WA, 98195-3527. Tel: 206-543-5635. Fax: 206-221-5298. p. 2533

Sheng, Hui, Mgr, E-Coll & Res Sharing, Westchester Library System, 540 White Plains Rd, Ste 200, Tarrytown, NY, 10591-5110. Tel: 914-231-3258. Fax: 914-674-4186. p. 1755

Sheng, Yi, Electronic Res, Wilson Elser Moskowitz Edelman & Dicker LLP, 150 E 42nd St, New York, NY, 10017. Tel: 212-490-3000. Fax: 212-490-3038. p. 1703

Sheng, Yilin, Asst Dir, Ridgefield Public Library, 527 Morse Ave, Ridgefield, NJ, 07657. Tel: 201-941-0192. Fax: 201-941-9354. p. 1526

Shenk, Audrey J, Acq, Syst Adminr, Eastern Mennonite University, 1200 Park Rd, Harrisonburg, VA, 22802-2462. Tel: 540-432-4175. Fax: 540-432-4977. p. 2470

Shenk, Diana, Archivist, Washington State Office of Secretary of State, 1129 Washington St SE, Olympia, WA, 98504-2283. Tel: 360-650-2813. Fax: 360-650-3323. p. 2523

Shenk, Howard, Exec Dir, Arabian Horse Owners Foundation, 4101 N Bear Canyon Rd, Tucson, AZ, 85749. Tel: 520-760-0682. Fax: 520-749-2572. p. 85

Shenk, Nadine, Cat, ILL Librn, New River Community College, 226 Martin Hall, Dublin, VA, 24084. Tel: 540-674-3600, Ext 4336. Fax: 540-676-3626. p. 2460

Shepard, Brian, Operations Dir, Arlington Heights Memorial Library, 500 N Dunton Ave, Arlington Heights, IL, 60004-5966. Tel: 847-506-2614. Fax: 847-506-2650. p. 589

Shepard, Cal, State Librn, State Library of North Carolina, 109 E Jones St, Raleigh, NC, 27601. Tel: 919-807-7400. Fax: 919-733-8748. p. 1817

Shepard, E Lee, Archivist, Virginia Historical Society Library, 428 North Blvd, Richmond, VA, 23220. Tel: 804-358-4901. Fax: 804-355-2399. p. 2492

Shepard, Elizabeth, Archivist, Cornell University Library, The Samuel J Wood Library & The C V Starr Biomedical Information Center, 1300 York Ave, C115, Box 67, New York, NY, 10065-4896. Tel: 212-746-6050. Fax: 212-746-6494. p. 1642

Shepard, Jim, Info Syst Coordr, Illinois State Library, Gwendolyn Brooks Bldg, 300 S Second St, Springfield, IL, 62701-9713. Tel: 217-782-5524. Fax: 217-785-4326. p. 705

Shepard, John, Head Librn, University of California, Berkeley, Jean Gray Hargrove Music Library, Hargrove Music Library, Berkeley, CA, 94720-6000. Tel: 510-642-2623. Fax: 510-642-8237. p. 128

Shepard, Nancy, Interim Asst Dean, Learning Res, College of the Siskiyous Library, 800 College Ave, Weed, CA, 96094. Tel: 530-938-5331. Fax: 530-938-5226. p. 282

Shepard, Phelps, Dir, Monmouth Public Library, 168 S Ecols St, Monmouth, OR, 97361. Tel: 503-838-1932. Fax: 503-838-3899. p. 2006

Shepard, Sharon, Dir, Cornell Public Library, 117 N Third St, Cornell, WI, 54732. Tel: 715-239-3709. Fax: 715-239-3704. p. 2586

Shepard, Virginia, Dir, Ogden Library, 220 Willow St, Ogden, KS, 66517. Tel: 785-537-0351. p. 886

Sheperdson, Amy, Ref, Carver Public Library, Two Meadowbrook Way, Carver, MA, 02330-1278. Tel: 508-866-3415. Fax: 508-866-3416. p. 1079

Shephard-Lupo, Pamela, Librn, Maine Department of Marine Resources, 180 McKown Point Rd, West Boothbay Harbor, ME, 04575. Tel: 207-633-9551. Fax: 207-633-9641. p. 1006

Shepherd, Anne, Dir, Charlotte County Library System, 2050 Forrest Nelson Blvd, Port Charlotte, FL, 33952. Tel: 941-613-3200. Fax: 941-613-3196. p. 484

Shepherd, Anne B, Ref Librn, Cincinnati Museum Center At Union Terminal, 1301 Western Ave, Cincinnati, OH, 45203. Tel: 513-287-7069. Fax: 513-287-7095. p. 1869

Shepherd, Kerry, Librn, Red River Public Library, 702 E Main St, Red River, NM, 87558. Tel: 505-754-6564. Fax: 505-754-6564. p. 1560

Shepherd, Linda, Bus Off Mgr, Glenview Public Library, 1930 Glenview Rd, Glenview, IL, 60025-2899. Tel: 847-729-7500. Fax: 847-729-7558. p. 650

Shepherd, Sarah, Librn, Clark Memorial Library, 538 Amity Rd, Bethany, CT, 06524-3015. Tel: 203-393-2103. p. 330

Shepherd, Susan, Head, Outreach Serv, Head, Ref & Instruction, University of California, San Diego, Science & Engineering, 9500 Gilman Dr, Dept 0175E, La Jolla, CA, 92093-0175. Tel: 858-534-4579. Fax: 858-534-5583. p. 162

Shephero, Marya, Head, Coll Develop, Suffolk County Community College, 533 College Rd, Selden, NY, 11784-2899. Tel: 631-451-4800. Fax: 631-451-4697. p. 1742

Shepkowski, Irene, Head, Ref, Coal City Public Library District, 85 N Garfield St, Coal City, IL, 60416. Tel: 815-634-4552. Fax: 815-634-2950. p. 630

Shepley, Jennifer, Br Mgr, Chesterfield County Public Library, Midlothian, 521 Coalfield Rd, Midlothian, VA, 23114. Tel: 804-768-7907. p. 2457

Sheplor, Madeline A, Head, Tech Serv, Bellingham Public Library, 210 Central Ave, CS-9710, Bellingham, WA, 98227-9710. Tel: 360-778-7323. p. 2508

Sheppard, Annette, Ref, Tech Serv, United States Air Force, Air Force Research Laboratory, Wright Research Site Technical Library, Det 1 AFRL/WSC, Bldg 642, Rm 1300, 2950 Hobson Way, Wright-Patterson AFB, OH, 45433-7765. Tel: 937-255-5511, Ext 4242. Fax: 937-656-7746. p. 1951

Sheppard, April, Head, Govt Doc, Arkansas State University, 322 University Loop West Circle, State University, AR, 72401. Tel: 870-972-3077. Fax: 870-972-3199. p. 115

Sheppard, Dave, Dir, Greig Memorial Library, 110 S Joy St, Oneida, IL, 61467. Tel: 309-483-3482. Fax: 309-483-3482. p. 685

Sheppard, Gail, Head, Youth Serv, Pittsburg Public Library, 308 N Walnut, Pittsburg, KS, 66762-4732. Tel: 620-231-8110. Fax: 620-232-2258. p. 890

Sheppard, Gladys, Supvr, Thomas H Leath Memorial Library, 412 E Franklin St, Rockingham, NC, 28379-4995. Tel: 910-895-6337. Fax: 910-895-5851. p. 1820

Sheppard, Heather, Acq, Cat, Pub Serv, Everett Community College, 2000 Tower St, Everett, WA, 98201-1352. Tel: 425-388-9964, Ext 7345. Fax: 425-388-9144. p. 2515

Sheppard, Heather, Librn, Cornish College of the Arts Library, 1000 Lenora St, Seattle, WA, 98121. Tel: 206-726-5041. Fax: 206-315-5811. p. 2527

Sheppard, Kathy, Fed Grants Coordr, South Carolina State Library, 1430-1500 Senate St, Columbia, SC, 29201. Tel: 803-734-8653. Fax: 803-734-8676. p. 2189

Sheppard, Kim, Tech Serv, Yolo County Library, Admin Off, 226 Buckeye St, Woodland, CA, 95695-2600. Tel: 530-666-8085. Fax: 530-666-8006. p. 284

Sheppard, Maureen, Coordr, Librn, Algonquin College Learning Resource Centre, 1385 Woodroffe Ave, Ottawa, ON, K2G 1V8, CANADA. Tel: 613-727-4723, Ext 5944. Fax: 613-727-7642. p. 2827

Sheppard, Nicole, Br Mgr, Bedford Public Library System, Stewartsville Library, 45 Cascade Dr, Vinton, VA, 24179. Tel: 540-890-4530. Fax: 434-525-9232. p. 2451

Sheppard, Ronald, Dir, Parkland Regional Library, 5404 56th Ave, Lacombe, AB, T4L 1G1, CANADA. Tel: 403-782-3850. Fax: 403-782-4650. p. 2709

Sheppard, Shirley, Chief Librn, Emo Public Library, Jesse St, Emo, ON, P0W 1E0, CANADA. Tel: 807-482-2575. Fax: 807-482-2575. p. 2804

Sheppard, Stacey, Librn, North Dakota Prevention Resource Center Library, 1237 W Divide Ave, Ste 1D, Bismarck, ND, 58501-1208. Tel: 701-328-8919. Fax: 701-328-8979. p. 1838

Shepson, Eleanore, Br Coordr, Chemung County Library District, 101 E Church St, Elmira, NY, 14901-2799. Tel: 607-733-9173. Fax: 607-733-9176. p. 1619

Shepstone, Carol, Univ Librn, Mount Royal University Library, 4825 Mount Royal Gate SW, Calgary, AB, T3E 6K6, CANADA. Tel: 403-440-6134. Fax: 403-440-6758. p. 2692

Sherbo, Laura, Br Mgr, Washington State Library, McNeil Island Correction Center, PO Box 88900, MS-WT-01, Steilacoom, WA, 98388-0900. Tel: 253-512-6586. Fax: 253-512-6587. p. 2545

Sherbo, Laura, Prog Mgr, Washington State Library, Eastern State Hospital, Maple St, Medical Lake, WA, 99022. Tel: 509-299-4276, 509-299-4500. Fax: 509-299-4555. p. 2545

Sherbondy, Patricia, Dir, Warren Library Association, 205 Market St, Warren, PA, 16365. Tel: 814-723-4650. Fax: 814-723-4521. p. 2150

Sherby, Louise S, Dr, Chief Librn, Hunter College Libraries, 695 Park Ave, New York, NY, 10065. Tel: 212-772-4143. Fax: 212-772-4142. p. 1682

Shere, Angie, Ch, Manchester Public Library, 304 N Franklin St, Manchester, IA, 52057. Tel: 563-927-3719. Fax: 563-927-3058. p. 829

Sherer, Joan, Ref Librn, United States Department of State, 2201 C St NW, Rm 3239, Washington, DC, 20520-2442. Tel: 202-647-1099. Fax: 202-647-2971. p. 419

Sheret, Larry, Info Literacy Librn, Western State College, 600 N Adams St, Gunnison, CO, 81231. Tel: 970-943-2898. Fax: 970-943-2042. p. 312

Sheret, Larry, Ref Serv Librn, Marshall University Libraries, One John Marshall Dr, Huntington, WV, 25755-2060. Tel: 304-696-6577. Fax: 304-696-5858. p. 2561

Sherfield, Jeanette, Br Mgr, Hancock County Public Library, Sugar Creek Branch, 5087 W US 52, New Palestine, IN, 46163. Tel: 317-861-6618, Ext 20. Fax: 317-861-2061. p. 746

Sheridan, Beth, Head, Adult/Teen/Outreach Serv, Orion Township Public Library, 825 Joslyn Rd, Lake Orion, MI, 48362. Tel: 248-693-3000, Ext 332. Fax: 248-693-3009. p. 1199

Sheridan, Christan, Pub Serv Librn, York Library Region, Four Carleton St, Fredericton, NB, E3B 5P4, CANADA. Tel: 506-444-2603. Fax: 506-457-4878. p. 2764

Sheridan, Claire, Dir, Spring Lake District Library, 123 E Exchange St, Spring Lake, MI, 49456-2018. Tel: 616-846-5770. Fax: 616-844-2129. p. 1229

Sheridan, Darlene, In Charge, Sheldon Library, 216 W Main St, Sheldon, MO, 64784. Tel: 417-884-2909. p. 1365

Sheridan, Donna, Circ, ILL, Milton-Freewater Public Library, Eight SW Eighth Ave, Milton-Freewater, OR, 97862-1501. Tel: 541-938-8239. Fax: 541-938-8254. p. 2006

Sheridan, Joan, Asst Librn, Windham Public Library, Church & Main Sts, Windham, NY, 12496. Tel: 518-734-4405. Fax: 518-734-4405. p. 1770

Sheridan, Kara, Dir, Long Island University, 70 Rte 340, Orangeburg, NY, 10962. Tel: 845-359-7200, Ext 5411. Fax: 845-359-2804. p. 1711

Sheridan, Natalie, Pub Serv Mgr, Cornell University Library, Mathematics, 420 Malott Hall, Ithaca, NY, 14853-4201. Tel: 607-254-3568. Fax: 607-254-5023. p. 1642

Sheridan, Rebecca, Head, Youth Serv, Easttown Library & Information Center, 720 First Ave, Berwyn, PA, 19312-1769. Tel: 610-644-0138. Fax: 610-251-9739. p. 2033

Sheridan, Susan, Head, Tech Serv, Amherst College, Amherst, MA, 01002. Fax: 413-542-2662. p. 1048

Sheridan, Terence, Libr Dir, Amridge University Library, 1200 Taylor Rd, Montgomery, AL, 36117. Tel: 334-387-7546. Fax: 334-387-3878. p. 28

Sheridan, Terri, Mus Librn, Santa Barbara Museum of Natural History Library, 2559 Puesta del Sol Rd, Santa Barbara, CA, 93105. Tel: 805-682-4711 ext. 134. p. 261

Sherif, Joan, Br Supvr, Tech Coordr, Northwestern Regional Library, 111 N Front St, Elkin, NC, 28621. Tel: 336-835-4894. Fax: 336-526-2270. p. 1791

Sherif, Sue, Head, Libr Develop, Alaska State Library, Library Development, 344 W Third Ave, Ste 125, Anchorage, AK, 99501. Tel: 907-269-6569. Fax: 907-269-6580. p. 44

Sherif, Sue, Head, Libr Develop, Alaska State Library, 333 Willoughby Ave, State Office Bldg, 8th Flr, Juneau, AK, 99801. Tel: 907-465-2910. Fax: 907-465-2151. p. 49

Sherkow, Shirley, Librn, Capital Area Library Consortium, c/o Minnesota Dept of Transportation, Library MS155, 395 John Ireland Blvd, Saint Paul, MN, 55155. Tel: 651-296-5272. Fax: 651-297-2354. p. 2946

Sherlock, Lisa J, Head, Reader Serv, University of Toronto Libraries, Victoria University Library, 71 Queens Park Crescent E, Toronto, ON, M5S 1K7, CANADA. Tel: 416-585-4471. Fax: 416-585-4591. p. 2867

Sherman, Brian, Head, Access Serv & Syst, Louisiana State University, One University Pl, Shreveport, LA, 71115-2399. Tel: 318-797-5382. Fax: 318-797-5156. p. 968

Sherman, Carla, Dir, Valley of the Tetons District Library, 56 N Main, Victor, ID, 83455. Tel: 208-787-2201. Fax: 208-787-2204. p. 585

Sherman, Carolyn, Librn, Genesee Public Library, 8351 Main St, Little Genesee, NY, 14754-9701. Tel: 585-928-1915. Fax: 585-928-1915. p. 1652

Sherman, Cathy, Dir, Cordova Public Library, 622 First St, Cordova, AK, 99574. Tel: 907-424-6667. Fax: 907-424-6666. p. 46

Sherman, Cynthia, Br Mgr, Iberia Parish Library, Loreauville Branch, 510 N Main St, Loreauville, LA, 70552. Tel: 337-229-6348. Fax: 337-229-6348. p. 959

Sherman, Dan, ILL, Tech Serv, Hinshaw & Culbertson Library, 222 N LaSalle, Ste 300, Chicago, IL, 60601-1081. Tel: 312-704-3000. Fax: 312-704-3951. p. 614

Sherman, Deanna, Libr Spec, Southeast Kentucky Community & Technical College, 207 Chrisman Hall, 700 College Rd, Cumberland, KY, 40823. Tel: 606-589-3072. Fax: 606-589-4941. p. 911

Sherman, Jacquelynn, Cat Librn, Campbell University, 113 Main St, Buies Creek, NC, 27506. Tel: 910-893-1460. Fax: 910-893-1470. p. 1778

Sherman, Janice, Dir, Morton Public Library District, 315 W Pershing St, Morton, IL, 61550. Tel: 309-263-2200. Fax: 309-266-9604. p. 676

Sherman, Jason, Syst Librn, University of Science & Arts of Oklahoma, 1901 S 17th St, Chickasha, OK, 73018. Tel: 405-574-1340. Fax: 405-574-1220. p. 1960

Sherman, Jessica, Librn, Monroe Public Library, 19 Plains Rd, Monroe, NH, 03771. Tel: 603-638-4736. p. 1458

Sherman, Joni, Info Spec, Society Promoting Environmental Conservation, 2150 Maple St, Vancouver, BC, V6J 3T3, CANADA. Tel: 604-736-7732. Fax: 604-736-7115. p. 2742

Sherman, Kris, Asst Mgr, Pub Serv, Chandler Public Library, 22 S Delaware, Chandler, AZ, 85225. Tel: 480-782-2818. Fax: 480-782-2823. p. 59

Sherman, Lee, Ref Librn, Kings County Library, 401 N Douty St, Hanford, CA, 93230. Tel: 559-582-0261. Fax: 559-583-6163. p. 156

Sherman, Marilyn, Adult Serv, Maury Loontjens Memorial Library, 35 Kingstown Rd, Narragansett, RI, 02882. Tel: 401-789-9507. Fax: 401-782-0677. p. 2168

Sherman, Marilyn A, Jr, Libr Tech, Upper River Valley Hospital Library, 11300 Rte 130, Waterville, NB, E7P 0A4, CANADA. Tel: 506-375-2740. Fax: 506-375-2680. p. 2767

Sherman, Roger, Info Spec, SRI International, 333 Ravenswood Ave, Menlo Park, CA, 94025. Tel: 650-859-5506. Fax: 650-859-2757. p. 185

Sherman, Susan, Ch, Derby Public Library, 313 Elizabeth St, Derby, CT, 06418. Tel: 203-736-1482. Fax: 203-736-1419. p. 336

Sherman, Ted, Syst Librn, D'Youville College, 320 Porter Ave, Buffalo, NY, 14201-1084. Tel: 716-829-7618. Fax: 716-829-7770. p. 1597

Sherman, Zakariya, Sr Librn, Tampa-Hillsborough County Public Library System, Thonotosassa Branch, 10715 Main St, Thonotosassa, FL, 33592-2831. Fax: 813-987-6217. p. 498

Shermer, Kerry, Asst Librn, Tech Serv, Central Baptist Theological Seminary, 22074 W 66th St, Shawnee, KS, 66226. Tel: 913-422-5789. Fax: 913-371-8110. p. 894

Shern, Vivian V, Ref Serv, Venable LLP Library, 750 E Pratt St, 9th Flr, Baltimore, MD, 21202. Tel: 410-244-7843. Fax: 410-244-7742. p. 1019

Sherod, James, Br Mgr, Los Angeles Public Library System, Baldwin Hills, 2906 S La Brea Ave, Los Angeles, CA, 90016-3902. Tel: 323-733-1196. Fax: 323 733-0774. p. 173

Sherrard, Karen L, Dir, Petoskey Public Library, 500 E Mitchell St, Petoskey, MI, 49770. Tel: 231-758-3100. Fax: 231-758-3106. p. 1217

Sherratt, Chris, Librn, Massachusetts Institute of Technology Libraries, Lindgren Library-Earth, Atmospheric & Planetary Sciences, Bldg 54-200, 77 Massachusetts Ave, Cambridge, MA, 02139-4307. Tel: 617-253-5648. Fax: 617-252-1621. p. 1078

Sherri, Kirschman, Dir, Frothingham Free Library, 28 W Main St, Fonda, NY, 12068. Tel: 518-853-3016. Fax: 518-853-3016. p. 1623

Sherriff, Graham, Pub Serv Librn, Lyndon State College, 1001 College Rd, Lyndonville, VT, 05851. Tel: 802-626-6366. Fax: 802-626-6331. p. 2427

Sherrill, Barbara, Acq, Amarillo College Library, 2201 S Washington, Amarillo, TX, 79109. Tel: 806-371-5400. Fax: 806-371-5470. p. 2274

Sherrill, Charles A, Archivist, State Librn, Tennessee State Library & Archives, 403 Seventh Ave N, Nashville, TN, 37243-0312. Tel: 615-741-2764. Fax: 615-532-2472, 615-741-6471. p. 2259

Sherrill, Denise, Asst Dir, Operations, Finance & Fac, Davidson College, 209 Ridge Rd, Davidson, NC, 28035-0001. Tel: 704-894-2331. Fax: 704-894-2625. p. 1786

Sherrill, Deresa, In Charge, Chiquita Brands International, Inc, 550 S Caldwell St, Charlotte, NC, 28202. Tel: 980-636-5000. Fax: 704-919-5230. p. 1782

Sherrill, Jacque, Dir, Jetmore Public Library, 310 Main St, Jetmore, KS, 67854. Tel: 620-357-8336. p. 874

Sherrill, Kate, Librn, Ivy Tech Community College, 3501 First Ave, Evansville, IN, 47710-3398. Tel: 812-429-1412. Fax: 812-429-9802. p. 739

Sherstad, Pam, Pub Relations, Right to Life of Michigan, 2340 Porter St SW, Grand Rapids, MI, 49509. Tel: 616-532-2300. Fax: 616-532-3461. p. 1185

Sherwood, Catella, Librn, Canadian Opera Co, 227 Front St E, Toronto, ON, M5A 1E8, CANADA. Tel: 416-363-6671. Fax: 416-363-5584. p. 2852

Sherwood, David, Dir, Nashotah House Library, 2777 Mission Rd, Nashotah, WI, 53058-9793. Tel: 262-646-6534. Fax: 262-646-6504. p. 2624

Sherwood, Joseph L, Exec Dir, Syst, Chester County Library System, 450 Exton Square Pkwy, Exton, PA, 19341-2496. Tel: 610-280-2611. Fax: 610-280-2688. p. 2056

Sherwood, Lawrence, Assoc Dean of Libr, Cuyamaca College Library, 900 Rancho San Diego Pkwy, El Cajon, CA, 92019-4304. Tel: 619-660-4416. Fax: 619-660-4493. p. 145

Sherwood, Louis, Jr, Univ Archivist, Texas Wesleyan University, 1201 Wesleyan St, Fort Worth, TX, 76105. Tel: 817-531-4822. Fax: 817-531-4806. p. 2324

Sherwood, Nancy, Dir, Auld Public Library, 537 N Webster St, Red Cloud, NE, 68970. Tel: 402-746-3352. p. 1417

Sherwood, Nancy, Tech Serv, Garden City Public Library, 60 Seventh St, Garden City, NY, 11530-2891. Tel: 516-742-8405. Fax: 516-742-2675. p. 1626

Sherwood, Sherrill, Coll Develop, Mkt, Haliburton County Public Library, Administrative Centre, 78 Maple Ave, Haliburton, ON, K0M 1S0, CANADA. Tel: 705-457-2241. Fax: 705-457-9586. p. 2807

Sherwood, William, Sr Librn, San Leandro Public Library, 300 Estudillo Ave, San Leandro, CA, 94577. Tel: 510-577-7964. Fax: 510-577-3967. p. 252

Sherwood, William, Sr Librn, San Leandro Public Library, Manor, 1307 Manor Blvd, San Leandro, CA, 94579-1501. Tel: 510-577-7970. p. 253

Sheryl, Ramer, Dir, Elmhurst Hospital Center, 79-01 Broadway, D3-52A, Elmhurst, NY, 11373. Tel: 718-334-2040. Fax: 718-334-5690. p. 1619

Shetter, Cynthia J, Dir, Los Lunas Public Library, 460 Main St NE, Los Lunas, NM, 87031. Tel: 505-839-3850. Fax: 505-352-3582. p. 1559

Shetuni, Spiro, Database Mgt, Winthrop University, 824 Oakland Ave, Rock Hill, SC, 29733. Tel: 803-323-2234. Fax: 803-323-2215. p. 2203

Sheviak, Jean K, Exec Dir, Capital District Library Council, 28 Essex St, Albany, NY, 12206. Tel: 518-438-2500. Fax: 518-438-2872. p. 2949

Shew, Anne, Dir, California Pacific Medical Center, 2395 Sacramento St, San Francisco, CA, 94115-2328. Tel: 415-600-3240. Fax: 415-600-6597. p. 241

Shew, Ellen, Dir, Rutherford Library, 2000 State Rte 129, South Bristol, ME, 04568. Tel: 207-644-1882. p. 1001

Shewberg, Caroline, Mgr, Libr Serv, West Perth Public Library, 105 Saint Andrew St, Mitchell, ON, N0K 1N0, CANADA. Tel: 519-348-9234. Fax: 519-348-4540. p. 2823

Shewchuk, Diane, Curator, Columbia County Historical Society Library, Columbia County Museum, Five Albany Ave, Kinderhook, NY, 12106. Tel: 518-758-9265. Fax: 518-758-2499. p. 1649

Shewfelt, Betty G, Tech Serv Dir, Wesleyan College, 4760 Forsyth Rd, Macon, GA, 31210-4462. Tel: 478-757-5202. Fax: 478-757-3898. p. 541

Shewfelt, John, Br Mgr, Markham Public Library, Milliken Mills Branch, 7600 Kennedy Rd, Unit 1, Unionville, ON, L3R 9S5, CANADA. Tel: 905-513-7977. Fax: 905-940-8326. p. 2820

Shgeir, Lee, Admin Serv Coordr, Arlington Public Library System, 101 E Abram St, MS 10-0100, Arlington, TX, 76010-1183. Tel: 817-459-6900. Fax: 817-459-6936. p. 2276

Shi, Xi, Dr, Head Librn, Rockland Community College Library, 145 College Rd, Suffern, NY, 10901. Tel: 845-574-4402. Fax: 845-574-4424. p. 1750

Shiarappa, Lorraine, Children's Coordr, Hopewell Public Library, 13 E Broad St, Hopewell, NJ, 08525. Tel: 609-466-1625. Fax: 609-466-1996. p. 1491

Shibuyama, Loni, Archivist, ONE Institute & Archives, 909 W Adams Blvd, Los Angeles, CA, 90007. Tel: 213-741-0094. Fax: lonis@onearchives.org. p. 176

Shiel, Teri, Info & Instruction Librn, Ref Librn, Westfield State University, 577 Western Ave, Westfield, MA, 01085-2580. Tel: 413-572-5251. Fax: 413-572-5520. p. 1138

Shields, Adrienne, Ref Serv, Southern University, Oliver B Spellman Law Library, 56 Roosevelt Steptoe, Baton Rouge, LA, 70813. Tel: 225-771-2139, 225-771-2315. Fax: 225-771-6254. p. 944

Shields, Catherine, Computer Serv, Ref Serv, East Lyme Public Library, Inc, 39 Society Rd, Niantic, CT, 06357-1100. Tel: 860-739-6926. Fax: 860-691-0020. p. 361

Shields, David, Chief Librn, Service Canada Library, 140 Promenade Du Portage, Phase 4-1, Ottawa, ON, K1A 0J9, CANADA. Fax: 819-953-5482. p. 2833

Shields, Diana, Librn, Gulf Correctional Institution Library, 500 Ike Steel Rd, Wewahitchka, FL, 32465. Tel: 850-639-1480. Fax: 850-639-1182. p. 504

Shields, Jeannette, Chief Librn, Bonfield Public Library, 365 Hwy 531, Bonfield, ON, P0H 1E0, CANADA. Tel: 705-776-2396. Fax: 705-776-1154. p. 2795

Shields, Jerri, Librn, Gabie Betts Burton Memorial Library, 217 S Kearney, Clarendon, TX, 79226. Tel: 806-874-3685. Fax: 806-874-9750. p. 2297

Shields, John, Coll Develop, Online Serv, Ref, United States Army, US Army Logistics University, Bldg 12420, 562 Quarters Rd, Fort Lee, VA, 23801-1705. Tel: 804-765-4722. Fax: 804-765-4660. p. 2465

Shields, Mickey, Asst Dir, Iowa League of Cities Library, 317 Sixth Ave, Ste 800, Des Moines, IA, 50309-4111. Tel: 515-244-7282. Fax: 515-244-0740. p. 809

Shields, Nicole, Supvr, Extn Serv, Napa City-County Library, 580 Coombs St, Napa, CA, 94559-3396. Tel: 707-253-4241. Fax: 707-253-4615. p. 192

Shields, Theodosia, Dr, Dir of Libr Serv, North Carolina Central University, 1801 Fayetteville St, Durham, NC, 27707-3129. Tel: 919-530-5233. Fax: 919-530-7612. p. 1789

Shiels, Margaret, Assoc Dir, FHI360 Library Services, 2224 E NC Hwy 54, Durham, NC, 27713. Tel: 919-544-7040. Fax: 919-544-7261. p. 1789

Shier, Andrea, Ref Librn, University of Toronto Libraries, Centre of Criminology, 14 Queens Park Crescent W, Toronto, ON, M5S 3K9, CANADA. Tel: 416-978-7068, Ext.245. Fax: 416-978-4195. p. 2865

Shifflet, Ann, Librn, Columbus College of Art & Design, 107 N Ninth St, Columbus, OH, 43215-3875. Tel: 614-222-3273, 614-224-9101. Fax: 614-222-6193. p. 1884

Shiflett, Barbara, Mgr, Sumter County Library System, 7375 Powell Rd, Ste 150, Wildwood, FL, 34785. Tel: 352-689-4560. Fax: 352-689-4561. p. 504

Shiflett, Orvin Lee, PhD, Dr, Chair, University of North Carolina at Greensboro, School of Education, 349 Curry Bldg, Greensboro, NC, 27402. Tel: 336-334-3481. Fax: 336-334-5060. p. 2971

Shifton, Anna, Info Tech Librn, North Brunswick Free Public Library, 880 Hermann Rd, North Brunswick, NJ, 08902. Tel: 732-246-3545. Fax: 732-246-1341. p. 1514

Shih, Chia-Chun, Librn, Kimbell Art Museum Library, 3333 Camp Bowie Blvd, Fort Worth, TX, 76107. Tel: 817-332-8451. Fax: 817-877-1264. p. 2322

Shih, Una, ILL, Res, SUNY Westchester Community College, 75 Grasslands Rd, Valhalla, NY, 10595-1693. Tel: 914-606-6573. Fax: 914-785-6513. p. 1760

Shih, Virginia Jing-yi, Librn, University of California, Berkeley, South-Southeast Asia Library, 120 Doe Library, Berkeley, CA, 94720-6000. Tel: 510-643-0850. Fax: 510-643-8817. p. 128

Shiles, Karen, Automation Syst Coordr, Gloucester County Library System, 389 Wolfert Station Rd, Mullica Hill, NJ, 08062. Tel: 856-223-6000. Fax: 856-223-6039. p. 1507

Shilkevich, Antoinette V, Librn, Blecher & Collins, 515 S Figueroa St, 17th Flr, Ste 1750, Los Angeles, CA, 90071. Tel: 213-622-4222. Fax: 213-622-1656. p. 168

Shilling, Dustin, Dir, Northern Tier Library Association, 4015 Dickey Rd, Gibsonia, PA, 15044-9713. Tel: 724-449-2665. Fax: 724-443-6755. p. 2060

Shillinglaw, Hank, Circ, Hancock County Public Library, 240 Court Sq, Hawesville, KY, 42348. Tel: 270-927-6760. Fax: 270-927-6847. p. 916

Shilts, Thomas, Youth Serv Librn, Capital Area District Libraries, Hope Borbas Okemos Library, 4321 Okemos Rd, Okemos, MI, 48864. Tel: 517-347-2021. Fax: 517-347-2034. p. 1200

Shimane, Linda, Commun Libr Mgr, County of Los Angeles Public Library, Lomita Library, 24200 Narbonne Ave, Lomita, CA, 90717-1188. Tel: 310-539-4515. Fax: 310-534-8649. p. 142

Shimek, Diane, Sr Info Spec, Conference Board, Inc, 845 Third Ave, New York, NY, 10022. Tel: 212-759-0900. Fax: 212-836-9750. p. 1676

Shimek, Gary S, Dir, Milwaukee School of Engineering, 500 E Kilbourn Ave, Milwaukee, WI, 53202. Tel: 414-277-7181. Fax: 414-277-7186. p. 2620

Shimer, Renee, Asst Law Librn, Madera County Law Library, County Government Ctr, 209 W Yosemite Ave, Madera, CA, 93637-3596. Tel: 559-673-0378. Fax: 559-673-0378. p. 181

Shimizu, Cindy, Libr Mgr, Pueblo City-County Library District, Pueblo West Library, 298 S Joe Martinez Blvd, Pueblo West, CO, 81007-2740. Tel: 719-562-5662. Fax: 719-562-5663. p. 321

Shimmin, Jo, Cat, Dir, Southeast Community College-Lincoln Campus, 8800 O St, Lincoln, NE, 68520. Tel: 402-437-2586. Fax: 402-437-2404. p. 1406

Shimmin, Nick, Dir, West Branch Public Library, 300 N Downey, West Branch, IA, 52358. Tel: 319-643-2633. Fax: 319-643-2845. p. 852

Shimon, Nancy, Tech Serv, Shorewood Public Library, 3920 N Murray Ave, Shorewood, WI, 53211-2385. Tel: 414-847-2670. p. 2638

Shimonishi, Melissa, Libr Asst, Hawaii State Archives, Iolani Palace Grounds, 364 S King St, Honolulu, HI, 96813. Tel: 808-586-0329. Fax: 808-586-0330. p. 561

Shimp, Andrew, Librn, Yale University Library, Engineering & Applied Science, 15 Prospect St, New Haven, CT, 06511. Tel: 203-432-7460. Fax: 203-432-7465. p. 357

Shimrock, Dana, Dir, Garrett College, 687 Mosser Rd, McHenry, MD, 21541. Tel: 301-387-3003. Fax: 301-387-3055. p. 1035

Shimunek, Jean, Ref Serv Mgr, Hayner Public Library District, 326 Belle St, Alton, IL, 62002. Tel: 618-462-0677. Fax: 618-462-0665. p. 588

Shin, Hee-sook, Coll Develop/Ref Librn, Columbia University, C V Starr East Asian Library, 300 Kent Hall, MC 3901, 1140 Amsterdam Ave, New York, NY, 10027. Tel: 212-854-4318. Fax: 212-662-6286. p. 1675

Shin, Helen, Librn, New Orleans Baptist Theological Seminary, 1000 Johnson Ferry Rd, Ste C115, Marietta, GA, 30068. Tel: 770-321-1606. Fax: 770-321-5363. p. 543

Shin, Helen, Extn Serv Librn, New Orleans Baptist Theological Seminary, 4110 Seminary Pl, New Orleans, LA, 70126. Tel: 770-321-1606. Fax: 770-321-5363. p. 961

Shincovich, Ann, Dir, Pocono Mountain Public Library, 5540 Memorial Blvd, Tobyhanna, PA, 18466. Tel: 570-894-8860. Fax: 570-894-8852. p. 2146

Shineton, Linda, Br Mgr, Burnaby Public Library, McGill Branch, 4595 Albert St, Burnaby, BC, V5C 2G6, CANADA. Tel: 604-299-8955. Fax: 604-299-7000. p. 2725

Shinnick, Joseph, Dir, Three Rivers Regional Library System, 208 Gloucester St, Brunswick, GA, 31520-7007. Tel: 912-267-1212. Fax: 912-267-9597. p. 522

Shinouda, Elizabeth, Commun Libr Mgr, Queens Borough Public Library, Douglaston-Little Neck Community Library, 249-01 Northern Blvd, Little Neck, NY, 11363. Tel: 718-225-8414. Fax: 718-631-8829. p. 1644

Shipe, Susan, Dir, Village Library of Morgantown, 207 N Walnut St, Morgantown, PA, 19543. Tel: 610-286-1022. Fax: 610-286-1024. p. 2092

Shipe, Susan L, Dir, Schuylkill Valley Community Library, 1310 Washington Rd, Leesport, PA, 19533-9708. Tel: 610-926-1555. Fax: 610-926-3710. p. 2080

Shipka, Katie, Assoc Librn, Saint Elizabeth Health Center, 1044 Belmont Ave, Youngstown, OH, 44501-1790. Tel: 330-480-3039. Fax: 330-480-3044. p. 1953

Shiplett, Darrell, Asst Librn, United States Air Force, Air Force Flight Test Center Technical Research Library, 812 TSS/ENTL, 307 E Popson Ave, Bldg 1400, Rm 106, Edwards AFB, CA, 93524-6630. Tel: 661-277-3606. Fax: 661-277-6451. p. 144

Shipley, Amy, Acq Librn, Garfield County Public Library System, 402 W Main, New Castle, CO, 81647. Tel: 970-984-2347. Fax: 970-984-2487. p. 319

Shipley, Brenda, Asst Librn, Greenfield Public Library, 515 Chestnut, Greenfield, IL, 62044-1305. Tel: 217-368-2613. Fax: 217-368-2613. p. 652

Shipley, Cindy, ILL, Dodge City Public Library, 1001 N Second Ave, Dodge City, KS, 67801-4484. Tel: 620-225-0248. Fax: 620-225-2761. p. 863

Shipley, Michele, Asst Dir, University of Rochester Medical Center, 601 Elmwood Ave, Rochester, NY, 14642. Tel: 585-275-3361. Fax: 585-756-7762. p. 1734

Shipley, Sam, Ref, Dodge City Public Library, 1001 N Second Ave, Dodge City, KS, 67801-4484. Tel: 620-225-0248. Fax: 620-225-2761. p. 863

Shipman, Charles, Ref Librn II, New Hampshire State Library, 20 Park St, Concord, NH, 03301-6314. Tel: 603-271-2392. Fax: 603-271-2205, 603-271-6826. p. 1443

Shipman, JoAnn, Librn, Guthrie CSD & King County Consolidated Library, Hwy 82, Guthrie, TX, 79236. Tel: 806-596-4466. Fax: 806-596-4088. p. 2330

Shipp, Connie, Br Mgr, Livingston Parish Library, Albany Springfield, 26941 Louisiana Hwy 43, Hammond, LA, 70403. Tel: 225-567-1441. Fax: 225-567-3768. p. 955

Shipp, Kelly, Ser & Electronic Res Librn, University of Maryland, Baltimore County, 1000 Hilltop Circle, Baltimore, MD, 21250. Tel: 410-455-2356. Fax: 410-455-1138. p. 1018

Shipp, Nadine, Acq Librn, Rainsville Public Library, 941 E Main St, Rainsville, AL, 35986. Tel: 256-638-3311. Fax: 256-638-3314. p. 34

Shippee, Jean, Ch, Wiscasset Public Library, 21 High St, Wiscasset, ME, 04578-4119. Tel: 207-882-7161. Fax: 207-882-6698. p. 1008

Shirazi, Bahman, Archives Coordr, California Institute of Integral Studies, 1453 Mission St, 2nd Flr, San Francisco, CA, 94103. Tel: 415-575-6253. Fax: 415-575-1264. p. 241

Shirdan, Rona, In Charge, First Presbyterian Church, 140 N Lansdowne Ave, Lansdowne, PA, 19050. Tel: 610-622-0800. Fax: 610-622-0881. p. 2078

Shire, Adam, Assoc & Syst Librn, Boston Architectural College, 320 Newbury St, Boston, MA, 02115. Tel: 617-585-0251. Fax: 617-585-0151. p. 1055

Shireman, Kimberly, Dir of Libr Serv, Rockingham Community College, 315 Wrenn Memorial Rd, Wentworth, NC, 27375. Tel: 336-342-4261, Ext 2250. Fax: 336-342-1203. p. 1829

Shirey, Chris, Cataloger, Natchez Adams Wilkinson Library Service, 220 S Commerce St, Natchez, MS, 39120-3502. Tel: 601-445-8862. Fax: 601-446-7795. p. 1309

Shiri, Ali, Dr, Assoc Prof, University of Alberta, 3-20 Rutherford S, Edmonton, AB, T6G 2J4, CANADA. Tel: 780-492-4578. Fax: 780-492-2430. p. 2977

Shirley, Angela, Dir, Wregie Memorial Library, 105 W Broadway, Oxford Junction, IA, 52323. Tel: 563-826-2450. Fax: 563-826-2450. p. 837

Shirley, Beverley, Consortia Serv, TexSHARE - Texas State Library & Archives Commission, 1201 Brazos, Austin, TX, 78701. Tel: 512-463-5433. Fax: 512-936-2306. p. 2956

Shirley, Donna, Supvr, Pub Serv, Rita & Truett Smith Public Library, 300 Country Club Rd, Bldg 300, Wylie, TX, 75098. Tel: 972-516-6250. p. 2401

Shirley, Eileen, Librn, Rochester General Hospital, 1425 Portland Ave, Rochester, NY, 14621. Tel: 585-922-4743. Fax: 585-544-1504. p. 1731

Shirley, Linda, Asst Librn, Orena Humphrey Public Library, 900 Main St, Ste 1, Whitwell, TN, 37397-5249. Tel: 423-658-6134. Fax: 423-658-7726. p. 2269

Shirley, Lynn, Librn, Grand County Library District, Hot Sulphur Springs Branch, 105 Moffat, Hot Sulphur Springs, CO, 80451. Tel: 970-725-3942. Fax: 970-725-0570. p. 310

Shirley, Philip, Tech Coordr, Cuyahoga Falls Library, 2015 Third St, Cuyahoga Falls, OH, 44221-3294. Tel: 330-928-2117, Ext 109. Fax: 330-928-2535. p. 1892

Shirshac, Cynthia, Asst Dir, Durham Public Library, Seven Maple Ave, Durham, CT, 06422. Tel: 860-349-9544. Fax: 860-349-1897. p. 337

Shiu, Julia, Info Analyst/Researcher, Association of Municipalities of Ontario, 200 University Ave, Ste 801, Toronto, ON, M5H 3C6, CANADA. Tel: 416-971-9856, Ext 321. Fax: 416-971-6191. p. 2850

Shive, Nancy, Libr Assoc, Illinois School for the Visually Impaired Library, 658 E State St, Jacksonville, IL, 62650-2184. Tel: 217-479-4400, Ext 4471. Fax: 217-479-4479. p. 658

Shively, Daniel C, Cat, Indiana University of Pennsylvania, 431 S 11th St, Indiana, PA, 15705-1096. Tel: 724-357-4864. Fax: 724-357-4891. p. 2071

Shively, Trisha, Adult Serv, Kokomo-Howard County Public Library, 220 N Union St, Kokomo, IN, 46901-4614. Tel: 765-457-3242. Fax: 765-457-3683. p. 758

Shivers, Chris, VPres, American Brahman Breeders Association Library, 3003 South Loop W, Ste 140, Houston, TX, 77054. Tel: 713-349-0854. Fax: 713-349-9795. p. 2333

Shives, Becky, Librn, York County Library System, Village, 35-C N Main St, Jacobus, PA, 17407. Tel: 717-428-1034. Fax: 717-428-3869. p. 2160

Shlaes, Nancy, Ref, Governors State University Library, One University Pkwy, University Park, IL, 60466-0975. Tel: 708-534-4137. Fax: 708-534-4564. p. 711

Shlah, Heather, Dir, Stickney-Forest View Public Library District, 6800 W 43rd St, Stickney, IL, 60402. Tel: 708-749-1050. Fax: 708-749-1054. p. 707

Shneyder, Elina, Librn, Colorado Department of Corrections, Youth Offender Services, PO Box 35010, Pueblo, CO, 81003. Tel: 719-544-4800, Ext 3507. Fax: 719-583-5909. p. 320

Shnidman, Avrohom S, Librn, Ner Israel Rabbinical College Library, 400 Mount Wilson Lane, Baltimore, MD, 21208. Tel: 410-484-7200. Fax: 410-484-3060. p. 1017

Shoaf, Eric, Assoc Dean, Clemson University Libraries, Box 343001, Clemson, SC, 29634-3001. Tel: 864-656-5731. Fax: 864-656-0758. p. 2186

Shoar, Shahin, Media Serv, Upper Arlington Public Library, 2800 Tremont Rd, Columbus, OH, 43221. Tel: 614-486-9621. Fax: 614-486-4530. p. 1891

Shoba, Doreen, Asst Dir, Wayne Public Library, 461 Valley Rd, Wayne, NJ, 07470. Tel: 973-694-4272, Ext 5102. Fax: 973-692-0637. p. 1540

Shochet, Michael, Head, Ref, University of Baltimore, 1420 Maryland Ave, Baltimore, MD, 21201. Tel: 410-837-4277. Fax: 410-837-4330. p. 1018

Shockey, Karen, Libr Instruction Coordr, State University of New York at Oswego, SUNY Oswego, 7060 State Rte 104, Oswego, NY, 13126-3514. Tel: 315-312-3566. Fax: 315-312-3194. p. 1713

Shockey, Leona, Govt Doc, McDaniel College, Two College Hill, Westminster, MD, 21157-4390. Tel: 410-857-4679. Fax: 410-857-2748. p. 1046

Shockey, Mindy, Librn, Price Brothers Co Library, 333 W First St, Ste 700, Dayton, OH, 45401. Tel: 937-226-8700. Fax: 937-226-8711. p. 1894

Shockley, Andrew, Librn, Oklahoma Library for the Blind & Physically Handicapped, 300 NE 18th St, Oklahoma City, OK, 73105. Tel: 405-521-3514. Fax: 405-521-4582. p. 1975

Shoemake, Linda, Ref Serv, American River College Library, 4700 College Oak Dr, Sacramento, CA, 95841. Tel: 916-484-8455. Fax: 916-484-8018, 916-484-8657. p. 220

Shoemaker, Jill, Ref, Lasell College, 80 A Maple Ave, Newton, MA, 02466. Tel: 617-243-2244. Fax: 617-243-2458. p. 1109

Shoemaker, Jim D, Br Mgr, Beaumont Public Library System, R C Miller Memorial, 1605 Dowlen Rd, Beaumont, TX, 77706. Tel: 409-866-9487. Fax: 409-866-3720. p. 2287

Shoemaker, Joy M, Librn, US Court of Appeals, Ninth Circuit Library, 125 S Grand Ave, Pasadena, CA, 91105. Tel: 626-229-7190. Fax: 626-229-7460. p. 207

Shoemaker, Lorna A, Dr, Dir, Christian Theological Seminary Library, 1000 W 42nd St, Indianapolis, IN, 46208. Tel: 317-924-1331. Fax: 317-931-2363. p. 750

Shoemaker, M Jeffrey, Dr, Librn, Pennsylvania State Department of Health, 110 Pickering Way, Lionville, PA, 19353. Tel: 610-280-3464. Fax: 610-450-1932. p. 2082

Shoemaker, Matt, Dir, Digital Coll, Historical Society of Pennsylvania, 1300 Locust St, Philadelphia, PA, 19107-5699. Tel: 215-732-6200, Ext 201. Fax: 215-732-2680. p. 2110

Shoemaker, Phyllis, Librn, University of Alaska Fairbanks, School of Fisheries & Ocean Sciences, 125 Third Ave, Seward, AK, 99664. Tel: 907-224-5261. Fax: 907-224-3392. p. 53

Shoemaker, Rene D, IV, Dir, University of Georgia, School of Environmental Design, G14 Caldwell Hall, Athens, GA, 30602. Tel: 706-542-8292. Fax: 706-542-4485. p. 510

Shoemaker, Sarah, ILL/Circ Supvr, Pacific Northwest National Laboratory, 2770 University Dr, Richland, WA, 99354. Tel: 509-372-7463. Fax: 509-372-7433. p. 2526

Shoemaker, Shane, Librn, Eastern State Hospital, 627 W Fourth, Lexington, KY, 40508. Tel: 859-246-7538. Fax: 859-246-7018. p. 920

Shoff, Patricia, Ch, Sinking Spring Public Library, 3940 Penn Ave, Sinking Spring, PA, 19608. Tel: 610-678-4311. Fax: 610-670-4826. p. 2140

Shofkom, Donna, Libr Asst, George F Johnson Memorial Library, 1001 Park St, Endicott, NY, 13760. Tel: 607-757-5350. Fax: 607-757-2491. p. 1620

Shofner, Pamela, Librn, Maine Department of Transportation Library, 16 State House Sta, Augusta, ME, 04333-0016. Tel: 207-624-3230. Fax: 207-624-3221. p. 974

Shoge, Ruth C, Dr, Dir, Washington College, 300 Washington Ave, Chestertown, MD, 21620-1197. Tel: 410-778-7292. Fax: 410-778-7288. p. 1023

Shogren, Deb, Br Librn, Albany County Public Library, 310 S Eighth St, Laramie, WY, 82070-3969. Tel: 307-721-2580. Fax: 307-721-2584. p. 2657

Shogren, Deb, Br Librn, Albany County Public Library, Centennial Valley Branch, PO Box 188, Centennial, WY, 82055-0188. Tel: 307-745-8393. p. 2657

Sholar, Kim, Ref Librn, Orange County Public Library, 137 W Margaret Lane, Hillsborough, NC, 27278. Tel: 919-245-2525. Fax: 919-644-3003. p. 1802

Sholtz, Barbara, Dir, Auld-Doudna Public Library, 155 W Grant St, Guide Rock, NE, 68942. Tel: 402-257-4015. p. 1400

Shone, Saralyn, Adminr, Info Tech, Arlington Public Library System, 101 E Abram St, MS 10-0100, Arlington, TX, 76010-1183. Tel: 817-459-6922. Fax: 817-459-6936. p. 2276

Shonek, Santosh, Librn, Durham Technical Community College, Northern Durham Center, 2401 Snow Hill Rd, Durham, NC, 27712. Tel: 919-536-7240. Fax: 919-686-3519. p. 1788

Shonouda, Hala, Br Mgr, Glendale Public Library, Library Connection @ Adams Square, 1100 E Chevy Chase Dr, Glendale, CA, 91205. Tel: 818-548-3833. Fax: 818-500-1039. p. 155

Shonouda, Hala, Br Mgr, Glendale Public Library, Pacific Park, 501 S Pacific Ave, Glendale, CA, 91204. Tel: 818-548-3760. Fax: 818-409-7154. p. 155

Shook, Julie D, Dir, The Louise & Lucille Hink-Tama Public Library, 401 Siegel St, Tama, IA, 52339. Tel: 641-484-2194. Fax: 641-484-4484. p. 847

Shoop, Jane, Librn, Seattle Central Community College, 1701 Broadway, 2BE2101, Seattle, WA, 98122. Tel: 206-587-4071. Fax: 206-587-3878. p. 2530

Shoop, Pam, Librn, Commonwealth Court Library, 603 Irvis Office Bldg, Commonwealth & Walnut Aves, Harrisburg, PA, 17120. Tel: 717-255-1615. Fax: 717-255-1784. p. 2064

Shoot, Judith Cunning, Ch, Livingston County Library, 450 Locust St, Chillicothe, MO, 64601-2597. Tel: 660-646-0547. Fax: 660-646-5504. p. 1323

Shope, Ginny, Dept Head, User Serv, US Army War College Library, 122 Forbes Ave, Carlisle, PA, 17013-5220. Tel: 717-245-4280. Fax: 717-245-3323. p. 2042

Shoppe, Anita, Instr, Big Horn County Public Library, 419 N Custer Ave, Hardin, MT, 59034. Fax: 406-665-1804. p. 1381

Shoptaugh, Terry, Archivist, Minnesota State University Moorhead, 1104 Seventh Ave S, Moorhead, MN, 56563. Tel: 218-477-2922. Fax: 218-477-5924. p. 1266

Shor, Cynthia, Dir, Walt Whitman Birthplace Association, 246 Old Walt Whitman Rd, Huntington Station, NY, 11746-4148. Tel: 631-427-5240. Fax: 631-427-5247. p. 1639

Shore, Christine, Ref Librn, College of Southern Nevada, 6375 W Charleston Blvd, W10I, Las Vegas, NV, 89146. Tel: 702-651-5069. Fax: 702-651-5718. p. 1429

Shore, Jeanna, ILL, Stillwater Public Library, 1107 S Duck St, Stillwater, OK, 74074. Tel: 405-372-3633. Fax: 405-624-0552. p. 1978

Shore, Monique, Syst Adminr, Drake Community Library, 930 Park St, Grinnell, IA, 50112-2016. Tel: 641-236-2661. Fax: 641-236-2667. p. 819

Shores, Elehna, Info Serv Librn, Northampton Community College, 3835 Green Pond Rd, Bethlehem, PA, 18020-7599. Tel: 610-861-5360. Fax: 610-861-5373. p. 2034

Shores, Mark L, Asst Dir, Miami University-Hamilton Campus, 1601 University Blvd, Hamilton, OH, 45011. Tel: 513-785-3235. Fax: 513-785-3231. p. 1904

Shorr, Risa, Librn, Ottawa Hospital, 501 Smyth Rd, Rm 1404, Ottawa, ON, K1H 8L6, CANADA. Tel: 613-737-8899, Ext 78530. Fax: 613-737-8521. p. 2832

Short, Ann Marie, Ch, Hamilton East Public Library, One Library Plaza, Cumberland Rd, Noblesville, IN, 46060-5639. Tel: 317-770-3218. Fax: 317-776-6936. p. 769

Short, Ann Marie, Assoc Dir, Pub Serv, Shawnee State University, 940 Second St, Portsmouth, OH, 45662-4344. Tel: 740-351-3462. Fax: 740-351-3432. p. 1931

Short, Becky, Dir, Samson Memorial Library, 107 Second St, Granton, WI, 54436. Tel: 715-238-5250. Fax: 715-238-8605. p. 2594

Short, Bradley, Librn, Washington University Libraries, Gaylord Music Library, Gaylord Hall, 6500 Forsyth Blvd, Saint Louis, MO, 63105. Tel: 314-935-5529. p. 1363

Short, Brent, Dir, Libr Serv, Saint Leo University, 33701 State Rd 52, Saint Leo, FL, 33574. Tel: 352-588-8260. Fax: 352-588-8484. p. 487

Short, Corinna A T, Purchasing, Peninsula Library & Historical Society, 6105 Riverview Rd, Peninsula, OH, 44264. Tel: 330-657-2291. Fax: 330-657-2311. p. 1928

Short, Debbie, Ref Serv, Ad, Utah Valley University Library, 800 W University Pkwy, Orem, UT, 84058-5999. Tel: 801-863-6336. Fax: 801-863-7065. p. 2409

Short, Doug, Online Serv Librn, Central Piedmont Community College Library, 1201 Elizabeth Ave, Charlotte, NC, 28235. Tel: 704-330-6845. Fax: 704-330-6887. p. 1781

Short, Janet, Mgr, The Library at Springfield Hospital Center, 6655 Sykesville Rd, Sykesville, MD, 21784. Tel: 410-970-7000, Ext 3481. Fax: 410-970-7197. p. 1043

Short, Jerri A, Dir, Salem Township Public Library, 535 W Pike St, Morrow, OH, 45152. Tel: 513-899-2588. Fax: 513-899-9420. p. 1918

Short, Mary, Dir, Granville Public Library, Two Granby Rd, Granville, MA, 01034-9539. Tel: 413-357-8531. Fax: 413-357-8531. p. 1091

Short, Sharon, Head, AV, Bexley Public Library, 2411 E Main St, Bexley, OH, 43209. Tel: 614-231-9709. p. 1860

Short, Stephanie, Cat, Young Harris College, One College St, Young Harris, GA, 30582. Tel: 706-379-4313. Fax: 706-379-4314. p. 558

Short, Vickie, Br Mgr, LaGrange County Public Library, Shipshewana Branch, 350 Depot St, Shipshewana, IN, 46565. Tel: 260-768-7444. Fax: 260-768-7290. p. 760

Short, Vickie, Head Librn, Lac Du Bonnet Regional Library, 84 Third St, Lac du Bonnet, MB, R0E 1A0, CANADA. Tel: 204-345-2653. Fax: 204-345-6827. p. 2749

Short, William, Assoc Dir, Libr Serv, Rhodes College, 2000 North Pkwy, Memphis, TN, 38112-1694. Tel: 901-843-3792. Fax: 901-843-3404. p. 2251

Short, Winnell, Tech Serv, Catawba College, 2300 W Innes St, Salisbury, NC, 28144-2488. Tel: 704-637-4209. Fax: 704-637-4304. p. 1822

Shorter, Marie, Librn, Bolivar County Library System, Dr Robert T Hollingsworth Public Library, Old Hwy 61, Shelby, MS, 38774. Tel: 662-398-7748. Fax: 662-398-7748. p. 1296

Shostack, Pauline, Electronic Res, Onondaga Community College, 4585 W Seneca Tpk, Syracuse, NY, 13215-4585. Tel: 315-498-2334. Fax: 315-498-7213. p. 1752

Shotts, Lesley N, Asst Librn, J F Drake State Technical College, 3421 Meridan St N, Huntsville, AL, 35811-1544. Tel: 256-551-5206. Fax: 256-551-3134. p. 22

Shotzbarger, Patricia, Tech Serv, Free Library of Philadelphia, Library for the Blind & Physically Handicapped, 919 Walnut St, Philadelphia, PA, 19107-5289. Tel: 215-683-3213. Fax: 215-683-3211. p. 2108

Shoup, Deborah, Youth Serv, Guilderland Public Library, 2228 Western Ave, Guilderland, NY, 12084-9701. Tel: 518-456-2400. Fax: 518-456-0923. p. 1632

Shovers, Brian, Libr Mgr, Montana Historical Society, 225 N Roberts St, Helena, MT, 59601-4514. Tel: 406-444-7415. Fax: 406-444-5297. p. 1382

Showalter, James D, Financial Mgr, Library System of Lancaster County, 1866 Colonial Village Lane, Ste 107, Lancaster, PA, 17601. Tel: 717-207-0500. Fax: 717-207-0504. p. 2077

Showalter, Janet, AV Coordr, Goshen Public Library, 601 S Fifth St, Goshen, IN, 46526-3994. Tel: 574-533-9531. Fax: 574-533-5211. p. 746

Showalter-Johnson, Deborah, Librn, US Court Library - Eighth Circuit, 9440 Charles Evans Whittaker US Courthouse, 400 E Ninth St, Kansas City, MO, 64106. Tel: 816-512-5790. Fax: 816-512-5799. p. 1341

Shrader, Marcia, Circ, Jefferson County Library, Arnold Branch, 1701 Missouri State Rd, Arnold, MO, 63010. Tel: 636-296-2204. Fax: 636-296-5975. p. 1331

Shrake, Richard, Asst Librn, Tech, American Philosophical Society Library, 105 S Fifth St, Philadelphia, PA, 19106-3386. Tel: 215-440-3400. Fax: 215-440-3423. p. 2102

Shrauger, Kristine, Head, ILL & Doc Delivery, University of Central Florida Libraries, 4000 Central Florida Blvd, Bldg 2, Orlando, FL, 32816-2666. Tel: 407-823-5422. Fax: 407-823-2529. p. 477

Shreeves, Edward, Assoc Univ Librn & Dir, Coll & Scholarly Communication, University of Iowa Libraries, 125 W Washington St, Iowa City, IA, 52242-1420. p. 823

Shreffler, Jean, Librn, Butler Institute of American Art, 524 Wick Ave, Youngstown, OH, 44502. Tel: 330-743-1711. Fax: 330-743-9567. p. 1952

Shreffler, Josh, Syst, Peninsula Libraries Automated Network, 2471 Flores St, San Mateo, CA, 94403-4000. Tel: 650-349-5538. Fax: 650-349-5089. p. 2938

Shreves, Thomas E, Med Librn, Pacific Hospital of Long Beach, 2776 Pacific Ave, Long Beach, CA, 90806. Tel: 562-997-2182. Fax: 562-595-0271. p. 167

Shridhar, Preeti, Communications Dir, Renton Public Library, 100 Mill Ave S, Renton, WA, 98057. Tel: 425-430-6610. Fax: 425-430-6833. p. 2525

Shrimplin, Aaron, Asst Dean, Res & Coll Serv, Miami University Libraries, 225 King Library, Oxford, OH, 45056. Tel: 513-529-6823. Fax: 513-529-3110. p. 1926

Shriner, Mary, Ref Librn, Park University Library, 8700 NW River Park Dr, Parkville, MO, 64152. Tel: 816-584-6464. Fax: 816-741-4911. p. 1349

Shriver, Margaret, Ref, Appleton Public Library, 225 N Oneida St, Appleton, WI, 54911-4780. Tel: 920-832-6170. Fax: 920-832-6182. p. 2578

Shriver, Mercedea, Ref & Web Serv Librn, Williams College, 55 Sawyer Library Dr, Williamstown, MA, 01267. Tel: 413-597-4716. Fax: 413-597-4106. p. 1141

Shrock, Daryl, Dir, Bristol-Washington Township Public Library, 505 W Vistula St, Bristol, IN, 46507. Tel: 574-848-7458. Fax: 574-848-4391. p. 729

Shrode, Flora, Head, Ref, Utah State University, 3000 Old Main Hill, Logan, UT, 84322-3000. Tel: 435-797-8033. Fax: 435-797-2880. p. 2407

Shrodes, Amber, Found Dir, Harford County Public Library, 1221-A Brass Mill Rd, Belcamp, MD, 21017-1209. Tel: 410-273-5600, Ext 2283. Fax: 410-273-5606. p. 1020

Shropshire, Laurie, Librn, Winkler County Library, 307 S Poplar St, Kermit, TX, 79745-4300. Tel: 432-586-3841. Fax: 432-586-2462. p. 2349

Shropshire, Sandra, Dean & Univ Librn, Idaho State University, Idaho State University, 850 S Ninth Ave, Pocatello, ID, 83209-8089. Tel: 208-282-2671. Fax: 208-282-5847. p. 581

Shrout, Bill, Collection Access Mgt, Kentucky Department for Libraries & Archives, 300 Coffee Tree Rd, Frankfort, KY, 40601. Tel: 502-564-8300. Fax: 502-564-5773. p. 913

Shroyer, Carol, Br Head, Saint Lucie County Library System, Lakewood Park, 7605 Santa Barbara Dr, Fort Pierce, FL, 34951. Tel: 772-462-6870. Fax: 772-462-6874. p. 447

Shtefan, Elena, Libr Asst, Northwestern College, Naperville Campus, 1809 N Mill St, Naperville, IL, 60563. Tel: 630-753-9091. Fax: 630-753-9823. p. 621

Shtulman, Robin, Asst Dir, Athol Public Library, 568 Main St, Athol, MA, 01331. Tel: 978-249-9515. Fax: 978-249-7636. p. 1050

Shu, Evena, Mgr, Tech Serv, Sr Librn, Monterey Park Bruggemeyer Library, 318 S Ramona Ave, Monterey Park, CA, 91754-3399. Tel: 626-307-1368. Fax: 626-288-4251. p. 190

Shu, Yue, Librn, Smithsonian Libraries, Freer Gallery of Art & Arthur M Sackler Gallery Library, Arthur M Sackler Gallery, Rm 2057, MRC 707, 12th St & Jefferson Dr SW, Washington, DC, 20560. Tel: 202-633-0479. Fax: 202-786-2936. p. 414

Shuey, Christine, In Charge, Klamath County Library Services District, Chemult Branch, 120 Damon St, Chemult, OR, 97731. Tel: 541-365-2412. Fax: 541-365-2412. p. 2002

Shuey, Lou Ellen, ILL, Freeport Public Library, 100 E Douglas St, Freeport, IL, 61032. Tel: 815-233-3000. Fax: 815-233-1099. p. 647

Shuffett-Todd, Sarah, Asst Dir, Circ, Green County Public Library, 112 W Court St, Greensburg, KY, 42743. Tel: 270-932-7081. Fax: 270-932-7081. p. 915

Shuffler, Ann, Dir, F M (Buck) Richards Memorial Library, 1106 S Blackburn St, Brady, TX, 76825. Tel: 325-597-2617. Fax: 325-597-0461. p. 2291

Shukitt, Pamela, Coll Develop Librn, Tech Serv Librn, Wilmington University Library, 320 DuPont Hwy, New Castle, DE, 19720. Tel: 302-328-9401. Fax: 302-328-0914. p. 385

Shuldman, Mitch, Head, Media Serv, University of Massachusetts Lowell Libraries, 61 Wilder St, Lowell, MA, 01854-3098. Tel: 978-934-4561. Fax: 978-934-3015. p. 1100

Shulik, Carolyn, Ch, Franklin Public Library, 421 12th St, Franklin, PA, 16323-0421. Tel: 814-432-5062. Fax: 814-432-8998. p. 2058

Shulkatis, Deborah, Libr Serv Mgr, Whittier Public Library, Whittwood Branch, 10537 Santa Gertrudes Ave, Whittier, CA, 90603-2760. Tel: 562-567-9950. Fax: 562-567-2881. p. 283

Shulkatis, Deborah, Mgr, Libr Serv, Whittier Public Library, 7344 S Washington Ave, Whittier, CA, 90602. Tel: 562-567-9900. Fax: 562-567-2880. p. 283

Shull, Hope, Dir, Freed-Hardeman University, 158 E Main St, Henderson, TN, 38340-2399. Tel: 731-989-6067. Fax: 731-989-6065. p. 2237

Shulman, Anne, Res Librn, Riker, Danzig, Scherer, Hyland & Perretti, Headquarters Plaza, One Speedwell Ave, Morristown, NJ, 07962. Tel: 973-538-0800. Fax: 973-538-1984. p. 1505

Shulman, Cindy, Regional Libr Mgr, Broward County Division of Libraries, Fort Lauderdale Branch, 1300 E Sunrise Blvd, Fort Lauderdale, FL, 33304. Tel: 954-765-4263. Fax: 954-765-4932. p. 441

Shulman, Frank Joseph, Curator, Asian Studies Newsletter Archives, 9225 Limestone Pl, College Park, MD, 20740-3943. Tel: 301-935-5614. p. 1024

Shulman, Stuart, Asst Prof, University of Pittsburgh, 135 N Bellefield Ave, Pittsburgh, PA, 15260. Tel: 412-624-5230. Fax: 412-624-5231. p. 2973

Shultes, Stephanie, Curator, Iroquois Indian Museum Library, 324 Caverns Rd, Howes Cave, NY, 12092. Tel: 518-296-8949. Fax: 518-296-8955. p. 1638

Shults, Charlene, Dir, University of Texas of the Permian Basin, 4901 E University Blvd, Odessa, TX, 79762. Tel: 432-552-2371. Fax: 432-552-2374. p. 2366

Shultz, Barbara J, Dir, Fort Dodge Public Library, 424 Central Ave, Fort Dodge, IA, 50501. Tel: 515-573-8167, Ext 231. Fax: 515-573-5422. p. 816

Shultz, Harriet, Dir, Jennings Carnegie Public Library, 303 Cary Ave, Jennings, LA, 70546-5223. Tel: 337-821-5517. Fax: 337-821-5527. p. 952

Shultz, Hazel, Asst Librn, Montezuma Public Library, 500 E Main St, Montezuma, IA, 50171. Tel: 641-623-3417. Fax: 641-623-3339. p. 833

Shultz, Mary, Librn, University of Illinois at Chicago, Library of the Health Sciences, Urbana, 102 Medical Sciences Bldg, MC-714, 506 S Mathews Ave, Urbana, IL, 61801. Tel: 217-244-2259. Fax: 217-333-9559. p. 627

Shultz, Suzanne M, Dir, Libr Serv, Wellspan Health at York Hospital, 1001 S George St, York, PA, 17405. Tel: 717-851-2495. Fax: 717-851-2487. p. 2159

Shuluk, William, Ref, Edison State College, 8099 College Pkwy SW, Bldg J, Fort Myers, FL, 33919. Tel: 239-489-9356. Fax: 239-489-9465. p. 444

Shum, Chun, Curator, Rare Bks, Harvard Library, Harvard-Yenching Library, Two Divinity Ave, Cambridge, MA, 02138. Tel: 617-495-2756. Fax: 617-496-6008. p. 1075

Shumaker, Deb, Dir, Kirtland Community College Library, 10775 N St Helen Rd, Roscommon, MI, 48653. Tel: 989-275-5000, Ext 235. Fax: 989-275-8510. p. 1223

Shuman, Brady, Tech Serv Spec, Covenant Theological Seminary, 12330 Conway Rd, Saint Louis, MO, 63141. Tel: 314-392-4100, 314-434-4044. Fax: 314-392-4116, 314-434-4819. p. 1354

Shuman, Elaine, Electronic Res Librn, Oregon Research Institute Library, 1715 Franklin Blvd, Eugene, OR, 97403-1983. Tel: 541-484-2123. Fax: 541-484-1108. p. 1997

Shuman, Jay, Assoc Dir, Res & Online Serv, New York University School of Law, 40 Washington Sq S, New York, NY, 10012-1099. Tel: 212-998-6300. Fax: 212-995-4559. p. 1695

Shumar, Alesha, Archivist, University of Tennessee, Knoxville, Special Collections, 121 Hodges Library, 1015 Volunteer Blvd, Knoxville, TN, 37996-1000. Tel: 865-974-4480. p. 2244

Shumate, Amanda, Ch, Guntersville Public Library, 1240 O'Brig Ave, Guntersville, AL, 35976. Tel: 256-571-7595. Fax: 256-571-7596. p. 19

Shumate, Connie L, Dir, Concord University, 1000 Vermillion St, Athens, WV, 24712. Tel: 304-384-5371. Fax: 304-384-7955. p. 2553

Shumate, Connie L, Dir, Princeton Public Library, 205 Center St, Princeton, WV, 24740-2932. Tel: 304-487-5045. Fax: 304-487-5046. p. 2570

Shumate, Debra, Mgr, District of Columbia Public Library, Cleveland Park, 3310 Connecticut Ave NW, Washington, DC, 20008. Tel: 202-282-3080. p. 398

Shumate, Ruth, Ref Librn, Tidewater Community College, 120 Campus Dr, Portsmouth, VA, 23701. Fax: 757-822-2149. p. 2485

Shumate, Vickie, Cataloger, Portales Public Library, 218 S Ave B, Portales, NM, 88130. Tel: 505-356-3940. Fax: 505-356-3964. p. 1560

Shumicky, Lisa, Asst Dir, Deer Park Public Library, 44 Lake Ave, Deer Park, NY, 11729-6047. Tel: 631-586-3000. Fax: 631-586-3006. p. 1613

Shumway, Heather, Dir, Hooksett Public Library, 1701B Hooksett Rd, Hooksett, NH, 03106-1852. Tel: 603-485-6092. Fax: 603-485-6193. p. 1451

Shung, Lily, Librn, Penfield Public Library, 1985 Baird Rd, Penfield, NY, 14526. Tel: 585-340-8720. Fax: 585-340-8748. p. 1716

Shupala, Christine, Dir, Texas A&M University-Corpus Christi, Mary & Jeff Bell Library, 6300 Ocean Dr, Corpus Christi, TX, 78412-5501. Tel: 361-825-2643. Fax: 361-825-5973. p. 2302

Shupe, Della, Dir, Libr Serv, Northwestern Health Sciences University, 2501 W 84th St, Bloomington, MN, 55431-1599. Tel: 952-885-5417. Fax: 952-884-3318. p. 1242

Shupe, Robert, Dir, Logan Library, 255 N Main, Logan, UT, 84321-3914. Tel: 435-716-9130. Fax: 435-716-9145. p. 2407

Shuping, Andrew, ILL/Circ Supvr, Ref Librn, Mercer University, Jack Tarver Library, 1300 Edgewood Ave, Macon, GA, 31207. Tel: 478-301-2251. Fax: 478-301-2111. p. 540

Shuping, Elizabeth, Youth Serv, Horry County Memorial Library, 1008 Fifth Ave, Conway, SC, 29526. Tel: 843-248-1544. Fax: 843-248-1548. p. 2191

Shupla, Martin, Ch, Sterling Municipal Library, Mary Elizabeth Wilbanks Ave, Baytown, TX, 77520. Tel: 281-427-7331. Fax: 281-420-5347. p. 2286

Shurden, Diane, Circ Asst, Sunflower County Library System, Horace Stansel Memorial, 112 S Ruby St, Ruleville, MS, 38771-3939. Tel: 662-756-2226. Fax: 662-756-2809. p. 1302

Shurden, Diane, Pub Serv, Sunflower County Library System, Drew Public, 290 W Park Ave, Drew, MS, 38737-3340. Tel: 662-745-2237. Fax: 662-745-2237. p. 1302

Shurden, Gail, Librn, Tombigbee Regional Library System, Mathiston Public Library, Scott St, Mathiston, MS, 39752-9214. Tel: 662-263-4772. Fax: 662-263-4772. p. 1318

Shurden, Lynn, Dir, Bolivar County Library System, 104 S Leflore Ave, Cleveland, MS, 38732. Tel: 662-843-2774. Fax: 662-843-4701. p. 1295

Shurly, Victoria M, Librn, Peninsula Community Library, Old Mission Peninsula School, 2735 Island View Rd, Traverse City, MI, 49686. Tel: 231-223-7700. Fax: 231-223-7708. p. 1231

Shurtleff, Jennie, Educ Coordr, Woodstock Historical Society, Inc, 26 Elm St, Woodstock, VT, 05091. Tel: 802-457-1822. Fax: 802-457-2811. p. 2441

Shurtleff, Lucy, Librn, Columbia County Library, Bearden Public Library, 210 N Cedar, Bearden, AR, 71720. Tel: 870-687-2634. p. 108

Shurtleff, William, Head Librn, Soyinfo Center Library, 1021 Dolores Dr, Lafayette, CA, 94549-2907. Tel: 925-283-2991. p. 163

Shuster, Laurie, Instrul Serv Librn, Ref, Pierce College Library, 9401 Farwest Dr SW, Lakewood, WA, 98498. Tel: 253-964-6305. Fax: 253-964-6713. p. 2519

Shute, Daniel J, Dr, Librn, Presbyterian College Library, 3495 University St, Montreal, QC, H3A 2A8, CANADA. Tel: 514-288-5256. Fax: 514-288-8072. p. 2900

Shutkin, Sara, Archivist, Rec Mgr, Ref Serv, Alverno College Library, 3401 S 39th St, Milwaukee, WI, 53215. Tel: 414-382-6202, Ext 2079. Fax: 414-382-6354. p. 2617

Shuttle, Jerry, Electronic Res, East Tennessee State University, Sherrod Library, Seehorn Dr & Lake St, Johnson City, TN, 37614-0204. Tel: 423-439-6996. Fax: 423-439-4410. p. 2239

Shuttleworth, Jeanne, Electronic Acq, University of Pennsylvania Libraries, 3420 Walnut St, Philadelphia, PA, 19104-6206. Tel: 215-898-7563. Fax: 215-898-0559. p. 2118

Shyam, Winnie, Ref, Southern Connecticut State University, 501 Crescent St, New Haven, CT, 06515. Tel: 203-392-5762. Fax: 203-392-5775. p. 356

Shyu, Ana, ILL, Dunlap Public Library District, 302 S First St, Dunlap, IL, 61525. Tel: 309-243-5716. Fax: 309-243-5874. p. 638

Siar, Janet, Head, Acq, University of Delaware Library, 181 S College Ave, Newark, DE, 19717-5267. Tel: 302-831-2231. Fax: 302-831-1046. p. 386

Siarny, William D, Dir, Charlotte Community Library, 226 S Bostwick St, Charlotte, MI, 48813-1801. Tel: 517-543-8859. Fax: 517-543-8868. p. 1162

Siasoco, Hope, Dir, Pinckney Community Public Library, 350 Mower Rd, Pinckney, MI, 48169. Tel: 734-878-3888. Fax: 734-878-2907. p. 1217

Siatunuu, Kopa, Librn, American Samoa Office of Library Services, Pavaiai Branch, Pavaiai Village, AS, 96799. Tel: 684-639-9605. Fax: 684-633-4240. p. 2665

Sibayan, Jessica, YA Serv, Franklin T Degroodt Library, 6475 Minton Rd SW, Palm Bay, FL, 32908. Tel: 321-952-6317. Fax: 321-952-6320. p. 479

Sibayan, Mary Jessica, Ch, Eau Gallie Public Library, 1521 Pineapple Ave, Melbourne, FL, 32935-6594. Tel: 321-255-4304. Fax: 321-255-4323. p. 463

Sibert, Michelle, Librn, Cumberland County Law Library, One Courthouse Sq, Carlisle, PA, 17013-3387. Tel: 717-240-6200. Fax: 717-240-6462. p. 2041

Sibley, Carol, Spec Coll Librn, Minnesota State University Moorhead, 1104 Seventh Ave S, Moorhead, MN, 56563. Tel: 218-477-2922. Fax: 218-477-5924. p. 1266

Sibley, Debbie, Dir, Libr Serv, Louisiana State University Health Sciences Center, 433 Bolivar St, Box B3-1, New Orleans, LA, 70112-2223. Tel: 504-568-7698. Fax: 504-568-7718. p. 961

Sibley, Donna, Asst Dir, Becker College, 61 Sever St, Worcester, MA, 01609. Tel: 508-373-9710. Fax: 508-849-5131. p. 1143

Sibley, Jean, Head, Ser, College of William & Mary in Virginia, Earl Gregg Swem Library, One Landrum Dr, Williamsburg, VA, 23187. Tel: 757-221-3103. Fax: 757-221-2635. p. 2502

Sibley, Jo, Circ, Plainfield-Guilford Township Public Library, 1120 Stafford Rd, Plainfield, IN, 46168-2230. Tel: 317-839-6602. Fax: 317-838-3805. p. 773

Sibley, Tina, Distance Educ, Arizona Western College & NAU Yuma Branch Campus, 2020 S Ave 8E, Yuma, AZ, 85366. Tel: 928-344-7777. Fax: 928-344-7751. p. 90

Sica, Deborah, Br Mgr, Harris County Public Library, Northwest, 11355 Regency Green Dr, Cypress, TX, 77429. Tel: 281-890-2665. Fax: 281-469-4718. p. 2336

Sicard, Paul, Head, Media Serv, Southwestern University, 1100 E University Ave, Georgetown, TX, 78626. Tel: 512-863-1561. Fax: 512-863-8198. p. 2327

Sicchio, Mary, Spec Coll & Archives Librn, Cape Cod Community College, 2240 Iyannough Rd, West Barnstable, MA, 02668-1599. Tel: 508-362-2131, Ext 4445. Fax: 508-375-4020. p. 1136

Sicchio, Mary E, Archivist, Falmouth Historical Society, Palmer Ave at the Village Green, Falmouth, MA, 02541. Tel: 508-548-4857. Fax: 508-540-0968. p. 1088

Sicignano, Charlie, Head, Tech Serv, Irvine Sullivan Ingram Library, University of West Georgia, 1601 Maple St, Carrollton, GA, 30118. Tel: 678-839-6498. Fax: 678-839-6511. p. 523

Siciliano, Sharon, Ref Serv, Ad, Burlington County Library, Pemberton Community Library, 16 Broadway, Browns Mills, NJ, 08015. Tel: 609-893-8262. Fax: 609-893-7547. p. 1543

Sickel, Joyce, Ref, Shook, Hardy & Bacon, 2555 Grand Blvd, 3rd Flr, Kansas City, MO, 64108-2613. Tel: 816-474-6550. Fax: 816-421-5547. p. 1341

Sickle, Ruth Van, Circ & Ref, Unicoi County Public Library, 201 Nolichucky Ave, Erwin, TN, 37650-1237. Tel: 423-743-6533. Fax: 423-743-0275. p. 2234

Siddiqui, Rashid, Syst Mgr, Carnegie Mellon University, Hunt Library, 4909 Frew St, Pittsburgh, PA, 15213-3890. Tel: 412-268-2446. Fax: 412-268-2793. p. 2123

Siddons, Jeff, Libr Mgr, Tulsa Community College Learning Resources Center, West Campus Library, 7505 W 41st St, Tulsa, OK, 74107-8633. Tel: 918-595-8010. Fax: 918-595-8016. p. 1983

Siders, David, Mgr, Public Library of Cincinnati & Hamilton County, Popular, South Bldg, 1st Flr, 800 Vine St, Cincinnati, OH, 45202-2009. Tel: 513-369-6919. Fax: 513-369-3123. p. 1872

Sides, Kate, Actg Librn, American Contract Bridge League, 2990 Airways Blvd, Memphis, TN, 38116-3847. Tel: 901-332-5586, Ext 1240. Fax: 901-398-7754. p. 2247

Sides, Patricia, Archivist, Willard Library of Evansville, 21 First Ave, Evansville, IN, 47710-1294. Tel: 812-425-4309. Fax: 812-421-9742. p. 739

Sides, Rachel, Dir, Guymon Public Library, 206 NW Fifth St, Guymon, OK, 73942. Tel: 580-338-7330. Fax: 580-338-2659. p. 1964

Sides-Renda, Rochelle, Librn, Birmingham Public Library, Springville Road, 1224 Springville Rd, Birmingham, AL, 35215. Tel: 205-226-4081. Fax: 205-856-0825. p. 7

Sidey, Diane, Asst Dir, Ch, Spalding Memorial Library, 724 S Main St, Athens, PA, 18810-1010. Tel: 570-888-7117. Fax: 570-882-9202. p. 2030

Sidford, Jill, Head Librn, Shearman & Sterling Library, 801 Pennsylvania Ave NW, Ste 900, Washington, DC, 20004-2634. Tel: 202-508-8055. Fax: 202-508-8100. p. 414

Sidie, Jennifer, Computer Serv, Ref Librn, Sr Serv, Clark Public Library, 303 Westfield Ave, Clark, NJ, 07066. Tel: 732-388-5999. Fax: 732-388-7866. p. 1479

Sidle, Michelle, Head, Tech Serv, Paulding County Carnegie Library, 205 S Main St, Paulding, OH, 45879-1492. Tel: 419-399-2032. Fax: 419-399-2114. p. 1928

Sidlek, Laura, Pub Serv Librn, Macomb Community College Libraries, Center Campus, C-Bldg, 44575 Garfield Rd, Clinton Township, MI, 48038-1139. Tel: 586-286-2106. Fax: 586-286-2002. p. 1234

Sidney, Peter, Asst VPres, Knowledge Mgt Coop Affairs, Cargill, Inc, 15407 McGinty Rd W, Wayzata, MN, 55391. Tel: 952-742-6498. Fax: 952-742-6062. p. 1287

Sidorick, Kim, Br Mgr, Mentor Public Library, Headlands, 4669 Corduroy Rd, Mentor, OH, 44060. Tel: 440-257-2000. p. 1917

Sidwell, Jean Louise, Dir, A T Still University of Health Sciences, Kirksville Campus, 800 W Jefferson St, Kirksville, MO, 63501. Tel: 660-626-2345. Fax: 660-626-2031, 660-626-2333. p. 1342

Siebelts, Barbara, Librn, First Lutheran Church Library, 327 S Dakota St, Sioux Falls, SD, 57104. Tel: 605-336-3734. Fax: 605-336-8370. p. 2218

Sieber, Richard, Asst Reader Serv Librn, Philadelphia Museum of Art Library, Ruth & Raymond G Perelman Bldg, 2525 Pennsylvania Ave, Philadelphia, PA, 19130. Tel: 215-684-7646. Fax: 215-236-0534. p. 2114

Siebers, Bruce, Head of Libr, Free Library of Philadelphia, Roxborough Branch, 6245 Ridge Ave, Philadelphia, PA, 19128-2630. Tel: 215-685-2550. Fax: 215-685-2551. p. 2109

Siebersma, Dan, State Librn, South Dakota State Library, 800 Governors Dr, Pierre, SD, 57501-2294. Tel: 605-773-3131. p. 2216

Siebert, Evelyn, Libr Mgr, La Glace Community Library, 9924 97 Ave, La Glace, AB, T0H 2J0, CANADA. Tel: 780-568-4696. Fax: 780-568-4707. p. 2708

Siebol, Mike, Curator, Yakima Valley Museum Archives, 2105 Tieton Dr, Yakima, WA, 98902. Tel: 509-248-0747. Fax: 509-453-4890. p. 2551

Sieck, Jane, Automation Serv, Dir, Ref Serv, Dunlap Public Library District, 302 S First St, Dunlap, IL, 61525. Tel: 309-243-5716. Fax: 309-243-5874. p. 638

Siecke, Elizabeth J, Col Librn, Dean, Ramapo College of New Jersey, 505 Ramapo Valley Rd, Mahwah, NJ, 07430-1623. Tel: 201-684-7575. p. 1498

Sieczkiewicz, Robert, Univ Archivist, Drexel University Libraries, Hagerty Library, 33rd & Market Sts, Philadelphia, PA, 19104-2875. Tel: 215-895-1757. Fax: 215-895-2070. p. 2105

Siedlecki, Armin, Cat, Emory University Libraries, Pitts Theology Library, Candler School of Theology, 505 S Kilgo Circle NE, Atlanta, GA, 30322-2810. Tel: 404-727-4166. Fax: 404-727-1219. p. 514

Siefken, Carol, Ch, Murrysville Community Library, 4130 Sardis Rd, Murrysville, PA, 15668-1120. Tel: 724-327-1102. Fax: 724-327-7142. p. 2094

Sieg, Julia, Dir, Marion County Public Library System, Headquarters-Ocala Public Library, 2720 E Silver Springs Blvd, Ocala, FL, 34470. Tel: 352-671-8551. Fax: 352-368-4545. p. 474

Sieg, Julia H, Dir, Marion County Public Library System, 2720 E Silver Springs Blvd, Ocala, FL, 34470. Tel: 352-671-8551. Fax: 352-368-4545. p. 474

Siegel, Adam, Actg Librn, University of California, Davis, Agricultural & Resource Economics Library, One Shields Ave, Davis, CA, 95616-8512. Tel: 530-752-1540. Fax: 530-752-5614. p. 139

Siegel, Bette, Govt Doc, The State Library of Massachusetts, State House, Rm 341, 24 Beacon St, Boston, MA, 02133. Tel: 617-727-6279. Fax: 617-727-5819. p. 1067

Siegel, Cheryl A, Librn, Vancouver Art Gallery Library, 750 Hornby St, Vancouver, BC, V6Z 2H7, CANADA. Tel: 604-662-4709. Fax: 604-682-1086. p. 2743

Siegel, Gretta, Sci Librn, Portland State University Library, 1875 SW Park Ave, Portland, OR, 97201-3220. Tel: 503-725-4708. Fax: 503-725-4524. p. 2014

Siegel, Jane Rogers, Bibliog Serv, Rare Bk Librn, Columbia University, Rare Book & Manuscript, Butler Library, 6th Flr E, 535 W 114th St, New York, NY, 10027. Tel: 212-854-8482. Fax: 212-854-1365. p. 1675

Siegel, John, Instruction Coordr, Ref Librn, University of Arkansas at Little Rock, 2801 S University Ave, Little Rock, AR, 72204. Tel: 501-569-3536. Fax: 501-569-3017. p. 107

Siegel, Karen, Chief Librn, Salem Township Public Library District, 115 W Main St, Yates City, IL, 61572. Tel: 309-358-1678. Fax: 309-358-1678. p. 722

Siegel, Lenny, Dir, Pacific Studies Center, 278A Hope St, Mountain View, CA, 94041. Tel: 650-969-1545. Fax: 650-961-8918. p. 192

Siegel, Leora O, Dir, Libr Serv, Lenhardt Library of the Chicago Botanic Garden, 1000 Lake Cook Rd, Glencoe, IL, 60022. Tel: 847-835-8202. Fax: 847-835-6885. p. 650

Siegel, Lori, Ref Librn, Washington University Libraries, George Warren Brown School of Social Work, One Brookings Dr, Campus Box 1196, Saint Louis, MO, 63130-4862. Tel: 314-935-4064. Fax: 314-935-8511. p. 1362

Siegel, Neil, Ref Librn, Truckee Meadows Community College, 7000 Dandini Blvd, Reno, NV, 89512-3999. Tel: 775-674-7608. Fax: 775-673-8231. p. 1432

Siegel, Robin, Librn, Centrastate Healthcare System Library, 901 W Main St, Freehold, NJ, 07728. Tel: 732-431-2000. p. 1487

Siegelman, Lynn, Dir, Aventis Pharmaceuticals Library, Rte 202-206, Bridgewater, NJ, 08807-0800. Tel: 908-231-2560. Fax: 908-231-2802. p. 1474

Siegelman, Lynn, Dir, Aventis Pharmaceuticals Library, Scientific Information & Library Services, 1041 Rt 202-206, Mail Stop: BRW K-303A, Bridgewater, NJ, 08807-6800. Tel: 908-231-4952. Fax: 908-231-2802. p. 1474

Siegfried, Cary, Dir, Arlington Public Library System, 101 E Abram St, MS 10-0100, Arlington, TX, 76010-1183. Tel: 817-459-6916. Fax: 817-459-6902. p. 2276

Siegmann, Starla, Dir of Libr Serv, Wisconsin Lutheran College Library, 8800 W Bluemound Rd, Milwaukee, WI, 53226. Tel: 414-443-8864. Fax: 414-443-8505. p. 2622

Siegner, Mary, Ch, Norelius Community Library, 1403 First Ave S, Denison, IA, 51442-2014. Tel: 712-263-9355. Fax: 712-263-8578. p. 808

Siegrist, Sarah, Asst Dir, Behringer-Crawford Museum, 1600 Montague Rd, Devou Park, Covington, KY, 41011. Tel: 859-491-4003. Fax: 859-491-4006. p. 910

Siem, Pauline, Dir, Faribault County Library Service, 120 S Main St, Ste C, Blue Earth, MN, 56013. Tel: 507-526-7182. p. 1242

Siemer, Barbara, Mgr, United States Navy, Naval Base Coronado Library, MWR Base Library, 2478 Munda Rd, San Diego, CA, 92155-5396. Tel: 619-437-3026. Fax: 619-437-3891. p. 238

Siemers, Jeff, Br Librn, Nicolet Area Technical College, 5364 College Dr, Rhinelander, WI, 54501. Tel: 715-356-6753. Fax: 715-365-4404. p. 2633

Siemers, Lynne, Dir, Washington Hospital Center, 110 Irving St NW, Rm 2A-21, Washington, DC, 20010-2975. Tel: 202-877-6221. Fax: 202-877-6757. p. 422

Siemon, Sherri, ILL Librn, West Perth Public Library, 105 Saint Andrew St, Mitchell, ON, N0K 1N0, CANADA. Tel: 519-348-9234. Fax: 519-348-4540. p. 2823

Siemons, Cynthia, Dir, Online Serv, Greene Public Library, 231 W Traer, Greene, IA, 50636-9406. Tel: 641-816-5642. Fax: 641-816-4838. p. 819

Sienczenko, Nina, Librn, New Kuban Education & Welfare Association, 228 Don Rd, Buena, NJ, 08310. Tel: 856-697-2255. Fax: 856-697-2255. p. 1476

Siepel, Marlene, Dir, Lordsburg-Hidalgo Library, 208 E Third St, Lordsburg, NM, 88045. Tel: 575-542-9646. Fax: 575-542-9646. p. 1559

Sieracki, Rita, Ref, Medical College of Wisconsin Libraries, Health Research Ctr, 3rd Flr, 8701 Watertown Plank Rd, Milwaukee, WI, 53226-0509. Tel: 414-955-8327. Fax: 414-955-6532. p. 2619

Sieradzki, Dorothy, Dir, Manchester-by-the-Sea Public Library, 15 Union St, Manchester-by-the-Sea, MA, 01944. Tel: 978-526-7711. Fax: 978-526-2018. p. 1102

Sierpe, Eino, Dr, Assoc Prof, Southern Connecticut State University, 501 Crescent St, New Haven, CT, 06515. Tel: 203-392-6883. Fax: 203-392-5780. p. 2963

Sierra, Carmen J, Ref Serv, Department of Veterans Affairs, Library Service 142D, Ten Calle Casia, San Juan, PR, 00921-3201. Tel: 787-641-7582, Ext 12163. Fax: 787-641-7582. p. 2676

Siers, Denise, Assoc Dir, Pub Serv, King County Library System, 960 Newport Way NW, Issaquah, WA, 98027. Tel: 425-482-9281. Fax: 425-369-3255. p. 2516

Sievers, Brooke, Head, Tech Serv, Addison Public Library, Four Friendship Plaza, Addison, IL, 60101. Tel: 630-458-3329. Fax: 630-543-6645. p. 587

Sievers, Pat, Asst Librn, Gladbrook Public Library, 301 Second St, Gladbrook, IA, 50635. Tel: 641-473-3236. Fax: 641-473-3236. p. 818

Sievers-Hill, Arlene Moore, Head, Acq, Case Western Reserve University, 11055 Euclid Ave, Cleveland, OH, 44106. Tel: 216-368-3328. Fax: 216-368-6950. p. 1876

Sievert, Charlotte, Med Librn, Summa Barberton Citizens Hospital, 155 Fifth St NE, Barberton, OH, 44203. Tel: 330-615-3104. Fax: 330-615-3103. p. 1857

Siftar, Tim, Ref Librn, Drexel University Libraries, Hagerty Library, 33rd & Market Sts, Philadelphia, PA, 19104-2875. Tel: 215-895-2762. Fax: 215-895-2070. p. 2105

Siga, Sharon, Dir, Strathcona County Library, 401 Festival Lane, Sherwood Park, AB, T8A 5P7, CANADA. Tel: 780-410-8600. Fax: 780-467-6861. p. 2716

Sigal, Ari, Dir, Catawba Valley Community College, 2550 Hwy 70 SE, Hickory, NC, 28602-9699. Tel: 828-327-7000, Ext 4229. Fax: 828-324-5130. p. 1801

Sigal, Myrna, Ch, West Nyack Free Library, 65 Strawtown Rd, West Nyack, NY, 10994. Tel: 845-358-6081. Fax: 845-358-4071. p. 1766

Sigalet, Jennifer, Pub Serv, Okanagan College Library, 1000 KLO Rd, Kelowna, BC, V1Y 4X8, CANADA. p. 2730

Sigl, Doris, Ser Librn, North Carolina Central University, 1801 Fayetteville St, Durham, NC, 27707-3129. Tel: 919-530-7317. Fax: 919-530-7612. p. 1789

Sigler, Kathi, Educ Librn, Saint John Fisher College, 3690 East Ave, Rochester, NY, 14618-3599. Tel: 585-385-8140. Fax: 585-385-8445. p. 1732

Signa, Simpson, Ch, Brunswick County Library, 109 W Moore St, Southport, NC, 28461. Tel: 910-457-6237. p. 1824

Sigsworth, Karen, Librn Supvr, Lorain Public Library System, North Ridgeville Branch, 35700 Bainbridge Rd, North Ridgeville, OH, 44039. Tel: 440-327-8326. Fax: 440-327-4443. p. 1911

Sigwald, John, Librn, Unger Memorial Library, 825 Austin St, Plainview, TX, 79072-7235. Tel: 806-296-1148. Fax: 806-291-1245. p. 2370

Siker, Nancy A, Asst Libr Dir, Milwaukee Institute of Art & Design Library, 273 E Erie St, Milwaukee, WI, 53202-6003. Tel: 414-847-3342. Fax: 414-291-8077. p. 2619

Sikes, Elaine, Br Mgr, East Central Georgia Regional Library, Burke County Library, 130 Hwy 24 S, Waynesboro, GA, 30830. Tel: 706-554-3277. Fax: 706-554-0313. p. 519

Sikes, Janice, Ref Librn, Atlanta-Fulton Public Library System, Auburn Avenue Research Library on African-American Culture & History, 101 Auburn Ave NE, Atlanta, GA, 30303. Tel: 404-730-4001, Ext 199. Fax: 404-730-5879. p. 511

Sikes, Mary, Br Mgr, Fort Worth Library, East Berry, 4300 E Berry St, Fort Worth, TX, 76105. Tel: 817-536-1945. Fax: 817-536-6253. p. 2322

Sikkink, Dianne, Librn, Spring Valley Public Library, 121 W Jefferson St, Spring Valley, MN, 55975-1244. Tel: 507-346-2100. Fax: 507-346-1908. p. 1285

Sikma, Renee, Assoc Librn, University of Wisconsin, 400 University Dr, West Bend, WI, 53095-3619. Tel: 262-335-5248. Fax: 262-335-5220. p. 2648

Sikora, David Allen, Br Head, Milwaukee Public Library, Atkinson, 1960 W Atkinson Ave, Milwaukee, WI, 53209. Tel: 414-286-3068. Fax: 414-286-8469. p. 2620

Sikora, Lisa, Exec Off Bus Mgr, Network of Illinois Learning Resources in Community Colleges, c/o Kishwaukee College, 21193 Malta Rd, Malta, IL, 60150. Tel: 608-523-4094. Fax: 608-523-4072. p. 2942

Sikora, Victoria, Br Mgr, Los Angeles Public Library System, Echo Park, 1410 W Temple St, Los Angeles, CA, 90026-5017. Tel: 213-250-7808. Fax: 213-580-3744. p. 173

Silberfarb, Stephen, Exec Dir, Jewish Community Relations Council of Minnesota & the Dakotas Library, 12 North 12th St, Ste 480, Minneapolis, MN, 55403-1331. Tel: 612-338-7816. Fax: 612-349-6569. p. 1260

Silberger, Kathryn, Head, Automation, Marist College, 3399 North Rd, Poughkeepsie, NY, 12601-1387. Tel: 845-575-3199. Fax: 845-575-3150. p. 1722

Silberman, Bonnie, Librn, Congregation Beth Emeth, 300 W Lea Blvd, Wilmington, DE, 19802. Tel: 302-764-2393. Fax: 302-764-2395. p. 387

Silberman, Carrie, Head, Children's Librn, The New York Society Library, 53 E 79th St, New York, NY, 10075. Tel: 212-288-6900, Ext 234. Fax: 212-744-5832. p. 1694

Silbersack, Barbara, Assoc Dir, Libr Operations, Thompson Hine LLP, 1400 Scripps Ctr, 312 Walnut St, Cincinnati, OH, 45202. Tel: 513-352-6528. Fax: 513-241-4771. p. 1873

Siler, Freddie, Tech Serv, Alabama State University, 915 S Jackson St, Montgomery, AL, 36104. Tel: 334-229-4106, 334-229-6890. Fax: 334-229-4911, 334-229-4940. p. 28

Siler, Sherry Daniel, Chief Librn, Lockheed Martin Missiles & Fire Control, 1701 W Marshall Dr, Grand Prairie, TX, 75051. Tel: 972-603-7155. Fax: 972-603-0182. p. 2329

Siles, Dorothy, Librn, Taylorville Public Library, 121 W Vine St, Taylorville, IL, 62568. Tel: 217-824-4736. Fax: 217-824-8921. p. 709

Silet, Scott, Dir, Libr & Media Serv, University of Wisconsin Colleges, 1500 University Dr, Waukesha, WI, 53188. Tel: 262-521-5473. Fax: 262-521-5116. p. 2645

Silfee, Jayne, Syst, Washington & Jefferson College Library, 60 S Lincoln St, Washington, PA, 15301. Tel: 724-223-6071. Fax: 724-223-5272. p. 2151

Silfen, Kate, Ref Librn, Boston College Libraries, Social Work Library, McGuinn Hall 038, 140 Commonwealth Ave, Chestnut Hill, MA, 02467-3810. Tel: 617-552-0792. Fax: 617-552-3199. p. 1081

Silic, Jeanette, Librn, Ref, Bingham McCutchen LLP, 150 Federal St, Boston, MA, 02110. Tel: 617-951-8313. Fax: 617-951-8543. p. 1055

Silk, Eleana, Librn, Saint Vladimir's Orthodox Theological Seminary Library, 575 Scarsdale Rd, Yonkers, NY, 10707-1699. Tel: 914-961-8313. Fax: 914-961-4507. p. 1771

Silliman, Nancy M, Dir, William K Kohrs Memorial Library, 501 Missouri Ave, Deer Lodge, MT, 59722-1152. Tel: 406-846-2622. Fax: 406-846-2622. p. 1377

Sillito, John, Curator, Spec Coll & Archives Librn, Weber State University, 2901 University Circle, Ogden, UT, 84408-2901. Tel: 801-626-6403. Fax: 801-626-7045. p. 2409

Sillius, Irene, Computer Support Spec, Sheridan College Library, 1430 Trafalgar Rd, Oakville, ON, L6H 2L1, CANADA. Tel: 905-845-9430. Fax: 905-815-4123. p. 2826

Sillius, Irene, Ref, Sheridan College Library, Davis Campus, 7899 McLaughlin Rd, Brampton, ON, L6V 1G6, CANADA. Tel: 905-459-7533. Fax: 905-874-4345. p. 2826

Sills, Diana, Ch, Bellwood Public Library, 600 Bohland Ave, Bellwood, IL, 60104-1896. Tel: 708-547-7393. Fax: 708-547-9352. p. 593

Silva, Carolyn, Acq, Taunton Public Library, 12 Pleasant St, Taunton, MA, 02780. Tel: 508-821-1410. Fax: 508-821-1414. p. 1130

Silva, Ed, Head, Doc Serv, University of Nevada, Las Vegas Libraries, 4505 Maryland Pkwy, Box 457001, Las Vegas, NV, 89154-7001. Tel: 702-895-2286. Fax: 702-895-2287. p. 1431

Silva, Elizabeth, Librn, Ohlone College, 43600 Mission Blvd, Fremont, CA, 94539. Tel: 510-659-6000, Ext 7484. Fax: 510-659-6265. p. 149

Silva, Erin, Doc Delivery & E-Reserves, University of Nevada-Reno, 1664 N Virginia St, Mailstop 0322, Reno, NV, 89557-0322. Tel: 775-682-5654. Fax: 775-784-4529. p. 1433

Silva, Judith, Archivist, Art Librn, Slippery Rock University of Pennsylvania, Slippery Rock, PA, 16057-9989. Tel: 724-738-2658. Fax: 724-738-2661. p. 2140

Silva, Kimberly, Instrul Design Consult, Mitchell College Library, 437 Pequot Ave, New London, CT, 06320-4498. Tel: 860-701-5150, Ext 5450. Fax: 860-701-5099. p. 360

Silva, Kimberly, Adult Serv, Circ, Fall River Public Library, 104 N Main St, Fall River, MA, 02720. Tel: 508-324-2700. Fax: 508-324-2707. p. 1088

Silva, Reagan, Dir, Clarendon College Library, 1122 College Dr, Clarendon, TX, 79226. Tel: 806-874-4813. Fax: 806-874-5080. p. 2297

Silva, Robin, Librn, Portsmouth Athenaeum, Six-Seven Market Sq, Portsmouth, NH, 03821. Tel: 603-431-2538. Fax: 603-431-7180. p. 1463

Silva, Sandra, Br Mgr, Riverside County Library System, Romoland Library, 26000 Briggs Rd, Romoland, CA, 92585. Tel: 951-325-2090. Fax: 951-926-7989. p. 218

Silva-Ortiz, Aidy, Libr Tech, Orlando Health, 1414 Kuhl Ave, MP 28, Orlando, FL, 32806-2134. Tel: 321-841-5454. Fax: 321-843-6825. p. 477

Silvan, Vicki, Librn, Chouteau County Library, Big Sandy Branch, 230 First St N, Big Sandy, MT, 59520. Tel: 406-378-2161. p. 1379

Silver, Cathy, Head Librn, Spruce Pine Public Library, 142 Walnut Ave, Spruce Pine, NC, 28777. Tel: 828-765-4673. p. 1825

Silver, Cheryl, Tech Serv, New York Medical College, Basic Science Bldg, 95 Grasslands Rd, Valhalla, NY, 10595. Tel: 914-594-4205. Fax: 914-594-3171. p. 1760

Silver, Howard, Head Librn, Massachusetts Institute of Technology Libraries, Barker Engineering, Bldg 10-500, 77 Massachusetts Ave, Cambridge, MA, 02139-4307. Tel: 617-253-9319. Fax: 617-258-5623. p. 1077

Silver, Howard, Head Librn, Massachusetts Institute of Technology Libraries, Science, Bldg 14S-134, 77 Massachusetts Ave, Cambridge, MA, 02139-4307. Tel: 617-253-9319. Fax: 617-253-6365. p. 1078

Silver, Ilana, Ch Serv Librn, West Babylon Public Library, 211 Rte 109, West Babylon, NY, 11704. Tel: 631-669-5445. Fax: 631-669-6539. p. 1765

Silver, Joel, Assoc Dir, Indiana University Bloomington, Lilly Library Rare Books & Manuscripts, 1200 E Seventh St, Bloomington, IN, 47405-5500. Tel: 812-855-2452. Fax: 812-855-3143. p. 728

Silver, Kaye, Mgr, Bonneville Power Administration Library - 1, 905 NE 11th Ave, Portland, OR, 97232. Tel: 503-230-4171. Fax: 503-230-5911. p. 2010

Silver, Marianne, Head, Adult Serv, Interim Dir, New City Free Library, 220 N Main St, New City, NY, 10956. Tel: 845-634-4997. p. 1664

Silver, Mary, Br Mgr, Atlanta-Fulton Public Library System, Peachtree Library, 1315 Peachtree St NE, Atlanta, GA, 30309. Tel: 404-885-7830. Fax: 404-855-7833. p. 512

Silver, Steve, Dir, Northwest Christian University, 1188 Kincade, Eugene, OR, 97401. Tel: 541-684-7237. Fax: 541-684-7307. p. 1997

Silver, Victoria, Head, Govt Doc, North Carolina Central University, 1801 Fayetteville St, Durham, NC, 27707-3129. Tel: 919-530-7307. Fax: 919-530-7612. p. 1789

Silver, Wendy, Br Mgr, Greenwich Library, Cos Cob Branch, Five Sinawoy Rd, Cos Cob, CT, 06807-2701. Tel: 203-622-6883. Fax: 203-661-5315. p. 342

Silvera, Vicki, Head, Spec Coll, Univ Archivist, Florida International University, 11200 SW Eighth St, Miami, FL, 33199. Tel: 305-348-3136. Fax: 305-348-4739. p. 465

Silverberg, Jean, Br Mgr, Dakota County Library System, Inver Glen, 8098 Blaine Ave, Inver Grove Heights, MN, 55076. Tel: 651-554-6840. Fax: 651-552-7522. p. 1249

Silverberg, Mary, Mgr, Saint-Gobain Abrasives Library, One New Bond St, Worcester, MA, 01606-2614. Tel: 508-795-2001. Fax: 508-795-5755. p. 1144

Silveria, Janie B, Coordr of Ref Serv, California State University-Monterey Bay, 100 Campus Ctr, Seaside, CA, 93955-8001. Tel: 831-582-3727. Fax: 831-582-3875. p. 268

Silverman, Alan, Dir, Easttown Library & Information Center, 720 First Ave, Berwyn, PA, 19312-1769. Tel: 610-644-0138. Fax: 610-251-9739. p. 2033

Silverman, Brian, In Charge, Box Butte County Law Library, Courthouse, 515 Box Butte Ave, Ste 302, Alliance, NE, 69301. Tel: 308-762-5354. Fax: 308-762-7703. p. 1391

Silverman, Carol, Asst Dir, Whelden Memorial Library, 2401 Meetinghouse Way, West Barnstable, MA, 02668-1403. Tel: 508-362-2262. Fax: 508-362-1344. p. 1136

Silverman, David, Pres, Charles E Stevens American Atheist Library & Archives, Inc, 225 Cristiani St, Cranford, NJ, 07016-3214. Tel: 908-276-7300. Fax: 908-276-7402. p. 1480

Silverman, Eleanor, Librn, East Orange General Hospital Medical Library, 300 Central Ave, East Orange, NJ, 07019. Tel: 973-395-4112. Fax: 973-266-8435. p. 1482

Silverman, Eleanor, Librn, Columbus Hospital, 495 N 13th St, Newark, NJ, 07107. Tel: 973-268-1400, Ext 2074. Fax: 973-268-1542. p. 1510

Silverman, Eleanor, Librn, Chilton Memorial Hospital, 97 West Pkwy, Pompton Plains, NJ, 07444. Tel: 973-831-5058. Fax: 973-831-5041. p. 1521

Silverman, Evelyn, Access Serv, ILL, Queens College, Benjamin S Rosenthal Library, 65-30 Kissena Blvd, Flushing, NY, 11367-0904. Tel: 718-997-3700. Fax: 718-997-3753. p. 1623

Silverman, Francine, Librn, Kennedy Memorial Hospitals-University Medical Center, 2201 Chapel Ave W, Cherry Hill, NJ, 08002-2048. Tel: 856-488-6500, 856-488-6865. Fax: 856-488-6606. p. 1478

Silverman, Judy, Head, Coll Cat, Centre Canadien d'Architecture/Canadian Centre for Architecture, 1920 rue Baile, Montreal, QC, H3H 2S6, CANADA. Tel: 514-939-7000. Fax: 514-939-7020. p. 2892

Silverman, Lisa, Dir, Sinai Temple, 10400 Wilshire Blvd, Los Angeles, CA, 90024. Tel: 310-474-1518, 310-481-3218. Fax: 310-474-6801. p. 177

Silverman, Reini, Librn, Temple Beth El, Congegation Sons of Israel & David, 70 Orchard Ave, Providence, RI, 02906. Tel: 401-331-6070. Fax: 401-521-6012. p. 2175

Silverman, Susan R, Head, Pub Serv, Winthrop University, 824 Oakland Ave, Rock Hill, SC, 29733. Tel: 803-323-2306. Fax: 803-323-2215. p. 2203

Silvernail, Janet, Automation Syst Coordr, Mobile Public Library, 700 Government St, Mobile, AL, 36602. Tel: 251-208-7106. Fax: 251-208-5865. p. 25

Silvers, Stephanie, Librn, Harmony Public Library, 225 Third Ave SW, Harmony, MN, 55939-6635. Tel: 507-886-8133. Fax: 507-886-1433. p. 1253

Silversides, Brock, Dir, University of Toronto Libraries, Media Commons, 130 St George St, Toronto, ON, M5S 1A5, CANADA. Tel: 416-978-7119. Fax: 416-978-8707. p. 2866

Silversides, Sabrina, Librn, Southeast Regional Library, Glenavon Branch, 311 Railway Ave, Glenavon, SK, S0G 1Y0, CANADA. Tel: 306-429-2180. p. 2929

Silverstein, Bruce, Electronic Res, Patchogue-Medford Library, 54-60 E Main St, Patchogue, NY, 11772. Tel: 631-654-4700, Ext 236. Fax: 631-289-3999. p. 1715

Silverstein, Linda, ILL, Syst Librn, Monmouth University, 400 Cedar Ave, West Long Branch, NJ, 07764. Tel: 732-571-3450, Ext 7521. Fax: 732-263-5124. p. 1541

Silverstine, Stanley, Head, Circ, Gulf Beaches Public Library, 200 Municipal Dr, Madeira Beach, FL, 33708. Tel: 727-391-2828. Fax: 727-399-2840. p. 462

Silverthorn, Janet, Br Mgr, Chippewa River District Library, Coe Township, 308 W Wright Ave, Shepherd, MI, 48883. Tel: 989-828-6801. Fax: 989-828-6801. p. 1211

Silverthorn, Karen, Circ Supvr, Atlantic Union College, 138 Main St, South Lancaster, MA, 01561. Tel: 978-368-2450. Fax: 978-368-2456. p. 1125

Silvestrini-Ruiz, Maria M, Info Literacy Librn, Inter-American University of Puerto Rico, 104 Parque Industrial Turpeaux, Rd 1, Mercedita, PR, 00715-1602. Tel: 787-284-1912. Fax: 787-841-0103. p. 2674

Silvey, Sandra, Br Mgr, Harris County Public Library, Katherine Tyra Branch, 16719 Clay Rd, Houston, TX, 77084. Tel: 281-550-0885. Fax: 281-550-3304. p. 2336

Silvia, Heather, Dir, North Bridgton Public Library, 113 Waterford Rd, North Bridgton, ME, 04057. Tel: 207-647-8563. p. 993

Silvia, Loretta, Head, Pub Serv, Joint Forces Staff College Library, 7800 Hampton Blvd, Norfolk, VA, 23511-1702. Tel: 757-443-6402. Fax: 757-443-6047. p. 2481

Silvis, Gregg, Assoc Univ Librn, Info Tech & Digital Initiatives, University of Delaware Library, 181 S College Ave, Newark, DE, 19717-5267. Tel: 302-831-2231. Fax: 302-831-1046. p. 386

Sim, Patrick, Librn, American Society of Anesthesiologists, 520 N Northwest Hwy, Park Ridge, IL, 60068-2573. Tel: 847-825-5586. Fax: 847-825-1692. p. 688

Simak, Ellen, Chief Curator, Hunter Museum of Art, Ten Bluff View, Chattanooga, TN, 37403-1197. Tel: 423-267-0968. Fax: 423-267-9844. p. 2227

Simard, Fabienne, Ref, Cegep de Jonquiere, 2505 rue St Hubert, Jonquiere, QC, G7X 7W2, CANADA. Tel: 418-547-2191. Fax: 418-547-0917. p. 2884

Simard, Guylaine, Libr Serv Mgr, Mediatheque, Institut de Tourisme et d'Hotellerie du Quebec, 3535, rue Saint-Denis, Local 1.97, Montreal, QC, H2X 3P1, CANADA. Tel: 514-282-5141. Fax: 514-282-5105. p. 2899

Simard, Jim, Head, Historical Coll, Librn, Alaska State Library, 333 Willoughby Ave, State Office Bldg, 8th Flr, Juneau, AK, 99801. Tel: 907-465-2910. Fax: 907-465-2151. p. 49

Simard, Jim, Hist Coll Librn, Alaska State Library, Alaska Historical Collections, 333 Willoughby Ave, Juneau, AK, 99801. Tel: 907-465-2926. Fax: 907-465-2990. p. 50

Simard, Katy, Prof, College de Maisonneuve, 3800, rue Sherbrooke Est, Montreal, QC, H1X 2A2, CANADA. Tel: 514-254-7131. Fax: 514-251-9741. p. 2978

Simard-Vermette, Helen, Libr Tech, Canada Agriculture & Agri-Food Canada, 3600 Blvd Casavant W, Saint-Hyacinthe, QC, J2S 8E3, CANADA. Tel: 450-768-3247, 450-773-1105. Fax: 450-773-8461. p. 2910

Simco, Kristie, Tech Serv Supvr, East Fishkill Public Library District, 348 Rte 376, Hopewell Junction, NY, 12533-6075. Tel: 845-221-9943, Ext 222. Fax: 845-226-1404. p. 1637

Simenson, Laurie, Sr Librn, Hennepin County Library, Augsburg Park, 7100 Nicollet Ave S, Richfield, MN, 55423-3117. Tel: 612-543-6203. Fax: 612-543-6202. p. 1263

Simeon, Cindy, Dir, Raymond A Whitwer Tilden Public Library, 202 S Center St, Tilden, NE, 68781. Tel: 402-368-5306. Fax: 402-368-5515. p. 1421

Simeone, Janet, Tech Serv, Sadie Pope Dowdell Library of South Amboy, 100 Harold G Hoffman Plaza, South Amboy, NJ, 08879. Tel: 732-721-6060. Fax: 732-721-1054. p. 1530

Simerl, Nancy, Librn, Sherburne Public Library, Two E State St, Sherburne, NY, 13460. Tel: 607-674-4242. Fax: 607-674-4242. p. 1743

Simes, Sharon, Dir, North Seattle Community College, 9600 College Way N, Seattle, WA, 98103. Tel: 206-527-3607. Fax: 206-527-3614. p. 2529

Simiele, Thomas, Dep Dir, Euclid Public Library, 631 E 222nd St, Euclid, OH, 44123-2091. Tel: 216-261-5300, Ext 116. Fax: 216-261-0575. p. 1898

Simmons, Lindsay, Evening Supvr, University of Wisconsin-Green Bay, 2420 Nicolet Dr, Green Bay, WI, 54311-7001. Tel: 920-465-2333. Fax: 920-465-2136. p. 2596

Simmerman, Rich, Syst Mgr, Dayton Metro Library, 215 E Third St, Dayton, OH, 45402-2103. Tel: 937-463-2665. Fax: 937-496-4300. p. 1892

Simmonds, Patience, Bibliog Instr, Penn State Erie, 4951 College Dr, Erie, PA, 16563-4115. Tel: 814-898-6106. Fax: 814-898-6350. p. 2056

Simmonds, Patricia, Ch, Piscataway Township Free Public Library, 500 Hoes Lane, Piscataway, NJ, 08854. Tel: 732-463-1633. Fax: 732-463-9022. p. 1520

Simmons, Andrea, Dir, Ballston Spa Public Library, 21 Milton Ave, Ballston Spa, NY, 12020. Tel: 518-885-5022. p. 1577

Simmons, Angelique, Family & Youth Serv Coordr, Newport News Public Library System, 700 Town Center Dr, Ste 300, Newport News, VA, 23606. Tel: 757-926-1350. Fax: 757-926-1365. p. 2480

Simmons, Beth, Mgr, Trion Public Library, 15 Bulldog Blvd, Trion, GA, 30753. Tel: 706-734-7594. Fax: 706-734-7504. p. 554

Simmons, Beverly, Ref & Instruction Librn, University of Tennessee at Chattanooga Library, 615 McCallie Ave, Dept 6456, Chattanooga, TN, 37403-2598. Tel: 423-425-4501. Fax: 423-425-4775. p. 2228

Simmons, Carolyn, Librn, Newport Public Library, 210 Howard Blvd, Newport, NC, 28570. Tel: 252-223-5108. Fax: 252-223-6116. p. 1813

Simmons, Celestia, Cluster Coordr, Hartford Public Library, Albany, 1250 Albany Ave, Hartford, CT, 06112. Tel: 860-695-7380. Fax: 860-722-6902. p. 346

Simmons, Cindy, Librn, North Central Regional Library, Manson Community, 80 Wapato Way, Manson, WA, 98831-9210. Tel: 509-687-3420. Fax: 509-687-3420. p. 2549

Simmons, Eileen D, Dir, Everett Public Library, 2702 Hoyt Ave, Everett, WA, 98201-3556. Tel: 425-257-8001. Fax: 425-257-8017. p. 2515

Simmons, Elizabeth, Ch, Richmond Heights Memorial Library, 8001 Dale Ave, Richmond Heights, MO, 63117. Tel: 314-645-6202. Fax: 314-781-3434. p. 1350

Simmons, Ellen, Govt Doc, Per, Hardin-Simmons University, 2341 Hickory St, Abilene, TX, 79698. Tel: 325-670-1236. Fax: 325-677-8351. p. 2272

Simmons, Ford, Ref & Info Serv Coordr, Webmaster, Sumter County Library, 111 N Harvin St, Sumter, SC, 29150. Tel: 803-773-7273. Fax: 803-773-4875. p. 2206

Simmons, Frances, Librn, Cochise County Law Library, 100 Quality Hill, Bisbee, AZ, 85603. Tel: 520-432-8513. Fax: 520-432-2630. p. 58

Simmons, Geraldine, Dir, Munford-Tipton Memorial Library, 87 College St, Munford, TN, 38058-6412. Tel: 901-837-2665. p. 2254

Simmons, Grace, Tech Serv Mgr, Shreve Memorial Library, 424 Texas St, Shreveport, LA, 71101. Tel: 318-226-4975. Fax: 318-226-4780. p. 969

Simmons, Gwen, Media Spec, Spec Coll, College of the Ozarks, Lyons Memorial Library, One Opportunity Ave, Point Lookout, MO, 65726. Tel: 417-690-3411. Fax: 417-334-3085. p. 1349

Simmons, Henry, Librn Supvr, Lakeland Public Library, Larry R Jackson Branch, 1700 N Florida Ave, Lakeland, FL, 33805. Tel: 863-834-4288. Fax: 863-834-4327. p. 459

Simmons, Henry, Dir, Union-PSCE, 3401 Brook Rd, Richmond, VA, 23227. Tel: 804-254-8045. Fax: 804-254-8060. p. 2490

Simmons, Jamie, Tech Serv Dir, Glen Ellyn Public Library, 400 Duane St, Glen Ellyn, IL, 60137-4508. Tel: 630-469-0879. Fax: 630-469-1086. p. 650

Simmons, Jamie, Archivist, Curator, Texarkana Museums System, 219 N State Line Ave, Texarkana, TX, 75501-5606. Tel: 903-793-4831. Fax: 903-793-7108. p. 2392

Simmons, John, Exec Dir, Rhode Island Public Expenditure Council Library, 86 Weybosset St, Providence, RI, 02903. Tel: 401-521-6320. Fax: 401-751-1915. p. 2174

Simmons, Karen, Asst Dir, Douglas County Library, 720 Fillmore St, Alexandria, MN, 56308-1763. Tel: 320-762-3014. Fax: 320-762-3036. p. 1239

Simmons, Kitty, Dir, La Sierra University Library, 4500 Riverwalk Pkwy, Riverside, CA, 92505-3344. Tel: 951-785-2397. Fax: 951-785-2445. p. 217

Simmons, Marianne, Head, Ref & Ser, Saint John Fisher College, 3690 East Ave, Rochester, NY, 14618-3599. Tel: 585-385-7399. Fax: 585-385-8445. p. 1732

Simmons, Marilyn, ILL, Jaffrey Public Library, 38 Main St, Jaffrey, NH, 03452-1196. Tel: 603-532-7301. Fax: 603-532-7301. p. 1452

Simmons, Mark, Librn, Phoenix VA Health Care System, 650 E Indian School Rd, Phoenix, AZ, 85012. Tel: 602-222-6411. Fax: 602-222-6472. p. 77

Simmons, Meriam D, Tech Serv, United States Army, Fort Stewart Main Post Library, 316 Lindquist Rd, Fort Stewart, GA, 31314-5126. Tel: 912-767-2260, 912-767-2828. Fax: 912-767-3794. p. 533

Simmons, Michael, Mgr, Libr Serv, Sparrow Health System, 1200 E Michigan Ave, Ste 111, Lansing, MI, 48912. Tel: 517-364-5660. Fax: 517-364-5665. p. 1202

Simmons, Michael, Ref Serv, Greensboro College, 815 W Market St, Greensboro, NC, 27401. Tel: 336-272-7102, Ext 378. Fax: 336-217-7233. p. 1796

Simmons, Michele, In Charge, National Park Service, 103 Monastery, Sitka, AK, 99835-7603. Tel: 907-747-6281. Fax: 907-747-5938. p. 53

Simmons, Nancy, Commun Partnerships Coordr, Larch Corrections Center Library, 15314 NE Dole Valley Rd, Yacolt, WA, 98765. Tel: 360-260-6300, Ext 215. Fax: 360-686-3892. p. 2550

Simmons, Nathan, Law Librn, Webmaster, Railway Mail Service Library, Inc, 117 E Main St, Boyce, VA, 22620-9639. Tel: 540-837-9090. p. 2452

Simmons, Rand, Actg State Librn, Washington State Library, 6880 Capitol Blvd S, Tumwater, WA, 98501-5513. Tel: 360-570-5585. Fax: 360-586-7575. p. 2544

Simmons, Rebecca, Archivist, Rochester Institute of Technology, 90 Lomb Memorial Dr, Rochester, NY, 14623-5604. Tel: 585-475-2557. Fax: 585-475-7007. p. 1731

Simmons, Sherrie, Head Librn, Charlotte Library, 115 Ferry Rd, Charlotte, VT, 05445. Tel: 802-425-3864. p. 2421

Simmons, Shirley, Br Supvr, Jackson/Hinds Library System, Medgar Evers Boulevard Library, 4215 Medgar Evers Blvd, Jackson, MS, 39213-5210. Tel: 601-982-2867. Fax: 601-982-2598. p. 1303

Simmons, Simmona, Serv Develop & Spec Projects Librn, University of Maryland, Baltimore County, 1000 Hilltop Circle, Baltimore, MD, 21250. Tel: 410-455-2356. p. 1018

Simmons, Susan, Mgr, Ref Serv, Mamie Doud Eisenhower Public Library, Three Community Park Rd, Broomfield, CO, 80020-3781. Tel: 720-887-2367. Fax: 720-887-1384. p. 292

Simmons, Teresa, Cat, Kettering College, 3737 Southern Blvd, Kettering, OH, 45429-1299. Tel: 937-395-8053, Ext 4. Fax: 937-395-8861. p. 1907

Simmons, Tom, Asst Dir, Los Lunas Public Library, 460 Main St NE, Los Lunas, NM, 87031. Tel: 505-839-3850. Fax: 505-352-3582. p. 1559

Simmons, Toni, Ch, Zula Bryant Wylie Public Library, 225 Cedar St, Cedar Hill, TX, 75104-2655. Tel: 972-291-7323, Ext 1312. Fax: 972-291-5361. p. 2296

Simmons-Henry, Linda, Dir, Spec Coll & Info Tech, Saint Augustine's College, 1315 Oakwood Ave, Raleigh, NC, 27610-2298. Tel: 919-516-4145. Fax: 919-516-4758. p. 1817

Simms, Christine, Doc, Tech Spec, Dartmouth College Library, Feldberg Business Administration & Engineering Library, 6193 Murdough Ctr, Hanover, NH, 03755-3560. Tel: 603-646-2354. Fax: 603-646-2384. p. 1450

Simms, Gail, Libr Tech, Atlantic Provinces Special Education Authority Library, 5940 South St, Halifax, NS, B3H 1S6, CANADA. Tel: 902-424-4614. Fax: 902-424-3808. p. 2780

Simms, Grace, Computer Librn, Samford University Library, Lucille Stewart Beeson Law Library, 800 Lakeshore Dr, Birmingham, AL, 35229. Tel: 205-726-2714. Fax: 205-726-2644. p. 9

Simms, Kelly, Cat, Laredo Public Library, 1120 E Calton Rd, Laredo, TX, 78041. Tel: 956-795-2400. Fax: 956-795-2403. p. 2354

Simms, Lisa, In Charge, Merced County Library, Winton Branch, 7057 W Walnut, Winton, CA, 95388. Tel: 209-358-3651. p. 186

Simms, Mary, Librn, Pleasant Grove Christian Church Library, 1324 Pleasant Dr, Dallas, TX, 75217. Tel: 214-391-3159. Fax: 214-391-3150. p. 2309

Simms, Sheree, Br Mgr, Putnam County Library System, Melrose Public Library, 312 Wynnwood Ave, Melrose, FL, 32666. Tel: 352-475-3382. Fax: 352-475-5779. p. 478

Simon, Alan C, Assoc Dir, HSLC/Access PA, 3600 Market St, Ste 550, Philadelphia, PA, 19104-2646. Tel: 215-222-1532. Fax: 215-222-0416. p. 2954

Simon, Aurelia, Ref, Delaware Technical & Community College, 400 Stanton-Christiana Rd, Newark, DE, 19713-2197. Tel: 302-454-3939. Fax: 302-453-3079. p. 385

Simon, Bashe, Dir of Libr, Touro College Libraries, 43 W 23rd St, Fifth Fl, New York, NY, 10010. Tel: 718-252-7800, Ext 226. Fax: 212-627-3696. p. 1701

Simon, Eva, Librn, California Department of Corrections Library System, Richard J Donovan Correctional Facility at Rock Mountain, 480 Alta Rd, San Diego, CA, 92179. Tel: 619-661-6500, Ext 5590. Fax: 619-661-7875. p. 221

Simon, Florence, Dir, The Canadian Zionist Federation, One Carre Cummings Sq, Ste 206, 5151 Cote St Catherine, Montreal, QC, H3W 1M6, CANADA. Tel: 514-739-7300, Ext 3100. Fax: 514-739-9412. p. 2892

Simon, Gary, Dir of Tech Serv, Public Library of Youngstown & Mahoning County, 305 Wick Ave, Youngstown, OH, 44503-1079. Tel: 330-744-8636. Fax: 330-744-3355. p. 1952

Simon, Heather, Dir, United Hospital Center, Three Hospital Plaza, Clarksburg, WV, 26302. Tel: 304-624-2230. Fax: 304-624-2358. p. 2557

Simon, Heidi, Ser, Harvard Library, Gordon McKay Library, School of Engineering & Applied Sciences, Pierce Hall, 29 Oxford St, Cambridge, MA, 02138. Tel: 617-495-2836. Fax: 617-495-9837. p. 1076

Simon, Jack, Presv/Exhibit Tech, Lloyd Library & Museum, 917 Plum St, Cincinnati, OH, 45202. Tel: 513-721-3707. Fax: 513-721-6575. p. 1870

Simon, Leslie, Dir, Archives, National Archives & Records Administration, 900 Market St, Philadelphia, PA, 19107-4292. Tel: 215-606-0100. Fax: 215-606-0116. p. 2113

Simon, Mae, Br Mgr, Cameron Parish Library, Hackberry Branch, 983 Main St, Hackberry, LA, 70645. Tel: 337-762-3978. Fax: 337-762-4115. p. 946

Simon, Margaret, Libr Supvr-Popular Libr, Saint James Parish Library, Vacherie Library, 2593 Hwy 20, Vacherie, LA, 70090-5601. Tel: 225-265-9066. Fax: 225-265-4691. p. 955

Simon, Margaret, Libr Supvr-Popular Libr, St James Parish Library, 1879 W Main St, Lutcher, LA, 70071-5140. Tel: 225-869-3618. Fax: 225-869-8435. p. 955

Simon, Mary, Asst Dir, Auburn Public Library, 749 E Thach Ave, Auburn, AL, 36830. Tel: 334-501-3190. p. 5

Simon, Mary, Mgr, Libr Serv, Prevention First Inc, 600 W Chicago Ave, Ste 200, Chicago, IL, 60654. Tel: 312-988-4646. Fax: 312-988-7096. p. 622

Simon, Mary, Libr Mgr, Lura Lynn Ryan Prevention Research Library, 33 W Grand Ave, Ste 300, Chicago, IL, 60654. Tel: 312-988-4646, Ext 252. Fax: 312-988-7096. p. 623

Simon, Meryl, Librn, Aesthetic Realism Foundation, Eli Siegel Collection, 141 Greene St, New York, NY, 10012-3201. Tel: 212-777-4490. Fax: 212-777-4426. p. 1667

Simon, Michael, Asst Dir, Long Beach Public Library, 111 W Park Ave, Long Beach, NY, 11561-3326. Tel: 516-432-7201. Fax: 516-889-4641. p. 1654

Simon, Michael, AV, Long Beach Public Library, 111 W Park Ave, Long Beach, NY, 11561-3326. Tel: 516-432-7201. Fax: 516-889-4641. p. 1654

Simon, Mindi, Mgr, Automation & Continuing Educ, Lee County Library System, 2345 Union St, Fort Myers, FL, 33901-3917. Tel: 239-533-4810. Fax: 239-485-1100. p. 445

Simon, Ralph R, Dr, Librn, Temple on the Heights, 27501 Fairmount Blvd, Pepper Pike, OH, 44124. Tel: 216-831-6555. Fax: 216-831-4599. p. 1929

Simon, Robert, Dir, Canton Public Library, 40 Dyer Ave, Canton, CT, 06019. Tel: 860-693-5800. Fax: 860-693-5804. p. 333

Simon, Rose, Dr, Dir, Salem College, 626 S Church St, Winston-Salem, NC, 27108. Tel: 336-917-5421. Fax: 336-917-5339. p. 1833

Simon, Rubi, Libr Dir, Burnham Memorial Library, 898 Main St, Colchester, VT, 05446. Tel: 802-879-7576. Fax: 802-879-5079. p. 2422

Simon, Stephanie, Pub Info Officer, Albany Public Library, 161 Washington Ave, Albany, NY, 12210. Tel: 518-427-4344. Fax: 518-449-3386. p. 1568

Simon, Stephen E, Archivist, Simsbury Historical Society Archives, 800 Hopmeadow St, Simsbury, CT, 06070. Tel: 860-658-2500. Fax: 860-651-4354. p. 367

Simon, Tracey, Dir, Floral Park Public Library, 17 Caroline Pl, Floral Park, NY, 11001. Tel: 516-326-6330. Fax: 516-437-6959. p. 1622

Simon, Tracey, Asst Dir, Head, Ref, Lynbrook Public Library, 56 Eldert St, Lynbrook, NY, 11563. Tel: 516-599-8630. Fax: 516-596-1312. p. 1655

Simonds, Mike, Chief Exec Officer, Bibliomation, 32 Crest Rd, Middlebury, CT, 06762. Tel: 203-577-4070, Ext 106. Fax: 203-577-4077. p. 2939

Simonds, Patricia, ILL, Ser, Florida State University Libraries, College of Law Library, 425 W Jefferson St, Tallahassee, FL, 32306. Tel: 850-644-4578. Fax: 850-644-5216. p. 494

Simone, Heather, Acq, Roger Williams University, Ten Metacom Ave, Bristol, RI, 02809-5171. Tel: 401-254-4537. Fax: 401-254-4543. p. 2163

Simoneau, Lorraine, Dir, Kurth Memorial Library, 706 S Raguet St, Lufkin, TX, 75904. Tel: 936-630-0560. Fax: 936-639-2487. p. 2358

Simoneaux, Julie, Ser, Iberville Parish Library, 24605 J Gerald Berret Blvd, Plaquemine, LA, 70764. Tel: 225-687-2520, 225-687-4397. Fax: 225-687-9719. p. 965

Simonelli, Marie, Acq, Info Serv, Northwestern Regional Library, 111 N Front St, Elkin, NC, 28621. Tel: 336-835-4894. Fax: 336-526-2270. p. 1791

Simonetta, Kathleen, Ch, Indian Trails Public Library District, 355 S Schoenbeck Rd, Wheeling, IL, 60090. Tel: 847-459-4100. Fax: 847-459-4760. p. 719

Simonovic, Vesna, Commun Libr Mgr, Queens Borough Public Library, Ridgewood Community Library, 20-12 Madison St, Ridgewood, NY, 11385. Tel: 718-821-4770. Fax: 718-628-6263. p. 1645

Simonovski, Larissa, Teen Librn, Merrick Library, 2279 Merrick Ave, Merrick, NY, 11566-4398. Tel: 516-377-6112. Fax: 516-377-1108. p. 1659

Simons, Ben, Curator, Nantucket Historical Association, Seven Fair St, Nantucket, MA, 02554-3737. Tel: 508-228-1655. Fax: 508-325-7968. p. 1107

Simons, Bo, Br Mgr, Sonoma County Library, Healdsburg Regional, 139 Piper St, Healdsburg, CA, 95448. Tel: 707-433-3772. Fax: 707-433-7946. p. 267

Simons, Brian, Dir, Verona Public Library, 500 Silent St, Verona, WI, 53593. Tel: 608-845-7180. Fax: 608-845-8917. p. 2643

Simons, Kirk, Adminr, Meserve, Mumper & Hughes, 300 S Grand Ave, 24th Flr, Los Angeles, CA, 90071-3185. Tel: 213-620-0300. Fax: 213-625-1930. p. 175

Simons, Mary Jo, Dir, Mars Area Public Library, 107 Grand Ave, Mars, PA, 16046. Tel: 724-625-9048. Fax: 724-625-2871. p. 2084

Simons, Michael F, Coll Develop & Res Mgt, University of Nevada-Reno, 1664 N Virginia St, Mailstop 0322, Reno, NV, 89557-0322. Tel: 775-682-5651. Fax: 775-784-4529. p. 1433

Simons, Nancy, Head, Coll Develop, Georgia Institute of Technology Library, 704 Cherry St, Atlanta, GA, 30332-0900. Tel: 404-894-4501. Fax: 404-894-6084. p. 515

Simons, Renee, Ch, Eagle Grove Memorial Library, 101 S Cadwell, Eagle Grove, IA, 50533. Tel: 515-448-4115. Fax: 515-448-5279. p. 813

Simons, Spencer, Dir, University of Houston, The O'Quinn Law Library, 12 Law Library, Houston, TX, 77204-6054. Tel: 713-743-2300. Fax: 713-743-2296. p. 2343

Simons, Sue, Mgr, East Central Georgia Regional Library, Warren County Library, Ten Warren St, Warrenton, GA, 30828. Tel: 706-465-2656. Fax: 706-465-2656. p. 520

Simons, Teresa, Librn, Madison Community Hospital, 917 N Washington Ave, Madison, SD, 57042. Tel: 605-256-6551. Fax: 605-256-6469. p. 2214

Simons-Oparah, Tanya, Mgr, Vols Serv - N Region, Broward County Division of Libraries, 100 S Andrews Ave, Fort Lauderdale, FL, 33301. Tel: 954-357-7514. Fax: 954-357-5733. p. 440

Simonsen, Cheryl, Assoc Dir, Texas Tech University Health Sciences Center at Amarillo, 1400 Wallace Blvd, Amarillo, TX, 79106. Tel: 806-354-5448. Fax: 806-354-5430. p. 2274

Simonsen, Doreen, Humanities Librn, Willamette University, 900 State St, Salem, OR, 97301. Tel: 503-375-5343. Fax: 503-370-6141. p. 2019

Simonsen, Lynette, Acq, University of South Dakota, McKusick Law Library, 414 E Clark St, Vermillion, SD, 57069-2390. Tel: 605-677-5259. Fax: 605-677-5417. p. 2220

Simonson, Lizeth, Commun Outreach Supvr-Bilingual, Carlsbad City Library, Library Learning Center, 3368 Eureka Pl, Carlsbad, CA, 92008. Tel: 760-931-4509. Fax: 760-729-8335. p. 132

Simpfendorfer, Linda, Ch, Ruth L Rockwood Memorial Library, Ten Robert Harp Dr, Livingston, NJ, 07039. Tel: 973-992-4600. Fax: 973-994-2346. p. 1496

Simpson, Angela, Sr Ref Librn, Atlanta-Fulton Public Library System, Buckhead Library, 269 Buckhead Ave NE, Atlanta, GA, 30305. Tel: 404-814-3500. Fax: 404-814-3503. p. 511

Simpson, Anita, Admin Serv, Tuolumne County Free Library, 480 Greenley Rd, Sonora, CA, 95370-5956. Tel: 209-533-5507. Fax: 209-533-0936. p. 269

Simpson, Anne, Dir, Black River Technical College Library, 1410 Hwy 304 E, Pocahontas, AR, 72455. Tel: 870-248-4060. Fax: 870-248-4100. p. 113

Simpson, Betsy, Head, Cat & Metadata Serv, University of Florida Libraries, 535 Library W, Gainesville, FL, 32611-7000. Tel: 352-273-2675. Fax: 352-392-7365. p. 450

Simpson, Bob, Librn, Atchison County Library, 200 S Main St, Rock Port, MO, 64482-1532. Tel: 660-744-5404. Fax: 660-744-2861. p. 1351

Simpson, Carol, Librn, National Park Service Library, 12795 W Alameda Pkwy, Lakewood, CO, 80228. Tel: 303-969-2534. Fax: 303-969-2557. p. 315

Simpson, Carol, Assoc Prof, Modified Serv, University of North Texas, 1155 Union Circle, Denton, TX, 76203-5017. Tel: 940-565-2445. Fax: 940-565-3101. p. 2975

Simpson, Charles W, Dean, Univ Libr, Adelphi University Libraries, One South Ave, Garden City, NY, 11530. Tel: 516-877-3570. Fax: 516-877-3592. p. 1625

Simpson, Cynthia, Ref Librn, Lawrence Technological University Library, 21000 W Ten Mile Rd, Southfield, MI, 48075-1058. Tel: 248-204-3000. Fax: 248-204-3005. p. 1228

Simpson, Cynthia, Librn, Middlesex Law Association, Ground Flr, Unit N, 80 Dundas St, London, ON, N6A 6A1, CANADA. Tel: 519-679-7046. Fax: 519-672-5917. p. 2818

Simpson, Debra, Librn, University of Guelph, Kemptville Campus, PO Box 2003, Kemptville, ON, K0G 1J0, CANADA. Tel: 613-258-8336, Ext 634. Fax: 613-258-8294. p. 2812

Simpson, Diane, Tech Serv, Supreme Court of the United States Library, One First St NE, Washington, DC, 20543. Tel: 202-479-3037. Fax: 202-479-3477. p. 416

Simpson, Evan, Head, Res & Instruction, Tufts University, 35 Professors Row, Medford, MA, 02155-5816. Tel: 617-627-6253. Fax: 617-627-3002. p. 1104

Simpson Gilmer, Margie, Asst Librn, Tombigbee Regional Library System, Choctaw County Public Library, 511 Louisville St, Ackerman, MS, 39735. Tel: 662-285-6348. Fax: 662-285-3042. p. 1318

Simpson, J Alan, Res Spec, Howard County Library System, Howard County Detention Center, 7301 Waterloo Rd, Columbia, MD, 20794. Tel: 410-313-5239. Fax: 410-313-5216. p. 1026

Simpson, Jane, Dir, Georgia Military College, 201 E Greene St, Milledgeville, GA, 31061. Tel: 478-445-2718. Fax: 478-445-5592. p. 544

Simpson, Jean, Head, Tech Serv, New Westminster Public Library, 716 Sixth Ave, New Westminster, BC, V3M 2B3, CANADA. Tel: 604-527-4671. Fax: 604-527-4674. p. 2734

Simpson, Jeff, Evening Ref Librn, Troy University, Montgomery Campus, 252 Montgomery St, Montgomery, AL, 36104-3425. Tel: 334-241-8605. Fax: 334-241-9590. p. 31

Simpson, Jenny, Cat, Nyssa Public Library, 319 Main St, Nyssa, OR, 97913-3845. Tel: 541-372-2978. Fax: 541-372-3278. p. 2008

Simpson, Julia, Mgr, Piedmont Regional Library, Auburn Public, 24 Fifth St, Auburn, GA, 30011-3280. Tel: 770-513-2925. p. 557

Simpson, Karen, Ref Serv/eRes, BCC-UCF Joint Use Library, 1519 Clearlake Rd, Cocoa, FL, 32922. Tel: 321-433-7264. Fax: 321-433-7678. p. 433

Simpson, King, Ref Librn, Logan County Public Library, 201 W Sixth St, Russellville, KY, 42276. Tel: 270-726-6129. Fax: 270-726-6127. p. 934

Simpson, Kristine, ILL, Marylhurst University, 17600 Pacific Hwy (Hwy 43), Marylhurst, OR, 97036-7036. Tel: 503-699-6261, Ext 4454. Fax: 503-636-1957. p. 2004

Simpson, Laura, Cataloger, University of Alabama at Birmingham, Mervyn H Sterne Library, 917 13th St S, Birmingham, AL, 35205. Tel: 205-934-6364. p. 10

Simpson, Laura, Syst Adminr, Tech Serv, Lambuth University, 705 Lambuth Blvd, Jackson, TN, 38301. Tel: 731-425-3292. Fax: 731-425-3200. p. 2238

Simpson, Leslie T, Dir, Winfred L & Elizabeth C Post Foundation, 300 Main St, Joplin, MO, 64801. Tel: 417-782-7678. p. 1336

Simpson, Linda, Librn, Los Medanos College Library, 2700 E Leland Rd, Pittsburg, CA, 94565. Tel: 925-439-2181, Ext 3396. p. 208

Simpson, Livy I, Instrul Serv Librn, Ref Serv, Volunteer State Community College Library, 1480 Nashville Pike, Gallatin, TN, 37066-3188. Tel: 615-230-3400, Ext 3414. Fax: 615-230-3410. p. 2235

Simpson, Lori, Asst Dir, Plumas County Museum Library, 500 Jackson St, Quincy, CA, 95971. Tel: 530-283-6320. Fax: 530-283-6081. p. 212

Simpson, Mae, Mgr, Southeast Arkansas Regional Library, Wilmar Branch, PO Box 415, Wilmar, AR, 71675. Tel: 870-367-8584. p. 110

Simpson, Martha, Head, Ch, Stratford Library Association, 2203 Main St, Stratford, CT, 06615. Tel: 203-385-4165. Fax: 203-381-2079. p. 371

Simpson, Melanee, Cat, Tech Serv, Fairport Harbor Public Library, 335 Vine St, Fairport Harbor, OH, 44077-5799. Tel: 440-358-0119. Fax: 440-354-6059. p. 1899

Simpson, Melissa, Dir, Adult Serv, Williamsburg Regional Library, 7770 Croaker Rd, Williamsburg, VA, 23188-7064. Tel: 757-259-4053. Fax: 757-259-4079, 757-259-7798. p. 2503

Simpson, Mona, Adminr, University of Mississippi, One Library Loop, University, MS, 38677. Tel: 662-915-7656. Fax: 662-915-5734. p. 1316

Simpson, Nancy J, Dir, Lepper Public Library, 303 E Lincoln Way, Lisbon, OH, 44432-1400. Tel: 330-424-3117. Fax: 330-424-7343. p. 1910

Simpson, Pamela, Librn, Orangeville Public Library, 301 Mill St, Orangeville, PA, 17859-0177. Tel: 570-683-5354. p. 2101

Simpson, Phoebe, Conserv Librn, Tech Serv, Rhode Island Historical Society Library, 121 Hope St, Providence, RI, 02906. Tel: 401-273-8107, Ext 24. Fax: 401-751-7930. p. 2174

Simpson, Shanda, Librn, Brunswick Community College Library, 50 College Rd, Supply, NC, 28462. Tel: 910-755-7331. Fax: 910-754-7805. p. 1826

Simpson, Sherry, Teen & Adult Serv Prog, Pope County Library System, 116 E Third St, Russellville, AR, 72801. Tel: 479-968-4368. Fax: 479-968-3222. p. 114

Simpson, Sonja, Librn, United States Courts Library, 46 E Ohio St, Rm 445, Indianapolis, IN, 46204. Tel: 317-229-3925. Fax: 317-229-3927. p. 755

Simpson, Susan, Dir, Huntington Hospital, 270 Park Ave, Huntington, NY, 11743. Tel: 631-351-2000, 631-351-2283. Fax: 631-351-2586. p. 1639

Simpson, Susan M, County Librn, Albany County Public Library, 310 S Eighth St, Laramie, WY, 82070-3969. Tel: 307-721-2580, Ext 5565. Fax: 307-721-2584. p. 2657

Simpson, Susan N, Assoc Dir, Libr Operations, East Carolina University, William E Laupus Health Sciences Library, 600 Moye Blvd, Health Sciences Bldg, Greenville, NC, 27834. Tel: 252-744-2904. Fax: 252-744-2672. p. 1799

Simpson, Susan W, Librn, Carteret County Public Library, 1702 Live Oak St, Beaufort, NC, 28516. Tel: 252-728-2050. Fax: 252-728-1857. p. 1776

Simpson, Susan W, Librn, Carteret County Public Library, Bogue Banks, 320 Salter Path Rd, Ste W, Pine Knoll Shores, NC, 28512. Tel: 252-247-4660. Fax: 252-247-2802. p. 1776

Simpson, Susan W, Librn, Carteret County Public Library, Western Carteret, 230 Taylor Notion Rd, Cape Carteret, NC, 28584. Tel: 252-393-6500. Fax: 252-393-6660. p. 1776

Simpson, Theresa, Circ, Sparta Public Library, 211 W Broadway, Sparta, IL, 62286. Tel: 618-443-5014. Fax: 618-443-2952. p. 704

Simpson, Tonya, Tech Info Spec/Fed Dep Libr, Naval History & Heritage, 805 Kidder-Breese St SE, Washington, DC, 20374-5060. Tel: 202-433-4132. Fax: 202-433-9553. p. 411

Simpson, Valrie, Regional Libr Mgr, Broward County Division of Libraries, South Regional/BC, 7300 Pines Blvd, Pembroke Pines, FL, 33024. Tel: 954-201-8834. Fax: 954-964-0282. p. 442

Simpson, William, Head Librn, Wallace State College, 801 Main St NW, Hanceville, AL, 35077-2000. Tel: 256-352-8260. Fax: 256-352-8254. p. 19

Simpson, William, ILL, Pasadena Public Library, 1201 Jeff Ginn Memorial Dr, Pasadena, TX, 77506-4895. Tel: 713-477-0276. Fax: 713-475-7005. p. 2368

Sims, Arlie, Head, Ref, Columbia College Chicago Library, 624 S Michigan Ave, Chicago, IL, 60605-1996. Tel: 312-369-7059. Fax: 312-344-8062. p. 611

Sims, Becky, Br Mgr, Siskiyou County Public Library, Montague Branch, City Hall, 230 S 13th St, Montague, CA, 96064. Tel: 530-459-5473. p. 286

Sims, Carmen Melinda, Dir, Bartow County Public Library System, 429 W Main St, Cartersville, GA, 30120. Tel: 770-382-4203, Ext 123. Fax: 770-386-3056. p. 524

Sims, Debra, Info Serv Mgr, Crain Communications Inc, 360 N Michigan Ave, 6th Flr, Chicago, IL, 60601. Tel: 312-649-5476. Fax: 312-649-5443. p. 612

Sims, Edward L, Syst Adminr, Saint John the Baptist Parish Library, 2920 New Hwy 51, LaPlace, LA, 70068. Tel: 985-652-2225, 985-652-6857. Fax: 985-652-8005. p. 954

Sims, Evelyn, Reserves Mgr, Longwood University, Redford & Race St, Farmville, VA, 23909. Tel: 434-395-2437. Fax: 434-395-2453. p. 2463

Sims, Gloria, Br Mgr, Maynard Public Library, 321 Mabel Ave, Maynard, MN, 56260. Tel: 320-367-2143. Fax: 320-367-2143. p. 1258

Sims, Iyanna, Electronic Res, North Carolina Agricultural & Technical State University, 1601 E Market St, Greensboro, NC, 27411-0002. Tel: 336-334-7640, Ext 3261. Fax: 336-334-7783. p. 1797

Sims, Jacquelyn, Head, Info Serv, Catawba College, 2300 W Innes St, Salisbury, NC, 28144-2488. Tel: 704-637-4379. Fax: 704-637-4304. p. 1821

Sims, Janice, Librn, Environmental Protection Agency, 960 College Station Rd, Athens, GA, 30605-2700. Tel: 706-355-8011. Fax: 706-355-8440. p. 509

Sims, Karen, Asst Librn, Deshler Public Library, 310 E Pearl St, Deshler, NE, 68340. Tel: 402-365-4107. Fax: 402-365-4107. p. 1397

Sims, Laurie A, Doc Delivery, Tech Spec, Kansas City University of Medicine & Biosciences D'Angelo Library, 1750 Independence Ave, Kansas City, MO, 64106-1453. Tel: 816-654-7266. Fax: 816-654-7261. p. 1338

Sims, Lee, Head, User Serv, Rutgers University Library for the Center for Law & Justice, 123 Washington St, Newark, NJ, 07102-3094. Tel: 973-353-3036. Fax: 973-353-1356. p. 1513

Sims, Linda, Mgr, Palm Beach County Law Library, County Courthouse, Rm 12200, 205 N Dixie Hwy, West Palm Beach, FL, 33401. Tel: 561-355-2928. Fax: 561-355-1654. p. 503

Sims, Linda, Ch, Hazel Park Memorial Library, 123 E Nine Mile Rd, Hazel Park, MI, 48030. Tel: 248-542-0940, 248-546-4095. Fax: 248-546-4083. p. 1189

Sims, Marcy, Dir, Virginia Beach Public Library Department, Bldg 19, Municipal Ctr, 2nd Flr, 2416 Courthouse Dr, Virginia Beach, VA, 23456. Tel: 757-385-4321. Fax: 757-385-4220. p. 2500

Sims, Mary, Tech Serv Librn, A T Still University of Health Sciences, Kirksville Campus, 800 W Jefferson St, Kirksville, MO, 63501. Tel: 660-626-2635. Fax: 660-626-2031, 660-626-2333. p. 1342

Sims, Patrice, Acq, Supvr, Mississippi College, 151 E Griffith St, Jackson, MS, 39201-1391. Tel: 601-925-7120. Fax: 601-925-7112. p. 1304

Sims, Rebecca, Dir, United States Air Force, 55 FSS/FSDL, Bldg 73, 510 Custer Dr, Offutt AFB, NE, 68113-2150. Tel: 402-294-5523. Fax: 402-294-7124. p. 1411

Sims, Richard, Librn, Centennial College of Applied Arts & Technology, Progress Campus Library, 941 Progress Ave, Scarborough, ON, M1G 3T8, CANADA. Tel: 416-289-5000, Ext 2600. Fax: 416-289-5242. p. 2840

Sims, Suzette S, Prog Serv Coordr, Craft Memorial Library, 600 Commerce St, Bluefield, WV, 24701. Tel: 304-325-3943. Fax: 304-325-3702. p. 2555

Sims, Willard, Dir, Mount Vernon Public Library, 1220 Military Rd, Mount Vernon, AL, 36560. Tel: 251-829-9497. Fax: 251-829-5546. p. 31

Simser, Jill, Circ/eRes, BCC-UCF Joint Use Library, 1519 Clearlake Rd, Cocoa, FL, 32922. Tel: 321-433-7252. Fax: 321-433-7678. p. 433

Simson, Angie, Librn, Lima Memorial Hospital, 1001 Bellefontaine Ave, Lima, OH, 45804. Tel: 419-228-3335. Fax: 419-226-5061. p. 1910

Simuel, Jahala, Ref Librn, Shaw University, 118 E South St, Raleigh, NC, 27601. Tel: 919-546-8407. Fax: 919-831-1161. p. 1817

Simundza, Gayle, Exec Dir, Cape Libraries Automated Materials Sharing Network, 270 Communication Way, Unit 4E, Hyannis, MA, 02601. Tel: 508-790-4399. Fax: 508-771-4533. p. 2945

Sin, Lauren, Broadcast Librn, NPR Library, 635 Massachusetts Ave NW, Washington, DC, 20001. Fax: 202-513-3056. p. 412

Sinard, Anne Marie, Tech Serv, Racine Louise Documentation Center, 500 Sherbrooke W, Montreal, QC, H3A 3G6, CANADA. Tel: 514-499-5188. Fax: 514-873-4900. p. 2897

Sinclair, Bryan, Head, Pub Serv, University of North Carolina at Asheville, One University Heights, CPO 1500, Asheville, NC, 28804-8504. Tel: 828-251-6336. p. 1775

Sinclair, Diane, Dir, Williams Public Library, 216 Main St, Williams, IA, 50271. Tel: 515-854-2643. Fax: 515-854-2643. p. 853

Sinclair, Jan, Librn, United Church of Los Alamos Library, 2525 Canyon Rd, Los Alamos, NM, 87544. Tel: 505-662-2971. Fax: 505-662-5927. p. 1559

Sinclair, Jen, Circ Supvr, Johnson County Public Library, Trafalgar Branch, 424 Tower St, Trafalgar, IN, 46181. Tel: 317-878-9560. Fax: 317-878-4093. p. 744

Sinclair, Kent, Dir, Norridgewock Public Library, 40 Mercer Rd, Norridgewock, ME, 04957. Tel: 207-634-2828. p. 993

Sinclair, Lorraine, Br Mgr, Muncie Public Library, Carnegie Library, 301 E Jackson St, Muncie, IN, 47305. Tel: 765-741-5157. p. 767

Sinclair, Mary Beth, Ch, Marshall-Lyon County Library, 301 W Lyon St, Marshall, MN, 56258. Tel: 507-537-7003. p. 1258

Sinclair, R Frank, Librn, Vance-Granville Community College, State Rd 1126, Poplar Creek Rd, Exit 209, Henderson, NC, 27536. Tel: 252-492-2061. Fax: 252-738-3372. p. 1800

Sinclair, Sharon, Librn, Allerton Public Library, 103 South Central Ave, Allerton, IA, 50008. Tel: 641-873-4575. p. 792

Sinclair, Wendy, Br Head, Regina Public Library, Albert, 1401 Robinson St, Regina, SK, S4T 2N7, CANADA. Tel: 306-777-6076. Fax: 306-949-7265. p. 2923

Sindelar, Norma, Archivist, Saint Louis Art Museum, One Fine Arts Dr, Forest Park, Saint Louis, MO, 63110-1380. Tel: 314-655-5452. Fax: 314-721-6172. p. 1357

Sinder, Janet, Assoc Dir, University of Maryland, Baltimore, Thurgood Marshall Law Library, 501 W Fayette St, Baltimore, MD, 21201-1768. Tel: 410-706-0792. Fax: 410-706-8354. p. 1019

Sindler, Elizabeth, Dir, City of Tavares Public Library, 314 N New Hampshire Ave, Tavares, FL, 32778. Tel: 352-742-6090. Fax: 352-742-6472. p. 499

Singarella, Thomas, Dr, Dir, University of Tennessee-Memphis, 877 Madison Ave, Memphis, TN, 38163. Tel: 901-448-5634. Fax: 901-448-7235. p. 2252

Singer, Braden, Ref, Center Moriches Free Public Library, 235 Main St, Center Moriches, NY, 11934. Tel: 631-878-0940. p. 1604

Singer, Joel, Cat, City University of New York, 365 Fifth Ave, New York, NY, 10016-4309. Tel: 212-817-7072. Fax: 212-817-2982. p. 1673

Singer, Madine, Librn, Insurance Information Institute Library, 110 William St, New York, NY, 10038. Tel: 212-346-5533. Fax: 212-267-9591. p. 1682

Singer, Marybelle, Librn, Alburg Public Library, 16 S Main St, Alburg, VT, 05440. Tel: 802-796-6077. Fax: 802-796-3089. p. 2417

Singer, Melanie, Circ Mgr, Washington County Public Library, 615 Fifth St, Marietta, OH, 45750-1973. Tel: 740-373-1057. p. 1913

Singerman, Susan, Librn, Johns Hopkins University, Applied Physics Laboratory, 11100 Johns Hopkins Rd, Laurel, MD, 20723-6099. Tel: 443-778-5151. Fax: 443-778-5353. p. 1035

Singh, Carolyn, Ref, Shasta College Library, 11555 Old Oregon Trail, Redding, CA, 96003-7692. Tel: 530-242-2347. p. 214

Singh, Devi, ILL, Miami Dade College, North Campus Learning Resources, 11380 NW 27th Ave, Miami, FL, 33167. Tel: 305-237-1142. Fax: 305-237-8276. p. 466

Singh, Genevieve, Cat, Washington Adventist University, 7600 Flower Ave, Takoma Park, MD, 20912-7796. Tel: 301-891-4221. Fax: 301-891-4204. p. 1043

Singh, H C, Head, Acq, Head, Ser, Brooklyn Law School Library, 250 Joralemon St, Brooklyn, NY, 11201. Tel: 718-780-7976. Fax: 718-780-0369. p. 1590

Singh, Harjit, Dr, Dir, Hackettstown Regional Medical Center, 651 Willow Grove St, Hackettstown, NJ, 07840. Tel: 908-850-7743. Fax: 908-850-6815. p. 1489

Singh, Indrajeet, Dir, Helene Fuld College of Nursing, 1879 Madison Ave, New York, NY, 10035. Tel: 212-616-7200, 212-616-7269. Fax: 212-616-7269. p. 1679

Singh, Judy, Librn, Canadian Tax Foundation, 595 Bay St, Ste 1200, Toronto, ON, M5G 2N5, CANADA. Tel: 416-599-0283. Fax: 416-599-9283. p. 2852

Singh, Lester, Network Mgr, John Jay College of Criminal Justice, 899 Tenth Ave, New York, NY, 10019. Tel: 212-237-8246, 212-237-8265. Fax: 212-237-8221. p. 1684

Singh, Lynnette, Mgr, Automation Serv, Geneva Public Library District, 127 James St, Geneva, IL, 60134. Tel: 630-232-0780. Fax: 630-232-0881. p. 649

Singh, Nalini, Ref & Web Content Coordr, University of Toronto Libraries, Faculty of Information Inforum, 140 Saint George St, 4th Flr, Toronto, ON, M5S 3G6, CANADA. Tel: 416-978-7069. Fax: 416-978-5769. p. 2865

Singh, Nan, Librn, California Christian College, 4881 E University Ave, Fresno, CA, 93703. Tel: 559-251-5025. Fax: 559-251-4231. p. 150

Singh, Rukshana, Librn, Southern California Library for Social Studies & Research, 6120 S Vermont Ave, Los Angeles, CA, 90044. Tel: 323-759-6063. Fax: 323-759-2252. p. 177

Singh, Sandra, City Librn, Vancouver Public Library, 350 W Georgia St, Vancouver, BC, V6B 6B1, CANADA. Tel: 604-331-3600. Fax: 604-331-3800. p. 2744

Singh, Shakuntala, Archit Librn, Tuskegee University, Hollis Burke Frissell Bldg, 1200 W Old Montgomery Rd, Tuskegee, AL, 36088. Tel: 334-727-4572. Fax: 334-727-9282. p. 39

Singh, Tischa, Info Tech, PricewaterhouseCoopers, National Tax Research Services, Royal Trust Tower, 77 King St W, Ste 3000, Toronto, ON, M5K 1G8, CANADA. Tel: 416-815-5103. Fax: 416-814-3200. p. 2857

Singh, Vandana, Asst Prof, University of Tennessee, Knoxville, 451 Communications Bldg, 1345 Circle Park Dr, Knoxville, TN, 37996-0341. Tel: 865-974-2785. Fax: 865-974-4967. p. 2974

Singla, Sanjeev, Info Syst Mgr, Santa Clara County Library District, 14600 Winchester Blvd, Los Gatos, CA, 95032. Tel: 408-293-2326, Ext 3051. Fax: 408-364-0161. p. 180

Singletary, Jon, Libr Syst Spec, Carnegie Mellon University, Hunt Library, 4909 Frew St, Pittsburgh, PA, 15213-3890. Tel: 412-268-2446. Fax: 412-268-2793. p. 2123

Singletary, Virginia, Dir, Stella Hill Memorial Library, 158 W San Antonio St, Alto, TX, 75925. Tel: 936-858-4343. p. 2273

Singleton, Alma Nickell, Dir, Florida Coastal School of Law, 8787 Baypine Rd, Jacksonville, FL, 32256. Tel: 904-680-7601. Fax: 904-680-7677. p. 452

Singleton, Brent, Coordr of Ref Serv, California State University, San Bernardino, 5500 University Pkwy, San Bernardino, CA, 92407-2318. Tel: 909-537-5083. Fax: 909-537-7048. p. 227

Singleton, Carol, Ref, Grove City College, 300 Campus Dr, Grove City, PA, 16127-2198. Tel: 724-450-4038. Fax: 724-458-2181. p. 2063

Singleton, Charnette, Dean of Libr, Trident Technical College, Berkeley Campus Learning Resources, LR-B, PO Box 118067, Charleston, SC, 29423-8067. Tel: 843-574-6088. Fax: 843-899-8100. p. 2185

Singleton, Charnette, Dean of Libr, Trident Technical College, Main Campus Learning Resources Center, LR-M, PO Box 118067, Charleston, SC, 29423-8067. Tel: 843-574-6087. Fax: 843-574-6484. p. 2185

Singleton, David, Dir, Charlotte Mecklenburg Library, 310 N Tryon St, Charlotte, NC, 28202-2176. Tel: 704-416-0101. Fax: 704-416-0130. p. 1781

Singleton, Eleanor, Ref Serv, Santa Monica College Library, 1900 Pico Blvd, Santa Monica, CA, 90405-1628. Tel: 310-434-4334, 310-434-4692. Fax: 310-434-4387. p. 266

Singleton, Erin, Youth Serv Librn, George F Johnson Memorial Library, 1001 Park St, Endicott, NY, 13760. Tel: 607-757-5350. Fax: 607-757-2491. p. 1621

Singleton, Joan, Dir, Bartlesville Public Library, 600 S Johnstone, Bartlesville, OK, 74003. Tel: 918-338-4163. Fax: 918-336-7495. p. 1957

Singleton, Laura, Librn, Western Nebraska Veterans Home Library, 1102 W 42nd St, Scottsbluff, NE, 69361-4713. Tel: 308-632-0300. Fax: 308-632-1384. p. 1419

Singleton, Margie, Chief Exec Officer, Vaughan Public Libraries, 900 Clark Ave W, Thornhill, ON, L4J 8C1, CANADA. Tel: 905-653-7323. Fax: 905-709-1530. p. 2847

Singleton, Paula R, Govt Doc Librn, Xavier University of Louisiana, One Drexel Dr, New Orleans, LA, 70125-1098. Tel: 504-520-7309. Fax: 504-520-7940. p. 964

Singleton, Susan, Exec Dir, Consortium of Academic & Research Libraries in Illinois, 100 Trade Ctr Dr, Ste 303, Champaign, IL, 61820. Tel: 217-244-5167. Fax: 217-244-7596. p. 2942

Singleton, Suzanne, Archivist, Spec Coll Librn, Francis Marion University, 4822 East Palmetto St, Florence, SC, 29506. Tel: 843-661-1319. Fax: 843-661-1309. p. 2194

Singlevich, Melissa, Head, Ref, Free Public Library of Hasbrouck Heights, 320 Boulevard, Hasbrouck Heights, NJ, 07604. Tel: 201-288-0484, 201-288-0488. Fax: 201-288-5467. p. 1490

Sinha, Dorothy, Mgr, Department of Veterans Affairs, One Veterans Dr, 142 D, Minneapolis, MN, 55417. Tel: 612-467-4200. Fax: 612-725-2046. p. 1259

Sinha, Luzviminda Navarro, Librn, Children's Medical Center, One Children's Plaza, Dayton, OH, 45404-1815. Tel: 937-641-3307. Fax: 937-461-5409. p. 1892

Siniak, Mary Ellen, Youth Serv, Seekonk Public Library, 410 Newman Ave, Seekonk, MA, 02771. Tel: 508-336-8230. Fax: 508-336-6437. p. 1123

Sininsky, Joanne, Dir, Haverstraw Kings Daughters Public Library, Village Library, 85 Main St, Haverstraw, NY, 10927. Tel: 845-429-3445. Fax: 845-429-7313. p. 1627

Sink, Martha, Tech Serv & Automation, Alamance County Public Libraries, 342 S Spring St, Burlington, NC, 27215. Tel: 336-513-4754. Fax: 336-229-3592. p. 1778

Sink, Thomas R, Dean of Libr Serv, Owens Community College Library, 30335 Oregon Rd, Perrysburg, OH, 43551. Tel: 567-661-7221. Fax: 567-661-7021. p. 1929

Sinn, Donghee, Dr, Asst Prof, University at Albany, State University of New York, Draper 116, 135 Western Ave, Albany, NY, 12222. Tel: 518-442-5117. Fax: 518-442-5367. p. 2970

Sinnett, Scott, Br Mgr, Saint Joseph County Public Library, River Park Branch, 2022 Mishawaka Ave, South Bend, IN, 46615. Tel: 574-282-4635. p. 779

Sinnott, Lindsey, Syst Librn, Tech Serv, Hope International University, 2500 E Nutwood Ave, Fullerton, CA, 92831. Tel: 714-879-3901, Ext 1218. Fax: 714-681-7515. p. 154

Sinon, Stephen, Archives, Head, Info Serv, ILL, The LuEsther T Mertz Library, The New York Botanical Garden, 2900 Southern Blvd, Bronx, NY, 10458-5126. Tel: 718-817-8728. Fax: 718-817-8956. p. 1587

Sinotte, Michelle, Info Serv, Mount Royal University Library, 4825 Mount Royal Gate SW, Calgary, AB, T3E 6K6, CANADA. Tel: 403-440-5683. Fax: 403-440-6758. p. 2692

Sinquefield, Katy, Librn for Blind & Physically Handicapped, Dougherty County Public Library, 300 Pine Ave, Albany, GA, 31701-2533. Tel: 229-420-3200. Fax: 229-420-3215. p. 507

Sinton, Ann, Ch, Town of Vail Public Library, 292 W Meadow Dr, Vail, CO, 81657. Tel: 970-479-2179. Fax: 970-479-2192. p. 325

Sioco, Deo, IT Mgr, Cargill, Inc, 15407 McGinty Rd W, Wayzata, MN, 55391. Tel: 952-742-6498. Fax: 952-742-6062. p. 1287

Sipe, Vicki, Cat Librn, University of Maryland, Baltimore County, 1000 Hilltop Circle, Baltimore, MD, 21250. Tel: 410-455-2356. Fax: 410-455-1598. p. 1018

Sipes, Jacqueline, Instrul Design Librn, George Mason University Libraries, 4400 University Dr, MSN 2FL, Fairfax, VA, 22030-4444. Tel: 703-993-2250. Fax: 703-993-2200. p. 2462

Sipman, Glorian, Coll Develop Librn, Tech Serv, MiraCosta College Library, One Barnard Dr, Oceanside, CA, 92056-3899. Tel: 760-795-6722. Fax: 760-795-6723. p. 199

Sipocz, Joseph, Literacy & Outreach Mgr, Saint Joseph County Public Library, 304 S Main, South Bend, IN, 46601-2125. Tel: 574-282-4646. Fax: 574-280-2763. p. 779

Sipocz, Joseph, Local & Family Hist Mgr, Saint Joseph County Public Library, 304 S Main, South Bend, IN, 46601-2125. Tel: 574-282-4646. Fax: 574-280-2763. p. 779

Sipple, Janice, Asst Dir, Powell County Public Library, 725 Breckenridge St, Stanton, KY, 40380. Tel: 606-663-4511. Fax: 606-663-4346. p. 936

Sippling, Kathy, Librn, Cayuga Community College, 806 W Broadway, Fulton, NY, 13069. Tel: 315-294-9019. Fax: 315-592-5055. p. 1625

Siracusa, Elizabeth, Outreach Serv Librn, Warner Library, 121 N Broadway, Tarrytown, NY, 10591. Tel: 914-631-7734. Fax: 914-631-2324. p. 1754

Siragusa, Debbie, Chief Financial Officer, The Kansas City Public Library, 14 W Tenth St, Kansas City, MO, 64105. Tel: 816-701-3515. Fax: 816-701-3401. p. 1338

Sirak, Jennifer E, Ch, Lambertville Free Public Library, Six Lilly St, Lambertville, NJ, 08530. Tel: 609-397-0275. Fax: 609-397-1784. p. 1494

Sirgey, Mary, Dir, Mansfield Free Public Library, 71 N Main St, Mansfield, PA, 16933. Tel: 570-662-3850. Fax: 570-662-7423. p. 2084

Sirianni, Edith, Ref, Bergen Community College, 400 Paramus Rd, Paramus, NJ, 07652-1595. Tel: 201-447-7131. Fax: 201-493-8167. p. 1517

Sirko, Ariana, Coll Develop, University of Manitoba Libraries, E K Williams Law Library, 401 Robson Hall, 224 Dysart Rd, Winnipeg, MB, R3T 2N2, CANADA. Tel: 204-474-6371. Fax: 204-474-7582. p. 2759

Sirney, Marie, Librn, American Graduate University Library, 733 N Dodsworth Ave, Covina, CA, 91724-2499. Tel: 626-966-4576, Ext 1003. Fax: 626-915-1709. p. 137

Sirochman, Casey, Dir, Carnegie Free Library, 299 S Pittsburgh St, Connellsville, PA, 15425-3580. Tel: 724-628-1380. Fax: 724-628-5636. p. 2047

Sirois, Jacinthe, ILL, Universite du Quebec en Outaouais, 283, Blvd Alexandre-Tache, Case postale 1250, succ Hull, Gatineau, QC, J8X 3X7, CANADA. Tel: 819-595-3900, Ext 1790. Fax: 819-773-1669. p. 2884

Sirois, Louise, Br Coordr, Cochise County Library District, Sunsites Community Library, 210 Ford Rd, Pearce, AZ, 85625. Tel: 520-826-3866. Fax: 520-826-3866. p. 58

Sisak, Christine A, ILL, Reserves, Ser, Nazareth College of Rochester Library, 4245 East Ave, Rochester, NY, 14618-3790. Tel: 585-389-2184. Fax: 585-389-2145. p. 1730

Sisco, Ellen, Asst Dir, Lincoln Public Library, Three Bedford Rd, Lincoln, MA, 01773. Tel: 781-259-8465. Fax: 781-259-1056. p. 1099

Sish, Ken, ILL, Dominican University of California, 50 Acacia Ave, San Rafael, CA, 94901-2298. Tel: 415-485-3251. Fax: 415-459-2309. p. 256

Sisk, Lisa, Dir, Park Hills Public Library, 16 S Coffman St, Park Hills, MO, 63601. Tel: 573-431-4842. Fax: 573-431-2110. p. 1349

Sisler, Seth, Libr Asst, Maysville Community & Technical College, 1755 US Hwy 68, Maysville, KY, 41056. Tel: 606-759-7141, Ext. 66124. Fax: 606-759-7176. p. 928

Sisneros, Caroline, Dir, Libr Serv, Phillips Graduate Institute Library, 19900 Plummer St, Chatsworth, CA, 91311. Tel: 818-386-5642. Fax: 818-386-5696. p. 133

Sison, Ruth, Instrul Serv Librn, Diablo Valley College Library, 321 Golf Club Rd, Pleasant Hill, CA, 94523-1576. Tel: 925-685-1230, Ext 2681. Fax: 925-798-3588. p. 210

Sissen, Melissa M, Pub Serv Librn, Siena Heights University Library, 1247 E Siena Heights Dr, Adrian, MI, 49221-1796. Tel: 517-264-7150. Fax: 517-264-7711. p. 1147

Sissom, Susan Faye, Dir, Palmer Public Library, 2115 Main St, Palmer, TN, 37365-9999. Tel: 931-779-5292. Fax: 931-779-2334. p. 2263

Sisson, Amy, Librn, Houston Community College Central College, Willie Lee Gay Hall ERC - South Campus, 1990 Airport Blvd, Houston, TX, 77051. Tel: 713-718-6693. Fax: 713-718-6655. p. 2337

Sisson, Gail, Libr Serv Dir, Miller & Martin PLLC, Volunteer Bldg, Ste 1000, 832 Georgia Ave, Chattanooga, TN, 37402-2289. Tel: 423-756-6600. Fax: 423-785-8480. p. 2227

Sisson, Lynn, Dir, Sodus Township Library, 3776 Naomi Rd, Sodus, MI, 49126-9783. Tel: 269-925-0903. Fax: 269-925-1823. p. 1227

Sisson, Stephen, Br Mgr, Ohoopee Regional Library System, Nelle Brown Memorial, 166 W Liberty St, Lyons, GA, 30436-1432. Tel: 912-526-6511. Fax: 912-526-6511. p. 555

Sissors, Jan, Circ Mgr, Arlington Heights Memorial Library, 500 N Dunton Ave, Arlington Heights, IL, 60004-5966. Tel: 847-506-2625. Fax: 847-506-2650. p. 589

Sisto, Vicky, Coordr, Youth Serv, Westminster Public Library, 3705 W 112th Ave, Westminster, CO, 80031. Tel: 303-658-2614. Fax: 303-404-5135. p. 326

Sistrunk, Wendy, Head, Spec Formats & Cat, University of Missouri-Kansas City Libraries, 800 E 51st St, Kansas City, MO, 64110. Tel: 816-235-5291. Fax: 816-333-5584. p. 1341

Sites, Martha, Assoc Univ Librn, Production & Tech Serv, University of Virginia, PO Box 400114, Charlottesville, VA, 22904-4114. Tel: 434-924-3021. Fax: 434-924-1431. p. 2454

Sitko, Michelle, Digital Ser & Scholarly Res Librn, Marywood University Library, 2300 Adams Ave, Scranton, PA, 18509-1598. Tel: 570-961-4707. Fax: 570-961-4769. p. 2137

Sitler, Lorraine C, Librn, United Network for Organ Sharing, 700 N Fourth St, Richmond, VA, 23219. Tel: 804-782-4846. Fax: 804-782-4893. p. 2491

Sitter, Clara, PhD, Chair, University of Denver, Morgridge College of Education, Katherine A Ruffatto Hall, 1999 E Evans Ave, Denver, CO, 80208. Tel: 303-871-3587. Fax: 303-871-2709. p. 2963

Sittler, Ryan, Info Literacy/Instrul Tech Librn, California University of Pennsylvania, 250 University Ave, California, PA, 15419-1394. Tel: 724-938-4923. Fax: 724-938-5901. p. 2040

Sitts, Jody, Ch, Field Library of Peekskill, Four Nelson Ave, Peekskill, NY, 10566-2138. Tel: 914-737-1212. Fax: 914-862-9710. p. 1716

Situ, Ping, Librn, University of Arizona, East Asian Collection, 1510 E University Blvd, Tucson, AZ, 85720. Tel: 520-307-2772. Fax: 520-621-3655. p. 89

Sitz, Emily, Dir, Southwest Kansas Library System, 100 Military Ave, Ste 210, Dodge City, KS, 67801-4484. Tel: 620-225-1231. Fax: 620-225-0252. p. 864

Siva, Nathan, Syst Adminr, University of Detroit Mercy Library, 4001 W McNichols Rd, Detroit, MI, 48221-3038. Tel: 313-993-1794. Fax: 313-993-1780. p. 1172

Six, Andrea, Circ, Starkville-Oktibbeha County Public Library System, 326 University Dr, Starkville, MS, 39759. Tel: 662-323-2766, 662-323-2783. Fax: 662-323-9140. p. 1315

Sixbey, Pete, Conservator, State Historical Society of Iowa, 402 Iowa Ave, Iowa City, IA, 52240-1806. Tel: 319-335-3916. Fax: 319-335-3935. p. 823

Sixt, Tina, Coll Develop, Ref Serv, Sierra Joint Community College District, 5000 Rocklin Rd, Rocklin, CA, 95677. Tel: 916-660-7230. Fax: 916-630-4539. p. 219

Sizemore, Ann, Dir, Apalachicola Municipal Library, 74 Sixth St, Gorrie Square, Apalachicola, FL, 32320. Tel: 850-653-8436. p. 425

Sizemore, Daardi, Archivist, Spec Coll Librn, Minnesota State University, Mankato, ML3097, Mankato, MN, 56001. Tel: 507-389-5952. Fax: 507-389-5155. p. 1257

Sizemore, Lisa, Mgr, Br Serv, Louisville Free Public Library, 301 York St, Louisville, KY, 40203-2205. Tel: 502-574-1718. Fax: 502-574-1666, 502-574-1693. p. 924

Sizemore, Mary M, Dir, High Point Public Library, 901 N Main St, High Point, NC, 27262. Tel: 336-883-3694. Fax: 336-883-3636. p. 1802

Sizemore, Mary Montgomery, Dir, Hickory Public Library, 375 Third St NE, Hickory, NC, 28601-5126. Tel: 828-304-0500, Ext 7275. Fax: 828-304-0023. p. 1801

Sizemore, Mary Montgomery, Dir, Hickory Public Library, Ridgeview, 706 First St SW, Hickory, NC, 28602. Tel: 828-304-0500, Ext 7275. Fax: 828-267-0485. p. 1801

Sizemore, Stacy, Br Head, Denton Public Library, South Branch, 3228 Teasley Lane, Denton, TX, 76210. Tel: 940-349-8761. Fax: 940-349-8383. p. 2312

Sizemore, Stephen, Dir, Admin & Finance, University of Kentucky Libraries, I-85, 401 Hilltop Ave, Lexington, KY, 40506-0456. Tel: 859-257-0500, Ext 2085. p. 921

Sizemore, Vicki, Br Mgr, West Georgia Regional Library, Mount Zion Public Library, 4455 Mount Zion Rd, Mount Zion, GA, 30150. Tel: 770-832-0056, Ext 104. Fax: 770-834-7228. p. 524

Sjoberg, Lisa, Col Archivist/Librn, Concordia College, 901 S Eighth St, Moorhead, MN, 56562. Tel: 218-299-3180. Fax: 218-299-4253. p. 1265

Sjoberg, Nilla, Syst Adminr, Rhinelander District Library, 106 N Stevens St, Rhinelander, WI, 54501-3193. Tel: 715-365-1070. Fax: 715-365-1076. p. 2633

Sjogren, Linda, Info Spec, UNESCO-Intergovernmental Oceanographic Commission & National Weather Service, 737 Bishop St, Ste 2200, Honolulu, HI, 96813. Tel: 808-532-6422. Fax: 808-532-5576. p. 565

Sjostrom, Eric, Assoc Principal Librn, Minnesota Orchestra Music Library, 1111 Nicollet Mall, Minneapolis, MN, 55403. Tel: 612-371-5623. Fax: 612-371-0838. p. 1261

Skaden, Anne, Dir, Kalona Public Library, 510 C Ave, Kalona, IA, 52247-9743. Tel: 319-656-3501. Fax: 319-656-3503. p. 825

Skaggs, Angela L, Asst Dir, Access Serv, Angelo State University Library, 2025 S Johnson, San Angelo, TX, 76904-5079. Tel: 325-486-6524. Fax: 325-942-2198. p. 2378

Skaggs, Jessica, YA Librn, North Suburban Library District, 6340 N Second St, Loves Park, IL, 61111. Tel: 815-633-4247. Fax: 815-633-4249. p. 668

Skaggs, Karen, Circ, Bartlett-Carnegie Sapulpa Public Library, 27 W Dewey, Sapulpa, OK, 74066. Tel: 918-224-5624. Fax: 918-224-3546. p. 1977

Skaggs, Melanie, Librn, West Florida Public Library, Southwest Branch Library, 12248 Gulf Beach Hwy, Pensacola, FL, 32507. Tel: 850-453-7780. Fax: 850-453-7782. p. 483

Skains, Barbara, Ref Serv Coordr, Shreve Memorial Library, Hamilton/South Caddo Branch, 2111 Bert Kouns Industrial Loop, Shreveport, LA, 71118. Tel: 318-687-6824. Fax: 318-686-0971. p. 969

Skaj, Jeanne, Librn, Department of Veterans Affairs Medical Center, 4801 Veterans Dr, Saint Cloud, MN, 56303. Tel: 320-255-6342. Fax: 320-255-6493. p. 1274

Skale, Linda Carnevale, Info Spec, United States Army, Wanamaker Bldg, 100 Penn Square E, Philadelphia, PA, 19107-3390. Tel: 215-656-6821. Fax: 215-656-6828. p. 2118

Skalitzky, Diana, Dir, Marshall Community Library, 605 Waterloo Rd, Marshall, WI, 53559. Tel: 608-655-3123. p. 2613

Skarbek, Kate, Libr Serv Mgr, Westminster Public Library, 3705 W 112th Ave, Westminster, CO, 80031. Tel: 303-658-2640. Fax: 303-404-5135. p. 326

Skarda, Mary Ann, Coordr, Ch Serv, Shreve Memorial Library, 424 Texas St, Shreveport, LA, 71101. Tel: 318-226-5880. Fax: 318-226-4780. p. 969

Skaronski, Myra, Mgr, Edmonton Public Library, Lois Hole Library, 17650-69 Ave NW, Edmonton, AB, T5T 3X9, CANADA. Tel: 780-442-0885. Fax: 780-442-0887. p. 2700

Skaugset, Chris, Dir, Longview Public Library, 1600 Louisiana St, Longview, WA, 98632-2993. Tel: 360-442-5309. Fax: 360-442-5954. p. 2520

Skeele, Devon, State Librn, New Mexico State Library, 1209 Camino Carlos Rey, Santa Fe, NM, 87507. Tel: 505-476-9700. Fax: 505-476-9701. p. 1563

Skeels, Suzanne, Asst Dir, Monroe Free Library, 44 Millpond Pkwy, Monroe, NY, 10950. Tel: 845-783-4411. Fax: 845-782-4707. p. 1662

Skeen, Carole, ILL, Elmwood Park Public Library, 210 Lee St, Elmwood Park, NJ, 07407. Tel: 201-796-8888. Fax: 201-703-1425. p. 1484

Skeen, Joseph, Dir, Farmland Public Library, 116 S Main St, Farmland, IN, 47340. Tel: 765-468-7292. Fax: 765-468-7292. p. 739

Skekloff, Susan, Ref Serv, Indiana University-Purdue University Fort Wayne, 2101 E Coliseum Blvd, Fort Wayne, IN, 46805-1499. Tel: 260-481-6011. Fax: 260-481-6509. p. 741

Skelly, Linda, Coordr, Spec Serv, Lititz Public Library, 651 Kissel Hill Rd, Lititz, PA, 17543. Tel: 717-626-2255. Fax: 717-627-4191. p. 2082

Skelton, Bill, Head, Info Serv, Coweta Public Library System, A Mitchell Powell Jr Public Library, 25 Hospital Rd, Newnan, GA, 30263. Tel: 770-253-3625. Fax: 770-254-7262. p. 546

Skelton, Frances H, Ref, New Haven Museum & Historical Society, 114 Whitney Ave, New Haven, CT, 06510-1025. Tel: 203-562-4183. Fax: 203-562-2002. p. 356

Skelton, Victoria, Librn, University of Toronto Libraries, Industrial Relations Centre, Jean & Dorothy Newman Library, 121 Saint George St, Toronto, ON, M5S 1A1, CANADA. Tel: 416-978-2928. Fax: 416-978-5694. p. 2866

Skevington, Wendy, Dir, Holbrook Public Library, 451 N First Ave, Holbrook, AZ, 86025. Tel: 928-524-3732. Fax: 928-524-2159. p. 65

Skewis, Charles A, Head, Coll & Res Serv, Georgia Southern University, 1400 Southern Dr, Statesboro, GA, 30458. Tel: 912-478-5114. Fax: 912-478-0093. p. 552

Skib, Bryan, Coll Develop, University of Michigan, 818 Hatcher Graduate Library, Ann Arbor, MI, 48109-1205. Tel: 734-764-9356. Fax: 734-763-5080. p. 1152

Skiba, Pauly, Dir, Oracle Public Library, 565 American Ave, Oracle, AZ, 85623. Tel: 520-896-2121. Fax: 520-896-2149. p. 70

Skibinsky, Orest, Asst Librn, St Vladimir's Library & Archives, 404 Meredith Rd NE, Calgary, AB, T2E 5A6, CANADA. Tel: 403-264-3437. Fax: 403-264-3438. p. 2692

Skica, Jan, Dir, University of Medicine & Dentistry of New Jersey, Academic Ctr, One Medical Center Dr, Stratford, NJ, 08084. Tel: 856-566-6800. Fax: 856-566-6380. p. 1532

Skidmore, Gail, Cat, Monterey Bay Aquarium Library, 886 Cannery Row, Monterey, CA, 93940-1085. Tel: 831-648-4849. Fax: 831-648-4884. p. 189

Skidmore, Kerry, Librn, Department of Veterans Affairs, 2360 E Pershing Blvd, Cheyenne, WY, 82001. Tel: 307-778-7321. Fax: 307-778-7356. p. 2652

Skidmore, Phyllis, Dir, Martha Canfield Memorial Free Library, 528 E Arlington Rd, Arlington, VT, 05250. Tel: 802-375-6153. Fax: 802-375-6153. p. 2417

Skidmore, Stephen C, Dir, Siuslaw Public Library District, 1460 Ninth St, Florence, OR, 97439-0022. Tel: 541-997-3132. Fax: 541-997-6473. p. 1998

Skidmore, Susan, Dir, Wilson Garnet A Public Library of Pike County, Piketon Branch, 200 E Second St, Piketon, OH, 45661-8047. Tel: 740-289-3064. Fax: 740-289-3064. p. 1945

Skillen, James W, Pres, Center for Public Justice Library, 2444 Solomon's Island Rd, Ste 201, Annapolis, MD, 21401. Tel: 410-571-6300. Fax: 410-571-6365. p. 1010

Skillin, Mary Lou, Br Mgr, Montclair Free Public Library, Bellevue, 185 Bellevue Ave, Upper Montclair, NJ, 07043. Tel: 973-744-2468. Fax: 973-744-3712. p. 1503

Skilton, Sarah, Dir, Oswego Public Library District, 32 W Jefferson St, Oswego, IL, 60543. Tel: 630-554-3150. Fax: 630-978-1307. p. 686

Skilton, Sarah, Dir, Oswego Public Library District, Montgomery Branch, 1111 Reading Dr, Montgomery, IL, 60538. Tel: 630-554-3150. Fax: 630-978-1307. p. 686

Skinner, Angela, Asst Librn, Swaney Memorial Library, 100 Court St, New Cumberland, WV, 26047. Tel: 304-564-3471. Fax: 304-564-3471. p. 2567

Skinner, Bernell, Librn, Grifton Public Library, 568 Queen St, Grifton, NC, 28530. Tel: 252-524-0345. Fax: 252-524-5545. p. 1799

Skinner, Geoffrey, Coordr, Tech Serv, Sonoma State University Library, 1801 E Cotati Ave, Rohnert Park, CA, 94928-3609. Tel: 707-664-3310. Fax: 707-664-2876. p. 219

Skinner, Jackie, Asst Dir, Otsego County Library, 700 S Otsego Ave, Gaylord, MI, 49735-1723. Tel: 989-732-5841, Ext 14. Fax: 989-732-9401. p. 1182

Skinner, Jenna, Commun Libr Mgr, Contra Costa County Library, Oakley Branch, 1050 Neroly Rd, Oakley, CA, 94561-3843. Tel: 925-625-2400. Fax: 925-625-8398. p. 209

Skinner, Jennifer, Asst Librn, Modale Public Library, 511 N Main St, Modale, IA, 51556. Tel: 712-645-2826. Fax: 712-645-2826. p. 832

Skinner, Kerry, Acq/Ser Librn, Arizona State University, College of Law, 110 S McAllister Ave, Tempe, AZ, 85287-7806. Tel: 480-965-4872. Fax: 480-965-4283. p. 83

Skinner, Robert E, Libr Dir, Xavier University of Louisiana, One Drexel Dr, New Orleans, LA, 70125-1098. Tel: 504-520-7305. Fax: 504-520-7940. p. 964

Skinner, Sherry, Ch, Lincoln County Library, Thayne Branch, 117 Peterson Pkwy, Thayne, WY, 83127. Tel: 307-883-7323. Fax: 307-883-7324. p. 2656

Skinner, Sophia, Circ/Shelving Supvr, Missouri State University-West Plains, 304 W Trish Knight St, West Plains, MO, 65775. Tel: 417-255-7945. Fax: 417-255-7944. p. 1372

Skinner, T C, Pres, MIT Science Fiction Society Library, 84 Massachusetts Ave, W20-473, Cambridge, MA, 02139-4307. Tel: 617-258-5126. p. 1078

Skinner, Timothy L, Libr Dir, Christ Central Institute, 110 Railroad Ave, Wagener, SC, 29164. Tel: 803-564-5902, Ext 5018. p. 2207

Skipper, Melissa, ILL, Marlboro County Library, 200 John Corry Rd, Bennettsville, SC, 29512. Tel: 843-479-5630. Fax: 843-479-5645. p. 2182

Skipper, Susan, Librn, Nora Sparks Warren Library, 210 N Willow St, Pauls Valley, OK, 73075. Tel: 405-238-5188. Fax: 405-238-5188. p. 1976

Skipworth, Vivian, Librn, United States Navy, Naval Weapons Stations, (WPNSTA) CHASN Library, Bldg 732, 2316 Red Bank Rd, Goose Creek, SC, 29445-8601. Tel: 843-764-7900. Fax: 843-764-4054. p. 2185

Skirpan, Rebecca, Interim Dir, Heritage Public Library, 52 Fourth St, McDonald, PA, 15057-1166. Tel: 724-926-8400. Fax: 724-926-4686. p. 2085

Skjong, Carla, Dir, Tyler Public Library, 230 N Tyler St, Tyler, MN, 56178-1161. Tel: 507-247-5556. Fax: 507-247-5557. p. 1286

Sklikas, Kate Stirk, N Metro Campus Librn, Chattahoochee Technical College Library, 980 S Cobb Dr SE, Marietta, GA, 30060-3300. Tel: 770-975-4054. Fax: 770-528-4454. p. 542

Skog, Aaron, Dir, System Wide Automated Network, c/o Metropolitan Library System, 125 Tower Dr, Burr Ridge, IL, 60527-5783. Tel: 630-734-5000. Fax: 630-734-5050. p. 2942

Skoglund, Sue, Mgr, Henry Ford Wyandotte Hospital, Rehabilitation Bldg, 4th Flr, 2333 Biddle Ave, Wyandotte, MI, 48192-4668. Tel: 734-246-7361. Fax: 734-246-6069. p. 1237

Skolarus, Linda, Mgr, Access Serv, The Henry Ford, 20900 Oakwood Blvd, Dearborn, MI, 48124-5029. Tel: 313-982-6057. Fax: 313-982-6244. p. 1167

Skold, Marlene, Librn, Our Redeemers Lutheran Church Library, 800 Tenth St S, Benson, MN, 56215. Tel: 320-843-3151. p. 1241

Skolnik, Amy E, Dir, Tyler Free Library, 81A Moosup Valley Rd, Foster, RI, 02825. Tel: 401-397-7930. Fax: 401-397-5830. p. 2166

Skolnik, Debbie, Librn, Mountain Area Health Education Center, 121 Hendersonville Rd, Asheville, NC, 28803. Tel: 828-257-4441. Fax: 828-257-4712. p. 1775

Skolrud, Emily, Circ, Northwest University, 5520 108th Ave NE, Kirkland, WA, 98083-0579. Tel: 425-889-5266. Fax: 425-889-7801. p. 2519

Skop, Vera, Dir, Inland Library System, 555 W Sixth St, San Bernardino, CA, 92140. Tel: 909-381-8257. Fax: 909-888-3171. p. 227

Skop, Vera, Exec Dir, San Bernardino, Inyo, Riverside Counties United Library Services, 555 W Sixth St, San Bernardino, CA, 92410. Tel: 909-381-8257. Fax: 909-888-3171. p. 2938

Skop, Vera, Syst Coordr, Serra Cooperative Library System, c/o San Diego Public Library, 820 E St, San Diego, CA, 92101. Tel: 619-232-1225. p. 2939

Skopelja, Elaine, Officer, Central Indiana Health Science Libraries Consortium, Indiana University School of Med Library, 975 W Walnut IB109, Indianapolis, IN, 46202. Tel: 317-274-8358. Fax: 317-274-4056. p. 2943

Skorina, Diane, Info Literacy, Instruction & Outreach, Ref, Ursinus College Library, 601 E Main St, Collegeville, PA, 19426. Tel: 610-409-3000, Ext 2302. Fax: 610-489-0634. p. 2046

Skornia, Arline, VPres, Gerald Area Library, 357 S Main St, Gerald, MO, 63037. Tel: 573-764-7323. p. 1329

Skorupsky, Anna, Cat, Circ Asst, Toronto Jewish Library, 4600 Bathurst St, 4th Flr, Toronto, ON, M2R 3V3, CANADA. Tel: 416-635-2996. Fax: 416-849-1005. p. 2859

Skory, Gary F, Dir, Midland County Historical Society Library, 3417 W Main St, Midland, MI, 48640. Tel: 989-631-5930, Ext 1300. p. 1208

Skousen, Diana, Dir, Summit County Library, 6505 N Landmark Dr, Ste 100, Park City, UT, 84098-6009. Tel: 435-615-3902. Fax: 435-615-3905. p. 2410

Skov, Catherina, Asst Librn, Waldoboro Public Library, 908 Main St, Waldoboro, ME, 04572-0768. Tel: 207-832-4484. Fax: 207-832-4484. p. 1004

Skovbjerg, Kelly W, Dir, Boerne Public Library, 451 N Main St, Bldg 100, Boerne, TX, 78006. Tel: 830-249-3053. Fax: 830-249-8410. p. 2290

Skove, Margaret, Dir, Blanden Memorial Art Museum, 920 Third Ave S, Fort Dodge, IA, 50501. Tel: 515-573-2316. Fax: 515-573-2317. p. 816

Skow, Dawn, Asst Librn, Jackson County Library, 311 Third St, Jackson, MN, 56143-1600. Tel: 507-847-4748. Fax: 507-847-5470. p. 1255

Skoworodko, Tracy, Librn, Spirit River Municipal Library, PO Box 490, Spirit River, AB, T0H 3G0, CANADA. Tel: 780-864-4038. p. 2717

Skowron, Agnes, Librn, Connecticut Clearinghouse, 334 Farmington Ave, Plainville, CT, 06062-1321. Tel: 860-793-9797. Fax: 860-793-9813. p. 364

Skowronek, Dolores, Ref Librn, Alverno College Library, 3401 S 39th St, Milwaukee, WI, 53215. Tel: 414-382-6184. Fax: 414-382-6354. p. 2617

Skpolja, Elaine, Knowledge Mgr, Outreach Coordr, Indiana University, Ruth Lilly Medical Library, 975 W Walnut St, IB 100, Indianapolis, IN, 46202-5121. Tel: 317-274-8358. Fax: 317-278-2349. p. 752

Skrade, Dennis, Head, Tech Serv, Minnesota State Law Library, Minnesota Judicial Ctr, Rm G25, 25 Rev Dr Martin Luther King Jr Blvd, Saint Paul, MN, 55155. Tel: 651-296-2775. Fax: 651-296-6740. p. 1280

Skrebutenas, Katherine, Ref, Princeton Theological Seminary, Mercer St & Library Pl, Princeton, NJ, 08542. Tel: 609-497-7940. Fax: 609-497-1826. p. 1522

Skreslet, Paula, Archives Librn, Ref Librn, Union Theological Seminary & Presbyterian School of Christian Education, 3401 Brook Rd, Richmond, VA, 23227. Tel: 804-278-4310. Fax: 804-278-4375. p. 2490

Skrimstad, Mark, Tech Serv, Supreme Court Law Library, 417 S King St, Rm 115, Honolulu, HI, 96813. Tel: 808-539-4964. Fax: 808-539-4974. p. 565

Skrodelis, Uldis, Br Mgr, Brooklyn Public Library, Brooklyn Heights, 280 Cadman Plaza W, Brooklyn, NY, 11201. Tel: 718-623-7100. Fax: 718-222-5681. p. 1591

Skrtic, John, Dir, Pub Serv, Cleveland Public Library, 325 Superior Ave, Cleveland, OH, 44114-1271. Tel: 216-623-2878. p. 1877

Skruch, Gail, Bus Mgr, Loutit District Library, 407 Columbus Ave, Grand Haven, MI, 49417. Tel: 616-842-5560, Ext 231. Fax: 616-847-0570. p. 1183

Skurdenis, Julie, Dep Librn, Bronx Community College Library & Learning Center, 106 Meister Hall, 2115 University Ave, Bronx, NY, 10453. Tel: 718-289-5439, 718-289-5548. Fax: 718-289-6063. p. 1586

Skuret, Daniel D, Jr, In Charge, Law Office of Daniel D Skuret Pc Library, 215 Division St, Ansonia, CT, 06401. Tel: 203-736-9934. Fax: 203-734-3484. p. 329

Skutnik, Samantha C, Dir, Case Western Reserve University, Lillian F & Milford J Harris Library, Mandel School of Applied Social Sciences, 11235 Bellflower Rd, Cleveland, OH, 44106-7164. Tel: 216-368-2283. Fax: 216-368-2106. p. 1876

Skvara, Mary, Curator, Whiting-Robertsdale Historical Society Museum, 1610 119th St, Whiting, IN, 46394. Tel: 219-659-1432. p. 788

Skwara, Dee, Head, Circ, Willingboro Public Library, Willingboro Town Ctr, 220 Willingboro Pkwy, Willingboro, NJ, 08046. Tel: 609-877-0476, 609-877-6668. Fax: 609-835-1699. p. 1544

Skwara, Michael, Circ, Pub Serv, Highland Community College Library, 2998 W Pearl City Rd, Freeport, IL, 61032-9341. Tel: 815-599-3657. Fax: 815-235-1366. p. 647

Skwerski, Jill, Br Mgr, Evanston Public Library, South, 949 Chicago Ave, Evanston, IL, 60202. Tel: 847-866-0333. Fax: 847-866-0332. p. 643

Skwor, Jeanette, Ser, University of Wisconsin-Green Bay, 2420 Nicolet Dr, Green Bay, WI, 54311-7001. Tel: 920-465-2670. Fax: 920-465-2136. p. 2596

Skypeck, James R, Head, Pub Serv, Boston University Libraries, School of Theology Library, 745 Commonwealth Ave, 2nd Flr, Boston, MA, 02215. Tel: 617-353-3034. Fax: 617-358-0699. p. 1058

Slachta, Karen, Head, Ch, Head, Youth Serv, Valley Community Library, 739 River St, Peckville, PA, 18452. Tel: 570-489-1765. p. 2102

Slack, Anita, Info Serv Librn, Vincennes University, Shake Learning Resources Center, 1002 N First St, Vincennes, IN, 47591. Tel: 812-888-5377. Fax: 812-888-5471. p. 784

Slack, Becky, Tech Serv, Brevard County Library System, 308 Forrest Ave, 2nd Flr, Cocoa, FL, 32922-7781. Tel: 321-633-1785. Fax: 321-633-1798. p. 433

Slack, Judy, Spec Coll Librn, Sheridan County Public Library System, 335 W Alger St, Sheridan, WY, 82801-3899. Tel: 307-674-8585, Ext 5. p. 2660

Slack, Marion, Ref Serv, Framingham State College, 100 State St, Framingham, MA, 01701. Tel: 508-626-4651. Fax: 508-626-4649. p. 1090

Slade, Alexander, Exec Dir, Council of Prairie & Pacific University Libraries, 2005 Sooke Rd, Victoria, BC, V9B 5Y2, CANADA. Tel: 250-391-2554. Fax: 250-391-2556. p. 2959

Slade, Eleanor, Br Mgr, San Diego County Library, Ramona Branch, 1275 Main St, Ramona, CA, 92065. Tel: 760-738-2434. Fax: 760-738-2475. p. 234

Slade, Grant, Sr Info Spec, American Water Works Association, 6666 W Quincy Ave, Denver, CO, 80235. Tel: 303-347-6170. Fax: 303-795-7603. p. 298

Slade, Kent, Dir, Highland City Library, 5400 W Civic Center Dr, Ste 2, Highland, UT, 84003. Tel: 801-772-4528. Fax: 801-756-6903. p. 2406

Sladger, Anne, Dir, Brigham & Women's Hospital, Thorn 127, 75 Francis St, Boston, MA, 02115. Tel: 617-732-5684. Fax: 617-975-0890. p. 1059

Slagell, Jeff M, Dir, Delta State University, Laflore Circle at Fifth Ave, Cleveland, MS, 38733-2599. Tel: 662-846-4440. Fax: 662-846-4443. p. 1296

Slagle, Anna P, Acq of Monographs, King College, 1350 King College Rd, Bristol, TN, 37620. Tel: 423-652-4716. Fax: 423-652-4871. p. 2225

Slagle, Lusetta, Br Mgr, Washington County - Jonesborough Library, 200 Sabin Dr, Jonesborough, TN, 37659-1306. Tel: 423-753-1800. Fax: 423-753-1802. p. 2240

Slagle, Lusetta, Br Mgr, Washington County - Jonesborough Library, Gray Branch, 5026 Bobby Hicks Hwy, Gray, TN, 37615-3461. Tel: 423-477-1559. Fax: 423-477-1553. p. 2240

Slagle, Vanessa, Librn, Clearwater Christian College, 3400 Gulf-to-Bay Blvd, Clearwater, FL, 33759-4595. Tel: 727-726-1153, Ext 218. Fax: 727-723-8566. p. 431

Slaight, Wilma, Archivist, Wellesley College, 106 Central St, Wellesley, MA, 02481-8275. Tel: 781-283-2128. Fax: 781-283-3796. p. 1135

Slais, Debbie, Dir, Williston Community Library, 1302 Davidson Dr, Williston, ND, 58801. Tel: 701-774-8805. Fax: 701-572-1186. p. 1849

Slamin, Mary, Ch, Greenburgh Public Library, 300 Tarrytown Rd, Elmsford, NY, 10523. Tel: 914-721-8200. Fax: 914-721-8201. p. 1620

Slaminski, Candace Hall, Sr Info Spec, Michael Best & Friedrich LLP, 100 E Wisconsin Ave, Milwaukee, WI, 53202-4108. Tel: 414-271-6560. Fax: 414-277-0656. p. 2619

Slaney, Jennifer, Dir, Sterling Public Library, 102 W Third St, Sterling, IL, 61081-3504. Tel: 815-625-1370. Fax: 815-625-7037. p. 707

Slanger, Nancy, Libr Syst Mgr, Alliant International University, One Beach St, Ste 100, San Francisco, CA, 94133. Tel: 415-955-2155. Fax: 415-955-2180. p. 240

Slaninka, Linda S, Dir, Swanton Local School District Public Library, 305 Chestnut St, Swanton, OH, 43558. Tel: 419-826-2760. Fax: 419-826-1020. p. 1937

Slapsys, Richard, Ref Librn, University of Massachusetts Lowell Libraries, 61 Wilder St, Lowell, MA, 01854-3098. Tel: 978-934-4593. Fax: 978-934-3015. p. 1100

Slaska, Karen, Mgr, Programming & Youth Serv, Citrus County Library System, Lakes Region, 1511 Druid Rd, Inverness, FL, 34452-4507. Tel: 352-726-2357. Fax: 352-726-2814. p. 427

Slate, Barbara, Automation Librn, Lubbock Christian University Library, 5601 19th St, Lubbock, TX, 79407-2009. Tel: 806-720-7326. p. 2357

Slate, John H, Archivist, Dallas Municipal Archives, City Hall, Rm 5-D South, 1500 Marilla St, Dallas, TX, 75201. Tel: 214-670-3738. Fax: 214-670-5029. p. 2306

Slate, Linda, Ch, Jonathan Trumbull Library, 580 Exeter Rd, Lebanon, CT, 06249. Tel: 860-642-2020, 860-642-7763. Fax: 860-642-4880. p. 349

Slate, Selina, Acq, Toccoa Falls College, PO Box 800749, Toccoa Falls, GA, 30598. Tel: 706-886-6831, Ext 5300. Fax: 706-282-6010. p. 554

Slaten, Marie, Tech Serv, Ruidoso Public Library, 107 Kansas City Rd, Ruidoso, NM, 88345. Tel: 505-258-3704. Fax: 505-258-4619. p. 1561

Slater Acosta, Elisa, Instruction Coordr, Ref & Instruction, Loyola Marymount University, One LMU Dr, MS 8200, Los Angeles, CA, 90045-2659. Tel: 310-338-7679. Fax: 310-338-4366. p. 175

Slater, Bill, Acq, Brigham Young University, Harold B Lee Library, 2060 HBLL, Provo, UT, 84602. Tel: 801-422-2927. Fax: 801-422-0466. p. 2411

Slater, Cindy, Dir, United States Olympic Committee, 1750 E Boulder, Colorado Springs, CO, 80909. Tel: 719-866-4622. Fax: 719-632-5352. p. 296

Slater, Cynthia, Bus Librn, Saint Joseph's University, Francis A Drexel Library, 5600 City Ave, Philadelphia, PA, 19131-1395. Tel: 610-660-1139. Fax: 610-660-1916. p. 2116

Slater, Darlene, Pub Serv, Ref, Virginia Baptist Historical Society & the Center for Baptist Heritage & Studies Library, PO Box 34, University of Richmond, Richmond, VA, 23173. Tel: 804-289-8434. Fax: 804-289-8953. p. 2492

Slater, John, Librn, Oklahoma State Reformatory Library, 1700 E First St, Granite, OK, 73547. Tel: 580-480-3700. Fax: 580-480-3989. p. 1964

Slater, Kay, Asst Dir, Sunflower County Library System, 201 Cypress Dr, Indianola, MS, 38751-2499. Tel: 662-887-1672. Fax: 662-887-1618. p. 1302

Slater, Linda, Pub Serv Mgr, University of Alberta, John W Scott Health Sciences Library, Walter C Mackenzie Health Sciences Ctr 2K3 28, Edmonton, AB, T6G 2R7, CANADA. Tel: 780-492-7948. Fax: 780-492-6960. p. 2702

Slater, Mary C, Librn, Murrell Memorial Library, Missouri Valley College, Tech Center Bldg, 500 E College St, Marshall, MO, 65340. Tel: 660-831-4180, 660-831-4181. Fax: 660-831-4068. p. 1344

Slater, Patricia, Head, Ch, Redford Township District Library, 25320 W Six Mile, Redford, MI, 48240. Tel: 313-531-5960. Fax: 313-531-1721. p. 1220

Slater, Sandy, Head, Genealogy Libr, Nebraska Prairie Museum, N Hwy 183, Holdrege, NE, 68949. Tel: 308-995-5015. Fax: 308-995-2241. p. 1402

Slater, Susan, Ch, Warren Library Association, 205 Market St, Warren, PA, 16365. Tel: 814-723-4650. Fax: 814-723-4521. p. 2151

Slating, Beth, Head, Tech Serv, Montgomery County-Norristown Public Library, 1001 Powell St, Norristown, PA, 19401-3817. Tel: 610-278-5100, Ext 118. p. 2098

Slaton, Debra, Dir, Marshall County Cooperative Library, 600 College St, Ste 100, Albertville, AL, 35950-2722. Tel: 256-878-8523. Fax: 256-878-9562. p. 3

Slaton, Gwendolyn C, Dir, Essex County College Library, 303 University Ave, Newark, NJ, 07102. Tel: 973-877-3238. Fax: 973-877-1887. p. 1510

Slaton, Gwendolyn C, Dir, Essex County College Library, Branch Campus, 730 Bloomfield Ave, West Caldwell, NJ, 07007. Tel: 973-877-1883. Fax: 973-877-6635. p. 1510

Slaton, Karen, Sr Librn, Tampa-Hillsborough County Public Library System, Seventy-Eighth Street Community Library, 7625 Palm River Rd, Tampa, FL, 33619-4131. Fax: 813-612-9125. p. 498

Slaton, Vanessa, Ch, Atlanta-Fulton Public Library System, Cleveland Avenue, 47 Cleveland Ave, Atlanta, GA, 30315. Tel: 404-762-4116. Fax: 404-762-4118. p. 511

Slatt, Vincent, Ref Serv, United States Holocaust Memorial Museum Library, 100 Raoul Wallenberg Pl SW, Washington, DC, 20024. Tel: 202-479-9717. Fax: 202-479-9726. p. 420

Slattery, Patrice, Archivist, University of North Carolina School of the Arts, 1533 S Main St, Winston-Salem, NC, 27127. Tel: 336-770-3270. Fax: 336-770-3271. p. 1834

Slattery-Thomas, Pamela, Librn, Soldiers Memorial Library, 85 Main St, Hiram, ME, 04041-3208. Tel: 207-625-4650. p. 988

Slauenwhite, Bill, Mgr, Novanet, 84 Chain Lake Dr, No 402, Halifax, NS, B3S 1A2, CANADA. Tel: 902-453-2470. Fax: 902-453-2369. p. 2959

Slaughter, Decca, Br Mgr, Forsyth County Public Library, Southside, 3185 Buchanan St, Winston-Salem, NC, 27127. Tel: 336-703-2980. Fax: 336-771-4724. p. 1832

Slaughter, Gloria, Tech Serv Librn, Hope College, Van Wylen Library, 53 Graves Pl, Holland, MI, 49422. Tel: 616-395-7793. Fax: 616-395-7965. p. 1190

Slaughter, Kerry, Circ Mgr, Central Washington University, 400 E University Way, Ellensburg, WA, 98926-7548. Tel: 509-963-1901. Fax: 509-963-3684. p. 2514

Slaughter, Paul, Br Mgr, Whitman County Rural Library District, Albion Branch, 310 F St, Albion, WA, 99102. Tel: 509-338-9641. p. 2512

Slaughter, Philenese H, Coordr, Instrul Serv, Austin Peay State University, 601 E College St, Clarksville, TN, 37044. Tel: 931-221-7741. Fax: 931-221-7296. p. 2228

Slaughter, Sharlene, Asst Librn, Belle Plaine City Library, 222 W Fifth Ave, Belle Plaine, KS, 67013. Tel: 620-488-3431. p. 857

Slaughter, Tanya, Ref & ILL Librn, Grand Prairie Public Library System, 901 Conover Dr, Grand Prairie, TX, 75051. Tel: 972-237-5700. Fax: 972-237-5750. p. 2329

Slaven, Donald, Commun Libr Mgr, County of Los Angeles Public Library, Claremont Library, 208 N Harvard Ave, Claremont, CA, 91711. Tel: 909-621-4902. Fax: 909-621-2366. p. 141

Slavick, Steven, Br Mgr, Algonquin Area Public Library District, 2600 Harnish Dr, Algonquin, IL, 60102-5900. Tel: 847-458-6060, 847-658-4343. Fax: 847-458-9370. p. 588

Slavin, Joan H, Librn, AmerGen Energy, Three Mile Island Nuclear Generating Sta, PO Box 480, Middletown, PA, 17057. Tel: 717-948-8105. Fax: 717-948-8824. p. 2089

Slay, Jana, Acq, Troy University Library, 309 Wallace Hall, 501 University Ave, Troy, AL, 36082. Tel: 334-670-3258. Fax: 334-670-3694. p. 37

Slaybaugh, Linda, Ch, Basalt Regional Library District, 14 Midland Ave, Basalt, CO, 81621-8305. Tel: 970-927-4311. Fax: 970-927-1351. p. 289

Sleasman, David, Supvr, Res Sharing Tech, Wisconsin Department of Public Instruction, Reference & Loan Library, 2109 S Stoughton Rd, Madison, WI, 53716-2899. Tel: 608-224-6179. Fax: 608-224-6178. p. 2610

Sled, Jill, Head Librn, Pioneer Pacific College Library, 27375 SW Parkway Ave, Wilsonville, OR, 97070. Tel: 503-682-1862. p. 2023

Sledd, Marcia, Ch, Delphi Public Library, 222 E Main St, Delphi, IN, 46923. Tel: 765-564-2929. Fax: 765-564-4746. p. 735

Sledge, Bridget, Ref, Benedict College Library, 1600 Harden St, Columbia, SC, 29204. Tel: 803-705-4364. Fax: 803-748-7539. p. 2186

Sledge, Sarah, Br Mgr, Huntsville-Madison Public Library, Madison Public Library, 130 Plaza Blvd, Madison, AL, 35758. Tel: 256-461-0046. Fax: 256-461-0530. p. 21

Slee, Joy, Librn, Dorothy Hull Windsor Township Library, 405 W Jefferson St, Dimondale, MI, 48821. Tel: 517-646-0633. Fax: 517-646-7061. p. 1174

Sleefe, Charles, Dir, Mineola Memorial Library, 195 Marcellus Rd, Mineola, NY, 11501. Tel: 516-746-8488. Fax: 516-294-6459. p. 1661

Sleeman, Bill, Asst Dir, Tech Serv, University of Maryland, Baltimore, Thurgood Marshall Law Library, 501 W Fayette St, Baltimore, MD, 21201-1768. Tel: 410-706-0783. Fax: 410-706-8354. p. 1019

Sleeth, James G, Dir, Chemung County Library District, 101 E Church St, Elmira, NY, 14901-2799. Tel: 607-733-8611. Fax: 607-733-9176. p. 1619

Sleeth, Peggy, Assoc Dir, Info Res, Dartmouth College Library, Biomedical Libraries (Dana Biomedical & Matthews-Fuller Health Sciences Library), Dana Biomedical Library/HB 6168, 64 College St, Hanover, NH, 03755-3563. Tel: 603-650-1635. p. 1450

Sleight, Kathie, Dir, Essential Club Free Library, 11 Pratt St, Canaseraga, NY, 14822. Tel: 607-545-6443. Fax: 607-545-6443. p. 1601

Sleister, Patricia, Dir, Mary Barnett Memorial Library, 400 Grand St, Guthrie Center, IA, 50115-1439. Tel: 641-747-8110. Fax: 641-747-8110. p. 820

Slemin, Charby, Br Mgr, Halifax Public Libraries, Woodlawn Public, 31 Eisener Blvd, Dartmouth, NS, B2W 0J1, CANADA. Tel: 902-435-8352. Fax: 902-435-8380. p. 2779

Slemmons, David, Librn, Oklahoma Library for the Blind & Physically Handicapped, 300 NE 18th St, Oklahoma City, OK, 73105. Tel: 405-521-3514. Fax: 405-521-4582. p. 1975

Slepian, Jean, Librn, Cheshire Medical Center, 580 Court St, Keene, NH, 03431. Tel: 603-354-6664. p. 1452

Slepian, Jean, Librn, Monadnock Community Hospital, 452 Old Street Rd, Peterborough, NH, 03458. Tel: 603-924-7191, Ext 1100. p. 1462

Slessor, Janet, Dir, Reinbeck Public Library, 501 Clark St, Reinbeck, IA, 50669. Tel: 319-788-2652. Fax: 319-788-2826. p. 840

Sletten, Marcelyn, Sr Librn, Hennepin County Library, Minneapolis Central, 300 Nicollet Mall, Minneapolis, MN, 55401. Tel: 612-543-8143. Fax: 612-543-8173. p. 1264

Slezak, Regina, Dir, Newport Public Library, 300 Spring St, Newport, RI, 02840. Tel: 401-847-8720. Fax: 401-842-0841. p. 2169

Slicer, Peggy, Librn, Shawano City-County Library, Tigerton Public, 221 Birch St, Tigerton, WI, 54486. Tel: 715-535-2194. Fax: 715-535-2666. p. 2637

Slife, Daniel, Dir, Huron Public Library, 333 Williams St, Huron, OH, 44839. Tel: 419-433-5009. Fax: 419-433-7228. p. 1906

Slife, Joye D P, Dir, Libr & Info Serv, Emmanuel College Library, 2261 W Main St, Franklin Springs, GA, 30639. Tel: 706-245-7226, Ext 2850. Fax: 706-245-4424. p. 534

Sligh, Jacqueline, Br Mgr, Richland County Public Library, Northeast Regional, 7490 Parklane Rd, Columbia, SC, 29223. Tel: 803-736-6575. p. 2188

Slight-Gibney, Nancy, Dir, Res Mgt & Assessment, University of Oregon Libraries, 1501 Kincaid St, Eugene, OR, 97403-1299. Tel: 541-346-3056. Fax: 541-346-3485. p. 1997

Slimman, Katherine, Coordr, Ontario Library Consortium, Owen Sound & North Grey Union Public Library, 824 First Ave W, Owen Sound, ON, N4K 4K4, CANADA. Tel: 905-627-8662. p. 2960

Slinger, Michael J, Assoc Dean, Info Serv & Tech, Dir, Legal Info Ctr, Widener University, School of Law Library, 4601 Concord Pike, Wilmington, DE, 19803. Tel: 302-477-2111. Fax: 302-477-2228. p. 389

Slinger, Michael J, Dir, Widener University, Harrisburg Campus Law Library, 3800 Vartan Way, Harrisburg, DE, 17110. Tel: 302-477-2111. Fax: 302-477-2228. p. 389

Slingluff, Deborah, Assoc Dir, Johns Hopkins University Libraries, The Sheridan Libraries, 3400 N Charles St, Baltimore, MD, 21218. Tel: 410-516-8254. Fax: 410-516-5080. p. 1014

Slingsby, Cecilia, Head, Tech Serv, Hastings Public Library, 517 W Fourth St, Hastings, NE, 68901-7560. Tel: 402-461-2346. Fax: 402-461-2359. p. 1401

Slipsky, Mary Jane, Res Librn, Nelson, Mullins, Riley & Scarborough, 1320 Main St, Ste 1700, Columbia, SC, 29201. Tel: 919-877-3858. Fax: 803-255-7500. p. 2188

Slive, Daniel, Head, Spec Coll, Southern Methodist University, Bridwell Library-Perkins School of Theology, 6005 Bishop Blvd, Dallas, TX, 75205. Tel: 214-768-3483. Fax: 214-768-4295. p. 2310

Slivers, Cindy, AV, Dine College, PO Box 1000, Tsaile, AZ, 86556. Tel: 928-724-6758. p. 85

Slivka, Krystal K, Chief Med Librn, Aultman Hospital, Aultman Education Ctr, C2-230, 2600 Seventh St SW, Canton, OH, 44710-1799. Tel: 330-363-5000. Fax: 330-363-2604. p. 1863

Slivka, Regina, Dir, E C Weber Fraser Public Library, 16330 Fourteen Mile Rd, Fraser, MI, 48026-2034. Tel: 586-293-2055. Fax: 586-294-5777. p. 1181

Slivken, David, Asst Dir, Dayton Metro Library, 215 E Third St, Dayton, OH, 45402-2103. Tel: 937-463-2665. Fax: 937-496-4300. p. 1892

Slizewski, Kathryn, Asst Librn, Gogebic Community College, E4946 Jackson Rd, Ironwood, MI, 49938. Tel: 906-932-4231, Ext 270. Fax: 906-932-0868. p. 1194

Sloam, Myrna, Archivist, Bryant Library, Two Paper Mill Rd, Roslyn, NY, 11576-2193. Tel: 516-621-2240. Fax: 516-621-7211. p. 1735

Sloan, Catherine, Librn, United States Navy, Naval Undersea Warfare Center Division, Newport Technical Library, 1176 Howell St, Bldg 101, Newport, RI, 02841. Tel: 401-832-4338. Fax: 401-832-3699. p. 2170

Sloan, Cindy, Librn, St Joseph Hospital, 172 Kinsley St, Nashua, NH, 03061. Tel: 603-595-3143. Fax: 603-595-3124. p. 1459

Sloan, D, Per, Sir Sandford Fleming College of Applied Arts & Technology Library, 599 Brealey Dr, Peterborough, ON, K9J 7B1, CANADA. Tel: 705-749-5530. Fax: 705-749-5542. p. 2836

Sloan, Lynette, Dir, Regional Libr, Planning & Develop, Tennessee State Library & Archives, 403 Seventh Ave N, Nashville, TN, 37243-0312. Tel: 615-741-3158. Fax: 615-532-2472, 615-741-6471. p. 2259

Sloan, Marcia, ILL, Indiana University East Campus Library, 2325 Chester Blvd, Richmond, IN, 47374. Tel: 765-973-8311. Fax: 765-973-8315. p. 775

Sloan, Nancy, Dir, Springfield Library, 129 County Hwy 29A, Springfield Center, NY, 13468. Tel: 315-858-5802. Fax: 315-858-5876. p. 1747

Sloan, Nancy, Cat, Furman University Libraries, 3300 Poinsett Hwy, Greenville, SC, 29613-4100. Tel: 864-294-2197. Fax: 864-294-3004. p. 2195

Sloan, Polly Anna, Librn, Haywood Community College, 185 Freedlander Dr, Clyde, NC, 28721. Tel: 828-565-4083. Fax: 828-627-4553. p. 1785

Sloan, Rebecca, Br Mgr, Mercer County Library System, Twin Rivers Branch, 276 Abbington Dr, East Windsor, NJ, 08520. Tel: 609-443-1880. Fax: 609-490-0186. p. 1494

Sloan, Robert C, Ref, Saint Mary's College of Maryland Library, 18952 E Fisher Rd, Saint Mary's City, MD, 20686-3001. Tel: 240-895-4268. Fax: 240-895-4914. p. 1040

Sloan, Shannon, Cat, Shelton State Community College, 9500 Old Greensboro Rd, Tuscaloosa, AL, 35405. Tel: 205-391-2440. Fax: 205-391-3926. p. 38

Sloan, Stephen, Head Librn, University of New Brunswick Libraries, Science & Forestry, Four Bailey Dr, Fredericton, NB, E3B 5H5, CANADA. Tel: 506-453-4601, 506-458-7759. Fax: 506-453-3518. p. 2764

Sloan, Steve, Admin Librn, Sunnyvale Public Library, 665 W Olive Ave, Sunnyvale, CA, 94086-7622. Tel: 408-730-7300. Fax: 408-735-8767. p. 273

Sloan, Tom, Mgr, Libr Serv, Boca Raton Public Library, 200 NW Boca Raton Blvd, Boca Raton, FL, 33432-3706. Tel: 561-393-7916. Fax: 561-393-7823. p. 428

Sloane, Ann, Libr Mgr, Kelley, Drye & Warren, Washington Harbour, 3050 K St, Ste 400, Washington, DC, 20007-5108. Tel: 202-342-8400. Fax: 202-342-8451. p. 406

Sloboden, Barbara, Librn, Anoka-Ramsey Community College, 11200 Mississippi Blvd NW, Coon Rapids, MN, 55433. Tel: 763-433-1466. p. 1246

Slocomb, Kim, Br Mgr, Pub Serv, Citrus County Library System, Central Ridge, 425 W Roosevelt Blvd, Beverly Hills, FL, 34465-4281. Tel: 352-746-6622. Fax: 352-746-4170. p. 427

Slocomb, Marianne, Dir, Rhode Island Hospital, 593 Eddy St, Providence, RI, 02902. Tel: 401-444-4671. p. 2174

Slocum, Kathleen, Continuing Educ Coordr, South Dakota State Library, 800 Governors Dr, Pierre, SD, 57501-2294. Tel: 605-773-3131. p. 2216

Slomka, Maggie, Libr Tech, Tech Serv, College of Southern Nevada, 6375 W Charleston Blvd, W10I, Las Vegas, NV, 89146. Tel: 702-651-5882. Fax: 702-651-7643. p. 1429

Slomski, Monica, Ref Serv, Milford Public Library, 57 New Haven Ave, Milford, CT, 06460. Tel: 203-783-3290. Fax: 203-877-1072. p. 352

Slone, Brian, Syst Librn, Fort Lewis College Library, 1000 Rim Dr, Durango, CO, 81301-3999. Tel: 970-247-7250. Fax: 970-247-7149. p. 305

Sloneker, Mark, Cataloger, Co-Dir, Ozark Christian College, 1111 N Main, Joplin, MO, 64801-4804. Tel: 417-626-1234, Ext 2713. Fax: 417-624-0090. p. 1336

Slopek, Linda, Dir, Carnegie Free Library, 61 Ninth St, Midland, PA, 15059-1503. Tel: 724-643-8980. Fax: 724-643-8985. p. 2089

Slossar, Bobbi Lee, Tech Res Librn, New Hampshire State Library, 20 Park St, Concord, NH, 03301-6314. Tel: 603-271-2143. Fax: 603-271-2205, 603-271-6826. p. 1443

Slote, Nancy, Br Mgr, Seattle Public Library, Capitol Hill, 425 Harvard Ave E, Seattle, WA, 98102. Tel: 206-684-4715. p. 2531

Slote, Nancy, Br Mgr, Seattle Public Library, Montlake, 2401 24th Ave E, Seattle, WA, 98112. Tel: 206-684-4720. p. 2531

Slotsve, Susan, Librn, Parkland Regional Library, Esterhazy Branch, 624 Main St, Esterhazy, SK, S0A 0X0, CANADA. Tel: 306-745-6406. p. 2932

Slough, Barbara, Librn, Rockbridge Regional Library, Glasgow Public, 1108 Blueridge Rd, Glasgow, VA, 24555. Tel: 540-258-2509. p. 2474

Slough, Eileen, Ch, Atlanta-Fulton Public Library System, Southwest Regional Library, 3665 Cascade Rd SW, Atlanta, GA, 30331. Tel: 404-699-6363. Fax: 404-699-6381. p. 512

Slough, Marlene, Head, Acq, Eastern Illinois University, 600 Lincoln Ave, Charleston, IL, 61920. Tel: 217-581-6021. Fax: 217-581-7379. p. 603

Slovasky, Stephen, Bibliog Serv, Connecticut State Library, 231 Capitol Ave, Hartford, CT, 06106. Tel: 860-757-6546. Fax: 860-757-6503. p. 345

Sloves, David H, Librn, Peckar & Abramson, 70 Grand Ave, River Edge, NJ, 07661. Tel: 201-343-3434. Fax: 201-343-6306. p. 1526

Sluck, Jeanie, Librn, Taylor Community Library, 710 Main St, Taylor, PA, 18517-1774. Tel: 570-562-3180. Fax: 570-562-3140. p. 2145

Sluis, Lisa Vander, Ch, Le Mars Public Library, 46 First St SW, Le Mars, IA, 51031-3696. Tel: 712-546-5004. Fax: 712-546-5797. p. 827

Sluss, Peggy, Circ Support, Malone University, 2600 Cleveland Ave NW, Canton, OH, 44709-3897. Tel: 330-471-8215. Fax: 330-454-6977. p. 1863

Slutsky, Carol, Ref Serv, Norton Rose Canada LLP Library, One Place Ville Marie, Ste 2500, Montreal, QC, H3B 1R1, CANADA. Tel: 514-847-4701. Fax: 514-286-5474. p. 2900

Slutzky, Amy, Ref Librn, SUNY Upstate Medical University, 766 Irving Ave, Syracuse, NY, 13210-1602. Tel: 315-464-7104. Fax: 315-464-4584. p. 1753

Sluzenski, Karen, Ref Librn, Dartmouth College Library, Feldberg Business Administration & Engineering Library, 6193 Murdough Ctr, Hanover, NH, 03755-3560. Tel: 603-646-2191. Fax: 603-646-2384. p. 1450

Slymon, Susan, Libr Dir, Turner Free Library, Two N Main St, Randolph, MA, 02368. Tel: 781-961-0932. Fax: 781-961-0933. p. 1120

Slyter, Dolores Jean, In Charge, Eastern Shore Hospital Center Professional Library, 5262 Woods Rd, Cambridge, MD, 21613-3796. Tel: 410-221-2485. Fax: 410-221-2475. p. 1022

Smail, Leslie, Dir, United States Air Force, 42 Ash Ave, Langley AFB, VA, 23665. Tel: 757-764-2906. Fax: 757-764-3315. p. 2473

Smailes, Suzanne, Head, Tech Serv, Wittenberg University, 807 Woodlawn Ave, Springfield, OH, 45504. Tel: 937-327-7020. Fax: 937-327-6139. p. 1936

Smaistrla, Geraldine, Asst Dir, Wharton County Library, 1920 N Fulton, Wharton, TX, 77488. Tel: 979-532-8080. p. 2400

Smale, Evan, Electronic Serv Librn, Novi Public Library, 45245 W Ten Mile Rd, Novi, MI, 48375. Tel: 248-349-0720. Fax: 248-349-6520. p. 1214

Small, Anne, Dir, Bethlehem Public Library, 32 Main St S, Bethlehem, CT, 06751. Tel: 203-266-7792. Fax: 203-266-7792. p. 330

Small, Carol, ILL, Independence Community College Library, 1057 W College Ave, Independence, KS, 67301. Tel: 620-331-4100. Fax: 620-331-6821. p. 873

Small, Carrie Mills, In Charge, Jewish Federation Libraries, Jewish Community Center Library, 801 Percy Warner Blvd, Nashville, TN, 37205. Tel: 615-354-1699. Fax: 615-352-0056. p. 2256

Small, Cheryl, Asst Br Mgr, Ch, Atlanta-Fulton Public Library System, South Fulton Regional Library, 4055 Flatshoals Rd SW, Union City, GA, 30291. Tel: 770-306-3092. Fax: 770-306-3127. p. 512

Small, Donna, Head, Ref, Hershey Public Library, 701 Cocoa Ave, Hershey, PA, 17033. Tel: 717-533-6555. Fax: 717-534-1666. p. 2069

Small, Kevin, ILL, Grayson County Public Library, 130 E Market St, Leitchfield, KY, 42754-1439. Tel: 270-259-5455. Fax: 270-259-4552. p. 920

Small, Sue, Exec Dir, Historic Schaefferstown, Inc, 111 N Market St, Schaefferstown, PA, 17088. Tel: 717-949-2444. p. 2136

Smallen, David, Dr, Dir, Hamilton College, 198 College Hill Rd, Clinton, NY, 13323-1299. Tel: 315-859-4489. Fax: 315-859-4578. p. 1607

Smallen, Tammy, Librn, Loudon Public Library, 210 River Rd, Loudon, TN, 37774. Tel: 865-458-3161. Fax: 865-458-3161. p. 2245

Smalley, Gene, Librn, Watchtower Bible School of Gilead Library, 100 Watchtower Dr, Patterson, NY, 12563-9204. Tel: 718-560-5000. p. 1715

Smalley, Lorraine, Tech Coordr, Pine Mountain Regional Library, 218 Perry St NW, Manchester, GA, 31816-1317. Tel: 706-846-3851. Fax: 706-846-8455, 706-846-9632. p. 542

Smalley, Martha Lund, Spec Coll Librn/Curator, Day Missions Coll, Syst Mgr, Yale University Library, Divinity School Library, 409 Prospect St, New Haven, CT, 06511-2108. Tel: 203-432-5289. Fax: 203-432-3906. p. 357

Smallidge, Elisabeth, Librn, United States Army, 72 Lyme Rd, Hanover, NH, 03755-1290. Tel: 603-646-4238. Fax: 603-646-4712. p. 1450

Smalling, Sheigla, Supvr, Montefiore Hospital-North Division, 600 E 233rd St, Rm B-11, Bronx, NY, 10466. Tel: 718-920-9869. Fax: 718-920-9407. p. 1588

Smalling, Sheigla, Dir, Montefiore Medical Center, 111 E 210th St, Bronx, NY, 10467. Tel: 718-920-4666. Fax: 718-920-4658. p. 1588

Smalt, Ruth, Exec Dir, Rye Historical Society Library, One Purchase St, Rye, NY, 10580. Tel: 914-967-7588. Fax: 914-967-6253. p. 1736

Smart, Anne, Librn, Boston Public Library, South End, 685 Tremont St, Boston, MA, 02118-3198. Tel: 617-536-8241. Fax: 617-266-8993. p. 1057

Smart, Carmen, Libr Mgr, Marwayne Public Library, PO Box 174, Marwayne, AB, T0B 2X0, CANADA. Tel: 780-847-3930. Fax: 780-847-3796. p. 2711

Smart, Emilie, Ref & Computer Serv Coordr, East Baton Rouge Parish Library, 7711 Goodwood Blvd, Baton Rouge, LA, 70806-7625. Tel: 225-231-3735. Fax: 225-231-3788. p. 942

Smart, J, Info Spec, Canadian Pacific Railway, 401 Ninth Ave SW, 7th Flr, Calgary, AB, T2P 4Z4, CANADA. Tel: 403-319-6189. Fax: 403-319-6257. p. 2691

Smart, Lana, Dir, National Business & Disability Council, 201 I U Willetts Rd, Albertson, NY, 11507-1599. Tel: 516-465-1519. Fax: 516-465-3730. p. 1571

Smart, Laura, Metadata Serv Mgr, California Institute of Technology, 1200 E California Blvd, M/C 1-32, Pasadena, CA, 91125-3200. Tel: 626-395-6149. Fax: 626-792-7540. p. 205

Smart, Nina, Ref Serv, Simon Fraser University Vancouver Library, 515 W Hastings St, Vancouver, BC, V6B 5K3, CANADA. Tel: 778-782-5050. Fax: 778-782-5052. p. 2742

Smart, Pamela, Asst Dir, D A Hurd Library, 41 High St, North Berwick, ME, 03906. Tel: 207-676-2215. Fax: 207-676-7976. p. 993

Smathers, Jennifer, Head, Tech Serv, State University of New York College at Brockport, 350 New Campus Dr, Brockport, NY, 14420-2997. Tel: 585-395-2151. Fax: 585-395-5651. p. 1585

Smathers-Barnes, Melissa, Dir, Mount Sterling Montgomery County Library, 241 W Locust St, Mount Sterling, KY, 40353. Tel: 859-498-2404. Fax: 859-498-7477. p. 930

Smayda, Susan, Dir, Southington Public Library & Museum, 255 Main St, Southington, CT, 06489. Tel: 860-628-0947. Fax: 860-628-0488. p. 368

Smedley, Marcie, Head, Youth Serv, Henderson District Public Libraries, James I Gibson Library, 100 W Lake Mead Pkwy, Henderson, NV, 89015. Tel: 702-565-8402. Fax: 702-565-8832. p. 1428

Smedstad, Deborah Barlow, Head Librn, Museum of Fine Arts, Boston, 300 Massachusetts Ave, Boston, MA, 02115. Tel: 617-369-3385. Fax: 617-369-4257. p. 1064

Smelcer, Desiree, Ref & Ad Serv Librn, South Hadley Public Library, 27 Bardwell St, South Hadley, MA, 01075. Tel: 413-538-5045. Fax: 413-539-9250. p. 1125

Smelts, Dorryce, Head, Govt Doc & Libr Syst, Legislative Library of Manitoba, 200 Vaughan St, Rm 100, Winnipeg, MB, R3C 1T5, CANADA. Tel: 204-945-1069. Fax: 204-948-1312. p. 2756

Smeltz, Angela, Br Mgr, Whitman County Rural Library District, Uniontown Branch, 110 S Montgomery, Uniontown, WA, 99179. Tel: 509-229-3880. p. 2513

Smeltzer, Becky, Tech Serv, Municipal Technical Advisory Service Library, Univ Tennessee Conference Ctr Bldg, 600 Henley St, Ste 120, Knoxville, TN, 37996-4105. Tel: 865-974-9841. Fax: 865-974-0423. p. 2242

Smernoff, Andrea, Tech Serv, Hempstead Public Library, 115 Nichols Ct, Hempstead, NY, 11550-3199. Tel: 516-481-6990. Fax: 516-481-6719. p. 1634

Smiddy, David, Exec Dir, Clark County Public Library, Warder Literacy Center, 137 E High St, Springfield, OH, 45502. Tel: 937-323-8617. p. 1935

Smigelski, Toni, Libr Mgr, Green Grove Public Library, PO Box 219, Niton Junction, AB, T0E 1S0, CANADA. Tel: 780-795-2474. Fax: 780-795-3933. p. 2712

Smigielski, Elizabeth, Asst Dir, University of Louisville Libraries, Kornhauser Health Sciences Library, Health Sciences Ctr, 500 S Preston St, Louisville, KY, 40202. Tel: 502-852-0754. Fax: 502-852-1631. p. 927

Smigielski, Sara, Ch, New Carlisle & Olive Township Public Library, 408 S Bray St, New Carlisle, IN, 46552. Tel: 574-654-3046. Fax: 574-654-8260. p. 768

Smikahl, Diane, Dir, Benicia Public Library, 150 East L St, Benicia, CA, 94510-3281. Tel: 707-746-4343. Fax: 707-747-8122. p. 126

Smiles-Haggerty, Courntey, Mgr, Online Searching, Aventis Pharmaceuticals Library, Scientific Information & Library Services, 1041 Rt 202-206, Mail Stop: BRW K-303A, Bridgewater, NJ, 08807-6800. Tel: 908-231-4952. Fax: 908-231-2802. p. 1474

Smiley, Cindy, Mgr, Salt Lake County Library Services, West Valley Branch, 2880 W 3650 South, West Valley City, UT, 84119-3743. Tel: 801-944-7621. Fax: 801-969-1782. p. 2414

Smiley, Jodi K, Br Librn, Jefferson County Library System, 202 S Main St, Boulder, MT, 59632. Tel: 406-225-3241. Fax: 406-225-3241. p. 1375

Smiley, Linda, Asst Librn, Bonnyville Municipal Library, 4804 49th Ave, Bonnyville, AB, T9N 2J3, CANADA. Tel: 780-826-3071. Fax: 780-826-2058. p. 2686

Smiley, Lucille, Asst Dir, Howard University Libraries, Business, 2600 Sixth St NW, Washington, DC, 20059. Tel: 202-806-1560. Fax: 202-797-6393. p. 404

Smiley, Rebecca, Ch Mgr, Citizens Library, 55 S College St, Washington, PA, 15301. Tel: 724-222-2400. Fax: 724-222-2606. p. 2151

Smiley, Trenton Marcus, Commun Relations Officer, Genesee District Library, G-4195 W Pasadena Ave, Flint, MI, 48504. Tel: 810-230-9613. Fax: 810-732-1161. p. 1179

Smilko, Jennifer, Asst Admin, Berks County Public Libraries, 1037F MacArthur Rd, Reading, PA, 19605. Tel: 610-378-5260. Fax: 610-378-1525. p. 2133

Smillie, John, Dir, Western Organization of Resource Councils Library, 220 S 27th St, Ste B, Billings, MT, 59101. Tel: 406-252-9672. Fax: 406-252-1092. p. 1375

Smilovitz, Jenny, Pub Serv, Spec Coll, The Boston Conservatory, Eight The Fenway, Boston, MA, 02215-4099. Tel: 617-912-9131. Fax: 617-912-9101. p. 1056

Smink, Nancy, Dir, Pottsville Free Public Library, 215 W Market St, Pottsville, PA, 17901-4304. Tel: 570-622-8105, 570-622-8880. Fax: 570-622-2157. p. 2131

Smirl, Christy, Coll Develop Mgr, Teton County Library, 125 Virginian Lane, Jackson, WY, 83001. Tel: 307-733-2164, Ext 260. Fax: 307-733-4568. p. 2656

Smirniw, Toni, Br Mgr, Ocean County Library, Tuckerton Branch, 380 Bay Ave, Tuckerton, NJ, 08087-2557. Tel: 609-296-1470. Fax: 609-296-6487. p. 1534

Smisek, Colleen, Adult Serv, Bay Shore-Brightwaters Public Library, One S Country Rd, Brightwaters, NY, 11718-1517. Tel: 631-665-4350. Fax: 631-665-4958. p. 1585

Smisek, Tom, Ref & Instrul Serv Librn, University of Wisconsin-River Falls, 410 S Third St, River Falls, WI, 54022. Tel: 715-425-3312. Fax: 715-425-0609. p. 2635

Smit, Danusia, Circ Supvr, Whistler Public Library, 4329 Main St, Whistler, BC, V0N 1B4, CANADA. Tel: 604-935-8433. Fax: 604-935-8434. p. 2746

Smit, Maria, Supvr, Elgin County Public Library, Belmont Branch, 14134 Belmont Rd, Belmont, ON, N0L 1B0, CANADA. Tel: 519-644-1560. Fax: 519-644-0533. p. 2844

Smit, Maria, Supvr, Elgin County Public Library, Springfield Branch, Malahida Community Place, 12105 Whittaker Rd, Springfield, ON, N0L 2J0, CANADA. Tel: 519-765-4515. Fax: 519-765-4453. p. 2844

Smith, Aaron, Circ, Kokomo-Howard County Public Library, 220 N Union St, Kokomo, IN, 46901-4614. Tel: 765-457-3242. Fax: 765-457-3683. p. 758

Smith, Adia, Br Mgr, Putnam County Library System, Crescent City Public Library, 610 N Summit, Crescent City, FL, 32112-2148. Tel: 386-698-2600. Fax: 386-698-4212. p. 478

Smith, Agatha, Cataloger, Atlanta-Fulton Public Library System, Auburn Avenue Research Library on African-American Culture & History, 101 Auburn Ave NE, Atlanta, GA, 30303. Tel: 404-730-4001, Ext 199. Fax: 404-730-5879. p. 511

Smith, Alan, Network Adminr, Allegan District Library, 331 Hubbard St, Allegan, MI, 49010. Tel: 269-673-4625. Fax: 269-673-8661. p. 1148

Smith, Alan, Head, Tech Serv, Ashtabula County District Library, 335 W 44th St, Ashtabula, OH, 44004-6897. Tel: 440-997-9341, Ext 232. Fax: 440-992-7714. p. 1855

Smith, Alan, Ref Librn, Horry County Memorial Library, Socastee, 141 707-Connector Rd, Myrtle Beach, SC, 29588. Tel: 843-215-4700. Fax: 843-215-2801. p. 2191

Smith, Alan, Mgr, Marion County Public Library, Mannington Public, 109 Clarksburg St, Mannington, WV, 26582. Tel: 304-986-2803. Fax: 304-986-3425. p. 2559

Smith, Aleta, Librn, New Mexico State Library, 423 W Nobles, Tucumcari, NM, 88401. Tel: 575-461-1206. Fax: 575-461-1824. p. 1566

Smith, Alex, Electronic Serv Librn, Wayne State College, 1111 Main St, Wayne, NE, 68787. Tel: 402-375-7261. Fax: 402-375-7538. p. 1423

Smith, Alice, Dir, Carbondale City Library, 234 Main St, Carbondale, KS, 66414-9635. Tel: 785-836-7638. Fax: 785-836-7789. p. 859

Smith, Alice, Circ, Coppin State College, 2500 W North Ave, Baltimore, MD, 21216-3698. Tel: 410-951-3400. Fax: 410-951-3430. p. 1012

Smith, Alice, Prog Coordr, North Seattle Community College, 9600 College Way N, Seattle, WA, 98103. Tel: 206-527-3610. Fax: 206-527-3614. p. 2529

Smith, Allen, Dir, Marion County Library, 101 E Court St, Marion, SC, 29571-3699. Tel: 843-423-8300. Fax: 843-423-8302. p. 2200

Smith, Amy, Circ Supvr, Troy University, Montgomery Campus, 252 Montgomery St, Montgomery, AL, 36104-3425. Tel: 334-241-9576. Fax: 334-241-9590. p. 31

Smith, Amy C, Librn, Raytheon Technical Library, Bldg 811/T, 1151 E Hermans Rd, Tucson, AZ, 85756. Tel: 520-794-8807. p. 87

Smith, Andrea, Librn, Minnesota Department of Corrections, 1010 W Sixth Ave, Shakopee, MN, 55379-2213. Tel: 952-496-4916. Fax: 952-496-4460. p. 1284

Smith, Andrew, Pres, American Forum for Global Education Library, 120 Wall St, Ste 2600, New York, NY, 10005-4001. Tel: 212-624-1300, Ext 341. Fax: 212-624-1412. p. 1668

Smith, Andrew W, Asst Dir, Michigan City Public Library, 100 E Fourth St, Michigan City, IN, 46360-3393. Tel: 219-873-3056. Fax: 219-873-3061. p. 764

Smith, Andy, Dir, Leetonia Community Public Library, 24 Walnut St, Leetonia, OH, 44431-1151. Tel: 330-427-6635. Fax: 330-427-2378. p. 1909

Smith, Angela, Br Mgr, Kenton County Public Library, Erlanger Branch, 401 Kenton Lands Rd, Erlanger, KY, 41018. Tel: 859-962-4001. Fax: 859-962-4010. p. 910

Smith, Angelina, Acq, Cat, Autauga-Prattville Public Library, 254 Doster St, Prattville, AL, 36067-3933. Tel: 334-365-3396. Fax: 334-365-3397. p. 34

Smith, Anita, Asst Librn, Henderson County Public Library District, 110 Hillcrest Dr, Biggsville, IL, 61418-9736. Tel: 309-627-2450. Fax: 309-627-2830. p. 595

Smith, Ann, Adult Serv, Franklin Township Free Public Library, 485 DeMott Lane, Somerset, NJ, 08873. Tel: 732-873-8700. Fax: 732-873-0746. p. 1529

Smith, Ann, Acad Librn, Acadia University, 50 Acadia St, Wolfville, NS, B4P 2R6, CANADA. Tel: 902-585-1249. Fax: 902-585-1748. p. 2786

Smith, Anna, Syst Mgr, Bartholomew County Public Library, 536 Fifth St, Columbus, IN, 47201-6225. Tel: 812-379-1279. Fax: 812-379-1275. p. 733

Smith, Anna, Br Librn, Sweetwater County Library System, Farson Branch Library, Farson Eden School Bldg, 30 Hwy 28, Farson, WY, 82932. Tel: 307-273-9301. Fax: 307-273-9313. p. 2655

Smith, Anne, Asst Dir, Pub Serv, Georgia Archives, 5800 Jonesboro Rd, Morrow, GA, 30260. Tel: 678-364-3731. Fax: 678-364-3856. p. 545

Smith, Anne, Librn, Walden Community Library, 135 Cahoon Farm Rd, West Danville, VT, 05873. Tel: 802-563-3000. Fax: 802-563-3030. p. 2439

Smith, Annette, Dr, Asst Prof, University of Wisconsin Oshkosh, 800 Algoma Blvd, Oshkosh, WI, 54901. Tel: 920-424-7252. Fax: 920-424-0858. p. 2977

Smith, Annice, Tech Serv, Cynthiana-Harrison County Public Library, 104 N Main St, Cynthiana, KY, 41031. Tel: 859-234-4881. Fax: 859-234-0059. p. 911

Smith, Annie, Ref, Utah Valley University Library, 800 W University Pkwy, Orem, UT, 84058-5999. Tel: 801-863-8752. Fax: 801-863-7065. p. 2409

Smith, Anthony, Dir, Digital Initiatives & Serv, University of Miami Libraries, 1300 Memorial Dr, Coral Gables, FL, 33146. Tel: 305-284-3233. Fax: 305-284-4027. p. 434

Smith, Anthony O, Libr Mgr, Chase Manhattan Bank, One Chase Manhattan Plaza, 25th Flr, New York, NY, 10081. Tel: 212-552-2499, 212-552-7820. Fax: 212-383-6626. p. 1672

Smith, Arnice, Br Mgr, Public Library of Cincinnati & Hamilton County, College Hill, 1400 W North Bend Rd, Cincinnati, OH, 45224. Tel: 513-369-6036. Fax: 513-369-6043. p. 1871

Smith, Arro, Head, Tech Serv, San Marcos Public Library, 625 E Hopkins, San Marcos, TX, 78666. Tel: 512-393-8200. p. 2384

Smith, Arthur, Dept Head, Royal Ontario Museum, 100 Queen's Park, Toronto, ON, M5S 2C6, CANADA. Tel: 416-586-5740. Fax: 416-586-5519. p. 2858

Smith, Ava M, Talking Bks, Texas State Library & Archives Commission, 1201 Brazos St, Austin, TX, 78701. Tel: 512-463-5428. Fax: 512-936-0685. p. 2282

Smith, Ava M, Regional Librn, Texas State Library & Archives Commission, 1201 Brazos, Austin, TX, 78711. Tel: 512-463-5428. Fax: 512-936-0685. p. 2283

Smith, Barbara, Asst Dir, Prospect Public Library, 17 Center St, Prospect, CT, 06712. Tel: 203-758-3001. Fax: 203-758-0080. p. 365

Smith, Barbara, Br Mgr, Public Library of Youngstown & Mahoning County, Canfield Branch, 43 W Main St, Canfield, OH, 44406. p. 1952

Smith, Barbara, Br Mgr, Public Library of Youngstown & Mahoning County, Greenford Branch, 7441 W South Range Rd, Greenford, OH, 44422. p. 1952

Smith, Barbara, Br Mgr, Public Library of Youngstown & Mahoning County, Sebring Branch, 195 W Ohio Ave, Sebring, OH, 44672. p. 1953

Smith, Barbara, Dir, Round Top Library Association Inc, 206 W Mill St, Round Top, TX, 78954. Tel: 979-249-2700. Fax: 979-249-2563. p. 2377

Smith, Barbara, Dir, Juneau Public Library, 250 N Fairfield Ave, Juneau, WI, 53039-1323. Tel: 920-386-4805. Fax: 920-386-4806. p. 2600

Smith, Bart Lind, Coordr, Libr Serv, Chicago Transit Authority-Law Library, 567 W Lake St, Chicago, IL, 60661-1498. Tel: 312-664-7200, Ext 12778, 312-681-2778. Fax: 312-681-2795. p. 611

Smith, Becky, Admin Senior Librn, United States Air Force, AFRL/RVIL, 3550 Aberdeen Ave SE Bldg 570, Kirtland AFB, NM, 87117-5776. Tel: 505-846-4767. Fax: 505-846-4790. p. 1557

Smith, Becky, Ch, Logan Library, 255 N Main, Logan, UT, 84321-3914. Tel: 435-716-9123. Fax: 435-716-9145. p. 2407

Smith, Becky G, Cataloger, Tygart Valley Community Library, Rte 219-250, Mill Creek, WV, 26280. Tel: 304-335-6277. Fax: 304-335-6277. p. 2565

Smith, Beth, Librn, Cohen & Grigsby PC, 11 Stanwix St, 15th Flr, Pittsburgh, PA, 15222-1319. Tel: 412-297-4870. Fax: 412-209-0672. p. 2124

Smith, Beth Roll, Libr Dir, West Bridgewater Public Library, 80 Howard St, West Bridgewater, MA, 02379-1710. Tel: 508-894-1255. Fax: 508-894-1258. p. 1137

Smith, Betty, Librn, Southwest Arkansas Regional Library, DeQueen Branch, 200 W Stillwell, DeQueen, AR, 71832. Tel: 870-584-4364. Fax: 870-642-8319. p. 103

Smith, Betty, Librn, Walnut Cove Public Library, 106 W Fifth St, Walnut Cove, NC, 27052. Tel: 336-591-7496. Fax: 336-591-8494. p. 1828

Smith, Betty Ann, Ref Librn, Lewis & Clark College, Aubrey R Watzek Library, 0615 SW Palatine Hill Rd, Portland, OR, 97219-7899. Tel: 503-768-7274. Fax: 503-768-7282. p. 2011

Smith, Beverly, Spec Coll Librn, Virgin Islands Division of Libraries, Archives & Museums, 23 Dronningens Gade, Saint Thomas, VI, 00802. Tel: 340-774-3407. Fax: 340-775-1887. p. 2679

Smith, Bill, Librn, North Carolina Department of Correction, Western Youth Institution Library, 5155 Western Ave, Morganton, NC, 28655-9696. Tel: 828-438-6037, Ext 270. Fax: 828-438-6076. p. 1811

Smith, Blossom, Br Mgr, Public Library of Cincinnati & Hamilton County, Reading Branch, 9001 Reading Rd, Reading, OH, 45215. Tel: 513-369-4465. Fax: 513-369-4466. p. 1873

Smith, Bonne, Br Mgr, West Georgia Regional Library, Maude P Ragsdale Public Library, 1815 Hiram-Douglasville Hwy, Hiram, GA, 30141. Tel: 770-439-3964. Fax: 770-943-8720. p. 524

Smith, Bonnie, Br Mgr, Sonoma County Library, Forestville Branch, 7050 Covey Rd, Forestville, CA, 95436. Tel: 707-887-7654. Fax: 707-887-7654. p. 267

Smith, Brandi, Librn, Acadia Municipal Library, PO Box 6, Acadia Valley, AB, T0J 0A0, CANADA. Tel: 403-972-3744. Fax: 403-972-2000. p. 2683

Smith, Brena, Ref, Outreach & Instruction Librn, California Institute of the Arts, 24700 McBean Pkwy, Valencia, CA, 91355. Tel: 661-253-7885. Fax: 661-254-4561. p. 278

Smith, Brenda, Libr Tech, Thaddeus Stevens College of Technology, 750 E King St, Lancaster, PA, 17602-3198. Tel: 717-391-3502. Fax: 717-396-7186. p. 2078

Smith, Brenda, Distance Learning Librn, Doc Delivery, Thompson Rivers University, 900 McGill Rd, Kamloops, BC, V2C 5N3, CANADA. Tel: 250-828-5300. Fax: 250-828-5313. p. 2730

Smith, Brian, Ref Librn, Delray Beach Public Library, 100 W Atlantic Ave, Delray Beach, FL, 33444. Tel: 561-819-6405. Fax: 561-266-9757. p. 437

Smith, Brian K, Syst Coordr, Erskine College & Theological Seminary, One Depot St, Due West, SC, 29639. Tel: 864-379-8789. Fax: 864-379-2900. p. 2193

Smith, Brigitte, Mgr, ILL, University of South Carolina Aiken, 471 University Pkwy, Aiken, SC, 29801. Tel: 803-641-3504. Fax: 803-641-3302. p. 2180

Smith, Bruce, Delivery Coordr, South Central Library System, 4610 S Biltmore Lane, Ste 101, Madison, WI, 53718-2153. Tel: 608-266-4695. Fax: 608-246-7958. p. 2607

Smith, Calvert, Br Mgr, Rockingham County Public Library, Reidsville Branch, 204 W Morehead St, Reidsville, NC, 27320. Tel: 336-349-8476. Fax: 336-342-4824. p. 1790

Smith, Candy, Head, Readers Advisory, Villa Park Public Library, 305 S Ardmore Ave, Villa Park, IL, 60181-2698. Tel: 630-834-1164. Fax: 630-834-0489. p. 714

Smith, Caren Jo, Circ, West Hartford Public Library, Bishop's Corner, 15 Starkel Rd, West Hartford, CT, 06117. Tel: 860-561-8210. p. 376

Smith, Carla, Ch, Colo Public Library, 309 Main St, Colo, IA, 50056. Tel: 641-377-2900. Fax: 641-377-2468. p. 804

Smith, Carol, Librn, Oberlin City Library, 104 E Oak, Oberlin, KS, 67749-1997. Tel: 785-475-2412. p. 885

Smith, Carol, Tech Coordr, Pulaski County Public Library System, 60 W Third St, Pulaski, VA, 24301. Tel: 540-980-7770. Fax: 540-980-7775. p. 2486

Smith, Carol Ann, Librn, Colorado Mental Health Institute of Pueblo, 1600 W 24th St, Pueblo, CO, 81003. Tel: 719-546-4197. Fax: 719-546-4484. p. 320

Smith, Carol Anne, Asst Librn, South Macon Public Library District, 451 W Glenn St, Macon, IL, 62544. Tel: 217-764-3356. Fax: 217-764-5490. p. 669

Smith, Carolyn, Cat & Govt Doc Asst, Rockhurst University, 1100 Rockhurst Rd, Kansas City, MO, 64110-2561. Tel: 816-501-4131. Fax: 816-501-4666. p. 1340

Smith, Catherine, Dir, Gulfport Public Library, 5501 28th Ave S, Gulfport, FL, 33707. Tel: 727-893-1075. Fax: 727-893-1072. p. 450

Smith, Catherine, Br Librn, Hardy County Public Library, East Hardy, 261 Cougar Dr, Baker, WV, 26801. Tel: 304-897-5544. Fax: 304-897-5544. p. 2566

Smith, Ceil, Acq Librn, Three Rivers Regional Library System, 208 Gloucester St, Brunswick, GA, 31520-7007. Tel: 912-267-1212. Fax: 912-267-9597. p. 522

Smith, Charlene, Asst Libr Serv Mgr, Lake County Library System, 2401 Woodlea Rd, Tavares, FL, 32778. Tel: 352-253-6160. Fax: 352-253-6184. p. 499

Smith, Charles, Head Librn, Free Library of Philadelphia, Business, Science & Industry, 1901 Vine St, Philadelphia, PA, 19103-1189. Tel: 215-686-5394. p. 2107

Smith, Charles, Dr, Sci, Western Kentucky University Libraries, Helm-Cravens Library Complex, 1906 College Heights Blvd, No 11067, Bowling Green, KY, 42101-1067. Tel: 270-745-2905. Fax: 270-745-6422. p. 908

Smith, Charlotte, Libr Mgr, Malvern-Hot Spring County Library, 202 E Third St, Malvern, AR, 72104. Tel: 501-332-5441. Fax: 501-332-6679. p. 108

Smith, Cheryl, Dir, O'Melveny & Myers LLP, 400 S Hope St, Los Angeles, CA, 90071-2899. Tel: 213-430-6000. Fax: 213-430-6407. p. 176

Smith, Cheryl, Dir, O'Melveny & Myers LLP, 610 Newport Center Dr, Newport Beach, CA, 92660-6429. Tel: 949-760-9600. Fax: 949-823-6994. p. 194

Smith, Cheryl, Tech Serv, St Clair College, 1001 Grand Ave W, Chatham, ON, N7M 5W4, CANADA. Tel: 519-354-9100, Ext 3232, 519-354-9100, Ext 3273. Fax: 519-354-5496. p. 2799

Smith, Christina, Adult Serv, Corona Public Library, 650 S Main St, Corona, CA, 92882. Tel: 951-736-2381. Fax: 951-736-2499. p. 136

Smith, Christine, Br Mgr, Lonesome Pine Regional Library, C Bascom Slemp Memorial, 11 Proctor St N, Big Stone Gap, VA, 24219. Tel: 276-523-1334. Fax: 276-523-5306. p. 2504

Smith, Christy, Librn, Texas Ranger Hall of Fame & Museum, 100 Texas Ranger Trail, Waco, TX, 76706. Tel: 254-750-8631. Fax: 254-750-8629. p. 2397

Smith, Cindy, Dir, Leonard A Good Community Library, 208 W Mulberry St, Ogden, IA, 50212. Tel: 515-275-4550. p. 836

Smith, Colleen, Head, Tech Serv, Albany Law School, 80 New Scotland Ave, Albany, NY, 12208. Tel: 518-445-2340. Fax: 518-472-5842. p. 1568

Smith, Colleen, Dir, Huron Public Library, 521 Dakota Ave S, Huron, SD, 57350. Tel: 605-353-8530. Fax: 605-353-8531. p. 2213

Smith, Connie, Dir, Gardendale Martha Moore Public Library, 995 Mt Olive Rd, Gardendale, AL, 35071. Tel: 205-631-6639. Fax: 205-631-0146. p. 18

Smith, Connie, Ch, Massapequa Public Library, 40 Harbor Lane, Massapequa Park, NY, 11762. Tel: 516-799-0770, Ext 320. Fax: 516-795-7528. p. 1658

Smith, Connie, Dir, Libr Serv, Head Librn, Morgan, Lewis & Bockius LLP, 1701 Market St, 13th Flr, Philadelphia, PA, 19103-2921. Tel: 215-963-5000. Fax: 215-963-5001. p. 2112

Smith, Cory, Librn, Abbott Memorial Library, 15 Library St, South Pomfret, VT, 05067. Tel: 802-457-2236. p. 2436

Smith, Cynthia, Dep City Librn, Escondido Public Library, 239 S Kalmia St, Escondido, CA, 92025. Tel: 760-839-4329. Fax: 760-741-4255. p. 146

Smith, Cynthia, Br Mgr, Peoria Public Library, Lincoln, 1312 W Lincoln, Peoria, IL, 61605-1976. Tel: 309-497-2601. Fax: 309-497-2611. p. 690

Smith, Cynthia, Dir, Limerick Public Library, 55 Washington St, Limerick, ME, 04048-3500. Tel: 207-793-8975. Fax: 207-793-8443. p. 990

Smith, D V, Pres, National Hunters Association Inc Library, 590 Wendell Blvd, Knightdale, NC, 27545-7886. Tel: 919-365-7157. Fax: 919-366-2142. p. 1805

Smith, Dale, Ch, Morse Institute Library, 14 E Central St, Natick, MA, 01760. Tel: 508-647-6520. Fax: 508-647-6527. p. 1107

Smith, Dan, Librn, Onondaga County Public Library, Southwest Community Center, 401 South Ave, Syracuse, NY, 13204. Tel: 315-671-5814. p. 1753

Smith, Dana, Mgr, Pioneer Hi-Bred International, Inc, 7300 NW 62nd Ave, Johnston, IA, 50131. Tel: 515-535-4199. Fax: 515-535-2184. p. 824

Smith, Daniel R, Dr, Admin Dir, Dean, Tech Serv Adminr, Western Piedmont Community College, 1001 Burkemont Ave, Morganton, NC, 28655-4504. Tel: 828-448-6195. Fax: 828-448-6173. p. 1811

Smith, Daniella, Dr, Asst Prof, University of North Texas, 1155 Union Circle, Denton, TX, 76203-5017. Tel: 940-565-2445. Fax: 940-565-3101. p. 2975

Smith, Danny, In Charge, Correctional Services of Canada, 4902 A Main St, Dorchester, NB, E4K 2Y9, CANADA. Tel: 506-379-4502, 506-379-4550. Fax: 506-379-4616. p. 2762

Smith, Daphne, Librn, CoxHealth Libraries, Cox Medical Ctr N, 1423 N Jefferson Ave, J-200, Springfield, MO, 65802. Tel: 417-269-8861. Fax: 417-269-3492. p. 1366

Smith, Daphne, Librn, CoxHealth Libraries, David Miller Memorial Library, Cox Medical Ctr S, 3801 S National Ave, Springfield, MO, 65807. Tel: 417-269-3460. Fax: 417-269-3492. p. 1366

Smith, Darlene, Dir, Winchester Public Library, 215 N Main St, Winchester, IL, 62694. Tel: 217-742-3150. Fax: 217-742-3150. p. 720

Smith, David, Tech Serv Librn, Kennebec Valley Community College, 92 Western Ave, Fairfield, ME, 04937-1367. Tel: 207-453-5004. Fax: 207-453-5194. p. 985

Smith, David, Dir of Tech, Saint Louis Public Library, 1415 Olive St, Saint Louis, MO, 63103-2315. Tel: 314-539-0300. Fax: 314-241-3840. p. 1359

Smith, David C, Cat, United States Forest Service, One Gifford Pinchot Dr, Madison, WI, 53726-2398. Tel: 608-231-9415. Fax: 608-231-9311. p. 2608

Smith, Dawn, Acq/Ser Librn, Loyola Law School, 919 S Albany St, Los Angeles, CA, 90015-1211. Tel: 213-736-1174. Fax: 213-487-2204. p. 175

Smith, Dawn, Librn, Illinois Prairie District Public Library, Benson Branch, 420 E Front, Benson, IL, 61516. Tel: 309-394-2542. Fax: 309-394-2542. p. 673

Smith, Dawn M, Asst Dean, Pub Serv, Florida Atlantic University, 777 Glades Rd, Boca Raton, FL, 33431. Tel: 561-297-1029. Fax: 561-297-2189. p. 428

Smith, Dean, Dir, Albuquerque-Bernalillo County Library System, North Valley, 7704 Second St NW, Albuquerque, NM, 87107. Tel: 505-897-8823. Fax: 505-897-8825. p. 1548

Smith, Dean P, Dir, Albuquerque-Bernalillo County Library System, 501 Copper Ave NW, Albuquerque, NM, 87102. Tel: 505-768-5122. Fax: 505-768-5191. p. 1548

Smith, Deb, Librn, Greensburg-Decatur County Public Library, Westport Branch, 205 W Main St, Westport, IN, 47283-9601. Tel: 812-591-2330. Fax: 812-591-2330. p. 747

Smith, Deb, ILL, Bloomfield Township Public Library, 1099 Lone Pine Rd, Bloomfield Township, MI, 48302-2410. Tel: 248-642-5800. Fax: 248-258-2555. p. 1159

Smith, Debara, Librn, Brownsdale Public Library, 103 E Main St, Brownsdale, MN, 55918-8817. Tel: 507-567-9951. Fax: 507-567-2250. p. 1243

Smith, Debbi, Coll Develop & Mgt Librn, Adelphi University Libraries, One South Ave, Garden City, NY, 11530. Tel: 516-877-3522. Fax: 516-877-3592. p. 1625

Smith, Debby, Librn, Robert W Rowe Public Library District, 120 E Si Johnson Ave, Sheridan, IL, 60551. Tel: 815-496-2031. Fax: 815-496-2067. p. 702

Smith, Deborah, Head of Libr, San Francisco Conservatory of Music, 1201 Ortega St, San Francisco, CA, 94122. Tel: 415-564-8086, 415-759-3413. Fax: 415-759-3499. p. 245

Smith, Deborah, Asst Mgr, Libr Serv, Niagara-on-the-Lake Public Library, Ten Anderson Lane, Niagara-on-the-Lake, ON, L0S 1J0, CANADA. Tel: 905-468-2023. Fax: 905-468-3334. p. 2824

Smith, Debra, Ref Librn, College of DuPage Library, 425 Fawell Blvd, Glen Ellyn, IL, 60137-6599. Tel: 630-942-2350. Fax: 630-858-8757. p. 649

Smith, Denise, Dir, Tipton Public Library, 206 Cedar St, Tipton, IA, 52772-1753. Tel: 563-886-6266. Fax: 563-886-6257. p. 847

Smith, Denise, Dir, Stanton County Library, 103 E Sherman, Johnson, KS, 67855. Tel: 620-492-2302. Fax: 620-492-2203. p. 874

Smith, Denise, Dir, Leroy Community Library, 104 W Gilbert, Le Roy, MI, 49655. Tel: 231-768-4493. Fax: 231-768-5024. p. 1203

Smith, Diana, Dir, New Salem Public Library, 24 S Main St, New Salem, MA, 01355. Tel: 978-544-6334. Fax: 978-544-6334. p. 1109

Smith, Diana, ILL, Saint Mary's Public Library, 127 Center St, Saint Marys, PA, 15857. Tel: 814-834-6141. Fax: 814-834-9814. p. 2135

Smith, Diane, Librn, Case Memorial Library, 911 Stetson Rd, Kenduskeag, ME, 04450. Tel: 207-884-8598. Fax: 207-884-3043. p. 988

Smith, Dianna, Cat, Beatty Library District, 400 N Fourth St, Beatty, NV, 89003. Tel: 775-553-2257. Fax: 775-553-2257. p. 1425

Smith, Dinah, Commun Health Info Ctr Coordr, Self Regional Healthcare, 1325 Spring St, Greenwood, SC, 29646. Tel: 864-725-4797. Fax: 864-725-4838. p. 2198

Smith, Dona, Head, Ch, Homewood Public Library, 1721 Oxmoor Rd, Homewood, AL, 35209-4085. Tel: 205-332-6616. Fax: 205-802-6424. p. 20

Smith, Donald R, Dean of Libr, University of Louisiana at Monroe Library, 700 University Ave, Monroe, LA, 71209-0720. Tel: 318-342-1051. Fax: 318-342-1075. p. 958

Smith, Donette, Libr Mgr, North Arkansas College Library, North Campus, 1320 Spring Rd, Harrison, AR, 72601. Tel: 870-391-3368. Fax: 870-391-3341. p. 102

Smith, Donna, Dir, Kankakee Community College, 100 College Dr, Kankakee, IL, 60901-6505. Tel: 815-802-8400. Fax: 815-802-8101. p. 660

Smith, Donna, Tech Serv Librn, Northern Kentucky University, University Dr, Highland Heights, KY, 41099. Tel: 859-572-6140. Fax: 859-572-5390. p. 917

Smith, Donna, Librn, Altus Public Library, 421 N Hudson, Altus, OK, 73521. Tel: 580-477-2890. Fax: 580-477-3626. p. 1955

Smith, Donna, Librn, Southern Prairie Library System, 421 N Hudson, Altus, OK, 73521. Tel: 580-477-2890. Fax: 580-477-3626. p. 1955

Smith, Donna, ILL, Eastfield College Library, 3737 Motley Dr, Mesquite, TX, 75150-2033. Tel: 972-860-7168. p. 2362

Smith, Doreen, Librn, Fairbanks Memorial Hospital Library, 1650 Cowles St, Fairbanks, AK, 99701-5998. Tel: 907-458-5584. p. 47

Smith, Doreen, Librn, Ater & Wynne, LLP, KOIN Ctr, Ste 1800, 222 SW Columbia, Portland, OR, 97201. Tel: 503-226-1191. Fax: 503-226-0079. p. 2010

Smith, Douglas, Dep Dir, Berkeley Public Library, 2090 Kittredge St, Berkeley, CA, 94704. Tel: 510-981-6100. Fax: 510-981-6111. p. 126

Smith, Douglas, Ref Serv, Oakland Public Library, 125 14th St, Oakland, CA, 94612. Tel: 510-238-6611. Fax: 510-238-2232. p. 197

Smith, Ed, Dir, Manville Public Library, 100 S Tenth Ave, Manville, NJ, 08835. Tel: 908-722-9722. Fax: 908-722-0631. p. 1499

Smith, Edward, III, Librn, Suffolk County Historical Society Library, 300 W Main St, Riverhead, NY, 11901-2894. Tel: 631-727-2881. Fax: 631-727-3467. p. 1728

Smith, Edward J, Exec Dir, Abilene Library Consortium, 3305 N Third St, Ste 301, Abilene, TX, 79603. Tel: 325-672-7081. Fax: 325-672-7082. p. 2955

Smith, Eileen, Ch, Clark Public Library, 303 Westfield Ave, Clark, NJ, 07066. Tel: 732-388-5999. Fax: 732-388-7866. p. 1479

Smith, Elaine, Dir, Treat Memorial Library, 56 Main St, Livermore Falls, ME, 04254. Tel: 207-897-3631. p. 990

Smith, Elizabeth, Librn, Maryland Department of Planning Library, 301 W Preston St, Rm 1101, Baltimore, MD, 21201-2365. Tel: 410-767-4500. Fax: 410-767-4480. p. 1015

Smith, Ellen, Tech Serv, Hinsdale Public Library, 20 E Maple St, Hinsdale, IL, 60521. Tel: 630-986-1976. Fax: 630-986-9654. p. 656

Smith, Ellen, Ref, Ramsey Free Public Library, 30 Wyckoff Ave, Ramsey, NJ, 07446. Tel: 201-327-1445. Fax: 201-327-3687. p. 1525

Smith, Ellen, Columbus Satellite Librn, US Court of Appeals for the Sixth Circuit Library, 312 Potter Stewart US Courthouse, Cincinnati, OH, 45202. Tel: 614-719-3181. Fax: 513-564-7329. p. 1873

Smith, Ellen, Librn, Tucker Ellis LLP, 925 Euclid Ave, Ste 1150, Cleveland, OH, 44115-1475. Tel: 216-592-5000. Fax: 216-592-5009. p. 1881

Smith, Ellis Gene, Acq, Tibetan Buddhist Resource Center, Inc, 150 W 17th St, New York, NY, 10011. Tel: 212-620-5000, Ext 306. Fax: 212-727-2997. p. 1701

Smith, Ellouise, Librn, Five Rivers Public Library, 301 Walnut St, Parsons, WV, 26287. Tel: 304-478-3880. Fax: 304-478-3880. p. 2569

Smith, Emily, In Charge, Christ Community Church, 1000 S Park Victoria Dr, Milpitas, CA, 95035-7099. Tel: 408-262-8000. Fax: 408-262-1635. p. 187

Smith, Eric, Dir, Libr Serv, Ontonagon Township Library, 311 N Steel St, Ontonagon, MI, 49953-1398. Tel: 906-884-4411. Fax: 906-884-2829. p. 1215

Smith, Erin, Ch, Fergus Falls Public Library, 205 E Hampden, Fergus Falls, MN, 56537-2930. Tel: 218-739-9387. Fax: 218-736-5131. p. 1251

Smith, Erin T, Cat, Syst Coordr, Westminster College, S Market St, New Wilmington, PA, 16172-0001. Tel: 724-946-7330. Fax: 724-946-6220. p. 2097

Smith, Eva, Cat Librn, Alcorn State University, 1000 ASU Dr, Alcorn State, MS, 39096-7500. Tel: 601-877-6353. Fax: 601-877-3885. p. 1293

Smith, Fan, Librn, Online Serv, Straub Clinic & Hospital, 888 S King St, Honolulu, HI, 96819. Tel: 808-522-4471. Fax: 808-522-4472. p. 565

Smith, Felicia, Br Librn, Sweetwater County Library System, Granger Branch Library, 60 Spruce, Granger, WY, 82934. Tel: 307-875-8038. Fax: 307-875-8038. p. 2655

Smith, Fran, Librn, Kapiolani Medical Center Library, 1319 Punahou St, Rm 611, Honolulu, HI, 96826. Tel: 808-983-8332. Fax: 808-983-6585. p. 564

Smith, Fran, Br Librn, Tombigbee Regional Library System, Webster County Public Library, 445 W Fox Ave, Eupora, MS, 39744. Tel: 662-258-7515. Fax: 662-258-7519. p. 1318

Smith, Frances, Librn, Deseronto Public Library, 358 Main St W, Deseronto, ON, K0K 1X0, CANADA. Tel: 613-396-2744. Fax: 613-396-3466. p. 2802

Smith, Frances, Librn, Tyendinaga Township Public Library, 852 Melrose Rd, RR1, Shannonville, ON, K0K 3A0, CANADA. Tel: 613-967-0606. Fax: 613-396-2080. p. 2841

Smith, Fred, Access Serv, Georgia Southern University, 1400 Southern Dr, Statesboro, GA, 30458. Tel: 912-478-5115. Fax: 912-478-0093. p. 552

Smith, Fred, Ref, New Jersey City University, 2039 Kennedy Blvd, Jersey City, NJ, 07305-1597. Tel: 201-200-3474. Fax: 201-200-2330, 201-200-2331. p. 1492

Smith, Gail R, Librn, Stephenson Memorial Library, 761 Forest Rd, Greenfield, NH, 03047-0127. Tel: 603-547-2790. p. 1449

Smith, Garrette, Br Mgr, Public Library of Cincinnati & Hamilton County, Norwood, 4325 Montgomery Rd, Cincinnati, OH, 45212. Tel: 513-369-6037. Fax: 513-369-6039. p. 1872

Smith, Gary, Librn, Massachusetts Trial Court, Court House, 76 East St, Pittsfield, MA, 01201. Tel: 413-442-5059. Fax: 413-448-2474. p. 1118

Smith, Gene, Dir, Shapleigh Community Library, Shapleigh Corner Rd, Shapleigh, ME, 04076. Tel: 207-636-3630. p. 1000

Smith, Genola, Dir, Fed Rec Ctr, National Archives & Records Administration, Denver Federal Ctr, Bldg 48, W Sixth Ave & Kipling St, Denver, CO, 80225-0307. Tel: 303-407-5740. Fax: 303-407-5707. p. 302

Smith, George W, Jr, Librn, Montana State Prison Library, 600 Conley Lake Rd, Deer Lodge, MT, 59722. Tel: 406-846-1320, Ext 2410. Fax: 406-846-2951. p. 1377

Smith, Gerry, County Historian, Broome County Historical Society Library, Broome County Public Library, 185 Court St, Binghamton, NY, 13901. Tel: 607-778-3572. Fax: 607-778-6429. p. 1582

Smith, Gina, Dir, Brookfield Public Library, 102 E Boston St, Brookfield, MO, 64628. Tel: 660-258-7439. Fax: 660-258-5626. p. 1321

Smith, Giselle, Br Mgr, Mesa County Public Library District, Fruita Branch, 324 N Coulson, Fruita, CO, 81521. Tel: 970-858-7703. p. 311

Smith, Gloria, Dir, Hartford Public Library District, 143 W Hawthorne, Hartford, IL, 62048. Tel: 618-254-9394. Fax: 618-254-6522. p. 653

Smith, Gloria, Br Supvr, Saint John the Baptist Parish Library, Reserve Branch, 170 W Tenth St, Reserve, LA, 70084. Tel: 985-536-4107. Fax: 985-536-4116. p. 955

Smith, Glynda, Librn, Newell Public Library, 208 Girard, Newell, SD, 57760. Tel: 605-456-2179. p. 2216

Smith, Greg, Assoc Dir-FMS, King County Library System, 960 Newport Way NW, Issaquah, WA, 98027. Tel: 425-369-3237. Fax: 425-369-3255. p. 2516

Smith, Gregory, Dir, Jacksboro Public Library, 585 Main St, Ste 201, Jacksboro, TN, 37757. Tel: 423-562-3675. Fax: 423-562-9587. p. 2237

Smith, Gretchen, Coll Develop, Georgia Southwestern State University, 800 Georgia Southwestern State University Dr, Americus, GA, 31709. Tel: 229-931-2789. Fax: 229-931-2265. p. 508

Smith, Gwen, Librn, Arnold's Cove Public Library, Five Highliner Dr, Arnold's Cove, NL, A0B 1A0, CANADA. Tel: 709-463-8707. p. 2769

Smith, Gwynne, Br Mgr, Wellington County Library, Mount Forest Branch, 118 Main St, Mount Forest, ON, N0G 2L0, CANADA. Tel: 519-323-4541. p. 2805

Smith Hale, F, Head, Info Serv, Canada Aviation Museum, 11 Aviation Pkwy, Ottawa, ON, K1K 4R3, CANADA. Tel: 613-993-2303. Fax: 613-990-3655. p. 2828

Smith Hale, Fiona, Dir, Libr & Archive Serv, Canada Science & Technology Museum, 2380 Lancaster Rd, Ottawa, ON, K1B 3W9, CANADA. Tel: 613-993-2303. Fax: 613-990-3636. p. 2829

Smith, Heather, Youth Serv Librn, Eastern Lancaster County Library, 11 Chestnut Dr, New Holland, PA, 17557-9437. Tel: 717-354-0525. Fax: 717-354-7787. p. 2096

Smith, Heather, Coll Develop, Info Literacy, Librn, University College of the North Libraries, Seventh & Charlebois, The Pas, MB, R9A 1M7, CANADA. Tel: 204-627-8561. Fax: 204-623-4597. p. 2753

Smith, Heidi, Asst Dir, Pub Serv, Waukegan Public Library, 128 N County St, Waukegan, IL, 60085. Tel: 847-623-2041. Fax: 847-623-2092, 847-623-2094. p. 716

Smith, Helen, Librn, Pennsylvania State University Libraries, Life Sciences, 401 Paterno Library, University Park, PA, 16802-1811. Tel: 814-865-3706. p. 2148

Smith, Herbert, Pres, Frances E Kennard Public Library, Auburn & Canal Sts, Meshoppen, PA, 18630. Tel: 570-833-5060. Fax: 570-833-4238. p. 2088

Smith, Hilda, Ref Librn, La Sierra University Library, 4500 Riverwalk Pkwy, Riverside, CA, 92505-3344. Tel: 951-785-2397. Fax: 951-785-2445. p. 217

Smith, Hope, Circ, Mississippi College, 101 W College St, Clinton, MS, 39058. Tel: 601-925-3232. Fax: 601-925-3435. p. 1296

Smith, Ina, Dir, Bonnyville Municipal Library, 4804 49th Ave, Bonnyville, AB, T9N 2J3, CANADA. Tel: 780-826-3071. Fax: 780-826-2058. p. 2686

Smith, Irma, Ref, Chatham College, Woodland Rd, Pittsburgh, PA, 15232. Tel: 412-365-1247. Fax: 412-365-1465. p. 2124

Smith, Ivan, Librn, Genesee District Library, Swartz Creek Area (Perkins Library), 8095 Civic Dr, Swartz Creek, MI, 48473. Tel: 810-635-3900. Fax: 810-635-4179. p. 1180

Smith, Jacqueline, Media Serv, University of the Sciences in Philadelphia, 4200 Woodland Ave, Philadelphia, PA, 19104-4491. Tel: 215-596-8994. Fax: 215-596-8760. p. 2120

Smith, James, Librn, Houston Community College Northeast College, Codwell Campus Library, 555 Community College Dr, Houston, TX, 77013-6127. Tel: 713-718-8354. Fax: 713-718-8330. p. 2337

Smith, James P, Dr, Dir, Libr Serv, St Francis College Library, 180 Remsen St, Brooklyn, NY, 11201. Tel: 718-489-5306. Fax: 718-489-3401. p. 1594

Smith, Jamie, Metadata/Cat Librn, Gallaudet University Library, 800 Florida Ave NE, Washington, DC, 20002-3095. Tel: 202-651-5217. p. 401

Smith, Jan, ILL, Rockville Public Library, Inc, 52 Union St, Vernon, CT, 06066-3155. Tel: 860-875-5892. Fax: 860-875-9795. p. 373

Smith, Jan, Librn, Commercial Appeal News Library, 495 Union Ave, Memphis, TN, 38103. Tel: 901-529-2781. Fax: 901-529-6460. p. 2248

Smith, Jane, Govt Doc, Instrul Serv Librn, Slippery Rock University of Pennsylvania, Slippery Rock, PA, 16057-9989. Tel: 724-738-2638. Fax: 724-738-2661. p. 2140

Smith, Janet, Div Mgr, Acq & Tech Serv, Humboldt County Library, 1313 Third St, Eureka, CA, 95501-0553. Tel: 707-269-1918. p. 147

Smith, Janet, Head, Support Serv, McMillan Memorial Library, 490 E Grand Ave, Wisconsin Rapids, WI, 54494-4898. Tel: 715-423-1040. Fax: 715-423-2665. p. 2650

Smith, Janet, Dir, Palliser Regional Library, 366 Coteau St W, Moose Jaw, SK, S6H 5C9, CANADA. Tel: 306-693-3669. Fax: 306-692-5657. p. 2918

Smith, Janet B, Acq, Nazareth College of Rochester Library, 4245 East Ave, Rochester, NY, 14618-3790. Tel: 585-389-2124. Fax: 585-389-2145. p. 1730

Smith, Jann, Br Mgr, Rusk County Library, McMillan Memorial, 401 S Commerce St, Overton, TX, 75684. Tel: 903-834-6318. Fax: 903-834-6937. p. 2332

Smith, Jean, Librn, Faulkner-Van Buren Regional Library System, Mayflower Branch, Six Ashmore Dr, Mayflower, AR, 72106. Tel: 501-470-9678. Fax: 501-470-9039. p. 96

Smith, Jean, Br Coordr, Phillips-Lee-Monroe Regional Library, West Helena Library, 721 Plaza St, West Helena, AR, 72390-2698. Tel: 870-572-2861. p. 103

Smith, Jean, Per, San Diego Mesa College Library, 7250 Mesa College Dr, San Diego, CA, 92111-4998. Tel: 619-388-2550. Fax: 619-388-2922. p. 235

Smith, Jean, Dir, Commonwealth of Massachusetts - Trial Court, 72 Belmont St, Brockton, MA, 02301. Tel: 508-586-7110. Fax: 508-588-8483. p. 1071

Smith, Jean, Ch, Clarion Free Library, 644 Main St, Clarion, PA, 16214. Tel: 814-226-7172. Fax: 814-226-6750. p. 2045

Smith, Jean, Dir, Libr Serv, Valley Forge Military Academy & College, 1001 Eagle Rd, Wayne, PA, 19087-3695. Tel: 610-989-1200, 610-989-1364. Fax: 610-975-9642. p. 2152

Smith, Jeanette, Ch, Romeo District Library, 65821 Van Dyke, Washington, MI, 48095. Tel: 586-752-0603. Fax: 586-752-8416. p. 1235

Smith, Jeanette K, Dir, Hardin County Library, 1365 Pickwick St, Savannah, TN, 38372. Tel: 731-925-4314, 731-925-6848. Fax: 731-925-7132. p. 2264

Smith, Jeanne, Mrg/Youth & Adult Serv, Cromaine District Library, 3688 N Hartland Rd, Hartland, MI, 48353. Tel: 810-632-5200, Ext 107. p. 1189

Smith, Jeannie, Adult Serv, Parker Public Library, 1001 S Navajo Ave, Parker, AZ, 85344. Tel: 928-669-2622. Fax: 928-669-8668. p. 70

Smith, Jeffrey, Assoc Curator, Columbia River Maritime Museum Library, 1792 Marine Dr, Astoria, OR, 97103. Tel: 503-325-2323. Fax: 503-325-2331. p. 1990

Smith, Jenn, Ref & Instruction Librn, School of the Art Institute of Chicago, 37 S Wabash Ave, Chicago, IL, 60603-3103. Tel: 312-899-5097. Fax: 312-899-1851. p. 624

Smith, Jennifer, Br Mgr, Monterey County Free Libraries, Carmel Valley Branch, 65 W Carmel Valley Rd, Carmel Valley, CA, 93924. Tel: 831-659-2377. Fax: 831-659-0589. p. 183

Smith, Jennifer, Asst Dir, Warren County-Vicksburg Public Library, 700 Veto St, Vicksburg, MS, 39180-3595. Tel: 601-636-6411. Fax: 601-634-4809. p. 1317

Smith, Jennifer, Head, Ch, Suffern Free Library, 210 Lafayette Ave, Suffern, NY, 10901. Tel: 845-357-1237. Fax: 845-357-3156. p. 1750

Smith, Jennifer, Dir, Cadott Community Library, 331 N Main St, Cadott, WI, 54727. Tel: 715-289-4950. Fax: 715-289-3149. p. 2584

Smith, Jennifer, PhD, Res & Instruction Librn, Northern Kentucky University, University Dr, Highland Heights, KY, 41099. Tel: 859-572-6620. Fax: 859-572-5390. p. 917

Smith, Jeremy, Ref, Davis, Graham & Stubbs LLP, 1550 17th St, Ste 500, Denver, CO, 80202. Tel: 303-892-7306. Fax: 303-893-1379. p. 300

Smith, Jill, Res Librn, University of Maryland, Baltimore, Thurgood Marshall Law Library, 501 W Fayette St, Baltimore, MD, 21201-1768. Tel: 410-706-6855. Fax: 410-706-8354. p. 1019

Smith, Jim, Exec Dir, BIO FOOD TECH (FTC Enterprises Limited), 101 Belvedere Ave, Charlottetown, PE, C1A 7N8, CANADA. Tel: 902-368-5548. Fax: 902-368-5549. p. 2875

Smith, Jo Ann, Asst Librn, Broken Bow Public Library, 404 Broadway, Broken Bow, OK, 74728. Tel: 580-584-2815. Fax: 580-584-9449. p. 1959

Smith, Joanie, Dir, Higgins Public Library, 201 N Main St, Higgins, TX, 79046. Tel: 806-852-2214. Fax: 806-852-2214. p. 2332

Smith, John A, Access Serv Librn, American University, 4801 Massachusetts Ave NW, Washington, DC, 20016-8182. Tel: 202-274-4354. Fax: 202-274-4365. p. 393

Smith, Jonathan, Head, Libr Info Tech, California State University, San Bernardino, 5500 University Pkwy, San Bernardino, CA, 92407-2318. Tel: 909-537-3492. Fax: 909-537-7048. p. 227

Smith, Joy, Tech Serv, Faulkner University, 5345 Atlanta Hwy, Montgomery, AL, 36109-3398. Tel: 334-386-7207. Fax: 334-386-7481. p. 28

Smith, Joyce, Pub Serv, Saint Johns River State College, 5001 St Johns Ave, Palatka, FL, 32177-3897. Tel: 386-312-4200. Fax: 386-325-4292. p. 478

Smith, Juanita, Asst Librn, Journal Gazette Library, 600 W Main St, Fort Wayne, IN, 46802. Tel: 260-461-8456. Fax: 260-461-8648. p. 742

Smith, Judie, Ref Serv Librn, Tarrant County College, 828 Harwood Rd, Hurst, TX, 76054-3219. Tel: 817-515-6625. p. 2346

Smith, Judith, Mgr, Geauga County Public Library, Chardon Library, 110 E Park St, Chardon, OH, 44024. Tel: 440-285-7601. Fax: 440-285-3808. p. 1867

Smith, Judith K, Librn, Larue D Carter Memorial Hospital, 2601 Cold Spring Rd, Indianapolis, IN, 46222-2202. Tel: 317-941-4154. Fax: 317-941-4385. p. 749

Smith, Judy, Dir, Graysville Public Library, 315 S Main St, Graysville, AL, 35073. Tel: 205-674-3040. Fax: 205-674-3296. p. 19

Smith, Judy, Br Mgr, Southwest Georgia Regional Library, Seminole County Public Library, 103 W Fourth St, Donalsonville, GA, 39845. Tel: 229-524-2665. Fax: 229-524-8913. p. 521

Smith, Judy, Dir, Chester Public Library, 623 Thayer Ave, Chester, NE, 68327. Tel: 402-324-5755. p. 1395

Smith, Julia, Mgr, Charlotte Mecklenburg Library, University City Regional, 301 East W T Harris Blvd, Charlotte, NC, 28262. Tel: 704-416-7200. Fax: 704-416-7300. p. 1782

Smith, Juliette S, Librn, Talladega College, 627 W Battle St, Talladega, AL, 35160. Tel: 256-761-6279. Fax: 256-362-0497. p. 37

Smith, Justin, Mgr, Nestle Purina Pet Care Co, Checkerboard Sq 2S, Saint Louis, MO, 63164. Tel: 314-982-2056. Fax: 314-982-3259. p. 1357

Smith, Karen M, YA Serv, Allen Park Public Library, 8100 Allen Rd, Allen Park, MI, 48101. Tel: 313-381-2425. Fax: 313-381-2124. p. 1149

Smith, Karen M, Dir, Whitesville Public Library, 500 Main St, Whitesville, NY, 14897-9703. Tel: 607-356-3645. Fax: 607-356-3645. p. 1769

Smith, Kate, Librn, Children's Hospital, Family Health Library, 1056 E 19th Ave, Denver, CO, 80218-1088. Tel: 303-861-6378. Fax: 303-864-5385. p. 299

Smith, Kathleen, Assoc Dir, Vanderbilt University, Special Collections & University Archives, 419 21st Ave S, Nashville, TN, 37203-2427. Tel: 615-322-2807. p. 2261

Smith, Kathy, Dir, San Manuel Public Library, 108 Fifth Ave, San Manuel, AZ, 85631. Tel: 520-385-4470. Fax: 520-385-2910. p. 80

Smith, Kathy, Dir, Garden Valley District Library, 342 Village Circle, Garden Valley, ID, 83622-8040. Tel: 208-462-3317. Fax: 208-462-3758. p. 574

Smith, Kathy, Br Mgr, Scottsville Free Library, Mumford Branch, 883 George St, Mumford, NY, 14511. Tel: 718-538-6124. p. 1742

Smith, Kathy, Librn, Jim Lucas Checotah Public Library, 626 W Gentry, Checotah, OK, 74426-2218. Tel: 918-473-6715. Fax: 918-473-6603. p. 1959

Smith, Kaye, Librn, Martin County Library, 200 N Saint Mary, Stanton, TX, 79782. Tel: 432-756-2472. Fax: 432-756-2681. p. 2389

Smith, Kevin L, Scholarly Communications Officer, Duke University Libraries, 411 Chapel Dr, Durham, NC, 27708. Tel: 919-668-4451. Fax: 919-684-2855. p. 1787

Smith, Kevin W, Libr Dir, York County Public Library, 100 Long Green Blvd, Yorktown, VA, 23693. Tel: 757-890-5134. Fax: 757-890-5127. p. 2505

Smith, Kile, Curator, Free Library of Philadelphia, Edwin A Fleisher Collection of Orchestral Music, 1901 Vine St, Philadelphia, PA, 19103-1189. Tel: 215-686-5313. Fax: 215-686-5314. p. 2107

Smith, Kim, Ch, Eunice Public Library, 1003 Ave N, Eunice, NM, 88231. Tel: 575-394-2336, 575-394-2338. Fax: 575-394-0970. p. 1555

Smith, Kim Ann, Circ Mgr, Northland Public Library, 300 Cumberland Rd, Pittsburgh, PA, 15237-5455. Tel: 412-366-8100, Ext 115. Fax: 412-366-2064. p. 2126

Smith, Kimberley, Asst Univ Librn, Coll Develop, California State University, Fresno, Henry Madden Library, 5200 N Barton Ave, Mail Stop ML-34, Fresno, CA, 93740-8014. Tel: 559-278-4578. Fax: 559-278-6952. p. 150

Smith, Kirsty, Dir, Great River Regional Library, 1300 W St Germain St, Saint Cloud, MN, 56301-3667. Tel: 320-650-2512. Fax: 320-650-2501. p. 1274

Smith, Kristen, Info Serv Librn, Loras College Library, 1450 Alta Vista St, Dubuque, IA, 52004-4327. Tel: 563-588-7189. Fax: 563-588-7147. p. 812

Smith, Kristi, Circ, Head, Ref, Ouachita Baptist University, 410 Ouachita, OBU Box 3742, Arkadelphia, AR, 71998-0001. Tel: 870-245-5119. Fax: 870-245-5245. p. 93

Smith, Kristin, Dir, Richmond Free Public Library, 2821 State Rd, Richmond, MA, 01254-9472. Tel: 413-698-3834. p. 1120

Smith, Krystal, Dir, Bell Memorial Public Library, 101 W Main St, Mentone, IN, 46539. Tel: 574-353-7234. Fax: 574-353-1307. p. 763

Smith, Lana, Asst Dir, Gentry County Library, 304 N Park, Stanberry, MO, 64489. Tel: 660-783-2335. Fax: 660-783-2335. p. 1368

Smith, Lana, Librn, Wayne County Public Library, Wayne Public, 325 Keyser St, Wayne, WV, 25570. Tel: 304-272-3756. Fax: 304-272-3756. p. 2563

Smith, Laura, Head, Circ, Santa Fe University of Art & Design, 1600 St Michael's Dr, Santa Fe, NM, 87505-7634. Tel: 505-473-6569. Fax: 505-473-6593. p. 1564

Smith, Laurie, Librn, Pasadena Presbyterian Church Library, 100 Pasadena Ave N, Saint Petersburg, FL, 33710-8315. Tel: 727-345-0148. Fax: 727-347-6836. p. 488

Smith, Lavada, Assoc Librn, ILL Librn, University of Michigan-Dearborn, 4901 Evergreen Rd, Dearborn, MI, 48128-2406. Tel: 313-593-5445. Fax: 313-593-5478. p. 1168

Smith, Lawrence, Patents Librn, Mississippi Library Commission, 3881 Eastwood Dr, Jackson, MS, 39211. Tel: 601-432-4111. Fax: 601-432-4480. p. 1304

Smith, Lawson, Br Head, Kemper-Newton Regional Library System, DeKalb Branch, PO Box 710, DeKalb, MS, 39328-0710. Tel: 601-743-5981. p. 1316

Smith, LeeRoy, Exec Dir, National Wrestling Hall of Fame Library & Museum, 405 W Hall of Fame Ave, Stillwater, OK, 74075. Tel: 405-377-5243. Fax: 405-377-5244. p. 1978

Smith, Leslie, Br Mgr, Brazoria County Library System, Sweeny Branch, 205 W Ashley-Wilson Rd, Sweeny, TX, 77480. Tel: 979-548-2567. Fax: 979-548-2597. p. 2276

Smith, Lesly M, Dir, Libr Serv, Haltom City Public Library, 4809 Haltom Rd, Haltom City, TX, 76117-3622. Tel: 817-222-7791. Fax: 817-834-1446. p. 2330

Smith, Lilly, Cat Mgr, Tyler Junior College, 1327 S Baxter St, Tyler, TX, 75701. Tel: 903-510-2645. Fax: 903-510-2639. p. 2393

Smith, Lilly F, Dir, Beauregard Parish Library, 205 S Washington Ave, DeRidder, LA, 70634. Tel: 337-463-6217. Fax: 337-462-5434. p. 948

Smith, Linda, Librn, Marissa Public Library, 212 N Main, Marissa, IL, 62257. Tel: 618-295-2825. Fax: 618-295-2435. p. 670

Smith, Linda, Br Mgr, Cape May County Library, Cape May City Branch, Ocean & Hughes St, Cape May, NJ, 08204. Tel: 609-884-9568. p. 1477

Smith, Linda, Assoc Dean, Prof, University of Illinois at Urbana-Champaign, Library & Information Science Bldg, 501 E Daniel St, Champaign, IL, 61820-6211. Tel: 217-333-3280. Fax: 217-244-3302. p. 2965

Smith, Linda K, Assoc Dean, Libr Serv, Menlo College, 1000 El Camino Real, Atherton, CA, 94027-4300. Tel: 650-543-3826. Fax: 650-543-3833. p. 122

Smith, Lisa, Ch, Lindenhurst Memorial Library, One Lee Ave, Lindenhurst, NY, 11757-5399. Tel: 631-957-7755. Fax: 631-957-7114. p. 1652

Smith, Lisa, Dep Dir, University of North Texas Health Science Center at Fort Worth, 3500 Camp Bowie Blvd, Fort Worth, TX, 76107-2699. Tel: 817-735-2589. Fax: 817-763-0325. p. 2324

Smith, Liz, Ref & Instruction Librn, Kalamazoo College, 1200 Academy St, Kalamazoo, MI, 49006-3285. Tel: 269-337-7153. Fax: 269-337-7143. p. 1197

Smith, Lois, Librn, Chinook Regional Library, Leader Branch, 151 First St W, Leader, SK, S0N 1H0, CANADA. Tel: 306-628-3830. p. 2928

Smith, Lorena L, Tech Serv Librn, Ardmore Public Library, 320 E St NW, Ardmore, OK, 73401. Tel: 580-223-8290. Fax: 580-221-3240. p. 1956

Smith, Lori Ward, Librn, Jackson-George Regional Library System, Pascagoula Public Library, 3214 Pascagoula St, Pascagoula, MS, 39567. Fax: 228-769-3113. p. 1310

Smith, Lori-Ellen, Ref & Teen Librn, Stafford Library, Ten Levinthal Run, Stafford, CT, 06075. Tel: 860-684-2852. Fax: 860-684-2128. p. 369

Smith, Lorna, Asst Dir, Cat, Madison Library District, 73 N Center, Rexburg, ID, 83440-1539. Tel: 208-356-3461. p. 582

Smith, Lorna, Librn, Winfield Public Library, PO Box 360, Winfield, AB, T0C 2X0, CANADA. Tel: 780-682-2498. Fax: 780-682-2490. p. 2722

Smith, Lorna, Asst Librn, Chinook Regional Library, Climax Branch, PO Box 323, Climax, SK, S0N 0N0, CANADA. Tel: 306-293-2229. p. 2928

Smith, Lorraine, Visual Res Curator, Pratt Institute Libraries, 200 Willoughby Ave, Brooklyn, NY, 11205-3897. Tel: 718-636-3716. Fax: 718-399-4401. p. 1594

Smith, Lorraine, Head of Libr, Canadian Agriculture Library-Harrow, 2585 County Rd 20 E, RR No 2, Harrow, ON, N0R 1G0, CANADA. Tel: 519-738-1204. Fax: 519-738-2929. p. 2811

Smith, Lorraine, Acq, John Bassett Memorial Library, 2600 College St, Sherbrooke, QC, J1M 0C8, CANADA. Tel: 819-822-9600, Ext 2283. Fax: 819-822-9644. p. 2912

Smith, Lorre, Digital Initiatives Librn, University at Albany, State University of New York, Science Library, 1400 Washington Ave, Albany, NY, 12222. Tel: 518-437-3948. Fax: 518-437-3952. p. 1571

Smith, Lucy, Chairperson, Triton College Library, 2000 N Fifth Ave, River Grove, IL, 60171. Tel: 708-456-0300, Ext 3215. Fax: 708-583-3120. p. 695

Smith, Lyn, Dir, Pittsfield Public Library, 110 Library St, Pittsfield, ME, 04967. Tel: 207-487-5880. p. 996

Smith, MacKenzie, Univ Librn, University of California, Davis, 100 NW Quad, Davis, CA, 95616-5292. Tel: 530-752-6561. Fax: 530-752-3148. p. 139

Smith, Maggie, Coordr, Pearl River Community College, Hancock Center Library, 454 Hwy 90, Ste D, Waveland, MS, 39756. Tel: 228-467-2761. Fax: 228-467-2763. p. 1312

Smith, Margaret, Archives Librn, Episcopal Diocese of Connecticut, 1335 Asylum Ave, Hartford, CT, 06105. Tel: 860-233-4481. Fax: 860-523-1410. p. 345

Smith, Margaret, Dir, Armada Free Public Library, 73930 Church St, Armada, MI, 48005-3331. Tel: 586-784-5921. p. 1154

Smith, Margaret, Dir, Hamlin-Lincoln County Public Library, 7999 Lynn Ave, Hamlin, WV, 25523. Tel: 304-824-5481. Fax: 304-824-7014. p. 2560

Smith, Margaret A, Asst Dir, Franklin Square Public Library, 19 Lincoln Rd, Franklin Square, NY, 11010. Tel: 516-488-3444. Fax: 516-354-3368. p. 1624

Smith, Margie, Asst Dir, Hudson Library & Historical Society, 96 Library St, Hudson, OH, 44236-5122. Tel: 330-653-6658. Fax: 330-650-3373. p. 1905

Smith, Margit, Head, Cat, University of San Diego, Helen K & James S Copley Library, 5998 Alcala Park, San Diego, CA, 92110. Fax: 619-260-4617. p. 239

Smith, Marilyn, Br Supvr, Flint River Regional Library, Monroe County Library, 62 W Main St, Forsyth, GA, 31029. Tel: 478-994-7025. p. 535

Smith, Marilyn, Librn, Onondaga County Public Library, Petit, 105 Victoria Pl, Syracuse, NY, 13210. Tel: 315-435-3636. Fax: 315-435-2731. p. 1753

Smith, Marilyn, Operations Dir, Southern Alberta Art Gallery Library, 601 Third Ave S, Lethbridge, AB, T1J 0H4, CANADA. Tel: 403-327-8770. Fax: 403-328-3913. p. 2710

Smith, Marji, Dir, Jonestown Community Library, 18649 FM1431, Ste 10A, Jonestown, TX, 78645. Tel: 512-267-7511. Fax: 512-267-4572. p. 2348

Smith, Mark, Dir, Sullivan Public Library, 104 W Vine St, Sullivan, MO, 63080. Tel: 573-468-4372. Fax: 573-860-4648. p. 1368

Smith, Mark, Head, Access Serv, Performing Arts Librn, State University of New York, 735 Anderson Hill Rd, Purchase, NY, 10577-1400. Tel: 914-251-6431. Fax: 914-251-6437. p. 1724

Smith, Mark A, Info Syst Librn, Alfred University, Scholes Library of Ceramics, New York State College of Ceramics at Alfred University, Two Pine St, Alfred, NY, 14802-1297. Tel: 607-871-2942. p. 1572

Smith, Marnie, Ref, Burlington Public Library, 22 Sears St, Burlington, MA, 01803. Tel: 781-270-1690. Fax: 781-229-0406. p. 1072

Smith, Marta, Asst City Librn, Fiske Free Library, 108 Broad St, Claremont, NH, 03743-2673. Tel: 603-542-7017. Fax: 603-542-7029. p. 1441

Smith, Martha, Assoc Dir, Florida Coastal School of Law, 8787 Baypine Rd, Jacksonville, FL, 32256. Tel: 904-680-7602. Fax: 904-680-7677. p. 452

Smith, Martha, Ref & Instrul Serv Librn, Elmira College, One Park Pl, Elmira, NY, 14901. Tel: 607-735-1866. Fax: 607-735-1158. p. 1620

Smith, Martie, Dir, Union County Public Library, 316 E Windsor St, Monroe, NC, 28112. Tel: 704-283-8184. Fax: 704-282-0657. p. 1810

Smith, Martin, Head, Automation, Redford Township District Library, 25320 W Six Mile, Redford, MI, 48240. Tel: 313-531-5960. Fax: 313-531-1721. p. 1220

Smith, Marva Mitchell, Fac Mgr, Chicago State University, 9501 S Martin Luther King Jr Dr, LIB 440, Chicago, IL, 60628-1598. Tel: 773-821-4950. Fax: 773-995-3772. p. 610

Smith, Mary, Head, Youth Serv, Mount Prospect Public Library, Ten S Emerson St, Mount Prospect, IL, 60056. Tel: 847-253-5675. Fax: 847-253-0642. p. 677

Smith, Mary, Asst Librn, Indian River Area Library, 3546 S Straits Hwy, Indian River, MI, 49749. Tel: 231-238-8581. Fax: 231-238-9494. p. 1193

Smith, Mary, Librn, Institute for Creation Research Library, 1806 Royal Lane, Dallas, TX, 75229. Tel: 214-615-8300. Fax: 214-615-8299. p. 2308

Smith, Mary Ann, Tech Serv, Imperial Valley College, 380 E Ira Aten Rd, Imperial, CA, 92251. Tel: 760-355-6380. Fax: 760-355-1090. p. 159

Smith, Mary Ann, ILL, Texas Biomedical Research Institute, 7620 NW Loop 410, San Antonio, TX, 78227-5301. p. 2383

Smith, Mary Jo, Ch, Gates Public Library, 902 Elmgrove Rd, Rochester, NY, 14624. Tel: 585-247-6446. Fax: 585-426-5733. p. 1729

Smith, Mary Kay, Ch, YA Serv, Safety Harbor Public Library, 101 Second St N, Safety Harbor, FL, 34695. Tel: 727-724-1525. Fax: 727-724-1533. p. 486

Smith, Mary Lee, Dep Dir, Farmington Public Library, 2101 Farmington Ave, Farmington, NM, 87401. Tel: 505-566-2205. Fax: 505-599-1257. p. 1555

Smith, Mary Morgan, Ch, YA Serv, Northland Public Library, 300 Cumberland Rd, Pittsburgh, PA, 15237-5455. Tel: 412-366-8100, Ext 120. Fax: 412-366-2064. p. 2126

Smith, Mary P, Assoc Dir, Tech Serv, Nova Southeastern University Libraries, Shepard Broad Law Center Library, 3305 College Ave, Fort Lauderdale, FL, 33314. Tel: 954-262-6100. p. 444

Smith, Marye, Librn, West Grey Public Library, Elmwood Branch, 25 Main St S, Elmwood, ON, N0G 1S0, CANADA. Tel: 519-363-3321. Fax: 519-363-3321. p. 2803

Smith, Matthew R, Access Serv Librn, Sullivan County Community College, 112 College Rd, Loch Sheldrake, NY, 12759-5108. Tel: 845-434-5750, Ext 4226. p. 1653

Smith, Melanie, Automation Syst Coordr, Washington County Public Library, 615 Fifth St, Marietta, OH, 45750-1973. Tel: 740-373-1057, Ext 213. p. 1913

Smith, Melanie F, Head, Circ, University of Akron Libraries, 315 Buchtel Mall, Akron, OH, 44325-1701. Tel: 330-972-7047. Fax: 330-972-5106. p. 1853

Smith, Melissa L, Dir, Martin Community College Library, 1161 Kehukee Park Rd, Williamston, NC, 27892-4425. Tel: 252-792-1521, Ext 280. Fax: 252-792-4425. p. 1830

Smith, Meme, Dir, Schuyler Public Library, 1123 A St, Schuyler, NE, 68661-1929. Tel: 402-352-2221. Fax: 402-352-5377. p. 1418

Smith, Merrill, In Charge, US Committee for Refugees & Immigrants Library, 1717 Massachusetts Ave NW, 2nd Flr, Washington, DC, 20036-2003. Tel: 202-347-3507. Fax: 202-347-3418. p. 417

Smith, Michael, Circ, College of Our Lady of the Elms, 291 Springfield St, Chicopee, MA, 01013-2839. Tel: 413-265-2280. Fax: 413-594-7418. p. 1082

Smith, Michael M, Assoc Prof, Bus Ref, Texas A&M University Libraries, West Campus Library, Olsen Blvd, Bldg 1511, College Station, TX, 77843-5001. Tel: 979-845-2902. Fax: 979-862-2977. p. 2299

Smith, Michael R, Dir, Hillsboro Public Library, 2850 NE Brookwood Pkwy, Hillsboro, OR, 97124-5327. Tel: 503-615-6500. Fax: 503-615-6601. p. 2000

Smith, Mike, Librn, Smithsonian Libraries, Freer Gallery of Art & Arthur M Sackler Gallery Library, Arthur M Sackler Gallery, Rm 2057, MRC 707, 12th St & Jefferson Dr SW, Washington, DC, 20560. Tel: 202-633-0480. Fax: 202-786-2936. p. 414

Smith, Misty, Circ, Pender County Public Library, 103 S Cowan St, Burgaw, NC, 28425. Tel: 910-259-1234. Fax: 910-259-0656. p. 1778

Smith, Mitchell, Br Mgr, Chicago Public Library, Whitney M Young Jr Branch, 7901 S King Dr, Chicago, IL, 60619. Tel: 312-747-0039. Fax: 312-747-1459. p. 610

Smith, Monica, Ch, Sandy Public Library, 38980 Proctor Blvd, Sandy, OR, 97055-8040. Tel: 503-668-5537. Fax: 503-668-3153. p. 2019

Smith, Monica L, Librn, Cairo Public Library, 1609 Washington Ave, Cairo, IL, 62914. Tel: 618-734-1840. Fax: 618-734-4799. p. 599

Smith, Morgan Inez, Circ Mgr, Stephens College, 1200 E Broadway, Columbia, MO, 65215. Tel: 573-876-7182. Fax: 573-876-7264. p. 1325

Smith, Moria, Librn, American Chemical Society Information Resource Center, 1155 16th St NW, Washington, DC, 20036. Tel: 202-872-4513. Fax: 202-872-6257. p. 392

Smith, Muriel, In Charge, United Nations Association In Canada, Winnipeg Branch, c/o The University of Winnipeg Library, 515 Portage Ave, Winnipeg, MB, R3B 2E9, CANADA. Tel: 204-586-0173. Fax: 204-783-8910. p. 2757

Smith, Myron J, Jr, Libr Dir, Tusculum College, Hwy 107, 60 Shiloh Rd, Greeneville, TN, 37743. Tel: 423-636-7320, Ext 5260, 5148. Fax: 423-787-8498. p. 2236

Smith, Nancy, Librn, Arkansas River Valley Regional Library System, Franklin County, 407 W Market St, Ozark, AR, 72949-2727. Tel: 479-667-2724. Fax: 479-667-9021. p. 97

Smith, Nancy, Br Mgr, Riverside County Library System, Sun City Library, 26982 Cherry Hills Blvd, Sun City, CA, 92586. Tel: 951-679-8672. Fax: 951-672-8293. p. 218

Smith, Nancy, Librn, Temple Beth Sholom, 1809 Whitney Ave, Hamden, CT, 06517. Tel: 203-288-7748. Fax: 203-288-0582. p. 344

Smith, Nancy, Visual Res, Trinity College Library, 300 Summit St, Hartford, CT, 06106. Tel: 860-297-4061. Fax: 860-297-2251. p. 347

Smith, Nancy, Assoc Dir, Pub Serv, King County Library System, 960 Newport Way NW, Issaquah, WA, 98027. Tel: 425-369-3309. Fax: 425-369-3255. p. 2516

Smith, Nancy Davis, Lead Librn, Kalamazoo Public Library, Washington Square, 1244 Portage Rd, Kalamazoo, MI, 49001. Tel: 269-553-7974. Fax: 269-342-9261. p. 1197

Smith, Nathan M, Librn, Utah State University, Young Educational Technology Center, UMC 2845 - 170 EDUC, Utah State University, Logan, UT, 84322-2845. Tel: 435-797-3377. p. 2407

Smith, Nina, Bus Librn, Lincoln-Lawrence-Franklin Regional Library, 100 S Jackson St, Brookhaven, MS, 39601-3347. Tel: 601-833-3369, 601-833-5038. Fax: 601-833-3381. p. 1294

Smith, Nora, Circ Supvr, Edmonds Community College Library, 20000 68th Ave W, Lynnwood, WA, 98036. Tel: 425-640-1529. p. 2520

Smith, Nordis, ILL, Pub Serv, Ref Serv, Huntingdon College, 1500 E Fairview Ave, Montgomery, AL, 36106. Tel: 334-833-4421. Fax: 334-263-4465. p. 29

Smith, Owen G, Head, Electronic Serv, University of San Diego, Katherine M & George M Pardee Jr Legal Research Center, 5998 Alcala Park, San Diego, CA, 92110-2492. Tel: 619-260-4542. Fax: 619-260-4616. p. 239

Smith, Owen G, Circuit Librn, US Court of Appeals for the Sixth Circuit Library, 312 Potter Stewart US Courthouse, Cincinnati, OH, 45202. Tel: 513-564-7321. Fax: 513-564-7329. p. 1873

Smith, Pam, Librn, Barton Library, Harper Memorial, 301 N Myrtle, Junction City, AR, 71749. Tel: 870-924-5556. Fax: 870-924-5556. p. 98

Smith, Pam, Head, Tech Serv, Syst Librn, Howe Library, 13 South St, Hanover, NH, 03755. Tel: 603-643-4120. Fax: 603-643-0725. p. 1450

Smith, Pam, Librn, Maud Public Library, 134 Main St, Maud, TX, 75567-0388. Tel: 903-585-5255. Fax: 903-585-5255. p. 2360

Smith, Pam, Circ Mgr, Park County Public Library, 1500 Heart Mountain St, Cody, WY, 82414. Tel: 307-527-1880. Fax: 307-527-1888. p. 2653

Smith, Pam Sandlian, Dir, Anythink Libraries, 5877 E 120th Ave, Thornton, CO, 80602. Tel: 303-288-2001. Fax: 303-451-0190. p. 323

Smith, Pat, Mgr, Thomas County Public Library System, Pavo Public Library, 219 E Harris St, Pavo, GA, 31778-2107. Tel: 229-859-2697. Fax: 229-859-2697. p. 554

Smith, Pat, Acq, ILL, Gwynedd-Mercy College, 1325 Sumneytown Pike, Gwynedd Valley, PA, 19437. Tel: 215-646-7300, Ext 493. Fax: 215-641-5596. p. 2063

Smith, Pat, Circ, Community College of Beaver County Library, One Campus Dr, Monaca, PA, 15061-2588. Tel: 724-775-8561. Fax: 724-728-8024. p. 2090

Smith, Patricia, Coordr, Coll Mgt, Colorado State University Libraries, Morgan Library, 1201 Center Avenue Mall, Fort Collins, CO, 80523-. Tel: 970-491-1838. Fax: 970-491-1195. p. 307

Smith, Patricia, Dir, Brimfield Public Library, 111 S Galena St, Brimfield, IL, 61517. Tel: 309-446-9575. Fax: 309-446-9357. p. 597

Smith, Patricia, Dir, Allen County Historical Society, 620 W Market St, Lima, OH, 45801-4604. Tel: 419-222-9426. Fax: 419-222-0649. p. 1909

Smith, Patricia, Dir, Beaver County Library System, One Campus Dr, Monaca, PA, 15061-2523. Tel: 724-728-3737. Fax: 724-728-8024. p. 2090

Smith, Patricia, Librn, Monaca Public Library, 609 Pennsylvania Ave, Monaca, PA, 15061. Tel: 724-775-9608. Fax: 724-775-1637. p. 2090

Smith, Patrick, Info Tech Mgr, DeKalb Public Library, 309 Oak St, DeKalb, IL, 60115-3369. Tel: 815-756-9568. Fax: 815-756-7837. p. 635

Smith, Patrick, Computer Serv, Broome County Public Library, 185 Court St, Binghamton, NY, 13901-3503. Tel: 607-343-8244. Fax: 607-778-6429. p. 1582

Smith, Patsy, Dir, Mancos Public Library, 211 W First St, Mancos, CO, 81328. Tel: 970-533-7600. Fax: 970-533-7289. p. 318

Smith, Patty, Ref Serv, Prairie Skies Public Library District, 125 W Editor St, Ashland, IL, 62612. Tel: 217-476-3417. Fax: 217-476-8076. p. 590

Smith, Paul M, Dir, Western Theological Seminary, 101 E 13th St, Holland, MI, 49423. Tel: 616-392-8555. p. 1191

Smith, Paula, Cat, State Historical Society of Iowa, 402 Iowa Ave, Iowa City, IA, 52240-1806. Tel: 319-335-3916. Fax: 319-335-3935. p. 823

Smith, Paula, Govt Doc, ILL, Great Basin College Library, 1500 College Pkwy, Elko, NV, 89801. Tel: 775-753-2222. Fax: 775-753-2296. p. 1427

Smith, Paula, Ref Librn, Pennsylvania State University, 1600 Woodland Rd, Abington, PA, 19001. Tel: 215-881-7424. Fax: 215-881-7423. p. 2025

Smith, Paulette, Ref, Valencia Community College, Raymer Maguire Jr Learning Resources Center, West Campus, 1800 S Kirkman Rd, Orlando, FL, 32811. Tel: 407-582-1210. Fax: 407-582-1686. p. 478

Smith, Pauline, Dir, South English Public Library, 407 Ives St, South English, IA, 52335. Tel: 319-667-2715. Fax: 319-667-4507. p. 845

Smith, Peggy, Librn, Putnam County Public Library District, Magnolia Branch, 114 N Chicago St, Magnolia, IL, 61336. Tel: 815-869-6038. Fax: 815-869-6038. p. 655

Smith, Peggy, Circ, Sampson-Clinton Public Library, Miriam B Lamb Memorial, 144 S Church Ave, Garland, NC, 28441. Tel: 910-529-2441. p. 1784

Smith, Peggy, Data Librn, University of Wisconsin-Madison, Business Library, Grainger Hall, Rm 2200, 975 University Ave, Madison, WI, 53706. Tel: 608-890-1901. Fax: 608-262-9001. p. 2608

Smith, Peggy E, Dean of Libr, Horry-Georgetown Technical College, 2050 Hwy 501 E, Conway, SC, 29526-9521. Tel: 843-349-5269. Fax: 843-347-0552. p. 2191

Smith, Peter, Ref & Digitization Librn, Western Washington University, 516 High St, MS 9103, Bellingham, WA, 98225. Tel: 360-650-3175. Fax: 360-650-3044. p. 2509

Smith, Peter, Coordr, Salem State University, Graduate School, 352 Lafayette St, Salem, MA, 01970. Tel: 978-542-6000, 978-542-7044. Fax: 978-542-7215. p. 2967

Smith, Philip, Ref, Bank of America Merrill Lynch & Co, 250 Vesey St, 24th Flr, New York, NY, 10080. Tel: 212-449-3814. Fax: 212-449-1379. p. 1669

Smith, Phyllis, Br Supvr, Saint Charles Parish Library, Norco Branch, 197 Good Hope St, Norco, LA, 70079-2516. Tel: 985-764-6581. p. 949

Smith, Phyllis, Supv Librn, New Hanover County Public Library, 201 Chestnut St, Wilmington, NC, 28401. Tel: 910-798-6300. Fax: 910-798-6312. p. 1830

Smith, R, Br Mgr, New Orleans Public Library, Mid-City Branch, 3700 Orleans Ave, New Orleans, LA, 70119. Tel: 504-596-2654. p. 962

Smith, Randy, Cat, Ref, Tech Serv, Lewiston City Library, 428 Thain Rd, Lewiston, ID, 83501-5399. Tel: 208-743-6519. Fax: 208-798-4446. p. 578

Smith, Randy, Spec Coll & Archives Librn, Goucher College Library, 1021 Dulaney Valley Rd, Baltimore, MD, 21204. Tel: 410-337-6360. Fax: 410-337-6419. p. 1014

Smith, Reagan, Head, Tech, Syst Adminr, Kendallville Public Library, 221 S Park Ave, Kendallville, IN, 46755-2248. Tel: 260-343-2010. Fax: 260-343-2011. p. 756

Smith, Rebecca, Head Librn, University of Illinois Library at Urbana-Champaign, Business & Economics, 101 Main Library, 1408 W Gregory, Urbana, IL, 61801. Tel: 217-244-0388. Fax: 217-244-1931. p. 712

Smith, Rebecca, Ch, Malden Public Library, 36 Salem St, Malden, MA, 02148-5291. Tel: 781-388-0803. Fax: 781-324-4467. p. 1102

Smith, Rebecca, Br Head, Lane Public Libraries, Oxford Lane Library, 15 S College Ave, Oxford, OH, 45056. Tel: 513-523-7531. Fax: 513-523-6661. p. 1904

Smith, Rebecca A, Librn, Historical Association of Southern Florida, 101 W Flagler St, Miami, FL, 33130. Tel: 305-375-1492. Fax: 305-372-6313. p. 465

Smith, Regina L, Exec Dir, Jenkins Law Library, 833 Chestnut St, Ste 1220, Philadelphia, PA, 19107-4429. Tel: 215-574-7904. Fax: 215-574-7920. p. 2111

Smith, Rhonda B, Circ Mgr, Waynesboro Public Library, 600 S Wayne Ave, Waynesboro, VA, 22980. Tel: 540-942-6746. Fax: 540-942-6753. p. 2501

Smith, Richard J, Dr, Dir, Missouri State Library, 600 W Main St, Jefferson City, MO, 65101-1532. Tel: 573-751-8720. Fax: 573-526-2985. p. 1335

Smith, Richard O, Br Mgr, Caroline County Public Library, North County Branch, 101 Cedar Lane, Greensboro, MD, 21639. Tel: 410-482-2173. Fax: 410-482-2634. p. 1027

Smith, Rise, Prof, Digital Design/Access Librn, Dakota State University, 820 N Washington Ave, Madison, SD, 57042-1799. Tel: 605-256-5203. Fax: 605-256-5208. p. 2214

Smith, Rita, Head, Res Serv, University of Tennessee, Knoxville, 1015 Volunteer Blvd, Knoxville, TN, 37996-1000. Tel: 865-974-4127. Fax: 865-974-9242. p. 2243

Smith, Rita, Librn, Wilford Hall Medical Center Library, 59MDW/SGN, Lackland AFB, TX, 78236-5300. Tel: 210-292-5771. Fax: 210-292-7030. p. 2352

Smith, Rita Hunt, Children's & Youth Serv, Hershey Public Library, 701 Cocoa Ave, Hershey, PA, 17033. Tel: 717-533-6555. Fax: 717-534-1666. p. 2069

Smith, Rita L, Ref Serv, Aiso Library, 543 Lawton Rd, Ste 617A, Monterey, CA, 93944-3214. Tel: 831-242-5553. Fax: 831-242-5816. p. 189

Smith, Robernette, Ref, Coppin State College, 2500 W North Ave, Baltimore, MD, 21216-3698. Tel: 410-951-3400. Fax: 410-951-3430. p. 1012

Smith, Robert, Curator, United States Cavalry Association, Bldg 247, Cameron Ave, Fort Riley, KS, 66442. Tel: 785-784-5797. Fax: 785-784-5797. p. 867

Smith, Robert, Ch, Stillwater County Library, 27 N Fourth St, Columbus, MT, 59019. Tel: 406-322-5009. Fax: 406-322-5009. p. 1377

Smith, Robert A, Dir, IT, Linda Hall Library, 5109 Cherry St, Kansas City, MO, 64110-2498. Tel: 816-926-8716. Fax: 816-926-8790. p. 1337

Smith, Robert C, Dr, Prof, Western Kentucky University, School of Teacher Education, 1092 Gary A Ransdell Hall, Normal St, WKU No 61030, Bowling Green, KY, 42101-1030. Tel: 270-779-4950. Fax: 270-745-6322. p. 2966

Smith, Robert E, Electronic Res Librn, Concordia Theological Seminary, 6600 N Clinton St, Fort Wayne, IN, 46825. Tel: 260-452-2145. Fax: 260-452-2126. p. 741

Smith, Roberta, Asst Librn, Arlington Public Library, 711 Main St, Arlington, IA, 50606. Tel: 563-633-3475. Fax: 563-633-3475. p. 794

Smith, Robin, Assoc Dir, Pub Serv, Indian Trails Public Library District, 355 S Schoenbeck Rd, Wheeling, IL, 60090. Tel: 847-459-4100. Fax: 847-459-4760. p. 719

Smith, Robin, Ch, Beaumont Public Library System, Beaumont Public, 801 Pearl St, Beaumont, TX, 77701. Tel: 409-838-6606. p. 2287

Smith, Rodger, Acq Mgr, Coll Mgr, Charleston County Public Library, 68 Calhoun St, Charleston, SC, 29401. Tel: 843-805-6866. p. 2183

Smith, Roger F, Exec Dir, Libr Serv, Wiregrass Georgia Technical College, 667 Perry House Rd, Fitzgerald, GA, 31750. Tel: 229-468-2012. Fax: 229-468-2110. p. 532

Smith, Ron, Archivist, RMS Foundation, Inc, 1126 Queens Hwy, Long Beach, CA, 90802. Tel: 562-435-3511. Fax: 562-437-4531. p. 167

Smith, Ronnie, Dir, Eufaula Carnegie Library, 217 N Eufaula Ave, Eufaula, AL, 36027. Tel: 334-687-2337. Fax: 334-687-8143. p. 16

Smith, Rosalyn Y, Libr Tech, Jewish Hospital, 4777 E Galbraith Rd, Cincinnati, OH, 45236. Tel: 513-686-5173. Fax: 513-686-5418. p. 1870

Smith, Rose E, Bus Mgr, Chicago State University, 9501 S Martin Luther King Jr Dr, LIB 440, Chicago, IL, 60628-1598. Tel: 773-995-2026. Fax: 773-995-3772. p. 610

Smith, Roxanne, Libr Tech, British Columbia Ministry of Forests Library, 722 Johnson St, 4th Flr, Victoria, BC, V8W 9C2, CANADA. Tel: 250-387-3628. Fax: 250-953-3079. p. 2745

Smith, Roya, Children's Coordr, Riverside County Library System, Lakeside Library, 32593 Riverside Dr, Lake Elsinore, CA, 92530. Tel: 951-678-7083. Fax: 951-678-7018. p. 217

Smith, Ruby, Ref Supvr, Public Library of Johnston County & Smithfield, 305 E Market St, Smithfield, NC, 27577-3919. Tel: 919-934-8146. Fax: 919-934-8084. p. 1824

Smith, Russell, Info Spec, University of Southern California Libraries, Norris Medical Library, 2003 Zonal Ave, Los Angeles, CA, 90089-9130. Tel: 323-442-1116. Fax: 323-221-1235. p. 179

Smith, Sabrina, Communications Facilitator, Citrus County Library System, 425 W Roosevelt Blvd, Beverly Hills, FL, 34465-4281. Tel: 352-746-9077. Fax: 352-746-9493. p. 427

Smith, Sadie E, Head, Ch, Licking County Library, 101 W Main St, Newark, OH, 43055-5054. Tel: 740-349-5551. Fax: 740-349-5575. p. 1922

Smith, Sallie, Syst & Cat Librn, University of Pittsburgh, Law Bldg, 3900 Forbes Ave, 4th Flr, Pittsburgh, PA, 15260. Tel: 412-648-1326. Fax: 412-648-1352. p. 2129

Smith, Sally, Assoc Librn, Ref Librn, University of Michigan-Dearborn, 4901 Evergreen Rd, Dearborn, MI, 48128-2406. Tel: 313-593-5617. Fax: 313-593-5478. p. 1168

Smith, Sally, Ser, Bethel University Library, 3900 Bethel Dr, Saint Paul, MN, 55112. Tel: 651-638-6222. Fax: 651-638-6001. p. 1277

Smith, Sally, Cat Mgr, King County Library System, 960 Newport Way NW, Issaquah, WA, 98027. Tel: 425-369-3340. Fax: 425-369-3255. p. 2516

Smith, Sally Decker, Head, Adult Serv, Indian Trails Public Library District, 355 S Schoenbeck Rd, Wheeling, IL, 60090. Tel: 847-459-4100. Fax: 847-459-4760. p. 719

Smith, SallyAnn M, Librn, John Graham Public Library, Nine Parsonage St, Newville, PA, 17241-1399. Tel: 717-776-5900. Fax: 717-776-4408. p. 2098

Smith, Sandra, Mgr, Brown County Public Library, Fayetteville-Perry Branch, 406 N East St, Fayetteville, OH, 45118. Tel: 513-875-2665. Fax: 513-875-2738. p. 1919

Smith, Sandra, Coordr, Libr Serv, New River Community College, 226 Martin Hall, Dublin, VA, 24084. Tel: 540-674-3600, Ext 4345. Fax: 540-676-3626. p. 2460

Smith, Sandy Sue, Ref Serv, Lodi Public Library, 201 W Locust St, Lodi, CA, 95240. Tel: 209-333-5566. Fax: 209-367-5944. p. 165

Smith, Sara, Day Circ Spec, Mount Vernon Nazarene University, 800 Martinsburg Rd, Mount Vernon, OH, 43050-9500. Tel: 740-397-9000, Ext 4240. Fax: 740-397-8847. p. 1919

Smith, Sarah, Asst Br Mgr, Baltimore County Public Library, Hereford, 16940 York Rd, Monkton, MD, 21111. Tel: 410-887-1919. Fax: 410-329-8203. p. 1044

Smith, Scott, Librn, URS Corp Library, 7650 W Courtney Campbell Causeway, Tampa, FL, 33607-1462. Tel: 813-675-6764. Fax: 813-636-2496. p. 499

Smith, Scott, Assoc Dean, University of Nevada, Las Vegas Libraries, 4505 Maryland Pkwy, Box 457001, Las Vegas, NV, 89154-7001. Tel: 702-895-2286. Fax: 702-895-2287. p. 1430

Smith, Scott, Tech Serv, Stevens Institute of Technology, Castle Point on Hudson, Hoboken, NJ, 07030. Tel: 201-216-5419. Fax: 201-216-8319. p. 1491

Smith, Sean, Media Spec, Marymount Manhattan College, 221 E 71st St, New York, NY, 10021. Tel: 212-774-4805. Fax: 212-458-8207. p. 1685

Smith, Seth, Ref Spec, State Historical Society of Missouri Library, 1020 Lowry St, Columbia, MO, 65201-7298. Tel: 573-882-7083. Fax: 573-884-4950. p. 1324

Smith, Shae, Head, Youth Serv, Oxford Public Library, 530 Pontiac Rd, Oxford, MI, 48371-4844. Tel: 248-628-3034. Fax: 248-628-5008. p. 1216

Smith, Shannon, Asst Coordr, Youth Serv, Fairfield County District Library, 219 N Broad St, Lancaster, OH, 43130-3098. Tel: 740-653-2745. Fax: 740-653-4199. p. 1908

Smith, Sharman, Exec Dir, Mississippi Library Commission, 3881 Eastwood Dr, Jackson, MS, 39211. Tel: 601-432-4039. Fax: 601-432-4480. p. 1304

Smith, Sharon, Area Res Mgr, W Region, Indianapolis-Marion County Public Library, 2450 N Meridian St, Indianapolis, IN, 46208. Tel: 317-275-4535. Fax: 317-269-5300. p. 753

Smith, Sharon, Br Mgr, Indianapolis-Marion County Public Library, Wayne, 198 S Girls School Rd, Indianapolis, IN, 46231-1120. Tel: 317-275-4530. p. 754

Smith, Sharon, Sr Mgr, American International Group, 70 Pine St, 6th Flr, New York, NY, 10270. Tel: 212-770-7911. Fax: 212-742-0949. p. 1668

Smith, Sharon, Dir, McDowell Technical Community College Library, 54 College Dr, Marion, NC, 28752-8728. Tel: 828-652-6021. Fax: 828-652-1014. p. 1809

Smith, Sharon, Dir, Southwestern Oregon Community College Library, 1988 Newmark Ave, Coos Bay, OR, 97420-2956. Tel: 541-888-7431. Fax: 541-888-7605. p. 1993

Smith, Sharron, Br Head, Muskegon Area District Library, Montague Branch, 8778 Ferry St, Montague, MI, 49437-1233. Tel: 231-893-2675. Fax: 231-737-6307. p. 1213

Smith, Sharyn, Adult Serv, Ref Serv, Eagle Valley Library District, 600 Broadway, Eagle, CO, 81631. Tel: 970-328-8800. Fax: 970-328-6901. p. 305

Smith, Shay, Ch, Meridian-Lauderdale County Public Library, 2517 Seventh St, Meridian, MS, 39301. Tel: 601-693-6771, Ext 234. Fax: 601-486-2260. p. 1308

Smith, Shelley, In Charge, Western Counties Regional Library, Clark's Harbour Branch, 2642 Main St, Clark's Harbour, NS, B0W 1P0, CANADA. Tel: 902-745-2885. p. 2787

Smith, Sherri, Libr Serv Supvr, Thousand Oaks Library, Newbury Park Branch, 2331 Borchard Rd, Newbury Park, CA, 91320-3206. Tel: 805-498-8488, Ext 7225. Fax: 805-498-7034. p. 275

Smith, Sherrie, Dir, Live Oak County Library, 402 N Houston St, George West, TX, 78022. Tel: 361-449-1124. p. 2327

Smith, Sherrie, Dir, Live Oak County Library, Three Rivers, 102 Leroy St, Three Rivers, TX, 78071. Tel: 361-449-1124. p. 2327

Smith, Sherry, Chief Librn, Granisle Public Library, Two Village Sq, McDonald Ave, Granisle, BC, V0J 1W0, CANADA. Tel: 250-697-2713. p. 2729

Smith, Shilo, Ref, United States Air Force, 8102 Condor St, MacDill AFB, FL, 33621-5408. Tel: 813-828-0434. Fax: 813-828-4416. p. 462

Smith, Shirley, Librn, Maryland Correctional Training Center Library, 18800 Roxbury Rd, Hagerstown, MD, 21746. Tel: 240-420-1607. Fax: 301-665-1813. p. 1031

Smith, Shirley, Br Librn, Albany County Public Library, 310 S Eighth St, Laramie, WY, 82070-3969. Tel: 307-721-2580. Fax: 307-721-2584. p. 2657

Smith, Shirley, Br Librn, Albany County Public Library, Rock River Branch, 386 Ave D, Rock River, WY, 82083. p. 2657

Smith, Stacey J, Head, Circ, University Libraries, University of Memphis, 126 Ned R McWherter Library, Memphis, TN, 38152-3250. Tel: 901-678-8201. p. 2252

Smith, Starr, Br Mgr, Fairfax County Public Library, Dolley Madison Branch, 1244 Oak Ridge Ave, McLean, VA, 22101-2818. Tel: 703-356-0770. p. 2461

Smith, Stefan, Outreach Serv Librn, University of Wisconsin-La Crosse, 1631 Pine St, La Crosse, WI, 54601-3748. Tel: 608-785-8396. Fax: 608-785-8639. p. 2603

Smith, Steffaney, Ch, Littleton Public Library, 92 Main St, Littleton, NH, 03561-1238. Tel: 603-444-5741. Fax: 603-444-1706. p. 1454

Smith, Steve, Admin Librn, Dearborn Public Library, 16301 Michigan Ave, Dearborn, MI, 48126. Tel: 313-943-2330. Fax: 313-943-2853. p. 1167

Smith, Steve, Coordr, Local Hist & Spec Coll, Spartanburg County Public Libraries, 151 S Church St, Spartanburg, SC, 29306-3241. Tel: 864-596-3500. Fax: 864-596-3518. p. 2205

Smith, Steven, Asst Dir, Knox County Public Library, 502 N Seventh St, Vincennes, IN, 47591-2119. Tel: 812-886-4380. Fax: 812-886-0342. p. 784

Smith, Steven A, Tech Serv Librn, Limestone College, 1115 College Dr, Gaffney, SC, 29340. Tel: 864-488-4611. Fax: 864-487-4613. p. 2194

Smith, Sue Ann, Head Librn, Borough of Folcroft Public Library, Delmar Dr & Ashland Ave, Folcroft, PA, 19032-2002. Tel: 610-586-1690. Fax: 610-586-2179. p. 2057

Smith, Susan, ILL, Olathe Public Library, 201 E Park St, Olathe, KS, 66061. Tel: 913-971-6854. Fax: 913-971-6809. p. 886

Smith, Susan, Assoc Dean, Wake Forest University, PO Box 7777, Winston-Salem, NC, 27109-7777. Tel: 336-758-5828. Fax: 336-758-3694, 336-758-8831. p. 1834

Smith, Susan, Ref/ILL, Sumter County Library, 111 N Harvin St, Sumter, SC, 29150. Tel: 803-773-7273. Fax: 803-773-4875. p. 2206

Smith, Susan, Circ Coordr, Dallas County Community College District, 1402 Corinth St, Dallas, TX, 75215. Tel: 214-860-5779. p. 2305

Smith, Susan, Commun Serv, Outreach Serv Librn, San Marcos Public Library, 625 E Hopkins, San Marcos, TX, 78666. Tel: 512-393-8200. p. 2384

Smith, Susan, Mgr, Weyerhaeuser Library & Information Resources, 32901 Weyerhaeuser Way S, Federal Way, WA, 98001. Tel: 253-924-6262. Fax: 253-924-3612. p. 2516

Smith, Susan, Librn, Madoc Public Library, 20 Davidson St, Madoc, ON, K0K 2K0, CANADA. Tel: 613-473-4456. Fax: 613-473-4456. p. 2819

Smith, Susan A, Coll Develop Librn, Irvine Sullivan Ingram Library, University of West Georgia, 1601 Maple St, Carrollton, GA, 30118. Tel: 678-839-6498. Fax: 678-839-6511. p. 523

Smith, Susan K, Head, Eng & Sci Libr, University of Kentucky Libraries, Science Library, 211 King Bldg, Lexington, KY, 40506-0039. Tel: 859-257-7176, 257-4364. Fax: 859-323-1911. p. 922

Smith, Susan K, Head, Eng & Sci Libr, University of Kentucky Libraries, Shaver Engineering Library, 355 Anderson Tower, Lexington, KY, 40506-0046. Tel: 859-257-7176. Fax: 859-323-1911. p. 922

Smith, Susan S, Mgr, Young Adult & Children's Serv, Bedford Public Library, 1323 K St, Bedford, IN, 47421. Tel: 812-275-4471. Fax: 812-278-5244. p. 726

Smith, Suzanne, Br Mgr, Johnson County Public Library, White River Library, 1664 Library Blvd, Greenwood, IN, 46142. Tel: 317-885-1330. Fax: 317-882-4117. p. 744

Smith, Suzanne, Ref Librn, Multnomah University, 8435 NE Glisan St, Portland, OR, 97220-5898. Tel: 503-251-5322, Fax: 503-254-1268. p. 2012

Smith, Suzi, Librn, Tulsa City-County Library, Sperry Branch, 15 E Main, Sperry, OK, 74073. Tel: 918-591-4690. Fax: 918-591-4691. p. 1983

Smith, Tamela M, Dir, Belington Public Library, 510 Elliott Ave, Belington, WV, 26250. Tel: 304-823-1026. Fax: 304-823-1026. p. 2554

Smith, Tanja, Dir, Marble Public Library, 302 Alice Ave, Marble, MN, 55764. Tel: 218-247-7676. Fax: 218-247-7676. p. 1258

Smith, Tarisa, Children's & Teen Serv Coordr, Hartley Public Library, 91 First St SE, Hartley, IA, 51346. Tel: 712-928-2080. Fax: 712-928-2823. p. 820

Smith, Teal, User Communication & Instruction Librn, University of California, Merced Library, 5200 N Lake Rd, Merced, CA, 95343-5001. Tel: 209-201-6485. Fax: 209-228-4271. p. 186

Smith, Ted, Librn, North Dakota Supreme Court, Judicial Wing, 2nd Flr, 600 E Boulevard Ave, Dept 182, Bismarck, ND, 58505-0540. Tel: 701-328-2227, 701-328-4496, 701-328-4594. Fax: 701-328-3609. p. 1838

Smith, Ted J, Libr Dir, Newport Public Library, 35 NW Nye St, Newport, OR, 97365-3714. Tel: 541-265-2153. Fax: 541-574-9496. p. 2007

Smith, Teresa, Ch, Euclid Public Library, 631 E 222nd St, Euclid, OH, 44123-2091. Tel: 216-261-5300, Ext 143. Fax: 216-261-9559. p. 1898

Smith, Terry, Circ, Greenfield Community College Library, One College Dr, Greenfield, MA, 01301-9739. Tel: 413-775-1830. Fax: 413-775-1838. p. 1092

Smith, Thomas J, Asst Teaching Prof, Drexel University, Rush Bldg, Rm 306, 30 N 33rd St, Philadelphia, PA, 19104-2875. Tel: 215-895-2474. Fax: 215-895-2494. p. 2973

Smith, Tienya, Commun Libr Mgr, Queens Borough Public Library, Long Island City Community Library, 37-44 21 St, Long Island City, NY, 11101. Tel: 718-752-3700. p. 1645

Smith, Tienya B, Asst Dir, Bosler Free Library, 158 W High St, Carlisle, PA, 17013-2988. Tel: 717-243-4642. Fax: 717-243-8281. p. 2041

Smith, Tiffany, Head of Libr, Free Library of Philadelphia, South Philadelphia Branch, 1700 S Broad St, Philadelphia, PA, 19145-2392. Tel: 215-685-1866, 215-685-1867. Fax: 215-685-1868. p. 2109

Smith, Tina, Commun Librn, Fort Vancouver Regional Library District, North Bonneville Community Library, 214 CBD Mall (Inside City Hall), North Bonneville, WA, 98639. Tel: 509-427-4439. p. 2546

Smith, Tina, Commun Librn, Fort Vancouver Regional Library District, Stevenson Community Library, 120 NW Vancouver Ave, Stevenson, WA, 98648. Tel: 509-427-5471. p. 2546

Smith, Tom, Asst Dir, Head Ref Librn, Frankfort Community Public Library, 208 W Clinton St, Frankfort, IN, 46041. Tel: 765-654-8746. Fax: 765-654-8747. p. 743

Smith, Tommie, Asst Librn, Mount Airy Public Library, 145 Rockford St, Mount Airy, NC, 27030-4759. Tel: 336-789-5108. Fax: 336-786-5838. p. 1811

Smith, Tori, ILL, Florida Institute of Technology, 150 W University Blvd, Melbourne, FL, 32901-6988. Tel: 321-674-8021. Fax: 321-724-2559. p. 463

Smith, Tracey, Br Adminr, Manatee Community College Library, Venice Campus, 8000 S Tamiami Trail, Venice, FL, 34293. Tel: 941-408-1434. Fax: 941-408-1445. p. 429

Smith, Tracey, Libr Tech, United States Court of Appeals, 1102 US Courthouse, 300 S Fourth St, Rm 1102, Minneapolis, MN, 55415. Tel: 612-664-5830. Fax: 612-664-5835. p. 1262

Smith, Tracey, Tech Serv, US Courts Library, 512 Federal Court Bldg, 316 N Robert St, Saint Paul, MN, 55101. Tel: 651-848-1320. Fax: 651-848-1325. p. 1282

Smith, Tracy D, Libr Dir, Arkansas State University, Palm & Iowa Sts, Beebe, AR, 72012. Tel: 501-882-8806. Fax: 501-882-8833. p. 94

Smith, Tracy H, Dir of Libr, Pearl River Community College, 101 Hwy 11 N, Poplarville, MS, 39470. Tel: 601-403-1331. Fax: 601-403-1135. p. 1312

Smith, Trista, Dir, Bitterroot Public Library, 306 State St, Hamilton, MT, 59840-2759. Tel: 406-363-1670. Fax: 406-363-1678. p. 1380

Smith, Vanessa, Libr Asst, Fisk University, Fisk University, 1000 17th Ave N, Nashville, TN, 37208-3051. Tel: 615-329-8646. Fax: 615-329-8761. p. 2256

Smith, Veronica, Automation Syst Coordr, Westminster Public Library, 3705 W 112th Ave, Westminster, CO, 80031. Tel: 303-658-2645. Fax: 303-404-5135. p. 326

Smith, Victor, Ref, La Grange Public Library, Ten W Cossitt Ave, La Grange, IL, 60525. Tel: 708-352-0576. p. 662

Smith, Violet, Adult Serv, Crook County Library, 414 Main St, Sundance, WY, 82729. Tel: 307-283-1006, 307-283-1008. Fax: 307-283-1006. p. 2660

Smith, Walt, Syst Adminr, Willingboro Public Library, Willingboro Town Ctr, 220 Willingboro Pkwy, Willingboro, NJ, 08046. Tel: 609-877-0476, 609-877-6668. Fax: 609-835-1699. p. 1544

Smith, Warren, Ref, Walpole Public Library, 65 Common St, Walpole, MA, 02081. Tel: 508-660-7340. Fax: 508-660-2714. p. 1132

Smith, Wendy, Mgr, El Dorado County Library, Pollock Pines Branch, 6210 Pony Express Trail, Pollock Pines, CA, 95726. Tel: 530-644-2498. Fax: 530-644-2498. p. 208

Smith, Whitney, Exec Dir, Flag Research Center Library, Three Edgehill Rd, Winchester, MA, 01890-3915. Tel: 781-729-9410. Fax: 781-721-4817. p. 1141

Smith, William, Asst Dir, Syst Adminr, Desoto Parish Library, 109 Crosby St, Mansfield, LA, 71052. Tel: 318-872-6100. Fax: 318-872-6120. p. 955

Smith, William L, Pub Serv, Wilmington University Library, 320 DuPont Hwy, New Castle, DE, 19720. Tel: 302-328-9401. Fax: 302-328-0914. p. 385

Smith, William L, Dr, Dir, Charles C Tandy MD Health Sciences Library, 1441 N Beckley Ave, Dallas, TX, 75203. Tel: 214-947-2330. Fax: 214-947-2334. p. 2310

Smith, Wilma, Dir, Gilman Public Library, 106 N Main St, Gilman, IA, 50106. Tel: 641-498-2120. p. 818

Smith, Wilma, Librn, Laurel County Public Library District, South Branch, 727 W Cumberland Gap Pkwy, Corbin, KY, 40701. Tel: 606-258-7000. p. 923

Smith, Zena, Head, Youth Serv, Midlothian Public Library, 14701 S Kenton Ave, Midlothian, IL, 60445-4122. Tel: 708-535-2027. Fax: 708-535-2053. p. 674

Smith-Borne, Holling, Libr Dir, Vanderbilt University, Anne Potter Wilson Music Library, Blair School of Music, 2400 Blakemore Ave, Nashville, TN, 37212. Tel: 615-322-5227. Fax: 615-343-0050. p. 2261

Smith-Collins, Heather, Curric Center Librn, Washburn University, Curriculum Resources Center, Carnegie Hall, Rm 101 & 103, Topeka, KS, 66621. Tel: 785-670-1956. Fax: 785-670-1085. p. 897

Smith-Cook, Cheryl, Libr Dir, United States Air Force, 97 FSS/FSDL, 109 E Ave, Bldg 65, Altus Air Force Base, OK, 73523-5134. Tel: 580-481-7693. Fax: 580-482-0469. p. 1956

Smith-Fyffe, Amy, Circ, Chillicothe & Ross County Public Library, Howard S Young Branch, 167 W Springfield St, Frankfort, OH, 45628. Tel: 740-702-4175. Fax: 740-702-4176. p. 1867

Smith-Gary, Kristin, Librn, Wyalusing Public Library, 202 Church St, Wyalusing, PA, 18853. Tel: 570-746-1711. Fax: 570-746-1671. p. 2158

Smith-Hunt, Patricia, Dr, Head, Presv Serv, University of California, Riverside Libraries, 900 University Ave, Riverside, CA, 92521. Tel: 951-827-7702. p. 218

Smith-Rapa, Melissa, Librn, Milbridge Public Library, 22 School St, Milbridge, ME, 04658. Tel: 207-546-3066. Fax: 207-546-3066. p. 992

Smithee, Jeannette, Exec Dir, SEFLIN - Southeast Florida Library Information Network, Inc, Wimberly Library, Office 452, Florida Atlantic University, 777 Glades Rd, Boca Raton, FL, 33431. Tel: 561-208-0984. Fax: 561-208-0995. p. 2940

Smither, Doris J, Dir, Bonne Terre Memorial Library, Five SW Main St, Bonne Terre, MO, 63628. Tel: 573-358-2260. Fax: 573-358-5941. p. 1320

Smitheram, Lou, Librn, Trinity Episcopal Church Library, 1500 State St, Santa Barbara, CA, 93101. Tel: 805-965-7419. Fax: 805-965-8840. p. 261

Smithers, Karen, Librn, Knoedler Memorial Library, 315 Main St, Augusta, KY, 41002. Tel: 606-756-3911. p. 906

Smithson, Janina, Libr Tech, Manitoba Department of Culture, Heritage & Tourism, 450 Broadway Ave, Rm 260, Winnipeg, MB, R3C 0V8, CANADA. Tel: 204-945-4243. Fax: 204-948-2167. p. 2756

Smithson, Paul G, Tech Serv Librn, Kalamazoo College, 1200 Academy St, Kalamazoo, MI, 49006-3285. Tel: 269-337-7147. Fax: 269-337-7143. p. 1197

Smithson, Suzanne, Dep Dir, Carlsbad City Library, Georgina Cole Library, 1250 Carlsbad Village Dr, Carlsbad, CA, 92008. Tel: 760-434-2870. Fax: 760-434-9975. p. 132

Smithson, Suzanne, Dep Libr Dir, Carlsbad City Library, 1775 Dove Lane, Carlsbad, CA, 92011-4048. Tel: 760-434-2876. Fax: 760-602-7942. p. 132

Smithwhite, Elva, Managing Librn, Pima County Public Library, Quincie Douglas, 1585 E 36th St, Tucson, AZ, 85713. Tel: 520-594-5335. Fax: 520-594-5336. p. 87

Smithwick, Mark, Dir, North Texas State Hospital, 4730 College Dr, Vernon, TX, 76384. Tel: 940-552-4117. Fax: 940-553-2515. p. 2395

Smoker, Sharon, Dir, Genesee Area Library, 301 Main St, Genesee, PA, 16923-8805. Tel: 814-228-3328. Fax: 814-228-3328. p. 2059

Smokey, Sheila, Head, Acq & Ser, Rochester Institute of Technology, 90 Lomb Memorial Dr, Rochester, NY, 14623-5604. Tel: 585-475-7283. Fax: 585-475-7007. p. 1731

Smolarek, Dennis, Ref Librn, Lake County Library System, Cooper Memorial Library, 2525 Oakley Seaver Dr, Clermont, FL, 34711. Tel: 352-536-2275. Fax: 352-536-2259. p. 500

Smolek, Janice M, Dir, Seafarer's Harry Lundeberg School of Seamanship, PO Box 75, Piney Point, MD, 20674-0075. Tel: 301-994-0010, Ext 5353. p. 1036

Smolen, David, Head, Tech Serv, Manchester City Library, 405 Pine St, Manchester, NH, 03104-6199. Tel: 603-624-6550. Fax: 603-628-6018. p. 1455

Smolinsky, Susan, Librn, Arvin A Brown Public Library, 88 Main St, Richford, VT, 05476-1133. Tel: 802-848-3313. p. 2433

Smolka, Martie, Adult Serv, Gunn Memorial Library, Inc, Five Wykeham Rd, Washington, CT, 06793-1308. Tel: 860-868-7586. Fax: 860-868-7247. p. 374

Smolow, Barbara, Tech Serv, Sarah Lawrence College, One Mead Way, Bronxville, NY, 10708. Tel: 914-395-2476. Fax: 914-395-2473. p. 1588

Smolzer, Jo, Head, Tech Serv, Huntley Area Public Library District, 11000 Ruth Rd, Huntley, IL, 60142-7155. Tel: 847-669-5386. Fax: 847-669-5439. p. 657

Smothers, Cathy, Automation Syst Coordr, Webmaster, Decatur Public Library, 504 Cherry St NE, Decatur, AL, 35601. Tel: 256-353-2993. Fax: 256-350-6736. p. 14

Smothers, Diann, Res & Instruction Librn, Northeastern University Libraries, Snell Library, 360 Huntington Ave, Boston, MA, 02115. Tel: 617-373-2363. p. 1065

Smus, Paula, Div Mgr, Libr Serv, Moreno Valley Public Library, 25480 Alessandro Blvd, Moreno Valley, CA, 92553. Tel: 951-413-3881. Fax: 951-413-3895. p. 191

Smuz, Kathy, Info Serv, Dunedin Public Library, 223 Douglas Ave, Dunedin, FL, 34698. Tel: 727-298-3080, Ext 222. Fax: 727-298-3088. p. 438

Smyczak, Rachael, Librn, Lapeer District Library, Clifford, 9530 Main St, Clifford, MI, 48727. Tel: 989-761-7393. Fax: 989-761-7541. p. 1202

Smyth, Elaine, Asst Dean, Libr, Louisiana State University Libraries, 295 Middleton Library, Baton Rouge, LA, 70803. Tel: 225-578-2217. Fax: 225-578-6825. p. 943

Smyth, Linda, Librn, Fraser Papers Inc Library, Central Tech Dept, 27 Rice St, Edmundston, NB, E3V 1S9, CANADA. Tel: 506-737-2252. Fax: 506-737-2137. p. 2762

Smyth, Maura, Libr Instruction, Ref Librn, Century College Library, 3300 N Century Ave, White Bear Lake, MN, 55110. Tel: 651-773-1762. Fax: 651-779-3963. p. 1288

Snapko, Belinda, Cat, Libr Tech, Tech Serv, Polk State College, 999 Ave H NE, Winter Haven, FL, 33881-4299. Tel: 863-297-1040. Fax: 863-297-1065. p. 504

Snapp, Dale, Head, Syst, University of California, Davis, 100 NW Quad, Davis, CA, 95616-5292. Tel: 530-752-6561. Fax: 530-752-3148. p. 139

Snapp, Heather, First Year Experience & Outreach Librn, Florida Gulf Coast University Library, 10501 FGCU Blvd S, Fort Myers, FL, 33965-6501. Tel: 239-745-4224. p. 445

Snarr, Alicia, Br Mgr, Maricopa County Library District, North Valley Regional, 40410 N Gavilan Peak Pkwy, Anthem, AZ, 85086. Tel: 602-652-3301. Fax: 602-652-3320. p. 75

Snavely, Loanne, Head, Learning Serv, Pennsylvania State University Libraries, Library Learning Services, 305 Pattee Library, Tower, University Park, PA, 16802-1803. Tel: 814-865-3064. Fax: 814-865-9256. p. 2148

Snavely, Sarah, Dir, Bowman Regional Public Library, 18 E Divide St, Bowman, ND, 58623. Tel: 701-523-3797. p. 1839

Snead, Barbara, Assoc Librn, Coll, Goucher College Library, 1021 Dulaney Valley Rd, Baltimore, MD, 21204. Tel: 410-337-6366. Fax: 410-337-6419. p. 1014

Snead, John, PhD, Dr, Asst Prof, University of Oklahoma, Bizzell Memorial Library, 401 W Brooks, Rm 120, Norman, OK, 73019-6032. Tel: 405-325-3921. Fax: 405-325-7648. p. 2972

Snead, Twila, Libr Mgr, St Luke's Cornwall Hospital, 70 Dubois St, Newburgh, NY, 12550-9986. Tel: 845-568-2220. Fax: 845-568-2913. p. 1705

Snediker, Kathy, Head of Libr, University of South Carolina, Elliot White Springs Business Library, Francis M Hipp-William H Close Bldg, 1705 College St, Columbia, SC, 29208. Tel: 803-777-6032. Fax: 803-777-6876. p. 2190

Snediker, Kathy, Assoc Dir, Pub Serv, Newberry College, 2100 College St, Newberry, SC, 29108-2197. Tel: 803-321-5229. Fax: 803-321-5232. p. 2201

Snee, Toni, Asst Dir, Scituate Town Library, 85 Branch St, Scituate, MA, 02066. Tel: 781-545-8727. Fax: 781-545-8728. p. 1123

Sneed, Jacqueline, Circ Supvr, Warren County Memorial Library, 119 South Front St, Warrenton, NC, 27589. Tel: 252-257-4990. Fax: 252-257-4089. p. 1828

Sneed, Nancy Darlene, Info Spec, Olin Corp, 1186 Lower River Rd, Charleston, TN, 37310. Tel: 423-336-4347. Fax: 423-336-4194. p. 2226

Sneff, Gretchen, Head of Libr, Temple University Libraries, Science, Engineering & Architecture Library, Engineering Bldg, Rm 201, 1947 N 12th St, Philadelphia, PA, 19122. Tel: 215-204-4724. Fax: 215-204-7720. p. 2117

Snell, Christeen, Br Supvr, Flint River Regional Library, Fayette County Public Library, 1821 Heritage Pkwy, Fayetteville, GA, 30214. Tel: 770-461-8841. p. 535

Snell, Gina, In Charge, Pictou - Antigonish Regional Library, Westville Library, 2020 Queen St, Westville, NS, B0K 2A0, CANADA. Tel: 902-396-5022. p. 2784

Snell, Jeremy, Web Librn, Mechanics' Institute Library, 57 Post St, San Francisco, CA, 94104-5003. Tel: 415-393-0111. Fax: 415-421-4192. p. 243

Snell, Shawana, Circ Mgr, Corcoran Gallery of Art/College of Art & Design Library, 500 17th St NW, Washington, DC, 20006. Tel: 202-478-1544. Fax: 202-628-7908. p. 396

Snell, Venus, Acq, Whittier Public Library, 7344 S Washington Ave, Whittier, CA, 90602. Tel: 562-567-9900. Fax: 562-567-2880. p. 283

Snellenberger, Diane, Dir, Taymouth Township Library, 2361 E Burt Rd, Burt, MI, 48417-9426. Tel: 989-770-4651. Fax: 989-770-4651. p. 1160

Sneller, Denise, Circ, Northwestern College, 101 Seventh St SW, Orange City, IA, 51041-1996. Tel: 712-707-7234. Fax: 712-707-7247. p. 836

Snelling, Brad, Coll Develop/Per Librn, College of Saint Scholastica Library, 1200 Kenwood Ave, Duluth, MN, 55811-4199. Tel: 218-723-6644. Fax: 218-723-5948. p. 1247

Snelling, Charlene, Coordr, Ref & Instrul Serv, Chicago State University, 9501 S Martin Luther King Jr Dr, LIB 440, Chicago, IL, 60628-1598. Tel: 773-995-2557. Fax: 773-995-3772. p. 610

Snelling, Lindsey, Generalist Librn, Rockwall County Library, 1215 E Yellowjacket Lane, Rockwall, TX, 75087. Tel: 972-204-7700. Fax: 972-204-7709. p. 2377

Snellman, Scott, Librn, Central Arizona College, 8470 N Overfield Rd, Coolidge, AZ, 85128. Tel: 520-494-5286. Fax: 520-494-5284. p. 60

Snelson, Lanty C, Supvry Librn, Mesa Public Library, Mesa Express Library, 2055 S Power Rd, Ste 1031, Mesa, AZ, 85209. Tel: 480-644-2713. p. 69

Snelson, Pamela, Dir, Franklin & Marshall College, 450 College Ave, Lancaster, PA, 17603-3318. Tel: 717-291-3896. Fax: 717-291-4160. p. 2076

Snelson, Pamela, Dir, Franklin & Marshall College, Martin Library of the Sciences, PO Box 3003, Lancaster, PA, 17604-3003. Tel: 717-291-3896. Fax: 717-291-4088. p. 2076

Snider, David, Dir, Lawton Public Library, 110 SW Fourth St, Lawton, OK, 73501-4034. Tel: 580-581-3450. Fax: 580-248-0243. p. 1967

Snider, Deanna, Mgr, Saint Thomas Library, 30 School House Lane, Saint Thomas, PA, 17252-9650. Tel: 717-369-4716. Fax: 717-369-4896. p. 2135

Snider, Jacqueline, Mgr, ACT Information Resource Center, 200 ACT Dr, Iowa City, IA, 52243. Tel: 319-337-1166. Fax: 319-337-1538. p. 822

Snider, Joyce, Asst Librn, Coffeeville Public Library, 714 Main St, Coffeeville, MS, 38922-2590. Tel: 662-675-8822. Fax: 662-675-2001. p. 1296

Snider, Linda L, Circ, University of Wisconsin, 1800 College Dr, Rice Lake, WI, 54868-2497. Tel: 715-234-1876, Ext 5461. Fax: 715-234-1975. p. 2634

Snider, Monroe C, Dr, Acq, Dir, University of West Alabama, UWA Station 12, Livingston, AL, 35470. Tel: 205-652-3613. Fax: 205-652-2332. p. 24

Snider, Sue D, Dir, Spencer County Public Library, 168 Taylorsville Rd, Taylorsville, KY, 40071. Tel: 502-477-8137. Fax: 502-477-5033. p. 936

Snider, William, Librn, Hobe Sound Bible College Library, 11440 SE Gomez Ave, Hobe Sound, FL, 33455-3378. Tel: 772-545-1400, Ext 1078. Fax: 772-545-1422. p. 451

Sniderman, Lynn, Assoc Librn, Federal Reserve Bank of Cleveland, 1455 E Sixth St, Cleveland, OH, 44114. Tel: 216-579-2052, 216-579-2961. Fax: 216-579-3172. p. 1880

Snidley, Mary, Cat, Tech Serv, Beth Israel Synagogue, 1015 E Park Ave, Vineland, NJ, 08360. Tel: 856-691-0852. Fax: 856-692-1957. p. 1538

Sniffin, David, Libr Develop Consult, South Carolina State Library, 1430-1500 Senate St, Columbia, SC, 29201. Tel: 803-734-8646. Fax: 803-734-8676. p. 2189

Snipes, Jill, ILL, Lynn Haven Public Library, 901 Ohio Ave, Lynn Haven, FL, 32444. Tel: 850-265-2781. Fax: 850-265-7311. p. 461

Snively, Ann, Dir, Wright Memorial Public Library, 1776 Far Hills Ave, Oakwood, OH, 45419-2598. Tel: 937-294-7171. Fax: 937-294-8578. p. 1924

Snively, Sharon, Dir, Delphos Public Library, 114 W Second, Delphos, KS, 67436. Tel: 785-523-4668. p. 863

Snoblen, Patricia, Br Mgr, Jackson District Library, Meijer, 2699 Airport Rd, Jackson, MI, 49202. Tel: 517-788-4480. Fax: 517-788-4481. p. 1196

Snodgrass, Jean, Coordr, Hendrick Medical Center, 1900 Pine St, Abilene, TX, 79601. Tel: 325-670-2375. Fax: 325-670-2422. p. 2272

Snoeberger, Mark A, Dir, Libr Serv, Detroit Baptist Theological Seminary Library, 4801 Allen Rd, Allen Park, MI, 48101. Tel: 313-381-0111, Ext 409. Fax: 313-381-0798. p. 1149

Snook, Myra, In Charge, Sussex County Historical Society Library, 82 Main St, Newton, NJ, 07860-2046. Tel: 973-383-6010. Fax: 973-383-6010. p. 1514

Snopek, Mary, Co-Dir, Preston Public Library, One W Gillet, Preston, IA, 52069. Tel: 563-689-3581. Fax: 563-689-3581. p. 839

Snow, Ann, Acq, Lincoln Memorial Library, 240 California Dr, Yountville, CA, 94599-1445. Tel: 707-944-4915. p. 285

Snow, Barbara, Asst Dir, University of Michigan, Law Library, 801 Monroe St, Ann Arbor, MI, 48109-1210. Tel: 734-763-3767. Fax: 734-615-0178. p. 1152

Snow, Beth, Br Mgr, Springfield-Greene County Library District, Ash Grove Branch, 101 E Main, Ash Grove, MO, 65604-0248. Tel: 417-751-2933. Fax: 417-751-2275. p. 1367

Snow, Beth, Br Mgr, Springfield-Greene County Library District, Willard Branch, East Shopping Ctr, Willard, MO, 65781-0517. Tel: 417-742-4258. Fax: 417-742-4589. p. 1368

Snow, Daria, Libr Adminr, University of Regina, Dr John Archer Library, 3737 Wascana Pkwy, Regina, SK, S4S 0A2, CANADA. Tel: 306-585-5110. Fax: 306-585-4878. p. 2925

Snow, Elinor, Dir, Mount Nittany Medical Center, 1800 E Park Ave, State College, PA, 16803. Tel: 814-234-6191. Fax: 814-231-7031. p. 2143

Snow, Helen M, Ref Serv, Greensboro Public Library, 219 N Church St, Greensboro, NC, 27402-3178. Tel: 336-373-2706. Fax: 336-333-6781. p. 1796

Snow, Linda, Head, Ref Serv, University of Texas at Dallas, 800 W Campbell Rd, Richardson, TX, 75080. Tel: 972-883-2626. Fax: 972-883-2473. p. 2374

Snow, Maureen, Librn, Carbonear Public Library, 256 Water St, Carbonear, NL, A1Y 1C4, CANADA. Tel: 709-596-3382. p. 2769

Snow, Richard, Coll Develop Librn, Loyola University New Orleans, 6363 Saint Charles Ave, New Orleans, LA, 70118-6195. Tel: 504-864-7111. Fax: 504-864-7247. p. 961

Snow, Sally, Asst Dir, Monroe County Library System, 115 South Ave, Rochester, NY, 14604. Tel: 585-428-8000. Fax: 585-428-8353. p. 1730

Snow, Timothy M, Ref Librn, University of Rio Grande, 218 N College Ave, Rio Grande, OH, 45674. Tel: 740-245-7005. Fax: 740-245-7096. p. 1931

Snowden, Helen, Br Mgr, Gloucester County Library System, Glassboro Public, Two Center St, Glassboro, NJ, 08028-1995. Tel: 856-881-0001, 856-881-5571. Fax: 856-881-9338. p. 1507

Snowden, Kent E, Libr Dir, Troy University, Montgomery Campus, 252 Montgomery St, Montgomery, AL, 36104-3425. Tel: 334-241-9783. Fax: 334-241-9590. p. 31

Snowder, Tereasa, Circ, Napa Valley College Library, 1700 Bldg, 2277 Napa-Vallejo Hwy, Napa, CA, 94558. Tel: 707-256-7457. Fax: 707-253-3015. p. 193

Snowhill, Lucia, Head, Coll Develop, University of California, Santa Barbara, Santa Barbara, CA, 93106-9010. Tel: 805-893-5383. Fax: 805-893-7010. p. 261

Snowman, Ann, Head, Access Serv, Pennsylvania State University Libraries, 510 Paterno Library, University Park, PA, 16802. Tel: 814-865-0401. Fax: 814-865-3665. p. 2148

Snowten, Renee, Ch, Reader Serv, Free Library of Philadelphia, Library for the Blind & Physically Handicapped, 919 Walnut St, Philadelphia, PA, 19107-5289. Tel: 215-683-3213. Fax: 215-683-3211. p. 2108

Snuff, Pamela, Cat, Niles District Library, 620 E Main St, Niles, MI, 49120. Tel: 269-683-8545, Ext 124. Fax: 269-683-0075. p. 1214

Snyder, Alisandra, Libr Dir, Tellico Plains Public Library, 209 Hwy 165, Tellico Plains, TN, 37385. Tel: 423-253-7388. Fax: 423-253-6274. p. 2267

Snyder, Amanda, Dir, Hampshire County Public Library, 153 W Main St, Romney, WV, 26757. Tel: 304-822-3185. Fax: 304-822-3955. p. 2570

Snyder, Bennett, Ser Librn, Notre Dame College, 4545 College Rd, South Euclid, OH, 44121. Tel: 216-373-5267. Fax: 216-381-3227. p. 1935

Snyder, Betty, Librn, Library District Number One, Doniphan County, Highland Branch, 306 W Main, Highland, KS, 66035. Tel: 785-442-3078. p. 898

Snyder, Bonnie, Dir, D R Evarts Library, 80 Second St, Athens, NY, 12015. Tel: 518-945-1417. Fax: 518-945-1417. p. 1575

Snyder, Chris, Librn, Snyder County Libraries, Middleburg Community Library, 13 N Main St, Middleburg, PA, 17842. Tel: 570-837-5931. Fax: 570-837-5931. p. 2138

Snyder, Christie, Dir, Ida Long Goodman Memorial Library, 406 N Monroe, Saint John, KS, 67576-1836. Tel: 620-549-3227. Fax: 620-549-6589. p. 892

Snyder, Christina M, Tech Serv Mgr, Bucks County Free Library, 150 S Pine St, Doylestown, PA, 18901-4932. Tel: 215-348-9083, Ext 1171. Fax: 215-348-4760. p. 2050

Snyder, Cindy, Ref & Info Serv, Claremont Colleges Library, 800 Dartmouth Ave, Claremont, CA, 91711. Tel: 909-621-8014. p. 134

Snyder, Colleen, Fiscal Officer, Mentor Public Library, 8215 Mentor Ave, Mentor, OH, 44060. Tel: 440-255-8811. Fax: 440-255-0520. p. 1917

Snyder, Cynthia, Pub Serv Librn, Rollins College, 1000 Holt Ave, Campus Box 2744, Winter Park, FL, 32789-2744. Tel: 407-646-2683. Fax: 407-646-1515. p. 505

Snyder, Effie, Asst Librn, Rushville Public Library, 104 N Monroe St, Rushville, IL, 62681-1364. Tel: 217-322-3030. Fax: 217-322-3030. p. 699

Snyder, Eileen, Legis Librn, Wisconsin Legislative Reference Bureau, One E Main St, Madison, WI, 53703-3373. Fax: 608-266-5648. p. 2611

Snyder, Fritz, Dir, University of Montana, William J Jameson Law Library, 32 Campus Dr, Missoula, MT, 59812. Tel: 406-243-2699. Fax: 406-243-6358. p. 1386

Snyder, Fritz, Interim Dean, Libr Operations, University of Montana, Maureen & Mike Mansfield Library, 32 Campus Dr, No 9936, Missoula, MT, 59812-9936. Tel: 406-243-6866. Fax: 406-243-4067. p. 1386

Snyder, Jacqueline, Librn, New Alexandria Public Library, Keystone Plaza, Rte 22, New Alexandria, PA, 15670-9703. Tel: 724-668-7747. p. 2095

Snyder, Jane, Librn, Underberg & Kessler Law Library, 300 Bausch & Lomb Pl, Rochester, NY, 14604. Tel: 585-258-2800. Fax: 585-258-2821. p. 1733

Snyder, Jenny, Librn, Dawson Creek Municipal Public Library, 1001 McKellar Ave, Dawson Creek, BC, V1G 4W7, CANADA. Tel: 250-782-4661. Fax: 250-782-4667. p. 2727

Snyder, Joshua, Asst Supvr, Access Serv, Judson University, 1151 N State St, Elgin, IL, 60123. Tel: 847-628-2030. Fax: 847-625-2045. p. 641

Snyder, Judi, Assoc Dir, Pub Serv, Martin County Library System, 2351 SE Monterey Rd, Stuart, FL, 34996. Tel: 772-219-4964. Fax: 772-219-4959. p. 491

Snyder, Judy, Asst Dir, Belle Center Free Public Library, 103 S Elizabeth St, Belle Center, OH, 43310. Tel: 937-464-3611. Fax: 937-464-3611. p. 1858

Snyder, Kathryn, Librn, Ozark Regional Library, Viburnum Branch, City Hall Missouri Ave, Viburnum, MO, 65566. Tel: 573-244-5986. p. 1334

Snyder, Kathy, Librn, Ray Brook Federal Correctional Institution Library, 128 Ray Brook Rd, Ray Brook, NY, 12977. Tel: 518-897-4167. Fax: 518-897-4220. p. 1726

Snyder, Lisa, Libr Tech, Alberta Association for Community Living, 11724 Kingsway Ave, Edmonton, AB, T5G 0X5, CANADA. Tel: 780-451-3055, Ext 225. Fax: 780-453-5779. p. 2697

Snyder, Lise, Ref, University of California Los Angeles Library, College Library, Powell Library Bldg, Los Angeles, CA, 90095. Tel: 310-825-5756. Fax: 310-206-9312. p. 178

Snyder, Louise, Asst Librn, Morris James LLP, 500 Delaware Ave, Ste 1500, Wilmington, DE, 19801-1494. Tel: 302-888-6881. Fax: 302-571-1750. p. 388

Snyder, Margaret, Librn, Centralia College, 600 Centralia College Blvd, Centralia, WA, 98531. Tel: 360-736-9391, Ext 423. Fax: 360-330-7502. p. 2511

Snyder, Mary, Dir, Mannsville Free Library, PO Box 156, Mannsville, NY, 13661. Tel: 315-465-4049. p. 1657

Snyder, Mary D, Admin Dir, Indian River County Library System, 1600 21st St, Vero Beach, FL, 32960. Tel: 772-770-5060. Fax: 772-770-5066. p. 501

Snyder, Mike, Dir, Louisville Public Library, 700 Lincoln Ave, Louisville, OH, 44641-1474. Tel: 330-875-1696. Fax: 330-875-3530. p. 1912

Snyder, Nancy, Info Spec, Motorola, Inc, 1301 E Algonquin Rd, Rm 1914, Schaumburg, IL, 60196-1078. Tel: 847-576-8580. Fax: 847-576-4716. p. 701

Snyder, Nancy, Ch, Wabash Carnegie Public Library, 188 W Hill St, Wabash, IN, 46992-3048. Tel: 260-563-2972. Fax: 260-563-0222. p. 785

Snyder, Nancy, Br Mgr, Wichita Public Library, Evergreen, 2601 N Arkansas, Wichita, KS, 67204. Tel: 316-303-8181. p. 901

Snyder, Pam, Librn, Marion General Hospital, 1000 McKinnly Park Dr, Marion, OH, 43302. Tel: 740-383-8668. Fax: 740-382-2978. p. 1914

Snyder, Peg, Circ, Framingham State College, 100 State St, Framingham, MA, 01701. Tel: 508-626-4027. Fax: 508-626-4469. p. 1090

Snyder, Rebecca, Assoc Dir, Dakota County Historical Society, 130 Third Ave N, South Saint Paul, MN, 55075. Tel: 651-552-7548. Fax: 651-552-7265. p. 1285

Snyder, Rob, Syst Coordr, Dixie State College of Utah, 225 S 700 E, Saint George, UT, 84770. Tel: 435-652-7719. Fax: 435-656-4169. p. 2412

Snyder, Robert, Br Mgr, Washington County Library System, Springdale Branch, 126 Lion Blvd, Springdale, UT, 84767. Tel: 435-772-3676. Fax: 435-772-3124. p. 2412

Snyder, Terry, Librn of the Col, Haverford College, 370 Lancaster Ave, Haverford, PA, 19041-1392. Tel: 610-896-1272. Fax: 610-896-1102. p. 2067

Snyder, Tina, Dir, Hancock County Public Library, 240 Court Sq, Hawesville, KY, 42348. Tel: 270-927-6760. Fax: 270-927-6847. p. 916

Snyder, Vicki, Res, Nevada Power Co Library, 6226 W Sahara Ave, Las Vegas, NV, 89151. Tel: 702-367-5055. Fax: 702-227-2023. p. 1430

Snyder, William E, Dir, Henderson County Public Library, 301 N Washington St, Hendersonville, NC, 28739. Tel: 828-697-4725. Fax: 828-692-8449, 828-697-4700. p. 1801

Snyder-Jones, Bonita, Managing Librn, Austin Public Library, Howson, 2500 Exposition Blvd, Austin, TX, 78703. Tel: 512-974-8800. Fax: 512-479-8554. p. 2279

Snyders, Christy, Head, Circ, Roselle Public Library District, 40 S Park St, Roselle, IL, 60172-2020. Tel: 630-529-1641, Ext 221. Fax: 630-529-7579. p. 699

Soapland, Bessie, Ref Serv, Payson Public Library, 328 N McLane Rd, Payson, AZ, 85541. Tel: 928-474-9260. Fax: 928-474-2679. p. 70

Soares, Danny, Head of Doc Delivery, San Jose State University, One Washington Sq, San Jose, CA, 95192-0028. Tel: 408-808-2078. Fax: 408-808-2141. p. 251

Soares, Geraldo, Tech Serv, Mount Vernon Public Library, 28 S First Ave, Mount Vernon, NY, 10550. Tel: 914-668-1840. Fax: 914-668-1018. p. 1664

Soares, Paula, Asst Head, Tech Serv, Russell Library, 123 Broad St, Middletown, CT, 06457. Tel: 860-347-2528, Ext 155. p. 352

Soares, Rodney, Librn II, Tulare County Library, Visalia Headquarters Branch, 200 W Oak Ave, Visalia, CA, 93291. Tel: 559-713-2708. Fax: 559-737-4586. p. 281

Soares, Zach, AV Tech Spec, College of the Atlantic, 109 Eden St, Bar Harbor, ME, 04609-1198. Tel: 207-288-5015, Ext 213. Fax: 207-288-2328. p. 976

Soash, April, Dir, Monrovia Public Library, 321 S Myrtle Ave, Monrovia, CA, 91016-2848. Tel: 626-256-8251. Fax: 626-256-8255. p. 189

Soave, Terry, Mgr, Outreach & Neighborhood Serv, Ann Arbor District Library, 343 S Fifth Ave, Ann Arbor, MI, 48104. Tel: 734-327-8327. Fax: 734-327-4255. p. 1150

Sobba, Andrea, Dir, Garnett Public Library, 125 W Fourth St, Garnett, KS, 66032-1350. Tel: 785-448-3388. Fax: 785-448-3936. p. 868

Sobczak, Elizabeth, Librn, Essentia Institute of Rural Health, 407 E Third St, Duluth, MN, 55805-1984. Tel: 218-786-4396. Fax: 218-786-4249. p. 1248

Sobel, Karen, Res & Instruction Librn, Auraria Library, 1100 Lawrence St, Denver, CO, 80204-2095. Tel: 303-352-3640. Fax: 303-556-3528. p. 298

Sobinski-Smith, Mary Jane, Head, Info Literacy & Instruction Serv, Western New England University, 1215 Wilbraham Rd, Springfield, MA, 01119. Tel: 413-782-1533. Fax: 413-796-2011. p. 1128

Sobon, Juliette, Dir, Township of Washington Public Library, 144 Woodfield Rd, Washington Township, NJ, 07676. Tel: 201-664-4586. Fax: 201-664-7331. p. 1539

Soborski, Sheryl, Tech Serv, Olean Public Library, 134 N Second St, Olean, NY, 14760-2583. Tel: 716-372-0200. Fax: 716-372-8651. p. 1710

Socha, Eileen, Dir, East Providence Public Library, 41 Grove Ave, East Providence, RI, 02914. Tel: 401-434-2453. Fax: 401-434-3324. p. 2166

Sochacka, E Tamara, Dir, Hamtramck Public Library, 2360 Caniff St, Hamtramck, MI, 48212. Tel: 313-365-7050. Fax: 313-365-0160. p. 1187

Sochats, Kenneth, Asst Prof, University of Pittsburgh, 135 N Bellefield Ave, Pittsburgh, PA, 15260. Tel: 412-624-5230. Fax: 412-624-5231. p. 2973

Socknat, Carmen, Head, Bibliog Serv, University of Toronto Libraries, Victoria University Library, 71 Queens Park Crescent E, Toronto, ON, M5S 1K7, CANADA. Tel: 416-585-4471. Fax: 416-585-4591. p. 2867

Soder, Nancy, Head Librn, Harrison County Library System, D'Iberville Public, 10391 AutoMall Pkwy, D'Iberville, MS, 39540. Tel: 228-392-2279. Fax: 228-396-9573. p. 1299

Soderberg, Simon, Youth Serv Librn, Fairfield Public Library, 104 W Adams, Fairfield, IA, 52556. Tel: 641-472-6551. Fax: 641-472-3249. p. 815

Soderdahl, Paul, Assoc Univ Librn & Dir, Libr Info Tech, University of Iowa Libraries, 125 W Washington St, Iowa City, IA, 52242-1420. p. 823

Soderquist, Janice, Dir, Axtell Public Library, 305 N Main St, Axtell, NE, 68924. Tel: 308-743-2592. p. 1392

Soderquist, Trina, Cat, Boston College Libraries, Educational Resource Center, 140 Commonwealth Ave, Chestnut Hill, MA, 02467. Tel: 617-552-4619. Fax: 617-552-1769. p. 1081

Sodha, Komal, Ref Serv, Belmont Abbey College, 100 Belmont-Mt Holly Rd, Belmont, NC, 28012. Tel: 704-461-6742. Fax: 704-461-6743. p. 1776

Sodoski, Marianne, Instruction & Ref Librn, King's College, 14 W Jackson St, Wilkes-Barre, PA, 18711-0850. Tel: 570-208-5840. Fax: 570-208-6022. p. 2155

Sodowsky, Kay, Libr Mgr, Metropolitan Community College, Blue River Library, 20301 E 78 Hwy, Independence, MO, 64057. Tel: 816-220-6642. Fax: 816-220-6751. p. 1339

Sodt, Jill, Coordr, Librn, Black Hawk College-East Campus, 26230 Black Hawk Rd, Galva, IL, 61434. Tel: 309-852-5671, Ext 1731. Fax: 309-852-0038. p. 648

Soehl, Kathy, Asst Dir, Dickinson Public Library, 4411 Hwy 3, Dickinson, TX, 77539. Tel: 281-534-3812. p. 2313

Soehner, Catherine, Dir, University of Michigan, Shapiro Science Library, 3175 Shapiro Library, 919 S University Ave, Ann Arbor, MI, 48109-1185. Tel: 734-936-7274. Fax: 734-763-9813. p. 1153

Soehner, Catherine, Assoc Dean, Res & Learning Serv, University of Utah, Marriott Library, 295 S 1500 East, Salt Lake City, UT, 84112-0860. Tel: 801-581-8558. Fax: 801-585-7185. p. 2415

Soehner, Catherine B, Dir, University of Michigan, Art, Architecture & Engineering Library, Duderstadt Ctr, 2281 Bonnisteel Blvd, Ann Arbor, MI, 48109-2094. Tel: 734-936-7274. Fax: 734-764-4487. p. 1152

Soehner, Kenneth, Chief Librn, Metropolitan Museum of Art, Thomas J Watson Library, 1000 Fifth Ave, New York, NY, 10028-0198. Tel: 212-570-3934. Fax: 212-570-3847. p. 1686

Soenksen, Cindy, Acq, Memphis Public Library & Information Center, 3030 Poplar Ave, Memphis, TN, 38111-3527. Tel: 901-415-2817. Fax: 901-323-7108. p. 2249

Soergel, Dagobert, Chair, University at Buffalo, State University of New York, 534 Baldy Hall, Buffalo, NY, 14260. Tel: 716-645-2412. Fax: 716-645-3775. p. 2971

Sofianos, Kathryn, Adult Serv, Chicago Ridge Public Library, 10400 S Oxford Ave, Chicago Ridge, IL, 60415. Tel: 708-423-7753. Fax: 708-423-2758. p. 628

Sogoian, Dottie, Ch, Livonia Public Library, Carl Sandburg Branch, 30100 W Seven Mile Rd, Livonia, MI, 48152-1918. Tel: 248-893-4010. Fax: 248-476-6230. p. 1204

Sogoian, Mariam, Acq, Pittsburgh Theological Seminary, 616 N Highland Ave, Pittsburgh, PA, 15206-2596. Tel: 412-924-1361. Fax: 412-362-2329. p. 2127

Sogunro, Abi, Librn, Montgomery College, Rockville Campus Library, Macklin Tower, 51 Mannakee St, Rockville, MD, 20850. Tel: 240-567-7114. Fax: 240-567-7153. p. 1037

Sohl, Morgan, Ref/Coll Librn, Rapid City Public Library, 610 Quincy St, Rapid City, SD, 57701-3630. Tel: 605-394-6139. Fax: 605-394-4064. p. 2217

Sohmer, Samantha, Res, KPMG Research, 2000 McGill College Ave Ste 1900, Montreal, QC, H3A 3H8, CANADA. Tel: 514-840-2252. Fax: 514-840-2162. p. 2897

Soileau, Debra, Br Mgr, Pointe Coupee Parish Library, Julian Poydras Branch, 4985 Poydras Lane, Rougon, LA, 70773. Tel: 225-627-5846. Fax: 225-627-5846. p. 965

Soini, Anne, Librn, New Ipswich Library, Six Main St, New Ipswich, NH, 03071. Tel: 603-878-4644. p. 1459

Sokol, Chris, Adult Serv, Latah County Library District, 110 S Jefferson, Moscow, ID, 83843-2833. Tel: 208-882-3925. Fax: 208-882-5098. p. 579

Sokol, Keyth, Tech Serv Dir, Jessamine County Public Library, 600 S Main St, Nicholasville, KY, 40356-1839. Tel: 859-885-3523, Ext 226. Fax: 859-885-5164. p. 931

Sokol, Peter, Circ Supvr, Santa Fe Community College, 3000 NW 83rd St, Bldg Y-100, Gainesville, FL, 32606. Tel: 352-395-5411. Fax: 352-395-5102. p. 449

Sokoll, Susan, Librn, Department of Veterans Affairs, Office of the General Counsel Law Library, 810 Vermont Ave NW, Washington, DC, 20420. Tel: 202-273-6558. Fax: 202-273-6645. p. 397

Sokolnicki, Marcia, Asst Dir, E C Scranton Memorial Library, 801 Boston Post Rd, Madison, CT, 06443. Tel: 203-245-7365. Fax: 203-245-7821. p. 349

Sokolowski, Lou Anne, Ch, Monroeville Public Library, 4000 Gateway Campus Blvd, Monroeville, PA, 15146-3381. Tel: 412-372-0500, Ext 21. Fax: 412-372-1168. p. 2091

Sola-Fernandez, Sylvia, Head Librn, University of Puerto Rico Library System, Periodicals Collection, Rio Piedras Campus, Edif Jose M Lazaro, San Juan, PR, 00931. Tel: 787-764-0000, Ext 5133. Fax: 787-772-1479. p. 2678

Sola-Fernandez, Sylvia, Head Librn, University of Puerto Rico Library System, Reference Collection, Rio Piedras Campus, Edif Jose M Lazaro, San Juan, PR, 00931. Tel: 787-764-0000, Ext 5133. Fax: 787-772-1479. p. 2678

Soland, Linda, Librn, Phoenix College, 1202 W Thomas Rd, Phoenix, AZ, 85013. Tel: 602-285-7457. Fax: 602-285-7368. p. 76

Solanke, Abiodun, Librn, Department of Correctional Education, 1954 State Farm Rd, State Farm, VA, 23160-9998. Tel: 804-784-3551, Ext 2259. Fax: 804-784-2480. p. 2496

Solar, Betty, Librn, Polsinelli Shughart PC, 700 W 47th St, Ste 1000, Kansas City, MO, 64112. Tel: 816-753-1000. Fax: 816-753-1536. p. 1340

Solar, Vivian, Cat Librn, Ascension Parish Library, 500 Mississippi St, Donaldsonville, LA, 70346-2535. Tel: 225-473-8052. Fax: 225-473-9522. p. 949

Solares, Gina, Cat Librn, Art Center College of Design, 1700 Lida St, Pasadena, CA, 91103. Tel: 626-396-2230. Fax: 626-568-0428. p. 205

Solberg, Dale W, Dir, Learning Res, Alaska Christian College, 35109 Royal Pl, Soldotna, AK, 99669. Tel: 907-260-7422. Fax: 907-260-6722. p. 53

Solberg, Judy, Dir, Instrul & Pub Serv, Seattle University, A A Lemieux Library, 901 12th Ave, Seattle, WA, 98122-4411. Tel: 206-296-6274. Fax: 206-296-2572. p. 2532

Solberg, Lea, ILL, Montana Historical Society, 225 N Roberts St, Helena, MT, 59601-4514. Tel: 406-444-2681. Fax: 406-444-5297. p. 1382

Solberg, Michelle, Admin Librn, Lutheran Brethren Seminary, 815 W Vernon Ave, Fergus Falls, MN, 56537. Tel: 218-739-1248. p. 1251

Solch, Ann Marie, Ch, Ringwood Public Library, 30 Cannici Dr, Ringwood, NJ, 07456. Tel: 973-962-6256. Fax: 973-962-7799. p. 1526

Soldano, Erika, Librn, Briger & Associates Library, 230 Park Ave, Ste 950, New York, NY, 10169. Tel: 212-953-4400. Fax: 212-953-2266. p. 1671

Soleic, Vanessa, Circ Supvr, Orange County Public Library, Carrboro Cybrary Branch, Carrboro Century Ctr, 100 N Greensboro St, Carrboro, NC, 27510. Tel: 919-918-7387. Fax: 919-918-3960. p. 1803

Soleil, Judith, Libr Dir, Anthroposophical Society in America, 65 Fern Hill Rd, Ghent, NY, 12075. Tel: 518-672-7690. Fax: 518-672-5827. p. 1628

Soles, Alice, ILL, Columbus County Public Library, 407 N Powell Blvd, Whiteville, NC, 28472. Tel: 910-642-3116. Fax: 910-642-3839. p. 1829

Solidum, Aleli, Circ Librn, Skagit Valley College, Whidbey Island Campus Library, 1900 SE Pioneer Way, Oak Harbor, WA, 98277-3099. Tel: 360-679-5322. Fax: 360-679-5341. p. 2521

Solis, Francisco, Tech Serv Librn, University of the Sacred Heart, Rosales St, PO Box 12383, Santurce, PR, 00914-0383. Tel: 787-728-1515, Ext 4364. Fax: 787-268-8868. p. 2678

Solis, Gloria O, Dir, Poteet Public Library, 500 Ave H, Poteet, TX, 78065. Tel: 830-742-8917. Fax: 830-742-3988. p. 2372

Solis, Josie, Libr Tech III, Lamar State College-Orange Library, 410 Front St, Orange, TX, 77630-5796. Tel: 409-882-3352. Fax: 409-883-7552. p. 2367

Soliz, Maria G, Dir, Laredo Public Library, 1120 E Calton Rd, Laredo, TX, 78041. Tel: 956-795-2400. Fax: 956-795-2403. p. 2353

Solla, Leah, Chem Librn, Coordr, Cornell University Library, Physical Sciences Library, Virtual Library, 283 Clark Hall, Ithaca, NY, 14853. Tel: 607-793-6217. Fax: 607-255-5288. p. 1642

Sollars, Sheryl A, Dir, Westfield Washington Public Library, 333 W Hoover St, Westfield, IN, 46074-9283. Tel: 317-896-9391. Fax: 317-896-3702. p. 787

Sollenberger, Julia, Dir, University of Rochester Medical Center, 601 Elmwood Ave, Rochester, NY, 14642. Tel: 716-275-5194. Fax: 585-756-7762. p. 1734

Solomon, Alan C, Head, Res Serv & Coll, Yale University Library, Sterling Memorial Library, 120 High St, New Haven, CT, 06520. Tel: 203-432-1778. Fax: 203-432-8527. p. 359

Solomon, Carolyn, Librn, United States Army, 819 Taylor St, Rm 2C02, Fort Worth, TX, 76102. Tel: 817-886-1013. Fax: 817-886-6401. p. 2324

Solomon, Dawn, Br Mgr, Shreve Memorial Library, Hollywood/Union Avenue, 2105 Hollywood Ave, Shreveport, LA, 71108. Tel: 318-636-5520. p. 969

Solomon, Geri, Asst Dean, Spec Coll & Univ Archivist, Hofstra University, 123 Hofstra University, Hempstead, NY, 11549. Tel: 516-463-6407. Fax: 516-463-6442. p. 1635

Solomon, Geri, Asst Dean, Hofstra University, Special Collections/Long Island Studies Institute, 032 Axinn Library, 123 Hofstra University, Hempstead, NY, 11549-1230. Tel: 516-463-6404, 516-463-6411. Fax: 516-463-6442. p. 1635

Solomon, Joel, Mgr, Libr Serv, Windels Marx Lane & Mittendorf, LLP Library, 156 W 56th St, New York, NY, 10019. Tel: 212-237-1000. Fax: 212-262-1215. p. 1703

Solomon, John, In Charge, Spaulding Rehabilitation Hospital, 125 Nashua St, 8th Flr, Boston, MA, 02114. Tel: 617-573-2415. Fax: 617-573-2419. p. 1067

Solomon, Joseph, Distance Educ, Piedmont Community College, 1715 College Dr, Roxboro, NC, 27573. Tel: 336-599-1181, Ext 253. Fax: 336-599-9146. p. 1821

Solomon, Judy, Archivist, Asst Librn, Temple Israel Libraries & Media Center, 5725 Walnut Lake Rd, West Bloomfield, MI, 48323. Tel: 248-661-5700. Fax: 248-661-1302. p. 1236

Solomon, Louise, Assoc Librn, Ch, Kinnelon Public Library, 132 Kinnelon Rd, Kinnelon, NJ, 07405-2393. Tel: 973-838-1321. Fax: 973-838-0741. p. 1493

Solomon, Meredith I, Libr Tech, Tuality Healthcare, Health Sciences Library, 335 SE Eighth Ave, Hillsboro, OR, 97123. Tel: 503-681-1121. Fax: 503-681-1729. p. 2000

Solomon, Miriam A, Asst Librn, Financial Accounting Foundation Library, 401 Merritt 7, Norwalk, CT, 06856-5116. Tel: 203-956-5238. Fax: 203-956-3492. p. 362

Solomon, Peter, Circ Supvr, Winthrop Public Library & Museum, Two Metcalf Sq, Winthrop, MA, 02152-3157. Tel: 617-846-1703. Fax: 617-846-7083. p. 1142

Solomon, Sandra, Coordr, Ch Serv, Saint Martin Parish Library, 201 Porter St, Saint Martinville, LA, 70582. Tel: 337-394-2207, Ext 23. Fax: 337-394-2248. p. 967

Solomon, Sandra, Librn Tech III, Virgin Islands Division of Libraries, Archives & Museums, Regional Library for the Blind & Physically Handicapped, 3012 Golden Rock, Christiansted, Saint Croix, VI, 00820. Tel: 340-772-2250. Fax: 340-772-3545. p. 2680

Solomon, Stephanie, Libr Instruction, Pub Serv Librn, Ref Librn, Columbia International University, 7435 Monticello Rd, Columbia, SC, 29203-1599. Tel: 803-807-5104. Fax: 803-744-1391. p. 2187

Solomon, Vicki, Asst Dir, Person County Public Library, 319 S Main St, Roxboro, NC, 27573. Tel: 336-597-7881. Fax: 336-597-5081. p. 1821

Solon, Melanie R, Law Librn, Berks County Law Library, Courthouse, Tenth Flr, 633 Court St, Reading, PA, 19601-4302. Tel: 610-478-3370. Fax: 610-478-6375. p. 2133

Solonika, Peg, In Charge, Multnomah County Library, Hillsdale, 1525 SW Sunset Blvd, Portland, OR, 97239. Tel: 503-988-5388. Fax: 503-988-5197. p. 2012

Solove, Dan, Head, Acq, Syst & Tech, Bethlehem Area Public Library, 11 W Church St, Bethlehem, PA, 18018. Tel: 610-867-3761, Ext 216. Fax: 610-867-2767. p. 2033

Soloway, Alene, Tech Serv, Dykema Gossett PLLC, 39577 N Woodward Ave, Ste 300, Bloomfield Hills, MI, 48304-2820. Tel: 248-203-0700. Fax: 248-203-0763. p. 1159

Soloway, Alene, Tech Serv, Dykema Gossett PLLC, 400 Renaissance Ctr, 38th Flr, Detroit, MI, 48243. Tel: 313-568-6714. Fax: 313-568-6735. p. 1171

Solowy, Kris, Tech Serv, Yellowknife Public Library, Centre Square Mall, 5022 49th St, 2nd Flr, Yellowknife, NT, X1A 2N5, CANADA. Tel: 867-669-3402. Fax: 867-920-5671. p. 2776

Soltau, Carolyn, Librn, Pacific Newspaper Group Library, 200 Granville St, Vancouver, BC, V6C 3N3, CANADA. Tel: 604-605-2584. Fax: 604-605-2353. p. 2742

Soltis, John, Info Serv Librn, Bridgeport Public Library, 925 Broad St, Bridgeport, CT, 06604. Tel: 203-576-7403. Fax: 203-576-8255. p. 331

Soltis, Regina, Human Res Mgr, Massillon Public Library, 208 Lincoln Way E, Massillon, OH, 44646-8416. Tel: 330-832-9831, Ext 309. Fax: 330-830-2182. p. 1915

Soltysiak, Caren, Head, Tech Serv, Vernon Area Public Library District, 300 Olde Half Day Rd, Lincolnshire, IL, 60069-2901. Tel: 847-634-3650. Fax: 847-634-8449. p. 666

Solyma, Alice, Mgr, Libr Serv, Natural Resources Canada-Canadian Forest Service, 506 W Burnside Rd, Victoria, BC, V8Z 1M5, CANADA. Tel: 250-363-0680. Fax: 250-363-6035. p. 2745

Soma, Amy, Access & Delivery Librn, Concordia College, 901 S Eighth St, Moorhead, MN, 56562. Tel: 218-299-4937. Fax: 218-299-4253. p. 1265

Somarelli, Rhonda, Asst Dir, Port Byron Library, 12 Mentz Dr, Port Byron, NY, 13140. Tel: 315-776-5694. Fax: 315-776-5693. p. 1720

Somathilake, Sheryl, Br Mgr, Mobile Public Library, Saraland Public, 111 Saraland Loop, Saraland, AL, 36571-2418. Tel: 251-675-2879. Fax: 251-679-5516. p. 26

Somchay, Debbie, Adult Serv, Lemont Public Library District, 50 E Wend St, Lemont, IL, 60439-6439. Tel: 630-257-6541. Fax: 630-257-7737. p. 664

Somerdin, Steve, Ref & Info Serv, Ames Free Library, 53 Main St, North Easton, MA, 02356. Tel: 508-238-2000. Fax: 508-238-2980. p. 1112

Somerhalder, Holly, Br Mgr, Door County Library, Fish Creek Branch, 4097 Hwy 42, Fish Creek, WI, 54212. Tel: 920-868-3471. Fax: 920-868-3072. p. 2640

Somerman, Nelly, Dir, Ref, Schaumburg Township District Library, 130 S Roselle Rd, Schaumburg, IL, 60193. Tel: 847-923-3326. Fax: 847-923-3335. p. 701

Somers, Denise, Mgr, Halifax Public Libraries, Musquodoboit Harbour Branch, Village Plaza, 7900 No 7 Hwy, Musquodoboit Harbour, NS, B0J 1L0, CANADA. Tel: 902-889-2227. Fax: 902-889-3799. p. 2779

Somers, Denise, Mgr, Halifax Public Libraries, Sheet Harbour Branch, Blue Water Business Ctr, 22756 Hwy No 7, Sheet Harbour, NS, B0J 3B0, CANADA. Tel: 902-885-2391. Fax: 902-885-2749. p. 2779

Somers, Jeanne, Dir, John Carroll University, 20700 N Park Blvd, University Heights, OH, 44118. Tel: 216-397-4233. Fax: 216-397-1768. p. 1942

Somers, Mary, Ref, Harford Community College Library, 401 Thomas Run Rd, Bel Air, MD, 21015. Tel: 410-836-4232. Fax: 410-836-4198. p. 1019

Somers, Michael, Dir, Bridgewater State College, Ten Shaw Rd, Bridgewater, MA, 02325. Tel: 508-531-1392. Fax: 508-531-1349, 508-531-6103. p. 1070

Somerset, Sherry, Asst Librn, Essex Free Library, Two Browns River Rd, Essex, VT, 05451. Tel: 802-879-0313. p. 2423

Somerton, Gloria, Librn, Whitbourne Public Library, Main St, Whitbourne, NL, A0B 3K0, CANADA. Tel: 709-759-2461. Fax: 709-759-2461. p. 2773

Somerton, Pat, ILL, British Columbia Legislative Library, Parliament Bldgs, Victoria, BC, V8V 1X4, CANADA. Tel: 250-387-6510. Fax: 250-356-1373. p. 2744

Somerville, Brooke, Multimedia, Webmaster, Redford Township District Library, 25320 W Six Mile, Redford, MI, 48240. Tel: 313-531-5960. Fax: 313-531-1721. p. 1220

Somerville, Jane, Dir, Stanley Community Public Library, 33 Ace of Diamonds Blvd, Stanley, ID, 83278. Tel: 208-774-2470. Fax: 208-774-2470. p. 584

Somerville, Mary M, Univ Librn/Libr Dir, Auraria Library, 1100 Lawrence St, Denver, CO, 80204-2095. Tel: 303-556-4587. Fax: 303-556-3528. p. 298

Sommer, Jamie, Student Serv Librn, The John Marshall Law School, 315 S Plymouth Ct, Chicago, IL, 60604. Tel: 312-427-2737. Fax: 312-427-8307. p. 618

Sommer, Jennifer, Youth Serv Coordr, Wright Memorial Public Library, 1776 Far Hills Ave, Oakwood, OH, 45419-2598. Tel: 937-294-7171. Fax: 937-294-8578. p. 1924

Sommer, Joan, Head, Access Serv, Marquette University Libraries, 1355 W Wisconsin Ave, Milwaukee, WI, 53233. Tel: 414-288-3606. Fax: 414-288-7813. p. 2618

Sommer, MaryAnne, Info Serv Librn, Cumberland County Public Library & Information Center, East Regional, 4809 Clinton Rd, Fayetteville, NC, 28301-8992. Tel: 910-485-2955. Fax: 910-485-5492. p. 1792

Sommer, Shelly, Mgr, University of Colorado Boulder, Institute of Arctic & Alpine Research Information Center, 1560 30th St, UCB 450, Boulder, CO, 80309-0450. Tel: 303-492-1867, 303-492-6387. Fax: 303-492-6388. p. 292

Sommer, Valerie, Dir, South San Francisco Public Library, 840 W Orange Ave, South San Francisco, CA, 94080-3125. Tel: 650-829-3872. Fax: 650-829-3866. p. 270

Sommers, Ann, Tech Serv, Norwalk Community College, 188 Richards Ave, Norwalk, CT, 06854-1655. Tel: 203-857-7200. Fax: 203-857-7380. p. 362

Sommers, Hannah, Librn, NPR Library, 635 Massachusetts Ave NW, Washington, DC, 20001. Fax: 202-513-3056. p. 412

Sommerville, April, Discovery & Access Mgr, SIT Graduate Institute/SIT Study Abroad, One Kipling Rd, Brattleboro, VT, 05302. Tel: 802-258-3354. Fax: 802-258-3248. p. 2420

Sommerville, James, Ref Librn, Somerville Library, 35 West End Ave, Somerville, NJ, 08876. Tel: 908-725-1336. Fax: 908-231-0608. p. 1530

Somrak, Holly, Mgr, Margaret Welch Memorial Library, 5051 State Hwy 84, Longville, MN, 56655. Tel: 218-363-2710. Fax: 218-363-2710. p. 1256

Soncrant, Roy, Librn, Genesee District Library, Clio Area, G-2080 W Vienna Rd, Clio, MI, 48420. Tel: 810-686-7130. Fax: 810-686-0071. p. 1179

Sonderman, Karen, Dir, North Canton Public Library, 185 N Main St, North Canton, OH, 44720-2595. Tel: 330-499-4712, Ext 315. Fax: 330-499-3452. p. 1923

Sondgeroth, Joyce, Dir, LaMoille-Clarion Public Library District, 81 Main St, LaMoille, IL, 61330. Tel: 815-638-2356. Fax: 815-638-2356. p. 663

Sondhi, Sabrina, Spec Coll Librn, Columbia University, Arthur W Diamond Law Library, 435 W 116th St, New York, NY, 10027. Tel: 212-854-3922. Fax: 212-854-3295. p. 1674

Soneberg, Sadie, Coll Develop, Dir, Big Bend Village Library, W230 S90175 Nevins St, Big Bend, WI, 53103-9722. Tel: 262-662-3571. Fax: 262-662-3459, 262-662-3751. p. 2582

Soneda, Brian M, Dir, Mount Vernon City Library, 315 Snoqualmie St, Mount Vernon, WA, 98273. Tel: 360-336-6249. Fax: 360-336-6259. p. 2521

Sonefeld, Patti, Tech Serv, Orangeburg-Calhoun Technical College, 3250 Saint Matthews Rd NE, Orangeburg, SC, 29118. Tel: 803-535-1262. Fax: 803-535-1240. p. 2201

Sones, Linda, Dir, Quimby Public Library, 201 N Main, Quimby, IA, 51049. Tel: 712-445-2413. Fax: 712-445-2688. p. 839

Song, Felicia, Head, Adult Serv, Lake Forest Library, 360 E Deerpath Ave, Lake Forest, IL, 60045-2252. Tel: 847-810-4611. Fax: 847-234-1453. p. 663

Song, Il-Yeol, PhD, Prof, Drexel University, Rush Bldg, Rm 306, 30 N 33rd St, Philadelphia, PA, 19104-2875. Tel: 215-895-2474. Fax: 215-895-2494. p. 2972

Song, Sophie, Info Tech Serv Mgr, Alberta Law Libraries, , Law Courts North, 5th Flr, 1A Sir Winston Churchill Sq, Edmonton, AB, T5J 0R2, CANADA. Tel: 780-427-3327. Fax: 780-427-0481. p. 2698

Song, Yiluo, Syst Librn, Rock Valley College Library, Educational Resources Center, 3301 N Mulford Rd, Rockford, IL, 61114. Tel: 815-921-4602. Fax: 815-921-4629. p. 697

Song, Yoo-Seong, Librn, University of Illinois Library at Urbana-Champaign, Labor & Industrial Relations, 147 ILIR, 504 E Armory Ave, Champaign, IL, 61820. Tel: 217-333-7993. Fax: 217-244-4091. p. 712

Song, Yoo-Seong, Librn, University of Illinois Library at Urbana-Champaign, Social Sciences, Health & Education Library, 100 Main Library, MC-522, 1408 W Gregory Dr, Urbana, IL, 61801. Tel: 217-333-8021. Fax: 217-333-2214. p. 713

Songster, Jennifer, Br Mgr, Long Beach Public Library, Dana, 3680 Atlantic Ave, Long Beach, CA, 90807. Tel: 562-570-1042. p. 167

Sonido, Eleanor, Bibliog Instr, Cat, Compton Community College Library, 1111 E Artesia Blvd, Compton, CA, 90221. Tel: 310-900-1600, Ext 2175. Fax: 310-900-1693. p. 136

Sonnek, Therese, Br Mgr, Ramsey County Library, White Bear Lake Branch, 4698 Clark Ave, White Bear Lake, MN, 55110-3415. Tel: 651-407-5302. Fax: 651-407-5305. p. 1284

Sonnenberg, Edmund, Govt Doc, Ref Serv, Widener University, Harrisburg Campus Law Library, 3800 Vartan Way, Harrisburg, DE, 17110. Tel: 717-541-3932. Fax: 717-541-3998. p. 389

Sonnesyn, Jill T, Librn, Gray, Plant, Mooty, 500 IDS Ctr, 800 S Eighth, Minneapolis, MN, 55402. Tel: 612-632-3000, 612-632-3122. p. 1260

Sonnichsen, Sanoy, Asst Librn, Shedd Free Library, 46 N Main, Washington, NH, 03280. Tel: 603-495-0410. Fax: 603-495-3592. p. 1467

Sonnier, Denice, Mgr, Davis Jefferson Parish Library, McBurney Memorial, 301 S Sarah St, Welsh, LA, 70591. Tel: 337-734-3262. Fax: 337-734-4540. p. 952

Sonnier, Mary, Librn, Acadia Parish Library, Morse Branch, 209 S Jules Ave, Morse, LA, 70559. Tel: 337-783-0784. Fax: 337-783-0784. p. 948

Sonntag, Gabriela, Dir, University of Redlands, 1200 E Colton Ave, Redlands, CA, 92374-3758. Tel: 909-748-8022. Fax: 909-335-5392. p. 215

Sonntag, Gabriela, Coordr, Instruction, Coordr, Ref (Info Serv), California State University, 333 S Twin Oaks Valley Rd, San Marcos, CA, 92096-0001. Tel: 760-750-4356. Fax: 760-750-3287. p. 254

Soofi, Janet, Tech Serv, Pauline Haass Public Library, N64 W23820 Main St, Sussex, WI, 53089-3120. Tel: 262-246-5180. Fax: 262-246-5236. p. 2642

Soohoo, Jason, Educ Res Librn, Salem State University Library, 352 Lafayette St, Salem, MA, 01970-5353. Tel: 978-542-6967. Fax: 978-542-6596. p. 1122

Sooter, Judy, Librn, Southwest Arkansas Regional Library, Hempstead County Library, 500 S Elm St, Hope, AR, 71801. Tel: 870-777-4564. Fax: 870-777-2915. p. 103

Sopalsky, Donna, Asst Dir, Haverstraw Kings Daughters Public Library, Ten W Ramapo Rd, Garnerville, NY, 10923. Tel: 845-786-3800. Fax: 845-786-3791. p. 1626

Sopko, Andrew J, Dr, Dir, Kenrick-Glennon Seminary, 5200 Glennon Dr, Saint Louis, MO, 63119. Tel: 314-792-6129. Fax: 314-792-6503. p. 1355

Soreide, Pamela, Dir, Holdrege Area Public Library, 604 East Ave, Holdrege, NE, 68949. Tel: 308-995-6556. Fax: 308-995-5732. p. 1402

Sorel, Lawrence J, Dir, Monroe County Seneca Park Zoo, 2222 St Paul St, Rochester, NY, 14621-1097. Tel: 585-266-6591. Fax: 585-266-5775. p. 1730

Sorensen, Gloria, Br Mgr, Omaha Public Library, Florence, 2920 Bondesson, Omaha, NE, 68112. Tel: 402-444-5299. Fax: 402-444-6607. p. 1414

Sorensen, Holly Richards, Asst Dir, Des Plaines Public Library, 1501 Ellinwood St, Des Plaines, IL, 60016-4553. Tel: 847-376-2789. Fax: 847-827-7974. p. 636

Sorensen, Janice, Librn, Kansas Geological Survey Library, 1930 Constant Ave, Lawrence, KS, 66047-3726. Tel: 785-864-4909. Fax: 785-864-5317. p. 877

Sorensen, Julie, Commun Libr Mgr, County of Los Angeles Public Library, San Gabriel Library, 500 S Del Mar Ave, San Gabriel, CA, 91776-2408. Tel: 626-287-0761. Fax: 626-285-2610. p. 143

Sorensen, Kristi, Dir, Belle Plaine Community Library, 904 12th St, Belle Plaine, IA, 52208-1711. Tel: 319-444-2902. Fax: 319-444-2902. p. 796

Sorensen, Luke E, Dir, Rumford Public Library, 56 Rumford Ave, Rumford, ME, 04276-1919. Tel: 207-364-3661. Fax: 207-364-7296. p. 999

Sorensen, Sally, Head, Cat, Texas Christian University, 2913 Lowden St, TCU Box 298400, Fort Worth, TX, 76129. Tel: 817-257-7106. Fax: 817-257-7282. p. 2323

Sorenson, Barbara, Librn, Amery Public Library, 801 Keller Ave S, Amery, WI, 54001-1096. Tel: 715-268-9340. Fax: 715-268-8659. p. 2577

Sorenson, Becky, Ref Serv, Ad, Pauline Haass Public Library, N64 W23820 Main St, Sussex, WI, 53089-3120. Tel: 262-246-5180. Fax: 262-246-5236. p. 2642

Sorenson, Cindy, Asst Dir, Kinney Memorial Library, 214 Main St, Hanlontown, IA, 50444. Tel: 641-896-2888. Fax: 641-896-2890. p. 820

Soret, Judy, Librn, Penn Wynne Library, 130 Overbrook Pkwy, Wynnewood, PA, 19096-3211. Tel: 610-642-7844. Fax: 610-642-2761. p. 2158

Sorg, Elizabeth, Dir, Norristown State Hospital, Kaleidoscope, Bldg 53 CR, 1001 Sterigere St, Norristown, PA, 19401. Tel: 610-313-1180, 610-313-5369. Fax: 610-313-5370. p. 2099

Soria, Lucila, Per, Saddleback College, 28000 Marguerite Pkwy, Mission Viejo, CA, 92692. Tel: 949-582-4873. Fax: 949-364-0284. p. 187

Soriano, Jo Ann, Ser, United States Department of the Army, CEHEC-ZL Casey Bldg, 7701 Telegraph Rd, Alexandria, VA, 22315-3860. Tel: 703-428-6388. Fax: 703-428-6310. p. 2446

Sorkness, Johanna, Librn, Supplee Memorial Presbyterian Church Library, 855 Welsh Rd, Maple Glen, PA, 19002. Tel: 215-646-4123. Fax: 215-646-8895. p. 2084

Sorn, Vickie, Youth & Commun Serv Librn, East Central Regional Library, 244 S Birch, Cambridge, MN, 55008-1588. Tel: 763-689-7390. Fax: 763-689-7389. p. 1243

Sorrell, Bethany, Asst Dir, Huntington Public Library, Seven E Main St, Huntington, MA, 01050. Tel: 413-667-3506. Fax: 413-667-0088. p. 1096

Sorrell, Eva, Principal Cataloger, California State University, San Bernardino, 5500 University Pkwy, San Bernardino, CA, 92407-2318. Tel: 909-537-7392. Fax: 909-537-7048. p. 227

Sorrell, Paul, Project Coordr, Union University, 1050 Union University Dr, Jackson, TN, 38305-3697. Tel: 731-661-5070. Fax: 731-661-5175. p. 2238

Sorrels, Ben, Managing Librn, Austin Public Library, Pleasant Hill, 211 E William Cannon Dr, Austin, TX, 78745. Tel: 512-974-3940. Fax: 512-444-6237. p. 2279

Sorrentino, Bobbi, Librn, Walworth Memorial Library, 101 Maple Ave, Walworth, WI, 53184-9530. Tel: 262-275-6322. Fax: 262-275-5315. p. 2643

Sorrentino, Connie, Circ, Greene County Public Library, 120 N 12th St, Paragould, AR, 72450. Tel: 870-236-8711. Fax: 870-236-1442. p. 111

Sorrentino, Jeneice, Librn, Hillsborough Community College, Ybor City Campus Learning Resources Center, 1502 E Ninth Ave, Tampa, FL, 33605. Tel: 813-253-7613. Fax: 813-259-6070. p. 496

Sorrough, Gail, Dir, UCSF Medical Center at Mount Zion, 1600 Divisadero St, Rm A-116, San Francisco, CA, 94115. Tel: 415-885-7378. p. 247

Sorth, Kristen, Asst Dir, Admin, Saint Louis County Library, 1640 S Lindbergh Blvd, Saint Louis, MO, 63131-3598. Tel: 314-994-3300, Ext 2155. Fax: 314-997-7602. p. 1358

Sosa, Aracelis, Ast Dir, Libr Dept, University of Puerto Rico Library System, University of Puerto Rico, Rio Piedras Campus, San Juan, PR, 00931. Tel: 787-764-0000, Ext 2790. Fax: 787-772-1479. p. 2677

Sosa, Richard, Dir, Finance & Planning, Denver Public Library, Ten W 14th Ave Pkwy, Denver, CO, 80204-2731. Tel: 720-865-1111. Fax: 720-865-2087. p. 300

Sosa-Arzuaga, Aracelis, Head Librn, University of Puerto Rico Library System, Public Administration Library, Rio Piedras Campus, San Juan, PR, 00931. Tel: 787-764-0000, Ext 5181, 787-764-0000, Ext 5182. Fax: 787-772-1479. p. 2678

Sosch, Mike, Archivist, Ref Serv, US National Park Service, 99 Warren St, Brookline, MA, 02445. Tel: 617-566-1689. Fax: 617-232-4073. p. 1072

Sosebee, Diane, Ch, Evergreen-Conecuh County Public Library, 119 Cemetery Ave, Evergreen, AL, 36401. Tel: 251-578-2670. Fax: 251-578-2316. p. 16

Sosnicki, Sheila, Admin Librn, Palos Park Public Library, 12330 S Forest Glen Blvd, Palos Park, IL, 60464. Tel: 708-448-1530. Fax: 708-448-3492. p. 688

Sosnowski, Carolyn, Dir, Educ & Info Serv, Special Libraries Association, 331 S Patrick St, Alexandria, VA, 22314-3501. Tel: 703-647-4914. Fax: 703-647-4901. p. 2446

Sosnowski, Maria, Librn, Clark County Law Library, 1200 Franklin St, Vancouver, WA, 98660. Tel: 360-397-2268. p. 2545

Sosnowski, Mark, Librn, Connecticut Correctional Institution, 900 Highland Ave, Cheshire, CT, 06410. Tel: 203-250-2600, Ext 2124. Fax: 203-250-2707. p. 334

Sostack, Maura, Health Sci Librn, Virtua Memorial Hospital of Burlington County, 175 Madison Ave, Mount Holly, NJ, 08060. Tel: 609-267-0700, Ext 43021. Fax: 609-267-8073. p. 1506

Sostack, Maura, Med Librn, Virtua Health System, Voorhees Division, 100 Bowman Dr, Medical Library, Garden Level Rm GD550, Voorhees, NJ, 08043. Tel: 856-247-3207. Fax: 856-247-3222. p. 1539

Sostrom, Heather, Libr Mgr, Alachua County Library District, Cone Park Branch, 2841 E University Ave, Gainesville, FL, 32641. Tel: 352-334-0720. Fax: 352-334-0310. p. 448

Sosulski, Nicolette Warisse, Bus Librn, Portage District Library, 300 Library Lane, Portage, MI, 49002. Tel: 269-329-4542, Ext 714. Fax: 269-324-9222. p. 1220

Sotak, Diane, Ref, University of Portland, 5000 N Willamette Blvd, Portland, OR, 97203-5743. Tel: 503-943-7111. Fax: 503-943-7491. p. 2015

Sotirelis, E Marilyn, Dir, Calais Free Library, Nine Union St, Calais, ME, 04619. Tel: 207-454-2758. Fax: 207-454-2765. p. 980

Soto, Adelaide, Head, Access Serv, Lehman College, City University of New York, 250 Bedford Park Blvd W, Bronx, NY, 10468-1589. Tel: 718-960-7773. Fax: 718-960-8952. p. 1587

Soto, Brian, Circ Mgr, Marymount Manhattan College, 221 E 71st St, New York, NY, 10021. Tel: 212-774-4804. Fax: 212-458-8207. p. 1685

Soto, Donna, Dir, Foley Public Library, 319 E Laurel Ave, Foley, AL, 36535. Tel: 251-943-7665. Fax: 251-943-8637. p. 17

Soto, Hilaria, II, Admin Serv, Department of Veterans Affairs, Library Service 142D, Ten Calle Casia, San Juan, PR, 00921-3201. Tel: 787-641-7582, Ext 12227. Fax: 787-641-4550. p. 2676

Soto, Jose, Law Librn, Saint Thomas University Library, Law Library, 16401 NW 37th Ave, Miami Gardens, FL, 33054. Tel: 305-623-2378. Fax: 305-623-2337. p. 469

Soto, Natalia, Librn, United States Army, 2218 Third St, Elmendorf AFB, AK, 99506-6898. Tel: 907-753-2527. Fax: 907-753-2526. p. 47

Soto, Sharon, Br Coordr, Indiana University, Indiana Institute on Disability & Community, 2853 E Tenth St, Bloomington, IN, 47408-2601. Tel: 812-855-9396. Fax: 812-855-9630. p. 727

Soto, Tricia N, Info Officer, Center for Advanced Study in the Behavioral Sciences Library, 75 Alta Rd, Stanford, CA, 94305. Tel: 650-736-0100. p. 270

Soto-Barra, Laura, Dir, NPR Library, 635 Massachusetts Ave NW, Washington, DC, 20001. Fax: 202-513-3056. p. 412

Souchock, Carol A, Dir, Adrian Public Library, 143 E Maumee St, Adrian, MI, 49221-2773. Tel: 517-265-2265. Fax: 517-265-8847. p. 1147

Soucie, Mary, Dir, Three Rivers Public Library District, 25207 W Channon Dr, Channahon, IL, 60410-5028. Tel: 815-467-6200. Fax: 815-467-4012. p. 603

Souers, Kathy, Head, Circ, Palm Harbor Library, 2330 Nebraska Ave, Palm Harbor, FL, 34683. Tel: 727-784-3332. Fax: 727-785-6534. p. 480

Soukup, Sara, Youth Serv, Lake Geneva Public Library, 918 W Main St, Lake Geneva, WI, 53147-1890. Tel: 262-249-5299. Fax: 262-249-5284. p. 2604

Soule, Jennifer, Dir, South Charleston Public Library, 312 Fourth Ave, South Charleston, WV, 25303-1297. Tel: 304-744-6561. Fax: 304-744-8808. p. 2572

Soules, Aline, Assoc Univ Librn, California State University, East Bay Library, 25800 Carlos Bee Blvd, Hayward, CA, 94542-3052. Tel: 510-885-4596. Fax: 510-885-2049. p. 157

Soulier, Norma J, Librn, Bad River Public Tribal Library, 72682 Maple St, Odanah, WI, 54861. Tel: 715-682-7111, Ext 1532. Fax: 715-682-7118. p. 2626

Soulliere, Robert, Digital Syst Librn, Mohawk College Library, 135 Fennell Ave W, Hamilton, ON, L9C 1E9, CANADA. Tel: 905-575-1212, Ext 3936. Fax: 905-575-2011. p. 2810

Soultoukis, Donna, Librn, Our Lady of Lourdes, School of Nursing Library, 1600 Haddon Ave, Camden, NJ, 08103. Tel: 856-757-3722. Fax: 856-757-3767. p. 1476

Sousa, Toni, Ref Librn, Mendocino College Library, 1000 Hensley Creek Rd, Ukiah, CA, 95482-7821. Tel: 707-468-3053. Fax: 707-468-3056. p. 277

Souter, Dennis G, Ref Serv, Oakland Community College, Auburn Hills Campus Library, 2900 Featherstone Rd, Bldg D, Auburn Hills, MI, 48326. Tel: 248-232-4125. Fax: 248-232-4136. p. 1154

South, Carmen, Dir, Walton Community Library, 122 Main St, Walton, KS, 67151. Tel: 620-837-3252. Fax: 620-837-3252. p. 899

South, Elisabeth G, Coll Develop & Automation Serv Librn, Florence-Lauderdale Public Library, 350 N Wood Ave, Florence, AL, 35630. Tel: 256-764-6564. Fax: 256-764-6629. p. 17

South, Kathy, Dir, Monroe County District Library, 96 Home Ave, Woodsfield, OH, 43793. Tel: 740-472-1954. Fax: 740-472-1110. p. 1949

Southall, Florence, Acq Asst, Longwood University, Redford & Race St, Farmville, VA, 23909. Tel: 434-395-2742. Fax: 434-395-2453. p. 2463

Southam, Pamela, Libr Tech, University of Manitoba Libraries, J W Crane Memorial Library, 2109 Portage Ave, Winnipeg, MB, R3J 0L3, CANADA. Tel: 204-831-2152. Fax: 204-888-1805. p. 2758

Southard, Christy, Tech Serv, Sequoyah Regional Library System, 116 Brown Industrial Pkwy, Canton, GA, 30114-2899. Tel: 770-479-3090, Ext 221. Fax: 770-479-3069. p. 523

Southard, Doug, Librn, CRA International Library, 200 Clarendon St T-33, Boston, MA, 02116. Tel: 617-425-3000. Fax: 617-425-3132. p. 1060

Southard, Greta, Dir, Boone County Public Library, 1786 Burlington Pike, Burlington, KY, 41005. Tel: 859-342-2665. Fax: 859-689-0435. p. 908

Souther, Randy, Ref Serv, University of San Francisco, 2130 Fulton St, San Francisco, CA, 94117-1080. Tel: 415-422-5388. Fax: 415-422-5949. p. 248

Southern, Debra, Tech Supvr, Honeywell Canada-Engine & Systems Knowledge Centre, 3333 Unity Dr, Mississauga, ON, L5L 3S6, CANADA. Tel: 905-608-6000, Ext 6139. Fax: 905-608-6001. p. 2822

Southern, Gordon T, Dir, Ref Librn, Walton & Tipton Township Public Library, 110 N Main St, Walton, IN, 46994-0406. Tel: 574-626-2234. Fax: 574-626-2234. p. 785

Southern, Melanie, Info Serv, Milton Public Library, 1010 Main St E, Milton, ON, L9T 6H7, CANADA. Tel: 905-875-2665, Ext 3265. Fax: 905-875-4324. p. 2822

Southwell, Dawn, Head, User Access Serv, Louisiana State University Health Sciences Center, 1501 Kings Hwy, Shreveport, LA, 71130. Tel: 318-675-4712. Fax: 318-675-5442. p. 968

Southwick, Leonora, Asst Dir, Madison Library, 1895 Village Rd, Madison, NH, 03849. Tel: 603-367-8545. Fax: 603-367-4479. p. 1455

Southwick, Shane, Network Coordr, Alaska State Library, Library Development, 344 W Third Ave, Ste 125, Anchorage, AK, 99501. Tel: 907-269-6570. Fax: 907-269-6580. p. 44

Southwood, Ev, Librn, Chinook Regional Library, Maple Creek Branch, 205 Jasper St, Maple Creek, SK, S0N 1N0, CANADA. Tel: 306-662-3522. p. 2928

Southworth, Heidi, Cat/Metadata Librn, University of Wisconsin-River Falls, 410 S Third St, River Falls, WI, 54022. Tel: 715-425-3924. Fax: 715-425-0609. p. 2635

Southworth, Marvin, Ref Serv, Coastal Bend College, 3800 Charco Rd, Beeville, TX, 78102-2110. Tel: 361-354-2737, 361-354-2740. Fax: 361-354-2719. p. 2288

Souza, Carol Jean, Br Mgr, Mineral County Public Library, Mina-Luning Library, 908 B St, Mina, NV, 89422. Tel: 775-573-2505. Fax: 775-573-2505. p. 1428

Sovanski, Vincent, Commun Ambassador & Sch Spec, Glenside Public Library District, 25 E Fullerton Ave, Glendale Heights, IL, 60139-2697. Tel: 630-260-1550. Fax: 630-260-1433. p. 650

Sowards, Steven, Assoc Dir, Coll, Michigan State University Library, 100 Library, East Lansing, MI, 48824-1048. Tel: 517-884-6391. Fax: 517-432-0487. p. 1175

Sowden, Mary Lou, Coordr, Keystone Library Network, Dixon University Ctr, 2986 N Second St, Harrisburg, PA, 17110-1201. Tel: 717-720-4088. Fax: 717-720-4453. p. 2954

Sowder, Steve, Head, Syst & Media Serv, Andrews University, 1400 Library Rd, Berrien Springs, MI, 49104-1400. Tel: 269-471-6242. Fax: 269-471-6166. p. 1157

Sowell, Cary, Ref Librn, Austin Community College, Eastview Campus Library, 3401 Webberville Rd, Austin, TX, 78702. Tel: 512-223-5232. Fax: 512-223-5111. p. 2278

Sowell, Pat, Head of Libr, Volusia County Public Library, Pierson Public, 115 N Volusia Ave, Pierson, FL, 32180. Tel: 386-749-6930. p. 436

Sowell, Val, Access Serv & Syst, Publ Librn, Web Serv, AIDS Library, 1233 Locust St, 2nd Flr, Philadelphia, PA, 19107. Tel: 215-985-4851. Fax: 215-985-4492. p. 2102

Sowers, Barb, Dir, Readlyn Community Library, 309 Main St, Readlyn, IA, 50668. Tel: 319-279-3432. Fax: 319-279-3432. p. 840

Sowers, Barbara, Head, Youth Serv, Freeport Public Library, 100 E Douglas St, Freeport, IL, 61032. Tel: 815-233-3000. Fax: 815-233-1099. p. 647

Sowers, Bill, Cataloging/State Docs, Librn, State Library of Kansas, State Capitol Bldg, Topeka, KS, 66612. Tel: 785-296-3296. Fax: 785-296-6650. p. 896

Sowers, Dawn, Pub Serv Mgr, Fauquier County Public Library, 11 Winchester St, Warrenton, VA, 20186-2825. Tel: 540-349-1253. Fax: 540-349-3278. p. 2500

Sowers, Margaret, Ch, Macomb Public Library District, 235 S Lafayette St, Macomb, IL, 61455-2231. Tel: 309-833-2714. Fax: 309-833-2714. p. 668

Sowers, Susan, Librn, Hoyt Lakes Public Library, 206 Kennedy Dr, Hoyt Lakes, MN, 55750. Tel: 218-225-2412. Fax: 218-225-2399. p. 1254

Sowles, Glen, Ad, Romeo District Library, 65821 Van Dyke, Washington, MI, 48095. Tel: 586-752-0603. Fax: 586-752-8416. p. 1235

Sox, Shauna, Librn, Beiseker Municipal Library, 700 First St, Beiseker, AB, T0M 0G0, CANADA. Tel: 403-947-3230. Fax: 403-947-2146. p. 2685

Soyars, Robin, Ser, Southside Virginia Community College Libraries, 109 Campus Dr, Alberta, VA, 23821. Tel: 434-949-1064. Fax: 434-949-0013. p. 2444

Sozansky, Basil, Dir, University of Minnesota Duluth Library, 416 Library Dr, Duluth, MN, 55812. Tel: 218-726-6562. Fax: 218-726-8019. p. 1248

Space, Cheryl, Youth Serv, State of Rhode Island Office of Library & Information Services, One Capitol Hill, 4th Flr, Providence, RI, 02908. Tel: 401-574-9309. Fax: 401-574-9320. p. 2175

Spadaccini, Linda, Dir, Waterbury Hospital, 64 Robbins St, Waterbury, CT, 06721. Tel: 203-573-6136. Fax: 203-573-6706. p. 375

Spadafora, David, Librn, Pres, Newberry Library, 60 W Walton St, Chicago, IL, 60610-3305. Tel: 312-255-3600. Fax: 312-255-3712. p. 620

Spadaro, Joanne, Sr Asst Librn, Ref, State University of New York, 223 Store Hill Rd, Old Westbury, NY, 11568. Tel: 516-876-2896. Fax: 516-876-3325. p. 1710

Spade, Elizabeth, Ch, Alexandria-Monroe Public Library, 117 E Church St, Alexandria, IN, 46001-2005. Tel: 765-724-2196. Fax: 765-724-2204. p. 723

Spadoni, Cindy, Head, Ref, O'Melveny & Myers LLP, 400 S Hope St, Los Angeles, CA, 90071-2899. Tel: 213-430-6000. Fax: 213-430-6407. p. 176

Spadoni, Cindy, Dir, Bibliog Serv, Dir, Coll Mgt, University of California Los Angeles Library, Hugh & Hazel Darling Law Library, 112 Law Bldg, Box 951458, 385 Charles E Young Dr E, Los Angeles, CA, 90095-1458. Tel: 310-825-7826. Fax: 310-825-1372. p. 178

Spady, Vanessa, Law Librn, Madera County Law Library, County Government Ctr, 209 W Yosemite Ave, Madera, CA, 93637-3596. Tel: 559-673-0378. Fax: 559-673-0378. p. 181

Spaeth, Paul J, Dir, Saint Bonaventure University, 3261 W State Rd, Saint Bonaventure, NY, 14778. Tel: 716-375-2323. Fax: 716-375-2389. p. 1737

Spafford, Susan L, Ref, Hoover Public Library, 200 Municipal Dr, Hoover, AL, 35216. Tel: 205-444-7810. Fax: 205-444-7878. p. 20

Spahn, Gary, Syst Librn, Thomas Jefferson University, 1020 Walnut St, Philadelphia, PA, 19107. Tel: 215-503-3123. Fax: 215-923-3203. p. 2118

Spaid, Melinda, Asst Librn, Orangeville Public Library, 301 Mill St, Orangeville, PA, 17859-0177. Tel: 570-683-5354. p. 2101

Spaid, Nancy, Syst Librn, New College of Florida University of South Florida Sarasota Manatee, 5800 Bay Shore Rd, Sarasota, FL, 34243-2109. Tel: 941-487-4402. Fax: 941-487-4307. p. 490

Spain, Patricia, Br Mgr, Puskarich Public Library, Clark Memorial, 102 W Main St, Freeport, OH, 43973. Tel: 740-658-3855. Fax: 740-658-3798. p. 1862

Spaine, Jamie, Admin Coordr, University of Puget Sound, 1500 N Warner St, Campus Mail Box 1021, Tacoma, WA, 98416-1021. Tel: 253-879-3243. Fax: 253-879-3670. p. 2541

Spak, Judy, Curric Support Librn, Yale University Library, Harvey Cushing/John Hay Whitney Medical Library, Sterling Hall of Medicine, 333 Cedar St, L110 SHM, New Haven, CT, 06520. Tel: 203-737-2961. Fax: 203-785-5636. p. 358

Spak, Karen L, Dir, Shenango Valley Community Library, 11 N Sharpsville Ave, Sharon, PA, 16146. Tel: 724-981-4360. Fax: 724-981-5208. p. 2139

Spakoski, Sandy, Cat, Southern New Hampshire University, 2500 N River Rd, Manchester, NH, 03106-1045. Tel: 603-645-9605, Ext 2169. Fax: 603-645-9685. p. 1456

Spalding, Donna, Br Mgr, Saint Louis County Library, Weber Road Branch, 4444 Weber Rd, Saint Louis, MO, 63123. Tel: 314-638-2210. Fax: 314-638-2212. p. 1359

Spalding, Jeff, Tech Serv, Florida Supreme Court Library, 500 S Duval St, Tallahassee, FL, 32399-1926. Tel: 850-488-8919. Fax: 850-922-5219. p. 495

Spale, Kathleen, Circ Serv, Tech Serv, North Riverside Public Library District, 2400 S DesPlaines Ave, North Riverside, IL, 60546. Tel: 708-447-0869, Ext 245. Fax: 708-447-0526. p. 682

Spalti, Michael, Assoc Univ Librn, Syst, Willamette University, 900 State St, Salem, OR, 97301. Tel: 503-370-6356. Fax: 503-370-6141. p. 2018

Spanfelner, Deborah, Librn, Broome Community College, 907 Front St, Binghamton, NY, 13905-1328. Tel: 607-778-5239. Fax: 607-778-5108. p. 1581

Spangle, Kathryn, Libr Mgr, Santa Fe Public Library, Oliver La Farge Branch Library, 1730 Llano St, Santa Fe, NM, 87505-5460. Tel: 505-955-4868. Fax: 505-955-4861. p. 1564

Spangler, Cheryl, Librn, Harrisburg Public Library, 354 Smith St, Harrisburg, OR, 97446. Tel: 541-995-6949. Fax: 541-995-9244. p. 2000

Spann, Catherine, Asst Librn, Fannie Brown Booth Memorial Library, 619 Tenaha St, Center, TX, 75935. Tel: 936-598-5522. Fax: fbbl.catherine@yahoo.com. p. 2296

Spann, Joseph E, Jr, Librn, Polk County Historical & Genealogical Library, Historic Courthouse, 100 E Main St, Bartow, FL, 33830. Tel: 863-534-4380. Fax: 863-534-4382. p. 426

Spann, Julie, Dir, Libr Serv, Blodgett Memorial Library, 37 Broad St, Fishkill, NY, 12524-1836. Tel: 845-896-9215. Fax: 845-896-9243. p. 1622

Spann, Marla, Head, Tech Serv, Pub Serv, East Chicago Public Library, 2401 E Columbus Dr, East Chicago, IN, 46312-2998. Tel: 219-397-2453. Fax: 219-397-6715. p. 736

Spano, Karen, Br Mgr, Palm Beach County Library System, Hagen Ranch Road, 14350 Hagen Ranch Rd, Delray Beach, FL, 33446. Tel: 561-894-7500. Fax: 561-495-5451. p. 503

Spanos, Sandra, ILL, Mitchell Public Library, 221 N Duff St, Mitchell, SD, 57301-2596. Tel: 605-995-8480. Fax: 605-995-8482. p. 2215

Spar, Ira, Librn, Hartford Medical Society, 236 Farmington Ave, PO Box 4003, Farmington, CT, 06034-4003. p. 340

Spare, Amy, Ref, Villanova University, Law Library, Garey Hall, 299 N Spring Mill Rd, Villanova, PA, 19085. Tel: 610-519-7188. Fax: 610-519-7033. p. 2150

Sparenberg, Connie, Dir, Earl Park Public Library, 102 E Fifth St, Earl Park, IN, 47942-8700. Tel: 219-474-6932. Fax: 219-474-6932. p. 736

Spark, Andrea, Br Mgr, Placer County Library, Colfax Branch, Two Church St, Colfax, CA, 95713. Tel: 530-346-8211. Fax: 530-346-8211. p. 123

Sparkman, Kathy, Coordr, Youth Serv, Central Mississippi Regional Library System, 104 Office Park Dr, Brandon, MS, 39042-2404. Tel: 601-825-0100. Fax: 601-825-0199. p. 1294

Sparks, Brian, Dir, Yellowstone Gateway Museum of Park County, 118 W Chinook, Livingston, MT, 59047. Tel: 406-222-4184. Fax: 406-222-4146. p. 1385

Sparks, Carolyn, Br Mgr, Franklin County Public Library, Carrabelle Branch, 311 Saint James Ave, Carrabelle, FL, 32322. Tel: 850-697-2366. Fax: 850-697-4562. p. 438

Sparks, David Hatfield, Head Librn/Tech Serv & Syst, College of Alameda, 555 Ralph Appezzato Memorial Pkwy, Alameda, CA, 94501. Tel: 510-748-2253. Fax: 510-748-2380. p. 119

Sparks, Diana K, Br Mgr, Robinson Public Library District, Oblong Branch, 110 E Main St, Oblong, IL, 62449. Tel: 618-592-3001. Fax: 618-592-3001. p. 695

Sparks, Heather, Br Mgr, Free Library of Philadelphia, Cecil B Moore Branch, 2320 W Cecil B Moore Ave, Philadelphia, PA, 19121-2927. Tel: 215-685-2766. Fax: 215-685-3893. p. 2108

Sparks, Helen, Br Mgr, Carroll County Public Library, Taneytown Branch, 10 Grand Dr, Taneytown, MD, 21787-2421. Tel: 410-386-4510. Fax: 410-386-4515. p. 1046

Sparks, Irene, Dir, Oxford Public Library, 213 Choccolocco St, Oxford, AL, 36203. Tel: 256-831-1750. Fax: 256-835-6798. p. 33

Sparks, Jonathan, Dr, Dir of Libr, Southwestern Oklahoma State University, 100 Campus Dr, Weatherford, OK, 73096-3002. Tel: 580-774-7023. Fax: 580-774-3112. p. 1985

Sparks, Karianne, Dir, Hampton University, 253 Town Center Dr, Virginia Beach, VA, 23462. Tel: 757-637-2422. Fax: 757-227-5979. p. 2499

Sparks, Kellie, Librn, Melbourne Campus, Keiser University Library System, 1500 NW 49th St, Fort Lauderdale, FL, 33309. Tel: 954-351-4035. Fax: 954-351-4051. p. 443

Sparks, Mary Ann, Libr Mgr, Edgerton Public Library, PO Box 180, Edgerton, AB, T0B 1K0, CANADA. Tel: 780-755-2666. Fax: 780-755-2666. p. 2697

Sparks, Millie, Br Mgr, Wilson County Public Library, Crocker-Stantonsburg Branch, 114 S Main St, Stantonsburg, NC, 27883. Tel: 252-238-3758. Fax: 252-238-3758. p. 1831

Sparks, Robert, Circ Supvr, Gannon University, 109 University Sq, Erie, PA, 16541. Tel: 814-871-7557. Fax: 814-871-5666. p. 2055

Sparks, Wesley, Cataloger, South Carolina State Library, 1430-1500 Senate St, Columbia, SC, 29201. Tel: 803-734-8662. Fax: 803-734-8676. p. 2189

Sparling, Kathy, Tech Serv, Ohlone College, 43600 Mission Blvd, Fremont, CA, 94539. Tel: 510-659-6160. Fax: 510-659-6265. p. 149

Sparrow, Joyce, Librn, JWB Children's Services Council of Pinellas County Resource Center, 6698 68th Ave N, Pinellas Park, FL, 33781-5015. Tel: 727-547-5671. Fax: 727-547-5689. p. 483

Spasser, Mark, Dir, Wayne State University Libraries, Vera P Shiffman Medical Library & Learning Resources Centers, Rackham Bldg Rm 044, 60 Farnsworth, Detroit, MI, 48202. Tel: 313-577-6663. Fax: 313-577-6668. p. 1173

Spatz, Michele, Dir, Mid-Columbia Medical Center, 200 E Fourth St, The Dalles, OR, 97058. Tel: 541-296-8444. Fax: 541-296-6054. p. 2021

Spaulding, Amy, Dr, Prof, Long Island University, C W Post Campus, 720 Northern Blvd, Brookville, NY, 11548-1300. Tel: 516-299-2172. Fax: 516-299-4168. p. 2970

Spaulding, Cheryl, Circ Coordr, Dyer Library, 371 Main St, Saco, ME, 04072. Tel: 207-283-3861. Fax: 207-283-0754. p. 999

Spaulding, Julie, Supvr, Victorian Village Health Center, 1087 Dennison Ave, Columbus, OH, 43201. Tel: 614-544-2016. Fax: 614-544-2015. p. 1891

Spaulding, Nancy, Youth Serv, Cedar Mill Community Library, 12505 NW Cornell Rd, Portland, OR, 97229. Tel: 503-644-0043. Fax: 503-644-3964. p. 2010

Spaw, Shawn, Teen Librn, Pulaski County Public Library, 304 S Main St, Somerset, KY, 42501-1402. Tel: 606-679-8401. Fax: 606-679-1779. p. 935

Speaker, Rinann, Media Spec, Wichita Public Library, Planeview Community, 2820 S Roosevelt, Wichita, KS, 67210. Tel: 316-973-7609. p. 901

Spear, Charlotte, Tech Serv, South Portland Public Library, 482 Broadway, South Portland, ME, 04106. Tel: 207-767-7660. Fax: 207-767-7626. p. 1002

Spear, Denise, Cultural Res Spec, Fort Frederica National Monument Library, 6515 Frederica Rd, Saint Simons Island, GA, 31522. Tel: 912-638-3639. Fax: 912-638-3639. p. 549

Spear, Jane, ILL Spec, Frederick County Public Libraries, 110 E Patrick St, Frederick, MD, 21701. Tel: 301-600-1613. Fax: 301-600-3789. p. 1028

Spear, Marge, Ch & Youth Librn, Pocahontas Public Library, 14 Second Ave NW, Pocahontas, IA, 50574. Tel: 712-335-4471. Fax: 712-335-4471. p. 839

Speare, April, Libr Serv Tech, Mohawk College Library, STARRT (Skilled Trades & Apprenticeship Research, Resources & Training) Library, 481 Barton St E, Stoney Creek, ON, L8E 2L7, CANADA. Tel: 905-575-2504, Ext 5028. Fax: 905-575-2549. p. 2810

Spearel, Janet, Principal Librn, Tampa-Hillsborough County Public Library System, Lutz Branch, 101 Lutz Lake Fern Rd W, Lutz, FL, 33548-7220. Fax: 813-264-3907. p. 497

Spearman, DeCarlous, Dir, Texas Southern University, Thurgood Marshall School of Law Library, 3100 Cleburne Ave, Houston, TX, 77004. Tel: 713-313-7328. Fax: 713-313-4483. p. 2342

Spearman, Leander, Dir, Belleville Public Library, 121 E Washington St, Belleville, IL, 62220. Tel: 618-234-0441. Fax: 618-234-9474. p. 593

Spearman, Patricia, In Charge, First Presbyterian Church Library, 200 W Trade St, Charlotte, NC, 28202-1623. Tel: 704-332-5123, Ext 269. Fax: 704-334-4135. p. 1783

Spearpoint, RoseMarie, Br Head, Toronto Public Library, Palmerston, 560 Palmerston Ave, Toronto, ON, M6G 2P7, CANADA. Tel: 416-393-7680. Fax: 416-393-7420. p. 2862

Spears, Barbara, Br Mgr, Prince George's County Memorial, Beltsville Branch, 4319 Sellman Rd, Beltsville, MD, 20705-2543. Tel: 301-937-0294. Fax: 301-595-3455. p. 1032

Spears, Donna Michelle, Res & Instruction Librn, Northern Kentucky University, Nunn Dr, Highland Heights, KY, 41099. Tel: 859-572-6035. Fax: 859-572-6529, 859-572-6664. p. 917

Spears, Joan, Librn, First United Methodist Church Library, 1115 S Boulder, Tulsa, OK, 74119-2492. Tel: 918-587-9481, Ext 152. Fax: 918-584-5228. p. 1980

Spears, John, Exec Dir, Naperville Public Library, 200 W Jefferson Ave, Naperville, IL, 60540-5374. Tel: 630-961-4100, Ext 6151. Fax: 630-637-6389. p. 679

Spears, Lisa, Dir, Attalla-Etowah County Public Library, 604 N Fourth St, Attalla, AL, 35954. Tel: 256-538-9266. Fax: 256-538-9223. p. 5

Spears, Melinda, Librn, MacEwan Grant University Library, South Campus Library, 7319 29th Ave, Edmonton, AB, T6K 2P1, CANADA. Tel: 780-497-4054. Fax: 780-497-4184. p. 2701

Spears, Paula, Circ, Gadsden Public Library, 254 College St, Gadsden, AL, 35901. Tel: 256-549-4699. p. 18

Spears, Shirley K, Dr, Dir, B B Comer Memorial Library, 314 N Broadway, Sylacauga, AL, 35150-2528. Tel: 256-249-0961. p. 36

Speas, Eric, Info Serv, University of Southern Mississippi Library, 118 College Dr, No 5053, Hattiesburg, MS, 39406. Tel: 601-214-3467. Fax: 601-266-6033. p. 1300

Speasl, Tim, Head, Ref, Union County Public Library, 316 E Windsor St, Monroe, NC, 28112. Tel: 704-283-8184. Fax: 704-282-0657. p. 1810

Specht, Alice, Dean, Hardin-Simmons University, 2341 Hickory St, Abilene, TX, 79698. Tel: 325-670-1229. Fax: 325-677-8351. p. 2272

Specht, Elizabeth, Operations Mgr, Roberts Wesleyan College & Northeastern Seminary, 2301 Westside Dr, Rochester, NY, 14624-1997. Tel: 585-594-6816. Fax: 585-594-6543. p. 1731

Specian, Ginger, Dir, LeTourneau University, 2100 S Mobberly Ave, Longview, TX, 75602-3524. Tel: 903-233-3260. Fax: 903-233-3263. p. 2357

Speck, Karen, Tech Support, Ozark-Dale County Public Library, Inc, 416 James St, Ozark, AL, 36360. Tel: 334-774-2399, 334-774-5480. p. 33

Speck, Michele, Electronic Res, Mission College Library, 3000 Mission College Blvd, Santa Clara, CA, 95054-1897. Tel: 408-855-5169. Fax: 408-855-5462. p. 262

Spector, Carol, Govt Doc, University of San Francisco, 2130 Fulton St, San Francisco, CA, 94117-1080. Tel: 415-422-2040. Fax: 415-422-5949. p. 248

Spector, Jennifer, Computer Serv, Thompson Coburn LLP, One US Bank Plaza, Saint Louis, MO, 63101. Tel: 314-552-6000. Fax: 314-552-7382. p. 1361

Speed, Beth, Librn, Woolworth Community Library, 100 E Utah Ave, Jal, NM, 88252. Tel: 505-395-3268. Fax: 505-395-2138. p. 1557

Speed, Tiffany, Br Mgr, Athens Regional Library System, Oglethorpe County, 858 Athens Rd, Lexington, GA, 30648. Tel: 706-743-8817. Fax: 706-743-8817. p. 509

Speer, Laura, Dir of Libr Serv, Fayetteville Public Library, 401 W Mountain St, Fayetteville, AR, 72701. Tel: 479-856-7000. Fax: 479-571-0222. p. 99

Speer, Lisa, Dr, Head, Spec Coll & Archives, Southeast Missouri State University, One University Plaza, Mail Stop 4600, Cape Girardeau, MO, 63701. Tel: 573-986-7446. Fax: 573-651-2666. p. 1322

Speer, Michael, Asst Dir/Ref Librn, Conneaut Public Library, 304 Buffalo St, Conneaut, OH, 44030-2658. Tel: 440-593-1608. Fax: 440-593-4470. p. 1891

Speer, Priscilla, Info Literacy & Ref Librn, Trevecca Nazarene University, 73 Lester Ave, Nashville, TN, 37210-4227. Tel: 615-248-1347. Fax: 615-248-1452. p. 2259

Speer, Priscilla, Asst Prof, Trevecca Nazarene University, School of Education, 333 Murfreesboro Rd, Nashville, TN, 37210-2877. Tel: 615-248-1201, 615-248-1205. Fax: 615-248-1597. p. 2974

Speer, Richard A, Dir, Lewiston Public Library, 200 Lisbon St, Lewiston, ME, 04240. Tel: 207-784-0135, Ext 208. Fax: 207-784-3011. p. 989

Speers, Beth, Librn, Altamont Public Library, 121 W Washington St, Altamont, IL, 62411. Tel: 618-483-5457. Fax: 618-483-5457. p. 588

Spehar, Mary Jane, Info Serv, Chattanooga-Hamilton County Bicentennial Library, 1001 Broad St, Chattanooga, TN, 37402-2652. Tel: 423-757-5429. Fax: 423-757-4994. p. 2226

Speidel, Daniel, Dir, Rivier College, 420 S Main St, Nashua, NH, 03060-5086. Tel: 603-897-8576. Fax: 603-897-8889. p. 1459

Speight, Judy, Dir, White House Inn Library & Museum, 412 Hwy 76, White House, TN, 37188. Tel: 615-672-0239. p. 2268

Speights, Faye, Librn, South Mississippi Regional Library, 900 Broad St, Columbia, MS, 39429. Tel: 601-736-5516. Fax: 601-736-1379. p. 1296

Speights, Faye, Librn, South Mississippi Regional Library, Prentiss Public, PO Box 1315, Prentiss, MS, 39474-1315. Tel: 601-792-5845. Fax: 601-792-8159. p. 1297

Speinmehl, Carrie, Tech Coordr, Hoover Public Library, 200 Municipal Dr, Hoover, AL, 35216. Tel: 205-444-7810. Fax: 205-444-7878. p. 20

Speir, Teresa, In Charge, Grandfield Public Library, 101 W Second St, Grandfield, OK, 73546-9449. Tel: 580-479-5598. Fax: 580-479-5534. p. 1964

Spellmon, Michael, Ref Librn, Groton Public Library, 52 Newtown Rd, Groton, CT, 06340. Tel: 860-441-6750. Fax: 860-448-0363. p. 342

Spelman, Michael, Br Supvr, Madison Public Library, South Madison Branch, 2222 S Park St, Madison, WI, 53713. Tel: 608-266-6395. Fax: 608-266-6303. p. 2607

Spelock, Deannia, Res Mgr, West Virginia Legislative Reference Library, Capitol Bldg, Rm MB 27, Charleston, WV, 25305-0591. Tel: 304-347-4830. Fax: 304-347-4901. p. 2557

Spence, Annie, Ref Librn, Bacon Memorial District Library, 45 Vinewood, Wyandotte, MI, 48192-5221. Tel: 734-246-8357. Fax: 734-282-1540. p. 1237

Spence, Dolly, Asst Dir, Quarryville Library, 357 Buck Rd, Quarryville, PA, 17566. Tel: 717-786-1336. Fax: 717-786-9220. p. 2132

Spence, Elaine, YA Serv, West Linn Public Library, 1595 Burns St, West Linn, OR, 97068-3231. Tel: 503-656-7853, Ext 3030. Fax: 503-656-2746. p. 2022

Spence, Heather, Libr Asst, Borgess Medical Center Library, 1521 Gull Rd, Kalamazoo, MI, 49048-1666. Tel: 269-226-7360. Fax: 269-226-6881. p. 1196

Spence, Judy, Col Librn, YA Librn, Van Alstyne Public Library, 151 W Cooper St, Van Alstyne, TX, 75495. Tel: 903-482-5991. Fax: 903-482-1316. p. 2395

Spence, Paul H, Coll Develop, University of Alabama at Birmingham, Mervyn H Sterne Library, 917 13th St S, Birmingham, AL, 35205. Tel: 205-934-6364. p. 10

Spence, Susan D, Ref Librn, Le Moyne College, 1419 Salt Springs Rd, Syracuse, NY, 13214-1301. Tel: 315-445-4332. Fax: 315-445-4642. p. 1751

Spence Wayne, Dir, Catahoula Parish Library, 300 Bushley St, Harrisonburg, LA, 71340. Tel: 318-744-5271. Fax: 318-744-5251. p. 950

Spence-Wilcox, Sharon, Librn, Seattle Central Community College, 1701 Broadway, 2BE2101, Seattle, WA, 98122. Tel: 206-587-4069. Fax: 206-587-3878. p. 2530

Spencer, Barton, Syst Adminr, University of Southern Mississippi Library, 118 College Dr, No 5053, Hattiesburg, MS, 39406. Tel: 601-266-6177. Fax: 601-266-6033. p. 1300

Spencer, Belinda, Asst Dir, Bedford Public Library, 507 Jefferson, Bedford, IA, 50833-1314. Tel: 712-523-2828. p. 796

Spencer, Beth, Info Res Spec, Fishbeck, Thompson, Carr & Huber, 1515 Arboretum Dr SE, Grand Rapids, MI, 49546. Tel: 616-464-3711. Fax: 616-464-6540. p. 1184

Spencer, Carla, Dir, Corrales Community Library, 84 W La Entrada, Corrales, NM, 87048. Tel: 505-897-0733. Fax: 505-897-0596. p. 1554

Spencer, Carol, Dir, Lahey Clinic Medical Center Library, 41 Mall Rd, Burlington, MA, 01805. Tel: 781-744-8253. Fax: 781-744-3615. p. 1072

Spencer, Cherie, Dir, Tipton County Public Library, 127 E Madison St, Tipton, IN, 46072-1993. Tel: 765-675-8761. Fax: 765-675-4475. p. 782

Spencer, Cherie, Dir, Tipton County Public Library, Windfall Branch, 109 McClellen St, Windfall, IN, 46076. Tel: 765-945-7655. Fax: 765-945-7655. p. 782

Spencer, Darron, Ch, Desoto Parish Library, 109 Crosby St, Mansfield, LA, 71052. Tel: 318-872-6100. Fax: 318-872-6120. p. 955

Spencer, Deirdre, Head of Libr, University of Michigan, Fine Arts Library, 260 Tappan Hall, 519 S State St, Ann Arbor, MI, 48109-1357. Tel: 734-764-5405. Fax: 734-764-5408. p. 1153

Spencer, Dirck, Ref, Sheppard Memorial Library, 530 S Evans St, Greenville, NC, 27858-2308. Tel: 252-329-4580. Fax: 252-329-4587. p. 1799

Spencer, Dorothy A, Dr, Dir, East Carolina University, William E Laupus Health Sciences Library, 600 Moye Blvd, Health Sciences Bldg, Greenville, NC, 27834. Tel: 252-744-2219. Fax: 252-744-2672. p. 1798

Spencer, Eric, Managing Librn II, Sno-Isle Libraries, Marysville Community Library, 6120 Grove St, Marysville, WA, 98270. Tel: 360-658-5000. Fax: 360-659-5050. p. 2542

Spencer, Heather, Circ, University of Wisconsin-Parkside Library, 900 Wood Rd, Kenosha, WI, 53141. Tel: 262-595-2356. Fax: 262-595-2545. p. 2602

Spencer, Heidi, Dir of Libr Serv, American International College, 1000 State St, Springfield, MA, 01109. Tel: 413-205-3461. Fax: 413-205-3904. p. 1126

Spencer, Jane, Dir, Bixby Memorial Free Library, 258 Main St, Vergennes, VT, 05491. Tel: 802-877-2211. Fax: 802-877-2411. p. 2437

Spencer, Jane, Dr, Dir, Libr Serv, Southwestern Michigan College, 58900 Cherry Grove Rd, Dowagiac, MI, 49047. Tel: 269-782-1204. Fax: 269-782-9575. p. 1174

Spencer, Jesse, ILL Librn, Christopher Newport University, One Avenue of the Arts, Newport News, VA, 23606. Tel: 757-594-7130. Fax: 757-594-7717. p. 2479

Spencer, John, Ref Coordr, Gonzaga University, 502 E Boone Ave, Spokane, WA, 99258-0095. Tel: 509-313-6110. Fax: 509-323-5904. p. 2536

Spencer, Judy, Head, Pub Serv, Amherst County Public Library, 382 S Main St, Amherst, VA, 24521. Tel: 434-946-9488. Fax: 434-946-9348. p. 2447

Spencer, LaRene, Coll Develop, Church of Jesus Christ of Latter-Day Saints, 4751 Neil Rd, Reno, NV, 89502. Tel: 775-826-1130. p. 1432

Spencer, Laura, Tech Serv, James V Brown Library of Williamsport & Lycoming County, 19 E Fourth St, Williamsport, PA, 17701-6390. Tel: 570-326-0536. Fax: 570-326-1671. p. 2156

Spencer, Linda, Dir, Carlock Public Library District, 202 E Washington, Carlock, IL, 61725. Tel: 309-376-5651. Fax: 309-376-4027. p. 600

Spencer, Loren, Dir, Church of Jesus Christ of Latter-Day Saints, 4751 Neil Rd, Reno, NV, 89502. Tel: 775-826-1130. p. 1432

Spencer, Marguerite, Asst Dir, Leavenworth Public Library, 417 Spruce St, Leavenworth, KS, 66048. Tel: 913-682-5666. Fax: 913-682-1248. p. 879

Spencer, Mark, In Charge, Hallmark Cards, Inc, 2501 McGee, No 146, Kansas City, MO, 64108. Tel: 816-274-7470. Fax: 816-545-2239. p. 1337

Spencer, Mary, Libr Mgr, Piedmont Regional Library, Statham Public, 1928 Railroad St, Statham, GA, 30666. Tel: 770-725-4785. p. 557

Spencer, Mary, Sci Librn, University of Kentucky Libraries, Science Library, 211 King Bldg, Lexington, KY, 40506-0039. Tel: 859-257-8359. Fax: 859-323-3225. p. 922

Spencer, Mary Ellen, Head, Ref & Res Serv, Virginia Commonwealth University Libraries, James Cabell Branch Library, Monroe Park Campus, 901 Park Ave, Richmond, VA, 23284-2033. Tel: 804-828-2729. Fax: 804-828-0151. p. 2492

Spencer, Meg, Sci Librn, Swarthmore College, 500 College Ave, Swarthmore, PA, 19081-1081. Tel: 610-328-7685. Fax: 610-328-7329. p. 2145

Spencer, Meg E, Sci, Swarthmore College, Cornell Science & Engineering, 500 College Ave, Swarthmore, PA, 19081-1399. Tel: 610-328-7685. Fax: 610-690-5776. p. 2145

Spencer, Megan, Div Mgr, Orem Public Library, 58 N State St, Orem, UT, 84057-5596. Tel: 801-229-7050. Fax: 801-229-7130. p. 2409

Spencer, Melanie, Br Supvr, Boonslick Regional Library, Boonville Branch, 618 Main St, Boonville, MO, 65233. Tel: 660-882-5864. Fax: 660-882-7953. p. 1365

Spencer, Nicole, Librn, Harrisville Free Library, 8209 Main St, Harrisville, NY, 13648. Tel: 315-543-2577. Fax: 315-543-2577. p. 1634

Spencer, Patricia, Pub Info Officer, Lewis & Clark Library, 120 S Last Chance Gulch, Helena, MT, 59601. Tel: 406-447-1690, Ext 124. Fax: 406-447-1687. p. 1382

Spencer, Richard, Mgr, NASA Headquarters Library, 300 E St SW, Rm 1J20, Washington, DC, 20546. Tel: 202-358-0172. Fax: 202-358-3251. p. 409

Spencer, Robert, Br Mgr, Arlington County Department of Libraries, Columbia Pike, 816 S Walter Reed Dr, Arlington, VA, 22204. Tel: 703-228-5711. Fax: 703-228-5559. p. 2448

Spencer, Roxanne, Coordr, Western Kentucky University Libraries, Educational Resources Center, Tate Page Hall, Rm 366, 1906 College Heights Blvd, No 31031, Bowling Green, KY, 42101. Tel: 270-745-4552, 270-745-4659. Fax: 270-745-4553. p. 908

Spencer, Roxanne, Asst Prof, Coordr of Educ Res Ctr, Western Kentucky University, School of Teacher Education, 1092 Gary A Ransdell Hall, Normal St, WKU No 61030, Bowling Green, KY, 42101-1030. Tel: 270-745-3147. Fax: 270-745-6322. p. 2966

Spencer, Sandy, Ref Librn, Mendocino College Library, 1000 Hensley Creek Rd, Ukiah, CA, 95482-7821. Tel: 707-468-3053. Fax: 707-468-3056. p. 277

Spencer, Scott, Librn, Philadelphia Corporation for Aging Library, 642 N Broad St, Philadelphia, PA, 19130-3049. Tel: 215-765-9000, Ext 5062. Fax: 215-765-9066. p. 2114

Spencer, Shannon, Per, Ref, University of Tampa, 401 W Kennedy Blvd, Tampa, FL, 33606-1490. Tel: 813-253-6231. Fax: 813-258-7426. p. 499

Spencer, Sonya, Dir, Lee County Public Library, 123 Center St, Beattyville, KY, 41311. Tel: 606-464-8014. Fax: 606-464-2052. p. 907

Spencer, Stephannie, Asst Librn, Maricopa Community Library, 44240 W Maricopa, Casa Grande Hwy, Maricopa, AZ, 85239. Tel: 520-568-2926. Fax: 520-568-2680. p. 68

Spencer, Stephen, Coll Develop, Wheaton College, 510 Irving Ave, Wheaton, IL, 60187-5593. Tel: 630-752-7104. Fax: 630-752-5855. p. 718

Spencer, Sue, Sch Libr Media, University of North Carolina at Greensboro, School of Education, 349 Curry Bldg, Greensboro, NC, 27402. Tel: 336-334-3373. Fax: 336-334-5060. p. 2971

Spencer, Tina, Ref Serv, Kingsport Public Library & Archives, 400 Broad St, Kingsport, TN, 37660-4292. Tel: 423-224-2539. Fax: 423-224-2558. p. 2240

Spencer, Vickie V, Head, Circ, Reserves, North Carolina Central University, 1801 Fayetteville St, Durham, NC, 27707-3129. Tel: 919-530-7305. Fax: 919-530-7612. p. 1789

Spender, Aurie, Ser, Lancaster Bible College Library, 901 Eden Rd, Lancaster, PA, 17601-5036. Tel: 717-560-8250. Fax: 717-560-8265. p. 2076

Spendlove, Sandra, Dir, Monroe Public Library, 55 N Main St, Monroe, UT, 84754. Tel: 435-527-4019. Fax: 435-527-4622. p. 2408

Spera, Andy, Fac Serv Coordr, Baltimore County Public Library, 320 York Rd, Towson, MD, 21204-5179. Tel: 410-887-6131. Fax: 410-887-6103. p. 1044

Speranza, Ginger, Librn, Washington School for the Deaf, McGill Library, 611 Grand Blvd, Vancouver, WA, 98661-4498. Tel: 360-696-6525, Ext 4352. Fax: 360-418-0418. p. 2546

Sperka, Shelley, Tech Serv, Wofford College, 429 N Church St, Spartanburg, SC, 29303-3663. Tel: 864-597-4300. Fax: 864-597-4329. p. 2206

Sperling, Marion, Archivist, Madison County Historical Museum & Archival Library, 715 N Main St, Edwardsville, IL, 62025-1111. Tel: 618-656-7562, 618-656-7569. Fax: 618-659-3457. p. 639

Sperry, Regina, Dir, Librn, Northwest Regional Library, Winfield Public Library, 185 Ashwood Dr, Winfield, AL, 35594. Tel: 205-487-2484. Fax: 205-487-5146. p. 41

Spetland, Charles G, Coll Develop, University of Minnesota Libraries-Twin Cities, 499 O Meredith Wilson Library, 309 19th Ave S, Minneapolis, MN, 55455-0414. Tel: 612-626-7960. Fax: 612-626-9353. p. 1262

Speyer, Anne, Asst Librn, South Dennis Free Public Library, 389 Main St, South Dennis, MA, 02660. Tel: 508-394-8954. Fax: 508-394-4392. p. 1125

Spice, Joan, Head Librn, Headingley Municipal Library, 49 Alboro St, Headingley, MB, R4J 1A3, CANADA. Tel: 204-888-5410. Fax: 204-831-7207. p. 2749

Spicehandler, Galinas, Librn, Saint John's University Library, Kathryn & Shelby Cullom Davis Library, 101 Murray St, 3rd Flr, New York, NY, 10007. Tel: 212-277-5135. Fax: 212-277-5140. p. 1725

Spicer, Lou, Ch Mgr, Wayne Township Library, 80 N Sixth St, Richmond, IN, 47374-3079. Tel: 765-966-8291. Fax: 765-962-1318. p. 775

Spicer, Udella, Dir of Libr Serv, Moultrie Technical College Library, 800 Veterans Pkwy N, Moultrie, GA, 31788. Tel: 229-891-7020. Fax: 229-891-7010. p. 546

Spickelmier, Pamela, Dir, Saint Luke's Health System Libraries, 190 E Bannock St, Boise, ID, 83712-6297. Tel: 208-381-2276. Fax: 208-381-4317. p. 572

Spickett, Donna, Supvr, Essex County Library, LaSalle Branch, 1555 Talbot Rd, Unit 400, LaSalle, ON, N9H 2N2, CANADA. Tel: 226-946-1529, Ext 210. p. 2804

Spicola, Lisa, Ref Librn, Johnson & Wales University Library, Culinary Library, 321 Harborside Blvd, Providence, RI, 02905. Tel: 401-598-1466. p. 2172

Spied, Vinell, Adult Ref Librn, Newark Public Library, Clinton, 739 Bergen St, Newark, NJ, 07108. Tel: 973-733-7754, 973-733-7757. Fax: 973-733-7757. p. 1512

Spiegel, Maggie, Br Head, Jones Library, Inc, 43 Amity St, Amherst, MA, 01002-2285. Tel: 413-259-3099. Fax: 413-256-4096. p. 1048

Spiegel, Maggie, Br Head, Jones Library, Inc, North Amherst Branch, Eight Montague Rd, Amherst, MA, 01002. Tel: 413-259-3099. p. 1049

Spiegel, Mary Alice, Head, Ch, Cleve J Fredricksen Library, 100 N 19th St, Camp Hill, PA, 17011-3900. Tel: 717-761-3900. Fax: 717-761-5493. p. 2040

Spiegel, Sara, Tech Serv Librn, Jewish Theological Seminary Library, 3080 Broadway, New York, NY, 10027. Tel: 212-678-8093. Fax: 212-678-8891, 212-678-8998. p. 1683

Spiegel, Sarah, Ref Librn, University of Arkansas Libraries, 365 N McIlroy Ave, Fayetteville, AR, 72701-4002. Tel: 479-575-8415. Fax: 479-575-6656. p. 99

Spiegelglass, Howard, AV, Head, Tech Serv, South Huntington Public Library, 145 Pidgeon Hill Rd, Huntington Station, NY, 11746. Tel: 631-549-4411. Fax: 631-549-1266. p. 1639

Spiegelman, Marsha, Ref, Nassau Community College, One Education Dr, Garden City, NY, 11530-6793. Tel: 516-572-7400. Fax: 516-572-7846. p. 1626

Spiegler, Julie, Br Mgr, Kanawha County Public Library, Cross Lanes, 5449 Big Tyler Rd, Charleston, WV, 25313. Tel: 304-776-5999. Fax: 304-776-6005. p. 2556

Spiel, Karen, Regional Mgr, Seattle Public Library, Green Lake, 7364 E Green Lake Dr N, Seattle, WA, 98115. Tel: 206-684-7547. p. 2531

Spiel, Karen, Regional Mgr, Seattle Public Library, Wallingford, 1501 N 45th St, Seattle, WA, 98103. Tel: 206-684-4088. p. 2532

Spieldenner, E Brooke, Libr Commun Serv Mgr, Richmond Public Library, West End, 5420 Patterson Ave, Richmond, VA, 23226. Tel: 804-646-1877. Fax: 804-646-3769. p. 2490

Spiese, Kelly, Cat Librn, Wilson College, 1015 Philadelphia Avenue, Chambersburg, PA, 17201-1285. Tel: 717-264-4141, Ext 3295. Fax: 717-263-7194. p. 2043

Spiess, Patricia, Dir, La Crosse Public Library, 307 E Main St, La Crosse, IN, 46348. Tel: 219-754-2606. Fax: 219-754-2606. p. 758

Spiess, Rhonda, Br Mgr, Saint Tammany Parish Library, Lacombe Branch, 28027 Hwy 190, Lacombe, LA, 70445. Tel: 985-882-7858. Fax: 985-882-8072. p. 948

Spiewak, Donna, Asst Dir, Green Hills Public Library District, 8611 W 103rd St, Palos Hills, IL, 60465. Tel: 708-598-8446, Ext 21. Fax: 708-598-0856. p. 687

Spiker, Susan, Info Serv Librn, Viterbo University, 900 Viterbo Dr, La Crosse, WI, 54601. Tel: 608-796-3267. Fax: 608-796-3275. p. 2603

Spikes, Denita, Acq, Middle Georgia Regional Library System, 1180 Washington Ave, Macon, GA, 31201-1790. Tel: 478-744-0817. Fax: 478-742-3161. p. 541

Spikes, Janet, Librn, Woodrow Wilson International Center for Scholars Library, 1300 Pennsylvania Ave NW, Washington, DC, 20004-3027. Tel: 202-691-4150. Fax: 202-691-4001. p. 423

Spikes, Janet, Librn, Woodrow Wilson International Center for Scholars Library, Kennan Institute for Advanced Russian Studies Library, 1300 Pennsylvania Ave NW, Washington, DC, 20004-3027. Tel: 202-691-4198. p. 423

Spiliopoulos, Gus, Ch, Parsons Memorial Library, 27 Saco Rd, Alfred, ME, 04002. Tel: 207-324-2001. Fax: 207-324-2001. p. 973

Spilker, Chris, Dir, Sacred Heart Major Seminary, 2701 Chicago Blvd, Detroit, MI, 48206. Tel: 313-883-8651. Fax: 313-868-8594. p. 1171

Spilker, Christopher, Dir of Libr, Detroit Area Consortium of Catholic Colleges, c/o Sacred Heart Seminary, 2701 Chicago Blvd, Detroit, MI, 48206. Tel: 313-883-8500. Fax: 313-883-8594. p. 2946

Spillane, Nancy, Ch, Flesh Public Library, 124 W Greene St, Piqua, OH, 45356-2399. Tel: 937-773-6753. Fax: 937-773-5981. p. 1930

Spiller, Virginia, Librn, Old York Historical Society Library, 207 York St, York, ME, 03909. Tel: 207-363-4974. Fax: 207-363-4021. p. 1008

Spillman, Alice, Librn, Santa Anna Library, 606 Wallis Ave, Santa Anna, TX, 76878-2031. Tel: 325-348-3395. p. 2385

Spillman, Brenda G, ILL, Brevard College, One Brevard College Dr, Brevard, NC, 28712-4283. Tel: 828-884-8268. p. 1777

Spillman, Effie, Tech Serv, Ohio State University LIBRARIES, John A Prior Health Sciences Library, 376 W Tenth Ave, Columbus, OH, 43210-1240. Tel: 614-688-4616. Fax: 614-292-1920. p. 1889

Spillman, Jennifer, Mgr, Ad Serv, Dayton Metro Library, 215 E Third St, Dayton, OH, 45402-2103. Tel: 937-463-2665. Fax: 937-496-4300. p. 1892

Spillman, Susan, Computer Instrul Serv Librn, South Texas College of Law, 1303 San Jacinto St, Houston, TX, 77002-7000. Tel: 713-646-1711. Fax: 713-659-2217. p. 2342

Spillum, Kirsten, Circ Mgr, University of Washington Libraries, Allen Library, 4th Flr, Rm 482, Box 352900, Seattle, WA, 98195-2900. Tel: 206-685-3987. Fax: 206-685-6972. p. 2533

Spilman, Karen, Librn, National Cowboy & Western Heritage Museum, 1700 NE 63rd St, Oklahoma City, OK, 73111. Tel: 405-478-2250. Fax: 405-478-6421. p. 1973

Spilver, Becky, Coll Spec, Douglas County Libraries, Roxborough, 8357 N Rampart Range Rd, Ste 200, Littleton, CO, 80125. Tel: 303-791-7323. p. 294

Spina, Marie, Archivist, Fiorello H LaGuardia Community College Library, 31-10 Thomson Ave, Long Island City, NY, 11101. Tel: 718-482-5421. Fax: 718-482-5444, 718-609-2011. p. 1654

Spinas, George, Ref Librn, Mendocino College Library, 1000 Hensley Creek Rd, Ukiah, CA, 95482-7821. Tel: 707-468-3053. Fax: 707-468-3056. p. 277

Spinazola, Madonna, Gen Mgr, Destination Southwest Nova Scotia Association Library, PO Box 416, Kentville, NS, B4N 3X1, CANADA. Tel: 902-697-3500. Fax: 902-697-3505. p. 2783

Spindel, Dale, Dir, Kenilworth Public Library, 548 Blvd, Kenilworth, NJ, 07033. Tel: 908-276-2451. Fax: 908-276-7897. p. 1493

Spindler, Robert, Archivist, Arizona State University Libraries, 300 E Orange Mall Dr, Tempe, AZ, 85287-1006. Tel: 480-965-9277. Fax: 480-965-9169. p. 83

Spinelli, Christopher, Visual Res, New York School of Interior Design Library, 170 E 70th St, New York, NY, 10021. Tel: 212-472-1500, Ext 215. Fax: 212-472-8175. p. 1694

Spinks, Jeff, Med Librn, Lutheran Medical Center School of Nursing & Medical Staff Library, 3547 S Jefferson, Saint Louis, MO, 63118. Tel: 314-577-5864. Fax: 314-268-6160. p. 1356

Spinney, John, Electronic Res, Ref Serv, Norfolk Public Library, 139 Main St, Norfolk, MA, 02056. Tel: 508-528-3380. Fax: 508-528-6417. p. 1111

Spinney, Molly P, Dir, Westminster College, S Market St, New Wilmington, PA, 16172-0001. Tel: 724-946-7330. Fax: 724-946-6220. p. 2097

Spires, Todd, Coll Develop Librn, Bradley University, 1501 W Bradley Ave, Peoria, IL, 61625. Tel: 309-677-2850. Fax: 309-677-2558. p. 690

Spirko, Gene, Dir, Communication & Power Industries, 150 Sohier Rd, Beverly, MA, 01915-5595. Tel: 978-922-6000. Fax: 978-922-8914. p. 1053

Spiro, Kathy, Libr Asst, Smithers Public Library, 3817 Alfred Ave, Box 55, Smithers, BC, V0J 2N0, CANADA. Tel: 250-847-3043. Fax: 250-847-1533. p. 2737

Spisak, Rita, Librn, Libr Instruction/Outreach, Kennesaw State University, 1000 Chastain Rd, Kennesaw, GA, 30144. Tel: 770-423-6188. Fax: 770-423-6185. p. 537

Spiteri, Louise, Dr, Assoc Prof, Dalhousie University, 6100 University Ave, Halifax, NS, B3H 3J5, CANADA. Tel: 902-494-3656. Fax: 902-494-2451. p. 2978

Spitler, Karen, Br Mgr, Campbell County Public Library District, Philip N Carrico Branch, 1000 Highland Ave, Fort Thomas, KY, 41075. Tel: 859-572-5033. Fax: 859-572-5038. p. 909

Spittler, Kay, Ch, Clinton Public Library, 306 Eighth Ave S, Clinton, IA, 52732. Tel: 563-242-8441. Fax: 563-242-8162. p. 803

Spitz, Kara, Dir, Longview Public Library, 222 W Cotton St, Longview, TX, 75601-6348. Tel: 903-237-1340. Fax: 903-237-1327. p. 2357

Spitzer, Nancy, Patents & Tech Rpt Librn, University of Wisconsin-Madison, Kurt Wendt Engineering Library, 215 N Randall Ave, Madison, WI, 53706. Tel: 608-262-3493. Fax: 608-262-4739, 608-265-8751. p. 2610

Spitzzeri, Paul R, Coll Mgr, Workman & Temple Family Homestead Museum Library, 15415 E Don Julian Rd, City of Industry, CA, 91745-1029. Tel: 626-968-8492. Fax: 626-968-2048. p. 134

Spivak, Howard, Dr, Info Tech Dir, Syst Coordr, Brooklyn College Library, 2900 Bedford Ave, Brooklyn, NY, 11210-2889. Tel: 718-951-5336. Fax: 718-951-4540. p. 1589

Spivey, Andrew, Brother, Ref Spec, Belmont Abbey College, 100 Belmont-Mt Holly Rd, Belmont, NC, 28012. Tel: 704-461-6748. Fax: 704-461-6743. p. 1776

Spivey, Debbie, Supvr, City of Kawartha Lakes Public Library, 190 Kent St W, Lindsay, ON, K9V 2Y6, CANADA. Tel: 705-324-9411, Ext 1291. Fax: 705-878-1859. p. 2816

Spivey, Debbie, Supvr, City of Kawartha Lakes Public Library, Fenelon Falls Branch, 19 Market St, Fenelon Falls, ON, K0M 1N0, CANADA. Tel: 705-887-6300. Fax: 705-887-1532. p. 2816

Spivey, Linda, Prog Mgr, Montgomery-Floyd Regional Library System, 125 Sheltman St, Christiansburg, VA, 24073. Tel: 540-382-6965. Fax: 540-382-6964. p. 2457

Spivey, Mark A, PhD, Info Literacy Librn, Bryant & Stratton College Library, 301 Centre Pointe Dr, Virginia Beach, VA, 23462. Tel: 757-499-7900. Fax: 757-499-9977. p. 2498

Spivey, Melissa, Br Mgr, Iredell County Public Library, Harmony Branch, 3393 Harmony Hwy, Harmony, NC, 28634. Tel: 704-546-7086. Fax: 704-546-7549. p. 1826

Spivey, Peggy, Librn, American Rose Society Library, 8877 Jefferson Paige Rd, Shreveport, LA, 71119-8817. Tel: 318-938-5402. Fax: 318-938-5405. p. 967

Spivey, Susan, Librn, Lorain Public Library System, North Ridgeville Branch, 35700 Bainbridge Rd, North Ridgeville, OH, 44039. Tel: 440-327-8326. Fax: 440-327-4443. p. 1911

Spivey, Theresa, Head, Mat Mgt, Lincoln Parish Library, 910 N Trenton St, Ruston, LA, 71270-3328. Tel: 318-513-6426. Fax: 318-251-5045. p. 966

Spleas, Denise, Admin Prog Mgr II, University of Wisconsin Colleges, 1500 University Dr, Waukesha, WI, 53188. Tel: 262-521-5473. Fax: 262-521-5116. p. 2645

Splitt, Kimberly, Children's Coll Develop, Walnut Public Library District, 101 Heaton, Walnut, IL, 61376. Tel: 815-379-2159. Fax: 815-379-2159. p. 715

Spoerri, Anselm, Asst Prof, Rutgers, The State University of New Jersey, Four Huntington St, New Brunswick, NJ, 08901-1071. Tel: 732-932-7500, Ext 8955. Fax: 732-932-2644. p. 2969

Spohn, Melissa, Acq Librn, Kent State University Libraries, 1125 Risman Dr, Kent, OH, 44242. Tel: 330-672-1682. Fax: 330-672-3463. p. 1907

Spohrer, Elisabeth, Head, Tech Serv, University of California, Berkeley, Jean Gray Hargrove Music Library, Hargrove Music Library, Berkeley, CA, 94720-6000. Tel: 510-642-2623. Fax: 510-642-8237. p. 128

Sponaugle, Carol, Librn, Raleigh County Public Library, Shady Spring Branch, 440 Flat Top Rd, Shady Spring, WV, 25918. Tel: 304-763-2681. Fax: 304-763-3940. p. 2554

Spongberg, Janet, Circ Coordr, Smith College Libraries, Werner Josten Performing Arts Library, Mendenhall Ctr for the Performing Arts, Northampton, MA, 01063. Tel: 413-585-2932. Fax: 413-585-3930. p. 1114

Spongberg, Larry, Supvr (Weekend), Assumption College, 500 Salisbury St, Worcester, MA, 01609. Tel: 508-767-7135. Fax: 508-767-7374. p. 1143

Sponsel, Eleanor, Librn, Cambridge Public Library District, 212 W Center St, Cambridge, IL, 61238-1239. Tel: 309-937-2233. Fax: 309-937-2873. p. 599

Sponsel, Mary, Access Serv, Regis University, 3333 Regis Blvd, Denver, CO, 80221-1099. Tel: 303-458-4030. Fax: 303-964-5497. p. 303

Spoo, Melanie, In Charge, United States National Park Service, 74485 National Park Dr, Twentynine Palms, CA, 92277. Tel: 760-367-5571. Fax: 760-367-5588. p. 277

Spoon, Buddy, Info Spec, Hickory Public Library, 375 Third St NE, Hickory, NC, 28601-5126. Tel: 828-304-0500, Ext 7279. Fax: 828-304-0023. p. 1801

Spooner, Geraldine, Librn, Buck Memorial Library, 47 Main St, Bucksport, ME, 04416. Tel: 207-469-2650. p. 980

Spooner, Jessica, Instrul Support Assoc, Tech Serv, State University of New York College of Technology, 34 Cornell Dr, Canton, NY, 13617-1098. Tel: 315-386-7054. Fax: 315-386-7931. p. 1602

Spooner, Marilyn, Librn, Patten-North Haverhill Library, 2885 Dartmouth College Hwy, North Haverhill, NH, 03774-4533. Tel: 603-787-2542. p. 1461

Spooner, Pam, Head Librn, Austin Community College, South Austin Campus Library, 1820 W Stassney Lane, Austin, TX, 78745. Tel: 512-223-9184. Fax: 512-223-9190. p. 2278

Spoor, Holly, Br Mgr, Cass District Library, Mason-Union, 17049 US 12 E, Edwardsburg, MI, 49112. Tel: 269-641-7674. Fax: 269-641-7674. p. 1161

Spoor, Nicole, Info Res Librn, Hampton University, 130 E Tyler St, Hampton, VA, 23668. Tel: 757-727-5179. Fax: 757-727-5952. p. 2468

Spoor, Pamela J, Head, Ref, Manistee County Library, 95 Maple St, Manistee, MI, 49660. Tel: 231-723-2510, 231-723-2519. Fax: 231-723-8270. p. 1205

Spotteck, Susan, Tech Info Spec, United States Department of Justice, MCB No 4, Quantico, VA, 22135. Tel: 703-632-3217. Fax: 703-632-3214. p. 2487

Spottswood, Veronica, Acq, Park University Library, 8700 NW River Park Dr, Parkville, MO, 64152. Tel: 816-741-2000, Ext 6284. Fax: 816-741-4911. p. 1349

Spozio, Catherine, Ref, Sr Info Res Spec, Federal Reserve Bank of Boston, 600 Atlantic Ave, Boston, MA, 02210-2204. Tel: 617-973-3393. Fax: 617-973-4221. p. 1061

Spracklen, Lisa Marie, Co-Dir, Marrowbone Public Library District, 216 W Main St, Bethany, IL, 61914. Tel: 217-665-3014. Fax: 217-665-3246. p. 595

Spradley, Patsy, Libr Dir, Doris Stanley Memorial Library, 1515 Bookmark Lane, Moody, AL, 35004. Tel: 205-640-2517. Fax: 205-640-2534. p. 31

Spradling, David, Cent Libr Serv Mgr, Austin Public Library, 800 Guadalupe St, Austin, TX, 78701. Tel: 512-974-7437. p. 2278

Spragen, Nancy, Librn, Logan County Libraries, West Liberty Branch, 117 N Detroit, West Liberty, OH, 43357. Tel: 937-465-3656. p. 1859

Spragg, Lorraine, Librn, Toronto Mendelssohn Choir Library, 60 Simcoe St, Toronto, ON, M5J 2H5, CANADA. Tel: 416-598-0422, Ext 26. Fax: 416-598-2992. p. 2859

Sprague, Arlene, Ch, The Morristown & Morris Township Library, One Miller Rd, Morristown, NJ, 07960. Tel: 973-538-6161. Fax: 973-267-4064. p. 1505

Sprague, Elaine, Asst Dir, Harlan Community Library, 718 Court St, Harlan, IA, 51537. Tel: 712-755-5934. Fax: 712-755-3952. p. 820

Sprague, Jennifer, Dir, Saint John's College, 1160 Camino Cruz Blanca, Santa Fe, NM, 87505. Tel: 505-984-6041. Fax: 505-984-6004. p. 1563

Sprague, Kelly, Circ, Framingham Public Library, 49 Lexington St, Framingham, MA, 01702-8278. Tel: 508-879-5570, Ext 4345. Fax: 508-820-7210. p. 1090

Sprague, Lisa, Pub Serv, Enfield Public Library, 104 Middle Rd, Enfield, CT, 06082. Tel: 860-763-7510. Fax: 860-763-7514. p. 338

Sprague, Michelle, Tech Serv, Culinary Institute of America, 1946 Campus Dr, Hyde Park, NY, 12538-1499. Tel: 845-451-1747. Fax: 845-451-1092. p. 1639

Sprague, Suzanne, Assoc Dir, Electronic Libr Serv, Embry-Riddle Aeronautical University, 600 S Clyde Morris Blvd, Daytona Beach, FL, 32114-3900. Tel: 386-226-6932. Fax: 386-226-6368. p. 436

Sprain, Mara, Librn, National Oceanic & Atmospheric Administration, 151 Patton Ave, Asheville, NC, 28801-5001. Tel: 828-271-4677. Fax: 828-271-4009. p. 1775

Spratlin Hasskarl, Marie, Libr Dir, Burlington Public Library, 34 Library Lane, Burlington, CT, 06013. Tel: 860-673-3331. Fax: 860-673-0897. p. 333

Spratt, Cathy, Ch, Carlisle Public Library, 135 School St, Carlisle, IA, 50047-8702. Tel: 515-989-0909. Fax: 515-989-4328. p. 798

Spratt, Debra, Dir, Lawrence Public Library, 15 Main St, Pepperell, MA, 01463. Tel: 978-433-0330. Fax: 978-433-0317. p. 1117

Spratt, Hazel, Mgr, Edmonton Public Library, Riverbend, 460 Riverbend Sq, Rabbit Hill Rd & Terwillegar Dr, Edmonton, AB, T6R 2X2, CANADA. Tel: 780-944-5311. Fax: 780-944-5327. p. 2700

Spratt, Jackie, Circ Mgr, Bellwood Public Library, 600 Bohland Ave, Bellwood, IL, 60104-1896. Tel: 708-547-7393. Fax: 708-547-9352. p. 593

Spreen, Marilyn, Ch, Northminster Presbyterian Church Library, 703 Compton Rd, Cincinnati, OH, 45231. Tel: 513-931-0243. Fax: 513-931-0260. p. 1871

Spreng, Kristy, Ch, Loudonville Public Library, 122 E Main St, Loudonville, OH, 44842-1267. Tel: 419-994-5531. Fax: 419-994-4321. p. 1911

Sprenkle, P Edward, Adjunct Fac Librn, HACC Central Pennsylvania's Community College, 731 Old Harrisburg Rd, Gettysburg, PA, 17325. Tel: 717-337-1644. Fax: 717-337-2329. p. 2060

Sprenne, Shirley, Br Mgr, Lexington County Public Library System, Pelion Branch, 206 Pine St, Pelion, SC, 29123. Tel: 803-785-3272. Fax: 803-785-7651. p. 2199

Sprick, Diane, Ref Serv, Ad, Ohio Township Public Library System, 4111 Lakeshore Dr, Newburgh, IN, 47630-2274. Tel: 812-853-5468. Fax: 812-853-0509. p. 768

Spriester, Rebecca, Dir, Ellsworth Community College, 1100 College Ave, Iowa Falls, IA, 50126-1199. Tel: 641-648-4611, Ext 233. Fax: 641-648-3128. p. 824

Spriggs, Joan, ILL, Eagle Public Library, 100 N Stierman Way, Eagle, ID, 83616-5162. Tel: 208-939-6814. Fax: 208-939-1359. p. 574

Spring, Martha, Head, Ser & Electronic Res, Loyola University Chicago Libraries, Elizabeth M Cudahy Memorial Library, 6525 N Sheridan Rd, Chicago, IL, 60626. Tel: 773-508-2650. p. 617

Spring, Michael, Assoc Prof, University of Pittsburgh, 135 N Bellefield Ave, Pittsburgh, PA, 15260. Tel: 412-624-5230. Fax: 412-624-5231. p. 2973

Spring, Peggy, Br Librn, Community District Library, Corunna/Caledonia Township Branch, 210 E Corunna Ave, Corunna, MI, 48817. Tel: 989-743-4800. Fax: 989-743-5502. p. 1166

Spring, Rosalyn, Br Mgr, Mid-Continent Public Library, Antioch Branch, 6060 N Chestnut Ave, Gladstone, MO, 64119-1845. Tel: 816-454-1306. Fax: 816-454-7111. p. 1332

Springer, Amy, Govt & Bus Info Librn, Saint John's University, 2835 Abbey Plaza, Collegeville, MN, 56321. Tel: 320-363-2601. Fax: 320-363-2126. p. 1246

Springer, Amy, Govt & Bus Info Librn, College of Saint Benedict, 37 S College Ave, Saint Joseph, MN, 56374. Tel: 320-363-2601. Fax: 320-363-5197. p. 1277

Springer, Cheryl, Dir, Dulany Memorial Library, 501 S Broadway, Salisbury, MO, 65281. Tel: 660-388-5712. Fax: 660-388-5712. p. 1364

Springer, Elizabeth, Ch, Alexandria Library, Kate Waller Barrett Branch, 717 Queen St, Alexandria, VA, 22314. Tel: 703-746-1703. Fax: 703-746-1709. p. 2444

Springer, Joe A, Curator, Goshen College, Mennonite Historical Library, 1700 S Main, Goshen, IN, 46526. Tel: 574-535-7418. Fax: 574-535-7438. p. 746

Springer, John, Computer Serv, Geauga County Public Library, 12701 Ravenwood Dr, Chardon, OH, 44024-1336. Tel: 440-286-6811, 440-564-7131, 440-834-1856. Fax: 440-286-7419. p. 1866

Springer, Judy, Librn, Hanover Public Library, 205 Jackson St, Hanover, KS, 66945-8874. Tel: 785-337-2424. p. 870

Springer, Kathy, Asst Librn, Chinook Regional Library, Gull Lake Branch, 1377 Conrad Ave, Gull Lake, SK, S0N 1A0, CANADA. Tel: 306-672-3277. p. 2928

Springer, Katie, Coordr, Indiana State Data Center, Indiana State Library, 315 W Ohio St, Indianapolis, IN, 46202. Tel: 317-232-3733. Fax: 317-232-3728. p. 2943

Springer, Kelley, County Librn, West Georgia Regional Library, Douglas County Public Library, 6810 Selman Dr, Douglasville, GA, 30134. Tel: 770-920-7125. Fax: 770-920-3121. p. 524

Springer, Kristine, Br Mgr, Saint Joseph County Public Library, German Township Branch Library, 52807 Lynnewood Ave, South Bend, IN, 46628. Tel: 574-271-5144. p. 779

Springer, Larry, Dir, Morgan County Public Library, 105 Congress St, Berkeley Springs, WV, 25411. Tel: 304-258-3350. Fax: 304-258-3350. p. 2554

Springer, Rosie, Ref Serv, State Historical Society of Iowa-Des Moines Library, 600 E Locust, Des Moines, IA, 50319-0290. Tel: 515-281-6200. Fax: 515-282-0502. p. 810

Springer, Susan, Dir of Libr, Belhaven University, 1500 Peachtree St, Jackson, MS, 39202. Tel: 601-968-5947. Fax: 601-968-5968. p. 1303

Springer, Tamara, Human Res Mgr, Salt Lake County Library Services, 2197 E Fort Union Blvd, Salt Lake City, UT, 84121-3139. Tel: 801-943-4636. Fax: 801-942-6323. p. 2413

Springer-Ali, Nadja, Librn, Ref, Oakland Community College, 27055 Orchard Lake Rd, Bldg K, Farmington Hills, MI, 48334-4579. Tel: 248-522-3531. Fax: 248-522-3530. p. 1178

Springfield, Edwin, Asst Librn, Little Big Horn College Library, One Forestry Lane, Crow Agency, MT, 59022. Tel: 406-638-3160. Fax: 406-638-3170. p. 1377

Springston, Lorna, Dir, Libr Serv, Ball Memorial Hospital, 2401 W University Ave, Muncie, IN, 47303-3499. Tel: 765-747-4229. Fax: 765-747-0137. p. 766

Sprinkle-Hamlin, Sylvia, Dir, Forsyth County Public Library, 660 W Fifth St, Winston-Salem, NC, 27101. Tel: 336-703-3016. Fax: 336-727-2549. p. 1832

Sproat, Rebeccah, Librn, Tacoma Community College Library, 6501 S 19th St, Tacoma, WA, 98466-6100. Tel: 253-566-6028. Fax: 253-566-5398. p. 2540

Sproles, Emily, Bus Mgr, Saline County Public Library, 1800 Smithers Dr, Benton, AR, 72015. Tel: 501-778-4766. Fax: 501-778-0536. p. 95

Sproule, Anne, Asst Librn, Chinook Regional Library, Lafleche Branch, 157 Main St, Lafleche, SK, S0H 2K0, CANADA. Tel: 306-472-5466. p. 2928

Sprowls, Pat, Adult Serv, Elk City Carnegie Library, 221 W Broadway, Elk City, OK, 73644. Tel: 580-225-0136. Fax: 580-225-1051. p. 1963

Sproxton, Karen, In Charge, City of Kawartha Lakes Public Library, Little Britain Branch, Nine Arena Rd, Little Britain, ON, K0M 2C0, CANADA. Tel: 705-786-2088. Fax: 705-786-0375. p. 2816

Spruill, Barbara, Div Dir, Br Serv, Gwinnett County Public Library, 1001 Lawrenceville Hwy NW, Lawrenceville, GA, 30046-4707. Tel: 678-985-6078. p. 538

Spruill, Octavious, Head, Access Serv, North Carolina Agricultural & Technical State University, 1601 E Market St, Greensboro, NC, 27411-0002. Tel: 336-334-7617, Ext 3221. Fax: 336-334-7783. p. 1797

Spurgeon, Katherine, Br Mgr, Lake County Library System, Marion Baysinger Memorial County Library, 756 W Broad St, Groveland, FL, 34736. Tel: 352-429-5840. Fax: 352-429-9924. p. 500

Spurlin, Candice, Ref, University of South Dakota, McKusick Law Library, 414 E Clark St, Vermillion, SD, 57069-2390. Tel: 605-677-5259. Fax: 605-677-5417. p. 2220

Spurlin, Sharon, Pub Serv, Polk County Public Library, 1289 W Mills St, Columbus, NC, 28722. Tel: 828-894-8721. Fax: 828-894-2761. p. 1785

Spurlock, Gayla, Br Mgr, Mid-Continent Public Library, Colbern Road Branch, 1000 NE Colbern Rd, Lee's Summit, MO, 64086-5811. Tel: 816-525-9924. Fax: 816-525-3682. p. 1332

Spurlock, Jackie, Librn, Fort Vancouver Regional Library District, Battle Ground Community Library, 1207 SE Eighth Way, Battle Ground, WA, 98604. Tel: 360-687-2322. p. 2546

Spurlock, Stephanie, Br Mgr, Lane Public Libraries, Fairfield Lane Library, 1485 Corydale Dr, Fairfield, OH, 45014. Tel: 513-858-3238. Fax: 513-858-3298. p. 1904

Spurr, Gary, Coll Archivist, Tarleton State University Library, 201 Saint Felix, Stephenville, TX, 76401. Tel: 254-968-1808. Fax: 254-968-9467. p. 2389

Spurrell, Julie, Chief Librn, New Westminster Public Library, 716 Sixth Ave, New Westminster, BC, V3M 2B3, CANADA. Tel: 604-527-4675. Fax: 604-527-4674. p. 2734

Spurrier, Jennifer, Assoc Dean of Libr, Texas Tech University Libraries, 18th & Boston Ave, Lubbock, TX, 79409-0002. Tel: 806-742-2261. Fax: 806-742-0737. p. 2358

Spurrier-Bright, Patricia, Exec Dir, United States Cavalry Association, Bldg 247, Cameron Ave, Fort Riley, KS, 66442. Tel: 785-784-5797. Fax: 785-784-5797. p. 867

Spybuck, Crystal, Librn, Blanco County South Library District, 1118 Main St, Blanco, TX, 78606. Tel: 830-833-4280. Fax: 830-833-2680. p. 2290

Spyra, Rosemarie, Cat, D'Youville College, 320 Porter Ave, Buffalo, NY, 14201-1084. Tel: 716-829-8106. Fax: 716-829-7770. p. 1597

Squicciarini, Lisa, Coordr, Peconic Bay Medical Center, 1300 Roanoke Ave, Riverhead, NY, 11901-2058. Tel: 631-548-6000. Fax: 631-727-0772. p. 1728

Squicciarini, Stephanie, Teen Serv, Fairport Public Library, One Fairport Village Landing, Fairport, NY, 14450. Tel: 585-223-9091. Fax: 585-223-3998. p. 1621

Squier, Carol, Asst Librn, Brenizer Public Library, 430 W Center Ave, Merna, NE, 68856. Tel: 308-643-2268. Fax: 308-643-2268. p. 1408

Squier-Klein, Cynthia, Dir, Chesterfield Public Library, 408 Main Rd, Chesterfield, MA, 01012-9708. Tel: 413-296-4735. p. 1080

Squillante, Michael, Dir, Elwood Public Library, 1929 Jericho Tpk, East Northport, NY, 11731. Tel: 631-499-3722. Fax: 631-499-0057. p. 1617

Squire, Martha, Mgr, Heald College, 2910 Prospect Park Dr, Rancho Cordova, CA, 95670. Tel: 916-638-1616. Fax: 916-414-2676. p. 212

Squires, Bradley, Pub Serv Librn, North Las Vegas Library District, Alexander Library, 1755 W Alexander Rd, North Las Vegas, NV, 89032. Tel: 702-633-2880. Fax: 702-399-9813. p. 1432

Squires, Elizabeth, Br Mgr, Timberland Regional Library, Packwood Branch, 109 W Main St, Packwood, WA, 98361. Tel: 360-494-5111. Fax: 360-494-9237. p. 2544

Squires, Lorraine, YA Serv, Mastics-Moriches-Shirley Community Library, 407 William Floyd Pkwy, Shirley, NY, 11967. Tel: 631-399-1511. Fax: 631-281-4442. p. 1743

Squires, Richard, Coll Develop, Monroe Community College, LeRoy V Good Library, 1000 E Henrietta Rd, Rochester, NY, 14692. Tel: 585-292-2314. p. 1730

Srebro, Michele, Dir, Johnson College Library, 3427 N Main Ave, Scranton, PA, 18508-1995. Tel: 570-702-8953. Fax: 570-348-2181. p. 2137

Sridaran, Geetha, Asst Dir, Life University, 1269 Barclay Circle, Marietta, GA, 30060. Tel: 770-426-2691. Fax: 770-426-2745. p. 543

Srikanth, Radha, Circ, University of Connecticut at Stamford, One University Pl, Stamford, CT, 06901-2315. Tel: 203-251-8438. Fax: 203-251-8501. p. 370

Sritongsook, Sondhaya, Med Librn, Scripps Mercy Hospital Medical Library, 4077 Fifth Ave, MER-36, San Diego, CA, 92103-2180. Tel: 619-260-7024. Fax: 619-260-7262. p. 238

Srivastava, Rosalind, Tech Serv, Paul, Hastings, Janofsky & Walker LLP, 515 S Flower, 25th Flr, Los Angeles, CA, 90071. Tel: 213-683-5037. Fax: 213-627-0705. p. 176

Srypek, Amy, Tech Coordr, Faegre & Benson, LLP, 2200 Wells Fargo Ctr, 90 South Seventh St, Minneapolis, MN, 55402-3901. Tel: 612-766-7000. Fax: 612-766-1600. p. 1259

St Amant, Kyara, Dir of Tech Serv, New Orleans Baptist Theological Seminary, 4110 Seminary Pl, New Orleans, LA, 70126. Tel: 504-282-4455, Ext 3227. Fax: 504-816-8429. p. 961

St Amour, Angele, Tech Serv, University of Sudbury Library, 935 Ramsey Lake Rd, Sudbury, ON, P3E 2C6, CANADA. Tel: 705-673-5661, Ext 207. Fax: 705-673-4912. p. 2847

St Amour, Cynthia, Dir, Swansea Free Public Library, 69 Main St, Swansea, MA, 02777. Tel: 508-674-9609. Fax: 508-675-5444. p. 1130

St Amour, Lyzane, Online Serv, Ref, Pratt & Whitney Canada, Inc Library, 1000 Blvd Marie-Victorin, MS 01RA4, Longueuil, QC, J4G 1A1, CANADA. Tel: 450-677-9411, Ext 2607. Fax: 450-647-9469. p. 2887

St Arnaud, Denise, Chief Librn, Prince Rupert Library, 101 Sixth Ave W, Prince Rupert, BC, V8J 1Y9, CANADA. Tel: 250-627-1345. Fax: 250-627-7743. p. 2736

St Aubin, Kendra, Coll Develop, Bridgewater State College, Ten Shaw Rd, Bridgewater, MA, 02325. Tel: 508-531-2035. Fax: 508-531-1349, 508-531-6103. p. 1070

St Clair, Ann, Dir, Montana Tech Library, 1300 W Park St, Butte, MT, 59701-8997. Tel: 406-496-4284. Fax: 406-496-4133. p. 1376

St Clair, Catherine, Librn, Anaheim Public Library, Sunkist, 901 S Sunkist St, Anaheim, CA, 92806-4739. Tel: 714-765-3576. Fax: 714-765-3574. p. 121

St Clair, Gloriana, Dr, Dean of Libr, Carnegie Mellon University, Hunt Library, 4909 Frew St, Pittsburgh, PA, 15213-3890. Tel: 412-268-2447. Fax: 412-268-2793. p. 2123

St Clair, Jeffery, Librn, Arizona Department of Corrections - Adult Institutions, 10000 S Wilmot Rd, Tucson, AZ, 85734. Tel: 520-574-0024, Ext 37919. Fax: 520-574-7308. p. 85

St Clair, Katherine, Dir, Friends Free Library of Germantown, 5418 Germantown Ave, Philadelphia, PA, 19144. Tel: 215-951-2355. Fax: 215-951-2697. p. 2109

St Clair, Valerie, Head, Circ, Western New England University, 1215 Wilbraham Rd, Springfield, MA, 01119. Tel: 413-782-1514. Fax: 413-796-2011. p. 1128

St Cyr, Gayle, Ref, George H & Ella M Rodgers Memorial Library, 194 Derry Rd, Hudson, NH, 03051. Tel: 603-886-6030. Fax: 603-816-4501. p. 1452

St Fort, Reginald, Librn, Norwalk Public Library, South Norwalk Branch, Ten Washington St, South Norwalk, CT, 06854. Tel: 203-899-2790. Fax: 203-899-2788. p. 362

St Germain, Jan, Dir, Richmond Township Library, Smith St, Palmer, MI, 49871. Tel: 906-475-5241. Fax: 906-475-7516. p. 1216

St Jacques, Donna, Circ, The Blue Mountains Public Library, 173 Bruce St S, Thornbury, ON, N0H 2P0, CANADA. Tel: 519-599-3681. Fax: 519-599-7951. p. 2847

St John, Caitlin, Mgr, University of California, Riverside Libraries, Music Library, Arts Bldg, Rm 54, Riverside, CA, 92521. Tel: 951-827-2268. Fax: 951-827-3948. p. 219

St John, Edward, Head, Tech Serv, Loyola Law School, 919 S Albany St, Los Angeles, CA, 90015-1211. Tel: 213-736-1146. Fax: 213-385-7614. p. 175

St John, Leslie, Asst Libr Dir, Newton County Library System, 7116 Floyd St NE, Covington, GA, 30014. Tel: 770-787-3231. Fax: 770-784-2092. p. 527

St John, Nicole, Br Operations Adminr, University of Mary Washington, 1801 College Ave, Fredericksburg, VA, 22401-4665. Tel: 540-286-8033. Fax: 540-654-1067. p. 2466

St John, Robert, Law Librn, Cape May County Law Library, Nine N Main St, Cape May Court House, NJ, 08210. Tel: 609-594-3429. Fax: 609-463-1656. p. 1477

St Laurent, Florina, Circ, Swansea Free Public Library, 69 Main St, Swansea, MA, 02777. Tel: 508-674-9609. Fax: 508-675-5444. p. 1130

St Laurent, Laurie, Dir, Marshall District Library, 124 W Green St, Marshall, MI, 49068. Tel: 269-781-7821. Fax: 269-781-7090. p. 1207

St Laurent, Laurie, Br Mgr, Saint Charles City County Library District, Spencer Road Branch, 427 Spencer Rd, Saint Peters, MO, 63376. Tel: 636-441-0522, 636-447-2320. Fax: 636-926-3948. p. 1364

St Onge, Anne L, Dir, Mackinac Island Public Library, 903 Main St, Mackinac Island, MI, 49757. Tel: 906-847-3421. Fax: 906-847-3368. p. 1204

St Pe, Todd R, Librn, United States Court of Appeals, 600 Camp St, Rm 106, New Orleans, LA, 70130. Tel: 504-310-7797. Fax: 504-310-7578. p. 964

St Pierre, Anne, Br Supvr, Saint Charles Parish Library, Paradis Branch, 307 Audubon St, Paradis, LA, 70080. Tel: 985-758-1868. Fax: 985-758-1869. p. 949

St Pierre, Nancy, Ch, Pascoag Free Public Library, 57 Church St, Pascoag, RI, 02859. Tel: 401-568-6226. Fax: 401-567-9372. p. 2170

St Pierre, Therese, Librn, Bibliotheque Municipale, 25 A Rue St Pierre, Saint-Clement, QC, G0L 2N0, CANADA. Tel: 418-963-2258. Fax: 418-963-2619. p. 2909

St-Aubin, Diane, Chief Librn, CHUM, Hôpital Notre-Dame, 1560 rue Sherbrooke Est, Montreal, QC, H2L 4M1, CANADA. Tel: 514-890-8000, Ext 14269. Fax: 514-412-7569. p. 2893

St-Aubin, Diane, Actg Dir, Hopital Hotel-Dieu du CHUM, 3840 rue St-Urbain, Montreal, QC, H2W 1T8, CANADA. Tel: 514-890-8000, Ext 14355. p. 2896

St-Jacques, Nathalie, Librn, Fasken Martineau DuMoulin LLP, 800 Victoria Sq, Montreal, QC, H4Z 1E9, CANADA. Tel: 514-397-7632. Fax: 514-397-7600. p. 2895

St-Jean, Monique, Dir, Association des Bibliotheques de la Sante Affiliees a L'Universite de Montreal, c/o Health Library Univ Montreal, Pavillon Roger-Gaudry, 2900 Boul Edouard-Montpetit, 6e Etage, Salle L-623, Montreal, QC, H3C 3J7, CANADA. Tel: 514-343-6826. Fax: 514-343-2350. p. 2960

St-Louis, Chantal, Head, Prof Serv, Universite Laval Bibliotheque, Bibliotheque des Sciences Humaines et Sociales, Pavillon Jean-Charles-Bonenfant, 2345, allée des Bibliothèques, Quebec, QC, G1V 0A6, CANADA. Fax: 418-656-3048. p. 2906

St-Martin, Helene, Pub Serv, Ref Serv, Bibliotheque Charles-Edouard-Mailhot, Bibliotheque Alcide-Fleury, 841, blvd des Bois-Francs Sud, Victoriaville, QC, G6P 5W3, CANADA. Tel: 819-357-8240. Fax: 819-357-2099. p. 2915

St-Onge, Christiane, Chef de Section, Bibliothèques de Montrèal, Robert-Bourassa, 41, avenue Saint-Just, Montreal, QC, H2V 4T7, CANADA. Tel: 514-495-6209. Fax: 514-495-6287. p. 2891

St-Onge, Lee-Ann, ILL, John Bassett Memorial Library, 2600 College St, Sherbrooke, QC, J1M 0C8, CANADA. Tel: 819-822-9600. Fax: 819-822-9644. p. 2912

St-Onge, Michel, Acq, Chateauguay Municipal Library, 25 Maple Blvd, Chateauguay, QC, J6J 3P7, CANADA. Tel: 450-698-3085. Fax: 450-698-3109. p. 2880

St-Pierre, Anne, Librn, Plantagenet Village Library System, Wendover, 3104 du Quai Ave, Wendover, ON, K0A 3K0, CANADA. Tel: 613-673-2923. Fax: 613-673-2923. p. 2837

St-Pierre, Jocelyn, Archivist, Assemblee Nationale du Quebec Bibliotheque, 1035 Rue des Parlementaires, Edifice Pamphile-Lemay, Quebec, QC, G1A 1A3, CANADA. Tel: 418-643-1272. Fax: 418-646-4873. p. 2903

St-Vincent, Nicole, Bibliothecaire Responsable, Bibliothèques de Montrèal, Pointe-aux-Trembles, 14001, rue Notre-Dame Est, Montreal, QC, H1A 1T9, CANADA. Tel: 514-872-0644. Fax: 514-872-0525. p. 2891

Staab, Denise, Tech Serv Librn, Hobbs Public Library, 509 N Shipp, Hobbs, NM, 88240. Tel: 575-397-9328. Fax: 575-397-1508. p. 1556

Staab, Pat, Librn, Illinois Prairie District Public Library, Germantown-Hills Branch, 101 Warrior Way, Metamora, IL, 61548. Tel: 309-383-2263. Fax: 309-383-2263. p. 673

Staal, Connie, Circ Mgr, Faulkner-Van Buren Regional Library System, 1900 Tyler St, Conway, AR, 72032. Tel: 501-327-7482. Fax: 501-327-9098. p. 96

Staal, Kathy, Br Head, Toronto Public Library, Northern District, 40 Orchard View Blvd, Toronto, ON, M4R 1B9, CANADA. Tel: 416-393-7610. Fax: 416-393-7742. p. 2862

Staats, Mary, Librn, Farella, Braun & Martel, 235 Montgomery St, 17th Flr, San Francisco, CA, 94104. Tel: 415-954-4451. Fax: 415-954-4480. p. 242

Stabe, Mary, Ch, Upham Memorial Library, 138 W Main St, Fredericksburg, IA, 50630. Tel: 563-237-6498. Fax: 563-237-6218. p. 817

Stabell, Sandra, Br Mgr, Amherst Public Library, Williamsville, 5571 Main St, Amherst, NY, 14221. Tel: 716-632-6176. Fax: 716-634-2927. p. 1573

Stabinski, Antoinette, Head of Ref & Instrul Serv, Marple Public Library, 2599 Sproul Rd, Broomall, PA, 19008-2399. Tel: 610-356-1510. Fax: 610-356-3589. p. 2038

Stabler, Elizabeth F, Librn, Congregation Emanu-El of the City of New York, One E 65th St, New York, NY, 10065-6596. Tel: 212-744-1400. Fax: 212-570-0826. p. 1676

Stabnau, Jeff, Info Spec, Syngenta Crop Protection Library, 410 Swing Rd, Greensboro, NC, 27409. Tel: 336-632-7570. Fax: 336-299-8318. p. 1797

Stabo, Kris, Ch, Youth Serv, Menomonee Falls Public Library, W156 N8436 Pilgrim Rd, Menomonee Falls, WI, 53051. Tel: 262-532-8900. Fax: 262-532-8939. p. 2614

Stabryla, Kathleen, Dir, National Institute for Occupational Safety & Health, Cochrans Mill Rd, Pittsburgh, PA, 15236. Tel: 412-386-4431. Fax: 412-386-4592. p. 2126

Stacey, Carolyn, Dir, Escanaba Public Library, 400 Ludington St, Escanaba, MI, 49829. Tel: 906-789-7323. Fax: 906-786-0942. p. 1177

Stacey, Curt, Info Tech Mgr, Oak Park Public Library, 834 Lake St, Oak Park, IL, 60301. Tel: 708-383-8200. Fax: 708-697-6900. p. 684

Stacey, John W, Dr, Dir, Learning Res, Sandhills Community College, 3395 Airport Rd, Pinehurst, NC, 28374. Tel: 910-695-3820. Fax: 910-695-3947. p. 1814

Stacey, Kathleen, Head, Tech Serv, University of Hawaii at Hilo Library, 200 W Kawili St, Hilo, HI, 96720-4091. Tel: 808-974-7759. Fax: 808-974-7329. p. 559

Stacey, Lynn, Dir, Ref & Libr Info Serv, Baker College of Flint, 1050 W Bristol Rd, Flint, MI, 48507-5508. Tel: 810-766-4240. Fax: 810-766-2013. p. 1179

Stachelhaus, Linda, Head, Circ, Harmony Library, 195 Putnam Pike, Harmony, RI, 02829. Tel: 401-949-2850. Fax: 401-949-2868. p. 2167

Stachnik, Charlene, Supvr, University of Michigan, Museums, 2500 Museums Bldg, 1108 Geddes Rd, Ann Arbor, MI, 48109-1079. Tel: 734-764-0467. Fax: 734-764-3829. p. 1153

Stachnik, Lu Ann, Dir, Potterville Benton Township District Library, 150 Library Lane, Potterville, MI, 48876. Tel: 517-645-2989. Fax: 517-645-0268. p. 1220

Stachokas, George, Electronic Res Librn, Indiana State University, 510 North 6 1/2 St, Terre Haute, IN, 47809. Tel: 812-237-3180. Fax: 812-237-3376. p. 781

Stachurski, Melissa, Librn, Ogemaw District Library, Skidway Lake, 2129 Greenwood Rd, Prescott, MI, 48756. Tel: 989-873-5086. Fax: 989-873-4646. p. 1223

Staci, Grasky, Assoc Dean, Southern Maine Community College Library, Two Fort Rd, South Portland, ME, 04106. Tel: 207-741-5521. Fax: 207-741-5522. p. 1002

Stacie, Cohen B, Librn, Camp, Dresser & Mckee, 50 Hampshire St, Cambridge, MA, 02139. Tel: 617-452-6824. Fax: 617-452-8824. p. 1073

Stack, Bryan, Ser, Creighton University, Health Sciences Library-Learning Resource Center, 2770 Webster St, Omaha, NE, 68178-0210. Tel: 402-280-5137. Fax: 402-280-5134. p. 1412

Stack, Elizabeth, Librn, Morris, Nichols, Arsht & Tunnell, LLP, 1201 N Market St, Wilmington, DE, 19801. Tel: 302-351-9240. Fax: 302-658-3989. p. 388

Stack, Robert J, Dir, Portage County Public Library, Charles M White Library Bldg, 1001 Main St, Stevens Point, WI, 54481-2860. Tel: 715-346-1544. Fax: 715-346-1239. p. 2640

Stack, Sharon, Dir, Mauney Memorial Library, 100 S Piedmont Ave, Kings Mountain, NC, 28086. Tel: 704-739-2371, Ext 1678. Fax: 704-734-4499. p. 1804

Stackel, Martha, Cat, College of Charleston, 205 Calhoun St, Charleston, SC, 29401-3519. Tel: 843-953-5530, Fax: 843-953-6319. p. 2184

Stackhouse, Doug, Libr Coordr, Health One Presbyterian-Saint Luke's Medical Center, 1719 E 19th Ave, Denver, CO, 80218-1281. Tel: 303-839-6670. Fax: 303-869-1643. p. 302

Stackhouse, Eric, Chief Librn, Pictou - Antigonish Regional Library, 182 Dalhousie, New Glasgow, NS, B2H 5E3, CANADA. Tel: 902-755-6031. Fax: 902-755-6775. p. 2784

Stackhouse, Rosemary, Librn, Centennial College of Applied Arts & Technology, Morningside Campus Library, 755 Morningside Ave, Rm 160, Scarborough, ON, M1C 5J9, CANADA. Tel: 416-289-5000, Ext 8000. Fax: 416-289-5156. p. 2840

Stackpole, Mark, Cat, Tech Serv & Syst Librn, The California Maritime Academy Library, 200 Maritime Academy Dr, Vallejo, CA, 94590. Tel: 707-654-1090. Fax: 707-654-1094. p. 278

Stacy, Bonnie, Archivist, Librn, Historic Bethlehem Partnership Library, 427 N New St, Bethlehem, PA, 18018-5802. Tel: 610-882-0450. p. 2034

Stacy, Deena, Br Mgr, Flathead County Library, Columbia Falls Branch, 130 Sixth St W, Columbia Falls, MT, 59912. Tel: 406-892-5919. Fax: 406-892-5919. p. 1384

Stacy, Julie, Youth Serv Mgr, Washington County Public Library, 615 Fifth St, Marietta, OH, 45750-1973. Tel: 740-373-1057, Ext 218. p. 1913

Stacy, Karen, ILL, Black Hills State University, 1200 University St, Unit 9676, Spearfish, SD, 57799-9676. Tel: 605-642-6357. Fax: 605-642-6298. p. 2220

Stade, Kelly, Sr Librn, Hennepin County Library, Saint Louis Park, 3240 Library Lane, Saint Louis Park, MN, 55426-4101. Tel: 612-543-6128. Fax: 612-543-6127. p. 1264

Stadheim, Ruth, Educ Dir, Minnesota Department of Corrections, 1101 Linden Lane, Faribault, MN, 55021-6400. Tel: 507-334-0753. Fax: 507-334-0880. p. 1251

Stadnick, Phyllis, Adminr, Flin Flon Public Library, 58 Main St, Flin Flon, MB, R8A 1J8, CANADA. Tel: 204-687-3397. Fax: 204-687-4233. p. 2748

Staerker, John, Info Res, Hudson Valley Community College, 80 Vandenburgh Ave, Troy, NY, 12180. Tel: 518-629-7323. Fax: 518-629-7509. p. 1756

Stafford, Bill, Adminr, Louisiana Office of the Secretary of State, 3851 Essen Lane, Baton Rouge, LA, 70809-2137. Tel: 225-922-1208. Fax: 225-922-0433. p. 943

Stafford, Cecilia D, Dir, New Mexico State University at Grants, 1500 N Third St, Grants, NM, 87020. Tel: 505-287-6639. Fax: 505-287-6676. p. 1556

Stafford, Claire, Libr Tech, Nevada County Library, Penn Valley Station, 11336 Pleasant Valley Rd, Penn Valley, CA, 95946. Tel: 530-432-5764. p. 194

Stafford, Darci, Ch, Fremont County Library System, Dubois Branch, 202 N First, Dubois, WY, 82513. Tel: 307-455-2992. Fax: 307-455-2032. p. 2657

Stafford, Janet, Librn, Thayer Friday Reading Club City Library, 200 W Neosho Ave, Thayer, KS, 66776. Tel: 620-839-5646. Fax: 620-839-5646. p. 896

Stafford, Jeffrey, Dir, Robert R Jones Public Library, 900 First St, Coal Valley, IL, 61240. Tel: 309-799-3047. Fax: 309-799-5528. p. 630

Stafford, Jill, Head, Adult Serv, Matawan-Aberdeen Public Library, 165 Main St, Matawan, NJ, 07747. Tel: 732-583-9100. Fax: 732-583-9360. p. 1500

Stafford, Leslie, Tech Support, Eastern Health, Addictions Services Library, Mount Pearl Sq, 760 Topsail Rd, St. John's, NL, A1B 4A4, CANADA. Tel: 709-752-4120, 709-752-4121. Fax: 709-752-4412. p. 2772

Stafford, Mick, Dir, Harris County Public Library, Cy-Fair College Branch, 9191 Barker Cypress Rd, Cypress, TX, 77433. Tel: 281-290-3210. Fax: 281-290-5288. p. 2336

Stafford, Mick, Libr Dir, Lone Star College System, CyFair Library, 9191 Barker Cypress Rd, Cypress, TX, 77433. Tel: 281-290-3214, 281-290-3219. p. 2340

Stafford, Sandra, Youth/Young Adult Librn, Northborough Free Library, 34 Main St, Northborough, MA, 01532-1942. Tel: 508-393-5025. Fax: 508-393-5027. p. 1114

Stafford, Sheila Oakes, Tech Serv, Norfolk State University Library, 700 Park Ave, Norfolk, VA, 23504-8010. Tel: 757-823-2423. Fax: 757-823-2431. p. 2482

Stafford, Stephen, Librn, Vernon College, 4400 College Dr, Vernon, TX, 76384. Tel: 940-552-6291, Ext 2220. Fax: 940-552-0288. p. 2395

Stagg, Barbara, Exec Dir, Historic Rugby, 5517 Rugby Hwy, Rugby, TN, 37733. Tel: 423-628-2441. Fax: 423-628-2266. p. 2264

Staggs, Geneva, Asst Dir, Hospital Serv, University of South Alabama, Biomedical Library, Biomedical Library Bldg, 5791 USA Dr N, Mobile, AL, 36688-0002. Tel: 251-460-7043. Fax: 251-460-6958. p. 26

Stagner, Jeffrey, Librn, Cedar Valley College Library, 3030 N Dallas Ave, Lancaster, TX, 75134-3799. Tel: 972-860-8140. Fax: 972-860-8221. p. 2353

Staheli, Kory, Coll Develop, Brigham Young University, Howard W Hunter Law Library, 256 JRCB, Provo, UT, 84602-8000. Tel: 801-422-3593. Fax: 801-422-0404. p. 2411

Staheli, Kory, Dir, Brigham Young University, Howard W Hunter Law Library, 256 JRCB, Provo, UT, 84602-8000. Tel: 801-422-3593. Fax: 801-422-0404. p. 2411

Staheli, Susan, Br Mgr, Washington County Library System, Enterprise Branch, 393 S 200 E, Enterprise, UT, 84725. Tel: 435-878-2574. Fax: 435-878-2725. p. 2412

Stahl, Belinda, Br Head, Tombigbee Regional Library System, Hamilton Public Library, Old Hwy 45 S, Hamilton, MS, 39746. Tel: 601-343-8962. Fax: 601-343-8962. p. 1318

Stahl, Don, Educ Dir, Minnesota Department of Corrections, 62741 County Rd 551, Togo, MN, 55723. Tel: 218-376-4411. Fax: 218-376-4489. p. 1286

Stahl, Donna, Librn, Luzerne County Medical Society Library, 130 S Franklin St, Wilkes-Barre, PA, 18701. Tel: 570-823-0917. Fax: 570-823-5458. p. 2155

Stahl, Gerry, PhD, Assoc Prof, Drexel University, Rush Bldg, Rm 306, 30 N 33rd St, Philadelphia, PA, 19104-2875. Tel: 215-895-2474. Fax: 215-895-2494. p. 2972

Stahl, Joan, Dir, Res & Instruction Serv, Catholic University of America, 620 Michigan Ave NE, 315 Mullen Library, Washington, DC, 20064. Tel: 202-319-6473. Fax: 202-319-4735. p. 395

Stahl, Linda, Info Spec, Mid-Columbia Medical Center, 200 E Fourth St, The Dalles, OR, 97058. Tel: 541-296-8444. Fax: 541-296-6054. p. 2021

Stahl, Lois, Cat, Tech Serv, Public Library of Anniston-Calhoun County, 108 E Tenth St, Anniston, AL, 36201. Tel: 256-237-8501, 256-237-8503. Fax: 256-238-0474. p. 4

Stahl, Marty, Dir, Kothe Memorial Library, 309 Third St, Parkersburg, IA, 50665-1030. Tel: 319-346-2442. Fax: 319-346-2442. p. 838

Stahl, Michelle M, Exec Dir, Peterborough Historical Society Library, 19 Grove St, Peterborough, NH, 03458-1422. Tel: 603-924-3235. Fax: 603-924-3200. p. 1462

Stahl, Nanette, Curator, Yale University Library, Sterling Memorial Library, 120 High St, New Haven, CT, 06520. Tel: 203-432-7207. Fax: 203-432-1294. p. 359

Stahl, Rae Ann, Head, Tech Serv, San Jose State University, One Washington Sq, San Jose, CA, 95192-0028. Tel: 408-808-2467. Fax: 408-808-2141. p. 251

Stahl, Ritarose, Sister, Dir, Libr Serv, Silver Lake College, 2406 S Alverno Rd, Manitowoc, WI, 54220. Tel: 920-686-6134. Fax: 920-684-7082. p. 2612

Stahl, Sheryl, Assoc Librn, Hebrew Union College-Jewish Institute of Religion, 3077 University Ave, Los Angeles, CA, 90007. Tel: 213-749-3424. Fax: 213-749-1937. p. 170

Stahla, Bonnie, Youth Serv, Crook County Library, 414 Main St, Sundance, WY, 82729. Tel: 307-283-1006, 307-283-1008. Fax: 307-283-1006. p. 2660

Stahlberg, Ralph, Dir, Ref, Los Angeles County Law Library, Mildred L Lillie Bldg, 301 W First St, Los Angeles, CA, 90012-3100. Tel: 213-785-2529. Fax: 213-613-1329. p. 172

Stahlecker, Sally, Head, Tech Serv, Norfolk Public Library, 308 Prospect Ave, Norfolk, NE, 68701-4138. Tel: 402-844-2107. Fax: 402-844-2102. p. 1410

Stahler, Kim R, Instrul Serv Librn, Ref Serv, Reading Area Community College, Ten S Second St, Reading, PA, 19602. Tel: 610-607-6237. Fax: 610-607-6254. p. 2133

Stahley, Mary Jane, Dir, Bemus Point Public Library, 13 Main St, Bemus Point, NY, 14712. Tel: 716-386-2274. Fax: 716-386-2176. p. 1580

Stahley, Mem, Dr, Dean, Learning Res, BCC-UCF Joint Use Library, 1519 Clearlake Rd, Cocoa, FL, 32922. Tel: 321-433-7804. Fax: 321-433-7678. p. 433

Stahlnecker, Celine, Info Tech, Ref Serv, YA Serv, Grand Island Public Library, 211 N Washington St, Grand Island, NE, 68801-5855. Tel: 308-385-5333, Ext 154. Fax: 308-385-5339. p. 1400

Stahr, Shelah, Br Mgr, Pickaway County District Public Library, Floyd E Younkin Branch, 51 Long St, Ashville, OH, 43103. Tel: 740-983-8856, Ext 23. Fax: 740-983-4287. p. 1875

Stainbrook, Lynn M, Dir, Brown County Library, 515 Pine St, Green Bay, WI, 54301. Tel: 920-448-5810. Fax: 920-448-4376. p. 2595

Staines, Gail, PhD, Asst VPres, Univ Libr, Saint Louis University, Medical Center Library, 1402 S Grand Blvd, Saint Louis, MO, 63104. Tel: 314-977-3102. Fax: 314-977-3587. p. 1361

Stairiker, Claire, Head, Circ, Haddonfield Public Library, 60 Haddon Ave, Haddonfield, NJ, 08033-2422. Tel: 856-429-1304. Fax: 856-429-3760. p. 1489

Stakeley, Robert, Acq, Historical Society of Western Pennsylvania, 1212 Smallman St, Pittsburgh, PA, 15222. Tel: 412-454-6364. Fax: 412-454-6028. p. 2125

Stakes, Robert, Assoc VPres, Info Res & Planning, University of Texas at El Paso Library, 500 W University Ave, El Paso, TX, 79968-0582. Tel: 915-747-6710. Fax: 915-747-5345. p. 2317

Stakley, Paula, Ref Serv, Ad, Maud Preston Palenske Memorial Library, 500 Market St, Saint Joseph, MI, 49085. Tel: 269-983-7167. Fax: 269-983-5804. p. 1225

Stalder, Kathy, Br Supvr, Boise Public Library, Library! at Cole & Ustick, 7557 W Ustick Rd, Boise, ID, 83704. Tel: 208-570-6900. Fax: 208-376-1043. p. 570

Staley, Don, Librn, Arizona Department of Corrections - Adult Institutions, 12610 W Silverbell Rd, Marana, AZ, 85653. Tel: 520-682-2077. Fax: 520-682-4080. p. 68

Staley, Jim, Mkt, Mid-Continent Public Library, 15616 E US Hwy 24, Independence, MO, 64050-2098. Tel: 816-836-5200. Fax: 816-521-7253. p. 1332

Staley, Stephanie, Tech Serv, Cabrillo College, 6500 Soquel Dr, Aptos, CA, 95003-3198. Tel: 831-479-6537. Fax: 831-479-6500. p. 121

Staley, Thomas F, Dr, Dir, University of Texas Libraries, Harry Ransom Center, 300 W 21st St, Austin, TX, 78712. Tel: 512-471-8944. p. 2284

Stalker, Laura, Assoc Dir, Huntington Library, 1151 Oxford Rd, San Marino, CA, 91108. Tel: 626-405-2190. Fax: 626-449-5720. p. 255

Stalker, Martha, Dir, Bartlett-Carnegie Sapulpa Public Library, 27 W Dewey, Sapulpa, OK, 74066. Tel: 918-224-5624. Fax: 918-224-3546. p. 1977

Stallard, Cam, Law Librn, Frost, Brown & Todd LLC, 400 W Market St, 32nd Flr, Louisville, KY, 40202-3363. Tel: 859-231-0000. Fax: 859-231-0011. p. 923

Stallard, Kathryn, Head, Spec Coll, Southwestern University, 1100 E University Ave, Georgetown, TX, 78626. Tel: 512-863-1561. Fax: 512-863-8198. p. 2327

Stallard, Melinda, Ch, Hazel M Lewis Library, 511 Third Ave, Powers, OR, 97466. Tel: 541-439-5311. Fax: 541-439-5311. p. 2015

Stalling, Marsha, Br Mgr, Perry County District Library, Crooksville Branch, 111 E Main St, Crooksville, OH, 43731. Tel: 740-982-4821. Fax: 740-982-3133. p. 1921

Stallings, Larry, Librn, Akerman, Senterfitt & Eidson PA, 420 S Orange Ave, Ste 1200, Orlando, FL, 32801. Tel: 407-423-4000. Fax: 407-843-6610. p. 475

Stallings, Melanie, Librn, Yancey County Public Library, 321 School Circle, Burnsville, NC, 28714. Tel: 828-682-2600. Fax: 828-682-3060. p. 1779

Stallkamp, Margaret, Coll Develop, Havre Hill County Library, 402 Third St, Havre, MT, 59501. Tel: 406-265-2123. Fax: 406-262-1091. p. 1381

Stallman, Andrea, Librn, Lomira Public Library, 1038 Main St, Lomira, WI, 53048-9515. Tel: 920-269-4115. Fax: 920-269-4115. p. 2605

Stalloch, Joan, Circ, Utica Public Library, 303 Genesee St, Utica, NY, 13501. Tel: 315-735-2279. Fax: 315-734-1034. p. 1760

Stalmach, Krystyna, Tech Serv, Lambton County Library, 787 Broadway St, Wyoming, ON, N0N 1T0, CANADA. Tel: 519-845-3324, Ext 5221. Fax: 519-845-0700. p. 2872

Stam, Deirdre, Dr, Assoc Prof, Long Island University, C W Post Campus, 720 Northern Blvd, Brookville, NY, 11548-1300. Tel: 212-998-2680. Fax: 516-299-4168. p. 2970

Stam, Julianne, Head of Mkt, Eisenhower Public Library District, 4613 N Oketo Ave, Harwood Heights, IL, 60706. Tel: 708-867-7828. Fax: 708-867-1535. p. 654

Stamatopoulos, Gus, Assoc Dir, Pub Serv, Richard Stockton College of New Jersey Library, 101 Vera King Farris Dr, Galloway, NJ, 08205-9441. Tel: 609-652-4343. Fax: 609-652-4964. p. 1487

Stamey, Leisa, Librn, Buncombe County Public Libraries, Enka-Candler Branch, 1404 Sandhill Rd, Enka, NC, 28715. Tel: 828-250-4758. p. 1774

Stamm, Andrea, Coll Serv, Northwestern University Library, 1970 Campus Dr, Evanston, IL, 60208-2300. Tel: 847-491-7658. p. 644

Stamm, Andrea, Head, Bibliog Serv, Northwestern University Library, 1970 Campus Dr, Evanston, IL, 60208-2300. Tel: 847-491-7658. p. 644

Stamm, Andy, Foreign & Intl Law Ref, Georgetown University, Georgetown Law Library (John Wolff & Edward Bennett Williams Libraries), 111 G St NW, Washington, DC, 20001. Fax: 202-662-9168. p. 403

Stampahar, Margie, Tech Serv Coordr, Point Park University Library, 414 Wood St, Pittsburgh, PA, 15222. Tel: 412-392-3167. Fax: 412-392-3168. p. 2127

Stamper, Harry Loren, Head, Tech Serv, University of San Diego, Katherine M & George M Pardee Jr Legal Research Center, 5998 Alcala Park, San Diego, CA, 92110-2492. Tel: 619-260-4543. Fax: 619-260-4616. p. 239

Stamper, Vaughn, Network Serv Coordr, Hickory Public Library, 375 Third St NE, Hickory, NC, 28601-5126. Tel: 828-304-0500, Ext 7269. Fax: 828-304-0023. p. 1801

Stampfl, Barbara, Cat, Bartow Public Library, 2150 S Broadway Ave, Bartow, FL, 33830. Tel: 863-534-0131. Fax: 863-534-0913. p. 426

Stampler, Carol, Dir, Mason-Dixon Public Library, 250 Bailey Dr, Stewartstown, PA, 17363. Tel: 717-993-2404. Fax: 717-993-9210. p. 2143

Stanaland, Hollie, Ch, San Rafael Public Library, 1100 E St, San Rafael, CA, 94901-1900. Tel: 415-485-3323. Fax: 415-485-3112. p. 257

Stanbery, Renee, Librn, Jennings, Strouss & Salmon, The Collier Center, 11th Flr, 201 E Washington St, Phoenix, AZ, 85004-2385. Tel: 602-262-5911. Fax: 602-253-3255. p. 73

Stanbery-Cotney, Gilda E, Dir, Peach Public Libraries, 315 Martin Luther King Jr Dr, Fort Valley, GA, 31030-4196. Tel: 478-825-1640. Fax: 478-825-2061. p. 533

Stanbery-Kellam, Nancy, Exec Dir, Gwinnett County Public Library, 1001 Lawrenceville Hwy NW, Lawrenceville, GA, 30046-4707. Tel: 770-978-5154. p. 538

Stancliff, Eric, Pub Serv Librn, Concordia Seminary Library, 801 Seminary Pl, Saint Louis, MO, 63105-3199. Tel: 314-505-7033. Fax: 314-505-7046. p. 1353

Stanczak, Cindy, Ad, Albion District Library, 501 S Superior St, Albion, MI, 49224. Tel: 517-629-3993. Fax: 517-629-5354. p. 1148

Stanczak, Cindy, Ad, Albion Public Library, 437 S Third St, Albion, NE, 68620. Tel: 402-395-2021. p. 1391

Stanczak, Sharon, Dir, Develop & Communications, Massachusetts Institute of Technology Libraries, Office of the Director, 160 Memorial Dr, Cambridge, MA, 02142. Tel: 617-452-2123. Fax: 617-253-8894. p. 1077

Standefer, Diane, Circ & Tech Serv Mgr, Yorba Linda Public Library, 18181 Imperial Hwy, Yorba Linda, CA, 92886-3437. Tel: 714-777-2873. Fax: 714-777-0640. p. 285

Standefer, Steve, City Librn, Mansfield Public Library, 104 S Wisteria St, Mansfield, TX, 76063. Tel: 817-473-4391. Fax: 817-453-4975. p. 2359

Standerfer, Amanda, Head, Adult Serv, Decatur Public Library, 130 N Franklin St, Decatur, IL, 62523-1327. Tel: 217-421-9771. Fax: 217-233-4071. p. 634

Standifird, Beth, Librn, San Antonio Conservation Society Foundation Library, 107 King William St, San Antonio, TX, 78204. Tel: 210-224-6163. Fax: 210-354-0070. p. 2381

Standish-Moran, Julie, Br Mgr, Delaware County District Library, 84 E Winter St, Delaware, OH, 43015. Tel: 614-888-9160. Fax: 740-369-0196. p. 1895

Standish-Moran, Julie, Br Mgr, Delaware County District Library, Powell Branch, 460 S Liberty Rd, Powell, OH, 43065. Tel: 614-888-9160. Fax: 614-888-7358. p. 1895

Standley, Jeanne, Libr Dir, University of Texas at Tyler Library, 3900 University Blvd, Tyler, TX, 75799. Tel: 903-566-7351. Fax: 903-566-2513. p. 2394

Standling, Elizabeth, Asst Librn, Gale Library, 16 S Main St, Newton, NH, 03858-3310. Tel: 603-382-4691. Fax: 603-382-2528. p. 1460

Standridge, Paula, Tech Serv Coordr, Motlow State Community College Libraries, Ledford Mill Rd, Tullahoma, TN, 37388. Tel: 931-393-1669. Fax: 931-393-1516. p. 2267

Stanfield, Andrea, Instrul Serv Librn, Irvine Sullivan Ingram Library, University of West Georgia, 1601 Maple St, Carrollton, GA, 30118. Tel: 678-839-6498. Fax: 678-839-6511. p. 523

Stanfield, Annette, Reserves/Per Supvr, Lamar University, 211 Redbird Lane, Beaumont, TX, 77705. Tel: 409-880-8980. Fax: 409-880-2318. p. 2287

Stanfield, Barrie, Head, Info Ctr, Agriculture & Agri-Food Canada, 440 University Ave, Charlottetown, PE, C1A 4N6, CANADA. Tel: 902-566-6861. Fax: 902-566-6821. p. 2875

Stanfield, Joanne, Librn, Chattanooga-Hamilton County Bicentennial Library, Ooltewah-Collegedale, 9318 Apison Pike, Ooltewah, TN, 37363. Tel: 423-396-9223. Fax: 423-396-9334. p. 2227

Stanford, Dan, Br Mgr, San Antonio Public Library, San Pedro, 1315 San Pedro Ave, San Antonio, TX, 78212. Tel: 210-733-1454. Fax: 210-738-9471. p. 2382

Stanford, Linda, Br Mgr, Bossier Parish Central Library, Plain Dealing Branch, 208 E Mary Lee St, Plain Dealing, LA, 71064. Tel: 318-326-4233. p. 946

Stanford, Monica, Bus Librn, Madison County Library System, 102 Priestley St, Canton, MS, 39046-4599. p. 1295

Stanford, Yvonne M, Dir, Libr Serv, Coahoma Community College, 3240 Friars Point Rd, Clarksdale, MS, 38614. Tel: 662-621-4161. Fax: 662-627-9530. p. 1295

Stangel, Vickie, Dir, Dodgeville Public Library, 139 S Iowa St, Dodgeville, WI, 53533. Tel: 608-935-3728. Fax: 608-935-9405. p. 2588

Stanger, Carole, Dir, Atlantic Public Library, 507 Poplar St, Atlantic, IA, 50022. Tel: 712-243-5466. Fax: 712-243-5011. p. 795

Stanger, Keith, Ref, Eastern Michigan University, 955 W Circle Dr Library, Rm 200, Ypsilanti, MI, 48197. Tel: 734-487-0020, Ext 2136. p. 1238

Stangle, Rita, Tech Serv, Carroll County Public Library, 136 Court St, Carrollton, KY, 41008. Tel: 502-732-7020. Fax: 502-732-7122. p. 909

Stangohr, Margaret, Syst Librn, Tech Serv, Buena Vista University Library, 610 W Fourth St, Storm Lake, IA, 50588. Tel: 712-749-2092. Fax: 712-749-2059. p. 846

Stangroom, Scott, Head, Acq, University of Massachusetts Amherst, 154 Hicks Way, Amherst, MA, 01003-9275. Tel: 413-545-6724. Fax: 413-545-6873. p. 1049

Stanhope, David, Dep Dir, National Archives & Records Administration, 441 Freedom Pkwy, Atlanta, GA, 30307. Tel: 404-865-7128. Fax: 404-865-7102. p. 517

Staniec, Jillian, Archivist, Red Deer & District Archives, 4525 47 A Ave, Red Deer, AB, T4N 3T4, CANADA. Tel: 403-309-8403. Fax: 403-340-8728. p. 2714

Staninger, Steve, Assoc Univ Librn, University of San Diego, Helen K & James S Copley Library, 5998 Alcala Park, San Diego, CA, 92110. Fax: 619-260-4617. p. 239

Stanis, Suzanne, In Charge, Historic Landmarks Foundation of Indiana, 340 W Michigan St, Indianapolis, IN, 46202-3204. Tel: 317-639-4534. Fax: 317-639-6734. p. 751

Stanishevskaya, Irina, Cataloger, University of Alabama at Birmingham, Mervyn H Sterne Library, 917 13th St S, Birmingham, AL, 35205. Tel: 205-934-6364. p. 10

Stanislao, Mary Jo, Head, Circ, Bozeman Public Library, 626 E Main St, Bozeman, MT, 59715. Tel: 406-582-2409. Fax: 406-582-2424. p. 1375

Stanislow, Gail, Librn, Brandywine Conservancy, Inc, US Rte 1, Box 141, Chadds Ford, PA, 19317. Tel: 610-388-2700. Fax: 610-388-1197. p. 2043

Stanislowski, Patricia, Ref, Menasha Public Library, 440 First St, Menasha, WI, 54952-3191. Tel: 920-967-3660. Fax: 920-967-5159. p. 2614

Stanke, Denise, Circ, Phillips Public Library, 286 Cherry St, Phillips, WI, 54555-1240. Tel: 715-339-2868. p. 2629

Stankrauff, Alison, Archivist, Indiana University South Bend, 1700 Mishawaka Ave, South Bend, IN, 46615. Tel: 574-520-4392. Fax: 574-520-4472. p. 778

Stankus, Tony, Life Sci Librn, University of Arkansas Libraries, 365 N McIlroy Ave, Fayetteville, AR, 72701-4002. Tel: 479-575-4031. Fax: 479-575-6656. p. 99

Stanley, Beatrice, Mgr, Illinois Department of Corrections, 23813 E 3200 N Rd, Dwight, IL, 60420. Tel: 815-584-2806, Ext 2228. Fax: 815-854-1432. p. 638

Stanley, Ben, Sr Librn, Syst Adminr, Cranford Free Public Library, 224 Walnut Ave, Cranford, NJ, 07016-2931. Tel: 908-709-7272. Fax: 908-709-1658. p. 1480

Stanley, C Vaughan, Rare Bks & Spec Coll Librn, Washington & Lee University, University Library, 204 W Washington St, Lexington, VA, 24450-2116. Tel: 540-458-8649. Fax: 540-458-8964. p. 2475

Stanley, Carol, Br Librn, Cat, ILL, Athens Technical College Library, Elbert County Campus, 1317 Athens Hwy, Elberton, GA, 30635. Tel: 706-213-2116. Fax: 706-213-2149. p. 509

Stanley, Carol, Dir, Libr Serv, Athens Technical College Library, 800 US Hwy 29 N, Athens, GA, 30601-1500. Tel: 706-355-5020. Fax: 706-355-5162. p. 509

Stanley, David H, Dir, Seton Hill University, One Seton Hill Dr, Greensburg, PA, 15601. Tel: 724-838-4291. Fax: 724-838-4203. p. 2062

Stanley, Elizabeth M, Coll Mgt, Appalachian School of Law Library, 1221 Edgewater Dr, Grundy, VA, 24614-7062. Tel: 276-935-6688, Ext 1302. Fax: 276-935-7138. p. 2467

Stanley, Jane, Dir, Highland Park Public Library, 31 N Fifth Ave, Highland Park, NJ, 08904. Tel: 732-572-2750. Fax: 732-819-9046. p. 1490

Stanley, Janet L, Librn, Smithsonian Libraries, Warren M Robbins Library, National Museum of African Art, Nat Museum of African Art, Rm 2138, MRC 708, 950 Independence Ave SW, Washington, DC, 20560. Tel: 202-633-4681. Fax: 202-357-4879. p. 415

Stanley, Karen, Head, Ch, Rosenberg Library, 2310 Sealy Ave, Galveston, TX, 77550. Tel: 409-763-8854, Ext 119. Fax: 409-763-0275. p. 2326

Stanley, Lee, Archivist, Philadelphia City Archives, 3101 Market St, 1st Flr, Philadelphia, PA, 19104. Tel: 215-685-9400. Fax: 215-685-9409. p. 2114

Stanley, Mary Anne, Youth Serv Mgr, Manheim Township Public Library, 595 Granite Run Dr, Lancaster, PA, 17601. Tel: 717-560-6441. Fax: 717-560-0570. p. 2077

Stanley, Patricia, Librn, Rainier City Library, 106 B St W, Rainier, OR, 97048. Tel: 503-556-7301. Fax: 503-556-3200. p. 2016

Stanley, Ray, Br Mgr, Sacramento Public Library, Rio Linda Neighborhood Library, 902 Oak Lane, Rio Linda, CA, 95673. Tel: 916-566-2138, 916-566-2139. Fax: 916-566-2140. p. 225

Stanley, Robyn, Res, Lucasfilm Research Library, PO Box 2009, San Rafael, CA, 94912. Tel: 415-662-1912. p. 257

Stanley, Sharon, Dir, Mount Morris Library, 121 Main St, Mount Morris, NY, 14510-1596. Tel: 585-658-4412. Fax: 585-658-3642. p. 1664

Stanley, Theresa, Dir, Pima Community College, Downtown, 1255 N Stone Ave, Tucson, AZ, 85709-3035. Tel: 520-206-7267. Fax: 520-206-7217. p. 86

Stanley, Thomas, Librn, The Bertrand Russell Society, Inc Library, 98 Gillette St, Wilder, VT, 05088. Tel: 802-295-9058. p. 2439

Stannard, Deborah, Dir, Leelanau Township Public Library, 119 E Nagonaba St, Northport, MI, 49670. Tel: 231-386-5131. Fax: 231-386-5874. p. 1214

Stannard, Teresa L, Dir, Parchment Community Library, 401 S Riverview Dr, Parchment, MI, 49004-1200. Tel: 269-343-7747, Ext 203. Fax: 269-343-7749. p. 1216

Stano, Terri, Dir, Thayer Public Library, 798 Washington St, Braintree, MA, 02184. Tel: 781-848-0405. Fax: 781-356-5447. p. 1069

Stansberry, Barbara, Dir, Dakota City Public Library, 1710 Broadway, Dakota City, NE, 68731. Tel: 402-987-3778. Fax: 402-987-3778. p. 1397

Stansbery, Jill, Asst Dir, Coordr, Youth Serv, Upper Sandusky Community Library, 301 N Sandusky Ave, Upper Sandusky, OH, 43351-1139. Tel: 419-294-1345. Fax: 419-294-4499. p. 1942

Stansbury-Sunday, Deborah, Admin Librn, University of Connecticut Library, 369 Fairfield Rd, Storrs, CT, 06269-1005. Tel: 860-486-2219. Fax: 860-486-0584. p. 370

Stansfield, Bryan, Dr, Dir, Southwest College of Naturopathic Medicine & Health Sciences Library, 2140 E Broadway Rd, Tempe, AZ, 85282-1751. Tel: 480-222-9247. Fax: 480-858-9116. p. 84

Stanton, Dan, Govt Doc, Arizona State University Libraries, 300 E Orange Mall Dr, Tempe, AZ, 85287-1006. Tel: 480-965-1798. Fax: 480-965-9169. p. 83

Stanton, Debbie, Dir, Washington Public Library, 115 W Washington St, Washington, IA, 52353. Tel: 319-653-2726. Fax: 319-653-3095. p. 849

Stanton, Debbie, Br Librn, Cadillac-Wexford Public Library, Mesick Branch, 117 Eugene St, Mesick, MI, 49668. Tel: 231-885-1120. Fax: 231-885-1120. p. 1160

Stanton, Leslie, Ch, Saint Helena Public Library, 1492 Library Lane, Saint Helena, CA, 94574-1143. Tel: 707-963-5244. Fax: 707-963-5264. p. 226

Stanton, Marianne J, Ch, Melrose Public Library, 69 W Emerson St, Melrose, MA, 02176. Tel: 781-665-2313. Fax: 781-662-4229. p. 1105

Stanton, Nancy, Coordr, Braille Institute Library Services, Orange County Center, 527 N Dale Ave, Anaheim, CA, 92801. Tel: 714-821-5000, Ext 2126. Fax: 714-527-7621. p. 168

Stanton, Natasha, Ch, Mary Meuser Memorial Library, 1803 Northampton St, Easton, PA, 18042-3183. Tel: 610-258-3040. p. 2052

Stanton, Ralph, Librn, University of British Columbia Library, Rare Books & Special Collections, Irving K Barber Learning Ctr, 1961 East Mall, Vancouver, BC, V6T 1Z1, CANADA. Tel: 604-822-4879. Fax: 604-822-9587. p. 2743

Stanton, Ruth, Dean, Learning & Tech Res, Northern Virginia Community College Libraries, Medical Education Campus, 6699 Springfield Center Dr, Rm 341, Springfield, VA, 22150. Tel: 703-822-6684. Fax: 703-822-6612. p. 2447

Stanton, Shelly, Dir, Hannibal Free Library, 162 Oswego St, Hannibal, NY, 13074. Tel: 315-564-5471. Fax: 315-564-5471. p. 1634

Stanton, Staci, Asst Dir, Knoxville Public Library, 213 E Montgomery St, Knoxville, IA, 50138-2296. Tel: 641-828-0585. Fax: 641-828-0513. p. 825

Stanton, Stephanie, Dir, Malverne Public Library, 61 Saint Thomas Pl, Malverne, NY, 11565. Tel: 516-599-0750. Fax: 516-599-3320. p. 1657

Stanton, Stephen, Librn, University of Missouri-Columbia, Geological Sciences Library, 201 Geological Sciences, Columbia, MO, 65211. Tel: 573-882-4860. Fax: 573-882-5458. p. 1326

Stanton, Susan, Tech Serv Coordr, Natrona County Public Library, 307 E Second St, Casper, WY, 82601. Tel: 307-237-4935, Ext 120. Fax: 307-266-3734. p. 2652

Stanton, Susan, Dir, Access & Presv Serv, Alberta Culture, 8555 Roper Rd, Edmonton, AB, T6E 5W1, CANADA. Tel: 780-427-1750. Fax: 780-427-4646. p. 2697

Stanton, Victoria, Head, Ser, University of North Florida, Bldg 12-Library, One UNF Dr, Jacksonville, FL, 32224-2645. Tel: 904-620-1512. Fax: 904-620-2719. p. 455

Stanton-Jones, Dianna, Libr Asst, Annie Porter Ainsworth Memorial Library, 6064 S Main St, Sandy Creek, NY, 13145. Tel: 315-387-3732. Fax: 315-387-2005. p. 1738

Stanwicks, Kabel, Head, Circ, University at Albany, State University of New York, 1400 Washington Ave, Albany, NY, 12222-0001. Tel: 518-442-3578. Fax: 518-442-3088. p. 1570

Stanwicks, Kabel, Head, Circ, University at Albany, State University of New York, Science Library, 1400 Washington Ave, Albany, NY, 12222. Tel: 518-442-3578. Fax: 518-437-3952. p. 1571

Stanyon, Kelly, Info Spec, Trudeau Institute Library, 154 Algonquin Ave, Saranac Lake, NY, 12983. Tel: 518-891-3084, Ext 127. Fax: 518-891-5126. p. 1738

Staples, Alice, Archivist, Spec Coll Librn, Plymouth State University, Highland St, Plymouth, NH, 03264-1595. Tel: 603-535-2258. Fax: 603-535-2445. p. 1462

Staples, Jane, Asst Librn, Ogunquit Memorial Library, 166 Shore Rd, Ogunquit, ME, 03907. Tel: 207-646-9024. p. 994

Staples, Kathleen, Asst Librn, Calais Free Library, Nine Union St, Calais, ME, 04619. Tel: 207-454-2758. Fax: 207-454-2765. p. 980

Stapleton, Carrie L, Dir, Metropolis Public Library, 317 Metropolis St, Metropolis, IL, 62960. Tel: 618-524-4312. Fax: 618-524-3675. p. 673

Stapleton, Dorthy, Librn, Green Tom County Library System, Angelo West, 3013 Vista del Arroyo, San Angelo, TX, 76904. Tel: 915-659-6436. p. 2378

Stapleton, Jennifer, Head, Circ, Middletown Public Library, 125 S Broad St, Middletown, OH, 45044. Tel: 513-424-1251. Fax: 513-424-6585. p. 1917

Stapleton, Leslie, Dir, Daughters of the Republic of Texas Library at the Alamo, 300 Alamo Plaza, San Antonio, TX, 78205. Tel: 210-225-1071. Fax: 210-212-8514. p. 2379

Stapleton, Mary, Dir, Rochester Public Library, 208 W Spring St, Rochester, WI, 53167. Tel: 262-534-3533. Fax: 262-534-3531. p. 2635

Stapleton, Melody Sample, Librn, Mississippi Delta Community College, GHEC Library, 2900A Hwy 1 S, Greenville, MS, 38701. Tel: 662-332-8467. Fax: 662-332-8931. p. 1309

Stapp, Alexis, Evening/Weekend Supvr, ILL, Pittsburgh Theological Seminary, 616 N Highland Ave, Pittsburgh, PA, 15206-2596. Tel: 412-924-1356. Fax: 412-362-2329. p. 2127

Stapp, Dale, Dir, Ch Serv, Putnam County Library System, 50 E Broad St, Cookeville, TN, 38501. Tel: 931-526-2416. Fax: 931-372-8517. p. 2231

Stapp, Jennie, State Librn, Montana State Library, 1515 E Sixth Ave, Helena, MT, 59620-1800. Tel: 406-444-3115. Fax: 406-444-0266. p. 1383

Star, Michelle P, Acq Librn, East Stroudsburg University, 216 Normal St, East Stroudsburg, PA, 18301-2999. Tel: 570-422-3541. Fax: 570-422-3151. p. 2051

Stara, Lauren, Dir, Whistler Public Library, 4329 Main St, Whistler, BC, V0N 1B4, CANADA. Tel: 604-935-8433. Fax: 604-935-8434. p. 2746

Starasta, Leslie, Info Serv Librn, Lincoln Christian College & Seminary, 100 Campus View Dr, Lincoln, IL, 62656. Tel: 217-732-7788, Ext 2234. Fax: 217-732-3785. p. 665

Starasta, Mike, Dir, Lincoln College, 300 Keokuk, Lincoln, IL, 62656. Tel: 217-732-3155, Ext 290. Fax: 217-732-4465. p. 665

Starbuck, Roxanne, Cat, California State University, 9001 Stockdale Hwy, Bakersfield, CA, 93311-1022. Tel: 661-654-3258. Fax: 661-654-3238. p. 123

Starcher, Bonnie G, Dir, Sabina Public Library, 11 E Elm St, Sabina, OH, 45169-1330. Tel: 937-584-2751. Fax: 937-584-2751. p. 1932

Starcher, Debbie, Br Supvr, Wayne County Public Library, West Salem Branch, 99 E Buckeye St, West Salem, OH, 44287. Tel: 419-853-4762. Fax: 419-853-4572. p. 1950

Starck, Martha, Ref Serv, Milwaukee Area Technical College, 5555 W Highland Rd, Rm A282, Mequon, WI, 53092-1199. Tel: 262-238-2301. p. 2615

Starer, Paul, Dean, Foothill College, 12345 El Monte Rd, Los Altos Hills, CA, 94022-4599. Tel: 650-949-7390. Fax: 650-949-7123. p. 167

Staresina, Lois, Dir, Michigan Department of Community Health, 8303 Platt Rd, Saline, MI, 48176. Tel: 734-429-2531, Ext 4296. Fax: 734-429-7951. p. 1225

Stark, Beverly, Dir, Watkins College of Art & Design Library, 2298 Rosa L Parks Blvd (MetroCenter), Nashville, TN, 37228. Tel: 615-277-7426. Fax: 615-383-4849. p. 2261

Stark, Judith, Head, Ref (Info Serv), Southbury Public Library, 100 Poverty Rd, Southbury, CT, 06488. Tel: 203-262-0626. Fax: 203-262-6734. p. 368

Stark, Karyn, Head Librn, Tiskilwa Public Library, 119 E Main, Tiskilwa, IL, 61368. Tel: 815-646-4511. Fax: 815-646-4247. p. 709

Stark, Kris, Ch, Elgin Public Library, 214 Main St, Elgin, IA, 52141, Tel: 563-426-5313. Fax: 563-426-5999. p. 814

Stark, LeAnn, Libr Assoc, Green Forest Public Library, 206 E Main St, Green Forest, AR, 72638-2627. Tel: 870-438-6700. Fax: 870-438-4586. p. 101

Stark, Linda, Librn, Florida Christian College Library, 1011 Bill Beck Blvd, Kissimmee, FL, 34744. Tel: 407-569-1318. Fax: 321-206-2007. p. 456

Stark, Sandra M, Sr Librn, Illinois Historic Preservation Agency, 112 N Sixth St, Springfield, IL, 62701. Tel: 217-524-7238. Fax: 217-558-1571. p. 705

Stark, Ted, Dir, Menomonie Public Library, 600 Wolske Bay Rd, Menomonie, WI, 54751. Tel: 715-232-2164. Fax: 715-232-2324. p. 2614

Stark, Tom, Br Mgr, Chicago Public Library, Budlong Woods, 5630 N Lincoln Ave, Chicago, IL, 60659. Tel: 312-742-9590. Fax: 312-742-9650. p. 608

Starkey, Alysia, Dir, Kansas State University at Salina, Technology Center Bldg, 2310 Centennial Rd, Rm 111, Salina, KS, 67401. Tel: 785-826-2616. Fax: 785-826-2937. p. 893

Starkey, Cristi, Dir, Fultondale Public Library, PO Box 549, Fultondale, AL, 35068-0549. Tel: 205-849-6335. Fax: 205-841-3620. p. 18

Starkey, Deborah, Librn, Lowe Public Library, 40 Bridge St, Shinnston, WV, 26431. Tel: 304-592-1700. Fax: 304-592-1700. p. 2572

Starkey, Edward D, Univ Librn, University of San Diego, Helen K & James S Copley Library, 5998 Alcala Park, San Diego, CA, 92110. Fax: 619-260-4617. p. 239

Starkey, Jennifer, Ref & Instrul Serv Librn, Alma College Library, 614 W Superior St, Alma, MI, 48801. Tel: 989-463-7409. Fax: 989-463-8694. p. 1149

Starkey, Neal, Br Mgr, Tippecanoe County Public Library, Klondike Branch, 3062 Lindberg Rd, West Lafayette, IN, 47906. Tel: 765-463-5893. Fax: 765-463-5894. p. 759

Starkey, Robin, Ref, East Orange Public Library, 21 S Arlington Ave, East Orange, NJ, 07018-3892. Tel: 973-266-5600. Fax: 973-674-1991. p. 1482

Starks, Bonnie, Ref Serv, Sacred Heart Medical Center at RiverBend, 3333 RiverBend Dr, Springfield, OR, 97477. Tel: 541-222-2280. p. 2020

Starks, Jan, Circ Coordr, Watonwan County Library, 125 Fifth St S, Saint James, MN, 56081. Tel: 507-375-1278. Fax: 507-375-5415. p. 1276

Starkus, Kristina, Acq Librn, Marquette University Libraries, 1355 W Wisconsin Ave, Milwaukee, WI, 53233. Tel: 414-288-1985. Fax: 414-288-3123. p. 2618

Starkweather, Wendy, Dir, User Serv, University of Nevada, Las Vegas Libraries, 4505 Maryland Pkwy, Box 457001, Las Vegas, NV, 89154-7001. Tel: 702-895-2286. Fax: 702-895-2287. p. 1431

Starling, Gretchen, Asst Coordr, Tech Serv, Delaware State University, 1200 N Dupont Hwy, Dover, DE, 19901-2277. Tel: 302-857-6194. Fax: 302-857-6177. p. 382

Starling, Rita, Librn, White County Regional Library System, Searcy Public, 113 E Pleasure Ave, Searcy, AR, 72143. Fax: 501-268-5682. p. 115

Starnes, Christie, Br Mgr, Wake County Public Library System, Express Library Fayetteville Street, Wake County Off Bldg, 334 Fayetteville St, Raleigh, NC, 27602. Tel: 919-856-6898. Fax: 919-856-6206. p. 1817

Starnes, Christie, Dir, Public Library of Johnston County & Smithfield, Hocutt-Ellington Memorial, 100 S Church St, Clayton, NC, 27520. Tel: 919-359-9366. Fax: 919-553-1529. p. 1824

Starnes, Leda, Br Mgr, Middle Georgia Regional Library System, Crawford County Public Library, 340 McCrary St, Roberta, GA, 31078. Tel: 478-836-4478. Fax: 478-836-4478. p. 541

Starnes, Mary Jane, Outreach Serv Librn, Danville Public Library, 319 N Vermilion St, Danville, IL, 61832. Tel: 217-477-5227. Fax: 217-477-5230. p. 633

Staron, Kathleen, Tech Serv, Bay Path College, 539 Longmeadow St, Longmeadow, MA, 01106. Tel: 413-565-1376. Fax: 413-567-8345. p. 1100

Starr, Daniel, Tech Serv Dir, Metropolitan Museum of Art, Thomas J Watson Library, 1000 Fifth Ave, New York, NY, 10028-0198. Tel: 212-650-2582. Fax: 212-570-3847. p. 1686

Starr, Karen, Asst Adminr, Libr & Develop Serv, Information Nevada, Interlibrary Loan Dept, Nevada State Library & Archives, 100 N Stewart St, Carson City, NV, 89701-4285. Tel: 775-684-3381. Fax: 775-684-3311. p. 2948

Starr, Lea, Assoc Univ Librn, Res Serv, University of British Columbia Library, 1961 East Mall, Vancouver, BC, V6T 1Z1, CANADA. Tel: 604-822-2826. p. 2742

Starr, Lee B, Acq Librn, Kootenai-Shoshone Area Libraries, 8385 N Government Way, Hayden, ID, 83835-9280. Tel: 208-772-5612, Ext 17. Fax: 208-772-2498. p. 575

Starr, Linda, Bus Librn, Coyle Free Library, 102 N Main St, Chambersburg, PA, 17201-1676. Tel: 717-263-1054. Fax: 717-709-0288. p. 2043

Starr, Melissa, Supvr, International Trademark Association Library, 655 Third Ave 10th Flr, New York, NY, 10017. Tel: 212-768-9887. Fax: 212-768-7796. p. 1683

Starr, Rebecca, Coll Develop Mgr, Meriden Public Library, 105 Miller St, Meriden, CT, 06450. Tel: 203-630-6351. Fax: 203-238-3647. p. 350

Starr, Sandy, Bus Mgr, Washington County Public Library, 615 Fifth St, Marietta, OH, 45750-1973. Tel: 740-373-1057, Ext 216. p. 1913

Starr, Sharon, Br Librn, Mingo County Library, Gilbert Branch, City Hall, Gilbert, WV, 25621. Tel: 304-664-8886. Fax: 304-664-8886. p. 2558

Starr, Sheri, Asst Librn, Prairie Trails Public Library District, 8449 S Moody, Burbank, IL, 60459-2525. Tel: 708-430-3688. Fax: 708-430-5596. p. 598

Starr, Susan, Assoc Dean, California State University, 333 S Twin Oaks Valley Rd, San Marcos, CA, 92096-0001. Tel: 760-750-4372. Fax: 760-750-3287. p. 254

Starr, Valorie, Libr Dir, Sterling College, 125 W Cooper, Sterling, KS, 67579-1533. Tel: 620-278-4234. Fax: 620-278-4414. p. 895

Starratt, Jay, Dean of Libr, Washington State University Libraries, 100 Dairy Rd, Pullman, WA, 99164. Tel: 509-335-4558. Fax: 509-335-6721. p. 2525

Starratt, Jay, Chair, Orbis Cascade Alliance, 2288 Oakmont Way, Eugene, OR, 97401-5519. Tel: 541-246-2470. Fax: 541-246-2477. p. 2953

Starrett, David, Dean, Acad Info Serv, Dir, Southeast Missouri State University, One University Plaza, Mail Stop 4600, Cape Girardeau, MO, 63701. Tel: 573-651-2235. Fax: 573-651-2666. p. 1322

Starrett, Pat, Librn, AkzoNobel, 16651 Sprague Rd, Strongsville, OH, 44136. Tel: 440-826-5538. Fax: 440-826-5431. p. 1937

Start, Amanda, Br Head, Librn, Leeds & the Thousand Islands Public Library, Seeley's Bay Branch, 150 Main St, Seeley's Bay, ON, K0H 2N0, CANADA. Tel: 613-387-3909. Fax: 613-387-2037. p. 2815

Start, Susan, Adult Serv, Info Serv, Woodstock Public Library, 445 Hunter St, Woodstock, ON, N4S 4G7, CANADA. Tel: 519-539-4801. Fax: 519-539-5246. p. 2872

Starzmann, Carol, Asst Dir, Cecil County Public Library, 301 Newark Ave, Elkton, MD, 21921-5441. Tel: 410-996-5600. Fax: 410-996-5604. p. 1027

Starzynski, Aimee, Supvr, Middlesex County Library, Strathroy Branch, 34 Frank St, Strathroy, ON, N7G 2R4, CANADA. Tel: 519-245-1290. Fax: 519-245-0647. p. 2845

Staskowski, Jim, Br Mgr, Richland County Public Library, Sandhills, One Summit Pkwy, @ Clemson Rd, Columbia, SC, 29229. Tel: 803-699-9230. Fax: 803-699-0491. p. 2188

Stassek, Debby, Asst Dir, Tech Coordr, Van Buren District Library, 200 N Phelps St, Decatur, MI, 49045-1086. Tel: 269-423-4771. Fax: 269-423-8373. p. 1168

Stater, Christopher, Dir, Ellis Hospital, 1101 Nott St, Schenectady, NY, 12308. Tel: 518-243-4000, 518-243-4381. Fax: 518-243-1429. p. 1740

Staton, Lori, ILL, Worcester County Library, 307 N Washington St, Snow Hill, MD, 21863. Tel: 410-632-5622. Fax: 410-632-1159. p. 1042

Staton, Vicky, Br Mgr, Calcasieu Parish Public Library, Moss Bluff, 261 Parish Rd, Lake Charles, LA, 70611. Tel: 337-721-7128. Fax: 337-855-1827. p. 954

Statton, Thomas M, Dir of Libr Serv, Kaplan University Hagerstown Library, 18618 Crestwood Dr, Hagerstown, MD, 21742. Tel: 301-766-3600, 301-766-3653. Fax: 301-791-7661. p. 1031

Statz, Mary, Librn, Nelson Public Library, Ten W Third St, Nelson, NE, 68961. Tel: 402-225-7111. Fax: 402-225-7111. p. 1409

Statz, Meagan, Ad, Prairie du Sac Public Library, 560 Park Ave, Prairie du Sac, WI, 53578-1199. Tel: 608-643-8318. Fax: 608-643-4897. p. 2631

Staub, Susan, Ch, Fanwood Memorial Library, 14 Tillotson Rd, Fanwood, NJ, 07023-1399. Tel: 908-322-6400. Fax: 908-322-5590. p. 1485

Stauble, Margaret J, Pub Serv Librn, Hinds Community College, 505 E Main St, Raymond, MS, 39154. Tel: 601-857-3743. Fax: 601-857-3293. p. 1313

Staudemeyer, George J, Sr Res Spec, Clausen Miller Research Services Dept, Ten S LaSalle St, 16th Flr, Chicago, IL, 60603-1098. Tel: 312-606-7887. Fax: 312-606-7777. p. 611

Stauffacher, Pam, Br Supvr, Ch, Concord Public Library, Penacook Branch, Three Merrimack St, Penacook, NH, 03303. Tel: 603-225-8670. p. 1442

Stauffacher, Pamela, Children's Mgr, Concord Public Library, 45 Green St, Concord, NH, 03301-4294. Tel: 603-230-3688. Fax: 603-230-3693. p. 1442

Stauffer, Julie, Head, Acq & Electronic Res, University of Chicago Library, D'Angelo Law Library, 1121 E 60th St, Chicago, IL, 60637-2786. Tel: 773-702-0692. Fax: 773-702-2889. p. 626

Stauffer, Ramona, Librn, Salmon Public Library, 204 Main St, Salmon, ID, 83467-4111. Tel: 208-756-2311. Fax: 208-756-2444. p. 583

Stauffer, Suzanne, Dr, Assoc Prof, Louisiana State University, 267 Coates Hall, Baton Rouge, LA, 70803. Tel: 225-578-3158. Fax: 225-578-4581. p. 2966

Staum-Kuniej, Sonja, Dir, Indiana University-Purdue University, Herron Art Library, Herron School of Art & Design, 735 W New York St, Indianapolis, IN, 46202. Tel: 317-278-9417. Fax: 317-278-9497. p. 753

Stave, Thomas A, Head, Doc Ctr, University of Oregon Libraries, 1501 Kincaid St, Eugene, OR, 97403-1299. Tel: 541-346-3056. Fax: 541-346-3485. p. 1997

Staveness, Roxanne, Outreach Librn, Wisconsin Talking Book & Braille Library, 813 W Wells St, Milwaukee, WI, 53233-1436. Tel: 414-286-6918. Fax: 414-286-3102. p. 2622

Stavenga, Mink, Dean, Southwestern College Library, 900 Otay Lakes Rd, Chula Vista, CA, 91910-7299. Tel: 619-482-6542. Fax: 619-482-6417. p. 134

Stavenhagen, Annis, Asst Dir, Clarendon College Library, 1122 College Dr, Clarendon, TX, 79226. Tel: 806-874-4813. Fax: 806-874-5080. p. 2297

Stavinoha, Anna, Dir, Estacada Public Library, 825 NW Wade St, Estacada, OR, 97023. Tel: 503-630-8273. Fax: 503-630-8282. p. 1996

Stavinoha, Anna, Mgr, Woodburn Public Library, 280 Garfield St, Woodburn, OR, 97071-4698. Tel: 503-982-5252. Fax: 503-982-2808. p. 2023

Stavola, Beth, Ref Supvr, Bristol Public Library, Five High St, Bristol, CT, 06010. Tel: 860-584-7787. Fax: 860-584-7696. p. 332

Stavole, Janet, Br Mgr, Akron-Summit County Public Library, Nordonia Hills, 9458 Olde Eight Rd, Northfield, OH, 44067-1952. Tel: 330-467-8595. Fax: 330-467-4332. p. 1852

Stavovy, Patricia, Asst Law Librn, Washington County Law Library, One S Main St, Ste G004, Washington, PA, 15301-6813. Tel: 724-250-4026. p. 2151

Stavros, Christine, Br Head, Lowell Public Library, Schneider Branch, 24002 Parrish Ave, Schneider, IN, 46376. Tel: 219-552-1000. Fax: 219-552-0137. p. 762

Stawick, Maureen, Head Librn, Westat, Inc Library, 1650 Research Blvd, Rockville, MD, 20850. Tel: 301-251-1500. Fax: 301-294-2034. p. 1040

Stawski, Nina, Access Serv, Stephens College, 1200 E Broadway, Columbia, MO, 65215. Tel: 573-876-7182. Fax: 573-876-7264. p. 1325

Stayton, Gonda, Head, Acq, West Texas A&M University, University Dr & 26th St, Canyon, TX, 79016. Tel: 806-651-2218. Fax: 806-651-2213. p. 2294

Stayton, Kevin, Chief Curator, Brooklyn Museum of Art, Wilbour Library of Egyptology, 200 Eastern Pkwy, Brooklyn, NY, 11238. Tel: 718-501-6219. Fax: 718-501-6125. p. 1590

Stayvas, Robin, Ref Librn, Scotch Plains Public Library, 1927 Bartle Ave, Scotch Plains, NJ, 07076-1212. Tel: 908-322-5007. Fax: 908-322-0490. p. 1528

Steadham, Chris, Fac Serv, Res Librn, University of Kansas Libraries, Wheat Law Library, Green Hall, Rm 200, 1535 W 15th St, Lawrence, KS, 66045-7608. Tel: 785-864-3025. Fax: 785-864-3680. p. 878

Steans, Josh, ILL, University of Wisconsin-Stout Library, 315 Tenth Ave, Menomonie, WI, 54751-0790. Tel: 715-232-1215. Fax: 715-232-1783. p. 2615

Stearley, Cheryl, Coordr, Union Hospital, 1606 N Seventh St, Terre Haute, IN, 47804. Tel: 812-238-7641. Fax: 812-238-7595. p. 781

Stearn, Gwenn, State Archivist, Rhode Island State Archives, 337 Westminster St, Providence, RI, 02903. Tel: 401-222-2353. Fax: 401-222-3199. p. 2175

Stearns, Barry, Ref Serv, New England School of Law Library, 154 Stuart St, Boston, MA, 02116-5687. Tel: 617-422-7282. Fax: 617-422-7303. p. 1065

Stearns, Charlene, Br Mgr, Humboldt County Library, Blue Lake Branch, City Hall, 111 Greenwood Ave, Blue Lake, CA, 95525. Tel: 707-668-4207. p. 147

Stearns, Elizabeth, Asst Dir, Commun Libr Serv, Waukegan Public Library, 128 N County St, Waukegan, IL, 60085. Tel: 847-623-2041. Fax: 847-623-2092, 847-623-2094. p. 716

Stearns, Heather, Libr Asst, Website Mgr, Columbia County Rural Library District, 111 S Third St, Dayton, WA, 99328-1342. Tel: 509-382-4131. Fax: 509-382-1059. p. 2514

Stearns, Leah, Digital Serv, Thomas Jefferson Foundation Inc, 1329 Kenwood Farm Lane, Charlottesville, VA, 22902. Tel: 434-984-7550. Fax: 434-984-7546. p. 2454

Stearns, Melissa, Tech Serv Librn, Franklin Pierce University Library, 40 University Dr, Rindge, NH, 03461-3114. Tel: 603-899-4143. Fax: 603-899-4375. p. 1463

Stebbins, Bill, Librn, Bremer Pond Memorial Library, One Main St, Pittsburg, NH, 03592. Tel: 603-538-7032. p. 1462

Stec, Eileen, Librn, Rutgers University Libraries, Mabel Smith Douglass Library, Eight Chapel Dr, New Brunswick, NJ, 08901-8527. Tel: 732-932-9407, Ext 25. Fax: 732-353-1133. p. 1509

Stech, Trisha, Asst Dir, John Wood Community College Library, 1301 S 48th St, Quincy, IL, 62305. Tel: 217-641-4535, 217-641-4537. Fax: 217-641-4197. p. 693

Steckel, Christine, Dir, Lower Merion Library System, 75 E Lancaster Ave, Ardmore, PA, 19003-2388. Tel: 610-645-6110. Fax: 610-649-8835. p. 2029

Stecklein, Heather, Archivist, Librn, Library of Rush University Medical Center, Armour Academic Ctr, 600 S Paulina St, 5th Flr, Chicago, IL, 60612-3874. Tel: 312-942-7214. Fax: 312-942-3342. p. 617

Steckler, Kelly, Dir, Morton Mandan Public Library, 609 W Main St, Mandan, ND, 58554. Tel: 701-667-5365. Fax: 701-667-5368. p. 1845

Steckler, Kelly, Dir, Central Dakota Library Network, Morton Mandan Public Library, 609 W Main St, Mandan, ND, 58554-3149. Tel: 701-667-5365. p. 2951

Steckman, Cynthia, Br Mgr, Great River Regional Library, Richmond Library, 63 Hall Ave SW, Richmond, MN, 56368-8108. Tel: 320-597-3739. Fax: 320-597-3739. p. 1275

Stedke, Kathy, Circ Supvr, Ohio State University LIBRARIES, Lima Campus Library, 4240 Campus Dr, Lima, OH, 45804. Tel: 419-995-8361. Fax: 419-995-8138. p. 1888

Steeby, Sue, Br Mgr, Willard Library, Helen Warner Branch, 36 Minges Creek Pl, Battle Creek, MI, 49015. Tel: 269-968-8166, Ext 600. Fax: 269-979-8072. p. 1155

Steeby, Sue, Ch, Willard Library, Seven W Van Buren St, Battle Creek, MI, 49017-3009. Tel: 269-968-8166. Fax: 269-968-3284. p. 1155

Steed, Diana, Br Mgr, Montgomery County Public Library, John C Currie Memorial Library Candor Branch, 138 S School Rd, Candor, NC, 27229. Tel: 910-974-4033. Fax: 910-974-4033. p. 1827

Steed, Jane, Commun Librn, Monroe County Library System, Blue Bush, 2210 Blue Bush, Monroe, MI, 48162-9643. Tel: 734-242-4085. Fax: 734-242-0023. p. 1210

Steed, Jane, Commun Librn, Monroe County Library System, Frenchtown-Dixie, 2881 Nadeau Rd, Monroe, MI, 48162-9334. Tel: 734-289-1035. Fax: 734-289-3867. p. 1210

Steed, Jane, Commun Librn, Monroe County Library System, Robert A Vivian Branch, 2664 Vivian Rd, Monroe, MI, 48162-9212. Tel: 734-241-1430. Fax: 734-241-1430. p. 1210

Steed, Patty, Assoc Dir, Br & Ch, Salt Lake City Public Library, 210 E 400 S, Salt Lake City, UT, 84111-3280. Tel: 801-524-8202. Fax: 801-322-8194. p. 2413

Steel, Jamie, Dir, Sunbury Shores Arts & Nature Centre, Inc Library, 139 Water St, Saint Andrews, NB, E5B 1A7, CANADA. Tel: 506-529-3386. Fax: 506-529-4779. p. 2766

Steel, Virginia, Univ Librn, University of California, 1156 High St, Santa Cruz, CA, 95064. Tel: 831-459-2076. Fax: 831-459-8206. p. 264

Steele, Catherine, ILL, Wilton Library Association, 137 Old Ridgefield Rd, Wilton, CT, 06897-3019. Tel: 203-762-3950. Fax: 203-834-1166. p. 378

Steele, Cheryl, Circ, The Parrott Centre, 376 Wallbridge-Loyalist Rd, Belleville, ON, K8N 5B9, CANADA. Tel: 613-969-1913, Ext 2339. Fax: 613-969-5183. p. 2795

Steele, Dale, Librn, Arizona Department of Transportation Library, 206 S 17th Ave, Rm 198, Phoenix, AZ, 85007. Tel: 602-712-3138. Fax: 602-712-3400. p. 71

Steele, Debbie S, Tech Serv Librn, Jackson County Law Library, Inc, 1125 Grand Blvd, Ste 1050, Kansas City, MO, 64106. Tel: 816-221-2221. Fax: 816-221-6607. p. 1337

Steele, Diane, Dir, Wood River Public Library, 326 E Ferguson Ave, Wood River, IL, 62095-2098. Tel: 618-254-4832. Fax: 618-254-4836. p. 721

Steele, Diane, ILL, Chamberlin Free Public Library, 46 Main St, Greenville, NH, 03048. Tel: 603-878-1105. Fax: 603-878-4092. p. 1449

Steele, Jackie, Br Supvr, Western Manitoba Regional Library, Glenboro/South Cypress Library Branch, 105 Broadway St, Glenboro, MB, R0K 0X0, CANADA. Tel: 204-827-2874. p. 2748

Steele, Jan, Dir, Lago Vista Public Library, 5803 Thunderbird, Ste 40, Lago Vista, TX, 78645. Tel: 512-267-3868. Fax: 512-267-4855. p. 2352

Steele, Julia, Librn, Georgia Department of Corrections, Office of Library Services, 9676 Hwy 301 N, Glennville, GA, 30427. Tel: 912-654-5090. Fax: 912-654-5131. p. 535

Steele, Karly, Ref Librn, Galesburg Public Library, 40 E Simmons St, Galesburg, IL, 61401-4591. Tel: 309-343-6118. Fax: 309-343-4877. p. 648

Steele, Kirstin, Head, Coll Mgt, The Citadel, 171 Moultrie St, Charleston, SC, 29409-6140. Tel: 843-953-5116. Fax: 843-953-5190. p. 2184

Steele, Linda, Grad Coordr, Sch Libr Media, East Tennessee State University, Dept Curriculum & Instruction, Warf-Pickel Hall, PO Box 70684, Johnson City, TN, 37614-1709. Tel: 423-439-7851. Fax: 423-439-8362. p. 2974

Steele, Marion, Dir, Globe Public Library, 339 S Broad St, Globe, AZ, 85501-1744. Tel: 928-425-6111. Fax: 928-425-3357. p. 65

Steele, Martha, Assoc Dir, University of Houston - Clear Lake, 2700 Bay Area Blvd, Houston, TX, 77058-1098. Tel: 281-283-3912. Fax: 281-283-3937. p. 2343

Steele, Nancy Katharine, Dir, Southcentral Minnesota Inter-Library Exchange, 1400 Madison Ave, No 622, Mankato, MN, 56001. Tel: 507-625-7555. Fax: 507-625-4049. p. 2947

Steele, Patricia A, Dean, University of Maryland Libraries, College Park, MD, 20742. Tel: 301-405-9128. Fax: 301-314-9408. p. 1024

Steele, Patricia A, Dean of Libr, University of Maryland Libraries, Theodore R McKeldin Library, College Park, MD, 20742-7011. Tel: 301-405-9128. Fax: 301-314-9408. p. 1025

Steele, Patty, ILL, Marshfield Public Library, 211 E Second St, Marshfield, WI, 54449. Tel: 715-387-8494, Ext 233. Fax: 715-387-6909. p. 2613

Steele, Paula, Librn, Orwell Library, 1999 County Rte 2, Orwell, NY, 13426. Tel: 315-298-5563. Fax: 315-298-5859. p. 1712

Steele, Paula, Br Head, Napoleon Public Library, Florida Public, 671 County Rd 17D, Napoleon, OH, 43545-9215. Tel: 419-762-5876. Fax: 419-762-5645. p. 1920

Steele, Richard, Librn, United States Environmental Protection Agency, 944 E Harmon Ave, POS 19, Las Vegas, NV, 89119-6794. Tel: 702-798-2218. Fax: 702-798-2622. p. 1430

Steele, Ruth, Asst Libr Dir, Rawson Memorial District Library, 6495 Pine St, Cass City, MI, 48726-4073. Tel: 989-872-2856. Fax: 989-872-4073. p. 1161

Steele, Ruth, Archivist, Ctr for Pac NW Studies, Western Washington University, 516 High St, MS 9103, Bellingham, WA, 98225. Tel: 360-650-7747. Fax: 360-650-3044. p. 2509

Steele, Sandy, Br Mgr, Crawford County Library System, Frederic Township Library, 6872 N Old US Rte 27, Frederic, MI, 49733. Tel: 989-348-4067. Fax: 989-348-4067. p. 1186

Steele, Sandy, Br Mgr, Crawford County Library System, Lovells Township Library, 8405 Twin Bridge Rd, Grayling, MI, 49738. Tel: 989-344-9343. Fax: 989-348-6437. p. 1186

Steele, Sarah, Head, Res & Instruction, Campbell University, 113 Main St, Buies Creek, NC, 27506. Tel: 910-893-1460. Fax: 910-893-1470. p. 1778

Steele, Tricia, ILL, University of Wisconsin-Parkside Library, 900 Wood Rd, Kenosha, WI, 53141. Tel: 262-595-2168. Fax: 262-595-2545. p. 2602

Steelman, Dorothy, Dir, Lakehills Area Library, 7200 FM 1283, Lakehills, TX, 78063. Tel: 830-510-2777. Fax: 830-510-2777. p. 2352

Steelman, Jeannie, ILL, Librn, WellStar Health Services, 677 Church St, Marietta, GA, 30060. Tel: 770-793-7178. Fax: 770-793-7956. p. 544

Steely, Jeff A, Asst Dean & Dir, Central Libr, Baylor University Libraries, Jesse H Jones Library, 1312 S Third, Waco, TX, 76798. Tel: 254-710-2464. Fax: 254-710-3116. p. 2396

Steely, Jeff A, Asst Dean & Dir, Central Libr, Baylor University Libraries, Moody Memorial Library, 1312 S Third, Waco, TX, 76798. Tel: 254-710-2464. Fax: 254-710-3116. p. 2396

Steely, Stephanie, Tech Serv, Kutztown University, 15200 Kutztown Rd, Bldg 5, Kutztown, PA, 19530-0735. Tel: 610-683-4484. Fax: 610-683-4747. p. 2075

Steeman, Gerald, Chief Librn, United States Department of the Navy, Office of Naval Intelligence Research Library, 4251 Suitland Rd, Washington, DC, 20395-5720. Tel: 301-669-4272. Fax: 301-669-4282. p. 419

Steen, Carolyn B, Tech Coordr, Mid-Mississippi Regional Library System, 201 S Huntington St, Kosciusko, MS, 39090-9002. Tel: 662-289-5151. Fax: 662-289-5106. p. 1306

Steen, Katherine Michniuk, Librn, Graydon, Head & Ritchey LLP, 1900 Fifth Third Center, 511 Walnut St, Cincinnati, OH, 45202. Tel: 513-621-6464. Fax: 513-651-3836. p. 1870

Steen, Nancy, Asst Dir, ILL, Manitou Springs Public Library, 701 Manitou Ave, Manitou Springs, CO, 80829-1887. Tel: 719-685-5206. Fax: 719-685-1169. p. 318

Steen, Patty, Libr Mgr, Rumsey Community Library, PO Box 113, Rumsey, AB, T0J 2Y0, CANADA. Tel: 403-368-3939. Fax: 403-368-3939. p. 2715

Steen, Sara J, Managing Librn, Hazen & Sawyer, PC, 498 Seventh Ave, New York, NY, 10018. Tel: 212-539-7164. Fax: 212-614-9049. p. 1681

Steenblock, Maureen, Ch, Austin Public Library, 323 Fourth Ave NE, Austin, MN, 55912-3370. Tel: 507-433-2391. Fax: 507-433-8787. p. 1240

Steenken, Beau, Instrul Serv Librn, University of Kentucky Libraries, Law Library, 620 S Limestone St, Lexington, KY, 40506-0048. Tel: 859-257-1578. Fax: 859-323-4906. p. 922

Steep, Melinda, Dir, Yorba Linda Public Library, 18181 Imperial Hwy, Yorba Linda, CA, 92886-3437. Tel: 714-777-2466. Fax: 714-777-0640. p. 285

Steere, David, Librn, Smithsonian Libraries, National Museum of Natural History Library, Nat Museum of Natural Hist, Rm 51, MRC 154, Tenth St & Constitution Ave NW, Washington, DC, 20013-0712. Tel: 202-633-1676. Fax: 202-357-1896. p. 415

Steets, Theresa, Librn, High Bridge Public Library, 71 Main St, High Bridge, NJ, 08829. Tel: 908-638-8231. p. 1490

Steever, Judy, Chief Librn, Department of Veterans Affairs, 130 W Kingsbridge Rd, Bronx, NY, 10468. Tel: 718-741-4229. Fax: 718-741-4608. p. 1586

Steeves, Brian, Libr Dir, York Library Region, Fredericton Public Library, 12 Carleton St, Fredericton, NB, E3B 5P4, CANADA. Tel: 506-460-2809. Fax: 506-460-2801. p. 2764

Stefanich, Aaron, Ch, Grand Forks Public Library, 2110 Library Circle, Grand Forks, ND, 58201-6324. Tel: 701-772-8116, Ext 13. Fax: 701-772-1379. p. 1842

Stefanko, Elaine, Head, Info Serv, Osterhout Free Library, 71 S Franklin St, Wilkes-Barre, PA, 18701-1287. Tel: 570-823-0156. Fax: 570-823-5477. p. 2155

Stefano, Debbie, Br Mgr, Camden County Library System, Anthony P Infanti Bellmawr Branch Library, 35 E Browning Rd, Bellmawr, NJ, 08031. Tel: 856-931-1400. Fax: 856-931-5338. p. 1538

Stefanovik, Andrea, Librn, Enzon Pharmaceuticals, Inc, 20 Kingsbridge Rd, Piscataway, NJ, 08854-3969. Tel: 732-980-4936. Fax: 732-885-2950. p. 1520

Stefanow, Meagan, Librn, Insurance Library Association of Boston, 156 State St, Boston, MA, 02109. Tel: 617-227-2087. Fax: 617-723-8524. p. 1062

Stefero, Karen L, Librn, United States Army, USACE, Omaha District Library, Rm 764, 1616 Capitol Ave, Omaha, NE, 68102-4909. Tel: 402-995-2534, 402-995-2535. Fax: 402-995-2623. p. 1414

Steffan, Cindi, Mgr, The Manitoba Museum, 190 Rupert Ave, Winnipeg, MB, R3B 0N2, CANADA. Tel: 204-988-0662. Fax: 204-942-3679. p. 2757

Steffel, Nicolas, Coordr, Instrul Tech, Saint Catherine University, 2004 Randolph Ave, Mailstop No 4125, Saint Paul, MN, 55105. Tel: 651-690-6802. Fax: 651-690-8724. p. 2968

Steffen, Beverly, Librn, Burdett Community Library, 207 Elm St, Burdett, KS, 67523. Tel: 620-525-6588. p. 859

Steffen, Janelle, Librn, Moody County Resource Center, Colman Branch, 120 N Main Ave, Colman, SD, 57017. Tel: 605-534-3154. p. 2212

Steffen, Linda R, Dir, Patterson Memorial Library, 500 Division St, Wild Rose, WI, 54984-6857. Tel: 920-622-3835. Fax: 920-622-5140. p. 2649

Steffen, Nicolle, Dir, Res Serv, Colorado State Library, 201 E Colfax Ave, Rm 309, Denver, CO, 80203-1799. Tel: 303-866-6927. Fax: 303-866-6940. p. 299

Steffen, Ruth Ann, Dir, Ashley District Library, 104 New St, Ashley, MI, 48806. Tel: 989-847-4283, Ext 6. Fax: 989-847-4204. p. 1154

Steffen, Susan Swords, Dir, Elmhurst College, 190 Prospect St, Elmhurst, IL, 60126. Tel: 630-617-3172. Fax: 630-617-3332. p. 642

Steffensen, Cindy, Asst Librn, Buffalo Center Public Library, 221 N Main St, Buffalo Center, IA, 50424. Tel: 641-562-2546. Fax: 641-562-2546. p. 797

Steffes, Dale, Mgr, Planning & Forecasting Consultants Library, PO Box 820228, Houston, TX, 77282-0228. Tel: 281-497-2179. Fax: 281-497-4128. p. 2341

Steffey, Shannon, Ref Librn, University of Virginia's College at Wise, One College Ave, Wise, VA, 24293. Tel: 276-328-0157. Fax: 276-328-0105. p. 2504

Steffy, Lauri, Youth Serv, Indiana Free Library, Inc, 845 Philadelphia St, Indiana, PA, 15701-3908. Tel: 724-465-8841. Fax: 724-465-9902. p. 2071

Stefko, Katherine, Dir, Archives & Spec Coll, Bates College, 48 Campus Ave, Lewiston, ME, 04240. Tel: 207-786-6272. Fax: 207-755-5911. p. 989

Stefl-Mabry, Joette, Dr, Assoc Prof, University at Albany, State University of New York, Draper 116, 135 Western Ave, Albany, NY, 12222. Tel: 518-442-5120. Fax: 518-442-5367. p. 2970

Steflik, Stephen, Circ Supvr, Broome County Public Library, 185 Court St, Binghamton, NY, 13901-3503. Tel: 607-778-6400. Fax: 607-778-6429. p. 1582

Stegenga, Marcia, ILL, NASA, 21000 Brookpark Rd, MS 60-3, Cleveland, OH, 44135. Fax: 216-433-5777. p. 1880

Steger, Richard, Libr Tech, Pub Info, San Francisco Botanical Garden Society at Strybing Arboretum, 1199 Ninth Ave, (Ninth Ave at Lincoln Way), San Francisco, CA, 94122-2384. Tel: 415-661-1316, Ext 303. Fax: 415-661-3539. p. 244

Steger, Sheila, Ch, ILL, Mayville Public Library, 111 N Main St, Mayville, WI, 53050. Tel: 920-387-7910. Fax: 920-387-7917. p. 2613

Steger, W A, Pres, Consad Research Corp Library, 121 N Highland Ave, Pittsburgh, PA, 15206. Tel: 412-363-5500. Fax: 412-363-5509. p. 2124

Stegner, Donna, Acq, US Courts Library, Byron Rogers Courthouse, 1929 Stout St, Rm 430, Denver, CO, 80294. Tel: 303-844-3591. Fax: 303-844-5958. p. 303

Stegner, Sally, Dir, Lawrenceburg Public Library District, 150 Mary St, Lawrenceburg, IN, 47025-1995. Tel: 812-537-2775. Fax: 812-537-2810. p. 760

Stehel, Kristen, ILL, Utah State Library Division, 250 N 1950 West, Ste A, Salt Lake City, UT, 84116-7901. Tel: 801-715-6753. Fax: 801-715-6767. p. 2415

Stehle, Douglas, Head, Access Serv, University of Colorado Denver, 12950 E Montview Blvd, Aurora, CO, 80045. Tel: 303-724-2152. Fax: 303-724-2166. p. 289

Stehn, Joan M, Librn, United States Army, USA MEDDAC, Keller Army Community Hospital, Bldg 900, US Military Academy, West Point, NY, 10996-1197. Tel: 845-938-4883. Fax: 845-938-0114. p. 1767

Stehr, Andy, Circ Serv Mgr, Rochester Public Library, 101 Second St SE, Rochester, MN, 55904-3776. Tel: 507-328-2322. Fax: 507-328-2384. p. 1273

Steigenga, Connie, Librn, University of Tennessee, Knoxville, George F DeVine Music Library, 301 Music Bldg, 1741 Volunteer Blvd, Knoxville, TN, 37996-2600. Tel: 865-974-9946. Fax: 865-974-0564. p. 2244

Steiger, Sharon, Br Mgr, Latah County Library District, Genesee Branch, 140 E Walnut St, Genesee, ID, 83832. Tel: 208-285-1398. Fax: 208-285-1398. p. 579

Steiger, Sue, Librn, Wayne County Regional Library for the Blind & Physically Handicapped, 30555 Michigan Ave, Westland, MI, 48186-5310. Tel: 734-727-7300. Fax: 734-727-7333. p. 1236

Steimle, Claire, Librn, NOAA, National Marine Fisheries Service, Northeast Fisheries Science Ctr, 74 Magruder Rd, Highlands, NJ, 07732. Tel: 732-872-3034, 732-872-3035. Fax: 732-872-3088. p. 1491

Stein, Allem, Spec Coll & Oral Hist Librn, Chicago State University, 9501 S Martin Luther King Jr Dr, LIB 440, Chicago, IL, 60628-1598. Tel: 773-995-2586. Fax: 773-995-3772. p. 610

Stein, Andrea, Librn, Hankinson Public Library, City Hall, Hankinson, ND, 58041. Tel: 701-242-7929. p. 1844

Stein, Anne, Asst Librn, Har Zion Temple, 1500 Hagys Ford Rd, Penn Valley, PA, 19072. Tel: 610-667-5000. Fax: 610-667-2032. p. 2102

Stein, Ardis J, Librn, Jefferson County Law Library Association, 301 Market St, Steubenville, OH, 43952. Tel: 740-283-8553. Fax: 740-283-8629. p. 1936

Stein, Christin L, Dir, The Museums of Oglebay Institute Library, Oglebay Institute, The Burton Center, Wheeling, WV, 26003. Tel: 304-242-7272. Fax: 304-242-7287. p. 2574

Stein, Irene, Ref, New College of Florida University of South Florida Sarasota Manatee, 5800 Bay Shore Rd, Sarasota, FL, 34243-2109. Tel: 941-487-4407. Fax: 941-487-4307. p. 490

Stein, Joan, Head, Access Serv, Carnegie Mellon University, Hunt Library, 4909 Frew St, Pittsburgh, PA, 15213-3890. Tel: 412-268-2446. Fax: 412-268-2793. p. 2123

Stein, K, Assoc Univ Librn, Dir, Pub Serv, Fairleigh Dickinson University, 1000 River Rd, Teaneck, NJ, 07666-1914. Tel: 201-692-2653. Fax: 201-692-9815. p. 1532

Stein, Lynne, Ch, Hinckley Public Library District, 100 N Maple St, Hinckley, IL, 60520. Tel: 815-286-3220. Fax: 815-286-3664. p. 656

Stein, Margaret, Cat, Nioga Library System, 6575 Wheeler Rd, Lockport, NY, 14094. Tel: 716-434-6167, Ext 18. Fax: 716-434-8231. p. 1653

Stein, Mary, Asst Dir, Adm Serv, East Baton Rouge Parish Library, 7711 Goodwood Blvd, Baton Rouge, LA, 70806-7625. Tel: 225-231-3710. Fax: 225-231-3788. p. 942

Stein, Nancy, Librn, Monmouth County Library, Allentown Branch, 16 S Main St, Allentown, NJ, 08501. Tel: 609-259-7565. Fax: 609-259-9620. p. 1499

Stein, Renata, Curator, Center for Jewish History, 15 W 16 St, New York, NY, 10011-6301. Tel: 212-744-6400. Fax: 212-988-1305. p. 1672

Stein, Sandy, ILL, Menomonee Falls Public Library, W156 N8436 Pilgrim Rd, Menomonee Falls, WI, 53051. Tel: 262-532-8900. Fax: 262-532-8939. p. 2614

Stein, Terri, Librn, Iosco-Arenac District Library, Tawas City Branch, 208 North St, Tawas City, MI, 48763. Tel: 989-362-6557. Fax: 989-362-6557. p. 1176

Stein, William, Ref, Washington County Public Library, 205 Oak Hill St, Abingdon, VA, 24210. Tel: 276-676-6389. Fax: 276-676-6235. p. 2443

Stein-Ham, Roberta, Bus & Human Res Mgr, Scarsdale Public Library, 54 Olmsted Rd, Scarsdale, NY, 10583. Tel: 914-722-1300. Fax: 914-722-1305. p. 1739

Stein-Martin, Barbara L, Dr, Prof Emeritus, University of North Texas, 1155 Union Circle, Denton, TX, 76203-5017. Tel: 940-565-2445. Fax: 940-565-3101. p. 2975

Steinbeck, Carla, Archivist, Culver-Stockton College, One College Hill, Canton, MO, 63435. Tel: 573-288-6369. Fax: 573-288-6615. p. 1321

Steinberg, Alison, Online Serv, San Diego Mesa College Library, 7250 Mesa College Dr, San Diego, CA, 92111-4998. Tel: 619-388-2938. Fax: 619-388-2922. p. 235

Steinberg, Ben, ILL, Public Library of Brookline, 361 Washington St, Brookline, MA, 02445. Tel: 617-730-2370. Fax: 617-730-2160. p. 1071

Steinberg, Desiree, Librn, Larsen Family Public Library, 7401 W Main St, Webster, WI, 54893-8209. Tel: 715-866-7697. Fax: 715-866-8842. p. 2647

Steinberg, Katherine, Librn, Congregation Emanuel Library, 51 Grape St, Denver, CO, 80220. Tel: 303-388-4013. Fax: 303-388-6328. p. 300

Steinberg, Maria, Dir, Brewster Public Library, 79 Main St, Brewster, NY, 10509. Tel: 845-279-6421. Fax: 845-279-0043. p. 1584

Steinberger, Naomi M, Dir, Libr Serv, Jewish Theological Seminary Library, 3080 Broadway, New York, NY, 10027. Tel: 212-678-8982. Fax: 212-678-8891, 212-678-8998. p. 1683

Steinborn, Cheryl, Librn, Coatesville-Clay Township Public Library, 4928 Milton St, Coatesville, IN, 46121. Tel: 765-386-2355. Fax: 765-386-6177. p. 732

Steinbower, Charles, Librn, State of Ohio Department of Corrections, 5993 Home Rd, Delaware, OH, 43015. Tel: 740-881-3250. Fax: 740-881-1324. p. 1896

Steinbrenner, Brigit, Dir, Vermillion County Public Library, 385 E Market St, Newport, IN, 47966. Tel: 765-492-3555. Fax: 765-492-9558. p. 769

Steinbrink, Michael, Ref Librn, College of Saint Mary Library, 7000 Mercy Rd, Omaha, NE, 68106-2606. Tel: 402-399-2471. Fax: 402-399-2686. p. 1411

Steiner, Beth, Youth Serv Coordr, Auglaize County Public District Library, 203 S Perry St, Wapakoneta, OH, 45895-1999. Tel: 419-738-2921. Fax: 419-738-5168. p. 1944

Steiner, Beth Ryker, Dir, Moore Memorial Public Library, 1701 Ninth Ave N, Texas City, TX, 77590. Tel: 409-643-5979. Fax: 409-948-1106. p. 2392

Steiner, Claire, Info Serv Mgr, Glenwood-Lynwood Public Library District, 19901 Stony Island Ave, Glenwood, IL, 60411. Tel: 708-758-0090. Fax: 708-758-0106. p. 651

Steiner, Heidi, Head, Digital & Distance Educ Serv, Norwich University, 23 Harmon Dr, Northfield, VT, 05663. Tel: 802-485-2170. Fax: 802-485-2173. p. 2431

Steiner, Janet E, Dir, Tompkins County Public Library, 101 E Green St, Ithaca, NY, 14850-5613. Tel: 607-272-4557, Ext 234. Fax: 607-272-8111. p. 1643

Steiner, Juanita, Librn, Douglas County Library System, C Giles Hunt Memorial, 210 E Central St, Sutherlin, OR, 97479. Tel: 541-459-9161. Fax: 541-459-9161. p. 2016

Steiner, Karen, Br Mgr, Akron-Summit County Public Library, Mogadore Branch, 144 S Cleveland Ave, Mogadore, OH, 44260. Tel: 330-628-9228. Fax: 330-628-3256. p. 1852

Steiner, Kathy, Head, Access Serv, The Henry Ford, 20900 Oakwood Blvd, Dearborn, MI, 48124-5029. Tel: 313-982-6100, Ext 2285. Fax: 313-982-6244. p. 1167

Steiner, Marilyn C, Libr Dir, Fairfield County District Library, 219 N Broad St, Lancaster, OH, 43130-3098. Tel: 740-653-2745. Fax: 740-653-4199. p. 1908

Steiner, Rachel, Br Mgr, Omaha Public Library, W Clarke Swanson Branch, 9101 W Dodge Rd, Omaha, NE, 68114-3305. Tel: 402-444-5492. Fax: 402-444-6651. p. 1414

Steiner, Susan J, Dir, Reedsburg Public Library, 370 Vine St, Reedsburg, WI, 53959-1917. Tel: 608-524-3316, 608-768-7323. Fax: 608-524-9024. p. 2633

Steinfeld, Camille V, Dir, Cliffside Park Free Public Library, 505 Palisade Ave, Cliffside Park, NJ, 07010. Tel: 201-945-2867. Fax: 201-945-1016. p. 1479

Steinford, Jennifer, Asst Librn, Nazarene Theological Seminary, 1700 E Meyer Blvd, Kansas City, MO, 64131. Tel: 816-268-5474. Fax: 816-822-9025. p. 1340

Steingass, Rikki, Youth Serv, Bluffton Public Library, 145 S Main St, Bluffton, OH, 45817. Tel: 419-358-5016. Fax: 419-358-9653. p. 1860

Steingrubey, Elaine, Dir, Morrison-Talbott Library, 215 Park St, Waterloo, IL, 62298-1305. Tel: 618-939-6232. Fax: 618-939-4974. p. 715

Steinhauser, Martin, Br Mgr, Rochester Public Library, Lyell, 956 Lyell Ave, Rochester, NY, 14606. Tel: 585-428-8218. p. 1732

Steinhoff, Cynthia, Dir, Anne Arundel Community College, 101 College Pkwy, Arnold, MD, 21012-1895. Tel: 410-777-2211. Fax: 410-777-2652. p. 1011

Steinhoff, Nancy, Asst Dir, Viterbo University, 900 Viterbo Dr, La Crosse, WI, 54601. Tel: 608-796-3278. Fax: 608-796-3275. p. 2603

Steiniger, Janet, Head, Ref, Bethpage Public Library, 47 Powell Ave, Bethpage, NY, 11714-3197. Tel: 516-931-3907. Fax: 516-931-3926. p. 1581

Steinke, Charis, Mgr, Auglaize County Public District Library, New Knoxville Community, 304 S Main St, New Knoxville, OH, 45871. Tel: 419-753-2724. Fax: 419-753-2594. p. 1944

Steinke, Glenn, Dir, Sanofi Aventis, Nine Great Valley Pkwy, Malvern, PA, 19355. Tel: 610-889-8655. Fax: 610-889-8988. p. 2083

Steinke, Matthew, Ref Serv, Ohio State University LIBRARIES, Michael E Moritz Law Library, 55 W 12th Ave, Columbus, OH, 43210-1391. Tel: 614-292-9476. Fax: 614-292-3202. p. 1888

Steinke, Pam, Librn, Mott Public Library, 203 Third St E, Mott, ND, 58646-7525. Tel: 701-824-2163. Fax: 701-824-4008. p. 1847

Steinle-McLain, Tammy, Digital Librn, Info Tech, University of Kansas Libraries, Wheat Law Library, Green Hall, Rm 200, 1535 W 15th St, Lawrence, KS, 66045-7608. Tel: 785-864-3025. Fax: 785-864-3680. p. 878

Steinman, Debbie, Mgr, Support Serv, Springfield Public Library, 225 Fifth St, Springfield, OR, 97477-4697. Tel: 541-726-3766. Fax: 541-726-3747. p. 2020

Steinman, Ruth, Asst Librn, Conrad Grebel University College Library, 140 Westmount Rd N, Waterloo, ON, N2L 3G6, CANADA. Tel: 519-885-0220, Ext 24238. Fax: 519-885-0014. p. 2869

Steinmayer, Lynn, Dir, Goshen Public Library, 42 North St, Goshen, CT, 06756-1509. Tel: 860-491-3234. Fax: 860-491-0100. p. 341

Steinmetz, Andrew, Librn, Ottawa Hospital, Civic Campus Library, 1053 Carling Ave, D-1, Ottawa, ON, K1Y 4E9, CANADA. Tel: 613-798-5555, Ext 14450. Fax: 613-761-5292. p. 2832

Steinmetz, Carol, Dir, Lone Star College System, 20515 State Hwy 249, Bldg 11, Rm 11437, Houston, TX, 77070-2607. Tel: 281-290-2843. Fax: 281-290-2979. p. 2340

Steinmetz, Stephanie, In Charge, Tyler Cooper & Alcorn, LLP, 555 Long Wharf Dr, 8th Flr, New Haven, CT, 06509. Tel: 203-784-8200. Fax: 203-777-1181. p. 356

Steins, Janet L, Assoc Librn, Coll, Harvard Library, Tozzer Library, 21 Divinity Ave, Cambridge, MA, 02138. Tel: 617-495-1481, 617-495-2253. Fax: 617-496-2741. p. 1076

Steinsultz, Erin, Dir, Benton Public Library District, 502 S Main St, Benton, IL, 62812. Tel: 618-438-7511. Fax: 618-439-6139. p. 594

Steistol, Leif, Libr Tech, Lutheran Theological Seminary Library, 114 Seminary Crescent, Saskatoon, SK, S7N 0X3, CANADA. Tel: 306-966-7869. Fax: 306-966-7852. p. 2925

Stelk, Roger, Head, Coll Mgt, Whitman College, 345 Boyer Ave, Walla Walla, WA, 99362. Tel: 509-527-5909. Fax: 509-527-5900. p. 2547

Stella, Colleen, Assoc Librn, Head, Circ, Ref Serv, State University of New York, PO Box 902, Morrisville, NY, 13408-0902. Tel: 315-684-6055. Fax: 315-684-6115. p. 1663

Steller, Sue, Head, Circ, Galesburg Public Library, 40 E Simmons St, Galesburg, IL, 61401-4591. Tel: 309-343-6118. Fax: 309-343-4877. p. 648

Stelling, Shari, ILL, Ref Librn, State Historical Society of Iowa-Des Moines Library, 600 E Locust, Des Moines, IA, 50319-0290. Tel: 515-281-6200. Fax: 515-282-0502. p. 810

Stelly, John, Asst Dir, Ascension Parish Library, 500 Mississippi St, Donaldsonville, LA, 70346-2535. Tel: 225-473-8052. Fax: 225-473-9522. p. 949

Stelly, Susan, Br Mgr, Vermilion Parish Library, 405 E Saint Victor, Abbeville, LA, 70510-5101. Tel: 337-893-2655. Fax: 337-898-0526. p. 939

Stelts, Sandra K, Curator of Rare Bks & Ms, Pennsylvania State University Libraries, Eberly Family Special Collections Library, 104 Paterno Library, University Park, PA, 16802-1808. Tel: 814-863-5388. Fax: 814-863-5318. p. 2148

Stelzer, Stuart P, Dir, University of the Ozarks, 415 N College Ave, Clarksville, AR, 72830. Tel: 479-979-1382. Fax: 479-979-1477. p. 96

Stelzle, James, Dir, Lancaster Public Library, 5466 Broadway, Lancaster, NY, 14086. Tel: 716-683-1197. Fax: 716-686-0749. p. 1651

Stembal, Mary Ellen, Assoc Dir, Cook Memorial Public Library District, 413 N Milwaukee Ave, Libertyville, IL, 60048-2280. Tel: 847-362-2330. Fax: 847-362-2354. p. 665

Stembridge, Koren, Dir, Cary Memorial Library, 1874 Massachusetts Ave, Lexington, MA, 02420. Tel: 781-862-6288, Ext 312. Fax: 781-862-7355. p. 1099

Stembridge, Matthew, Librn, Ogeechee Technical College Library, One Joe Kennedy Blvd, Statesboro, GA, 30458. Tel: 912-871-3524. Fax: 912-486-7003. p. 552

Stemlar, Anne, Ref, Hale & Dorr Library, 60 State St, Boston, MA, 02109. Tel: 617-526-5900. Fax: 617-526-5000. p. 1061

Stemm, Mary A, ILL, Ref, Res, Gila County Library District, 1400 E Ash St, Globe, AZ, 85501-1414. Tel: 928-402-8768, 928-402-8770. Fax: 928-425-3462. p. 65

Stemmer, John, PhD, Dir, Bellarmine University, 2001 Newburg Rd, Louisville, KY, 40205-0671. Tel: 502-272-8140. Fax: 502-272-8038. p. 923

Stemmer, Pete, ILL, Bass River Community Library, Bass River Elementary School, 11 N Maple Ave, New Gretna, NJ, 08224. Tel: 609-296-6942. Fax: 609-296-4953. p. 1510

Stempeck, Marilyn M, Database Mgr, Clarion University of Pennsylvania, 840 Wood St, Clarion, PA, 16214. Tel: 814-393-2178. Fax: 814-393-2344. p. 2045

Stempel, Kathleen, Libr Asst/Youth Serv, Berne Public Library, 1656 Helderberg Trail, Berne, NY, 12023-0209. Tel: 518-872-1246. Fax: 518-872-9024. p. 1581

Stenbak, Judy, Youth Serv, Crook County Library, Moorcroft Branch, 105 E Converse, Moorcroft, WY, 82721. Tel: 307-756-3232. Fax: 307-756-3232. p. 2661

Stenberg, Beth, Ref Librn, Fauquier County Public Library, Bealeton Branch, 10877 Willow Dr N, Bealeton, VA, 22712. Tel: 540-439-9728. Fax: 540-439-9731. p. 2501

Stenberg, Brenda, Head, Ch, Bexley Public Library, 2411 E Main St, Bexley, OH, 43209. Tel: 614-231-9709. p. 1860

Stengel, Katherine A, Dir, Human Res, Middletown Public Library, 125 S Broad St, Middletown, OH, 45044. Tel: 513-424-1251. Fax: 513-424-6585. p. 1917

Stengel, Mark, Libr Dir, Cuesta College Library, Hwy 1, San Luis Obispo, CA, 93401. Tel: 805-546-3155. Fax: 805-546-3109. p. 253

Stenger, Brenda, Mgr, Knowledge Res, Abbott, 100 Abbott Park Rd, AP 6B, Abbott Park, IL, 60064-6107. Tel: 847-937-6959. Fax: 847-937-6333. p. 587

Stenger, Mary, Dir, Southern Area Library, Old Bank Bldg, Main St, Lost Creek, WV, 26385. Tel: 304-745-4865. Fax: 304-745-4865. p. 2564

Stenner, Julie, Librn, California Department of Corrections Library System, Correctional Training Facility, Hwy 101 N, Soledad, CA, 93960. Tel: 831-678-3951. Fax: 831-678-5910. p. 221

Stensen, Eileen, Asst Librn, Augusta Memorial Public Library, 113 N Stone St, Augusta, WI, 54722-6000. Tel: 715-286-2070. Fax: 715-286-5367. p. 2579

Stenson, Monique, Br Head, Clarence-Rockland Public Library, Bourget Branch, 2240 Dollard St, Bourget, ON, K0A 1E0, CANADA. Tel: 613-487-9488. p. 2839

Stensrud, Connie, ILL, Southwest Minnesota State University Library, 1501 State St, Marshall, MN, 56258. Tel: 507-537-6127. Fax: 507-537-6200. p. 1258

Stepanek, Donald, Br Mgr, Watertown Library Association, Oakville Branch, 55 Davis St, Oakville, CT, 06779. Tel: 860-945-5368. Fax: 860-945-7199. p. 375

Stepaniuk, Sandra, Librn, Darwell Public Library, 54225B Hwy 765, Darwell, AB, T0E 0L0, CANADA. Tel: 780-892-3746. Fax: 780-892-3743. p. 2696

Stepanova, Rita, Ch, Nahant Public Library, 15 Pleasant St, Nahant, MA, 01908. Tel: 781-581-0306. p. 1107

Stepanova, Tatiana, Archivist, Alaska State Archives, 141 Willoughby Ave, Juneau, AK, 99801-1720. Tel: 907-465-2270. Fax: 907-465-2465. p. 49

Stephan, Elizabeth, Librn, Col of Bus & Econ, Western Washington University, 516 High St, MS 9103, Bellingham, WA, 98225. Tel: 360-650-2061. Fax: 360-650-3044. p. 2509

Stephanian, Charles, Librn, San Francisco Art Institute, 800 Chestnut St, San Francisco, CA, 94133. Tel: 415-749-4562. p. 244

Stephen, Cherryl, Info Spec, Kaye Scholer LLP, 425 Park Ave, New York, NY, 10022. Tel: 212-836-7217. Fax: 212-836-6613. p. 1684

Stephens, Amy, Librn, Oklahoma City Zoo, 2101 NE 50th, Oklahoma City, OK, 73111. Tel: 405-424-3344, Ext 288, 405-425-0277. Fax: 405-425-0207, 405-425-0243. p. 1974

Stephens, Amy, Librn, Tulsa City-County Library, Outreach Services, 400 Civic Ctr, Tulsa, OK, 74103. Tel: 918-596-7922. Fax: 918-596-7283. p. 1983

Stephens, Antonia, Ad, Asst Dir, Sturgis Library, 3090 Main St, Barnstable, MA, 02630. Tel: 508-362-6636. Fax: 508-362-5467. p. 1051

Stephens, Betty, Circ, Montrose Regional Library District, Naturita Branch, Naturita, CO, 81422. Tel: 970-865-2848. Fax: 970-865-2157. p. 319

Stephens, Bradley K, Dir, Salem Public Library, 821 E State St, Salem, OH, 44460-2298. Tel: 330-332-2458. Fax: 330-332-4488. p. 1934

Stephens, Brenda W, Dir, Hyconeechee Regional Library, 300 W Tryon St, Hillsborough, NC, 27278. Tel: 919-644-3011. Fax: 919-644-3003. p. 1802

Stephens, Daylan, Circ Librn, Belhaven University, 1500 Peachtree St, Jackson, MS, 39202. Tel: 601-968-5948. Fax: 601-968-5968. p. 1303

Stephens, Debbie, Dir, Jasper Free Library, 3807 Preacher St, Jasper, NY, 14855. Tel: 607-792-3494. Fax: 607-792-3494. p. 1647

Stephens, Debra, Circ Supvr, Vanderbilt University, Science & Engineering, 3200 Stevenson Ctr, 419 21st Ave S, Nashville, TN, 37240-0007. Tel: 615-322-4905. Fax: 615-343-7249. p. 2261

Stephens, Gretchen, Librn, Purdue University Libraries, Veterinary Medical, Lynn Hall of Veterinary Medicine 1133, 625 Harrison St, West Lafayette, IN, 47907-2058. Tel: 765-494-2852. p. 787

Stephens, James, Info Tech Librn, University of Maryland, Baltimore County, 1000 Hilltop Circle, Baltimore, MD, 21250. Tel: 410-455-2356. p. 1018

Stephens, Jane, Circ, Chipola College Library, 3094 Indian Circle, Marianna, FL, 32446. Tel: 850-718-2279. Fax: 850-718-2349. p. 462

Stephens, Jay, Dir, Rockingham County Public Library, 527 Boone Rd, Eden, NC, 27288. Tel: 336-627-1106. Fax: 336-623-1258. p. 1790

Stephens, Jay, Dir, H Leslie Perry Memorial Library, 205 Breckenridge St, Henderson, NC, 27536. Tel: 252-438-3316. Fax: 252-438-3744. p. 1800

Stephens, Jeffrey, Div Mgr, Queens Borough Public Library, Fine Arts & Recreation Division, 89-11 Merrick Blvd, Jamaica, NY, 11432. Tel: 718-990-0756. Fax: 718-658-8342. p. 1644

Stephens, Jenelle, Mgr, Coll Develop Serv, Arkansas State Library, 900 W Capitol, Ste 100, Little Rock, AR, 72201-3108. Tel: 501-682-2550. Fax: 501-682-1529. p. 105

Stephens, Jennifer, Librn, Haynes & Boone LLP, 2323 Victory Ave, Ste 700, Dallas, TX, 75219. Tel: 214-651-5233. p. 2308

Stephens, Jerry, Br Mgr, US Courts Library, Byron Rogers Courthouse, 1929 Stout St, Rm 430, Denver, CO, 80294. Tel: 303-844-3591. Fax: 303-844-5958. p. 303

Stephens, Jerry E, Librn, US Courts Library, 2305 US Courthouse, 200 NW Fourth St, Oklahoma City, OK, 73102. Tel: 405-609-5462. Fax: 405-609-5461. p. 1975

Stephens, Jerry W, Dir/Librn, University of Alabama at Birmingham, Mervyn H Sterne Library, 917 13th St S, Birmingham, AL, 35205. Tel: 205-934-6364. p. 10

Stephens, Kelly, Dir, First Baptist Church Library, 100 W Friendly Ave, Greensboro, NC, 27401. Tel: 336-274-3286. Fax: 336-274-3288. p. 1796

Stephens, Kent, Curator, Historian, National Football Foundation's College, 111 S St Joseph St, South Bend, IN, 46601. Tel: 574-235-5711, 574-235-9999. Fax: 574-235-5720. p. 779

Stephens, Larry, Pub Serv, Georgia Highlands College Libraries, 3175 Cedartown Hwy SE, Rome, GA, 30161. Tel: 706-295-6318. Fax: 706-295-6365. p. 548

Stephens, Linda, Tech Serv, Enterprise State Community College, 600 Plaza Dr, Enterprise, AL, 36330. Tel: 334-347-2623, Ext 2271. Fax: 334-347-0146. p. 16

Stephens, Mary L, Librn, Davis Community Church Library, 412 C St, Davis, CA, 95616. Tel: 530-753-2894. Fax: 530-753-0182. p. 139

Stephens, Maureen, Cat/Acq Tech, Stormont, Dundas & Glengarry County Library, 26 Pitt St, Cornwall, ON, K6J 3P2, CANADA. Tel: 613-936-8777, Ext 225. Fax: 613-936-2532. p. 2801

Stephens, Randy, Exec Dir, The Gay, Lesbian, Bisexual, & Transgender Community Center, 946 N Mills Ave, Orlando, FL, 32803. Tel: 407-228-8272. Fax: 407-228-8230. p. 476

Stephens, Raylene, Librn, Cordelia B Preston Memorial Library, 510 Orleans Ave, Orleans, NE, 68966. Tel: 308-473-3425. Fax: 308-473-3425. p. 1415

Stephens, Robin, Asst Librn, Cambridge Community Library, Superior St, Cambridge, ID, 83610. Tel: 208-257-3434. p. 572

Stephens, Ruth, Br Mgr, Kansas City Public Library, Southeast, 6242 Swope Pkwy, Kansas City, MO, 64130-4447. Tel: 816-701-3584. Fax: 816-701-3494. p. 1338

Stephens, Sally, Br Head, Winnipeg Public Library, River Heights, 1520 Corydon Ave, Winnipeg, MB, R3N 0J6, CANADA. Tel: 204-986-4934. Fax: 204-986-3544. p. 2760

Stephens, Sara T, Mgr, Libr Serv, Sutherland, Asbill & Brennan LLP Library, 1275 Pennsylvania Ave NW, 6th Flr, Washington, DC, 20004-2415. Tel: 202-383-0100. Fax: 202-637-3593. p. 416

Stephens, Sarah, Dir, Scranton Public Library, 1102 Main St, Scranton, IA, 51462. Tel: 712-652-3453. p. 842

Stephens, Seth, Dir, Jefferson Township Public Library, 1031 Weldon Rd, Oak Ridge, NJ, 07438. Tel: 973-208-6244. Fax: 973-697-7051. p. 1515

Stephens, Sue, Mgr, Sequoyah Regional Library System, Woodstock Public, 7735 Main St, Woodstock, GA, 30188. Tel: 770-926-5859. Fax: 770-591-8476. p. 523

Stephens, Susan, Dir, Chattooga County Library, 360 Farrar Dr, Summerville, GA, 30747-2016. Tel: 706-857-2553. Fax: 706-857-7841. p. 552

Stephens, Todd, Dir, Spartanburg County Public Libraries, 151 S Church St, Spartanburg, SC, 29306-3241. Tel: 864-596-3500. Fax: 864-596-3518. p. 2205

Stephenson, Barbara, Chief Librn, Port Hope Public Library, 31 Queen St, Port Hope, ON, L1A 2Y8, CANADA. Tel: 905-885-4712. Fax: 905-885-4181. p. 2837

Stephenson, Charlotte, Ch, Augusta County Library, Churchville Branch, 3714 Churchville Ave, Churchville, VA, 24421. Tel: 540-245-5287. Fax: 540-245-5290. p. 2464

Stephenson, Cheryl E, In Charge, 3M Canada Co, 1840 Oxford St E, London, ON, N5V 3R6, CANADA. Tel: 519-451-2500, Ext 2486. Fax: 519-452-4714. p. 2818

Stephenson, Chris, Libr Syst Adminr, Law Society of Upper Canada, Osgoode Hall, 130 Queen St W, Toronto, ON, M5H 2N6, CANADA. Tel: 416-947-3315. Fax: 416-869-0331. p. 2855

Stephenson, Deb, Circ, Carnegie-Stout Public Library, 360 W 11th St, Dubuque, IA, 52001. Tel: 563-589-4139. Fax: 563-589-4217. p. 811

Stephenson, Doris, Tech & Sci Librn, Manchester College, 604 E College Ave, North Manchester, IN, 46962. Tel: 260-982-5028. Fax: 260-982-5362. p. 769

Stephenson, Gary, Media Spec, Hardin-Simmons University, 2341 Hickory St, Abilene, TX, 79698. Tel: 325-670-1236. Fax: 325-677-8351. p. 2272

Stephenson, Graham, Indexer, Production Coordr, Alternative Press Center Library, 2040 N Milwaukee Ave, 2nd Flr, Chicago, IL, 60647. Tel: 312-451-8133. Fax: 773-772-4180. p. 605

Stephenson, Heather, Info Serv Librn, Siouxland Libraries, 200 N Dakota Ave, Sioux Falls, SD, 57104. Tel: 605-367-8718. Fax: 605-367-4312. p. 2218

Stephenson, Jenniffer, Dir, Greenwood-Leflore Public Library System, 405 W Washington St, Greenwood, MS, 38930-4297. Tel: 662-453-3634. Fax: 662-453-0683. p. 1299

Stephenson, Linda, Coordr, Pub Serv, Ref Librn, Dallas Baptist University, 3000 Mountain Creek Pkwy, Dallas, TX, 75211-9299. Tel: 214-333-5522. Fax: 214-333-5323. p. 2305

Stephenson, Linda, Head, Info Serv, University of Utah, S J Quinney Law Library, 332 S 1400 East, Salt Lake City, UT, 84112-0731. Tel: 801-581-5800. Fax: 801-585-3033. p. 2415

Stephenson, Martha, Instrul Serv Librn, Ref Serv, University of Wisconsin-Whitewater Library, 800 W Main St, Whitewater, WI, 53190. Tel: 262-472-4366. Fax: 262-472-5727. p. 2649

Stephenson, Mary Sue, Sr Instr, University of British Columbia, The Irving K Barber Centre, 1961 E Mall, Ste 470, Vancouver, BC, V6T 1Z1, CANADA. Tel: 604-822-2404. Fax: 604-822-6006. p. 2977

Stephenson, Priscilla L, Chief, Philadelphia VA Medical Center, 3900 Woodland Ave, Philadelphia, PA, 19104. Tel: 215-823-5860. Fax: 215-823-5108. p. 2115

Stephenson, Sue, Librn, Southwest Georgia Technical College Library, 15689 US Hwy 19 N, Thomasville, GA, 31792. Tel: 229-225-3958. Fax: 229-225-3959. p. 553

Stephenson, Warren, Tech Serv, University of Maryland Libraries, Architecture Library, College Park, MD, 20742-7011. Tel: 301-405-6317. Fax: 301-314-9583. p. 1025

Stephenson, Wenda, Head, Cat, University of the Virgin Islands, RR 2, Box 10000, Kingshill, VI, 00850-9781. Tel: 340-692-4136. Fax: 340-692-4135. p. 2679

Stephenson, Wilma, Asst Libr Dir, Garrett Memorial Library, 123 S Main, Moulton, IA, 52572-1327. Tel: 641-642-3664. Fax: 641-642-3664. p. 833

Stepina, Barbara, Adult Serv, Clarendon Hills Public Library, Seven N Prospect Ave, Clarendon Hills, IL, 60514. Tel: 630-323-8188. Fax: 630-323-8189. p. 629

Stepp, Tina, Youth/Young Adult Librn, Henderson County Public Library, 301 N Washington St, Hendersonville, NC, 28739. Tel: 828-697-4725. Fax: 828-692-8449, 828-697-4700. p. 1801

Stepp, Tina, Dir, Robeson County Public Library, 101 N Chestnut St, Lumberton, NC, 28358-5639. Tel: 910-738-4859. Fax: 910-739-8321. p. 1808

Steptoe, Chantay, Spec Coll & Archives Librn, Tennessean Library & Archives, 1100 Broadway, Nashville, TN, 37203. Tel: 615-259-8000. p. 2258

Sterbenz, John, Tech Serv, University of Michigan, Kresge Business Administration Library, Stephen M Ross School of Business, 701 Tappan St, K3330, Ann Arbor, MI, 48109-1234. Tel: 734-764-5746. Fax: 734-764-3839. p. 1152

Stere, Robert, Coll Mgt Librn, Mount Aloysius College Library, 7373 Admiral Peary Hwy, Cresson, PA, 16630-1999. Tel: 814-886-6445. Fax: 814-886-5767. p. 2048

Sterle, Christine, Head, Adult Serv, Thorntown Public Library, 124 N Market St, Thorntown, IN, 46071-1144. Tel: 765-436-7348. Fax: 765-436-7011. p. 782

Sterling, Bonnie, Dir, Milltown Public Library, 20 W Church St, Milltown, NJ, 08850. Tel: 732-247-2270. Fax: 732-745-9493. p. 1502

Sterling, Buck, Pub Serv Librn, Alaska State Court Law Library, 303 K St, Anchorage, AK, 99501. Tel: 907-264-0585. Fax: 907-264-0733. p. 44

Sterling, Buck C, Sr Ref Librn, Gonzaga University School of Law, 721 N Cincinnati St, Spokane, WA, 99202. Tel: 509-323-3753. Fax: 509-323-5733. p. 2536

Sterling, Carol, Dir, Eastpointe Memorial Library, 15875 Oak St, Eastpointe, MI, 48021-2390. Tel: 586-445-5096. Fax: 586-775-0150. p. 1176

Sterling, Carolin, Syst Adminr, Central State University, 1400 Brush Row Rd, Wilberforce, OH, 45384. Tel: 937-376-6396. Fax: 937-376-6132. p. 1948

Sterling, Julie, Br Coordr, Vance-Granville Community College, Franklin Campus, 8100 NC 56 Hwy, Louisburg, NC, 27549. Tel: 919-496-1567, Ext 3606. Fax: 919-496-6604. p. 1800

Sterling, Rick, Dir, Richard C Sullivan Public Library of Wilton Manors, 500 NE 26th St, Wilton Manors, FL, 33305. Tel: 954-390-2195. Fax: 954-390-2183. p. 504

Sterling, Susan, Dir, Dimmick Memorial Library, 54 Broadway, Jim Thorpe, PA, 18229-2022. Tel: 570-325-2131. Fax: 570-325-9339. p. 2073

Sterling, Susan Fisher, Dir, National Museum of Women in the Arts, 1250 New York Ave NW, Washington, DC, 20005-3920. Tel: 202-266-2806. Fax: 202-393-3234. p. 410

Sterling, Terry, Supvr, Coll Develop, Fresno County Public Library, 2420 Mariposa St, Fresno, CA, 93721-2285. Tel: 559-600-6243. p. 151

Sterma, Kathy, Head Librn, North-West Regional Library, 610 First St N, Swan River, MB, R0L 1Z0, CANADA. Tel: 204-734-3880. Fax: 204-734-3880. p. 2752

Stern, Carole, Dir, Annawan-Alba Township Library, 200 N Meadow Lane, Ste 2, Annawan, IL, 61234-7607. Tel: 309-935-6483. Fax: 309-935-6483. p. 589

Stern, Catherine, Electronic Res, Fiorello H LaGuardia Community College Library, 31-10 Thomson Ave, Long Island City, NY, 11101. Tel: 718-482-5421. Fax: 718-482-5444, 718-609-2011. p. 1654

Stern, David, Librn, Yale University Library, Geology, Kline Science, 210 Whitney Ave Rm 328, New Haven, CT, 06520. Tel: 203-432-3157. Fax: 203-432-3134. p. 357

Stern, David, Dir, Yale University Library, Kline Science Library, 219 Prospect St, New Haven, CT, 06511-2106. Tel: 203-432-3439. Fax: 203-432-3441. p. 358

Stern, David, Librn, Yale University Library, Sterling Chemistry Library, 225 Prospect St, New Haven, CT, 06511-8499. Tel: 203-432-3960. Fax: 203-432-3049. p. 359

Stern, Deborah, Dir, Reconstructionist Rabbinical College Library, 1299 Church Rd, Wyncote, PA, 19095. Tel: 215-576-0800, Ext 232. Fax: 215-576-6143. p. 2158

Stern, Diana B, Dir, Woodstock Library, Five Library Lane, Woodstock, NY, 12498-1299. Tel: 845-679-2213. Fax: 845-679-7149. p. 1771

Stern, Jill, Ref Assoc, Richland Community College, One College Park, Decatur, IL, 62521. Tel: 217-875-7200, Ext 296. Fax: 217-875-6961. p. 634

Stern, Joanne, Librn, Martinsburg Community Library, 201 S Walnut St, Martinsburg, PA, 16662-1129. Tel: 814-793-3335. Fax: 814-793-9755. p. 2084

Stern, Kelly, Youth Serv Librn, Waterloo Public Library, 415 Commercial St, Waterloo, IA, 50701-1385. Tel: 319-291-4521. Fax: 319-291-6736. p. 850

Stern, Margie, Youth Serv, Delaware County Library System, 340 N Middletown Rd, Bldg 19, Media, PA, 19063-5597. Tel: 610-891-8622. Fax: 610-891-8641. p. 2087

Stern, Marilyn, Tech Serv, United States Merchant Marine Academy, 300 Steamboat Rd, Kings Point, NY, 11024-1699. Tel: 516-726-5749. Fax: 516-726-5900. p. 1649

Stern, Marjorie, Instr, Northampton Community College, 3835 Green Pond Rd, Bethlehem, PA, 18020. Tel: 610-861-5358. Fax: 610-861-5373. p. 2973

Stern, Mark, In Charge, American Jewish Congress, 825 Third Ave, Ste 1800, New York, NY, 10022. Tel: 212-879-4500. Fax: 212-758-1633. p. 1668

Stern, Peter, Bibliographer, University of Massachusetts Amherst, 154 Hicks Way, Amherst, MA, 01003-9275. Tel: 413-545-3967. Fax: 413-545-6873. p. 1049

Stern, Richard, Bus Librn, Seton Hall University Libraries, Walsh Libary Bldg, 400 S Orange Ave, South Orange, NJ, 07079. Tel: 973-275-2046. Fax: 973-761-9432. p. 1530

Sternberg, Guy, Dir, Illinois College, 12000 Boy Scout Trail, Petersburg, IL, 62675-9736. Tel: 217-632-3685. p. 691

Sternberg, Patricia, Bus Mgr, Lewis & Clark Library, 120 S Last Chance Gulch, Helena, MT, 59601. Tel: 406-447-1690, Ext 121. Fax: 406-447-1687. p. 1382

Sterne, John, Head Librn, National Guard Memorial Library, One Massachusetts Ave NW, Washington, DC, 20001. Tel: 202-408-5890. Fax: 202-682-9358. p. 410

Sterner, Kathleen, Tech Serv, Mount Saint Mary's University, 16300 Old Emmitsburg Rd, Emmitsburg, MD, 21727-7799. Tel: 301-447-5244. Fax: 301-447-5099. p. 1028

Sternhagen, LaVonne, Dir, Beaman Community Memorial Library, 223 Main St, Beaman, IA, 50609. Tel: 641-366-2912. Fax: 641-366-2912. p. 796

Sterns, Cassandra, YA Serv, Altadena Library District, 600 E Mariposa St, Altadena, CA, 91001. Tel: 626-798-0833. Fax: 626-798-5351. p. 120

Sterrett, Myra, Dir, Santa Fe Community College, 3000 NW 83rd St, Bldg Y-100, Gainesville, FL, 32606. Tel: 352-395-5406. Fax: 352-395-5102. p. 449

Sterthaus, Elizabeth, ILL Librn, Embry-Riddle Aeronautical University, 600 S Clyde Morris Blvd, Daytona Beach, FL, 32114-3900. Tel: 386-226-6595. Fax: 386-226-6368. p. 436

Stesenko, Gloria, Librn, North-West Regional Library, Benito Branch, 141 Main St, Benito, MB, R0L 0C0, CANADA. Tel: 204-539-2446. Fax: 204-539-2446. p. 2752

Stetson, Catherine, AV, Needham Free Public Library, 1139 Highland Ave, Needham, MA, 02494-3298. Tel: 781-455-7559. Fax: 781-455-7591. p. 1108

Stetson, Daniel E, Exec Dir, Polk Museum of Art, 800 E Palmetto St, Lakeland, FL, 33801-5529. Tel: 863-688-7743. Fax: 863-688-2611. p. 459

Stetson, Deb, Asst Librn, Putney Public Library, 55 Main St, Putney, VT, 05346. Tel: 802-387-4407. p. 2433

Stetson, Jean, Dir, Head Librn, Edward Chipman Public Library, 126 N Locust St, Momence, IL, 60954. Tel: 815-472-2581. Fax: 815-472-2581. p. 675

Stetson, Keith, Coll Develop, Fairfield University, 1073 N Benson Rd, Fairfield, CT, 06430-5195. Tel: 203-254-4044. Fax: 203-254-4135. p. 339

Stetson, Linda, Dir, Morse Institute Library, 14 E Central St, Natick, MA, 01760. Tel: 508-647-6523. Fax: 508-647-6527. p. 1107

Stetson, Ruth, Dir, Tarkington Community Library, 3032 Fm 163 Rd, Cleveland, TX, 77327. Tel: 281-592-5136. Fax: 281-592-5136. p. 2298

Stevanus, Mary, Librn, Maryland Correctional Institution-Hagestown Library, 18601 Roxbury Rd, Hagerstown, MD, 21746. Tel: 240-420-1000, Ext 2347, 301-733-2800, Ext 2347. Fax: 301-797-8448. p. 1031

Steve, Sickels, ILL, Kirkwood Community College Library, Benton Hall, 6301 Kirkwood Blvd SW, Cedar Rapids, IA, 52404-5260. Tel: 319-398-5553. Fax: 319-398-4908. p. 800

Steven, Dunlap, Head, Tech Serv, Golden Gate University, 536 Mission St, San Francisco, CA, 94105-2967. Tel: 415-442-7242. Fax: 415-543-6779. p. 242

Steven, Moira, Dir, Maine College of Art, 522 Congress St, Portland, ME, 04101. Tel: 207-775-5153, Ext 5090. Fax: 207-772-5069. p. 996

Steven, Rockey, Dir, Cornell University Library, Engineering, Virtual Library, Carpenter Hall, Ithaca, NY, 14853-2201. Tel: 607-254-6261. p. 1641

Stevens, Andrew, Web Serv Librn, George Mason University Libraries, 4400 University Dr, MSN 2FL, Fairfax, VA, 22030-4444. Tel: 703-993-2250. Fax: 703-993-2200. p. 2462

Stevens, Anne, Librn, Stockton-San Joaquin County Public Library, Manteca Branch, 320 W Center St, Manteca, CA, 95336. Fax: 209-825-2394. p. 273

Stevens, Arena, Coordr of Ref Serv, Libr Instruction, Indiana University Northwest Library, 3400 Broadway, Gary, IN, 46408. Tel: 219-980-6625. Fax: 219-980-6558. p. 745

Stevens, Brian, Archives & Spec Coll Librn, Western Connecticut State University, 181 White St, Danbury, CT, 06810. Tel: 203-837-9100. Fax: 203-837-9108. p. 335

Stevens, Brooke, Ch, Starr Library, 68 W Market St, Rhinebeck, NY, 12572. Tel: 845-876-4030. Fax: 845-876-4030. p. 1727

Stevens, Cathy, ILL, Saratoga Springs Public Library, 49 Henry St, Saratoga Springs, NY, 12866. Tel: 518-584-7860. Fax: 518-584-7866. p. 1738

Stevens, Cory, Head, Pub Serv, Lake Forest College, 555 N Sheridan, Lake Forest, IL, 60045. Tel: 847-735-5072. Fax: 847-735-6297. p. 663

Stevens, Daniel, Ref Serv, Lone Star College System, Montgomery College Library, 3200 College Park Dr, Conroe, TX, 77384. Tel: 936-273-7487. Fax: 936-273-7395. p. 2340

Stevens, Deanna, Libr Tech-ILLO, Wellington County Library, 552 Wellington Rd 18, RR1, Fergus, ON, N1M 2W3, CANADA. Tel: 519-846-0918, Ext 225. Fax: 519-846-2066. p. 2805

Stevens, Deanna, Pres, Tampa Bay Medical Library Network, Florida Hospital College of Health Sciences, 671 Winyah Dr, Orlando, FL, 32803-1226. Tel: 407-303-9798. Fax: 407-303-9408. p. 2941

Stevens, Deanna L, Acq, Dir, Florida Hospital College of Health Sciences, 671 Winyah Dr, Orlando, FL, 32803. Tel: 407-303-7747, Ext 9878. Fax: 407-303-9622. p. 475

Stevens, Debra, Br Mgr, Memphis Public Library, East Shelby Branch, 7200 E Shelby Dr, Memphis, TN, 38125. Tel: 901-751-7360. p. 2250

Stevens, Denise, Info Spec, Prevention First, 1405 State Hwy 35N, Ocean, NJ, 07712. Tel: 732-663-1800. Fax: 732-663-1698. p. 1515

Stevens, Giselle, Asst Head Librn, Newburyport Public Library, 94 State St, Newburyport, MA, 01950-6619. Tel: 978-465-4428, Ext 224. Fax: 978-463-0394. p. 1109

Stevens, John, Libr Dir, Fairfield Library Association, Inc, 350 W Main, Fairfield, TX, 75840. Tel: 903-389-3574. Fax: 903-389-5636. p. 2318

Stevens, Karen, Archivist, Libr Mgr, National Park Service Independence National Historical Park, Merchants Exchange Bldg, 3rd Flr, 143 S Third St, Philadelphia, PA, 19106. Tel: 215-597-2069. Fax: 215-597-3969. p. 2113

Stevens, Katherine M, Circ, Portland Community College Library, 12000 SW 49th AV, Portland, OR, 97219. Tel: 503-977-4678. Fax: 971-722-8397. p. 2013

Stevens, Kathy, Youth Serv Librn, Baxter Memorial Library, 71 South St, Gorham, ME, 04038. Tel: 207-222-1190. Fax: 207-839-7749. p. 986

Stevens, Katie, Librn, Bonner General Hospital, 520 N Third Ave, Sandpoint, ID, 83864. Tel: 208-263-1441. Fax: 208-265-1266. p. 583

Stevens, Kim, Cat Librn, Jacksonville State University Library, 700 Pelham Rd N, Jacksonville, AL, 36265. Tel: 256-782-5255. Fax: 256-782-5872. p. 22

Stevens, Leon, Librn, Walter & Haverfield LLP, The Tower at Erieview, Ste 3500, 1301 E Ninth St, Cleveland, OH, 44114-1821. Tel: 216-781-1212. Fax: 216-575-0911. p. 1881

Stevens, Lisa, Mgr, Wayne County Public Library, Pikeville Public, 107 W Main St, Pikeville, NC, 27863. Tel: 919-705-1892. p. 1795

Stevens, Lora-Lynn, Coll Develop, Head, Tech Serv, Martin Memorial Library, 159 E Market St, York, PA, 17401-1269. Tel: 717-846-5300. Fax: 717-848-2330. p. 2159

Stevens, Marilyn, Mgr, California State Department of Corporations Library, 1515 K St, Ste 200, Sacramento, CA, 95814. Tel: 916-324-9600. Fax: 916-445-7975. p. 222

Stevens, Mark, Syst, Utah Valley University Library, 800 W University Pkwy, Orem, UT, 84058-5999. Tel: 801-863-8155. Fax: 801-863-7065. p. 2409

Stevens, Mary P, Librn, Mississippi Museum of Natural Science Library, 2148 Riverside Dr, Jackson, MS, 39202. Tel: 601-354-7303. Fax: 601-354-7227. p. 1305

Stevens, Michael, Tech Serv, Springfield College, 263 Alden St, Springfield, MA, 01109-3797. Tel: 413-748-3360. Fax: 413-748-3631. p. 1128

Stevens, Michelle, Circ Librn, ILL Librn, Lee Public Library, Seven Mast Rd, Lee, NH, 03824. Tel: 603-659-2626. Fax: 603-659-2986. p. 1454

Stevens, Nathan, Asst Dir, North Carolina State University Libraries, College of Education Media Center, 400 Poe Hall, Campus Box 7801, Raleigh, NC, 27695-7801. Tel: 919-515-3191. Fax: 919-515-7634. p. 1816

Stevens, Norman, Exec Dir, Kankakee County Historical Society Museum Library, 801 S Eighth Ave, Kankakee, IL, 60901-4744. Tel: 815-932-5279. Fax: 815-932-5204. p. 661

Stevens, Paula, Ref Serv, Arizona Republic Library, 200 E Van Buren, Phoenix, AZ, 85004. Tel: 602-444-4446. Fax: 602-444-4294. p. 71

Stevens, Phyllis, Asst Librn, Hughesville Area Public Library, 146 S Fifth St, Hughesville, PA, 17737. Tel: 570-584-3762. Fax: 570-584-2689. p. 2070

Stevens, Rene, Tech Serv, United States Air Force, 45th Space Wing Technical Library FL2513, Bldg 989, Rm A1-S3, 1030 S Hwy A1A, Patrick AFB, FL, 32925-3002. Tel: 321-494-6638, 321-494-7220. Fax: 321-494-6636. p. 481

Stevens, Russell, Supvr, Ventura County Library, Saticoy Library, 11426 Violeta St, Saticoy, CA, 93004. Tel: 805-647-5736. Fax: 805-672-0406. p. 280

Stevens, Scott, Assoc Librn, Baltimore County Circuit Court Library, 401 Bosley Ave, Towson, MD, 21204. Tel: 410-887-3086. Fax: 410-887-4807. p. 1044

Stevens, Shelen A, Dir, Weston Public Library, 13153 Main St, Weston, OH, 43569. Tel: 419-669-3415. Fax: 419-669-3216. p. 1947

Stevens, Sheryl, Coordr, Cat, University of Toledo, 2801 W Bancroft St, Mail Stop 509, Toledo, OH, 43606-3390. Tel: 419-530-7981. Fax: 419-530-2726. p. 1941

Stevens, Spencer, Info Serv Spec, Alberta Children's Hospital Knowledge Centre, 2888 Shaganappi Trail NW, A2-908, 2nd Flr, Calgary, AB, T3B 6AB, CANADA. Tel: 403-955-7077. Fax: 403-955-2799. p. 2687

Stevens, Stacy, Dir, T B Scott Library, 106 W First St, Merrill, WI, 54452-2398. Tel: 715-536-7191. Fax: 715-536-1705. p. 2616

Stevens, Sue, Br Mgr, Rockford Public Library, East, 6685 E State St, Rockford, IL, 61108. Tel: 815-965-7606. Fax: 815-226-1538. p. 697

Stevens, Sue, ILL, Ref, Hartwick College, One Hartwick Dr, Oneonta, NY, 13820. Tel: 607-431-4440. Fax: 607-431-4457. p. 1710

Stevens, Suzanne, Circ, Allendale Township Library, 6175 Library Ln, Allendale, MI, 49401. Tel: 616-895-4178. Fax: 616-895-5178. p. 1149

Stevenson, Ann, Dept Head, Info Mgr, Audrey & Harry Hawthorn Library & Archives at the UBC Museum of Anthropology, 6393 NW Marine Dr, Vancouver, BC, V6T 1Z2, CANADA. Tel: 604-822-4834. Fax: 604-822-2974. p. 2741

Stevenson, Cara Beth, Libr Spec, Media Serv, Tech Serv, Grays Harbor College, 1620 Edward P Smith Dr, Aberdeen, WA, 98520-7599. Tel: 360-538-4050. Fax: 360-538-4294. p. 2507

Stevenson, Claire, Head, Circ, Wilbraham Public Library, 25 Crane Park Dr, Wilbraham, MA, 01095-1799. Tel: 413-596-6141. Fax: 413-596-5090. p. 1140

Stevenson, Janis K, Dir, Presque Isle District Library, 181 E Erie St, Rogers City, MI, 49779-1709. Tel: 989-734-2477, Ext 222. Fax: 989-734-4899. p. 1222

Stevenson, Karen, Asst Librn, Potomac Public Library, 110 E State St, Potomac, IL, 61865. Tel: 217-987-6457. Fax: 217-987-6457. p. 692

Stevenson, Lacy, Br Mgr, Portsmouth Public Library, South Webster Branch, 496 Webster St, South Webster, OH, 45682. Tel: 740-778-2122. Fax: 740-778-3436. p. 1931

Stevenson, Lori V, Libr Tech, Townsend Public Library, 276 Main St, Townsend, MA, 01469-1513. Tel: 978-597-1714. Fax: 978-597-2779. p. 1131

Stevenson, Lucy, Libr Spec, Saint Dominic-Jackson Memorial Hospital, 969 Lakeland Dr, Jackson, MS, 39216. Tel: 601-200-6944. Fax: 601-200-8075. p. 1305

Stevenson, Marilyn, Head Librn, Pinellas Talking Book Library, 1330 Cleveland St, Clearwater, FL, 33755-5103. Tel: 727-441-9958. Fax: 727-441-9068. p. 432

Stevenson, Marilyn, Supvr, New Hampshire State Library, Gallen State Office Park, Dolloff Bldg, 117 Pleasant St, Concord, NH, 03301-3852. Tel: 603-271-2417, 603-271-3429. Fax: 603-271-8370. p. 1443

Stevenson, Martha, Instr, Northampton Community College, 3835 Green Pond Rd, Bethlehem, PA, 18020. Tel: 610-861-5358. Fax: 610-861-5373. p. 2973

Stevenson, Michael, Coll Develop, Quinsigamond Community College, 670 W Boylston St, Worcester, MA, 01606-2092. Tel: 508-854-2793. Fax: 508-854-4204. p. 1144

Stevenson, Roxanne, Ch, Stubbs Memorial Library, 207 E Second St, Holstein, IA, 51025. Tel: 712-368-4563. Fax: 712-368-4483. p. 821

Stevenson, Sherri, Dir, Aurelia Public Library, 232 Main St, Aurelia, IA, 51005. Tel: 712-434-5330. Fax: 712-434-5330. p. 795

Stevenson, Wendy, Youth Serv, West Melbourne Public Library, 2755 Wingate Blvd, West Melbourne, FL, 32904. Tel: 321-952-4508. Fax: 321-952-4510. p. 502

Stever, Vicky, Dir, United States Air Force, 305 W F St, Bldg 278, Eglin AFB, FL, 32542-6842. Tel: 850-882-5016. Fax: 850-882-2621. p. 439

Stevick, David, Libr Dir, Houghton College, One Willard Ave, Houghton, NY, 14744. Tel: 585-567-9242. Fax: 585-567-9248. p. 1638

Steward, Barbara, Librn, Kansas State University Libraries, Mathematics & Physics Library, 105 Cardwell Hall, Manhattan, KS, 66506. Tel: 785-532-6827. Fax: 785-532-6806. p. 881

Steward, Bethan, Librn, Boston Public Library, Egleston Square, 2044 Columbus Ave, Roxbury, MA, 02119-1123. Tel: 617-445-4340. Fax: 617-445-3978. p. 1057

Steward, Karilyn, Librn, City of Calabasas Library, 200 Civic Center Way, Calabasas, CA, 91302. Tel: 818-225-7616. Fax: 818-225-7728. p. 131

Steward, Lloyd, Educ Coordr, Wildwood Correctional Complex Library, Ten Chugach Ave, Kenai, AK, 99611. Tel: 907-260-7200. Fax: 907-260-7208. p. 50

Steward, Noreen, Librn, Saranac Public Library, Clarksville Branch, 130 S Main St, Clarksville, MI, 48815. Tel: 616-693-1001. Fax: 616-693-2365. p. 1226

Stewart, Alan, Mgr, Coll Develop, Memphis Public Library & Information Center, 3030 Poplar Ave, Memphis, TN, 38111-3527. Tel: 901-415-2700. Fax: 901-323-7108. p. 2249

Stewart, Amanda, Dir, Richland Parish Library, 1410 Louisa St, Rayville, LA, 71269-3299. Tel: 318-728-4806. Fax: 318-728-6108. p. 966

Stewart, Amber, Ch, Mary Wood Weldon Memorial Library, 107 W College St, Glasgow, KY, 42141. Tel: 270-651-2824. Fax: 270-651-2824. p. 915

Stewart, Andrea W, Interim Univ Librn, The George Washington University, 2130 H St NW, Ste 201, Washington, DC, 20052. Tel: 202-994-6455. Fax: 202-994-6464. p. 401

Stewart, Angela, Librn, Palliser Regional Library, Rockglen Branch, 1018 Centre St, Rockglen, SK, S0H 3R0, CANADA. Tel: 306-476-2350. Fax: 306-476-2339. p. 2919

Stewart, Ann, Chairperson, High Prairie Municipal Library, 4723 53rd Ave, High Prairie, AB, T0G 1E0, CANADA. Tel: 780-523-3838. Fax: 780-523-3838. p. 2707

Stewart, Anna, Libr Instruction, Saint Edwards University, 3001 S Congress Ave, Austin, TX, 78704-6489. Tel: 512-428-1096. Fax: 512-448-8737. p. 2281

Stewart, Anne W, Res Librn, Crawford County Historical Society, 411 Chestnut St, Meadville, PA, 16335. Tel: 814-724-6080. Fax: 814-724-6080. p. 2086

Stewart, Barbara, Librn, Saint Clair County Public Library, Ashville Branch, Sixth Ave, Ashville, AL, 35953. Tel: 205-594-7954. p. 5

Stewart, Barbara, Librn, Webster Free Library, 22 Depot St, Kingfield, ME, 04947. Tel: 207-265-2052. p. 989

Stewart, Barbara, Cataloger, Capitan Public Library, 101 E Second St, Capitan, NM, 88316. Tel: 575-354-3035. Fax: 575-354-3223. p. 1552

Stewart, Bonnie, Dir, Maclure Library, 840 Arch St, Pittsford, VT, 05763-0060. Tel: 802-483-2972. Fax: 802-483-2703. p. 2432

Stewart, Brandi, Cataloger, Ch, Monroe County Public Library, 500 W Fourth St, Tompkinsville, KY, 42167. Tel: 270-487-5301. Fax: 270-487-5309. p. 936

Stewart, Brenton, Cat, Southern Polytechnic State University, 1100 S Marietta Pkwy, Marietta, GA, 30060-2896. Tel: 678-915-7465. Fax: 678-915-4944. p. 543

Stewart, Bruce, Libr Mgr, Alachua County Library District, Waldo Branch, 14257 Cole St, Waldo, FL, 32694. Tel: 352-468-3298. Fax: 352-468-3299. p. 449

Stewart, Byron, Asst Prof, Missouri State University, Duane G Meyer Library, 901 S National Ave, Springfield, MO, 65897. Tel: 417-836-4525. Fax: 417-836-4764. p. 2968

Stewart, Byron Y, Head, Ref & Govt Serv, Missouri State University, 850 S John Q Hammons Pkwy, Springfield, MO, 65807. Tel: 417-836-4533. Fax: 417-836-4764. p. 1367

Stewart, Carol Johnson, Dir, Libr Serv, Clayton County Library System, 865 Battlecreek Rd, Jonesboro, GA, 30236. Tel: 770-473-3850. Fax: 770-473-3858. p. 536

Stewart, Carolyn, Dir, Jasper Public Library, 14 W Second St, Jasper, TN, 37347-3409. Tel: 423-942-3369. Fax: 423-942-6383. p. 2239

Stewart, Cassandra, Librn, Sumpter Township Library, 148 Courthouse Sq, Toledo, IL, 62468. Tel: 217-849-2072. Fax: 217-849-2072. p. 710

Stewart, Catherine, Asst Dir, Ch, Memorial Library of Nazareth & Vicinity, 295 E Center St, Nazareth, PA, 18064-2298. Tel: 610-759-4932. Fax: 610-759-9513. p. 2095

Stewart, Celesta, Ch, Ch, Hobbs Public Library, 509 N Shipp, Hobbs, NM, 88240. Tel: 575-397-9328. Fax: 575-397-1508. p. 1556

Stewart, Charles, Head, Tech Serv, City College of the City University of New York, North Academic Ctr, 160 Convent Ave, New York, NY, 10031. Tel: 212-650-5369. Fax: 212-650-7604. p. 1672

Stewart, Cherilyn, Dir, Manitowoc Public Library, 707 Quay St, Manitowoc, WI, 54220. Tel: 920-686-3000. p. 2612

Stewart, Christina, Br Mgr, Florence County Library System, Pamplico Public Library, 100 E Main St, Pamplico, SC, 29583. Tel: 843-493-5441. Fax: 843-493-0361. p. 2193

Stewart, Christina, Sr Ref Librn, Florence County Library System, 509 S Dargan St, Florence, SC, 29506. Tel: 843-662-8424. Fax: 843-661-7544. p. 2193

Stewart, Christina A, Dir, Wilmington Memorial Library, 175 Middlesex Ave, Wilmington, MA, 01887-2779. Tel: 978-658-2967. Fax: 978-658-9699. p. 1141

Stewart, Christine, Dir, Caseyville Public Library District, 419 S Second St, Caseyville, IL, 62232. Tel: 618-345-5848. Fax: 618-345-0081. p. 602

Stewart, Christopher, Dean, Illinois Institute of Technology, 35 W 33rd St, Chicago, IL, 60616. Tel: 312-567-3293. Fax: 312-567-5318. p. 615

Stewart, Christopher, Web Coordr, State University of New York Downstate Medical Center, 395 Lenox Rd, Brooklyn, NY, 11203. Tel: 718-270-7400. Fax: 718-270-7413, 718-270-7468. p. 1595

Stewart, Cindy, Assoc Dir, Health Sci Libr, Dartmouth College Library, Biomedical Libraries (Dana Biomedical & Matthews-Fuller Health Sciences Library), Dana Biomedical Library/HB 6168, 64 College St, Hanover, NH, 03755-3563. Tel: 603-650-4967. p. 1450

Stewart, Cindy, Actg Dir, Central Vermont Medical Center, 130 Fisher Rd, Berlin, VT, 05602. Tel: 802-371-4205. Fax: 803-371-4575. p. 2419

Stewart, Cortiz, In Charge, United States Navy, Medical Library, Code 185, 6000 W Hwy 98, Code 185, Pensacola, FL, 32512-0003. Tel: 850-505-6635. Fax: 850-505-7063. p. 482

Stewart, Danny, Dir, Pell City Library, 1923 First Ave N, Pell City, AL, 35125. Tel: 205-884-1015. Fax: 205-814-4798. p. 33

Stewart, David, Dir, Bethel University Library, 3900 Bethel Dr, Saint Paul, MN, 55112. Tel: 651-638-6222. Fax: 651-638-6001. p. 1277

Stewart, David, Pub Serv, Wake Forest University, Coy C Carpenter School of Medicine Library, Medical Center Blvd, Winston-Salem, NC, 27157-1069. Tel: 336-716-4691. Fax: 336-716-2186. p. 1834

Stewart, David, Chair, Minnesota Theological Library Association, Luther Seminary Library, 2375 Como Ave, Saint Paul, MN, 55108. Tel: 651-641-3447. p. 2947

Stewart, David R, Dir, Luther Seminary Library, Gullixson Hall, 2375 Como Ave, Saint Paul, MN, 55108. Tel: 651-641-3592. Fax: 651-641-3280. p. 1278

Stewart, Debora A, Ref Serv, Palm Beach Atlantic University, 300 Pembroke Pl, West Palm Beach, FL, 33401-6503. Tel: 561-803-2224. Fax: 561-803-2235. p. 503

Stewart, Deborah, Asst Dir, Elkhart Public Library, 300 S Second St, Elkhart, IN, 46516-3184. Tel: 574-522-3333. Fax: 574-293-9213, 574-522-2174. p. 737

Stewart, Donetta, Dir, Auburn Public Library, 209 Pine St, Auburn, IA, 51433. Tel: 712-688-2264. Fax: 712-688-2264. p. 795

Stewart, Elaina B, Digital Initiatives Librn, Syst & Web Develop Librn, Youth Serv Librn, Oklahoma Panhandle State University, 409 W Sewell, Goodwell, OK, 73939. Tel: 580-349-1544. Fax: 580-349-1541. p. 1964

Stewart, Gina, Head, Circ, Pleasanton Public Library, 321 N Main, Pleasanton, TX, 78064. Tel: 830-569-3622. Fax: 830-569-6082. p. 2371

Stewart, Glenna, Tech Serv Mgr, North Madison County Public Library System, 1600 Main St, Elwood, IN, 46036. Tel: 765-552-5001. Fax: 765-552-0955. p. 737

Stewart, Hazel, Tech Serv, Parkersburg & Wood County Public Library, 3100 Emerson Ave, Parkersburg, WV, 26104-2414. Tel: 304-420-4587, Ext 23. Fax: 304-420-4589. p. 2568

Stewart, Henry R, Dr, Dean, Univ Libr, Troy University Library, 309 Wallace Hall, 501 University Ave, Troy, AL, 36082. Tel: 334-670-3263. Fax: 334-670-3694. p. 37

Stewart, James, Mgr, Montgomery County Public Libraries, Marilyn J Praisner Branch, 14910 Old Columbia Pike, Burtonsville, MD, 20866. Tel: 240-773-9430. Fax: 301-421-5407. p. 1039

Stewart, Jamie, Asst Librn, Chapman & Cutler, 111 W Monroe, Chicago, IL, 60603-4096. Tel: 312-845-3435. Fax: 312-701-6620. p. 607

Stewart, Janet, Syst Coordr, Shawnee State University, 940 Second St, Portsmouth, OH, 45662-4344. Tel: 740-351-3197. Fax: 740-351-3432. p. 1931

Stewart, Jean, Asst Librn, Regional Medical Center, 1001 Towson Ave, Fort Smith, AR, 72901-4915. Tel: 479-441-5337. Fax: 479-441-5339. p. 101

Stewart, Jeanie, Dir, Conran Memorial Library, 302 E Main St, Hayti, MO, 63851. Tel: 573-359-0599. p. 1330

Stewart, Jennifer, Med Librn, Sacred Heart Health System, 5151 N Ninth Ave, Pensacola, FL, 32504. Tel: 850-416-7109. Fax: 850-416-6864. p. 482

Stewart, John, Info Tech Supvr, State Library of Ohio, SEO Library Center, 40780 Marietta Rd, Caldwell, OH, 43724. Tel: 740-783-5705. p. 1890

Stewart, June, Dir, Reader Serv, University of Arkansas at Little Rock, Pulaski County Law Library, 1203 McMath Ave, Little Rock, AR, 72202-5142. Tel: 501-324-9975. Fax: 501-324-9447. p. 107

Stewart, Kathleen, Mgr, Ser, Oregon Health & Science University Library, 3181 SW Sam Jackson Park Rd, Portland, OR, 97239-3098. Tel: 503-494-3460. Fax: 503-494-3227. p. 2013

Stewart, Kristen, Asst Br Librn/Ref, Brazoria County Library System, Pearland Branch, 3522 Liberty Dr, Pearland, TX, 77581. Tel: 281-485-4876. Fax: 281-485-5576. p. 2276

Stewart, Laura, Adult Serv, Iberville Parish Library, 24605 J Gerald Berret Blvd, Plaquemine, LA, 70764. Tel: 225-687-2520, 225-687-4397. Fax: 225-687-9719. p. 965

Stewart, Linda, Librn, Fayette County Public Libraries, Fayetteville Branch, 200 W Maple Ave, Fayetteville, WV, 25840. Tel: 304-574-0070. Fax: 304-574-0070. p. 2568

Stewart, Lynn, Br Librn, Granby Public Library, Frederick H Cossitt Library, 388 N Granby Rd, North Granby, CT, 06060. Tel: 860-653-8958. Fax: 860-653-8958. p. 341

Stewart, Margaret, Ref Serv, Widener University, School of Law Library, 4601 Concord Pike, Wilmington, DE, 19803. Tel: 302-477-2039. Fax: 302-477-2240. p. 389

Stewart, Margaret Z, Exec Dir, Erie County Public Library, 160 E Front St, Erie, PA, 16507. Tel: 814-451-6900. Fax: 814-451-6907. p. 2055

Stewart, Martha M, Head, Syst, United States Air Force, Air University - Muir S Fairchild Research Information Center, 600 Chennault Circle, Maxwell AFB, AL, 36112-6010. Tel: 334-953-2474. p. 24

Stewart, Marvin, In Charge, Charleston County Public Library, Village Branch, 430 Whilden St, Mount Pleasant, SC, 29464. Tel: 843-884-9741. Fax: 843-884-5396. p. 2183

Stewart, Mary, Sr City Librn, Ventura County Library, E P Foster Library, 651 E Main St, Ventura, CA, 93001. Tel: 805-641-4414. Fax: 805-648-3696. p. 280

Stewart, Mary, Dean, Indian Hills Community College, 525 Grandview Ave, Bldg 10, Ottumwa, IA, 52501-1398. Tel: 641-683-5199. Fax: 641-683-5184. p. 837

Stewart, Mary Jane, Dir, Sutton Public Library, 450 Fourth St, No C, Sutton, WV, 26601. Tel: 304-765-7224. Fax: 304-765-7224. p. 2572

Stewart, Melissa, Head of Outreach, Hamilton East Public Library, One Library Plaza, Cumberland Rd, Noblesville, IN, 46060-5639. Tel: 317-770-3235. Fax: 317-776-6936. p. 769

Stewart, Nancy, Law Librn, Plumas County Law Library, 520 W Main St, Rm 414, Quincy, CA, 95971. Tel: 530-283-6325. p. 212

Stewart, Nancy, Librn, Providence Historical Society, 3980 Tampa Rd, Ste 207, Tampa, FL, 34677. Tel: 813-855-4635. Fax: 813-855-2309. p. 497

Stewart, Nancy Rhea, Dir, Carbon Hill City Library, 414 NW Fifth Ave, Carbon Hill, AL, 35549. Tel: 205-924-4254. p. 11

Stewart, Rick, Mgr, W E Sears Youth Center, 9400 Sears Lane, Poplar Bluff, MO, 63901-9716. Tel: 573-840-9280. Fax: 573-840-9352. p. 1349

Stewart, Robert, In Charge, Wilton Historical Society, Inc Library, 224 Danbury Rd, Wilton, CT, 06897. Tel: 203-762-7257. Fax: 203-762-3297. p. 378

Stewart, Robert W, Dir, Asbury Park Public Library, 500 First Ave, Asbury Park, NJ, 07712. Tel: 732-774-4221. Fax: 732-988-6101. p. 1469

Stewart, Sandra, Actg Div Mgr, San Jose Public Library, 150 E San Fernando St, San Jose, CA, 95112-3580. Tel: 408-808-2186. p. 250

Stewart, Shannon, Assoc Librn, Concordia College, 1804 Green St, Selma, AL, 36703-3323. Tel: 334-874-5700, Ext 19731. Fax: 334-874-5755. p. 35

Stewart, Shannon, Librn, North Central Regional Library, Royal City Community, 136 Camelia St, Royal City, WA, 99357. Tel: 509-346-9281. Fax: 509-346-9281. p. 2549

Stewart, Sharon, Librn, B Elizabeth Strong Memorial Library, 6312 E Main St, Turin, NY, 13473-9998. Tel: 315-348-6433. Fax: 315-348-6433. p. 1757

Stewart, Sia, Dir, Kingston Public Library, Six Green St, Kingston, MA, 02364. Tel: 781-585-0517. Fax: 781-585-0521. p. 1097

Stewart, Steven, Libr Tech Assoc for Outreach & Pub Serv, Barton College, 400 Atlantic Christian College Dr NE, Wilson, NC, 27893. Tel: 252-399-6500. Fax: 252-399-6571. p. 1831

Stewart, Susan, Ref Serv, Ch, Wallingford Public Library, 200 N Main St, Wallingford, CT, 06492-3791. Tel: 203-265-6754. Fax: 203-269-5698. p. 373

Stewart, Susan, Ch, Allen County Public Library, 106 W Main, Scottsville, KY, 42164. Tel: 270-237-3861. Fax: 270-237-4095. p. 934

Stewart, Susan, Br Mgr, Jersey City Free Public Library, Five Corners, 678 Newark Ave, Jersey City, NJ, 07306. Tel: 201-547-4548. Fax: 201-656-1517. p. 1492

Stewart, Susan, Br Mgr, Jersey City Free Public Library, Watters Media Arts Department, 678 Newark Ave, Jersey City, NJ, 07306. Tel: 201-547-4546. Fax: 201-656-1517. p. 1492

Stewart, Susan A, Dir, Life University, 1269 Barclay Circle, Marietta, GA, 30060. Tel: 770-426-2692. Fax: 770-426-2745. p. 543

Stewart, Tammy, Tech Serv, Fayetteville Technical Community College, 2201 Hull Rd, Fayetteville, NC, 28303. Tel: 910-678-8253. Fax: 910-678-8401. p. 1793

Stewart, Tammy, Asst Prof, Missouri State University, Duane G Meyer Library, 901 S National Ave, Springfield, MO, 65897. Tel: 417-836-4525. Fax: 417-836-4764. p. 2968

Stewart, Valerie Rice, Librn, Cascade Public Library, 105 Front St, Cascade, ID, 83611. Tel: 208-382-4757. Fax: 208-382-4757. p. 572

Stewart, Vivian, Assoc Dir, Libr Admin, Southwest Tennessee Community College, George Freeman Library, 5983 Macon Cove, Memphis, TN, 38134. Tel: 901-333-4706. Fax: 901-333-5141. p. 2251

Stewart, Vivian, Assoc Dir, Southwest Tennessee Community College, 170 Myrtle St, Memphis, TN, 38103. Tel: 901-333-5067. Fax: 901-333-5141. p. 2251

Stewart, Vivian, Assoc Dir, Southwest Tennessee Community College, Gill Library, 3833 Mountain Terrace, Memphis, TN, 38127. Tel: 901-333-5979. Fax: 901-333-5980. p. 2251

Stewart, Vivian, Assoc Dir, Southwest Tennessee Community College, Southeast Center Library, 5396 Mendenhall Mall, Memphis, TN, 38115. Tel: 901-333-6037. Fax: 901-333-6038. p. 2252

Stewart, Vivian, Assoc Dir, Southwest Tennessee Community College, Whitehaven Center Library, 3035 Directors Row, Bldg 6, Memphis, TN, 38131. Tel: 901-333-6442. Fax: 901-333-6441. p. 2252

Stewart, Wanda, Librn, Middle Georgia Regional Library System, Charles A Lanford MD Library, 6504 Houston Rd, Macon, GA, 31216-6702. Tel: 478-621-6970. Fax: 478-621-6985. p. 541

Stewart, Wendy, Res Serv/Spec Projects Librn, Portland State University Library, 1875 SW Park Ave, Portland, OR, 97201-3220. Tel: 503-725-5785. Fax: 503-725-4524. p. 2014

Steytler, Jessica, Archivist, American Congregational Association, 14 Beacon St, 2nd Flr, Boston, MA, 02108-9999. Tel: 617-523-0470. Fax: 617-523-0491. p. 1054

Stiassny, Melanie, Curator, American Museum of Natural History Library, Bashford Dean Memorial Library, Department of Ichthyology, 79th St at Central Park W, New York, NY, 10024-5192. Tel: 212-769-5796. Fax: 212-769-5642. p. 1668

Stichert, Sara, ILL, University of Wisconsin Oshkosh, 801 Elmwood Ave, Oshkosh, WI, 54901. Tel: 920-424-3348. Fax: 920-424-7338. p. 2628

Stick, Malcolm, Libr Mgr, Thelma Fanning Memorial Library, 1907 21 Ave, Nanton, AB, T0L 1R0, CANADA. Tel: 403-646-5535. p. 2712

Stickel, Rebecca, Fiscal Officer, London Public Library, 20 E First St, London, OH, 43140. Tel: 740-852-9543. Fax: 740-852-3691. p. 1911

Stickman, James S, Ser, University of Washington Libraries, Allen Library, 4th Flr, Rm 482, Box 352900, Seattle, WA, 98195-2900. Tel: 206-543-1760. Fax: 206-685-8727. p. 2533

Stickney, Stephen, Br Mgr, Brooklyn Public Library, Coney Island, 1901 Mermaid Ave, Brooklyn, NY, 11224. Tel: 718-265-3220. Fax: 718-265-5026. p. 1591

Stickney, Zephorene L, Col Archivist/Spec Coll Curator, Wheaton College Library, 26 E Main St, Norton, MA, 02766-2322. Tel: 508-286-3712. p. 1115

Stidham, Jennifer, Librn, Houston Community College Northeast College, Northline Library, 8001 Fulton St, Houston, TX, 77022. Tel: 713-718-8045. Fax: 713-718-8063. p. 2338

Stidham, Linda, Head, Ref, Grand Prairie Public Library System, 901 Conover Dr, Grand Prairie, TX, 75051. Tel: 972-237-5700. Fax: 972-237-5750. p. 2329

Stidsen, Carl, Res Librn, New England Air Museum, Bradley Int Airport, Windsor Locks, CT, 06096. Tel: 860-623-3305. Fax: 860-627-2820. p. 379

Stieber, Dale, Spec Coll Librn, Occidental College Library, 1600 Campus Rd, Los Angeles, CA, 90041. Tel: 323-259-2852. Fax: 323-341-4991. p. 176

Stief, Denise, Librn, Cereal & District Municipal Library, 415 Main St, Cereal, AB, T0J 0N0, CANADA. Tel: 403-326-3853. p. 2694

Stieglitz, Tara, Ref Librn, Grant MacEwan University Library, 10700 104th Ave, Edmonton, AB, T5J 4S2, CANADA. Tel: 780-497-5850. Fax: 780-497-5895. p. 2701

Stielstra, Julie, Mgr, Libr of Cadence Health, Cadence Health - Central DuPage Hospital, 25 N Winfield Rd, Winfield, IL, 60190. Tel: 630-933-4536. Fax: 630-933-4530. p. 720

Stiens, Mary Jane, Librn, Northwest Missouri State University, Horace Mann Library, Brown Hall 121, 800 University Dr, Maryville, MO, 64468. Tel: 660-562-1271. Fax: 660-562-1992. p. 1345

Stier Pulver, Karen, Mgr, Pub Serv, Wood Dale Public Library District, 520 N Wood Dale Rd, Wood Dale, IL, 60191. Tel: 630-766-6762. Fax: 630-766-5715. p. 721

Stier, Rosie, Librn, Allen County Public Library, Little Turtle, 2201 Sherman Blvd, Fort Wayne, IN, 46808. Tel: 260-421-1335. Fax: 260-424-5170. p. 741

Stierholz, Katrina L, Dir, Federal Reserve Bank of Saint Louis, One Federal Reserve Bank Plaza, Saint Louis, MO, 63102-2005. Tel: 314-444-8552. Fax: 314-444-8694. p. 1354

Stierman, Jeanne, Ref Librn, Western Illinois University Libraries, One University Circle, Macomb, IL, 61455. Tel: 309-298-2744, Ext 4. Fax: 309-298-2791. p. 669

Stierman, John, Ref Librn, Western Illinois University Libraries, One University Circle, Macomb, IL, 61455. Tel: 309-298-2756, Ext 5. Fax: 309-298-2791. p. 669

Stiffler, Joan, Br Mgr, Harford County Public Library, Norrisville Branch, 5310 Norrisville Rd, White Hall, MD, 21161-8924. Tel: 410-692-7850. Fax: 410-692-7851. p. 1020

Stifler, Luke, Asst Br Mgr, Louisville Free Public Library, Southwest Regional, 10375 Dixie Hwy, Louisville, KY, 40272. Tel: 502-933-0029. Fax: 502-933-2782. p. 925

Stigleman, Sue, Librn, Mountain Area Health Education Center, 121 Hendersonville Rd, Asheville, NC, 28803. Tel: 828-257-4451. Fax: 828-257-4712. p. 1775

Stigler, Brad, Dir, Libr Serv, Westville Correctional Facility, 5501 S 1100 W, Westville, IN, 46391. Tel: 219-785-2511, Ext 4672. Fax: 219-785-4864. p. 787

Stiles, Cheryl, Librn/Grad Libr Instruction, Kennesaw State University, 1000 Chastain Rd, Kennesaw, GA, 30144. Tel: 770-423-6003. Fax: 770-423-6185. p. 537

Stiles, Peggy, Circ, Stanton County Library, 103 E Sherman, Johnson, KS, 67855. Tel: 620-492-2302. Fax: 620-492-2203. p. 874

Stiles, Robert, Principal Librn, Detroit Symphony Orchestra Library, 3711 Woodward Ave, Detroit, MI, 48201. Tel: 313-576-5100, 313-576-5172. Fax: 313-576-5593. p. 1170

Still, Echo, Admin Serv, Western Iowa Technical Community College, 4647 Stone Ave, Sioux City, IA, 51106. Tel: 712-274-8733, Ext 1211. Fax: 712-274-6423. p. 844

Still, Julie, Ref, Rutgers University Libraries, Paul Robeson Library, Camden, 300 N Fourth St, Camden, NJ, 08102-1404. Tel: 856-225-6033. Fax: 856-225-6428. p. 1477

Stille, Angie, Info Spec, University of Bridgeport, 126 Park Ave, Bridgeport, CT, 06604-5620. Tel: 203-576-4527. Fax: 203-576-4791. p. 332

Stiller, Jeanne, Ref, Newburgh Free Library, 124 Grand St, Newburgh, NY, 12550. Tel: 845-563-3600. Fax: 845-563-3602. p. 1705

Stiller, Marcia, Libr Dir, Corry Public Library, 117 W Washington St, Corry, PA, 16407. Tel: 814-664-4404, 814-664-7611. Fax: 814-663-0742. p. 2047

Stiller, Shannon, Adult Serv, Ripon Public Library, 120 Jefferson St, Ripon, WI, 54971-1395. Tel: 920-748-6160. Fax: 920-748-6298. p. 2634

Stilley, Bettye W, Librn, United States Navy, 2080 Child St, Jacksonville, FL, 32214. Tel: 904-542-7300. Fax: 904-542-7093. p. 455

Stilley, Judith, Librn, Grand Rapids Public Library, Van Belkum Branch, 1563 Plainfield Ave NE, Grand Rapids, MI, 49505. Tel: 616-988-5410. Fax: 616-365-2615. p. 1185

Stillinger, Linda, Libr Mgr, Big Valley Municipal Library, 29 First Ave S, Big Valley, AB, T0J 0G0, CANADA. Tel: 403-876-2642. Fax: 403-876-2401. p. 2685

Stillings, Craig, Dep Dir, Winter Park Public Library, 460 E New England Ave, Winter Park, FL, 32789-4493. Tel: 407-623-3458. Fax: 407-623-3489. p. 505

Stillman, Ann, Mgr, Montgomery County Public Libraries, Quince Orchard Library, 15831 Quince Orchard Rd, Gaithersburg, MD, 20878. Tel: 240-777-0212. Fax: 240-777-0202. p. 1039

Stillman, Garry, Ref, Saint Mary's University, Sarita Kennedy East Law Library, One Camino Santa Maria, San Antonio, TX, 78228-8605. Tel: 210-436-3435, Ext 1366. Fax: 210-436-3240. p. 2381

Stillman, Patti, Mgr, ILL, Pembroke Public Library, 237 Victoria St, Pembroke, ON, K8A 4K5, CANADA. Tel: 613-732-8844. Fax: 613-732-1116. p. 2835

Stillson, Cheryl, Asst Dir, Mark Skinner Library, 48 West Rd, Manchester, VT, 05254. Tel: 802-362-2607. p. 2427

Stillwagon, Ingrid, In Charge, Long Beach Public Library, Point Lookout Branch, 26B Lido Blvd, Point Lookout, NY, 11569. Tel: 516-432-3409. p. 1654

Stillwell, Kristine, Dr, Ref Serv, Troy University Library, 309 Wallace Hall, 501 University Ave, Troy, AL, 36082. Tel: 334-670-3261. Fax: 334-670-3694. p. 37

Stillwell, Lisa, Info Literacy, Franklin & Marshall College, 450 College Ave, Lancaster, PA, 17603-3318. Tel: 717-291-3844. Fax: 717-291-4160. p. 2076

Stilson, Scott, Libr Supvr, South Puget Sound Community College Library, 2011 Mottman Rd SW, Olympia, WA, 98512. Tel: 360-596-5271. Fax: 360-596-5714. p. 2522

Stilwell, Arlene, Dir, New Sharon Public Library, 107 W Maple, New Sharon, IA, 50207. Tel: 641-637-2689. p. 835

Stilwell, Martha A, Acq/Ref Serv, Dir, Kellogg Community College, 450 North Ave, Battle Creek, MI, 49017-3397. Tel: 269-965-4122, Ext 2380. Fax: 269-965-4133. p. 1155

Stimson, Jane, Ref, San Jacinto College South, 13735 Beamer Rd, Houston, TX, 77089-6099. Tel: 281-922-3416. Fax: 281-922-3470. p. 2342

Stinchfield, Karen, Dir, Cushman Library, 28 Church St, Bernardston, MA, 01337. Tel: 413-648-5402. Fax: 413-648-0168. p. 1053

Stinchfield, Mary Ellen, Vols Serv Coordr, Cleveland Bradley County Public Library, 795 Church St NE, Cleveland, TN, 37311-5295. Tel: 423-472-2163. Fax: 423-339-9791. p. 2229

Stinchfield, Pat, Mgr, Auglaize County Public District Library, Edward R & Minnie D White Memorial, 108 E Wapakoneta St, Waynesfield, OH, 45896. Tel: 419-568-5851. Fax: 419-568-2368. p. 1944

Stinchfield, Patricia, Mgr, Auglaize County Public District Library, Cridersville Public Library, 116 W Main St, Cridersville, OH, 45895. Tel: 419-645-5447. Fax: 419-645-6019. p. 1944

Stincic, Anne, Dir, Waterloo Library & Historical Society, 31 E Williams St, Waterloo, NY, 13165. Tel: 315-539-3313. Fax: 315-539-7798. p. 1763

Stine, Joni, Dir, Bella Vista Public Library, 11 Dickens Pl, Bella Vista, AR, 72714-4603. Tel: 479-855-1753. Fax: 479-855-4475. p. 94

Stine, Nancy, Coordr, Northwest AHEC Library at Salisbury, c/o Rowan Regional Medical Ctr, 612 Mocksville Ave, Salisbury, NC, 28144. Tel: 704-210-5069. Fax: 704-636-5050. p. 2951

Stine, Walter, Exec Dir, Fenway Libraries Online, Inc, c/o Wentworth Institute Technology, 550 Huntington Ave, Boston, MA, 02115. Tel: 617-442-2384. Fax: 617-442-1519. p. 2945

Stinehour, Donna, Librn, Davies Memorial Library, 532 Maple St, Lower Waterford, VT, 05848. Tel: 802-748-4609. p. 2427

Stiner, Janis, Circ, ILL, Grove City Community Library, 125 W Main St, Grove City, PA, 16127-1569. Tel: 724-458-7320. Fax: 724-458-7332. p. 2063

Stines, Joe, Dir of Libr, Tampa-Hillsborough County Public Library System, 900 N Ashley Dr, Tampa, FL, 33602-3704. Tel: 813-273-3652. Fax: 813-273-3707. p. 497

Stinnett, Judy, ILL, Athens State University Library, 407 E Pryor St, Athens, AL, 35611. Tel: 256-233-8218. Fax: 256-233-6547. p. 5

Stinson, Amanda, Cat, Ardmore Higher Education Center Library, 611 Veterans Blvd, Ardmore, OK, 73401. Tel: 580-220-2872. Fax: 580-223-5611. p. 1956

Stinson, Betty Jean, Librn, Catawba County Library, Maiden Branch, 11 S A Ave, Maiden, NC, 28650. Tel: 828-428-2712. Fax: 828-428-3845. p. 1813

Stinson, Judy, Doc/Ref Serv, Washington & Lee University, Wilbur C Hall Law Library, Lewis Hall, E Denny Circle, Lexington, VA, 24450. Tel: 540-458-8544. Fax: 540-458-8967. p. 2474

Stinson, Peggy, Cat, Catawba County Library, 115 West C St, Newton, NC, 28658. Tel: 828-465-8664. Fax: 828-465-8983. p. 1813

Stipo, Ellen, Commun Libr Mgr, Queens Borough Public Library, South Jamaica Community Library, 108-41 Guy Brewer Blvd, Jamaica, NY, 11433. Tel: 718-739-4088. p. 1645

Stirk, Kate, Librn, North Metro Technical College/Georgia Highlands College Library, 5198 Ross Rd, Acworth, GA, 30102. Tel: 770-975-4054. Fax: 770-975-4284. p. 507

Stirling, Isabel, Assoc Univ Librn, University of California, Berkeley, 255 Doe Library, Berkeley, CA, 94720-6000. Tel: 510-642-3773. Fax: 510-643-8179. p. 127

Stirling, Marlene, Dir, Nora Springs Public Library, 45 N Hawkeye, Nora Springs, IA, 50458. Tel: 641-749-5569. p. 835

Stirnaman, Jason, Digital Projects Librn, University of Kansas Medical Center, 2100 W 39th Ave, Kansas City, KS, 66160-7180. Tel: 913-588-7319. Fax: 913-588-7304. p. 876

Stites, Amanda, Coop Librn, IBM Corp, 11501 Burnet Rd, Austin, TX, 78758. Tel: 512-833-9279. p. 2280

Stites, Barbara, Dr, Assoc Dir, Florida Gulf Coast University Library, 10501 FGCU Blvd S, Fort Myers, FL, 33965-6501. Tel: 239-590-7602. p. 444

Stites, Jill, Mgr, Ryerson Nature Library, 21950 N Riverwoods Rd, Deerfield, IL, 60015. Tel: 847-968-3321. Fax: 847-948-7712. p. 635

Stith, Bobbie Jo, Dir, Anna Miller Museum Library, 401 Delaware, Newcastle, WY, 82701. Tel: 307-746-4188. Fax: 307-746-4629. p. 2658

Stith, Janet, Assoc Dean/Dir, University of Kentucky Libraries, Medical Center Library, 800 Rose St, Lexington, KY, 40536-0298. Tel: 859-323-5300. Fax: 859-323-1040. p. 922

Stith, Megan, Ch, Meade County Public Library, 400 Library Pl, Brandenburg, KY, 40108-1045. Tel: 270-422-2094. Fax: 270-422-3133. p. 908

Stitson, Jessica, Acq, Woburn Public Library, 45 Pleasant St, Woburn, MA, 01801. Tel: 781-933-0148. Fax: 781-938-7860. p. 1142

Stitt, Walter, Dir, Attleboro Public Library, 74 N Main St, Attleboro, MA, 02703. Tel: 508-222-0157, 508-222-0159. Fax: 508-226-3326. p. 1050

Stivers, Beverly, Dir, Nigel Sprouse Memorial Library, 102 E Kimball, Callaway, NE, 68825. Tel: 308-836-2610. Fax: 308-836-2610. p. 1395

Stivers, Rachelle, Dir, Heartland Community College Library, 1500 W Raab Rd, Normal, IL, 61761. Tel: 309-268-8274. Fax: 309-268-7989. p. 681

Stivers, Robert, Dir, Kilpatrick Stockton, 1100 Peachtree St, Ste 2800, Atlanta, GA, 30309. Tel: 404-815-6261. Fax: 404-815-6555. p. 516

Stivers, Robert, Mgr, Info Serv, Harter, Secrest & Emery LLP, 1600 Bausch & Lomb Pl, Rochester, NY, 14604. Tel: 585-231-1230. Fax: 585-232-2152. p. 1729

Stivers, Tracey, Archives, Database Coordr, Tech Serv, Cincinnati State Technical & Community College, 3520 Central Pkwy, Cincinnati, OH, 45223-2612. Tel: 513-569-1608. Fax: 513-559-1527. p. 1869

Stiverson, Cynthia, Acq Mgr, Maryland Department of Legislative Services Library, 90 State Circle, Annapolis, MD, 21401. Tel: 410-946-5400. Fax: 410-946-5405. p. 1010

Stiverson, Keith Ann, Libr Dir, Illinois Institute of Technology, Chicago-Kent College of Law Library, 565 W Adams St, Chicago, IL, 60661. Tel: 312-906-5610. Fax: 312-906-5679. p. 615

Stiwinter, Katherine Knott, Pub Serv Librn, Spartanburg Community College Library, 800 Brisack Rd, Spartanburg, SC, 29305. Tel: 864-592-4615. Fax: 864-592-4762. p. 2205

Stoan, Stephen K, Dir, Drury University, 900 N Benton Ave, Springfield, MO, 65802. Tel: 417-873-7282. Fax: 417-873-7432. p. 1366

Stobbe, Julie, Dir, Omro Public Library, 405 E Huron St, Omro, WI, 54963-1405. Tel: 920-685-7016. Fax: 920-685-7017. p. 2627

Stobbe, Linda, Bus Mgr, Northern Waters Library Service, 3200 E Lakeshore Dr, Ashland, WI, 54806-2510. Tel: 715-682-2365, Ext 14. Fax: 715-685-2704. p. 2579

Stoch, Ronald V, Dir, Eisenhower Public Library District, 4613 N Oketo Ave, Harwood Heights, IL, 60706. Tel: 708-867-7828. Fax: 708-867-1535. p. 654

Stock, Lisa, Dean, Learning Res, College of DuPage Library, 425 Fawell Blvd, Glen Ellyn, IL, 60137-6599. Tel: 630-942-2350. Fax: 630-858-8757. p. 649

Stock, Matt, Librn, University of Oklahoma, Architecture, Architecture Library, LLG8, 830 Van Vleet Oval, Norman, OK, 73019. Tel: 405-325-5521. Fax: 405-325-6637. p. 1971

Stock, Matt, Librn, University of Oklahoma, Fine Arts, Fine Arts Library, 20, 500 W Boyd St, Norman, OK, 73019. Tel: 405-325-4243. Fax: 405-325-4243. p. 1971

Stockamp, Steve, Circ Supvr, University of Washington Libraries, Engineering Library, Engineering Library Bldg, Box 352170, Seattle, WA, 98195-2170. Tel: 206-543-0740. Fax: 206-543-3305. p. 2533

Stockdale, June, Chief Librn, Nelson Public Library, 602 Stanley St, Nelson, BC, V1L 1N4, CANADA. Tel: 250-352-6333. Fax: 250-354-1799. p. 2733

Stocker, Gina, Acq, Northwest University, 5520 108th Ave NE, Kirkland, WA, 98083-0579. Tel: 425-889-5301. Fax: 425-889-7801. p. 2519

Stocker, Jennifer, Dir, Easton Area Public Library & District Center, 515 Church St, Easton, PA, 18042-3587. Tel: 610-258-2917, Ext 310. Fax: 610-253-2231. p. 2052

Stockert, Vera, Commun Librn, Roundup Community Library, 601 Sixth Ave W, Roundup, MT, 59072. Tel: 406-323-1802. Fax: 406-323-1346. p. 1388

Stocking, Pamela, Dir, Ellenville Public Library & Museum, 40 Center St, Ellenville, NY, 12428-1396. Tel: 845-647-5530. Fax: 845-647-3554. p. 1619

Stockinger, Jill, Br Mgr, Sacramento Public Library, Rancho Cordova Community Library, 9845 Folsom Blvd, Sacramento, CA, 95827. p. 225

Stockman, Cyndi, Librn, Elk Lake Public Library, First St, Elk Lake, ON, P0J 1G0, CANADA. Tel: 705-678-2340. Fax: 705-678-2340. p. 2803

Stockman, Ginny, Mgr, Lyon County Library System, Smith Valley Branch, 22 Day Lane, Smith, NV, 89430-9707. Tel: 775-465-2369. Fax: 775-465-2309. p. 1435

Stockman, Jeanne, Libr Mgr, Lyon County Library System, 20 Nevin Way, Yerington, NV, 89447. Tel: 775-463-6645. Fax: 775-463-6646. p. 1435

Stockstill, Judy, Dir, Libr Serv, Central Christian College of Kansas, 1200 S Main, McPherson, KS, 67460. Tel: 620-241-0723, Ext 359. Fax: 620-241-6032. p. 883

Stockton, David, Cat, Oglethorpe University, 4484 Peachtree Rd NE, Atlanta, GA, 30319. Tel: 404-364-8511. Fax: 404-364-8517. p. 517

Stockton, David, Assoc Dir, Mat Proc, United States Military Academy Library, Jefferson Hall Library & Learning Center, 758 Cullum Rd, West Point, NY, 10996. Tel: 845-938-3833. Fax: 845-938-4000. p. 1767

Stockton, Gary, Acq, Archivist, Illinois Historic Preservation Agency, 112 N Sixth St, Springfield, IL, 62701. Tel: 217-524-5939. Fax: 217-785-6250. p. 705

Stockwell, Angela N, Coll Spec, University of Maine, 56 Norridgewock Ave, Skowhegan, ME, 04976. Tel: 207-474-7133. Fax: 207-474-8878. p. 1001

Stockwell, Patricia, Head, Tech Serv, Pikes Peak Community College Library, 5675 S Academy Blvd, C7, Colorado Springs, CO, 80906-5498. Tel: 719-502-3238. p. 296

Stoddard, Barbara J, Asst Librn, Sugar Grove Free Library, Harmon & School Sts, Sugar Grove, PA, 16350. Tel: 814-489-7872. Fax: 814-489-7826. p. 2144

Stoddard, Kim, Coordr, Mohave County Library District, Golden Shores Community Library, 13169 S Golden Shores Pkwy, Topock, AZ, 86436-1086. Tel: 928-768-2235. Fax: 928-768-2235. p. 67

Stoddard, Lauren, Br Mgr, Washington County Library System, Hurricane Branch, 36 S 300 West, Hurricane, UT, 84737-2100. Tel: 435-635-4621. Fax: 435-635-3845. p. 2412

Stoddard, Laurie, Librn, Renfrew County Law Association, 297 Pembroke St E, Pembroke, ON, K8A 3K2, CANADA. Tel: 613-732-4880. Fax: 613-732-2262. p. 2835

Stoddard, Mari, Info Serv Librn, University of Arizona, Arizona Health Sciences Library, 1501 N Campbell Ave, Tucson, AZ, 85724. Tel: 520-626-2925. Fax: 520-626-2922. p. 88

Stoddard, Morgan, Ref Librn, Georgetown University, Georgetown Law Library (John Wolff & Edward Bennett Williams Libraries), 111 G St NW, Washington, DC, 20001. Fax: 202-662-9168. p. 403

Stoddard, Robert, Acq, Holyoke Community College Library, Donahue Bldg, 2nd Flr, 303 Homestead Ave, Holyoke, MA, 01040-1099. Tel: 413-552-2376. Fax: 413-552-2729. p. 1095

Stoddard, William, Circ, Otterbein University, 138 W Main St, Westerville, OH, 43081. Tel: 614-823-1985. Fax: 614-823-1921. p. 1946

Stoddart, Joan, Dep Dir, University of Utah, Spencer S Eccles Health Sciences Library, Bldg 589, 10 N 1900 E, Salt Lake City, UT, 84112-5890. Tel: 801-581-8771. Fax: 801-581-3632. p. 2415

Stodola, Deborah, Librn, Fisher-Whiting Memorial Library, 609 Courtright St, Mapleton, IA, 51034. Tel: 712-881-1312. Fax: 712-881-1312. p. 829

Stoebner, Mark, Librn, Mike Durfee State Prison, 1412 Wood St, Springfield, SD, 57062. Tel: 605-369-2201, 605-369-4318. Fax: 604-369-2813. p. 2220

Stoelb, Barbara, ILL, Edwin A Bemis Public Library, 6014 S Datura St, Littleton, CO, 80120-2636. Tel: 303-795-3961. Fax: 303-795-3996. p. 316

Stoesz, Conrad, Archivist, Centre for Mennonite Brethren Studies Archive, 1310 Taylor Ave, Winnipeg, MB, R3M 3Z6, CANADA. Tel: 204-669-6575. Fax: 204-654-1865. p. 2755

Stoesz, Rachel, Libr Mgr, DeBolt Public Library, PO Box 480, DeBolt, AB, T0H 1B0, CANADA. Tel: 780-957-3770. p. 2696

Stoffel, Ann, Acq, Librn I, Louisville Public Library, 951 Spruce St, Louisville, CO, 80027. Tel: 303-335-4849. Fax: 303-335-4833. p. 317

Stoffela, Peter J, Dir, Prof, University of Florida, 2199 S Rock Rd, Fort Pierce, FL, 34945. Tel: 772-468-3922. Fax: 772-468-5668. p. 447

Stoffer, Rhonda, Head, Genealogical Serv, Marion Public Library, 600 S Washington St, Marion, IN, 46953-1992. Tel: 765-668-2900. Fax: 765-668-2911. p. 763

Stoffers, Margaret, Br Mgr, Great River Regional Library, Elk River Library, 13020 Orono Pkwy, Elk River, MN, 55330. Tel: 763-441-1641. Fax: 763-241-9286. p. 1275

Stoffle, Carla, Dean of Libr, University of Arizona, 1510 E University Blvd, Tucson, AZ, 85721. Tel: 520-621-6441. p. 88

Stofocik, Jai, Ref Serv, Tidewater Community College Learning Resources Center, 300 Granby St, Norfolk, VA, 23510. Tel: 757-822-1100. Fax: 757-822-1106. p. 2483

Stofregen, Kathleen, Asst Librn, Ch, Broken Bow Public Library, 404 Broadway, Broken Bow, OK, 74728. Tel: 580-584-2815. Fax: 580-584-9449. p. 1959

Stohl, Valerie, Adult Serv, Tech Serv, Madison Library District, 73 N Center, Rexburg, ID, 83440-1539. Tel: 208-356-3461. p. 582

Stohr, Nicki, Dir, Sam Fore Jr Wilson County Public Library, One Library Lane, Floresville, TX, 78114. Tel: 830-393-7361. Fax: 830-393-7337. p. 2319

Stohr, S, Asst Dir, Nissen Public Library, 217 W Fifth, Saint Ansgar, IA, 50472-0040. Tel: 641-713-2218. Fax: 641-713-4716. p. 842

Stohs, Cindy, Dir, Coffey County Library, LeRoy Branch, 725 Main St, LeRoy, KS, 66857. Tel: 620-964-2321. Fax: 620-964-2394. p. 859

Stojakovic, Tamara, Br Mgr, Mississauga Library System, South Common, 2233 S Millway Dr, Mississauga, ON, L5L 3H7, CANADA. Tel: 905-615-4770. Fax: 905-615-4771. p. 2823

Stojanovic-Lewis, Diana, Sr Libr Tech, University of Manitoba Libraries, J W Crane Memorial Library, 2109 Portage Ave, Winnipeg, MB, R3J 0L3, CANADA. Tel: 204-831-2152. Fax: 204-888-1805. p. 2758

Stokanovich, Bree, Adult Serv, Hamburg Township Library, 10411 Merrill Rd, Hamburg, MI, 48139. Tel: 810-231-1771. Fax: 810-231-1520. p. 1187

Stoker, Mike, Assoc Dir, Finance & Operations, Salt Lake County Library Services, 2197 E Fort Union Blvd, Salt Lake City, UT, 84121-3139. Tel: 801-943-4636. Fax: 801-942-6323. p. 2413

Stoker, R Wayne, Dir, Las Vegas FamilySearch Library, 509 S Ninth St, Las Vegas, NV, 89101. Tel: 702-528-2348. Fax: 702-243-4228. p. 1430

Stokes, Alan, Interim Dir, University of South Carolina, South Caroliniana, Columbia, SC, 29208-0103. Tel: 803-777-3131. Fax: 803-777-5747. p. 2190

Stokes, Betty, Br Mgr, Vernon Parish Library, Paul Lawrence Dunbar Branch, 1003 N Gladys, Leesville, LA, 71446. Tel: 337-239-7037. p. 955

Stokes, Carol, Archivist, The City of Calgary, Corporate Records, Archives, 313 Seventh Ave SE, Calgary, AB, T2G 0J1, CANADA. Tel: 403-268-8180. Fax: 403-268-6731. p. 2691

Stokes, Cossandra, Head, Circ, Peoria Public Library, 107 NE Monroe St, Peoria, IL, 61602-1070. Tel: 309-497-2165. Fax: 309-497-2007. p. 690

Stokes, David, Ref Serv, Hazel Park Memorial Library, 123 E Nine Mile Rd, Hazel Park, MI, 48030. Tel: 248-542-0940, 248-546-4095. Fax: 248-546-4083. p. 1189

Stokes, Elizabeth, Head, Circ, Riverhead Free Library, 330 Court St, Riverhead, NY, 11901-2885. Tel: 631-727-3228. Fax: 631-727-4762. p. 1728

Stokes, Glenda, Librn, Spiro Public Library, 208 S Main, Spiro, OK, 74959. Tel: 918-962-3461. Fax: 918-962-5320. p. 1978

Stokes, Hellena, Mgr, Houston Public Library, The African American Library at the Gregory School, 1300 Victor St, Houston, TX, 77019. Tel: 832-393-1440. p. 2339

Stokes, Joan, Asst Dir, Ch, Southbury Public Library, 100 Poverty Rd, Southbury, CT, 06488. Tel: 203-262-0626. Fax: 203-262-6734. p. 368

Stokes, Judith, Ser, Rhode Island College, 600 Mt Pleasant Ave, Providence, RI, 02908-1924. Tel: 401-456-8126. Fax: 401-456-9646. p. 2174

Stokes, Leslie, Br Mgr, West Georgia Regional Library, Heard County Public Library, 564 Main St, Franklin, GA, 30217. Tel: 706-675-6501. Fax: 706-675-1065. p. 524

Stokes, Linda, Librn, Live Oak Public Libraries, Library for the Blind & Physically Handicapped, 14097 Abercorn St, Savannah, GA, 31419. Tel: 912-925-7774. Fax: 912-925-8310. p. 550

Stokes, Marg, Head Librn, Pinawa Public Library, Vanier Rd, Pinawa, MB, R0E 1L0, CANADA. Tel: 204-753-2496. Fax: 204-753-2770. p. 2750

Stokes, Mary, Br Coordr, Ashtabula County District Library, Geneva Public, 860 Sherman St, Geneva, OH, 44041. Tel: 440-466-4521. Fax: 440-466-0162. p. 1855

Stokes, Nancy L, Asst Dean, Univ Libr, University of Akron Libraries, 315 Buchtel Mall, Akron, OH, 44325-1701. Tel: 330-972-7017. Fax: 330-972-5106. p. 1853

Stokes, Perry N, Chief Librn/CEO, County Librn, Libr Dir, Baker County Public Library, 2400 Resort St, Baker City, OR, 97814-2798. Tel: 541-523-6419. Fax: 541-523-9088. p. 1990

Stokes, Susan, Circ Librn, Moultonborough Public Library, Four Holland St, Moultonborough, NH, 03254. Tel: 603-476-8895. p. 1458

Stokes, Thomas E, Librn, Emmanuel School of Religion Library, One Walker Dr, Johnson City, TN, 37601-9438. Tel: 423-926-1186. Fax: 423-926-6198. p. 2239

Stokloza, Kristin, Coordr, Electronic Res, Harvard Library, History of Science Library - Cabot Science Library, Science Center, One Oxford St, Cambridge, MA, 02138. Tel: 617-495-5355. Fax: 617-495-5324. p. 1075

Stoldt, Stacy, Ref Librn, Lenhardt Library of the Chicago Botanic Garden, 1000 Lake Cook Rd, Glencoe, IL, 60022. Tel: 847-835-8201. Fax: 847-835-6885. p. 650

Stolfer, Karen, Ref Serv, Hanson Public Library, 132 Maquan St, Hanson, MA, 02341. Tel: 781-293-2151. Fax: 781-293-6801. p. 1093

Stolfi, Maria, Tech Serv, John C Hart Memorial Library, 1130 Main St, Shrub Oak, NY, 10588. Tel: 914-245-5262. Fax: 914-245-2216. p. 1743

Stoll, Christina, Prog Mgr, Arlington Heights Memorial Library, 500 N Dunton Ave, Arlington Heights, IL, 60004-5966. Tel: 847-870-4429. Fax: 847-506-2650. p. 589

Stoll, Kaye, Mgr, Crowheart Public Library, 33 Old Yellowstone Hwy, Crowheart, WY, 82512. Tel: 307-486-2280. p. 2654

Stolt, Wilbur, Dir, University of North Dakota, 3051 University Ave, Stop 9000, Grand Forks, ND, 58202-9000. Tel: 701-777-2189. Fax: 701-777-3319. p. 1843

Stoltenberg, Jaime, Librn, University of
Wisconsin-Madison, Arthur H Robinson Map
Library, 310 Science Hall, 550 N Park St,
Madison, WI, 53706-1491. Tel: 608-262-1471.
Fax: 608-265-3991. p. 2609

Stoltenburg, Jeanne M, Libr Dir, Supvry Librn,
United States Air Force, 28 FSS/FSDL, 2650
Doolittle Dr, Bldg 3910, Ellsworth AFB, SD,
57706-4820. Tel: 605-385-1686, 605-385-1688.
Fax: 605-385-4467. p. 2212

Stoltz, Dorothy, Outreach Serv Librn, Prog Serv,
Carroll County Public Library, 115 Airport Dr,
Westminster, MD, 21157. Tel: 410-386-4450,
Ext 733. Fax: 410-386-4497. p. 1045

Stoltz, Jennie, Dir, Pewaukee Public Library, 210
Main St, Pewaukee, WI, 53072-3596. Tel:
262-691-5670. Fax: 262-691-5673. p. 2629

Stoltz, Zoe Ann, Ref Historian, Montana
Historical Society, 225 N Roberts St, Helena,
MT, 59601-4514. Tel: 406-444-1988. Fax:
406-444-5297. p. 1382

Stolworthy, Rachel, Ch, Franklin Public Library,
310 Central St, Franklin, NH, 03235. Tel:
603-934-2911. Fax: 603-934-7413. p. 1447

Stolys, Barb, Br Mgr, West Lincoln Public Library,
Caistorville Branch, 9549 Reg Rd 9, York St,
Caistorville, ON, N0A 1C0, CANADA. Tel:
905-692-4290. Fax: 905-692-4290. p. 2842

Stolz, William, Asst Dir, Ref, University of
Missouri, 23 Ellis Library, Columbia, MO,
65201-5149. Tel: 573-882-0188. Fax:
573-884-0345. p. 1325

Stombres, Debra, Br Coordr, Aurora Public Library,
West Branch, 233 S Constitution Dr, Aurora,
IL, 60506-0506. Tel: 630-264-3600. Fax:
630-844-8695. p. 591

Stonberg, Dee, Assoc Dir, Access Serv, Babson
College, 231 Forest St, Babson Park, MA,
02457-0310. Tel: 781-239-4391. Fax:
781-239-5226. p. 1051

Stone, Aingeal, Info Coordr, Government of the
Northwest Territories, 600, 5102 50th Ave,
Yellowknife, NT, X1A 3S8, CANADA. Tel:
867-920-8606. Fax: 867-873-0293. p. 2775

Stone, Amanda, Librn, South Carolina State Library,
1430-1500 Senate St, Columbia, SC, 29201. Tel:
803-734-4816. Fax: 803-734-8676. p. 2189

Stone, Bethany, Br Mgr, Orange County Library
District, Southwest, 7255 Della Dr, Orlando, FL,
32819. p. 476

Stone, Bonnie, Librn, Thunderchild Library,
Thunderchild First Nation, 1032 100th St,
Turtleford, SK, S0M 2Y0, CANADA. Tel:
306-845-3779. Fax: 306-845-3866. p. 2929

Stone, Cara, Fac Develop & Instruction Librn, Grand
View University Library, 1350 Morton Ave, Des
Moines, IA, 50316-1494. Tel: 515-263-2877.
Fax: 515-263-2998. p. 809

Stone, Cynthia, Dir, Newton History Museum at
The Jackson Homestead, 527 Washington St,
Newton, MA, 02458. Tel: 617-796-1450. Fax:
617-552-7228. p. 1110

Stone, Deborah M, Dir, Orleans Town & Township
Public Library, 174 N Maple St, Orleans,
IN, 47452-1424. Tel: 812-865-3270. Fax:
812-865-3270. p. 771

Stone, Erica, Ref Librn II, Grapevine Public Library,
1201 Municipal Way, Grapevine, TX, 76051.
Tel: 817-410-3403. Fax: 817-410-3084. p. 2329

Stone, Glenice, Dir, Northeast Mississippi
Community College, 101 Cunningham Blvd,
Booneville, MS, 38829. Tel: 662-720-7237,
662-728-7751. Fax: 662-728-2428. p. 1294

Stone, Heather, Tech Serv Librn, New England
College of Optometry Library, 424 Beacon St,
Boston, MA, 02115. Tel: 617-587-5579. Fax:
617-587-5573. p. 1064

Stone, Idelle, Res Assoc, Ford Foundation Research
Center, 320 E 43rd St, New York, NY, 10017.
Tel: 212-573-5000. p. 1678

Stone, James, Managing Librn, The Natalie A &
Louis D Boshes Library for the Neurosciences,
912 S Wood St, Chicago, IL, 60612-7325. Tel:
312-996-4842. Fax: 312-996-9018. p. 607

Stone, Jan, Head, Fac Serv, University of North
Dakota, 215 Centennial Dr, Grand Forks, ND,
58202. Tel: 701-777-2204. Fax: 701-777-2217.
p. 1843

Stone, Janet, Mgr, Ad Serv, Sr Librn, Web Serv,
Glendora Public Library & Cultural Center, 140
S Glendora Ave, Glendora, CA, 91741. Tel:
626-852-4896. Fax: 626-852-4899. p. 156

Stone, Jeanette, Librn, Northwest Mississippi
Community College, 1310 Belk Dr, Oxford, MS,
38655. Tel: 662-238-7953. Fax: 662-236-4764.
p. 1310

Stone, Jeannie, Dir, Bayard Public Library, 315
Main St, Bayard, IA, 50029. Tel: 712-651-2238.
Fax: 712-651-2238. p. 796

Stone, Joan, Dir, Crosby County Library,
Lorenzo Branch, 409 Van Buren, Lorenzo,
TX, 79343-2553. Tel: 806-634-5639. Fax:
806-634-5639. p. 2303

Stone, John, Librn, Santa Clarita Interlibrary
Network, Powell Library, 21726 Placerita
Canyon Rd, Santa Clarita, CA, 91321. Tel:
661-362-2271. Fax: 661-362-2719. p. 2938

Stone, John W, Dir, Robert L Powell Library
(The Master's College), 21726 W Placerita
Canyon Rd, Santa Clarita, CA, 91321-1200. Tel:
661-259-3540. Fax: 661-362-2719. p. 263

Stone, Judy, Librn, Jasonville Public Library, 611
W Main St, Jasonville, IN, 47438-0105. Tel:
812-665-2025. p. 756

Stone, Judy, Circ, Luther Seminary Library,
Gullixson Hall, 2375 Como Ave, Saint
Paul, MN, 55108. Tel: 651-641-3624. Fax:
651-641-3280. p. 1278

Stone, Katherine, Br Mgr, Dallas Public Library,
Forest Green, 9015 Forest Lane, Dallas,
TX, 75243-4114. Tel: 214-670-1335. Fax:
214-670-5597. p. 2306

Stone, Kathy, Librn, Jefferson Public Library, 48
Washington Rd, Jefferson, ME, 04348. Tel:
207-549-7491. p. 988

Stone, Kenneth H, Dep Dir-Chief Financial Officer,
Buffalo & Erie County Public Library System,
One Lafayette Sq, Buffalo, NY, 14203-1887.
Tel: 716-858-8900. Fax: 716-858-6211. p. 1596

Stone, Kitty, Br Mgr, Dallas Public Library,
Fretz Park, 6990 Belt Line Rd, Dallas,
TX, 75240-7963. Tel: 214-670-6421. Fax:
214-670-6621. p. 2306

Stone, Libby, ILL, Pub Serv, Gaston College, 201
Hwy 321 S, Dallas, NC, 28034-1499. Tel:
704-922-6359. Fax: 704-922-2342. p. 1786

Stone, Linda, Curator, Woolaroc Museum Library,
1925 Woolaroc Ranch Rd, Bartlesville, OK,
74003. Tel: 918-336-0307, Ext 32. Fax:
918-336-0084. p. 1958

Stone, Margaret, Mgr, Washington County
Library, Wildwood Branch, 763 Stillwater
Rd, Mahtomedi, MN, 55115-2008. Tel:
651-426-2042. Fax: 651-275-8541. p. 1291

Stone, Martha, Ref, Massachusetts General Hospital,
Treadwell Library, Bartlett Hall Ext - I, 55
Fruit St, Boston, MA, 02114-2696. Tel:
617-726-8600. Fax: 617-726-6784. p. 1063

Stone, Mary, Br Head, Toronto Public Library,
Hillcrest, 5801 Leslie St, Toronto, ON, M2H
1J8, CANADA. Tel: 416-395-5830. Fax:
416-395-5439. p. 2862

Stone, Mary Ann, Dir, Sunflower County
Library System, 201 Cypress Dr, Indianola,
MS, 38751-2499. Tel: 662-887-1672. Fax:
662-887-1618. p. 1302

Stone, Maude M, Librn, Fobes Memorial Library,
Four Maple St, Oakham, MA, 01068. Tel:
508-882-3372. Fax: 508-882-3372. p. 1116

Stone, John Michael, Archives Mgr, University of
California Los Angeles Library, Chicano Studies
Research Center Library & Archive, 144 Haines
Hall, Los Angeles, CA, 90095-1544. Tel:
310-206-6052. Fax: 310-206-1784. p. 178

Stone, Patricia, Dir, Rodman Public Library, 215 E
Broadway St, Alliance, OH, 44601-2694. Tel:
330-821-2665. Fax: 330-821-5053. p. 1854

Stone, Phillip, Archivist, Wofford College, 429 N
Church St, Spartanburg, SC, 29303-3663. Tel:
864-597-4300. Fax: 864-597-4329. p. 2206

Stone, Rebecca, Librn, Conception Bay South Public
Library, 110 Conception Bay Hwy, Conception
Bay South, NL, A1W 1N1, CANADA. Tel:
709-834-4241. p. 2769

Stone, Roberta, Mgr, Collier County Public Library,
Everglades Branch, City Hall, Everglades
City, FL, 34139. Tel: 239-695-2511. Fax:
239-695-2511. p. 471

Stone, Roy, Br Mgr, Los Angeles Public Library
System, Fairfax, 161 S Gardner St, Los Angeles,
CA, 90036-2717. Tel: 323-936-6191. Fax:
323-934-2675. p. 173

Stone, September, Dir, Libr & Info Serv, Nebraska
Health Care Association Library, 3900 NW
12th St, Ste 100, Lincoln, NE, 68521. Tel:
402-435-3551. Fax: 402-475-6289. p. 1405

Stone, Steven, Extended Campus Librn, Bluegrass
Community & Technical College, Oswald Bldg,
470 Cooper Dr, Lexington, KY, 40506-0235.
Tel: 859-246-6387. Fax: 859-246-4675. p. 920

Stone, Sue, Librn, Missoula Public Library, Seeley
Lake Community, 456 Airport Rd, Seeley
Lake, MT, 59868. Tel: 406-677-8995. Fax:
406-677-2949. p. 1386

Stone, Susan, Dir, Susquehanna County Historical
Society & Free Library Association, Two
Monument Sq, Montrose, PA, 18801-1115. Tel:
570-278-1881. Fax: 570-278-9336. p. 2092

Stone, Susie, Dir, Leon County Library, 207 E
Saint Mary's, Centerville, TX, 75833. Tel:
903-536-3726. Fax: 903-536-2329. p. 2296

Stone, Terrie, Libr Mgr, Wildwood Public
Library, 5215-50th St, Wildwood, AB, T0E
2M0, CANADA. Tel: 780-325-3882. Fax:
780-325-3880. p. 2722

Stone, Tina, Dir, Julesburg Public Library, 320
Cedar St, Julesburg, CO, 80737-1545. Tel:
970-474-2608. Fax: 970-474-2787. p. 314

Stoneberg, John, Dir, L E Phillips Memorial Public
Library, 400 Eau Claire St, Eau Claire, WI,
54701. Tel: 715-839-5001. Fax: 715-839-5310.
p. 2590

Stonehocker, Lori, Librn, Redfield Public Library,
1112 Thomas St, Redfield, IA, 50233. Tel:
515-833-2200. p. 840

Stoneman, William P, Head Librn, Harvard Library,
Houghton Library-Rare Books & Manuscripts,
Houghton Library, Cambridge, MA, 02138. Tel:
617-495-2441. Fax: 617-495-1376. p. 1075

Stoner, Connie Salyers, Dir, Shawnee State
University, 940 Second St, Portsmouth,
OH, 45662-4344. Tel: 740-351-3323. Fax:
740-351-3432. p. 1931

Stoner, David, Head, Ref (Info Serv), Clearwater
Public Library System, 100 N Osceola Ave,
Clearwater, FL, 33755. Tel: 727-562-4970. Fax:
727-562-4975. p. 432

Stoner, Gregory, Curator, George Washington
Foundation, 1201 Washington Ave,
Fredericksburg, VA, 22401. Tel: 540-373-3381.
Fax: 540-371-6066. p. 2466

Stoner, Karen J, Librn, Decatur Memorial Hospital,
2300 N Edward St, Decatur, IL, 62526. Tel:
217-876-2940. Fax: 217-876-2945. p. 633

Stoner, Marcie, In Charge, Madonna Rehabilitation
Hospital, 5401 South St, Lincoln, NE,
68506-2134. Tel: 402-489-7102. Fax:
402-486-8381. p. 1405

Stoner, Marian, Circ Serv Coordr, Rogue
Community College, Wiseman Ctr, 3345
Redwood Hwy, Grants Pass, OR, 97527. Tel:
541-956-7150. Fax: 541-471-3588. p. 1999

Stoner, Marian, Syst Adminr, Southern Oregon
Library Information System, 724 S Central
Ave, Ste 112, Medford, OR, 97501. Tel:
541-772-2141. Fax: 541-772-2144. p. 2953

Stoner, Ruth, Librn, Niagara Parks Botanical
Gardens & School of Horticulture, 2565
Niagara Pkwy N, Niagara Falls, ON, L2E 6S4,
CANADA. Tel: 905-356-8554, Ext 226. Fax:
905-356-5488. p. 2824

Stonesifer, Lynn, Coll Develop, Enoch Pratt Free Library, 400 Cathedral St, Baltimore, MD, 21201-4484. Tel: 410-396-5430. Fax: 410-396-1441. p. 1012

Stonesifer, Susan, Br Mgr, Howard County Library System, Miller Branch & Historical Center, 9421 Frederick Rd, Ellicott City, MD, 21042-2119. Tel: 410-313-1978. Fax: 410-313-1999. p. 1026

Stonewell, Steve, Circ Serv Supvr, Saint Mary's College Library, 1928 Saint Mary's Rd, Moraga, CA, 94575. Tel: 925-631-4229. Fax: 925-376-6097. p. 191

Stooksbury, Marie, Asst Dir, Oak Ridge Public Library, 1401 Oak Ridge Tpk, Oak Ridge, TN, 37830-6224. Tel: 865-425-3455. Fax: 865-425-3429. p. 2262

Stoops, Jaime, Br Mgr, Pamunkey Regional Library, Mechanicsville Branch, 7179 Stonewall Pkwy, Mechanicsville, VA, 23111. Tel: 804-746-9615. Fax: 804-730-4292. p. 2469

Stopka, Christina, Dep Dir, Texas Ranger Hall of Fame & Museum, 100 Texas Ranger Trail, Waco, TX, 76706. Tel: 254-750-8631. Fax: 254-750-8629. p. 2397

Storch, Barbara, Tech Mgr, West Palm Beach Public Library, 411 Clematis St, West Palm Beach, FL, 33401. Tel: 561-868-7721. Fax: 561-868-7706. p. 504

Storen, JoAnne, Br Mgr, Mississauga Library System, Woodlands, 1030 McBride Ave, Mississauga, ON, L5C 1L6, CANADA. Tel: 905-615-4825. Fax: 905-615-4826. p. 2823

Storer, Gail, Librn, Columbus College of Art & Design, 107 N Ninth St, Columbus, OH, 43215-3875. Tel: 614-222-3273, 614-224-9101. Fax: 614-222-6193. p. 1884

Storer, Maryruth, Dir, Orange County Public Law Library, 515 N Flower St, Santa Ana, CA, 92703-2354. Tel: 714-834-3397. Fax: 714-834-4375. p. 259

Storey, Melodie Rae, Ser, Regent College, 5800 University Blvd, Vancouver, BC, V6T 2E4, CANADA. Tel: 604-221-3397. Fax: 604-224-3097. p. 2742

Storey-Ewoldt, Ronnie, Pub Serv Dir, Anythink Libraries, 5877 E 120th Ave, Thornton, CO, 80602. Tel: 303-288-2001. Fax: 303-451-0190. p. 323

Storie, Monique, Ref, University of Guam, Guam & Micronesia Collection, UOG Sta, Mangilao, GU, 96923. Tel: 671-735-2157, 671-735-2160. Fax: 671-734-7403. p. 2667

Stork, Ellen, Supv Librn, Ch, Bernards Township Library, 32 S Maple Ave, Basking Ridge, NJ, 07920-1216. Tel: 908-204-3031. Fax: 908-766-1580. p. 1470

Stork, Jackie, Head, Youth Serv, Itasca Community Library, 500 W Irving Park Rd, Itasca, IL, 60143. Tel: 630-773-1699. Fax: 630-773-1707. p. 658

Stork, Kay, Dir, Arlington Public Library, 410 W Elm, Arlington, NE, 68002. Tel: 402-478-4545. p. 1392

Storm, Mary, Librn, Moultrie County Historical & Genealogical Society Library, 117 E Harrison St, Sullivan, IL, 61951. Tel: 217-728-4085. p. 708

Stormes, Sheridan, Music Librn, Butler University Libraries, 4600 Sunset Ave, Indianapolis, IN, 46208. Tel: 317-940-9218. Fax: 317-940-9711. p. 749

Stormont, Samuel R, Head Librn, Pennsylvania State University, 1600 Woodland Rd, Abington, PA, 19001. Tel: 215-881-7425. Fax: 215-881-7423. p. 2025

Stormont, Trish, Vols Serv Coordr, Tigard Public Library, 13500 SW Hall Blvd, Tigard, OR, 97223-8111. Tel: 503-684-6537, Ext 2516. Fax: 503-598-7515, 503-718-2797. p. 2021

Storms, Robbi, Dir, Ivoryton Library Association, 106 Main St, Ivoryton, CT, 06442. Tel: 860-767-1252. Fax: 860-767-3157. p. 348

Storrer, Karla B, Exec Dir, Blind Children's Fund Library, 201 S University St, Mount Pleasant, MI, 48858. Tel: 989-779-9966. Fax: 989-779-0015. p. 1211

Storring, Gail, Br Support, Stormont, Dundas & Glengarry County Library, Winchester Branch, 547 St Lawrence St, Winchester, ON, K0C 2K0, CANADA. Tel: 613-774-2612. Fax: 613-774-5866. p. 2802

Storti, Teresa, Circ Coordr, Chillicothe Public Library District, 430 N Bradley Ave, Chillicothe, IL, 61523-1920. Tel: 309-274-2719. Fax: 309-274-3000. p. 628

Story, Andrew, Programming, Elwood Public Library, 1929 Jericho Tpk, East Northport, NY, 11731. Tel: 631-499-3722. Fax: 631-499-0057. p. 1617

Story, Carolyn, Circ Supvr, Covington-Veedersburg Public Library, 622 Fifth St, Covington, IN, 47932. Tel: 765-793-2572. Fax: 765-793-2621. p. 734

Story, Edwynne, Librn, Phillips-Lee-Monroe Regional Library, Marvell Library, 806 Carruth, Marvell, AR, 72366. Tel: 870-829-3183. p. 103

Story, Howard, Fac Coordr, El Camino College, 16007 S Crenshaw Blvd, Torrance, CA, 90506. Tel: 310-660-3525. Fax: 310-660-3513. p. 275

Story, Steve, Librn, Fayette County Historical Society Library, 100 N Walnut St, West Union, IA, 52175-1347. Tel: 563-422-5797. p. 852

Story-Huffman, Ru, Ref, Georgia Southwestern State University, 800 Georgia Southwestern State University Dr, Americus, GA, 31709. Tel: 229-931-2850. Fax: 229-931-2265. p. 508

Stott, Barbara, Access Serv, Chandler-Gilbert Community College Library, 2626 E Pecos Rd, Chandler, AZ, 85225-2499. Tel: 480-857-5137. Fax: 480-857-5136. p. 59

Stottlemyre, Liz, Dir, Andrews County Library, 109 NW First St, Andrews, TX, 79714. Tel: 432-523-9819. Fax: 432-523-4570. p. 2275

Stottler, Marge, Asst Dir, Bloomfield Public Library, 121 S Broadway, Bloomfield, NE, 68718. Tel: 402-373-4588. Fax: 402-373-2601. p. 1394

Stottrup, Jeanette, Head Librn, Dassel Public Library, 460 Third St N, Dassel, MN, 55325. Tel: 320-275-3756. Fax: 320-275-3756. p. 1247

Stottrup, Jeanette, Head Librn, Grove City Public Library, 210 Atlantic Ave W, Grove City, MN, 56243. Tel: 320-857-2550. Fax: 320-857-2322. p. 1253

Stotts, Lorri Ane, Ch, Peoria Heights Public Library, 816 E Glen Ave, Peoria Heights, IL, 61616. Tel: 309-682-5578. Fax: 309-682-4457. p. 690

Stoudenmire, Vernice, Librn, Wilsonville Public Library, PO Box 70, Wilsonville, AL, 35186-0070. Tel: 205-669-6180. Fax: 205-669-6205. p. 40

Stoudt, Carol, Dir, McCoy Public Library, 190 N Judgement St, Shullsburg, WI, 53586. Tel: 608-965-4424, Ext 5. Fax: 608-965-4809. p. 2638

Stoudt, Carol, Dir, McCoy Public Library, Gratiot Annex, 3895 Main St, Gratiot, WI, 53541. Tel: 608-922-3803. p. 2638

Stoudt, Lynette, Sr Archivist, Georgia Historical Society Library, 501 Whitaker St, Savannah, GA, 31401. Tel: 912-651-2128. Fax: 912-651-2831. p. 550

Stouffer, David, Mgr, Info Sys, Broward County Division of Libraries, 100 S Andrews Ave, Fort Lauderdale, FL, 33301. Tel: 954-357-6287. Fax: 954-357-5749. p. 440

Stough, Tom, Assoc Librn, Oxnard College Library, 4000 S Rose Ave, Oxnard, CA, 93033-6699. Tel: 805-986-5949. Fax: 805-986-5888. p. 202

Stoughton, Judy, Ch, Mansfield Public Library, 54 Warrenville Rd, Mansfield Center, CT, 06250. Tel: 860-423-2501. Fax: 860-423-9856. p. 350

Stoupenos, Viki, Fla & Cent Region Librn, Saint Leo University, 33701 State Rd 52, Saint Leo, FL, 33574. Tel: 912-352-7970. Fax: 352-588-8484. p. 487

Stout, Anna, Educ Outreach, University of Miami Libraries, 1300 Memorial Dr, Coral Gables, FL, 33146. Tel: 305-284-3233. Fax: 305-284-4027. p. 434

Stout, Cathy, Head, Ref, Trenton Free Public Library, 120 Academy St, Trenton, NJ, 08608-1302. Tel: 609-392-7188. Fax: 609-396-7655. p. 1536

Stout, Cathy, Per, Trenton Free Public Library, 120 Academy St, Trenton, NJ, 08608-1302. Tel: 609-392-7188. Fax: 609-396-7655. p. 1536

Stout, Claire, Dir, Tri-County Library, 132 E Market St, Mabank, TX, 75147-2307. Tel: 903-887-9622. Fax: 903-887-3396. p. 2359

Stout, Denise Pulgino, Head, Youth Serv, Montgomery County-Norristown Public Library, 1001 Powell St, Norristown, PA, 19401-3817. Tel: 610-278-5100, Ext 205. p. 2098

Stout, Doug, Head, Circ, Licking County Library, 101 W Main St, Newark, OH, 43055-5054. Tel: 740-349-5571. Fax: 740-349-5535. p. 1922

Stout, Heather, Ch, YA Serv, Lewiston City Library, 428 Thain Rd, Lewiston, ID, 83501-5399. Tel: 208-743-6519. Fax: 208-798-4446. p. 578

Stout, Jill, Circ, Tremont District Public Library, 215 S Sampson St, Tremont, IL, 61568. Tel: 309-925-5432, 309-925-5597. Fax: 309-925-9953. p. 710

Stout, Julie, Circ, Charles A Ransom District Library, 180 S Sherwood Ave, Plainwell, MI, 49080-1896. Tel: 269-685-8024. Fax: 269-685-2266. p. 1218

Stout, Katrina, Librn, Missoula Public Library, Seeley Lake Community, 456 Airport Rd, Seeley Lake, MT, 59868. Tel: 406-677-8995. Fax: 406-677-2949. p. 1386

Stout, Kristin, Ref & Instruction Librn, Armstrong Atlantic State University, 11935 Abercorn St, Savannah, GA, 31419. Tel: 912-344-3027. Fax: 912-344-3457. p. 549

Stout, Mary J, Dir, Ohio University, 1804 Liberty Ave, Ironton, OH, 45638-2296. Tel: 740-533-4649. Fax: 740-533-4631. p. 1906

Stout, Nancy, Ref Librn, Fordham University Libraries, 441 E Fordham Rd, Bronx, NY, 10458-5151. Tel: 718-817-3570. Fax: 718-817-3582. p. 1586

Stout, Terry, Librn, Jackson County Library, 910 Main St, Kadoka, SD, 57543. Tel: 605-837-2689. p. 2213

Stout, Tracy, Asst Prof, Missouri State University, Duane G Meyer Library, 901 S National Ave, Springfield, MO, 65897. Tel: 417-836-4525. Fax: 417-836-4764. p. 2968

Stoutjesdyk, Carol, Circ, Central Lake District Library, 7900 Maple St, Central Lake, MI, 49622. Tel: 231-544-2517. Fax: 231-544-5016. p. 1162

Stovall, Ann, Computer Serv, Tech Serv, Indian Prairie Public Library District, 401 Plainfield Rd, Darien, IL, 60561-4207. Tel: 630-887-8760. Fax: 630-887-8801. p. 633

Stovall, Jerry, Dir, South Georgia Technical College, 900 S Georgia Tech Pkwy, Americus, GA, 31709. Tel: 229-931-2562. Fax: 229-931-2732. p. 508

Stovall, Jerry, Dir, South Georgia Technical College, 402 N Midway Rd, Cordele, GA, 31015. Tel: 229-271-4071. Fax: 229-271-4050. p. 527

Stovall, Judy, Sr Librn, Denver Public Library, Decker, 1501 S Logan, Denver, CO, 80210-2632. Tel: 303-733-7584. Fax: 303-733-8665. p. 301

Stovall, Pamela, Assoc Dir, District of Columbia Public Library, Martin Luther King Jr Memorial, 901 G St NW, Washington, DC, 20001-4599. Tel: 202-727-1222. Fax: 202-727-3856. p. 398

Stovall, Sheila, Dir, Allen County Public Library, 106 W Main, Scottsville, KY, 42164. Tel: 270-237-3861. Fax: 270-237-4095. p. 934

Stovall, Susan, Dir, Coffee County Lannom Memorial Public Library, 312 N Collins St, Tullahoma, TN, 37388-3229. Tel: 931-454-2404, 931-455-2460. Fax: 931-454-2300. p. 2267

Stoveken, Theresa, Librn, Three Bridges Public Library, 449 Main St, Three Bridges, NJ, 08887. Tel: 908-782-2908. Fax: 908-782-2908. p. 1533

Stover, Doug, In Charge, Cape Hatteras National Seashore, 1401 National Park Dr, Manteo, NC, 27954-9708. Tel: 252-473-2111, Ext 153. Fax: 252-473-2595. p. 1808

Stover, Joan, Asst Dir, Central Delaware Library Consortium, Dover Public Library, 45 S State St, Dover, DE, 19901. Tel: 302-736-4220. Fax: 302-736-5087. p. 2940

Stover, Kathy, Dir, Otis Health Care Center, 185 Graston Rd, Townshend, VT, 05353. Tel: 802-365-7920, Ext 119. p. 2437

Stover, Mark, PhD, Dean, California State University, Northridge, 18111 Nordhoff St, Northridge, CA, 91330. Tel: 818-677-2285. Fax: 818-677-2676. p. 195

Stover, Nancy, Dir, Williamsburg Community Library, 107 S Louisa, Williamsburg, KS, 66095. Tel: 785-746-5407. p. 902

Stover, Sheila, Librn, Fish Lake Library, Hwy 264 Bluebird Lane, Dyer, NV, 89010. Tel: 775-572-3311. Fax: 775-572-3311. p. 1426

Stover, Stephanie, Librn, Marion Correctional Institution Library, 3269 NW 105th St, Ocala, FL, 34482. Tel: 352-401-6813. Fax: 352-840-5657. p. 474

Stover, Susan M, Sr Librn, Mote Marine Laboratory Library, 1600 Ken Thompson Pkwy, Sarasota, FL, 34236-1096. Tel: 941-388-4441, Ext 333. p. 489

Stover, Teri, Dir, Texas A&M University-Texarkana, 7101 University Ave, Texarkana, TX, 75503. Tel: 903-223-3088. Fax: 903-334-6695. p. 2392

Stovin, Lorraine, Librn, Bren Del Win Centennial Library, 211 N Railway W, Deloraine, MB, R0M 0M0, CANADA. Tel: 204-747-2415. p. 2748

Stow, Betsy, Mgr, Live Oak Public Libraries, Hinesville Branch, 236 Memorial Dr, Hinesville, GA, 31313. Tel: 912-368-4003. Fax: 912-369-7148. p. 550

Stow, Betsy, Mgr, Live Oak Public Libraries, Midway-Riceboro Branch, 1165 Bill Martin Rd, Midway, GA, 31320. Tel: 912-884-5742. Fax: 912-884-5741. p. 550

Stowe, Donna, Asst Librn, Leland Township Public Library, 203 E Cedar, Leland, MI, 49654. Tel: 231-256-9152. Fax: 231-256-8847. p. 1203

Stowe, Stephanie, Chief Librn/CEO, Pelham Public Library, 43 Pelham Town Sq, Fonthill, ON, L0S 1E0, CANADA. Tel: 905-892-6443. Fax: 905-892-3392. p. 2805

Stowell, Michael C, Dir, Tulare Public Library, 475 North M St, Tulare, CA, 93274-4142. Tel: 559-685-4515. Fax: 559-685-2345. p. 276

Stower, Brye, Head of Libr, Archer Daniels Midland Co, 1001 N Brush College Rd, Decatur, IL, 62521-1656. Tel: 217-451-4249. Fax: 217-451-4253. p. 633

Stoyanova, Penka I, Head of Libr, Credit Valley Hospital, 2200 Eglinton Ave W, Mississauga, ON, L5M 2N1, CANADA. Tel: 905-813-2411. Fax: 905-813-3969. p. 2822

Stoyke, Rachel, Adult Serv, Plymouth Public Library, 130 Division St, Plymouth, WI, 53073-1802. Tel: 920-892-4416. Fax: 920-892-6295. p. 2631

Strachan, Elisabeth, Ch, Thayer Public Library, 798 Washington St, Braintree, MA, 02184. Tel: 781-848-0405, Ext 4426. Fax: 781-356-5447. p. 1069

Strachan, Pamela, Dir, Irvington Public Library, 12 S Astor St, Irvington, NY, 10533. Tel: 914-591-7840. Fax: 914-591-0347. p. 1640

Strack, Sharon, Br Mgr, East Central Regional Library, Milaca Community Library, 145 S Central, Milaca, MN, 56353-1122. Tel: 320-983-3677. Fax: 320-983-3677. p. 1244

Stracke, David, Br Mgr, Kent District Library, Plainfield Township Branch, 2650 Five Mile Rd NE, Grand Rapids, MI, 49525. Tel: 616-784-2007. Fax: 616-647-3934. p. 1166

Strader, Jean, Dir, Parsons Public Library, 311 S 17th St, Parsons, KS, 67357. Tel: 620-421-5920. Fax: 620-421-3951. p. 889

Strader, Linda, Librn, Belleville Public Library, 8086 County Rd 75, Belleville, NY, 13611. Tel: 315-846-5103. Fax: 315-846-5103. p. 1580

Stradwer, William, Libr Tech, VA Long Beach Health Care System, 5901 E Seventh St, Bldg 2, Rm 345, Long Beach, CA, 90822-5201. Tel: 562-826-8000, ext 5463. Fax: 562-826-5447. p. 167

Strahan, Michael, Coordr, Instruction, Northern Michigan University, 1401 Presque Isle, Marquette, MI, 49855. Tel: 906-227-2463. Fax: 906-227-1333. p. 1206

Straight, Joanne, Librn, Craven-Pamlico-Carteret Regional Library System, 400 Johnson St, New Bern, NC, 28560. Tel: 252-638-7800. Fax: 252-638-7817. p. 1812

Straight, Joanne, Head Librn, New Bern-Craven County Public Library, 400 Johnson St, New Bern, NC, 28560-4098. Tel: 252-638-7800. Fax: 252-638-7817. p. 1812

Strain, Judson, Ref Librn, Olivet Nazarene University, One University Ave, Bourbonnais, IL, 60914-2271. Tel: 815-928-5438. Fax: 815-939-5170. p. 596

Strain, Maxine, Dir, Tucker Memorial Public Library, 313 Harbine St, Alexandria, NE, 68303. Tel: 402-749-3750. p. 1391

Strait, Angela D, Asst Dir, Cabell County Public Library, 455 Ninth Street Plaza, Huntington, WV, 25701. Tel: 304-528-5700. Fax: 304-528-5701. p. 2561

Strait, Constance, Head, Tech Serv, Decatur Public Library, 130 N Franklin St, Decatur, IL, 62523-1327. Tel: 217-421-9739. Fax: 217-233-4071. p. 634

Straith, Ruth, Circ Mgr, Carnegie Public Library, 712 Sixth St, Charleston, IL, 61920. Tel: 217-345-4913. Fax: 217-348-5616. p. 603

Straka, Mary, Sr Ref Librn, Argonne National Laboratory, 9700 S Cass Ave, Bldg 240, Argonne, IL, 60439-4801. Tel: 630-252-7770. Fax: 630-252-5024. p. 589

Straley, Jo Ella, Broadcast & Ref Librn, NPR Library, 635 Massachusetts Ave NW, Washington, DC, 20001. Fax: 202-513-3056. p. 412

Stranc, Susanne, Automation Syst Coordr, Ref, La Crosse County Library, Holmen Area, 103 State St, Holmen, WI, 54636. Tel: 608-526-4198. Fax: 608-526-3299. p. 2598

Strand, Jennifer, Librn, Osceola Township Public & School Library, 48475 Maple St, Dollar Bay, MI, 49922. Tel: 906-482-5800. Fax: 906-487-5931. p. 1174

Strand, Jill, Res Librn, Faegre & Benson, LLP, 2200 Wells Fargo Ctr, 90 South Seventh St, Minneapolis, MN, 55402-3901. Tel: 612-766-7000. Fax: 612-766-1600. p. 1259

Strand, Rose, Cat Tech, Alamosa Public Library, 300 Hunt Ave, Alamosa, CO, 81101. Tel: 719-589-6592, Ext 2539. Fax: 719-589-3786. p. 287

Strandlund, Kelly, Librn, Roosevelt County Library, Froid Public, 110 Main, Froid, MT, 59226. Tel: 406-766-2492. p. 1390

Strandt, Laura, Youth Serv, Hamburg Township Library, 10411 Merrill Rd, Hamburg, MI, 48139. Tel: 810-231-1771. Fax: 810-231-1520. p. 1187

Strang, Anne, Ch, Ogden Farmers' Library, 269 Ogden Center Rd, Spencerport, NY, 14559. Tel: 585-617-6181. Fax: 585-352-3406. p. 1746

Strang, Jane, Libr Asst, Cascade Public Library, 310 First Ave W, Cascade, IA, 52033. Tel: 563-852-3201. Fax: 563-852-6011. p. 799

Strange, Alan D, Theological Librn, Mid-America Reformed Seminary Library, 229 Seminary Dr, Dyer, IN, 46311. Tel: 219-864-2400. Fax: 219-864-2410. p. 736

Strange, Jennifer, Head Librn, Plano Public Library System, L E R Schimelpfenig Library, 5024 Custer Rd, Plano, TX, 75023. Tel: 972-769-4200. Fax: 972-769-4210. p. 2371

Strange, Kathleen, ILL, Ref, Clarendon Hills Public Library, Seven N Prospect Ave, Clarendon Hills, IL, 60514. Tel: 630-323-8188. Fax: 630-323-8189. p. 629

Strange, Mariann, Mgr, Rapides Parish Library, J L Robertson Branch, 809 Tioga High School Rd, Ball, LA, 71405. Tel: 318-640-3098. Fax: 318-640-8713. p. 940

Strange, Michele, Circ, University of Wisconsin-La Crosse, 1631 Pine St, La Crosse, WI, 54601-3748. Tel: 608-785-8943. Fax: 608-785-8639. p. 2603

Strank, Carol, Head, Tech Serv, Indian River County Library System, 1600 21st St, Vero Beach, FL, 32960. Tel: 772-770-5060. Fax: 772-770-5066. p. 501

Stransky, Barbara, Ref Librn, Kansas City Kansas Community College Library, 7250 State Ave, Kansas City, KS, 66112-3098. Tel: 913-288-7650. Fax: 913-288-7606. p. 875

Strapko, Maureen, Dir, Sargent Memorial Library, 427 Massachusetts Ave, Boxborough, MA, 01719. Tel: 978-263-4680. Fax: 978-263-1275. p. 1069

Strasser, Dennis, Head of Libr, Western Michigan University, Education Library, 2800 Sangren Hall, 1903 W Michigan Ave, Kalamazoo, MI, 49008. Tel: 269-387-5230. Fax: 268-387-5231. p. 1198

Strasser, Mike, In Charge, Watertown Memorial Hospital, 125 Hospital Dr, Watertown, WI, 53098-3384. Tel: 920-262-4278. Fax: 920-262-4266. p. 2644

Stratford, Jean, Res, University of California, Davis, Institute of Governmental Affairs Library & Data Archive, Shields Library, Rm 360, One Shields Ave, Davis, CA, 95616-8617. Tel: 530-752-2042. Fax: 530-752-2835. p. 139

Stratman, Jason D, Ref & Info Serv, Web Coordr, Missouri History Museum, 225 S Skinker Blvd, Saint Louis, MO, 63105. Tel: 314-746-4500. Fax: 314-746-4548. p. 1356

Stratton, Bryan, Br Mgr 1, Sno-Isle Libraries, Darrington Community Library, 1005 Cascade St, Darrington, WA, 98241. Tel: 360-436-1600. Fax: 360-436-1659. p. 2542

Stratton, Casey, Ch, Teen Serv, Martins Ferry Public Library, 20 James Wright Pl, Martins Ferry, OH, 43935. Tel: 740-633-0314. Fax: 740-633-6242. p. 1914

Stratton, Dian, Pub Serv Librn, Eastern Maine Community College Library, Katahdin Hall, 354 Hogan Rd, Bangor, ME, 04401-4280. Tel: 207-974-4640. Fax: 207-974-4641. p. 975

Stratton, Lindsay, Training Coordr, Pioneer Library System, 2557 State Rte 21, Canandaigua, NY, 14424. Tel: 585-394-8260. Fax: 585-394-1935. p. 1601

Stratton, Lisa, Ch, YA Serv, Upton Town Library, Two Main St, Upton, MA, 01568-1608. Tel: 508-529-6272. Fax: 508-529-2453. p. 1131

Stratton, Traci, Head, ILL, Tech Serv Librn, Cordova District Library, 402 Main Ave, Cordova, IL, 61242-9790. Tel: 309-654-2330. Fax: 309-654-2290. p. 631

Straub, William, Digital Serv, University of Minnesota-Morris, 600 E Fourth St, Morris, MN, 56267. Tel: 320-589-6164. Fax: 320-589-6168. p. 1267

Straube, Karen, Tech Serv Librn, Longview Public Library, 1600 Louisiana St, Longview, WA, 98632-2993. Tel: 360-442-5316. Fax: 360-442-5954. p. 2520

Straubel, Danielle, Librn, Michigan Department of Corrections, 1500 Caberfae Way, Manistee, MI, 49660-0038. Tel: 231-723-8272. Fax: 231-723-8430. p. 1206

Strauber, Chris, Ref, Wofford College, 429 N Church St, Spartanburg, SC, 29303-3663. Tel: 864-597-4300. Fax: 864-597-4329. p. 2206

Strauch, Katina, Coll Develop, College of Charleston, 205 Calhoun St, Charleston, SC, 29401-3519. Tel: 843-953-5530. Fax: 843-953-6319. p. 2184

Strauch, Susan, Circ, Pontiac Public Library, 211 E Madison St, Pontiac, IL, 61764. Tel: 815-844-7229. Fax: 815-844-3475. p. 692

Straumann, Jenn, Br Librn, Anoka County Library, Crooked Lake, 11440 Crooked Lake Blvd, Coon Rapids, MN, 55433-3441. Tel: 763-576-5972. Fax: 763-576-5973. p. 1241

Strausman, Jeanne, Chief Librn, New York Institute of Technology, Northern Blvd, Old Westbury, NY, 11568-8000. Tel: 516-686-3779. Fax: 516-686-3709. p. 1710

Strauss, Barbara, Asst Dir, Tech Serv, Cleveland State University, University Library, Rhodes Tower, 2121 Euclid Ave, Cleveland, OH, 44115-2214. Tel: 216-687-2362. Fax: 216-687-9380. p. 1879

Strauss, Carol Kahn, Exec Dir, Center for Jewish History, 15 W 16 St, New York, NY, 10011-6301. Tel: 212-744-6400. Fax: 212-988-1305. p. 1671

Strauss, Catina, Ref, Monroe Free Library, 44 Millpond Pkwy, Monroe, NY, 10950. Tel: 845-783-4411. Fax: 845-782-4707. p. 1662

Strauss, Grace, Dir, Clinton Township Public Library, 100 Brown St, Clinton, MI, 49236. Tel: 517-456-4141. Fax: 517-456-4142. p. 1163

Strauss, Jason, Dir of Libr Serv, Wright Institute Library, 2728 Durant Ave, Berkeley, CA, 94704. Tel: 510-841-9230, Ext 140. Fax: 510-841-0167. p. 128

Strauss, Karen, Actg Chief, San Francisco Public Library, 100 Larkin St, San Francisco, CA, 94102-4733. Tel: 415-557-4200. Fax: 415-557-4424. p. 246

Strauss, Kathy, Genealogy Serv, Denton Public Library, 502 Oakland St, Denton, TX, 76201. Tel: 940-349-8257. Fax: 940-349-8101. p. 2312

Strauss, Kelly, Youth Serv, Edward U Demmer Memorial Library, 6961 W School St, Three Lakes, WI, 54562. Tel: 715-546-3391. Fax: 715-546-2930. p. 2642

Strauss, Todd, Computer Serv, Waltham Public Library, 735 Main St, Waltham, MA, 02451. Tel: 781-314-3425. Fax: 781-314-3426. p. 1133

Stravets, Rita, Librn, Touro College Libraries, 43 W 23rd St, Fifth Fl, New York, NY, 10010. Tel: 212-463-0400, Ext 5321. Fax: 212-627-3696. p. 1701

Straw, John B, Asst Dean, Digital Initiatives & Spec Coll, Ball State University Libraries, 2000 W University Ave, Muncie, IN, 47306-1099. Tel: 765-285-5277. Fax: 765-285-2008. p. 766

Straw, John B, Jr, Asst Dean, Spec Coll, Ball State University Libraries, Archives & Special Collections, Bracken Library, Rm 210, Muncie, IN, 47306-0161. Tel: 765-285-5078. Fax: 765-285-8149. p. 767

Straw, Joseph, Ref & Instruction Librn, Marietta College, 220 Fifth St, Marietta, OH, 45750. Tel: 740-376-4541. Fax: 740-376-4843. p. 1913

Straw, Linda, Sr Libr Asst, Baxter Memorial Library, 71 South St, Gorham, ME, 04038. Tel: 207-222-1190. Fax: 207-839-7749. p. 986

Straw, Melissa, Dir, Libr Presv, Goucher College Library, 1021 Dulaney Valley Rd, Baltimore, MD, 21204. Tel: 410-337-6368. Fax: 410-337-6419. p. 1014

Strawhun, Lori, Human Res Mgr, Springfield-Greene County Library District, 4653 S Campbell, Springfield, MO, 65810-1723. Tel: 417-882-0714. Fax: 417-883-9348. p. 1367

Strawn, Shirley, Tech Serv, Ardmore Public Library, 320 E St NW, Ardmore, OK, 73401. Tel: 580-223-8290. Fax: 580-221-3240. p. 1956

Strawn, Timothy, Dir, Info Res & Archives, California Polytechnic State University, One Grand Ave, San Luis Obispo, CA, 93407. Tel: 805-756-1485. Fax: 805-756-2346. p. 253

Strayton, Melissa, Librn, Charles B Danforth Public Library, 6208 VT Rte 12, Barnard, VT, 05031. Tel: 802-234-9408. p. 2417

Strazhnik, Lana, Dir, JFK Medical Center, 65 James St, Edison, NJ, 08818-3059. Tel: 732-321-7181. Fax: 732-744-5639. p. 1483

Strazhnik, Lana, Librn, Muhlenberg Regional Medical Center, Park Ave & Randolph Rd, Plainfield, NJ, 07061. Tel: 908-668-2005. Fax: 908-753-3723. p. 1521

Straziuso, Louisa, Ref Serv, Tiffin University, 139 Miami St, Tiffin, OH, 44883-2162. Tel: 419-448-3435. Fax: 419-443-5013. p. 1938

Streb, Theresa, Libr Dir, Lyons Public Library, 67 Canal St, Lyons, NY, 14489. Tel: 315-946-9262. Fax: 315-946-3320. p. 1656

Streber, Joni, Circ Mgr, Mgr, ILL, Wilmington College, Pyle Ctr 1227, 1870 Quaker Way, Wilmington, OH, 45177-2473. Tel: 937-382-6661, Ext 345. Fax: 937-383-8571. p. 1949

Streby, Paul, Coll Develop Librn, Webmaster, University of Michigan-Flint, 303 E Kearsley St, Flint, MI, 48502-1950. Tel: 810-762-3405. Fax: 810-762-3133. p. 1181

Strecker, Bill, Dir, Lisle Library District, 777 Front St, Lisle, IL, 60532-3599. Tel: 630-971-1675. Fax: 630-971-1701. p. 666

Strecker, Shawn, Dir, Elmwood Park Public Library, One Conti Pkwy, Elmwood Park, IL, 60707. Tel: 708-395-1230. Fax: 708-453-4671. p. 643

Streeper, Nate, Coordr, Braille Institute Library Services, Santa Barbara Center, 2031 De La Vina St, Santa Barbara, CA, 93105. Tel: 805-682-6222. Fax: 805-687-6141. p. 169

Streese, Germano, First Year Experience Librn, Luther College, 700 College Dr, Decorah, IA, 52101. Tel: 563-387-2223. Fax: 563-387-1657. p. 807

Street, Aiden, Br Mgr, Pioneer Library System, Southwest Oklahoma City Public Library, 2201 SW 134th St, Oklahoma City, OK, 73170. Tel: 405-979-2200. Fax: 405-692-6394. p. 1970

Street, Patti, Br Mgr, Columbia County Public Library, Fort White Branch, 17700 SW State Rd 47, Fort White, FL, 32038. Tel: 386-497-1108. Fax: 386-497-2066. p. 457

Street, Sheila, Dir, Alamance Community College, 1247 Jimmie Kerr Rd, Graham, NC, 27253. Tel: 336-506-4186. Fax: 336-578-5561. p. 1795

Street, Suzanne, Dir, Leanna Hicks Public Library, 2005 Inkster Rd, Inkster, MI, 48141. Tel: 313-563-2822. Fax: 313-274-5130. p. 1193

Street, Wendy, Dir, Pella Public Library, 603 Main St, Pella, IA, 50219-1592. Tel: 641-628-4268. Fax: 641-628-1735. p. 838

Streeter, Anita, Exec Dir, Embroiderers Guild of America Inc Library, 426 W Jefferson St, Louisville, KY, 40202-3202. Tel: 502-589-6956. Fax: 502-584-7900. p. 923

Streeter, Gwenell, Br Librn, Riverside Regional Library, Benton Branch, 54 N Winchester, Benton, MO, 63736. Tel: 573-545-3581. Fax: 573-545-3581. p. 1334

Streeter, Kim, Dir, Linn County Library District No 5, 904 Main St, Pleasanton, KS, 66075. Tel: 913-352-8554. Fax: 913-352-8554. p. 890

Streeton, Shellie, In Charge, Suncor Energy Library, 150-Sixth Ave SW, Calgary, AB, T2P 3E3, CANADA. Tel: 403-296-4413. Fax: 403-296-3030. p. 2693

Strege, Reed, Commun Libr Mgr, County of Los Angeles Public Library, Westlake Village Library, 31220 W Oak Crest Dr, Westlake Village, CA, 91361. Tel: 818-865-9230. Fax: 818-865-0724. p. 143

Streibel, Janna, Dir, Lizard Butte Public Library, 429 Main St, Ste 105, Marsing, ID, 83639. Tel: 208-896-4690. Fax: 208-896-4472. p. 578

Streif, Kim F, Cat, Southwest Wisconsin Library System, 1775 Fourth St, Fennimore, WI, 53809-1137. Tel: 608-822-2055. Fax: 608-822-6251. p. 2591

Streiff, Marian, Mgr, Carnegie Library of Pittsburgh, Mount Washington, 315 Grandview Ave, Pittsburgh, PA, 15211-1549. Tel: 412-381-3380. p. 2123

Streiker, Susan, Head Librn, Paul, Hastings, Janofsky & Walker LLP, 515 S Flower, 25th Flr, Los Angeles, CA, 90071. Tel: 213-683-5057. Fax: 213-627-0705. p. 176

Strein, Sharon R, Circ Supvr, United States Army, Combined Arms Research Library, US Army Command & General Staff College, Eisenhower Hall, 250 Gibbon Ave, Fort Leavenworth, KS, 66027-2314. Tel: 913-758-3005. Fax: 913-758-3014. p. 867

Streit, Pansy, Dir, Livermore Public Library, 402 Fifth St, Livermore, IA, 50558. Tel: 515-379-2078. Fax: 515-379-2078. p. 828

Strelka, Debra, Coordr, Cat, University of Wisconsin-Green Bay, 2420 Nicolet Dr, Green Bay, WI, 54311-7001. Tel: 920-465-2154. Fax: 920-465-2136. p. 2596

Stremming, Stacey, Libr Dir, Windsor Storm Memorial Public Library District, 102 S Maple, Windsor, IL, 61957. Tel: 217-459-2498. Fax: 217-459-2499. p. 720

Strength, Bonnie L, Asst Dir, H Grady Bradshaw Chambers County Library, 3419 20th Ave, Valley, AL, 36854. Tel: 334-768-2161. Fax: 334-768-7272. p. 39

Strescino, Margie, Librn, Pueblo Chieftain Newspaper Library, 825 W Sixth St, Pueblo, CO, 81003-2313. Tel: 719-404-2774, 719-544-3520, Ext 491. p. 320

Stretsberry, Sonya, Adult Serv, Circ, Bartholomew County Public Library, 536 Fifth St, Columbus, IN, 47201-6225. Tel: 812-379-1255. Fax: 812-379-1275. p. 733

Streyle, Linda, Circ, Door County Library, Central Library, 107 S Fourth Ave, Sturgeon Bay, WI, 54235. p. 2640

Stribe, Judi, Ch, Manning Public Library, 310 Main St, Manning, IA, 51455. Tel: 712-655-2260. Fax: 712-655-2260. p. 829

Stricker, Linda, Librn, Memorial Hospital, 715 S Taft Ave, Fremont, OH, 43420. Tel: 419-332-7321, Ext 3497. Fax: 419-334-6691. p. 1900

Stricker, Michele, Assoc Dir, Libr Develop Bur, New Jersey State Library, 185 W State St, Trenton, NJ, 08618. Tel: 609-278-2640, Ext 113. Fax: 609-278-2652. p. 1536

Stricker, Patti, Circ, William Rainey Harper College Library, 1200 W Algonquin Rd, Palatine, IL, 60067. Tel: 847-925-6767. Fax: 847-925-6164. p. 687

Stricker, Warren, Dir, Res, Panhandle-Plains Historical Museum, 2503 Fourth Ave, Canyon, TX, 79015. Tel: 806-651-2254. Fax: 806-651-2260. p. 2294

Strickland, Carolyn, Head, Ref, Lake County Public Library, 1919 W 81st Ave, Merrillville, IN, 46410-5488. Tel: 219-769-3541. Fax: 219-756-9358. p. 763

Strickland, Christine, Media Spec, College of Coastal Georgia, One College Way, Brunswick, GA, 31520-3644. Tel: 912-279-5700. p. 521

Strickland, Denise, Dir, Mooneyham Public Library, 240 E Main St, Forest City, NC, 28043. Tel: 828-248-5224. Fax: 828-248-5224. p. 1794

Strickland, Elaine, Cat, Nassau County Public Library System, 25 N Fourth St, Fernandina Beach, FL, 32034-4123. Tel: 904-548-4860. Fax: 904-277-7366. p. 439

Strickland, Elizabeth, Ser/Accounts Librn, State University of New York College at New Paltz, 300 Hawk Dr, New Paltz, NY, 12561-2493. Tel: 845-257-3662. Fax: 845-257-3888. p. 1666

Strickland, Janice, Ref, Statesboro Regional Public Libraries, 124 S Main St, Statesboro, GA, 30458. Tel: 912-764-1341. Fax: 912-764-1348. p. 552

Strickland, Janice, Spec Coll Librn, Statesboro Regional Public Libraries, 124 S Main St, Statesboro, GA, 30458. Tel: 912-764-1340. Fax: 912-764-1348. p. 552

Strickland, Jay, Off-Campus Librn, Paris Junior College, 2400 Clarksville St, Paris, TX, 75460. Tel: 903-453-6435. Fax: 903-454-3380. p. 2368

Strickland, Karla, Curator, Memphis College of Art, 1930 Poplar Ave, Memphis, TN, 38104. Tel: 901-272-5131. Fax: 901-272-5104. p. 2249

Strickland, Lori, Ch, Darlington County Library, Hartsville Memorial, 147 W College St, Hartsville, SC, 29550. Tel: 843-332-5115. Fax: 843-332-7071. p. 2192

Strickland, Michele, Coordr, Elsie Quirk Public Library of Englewood, 100 W Dearborn St, Englewood, FL, 34223-3309. Tel: 941-861-1215. p. 439

Strickland, Norma, Asst Librn, Grant County Library, 215 E Grant Ave, Ulysses, KS, 67880-2958. Tel: 620-356-1433. Fax: 620-356-1344. p. 898

Strickland, Patricia, Dir, Marlow Town Library, 12 Church St, Marlow, NH, 03456. Tel: 603-446-3466. Fax: 603-446-3466. p. 1457

Strickland, Patricia, Br Mgr, Columbus County Public Library, Tabor City Public, 101 E Fifth St, Tabor City, NC, 28463. Tel: 910-653-3774. Fax: 910-653-3788. p. 1829

Strickland, Regina, Asst Dir, Horseshoe Bend Regional Library, 207 N West St, Dadeville, AL, 36853. Tel: 256-825-9232. Fax: 256-825-4314. p. 14

Strickland, Stacey L, Asst Dir, Youth Serv, Stevens County Library, 500 Monroe, Hugoton, KS, 67951-2639. Tel: 620-544-2301. Fax: 620-544-2322. p. 872

Strickland, Stephanie, Br Mgr, Hawaii State Public Library System, Waikiki-Kapahulu Public Library, 400 Kapahulu Ave, Honolulu, HI, 96815. Tel: 808-733-8488. Fax: 808-733-8490. p. 563

Strickland, Vicki, In Charge, Saskatchewan Justice, Civil Law Library, 900 - 1874 Scarth St, Regina, SK, S4P 4B3, CANADA. Tel: 306-787-8382. Fax: 306-787-0581. p. 2924

Strickland, Victoria, Circ, Sampson-Clinton Public Library, 217 Graham St, Clinton, NC, 28328. Tel: 910-592-4153. Fax: 910-590-3504. p. 1784

Strickland-Naczi, Bonnie, Ref Serv, Ch, Wallingford Public Library, 200 N Main St, Wallingford, CT, 06492-3791. Tel: 203-265-6754. Fax: 203-269-5698. p. 373

Strickler, Christa, Cat, Northwest University, 5520 108th Ave NE, Kirkland, WA, 98083-0579. Tel: 425-889-5267. Fax: 425-889-7801. p. 2519

Stricklett, Rhonda, Instrul Tech, Ref Librn, McDaniel College, Two College Hill, Westminster, MD, 21157-4390. Tel: 410-857-2283. Fax: 410-857-2748. p. 1046

Stricklin, Betty, Ch, Hardin County Library, 1365 Pickwick St, Savannah, TN, 38372. Tel: 731-925-4314, 731-925-6848. Fax: 731-925-7132. p. 2264

Stricklin, David, Dr, Curator, Central Arkansas Library System, 100 Rock St, Little Rock, AR, 72201-4698. Tel: 501-320-5710. p. 106

Strickman, Donna, Ref, Cumberland County Library, 800 E Commerce St, Bridgeton, NJ, 08302-2295. Tel: 856-453-2210. Fax: 856-451-1940. p. 1474

Striebel, Heather, Librn, Curtis, Mallet-Prevost, Colt & Mosle Library, 101 Park Ave, New York, NY, 10178-0061. Tel: 212-696-6138. Fax: 212-697-1559. p. 1676

Striepe, Claudia, Bibliog Instruction Librn, El Camino College, 16007 S Crenshaw Blvd, Torrance, CA, 90506. Tel: 310-660-3525. Fax: 310-660-3513. p. 275

Striepe, Thomas J, Fac Serv Librn, University of Georgia, 225 Herty Dr, Athens, GA, 30602-6018. Tel: 706-542-5077. Fax: 706-542-5001. p. 510

Strife, Mary, Dir, West Virginia University Libraries, Evansdale Library, One Evansdale Dr, Morgantown, WV, 26506. Tel: 304-293-4696. Fax: 304-293-7330. p. 2566

Strife, Mary, Dir, West Virginia University Libraries, WVU Libraries, 1549 University Ave, Morgantown, WV, 26506. Tel: 904-293-4696, Ext 5112. Fax: 304-293-6638. p. 2566

Strimaitis, Ona, Librn, Sisters of The Immaculate Conception Convent Library, 600 Liberty Hwy, Putnam, CT, 06260. Tel: 860-928-7955. Fax: 860-928-1930. p. 365

Striman, Brian D, Tech Serv, University of Nebraska-Lincoln, Marvin & Virginia Schmid Law Library, 40 Fair St, Lincoln, NE, 68583. Tel: 402-472-3547. Fax: 402-472-8260. p. 1407

Stringer, Colleen, Head, Adult Serv, Brandon Township Public Library, 304 South St, Ortonville, MI, 48462. Tel: 248-627-1474. Fax: 248-627-9880. p. 1215

Stringer, Elaine, Circ Serv, Somerset County Library System, Watchung Public, 12 Stirling Rd, Watchung, NJ, 07069. Tel: 908-561-0117. Fax: 908-769-1145. p. 1475

Stringer, Ellen, YA Serv, Lexington County Public Library System, 5440 Augusta Rd, Lexington, SC, 29072. Tel: 803-785-2632. Fax: 803-785-2601. p. 2199

Stringer, Erin, Interim Dir, Columbus-Lowndes Public Library, 314 N Seventh St, Columbus, MS, 39701. Tel: 662-329-5300. Fax: 662-329-5156. p. 1297

Stringer, Joyce, Br Mgr, Mize Public Library, 210 Hwy 28, Mize, MS, 39116. Tel: 601-733-9414. p. 1309

Stringer, Minnie, Asst Br Mgr, Ch, Librn I, Montgomery City-County Public Library System, Rufus A Lewis Regional Branch Library, 3095 Mobile Hwy, Montgomery, AL, 36108. Tel: 334-240-4848. Fax: 334-240-4847. p. 30

Stringer, Peggy, In Charge, Schenectady County Public Library, Hamilton Hill, 700 Craig St, Schenectady, NY, 12307. Tel: 518-386-2244. p. 1741

Stringer, Sybyl, Librn, Hinds Community College, Jackson Nursing Allied Health Center Learning Resources/Library, 1750 Chadwick Dr, Jackson, MS, 39204-3490. Tel: 601-376-4816. Fax: 601-371-3703. p. 1313

Stringer-Hye, Richard, Ref Librn, Tech Coordr, Vanderbilt University, Science & Engineering, 3200 Stevenson Ctr, 419 21st Ave S, Nashville, TN, 37240-0007. Tel: 615-343-4395. Fax: 615-343-7249. p. 2261

Stringfellow, Patty, Dir, Jasper County Public Library, 208 W Susan St, Rensselaer, IN, 47978. Tel: 219-866-5881. Fax: 219-866-7378. p. 774

Stringham, Fern, Pub Serv, Western Wyoming Community College, 2500 College Dr, Rock Springs, WY, 82902. Tel: 307-382-1700. Fax: 307-382-7665. p. 2659

Striplin-Cova, Lanelle, Ch, YA Serv, Public Library of Anniston-Calhoun County, 108 E Tenth St, Anniston, AL, 36201. Tel: 256-237-8501, 256-237-8503. Fax: 256-238-0474. p. 4

Stripnieks, Lilita, Chief Exec Officer, St Catharines Public Library, 54 Church St, St. Catharines, ON, L2R 7K2, CANADA. Tel: 905-688-6103, Ext 235. Fax: 905-688-6292. p. 2843

Strizhevsky, Vladimir, Asst Librn, Mercy College Libraries, Bronx Campus, 1200 Waters Pl, Bronx, NY, 10461. Tel: 718-678-8392. p. 1615

Strizzi, Paul, Dir, Pennsylvania Board of Probation & Parole Library, 1101 S Front St, Ste 5600, Harrisburg, PA, 17104-2552. Tel: 717-787-6151. Fax: 717-772-4185. p. 2065

Strlich, Christine, Ref & Media Ctr Librn, Lake Erie College, 391 W Washington St, Painesville, OH, 44077-3309. Tel: 440-375-7400. p. 1926

Strniste, Bryan, Ref & Instrul Serv Librn, Southern Maine Community College Library, Two Fort Rd, South Portland, ME, 04106. Tel: 207-741-5521. Fax: 207-741-5522. p. 1002

Strobel, Tracy, Dep Dir, Cuyahoga County Public Library, 2111 Snow Rd, Parma, OH, 44134-2728. Tel: 216-398-1800. Fax: 216-398-1748. p. 1927

Stroben, Anna, Finance & Bus Dir, Mid-Columbia Libraries, 405 S Dayton, Kennewick, WA, 99336. Tel: 509-582-4745. Fax: 509-737-6349. p. 2518

Strock, Adrienne, Br Mgr, Maricopa County Library District, Guadalupe Branch, 9241 S Avenida del Yaqui, Guadalupe, AZ, 85283. Tel: 602-652-3291. Fax: 602-652-3296. p. 74

Strode, Cindy, Pub Serv Librn, Monroe County Public Library, 500 W Fourth St, Tompkinsville, KY, 42167. Tel: 270-487-5301. Fax: 270-487-5309. p. 936

Strodtman, Leasa, Tech Serv, Central Methodist College, 411 Central Methodist Sq, Fayette, MO, 65248. Tel: 660-248-6271. Fax: 660-248-6226. p. 1327

Strohl, Bonnie, Assoc Dean, University of Scranton, Monroe & Linden, Scranton, PA, 18510-4634. Tel: 570-941-4006. Fax: 570-941-7817. p. 2138

Strohm, Robert F, Rare Bks, VPres, Virginia Historical Society Library, 428 North Blvd, Richmond, VA, 23220. Tel: 804-358-4901. Fax: 804-355-2399. p. 2492

Strohm, Shelley, Dir, Housatonic Community College Library, 900 Lafayette Blvd, Bridgeport, CT, 06604. Tel: 203-332-5072. Fax: 203-332-5252. p. 331

Strohmeyer, Julia, YA Serv, Free Public Library of the Borough of Fort Lee, 320 Main St, Fort Lee, NJ, 07024. Tel: 201-592-3614. Fax: 201-585-0375. p. 1486

Strohmeyer, Kristin, Ref Librn, Hamilton College, 198 College Hill Rd, Clinton, NY, 13323-1299. Tel: 315-859-4481. Fax: 315-859-4578. p. 1607

Strojny, Duane, Assoc Dean, Thomas M Cooley Law School Libraries, 300 S Capitol Ave, Lansing, MI, 48901. Tel: 517-371-5140, Ext 3401. Fax: 517-334-5715, 517-334-5717. p. 1202

Stroker, Frank, Asst Librn, Pittsburgh History & Landmarks Foundation, 100 W Station Square Dr, Ste 450, Pittsburgh, PA, 15219. Tel: 412-471-5808. Fax: 412-471-1633. p. 2127

Strom, Kelly S, Coll Develop, Champaign Public Library, 200 W Green St, Champaign, IL, 61820-5193. Tel: 217-403-2050. Fax: 217-403-2053. p. 602

Strombo, Cathryn, Librn, Mineral County Museum & Historical Society Library, 301 Second Ave E, Superior, MT, 59872. Tel: 406-822-3543. p. 1389

Stromgren, Jeanette, Dir, Osage City Public Library, 515 Main St, Osage City, KS, 66523. Tel: 785-528-2620, 785-528-3727. Fax: 785-528-4502. p. 886

Stromme, Elizabeth, Ref Serv, Alexandria Library, Charles E Beatley Jr Central (Hqtrs), 5005 Duke St, Alexandria, VA, 22304-2903. Tel: 703-746-1746. p. 2444

Stromseth, Sally, Ch, Decorah Public Library, 202 Winnebago St, Decorah, IA, 52101, Tel: 563-382-3717. Fax: 563-382-4524. p. 807

Strong, Angie, Dir, Madrid Public Library, 100 W Third St, Madrid, IA, 50156. Tel: 515-795-3846. Fax: 515-795-3697. p. 828

Strong, Barbara, Youth Serv Coordr, Craftsbury Public Library, 12 Church St, Craftsbury Common, VT, 05827-9696. Tel: 802-586-9683. Fax: 802-586-9683. p. 2422

Strong, Brenda, Cat, Duncan Public Library, 2211 N Hwy 81, Duncan, OK, 73533. Tel: 580-255-0636. Fax: 580-255-6136. p. 1961

Strong, Cat, Tech Librn, Oro Valley Public Library, 1305 W Naranja Dr, Oro Valley, AZ, 85737-9762. Tel: 520-229-5300. Fax: 520-229-5319. p. 70

Strong, Catherine, Managing Librn, Pima County Public Library, Mission, 3770 S Mission Rd, Tucson, AZ, 85713. Tel: 520-594-5325. Fax: 520-594-5326. p. 87

Strong, Dustin Lance, Br Mgr, Louisville Free Public Library, Iroquois, 601 W Woodlawn, Louisville, KY, 40215. Tel: 502-574-1720. Fax: 502-367-1468. p. 934

Strong, Gary E, Univ Librn, University of California Los Angeles Library, PO Box 951575, Los Angeles, CA, 90095-1575. Tel: 310-825-1201. Fax: 310-206-4109. p. 178

Strong, Marjorie, Asst Librn, Vermont Historical Society Library, Vermont History Ctr, 60 Washington St, Barre, VT, 05641-4209. Tel: 802-479-8509. Fax: 802-479-8510. p. 2418

Strong, Patricia, ILL, Tougaloo College, Tougaloo College, 500 W County Line Rd, Tougaloo, MS, 39174-9799. Tel: 601-977-7706. Fax: 601-977-7714. p. 1315

Stronks, Rick, In Charge, Algonquin Park Visitor Centre, PO Box 219, Whitney, ON, K0J 2M0, CANADA. Tel: 613-637-2828. Fax: 613-637-2138. p. 2871

Stroomer, Betsy, Dir, Lafayette Public Library, 775 W Baseline Rd, Lafayette, CO, 80026. Tel: 303-665-5200. Fax: 303-665-8936. p. 314

Stroot, Joy, Asst Librn, Kingman Carnegie Public Library, 455 N Main St, Kingman, KS, 67068-1395. Tel: 620-532-3061. Fax: 620-532-2528. p. 876

Stroshane, Eric, Coordr, Field Serv Prog, North Dakota State Library, Library Memorial Bldg, 604 East Blvd Ave, Dept 250, Bismarck, ND, 58505-0800. Tel: 701-328-4661. Fax: 701-328-2040. p. 1838

Strother, B, Br Mgr, New Orleans Public Library, Algiers Regional, 3014 Holiday Dr, New Orleans, LA, 70131. Tel: 504-596-2641. Fax: 504-596-2661. p. 962

Strother, Donna, Br Mgr, Vernon Parish Library, Pitkin Branch, 7277 Hwy 463, Pitkin, LA, 70656. Tel: 318-358-3294. Fax: 318-358-3294. p. 955

Strother, Elizabeth, Head of Libr, Louisiana State University Health Sciences Center, School of Dentistry Library, 1100 Florida Ave, New Orleans, LA, 70119-2799. Tel: 504-941-8158. Fax: 504-941-8161. p. 961

Strother, Elizabeth A, Br Coordr, Louisiana State University Health Sciences Center, 433 Bolivar St, Box B3-1, New Orleans, LA, 70112-2223. Tel: 504-619-8507. Fax: 504-619-8783. p. 961

Strother, Joan, Circ Supvr, Tippecanoe County-Ivy Tech Library, 3101 S Creasy Lane, Lafayette, IN, 47903. Tel: 765-269-5380. Fax: 765-269-5383. p. 759

Strother, Lara, Librn, Mary Lou Reddick Public Library, 7005 Charbonneau Rd, Lake Worth, TX, 76135. Tel: 817-237-9681. Fax: 817-237-9671. p. 2352

Stroud, Diana, Asst Dean, University of Illinois at Urbana-Champaign, Library & Information Science Bldg, 501 E Daniel St, Champaign, IL, 61820-6211. Tel: 217-333-3280. Fax: 217-244-3302. p. 2965

Stroud, Lucille, Music Libr Tech, West Chester University, Presser Music Library, School of Music & Performing Arts Center, West Chester, PA, 19383. Tel: 610-436-2379, 610-436-2430. Fax: 610-436-2873. p. 2154

Stroud, P, Info Serv, Parkland Regional Library, Hwy 52 W, Yorkton, SK, S3N 3Z4, CANADA. Tel: 306-783-7022. Fax: 306-782-2844. p. 2931

Stroud, Pat, Dir, West Virginia Northern Community College Library, New Martinsville Campus, 141 Main St, New Martinsville, WV, 26155. Tel: 304-455-4684, Ext 4727. p. 2575

Stroud, Patricia, Dir, West Virginia Northern Community College Library, 1704 Market St, Wheeling, WV, 26003-3699. Tel: 304-723-2210, Ext 5621. Fax: 304-232-0965. p. 2575

Strougal, Pat, Dir, United States Environmental Protection Agency, Region 4 OEA Information-Research Center, 61 Forsyth St SW, Atlanta, GA, 30303-3104. Tel: 404-562-9654. Fax: 404-562-9663. p. 518

Stroup, Debbie, Head, Circ, Southampton Free Library, 947 Street Rd, Southampton, PA, 18966. Tel: 215-322-1415. Fax: 215-396-9375. p. 2142

Stroup, Karen, Librn, State Correctional Institution, 660 State Rte 11, Hunlock Creek, PA, 18621. Tel: 570-735-8754, Ext 373. Fax: 570-740-2406. p. 2070

Stroup, Meg, Circ Mgr, Cherokee County Public Library, 300 E Rutledge Ave, Gaffney, SC, 29340-2227. Tel: 864-487-2711. Fax: 864-487-2752. p. 2194

Stroup, Richard, Pub Serv, King County Law Library, W 621 King County Courthouse, 516 Third Ave, Seattle, WA, 98104. Tel: 206-296-0940. Fax: 206-205-0513. p. 2528

Strouse, Lisa, Asst Librn, Boone Area Library, 129 N Mill St, Birdsboro, PA, 19508-2340. Tel: 610-582-5666. Fax: 610-582-6826. p. 2035

Strouse, Mary, Assoc Dir, Catholic University of America, Judge Kathryn J DuFour Law Library, 3600 John McCormack Rd NE, Washington, DC, 20064-8206. Tel: 202-319-5547. Fax: 202-319-5581. p. 396

Strouse, Sue, Circ Mgr, Cromaine District Library, 3688 N Hartland Rd, Hartland, MI, 48353. Tel: 810-632-5200, Ext 102. p. 1189

Strouse, Sue, Circ Mgr, Cromaine District Library, Crossroads, 1788 N Old US 23, Howell, MI, 48843. Tel: 810-632-7480. p. 1189

Strout, Gweneth, Dir, Gallison Memorial Library, 1292 Main St, Harrington, ME, 04643. Tel: 207-483-4547. p. 987

Strow, Laurie, Assoc Librn, New Jersey Department of Transportation, 1035 Parkway Ave, Trenton, NJ, 08618-2309. Tel: 609-530-5289. Fax: 609-530-2052. p. 1535

Strube, Kathleen, Dir, Aurora Health Care Libraries, 2900 W Oklahoma Ave, Milwaukee, WI, 53215-4330. Tel: 414-649-7356. Fax: 414-649-7037. p. 2617

Strubel, Gary, Librn, Southwestern Vermont Health Care, 100 Hospital Dr, Bennington, VT, 05201. Tel: 802-447-5120. Fax: 802-447-5388. p. 2419

Strubin, Kathleen, Acq, Palos Park Public Library, 12330 S Forest Glen Blvd, Palos Park, IL, 60464. Tel: 708-448-1530. Fax: 708-448-3492. p. 688

Struble, Pat, Acq Mgr, Saline County Public Library, 1800 Smithers Dr, Benton, AR, 72015. Tel: 501-778-4766. Fax: 501-778-0536. p. 95

Struck, Kathyleen, ILL Coordr, Calvin College & Calvin Theological Seminary, 1855 Knollcrest Circle SE, Grand Rapids, MI, 49546-4402. Tel: 616-526-8573. Fax: 616-526-6470. p. 1184

Struckmeyer, Amanda, Youth Serv, Middleton Public Library, 7425 Hubbard Ave, Middleton, WI, 53562-3117. Tel: 608-827-7407. Fax: 608-836-5724. p. 2616

Struecker, Chris, Dir, Fenton Public Library, 605 Maple, Fenton, IA, 50539-0217. Tel: 515-889-2333. Fax: 515-889-2333. p. 816

Struecker, Chris, Librn, Ringsted Public Library, Eight W Maple St, Ringsted, IA, 50578. Tel: 712-866-0878. Fax: 712-866-0879. p. 840

Strum, Leanne G, Assoc Dean, Regent University Library, 1000 Regent University Dr, Virginia Beach, VA, 23464. Tel: 757-352-4172. Fax: 757-352-4167. p. 2499

Strunk, Sheila, Br Coordr, Shelby County Libraries, Anna Community, 304 N Second St, Anna, OH, 45302. Tel: 937-394-2761. Fax: 937-394-2761. p. 1935

Strunk, Susan, Dir, Palatine Public Library District, 700 N North Ct, Palatine, IL, 60067-8159. Tel: 847-358-5881. p. 686

Strunz, Marah, Dir, Orfordville Public Library, 203 W Beloit St, Orfordville, WI, 53576-8749. Tel: 608-879-9229. Fax: 608-879-2031. p. 2627

Struthers, Lisa A, Dir, San Jacinto Museum of History, One Monument Circle, La Porte, TX, 77571-9585. Tel: 281-479-2421. Fax: 281-479-2866. p. 2352

Struthers, Randy, Head, Circ, Plano Community Library District, 15 W North St, Plano, IL, 60545. Tel: 630-552-2009. Fax: 630-552-1008. p. 691

Strutin, Michal, Assoc Librn, Santa Clara University, 500 El Camino Real, Santa Clara, CA, 95053-0500. Tel: 408-554-6830. Fax: 408-554-6827. p. 263

Struttmann, Patricia, Asst Dir, Hiawatha Public Library, 150 W Willman St, Hiawatha, IA, 52233. Tel: 319-393-1414. Fax: 319-393-6005. p. 821

Strycharz, Jaclyn, Head, Circ, Lucius Beebe Memorial Library, 345 Main St, Wakefield, MA, 01880-5093. Tel: 781-246-6334. Fax: 781-246-6385. p. 1132

Strykowski, Jill, Media & Digital Res Librn, Iona College, 715 North Ave, New Rochelle, NY, 10801-1890. Tel: 914-633-2353. Fax: 914-633-2136. p. 1666

Stuart, Alicia, Dir, Beene-Pearson Public Library, 208 Elm Ave, South Pittsburg, TN, 37380-1312. Tel: 423-837-6513. Fax: 423-837-6612. p. 2266

Stuart, Gail, Coordr, Ref (Info Serv), Northern Essex Community College, 100 Elliott St, Haverhill, MA, 01830. Tel: 978-556-3421. Fax: 978-556-3738. p. 1094

Stuart, Jason, Affiliate Librn, Regent University Library, 1000 Regent University Dr, Virginia Beach, VA, 23464. Tel: 757-352-4184. Fax: 757-352-4167. p. 2499

Stuart, Jeanne, Librn, Bodman PLC Law Library, Ford Field, 6th Flr, 1901 Saint Antoine St, Detroit, MI, 48226. Tel: 313-259-7777. Fax: 313-393-7579. p. 1169

Stuart, Jennifer, Librn, Mountain Area Health Education Center, 121 Hendersonville Rd, Asheville, NC, 28803. Tel: 828-257-4449. Fax: 828-257-4712. p. 1775

Stuart, Joan, Dir, New Virginia Public Library, 504 Book Alley, New Virginia, IA, 50210. Tel: 641-449-3614. p. 835

Stuart, Lorraine A, Archivist, Hirsch Library, Museum of Fine Arts, Houston, 1001 Bissonnet St, Houston, TX, 77005-1803. Tel: 713-639-7325. Fax: 713-639-7707. p. 2337

Stuart, Mary, Librn, University of Illinois Library at Urbana-Champaign, History, Philosophy & Newspaper, 246 Main Library, 1408 W Gregory Dr, Urbana, IL, 61801. Tel: 217-244-0797. p. 712

Stuart, Memree, Libr Mgr, Alachua County Library District, Hawthorne Branch, 6640 SE 221 St, Hawthorne, FL, 32640-3815. Tel: 352-481-1920. Fax: 352-481-1921. p. 448

Stuart, Myla, Ch, Comstock Township Library, 6130 King Hwy, Comstock, MI, 49041. Tel: 269-345-0136. Fax: 269-345-0138. p. 1165

Stuart, Nancy, Coordr, ILL, University of Victoria Libraries, McPherson Library, PO Box 1800, Victoria, BC, V8W 3H5, CANADA. Tel: 250-721-8211. Fax: 250-721-8215. p. 2746

Stuart, Sandra, Ref, Kelley Drye & Warren, 101 Park Ave, New York, NY, 10178. Tel: 212-808-7800. Fax: 212-808-7897. p. 1684

Stuart, Sara, Dir, Communications & Develop, Citizens Union Foundation Library, 299 Broadway, Ste 700, New York, NY, 10007. Tel: 212-227-0342. Fax: 212-227-0345. p. 1672

Stubblefield, Gail, Librn, Murray-Colloway County Hospital, 803 Poplar St, Murray, KY, 42071-2467. Tel: 270-762-1572. Fax: 270-762-1770. p. 930

Stubblefield, Laura, Coll Develop, Head of Libr, Sharp HealthCare, 7901 Frost St, San Diego, CA, 92123. Tel: 858-939-3242. Fax: 858-939-3248. p. 238

Stubbs, Janis T, Asst Dir, Delaware County Library System, 340 N Middletown Rd, Bldg 19, Media, PA, 19063-5597. Tel: 610-891-8622. Fax: 610-891-8641. p. 2087

Stubbs, Judy, Asst Dir, Tech Serv, Oral Roberts University Library, 7777 South Lewis Ave, Tulsa, OK, 74171. Tel: 918-495-6889. Fax: 918-495-6727. p. 1981

Stubbs, Walter O, Admin Librn, Opelousas-Eunice Public Library, 212 E Grolee St, Opelousas, LA, 70570. Tel: 337-948-3693. Fax: 337-948-5200. p. 965

Stuber, Sarah, Libr Assoc, La Crosse County Library, Campbell, Campbell Town Hall, 2219 Bainbridge St, LaCrosse, WI, 54603. Tel: 608-783-0052. p. 2598

Stuchel, Karen, Librn, Missouri Department of Corrections, Farmington Correctional Center, 1012 W Columbia St, Farmington, MO, 63640-2902. Tel: 573-218-7100, Ext 346. Fax: 573-218-7106. p. 1334

Stucke, Alison, Libr Tech, Wisconsin Indianhead Technical College, 600 N 21st St, Superior, WI, 54880-5296. Tel: 715-394-6677, Ext 6276. Fax: 715-394-3771. p. 2641

Stuckel, Jon, Info Tech Dir, Mid-Columbia Libraries, 405 S Dayton, Kennewick, WA, 99336. Tel: 509-582-4745. Fax: 509-737-6349. p. 2518

Stuckemeyer, Mickee, ILL, Walter E Olson Memorial Library, 203 N Main St, Eagle River, WI, 54521. Tel: 715-479-8070, Ext 23. Fax: 715-479-2435. p. 2589

Stuckey, Ellen, Dir, Butler Public Library, 340 S Broadway, Butler, IN, 46721. Tel: 260-868-2351. Fax: 260-868-5491. p. 730

Stuckey, Gabriel, Librn, Somerset County Library System, Corbin Memorial Library, Four E Main St, Crisfield, MD, 21817. Tel: 410-968-0955. Fax: 410-968-2363. p. 1036

Stuckey, Jeannie, In Charge, Oaklawn Community Mental Health Center, 2600 Oakland Ave, Elkhart, IN, 46517. Tel: 574-537-2690. Fax: 574-537-2605. p. 737

Stuckey, Sheila A, Dir, Libr Serv, Kentucky State University, 400 E Main St, Frankfort, KY, 40601-2355. Tel: 502-597-6852. Fax: 502-597-5068. p. 914

Stuckey, Susan, Tech Serv, Normal Memorial Library, 301 N Eagle St, Fayette, OH, 43521. Tel: 419-237-2115. Fax: 419-237-2002. p. 1899

Stucky, Gail, Co-Dir, Libr & Dir Pub Serv, Bethel College Library, 300 E 27th St, North Newton, KS, 67117-0531. Tel: 316-284-5361. Fax: 316-284-5843. p. 885

Studebaker, Nancy, Dir, Niles District Library, 620 E Main St, Niles, MI, 49120. Tel: 269-683-8545. Fax: 269-683-0075. p. 1214

Studer, Jody, Circ Supvr, Homer Township Public Library District, 14320 W 151st St, Homer Glen, IL, 60491. Tel: 708-301-7908. Fax: 708-301-4535. p. 657

Studer, Lisa, Dir, Bennett Public Library, 203 Main St, Bennett, IA, 52721. Tel: 563-890-2238. Fax: 563-890-2711. p. 796

Studer, Lou Ann, Ch, Lebanon Public Library, 101 S Broadway, Lebanon, OH, 45036. Tel: 513-932-2665. Fax: 513-932-7323. p. 1909

Studer, Louise E, Mgr, Fish & Neave IP Group of Ropes Gray LLP Library, 1211 Avenue of the Americas, New York, NY, 10036. Tel: 212-596-9200. Fax: 212-596-9090. p. 1678

Studley, Mary, Circ, Knox County Public Library, 502 N Seventh St, Vincennes, IN, 47591-2119. Tel: 812-886-4380. Fax: 812-886-0342. p. 784

Studwell, Lorene, Info Serv Spec II, Newport News Public Library System, Law Library, 2501 Washington Ave, Newport News, VA, 23607. Tel: 757-926-8678. Fax: 757-926-8824. p. 2480

Study, Cheryl, Dir, Ch Serv, Winchester Community Library, 125 N East St, Winchester, IN, 47394-1698. Tel: 765-584-4824. Fax: 765-584-3624. p. 788

Stuehrenberg, Paul F, Librn, Yale University Library, Divinity School Library, 409 Prospect St, New Haven, CT, 06511-2108. Tel: 203-432-5292. Fax: 203-432-3906. p. 357

Stuffles, Pamela, Librn, Westport Public Library, Three Spring St, Westport, ON, K0G 1X0, CANADA. Tel: 613-273-3223. Fax: 613-273-3460. p. 2870

Stuhlman, Rachel, Librn, George Eastman House, 900 East Ave, Rochester, NY, 14607. Tel: 585-271-3361, Ext 313. Fax: 585-271-3970. p. 1729

Stuhlmann, Jason, Head, Youth Serv, Elmwood Park Public Library, One Conti Pkwy, Elmwood Park, IL, 60707. Tel: 708-395-1237. Fax: 708-453-4671. p. 643

Stuhr, Rebecca, Coll Develop, Presv Librn, Grinnell College Libraries, 1111 Sixth Ave, Grinnell, IA, 50112-1770. Tel: 641-269-3674. Fax: 641-269-4283. p. 819

Stuhr, Sharon, Asst Librn, Marion Public Library, 120 N Main, Marion, WI, 54950. Tel: 715-754-5368. Fax: 715-754-4610. p. 2613

Stukey, Carol, Med Librn, Rehabilitation Institute of Chicago, 345 E Superior St, 1st Flr, Chicago, IL, 60611. Tel: 312-238-5433. Fax: 312-238-2860. p. 622

Stula, Nancy, Curator, Dir, Lyman Allyn Art Museum Library, 625 Williams St, New London, CT, 06320-4199. Tel: 860-443-2545. Fax: 860-442-1280. p. 359

Stulack, Nancy, Librn, United States Golf Association Museum & Archives, Golf House, 77 Liberty Corner Rd, Far Hills, NJ, 07931-2570. Tel: 908-234-2300. Fax: 908-470-5013. p. 1485

Stuller, Linda, Ch, Public Library of Steubenville & Jefferson County, 407 S Fourth St, Steubenville, OH, 43952-2942. Tel: 740-282-9782. Fax: 740-282-2919. p. 1936

Stuller, Linda, Librn, Public Library of Steubenville & Jefferson County, Schiappa Branch, 4141 Mall Dr, Steubenville, OH, 43952. Tel: 740-264-6166. Fax: 740-264-7397. p. 1937

Stults, Carol, Head, Youth Serv, Tippecanoe County Public Library, 627 South St, Lafayette, IN, 47901-1470. Tel: 765-429-0100. Fax: 765-429-0150. p. 759

Stultz, Amy, Youth Serv Librn, Lake County Library System, Cooper Memorial Library, 2525 Oakley Seaver Dr, Clermont, FL, 34711. Tel: 352-536-2275. Fax: 352-536-2259. p. 500

Stumbough, Doug, Br Serv Mgr, Spokane County Library District, 4322 N Argonne Rd, Spokane, WA, 99212-1868. Tel: 509-893-8200. Fax: 509-893-8472. p. 2536

Stumme, Mark, Ref Librn, Drake University, 2725 University Ave, Des Moines, IA, 50311. Tel: 515-271-3192. Fax: 515-271-3933. p. 809

Stump, Jason, Br Mgr, Portsmouth Public Library, Northwest, 13056 State Rte 73, Rm 12, McDermott, OH, 45652. Tel: 740-372-8314. Fax: 740-372-4315. p. 1930

Stump, Sandra L, Ref, Albright College, 13th & Exeter Sts, Reading, PA, 19604. Tel: 610-921-7205. Fax: 610-921-7509. p. 2132

Stump, Sheryl, Cat, Tech Serv, Delta State University, Laflore Circle at Fifth Ave, Cleveland, MS, 38733-2599. Tel: 662-846-4458. Fax: 662-846-4443. p. 1296

Stumpff, Julia C, Dir, Ivy Tech Libr Serv, University Library of Columbus, 4555 Central Ave, LC 1600, Columbus, IN, 47203. Tel: 812-314-8711. Fax: 812-314-8722. p. 733

Stumpff, Lindy, Librn, Western State Hospital, 2400 Russellville Rd, Hopkinsville, KY, 42241. Tel: 270-889-6025. Fax: 270-885-5257. p. 918

Stundon, Liz, In Charge, URS Greiner Woodward-Clyde Consultants Library, 201 Willowbrook Blvd, Wayne, NJ, 07470-0290. Tel: 973-785-0700, Ext 281, 973-812-3100. Fax: 973-785-0023. p. 1540

Stuntz, Christina, Librn, Mid-Coast Hospital, 123 Medical Center Dr, Brunswick, ME, 04011. Tel: 207-373-6571. Fax: 207-373-6572. p. 979

Stupegia, Cristy, Admin Dir, Sparta Public Library, 211 W Broadway, Sparta, IL, 62286. Tel: 618-443-5014. Fax: 618-443-2952. p. 704

Stupski, Betsy L, Dir, Libr Serv, Florida Attorney General's Law Library, Collins Bldg, 107 W Gaines St, Rm 437, Tallahassee, FL, 32399-1050. Tel: 850-414-3300. Fax: 850-921-5784. p. 493

Sturdevant, Deborah, Dir, Lisle Free Library, 8998 Main St, Lisle, NY, 13797. Tel: 607-692-3115. Fax: 607-692-3115. p. 1652

Sturdivant, Jauquina, Interim Dean of Libr, Florida Memorial University, 15800 NW 42nd Ave, Miami Gardens, FL, 33054. Tel: 305-626-3641. Fax: 305-626-3625. p. 469

Sturdivant, Lois, Librn, Richmond Community College Library, 1042 W Hamlet Ave, Hamlet, NC, 28345. Tel: 910-410-1753. Fax: 910-582-7045. p. 1800

Sturgeon, Holly, Circ Mgr, Seattle University, A Lemieux Library, 901 12th Ave, Seattle, WA, 98122-4411. Tel: 206-296-6234. Fax: 206-296-2572. p. 2532

Sturgeon, Melanie, PhD, Dir, Hist & Archives, Arizona State Library, Archives & Public Records, 1700 W Washington, Rm 200, Phoenix, AZ, 85007. Tel: 602-926-3720. Fax: 602-256-7983. p. 72

Sturgeon, Roy, Instruction Coordr, Ref Librn, Tulane University, Law Library, 6329 Freret St, New Orleans, LA, 70118-6231. Tel: 504-865-5953. Fax: 504-865-5917. p. 963

Sturgeon, Roy, Ref, Touro College, 225 Eastview Dr, Central Islip, NY, 11722-4539. Tel: 631-761-7000, 631-761-7150. Fax: 631-761-7159. p. 1605

Sturgeon, Tammy, Cataloger, Hancock County Public Library, 240 Court Sq, Hawesville, KY, 42348. Tel: 270-927-6760. Fax: 270-927-6847. p. 916

Sturgeon, Walter B, Librn, International Wild Waterfowl Association, 1633 Bowden Rd, Spring Hope, NC, 27882. Tel: 252-478-5610. Fax: 252-478-7286. p. 1825

Sturges, David, Dir, Vermont Technical College, Main St, Randolph Center, VT, 05061. Tel: 802-728-1237. Fax: 802-728-1506. p. 2433

Sturges, Debra, Head, Access Serv, Creighton University, 2500 California Plaza, Omaha, NE, 68178-0209. Tel: 402-280-4756. Fax: 402-280-2435. p. 1412

Sturges, Marjorie, Ref, Pinellas Park Public Library, 7770 52nd St, Pinellas Park, FL, 33781-3498. Tel: 727-541-0718. Fax: 727-541-0818. p. 483

Sturges, Michelle, Head, Cat, Kapiolani Community College Library, 4303 Diamond Head Rd, Honolulu, HI, 96816. Tel: 808-734-9163. Fax: 808-734-9453. p. 564

Sturgill, Carrie, Head, Ch, Radnor Memorial Library, 114 W Wayne Ave, Wayne, PA, 19087-4098. Tel: 610-687-1124. Fax: 610-687-1454. p. 2152

Sturgis, Sharon, Librn, Ellinwood School & Community Library, 210 N Schiller Ave, Ellinwood, KS, 67526-1651. Tel: 620-564-2306. Fax: 620-564-2848. p. 865

Sturkey, Monique Delatte, Acq Librn, Fullerton College, 321 E Chapman Ave, Fullerton, CA, 92832-2095. Tel: 714-992-7379. Fax: 714-992-9961. p. 153

Sturm, Danna, Librn, Western Nevada Community College, 2201 W College Pkwy, Carson City, NV, 89703. Tel: 775-445-3229. Fax: 775-445-3363. p. 1426

Sturm, David, Chief Info Officer, VPres, The New York Public Library - Astor, Lenox & Tilden Foundations, 476 Fifth Ave, (@ 42nd St), New York, NY, 10018-2788. Tel: 212-621-0661. Fax: 212-592-7440. p. 1690

Sturm, Glynis, Assoc Librn, ILL, Stewartville Public Library, 110 Second St SE, Stewartville, MN, 55976-1306. Tel: 507-533-4902. Fax: 507-533-4746. p. 1285

Sturm, Heather, Dir, Manchester District Library, 912 City Rd (M-52), Manchester, MI, 48158-0540. Tel: 734-428-8045. p. 1205

Sturm, Maria, Dr, VPres, Culture & Heritage, German Society of Pennsylvania, 611 Spring Garden St, Philadelphia, PA, 19123. Tel: 215-627-2332. Fax: 215-627-5297. p. 2110

Sturm, Shannon, Asst Head, Spec Coll & Prog, Univ Archivist, Angelo State University Library, 2025 S Johnson, San Angelo, TX, 76904-5079. Tel: 325-486-6555. Fax: 325-942-2198. p. 2378

Sturm, Tim, Ref Serv, American River College Library, 4700 College Oak Dr, Sacramento, CA, 95841. Tel: 916-484-8455. Fax: 916-484-8018, 916-484-8657. p. 220

Sturman, Debbie, Dir, Niobrara County Library, 425 S Main, Lusk, WY, 82225. Tel: 307-334-3490. Fax: 307-334-3490. p. 2658

Sturman, Tree, VPres, Prog, Vermont Institute of Natural Science Library, 6565 Woodstock Rd, Quechee, VT, 05059. Tel: 802-359-5000. Fax: 802-359-5001. p. 2433

Sturr, Natalie, Coordr, Libr Tech, State University of New York at Oswego, SUNY Oswego, 7060 State Rte 104, Oswego, NY, 13126-3514. Tel: 315-312-3565. Fax: 315-312-3194. p. 1713

Sturtz, Brenda, ILL, Libr Tech, Clarion University of Pennsylvania, 1801 W First St, Oil City, PA, 16301. Tel: 814-676-6591, Ext 1244. Fax: 814-677-3987. p. 2100

Sturtz, Carmaline, Br Mgr, Muskingum County Library System, New Concord Branch, 77 W Main St, New Concord, OH, 43762. Tel: 740-826-4184. p. 1954

Sturz, Carol, Coordr, College of Dupage, 425 Fawell Blvd, Glen Ellyn, IL, 60137. Tel: 630-942-2597. Fax: 630-858-8757. p. 2964

Stuter, Cathy J, Asst Dir, Shenandoah County Library, 514 Stoney Creek Blvd, Edinburg, VA, 22824. Tel: 540-984-8200, Ext 205. Fax: 540-984-8207. p. 2460

Stutes, Angela, Dir, Human Res, Calcasieu Parish Public Library, 301 W Claude St, Lake Charles, LA, 70605-3457. Tel: 337-721-7155. Fax: 337-475-8806. p. 953

Stutesman, Jennifer, Circ/ILL/Media, University of Alaska Fairbanks, 310 Tanana Dr, Fairbanks, AK, 99775. Tel: 907-474-2676. Fax: 907-474-6841. p. 48

Stutler, Tim, Tech Serv, Madisonville Community College, 2000 College Dr, Madisonville, KY, 42431. Tel: 270-824-8678. Fax: 270-825-8553. p. 928

Stutsman, Rachel, Adminr, United Presbyterian Church, 4701 N Central Ave, Indianapolis, IN, 46205. Tel: 317-283-1305. Fax: 317-921-2266. p. 755

Stutz, Dudley, Asst Librn, ILL, University of South Carolina at Beaufort Library, One University Blvd, Bluffton, SC, 29909-6085. Tel: 843-208-8160. Fax: 843-208-8296. p. 2182

Stutz, Lynne, Dir, Cheyenne Wells Public Library, 151 S First St W, Cheyenne Wells, CO, 80810. Tel: 719-767-5138. Fax: 719-767-5379. p. 294

Stutzenberger, Helen, Ch, Oberlin Public Library, 65 S Main St, Oberlin, OH, 44074-1626. Tel: 440-775-4790. Fax: 440-774-2880. p. 1925

Stutzman, Anne, ILL, The William K Sanford Town Library, 629 Albany Shaker Rd, Loudonville, NY, 12211-1196. Tel: 518-458-9274. Fax: 518-438-0988. p. 1655

Stutzman, Karl, Access Serv Librn, Associated Mennonite Biblical Seminary Library, 3003 Benham Ave, Elkhart, IN, 46517. Tel: 574-296-6280. Fax: 574-295-0092. p. 737

Stutzman, Rebecca, Ch, North Tonawanda Public Library, 505 Meadow Dr, North Tonawanda, NY, 14120-2888. Tel: 716-693-4132. Fax: 716-693-0719. p. 1707

Stuver, Diane, Dir, Henry A Malley Memorial Library, 101 S Lincoln, Broadus, MT, 59317. Tel: 406-436-2812. p. 1375

Styles, Julie, Coll Mgr, Tech Serv, Avon Free Public Library, 281 Country Club Rd, Avon, CT, 06001. Tel: 860-673-9712. Fax: 860-675-6364. p. 329

Styles, Laureen, Chief Exec Officer, BC Academic Health Council, 402-1770 W Seventh Ave, Vancouver, BC, V6J 4Y6, CANADA. Tel: 604-739-3910, Ext 228. Fax: 604-739-3931. p. 2959

Stylianopoulos, Lucie, Head Librn, University of Virginia, Fiske Kimball Fine Arts, Bayly Dr, Charlottesville, VA, 22904-4131. Tel: 434-924-6938. Fax: 434-982-2678. p. 2455

Styons, Jessica, Assoc Dir, Br Serv, New Orleans Public Library, 219 Loyola Ave, New Orleans, LA, 70112-2044. Tel: 504-529-7323, 504-596-2570. Fax: 504-596-2609. p. 962

Stypka, Joseph A, In Charge, Murphy-Jahn Library, 35 E Wacker Dr, Chicago, IL, 60601. Tel: 312-427-7300. Fax: 312-332-0274. p. 619

Su, Brian, Dir, Taiwan Resource Library, One E 42nd St, 5th Flr, New York, NY, 10017-6904. Tel: 212-317-7342. Fax: 212-557-3043. p. 1700

Su, Di, Head, Ref Serv, York College Library, 94-20 Guy R Brewer Blvd, Jamaica, NY, 11451. Tel: 718-262-2031. Fax: 718-262-2027, 718-262-2997. p. 1646

Su, Julie, Head, Ser, San Diego State University Library & Information Access, 5500 Campanile Dr, San Diego, CA, 92182-8050. Tel: 619-594-0904. Fax: 619-594-3270. p. 237

Su, Meng-fen, Head Librn, University of Texas Libraries, East Asian Library Program, PO Box P, PCL4-114, S5431, Austin, TX, 78713-8916. Tel: 512-495-4325. p. 2284

Su, Mila, Assoc Librn, Coordr, Access Serv, State University of New York College at Plattsburgh, Two Draper Ave, Plattsburgh, NY, 12901-2697. Tel: 518-564-5306. Fax: 518-564-5209. p. 1719

Su, Mila, Ref, Pennsylvania State University, Altoona College, 3000 Ivyside Park, Altoona, PA, 16601-3760. Tel: 814-949-5255. Fax: 814-949-5246, 814-949-5520. p. 2028

Su, Min, Librn, Lanier Technical College, 7745 Majors Rd, Cumming, GA, 30041. Tel: 770-781-6895. Fax: 770-781-6988. p. 527

Suarez, Dora, Br Mgr, Los Angeles Public Library System, Arroyo Seco Regional, 6145 N Figueroa St, Los Angeles, CA, 90042-3593. Tel: 323-255-0537. Fax: 323-255-1710. p. 173

Suarez, Mari, Dir, Highland Beach Library, 3618 S Ocean Blvd, Highland Beach, FL, 33487. Tel: 561-278-5455. Fax: 561-278-0156. p. 451

Suarez, Mona, Sr Res Spec, Group Technology Library & Information Services, 150 W Warrenville Rd, MC F1, Naperville, IL, 60563. Tel: 281-366-3387. Fax: 630-420-3697. p. 678

Suarez, Shari, Librn, Genesee District Library, Genesee Township (Johnson Memorial Library), 7397 N Genesee Rd, Genesee, MI, 48437. Tel: 810-640-1410. Fax: 810-640-2413. p. 1180

Suarez, Steven, AV, Valencia Community College, East Campus, 701 N Econlockhatchee Trail, Orlando, FL, 32825. Tel: 407-582-2467. Fax: 407-582-8914. p. 478

Suarez, Tanya, Youth Serv Librn, Long Beach Public Library, 111 W Park Ave, Long Beach, NY, 11561-3326. Tel: 516-432-7201. Fax: 516-889-4641. p. 1654

Suarez, Yamil, Libr Syst Adminr, Berklee College of Music Library, 150 Massachusetts Ave, Boston, MA, 02115. Tel: 617-747-2617. Fax: 617-747-2050. p. 1055

Suarez, Yamil, Libr Syst Support, Berklee College of Music Library, 150 Massachusetts Ave, Boston, MA, 02115. Tel: 617-747-2617. Fax: 617-747-2050. p. 1055

Subach, Jillian, Br Supvr, Boise Public Library, Library! at Collister, 4724 W State St, Boise, ID, 83703. Tel: 208-562-4917. p. 570

Subasic, Kate, Librn, Belmont County Law Library, Court House, 101 W Main St, Saint Clairsville, OH, 43950. Tel: 740-695-2121, Ext 248. Fax: 740-695-4968. p. 1933

Subbio, Helen, Ref, Delaware County Library System, 340 N Middletown Rd, Bldg 19, Media, PA, 19063-5597. Tel: 610-891-8622. Fax: 610-891-8641. p. 2087

Subramanian, Jane, Archives & Spec Coll Librn, State University of New York College at Potsdam, 44 Pierrepont Ave, Potsdam, NY, 13676-2294. Tel: 315-267-3326. Fax: 315-267-2744. p. 1722

Suby, Nancy, Dir, Fertile Public Library, 204 W Main St, Fertile, IA, 50434-1020. Tel: 641-797-2787. Fax: 641-797-2787. p. 816

Suchy, Catherine, Info Literacy Librn, Pub Serv, Joliet Junior College, J-Bldg, 3rd Flr, 1215 Houbolt Rd, Joliet, IL, 60431-8938. Tel: 815-729-9020, Ext 6604. Fax: 815-744-2465. p. 660

Suchy, Mary Jo, Asst Dir, Fred C Fischer Library, 167 Fourth St, Belleville, MI, 48111. Tel: 734-699-3291. Fax: 734-699-6352. p. 1156

Suda, Jane, Bibliog Instr, Fordham University Libraries, 441 E Fordham Rd, Bronx, NY, 10458-5151. Tel: 718-817-3570. Fax: 718-817-3582. p. 1586

Suda, Kristin, Tech Serv, Delaware County Library System, 340 N Middletown Rd, Bldg 19, Media, PA, 19063-5597. Tel: 610-891-8622. Fax: 610-891-8641. p. 2087

Suda, Virginia, Outreach Serv Librn, Elyria Public Library System, 320 Washington Ave, Elyria, OH, 44035-5199. Tel: 440-323-5747. Fax: 440-323-5788. p. 1898

Sudbeck, Pat, Dir, Queen of Peace Hospital Library, 525 N Foster, Mitchell, SD, 57301. Tel: 605-995-2462. Fax: 605-995-2441. p. 2215

Suddarth, Matthew, Dir, Winfield Public Library, OS-291 Winfield Rd, Winfield, IL, 60190. Tel: 630-653-7599. Fax: 630-653-7781. p. 720

Suddeth, Jewel, Mgr, Rabun County Public Library, 73 Jo Dotson Circle, Clayton, GA, 30525. Tel: 706-782-3731. Fax: 706-782-6514. p. 525

Sudduth, Elizabeth, Spec Coll Librn, University of South Carolina, 1322 Greene St, Columbia, SC, 29208-0103. Tel: 803-777-3142. p. 2189

Suder, Joy, Circ, Elkins-Randolph County Public Library, 416 Davis Ave, Elkins, WV, 26241. Tel: 304-637-0287. Fax: 304-637-0288. p. 2558

Sudine, Nancy L, Br Mgr, Allegany County Library System, Westernport Branch, 66 Main St, Westernport, MD, 21562. Tel: 301-359-0455. Fax: 301-359-0046. p. 1026

Suellentrop, Tricia, Dep County Librn, Johnson County Library, 9875 W 87th St, Overland Park, KS, 66212. Tel: 913-495-2400. Fax: 913-495-2460. p. 888

Suelzer, Elizabeth, ILL Librn, Milwaukee School of Engineering, 500 E Kilbourn Ave, Milwaukee, WI, 53202. Tel: 414-277-7182. Fax: 414-277-7186. p. 2620

Sueper, Betty, Asst Librn, Humphrey Public Library, 307 Main St, Humphrey, NE, 68642. Tel: 402-923-0957. Fax: 402-923-0957. p. 1402

Sueppel, Stephanie, Asst Dir, Drake Community Library, 930 Park St, Grinnell, IA, 50112-2016. Tel: 641-236-2661. Fax: 641-236-2667. p. 819

Suerst, Cynthia, Dir, Vernon Area Public Library District, 300 Olde Half Day Rd, Lincolnshire, IL, 60069-2901. Tel: 847-634-3650. Fax: 847-634-8449. p. 666

Suess, Jeff, In Charge, Cincinnati Enquirer Library, 312 Elm St, Cincinnati, OH, 45202. Tel: 513-768-8462. Fax: 513-768-8340. p. 1869

Suessmuth, Charles, Dir, Nancy Carol Roberts Memorial Library, 100 W MLK Jr Pkwy, Brenham, TX, 77833. Tel: 979-337-7202. Fax: 979-337-7209. p. 2291

Suffecool, Tracy, Ch, Nanuet Public Library, 149 Church St, Nanuet, NY, 10954. Tel: 845-623-4281. Fax: 845-623-2415. p. 1664

Suffoletta, Kathryn, Supvr, Middlesex County Library, Dorchester Branch, 2123 Dorchester Rd, Dorchester, ON, N0L 1G0, CANADA. Tel: 519-268-3451. Fax: 519-268-1047. p. 2845

Suffren, Jay, Librn, Department of Veterans Affairs, 1111 E End Blvd, Wilkes-Barre, PA, 18711. Tel: 570-824-3521. Fax: 570-821-7264. p. 2155

Sufic, Joanna, Br Mgr, Jefferson Parish Library, Charles A Wagner Branch, 6646 Riverside Dr, Metairie, LA, 70003. Tel: 504-838-1193. p. 957

Sugarman, Tammy, Assoc Univ Librn, Res Serv, Georgia State University Library, 100 Decatur St SE, Atlanta, GA, 30303-3202. Tel: 404-413-2705. Fax: 404-413-2701. p. 516

Sugawara, Sumiye, Librn, Corporation of the Township of Nipigon Public Library Board, 52 Front St, Nipigon, ON, P0T 2J0, CANADA. Tel: 807-887-3142. Fax: 807-887-3142. p. 2825

Sugden, Sarah, Dir, Waterville Public Library, 73 Elm St, Waterville, ME, 04901-6078. Tel: 207-872-5433. Fax: 207-873-4779. p. 1006

Suggs, Cindy, Dir, Brent-Centreville Public Library, 20 Library St, Centreville, AL, 35042. Tel: 205-926-4736. Fax: 205-926-4736. p. 11

Suggs, Pamela, Dir, Claiborne Parish Library,
909 Edgewood Dr, Homer, LA, 71040. Tel:
318-927-3845. Fax: 318-927-2016. p. 951

Suggs, Patti, Br Mgr, Moultrie-Colquitt County
Library, Doerun Municipal Library, PO Box 427,
Doerun, GA, 31744. Tel: 229-782-5507. p. 546

Sugimura, Sue, Actg Managing Librn, Hawaii State
Public Library System, 402 Kapahulu Ave,
Honolulu, HI, 96815. Tel: 808-733-8444. Fax:
808-733-8449. p. 561

Sugnet, Chris, Asst Dean, Scholarly
Communications, Colorado State University
Libraries, Morgan Library, 1201 Center
Avenue Mall, Fort Collins, CO, 80523-. Tel:
970-491-1838. Fax: 970-491-1195. p. 307

Suhadolnik, Maria, Librn, State Correctional
Institution, PO Box 256, Waymart, PA,
18472-0256. Tel: 570-488-5811. Fax:
570-488-2551, 570-488-2609. p. 2152

Suhfras, Martha, Dir, Plymouth Public Library, 130
Division St, Plymouth, WI, 53073-1802. Tel:
920-892-4416. Fax: 920-892-6295. p. 2631

Suholutsky, Inna, Librn, JBI International, 110
E 30th St, New York, NY, 10016. Tel:
212-889-2525. Fax: 212-689-3692. p. 1683

Suhr, Susan, Tech Serv Coordr, North Kawartha
Public Library, 175 Burleigh St, Apsley, ON,
K0L 1A0, CANADA. Tel: 705-656-4333. Fax:
705-656-2538. p. 2792

Suhre, Carol A, Dir, Clermont County Law Library
Association, 270 Main St, Batavia, OH, 45103.
Tel: 513-732-7109. Fax: 513-732-0974. p. 1857

Suhre, Marie, Coll Develop Librn, Idaho National
Laboratory, 1765 N Yellowstone Hwy, Idaho
Falls, ID, 83415-2300. Tel: 208-526-1194. Fax:
208-526-1697. p. 576

Suhsen, Robin B, Librn, Princeton Area Library,
100 S Fourth Ave, Princeton, MN, 55371. Tel:
763-389-3753. Fax: 763-389-3753. p. 1271

Suite, Cynde, Br Mgr, Bartow County Public Library
System, Adairsville Branch, 202 N Main St,
Adairsville, GA, 30123. Tel: 770-769-9200. Fax:
770-769-9201. p. 524

Suiter, David, Dir, United States Department of
Defense, Washington Headquarters Services,
1155 Defense Pentagon, Washington, DC,
20301-1155. Fax: 703-695-3999. p. 418

Suiter, Jody, Dir, Macksville City Library, 333
N Main St, Macksville, KS, 67557. Tel:
620-348-3555. Fax: 620-348-3555. p. 881

Sukalski, Pam, Dir, Minnesota West Community
& Technical College Libraries, 1450 College
Way, Worthington, MN, 56187-3024. Tel:
507-372-3462. p. 1291

Sukalski, Pam, Librn, Minnesota West Community
& Technical College, Canby Campus, 1011 First
St W, Canby, MN, 56220. Tel: 507-223-7252.
Fax: 507-223-5291. p. 1291

Sukalski, Pam, Librn, Minnesota West Community
& Technical College, Granite Falls Campus,
1593 11th Ave, Granite Falls, MN, 56241. Tel:
320-564-4511. Fax: 320-564-2318. p. 1291

Sukalski, Pam, Librn, Minnesota West Community
& Technical College, Pipestone Campus, 1314
N Hiawatha Ave, Pipestone, MN, 56164. Tel:
507-825-6832. Fax: 507-825-4656. p. 1291

Sukenic, Harvey, Libr Dir, Hebrew College, 160
Herrick Rd, Newton Centre, MA, 02459. Tel:
617-559-8750. Fax: 617-559-8751. p. 1110

Sulgar, Anna, ILL, William B Ogden Free Library,
42 Gardiner Pl, Walton, NY, 13856. Tel:
607-865-5929. Fax: 607-865-6821. p. 1762

Sulkers, Richard, Chief Exec Officer, Parry Sound
Public Library, 29 Mary St, Parry Sound, ON,
P2A 1E3, CANADA. Tel: 705-746-9601. Fax:
705-746-9601. p. 2835

Sulkes, Emilie, Librn, Cincinnati Psychoanalytic
Institute, 3001 Highland Ave, Cincinnati, OH,
45219. Tel: 513-961-8886. Fax: 513-961-0308.
p. 1869

Sullenger, Paula, Head, Acq, Auburn University,
Ralph Brown Draughon Library, 231 Mell St,
Auburn, AL, 36849. Tel: 334-844-1725. Fax:
334-844-4424. p. 5

Sullivan, Amy, Res Serv Librn, West Kentucky
Community & Technical College, 4810
Alben Barkley Dr, Paducah, KY, 42001. Tel:
270-534-3171. Fax: 270-554-6218. p. 932

Sullivan, Andrea, Head, Ref & Instruction,
Daemen College Library, Research &
Information Commons, 4380 Main St, Amherst,
NY, 14226-3592. Tel: 716-839-8243. Fax:
716-839-8475. p. 1573

Sullivan, Ann, Outreach Serv Librn, Sheppard
Memorial Library, 530 S Evans St, Greenville,
NC, 27858-2308. Tel: 252-329-4251. Fax:
252-329-4521. p. 1799

Sullivan, April, Archivist, Curator, Spec Coll, Saint
Edwards University, 3001 S Congress Ave,
Austin, TX, 78704-6489. Tel: 512-448-8469.
Fax: 512-448-8737. p. 2281

Sullivan, Barbara, Tech Serv Librn, Norwell Public
Library, 64 South St, Norwell, MA, 02061-2433.
Tel: 781-659-2015. Fax: 781-659-6755. p. 1115

Sullivan, Barbara, Tech Serv, Maxfield Public
Library, Eight Rte 129, Loudon, NH, 03307. Tel:
603-798-5153. p. 1454

Sullivan, Barbara, Librn, Center for Health,
Environment & Justice, 150 S Washington
St, Ste 300, Falls Church, VA, 22046. Tel:
703-237-2249. Fax: 703-237-8389. p. 2462

Sullivan, Bessie, Chief Exec Officer, County
Librn, Haliburton County Public Library,
Administrative Centre, 78 Maple Ave,
Haliburton, ON, K0M 1S0, CANADA. Tel:
705-457-2241. Fax: 705-457-9586. p. 2807

Sullivan, Beth, Dir, Bloomfield Public Library, 107
N Columbia St, Bloomfield, IA, 52537-1431.
Tel: 641-664-2209. Fax: 641-664-2506. p. 797

Sullivan, Brian, Instrul Librn, Alfred University,
Herrick Memorial Library, One Saxon Dr,
Alfred, NY, 14802. Tel: 607-871-2268. Fax:
607-871-2299. p. 1572

Sullivan, Bruce, Network Adminr, Poughkeepsie
Public Library District, 93 Market St,
Poughkeepsie, NY, 12601. Tel: 845-485-3445.
Fax: 845-485-3789. p. 1723

Sullivan, Carol, Asst Dir, Libr Serv, State Education
Resource Center Library, 25 Industrial Park
Rd, Middletown, CT, 06457-1516. Tel:
860-632-1485, Ext 341. Fax: 860-632-0438.
p. 352

Sullivan, Casey, Asst Librn, Bremer Pond Memorial
Library, One Main St, Pittsburg, NH, 03592. Tel:
603-538-7032. p. 1462

Sullivan, Charles A, Dir, Seton Hall University, One
Newark Ctr, Newark, NJ, 07102. p. 1513

Sullivan, Charles M, Exec Dir, Cambridge Historical
Commission Archive, 831 Massachusetts
Ave, 2nd Flr, Cambridge, MA, 02139. Tel:
617-349-4683. Fax: 617-349-3116. p. 1072

Sullivan, Chris, Adult Serv, Franklin T Degroodt
Library, 6475 Minton Rd SW, Palm Bay, FL,
32908. Tel: 321-952-6317. Fax: 321-952-6320.
p. 479

Sullivan, Connie, Br Mgr, Porter County Public
Library System, Valparaiso Public (Central), 103
Jefferson St, Valparaiso, IN, 46383-4820. Tel:
219-462-0524. Fax: 219-477-4867. p. 783

Sullivan, Connie, Prog Asst, Braille & Talking Bks,
South Dakota State Library, Braille & Talking
Book Program, McKay Bldg, 800 Governors
Dr, Pierre, SD, 57501-2294. Tel: 605-773-3131.
p. 2216

Sullivan, Dan, Govt Doc, Ref Serv, Colorado State
University Pueblo Library, 2200 Bonforte Blvd,
Pueblo, CO, 81001-4901. Tel: 719-549-2361.
Fax: 719-549-2738. p. 320

Sullivan, Dean, Govt Doc Librn, Irvine Sullivan
Ingram Library, University of West Georgia,
1601 Maple St, Carrollton, GA, 30118. Tel:
678-839-6498. Fax: 678-839-6511. p. 523

Sullivan, Debra S, Librn, Norton Audubon Hospital,
One Audubon Plaza Dr, Louisville, KY, 40217.
Tel: 502-636-7296. Fax: 502-636-7257. p. 925

Sullivan, Donna, Libr Assoc, Maine State Law
& Legislative Reference Library, 43 State
House Sta, Augusta, ME, 04333-0043. Tel:
207-287-1600. Fax: 207-287-6467. p. 974

Sullivan, Eileen, Children's Coll Develop Mgr,
Cook Memorial Public Library District, 413 N
Milwaukee Ave, Libertyville, IL, 60048-2280.
Tel: 847-362-2330. Fax: 847-362-2354. p. 665

Sullivan, Elizabeth, Bus Intelligence Librn,
McKenna, Long & Aldridge LLP, 1900
K St NW, Washington, DC, 20006. Tel:
202-496-7579. Fax: 202-496-7756. p. 408

Sullivan, Elizabeth, Sister, ILL, College of Our
Lady of the Elms, 291 Springfield St, Chicopee,
MA, 01013-2839. Tel: 413-265-2280. Fax:
413-594-7418. p. 1082

Sullivan, Jane, Br Mgr, Martinsburg-Berkeley
County Public Library, North Berkeley
Public Library, 125 T J Jackson Dr, Falling
Waters, WV, 25419. Tel: 304-274-3443. Fax:
304-274-3443. p. 2565

Sullivan, Janelle, Cat, Oral Roberts University
Library, 7777 South Lewis Ave, Tulsa, OK,
74171. Tel: 918-495-6882. Fax: 918-495-6893.
p. 1981

Sullivan, Jean, Librn, Arizona Department of
Corrections - Adult Institutions, PO Box 2799,
Globe, AZ, 85502-2799. Tel: 928-425-8141.
Fax: 928-425-0621. p. 64

Sullivan, Jessica A, Tech Serv Librn, Sullivan
& Worcester, LLP, One Post Office Sq,
Boston, MA, 02109. Tel: 617-338-2800. Fax:
617-338-2880. p. 1067

Sullivan, Joanne, Dir, Saint Agnes Healthcare,
900 Caton Ave, Baltimore, MD, 21229.
Tel: 410-368-3123, 410-368-3124. Fax:
410-368-3298. p. 1017

Sullivan, John, Imaging Serv, Huntington Library,
1151 Oxford Rd, San Marino, CA, 91108. Tel:
626-405-3435. Fax: 626-449-5720. p. 255

Sullivan, John, Dr, Instr, University of South
Florida, 4202 Fowler Ave, CIS 1040, Tampa,
FL, 33620-7800. Tel: 813-974-2370. Fax:
813-974-6840. p. 2964

Sullivan, Joyce, Dir, Elgin Public Library, 503
S Second St, Elgin, NE, 68636-3222. Tel:
402-843-2460. Fax: 402-843-2460. p. 1398

Sullivan, Katherine, Librn, Audubon Park Public
Library, 20 Road C, Audubon Park, NJ, 08106.
Tel: 856-547-5236. p. 1470

Sullivan, Kathleen, Br Mgr, Cuyahoga County
Public Library, Parma-Ridge Branch, 5850
Ridge Rd, Parma, OH, 44129-3166. Tel:
440-888-4300. Fax: 440-884-2097. p. 1928

Sullivan, Kathleen, Br Mgr, Cuyahoga County
Public Library, Parma-South Branch, 7335 Ridge
Rd, Parma, OH, 44129-6602. Tel: 440-885-5362.
Fax: 440-884-2263. p. 1928

Sullivan, Kathryn, Asst Head, Ref Serv, University
of Maryland, Baltimore County, 1000
Hilltop Circle, Baltimore, MD, 21250. Tel:
410-455-2356. p. 1018

Sullivan, Ken, Dir, Western Nevada Community
College, 2201 W College Pkwy, Carson
City, NV, 89703. Tel: 775-445-4246. Fax:
775-445-3363. p. 1426

Sullivan, Kerry, Health Sci Librn, Walden University
Library, 100 Washington Ave S, Ste 900,
Minneapolis, MN, 55401. p. 1262

Sullivan, Kevin, Digital Serv Coordr, Manhattanville
College Library, 2900 Purchase St, Purchase,
NY, 10577. Tel: 914-323-5453. Fax:
914-323-8139. p. 1724

Sullivan, Kristen, Pub Serv, Pocono Mountain Public
Library, 5540 Memorial Blvd, Tobyhanna, PA,
18466. Tel: 570-894-8860. Fax: 570-894-8852.
p. 2146

Sullivan, Larry E, Dr, Chief Librn, John Jay College
of Criminal Justice, 899 Tenth Ave, New York,
NY, 10019. Tel: 212-237-8246, 212-237-8265.
Fax: 212-237-8221. p. 1683

Sullivan, Laura, Grants Coordr, Librn, Northern
Kentucky University, University Dr, Highland
Heights, KY, 41099. Tel: 859-572-5724. Fax:
859-572-5390. p. 917

Sullivan, Lee, Head, Coll Serv, Lesley University, 89
Brattle St, Cambridge, MA, 02138-2790. Tel:
617-349-8840. Fax: 617-349-8849. p. 1077

Sullivan, Lester, Univ Archivist, Xavier University of Louisiana, One Drexel Dr, New Orleans, LA, 70125-1098. Tel: 504-520-7305. Fax: 504-520-7940. p. 964

Sullivan, Louise, Librn, Sullivan County Public Library, Dugger Public, 8007 E Main St, Dugger, IN, 47848. Tel: 812-648-2822. p. 780

Sullivan, Louise, Br Mgr, Spokane Public Library, South Hill, 3324 S Perry Ave, Spokane, WA, 99203. Tel: 509-444-5386. Fax: 509-444-5371. p. 2538

Sullivan, Maggie, Adult Serv, ILL, Park County Public Library, Powell Branch, 217 E Third, Powell, WY, 82435-1903. Tel: 307-754-8828. Fax: 307-754-8824. p. 2654

Sullivan, Margot, Adult Serv, Morrill Memorial Library, 33 Walpole St, Norwood, MA, 02062-1206. Tel: 781-769-0200. Fax: 781-769-6083. p. 1115

Sullivan, Marina, Dir, Babylon Public Library, 24 S Carll Ave, Babylon, NY, 11702. Tel: 631-669-1624. Fax: 631-669-7826. p. 1577

Sullivan, Mark G, Legal Info Librn, Boston College, 885 Centre St, Newton Centre, MA, 02459. Tel: 617-552-2896. Fax: 617-552-2889. p. 1110

Sullivan, Michael, Admin Supvr, Jacksonville Public Library, 303 N Laura St, Jacksonville, FL, 32202-3505. Tel: 904-630-2434. Fax: 904-630-2431. p. 453

Sullivan, Michael, Br Mgr, Jacksonville Public Library, Murray Hill, 918 Edgewood Ave S, Jacksonville, FL, 32205-5341. Tel: 904-384-2665. Fax: 904-381-1104. p. 454

Sullivan, Nancy, Circ, University of Puget Sound, 1500 N Warner St, Campus Mail Box 1021, Tacoma, WA, 98416-1021. Tel: 253-879-2665. Fax: 253-879-3670. p. 2541

Sullivan, Olivia, Acq, University of Nevada-Reno, 1664 N Virginia St, Mailstop 0322, Reno, NV, 89557-0322. Tel: 775-682-5582. Fax: 775-784-1328. p. 1433

Sullivan, Patricia, Asst Dir, Assoc Librn, Instrul Serv, Molloy College, 1000 Hempstead Ave, Rockville Centre, NY, 11571. Tel: 516-678-5000, Ext 6386. Fax: 516-678-8908. p. 1734

Sullivan, Paulette, Br Mgr, Monroe County Public Library, Key Largo Branch, Tradewinds Shopping Ctr, 101485 Overseas Hwy, Key Largo, FL, 33037. Tel: 305-451-2396. Fax: 305-853-7311. p. 456

Sullivan, Rania S, Dir, Avalon Public Library, 317 S Home Ave, Avalon, PA, 15202. Tel: 412-761-2288. Fax: 412-761-7745. p. 2030

Sullivan, Rebecca, Instrul Tech Librn, Luther College, 700 College Dr, Decorah, IA, 52101. Tel: 563-387-2212. Fax: 563-387-1657. p. 807

Sullivan, Rebecca W, Dir, Riter C Hulsey Public Library, 301 N Rockwall, Terrell, TX, 75160-2618. Tel: 972-551-6663. Fax: 972-551-6662. p. 2391

Sullivan, Rose, Dir, National Center for Appropriate Technology, 3040 Continental Dr, Butte, MT, 59701. Tel: 406-494-8643. Fax: 406-494-2905. p. 1376

Sullivan, Ruth, Dean, Community College of Rhode Island, 1762 Louisquisset Pike, Lincoln, RI, 02865. Tel: 401-333-7058. Fax: 401-331-7115. p. 2168

Sullivan, Ruth, Dean, Community College of Rhode Island, One John H Chafee Blvd, Newport, RI, 02840. Tel: 401-825-1000. p. 2169

Sullivan, Ruth, Dean, Learning Res, Community College of Rhode Island, 400 East Ave, Warwick, RI, 02886-1807. Tel: 401-825-2488. Fax: 401-825-2421. p. 2177

Sullivan, Sarah, Chief Financial Officer, Richland County Public Library, 1431 Assembly St, Columbia, SC, 29201-3101. Tel: 803-799-9084. Fax: 803-929-3448. p. 2188

Sullivan, Sharon, Adult Serv, Ref, Truro Public Library, Five Library Lane, North Truro, MA, 02652. Tel: 508-487-1125. Fax: 508-487-3571. p. 1113

Sullivan, Sheila, Ch, Georgetown County Library, 405 Cleland St, Georgetown, SC, 29440-3200. Tel: 843-545-3300. Fax: 843-545-3395. p. 2194

Sullivan, Steve, Curator, Chicago Academy of Sciences, 2430 N Cannon Dr, Chicago, IL, 60614. Tel: 773-525-0166. Fax: 773-755-5199. p. 607

Sullivan, Steve, Operations Supvr, Richland County Public Library, 1431 Assembly St, Columbia, SC, 29201-3101. Tel: 803-799-9084. Fax: 803-929-3448. p. 2188

Sullivan, Susan C, Librn, United States Courts, John Joseph Moakley US Courthouse, Ste 9400, One Courthouse Way, Boston, MA, 02210. Tel: 617-748-9044. Fax: 617-748-9358. p. 1068

Sullivan, Suzanne, Head, Coll Serv, Auburn Public Library, 49 Spring St, Auburn, ME, 04210. Tel: 207-333-6640. Fax: 207-333-6644. p. 974

Sullivan, Syd, Librn, Tacoma Community College Library, 6501 S 19th St, Tacoma, WA, 98466-6100. Tel: 253-566-5103. Fax: 253-566-5398. p. 2540

Sullivan, Thomas, Brother, Acq, Libr Dir, Conception Abbey & Seminary Library, 37174 State Hwy W, Conception, MO, 64433. Tel: 660-944-2803. Fax: 660-944-2833. p. 1326

Sullivan, Tracy, Circ Mgr, Drury University, 900 N Benton Ave, Springfield, MO, 65802. Tel: 417-873-7481. Fax: 417-873-7432. p. 1366

Sullivan, Vicki, Dep Dir, Oklahoma Department of Libraries, 200 NE 18th St, Oklahoma City, OK, 73105. Tel: 405-521-2502. Fax: 405-525-7804. p. 1974

Sullivan, Wanda, Dir, Tryon Public Library, 25 S Main St, Tryon, OK, 74875. Tel: 918-374-2227. Fax: 918-374-2228. p. 1980

Sullivan-Seblonka, Cathy, Ch, Peter White Public Library, 217 N Front St, Marquette, MI, 49855. Tel: 906-228-9510. Fax: 906-226-1783. p. 1207

Suloff Laughlin, Jean, Librn, Mifflin County Historical Society Library & Museum, One W Market St, Lewistown, PA, 17044. Tel: 717-242-1022. Fax: 717-242-3488. p. 2081

Sulonen, Dana, Librn, Tribune Chronicle Library, 240 Franklin St SE, Warren, OH, 44482-5711. Tel: 330-841-1734. Fax: 330-841-1717. p. 1944

Sulouff, Patricia, Actg Dir, University of Rochester, Carlson Science & Engineering Library, 160 Trustee Rd, Rochester, NY, 14627-0236. Tel: 585-275-4488. Fax: 585-273-4656. p. 1733

Sultan, Sushma, Libr Tech, Hicks Morley Hamilton Stewart & Storie LLP, TD Ctr, 39th Flr, 77 King St W, Toronto, ON, M5H 1K8, CANADA. Tel: 416 362-1011, Ext 7118. Fax: 416-362-9680. p. 2854

Sultan, Terrie, Dir, Parrish Art Museum Library, 25 Jobs Lane, Southampton, NY, 11968. Tel: 631-283-2118, Ext 12. Fax: 631-283-7006. p. 1745

Sulzbach, Deborah E, Acq, Drake University, Drake Law Library, Opperman Hall, 2615 Carpenter Ave, Des Moines, IA, 50311-4505. Tel: 515-271-3784. Fax: 515-271-2530. p. 809

Sulzer, Jack, Assoc Dean, Undergrad & Learning Serv, Pennsylvania State University Libraries, 510 Paterno Library, University Park, PA, 16802. Tel: 814-865-0401. Fax: 814-865-3665. p. 2148

Sumblin, Susan, Dir, Enterprise State Community College, 600 Plaza Dr, Enterprise, AL, 36330. Tel: 334-347-2623, Ext 2271. Fax: 334-347-0146. p. 16

Sumerford, Steven L, Asst Dir, Commun Relations Librn, Greensboro Public Library, 219 N Church St, Greensboro, NC, 27402-3178. Tel: 336-373-3636. Fax: 336-333-6781. p. 1796

Sumida, Jerilyn, Head, Cat, East-West Center, 1601 East-West Rd, Honolulu, HI, 96848-1601. Tel: 808-944-7379. Fax: 808-944-7600. p. 560

Sumler, Claudia, Sr Adminr, Pub Serv, Harford County Public Library, 1221-A Brass Mill Rd, Belcamp, MD, 21017-1209. Tel: 410-273-5600, Ext 2249. Fax: 410-273-5606. p. 1020

Summars, Kathy, Dir, Buffalo Public Library, 11 E Turner, Buffalo, OK, 73834. Tel: 580-735-2995. Fax: 580-735-6157. p. 1959

Summer, Jessica, Youth Serv Dir, Jeudevine Memorial Library, 93 N Main St, Hardwick, VT, 05843. Tel: 802-472-5948. Fax: 802-472-3793. p. 2425

Summerfield, Terri, Dir, Clearwater County Free Library District, 204 Wood St, Weippe, ID, 83553. Tel: 208-435-4058. Fax: 208-435-4374. p. 585

Summers, Anita D, Asst Dir, Sequoyah Regional Library System, 116 Brown Industrial Pkwy, Canton, GA, 30114-2899. Tel: 770-479-3090, Ext 221. Fax: 770-479-3069. p. 523

Summers, Barbara, Automation Syst Coordr, York County Library System, 159 E Market St, 3rd Flr, York, PA, 17401. Tel: 717-840-7435. Fax: 717-849-6999. p. 2160

Summers, Bryan, Teen Serv Mgr, Yuma County Library District, 2951 S 21st Dr, Yuma, AZ, 85364. Tel: 928-373-6487. Fax: 928-782-9420. p. 91

Summers, Charlotte, Libr Dir, Florence Public Library, 207 E Main St, Florence, TX, 76527-4048. Tel: 254-793-2672. Fax: 254-793-2102. p. 2319

Summers, Linda, Libr Dir, Nashville Public Library, 219 E Elm St, Nashville, IL, 62263-1711. Tel: 618-327-3827. Fax: 618-327-4820. p. 679

Summers, Lucy, Ch, Holly Township Library, 1116 N Saginaw St, Holly, MI, 48442-1395. Tel: 248-634-1754. Fax: 248-634-8088. p. 1191

Summers-Ables, Joy, Assoc Dir, University of Oklahoma Health Sciences Center, 1000 Stanton L Young Blvd, Oklahoma City, OK, 73117-1213. Tel: 405-271-2285. Fax: 405-271-6186. p. 1975

Summersgill, Roberta, Br Mgr, Burnaby Public Library, Tommy Douglas Branch, 7311 Kingsway, Burnaby, BC, V5E 1G8, CANADA. Tel: 604-522-3971. p. 2725

Summerville, Sarah, Dir, Unexpected Wildlife Refuge Library, 110 Unexpected Rd, Newfield, NJ, 08344. Tel: 856-697-3541. p. 1513

Summey, Jane, Dir, Libr Serv, Southeastern Technical College Library, 346 Kite Rd, Swainsboro, GA, 30401. Tel: 478-289-2322. Fax: 478-289-2322. p. 553

Summey, Jane L, Dir, Libr Serv, Southeastern Technical College, 211 S Tillman St, Glennville, GA, 30427. Tel: 912-654-5276, Ext 4125. Fax: 912-654-5223. p. 535

Summey, Jane L, Dir, Libr Serv, Southeastern Technical College, 3001 E First St, Vidalia, GA, 30474. Tel: 912-538-3132. Fax: 912-538-3156. p. 556

Summey, Terri, Access Serv, Emporia State University, 1200 Commercial St, Box 4051, Emporia, KS, 66801. Tel: 620-341-5207. Fax: 620-341-5997. p. 866

Sumner, Bettie, ILL, Shorter College, 315 Shorter Ave, Rome, GA, 30165. Tel: 706-291-2121, Ext 7296. Fax: 706-236-1512. p. 549

Sumner, Cheryl, Librn, Lilly Pike Sullivan Municipal Library, 103 Railroad St, Enfield, NC, 27823. Tel: 252-445-5203. Fax: 252-445-4321. p. 1792

Sumner, Delores, Spec Coll Librn, Northeastern State University, 711 N Grand Ave, Tahlequah, OK, 74464-2333. Tel: 918-456-5511, Ext 3200. Fax: 918-458-2197. p. 1979

Sumner, Elaine, Tech Serv, Cumberland Public Library, 1464 Diamond Hill Rd, Cumberland, RI, 02864-5510. Tel: 401-333-2552, Ext 131. Fax: 401-334-0578. p. 2165

Sumner, Katie, Librn, Marquette Heights Public Library, 715 Lincoln Rd, Marquette Heights, IL, 61554-1313. Tel: 309-382-3778. p. 671

Sumner, Sandy, Instruction & Outreach Librn, Morehead State University, 150 University Blvd, Morehead, KY, 40351. Tel: 606-783-5110. Fax: 606-783-5037. p. 929

Sumners, Bill, Dir, Southern Baptist Historical Library & Archives, 901 Commerce St, Ste 400, Nashville, TN, 37203-3630. Tel: 615-244-0344. Fax: 615-782-4821. p. 2258

Sumpter, Debbie, Media Spec, Burlington Public Library, 2331 New St, Burlington, ON, L7R 1J4, CANADA. Tel: 905-639-3611. Fax: 905-681-7277. p. 2797

Sumpter, Jill, Tech Coordr, Fort Bend County Libraries, 1001 Golfview Dr, Richmond, TX, 77469-5199. Tel: 281-341-2630. Fax: 281-341-2688. p. 2374

Sumrall, Richard, Dir, Lincoln Public Library District, 725 Pekin, Lincoln, IL, 62656. Tel: 217-732-5732, 217-732-8878. Fax: 217-732-6273. p. 666

Sumruld, Sharon, Asst Dir, Scurry County Library, 1916 23rd St, Snyder, TX, 79549-1910. Tel: 325-573-5572. Fax: 325-573-1060. p. 2388

Sun, Hongyan, Automation Librn, Delta State University, Laflore Circle at Fifth Ave, Cleveland, MS, 38733-2599. Tel: 662-846-4440. Fax: 662-846-4443. p. 1296

Sun, Hongyi, Librn, Kean University, 1000 Morris Ave, Union, NJ, 07083. Tel: 908-737-4600. Fax: 908-737-4620. p. 1537

Sun, Jinong, Govt Doc, Fayetteville State University, 1200 Murchison Rd, Fayetteville, NC, 28301-4298. Tel: 910-672-1752. Fax: 910-672-1746. p. 1793

Sun, Xianghua, Mgr, Carnegie Museum of Natural History Library, 4400 Forbes Ave, Pittsburgh, PA, 15213-4080. Tel: 412-622-3264, 412-622-8870. Fax: 412-622-8837. p. 2124

Sun, Ying, Dr, Asst Prof, University at Buffalo, State University of New York, 534 Baldy Hall, Buffalo, NY, 14260. Tel: 716-645-2412. Fax: 716-645-3775. p. 2971

Sundaram, Justine, Ref, Boston College Libraries, John J Burns Library of Rare Books & Special Collections, 140 Commonwealth Ave, Chestnut Hill, MA, 02467. Tel: 617-552-4861. Fax: 617-552-2465. p. 1080

Sundberg, Jane M, In Charge, National Park Service, PO Box 210, Yorktown, VA, 23690-0210. Tel: 757-898-2415. Fax: 757-898-6346. p. 2505

Sundborg, Laurie, Chief Operating Officer, Tulsa City-County Library, 400 Civic Ctr, Tulsa, OK, 74103. Tel: 918-596-7977, Fax: 918-596-7964. p. 1982

Sunde, Esther, Ref, South Seattle Community College, 6000 16th Ave SW, Seattle, WA, 98106-1499. Tel: 206-768-6663. Fax: 206-763-5155. p. 2532

Sunderland, Holli, Br Mgr, Mifflin County Library, Kishacoquillas Branch, 194 N Penn St, Belleville, PA, 17004. Tel: 717-935-2880. Fax: 717-935-2880. p. 2081

Sunderman, Delores, Asst Librn, Kingman Public Library, 123 W State St, Kingman, IN, 47952. Tel: 765-397-3138. Fax: 765-397-3566. p. 757

Sundheim, Jennifer, Asst Dir, Head, Coll & Access Serv, University of Washington Libraries, Tacoma Library, 1900 Commerce St, Box 358460, Tacoma, WA, 98402-3100. Tel: 253-692-4860. Fax: 253-692-4445. p. 2535

Sundin, Kelly, Ref Serv, Syst Librn, California Institute of Integral Studies, 1453 Mission St, 2nd Flr, San Francisco, CA, 94103. Tel: 415-575-6187. Fax: 415-575-1264. p. 241

Sundstrand, Jacque, Spec Coll, University of Nevada-Reno, 1664 N Virginia St, Mailstop 0322, Reno, NV, 89557-0322. Tel: 775-682-5667. Fax: 775-784-4529. p. 1433

Sung, Myung, Tech Serv Mgr, St Charles Public Library District, One S Sixth Ave, Saint Charles, IL, 60174-2105. Tel: 630-584-0076, Ext 237. Fax: 630-584-3448. p. 699

Sung, Nackil, Head, Tech Serv, Eastern Illinois University, 600 Lincoln Ave, Charleston, IL, 61920. Tel: 217-581-6094. p. 603

Sunhachawi-Taylor, Poom, Head, Adult Serv, Head, Tech Serv, Rosenberg Library, 2310 Sealy Ave, Galveston, TX, 77550. Tel: 409-763-8854, Ext 140. Fax: 409-763-0275. p. 2326

Sunio, Maria, Principal Librn, Upland Public Library, 450 N Euclid Ave, Upland, CA, 91786-4732. Tel: 909-931-4200. Fax: 909-931-4209. p. 278

Sup, Susan, Librn, Arnolds Park Public Library, Hwy 71, Arnolds Park, IA, 51331. Tel: 712-332-2033. p. 794

Supancic, Allison, Librn, Regional Foundation Library, 1009 E 11th St, 2nd Flr, Austin, TX, 78702. Tel: 512-475-7373. p. 2281

Supinski, Stephanie, Br Mgr, Easton Area Public Library & District Center, Palmer Memorial Library, One Weller Pl, Easton, PA, 18045. Tel: 610-258-7492. p. 2052

Supnick, Patricia, Librn, Children's Hospital of Michigan, Phyllis Ann Colburn Memorial Family Library, 3901 Beaubien Blvd, 5th Flr, Detroit, MI, 48201. Tel: 313-745-5437. Fax: 313-993-0148. p. 1169

Suppiah, Selva, Coordr, Coll Serv, Alberta Legislature Library, 216 Legislature Bldg, 10800-97 Ave, Edmonton, AB, T5K 2B6, CANADA. Tel: 780-644-5605. Fax: 780-427-6016. p. 2699

Sura, Michele, Mgr, Privy Council Office, 85 Sparks St, Rm 1000, Ottawa, ON, K1A 0A3, CANADA. Tel: 613-957-5125. Fax: 613-957-5043. p. 2832

Surabian, Bettyjane, Teen Librn, Rye Free Reading Room, 1061 Boston Post Rd, Rye, NY, 10580. Tel: 914-967-0480. Fax: 914-967-5522. p. 1736

Surber, Erik, Dir, Waukee Public Library, 950 Warrior Lane, Waukee, IA, 50263. Tel: 515-987-1280. Fax: 515-987-5262. p. 850

Surface, Mitchell, Webmaster, Journal Gazette Library, 600 W Main St, Fort Wayne, IN, 46802. Tel: 260-461-8196. Fax: 260-461-8648. p. 742

Suri, Manisha, Dir, Support Serv, Westmont Public Library, 428 N Cass, Westmont, IL, 60559-1502. Tel: 630-969-5625. Fax: 630-969-6490. p. 717

Surles, Alma, Pub Serv Librn, Alabama Supreme Court & State Law Library, Heflin-Torbert Judicial Bldg, 300 Dexter Ave, Montgomery, AL, 36104. Tel: 334-229-0569. Fax: 334-229-0543. p. 28

Surles, Donna, Ref Serv, Haywood County Public Library, 678 S Haywood St, Waynesville, NC, 28786-4398. Tel: 828-452-5169, Ext 2508. Fax: 828-452-6746. p. 1828

Surman, Melba, Pub Serv Asst, Texarkana College, 2500 N Robison Rd, Texarkana, TX, 75599. Tel: 903-832-5565, Ext 3075. Fax: 903-831-7429. p. 2391

Surniak, Laura, Ch, Norwood Public Library, 198 Summit St, Norwood, NJ, 07648-1835. Tel: 201-768-9555. Fax: 201-767-2176. p. 1515

Suroosh, Monica, Librn, Virginia State Police Academy Library, 7700 Midlothian Tpke, Richmond, VA, 23235. Tel: 804-674-2258. Fax: 804-674-2089. p. 2493

Surovik-Bohnert, Margo, Librn, Georgia Power Co-Southern Co, 241 Ralph McGill Blvd NE, Bin 10044, Atlanta, GA, 30308. Tel: 404-506-6633. Fax: 404-506-6652. p. 515

Surprenant, Neil, Dir, Educ Res, Paul Smiths College of Arts & Sciences, Rte's 30 & 86, Paul Smiths, NY, 12970. Tel: 518-327-6353. Fax: 518-327-6350. p. 1715

Surprenant, Thomas T, Prof, Queens College of the City University of New York, Benjamin Rosenthal Library, Rm 254, 65-30 Kissena Blvd, Flushing, NY, 11367. Tel: 718-997-3790. Fax: 718-997-3797. p. 2970

Surratt, Greg, Tech Serv, United States Courts Library, 333 Lomas Blvd NW, Ste 360, Albuquerque, NM, 87102. Tel: 505-348-2135. Fax: 505-348-2795. p. 1550

Surss, Stephanie, Ch, Madison County Library System, Ridgeland Public Library, 397 Hwy 51 N, Ridgeland, MS, 39157. Tel: 601-856-4536. Fax: 601-856-3748. p. 1295

Susa, Bryant, Commun Libr Mgr, County of Los Angeles Public Library, Dr Martin Luther King, Jr Library, 17906 S Avalon Blvd, Carson, CA, 90746-1598. Tel: 310-327-4830. Fax: 310-327-3630. p. 142

Susan, Odencrantz, Libr Dir, Tacoma Public Library, 1102 Tacoma Ave S, Tacoma, WA, 98402-2098. Tel: 253-292-2001. Fax: 253-344-5584. p. 2540

Susan, Perretta, Law Librn, Delaware County Library System, 340 N Middletown Rd, Bldg 19, Media, PA, 19063-5597. Tel: 610-891-8622. Fax: 610-891-8641. p. 2087

Suscovich, Karen, Dir, Fallsington Library, 139 Yardley Ave, Fallsington, PA, 19054-1119. Tel: 215-295-4449. p. 2057

Susko, Margaret, Bus Librn, Back Mountain Memorial Library, 96 Huntsville Rd, Dallas, PA, 18612. Tel: 570-675-1182. Fax: 570-674-5863. p. 2048

Suson, Gina, Librn, Walters Public Library, 202 N Broadway St, Walters, OK, 73572-1226. Tel: 580-875-2006. Fax: 580-875-2023. p. 1985

Sussman, Diana Brawley, Dir, Carbondale Public Library, 405 W Main St, Carbondale, IL, 62901-2995. Tel: 618-457-0354. Fax: 618-457-0353. p. 600

Sussman, Marge, Br Mgr, Berkeley Public Library, North Branch, 1170 The Alameda, Berkeley, CA, 94707. Tel: 510-981-6250. Fax: 510-528-8975. p. 126

Sustache, Rafael, Coordr, AV, Amaury Veray Music Library, 350 Rafael Lamar, Hato Rey, PR, 00918. Tel: 787-751-0160, Ext 279. Fax: 787-754-5934. p. 2673

Suter, Gwen, Br Mgr, Portsmouth Public Library, W Gordon Ryan Branch, 103 Lucasville-Minford Rd, Lucasville, OH, 45648-0744. Tel: 740-259-6119. Fax: 740-259-3168. p. 1931

Suter, Marcia, Dir, Libr Serv, University of Toledo, 2801 W Bancroft St, Mail Stop 509, Toledo, OH, 43606-3390. Tel: 419-530-2629. Fax: 419-530-2726. p. 1941

Suter, Sally, Br Mgr, Louisville Free Public Library, Middletown, 200 N Juneau Dr, Louisville, KY, 40243. Tel: 502-245-7332. Fax: 502-245-7038. p. 924

Suteu, Corina, Dir, Romanian Cultural Institute, 200 E 38th St, New York, NY, 10016. Tel: 212-687-0180. Fax: 212-687-0181. p. 1698

Sutherland, Cindy, Pub Serv, Thomas Beaver Free Library, 205 Ferry St, Danville, PA, 17821-1939. Tel: 570-275-4180. Fax: 570-275-8480. p. 2049

Sutherland, Leslie, Youth Serv, Carroll County Public Library, 136 Court St, Carrollton, KY, 41008. Tel: 502-732-7020. Fax: 502-732-7122. p. 909

Sutherland, Leslie, Br Mgr, Oakville Public Library, Iroquois Ridge, 1051 Glenashton Dr, Oakville, ON, L6H 6Z4, CANADA. Tel: 905-338-4247. Fax: 905-338-4248. p. 2825

Sutherland, Linda, Fiscal Officer, Stow-Munroe Falls Public Library, 3512 Darrow Rd, Stow, OH, 44224. Tel: 330-688-3295. p. 1937

Sutherland, Michael, Web Serv Librn, University of Nebraska at Kearney, 2508 11th Ave, Kearney, NE, 68849-2240. Tel: 308-865-8544. Fax: 308-865-8722. p. 1403

Sutherland Mills, Kimberly, Mgr, Prog & Outreach, Kingston Frontenac Public Library, 130 Johnson St, Kingston, ON, K7L 1X8, CANADA. Tel: 613-549-8888, Ext 1520. Fax: 613-549-8476. p. 2813

Sutherland, Peggy, Br Mgr, Sullivan County Public Library, Sullivan Gardens Branch, 104 Bluegrass Dr, Kingsport, TN, 37660. Tel: 423-349-5990. Fax: 423-349-5990. p. 2225

Sutherland, Robert, Managing Librn, Yukon College Library, 500 College Dr, Whitehorse, YT, Y1A 5K4, CANADA. Tel: 867-668-8888. Fax: 867-668-8808. p. 2934

Sutherland, Robert, Dr, Dir, Southwest Virginia Community College Library, Russell Hall, 599 Community College Rd, Cedar Bluff, VA, 24609. Tel: 276-964-7265. Fax: 276-964-7259. p. 2453

Sutherland, Timothy, Dir of Libr Serv, Indiana University Northwest Library, 3400 Broadway, Gary, IN, 46408. Tel: 219-980-6946. Fax: 219-980-6558. p. 745

Sutherland, Timothy, Dir, Lake County Central Law Library, Indiana University Northwest, 3400 Broadway, Gary, IN, 46408. Tel: 219-980-6946. Fax: 219-980-6558. p. 745

Sutherland, Tracy, ILL, Eastern Connecticut State University, 83 Windham St, Willimantic, CT, 06226-2295. Tel: 860-465-5719. Fax: 860-465-5521. p. 378

Sutorus, Jessica, Br Mgr, San Bernardino County Library, Sam J Racadio Library & Environmental Learning Center, 7863 Central Ave, Highland, CA, 92346-4107. Tel: 909-425-4700. Fax: 909-864-0816. p. 229

Sutphin, Allison, Br Adminr, Southern Illinois University School of Medicine Library, 801 N Rutledge, Springfield, IL, 62702. Tel: 217-545-2658. Fax: 217-545-0988. p. 706

Sutter, Amy, Reserves & Digital Serv Coordr, Illinois Wesleyan University, One Ames Plaza, Bloomington, IL, 61701-7188. Tel: 309-556-3728. Fax: 309-556-3706. p. 595

Sutter, Cynthia, Youth Serv, Agawam Public Library, 750 Cooper St, Agawam, MA, 01001. Tel: 413-789-1550. Fax: 413-789-1552. p. 1048

Sutter, Randi, Info & Instruction Librn, Heartland Community College Library, 1500 W Raab Rd, Normal, IL, 61761. Tel: 309-268-8275. Fax: 309-268-7989. p. 681

Sutter, Sandra, Mgr, Johnson County Library, Leawood Pioneer Branch, 4700 Town Center Dr, Leawood, KS, 66211. Tel: 913-344-0255. Fax: 913-344-0253. p. 888

Sutterfield, Debra, Dir, White River Regional Library, 368 E Main St, Batesville, AR, 72501. Tel: 870-793-8814. Fax: 870-793-8896. p. 94

Sutterfield, Suzanne, Librn, Stockton-San Joaquin County Public Library, Lathrop Branch, 15461 Seventh St, Lathrop, CA, 95366. Fax: 209-858-5239. p. 273

Sutterlin, Edith, Head, Tech Serv, Northland Public Library, 300 Cumberland Rd, Pittsburgh, PA, 15237-5455. Tel: 412-366-8100, Ext 125. Fax: 412-366-2064. p. 2126

Suttle, George, Ref Librn, Spokane Falls Community College, 3410 Ft George Wright Dr, MS 3020, Spokane, WA, 99224-5288. Tel: 509-533-3807. Fax: 509-533-3144. p. 2537

Suttle, Heather, In Charge, Western Counties Regional Library, Lockeport Branch, 35 North St, Lockeport, NS, B0T 1L0, CANADA. Tel: 902-656-2817. p. 2787

Suttle, Jennie, Circ Mgr, New Lenox Public Library District, 120 Veterans Pkwy, New Lenox, IL, 60451. Tel: 815-485-2605. Fax: 815-485-2548. p. 680

Suttles, Cheryl, Mgr, Libr Serv, Integris Baptist Medical Center, 3300 Northwest Expressway, Oklahoma City, OK, 73112. Tel: 405-949-3766. Fax: 405-949-3883. p. 1972

Suttles, Dennis, Libr Spec, Lincoln Land Community College Library, 5250 Shepherd Rd, Springfield, IL, 62794. Tel: 217-786-2354. Fax: 217-786-2251. p. 705

Sutton, Anglea, Libr Coordr, National Park Service, One Indian Well Headquarters, Tulelake, CA, 96134. Tel: 530-667-8113, 530-667-8119. Fax: 530-667-2737. p. 276

Sutton, Anna, Br Mgr, Anderson County Library, Powdersville, Four Civic Ct, Easley, SC, 29642. Tel: 864-295-2961. Fax: 864-295-2961. p. 2181

Sutton, Anne, Dir, Riviera Beach Public Library, 600 W Blue Heron Blvd, Riviera Beach, FL, 33404-4398. Tel: 561-845-4195. Fax: 561-881-7308. p. 485

Sutton, Barbara, Br Mgr, San Diego County Library, Bonita-Sunnyside Branch, 4375 Bonita Rd, Bonita, CA, 91902-2698. Tel: 619-475-3867. Fax: 619-475-4366. p. 233

Sutton, Chelsea, Librn, Principia College, One Maybeck Pl, Elsah, IL, 62028-9703. Tel: 618-374-5235. Fax: 618-374-5107. p. 643

Sutton, Connie, Dir, Keyser-Mineral County Public Library, 105 N Main St, Keyser, WV, 26726. Tel: 304-788-3222. Fax: 304-788-3222. p. 2563

Sutton, Dionci, Circ Mgr, Shreve Memorial Library, 424 Texas St, Shreveport, LA, 71101. Tel: 318-226-5897. Fax: 318-226-4780. p. 969

Sutton, Dorothy L, Acq, Head, Tech Serv, Purchasing, Cheltenham Township Library System, 215 S Keswick Ave, Glenside, PA, 19038-4420. Tel: 215-885-0457. Fax: 215-885-1239. p. 2061

Sutton, Dorothy L, Head, Tech Serv, Cheltenham Township Library System, East Cheltenham Free Library, 400 Myrtle Ave, Cheltenham, PA, 19012-2038. Tel: 215-885-0457. Fax: 215-885-1239. p. 2061

Sutton, Dorothy L, Head, Tech Serv, Cheltenham Township Library System, Elkins Park Free Library, 563 E Church Rd, Elkins Park, PA, 19027-2499. Tel: 215-885-0457. Fax: 215-885-1239. p. 2061

Sutton, Dorothy L, Head, Tech Serv, Cheltenham Township Library System, Glenside Free Library, 215 S Keswick Ave, Glenside, PA, 19038-4420. Tel: 215-885-0457. Fax: 215-885-1239. p. 2061

Sutton, Dorothy L, Head, Tech Serv, Cheltenham Township Library System, LaMott Free Library, 7420 Sycamore Ave, LaMott, PA, 19027-1005. Tel: 215-885-0457. Fax: 215-885-1239. p. 2062

Sutton, Ellen, Assoc Dean of Libr, Pub Serv Adminr, College of DuPage Library, 425 Fawell Blvd, Glen Ellyn, IL, 60137-6599. Tel: 630-942-2659. Fax: 630-858-8757. p. 649

Sutton, James, Technology Tech, Crockett Public Library, 709 E Houston Ave, Crockett, TX, 75835-2124. Tel: 936-544-3089. Fax: 936-544-4139. p. 2303

Sutton, Janice, Dir, Trinity Valley Community College Library, 100 Cardinal Dr, Athens, TX, 75751-2765. Tel: 903-675-6229. Fax: 903-675-6207. p. 2277

Sutton, Joan, Libr Tech, Prince Edward Island Public Library Service, Breadalbane Public, 4023 Dixon Rd, Breadalbane, PE, C0A 1E0, CANADA. Tel: 902-964-2520. p. 2876

Sutton, Kay, Librn, Galeton Public Library, Five Park Ln, Galeton, PA, 16922. Tel: 814-435-2321. Fax: 814-435-2321. p. 2059

Sutton, Ken, Network Adminr, Library Connection, Inc, 599 Matianuck Ave, Windsor, CT, 06095-3567. Tel: 860-298-5322. Fax: 860-298-5328. p. 2939

Sutton, Kristine, Dir, Newstead Public Library, 33 Main St, Akron, NY, 14001-1020. Tel: 716-542-2327. Fax: 716-542-3703. p. 1567

Sutton, Linda, Assoc Dir of Libr, Seminole Community College Library, 100 Weldon Blvd, Sanford, FL, 32773-6199. Fax: 407-328-2233. p. 489

Sutton, Lynn, Dean, Wake Forest University, PO Box 7777, Winston-Salem, NC, 27109-7777. Tel: 335-758-5480. Fax: 336-758-3694, 336-758-8831. p. 1834

Sutton, Mary J, Librn, Upper Valley Medical Center, 3130 N Dixie Hwy, Troy, OH, 45373. Tel: 937-440-4594. Fax: 937-440-4591. p. 1941

Sutton, Norma, Ref Serv, North Park University, Brandel Library, 5114 N Christiana Ave, Chicago, IL, 60625. Tel: 773-244-6239. Fax: 773-244-4891. p. 620

Sutton, Sandra, Br Librn, Brooklyn Public Library, Eastern Parkway, 1044 Eastern Pkwy, Brooklyn, NY, 11213. Tel: 718-953-4225. Fax: 718-953-3970. p. 1591

Sutton, Sandra K, Neighborhood Libr Supvr, Brooklyn Public Library, Red Hook, Seven Wolcott St, Brooklyn, NY, 11231. Tel: 718-935-0203. Fax: 718-935-0160. p. 1592

Sutton, Shan, Assoc Univ Librn, Res & Scholarly Communication, Oregon State University Libraries, 121 The Valley Library, Corvallis, OR, 97331-4501. Tel: 541-908-1655. Fax: 541-737-3453. p. 1994

Sutton, Stephanie, Dir of Tech Serv, Tennessee State Library & Archives, 403 Seventh Ave N, Nashville, TN, 37243-0312. Tel: 615-253-3462. Fax: 615-532-2472, 615-741-6471. p. 2259

Sutton, Stuart, Assoc Prof, University of Washington, Mary Gates Hall, Ste 370, Campus Box 352840, Seattle, WA, 98195-2840. Tel: 206-685-9937. Fax: 206-616-3152. p. 2976

Sutton, T, Asst Dir, Carl Albert State College, 1507 S McKenna, Poteau, OK, 74953. Tel: 918-647-1310. Fax: 918-647-1314. p. 1976

Suvak, Daniel, Dean, Institutional Effectiveness & Libr Serv, Walsh University, 2020 E Maple St NW, North Canton, OH, 44720-3336. Tel: 330-490-7183. Fax: 330-490-7270. p. 1923

Suvak, William A, Jr, Librn, Mayview State Hospital, 1601 Mayview Rd, Bridgeville, PA, 15017-1599. Tel: 412-257-6496. Fax: 412-257-6320. p. 2037

Suzuki, Linda, Br Mgr, San Francisco Public Library, Western Addition Branch Library, 1550 Scott St, San Francisco, CA, 94115-3512. Tel: 415-355-5727. Fax: 415-440-4527. p. 247

Svadjian, Armen, Pub Serv, Tyndale University College & Seminary, 25 Ballyconnor Ct, Toronto, ON, M2M 4B3, CANADA. Tel: 416-226-6380. Fax: 416-218-6765. p. 2864

Svarckopf, Jennifer, Mgr, Syst & Tech Serv, Canada Department of Justice Library, EMB, Rm A-370, 284 Wellington St, Ottawa, ON, K1A 0H8, CANADA. Tel: 613-957-4606. p. 2828

Sveinsson, Joan L, Dir, The Colony Public Library, 6800 Main St, The Colony, TX, 75056-1133. Tel: 972-625-1900. Fax: 972-624-2245. p. 2392

Svenningsen, Julie, Libr Assoc, Scott County Library System, 13090 Alabama Ave S, Savage, MN, 55378-1479. Tel: 952-707-1760. Fax: 952-707-1775. p. 1283

Svenningsen, Tammy, Dir, Spruce Grove Public Library, 35 Fifth Ave, Spruce Grove, AB, T7X 2C5, CANADA. Tel: 780-962-4423, Ext 107. Fax: 780-962-4826. p. 2717

Svetahor, Lillian, Br Mgr, Middlesex County Public Library, Deltaville Branch, 35 Lover's Lane, Deltaville, VA, 23043. Tel: 804-776-7362. Fax: 804-776-7423. p. 2498

Sviantek, Donna, Librn, United States Army, APVG-GAF-RL (FS), Bldg 650, Fort Shafter, HI, 96858-5009. Tel: 808-438-9521. Fax: 808-438-3100. p. 559

Svitavsky, William, Electronic Res, Rollins College, 1000 Holt Ave, Campus Box 2744, Winter Park, FL, 32789-2744. Tel: 407-646-2679. Fax: 407-646-1515. p. 505

Svoboda, Barb, Ref Serv, Hartland Public Library, 110 E Park Ave, Hartland, WI, 53029. Tel: 262-367-3350. Fax: 262-369-2251. p. 2597

Svoboda, Barbara, Ref/YA, Horsham Township Library, 435 Babylon Rd, Horsham, PA, 19044-1224. Tel: 215-443-2609, Ext 208. Fax: 215-443-2697. p. 2069

Svoboda, Cynthia J W, Ref, Ref Serv, Ad, Bridgewater State College, Ten Shaw Rd, Bridgewater, MA, 02325. Tel: 508-531-1256. Fax: 508-531-1349, 508-531-6103. p. 1070

Swafford, Carolyn J, Dir, Canton Free Library, Eight Park St, Canton, NY, 13617. Tel: 315-386-3712. Fax: 315-386-4131. p. 1602

Swafford, James, Head, Info Tech, Pittsburg Public Library, 308 N Walnut, Pittsburg, KS, 66762-4732. Tel: 620-231-8110. Fax: 620-232-2258. p. 890

Swafford, Kristi, Dir, Calhoun Public Library, 746 Hwy 163, Calhoun, TN, 37309. Tel: 423-336-2348. Fax: 423-336-1527. p. 2226

Swafford, Peggy, ILL, Artesia Public Library, 306 W Richardson Ave, Artesia, NM, 88210-2499. Tel: 575-746-4252. Fax: 575-746-3075. p. 1551

Swafford, William M, Sr Librn, California Department of Corrections & Rehabilitation, Fifth St & Western Ave, Norco, CA, 92860. Tel: 951-737-2683, Ext 4504. Fax: 951-273-2380. p. 194

Swaggerty, Carol, Br Mgr, Knox County Public Library System, Powell Branch, 330 W Emory Rd, Knoxville, TN, 37938-4010. Tel: 865-947-6210. Fax: 865-938-6466. p. 2242

Swails, Mark, Ref/Copyright Librn, Johnson County Community College, 12345 College Blvd, Box 21, Overland Park, KS, 66210. Tel: 913-469-8500, Ext 3773. Fax: 913-469-3816. p. 888

Swaim, Janet, ILL, White River Regional Library, 368 E Main St, Batesville, AR, 72501. Tel: 870-793-8814. Fax: 870-793-8896. p. 94

Swain, Al, Acq, Chowan University, One University Pl, Murfreesboro, NC, 27855. Tel: 252-398-6203. Fax: 252-398-1301. p. 1811

Swain, Deborah, Asst Prof, North Carolina Central University, 1801 Fayetteville St, Durham, NC, 27707. Tel: 919-530-6485. Fax: 919-530-6402. p. 2971

Swain, Donald, Access Serv, University of Oregon Libraries, Mathematics, 210 Fenton Hall, University of Oregon, Eugene, OR, 97403. Tel: 541-346-2656. Fax: 541-346-3012. p. 1997

Swain, Dorothy, Asst Dir, Greenville Public Library, 573 Putnam Pike, Greenville, RI, 02828-2195. Tel: 401-949-3630. Fax: 401-949-0530. p. 2166

Swain, Melissa, Circ Librn, Wythe-Grayson Regional Library, Rural Retreat Public, 119 N Greever St, Rural Retreat, VA, 24368-2450. Tel: 276-686-8337. Fax: 276-686-8337. p. 2472

Swain, Monique, Librn, Johnson & Wales University, 1701 NE 127th St, North Miami, FL, 33181. Tel: 305-892-7043. p. 472

Swain, Richard H, Dir, West Chester University, 25 W Rosedale Ave, West Chester, PA, 19383. Tel: 610-436-2747. p. 2153

Swalboski, Marlys, Dir, Silver Falls Library District, 410 S Water St, Silverton, OR, 97381-2137. Tel: 503-873-5173. Fax: 503-873-6227. p. 2020

Swalboski, Martin, Tech Serv, Chautauqua-Cattaraugus Library System, 106 W Fifth St, Jamestown, NY, 14701. Tel: 716-484-7136. p. 1646

Swan, Bruce, Actg Head, University of Illinois Library at Urbana-Champaign, Modern Languages & Linguistics, 425 Main Library, MC-522, 1408 W Gregory Dr, Urbana, IL, 61801. Tel: 217-333-0076. Fax: 217-333-2214. p. 712

Swan, Deba, Dean of Libr, Central Texas College, Bld 102, 6200 W Central Texas Expressway, Killeen, TX, 76549. Tel: 254-526-1475. Fax: 254-526-1878. p. 2350

Swan, Loydell, Librn, Plainview Carnegie Public Library, 102 Main St, Plainview, NE, 68769. Tel: 402-582-4507. Fax: 402-582-4813. p. 1417

Swan, Marilyn S, Dir, Effingham Public Library, 30 Town House Rd, Effingham, NH, 03882. Tel: 603-539-1537. p. 1446

Swan, Michael, Chief Librn, Aiken-Bamberg-Barnwell-Edgefield Regional Library System, Aiken County, 314 Chesterfield St SW, Aiken, SC, 29801. Tel: 803-642-2020. Fax: 803-642-7570. p. 2179

Swan, Paula D, Prog Lead/Mgr, Spokane Falls Community College, Bldg 2 MS 3020, W3410 Fort George Wright Dr, Spokane, WA, 99224-5288. Tel: 509-533-3809. Fax: 509-533-3144. p. 2975

Swan, Phil, Head Librn, Soc Work Libr, Hunter College Libraries, 695 Park Ave, New York, NY, 10065. Tel: 212-452-7078. Fax: 212-772-4142. p. 1682

Swan, Philip, Head Librn, Hunter College Libraries, Schools of Social Work & Public Health Library, 2180 Third Ave, New York, NY, 10035. Tel: 212-396-7654. p. 1682

Swan, Ruth M, Dr, Assoc Dir, Florida Agricultural & Mechanical University Libraries, 1500 S Martin Luther King Blvd, Tallahassee, FL, 32307-4700. Tel: 850-599-3370. Fax: 850-561-2293. p. 492

Swan, Sally A, Librn, United States Army, Seven Bernard Rd, Fort Monroe, VA, 23651-5124. Tel: 757-788-2909. Fax: 757-788-2931. p. 2465

Swan, Susan, YA Serv, Western Allegheny Community Library, 8042 Steubenville Pike, Oakdale, PA, 15071-9375. Tel: 724-695-8150. Fax: 724-695-2860. p. 2100

Swanay, Robert, Dir, Johnson City Public Library, 100 W Millard St, Johnson City, TN, 37604. Tel: 423-434-4457. Fax: 423-434-4469. p. 2240

Swanbeck, Jan, Chair, Govt Doc, University of Florida Libraries, 535 Library W, Gainesville, FL, 32611-7000. Tel: 352-273-0367. Fax: 352-392-3357. p. 449

Swanekamp, Joan E, Head, Cat, Yale University Library, Sterling Memorial Library, 120 High St, New Haven, CT, 06520. Tel: 203-432-1701. Fax: 203-432-1294. p. 359

Swaney, Ann, Govt Doc Librn, Northwestern Michigan College, 1701 E Front St, Traverse City, MI, 49686-3061. Tel: 231-995-1065. Fax: 231-995-1056. p. 1231

Swanger, Maggie, Ref, Laramie County Community College Library, 1400 E College Dr, Cheyenne, WY, 82007-3204. Tel: 307-778-1283. Fax: 307-778-1399. p. 2652

Swanick, Eric, Spec Coll Librn, Simon Fraser University Library, 8888 University Dr, Burnaby, BC, V5A 1S6, CANADA. Tel: 778-782-4626. Fax: 778-782-3023. p. 2726

Swank, Kris, Librn, Pima Community College, 2202 W Anklam Rd, Tucson, AZ, 85709-0001. Tel: 520-206-6821. Fax: 520-206-3059. p. 86

Swank-Letkeman, Laurie, Ref Serv, Peoria Public Library, 107 NE Monroe St, Peoria, IL, 61602-1070. Tel: 309-497-2125. Fax: 309-497-2007. p. 690

Swann, Bruce W, Librn, University of Illinois Library at Urbana-Champaign, Classics, 1408 W Gregory Dr, 419A, Urbana, IL, 61801. Tel: 217-244-1872. Fax: 217-333-2214. p. 712

Swann, Julie, Coordr, Content, Access & Delivery Serv, Northern Arizona University, Bldg 028, Knoles Dr, Flagstaff, AZ, 86011. Tel: 928-523-4939. Fax: 928-523-3770. p. 62

Swann, Linda, Mgr, Suwannee River Regional Library, Lee Public Library, 190 SE County Rd 255, Lee, FL, 32059-0040. Tel: 850-971-5665. Fax: 850-971-4333. p. 461

Swanner, Alex, Access Serv Librn, De Anza College, 21250 Stevens Creek Blvd, Cupertino, CA, 95014-5793. Tel: 408-864-8486. Fax: 408-864-8603. p. 138

Swanner, Ronnie C, Dir, Ctr for Learning & Tech, Trinity University, One Trinity Pl, San Antonio, TX, 78212-7200. Tel: 210-999-7356. Fax: 210-999-8182. p. 2383

Swanson, Andy, Dir, Klamath County Library Services District, 126 S Third St, Klamath Falls, OR, 97601-6394. Tel: 541-882-8896. Fax: 541-882-6166. p. 2001

Swanson, Andy, Dir, Southern Oregon Library Federation, c/o Klamath County Library, 126 S Third St, Klamath Falls, OR, 97601. Tel: 541-882-8894. Fax: 541-882-6166. p. 2953

Swanson, Anny, Circ & Staff Develop Coordr, United States Navy, Bldg 160, 2601E Paul Jones St, Great Lakes, IL, 60088-2845. Tel: 847-688-4617. Fax: 847-688-3602. p. 652

Swanson, Bernadette, Ref Librn, University of California, Davis, Loren D Carlson Health Sciences Library, Med Sci 1B, One Shields Ave, Davis, CA, 95616-5291. Tel: 530-752-7637. Fax: 530-752-4718. p. 139

Swanson, Carol, Br Supvr, Lincoln City Libraries, Charles H Gere Branch, 2400 S 56th St, Lincoln, NE, 68506-3599. Tel: 402-441-8560. Fax: 402-441-8563. p. 1405

Swanson, Catherine, Archivist, Scottish Rite Masonic Museum & Library, Inc, 33 Marrett Rd, Lexington, MA, 02421. Tel: 781-457-4116. Fax: 781-861-9846 (call first). p. 1099

Swanson, Cecilia, Dir, Portage County District Library, 10482 South St, Garrettsville, OH, 44231. Tel: 330-527-5082. Fax: 330-527-4370. p. 1901

Swanson, Charlene, Librn, Riverside Public Library, Arlington, 9556 Magnolia, Riverside, CA, 92503-3698. Tel: 951-689-6612. Fax: 951-689-6612. p. 218

Swanson, Connie Jo, Dir, Walkerton-Lincoln Township Public Library, 300 Michigan St, Walkerton, IN, 46574. Tel: 574-586-2933. Fax: 574-586-2933. p. 785

Swanson, Constance L, Tech Serv Librn, Atlantic City Free Public Library, One N Tennessee Ave, Atlantic City, NJ, 08401. Tel: 609-345-2269, Ext 3040. Fax: 609-345-5570. p. 1470

Swanson, Dayle, Librn, Clementon Memorial Library, 195 Gibbsboro Rd, Clementon, NJ, 08021. Tel: 856-783-3233. Fax: 856-784-8794. p. 1479

Swanson, Dennis M, Dir of Libr, The Master's Seminary Library, 13248 Roscoe Blvd, Sun Valley, CA, 91352. Tel: 818-909-5634. Fax: 818-909-5680. p. 273

Swanson, Dona, Br Mgr, Prince William Public Library System, Nokesville Neighborhood, 12993 Fitzwater Dr, Nokesville, VA, 20181-2229. Tel: 703-792-5665. Fax: 703-594-2250. p. 2486

Swanson, Ellie, Tech Serv Librn, Elgin Community College, 1700 Spartan Dr, Elgin, IL, 60123. Tel: 847-214-7337. p. 641

Swanson, Joe, Jr, Dept Head, Interim Dir, Morehouse School of Medicine Library, 720 Westview Dr SW, Atlanta, GA, 30310-1495. Tel: 404-752-1530. Fax: 404-752-1049. p. 517

Swanson, Karen, Supvry Librn, United States Environmental Protection Agency, 77 W Jackson Blvd (PL-16J), Chicago, IL, 60604. Tel: 312-886-6822. Fax: 312-886-1492. p. 626

Swanson, Kathleen, Librn, Montgomery College, Takoma Park Campus Library, 7600 Takoma Ave, Takoma Park, MD, 20912. Tel: 240-567-1537. Fax: 240-567-5820. p. 1037

Swanson, LaVerne, Circ Mgr, Columbus Metropolitan Library, Northwest, 2280 Hard Rd, Columbus, OH, 43235. Tel: 614-807-2659. Fax: 614-807-2659. p. 1885

Swanson, Linda, Head, Info Serv, Concordia College, 901 S Eighth St, Moorhead, MN, 56562. Tel: 219-299-4402. Fax: 218-299-4253. p. 1265

Swanson, Marnie, Univ Librn, University of Victoria Libraries, McPherson Library, PO Box 1800, Victoria, BC, V8W 3H5, CANADA. Tel: 250-721-8211. Fax: 250-721-8215. p. 2746

Swanson, Patricia, Librn, Bladen County Public Library, Clarkton Public, 10413 N College St, Clarkton, NC, 28433. Tel: 910-647-3661. p. 1791

Swanson, Penny, Head, Cat, Simon Fraser University Library, 8888 University Dr, Burnaby, BC, V5A 1S6, CANADA. Tel: 778-782-3184. Fax: 604-291-6579. p. 2726

Swanson, Regina, Coordr, Miriam Hospital, 164 Summit Ave, Providence, RI, 02906. Tel: 401-793-2291. Fax: 401-274-9568. p. 2173

Swanson, Ruthann, Dir, Alsip-Merrionette Park Public Library District, 11960 S Pulaski Rd, Alsip, IL, 60803-1197. Tel: 708-371-5666. Fax: 708-371-5672. p. 588

Swanson, Sandra, Med Librn, Mercy Health Partners, 1500 E Sherman Blvd, Muskegon, MI, 49443. Tel: 231-672-3972. Fax: 231-672-3842. p. 1212

Swanson, Sara, Info Literacy Librn, Davidson College, 209 Ridge Rd, Davidson, NC, 28035-0001. Tel: 704-894-2331. Fax: 704-894-2625. p. 1786

Swanson, Treasure, Archives Mgr, Cleveland Bradley County Public Library, History Branch & Archives, 833 N Ocoee St, Cleveland, TN, 37311. Tel: 423-479-8367. p. 2229

Swanson, Troy, Dept Chair, Pub Serv, Teaching & Learning Librn, Moraine Valley Community College Library, 9000 W College Pkwy, Palos Hills, IL, 60465. Tel: 708-974-5439. Fax: 708-974-1184. p. 687

Swanson-Farmarco, Cindy, Asst Libr Mgr, Baltimore County Public Library, Lansdowne, 500 Third Ave, Baltimore, MD, 21227. Tel: 410-887-5602. Fax: 410-887-5633. p. 1044

Swantek, Shauna Lea, Dir, Putnam District Library, 327 N Main St, Nashville, MI, 49073-9578. Tel: 517-852-9723. Fax: 517-852-9723. p. 1213

Swanto, Pam, Head of Libr, Volusia County Public Library, Lake Helen Public, 221 N Euclid Ave, Lake Helen, FL, 32744. Tel: 386-228-1152. Fax: 386-228-1154. p. 436

Swanton, Abby, Wis Doc Dep Prog/Wis Digital Archives, Wisconsin Department of Public Instruction, Reference & Loan Library, 2109 S Stoughton Rd, Madison, WI, 53716-2899. Tel: 608-224-6167. Fax: 608-224-6178. p. 2610

Swanton, James, Dir, Harlem Hospital Medical Center, 506 Lenox Ave, KP6108, New York, NY, 10037. Tel: 212-939-1685. p. 1680

Swanwick, Maureen, Head, Circ, Romeo District Library, 65821 Van Dyke, Washington, MI, 48095. Tel: 586-752-0603. Fax: 586-752-8416. p. 1235

Swanzy, Geri, Ch, Brazoria County Library System, Manvel Branch, 20514B Hwy 6, Manvel, TX, 77578. Tel: 281-489-7596. Fax: 281-489-7596. p. 2275

Swarbrick, Maria, Mem Serv Librn, Saskatchewan Legislative Library, 234-2405 Legislative Dr, Regina, SK, S4S 0B3, CANADA. Tel: 306-787-7663. Fax: 306-787-5856. p. 2924

Swark, Jamie, Circ, Mount Aloysius College Library, 7373 Admiral Peary Hwy, Cresson, PA, 16630-1999. Tel: 814-886-6445. Fax: 814-886-5767. p. 2048

Swarm, Darryl, Assessment Librn, Asst Prof, University of La Verne, 2040 Third St, La Verne, CA, 91750. Tel: 909-593-3511, Ext 4305. Fax: 909-392-2733. p. 162

Swarr, Lisa, Acq Asst, Lancaster Bible College Library, 901 Eden Rd, Lancaster, PA, 17601-5036. Tel: 717-560-8250. Fax: 717-560-8265. p. 2076

Swart, Colleen, Asst Dir, Oostburg Public Library, 213 N Eighth St, Oostburg, WI, 53070. Tel: 920-564-2934. p. 2627

Swart, Kathy, Ref & Instruction, Pierce College Library, Puyallup Campus, 1601 39th Ave SE, Puyallup, WA, 98374. Tel: 253-840-8305. Fax: 253-840-8316. p. 2520

Swart, Natalie, Br Mgr, Fauquier County Public Library, Bealeton Branch, 10877 Willow Dr N, Bealeton, VA, 22712. Tel: 540-439-9728. Fax: 540-439-9731. p. 2501

Swarthout, Judy L, Assoc Law Librn, Ref, Pennsylvania State University - Dickinson School of Law (University Libraries), 1170 Harrisburg Pike, Carlisle, PA, 17013-1617. Tel: 717-240-5229. Fax: 717-240-5127. p. 2042

Swartout, Daniel, Dir, Edgecombe County Memorial Library, 909 Main St, Tarboro, NC, 27886. Tel: 252-823-1141. Fax: 252-823-7699. p. 1826

Swartout, Dennis, Dir, Tri-Cities Historical Society Museum, 200 Washington Ave, Grand Haven, MI, 49417. Tel: 616-842-0700. Fax: 616-842-3698. p. 1183

Swartwout, Laurie, Curator, Operations Mgr, Cardinal Stritch University Library, 6801 N Yates Rd, Milwaukee, WI, 53207-3985. Tel: 414-410-4263. Fax: 414-410-4268. p. 2617

Swartz, Bridget, Librn, Parish Public Library, Main & Church St, Parish, NY, 13131. Tel: 315-625-7130. p. 1714

Swartz, Jane, Librn, Missouri Department of Corrections, Fulton Reception & Diagnostic Center, PO Box 190, Fulton, MO, 65251-0190. Tel: 573-592-4040. Fax: 573-592-4020. p. 1334

Swartz, Pat, Archivist, Librn, Fairbanks Museum & Planetarium, 1302 Main St, Saint Johnsbury, VT, 05819. Tel: 802-748-2372, Ext 105. Fax: 802-748-3347. p. 2434

Swartz, Pauline, Bibliog Instr, Mt San Antonio College Library, 1100 N Grand Ave, Walnut, CA, 91789. Tel: 909-274-4260. Fax: 909-468-4011. p. 282

Swartz-Truesdell, Lin, Asst Libr Dir, Kenosha Public Library, 812 56th St, Kenosha, WI, 53140-3735. Tel: 262-564-6326. Fax: 262-564-6370. p. 2601

Swartzbaugh, Roger, Ref, St John's Hospital, 800 E Carpenter, Springfield, IL, 62769. Tel: 217-544-6464, Ext 44563. Fax: 217-525-2895. p. 706

Swartzel, Judith, Tech Serv, The Citadel, 171 Moultrie St, Charleston, SC, 29409-6140. Tel: 843-953-5116. Fax: 843-953-5190. p. 2184

Swartzel, Linda, Dir, Mary L Cook Public Library, 381 Old Stage Rd, Waynesville, OH, 45068. Tel: 513-897-4826. Fax: 513-897-9215. p. 1945

Swartzendruber, Rozella, Chairperson, Bethesda Mennonite Church Library, PO Box 130, Henderson, NE, 68371-0130. Tel: 402-723-4562. Fax: 402-723-4567. p. 1402

Swartzlander, Barbara, Dir, Pub Serv, University of New England Libraries, 11 Hills Beach Rd, Biddeford, ME, 04005. Tel: 207-602-2315. Fax: 207-602-5922. p. 978

Swary, Lynn, Librn, Holgate Community Library, 204 Railway Ave, Holgate, OH, 43527. Tel: 419-264-7965. Fax: 419-264-1261. p. 1905

Swasey, Ashley, Adult Serv, North Hampton Public Library, 237A Atlantic Ave, North Hampton, NH, 03862-2341. Tel: 603-964-6326. Fax: 603-964-1107. p. 1461

Swasta, Susan, Database Coordr, ILL, Webmaster, Mark Skinner Library, 48 West Rd, Manchester, VT, 05254. Tel: 802-362-2607. p. 2427

Swatski, Joseph, Ref Librn, State University of New York, 735 Anderson Hill Rd, Purchase, NY, 10577-1400. Tel: 914-251-6411. Fax: 914-251-6437. p. 1724

Swauncy, Emmer T, Tech Serv Team Leader, Southwest Tennessee Community College, George Freeman Library, 5983 Macon Cove, Memphis, TN, 38134. Tel: 901-333-4437. Fax: 901-333-4566. p. 2251

Sway, Pamela, Youth Serv Librn, Wayland Free Public Library, Five Concord Rd, Wayland, MA, 01778. Tel: 508-358-2311. Fax: 508-358-5249. p. 1134

Swayney, Robin, Libr Mgr, Qualla Boundary Public Library, 810 Acquoni Rd, Cherokee Indian Reservation, Cherokee, NC, 28719. Tel: 828-497-1764. Fax: 828-497-1763. p. 1784

Sweany, Diana, Electronic Serv, Regis University, 3333 Regis Blvd, Denver, CO, 80221-1099. Tel: 303-458-4030. Fax: 303-964-5497. p. 303

Swearengen, John, Br Mgr, University Libraries, University of Memphis, Communication Sciences, 807 Jefferson St, Rm 110, Memphis, TN, 38105-5042. Tel: 901-678-5846. Fax: 901-678-8281. p. 2252

Swearingen, Brent, Instrul Serv Librn, John Brown University Library, 2000 W University, Siloam Springs, AR, 72761. Tel: 479-524-7207. Fax: 479-524-7335. p. 115

Swearingen, John, Med Librn, Charlotte AHEC Library, Medical Education Bldg, 1000 Blythe Blvd, Charlotte, NC, 28203. Tel: 704-355-3129. Fax: 704-355-7138. p. 1781

Sweatlock, Diane, Ref Librn, River Vale Free Public Library, 412 Rivervale Rd, River Vale, NJ, 07675. Tel: 201-391-2323. Fax: 201-391-6599. p. 1526

Sweatlock, Donna Z, Circ Mgr, Oradell Free Public Library, 375 Kinderkamack Rd, Oradell, NJ, 07649-2122. Tel: 201-262-2613. Fax: 201-262-9112. p. 1516

Swedberg, Donna, Mgr, Santa Cruz City-County Library System Headquarters, Central, 224 Church St, Santa Cruz, CA, 95060-3873, Tel: 831-427-7706, Ext 7750. Fax: 831-427-7701. p. 264

Swedlund, Iris, Librn, Velva School & Public Library, 101 W Fourth St, Velva, ND, 58790-7045. Tel: 701-338-2022. Fax: 701-338-2023. p. 1848

Sweeney, Charlotte, Circ, Ref & Instrul Serv Librn, Pensacola State College, 1000 College Blvd, Pensacola, FL, 32504-8998. Tel: 850-484-2007. Fax: 850-484-1991. p. 482

Sweeney, Debbie, Asst Dir, Augusta County Library, 1759 Jefferson Hwy, Fishersville, VA, 22939. Tel: 540-885-3961, 540-949-6354. Fax: 540-943-5965. p. 2464

Sweeney, Frances, Tech Serv, United States Army, 1325 J St, Ste 820, Sacramento, CA, 95814-2922. Tel: 916-557-6657. Fax: 916-557-7091. p. 225

Sweeney, J Mark, Div Chief, Library of Congress, Serial & Government Publications Division, James Madison Memorial Bldg, Rm LM-133, LM-131, Washington, DC, 20540-4760. Tel: 202-707-2958. Fax: 202-707-6128. p. 408

Sweeney, Kathleen, Dir, Semmes, Bowen & Semmes Library, 25 S Charles St, Ste 1400, Baltimore, MD, 21201. Tel: 410-385-3936. Fax: 410-539-5223. p. 1017

Sweeney Marsh, Joan, Dir, Sheridan College Library, 1430 Trafalgar Rd, Oakville, ON, L6H 2L1, CANADA. Tel: 905-845-9430, Ext 2480. Fax: 905-815-4123. p. 2826

Sweeney, Michael, Ref Librn, Jenkins Law Library, 833 Chestnut St, Ste 1220, Philadelphia, PA, 19107-4429. Tel: 215-574-7946. Fax: 215-574-7920. p. 2111

Sweeney, Patrick, Mgr, San Mateo County Library, East Palo Alto Library, 2415 University Ave, East Palo Alto, CA, 94303. Tel: 650-321-7712. Fax: 650-326-8961. p. 255

Sweeney, Richard T, Univ Librn, New Jersey Institute of Technology, University Heights, Newark, NJ, 07102-1982. Tel: 973-596-3206. Fax: 973-643-5601. p. 1511

Sweeney, S, Archivist, Spec Coll Librn, University of Manitoba Libraries, Elizabeth Dafoe Libr, Rm 156, Winnipeg, MB, R3T 2N2, CANADA. Tel: 204-474-9881. Fax: 204-474-7583. p. 2758

Sweeney, Sarah, Metadata Librn, Northeastern University Libraries, Snell Library, 360 Huntington Ave, Boston, MA, 02115. Tel: 617-373-5062. p. 1065

Sweeney, Shelley, Head, Archives & Spec Coll, University of Manitoba Libraries, Elizabeth Dafoe Library, 25 Chancellor's Circle, Winnipeg, MB, R3T 2N2, CANADA. Tel: 204-474-6350. Fax: 204-474-7577. p. 2758

Sweeney, Stephen, Libr Dir, Cardinal Stafford Library, 1300 S Steele St, Denver, CO, 80210. Tel: 303-715-3192. Fax: 303-715-2037. p. 298

Sweeney, Timothy E, Librn, Whiting Forensic Institute Library, 70 O'Brien Dr, Middletown, CT, 06457. Tel: 860-262-5400, Ext 2522, 860-262-5469. Fax: 860-262-5470. p. 352

Sweeny, Sally, Libr Supvr-Popular Libr, Sacramento Public Library, Courtland Community Operated Neighborhood Library, 170 Primasing Ave, Courtland, CA, 95615. p. 224

Sweeper, Darren, Govt Doc Librn, Seton Hall University Libraries, Walsh Libary Bldg, 400 S Orange Ave, South Orange, NJ, 07079. Tel: 973-275-2058. Fax: 973-761-9432. p. 1530

Sweet, Arlene, Asst Librn, Aldrich Free Public Library, 299 Main St, Moosup, CT, 06354. Tel: 860-564-8760. Fax: 860-564-8491. p. 353

Sweet, Barbara, Dir, County of Prince Edward Libraries, 208 Main St, Picton, ON, K0K 2T0, CANADA. Tel: 613-476-5962. Fax: 613-476-3325. p. 2836

Sweet, Beth, Dir, D A Hurd Library, 41 High St, North Berwick, ME, 03906. Tel: 207-676-2215. Fax: 207-676-7976. p. 993

Sweet, Bob, Mgr, University of Michigan, Transportation Research Institute Library, 2901 Baxter Rd, Ann Arbor, MI, 48109-2150. Tel: 734-936-1073. Fax: 734-936-1081. p. 1152

Sweet, Chris, Info & Instruction Librn, Heartland Community College Library, 1500 W Raab Rd, Normal, IL, 61761. Tel: 309-268-8277. Fax: 309-268-7989. p. 681

Sweet, Christopher, Info Literacy Librn, Illinois Wesleyan University, One Ames Plaza, Bloomington, IL, 61701-7188. Tel: 309-556-3984. Fax: 309-556-3706. p. 595

Sweet Cloud, Angela, Ref, Utica Public Library, 303 Genesee St, Utica, NY, 13501. Tel: 315-735-2279. Fax: 315-734-1034. p. 1760

Sweet, David A, Dir, Libr Serv, American Health Information Management Association, 233 N Michigan Ave, Ste 2150, Chicago, IL, 60601. Tel: 312-233-1501. Fax: 312-233-1901. p. 605

Sweet, Doris Ann, Dir of Libr Serv, Assumption College, 500 Salisbury St, Worcester, MA, 01609. Tel: 508-767-7272. Fax: 508-767-7374. p. 1143

Sweet, Fred, Dr, Dir, Cornerstone University, 1001 E Beltline Ave NE, Grand Rapids, MI, 49525. Tel: 616-949-5300. Fax: 616-222-1405. p. 1184

Sweet, Gale, Coordr, Burlington Libraries Information Consortium, Five Pioneer Blvd, Westampton, NJ, 08060. Tel: 609-267-9660. Fax: 609-267-4091. p. 2948

Sweet, Jane, Coordr, Toronto Monthly Meeting of the Religious Society of Friends (Quakers), 60 Lowther Ave, Toronto, ON, M5R 1C7, CANADA. Tel: 416-921-0368. Fax: 416-920-5214. p. 2859

Sweet, Kimberly, Pub Serv, Ropes & Gray LLP Library, Prudential Tower, 800 Boylston St, Boston, MA, 02199. Tel: 617-951-7855. Fax: 617-951-7050. p. 1066

Sweet, Robert, Assoc Dean of Libr, Texas Tech University Libraries, 18th & Boston Ave, Lubbock, TX, 79409-0002. Tel: 806-742-2261. Fax: 806-742-0737. p. 2358

Sweet, Russell, Assoc Dir, Boston University Libraries, Pappas Law Library, 765 Commonwealth Ave, Boston, MA, 02215. Tel: 617-353-8877. Fax: 617-353-5995. p. 1058

Sweeter, Kristine, Librn, Whitingham Free Public Library, 2948 Vt Rte 100, Jacksonville, VT, 05342. Tel: 802-368-7506. p. 2426

Sweetgall, Susan, Pub Serv, Suffolk University, John Joseph Moakley Law Library, 120 Tremont St, Boston, MA, 02108-4977. Tel: 617-573-8177. p. 1067

Sweetkind-Singer, Julie, Bibliographer, Head Librn, Stanford University Libraries, Branner Earth Sciences & Map Collections, Mitchell Bldg, 2nd Flr, Stanford, CA, 94305-2174. Tel: 650-723-2746, 650-725-1102, 650-725-1103, Fax; 650-725-2534. p. 271

Sweetman, Sherry, Archivist, Olmsted County Historical Society, 1195 W Circle Dr SW, Rochester, MN, 55902. Tel: 507-282-9447. Fax: 507-289-5481. p. 1272

Sweetser, Robin, Asst Librn, Fuller Public Library, 29 School St, Hillsboro, NH, 03244. Tel: 603-464-3595. Fax: 603-464-4572. p. 1451

Sweezie, Beverly, Syst Coordr, Middlesex County Library, 34B Frank St, Strathroy, ON, N7G 2R4, CANADA. Tel: 519-245-8237. Fax: 519-245-8238. p. 2845

Sweigert, Donna, Ch, Hamburg Public Library, 35 N Third St, Hamburg, PA, 19526-1502. Tel: 610-562-2843. Fax: 610-562-8136. p. 2064

Sweley, Pam, Librn, Scotia Public Library, PO Box 188, Scotia, NE, 68875-0188. Tel: 308-245-3191. Fax: 308-245-3191. p. 1418

Swelland, Shelley, Head, Acq, Evergreen State College, Library Bldg, Rm 2300, 2700 Evergreen Pkwy NW, Olympia, WA, 98505-0002. Tel: 360-867-6127. Fax: 360-867-6790. p. 2522

Swensen, Rolf, Web Coordr, Queens College, Benjamin S Rosenthal Library, 65-30 Kissena Blvd, Flushing, NY, 11367-0904. Tel: 718-997-3700. Fax: 718-997-3753. p. 1623

Swenson Danowitz, Erica, Ref, Delaware County Community College Library, 901 S Media Line Rd, Media, PA, 19063-1094. Tel: 610-359-5149, 610-359-5326. Fax: 610-359-5272. p. 2087

Swenson, Mark, Tech Librn, Winnetka-Northfield Public Library District, 768 Oak St, Winnetka, IL, 60093-2583. Tel: 847-446-7220. Fax: 847-446-5085. p. 720

Swenson, Terry, Asst Dir, Copperas Cove Public Library, 501 S Main St, Copperas Cove, TX, 76522. Tel: 254-547-3826. Fax: 254-542-7279. p. 2301

Swertz, Stella, Librn, Tatagwa View, 808 Souris Valley Rd, Weyburn, SK, S4H 2Z9, CANADA. Tel: 306-842-8360. Fax: 306-842-8341. p. 2931

Swetish, Kathleen, Dir, Whelden Memorial Library, 2401 Meetinghouse Way, West Barnstable, MA, 02668-1403. Tel: 508-362-2262. Fax: 508-362-1344. p. 1136

Swetland, Karen, Pub Serv Librn, Ref Serv Coordr, University of South Carolina Upstate Library, 800 University Way, Spartanburg, SC, 29303. Tel: 864-503-5034. Fax: 864-503-5601. p. 2205

Swetman, Barbara, Acq/Ser Librn, Hamilton College, 198 College Hill Rd, Clinton, NY, 13323-1299. Tel: 315-859-4470. Fax: 315-859-4578. p. 1607

Swets, Heidi, Youth Serv Coordr, Decorah Public Library, 202 Winnebago St, Decorah, IA, 52101. Tel: 563-382-3717. Fax: 563-382-4524. p. 807

Swett, Donna, Asst Dir, Ch, New Durham Public Library, Two Old Bay Rd, New Durham, NH, 03855-2214. Tel: 603-859-2201. Fax: 603-859-2201. p. 1459

Swett, Ronnie, Dir, Island Park Public Library, 176 Long Beach Rd, Island Park, NY, 11558. Tel: 516-432-0122. Fax: 516-889-3584. p. 1640

Swickard, Kelly, Cataloger, Maryland Institute College of Art, 1401 Mount Royal Ave, Baltimore, MD, 21217. Tel: 410-225-2248. Fax: 410-225-2316. p. 1015

Swider, Colleen, Ser Librn, Keene Public Library, 60 Winter St, Keene, NH, 03431-3360. Tel: 603-352-0157. Fax: 866-743-0446. p. 1452

Swierat, Catherine, Circ Supvr, East Fishkill Public Library District, 348 Rte 376, Hopewell Junction, NY, 12533-6075. Tel: 845-221-9943, Ext 228. Fax: 845-226-1404. p. 1637

Swiercinsky, Lori, Dir, Hillcrest Public Library, 804 Bristol, Cuba, KS, 66940-3024. Tel: 785-729-3333, 785-729-3355. Fax: 785-729-3692. p. 862

Swierczek, Julie, Cat, Salve Regina University, 100 Ochre Point Ave, Newport, RI, 02840-4192. Tel: 401-341-2330. Fax: 401-341-2951. p. 2169

Swift, Carole, Dir, Kaplan University, 1801 E Kimberly Rd, Ste 1, Davenport, IA, 52807. Tel: 563-441-2467. Fax: 563-355-1320. p. 806

Swift, Colleen, Dir, Williams Lake Library, 180 N Third Ave, Ste A, Williams Lake, BC, V2G 2A4, CANADA. Tel: 250-392-3630. Fax: 250-392-3518. p. 2746

Swift, Elizabeth, Archivist, Wabash College, PO Box 352, Crawfordsville, IN, 47933. Tel: 765-361-6378. Fax: 765-361-6295. p. 734

Swift, Janet M, Librn, University of Connecticut, 99 E Main St, Waterbury, CT, 06702-2311. Tel: 203-236-9900. Fax: 203-236-9905. p. 375

Swift, Jim, Info Tech Librn, Fairfield Public Library, 1080 Old Post Rd, Fairfield, CT, 06824. Tel: 203-256-3155. p. 339

Swift, June, In Charge, Western Counties Regional Library, Westport Branch, 17 Second St, Westport, NS, B0V 1H0, CANADA. Tel: 902-839-2955. p. 2787

Swift, L G, Br Mgr, Fort Worth Library, Southwest Regional, 4001 Library Lane, Fort Worth, TX, 76109. Tel: 817-782-9853. Fax: 817-732-8714. p. 2322

Swift, L G, Librn, Fort Worth Library, eSkills Library & Job Center, 5651 E Lancaster, Fort Worth, TX, 76112. Tel: 817-451-0916. Fax: 817-496-8931. p. 2322

Swift, Leah, Mkt Researcher, R V Anderson Associates Ltd Library, 2001 Sheppard Ave E, Ste 400, Toronto, ON, M2J 4Z8, CANADA. Tel: 416-497-8600, Ext 212. Fax: 416-497-0342. p. 2849

Swift, Stephanie, Cat, Head, Tech Serv, University of Toronto Libraries, 252 Bloor St W, Toronto, ON, M5S 1V6, CANADA. Tel: 416-978-1850. Fax: 416-926-4737. p. 2867

Swigart, Patricia B, Pres, Swigart Museum Library, Museum Park, Rte 22 E, Huntingdon, PA, 16652. Tel: 814-643-0885. Fax: 814-643-2857. p. 2070

Swihart, Cheryl, Librn, Crestline Public Library, 324 N Thoman St, Crestline, OH, 44827-1410. Tel: 419-683-3909. Fax: 419-683-3022. p. 1892

Swincicki, Holly Jo, Asst Libr Dir, Morton Township Public Library, 110 S James, Mecosta, MI, 49332-9334. Tel: 231-972-8583. Fax: 231-972-4332. p. 1207

Swindells, Geoffrey, Interim Mgr, Northwestern University Library, Seeley G Mudd Library for Science & Engineering, 2233 Tech Dr, Evanston, IL, 60208. Tel: 847-491-3362. Fax: 847-491-4655. p. 644

Swindle, Ginann, Br Mgr, Central Arkansas Library System, Amy Sanders Branch, 31 Shelby Dr, Sherwood, AR, 72120-3197. Tel: 501-835-7756. p. 106

Swindlehurst, Diane, Ref, East Providence Public Library, 41 Grove Ave, East Providence, RI, 02914. Tel: 401-434-2453. Fax: 401-434-3324. p. 2166

Swingen, Lisa, Dir, Juanita Earp Media Center Library, 120 E Fifth & Summit St, Crystal Lake, IA, 50432. Tel: 641-565-3325. Fax: 641-565-3325. p. 805

Swingle, Delia, Dir, Zenda Public Library, 215 N Main, Zenda, KS, 67159. Tel: 620-243-5791. p. 903

Swink, Esther, Dr, Dean, Trevecca Nazarene University, School of Education, 333 Murfreesboro Rd, Nashville, TN, 37210-2877. Tel: 615-248-1201, 615-248-1205. Fax: 615-248-1597. p. 2974

Swink, Lila, Head Librn, Choctaw County Public Library, 703 E Jackson St, Hugo, OK, 74743. Tel: 580-326-5591. Fax: 580-326-7388. p. 1966

Swink, Selena, Br Mgr, Lake Public Library, City Hall, 100 Front St, Lake, MS, 39092. Tel: 601-775-3560. p. 1306

Swink, Toni, Circ, Cleveland Bradley County Public Library, 795 Church St NE, Cleveland, TN, 37311-5295. Tel: 423-472-2163. Fax: 423-339-9791. p. 2229

Swinnerton, Linda, Acq, Huntingdon County Library, 330 Penn St, Huntingdon, PA, 16652-1487. Tel: 814-643-0200. Fax: 814-643-0132. p. 2070

Swinney, Victoria, Dr, Dir, Oklahoma City University, Dulaney-Browne Library, 2501 N Blackwelder, Oklahoma City, OK, 73106. Tel: 405-208-5068. Fax: 405-208-5291. p. 1974

Swinson, Bara, Circ Mgr, Monroe County Public Library, 303 E Kirkwood Ave, Bloomington, IN, 47408. Tel: 812-349-3050. Fax: 812-349-3051. p. 728

Swinson, William, Dir, Millburn Free Public Library, 200 Glen Ave, Millburn, NJ, 07041. Tel: 973-376-1006, Ext 26. Fax: 973-376-0104. p. 1502

Swischer, Donna, Dir, Digital Asset Mgt/Spec Projects, Linda Hall Library, 5109 Cherry St, Kansas City, MO, 64110-2498. Tel: 816-926-8718. Fax: 816-926-8790. p. 1337

Swisher, Carol, Ch, Sullivan County Public Library, 100 S Crowder St, Sullivan, IN, 47882. Tel: 812-268-4957. Fax: 812-268-5370. p. 780

Swisher, Susan, Librn, Holden Arboretum, 9500 Sperry Rd, Kirtland, OH, 44094. Tel: 440-946-4400, Ext 225. Fax: 440-256-5836. p. 1908

Swisstack, Suzzane, Circ Asst, Longwood University, Redford & Race St, Farmville, VA, 23909. Tel: 434-395-2451. Fax: 434-395-2453. p. 2463

Swiszcz, B Douglas, Tech Serv, Barrington Public Library, 281 County Rd, Barrington, RI, 02806. Tel: 401-247-1920. Fax: 401-247-3763. p. 2163

Swiszcz, Jane, Govt Doc, Ref Serv, Stonehill College, 320 Washington St, Easton, MA, 02357-4015. Tel: 508-565-1452. Fax: 508-565-1424. p. 1086

Swityk, Wasyl, Asst Librn, St Vladimir's Library & Archives, 404 Meredith Rd NE, Calgary, AB, T2E 5A6, CANADA. Tel: 403-264-3437. Fax: 403-264-3438. p. 2692

Switzer, Amy, Dep Dir, Shaker Heights Public Library, 16500 Van Aken Blvd, Shaker Heights, OH, 44120-5318. Tel: 216-991-2030. Fax: 216-991-5951. p. 1934

Switzer, Anne, Outreach Librn, Oakland University Library, 2200 N Squirrel Rd, Rochester, MI, 48309-4402. Tel: 248-370-2475. Fax: 248-370-2474. p. 1221

Switzer, Cheryl, Head Librn, Arcola Public Library District, 407 E Main St, Arcola, IL, 61910-1513. Tel: 217-268-4477. Fax: 217-268-4478. p. 589

Switzer, Kim, Br Coordr, Lennox & Addington County Public Library, Napanee Branch, 25 River Rd, Napanee, ON, K7R 3S6, CANADA. Tel: 613-354-2525. Fax: 613-354-7527. p. 2824

Switzer, Linda, Librn, Greater West Central Public Library District, Plymouth Branch, 103 W Side Sq, Plymouth, IL, 62367. Tel: 309-458-6616. Fax: 309-458-6616. p. 591

Switzer, Teri R, Dean of Libr, University of Colorado at Colorado Springs, 1420 Austin Bluffs Pkwy, Colorado Springs, CO, 80918. Tel: 719-255-3115. Fax: 719-528-5227. p. 296

Swonger, Stephanie, Librn, Minneola City Library, 112 Main St, Minneola, KS, 67865-8544. Tel: 620-885-4749. Fax: 620-885-4278. p. 883

Swope, Jeff, Ch, James V Brown Library of Williamsport & Lycoming County, 19 E Fourth St, Williamsport, PA, 17701-6390. Tel: 570-326-0536. Fax: 570-326-1671. p. 2156

Sword, Catherine, Coordr, Pub Serv, Whitchurch-Stouffville Public Library, 30 Burkholder St, Stouffville, ON, L4A 4K1, CANADA. Tel: 905-642-7323. Fax: 905-640-1384. p. 2845

Sword, Mildred R, Librn, Rocky Hill Historical Society, 785 Old Main St, Rocky Hill, CT, 06067-1519. Tel: 860-563-6704. p. 366

Sword, Shannan, Dir, Sylvan Lake Municipal Library, 4715-50 Ave, Sylvan Lake, AB, T4S 1A2, CANADA. Tel: 403-887-2130. Fax: 403-887-0537. p. 2719

Swoverland, Kim, Admin Serv Mgr, Dexter District Library, 3255 Alpine St, Dexter, MI, 48130. Tel: 734-426-4477. Fax: 734-426-1217. p. 1174

Swyers, Barbara, Librn, Georgian Bay Township Library, 2587 Honey Harbour Rd, Honey Harbour, ON, P0E 1H0, CANADA. Tel: 705-756-8851. Fax: 705-756-8851. p. 2811

Sydelko, Bette, Head, Ref (Info Serv), Wright State University Libraries, 126 Dunbar Library, 3640 Colonel Glenn Hwy, Dayton, OH, 45435-0001. Tel: 937-775-3840. Fax: 937-775-4109. p. 1895

Sydorenko, Wasyl, Res Spec, University of Toronto Libraries, Petro Jacyk Central & East European Resource Centre, 130 St George St, Rm 3008, Toronto, ON, M5S 1A5, CANADA. Tel: 416-978-0588. Fax: 416-971-2636. p. 2866

Sykeny, Karen, Coll, Acq & Proc Mgr, Massillon Public Library, 208 Lincoln Way E, Massillon, OH, 44646-8416. Tel: 330-832-9831, Ext 318. Fax: 330-830-2182. p. 1915

Sykes, Claudette, Br Head, Chatham-Kent Public Library, Wheatley Branch, 35 Talbot St W, Wheatley, ON, N0P 2P0, CANADA. Tel: 519-825-7131. Fax: 519-825-7537. p. 2799

Sykes, Faye, Br Librn, Bladen County Public Library, Bridger Memorial, 313 S Main St, Bladenboro, NC, 28320. Tel: 910-863-4586. p. 1791

Sykes, Frank, Mgr, Livonia Public Library, Two Washington St, Livonia, NY, 14487-9738. Tel: 585-346-3450. Fax: 585-346-5911. p. 1653

Sykes, Gay, Dir, Nickerson Public Library, 23 N Nickerson, Nickerson, KS, 67561. Tel: 620-422-3361. Fax: 620-422-3361. p. 885

Sykes, Rebecca, Libr Dir, Montana Bible College Library, 20 Cornerstone Way, Bozeman, MT, 59718. Tel: 406-556-7215. Fax: 406-586-3585. p. 1375

Sykes-Austin, Barbara, Ref Librn, Columbia University, Avery Architectural & Fine Arts Library, 1172 Amsterdam Ave, MC 0301, New York, NY, 10027. Tel: 212-854-6199. Fax: 212-854-8904. p. 1674

Syler, Heidi, Ref Serv, University of the South, 735 University Ave, Sewanee, TN, 37383-1000. Tel: 931-598-1709. Fax: 931-598-1702. p. 2265

Sylvain, Dennis, Libr Mgr, Colorado State University Libraries, Veterinary Medical Center, 300 West Drake Rd, Fort Collins, CO, 80523-1620. Tel: 970-297-1213. Fax: 970-297-4141. p. 307

Sylvester, Cecelia, Librn, Big Horn County Library, Hyattville Library, 2045 Hwy 31, Hyattville, WY, 82428. Tel: 307-469-2444. p. 2651

Sylvester, Diane, Librn, Lakeland Library Region, Borden Branch, 303 First Ave, Borden, SK, S0K 0N0, CANADA. Tel: 306-997-2220. p. 2920

Sylvester, Ginny, Access Serv, ILL, Arizona State University Libraries, 300 E Orange Mall Dr, Tempe, AZ, 85287-1006. Tel: 480-965-4919. Fax: 480-965-9169. p. 83

Sylvester, Jeanne, Supv Librn, Circ, Nutley Free Public Library, 93 Booth Dr, Nutley, NJ, 07110-2782. Tel: 973-667-0405. p. 1515

Sylvestre, Ruth, Supvr, Essex County Library, Lakeshore, 304 Rourke Line Rd, RR No 3, Belle River, ON, N0R 1A0, CANADA. Tel: 226-946-1529, Ext 280. p. 2804

Sylvia, Lorna, Head, Tech Serv, Raynham Public Library, 760 S Main St, Raynham, MA, 02767. Tel: 508-823-1344. Fax: 508-824-0494. p. 1120

Sylvia, Margaret, Asst Dir, Tech Serv, Saint Mary's University, Louis J Blume Library, One Camino Santa Maria, San Antonio, TX, 78228-8608. Tel: 210-436-3441. Fax: 210-436-3782. p. 2381

Symansky, Judy, Librn, McGill University Libraries, Howard Ross Library of Management, Samuel Bronfman Bldg, 1001 Sherbrooke St W, 2nd Flr, Montreal, QC, H3A 1G5, CANADA. Tel: 514-398-4690. Fax: 514-398-5046. p. 2899

Symington, Nancy, Dir, Dennis Memorial Library Association, 1020 Old Bass River Rd, Dennis, MA, 02638-2523. Tel: 508-385-2255. Fax: 508-385-7322. p. 1084

Symon, Beverly Jo, Dir, Spencer County Public Library, 210 Walnut St, Rockport, IN, 47635-1398. Tel: 812-649-4866. Fax: 812-649-4018. p. 776

Symons, Diana, Soc Sci Librn, Saint John's University, 2835 Abbey Plaza, Collegeville, MN, 56321. Tel: 320-363-5296. Fax: 320-363-5197. p. 1246

Symons, Diana, Soc Sci Librn, College of Saint Benedict, 37 S College Ave, Saint Joseph, MN, 56374. Tel: 320-363-5296. Fax: 320-363-5197. p. 1277

Symons, Ken, Mgr, Bus Serv, Brantford Public Library, 173 Colborne St, Brantford, ON, N3T 2G8, CANADA. Tel: 519-756-2220, Ext 320. Fax: 519-756-4979. p. 2796

Simpson, Penny, Librn, Wiss, Janney, Elstner Associates, Inc, 330 Pfingsten Rd, Northbrook, IL, 60062. Tel: 847-272-7400, Ext 4202, 847-753-7202. Fax: 847-498-0358. p. 682

Syms, Laura, Librn, Cape Breton University Library, 1250 Grand Lake Rd, Sydney, NS, B1P 6L2, CANADA. Tel: 902-563-1421. Fax: 902-563-1826. p. 2785

Synder, Mary, Dir, North Indian River County Library, 1001 Sebastian Blvd, CR 512, Sebastian, FL, 32958. Tel: 772-589-1355. Fax: 772-388-3697. p. 490

Synnestvedt, Betty, Coord, Ad Serv, Minor Memorial Library, 23 South St, Roxbury, CT, 06783. Tel: 860-350-2181. Fax: 860-350-6882. p. 366

Synott, Johannah, Librn, Plymouth Library Association, 692 Main St, Plymouth, CT, 06782. Tel: 860-283-5977. p. 364

Sypko, Liz, Br Mgr, Mid-Continent Public Library, Oak Grove Branch, 2320 S Broadway, Oak Grove, MO, 64075-9369. Tel: 816-690-3213. Fax: 816-690-5681. p. 1333

Sypniewski, Ted, Acq, Ser, Canadian Museum of Nature Library & Archives, PO Box 3443, Sta D, Ottawa, ON, K1P 6P4, CANADA. Tel: 613-566-4734. Fax: 613-364-4026. p. 2829

Syracuse, Dedree, Asst Librn, Charleston Library Society, 164 King St, Charleston, SC, 29401. Tel: 843-723-9912. Fax: 843-723-3500. p. 2183

Syrett, Matt, Ref, Mansfield University, Mansfield, PA, 16933. Tel: 570-662-4679. Fax: 570-662-4993. p. 2084

Syrianos, Gregory, Libr Dir, George C Bullis Memorial Library, 101 Main St, Maybrook, NY, 12543. Tel: 845-427-2914. Fax: 845-427-2881. p. 1659

Sysak, H Maria, Dir, Baldwin Public Library, 2385 Grand Ave, Baldwin, NY, 11510-3289. Tel: 516-223-6228. Fax: 516-623-7991. p. 1577

Syseskey, Thomas W, Col Librn, Thomas More College of Liberal Arts, Six Manchester St, Merrimack, NH, 03054-4805. Tel: 603-880-0425. Fax: 603-880-9280. p. 1457

Syvertson, Barb, ILL Supvr, Messiah College, One College Ave, Ste 3002, Mechanicsburg, PA, 17055. Tel: 717-691-6006. Fax: 717-691-2356. p. 2087

Syvertson, Deb M, Dir, Dakota College at Bottineau Library, 105 Simrall Blvd, Bottineau, ND, 58318. Tel: 701-228-5425. Fax: 701-228-5438. p. 1839

Szabo, Alesia, Cat Librn, Western Connecticut State University, 181 White St, Danbury, CT, 06810. Tel: 203-837-9100. Fax: 203-837-9108. p. 335

Szabo, John F, City Librn, Los Angeles Public Library System, 630 W Fifth St, Los Angeles, CA, 90071-2097. Tel: 213-228-7000. Fax: 213-228-7519. p. 172

Szabo, Kristine, Ser Librn, Ohio Wesleyan University, 43 Rowland, Delaware, OH, 43015-2370. Tel: 740-368-3252. Fax: 740-368-3222. p. 1896

Szabo, Peter, Music Librn, Ref, Ohio Wesleyan University, 43 Rowland, Delaware, OH, 43015-2370. Tel: 740-368-3709. Fax: 740-368-3222. p. 1896

Szafran, Kathleen, In Charge, Osterhout Free Library, Plains Township, 126 N Main St, Plains, PA, 18705. Tel: 570-824-1862. Fax: 570-824-1862. p. 2156

Szafran, Melissa, Dir, Pittston Memorial Library, 47 Broad St, Pittston, PA, 18640. Tel: 570-654-9565. Fax: 570-654-6078. p. 2130

Szafran, Melissa A, Exec Dir, Hoyt Library, 284 Wyoming Ave, Kingston, PA, 18704-3597. Tel: 570-287-2013. Fax: 570-283-2081. p. 2074

Szaley, Ann, Ch, Seymour Public Library, 46 Church St, Seymour, CT, 06483. Tel: 203-888-3903. Fax: 203-888-4099. p. 366

Szalkowski, Barbara, Sr Cat Librn, South Texas College of Law, 1303 San Jacinto St, Houston, TX, 77002-7000. Tel: 713-646-1711. Fax: 713-659-2217. p. 2342

Szarejko, Celia, Syst Librn, East Tennessee State University, Sherrod Library, Seehorn Dr & Lake St, Johnson City, TN, 37614-0204. Tel: 423-439-4337. Fax: 423-439-5222. p. 2239

Szarmach, Janet, Dir, Kensington Social & Public Library, 126 Amesbury Rd, Kensington, NH, 03833-5621. Tel: 603-772-5022. Fax: 603-778-2953. p. 1453

Szary, Rich, Assoc Univ Librn, Spec Coll, Dir, Louis Round Wilson Librn, University of North Carolina at Chapel Hill, Davis Library, 208 Raleigh St, Campus Box 3900, Chapel Hill, NC, 27514-8890. Tel: 919-962-8125. p. 1780

Szasz, Debby, Acq, Washington Adventist University, 7600 Flower Ave, Takoma Park, MD, 20912-7796. Tel: 301-891-4217. Fax: 301-891-4204. p. 1043

Szczepaniak, Adam, Jr, Assoc State Librn, Dir, New Jersey State Library, Talking Book & Braille Center, 2300 Stuyvesant Ave, Trenton, NJ, 08618. Tel: 604-406-7179, Ext 801. Fax: 609-406-7181. p. 1536

Szczepanski, Nancy, Head, Circ Serv, Canton Public Library, 1200 S Canton Center Rd, Canton, MI, 48188-1600. Tel: 734-397-0999. Fax: 734-397-1130. p. 1160

Szczygiel, Rosemary, Libr Mgr, Nassau County Public Library System, Hilliard Branch, 15821 CR 108, Hilliard, FL, 32046. Tel: 904-845-2495. Fax: 904-845-2449. p. 440

Sze, Elisa, Coll & Pub Serv Coordr, University of Toronto Libraries, Faculty of Information Inforum, 140 Saint George St, 4th Flr, Toronto, ON, M5S 3G6, CANADA. Tel: 416-978-7071. Fax: 416-978-5769. p. 2865

Szelag, Joanne, Adult Serv, Agawam Public Library, 750 Cooper St, Agawam, MA, 01001. Tel: 413-789-1550. Fax: 413-789-1552. p. 1048

Szeles, Lisa, Br Mgr, Stark County District Library, Perry Sippo Branch, 5710 12th St NW, Canton, OH, 44708. Tel: 330-477-8482. Fax: 330-479-0015. p. 1865

Szentkiralyi, Irene, Librn, Fairview Hospital, 18101 Lorain Ave, Cleveland, OH, 44111. Tel: 216-476-7117. Fax: 216-476-7803. p. 1879

Szep, Jutta, Librn, Walker Nott Dragicevic Associates Ltd Library, 90 Eglinton Ave E, Ste 701, Toronto, ON, M4P 2Y3, CANADA. Tel: 416-968-3511. Fax: 416-960-0172. p. 2867

Szitas, Emily M, Pub Serv, Carlow University, 3333 Fifth Ave, Pittsburgh, PA, 15213. Tel: 412-578-2049. Fax: 412-578-6242. p. 2122

Szoke, Deborah, Archives, Tech, Florida Southern College, 111 Lake Hollingsworth Dr, Lakeland, FL, 33801-5698. Tel: 863-616-6487. Fax: 863-680-4126. p. 459

Szolomayer, Kathy, Librn, Washington State Library, Department of Transportation, Department of Transportation, Olympia, WA, 98504. Tel: 360-705-7750. Fax: 360-705-6831. p. 2545

Szot, Pam, Supv Librn, Aurora Public Library, Mission Veijo Branch, 15324 E Hampden Circle, Aurora, CO, 80013-2408. Tel: 303-326-8600. Fax: 303-680-4041. p. 288

Szot, Pam, Supvr, S Region Libr, Aurora Public Library, Tallyns Reach, 23911 E Arapahoe Rd, Aurora, CO, 80016. Tel: 303-627-3050. Fax: 303-627-3060. p. 288

Szoyka, Audrey, Librn, Greene County Law Library, Court House, Waynesburg, PA, 15370. Tel: 412-852-5237. Fax: 412-627-4716. p. 2152

Szpila, Jerome, Br Mgr, Camden County Library System, Riletta L Cream Ferry Avenue Branch, 852 Ferry Ave, Camden, NJ, 08104. Tel: 856-342-9789. Fax: 856-342-9791. p. 1538

Szudy, Lois F, Dir, Otterbein University, 138 W Main St, Westerville, OH, 43081. Tel: 614-823-1414. Fax: 614-823-1921. p. 1946

Szwajcer, Andrea, Clinical Librn, University of Manitoba Libraries, Carolyn Sifton-Helene Fuld Library, St Boniface Hospital, 409 Tache Ave, Winnipeg, MB, R2H 2A6, CANADA. Tel: 204-237-2991. Fax: 204-235-3339. p. 2759

Szydlowski, Nick, Digital Serv & Institutional Repository Librn, Boston College, 885 Centre St, Newton Centre, MA, 02459. Tel: 617-552-4474. Fax: 617-552-2889. p. 1110

Szylivan, Kristin, PhD, Assoc Prof, Saint John's University, Saint Augustine Hall, Rm 408, 8000 Utopia Pkwy, Jamaica, NY, 11439. Tel: 718-990-5239. Fax: 718-990-2071. p. 2970

Szymanik, Elizabeth, Librn, Brainerd Memorial Library, 4215 Bruce Badger Memorial Hwy, Danville, VT, 05828. Tel: 802-748-4423. p. 2422

Szymanik, Susan, Br Mgr, Ref Librn, Burlington County Library, Evesham Branch, Evesham Municipal Complex, 984 Tuckerton Rd, Marlton, NJ, 08053. Tel: 856-983-1444. Fax: 856-983-4939. p. 1543

Szymanski, Cynthia, Head, Tech Serv, Indiana University Northwest Library, 3400 Broadway, Gary, IN, 46408. Tel: 219-980-6521. Fax: 219-980-6558. p. 745

Szymanski, Gerry, Dir, Gay Alliance of the Genessee Valley, Inc Library & Archives, 875 E Main St, Ste 500, Rochester, NY, 14605. Tel: 585-244-8640. Fax: 585-244-8246. p. 1729

Szymanski, Sheri, Asst Dir, Stratford Library Association, 2203 Main St, Stratford, CT, 06615. Tel: 203-381-2063. Fax: 203-381-2079. p. 371

Szymula, Susan E, Dir, Mims/Scottsmoor Public Library, 3615 Lionel Rd, Mims, FL, 32754. Tel: 321-264-5080. Fax: 321-264-5081. p. 470

Szynaka, Edward, Dir, Peoria Public Library, 107 NE Monroe St, Peoria, IL, 61602-1070. Tel: 309-497-2140. Fax: 309-497-2007. p. 690

Szypulski, Ann, Dir, Laurens County Library, 1017 W Main St, Laurens, SC, 29360. Tel: 864-681-7323. Fax: 864-681-0598. p. 2199

Tabachnick, Sharon E, Dr, Dir of Libr Serv, Southern College of Optometry Library, 1245 Madison Ave, Memphis, TN, 38104. Tel: 901-722-3238. Fax: 901-722-3292. p. 2251

Tabaei, Sara, Info Literacy Librn, Touro College Libraries, 43 W 23rd St, Fifth Fl, New York, NY, 10010. Tel: 212-463-0400, Ext 5321. Fax: 212-627-3696. p. 1701

Tabakin, Rebecca, Libr Dir, ECPI University, 5555 Greenwich Rd, Virginia Beach, VA, 23462. Tel: 757-671-7171, Ext 55382. Fax: 757-671-8661. p. 2498

Tabatabai, Habib, Dir, Libr Syst & Tech Serv, University of Central Oklahoma, 100 N University Dr, Edmond, OK, 73034. Tel: 405-974-2884. Fax: 405-974-3806, 405-974-3874. p. 1962

Tabb, Winston, Dean, Johns Hopkins University Libraries, The Sheridan Libraries, 3400 N Charles St, Baltimore, MD, 21218. Tel: 410-516-8328. Fax: 410-516-5080. p. 1014

Tabechian, Hechmat, Exec Dir, Rochester Academy of Medicine Library, 1441 East Ave, Rochester, NY, 14610-1665. Tel: 585-271-1313. Fax: 585-271-4172. p. 1731

Taber, Gay, Head, Ref, Instr, Texas Health Harris Methodist Fort Worth Hospital, 1301 Pennsylvania Ave, Fort Worth, TX, 76104. Tel: 817-250-2118. Fax: 817-250-5119. p. 2324

Taber, Kolette, Mgr, Libr Serv, Canadian Life & Health Insurance Association, Inc, One Queen St E, Ste 1700, Toronto, ON, M5C 2X9, CANADA. Tel: 416-777-2221, Ext 3070. Fax: 416-777-1895. p. 2851

Taber, Lucinda, Adult Serv, Cecil County Public Library, 301 Newark Ave, Elkton, MD, 21921-5441. Tel: 410-996-5600. Fax: 410-996-5604. p. 1027

Tabereaux, Christina, Dir, Balch & Bingham Attorneys Library, 1901 Sixth Ave N, Ste 1500, Birmingham, AL, 35203. Tel: 205-226-8710. Fax: 205-226-8798. p. 6

Tabib, Ahmed, Mgr, Henrico County Public Library, Twin Hickory Area Library, 5001 Twin Hickory Rd, Glen Allen, VA, 23059-2509. Tel: 804-290-9200. Fax: 804-364-4624. p. 2471

Tabish, Colleen, Librn, Kitscoty Public Library, 4910 51 St, Kitscoty, AB, T0B 2P0, CANADA. Tel: 780-846-2822. Fax: 780-846-2215. p. 2708

Tablish, Karen, Cat, North Arkansas College Library, 1515 Pioneer Dr, Harrison, AR, 72601. Tel: 870-391-3359. Fax: 870-391-3245. p. 102

Taboh-Bley, Beth, Dir, Holocaust Memorial & Tolerance Center of Nassau County, Welwyn Preserve, 100 Crescent Beach Rd, Glen Cove, NY, 11542. Tel: 516-571-8043. Fax: 516-571-8041. p. 1628

Tabor, Janet, Librn, Arizona Department of Corrections - Adult Institutions, 26700 S Hwy 85, Buckeye, AZ, 85326. Tel: 623-386-6160, Ext 4908. Fax: 623-386-6160, Ext 4910. p. 58

Tabor, Jeannie, Asst Librn, Thompson Free Library, 186 E Main St, Dover-Foxcroft, ME, 04426. Tel: 207-564-3350. Fax: 207-564-3531. p. 983

Tabor, Leslie, Br Mgr, Pioneer Library System, Norman Public, 225 N Webster, Norman, OK, 73069. Tel: 405-701-2600. Fax: 405-701-2608. p. 1970

Tabor, Stephen, Curator, Huntington Library, 1151 Oxford Rd, San Marino, CA, 91108. Tel: 626-405-2179. Fax: 626-449-5720. p. 255

Tabri, Lara, Coll Develop Assoc, Tyler Public Library, 201 S College Ave, Tyler, TX, 75702-7381. Tel: 903-593-7323. Fax: 903-531-1329. p. 2394

Tabusa, Phyllis, Head Librn, East-West Center, 1601 East-West Rd, Honolulu, HI, 96848-1601. Tel: 808-944-7450. Fax: 808-944-7600. p. 560

Tacey, Sheila, Libr Tech, United States Navy, Naval Hospital Library, HP01 One Boone Rd, Bremerton, WA, 98312-1898. Tel: 360-475-4316. Fax: 360-475-4324. p. 2511

Tack, Barbara, Head, Youth Serv, Ashtabula County District Library, 335 W 44th St, Ashtabula, OH, 44004-6897. Tel: 440-997-9341, Ext 230. Fax: 440-992-7714. p. 1855

Tacke, Kathy, Media & Res Spec, Memorial Hospital of Sweetwater County, 1200 College Dr, Rock Springs, WY, 82901-5868. Tel: 307-352-8433. Fax: 307-352-8173. p. 2659

Tacke, Melissa, Archivist, Librn, Schenectady County Historical Society, 32 Washington Ave, Schenectady, NY, 12305. Tel: 518-374-0263. Fax: 518-688-2825. p. 1740

Tackenberg, William David, Archivist, Arizona Historical Society, 949 E Second St, Tucson, AZ, 85719. Tel: 520-628-5774. Fax: 520-629-8966. p. 85

Tackett, Charles, Libr Tech, Department of Veterans Affairs, 17273 State Rte 104, Chillicothe, OH, 45601. Tel: 740-773-1141 Ext 7623. Fax: 740-772-7041. p. 1867

Tackett, Elizabeth, Librn, Buffalo Creek Memorial Library, 511 E McDonald Ave, Man, WV, 25635. Tel: 304-583-7887. Fax: 304-583-0182. p. 2564

Tackett, Sarilda, Pub Serv Adminr, Jackson District Library, 290 W Michigan Ave, Jackson, MI, 49201. Tel: 517-788-4087. Fax: 517-782-8635. p. 1195

Tackett, Sherry, Ch, White House Inn Library & Museum, 412 Hwy 76, White House, TN, 37188. Tel: 615-672-0239. p. 2268

Tackitt, Suzanne, Libr Coordr, Flagstaff Medical Center, 1200 N Beaver St, Flagstaff, AZ, 86001. Tel: 928-773-2418. Fax: 928-773-2253. p. 62

Tacoma, Cathy, Dir, Cadillac-Wexford Public Library, 411 S Lake St, Cadillac, MI, 49601. Tel: 231-775-6541. Fax: 231-775-6778. p. 1160

Tacsik, Kris, Curator, California State University, Northridge, Geography Map Library, Sierra Hall 171, 18111 Nordhoff St, Northridge, CA, 91330-8249. Tel: 818-677-3465. Fax: 818-677-7840. p. 195

Taddonio, Beth, ILL, Henry Carter Hull Library, Inc, Ten Killingworth Tpk, Clinton, CT, 06413. Tel: 860-669-2342. Fax: 860-669-8318. p. 334

Taddonio, Jacqueline, Dir, Cat, Historical Society of Pennsylvania, 1300 Locust St, Philadelphia, PA, 19107-5699. Tel: 215-732-6200, Ext 206. Fax: 215-732-2680. p. 2110

Tadeo, Carmen, Circ, Port Isabel Public Library, 213 Yturria St, Port Isabel, TX, 78578. Tel: 956-943-1822. Fax: 956-943-4638. p. 2371

Taffe, Michael, Brother, Asst Librn, Assumption Abbey Library, 418 Third Ave W, Richardton, ND, 58652-7100. Tel: 701-974-3315. Fax: 701-974-3317. p. 1847

Tafoya, Sharon, Librn, Federal Law Enforcement Training Center Library, Bldg 262, 1131 Chapel Crossing Rd, Glynco, GA, 31524. Tel: 912-267-2320. p. 535

Taft, Gretchen, Dir, Memorial Library of Little Valley, 110 Rock City St, Little Valley, NY, 14755. Tel: 716-938-6301. Fax: 716-938-6301. p. 1653

Tafuri, Narda, Acq & Continuing Res, University of Scranton, Monroe & Linden, Scranton, PA, 18510-4634. Tel: 570-941-7811. Fax: 570-941-7809. p. 2138

Tag, Sylvia, Librn, Woodring Col, Western Washington University, 516 High St, MS 9103, Bellingham, WA, 98225. Tel: 360-650-7992. Fax: 360-650-3044. p. 2509

Tagak-Devries, Katharine, Libr Tech, Nunavut Arctic College, Tunnganaqsarvik Bldg, 1st Flr, Iqaluit, NU, X0A 0H0, CANADA. Tel: 867-979-7220. Fax: 867-979-7102. p. 2789

Tagblom, Dawn, Chief Librn, Port St Lucie Campus Col of Golf, Keiser University Library System, 1500 NW 49th St, Fort Lauderdale, FL, 33309. Tel: 954-351-4035. Fax: 954-351-4051. p. 443

Tagg, John, Librn, West Park Healthcare Centre, 82 Buttonwood Ave, Toronto, ON, M6M 2J5, CANADA. Tel: 416-243-3600, Ext 2048. Fax: 416-243-8947. p. 2867

Taggart, Bruce M, Vice Provost for Libr & Tech Serv, Lehigh University, Fairchild-Martindale Library, Eight A E Packer Ave, Bethlehem, PA, 18015-3170. Fax: 610-758-6524. p. 2034

Taggart, Eric, Dir, Coshocton Public Library, 655 Main St, Coshocton, OH, 43812-1697. Tel: 740-622-0956. Fax: 740-622-4331. p. 1891

Taggart, Katherine, Sr Res Serv Librn, Lowenstein Sandler PC Library, 65 Livingston Ave, Roseland, NJ, 07068. Tel: 973-422-6442. Fax: 973-422-6443. p. 1527

Taginski, Toni, Circ Mgr, Fletcher Free Library, 235 College St, Burlington, VT, 05401. Tel: 802-863-3403. Fax: 802-865-7227. p. 2420

Tagliaferro, Jessica, Electronic Res Librn, SUNY Westchester Community College, 75 Grasslands Rd, Valhalla, NY, 10595-1693. Tel: 914-606-6808. Fax: 914-785-6513. p. 1760

Tagtmeyer, Peter, Asst Librn, Colgate University, George R Cooley Science Library, 13 Oak Dr, Hamilton, NY, 13346-1338. Tel: 315-228-7402. Fax: 315-228-7029. p. 1633

Tahaney, Erin, Librn, Princeton Library in New York, 15 W 43rd St, New York, NY, 10036. Tel: 212-596-1250. Fax: 212-596-1399. p. 1697

Tahir, Peggy, Librn, Theosophical Society Library, 809 Mason St, San Francisco, CA, 94108-2210. Tel: 415-771-8777. p. 247

Tahir, Peggy, Mgr, Pub Serv, University of California San Francisco, 530 Parnassus Ave, San Francisco, CA, 94143-0840. Tel: 415-476-5765. p. 248

Tahir, Peggy, Mgr, Pub Serv, University of California San Francisco, Mission Bay FAMRI Library, William J Rutter Conference Ctr, Rm 150, 1675 Owens St, San Francisco, CA, 94143-2119. Tel: 415-476-5765. p. 248

Tahirkheli, Sharon, Dir, American Geological Institute Library, 4220 King St, Alexandria, VA, 22302-1502. Tel: 703-379-2480, Ext 239. Fax: 703-379-7563. p. 2445

Tahman, Tiffany, Librn, Oshawa Public Library, Northview, 250 Beatrice St E, Oshawa, ON, L1G 7T6, CANADA. Tel: 905-576-6040. p. 2827

Tahtinen, Trixine, Ch, Dir, Oostburg Public Library, 213 N Eighth St, Oostburg, WI, 53070. Tel: 920-564-2934. p. 2627

Tai, Andrew, Youth Serv Librn, Chester C Corbin Public Library, Two Lake St, Webster, MA, 01570. Tel: 508-949-3880. Fax: 508-949-0537. p. 1134

Tai, Elizabeth L, Dir, Poquoson Public Library, 500 City Hall Ave, Poquoson, VA, 23662-1996. Tel: 757-868-3066. Fax: 757-868-3106. p. 2485

Tai, I-Chene, Tech Serv Librn, Le Moyne College, 1419 Salt Springs Rd, Syracuse, NY, 13214-1301. Tel: 315-445-4331. Fax: 315-445-4642. p. 1751

Tai-Lauria, Elaine, Exec Dir, Wilton Library Association, 137 Old Ridgefield Rd, Wilton, CT, 06897-3019. Tel: 203-762-3950. Fax: 203-834-1166. p. 378

Taillon, Marie-Claude, Ref Serv, Bibliotheques de Trois-Rivieres, 1425 Place de l'Hotel de Ville, CP 1713, Trois-Rivieres, QC, G9A 5L9, CANADA. Tel: 819-372-4645. Fax: 819-693-1892. p. 2913

Tairov, Giovanni, Dir, Livingston Parish Library, 13986 Florida Blvd, Livingston, LA, 70754-6340. Tel: 225-686-2436. Fax: 225-686-3888. p. 955

Tait, Jonathan, Libr Mgr, Haut-Saint-Jean Regional Library, L P Fisher Public Library, 679 Main St, Woodstock, NB, E7M 2E1, CANADA. Tel: 506-325-4777. Fax: 506-325-4811. p. 2762

Tait, Sue, Dir, Diocese of Olympia, 1551 Tenth Ave E, Seattle, WA, 98102-4210. Tel: 206-325-4200. Fax: 206-325-4631. p. 2527

Taitano, M, Dir, United States Air Force, 36 FSS/FSDL (FL 5240), Unit 14004, Box 28, APO AP, GU, 96543-4004. Tel: 671-366-4291. Fax: 671-366-2728. p. 2667

Tajeda, Paula, Treas, Southeastern Chapter of the American Association of Law Libraries, c/o University of Kentucky, Law Library, 620 S Limestone St, Lexington, KY, 40506-0048. Tel: 859-257-8347. Fax: 859-323-4906. p. 2944

Takala, Paul, Chief Librn, Hamilton Public Library, 55 York Blvd, Hamilton, ON, L8R 3K1, CANADA. Tel: 905-546-3215. Fax: 905-546-3202. p. 2808

Takata, Linda, Head, Tech Serv, Harvard Library, Fine Arts Library, Fogg Art Museum, 32 Quincy St, Cambridge, MA, 02138. Tel: 617-495-3374. Fax: 617-496-4889. p. 1075

Takatani, Grace, Cat, University of California, 200 McAllister St, San Francisco, CA, 94102-4978. Tel: 415-565-4757. Fax: 415-581-8849. p. 248

Takishita, Faith, Ref, Malaspina University-College Library, 900 Fifth St, Nanaimo, BC, V9R 5S5, CANADA. Tel: 250-753-3245, Ext 2268. Fax: 250-740-6473. p. 2732

Takorian, Holly, Adult Serv, Asst Librn, Merriam-Gilbert Public Library, Three W Main St, West Brookfield, MA, 01585. Tel: 508-867-1410. Fax: 508-867-1409. p. 1137

Talbert, Annette, Head, Circ, Ohio University Libraries, 30 Park Pl, Athens, OH, 45701-2978. Tel: 740-593-2906. Fax: 740-593-2708. p. 1856

Talbert, Carol, Libr Tech, Big Sandy Community & Technical College, Mayo-Paintsville Campus, Bldg F, 513 Third St, Rm 206A, Paintsville, KY, 41240. Tel: 606-789-5321, Ext 82831. p. 933

Talbert, James E, Archivist, Greenbrier Historical Society Archives, 301 W Washington St, Lewisburg, WV, 24901. Tel: 304-645-3398. Fax: 304-645-5201. p. 2564

Talbert, Penny, Pub Relations, Ephrata Public Library, 550 S Reading Rd, Ephrata, PA, 17522. Tel: 717-738-9291. Fax: 717-721-3003. p. 2054

Talbot, Christiane, Librn, National Film Board of Canada, 3155 Cote de Liesse, Montreal, QC, H4N 2N4, CANADA. Tel: 514 283-9046. Fax: 514-283-9811. p. 2900

Talbot, Lauren, Actg Commun Libr Mgr, County of Los Angeles Public Library, Paramount Library, 16254 Colorado Ave, Paramount, CA, 90723-5085. Tel: 562-630-3171. Fax: 562-630-3968. p. 143

Talbot-Stanaway, Susan, Dir, Zanesville Museum of Art Library, 620 Military Rd, Zanesville, OH, 43701. Tel: 740-452-0741. Fax: 740-452-0797. p. 1954

Talbott, Bill, Dir, Sheridan Public Library, 109 E Hamilton, Sheridan, MT, 59749. Tel: 406-842-5770. Fax: 317-758-0045. p. 1388

Talbott, Edgar F, III, Actg Dir, Cat, Tech Serv, Buchanan County Public Library, Rte 2, Poetown Rd, Grundy, VA, 24614-9613. Tel: 276-935-6581. Fax: 276-935-6292. p. 2467

Talbott, Lauren, Commun Libr Mgr, County of Los Angeles Public Library, Graham Library, 1900 E Firestone Blvd, Los Angeles, CA, 90001-4126. Tel: 323-582-2903. Fax: 323-581-8478. p. 141

Talchik, Rita, Br Mgr, Broward County Division of Libraries, Stirling Road, 3151 Stirling Rd, Hollywood, FL, 33312-6526. Tel: 954-985-2689. Fax: 954-985-4095. p. 442

Talens, Mary Lou, Librn, Fresno County Genealogical Society Library, Fresno Public Library, 2420 Mariposa St, Fresno, CA, 93721-2285. Tel: 559-600-6230. Fax: 559-448-1971. p. 151

Tales, Matt, Head, Cat, Wilfrid Laurier University Library, 75 University Ave W, Waterloo, ON, N2L 3C5, CANADA. Tel: 519-884-0710, Ext 3839. Fax: 519-884-3209. p. 2869

Tallen, Carolyn L, Libr Asst, Bixby Memorial Free Library, 258 Main St, Vergennes, VT, 05491. Tel: 802-877-2211. Fax: 802-877-2411. p. 2437

Tallent, Edward, Head, Ref, Boston College Libraries, Thomas P O'Neill Jr Library (Central Library), 140 Commonwealth Ave, Chestnut Hill, MA, 02467. Tel: 617-552-2854. Fax: 617-552-0599. p. 1081

Tallent, Tony, Dir, Literacy & Learning, Richland County Public Library, 1431 Assembly St, Columbia, SC, 29201-3101. Tel: 803-799-9084. Fax: 803-929-3448. p. 2188

Talley, Brenda, Adult Serv, North Richland Hills Public Library, 9015 Grand Ave, North Richland Hills, TX, 76180. Tel: 817-427-6800. Fax: 817-427-6808. p. 2366

Talley, Kaye, Coordr, Tech Serv, University of Central Arkansas, 201 Donaghey Ave, Conway, AR, 72035. Tel: 501-450-3174. Fax: 501-450-5208. p. 97

Tallman, Eve, Dir, Mesa County Public Library District, 443 North 6th St, Grand Junction, CO, 81501. Tel: 970-243-4442. p. 310

Tallman, Jennifer, Dir, Jane Morgan Memorial Library, 109 W Edgewater St, Cambria, WI, 53923. Tel: 920-348-4030. p. 2584

Tallman, Jonathan, Dir, Libr Serv, Virginia Intermont College, 1013 Moore St, Bristol, VA, 24201. Tel: 276-466-7959. p. 2453

Tally, Joseph, Libr Dir, Alliant International University, One Beach St, Ste 100, San Francisco, CA, 94133. Tel: 415-955-2157. Fax: 415-955-2180. p. 240

Tally, Linda, Libr Asst, Bastyr University Library, 14500 Juanita Dr NE, Kenmore, WA, 98028. Tel: 425-602-3020. Fax: 425-602-3188. p. 2518

Talman, Martha, Ref Serv, Dixie State College of Utah, 225 S 700 E, Saint George, UT, 84770. Tel: 435-652-7722. Fax: 435-656-4169. p. 2412

Taloff, John, Circ Supvr, Humboldt State University Library, One Harpst St, Arcata, CA, 95521-8299. Tel: 707-826-5599. Fax: 707-826-3440. p. 122

Talon, Leslie, Ch, Free Library of Springfield Township, 1600 Paper Mill Rd, Wyndmoor, PA, 19038. Tel: 215-836-5300. Fax: 215-836-2404. p. 2158

Talty, Catherine, Ch, Gloucester, Lyceum & Sawyer Free Library, Two Dale Ave, Gloucester, MA, 01930-5906. Tel: 978-281-9763. Fax: 978-281-9770. p. 1091

Tam, Jessie, Head, Tech Serv, Maryland State Law Library, Courts of Appeal Bldg, 361 Rowe Blvd, Annapolis, MD, 21401-1697. Tel: 410-260-1430. Fax: 410-260-1572, 410-974-2063. p. 1010

Tam, Michael, Br Mgr, Brooklyn Public Library, Kings Bay, 3650 Nostrand Ave, Brooklyn, NY, 11229. Tel: 718-368-1709. Fax: 718-368-1410. p. 1591

Tamachi, Shabira, Libr Tech, Oxford Law Association Library, Courthouse, 415 Hunter St, Woodstock, ON, N4S 4G6, CANADA. Tel: 519-539-7711. Fax: 519-539-7962. p. 2872

Tamanaha, Inez, Br Mgr, Manatee County Public Library System, Island Branch, 5701 Marina Dr, Holmes Beach, FL, 34217. Tel: 941-778-6341. Fax: 941-749-7184. p. 430

Tamares, Shan, Ref, Loma Linda University, 11072 Anderson St, Loma Linda, CA, 92350-0001. Tel: 909-558-4581. Fax: 909-558-4121. p. 165

Tamarkin, Molly, Assoc Univ Librn, Info Tech, Duke University Libraries, 411 Chapel Dr, Durham, NC, 27708. Tel: 919-660-5802. Fax: 919-660-5923. p. 1787

Tambini, Rob, Dir, Dover Free Public Library, 32 E Clinton St, Dover, NJ, 07801. Tel: 973-366-0172. Fax: 973-366-0175. p. 1481

Tambo, David, Spec Coll & Archives Librn, University of California, Santa Barbara, Santa Barbara, CA, 93106-9010. Tel: 805-893-3420. Fax: 805-893-7010. p. 262

Tamburello, Paula, Mat Access & Acq Coordr, Goddard College, 123 Pitkin Rd, Plainfield, VT, 05667. Tel: 802-322-1607. p. 2432

Tamez, Jose, Asst Dir, Dustin Michael Sekula Memorial Library, 1906 S Closner Blvd, Edinburg, TX, 78539. Tel: 956-383-6246. Fax: 956-318-3123. p. 2315

Tammany, Rosina, Archivist, Spec Coll Coordr, Eastern Michigan University, 955 W Circle Dr Library, Rm 200, Ypsilanti, MI, 48197. Tel: 734-487-0020 Ext 2301. p. 1238

Tan, Chengjiao, Commun Libr Mgr, Queens Borough Public Library, Windsor Park Community Library, 79-50 Bell Blvd, Bayside, NY, 11364. Tel: 718-468-8300. Fax: 718-264-0376. p. 1645

Tan, Felipe, Head, Cat, Andrews University, 1400 Library Rd, Berrien Springs, MI, 49104-1400. Tel: 269-471-6262. Fax: 269-471-6166. p. 1157

Tan, Jian, Head, Tech Serv, Lake Forest Library, 360 E Deerpath Ave, Lake Forest, IL, 60045-2252. Tel: 847-810-4624. Fax: 847-234-1453. p. 663

Tan, Leticia, Commun Libr Mgr, County of Los Angeles Public Library, Carson Library, 151 E Carson St, Carson, CA, 90745-2797. Tel: 310-830-0901. Fax: 310-830-6181. p. 141

Tan, Wendy, Cat, Hunter College Libraries, 695 Park Ave, New York, NY, 10065. Tel: 212-772-4173. Fax: 212-772-4142. p. 1682

Tanaka, Kirsten, Archivist, Head Librn, San Francisco Performing Arts Library & Museum, 401 Van Ness Ave, 4th Flr, San Francisco, CA, 94102. Tel: 415-255-4800. Fax: 415-255-1913. p. 246

Tanaka, Shirley L, Mgr, Tech Serv, Aerospace Corp, 2360 E El Segundo Blvd, El Segundo, CA, 90245-4691. Tel: 310-336-6093. Fax: 310-336-0624. p. 146

Tancin, Charlotte A, Librn, Carnegie Mellon University, Hunt Institute for Botanical Documentation, Hunt Library Bldg, 5th Flr, 4909 Frew St, Pittsburgh, PA, 15213-3890. Tel: 412-268-7301. Fax: 412-268-5677. p. 2124

Tancred, Jean, Librn, Virginia Beach Public Library Department, Wahab Public Law Library, Municipal Ctr, Judicial Ctr, Court Support Bldg 10B, 2425 Nimmo Pkwy, Virginia Beach, VA, 23456. Tel: 757-385-4419. Fax: 757-385-8742. p. 2500

Tandy, Martha, Dir, Weatherford College Library, 225 College Park Dr, Weatherford, TX, 76086. Tel: 817-594-5471, 817-598-6252. Fax: 817-598-6369, 817-599-9305. p. 2399

Tang, Alice, Commun Libr Mgr, County of Los Angeles Public Library, Willowbrook Library, 11838 Wilmington Ave, Los Angeles, CA, 90059-3016. Tel: 323-564-5698. Fax: 323-564-7709. p. 144

Tang, Florence, Electronic Res, Mercer University Atlanta, 3001 Mercer University Dr, Atlanta, GA, 30341. Tel: 678-547-6261. Fax: 678-547-6270. p. 517

Tang, Jennifer, Acq, Ser, Hostos Community College Library, 475 Grand Concourse, A-207, Bronx, NY, 10451. Tel: 718-518-4298. Fax: 718-518-4206. p. 1587

Tang, Lorna, Assoc Librn, Tech Serv, University of Chicago Library, D'Angelo Law Library, 1121 E 60th St, Chicago, IL, 60637-2786. Tel: 773-702-9619. Fax: 773-702-2889. p. 626

Tang, Luan, Libr Tech, United States Department of Health & Human Services, Rm 4541, Cohen Bldg, 330 Independence Ave SW, Washington, DC, 20201. Tel: 202-619-0190. Fax: 202-619-3719. p. 419

Tang, Qin, Tech Serv Librn, Minnesota Department of Transportation Library, 395 John Ireland Blvd, MS 155, Saint Paul, MN, 55155. Tel: 651-366-3784. Fax: 651-366-3789. p. 1279

Tang, Rong, Asst Prof, Simmons College, 300 The Fenway, Boston, MA, 02115. Tel: 617-521-2800. Fax: 617-521-3192. p. 2967

Tang, Stella, Ser, Mills College, 5000 MacArthur Blvd, Oakland, CA, 94613. Tel: 510-430-2382. Fax: 510-430-2278. p. 197

Tang, Stella, Tech Serv, California Academy of Sciences Library, Golden Gate Park, 55 Music Concourse Dr, San Francisco, CA, 94118. Tel: 415-379-5492. Fax: 415-379-5729. p. 240

Tang, Vinh, Dr, Pres, Vietnamese Canadian Federation Library, 249 Rochester St, Ottawa, ON, K1R 7M9, CANADA. Tel: 613-230-8282. Fax: 613-230-8281. p. 2834

Tang, Yingqi, Electronic Res Librn, Jacksonville State University Library, 700 Pelham Rd N, Jacksonville, AL, 36265. Tel: 256-782-5255. Fax: 256-782-5872. p. 22

Tangalos, Sofia A, Dir, Multidisciplinary Center for Earthquake Engineering Research, State University of New York at Buffalo, 304 Capen Hall, Buffalo, NY, 14260. Tel: 716-645-3377. Fax: 716-645-3399. p. 1598

Tangeman, Suzanne, Dir, Sikeston Public Library, 121 E North St, Sikeston, MO, 63801. Tel: 573-471-4140. Fax: 573-471-6048. p. 1365

Tanghlyn, Wanda, Sr Librn, University of Texas at Dallas, Callier Library, 1966 Inwood Rd, Dallas, TX, 75235. Tel: 214-905-3165. Fax: 214-905-3143. p. 2374

Tangri, Shayeri, Br Mgr, Los Angeles Public Library System, Porter Ranch, 11371 Tampa Ave, Northridge, CA, 91326. Tel: 818-360-5706. Fax: 818-360-3106. p. 174

Tanguay, Annette, Librn, York County Community College Library, 112 College Dr, Wells, ME, 04090. Tel: 207-646-9282. Fax: 207-641-2770. p. 1006

Tanguay, Donna, Access Serv, University of Massachusetts Lowell Libraries, Lydon Library, 84 University Ave, Lowell, MA, 01854-2896. Tel: 978-934-3204. Fax: 978-934-3014. p. 1101

Tanguay, Marlene, Info Spec, Res Serv Spec, Societe Generale de Financement du Quebec, 600 de La Gauchetiere ouest, Bureau 1500, Montreal, QC, H3B 4L8, CANADA. Tel: 418-876-9290. Fax: 418-395-8055. p. 2901

Tanguay, Yves, Admin Dir, Mediatheque Maskoutaine, 2720 rue Dessaulles, Saint-Hyacinthe, QC, J2S 2V7, CANADA. Tel: 450-773-1830. Fax: 450-773-3398. p. 2910

Tani, Ernest, Librn, National Opinion Research Center Library, 1155 E 60th St, Rm 281, Chicago, IL, 60637-2667. Tel: 773-256-6206. Fax: 773-753-7886. p. 620

Taniguchi, Marilyn, Libr Serv Mgr/Pub Serv, Beverly Hills Public Library, 444 N Rexford Dr, Beverly Hills, CA, 90210-4877. Tel: 310-288-2220. Fax: 310-278-3387. p. 129

Tanji, Lorelei, Univ Librn, University of California Library, PO Box 19557, Irvine, CA, 92623-9557. Tel: 949-824-6836. p. 160

Tanji, Virginia M, Dir, John A Burns School of Medicine, 651 Ilalo St, MEB, Honolulu, HI, 96813. Tel: 808-692-0823. Fax: 808-692-1244. p. 564

Tankersley, Janice, Head, Cat, Rhodes College, 2000 North Pkwy, Memphis, TN, 38112-1694. Tel: 901-843-3891. Fax: 901-843-3404. p. 2251

Tannenbaum, Sabina D, Librn, LTK Engineering Services Library, 100 W Butler Ave, Ambler, PA, 19002. Tel: 215-641-8833. Fax: 215-542-7676. p. 2028

Tanner, Caryn, Ch, Putnam County District Library, The Educational Service Ctr, 124 Putnam Pkwy, Ottawa, OH, 45875-1471. Tel: 419-523-3747. Fax: 419-523-6477. p. 1926

Tanner, Cindy, Coll Develop, British Columbia Legislative Library, Parliament Bldgs, Victoria, BC, V8V 1X4, CANADA. Tel: 250-953-4718. Fax: 250-356-1373. p. 2745

Tanner, Daniel, Asst Dir/ILL/Homebound, Grand Valley Public Library, One N School St, Orwell, OH, 44076. Tel: 440-437-6545, 440-536-9159. Fax: 440-437-1017. p. 1925

Tanner, Darci, Res, Jenner & Block Library, 353 N Clark St, Ste 4300, Chicago, IL, 60654. Tel: 312-222-9350. Fax: 312-527-0484. p. 616

Tanner, Donna Gaye, Br Mgr, Librn II, Florence County Library System, Johnsonville Public Library, 242 S Georgetown Hwy, Johnsonville, SC, 29555. Tel: 843-386-2052. Fax: 843-380-1302. p. 2193

Tanner, Ellen, Br Mgr, Los Angeles Public Library System, Ascot, 120 W Florence Ave, Los Angeles, CA, 90003. Tel: 323-759-4817. Fax: 323-758-6578. p. 173

Tanner, Fonda, Mgr, Northwest Regional Library System, Harrell Memorial Library of Liberty County, 12818 NW Hwy 12, Bristol, FL, 32321. Tel: 850-643-2247. Fax: 850-643-2208. p. 481

Tanner, Jessie, Ch, Gilford Public Library, 31 Potter Hill Rd, Gilford, NH, 03249-6803. Tel: 603-524-6042. Fax: 603-524-1218. p. 1448

Tanner, Linda, Librn, Wentworth Military Academy, 1880 Washington Ave, Lexington, MO, 64067. Tel: 660-259-2221. Fax: 660-259-2677. p. 1343

Tanner, Melinda, Asst Dir, District Consult Librn, Citizens Library, 55 S College St, Washington, PA, 15301. Tel: 724-222-2400. Fax: 724-222-2606. p. 2151

Tanner, Phyllis, Bibliog Instr, Enterprise State Community College, 600 Plaza Dr, Enterprise, AL, 36330. Tel: 334-347-2623, Ext 2271. Fax: 334-347-0146. p. 16

Tanner, Tracy, Librn, Bodman Memorial Library, Eight Aldrich St, Philadelphia, NY, 13673. Tel: 315-642-3323. Fax: 315-642-0617. p. 1717

Tanner, Walt, Coordr, Saint Mary's University, Ferguson Library for Print Handicapped Students, 923 Robie, Halifax, NS, B3H 3C3, CANADA. Tel: 902-420-5553. Fax: 902-420-5561. p. 2783

Tannler, Albert M, Hist Coll Dir, Pittsburgh History & Landmarks Foundation, 100 W Station Square Dr, Ste 450, Pittsburgh, PA, 15219. Tel: 412-471-5808. Fax: 412-471-1633. p. 2127

Tannous, John, Dir, Smoki Museum, American Indian Art & Culture, 147 N Arizona St, Prescott, AZ, 86301. Tel: 928-445-1230. Fax: 928-777-0573. p. 78

Tano, Pete, Librn, Douglas County Library System, Paul B & Dorothy F Hult Library, 440 SE Grape, Winston, OR, 97496. Tel: 541-679-5501. p. 2016

Tanski, Anne, Dir, Community College of Allegheny County, 808 Ridge Ave, Pittsburgh, PA, 15212-6003. Tel: 412-237-2585. Fax: 412-237-6563. p. 2124

Tanski, Anne, Operations Mgr, Community College of Allegheny County, 8701 Perry Hwy, Pittsburgh, PA, 15237-5372. Tel: 412-369-3681. Fax: 412-369-3626. p. 2124

Tansley, Sarah, Br Mgr, Chicago Public Library, Humboldt Park, 1605 N Troy St, Chicago, IL, 60647. Tel: 312-744-2244. Fax: 312-742-5522. p. 609

Tantillo, Rebecca, Dir, Parma Public Library, Seven West Ave, Hilton, NY, 14468-1214. Tel: 585-392-8350. Fax: 585-392-9870. p. 1636

Tanton, Stephanie, Dir, Libr & Cultural Serv, Mission Viejo Library, 100 Civic Ctr, Mission Viejo, CA, 92691. Tel: 949-470-3076. Fax: 949-586-8447. p. 187

Tanzer, Sharon, Ch, Whiting Library, 117 Main St, Chester, VT, 05143. Tel: 802-875-2277. Fax: 802-875-2277. p. 2421

Tanzy, Robert, Br Mgr, Ouachita Parish Public Library, Ollie Burns Branch, 5601 Hwy 165 S, Richwood, LA, 71202. Tel: 318-327-1235. Fax: 318-329-8255. p. 957

Taormina, Kristy, Pub Serv, Mount Clemens Public Library, 150 Cass Ave, Mount Clemens, MI, 48043. Tel: 586-469-6200. Fax: 586-469-6668. p. 1210

Tapak, Laraine, Dir, Confederation College Library, 1450 Nakina Dr, Thunder Bay, ON, P7C 4W1, CANADA. Tel: 807-475-6241. Fax: 807-622-3258. p. 2848

Tapley, Denise, Librn, Sherman Public Library, Nine Church St, Sherman, ME, 04776. Tel: 207-365-4882. p. 1000

Tapley, Sylvia, Librn, Brooksville Free Public Library, Inc, Townhouse Bldg, One Townhouse Rd, Brooksville, ME, 04617-3647. Tel: 207-326-4560. Fax: 207-326-4560. p. 979

Taplin, Ronda, Dir, Krabbenhoft Public Library, 512 Elk St, Sabula, IA, 52070. Tel: 563-687-2950. Fax: 563-687-2950. p. 841

Tapp, Andrea, Librn, Warner Memorial Library, PO Box 270, Warner, AB, T0K 2L0, CANADA. Tel: 403-642-3988. p. 2721

Tapp, Lizzette, Circ Librn, Shaw University, 118 E South St, Raleigh, NC, 27601. Tel: 919-546-8407. Fax: 919-831-1161. p. 1817

Tapper, Janet, Univ Librn, University of Western States, 2900 NE 132nd Ave, Portland, OR, 97230-3099. Tel: 503-251-5752. Fax: 503-251-5759. p. 2015

Tappy, Victoria, Dir, Warren County Historical Society, 105 S Broadway, Lebanon, OH, 45036. Tel: 513-932-1817. Fax: 513-932-8560. p. 1909

Taraba, Suzy, Archivist, Spec Coll Librn, Wesleyan University, 252 Church St, Middletown, CT, 06459-3199. Tel: 860-685-3844. Fax: 860-685-2661. p. 352

Tarabula, Jill M, Syst & Tech Serv Librn, Clinton Community College, 136 Clinton Point Dr, Plattsburgh, NY, 12901-5690. Tel: 518-562-4247. Fax: 518-562-4116. p. 1718

Tarala, Georgy, VPres, Museum of Russian Culture, Inc Library, 2450 Sutter St, San Francisco, CA, 94115. Tel: 415-921-4082. Fax: 415-921-4082. p. 244

Tarantino, Jane, Ch Serv Librn, Rutherford Public Library, 150 Park Ave, Rutherford, NJ, 07070. Tel: 201-939-8600. Fax: 201-939-4108. p. 1528

Tarantino, Linda, Br Mgr, Mid-Continent Public Library, Grandview Branch, 12930 Booth Lane, Grandview, MO, 64030-2682. Tel: 816-763-0550. Fax: 816-763-3924. p. 1332

Taranto, Cheryl, Head of Libr, University of Nevada, Las Vegas Libraries, Music, 4505 S Maryland Pkwy, Las Vegas, NV, 89154-7002. Tel: 702-895-2549. p. 1431

Taranto, Elaine, Circ, Ref, Santa Clara County Law Library, 360 N First St, San Jose, CA, 95113. Tel: 408-299-3568. Fax: 408-286-9283. p. 252

Taranto, Lisa, Ch, Southborough Public Library, 25 Main St, Southborough, MA, 01772. Tel: 508-485-5031. Fax: 508-229-4451. p. 1126

Taranto, Pam, Law Librn, Frost, Brown & Todd LLC, 400 W Market St, 32nd Flr, Louisville, KY, 40202-3363. Tel: 502-589-5400. Fax: 502-581-1087. p. 923

Tarantowicz, Thomas A, Dir, Brentwood Public Library, 34 Second Ave, Brentwood, NY, 11717. Tel: 631-273-7883. Fax: 631-273-7896. p. 1584

Tarascio, Jean, Youth Serv Librn, Port Townsend Public Library, 1220 Lawrence St, Port Townsend, WA, 98368-6527. Tel: 360-344-3059. Fax: 360-385-5805. p. 2524

Tarasevich, Elizabeth, Ref Librn, Prince Memorial Library, 266 Main St, Cumberland, ME, 04021-9754. Tel: 207-829-2215. Fax: 207-829-2221. p. 982

Tarbox, Karen, Librn, Towers Perrin Information Centre, South Tower, Ste 1501, 175 Bloor St E, Toronto, ON, M4W 3T6, CANADA. Tel: 416-960-2609. Fax: 416-960-2819. p. 2864

Tarbox, Scott, Ref Librn, Santa Fe Community College, 3000 NW 83rd St, Bldg Y-100, Gainesville, FL, 32606. Tel: 352-395-5233. Fax: 352-395-5102. p. 449

Tarczy, Matt, Head, Ref, Hudson Library & Historical Society, 96 Library St, Hudson, OH, 44236-5122. Tel: 330-653-6658. Fax: 330-650-3373. p. 1905

Tardif, Josée, Chief Librn, Bibliotheque Gabrielle-Roy, Vieux-Quebec, 37 rue Sainte-Angele, Quebec, QC, G1R 4G5, CANADA. Tel: 418-641-6797. p. 2903

Tardiff, Kristine, Libr Mgr, San Luis Obispo County Library, 995 Palm St, San Luis Obispo, CA, 93401. Tel: 805-781-5783. Fax: 805-781-1320. p. 253

Tarelli-Falcon, Maggie, Asst Dir, Omaha Public Library, 215 S 15th St, Omaha, NE, 68102-1629. Tel: 402-444-4854. Fax: 402-444-4504. p. 1413

Tarita, Teri, Librn, Pacific Salmon Commission Library, 1155 Robson St, Ste 600, Vancouver, BC, V6E 1B5, CANADA. Tel: 604-684-8081. Fax: 604-666-8707. p. 2742

Tarpinian, Lori, Dir, Libr Serv, Mintz, Levin, Cohn, Ferris, Glovsky & Popeo, One Financial Ctr, Boston, MA, 02111. Tel: 617-348-4851. Fax: 617-542-2241. p. 1064

Tarr, Sharon, ILL, Spooner Memorial Library, 421 High St, Spooner, WI, 54801-1431. Tel: 715-635-2792. Fax: 715-635-2147. p. 2639

Tarrio, Christine, Ch, Stephenson Memorial Library, 761 Forest Rd, Greenfield, NH, 03047-0127. Tel: 603-547-2790. p. 1449

Tarry, Craig, Asst Dir, Indian River County Library System, 1600 21st St, Vero Beach, FL, 32960. Tel: 772-770-5060. Fax: 772-770-5066. p. 501

Tarter, Patty, Acq, ILL, Berea College, 100 Campus Dr, Berea, KY, 40404. Tel: 859-985-3364. Fax: 859-985-3912. p. 907

Tarzanin, Sylvia, Coordr, Ref (Info Serv), University of the Sciences in Philadelphia, 4200 Woodland Ave, Philadelphia, PA, 19104-4491. Tel: 215-596-8731. Fax: 215-596-8760. p. 2120

Tash, Steve, AV, Distance Educ, Saddleback College, 28000 Marguerite Pkwy, Mission Viejo, CA, 92692. Tel: 949-582-4543. Fax: 949-364-0284. p. 187

Tassa, Lisa, Br Mgr, Calvert County Public Library, Fairview, 8120 Southern Maryland Blvd, Owings, MD, 20736. Tel: 410-257-2101. Fax: 410-257-0662. p. 1036

Tassi, Isabelle, Ref Serv, Clearwater Public Library System, Countryside, 2741 State Rd 580, Clearwater, FL, 33761. Tel: 727-562-4970. Fax: 727-669-1289. p. 432

Tassin, Daphine, Libr Assoc, Law Library of Louisiana, Louisiana Supreme Court, 2nd Flr, 400 Royal St, New Orleans, LA, 70130-2104. Tel: 504-310-2400. Fax: 504-310-2419. p. 960

Tassin, Karen, ILL Librn, Saint John the Baptist Parish Library, 2920 New Hwy 51, LaPlace, LA, 70068. Tel: 985-652-2225, 985-652-6857. Fax: 985-652-8005. p. 954

Tassini, Katherine Mansfield, Librn, Historical Society of Haddonfield Library, 343 King's Hwy E, Haddonfield, NJ, 08033. Tel: 856-429-7375. p. 1489

Taste, Sharon, Mgr, Dayton Metro Library, Dayton View, 1515 Salem Ave, Dayton, OH, 45406. Tel: 937-496-8926. Fax: 937-496-4326. p. 1893

Tatar, Colleen, Librn, Hazleton Area Public Library, Freeland Branch, 515 Front St, Freeland, PA, 18224. Tel: 570-636-2125. p. 2068

Tatarka, Karen, Dir, Weston Public Library, 56 Norfield Rd, Weston, CT, 06883-2225. Tel: 203-222-2650. Fax: 203-222-2560. p. 377

Tate, Albert Jules, III, Dir, Libr Serv, Louisiana State University at Alexandria, 8100 Hwy 71 S, Alexandria, LA, 71302. Tel: 318-473-6438. Fax: 318-473-6556. p. 939

Tate, Allen, Head, Computer Serv, Ohio Township Public Library System, 4111 Lakeshore Dr, Newburgh, IN, 47630-2274. Tel: 812-853-5468. Fax: 812-853-0509. p. 768

Tate, Carolyn, Dir, Country Music Hall of Fame & Museum, 222 Fifth Ave S, Nashville, TN, 37203. Tel: 615-416-2009. Fax: 615-255-2245. p. 2255

Tate, Darcie, Librn, Calgary Academy Library, 1677 93rd St SW, Calgary, AB, T3H 0R3, CANADA. Tel: 403-686-6444, Ext 258. Fax: 403-240-3427. p. 2688

Tate, Debbra, Acq Librn, Kentucky State University, 400 E Main St, Frankfort, KY, 40601-2355. Tel: 502-597-6862. Fax: 502-597-5068. p. 914

Tate, Denise, Libr Res Mgr - Coll Develop, Tech Serv, Seminole County Public Library System, 215 N Oxford Rd, Casselberry, FL, 32707. Tel: 407-665-1507. Fax: 407-665-1510. p. 431

Tate, Diane, Actg Librn, Axtell Public Library, 401 Maple, Axtell, KS, 66403. Tel: 785-736-2858. p. 857

Tate, Geneva, Libr Spec, Piedmont Technical College Library, 620 N Emerald Rd, Bldg K, Greenwood, SC, 29646. Tel: 864-941-8793. Fax: 864-941-8558. p. 2197

Tate, Mary Lue, Librn, Sidell District Library, 101 E Market St, Sidell, IL, 61876. Tel: 217-288-9031. Fax: 217-288-9031. p. 702

Tate, Maurice T, Dir, Brunswick County Library, 109 W Moore St, Southport, NC, 28461. Tel: 910-457-6237. p. 1824

Tate, Michelle, Librn, Northrop Grumman Corp, Corporate Research Library, 1840 Century Park E, Los Angeles, CA, 90067-2199. Tel: 310-201-3132, 310-201-3231. Fax: 310-201-3023. p. 176

Tate, Vicki, Head, Govt Doc, University of South Alabama, 5901 USA Drive N, Rm 145, Mobile, AL, 36688. Tel: 251-460-2822. Fax: 251-460-7181. p. 26

Tatman, Karissa, Ref Librn, Richton Park Public Library District, 4045 Sauk Trail, Richton Park, IL, 60471. Tel: 708-481-5333. Fax: 708-481-4343. p. 694

Tatman, Sandra L, PhD, Dir, Athenaeum of Philadelphia, 219 S Sixth St, East Washington Square, Philadelphia, PA, 19106-3794. Tel: 215-925-2688. Fax: 215-925-3755. p. 2103

Tatnall, Amber, Dir, York County Community College Library, 112 College Dr, Wells, ME, 04090. Tel: 207-646-9282. Fax: 207-641-2770. p. 1006

Tatro, Fred, Dir, Boston Baptist College Library, 950 Metropolitan Ave, Boston, MA, 02136. Tel: 617-364-3510, Ext 216. p. 1056

Tatro, Mary, Tech Serv, Augustana College Library, 3435 9 1/2 Ave, Rock Island, IL, 61201-2296. Tel: 309-794-7266. Fax: 309-794-7640. p. 696

Tatta, Antonietta, Librn, Condon & Forsyth Library, Seven Times Sq, 18th Flr, New York, NY, 10036. Tel: 212-490-9100. Fax: 212-370-4453. p. 1676

Taub, Joan Barbara, Dir, Belleville Public Library & Information Center, 221 Washington Ave, Belleville, NJ, 07109-3189. Tel: 973-450-3434. Fax: 973-450-9518, 973-759-6731. p. 1471

Taube, John, Dir, Allegany County Library System, 31 Washington St, Cumberland, MD, 21502. Tel: 301-777-1200. Fax: 301-777-7299. p. 1026

Taubeneck, Brian, Ref Serv, Pew Charitable Trusts Library, 901 E St NW, Washington, DC, 20004. Tel: 202-540-6589. p. 413

Tauber, Chestene, Asst Dir, Fentress County Public Library, 306 S Main St, Jamestown, TN, 38556-3845. Tel: 931-879-7512. Fax: 931-879-6984. p. 2239

Tauber, Jean Ann, Librn, First Presbyterian Church of the Covenant, 250 W Seventh St, Erie, PA, 16501. Tel: 814-456-4243. Fax: 814-454-3350. p. 2055

Taul, Glen, Archivist, Campbellsville University, One University Dr, Campbellsville, KY, 42718-2799. Tel: 270-789-5024. Fax: 270-789-5336. p. 909

Taulbee, Joan T, Head Librn, Hodgson Russ LLP, 140 pearl St, Ste 100, Buffalo, NY, 14202-4040. Tel: 716-848-1282, 716-856-4000. Fax: 716-849-0349. p. 1598

Tauler, Sandra, Dir, Commun Serv, Camarena Memorial Library, 850 Encinas Ave, Calexico, CA, 92231. Tel: 760-768-2170. Fax: 760-357-0404. p. 131

Taupier, Andrea S, Dir, Springfield College, 263 Alden St, Springfield, MA, 01109-3797. Tel: 413-748-3315. Fax: 413-748-3631. p. 1128

Tautchier, Christian, Pub Serv, Chateauguay Municipal Library, 25 Maple Blvd, Chateauguay, QC, J6J 3P7, CANADA. Tel: 450-698-3085. Fax: 450-698-3109. p. 2880

Tautkus, Mike, Dir, Kingfisher Memorial Library, 505 W Will Rogers St, Kingfisher, OK, 73750. Tel: 405-375-3384. Fax: 405-375-3306. p. 1966

Tauvette, Sophie, Libr Tech, Canada Industrial Relations Board Library, C D Howe Bldg, 4th Flr W, 240 Sparks St, Ottawa, ON, K1A 0X8, CANADA. p. 2828

Tavares, Jocelyn, Dir, Dighton Public Library, 395 Main St, Dighton, MA, 02715. Tel: 508-669-6421. Fax: 508-669-6963. p. 1084

Tavenner, Debbie, Adminr, Ohio Legislative Service Commission Library, 77 S High St, 9th Flr, Columbus, OH, 43215-6136. Tel: 614-466-2241. Fax: 614-644-1721. p. 1887

Tavernier, Joan Elizabeth, Libr Mgr, Wide Awake Club Library, 46 W Main St, Fillmore, NY, 14735-8706. Tel: 585-567-8301. Fax: 585-567-8301. p. 1622

Tawil, Adrienne, Adult Serv & Tech Serv/ILL, Madison Public Library, 39 Keep St, Madison, NJ, 07940. Tel: 973-377-0722. Fax: 973-377-3142. p. 1498

Tawyea, Edward W, Univ Librn, Thomas Jefferson University, 1020 Walnut St, Philadelphia, PA, 19107. Tel: 215-503-6994. Fax: 215-923-3203. p. 2118

Taxakis, Brooke, Ref & Instruction Libr, Campbell University, 113 Main St, Buies Creek, NC, 27506. Tel: 910-893-1460. Fax: 910-893-1470. p. 1778

Taxman, Jennifer, Head, Circ, Dartmouth College Library, Baker-Berry Library, 6025 Baker-Berry Library, Hanover, NH, 03755-3525. Tel: 603-646-2560. Fax: 603-646-2167. p. 1450

Tay, Endrina, Assoc Found Librn, Tech Serv, Thomas Jefferson Foundation Inc, 1329 Kenwood Farm Lane, Charlottesville, VA, 22902. Tel: 434-984-7541. Fax: 434-984-7546. p. 2454

Taychert, Alice Marie, Dir, Hornell Public Library, 64 Genesee St, Hornell, NY, 14843-1651. Tel: 607-324-1210. Fax: 607-324-2570. p. 1638

Taylir, Vanessa, YA Serv, Menasha Public Library, 440 First St, Menasha, WI, 54952-3191. Tel: 920-967-3660. Fax: 920-967-5159. p. 2614

Taylor, Amanda, Dir, Concordia Parish Library, 1609 Third St, Ferriday, LA, 71334-2298. Tel: 318-757-3550. Fax: 318-757-1941. p. 949

Taylor, Amber Ruth, Cat, Decatur County Library, Court Sq, 20 W Market St, Decaturville, TN, 38329. Tel: 731-852-3325. Fax: 731-852-2351. p. 2232

Taylor, Amy, Libr Mgr, Stanislaus County Free Library, 1500 I St, Modesto, CA, 95354-1166. Tel: 209-558-7800. Fax: 209-529-4779. p. 188

Taylor, Amy, Librn, Spindale Public Library, 131 Tanner St, Spindale, NC, 28160. Tel: 828-286-3879. Fax: 828-286-8338. p. 1825

Taylor, Andrea, Div Mgr, Tech Serv, Fullerton Public Library, 353 W Commonwealth Ave, Fullerton, CA, 92832-1796. Tel: 714-738-6392. Fax: 714-447-3280. p. 154

Taylor, Andy, Digital Tech Librn, University of North Alabama, One Harrison Plaza, Box 5028, Florence, AL, 35632-0001. Tel: 256-765-4470. Fax: 256-765-4438. p. 17

Taylor, Angela, Br Mgr, Sullivan County Public Library, Bloomingdale Branch, 3230 Van Horn St, Kingsport, TN, 37660. Tel: 423-288-1310. Fax: 423-288-1310. p. 2224

Taylor, Ann, Sr Librn, Marin County Free Library, Bolinas Branch, Wharf Rd, Bolinas, CA, 94924. Tel: 415-868-1171. p. 257

Taylor, Ann, Sr Librn, Marin County Free Library, Inverness Branch, 15 Park Ave, Inverness, CA, 94937. Tel: 415-669-1288. p. 257

Taylor, Ann, Sr Librn, Marin County Free Library, Point Reyes Station Branch, 11431 State Rte 1, Point Reyes Station, CA, 94956. Tel: 415-663-8375. p. 257

Taylor, Ann M, Ref Librn, Duke University Libraries, School of Law Library, 210 Science Dr, Durham, NC, 27708. Tel: 919-613-7113. Fax: 919-613-7237. p. 1788

Taylor, Anne Cleester, Ref, Washington University Libraries, Law Library, Washington Univ Sch Law, Anheuser-Busch Hall, One Brookings Dr, Campus Box 1171, Saint Louis, MO, 63130. Tel: 314-935-4829. Fax: 314-935-7125. p. 1363

Taylor, Anneliese, Mgr, Coll Mgt, University of California San Francisco, 530 Parnassus Ave, San Francisco, CA, 94143-0840. Tel: 415-476-8415. p. 248

Taylor, Ara, Circ, Reserves, Whatcom Community College Library, 237 W Kellogg Rd, Bellingham, WA, 98226. Tel: 360-383-3300. p. 2509

Taylor, Ashley Kay, Dir, Choctaw County Public Library, 124 N Academy Ave, Butler, AL, 36904. Tel: 205-459-2542. p. 11

Taylor, Athalia Boroughs, Dir, Decatur County Library, Court Sq, 20 W Market St, Decaturville, TN, 38329. Tel: 731-852-3325. Fax: 731-852-2351. p. 2232

Taylor, Audrey, Dir, Elkins-Randolph County Public Library, 416 Davis Ave, Elkins, WV, 26241. Tel: 304-637-0287. Fax: 304-637-0288. p. 2558

Taylor, Barbara, Head, Cat, Tennessee State University, 3500 John A Merritt Blvd, Nashville, TN, 37209. Tel: 615-963-5236. Fax: 615-963-1368. p. 2259

Taylor, Beth, Head, Tech Serv, Librn, University of Michigan-Dearborn, 4901 Evergreen Rd, Dearborn, MI, 48128-2406. Tel: 313-593-5402. Fax: 313-593-5478. p. 1168

Taylor, Betty Louise, Dir, Mount Carmel Public Library, 727 Mulberry St, Mount Carmel, IL, 62863-2047. Tel: 618-263-3531. Fax: 618-262-4243. p. 676

Taylor, Bill, Ser, Southwestern Baptist Theological Seminary Libraries, 2001 W Seminary Dr, Fort Worth, TX, 76115-2157. Tel: 817-923-1921, Ext 4000. Fax: 817-921-8765. p. 2323

Taylor, Bonnie, Dir, Lenox Public Library, 101 N Main St, Lenox, IA, 50851. Tel: 641-333-4411. Fax: 641-333-2506. p. 827

Taylor, Brandon, Dr, Instructional Technologist, Chicago State University, 9501 S Martin Luther King Jr Dr, LIB 440, Chicago, IL, 60628-1598. Tel: 773-821-2782. Fax: 773-995-3772. p. 610

Taylor, Brenda, Archivist, Prescott Historical Society, 415 W Gurley St, Prescott, AZ, 86301. Tel: 928-445-3122. Fax: 928-776-9053. p. 78

Taylor, Carol, Dir, Connecticut State Library, 198 West St, Rocky Hill, CT, 06067. Tel: 860-721-2020. Fax: 860-721-2056. p. 365

Taylor, Carol, Ch, Atlanta-Fulton Public Library System, Sandy Springs Regional Library, 395 Mount Vernon Hwy, Sandy Springs, GA, 30328. Tel: 404-303-6130. Fax: 404-303-6133. p. 512

Taylor, Carol, Asst Dir, Jefferson County Library System, 306 E Broad St, Louisville, GA, 30434. Tel: 478-625-3751. Fax: 478-625-7683. p. 539

Taylor, Carol, Librn, Owensboro Medical Health System, 811 E Parish Ave, Owensboro, KY, 42303. Tel: 270-688-2167. Fax: 270-688-2168. p. 931

Taylor, Caroline, Circ, University of South Carolina, 1322 Greene St, Columbia, SC, 29208-0103. Tel: 803-777-3142. p. 2189

Taylor, Carrie, Ref, Pasquotank-Camden Library, 100 E Colonial Ave, Elizabeth City, NC, 27909. Tel: 252-335-2473, 252-335-7536. Fax: 252-331-7449. p. 1791

Taylor, Cathy, Br Supvr, Guelph Public Library, Westminster Square Branch, 100-31 Farley Dr, Guelph, ON, N1L 0B7, CANADA. Tel: 519-829-4404. p. 2807

Taylor, Chantelle, Youth Serv Librn, Cumberland Public Libraries, 21 Acadia St, 2nd Flr, Amherst, NS, B4H 4W3, CANADA. Tel: 902-667-2135. Fax: 902-667-1360. p. 2777

Taylor, Charlene, Librn, Dry Point Township Library, S Rte 128, Cowden, IL, 62422. Tel: 217-783-2616. p. 631

Taylor, Charlene, Head, Ref & Adult Serv, Englewood Public Library, 31 Engle St, Englewood, NJ, 07631. Tel: 201-568-2215. Fax: 201-568-6895. p. 1484

Taylor, Cheri, Asst Dir, Leetonia Community Public Library, 24 Walnut St, Leetonia, OH, 44431-1151. Tel: 330-427-6635. Fax: 330-427-2378. p. 1909

Taylor, Chris, Dir, Upper Arlington Public Library, 2800 Tremont Rd, Columbus, OH, 43221. Tel: 614-486-9621. Fax: 614-486-4530. p. 1891

Taylor Coombs, Melanie, Dir, Farmington Public Library, 117 Academy St, Farmington, ME, 04938. Tel: 207-778-4312. p. 985

Taylor, Cornelia A, Bibliographer, Florida Agricultural & Mechanical University Libraries, 1500 S Martin Luther King Blvd, Tallahassee, FL, 32307-4700. Tel: 850-599-3370. Fax: 850-561-2293. p. 492

Taylor, Cory, Dir, Walton Erickson Public Library, 4808 Northland Dr, Morley, MI, 49336-9522. Tel: 231-856-4298. Fax: 231-856-0307. p. 1210

Taylor, Crystal, Libr Spec, Inyo County Free Library, Furnace Creek, 201 Nevares Rd, Cow Creek, Death Valley, CA, 92328. Tel: 760-786-2408. p. 159

Taylor, Cynthia, Dir, Antigo Public Library, 617 Clermont St, Antigo, WI, 54409-1894. Tel: 715-623-3724. Fax: 715-627-2317. p. 2578

Taylor, Damita, Electronic Res & Copyright Librn, North Carolina Central University, School of Law Library, 1512 S Alston Ave, Durham, NC, 27707. Tel: 919-530-7176. Fax: 919-530-7926. p. 1789

Taylor, Dan, Libr Tech Spec, Ithaca College Library, 953 Danby Rd, Ithaca, NY, 14850-7060. Tel: 607-274-3206. Fax: 607-274-1539. p. 1643

Taylor, Danielle, Ch, Shorewood-Troy Public Library District, 650 Deerwood Dr, Shorewood, IL, 60431. Tel: 815-725-4368. Fax: 815-725-1722. p. 702

Taylor, DeAnn, Dir, Clark County District Library, 160 Main St, Dubois, ID, 83423. Tel: 208-374-5267. p. 573

Taylor, Deborah, Actg Librn, Huntsville Museum of Art Library, 300 Church St S, Huntsville, AL, 35801. Tel: 256-535-4350, Ext 217. Fax: 256-532-1743, 256-533-6748. p. 21

Taylor, Deborah, Coord, Ad Serv, Enoch Pratt Free Library, 400 Cathedral St, Baltimore, MD, 21201-4484. Tel: 410-396-5430. Fax: 410-396-1441. p. 1012

Taylor, Donn V, Br Supvr, Flint River Regional Library, Jackson-Butts County Public Library, 436 E College St, Jackson, GA, 30233. Tel: 770-775-7524. p. 535

Taylor, Donna, Dir, Bridgeville Public Library, 505 McMillen St, Bridgeville, PA, 15017. Tel: 412-221-3737. Fax: 412-220-8124. p. 2037

Taylor, Dorian, Cat, Kent Memorial Library, 50 N Main St (Junction of Rtes 75 & 168), Suffield, CT, 06078-2117. Tel: 860-668-3896. Fax: 860-668-3895. p. 371

Taylor, Doug, Ref Librn, Jacksonville State University Library, 700 Pelham Rd N, Jacksonville, AL, 36265. Tel: 256-782-5255. Fax: 256-782-5872. p. 22

Taylor, Emily, Br Mgr, Dixie Regional Library System, Jesse Yancy Memorial Library, 314 N Newberger Ave, Bruce, MS, 38915. Tel: 662-983-2220. Fax: 662-983-2220. p. 1312

Taylor, Erin, Dir, Gnadenhutten Public Library, 160 N Walnut St, Gnadenhutten, OH, 44629. Tel: 740-254-9224. Fax: 740-254-9841. p. 1902

Taylor, Gabrielle, YA Serv, Atlanta-Fulton Public Library System, South Fulton Regional Library, 4055 Flatshoals Rd SW, Union City, GA, 30291. Tel: 770-306-3092. Fax: 770-306-3127. p. 512

Taylor, Gary, Circ, Corban University Library, 5000 Deer Park Dr SE, Salem, OR, 97317-9392. Tel: 503-375-7016. Fax: 503-375-7196. p. 2017

Taylor, Gayle, Librn, Scott-Sebastian Regional Library, Sebastian County Library, 18 N Adair, Greenwood, AR, 72936. Tel: 479-996-2856. p. 102

Taylor, Gil, Librn, Smithsonian Libraries, Museum Support Center Library, Smithsonian Museum Support Center, Rm C-2000, MRC 534, 4210 Silver Hill Rd, Suitland, DC, 20746-2863. Tel: 301-238-1026. Fax: 301-238-3661. p. 415

Taylor, Gloria, Br Supvr, Southside Regional Library, R T Arnold Public, 110 E Danville St, South Hill, VA, 23970. Tel: 434-447-8162. Fax: 434-447-4050. p. 2452

Taylor, Hali, Dir, Shepherdstown Public Library, German & King Sts, Shepherdstown, WV, 25443. Tel: 304-876-2783. Fax: 304-876-6213. p. 2571

Taylor, Hazel, Asst Prof, University of Washington, Mary Gates Hall, Ste 370, Campus Box 352840, Seattle, WA, 98195-2840. Tel: 206-685-9937. Fax: 206-616-3152. p. 2976

Taylor, James, Archivist, Museum of the Cherokee Indian, 589 Tsali Blvd, Cherokee, NC, 28719. Tel: 828-497-3481. Fax: 828-497-4985. p. 1784

Taylor, Jane, Br Mgr, Siouxland Libraries, Ronning Branch, 3100 E 49th St, Sioux Falls, SD, 57103-5877. Tel: 605-367-8715. Fax: 605-371-4144. p. 2219

Taylor, Jane, Dir, British Columbia Legislative Library, Parliament Bldgs, Victoria, BC, V8V 1X4, CANADA. Tel: 250-387-6500. Fax: 250-356-1373. p. 2744

Taylor, Janet L, Bus & Finance Mgr, Coordr, Outreach Serv, Coordr, Pub Serv, South Dakota School of Mines & Technology, 501 E Saint Joseph St, Rapid City, SD, 57701-3995. Tel: 605-394-1262. Fax: 605-394-1256. p. 2217

Taylor, Jean, Ref Librn, Mark Twain Library, Rte 53 & Diamond Hill Rd, Redding, CT, 06896. Tel: 203-938-2545. Fax: 203-938-4026. p. 365

Taylor, Jeff, Curator, Sloan Museum, Flint Cultural Ctr, 303 Walnut St, Flint, MI, 48503. Tel: 810-237-3435. Fax: 810-237-3433. p. 1181

Taylor, Jennifer, Asst Librn, Wellsville City Library, 115 W Sixth St, Wellsville, KS, 66092. Tel: 785-883-2870. Fax: 785-883-2870. p. 899

Taylor, Jennifer, Educ Supvr, Tulsa Zoo & Living Museum, 5701 E 36th St N, Tulsa, OK, 74115. Tel: 918-669-6219. Fax: 918-669-6875. p. 1984

Taylor, Jill, Librn, Southeast Regional Library, Windthorst Branch, 202 Angus St, Windthorst, SK, S0G 5G0, CANADA. Tel: 306-224-2159. p. 2931

Taylor, Joan, Pub Serv Librn, Clayton State University, 2000 Clayton State Blvd, Morrow, GA, 30260. Tel: 678-466-4340. Fax: 678-466-4349. p. 545

Taylor, Joan Bessman, Dr, Asst Prof, University of Iowa, 3087 Main Library, Iowa City, IA, 52242-1420. Tel: 319-335-5707. Fax: 319-335-5374. p. 2965

Taylor, Joanna, Instrul Res, Eastern Nazarene College, 23 E Elm Ave, Quincy, MA, 02170. Tel: 617-745-3850. Fax: 617-745-3913. p. 1119

Taylor, Johna, Admin Support Coordr, California State University Dominguez Hills, 1000 E Victoria St, Carson, CA, 90747. Tel: 310-243-2305. Fax: 310-516-4219. p. 132

Taylor, Jolyn, Tech Coordr, Hudson Library & Historical Society, 96 Library St, Hudson, OH, 44236-5122. Tel: 330-653-6658. Fax: 330-650-3373. p. 1905

Taylor, Judy, Dir, Butler County Historical-Genealogical Society Library, 309 Fort Dale St, Greenville, AL, 36037. Tel: 334-382-6852. p. 19

Taylor, Julia, Legis Librn, Dickstein Shapiro LLP, Research Services, 1825 Eye St NW, Washington, DC, 20006. Tel: 202-420-4999. Fax: 202-420-2201. p. 398

Taylor, Julie, Tech Serv, Vermont Technical College, Main St, Randolph Center, VT, 05061. Tel: 802-728-1237. Fax: 802-728-1506. p. 2433

Taylor, Karan Lea, Librn, Jack McConnico Memorial Library, 225 Oak Grove Rd, Selmer, TN, 38375. Tel: 731-645-5571. Fax: 731-645-4874. p. 2265

Taylor, Karen, Head, Access Serv, University of South Carolina, Coleman Karesh Law Library, USC Law Ctr, 701 Main St, Columbia, SC, 29208. Tel: 803-777-5942. Fax: 803-777-9405. p. 2190

Taylor, Karen, Mgr, Info & Libr Serv, Purdue Pharma Library, 575 Granite Ct, Pickering, ON, L1W 3W8, CANADA. Tel: 905-420-4991. Fax: 905-420-5036. p. 2836

Taylor, Karen A, Dir, East Greenwich Free Library, 82 Peirce St, East Greenwich, RI, 02818. Tel: 401-884-9510. Fax: 401-884-3790. p. 2165

Taylor, Karin, Dir, Andalusia Public Library, 212 S Three Notch St, Andalusia, AL, 36420. Tel: 334-222-6612. Fax: 334-222-6612. p. 4

Taylor, Karin, Ch, Beardsley & Memorial Library, 40 Munro Pl, Winsted, CT, 06098. Tel: 860-379-6043. Fax: 860-379-3621. p. 379

Taylor, Kathleen, Asst Librn, Bloomsburg Public Library, 225 Market St, Bloomsburg, PA, 17815-1726. Tel: 570-784-0883. Fax: 570-784-8541. p. 2035

Taylor, Kathryn T, Dir, Westerly Public Library, 44 Broad St, Westerly, RI, 02891. Tel: 401-596-2877, Ext 303. Fax: 401-596-5600. p. 2178

Taylor, Kathy, Br Mgr, Public Library of Cincinnati & Hamilton County, Green Township, 6525 Bridgetown Rd, Cincinnati, OH, 45248. Tel: 513-369-6095. Fax: 513-369-4482. p. 1872

Taylor, Kay, Ch, Craighead County Jonesboro Public Library, 315 W Oak Ave, Jonesboro, AR, 72401-3513. Tel: 870-935-5133, Ext 12. Fax: 870-935-7987. p. 104

Taylor, Kolleen, Dir, The Bertha Bartlett Public Library, 503 Broad St, Story City, IA, 50248-1133. Tel: 515-733-2685. Fax: 515-733-2843. p. 846

Taylor, Larry, Extn Serv, Rochester Public Library, 115 South Ave, Rochester, NY, 14604-1896. Tel: 585-428-7300. Fax: 585-428-8353. p. 1732

Taylor, Laura, Asst Dir, Marigold Library System, 710-Second St, Strathmore, AB, T1P 1K4, CANADA. Tel: 403-934-5334, Ext 242. Fax: 403-934-5331. p. 2718

Taylor, Laurie, Interim Dir, Digital Libr Ctr, University of Florida Libraries, 535 Library W, Gainesville, FL, 32611-7000. Tel: 352-273-2900. Fax: 352-846-3702. p. 449

Taylor, Linda, Br Mgr, Riverside Public Library, La Sierra, 4600 La Sierra, Riverside, CA, 92505-2722. Tel: 951-688-7740. Fax: 951-352-7578. p. 218

Taylor, Linda, Pub Serv Mgr, Rappahannock Community College, 52 Campus Dr, Warsaw, VA, 22572. Tel: 804-333-6710. Fax: 804-333-0589. p. 2501

Taylor, Linda Stiles, Ch, Forest Grove City Library, 2114 Pacific Ave, Forest Grove, OR, 97116-9019. Tel: 503-992-3245. Fax: 503-992-3333. p. 1998

Taylor, Loren, Sr Librn, Hennepin County Library, Ridgedale, 12601 Ridgedale Dr, Minnetonka, MN, 55305-1909. Tel: 612-543-8820. Fax: 612-543-8819. p. 1264

Taylor, Lorrie, Circ Serv, Allerton Public Library District, 201 N State St, Monticello, IL, 61856. Tel: 217-762-4676. Fax: 217-762-2021. p. 675

Taylor, Lorrie, Head, Circ, Alma Public Library, 351 N Court, Alma, MI, 48801-1999. Tel: 989-463-3966, Ext 101. Fax: 989-466-5901. p. 1149

Taylor, Louise, Br Mgr, Lexington County Public Library System, Gilbert-Summit Branch, 405 Broad St, Gilbert, SC, 29054. Tel: 803-785-5387. Fax: 803-785-5387. p. 2199

Taylor, Margaret, Coll Develop, Oceanside Public Library, 330 N Coast Hwy, Oceanside, CA, 92054-2824. Tel: 760-435-5579. Fax: 760-435-9614. p. 199

Taylor, Mark Allen, Dir, Temple University Libraries, Health Science Center Libraries, 3440 N Broad St, Philadelphia, PA, 19140. Tel: 215-707-2402. Fax: 215-707-4135. p. 2117

Taylor, Martha, Libr Serv Supvr, Central Piedmont Community College Library, 1201 Elizabeth Ave, Charlotte, NC, 28235. Tel: 704-330-6872. Fax: 704-330-6887. p. 1781

Taylor, Marvin, Dir, New York University, Fales Library & Special Collections, 70 Washington Sq S, New York, NY, 10012. Tel: 212-998-2599. Fax: 212-995-3835. p. 1695

Taylor, Marvin, Spec Coll Librn, New York University, 70 Washington Sq S, New York, NY, 10012-1091. Tel: 212-998-2505. Fax: 212-995-4070. p. 1695

Taylor, Mary, Dir, Minocqua Public Library, 415 Menominee St, Minocqua, WI, 54548. Tel: 715-356-4437. Fax: 715-358-2873. p. 2622

Taylor, Mary Virginia, Chief Librn, Department of Veterans Affairs-Memphis, 1030 Jefferson Ave, Memphis, TN, 38104-2193. Tel: 901-523-8990, Ext 5883. Fax: 901-577-7338. p. 2248

Taylor, Mayo, Access Serv Librn, Middle Tennessee State University, MTSU, PO Box 13, Murfreesboro, TN, 37132. Tel: 615-898-5605. p. 2254

Taylor, Megan, Circ Serv Mgr, The Seattle Public Library, 1000 Fourth Ave, Seattle, WA, 98104-1109. Tel: 206-386-4636. p. 2531

Taylor, Michael, Librn, Herzing College Library, 1595 S Semoran Blvd, Ste 1501, Winter Park, FL, 32792. Tel: 407-478-0500. Fax: 407-478-0501. p. 505

Taylor, Michael, Dir, Pender County Public Library, 103 S Cowan St, Burgaw, NC, 28425. Tel: 910-259-1234. Fax: 910-259-0656. p. 1778

Taylor, Michael, Coordr, Remote Serv, Vermont Technical College, Main St, Randolph Center, VT, 05061. Tel: 802-728-1237. Fax: 802-728-1506. p. 2433

Taylor, Mildretha, Librn, Mammoth Public Library, 125 N Clark St, Mammoth, AZ, 85618. Tel: 520-487-2026. Fax: 520-487-2364. p. 68

Taylor, Nick, Adult Serv, Web Serv, Free Public Library of the Borough of Fort Lee, 320 Main St, Fort Lee, NJ, 07024. Tel: 201-592-3614. Fax: 201-585-0375. p. 1486

Taylor, Noreen, Librn, Canyon Area Library, 1501 Third Ave, Canyon, TX, 79015. Tel: 806-655-5015. Fax: 806-655-5032. p. 2294

Taylor, Ona, Circ Supvr, Carnegie Mellon University, Hunt Library, 4909 Frew St, Pittsburgh, PA, 15213-3890. Tel: 412-268-2446. Fax: 412-268-2793. p. 2123

Taylor, Opal, Librn, Pigeon Lake Public Library, 603-2 Second Ave, Ma-Me-O Beach, AB, T0C 1X0, CANADA. Tel: 780-586-3778. p. 2710

Taylor, Pam, Circ Supvr, Delaware County District Library, 84 E Winter St, Delaware, OH, 43015. Tel: 740-362-3861. Fax: 740-369-0196. p. 1895

Taylor, Pam, Librn, Clear Lake City Library, 125 Third Ave S, Clear Lake, SD, 57226. Tel: 605-874-2013. p. 2211

Taylor, Pat, Br Mgr, Llano County Library System, Lake Shore, 7346 Ranch Rd 261, Buchanan Dam, TX, 78609. Tel: 325-379-1174. Fax: 325-379-3054. p. 2356

Taylor, Patience, Ad, ILL Coordr, Goodwin Library, 422 Main St, Farmington, NH, 03835-1519. Tel: 603-755-2944. Fax: 603-755-2944. p. 1447

Taylor, Patrick, Dir of Finance, Capital Area District Libraries, 401 S Capitol Ave, Lansing, MI, 48933. Tel: 517-367-6337. Fax: 517-374-1068. p. 1200

Taylor, Paula, Circ Mgr, Davis & Elkins College, 100 Campus Dr, Elkins, WV, 26241. Tel: 304-637-1200. Fax: 304-637-1415. p. 2558

Taylor, Peggy, Librn, White County Regional Library System, Pangburn Public, 914 Main St, Pangburn, AR, 72121. Tel: 501-728-4612. Fax: 501-728-4612. p. 115

Taylor, Penny, Br Mgr, San Diego County Library, Santee Branch, 9225 Carlton Hills Blvd, No 17, Santee, CA, 92071-3192. Tel: 619-448-1863. Fax: 619-448-1497. p. 234

Taylor, Prudence A, Dir, Greenwood County Library, 600 S Main St, Greenwood, SC, 29646. Tel: 864-941-3030. Fax: 864-941-4651. p. 2197

Taylor, Rebbecca, Dir, Ector County Library, 321 W Fifth St, Odessa, TX, 79761-5066. Tel: 432-332-0633. Fax: 432-377-6502. p. 2366

Taylor, Rhonda Harris, PhD, Dr, Assoc Prof, University of Oklahoma, Bizzell Memorial Library, 401 W Brooks, Rm 120, Norman, OK, 73019-6032. Tel: 405-325-3921. Fax: 405-325-7648. p. 2972

Taylor, Robert, Mgr, West Virginia Archives & History Library, Cultural Ctr, 1900 Kanawha Blvd E, Charleston, WV, 25305-0300. Tel: 304-558-0230. Fax: 304-558-4193. p. 2556

Taylor, Robin, Librn, Philmont Museum & Seton Memorial Library, Philmont Scout Ranch, 17 Deer Run Rd, Cimarron, NM, 87714. Tel: 575-376-1136. Fax: 575-376-2602. p. 1553

Taylor, Rose, Dir, Bridgeview Public Library, 7840 W 79th St, Bridgeview, IL, 60455-1496. Tel: 708-458-2880, Ext 100. Fax: 708-458-3553. p. 597

Taylor, Rosemarie Kazda, Mgr, Wilkes-Barre General Hospital, 575 N River St, Wilkes-Barre, PA, 18764. Tel: 570-552-1175. Fax: 570-552-1183. p. 2156

Taylor, Russell, Dir of Libr, Lees-McRae College, 191 Main St W, Banner Elk, NC, 28604-9238. Tel: 828-898-8727. Fax: 828-898-8710. p. 1775

Taylor, Salai, Libr Mgr, Alamosa Public Library, 300 Hunt Ave, Alamosa, CO, 81101. Tel: 719-589-6592, Ext 2543. Fax: 719-589-3786. p. 287

Taylor, Samuel, Automation Syst Coordr, Northland Public Library, 300 Cumberland Rd, Pittsburgh, PA, 15237-5455. Tel: 412-366-8100, Ext 130. Fax: 412-366-2064. p. 2126

Taylor, Sarah, Mgr, Ch Serv, Johnson County Public Library, 401 State St, Franklin, IN, 46131-2545. Tel: 317-738-2833. Fax: 317-738-9635. p. 744

Taylor, Sean, Access Serv, King College, 1350 King College Rd, Bristol, TN, 37620. Tel: 423-652-4790. Fax: 423-652-4871. p. 2225

Taylor, Shari, Dir, Earlville Free Library, Four N Main St, Earlville, NY, 13332. Tel: 315-691-5931. Fax: 315-691-5931. p. 1616

Taylor, Sharon, Asst Dir, Weeks Public Library, 36 Post Rd, Greenland, NH, 03840-2312. Tel: 603-436-8548. Fax: 603-427-0913. p. 1449

Taylor, Sharon, Dir, Pittsburgh Theological Seminary, 616 N Highland Ave, Pittsburgh, PA, 15206-2596. Tel: 412-924-1350. Fax: 412-362-2329. p. 2127

Taylor, Shelia, Librn, United States Department of Transportation, Federal Highway Administration-Chief Counsel's Law Library, 1200 New Jersy Ave SE, Rm E84-464, Washington, DC, 20590. Tel: 202-366-1387. Fax: 202-366-1380. p. 419

Taylor, Sheryl Sheeres, Dir, Libr Serv, Dordt College, 498 Fourth Ave NE, Sioux Center, IA, 51250. Tel: 712-722-6047. Fax: 712-722-1198. p. 843

Taylor, Sondra, Ch, Camanche Public Library, 102 12th Ave, Camanche, IA, 52730. Tel: 563-259-1106. Fax: 563-259-1106. p. 798

Taylor, Sue, In Charge, Founding Church of Scientology, 1701 20th St NW, Washington, DC, 20009. Tel: 202-797-9826. Fax: 202-797-9813. p. 401

Taylor, Sue Ann, Head, Tech Serv, Rogers Memorial Library, 91 Coopers Farm Rd, Southampton, NY, 11968. Tel: 631-283-0774. Fax: 631-287-6539. p. 1746

Taylor, Susan, Educ Coordr, Yukon-Kuskokwim Correctional Center Library, PO Box 400, Bethel, AK, 99559. Tel: 907-543-5245. Fax: 907-543-3097. p. 46

Taylor, Susan, Br Mgr, Long Beach Public Library, Mark Twain Branch, 1401 E Anaheim St, Long Beach, CA, 90813. Tel: 562-570-1046. p. 167

Taylor, Susan, Ch, Oldsmar Library, 400 St Petersburg Dr E, Oldsmar, FL, 34677. Tel: 813-749-1178. Fax: 813-854-1881. p. 474

Taylor, Tammy, Circ Supvr, University of Baltimore, 1420 Maryland Ave, Baltimore, MD, 21201. Tel: 410-837-4263. Fax: 410-837-4330. p. 1018

Taylor, Terry, Librn, Shakespeare Society of America, 7981 Moss Landing Rd, Moss landing, CA, 95039. Tel: 831-633-2989. p. 192

Taylor, Terry, Assoc Dir, Res & Info Serv, DePaul University Libraries, 2350 N Kenmore, Chicago, IL, 60614. Tel: 773-325-3725, 773-325-7862. Fax: 773-325-7870. p. 612

Taylor, Tom, Mem Serv Coordr, South Central Kansas Library System, 321 N Main St, South Hutchinson, KS, 67505-1146. Tel: 620-663-3211. Fax: 620-663-9797. p. 895

Taylor, Traci, Librn, Bellingham Technical College Library, 3028 Lindbergh Ave, Bellingham, WA, 98225-1599. Tel: 360-752-8488. Fax: 360-752-8384. p. 2508

Taylor, Trish, Adult Serv Mgr, Santa Clara City Library, 2635 Homestead Rd, Santa Clara, CA, 95051. Tel: 408-615-2902. Fax: 408-247-9657. p. 262

Taylor, Tucker Neel, Dir, Newberry County Library, 1300 Friend St, Newberry, SC, 29108-3400. Tel: 803-276-0854. Fax: 803-276-7478. p. 2201

Taylor, Valerie, Librn, Chester County Library, Lewisville Community Library, 3771 Lancaster Hwy, Richburg, SC, 29729. Tel: 803-789-7800. Fax: 803-789-7801. p. 2186

Taylor, Vickie H, Sr VPres, Capital Group Companies, Inc, 333 S Hope St, Los Angeles, CA, 90071. Tel: 213-486-9261. Fax: 213-486-9571. p. 169

Taylor, Wendy, Ch, Kent Memorial Library, 50 N Main St (Junction of Rtes 75 & 168), Suffield, CT, 06078-2117. Tel: 860-668-3896. Fax: 860-668-3895. p. 371

Taylor-Bandele, Leola, Ref, Essex County College Library, 303 University Ave, Newark, NJ, 07102. Tel: 973-877-3238. Fax: 973-877-1887. p. 1510

Taylor-Furbee, Sondra, Exec Dir, Southwest Florida Library Network, Bldg III, Unit 7, 12751 Westlinks Dr, Fort Myers, FL, 33913. Tel: 239-225-4225. Fax: 239-225-4229. p. 2940

Taylor-Hille, Kandy, Br Mgr, Brazoria County Library System, Danbury Branch, 1702 N Main St, Danbury, TX, 77534. Tel: 979-922-1905. Fax: 979-922-1905. p. 2275

Taylor-Pruitt, Christy, Assoc Dean, Florida State College at Jacksonville, 3939 Roosevelt Blvd, C-100, Jacksonville, FL, 32205. Tel: 904-381-3626. Fax: 904-381-3579. p. 452

Taylor-Samuel, Valerie, Head of Libr, Free Library of Philadelphia, West Oak Lane Branch, 2000 Washington Lane, Philadelphia, PA, 19138-1344. Tel: 215-685-2843. Fax: 215-685-2844. p. 2109

Taylor-Smith, Cheryl, Asst Librn, High River Centennial Library, 909 First St SW, High River, AB, T1V 1A5, CANADA. Tel: 403-652-2917. Fax: 403-652-7203. p. 2707

Taylor-Veisey, Anne, Ref Serv, Canadian Memorial Chiropractic College, 6100 Leslie St, Toronto, ON, M2H 3J1, CANADA. Tel: 416-482-2340, Ext 158. Fax: 416-482-4816. p. 2851

Taylor-Watkins, Jody, Asst Librn, Ref, Saint Joseph's College, Hwy 231 S, Rensselaer, IN, 47978. Tel: 219-866-6210. Fax: 219-866-6135. p. 774

Taysom, Dan, Computer Serv, Spec Coll, University of California, 200 McAllister St, San Francisco, CA, 94102-4978. Tel: 415-565-4757. Fax: 415-581-8849. p. 248

Tchangalova, Nedelina, Ref, University of Maryland Libraries, Engineering & Physical Sciences Library, College Park, MD, 20742-7011. Tel: 301-405-9151. p. 1025

Tchida, Jennifer, Youth Serv, Bartholomew County Public Library, 536 Fifth St, Columbus, IN, 47201-6225. Tel: 812-379-1288. Fax: 812-379-1275. p. 733

Tchiyuka, Evelyn, Assoc Dir, Pub Serv, Prince George's County Memorial Library System, 6532 Adelphi Rd, Hyattsville, MD, 20782-2098. Tel: 301-699-3500. Fax: 301-699-0122. p. 1032

Tckazuk, Diana, ILL, Oshawa Public Library, 65 Bagot St, Oshawa, ON, L1H 1N2, CANADA. Tel: 905-579-6111. Fax: 905-433-8107. p. 2827

Te Tan, Robert, ILL, Bureau of National Affairs, Inc Library, 1801 S Bell St, Rm 3200, Arlington, VA, 22202. Tel: 703-341-3315. Fax: 703-341-1636. p. 2449

Teachout, Laurenne, Dir, Stephentown Memorial Library, 472 State Rte 43, Stephentown, NY, 12168. Tel: 518-733-5750. p. 1748

Teachworth, Connie, Dir, Lake Odessa Community Library, 1007 Fourth Ave, Lake Odessa, MI, 48849-1023. Tel: 616-374-4591. Fax: 616-374-3054. p. 1199

Teaff, Elizabeth Anne, Access Serv Librn, Washington & Lee University, University Library, 204 W Washington St, Lexington, VA, 24450-2116. Tel: 540-458-8640. Fax: 540-458-8964. p. 2475

Teaford, Ellie, Br Mgr, Kanawha County Public Library, Elk Valley, 4636 Pennsylvania Ave, Charleston, WV, 25302. Tel: 304-965-3636. Fax: 304-965-3702. p. 2556

Teague, Edward, Dir, University of Oregon Libraries, Architecture & Allied Arts, 200 Lawrence Hall, Eugene, OR, 97403. Tel: 541-346-3637. Fax: 541-346-2205. p. 1997

Teague, Gypsey, Head of Libr, Clemson University Libraries, Gunnin Architecture Library, 112 Lee Hall, Clemson University, Clemson, SC, 29634-0501. Tel: 864-656-3933. Fax: 864-656-3932. p. 2186

Teague, Janie, Dir, Trumann Public Library, 1200 W Main St, Trumann, AR, 72472. Tel: 870-483-7744. Fax: 870-483-7744. p. 116

Teague, Phil, Coordr, Info Tech, Birmingham Public Library, 2100 Park Pl, Birmingham, AL, 35203. Tel: 205-226-3701. Fax: 205-226-3703. p. 7

Teague, Teresa, Asst Librn, Tech Serv, Campbell University, Norman Adrian Wiggins School of Law Library, 225 Hillsborough St, Ste 203, Raleigh, NC, 27603. Tel: 919-865-5872. Fax: 919-865-5995. p. 1778

Teahan, John, Librn, Wadsworth Atheneum, 600 Main St, Hartford, CT, 06103. Tel: 860-278-2670, Ext 3115. Fax: 860-527-0803. p. 348

Teal Lovely, Victoria, ILS Project Mgr, South Central Library System, 4610 S Biltmore Lane, Ste 101, Madison, WI, 53718-2153. Tel: 608-242-4713. Fax: 608-246-7958. p. 2607

Teale, Susan, Asst Dir, Ref Librn, East Longmeadow Public Library, 60 Center Sq, East Longmeadow, MA, 01028-2459. Tel: 413-525-5400. Fax: 413-525-0344. p. 1086

Tear, Lindsey L, Cat, Salem Public Library, 28 E Main St, Salem, VA, 24153. Tel: 540-375-3089. Fax: 540-389-7054. p. 2496

Teasdale, Gilles, Librn, Saint Mary's Hospital, 3830 Lacombe Ave, Montreal, QC, H3T 1M5, CANADA. Tel: 514-345-3511, Ext 3317. Fax: 514-734-2695. p. 2901

Teasdale, Rebecca, Assoc Dir, Pub Serv, Oak Park Public Library, 834 Lake St, Oak Park, IL, 60301. Tel: 708-383-8200. Fax: 708-697-6900. p. 684

Teasdle, Holly, Dir, Lyon Township Public Library, 27005 S Milford Rd, South Lyon, MI, 48178. Tel: 248-437-8800. Fax: 248-437-4621. p. 1227

Teasley, Christina, Librn, North Georgia Technical College Library, 1500 Hwy 197 N, Clarkesville, GA, 30523. Tel: 706-754-7720. Fax: 706-754-7777. p. 524

Teaster, Gale, Head, Ser, Acq & Cat, Winthrop University, 824 Oakland Ave, Rock Hill, SC, 29733. Tel: 803-323-2131, 803-323-2274, 803-323-2311. Fax: 803-323-2215. p. 2203

Teaster, Neena, Computing Coordr/Evening Supvr, Maryville College, 502 E Lamar Alexander Pkwy, Maryville, TN, 37804-5907. Tel: 865-981-8258. Fax: 865-981-8267. p. 2247

Teatero, Barbara, Head, Spec Coll, Queen's University, W D Jordan Special Collections - Music, Douglas Library, 6th Level, Kingston, ON, K7L 5C4, CANADA. Tel: 613-533-6320. Fax: 613-533-2584. p. 2814

Teaze, Kathleen, Dir, Prince George's County Memorial Library System, 6532 Adelphi Rd, Hyattsville, MD, 20782-2098. Tel: 301-699-3500. Fax: 301-985-5494. p. 1032

Tebault, Hugh H, III, Pres, Latham Foundation Library, Latham Plaza Bldg, 1826 Clement Ave, Alameda, CA, 94501-1397. Tel: 510-521-0920. Fax: 510-521-9861. p. 119

Tebbe, Michael, Assoc Librn, Duff & Phelps, 311 S Wacker Dr, Ste 4200, Chicago, IL, 60606. Tel: 312-697-4535. Fax: 312-697-4609. p. 613

Tebben, Cindy, Dir, Wesley Public Library, 206 W Main St, Wesley, IA, 50483. Tel: 515-679-4214. Fax: 515-679-4214. p. 851

Tebo, Ginger, Ch, Roswell P Flower Memorial Library, 229 Washington St, Watertown, NY, 13601-3388. Tel: 315-785-7705. Fax: 315-788-2584. p. 1763

Tebo, John, Head of Libr, University of Cincinnati Libraries, Chemistry-Biology, 503 Rieveschl, A-3, Cincinnati, OH, 45221. Tel: 513-556-1494. Fax: 513-556-1103. p. 1874

Tecumseh, Ramona, Head Librn, Ira H Hayes Memorial Library, Gila River Indian Community Church & Pima, Sacaton, AZ, 85247. Tel: 520-562-3225. Fax: 520-562-3903. p. 79

Tedesco-Blair, Graham, Ref Librn, Wichita Falls Public Library, 600 11th St, Wichita Falls, TX, 76301-4604. Tel: 940-767-0868, Ext 232. Fax: 940-720-6672. p. 2401

Tedford, Rosalind, Dir, Res & Instruction Serv, Wake Forest University, PO Box 7777, Winston-Salem, NC, 27109-7777. Tel: 336-758-5910. Fax: 336-758-3694, 336-758-8831. p. 1834

Teed, Mary, Head, Circ, Mid-America Baptist Theological Seminary, 2095 Appling Rd, Cordova, TN, 38016. Tel: 901-751-3007. Fax: 901-751-8454. p. 2232

Teegarden, Greg, Archives Dir, Wesleyan Church, 13300 Olio Rd, Fishers, IN, 46037. Tel: 317-774-7996. Fax: 317-774-7998. p. 740

Teel, April, Dir, Emily Taber Public Library, 14 McIver Ave W, Macclenny, FL, 32063. Tel: 904-259-6464. p. 461

Teel, Eunice, Librn, North Central Michigan College Library, 1515 Howard St, Petoskey, MI, 49770. Tel: 231-348-6715. Fax: 231-348-6629. p. 1217

Teel, Linda M, Dir, Libr Serv, Pitt Community College, Hwy 11 S, Greenville, NC, 27835. Tel: 252-321-4359. Fax: 252-321-4449. p. 1799

Teel, Linda M, Circ, Oxford Public Library, 48 S Second St, Oxford, PA, 19363-1377. Tel: 610-932-9625. Fax: 610-932-9251. p. 2101

Teeple, Andrew, Head, Tech Serv, Lake County Public Library, 1919 W 81st Ave, Merrillville, IN, 46410-5488. Tel: 219-769-3541. Fax: 219-756-9358. p. 763

Teeter, Kyle, Admin Serv Mgr, Whatcom County Library System, 5205 Northwest Dr, Bellingham, WA, 98226-9050. Tel: 360-384-3150. Fax: 360-384-4947. p. 2509

Teeter, Robert J, Librn, Santa Clara Valley Water District Library, 1020 Blossom Hill Rd, San Jose, CA, 95123. Tel: 408-265-2600, Ext 3748. Fax: 408-979-5693. p. 252

Teets, Carin, Cat, Bridgewater College, 402 E College St, Bridgewater, VA, 22812. Tel: 540-828-5414. Fax: 540-828-5482. p. 2452

Tegegne, Bekele, Govt Doc/Ref Librn, Kentucky State University, 400 E Main St, Frankfort, KY, 40601-2355. Tel: 502-597-6858. Fax: 502-597-5068. p. 914

Tegel, Peggy, Adult Serv, Oswego Public Library District, 32 W Jefferson St, Oswego, IL, 60543. Tel: 630-554-3150. Fax: 630-978-1307. p. 686

Tegge, Susan, Head, Adult Serv, Springfield Free Public Library, 66 Mountain Ave, Springfield, NJ, 07081-1786. Tel: 973-376-4930. Fax: 973-376-1334. p. 1532

Teghtmeyer, Anne, Dir, Council Grove Public Library, 829 W Main St, Council Grove, KS, 66846. Tel: 620-767-5716. Fax: 620-767-7312. p. 862

Teh-Frenette, Lillian, Media Spec, Red Deer College Library, 100 College Blvd, Red Deer, AB, T4N 5H5, CANADA. Tel: 403-342-3344. Fax: 403-346-8500. p. 2714

Tehrani, Mahnaz, ILL, New York Institute of Technology, Northern Blvd, Old Westbury, NY, 11568-8000. Tel: 516-686-3743. Fax: 516-686-3709. p. 1710

Teich, Steve, Ref/Outreach Coordr, Oregon Health & Science University Library, 3181 SW Sam Jackson Park Rd, Portland, OR, 97239-3098. Tel: 503-494-3444. Fax: 503-494-3227. p. 2013

Teichert, Richard, Dep Dir, Admin, Sacramento Public Library, 828 I St, Sacramento, CA, 95814. Tel: 916-264-2737. Fax: 916-264-2755. p. 224

Teitelbaum, Jeff, Librn, Forensic Laboratory Services Bureau Library, 2203 Airport Way S, Ste 250, Seattle, WA, 98134. Tel: 206-262-6027. Fax: 206-262-6018. p. 2527

Teitzel, Marion, In Charge, Trinity County Library, Trinity Center Branch, Trinity Center, CA, 96091. Tel: 530-266-3242. p. 282

Teixeira, Monica, Ref, Monroe Township Public Library, Four Municipal Plaza, Monroe Township, NJ, 08831-1900. Tel: 732-521-5000. Fax: 732-521-4766. p. 1503

Tekautz, Laurel, Librn, Mesabi Range Community & Technical College Library, 1001 Chestnut St W, Virginia, MN, 55792. Tel: 218-749-7778. Fax: 218-748-2419. p. 1286

Tekin, Kathy, Libr Supvr, Youth Serv, Jacksonville Public Library, 303 N Laura St, Jacksonville, FL, 32202-3505. Tel: 904-630-1627. Fax: 904-630-1435. p. 453

Tekulve, Nicole, Instrul Serv Librn, University of Southern Indiana, 8600 University Blvd, Evansville, IN, 47712. Tel: 812-465-1277. Fax: 812-465-1693. p. 739

Telatnik, George, Librn, Niagara Falls Public Library, 1425 Main St, Niagara Falls, NY, 14305. Tel: 716-286-4881. Fax: 716-286-4912. p. 1705

Teleglow, Fern, Br Head Librn, Okanagan Regional Library, 1430 KLO Rd, Kelowna, BC, V1W 3P6, CANADA. Tel: 250-860-4033. Fax: 250-861-8696. p. 2730

Teleha, John, Ref Librn, North Carolina Agricultural & Technical State University, 1601 E Market St, Greensboro, NC, 27411-0002. Tel: 336-334-7159, Ext 3213. Fax: 336-334-7783. p. 1797

Teleha, Sheri, Cat, Ser, High Point University, 833 Montlieu Ave, High Point, NC, 27262-4221. Tel: 336-841-4549. Fax: 336-841-5123. p. 1802

Telesca, Sue, Head, Tech Serv, New City Free Library, 220 N Main St, New City, NY, 10956. Tel: 845-634-4997. p. 1664

Teliha, James, Head, Access Serv, Robert L Carothers Library & Learning Commons, 15 Lippitt Rd, Kingston, RI, 02881. Tel: 406-874-4619. Fax: 401-874-4608. p. 2168

Tella, Liisa, Librn, Harper Grey LLP Library, 3200-650 W Georgia St, Vancouver, BC, V6B 4P7, CANADA. Tel: 604-895-2861. Fax: 604-669-9385. p. 2741

Telles, James, Librn, Folsom Lake College Library, Ten College Pkwy, Folsom, CA, 95630. Tel: 916-608-6528. Fax: 916-608-6533. p. 148

Tellez, Anna, Tech Support, United States Geological Survey Library, 345 Middlefield Rd, Bldg 15 (MS-955), Menlo Park, CA, 94025-3591. Tel: 650-329-5128. Fax: 650-329-5132. p. 185

Tellez, Ida, Asst Dir, Port Isabel Public Library, 213 Yturria St, Port Isabel, TX, 78578. Tel: 956-943-1822. Fax: 956-943-4638. p. 2371

Telli, Andrea, Asst Commissioner, Neighborhood Serv, Chicago Public Library, 400 S State St, Chicago, IL, 60605. Tel: 312-747-4212. Fax: 312-747-4076. p. 608

Tellier, Diane, Head of Libr, West Nipissing Public Library, Verner Branch, 11790 Hwy 64, Verner, ON, P0H 2M0, CANADA. Tel: 705-594-2800. Fax: 705-594-2800. p. 2846

Tellier, Raymond, Librn, Pascoag Free Public Library, 57 Church St, Pascoag, RI, 02859. Tel: 401-568-6226. Fax: 401-567-9372. p. 2170

Tellman, Patricia Elaine, Dir, Navy General Library Program, 1802 Doolittle Ave, NAS Fort Worth JRB, Fort Worth, TX, 76127. Tel: 817-782-7735. Fax: 817-782-7219. p. 2322

Tello, Humberto, Supvr, Ventura County Library, Albert H Soliz Library, 2820 Jourdan St, Oxnard, CA, 93036. Tel: 805-485-4515. Fax: 805-604-7966. p. 280

Temanson, Brock, Libr Mgr, Northrop Grumman IT-TASC, 4801 Stonecroft Blvd, Chantilly, VA, 20151-3822. Tel: 703-633-8300, Ext 4654. Fax: 703-449-7648. p. 2453

Temko, Wendy, Human Res Officer, Mount Prospect Public Library, Ten S Emerson St, Mount Prospect, IL, 60056. Tel: 847-253-5675. Fax: 847-253-0642. p. 677

Temoin, Sher, Asst Librn, Parkland Regional Library, Hwy 52 W, Yorkton, SK, S3N 3Z4, CANADA. Tel: 306-783-7022. Fax: 306-782-2844. p. 2931

Tempest, Jill, Assoc Dir, Cobb County Public Library System, 266 Roswell St, Marietta, GA, 30060-2004. Tel: 770-528-2330. Fax: 770-528-2349. p. 542

Tempest, Jill, Mgr, Cobb County Public Library System, Kennesaw Branch, 2250 Lewis St, Kennesaw, GA, 30144. Tel: 770-528-2529. Fax: 770-528-2593. p. 543

Temple, Bonnie, ILL, Asbury University, One Macklem Dr, Wilmore, KY, 40390-1198. Tel: 859-858-3511. Fax: 859-858-3921. p. 938

Temple, Christy, Ref & Info Serv, Daviess County Public Library, 2020 Frederica St, Owensboro, KY, 42301. Tel: 270-684-0211. Fax: 270-684-0218. p. 931

Temple, Kenton, Dir, Anna Porter Public Library, 207 Cherokee Orchard Rd, Gatlinburg, TN, 37738-3417. Tel: 865-436-5588. Fax: 865-436-5588. p. 2235

Temple, Pamela P, Tech Serv, Chattanooga State Community College, 4501 Amnicola Hwy, Chattanooga, TN, 37406-1097. Tel: 423-697-3291. Fax: 423-697-4409. p. 2227

Temple, Sharon, Ref & Prog Librn, Westbank Community Library District, 1309 Westbank Dr, Austin, TX, 78746. Tel: 512-327-3045. Fax: 512-327-3074. p. 2285

Temple, Wayne, Chief Dep, Illinois State Archives, Two W Margaret Cross Norton Bldg, Springfield, IL, 62756. Tel: 217-782-3492. Fax: 217-524-3930. p. 705

Templer, Peggy, Dir, Mendocino Art Center Library, 45200 Little Lake St, Mendocino, CA, 95460. Tel: 707-937-5818. Fax: 707-937-1764. p. 184

Templeton, Etheldra, Dir, Philadelphia College of Osteopathic Medicine, 4170 City Ave, Philadelphia, PA, 19131-1694. Tel: 215-871-6470. Fax: 215-871-6478. p. 2114

Templeton, Rijn, Head Librn, University of Iowa Libraries, Art, 235 Art Bldg W, 141 N Riverside Dr, Iowa City, IA, 52242. Tel: 319-335-3089. Fax: 319-335-5900. p. 823

Templeton, Virginia, Ref/Publ Librn, University of Miami, 1311 Miller Dr, Coral Gables, FL, 33146. Tel: 305-284-2251. Fax: 305-284-3554. p. 434

Templin, Barbara, In Charge, Leon Public Library, 113 S Main St, Leon, KS, 67074-9785. Tel: 316-742-3438. p. 879

Ten Brink, Charles, Dir, Michigan State University, 115 Law College Bldg, East Lansing, MI, 48824-1300. Tel: 517-432-6862. Fax: 517-432-6861. p. 1175

Ten Have, Elizabeth, Dir, Libr Acad Partnerships, Drexel University Libraries, Hagerty Library, 33rd & Market Sts, Philadelphia, PA, 19104-2875. Tel: 215-895-2751. Fax: 215-895-2070. p. 2105

Tencate, Sri P, Br Mgr, Hawaii State Public Library System, Molokai Public Library, 15 Ala Malama St, Kaunakakai, HI, 96748. Tel: 808-553-1765. Fax: 808-553-1766. p. 563

Tench, Frederick, Acq & Presv Serv Librn, Old Dominion University Libraries, 4427 Hampton Blvd, Norfolk, VA, 23529-0256. Tel: 757-683-4144. Fax: 757-683-5767. p. 2482

Tendulkar, Sulbha, Librn, Baker College of Flint, 1050 W Bristol Rd, Flint, MI, 48507-5508. Tel: 810-766-2016. Fax: 810-766-2013. p. 1179

Tenenholtz, David, Music Libr Assoc, University of Richmond, Parsons Music Library, Modlin Center for the Arts, Webb Tower, University of Richmond, VA, 23173. Tel: 804-289-8286. Fax: 804-287-6899. p. 2491

Teneycke, Peggy, Libr Mgr, Bon Accord Public Library, PO Box 749, Bon Accord, AB, T0A 0K0, CANADA. Tel: 780-921-2540. Fax: 780-921-2580. p. 2685

Tenglund, Ann M, Computer Serv & Info Literacy Instruction, Saint Bonaventure University, 3261 W State Rd, Saint Bonaventure, NY, 14778. Tel: 716-375-2378. Fax: 716-375-2389. p. 1737

Tenhage, Joyce, Br Mgr, Wellington County Library, Aboyne, 552 Wellington Rd 18, RR 1, Fergus, ON, N1M 2W3, CANADA. Tel: 519-846-0918, Ext 222. p. 2805

Tennant, Bruce, Evening/Weekend Supvr, University of Maryland Libraries, Michelle Smith Performing Arts Library, 2511 Clarice Smith Performing Arts Library, College Park, MD, 20742-1630. Tel: 301-405-9218. Fax: 301-314-7170. p. 1025

Tennant, Carolyn, Br Mgr, Manistee County Library, Kaleva Branch, 14618 Walta St, Kaleva, MI, 49645. Tel: 231-362-3178. Fax: 231-362-3180. p. 1205

Tennant, Elaine C, Dir, University of California, Berkeley, Bancroft Library, Berkeley, CA, 94720-6000. Tel: 510-642-3781. Fax: 510-642-7589. p. 127

Tennant, Shannon, Cat Librn, Elon University, 308 N O'Kelly Ave, Elon, NC, 27244-0187. Tel: 336-278-6585. Fax: 336-278-6637. p. 1791

Tennant, Susan Miller, Dir, Lititz Public Library, 651 Kissel Hill Rd, Lititz, PA, 17543. Tel: 717-626-2255. Fax: 717-627-4191. p. 2082

Tenney, David, IT & Fac Mgr, Wayne County Public Library, 220 W Liberty St, Wooster, OH, 44691-3593. Tel: 330-804-4684. Fax: 330-262-1352. p. 1950

Tenney, Joyce, Assoc Dir, University of Maryland, Baltimore County, 1000 Hilltop Circle, Baltimore, MD, 21250. Tel: 410-455-2356. Fax: 410-455-1138. p. 1018

Tenney, Robin, Dir, Lewis Egerton Smoot Memorial Library, 8562 Dahlgren Rd, King George, VA, 22485-3503. Tel: 540-775-7951. Fax: 540-775-5292. p. 2472

Tennis, Joseph, Asst Prof, University of Washington, Mary Gates Hall, Ste 370, Campus Box 352840, Seattle, WA, 98195-2840. Tel: 206-685-9937. Fax: 206-616-3152. p. 2976

Tennis, Laura, Coordr, Ch Serv, Page Public Library, 479 S Lake Powell Blvd, Page, AZ, 86040. Tel: 928-645-5802. Fax: 928-645-5804. p. 70

Tennyson, Jodee, Acq Librn, Tarleton State University Library, 201 Saint Felix, Stephenville, TX, 76401. Tel: 254-968-9475. Fax: 254-968-9467. p. 2389

Tenopir, Carol, Prof, University of Tennessee, Knoxville, 451 Communications Bldg, 1345 Circle Park Dr, Knoxville, TN, 37996-0341. Tel: 865-974-2148. Fax: 865-974-4967. p. 2974

Tenpas, Cid, Dean, Tech & Instrul Support Serv, Riverside Community College District, 16130 Lasselle St, Moreno Valley, CA, 92551-2045. Tel: 951-571-6344. Fax: 951-571-6191. p. 191

Tenpenny, Brent, Mgr, Access Serv, Vanderbilt University, Walker Management Library, Owen Graduate School of Management, 401 21st Ave S, Nashville, TN, 37203. Tel: 615-343-7324. Fax: 615-343-0061. p. 2261

Tensae, Andeberhan, Libr Commun Serv Mgr, Richmond Public Library, North Avenue, 2901 North Ave, Richmond, VA, 23222. Tel: 804-646-6675. Fax: 804-646-3768. p. 2490

Teo, Kam, Librn, Southeast Regional Library, Weyburn Branch, 45 Bison Ave NE, Weyburn, SK, S4H 0H9, CANADA. Tel: 306-842-4352, 306-848-3950. Fax: 306-842-1255. p. 2931

Teolis, Marilyn, Librn, Baptist Hospital, 2000 Church St, Nashville, TN, 37236. Tel: 615-284-5373. Fax: 615-284-5861. p. 2255

Tepavcevich, Leposava, Br Mgr, Newton County Public Library, Roselawn Library, 4421 East State Rd 10, Roselawn, IN, 46372. Tel: 219-345-2010. Fax: 219-345-2117. p. 760

Tepe, Chaba Hocine, Dir, Logan University/College of Chiropractic Library, 1851 Schoettler Rd, Chesterfield, MO, 63006. Tel: 636-227-2100. Fax: 636-207-2448. p. 1323

Tepe, Nick, Head, Circ, Columbus Metropolitan Library, 96 S Grant Ave, Columbus, OH, 43215-4781. Tel: 614-645-2275. Fax: 614-849-1157. p. 1884

Teran, Hector, Asst Librn, Kuskokwim Consortium Library, 420 State Hwy, Bethel, AK, 99559. Tel: 907-543-4516. Fax: 907-543-4503. p. 46

Terbeek, Wendy L, Dir, Hammond Library of Crown Point NY, 2732 Main St, Crown Point, NY, 12928. Tel: 518-597-3616. Fax: 518-597-3166. p. 1612

Teresa, Sayers, Br Mgr, Boone County Public Library, Lents Branch, 3215 Cougar Path, Hebron, KY, 41048-9642. Fax: 859-586-8215. p. 909

Teresi, Lucia, Coll Develop Librn, Ref Librn, James Prendergast Library Association, 509 Cherry St, Jamestown, NY, 14701. Tel: 716-484-7135. Fax: 716-487-1148. p. 1647

Terhorst, Jodi, Libr Tech, Alex Robb Resource Center, 1600 Fourth Ave, Regina, SK, S4R 8C8, CANADA. Tel: 306-523-3055. Fax: 306-523-3031. p. 2923

Terhorst, John, Syst, Weil, Gotshal & Manges Library, 767 Fifth Ave, New York, NY, 10153. Tel: 212-310-8626. Fax: 212-310-8007. p. 1702

Terhune, Dorothy, Ref Serv, Grand Rapids Community College, 140 Ransom NE Ave, Grand Rapids, MI, 49503. Tel: 616-234-3849. Fax: 616-234-3878. p. 1185

Terhune, Joyce, Dir, Webster County Historical Museum Library, 721 W Fourth Ave, Red Cloud, NE, 68970. Tel: 402-746-2444. p. 1418

Terhune, Stanford, Ref Librn, Malone University, 2600 Cleveland Ave NW, Canton, OH, 44709-3897. Tel: 330-471-8318. Fax: 330-454-6977. p. 1863

Terifay, Lora, Head, Ch, Southampton Free Library, 947 Street Rd, Southampton, PA, 18966. Tel: 215-322-1415. Fax: 215-396-9375. p. 2142

Terkelsen, Penelope, Youth Serv Dir, Centerville Public Library Association, Inc, 585 Main St, Centerville, MA, 02632. Tel: 508-790-6220. Fax: 508-790-6218. p. 1079

Terlaga, Amy, Asst Dir, Bibliomation, 32 Crest Rd, Middlebury, CT, 06762. Tel: 203-577-4070, Ext 101. Fax: 203-577-4077. p. 2939

Terlecky, John, Librn, Saint Basil College Library, 39 Clovelly Rd, Stamford, CT, 06902-3004. Tel: 203-327-7899. Fax: 203-967-9948. p. 369

Terlinsky, Katherine, Dir, Altoona Hospital, 620 Howard Ave, Altoona, PA, 16601-4899. Tel: 814-946-2318. Fax: 814-889-3176. p. 2028

Termine, Jack, Archivist, State University of New York Downstate Medical Center, 395 Lenox Rd, Brooklyn, NY, 11203. Tel: 718-270-7400. Fax: 718-270-7413, 718-270-7468. p. 1595

Terminella, Sue E, Med Librn, J Stephen Lindsey Medical Library, 1602 Skipwith Rd, Richmond, VA, 23229-5298. Tel: 804-289-4728. Fax: 804-289-4960. p. 2489

Ternak, Armand, Libr Dir, Temple Terrace Public Library, 202 Bullard Pkwy, Temple Terrace, FL, 33617-5512. Tel: 813-506-6772. p. 500

Ternes, Jane, Libr Spec, Walla Walla Public Library, 238 E Alder, Walla Walla, WA, 99362. Tel: 509-524-4441. Fax: 509-524-7950. p. 2547

Ternes, Mary, Librn, National School Boards Association Library, 1680 Duke St, Alexandria, VA, 22314-3493. Tel: 703-838-6731. Fax: 703-548-5516. p. 2446

Terpening, Nancy, Head, Tech Serv, Galesburg Public Library, 40 E Simmons St, Galesburg, IL, 61401-4591. Tel: 309-343-6118. Fax: 309-343-4877. p. 648

Terpstra, Anne, Librn, McKay Library, 105 S Webster St, Augusta, MI, 49012-9601. Tel: 616-731-4000. Fax: 616-731-5323. p. 1154

Terrance, McArthur, Librn, Fresno County Public Library, Sanger Branch, 1812 Seventh St, Sanger, CA, 93657-2805. Tel: 559-875-2435. p. 152

Terranova, Marie, Ch, Malverne Public Library, 61 Saint Thomas Pl, Malverne, NY, 11565. Tel: 516-599-0750. Fax: 516-599-3320. p. 1657

Terrazas, Sara, Dir, Kinney County Public Library, 510 S Ellen, Brackettville, TX, 78832. Tel: 830-563-2884. Fax: 830-563-2312. p. 2291

Terrazas, Selena, Br Mgr, Los Angeles Public Library System, West Valley Regional, 19036 Vanowen St, Receda, CA, 91335. Tel: 818-345-9806. Fax: 818-345-4288. p. 174

Terrell, Amy, Librn, United States Marine Corps, MCAGCC, Box 788150, Twentynine Palms, CA, 92278-8150. Tel: 760-830-6875. Fax: 760-830-4497. p. 277

Terrell, Annetta, Ch, Muncie Public Library, John F Kennedy Branch, 1700 W McGalliard Rd, Muncie, IN, 47304. Tel: 765-741-7333. Fax: 765-747-8213. p. 767

Terrell, Carrie M, Dir, Plains Public Library District, 108 W Railroad, Plains, MT, 59859. Tel: 406-826-3101. Fax: 406-826-3101. p. 1387

Terrell, Danielle, Govt Doc Librn, Alcorn State University, 1000 ASU Dr, Alcorn State, MS, 39096-7500. Tel: 601-877-6358. Fax: 601-877-3885. p. 1293

Terrell, Walter D, Jr, Exec Dir, Weinberg Nature Center Library, 455 Mamaroneck Rd, Scarsdale, NY, 10583. Tel: 914-722-1289. Fax: 914-723-4784. p. 1739

Terrill, Nancy J, Librn, Ridgemont Public Library, 124 E Taylor St, Mount Victory, OH, 43340-8811. Tel: 937-354-4445. Fax: 937-354-4445. p. 1919

Terrio, Robert, Ser, Rider University, Katharine Houk Talbott Library, Westminster Choir College, 101 Walnut Lane, Princeton, NJ, 08540-3899. Tel: 609-921-7100, Ext 8296. Fax: 609-497-0243. p. 1494

Territo, Stephen D, Circ Mgr, Extn Serv, Vernon Area Public Library District, 300 Olde Half Day Rd, Lincolnshire, IL, 60069-2901. Tel: 847-634-3650. Fax: 847-634-8449. p. 666

Terrones, Vicky, Circ Mgr, Plainfield Public Library, 800 Park Ave, Plainfield, NJ, 07060-2594. Tel: 908-757-1111. Fax: 908-754-0063. p. 1521

Terry, Aileen, Librn, Wharton County Library, El Campo Branch, 200 W Church St, El Campo, TX, 77437-3316. Tel: 979-543-2362. p. 2400

Terry, Allison, Librn, Hawley Troxell Ennis & Hawley, 877 Main St, Ste 1000, Boise, ID, 83702-1617. Tel: 208-344-6000. Fax: 208-342-3829. p. 571

Terry, Beverly, Outreach Serv Librn, Logan County Public Library, 201 W Sixth St, Russellville, KY, 42276. Tel: 270-726-6129. Fax: 270-726-6127. p. 934

Terry, Carol S, Dir, Libr Serv, Rhode Island School of Design Library, 15 Westminster St, Providence, RI, 02903. Tel: 401-709-5900. Fax: 401-709-5932. p. 2174

Terry, Cindy, ILL & Distance Libr Serv Spec, Maryland State Law Library, Courts of Appeal Bldg, 361 Rowe Blvd, Annapolis, MD, 21401-1697. Tel: 410-260-1430. Fax: 410-260-1572, 410-974-2063. p. 1010

Terry, Cindy, Tech Serv, Museum of Western Art Library, 1550 Bandera Hwy, Kerrville, TX, 78028-9547. Tel: 830-896-2553. Fax: 830-257-5206. p. 2349

Thalacker, Reagen A, Librn, United States Geological Survey, 8711 37th St SE, Jamestown, ND, 58401-9736. Tel: 701-253-5566. Fax: 701-253-5553. p. 1845

Thaler, Susan, Adminr, Yonkers Public Library, Riverfront, One Larkin Ctr, Yonkers, NY, 10701. Tel: 914-337-1500. Fax: 914-376-3004. p. 1772

Thalhimer, Sheila, Dir, Johns Hopkins University School of Advanced International Studies, 1740 Massachusetts Ave NW, Washington, DC, 20036. Tel: 202-663-5900. Fax: 202-663-5916. p. 405

Thalman, Jennifer, ILL, Virginia Beach Public Library Department, Interlibrary Loan Division, 4100 Virginia Beach Blvd, Virginia Beach, VA, 23452. Tel: 757-385-0167. p. 2500

Thamm, Mark, Media Spec, Franklin Pierce University Library, 40 University Dr, Rindge, NH, 03461-3114. Tel: 603-899-4141. Fax: 603-899-4375. p. 1463

Thampi-Lukose, Usha, Head Librn, Cedar Grove Free Public Library, One Municipal Plaza, Cedar Grove, NJ, 07009. Tel: 973-239-1447. Fax: 973-239-1275. p. 1478

Thams, Heather, Librn, Yellowstone National Park, Yellowstone Heritage & Research Ctr, 200 Old Yellowstone Trail, Gardiner, MT, 59030. Tel: 307-344-2264. Fax: 406-848-9958. p. 1379

Thangarajah, Jeya, Ref Serv, Huntington Memorial Hospital, 100 W California Blvd, Pasadena, CA, 91105-3010. Tel: 626-397-5161. Fax: 626-397-2908. p. 206

Thanh, Quang, Syst Coordr, De Anza College, 21250 Stevens Creek Blvd, Cupertino, CA, 95014-5793. Tel: 408-864-8494. Fax: 408-864-8603. p. 138

Tharan, Lynne E, Libr Dir, Uniontown Public Library, 24 Jefferson St, Uniontown, PA, 15401-3602. Tel: 724-437-1165. Fax: 724-439-5689. p. 2147

Tharp, Barb, Coordr, Genesis Medical Center, Illini Campus, 855 Illini Dr, Ste 102, Silvis, IL, 61282. Tel: 309-792-4360. Fax: 309-792-4362. p. 702

Tharp, Connie, Info Serv Assoc, Trine University, 720 Park Ave, Angola, IN, 46703. Tel: 260-665-4163. Fax: 260-665-4283. p. 724

Tharp, Lisa, Br Mgr, Phoenix Public Library, Century Library, 1750 E Highland Ave, Phoenix, AZ, 85016-4619. Tel: 602-262-4636. p. 76

Tharrington, Tom, Cat Librn, New College of Florida University of South Florida Sarasota Manatee, 5800 Bay Shore Rd, Sarasota, FL, 34243-2109. Tel: 941-487-4416. Fax: 941-487-4307. p. 490

Thatcher, Shirley, Acq, Samuel Roberts Noble Foundation, Inc, 2510 Sam Noble Pkwy, Ardmore, OK, 73401. Tel: 580-224-6262. Fax: 580-224-6265. p. 1957

Thatcher, Wendy, ILL, Ref Librn, Topsfield Town Library, One S Common St, Topsfield, MA, 01983-1496. Tel: 978-887-1528. Fax: 978-887-0185. p. 1131

Thayer, Cindy, Asst Librn, Lyons Township District Library, 309 Bridge St, Lyons, MI, 48851. Tel: 989-855-3414. Fax: 989-855-2069. p. 1204

Thayer, Cola, Circ, Chemung County Library District, 101 E Church St, Elmira, NY, 14901-2799. Tel: 607-733-9173. Fax: 607-733-9176. p. 1619

Thayer, J Peter, Ref & Access Serv Librn, Marietta College, 220 Fifth St, Marietta, OH, 45750. Tel: 740-376-4361. Fax: 740-376-4843. p. 1913

Thayer, Marika, Br Librn, Lincoln County Library, LaBarge Branch, 262 Main St, LaBarge, WY, 83123. Tel: 307-386-2571. Fax: 307-386-2569. p. 2656

Thayer, Marilyn, Youth Serv, Middleborough Public Library, 102 N Main St, Middleborough, MA, 02346. Tel: 508-946-2470. Fax: 508-946-2473. p. 1105

Thayer, Martha, Librn, NIH, National Institute of Allergy & Infectious Diseases, 903 S Fourth St, Hamilton, MT, 59840-2932. Tel: 406-363-9212. Fax: 406-363-9336. p. 1381

Thayer-Coleman, Gina, Circ Mgr, Johnson City Public Library, 100 W Millard St, Johnson City, TN, 37604. Tel: 423-434-4465. Fax: 423-434-4469. p. 2240

Theeke, Tina M, Dir, Farmington Community Library, 32737 W 12 Mile Rd, Farmington Hills, MI, 48334-3302. Tel: 248-848-4301. Fax: 248-553-3228. p. 1177

Theilade, Frances, Asst Librn, Circ, Ref, Saint Peter's Seminary, 1040 Waterloo St N, London, ON, N6A 3Y1, CANADA. Tel: 519-432-1824. Fax: 519-439-5172. p. 2818

Theinert, Leo, Ref Librn, Borough of Manhattan Community College Library, 199 Chambers St, New York, NY, 10007. Tel: 212-220-1449. Fax: 212-748-7466. p. 1671

Theis, Ann, Coll Develop Coordr, Henrico County Public Library, 1001 N Laburnum Ave, Henrico, VA, 23223-2705. Tel: 804-290-9000. Fax: 804-222-5566. p. 2471

Theising, Joan, Librn, Germantown Public Library District, 403 Munster St, Germantown, IL, 62245. Tel: 618-523-4820. Fax: 618-523-4599. p. 649

Theison, Rose, Asst Librn, Danvers Township Library, 117 E Exchange St, Danvers, IL, 61732-9347. Tel: 309-963-4269. Fax: 309-963-4269. p. 632

Theiss, Danielle, Head, Pub Serv, Rockhurst University, 1100 Rockhurst Rd, Kansas City, MO, 64110-2561. Tel: 816-501-4189. Fax: 816-501-4666. p. 1340

Theiss, Edlyn, Librn, United Church of Christ, 415 S Main St, North Canton, OH, 44720. Tel: 330-499-8191. Fax: 330-499-8194. p. 1923

Theiss, Michelle, Mgr, Holzer Medical Center, 100 Jackson Pike, Gallipolis, OH, 45631. Tel: 740-446-5313. Fax: 740-446-5281. p. 1901

Theissen, Jane, Ref & Learning Commons Librn, Fontbonne University, 6800 Wydown Blvd, Saint Louis, MO, 63105. Tel: 314-889-4570. Fax: 314-719-8040. p. 1354

Theivagt, Pat, Head Librn, Greenfield Public Library, 515 Chestnut, Greenfield, IL, 62044-1305. Tel: 217-368-2613. Fax: 217-368-2613. p. 652

Thelen, Nancy, Teen Serv, Allegan District Library, 331 Hubbard St, Allegan, MI, 49010. Tel: 269-673-4625. Fax: 269-673-8661. p. 1148

Theobald, Maureen, Exec Dir, Black Gold Cooperative Library System, 3437 Empresa Dr, Ste C, San Luis Obispo, CA, 93401. Tel: 805-543-1093. p. 253

Theobald, Maureen, Admin Dir, Gold Coast Library Network, 3437 Empresa Dr, Ste C, San Luis Obispo, CA, 93401-7355. Tel: 805-543-6082. Fax: 805-543-9487. p. 2938

Theodore-McIntosh, Roslyn, Dir, Gowling Lafleur Henderson LLP, One First Canadian Pl, 100 King St W, Ste 1600, Toronto, ON, M5X 1G5, CANADA. Tel: 416-862-5735. Fax: 416-862-7661. p. 2854

Theodore-Shusta, Eileen, Human Res, Ohio University Libraries, 30 Park Pl, Athens, OH, 45701-2978. Tel: 740-593-2989. Fax: 740-593-2708. p. 1856

Theriault, Bonnie, Asst Dir, ILL Librn, Aldrich Free Public Library, 299 Main St, Moosup, CT, 06354. Tel: 860-564-8760. Fax: 860-564-8491. p. 353

Thériault, Geneviève, Librn Dir, York Library Region, Mediatheque Pere Louis Lamontagne, Carrefour-Beausoleil, 300 Chemin Beaverbrook, Miramichi, NB, E1V 1A1, CANADA. Tel: 506-627-4084. Fax: 506-627-4592. p. 2764

Theriault, Ken, Dir, Madawaska Public Library, 393 Main St, Madawaska, ME, 04756-1126. Tel: 207-728-3606. p. 991

Theriault, Lise, Dir, Bibliotheque Municipale de Sainte-Therese, 150 Boul du Seminaire, Sainte Therese, QC, J7E 1Z2, CANADA. Tel: 450-434-1442. Fax: 450-434-6070. p. 2909

Theriot, Betsy, Br Mgr, Assumption Parish Library, Bayou L'ourse, 4174 Hwy 662, Morgan City, LA, 70380. Tel: 985-631-3200. Fax: 985-631-3200. p. 958

Theriot, Clifton, Head, Archives, Nicholls State University, 906 E First St, Thibodaux, LA, 70310. Tel: 985-448-4621. Fax: 985-448-4925. p. 971

Thero, Stephanie, Client Serv Mgr, Yellowhead Regional Library, 433 King St, Spruce Grove, AB, T7X 2Y1, CANADA. Tel: 780-962-2003, Ext 224. Fax: 780-962-2770. p. 2717

Theroux, Gisele, Librn, Bibliotheque Pere Champagne, 44 Rue Rogers, Notre Dame de Lourdes, MB, R0G 1M0, CANADA. Tel: 204-248-2386. p. 2750

Theroux, Shari, Librn, Northern State University, 1200 S Jay St, Aberdeen, SD, 57401-7198. Tel: 605-626-2645. Fax: 605-626-2473. p. 2209

Therrien, Tracey, Dir, Smithers Public Library, 3817 Alfred Ave, Box 55, Smithers, BC, V0J 2N0, CANADA. Tel: 250-847-3043. Fax: 250-847-1533. p. 2737

Theunissen, Yolanda, Curator, University of Southern Maine, 314 Forest Ave, Portland, ME, 04104. Tel: 207-780-4616. Fax: 207-780-4042. p. 998

Theus, Pamela, Asst Dir, Res Mgt, William Paterson University of New Jersey, 300 Pompton Rd, Wayne, NJ, 07470. Tel: 973-720-2160. Fax: 973-720-3171. p. 1540

Thevenote, Theresa, Dir, Avoyelles Parish Library, 104 N Washington St, Marksville, LA, 71351-2496. Tel: 318-253-7559. Fax: 318-253-6361. p. 956

Thew, Candia, Pub Serv, Texas Tech University Health Sciences Center, 3601 Fourth St, Lubbock, TX, 79430-7781. Tel: 806-743-2200. Fax: 806-743-2218. p. 2357

Thewis, Jennifer, Dir, Legion Memorial Library, 102 E Bennett Ave, Mellen, WI, 54546. Tel: 715-274-8331. Fax: 715-274-3707. p. 2614

Thexton, Helen, Br Mgr, Halifax Public Libraries, Alderney Gate, 60 Alderney Dr, Dartmouth, NS, B3H 3C3, CANADA. Tel: 902-490-5840. Fax: 902-490-5842. p. 2779

Theyer, Hillary, City Librn, Torrance Public Library, 3301 Torrance Blvd, Torrance, CA, 90503. Tel: 310-618-5950. Fax: 310-618-5952. p. 276

Thibaudeau, Louise, Coll Develop, Dir, Ecole de Technologie Superieure (Service de la bibliotheque), 1100 rue Notre-Dame Ouest, Montreal, QC, H3C 1K3, CANADA. Tel: 514-396-8946. Fax: 514-396-8633. p. 2895

Thibault, Beth, Educ Adminr, Valley Regional Hospital, 243 Elm St, Claremont, NH, 03743. Tel: 603-542-1839, 603-542-7771. Fax: 603-542-1814. p. 1442

Thibault, Denis, AV, Media Spec, Cegep de Sainte-Foy Bibliotheque, 2410 Chemin Sainte-Foy, Sainte-Foy, QC, G1V 1T3, CANADA. Tel: 418-659-6600, Ext 3714. Fax: 418-659-4563. p. 2910

Thibault, Joan, Dir, Cushing Public Library, 39 Cross Rd, Cushing, ME, 04563. Tel: 207-354-8860. p. 983

Thibault, Marguerite, In Charge, Western Counties Regional Library, Weymouth Branch, No 4609, Hwy One, Weymouth, NS, B0W 3T0, CANADA. Tel: 902-837-4596. p. 2787

Thibault, Steven, Librn, Field Memorial Library, One Elm St, Conway, MA, 01341. Tel: 413-369-4646. p. 1083

Thibault, Suzanne, Chef de Section, Bibliothèques de Montrèal, Saint-Michel, 7601, rue François-Perrault, Montreal, QC, H2A 3L6, CANADA. Tel: 514-872-3910. Fax: 514-872-0528. p. 2891

Thibault, Sylvie, Dir Gen, Reseau BIBLIO de l'Outaouais, 2295 Saint-Louis St, Gatineau, QC, J8T 5L8, CANADA. Tel: 819-561-6008. Fax: 819-561-6767. p. 2960

Thibault, Theresa, Div Chief, United States National Park Service, Park Headquarters, Second Ave & Broadway, Skagway, AK, 99840. Tel: 907-983-9236. Fax: 907-983-9249. p. 53

Thibeault, Alan, Chief Librn, Boston Herald, One Herald Sq, Boston, MA, 02118. Tel: 617-619-6680. Fax: 617-619-6450. p. 1056

Thibeault, Alan, Dir, Winthrop Public Library & Museum, Two Metcalf Sq, Winthrop, MA, 02152-3157. Tel: 617-846-1703. Fax: 617-846-7083. p. 1142

Thibodeau, Clay, Archivist, George Brown College of Applied Arts & Technology Archives, 500 Macpherson Ave, Rm F-103, Toronto, ON, M5R 1M3, CANADA. Tel: 416-415-5000, Ext 4771. Fax: 416-415-4772. p. 2853

Thibodeau, David, Coordr, Acq, Coordr, Ser, Georgia College & State University, 320 N Wayne St, Milledgeville, GA, 31061-3397. Tel: 478-445-4047. Fax: 478-445-6847. p. 544

Thibodeau, Linda, Dir, Libr, Archives & Mus, Alaska State Library, 333 Willoughby Ave, State Office Bldg, 8th Flr, Juneau, AK, 99801. Tel: 907-465-2911. Fax: 907-465-2151. p. 49

Thibodeau, Michelle, Librn, Bibliotheque Municipale de Saint-Fabien de Panet, 199, Saint Bilodeau, Saint-Fabian de Panet, QC, G0R 2J0, CANADA. Tel: 418-249-4471. Fax: 418-249-2507. p. 2910

Thibodeau, Patricia, Assoc Dean, Libr Serv, Duke University Libraries, Medical Center Library, DUMC Box 3702, Ten Bryan-Searle Dr, Durham, NC, 27710-0001. Tel: 919-660-1148. Fax: 919-681-7599. p. 1788

Thibodeau, Sarah, Ref, Marian University, 45 S National Ave, Fond du Lac, WI, 54935. Tel: 920-923-8096. Fax: 920-923-7154. p. 2592

Thibodeau, Sean, Commun Planning Librn, Pollard Memorial Library, 401 Merrimack St, Lowell, MA, 01852. Tel: 978-970-4120. Fax: 978-970-4117. p. 1100

Thibodeau, Sean C, Acq & Cat, Nutter McClennen & Fish LLP, World Trade Center W, 155 Seaport Blvd, Boston, MA, 02210. Tel: 617-439-2000. Fax: 617-310-9000. p. 1066

Thibodeaux, Carolyn, Ch, Port Arthur Public Library, 4615 Ninth Ave, Port Arthur, TX, 77642. Tel: 409-985-8838, Ext 2237. Fax: 409-985-5969. p. 2371

Thibodeaux, Margaret, Regional Br Mgr, Lafayette Public Library, North Regional Branch, 5101 N University Ave, Carencro, LA, 70520-3004. Tel: 337-896-6323. p. 953

Thibodeaux, Marie, Asst Br Mgr, Vermilion Parish Library, Kaplan Branch, 815 N Cushing Ave, Kaplan, LA, 70548-2614. Tel: 337-643-7209. Fax: 337-643-7250. p. 939

Thibodeaux, Peggy, Regional Br Mgr, Lafayette Public Library, 301 W Congress, Lafayette, LA, 70501-6866. Tel: 337-896-6323. Fax: 337-261-5782. p. 952

Thibodeaux, Teresa, Coll Develop, Saint Martin Parish Library, 201 Porter St, Saint Martinville, LA, 70582. Tel: 337-394-2207, Ext 23. Fax: 337-394-2248. p. 967

Thiebaud, James, Media Spec, Xavier University of Louisiana, One Drexel Dr, New Orleans, LA, 70125-1098. Tel: 504-520-6785. Fax: 504-520-7940. p. 964

Thiede, Beth, Financial Dir, Michigan City Public Library, 100 E Fourth St, Michigan City, IN, 46360-3393. Tel: 219-873-3047. Fax: 219-873-3068. p. 764

Thiede, Tiffany, Ch, Verona Public Library, 500 Silent St, Verona, WI, 53593. Tel: 608-845-7180. Fax: 608-845-8917. p. 2643

Thiele, Jennifer, Dir, Marinette County Library System, 1700 Hall Ave, Marinette, WI, 54143-1799. Tel: 715-732-7572. Fax: 715-732-7575. p. 2612

Thiele, Ronald L, Asst Dean, Advan, Syracuse University Library, 222 Waverly Ave, Syracuse, NY, 13244-2010. Tel: 315-443-2573. p. 1754

Thieling, Kaileen, Dir, Central Mississippi Regional Library System, 104 Office Park Dr, Brandon, MS, 39042-2404. Tel: 601-825-0100. Fax: 601-825-0199. p. 1294

Thiem, Donna, Info Tech, Columbus Public Library, 2504 14th St, Columbus, NE, 68601-4988. Tel: 402-564-7116. Fax: 402-563-3378. p. 1396

Thieman, Lindsey, Curator, International Museum of Surgical Science Library, 1524 N Lake Shore Dr, Chicago, IL, 60610. Tel: 312-642-6502. Fax: 312-642-9516. p. 616

Thierichen, Jan, Dir, Las Animas - Bent County Public Library, 306 Fifth St, Las Animas, CO, 81054. Tel: 719-456-0111. Fax: 719-456-0112. p. 316

Thiesen, Barbara, Cat, Bethel College Library, Mennonite Library & Archives, 300 E 27th St, North Newton, KS, 67117-0531. Tel: 316-284-5304. Fax: 316-284-5843. p. 885

Thiesen, Barbara, Co-Dir, Libr & Dir Tech Serv, Bethel College Library, 300 E 27th St, North Newton, KS, 67117-0531. Tel: 316-284-5361. Fax: 316-284-5843. p. 885

Thiesen, John, Archivist, Dir, Bethel College Library, Mennonite Library & Archives, 300 E 27th St, North Newton, KS, 67117-0531. Tel: 316-284-5304. Fax: 316-284-5843. p. 885

Thiessen, Charlotte, Librn, Nipawin Bible College Library, Hwy 35 S, Nipawin, SK, S0E 1E0, CANADA. Tel: 306-862-5095. Fax: 306-862-3651. p. 2919

Thiessen, David, Libr Mgr, Fraser Valley Regional Library, Aldergrove Branch, 26770 - 29th Ave, Aldergrove, BC, V4W 3B8, CANADA. Tel: 604-856-6415. Fax: 604-856-6816. p. 2723

Thiessen, David, Libr Mgr, Fraser Valley Regional Library, Brookswood Library, 20045 - 40th Ave, Langley, BC, V3A 2W2, CANADA. Tel: 604-534-7055. Fax: 604-532-7432. p. 2723

Thiessen, David, Libr Mgr, Fraser Valley Regional Library, Fort Langley Library, Box 312, 9167 Glover Rd, Fort Langley, BC, V1M 2R6, CANADA. Tel: 604-888-0722. Fax: 604-882-0729. p. 2723

Thiessen, David, Libr Mgr, Fraser Valley Regional Library, Muriel Arnason Library (Willowbrook), Township of Langley Civic Centre, 130 - 20338 65 Ave, Langley, BC, V2Y 2X3, CANADA. Tel: 604-532-3590. Fax: 604-534-3141. p. 2723

Thiessen, David, Libr Mgr, Fraser Valley Regional Library, Murrayville Library, Unit 100 - 22071 48 Ave, Langley, BC, V3A 3N1, CANADA. Tel: 604-533-0339. Fax: 604-514-7260. p. 2724

Thiessen, David, Libr Mgr, Fraser Valley Regional Library, Walnut Grove Library, Walnut Grove Community Centre, 8889 Walnut Grove Dr, Langley, BC, V1M 2N7, CANADA. Tel: 604-882-0410. Fax: 604-882-3754. p. 2724

Thiessen, David, Libr Mgr, Fraser Valley Regional Library, White Rock Library, 15342 Buena Vista Ave, White Rock, BC, V4B 1Y6, CANADA. Tel: 604-541-2201. Fax: 604-541-2209. p. 2724

Thiessen, Jannay, Br Pub Serv Mgr, Saskatoon Public Library, 311-23rd St E, Saskatoon, SK, S7K 0J6, CANADA. Tel: 306-975-8131. Fax: 306-975-7542. p. 2926

Thiessen, Jean, Dir, Whitewater Memorial Library, 118 E Topeka, Whitewater, KS, 67154. Tel: 316-799-2471. Fax: 316-799-1099. p. 900

Thiessen, Jonquil, Mgr, Acme Municipal Library, 610 Walsh Ave, Acme, AB, T0M 0A0, CANADA. Tel: 403-546-3845. Fax: 403-546-2248. p. 2683

Thiessen, Richard, Dir, Libr Serv, Columbia Bible College Library, 2940 Clearbrook Rd, Abbotsford, BC, V2T 2Z8, CANADA. Tel: 604-853-3358. Fax: 604-853-3063. p. 2723

Thiessen, Sonya, Asst Librn, Belle Plaine Community Library, 904 12th St, Belle Plaine, IA, 52208-1711. Tel: 319-444-2902. Fax: 319-444-2902. p. 796

Thiessen, Stacia S, Librn, Folsom Lake College Library, Ten College Pkwy, Folsom, CA, 95630. Tel: 916-608-6557. Fax: 916-608-6533. p. 148

Thiffeault, Julie, Librn, Prince Edward Island Public Library Service, Bibliotheque J-Henri-Blanchard, Five Maris Stella, Summerside, PE, C1N 3Y5, CANADA. Tel: 902-432-2748. Fax: 902-888-1686. p. 2876

Thigpen, Sara, Extn Serv, Aiken-Bamberg-Barnwell-Edgefield Regional Library System, 314 Chesterfield St SW, Aiken, SC, 29801-7171. Tel: 803-642-7575. Fax: 803-642-7597. p. 2179

Thiim, Teresa, YA Serv, Fort Bend County Libraries, 1001 Golfview Dr, Richmond, TX, 77469-5199. Tel: 281-341-2613. Fax: 281-341-2688. p. 2375

Thill, Mary, Humanities Librn, Northeastern Illinois University, 5500 N Saint Louis Ave, Chicago, IL, 60625-4699. Tel: 773-442-4405. Fax: 773-442-4531. p. 621

Thilmany, Beth, Dir, Camanche Public Library, 102 12th Ave, Camanche, IA, 52730. Tel: 563-259-1106. Fax: 563-259-1106. p. 798

Thimons, Dana, Libr Dir, Southwest Florida College, 1685 Medical Lane, Fort Myers, FL, 33907. Tel: 239-939-4766. Fax: 239-936-4040. p. 446

Thimsen, Janice, Librn, Mount Olive Public Library, 100 N Plum St, Mount Olive, IL, 62069-1755. Tel: 217-999-7311. Fax: 217-999-7360. p. 677

Thirlwall, David, Assoc Univ Librn, Personnel & Communications, Concordia University Libraries, 1400 de Maisonneuve Blvd W, LB 209, Montreal, QC, H3G 1M8, CANADA. Tel: 514-848-2424, Ext 7693. Fax: 514-848-2882. p. 2894

Thirsk, Patricia, ILL, Nassau County Public Library System, 25 N Fourth St, Fernandina Beach, FL, 32034-4123. Tel: 904-548-4465. Fax: 904-548-4426. p. 439

Thirsk, Patti, Circ, Nassau County Public Library System, Yulee Branch, 76346 William Burgess Blvd, Yulee, FL, 32097. Tel: 904-548-4467. Fax: 904-548-4426. p. 440

Thirunavukarasu, Meera, Ser & Acq Tech, University of Toronto Libraries, Faculty of Information Inforum, 140 Saint George St, 4th Flr, Toronto, ON, M5S 3G6, CANADA. Tel: 416-978-5542. Fax: 416-978-5769. p. 2866

Thiry, Christopher J J, Maps Librn, Colorado School of Mines, 1400 Illinois St, Golden, CO, 80401-1887. Tel: 303-273-3697. Fax: 303-273-3199. p. 309

Thiss, Ramona, Dir, Jefferson College of Health Sciences, 920 S Jefferson St, Roanoke, VA, 24016. Tel: 540-985-9828. Fax: 540-224-4404. p. 2494

Thisse, Karen, Br Mgr, Blue Ridge Regional Library, Bassett Branch, 3969 Fairystone Park Hwy, Bassett, VA, 24055. Tel: 276-629-2426. Fax: 276-629-3808. p. 2478

Thissell, Cara, Circ, Burlington Public Library, 22 Sears St, Burlington, MA, 01803. Tel: 781-270-1690. Fax: 781-229-0406. p. 1072

Thistle, Dawn, Librn, Vassalboro Public Library, 930 Bog Rd, East Vassalboro, ME, 04935. Tel: 207-923-3233. p. 984

Thistle, Dawn, Spec Coll Librn, Gardiner Public Library, 152 Water St, Gardiner, ME, 04345. Tel: 207-582-3312. Fax: 207-582-6104. p. 986

Thistlethwaite, Polly, Actg Chief Librn, City University of New York, 365 Fifth Ave, New York, NY, 10016-4309. Tel: 212-817-7040. Fax: 212-817-2982. p. 1673

Thivierge, Lynda, Chief Librn, Snc-Lavalin, Inc Library, 455 boul Rene-Levesque ouest, Montreal, QC, H2Z 1Z3, CANADA. Tel: 514-393-1000, Ext 2888. Fax: 514-866-6709. p. 2901

Thode, Ernie, Br Mgr, Washington County Public Library, Local History & Genealogy, 418 Washington St, Marietta, OH, 45750. Tel: 740-376-2172. Fax: 740-376-2175. p. 1914

Thogode, Sarah, Govt Doc, Saint Petersburg Public Library, 3745 Ninth Ave N, Saint Petersburg, FL, 33713. Tel: 727-893-7724. Fax: 727-892-5432. p. 488

Thom, Julie, Libr Mgr, Mary Hower Medical Library, One Perkins Sq, Akron, OH, 44308-1062. Tel: 330-543-8250. p. 1853

Thoma, Jane, Br Mgr, Toledo-Lucas County Public Library, South, 1736 Broadway, Toledo, OH, 43609. Tel: 419-259-5395. Fax: 419-243-4217. p. 1940

Thoman, Sheila, Librn, Saint Mary's School for the Deaf, 2253 Main St, Buffalo, NY, 14214. Tel: 716-834-7200, Ext 152. Fax: 716-837-2080. p. 1598

Thomas, Alice, Asst Dir, Pub Serv, Southern Pines Public Library, 170 W Connecticut Ave, Southern Pines, NC, 28387-4819. Tel: 910-692-8235. Fax: 910-695-1037. p. 1824

Thomas, Alice C, Dir, Vienna Public Library, 2300 River Rd, Vienna, WV, 26105. Tel: 304-295-7771. Fax: 304-295-7776. p. 2573

Thomas, Amanda, Asst Librn, Center for Advanced Study in the Behavioral Sciences Library, 75 Alta Rd, Stanford, CA, 94305. Tel: 650-736-0100. p. 270

Thomas, Amie, Pub Serv, Brownsburg Public Library, 450 S Jefferson St, Brownsburg, IN, 46112-1310. Tel: 317-852-3167, Ext 108. Fax: 317-852-7734. p. 730

Thomas, Anna, Mgr, Vols Serv, Lancaster Public Library, 125 N Duke St, Lancaster, PA, 17602-2883. Tel: 717-394-2651, Ext 273. Fax: 717-394-3083. p. 2077

Thomas, Anne, Librn, Oswego County Supreme Court, 25 E Oneida St, Oswego, NY, 13126. Tel: 315-349-3297. Fax: 315-349-3273. p. 1713

Thomas, Ashli, Libr Asst, Cumberland University, One Cumberland Sq, Lebanon, TN, 37087. Tel: 615-547-1354. Fax: 615-444-2569. p. 2244

Thomas, Audrey J, Cat, United States Department of the Army, CEHEC-ZL Casey Bldg, 7701 Telegraph Rd, Alexandria, VA, 22315-3860. Tel: 703-428-6388. Fax: 703-428-6310. p. 2446

Thomas, Barbara, Tech Serv, Oceanside Library, 30 Davison Ave, Oceanside, NY, 11572-2299. Tel: 516-766-2360. Fax: 516-766-1895. p. 1709

Thomas, Barbara, Pub Serv, Graduate Institute of Applied Linguistics Library, 7500 W Camp Wisdom Rd, Dallas, TX, 75236-5699. Tel: 972-708-7416. Fax: 972-708-7292. p. 2308

Thomas, Bob, Circ, Linn County Library District No 5, 904 Main St, Pleasanton, KS, 66075. Tel: 913-352-8554. Fax: 913-352-8554. p. 890

Thomas, Bob, Integrated Syst Librn & Principal Cataloger, Western Washington University, 516 High St, MS 9103, Bellingham, WA, 98225. Tel: 360-650-7458. Fax: 360-650-3044. p. 2509

Thomas, Bonita, Tech Serv, Pine Mountain Regional Library, 218 Perry St NW, Manchester, GA, 31816-1317. Tel: 706-846-3851. Fax: 706-846-8455, 706-846-9632. p. 542

Thomas, Carolyn, Dir, Sierra Madre Public Library, 440 W Sierra Madre Blvd, Sierra Madre, CA, 91024-2399. Tel: 626-355-7186, 626-355-7187. Fax: 626-355-6218. p. 269

Thomas, Carrie P, Col Librn, Colby-Sawyer College, 541 Main St, New London, NH, 03257-4648. Tel: 603-526-3686. Fax: 603-526-3777. p. 1459

Thomas, Catherine, Tech Serv, University of Hawaii, 2525 Dole St, Honolulu, HI, 96822-2328. Tel: 808-956-5581, 808-956-7583. Fax: 808-956-4615. p. 565

Thomas, Charlene, Circ, Sheppard Memorial Library, 530 S Evans St, Greenville, NC, 27858-2308. Tel: 252-329-4580. Fax: 252-329-4587. p. 1799

Thomas, Cornel, Libr Dir/Br Mgr, Duchesne Library, 130 S Center St, Duchesne, UT, 84021. Tel: 435-738-2800. Fax: 435-738-2802. p. 2404

Thomas, Cornell, Br Mgr, Calcasieu Parish Public Library, Iowa Branch, 107 First St, Iowa, LA, 70647. Tel: 337-721-7101. Fax: 337-582-3597. p. 954

Thomas, Craig, Syst Librn, University of Wisconsin Oshkosh, 801 Elmwood Ave, Oshkosh, WI, 54901. Tel: 920-424-7323. Fax: 920-424-7338. p. 2628

Thomas, Deanna, Librn, Moose Pass Public Library, Depot Rd, Moose Pass, AK, 99631. Tel: 907-288-3111. Fax: 907-288-3111. p. 51

Thomas, Deb, Br Mgr, Burnaby Public Library, Bob Prittie Metrotown Branch, 6100 Willingdon Ave, Burnaby, BC, V5H 4N5, CANADA. Tel: 604-436-5432. Fax: 604-436-2961. p. 2725

Thomas, Debbie, Asst Dir, Derby Public Library, 1600 E Walnut Grove, Derby, KS, 67037. Tel: 316-788-0760. Fax: 316-788-7313. p. 863

Thomas, Deborah, Dir, Greater Baltimore Medical Center, 6701 N Charles St, Baltimore, MD, 21204. Tel: 443-849-2530. Fax: 443-849-2664. p. 1014

Thomas, Deborah, Sr Libr Tech, United States Air Force, Wright-Patterson Air Force Base Library FL2300, 88 MSG/SVMG, Bldg 1226, 5435 Hemlock St, Wright-Patterson AFB, OH, 45433-5420. Tel: 937-257-4340, 937-257-4815. Fax: 937-656-1776. p. 1951

Thomas, Deborah, Coordr, Maryland Association of Health Science Librarians, VA Medical HealthCare System, Medical Library, Ten N Greene St, Baltimore, MD, 21201. Tel: 443-849-2531. p. 2944

Thomas, Dena, Archivist, Librn, Venito Garcia Public Library & Archives, PO Box 837, Sells, AZ, 85634-0837. Tel: 520-383-5756. Fax: 520-383-2429. p. 81

Thomas, Dia, Computer Classes & AV, Barberton Public Library, 602 W Park Ave, Barberton, OH, 44203-2458. Tel: 330-745-1194. Fax: 330-745-8261. p. 1857

Thomas, Diane, Sr Librn, Mono County Free Library, Crowley Lake, 3627 Crowley Lake Dr, Crowley Lake, CA, 93546. Tel: 760-935-4505. Fax: 760-935-4560. p. 182

Thomas, Diane, Access Serv, Central Michigan University, Park 407, Mount Pleasant, MI, 48859. Tel: 989-774-2286. Fax: 989-774-2179. p. 1211

Thomas, Diane, Br Mgr, Warren-Trumbull County Public Library, Howland Branch, 9095 E Market St, Warren, OH, 44484. Tel: 330-856-2011. p. 1945

Thomas, Donna, Br Mgr, Jacksonville Public Library, Highlands Regional, 1826 Dunn Ave, Jacksonville, FL, 32218-4712. Tel: 904-757-7702. Fax: 904-696-4328. p. 453

Thomas, Dorothy, Br Head, East Baton Rouge Parish Library, Eden Park, 5131 Greenwell Springs Rd, Baton Rouge, LA, 70806. Tel: 225-231-3240. Fax: 225-231-3289. p. 943

Thomas, Dottie, Dir, Ohio County Public Library, 52 16th St, Wheeling, WV, 26003-3696. Tel: 304-232-0244. Fax: 304-232-6848. p. 2574

Thomas, Douglas J, Exec Dir, The Navy League of Canada Library, 305 Rideau St, 1st Flr, Ottawa, ON, K1N 9E5, CANADA. Tel: 613-993-5415. Fax: 613-990-8701. p. 2832

Thomas, Elaine, Asst Librn, US Court of Appeals Library, Pioneer Courthouse, 700 SW Sixth Ave, Ste 109, Portland, OR, 97204. Tel: 503-833-5310. Fax: 503-833-5315. p. 2015

Thomas, Elaine, Asst Librn, United States Courts Libraries, 7A40 Mark O Hatfield, US Courthouse, 1000 SW Third Ave, Portland, OR, 97204. Tel: 503-326-8140. Fax: 503-326-8144. p. 2015

Thomas, Felton, Jr, Exec Dir, CEO, Cleveland Public Library, 325 Superior Ave, Cleveland, OH, 44114-1271. Tel: 216-623-2800. p. 1877

Thomas, Florida, Librn, Hendry County Library System, Harlem Library, 1010J Harlem Academy Ave, Clewiston, FL, 33440. Tel: 863-902-3322. Fax: 863-902-3323. p. 433

Thomas, Frances, Librn, Louisiana House of Representatives, PO Box 94012, Baton Rouge, LA, 70804-9012. Tel: 225-342-2430. Fax: 225-342-2431. p. 943

Thomas, Gaile, ILL, Tulane University, 7001 Freret St, New Orleans, LA, 70118-5682. Tel: 504-865-5683. Fax: 504-865-6773. p. 963

Thomas, Gayleen, Sr Librn, San Jose Public Library, Cambrian, 1780 Hillsdale Ave, San Jose, CA, 95124-3199. Tel: 408-808-3080. Fax: 408-264-1894. p. 251

Thomas, Gayleen, Sr Librn, San Jose Public Library, West Valley, 1243 San Tomas Aquino Rd, San Jose, CA, 95117-3399. Tel: 408-244-4747. Fax: 408-984-3736. p. 251

Thomas, Glennis, Dir, Boise Bible College Library, 8695 W Marigold St, Boise, ID, 83714-1220. Tel: 208-376-7731. Fax: 208-376-7743. p. 570

Thomas, Hannah, Head, Cat & Coll, Saint Mary's College Library, 1928 Saint Mary's Rd, Moraga, CA, 94575. Tel: 925-631-4229. Fax: 925-376-6097. p. 191

Thomas, Helen, Co-Librn, First United Methodist Church Library, 400 S Main St, Mount Pleasant, MI, 48858. Tel: 989-773-6934. Fax: 989-773-1855. p. 1211

Thomas, Ima, Librn, Terra Alta Public Library, 701-B E State Ave, Terra Alta, WV, 26764-1204. Tel: 304-789-2724. Fax: 304-789-2724. p. 2572

Thomas, Jackie, Dir, Poplar Bluff Public Library, 318 N Main St, Poplar Bluff, MO, 63901. Tel: 573-686-8639. Fax: 573-785-6876. p. 1349

Thomas, James A, Dir, Verona Public Library, 17 Gould St, Verona, NJ, 07044-1928. Tel: 973-857-4848. Fax: 973-857-4851. p. 1537

Thomas, Jan, Dir, Breese Public Library, 530 N Third St, Breese, IL, 62230. Tel: 618-526-7361. Fax: 618-526-0143. p. 597

Thomas, Jane, Head, Ref, Rodman Public Library, 215 E Broadway St, Alliance, OH, 44601-2694. Tel: 330-821-2665. Fax: 330-821-5053. p. 1854

Thomas, Janet K, Tech Serv, Ringling College of Art & Design, 2700 N Tamiami Trail, Sarasota, FL, 34234. Tel: 941-359-7586. Fax: 941-359-7632. p. 490

Thomas, Jean, Coordr, Libr Serv, Saint Louis Community College, Forest Park Campus Library, 5600 Oakland Ave, Saint Louis, MO, 63110-1316. Tel: 314-644-9206. Fax: 314-644-9240. p. 1357

Thomas, Jeff, Photo Archivist, Mazamas Library & Archives, 527 SE 43rd Ave, Portland, OR, 97215. Tel: 503-227-2345, Ext 2. Fax: 503-227-0862. p. 2011

Thomas, Jen, Syst Librn, Preble County District Library, 450 S Barron St, Eaton, OH, 45320-2402. Tel: 937-456-4250. Fax: 937-456-6092. p. 1897

Thomas, Jennie, Pub Serv, Athenaeum of Ohio, 6616 Beechmont Ave, Cincinnati, OH, 45230-2091. Tel: 513-231-2223, Ext 136. Fax: 513-231-3254. p. 1868

Thomas, Jennifer, Dir, Dexter Free Library, 120 E Kirby St, Dexter, NY, 13634. Tel: 315-639-6785. Fax: 315-639-6785. p. 1614

Thomas, Jennifer, Chair, Grande Prairie Regional College, 10726 106th Ave, Grande Prairie, AB, T8V 4C4, CANADA. Tel: 780-539-2939. Fax: 780-539-2730. p. 2705

Thomas, Jill, Dir of Tech Serv, Lawrence University, 113 S Lawe St, Appleton, WI, 54911-5683. Fax: 920-832-6967. p. 2578

Thomas, Jo Helen, Librn, Lawrence County Law Library, 430 Court St, New Castle, PA, 16101. Tel: 724-656-2136. Fax: 724-658-4489. p. 2096

Thomas, Jody, In Charge, Santa Barbara Public Library, Montecito, 1469 E Valley Rd, Santa Barbara, CA, 93108. Tel: 805-969-5063. p. 261

Thomas, John, Info Literacy, State University of New York - Jefferson Community College, 1220 Coffeen St, Watertown, NY, 13601-1897. Tel: 315-786-2314. Fax: 315-788-0716. p. 1764

Thomas, John M, Asst Dir, Network Adminr, Spanish Peaks Library District, 415 Walsen Ave, Walsenburg, CO, 81089. Tel: 719-738-2774. Fax: 719-738-2468. p. 325

Thomas, Joseph, Head, Tech Serv, University of Notre Dame, 2345 Biolchini Hall of Law, Notre Dame, IN, 46556-4640. Tel: 574-631-5992. Fax: 574-631-6371. p. 771

Thomas, Josy, Coordr, Access Serv, El Centro College, 801 Main St, Dallas, TX, 75202-3605. Tel: 214-860-2174. Fax: 214-860-2440. p. 2308

Thomas, Juanita, ILL, Wisconsin Valley Library Service, 300 N First St, Wausau, WI, 54403. Tel: 715-261-7250. Fax: 715-261-7259. p. 2647

Thomas, Julie A, Tech Serv, Drake University, Drake Law Library, Opperman Hall, 2615 Carpenter Ave, Des Moines, IA, 50311-4505. Tel: 515-271-2052. Fax: 515-271-2530. p. 809

Thomas, Karen, Ser & Tech Serv, Lake City Community College, 149 SE College Pl, Lake City, FL, 32025-2006. Tel: 386-754-4339. Fax: 386-754-4839. p. 457

Thomas, Karen, Libr Tech, Shippensburg University, 1871 Old Main Dr, Shippensburg, PA, 17257-2299. Tel: 717-477-1123, Ext 3597. Fax: 717-477-1389. p. 2140

Thomas, Kate, Asst Librn, Fitzwilliam Town Library, 11 Templeton Tpk, Fitzwilliam, NH, 03447. Tel: 603-585-6503. Fax: 603-585-6738. p. 1447

Thomas, Kathie, Mgr, Pioneer Library System, Newcastle Public, 705 NW Tenth, Newcastle, OK, 73065. Tel: 405-387-5076. Fax: 405-387-5204. p. 1970

Thomas, Kathie, Exec Dir, Multicultural Council of Windsor & Essex County Library, 245 Janette Ave, Windsor, ON, N9A 4Z2, CANADA. Tel: 519-255-1127. Fax: 519-255-1435. p. 2871

Thomas, Kathy, Govt Doc, North Dakota State University Libraries, 1201 Albrecht Blvd, Fargo, ND, 58108. Tel: 701-231-8863. Fax: 701-231-6128. p. 1841

Thomas, Kay, Dir, Cooper Landing Community Library, Mile .8 Bean Creek Rd, Cooper Landing, AK, 99572. Tel: 907-599-1643. p. 46

Thomas, Kelly, Info Syst Analyst, California Environmental Protection Agency Public Library, 1001 I St, Sacramento, CA, 95812. Tel: 916-322-8598. p. 222

Thomas, Kirsti, Tech Serv, Saint Martin's University, 5300 Pacific Ave SE, Lacey, WA, 98503. Tel: 360-486-8827. Fax: 360-486-8825. p. 2519

Thomas, Laquisha, Libr Asst II, Montgomery City-County Public Library System, Pintlala Branch Library, 255 Federal Rd, Pintlala, AL, 36043-9781. Tel: 334-281-8069. Fax: 334-240-4860. p. 30

Thomas, LaTarsha, Librn, Halifax County Library, Weldon Memorial, Six W First St, Weldon, NC, 27890. Tel: 252-536-3837. Fax: 252-536-2477. p. 1800

Thomas, Leigh, Librn, Salt River Tribal Library, 1880 N Longmore Rd, Scottsdale, AZ, 85256. Tel: 480-850-8339. Fax: 480-850-2931. p. 80

Thomas, Linda, Librn, Schleicher County Public Library, 201 SW Main St, Eldorado, TX, 76936. Tel: 325-853-3767. Fax: 325-853-2963. p. 2317

Thomas, Lisa, Circ Serv, Weston County Public Library, 23 W Main St, Newcastle, WY, 82701. Tel: 307-746-2206. Fax: 307-746-2218. p. 2658

Thomas, Louise, Dir, Kalama Public Library, 312 First St, Kalama, WA, 98625. Tel: 360-673-4568. Fax: 360-673-4560. p. 2518

Thomas, Lynn, Youth Serv Coordr, Westmont Public Library, 428 N Cass, Westmont, IL, 60559-1502. Tel: 630-969-5625. Fax: 630-969-6490. p. 717

Thomas, Lynne, Rare Bks, Spec Coll Librn, Northern Illinois University Libraries, DeKalb, IL, 60115-2868. Tel: 815-753-0255. p. 635

Thomas, Marcia, Dir, Commun & Tech Serv, Illinois Wesleyan University, One Ames Plaza, Bloomington, IL, 61701-7188. Tel: 309-556-3808. Fax: 309-556-3706. p. 595

Thomas, Marcia M, Dir, Cleveland Chiropractic College, 10850 Lowell Ave, Overland Park, KS, 66210. Tel: 913-234-0809. Fax: 913-234-0901. p. 887

Thomas, Margaret, Librn, Orangeburg County Library, Holly Hill Branch, 8441 Old State Rd, Hwy 176, Holly Hill, SC, 29059. Tel: 803-531-4636. p. 2201

Thomas, Margaret, Librn, Orangeburg County Library, Mentor Branch, 2626 Cleveland St, Elloree, SC, 29047. Tel: 803-531-4636. p. 2201

Thomas, Margaret, Librn, Orangeburg County Library, North Branch, 9316 North Rd, Hwy 178, North, SC, 29112. Tel: 803-531-4636. p. 2201

Thomas, Margaret, Librn, South Puget Sound Community College Library, 2011 Mottman Rd SW, Olympia, WA, 98512. Tel: 360-596-5271. Fax: 360-596-5714. p. 2522

Thomas, Margaret A, Dir, MacDonald Public Library, 36480 Main St, New Baltimore, MI, 48047-2509. Tel: 586-725-0273. Fax: 586-725-8360. p. 1213

Thomas, Marie, Head, Circ Serv, Barrington Public Library District, 505 N Northwest Hwy, Barrington, IL, 60010. Tel: 847-382-1300. Fax: 847-382-1261. p. 592

Thomas, Mark, Dir, Worcester County Library, 307 N Washington St, Snow Hill, MD, 21863. Tel: 410-632-2600. Fax: 410-632-1159. p. 1042

Thomas, Mary, Librn, Foothill College, 12345 El Monte Rd, Los Altos Hills, CA, 94022-4599. Tel: 650-949-7390. Fax: 650-949-7123. p. 167

Thomas, Mary, Librn, Foothill College, 12345 El Monte Rd, Los Altos Hills, CA, 94022-4599. Tel: 650-949-7086. Fax: 650-949-7123. p. 2962

Thomas, Mary Augusta, Dep Dir, Smithsonian Libraries, Nat Museum of Natural Hist, Rm 22, MRC154, Tenth St & Constitution Ave NW, Washington, DC, 20002. Tel: 202-633-2240. Fax: 202-633-4315. p. 414

Thomas, Mary Ellen, Librn, Lapeer District Library, Elba, 5508 Davison Rd, Lapeer, MI, 48446. Tel: 810-653-7200. Fax: 810-653-4267. p. 1202

Thomas, Mary Lynn, Ch, Newberg Public Library, 503 E Hancock St, Newberg, OR, 97132-2899. Tel: 503-537-0304. Fax: 503-538-9720. p. 2007

Thomas, Mary Trev, Circ, Bethlehem Public Library, 451 Delaware Ave, Delmar, NY, 12054-3042. Tel: 518-439-9314. Fax: 518-478-0901. p. 1614

Thomas, Matthew, ILL Coordr, Jenkins Law Library, 833 Chestnut St, Ste 1220, Philadelphia, PA, 19107-4429. Tel: 215-574-7933. Fax: 215-574-7920. p. 2111

Thomas, Megan, Ref Librn, Montana State University, 1500 University Dr, Billings, MT, 59101-0298. Tel: 406-657-1663. Fax: 406-657-2037. p. 1374

Thomas, Melanie, Librn, Mississippi State University, Meridian Campus, 1000 Hwy 19 N, Meridian, MS, 39307. Tel: 601-484-0236. Fax: 601-484-0139. p. 1309

Thomas, Michael, Adult Serv, Neenah Public Library, 240 E Wisconsin Ave, Neenah, WI, 54956-3010. Tel: 920-886-6311. Fax: 920-886-6324. p. 2624

Thomas, Mike, Dir, Winfield Public Library, 112 W Ash, Winfield, IA, 52659-9511. Tel: 319-257-3247. Fax: 319-257-3247. p. 853

Thomas, Nicole, Circ Supvr, Cleveland Institute of Music, 11021 East Blvd, Cleveland, OH, 44106-1776. Tel: 216-707-4508. Fax: 216-791-3063. p. 1877

Thomas, Pam, LSTA Coordr, Illinois Central College, One College Dr, L445, East Peoria, IL, 61635-0001. Tel: 309-694-5508. Fax: 309-694-5473. p. 2965

Thomas, Pamela, Cat, Illinois Central College, One College Dr, East Peoria, IL, 61635-0001. Tel: 309-694-5461. Fax: 309-694-5473. p. 638

Thomas, Patricia, Dir, Plymouth District Library, 223 S Main St, Plymouth, MI, 48170-1687. Tel: 734-453-0750, Ext 218. Fax: 734-453-0733. p. 1218

Thomas, Paul, Librn, Stanford University Libraries, Hoover Institution on War, Revolution & Peace Library, Stanford, CA, 94305-6004. Tel: 650-723-1754. Fax: 650-723-1687. p. 271

Thomas, Phyllis, Tech Serv, United States Army, Ray Bldg, 1222 Spruce St, Rm No 4202, Saint Louis, MO, 63103-2833. Tel: 314-331-8883. Fax: 314-331-8677. p. 1361

Thomas, Princess, Head, Ch, Morris County Library, 30 E Hanover Ave, Whippany, NJ, 07981. Tel: 973-285-6981. p. 1544

Thomas, Raye Lynn, Coordr, Access Serv, Coordr, ILL, Sonoma State University Library, 1801 E Cotati Ave, Rohnert Park, CA, 94928-3609. Tel: 707-664-2951. Fax: 707-664-2090. p. 219

Thomas, Rita, Asst Dir, Menifee County Public Library, 1585 Main St, Frenchburg, KY, 40322. Tel: 606-768-2212. Fax: 606-768-9676. p. 914

Thomas, Roberta, Dir, Grayslake Area Public Library District, 100 Library Lane, Grayslake, IL, 60030-1684. Tel: 847-223-5313. Fax: 847-223-6482. p. 652

Thomas, Roger, Libr Serv Supvr, Saint Louis Community College, Florissant Valley Campus Library, 3400 Pershall Rd, Ferguson, MO, 63135-1408. Tel: 314-513-4529. Fax: 314-513-4053. p. 1357

Thomas, Sabrina, Res & Instruction Librn, Marshall University Libraries, One John Marshall Dr, Huntington, WV, 25755-2060. Tel: 304-696-3627. Fax: 304-696-5858. p. 2562

Thomas, Sandra, Electronic Res & ILL Librn, Ser Librn, Southeastern Oklahoma State University, 1405 N Fourth Ave, PMB 4105, Durant, OK, 74701-0609. Tel: 580-745-2933. Fax: 580-745-7463. p. 1961

Thomas, Sandra, Dir, Dublin Public Library, 206 W Blackjack St, Dublin, TX, 76446. Tel: 254-445-4141. Fax: 254-445-2176. p. 2314

Thomas, Sara, Mgr, Whiteford, Taylor & Preston, Seven St Paul St, Ste 1500, Baltimore, MD, 21202. Tel: 410-347-8700. Fax: 410-752-7092. p. 1019

Thomas, Sarah K, Dir, Embry-Riddle Aeronautical University, 3700 Willow Creek Rd, Prescott, AZ, 86301-3720. Tel: 928-777-3812. p. 78

Thomas, Scott, Tech Coordr, Scranton Public Library, Albright Memorial Bldg, 500 Vine St, Scranton, PA, 18509-3298. Tel: 570-348-3000. Fax: 570-348-3020. p. 2138

Thomas, Scott, Instr, Northampton Community College, 3835 Green Pond Rd, Bethlehem, PA, 18020. Tel: 610-861-5358. Fax: 610-861-5373. p. 2973

Thomas, Selena, Ref Librn, IBM Corp, 1101 Kitchawan Rd, Yorktown Heights, NY, 10598. Tel: 914-784-6842. Fax: 914-945-4144. p. 1772

Thomas, Sharon, ILL, Tech Serv, Salem Free Public Library, 112 W Broadway, Salem, NJ, 08079-1302. Tel: 856-935-0526. Fax: 856-935-5110. p. 1528

Thomas, Sharon, Librn, St Joseph Township Public Library, 1240 Richard St, Richards Landing, ON, P0R 1J0, CANADA. Tel: 705-246-2353. Fax: 705-246-2353. p. 2838

Thomas, Sheila, Librn, Saint Francis Hospital, Inc, 701 N Clayton St, Wilmington, DE, 19805. Tel: 302-421-4834. Fax: 302-575-8080. p. 388

Thomas, Sherri, Law Librn, University of New Mexico, Law Library, 1117 Stanford Dr NE, Albuquerque, NM, 87131-1441. Tel: 505-277-6236. Fax: 505-277-0068. p. 1551

Thomas, Stephanie S, ILL, Ref Librn, Francis Marion University, 4822 East Palmetto St, Florence, SC, 29506. Tel: 843-661-4674. Fax: 843-661-1309. p. 2194

Thomas, Stephen, Dir, Ohio Township Public Library System, 4111 Lakeshore Dr, Newburgh, IN, 47630-2274. Tel: 812-853-5468. Fax: 812-853-0509. p. 768

Thomas, Steve, Supvr, Automation Serv, Central Kansas Library System, 1409 Williams St, Great Bend, KS, 67530-4020. Tel: 620-792-4865. Fax: 620-792-5495. p. 869

Thomas, Steven, Asst Dir, Washington County Library System, 1080 W Clydesdale Dr, Fayetteville, AR, 72701. Tel: 479-442-6253. Fax: 479-442-6812. p. 100

Thomas, Sue, Br Mgr, Paulding County Carnegie Library, Cooper Community, 206 N First St, Oakwood, OH, 45873. Tel: 419-594-3337. Fax: 419-594-3337. p. 1928

Thomas, Susan, Head, Coll Serv, Indiana University South Bend, 1700 Mishawaka Ave, South Bend, IN, 46615. Tel: 574-520-5500. Fax: 574-520-4472. p. 778

Thomas, Susan, Librn, Montgomery Area Public Library, One S Main St, Montgomery, PA, 17752-1150. Tel: 570-547-6212. Fax: 570-547-0648. p. 2092

Thomas, Sylvia Sue, Libr Serv Dir, Indiana Business College Library System, 550 E Washington St, Indianapolis, IN, 46204. Tel: 317-656-4740. Fax: 317-264-5650. p. 751

Thomas, Tamela, Acq, Uncle Remus Regional Library System, 1121 East Ave, Madison, GA, 30650. Tel: 706-342-4974, Ext 14. Fax: 706-342-4510. p. 541

Thomas, Tara, Dir, Conway Public Library, 15 Main St, Conway, NH, 03818. Tel: 603-447-5552. Fax: 603-447-6921. p. 1444

Thomas, Tara, Teen Serv, Upper Dublin Public Library, 805 Loch Alsh Ave, Fort Washington, PA, 19034. Tel: 215-628-8744. p. 2058

Thomas, Tracey, Asst Dir, B B Comer Memorial Library, 314 N Broadway, Sylacauga, AL, 35150-2528. Tel: 256-249-0961. p. 36

Thomas, Valerie, Asst Librn, State Transportation Library, Ten Park Plaza, Boston, MA, 02116. Tel: 617-973-8000. Fax: 617-973-7153. p. 1067

Thomas, Vanrea, Dep Chief Librn, Medgar Evers College, 1650 Bedford Ave, Brooklyn, NY, 11225-2010. Tel: 718-270-4885. Fax: 718-270-5182. p. 1593

Thomas, Vanrea, Head, Ref Serv, Medgar Evers College, 1650 Bedford Ave, Brooklyn, NY, 11225-2010. Tel: 718-270-4885. Fax: 718-270-5182. p. 1593

Thomas, Verna E, Libr Dir, Res Coordr, Trinity International University, 8190 W State Rd 84, Davie, FL, 33324-4611. Tel: 954-382-6561. Fax: 954-382-6421. p. 435

Thomas, Virginia C, Dir, Wayne State University Libraries, Arthur Neef Law Library, 474 Ferry Mall, Detroit, MI, 48202. Tel: 313-577-3925. Fax: 313-577-5498. p. 1173

Thomas, Vose, Br Mgr, Riverside County Library System, Lake Elsinore Library, 600 W Graham, Lake Elsinore, CA, 92530. Tel: 951-245-3918. Fax: 951-245-7715. p. 217

Thomas, Yvonne, Libr Tech, Los Robles Regional Medical Center, 215 W Janss Rd, Thousand Oaks, CA, 91360. Tel: 805-370-4609. Fax: 805-370-4843. p. 274

Thomas-Burbank, Coleen, In Charge, Klamath County Library Services District, Gilchrist Branch, 138306 Michigan Ave, Gilchrist, OR, 97737. Tel: 541-433-2186. Fax: 541-433-2186. p. 2002

Thomasian, Ruth, Exec Dir, Project SAVE Armenian Photograph Archives, 65 Main St, 3rd Flr, Watertown, MA, 02472-4400. Tel: 617-923-4542. Fax: 617-924-0434. p. 1134

Thomason, Anne, Col Archivist, Earlham College, 801 National Rd W, Richmond, IN, 47374-4095. Tel: 765-983-1743. Fax: 765-983-1304. p. 774

Thomason, Beth, Librn, Carrier Mills-Stonefort Public Library District, 109 W Oak St, Carrier Mills, IL, 62917. Tel: 618-994-2011. Fax: 618-994-2303. p. 601

Thomason, Christia, Cat & Digital Res Librn, University of North Carolina School of the Arts, 1533 S Main St, Winston-Salem, NC, 27127. Tel: 336-770-3270. Fax: 336-770-3271. p. 1833

Thomason, Marlene, Br Mgr, Monterey County Free Libraries, Parkfield, 70643 Parkfield-Coalinga Rd, San Miguel, CA, 93451. Tel: 805-463-2347. Fax: 805-463-2347. p. 183

Thomason, Sheila, Librn, Meriden Library, 22 Bean Rd, Meriden, NH, 03770. Tel: 603-469-3252. p. 1457

Thomasson, Nadine, Asst Librn, Belle Plaine Community Library, 904 12th St, Belle Plaine, IA, 52208-1711. Tel: 319-444-2902. Fax: 319-444-2902. p. 796

Thomasson, Rose, Libr Asst I, Marshall-Lyon County Library, 301 W Lyon St, Marshall, MN, 56258. Tel: 507-537-7003. p. 1258

Thomaswick, Tracey, Br Mgr, Chestatee Regional Library System, Lumpkin County Library, 342 Courthouse Hill, Dahlonega, GA, 30533. Tel: 706-864-3668. Fax: 706-864-3937. p. 529

Thomlison, Paula, Mgr, Mkt, Communications & Develop, Brantford Public Library, 173 Colborne St, Brantford, ON, N3T 2G8, CANADA. Tel: 519-756-2220, Ext 343. Fax: 519-756-4979. p. 2796

Thompkins, Harriet, ILL, Ref Serv, Ch, Gulf Beaches Public Library, 200 Municipal Dr, Madeira Beach, FL, 33708. Tel: 727-391-2828. Fax: 727-399-2840. p. 462

Thompson, Adonna, Asst Dir, Archival Coll & Serv, Duke University Libraries, Medical Center Library, DUMC Box 3702, Ten Bryan-Searle Dr, Durham, NC, 27710-0001. Tel: 919-383-2653. Fax: 919-681-7599. p. 1788

Thompson, Alice, Librn, Southwest Tennessee Community College, 170 Myrtle St, Memphis, TN, 38103. Tel: 901-333-5945. Fax: 901-333-5141. p. 2251

Thompson, Amelia, Asst Dir, Oklahoma Wesleyan University Library, 2201 Silver Lake Rd, Bartlesville, OK, 74006-6299. Tel: 918-335-6274. Fax: 918-335-6220. p. 1958

Thompson, Ann, Head, Adult Serv, Essex Library Association, Inc, 33 West Ave, Essex, CT, 06426-1196. Tel: 860-767-1560. Fax: 860-767-2500. p. 338

Thompson, Ann, Head, Cat, Shenandoah County Library, 514 Stoney Creek Blvd, Edinburg, VA, 22824. Tel: 540-984-8200. Fax: 540-984-8207. p. 2460

Thompson, Ann B, Dir, Elizabethtown Community & Technical College Library, 600 College Street Rd, Elizabethtown, KY, 42701. Tel: 270-706-8812. Fax: 270-769-1618. p. 912

Thompson, Arieta, Rare Bks, Spec Coll Librn, American Samoa Office of Library Services, American Library Bldg, Pago Pago, AS, 96799. Tel: 684-699-2170. Fax: 684-633-4240, 684-699-2193. p. 2665

Thompson, Barbara, Mrg/Youth & Adult Serv, Springfield Public Library, 225 Fifth St, Springfield, OR, 97477-4697. Tel: 541-726-3766. Fax: 541-726-3747. p. 2020

Thompson, Barbara, Dept Head, Librn, Community College of Allegheny County, 8701 Perry Hwy, Pittsburgh, PA, 15237-5372. Tel: 412-369-3671. Fax: 412-369-3626. p. 2124

Thompson, Barbara, Dir, Lake Cities Library, 302 S Shady Shores Rd, Lake Dallas, TX, 75065-3609. Tel: 940-497-3566. Fax: 940-497-3567. p. 2352

Thompson, Becky, Br Mgr, Anderson County Library, Iva Branch, 203 W Cruette St, Iva, SC, 29655. Tel: 864-348-6150. Fax: 864-348-6150. p. 2180

Thompson, Betsy, Chairperson, Sioux City Library Cooperative, c/o Sioux City Public Library, 529 Pierce St, Sioux City, IA, 51101-1203. Tel: 712-255-2933, Ext 255. Fax: 712-279-6432. p. 2943

Thompson, Betsy J, Dir, Sioux City Public Library, 529 Pierce St, Sioux City, IA, 51101-1203. Tel: 712-255-2933. p. 844

Thompson, Beverly, Cat, Tech Serv, Woburn Public Library, 45 Pleasant St, Woburn, MA, 01801. Tel: 781-933-0148. Fax: 781-938-7860. p. 1142

Thompson, Brenda, Br Mgr, Jasper County Public Library, DeMotte Branch, 901 Birch St SW, DeMotte, IN, 46310. Tel: 219-987-2221. Fax: 219-987-2220. p. 774

Thompson, Brian, Curator, Mgr, University of Washington Botanic Gardens, 3501 NE 41st St, Seattle, WA, 98105. Tel: 206-543-0415. Fax: 206-897-1435. p. 2533

Thompson, Bruce, Mgr, Cobb County Public Library System, Powder Springs Branch, 4181 Atlanta St, Bldg 1, Powder Springs, GA, 30127. Tel: 770-439-3600. Fax: 770-439-3620. p. 543

Thompson, Bruce, Sr Librn, Oneida Correctional Facility Library, 6100 School Rd, Rome, NY, 13440. Tel: 315-339-6880, Ext 4600. Fax: 315-339-6880, Ext 3299. p. 1735

Thompson, Camille, Youth Serv Coordr, New Brunswick Free Public Library, 60 Livingston Ave, New Brunswick, NJ, 08901-2597. Tel: 732-745-5108, Ext 32. Fax: 732-846-0226. p. 1508

Thompson, Candy, ILL, Lynchburg Public Library, 2315 Memorial Ave, Lynchburg, VA, 24501. Tel: 434-455-6300. p. 2476

Thompson, Carmel, Supvr, Acq, University of Puget Sound, 1500 N Warner St, Campus Mail Box 1021, Tacoma, WA, 98416-1021. Tel: 253-879-3240. Fax: 253-879-3670. p. 2541

Thompson, Carol J, Dir, Kling Memorial Library, 708 Seventh St, Grundy Center, IA, 50638-1430. Tel: 641-473-2314. Fax: 319-825-5863. p. 819

Thompson, Carole, Asst Librn, J A Tarbell Library, 136 Forest Rd, Lyndeborough, NH, 03082. Tel: 603-654-6790. Fax: 603-654-6790. p. 1454

Thompson, Caroline, ILL, University of West Florida, 11000 University Pkwy, Pensacola, FL, 32514-5750. Tel: 850-474-2412. Fax: 850-474-3338. p. 482

Thompson, Cassandra, Dir, Bloomfield-Eastern Greene County Public Library, 125 S Franklin St, Bloomfield, IN, 47424-1406. Tel: 812-384-4125. Fax: 812-384-0820. p. 726

Thompson, Catherine A, Libr Dir, Aquinnah Public Library, One Church St, Aquinnah, MA, 02535. Tel: 508-645-2314. Fax: 508-645-2188. p. 1050

Thompson, Catherine A, Dir, Chilmark Free Public Library, 522 South Rd, Chilmark, MA, 02535. Tel: 508-645-3360. Fax: 508-645-3737. p. 1082

Thompson, Charlene, Ref & Instrul Serv, Instr Coordr, Judson University, 1151 N State St, Elgin, IL, 60123. Tel: 847-628-2033. Fax: 847-625-2045. p. 641

Thompson, Christina, Col Archivist, Pub Serv Librn, Hendrix College, 1600 Washington Ave, Conway, AR, 72032. Tel: 501-450-4558. Fax: 501-450-3800. p. 97

Thompson, Clinton M, Dir, University of Oklahoma Health Sciences Center, 1000 Stanton L Young Blvd, Oklahoma City, OK, 73117-1213. Tel: 405-271-2285. Fax: 405-271-3297. p. 1975

Thompson, Clinton M, Jr, Dir, Oklahoma Health Sciences Library Association, University of Oklahoma - HSC Bird Health Science Library, 1000 S L Young Blvd, Oklahoma City, OK, 73190. Tel: 405-271-2285, Ext 48755. Fax: 405-271-3297. p. 2953

Thompson, Colin, Librn, Sons of Norway, 1455 W Lake St, Minneapolis, MN, 55408. Tel: 612-827-3611. Fax: 612-827-0658. p. 1261

Thompson, Cynthia, Dir, Pub Serv, University of Missouri-Kansas City Libraries, 800 E 51st St, Kansas City, MO, 64110. Tel: 816-235-1511. Fax: 816-333-5584. p. 1341

Thompson, D Leigh, Instrul Serv Librn, University of North Alabama, One Harrison Plaza, Box 5028, Florence, AL, 35632-0001. Tel: 256-765-4466. Fax: 256-765-4438. p. 17

Thompson, D Lynn, Dir, Southern Pines Public Library, 170 W Connecticut Ave, Southern Pines, NC, 28387-4819. Tel: 910-692-8235. Fax: 910-695-1037. p. 1824

Thompson, Dale, Dir, Providence Public Library, 150 Empire St, Providence, RI, 02903-3283. Tel: 401-455-8100. Fax: 401-455-8065, 401-455-8080. p. 2173

Thompson, Dale, Asst Prof, University of North Texas, 1155 Union Circle, Denton, TX, 76203-5017. Tel: 940-565-2445. Fax: 940-565-3101. p. 2975

Thompson, Darryl, Librn, Eastern Kentucky Correctional Complex Library, 200 Road to Justice, West Liberty, KY, 41472. Tel: 606-743-2800. Fax: 606-743-2811. p. 937

Thompson, Dawn, Dir, Wadena Public Library, 136 S Mill St, Wadena, IA, 52169. Tel: 563-774-2039. Fax: 563-774-2039. p. 849

Thompson, Dean, Coll Develop Librn, Dona Ana Community College Library, 3400 S Espina, Rm 260, Las Cruces, NM, 88003. Tel: 575-528-7064. Fax: 575-527-7636. p. 1558

Thompson, Deanna, Librn, Trinity Valley Community College Library, Kaufman County, PO Box 668, Terrell, TX, 75160-0668. Tel: 972-563-4929. Fax: 972-563-1667. p. 2277

Thompson, Debbie, Tech Spec, University of Charleston, 2300 MacCorkle Ave SE, Charleston, WV, 25304-1099. Tel: 304-357-4997. Fax: 304-357-4715. p. 2556

Thompson, Deborah, E-Learning Librn, University of Central Oklahoma, 100 N University Dr, Edmond, OK, 73034. Tel: 405-974-2880. Fax: 405-974-3806, 405-974-3874. p. 1962

Thompson, Deborah T, Access Serv & Coll Maintenance Assoc, University of Rio Grande, 218 N College Ave, Rio Grande, OH, 45674. Tel: 740-245-7005. Fax: 740-245-7096. p. 1931

Thompson, Devona, Cat, Greenville Area Public Library, 330 Main St, Greenville, PA, 16125-2619. Tel: 724-588-5490. Fax: 724-588-5481. p. 2063

Thompson, Diana, Librn, Annapolis Valley Regional Library, Hantsport Branch, 11 School St, Hantsport, NS, B0P 1P0, CANADA. Tel: 902-684-4005. p. 2778

Thompson, Diane, Head Librn, Natural Resources Canada, 625 Robson St, Vancouver, BC, V6B 5J3, CANADA. Tel: 604-666-3812. Fax: 604-666-7186. p. 2741

Thompson, Diane, Libr Mgr, Haut-Saint-Jean Regional Library, Kedgwick Public, 116 Notre-Dame St, Unit P, Kedgwick, NB, E8B 1H8, CANADA. Tel: 506-284-2757. Fax: 506-284-4557. p. 2762

Thompson, Donald, Br Mgr, Chicago Public Library, Mabel Manning Branch, Six S Hoyne Ave, Chicago, IL, 60612. Tel: 312-746-6800. Fax: 312-746-6806. p. 609

Thompson, Elizabeth, Dir, Gorham Public Library, 35 Railroad St, Gorham, NH, 03581. Tel: 603-466-2525. p. 1448

Thompson, Ellen, Asst Dir, Coos Bay Public Library, 525 Anderson St, Coos Bay, OR, 97420-1678. Tel: 541-269-1101. Fax: 541-269-7567. p. 1993

Thompson, Emily, Learning Tech Librn, State University of New York at Oswego, SUNY Oswego, 7060 State Rte 104, Oswego, NY, 13126-3514. Tel: 315-312-3563. Fax: 315-312-3194. p. 1713

Thompson, Eridan J, Access Serv Librn, Florida Southern College, 111 Lake Hollingsworth Dr, Lakeland, FL, 33801-5698. Tel: 863-616-6450. Fax: 863-680-4126. p. 459

Thompson, Erin E, Dir, Boulder County Corrections Library, 3200 Airport Rd, Boulder, CO, 80301. Tel: 303-441-4686. Fax: 303-441-4608. p. 290

Thompson, Gary B, Dir, Siena College, 515 Loudon Rd, Loudonville, NY, 12211-1462. Tel: 518-783-6717. Fax: 518-783-2570. p. 1655

Thompson, Gen, Outreach Serv Librn, Harrison County Library System, 2600 24th Ave, No 6, Gulfport, MS, 39501-2081. Tel: 228-868-1383. Fax: 228-863-7433. p. 1299

Thompson, George, Head, Spec Coll & Archives, California State University, Chico, 400 W First St, Chico, CA, 95929-0295. Tel: 530-898-6603. Fax: 530-898-4443. p. 133

Thompson, Glenda, Head Librn, Houston County Public Library System, Nola Brantley Memorial Library, 721 Watson Blvd, Warner Robins, GA, 31093. Tel: 478-923-0128. Fax: 478-929-8611. p. 547

Thompson, Gregory C, Assoc Dean, Spec Coll, University of Utah, Marriott Library, 295 S 1500 East, Salt Lake City, UT, 84112-0860. Tel: 801-581-8863. Fax: 801-585-7185. p. 2415

Thompson, Harry F, Dir, Augustana College, Center for Western Studies, 2201 S Summit Ave, Sioux Falls, SD, 57197. Tel: 605-274-4007. Fax: 605-274-4999. p. 2218

Thompson, Henrietta, Librn, Ashley County Library, 211 E Lincoln, Hamburg, AR, 71646. Tel: 870-853-2078. Fax: 870-853-2079. p. 102

Thompson, Holly, Dir, Rantoul Public Library, 106 W Flessner, Rantoul, IL, 61866. Tel: 217-893-3955. Fax: 217-893-3961. p. 693

Thompson, Jan, Librn, Renwick Public Library, 204 Stoddard St, Renwick, IA, 50577-0038. Tel: 515-824-3209. Fax: 515-824-3209. p. 840

Thompson, Jane, Asst Dir, Fac Serv, University of Colorado Boulder, The William A Wise Law Library, 2450 Kittredge Loop Dr, 402 UCB, Boulder, CO, 80309-0402. Tel: 303-492-2705. Fax: 303-492-2707. p. 292

Thompson, Jane, Youth Serv Dir, Belfast Free Library, 106 High St, Belfast, ME, 04915. Tel: 207-338-3884. Fax: 207-338-3895. p. 977

Thompson, Jeaniter, Accounts Supvr, Northeastern University Libraries, Snell Library, 360 Huntington Ave, Boston, MA, 02115. Tel: 617-373-5933. p. 1065

Thompson, Jeff, Dir, Merritt Island Public Library, 1195 N Courtenay Pkwy, Merritt Island, FL, 32953-4596. Tel: 321-455-1369. p. 464

Thompson, Jennifer, Asst Dir, Mercy College of Health Sciences Library, 928 Sixth Ave, Des Moines, IA, 50309-1239. Tel: 515-643-6613. Fax: 515-643-6695. p. 810

Thompson, Jo, Acq, Enterprise Public Library, 101 E Grubbs St, Enterprise, AL, 36330. Tel: 334-347-2636. Fax: 334-393-6477. p. 15

Thompson, Joanna M, Dir, Libr Serv, Bluefield State College, 219 Rock St, Bluefield, WV, 24701. Tel: 304-327-4054. Fax: 304-327-4203. p. 2554

Thompson, Jocelyne, Assoc Dir of Libr/Coll Serv, University of New Brunswick Libraries, Five Macaulay Dr, Fredericton, NB, E3B 5H5, CANADA. Tel: 506-458-7053. Fax: 506-453-4595. p. 2763

Thompson, Jody, Head, Archives & Rec Mgt, Georgia Institute of Technology Library, 704 Cherry St, Atlanta, GA, 30332-0900. Tel: 404-894-4501. Fax: 404-894-6084. p. 515

Thompson, John, Dir, Indianhead Federated Library System, 1538 Truax Blvd, Eau Claire, WI, 54703. Tel: 715-839-5082. Fax: 715-839-5151. p. 2589

Thompson, John R, Dean, Citrus College, 1000 W Foothill Blvd, Glendora, CA, 91741-1899. Tel: 626-914-8643. Fax: 626-963-2531. p. 2962

Thompson, John Walters, ILL, Syst Librn, Waynesburg College, 93 Locust Ave, Waynesburg, PA, 15370-1242. Tel: 724-852-7668. Fax: 724-627-4188. p. 2152

Thompson, Jolene, Online Serv & Tech, Zelienople Area Public Library, 227 S High St, Zelienople, PA, 16063-1319. Tel: 724-452-9330. Fax: 724-452-9318. p. 2160

Thompson, Joseph, Assoc Dir, Western Md Regional Libr, Washington County Free Library, 100 S Potomac St, Hagerstown, MD, 21740. Tel: 301-739-3250. Fax: 301-739-7603. p. 1031

Thompson, Joseph, Assoc Dir, Western Maryland Public Libraries, 100 S Potomac St, Hagerstown, MD, 21740. Tel: 301-739-3250, Ext 140. Fax: 301-739-7603. p. 1032

Thompson, Judy, Ref Librn, Berry College, 2277 Martha Berry Hwy, Mount Berry, GA, 30149. Tel: 706-233-4057. p. 546

Thompson, Judy, Ref Librn, Edwardsville Public Library, 112 S Kansas St, Edwardsville, IL, 62025. Tel: 618-692-7556. Fax: 618-692-9566. p. 639

Thompson, June, Br Supvr, Gaston County Public Library, Ferguson-Erwin Center, 913 N Pryor St, Gastonia, NC, 28052. Tel: 704-868-8046. Fax: 704-868-8046. p. 1794

Thompson, Karolyn, Doc Delivery, University of Southern Mississippi Library, 118 College Dr, No 5053, Hattiesburg, MS, 39406. Tel: 601-266-5111. Fax: 601-266-6033. p. 1300

Thompson, Kelly, Dep Chief Exec Officer, Mgr, Young Adult & Children's Serv, Petawawa Public Library, 16 Civic Centre Rd, Petawawa, ON, K8H 3H5, CANADA. Tel: 613-687-2227. Fax: 613-687-2527. p. 2835

Thompson, Kenneth, Br Mgr, Atlanta-Fulton Public Library System, East Atlanta Library, 400 Flat Shoals Ave SE, Atlanta, GA, 30318-1938. Tel: 404-730-5438. Fax: 404-730-5436. p. 512

Thompson, Kirsten, Br Mgr, Milwaukee Public Library, Center Street, 2727 W Fond du Lac Ave, Milwaukee, WI, 53210. Tel: 414-286-3090. Fax: 414-286-8467. p. 2620

Thompson, Konny, Acq Librn, Gonzaga University, 502 E Boone Ave, Spokane, WA, 99258-0095. Tel: 509-313-6546. Fax: 509-323-5904. p. 2536

Thompson, Lana, Mgr, MacEwan Grant University Library, Alberta College Campus Library, 10050 MacDonald Dr, Edmonton, AB, T5J 2B7, CANADA. Tel: 780-423-3738. Fax: 780-424-6371. p. 2701

Thompson, Laurie L, Asst VPres, Libr Serv, University of Texas Southwestern Medical Center Library, 5323 Harry Hines Blvd, Dallas, TX, 75390-9049. Tel: 214-648-2626. Fax: 214-648-2826. p. 2311

Thompson, Leanne, Presv Librn, Res Librn, Alberta Legislature Library, 216 Legislature Bldg, 10800-97 Ave, Edmonton, AB, T5K 2B6, CANADA. Tel: 780-422-9316. Fax: 780-427-6016. p. 2699

Thompson, Lilla, Cat, Hollins University, 7950 E Campus Dr, Roanoke, VA, 24020-1000. Tel: 540-362-7467. Fax: 540-362-6756. p. 2493

Thompson, Linda, Librn, Walton County Public Library System, Coastal, 437 Greenway Trail, Santa Rosa Beach, FL, 32459-5589. Tel: 850-267-2809. Fax: 850-267-9452. p. 437

Thompson, Linda, Assoc Dean of Libr, University of Houston, M D Anderson Library, 114 University Libraries, Houston, TX, 77204-2000. Tel: 713-743-9800. Fax: 713-743-9811. p. 2343

Thompson, Linda, Dir, Springlake-Earth Community Library, 472 Farm Rd 302, Springlake, TX, 79082. Tel: 806-257-3357. Fax: 806-257-3927. p. 2388

Thompson, Liz, Info Processing Librn, State of Mississippi Judiciary, Carroll Gartin Justice Bldg, 450 High St, Jackson, MS, 39201. Tel: 601-359-3672. Fax: 601-359-2912. p. 1305

Thompson, Lois Langer, Dir, Hennepin County Library, 12601 Ridgedale Dr, Minnetonka, MN, 55305-1909. Tel: 612-543-8541. Fax: 612-543-8600. p. 1263

Thompson, Lolana, Pub Serv, Spec Coll, Dallas Theological Seminary, 3909 Swiss Ave, Dallas, TX, 75204. Tel: 214-841-3755. Fax: 214-841-3745. p. 2307

Thompson, Lorenza Tejada, Mrs, Mgr, Hicks Morley Hamilton Stewart & Storie LLP, TD Ctr, 39th Flr, 77 King St W, Toronto, ON, M5H 1K8, CANADA. Tel: 416 362-1011, Ext 7119. Fax: 416-362-9680. p. 2854

Thompson, Lynn, Dir, Clark Memorial Library, Seven Pinehurst Dr, Carolina, RI, 02812. Tel: 401-364-6100. Fax: 401-364-7675. p. 2164

Thompson, Lynn, Pub Serv, New Braunfels Public Library, 700 E Common St, New Braunfels, TX, 78130-5689. Tel: 830-221-4315. Fax: 830-608-2151. p. 2365

Thompson, Madeleine, Librn & Archivist, Wildlife Conservation Society Library, 2300 Southern Blvd, Bronx, NY, 10460. Tel: 718-220-6874. p. 1588

Thompson, Marcy, Local Hist Librn, Transylvania County Library, 212 S Gaston, Brevard, NC, 28712. Tel: 828-884-3151. Fax: 828-877-4230. p. 1777

Thompson, Margaret, Communications Mgr, Teton County Library, 125 Virginian Lane, Jackson, WY, 83001. Tel: 307-733-2164, Ext 112. Fax: 307-733-4568. p. 2656

Thompson, Marianne M, Asst Dir, Pub Serv, Fountaindale Public Library District, 300 W Briarcliff Rd, Bolingbrook, IL, 60440-2844. Tel: 630-759-2102, Ext 4202. Fax: 630-759-9519. p. 596

Thompson, Marie, Librn, Saint Luke's Hospital, 4141 Mill St, Kansas City, MO, 64111. Tel: 816-531-0560. Fax: 816-531-6316. p. 1340

Thompson, Marie, Dental Librn, University of Missouri-Kansas City Libraries, 800 E 51st St, Kansas City, MO, 64110. Tel: 816-235-2063. Fax: 816-333-5584. p. 1341

Thompson, Marie, Librn, University of Missouri-Kansas City Libraries, Dental Library, 650 E 25th St, Kansas City, MO, 64108. Tel: 816-235-2063. Fax: 816-235-6540. p. 1341

Thompson, Mark, Dir, Middlesex County College Library, 2600 Woodbridge Ave, Edison, NJ, 08818. Tel: 732-906-4252. Fax: 732-906-4159. p. 1483

Thompson, Marvelyn E, Ref Librn, Consortium of Southern Biomedical Libraries, Meharry Medical College, 1005 Dr D B Todd Blvd, Nashville, TN, 37208. Tel: 615-327-6728. Fax: 615-327-6448. p. 2955

Thompson, Mary, Ft Myers Campus Libr Dir, Keiser University Library System, 1500 NW 49th St, Fort Lauderdale, FL, 33309. Tel: 954-351-4035. Fax: 954-351-4051. p. 443

Thompson, Mary, Dir, Sisters of Saint Mary of Namur, 241 Layfette Ave, Buffalo, NY, 14213. Tel: 716-885-6252. Fax: 716-884-6598. p. 1599

Thompson, Mary, Pub Serv, Gardner-Webb University, 110 S Main St, Boiling Springs, NC, 28017. Tel: 704-406-4294. Fax: 704-406-4623. p. 1776

Thompson, Mary Agnes, Librn, Catholic University of America, Reference & Instructional Services Division, 124 Mullen Library, 620 Michigan Ave NE, Washington, DC, 20064. Tel: 292-319-6421. Fax: 202-319-6054. p. 396

Thompson, Mary Ann, Spec Coll Librn, Hays Public Library, 1205 Main, Hays, KS, 67601-3693. Tel: 785-625-9014. Fax: 785-625-8683. p. 871

Thompson, Michel, Bus Mgr, New Orleans Public Library, 219 Loyola Ave, New Orleans, LA, 70112-2044. Tel: 504-529-7323, 504-596-2570. Fax: 504-596-2609. p. 962

Thompson, Miriam, Coll Develop, Ref Serv, Grand Rapids Community College, 140 Ransom NE Ave, Grand Rapids, MI, 49503. Tel: 616-234-3865. Fax: 616-234-3878. p. 1185

Thompson, Miriam, Ch, Baraboo Public Library, 230 Fourth Ave, Baraboo, WI, 53913. Tel: 608-356-6166. Fax: 608-355-2779. p. 2580

Thompson, Myra A, ILL, Lamar State College, 317 Stilwell Blvd, Port Arthur, TX, 77640. Tel: 409-984-6222. Fax: 409-984-6008. p. 2371

Thompson, Pam, Br Mgr, Jacksonville Public Library, San Marco, 1513 LaSalle St, Jacksonville, FL, 32207-8653. Tel: 904-858-2907. Fax: 904-306-2182. p. 454

Thompson, Pam, Circ, Butler Public Library, 100 W Atkinson, Butler, MO, 64730. Tel: 660-679-4321. Fax: 660-679-4321. p. 1321

Thompson, Pam, Br Supvr II, Pend Oreille County Library District, Calispel Valley Library, 107 First Ave, Cusick, WA, 99119. Tel: 509-445-1215. Fax: 509-445-1215. p. 2522

Thompson, Pamela, Librn, Mason County Library System, Mason City Public, Eight Brown St, Mason, WV, 25260. Tel: 304-773-5580. Fax: 304-773-5580. p. 2570

Thompson, Pamela, Librn, Mason County Library System, New Haven Public, 106 Main St, New Haven, WV, 25265. Tel: 304-882-3252. Fax: 304-882-3252. p. 2570

Thompson, Pat, In Charge, National Park Service, One Park Rd, Petrified Forest National Park, AZ, 86028. Tel: 928-524-6228. Fax: 928-524-3567. p. 71

Thompson, Pat, Librn, Chewelah Public Library, 307 E Clay Ave, Chewelah, WA, 99109. Tel: 509-935-6805. Fax: 509-935-4564. p. 2512

Thompson, Patricia, Asst Univ Librn, University of the South, 735 University Ave, Sewanee, TN, 37383-1000. Tel: 931-598-1657. Fax: 931-598-1702. p. 2265

Thompson, Peggy, Librn, Sullivan County Public Library, Shelburn Public, 17 W Griffith, Shelburn, IN, 47879. Tel: 812-397-2210. p. 780

Thompson, Priscilla C, Pub Serv, Prince George's Community College Library, 301 Largo Rd, Largo, MD, 20774-2199. Tel: 301-322-0468. Fax: 301-808-8847. p. 1034

Thompson, Randall, Dir, University of Arkansas Libraries, Robert A & Vivian Young Law Library, School of Law, Waterman Hall 107, Fayetteville, AR, 72701-1201. Tel: 479-575-5831. Fax: 479-575-2053. p. 100

Thompson, Rebecca, Asst Prof, Missouri State University, Duane G Meyer Library, 901 S National Ave, Springfield, MO, 65897. Tel: 417-836-4525. Fax: 417-836-4764. p. 2968

Thompson, Renee, Asst Librn, State Education Resource Center Library, 25 Industrial Park Rd, Middletown, CT, 06457-1516. Tel: 860-632-1485, Ext 213. Fax: 860-632-0438. p. 352

Thompson, Richard A, Prof, University of Pittsburgh, 135 N Bellefield Ave, Pittsburgh, PA, 15260. Tel: 412-624-5230. Fax: 412-624-5231. p. 2973

Thompson, Robert, Computer Serv, York University Libraries, 4700 Keele St, Toronto, ON, M3J 1P3, CANADA. Tel: 416-736-5601. Fax: 416-736-5451. p. 2868

Thompson, Ronelle, Dir, Libr Serv, Augustana College, 2001 S Summit Ave, Sioux Falls, SD, 57197-0001. Tel: 605-274-4921. Fax: 605-274-5447. p. 2218

Thompson, Rosanna, Circ Mgr, Union County Public Library, 316 E Windsor St, Monroe, NC, 28112. Tel: 704-283-8184. Fax: 704-282-0657. p. 1810

Thompson, Rose, Interim Dir, Leepertown Township Public Library, 201 E Nebraska, Bureau, IL, 61315. Tel: 815-659-3283. Fax: 815-659-3263. p. 598

Thompson, Roslin I, Dir, Knoxville Public Library, 213 E Montgomery St, Knoxville, IA, 50138-2296. Tel: 641-828-0585. Fax: 641-828-0513. p. 825

Thompson, Sandi, Dir, Puskarich Public Library, 200 E Market St, Cadiz, OH, 43907-1185. Tel: 740-942-2623. Fax: 740-942-8047. p. 1862

Thompson, Sandra, Head of Libr, Temple University Libraries, Ambler, 580 Meetinghouse Rd, Ambler, PA, 19002. Tel: 267-468-8642. Fax: 267-468-8641. p. 2117

Thompson, Sandy, Cat, Mary Lou Johnson Hardin County District Library, 325 E Columbus St, Kenton, OH, 43326-1546. Tel: 419-673-2278. Fax: 419-674-4321. p. 1907

Thompson, Sarah, Librn, Parkland Regional Library, LeRoy Branch, PO Box 310, LeRoy, SK, S0K 2P0, CANADA. Tel: 306-286-3356. p. 2932

Thompson, Shari, Tech Serv, Windsor-Severance Library, 720 Third St, Windsor, CO, 80550-5109. Tel: 970-686-5603. Fax: 970-686-2502. p. 326

Thompson, Sharon, Mgr, Bartholomew County Public Library, Subregional Library for the Blind & Physically Handicapped, 536 Fifth St, Columbus, IN, 47201. Tel: 812-379-1277. Fax: 812-379-1275. p. 733

Thompson, Shirley, Dir, Goodwater Public Library, 36 Weogufka St, Goodwater, AL, 35072. Tel: 256-839-5741. Fax: 256-839-5741. p. 18

Thompson, Stacy, Dean of Instruction, Merritt College Library, 12500 Campus Dr, Oakland, CA, 94619. Tel: 510-436-2461. Fax: 510-531-4960. p. 197

Thompson, Steven, Archivist, Outreach Librn, Rock Valley College Library, Educational Resources Center, 3301 N Mulford Rd, Rockford, IL, 61114. Tel: 815-921-4612. Fax: 815-921-4629. p. 697

Thompson, Sue, Ch, Lynn Murray Memorial Library, 601 Railroad St, Chester, WV, 26034. Tel: 304-387-1010. Fax: 304-387-1010. p. 2557

Thompson, Susan M, Coordr, Info Tech, California State University, 333 S Twin Oaks Valley Rd, San Marcos, CA, 92096-0001. Tel: 760-750-4373. Fax: 760-750-3287. p. 254

Thompson, Swannie, Librn, Virginia University of Lynchburg, 2058 Garfield Ave, Lynchburg, VA, 24501-6417. Tel: 434-528-5276. Fax: 434-528-4257. p. 2476

Thompson, Teresa, Mgr, Haldimand County Public Library, Caledonia Branch, 100 Haddington St, Unit 2, Caledonia, ON, N3W 2N4, CANADA. Tel: 905-765-2634. Fax: 905-765-2634. p. 2802

Thompson, Teresa, Sr Librn, Pub, Haldimand County Public Library, Hagersville Branch, 13 Alma St N, Hagersville, ON, N0A 1H0, CANADA. Tel: 905-768-5941. Fax: 905-768-5941. p. 2803

Thompson, Teresa W, AV, Pitt Community College, Hwy 11 S, Greenville, NC, 27835. Tel: 252-321-4357. Fax: 252-321-4404. p. 1799

Thompson, Terry, Librn, Siskiyou County Public Library, Mount Shasta Branch, 515 E Alma St, Mount Shasta, CA, 96067. Tel: 530-926-2031. Fax: 530-926-2031. p. 286

Thompson, Theresa, Br Supvr, Kern County Library, Frazier Park Branch, 3732 Park Dr, Frazier Park, CA, 93225. Tel: 661-245-1267. p. 124

Thompson, Thomas A, Brother, Dir, University of Dayton Libraries, Marian Library, 300 College Park Dr, Dayton, OH, 45469-1390. Tel: 937-229-4214. Fax: 937-229-4258. p. 1894

Thompson, Thomas, Fr, Dir, Spec Libr, University of Dayton Libraries, 300 College Park Dr, Dayton, OH, 45469-1360. Tel: 937-229-4252. Fax: 937-229-4215. p. 1894

Thompson, Tim, Librn, Holley A G State Hospital, Patients Library, 1199 W Lantana Rd, Lantana, FL, 33465. Tel: 561-582-5666, Ext 3799. Fax: 561-540-3753. p. 460

Thompson, Todd M, Asst Librn, Racquet & Tennis Club Library, 370 Park Ave, New York, NY, 10022-5968. Tel: 212-753-9700. p. 1698

Thompson, Wanda, Librn, Clarkson Public Library, 318 Pine St, Clarkson, NE, 68629. Tel: 402-892-3235. Fax: 402-892-3235. p. 1396

Thompson, Wendell, Dir, Libr Serv, Oklahoma Wesleyan University Library, 2201 Silver Lake Rd, Bartlesville, OK, 74006-6299. Tel: 918-335-6285. Fax: 918-335-6220. p. 1958

Thompson, William, Instrul Serv Librn, Western Illinois University Libraries, One University Circle, Macomb, IL, 61455. Tel: 309-298-2785, Ext 7. Fax: 309-298-2791. p. 669

Thompson, William, Computer Serv, Northwest Mississippi Community College, 5197 WE Ross Pkwy, Southaven, MS, 38671. Tel: 662-280-6164. Fax: 662-280-6161. p. 1315

Thompson-Allen, Gail, Head, Media Serv, Russell Library, 123 Broad St, Middletown, CT, 06457. Tel: 860-347-2528, Ext 132. p. 352

Thompson-Franklin, Samantha, Coll Mgt, Librn, Lewis-Clark State College Library, 500 Eighth Ave, Lewiston, ID, 83501. Tel: 208-792-2557. Fax: 208-792-2831. p. 578

Thompson-Przylucki, Tracy L, Exec Dir, New England Law Library Consortium, Inc, Nine Drummer Rd, Keene, NH, 03431. Tel: 603-357-3385. Fax: 603-357-2075. p. 2948

Thoms, Beth, Librn, Montgomery College, Rockville Campus Library, Macklin Tower, 51 Mannakee St, Rockville, MD, 20850. Tel: 240-567-7128. Fax: 240-567-7153. p. 1037

Thoms, Beth, Ref & Instruction, Pierce College Library, Puyallup Campus, 1601 39th Ave SE, Puyallup, WA, 98374. Tel: 253-840-8303. Fax: 253-840-8316. p. 2520

Thoms, Bill, Asst Dir, Fac & Tech, Trails Regional Library, 432 N Holden St, Warrensburg, MO, 64093. Tel: 660-747-1699. Fax: 660-747-5774. p. 1371

Thomsen, Cheryl, Sr Mgt Analyst, Scottsdale Public Library, 3839 N Drinkwater Blvd, Scottsdale, AZ, 85251-4467. Tel: 480-312-7323. Fax: 480-312-7993. p. 81

Thomsen, Cristina, Dir, Univ Librn, Southwestern Adventist University, 101 W Magnolia St, Keene, TX, 76059. Tel: 817-202-6242. Fax: 817-556-4722. p. 2349

Thomsen, Elizabeth B, Mgr, Libr Serv, North of Boston Library Exchange, Inc, 26 Cherry Hill Dr, Danvers, MA, 01923. Tel: 978-777-8844. Fax: 978-750-8472. p. 2945

Thomsen, Jan, Dir, Alice M Farr Library, 1603 L St, Aurora, NE, 68818-2132. Tel: 402-694-2272. Fax: 402-694-2273. p. 1392

Thomsen, Jill, Circ, Peoria Public Library, 8463 W Monroe St, Peoria, AZ, 85345. Tel: 623-773-7566. Fax: 623-773-7567. p. 71

Thomsen, Kathleen, Dir, Lexington Public Library, 907 N Washington, Lexington, NE, 68850. Tel: 308-324-2151. Fax: 308-324-2140. p. 1404

Thomsen, Linda, Tech Serv, Department of Veterans Affairs, Northern Arizona VA Health Care System General Library, 500 Hwy 89 N, Prescott, AZ, 86313. Tel: 520-776-6031. Fax: 928-776-6094. p. 78

Thomsen, Sandy, Librn, Los Angeles Mission College Library, 13356 Eldridge Ave, Sylmar, CA, 91342-3200. Tel: 818-364-7750. Fax: 818-364-7749. p. 274

Thomson, Allison, Mgr, Calgary Public Library, Bowness, 7930 Bowness Rd NW, Calgary, AB, T3B 0H3, CANADA. p. 2688

Thomson, Allison, Mgr, Calgary Public Library, Crowfoot, 8665 Nose Hill Dr, Calgary, AB, T3G 5T3, CANADA. p. 2689

Thomson, Ashley, Librn, Laurentian University, 935 Ramsey Lake Rd, Sudbury, ON, P3E 2C6, CANADA. Tel: 705-675-1151, Ext 3322. Fax: 705-675-4877. p. 2846

Thomson, Betty, Tech Librn, Taylor Public Library, 801 Vance St, Taylor, TX, 76574. Tel: 512-352-3434. Fax: 512-352-8080. p. 2390

Thomson, Bob, In Charge, Woodland Hills Presbyterian Church, 5751 Platt Ave, Woodland Hills, CA, 91367. Tel: 818-346-7894. Fax: 818-346-7826. p. 285

Thomson, Brenda, Commun Relations Coordr, Natrona County Public Library, 307 E Second St, Casper, WY, 82601. Tel: 307-237-4935. Fax: 307-266-3734. p. 2652

Thomson, Christine, Ch, Mesquite Public Library, 300 W Grubb Dr, Mesquite, TX, 75149. Tel: 972-216-6220. Fax: 972-216-6740. p. 2362

Thomson, Cynthia Stratton, Dir, Amelia S Givin Free Library, 114 N Baltimore Ave, Mount Holly Springs, PA, 17065-1201. Tel: 717-486-3688. Fax: 717-486-7170. p. 2093

Thomson, Gordon, Chief Exec Officer, Fort Erie Public Library, 136 Gilmore Rd, Fort Erie, ON, L2A 2M1, CANADA. Tel: 905-871-2546. Fax: 905-871-9884. p. 2806

Thomson, Gwen, Mgr, Adult & Info Serv, Saskatoon Public Library, 311-23rd St E, Saskatoon, SK, S7K 0J6, CANADA. Tel: 306-975-7564. Fax: 306-975-7542. p. 2926

Thomson, Joyce, Dir, Atlantic School of Theology Library, 624 Francklyn St, Halifax, NS, B3H 3B5, CANADA. Tel: 902-496-7948. Fax: 902-423-7941. p. 2780

Thomson, Karen, Asst Librn, Penhold & District Public Library, Penhold Regional Multi-Plex, One Waskasoo Ave, Penhold, AB, T0M 1R0, CANADA. Tel: 403-886-2636. Fax: 403-886-2638. p. 2713

Thomson, Laura, Dir of Proc, Amistad Research Center, Tulane University, Tilton Hall, 6823 St Charles Ave, New Orleans, LA, 70118. Tel: 504-314-2137. Fax: 504-862-8961. p. 959

Thomson, Lisa, Dir, Barker Free Library, 8706 Main St, Barker, NY, 14012. Tel: 716-795-3344. Fax: 716-795-3344. p. 1577

Thomson, Mary, Librn, CMC Electronics Inc Library, 600 Dr Frederik Philips Blvd, Montreal, QC, H4M 2S9, CANADA. Tel: 514-748-3000, Ext 4577, 514-748-3148. Fax: 514-748-3100. p. 2893

Thomson, Mary Beth, Assoc Dean, Coll & Tech Serv, University of Kentucky Libraries, I-85, 401 Hilltop Ave, Lexington, KY, 40506-0456. Tel: 859-257-0500, Ext 2143. p. 921

Thomson, Patricia, Head, Cat, Juilliard School, 60 Lincoln Center Plaza, New York, NY, 10023-6588. Tel: 212-799-5000, Ext 265. Fax: 212-769-6421. p. 1684

Thomson, Sharon, Librn, York Central Hospital, Ten Trench St, Richmond Hill, ON, L4C 4Z3, CANADA. Tel: 905-883-2018. Fax: 905-883-2135. p. 2839

Thomure, Rose, Asst Librn, Crystal City Public Library, 736 Mississippi Ave, Crystal City, MO, 63019-1646. Tel: 636-937-7166. Fax: 636-937-3193. p. 1327

Thor, Dianna, Managing Librn, Pima County Public Library, Dusenberry River Center, 5605 E River Rd, No 105, Tucson, AZ, 85750. Tel: 520-594-5345. Fax: 520-594-5346. p. 87

Thorbjornsen, Barbara, Ch, Kingston Public Library, 10004 Bradford Way, Kingston, TN, 37763. Tel: 865-376-9905. Fax: 865-376-2301. p. 2241

Thorburn, Colleen, Tech Serv, Tallahassee Community College Library, 444 Appleyard Dr, Tallahassee, FL, 32304-2895. Tel: 850-201-8396. Fax: 850-201-8380. p. 495

Thoreson, Joel, Chief Archivist, Mgt Ref & Tech, Archives of the Evangelical Lutheran Church in America, 321 Bonnie Lane, Elk Grove Village, IL, 60007. Tel: 773-380-2818, 847-690-9410. Fax: 847-690-9502. p. 641

Thoreson, Mary J, Dir, Crystal Falls District Community Library, 237 Superior Ave, Crystal Falls, MI, 49920-1331. Tel: 906-875-3344. Fax: 906-874-0077. p. 1167

Thorisch, Thomas, Coordr, Libr Instruction, Ref Librn, Oklahoma State University - Tulsa Library, 700 N Greenwood Ave, Tulsa, OK, 74106-0700. Tel: 918-594-8146. Fax: 918-594-8145. p. 1981

Thorleifson, Harvey, Dir, Minnesota Geological Survey Library, 2642 University Ave W, Saint Paul, MN, 55114-1032. Tel: 612-627-4780. Fax: 612-627-4778. p. 1280

Thornberry, Evan, Interim Dir, Huxley College of the Environment, Western Washington University, AH 101, 516 High St, Bellingham, WA, 98225-9085. Tel: 360-650-3272. Fax: 360-778-0273. p. 2508

Thornberry, Stacey, Ref Librn, Birmingham-Southern College, 900 Arkadelphia Rd, Birmingham, AL, 35254. Tel: 205-226-4740. Fax: 205-226-4743. p. 8

Thornborough, Kathy, Chief Librn, Western Manitoba Regional Library, 710 Rosser Ave, Unit 1, Brandon, MB, R7A 0K9, CANADA. Tel: 204-727-6648. Fax: 204-727-4447. p. 2748

Thornborough, Kathy, Chief Librn, Western Manitoba Regional Library, Brandon Branch, 710 Rosser Ave, Unit 1, Brandon, MB, R7A 0K9, CANADA. Tel: 204-727-6648. Fax: 204-727-4447. p. 2748

Thornbury, Don, Head, Tech Serv, Princeton University, Department of Rare Books, One Washington Rd, Princeton, NJ, 08544. Tel: 609-258-3184. p. 1523

Thornbury, Donald, Cat, Tech Serv, Princeton University, One Washington Rd, Princeton, NJ, 08544-2098. Tel: 609-258-3177. Fax: 609-258-0441. p. 1523

Thornbury, Nancy, Literacy Coordr - Franklin Learning Ctr, Hennepin County Library, Franklin, 1314 E Franklin Ave, Minneapolis, MN, 55404-2924. Tel: 612-543-6939. Fax: 612-543-6927. p. 1263

Thorne, Abby, Pub Serv Librn, Bluegrass Community & Technical College, Oswald Bldg, 470 Cooper Dr, Lexington, KY, 40506-0235. Tel: 859-246-6380. Fax: 859-246-4675. p. 920

Thorne, Alissa, Librn, Annapolis Valley Regional Library, Berwick Branch, 210 Commercial St, Berwick, NS, B0P 1E0, CANADA. Tel: 902-538-4030. p. 2778

Thorne, Barbara, Tech Serv Mgr, Mamie Doud Eisenhower Public Library, Three Community Park Rd, Broomfield, CO, 80020-3781. Tel: 720-887-2326. Fax: 720-887-1384. p. 292

Thorne, Laura, Dir, Jackson City Library, 21 Broadway St, Jackson, OH, 45640-1695. Tel: 740-286-4111. Fax: 740-286-3438. p. 1906

Thorne, Nancy, Evening/Weekend Ref Librn, Drexel University Libraries, Hagerty Library, 33rd & Market Sts, Philadelphia, PA, 19104-2875. Tel: 215-895-2750. Fax: 215-895-2070. p. 2105

Thorne, Sheila, Libr Dir, Clay County Public Library, 614 Main St, Clay, WV, 25043. Tel: 304-587-4254. Fax: 304-587-7668. p. 2558

Thorner, Kathleen, Ch, Dover Public Library, 73 Locust St, Dover, NH, 03820-3785. Tel: 603-516-6050. Fax: 603-516-6053. p. 1445

Thornhill, Robert, Br Mgr, Los Angeles Public Library System, Alma Reaves Woods-Watts Branch, 10205 Compton Ave, Los Angeles, CA, 90002-3308. Tel: 323-789-2859. Fax: 323-789-2850. p. 174

Thornley, Cynthia, Br Mgr, Charles County Public Library, P D Brown Memorial, 50 Village St, Waldorf, MD, 20602-1837. Tel: 301-645-2864. Fax: 301-843-4869. p. 1034

Thornley, Richard, Mgr, Edmonton Public Library, Idylwylde, 8310 88th Ave NW, Edmonton, AB, T6C 1L1, CANADA. Tel: 780-496-1808. Fax: 780-496-7092. p. 2700

Thornsbury, Michael, Tech Coordr, Rowan County Public Library, 175 Beacon Hill Dr, Morehead, KY, 40351. Tel: 606-784-7137. Fax: 606-784-2130. p. 929

Thornton, Amy J, Law Librn, Wisconsin Department of Justice, 17 W Main St, Madison, WI, 53703. Tel: 608-266-1546. p. 2610

Thornton, Angela, Mgr, Metropolitan Library System in Oklahoma County, Ronald J Norick Downtown Library, 300 Park Ave, Oklahoma City, OK, 73102. Tel: 405-231-8650. Fax: 405-606-3895. p. 1973

Thornton, Ann, Dir, Res & Ref Serv, The New York Public Library - Astor, Lenox & Tilden Foundations, 476 Fifth Ave, (@ 42nd St), New York, NY, 10018-2788. Tel: 212-930-9286. Fax: 212-869-3567. p. 1690

Thornton, Belita, Head of Libr, Free Library of Philadelphia, Logan Branch, 1333 Wagner Ave, Philadelphia, PA, 19141-2916. Tel: 215-685-9156, 215-686-9157. Fax: 215-456-2285. p. 2108

Thornton, Christopher, Head, Ser, Case Western Reserve University, 11055 Euclid Ave, Cleveland, OH, 44106. Tel: 216-368-6229. Fax: 216-368-3669. p. 1876

Thornton, Christopher, Head, Cat, Cleveland Botanical Garden, 11030 East Blvd, Cleveland, OH, 44106. Tel: 216-707-2812. Fax: 216-721-1694, 216-721-2056. p. 1876

Thornton, Corey, Curator, Portsmouth Naval Shipyard Museum, Two High St, Portsmouth, VA, 23704-3830. Tel: 757-393-8591. Fax: 757-393-5244. p. 2485

Thornton, Dana, Asst Dir, Columbia County Library, 2057 N Jackson St, Box 668, Magnolia, AR, 71753. Tel: 870-234-1991. Fax: 870-234-5077. p. 108

Thornton, Elizabeth E, Dir, Bentley Memorial Library, 206 Bolton Center Rd, Bolton, CT, 06043. Tel: 860-646-7349. Fax: 860-649-9059. p. 331

Thornton, Glenda A, Dr, Dir, Cleveland State University, University Library, Rhodes Tower, 2121 Euclid Ave, Cleveland, OH, 44115-2214. Tel: 216-687-2475. Fax: 216-687-9380. p. 1879

Thornton, Joel, Archivist, Wyandotte County Museum, 631 N 126th St, Bonner Springs, KS, 66012. Tel: 913-721-1078. Fax: 913-721-1394. p. 858

Thornton, Joel, Asst Prof, Bus Ref, Texas A&M University Libraries, West Campus Library, Olsen Blvd, Bldg 1511, College Station, TX, 77843-5001. Tel: 979-862-8933. Fax: 979-862-2977. p. 2299

Thornton, Joseph, Libr Tech, United States Department of the Treasury, United States Department of the Treasury, 250 E St SW, Washington, DC, 20219. Tel: 202-874-4722. Fax: 202-874-5138. p. 419

Thornton, Joseph, Automation Serv, Upper Hudson Library System, 28 Essex St, Albany, NY, 12206. Tel: 518-437-9880, Ext 230. Fax: 518-437-9884. p. 1571

Thornton, Karen, Govt Doc, Case Western Reserve University, 11055 Euclid Ave, Cleveland, OH, 44106. Tel: 216-368-6511. Fax: 216-368-6950. p. 1876

Thornton, Lark, Br Mgr, Sampson-Clinton Public Library, Bryan Memorial, 302 W Weeksdale St, Newton Grove, NC, 28366. Tel: 910-594-1260. p. 1784

Thornton, Linda, Outreach Serv Librn, Auburn University, Ralph Brown Draughon Library, 231 Mell St, Auburn, AL, 36849. Tel: 334-844-4500. Fax: 334-844-4424. p. 5

Thornton, Lori, Tech Serv, Carson-Newman College, 1634 Russell Ave, Jefferson City, TN, 37760. Tel: 865-471-3339. Fax: 865-471-3450. p. 2239

Thornton, Mary, Br Mgr, Timberland Regional Library, Hoquiam Branch, 420 Seventh St, Hoquiam, WA, 98550-3616. Tel: 360-532-1710. Fax: 360-538-9608. p. 2543

Thornton, Michael, Dir, Loudonville Public Library, 122 E Main St, Loudonville, OH, 44842-1267. Tel: 419-994-5531. Fax: 419-994-4321. p. 1911

Thornton, Pamela, Dir, Chappaqua Public Library, 195 S Greeley Ave, Chappaqua, NY, 10514. Tel: 914-238-4779, Ext 108. Fax: 914-238-3597. p. 1605

Thornton, Phyllis, Dir, Libr Serv, McCarthy Tetrault LLP Library, 421 Seventh Ave SW, Ste 3300, Calgary, AB, T2P 4K9, CANADA. Tel: 403-260-3670. Fax: 403-260-3501. p. 2692

Thornton, Sharon, Librn, Illinois Prairie District Public Library, Metamora Branch, 208 E Partridge, Metamora, IL, 61548. Tel: 309-367-4594. Fax: 309-367-2687. p. 673

Thornton, Susan, Br Mgr, Omaha Public Library, Milton R Abrahams Branch, 5111 N 90th St, Omaha, NE, 68134. Tel: 402-444-6284. Fax: 402-444-6590. p. 1414

Thornton, Valencia, Circ, Elbert County Public Library, 345 Heard St, Elberton, GA, 30635. Tel: 706-283-5375. Fax: 706-283-5456. p. 532

Thorp, David, Br Mgr, Hawaii State Public Library System, Koloa Public & School Library, 3451 Poipu Rd, Koloa, HI, 96756. Tel: 808-742-8455. Fax: 808-742-8454. p. 562

Thorp, Doreen, Circ, Peninsula Public Library, 280 Central Ave, Lawrence, NY, 11559. Tel: 516-239-3262. Fax: 516-239-8425. p. 1651

Thorp, Mark, Coordr, Financial & Auxiliary Serv, Florida State University Libraries, John A Degen Resource Room, School of Theater, Fine Arts Bldg, 540 W Call St, Tallahassee, FL, 32306. Tel: 850-644-7259. p. 494

Thorpe, Andrea, Dir, Richards Free Library, 58 N Main St, Newport, NH, 03773-1597. Tel: 603-863-3430. Fax: 603-863-3022. p. 1460

Thorpe, Angie, Digital User Experience Librn, Indiana University Kokomo Library, 2300 S Washington St, Kokomo, IN, 46904. Tel: 765-455-9265. Fax: 765-455-9276. p. 758

Thorpe, Barbara, Dir, Raymond Village Library, Three Meadow Rd, Raymond, ME, 04071-6461. Tel: 207-655-4283. p. 999

Thorpe, Connie, Tech Serv, Elmont Public Library, 700 Hempstead Tpk, Elmont, NY, 11003-1896. Tel: 516-354-5280. Fax: 516-354-3276. p. 1620

Thorpe, Gillian, Dir, Julia L Butterfield Memorial Library, Ten Morris Ave, Cold Spring, NY, 10516. Tel: 845-265-3040. Fax: 845-265-4852. p. 1608

Thorpe, Mary, Ref, East Rockaway Public Library, 477 Atlantic Ave, East Rockaway, NY, 11518. Tel: 516-599-1664. Fax: 516-596-0154. p. 1617

Thorpe, Nancy, In Charge, The Aspen Institute, 1000 N Third St, Aspen, CO, 81611-1361. Tel: 970-925-7010. Fax: 970-925-4188. p. 288

Thorrat, Lori Ann, Cat Mgr, Cuyahoga County Public Library, 2111 Snow Rd, Parma, OH, 44134-2728. Tel: 216-398-1800. Fax: 216-398-1748. p. 1927

Thorsen, Don, Dir, Philo Public Library District, 115 E Washington St, Philo, IL, 61864. Tel: 217-684-2896. Fax: 217-684-2719. p. 691

Thorseth, Liv, Br Head, Winnipeg Public Library, Charleswood, 5014 Roblin Blvd, Winnipeg, MB, R3R 0G7, CANADA. Tel: 204-986-3072. Fax: 204-986-3545. p. 2760

Thorson, Coleen, Br Mgr, Broward County Division of Libraries, Beach Branch, 221 Pompano Beach Blvd, Pompano Beach, FL, 33062. Tel: 954-786-2197. Fax: 954-786-2146. p. 441

Thorsen, Elizabeth, Mgr, Ref & Coll Serv, Laramie County Library System, 2200 Pioneer Ave, Cheyenne, WY, 82001-3610. Tel: 307-773-7230. Fax: 307-634-2082. p. 2652

Thorson, Janet, Librn, Cambridge Memorial Library, 224 Water St, Cambridge, IA, 50046. Tel: 515-220-4542. Fax: 515-220-4542. p. 798

Thorson, Marsha, Tech Info Spec, Carus Chemical Co, 1500 Eighth St, La Salle, IL, 61301-3500. Tel: 815-224-6886. Fax: 815-224-6896. p. 662

Thorson, Nancy, Librn, First Lutheran Church, 615 W Fifth St, Red Wing, MN, 55066. Tel: 651-388-9311. Fax: 651-388-1714. p. 1271

Thorson, Shirley, Dir, Southbury Public Library, 100 Poverty Rd, Southbury, CT, 06488. Tel: 203-262-0626. Fax: 203-262-6734. p. 368

Thorstensen, Mary, Librn, Cumberland County College Library, 3322 College Dr, Vineland, NJ, 08360. Tel: 856-691-8600, Ext 261. Fax: 856-691-1969. p. 1538

Thorton, Tammy, Actg Mgr, Algonquin College Learning Resource Centre, 1385 Woodroffe Ave, Ottawa, ON, K2G 1V8, CANADA. Tel: 613-727-4723, Ext 5062. Fax: 613-727-7642. p. 2827

Thorusen, Yvonne, Librn, Idaho Power Co, 1221 W Idaho St, Boise, ID, 83702. Tel: 208-388-2696. Fax: 208-388-5505. p. 571

Thouin, Deborah, Asst Dir, Minot-Sleeper Library, 35 Pleasant St, Bristol, NH, 03222-1407. Tel: 603-744-3352. p. 1439

Thrash, David, Asst Br Mgr, Atlanta-Fulton Public Library System, Alpharetta Library, 238 Canton St, Alpharetta, GA, 30004. Tel: 770-740-2425. Fax: 770-740-2427. p. 511

Thrash, Kathy, Tech Serv, Southern Union State Community College, 750 Robert St, Wadley, AL, 36276. Tel: 256-395-2211, Ext 5130. Fax: 256-395-2215. p. 40

Thrash, Melinda, Librn, Mound Valley Public Library, 411 Hickory, Mound Valley, KS, 67354. Tel: 620-328-3341. Fax: 620-328-3341. p. 884

Thrasher, Jill, Librn, Sherman Research Library & Gardens, 2647 E Pacific Coast Hwy, Corona del Mar, CA, 92625. Tel: 949-673-1880. Fax: 949-675-5458. p. 136

Thrasher, Laurel, Bibliog Instr, Ref, Mount Saint Mary's University, 16300 Old Emmitsburg Rd, Emmitsburg, MD, 21727-7799. Tel: 301-447-5244. Fax: 301-447-5099. p. 1027

Thrasher, Lucy, Mgr, District of Columbia Public Library, Palisades, 4901 V St NW, Washington, DC, 20007. Tel: 202-282-3139. p. 398

Thrasher, Shawn, YA Serv, Monrovia Public Library, 321 S Myrtle Ave, Monrovia, CA, 91016-2848. Tel: 626-256-8254. Fax: 626-256-8255. p. 189

Thrasher-Hanson, Aimee, Head of Libr, Free Library of Philadelphia, Lillian Marrero Branch, 601 W Lehigh Ave, Philadelphia, PA, 19133-2228. Tel: 215-685-9794. Fax: 215-685-9689. p. 2108

Thrawley, Charles, Br Mgr, Morgan County Public Library, Northeast Branch, 9410 State Rd 144, Martinsville, IN, 46151. Tel: 317-422-9915. Fax: 317-422-9451. p. 763

Threadgill, Catherine H, Dir, Brazoria County Library System, 451 N Velasco, Ste 250, Angleton, TX, 77515. Tel: 979-864-1509. Fax: 979-864-1298. p. 2275

Threatt, Pati, Archives & Spec Coll Librn, Asst Prof, McNeese State University, 4205 Ryan St, Lake Charles, LA, 70609. Tel: 337-475-5731. Fax: 337-475-5719, 337-475-5727. p. 954

Threet, Darla, Librn, Gentry Public Library, 105 E Main St, Gentry, AR, 72734. Tel: 479-736-2054. Fax: 479-736-8567. p. 101

Threlkeld, Lori, Project Leader, Maricopa County Community College District, 2411 W 14th St, Tempe, AZ, 85281-6942. Tel: 480-731-8776. Fax: 480-731-8787. p. 2937

Thren, Kathy, Dir, Adamstown Area Library, 3000 N Reading Rd, Rte 272, Adamstown, PA, 19501. Tel: 717-484-4200. Fax: 717-484-0738. p. 2025

Thresher, Jacquelyn, Dir, Nassau Library System, 900 Jerusalem Ave, Uniondale, NY, 11553-3039. Tel: 516-292-8920, Ext 220. Fax: 516-565-0950. p. 1758

Throckmorton, Sandra, Librn, Morgantown Public Library, Clay-Battelle Public Library, 6059 Mason Dixon Hwy, Blacksville, WV, 26521. Tel: 304-432-8531. Fax: 304-432-8288. p. 2566

Throgmorton, Nason, Syst Librn, Columbia College, 1001 Rogers St, Columbia, MO, 65216. Tel: 573-875-7231. Fax: 573-875-7379. p. 1324

Throndset Kruk, Dawn, Dir, Cavalier County Library, 600 Fifth Ave, Langdon, ND, 58249. Tel: 701-256-5353. Fax: 701-256-5361. p. 1845

Thronson, Linda, Br Mgr, Iberia Parish Library, Parkview Branch, 500 Grand Pre Blvd, New Iberia, LA, 70563. Tel: 337-364-7480. Fax: 337-364-7714. p. 959

Throssell, Jennifer, Asst Librn, Southeast Regional Library, Lake Alma Branch, Hwy 18, Lake Alma, SK, S0C 1M0, CANADA. Tel: 306-447-2061. p. 2930

Thrower, Jane B, Librn, McMillan Memorial Library, 205 E Second Ave, Red Springs, NC, 28377. Tel: 910-843-4205. p. 1819

Thul, Betty, Per, Lower Providence Community Library, 50 Parklane Dr, Eagleville, PA, 19403-1171. Tel: 610-666-6640. Fax: 610-666-5109. p. 2051

Thulin, Kendra, Librn, St Joseph Hospital Library, 2901 Squalicum Pkwy, Bellingham, WA, 98225. Tel: 360-738-6786. Fax: 360-715-4106. p. 2509

Thuma, Jessie, Librn, Crane Thomas Public Library, North Quincy Branch, 381 Hancock St, Quincy, MA, 02171. Tel: 617-376-1320, 617-376-1321. Fax: 617-376-1432. p. 1119

Thumin, Ling, Circ, Missouri Baptist University, One College Park Dr, Saint Louis, MO, 63141-8698. Tel: 314-434-1115. Fax: 314-392-2343. p. 1356

Thurber, Amy, Dir, Canaan Town Library, 1173 US Rte 4, Canaan, NH, 03741. Tel: 603-523-9650. p. 1440

Thurlow, Hugh, Dir, Rocky Mountain College of Art & Design Library, 1600 Pierce St, Lakewood, CO, 80214. Tel: 303-225-8584, 303-753-6046, Ext 8584. Fax: 303-759-4970. p. 315

Thurlow, Susannah, Archivist, Milton L Rock Resource Center, 1720 Locust St, Philadelphia, PA, 19103. Tel: 215-717-3148. Fax: 215-717-3170. p. 2116

Thurlow, Theresa, Librn, Cole Memorial Library, 789 Hammett Rd, Enfield, ME, 04493-4347. Tel: 207-732-4270. Fax: 207-732-5335. p. 984

Thurman, Bob, Librn, New Providence Presbyterian Church, 703 W Broadway Ave, Maryville, TN, 37801. Tel: 865-983-0182. Fax: 865-681-0804. p. 2247

Thurman, Erik, Br Mgr, Monterey County Free Libraries, Gonzales Branch, 851 Fifth St, Ste T, Gonzales, CA, 93926. Tel: 831-675-2209. Fax: 831-675-9525. p. 183

Thurman, Mitzi, Br Mgr, Neosho/Newton County Library, Seneca Branch, 1216 Cherokee, Seneca, MO, 64865. Tel: 417-776-2705. Fax: 417-776-8003. p. 1347

Thurman, Rebecca, Dir, Tillamook Bay Community College Library, 2510 First St, Rm 7, Tillamook, OR, 97141. Tel: 503-842-8222, Ext 1126. Fax: 503-842-2214. p. 2021

Thurman, Ryanna, Computer Serv, Ref Serv, Kenai Community Library, 163 Main St Loop, Kenai, AK, 99611-7723. Tel: 907-283-4378. Fax: 907-283-2266. p. 50

Thurman, Sharon, Librn, South Pekin Public Library, 208 W Main St, South Pekin, IL, 61564. Tel: 309-348-2446. Fax: 309-348-2419. p. 704

Thurman, Vaughn, Br Mgr, New Tecumseth Public Library, Memorial Branch, 17 Victoria St E, Alliston, ON, L9R 1V6, CANADA. Tel: 705-435-5651. Fax: 705-435-0750. p. 2792

Thurrott, Nancy, Acq, Ser, Godfrey Memorial Library, 134 Newfield St, Middletown, CT, 06457-2534. Tel: 860-346-4375. Fax: 860-347-9874. p. 351

Thurston, David, Acq Librn, Asst Dir, Texas Wesleyan University, 1201 Wesleyan St, Fort Worth, TX, 76105. Tel: 817-531-4813. Fax: 817-531-4806. p. 2324

Thurston, Michele, Assoc Librn, Annawan-Alba Township Library, 200 N Meadow Lane, Ste 2, Annawan, IL, 61234-7607. Tel: 309-935-6483. Fax: 309-935-6483. p. 589

Thweatt, Elizabeth, Interim Dir, Gonzaga University School of Law, 721 N Cincinnati St, Spokane, WA, 99202. Tel: 509-323-5792. Fax: 509-323-5733. p. 2536

Tiampetti, Fran, Br Mgr, Cape May County Library, Wildwood Crest Branch, 6301 Ocean Ave, Wildwood Crest, NJ, 08260. Tel: 609-522-0564. p. 1477

Tian, Lijun, Dir, Presbyterian Hospital, Edward S Harkness Eye Institute, 635 W 165th St, New York, NY, 10032. Tel: 212-305-2916, 212-305-9855. Fax: 212-305-3173. p. 1697

Tibbals, Melanie, Circ, Franklin T Degroodt Library, 6475 Minton Rd SW, Palm Bay, FL, 32908. Tel: 321-952-6317. Fax: 321-952-6320. p. 479

Tibbetts, Cherie, Br Mgr, Trails Regional Library, Leeton Express Branch, 500 N Main St, Leeton, MO, 64761. Tel: 660-653-2301, Ext 125, 660-653-4314. p. 1371

Tibbits, Randolph, Head of Doc Delivery, Rice University, 6100 Main, MS-44, Houston, TX, 77005. Tel: 713-348-8827. Fax: 713-348-5258. p. 2341

Tibbits, Victoria, Librn, Westford Library, 1718 Vermont Rte 128, Westford, VT, 05494. Tel: 802-878-5639. p. 2439

Tiberg, James, Ref, Peninsula Public Library, 280 Central Ave, Lawrence, NY, 11559. Tel: 516-239-3262. Fax: 516-239-8425. p. 1651

Tiberii, Corinna, Circ Librn, Jacob Edwards Library, 236 Main St, Southbridge, MA, 01550-2598. Tel: 508-764-5426. Fax: 508-764-5428. p. 1126

Ticen, David, Bibliog Instr, University of Houston, 2602 N Ben Jordan St, Victoria, TX, 77901-5699. Tel: 361-570-4177. Fax: 361-570-4155. p. 2395

Tichenor, Jerie, Dir, Meriden Community Library, 100 Main St, Meriden, KS, 66512. Tel: 785-484-3393. Fax: 785-484-3393. p. 883

Tichgelaar, Shaunda, Coll & Liaison Serv Librn, Ohio Dominican University Library, 1216 Sunbury Rd, Columbus, OH, 43219. Tel: 614-251-4755. Fax: 614-252-2650. p. 1886

Tichy, Brenda, Br Mgr, Parish Allen Libraries, Oakdale Branch, 405 E Sixth Ave, Oakdale, LA, 71463. Tel: 318-335-2690. Fax: 318-335-4743. p. 965

Tickner, Lorraine, Dir, Tully Free Library, 12 State St, Tully, NY, 13159-3254. Tel: 315-696-8606. Fax: 315-696-8120. p. 1757

Ticoll, Miriam, Pres, Canadian Health Libraries Association, 39 River St, Toronto, ON, M5A 3P1, CANADA. Tel: 416-646-1600. Fax: 416-646-9460. p. 2959

Ticoll, Miriam, Exec Dir, Health Science Information Consortium of Toronto, c/o Gerstein Sci Info Ctr, Univ Toronto, Nine King's College Circle, Toronto, ON, M5S 1A5, CANADA. Tel: 416-978-6359. Fax: 416-971-2637. p. 2960

Tidal, Angelina, Dir, Letcher County Public Libraries, 220 Main St, Whitesburg, KY, 41858. Tel: 606-633-7547. Fax: 606-633-3407. p. 937

Tidd, Elizabeth, Asst Librn, Gilford Public Library, 31 Potter Hill Rd, Gilford, NH, 03249-6803. Tel: 603-524-6042. Fax: 603-524-1218. p. 1448

Tiddes, Heather, Asst Dir, Pembroke Town Library, 313 Pembroke St, Pembroke, NH, 03275. Tel: 603-485-7851. Fax: 603-485-3351. p. 1461

Tidline, Tonyia J, Assoc Prof, Dir, PhD Prog, Dominican University, 7900 W Division St, River Forest, IL, 60305. Tel: 708-524-6845. Fax: 708-524-6657. p. 2965

Tidona, Francine, Chief Librn, Department of Veterans Affairs, 800 Poly Pl, Brooklyn, NY, 11209. Tel: 718-836-6600, Ext 3559. Fax: 718-630-3573. p. 1592

Tidwell, Allyssa, In Charge, Merced County Library, Delhi Educational Park Community, 16881 Schendal Rd, Delhi, CA, 95315-9543. Tel: 209-656-2049. p. 185

Tidwell, Judy, Dir, Adelia McConnell Russell Library, 318 Church St, Alexander City, AL, 35010-2516. Tel: 256-329-6796. Fax: 256-329-6797. p. 4

Tidwell, Mark J, Dir, Jellico Public Library, 104 N Main St, Jellico, TN, 37762-2004. Tel: 423-784-7488. Fax: 423-784-8745. p. 2239

Tidwell, Sharon, Br Mgr, Brooklyn Public Library, Clinton Hill, 380 Washington Ave, Brooklyn, NY, 11238. Tel: 718-398-8713. Fax: 718-398-8715. p. 1591

Tiedt, Karen, Dir, Fairbank Public Library, 212 Main St, Fairbank, IA, 50629. Tel: 319-635-2487. Fax: 319-635-2487. p. 815

Tiegel, Mitch, Librn, Onondaga County Public Library, Soule, 101 Springfield Rd, Syracuse, NY, 13214. Tel: 315-435-5320. Fax: 315-449-4239. p. 1753

Tieger, Helene, Archivist, Bard College, One Library Rd, Annandale-on-Hudson, NY, 12504. Tel: 845-758-7396. Fax: 845-758-5801. p. 1574

Tiegs, Ed, Ch, Brewer Public Library, 325 N Central Ave, Richland Center, WI, 53581-1802. Tel: 608-647-6444. Fax: 608-647-6797. p. 2634

Tiegs, Tracie, Law Librn, Frost, Brown & Todd LLC, 400 W Market St, 32nd Flr, Louisville, KY, 40202-3363. Tel: 513-651-6800. Fax: 513-651-6981. p. 923

Tiegs, Tracie, Librn, Frost Brown Todd LLC, 3300 Great American Tower, 301 E Fourth St, Cincinnati, OH, 45202. Tel: 513-651-6982. Fax: 513-651-6981. p. 1870

Tieman, Barbara, Cat, Prescott Valley Public Library, 7401 E Civic Circle, Prescott Valley, AZ, 86314. Tel: 928-759-3040. Fax: 928-759-3121. p. 79

Tiemann, Melissa, Circ Supvr, Ser Librn, College of Saint Mary Library, 7000 Mercy Rd, Omaha, NE, 68106-2606. Tel: 402-399-2466. Fax: 402-399-2686. p. 1411

Tiemeyer, Jamie, Electronic Res Librn, Cornerstone University, 1001 E Beltline Ave NE, Grand Rapids, MI, 49525. Tel: 616-949-5300. Fax: 616-222-1405. p. 1184

Tierce, Jill, Dir, Waldport Public Library, 460 Hemlock St, Waldport, OR, 97394. Tel: 541-563-5880. Fax: 541-563-6237. p. 2022

Tierce, Jill, Pres, Coastal Resource Sharing Network, c/o Tillamook County Library, 1716 Third St, Tillamook, OR, 97141. Tel: 503-842-4792. Fax: 503-815-8194. p. 2953

Tierce, Joan E, District Librn, Holmes Community College, 1180 W Monroe St, Grenada, MS, 38901. Tel: 662-227-2312. Fax: 662-227-2290. p. 1299

Tierney, Barbara, Head, Res & Info Serv, University of Central Florida Libraries, 4000 Central Florida Blvd, Bldg 2, Orlando, FL, 32816-2666. Tel: 407-823-2564. Fax: 407-823-2529. p. 477

Tierney, Catherine, Assoc Univ Librn, Tech Serv, Stanford University Libraries, 557 Escondido Mall, Stanford, CA, 94305-6004. Tel: 650-725-1064. p. 270

Tierney, Catie, Ref Librn, Middle Georgia Regional Library System, 1180 Washington Ave, Macon, GA, 31201-1790. Tel: 478-744-0825. Fax: 478-742-3161. p. 541

Tierney, Eileen, Media Spec, Robert L Carothers Library & Learning Commons, 15 Lippitt Rd, Kingston, RI, 02881. Tel: 401-874-4267. Fax: 401-874-4608. p. 2168

Tietje, Lori, Dir, Patrick Henry School District Public Library, 208 NE Ave, Deshler, OH, 43516. Tel: 419-278-3616. Fax: 419-278-3616. p. 1896

Tietjen, Linda, Coll Develop Librn, Auraria Library, 1100 Lawrence St, Denver, CO, 80204-2095. Tel: 303-556-4298. Fax: 303-556-3528. p. 298

Tietolman, Angela, Librn, Robinson, Sheppard & Shapiro, 800 Place Victoria, Ste 4700, Montreal, QC, H4Z 1H6, CANADA. Tel: 514-393-4009. Fax: 514-878-1865. p. 2901

Tiffany, Georgia, Ch, Cambria County Library System & District Center, 248 Main St, Johnstown, PA, 15901. Tel: 814-536-5131. Fax: 814-536-6905. p. 2073

Tiffin, John, Tech Serv Librn, Biola University Library, 13800 Biola Ave, La Mirada, CA, 90639. Tel: 562-944-0351, Ext 5153. Fax: 562-903-4840. p. 162

Tighe, Chris, Librn, United States Courts Library, 750 Missouri Ave, East Saint Louis, IL, 62202. Tel: 618-482-9477. Fax: 618-482-9234. p. 639

Tighe, Rebecca, Head, Ch, Wilson County Public Library, 249 Nash St W, Wilson, NC, 27893-3801. Tel: 252-237-5355. p. 1831

Tigner, Janette, Local Hist Librn, Bolivar-Hardeman County Library, 213 N Washington St, Bolivar, TN, 38008-2020. Tel: 731-658-3436. Fax: 731-658-4660. p. 2225

Tigue, Roxanne, ILL, Scranton Public Library, Albright Memorial Bldg, 500 Vine St, Scranton, PA, 18509-3298. Tel: 570-348-3000. Fax: 570-348-3020. p. 2138

Tikovitsch, Terry, Dir, Robert W Barlow Memorial Library, 921 Washington Ave, Iowa Falls, IA, 50126. Tel: 641-648-2872. Fax: 641-648-2872. p. 824

Tilbe, Janet, Mgr, Bridgewater Free Library, 404 Pritchard Ave, Bridgewater, NY, 13313. Tel: 315-822-6475. p. 1585

Tilden, Juliana, Coordr, Cat, Assemblies of God Theological Seminary, 1435 N Glenstone Ave, Springfield, MO, 65802-2131. Tel: 417-268-1061. Fax: 417-268-1001. p. 1365

Tilden, Penny, Librn, Rolfe Public Library, 319 Garfield St, Rolfe, IA, 50581-1118. Tel: 712-848-3143. Fax: 712-848-3143. p. 841

Tileston, Nancy, Coordr, Tech Serv, Anchorage Public Library, 3600 Denali St, Anchorage, AK, 99503. Tel: 907-343-2998. Fax: 907-343-2930. p. 44

Tilito, Mata, Librn, American Samoa Office of Library Services, Lupelele, Iliili Village, Pago Pago, AS, 96799. Tel: 684-688-7832. Fax: 684-633-4240. p. 2665

Tillander, Andrea, Mgr, Res, Clausen Miller Research Services Dept, Ten S LaSalle St, 16th Flr, Chicago, IL, 60603-1098. Tel: 312-606-7887. Fax: 312-606-7777. p. 611

Tillequots, Jolena, Asst Head Librn, Yakama Nation Library, Yakama Nation Cultural Ctr, Hwy 97 at Fort Rd, Toppenish, WA, 98948. Tel: 509-865-2800, Ext 6, 509-865-5121, Ext 4721, 509-865-5121, Ext 4747. Fax: 509-865-6101. p. 2541

Tillequots, Jolena, Libr Tech, Yakama Nation Library, Yakama Nation Cultural Ctr, Hwy 97 at Fort Rd, Toppenish, WA, 98948. Tel: 509-865-2800, Ext 6, 509-865-5121, Ext 4721, 509-865-5121, Ext 4747. Fax: 509-865-6101. p. 2541

Tiller, Phyllis, Bus Librn, Circ, ILL, Buchanan County Public Library, Rte 2, Poetown Rd, Grundy, VA, 24614-9613. Tel: 276-935-6581. Fax: 276-935-6292. p. 2467

Tillery, Phyllis, Dir, Pilot Point Community Library, 324 S Washington St, Pilot Point, TX, 76258. Tel: 940-686-5004. Fax: 940-686-2833. p. 2369

Tillery, Theresa, Dir, Richland Hills Public Library, 6724 Rena Dr, Richland Hills, TX, 76118-6297. Tel: 817-299-1860. Fax: 817-299-1863. p. 2374

Tillett, Ellen, Pub Serv, Wofford College, 429 N Church St, Spartanburg, SC, 29303-3663. Tel: 864-597-4300. Fax: 864-597-4329. p. 2206

Tilley, Carol, Asst Prof, University of Illinois at Urbana-Champaign, Library & Information Science Bldg, 501 E Daniel St, Champaign, IL, 61820-6211. Tel: 217-333-3280. Fax: 217-244-3302. p. 2965

Tilley, Marilyn, Youth Serv Dir, Churdan City Library, 414 Sand St, Churdan, IA, 50050. Tel: 515-389-3423. Fax: 515-389-3401. p. 802

Tilley, Sheryl, Br Mgr, Region of Waterloo Library, Elmira Branch, 65 Arthur St S, Elmira, ON, N3B 2M6, CANADA. Tel: 519-669-5477. p. 2793

Tillinghast, Nancy, Dir, Thomas County Public Library System, 201 N Madison St, Thomasville, GA, 31792-5414. Tel: 229-225-5252. Fax: 229-225-5258. p. 553

Tillinghast-Thompson, Andrea, Dir, Red Jacket Community Library, Seven Lehigh Ave, Shortsville, NY, 14548. Tel: 585-289-3559. Fax: 585-289-9845. p. 1743

Tillman, Adriene, Br Mgr, Live Oak Public Libraries, Carnegie Branch, 537 E Henry St, Savannah, GA, 31401. Tel: 912-231-9921. Fax: 912-231-9575. p. 550

Tillman, Hope N, Dir, Babson College, 231 Forest St, Babson Park, MA, 02457-0310. Tel: 781-239-4259. Fax: 781-239-5226. p. 1051

Tillman, Janet L, Ref Librn, Robert L Powell Library (The Master's College), 21726 W Placerita Canyon Rd, Santa Clarita, CA, 91321-1200. Tel: 661-259-3540. Fax: 661-362-2719. p. 263

Tillman, Leta, ILL, Hardin-Simmons University, 2341 Hickory St, Abilene, TX, 79698. Tel: 325-670-1236. Fax: 325-677-8351. p. 2272

Tillman, Marilyn, Librn, Lauderdale County Library, 120 Lafayette St, Ripley, TN, 38063-1321. Tel: 731-635-1872. Fax: 731-635-8568. p. 2264

Tillman, Marvin, Head, Libr Serv Ctr, Duke University Libraries, 411 Chapel Dr, Durham, NC, 27708. Tel: 919-596-3962, Ext 10. Fax: 919-598-3103, p. 1787

Tillman, Mike, Teacher Res Ctr Librn, California State University, Fresno, Henry Madden Library, 5200 N Barton Ave, Mail Stop ML-34, Fresno, CA, 93740-8014. Tel: 559-278-2054. Fax: 559-278-6952. p. 150

Tillotson, Jan, ILL Supvr, Friends University, 2100 W University St, Wichita, KS, 67213-3397. Tel: 316-295-5603. Fax: 316-295-5080. p. 900

Tillson, Joanna, Ref, Delaware County Community College Library, 901 S Media Line Rd, Media, PA, 19063-1094. Tel: 610-359-5149, 610-359-5326. Fax: 610-359-5272. p. 2087

Tillson, Linda L, Dir, Park City Library, 1255 Park Ave, Park City, UT, 84060. Tel: 435-615-5605. Fax: 435-615-4903. p. 2410

Tilsner, Florence, Acq/Ser Asst, Holy Family University Library, 9801 Frankford Ave, Philadelphia, PA, 19114. Tel: 267-341-3315, 267-341-3316. Fax: 215-632-8067. p. 2111

Tilson, Glenda, Dir, Libr Serv Bur, Mississippi Library Commission, 3881 Eastwood Dr, Jackson, MS, 39211. Tel: 601-432-4124. Fax: 601-432-4480. p. 1304

Tilsy, Emily, Per, Supvr, Access Serv, Judson University, 1151 N State St, Elgin, IL, 60123. Tel: 847-628-2040. Fax: 847-625-2045. p. 641

Tilton, Bart, Asst Librn, Colorado Department of Corrections, 12750 Hwy 96, Lane 13, Crowley, CO, 81034. Tel: 719-267-3520, Ext 3251. Fax: 719-267-5024. p. 297

Timberlake, Mona, Librn, Bullitt County Public Library, Dorothea Stottman Branch, 1251 Hillview Blvd, Louisville, KY, 40229. Tel: 502-957-5759. Fax: 502-957-5759. p. 935

Timblin, Caroll, Asst Dir, Foxburg Free Library, 31 Main St, Foxburg, PA, 16036. Tel: 724-659-3431. Fax: 724-659-3214. p. 2058

Timbs, Jeff, Dir, Allen Public Library, 300 N Allen Dr, Allen, TX, 75013. Tel: 214-509-4900. Fax: 214-509-4950. p. 2273

Timko, Christine, Asst Librn, Coll Develop, Nevada Supreme Court Library, Supreme Court Bldg, 201 S Carson St, Ste 100, Carson City, NV, 89701-4702. Tel: 775-684-1640. Fax: 775-684-1662. p. 1426

Timm, Donna, Head, User Educ/Outreach, Louisiana State University Health Sciences Center, 1501 Kings Hwy, Shreveport, LA, 71130. Tel: 318-675-5474. Fax: 318-675-5442. p. 968

Timm, Heidi, Librn, Northwest Regional Library, Thief River Falls Public Library, 102 Main Ave S, Thief River Falls, MN, 56701. Tel: 218-681-4325. Fax: 218-681-4355. p. 1286

Timm, Helen, In Charge, Alcona County Library System, Caledonia Township, 1499 Hurbert Rd, Hubbard Lake, MI, 49747-9611. Tel: 989-724-6796. Fax: 989-724-6173. p. 1188

Timm, Marcia, Supv Librn, Albany Public Library, 1390 Waverly Dr SE, Albany, OR, 97322. Tel: 541-917-7592. Fax: 541-917-7586. p. 1989

Timm, Randy, Librn, Cowen Library, 47 Mill St, Cowen, WV, 26206. Tel: 304-226-5332. Fax: 304-226-5332. p. 2558

Timm, Robert M, Mgr, Hopland Research & Extension Center Library, 4070 University Rd, Hopland, CA, 95449. Tel: 707-744-1424. Fax: 707-744-1040. p. 158

Timmer, Nancy, Asst Dir, Lake Alfred Public Library, 195 E Pomelo St, Lake Alfred, FL, 33850. Tel: 863-291-5378. Fax: 863-965-6386. p. 457

Timmerman, Dot, Asst Librn, Signal Mountain Public Library, 1114 James Blvd, Signal Mountain, TN, 37377-2509. Tel: 423-886-7323. Fax: 423-886-3735. p. 2265

Timmerman, Sonja, ILL/E-Reserves, Gustavus Adolphus College, 800 W College Ave, Saint Peter, MN, 56082. Tel: 507-933-7556. Fax: 507-933-6292. p. 1283

Timmins, Elizabeth M, Libr Dir, Programmer, Muehl Public Library, 436 N Main, Seymour, WI, 54165-1021. Tel: 920-833-2725. Fax: 920-833-9804. p. 2636

Timmons, Mary, Managing Librn, Monroe Community College, Damon City Campus Library, 228 E Main St, 4th Flr 4-101, Rochester, NY, 14604. Tel: 585-262-1413. Fax: 585-262-1516. p. 1730

Timmons, Mindy, Asst Librn, Cat, Broken Bow Public Library, 404 Broadway, Broken Bow, OK, 74728. Tel: 580-584-2815. Fax: 580-584-9449. p. 1959

Timmons, Traci, Librn, Mgr, Libr Serv, Seattle Art Museum, Dorothy Stimson Bullitt Library, 1300 First Ave, Seattle, WA, 98101. Tel: 206-654-3220. Fax: 206-654-3135. p. 2530

Timony, Patrick, Adaptive Tech Librn, DC Regional Library for the Blind & Physically Handicapped, Adaptive Services Division, Rm 215, 901 G St NW, Washington, DC, 20001. Tel: 202-559-5368 (videophone), 202-727-2142. Fax: 202-727-0322. p. 397

Timothy, Lisa, Asst Dir, East Lyme Public Library, Inc, 39 Society Rd, Niantic, CT, 06357-1100. Tel: 860-739-6926. Fax: 860-691-0020. p. 361

Tims, Barbara, Librn, Texas Medical Association, 401 W 15th, Austin, TX, 78701-1680. Tel: 512-370-1300. p. 2282

Tin, Tony, Head, Digital Initiatives & Electronic Res, Athabasca University Library, One University Dr, Athabasca, AB, T9S 3A3, CANADA. Tel: 780-675-6486. Fax: 780-675-6478. p. 2684

Tincher, Tina M, Librn, Michigan Department of Natural Resources, Institute for Fisheries Research, 212 Museums Annex Bldg, 1109 N University Ave, Ann Arbor, MI, 48109-1084. Tel: 734-663-3554, Ext 10555. Fax: 734-663-9399. p. 1151

Tinder, James, Ch, Lodi Public Library, 201 W Locust St, Lodi, CA, 95240. Tel: 209-333-6800, Ext 2008. Fax: 209-367-5944. p. 165

Tinerella, Sherry, Electronic Res Librn, Arkansas Tech University, 305 West Q St, Russellville, AR, 72801-2222. Tel: 479-968-0288. Fax: 479-964-0559. p. 113

Tinerella, Vince, Pub Serv, Arkansas Tech University, 305 West Q St, Russellville, AR, 72801-2222. Tel: 479-964-0571. Fax: 479-964-0559. p. 113

Ting, Ching-Cheng C, Librn, United States Courts Library, 515 Rusk Ave, Rm 6311, Houston, TX, 77002. Tel: 713-250-5696. Fax: 713-250-5091. p. 2343

Ting, Ching-yi, Librn, Taiwan Resource Library, One E 42nd St, 5th Flr, New York, NY, 10017-6904. Tel: 212-317-7342. Fax: 212-557-3043. p. 1700

Tingen, James D, Coordr, Pub Serv, Flint River Regional Library, 800 Memorial Dr, Griffin, GA, 30223. Tel: 770-412-4770. p. 535

Tingen, James D, Coordr, Pub Serv, Flint River Regional Library, Griffin-Spalding County Library, 800 Memorial Dr, Griffin, GA, 30223. Tel: 770-412-4770. p. 535

Tingle, Natalia, Bus Ref & Instruction Librn, University of Colorado Boulder, William M White Business Library, Koelbel Bldg, Leeds College of Business, Boulder, CO, 80309. Tel: 303-492-3034. Fax: 303-735-0333. p. 292

Tingley, Charles, Sr Res Librn, Saint Augustine Historical Society, Six Artillery Lane, 2nd Flr, Saint Augustine, FL, 32084. Tel: 904-825-2333. p. 486

Tinius, Dara, Libr Instruction, Ref Librn, Oklahoma Christian University, 2501 E Memorial Rd, Edmond, OK, 73013. Tel: 405-425-5315. Fax: 405-425-5313. p. 1962

Tinker, Barbara Elizabeth, Dir, Old Charles Town Library, Inc, 200 E Washington St, Charles Town, WV, 25414. Tel: 304-725-2208. Fax: 304-725-6618. p. 2556

Tinkham, Debra, Librn, Bradford Public Library, 21 S Main St, Bradford, VT, 05033. Tel: 802-222-4536. p. 2419

Tinney, Gail, Librn, Legal Assistance Foundation of Metropolitan Chicago Library, 111 W Jackson, 3rd Flr, Chicago, IL, 60604. Tel: 312-341-1070, Ext 8337. Fax: 312-341-1041. p. 616

Tinney, Nancy, Librn, East Orange Public Library, Ampere, 39 Ampere Plaza, East Orange, NJ, 07017. Tel: 973-266-7047, 973-266-7048. Fax: 973-674-1991. p. 1482

Tinney, Nancy, Librn, East Orange Public Library, Elmwood, 317 S Clinton St, East Orange, NJ, 07018. Tel: 973-266-7050. p. 1482

Tinney, Nancy, Librn, East Orange Public Library, Franklin, 192 Dodd St, East Orange, NJ, 07017. Tel: 973-266-7053. Fax: 973-674-1991. p. 1482

Tinnin, Nathan, Ref Librn, Austin Community College, Pinnacle Campus Library, 7748 Hwy 290 W, Austin, TX, 78736. Tel: 512-223-8130. Fax: 512-223-8223. p. 2278

Tinsley, Ann Marie, Circ, Hudson Valley Community College, 80 Vandenburgh Ave, Troy, NY, 12180. Tel: 518-629-7336. Fax: 518-629-7509. p. 1756

Tinsley, Sherry L, Libr Spec, Southeast Kentucky Community & Technical College, 207 Chrisman Hall, 700 College Rd, Cumberland, KY, 40823. Tel: 606-589-3074. Fax: 606-589-4941. p. 911

Tinsoey, Adrianne, Librn, Crucible Materials Corp, 6003 Campbells Run Rd, Pittsburgh, PA, 15205. Tel: 412-923-2955, Ext 255. Fax: 412-788-4665. p. 2125

Tinter, Marilyn, Dir, Pound Ridge Library, 271 Westchester Ave, Pound Ridge, NY, 10576-1714. Tel: 914-764-5085. Fax: 914-764-5319. p. 1724

Tinther, Miklos, Librn, Collectors Club Library, 22 E 35th St, New York, NY, 10016-3806. Tel: 212-683-0559. Fax: 212-481-1269. p. 1674

Tipler, Stephen, Web Serv Librn, Marshall University Libraries, One John Marshall Dr, Huntington, WV, 25755-2060. Tel: 304-696-2907. Fax: 304-696-5858. p. 2562

Tipper, David, Assoc Prof, University of Pittsburgh, 135 N Bellefield Ave, Pittsburgh, PA, 15260. Tel: 412-624-5230. Fax: 412-624-5231. p. 2973

Tippets, Kathy, Head, Tech Serv, Show Low Public Library, 180 N Ninth St, Show Low, AZ, 85901. Tel: 928-532-4076. Fax: 928-532-4079. p. 82

Tippetts, Laura, Tech Info Spec, United States Department of Labor, 1111 Third Ave, Ste 715, Seattle, WA, 98101-3212. Tel: 206-553-5930. Fax: 206-553-6499. p. 2533

Tippey, Paul, Mgr, Libr Serv, Asbury Theological Seminary, 204 N Lexington Ave, Wilmore, KY, 40390-1199. Tel: 859-858-2233. Fax: 859-858-2330. p. 938

Tippin, Keith, Ref, Collingwood Public Library, 55 St Marie St, Collingwood, ON, L9Y 0W6, CANADA. Tel: 705-445-1571, Ext 6227. Fax: 705-445-3704. p. 2800

Tipping, Erin, Children & Youth Serv Librn, Andrew Carnegie Free Library & Music Hall, 300 Beechwood Ave, Carnegie, PA, 15106-2699, Tel: 412-276-3456. Fax: 412-276-9472. p. 2042

Tippins, Carol, Principal Asst Librn, Ned R McWherter Weakley County Library, 341 Linden St, Dresden, TN, 38225-1400. Tel: 731-364-2678. Fax: 731-364-2599. p. 2233

Tipton, Ashley, ILL, Midwestern State University, 3410 Taft Ave, Wichita Falls, TX, 76308-2099. Fax: 940-397-4689. p. 2400

Tipton, Carol, Dr, Libr Dir, Texas A&M University-Kingsville, 700 University Blvd, MSC 197, Kingsville, TX, 78363-8202. Tel: 361-539-3528. Fax: 361-593-4093. p. 2351

Tipton, David, Sr Assoc Librn, Admin & User Serv, Webmaster, Spalding University Library, 853 Library Lane, Louisville, KY, 40203-9986. Tel: 502-585-7130. Fax: 502-585-7156. p. 925

Tipton, Jessica, Evening/Weekend Ref Librn, Johnson County Community College, 12345 College Blvd, Box 21, Overland Park, KS, 66210. Tel: 913-469-8500, Ext 3286. Fax: 913-469-3816. p. 888

Tipton, Jocelyn, Head, Ref, Eastern Illinois University, 600 Lincoln Ave, Charleston, IL, 61920. Tel: 217-581-7542. p. 603

Tipton, Noah, Head Bldg Serv, Decatur Public Library, 130 N Franklin St, Decatur, IL, 62523-1327. Tel: 217-421-9738. Fax: 217-233-4071. p. 634

Tipton, Rebecca, Librn, Del Norte County Library District, 190 Price Mall, Crescent City, CA, 95531-4395. Tel: 707-464-9793. Fax: 707-464-6726. p. 137

Tipton, Roberta, Ref, Rutgers University Libraries, John Cotton Dana Library, 185 University Ave, Newark, NJ, 07102. Tel: 973-353-5222. Fax: 973-353-1133. p. 1512

Tirado, Amílcar, Asst Dir, University of Puerto Rico Library System, University of Puerto Rico, Rio Piedras Campus, San Juan, PR, 00931. Tel: 787-764-0000, Ext 5090. Fax: 787-772-1479. p. 2676

Tirapelle, Leslie A, Syst & Web Develop Librn, Pasadena City College Library, 1570 E Colorado Blvd, Pasadena, CA, 91106-2003. Tel: 626-585-7839. Fax: 626-585-7913. p. 206

Tirey, Alisha, Mgr of Computing, Putnam County District Library, The Educational Service Ctr, 124 Putnam Pkwy, Ottawa, OH, 45875-1471. Tel: 419-523-3747. Fax: 419-523-6477. p. 1926

Tirey, Judy, LSTA Coordr, Oklahoma Department of Libraries, 200 NE 18th St, Oklahoma City, OK, 73105. Tel: 405-521-2502. Fax: 405-525-7804. p. 1974

Tisani, Deborah, Br Mgr, East Central Georgia Regional Library, Sardis County Library, 750 Charles Perry Ave, Sardis, GA, 30456. Tel: 478-569-4866. Fax: 478-569-9510. p. 520

Tiscareno, Joe, Network Adminr, Lemont Public Library District, 50 E Wend St, Lemont, IL, 60439-6439. Tel: 630-257-6541. Fax: 630-257-7737. p. 664

Tish, Becky, Br Mgr, Martin County Library, Sherburn Branch, 21 N Main St, Sherburn, MN, 56171-1052. Tel: 507-764-7611. p. 1250

Tish, Emily, Dir, Trussville Public Library, 201 Parkway Dr, Trussville, AL, 35173. Tel: 205-655-6022. Fax: 205-661-1645. p. 38

Tisi, Madel, Access Serv, Ramapo College of New Jersey, 505 Ramapo Valley Rd, Mahwah, NJ, 07430-1623. Tel: 201 684 7510. p. 1498

Titmus, Joy, Circ Librn, Center Moriches Free Public Library, 235 Main St, Center Moriches, NY, 11934. Tel: 631-878-0940. p. 1604

Titone, Angela, Mgr, Consumer Electronics Association, 1919 S Eads St, Arlington, VA, 22202. Tel: 703-907-7763. p. 2449

Titonis, Georgia, Librn, Boston Public Library, Uphams Corner, 500 Columbia Rd, Dorchester, MA, 02125-2389. Tel: 617-265-0139. Fax: 617-282-2623. p. 1057

Titschinger, Casey, Br Mgr, Public Library of Cincinnati & Hamilton County, Walnut Hills, 2533 Kemper Lane, Cincinnati, OH, 45206. Tel: 513-369-6053. Fax: 513-369-4492. p. 1873

Tittemore, Cecilia, Cat, Dartmouth College Library, 6025 Baker Berry Library, Rm 115, Hanover, NH, 03755-3525. Tel: 603-646-2236. Fax: 603-646-3702. p. 1450

Tittle, Beth, Circ Serv, ILL, Jerseyville Public Library, 105 N Liberty St, Jerseyville, IL, 62052-1512. Tel: 618-498-9514. Fax: 618-498-3036. p. 659

Tittle, Debbie, Asst Dir, Pioneer Memorial Library, 375 W Fourth St, Colby, KS, 67701-2197. Tel: 785-460-4470. Fax: 785-460-4472. p. 861

Tittle, Karen, Dir, May Justus Memorial Library, 24 Dixie Lee Ave, Monteagle, TN, 37356. Tel: 931-924-2638. Fax: 931-924-3628. p. 2253

Tittlemore, Cecilia, Head, Cat & Metadata Serv, Dartmouth College Library, Baker-Berry Library, 6025 Baker-Berry Library, Hanover, NH, 03755-3525. Tel: 603-646-2560. Fax: 603-646-2167. p. 1450

Titus, Elizabeth A, Dr, Dean, New Mexico State University Library, 2911 McFie Circle, Las Cruces, NM, 88003. Tel: 575-646-1508. Fax: 575-646-6940. p. 1558

Titus, Ernestine, Dir, Fairview City Library, 115 S Sixth Ave, Fairview, OK, 73737-2141. Tel: 580-227-2190. Fax: 580-227-2187. p. 1963

Titus, John, Tech Serv, Amarillo Public Library, 413 E Fourth Ave, Amarillo, TX, 79101. Tel: 806-378-9331. Fax: 806-378-9327. p. 2274

Titus, Judy, Media Serv, Cedar Crest College, 100 College Dr, Allentown, PA, 18104-6196. Tel: 610-606-4666, Ext 3387. Fax: 610-740-3769. p. 2026

Titus, Mark, Dir, Hunterdon County Library, 314 State Rte 12, Flemington, NJ, 08822. Tel: 908-788-1444. Fax: 908-806-4862. p. 1486

Titus, Ron, Electronic Serv Librn, Marshall University Libraries, One John Marshall Dr, Huntington, WV, 25755-2060. Tel: 304-696-6575. Fax: 304-696-5858. p. 2561

Titus, Susanne, Head, Libr Serv, Swenson Swedish Immigration Research Center, Augustana College, 3520 Seventh Ave, Rock Island, IL, 61201. Tel: 309-794-7807. Fax: 309-794-7443. p. 696

Tiumalu, Mary, Asst Librn, Feleti Barstow Public Library, PO Box 997687, Pago Pago, AS, 96799. Tel: 684-633-5816. Fax: 684-633-5823. p. 2666

Tiwana, Bashir, Mgr, Tech Serv, University of Texas at Brownsville & Texas Southmost College Library, 80 Fort Brown St, Brownsville, TX, 78521. Tel: 956-882-7757. Fax: 956-882-5495. p. 2292

Tiwana, Shah, Mgr, Chicago Public Library, Government Publications, 400 S State St, Chicago, IL, 60605. Tel: 312-747-4524. Fax: 312-747-4516. p. 608

Tizzard, Judy, Per, Warren Wilson College, 701 Warren Wilson Rd, Swannanoa, NC, 28778. Tel: 828-771-3060. Fax: 828-771-7085. p. 1826

Tjepkes, Julie, Ch, Atlantic Public Library, 507 Poplar St, Atlantic, IA, 50022. Tel: 712-243-5466. Fax: 712-243-5011. p. 795

Tkach, Mary, Librn, Harrison Memorial Library, Seventh Ave SW, Moose Jaw, SK, S6H 4R2, CANADA. Tel: 306-694-3000. Fax: 306-694-3003. p. 2918

Tkacik, Renee, Educ Librn, Instrul Mat Coordr, Slippery Rock University of Pennsylvania, Slippery Rock, PA, 16057-9989. Tel: 724-738-2058. Fax: 724-738-2661. p. 2140

Tkaczuk, Lydia, Chief Librn, Jesse Brown VA Medical Center, 820 S Damen Ave, Chicago, IL, 60612. Tel: 312-569-6116. Fax: 312-569-6110. p. 607

Tkaczyx, Christine, Ch, Waterford Public Library, 49 Rope Ferry Rd, Waterford, CT, 06385. Tel: 860-444-5805. Fax: 860-437-1685. p. 375

Tobar, Kathy, Dir, Libr & Med Staff Serv, MetroSouth Medical Center, 12935 S Gregory St, Blue Island, IL, 60406. Tel: 708-597-2000, Ext 5388. Fax: 708-824-4494. p. 596

Tobey, Carrie, Ref & Instruction Librn, Cape Cod Community College, 2240 Iyannough Rd, West Barnstable, MA, 02668-1599. Tel: 508-362-2131 Ext 4753. Fax: 508-375-4020. p. 1136

Tobey, Judy, Librn, Dean College, 99 Main St, Franklin, MA, 02038-1994. Tel: 508-541-1771. Fax: 508-541-1918. p. 1090

Tobia, Rajia, Executive Dir of Libr, University of Texas Health Science Center at San Antonio Libraries, 7703 Floyd Curl Dr, MSC 7940, San Antonio, TX, 78229-3900. Tel: 210-567-2400. Fax: 210-567-2490. p. 2383

Tobias, Arnie, Sr Libr Asst, Englewood Public Library, 31 Engle St, Englewood, NJ, 07631. Tel: 201-568-2215. Fax: 201-568-6895. p. 1484

Tobias, Betty, ILL, University of Richmond, 28 Westhampton Way, Richmond, VA, 23173. Tel: 804-289-8454. Fax: 804-289-8757. p. 2491

Tobias, Elaine, Librn, Pilger Public Library, 120 Main St, Pilger, NE, 68768. Tel: 402-396-3550. Fax: 402-396-3550. p. 1416

Tobias, Jennifer, Reader Serv Librn, Museum of Modern Art Library, 11 W 53rd St, New York, NY, 10019-5498. Tel: 212-708-9433. Fax: 212-333-1122. p. 1687

Tobias, Nanci, Br Supvr, Lake Agassiz Regional Library, Breckenridge Public Library, 205 N Seventh St, Breckenridge, MN, 56520-1519. Tel: 218-643-2113. Fax: 218-643-2113. p. 1266

Tobias, Sarah, Dir, Sycamore Public Library, 103 E State St, Sycamore, IL, 60178-1440. Tel: 815-895-2500. Fax: 815-895-9816. p. 709

Tobias, Sarah, Ch, Franklin Lakes Free Public Library, 470 DeKorte Dr, Franklin Lakes, NJ, 07417. Tel: 201-891-2224. Fax: 201-891-5102. p. 1487

Tobias, Vicky, Ref Serv, Algonquin Area Public Library District, 2600 Harnish Dr, Algonquin, IL, 60102-5900. Tel: 847-458-6060, 847-658-4343. Fax: 847-458-9370. p. 588

Tobichuk, Mary, Dir, Fiske Public Library, 110 Randall Rd, Wrentham, MA, 02093. Tel: 508-384-5440. Fax: 508-384-5443. p. 1146

Tobin, Brian, Mgr, Coll Mgt, Ontario Legislative Library, Legislative Bldg, Queen's Park, Toronto, ON, M7A 1A9, CANADA. Tel: 416-325-3910. Fax: 416-325-3925. p. 2856

Tobin, Carol, Head, Res & Instrul Serv, University of North Carolina at Chapel Hill, Davis Library, 208 Raleigh St, Campus Box 3900, Chapel Hill, NC, 27514-8890. p. 1780

Tobin, Eldbjorg, Librn, Chippewa Valley Museum, Inc, 1204 Carson Park Dr, Eau Claire, WI, 54702. Tel: 715-834-7871. Fax: 715-834-6624. p. 2589

Tobin, Frances, Commun Libr Mgr, Queens Borough Public Library, North Forest Park Community Library, 98-27 Metropolitan Ave, Forest Hills, NY, 11375. Tel: 718-261-5512. p. 1645

Tobin, Gail, Br Coordr, Schaumburg Township District Library, Hanover Park Branch, 1266 Irving Park Rd, Hanover Park, IL, 60133. Tel: 847-923-3470. Fax: 847-923-3488. p. 701

Tobin, Helen, In Charge, Mid-Columbia Libraries, Connell Branch, 118 N Columbia, Connell, WA, 99326. Tel: 509-234-4971. Fax: 509-234-4902. p. 2518

Tobin, Karen, Asst Dir, Goodnow Library, 21 Concord Rd, Sudbury, MA, 01776-2383. Tel: 978-443-1035. Fax: 978-443-1047. p. 1129

Tobin, Mary, Ref Serv, Ridley Township Public Library, 100 E MacDade Blvd, Folsom, PA, 19033-2592. Tel: 610-583-0593. Fax: 610-583-9505. p. 2057

Tobin, Renee, Principal Librn, Rancho Cucamonga Public Library, 7368 Archibald Ave, Rancho Cucamonga, CA, 91730. Tel: 909-477-2720, Ext 5024. Fax: 909-477-2721. p. 213

Tobin, Theresa A, Head Librn, Massachusetts Institute of Technology Libraries, Humanities, Bldg 145-200, Hayden Library Bldg, 77 Massachusetts Ave, Cambridge, MA, 02139-4307. Tel: 617-253-5674. Fax: 617-253-3109. p. 1078

Tobiska, Linda, Mgr, Lane Powell PC, 601 SW Second Ave, No 2100, Portland, OR, 97204. Tel: 503-778-2100. Fax: 503-778-2200. p. 2011

Toby, Benjamin, Info Serv Mgr, Librn, Freshfields Bruckhaus Deringer US LLP, 520 Madison Ave, 34th Flr, New York, NY, 10022. Tel: 212-277-4084. Fax: 646-521-5684. p. 1679

Toch, Uri, Ref/Instruction Librn, College of Lake County, 19351 W Washington St, Grayslake, IL, 60030. Tel: 847-543-2466. Fax: 847-223-7690. p. 652

Todaro, Don, Asst Dir, Library of Michigan, 702 W Kalamazoo St, Lansing, MI, 48915. Tel: 517-373-1395. Fax: 517-373-5700. p. 1201

Todaro, Julie, Dean, Libr Serv, Austin Community College, 1212 Rio Grande, Austin, TX, 78701. Tel: 512-223-3071. Fax: 512-223-3431. p. 2278

Todd, Alexander, Adult Serv, Prospect Heights Public Library District, 12 N Elm St, Prospect Heights, IL, 60070-1450. Tel: 847-259-3500. Fax: 847-259-4602. p. 692

Todd, Anna, Librn, Houston Love Memorial Library, Ashford Branch, 305 Sixth Ave, Ashford, AL, 36312. Tel: 334-899-3121. p. 15

Todd, Ashley, Mgr, Info & Libr Serv, Harness Racing Museum & Hall of Fame, 240 Main St, Goshen, NY, 10924-2157. Tel: 845-294-6330. Fax: 845-294-3463. p. 1629

Todd, Carl, Tech Serv, Holyoke Community College Library, Donahue Bldg, 2nd Flr, 303 Homestead Ave, Holyoke, MA, 01040-1099. Tel: 413-552-2374. Fax: 413-552-2729. p. 1095

Todd, Carla, Circ Coordr, Calvin College & Calvin Theological Seminary, 1855 Knollcrest Circle SE, Grand Rapids, MI, 49546-4402. Tel: 616-526-6256. Fax: 616-526-6470. p. 1184

Todd, Debbie, Ref Librn, Montana Tech Library, 1300 W Park St, Butte, MT, 59701-8997. Tel: 406-496-4286. Fax: 406-496-4133. p. 1376

Todd, Dorothy, Asst Librn, Cherokee Public Library, 118 Church St, Cherokee, AL, 35616. Tel: 256-359-4384. Fax: 256-359-4016. p. 12

Todd, Edward, Br Mgr, Nashville Public Library, Southeast, 2325 Hickory Highlands Dr, Antioch, TN, 37013-2101. Tel: 615-862-5871. Fax: 615-862-5756. p. 2258

Todd, Eugenie, Libr Asst III, Kings County Library, Kettleman City Branch, PO Box 158, Kettleman City, CA, 93239-0158. Tel: 559-386-9804. p. 156

Todd, Ginny, Ch, Rumford Public Library, 56 Rumford Ave, Rumford, ME, 04276-1919. Tel: 207-364-3661. Fax: 207-364-7296. p. 999

Todd, K J, Circ, Mendocino College Library, 1000 Hensley Creek Rd, Ukiah, CA, 95482-7821. Tel: 707-468-3053. Fax: 707-468-3056. p. 277

Todd, Leslie, Head, Ch, Haverhill Public Library, 99 Main St, Haverhill, MA, 01830-5092. Tel: 978-373-1586, Ext 626. Fax: 978-372-8508. p. 1094

Todd, Leslie, Info Literacy Librn, University of the Incarnate Word, 4301 Broadway, UPO Box 297, San Antonio, TX, 78209-6397. Tel: 210-829-3841. Fax: 210-829-6041. p. 2384

Todd, Linda, Librn, Catholic University of America, Nursing-Biology Library, 212 Gowan Hall, 620 Michigan Ave NE, Washington, DC, 20064. Tel: 202-319-6695. Fax: 202-319-5410. p. 396

Todd, Lonni, Dir, Island Free Library, PO Box 1830, Block Island, RI, 02807-1830. Tel: 401-466-3233. Fax: 401-466-3236. p. 2163

Todd, Margaret Donnellan, County Librn, County of Los Angeles Public Library, 7400 E Imperial Hwy, Downey, CA, 90242-3375. Tel: 562-940-8400. Fax: 562-803-3032. p. 140

Todd, Mary P, Dir, Stoneham Public Library, 431 Main St, Stoneham, MA, 02180. Tel: 781-438-1324. Fax: 781-279-3836. p. 1129

Todd, Melanie, Dir, Lucy Hill Patterson Memorial Library, 201 Ackerman St, Rockdale, TX, 76567. Tel: 512-446-3410. Fax: 512-446-5597. p. 2376

Todd, Patricia, Ref, Alhambra Public Library, 101 S First St, Alhambra, CA, 91801-3432. Tel: 626-570-5008. Fax: 626-457-1104. p. 120

Todd, Ross, Assoc Prof, Rutgers, The State University of New Jersey, Four Huntington St, New Brunswick, NJ, 08901-1071. Tel: 732-932-7500, Ext 8955. Fax: 732-932-2644. p. 2969

Todd, Sandra, Mgr, Jack C Montgomery VA Medical Center, 1011 Honor Heights Dr, Muskogee, OK, 74401. Tel: 918-680-3753. Fax: 918-680-3752. p. 1969

Todd, Stella, Dir, Heuvelton Free Library, 57 State St, Heuvelton, NY, 13654. Tel: 315-344-6550. Fax: 315-344-6550. p. 1636

Todd, Sue, Actg Children's Librn, Asst Dir, YA Librn, Eastpointe Memorial Library, 15875 Oak St, Eastpointe, MI, 48021-2390. Tel: 586-445-5096. Fax: 586-775-0150. p. 1176

Todd, Susan, Dir, Athens-Limestone Public Library, 405 E South St, Athens, AL, 35611. Tel: 256-232-1233. Fax: 256-232-1250. p. 5

Todd, Vance, Computer Librn, Fairport Harbor Public Library, 335 Vine St, Fairport Harbor, OH, 44077-5799. Tel: 440-354-8191. Fax: 440-354-6059. p. 1899

Todd, Vonda K, Head Librn, Texas Commission on Environment Quality Library, 12100 Park 35 Circle, MC-196, Austin, TX, 78753. Tel: 512-239-0024. Fax: 512-239-0022. p. 2281

Todd-Roberts, Vera, Br Head, Chatham-Kent Public Library, Ridgetown Branch, 54 Main St, Ridgetown, ON, N0P 2C0, CANADA. Tel: 519-674-3121. p. 2799

Todman, Judith, Div Mgr, Queens Borough Public Library, Long Island Division, 89-11 Merrick Blvd, Jamaica, NY, 11432. Tel: 718-990-0770. Fax: 718-658-8312. p. 1645

Todtman, Rhonda, YA Librn, Peninsula Public Library, 280 Central Ave, Lawrence, NY, 11559. Tel: 516-239-3262. Fax: 516-239-8425. p. 1651

Todwong, Janet, Digital Projects, Washburn University, School of Law Library, 1700 SW College Ave, Topeka, KS, 66621. Tel: 785-670-3191. Fax: 785-670-3194. p. 897

Toebbe, Kate, Br Mgr, Public Library of Cincinnati & Hamilton County, Avondale, 3566 Reading Rd, Cincinnati, OH, 45229. Tel: 513-369-4440. Fax: 513-369-4539. p. 1871

Toelle, Judith, Cat, Minot Public Library, 516 Second Ave SW, Minot, ND, 58701-3792. Tel: 701-852-1045. Fax: 701-852-2595. p. 1846

Toelle, Mae, Asst Dir, Lied Battle Creek Public Library, 100 S Fourth St, Battle Creek, NE, 68715. Tel: 402-675-6934. Fax: 402-675-3911. p. 1392

Toennis, Nick, Libr Asst, Idaho State Law Library, 322 E Front St, Ste 560, Boise, ID, 83702. Tel: 208-364-4070. Fax: 208-334-2467. p. 571

Toepper, Steve, Librn, United States Navy, 114 Porter Ave, Newport, RI, 02841-1219. Tel: 706-354-7183. Fax: 706-354-7318. p. 2170

Toewe, BJ, Libr Adminr, Salem Public Library, 585 Liberty St SE, Salem, OR, 97301. Tel: 503-588-6084. Fax: 503-588-6055. p. 2018

Toews, Lorraine, Veterinary Med Librn, University of Calgary Library, Health Sciences Library, Health Sci Ctr, 3330 Hospital Dr NW, Calgary, AB, T2N 4N1, CANADA. Tel: 403-220-3750. Fax: 403-210-9847. p. 2693

Toews, Teresa, Librn, Lakeland Library Region, Mayfair Branch, PO Box 70, Mayfair, SK, S0M 1S0, CANADA. Tel: 306-246-4465. p. 2920

Toews-Neufeldt, Lynette, Info Serv Coordr, Concordia University College of Alberta, 7128 Ada Blvd, Edmonton, AB, T5B 4E4, CANADA. Tel: 780-479-9339. Fax: 780-471-6796. p. 2700

Tofalo, Ann, Tech Serv Supvr, Winter Park Public Library, 460 E New England Ave, Winter Park, FL, 32789-4493. Tel: 407-623-3300. Fax: 407-623-3489. p. 505

Tofanelli, John, Coll Librn, Columbia University, Anglo-American, 309 Butler Library, 535 W 114th St, New York, NY, 10027. Tel: 212-854-4356. p. 1674

Tofferi, Jill, Dir, Fletcher Memorial Library, 257 Main St, Hampton, CT, 06247. Tel: 860-455-1086. p. 344

Tofferi, Jill, Dir, Fletcher Memorial Library, 88 Main St, Ludlow, VT, 05149. Tel: 802-228-3517, 802-228-8921. p. 2427

Toffoli, Garry, Exec Dir, Canadian Royal Heritage Trust, The Fealty Heritage Ctr, 3050 Yonge St, Ste 206A, Toronto, ON, M4N 2K4, CANADA. Tel: 416-482-4909. Fax: 416-482-4909, 416-544-8082. p. 2852

Tokarczyk, Bill, Dir, Ashtabula County District Library, Geneva Public, 860 Sherman St, Geneva, OH, 44041. Tel: 440-997-9341, Ext 224. Fax: 440-998-1198. p. 1855

Tokarczyk, William J, Dir, Ashtabula County District Library, 335 W 44th St, Ashtabula, OH, 44004-6897. Tel: 440-997-9341, Ext 224. Fax: 440-992-7714. p. 1855

Tolan, Michael, Cat, Black Hills State University, 1200 University St, Unit 9676, Spearfish, SD, 57799-9676. Tel: 605-642-6356. Fax: 605-642-6298. p. 2220

Tolan, Michael, Bibliog Serv, Black Hills State University, E Y Berry Library Learning Ctr, 1200 University St, Unit 9676, Spearfish, SD, 57799-9676. Tel: 605-642-6356. Fax: 605-642-6298. p. 2973

Toland, Virginia L, Libr Supvr-Popular Libr, Spokane Community College Library, Mailstop 2160, Learning Resources Ctr, Bldg 16, 1810 N Greene St, Spokane, WA, 99217-5399. Tel: 509-533-8170. Fax: 509-533-8818. p. 2536

Toledo, Ivan, Asst Dir, Miami Dade College, Medical Center Campus Library & Information Resource Center, 950 NW 20th St, Miami, FL, 33127. Tel: 305-237-4325. Fax: 305-237-4301. p. 466

Toliver, Lee, Head Librn, Talihina Public Library, 900 Second St, Talihina, OK, 74571. Tel: 918-567-2002. Fax: 918-567-2921. p. 1980

Tollagsen, Jeanne, Dir, Woden Public Library, 304 Main St, Woden, IA, 50484. Tel: 641-926-5716. Fax: 641-926-5716. p. 853

Tolle, Sherry, Librn, Barnet Public Library, 147 Church St, Barnet, VT, 05821. Tel: 802-633-4436. Fax: 802-633-4436. p. 2417

Tollefson, Alan M, Dir, Schreiner Memorial Library, 113 W Elm St, Lancaster, WI, 53813-1202. Tel: 608-723-7304. Fax: 608-723-7304. p. 2605

Tolleson, Mark, Assoc Dir, County College of Morris, 214 Center Grove Rd, Randolph, NJ, 07869-2086. Tel: 973-328-5311. p. 1525

Tolley-Stokes, Rebecca, Fac Outreach Librn, East Tennessee State University, Sherrod Library, Seehorn Dr & Lake St, Johnson City, TN, 37614-0204. Tel: 423-439-4365. Fax: 423-439-5222. p. 2239

Tollie-Porter, Michele, Dir, Clifton Forge Public Library, 535 Church St, Clifton Forge, VA, 24422. Tel: 540-863-2519. Fax: 540-863-2520. p. 2457

Tollison, Rena S, Cat, Kingfisher Memorial Library, 505 W Will Rogers St, Kingfisher, OK, 73750. Tel: 405-375-3384. Fax: 405-375-3306. p. 1966

Tollison, Sharon, Dir, Carrollton-North Carrollton Public Library, 1102 Lexington St, Carrollton, MS, 38951. Tel: 662-237-6268. Fax: 662-237-6268. p. 1295

Tollison, Sharon, Librn, Vaiden Public Library, PO Box 108, Vaiden, MS, 39176-0108. Tel: 662-464-7736. Fax: 662-464-7736. p. 1317

Tolliver, Carol, Libr Assoc, Desoto Parish Library, Stonewall Branch, 808 Hwy 171, Stonewall, LA, 71078. Tel: 318-925-9191. Fax: 318-925-3392. p. 956

Tolliver, Dorothy, Ref Librn, University of Hawaii, 310 Kaahumanu Ave, Kahului, HI, 96732. Tel: 808-984-3233. Fax: 808-244-9644. p. 566

Tolliver, Patricia, Dir, Upshur County Public Library, Rte 6, PO Box 480, Tennerton Rd, Buckhannon, WV, 26201. Tel: 304-473-4219. Fax: 304-473-4222. p. 2555

Tolliver, Robert, Librn, University of Michigan, Art, Architecture & Engineering Library, Duderstadt Ctr, 2281 Bonnisteel Blvd, Ann Arbor, MI, 48109-2094. Tel: 734-647-5747. Fax: 734-764-4487. p. 1152

Tolliver, Robert L, Sci Librn, Pennsylvania State University Libraries, Fletcher L Byrom Earth & Mineral Sciences Library, 105 Deike Bldg, University Park, PA, 16802. Tel: 814-865-9517. Fax: 814-865-1379. p. 2148

Tollman, Tom, Ref, Normandale Community College Library, 9700 France Ave S, Bloomington, MN, 55431. Tel: 952-487-8294. Fax: 952-487-8101. p. 1242

Tolly, Lynda, Librn, University of California Los Angeles Library, Grace M Hunt Memorial English Reading Room, 235 Humanities Bldg, 415 Portola Plaza, Los Angeles, CA, 90095. Tel: 310-825-4511. p. 178

Tolman, Lorraine E, Dr, Librn, Wellesley Hills Congregational Church Library, 207 Washington St, Wellesley Hills, MA, 02481-3105. Tel: 781-235-4424. Fax: 781-235-9838. p. 1135

Tolman, Margaret, Librn, Emma Humphrey Library, 150 A St E, Vale, OR, 97918-1345. Tel: 541-473-3902. p. 2022

Tolppanen, Bradley, Head, Circ, Eastern Illinois University, 600 Lincoln Ave, Charleston, IL, 61920. Tel: 217-581-6006. p. 603

Tolson, Donna, Head of Libr, University of Virginia, Clemons Library, PO Box 400710, Charlottesville, VA, 22904-4710. Tel: 434-982-2957. Fax: 434-924-7468. p. 2455

Tolson, Stephanie, Dr, Dean, Learning Res, St Charles Community College, 4601 Mid Rivers Mall Dr, Cottleville, MO, 63376. Tel: 636-922-8000. Fax: 636-922-8433. p. 1326

Tolstrup, Barbara, Pres, Malden Historical Society, c/o Malden Public Library, 36 Salem St, Malden, MA, 02148-5291. Tel: 781-338-9365. Fax: 781-324-4467. p. 1102

Tolzman, Ann, Access Serv Librn, Mesa Community College Library, 1833 W Southern Ave, Mesa, AZ, 85202. Tel: 480-461-7982. Fax: 480-461-7681. p. 68

Tom, Anne Marie, Ch, Monessen Public Library & District Center, 326 Donner Ave, Monessen, PA, 15062-1182. Tel: 724-684-4750. Fax: 724-684-7077. p. 2091

Tom, Atkinson, Dr, Asst Prof, University of Central Florida, College of Education, PO Box 161250, Orlando, FL, 32816. Tel: 407-823-3763. Fax: 407-823-4880. p. 2963

Tom, Blair, Customer Serv Mgr, Muskingum County Library System, 220 N Fifth St, Zanesville, OH, 43701-3587. Tel: 740-453-0391, Ext 131. Fax: 740-455-6937. p. 1953

Tom, Gene, Chief Financial Officer, Oakland Public Library, 125 14th St, Oakland, CA, 94612. Tel: 510-238-6609. Fax: 510-238-6866. p. 197

Tom, Gene, Chief Financial Officer, Oakland Public Library, Main Library, 125 14th St, Oakland, CA, 94612. Tel: 510-238-3134. Fax: 510-238-2232. p. 198

Tom, Jimmy, Dir, Foundation Center Library, 79 Fifth Ave, New York, NY, 10003-3076. Tel: 212-620-4230. Fax: 212-691-1828. p. 1679

Tom, Robert, In Charge, Hawaii Chinese History Center Library, 111 N King St, Ste 410, Honolulu, HI, 96817-4703. Tel: 808-521-5948. p. 560

Tom, Tracy, Br Mgr, Muskingum County Library System, Dresden Branch, 816 Main St, Dresden, OH, 43821. Tel: 740-754-1003. p. 1954

Toma, Carmen, Libr Mgr, Amisk Public Library, 5005 50 St, Amisk, AB, T0B 0B0, CANADA. Tel: 780-628-5457. Fax: 780-856-3980. p. 2683

Toma, Mary, Head Librn, South Central Regional Library, 160 Main St, Winkler, MB, R6W 4B4, CANADA. Tel: 204-325-5864. Fax: 204-331-1847. p. 2753

Toma, Yan, Ref, Danbury Public Library, 170 Main St, Danbury, CT, 06810. Tel: 203-797-4505. Fax: 203-797-4501. p. 335

Tomaiuolo, Nick, Bibliog Instr, Central Connecticut State University, 1615 Stanley St, New Britain, CT, 06050. Tel: 860-832-2068. Fax: 860-832-3409. p. 353

Tomajko, Kathy, Assoc Dean, Partnerships, Communications & Assessment, Georgia Institute of Technology Library, 704 Cherry St, Atlanta, GA, 30332-0900. Tel: 404-894-4501. Fax: 404-894-6084. p. 515

Tomalee, Doan, Head of Libr, Purdue University Libraries, John W Hicks Undergraduate Library, Hicks Undergraduate Library, Ground Flr, 504 W State St, West Lafayette, IN, 47907-2058. Tel: 765-494-6728. Fax: 765-494-6744. p. 786

Tomas, Barbara, Br Mgr, Presque Isle District Library, Posen Branch, 6987 Turtle St, Posen, MI, 49776. Tel: 989-766-2233. Fax: 989-766-9977. p. 1222

Tomaseski, Kelly L, Dir, Town of Esopus Public Library, 128 Canal St, Port Ewen, NY, 12466. Tel: 845-338-5580. Fax: 845-338-5583. p. 1720

Tomasicchio, John, Archivist, Metropolitan Opera Archives, Lincoln Center Plaza, New York, NY, 10023. Tel: 212-799-3100, Ext 2525. Fax: 212-870-7657. p. 1687

Tomasik, Betsy, Tech Serv, Mifflin County Library, 123 N Wayne St, Lewistown, PA, 17044-1794. Tel: 717-242-2391. Fax: 717-242-2825. p. 2081

Tomasik, Tim, Br Mgr, Sacramento Public Library, North Sacramento-Hagginwood Neighborhood Library, 2109 Del Paso Blvd, Sacramento, CA, 95815. p. 225

Tomasini, Chris, Librn, Lakehead University Library, Orillia, 500 University Ave, Orillia, ON, L3Z 0B9, CANADA. Tel: 705-330-4008. p. 2848

Tomassi, Noreen, Dir, Center for Fiction, 17 E 47th St, New York, NY, 10017. Tel: 212-755-6710. Fax: 212-824-0831. p. 1671

Tomasso, Peggy, Commun Librn, Santa Clara County Library District, Morgan Hill Branch, 660 W Main Ave, Morgan Hill, CA, 95037-4128. Tel: 408-779-3196. Fax: 408-779-0883. p. 181

Tombarge, John, Head, Pub Serv, Ref, Washington & Lee University, University Library, 204 W Washington St, Lexington, VA, 24450-2116. Tel: 540-458-8134. Fax: 540-458-8964. p. 2475

Tomblin, Linda, Circ, Garrett College, 687 Mosser Rd, McHenry, MD, 21541. Tel: 301-387-3009. Fax: 301-387-3055. p. 1035

Tomczak, Justine, Sr Librn, Clifton Public Library, 292 Piaget Ave, Clifton, NJ, 07011. Tel: 973-772-5500. p. 1479

Tomczak, Patricia, Dean of Libr, Quincy University, 1800 College Ave, Quincy, IL, 62301-2699. Tel: 217-228-5432, Ext 3801. Fax: 217-228-5354. p. 693

Tomczyk, Bob, Asst Dir, Marion Public Library, 120 N Main, Marion, WI, 54950. Tel: 715-754-5368. Fax: 715-754-4610. p. 2613

Tomek, Nancy, Libr Assoc II, Lorain Public Library System, Avon Branch, 37485 Harvest Dr, Avon, OH, 44011-2812. Tel: 440-934-4743. Fax: 440-934-4165. p. 1911

Tomeo, Megan, Ref Librn, Colorado School of Mines, 1400 Illinois St, Golden, CO, 80401-1887. Tel: 303-273-3689. Fax: 303-273-3199. p. 309

Tomeo, Susan, Ch, Medford Public Library, 111 High St, Medford, MA, 02155. Tel: 781-395-7950. Fax: 781-391-2261. p. 1104

Tomer, Christinger, Assoc Prof, University of Pittsburgh, 135 N Bellefield Ave, Pittsburgh, PA, 15260. Tel: 412-624-5230. Fax: 412-624-5231. p. 2973

Tomerlin, Rebecca, IT Mgr, La Porte County Public Library, 904 Indiana Ave, La Porte, IN, 46350-3435. Tel: 219-362-6156. Fax: 219-362-6158. p. 758

Tomes, Ann M, Librn, Beverly Hospital Library, 85 Herrick St, Beverly, MA, 01915-1777. Tel: 978-922-3000, Ext 2920. p. 1053

Tomes, Sue, Tech Support, Veterans Affairs Medical Center Library, 800 Zorn Ave, Louisville, KY, 40206-1499. Tel: 502-287-6240. Fax: 502-287-6134. p. 927

Tomich, Nicholas, Librn, Union County Law Library, Union County Courthouse Annex, Rm 407, Elizabeth, NJ, 07207. Tel: 908-659-4625. p. 1484

Tominaga, Mana, Actg Sr Librn, San Jose Public Library, 150 E San Fernando St, San Jose, CA, 95112-3580. Tel: 408-808-2035. p. 250

Tomita, Kellie, Mkt & Communications Mgr, Cumberland County Public Library & Information Center, 300 Maiden Lane, Fayetteville, NC, 28301-5000. Tel: 910-483-7727. Fax: 910-486-5372. p. 1792

Tomka, Pam, Dir, Washington District Library, Sunnyland, Sunnyland Plaza, Washington, IL, 61571. Tel: 309-745-3023. Fax: 309-745-3023. p. 715

Tomkinson, Victoria, Librn, Jamaica Memorial Library, 17 Depot St, Jamaica, VT, 05343. Tel: 802-874-4901. p. 2426

Tomlianovich, Julie, Youth Serv Consult, South Central Kansas Library System, 321 N Main St, South Hutchinson, KS, 67505-1146. Tel: 620-663-3211. Fax: 620-663-9797. p. 895

Tomlin, Kathryn, Dir, Luverne Public Library, 148 E Third St, Luverne, AL, 36049. Tel: 334-335-5326. Fax: 334-335-6402. p. 24

Tomlin, Mary E, Archivist, National Archives & Records Administration, 5780 Jonesboro Rd, Morrow, GA, 30260. Tel: 770-968-2100. Fax: 770-968-2457. p. 545

Tomlin, Patrick, Br Head, Virginia Polytechnic Institute & State University Libraries, Drill Field Dr, Blacksburg, VA, 24062-9001. Tel: 540-231-9272. Fax: 540-231-3946. p. 2451

Tomlinson, Andrea, Tech Serv Librn, Donald F & Mildred Topp Othmer Library of Chemical History, 315 Chestnut St, Philadelphia, PA, 19106. Tel: 215-873-8205. Fax: 215-629-5205. p. 2113

Tomlinson, Brian, Fiscal Officer, Atlantic County Library System, 40 Farragut Ave, Mays Landing, NJ, 08330-1750. Tel: 609-625-2776. Fax: 609-625-8143. p. 1500

Tomlinson, Clint, Circ, Ohio State University LIBRARIES, Fine Arts, Wexner Center for the Arts, 1871 N High St, Columbus, OH, 43210. Tel: 614-292-6184. Fax: 614-292-4573. p. 1887

Tomlinson, Elise, Instrul Serv Librn, University of Alaska Southeast, 11120 Glacier Hwy, Juneau, AK, 99801-8676. Tel: 907-796-6440. Fax: 907-796-6249. p. 50

Tomlinson, Ellen, Dir, Clearwater Memorial Public Library, 402 Michigan Ave, Orofino, ID, 83544. Tel: 208-476-3411. Fax: 208-476-4527. p. 581

Tomlinson, Kathryn S, Dir, Circ & Archives, Wiregrass Georgia Technical College Library, 4089 Val Tech Rd, Valdosta, GA, 31602. Tel: 229-259-5178. Fax: 229-259-5179. p. 555

Tomlinson, Kimberly, Ref Librn, Wisconsin Talking Book & Braille Library, 813 W Wells St, Milwaukee, WI, 53233-1436. Tel: 414-286-3045. Fax: 414-286-3102. p. 2622

Tomlinson, Martin, Mgr, Osler, Hoskin & Harcourt Library, One First Canadian Pl, 64th Flr, Toronto, ON, M5X 1B8, CANADA. Tel: 416-862-4239. Fax: 416-862-6666. p. 2857

Tomlinson, Robert, Librn, Grand Lodge of Kansas Library, 320 S W Eight Ave, Topeka, KS, 66601. Tel: 785-234-5518. Fax: 785-357-4036. p. 896

Tommerdahl, Eric, Dir, Hendry County Library System, 120 W Osceola Ave, Clewiston, FL, 33440. Tel: 863-983-1493. Fax: 863-983-9194. p. 433

Tommila, Kiki, Coll Develop Librn, Instruction Librn, Whatcom Community College Library, 237 W Kellogg Rd, Bellingham, WA, 98226. Tel: 360-383-3300. p. 2509

Tompkins, Allen, Dir, Red Creek Free Library, 6817 Main St, Red Creek, NY, 13143. Tel: 315-754-6679. Fax: 315-754-6679. p. 1726

Tompkins, Beth, Dir, Oak Park Public Library, 14200 Oak Park Blvd, Oak Park, MI, 48237-2089. Tel: 248-691-7480. Fax: 248-691-7155. p. 1215

Tompkins, Bonnie, Librn, South Haven Township Library, 104 W Baird, South Haven, KS, 67140. Tel: 620-892-5268. p. 895

Tompkins, Elizabeth, Electronic Serv Librn, Kingsborough Community College, 2001 Oriental Blvd, Brooklyn, NY, 11235. Tel: 718368-6541. Fax: 718-368-5482. p. 1592

Tompkins, SaraJane, Librn, Northern Michigan University, 1401 Presque Isle, Marquette, MI, 49855. Tel: 906-227-2431. Fax: 906-227-1333. p. 1206

Tompkins-Baldwin, Linda, Libr Dir, Baltimore Museum of Art, Ten Art Museum Dr, Baltimore, MD, 21218-3898. Tel: 443-573-1779. Fax: 443-573-1781. p. 1012

Tompoulidis, Stella, Head, Info Serv, Head, Ref, Middletown Public Library, 125 S Broad St, Middletown, OH, 45044. Tel: 513-424-1251. Fax: 513-424-6585. p. 1917

Toms, Robin, Libr Dir, Ouachita Parish Public Library, 1800 Stubbs Ave, Monroe, LA, 71201. Tel: 318-327-1490. Fax: 318-327-1373. p. 957

Tomshinsky, Ida, Adminr, ITT Educational Services, Inc, 7955 NW 12th St, Ste 119, Doral, FL, 33126. Tel: 305-477-3080, Ext 150. Fax: 305-463-0893. p. 438

Tomzik, Peggy, Head, Circ, Eisenhower Public Library District, 4613 N Oketo Ave, Harwood Heights, IL, 60706. Tel: 708-867-7828. Fax: 708-867-1535. p. 654

Toner, Janelle, Librn, Sisters of Charity Hospital Medical Library, 2157 Main St, Buffalo, NY, 14214. Tel: 716-862-1256. Fax: 716-862-1883. p. 1598

Toner, Janelle, Librn, Sisters of Charity Hospital, 2605 Harlem Rd, Cheektowaga, NY, 14225. Tel: 716-633-0705. Fax: 716-891-2616. p. 1606

Toner, Jessica, Ch, Elwood Public Library, 1929 Jericho Tpk, East Northport, NY, 11731. Tel: 631-499-3722. Fax: 631-499-0057. p. 1617

Toner, Neil, Circ, University of New Brunswick Libraries, Engineering, Sir Edmund Head Hall, Rm C-15, 15 Dineen Dr, Fredericton, NB, E3B 5A3, CANADA. Tel: 506-453-4747. Fax: 506-453-4829. p. 2764

Toner, Valerie, Supvr, Ch Serv, Bristol Public Library, Five High St, Bristol, CT, 06010. Tel: 860-584-7787. Fax: 860-584-7696. p. 332

Toner-Rogala, Edel, Chief Librn, Burnaby Public Library, 6100 Willingdon Ave, Burnaby, BC, V5H 4N5, CANADA. Tel: 604-436-5427. Fax: 604-436-2961. p. 2725

Toney, Angela, Libr Assoc, Desoto Parish Library, Logansport Branch, 203 Hwy 5, Logansport, LA, 71049. Tel: 318-697-2311. Fax: 318-697-4081. p. 955

Toney, Jason, Curator, Catawba County Historical Museum, 30 N College Ave, Newton, NC, 28658. Tel: 828-465-0383. Fax: 828-465-9813. p. 1813

Tong, Darlene, Head, Info, Res & Instrul Serv/Dept Co-Chair, San Francisco State University, 1630 Holloway Ave, San Francisco, CA, 94132-4030. Tel: 415-338-2188. p. 247

Tong, Frances, Info Tech Mgr, Naperville Public Library, 200 W Jefferson Ave, Naperville, IL, 60540-5374. Tel: 630-961-4100, Ext 4980. Fax: 630-637-6389. p. 679

Tong, Helen (Qi), Digital Serv, United States Geological Survey Library, National Ctr, Rm 1D100, 12201 Sunrise Valley Dr, Reston, VA, 20192. Fax: 703-648-6373. p. 2487

Tong, Jenny, Acq, Cat, Tech Serv, East Orange Public Library, 21 S Arlington Ave, East Orange, NJ, 07018-3892. Tel: 973-266-5600. Fax: 973-674-1991. p. 1482

Tonjes, Chris, Dir, Info Tech, District of Columbia Public Library, 901 G St NW, Washington, DC, 20001-4599. Tel: 202-727-5725. Fax: 202-727-1129. p. 398

Tonkonow, Dana, Cat, Metadata Serv, Central Connecticut State University, 1615 Stanley St, New Britain, CT, 06050. Tel: 860-832-2058. Fax: 860-832-3409. p. 353

Tonn, Anke, Head, ILL, Nicholls State University, 906 E First St, Thibodaux, LA, 70310. Tel: 985-448-4646, 985-448-4660. Fax: 985-448-4925. p. 971

Tonner, Paulette, Libr Mgr, Haut-Saint-Jean Regional Library, Nackawic Public-School Library, 30 Landegger Dr, Nackawic, NB, E6G 1E9, CANADA. Tel: 506-575-2136. Fax: 506-575-2336. p. 2762

Tonner, Shawn, Dir, Libr Serv, North Georgia College & State University, 238 Georgia Circle, Dahlonega, GA, 30597-3001. Tel: 706-864-1514. p. 527

Tonsing, Joan, Youth Serv Librn, Kendallville Public Library, Limberlost Public, 164 Kelly St, Rome City, IN, 46784. Tel: 260-854-2775. Fax: 260-854-3382. p. 757

Tonyan, Joel, Librn, Northwest Arkansas Community College Library, One College Dr, Bentonville, AR, 72712-5091. Tel: 479-619-4244. Fax: 479-619-4115. p. 95

Tooey, M J, Exec Dir, University of Maryland, Baltimore, Health Sciences & Human Services Library, 601 W Lombard St, Baltimore, MD, 21201. Tel: 410-706-7545. Fax: 410-706-3101. p. 1019

Tooey, Mary J, Dir, National Network of Libraries of Medicine Southeastern Atlantic Region, Univ Md Health Scis & Human Servs Libr, 601 W Lombard St, Baltimore, MD, 21201-1512. Tel: 410-706-2855. Fax: 410-706-0099. p. 2944

Tooker, Sue, Asst Librn, O'Neill Public Library, 601 E Douglas, O'Neill, NE, 68763. Tel: 402-336-3110. Fax: 402-336-3268. p. 1415

Tookes, Amos, Librn, United States Navy, Base Library, Bldg 7122, 814 Radford Blvd, Ste 20311, Albany, GA, 31704-0311. Tel: 229-639-5242. Fax: 229-639-5197. p. 507

Toole, Laurel, Tech Serv, Lynnfield Public Library, 18 Summer St, Lynnfield, MA, 01940-1837. Tel: 781-334-5411. Fax: 781-334-2164. p. 1101

Toole, Susan, Br Mgr, Aiken-Bamberg-Barnwell-Edgefield Regional Library System, New Ellenton Branch, 407 Main St, New Ellenton, SC, 29809. Tel: 803-652-7845. Fax: 803-652-7845. p. 2179

Tooley, Helen, Libr Mgr, Evans Mills Public Library, 8706 Noble St, Evans Mills, NY, 13637. Tel: 315-629-4483. Fax: 315-629-5198. p. 1621

Toolis, Lorna, Br Head, Toronto Public Library, Merril Collection of Science Fiction, Speculation & Fantasy, 239 College St, 3rd Flr, Toronto, ON, M5T 1R5, CANADA. Tel: 416-393-7748. Fax: 416-393-7741. p. 2862

Toombs, Jean, Dir, Cleveland Institute of Music, 11021 East Blvd, Cleveland, OH, 44106-1776. Tel: 216-795-3181. Fax: 216-791-3063. p. 1877

Toombs, Michelle, Dir, Marigold Library System, 710-Second St, Strathmore, AB, T1P 1K4, CANADA. Tel: 403-934-5334, Ext 224. Fax: 403-934-5331. p. 2718

Toombs, Nancy, Managing Librn, Austin Public Library, Spicewood Springs, 8637 Spicewood Springs Rd, Austin, TX, 78759. Tel: 512-974-3800. Fax: 512-974-3801. p. 2279

Toombs, Stephen, Head Music Librn, Case Western Reserve University, 11055 Euclid Ave, Cleveland, OH, 44106. Tel: 216-368-2403. Fax: 216-368-6950. p. 1876

Toombs, Stephen, Music Librn, Case Western Reserve University, Kulas Music Library, Hayden Hall, 11118 Bellflower Rd, Cleveland, OH, 44106-7106. Tel: 216-368-2403. p. 1876

Toombs, Sylvia, Dir, Washington University Libraries, George Warren Brown School of Social Work, One Brookings Dr, Campus Box 1196, Saint Louis, MO, 63130-4862. Tel: 314-935-8644. Fax: 314-935-8511. p. 1362

Toombs, William W, Syst, Tech Serv, Kenrick-Glennon Seminary, 5200 Glennon Dr, Saint Louis, MO, 63119. Tel: 314-792-6133. Fax: 314-792-6503. p. 1355

Toombs, Yvonne, Asst Librn, DeKalb County Public Library, 504 Grand Ave NW, Fort Payne, AL, 35967. Tel: 256-845-2671. Fax: 256-845-2671. p. 17

Toomer, Patrice, Libr Serv Coordr, Wiregrass Georgia Technical College, 706 Baker Hwy, Douglas, GA, 31533. Tel: 912-389-2226. Fax: 912-389-4308. p. 531

Toomey, Trudy, ILL Coordr, Wasilla Meta-Rose Public Library, 391 N Main St, Wasilla, AK, 99654-7085. Tel: 907-864-9175. Fax: 907-376-2347. p. 55

Toon, Michael, Librn, Baylor University Libraries, Texas Collection, 1429 S Fifth St, Waco, TX, 76706. Tel: 254-710-1268. Fax: 254-710-1368. p. 2397

Tooth, John, Coordr, Manitoba Department of Education, 1181 Portage Ave, Winnipeg, MB, R3G 0T3, CANADA. Tel: 204-945-7833. Fax: 204-945-8756. p. 2756

Tooulias-Santolin, Christina, Librn, University of Toronto Libraries, Noranda Earth Sciences Library, Five Bancroft Ave, 2nd Flr, Toronto, ON, M5S 1A5, CANADA. Tel: 416-978-3024. Fax: 416-971-2101. p. 2867

Topcik, Heather, Chief Librn, Bard Graduate Center Library, 38 W 86th St, New York, NY, 10024. Tel: 212-501-3036. Fax: 212-501-3098. p. 1669

Topel, Adriana, Ref Serv, Clearwater Public Library System, East, 2251 Drew St, Clearwater, FL, 33765. Tel: 727-562-4970. p. 432

Toperoff, Elizabeth, Commun Libr Mgr, Queens Borough Public Library, Howard Beach Community Library, 92-06 156th Ave, Howard Beach, NY, 11414. Tel: 718-641-7086. p. 1644

Topete, Connie, Br Mgr, Los Angeles Public Library System, Malabar, 2801 Wabash Ave, Los Angeles, CA, 90033-2604. Tel: 323-263-1497, 323-268-0874. Fax: 323-612-0416. p. 173

Topoleski, David, Bus Tech Mgr, Toledo-Lucas County Public Library, 325 N Michigan St, Toledo, OH, 43604-6614. Tel: 419-259-5209. Fax: 419-259-5243. p. 1939

Topolnyski, Nick, Asst Librn, St Vladimir's Library & Archives, 404 Meredith Rd NE, Calgary, AB, T2E 5A6, CANADA. Tel: 403-264-3437. Fax: 403-264-3438. p. 2692

Toppen, C L, Dir, Buhl Public Library, 215 Broadway N, Buhl, ID, 83316-1624. Tel: 208-543-6500. Fax: 208-543-2318. p. 572

Topper, Joby, Tech Serv Librn, Lock Haven University of Pennsylvania, 401 N Fairview Ave, Lock Haven, PA, 17745-2390. Tel: 570-484-2465. Fax: 570-484-2506. p. 2082

Topper, Joby, Interim Dir, Libr & Info Serv, Susquehanna Library Cooperative, Lock Haven University, Stevenson Library, 401 N Fairview St, Lock Haven, PA, 17745. Tel: 570-484-2465. Fax: 570-484-2506. p. 2955

Topping, Irina, Cat Librn, Ser Librn, Union Theological Seminary & Presbyterian School of Christian Education, 3401 Brook Rd, Richmond, VA, 23227. Tel: 804-278-4314. Fax: 804-278-4375. p. 2490

Topping, Mary, In Charge, First Christian Church, 211 W Fifth Ave, Knoxville, TN, 37917. Tel: 865-522-0545. Fax: 865-521-6266. p. 2241

Topps, Stella, Circ, Elizabeth Jones Library, 1050 Fairfield Ave, Grenada, MS, 38901-3605. Tel: 662-226-2072. Fax: 662-226-8747. p. 1299

Topritzhofer, William A, Coordr, Southeastern Wisconsin Information Technology Exchange, Inc, 6801 N Yates Rd, Milwaukee, WI, 53217-3985. Tel: 414-351-2423. Fax: 414-228-4146. p. 2958

Tordoff, Dirk, Film Archivist, University of Alaska Fairbanks, 310 Tanana Dr, Fairbanks, AK, 99775. Tel: 907-474-5357. Fax: 907-474-6841. p. 48

Torello, Lesley, Ch, Granville Public Library, 217 E Broadway, Granville, OH, 43023-1398. Tel: 740-587-0196. Fax: 740-587-0197. p. 1903

Toren, Hilary, Librn, Scott County Library System, Prior Lake Public Library, 16210 Eagle Creek Ave SE, Prior Lake, MN, 55372-9202. Tel: 952-447-3375. Fax: 952-447-3375. p. 1284

Torgerson Lundin, Jessica, Cat/Acq Tech, Montana State University, 1500 University Dr, Billings, MT, 59101-0298. Tel: 406-657-1664. Fax: 406-657-2037. p. 1374

Torgerson, Rick, Tech Serv, Delta State University, Laflore Circle at Fifth Ave, Cleveland, MS, 38733-2599. Tel: 662-846-4438. Fax: 662-846-4443. p. 1296

Torgeson, Mary Jo, Dir, Puyallup Public Library, 324 S Meridian, Puyallup, WA, 98371. Tel: 253-841-5454. Fax: 253-841-5483. p. 2525

Torgormey, Jason, ILL, Fort Valley State University, 1005 State University Dr, Fort Valley, GA, 31030-4313. Tel: 478-825-6343. Fax: 478-825-6663, 478-825-6916. p. 533

Torian, R, Sr Librn, Greene Correctional Facility, Plank Rd, Coxsackie, NY, 12051. Tel: 518-731-2741, Ext 4600. Fax: 518-741-2099. p. 1612

Torkelson, Jon, Interim Dir, Lincoln Public Library, 485 Twelve Bridges Dr, Lincoln, CA, 95648. Tel: 916-434-2410. Fax: 919-409-9235. p. 164

Tornabene, Charles, Librn, Southwest Florida Water Management District Library, 2379 Broad St, Brooksville, FL, 34604-6899. Tel: 352-796-7211, Ext 4051. Fax: 352-797-5807. p. 431

Tornatore, Jeane, Tech Serv Mgr, Jefferson County Library, 5678 State Rd PP, High Ridge, MO, 63049-2216. Tel: 636-677-8689. Fax: 636-677-1769. p. 1331

Tornquist, Kristi, Chief Univ Librn, South Dakota State University, 1300 N Campus Dr, Box 2115, Brookings, SD, 57007-1098. Tel: 605-688-5106. Fax: 605-688-6133. p. 2210

Toro, Cirilo, Info Literacy, Pontifical Catholic University Of Puerto Rico, Encarnacion Valdes Library, 2250 Avenida Las Americas, Ste 509, Ponce, PR, 00717-0777. Tel: 787-841-2000, Ext 1814. Fax: 787-284-0235. p. 2675

Toro, Orlando, Acq, Asst Librn, Amaury Veray Music Library, 350 Rafael Lamar, Hato Rey, PR, 00918. Tel: 787-751-0160, Ext 225. Fax: 787-754-5934. p. 2673

Torowski, Nancy, ILL, Worcester Public Library, Three Salem Sq, Worcester, MA, 01608. Tel: 508-799-1655. Fax: 508-799-1652. p. 1145

Torphy, Nancy, Br Mgr, Milwaukee Public Library, East, 1910 E North Ave, Milwaukee, WI, 53202. Tel: 414-286-3058. Fax: 414-286-8431. p. 2620

Torralbas, Grisel, Acq Librn, Hialeah-John F Kennedy Library, 190 W 49th St, Hialeah, FL, 33012-3798. Tel: 305-821-2700. Fax: 305-818-9144. p. 450

Torrance, Amy, Acq, Colby Community College, 1255 S Range Ave, Colby, KS, 67701. Tel: 785-460-4689. Fax: 785-460-4600. p. 861

Torrance, Millie, Br Mgr, Sacramento Public Library, Belle Cooledge Community Library, 5600 S Land Park Dr, Sacramento, CA, 95822. p. 224

Torrens, Carol, Outreach Serv Librn, Bloomington Public Library, 205 E Olive St, Bloomington, IL, 61701. Tel: 309-828-6091. Fax: 309-828-7312. p. 595

Torres, Amparo, Ref, Marshall Memorial Library, 110 S Diamond St, Deming, NM, 88030-3698. Tel: 505-546-9202. Fax: 505-546-9649. p. 1554

Torres, Ana Aurelia, Asst Dir, Pontifical Catholic University Of Puerto Rico, Encarnacion Valdes Library, 2250 Avenida Las Americas, Ste 509, Ponce, PR, 00717-0777. Tel: 787-841-2000, Ext 1811. Fax: 787-284-0235. p. 2674

Torres, Anita, Supvr, Circ, City of Calabasas Library, 200 Civic Center Way, Calabasas, CA, 91302. Tel: 818-225-7616. Fax: 818-225-7728. p. 131

Torres, Arturo L, Dir, Texas Tech University, School of Law Bldg, 1802 Hartford Ave, Lubbock, TX, 79409. Tel: 806-742-3957. Fax: 806-742-1629. p. 2357

Torres, Bessy, In Charge, University of Florida, Tropical Research & Education Center, 18905 SW 280th St, Homestead, FL, 33031. Tel: 305-246-6340. Fax: 305-246-7003. p. 451

Torres, Bonnie, Instrul Media Ctr Mgr, Elmhurst College, 190 Prospect St, Elmhurst, IL, 60126. Tel: 630-617-3153. Fax: 630-617-3332. p. 642

Torres, Christine, Circ, Pueblo Community College Library, 900 W Orman Ave, Pueblo, CO, 81004-1430. Tel: 719-549-3308. Fax: 719-549-3309. p. 321

Torres, Deborah, Asst Prog Dir, Saint Catherine University, 2004 Randolph Ave, Mailstop No 4125, Saint Paul, MN, 55105. Tel: 651-690-6802. Fax: 651-690-8724. p. 2968

Torres, Elsie, Circ, Wells College, 170 Main St, Aurora, NY, 13026-0500. Tel: 315-364-3351. Fax: 315-364-3412. p. 1576

Torres, Ivy, LTA Supvr, Acq, Florida International University, 3000 NE 151st St, North Miami, FL, 33181-3600. Tel: 305-919-5717. Fax: 305-919-5914. p. 472

Torres, Joni J, Librn, Hawaii Employers Council Library, 2682 Waiwai Loop, Honolulu, HI, 96819. Tel: 808-836-1511. Fax: 808-836-1649. p. 560

Torres, Karrie, Sr Librn, Otisville State Correctional Facility Library, PO Box 8, Otisville, NY, 10963-0008. Tel: 845-386-1490, Ext 4600. p. 1713

Torres, Luisa, Dir, Universidad del Turabo, PO Box 3030, Gurabo, PR, 00778-3030. Tel: 787-743-7979, Ext 4501. Fax: 787-743-7924. p. 2673

Torres, Marjorie, Cat, Universidad del Turabo, PO Box 3030, Gurabo, PR, 00778-3030. Tel: 787-743-7979, Ext 4501. Fax: 787-743-7924. p. 2673

Torres, Mia, Circ, Belleville Public Library & Information Center, 221 Washington Ave, Belleville, NJ, 07109-3189. Tel: 973-450-3434. Fax: 973-450-9518, 973-759-6731. p. 1471

Torres, Myrna, Ref Librn, University of Puerto Rico, Minillas Park, 170, 174 Rd, Bayamon, PR, 00959-1919. Tel: 787-993-0000, Ext 3222, 787-993-8857. Fax: 787-993-8914. p. 2672

Torres, Ramona, Ref Serv, Bay City Public Library, 1100 Seventh St, Bay City, TX, 77414. Tel: 979-245-6931. Fax: 979-245-2614. p. 2286

Torres, Teresa, Commun Librn, Fort Vancouver Regional Library District, Cascade Park Community Library, 600 NE 136th Ave, Vancouver, WA, 98684. Tel: 360-256-7782. Fax: 360-256-7987. p. 2546

Torres, Tracy, Ch, Groton Public Library, 52 Newtown Rd, Groton, CT, 06340. Tel: 860-441-6750. Fax: 860-448-0363. p. 342

Torres, Yarelis, Head Librn, University of Puerto Rico Library System, Library Services for the Physically Handicapped, Rio Piedras Campus, Edif Jose M Lazaro, San Juan, PR, 00931. Tel: 787-764-0000, Ext 5173. Fax: 787-772-1479. p. 2677

Torres-Alvarez, Ivette, Dir, Supreme Court Library of Puerto Rico, Munoz Rivera Ave, Puerta de Tierra, San Juan, PR, 00902. Tel: 787-289-0179, 787-723-3550. Fax: 787-724-5090. p. 2676

Torres-Aveillez, Magdalena, Ref Librn, Inter-American University of Puerto Rico, San German Campus, Ave Inter-American University, Rd 102, K 30 6, San German, PR, 00683-9801. Tel: 787-264-1912, Ext 7521. Fax: 787-264-2544. p. 2675

Torres-Hanley, Jeannette, Ref Librn, Free Public Library of Bayonne, 697 Avenue C, Bayonne, NJ, 07002. Tel: 201-858-6970. Fax: 201-437-6928. p. 1470

Torres-Zayas, Adalin, Tech Serv Supvr, Inglewood Public Library, 101 W Manchester Blvd, Inglewood, CA, 90301-1771. Tel: 310-412-5397. Fax: 310-412-8848. p. 159

Torrie, Susan, Libr Mgr, Barnwell Public Library, 500 Second St W, Barnwell, AB, T0K 0B0, CANADA. Tel: 403-223-3626. p. 2684

Torstad, Julie, Tech Serv Mgr, Plano Public Library System, Library Administration, 2501 Coit Rd, Plano, TX, 75075. Tel: 972-769-4291. Fax: 972-769-4121. p. 2370

Torv, Denise, Exec Dir, Westport Historical Society Library, 25 Avery Pl, Westport, CT, 06880-3215. Tel: 203-222-1424. Fax: 203-221-0981. p. 377

Torvik, Vetle, Asst Prof, University of Illinois at Urbana-Champaign, Library & Information Science Bldg, 501 E Daniel St, Champaign, IL, 61820-6211. Tel: 217-333-3280. Fax: 217-244-3302. p. 2965

Tosa, Yukiko, Librn, Vancouver Public Library, Kensington Community, 3927 Knight St, Vancouver, BC, V5N 3L8, CANADA. Tel: 604-665-3961. Fax: 604-665-3385. p. 2744

Tosaka, Yuji, Cat Librn, The College of New Jersey Library, 2000 Pennington Rd, Ewing, NJ, 08628-0718. Tel: 609-771-2311, 609-771-2332. Fax: 609-637-5177. p. 1484

Toscano, Josie, Librn, North Central Regional Library, Mattawa Community, 101 Manson Lane, Mattawa, WA, 99349. Tel: 509-932-5507. Fax: 509-932-5507. p. 2549

Toscano, Juan Carlos, Info Spec, Academy for Educational Development, 1825 Connecticut Ave NW, Washington, DC, 20009-5721. Tel: 202-884-8000, 202-884-8118. Fax: 202-884-8491. p. 391

Toscano, Sandra, Br Mgr, Oakland Public Library, Melrose, 4805 Foothill Blvd, Oakland, CA, 94601. Tel: 510-535-5623. p. 198

Tosh, Christopher, Hospital Libr Serv Coordr, Capital District Library Council, 28 Essex St, Albany, NY, 12206. Tel: 518-438-2500. Fax: 518-438-2872. p. 2949

Tosi, Brooke, Librn, Federal Reserve Bank of Minneapolis, 90 Hennepin Ave, Minneapolis, MN, 55401-2171. Tel: 612-204-5509. p. 1259

Tosi, Laura, Librn, Bronx County Historical Society, 3309 Bainbridge Ave, Bronx, NY, 10467. Tel: 718-881-8900. Fax: 718-881-4827. p. 1586

Tosko, Michael P, Head, Teaching & Training, University of Akron Libraries, 315 Buchtel Mall, Akron, OH, 44325-1701. Tel: 330-972-2648. Fax: 330-972-5106. p. 1853

Toston, Shirley, Asst Br Mgr, Ch, Librn I, Montgomery City-County Public Library System, E L Lowder Regional Branch Library, 2590 Bell Rd, Montgomery, AL, 36117. Tel: 334-244-5717. Fax: 334-240-4893. p. 30

Toth, Carolyn, Dir, Sewickley Public Library, Inc, 500 Thorn St, Sewickley, PA, 15143-1333. Tel: 412-741-6920. Fax: 412-741-6099. p. 2139

Toth, Freida, YA Serv, Crandall Public Library, 251 Glen St, Glens Falls, NY, 12801-3593. Tel: 518-792-6508. Fax: 518-792-5251. p. 1629

Toth, Gabrielle, Govt Info & Maps Librn, Chicago State University, 9501 S Martin Luther King Jr Dr, LIB 440, Chicago, IL, 60628-1598. Tel: 773-995-2562. Fax: 773-995-3772. p. 610

Toth, Gregory, Ref Serv, State University of New York College at Brockport, 350 New Campus Dr, Brockport, NY, 14420-2997. Tel: 585-395-2450. Fax: 585-395-5651. p. 1585

Toth, Joe, Dir of Libr Serv, Ocean County College Library, College Dr, Toms River, NJ, 08754. Tel: 732-255-0392. Fax: 732-255-0421. p. 1533

Toth, Michelle, Assoc Librn, Coordr, Libr Courses, State University of New York College at Plattsburgh, Two Draper Ave, Plattsburgh, NY, 12901-2697. Tel: 518-564-5225. Fax: 518-564-5209. p. 1719

Toth, Paulette, Libr Serv Mgr, Kirkland & Ellis, 153 E 53rd St, New York, NY, 10022. Tel: 212-446-4990. Fax: 212-446-4900. p. 1684

Totilo, Janice, Librn, FM Global Library, 1301 Atwood Ave, Johnston, RI, 02919. Tel: 401-275-3000, Ext 1464. Fax: 401-275-3029. p. 2167

Totman, Jill, Librn, Buncombe County Public Libraries, Weaverville Branch-Sprinkle Memorial Library, 41 N Main St, Weaverville, NC, 28787. Tel: 828-250-6482. p. 1774

Totten, Herman L, PhD, Dr, Dean, University of North Texas, 1155 Union Circle, Denton, TX, 76203-5017. Tel: 940-565-2445. Fax: 940-565-3101. p. 2975

Totten, Kathy, Br Mgr, Anythink Libraries, Anythink Washington Street, 8992 Washington St, Thornton, CO, 80229. Tel: 303-287-2514. Fax: 303-286-8467. p. 324

Totten, Mark, Commun Libr Mgr, County of Los Angeles Public Library, La Canada Flintridge Library, 4545 N Oakwood Ave, La Canada Flintridge, CA, 91011-3358. Tel: 818-790-3330. Fax: 818-952-1754. p. 142

Totten, Nancy T, Coordr, Pub Serv, Indiana University Southeast Library, 4201 Grant Line Rd, New Albany, IN, 47150. Tel: 812-941-2262. Fax: 812-941-2656. p. 767

Tottenhoff, Jeffrey, Libr Bus Adminr, Broward County Division of Libraries, 100 S Andrews Ave, Fort Lauderdale, FL, 33301. Tel: 954-357-7237. Fax: 954-357-5771. p. 441

Totter, Susan, Dir, Dover Plains Library, 1797 Rte 22, Wingdale, NY, 12594-1444. Tel: 845-832-6605. Fax: 845-832-6616. p. 1770

Totton, Victoria, Asst Dir, Bus Mgr, Cicero Public Library, 5225 W Cermak Rd, Cicero, IL, 60804. Tel: 708-652-8084. Fax: 708-652-8095. p. 629

Touchet, Angela, Br Mgr, Vermilion Parish Library, Gueydan Branch, 704 Tenth St, Gueydan, LA, 70542-3806. Tel: 337-536-6781. Fax: 337-536-0112. p. 939

Toupin, Claude, Chef de Div, Bibliothèques de Montrèal, Pointe-aux-Trembles, 14001, rue Notre-Dame Est, Montreal, QC, H1A 1T9, CANADA. Tel: 514-872-2102. Fax: 514-872-0525. p. 2891

Toupin, Claude, Chef de Div, Bibliothèques de Montrèal, Riviere-des-Prairies, 9001, boulevard Perras, Montreal, QC, H1E 3J7, CANADA. Tel: 514-872-2102. Fax: 514-872-9650. p. 2891

Toupin, Mary, Ref Serv, Titusville Public Library, 2121 S Hopkins Ave, Titusville, FL, 32780. Tel: 321-264-5026. Fax: 321-264-5030. p. 500

Tour, Debra, Acq Mgr, Orange County Library District, 101 E Central Blvd, Orlando, FL, 32801. Tel: 407-835-7323. p. 476

Tourigny, Nancy, Circ, Leominster Public Library, 30 West St, Leominster, MA, 01453. Tel: 978-534-7522. Fax: 978-840-3357. p. 1098

Tourjee, Mary Anne, Dir, Lilly Library, 19 Meadow St, Florence, MA, 01062. Tel: 413-587-1500. Fax: 413-587-1504. p. 1089

Tourville, Elaine, Librn, Holy Apostles Catholic Church Library, 4925 N Carefree Circle, Colorado Springs, CO, 80917. Tel: 719-597-4249. Fax: 719-591-1816. p. 295

Tousey, J, Ch, North Shore Public Library, 250 Rte 25A, Shoreham, NY, 11786-9677. Tel: 631-929-4488. Fax: 631-929-4551. p. 1743

Tousignant, Claude, Actg Univ Librn, Tele-Universite, 455 rue du Parvis, Quebec, QC, G1K 9H6, CANADA. Tel: 418-657-2747. Fax: 418-657-2094. p. 2906

Tout, Robert, ILL, Ref Serv, Bridgewater College, 402 E College St, Bridgewater, VA, 22812. Tel: 540-828-5672. Fax: 540-828-5482. p. 2452

Tovar, Cecilia, Br Mgr, Yuma County Library District, San Luis Branch, 1075 N Sixth Ave, San Luis, AZ, 85349. Tel: 928-314-2447. Fax: 928-627-8296. p. 92

Tovish, Maureen, Librn, East Norwalk Improvement Association Library, 51 Van Zant St, Norwalk, CT, 06855. Tel: 203-838-0408. p. 362

Tovrea, Roxanne, Dir, Bartow Public Library, 2150 S Broadway Ave, Bartow, FL, 33830. Tel: 863-534-0131. Fax: 863-534-0913. p. 426

Tow, Jennifer, Ch, Martin County Library, 110 N Park St, Fairmont, MN, 56031-2822. Tel: 507-238-4207. Fax: 507-238-4208. p. 1250

Tow, Kenneth, Librn, Callahan Eye Foundation Hospital, 1720 University Blvd, Birmingham, AL, 35233-1895. Tel: 205-325-8505. Fax: 205-325-8506. p. 8

Towanda, Mathurin, Per, SUNY Westchester Community College, 75 Grasslands Rd, Valhalla, NY, 10595-1693. Tel: 914-606-8529. Fax: 914-785-6513. p. 1760

Towell, Fay, Dir, Greenville Hospital System, 701 Grove Rd, Greenville, SC, 29605. Tel: 864-455-3099. Fax: 864-455-5696. p. 2196

Tower, Karen, Librn, Huntington Woods Public Library, 26415 Scotia, Huntington Woods, MI, 48070-1198. Tel: 248-543-9720. Fax: 248-543-2559. p. 1193

Towers, Sha, Fine Arts Librn, Baylor University Libraries, Crouch Fine Arts Library, 1312 S Third St, Waco, TX, 76798. Tel: 254-710-6673. p. 2396

Towery, Stephanie, Librn, Haynes & Boone LLP, 2323 Victory Ave, Ste 700, Dallas, TX, 75219. Tel: 512-867-8473. p. 2308

Towey, Cathleen, Dir, Westbury Memorial Public Library, 445 Jefferson St, Westbury, NY, 11590. Tel: 516-333-0176. Fax: 516-333-1752. p. 1767

Towey, Cathleen, Dir, Westbury Memorial Public Library, Children's Library - Robert Bacon Memorial, 374 School St, Westbury, NY, 11590. Tel: 516-333-0176. p. 1767

Towle, Evan, Reader Serv Librn, Philadelphia Museum of Art Library, Ruth & Raymond G Perelman Bldg, 2525 Pennsylvania Ave, Philadelphia, PA, 19130. Tel: 215-684-7645. Fax: 215-236-0534. p. 2114

Towles, Carole, Br Mgr, Phoenix Public Library, Palo Verde Library, 4402 N 51st Ave, Phoenix, AZ, 85031. p. 76

Towlson, Diane, Commun Relations Coordr, Liverpool Public Library, 310 Tulip St, Liverpool, NY, 13088-4997. Tel: 315-457-0310. Fax: 315-453-7867. p. 1653

Town, Marie, Youth Serv, Oceanside Public Library, 330 N Coast Hwy, Oceanside, CA, 92054-2824. Tel: 760-435-5597. Fax: 760-435-9614. p. 199

Towne, Cheryl, Br Mgr, Tacoma Public Library, Wheelock Branch, 3722 N 26th St, Tacoma, WA, 98407. p. 2540

Towne, Daniel, Syst/Electronic Serv Librn, Fulton-Montgomery Community College, 2805 State Hwy 67, Johnstown, NY, 12095-3790. Tel: 518-762-4651, Ext 5601. Fax: 518-762-3834. p. 1648

Townley, Megan, Cataloger, Bob Jones University, 1700 Wade Hampton Blvd, Greenville, SC, 29614. Tel: 864-242-5100, Ext 6000. Fax: 864-232-1729. p. 2195

Townley, Sandra, Circ Supvr, Tacoma Community College Library, 6501 S 19th St, Tacoma, WA, 98466-6100. Tel: 253-566-5089. Fax: 253-566-5398. p. 2540

Towns, Bobby, Libr Serv Mgr, Mayer Brown LLP, 71 S Wacker Dr, Chicago, IL, 60606. Tel: 312-782-0600. Fax: 312-701-7711. p. 618

Towns-Campbell, Julia, Librn, Columbia Environmental Research Center Library, US Geological Survey, 4200 New Haven Rd, Columbia, MO, 65201. Tel: 573-876-1853. Fax: 573-876-1833. p. 1324

Townsel, Melinda, Head Librn, Austin Community College, Northridge Campus Library, 11928 Stone Hollow Dr, Austin, TX, 78758. Tel: 512-223-4741. Fax: 512-223-4902. p. 2278

Townsend, Allen, Dir, Yale University Library, Robert B Haas Family Arts Library, Loria Ctr, 180 York St, New Haven, CT, 06520. Tel: 203-432-2642. Fax: 203-432-0549. p. 358

Townsend, Bette, Librn, Norton Public Library, One Washington Sq, Norton, KS, 67654-1615. Tel: 785-877-2481. p. 885

Townsend, Carla, Librn, Central Baptist Hospital Library, 1740 Nicholasville Rd, Lexington, KY, 40503. Tel: 859-260-6297. Fax: 859-260-6442. p. 920

Townsend, Carol, Br Mgr, Alpine Public Library, Marathon Public, 106 N Third St E, Marathon, TX, 79842. Tel: 432-386-4136. Fax: 432-386-4136. p. 2273

Townsend, Charles, Br Librn, Kiowa County Library, Haviland Branch, PO Box 295, Haviland, KS, 67059. Tel: 620-862-5350. p. 869

Townsend, Darlene, Head, Cat, University of North Alabama, One Harrison Plaza, Box 5028, Florence, AL, 35632-0001. Tel: 256-765-4473. Fax: 256-765-4438. p. 17

Townsend, Debby, IT Tech, Gaston Community Library, 116 Front St, Gaston, OR, 97119. Tel: 503-662-4104. Fax: 503-985-1014. p. 1999

Townsend, Gregory, Br Mgr, US Courts Library, Byron Rogers Courthouse, 1929 Stout St, Rm 430, Denver, CO, 80294. Tel: 303-844-3591. Fax: 303-844-5958. p. 303

Townsend, Gregory L, Librn, United States Courts Library, 333 Lomas Blvd NW, Ste 360, Albuquerque, NM, 87102. Tel: 505-348-2135. Fax: 505-348-2795. p. 1550

Townsend, Jerrie, Dir, Phillips Community College of the University of Arkansas, 1210 Ricebelt Ave, DeWitt, AR, 72042. Tel: 870-946-3506, Ext 1818. Fax: 870-946-2644. p. 98

Townsend, Jerrie, Dir, Phillips Community College of the University of Arkansas, 1000 Campus Dr, Helena, AR, 72342. Tel: 870-338-6474. Fax: 870-338-2783. p. 103

Townsend, Jerrie, Dir, Phillips Community College of the University of Arkansas, 2807 Hwy 165 S, Box A, Stuttgart, AR, 72160. Tel: 870-673-4201, Ext 1819. Fax: 870-673-8166. p. 116

Townsend, Julie, Ch, Fort Scott Public Library, 201 S National, Fort Scott, KS, 66701. Tel: 620-223-2882. p. 867

Townsend, Margaret A, Youth Serv Librn, Ritter Public Library, 5680 Liberty Ave, Vermilion, OH, 44089-1198. Tel: 440-967-3798, Ext 18. Fax: 440-967-5482. p. 1943

Townsend, Mary Ann, Dir, Floyd County Historical Society Museum Library, 500 Gilbert St, Charles City, IA, 50616-2738. Tel: 641-228-1099. Fax: 641-228-1157. p. 801

Townsend, Phyllis, Acq of Monographs & Journals, Hood College, 401 Rosemont Ave, Frederick, MD, 21701. Tel: 301-696-3933. Fax: 301-696-3796. p. 1029

Townsend, Ronald, Acq, ILL Librn, Lutheran Theological Seminary, 7301 Germantown Ave, Philadelphia, PA, 19119-1794. Tel: 215-248-6329. Fax: 215-248-6327. p. 2112

Townsend, Rosa, Libr Spec, Southside Virginia Community College, 200 Daniel Rd, Keysville, VA, 23947. Tel: 434-736-2045. Fax: 434-736-2079. p. 2472

Townsend, Sarah, Br Mgr, Norfolk Public Library, Van Wyck, 1368 DeBree Ave, Norfolk, VA, 23517. Tel: 757-441-2844. Fax: 757-441-1456. p. 2482

Townsend, Shawn, Principal Librn, Upland Public Library, 450 N Euclid Ave, Upland, CA, 91786-4732. Tel: 909-931-4200. Fax: 909-931-4209. p. 278

Townsend, Shirley, Librn, Wyoming State Training School Medical Library, 8204 State Hwy 789, Lander, WY, 82520-9499. Tel: 307-335-6804. Fax: 307-335-6990. p. 2657

Townsend, Teri, Res Librn, Troutman Sanders LLP, 600 Peachtree St NE, Ste 5200, Atlanta, GA, 30308-2216. Tel: 404-885-3794. Fax: 404-962-6783. p. 518

Townsend, Terrie, Ch, Pine Mountain Regional Library, 218 Perry St NW, Manchester, GA, 31816-1317. Tel: 706-846-3851. Fax: 706-846-8455, 706-846-9632. p. 542

Townsend, Valerie, Asst Librn, Head, ILL, Inuvik Centennial Library, 100 Mackenzie Rd, Inuvik, NT, X0E 0T0, CANADA. Tel: 867-777-8620. Fax: 867-777-8621. p. 2775

Townsend, Wilma, Curator, Ontario County Historical Society Library, 55 N Main St, Canandaigua, NY, 14424. Tel: 585-394-4975. Fax: 585-394-9351. p. 1601

Townson, Sharon, Asst Dir, Cullman County Public Library System, 200 Clark St NE, Cullman, AL, 35055. Tel: 256-734-1068. Fax: 256-734-6902. p. 13

Toy, Renee, Librn, Texas School for the Blind, 1100 W 45th St, Austin, TX, 78756. Tel: 512-454-8631. Fax: 512-206-9450. p. 2282

Toy, Terry, Head, Syst, University of California, Riverside Libraries, 900 University Ave, Riverside, CA, 92521. Tel: 951-827-4319. p. 218

Toyama, Ralph, Head Librn, Syst Librn, Leeward Community College Library, 96-045 Ala Ike, Pearl City, HI, 96782-3393. Tel: 808-455-0682. Fax: 808-453-6729. p. 567

Toze, Sandra, Lecturer, Dalhousie University, 6100 University Ave, Halifax, NS, B3H 3J5, CANADA. Tel: 902-494-3656. Fax: 902-494-2451. p. 2978

Tozer, Rosemary, Sr Librn, Richard T Liddicoat Gemological Library & Information Center, 5345 Armada Dr, Carlsbad, CA, 92008. Tel: 760-603-4016. Fax: 760-603-4256. p. 132

Tozier, Glenn, Electronic Res & ILL Librn, Alliant International University, 5130 E Clinton Way, Fresno, CA, 93727. Tel: 559-253-2265. Fax: 559-253-2223. p. 150

Traber, Sue, Libr Asst, Wickenburg Public Library, 164 E Apache St, Wickenburg, AZ, 85390. Tel: 928-684-2665. p. 89

Trace, Ciaran, Asst Prof, University of Wisconsin-Madison, 4217 H C White Hall, 600 N Park St, Madison, WI, 53706. Tel: 608-262-2955. Fax: 608-263-4849. p. 2976

Trace, Howard, Dir, Libr & Mus Serv, American Legion National Headquarters Library, 700 N Pennsylvania St, 4th Flr, Indianapolis, IN, 46204-1172. Tel: 317-630-1366. Fax: 317-630-1241. p. 749

Tracey, Barbara, IT & Security Mgr, Warren Library Association, 205 Market St, Warren, PA, 16365. Tel: 814-723-4650. Fax: 814-723-4521. p. 2150

Tracey, Leslie E, Acq, New England Institute of Technology Library, 1408 Division Rd, East Greenwich, RI, 02818-1205. Tel: 401-739-5000, Ext 3473. Fax: 401-886-0861. p. 2166

Tracey, Stephen, Electronic Res, Bentley College, 175 Forest St, Waltham, MA, 02452-4705. Tel: 781-891-2168. Fax: 781-891-2830. p. 1132

Tracht, Frances, Actg Libr Mgr, Inglewood Public Library, 101 W Manchester Blvd, Inglewood, CA, 90301-1771. Tel: 310-412-5397. Fax: 310-412-8848. p. 159

Trachta, Kendra, Dep Dir, Sno-Isle Libraries, 7312 35th Ave NE, Tulalip, WA, 98271-7417. Tel: 360-651-7066. Fax: 360-651-7151. p. 2541

Tracy, Carla, Dir, Augustana College Library, 3435 9 1/2 Ave, Rock Island, IL, 61201-2296. Tel: 309-794-7266. Fax: 309-794-7640. p. 696

Tracy, Carol, Ref Serv, Mokena Community Public Library District, 11327 W 195th St, Mokena, IL, 60448. Tel: 708-479-9663. Fax: 708-479-9684. p. 674

Tracy, Elizabeth, Mgr, Children's Dept, San Miguel County Public Library District 1, 100 W Pacific Ave, Telluride, CO, 81435-2189. Tel: 970-728-4519. Fax: 970-728-3340. p. 323

Tracy, Hannah, Libr Dir, Fairlee Public Library, 221 US Rte 5N, Fairlee, VT, 05045-9584. Tel: 802-333-4716. Fax: 802-333-4152. p. 2424

Tracy, Jami Frazier, Curator, Wichita-Sedgwick County Historical Museum Library, 204 S Main St, Wichita, KS, 67202. Tel: 316-265-9314. Fax: 316-265-9319. p. 901

Tracy, Jeannette, Dir, Libr Serv, Foley & Hoag LLP Library, 155 Seaport Blvd, Boston, MA, 02210. Tel: 617-832-7070. Fax: 617-832-7000. p. 1061

Tracy, Joyce, Ref & ILL Librn, Northwestern College, Bridgeview Campus, 7725 S Harlem Ave, Bridgeview, IL, 60455. Tel: 708-237-5000. Fax: 708-237-5005. p. 621

Tracy, Morgan, Dir of Libr Serv, Asbury University, One Macklem Dr, Wilmore, KY, 40390-1198. Tel: 859-858-3511, Ext 2126. Fax: 859-858-3921. p. 938

Tracy, Nancy, Asst Dir, Salem Public Library, 370 Essex St, Salem, MA, 01970-3298. Tel: 978-744-0860. Fax: 978-745-8616. p. 1122

Tracy, Roberta, Asst Librn, Ainsworth Public Library, 2338 VT Rte 14, Williamstown, VT, 05679. Tel: 802-433-5887. Fax: 802-433-2161. p. 2440

Tracy, T, Ref Librn, Prairie State College Library, 202 S Halsted St, Chicago Heights, IL, 60411-8200. Tel: 708-709-3550. Fax: 708-709-3940. p. 628

Tracy, Thelma, Asst Librn, Weare Public Library, Ten Paige Memorial Lane, Weare, NH, 03281. Tel: 603-529-2044. Fax: 603-529-7341. p. 1467

Traczek, Rozanne, Librn, Fairchild Public Library, 208 Huron St, Fairchild, WI, 54741. Tel: 715-334-4007. p. 2591

Trafford, Mabel, Librn, Tripler Army Medical Center, One Jarrett White Rd, Honolulu, HI, 96859-5000. Tel: 808-433-4534. Fax: 808-433-4892. p. 565

Trafford, Mabel, Continuing Educ Chair, Hawaii-Pacific Chapter of the Medical Library Association, Health Sciences Library, 651 Ilalo St MEB, Honolulu, HI, 96813. Tel: 808-692-0810. Fax: 808-692-1244. p. 2941

Trafton, William, Tech Serv, Verona Public Library, 17 Gould St, Verona, NJ, 07044-1928. Tel: 973-857-4848. Fax: 973-857-4851. p. 1537

Tragemann, Rita, Acq & Acctg, Shelton State Community College, 9500 Old Greensboro Rd, Tuscaloosa, AL, 35405. Tel: 205-391-3911. Fax: 205-391-3926. p. 38

Trahan, Angel, Br Mgr, Calcasieu Parish Public Library, Hayes Branch, 7709 Perier St, Hayes, LA, 70646. Tel: 337-721-7098. Fax: 337-622-3605. p. 954

Trahan, Eric, Dir, Canajoharie Library & Art Gallery, Two Erie Blvd, Canajoharie, NY, 13317. Tel: 518-673-2314. Fax: 518-673-5243. p. 1601

Trahan, Eric, Dir, Mohawk Valley Library System, 858 Duanesburg Rd, Schenectady, NY, 12306-1057. Tel: 518-355-2010. Fax: 518-355-0674. p. 1740

Trahan, Kristie Rose, Commun Relations Coordr, Iberia Parish Library, 445 E Main St, New Iberia, LA, 70560-3710. Tel: 337-364-7024, 337-364-7074. Fax: 337-364-7042. p. 959

Trahan, Sue, Asst Br Mgr, Vermilion Parish Library, 405 E Saint Victor, Abbeville, LA, 70510-5101. Tel: 337-893-2655. Fax: 337-898-0526. p. 939

Trahan-Liptak, Joy, ILL, Rutland Free Public Library, 280 Main St, Rutland, MA, 01543. Tel: 508-886-4108. Fax: 508-886-4141. p. 1121

Train, Robyn, Adult Serv, Ref, William Jeanes Memorial Library, 4051 Joshua Rd, Lafayette Hill, PA, 19444-1400. Tel: 610-828-0441. Fax: 610-828-4049. p. 2075

Trainer, Karen, Univ Librn, Princeton University, One Washington Rd, Princeton, NJ, 08544-2098. Tel: 609-258-3170. Fax: 609-258-0441. p. 1523

Trainor, Charlene, Librn, Fennemore Craig, 3003 N Central Ave, Ste 2600, Phoenix, AZ, 85012-2913. Tel: 602-916-5280. Fax: 602-916-5999. p. 73

Traister, Daniel, Curator of Res Serv, University of Pennsylvania Libraries, Rare Book & Manuscript Library, 3420 Walnut St, Philadelphia, PA, 19104. Tel: 215-898-7089. p. 2119

Tramdack, Philip, Dir, Slippery Rock University of Pennsylvania, Slippery Rock, PA, 16057-9989. Tel: 724-738-2630. Fax: 724-738-2661. p. 2140

Tramdack, Philip, Dir, State System of Higher Education Library Cooperative, c/o Bailey Library, Slippery Rock Univ of Pennsylvania, Slippery Rock, PA, 16057. Tel: 724-738-2630. Fax: 724-738-2661. p. 2955

Tramel, Gregory, Adult Serv Coordr, Montgomery County Memorial Library System, 104 I-45 N, Conroe, TX, 77301-2720. Tel: 936-788-8377, Ext 250. Fax: 936-788-8398. p. 2300

Trammell, Carolyn, Librn, Tulsa City-County Library, Bixby Branch, 20 E Breckinridge, Bixby, OK, 74008. Tel: 918-366-3397. Fax: 918-366-3392. p. 1982

Trammell, Pamela, Dir, Keller Public Library, 402 W Grant St, Dexter, MO, 63841. Tel: 573-624-3764. Fax: 573-614-1051. p. 1327

Trammell, Rebecca S, Dir, Stetson University College of Law Library, 1401 61st St S, Gulfport, FL, 33707. Tel: 727-562-7820. Fax: 727-345-8973. p. 450

Tramondozzi, John E, Curator, Malden Historical Society, c/o Malden Public Library, 36 Salem St, Malden, MA, 02148-5291. Tel: 781-338-9365. Fax: 781-324-4467. p. 1102

Tramontana, Alice F, Mgr, McCormick & Co, Inc, 204 Wight Ave, Hunt Valley, MD, 21031. Tel: 410-771-7983. Fax: 410-785-7439. p. 1032

Tramte, Helen, Acq, Ursuline College, 2550 Lander Rd, Pepper Pike, OH, 44124-4398. Tel: 440-449-4202. Fax: 440-449-3180. p. 1929

Tran, Alice Y, Archivist, Hawaii State Archives, Iolani Palace Grounds, 364 S King St, Honolulu, HI, 96813. Tel: 808-586-0329. Fax: 808-586-0330. p. 561

Tran, Candice, Sr Librn, San Jose Public Library, Berryessa, 3355 Noble Ave, San Jose, CA, 95132-3198. Tel: 408-808-3050. Fax: 408-923-3222. p. 251

Tran, Candice, Sr Librn, San Jose Public Library, Evergreen, 2635 Aborn Rd, San Jose, CA, 95121-1294. Tel: 408-808-3060. Fax: 408-238-0548. p. 251

Tran, Hieu, Network Adminr, Milwaukee County Federated Library System, 709 N Eighth St, Milwaukee, WI, 53233-2414. Tel: 414-286-8684. Fax: 414-286-3209. p. 2619

Tran, Kim-Uyen, Dir, Initiatives & Stragegies, New Orleans Public Library, 219 Loyola Ave, New Orleans, LA, 70112-2044. Tel: 504-529-7323, 504-596-2570. Fax: 504-596-2609. p. 962

Tran, Lan, Librn, Musee de la Civilisation - Bibliotheque du Seminaire de Quebec, Nine rue de l'Universite, Quebec, QC, G1R 5K1, CANADA. Tel: 418-643-2158. Fax: 418-692-5206. p. 2906

Tran, Naomi, Circ, Waco-McLennan County Library System, 1717 Austin Ave, Waco, TX, 76701-1794. Tel: 254-750-5941. Fax: 254-750-5940. p. 2397

Tran, Truc, Head, Syst, Salt Lake Community College Libraries, 4600 S Redwood Rd, Salt Lake City, UT, 84123-3197. Tel: 801-957-4607. Fax: 801-957-4414. p. 2413

Trangsrud, Cynthia, Pres, Knapp, Petersen & Clarke, 550 N Brand Blvd, Ste 1500, Glendale, CA, 91203-1922. Tel: 818-547-5000. Fax: 818-547-5329. p. 155

Tranquada, Katherine, Dir, Waltham Public Library, 735 Main St, Waltham, MA, 02451. Tel: 781-314-3430. Fax: 781-314-3426. p. 1133

Transue, Beth, Coll Develop Coordr, Messiah College, One College Ave, Ste 3002, Mechanicsburg, PA, 17055. Tel: 717-691-6006, Ext 3810. Fax: 717-691-2356. p. 2087

Trant, Gene Ann, Dir, Wellington Public Library, 3800 Wilson Ave, Wellington, CO, 80549. Tel: 970-568-3040. Fax: 970-568-9713. p. 325

Trantham, Cheryl, Acq, Hudson Valley Community College, 80 Vandenburgh Ave, Troy, NY, 12180. Tel: 518-629-7391. Fax: 518-629-7509. p. 1756

Traore, Jennifer, Instr, Ivy Tech Community College of Indiana, Northeast, 3800 N Anthony Blvd, Fort Wayne, IN, 46805-1430. Tel: 260-480-4176. Fax: 260-480-4121. p. 742

Trapasso, James, Head, Pub Serv, Ossining Public Library, 53 Croton Ave, Ossining, NY, 10562-4903. Tel: 914-941-2416. Fax: 914-941-7464. p. 1712

Trapp, Janice, Dir, James V Brown Library of
Williamsport & Lycoming County, 19 E
Fourth St, Williamsport, PA, 17701-6390. Tel:
570-326-0536. Fax: 570-327-3005. p. 2156

Trapp, Naomi, Librn, Southwestern College
Library, 900 Otay Lakes Rd, Chula Vista, CA,
91910-7299. Tel: 619-421-6700, Ext 5893. Fax:
619-482-6417. p. 134

Trapp, Rachel, Librn, Northwest-Shoals Community
College, 800 George Wallace Blvd, Muscle
Shoals, AL, 35661-3206. Tel: 256-331-5283.
Fax: 256-331-5269. p. 32

Trapp, Rachel, Coll Develop, Librn,
Northwest-Shoals Community College, 2080
College Rd, Phil Campbell, AL, 35581. Tel:
256-331-6271. Fax: 256-331-6202. p. 34

Traquair, Jesse, Libr Mgr, Strathmore Municipal
Library, 85 Lakeside Blvd, Strathmore, AB,
T1P 1A1, CANADA. Tel: 403-934-5440. Fax:
403-934-1908. p. 2718

Trask, Carolyn, Dir, Hinckley, Allen & Snyder LLP,
50 Kennedy Plaza, Providence, RI, 02903. Tel:
401-274-2000. Fax: 401-277-9600. p. 2172

Trask, Nancy, Dir, Winterset Public Library, 123 N
Second St, Winterset, IA, 50273-1508. Tel:
515-462-1731. Fax: 515-462-4196. p. 853

Trask, Richard, Archivist, Peabody Institute
Library of Danvers, 15 Sylvan St, Danvers,
MA, 01923-2735. Tel: 978-774-0554. Fax:
978-762-0251. p. 1083

Trask, Susan, Head, Youth Serv, York County Public
Library, 100 Long Green Blvd, Yorktown, VA,
23693. Tel: 757-890-5110. Fax: 757-890-5127.
p. 2505

Traub, Barbara G, Head of Ref & Instrul Serv,
Saint John's University Library, Rittenberg Law
Library, 8000 Utopia Pkwy, Queens, NY, 11439.
Tel: 718-990-1668. Fax: 718-990-6649. p. 1725

Trauceniek, Kim, Outreach & Develop Mgr,
University of Massachusetts at Boston, 100
Morrissey Blvd, Boston, MA, 02125-3300. Tel:
617-287-5921. p. 1068

Trauernicht, Marcia, Head, Cat, Rochester Institute
of Technology, 90 Lomb Memorial Dr,
Rochester, NY, 14623-5604. Tel: 585-475-7292.
Fax: 585-475-7007. p. 1731

Traugott, Joan, Tech Serv, Amityville Public Library,
Oak & John Sts, Amityville, NY, 11701. Tel:
631-264-0567. Fax: 631-264-2006. p. 1573

Trauner, Meg, Dir, Duke University Libraries, Ford
Library, One Towerview Rd, Durham, NC,
27708. Tel: 919-660-7869. Fax: 919-660-7950.
p. 1787

Trause, John J, Dir, Oradell Free Public Library, 375
Kinderkamack Rd, Oradell, NJ, 07649-2122.
Tel: 201-262-2613. Fax: 201-262-9112. p. 1516

Traveny, Carol, Tech Serv Librn, Bryn Athyn
College, 2925 College Dr, Bryn Athyn, PA,
19009. Tel: 267-502-2547. Fax: 267-502-2637.
p. 2038

Travers, Carolyn Freeman, Genealogist, Librn/Head,
Cat, Librn/Head, Ref Coll Develop, General
Society of Mayflower Descendants, Four
Winslow St, Plymouth, MA, 02360. Tel:
508-746-3188. Fax: 508-746-2488. p. 1118

Travers, Chris, Dir of Booth Hist Archives, Spec
Coll Librn, San Diego Historical Society,
Balboa Park, 1649 El Prado, Ste 3, San Diego,
CA, 92101. Tel: 619-232-6203, Ext 116. Fax:
619-232-1059. p. 235

Travis, Carol, Acq, Collier County Public Library,
2385 Orange Blossom Dr, Naples, FL, 34109.
Tel: 239-593-0334. Fax: 239-254-8167. p. 471

Travis, Eric, Managing Librn, Austin Public Library,
Terrazas, 1105 E Cesar Chavez St, Austin, TX,
78702. Tel: 512-974-3636. Fax: 512-479-8558.
p. 2279

Travis, Linda, Dir, Bibliotheque Municipale
Eva-Senecal, 450 Marquette St, Sherbrooke, QC,
J1H 1M4, CANADA. Tel: 819-821-5861. Fax:
819-822-6110. p. 2912

Travis, Maureen, Chief Librn, Chapleau Public
Library, 20 Pine St, Chapleau, ON, P0M
1K0, CANADA. Tel: 705-864-0852. Fax:
705-864-0295. p. 2799

Travis, Richard, Archivist, Florida State University
Libraries, Film School Resource & Research
Center, 3100 University Center, Bldg A,
Tallahassee, FL, 32306-2350. Tel: 850-644-0693.
Fax: 850-644-2626. p. 495

Travis, Terry, Tech Serv, Tippecanoe County
Public Library, 627 South St, Lafayette,
IN, 47901-1470. Tel: 765-429-0100. Fax:
765-429-0150. p. 759

Travis, Tina, Br Supvr, Warwick Public Library,
Norwood, 328 Pawtuxet Ave, Warwick, RI,
02888. Tel: 401-941-7545. p. 2177

Trawick, Theresa C, Learning Res Coordr, Lurleen
B Wallace Community College Library, 1000
Danalley Blvd, Andalusia, AL, 36420. Tel:
334-493-5368. Fax: 334-493-7003. p. 4

Traxler, Amy, Librn, The Whale Museum Library,
62 First St N, Friday Harbor, WA, 98250-7973.
Tel: 360-378-4710, Ext 27. Fax: 360-378-5790.
p. 2516

Traylor, Michelle, Librn, Levy County Public
Library System, Williston Public, Ten SE
First St, Williston, FL, 32696-2671. Tel:
352-528-2313. Fax: 352-528-2313. p. 430

Traynor, Karen, Dir, Sullivan Free Library, 101
Falls Blvd, Chittenango, NY, 13037-1699. Tel:
315-687-6331. Fax: 315-687-6512. p. 1606

Traynor, Karen, Librn, Sullivan Free Library,
Bridgeport Branch, North Rd, Bridgeport, NY,
13030. Tel: 315-633-2253. Fax: 315-633-2945.
p. 1606

Traynor, Marian, Operations Mgr, Sheridan College
Library, Davis Campus, 7899 McLaughlin Rd,
Brampton, ON, L6V 1G6, CANADA. Tel:
905-459-7533, Ext 5283. Fax: 905-874-4345.
p. 2826

Treacy, Thomas, Dr, Pres, Antonelli Institute, 300
Montgomery Ave, Erdenheim, PA, 19038. Tel:
215-836-2222. Fax: 215-836-2794. p. 2055

Treadway, Jody C, Dir, Wayne Public Library,
461 Valley Rd, Wayne, NJ, 07470. Tel:
973-694-4272, Ext 5101. Fax: 973-692-0637.
p. 1540

Treadway, Sandra G, State Archivist, State Librn,
The Library of Virginia, 800 E Broad St,
Richmond, VA, 23219-8000. Tel: 804-692-3597.
Fax: 804-692-3594. p. 2489

Treadwell, Irving, Librn, Pilgrim Psychiatric Center,
Medical Library, Bldg 82, 998 Crooked Hill
Rd, West Brentwood, NY, 11717-1087. Tel:
631-761-3500. p. 1765

Treadwell, Jane, Dean, Libr Instrul Serv, University
of Illinois at Springfield, One University Plaza,
MS BRK-140, Springfield, IL, 62703-5407. Tel:
217-206-6597. Fax: 217-206-6354. p. 707

Treadwell, Lawrence, IV, Ref Serv, St Thomas
University Library, 16401 NW 37th Ave, Miami
Gardens, FL, 33054. Tel: 305-474-6860. Fax:
305-628-6666. p. 469

Treadwell, Maria, Instr, University of South
Florida, 4202 Fowler Ave, CIS 1040, Tampa,
FL, 33620-7800. Tel: 813-974-3520. Fax:
813-974-6840. p. 2964

Treadwell, Rita, Head, Ref, Powell, Goldstein LLP,
1201 W Peachtree St, 14th Flr, Atlanta, GA,
30309. Tel: 404-572-6696. Fax: 404-572-6999.
p. 518

Treager, Maggi, Librn, Horace J & Idabell Rosen
Library, 2909 W Mequon Rd, Mequon, WI,
53092. Tel: 262-242-6900. Fax: 262-242-3952.
p. 2615

Treanor, Brian, Mgr, Libr Serv, Peabody & Arnold
LLP, Federal Reserve Plaza, 600 Atlantic Ave,
Boston, MA, 02110. Tel: 617-261-5051, Ext
7157. Fax: 617-951-2125. p. 1066

Treaster, Beth, Dir, Centerville-Center Township
Public Library, 126 E Main St, Centerville,
IN, 47330-1206. Tel: 765-855-5223. Fax:
765-855-2009. p. 731

Treaster, Beth, Librn, Saint Francis Health System,
6161 S Yale Ave, Tulsa, OK, 74136. Tel:
918-494-1210. Fax: 918-494-1893. p. 1982

Treat, Benjamin, Re/Ser Librn, Franklin Pierce
University Library, 40 University Dr, Rindge,
NH, 03461-3114. Tel: 603-899-4149. Fax:
603-899-4375. p. 1463

Trebbe, Jill, Archivist, US National Park Service,
99 Warren St, Brookline, MA, 02445. Tel:
617-566-1689. Fax: 617-232-4073. p. 1072

Trede, Gayle, Dir, Mount Pleasant Public Library,
307 E Monroe, Ste 101, Mount Pleasant, IA,
52641. Tel: 319-385-1490. Fax: 319-385-1491.
p. 833

Treen, Christine, Librn, Estancia Public Library,
Tenth & Highland, Estancia, NM, 87016. Tel:
505-384-9655. Fax: 505-384-9655. p. 1555

Treesh, Zane, Br Mgr, Anchorage Public Library,
Chugiak-Eagle River Branch, 12400 Old
Glenn Hwy, Eagle River, AK, 99577. Tel:
907-343-1533. Fax: 907-694-2955. p. 44

Treggett, Janice, Sr Coll Develop Librn, Recording
for the Blind & Dyslexic, 20 Roszel Rd,
Princeton, NJ, 08540. Tel: 609-452-0606. Fax:
609-520-7990, 609-987-8116. p. 1524

Trehaeven, Robin, Tech Serv, Edwin A Bemis
Public Library, 6014 S Datura St, Littleton,
CO, 80120-2636. Tel: 303-795-3961. Fax:
303-795-3996. p. 316

Trehub, Aaron, Head, Syst, Auburn University,
Ralph Brown Draughon Library, 231 Mell St,
Auburn, AL, 36849. Tel: 334-844-1716. Fax:
334-844-4424. p. 5

Treichel, Melissa, Access Serv Mgr, Willamette
University, 900 State St, Salem, OR, 97301. Tel:
503-370-4217. Fax: 503-370-6141. p. 2019

Treihaft, Margo, Librn, URS Corp, 1615
Murray Canyon Rd, Ste 1000, San Diego,
CA, 92108-4324. Tel: 619-294-9400. Fax:
619-293-7920. p. 239

Treimer, Ellen, Adult Coordr, Hartley Public
Library, 91 First St SE, Hartley, IA, 51346. Tel:
712-928-2080. Fax: 712-928-2823. p. 820

Trejo, Armando, Archivist, ILL Librn, Elgin
Community College, 1700 Spartan Dr, Elgin, IL,
60123. Tel: 847-214-7337. p. 641

Trejo, Ninfa, Dir, Pima Community College, District
Library Services, 4905B E Broadway Blvd,
Tucson, AZ, 85709-1140. Tel: 520-206-2238.
Fax: 520-206-2022. p. 86

Trejo, Stephen, Asst Dir, University of Texas
Libraries, Population Research Center Library,
Main Bldg 1800, G1800, Austin, TX, 78712.
Tel: 512-471-8332. Fax: 512-471-4886. p. 2284

Trela, Doris, Mgr, Circ & Tech Serv,
Alsip-Merrionette Park Public Library District,
11960 S Pulaski Rd, Alsip, IL, 60803-1197. Tel:
708-371-5666. Fax: 708-371-5672. p. 588

Tremain, Robert, Gen Mgr, Lambton County
Library, 787 Broadway St, Wyoming, ON, N0N
1T0, CANADA. Tel: 519-845-3324, Ext 5236.
Fax: 519-845-0700. p. 2872

Tremaine, Jayne, Dir, Lebanon Community Library,
125 N Seventh St, Lebanon, PA, 17046-5000.
Tel: 717-273-7624. Fax: 717-273-2719. p. 2079

Tremaine, Jayne, Syst Adminr, Lebanon County
Library System, 125 N Seventh St, Lebanon,
PA, 17046. Tel: 717-273-7624. Fax:
717-273-2719. p. 2080

Tremaine, Laurine, Chair, Parry Sound & Area
Access Network, c/o Parry Sound Public
Library, 29 Mary St, Parry Sound, ON, P2A
1E3, CANADA. Tel: 705-746-9601. Fax:
705-746-9601. p. 2960

Tremayne, Virginia, Dir, Hyrum Library, 50 W
Main, Hyrum, UT, 84319. Tel: 435-245-6411.
Fax: 435-245-0180. p. 2406

Trembath, Andrea, Librn, Lakeland Regional
Library, Cartwright Branch, 483 N Railway Ave,
Cartwright, MB, R0K 0L0, CANADA. Tel:
204-529-2261. p. 2749

Tremblay, Andrée, Chef de Div, Bibliothèques de
Montrèal, Saint-Laurent, 1380, rue de l'Église,
Montreal, QC, H4L 2H2, CANADA. Tel:
514-855-6130, Ext 4722. Fax: 514-855-6129.
p. 2891

Tremblay, Brigitte, Chief Exec Officer, Dubreuilville Public Library, 120 Magpie St, Dubreuilville, ON, P0S 1B0, CANADA. Tel: 705-884-1435. Fax: 705-884-1437. p. 2802

Tremblay, Brigitte, Librn, Dubreuilville Public Library, 120 Magpie St, Dubreuilville, ON, P0S 1B0, CANADA. Tel: 705-884-1435. Fax: 705-884-1437. p. 2802

Tremblay, Carrie, Ref Librn, Dover Public Library, 73 Locust St, Dover, NH, 03820-3785. Tel: 603-516-6050. Fax: 603-516-6053. p. 1445

Tremblay, Cindy, Tech Serv Librn, University of New Hampshire at Manchester Library, 400 Commercial St, Manchester, NH, 03101. Tel: 603-641-4173. Fax: 603-641-4124. p. 1456

Tremblay, Claire, Cat, Conservatoire de Musique de Quebec Bibliotheque, 270 rue Saint-Amable, Quebec, QC, G1R 5G1, CANADA. Tel: 418-643-2190, Ext 232. Fax: 418-644-9658. p. 2904

Tremblay, Lino, Dr, Coordr, Acq, Coordr, Circ, Coordr, Ser, Universite du Quebec a Rimouski - Bibliotheque, 300 Allee des Ursulines, Rimouski, QC, G5L 3A1, CANADA. Tel: 418-723-1986, Ext 1474. Fax: 418-724-1621. p. 2907

Tremblay, Nathalie, ILL, Bibliotheque Municipale de Saint Felicien, 1209 Blvd Sacre-Coeur, Saint Felicien, QC, G8K 2R5, CANADA. Tel: 418-679-5334. Fax: 418-679-2178. p. 2908

Tremblay, Nicole, Coll Develop, Bibliotheque de Beaconsfield, 303 Boulevard, Beaconsfield, QC, H9W 4A7, CANADA. Tel: 514-428-4460. Fax: 514-428-4477. p. 2880

Tremblay, Paul, Head, Ref Serv, Long Island University, One University Plaza, Brooklyn, NY, 11201-9926. Tel: 718-488-1081. Fax: 718-780-4057. p. 1593

Tremblay, Paul, Dir, College Militaire Royal de Saint-Jean Library, 15 rue Jaques-Cartier Nord, Saint-Jean-Sur-Richelieu, QC, J3B 8R8, CANADA. Tel: 450-358-6608. Fax: 450-358-6929. p. 2911

Tremblay, Regina, Libr Asst, Naples Public Library, 940 Roosevelt Trail, Naples, ME, 04055. Tel: 207-693-6841. Fax: 207-693-7098. p. 993

Tremblay, Susanne, Libr Mgr, Valleyview Municipal Library, 4804 50th Ave, Valleyview, AB, T0H 3N0, CANADA. Tel: 780-524-3033. Fax: 780-524-4563. p. 2720

Tremblay, Yolanda, Librn, Wapiti Regional Library, Mistatim Public Library, Railway Ave, Mistatim, SK, S0E 1B0, CANADA. Tel: 306-889-2008. p. 2921

Trembley, Cyndi, Computer Serv, Ref, Harris, Beach PLLC, 99 Garnsey Rd, Pittsford, NY, 14534. Tel: 585-419-8800, Ext 8917. Fax: 585-419-8814. p. 1718

Trenam, Jami, Regional Supvr, Great River Regional Library, 1300 W St Germain St, Saint Cloud, MN, 56301-3667. Tel: 320-650-2527. Fax: 320-650-2501. p. 1274

Trenblay, Margarite, Dir, College de Montreal Bibliotheque, 1931 Ouest rue Sherbrooke, Montreal, QC, H3H 1E3, CANADA. Tel: 514-933-7397. Fax: 514-933-3225. p. 2893

Trendler, Amy E, Archit Librn, Ball State University Libraries, Architecture, Architecture Bldg, Rm 116, Muncie, IN, 47306. Tel: 765-285-5858. Fax: 765-285-2644. p. 766

Trenholm, Jerry, Mgr, McDermott, Will & Emery Law Library, 227 W Monroe St, 46th Flr, Chicago, IL, 60606-5096. Tel: 312-984-3289. Fax: 312-984-2094. p. 618

Trenholme, Anne, Art Bibliogr/Western Lang, Cleveland Museum of Art, 11150 East Blvd, Cleveland, OH, 44106-1797. Tel: 216-707-2557. Fax: 216-421-0921. p. 1877

Trent, Joyce Miller, Librn, Leon Valley Public Library, 6425 Evers Rd, Leon Valley, TX, 78238-1453. Tel: 210-684-0720. Fax: 210-684-2088. p. 2355

Trent, Linda, Head, Circ, Harrison County Library System, D'Iberville Public, 10391 AutoMall Pkwy, D'Iberville, MS, 39540. Tel: 228-392-2279. Fax: 228-396-9573. p. 1299

Trent, Renolds, Dir, United States Army, Sayers Memorial Library, Bldg 93, Wold Ave, Fort Benning, GA, 31905. Tel: 706-545-8932. Fax: 706-545-6363. p. 532

Trentham, JoAn, Dr, Dir, Pigeon Forge Public Library, 2449 Library Dr, Pigeon Forge, TN, 37876. Tel: 865-429-7490. Fax: 865-429-7495. p. 2263

Trenthem, Wendy, Librn, Memphis Brooks Museum of Art Library, Overton Park, 1934 Poplar Ave, Memphis, TN, 38104. Tel: 901-544-6200. Fax: 901-725-4071. p. 2249

Trepal, Amy, Dept Head, University of South Carolina, Educational Films, Thomas Cooper Library, Level 3, Rm 317, Columbia, SC, 29208. Tel: 803-777-0322, 803-777-2858. p. 2190

Trépanier, Marik, Chief Librn, Bibliotheque Gabrielle-Roy, Saint-André, 2155 Blvd Bastien, Quebec, QC, G2B 1B8, CANADA. Tel: 418-641-6790. p. 2903

Trépanier, Marik, Librn, Bibliotheque Gabrielle-Roy, Lebourgneuf, 1650 Blvd la Morille, Quebec, QC, G2K 2L2, CANADA. Tel: 418-641-6794. p. 2903

Trepanier, Peter, Reader Serv, National Gallery of Canada Library, 380 Sussex Dr, Ottawa, ON, K1N 9N4, CANADA. Tel: 613-990-0587. Fax: 613-990-9818. p. 2832

Trepp, Deborah, Co-Dir, Coll & Circ Operations, The New York Public Library - Astor, Lenox & Tilden Foundations, 476 Fifth Ave, (@ 42nd St), New York, NY, 10018-2788. Tel: 212-340-0811. Fax: 212-576-0034. p. 1690

Trepp, George, Dir, Long Beach Public Library, 111 W Park Ave, Long Beach, NY, 11561-3326. Tel: 516-432-7201. Fax: 516-889-4641. p. 1654

Treptow, Barbara, Ref & Libr Instruction, Blinn College Library, 800 Blinn Blvd, Brenham, TX, 77833. Tel: 979-830-4250. Fax: 979-830-4222. p. 2291

Treptow, Sheila, Dir, Wells Public Library, 54 First St SW, Wells, MN, 56097-1913. Tel: 507-553-3702. Fax: 507-553-6141. p. 1288

Tresnan, Joseph, Ref & Ser Librn, Rosemont College Library, 1400 Montgomery Ave, Rosemont, PA, 19010-1631. Tel: 610-527-0200, Ext 2206. Fax: 610-525-2930. p. 2135

Tresp, Teresa, Head of Libr, Saint Mary's County Memorial Library, Lexington Park Branch, 21677 FDR Blvd, Lexington Park, MD, 20653. Tel: 301-863-8188, Ext 1012. Fax: 301-863-2550. p. 1035

Tress, Will, Dir, University of Baltimore, Law Library, 1415 Maryland Ave, Baltimore, MD, 21201. Tel: 410-837-4554. Fax: 410-837-4570. p. 1018

Tressler, Alexa, Ch, Dustin Michael Sekula Memorial Library, 1906 S Closner Blvd, Edinburg, TX, 78539. Tel: 956-383-6246. Fax: 956-318-3123. p. 2315

Tretiakova, Marie, Libr Assoc, Center for Creative Leadership Library, One Leadership Pl, Greensboro, NC, 27410. Tel: 336-286-4083. Fax: 336-286-4087. p. 1795

Tretter, Laura, Cataloger, State Law Library of Montana, 215 N Sanders, Helena, MT, 59601-4522. Tel: 406-444-3660. Fax: 406-444-3603. p. 1383

Trevino, Annabel, Univ Librn, University of Texas at Brownsville & Texas Southmost College Library, 80 Fort Brown St, Brownsville, TX, 78521. Tel: 956-882-8296. Fax: 956-882-5495. p. 2292

Trevino, Brenda, Ch, Brownsville Public Library System, 2600 Central Blvd, Brownsville, TX, 78520-8824. Tel: 956-548-1055. Fax: 956-548-0684. p. 2292

Trevino, Gail, Dr, Dir, United States Air Force, Bldg 598, Fifth St E, Randolph AFB, TX, 78150-4424. Tel: 210-652-8901. Fax: 210-652-3261. p. 2373

Trevino, San, Tech Asst, Western Oklahoma State College, 2801 N Main St, Altus, OK, 73521. Tel: 580-477-7951. Fax: 580-477-7777. p. 1956

Trevvett, Melissa, Exec Dir, Boston Library Consortium, Inc, McKim Bldg, 700 Boylston St, Boston, MA, 02117. Tel: 617-262-0380. Fax: 617-262-0163. p. 2945

Tri, Ben, Librn, Saint Paul College Library, 235 Marshall Ave, Saint Paul, MN, 55102. Tel: 651-846-1410. Fax: 651-221-1416. p. 1281

Triance, Robert, Ser, Geneva College, 3200 College Ave, Beaver Falls, PA, 15010-3599. Tel: 724-847-6693. Fax: 724-847-6687. p. 2031

Triandafilou, Mary, Br Mgr, Enoch Pratt Free Library, Light Street, 1251 Light St, Baltimore, MD, 21230-4305. Tel: 410-396-1096. Fax: 410-396-1097. p. 1013

Triandaflyllis, Margaret Ann, Br Mgr, Harris County Public Library, West University, 6108 Auden, Houston, TX, 77005. Tel: 713-668-8273. Fax: 713-667-2264. p. 2336

Tribble, Judith, Dir, Saint Mary-of-the-Woods College Library, 3301 Saint Mary's Rd, Saint Mary-of-the-Woods, IN, 47876. Tel: 812-535-5255. Fax: 812-535-5127. p. 777

Tribble, Nettie, Librn, Columbia County Library, Stephens Public Library, 108 W Ruby St, Stephens, AR, 71764. Tel: 870-786-5231. p. 108

Tribby, Rita, In Charge, Washington Carnegie Public Library, Plainville Branch, 858 Second St, Plainville, IN, 47568. Tel: 812-687-7271. Fax: 812-687-7271. p. 786

Tricarico, Mary Ann, Dir, Dedham Public Library, 43 Church St, Dedham, MA, 02026. Tel: 781-751-9284. Fax: 781-751-9289. p. 1084

Trice, Clint, Mgr, Info Tech, North Madison County Public Library System, 1600 Main St, Elwood, IN, 46036. Tel: 765-552-5001. Fax: 765-552-0955. p. 737

Trice, Jeanne, Br Mgr, Caroline County Public Library, Federalsburg Branch, 123 Morris Ave, Federalsburg, MD, 21632. Tel: 410-754-8397. Fax: 410-754-3058. p. 1027

Trice, Roselyn, Libr Assoc, Fulton County Law Library, Justice Center Tower, Ste 7000, 185 Central Ave, Atlanta, GA, 30303. Tel: 404-730-4544. Fax: 404-730-4565. p. 515

Triche, Charles W, III, Dr, Dean of Libr, University of Louisiana at Lafayette, PO Box 40199, Lafayette, LA, 70504-0199. Tel: 337-482-6396. Fax: 337-482-6399. p. 953

Triebwasser, Glenda, Dir, Molalla Public Library, 201 E Fifth St, Molalla, OR, 97038. Tel: 503-829-2593. Fax: 503-759-3486. p. 2006

Trigg, Elizabeth, Youth Serv, Paola Free Library, 101 E Peoria, Paola, KS, 66071-1798. Tel: 913-259-3655. Fax: 913-259-3656. p. 889

Triller, Malinda, Spec Coll Librn, Dickinson College, 333 W High St, Carlisle, PA, 17013-2896. Tel: 717-245-1397. Fax: 717-245-1439. p. 2042

Trimarchi, Michaeleen, Ref Serv, The Scripps Research Institute, 10550 N Torrey Pines Rd, La Jolla, CA, 92037. Tel: 858-784-8705. Fax: 858-784-2035. p. 161

Trimble, Annika, Librn, Aurora College, 191 Mackenzie Rd, Inuvik, NT, X0E 0T0, CANADA. Tel: 867-777-3298, Ext 207. Fax: 867-777-4264. p. 2775

Trimble, Carolyn, Librn, Wewoka Public Library, 118 W Fifth, Wewoka, OK, 74884. Tel: 405-257-3225. Fax: 405-257-5049. p. 1986

Trimble, Donna, Librn, Bowman & Brooke, 150 S Fifth St, Ste 2600, Minneapolis, MN, 55402. Tel: 612-339-8682. Fax: 612-672-3200. p. 1259

Trimble, Frances, Br Mgr, Carnegie Library of McKeesport, White Oak Branch, McAllister Lodge, 169 Victoria Dr, White Oak, PA, 15131. Tel: 412-678-2002. p. 2085

Trimble, Jane, Circ, Elkins-Randolph County Public Library, 416 Davis Ave, Elkins, WV, 26241. Tel: 304-637-0287. Fax: 304-637-0288. p. 2558

Trimble, Jeffrey, Syst Librn, Youngstown State University, One University Plaza, Youngstown, OH, 44555-0001. Tel: 330-941-2483. Fax: 330-941-3734. p. 1953

Trimble, William, AV Coordr, Syst Mgr, Clarion University of Pennsylvania, 840 Wood St, Clarion, PA, 16214. Tel: 814-393-2017. Fax: 814-393-2344. p. 2045

Trimboli, Teresa, Librn, North American Center for Marianist Studies Library, 4435 E Patterson Rd, Dayton, OH, 45430-1083. Tel: 937-429-2521. Fax: 937-429-3195. p. 1894

Trimper, Wendy, In Charge, Annapolis Valley Regional Library, PO Box 640, Bridgetown, NS, B0S 1C0, CANADA. Tel: 902-665-2995. Fax: 902-665-4899. p. 2778

Trinchitella, Carol, Ser, Connecticut State Library, 231 Capitol Ave, Hartford, CT, 06106. Tel: 860-757-6562. Fax: 860-757-6503. p. 345

Trinh, Diep, Exec Dir, Vietnamese Canadian Federation Library, 249 Rochester St, Ottawa, ON, K1R 7M9, CANADA. Tel: 613-230-8282. Fax: 613-230-8281. p. 2834

Trinidad-Christensen, Jeremiah, Maps Librn, Columbia University, Lehman Library, 420 W 118th St, New York, NY, 10027. Tel: 212-854-3794. Fax: 212-854-2495. p. 1675

Trinkle, Diane, Dir, Nortonville Public Library, 407 Main, Nortonville, KS, 66060-4001. Tel: 913-886-2060. Fax: 913-886-3070. p. 885

Trinkle, Jeff, Pub & Info Serv Coordr, Vigo County Public Library, One Library Sq, Terre Haute, IN, 47807. Tel: 812-232-1113, Ext 2214. Fax: 812-232-3208. p. 782

Triplehorn, Julia, Librn, Geophysical Institute, Int Arctic Research Ctr, 930 Koyukuk, Fairbanks, AK, 99775. Tel: 907-474-7503. Fax: 907-474-7290. p. 48

Triplett, John, Cataloger/Ref Librn, United States Army, Fort Riley Post Library, Bldg 5306, Hood Dr, Fort Riley, KS, 66442-6416. Tel: 785-239-9582. Fax: 785-239-4422. p. 867

Triplett, Liz, Dep Dir, Richmond Public Library, 38 W Main, Richmond, UT, 84333-1409, Tel: 435-258-5525. Fax: 435-258-3604. p. 2411

Triplett, Lynn, Libr Dir, Regis College Library, 235 Wellesley St, Weston, MA, 02493. Tel: 781-768-7000, Ext 7307. Fax: 781-768-7323. p. 1139

Triplett, Nancy, Br Mgr, Timberland Regional Library, Hoodsport Branch, N 40 Schoolhouse Hill Rd, Hoodsport, WA, 98548. Tel: 360-877-9339. Fax: 360-877-9695. p. 2543

Triplett, Robert K, Ref Serv, Palm Beach Atlantic University, 300 Pembroke Pl, West Palm Beach, FL, 33401-6503. Tel: 561-803-2234. Fax: 561-803-2235. p. 503

Triplett, Tonya, Info Serv, Northwestern Regional Library, 111 N Front St, Elkin, NC, 28621. Tel: 336-835-4894. Fax: 336-526-2270. p. 1791

Tripodes, Brenda, Ch, YA Librn, Fiske Free Library, 108 Broad St, Claremont, NH, 03743-2673. Tel: 603-542-7017. Fax: 603-542-7029. p. 1441

Tripp, Ann, Br Mgr, Roanoke County Public Library, Hollins, 6624 Peters Creek Rd, Roanoke, VA, 24019. Tel: 540-561-8024. Fax: 540-563-8902. p. 2494

Tripp, Audrey, Br Mgr, Darlington County Library, 204 N Main St, Darlington, SC, 29532. Tel: 843-398-4940. Fax: 843-398-4942. p. 2192

Tripp, Audrey, Br Mgr, Darlington County Library, Hartsville Memorial, 147 W College St, Hartsville, SC, 29550. Tel: 843-332-5115. Fax: 843-332-7071. p. 2192

Tripp, Billy, Asst Dir, Peach Public Libraries, 315 Martin Luther King Jr Dr, Fort Valley, GA, 31030-4196. Tel: 478-825-1640. Fax: 478-825-2061. p. 533

Tripp, Carol, Librn, Intermountain Health Care, Eighth Ave & C St, Salt Lake City, UT, 84143-0001. Tel: 801-408-1054. Fax: 801-408-5287. p. 2412

Tripp, Holly, ILL Librn, Concord Public Library, 45 Green St, Concord, NH, 03301-4294. Tel: 603-225-8670. Fax: 603-230-3693. p. 1442

Tripp, Jenny, Adult Prog & Serv, Essex Library Association, Inc, 33 West Ave, Essex, CT, 06426-1196. Tel: 860-767-1560. Fax: 860-767-2500. p. 338

Tripp, Maureen, Media Librn, Emerson College Library, 120 Boylston St, Boston, MA, 02116-4624. Tel: 617-824-8407. Fax: 617-824-7817. p. 1060

Tripp, Teresa D, Asst Dir, Admin, East Carolina University, William E Laupus Health Sciences Library, 600 Moye Blvd, Health Sciences Bldg, Greenville, NC, 27834. Tel: 252-744-3495. Fax: 252-744-2672. p. 1799

Tripp-Melby, Pamela, Chief Librn, Joint World Bank-International Monetary Fund Library, 700 19th St NW, Washington, DC, 20431. Tel: 202-623-7054. Fax: 202-623-6417. p. 405

Trippensee, Honey, Youth Serv Mgr, Wake County Public Library System, Eva H Perry Regional Library, 2100 Shepherd's Vineyard Dr, Apex, NC, 27502. Tel: 919-387-4311. Fax: 919-387-4320. p. 1818

Trippler, Elizabeth, Ch, Shenandoah Public Library, 201 S Elm St, Shenandoah, IA, 51601. Tel: 712-246-2315. Fax: 712-246-5847. p. 843

Tripuraneni, Vinaya, Prof, Univ Librn, University of La Verne, 2040 Third St, La Verne, CA, 91750. Tel: 909-593-3511, Ext 4305. Fax: 909-392-2733. p. 162

Trischitti, John, III, Dir, Midland County Public Library, 301 W Missouri, Midland, TX, 79701. Tel: 432-688-4320. Fax: 432-688-4939. p. 2363

Trish, Maggie, Interim Dir, Curtis Laws Wilson Library, 400 W 14th St, Rolla, MO, 65409-0060. Tel: 573-341-4011. Fax: 573-341-4233. p. 1351

Trish, Reid, Librn, Somerville Hospital, 230 Highland Ave, Somerville, MA, 02143. Tel: 617-591-4288. Fax: 617-591-4286. p. 1124

Tristano, Debra Ann, Mgr, Ad Serv, Tuscarawas County Public Library, 121 Fair Ave NW, New Philadelphia, OH, 44663-2600. Tel: 330-364-4474. Fax: 330-364-8217. p. 1921

Trithart, David, Govt Doc Coordr, State University of New York College at Potsdam, 44 Pierrepont Ave, Potsdam, NY, 13676-2294. Tel: 315-267-3311. Fax: 315-267-2744. p. 1722

Tritsch, Jon, Coordr, Cat, Lamar University, 211 Redbird Lane, Beaumont, TX, 77705. Tel: 409-880-7299. Fax: 409-880-2318. p. 2287

Tritt, Deborah, Instruction & Ref Librn, University of South Carolina Aiken, 471 University Pkwy, Aiken, SC, 29801. Tel: 803-641-3589. Fax: 803-641-3302. p. 2180

Trivedi, Himanshu, Ref Librn, Elgin Community College, 1700 Spartan Dr, Elgin, IL, 60123. Tel: 847-214-7337. p. 641

Trivett, Heidi, Br Mgr, LaGrange County Public Library, Topeka Branch, 133 N Main St, Topeka, IN, 46571. Tel: 260-593-3030. Fax: 260-593-3032. p. 760

Trocaru, Alina, Cat & Ref, Addictions Foundation of Manitoba, 1031 Portage Ave, Winnipeg, MB, R3G 0R8, CANADA. Tel: 204-944-6275. Fax: 204-772-0225. p. 2753

Trochta, Jill, Ch, Suring Area Public Library, 604 E Main St, Suring, WI, 54174. Tel: 920-842-4451. p. 2641

Trodler, Sharon, YA Serv, Dunham Public Library, 76 Main St, Whitesboro, NY, 13492. Tel: 315-736-9734. Fax: 315-736-3265. p. 1769

Troeger, Nancy, Dir, Abel J Morneault Memorial Library, 153 Main St, Van Buren, ME, 04785. Tel: 207-868-5076. p. 1004

Troendle, Mark, Librn, Great River Regional Library, Saint Cloud Public Library, 1300 W Saint Germain St, Saint Cloud, MN, 56301-3667. Tel: 320-650-2533. Fax: 320-650-2501. p. 1275

Troendle, Mark, Asst Dir, L E Phillips Memorial Public Library, 400 Eau Claire St, Eau Claire, WI, 54701. Tel: 715-839-6225. Fax: 715-839-5310. p. 2590

Troese, Carol B, Dir, Cranberry Public Library, 2525 Rochester Rd, Ste 300, Cranberry Township, PA, 16066-6423. Tel: 724-776-9100, Ext 1125. Fax: 724-776-2490. p. 2047

Trojan, Bogusia, Dir, University Health Network, Health Sciences Library, 610 University Ave, 5th Flr, Toronto, ON, M5G 2M9, CANADA. Tel: 416-946-4482. Fax: 416-946-2084. p. 2864

Trojan, Bogusia, Dir, University Health Network, Toronto General Hospital Health Sciences Library, University Health Network, 200 Elizabeth St, ENI 418, Toronto, ON, M5G 2C4, CANADA. Tel: 416-340-3429. Fax: 416-340-4384. p. 2864

Trojanowski, Hermann, Archivist, University of North Carolina at Greensboro, 320 Spring Garden St, Greensboro, NC, 27402. Tel: 336-334-4045. Fax: 336-334-5399. p. 1798

Trojanowski, Jim, Dir, Northern Waters Library Service, 3200 E Lakeshore Dr, Ashland, WI, 54806-2510. Tel: 715-682-2365, Ext 11. Fax: 715-685-2704. p. 2579

Trojanowski, Julia, Dir, Instrul Serv Librn, Ref Serv, Northland College, 1411 Ellis Ave, Ashland, WI, 54806-3999. Tel: 715-682-1279. Fax: 715-682-1693. p. 2579

Trombatore, Dennis, Librn, University of Texas Libraries, Walter Geology Library, Geology 4-202, Austin, TX, 78713-8916. Tel: 512-495-4680. Fax: 512-495-4102. p. 2285

Trombetta, Amy, Br Mgr, Old Bridge Public Library, Laurence Harbor Branch, 277 Shoreland Circle, Laurence Harbor, NJ, 08879. Tel: 732-566-2227. Fax: 732-583-8829. p. 1516

Trombetta, Christian, Digital Serv Librn, Bristol Public Library, 701 Goode St, Bristol, VA, 24201-4199. Tel: 276-645-8792. Fax: 276-669-5593. p. 2452

Tromblee, Stacey, Dir, Cannon Free Library, 40 Elm St, Delhi, NY, 13753. Tel: 607-746-2662. Fax: 607-746-2662. p. 1613

Tromp, Kathleen, Circ, Nicolet Area Technical College, 5364 College Dr, Rhinelander, WI, 54501. Tel: 715-365-4479. Fax: 715-365-4404. p. 2633

Trone, Thomas, Ref, Montclair State University, One Normal Ave, Montclair, NJ, 07043-1699. Tel: 973-655-7146. Fax: 973-655-7780. p. 1503

Tronier, Suzanne, Mgr, Salt Lake County Library Services, Calvin S Smith Branch, 810 E 3300 South, Salt Lake City, UT, 84106-1534. Tel: 801-944-7630. Fax: 801-485-3243. p. 2414

Tronier, Suzanne, Mgr, Salt Lake County Library Services, East Millcreek, 2266 E Evergreen Ave, Salt Lake City, UT, 84109-2927. Tel: 801-944-7510. Fax: 801-278-9016. p. 2414

Tronrud, Tory J, Curator, Thunder Bay Historical Museum Society Library, 425 Donald St E, Thunder Bay, ON, P7E 5V1, CANADA. Tel: 807-623-0801. Fax: 807-622-6880. p. 2849

Troost, Kristina, PhD, Head, Intl & Area Studies, Duke University Libraries, 411 Chapel Dr, Durham, NC, 27708. Tel: 919-660-5844. Fax: 919-660-5923. p. 1787

Troppmann, Kathleen, Circ, St Albert Public Library, Five Saint Anne St, St. Albert, AB, T8N 3Z9, CANADA. Tel: 780-459-1530. Fax: 780-458-5772. p. 2717

Trosclair, Charlotte, Dir, Vermilion Parish Library, 405 E Saint Victor, Abbeville, LA, 70510-5101. Tel: 337-893-2655. Fax: 337-898-0526. p. 939

Trosino, Janet, Ch, Flint Public Library, 1026 E Kearsley St, Flint, MI, 48502-1994. Tel: 810-249-2175. Fax: 810-249-2635. p. 1179

Trosper, Marilyn M, Dir, Polson City Library, Two First Ave E, Polson, MT, 59860. Tel: 406-883-8225. Fax: 406-883-8239. p. 1387

Trost, Bari, Asst Dir, Rigby Public Library, 110 N State St, Rigby, ID, 83442. Tel: 208-745-8231. Fax: 208-745-8231. p. 582

Trost, Elaine, Monographs Cataloger, Missouri Baptist University, One College Park Dr, Saint Louis, MO, 63141-8698. Tel: 314-392-2342. Fax: 314-392-2343. p. 1356

Trott, Avis, In Charge, Elk River Free Library District, 203 Main St, Elk River, ID, 83827. Tel: 208-826-3539. p. 574

Trott, Barry, Digital Serv Dir, Williamsburg Regional Library, 7770 Croaker Rd, Williamsburg, VA, 23188-7064. Tel: 757-259-7747. Fax: 757-259-4079, 757-259-7798. p. 2503

Trott, Garrett, ILL, Ref Serv, Corban University Library, 5000 Deer Park Dr SE, Salem, OR, 97317-9392. Tel: 503-375-7016. Fax: 503-375-7196. p. 2017

Trott, Guy, ILL, Online Serv, Ref, Alberta Innovates-Technology Futures, Calgary Branch, 3608 33rd St NW, Calgary, AB, T2L 2A6, CANADA. Tel: 403-210-5292. Fax: 403-210-5380. p. 2698

Trott, Lewis, Cat Librn, Fayetteville State University, 1200 Murchison Rd, Fayetteville, NC, 28301-4298. Tel: 910-672-1549. Fax: 910-672-1746. p. 1793

Trotta, Marcia, Librn, Berlin Free Library, 834 Worthington Ridge, Berlin, CT, 06037-3203, Tel: 860-828-3344. p. 330

Trotta, Victoria, Assoc Dean, Arizona State University, College of Law, 110 S McAllister Ave, Tempe, AZ, 85287-7806. Tel: 480-965-2521. Fax: 480-965-4283. p. 83

Trotter, Amy L, Ref Librn, Ritter Public Library, 5680 Liberty Ave, Vermilion, OH, 44089-1198. Tel: 440-967-3798, Ext 15. Fax: 440-967-5482. p. 1943

Trotter, Janet, Librn, Monmouth County Library, Wall Township, 2700 Allaire Rd, Wall, NJ, 07719. Tel: 732-449-8877. Fax: 732-449-1732. p. 1499

Trotter, Jessica, Pub Serv, Capital Area District Libraries, Downtown Lansing Library, 401 S Capitol Ave, Lansing, MI, 48933. Tel: 517-367-6302. Fax: 517-374-1068. p. 1200

Trotter, Margaret Ann, Pub Serv Coordr, Vanderbilt University, Divinity Library, 419 21st Ave S, Nashville, TN, 37203-2427. Tel: 615-322-2865. Fax: 615-343-8279. p. 2260

Trotter, Patsy, Librn, Macfee & Taft Law Offices, Two Leadership Sq, 10th Flr, 211 N Robinson, Oklahoma City, OK, 73102. Tel: 405-235-9621. Fax: 405-235-0439. p. 1972

Trotter, Tracy, Dir, Adams Memorial Library, 1112 Ligonier St, Latrobe, PA, 15650. Tel: 724-539-1972. Fax: 724-537-0338. p. 2078

Trottier, Chantal, Chef de Section, Bibliothèques de Montrèal, Parc-Extension, 421, rue Saint-Roch, Montreal, QC, H3N 1K2, CANADA. Tel: 514-872-7416. Fax: 514-872-6152. p. 2890

Trottier, Dominique, Prof, College Francois-Xavier-Garneau, 1660 blvd de l'Entente, Quebec, QC, G1S 4S3, CANADA. Tel: 418-688-8310, Ext 3504. Fax: 418-681-9384. p. 2978

Trottier, Jacques, Head, Circ, University of Sudbury Library, 935 Ramsey Lake Rd, Sudbury, ON, P3E 2C6, CANADA. Tel: 705-673-5661, Ext 216. Fax: 705-673-4912. p. 2847

Trottier, Kerry, Libr Mgr, Saint Paul Municipal Library, 4802-53 St, St. Paul, AB, T0A 3A0, CANADA. Tel: 780-645-4904. Fax: 780-645-5198. p. 2717

Troup, Holly, Librn, Clearwater Public Library, 626 Main St, Clearwater, NE, 68726. Tel: 402-485-2365. Fax: 402-485-2365. p. 1396

Troup, Karen S, Librn, Monroeton Public Library, 110 College Ave, Monroeton, PA, 18832. Tel: 570-265-2871. Fax: 570-265-7995. p. 2091

Trout, Amy, Curator, Connecticut River Museum, 67 Main St, Essex, CT, 06426. Tel: 860-767-8269. Fax: 860-767-7028. p. 338

Trout, Kimberly, Dep Fiscal Officer, Gallia County District Library, Seven Spruce St, Gallipolis, OH, 45631. Tel: 740-446-7323. Fax: 740-446-1701. p. 1901

Trout, Linda S, Commun Serv Mgr, Omaha Public Library, 215 S 15th St, Omaha, NE, 68102-1629. Tel: 402-444-4838. Fax: 402-444-4504. p. 1413

Trout, Paula, Tech Serv, Okanagan Regional Library, 1430 KLO Rd, Kelowna, BC, V1W 3P6, CANADA. Tel: 250-860-4033. Fax: 250-861-8696. p. 2730

Trout, Peggy, Circ Serv, Rochester Public Library, 65 S Main St, Rochester, NH, 03867-2707. Tel: 603-332-1428. Fax: 603-335-7582. p. 1464

Troutman, Charles R, Dir, AHEC Med Media & Libr Serv, Charlotte AHEC Library, Medical Education Bldg, 1000 Blythe Blvd, Charlotte, NC, 28203. Tel: 704-355-3129. Fax: 704-355-7138. p. 1781

Troutman, Christine, Ser, Edinboro University of Pennsylvania, 200 Tartan Ave, Edinboro, PA, 16444. Tel: 814-732-2779. Fax: 814-732-2883. p. 2053

Trouwhorst, Sue, Librn, Bremen Public Library, 204 Waldoboro Rd, Bremen, ME, 04551. Tel: 207-529-5572. p. 978

Trovillo, Michelle, Law Librn, Dinsmore & Shohl Library, 255 E Fifth St, 1900 Chemed Ctr, Cincinnati, OH, 45202-3172. Tel: 513-977-8433. Fax: 513-977-8141. p. 1870

Trow, Ginger, Info Serv Librn, Menlo College, 1000 El Camino Real, Atherton, CA, 94027-4300. Tel: 650-543-3826. Fax: 650-543-3833. p. 122

Trowbridge, Norma J, Dir, Mehoopany Area Library, Schoolhouse Hill Rd, Mehoopany, PA, 18629. Tel: 570-833-2818. Fax: 570-833-2818. p. 2088

Troxler, Engle, Circ, Ref Serv, Isothermal Community College Library, 286 ICC Loop Rd, Spindale, NC, 28160. Tel: 828-286-3636, Ext 217. Fax: 828-286-8208. p. 1825

Troy, Christy, Commun Libr Supvr, Yakima Valley Libraries, Toppenish Library, One South Elm, Toppenish, WA, 98948. Tel: 509-865-3600. Fax: 509-865-3600. p. 2551

Troy, Shawn R, Dir, Libr Serv, Mid Michigan Community College, 1375 S Clare Ave, Harrison, MI, 48625. Tel: 989-386-6616. Fax: 989-386-2411. p. 1188

Troyer, April, Ref, Clearwater Public Library System, East, 2251 Drew St, Clearwater, FL, 33765. Tel: 727-562-4970. p. 432

Troyer, Jessica, Br Supvr, Wood County District Public Library, Walbridge Branch, 108 N Main, Walbridge, OH, 43465. Tel: 419-666-9900. Fax: 419-666-8217. p. 1861

Troyer, Jessica, Dir, Liberty Center Public Library, 124 East St, Liberty Center, OH, 43532. Tel: 419-533-5721. Fax: 419-533-4849. p. 1909

Trozzi, Yvette, In Charge, Federal Bureau of Investigation, 2501 Investigation Pkwy, Quantico, VA, 22135. Tel: 703-632-8375. Fax: 703-632-8374. p. 2486

Truax, Morgan, Librn, Royal Alexandra Hospital, 10240 Kingsway, Edmonton, AB, T5H 3V9, CANADA. Tel: 780-735-5832. Fax: 780-735-4136. p. 2702

Truax, Penny, ILL, Per, United Theological Seminary of the Twin Cities, 3000 Fifth St NW, New Brighton, MN, 55112-2598. Tel: 651-255-6142. Fax: 651-633-4315. p. 1267

Truby, Mary, Dir, Angola Public Library, 34 N Main St, Angola, NY, 14006. Tel: 716-549-1271. Fax: 716-549-3954. p. 1574

Truckenmiller, Diane, Co-Dir, Ocheyedan Public Library, 874 Main St, Ocheyedan, IA, 51354. Tel: 712-758-3352. Fax: 712-758-3352. p. 836

Truckey, Jean, Br Mgr, Montague Public Libraries, Millers Falls Branch, 23 Bridge St, Millers Falls, MA, 01349. Tel: 413-659-3801. p. 1131

Trudeau, Loraine M, Head Librn, Jake Epp Library, 255 Elmdale Dr, Steinbach, MB, R5G 1N6, CANADA. Tel: 204-326-6841. Fax: 204-326-6859. p. 2752

Trudeau, Mike, Librn, Legislative Reference Bureau Law Library, State Capitol, Rm 112, Springfield, IL, 62706. Tel: 217-782-6625. Fax: 217-785-4583. p. 705

Trudeau, Robin, In Charge, Ticonderoga Historical Society Library, Hancock House, Six Moses Circle, Ticonderoga, NY, 12883. Tel: 518-585-7868. Fax: 518-585-6367. p. 1755

Trudel, Normand, Coll Mgr, Stewart Museum, The Old Fort St Helen's Island, Montreal, QC, H3C 4G6, CANADA. Tel: 514-861-6701. Fax: 514-284-0123. p. 2901

True, Caroline, Ch, Blair Public Library, 210 S 17th St, Blair, NE, 68008. Tel: 402-426-3617. p. 1394

True, Curt, Interim Dir, Obion County Public Library, 1221 E Reelfoot Ave, Union City, TN, 38261-5097. Tel: 731-885-7000, 731-885-9411. Fax: 731-885-9638. p. 2268

Trueblood, Dianne, Media Spec, South Georgia Technical College, 402 N Midway Rd, Cordele, GA, 31015. Tel: 229-271-4071. Fax: 229-271-4050. p. 527

Trueblood, Sherri, Coordr, Outreach Serv, Shepard-Pruden Memorial Library, 106 W Water St, Edenton, NC, 27932. Tel: 252-482-4112. Fax: 252-482-5451. p. 1790

Truelove, Linda, Principal Cataloger, Tech Serv, Huachuca City Public Library, 506 N Gonzales Blvd, Huachuca City, AZ, 85616-9610. Tel: 520-456-1063. Fax: 520-456-1063. p. 65

Trueman, Rhonda, Access Serv Librn, Circ, Northwest Florida State College, 100 College Blvd, Niceville, FL, 32578. Tel: 850-729-5392. Fax: 850-729-5295. p. 472

Truesdale, Beverly, Per, Southern California Genealogical Society, 417 Irving Dr, Burbank, CA, 91504-2408. Tel: 818-843-7247. Fax: 818-843-7262. p. 130

Truesdell, Bobbi, Dir, Schoolcraft Community Library, 330 N Centre St, Schoolcraft, MI, 49087. Tel: 616-679-5959. Fax: 616-679-5599. p. 1226

Truesdell, Cheryl, Dean, Indiana University-Purdue University Fort Wayne, 2101 E Coliseum Blvd, Fort Wayne, IN, 46805-1499. Tel: 260-481-6512. Fax: 260-481-6509. p. 741

Truett, Carol, Dr, Prof, Appalachian State University, RCOE, Dept of LES, 311 Edwin Duncan Hall, Boone, NC, 28608. Tel: 828-262-7236. Fax: 828-262-6035. p. 2971

Truex, Eleanor, Med Librn, Resurrection Health Care, 2900 N Lake Shore Dr, Chicago, IL, 60657. Tel: 773-665-3038. Fax: 773-665-3416. p. 622

Trufanow, Mike, ILL, United States Agency for International Development, 1300 Pennsylvania Ave NW, Rm M01-010, Washington, DC, 20523-1000. Tel: 202-712-0579. Fax: 202-216-3515. p. 417

Truitt, Tabitha, Ch, H Grady Bradshaw Chambers County Library, 3419 20th Ave, Valley, AL, 36854. Tel: 334-768-2161. Fax: 334-768-7272. p. 39

Trujillio, Virginia, Br Mgr, Eagle Valley Library District, Gypsum Public, 48 Lundgren Blvd, Gypsum, CO, 81637. Tel: 970-524-5080. Fax: 970-524-5082. p. 305

Trujillo, Barbara, Dir, Libr Serv Mgr, Cuba Public Library, 13 E Cordova Ave, Cuba, NM, 87013. Tel: 505-289-3100. Fax: 575-289-9187. p. 1554

Trujillo, Christine, Dir, El Rito Public Library, 182 Placitas Rd, El Rito, NM, 87530. Tel: 575-581-4608. Fax: 575-581-9591. p. 1554

Trujillo, Enrico, Info Spec I, University of New Mexico, Taos Campus, 115 Civic Plaza Dr, Taos, NM, 87571. Tel: 575-737-6242. Fax: 575-737-6292. p. 1551

Trujillo, Flo, Youth Serv Coordr, Farmington Public Library, 2101 Farmington Ave, Farmington, NM, 87401. Tel: 505-599-1261. Fax: 505-599-1257. p. 1555

Trujillo, Isabel, Dir, Abiquiu Public Library, 29 Abiquiu Pueblo, County Rd 187, Abiquiu, NM, 87510. Tel: 505-685-4884. Fax: 505-685-0754. p. 1547

Trujillo, Julie C, Dir of Libr, Truchas Community Library, No 60 County Rd 75, Truchas, NM, 87578. Tel: 505-689-2683. Fax: 505-689-1155. p. 1566

Trulson, Shelly, Librn, United States Army Corps of Engineers, 4735 E Marginal Way, Seattle, WA, 98134. Tel: 206-316-3728. Fax: 206-766-6444. p. 2533

Truman, Meg, Dir, Judson College, 306 E Dekalb, Marion, AL, 36756. Tel: 334-683-5182. Fax: 334-683-5188. p. 24

Truman, Rob, Electronic Res, Lewis & Clark College, Paul L Boley Law Library, Lewis & Clark Law School, 10015 SW Terwilliger Blvd, Portland, OR, 97219. Tel: 503-768-6776. Fax: 503-768-6760. p. 2011

Trumble, Paul, Head, Ser, Amherst College, Amherst, MA, 01002. Fax: 413-542-2662. p. 1048

Trumble, Stephen, Commun Libr Mgr, County of Los Angeles Public Library, Norwood Library, 4550 N Peck Rd, El Monte, CA, 91732-1998. Tel: 626-443-3147. Fax: 626-350-6099. p. 143

Trumbo, Gerri, Libr Mgr, United States Army, Institute of Surgical Research Library, 3698 Chambers Pass, Bldg 3611, Fort Sam Houston, TX, 78234-6315. Tel: 210-539-4559. Fax: 210-539-1460. p. 2321

Trumbull, Donna, Libr Asst, Townshend Public Library, 1971 Rte 30, Townshend, VT, 05353. Tel: 802-365-4039. p. 2437

Trump, Betty, Ch, Mount Sterling Montgomery County Library, 241 W Locust St, Mount Sterling, KY, 40353. Tel: 859-498-2404. Fax: 859-498-7477. p. 930

Trunley, Robert, Dir, Elm Grove Public Library, 13600 W Juneau Blvd, Elm Grove, WI, 53122-1679. Tel: 262-782-6717. Fax: 262-780-4827. p. 2591

Truong, Kathleen, In Charge, Pierce, Goodwin, Alexander & Linville Library, 3131 Briarpark, Ste 200, Houston, TX, 77042. Tel: 713-622-1444. Fax: 713-968-9333. p. 2341

Truong, Susan, Br Head, Toronto Public Library, Main Street, 137 Main St, Toronto, ON, M4E 2V9, CANADA. Tel: 416-393-7700. Fax: 416-393-7505. p. 2862

Trupiano, Vicky, Dir, Fountaindale Public Library District, 300 W Briarcliff Rd, Bolingbrook, IL, 60440-2844. Tel: 630-759-2102, Ext 4157. Fax: 630-759-9519. p. 596

Trupp, Beth, Youth Serv Librn, Gering Public Library, 1055 P St, Gering, NE, 69341. Tel: 308-436-7433. Fax: 308-436-6869. p. 1399

Truppo, Debra, Ch, Edison Township Free Public Library, 340 Plainfield Ave, Edison, NJ, 08817. Tel: 732-287-2298. Fax: 732-819-9134. p. 1483

Trushenski, Jenny, Dir, Martin County Library, 110 N Park St, Fairmont, MN, 56031-2822. Tel: 507-238-4207. Fax: 507-238-4208. p. 1250

Truslow, Hugh K, Librn, Harvard Library, Davis Center for Russian & Eurasian Studies Fung Library, Knafel Bldg, Concourse Level, 1737 Cambridge St, Cambridge, MA, 02138. Tel: 617-496-0485. Fax: 617-496-0091. p. 1074

Truslow, Robyn, Pub Relations Coordr, Calvert County Public Library, 850 Costley Way, Prince Frederick, MD, 20678. Tel: 410-535-0291. Fax: 410-535-3022. p. 1036

Trust, Nancy, Dir, Bass River Community Library, Bass River Elementary School, 11 N Maple Ave, New Gretna, NJ, 08224. Tel: 609-296-6942. Fax: 609-296-4953. p. 1510

Trusty, Jennifer, Ch, Brazoria County Library System, Pearland Branch, 3522 Liberty Dr, Pearland, TX, 77581. Tel: 281-485-4876. Fax: 281-485-5576. p. 2276

Trutna, Carrie, Children's Serv Coordr, Wahoo Public Library, 637 N Maple St, Wahoo, NE, 68066-1673. Tel: 402-443-3871. Fax: 402-443-3877. p. 1422

Truty, Heidi, Archivist, Head, Pub Serv, Wheaton College, Marion E Wade Center, 351 E Lincoln, Wheaton, IL, 60187-4213. Tel: 630-752-5908. Fax: 630-752-5459. p. 718

Trybulski, Mary Jane, Asst Dir, Chicopee Public Library, 449 Front St, Chicopee, MA, 01013. Tel: 413-594-1800. Fax: 413-594-1819. p. 1081

Tryon, Alys, Librn, Lane Powell PC, 601 SW Second Ave, No 2100, Portland, OR, 97204. Tel: 503-778-2100. Fax: 503-778-2200. p. 2011

Tryon, Julia, Govt Doc, Providence College, One Cunningham Sq, Providence, RI, 02918-0001. Tel: 401 865-1990. Fax: 401-865-2823. p. 2173

Tryon, Rusty, Head, Acq, Midwestern Baptist Theological Seminary Library, 5001 N Oak Trafficway, Kansas City, MO, 64118-4620. Tel: 816-414-3726. Fax: 816-414-3790. p. 1339

Trzcinski, Christine, AV Coordr, Ref Librn, Chappaqua Public Library, 195 S Greeley Ave, Chappaqua, NY, 10514. Tel: 914-238-4779, Ext 115. Fax: 914-238-3597. p. 1605

Trzeciak, Jeffrey, Univ Librn, Washington University Libraries, One Brookings Dr, Campus Box 1061, Saint Louis, MO, 63130-4862. Tel: 314-935-5400. Fax: 314-935-4045. p. 1362

Trzepacz, Martha, Evening Ref Librn, Helen Kate Furness Free Library, 100 N Providence Rd, Wallingford, PA, 19086. Tel: 610-566-9331. Fax: 610-566-9337. p. 2150

Tsai, Victoria, Asst Dir, Campus Serv, Central Piedmont Community College Library, 1201 Elizabeth Ave, Charlotte, NC, 28235. Tel: 704-330-6106. Fax: 704-330-6887. p. 1781

Tsang, Jean, Dir, Milford Public Library, 57 New Haven Ave, Milford, CT, 06460. Tel: 203-783-3399. Fax: 203-877-1072. p. 352

Tsang, Katherine, Head Librn, United States Railroad Retirement Board Library, 844 N Rush St, Chicago, IL, 60611-2031. Tel: 312-751-4926. Fax: 312-751-4924. p. 626

Tsao, Jennifer, Ref, New York Institute of Technology, 1855 Broadway, New York, NY, 10023. Tel: 212-261-1526. Fax: 212-261-1681. p. 1689

Tsapina, Olga, Curator, Huntington Library, 1151 Oxford Rd, San Marino, CA, 91108. Tel: 626-405-2209. Fax: 626-449-5720. p. 255

Tsaur, Wanlin Chang, Acq, New Brunswick Theological Seminary, 21 Seminary Pl, New Brunswick, NJ, 08901-1159. Tel: 732-247-5243. Fax: 732-249-5412. p. 1508

Tschinkel, Andrew, Dir, Queens County Supreme Court Library, Kew Gardens Branch, 125-01 Queens Blvd, 7th Flr, Kew Gardens, NY, 11415. Tel: 718-298-1327. Fax: 718-520-4661. p. 1646

Tschorke, Shirley, Librn, Aldersgate United Methodist Church Library, 4115 Dewey Ave, Rochester, NY, 14616. Tel: 585-663-3665. Fax: 585-865-8442. p. 1728

Tschudny, Kathy, In Charge, Immanuel Evangelical Lutheran Church Library, 645 Poplar St, Terre Haute, IN, 47807. Tel: 812-232-4972. Fax: 812-234-3935. p. 781

Tse, Angela, Br Mgr, Markham Public Library, Angus Glen Branch, 3990 Major Mackenzie Dr E, Markham, ON, L6C 1P8, CANADA. Tel: 905-513-7977, Ext 7150. Fax: 905-944-3801. p. 2820

Tseng, Louisa, Ref Librn, University of Massachusetts at Boston, 100 Morrissey Blvd, Boston, MA, 02125-3300. Tel: 617-287-5924. p. 1068

Tseng, Peggy, District Consult Librn, Monessen Public Library & District Center, 326 Donner Ave, Monessen, PA, 15062-1182. Tel: 724-684-4750. Fax: 724-684-7077. p. 2091

Tseng, Wenling, Distance Educ Librn, Chapman University, One University Dr, Orange, CA, 92866-1099. Tel: 714-532-7756. Fax: 714-532-7743. p. 200

Tseng, Winnie, Bibliog Instr, Online Serv, Per, Sinclair Community College Library, 444 W Third St, Dayton, OH, 45402-1460. Tel: 937-512-5349. Fax: 937-512-4564. p. 1894

Tsirigotis, Marilyn, Dir, Harvin Clarendon County Library, 215 N Brooks St, Manning, SC, 29102. Tel: 803-435-8633. Fax: 803-435-8101. p. 2199

Tso, Chin, Mgr, Vaughan Public Libraries, Bathurst Clark Resource Library, 900 Clark Ave W, Thornhill, ON, L4J 8C1, CANADA. Tel: 905-653-7323. Fax: 905-709-1099. p. 2848

Tsou, Judy, Head Music Libr, University of Washington Libraries, Music, 113 Music Bldg, Box 353450, Seattle, WA, 98195-3450. Tel: 206-685-3140. p. 2534

Tsui, Tracy, Syst Librn, Southwestern Law School, 3050 Wilshire Blvd, Los Angeles, CA, 90010. Tel: 213-738-5771. Fax: 213-738-5792. p. 177

Tsung, Shu-Chen, Assoc Univ Librn, Digital Serv & Tech Planning, Georgetown University, 37th & N St NW, Washington, DC, 20057-1174. Tel: 202-687-7429. Fax: 202-687-7501. p. 402

Tsurikov, Vladimir, Dir, Libr Serv, Holy Trinity Orthodox Seminary Library, 1407 Robinson Rd, Jordanville, NY, 13361-0036. Tel: 315-858-3116. Fax: 315-858-0945. p. 1648

Tsutsui, Ilona, Coll Librn, University of Oregon Libraries, John E Jaqua Law Library, William W Knight Law Ctr, 2nd Flr, 1515 Agate St, Eugene, OR, 97403-1221. Tel: 541-346-1657. Fax: 541-346-1669. p. 1997

Tu, Carol, Librn, First Baptist Church Library, 425 W University Ave, Gainesville, FL, 32601. Tel: 352-376-4681. Fax: 352-374-7269. p. 449

Tu, Feili, Asst Prof, University of South Carolina, 1501 Greene St, Columbia, SC, 29208. Tel: 803-777-3858. Fax: 803-777-7938. p. 2973

Tubb, Lillian, Librn, Attica City Library, 125 N Main St, Attica, KS, 67009. Tel: 620-254-7683. p. 857

Tubbs, Barbara C, ILL, Warren Library Association, 205 Market St, Warren, PA, 16365. Tel: 814-723-4650. Fax: 814-723-4521. p. 2151

Tubbs, Leah, Cat Spec, Inyo County Free Library, 168 N Edwards St, Independence, CA, 93526. Tel: 760-878-0260. Fax: 760-878-0360. p. 159

Tubbs, Marsha, Ch, Columbia Heights Public Library, 820 40th Ave NE, Columbia Heights, MN, 55421. Tel: 763-706-3690. Fax: 763-706-3691. p. 1246

Tubinis, Jason, Info Tech Librn, University of Georgia, 225 Herty Dr, Athens, GA, 30602-6018. Tel: 706-542-7365. Fax: 706-542-5001. p. 510

Tubolino, Karen, Dir, Department of Veterans Affairs Library Service, 4646 John R St, Detroit, MI, 48201. Tel: 313-576-1085. Fax: 313-576-1048. p. 1169

Tubridy, Michael, Librn, International Council of Shopping Centers, 1221 Avenue of the Americas, 41st Flr, New York, NY, 10020-1099. Tel: 646-728-3800. Fax: 732-694-1714. p. 1683

Tucci, Valerie, Librn, The College of New Jersey Library, 2000 Pennington Rd, Ewing, NJ, 08628-0718. Tel: 609-771-2311, 609-771-2332. Fax: 609-637-5177. p. 1484

Tuchmayer, Harry, Dir, New Hanover County Public Library, 201 Chestnut St, Wilmington, NC, 28401. Tel: 910-798-6321. Fax: 910-798-6312. p. 1830

Tuck, Coralee, Dep Dir, Campbell County Public Library, 684 Village Hwy, Lower Level, Rustburg, VA, 24588. Tel: 434-332-9660. Fax: 434-332-9697. p. 2495

Tuck, Nikki, Librn, United States Army, Military Occupational Specialty Library, Bldg 2110, Fort Wainwright, AK, 99703. Tel: 907-353-7297. Fax: 907-353-7472. p. 48

Tuck, Sue, Supvr, Essex County Library, Leamington Branch, One John St, Leamington, ON, N8H 1H1, CANADA. Tel: 226-946-1529, Ext 220. p. 2804

Tucker, Adam, Ref Librn, Jefferson County Library, Windsor, 7479 Metropolitian Blvd, Barnhart, MO, 63012. Tel: 636-461-1914. Fax: 636-461-1915. p. 1331

Tucker, Betty, Head, Coll Mgt, Louisiana State University Health Sciences Center, 1501 Kings Hwy, Shreveport, LA, 71130. Tel: 318-675-5457. Fax: 318-675-5442. p. 968

Tucker, Betty, Ch, Onondaga Free Library, 4840 W Seneca Tpk, Syracuse, NY, 13215. Tel: 315-492-1727. Fax: 315-492-1323. p. 1753

Tucker, Carolyn, Cat, Tech Serv, Natchitoches Parish Library, 450 Second St, Natchitoches, LA, 71457-4649. Tel: 318-357-3280. Fax: 318-357-7073. p. 958

Tucker, Catherine, Librn, Brooklyn Town Library Association, Ten Canterbury Rd, Brooklyn, CT, 06234. Tel: 860-774-0649. Fax: 860-774-0649. p. 332

Tucker, Catherine, Librn, Mirick O'Connell, 100 Front St, Worcester, MA, 01608-1477. Tel: 508-860-1520. Fax: 508-983-6230. p. 1144

Tucker, Catherine, Librn, Hartshorne Public Library, 720 Penn Ave, Hartshorne, OK, 74547. Tel: 918-297-2113. Fax: 918-297-7004. p. 1964

Tucker, Cory, Head, Coll Mgt, University of Nevada, Las Vegas Libraries, 4505 Maryland Pkwy, Box 457001, Las Vegas, NV, 89154-7001. Tel: 702-895-2286. Fax: 702-895-2287. p. 1431

Tucker, David, Coll Mgt, DeKalb County Public Library, Administrative Office, 215 Sycamore St, 4th Flr, Decatur, GA, 30030. Tel: 404-508-7190. Fax: 404-508-7184. p. 529

Tucker, Dawnn, Dir, Lied Pierce Public Library, 207 W Court St, Pierce, NE, 68767. Tel: 402-329-6324. Fax: 402-329-6442. p. 1416

Tucker, Dayna, Ch, River Grove Public Library District, 8638 W Grand Ave, River Grove, IL, 60171. Tel: 708-453-4484. Fax: 708-453-4517. p. 694

Tucker, Diana, Br Mgr, Saint Charles City County Library District, Corporate Parkway Branch, 1200 Corporate Pkwy, Wentzville, MO, 63385-4828. Tel: 636-327-4010, 636-332-8280. Fax: 636-327-0548. p. 1364

Tucker, Elissa, Librn, Sharkey-Issaquena County Library, 116 E China St, Rolling Fork, MS, 39159. Tel: 662-873-4076. Fax: 662-873-0614. p. 1314

Tucker, Elizabeth, Dir, DeKalb County Public Library, 504 Grand Ave NW, Fort Payne, AL, 35967. Tel: 256-845-2671. Fax: 256-845-2671. p. 17

Tucker, Gayle, Human Res Mgr, Bloomington Public Library, 205 E Olive St, Bloomington, IL, 61701. Tel: 309-828-6091. Fax: 309-828-7312. p. 595

Tucker, Heather, Tech Serv Coordr, Mount Hood Community College Library, 26000 SE Stark St, Gresham, OR, 97030. Tel: 503-491-7106. Fax: 503-491-7389. p. 1999

Tucker, James, Librn, Johns Hopkins University Libraries, Adolf Meyer Library, 600 N Wolfe St, Baltimore, MD, 21205. Tel: 410-955-5819. Fax: 410-955-0860. p. 1014

Tucker, Jane, Dir, Astoria Public Library, 450 Tenth St, Astoria, OR, 97103. Tel: 503-325-7323. p. 1990

Tucker, Joe, Instruction Coordr, Ref & Instrul Serv Librn, Bennington College, One College Dr, Bennington, VT, 05201-6001. Tel: 802-440-4610. Fax: 802-440-4580. p. 2418

Tucker, Kari, Asst Dir, Jervis Public Library Association, Inc, 613 N Washington St, Rome, NY, 13440-4296. Tel: 315-336-4570. p. 1734

Tucker, Karly, Br Mgr, Whatcom County Library System, Island Branch, 2144 S Nugent Rd, Lummi Island, WA, 98262. Tel: 360-758-7145. Fax: 360-758-7145. p. 2509

Tucker, Kathy, Dir, Gleason Memorial Library, 105 College St, Gleason, TN, 38229. Tel: 731-648-9020. Fax: 731-648-9020. p. 2235

Tucker, Kim, Dir, Sonoma County Law Library, Hall of Justice, Rm 213-J, 600 Administration Dr, Santa Rosa, CA, 95403-2879. Tel: 707-565-2668. Fax: 707-565-1126. p. 267

Tucker, Kristi, Dir, Marshall County Public Library System, 1003 Poplar St, Benton, KY, 42025. Tel: 270-527-9969. Fax: 270-527-0506. p. 907

Tucker, Laura Ayling, Cat Librn, Lewis & Clark College, Aubrey R Watzek Library, 0615 SW Palatine Hill Rd, Portland, OR, 97219-7899. Tel: 503-768-7274. Fax: 503-768-7282. p. 2011

Tucker, Lawren, Chief Dep, Illinois State Library, Gwendolyn Brooks Bldg, 300 S Second St, Springfield, IL, 62701-9713. Tel: 217-524-4200. Fax: 217-785-4326. p. 705

Tucker, Louise, Librn, Connecticut Judicial Branch Law Libraries, Litchfield Law Library, Litchfield Courthouse, 15 West St, Litchfield, CT, 06759-3501. Tel: 860-567-0598. Fax: 860-567-4533. p. 344

Tucker, Marcia, Librn, Institute for Advanced Study Libraries, Einstein Dr, Princeton, NJ, 08540. Tel: 609-734-8181, 609-734-8276. Fax: 609-924-8399, 609-951-4515. p. 1522

Tucker, Mark, Dr, Dean of Libr, Abilene Christian University, 221 Brown Library, ACU Box 29208, Abilene, TX, 79699-9208. Tel: 325-674-2344. Fax: 325-674-2202. p. 2271

Tucker, Mary Ellen, Librn, University of North Carolina at Chapel Hill, Highway Safety Research Center, 730 Martin Luther King Jr Blvd, CB No 3430, Chapel Hill, NC, 27599-3430. Tel: 919-962-2202. Fax: 919-962-8710. p. 1781

Tucker, Robert, ILL, Pearl River County Library System, 900 Goodyear Blvd, Picayune, MS, 39466. Tel: 601-798-5081. Fax: 601-798-5082. p. 1311

Tucker, Rodney, Libr Tech, Nova Scotia Community College, 80 Mawiomi Pl, Dartmouth, NS, B2Y 0A5, CANADA. Tel: 902-491-1035. Fax: 902-491-1037. p. 2780

Tucker, Sandra, Sci, Eng & Liaison Serv, Texas A&M University Libraries, 5000 TAMU, College Station, TX, 77843-5000. Tel: 979-862-1043. Fax: 979-845-6238. p. 2298

Tucker, Sharron, Doc, Jersey City Free Public Library, 472 Jersey Ave, Jersey City, NJ, 07302-3499. Tel: 201-547-4517. Fax: 201-547-4584. p. 1492

Tucker, Sheila, County Historian, Cayuga County Historian's Office, Historic Old Post Off Bldg, 157 Genesee St, Auburn, NY, 13021-3490. Tel: 315-253-1300. p. 1576

Tucker, Taneishe, Dir, Vestavia Hills Library in the Forest, 1112 Montgomery Hwy, Vestavia Hills, AL, 35216. Tel: 205-978-0155. Fax: 205-978-0156. p. 39

Tucker, Theresa Marie, Dir, Lawrence Public Library District, 814 12th St, Lawrenceville, IL, 62439. Tel: 618-943-3016. Fax: 618-943-3215. p. 664

Tucker, Tina, Dir, Commun Develop, Thunder Bay Public Library, 285 Red River Rd, Thunder Bay, ON, P7B 1A9, CANADA. Tel: 807-684-6813. Fax: 807-345-8727. p. 2849

Tucker, Virginia, Law Librn, Whatcom County Law Library, Courthouse, Ste B-03, 311 Grand Ave, Bellingham, WA, 98225. Tel: 360-676-6556. Fax: 360-676-7727. p. 2509

Tucker-Watt, Carol-Anne, In Charge, Contra Costa County Library, Rodeo Community Library, 220 Pacific Ave, Rodeo, CA, 94572-1118. Tel: 510-799-2606. Fax: 510-799-3349. p. 209

Tuckman, Joel, Res, The Beasley Firm, LLC, 1125 Walnut St, Philadelphia, PA, 19107-4997. Tel: 215-592-1000. Fax: 215-592-8360. p. 2103

Tudor, Gail, Libr Tech, Michigan Department of Corrections, 2400 S Sheridan Dr, Muskegon, MI, 49442. Tel: 231-773-3201, Ext 271. Fax: 616-773-3657. p. 1212

Tudor, Jennifer, Circ, Clearwater Public Library System, East, 2251 Drew St, Clearwater, FL, 33765. Tel: 727-562-4970. p. 432

Tudor, Rhynda, In Charge, Pictou - Antigonish Regional Library, Antigonish Library, College St, Antigonish, NS, B2G 2M5, CANADA. Tel: 902-863-4276. p. 2784

Tufano, Eleanor, Dir, Shrewsbury Public Library, 98 Town Hill Rd, Cuttingsville, VT, 05738. Tel: 802-492-3410. p. 2422

Tufano, Vivian, Head, Circ, Henderson District Public Libraries, James I Gibson Library, 100 W Lake Mead Pkwy, Henderson, NV, 89015. Tel: 702-565-8402. Fax: 702-565-8832. p. 1428

Tufaro, Linda, Dir, Pearl River County Library System, 900 Goodyear Blvd, Picayune, MS, 39466. Tel: 601-798-5081. Fax: 601-798-5082. p. 1311

Tuff, Dianne, Asst Librn, Heart of America Library, 201 Third St SW, Rugby, ND, 58368-1793. Tel: 701-776-6223. Fax: 701-776-6897. p. 1848

Tufts, Sarah, Ch, Windsor Public Library, 43 State St, Windsor, VT, 05089. Tel: 802-674-2556. Fax: 802-674-5767. p. 2440

Tugarina, Olga, Tech Serv, New England Historic Genealogical Society Library, 99-101 Newbury St, Boston, MA, 02116-3007. Tel: 617-226-1228. Fax: 617-536-7307. p. 1065

Tuggle, Donna, Ch, Wayne County Public Library, 150 S Main St, Monticello, KY, 42633. Tel: 606-348-8565. Fax: 606-348-3829. p. 929

Tuggle, Herbert, Librn, Mount Rushmore National Memorial Library, Bldg 31, Ste 1, 13000 Hwy 244, Keystone, SD, 57751. Tel: 605-574-2523. Fax: 605-574-2307. p. 2213

Tuggle, John, Asst Dir, Pub Serv, Live Oak Public Libraries, 2002 Bull St, Savannah, GA, 31401. Tel: 912-652-3600. Fax: 912-652-3638. p. 550

Tuggle, Robert, Dir, Metropolitan Opera Archives, Lincoln Center Plaza, New York, NY, 10023. Tel: 212-799-3100, Ext 2525. Fax: 212-870-7657. p. 1687

Tugwell, Cindy, Exec Dir, Heritage Winnipeg Corp Library, 63 Albert St, Ste 509, Winnipeg, MB, R3B 1G4, CANADA. Tel: 204-942-2663. Fax: 204-942-2094. p. 2755

Tuisku, Connie, Ref, Palm Beach State College, 4200 Congress Ave, Mail Sta 17, Lake Worth, FL, 33461. Tel: 561-868-3800. Fax: 561-868-3708. p. 459

Tuite, Lisa, Librn, Boston Globe, 135 Morrissey Blvd, Boston, MA, 02107. Tel: 617-929-2540. Fax: 617-929-3314. p. 1056

Tukhareli, Natalia, Librn, Rouge Valley Health System-Centenary Health Centre, 2867 Ellesmere Rd, Toronto, ON, M1E 4B9, CANADA. Tel: 416-281-7101. Fax: 416-281-7360. p. 2858

Tulanian, David, Actg Br Mgr, Los Angeles Public Library System, Angeles Mesa, 2700 W 52nd St, Los Angeles, CA, 90043-1999. Tel: 323-292-4328. Fax: 323-296-3508. p. 173

Tuley-Williams, Dana, Syst Librn, Oklahoma City Community College, 7777 S May Ave, Oklahoma City, OK, 73159. Tel: 405-682-1611, Ext 7390. Fax: 405-682-7585. p. 1973

Tull, Betty, Librn, Central United Methodist Church Library, 616 Jackson St SE, Decatur, AL, 35601-3124. Tel: 256-353-6941. p. 14

Tull, Pamela, Head, Pub Serv, University of Kansas Libraries, Wheat Law Library, Green Hall, Rm 200, 1535 W 15th St, Lawrence, KS, 66045-7608. Tel: 785-864-3025. Fax: 785-864-3680. p. 878

Tull, Rita, Actg Br Mgr, Montgomery County Public Libraries, Davis Library, 6400 Democracy Blvd, Bethesda, MD, 20817-1638. Tel: 240-777-0922. Fax: 301-564-5055. p. 1038

Tullis, Kim, Tech Serv, Saint Joseph Public Library, East Hills Library, 502 N Woodbine Rd, Saint Joseph, MO, 64506. Tel: 816-236-1423. Fax: 816-236-1429. p. 1353

Tulloch, Meg, Dir, US Department of Defense, Fort McNair, Marshall Hall, Washington, DC, 20319-5066. Tel: 202-685-3948. Fax: 202-685-3733. p. 418

Tully, Patricia, Univ Librn, Wesleyan University, 252 Church St, Middletown, CT, 06459-3199. Tel: 860-685-3887. Fax: 860-685-2661. p. 352

Tully, Patricia, Managing Dir, CTW Library Consortium, Olin Memorial Library, Wesleyan University, Middletown, CT, 06459-6065. Tel: 860-685-3887. Fax: 860-685-2661. p. 2939

Tully, Teresa, Ref Librn, Sullivan & Cromwell LLP, 125 Broad St, New York, NY, 10004. Tel: 212-558-3780. Fax: 212-558-3346. p. 1700

Tumber, Edward, Ref, Ser, Clearwater Public Library System, 100 N Osceola Ave, Clearwater, FL, 33755. Tel: 727-562-4970. Fax: 727-562-4977. p. 432

Tumbleson, Beth, Asst Dir, Miami University-Middletown, 4200 N University Blvd, Middletown, OH, 45042-3497. Tel: 513-727-3232. p. 1917

Tuminello, Kathy, Admin Serv, Shreve Memorial Library, 424 Texas St, Shreveport, LA, 71101. Tel: 318-226-5897. Fax: 318-226-4780. p. 969

Tunai, Lily, Circ Serv Coordr, Feleti Barstow Public Library, PO Box 997687, Pago Pago, AS, 96799. Tel: 684-633-5816. Fax: 684-633-5823. p. 2666

Tunches, Cynthia, Librn, Corpus Christi Public Libraries, Janet F Harte Public, 2629 Waldron Rd, Corpus Christi, TX, 78418. Tel: 361-937-6569. Fax: 361-937-5222. p. 2301

Tune, Sheryl, Br Mgr, Kings County Library, Avenal Branch, 501 E King St, Avenal, CA, 93204. Tel: 559-386-5741. Fax: 559-386-1418. p. 156

Tunis, Cortney, Res Ctr Mgr, Wheelock College Library, 132 The Riverway, Boston, MA, 02215-4815. Tel: 617-879-2142. Fax: 617-879-2408. p. 1068

Tunnell, Julie, Head Librn, Metropolitan Transportation Commission, 101 Eighth St, Oakland, CA, 94607. Tel: 510-817-5836. Fax: 510-817-5932. p. 197

Tunney, Robin, Br Dir, Guelph Public Library, Scottsdale Centre Branch, 650 Scottsdale Dr, Guelph, ON, N1G 3M2, CANADA. Tel: 519-829-4402. p. 2807

Tunon, Johanna, Head, Distance & Instrul Libr Serv, Nova Southeastern University Libraries, 3100 Ray Ferrero Jr Blvd, Fort Lauderdale, FL, 33314. Tel: 954-262-4608. Fax: 954-262-3805. p. 444

Tunrbill, Nancy, Tech Serv Librn, Fitchburg State College, 160 Pearl St, Fitchburg, MA, 01420. Tel: 978 665-4338. Fax: 978-665-3069. p. 1089

Tunstall, Charles, Ref Librn, Tusculum College, Hwy 107, 60 Shiloh Rd, Greeneville, TN, 37743. Tel: 423-636-7320, Ext 5124. Fax: 423-787-8498. p. 2236

Tunstall, Margaret, Acq Librn, Texas Southern University, 3100 Cleburne Ave, Houston, TX, 77004. Tel: 713-313-7152. Fax: 713-313-1080. p. 2342

Tuohey, Jeanne, Ref, Niagara County Community College, 3111 Saunders Settlement Rd, Sanborn, NY, 14132. Tel: 716-614-6791. Fax: 716-614-6816, 716-614-6828. p. 1737

Tuohig, Paul, Res Analyst, United States Army, The Institute of Heraldry Library, 9325 Gunston Rd, Ste S113, Fort Belvoir, VA, 22060-5579. Tel: 703-806-4967, 703-806-4975. Fax: 703-656-4964. p. 2464

Tuohy, Catherine, Asst Dir, Technology & Tech Serv, Emmanuel College, 400 The Fenway, Boston, MA, 02115. Tel: 617-264-7658. Fax: 617-735-9763. p. 1060

Tuohy, Nancy L, Dir, Res Serv, Clausen Miller Research Services Dept, Ten S LaSalle St, 16th Flr, Chicago, IL, 60603-1098. Tel: 312-606-7535. Fax: 312-606-7777. p. 611

Tuohy, Patricia, Exec Dir, Central Texas Library System, Inc, 5555 N Lamar Blvd, Ste L115, Austin, TX, 78751. Tel: 512-583-0704, Ext 12. Fax: 512-583-0709. p. 2280

Tuominen, Lisa, Chief Librn, Ottawa Citizen Library, 1101 Baxter Rd, Ottawa, ON, K2C 3M4, CANADA. Tel: 613-596-3744. Fax: 613-726-1198. p. 2832

Tupper, Judy, Librn, Muir Library, 36 Main St N, Winnebago, MN, 56098-2097. Tel: 507-893-3196. Fax: 507-893-4766. p. 1289

Turbak, Jamie, Br Mgr, Oakland Public Library, Piedmont Avenue, 160 41st St, Oakland, CA, 94611. Tel: 510-597-5011. Fax: 510-597-5078. p. 198

Turbak, Jamie, Supv Librn, Main Libr Pub Serv, Oakland Public Library, Main Library, 125 14th St, Oakland, CA, 94612. Tel: 510-238-3134. Fax: 510-238-2232. p. 198

Turbes, Mike, Tech Mgr, Dakota County Library System, 1340 Wescott Rd, Eagan, MN, 55123-1099. Tel: 651-450-2991. Fax: 651-450-2915. p. 1249

Turbide, Candice, Ch, Teck Centennial Library, Ten Kirkland St E, Kirkland Lake, ON, P2N 1P1, CANADA. Tel: 705-567-7966. Fax: 705-568-6303. p. 2814

Turbyne, Susan, Dir, Byron G Merrill Library, Ten Buffalo Rd, Rumney, NH, 03266. Tel: 603-786-9520. p. 1464

Turcott, Irene, Ref & Instrul Serv Librn, Kalamazoo Valley Community College Libraries, 6767 West O Ave, Kalamazoo, MI, 49003. Tel: 269-488-4328, 269-488-4380. Fax: 269-488-4488. p. 1197

Turcotte, Dawna, Librn, Northern Lights College, 9820 120 Ave, Fort Saint John, BC, V1J 6K1, CANADA. Tel: 250-787-6213. Fax: 250-785-1294. p. 2728

Turcotte, Joceline-Andree, Dir, Bibliotheque Municipale Come-Saint-Germain, 545 rue des Ecoles, Drummondville, QC, J2B 1J6, CANADA. Tel: 819-478-6588. Fax: 819-478-0399. p. 2881

Turcotte, Vickie, Head, Tech Serv, Chelmsford Public Library, 25 Boston Rd, Chelmsford, MA, 01824-3088. Tel: 978-256-5521. Fax: 978-256-8511. p. 1079

Tureski, Shannon, Human Res Officer, Queen's University, 101 Union St, Kingston, ON, K7L 5C4, CANADA. Tel: 613-533-6000, Ext 75270. Fax: 613-533-6362. p. 2814

Tureson, Tamara, Electronic Res, Holland & Hart, 555 17th St, Ste 3200, Denver, CO, 80201-3950. Tel: 303-295-8091. Fax: 303-295-8261. p. 302

Turgeon, Lisa, Ch, Berlin Free Library, 834 Worthington Ridge, Berlin, CT, 06037-3203. Tel: 860-828-3344. p. 330

Turgeon, Marilyn, Librn, Chinook Regional Library, Abbey Branch, 133 Main St, Abbey, SK, S0N 0A0, CANADA. Tel: 306-689-2202. p. 2928

Turgeon, Marla, Cat & Circ Supvr, Spoon River College Library, 23235 N County Rd 22, Canton, IL, 61520. Tel: 309-649-6222. Fax: 309-649-6235. p. 599

Turgeon, Tammy, Dir, Sterling Heights Public Library, 40255 Dodge Park Rd, Sterling Heights, MI, 48313-4140. Tel: 586-446-2640. Fax: 586-276-4067. p. 1229

Turgeon, Trudy, Librn, Chinook Regional Library, Kincaid Branch, Village Office, Kincaid, SK, S0H 2J0, CANADA. Tel: 306-264-3910. p. 2928

Turhollow, C Anne, Interim Assoc Dean, San Diego State University Library & Information Access, 5500 Campanile Dr, San Diego, CA, 92182-8050. Tel: 619-594-6728. Fax: 619-594-3270. p. 237

Turitz, Debra, Dir, Jewish Community Center on the Palisades, 411 E Clinton Ave, Tenafly, NJ, 07670. Tel: 201-569-7900, Ext 234. Fax: 201-569-7448. p. 1533

Turk, Gloria, Librn, San Jose Museum of Art Library, 110 S Market St, San Jose, CA, 95113. Tel: 408-271-6840. Fax: 408-294-2977. p. 250

Turkalj, Heidi, Cat, Libr Tech, Moody Bible Institute, 820 N La Salle Blvd, Chicago, IL, 60610-3284. Tel: 312-329-4136. Fax: 312-329-8959. p. 619

Turkalo, Laury, Syst Coordr, Robert L Carothers Library & Learning Commons, 15 Lippitt Rd, Kingston, RI, 02881. Tel: 401-874-2820. Fax: 401-874-4608. p. 2168

Turkington, Barbara, Asst Dir, Advan, Saint Louis County Library, 1640 S Lindbergh Blvd, Saint Louis, MO, 63131-3598. Tel: 314-994-3300, Ext 2152. Fax: 314-997-7602. p. 1358

Turkos, Joseph, Acq, Loyola-Notre Dame Library, Inc, 200 Winston Ave, Baltimore, MD, 21212. Tel: 410-617-6800. Fax: 410-617-6895. p. 1015

Turman, Alice, Youth Serv, Huntingdon Valley Library, 625 Red Lion Rd, Huntingdon Valley, PA, 19006-6297. Tel: 215-947-5138. Fax: 215-938-5894. p. 2070

Turman, Lynne, Head, Coll, Virginia Commonwealth University Libraries, Tompkins-McCaw Library, Medical College of Virginia Campus, 509 N 12th St, Richmond, VA, 23298-0582. Tel: 804-828-0638. Fax: 804-828-6089. p. 2492

Turn, Jean, Dir, Kinchafoonee Regional Library System, 913 Forrester Dr SE, Dawson, GA, 39842-2106. Tel: 229-995-6331. Fax: 229-995-3383. p. 528

Turn, Jean O, Head Librn, Kinchafoonee Regional Library System, Clay County Library, 208 S Hancock St, Fort Gaines, GA, 39851-9506. Tel: 229-768-2248. Fax: 229-768-2248. p. 528

Turnage, Karen, In Charge, Lincoln-Lawrence-Franklin Regional Library, New Hebron Public Library, 209 Jones St, New Hebron, MS, 39140-3986. Tel: 601-694-2623. Fax: 601-694-2623. p. 1295

Turnbaugh, Rebecca, Mgr, Ref & Tech Serv, South Kingstown Public Library, 1057 Kingstown Rd, Peace Dale, RI, 02879-2434. Tel: 401-783-4085, 401-789-1555. Fax: 401-782-6370. p. 2171

Turnbow, Dominique, Undergrad Serv Librn, University of California, San Diego, Biomedical Library, 9500 Gilman Dr, 0699, La Jolla, CA, 92093-0699. Tel: 858-534-3418. Fax: 858-822-2219. p. 162

Turnbull, Ann, Head, Info Serv, Kewanee Public Library District, 102 S Tremont St, Kewanee, IL, 61443. Tel: 309-852-4505. Fax: 309-852-4466. p. 661

Turnbull, Caren, Asst Mgr, Geneva College, 3200 College Ave, Beaver Falls, PA, 15010-3599. Tel: 724-847-6563. Fax: 724-847-6687. p. 2031

Turnbull, Donald, Asst Prof, University of Texas at Austin, One University Sta, D7000, Austin, TX, 78712-0390. Tel: 512-471-3821. Fax: 512-471-3971. p. 2975

Turner, Ali, Div Mgr, Communications & Commun Engagement, Hennepin County Library, 12601 Ridgedale Dr, Minnetonka, MN, 55305-1909. Tel: 612-543-8516. Fax: 612-543-8600. p. 1263

Turner, Alissa, Head, Coll & Tech, Saline County Public Library, 1800 Smithers Dr, Benton, AR, 72015. Tel: 501-778-4766. Fax: 501-778-0536. p. 94

Turner, Amanda, Librn, Raleigh County Public Library, Sophia Branch, General Delivery, 103 First St, Sophia, WV, 25921. Tel: 304-683-5990. Fax: 304-683-3124. p. 2554

Turner, Amber, Mgr, Human Res, Johnson County Public Library, 401 State St, Franklin, IN, 46131-2545. Tel: 317-738-2833. Fax: 317-738-9635. p. 744

Turner, Amos, Head, Ref, School of Visual Arts, 380 Second Ave, 2nd Flr, New York, NY, 10010-3994. Tel: 212-592-2660. Fax: 212-592-2655. p. 1699

Turner, Amy, Film, Theatre & Communications Librn, Head, Jones Film & Video Coll, Southern Methodist University, Hamon Arts Library, 6101 N Bishop Blvd, Dallas, TX, 75275. Tel: 214-768-1855. Fax: 214-768-1800. p. 2310

Turner, Angela, Ref Librn, Clark County Public Library, 370 S Burns Ave, Winchester, KY, 40391-1876. Tel: 859-744-5661. Fax: 859-744-5993. p. 938

Turner, Angela, Asst Librn, Rutherford County Library, Mountains Branch, 150 Bills Creek Rd, Lake Lure, NC, 28746. Tel: 828-625-0456. Fax: 828-625-0453. p. 1825

Turner, Ann, ILL Librn, Flint River Regional Library, 800 Memorial Dr, Griffin, GA, 30223. Tel: 770-412-4770. p. 535

Turner, Annie, Head Librn, Ref Librn, Ministere des Ressources naturelles et de la Faune, 5700 4e Ave Ouest, B-201, Quebec, QC, G1H 6R1, CANADA. Tel: 418-627-8686, Ext 3552. Fax: 418-644-1124. p. 2906

Turner, Ashley, Librn, Edna Ralston Public Library, 116 1/2 Towner Ave, Larimore, ND, 58251. Tel: 701-343-2181. p. 1845

Turner, Bronsene, Cat, ILL, Rappahannock Community College Library, 12745 College Dr, Glenns, VA, 23149. Tel: 804-758-6710. Fax: 804-758-0213. p. 2467

Turner, Camille, Librn, Fresno County Public Library, Auberry Branch, 33049 Auberry Rd, Auberry, CA, 93602. Tel: 559-855-8523. Fax: 559-855-8523. p. 152

Turner, Carrie L, Admin Dir, Cheltenham Township Library System, 215 S Keswick Ave, Glenside, PA, 19038-4420. Tel: 215-885-0457. Fax: 215-885-1239. p. 2061

Turner, Cheryl, Dir, Wilderness Coast Public Libraries, 1180 W Washington St, Monticello, FL, 32344. Tel: 850-997-7400. Fax: 850-997-7403. p. 470

Turner, Colette, Dir, Vidor Public Library, 440 E Bolivar, Vidor, TX, 77662. Tel: 409-769-7148. Fax: 409-769-5782. p. 2395

Turner, Debbie, Mgr, Three Rivers Regional Library System, Wayne County Library, 759 Sunset Blvd, Jesup, GA, 31545-4409. Tel: 912-427-2500. Fax: 912-427-0071. p. 522

Turner, Debra, Commun Relations Librn, York County Library, 138 E Black St, Rock Hill, SC, 29731. Tel: 803-981-5837. Fax: 803-981-5866. p. 2203

Turner, Diane, Res & Instruction Librn, Auraria Library, 1100 Lawrence St, Denver, CO, 80204-2095. Tel: 303-556-2719. Fax: 303-556-3528. p. 298

Turner, Don, Ref Serv, Jefferson County Library, Windsor, 7479 Metropolitian Blvd, Barnhart, MO, 63012. Tel: 636-461-1914. Fax: 636-461-1915. p. 1331

Turner, Donald, Br Mgr, Live Oak Public Libraries, West Broad Branch, 1110 May St, Savannah, GA, 31415. Tel: 912-232-6395. Fax: 912-232-6395. p. 550

Turner, Elizabeth, Bus Librn, Lee County Library, 219 N Madison St, Tupelo, MS, 38804-3899. Tel: 662-841-9027. Fax: 662-840-7615. p. 1316

Turner, Ellen, Ref Serv, Tech Serv, Widener University, Harrisburg Campus Law Library, 3800 Vartan Way, Harrisburg, DE, 17110. Tel: 717-541-3929. Fax: 717-541-3998. p. 389

Turner, Emily, Libr Dir, DeVry College of New York Library, 180 Madison Ave, 16th Flr, New York, NY, 10016-5267. Tel: 212-312-4414. p. 1677

Turner, Frances, Circ, Dolton Public Library District, 14037 Lincoln, Dolton, IL, 60419-1091. Tel: 708-849-2385. Fax: 708-841-2725. p. 637

Turner, Frank M, Univ Librn, Yale University Library, Sterling Memorial Library, 120 High St, New Haven, CT, 06520. Tel: 203-432-2798. Fax: 203-432-1294. p. 359

Turner, Heather, Tech Serv Librn, Bethany College, Mary Cutlip Center for Library & Information Technology, 300 Main St, Bethany, WV, 26032. Tel: 304-829-7321. Fax: 304-829-7333. p. 2554

Turner, Heidi, Librn, Kirklin Public Library, 115 N Main, Kirklin, IN, 46050. Tel: 765-279-8308. Fax: 765-279-8258. p. 757

Turner, I Bruce, Dr, Archivist, University of Louisiana at Lafayette, PO Box 40199, Lafayette, LA, 70504-0199. Tel: 337-482-5702. Fax: 337-482-6399. p. 953

Turner, James, Prof, Universite de Montreal, 3150, rue Jean-Brillant, bur C-2004, Montreal, QC, H3T 1N8, CANADA. Tel: 514-343-6044. Fax: 514-343-5753. p. 2979

Turner, Jamie, Librn, Stockton-San Joaquin County Public Library, Escalon Branch, 1540 Second St, Escalon, CA, 95320. Tel: 209-838-2494. Fax: 209-838-2032. p. 273

Turner, Jane, Univ Archivist, University of Victoria Libraries, McPherson Library, PO Box 1800, Victoria, BC, V8W 3H5, CANADA. Tel: 250-721-8211. Fax: 250-721-8215. p. 2746

Turner, Janet, Adult Serv, Ref, Amherst Public Library, 221 Spring St, Amherst, OH, 44001. Tel: 440-988-4230. Fax: 440-988-4115. p. 1854

Turner, Jess, Sr Librn, Denton Public Library, South Branch, 3228 Teasley Lane, Denton, TX, 76210. Tel: 940-349-8256. Fax: 940-349-8383. p. 2312

Turner, Joy, Libr Dir, Tellico Plains Public Library, 209 Hwy 165, Tellico Plains, TN, 37385. Tel: 423-253-7388. Fax: 423-253-6274. p. 2267

Turner, June, Librn, Palo Verde College, One College Dr, Blythe, CA, 92225-9561. Tel: 760-921-5518. Fax: 760-921-5581. p. 129

Turner, Kathleen, Evening Supvr, Outreach Librn, Drexel University Health Sciences Libraries, 245 N 15th St MS 449, Philadelphia, PA, 19102-1192. Fax: 215-762-8180. p. 2105

Turner, Kathryn Bates, Libr Dir, Yolo County Law Library, 204 Fourth St, Ste A, Woodland, CA, 95695. Tel: 530-666-8918. Fax: 530-666-8618. p. 284

Turner, Kathy, Dir, Instrul Serv, Florida Institute of Technology, 150 W University Blvd, Melbourne, FL, 32901-6988. Tel: 321-674-8021. Fax: 321-724-2559. p. 463

Turner, Kathy M, Tech Serv Librn, Elizabeth City State University, 1704 Weeksville Rd, Elizabeth City, NC, 27909. Tel: 252-335-3428. Fax: 252-335-3408. p. 1790

Turner, Leigh, Mgr, Albuquerque-Bernalillo County Library System, Cherry Hills, 6901 Barstow NE, Albuquerque, NM, 87111. Tel: 505-857-8321. Fax: 505-857-8323. p. 1548

Turner, Lillian, Chair, St Philip's College, 1801 Martin Luther King Dr, San Antonio, TX, 78203-2098. Tel: 210-486-2330. Fax: 210-486-2335. p. 2381

Turner, Liz, Librn, Oswego Public Library, 704 Fourth St, Oswego, KS, 67356. Tel: 620-795-4921. Fax: 620-795-4921. p. 887

Turner, Liz, Ch, Madison County Library System, Madison Public Library, 994 Madison Ave, Madison, MS, 39110. Tel: 601-856-2749. Fax: 601-856-2681. p. 1295`

Turner, Lynne, Librn, Blue Rapids Public Library, 14 Public Sq, Blue Rapids, KS, 66411. Tel: 785-363-7709. p. 858

Turner, Marcellus, City Librn, The Seattle Public Library, 1000 Fourth Ave, Seattle, WA, 98104-1109. Tel: 206-386-4636. p. 2531

Turner, Maria, Dir, Rio Hondo Public Library, 121 N Arroyo Blvd, Rio Hondo, TX, 78583. Tel: 956-748-3322. Fax: 956-748-3322. p. 2376

Turner, Mary, In Charge, Department of Corrections, 12279 Brady Dr, Custer, SD, 57730. Tel: 605-673-2521. Fax: 605-673-5489. p. 2211

Turner, Pamela E, Dir, Baxter Memorial Library, 71 South St, Gorham, ME, 04038. Tel: 207-222-1190. Fax: 207-839-7749. p. 986

Turner, Pat, Dir, Marshall Memorial Library, 110 S Diamond St, Deming, NM, 88030-3698. Tel: 505-546-9202. Fax: 505-546-9649. p. 1554

Turner, Penelope A, Dir, Info Serv, Smith, Haughey, Rice & Roegge, 200 Calder Plaza Bldg, 250 Monroe Ave NW, Grand Rapids, MI, 49503. Tel: 614-458-5315. Fax: 616-774-2461. p. 1186

Turner, Phillip, Dr, Prof, University of North Texas, 1155 Union Circle, Denton, TX, 76203-5017. Tel: 940-565-4462. Fax: 940-565-3101. p. 2975

Turner, Ramsey, Circ & ILL Coordr, Bethany Lutheran College Memorial Library, 700 Luther Dr, Mankato, MN, 56001-4490. Tel: 507-344-7000. Fax: 507-344-7376. p. 1257

Turner, Rebecca, Head, Circ, Suffolk County Community College, 533 College Rd, Selden, NY, 11784-2899. Tel: 631-451-4800. Fax: 631-451-4697. p. 1742

Turner, Robyn, Dir, Caryville Public Library, 4839 Old Hwy 63, Ste 2, Caryville, TN, 37714-4105. Tel: 423-562-1108. Fax: 423-562-1096. p. 2226

Turner, Ruth, Dir, First Baptist Church of Dallas, 1707 San Jacinto, Dallas, TX, 75201. Tel: 214-969-2442. p. 2308

Turner, Sandy, Asst Coordr, Mondak Heritage Center, 120 Third Ave SE, Sidney, MT, 59270-0050. Tel: 406-433-3500. Fax: 406-433-3503. p. 1388

Turner, Shad, Pub Serv, Yellowknife Public Library, Centre Square Mall, 5022 49th St, 2nd Flr, Yellowknife, NT, X1A 2N5, CANADA. Tel: 867-920-5642. Fax: 867-920-5671. p. 2776

Turner, Sharon, Dir, Morgantown Public Library System, 373 Spruce St, Morgantown, WV, 26505. Tel: 304-291-7425. Fax: 304-291-7427. p. 2566

Turner, Sharon, Br Supvr, Guelph Public Library, West End Branch, 21 Imperial Rd S, Guelph, ON, N1K 1X3, CANADA. Tel: 519-829-4403. p. 2807

Turner, Sherlonya, Mgr, Youth & Adult Serv & Coll, Ann Arbor District Library, 343 S Fifth Ave, Ann Arbor, MI, 48104. Tel: 734-327-4268. Fax: 734-327-8307. p. 1150

Turner, Sherri, Asst Dir, Lawrence Public Library, 707 Vermont St, Lawrence, KS, 66044-2371. Tel: 785-843-3833, Ext 126. Fax: 785-843-3368. p. 877

Turner, Suzanne, Librn, Testing Engineers International, Inc, 3455 S 500 West, South Salt Lake, UT, 84115-4234. Tel: 801-262-2332. Fax: 801-262-2363. p. 2416

Turner-Harris, Carolyn, Br Mgr, Cheltenham Township Library System, LaMott Free Library, 7420 Sycamore Ave, LaMott, PA, 19027-1005. Tel: 215-635-4419. Fax: 215-635-4419. p. 2062

Turner-Hatchett, Lisa, Youth Serv, Clearwater Public Library System, 100 N Osceola Ave, Clearwater, FL, 33755. Tel: 727-562-4970. Fax: 727-562-4977. p. 432

Turney, Linda, Coordr, Cat, Sam Houston State University, 1830 Bobby K Marks Dr, Huntsville, TX, 77340. Tel: 936-294-3503. Fax: 936-294-3780. p. 2345

Turney, Peg, Per, Paola Free Library, 101 E Peoria, Paola, KS, 66071-1798. Tel: 913-259-3655. Fax: 913-259-3656. p. 889

Turney, Sayre, Adjunct Fac Librn, Harrisburg Area Community College, 1641 Old Philadelphia Pike, Lancaster, PA, 17602. Tel: 717-358-2986. Fax: 717-358-2952. p. 2076

Turnquist, Jan, Exec Dir, Louisa May Alcott Memorial Association Library, 399 Lexington Rd, Concord, MA, 01742. Tel: 978-369-4118. Fax: 978-369-1367. p. 1082

Turnquist, Laura, Ch, Alta Community Library, 1009 Main St, Alta, IA, 51002. Tel: 712-200-1250. p. 792

Turnquist, Reba, Coll Develop Librn, University of Washington Libraries, Marian Gould Gallagher Law Library, William H Gates Hall, Box 353025, Seattle, WA, 98195-3025. Tel: 206-543-4098. Fax: 206-685-2165. p. 2534

Turock, Betty J, Assoc Dean, Prof, Rutgers, The State University of New Jersey, Four Huntington St, New Brunswick, NJ, 08901-1071. Tel: 732-932-7500, Ext 8955. Fax: 732-932-2644. p. 2969

Turosik, Diane, ILL, California University of Pennsylvania, 250 University Ave, California, PA, 15419-1394. Tel: 724-938-5539. Fax: 724-938-5901. p. 2040

Turrell, Susan, Librn, Tunkhannock Public Library, 220 W Tioga St, Tunkhannock, PA, 18657-6611. Tel: 570-836-1677. Fax: 570-836-2148. p. 2147

Turrini, Joseph M, Dr, Asst Prof, Wayne State University, 106 Kresge Library, Detroit, MI, 48202. Tel: 313-577-1825. Fax: 313-577-7563. p. 2968

Turrubiarte, Elaine, Admin Serv, Aubrey Area Library, 226 Countryside Dr, Aubrey, TX, 76227. Tel: 940-365-9162. Fax: 940-365-9411. p. 2277

Turse, Trinidad, Ref Serv, Ch, Livonia Public Library, Civic Center, 32777 Five Mile Rd, Livonia, MI, 48154-3045. Tel: 734-466-2454. Fax: 734-458-6011. p. 1203

Tursi, Laraine, Dir, Coney Island Hospital, 2601 Ocean Pkwy, Brooklyn, NY, 11235. Tel: 718-616-3000, 718-616-4158. Fax: 718-616-4178. p. 1592

Turtell, Neal, Exec Librn, National Gallery of Art Library, Fourth St & Constitution Ave NW, Washington, DC, 20565. Tel: 202-842-6511. Fax: 202-789-3068. p. 409

Turtle, Rita, Chief Exec Officer, Quinte West Public Library, Seven Creswell Dr, Trenton, ON, K8V 6X5, CANADA. Tel: 613-394-3381. Fax: 613-394-2079. p. 2868

Turton, Trina, Circ, Selby Public Library, 1331 First St, Sarasota, FL, 34236-4899. Tel: 941-861-1100. Fax: 941-316-1188. p. 490

Turvill, Gretchen, ILL, Illinois Central College, One College Dr, East Peoria, IL, 61635-0001. Tel: 309-694-5461. Fax: 309-694-5473. p. 638

Tusa, Sarah, Coordr, Coll Develop & Acq, Lamar University, 211 Redbird Lane, Beaumont, TX, 77705. Tel: 409-880-8125. Fax: 409-880-2318. p. 2287

Tusack, Karen, Network Serv, University of Wisconsin-Madison, L & S Learning Support Services, Van Hise Hall, 1220 Linden Dr, Madison, WI, 53706. Tel: 608-262-1408. Fax: 608-262-7579. p. 2609

Tusche, Jennifer Schroth, Electronic Serv, Drinker Biddle & Reath LLP, One Logan Sq, 18th & Cherry St, Philadelphia, PA, 19103. Tel: 215-988-3368. Fax: 215-564-1329, 215-988-2757. p. 2106

Tush, Peter, Librn, Salvador Dali Foundation Inc, 1000 Third St S, Saint Petersburg, FL, 33701. Tel: 727-823-3767. Fax: 727-823-8532. p. 487

Tusing, Holly, Pres, Hyde Park Public Library, 700 Main St, Hyde Park, PA, 15641. Tel: 724-845-1944. p. 2070

Tusinski, Nancy, Adult Serv, Springfield Town Library, 43 Main St, Springfield, VT, 05156. Tel: 802-885-3108. Fax: 802-885-4906. p. 2436

Tuske, Richard, Dir, Association of the Bar of the City of New York Library, 42 W 44th St, New York, NY, 10036. Tel: 212-382-6666. Fax: 212-382-6790. p. 1669

Tustin, Deborah, Cat, Cape Cod Hospital, 27 Park St, Hyannis, MA, 02601-5230. Tel: 508-862-5443. Fax: 774-552-6904. p. 1096

Tuten, Jane H, Dir, University of South Carolina Aiken, 471 University Pkwy, Aiken, SC, 29801. Tel: 803-648-6851, Ext 3465. Fax: 803-641-3302. p. 2180

Tuthill, Dawn, Librn, Eastern Long Island Hospital, 201 Manor Pl, Greenport, NY, 11944. Tel: 631-477-1000, Ext 273. Fax: 631-477-1670. p. 1631

Tuthill, Jeffrey, Head, Tech Serv, East Carolina University, Music Library, A J Fletcher Music Ctr, Rm A110, Greenville, NC, 27858. Tel: 252-328-1240. Fax: 252-328-1243. p. 1799

Tutt, Patrice, Per, Miles College, 5500 Myron Massey Blvd, Fairfield, AL, 35064. Tel: 205-929-1711. Fax: 205-929-1635. p. 16

Tuttle, Barbara, Ref & Instruction Librn, Dakota County Technical College Library, 1300 E 145th St, Rosemount, MN, 55068. Tel: 651-423-8366. Fax: 651-423-8043. p. 1273

Tuttle, Brandi, Info & Educ Serv Librn/Pub Serv, Duke University Libraries, Medical Center Library, DUMC Box 3702, Ten Bryan-Searle Dr, Durham, NC, 27710-0001. Tel: 919-660-1126. Fax: 919-681-7599. p. 1788

Tuttle, Craig, Archivist, Fayetteville State University, 1200 Murchison Rd, Fayetteville, NC, 28301-4298. Tel: 910-672-1613. Fax: 910-672-1746. p. 1793

Tuttle, Elvia, Br Mgr, Public Library of Cincinnati & Hamilton County, Price Hill, 3215 Warsaw Ave, Cincinnati, OH, 45205. Tel: 513-369-4490. Fax: 513-369-4538. p. 1872

Tuttle, George, Computer Serv Librn, Piedmont Regional Library, 189 Bell View St, Winder, GA, 30680-1706. Tel: 770-867-2762. Fax: 770-867-7483. p. 557

Tuttle, Idella, Librn, Ewing Township Library, 202 E Nebraska, Ewing, NE, 68735. p. 1398

Tuttle, Jane, Head, User Serv, Columbia College, 1301 Columbia College Dr, Columbia, SC, 29203-9987. Tel: 803-786-3337. Fax: 803-786-3700. p. 2187

Tuttle, Joe, Head Librn, Sussex County Law Library, 4347 High St, Newton, NJ, 07860. Tel: 973-579-0702. Fax: 973-579-0679. p. 1514

Tuttle, Steve D, Dir, Archives Div, South Carolina Department of Archives & History, 8301 Parklane Rd, Columbia, SC, 29223. Tel: 803-896-6104. Fax: 803-896-6198. p. 2189

Tuttrup, Cathy, Pub Serv Mgr, Brookfield Public Library, 1900 N Calhoun Rd, Brookfield, WI, 53005. Tel: 262-782-4140. Fax: 262-796-6670. p. 2583

Tuveson, Anne, Ref & Instrul Serv Librn, University of Wisconsin-River Falls, 410 S Third St, River Falls, WI, 54022. Tel: 715-425-3321. Fax: 715-425-0609. p. 2635

Tuytschaevers, Mary, Dir, Libr Serv, New Mexico Junior College, One Thunderbird Circle, Hobbs, NM, 88240. Tel: 575-492-2870. Fax: 575-492-2883. p. 1556

Tvaruzka, Kathryn, Educ Librn, Head, Access Serv, University of Wisconsin-Eau Claire, 105 Garfield Ave, Eau Claire, WI, 54702-4004. Tel: 715-836-4522. Fax: 715-836-2949. p. 2590

Tvedten, Lenny, Exec Dir, Martin County Historical Society, Inc, 304 E Blue Earth Ave, Fairmont, MN, 56031. Tel: 507-235-5178. Fax: 507-235-5179. p. 1250

Twait, Michelle, Ref Librn, Gustavus Adolphus College, 800 W College Ave, Saint Peter, MN, 56082. Tel: 507-933-7563. Fax: 507-933-6292. p. 1283

Twarkins, Elizabeth, Coll Develop, Welles-Turner Memorial Library, 2407 Main St, Glastonbury, CT, 06033. Tel: 860-652-7727. Fax: 860-652-7721. p. 340

Tweed, Heather, Youth Ref Librn, Fruitville Public Library, 100 Coburn Rd, Sarasota, FL, 34240. Tel: 941-861-2500. Fax: 941-861-2528. p. 489

Tweed, Larry, Librn, Holland College Library Services, 140 Weymouth St, Charlottetown, PE, C1A 4Z1, CANADA. Tel: 902-566-9558. Fax: 902-566-9522. p. 2875

Tweedie, Lynne, Ref, Putnam County Public Library, 103 E Poplar St, Greencastle, IN, 46135-1655. Tel: 765-653-2755. Fax: 765-653-2756. p. 746

Twentier, Steven, Dir, Saxonburg Area Library, 240 W Main St, Saxonburg, PA, 16056. Tel: 724-352-4810. Fax: 724-352-1815. p. 2136

Twidale, Michael, Prof, University of Illinois at Urbana-Champaign, Library & Information Science Bldg, 501 E Daniel St, Champaign, IL, 61820-6211. Tel: 217-333-3280. Fax: 217-244-3302. p. 2965

Twigg, Martha, Exec Dir, South Shore Natural Science Center, 48 Jacob's Lane, Norwell, MA, 02061-1149. Tel: 781-659-2559. Fax: 781-659-5924. p. 1115

Twine, Jeff, Librn, American Society for Psychical Research Inc Library, Five W 73rd St, New York, NY, 10023. Tel: 212-799-5050. Fax: 212-496-2497. p. 1668

Twing, Cynthia R, Dir, Johnson County Library, 171 N Adams Ave, Buffalo, WY, 82834. Tel: 307-684-5546. Fax: 307-684-7888. p. 2651

Twingley, Carolyn, Archives, ILL, Ser, Bismarck State College Library, 1500 Edwards Ave, Bismarck, ND, 58501. Tel: 701-224-5450. Fax: 701-224-5551. p. 1837

Twiss, Jean, Dir, Libr Serv, Spoon River Public Library District, 201 S Third St, Cuba, IL, 61427. Tel: 309-785-5496. Fax: 309-785-5439. p. 632

Twiss-Brooks, Andrea, Co-Dir, Coll Develop, Head of Libr, University of Chicago Library, John Crerar Library, 5730 S Ellis Ave, Chicago, IL, 60637. Tel: 773-702-8777. p. 626

Twiss-Brooks, Andrea, Co-Dir, Sci Libr, Head, Coll Serv, University of Chicago Library, 1100 E 57th St, Chicago, IL, 60637-1502. Tel: 773-702-8777. Fax: 773-702-3317. p. 626

Twito, Tina, Dir, Callender Heritage Library, 505 Thomas St, Callender, IA, 50523. Tel: 515-548-3803. Fax: 515-548-3801. p. 798

Twombly, John, Br Mgr, Chesterfield County Public Library, Bon Air, 9103 Rattlesnake Rd, Richmond, VA, 23235. Tel: 804-320-2461. p. 2457

Twombly, Laura, Assoc Dir, Arvilla E Diver Memorial Library, 136 Main St, Schaghticoke, NY, 12154. Tel: 518-753-4344. Fax: 518-753-4344. p. 1740

Twombly, Lee, Media Librn, Outreach Librn, Ref Librn, Mercer University, Jack Tarver Library, 1300 Edgewood Ave, Macon, GA, 31207. Tel: 478-301-2852. Fax: 478-301-2111. p. 540

Twombly, Wylene, Dir, Ceresco Community Library, 425 S Second St, Ceresco, NE, 68017. Tel: 402-785-2585. Fax: 402-665-2036. p. 1395

Twomey, Beth, Educ Serv Librn, North Dakota State University Libraries, 1201 Albrecht Blvd, Fargo, ND, 58108. Tel: 701-231-8141. Fax: 701-231-6128. p. 1841

Twyford, Nancy, Libr Spec, Inyo County Free Library, Tecopa Branch, 408 Tecopa Hot Springs Rd, Tecopa, CA, 92389. Tel: 760-852-4171. Fax: 760-852-4171. p. 159

Tyburski, Eugenie, Admin Mgr, Ballard, Spahr LLP Library, 1735 Market St, 51st Flr, Philadelphia, PA, 19103-7599. Tel: 215-864-8150. Fax: 215-864-8999. p. 2103

Tychnowicz, Susan, Head, Teen Serv, Sachem Public Library, 150 Holbrook Rd, Holbrook, NY, 11741. Tel: 631-588-5024. Fax: 631-588-5064. p. 1637

Tyckoson, Dave, Assoc Univ Librn, California State University, Fresno, Henry Madden Library, 5200 N Barton Ave, Mail Stop ML-34, Fresno, CA, 93740-8014. Tel: 559-278-5678. Fax: 559-278-6952. p. 150

Tyle-Annen, Alex, Dir, Adult Serv, Homer Township Public Library District, 14320 W 151st St, Homer Glen, IL, 60491. Tel: 708-301-7908. Fax: 708-301-4535. p. 657

Tyler, Cheryl, Librn, Iosco-Arenac District Library, Plainfield Township, 220 N Washington, Hale, MI, 48739-9578. Tel: 989-728-2811. Fax: 989-728-4086. p. 1176

Tyler, Cynthia K, Asst Dir, Reed City Public Library, 410 W Upton Ave, Reed City, MI, 49677-1152. Tel: 231-832-2131. Fax: 231-832-2131. p. 1221

Tyler, Elisabeth A, Head Librn, God's Bible School & College Library, 513 Ringgold St, Cincinnati, OH, 45202. Tel: 513-721-7944, Ext 261. p. 1870

Tyler, Jeanie, Br Mgr, Grant Parish Library, Pollock Branch, 1316 Pine St, Pollock, LA, 71467. Tel: 318-765-9616. Fax: 318-765-9616. p. 947

Tyler, Kim, Dir, Sacred Heart Medical Center at RiverBend, 3333 RiverBend Dr, Springfield, OR, 97477. Tel: 541-222-2280. p. 2020

Tyler, Laura, Res, LMI Library, 2000 Corporate Ridge, McLean, VA, 22102-7805. Tel: 703-917-7214. Fax: 703-917-7474. p. 2478

Tyler, Mary, Librn, Laceyville Public Library, W Main St, Laceyville, PA, 18623. Tel: 570-869-1958. p. 2075

Tyler, Roland, Circ, Sierra Vista Public Library, 2600 E Tacoma, Sierra Vista, AZ, 85635-1399. Tel: 520-458-4225. Fax: 520-458-5377. p. 82

Tyler, Sharon, Ref Librn, Keuka College, 141 Central Ave, Keuka Park, NY, 14478-0038. Tel: 315-279-5224, 315-279-5632. Fax: 315-279-5334. p. 1649

Tyler, Shirley, Circ Supvr, Newport Public Library, 300 Spring St, Newport, RI, 02840. Tel: 401-847-8720. Fax: 401-842-0841. p. 2169

Tymciurak, Olya, Mgr, Naperville Public Library, 95th Street, 3015 Cedar Glade Dr, Naperville, IL, 60564. Tel: 630-961-4100, Ext 4900. Fax: 630-637-4870. p. 679

Tynan, Laurie, Libr Dir, Horsham Township Library, 435 Babylon Rd, Horsham, PA, 19044-1224. Tel: 215-443-2609, Ext 205. Fax: 215-443-2697. p. 2069

Tynan, Mary, Ref, Mansfield Public Library, 255 Hope St, Mansfield, MA, 02048-2353. Tel: 508-261-7380. Fax: 508-261-7422. p. 1102

Tynan, Peter, Brother, Spec Coll & Archives Librn, Saint Martin's University, 5300 Pacific Ave SE, Lacey, WA, 98503. Tel: 360-486-8828. Fax: 360-486-8825. p. 2519

Tynan, Stacy, Town Librn, Rockford Public Library, 202 W Main Ave, Rockford, IA, 50468-1212. Tel: 641-756-3725. Fax: 641-756-3725. p. 841

Tyndall, John, Mgr, Info Tech, Fontana Regional Library, 33 Fryemont St, Bryson City, NC, 28713. Tel: 828-488-2382. Fax: 828-488-2638. p. 1778

Tyne, Sarah Gellard, Info & Communications Officer, Western Canadian Universities Marine Sciences Society, 100 Pachena Rd, Bamfield, BC, V0R 1B0, CANADA. Tel: 250-728-3301, Ext 213. Fax: 250-728-3452. p. 2724

Tyner, Jamie, Dir, Linton Public Library, 95 SE First St, Linton, IN, 47441. Tel: 812-847-7802. Fax: 812-847-4695. p. 761

Tyner, Ross, Libr Dir, Okanagan College Library, 1000 KLO Rd, Kelowna, BC, V1Y 4X8, CANADA. p. 2730

Tyner, Susan, Children/Youth Librn, Benton County Public Library, 121 S Forrest Ave, Camden, TN, 38320-2055. Tel: 731-584-4772. Fax: 731-584-1098. p. 2226

Tyner, Theresa, Dir, North Manchester Public Library, 405 N Market St, North Manchester, IN, 46962. Tel: 260-982-4773. Fax: 260-982-6342. p. 769

Tyree, Janet, Librn, Springdale Free Public Library, 331 School St, Springdale, PA, 15144-1343. Tel: 724-274-9729. Fax: 724-274-6125. p. 2142

TyRee, Jenks, Instruction Coordr, Ref Librn, Montana State University, 1500 University Dr, Billings, MT, 59101-0298. Tel: 406-657-1654. Fax: 406-657-2037. p. 1374

Tyrrel, Penny, Pub Serv & Coll Supvr, Algoma University College, 1520 Queen St E, Sault Ste. Marie, ON, P6A 2G4, CANADA. Tel: 705-949-2101. Fax: 705-949-6583. p. 2840

Tyrrell, Kay J, Res & Automation Serv Librn, National Association of Insurance Commissioners, 1100 Walnut St, Ste 1500, Kansas City, MO, 64106-2197. Tel: 816-783-8253. Fax: 816-460-7682. p. 1340

Tysall, Cindy, Mgr, Lafayette County Public Library, 120 NE Crawford St, Mayo, FL, 32066. Tel: 386-294-1021. Fax: 386-294-3396. p. 463

Tyson, Bryan, Head, Tech Serv, Bob Jones University, 1700 Wade Hampton Blvd, Greenville, SC, 29614. Tel: 864-242-5100, Ext 6000. Fax: 864-232-1729. p. 2195

Tyson, Roberta, Libr Spec, Horry-Georgetown Technical College, 2050 Hwy 501 E, Conway, SC, 29526-9521. Tel: 843-349-5396. Fax: 843-347-0552. p. 2191

Tyson, Stephanie, Outreach Serv Librn, Youth Serv, Columbia County Public Library, 308 NW Columbia Ave, Lake City, FL, 32055. Tel: 386-758-2101. Fax: 386-758-2135. p. 457

U, Anna, Librn, University of Toronto Libraries, Cheng Yu Tung East Asian Library, John P Robarts Research Library, 130 St George St, Rm 8049, Toronto, ON, M5S 1A5, CANADA. Tel: 416-978-7690. Fax: 416-978-0863. p. 2865

Ubl, Chad, Dir, Commun Serv, Winona Public Library, 151 W Fifth St, Winona, MN, 55987-3170. Tel: 507-452-4582. Fax: 507-452-5842. p. 1290

Uchida, Tammy, Supvr, Circ, Bellarmine University, 2001 Newburg Rd, Louisville, KY, 40205-0671. Tel: 502-272-8308. Fax: 502-272-8038. p. 923

Uchino, Martha, Ch, Natchitoches Parish Library, 450 Second St, Natchitoches, LA, 71457-4649. Tel: 318-357-3280. Fax: 318-357-7073. p. 958

Udd, Stanley, Dir, Grace University Library, 823 Worthington, Omaha, NE, 68108-3642. Tel: 402-449-2893. Fax: 402-449-2919. p. 1413

Uden, Ryann, Head, Youth Serv, Barrington Public Library District, 505 N Northwest Hwy, Barrington, IL, 60010. Tel: 847-382-1300. Fax: 847-382-1261. p. 592

Udovic, Edward, VPres, Teaching & Learning Res, DePaul University Libraries, 2350 N Kenmore, Chicago, IL, 60614. Tel: 773-325-3725, 773-325-7862. Fax: 773-325-7870. p. 612

Uecker-Hettinga, Mary Jane, Dir, Marathon County Historical Society Library, 410 McIndoe St, Wausau, WI, 54403. Tel: 715-848-0378. Fax: 715-848-0576. p. 2646

Ueckert, Bonnie, Ch, Bastrop Public Library, 1100 Church St, Bastrop, TX, 78602. Tel: 512-321-5441. Fax: 512-321-3163. p. 2286

Uehara, Shane, Coordr, Heald College, 1500 Kapiolani Blvd, Honolulu, HI, 96814. Tel: 808-628-5525. Fax: 808-955-6964. p. 564

Uehlein, Sara, Librn, King & Spalding, 1700 Pennsylvania Ave NW, Ste 200, Washington, DC, 20006-4706. Tel: 202-737-0500. Fax: 202-626-3737. p. 406

Uffner, Laura, Doc, NASA, Kennedy Space Center, FL, 32899. Tel: 321-867-3600. Fax: 321-867-4534. p. 455

Ugorowski, Michael, Coordr, Pub Serv, Mott Community College, 1401 E Court St, Flint, MI, 48503. Tel: 810-762-5662. Fax: 810-762-0407. p. 1180

Uhde, Tonya, Dir, Meservey Public Library, 719 First St, Meservey, IA, 50457. Tel: 641-358-6274. Fax: 641-358-6274. p. 832

Uhden, Felicia, Head, Access Serv, Corvallis-Benton County Public Library, 645 NW Monroe Ave, Corvallis, OR, 97330. Tel: 541-766-6997. p. 1994

Uhler, Linda, Mgr, Youth Serv, Westerville Public Library, 126 S State St, Westerville, OH, 43081-2095. Tel: 614-882-7277, Ext 2130. Fax: 614-882-4160. p. 1947

Uhlhorn, Melissa, Libr Mgr, Schertz Public Library, 798 Schertz Pkwy, Schertz, TX, 78154. Tel: 210-619-1700. Fax: 210-619-1711. p. 2385

Uhlinger, Eleanor, Univ Librn, Naval Postgraduate School, 411 Dyer Rd, Monterey, CA, 93943. Tel: 831-656-2975. Fax: 831-656-2050. p. 190

Uhlman, Carol, Librn, Williamsburg Public Library, 214 W State St, Williamsburg, IA, 52361. Tel: 319-668-1195. Fax: 319-668-9621. p. 853

Uhre, Lea, Dir, Executive Office of the President Libraries, 725 17th St NW, Rm G-007, Washington, DC, 20503. Tel: 202-395-4690. Fax: 202-395-6137. p. 399

Uhrig, Sue, Circ, Chillicothe & Ross County Public Library, 140 S Paint St, Chillicothe, OH, 45601. Tel: 740-702-4145. Fax: 740-702-4153. p. 1867

Uhte, Carol, In Charge, Multnomah County Library, Woodstock, 6008 SE 49th Ave, Portland, OR, 97206-6117. Tel: 503-988-5399. Fax: 503-988-5173. p. 2012

Uko, Kenneth, Br Mgr, Jersey City Free Public Library, Greenville, 1841 Kennedy Blvd, Jersey City, NJ, 07305. Tel: 201-547-4553. Fax: 201-433-1708. p. 1492

Ukwu, Dele, Cat Librn, Long Beach City College, 4901 E Carson St, Long Beach, CA, 90808. Tel: 562-938-4581. Fax: 562-938-3062, 562-938-4777. p. 166

Ulbrich, Sharon, Dir, Bayard Public Library, 509 Ave A, Bayard, NE, 69334. Tel: 308-586-1144. Fax: 308-586-1061. p. 1393

Uleryk, Elizabeth, Dir, Hospital for Sick Children, 555 University Ave, Toronto, ON, M5G 1X8, CANADA. Tel: 416-813-6695. Fax: 416-813-7523. p. 2854

Ulibarri, Beatrice, Libr Assoc/Acq Section, New Mexico Highlands University, Ninth & National Ave, Las Vegas, NM, 87701. Tel: 505-454-3336. Fax: 505-454-0026. p. 1559

Ulincy, Loretta, Pub Serv, DeSales University, 2755 Station Ave, Center Valley, PA, 18034. Tel: 610-282-1100, Ext 1266. Fax: 610-282-2342. p. 2043

Ullah, Joyce, Youth Serv Coordr, Denison Public Library, 300 W Gandy St, Denison, TX, 75020-3153. Tel: 903-465-1797. Fax: 903-465-1130. p. 2312

Ullman, Melanie, Librn, Temple Emanuel Library, 280 May St, Worcester, MA, 01602-2599. Tel: 508-755-1257. Fax: 508-795-0417. p. 1144

Ullrich, Dieter, Dir, Archives & Spec Coll, Murray State University, 205 Waterfield Library, Dean's Office, Murray, KY, 42071-3307. Tel: 270-809-4295. Fax: 270-809-3736. p. 930

Ullrich, Melanie, Circ, Johnsburg Public Library District, 3000 N Johnsburg Rd, Johnsburg, IL, 60051. Tel: 815-344-0077. Fax: 815-344-3524. p. 659

Ullrich, Rikki, Dir, Ida Grove Public Library, 100 E Second St, Ida Grove, IA, 51445. Tel: 712-364-2306. Fax: 712-364-3228. p. 822

Ulm, Scott, Librn, Tennessee Correction Academy Library, 1314 S Jackson St, Tullahoma, TN, 37388. Tel: 931-461-7693. Fax: 931-461-7757. p. 2268

Ulman, Mildred, ILL, Moundsville-Marshall County Public Library, 700 Fifth St, Moundsville, WV, 26041-1993. Tel: 304-845-6911. Fax: 304-845-6912. p. 2567

Ulmer, Katherine, Commun Libr Supvr, Yakima Valley Libraries, Naches Library, 303 Naches Ave, Naches, WA, 98937. Tel: 509-653-2005. Fax: 509-653-2005. p. 2550

Ulmer, Mary Jane, Asst Librn, Beaver Area Memorial Library, 100 College Ave, Beaver, PA, 15009-2794. Tel: 724-775-1132. Fax: 724-775-6982. p. 2031

Ulmschneider, John E, Univ Librn, Virginia Commonwealth University Libraries, 901 Park Ave, Richmond, VA, 23284-2033. Tel: 804-828-1110. Fax: 804-828-0151. p. 2492

Ulmschneider, John E, Officer, Univ Librn, Richmond Academic Library Consortium, Virginia Commonwealth University, James Branch Cabell Library, 901 Park Ave, Richmond, VA, 23284. Tel: 804-828-1107, 804-828-1110. Fax: 804-828-0151, 804-828-1105. p. 2957

Ulrey, Becky, Ref Librn, Baker College of Muskegon Library, 1903 Marquette Ave, Muskegon, MI, 49442-3404. Tel: 231-777-5330. Fax: 231-777-5334. p. 1212

Ulrich, Erin, Coordr, Youth Serv, Santa Clara City Library, 2635 Homestead Rd, Santa Clara, CA, 95051. Tel: 408-615-2918. Fax: 408-247-9657. p. 262

Ulrich, Jennifer M, Tech Serv Librn, Eastern Mennonite University, 1200 Park Rd, Harrisonburg, VA, 22802-2462. Tel: 540-432-4175. Fax: 540-432-4977. p. 2470

Ulrich, Lise, Acq, ILL, College de Maisonneuve Centre des Medias, 3800 Est rue Sherbrooke E, Montreal, QC, H1X 2A2, CANADA. Tel: 514-254-7131. Fax: 514-254-2517. p. 2893

Ulrich, Rita, Libr Asst, Saint Peter's Seminary, 1040 Waterloo St N, London, ON, N6A 3Y1, CANADA. Tel: 519-432-1824. Fax: 519-439-5172. p. 2818

Ultan Boudewyns, Deborah K, Librn, University of Minnesota Libraries-Twin Cities, Architecture & Landscape Architecture Library, 210 Rapson Hall, 89 Church St SE, Minneapolis, MN, 55455. Tel: 612-624-6383. Fax: 612-625-5597. p. 1262

Ulveland, Dana, Coordr, Western Oregon University, 345 N Monmouth Ave, Monmouth, OR, 97361-1396. Tel: 503-838-8039, 503-838-8492. Fax: 503-838-8228. p. 2972

Ulvestad, Judy, Circ, Rawlins Municipal Library, 1000 E Church St, Pierre, SD, 57501. Tel: 605-773-7421. Fax: 605-773-7423. p. 2216

Umali, Jennifer L, Librn, W R Grace & Co Library, 62 Whittemore Ave, Cambridge, MA, 02140. Tel: 617-498-4595. Fax: 617-864-7198. p. 1073

Umansky, Olga, Librn & Archivist, Boston Psychoanalytic Society & Institute, Inc, 169 Herrick Rd, Newton, MA, 02459. Tel: 617-266-0953, Ext 104. Fax: 857-255-3253. p. 1109

Umba, Marc Mambuku, Dir, Librn, Bibliothèque de la Compagnie de Jésus, Collège Jean-de-Brebeuf, L B4-25, 3200, Ch Côte-Sainte-Catherine, Montreal, QC, H3T 1C1, CANADA. Tel: 514-342-9342, Ext 5466. p. 2888

Umbarger, Brenda J, Exec Asst of Operations, Smyth-Bland Regional Library, 118 S Sheffey St, Marion, VA, 24354. Tel: 276-783-2323. Fax: 276-783-5279. p. 2477

Umbaugh, Betsy, Asst Librn, Chatfield Brass Band, Inc, 81 Library Lane, Chatfield, MN, 55923. Tel: 507-867-3275. p. 1245

Umbayemake, Linda, Librn, East Cleveland Public Library, Caledonia Branch, 960 Caledonia Rd, Cleveland Heights, OH, 44112. Tel: 216-268-6280. Fax: 216-268-6294. p. 1897

Umberger, Sheila, Dir, Roanoke Public Libraries, 706 S Jefferson St, Roanoke, VA, 24016-5191. Tel: 540-853-2473. Fax: 540-853-1781. p. 2494

Umberger, Stan, Dir, Roanoke College, 220 High St, Salem, VA, 24153. Tel: 540-375-2295. p. 2495

Umhauer, Joseph, Head, Cat, Niagara University Library, 5795 Lewiston Rd, Niagara University, NY, 14109. Tel: 716-286-8015. Fax: 716-286-8030. p. 1705

Umpleby, Susan, Ch, Ontario City Library, 215 East C St, Ontario, CA, 91764. Tel: 909-395-2208. Fax: 909-395-2043. p. 200

Umstead, Wes, Br Mgr, Chippewa River District Library, Fremont Township, 2833 W Blanchard Rd, Winn, MI, 48896. Tel: 989-866-2550. Fax: 989-866-2550. p. 1211

Underhill, Janelle, Librn, Rio Salado College, 2323 W 14th St, Tempe, AZ, 85281. Tel: 480-517-8424. Fax: 480-517-8449. p. 84

Underhill, Jeanne, Dir, Lamar Warren Law Library of Broward County, 1800 Broward County Judicial Complex, 201 SE Sixth St, Fort Lauderdale, FL, 33301. Tel: 954-831-6226. p. 444

Underhill, Karen J, Spec Coll & Archives Librn, Northern Arizona University, Bldg 028, Knoles Dr, Flagstaff, AZ, 86011. Tel: 928-523-6502. Fax: 928-523-3770. p. 62

Underhill, Tracy, Dir, Crawford County Public Library, 203 Indiana Ave, English, IN, 47118. Tel: 812-338-2606. Fax: 812-338-3034. p. 737

Underwood, A, Mrs, Cat Mgr, ILL, Ohio University-Zanesville/ Zane State College, 1425 Newark Rd, Zanesville, OH, 43701. Tel: 740-588-1404. Fax: 740-453-0706. p. 1954

Underwood, Jack, Br Librn, Spartanburg County Public Libraries, Chesnee Library, 100 Pickens Ave, Chesnee, SC, 29323. Tel: 864-461-2423. p. 2205

Underwood, Jane, Online Serv, Res Serv, Northern Kentucky University, Nunn Dr, Highland Heights, KY, 41099. Tel: 859-572-6485. Fax: 859-572-6529, 859-572-6664. p. 917

Underwood, Jonna, Librn, Northern State University, 1200 S Jay St, Aberdeen, SD, 57401-7198. Tel: 605-626-2645. Fax: 605-626-2473. p. 2209

Underwood, Kent, Media Spec, New York University, 70 Washington Sq S, New York, NY, 10012-1091. Tel: 212-998-2505. Fax: 212-995-4070. p. 1695

Underwood, Kirsten, Head, Ref, Nevins Memorial Library, 305 Broadway, Methuen, MA, 01844-6898. Tel: 978-686-4080. Fax: 978-686-8669. p. 1105

Underwood, Patricia P, Asst Dir, Orange Beach Public Library, 26267 Canal Rd, Orange Beach, AL, 36561-3917. Tel: 251-981-2923. Fax: 251-981-2920. p. 33

Underwood, Sandra, Acq, Public Library of Anniston-Calhoun County, 108 E Tenth St, Anniston, AL, 36201. Tel: 256-237-8501, 256-237-8503. Fax: 256-238-0474. p. 4

Underwood, Sandra, Dir, Carl Elliott Regional Library System, 98 E 18th St, Jasper, AL, 35501. Tel: 205-221-2568. p. 23

Underwood, Stephen, Syst Adminr, Carl Elliott Regional Library System, 98 E 18th St, Jasper, AL, 35501. Tel: 205-221-2568. p. 23

Ungar, Judi, Ref & Instruction Librn, Harrisburg Area Community College, One HACC Dr, Harrisburg, PA, 17110-2999. Tel: 717-780-2460. Fax: 717-780-2462. p. 2065

Ungarelli, Donald, Dr, Dean, Univ Libr, Long Island University, One University Plaza, Brooklyn, NY, 11201-9926. Tel: 718-488-1081. Fax: 718-780-4057. p. 1593

Ungarelli, Lou, Dir, Lebanon Public Library, Nine E Park St, Lebanon, NH, 03766. Tel: 603-448-2459. p. 1454

Unger, Barbara, Libr Tech, University of Manitoba Libraries, Father Harold Drake Library - St Pauls College, 70 Dysart Rd, Winnipeg, MB, R3T 2M6, CANADA. Tel: 204-474-8585. Fax: 204-474-7615. p. 2758

Unger, Kelley Rae, Adult Serv, Peabody Institute Library, 82 Main St, Peabody, MA, 01960-5592. Tel: 978-531-0100. Fax: 978-532-1797. p. 1116

Unger, Melvin P, Dr, Dir, Baldwin Wallace University, Riemenschneider Bach Institute, Boesel Musical Arts Bldg., 49 Seminary St, Berea, OH, 44017-2088. Tel: 440-826-2207. Fax: 440-826-8138. p. 1859

Unger, Susan, Dir, Elkins Public Library, 162 Doolin Dr, Elkins, AR, 72727. Tel: 479-643-2904. p. 98

Ungerleider, Vivian, Ch, Clifton Public Library, Allwood Branch, 44 Lyall Rd, Clifton, NJ, 07012. Tel: 973-471-0555. Fax: 973-471-9284. p. 1479

Ungham, Susan, Mgr, Medina County District Library, Brunswick Community, 3649 Center Rd, Brunswick, OH, 44212-0430. Tel: 330-273-4150. Fax: 330-225-0310. p. 1916

Ungs, Kim, Dir, Hopkinton Public Library, 110 First St SE, Hopkinton, IA, 52237. Tel: 563-926-2514. Fax: 563-926-2065. p. 821

Unni, Asha, Asst Dir, TCI College of Technology, 320 W 31st St, New York, NY, 10001. Tel: 212-594-4000, Ext 5279. Fax: 212-330-0894. p. 1700

Unrath, Kevin, Head, Borrower Serv, Middletown Public Library, 55 New Monmouth Rd, Middletown, NJ, 07748. Tel: 732-671-3700, Ext 317. Fax: 732-671-5839. p. 1501

Unrath, Kevin, Head, Access Serv, Western Carolina University, 176 Central Dr, Cullowhee, NC, 28723. Tel: 828-227-3405. Fax: 828-227-7015. p. 1786

Unruh, Doris, Chair, Department of Community Services, Government of Yukon, Faro Community, Del Van Gorder School, Faro, YT, Y0B 1K0, CANADA. Tel: 867-994-2684. Fax: 867-994-2236, 867-994-3342. p. 2933

Unruh, Janice, Librn, Taylor Public Library, 106 Williams St, Taylor, NE, 68879-0206. Tel: 308-942-6213. p. 1421

Unruh, Lysianne, Dir, Mount Horeb Public Library, 105 Perimeter Rd, Mount Horeb, WI, 53572. Tel: 608-437-5021. Fax: 608-437-6264. p. 2623

Unruh, Sandy, Asst Librn, Cimarron City Library, 120 N Main, Cimarron, KS, 67835. Tel: 620-855-3808. Fax: 620-855-3884. p. 860

Unseth, Carole, ILL, Graduate Institute of Applied Linguistics Library, 7500 W Camp Wisdom Rd, Dallas, TX, 75236-5699. Tel: 972-708-7416. Fax: 972-708-7292. p. 2308

Unsworth, Alan, Ref & Web Serv Librn, Surry Community College, 630 S Main St, Dobson, NC, 27017-8432. Tel: 336-386-3317. Fax: 336-386-3692. p. 1787

Unterborn, Lee, Cat, Saint Mary's University, Sarita Kennedy East Law Library, One Camino Santa Maria, San Antonio, TX, 78228-8605. Tel: 210-436-3435. Fax: 210-436-3240. p. 2381

Unterholzner, Dennis, Head, Pub Serv, Carthage College, 2001 Alford Park Dr, Kenosha, WI, 53140-1900. Tel: 262-551-5900. Fax: 262-551-5904. p. 2601

Unver, Amira, Dir, College of Saint Elizabeth, Two Convent Rd, Morristown, NJ, 07960-6989. Tel: 973-290-4233. Fax: 973-290-4226. p. 1504

Upchurch, Inger, Br Mgr, Memphis Public Library, Gaston Park, 1040 S Third, Memphis, TN, 38106-2002. Tel: 901-942-0836. Fax: 901-942-5667. p. 2250

Upchurch, Inger, Mgr, Memphis Public Library, Cornelia Crenshaw Memorial Library, 531 Vance Ave, Memphis, TN, 38126-2116. Tel: 901-525-1643. Fax: 901-525-0390. p. 2250

Upchurch, Inger, Mgr, Memphis Public Library, Cossitt Branch, 33 S Front, Memphis, TN, 38103-2499. Tel: 901-526-1712. Fax: 901-526-0730. p. 2250

Upchurch, Mary Ann, Librn, Covenant Medical Center, 3421 W Ninth St, Waterloo, IA, 50702. Tel: 319-272-7385. Fax: 319-272-7313. p. 850

Upchurch, Mitchelle, Librn, Dorchester County Circuit Court, 206 High St, Cambridge, MD, 21613. Tel: 410-228-6300. Fax: 410-221-5003. p. 1022

Upchurch, Sharon K, Libr Dir, Culver-Stockton College, One College Hill, Canton, MO, 63435. Tel: 573-288-6321. Fax: 573-288-6615. p. 1321

Updegrove, Mark K, Dir, Lyndon Baines Johnson Library & Museum, 2313 Red River St, Austin, TX, 78705. Tel: 512-721-0200. p. 2281

Upell, Joan, Sch Libr Coordr, South Dakota State Library, 800 Governors Dr, Pierre, SD, 57501-2294. Tel: 605-773-3131. p. 2216

Upole, Susan, Dir, Delmar Public Library, 101 N Bi-State Blvd, Delmar, DE, 19940. Tel: 302-846-9894. Fax: 302-846-3408. p. 381

Uppena, Susan, Dir, Eckstein Memorial Library, 1034 E Dewey St, Cassville, WI, 53806. Tel: 608-725-5838. Fax: 608-725-5152. p. 2584

Upshaw, Nancy, Librn, Mid-Mississippi Regional Library System, Goodman Public, 9792 Main St, Goodman, MS, 39079. Tel: 662-472-0550. Fax: 662-472-0599. p. 1306

Upshaw, Suzanne, Br Mgr, Jefferson Parish Library, Old Metairie, 2350 Metairie Rd, Metairie, LA, 70001. Tel: 504-838-4353. Fax: 504-838-1014. p. 957

Upson, Matt, Dir of Libr Serv, McPherson College, 1600 E Euclid, McPherson, KS, 67460-3899. Tel: 620-242-0487, 620-242-0490. Fax: 620-241-8443. p. 883

Upton, Ann, Spec Coll Librn, Haverford College, 370 Lancaster Ave, Haverford, PA, 19041-1392. Tel: 610-896-1158. Fax: 610-896-1102. p. 2067

Upton, Connie Jean, Mgr, Libr Serv, Olin Corp, 1186 Lower River Rd, Charleston, TN, 37310. Tel: 423-336-4347. Fax: 423-336-4194. p. 2226

Upton, Diana, In Charge, Porterville Developmental Center, Professional Library, 26501 Ave 140, Porterville, CA, 93257. Tel: 559-782-2609. Fax: 559-782-2364. p. 212

Urbain, Carole, Assoc Dir, Client Serv, Humanities, Law, Mgt & Soc Sci, McGill University Libraries, 3459 McTavish St, Montreal, QC, H3A 1Y1, CANADA. Tel: 514-398-5725. Fax: 514-398-7184. p. 2898

Urbain, Carole Urbain, Assoc Dir, McGill University Libraries, Humanities & Social Sciences, McLennan Library Bldg, 3459 McTavish St, Montreal, QC, H3A 1Y1, CANADA. Tel: 514-398-4734. Fax: 514-398-7184. p. 2898

Urban, Barb, Br Mgr, Saint Louis County Library, Daniel Boone Branch, 300 Clarkson Rd, Ellisville, MO, 63011. p. 1358

Urban, Barbara, Br Mgr, Richland County Public Library, Wheatley, 931 Woodrow St, Columbia, SC, 29205. Tel: 803-799-5873. p. 2188

Urban, Chris, Dir, Technomic, Inc, 300 S Riverside Plaza, Ste 1200, Chicago, IL, 60606. Tel: 312-876-3929. Fax: 312-876-1158. p. 625

Urban, Clara Beth, Librn, Wildwood Heritage Museum & Library, 92 Cypress Bend Dr, Village Mills, TX, 77663. Tel: 409-834-2924. p. 2395

Urban, Gloria, Dir, Vineland Public Library, 1058 E Landis Ave, Vineland, NJ, 08360. Tel: 856-794-4244. Fax: 856-691-0366. p. 1538

Urban, Marion, Info Serv, Southington Public Library & Museum, 255 Main St, Southington, CT, 06489. Tel: 860-628-0947. Fax: 860-628-0488. p. 368

Urban, Nancy, Ch, Sheridan Public Library, 103 W First St, Sheridan, IN, 46069. Tel: 317-758-5201. Fax: 317-758-0045. p. 778

Urban, Pam, Libr Dir, Du Quoin Public Library, 28 S Washington St, Du Quoin, IL, 62832. Tel: 618-542-5045. Fax: 618-542-4735. p. 637

Urban, Sandra, Head, Cat, York College Library, 94-20 Guy R Brewer Blvd, Jamaica, NY, 11451. Tel: 718-262-2022. Fax: 718-262-2027, 718-262-2997. p. 1646

Urban, Shannon, Head of Libr, Rockwell Automation Library, 1201 S Second St, Milwaukee, WI, 53204. Tel: 414-382-2342. Fax: 414-382-2462. p. 2621

Urbanek, Laura, Dir, Roland Public Library, 218 N Main, Roland, IA, 50236. Tel: 515-388-4086. p. 841

Urbanek, Mark, Libr Dir, Pinckneyville Public Library, 312 S Walnut St, Pinckneyville, IL, 62274. Tel: 618-357-2410. Fax: 618-357-2410. p. 691

Urbaniak, Sandy, ILL, Presentation College Library, 1500 N Main, Aberdeen, SD, 57401-1299. Tel: 605-229-8468. Fax: 605-229-8430. p. 2209

Urbank, Aaron, Circ, Buckley Public Library, 408 Dewey Ave, Poteau, OK, 74953. Tel: 918-647-3833, 918-647-4444. Fax: 918-647-8910. p. 1976

Urbanski, Denise, Br Mgr, Oregon National Primate Research Center, 505 NW 185th Ave, Beaverton, OR, 97006. Tel: 503-690-5311. Fax: 503-690-5243. p. 1991

Urbashich, Mary Ann, Assoc Dir, Alzheimer's Association, 225 N Michigan Ave, 17th Flr, Chicago, IL, 60601. Tel: 312-335-5199. p. 605

Urbiel, Martha, Dir, Westwood Free Public Library, 49 Park Ave, Westwood, NJ, 07675. Tel: 201-664-0583. Fax: 201-664-6088. p. 1543

Urbizagastegui, Shelley, Asst Prof, Info Literacy Librn, University of La Verne, 2040 Third St, La Verne, CA, 91750. Tel: 909-593-3511, Ext 4305. Fax: 909-392-2733. p. 162

Urbizu, William, Asst Dir, Miami-Dade Public Library System, 101 W Flagler St, Miami, FL, 33130-1523. Tel: 305-375-5016. Fax: 305-375-3048. p. 466

Urciuoli, Wendy, Librn, Mid State Medical Center, 435 Lewis Ave, Meriden, CT, 06451. Tel: 203-694-8131. Fax: 203-694-7618. p. 351

Ureel, Desta, Dir, Dryden Township Library, 5480 Main St, Dryden, MI, 48428-9968. Tel: 810-796-3586. Fax: 810-796-2634. p. 1174

Urell, Ruth, Dir, Reading Public Library, 64 Middlesex Ave, Reading, MA, 01867-2550. Tel: 781-942-6725. Fax: 781-942-9113. p. 1120

Urell, Thomas, Communications Officer, Northeastern University Libraries, Snell Library, 360 Huntington Ave, Boston, MA, 02115. Tel: 617-373-2821. p. 1065

Urfer, Bonnie, Dir, Progressive Foundation, 740 Round Lake Rd, Luck, WI, 54853. Tel: 715-472-4185. Fax: 715-472-4184. p. 2606

Urian, John, Info Tech, Hood College, 401 Rosemont Ave, Frederick, MD, 21701. Tel: 301-696-3858. Fax: 301-696-3796. p. 1029

Urian, Kevin, Digital & Training Serv Librn, Cecil County Public Library, 301 Newark Ave, Elkton, MD, 21921-5441. Tel: 410-996-5600. Fax: 410-996-5604. p. 1027

Uriarte, Sheila, Br Head, Daly City Public Library, Westlake, 275 Southgate Ave, Daly City, CA, 94015-3471. Tel: 650-991-8071. Fax: 650-991-8180. p. 139

Uribe, Wendy, Ref Serv, Washington County Library System, 88 West 100 South, Saint George, UT, 84770-3490. Tel: 435-256-6320. Fax: 435-634-5741. p. 2412

Uricchio, William, Dir, University of Connecticut Library, Harleigh B Trecker Library, 1800 Asylum Ave, West Hartford, CT, 06117. Tel: 860-570-9028. Fax: 860-570-9036. p. 371

Urich, Carmen, Librn, North Colorado Medical Center, 1801 16th St, Greeley, CO, 80631-5199. Tel: 970-350-6471. Fax: 970-350-6475. p. 312

Urie, Sherry, Librn, John Woodruff Simpson Memorial Library, 1972 E Craftsbury Rd, East Craftsbury, VT, 05826. Tel: 802-586-9692. p. 2423

Urquhart, Dawn, Librn, Aird & Berlis LLP Law Library, 181 Bay St, Ste 1800, Brooksfield Pl, Toronto, ON, M5J 2T9, CANADA. Tel: 416-865-7756. Fax: 416-863-1515. p. 2849

Urquiaga, Laurie, Assoc Dir, Access Serv, Brigham Young University, Howard W Hunter Law Library, 256 JRCB, Provo, UT, 84602-8000. Tel: 801-422-3593. Fax: 801-422-0404. p. 2411

Urquizu, Linda, Per, Riverside Community College District, 4800 Magnolia Ave, Riverside, CA, 92506-1299. Tel: 951-222-8651. Fax: 951-328-3679. p. 217

Urrea, Olga, Cat, St Thomas University Library, 16401 NW 37th Ave, Miami Gardens, FL, 33054. Tel: 305-474-6863. Fax: 305-628-6666. p. 469

Urrizola, Manuel, Head, Cat & Metadata Serv, University of California, Riverside Libraries, 900 University Ave, Riverside, CA, 92521. Tel: 951-827-5051. p. 218

Urso, Lori, Dir, Pettaquamscutt Historical Society, 2636 Kingstown Rd, Kingston, RI, 02881. Tel: 401-783-1328. p. 2167

Ursulak, Nick, Mgr, Borrower Serv, Grant MacEwan University Library, 10700 104th Ave, Edmonton, AB, T5J 4S2, CANADA. Tel: 780-497-5850. Fax: 780-497-5895. p. 2701

Urtz, Joyce, Asst Librn, Richfield Springs Public Library, 102 Main St, Richfield Springs, NY, 13439. Tel: 315-858-0230. Fax: 315-858-0230. p. 1727

Urwiler, Sheila, Head, Multimedia, Deerfield Public Library, 920 Waukegan Rd, Deerfield, IL, 60015. Tel: 847-945-3311. Fax: 847-945-3402. p. 634

Urwiler, Sheila R, Dir, Starke County Public Library System, 152 W Culver Rd, Knox, IN, 46534-2220. Tel: 574-772-7323. p. 757

Uscio, Joseph, Ref, North Providence Union Free Library, 1810 Mineral Spring Ave, North Providence, RI, 02904. Tel: 401-353-5600. p. 2170

Usher, Brian, Info Syst Coordr, Auburn Public Library, 49 Spring St, Auburn, ME, 04210. Tel: 207-333-6640. Fax: 207-333-6644. p. 974

Usher, Olivia, YA Librn, Portales Public Library, 218 S Ave B, Portales, NM, 88130. Tel: 505-356-3940. Fax: 505-356-3964. p. 1560

Usina, Phyllis, Librn, Santa Rosa Junior College, 1501 Mendocino Ave, Santa Rosa, CA, 95401. Tel: 707-778-4773. Fax: 707-527-4545. p. 267

Uslan, Niza, Ch, Cabell County Public Library, 455 Ninth Street Plaza, Huntington, WV, 25701. Tel: 304-528-5700. Fax: 304-528-5701. p. 2561

Usova, Tatiana, Librn, University of Alberta, Bibliotheque Saint-Jean, 8406 rue Marie-Anne Gaboury (91 St), Edmonton, AB, T6C 4G9, CANADA. Tel: 780-465-8710. Fax: 780-468-2550. p. 2702

Utchel, Christine, Ref Librn, Bronxville Public Library, 201 Pondfield Rd, Bronxville, NY, 10708. Tel: 914-337-7680. Fax: 914-337-0332. p. 1588

Uthoff, Sarah, Dir, Oxford Public Library, 112 Augusta Ave, Oxford, IA, 52322. Tel: 319-828-4087. Fax: 319-828-4087. p. 837

Utley, Betty, Coll Develop Serv Mgr, Wake County Public Library System, 4020 Carya Dr, Raleigh, NC, 27610-2900. Tel: 919-250-3972. p. 1817

Utley, Ellen, Br Mgr, Prince George's County Memorial, Greenbelt Branch, 11 Crescent Rd, Greenbelt, MD, 20770-1898. Tel: 301-345-5800. Fax: 301-982-5018. p. 1032

Utley, Lance, Librn, National Radio Astronomy Observatory Library, 520 Edgemont Rd, Charlottesville, VA, 22903-2475. Tel: 434-296-0215. Fax: 434-296-0278. p. 2454

Utsunomiya, Leslie, Adult Serv, ILL, Coquitlam Public Library, 575 Poirier St, Coquitlam, BC, V3J 6A9, CANADA. Tel: 604-937-4140. Fax: 604-931-6739. p. 2727

Uttangi-Matsos, Meg, Br Mgr, Hamilton Public Library, Barton, 571 Barton St E, Hamilton, ON, L8L 2Z4, CANADA. Tel: 905-546-3200, Ext 3452. p. 2808

Uttangi-Matsos, Meg, Br Mgr, Hamilton Public Library, Kenilworth, 103 Kenilworth Ave N, Hamilton, ON, L8H 4R6, CANADA. Tel: 905-546-3200, Ext 3473. p. 2809

Uttaro, Patricia, Dir, Monroe County Library System, 115 South Ave, Rochester, NY, 14604. Tel: 585-428-8000. Fax: 585-428-8353. p. 1730

Utter, Susan, Br Librn, Cadillac-Wexford Public Library, Buckley Branch, 305 S First St, Buckley, MI, 49620-9526. Tel: 231-269-3325, Ext 3020. Fax: 231-269-3625. p. 1160

Utterback, Martha, Asst Dir, Daughters of the Republic of Texas Library at the Alamo, 300 Alamo Plaza, San Antonio, TX, 78205. Tel: 210-225-1071. Fax: 210-212-8514. p. 2379

Utterback, Nancy, Dep Dir, University of Louisville Libraries, Kornhauser Health Sciences Library, Health Sciences Ctr, 500 S Preston St, Louisville, KY, 40202. Tel: 502-852-1627. Fax: 502-852-1631. p. 927

Uttich, Richard M, Univ Librn, Roosevelt University, 430 S Michigan Ave, Chicago, IL, 60605. Tel: 312-341-3640. Fax: 312-341-2425. p. 623

Uttich, Richard M, Univ Librn, Roosevelt University, Robert R McCormick Tribune Foundation Library, 1400 N Roosevelt Blvd, Schaumburg, IL, 60173. Tel: 312-341-3540. Fax: 847-619-7983. p. 623

Utz, Bonnie, Dir, Madison County Library, Inc, 402 N Main St, Madison, VA, 22727. Tel: 540-948-4720. Fax: 540-948-4919. p. 2477

Utz, Joy, Asst Dir, Acq, Free Library of Springfield Township, 1600 Paper Mill Rd, Wyndmoor, PA, 19038. Tel: 215-836-5300. Fax: 215-836-2404. p. 2158

Utz, Sharon, Circ, Shelbina Carnegie Public Library, 102 N Center, Shelbina, MO, 63468. Tel: 573-588-2271. Fax: 573-588-2271. p. 1365

Uvalles, Debbie, Coordr, Libr Serv, CTB/Mcgraw-Hill Library, 20 Ryan Ranch Rd, Monterey, CA, 93940-5703. Tel: 831-393-6555. Fax: 831-393-7825. p. 189

Uyehara, Alan, Dr, Dir, Libr & Learning Res, Galveston College, 4015 Ave Q, Galveston, TX, 77550. Tel: 409-944-1240. Fax: 409-944-1521. p. 2326

Uyengco-Harooch, Myrna Y, Med Librn, White Memorial Medical Center, 1720 Cesar E Chavez Ave, Los Angeles, CA, 90033-2462. Tel: 323-260-5715. Fax: 323-260-5748. p. 180

Uzuner, Ozlem, Dr, Asst Prof, University at Albany, State University of New York, Draper 116, 135 Western Ave, Albany, NY, 12222. Tel: 518-442-4687. Fax: 518-442-5367. p. 2970

Vacant, Head, Cat & Metadata Serv, Siena College, 515 Loudon Rd, Loudonville, NY, 12211-1462. Tel: 518-783-2591. Fax: 518-783-2570. p. 1655

Vaccaro, Beth, Dir, Operations, Donora Public Library, 510 Meldon Ave, Donora, PA, 15033-1333. Tel: 724-379-7940. Fax: 724-379-8809. p. 2049

Vaccaro, Beth, Librn, Smithton Public Library, Center & Second St, Smithton, PA, 15479. Tel: 724-872-0701. Fax: 724-872-0701. p. 2141

Vacek, Nancy, Dir, Dvoracek Memorial Library, 419 W Third, Wilber, NE, 68465. Tel: 402-821-2832. p. 1423

Vache, Jaime, Libr Dir, Stoughton Public Library, 304 S Fourth St, Stoughton, WI, 53589-0191. Tel: 608-873-6281. Fax: 608-873-0108. p. 2640

Vachon, Pat, Asst Librn, Blaisdell Memorial Library, 129 Stage Rd, Nottingham, NH, 03290. Tel: 603-679-8484. Fax: 603-679-6774. p. 1461

Vachon, Stephanie, Libr Tech, Emploi Quebec, 276 rue St-Jacques, 6e etage, Montreal, QC, H2Y 1N3, CANADA. Tel: 514-864-3086. Fax: 514-864-3239. p. 2895

Vacovich, Lee, Pres, Alabama Health Libraries Association, Inc, University of Alabama, Lister Hill Library, 1530 Third Ave S, Birmingham, AL, 35294-0013. Tel: 205-975-8313. Fax: 205-934-2230. p. 2937

Vaden, Deborah, Libr Serv Mgr-Br, Irving Public Library, 801 W Irving Blvd, Irving, TX, 75015. Tel: 972-721-2457. Fax: 972-721-2463. p. 2346

Vaden, Grant, Sr Librn, Coll Develop, Haltom City Public Library, 4809 Haltom Rd, Haltom City, TX, 76117-3622. Tel: 817-222-7813. Fax: 817-834-1446. p. 2330

Vader, Patricia A, Dir, Western University of Health Sciences, 287 E Third St, Pomona, CA, 91766-1854. Tel: 909-469-5323. Fax: 909-469-5486. p. 211

Vadnais, Ethel, Dir, Jefferson County District Library, Hamer Branch, 2450 E 2100 North, Hamer, ID, 83425. Tel: 208-662-5275. Fax: 208-662-5213. p. 578

Vadnais, Martine, Librn, Ref, Morneau Sobeco Library, 500 Rene-Levesque Blvd W, Ste 1200, Montreal, QC, H2Z 1W7, CANADA. Tel: 514-878-9090, Ext 8299. Fax: 514-875-2673. p. 2900

Vadnais, Sandra, Librn, Minnesota Department of Corrections, 7525 Fourth Ave, Lino Lakes, MN, 55014. Tel: 651-717-6684. Fax: 651-717-6598. p. 1256

Vaeth, Carol, Bk & Doc Delivery Supvr, University of Baltimore, 1420 Maryland Ave, Baltimore, MD, 21201. Tel: 410-837-4260. Fax: 410-837-4330. p. 1018

Vagts, Rachel, Col Archivist, Luther College, 700 College Dr, Decorah, IA, 52101. Tel: 563-387-1805. Fax: 563-387-1657. p. 807

Vahey, Patty, Head, Adult Serv, Alexandrian Public Library, 115 W Fifth St, Mount Vernon, IN, 47620. Tel: 812-838-3286. Fax: 812-838-9639. p. 766

Vail, Deana, In Charge, First Congregational Church, 640 Millsboro Rd, Mansfield, OH, 44903. Tel: 419-756-3046. Fax: 419-756-5834. p. 1912

Vail, Evelyn J, Librn, North Kansas City Hospital, 2800 Clay Edwards Dr, North Kansas City, MO, 64116. Tel: 816-691-1692. Fax: 816-346-7192. p. 1348

Vail, Virginia, ILL, Ref & Instrul Serv Librn, Pensacola State College, 1000 College Blvd, Pensacola, FL, 32504-8998. Tel: 850-484-2084. Fax: 850-484-1991. p. 482

Vaillancourt, Joan, Ch, Hastings-on-Hudson Public Library, Seven Maple Ave, Hastings-on-Hudson, NY, 10706. Tel: 914-478-3307. Fax: 914-478-4813. p. 1634

Vaillancourt, Nancy, Br Mgr, Owatonna Public Library, Blooming Prairie Branch, 138 Highway Ave S, Blooming Prairie, MN, 55917. Tel: 507-583-7750. Fax: 507-583-4520. p. 1270

Vaillant, Carol, Asst Librn, St Charles Public Library, 22 St Anne, Rm 216-217, Saint Charles, ON, P0M 2W0, CANADA. Tel: 705-867-5332. Fax: 705-867-2511. p. 2839

Vajs, Kristin, Chief Librn, Board of Governors of The Federal Reserve System, Research Library, 20th & C St NW, MS 102, Washington, DC, 20551. Tel: 202-452-3333. Fax: 202-530-6222. p. 394

Val Cleave, Tim, In Charge, US National Park Service, 5646 Carver Rd, Diamond, MO, 64840-8314. Tel: 417-325-4151. Fax: 417-325-4231. p. 1327

Valade, Rita M, Dir, Roseville Public Library, 29777 Gratiot Ave, Roseville, MI, 48066. Tel: 586-445-5407. Fax: 586-445-5499. p. 1223

Valadez, Elva, County Librn, Dir, Fort Stockton Public Library, 500 N Water St, Fort Stockton, TX, 79735. Tel: 432-336-3374. Fax: 432-336-6648. p. 2321

Valantinas, Helen, Asst Dir, Admin, Fountaindale Public Library District, 300 W Briarcliff Rd, Bolingbrook, IL, 60440-2844. Tel: 630-759-2102, Ext 4210. Fax: 630-759-9519. p. 596

Valasek, Jana Marie, Librn, Bibliotheque Commemorative Pettes, 276 rue Knowlton, Knowlton, QC, J0E 1V0, CANADA. Tel: 450-243-6128. Fax: 450-243-5272. p. 2885

Valauskas, Edward J, Curator, Rare Bks, Lenhardt Library of the Chicago Botanic Garden, 1000 Lake Cook Rd, Glencoe, IL, 60022. Tel: 847-835-8206. Fax: 847-835-6885. p. 650

Valbuena, Andrew, Head, Ser, Chapman University, One University Dr, Orange, CA, 92866-1099. Tel: 714-532-7756. Fax: 714-532-7743. p. 200

Valbuena, Andrew, Head, Ser, California State University, Sacramento Library, 2000 State University Dr E, Sacramento, CA, 95819-6039. Tel: 916-278-5679. Fax: 916-278-5917. p. 223

Valdes, Barbara, Tech Serv, Halifax County Library, 33 S Granville St, Halifax, NC, 27839. Tel: 252-583-3631. Fax: 252-583-8661. p. 1799

Valdes, Carrie, Dir, Grand County Public Library, 257 E Center St, Moab, UT, 84532. Tel: 435-259-5421. Fax: 435-259-1380. p. 2407

Valdes, Lauren, Electronic Res, Ref Serv, Los Angeles Pierce College Library, 6201 Winnetka Ave, Woodland Hills, CA, 91371. Tel: 818-719-6409. Fax: 818-719-9058. p. 285

Valdez, Arlene, Librn, Vallejo Naval & Historical Museum, 734 Marin St, Vallejo, CA, 94590. Tel: 707-643-0077. Fax: 707-643-2443. p. 278

Valdez, Ismael, Br Mgr, Zapata County Public Library, A L Bennavides Branch, 301 Lincoln Ave, San Ygnacio, TX, 78067. Tel: 956-765-5611, Ext 26. p. 2402

Valdez, Joseph, Head, External Prog Div, New Mexico Highlands University, Ninth & National Ave, Las Vegas, NM, 87701. Tel: 505-891-6914. Fax: 505-891-2972. p. 1559

Valdez, Judith, Disability Serv Librn, Auraria Library, 1100 Lawrence St, Denver, CO, 80204-2095. Tel: 303-556-4999. Fax: 303-556-3528. p. 298

Valdez, Ruth, Asst Admin, Robert J Kleberg Public Library, 220 N Fourth St, Kingsville, TX, 78363. Tel: 361-592-6381. p. 2350

Valdez, Veronica Marie, Med Librn, Department of Veterans Affairs Medical Center Library, 385 Tremont Ave, East Orange, NJ, 07018-1095. Tel: 973-676-1000, Ext 1962. Fax: 973-395-7234. p. 1482

Valdivia, Aaron, Managing Librn, Pima County Public Library, El Pueblo, 101 W Irvington Rd, Tucson, AZ, 85714. Tel: 520-594-5250. Fax: 520-594-5251. p. 87

Valdivia, Alex, Evening/Weekend Librn, University of La Verne, 2040 Third St, La Verne, CA, 91750. Tel: 909-593-3511, Ext 4305. Fax: 909-392-2733. p. 162

Valdivia, Ximena, Mgr, Archives & Spec Coll, Barry University, 11300 NE Second Ave, Miami, FL, 33161. Tel: 305-899-3027. Fax: 305-899-4792. p. 464

Valdiviezo, Geraldine, Media Serv, Allan Hancock College, 800 S College Dr, Santa Maria, CA, 93454. Tel: 805-922-6966, Ext 3224. Fax: 805-922-3763. p. 265

Valdovinos, Louise, Ch, DeForest Area Public Library, 203 Library St, DeForest, WI, 53532. Tel: 608-846-5482. Fax: 608-846-6875. p. 2588

Valdry, Andree, Acq, Compton Community College Library, 1111 E Artesia Blvd, Compton, CA, 90221. Tel: 310-900-1600, Ext 2175. Fax: 310-900-1693. p. 136

Valencia, Dave, Interim Br Mgr, Seattle Public Library, Ballard, 5614 22nd Ave NW, Seattle, WA, 98107. Tel: 206-684-4089. p. 2531

Valencia, Dave, Regional Mgr, Seattle Public Library, Fremont, 731 N 35th St, Seattle, WA, 98103. Tel: 206-684-4084. p. 2531

Valencia, Dave, Regional Mgr, Seattle Public Library, Magnolia, 2801 34th Ave W, Seattle, WA, 98199. Tel: 206-386-4225. p. 2531

Valencia, Diego F, Digitization Coordr, Hunter College Libraries, Centro - Center for Puerto Rican Studies Library, 2180 Third Ave, Rm 121, New York, NY, 10035. Tel: 212-396-7874. Fax: 212-396-7707. p. 1682

Valencia, Dorothy, Evening Supvr, University of Arkansas Libraries, Fine Arts, 104 Fine Arts Bldg, Fayetteville, AR, 72701. Tel: 479-575-4236. p. 100

Valencia, Ernesto, Syst Librn, Northeastern University Libraries, Snell Library, 360 Huntington Ave, Boston, MA, 02115. Tel: 617-373-3398. p. 1065

Valente, Mario, Dean, MiraCosta College Library, One Barnard Dr, Oceanside, CA, 92056-3899. Tel: 760-795-6720. Fax: 760-795-6723. p. 199

Valenti, Dorothy, Libr Mgr, Constableville Village Library, 3158 Main St, Constableville, NY, 13325. Tel: 315-397-2801. Fax: 315-397-2801. p. 1609

Valenti, Gloria, Librn, Pendle Hill Library, 338 Plush Mill Rd, Wallingford, PA, 19086. Tel: 610-566-4507. Fax: 610-566-3679. p. 2150

Valenti, Teresa, Tech Serv, Pueblo City-County Library District, 100 E Abriendo Ave, Pueblo, CO, 81004-4290. Tel: 719-562-5629. Fax: 719-562-5619. p. 320

Valenti, Tony, Dir, Edison State College, 7007 Lely Cultural Pkwy, Naples, FL, 34113-8976. Tel: 239-732-3774. Fax: 239-732-3777. p. 471

Valentin, Annette, Dir, Universidad Central De Bayamon Library, PO Box 1725, Bayamon, PR, 00960-1725. Tel: 787-786-3030, Ext 2136. Fax: 787-740-2200. p. 2672

Valentin, Blanca, Spec Coll & Archives Librn, Pontifical Catholic University Of Puerto Rico, Encarnacion Valdes Library, 2250 Avenida Las Americas, Ste 509, Ponce, PR, 00717-0777. Tel: 787-841-2000, Ext 1808. Fax: 787-284-0235. p. 2675

Valentin, Ryan, Head, Pub Serv, University of Kentucky Libraries, Law Library, 620 S Limestone St, Lexington, KY, 40506-0048. Tel: 859-257-8347. Fax: 859-323-4906. p. 922

Valentin, Violet Jean, Dir, Gill Memorial Library, 145 E Broad St, Paulsboro, NJ, 08066. Tel: 856-423-5155. Fax: 856-423-9162. p. 1519

Valentine, Alexander, Media Serv, City College of San Francisco, 50 Phelan Ave, San Francisco, CA, 94112. Tel: 415-452-5426. Fax: 415-452-5588. p. 241

Valentine, Barbara, Librn, Linfield College, 900 S Baker St, McMinnville, OR, 97128. Tel: 503-883-2573. Fax: 503-883-2566. p. 2005

Valentine, Cathy, Librn, Watertown Township Fostoria Library, 9405 Foster St, Fostoria, MI, 48435. Tel: 989-795-2794. Fax: 989-795-2892. p. 1181

Valentine, Deanna, Head, Tech Serv, Whiting Public Library, 1735 Oliver St, Whiting, IN, 46394-1794. Tel: 219-473-4700, Ext 15. Fax: 219-659-5833. p. 788

Valentine, Diane, Teen Serv, Somerset County Library System, Hillsborough Public, Hillsborough Municipal Complex, 379 S Branch Rd, Hillsborough, NJ, 08844. Tel: 908-369-2200. Fax: 908-369-8242. p. 1475

Valentine, Friday, Metadata Librn, Ser Librn, Oregon Health & Science University Library, 3181 SW Sam Jackson Park Rd, Portland, OR, 97239-3098. Tel: 503-494-0883. Fax: 503-494-3227. p. 2013

Valentine, Jeanne, Mgr, Ad Serv, Plano Community Library District, 15 W North St, Plano, IL, 60545. Tel: 630-552-2009. Fax: 630-552-1008. p. 691

Valentine, Jo-Anne, Chief Librn, Dep Dir, Foreign Affairs Canada & International Trade Canada, Lester B Pearson Bldg, 125 Sussex Drive, Ottawa, ON, K1A 0G2, CANADA. Tel: 613-996-4042. Fax: 613-944-0222. p. 2831

Valentine, June, Librn, Chester Mental Health Center, 1315 Lehmen Rd, Chester, IL, 62233-2542. Tel: 618-826-4571, Ext 539. Fax: 618-826-3581. p. 604

Valentine, Patrick, Dr, Asst Prof, East Carolina University, 101 Umstead Residence Hall, Greenville, NC, 27858-4353. Tel: 252-737-1570. Fax: 252-328-4368. p. 2971

Valentine, Peter, Librn, Linklaters, 1345 Sixth Ave, 19th Flr, New York, NY, 10105. Tel: 212-424-9000. Fax: 212-424-9100. p. 1685

Valentine, Susan, Dir, Smithton Public Library District, 109 S Main, Smithton, IL, 62285-1707. Tel: 618-233-8057. Fax: 618-233-3670. p. 703

Valentino, Camille, Dir, Emerson Public Library, 20 Palisade Ave, Emerson, NJ, 07630. Tel: 201-261-5604. Fax: 201-262-7999. p. 1484

Valentino, Erin, Res & Instrul Serv, Trinity College Library, 300 Summit St, Hartford, CT, 06106. Tel: 860-297-5211. Fax: 860-297-2251. p. 347

Valenzuela, David, Libr Dir, Buffalo News Library, One News Plaza, Buffalo, NY, 14203. Tel: 716-849-4401. Fax: 716-856-5150. p. 1597

Valenzuela, Elisa, Librn, Lockheed Martin, 199 Borton Landing Rd, Moorestown, NJ, 08057-0927. Tel: 609-326-4750. Fax: 609-326-5301. p. 1504

Valenzuela, Leah, Tech Asst, California Department of Corrections Library System, California Correctional Institution, 24900 Hwy 202, Tehachapi, CA, 93561. Tel: 661-822-4402. Fax: 661-823-3358, 661-823-5016. p. 221

Valenzuela, Ross, Assoc Librn, Mount San Jacinto College, 1499 N State St, San Jacinto, CA, 92583-2399. Tel: 951-487-6752, Ext 1580. Fax: 951-654-8387. p. 249

Valerio-Nowc, Lisa, Youth Serv Librn, Saint Clair Shores Public Library, 22500 11 Mile Rd, Saint Clair Shores, MI, 48081-1399. Tel: 586-771-9020. Fax: 586-771-8935. p. 1224

Valero, Carmen, Librn, Luce, Forward, Hamilton & Scripps, 600 W Broadway, Ste 2600, San Diego, CA, 92101. Tel: 619-236-1414. Fax: 619-232-8311. p. 231

Valero, Elizabeth, Dir, Millbury Public Library, 128 Elm St, Millbury, MA, 01527. Tel: 508-865-1181. Fax: 508-865-0795. p. 1106

Valeski, Janet L, Ref, Quinnipiac University, 275 Mount Carmel Ave, Hamden, CT, 06518. Tel: 203-582-8943. Fax: 203-582-3451. p. 343

Valiquette, Josée, Chef de Section, Bibliothèques de Montrèal, Langelier, 6473, rue Sherbrooke Est, Montreal, QC, H1N 1C5, CANADA. Tel: 514-872-1529. Fax: 514-872-0523. p. 2890

Vallaincourt, Anna, Br Mgr, Las Vegas-Clark County Library District, Sunrise Library, 5400 Harris Ave, Las Vegas, NV, 89110. Tel: 702-507-3900. Fax: 702-507-3914. p. 1430

Vallazza, Magaly, Mgr, Johnson County Library, Oak Park, 9500 Bluejacket, Overland Park, KS, 66214. Tel: 913-752-8705. Fax: 913-752-8709. p. 888

Valle, Barbara, Coordr, Texas Trans-Pecos Regional Library System, El Paso Public Library, 501 Oregon St N, El Paso, TX, 79901-1103. Tel: 915-543-5465. Fax: 915-543-5473. p. 2317

Valle, Blair, Children's Consult, Chautauqua-Cattaraugus Library System, 106 W Fifth St, Jamestown, NY, 14701. Tel: 716-484-7136. p. 1646

Vallejo, Christina, Acq, ILL, Arcadia Public Library, 20 W Duarte Rd, Arcadia, CA, 91006. Tel: 626-821-5567. Fax: 626-447-8050. p. 121

Vallejos, James, Circ Supvr, Edwin A Bemis Public Library, 6014 S Datura St, Littleton, CO, 80120-2636. Tel: 303-795-3961. Fax: 303-795-3996. p. 316

Vallejos, Victoria, Commun Libr Mgr, County of Los Angeles Public Library, Quartz Hill Library, 42018 N 50th St W, Quartz Hill, CA, 93536-3509. Tel: 661-943-2454. Fax: 661-943-6337. p. 143

Vallerand, Josee, Archivist, EXPORAIL Archives Library, The Canadian Railway Museum, 110 St Pierre, Saint Constant, QC, J5A 1G7, CANADA. Tel: 450-638-1522, Ext 237. Fax: 450-638-1563. p. 2908

Valles, Christina, Dir, Terrell County Public Library, Courthouse Sq, 109 Hackberry, Sanderson, TX, 79848. Tel: 432-345-2294. Fax: 432-345-2144. p. 2385

Valles, Joseph, Tech Serv, Conyers-Rockdale Library System, 864 Green St, Conyers, GA, 30012. Tel: 770-388-5040. Fax: 770-388-5043. p. 527

Valley, Karen, Dir, Walker Memorial Library, 800 Main St, Westbrook, ME, 04092. Tel: 207-854-0630. Fax: 207-854-0629. p. 1006

Valley, Paula, Ref Librn, Supvr, ILL, Houghton College, One Willard Ave, Houghton, NY, 14744. Tel: 585-567-9245. Fax: 585-567-9248. p. 1638

Valliant, Merrie, Librn, Johnson & Wales University, College of Business, 7150 Montview Blvd, Denver, CO, 80220. Tel: 303-256-9345. Fax: 303-256-9459. p. 302

Vallier, John, Head, Distributed Media Serv, University of Washington Libraries, Media Center, Odegaard Undergraduate Library, Mezzanine Level, Box 353080, Seattle, WA, 98195-3080. Tel: 206-618-1210. Fax: 206-685-8485. p. 2534

Vallières, Nicole, Dir, Bibliotheque et Archives nationales du Quebec, 475 de Maisonneuve E, Montreal, QC, H2L 5C4, CANADA. Tel: 514-873-1101, Ext 6714. Fax: 514-873-9312. p. 2888

Vallone, Richard, Pub Serv, New England Conservatory of Music, 33 Gainsborough St, Boston, MA, 02115. Tel: 617-585-1251. Fax: 617-585-1245. p. 1064

Valois, Richard-Alain, Media Spec, Bibliotheques de Trois-Rivieres, Bibliotheque Maurice-Loranger, 70 rue Pare, Trois-Rivieres, QC, G8T 6V8, CANADA. Tel: 819-378-8826. Fax: 819-378-5539. p. 2914

Valosin, Chris, Curator, National Park Service, 648 Rte 32, Stillwater, NY, 12170. Tel: 518-664-9821, Ext 221. Fax: 518-664-9830. p. 1749

Valvano, Sandra, Adminr, Lyndhurst Free Public Library, 355 Valley Brook Ave, Lyndhurst, NJ, 07071. Tel: 201-804-2478. Fax: 201-939-7677. p. 1497

Valverde, Mary Ellen, Asst Librn, Saint Peter's College, Hudson Terrace, Englewood Cliffs, NJ, 07632. Tel: 201-568-7730. Fax: 201-568-6614. p. 1484

Valverde, Victoria, Librn, Los Angeles Institute & Society for Psychoanalytic Studies, 12011 San Vicente Blvd, Ste 310, Los Angeles, CA, 90049. Tel: 310-440-0333, 310-440-4065. p. 172

Valyi-Hax, Kristen, Librn, Hughes Ruth Memorial District Library, Attica Township Library, 4352 Peppermill Rd, Attica, MI, 48412-9624. Tel: 810-724-2007. Fax: 810-724-2007. p. 1193

Valyi-Hax, Kristen, Dir, Romeo District Library, 65821 Van Dyke, Washington, MI, 48095. Tel: 586-752-0603. Fax: 586-752-8416. p. 1235

Van Achterberg, Barbara, Adult Serv, Bethel Public Library, 189 Greenwood Ave, Bethel, CT, 06801-2598. Tel: 203-794-8756. Fax: 203-794-8761. p. 330

Van Acker, Jill, Interim Dir, Princeton Public Library, 698 E Peru St, Princeton, IL, 61356. Tel: 815-875-1331. Fax: 815-872-1376. p. 692

van Aken, Cornelia, Asst Dir, Pub Serv, Palo Alto City Library, 1213 Newell Rd, Palo Alto, CA, 94303-2907. Tel: 650-329-2668. Fax: 650-327-2033. p. 204

Van Allen, Cathy, Head Librn, Sharon Springs Public Library, 113 W Second St, Sharon Springs, KS, 67758. Tel: 785-852-4685. Fax: 785-852-4687. p. 894

Van Allen, Deborah, Circ, ILL, Heritage University, 3240 Fort Rd, Toppenish, WA, 98948. Tel: 509-865-8500, Ext 3430. Fax: 509-865-4144. p. 2541

Van Arsdale, Bill, Circ, Govt Doc, Syst, Wayne State College, 1111 Main St, Wayne, NE, 68787. Tel: 402-375-7259. Fax: 402-375-7538. p. 1423

Van Arsdale, Dennis G, Cat, Coll Develop, Tech Serv, University of Arkansas Fort Smith, 5210 Grand Ave, Fort Smith, AR, 72903. Tel: 479-788-7206. Fax: 479-788-7209. p. 101

Van Arsdale, William, Access Serv, University of Wyoming Libraries, Library Annex, Dept 3262, 1000 E University Ave, Laramie, WY, 82071. Tel: 307-766-2499. p. 2658

Van Arsdale, William, Head, Access Serv, University of Wyoming Libraries, 13th & Ivinson, Laramie, WY, 82071. Tel: 307-766-3279. Fax: 307-766-2510. p. 2658

Van Auken, Kate, Dir, Rawson Memorial District Library, 6495 Pine St, Cass City, MI, 48726-4073. Tel: 989-872-2856. Fax: 989-872-4073. p. 1161

Van Beers, Aaron, Chairperson, Devon Public Library, 101, 17 Athabasca Ave, Devon, AB, T9G 1G5, CANADA. Tel: 780-987-3720. p. 2696

Van Benschoten, Mary Ann, Coll Develop, Orange County Community College Library, 115 South St, Middletown, NY, 10940. Tel: 845-341-4258. Fax: 845-341-4424. p. 1660

van Beynen, Kaya, Ref Librn, University of South Florida Saint Petersburg, 140 Seventh Ave S, POY118, Saint Petersburg, FL, 33701. Tel: 727-873-4401. Fax: 727-873-4196. p. 489

Van Biert, Tamara, Dir, Stony Plain Public Library, 4613-52 Ave, No 112, Stony Plain, AB, T7Z 1E7, CANADA. Tel: 780-963-5440. Fax: 780-963-1746. p. 2718

van Blokand, P J, Librn, University of Florida, 2199 S Rock Rd, Fort Pierce, FL, 34945. Tel: 772-468-3922. Fax: 772-468-5668. p. 447

Van Bruggen, Sharon, Acq, ILL, Alberta Department of Environment Library, 9920 108th St, 6th Flr, Edmonton, AB, T5K 2M4, CANADA. Tel: 780-422-7549. Fax: 780-422-0170. p. 2698

Van Buren, Jessica, Dir, Utah State Law Library, 450 S State St, W-13, Salt Lake City, UT, 84111-3101. Tel: 801-238-7990. Fax: 801-238-7993. p. 2415

Van Buren, Stephen, Archives, Spec Coll, South Dakota State University, 1300 N Campus Dr, Box 2115, Brookings, SD, 57007-1098. Tel: 605-688-4906. Fax: 605-688-6133. p. 2210

Van Burgh, Chris, Outreach Librn, Wyoming State Library, 2800 Central Ave, Cheyenne, WY, 82002. Tel: 307-777-6333. Fax: 307-777-6289. p. 2653

Van Buskirk, Neli, Asst Dir, Nederland Community Library, 200 Hwy 72 N, Nederland, CO, 80466. Tel: 303-258-1101. p. 319

Van Camp, Holly, Ch, Vienna Public Library, 2300 River Rd, Vienna, WV, 26105. Tel: 304-295-7771. Fax: 304-295-7776. p. 2573

Van Cleave, Barbara, Tech Serv, University of Montana Western, 710 S Atlantic St, Dillon, MT, 59725. Tel: 406-683-7491. Fax: 406-683-7493. p. 1378

Van Cleave, Benita, Circ, Salem Public Library, 28 E Main St, Salem, VA, 24153. Tel: 540-375-3089. Fax: 540-389-7054. p. 2496

Van Cleave, Richard H, Curator, Tongass Historical Museum, 629 Dock St, Ketchikan, AK, 99901. Tel: 907-225-5600. Fax: 907-225-5602. p. 50

Van Cleve, Gib, Info Tech, Saint Louis County Library, 1640 S Lindbergh Blvd, Saint Louis, MO, 63131-3598. Tel: 314-994-3300, Ext 2201. Fax: 314-997-7602. p. 1358

Van Dam, Edwina, Ref, Floral Park Public Library, 17 Caroline Pl, Floral Park, NY, 11001. Tel: 516-326-6330. Fax: 516-437-6959. p. 1622

Van Dan, Rebecca, YA Serv, Middleton Public Library, 7425 Hubbard Ave, Middleton, WI, 53562-3117. Tel: 608-827-7410. Fax: 608-836-5724. p. 2616

Van De Cappelle, Maria, Br Librn, Prince Edward Island Public Library Service, Morell Public, 89 Red Head Rd, Morell, PE, C0A 1S0, CANADA. Tel: 902-961-3389. p. 2876

Van De Cappelle, Maria, Br Librn, Prince Edward Island Public Library Service, Mount Stewart Public, 104 Main St, Mount Stewart, PE, C0A 1T0, CANADA. Tel: 902-676-2050. p. 2876

Van De Carr, Janet, Dir, Park Ridge Public Library, 20 S Prospect, Park Ridge, IL, 60068-4188. Tel: 847-720-3203. Fax: 847-825-0001. p. 688

Van de Castle, Debbie, Librn, York County Library System, Dover Area Community, 3700-3 Davidsburg Rd, Dover, PA, 17315. Tel: 717-292-6814. Fax: 717-292-9774. p. 2160

Van de Castle, Deborah, Dir, Glatfelter Memorial Library, 101 Glenview Rd, Spring Grove, PA, 17362. Tel: 717-225-3220. Fax: 717-225-9808. p. 2142

van de Voort, Colleen, Circ & AV Serv Librn, Kwantlen Polytechnic University Library, 12666 72 Ave., Surrey, BC, V3W 2M8, CANADA. Tel: 604-599-2090. Fax: 604-599-2106. p. 2738

Van Dee, Crystal, Curator of Ms & Libr, Nevada State Museum, 700 Twin Lakes Dr, Las Vegas, NV, 89107. Tel: 702-486-5205, Ext 240. p. 1430

Van Den Hul, Dawn, ILL, Dordt College, 498 Fourth Ave NE, Sioux Center, IA, 51250. Tel: 712-722-6040. Fax: 712-722-1198. p. 843

Van der Heuvel, Heidi, Acq, Ref Serv, Ottawa Library, 105 S Hickory St, Ottawa, KS, 66067-2306. Tel: 785-242-3080. Fax: 785-242-8789. p. 887

Van Der Meer, Rebecca, Br Mgr, Kanawha County Public Library, Saint Albans Branch, 602 Fourth St, Saint Albans, WV, 25177. Tel: 304-722-4244. Fax: 304-722-4276. p. 2556

Van der Reyden, Dianne, Dir, Library of Congress, Preservation Directorate, Madison Memorial Bldg, Rm 642, Washington, DC, 20540-4500. Tel: 202-707-5213. Fax: 202-707-6269. p. 407

van der Valk, Linda, Pres, Chatsworth Historical Society, 10385 Shadow Oak Dr, Chatsworth, CA, 91311. Tel: 818-882-5614. Fax: 818-882-5614. p. 133

Van Der Veen, Kirsten, Libr Tech, Smithsonian Libraries, The Dibner Library of the History of Science & Technology, Nat Museum of American Hist, Rm 1041, MRC 672, 12th St & Constitution Ave NW, Washington, DC, 20560-0672. Tel: 202-633-3872. p. 414

Van der Velde, Margaret, Librn, Theological College of the Canadian Reformed Churches Library, 110 W 27th St, Hamilton, ON, L9C 5A1, CANADA. Tel: 905-575-3688. Fax: 905-575-0799. p. 2811

Van Diepen, Melissa, Chief Librn, The Modesto Bee, 1325 H St, Modesto, CA, 95354. Tel: 209-578-2333, 209-578-2370. Fax: 209-578-2207. p. 188

Van Doornik, Sally, Asst Br Mgr, Huron County Library, Clinton Branch, 27 Albert St, Clinton, ON, N0M 1L0, CANADA. Tel: 519-482-3673. p. 2799

Van Doren, Mary, Ch, Nelsonville Public Library, 95 W Washington, Nelsonville, OH, 45764-1177. Tel: 740-753-2118. Fax: 740-753-3543. p. 1920

Van Dorn, Nicholas, Libr Assoc, Nutley Free Public Library, 93 Booth Dr, Nutley, NJ, 07110-2782. Tel: 973-667-0405. p. 1515

Van Duzer, Lee, Librn, United States District Court Library, 280 S First St, San Jose, CA, 95113. Tel: 408-535-5323. Fax: 408-535-5322. p. 252

Van Dyk, Jacqueline, Head, Syst, Vancouver Community College, 250 W Pender St, Vancouver, BC, V6B 1S9, CANADA. Tel: 604-871-7157. Fax: 604-443-8588. p. 2743

van Dyk, Jacqueline, Dir, British Columbia Ministry of Education, 620 Superior St, 5th Flr, Victoria, BC, V8V 1V2, CANADA. Tel: 250-356-1791. Fax: 250-953-3225. p. 2745

Van Dyk, Stephen H, Librn, Smithsonian Libraries, Cooper-Hewitt, National Design Museum Library, Two E 91st St, 3rd Flr, New York City, DC, 10128. Tel: 212-849-8335. Fax: 212-849-8339. p. 414

Van Dyke, Dan, Exec Dir, Nebraska Prairie Museum, N Hwy 183, Holdrege, NE, 68949. Tel: 308-995-5015. Fax: 308-995-2241. p. 1402

Van Eaton, Lori, In Charge, Norton Correctional Facility, PO Box 546, Norton, KS, 67654. Tel: 785-877-3389, Ext 333. Fax: 785-877-3972. p. 885

Van Epps, Michele, Dir, Acton Public Library, 60 Old Boston Post Rd, Old Saybrook, CT, 06475-2200. Tel: 860-395-3184. Fax: 860-395-2462. p. 363

Van Erem, Rochelle, Ser, Todd Wehr Library, St Norbert College, 301 Third St, De Pere, WI, 54115. Tel: 920-403-3270. Fax: 920-403-4064. p. 2587

Van Ert, Cindy, Librn, New Page Corp, 300 N Biron Dr, Wisconsin Rapids, WI, 54494. Tel: 715-422-2368. Fax: 715-422-2227. p. 2650

Van Es, Rhonda, Head, Circ, Sioux Center Public Library, 102 S Main Ave, Sioux Center, IA, 51250-1801. Tel: 712-722-2138. Fax: 712-722-1235. p. 843

Van Essen-Fishman, Sam, Libr Assoc, New York School of Interior Design Library, 170 E 70th St, New York, NY, 10021. Tel: 212-472-1500, Ext 214. Fax: 212-472-8175. p. 1694

Van Fleet, Connie J, PhD, Dr, Prof, University of Oklahoma, Bizzell Memorial Library, 401 W Brooks, Rm 120, Norman, OK, 73019-6032. Tel: 405-325-3921. Fax: 405-325-7648. p. 2972

Van Gelder, Marinke, Librn, Alaska State Court Law Library, Juneau Branch, Dimond Court Bldg, 123 Fourth St, Juneau, AK, 99811. Tel: 907-463-4761. Fax: 907-463-4784. p. 44

Van Gemert, Edward, Dep Dir, University of Wisconsin-Madison, 728 State St, Madison, WI, 53706. Tel: 608-262-0950. Fax: 608-265-2754. p. 2608

van Haaften, Jami, Librn, Health Sciences North, 41 Ramsey Lake Rd, Sudbury, ON, P3E 5J1, CANADA. Tel: 705-523-7100, Ext 3375. Fax: 705-523-7317. p. 2846

Van Herreweghe, Christa, Info Tech, University City Public Library, 6701 Delmar Blvd, University City, MO, 63130. Tel: 314-727-3150. Fax: 314-727-6005. p. 1370

Van Hine, Pamela M, Ref Serv, American College of Obstetricians & Gynecologists, 409 12th St SW, Washington, DC, 20024-2188. Tel: 202-863-2518. Fax: 202-484-1595. p. 392

Van Hoeck, Michelle, Res, Santa Rosa Press Democrat, 427 Mendocino Ave, Santa Rosa, CA, 95401-6385. Tel: 707-526-8520. Fax: 707-521-5411. p. 267

Van Hook, Lorie, Ch, Dighton Public Library, 395 Main St, Dighton, MA, 02715. Tel: 508-669-6421. Fax: 508-669-6963. p. 1084

Van Hoose, Reva, Cat, Lewis & Clark Community College, 5800 Godfrey Rd, Godfrey, IL, 62035. Tel: 618-466-3411, Ext 4306. Fax: 618-468-4301. p. 651

Van Horn, Brian, Librn, Winhall Memorial Library, Two Lower Tayler Hill Rd, Bondville, VT, 05340. Tel: 802-297-9741. p. 2419

Van Horn, Margaret, Circ, O'Fallon Public Library, 120 Civic Plaza, O'Fallon, IL, 62269-2692. Tel: 618-632-3783. Fax: 618-632-3759. p. 684

Van Horne, John C, Dir, Library Company of Philadelphia, 1314 Locust St, Philadelphia, PA, 19107-5698. Tel: 215-546-3181. Fax: 215-546-5167. p. 2112

Van Houten, Carol, Ref Librn, Web Coordr, Bank Street College of Education Library, 610 W 112th St, 5th Flr, New York, NY, 10025. Tel: 212-875-4455. Fax: 212-875-4558. p. 1669

Van Houtte, Philippe, Syst Librn, Arkansas Tech University, 305 West Q St, Russellville, AR, 72801-2222. Tel: 479-498-6042. Fax: 479-964-0559. p. 113

Van Houweling, Douglas E, Prof, University of Michigan, 304 West Hall, 1085 S University, Ann Arbor, MI, 48109-1107. Tel: 734-763-2285. Fax: 734-764-2475. p. 2967

Van Iderstine, Anne, Mgr, Info Serv, Legislative Library of Nova Scotia, Province House, 2nd Flr, Halifax, NS, B3J 2P8, CANADA. Tel: 902-424-5932. Fax: 902-424-0220. p. 2781

Van Ingen, Rosary, Adult Serv, Hoboken Public Library, 500 Park Ave, Hoboken, NJ, 07030. Tel: 201-420-2346. Fax: 201-420-2299. p. 1491

van Kalmthout, Frank, Librn, Archives of Ontario Library, 134 Ian Macdonald Blvd, Toronto, ON, M7A 2C5, CANADA. Tel: 416-327-1553. Fax: 416-327-1999. p. 2850

Van Kampen, Doris, Fac Develop Librn, Saint Leo University, 33701 State Rd 52, Saint Leo, FL, 33574. Tel: 352-588-8485. Fax: 352-588-8484. p. 487

Van Keuren, Linda, Asst Dir, Res & Access Mgt, Georgetown University, Dahlgren Memorial Library, Preclinical Science Bldg GM-7, 3900 Reservoir Rd NW, Washington, DC, 20007. Tel: 202-687-1168. Fax: 202-687-1862. p. 402

Van Kirk, Karen, Tech Serv, Corpus Christi Public Libraries, 805 Comanche, Corpus Christi, TX, 78401. Tel: 361-826-7000. Fax: 361-826-7046. p. 2301

Van Kirk, Shannon, Dir, Blue Mountain Community College Library, 2411 NW Carden Ave, Pendleton, OR, 97801. Tel: 541-278-5915. Fax: 541-276-6119. p. 2009

Van Kleek, Laurence M, Librn, Summit Pacific College, 35235 Straiton Rd, Abbotsford, BC, V2S 7Z1, CANADA. Tel: 604-851-7230. Fax: 604-853-8951. p. 2724

Van Laningham, Ruth, Librn, Middle East Institute, 1761 N St NW, Washington, DC, 20036. Tel: 202-785-0183. Fax: 202-331-8861. p. 408

Van Leeuwen, Katherine, Adult Serv, The Brookfield Library, 182 Whisconier Rd, Brookfield, CT, 06804. Tel: 203-775-6241. Fax: 203-740-7723. p. 332

Van Leeuwen, Peter, Online Serv, International College Library, 2655 Northbrooke Dr, Naples, FL, 34119. Tel: 239-598-6109, 239-938-7812. Fax: 239-598-6250, 239-938-7886. p. 471

Van Maanen, Lorna, Dir, Rock Valley Public Library, 1531 Main St, Rock Valley, IA, 51247-1127. Tel: 712-476-5651. Fax: 712-476-5261. p. 841

Van Meter, Dana, Tech Serv Librn, Institute for Advanced Study Libraries, Einstein Dr, Princeton, NJ, 08540. Tel: 609-734-8376. Fax: 609-924-8399, 609-951-4515. p. 1522

Van Meter, Rozella, Dir, Fern Ridge Library District, 88026 Territorial Rd, Veneta, OR, 97487. Tel: 541-935-7512. Fax: 541-935-8013. p. 2022

Van Minnen, Ania, Br Mgr, Hamilton Public Library, Carlisle Branch, 1496 Centre Rd, Carlisle, ON, L0R 1H0, CANADA. Tel: 905-546-3200, Ext 6603. p. 2809

Van Minnen, Ania, Br Mgr, Hamilton Public Library, Freelton Branch, 1803 Brock Rd, Freelton, ON, L0R 1K0, CANADA. Tel: 905-546-3200, Ext 6603. p. 2809

Van Minnen, Ania, Br Mgr, Hamilton Public Library, Lynden Branch, 79 Lynden Rd, Lynden, ON, L0R 1T0, CANADA. Tel: 905-546-3200, Ext 6603. p. 2809

Van Minnen, Ania, Br Mgr, Hamilton Public Library, Millgrove Branch, 857 Millgrove Side Rd, Millgrove, ON, L0R 1V0, CANADA. Tel: 905-546-3200, Ext 6603. p. 2809

Van Minnen, Ania, Br Mgr, Hamilton Public Library, Rockton Branch, 795 Old Hwy 8, Rockton, ON, L0R 1X0, CANADA. Tel: 905-546-3200, Ext 6603. p. 2809

Van Minnen, Ania, Br Mgr, Hamilton Public Library, Waterdown Branch, 25 Mill St N, Waterdown, ON, L0R 2H0, CANADA. Tel: 905-546-3200, Ext 6603. p. 2810

Van Moorsel, Guillaume, Dir, Stamford Hospital, Shelborne Rd at W Broad, Stamford, CT, 06904. Tel: 203-325-7523. Fax: 203-276-7109. p. 370

Van Ness, Beth, Ref Serv, Canton Public Library, 40 Dyer Ave, Canton, CT, 06019. Tel: 860-693-5800. Fax: 860-693-5804. p. 333

Van Ness, Cynthia M, Dir, Libr & Archives, Buffalo History Museum Research Library, One Museum Ct, Buffalo, NY, 14216-3199. Tel: 716-873-9644. Fax: 716-873-8754. p. 1597

Van Nest, Dee, Coordr, Ref (Info Serv), Maryland State Law Library, Courts of Appeal Bldg, 361 Rowe Blvd, Annapolis, MD, 21401-1697. Tel: 410-260-1430. Fax: 410-260-1572, 410-974-2063. p. 1010

Van Niekerken, Bill, Archives Dir, San Francisco Chronicle Library, 901 Mission St, San Francisco, CA, 94103. Tel: 415-777-7231. Fax: 415-896-0668. p. 245

Van Norden, Marshall, In Charge, Thetford Town Library, Thetford Historical, PO Box 33, Thetford, VT, 05074-0033. Tel: 802-785-2068. p. 2437

Van Nort, Sydney, Archivist, City College of the City University of New York, North Academic Ctr, 160 Convent Ave, New York, NY, 10031. Tel: 212-650-7609. Fax: 212-650-7604. p. 1672

Van Nort, Sydney, Archivist, City College of the City University of New York, College Archives & Special Collections, North Academic

Ctr-Cohen Library, 160 Convent Ave, New York, NY, 10031. Tel: 212-650-7609. Fax: 212-650-7604. p. 1673

Van Olpen, Daniel, Libr Dir, Westport Library Association, PO Box 436, Westport, NY, 12993-0436. Tel: 518-962-8219. Fax: 518-962-8219. p. 1768

van Oosten, Janet, Pub Serv, Crown College, 8700 College View Dr, Saint Bonifacius, MN, 55375-9002. Tel: 952-446-4240. Fax: 952-446-4149. p. 1274

Van Patten, Margaret A, Ref Serv, Ad, Baldwinsville Public Library, 33 E Genesee St, Baldwinsville, NY, 13027-2575. Tel: 315-635-5631. Fax: 315-635-6760. p. 1577

Van Pelt, Martha, Dir, South Central Library System, 4610 S Biltmore Lane, Ste 101, Madison, WI, 53718-2153. Tel: 608-246-7975. Fax: 608-246-7958. p. 2607

Van Pottelsberghe, Brian, Ref Librn, Thomas M Cooley Law School Libraries, 300 S Capitol Ave, Lansing, MI, 48901. Tel: 517-371-5140, Ext 3309. Fax: 517-334-5715, 517-334-5717. p. 1202

Van Riddle, Martha, Librn, Malden Public Library, Linden Branch, Oliver & Clapp Sts, Malden, MA, 02148. Tel: 781-397-7067. p. 1102

Van Rij, Karen, Mgr, Knox County Public Library System, Karns Branch, 7516 Oak Ridge Hwy, Knoxville, TN, 37931-3333. Tel: 865-470-8663. Fax: 865-693-7858. p. 2242

Van Rossem, Karen, Info Serv, Ref Librn, Scholastic Inc Library, 557 Broadway, New York, NY, 10012. Tel: 212-343-6171. Fax: 212-389-3317. p. 1699

Van Sickle, Adam, Patron Serv Mgr, Teton County Library, 125 Virginian Lane, Jackson, WY, 83001. Tel: 307-733-2164, Ext 257. Fax: 307-733-4568. p. 2656

Van Sickle, Elaine, Asst Librn, Knoxville Public Library, 112 E Main St, Knoxville, PA, 16928. Tel: 814-326-4448. Fax: 814-326-4448. p. 2075

van Sickle, Jennifer, Ser, Trinity College Library, 300 Summit St, Hartford, CT, 06106. Tel: 860-297-2250. Fax: 860-297-2251. p. 347

Van Sickle, Mary, Tech Serv & Automation, Crystal Lake Public Library, 126 Paddock St, Crystal Lake, IL, 60014. Tel: 815-459-1687. Fax: 815-459-9581. p. 632

Van Skaik, Patricia, Mgr, Public Library of Cincinnati & Hamilton County, Genealogy & Local History, South Bldg, 3rd Flr, 800 Vine St, Cincinnati, OH, 45202-2009. Tel: 513-369-6905. Fax: 513-369-3123. p. 1872

Van Soest, Bertha, Br Mgr, Wellington County Library, Drayton Branch, 24 Wood St, Drayton, ON, N0G 1P0, CANADA. Tel: 519-638-3788. p. 2805

Van Stempvoort, Mary Ellen, Libr Dir, Patmos Library, 2445 Riley St, Jamestown, MI, 49427. Tel: 616-896-9798. Fax: 616-896-7645. p. 1196

Van Swol, Constance, Ch, Chicago Ridge Public Library, 10400 S Oxford Ave, Chicago Ridge, IL, 60415. Tel: 708-423-7753. Fax: 708-423-2758. p. 628

Van Tuyl, Elizabeth, Hist Coll Librn, Bridgeport Public Library, 925 Broad St, Bridgeport, CT, 06604. Tel: 203-576-7403. Fax: 203-576-8255. p. 331

Van Ullen, Mary, Assoc Dir, Coll Develop, University at Albany, State University of New York, 1400 Washington Ave, Albany, NY, 12222-0001. Tel: 518-442-3559. Fax: 518-442-3088. p. 1570

Van Vactor, Myra, Dean, Bellevue College, 3000 Landerholm Circle SE, Bellevue, WA, 98007-6484. Tel: 425-564-2252. Fax: 425-564-6186. p. 2508

Van Velzen, Lina, Br Mgr, Mississauga Library System, Courtneypark, 730 Courtneypark Dr W, Mississauga, ON, L5W 1L9, CANADA. Tel: 905-615-4745. p. 2823

Van Volkingburg, Heather, Res & Instruction Librn, Barnard College, 3009 Broadway, New York, NY, 10027-6598. Tel: 212-851-9692. p. 1670

Van Vranken, JoAnn, Reader Serv, New York State Historical Association, 5798 State Hwy 80, Cooperstown, NY, 13326. Tel: 607-547-1470. Fax: 607-547-1405. p. 1610

Van Weelden, Katherine, Dir, New England College, 28 Bridge St, Henniker, NH, 03242-3298. Tel: 603-428-2344. Fax: 603-428-4273. p. 1451

Van Wingen, June L, Librn, United States Department of Justice, 330 Ionia, Ste 501, Grand Rapids, MI, 49503. Tel: 616-456-2404, Ext 2050. Fax: 616-456-2408. p. 1186

Van Winkle, Amanda, Ch, Franklin County Public Library District, 919 Main St, Brookville, IN, 47012-1498. Tel: 765-647-4031. Fax: 765-647-0278. p. 730

Van Winkle, Ed, Libr Mgr, Maricopa County Jail Library, 3150 W Lower Buckeye Rd, Phoenix, AZ, 85009. Tel: 602-876-5633, 602-876-5638. Fax: 602-353-1546. p. 74

Van Winkle, Joan, In Charge, First United Methodist Church, Laura Knight Children's Library, 419 NE First St, Gainesville, FL, 32601. Tel: 352-372-8523. Fax: 352-372-2524. p. 449

Van Zandt, Patricia, Dean, East Tennessee State University, Sherrod Library, Seehorn Dr & Lake St, Johnson City, TN, 37614-0204. Tel: 423-439-4337. Fax: 423-439-5222. p. 2239

Van Zandt, Patricia, Dir, Scholarly Resources & Res Serv, Southern Methodist University, Central University Libraries, 6414 Robert S Hyer Lane, Dallas, TX, 75275. Tel: 214-768-4960. Fax: 214-768-3815. p. 2310

Van Zandt, Patricia, Dir, Scholarly Resources & Res Serv, Southern Methodist University, Fondren Library, 6414 Robert S Hyer Lane, Dallas, TX, 75275. Tel: 214-768-4960. Fax: 214-768-3815. p. 2310

van Zanten, Denise, Dir, Manchester City Library, 405 Pine St, Manchester, NH, 03104-6199. Tel: 603-624-6550. Fax: 603-624-6559. p. 1455

VanAntwerp, Deb, Ch, Pittsfield Public Library, 205 N Memorial, Pittsfield, IL, 62363-1406. Tel: 217-285-2200. Fax: 217-285-9423. p. 691

VanAntwerp, Thomas, Librn Spec F/C, Florida Department of Corrections, 2739 Gall Blvd, Zephyrhills, FL, 33541. Tel: 813-782-5221, Ext 439. Fax: 813-780-0123. p. 505

VanBibber, Dawn, Adult Coll Develop Librn, Kokomo-Howard County Public Library, 220 N Union St, Kokomo, IN, 46901-4614. Tel: 765-457-3242. Fax: 765-457-3683. p. 758

Vancavage, Susan, Head, Acq, North Canton Public Library, 185 N Main St, North Canton, OH, 44720-2595. Tel: 330-499-4712. Fax: 330-499-7356. p. 1923

Vance, Brian, IT Serv Mgr, Oklahoma Water Resources Board Library, 3800 N Classen Blvd, Oklahoma City, OK, 73118. Tel: 405-530-8800. Fax: 405-530-8900. p. 1975

Vance, Candace, Head, Lending Serv, University of Mississippi Medical Center, 2500 N State St, Jackson, MS, 39216-4505. Tel: 601-984-1234. Fax: 601-984-1251. p. 1305

Vance, Carole, Dir, Paoli Public Library, Ten E Court, Paoli, IN, 47454. Tel: 812-723-3841. Fax: 812-723-3841. p. 772

Vance, Carolyn J, Head Librn, News-Gazette Library, 15 Main St, Champaign, IL, 61820. Tel: 217-351-5228. Fax: 217-351-5374. p. 603

Vance, Dorothy, Pub Relations Coordr, Central Mississippi Regional Library System, 104 Office Park Dr, Brandon, MS, 39042-2404. Tel: 601-825-0100. Fax: 601-825-0199. p. 1294

Vance, Jackson Q, Clarkston Ctr Libr Coordr, Walla Walla Community College Library, 500 Tausick Way, Walla Walla, WA, 99362-9267. Tel: 509-758-1714. Fax: 509-527-4480. p. 2547

Vance, Janet, Commun Serv Supvr, Richardson Public Library, 900 Civic Center Dr, Richardson, TX, 75080. Tel: 972-744-4376. Fax: 972-744-5806. p. 2374

Vance, Karen, Asst Librn, Indian River Area Library, 3546 S Straits Hwy, Indian River, MI, 49749. Tel: 231-238-8581. Fax: 231-238-9494. p. 1193

Vance, Kathryn A, Dir, Libr Serv, Miller, Johnson, Snell & Cummiskey, 250 Monroe NW, Ste 800, Grand Rapids, MI, 49503-2250. Tel: 616-831-1875. Fax: 616-988-1875. p. 1185

Vance, Kendall, ILL, Waubonsee Community College, State Rte 47 at Waubonsee Dr, Sugar Grove, IL, 60554. Tel: 630-466-2333. Fax: 630-466-7799. p. 708

Vance, Mona, Archivist, Columbus-Lowndes Public Library, 314 N Seventh St, Columbus, MS, 39701. Tel: 662-329-5300. Fax: 662-329-5158. p. 1297

Vance, Patrice, Dir, Eckels Memorial Library, 207 S Hwy, Oakland, IA, 51560. Tel: 712-482-6668. Fax: 712-482-6668. p. 836

Vance, Robin-Lee, Prog Coordr, Rotary Club of Slave Lake Public Library, 101 Main St SE, Slave Lake, AB, T0G 2A0, CANADA. Tel: 780-849-5250. Fax: 780-849-3275. p. 2716

Vancil, David, Dr, Dept Chair, Spec Coll, Indiana State University, 510 North 6 1/2 St, Terre Haute, IN, 47809. Tel: 812-237-2611. Fax: 812-237-3376. p. 781

Vancil, Marie, Tech Serv, Milton-Freewater Public Library, Eight SW Eighth Ave, Milton-Freewater, OR, 97862-1501. Tel: 541-938-8247. Fax: 541-938-8254. p. 2006

VanCourt, Janis, Coordr, Ref (Info Serv), Utica College, 1600 Burrstone Rd, Utica, NY, 13502-4892. Tel: 315-792-3351. Fax: 315-792-3361. p. 1759

VandaLinda, Ellen, Ch, Everett Public Libraries, 410 Broadway, Everett, MA, 02149. Tel: 617-394-2305. Fax: 617-389-1230. p. 1087

VanDam, Gretchen, Circuit Librn, William J Campbell Library of the US Courts, 219 S Dearborn St, Rm 1637, Chicago, IL, 60604-1769. Tel: 312-435-5660. Fax: 312-408-5031. p. 607

Vande Vusse, Bob, Interim Dir, Fennville District Library, 400 W Main St, Fennville, MI, 49408. Tel: 269-561-5050. Fax: 269-561-5251. p. 1178

VandeBurgt, Melissa Minds, Digital Serv Librn, Florida Gulf Coast University Library, 10501 FGCU Blvd S, Fort Myers, FL, 33965-6501. Tel: 239-590-7658. p. 445

VandeCreek, Leanne, Bibliographer, Northern Illinois University Libraries, DeKalb, IL, 60115-2868. Tel: 815-753-4025. p. 635

VandeLinde, Dotte, Coordr, Sedona Public Library, 3250 White Bear Rd, Sedona, AZ, 86336. Tel: 928-282-7714. Fax: 928-282-5789. p. 81

Vanden Heuvel, Eric, Archivist, Waukesha County Historical Society & Museum, 101 W Main St, Waukesha, WI, 53186. Tel: 262-521-2859. Fax: 262-521-2865. p. 2645

Vandenberg, Beth, Ch, Rock Valley Public Library, 1531 Main St, Rock Valley, IA, 51247-1127. Tel: 712-476-5651. Fax: 712-476-5261. p. 841

Vandenberg, John, Libr Tech, Truckee Meadows Community College, Meadowood Library, 5270 Neil Rd, Reno, NV, 89502. Tel: 775-824-3816. Fax: 775-824-3806. p. 1433

Vandenberg, Victoria, Circ, Oshkosh Public Library, 106 Washington Ave, Oshkosh, WI, 54901-4985. Tel: 920-236-5201, 920-236-5205. Fax: 920-236-5228. p. 2628

Vandenbogaard, Anne, Supvr, Middlesex County Library, Ailsa Craig Branch, 147 Main St, Ailsa Craig, ON, N0M 1A0, CANADA. Tel: 519-293-3441. Fax: 519-293-9319. p. 2845

VanDenBosch, Glenda, Dir, Howe Memorial Library, 128 E Saginaw St, Breckenridge, MI, 48615. Tel: 989-842-3202. Fax: 989-842-3202. p. 1159

Vandenburg, Michael, Assoc Univ Librn, Queen's University, 101 Union St, Kingston, ON, K7L 5C4, CANADA. Tel: 613-533-6000, Ext 74536. Fax: 613-533-6362. p. 2814

Vander Esch, Marge, Ch, Hull Public Library, 1408 Main St, Hull, IA, 51239. Tel: 712-439-1321. Fax: 712-439-1534. p. 821

Vander Heide, Erna, Asst Librn, Houston Public Library, 3150 14th St, Houston, BC, V0J 1Z0, CANADA. Tel: 250-845-2256. Fax: 250-845-2088. p. 2729

Vander Pyl, Jeanie M, Dir, Cape Cod Hospital, 27 Park St, Hyannis, MA, 02601-5230. Tel: 508-862-5866. Fax: 774-552-6904. p. 1096

Vanderbosch, Donna, Ser, Athenaeum of Ohio, 6616 Beechmont Ave, Cincinnati, OH, 45230-2091. Tel: 513-231-2223, Ext 134. Fax: 513-231-3254. p. 1868

Vandergrift, Kay, Prof, Rutgers, The State University of New Jersey, Four Huntington St, New Brunswick, NJ, 08901-1071. Tel: 732-932-7500, Ext 8955. Fax: 732-932-2644. p. 2969

Vanderhaak, Rosie, Br Mgr, Riverside County Library System, Temecula Public Library, 30600 Pauba Rd, Temecula, CA, 92592. Tel: 951-693-8900. Fax: 951-693-8998. p. 218

VanderHeijden, Michael, Ref, Yale University Library, Lillian Goldman Library Yale Law School, 127 Wall St, New Haven, CT, 06511. Tel: 203-432-1600. Fax: 203-432-2112. p. 358

Vanderhoef, Richard, Syst Librn, Hellenic College-Holy Cross Greek Orthodox School of Theology, 50 Goddard Ave, Brookline, MA, 02445-7496. Tel: 617-850-1245. Fax: 617-850-1470. p. 1071

Vanderhooft, Eloise G, Head, Tech Serv, Salt Lake Community College Libraries, 4600 S Redwood Rd, Salt Lake City, UT, 84123-3197. Tel: 801-957-4588. Fax: 801-957-4414. p. 2413

Vanderhorst, Sheila, Asst Dir, Ch, Jaffrey Public Library, 38 Main St, Jaffrey, NH, 03452-1196. Tel: 603-532-7301. Fax: 603-532-7301. p. 1452

VanderHye, Colleen, Outreach Librn, Matteson Public Library, 801 S School St, Matteson, IL, 60443-1897. Tel: 708-748-4431. Fax: 708-748-0510. p. 671

Vanderkooi, Joanne, Ch, YA Serv, King County Library System, 960 Newport Way NW, Issaquah, WA, 98027. Tel: 425-369-3320. Fax: 425-369-3255. p. 2516

Vanderkooy, Mary, Librn, Herrick District Library, 300 S River Ave, Holland, MI, 49423-3290. Tel: 616-355-3100. p. 1190

Vanderlaan, Robert J, Cataloger/Ref Librn, Muskegon Community College, 221 S Quarterline Rd, Muskegon, MI, 49442. Tel: 231-777-0267. Fax: 231-777-0279. p. 1213

Vanderlin, Scott, Res/Fac Serv Librn, Illinois Institute of Technology, Chicago-Kent College of Law Library, 565 W Adams St, Chicago, IL, 60661. Tel: 312-906-5600. Fax: 312-906-5679. p. 615

Vanderloh, Shannon, Mgr, Duchess & District Public Library, 256A Louise Ave, Box 88, Duchess, AB, T0J 0Z0, CANADA. Tel: 403-378-4369. Fax: 403-378-4369. p. 2697

Vanderloo, Tom, Digital Serv Librn, US Court of Appeals for the Sixth Circuit Library, 312 Potter Stewart US Courthouse, Cincinnati, OH, 45202. Tel: 513-564-7321. Fax: 513-564-7329. p. 1873

Vandermeer, Philip, Head of Libr, University of North Carolina at Chapel Hill, Music, 300 Wilson Library, Campus Box 3906, Chapel Hill, NC, 27514-8890. Tel: 919-966-1113. Fax: 919-843-0418. p. 1781

VanderPloeg, Sondra, Cat, Ref Librn, Colby-Sawyer College, 541 Main St, New London, NH, 03257-4648. Tel: 603-526-3375. Fax: 603-526-3777. p. 1459

VanderPol, Diane, Govt Doc, Calvin College & Calvin Theological Seminary, 1855 Knollcrest Circle SE, Grand Rapids, MI, 49546-4402. Tel: 616-526-7072. Fax: 616-526-6470. p. 1184

VanderPol, Diane, Dir, Westminster College, 1840 S 1300 East, Salt Lake City, UT, 84105-3697. Tel: 801-832-2250. Fax: 801-832-3109. p. 2415

Vanderpool, Sarah, ILL, Tech Serv, Whatcom Community College Library, 237 W Kellogg Rd, Bellingham, WA, 98226. Tel: 360-383-3300. p. 2509

Vanderree, Cara, Dir, Ashland City Library, 604 Main St, Ashland, KS, 67831. Tel: 620-635-2589. Fax: 620-635-2931. p. 856

Vandersteen, Beth, Dir, West Baton Rouge Parish Library, 830 N Alexander Ave, Port Allen, LA, 70767-2327. Tel: 225-342-7920. Fax: 225-342-7918. p. 966

Vandertorn, Vicki, Dir, Simi Valley Hospital & Health Cares Services, 2975 N Sycamore Dr, Simi Valley, CA, 93065. Tel: 805-955-6900. Fax: 805-955-6063. p. 269

Vanderveen, Janet, Coordr, Br Serv, Clarington Public Library, Courtice Branch, 2950 Courtice Rd, Courtice, ON, L1E 2H8, CANADA. Tel: 905-404-0707. p. 2796

Vandervest, Gail Ann, Ch, Jefferson County Public Library, 375 S Water St, Monticello, FL, 32344. Tel: 850-342-0205. Fax: 850-342-0207. p. 470

Vandervorst, Kathleen, Ref & Teen Serv, Bismarck Veterans Memorial Public Library, 515 N Fifth St, Bismarck, ND, 58503-4081. Tel: 701-355-1480. Fax: 701-221-3729. p. 1837

VanderWagen, Sheryl, Syst Coordr, Lakeland Library Cooperative, 4138 Three Mile Rd NW, Grand Rapids, MI, 49534-1134. Tel: 616-559-5253. Fax: 616-559-4329. p. 2946

Vanderwall, Susan, Bus Mgr, Rochester Regional Library Council, 390 Packetts Landing, Fairport, NY, 14450. Tel: 585-223-7570. Fax: 585-223-7712. p. 2950

VanderWerff, Dennis I, Dr, Dir, Cerro Coso Community College Library, 3000 College Heights Blvd, Ridgecrest, CA, 93555-9571. Tel: 760-384-6132. Fax: 760-384-6139. p. 216

Vanderwiel, Paul, Dir, Human Res, Carnegie Library of Pittsburgh, 4400 Forbes Ave, Pittsburgh, PA, 15213-4080. Tel: 412-622-5781. Fax: 412-622-6278. p. 2122

Vanderzande, Jane, Br Mgr, Lennox & Addington County Public Library, Amherstview Branch, 322 Amherst Dr, Amherstview, ON, K7N 1S9, CANADA. Tel: 613-389-6006. Fax: 613-389-0077. p. 2824

Vandeveer, Karen, Adult Serv, Warren County Public Library District, 62 Public Sq, Monmouth, IL, 61462. Tel: 309-734-3166. Fax: 309-734-5955. p. 675

Vandivort, MaryAnne, Br Mgr, Norfolk Public Library, Horace C Downing Branch, 555 E Liberty St, Norfolk, VA, 23523. Tel: 757-441-1968. Fax: 757-441-1994. p. 2481

VanDoran, Chris, Pub Serv Mgr, Martin Methodist College, 433 W Madison St, Pulaski, TN, 38478-2799. Tel: 931-363-9844. Fax: 931-363-9844. p. 2264

VanDoren, Wayne, Supvr, Mountain View Youth Correctional Facility Library, 31 Petticoat Lane, Annandale, NJ, 08801-4097. Tel: 908-638-6191, Ext 7316. Fax: 908-638-6143. p. 1469

VanDoren, Wayne, Supvr, Mountain View Youth Correctional Facility Library, Minimum Unit, 31 Petticoat Lane, Annandale, NJ, 08801-4097. Tel: 908-638-6191, Ext 7384. p. 1469

VanDusen, Sandy, Librn, Sterling Public Library, 420 N Fifth St, Sterling, CO, 80751-3363. Tel: 970-522-2023. Fax: 970-522-2657. p. 323

VanDyk, Margaret, Librn, Santa Fe University of Art & Design, 1600 St Michael's Dr, Santa Fe, NM, 87505-7634. Tel: 505-473-6569. Fax: 505-473-6593. p. 1564

Vanek, Elissia, Librn, Township Library of Silver Creek, 309 Vine St, Silver Creek, NE, 68663. Tel: 308-773-2594. p. 1419

VanEtt, Sharon, Interim Dir, Ionia Community Library, 126 E Main St, Ionia, MI, 48846. Tel: 616-527-3680. Fax: 616-527-6210. p. 1193

VanFelton, Joan, Tech Serv Mgr, Pike County Public Library, 201 Broad St, Milford, PA, 18337-1398. Tel: 570-296-8211. Fax: 570-296-8987. p. 2090

VanFleet, Heather, Ad, Romeo District Library, 65821 Van Dyke, Washington, MI, 48095. Tel: 586-752-0603. Fax: 586-752-8416. p. 1235

VanFossen, Evelyn, Asst Librn, Potterville Benton Township District Library, 150 Library Lane, Potterville, MI, 48876. Tel: 517-645-2989. Fax: 517-645-0268. p. 1220

VanGilder, Catherine, Dir, Columbus Public Library, 205 N Kansas, Columbus, KS, 66725-1221. Tel: 620-429-2086. Fax: 620-429-1950. p. 862

VanGorden, Janice, Librn, Pennsylvania School for the Deaf Library, 100 W School House Lane, Philadelphia, PA, 19144. Tel: 215-951-4743. Fax: 215-951-4708. p. 2114

VanGundy, Amelia C, Cat Librn, University of Virginia's College at Wise, One College Ave, Wise, VA, 24293. Tel: 276-328-0154. Fax: 276-328-0105. p. 2504

VanHess, Regina, Adult Serv, Anacortes Public Library, 1220 Tenth St, Anacortes, WA, 98221-1922. Tel: 360-293-1910, Ext 24. Fax: 360-293-1929. p. 2507

VanHorn, Adrienne, Asst Librn, Marion Public Library, 4036 Maple Ave, Marion, NY, 14505. Tel: 315-926-4933. Fax: 315-926-7038. p. 1658

VanHorsen, Jackie, Ch, Nobles County Library, 407 12th St, Worthington, MN, 56187. Tel: 507-372-2981. Fax: 507-372-2982. p. 1291

VanHouten, Michael, Co-Dir, Albion College, 602 E Cass St, Albion, MI, 49224-1879. Tel: 517-629-0293. Fax: 517-629-0504. p. 1148

VanKessel, Karla, Libr Mgr, London Health Sciences Centre Library Services, 800 Commissioners Rd E, London, ON, N6A 4G5, CANADA. Tel: 519-685-8500, Ext 75934. Fax: 519-667-6641. p. 2817

Vanlaanen, Sue, Communications Dir, Fort Vancouver Regional Library District, 1007 E Mill Plain Blvd, Vancouver, WA, 98663. Tel: 360-699-8815. Fax: 360-693-2681. p. 2546

VanMarter, Dianne Helene, Dir, Libr Serv, Ecumenical Theological Seminary, 2930 Woodward Ave, Detroit, MI, 48201. Tel: 313-831-5200, Ext 222. Fax: 313-831-1353. p. 1171

VanNess, Carolyn, Coll Develop, Librn, Rochester Civic Garden Center, Inc Library, Five Castle Park, Rochester, NY, 14620. Tel: 716-473-5130. Fax: 716-473-8136. p. 1731

Vanness, Kaye, Dir, Alexander Public Library, 409 Harriman St, Alexander, IA, 50420. Tel: 641-692-3238. Fax: 641-692-3238. p. 792

Vanni, Robert J, VPres, Gen Counsel & Secy of the Corp, The New York Public Library - Astor, Lenox & Tilden Foundations, 476 Fifth Ave, (@ 42nd St), New York, NY, 10018-2788. Tel: 212-930-0744. Fax: 212-592-7440. p. 1690

Vannoy, Julie, ILL, Fort Morgan Public Library, 414 Main St, Fort Morgan, CO, 80701. Tel: 970-542-4000. Fax: 970-542-4013. p. 308

Vano, Jennie, Librn, Bates Technical College Library, 2201 S 78th St, E201, Tacoma, WA, 98409-9000. Tel: 253-680-7543. Fax: 253-680-7551. p. 2538

Vanola, Tiziano, Br Head, Toronto Public Library, Yorkville, 22 Yorkville Ave, Toronto, ON, M4W 1L4, CANADA. Tel: 416-393-7660. Fax: 416-393-7725. p. 2864

vanOosten, Roger, Instruction & Outreach, Ref, Moody Bible Institute, 820 N La Salle Blvd, Chicago, IL, 60610-3284. Tel: 312-329-4136. Fax: 312-329-8959. p. 619

VanOrsdel, Lee, Dean, Univ Libr, Grand Valley State University Libraries, One Campus Dr, Allendale, MI, 49401-9403. Tel: 616-331-2621. p. 1149

VanOstran, Sue, Librn, Witt Memorial Public Library, 18 N Second St, Witt, IL, 62094. Tel: 217-594-7333. Fax: 217-594-7333. p. 720

Vanotta, Judith, Librn, Murtha Cullina LLP Library, City Pl, Hartford, CT, 06103. Tel: 860-240-6092. Fax: 860-240-6150. p. 347

Vanover, Mary, Librn, Clayton City Library, HC 1, Box 76, Clayton, KS, 67629. p. 861

VanScoyoc, Lilas, Librn, Evart Public Library, 104 N Main St, Evart, MI, 49631. Tel: 231-734-5542. Fax: 231-734-5542. p. 1177

Vansteen, John, Assoc Librn, Dir, Info Literacy, Five Towns College Library, 305 N Service Rd, Dix Hills, NY, 11746. Tel: 631-656-2144. Fax: 631-656-2171. p. 1614

VanStempvoort, Mary Ellen, Adjunct Ref Librn, Muskegon Community College, 221 S Quarterline Rd, Muskegon, MI, 49442. Tel: 231-777-0268. Fax: 231-777-0279. p. 1213

Vanstone, Catherine, Asst Dir, Tech, Training & Develop, Southwest Georgia Regional Library, 301 S Monroe St, Bainbridge, GA, 39819. Tel: 229-248-2665. Fax: 229-248-2670. p. 521

VanSwol, Mary, Admin Serv Coordr, Park Forest Public Library, 400 Lakewood Blvd, Park Forest, IL, 60466. Tel: 708-748-3731. Fax: 708-748-8127. p. 688

Vant Sant, Susanna, Librn, Tompkins Cortland Community College, 170 North St, Dryden, NY, 13053-8504. Tel: 607-844-8222. Fax: 607-844-6540. p. 1615

Vanterpool, Karen, Electronic Res, SUNY Westchester Community College, 75 Grasslands Rd, Valhalla, NY, 10595-1693. Tel: 914-785-8536. Fax: 914-785-6513. p. 1760

Vantine, Meg, Dir, Slater Library, 26 Main St, Jewett City, CT, 06351. Tel: 860-376-0024. Fax: 860-376-0024. p. 348

Vantran, Anne, Ch, East Bridgewater Public Library, 32 Union St, East Bridgewater, MA, 02333-1598. Tel: 508-378-1616. Fax: 508-378-1617. p. 1085

Vantrease, Sarah, Br Librn, Butte County Library, Chico Branch, 1108 Sherman Ave, Chico, CA, 95926-3575. Tel: 530-891-2762. Fax: 530-891-2978. p. 202

VanValkenburg, Trevor, Librn, Lenawee County Library, 4459 W US Rte 223, Adrian, MI, 49221-1294. Tel: 517-263-1011. Fax: 517-263-7109. p. 1147

VanVickle, Kathleen, Tech Serv Supvr, College of Lake County, 19351 W Washington St, Grayslake, IL, 60030. Tel: 847-543-2893. Fax: 847-223-7690. p. 652

VanWaardhuizen, Lauren, Cat Librn, University of Kansas Libraries, Wheat Law Library, Green Hall, Rm 200, 1535 W 15th St, Lawrence, KS, 66045-7608. Tel: 785-864-3025. Fax: 785-864-3680. p. 878

VanWaart, Ellen, Dir, Iowa Western Community College, 2700 College Rd, Council Bluffs, IA, 51503-7057. Tel: 712-325-3247. Fax: 712-325-3244. p. 805

VanWeelden, Beth, Librn, Public Library of Steubenville & Jefferson County, Toronto Branch, 607 Daniels St, Toronto, OH, 43964. Tel: 740-537-1262. Fax: 740-537-5447. p. 1937

Vanzant-Salyer, Michelle, Librn, Highland County Law Library, Courthouse, High & Main Sts, Hillsboro, OH, 45133. Tel: 937-393-4863. Fax: 937-393-6878. p. 1904

Vanzetti, Dakshina, Librn, Sri Aurobindo Sadhana Peetham Library, 2621 W Hwy 12, Lodi, CA, 95242. Tel: 209-339-1342, 209-339-3710. Fax: 209-339-3715. p. 165

Varady, Kathy, Circ, Lyme Public Library, 482 Hamburg Rd, Lyme, CT, 06371-3110. Tel: 860-434-2272. Fax: 860-434-9972. p. 349

Vardaman, Lisa, Ref Serv, Troy University Library, 309 Wallace Hall, 501 University Ave, Troy, AL, 36082. Tel: 334-670-3262. Fax: 334-670-3694. p. 37

Varee, Telce, Librn, Linesville Community Public Library, 111 Penn St, Linesville, PA, 16424. Tel: 814-683-4354. Fax: 814-683-4354. p. 2082

Vargas, Gwen, Dir of Libr Serv, K&L Gates Library, The K&L Gates Ctr, 210 Sixth Ave, Pittsburgh, PA, 15222. Tel: 412-355-6718. Fax: 412-355-6501. p. 2126

Vargas, Jenny, Instrul Serv Librn, Scottsdale Community College Library, 9000 E Chaparral Rd, Scottsdale, AZ, 85256. Tel: 480-423-6654. Fax: 480-423-6666. p. 80

Vargas, Luz E, Dir, Sunland Park Community Library, 984 McNutt Rd, Sunland Park, NM, 88063-9039. Tel: 505-874-0873. Fax: 505-589-1222. p. 1565

Vargas, Magda, Acq, Pontifical Catholic University Of Puerto Rico, Encarnacion Valdes Library, 2250 Avenida Las Americas, Ste 509, Ponce, PR, 00717-0777. Tel: 787-841-2000, Ext 1816. Fax: 787-284-0235. p. 2674

Vargas, Mark, Dir, Saint Xavier University, 3700 W 103rd St, Chicago, IL, 60655-3105. Tel: 773-298-3350. Fax: 773-779-5231. p. 623

Vargas, Mark, Pres, LIBRAS, Inc, North Park University, 3225 W Foster Ave, Chicago, IL, 60625-4895. Tel: 773-298-3350. Fax: 773-244-4891. p. 2942

Vargas, Monse, Commun Libr Supvr, Yakima Valley Libraries, Southeast Yakima Library, 1211 S Seventh St, Yakima, WA, 98901. Tel: 509-576-0723. Fax: 509-576-0723. p. 2551

Vargas, Oscar, Head, Circ, Somerville Library, 35 West End Ave, Somerville, NJ, 08876. Tel: 908-725-1336. Fax: 908-231-0608. p. 1530

Vargas Robinson, Jessica, Circ, Todd Wehr Library, St Norbert College, 301 Third St, De Pere, WI, 54115. Tel: 920-403-3280. Fax: 920-403-4064. p. 2587

Vargha, Rebecca, Librn, University of North Carolina at Chapel Hill, Information & Library Science, 114 Manning Hall, CB No 3360, Chapel Hill, NC, 27599. Tel: 919-962-8361. Fax: 919-962-8071. p. 1781

Vargha, Rebecca, Univ Librn, University of North Carolina at Chapel Hill, CB No 3360, 100 Manning Hall, Chapel Hill, NC, 27599-3360. Tel: 919-962-8366. Fax: 919-962-8071. p. 2971

Vargo, Jackie, Syst Coordr, Hialeah-John F Kennedy Library, 190 W 49th St, Hialeah, FL, 33012-3798. Tel: 305-821-2700. Fax: 305-818-9144. p. 450

Vargo, Vicki, Exec Dir, Braddock Carnegie Library, 419 Library St, Braddock, PA, 15104-1609. Tel: 412-351-5356. Fax: 412-351-6810. p. 2037

Varick, Vicki, Dir, Aaron Cutler Memorial Library, 269 Charles Bancroft Hwy, Litchfield, NH, 03052. Tel: 603-424-4044. Fax: 603-424-4044. p. 1454

Varipapa, Carol, ILL, Eastern Monroe Public Library, 1002 N Ninth St, Stroudsburg, PA, 18360. Tel: 570-421-0800. Fax: 570-421-0212. p. 2143

Varland, Janet, Br Mgr, Lewis & Clark Library, Augusta Branch, 205 Main St, Augusta, MT, 59410. Tel: 406-362-4300. Fax: 406-562-3358. p. 1382

Varlejs, Jana, Assoc Prof, Rutgers, The State University of New Jersey, Four Huntington St, New Brunswick, NJ, 08901-1071. Tel: 732-932-7500, Ext 8955. Fax: 732-932-2644. p. 2969

Varley, Elaine, Curator, Dighton Historical Society Museum Library, 1217 Williams St, Dighton, MA, 02715-1013. Tel: 508-669-5514. p. 1084

Varley, Holly, Coll Develop, Public Library of Cincinnati & Hamilton County, 800 Vine St, Cincinnati, OH, 45202-2009. Tel: 513-369-6952. Fax: 513-369-6993. p. 1871

Varley, Rita, Head Librn, Philadelphia Yearly Meeting of the Religious Society of Friends, 1515 Cherry St, Philadelphia, PA, 19102. Tel: 215-241-7219. Fax: 215-567-2096. p. 2115

Varnado, Constance P, Asst Dean, Delgado Community College, Bldg 10, Rm 116, 615 City Park Ave, New Orleans, LA, 70119. Tel: 504-671-5332. p. 959

Varnado, Denise, In Charge, San Bernardino County Sun Library, 2239 Gannett Pkwy, San Bernardino, CA, 92407. Tel: 909-889-9666, Ext 3843. Fax: 909-885-8741. p. 229

Varnavas, Anna, Librn, American Council of Life Insurers Library, 101 Constitution Ave NW, Washington, DC, 20001. Tel: 202-624-2000. Fax: 202-624-2319. p. 392

Varner, Douglas, Sr Assoc Dir/Biomedical Informationist, Georgetown University, Dahlgren Memorial Library, Preclinical Science Bldg GM-7, 3900 Reservoir Rd NW, Washington, DC, 20007. Tel: 202-687-1328. Fax: 202-687-1862. p. 402

Varner, Elizabeth, Asst Librn, Boswell & Grant Township Public Library, 101 E Main St, Boswell, IN, 47921. Tel: 765-869-5428. Fax: 765-869-5428. p. 729

Varner, Karen, Dir, Lamb County Library, 110 E Sixth St, Littlefield, TX, 79339. Tel: 806-385-5223. Fax: 806-385-0030. p. 2356

Varnet, Eleanor, ILL, Enfield Public Library, 104 Middle Rd, Enfield, CT, 06082. Tel: 860-763-7510. Fax: 860-763-7514. p. 338

Varnet, Michael, Chief, Financial & Bus Officer, Pikes Peak Library District, 20 N Cascade Ave, Colorado Springs, CO, 80903. Tel: 719-531-6333. p. 296

Varney, Ann, Dir, Zadoc Long Free Library, Five Turner St, Rte 117, Buckfield, ME, 04220. Tel: 207-336-2171. p. 980

Varney, Vicki, Librn, Turner Public Library, 98 Matthews Way, Turner, ME, 04282-3930. Tel: 207-225-2030. p. 1004

Varno, Edward, Dir, Ontario County Historical Society Library, 55 N Main St, Canandaigua, NY, 14424. Tel: 585-394-4975. Fax: 585-394-9351. p. 1601

Varscsak, Susan, Transitions Coordr, Maricopa County Library District, 2700 N Central Ave, Ste 700, Phoenix, AZ, 85004. Tel: 602-651-2016. Fax: 602-652-3071. p. 74

Varvarikos, Maria, Head Librn, Lower Canada College Library, 4090 Royal Ave, Montreal, QC, H4A 2M5, CANADA. Tel: 514-482-9916. Fax: 514-482-0195. p. 2897

Vasconi, Jeffrey, Ch, Gold Coast Public Library, 50 Railroad Ave, Glen Head, NY, 11545. Tel: 516-759-8300. Fax: 516-759-8308. p. 1628

Vasconi, Linda, Pub Relations, North Merrick Public Library, 1691 Meadowbrook Rd, North Merrick, NY, 11566. Tel: 516-378-7474. Fax: 516-378-0876. p. 1706

Vaselaar, Meredith, Librn, Nobles County Library, Adrian Branch, 214 Maine Ave, Adrian, MN, 56110-1056. Tel: 507-483-2541. Fax: 507-483-2541. p. 1291

Vash, Kerry, Online Librn, Saint Leo University, 33701 State Rd 52, Saint Leo, FL, 33574. Tel: 352-588-8267. Fax: 352-588-8484. p. 487

Vasil, Nick, Asst Mgr, Tech Serv, Ivy Tech State Community College-Northwest, 1440 E 35th Ave, Gary, IN, 46409-1499. Tel: 219-981-4410. Fax: 219-981-4415. p. 745

Vasilik, Kate, YA Serv, Franklin Lakes Free Public Library, 470 DeKorte Dr, Franklin Lakes, NJ, 07417. Tel: 201-891-2224. Fax: 201-891-5102. p. 1487

Vasilik, Patricia, Principal Librn, Clifton Public Library, 292 Piaget Ave, Clifton, NJ, 07011. Tel: 973-772-5500. p. 1479

Vasinda, Kathleen Ann, Dir, Runnemede Free Public Library, Broadway & Black Horse Pike, Runnemede, NJ, 08078. Tel: 856-939-4688. Fax: 856-939-6371. p. 1528

Vaska, Marcus, Librn, Tom Baker Cancer Ctr Knowledge Ctr, Holy Cross Site, University of Calgary Library, Health Sciences Library, Health Sci Ctr, 3330 Hospital Dr NW, Calgary, AB, T2N 4N1, CANADA. Tel: 403-698-8016. Fax: 403-210-9847. p. 2693

Vasquez, Alison, Dir, United States Air Force, Edwards Air Force Base Library, Five W Yeager Blvd, Edwards AFB, CA, 93524-1295. Tel: 661-275-2665. Fax: 661-277-6100. p. 145

Vasquez, Barbara J, Chair, Los Angeles City College Library, 855 N Vermont Ave, Los Angeles, CA, 90029. Tel: 323-953-4000. Fax: 323-953-4013. p. 171

Vasquez, Clare, Pub Serv, Saint Louis Art Museum, One Fine Arts Dr, Forest Park, Saint Louis, MO, 63110-1380. Tel: 314-655-5252. Fax: 314-721-6172. p. 1357

Vasquez, Manuel, Librn, California Department of Alcohol & Drug Programs, 1700 K St, 1st Flr, Sacramento, CA, 95814-4037. Tel: 916-324-5439. Fax: 916-323-1270. p. 220

Vasquez, Rosemary, Coordr, Council of Research & Academic Libraries, PO Box 290236, San Antonio, TX, 78280-1636. Tel: 210-458-4885. p. 2956

Vasquez, Valerie, Librn, University of Wyoming at Cheyenne, 821 E 18th St, Cheyenne, WY, 82001-4775. Tel: 307-777-7911, Ext 116. Fax: 307-638-3616. p. 2653

Vass, Tharen, Circ, Hart County Library, 150 Benson St, Hartwell, GA, 30643. Tel: 706-376-4655. Fax: 706-376-1157. p. 536

Vassallo, John Anthony, Chief Librn, United States Army, Fort Jackson Main Post Library, Thomas Lee Hall Main Post Library, Bldg 4679, Fort Jackson, SC, 29207. Tel: 803-751-4816, 803-751-5589. Fax: 803-751-1065. p. 2194

Vassar, David, Educ Spec, Ref, Fordham University Library at Lincoln Center, Leon Lowenstein Bldg, 113 W 60th St, New York, NY, 10023-7480. Tel: 212-636-6050. Fax: 212-636-6766. p. 1678

Vassilakos-Long, Jill, Coordr, Spec Coll, Govt Doc, California State University, San Bernardino, 5500 University Pkwy, San Bernardino, CA, 92407-2318. Tel: 909-537-7541. Fax: 909-537-7048. p. 227

Vassios, Dora Mae, Dir, Hugo Public Library, 522 Second Ave, Hugo, CO, 80821. Tel: 719-743-2325. p. 313

Vater-Olsen, Susan, Librn, Scandinavia Public Library, 349 N Main St, Scandinavia, WI, 54977. Tel: 715-467-4636. p. 2636

Vaughan, Catharine, Chief Librn, West Lincoln Public Library, 318 Canborough St, Smithville, ON, L0R 2A0, CANADA. Tel: 905-957-3756. Fax: 905-957-3219. p. 2842

Vaughan, Colleen, Librn, Provost Municipal Library, PO Box 120, Provost, AB, T0B 3S0, CANADA. Tel: 780-753-2801. Fax: 780-753-2801. p. 2714

Vaughan, Debbie, Chief Librn, Dir of Res & Access, Chicago History Museum, 1601 N Clark St, Chicago, IL, 60614-6099. Tel: 312-799-2030. Fax: 312-266-2076. p. 607

Vaughan, Emily, Libr Asst, National Endowment for Democracy Library, 1025 F St NW, Ste 800, Washington, DC, 20004. Tel: 202-378-9700. Fax: 202-378-9407. p. 409

Vaughan, James, Assoc Univ Librn, User Serv, University of Chicago Library, 1100 E 57th St, Chicago, IL, 60637-1502. Tel: 773-702-8351. Fax: 773-702-6623. p. 626

Vaughan, Jason, Dir of Tech, University of Nevada, Las Vegas Libraries, 4505 Maryland Pkwy, Box 457001, Las Vegas, NV, 89154-7001. Tel: 702-895-2179. Fax: 702-895-2287. p. 1431

Vaughan, Ken, Librn, Westat, Inc Library, 1650 Research Blvd, Rockville, MD, 20850. Tel: 301-251-1500. Fax: 301-294-2034. p. 1040

Vaughan, Nancy P, Librn, Du Pont De Nemours & Co, Inc, 800 DuPont Rd, Rte 23 S, Circleville, OH, 43113. Tel: 740-474-0111. Fax: 740-474-0244. p. 1875

Vaughan, Richard, Acq Librn, Indiana University, School of Law Library, Maurer School of Law, 211 S Indiana Ave, Bloomington, IN, 47405. Tel: 812-855-4199. Fax: 812-855-7099. p. 727

Vaughan, Sandy, Asst Librn, Mary Barnett Memorial Library, 400 Grand St, Guthrie Center, IA, 50115-1439. Tel: 641-747-8110. Fax: 641-747-8110. p. 820

Vaughan, Susan, Ser, University of Dallas, 1845 E Northgate Dr, Irving, TX, 75062-4736. Tel: 972-721-4130. Fax: 972-721-4010. p. 2347

Vaughn, Angel, YA Spec, Massillon Public Library, 208 Lincoln Way E, Massillon, OH, 44646-8416. Tel: 330-832-9831, Ext 321. Fax: 330-830-2182. p. 1915

Vaughn, Betty H, Dir, Dora Public Library, 56125 Goldbrick Rd, Myrtle Point, OR, 97458. Tel: 541-572-6009. Fax: 541-572-3084. p. 2007

Vaughn, Cynthia, Circ, Med Librn, Ref, University of Tennessee Graduate School of Medicine, 1924 Alcoa Hwy, Box U-111, Knoxville, TN, 37920. Tel: 865-305-9526. Fax: 865-305-9527. p. 2243

Vaughn, Cynthia, Pres, Knoxville Area Health Sciences Library Consortium, UT Preston Med Libr, 1924 Alcoa Hwy, Knoxville, TN, 37920. Tel: 865-305-9526. Fax: 865-305-9527. p. 2955

Vaughn, Eileen, Librn, Beebe Medical Center, 424 Savannah Rd, Lewes, DE, 19958. Tel: 302-645-3100, Ext 5472. Fax: 302-644-2319. p. 384

Vaughn, Eileen, Librn, Beebe Medical Center, Nursing School Library, 424 Savannah Rd, Lewes, DE, 19958. Tel: 302-645-3100, Ext 5667. Fax: 302-645-3488. p. 384

Vaughn, Evangeline, Circ, Concord University, 1000 Vermillion St, Athens, WV, 24712. Tel: 304-384-5371. Fax: 304-384-7955. p. 2553

Vaughn, Faye, Tech Serv, Nashville State Technical Community College, 120 White Bridge Rd, Nashville, TN, 37209-4515. Tel: 615-353-3560. Fax: 615-353-3558. p. 2258

Vaughn, Jan, Asst Dir, Warren-Trumbull County Public Library, 444 Mahoning Ave NW, Warren, OH, 44483. Tel: 330-399-8807. Fax: 330-395-3988. p. 1944

Vaughn, Joy, Tech Serv Supvr, Public Library of Johnston County & Smithfield, 305 E Market St, Smithfield, NC, 27577-3919. Tel: 919-934-8146. Fax: 919-934-8084. p. 1824

Vaughn, Judith, Ref, Johnson County Community College, 12345 College Blvd, Box 21, Overland Park, KS, 66210. Tel: 913-469-3871. Fax: 913-469-3816. p. 888

Vaughn, Pamela, Dir, Springville Public Library, 50 S Main St, Springville, UT, 84663. Tel: 801-489-2720. Fax: 801-489-2709. p. 2416

Vaughn, Phyllis, Adminr, Bureau of Braille & Talking Book Library Services, 420 Platt St, Daytona Beach, FL, 32114-2804. Tel: 386-239-6000. Fax: 386-239-6069. p. 435

Vaughn, Priscilla, Asst Dir, Billerica Public Library, 15 Concord Rd, Billerica, MA, 01821. Tel: 978-671-0948. Fax: 978-667-4242. p. 1054

Vaughn, Ruth, Circ Mgr, Platte County Public Library, 904 Ninth St, Wheatland, WY, 82201-2699. Tel: 307-322-2689. Fax: 307-322-3540. p. 2661

Vaughn, Sondra C, Br Mgr, Mountain Regional Library System, 698 Miller St, Young Harris, GA, 30582. Tel: 706-379-3732. Fax: 706-379-2047. p. 558

Vaughn, Susan, Legal Info Librn, Boston College, 885 Centre St, Newton Centre, MA, 02459. Tel: 617-552-8607. Fax: 617-552-2889. p. 1110

Vaughn, Susan, Assoc Librn, Coll Mgt, Brooklyn College Library, 2900 Bedford Ave, Brooklyn, NY, 11210-2889. Tel: 718-951-5348. Fax: 718-951-4540. p. 1589

Vaughn, Vida, Dir, Meyersdale Public Library, 210 Center St, Meyersdale, PA, 15552-1323. Tel: 814-634-0512. Fax: 814-634-0512. p. 2088

Vaughn-Tucker, Daenel, Head, Access Serv, Southeast Missouri State University, One University Plaza, Mail Stop 4600, Cape Girardeau, MO, 63701. Tel: 573-651-2797. Fax: 573-651-2666. p. 1322

Vaught, Georgia, Mgr, Info Tech, Johnson County Public Library, 401 State St, Franklin, IN, 46131-2545. Tel: 317-738-2833. Fax: 317-738-9635. p. 744

Vaught, Georgia, Mgr, Info Tech, Johnson County Public Library, White River Library, 1664 Library Blvd, Greenwood, IN, 46142. Tel: 317-885-1330. Fax: 317-882-4117. p. 744

Vavala, Jane, Info Serv, Ref Serv, State University of New York, College of Technology, Upper Colleg Dr, Alfred, NY, 14802. Tel: 607-587-4313. Fax: 607-587-4351. p. 1572

Vavala, Jane, Dir, Tech Serv, Saint Mary's Public Library, 127 Center St, Saint Marys, PA, 15857. Tel: 814-834-6141. Fax: 814-834-9814. p. 2135

Vavra, Verlas, Librn, Tripp County Library-Grossenburg Memorial, Colome Branch, 217 Main St, Colome, SD, 57528. p. 2222

Vazquez, Donna, Asst Dir, Libr Bus Serv, Florida Gulf Coast University Library, 10501 FGCU Blvd S, Fort Myers, FL, 33965-6501. Tel: 239-590-7603. p. 444

Vazquez-Garcia, Homero, Asst Dir, Laredo Public Library, 1120 E Calton Rd, Laredo, TX, 78041. Tel: 956-795-2420. Fax: 956-795-2403. p. 2353

Veach, Carol L, Ch, City of Tonawanda Public Library, 333 Main St, Tonawanda, NY, 14150. Tel: 716-693-5043. Fax: 716-693-0825. p. 1755

Veach, Christopher, Circ, Tech Serv, Lake County Library, 1425 N High St, Lakeport, CA, 95453-3800. Tel: 707-263-8816. Fax: 707-263-6796. p. 163

Veach, Grace, Dean of Libr Serv, Southeastern University, 1000 Longfellow Blvd, Lakeland, FL, 33801. Tel: 863-667-5089. Fax: 863-669-4160. p. 460

Veale, Miriam, Libr Assoc/Tech Serv, Coweta Public Library System, 85 Literary Lane, Newnan, GA, 30265. Tel: 770-683-2052. Fax: 770-683-0065. p. 546

Vear, Ruslyn, Head, Ref, Amherst Town Library, 14 Main St, Amherst, NH, 03031-2930. Tel: 603-673-2288. Fax: 603-672-6063. p. 1437

Veasey, Susan, ILL, Ref, Houston Love Memorial Library, 212 W Burdeshaw St, Dothan, AL, 36303. Tel: 334-793-9767. Fax: 334-793-6645. p. 15

Veatch, Gisela, Dir, Mitchellville Public Library, 204 Center Ave N, Mitchellville, IA, 50169. Tel: 515-967-3339. Fax: 515-967-1868. p. 832

Veatch, Jim, Tech Serv, Bartram Trail Regional Library, 204 E Liberty St, Washington, GA, 30673. Tel: 706-678-7736. Fax: 706-678-1615. p. 556

Veatch, Lamar J, Dr, State Librn, Georgia Public Library Service, 1800 Century Place, Ste 150, Atlanta, GA, 30345-4304. Tel: 404-235-7177. Fax: 404-235-7201. p. 515

Vecchio, Anna, Ser, University of New Haven, 300 Boston Post Rd, West Haven, CT, 06516. Tel: 203-932-7188. Fax: 203-932-1469. p. 377

Vecchio, Helen, Ref, Manlius Library, One Arkie Albanese Ave, Manlius, NY, 13104. Tel: 315-682-6400. Fax: 315-682-4490. p. 1657

Vecchiola, Rina, Supv Librn, Washington University Libraries, Art & Architecture, One Brookings Dr, Campus Box 1061, Saint Louis, MO, 63130-4862. Tel: 314-935-7658. Fax: 314-935-4362. p. 1362

Veenstra, Jolene, Circ Serv Supvr, Redeemer College Library, 777 Garner Rd E, Ancaster, ON, L9K 1J4, CANADA. Tel: 905-648-2131. Fax: 905-648-2134. p. 2792

Vega, Aixa, Dir, Universidad Adventista de las Antillas, Carr 106 Km 2 Interior, Bo La Quinta, Mayaguez, PR, 00680. Tel: 787-834-9595, Ext 2314. Fax: 787-834-6015. p. 2674

Vega Garcia, Susan, Libr Instruction, Iowa State University Library, 302 Parks Library, Ames, IA, 50011-2140. Tel: 515-294-1442, 515-294-1443. Fax: 515-294-5525. p. 793

Vega, Kacy, Juv Serv Coordr, Union County Public Library, 316 E Windsor St, Monroe, NC, 28112. Tel: 704-283-8184. Fax: 704-282-0657. p. 1810

Vega, Lupita, Principal Librn, Youth Serv, Santa Ana Public Library, 26 Civic Center Plaza, Santa Ana, CA, 92701-4010. Tel: 714-647-5250. Fax: 714-647-5296. p. 259

Vega, Patricia, Br Mgr, Biblioteca Criolla, Jersey City Free Public Library, 472 Jersey Ave, Jersey City, NJ, 07302-3499. Tel: 201-547-4541. Fax: 201-547-5889. p. 1492

Vega-DeJoseph, Juanita, Head of Libr, Free Library of Philadelphia, Wadsworth Avenue Branch, 1500 Wadsworth Ave, Philadelphia, PA, 19150-1699. Tel: 215-685-9293. Fax: 215-685-9295. p. 2109

Vegelante, Tina, ILL, The State Library of Massachusetts, State House, Rm 341, 24 Beacon St, Boston, MA, 02133. Tel: 617-727-2590. Fax: 617-727-5819. p. 1067

Veghts, Darlene, Asst Dir, La Roche College, 9000 Babcock Blvd, Pittsburgh, PA, 15237. Tel: 412-536-1055. Fax: 412-536-1062. p. 2126

Veglas, Beverly, Librn, Massachusetts Department of Corrections, PO Box 100, South Walpole, MA, 02071-0100. Tel: 508-668-2100. p. 1126

Vehorn, Jane, Br Coordr, Shelby County Libraries, Philip Sheets Family Botkins Branch, 109 E Lynn St, Botkins, OH, 45306. Tel: 937-693-6671. Fax: 937-693-6671. p. 1935

Vehre, John L, Jr, Dir, Greenville Public Library, 520 Sycamore St, Greenville, OH, 45331-1438. Tel: 937-548-3915. Fax: 937-548-3837. p. 1903

Veilleux, Ruth, Librn, De Grandpre Chait Library, 1000 de la Gauchetiere Ouest, Ste 2900, Montreal, QC, H3B 4W5, CANADA. Tel: 514-878-4311. Fax: 514-878-4333. p. 2895

Veinot, Tiffany, Asst Prof, University of Michigan, 304 West Hall, 1085 S University, Ann Arbor, MI, 48109-1107. Tel: 734-763-2285. Fax: 734-764-2475. p. 2967

Veinus, Janine, Tech Serv, Flagstaff City-Coconino County Public Library System, 300 W Aspen, Flagstaff, AZ, 86001. Tel: 928-213-2331. Fax: 928-774-9573. p. 62

Veit, Frances, Ch, Buckham Memorial Library, 11 Division St E, Faribault, MN, 55021-6000. Tel: 507-334-2089. Fax: 507-384-0503. p. 1250

Veit, Richard, Actg Librn, Archaeological Society of New Jersey Library, Department of History & Anthropology, Monmouth University, West Long Branch, NJ, 07764-1898. Tel: 732-263-5699. p. 1541

Veith, Kathleen H, Dir, Libr Serv, Potter Anderson & Corroon LLP, Hercules Plaza, 1313 N Market St, Wilmington, DE, 19801. Tel: 302-984-6195. Fax: 302-778-6195. p. 388

Vejnar, Robert, Archivist, Spec Coll Librn, Emory & Henry College, 30480 Armbrister Dr, Emory, VA, 24327. Tel: 276-944-6208. Fax: 276-944-4592. p. 2460

Vekerdy, Lilla, Curator, Head, Spec Coll, Smithsonian Libraries, The Dibner Library of the History of Science & Technology, Nat Museum of American Hist, Rm 1041, MRC 672, 12th St & Constitution Ave NW, Washington, DC, 20560-0672. Tel: 202-633-3872. p. 414

Vekerdy, Lilla, Rare Bk Librn, Washington University Libraries, Bernard Becker Medical Library, 660 S Euclid Ave, Campus Box 8132, Saint Louis, MO, 63110. Tel: 314-362-4235. Fax: 314-454-6606. p. 1362

Vela, Hector, Acq, Robert J Kleberg Public Library, 220 N Fourth St, Kingsville, TX, 78363. Tel: 361-592-6381. p. 2350

Velarde, Lisa, Info Serv Librn, Menlo College, 1000 El Camino Real, Atherton, CA, 94027-4300. Tel: 650-543-3826. Fax: 650-543-3833. p. 122

Velasquez, Alan, Head Librn, Tulane University, Architecture Library, Richardson Memorial Bldg, Rm 202, 6823 St Charles Ave, New Orleans, LA, 70118. Tel: 504-865-5391. Fax: 504-862-8966. p. 963

Velasquez, Jennifer, Coordr, Teen Serv, San Antonio Public Library, 600 Soledad, San Antonio, TX, 78205-2786. Tel: 210-207-2567. Fax: 210-207-2603. p. 2382

Velasquez, Jennifer, Mgr, San Antonio Public Library, Teen Services, 600 Soledad, San Antonio, TX, 78205-2786. Tel: 210-207-2678. Fax: 210-207-2553. p. 2382

Velasquez, Terry, Mgr, Johnson County Library, Edgerton Branch, 319 E Nelson, Edgerton, KS, 66021. Tel: 913-495-3888. Fax: 913-893-6723. p. 888

Velasquez, Terry, Mgr, Johnson County Library, Gardner Branch, 137 E Shawnee, Gardner, KS, 66030. Tel: 913-495-3888. Fax: 913-495-3881. p. 888

Velasquez, Terry, Mgr, Johnson County Library, Spring Hill Branch, 109 S Webster, Spring Hill, KS, 66083. Tel: 913-495-3888. Fax: 913-686-2004. p. 888

Velder, Linda, Curator, Newell Public Library, 208 Girard, Newell, SD, 57760. Tel: 605-456-2179. p. 2216

Velez, Julia Y, Dir, University of Puerto Rico Library, Rio Piedras Campus, San Juan, PR, 00931. Tel: 787-764-0000, Ext 5983. Fax: 787-764-2890. p. 2676

Velez, Magali, Asst Librn, Ref, Prudential Financial, Prudential Insurance Law Library, Four Plaza, 751 Broad St, Newark, NJ, 07102-3714. Tel: 973-802-6811. Fax: 973-802-2298. p. 1512

Velez, Nancy, Br Head, Toronto Public Library, Black Creek, North York Sheridan Mall, 1700 Wilson Ave, Toronto, ON, M3L 1B2, CANADA. Tel: 416-395-5470. Fax: 416-395-5435. p. 2860

Velez-Natal, Betsaida, Dir, McConnell Valdes, 270 Munoz Rivera Ave, Hato Rey, PR, 00918. Tel: 787-250-5147, 787-759-9292. Fax: 787-759-9225. p. 2673

Velez-Natal, Betsaida, Assoc Prof, University of Puerto Rico, Rio Piedras Campus, PO Box 21906, San Juan, PR, 00931-1906. Tel: 787-764-0000, Ext 1286, 787-764-0000, Ext 5028. Fax: 787-764-2311. p. 2977

Velez-Rubio, Daniel, Libr Serv Supvr, Hernando County Public Library System, East Hernando, 6457 Windemere Rd, Brooksville, FL, 34602. Tel: 352-754-4043. Fax: 352-754-4445. p. 430

Veli, Gail, Reserves, McGill University Libraries, Howard Ross Library of Management, Samuel Bronfman Bldg, 1001 Sherbrooke St W, 2nd Flr, Montreal, QC, H3A 1G5, CANADA. Tel: 514-398-4690, Ext 04553. Fax: 514-398-5046. p. 2899

Veli, Ravil, Dir of Libr Serv, Asnuntuck Community College, 170 Elm St, Enfield, CT, 06082-0068. Tel: 860-253-3171. Fax: 860-253-9310. p. 338

Veli, Ravil, Dir, Norwich University, 23 Harmon Dr, Northfield, VT, 05663. Tel: 802-485-2169. Fax: 802-485-2173. p. 2431

Veligitone, Alofa, Librn, American Samoa Office of Library Services, Manu'a, Tau Community School, Manu'a Island, AS, 96799. Tel: 684-732-3512. Fax: 684-633-4240. p. 2665

Vellam, Kathleen, Dir, Public Library for Union County, 255 Reitz Blvd, Lewisburg, PA, 17837-9211. Tel: 570-523-1172. Fax: 570-524-7771. p. 2081

Vellam, Kathleen O'Brien, Adminr, Union County Library System, 255 Reitz Blvd, Lewisburg, PA, 17837-9211. Tel: 570-523-1172. Fax: 570-524-7771. p. 2081

Vellanoweth, Vivian, Media Spec, Whittier Public Library, 7344 S Washington Ave, Whittier, CA, 90602. Tel: 562-567-9900. Fax: 562-567-2880. p. 283

Vellucci, Margaret, Br Mgr, Edison Township Free Public Library, Clara Barton Branch, 141 Hoover Ave, Edison, NJ, 08837. Tel: 732-738-0096. Fax: 732-738-8325. p. 1483

Vellucci, Penny, Br Mgr, Edison Township Free Public Library, 340 Plainfield Ave, Edison, NJ, 08817. Tel: 732-738-0096. Fax: 732-738-8325. p. 1483

Vellucci, Sherry, Dr, Dean, Univ Libr, University of New Hampshire Library, 18 Library Way, Durham, NH, 03824. Tel: 603-862-1506. Fax: 603-862-0247. p. 1445

Vellutini, Susan, Asst Librn, Beaver Valley Public Library, 1847 First St, Fruitvale, BC, V0G 1L0, CANADA. Tel: 250-367-7114. Fax: 250-367-7130. p. 2728

Velnich, Doreen, Br Supvr, Worcester Public Library, Frances Perkins Branch, 470 W Boylston St, Worcester, MA, 01606-3226. Tel: 508-799-1687. Fax: 508-799-1693. p. 1145

Velnich, Doreen, Head, Ref, Worcester Public Library, Three Salem Sq, Worcester, MA, 01608. Tel: 508-799-1655. Fax: 508-799-1652. p. 1145

Veltze, Linda, Dr, Prof, Appalachian State University, RCOE, Dept of LES, 311 Edwin Duncan Hall, Boone, NC, 28608. Tel: 828-262-7236. Fax: 828-262-6035. p. 2971

Venanzi, Kirstie, Acq Librn, Institute for Advanced Study Libraries, Einstein Dr, Princeton, NJ, 08540. Tel: 609-734-8374. Fax: 609-924-8399, 609-951-4515. p. 1522

Venard, Paul D, Ref Librn, University of Dayton School of Law, 300 College Park, Dayton, OH, 45469-2780. Tel: 937-229-2314. Fax: 937-229-2555. p. 1894

Venditti, Kathern, Ref Librn, Ashland University Library, 509 College Ave, Ashland, OH, 44805-3796. Tel: 419-289-5400. Fax: 419-289-5422. p. 1855

Venechanos, Rachel, Assoc Librn, Highland Park Presbyterian Church, 3821 University Blvd, Dallas, TX, 75205. Tel: 214-526-4277. p. 2308

Venegas, E Frances, Librn, Garcia Venito Public Library & Archives, San Lucy District, 1125 C St, Gila Bend, AZ, 85337. Tel: 928-683-2012, 928-683-2796. Fax: 928-683-2802. p. 81

Veneziani, Mitsy, Ch, Avonmore Public Library, 619 Allegheny Ave, Avonmore, PA, 15618. Tel: 724-697-4828. Fax: 724-697-1322. p. 2030

Venhor, Sandra, ILL, Carleton A Friday Memorial Library, 155 E First St, New Richmond, WI, 54017. Tel: 715-243-0431. Fax: 715-246-2691. p. 2625

Venie, Todd, Ref Librn, Georgetown University, Georgetown Law Library (John Wolff & Edward Bennett Williams Libraries), 111 G St NW, Washington, DC, 20001. Fax: 202-662-9168. p. 403

Venis, Linda, Supvr, Libr Serv, WellStar Library Services, 677 Church St, Marietta, GA, 30060. Tel: 770-793-7178. Fax: 770-793-7956. p. 544

Venkat, Girija, Ref & Instruction Librn, Hampton University, 130 E Tyler St, Hampton, VA, 23668. Tel: 757-727-5371. Fax: 757-727-5952. p. 2468

Vennerbeck, Ann H, Libr Asst, Philbrick-James Library, Four Church St, Deerfield, NH, 03037-1426. Tel: 603-463-7187. p. 1444

Vente, Kathy, Dir, Thornton Public Library, 115 E Margaret St, Thornton, IL, 60476. Tel: 708-877-2579. Fax: 708-877-2608. p. 709

Ventgen, Carol, Dir, Coos Bay Public Library, 525 Anderson St, Coos Bay, OR, 97420-1678. Tel: 541-269-1101. Fax: 541-269-7567. p. 1993

Ventline, Madeline, Dir, Community Health Partners, 3700 Kolbe Rd, Lorain, OH, 44053. Tel: 440-960-3327. Fax: 440-960-3298. p. 1911

Vento, Jane, Dir, Milan Public Library, 20 Bridge St, Milan, NH, 03588. Tel: 603-449-7307. p. 1457

Venton, Maureen, Chief Librn, Brighton Public Library, 35 Alice St, Brighton, ON, K0K 1H0, CANADA. Tel: 613-475-2511. p. 2797

Ventresca, Jordy, Librn, Worthington Historical Society Library, 50 W New England Ave, Worthington, OH, 43085-3536. Tel: 614-885-1247. Fax: 614-885-1040. p. 1950

Ventrudo, Meg, Dir, Jacques Marchais Museum of Tibetan Art Library, 338 Lighthouse Ave, Staten Island, NY, 10306. Tel: 718-987-3500. Fax: 718-351-0402. p. 1747

Ventura, James A, Circ, Somerville Public Library, 79 Highland Ave, Somerville, MA, 02143. Tel: 617-623-5000, Ext 2905. Fax: 617-628-4052. p. 1124

Ventura, Julie, Br Mgr, Orange County Library District, South Creek, 1702 Deerfield Blvd, Orlando, FL, 32837. p. 476

Ventura, Katie, Asst Dir, Kent Public Library, 17 Sybil's Crossing, Kent Lakes, NY, 10512. Tel: 845-225-8585. Fax: 845-225-8549. p. 1649

Ventura, Sheri, Distance Learning Serv, County College of Morris, 214 Center Grove Rd, Randolph, NJ, 07869-2086. p. 1525

Venturella, Anna, Info Serv, Hershey Foods Corp, 1025 Reese Ave, Hershey, PA, 17033-2272. Tel: 717-534-5106. Fax: 717-534-5069. p. 2069

Venzor, Ezie, Youth Serv, Lovington Public Library, 115 Main St, Lovington, NM, 88260. Tel: 575-396-3144, 575-396-6900. Fax: 575-396-7189. p. 1559

Veomett, Colleen, Ref Serv, Tech Serv, Heritage University, 3240 Fort Rd, Toppenish, WA, 98948. Tel: 509-865-8500, Ext 3427. Fax: 509-865-4144. p. 2541

Vepari, Gertrud, ILL, Glenview Public Library, 1930 Glenview Rd, Glenview, IL, 60025-2899. Tel: 847-729-7500. Fax: 847-729-7558. p. 651

Ver Steeg, Jennie, Dir of Libr Serv, Walden University Library, 100 Washington Ave S, Ste 900, Minneapolis, MN, 55401. Tel: 612-312-2379. Fax: 612-338-5092. p. 1262

Vera, Leslie, Libr Tech, Nevada County Library, Doris Foley Library for Historical Research, 211 N Pine St, Nevada City, CA, 95959-2592. Tel: 530-265-4606. p. 193

Veracka, Peter G, Dir, Pontifical College Josephinum, 7625 N High St, Columbus, OH, 43235-1498. Tel: 614-985-2295. Fax: 614-885-2307. p. 1890

Veramay, Karen, Br Mgr, Jackson District Library, Concord Branch, 108 S Main St, Concord, MI, 49237. Tel: 517-905-1379. Fax: 517-524-6971. p. 1195

Verba, Sharon, Ref, University of South Carolina, 1322 Greene St, Columbia, SC, 29208-0103. Tel: 803-777-3142. p. 2189

Verbeck, Alison, Librn, Washington University Libraries, Pfeiffer Physics Library, One Brookings Dr, 340 Compton Lab, Saint Louis, MO, 63130. Tel: 314-935-6215. Fax: 314-935-6219. p. 1363

Verberne, Linda, Supvr, Middlesex County Library, Delaware Branch, 29 Young St, Delaware, ON, N0L 1E0, CANADA. Tel: 519-652-9978. Fax: 519-652-0166. p. 2845

Verbesey, Kevin, Dir, Suffolk Cooperative Library System, 627 N Sunrise Service Rd, Bellport, NY, 11713. Tel: 631-286-1600. Fax: 631-286-1647. p. 1580

Verble, Carol S, ILL, Missouri History Museum, 225 S Skinker Blvd, Saint Louis, MO, 63105. Tel: 314-746-4500. Fax: 314-746-4548. p. 1356

Verble, Melissa, ILL & Evening Circ Coordr, Christian Brothers University, 650 E Pkwy South, Memphis, TN, 38104. Tel: 901-321-3432. Fax: 901-321-3219. p. 2248

Verburg, Fay, Coll Develop Coordr, Head, Ref, Augusta State University, 2500 Walton Way, Augusta, GA, 30904-2200. Tel: 706-737-1745. Fax: 706-667-4415. p. 518

Verdeck, Jamie, Librn, Tracy Public Library, 117 Third St, Tracy, MN, 56175-1211. Tel: 507-629-5548. Fax: 507-629-5549. p. 1286

Verderame, Concetta, Ref Librn, Burlington County Library, Maple Shade Branch, 200 Stiles Ave, Maple Shade, NJ, 08052. Tel: 856-779-9767. Fax: 856-779-0033. p. 1543

Verdesca, Anthony, Ref Serv, Palm Beach Atlantic University, 300 Pembroke Pl, West Palm Beach, FL, 33401-6503. Tel: 561-803-2238. Fax: 561-803-2235. p. 503

Verdibello, Muriel, Dir, Newburgh Free Library, 124 Grand St, Newburgh, NY, 12550. Tel: 845-563-3600. Fax: 845-563-3602. p. 1705

Verdine, Guillory, Br Mgr, Calcasieu Parish Public Library, Carnegie Memorial, 411 Pujo St, Lake Charles, LA, 70601-4254. Tel: 337-721-7084. Fax: 337-437-3480. p. 953

Verdini, Jim, Access Serv, Ref Serv, Averett University Library, 344 W Main St, Danville, VA, 24541-2849. Tel: 434-791-5694. Fax: 434-791-5637. p. 2459

Verdone, Joyce, Libr Tech, New Hampshire Division of Public Health Services, 29 Hazen Dr, Concord, NH, 03301. Tel: 603-271-0562, 603-271-7060. Fax: 603-271-0542. p. 1442

Verdone, Joyce, Ser, NHTI, Concord's Community College, 31 College Dr, Concord, NH, 03301-7425. Tel: 603-271-7186. Fax: 603-271-7189. p. 1443

Verdugo, Karen, Assoc Dir, Loyola Law School, 919 S Albany St, Los Angeles, CA, 90015-1211. Tel: 213-736-1181. Fax: 213-487-2204. p. 175

Veregge, Audrey, Librn, Shadelands Ranch Historical Museum, 2660 Ygnacio Valley Rd, Walnut Creek, CA, 94598. Tel: 925-935-7871. Fax: 925-935-7885. p. 282

Verellen, Lou, Librn, North Central Regional Library, Chelan Community, 417 S Bradley St, Chelan, WA, 98816. Tel: 509-682-5131. Fax: 509-682-5131. p. 2548

Veress, Eugene S, Sr Librn, New York State Department of Correctional Services, 3595 State School Rd, Albion, NY, 14411. Tel: 585-589-5511, Ext 4600. p. 1571

Vergara, Deborah, Sr Res Librn, McKenna, Long & Aldridge LLP, 1900 K St NW, Washington, DC, 20006. Tel: 202-496-7125. Fax: 202-496-7756. p. 408

Vergara-Bautista, Gina S, Head, Coll Mgt, Hawaii State Archives, Iolani Palace Grounds, 364 S King St, Honolulu, HI, 96813. Tel: 808-586-0329. Fax: 808-586-0330. p. 561

Verge, Colleen, Dir, Albion Public Library, 437 S Third St, Albion, NE, 68620. Tel: 402-395-2021. p. 1391

Verge, Colleen Richards, Dir, Albion District Library, 501 S Superior St, Albion, MI, 49224. Tel: 517-629-3993. Fax: 517-629-5354. p. 1148

Verge, Laurie, Dir, Maryland National Capital Park & Planning Commission, 9118 Brandywine Rd, Clinton, MD, 20735. Tel: 301-868-1121. Fax: 301-868-8177. p. 1024

Verge, Lynn, Exec Dir, Atwater Library & Computer Centre, 1200 Atwater Ave, Westmount, QC, H3Z 1X4, CANADA. Tel: 514-935-7344. Fax: 514-935-1960. p. 2915

Vergel, Alfredo, Assoc Librn, Pub Serv & Spec Coll, Southwestern Adventist University, 101 W Magnolia St, Keene, TX, 76059. Tel: 817-202-6521. Fax: 817-556-4722. p. 2349

Verguizas, Luz, Acq Librn, Columbia University, Arthur W Diamond Law Library, 435 W 116th St, New York, NY, 10027. Tel: 212-854-3922. Fax: 212-854-3295. p. 1674

Verhey, Barbara, Circ, Rock County Community Library, 201 W Main, Luverne, MN, 56156. Tel: 507-449-5040. Fax: 507-449-5034. p. 1256

Verhoff, Andrew J, Mgr, Ohio Historical Society, 601 Second St, Marietta, OH, 45750-2122. Tel: 740-373-3750. Fax: 740-373-3680. p. 1913

Verhoff, Debbie, Head Librn, Lesley University, 700 Beacon St, Boston, MA, 02215-2598. Tel: 617-585-6671. Fax: 617-585-6655. p. 1062

Verlaque, Laura, Dir of Coll, Pasadena Museum of History, 470 W Walnut St, Pasadena, CA, 91103-3594. Tel: 626-577-1660. Fax: 626-577-1662. p. 206

Verma, Asha, Head, Circ, Montgomery County-Norristown Public Library, 1001 Powell St, Norristown, PA, 19401-3817. Tel: 610-278-5100, Ext 110. p. 2098

Verma, Louisa, Ref Serv, Huntington Memorial Hospital, 100 W California Blvd, Pasadena, CA, 91105-3010. Tel: 626-397-5161. Fax: 626-397-2908. p. 206

Vermeulen, Susan, Mgr, Greensboro Public Library, Kathleen Clay Edwards Family Branch, 1420 Price Park Rd, Greensboro, NC, 27410. Tel: 336-373-2923. Fax: 336-851-5047. p. 1796

Vermeychuk, Sandy, ILL, Swarthmore College, 500 College Ave, Swarthmore, PA, 19081-1081. Tel: 610-328-8489. Fax: 610-328-7329. p. 2145

Verna, Gaetane, Dir, Musee d'art de Joliette, 145 Wilfrid-Corbeil St, Joliette, QC, J6E 4T4, CANADA. Tel: 450-756-0311. Fax: 450-756-6511. p. 2884

Vernau, Mary, Dir, Altoona Public Library, 1303 Lynn Ave, Altoona, WI, 54720-0278. Tel: 715-839-5029. Fax: 715-830-5119. p. 2577

Vernon, Gail, Br Mgr, Public Library Association of Annapolis & Anne Arundel County, Inc, Maryland City at Russett, 3501 Russett Common, Laurel, MD, 20724. Tel: 301-725-2390. Fax: 301-498-5749. p. 1010

Vernoy, Mark W, Dr, Dean, Palomar College, 1140 W Mission Rd, San Marcos, CA, 92069-1487. Tel: 760-744-1150, Ext 2759. Fax: 760-761-3500. p. 2962

Verny, Carol, Dir, Haverhill Public Library, 99 Main St, Haverhill, MA, 01830-5092. Tel: 978-373-1586, Ext 621. Fax: 978-372-8508. p. 1094

Verone, Amy, Curator, Sagamore Hill National Historic Site Library, 20 Sagamore Hill Rd, Oyster Bay, NY, 11771-1899. Tel: 516-922-4788. Fax: 516-922-4792. p. 1714

Veronica, Padilla, In Charge, University of California, Berkeley, Philosophy, 305 Moses Hall, Berkeley, CA, 94720. Tel: 510-642-6516. p. 128

Veronique, Marcotta, Librn, Chateauguay Municipal Library, 25 Maple Blvd, Chateauguay, QC, J6J 3P7, CANADA. Tel: 450-698-3085. Fax: 450-698-3109. p. 2880

Verret, Denyse, Dir of Educ, College de l'Assomption, 270 boul l'Ange-Gardien, L'Assomption, QC, J5W 1R7, CANADA. Tel: 450-589-5621, Ext 258. Fax: 450-589-2910. p. 2885

Verrilla, Marlo, ILL, Saint Vincent College & Seminary Library, 300 Fraser Purchase Rd, Latrobe, PA, 15650-2690. Tel: 724-805-2966. Fax: 724-805-2905. p. 2079

Verrilla, Marlo, Ref Serv, YA Serv, Ligonier Valley Library Association, Inc, 120 W Main St, Ligonier, PA, 15658-1243. Tel: 724-238-6451. Fax: 724-238-6989. p. 2081

Verry, Tim, Libr Tech, Canadian Agriculture Library - Winnipeg, 195 Dafoe Rd, Winnipeg, MB, R3T 2M9, CANADA. Tel: 204-983-0721, 204-983-0755. Fax: 204-983-4604. p. 2754

Verscaj, Valerie, Youth Serv Librn, St Charles Public Library District, One S Sixth Ave, Saint Charles, IL, 60174-2105. Tel: 630-584-0076, Ext 207. Fax: 630-584-3448. p. 699

Versluis, Jan, Ref Serv, Dordt College, 498 Fourth Ave NE, Sioux Center, IA, 51250. Tel: 712-722-6040. Fax: 712-722-1198. p. 843

Vertz, Rosina, Commun Br Supvr, Pierce County Library System, Key Center, 8905 Key Peninsula Hwy N, Lakebay, WA, 98349. Tel: 253-548-3309. Fax: 253-884-3706. p. 2539

Vesci, Thomas, Dir, Media Serv, Asnuntuck Community College, 170 Elm St, Enfield, CT, 06082-0068. Tel: 860-253-3173. Fax: 860-253-9310. p. 338

Veselovsky, Cassie, Youth Serv, Capital Area District Libraries, Downtown Lansing Library, 401 S Capitol Ave, Lansing, MI, 48933. Tel: 517-367-6363. Fax: 517-374-1068. p. 1200

Vesely, Suzanne Araas, Dir, Maharishi University of Management Library, 1000 N Fourth St, Fairfield, IA, 52557. Tel: 641-472-1148. Fax: 641-472-1137. p. 815

Vespa, Rose, Chief Exec Officer, Brantford Public Library, 173 Colborne St, Brantford, ON, N3T 2G8, CANADA. Tel: 519-756-2220, Ext 319. Fax: 519-756-4979. p. 2796

Vesper, Virginia, Coordr, Coll Mgt, Middle Tennessee State University, MTSU, PO Box 13, Murfreesboro, TN, 37132. Tel: 615-898-2806. p. 2254

Vess, Jennifer, Ref Serv Supvr, Pearl Public Library, 2416 Old Brandon Rd, Pearl, MS, 39208-4601. Tel: 601-932-2562. Fax: 601-932-3535. p. 1311

Vess, Ron, Librn, Southwestern College Library, 900 Otay Lakes Rd, Chula Vista, CA, 91910-7299. Tel: 619-216-6619, 619-482-6373. Fax: 619-482-6417. p. 134

Vessella, A, Ch, Young Men's Library Association, 37 Main St, Ware, MA, 01082-1317. Tel: 413-967-5491. Fax: 413-967-6060. p. 1133

Vest, John, Br Mgr, Roanoke County Public Library, Glenvar, 3917 Daugherty Rd, Salem, VA, 24153. Tel: 540-387-6163. Fax: 540-380-3951. p. 2494

Vest, Stephen C, Dir, Botetourt County Library, 28 Avery Row, Roanoke, VA, 24012. Tel: 540-977-3433. Fax: 540-977-2407. p. 2493

Vest, Steven, Head, Ref & Res Serv, Alma College Library, 614 W Superior St, Alma, MI, 48801. Tel: 989-463-7344. Fax: 989-463-8694. p. 1149

Vestal, Betty, ILL, Park University Library, 8700 NW River Park Dr, Parkville, MO, 64152. Tel: 816-584-6283. Fax: 816-741-4911. p. 1349

Vestal, Maureen, Librn, San Luis Obispo County Library, Shandon Branch, 240 E Centre St, Shandon, CA, 93461. Tel: 805-237-3009. Fax: 805-237-3022. p. 254

Vestal, Maureen, Librn, San Luis Obispo County Library, Simmler Branch, 13080 Soda Lake Rd, Simmler, CA, 93453. Tel: 805-475-2603. Fax: 805-475-2759. p. 254

Vestermark, Paula, Per, Luther Seminary Library, Gullixson Hall, 2375 Como Ave, Saint Paul, MN, 55108. Tel: 651-641-3231. Fax: 651-641-3280. p. 1278

Vetsch, Rick, Br Mgr, Uncle Remus Regional Library System, O'Kelly Memorial Library, 363 Conyers Rd, Loganville, GA, 30052. Tel: 770-466-2895. Fax: 770-466-3700. p. 542

Vetter, Imelda, Ref Librn, University of Alabama at Birmingham, Mervyn H Sterne Library, 917 13th St S, Birmingham, AL, 35205. Tel: 205-934-6364. p. 10

Vetter, Suzanne, Dir, Kellogg Free Library, 5681 Telephone Rd Exten, Cincinnatus, NY, 13040. Tel: 607-863-4300. Fax: 607-863-3430. p. 1606

Vezina, Alain, Coordr, Cegep Marie-Victorin Bibliotheque, 7000 rue Marie-Victorin, Montreal, QC, H1G 2J6, CANADA. Tel: 514-325-0150, Ext 2363. Fax: 514-328-3840. p. 2892

Vezina, Claire, Librn, Association paritaire pour la sante et la securite du travail - secteur affaires municipales, 715 Square Victoria, Ste 710, Montreal, QC, H2Y 2H7, CANADA. Tel: 514-849-8373, Ext 230. Fax: 514-849-8873. p. 2888

Vézina, Sylvie, Chef de Div, Bibliothèques de Montrèal, Saint-Léonard, 8420, boulevard Lacordaire, Montreal, QC, H1R 3G5, CANADA. Tel: 514-328-8500, Ext 8517. Fax: 514-328-7002. p. 2891

Viana, Amanda, Info Serv Librn, Norton Public Library, 68 E Main St, Norton, MA, 02766. Tel: 508-285-0265. Fax: 508-285-0266. p. 1114

Viands, Janlee, Head, County Serv, Washington County Free Library, 100 S Potomac St, Hagerstown, MD, 21740. Tel: 301-739-3250. Fax: 301-739-7603. p. 1031

Viator, Van P, Info Literacy/Ref, Nicholls State University, 906 E First St, Thibodaux, LA, 70310. Tel: 985-448-4646, 985-448-4660. Fax: 985-448-4925. p. 971

Viau, France, ILL, Canada School of Public Service Library, 241 Cité des jeunes Blvd, Gatineau, QC, K1N 6Z2, CANADA. Tel: 819-953-5295. Fax: 819-953-1702. p. 2882

Vicarel, Diane, Digital Serv Mgr, Public Library of Youngstown & Mahoning County, 305 Wick Ave, Youngstown, OH, 44503-1079. Tel: 330-744-8636. Fax: 330-744-3355. p. 1952

Vicchiarelli, Michael, In Charge, Florida Department of Corrections, 19225 US Hwy 27, Clermont, FL, 34715. Tel: 352-394-6146, Ext 295. Fax: 352-394-1313. p. 432

Vice, James, Librn, Northwest Regional Library, Kennedy Public Library, 17885 Hwy 96, Kennedy, AL, 35574. Tel: 205-596-3670. Fax: 205-596-3956. p. 40

Vicente, Miguel J, Libr Mgr, Piedmont Regional Library, Commerce Public, 1344 S Broad St, Commerce, GA, 30529-2053. Tel: 706-335-5946. Fax: 706-335-6879. p. 557

Vick, Liza, Res Serv Librn, Harvard Library, Eda Kuhn Loeb Music Library, Music Bldg, Harvard University, Cambridge, MA, 02138. Tel: 617-495-2794. Fax: 617-496-4636. p. 1076

Vick, Mary Ellen, Interim Dir, Whittier College, Bonnie Bell Wardman Library, 7031 Founders Hill Rd, Whittier, CA, 90608-9984. Tel: 562-907-4247. Fax: 562-698-7168. p. 283

Vick, Natalee, Tech Serv Coordr, Seattle Pacific University Library, 3307 Third Ave W, Seattle, WA, 98119. Tel: 206-281-2735. Fax: 206-281-2936. p. 2530

Vickers, Adrian, Mgr, Info Tech, Octavia Fellin Public Library, 115 W Hill Ave, Gallup, NM, 87301. Tel: 505-863-1291. Fax: 505-722-5090. p. 1556

Vickers, Jacqueline H, Dir, South Georgia College, 100 W College Park Dr, Douglas, GA, 31533-5098. Tel: 912-260-4323. Fax: 912-260-4452. p. 531

Vickers, Margaret, Periodicals Librn, Belmont Abbey College, 100 Belmont-Mt Holly Rd, Belmont, NC, 28012. Tel: 704-461-6747. Fax: 704-461-6743. p. 1776

Vickers, Neal, Financial Dir, Live Oak Public Libraries, 2002 Bull St, Savannah, GA, 31401. Tel: 912-652-3600. Fax: 912-652-3638. p. 550

Vickers, Rebecca, Dir, Lubbock Christian University Library, 5601 19th St, Lubbock, TX, 79407-2009. Tel: 806-720-7326. p. 2357

Vickery, Cynthia, Dir, Shawneetown Public Library, 320 N Lincoln Blvd E, Shawneetown, IL, 62984. Tel: 618-269-3761. Fax: 618-269-3761. p. 701

Vickery, Laura, Children's Coordr, Dyer Library, 371 Main St, Saco, ME, 04072. Tel: 207-283-3861. Fax: 207-283-0754. p. 999

Vickrey, Carolyn, Dr, Assoc Dir, Austin College, 900 N Grand Ave, Ste 6L, Sherman, TX, 75090-4402. Tel: 903-813-2490. Fax: 903-813-2297. p. 2387

Victor, Jane, Ref & Instruction Librn, Pittsburg State University, 1605 S Joplin St, Pittsburg, KS, 66762-5889. Tel: 620-235-4886. Fax: 620-235-4090. p. 890

Victoria, Margaret, Libr Dir, Stonington Free Library, 20 High St, Stonington, CT, 06378. Tel: 860-535-0658. Fax: 860-535-3945. p. 370

Victoria, Melek, Dir of Libr, Cambridge City Public Library, 33 W Main St, Cambridge City, IN, 47327. Tel: 765-478-3335. Fax: 765-478-6144. p. 731

Victoria, Van, Asst Dir, Kent Free Library, 312 W Main, Kent, OH, 44240-2493. Tel: 330-673-4414. Fax: 330-673-0226. p. 1906

Victorin, Andres, ILL, Ref, Paul, Hastings, Janofsky & Walker LLP, 515 S Flower, 25th Flr, Los Angeles, CA, 90071. Tel: 213-683-6000. Fax: 213-627-0705. p. 176

Vidal, Anna, Head, Adult Serv, Royal Oak Public Library, 222 E Eleven Mile Rd, Royal Oak, MI, 48067-2633. Tel: 248-246-3716. Fax: 248-246-3701. p. 1223

Vidales, Marisol, Br Mgr, Brownsville Public Library System, 2600 Central Blvd, Brownsville, TX, 78520-8824. Tel: 956-548-1055. Fax: 956-548-0684. p. 2292

Vidales, Marisol, Dir, Dr Hector P Garcia Memorial Library, 434 S Ohio St, Mercedes, TX, 78570. Tel: 956-565-2371. Fax: 956-565-9458. p. 2362

Vidas, Chris, Coordr, Electronic Res, Pub Serv Librn, University of South Carolina Upstate Library, 800 University Way, Spartanburg, SC, 29303. Tel: 864-503-5672. Fax: 864-503-5601. p. 2205

Vidaurri, Amada, Evening/Weekend Librn, West Texas A&M University, University Dr & 26th St, Canyon, TX, 79016. Tel: 806-651-2229. Fax: 806-651-2213. p. 2294

Vidaurri, Andrea, Circ, Robert J Kleberg Public Library, 220 N Fourth St, Kingsville, TX, 78363. Tel: 361-592-6381. p. 2350

Viden, Francine, Librn, Capehart & Scatchard, PA Library, 8000 Midlantic Dr, Ste 300 S, Mount Laurel, NJ, 08054. Tel: 856-234-6800, Ext 2151. Fax: 856-235-2786. p. 1506

Videon, Carol, Ref, Delaware County Community College Library, 901 S Media Line Rd, Media, PA, 19063-1094. Tel: 610-359-5149, 610-359-5326. Fax: 610-359-5272. p. 2087

Vidmar, Dale, Bibliog Instr, Southern Oregon University, 1250 Siskiyou Blvd, Ashland, OR, 97520-5076. Tel: 541-552-6842. Fax: 541-552-6429. p. 1990

Vidrine, Elizabeth, Info Tech, Randolph Community College, 629 Industrial Park Ave, Asheboro, NC, 27205-7333. Tel: 336-633-0204. Fax: 336-629-4695. p. 1773

Vidrine, Rachel, Librn, Wake Technical Community College, Western Wake Library, 3434 Kildaire Farms Rd, Cary, NC, 27518-2277. Tel: 919-335-1029. p. 1819

Vidunas, Gail, Br Mgr, Hawaii State Public Library System, Pahoa Public & School Library, 15-3070 Pahoa-Kalapana Rd, Pahoa, HI, 96778. Tel: 808-965-2171. Fax: 808-965-2199. p. 563

Viehmeyer, Allen L, Assoc Dir, Schwenkfelder Library & Heritage Center, 105 Seminary St, Pennsburg, PA, 18073. Tel: 215-679-3103, Ext 17. Fax: 215-679-8175. p. 2102

Vieira, Karen M, Circ, South Dakota School of Mines & Technology, 501 E Saint Joseph St, Rapid City, SD, 57701-3995. Tel: 605-394-2418. Fax: 605-394-1256. p. 2217

Viel, Michelle, Coordr, Access Serv, Bradley University, 1501 W Bradley Ave, Peoria, IL, 61625. Tel: 309-677-2850. Fax: 309-677-2558. p. 690

Vielma, Sulema, Managing Librn, Austin Public Library, Eustasio Cepeda, 651 N Pleasant Valley Rd, Austin, TX, 78702. Tel: 512-974-7372. Fax: 512-974-7329. p. 2279

Vielot, Marie, Br Mgr, Coweta Public Library System, Grantville Public Library, 100 Park Dr, Grantville, GA, 30220-1708. Tel: 770-683-0535. p. 546

Vielot, Marie, Br Mgr, Coweta Public Library System, Senoia Area Public Library, 70 Main St, Senoia, GA, 30276. Tel: 770-599-3537. Fax: 770-599-3537. p. 546

Vien, Lindsey, Educ Serv Coordr, Hayward Public Library, 835 C St, Hayward, CA, 94541-5120. Tel: 510-881-7935. p. 157

Viens, Manon, Ref, Cinematheque Quebecoise, 335 boul de Maisonneuve est, Montreal, QC, H2X 1K1, CANADA. Tel: 514-842-9768, Ext 262. Fax: 514-842-1816. p. 2893

Viera, Ann, Ref Serv Librn, University of Tennessee, Knoxville, Agriculture-Veterinary Medicine, A-113 Veterinary Teaching Hospital, 2407 Joe Johnson Dr, Knoxville, TN, 37996-4541. Tel: 865-974-9015. Fax: 865-974-4732. p. 2244

Vierck, Marcia, Assoc Dir, Elkhart Public Library, Pierre Moran Branch, 2400 Benham Ave, Elkhart, IN, 46517. Tel: 574-294-6418. Fax: 574-294-6419. p. 737

Viereck, Barb, Asst Dir, Admin, Larchwood Public Library, 1020 Broadway, Larchwood, IA, 51241. Tel: 712-477-2583. Fax: 712-477-2366. p. 827

Vierra, Bobbie, Tech Serv, Saint Helena Public Library, 1492 Library Lane, Saint Helena, CA, 94574-1143. Tel: 707-963-5244. Fax: 707-963-5264. p. 226

Vierra, Martha, Cat, Howard County Library, 500 Main St, Big Spring, TX, 79720-2532. Tel: 432-264-2260. Fax: 432-264-2263. p. 2289

Viers, Valerie, Archivist, Ref Serv, Ripon College, 300 Seward St, Ripon, WI, 54971. Tel: 920-748-8752. Fax: 920-748-7243. p. 2634

Vierthaler, Patricia, Cat, Circ, Ser, Trident Technical College, Main Campus Learning Resources Center, LR-M, PO Box 118067, Charleston, SC, 29423-8067. Tel: 843-574-6089. Fax: 843-574-6484. p. 2185

Viestenz, Jackie, Dir, Sherman Free Library, 20 Church St, Port Henry, NY, 12974. Tel: 518-546-7461. Fax: 518-546-7461. p. 1720

Vieth, Lynne, Instrul & Res Librn, Whitman College, 345 Boyer Ave, Walla Walla, WA, 99362. Tel: 509-527-4905. Fax: 509-527-5900. p. 2547

Viezbicke, Lisa, Asst Dir, Libr Serv, Beloit College, 731 College St, Beloit, WI, 53511-5595. Tel: 608-363-2486. Fax: 608-363-2487. p. 2581

Vigeland, Bonnie, Bibliog Instr, Ref, Hampshire College Library, 893 West St, Amherst, MA, 01002-5001. Tel: 413-559-5440. Fax: 413-559-5419. p. 1048

Vigezzi, Nancy, Head, Tech Serv, Merrimack Public Library, 470 Daniel Webster Hwy, Merrimack, NH, 03054-3694. Tel: 603-424-5021. Fax: 603-424-7312. p. 1457

Viggiano, Ellen, Evening Librn, Central Carolina Community College Libraries, 1105 Kelly Dr, Sanford, NC, 27330. Tel: 919-718-7244. Fax: 919-718-7378. p. 1823

Viggiano, Leonard, Evening Librn, Central Carolina Community College Libraries, 1105 Kelly Dr, Sanford, NC, 27330. Tel: 919-718-7244. Fax: 919-718-7378. p. 1823

Viggiano, Steve, Head, Info & Tech, Manchester City Library, 405 Pine St, Manchester, NH, 03104-6199. Tel: 603-624-6550. Fax: 603-624-6559. p. 1455

Viggiano, Steve, Evening Ref Librn, Southern New Hampshire University, 2500 N River Rd, Manchester, NH, 03106-1045. Tel: 603-645-9605. Fax: 603-645-9685. p. 1456

Vigil, Annette, Co-Mgr, Phoenix Public Library, South Mountain Community Library, 7050 S 24th St, Phoenix, AZ, 85042. Tel: 602-262-4636. p. 76

Vigil, Debra, Circ Supvr, ILL, North Idaho College Library, 1000 W Garden Ave, Coeur d'Alene, ID, 83814-2199. Tel: 208-769-3355. Fax: 208-769-3428. p. 573

Vigil, Doris, Circ, Pueblo of Pojoaque Public Library, 37 Camino del Rincon, Ste 2, Santa Fe, NM, 87506-9810. Tel: 505-455-7511. Fax: 505-455-0501. p. 1563

Vigil, Joan, Sr Librn, Denver Public Library, Valdez Perry Branch, 4690 Vine St, Denver, CO, 80216-2823. Tel: 303-295-4302. Fax: 303-295-4307. p. 301

Vigil, Merle F, Res, USDA Agricultural Research Service, 40335 County Rd GG, Akron, CO, 80720. Tel: 970-345-2259. Fax: 970-345-2088. p. 287

Vigil, Norma, Librn, Fred Macaron Library, 600 Colbert, Springer, NM, 87747. Tel: 575-483-2848. Fax: 575-483-2471. p. 1565

Vigil, Patricia, Librn, Colorado Department of Corrections, 4102 Sawmill Mesa Rd, Delta, CO, 81416. Tel: 970-874-7614, Ext 2950, 970-874-7614, Ext 2955. Fax: 970-874-5810, 970-874-5890. p. 298

Vigneau, Andre, Archivist, Chief Librn, Societe de Transport de Montreal, 800 Gauchetiere St O, Bureau 9740, Montreal, QC, H5A 1J6, CANADA. Tel: 514-280-6109. Fax: 514-280-6126. p. 2901

Vigness, Jane, Br Librn, Lake Agassiz Regional Library, Climax Public Library, 104 W Broadway, Climax, MN, 56523-0006. Tel: 218-857-2455. Fax: 218-857-2455. p. 1266

Vigo-Cepeda, Luisa, Prof, University of Puerto Rico, Rio Piedras Campus, PO Box 21906, San Juan, PR, 00931-1906. Tel: 787-764-0000, Ext 1286, 787-764-0000, Ext 5028. Fax: 787-764-2311. p. 2977

Vigorito, Patricia M, Librn, Morton Hospital, a Steward Family Hospital, 88 Washington St, Taunton, MA, 02780-2499. Tel: 508-828-7407. Fax: 508-828-7408. p. 1130

Vigue, Meta, ILL, Waterville Public Library, 73 Elm St, Waterville, ME, 04901-6078. Tel: 207-872-5433. Fax: 207-873-4779. p. 1006

Vik, Jean, Assoc Dir, Syst, University of Texas at Dallas, 800 W Campbell Rd, Richardson, TX, 75080. Tel: 972-883-2623. Fax: 972-883-2988. p. 2374

Vilander, Debbie, Br Mgr, Long Beach Public Library, Bay Shore, 195 Bay Shore Ave, Long Beach, CA, 90803. Tel: 562-570-1039. p. 167

Vilelle, Luke, Actg Univ Librn, Pub Serv, Hollins University, 7950 E Campus Dr, Roanoke, VA, 24020-1000. Tel: 540-362-6592. Fax: 540-362-6756. p. 2493

Viles, Ann, Assoc Univ Librn, Appalachian State University, 218 College St, Boone, NC, 28608. Tel: 828-262-2777. Fax: 828-262-3001. p. 1776

Viles, Deborah, Acq Mgr, Maryland Institute College of Art, 1401 Mount Royal Ave, Baltimore, MD, 21217. Tel: 410-225-2304, 410-225-2311. Fax: 410-225-2316. p. 1015

Villa, Dario, Archivist, Ref Librn, Northeastern Illinois University, 5500 N Saint Louis Ave, Chicago, IL, 60625-4699. Tel: 773-442-4416. Fax: 773-442-4531. p. 621

Villa, Mara, Supvr, Youth Serv, Pearl Public Library, 2416 Old Brandon Rd, Pearl, MS, 39208-4601. Tel: 601-932-2562. Fax: 601-932-3535. p. 1311

Villa, Mayte, Librn, Hispanic Culture Foundation Resource Library, 1701 Fourth St SW, Albuquerque, NM, 87102. Tel: 505-246-2261, Ext 165. Fax: 505-724-4778. p. 1549

Villa, Samantha, Tech Serv Librn, Carlsbad Public Library, 101 S Halagueno St, Carlsbad, NM, 88220. Tel: 575-885-6776. Fax: 575-887-7706. p. 1552

Villagran, Stella, Ref, Organization of American States, 19th & Constitution Ave NW, Washington, DC, 20006-4499. Tel: 202-458-6041. Fax: 202-458-3914. p. 412

Villamil, Maria E, Ref, Inter-American University of Puerto Rico, 500 Carretera Dr, Bayamon, PR, 00957-6257. Tel: 787-279-1912. Fax: 787-279-2205. p. 2671

Villanueva, Julie, Circ Supvr, Monterey Park Bruggemeyer Library, 318 S Ramona Ave, Monterey Park, CA, 91754-3399. Tel: 626-307-1368. Fax: 626-288-4251. p. 190

Villarino, Esther, Head, Cat, University of Puerto Rico, Law School Library, Avenidas Ponce de Leon & Gandara, San Juan, PR, 00931. Tel: 787-999-9709. Fax: 787-999-9680. p. 2676

Villarma, Margaret, Assoc Librn, Irene Ingle Public Library, 124 Second Ave, Wrangell, AK, 99929. Tel: 907-874-3535. Fax: 907-874-2520. p. 55

Villarreal, Melina, Cat Tech, Laredo Community College, West End Washington St, Laredo, TX, 78040. Tel: 956-721-5269. Fax: 956-721-5447. p. 2353

Villarreal, Raymond, Br Mgr, San Antonio Public Library, Bazan, 2200 W Commerce St, San Antonio, TX, 78207. Tel: 210-225-1614. p. 2382

Villasana, Janie, Br Mgr, El Paso Public Library, Memorial Park, 3200 Copper Ave, El Paso, TX, 79930. Tel: 915-566-1034. Fax: 915-564-3944. p. 2316

Villegas, Alberto, Head Librn, El Paso Community College Library, Transmountain Campus Library, 9570 Gateway Blvd N, El Paso, TX, 79924. Tel: 915-831-5198. p. 2316

Villegas, Susana, Libr Dir, La Joya Municipal Library, 925 S Leo Ave, La Joya, TX, 78560. Tel: 956-581-4533. Fax: 956-580-7023. p. 2351

Villegas, Victoria, Libr Asst, City of Melissa Public Library, 3411 Barker Ave, Melissa, TX, 75454. Tel: 972-837-4540. Fax: 972-837-2006. p. 2361

Villella, Therese, Tech Serv Librn, Rivkin Radler LLP, 926 RexCorp Plaza, Uniondale, NY, 11556-0926. Tel: 516-357-3453, 516-357-3454, 516-357-3455. Fax: 516-357-3333. p. 1758

Villigrana, Rosa, Librn, Lake County Library District, Silver Lake Branch, Hwy 31, Silver Lake, OR, 97638. Tel: 541-576-2146. Fax: 541-576-2146. p. 2003

Villines, Annette, Pub Serv Asst, Oral Roberts University Library, 7777 South Lewis Ave, Tulsa, OK, 74171. Tel: 918-495-7378. Fax: 918-495-6893. p. 1981

Vinals, Jose, Librn, Quebec Ministere des Transports, 700 est boul Rene-Levesque, Quebec, QC, G1R 5H1, CANADA. Tel: 418-643-3578. Fax: 418-646-2343. p. 2906

Vince, Jeanne, Pub Serv, Ref, University of Tampa, 401 W Kennedy Blvd, Tampa, FL, 33606-1490. Tel: 813-253-6231. Fax: 813-258-7426. p. 499

Vincelli, Deborah, Electronic Res, Metropolitan Museum of Art, Thomas J Watson Library, 1000 Fifth Ave, New York, NY, 10028-0198. Tel: 212-650-2912. Fax: 212-570-3847. p. 1686

Vincelli, Nick J, Head Librn, North Carolina Department of Labor, 111 Hillsborough St, Rm C510, Raleigh, NC, 27603-1762. Tel: 919-807-2848, 919-807-2850. Fax: 919-807-2849. p. 1815

Vincent, Annette, Circ Mgr, Coordr, University of Arkansas-Monticello Library, 514 University Dr, Monticello, AR, 71656. Tel: 870-460-1080. Fax: 870-460-1980. p. 110

Vincent, Bonnie, Circ, Pinellas Park Public Library, 7770 52nd St, Pinellas Park, FL, 33781-3498. Tel: 727-541-0718. Fax: 727-541-0818. p. 483

Vincent, Carol, Head Librn, Temple University School of Podiatric Medicine, Eighth St at Race, Philadelphia, PA, 19107. Tel: 215-625-5275. Fax: 215-629-1622. p. 2117

Vincent, Carol, Dir, Eastern Shore Public Library, 23610 Front St, Accomac, VA, 23301. Tel: 757-678-7800, 757-787-3400, 757-824-5151. Fax: 757-787-2241. p. 2443

Vincent, Carol, Dir, Eastern Shore Public Library, Northampton Free Library, 7745 Seaside Rd, Nassawadox, VA, 23413. Tel: 757-414-0010. Fax: 757-414-0424. p. 2443

Vincent, Charl, Libr Mgr, Empress Municipal Library, 613 Third Ave, Empress, AB, T0J 1E0, CANADA. Tel: 403-565-3936. Fax: 403-565-2010. p. 2703

Vincent, Danielle, Librn, Bibliotheque Montcalm Library, 113 B, Second Ave, Saint-Jean-Baptiste, MB, R0G 2B0, CANADA. Tel: 204-758-3137. Fax: 204-758-3574. p. 2751

Vincent, Dena, Librn, Edward A Block Family Library, Riley Hospital, 702 Barnhill Dr, Rm 1719, Indianapolis, IN, 46202-5128. Tel: 317-274-1149, 317-278-1645. Fax: 317-278-1631. p. 749

Vincent, John, Pres, Downey Historical Society, 12540 Rives Ave, Downey, CA, 90242-3444. Tel: 562-862-2777. p. 144

Vincent, Linda, Br Mgr, Milwaukee Public Library, Zablocki, 3501 W Oklahoma Ave, Milwaukee, WI, 53215. Tel: 414-286-3055. Fax: 414-286-8430. p. 2620

Vincent, Linda S, Mgt Librn, Wisconsin Talking Book & Braille Library, 813 W Wells St, Milwaukee, WI, 53233-1436. Tel: 414-286-3010. Fax: 414-286-3102. p. 2622

Vincent, Lise, Coordr, Cegep du Vieux Montreal Library, 255 Ontario St E, Montreal, QC, H2X 1X6, CANADA. Tel: 514-982-3437, Ext 2580. Fax: 514-982-3448. p. 2892

Vincent, Lynda A, Pub Serv, Volunteer State Community College Library, 1480 Nashville Pike, Gallatin, TN, 37066-3188. Tel: 615-230-3400, Ext 3415. Fax: 615-230-3410. p. 2235

Vincent, Monica, Circ Serv, Liverpool Public Library, 310 Tulip St, Liverpool, NY, 13088-4997. Tel: 315-457-0310. Fax: 315-453-7867. p. 1653

Vincent, Nancy, Dir, Keene Public Library, 60 Winter St, Keene, NH, 03431-3360. Tel: 603-352-0157. Fax: 866-743-0446. p. 1452

Vincent, Pam, Dir, Henderson County Public Library, 101 S Main St, Henderson, KY, 42420-3599. Tel: 270-826-3712. Fax: 270-827-4226. p. 917

Vincent, Patti, In Charge, Multnomah County Library, Capitol Hill, 10723 SW Capitol Hwy, Portland, OR, 97219-6816. Tel: 503-988-5385. Fax: 503-988-5479. p. 2012

Vincent, Rachel, Librn, Sterling Public Library, 1183 Plainfield Pike, Oneco, CT, 06373. Tel: 860-564-2692. Fax: 860-564-0789. p. 363

Vincent, Sandy, Spec Coll Librn, Fremont Area District Library, 104 E Main, Fremont, MI, 49412. Tel: 231-928-0253. Fax: 231-924-2355. p. 1182

Vincent, Sharla A, Dir, Tekonsha Public Library, 230 S Church St, Tekonsha, MI, 49092. Tel: 517-767-4769. Fax: 517-767-4769. p. 1230

Vincent, Sharon, Br Head, Farmington Community Library, 32737 W 12 Mile Rd, Farmington Hills, MI, 48334-3302. Tel: 248-848-4307. Fax: 248-553-3228. p. 1178

Vincent, Steven, Head, Ref, ILL, Southern Polytechnic State University, 1100 S Marietta Pkwy, Marietta, GA, 30060-2896. Tel: 678-915-7276. Fax: 678-915-4944. p. 543

Vincent, Steven, Pres, Metro Atlanta Library Association, PO Box 14948, Atlanta, GA, 30324. Tel: 404-371-8072. Fax: 678-915-7471. p. 2941

Vincent, Sue, ILL Librn, Dover Public Library, 73 Locust St, Dover, NH, 03820-3785. Tel: 603-516-6050. Fax: 603-516-6053. p. 1445

Vincevic, Cathy, Librn, Allenstown Public Library, 59 Main St, Allenstown, NH, 03275-1716. Tel: 603-485-7651. p. 1437

Vinci, Laura J, Ref, Wilentz, Goldman & Spitzer, 90 Woodbridge Center Dr, Woodbridge, NJ, 07095. Tel: 732-855-6140. Fax: 732-726-6503. p. 1545

Vincz, Sharon, Dir, Library Company of Burlington, 23 W Union St, Burlington, NJ, 08016. Tel: 609-386-1273. Fax: 609-386-1273. p. 1476

Vincze, Georgette, Librn, Abbott Laboratories Ltd Library, 8401 Trans Canada Hwy, Ville St'Laurent, Saint Laurent, QC, H4S 1Z1, CANADA. Tel: 514-832-7000. Fax: 514-832-7800. p. 2909

Vine, Scott, Ref Serv, Franklin & Marshall College, 450 College Ave, Lancaster, PA, 17603-3318. Tel: 717-291-3840. Fax: 717-291-4160. p. 2076

Vine, William A, Coll Mgt Librn, Madonna University Library, 36600 Schoolcraft Rd, Livonia, MI, 48150-1173. Tel: 734-432-5685. Fax: 734-432-5687. p. 1204

Vineis, Pat, Acq, Media Spec, Sandwich Public Library, 142 Main St, Sandwich, MA, 02563. Tel: 508-888-0625. Fax: 508-833-1076. p. 1122

Vines, Hattie, Info & Educ Serv Librn/Pub Serv, Duke University Libraries, Medical Center Library, DUMC Box 3702, Ten Bryan-Searle Dr, Durham, NC, 27710-0001. Tel: 919-660-1125. Fax: 919-681-7599. p. 1788

Vines, Susan, Pub Serv, Georgia Highlands College Libraries, 3175 Cedartown Hwy SE, Rome, GA, 30161. Tel: 706-295-6318. Fax: 706-295-6365. p. 548

Vinet, France, Prof, College de Maisonneuve, 3800, rue Sherbrooke Est, Montreal, QC, H1X 2A2, CANADA. Tel: 514-254-7131. Fax: 514-251-9741. p. 2978

Vineyard, Judy, Assoc Dean, John A Logan College, 700 Logan College Rd, Carterville, IL, 62918. Tel: 618-985-3741, Ext 8404. Fax: 618-985-3899. p. 601

Vink, Barbara, Pub Relations, Voorheesville Public Library, 51 School Rd, Voorheesville, NY, 12186. Tel: 518-765-2791. Fax: 518-765-3007. p. 1761

Vinke, Dana, Principal Librn, Torrance Public Library, 3301 Torrance Blvd, Torrance, CA, 90503. Tel: 310-618-5974. Fax: 310-618-5952. p. 276

Vinopal, Kelly, Dir, Info Res, American Society of International Law Library, 2223 Massachusetts Ave NW, Washington, DC, 20008-2864. Tel: 202-939-6005. Fax: 202-319-1670. p. 393

Vinson, Bill, Pub Serv, Georgia Highlands College Libraries, 3175 Cedartown Hwy SE, Rome, GA, 30161. Tel: 706-295-6318. Fax: 706-295-6365. p. 548

Vinson, Chris, Head, Digital Initiatives & Info Tech, Clemson University Libraries, Box 343001, Clemson, SC, 29634-3001. Tel: 864-656-3039. Fax: 864-656-0758. p. 2186

Vinson, Debra, Librn, Louisville Public Library, 1951 Main St, Louisville, AL, 36048. Tel: 334-266-5210. Fax: 334-266-5630. p. 24

Vinson, Dyan, Acq, Thomas Nelson Community College Library, Wythe Hall 228, 99 Thomas Nelson Dr, Hampton, VA, 23666. Tel: 757-825-2872. Fax: 757-825-2870. p. 2468

Vinton, Cab, Dir, Sanbornton Public Library, 27 Meetinghouse Hill Rd, Sanbornton, NH, 03269. Tel: 603-286-8288. Fax: 603-286-9544. p. 1464

Vinyard, Anne, Per, West Virginia University Institute of Technology, 405 Fayette Pike, Montgomery, WV, 25136-2436. Tel: 304-442-3218. Fax: 304-442-3091. p. 2565

Vinyard, Carolyn, Ref & Info Serv, Capital University, Law School Library, 303 E Broad St, Columbus, OH, 43215. Tel: 614-236-6464. Fax: 614-236-6957. p. 1883

Vinyard, Marc, Ref, Pepperdine University Libraries, 24255 Pacific Coast Hwy, Malibu, CA, 90263. Tel: 310-506-4252. Fax: 310-506-7225. p. 182

Vinyard, Sue, Adult Serv, Clinton Public Library, 313 S Fourth St, Clinton, IN, 47842-2398. Tel: 765-832-8349. Fax: 765-832-3823. p. 732

Violetto, Caroline, Br Mgr, Cook County Law Library, Markham Branch, 16501 S Kedzie Pkwy, Markham, IL, 60426. Tel: 708-210-4125. Fax: 708-210-4374. p. 612

Vioreanu, Judy, Adult Serv, Coll Develop, Ref, Kinnelon Public Library, 132 Kinnelon Rd, Kinnelon, NJ, 07405-2393. Tel: 973-838-1321. Fax: 973-838-0741. p. 1493

Vipperman, Betsy, Pub Serv, New York State Judicial Department, M Dolores Denman Courthouse, 50 East Ave, Ste 100, Rochester, NY, 14604-2214. Tel: 585-530-3250. Fax: 585-530-3270. p. 1731

Viramontes, Christina, Tech Serv Librn, La Sierra University Library, 4500 Riverwalk Pkwy, Riverside, CA, 92505-3344. Tel: 951-785-2397. Fax: 951-785-2445. p. 217

Viramontes, Soledad, In Charge, Mexican American Opportunity Foundation, 401 N Garfield Ave, Montebello, CA, 90640. Tel: 323-890-9600. Fax: 323-890-9632. p. 189

Virgil, Candance, Asst Dean, Libr Serv, Lindenwood University, 209 S Kingshighway, Saint Charles, MO, 63301. Tel: 636-949-4194. Fax: 636-949-4822. p. 1351

Virgil-Call, Nancy, Asst Libr Dir, Utica College, 1600 Burrstone Rd, Utica, NY, 13502-4892. Tel: 315-792-3151. Fax: 315-792-3361. p. 1759

Virkler, Darlene, Dir, Macedon Public Library, 30 Main St, Macedon, NY, 14502-9101. Tel: 315-986-5932. Fax: 315-986-2952. p. 1656

Virks, Ulla Merike, Dir, Cross' Mills Public Library, 4417 Old Post Rd, Charlestown, RI, 02813. Tel: 401-364-6211. Fax: 401-364-0609. p. 2164

Virr, Richard, Dr, Archivist, Anglican Church of Canada Archives, 1444 Union Ave, Montreal, QC, H3A 2B8, CANADA. Tel: 514-843-6577, Ext 254. Fax: 514-843-6344. p. 2887

Virta, Alan, Head, Spec Coll, Boise State University, 1865 Cesar Chavez Lane, Boise, ID, 83725-1430. Tel: 208-426-3958. Fax: 208-334-2111. p. 570

Virtue, Alicia, Electronic Serv Librn, Santa Rosa Junior College, 1501 Mendocino Ave, Santa Rosa, CA, 95401. Tel: 707-527-4773. Fax: 707-527-4545. p. 267

Viscount, Heather, Access Serv, Cobourg Public Library, 200 Ontario St, Cobourg, ON, K9A 5P4, CANADA. Tel: 905-372-9271. Fax: 905-372-4538. p. 2800

Viser, Helen, Br Mgr, Lubbock Public Library, Bobbie Gean & T J Patterson Branch, 1836 Parkway Dr, Lubbock, TX, 79403. Tel: 806-767-3300. Fax: 806-767-3302. p. 2357

Vision, Sue, Head, Ref, Haverford Township Free Library, 1601 Darby Rd, Havertown, PA, 19083-3798. Tel: 610-446-3082. Fax: 610-853-3090. p. 2067

Visione, Jennifer, Admin Serv, West Nyack Free Library, 65 Strawtown Rd, West Nyack, NY, 10994. Tel: 845-358-6081. Fax: 845-358-4071. p. 1766

Visnesky, Holly, Sr Librn, Ch Serv, Mt Lebanon Public Library, 16 Castle Shannon Blvd, Pittsburgh, PA, 15228-2252. Tel: 412-531-1912. Fax: 412-531-1161. p. 2126

Visnich, Claudia, Mgr, Kansas City Public Library, North-East, 6000 Wilson Rd, Kansas City, MO, 64123. Tel: 816-701-3589. Fax: 816-701-3495. p. 1338

Visnich, Claudia, Mgr, Kansas City Public Library, Sugar Creek Branch, 102 S Sterling, Sugar Creek, MO, 64054. Tel: 816-701-3589. Fax: 816-701-3499. p. 1338

Visser, Dagmar, Librn, Neerlandia Public Library, PO Box 10, Neerlandia, AB, T0G 1R0, CANADA. Tel: 780-674-5384. Fax: 780-674-2927. p. 2712

Visser, Murray R, Supvry Librn, Marine Corps Base Hawaii Libraries, Marine Corps Base Hawaii, Bldg 219, Kaneohe Bay, HI, 96863. Tel: 808-254-7624. Fax: 808-254-7623. p. 566

Visser, Susan, Dir, South Bend Museum of Art Library, 120 S St Joseph St, South Bend, IN, 46601. Tel: 574-235-9102. Fax: 574-235-5782. p. 779

Vita, Frances, Dir, Quarryville Library, 357 Buck Rd, Quarryville, PA, 17566. Tel: 717-786-1336. Fax: 717-786-9220. p. 2132

Vital, Sarah, Ref & Instruction Librn, Saint Mary's College Library, 1928 Saint Mary's Rd, Moraga, CA, 94575. Tel: 925-631-4229. Fax: 925-376-6097. p. 191

Vitale, Whitney, Info Literacy/Distance Educ Librn, Boston Architectural College, 320 Newbury St, Boston, MA, 02115. Tel: 617-585-7337. Fax: 617-585-0151. p. 1055

Vitali, John, Chief Financial Officer, Dep Dir, Bus Admin, Brooklyn Public Library, Grand Army Plaza, Brooklyn, NY, 11238-5698. Tel: 718-230-2407. Fax: 718-398-3947. p. 1590

Vitamvas, Sally, Dir, Silver City Public Library, 408 Main St, Silver City, IA, 51571. Tel: 712-525-9053. Fax: 712-525-9053. p. 843

Vitas, Robertas, Dr, VPres, Lithuanian Research & Studies Center, Inc, 5600 S Claremont Ave, Chicago, IL, 60636-1039. Tel: 773-434-4545. Fax: 773-434-9363. p. 617

Vitek, Bill, Chief Librn, Social Security Administration Library, Annex Bldg 1520, Baltimore, MD, 21235-6401. Fax: 410-966-2027. p. 1017

Viti, Thomas P, Dir, Westwood Public Library, 668 High St, Westwood, MA, 02090. Tel: 781-326-7562. Fax: 781-326-5383. p. 1139

Vitovec, Ernst, Br Supvr, Fresno County Public Library, 2420 Mariposa St, Fresno, CA, 93721-2285. Tel: 559-600-7323. p. 151

Vits, Inez, Librn, Pankhurst Memorial Library, Three S Jefferson Ave, Amboy, IL, 61310-1400. Tel: 815-857-3925. Fax: 815-857-3065. p. 588

Vittitoe, Margaret, Librn, Modale Public Library, 511 N Main St, Modale, IA, 51556. Tel: 712-645-2826. Fax: 712-645-2826. p. 832

Vittum-Jones, Leona, Librn, Henderson District Public Libraries, Lydia Malcolm Library, 2960 Sunridge Heights Pkwy, Ste 100, Henderson, NV, 89052. Tel: 702-263-7522, 702-263-7523. Fax: 702-263-7402. p. 1428

Viveiros, Jayme Z, Dir, Russell Memorial Library, 88 Main St, Acushnet, MA, 02743. Tel: 508-998-0270. Fax: 508-998-0271. p. 1047

Viverette, Lee B, Art Librn, Ref Serv Coordr, Virginia Museum of Fine Arts Library, 200 N Boulevard, Richmond, VA, 23220-4007. Tel: 804-340-1496. Fax: 804-340-1431. p. 2492

Vivian, Jean-Paul, Principal Law Librn, Nassau County Supreme Court, 100 Supreme Court Dr, Mineola, NY, 11501. Tel: 516-442-8580. Fax: 516-442-8578. p. 1661

Vivian, Mary E, Chief Librn, Pearl City Public Library District, 221 S Main St, Pearl City, IL, 61062. Tel: 815-443-2832. Fax: 815-443-2832. p. 689

Vivican, Dorothea, Librn Tech I, Virgin Islands Division of Libraries, Archives & Museums, Regional Library for the Blind & Physically Handicapped, 3012 Golden Rock, Christiansted, Saint Croix, VI, 00820. Tel: 340-772-2250. Fax: 340-772-3545. p. 2680

Vivier, Brian, Coordr, Pub Serv, University
of Michigan, Asia, Hatcher Library, 920
N University St, Rm 418, Ann Arbor,
MI, 48109-1205. Tel: 734-764-0406. Fax:
734-647-2885. p. 1152

Vizecky, Susan, Librn, Ivanhoe Public Library,
401 N Harold, Ivanhoe, MN, 56142. Tel:
507-694-1555. Fax: 507-694-1738. p. 1255

Vizzini, Beth, Head, Circ, West Texas A&M
University, University Dr & 26th St, Canyon,
TX, 79016. Tel: 806-651-2223. Fax:
806-651-2213. p. 2294

Vlachos, Helen, Info Spec, Brown, Rudnick,
Berlack, Israels LLP, One Financial Ctr,
Boston, MA, 02111. Tel: 617-856-8213. Fax:
617-856-8201. p. 1059

Vlahos, Len, Dir, American Booksellers Association,
200 White Plains Rd, Tarrytown, NY, 10591.
Tel: 914-591-2665. Fax: 914-591-2720. p. 1754

Vlcek, Laurel, Head, Ref, Vernon Area Public
Library District, 300 Olde Half Day
Rd, Lincolnshire, IL, 60069-2901. Tel:
847-634-3650. Fax: 847-634-8449. p. 666

Vloeberghs, Sonja, Mgr, Access Serv, Princeton
Public Library, 65 Witherspoon St, Princeton,
NJ, 08542. Tel: 609-924-9529, Ext 213. Fax:
609-924-6109. p. 1522

Vnuk, Rebecca, Dir, Adult Serv, Glen Ellyn
Public Library, 400 Duane St, Glen Ellyn,
IL, 60137-4508. Tel: 630-469-0879. Fax:
630-469-1086. p. 650

Vocino, Michael, Coll Develop, Robert L Carothers
Library & Learning Commons, 15 Lippitt Rd,
Kingston, RI, 02881. Tel: 401-874-4605. Fax:
401-874-4608. p. 2168

Vodraska, Curtis, Asst Librn, Ely Public
Library, 1595 Dows St, Ely, IA, 52227. Tel:
319-848-7616. Fax: 319-848-4056. p. 814

Voegler, Carolyn, Dir, Garden City Public Library,
60 Seventh St, Garden City, NY, 11530-2891.
Tel: 516-742-8405. Fax: 516-742-2675. p. 1626

Voelck, Julie, Dean, Oakland University Library,
2200 N Squirrel Rd, Rochester, MI, 48309-4402.
Tel: 248-370-4426. Fax: 248-370-2474. p. 1221

Voelkel, James, Curator, Rare Bks, Donald F &
Mildred Topp Othmer Library of Chemical
History, 315 Chestnut St, Philadelphia, PA,
19106. Tel: 215-873-8271. Fax: 215-629-5271.
p. 2113

Voelker, Charley, Ref Serv, Ad, Morley Library, 184
Phelps St, Painesville, OH, 44077-3926. Tel:
440-352-3383. Fax: 440-352-9097. p. 1927

Voelker, James R, Dep Dir, United States Court
of Appeals Library, Thomas F Eagleton US
Courthouse, 111 S Tenth St, Rm 22-300, Saint
Louis, MO, 63102. Tel: 314-244-2665. Fax:
314-244-2675. p. 1361

Voelker, Joan, Archivist, United States Court of
Appeals Library, Thomas F Eagleton US
Courthouse, 111 S Tenth St, Rm 22-300, Saint
Louis, MO, 63102. Tel: 314-244-2665. Fax:
314-244-2675. p. 1361

Voelkl, Roberta, YA Serv, Ogden Farmers' Library,
269 Ogden Center Rd, Spencerport, NY, 14559.
Tel: 585-617-6181. Fax: 585-352-3406. p. 1746

Voeller, Stacy, Electronic Res, Minnesota State
University Moorhead, 1104 Seventh Ave S,
Moorhead, MN, 56563. Tel: 218-477-2922. Fax:
218-477-5924. p. 1266

Vogan, Wayne, Librn, Canadian Opera Co, 227 Front
St E, Toronto, ON, M5A 1E8, CANADA. Tel:
416-363-6671. Fax: 416-363-5584. p. 2852

Voge, Susan, Head, Ref, Lehman College, City
University of New York, 250 Bedford Park Blvd
W, Bronx, NY, 10468-1589. Tel: 718-960-7765.
Fax: 718-960-8952. p. 1587

Vogel, Anita, Ref Serv, Northwestern College, 101
Seventh St SW, Orange City, IA, 51041-1996.
Tel: 712-707-7249. Fax: 712-707-7247. p. 836

Vogel, Betsy, Librn, Rayovac, 601 Rayovac Dr,
Madison, WI, 53711. Tel: 608-275-4714. Fax:
608-275-4992. p. 2607

Vogel, Carissa, Head, Pub Serv, Columbia
University, Arthur W Diamond Law Library,
435 W 116th St, New York, NY, 10027. Tel:
212-854-3922. Fax: 212-854-3295. p. 1674

Vogel, Chris, Pub Serv, Rainbow Resource Centre
Library, 170 Scott St, Winnipeg, MB, R3C
2Z6, CANADA. Tel: 204-474-0212. Fax:
204-478-1160. p. 2757

Vogel, Gerald, Asst Dir, Avon Lake Public
Library, 32649 Electric Blvd, Avon Lake,
OH, 44012-1669. Tel: 440-933-8128. Fax:
440-933-5659. p. 1856

Vogel, Joanne C, Access Serv Librn, Saint
Louis University, Omer Poos Law Library,
Morrissey Hall, 3700 Lindell Blvd, Saint Louis,
MO, 63108-3478. Tel: 314-977-2758. Fax:
314-977-3966. p. 1361

Vogel, John, Head Librn, National Clearinghouse
on Child Abuse & Neglect Information, 10530
Rosehaven St, Ste 400, Fairfax, VA, 22030. Tel:
703-279-6275. Fax: 703-385-3206. p. 2462

Vogel, Mary, Cat, Lenhardt Library of the
Chicago Botanic Garden, 1000 Lake Cook Rd,
Glencoe, IL, 60022. Tel: 847-835-8381. Fax:
847-835-6885. p. 650

Vogel, Maureen, Libr Asst, Camanche Public
Library, 102 12th Ave, Camanche, IA, 52730.
Tel: 563-259-1106. Fax: 563-259-1106. p. 798

Vogel, Pamela Jean, Ch Serv Librn, Rushville
Public Library, 130 W Third St, Rushville,
IN, 46173-1899. Tel: 765-932-3496. Fax:
765-932-4528. p. 776

Vogel, Petra, Librn, Sterling College, 1205 N
Craftsbury Rd, Craftsbury Common, VT, 05827.
Tel: 802-586-7711, Ext 129. Fax: 802-586-2596.
p. 2422

Vogel, Petra, Librn, Sterling College, 479 Cross Rd,
Wolcott, VT, 05680-4088. Tel: 802-586-7711,
Ext 129. Fax: 802-586-2596. p. 2440

Vogel, Phyllis, Tech Serv Dir, DeSales University,
2755 Station Ave, Center Valley, PA, 18034. Tel:
610-282-1100, Ext 1266. Fax: 610-282-2342.
p. 2043

Vogel, Rita, Br Mgr, York County Library, York
Public, 21 E Liberty St, York, SC, 29745. Tel:
803-684-3751. Fax: 803-684-6223. p. 2203

Vogel, Sharon, Librn, Farnhamville Public Library,
240 Hardin, Farnhamville, IA, 50538. Tel:
515-544-3660. Fax: 515-544-3703. p. 816

Vogel, Sharon, Dir, Berlin Free Town Library,
Whitehouse Memorial Bldg, 47 Main St,
Berlin, NY, 12022. Tel: 518-658-2231. Fax:
518-658-9565. p. 1581

Vogelgesang, Jan, Circ, ILL, Illinois Valley
Community College, 815 N Orlando Smith Ave,
Oglesby, IL, 61348-9692. Tel: 815-224-0306.
Fax: 815-224-9147. p. 684

Vogelsang, Marlene, In Charge, Pacific Gas &
Electric Co, 851 Howard St, San Francisco, CA,
94103. Tel: 415-973-7206. Fax: 415-896-1280.
p. 244

Voges, Judy, Tech Serv Dir, Marylhurst University,
17600 Pacific Hwy (Hwy 43), Marylhurst, OR,
97036-7036. Tel: 503-699-6261, Ext 3374. Fax:
503-636-1957. p. 2004

Vogh, Bryan, Head, Syst, University of
Wisconsin-Eau Claire, 105 Garfield Ave, Eau
Claire, WI, 54702-4004. Tel: 715-836-4962. Fax:
715-836-2949. p. 2590

Vogl, Ann, Assoc Librn, University of Wisconsin
Baraboo-Sauk County, 1006 Connie Rd,
Baraboo, WI, 53913. Tel: 608-355-5251. Fax:
608-355-5291. p. 2580

Vogler, Brad, Ref Librn, Catawba Valley Community
College, 2550 Hwy 70 SE, Hickory, NC,
28602-9699. Tel: 828-327-7000, Ext 4457. Fax:
828-324-5130. p. 1801

Vogler, Laura, Mgr, Ser, Wabash College, PO
Box 352, Crawfordsville, IN, 47933. Tel:
765-361-6215. Fax: 765-361-6295. p. 734

Vogt, Karen, Asst Librn, Hennessey Public Library,
525 S Main, Hennessey, OK, 73742. Tel:
405-853-2073. Fax: 405-853-2073. p. 1965

Vogt, Lori, Dir, Bailey H Dunlap Memorial Public
Library, 400 S Main St, La Feria, TX, 78559.
Tel: 956-797-1242. Fax: 956-797-5408. p. 2351

Vogt, Sharon L, Dir, Kanabec County Historical
Society, 805 W Forest Ave, Mora, MN,
55051-1466. Tel: 320-679-1665. Fax:
320-679-1673. p. 1267

Vogt, Valerie, Ref, Shook, Hardy & Bacon,
2555 Grand Blvd, 3rd Flr, Kansas City,
MO, 64108-2613. Tel: 816-474-6550. Fax:
816-421-5547. p. 1341

Vogus, Brad, Head of Libr, Arizona State
University Libraries, Daniel E Noble Science
& Engineering Library, 601 E Tyler, Tempe,
AZ, 85287-1006. Tel: 480-965-2600. Fax:
480-965-0883. p. 84

Voight, Karen, Librn, Audubon Naturalist Society
Library, 8940 Jones Mill Rd, Chevy Chase, MD,
20815. Tel: 301-652-9188. Fax: 301-951-7179.
p. 1024

Voigts, Leila, Sr Res Spec, Clausen Miller Research
Services Dept, Ten S LaSalle St, 16th Flr,
Chicago, IL, 60603-1098. Tel: 312-606-7887.
Fax: 312-606-7777. p. 611

Voisinet, David, Dir, New York State Judicial
Department, M Dolores Denman Courthouse, 50
East Ave, Ste 100, Rochester, NY, 14604-2214.
Tel: 585-530-3250. Fax: 585-530-3270. p. 1731

Voitko, Nancy, Br Mgr, Ocean County Library,
Beachwood Branch, 126 Beachwood
Blvd, Beachwood, NJ, 08722-2810. Tel:
732-244-4573. Fax: 732-736-1025. p. 1534

Vokey, Sherri, Instr, Red River College,
W210B-160 Princess St, Winnipeg, MB, R3B
1K9, CANADA. Tel: 204-949-8477. Fax:
204-949-0032. p. 2978

Volano, Claudia, Asst Dir, West Haven Public
Library, 300 Elm St, West Haven, CT,
06516-4692. Tel: 203-937-4233. p. 377

Volat, Helene, Head, Ref, Stony Brook University,
W-1502 Melville Library, John S Toll Rd, Stony
Brook, NY, 11794-3300. Tel: 631-632-7100.
Fax: 631-632-7116. p. 1749

Volenik, Kimberly, Patron Serv Mgr, Marion
Public Library, 445 E Church St, Marion,
OH, 43302-4290. Tel: 740-387-0992. Fax:
740-382-9954. p. 1914

Volin, Eva, Supvr, Ch Serv, Alameda Free Library,
1550 Oak St, Alameda, CA, 94501-2932. Tel:
510-747-7707. p. 119

Volk, Carrie, Syst Librn, Winthrop University,
824 Oakland Ave, Rock Hill, SC, 29733. Tel:
803-323-2131, 803-323-2274, 803-323-2311.
Fax: 803-323-2215. p. 2203

Volk, Ulla, Dir, Libr Serv, Cooper Union for
Advancement of Science & Art Library, Seven
E Seventh St, New York, NY, 10003. Tel:
212-353-4184. Fax: 212-353-4017. p. 1676

Volkening, Tom, Librn, Michigan State University
Library, Engineering Library, 1515 Engineering
Bldg, East Lansing, MI, 48824. Tel:
517-355-8536. Fax: 517-353-9041. p. 1175

Volkman, Virginia, Dir, Sedona Public Library,
3250 White Bear Rd, Sedona, AZ, 86336. Tel:
928-282-7714. Fax: 928-282-5789. p. 81

Vollin, Lida, ILL, Natrona County Public Library,
307 E Second St, Casper, WY, 82601. Tel:
307-237-4935, Ext 121. Fax: 307-266-3734.
p. 2652

Vollmar-Grone, Michael, AV, Shelby County
Libraries, 230 E North St, Sidney, OH,
45365-2785. Tel: 937-492-8354. Fax:
937-492-9229. p. 1934

Vollmer, Helen, Librn, Francesville-Salem
Township Public Library, 201 W Montgomery,
Francesville, IN, 47946. Tel: 219-567-9433. Fax:
219-567-9433. p. 743

Vollrath, Justeen, Circ, University of Wisconsin
Center-Marathon County Library, 518 S
Seventh Ave, Wausau, WI, 54401-5396. Tel:
715-261-6202. Fax: 715-261-6330. p. 2647

Volo, Barbara, Monographs Librn, Tulane University, Rudolph Matas Library of the Health Sciences, Tulane Health Sciences Campus, 1430 Tulane Ave, SL-86, New Orleans, LA, 70112-2699. Tel: 504-988-2404. Fax: 504-988-7417. p. 963

Volosin, Cheryl, Supvr, Ch Serv, Ruidoso Public Library, 107 Kansas City Rd, Ruidoso, NM, 88345. Tel: 505-258-3704. Fax: 505-258-4619. p. 1561

Volpe, Paul, Br Mgr, Newark Public Library, Clinton, 739 Bergen St, Newark, NJ, 07108. Tel: 973-733-7754, 973-733-7757. Fax: 973-733-7757. p. 1512

Volpini, Deborah, Circ, Boyden Library, Ten Bird St, Foxborough, MA, 02035. Tel: 508-543-1245. Fax: 508-543-1193. p. 1089

Voltin, Rose Mary, Asst Librn, Lyons Public Library, 448 Cedar St, Lyons, OR, 97358-2122. Tel: 503-859-2366. p. 2004

Voltmer, Nancy, Circ Supvr, Ames Public Library, 515 Douglas Ave, Ames, IA, 50010. Tel: 515-239-5658. Fax: 515-233-9001. p. 792

Volz, Carolynn, Access Serv, International College Library, 2655 Northbrooke Dr, Naples, FL, 34119. Tel: 239-598-6109, 239-938-7812. Fax: 239-598-6250, 239-938-7886. p. 471

Volz, Robert L, Custodian of the Chapin Libr, Williams College, Chapin Library, 96 School St, Apt 3, Williamstown, MA, 01267. Tel: 413-597-2930. Fax: 413-597-2929. p. 1141

Vomund, Paula, Br Mgr, Mexico-Audrain County Library District, Martinsburg Branch, 201 E Washington St, Martinsburg, MO, 65264. Tel: 573-492-6254. Fax: 573-492-6254. p. 1345

Von Arb, Phyllis, Dir, Colona District Public Library, 911 First St, Colona, IL, 61241. Tel: 309-792-0548. Fax: 309-792-2143. p. 631

Von Braun, Bonnie, Br Mgr, Humboldt County Library, Ferndale Branch, 807 Main St, Ferndale, CA, 95536. Tel: 707-786-9559. p. 147

von Daum Tholl, Susan E, Dr, Dir, Emmanuel College, 400 The Fenway, Boston, MA, 02115. Tel: 617-264-7659. Fax: 617-735-9763. p. 1060

Von Der Heide, Connie, Dir of Ref & Outreach Serv, Wisconsin State Law Library, 120 Martin Luther King Jr Blvd, 2nd Flr, Madison, WI, 53703. Tel: 608-267-2202. Fax: 608-267-2319. p. 2611

Von der Lancken, Paula, Cat, Hudson Valley Community College, 80 Vandenburgh Ave, Troy, NY, 12180. Tel: 518-629-7393. Fax: 518-629-7509. p. 1756

Von Drasek, Lisa, Ch, Bank Street College of Education Library, 610 W 112th St, 5th Flr, New York, NY, 10025. Tel: 212-875-4452. Fax: 212-875-4558. p. 1669

Von Hendy, Matthew, Res Librn, The National Academies, 500 Fifth St NW, Keck 304, Washington, DC, 20001-2721. Tel: 202-334-2125. Fax: 202-334-1651. p. 409

Von Holtz, Judy, Head, Tech Serv, Southbury Public Library, 100 Poverty Rd, Southbury, CT, 06488. Tel: 203-262-0626. Fax: 203-262-6734. p. 368

Von Iderstein, Joey, Ch, Scituate Town Library, 85 Branch St, Scituate, MA, 02066. Tel: 781-545-8727. Fax: 781-545-8728. p. 1123

Von Isenburg, Megan, Assoc Dir, Info Serv/Pub Serv, Duke University Libraries, Medical Center Library, DUMC Box 3702, Ten Bryan-Searle Dr, Durham, NC, 27710-0001. Tel: 919-660-1131. Fax: 919-681-7599. p. 1788

Von Kann, Lisa, Dir, Saint Johnsbury Athenaeum, 1171 Main St, Saint Johnsbury, VT, 05819-2289. Tel: 802-748-8291. Fax: 802-748-8086. p. 2435

Von Segen, Ann M, Dir, Providence Saint Vincent Hospital & Medical Center, 9205 SW Barnes Rd, Portland, OR, 97225. Tel: 503-216-2257. Fax: 503-216-6085. p. 2014

Von Swearingen, Rachel Fox, Evening Librn, Metadata Librn, The Boston Conservatory, Eight The Fenway, Boston, MA, 02215-4099. Tel: 617-912-9131. Fax: 617-912-9101. p. 1056

Von Unwerth, Matthew, Dir, New York Psychoanalytic Institute, 247 E 82nd St, New York, NY, 10028. Tel: 212-879-6900. Fax: 212-879-0588. p. 1690

Von Wittgenstein, Karin, Dir, Kimberley Public Library, 115 Spokane St, Kimberley, BC, V1A 2E5, CANADA. Tel: 250-427-3112. Fax: 250-427-7157. p. 2731

Von Zweck, Claudia, Exec Dir, Canadian Association of Occupational Therapists, CTTC Bldg, Ste 3400, 1125 Colonel By Dr, Ottawa, ON, K1S 5R1, CANADA. Tel: 613-523-2268. Fax: 613-523-2552. p. 2829

Vonasek, Toni Engelhardt, Adult Serv, Ref Supvr (Info Serv), Grand Forks Public Library, 2110 Library Circle, Grand Forks, ND, 58201-6324. Tel: 701-772-8116. Fax: 701-772-1379. p. 1842

VonBehren, Sue, Librn, Morley Public Library, 507 Vine St, Morley, IA, 52312. Tel: 319-489-9271. Fax: 319-489-9271. p. 833

Vonderhaar, Shirley J, Dir, James Kennedy Public Library, 320 First Ave E, Dyersville, IA, 52040. Tel: 563-875-8912. Fax: 563-875-6162. p. 812

Vonderscheer, Christel, Assoc Dir, Harford Community College Library, 401 Thomas Run Rd, Bel Air, MD, 21015. Tel: 410-836-4145. Fax: 410-836-4198. p. 1019

Vondracek, Lila, Librn, Bison Community Library, 202 Main St, Bison, KS, 67520. Tel: 785-356-4803. Fax: 785-356-2403. p. 858

Vondruska, Eloise M, Interim Dir, Northwestern University, Chicago, Pritzker Legal Research Center, 375 E Chicago Ave, Chicago, IL, 60611. Tel: 312-503-7369. Fax: 312-503-9230. p. 621

VonHein, Charlotte, Circ, Haverstraw Kings Daughters Public Library, Village Library, 85 Main St, Haverstraw, NY, 10927. Tel: 845-429-3445. Fax: 845-429-7313. p. 1627

Vonk, Teresa, Bus Mgr, Prescott Public Library, 215 E Goodwin St, Prescott, AZ, 86303. Tel: 928-777-1504. Fax: 928-771-5829. p. 78

Vonka, Stephanie, Librn, Material Handling Association of Quebec, 62A Labelle, Laval-des-Rapides, QC, H7N 2S3, CANADA. Tel: 450-662-3717. Fax: 450-662-6096. p. 2886

VonSeggern, Merry, Ch, Grand Island Public Library, 211 N Washington St, Grand Island, NE, 68801-5855. Tel: 308-385-5333, Ext 125. Fax: 308-385-5339. p. 1400

VonTauffkirchen, Elizabeth, Head, Ch, Info Tech, Pine River Public Library District, 395 Bayfield Center Dr, Bayfield, CO, 81122. Tel: 970-884-2222. Fax: 970-884-7155. p. 289

VonVille, Helena M, Dir, Ref, University of Texas, School of Public Health Library, 1200 Herman Pressler Blvd, Houston, TX, 77030-3900. Tel: 713-500-9121. Fax: 713-500-9125. p. 2344

Voogd, Jan, Head, Coll Mgt, Harvard Library, Social Sciences Program, Lamont Library, Level B, Harvard University, Cambridge, MA, 02138. Tel: 617-495-2106. Fax: 617-496-5570. p. 1076

Voorhees, Jane, Dir, Libr Serv, Kinney Memorial Library, 3140 County Hwy 11, Hartwick, NY, 13348-3007. Tel: 607-293-6600. Fax: 607-293-6600. p. 1634

Voorhees, Jane, Dir, Kirby Free Library of Salisbury Center, 105 Rte 29A, Salisbury Center, NY, 13454. Tel: 315-429-9006. Fax: 315-429-9006. p. 1737

Voorhees, Linda, Libr Dir, Cape Vincent Community Library, 157 N Real St, Cape Vincent, NY, 13618. Tel: 315-654-2132. Fax: 315-654-2132. p. 1603

Voorhees, Renee, Dir, Marstons Mills Public Library, 2160 Main St, Marstons Mills, MA, 02648. Tel: 508-428-5175. Fax: 508-420-5194. p. 1103

Voorhies, Marguerite, Tech Serv, Volunteer State Community College Library, 1480 Nashville Pike, Gallatin, TN, 37066-3188. Tel: 615-230-3400, Ext 3404. Fax: 615-230-3410. p. 2235

Voors, Mary, Mgr, Ch Serv, Allen County Public Library, 900 Library Plaza, Fort Wayne, IN, 46802. Tel: 260-421-1221. Fax: 260-421-1386. p. 740

Vopalensky, Jan, Librn, North Bend Public Library, 140 E Eighth St, North Bend, NE, 68649. Tel: 402-652-8356. Fax: 402-652-8356. p. 1410

Vorbach, James, PhD, Assoc Prof, Saint John's University, Saint Augustine Hall, Rm 408, 8000 Utopia Pkwy, Jamaica, NY, 11439. Tel: 718-990-1834. Fax: 718-990-2071. p. 2970

Vorce, Damon, Br Mgr, Brooklyn Public Library, Marcy, 617 DeKalb Ave, Brooklyn, NY, 11216. Tel: 718-935-0032. Fax: 718-935-0045. p. 1591

Vorhies, Holly, Cat, United States Holocaust Memorial Museum Library, 100 Raoul Wallenberg Pl SW, Washington, DC, 20024. Tel: 202-479-9717. Fax: 202-479-9726. p. 420

Vork, Gretchen, Br Mgr, Great River Regional Library, Paynesville Library, 119 Washburne Ave, Paynesville, MN, 56362. Tel: 320-243-7343. Fax: 320-243-7343. p. 1275

Voros, David Stephen, Dean, Libr Serv, Lehigh Carbon Community College Library, 4525 Education Park Dr, Schnecksville, PA, 18078-9372. Tel: 610-799-1164. Fax: 610-779-1159. p. 2136

Vorp, Donald M, Coll Develop, Princeton Theological Seminary, Mercer St & Library Pl, Princeton, NJ, 08542. Tel: 609-497-7940. Fax: 609-497-1826. p. 1522

Vorwald, Pat, Head, Adult Serv, Freeport Public Library, 100 E Douglas St, Freeport, IL, 61032. Tel: 815-233-3000. Fax: 815-233-1099. p. 647

Vos, Larry, Mgr, Ref Serv & Coll Develop, Wichita Public Library, 223 S Main St, Wichita, KS, 67202. Tel: 316-261-8540. Fax: 316-262-4540. p. 901

Vos, Lauren, Customer Serv Supvr, Evansville Vanderburgh Public Library, West, 2000 W Franklin St, Evansville, IN, 47712. Tel: 812-428-8232. Fax: 812-428-8230. p. 738

Vosatka, Diane, Head, Ref, Central Brevard Library & Reference Center, 308 Forrest Ave, Cocoa, FL, 32922. Tel: 321-633-1792. Fax: 321-633-1806. p. 433

Vosatka, Diane, Dir, South Mainland Library, 7921 Ron Beatty Blvd, Micco, FL, 32976. Tel: 772-664-4066. Fax: 772-664-0534. p. 470

Vose, David, Coordr, Info Commons, State University of New York at Binghamton, University Downtown Center Library Information Commons & Services, 67 Washington St, Binghamton, NY, 13902-6000. Tel: 607-777-9275. Fax: 607-777-9136. p. 1582

Vose, Jeanne, Libr Asst II, University of Maine at Machias, 116 O'Brien Ave, Machias, ME, 04654-1397. Tel: 207-255-1234. Fax: 207-255-1356. p. 991

Voskuil, Bart, Assoc Librn, Mid-America Reformed Seminary Library, 229 Seminary Dr, Dyer, IN, 46311. Tel: 219-864-2400. Fax: 219-864-2410. p. 736

Voskuil, Bart, Ref Librn/Geosciences Liaison, Western Carolina University, 176 Central Dr, Cullowhee, NC, 28723. Tel: 828-227-3493. Fax: 828-227-7015. p. 1786

Vosoughi, Annalyn, Coordr, Heald College, 1605 E March Lane, Stockton, CA, 95210. Tel: 209-473-5200. Fax: 209-473-5287. p. 272

Voss, Anke, Archives Dir, The Urbana Free Library, 210 W Green St, Urbana, IL, 61801-5326. Tel: 217-367-4025. Fax: 217-367-4061. p. 713

Voss, Barbara, Regional Dir, National Archives & Records Administration, Denver Federal Ctr, Bldg 48, W Sixth Ave & Kipling St, Denver, CO, 80225-0307. Tel: 303-407-5701. Fax: 303-407-5707. p. 302

Voss, Brian, Librn, National Environmental Satellite Data & Information Services, Bldg 3, 7600 Sand Point Way NE, Seattle, WA, 98115. Tel: 206-526-6241. Fax: 206-526-4535. p. 2529

Voss, Debbra L, Mgr, Ad Serv, Ref, Mead Public Library, 710 N Eighth St, Sheboygan, WI, 53081-4563. Tel: 920-459-3400, Ext 3420. Fax: 920-459-0204. p. 2637

Voss, Julie, Asst Librn, Bertolet Memorial Library District, 705 S Main St, Leaf River, IL, 61047. Tel: 815-738-2742. Fax: 815-738-2742. p. 664

Voss, Karlyn, Dir, External & Govt Relations, Carnegie Library of Pittsburgh, 4400 Forbes Ave, Pittsburgh, PA, 15213-4080. Tel: 412-578-2452. Fax: 412-622-6278. p. 2122

Voss, Kathleen, Dir, Bruce Area Library, 102 W River Ave, Bruce, WI, 54819. Tel: 715-868-2005. p. 2584

Voss, Ruth Ann, Dir, Faulkner-Van Buren Regional Library System, 1900 Tyler St, Conway, AR, 72032. Tel: 501-327-7482. Fax: 501-327-9098. p. 96

Voss, Valerie, Ch, Tulare County Library, Visalia Headquarters Branch, 200 W Oak Ave, Visalia, CA, 93291. Tel: 559-713-2732. Fax: 559-737-4586. p. 281

Vossberg, Susan J, Ref Librn, Web Develop Librn, Hamline University, School of Law Library, 1536 Hewitt Ave, Saint Paul, MN, 55104-1237. Tel: 651-523-2379. Fax: 651-523-2863. p. 1278

Votaw, Floyd M, Dir, Corban University Library, 5000 Deer Park Dr SE, Salem, OR, 97317-9392. Tel: 503-375-7016. Fax: 503-375-7196. p. 2017

Voth, Althea, Admin Serv, Supvr, Circ, Red Wing Public Library, 225 East Ave, Red Wing, MN, 55066-2298. Tel: 651-385-3673. Fax: 651-385-3644. p. 1272

Votipka, Jessica, Dir, Exeter Public Library, 202 S Exeter Ave, Exeter, NE, 68351. Tel: 402-266-3031. Fax: 402-266-3061. p. 1398

Voves, Ed, Head of Libr, Free Library of Philadelphia, Kingsessing Branch, 1201 S 51st, Philadelphia, PA, 19143-4353. Tel: 215-685-2690. Fax: 215-685-2691. p. 2108

Vovos, Jean Marie, Circ, United States Book Exchange Library, 2969 W 25th St, Cleveland, OH, 44113-5393. Tel: 216-241-6960. Fax: 216-241-6966. p. 1881

Vrabel, Donald A, Govt Doc, Ref, Allegheny College Library, 555 N Main St, Meadville, PA, 16335. Tel: 814-332-3317. Fax: 814-337-5673. p. 2086

Vrattos, Constance, Assoc Dir, Lesley University, 89 Brattle St, Cambridge, MA, 02138-2790. Tel: 617-349-8840. Fax: 617-349-8849. p. 1077

Vreeke, Tracy, Cataloger, Tech Serv, Door County Library, 107 S Fourth Ave, Sturgeon Bay, WI, 54235. Tel: 920-746-7116. Fax: 920-743-6697. p. 2640

Vreeland, Kate, Adult Serv, Ogden Farmers' Library, 269 Ogden Center Rd, Spencerport, NY, 14559. Tel: 585-617-6181. Fax: 585-352-3406. p. 1746

Vrieze, Scott, Dir, Carleton A Friday Memorial Library, 155 E First St, New Richmond, WI, 54017. Tel: 715-243-0431. Fax: 715-246-2691. p. 2625

Vroegh, Vicki, Dir, Eddyville Public Library, Akers Memorial Bldg, 202 S Second St, Eddyville, IA, 52553. Tel: 641-969-4815. Fax: 641-969-4040. p. 813

Vrona, Patrice, Br Mgr, Kent District Library, Grandville Branch, 4055 Maple St SW, Grandville, MI, 49418. Tel: 616-784-2007. Fax: 616-647-3894. p. 1165

Vukelic, Snezana, Mgr, Info Serv, Association of Municipalities of Ontario, 200 University Ave, Ste 801, Toronto, ON, M5H 3C6, CANADA. Tel: 416-971-9856, Ext 322. Fax: 416-971-6191. p. 2850

Vukovich, Nick, Educ Spec, Charlotte AHEC Library, Medical Education Bldg, 1000 Blythe Blvd, Charlotte, NC, 28203. Tel: 704-355-3129. Fax: 704-355-7138. p. 1781

Vulcu, Luminita, Asst Librn, Pennsylvania College of Optometry, 8360 Old York Rd, Elkins Park, PA, 19027. Tel: 215-780-1262. Fax: 215-780-1263. p. 2054

Vuncannon, Carl, Curator, Bernice Bienenstock Furniture Library, 1009 N Main St, High Point, NC, 27262. Tel: 336-883-4011. Fax: 336-883-6579. p. 1802

Vuori, Tencil, Coll Mgt, Red Deer College Library, 100 College Blvd, Red Deer, AB, T4N 5H5, CANADA. Tel: 403-342-3344. Fax: 403-346-8500. p. 2714

Vyortkina, Dina, Dir, Florida State University Libraries, Curriculum Resource Center, College of Education, 002 Stone Bldg, Tallahassee, FL, 32306-4450. Tel: 850-644-1583. Fax: 850-644-2725. p. 494

Waage, Steven, Syst Adminr, Cooperating Libraries in Consortium, 1619 Dayton Ave, Ste 204, Saint Paul, MN, 55104. Tel: 651-644-3878. Fax: 651-644-6258. p. 2946

Waage, Thomas, Libr Res Coordr, St Andrews University, 1700 Dogwood Mile, Laurinburg, NC, 28352. Tel: 910-277-5025. Fax: 910-277-5050. p. 1805

Waarala, Karrie, Dir, Auburn Hills Public Library, 3400 E Seyburn Dr, Auburn Hills, MI, 48326-2759. Tel: 248-364-6705. Fax: 248-370-9364. p. 1154

Waarvik, Mary, Dir, Elroy Public Library, 501 Second Main St, Elroy, WI, 53929-1255. Tel: 608-462-2407. Fax: 608-462-2407. p. 2591

Wacek, Dawn, Dir, Rice Lake Public Library, Two E Marshall St, Rice Lake, WI, 54868. Tel: 715-234-4861. Fax: 715-234-5026. p. 2633

Wacha, Megan, Res & Instruction Librn, Barnard College, 3009 Broadway, New York, NY, 10027-6598. Tel: 212-854-7652. p. 1670

Wacholder, Nina, Asst Prof, Rutgers, The State University of New Jersey, Four Huntington St, New Brunswick, NJ, 08901-1071. Tel: 732-932-7500, Ext 8955. Fax: 732-932-2644. p. 2969

Wachtel, Sylvia, Mgr, Omnicom, 1285 Avenue of the Americas, New York, NY, 10019. Tel: 212-459-5103. Fax: 212-459-6417. p. 1696

Wachter, Misty, Librn, Takotna Community Library, PO Box 86, Takotna, AK, 99675. Tel: 907-298-2229. Fax: 907-298-2325. p. 54

Wachter-Nelson, Ruth, Archivist, University of Wisconsin-Stevens Point, 900 Reserve St, Stevens Point, WI, 54481-1985. Tel: 715-346-2586. Fax: 715-346-3857. p. 2640

Wachuta-Breckel, Rita, Dir, Lawton Memorial Library, 118 N Bird St, La Farge, WI, 54639. Tel: 608-625-2015. Fax: 608-625-2329. p. 2604

Wack, Colleen, Libr Mgr, Edberg Municipal Library, 48 First Ave W, Edberg, AB, T0B 1J0, CANADA. Tel: 780-678-5606. Fax: 780-877-2562. p. 2697

Wacondo, Elizabeth, Dir, Laguna Public Library, PO Box 194, Laguna, NM, 87026-0194. Tel: 505-552-6280. Fax: 505-552-6941. p. 1557

Wada, Sandra, Librn, Maui Correctional Center Library, 600 Waiale Dr, Wailuku, HI, 96753. Tel: 808-243-5855. Fax: 808-242-7867. p. 567

Wadas, Linda, Acq, Borough of Manhattan Community College Library, 199 Chambers St, New York, NY, 10007. Tel: 212-220-1443. Fax: 212-748-7466. p. 1671

Waddell, Carolyn, Br Mgr, Columbus County Public Library, Fair Bluff Community, 315 Railroad St, Fair Bluff, NC, 28469. Tel: 910-649-7098. Fax: 910-649-7733. p. 1829

Waddell, Cherry, Br Mgr, West Georgia Regional Library, Crossroads Public Library, 909 Harmony Grove Church Rd, Acworth, GA, 30101. Tel: 770-975-0197. p. 524

Waddell, Christine, Dir, Linn County Library District No 2, 209 N Broadway, La Cygne, KS, 66040. Tel: 913-757-2151. Fax: 913-757-2405. p. 877

Waddell, Janice, Br Librn, Tay Township Public Library, Waubaushene Branch, 17 Thiffault St, Waubaushene, ON, L0K 2C0, CANADA. Tel: 705-538-1122. Fax: 705-538-1122. p. 2838

Waddell, Stacie, Chief, Libr Serv, Piedmont Healthcare, Inc, 1968 Peachtree Rd NW, Atlanta, GA, 30309. Tel: 404-605-3305. Fax: 404-609-6641. p. 517

Waddell, Suzanne, Librn, Thaddeus Stevens College of Technology, 750 E King St, Lancaster, PA, 17602-3198. Tel: 717-396-7176. Fax: 717-396-7186. p. 2078

Waddingham, Nola, Librn, Clarion Public Library, 302 N Main St, Clarion, IA, 50525. Tel: 515-532-3673. Fax: 515-532-6322. p. 802

Waddle, Keith, Dr, ILL/Ref Librn, McMurry University, Sayles Blvd & S 14th, Abilene, TX, 79605. Tel: 325-793-4683. Fax: 325-793-4930. p. 2272

Waddle, Sue, Librn, College of New Caledonia, 545 Hwy 16, Burns Lake, BC, V0J 1E0, CANADA. Tel: 250-692-1700. Fax: 250-692-1750. p. 2726

Wade, Dale, Mgr, Georgetown County Library, Andrews Branch, 105 N Morgan St, Andrews, SC, 29510. Tel: 803-264-8785. Fax: 803-264-8785. p. 2195

Wade, Dana, Librn, Culbertson Public Library, 507 New York St, Culbertson, NE, 69024. Tel: 308-278-2135. p. 1397

Wade, Dianna J, Dir, Beacon College Library, 101 W Main St, Leesburg, FL, 34748. Tel: 352-787-1207. Fax: 352-787-7924. p. 460

Wade, Eric D, Dir, United States Courts for the Ninth Circuit Library, 95 Seventh St, San Francisco, CA, 94103. Tel: 415-556-9500. Fax: 415-556-9927. p. 247

Wade, Heather A, Archivist, Emporia State University, Anderson Memorial Library & Archives, 1200 Commercial St, Box 4051, Emporia, KS, 66801. Tel: 620-341-5034. Fax: 620-341-5587. p. 866

Wade, Helen, Sister, Ref, College of Mount Saint Vincent, 6301 Riverdale Ave, Bronx, NY, 10471-1093. Tel: 718-405-3395. Fax: 718-601-2091. p. 1586

Wade, Jennifer, Br Librn, Duplin County Library, Phillip Leff Memorial Library, 807 Broad St, Beulaville, NC, 28518. Tel: 910-298-4677. Fax: 910-298-5069. p. 1804

Wade, John Mark, Asst Librn, Emmanuel School of Religion Library, One Walker Dr, Johnson City, TN, 37601-9438. Tel: 423-926-1186. Fax: 423-926-6198. p. 2239

Wade, Karen, Dir, Workman & Temple Family Homestead Museum Library, 15415 E Don Julian Rd, City of Industry, CA, 91745-1029. Tel: 626-968-8492. Fax: 626-968-2048. p. 134

Wade, Katherine, Librn, Federal Aviation Administration, Civil Aerospace Medical Institute Library, 6500 S MacArthur, AAM-400a, Oklahoma City, OK, 73169. Tel: 405-954-4398. Fax: 405-954-4379. p. 1972

Wade, Kathy, Librn, Washington County Historical Society Library, 307 E Market St, Salem, IN, 47167. Tel: 812-883-6495. p. 777

Wade, Kim, Librn, Montmorency County Public Libraries, Hillman Wright Branch, 121 W Second St, Hillman, MI, 49746-9024. Tel: 989-742-4021. Fax: 989-742-4021. p. 1154

Wade, Liz, Tech Serv Librn, Guilford College, 5800 W Friendly Ave, Greensboro, NC, 27410-4175. Tel: 336-316-2450. Fax: 336-316-2950. p. 1796

Wade, Marialice, ILL, Waltham Public Library, 735 Main St, Waltham, MA, 02451. Tel: 781-314-3425. Fax: 781-314-3426. p. 1133

Wade, Patricia, Coordr, Ref Serv-Adult, Saint Mary's College Library, 1928 Saint Mary's Rd, Moraga, CA, 94575. Tel: 925-631-4229. Fax: 925-376-6097. p. 191

Wade, Rebecca, Literacy Coordr, Fresno County Public Library, 2420 Mariposa St, Fresno, CA, 93721-2285. Tel: 559-224-7094. p. 151

Wade, Rebecca, Coordr, Fresno County Public Library, Literacy Services Center, 2420 Mariposa St, Fresno, CA, 93721. Tel: 559-600-9240. p. 152

Wade, Rosalind S, Librn, Louis T Graves Memorial Public Library, 18 Maine St, Kennebunkport, ME, 04046-6173. Tel: 207-967-2778. p. 989

Wade, Shana, Pub Serv Dir, Mesa County Public Library District, 443 North 6th St, Grand Junction, CO, 81501. Tel: 970-243-4442. p. 310

Wade, Sherry, Br Mgr, Kern County Library, Baker Branch, 1400 Baker St, Bakersfield, CA, 93305-3731. Tel: 661-861-2390. p. 124

Wadelius, Lauren, Adminr, The Pas Regional Library, 53 Edwards Ave, The Pas, MB, R9A 1R2, CANADA. Tel: 204-623-2023. Fax: 204-623-4594. p. 2752

Wadian, Becky, Dir, Upper Iowa University, 605 Washington St, Fayette, IA, 52142. Tel: 563-425-5270. Fax: 563-425-5271. p. 816

Wadick, Patricia, Computer Serv, Riley County Kansas Genealogical Society Library, 2005 Claflin, Manhattan, KS, 66502-3415. Tel: 785-565-6495. p. 882

Wadland, Justin, Head, Media & Visual Res, University of Washington Libraries, Tacoma Library, 1900 Commerce St, Box 358460, Tacoma, WA, 98402-3100. Tel: 253-692-5741. Fax: 253-692-4445. p. 2535

Wadleigh, Deborah, Tech Serv, Onslow County Public Library, 58 Doris Ave E, Jacksonville, NC, 28540. Tel: 910-455-7350, Ext 237. Fax: 910-455-1661. p. 1803

Wadler, Karen, Librn, Congregation Beth Shalom, 3433 Walters Ave, Northbrook, IL, 60062-3298. Tel: 847-498-4100. Fax: 847-498-9160. p. 682

Wadley, Deborah, Br Mgr, Las Vegas-Clark County Library District, Sandy Valley Library, 650 W Quartz Ave, HCR 31 Box 377, Sandy Valley, NV, 89019. Tel: 702-723-5333. Fax: 702-723-1010. p. 1430

Wadman, Linda J, Dir, North Country Library Cooperative, 5528 Emerald Ave, Mountain Iron, MN, 55768-2069. Tel: 218-741-1907. Fax: 218-741-1908. p. 2947

Wadsworth, David H, Historian, Cohasset Historical Society Library, 106 S Main St, Cohasset, MA, 02025. Tel: 781-383-1434. Fax: 781-383-1190. p. 1082

Wadsworth, Marissa, Head, Adult Serv, Lower Providence Community Library, 50 Parklane Dr, Eagleville, PA, 19403-1171. Tel: 610-666-6640. Fax: 610-666-5109. p. 2051

Waelchli, Paul, Info Literacy Librn, Todd Wehr Library, St Norbert College, 301 Third St, De Pere, WI, 54115. Tel: 920-403-3291. Fax: 920-403-4064. p. 2587

Waelde, Kaye, Regional Mgr, Faegre & Benson, LLP, 3200 Wells Fargo Ctr, 1700 Lincoln St, Denver, CO, 80203. Tel: 303-607-3722. Fax: 303-607-3600. p. 302

Waer, Becky L, Mgr, Isabelle Hunt Memorial Public Library, 6124 N Randall Pl, Pine, AZ, 85544. Tel: 928-476-3678. Fax: 928-476-2914. p. 77

Wagar, Cathy, Cat Librn, Loyola University New Orleans, Loyola Law Library, School of Law, 7214 St Charles Ave, New Orleans, LA, 70118. Tel: 504-861-5539. Fax: 504-861-5895. p. 961

Wagenaar, Larry J, Exec Dir, Historical Society of Michigan, 1305 Abbott Rd, East Lansing, MI, 48823. Tel: 517-324-1828. Fax: 517-324-4370. p. 1175

Wagener, Beverly, Asst Dir, Lucas County Law Library, Lucas County Family Court Center, 905 Jackson St, Toledo, OH, 43604-5512. Tel: 419-213-4747. Fax: 419-213-4287. p. 1939

Wagener, Roberta, ILL, Nelson-Atkins Museum of Art, 4525 Oak St, Kansas City, MO, 64111-1873. Tel: 817-751-1287. Fax: 816-751-0498. p. 1340

Wagenseil, Lois, Librn, Brookhaven College, 3939 Valley View, Farmers Branch, TX, 75244-4997. Tel: 972-860-4854. Fax: 972-860-4675. p. 2319

Wager, Judy, Tech Serv, Saint Clair County Community College, 323 Erie St, Port Huron, MI, 48060. Tel: 810-984-3881, 810-989-5640. Fax: 810-984-2852. p. 1219

Wages, Georgia, Head, Support Serv, Kern County Library, 701 Truxtun Ave, Bakersfield, CA, 93301-4816. Tel: 661-868-0700. Fax: 661-868-0799. p. 124

Wagg, Caryl, Librn, Brownville Free Public Library, 27 Church St, Brownville, ME, 04414-3235. Tel: 207-965-8318. p. 979

Waggener, Terry, Bus Mgr, American Electric Power Service Corp, Legal Library, One Riverside Plaza, Flr 29, Columbus, OH, 43215. Tel: 614-716-1690. Fax: 614-716-1687. p. 1883

Waggoner, Elizabeth, Dir, Tensas Parish Library, 135 Plank Rd, Saint Joseph, LA, 71366. Tel: 318-766-3781. Fax: 318-766-0098. p. 967

Waggoner, Margaret J, Dir, Kaukauna Public Library, 111 Main Ave, Kaukauna, WI, 54130-2436. Tel: 920-766-6340. Fax: 920-766-6343. p. 2600

Waggoner, Mary Helen, Dir, Tombigbee Regional Library System, 338 Commerce, West Point, MS, 39773. Tel: 662-494-4872. Fax: 662-494-0300. p. 1317

Waghalter, Lynn, In Charge, Congregation Agudas Achim, 16550 Huebner Rd, San Antonio, TX, 78248. Tel: 210-479-0307. Fax: 210-479-0295. p. 2379

Wagle, Sandee, Managing Librn, Columbus Metropolitan Library, Parsons, 845 Parsons Ave, Columbus, OH, 43206. Tel: 614-645-2275. Fax: 614-479-4319. p. 1885

Wagle, Sandee, Managing Librn, Columbus Metropolitan Library, South High, 3540 S High St, Columbus, OH, 43207. Tel: 614-645-2275. Fax: 614-479-4369. p. 1885

Wagle, Sandee, Managing Librn, Columbus Metropolitan Library, Southeast, 3980 S Hamilton Rd, Groveport, OH, 43125. Tel: 614-645-2275. Fax: 614-479-4359. p. 1885

Wagner, Alda, Br Mgr, Briggs Lawrence County Public Library, Southern, 317 Solida Rd, South Point, OH, 45680. Tel: 740-377-2288, 740-867-2506. Fax: 740-377-9298. p. 1906

Wagner, Barb, Librn, Coudersport Public Library, 502 Park Ave, Coudersport, PA, 16915-1672. Tel: 814-274-9382. Fax: 814-274-9137. p. 2047

Wagner, Beth, Librn, Environmental Protection Agency, EPA Region 6, 1445 Ross Ave, Ste 1200, Dallas, TX, 75202. Tel: 214-665-6424. Fax: 214-665-8574. p. 2308

Wagner, Brent, Sr Librn, Denver Public Library, Ross-Cherry Creek, 305 Milwaukee St, Denver, CO, 80206-4329. Tel: 303-331-4016. Fax: 303-331-3860. p. 301

Wagner, Carolyn, Asst Dir, Chicago Heights Public Library, 25 W 15th St, Chicago Heights, IL, 60411-3488. Tel: 708-754-0323. Fax: 708-754-0325. p. 628

Wagner, Charlene M, Ch, Gardiner Public Library, 152 Water St, Gardiner, ME, 04345. Tel: 207-582-3312. Fax: 207-582-6104. p. 986

Wagner, Charles A, Dir, Peru Public Library, 102 E Main St, Peru, IN, 46970-2338. Tel: 765-473-3069. Fax: 765-473-3060. p. 772

Wagner, Christina, Librn, Foley & Lardner, 321 N Clark St, Ste 2800, Chicago, IL, 60610. Tel: 312-832-4500. Fax: 312-832-4700. p. 613

Wagner, Clarissa, Circ, Long Hill Township Public Library, 917 Valley Rd, Gillette, NJ, 07933. Tel: 908-647-2088. Fax: 908-647-2098. p. 1488

Wagner, Dan, Circ, Westminster Seminary California Library, 1725 Bear Valley Pkwy, Escondido, CA, 92027. Tel: 760-480-8474. Fax: 760-480-0252. p. 147

Wagner, Darla, Tech Serv, Westfield Memorial Library, 550 E Broad St, Westfield, NJ, 07090. Tel: 908-789-4090. Fax: 908-789-0921. p. 1543

Wagner, Darlene, Librn, Chinook Regional Library, Prelate Branch, Village Office, Main St, Prelate, SK, S0N 2B0, CANADA. Tel: 306-673-2340. p. 2928

Wagner, David, Circ & ILL, Drexel University Libraries, Queen Lane Library, 2900 Queen Lane, Philadelphia, PA, 19129. Tel: 215-991-8740. Fax: 215-843-0840. p. 2105

Wagner, Donna, Asst Librn, Twin Bridges Public Library, 206 S Main St, Twin Bridges, MT, 59754. Tel: 406-684-5416. Fax: 406-684-5260. p. 1389

Wagner, Dora, Archivist, Northwestern College, 3003 Snelling Ave N, Saint Paul, MN, 55113. Tel: 651-631-5241. Fax: 651-631-5598. p. 1280

Wagner, Gerald, Head, ILL & Doc Delivery, University of Cincinnati Libraries, Donald C Harrison Health Sciences Library, PO Box 670574, Cincinnati, OH, 45267-0574. Tel: 513-558-8389. Fax: 513-558-2682. p. 1874

Wagner, Jack, Cat, University of Oklahoma Health Sciences Center, 1000 Stanton L Young Blvd, Oklahoma City, OK, 73117-1213. Tel: 405-271-2285, Ext 48758. Fax: 405-271-3297. p. 1975

Wagner, Janice, In Charge, Bayliss Public Library, Engadine Branch, W13920 Melville St, Engadine, MI, 49827. Tel: 906-477-6313, Ext 140. Fax: 906-477-6643. p. 1226

Wagner, Jason, Info Spec/Archives, Educational Testing Service, Rosedale Rd, Princeton, NJ, 08541. Tel: 609-734-5296. Fax: 609-683-7186. p. 1522

Wagner, Jeanne, Ref, Ser, Washington State University, 600 N Riverpoint Blvd, Spokane, WA, 99202. Tel: 509-358-7930. Fax: 509-358-7928. p. 2538

Wagner, Joyce, YA Serv, Poplar Creek Public Library District, 1405 S Park Ave, Streamwood, IL, 60107-2997. Tel: 630-837-6800. Fax: 630-837-6823. p. 708

Wagner, Karen, Res Sharing Librn, University of Wisconsin-Madison, Kurt Wendt Engineering Library, 215 N Randall Ave, Madison, WI, 53706. Tel: 608-262-3493. Fax: 608-262-4739, 608-265-8751. p. 2610

Wagner, Karen, Archivist, Wellington County Museum & Archives, 0536 Wellington Rd 18, RR 1, Fergus, ON, N1M 2W3, CANADA. Tel: 519-846-0916. Fax: 519-846-9630. p. 2805

Wagner, Kathi, Dir, Red Oak Public Library, 400 N Second St, Red Oak, IA, 51566-2251. Tel: 712-623-6516. Fax: 712-623-6518. p. 840

Wagner, Kenneth, AV, Schenectady County Public Library, 99 Clinton St, Schenectady, NY, 12305-2083. Tel: 518-388-4502. Fax: 518-386-2241. p. 1740

Wagner, Kurt, Asst Dir, Libr & Info Syst, William Paterson University of New Jersey, 300 Pompton Rd, Wayne, NJ, 07470. Tel: 973-720-2285. Fax: 973-720-3171. p. 1540

Wagner, Leah, Asst Dir, Monroe Township Public Library, Four Municipal Plaza, Monroe Township, NJ, 08831-1900. Tel: 732-521-5000, Ext 108. Fax: 732-521-4766. p. 1503

Wagner, Lori, Ch, Mitchell Public Library, 221 N Duff St, Mitchell, SD, 57301-2596. Tel: 605-995-8480. Fax: 605-995-8482. p. 2215

Wagner, Madelyn, Adminr, Kaplan University, 3165 Edgewood Pkwy SW, Cedar Rapids, IA, 52404. Tel: 319-363-0481, Ext 123. Fax: 319-363-3812. p. 800

Wagner, Maria, Tech Mgr, Portland Community College Library, 12000 SW 49th AV, Portland, OR, 97219. Tel: 503-977-4631. Fax: 971-722-8397. p. 2013

Wagner, Marsha, Libr Dir, Canal Fulton Public Library, 154 Market St NE, Canal Fulton, OH, 44614-1196. Tel: 330-854-4148. Fax: 330-854-9520. p. 1863

Wagner, Mary Ann, Libr Tech, Department of Veterans Affairs, 325 New Castle Rd, Butler, PA, 16001. Tel: 724-477-5024. Fax: 724-477-5073. p. 2040

Wagner, Meredith, Br Mgr, Kokomo-Howard County Public Library, Russiaville Branch, 315 Mesa Dr, Russiaville, IN, 46979. Tel: 765-883-5112. Fax: 765-883-5974. p. 758

Wagner, Meredith, Assoc Dir, Jefferson County Rural Library District, 620 Cedar Ave, Port Hadlock, WA, 98339-9514. Tel: 360-385-6544. Fax: 360-385-7921. p. 2524

Wagner, Michael, Mgr, Nashville Public Library, Nashville Talking Library, 505 Heritage Dr, Madison, TN, 37115-2688. Tel: 615-862-5874. Fax: 615-862-5796. p. 2258

Wagner, Nancy, Asst Librn, Dryden Township Library, 5480 Main St, Dryden, MI, 48428-9968. Tel: 810-796-3586. Fax: 810-796-2634. p. 1174

Wagner, Nancy, ILL, Washington State University, 600 N Riverpoint Blvd, Spokane, WA, 99202. Tel: 509-358-7930. Fax: 509-358-7928. p. 2538

Wagner, Rachel, Librn, Alabama League of Municipalities Library, PO Box 1270, Montgomery, AL, 36102-1270. Tel: 334-262-2566. Fax: 334-263-0200. p. 27

Wagner, Robin, Dir, Libr Serv, Gettysburg College, 300 N Washington St, Gettysburg, PA, 17325. Tel: 717-337-6768. Fax: 717-337-7001. p. 2059

Wagner, Rod, Dir, Nebraska Library Commission, The Atrium, 1200 N St, Ste 120, Lincoln, NE, 68508-2023. Tel: 402-471-4001. Fax: 402-471-2083. p. 1406

Wagner, Sandy, Ch, Monticello Union Township Public Library, 321 W Broadway, Monticello, IN, 47960-2047. Tel: 574-583-2665, 574-583-5643. Fax: 574-583-2782. p. 766

Wagner, Sue, Mgr, Kootenai-Shoshone Area Libraries, Athol Branch, 30399 Third St, Athol, ID, 83801. Tel: 208-683-2979. Fax: 208-683-2979. p. 575

Wagner, Victoria, Head, Circ, William Paterson University of New Jersey, 300 Pompton Rd, Wayne, NJ, 07470. Tel: 973-720-3190. Fax: 973-720-3171. p. 1540

Wagner, Wanda, Br Mgr, Public Library Association of Annapolis & Anne Arundel County, Inc, North County Area, 1010 Eastway, Glen Burnie, MD, 21061. Tel: 410-222-6270. Fax: 410-222-6276. p. 1011

Wagner, Wanda, Chairperson, Clive Public Library, 5115 50th St, Clive, AB, T0C 0Y0, CANADA. Tel: 403-784-3131. Fax: 403-784-3131. p. 2695

Wagness, Gerry, Librn, Lakota City Library, 116 West B Ave, Lakota, ND, 58344. Tel: 701-247-2543. p. 1845

Wagoner-Perry, Morganne, Dir, DeVry University, 1870 W 122nd Ave, Westminster, CO, 80234. Tel: 303-280-7621. p. 325

Wagstaff, Ellen, Librn, ATK Launch Systems, PO Box 707, Brigham City, UT, 84302-0707. Tel: 435-863-6819. Fax: 435-863-6023. p. 2403

Wagstaff, John, Head Librn, University of Illinois Library at Urbana-Champaign, Music & Performing Arts, 2146 Music Bldg, MC-056, 1114 W Nevada St, Urbana, IL, 61801-3859. Tel: 217-244-5070. Fax: 217-244-9097. p. 712

Wagstaff, Rita, Librn, San Diego County Public Law Library, South Bay, 500 Third Ave, Chula Vista, CA, 91910-5617. Tel: 619-691-4929. Fax: 619-427-7521. p. 234

Wagy, Milton L, Hist Coll Librn, Ref Serv, Ad, Ellensburg Public Library, 209 N Ruby St, Ellensburg, WA, 98926-3397. Tel: 509-962-7250. Fax: 509-962-7295. p. 2514

Waheed, Jawadi, Supv Librn, California Department of Justice, CCI Forensic Library, 4949 Broadway, Rm A-107, Sacramento, CA, 95820. Tel: 916-227-3575. Fax: 916-454-5433. p. 222

Wahl, B J, Coll Develop, Electronic Res, Keene Public Library, 60 Winter St, Keene, NH, 03431-3360. Tel: 603-352-0157. Fax: 866-743-0446. p. 1452

Wahl, Donna, Dir, Libr Serv, Johnson & Johnson Pharmaceutical Research & Development, 1003 US Hwy 202 P, Raritan, NJ, 08869-0602. Tel: 908-704-4919, 908-704-8998. Fax: 908-707-9860. p. 1525

Wahl, Richard, Librn, National Rifle Association, 11250 Waples Mill Rd, Fairfax, VA, 22030. Tel: 703-267-3859. Fax: 703-267-3980. p. 2462

Wahlstrom, Nancy, Tech Serv, United States Army, Sayers Memorial Library, Bldg 93, Wold Ave, Fort Benning, GA, 31905. Tel: 706-545-7141. Fax: 706-545-6363. p. 532

Wahnefried, Cathy, Libr Assoc, New Hanover County Public Library, Carolina Beach Branch, 300 Cape Fear Blvd, Carolina Beach, NC, 28428. Tel: 910-798-6385. Fax: 910-458-9422. p. 1830

Wai, Zoe, Mgr, NASA Goddard Institute for Space Studies Library, 2880 Broadway, Rm 710, New York, NY, 10025. Tel: 212-678-5613. Fax: 212-678-5552. p. 1687

Waibel, Sue, Dir, Remington-Carpenter Township Public Library, 105 N Ohio St, Remington, IN, 47977. Tel: 219-261-2543. Fax: 219-261-3800. p. 774

Waide, John, Univ Archivist, Saint Louis University, 3650 Lindell Blvd, Saint Louis, MO, 63108-3302. Tel: 314-977-3091. Fax: 314-977-3108. p. 1360

Waidelich, Kim, Librn, US Environmental Protection Agency, 701 Mapes Rd, Fort George G Meade, MD, 20755-5350. Tel: 410-305-2603, 410-305-3031. Fax: 410-305-3092. p. 1028

Waigand, Helen, ILL, Southwestern Community College, 1501 W Townline, Creston, IA, 50801. Tel: 641-782-1462. Fax: 641-782-1301. p. 805

Wainwright, Barbara, Coll Develop, Washington County Public Library, 615 Fifth St, Marietta, OH, 45750-1973. Tel: 740-373-1057, Ext 211. p. 1913

Wainwright, Francesca, Br Mgr, Seattle Public Library, Greenwood, 8016 Greenwood Ave N, Seattle, WA, 98103. Tel: 206-684-4086. p. 2531

Wainwright, Francesca, Regional Mgr, Seattle Public Library, North East, 6801 35th Ave NE, Seattle, WA, 98115. Tel: 206-684-7539. p. 2531

Wainwright, Francesca, Regional Mgr, Seattle Public Library, Northgate, 10548 Fifth Ave NE, Seattle, WA, 98125. Tel: 206-386-1980. p. 2531

Waiss, Gayle, Asst Libr Dir, Ch, Siuslaw Public Library District, 1460 Ninth St, Florence, OR, 97439-0022. Tel: 541-997-3132. Fax: 541-997-6473. p. 1998

Wait, Tiffany, YA Serv, Shorewood Public Library, 3920 N Murray Ave, Shorewood, WI, 53211-2385. Tel: 414-847-2670. p. 2638

Waite, Amy, Access Serv Mgr, Circ, Clark College, Mail Stop LIB 112, 1933 Fort Vancouver Way, Vancouver, WA, 98663-3598. Tel: 360-992-2152. Fax: 360-992-2869. p. 2545

Waite, Chris, YA Serv, West Chicago Public Library District, 118 W Washington St, West Chicago, IL, 60185. Tel: 630-231-1552. Fax: 630-231-1709. p. 717

Waite, Dianna, Circ, Salina Public Library, 301 W Elm St, Salina, KS, 67401. Tel: 785-825-4624. Fax: 785-823-0706. p. 893

Waite, James, Dir of Develop, University of Toledo, 2801 W Bancroft St, Mail Stop 509, Toledo, OH, 43606-3390. Tel: 419-530-5414. Fax: 419-530-2726. p. 1941

Waite, Margaret A, Dir, North Tonawanda Public Library, 505 Meadow Dr, North Tonawanda, NY, 14120-2888. Tel: 716-693-4132. Fax: 716-693-0719. p. 1707

Waithe, Lisette, Head, Ch, Plainfield Public Library, 800 Park Ave, Plainfield, NJ, 07060-2594. Tel: 908-757-1111, Ext 129. Fax: 908-754-0063. p. 1521

Waitman, Lorraine, Chief, Libr User Serv, United Nations Dag Hammarskjold Library, United Nations, New York, NY, 10017. Fax: 212-963-2261. p. 1702

Waitz, Emily, Head, Tech Serv, Hamline University, School of Law Library, 1536 Hewitt Ave, Saint Paul, MN, 55104-1237. Tel: 651-523-2379. Fax: 651-523-2863. p. 1278

Wakashige, Ben, Dir of Libr, Central New Mexico Community College Libraries, 525 Buena Vista SE, Albuquerque, NM, 87106-4023. Tel: 505-224-3286. Fax: 505-224-3321. p. 1548

Wakashige, Ben, Dir of Libr, Central New Mexico Community College Libraries, Montoya Campus Library, J Bldg, Rm 123, 4700 Morris NE, Albuquerque, NM, 87111. Tel: 505-224-3286. Fax: 505-224-5727. p. 1548

Wakashige, Benjamin, Syst Dir of Libr, National American University, 1601 Rio Rancho Blvd, Ste 200, Rio Rancho, NM, 87124. Tel: 505-348-3746. Fax: 505-348-3705. p. 2969

Wakefield, Angela, Dir, Killgore Memorial Library, 124 S Bliss Ave, Dumas, TX, 79029-3889. Tel: 806-935-4941. Fax: 806-935-3324. p. 2314

Wakefield, Ann, Ref Librn, Pension Benefit Guaranty Corporation, 1200 K St NW, Ste 360, Washington, DC, 20005-4026. Tel: 202-326-4000, Ext 3550. Fax: 202-326-4011. p. 412

Wakefield, Diane, Dir, Beaver Area Memorial Library, 100 College Ave, Beaver, PA, 15009-2794. Tel: 724-775-1132. Fax: 724-775-6982. p. 2031

Wakefield, Heather J, Dir, Saegertown Area Library, 325 Broad St, Saegertown, PA, 16433. Tel: 814-763-5203. Fax: 814-763-4979. p. 2135

Wakefield, Wesley H, Pres, Bible Holiness Movement Library, 311 Falcon Pl, Penticton, BC, V2A 8K6, CANADA. Tel: 250-492-3376. p. 2735

Wakeford, Leslie, Tech Serv Librn, Wake Forest University, Professional Center Library, Worrell Professional Ctr for Law & Management, 1834 Wake Forest Rd, Winston-Salem, NC, 27106. Tel: 336-758-5932. Fax: 336-758-6077. p. 1834

Wakeling, William M, Dean, Univ Libr, Northeastern University Libraries, Snell Library, 360 Huntington Ave, Boston, MA, 02115. Tel: 617-373-8778. p. 1065

Wakimoto, Jina, Assoc Prof, Dir, Metadata Serv, University of Colorado Boulder, 1720 Pleasant St, 184 UCB, Boulder, CO, 80309-0184. Tel: 303-492-3920. Fax: 303-492-3340. p. 291

Wakin, Eric, Lehman Curator, Am Hist, Columbia University, Rare Book & Manuscript, Butler Library, 6th Flr E, 535 W 114th St, New York, NY, 10027. Tel: 212-854-9616. Fax: 212-854-1365. p. 1675

Waks, Jane B, Sr Librn, Concepts NREC Library, 39 Olympia Ave, Woburn, MA, 01801-2073. Tel: 781-935-9050. Fax: 781-935-9052. p. 1142

Waks, Robert, ILL, College of Saint Elizabeth, Two Convent Rd, Morristown, NJ, 07960-6989. Tel: 973-290-4240. Fax: 973-290-4226. p. 1504

Walas, Nadine, ILL Tech, Department of Veterans Affairs, Medical Library 142D, 4150 Clement St, San Francisco, CA, 94121. Tel: 415-221-4810, Ext 3302. Fax: 415-750-6919. p. 241

Walaskay, Ann, Govt Doc, Ref, Oakland Community College, 27055 Orchard Lake Rd, Bldg K, Farmington Hills, MI, 48334-4579. Tel: 248-522-3528. Fax: 248-522-3530. p. 1178

Walch, Darlene M, Dean, Northern Michigan University, 1401 Presque Isle, Marquette, MI, 49855. Tel: 906-227-2117. Fax: 906-227-1333. p. 1206

Walch, Irene, Head, Ref, Clark University, 950 Main St, Worcester, MA, 01610-1477. Tel: 508-793-7711. Fax: 508-793-8871. p. 1143

Walchak, Shelley, Commun Prog Consult, Colorado State Library, 201 E Colfax Ave, Rm 309, Denver, CO, 80203-1799. Tel: 303-866-6891. Fax: 303-866-6940. p. 299

Walcott, Barbara, Ref, Bergen Community College, 400 Paramus Rd, Paramus, NJ, 07652-1595. Tel: 201-447-5243. Fax: 201-493-8167. p. 1517

Walcott, Richard, Circ, Thiel College, 75 College Ave, Greenville, PA, 16125-2183. Tel: 724-589-2118. Fax: 724-589-2122. p. 2063

Walczak, Jerome, Head, Ref, Agawam Public Library, 750 Cooper St, Agawam, MA, 01001. Tel: 413-789-1550. Fax: 413-789-1552. p. 1048

Walczak, Kathleen Ann, Mgr, Howard C Raether Library, 13625 Bishop's Dr, Brookfield, WI, 53005-6607. Tel: 262-814-1556. Fax: 262-789-6977. p. 2583

Wald, Betsy, Br Mgr, Maplewood Memorial Library, Hilton, 1688 Springfield Ave, Maplewood, NJ, 07040-2923. Tel: 973-762-1688. p. 1499

Wald, Jean, Music, Stetson University, 421 N Woodland Blvd, Unit 8418, DeLand, FL, 32723. Tel: 386-822-8958. p. 437

Waldemer, Susan, Librn, Wilder Public Library District, 207 A Ave, Wilder, ID, 83676-6099. Tel: 208-482-7880. Fax: 208-482-7880. p. 585

Walden, Carolyn, Head, Cat & Coll Mgt, University of Alabama at Birmingham, Mervyn H Sterne Library, 917 13th St S, Birmingham, AL, 35205. Tel: 205-934-0633. p. 10

Walden, Diane, Regional Librn, Colorado Department of Corrections, 12750 Hwy 96, Lane 13, Crowley, CO, 81034. Tel: 719-269-5607. Fax: 719-267-5024. p. 297

Walden, Diane, Coordr, Institutional Libr, Colorado State Library, 201 E Colfax Ave, Rm 309, Denver, CO, 80203-1799. Tel: 303-866-6341. Fax: 303-866-6940. p. 299

Walden, Glenn, Libr Assoc, Louisiana State University Libraries, Carter Music Resources Center, 202 Middleton Library, Baton Rouge, LA, 70803-3300. Tel: 225-578-4674. Fax: 225-578-6825. p. 943

Walden, Julia, Head, Info & Prog Serv, Granville Public Library, 217 E Broadway, Granville, OH, 43023-1398. Tel: 740-587-0196. Fax: 740-587-0197. p. 1902

Walden, Marilyn, Dir, Arcanum Public Library, 101 W North St, Arcanum, OH, 45304-1126. Tel: 937-692-8484. Fax: 937-692-8916. p. 1854

Waldera, Kate, Head, Ref, Bismarck Veterans Memorial Public Library, 515 N Fifth St, Bismarck, ND, 58503-4081. Tel: 701-355-1492. Fax: 701-221-3729. p. 1837

Waldman Forczek, Casse, Law Librn, Lake County Law Library, 175 Third St, Lakeport, CA, 95453. Tel: 707-263-2205. Fax: 707-263-2207. p. 163

Waldman, Glenys A, Dr, Librn, The Masonic Library & Museum of Pennsylvania, Masonic Temple, One N Broad St, Philadelphia, PA, 19107-2520. Tel: 215-988-1908. Fax: 215-988-1953. p. 2112

Waldman, Michael, Head, Coll Mgt, Baruch College-CUNY, 151 E 25 St, Box H-0520, New York, NY, 10010-2313. Tel: 646-312-1689. Fax: 646-312-1691. p. 1670

Waldman, Peggy, Librn, Overbrook Public Library, 317 Maple St, Overbrook, KS, 66524. Tel: 785-665-7266. Fax: 785-665-7973. p. 887

Waldman, Robert, Dir, York Public Library, 15 Long Sands Rd, York, ME, 03909. Tel: 207-363-2818. Fax: 207-363-7250. p. 1008

Waldo, Suzy, Mgr, Carnegie Library of Pittsburgh, Knoxville, 400 Brownsville Rd, Pittsburgh, PA, 15210-2251. Tel: 412-381-6543. p. 2123

Waldorf, Donna, Head, Tech Serv, Geauga County Public Library, 12701 Ravenwood Dr, Chardon, OH, 44024-1336. Tel: 440-286-6811, 440-564-7131, 440-834-1856. Fax: 440-286-7419. p. 1866

Waldrep, Brenda, Coordr, Circ, Cullman County Public Library System, 200 Clark St NE, Cullman, AL, 35055. Tel: 256-734-1068. Fax: 256-734-6902. p. 13

Waldrep, Pam, Br Mgr, South San Francisco Public Library, Grand Avenue, 306 Walnut Ave, South San Francisco, CA, 94080-2700. Tel: 650-877-8530. Fax: 650-829-6615. p. 270

Waldron, Anne, Res, Kirkland & Ellis LLP Library, 300 N LaSalle St, 11th Flr, Chicago, IL, 60654. Tel: 312-862-2346. Fax: 312-862-2200. p. 616

Waldron, Betty, Sr Librn, Ch Serv, Wanaque Public Library, 616 Ringwood Ave, Wanaque, NJ, 07465. Tel: 973-839-4434. Fax: 973-839-8904. p. 1539

Waldron, Melanie, Youth Serv Librn, Black Creek Village Library, 507 S Maple St, Black Creek, WI, 54106-9304. Tel: 920-984-3094. Fax: 920-984-3559. p. 2582

Waldron, Tamera, ILL, Battelle Energy Alliance, LLC, 1776 Science Center Dr, MS 2300, Idaho Falls, ID, 83415-2300. Tel: 208-526-1185. Fax: 208-526-0211. p. 576

Waldron, Tracy, Dir, East Kingston Public Library, 47 Maplevale Rd, East Kingston, NH, 03827. Tel: 603-642-8333. p. 1446

Waldrop, Cordelia H, Dir, Florala Public Library, 1214 Fourth St, Florala, AL, 36442-3810. Tel: 334-858-3525. Fax: 334-858-3525. p. 17

Waldrop, Jean, E-Res & Ser Librn, Harding University, 915 E Market St, Searcy, AR, 72149-2267. Tel: 501-279-4011. p. 114

Waldrop, Patricia, Ch, Tombigbee Regional Library System, Evans Memorial Library, 105 N Long St, Aberdeen, MS, 39730. Tel: 662-369-4601. Fax: 662-369-2971. p. 1318

Waldrop, Susan O, Libr Tech, United States Army, Martin Army Community Hospital Medical Library, Bldg 9200, Rm 010 MCXB-IL, 7950 Martin Loop, Fort Benning, GA, 31905-5637. Tel: 706-544-3533. Fax: 706-544-3215. p. 532

Waldrup, Jane, Head, Circ, Delta State University, Laflore Circle at Fifth Ave, Cleveland, MS, 38733-2599. Tel: 662-846-4440. Fax: 662-846-4443. p. 1296

Wale, Carla, Res & Electronic Technologies Librn, Northern Illinois University Libraries, David C Shapiro Memorial Law Library, Normal Rd, DeKalb, IL, 60115-2890. Tel: (815) 753-9487. Fax: 815-753-9499. p. 636

Walenta, Peter, Circ, Yeshiva University Libraries, Dr Lillian & Dr Rebecca Chutick Law Library, Benjamin N Cardozo School of Law, 55 Fifth Ave, New York, NY, 10003-4301. Tel: 212-790-0223. Fax: 212-790-0236. p. 1703

Walenter, Stacy, Librn, Lincoln County Public Libraries, Troy Branch, Third & Kalispell Ave, Troy, MT, 59935. Tel: 406-295-4040. Fax: 406-295-4040. p. 1385

Wales, John, Libr Serv Coordr, Trent University, Oshawa Campus Library, 55 Thornton Rd S, Oshawa, ON, L1J 5Y1, CANADA. Tel: 905-435-5102 Ext 5062. p. 2836

Wales, Patricia L, Mgr, YNHH Saint Raphael Campus, 1450 Chapel St, New Haven, CT, 06511. Tel: 203-789-3330. Fax: 203-789-5176. p. 359

Walia, Sandra, Librn, Maryland National Capital Park & Planning Commission, 9118 Brandywine Rd, Clinton, MD, 20735. Tel: 301-868-1121. Fax: 301-868-8177. p. 1024

Walizer, Beth, Dr, Asst Prof, Fort Hays State University, Rarick Hall, Rm 243, 600 Park St, Hays, KS, 67601-4099. Tel: 785-628-4204. Fax: 785-628-4140. p. 2966

Walk, Maggie, Tech Serv Librn, Helen Hall Library, 100 W Walker, League City, TX, 77573-3899. Tel: 281-554-1127. Fax: 281-554-1118. p. 2354

Walker, Angie, Asst Librn, Boonville Community Public Library, 121 W Main St, Boonville, NC, 27011-9125. Tel: 336-367-7737. Fax: 336-367-7767. p. 1777

Walker, Anna, Asst Librn, Buffalo Creek Memorial Library, 511 E McDonald Ave, Man, WV, 25635. Tel: 304-583-7887. Fax: 304-583-0182. p. 2564

Walker, Anne C, Co-Dir, Cabot Public Library, 3084 Main St, Cabot, VT, 05647. Tel: 802-563-2721. p. 2421

Walker, Arlene, Chmn, Boyle Public Library, PO Box 450, Boyle, AB, T0A 0M0, CANADA. Tel: 780-689-4161. Fax: 780-689-5660. p. 2686

Walker, Aspen, Br Mgr, Douglas County Libraries, Lone Tree Library, 8827 Lone Tree Pkwy, Lone Tree, CO, 80124-8961. Tel: 303-791-7323. Fax: 303-799-4275. p. 294

Walker, Azurinthia, Mgr, Dougherty County Public Library, Westtown, 2124 Waddell Ave, Albany, GA, 31707. Tel: 229-420-3280. p. 507

Walker, Barbara, Admin Serv, Lakeview Public Library, 1120 Woodfield Rd, Rockville Centre, NY, 11570. Tel: 516-536-3071. Fax: 516-536-6260. p. 1734

Walker, Barbara, Br Mgr, Aiken-Bamberg-Barnwell-Edgefield Regional Library System, Nancy Carson - North Augusta Library, 135 Edgefield Rd, North Augusta, SC, 29841-2423. Tel: 803-279-5767. Fax: 803-202-3588. p. 2179

Walker, Becky S, Libr & Syst Tech Mgr, Meherrin Regional Library, William E Richardson Jr Memorial Library, 100 Spring St, Emporia, VA, 23847. Tel: 804-634-2539. Fax: 804-634-5489. p. 2473

Walker, Ben, Head, Educ Libr, University of Florida Libraries, 535 Library W, Gainesville, FL, 32611-7000. Tel: 352-273-2780. Fax: 352-392-4789. p. 450

Walker, Beth, Principal Librn, Pasadena Public Library, 285 E Walnut St, Pasadena, CA, 91101. Tel: 626-744-4066. Fax: 626-585-8396. p. 207

Walker, Beth E, Dir, College for Creative Studies Library, Manoogian Visual Resource Ctr, 301 Frederick Douglass Dr, Detroit, MI, 48202-4034. Tel: 313-664-7641. Fax: 313-664-7880. p. 1169

Walker, Bill, Librn, Stockton-San Joaquin County Public Library, Margaret K Troke Branch, 502 W Benjamin Holt Dr, Stockton, CA, 95207. Fax: 209-937-7721. p. 273

Walker, Billie E, Ref Librn, Pennsylvania State University, Berks Campus, Tulpehocken Rd, Reading, PA, 19610. Tel: 610-396-6242. Fax: 610-396-6249. p. 2133

Walker, Bobbie Jo, Ref Librn, Atlanta-Fulton Public Library System, Roswell Regional Library, 115 Norcross St, Roswell, GA, 30075. Tel: 770-640-3075. Fax: 770-640-3077. p. 512

Walker, Byron, Pub Serv Librn, Spruce Grove Public Library, 35 Fifth Ave, Spruce Grove, AB, T7X 2C5, CANADA. Tel: 780-962-4423, Ext 107. Fax: 780-962-4826. p. 2717

Walker, Carolyn, Br Mgr, Alberta Law Libraries, Judicial, Calgary Courts Ctr, 2001-N, 601 - 5 St SW, Calgary, AB, T2P 5P7, CANADA. Tel: 403-297-3959. Fax: 403-297-2981. p. 2687

Walker, Celia, Spec Project Dir, Vanderbilt University, 419 21st Ave S, Nashville, TN, 37203-2427. Tel: 615-322-7100. Fax: 615-343-8279. p. 2260

Walker, Christine, Info Mgt Team Leader, Deere & Co Library, One John Deere Pl, Moline, IL, 61265. Tel: 309-765-4733. Fax: 309-765-4088. p. 674

Walker, Christine M, Asst Dir, Capital District Library Council, 28 Essex St, Albany, NY, 12206. Tel: 518-438-2500. Fax: 518-438-2872. p. 2949

Walker, Clint, Dir, Herbert Wescoat Memorial Library, 120 N Market St, McArthur, OH, 45651-1218. Tel: 740-596-5691. Fax: 740-596-2477. p. 1916

Walker, Courtney, Acq & Cat, National Energy Board Library, 444 Seventh Ave SW, Calgary, AB, T2P 0X8, CANADA. Tel: 403-299-3561. Fax: 403-292-5576. p. 2692

Walker, Cynthia, Head, Ch, Waterford Township Public Library, 5168 Civic Center Dr, Waterford, MI, 48329. Tel: 248-674-4831. Fax: 248-674-1910. p. 1235

Walker, Dana, Head, Ser, University of Georgia Libraries, Athens, GA, 30602-1641. Tel: 706-542-0605. Fax: 706-542-4144. p. 510

Walker, Danny, Sr Librn, Denver Public Library, Blair-Caldwell African American Research Library, 2401 Welton St, Denver, CO, 80205-3015. Tel: 720-865-2401. Fax: 720-865-2418. p. 301

Walker, Darlene, Archivist, Ref Serv, Res, Putnam County Library System, 601 College Rd, Palatka, FL, 32177-3873. Tel: 386-329-0126. Fax: 386-329-1240. p. 478

Walker, Darlene, Interim Libr Mgr, Yeadon Public Library, 809 Longacre Blvd, Yeadon, PA, 19050-3398. Tel: 610-623-4090. Fax: 610-394-9374. p. 2159

Walker, Davis, Mgr, Harcourt Inc, 6277 Sea Harbor Dr, Orlando, FL, 32887. Tel: 407-345-3113. Fax: 407-351-9906. p. 476

Walker, Debbie, Br Serv Coordr, Coordr, Circ, Tech Serv Coordr, Newport Beach Public Library, 1000 Avocado Ave, Newport Beach, CA, 92660-6301. Tel: 949-717-3829. Fax: 949-640-5681. p. 194

Walker, Deborah, Libr Mgr, Elbert County Public Library, Bowman Branch, 21 Prince Ave, Bowman, GA, 30624. Tel: 706-246-0046. p. 532

Walker, Demetra, Dir, Williamsburg Technical College Library, 601 MLK Jr Ave, Kingstree, SC, 29556. Tel: 843-355-4131. Fax: 843-355-4291. p. 2198

Walker, Denise, Librn, Virginia Beach Public Library Department, Kempsville Area, 832 Kempsville Rd, Virginia Beach, VA, 23464-2793. Tel: 757-385-2614. Fax: 757-495-5401. p. 2500

Walker, Devin, Web Developer, Lawrence Public Library, 707 Vermont St, Lawrence, KS, 66044-2371. Tel: 785-843-3833, Ext 135. Fax: 785-843-3368. p. 878

Walker, Diana, Circ, Lakeview Public Library, 1120 Woodfield Rd, Rockville Centre, NY, 11570. Tel: 516-536-3071. Fax: 516-536-6260. p. 1734

Walker, Diane, Dep Univ Librn, University of Virginia, PO Box 400114, Charlottesville, VA, 22904-4114. Tel: 434-924-3021. Fax: 434-924-1431. p. 2454

Walker, Diane, Pub Serv, Virginia Institute of Marine Science, College of William & Mary, Rte 1208, Greate Rd, Gloucester Point, VA, 23062. Tel: 804-684-7116. Fax: 804-684-7113. p. 2467

Walker, Diane Parr, Edward H Arnold Univ Librn, Hesburgh Libraries, 221 Hesburgh Library, University of Notre Dame, Notre Dame, IN, 46556. Tel: 574-631-5252. Fax: 574-631-6772. p. 770

Walker, Donna, Mgr, Arapahoe Library District, Davies Public Library, 303 Third Ave, Deer Trail, CO, 80105. Tel: 303-769-4310. Fax: 303-769-4350. p. 305

Walker, Donna, Mgr, Arapahoe Library District, Kelver Public Library, 404 E Front St, Byers, CO, 80103. Fax: 303-822-9393. p. 306

Walker, Donna, Mgr, Arapahoe Library District, Sheridan Public Library, 3201 W Oxford Ave, Sheridan, CO, 80236. Fax: 303-789-2611. p. 306

Walker, Elaine, Circ, Claremont School of Theology Library, 1325 N College Ave, Claremont, CA, 91711. Tel: 909-447-2510. p. 134

Walker, Elaine, Librn, Dechert Library, Cira Ctr, 2929 Arch St, Philadelphia, PA, 19104. Tel: 215-994-4000. Fax: 215-994-2222. p. 2105

Walker, Elaine E, Circ, Media Serv, Lambuth University, 705 Lambuth Blvd, Jackson, TN, 38301. Tel: 731-425-3298. Fax: 731-425-3200. p. 2238

Walker, Elizabeth, Dir, Milton L Rock Resource Center, 1720 Locust St, Philadelphia, PA, 19103. Tel: 215-893-5265. Fax: 215-717-3170. p. 2115

Walker, Elizabeth, Archivist, City of Edmonton, Archives, 10440 - 108 Ave, 2nd Flr, Prince of Wales Armouries Heritage Centre, Edmonton, AB, T5H 3Z9, CANADA. Tel: 780-496-8714. Fax: 780-496-8732. p. 2699

Walker, Ella Mae, Circ, Fort Morgan Public Library, 414 Main St, Fort Morgan, CO, 80701. Tel: 970-542-4000. Fax: 970-542-4013. p. 308

Walker, Evelyn, Librn, Daughters of Charity Health Care System, 2131 W Third St, Los Angeles, CA, 90057. Tel: 213-484-5530. Fax: 213-484-7092. p. 169

Walker, Evelyn, Dir, Mountainair Public Library, 109 Roosevelt Ave, Mountainair, NM, 87036. Tel: 505-847-9676. p. 1560

Walker, Felecia, Br Mgr, Livingston Parish Library, Denham Springs - Walker Branch, 8101 US Hwy 190, Denham Springs, LA, 70726. Tel: 225-665-8118. Fax: 225-791-6325. p. 955

Walker, Frank, Mgr, Northwest Regional Library System, Robert L Young Public Library, 116 S Arnold Rd, Panama City Beach, FL, 32413. Tel: 850-233-5055. Fax: 850-233-5019. p. 481

Walker, Gail, Mgr, Edmonton Public Library, Calder, 12522 132nd Ave, Edmonton, AB, T5L 3P9, CANADA. Tel: 780-496-7090. Fax: 780-496-1453. p. 2700

Walker, Gay, Spec Coll & Archives Librn, Reed College, 3203 SE Woodstock Blvd, Portland, OR, 97202-8199. Tel: 503-777-7702. Fax: 503-777-7786. p. 2014

Walker, Glenda, Br Mgr, Librn III, Montgomery City-County Public Library System, Rufus A Lewis Regional Branch Library, 3095 Mobile Hwy, Montgomery, AL, 36108. Tel: 334-240-4848. Fax: 334-240-4847. p. 29

Walker, Glenda, Br Mgr, Librn III, Montgomery City-County Public Library System, Bertha Pleasant Williams Library - Rosa L Parks Avenue Branch, 1276 Rosa L Parks Ave, Montgomery, AL, 36108. Tel: 334-240-4979. Fax: 334-240-4925. p. 31

Walker, Hazel J, Ref, Pitt Community College, Hwy 11 S, Greenville, NC, 27835. Tel: 252-321-4357. Fax: 252-321-4404. p. 1799

Walker, Heather, Librn, Coldwater Memorial Public Library, 31 Coldwater Rd, Coldwater, ON, L0K 1E0, CANADA. Tel: 705-686-3601. Fax: 705-686-3741. p. 2800

Walker, Heather, Head, Libr Serv, Tay Township Public Library, 715 Fourth Ave, Port McNicoll, ON, L0K 1R0, CANADA. Tel: 705-534-3511. Fax: 705-534-3511. p. 2838

Walker, Heather, Dir, Chinook Regional Library, 1240 Chaplin St W, Swift Current, SK, S9H 0G8, CANADA. Tel: 306-773-3186. Fax: 306-773-0434. p. 2927

Walker, Helen, Librn, Burr & Forman Library, Southtrust Tower, Ste 3100, 420 20th St N, Birmingham, AL, 35203. Tel: 205-251-3000. Fax: 205-458-5100. p. 8

Walker, Jacqueline C, Outreach Serv Librn, Aldrich Public Library, Six Washington St, Barre, VT, 05641-4227. Tel: 802-476-7550. Fax: 802-479-0450 (Call before sending fax). p. 2418

Walker, James, Tech Serv Adminr, Colorado Mesa University, 1200 College Pl, Grand Junction, CO, 81501. Tel: 970-248-1863. Fax: 970-248-1930. p. 310

Walker, Jane, Dir, Elm Creek Public Library, 241 N Tyler St, Elm Creek, NE, 68836. Tel: 308-856-4394. p. 1398

Walker, Janet, Dir, South Cheatham Public Library, 358 N Main St, Kingston Springs, TN, 37082. Tel: 615-952-4752. Fax: 615-952-3803. p. 2241

Walker, Jason, Supvr, Rapid City Public Library, 610 Quincy St, Rapid City, SD, 57701-3630. Tel: 605-394-6139, Ext 243. Fax: 605-394-4064. p. 2217

Walker, Jean, Pub Serv, Ser/ILL, The California Maritime Academy Library, 200 Maritime Academy Dr, Vallejo, CA, 94590. Tel: 707-654-1090. Fax: 707-654-1094. p. 278

Walker, Jennifer, Dir, Develop Serv Bur, Mississippi Library Commission, 3881 Eastwood Dr, Jackson, MS, 39211. Tel: 601-432-4068. Fax: 601-432-4480. p. 1304

Walker, Jennifer, Libr Serv Mgr, Grand Prairie Public Library System, 901 Conover Dr, Grand Prairie, TX, 75051. Tel: 972-237-5700. Fax: 972-237-5750. p. 2329

Walker, Jennifer, Head Librn, County of Carleton Law Library, Ottawa Court House, 2004-161 Elgin St, Ottawa, ON, K2P 2K1, CANADA. Tel: 613-233-7386, Ext 225. Fax: 613-238-3788. p. 2830

Walker, Jerri, Br Mgr, Sabine Parish Library, Converse Branch, 400 Wildcat Dr, Converse, LA, 71419. Tel: 318-567-3121. p. 956

Walker, Jim, Dir, Oxford Public Library, 129 S Franklin St, Oxford, WI, 53952. Tel: 608-586-4458. Fax: 608-586-4459. p. 2628

Walker, Jon, Exec Dir, Pueblo City-County Library District, 100 E Abriendo Ave, Pueblo, CO, 81004-4290. Tel: 719-562-5625. Fax: 719-562-5619. p. 320

Walker, Juanita, Asst Dir, Pub Serv, Prairie View A&M University, PO Box 519, MS 1040, Prairie View, TX, 77446-0519. Tel: 936-261-1531. Fax: 936-261-1539. p. 2372

Walker, Judi, Br Head, Vancouver Public Library, Mount Pleasant, One Kingsway, Vancouver, BC, V5T 3H7, CANADA. Tel: 604-665-3962. Fax: 604-665-3495. p. 2744

Walker, Judith A, Dir, Naval Air Station Pensacola Library, 250 Chambers Ave, Bldg 634, Pensacola, FL, 32508-5217. Tel: 850-452-4362. Fax: 850-452-3961. p. 481

Walker, Julia, Youth Serv Coordr, Alamance County Public Libraries, May Memorial Library, 342 S Spring St, Burlington, NC, 27215. Tel: 336-229-3588. Fax: 336-229-3592. p. 1779

Walker, Julie, Dep State Librn, Georgia Public Library Service, 1800 Century Place, Ste 150, Atlanta, GA, 30345-4304. Tel: 404-235-7140. Fax: 404-235-7201. p. 515

Walker, Karen, Dir, Alanson Area Public Library, 7631 Burr Ave, Alanson, MI, 49706. Tel: 231-548-5465. Fax: 231-548-5465. p. 1148

Walker, Karen, Dir, Crooked Tree District Library, 2203 Walloon St, Walloon Lake, MI, 49796. Tel: 231-535-2111. Fax: 231-535-2790. p. 1234

Walker, Karen, Dir, Crooked Tree District Library, Boyne Falls Branch, 3008 Railroad St, Boyne Falls, MI, 49713. Tel: 231-549-2277. p. 1234

Walker, Karen E, Dir, Clinton Public Library, 313 S Fourth St, Clinton, IN, 47842-2398. Tel: 765-832-8349. Fax: 765-832-3823. p. 732

Walker, Kate, Ref Serv, YA, Anderson County Library, 300 N McDuffie St, Anderson, SC, 29621-5643. Tel: 864-260-4500. Fax: 864-260-4510. p. 2180

Walker, Keith, Dir of Libr Serv, Medicine Hat College Library, 299 College Dr SE, Medicine Hat, AB, T1A 3Y6, CANADA. Tel: 403-504-3539. Fax: 403-504-3634. p. 2711

Walker, Kent, Automation Syst Coordr, Clearwater Public Library System, 100 N Osceola Ave, Clearwater, FL, 33755. Tel: 727-562-4970. Fax: 727-562-4977. p. 432

Walker, Kevin, Acq, Alabama State University, 915 S Jackson St, Montgomery, AL, 36104. Tel: 334-229-4106, 334-229-6890. Fax: 334-229-4911, 334-229-4940. p. 28

Walker, Kim, Ser Tech, University of the District of Columbia, David A Clarke School of Law, Charles N & Hilda H M Mason Law Library, Bldg 39, Rm B-16, 4200 Connecticut Ave NW, Washington, DC, 20008. Tel: 202-274-7310. Fax: 202-274-7311. p. 421

Walker, Kim, Archives Mgr, Shelburne County Archives & Genealogical Society Library, 168 Water St, Shelburne, NS, B0T 1W0, CANADA. Tel: 902-875-4299. Fax: 902-875-3267. p. 2784

Walker, Larrisa, Libr Dir, Oliver Springs Public Library, 610 Walker Ave, Oliver Springs, TN, 37840. Tel: 865-435-2509. Fax: 865-730-6476. p. 2262

Walker, Laura Beth, Ref Librn, First Regional Library, Lafayette County-Oxford Public Library, 401 Bramlett Blvd, Oxford, MS, 38655. Tel: 662-234-5751. Fax: 662-234-3155. p. 1302

Walker, Lena, Dir, McNary Community Library, 14 S Cady Ave, McNary, AZ, 85930. Tel: 928-334-2116. p. 68

Walker, Leslie, Assoc Librn, Lutheran Theological Southern Seminary, 4201 N Main St, Columbia, SC, 29203. Tel: 803-461-3220, 803-786-5150. Fax: 803-461-3278. p. 2188

Walker, Libby, Admin Coordr, Vigo County Public Library, One Library Sq, Terre Haute, IN, 47807. Tel: 812-232-1113, Ext 2203. Fax: 812-232-3208. p. 782

Walker, Lottie, Ch, Warren County-Vicksburg Public Library, 700 Veto St, Vicksburg, MS, 39180-3595. Tel: 601-636-6411. Fax: 601-634-4809. p. 1317

Walker, Lucinda H, Dir, Norwich Public Library, 368 Main St, Norwich, VT, 05055-9453. Tel: 802-649-1184. Fax: 802-649-3470. p. 2431

Walker, Madge, Dir, Greeneville Green County Public Library, 210 N Main St, Greeneville, TN, 37745-3816. Tel: 423-638-5034. Fax: 423-638-3841. p. 2236

Walker, Margie, YA Serv, Amesbury Public Library, 149 Main St, Amesbury, MA, 01913. Tel: 978-388-8148. p. 1048

Walker, Marshia, Head, Circ, Jacksonville Public Library, 502 S Jackson St, Jacksonville, TX, 75766. Tel: 903-586-7664. Fax: 903-586-3397. p. 2347

Walker, Martaire, Ref Librn, Atlanta-Fulton Public Library System, Southwest Regional Library, 3665 Cascade Rd SW, Atlanta, GA, 30331. Tel: 404-699-6363. Fax: 404-699-6381. p. 512

Walker, Martha, Dir, Cornell University Library, Fine Arts, 235 Sibley Dome, Ithaca, NY, 14853-6701. Tel: 607-255-3710. Fax: 607-255-6718. p. 1641

Walker, Mary, Electronic Res Librn, Wichita State University Libraries, 1845 Fairmount, Wichita, KS, 67260-0068. Tel: 316-978-5792. Fax: 316-978-3048. p. 902

Walker, Mary O, Librn, Greystone Park Psychiatric Hospital, 59 Koch Ave, Morris Plains, NJ, 07950. Tel: 973-538-1800, Ext 5262. p. 1504

Walker, Mattie, Coll Develop, Rust College, 150 E Rust Ave, Holly Springs, MS, 38635. Tel: 662-252-8000, Ext 4100. Fax: 662-252-8873. p. 1302

Walker, Melissa, Youth Serv, Clearwater Public Library System, East, 2251 Drew St, Clearwater, FL, 33765. Tel: 727-562-4970. p. 432

Walker, Melissa, Asst Librn, Stevens Memorial Library, 20 Memorial Dr, Ashburnham, MA, 01430. Tel: 978-827-4115. Fax: 978-827-4116. p. 1050

Walker, Melveta, Dir, Eastern New Mexico University, 1300 S Ave K, Sta 32, Portales, NM, 88130-7402. Tel: 575-562-2626. Fax: 575-562-2647. p. 1560

Walker, Mercede, Ch, Gaston-Lincoln Regional Library, 1555 E Garrison Blvd, Gastonia, NC, 28054. Tel: 704-868-2164. Fax: 704-853-6012. p. 1794

Walker, Michael C, Assoc Librn, Pub Serv, Virginia State University, One Hayden Dr, Petersburg, VA, 23806-0001. Tel: 804-524-6946. Fax: 804-524-6959. p. 2484

Walker, Michelle, Dir, Omnicom Management Services, 1999 Bryan St, Ste 3200, Dallas, TX, 75201. Tel: 214-259-2517. Fax: 214-259-2508. p. 2309

Walker, Nancy A, Dir, Berkshire Community College, 1350 West St, Pittsfield, MA, 01201. Tel: 413-236-2151. Fax: 413-448-2700. p. 1117

Walker, Pam, Dir, Crichton College, 255 N Highland St, Memphis, TN, 38111. Tel: 901-320-9770. Fax: 901-320-9785. p. 2248

Walker, Patricia, Asst Libr Dir, Plaquemines Parish Library, 8442 Hwy 23, Belle Chasse, LA, 70037. Tel: 504-398-7302. Fax: 504-398-4580. p. 945

Walker, Patricia, Ad, Nichols Memorial Library, 169 Main St, Kingston, NH, 03848-0128. Tel: 603-642-3521. Fax: 603-642-3135. p. 1453

Walker, Patricia Sue, Br Mgr, Knox County Public Library System, Corryton Branch, 7733 Corryton Rd, Corryton, TN, 37721-9802. Tel: 865-688-1501. Fax: 865-687-7568. p. 2242

Walker, Paul, Chief Exec Officer, North Bay Public Library, 271 Worthington St E, North Bay, ON, P1B 1H1, CANADA. Tel: 705-474-4830. Fax: 705-495-4010. p. 2825

Walker, Paula, Communications Coordr, Tigard Public Library, 13500 SW Hall Blvd, Tigard, OR, 97223-8111. Tel: 503-684-6537, Ext 2508. Fax: 503-598-7515, 503-718-2797. p. 2021

Walker, Phillip Ira, Evening Supvr, Transylvania University Library, 300 N Broadway, Lexington, KY, 40508. Tel: 859-246-5006. Fax: 859-233-8779. p. 921

Walker, Rhita, Purchasing, Phillips Community College of the University of Arkansas, 1000 Campus Dr, Helena, AR, 72342. Tel: 870-338-6474. Fax: 870-338-2783. p. 103

Walker, Rhonda, Br Mgr, Broward County Division of Libraries, Northwest Branch, 1580 NW Third Ave, Pompano Beach, FL, 33060. Tel: 954-786-2186. Fax: 954-786-2167. p. 442

Walker, Rick, Mgr, Libr Serv, Winnipeg Public Library, 251 Donald St, Winnipeg, MB, R3C 3P5, CANADA. Tel: 204-986-6462. Fax: 204-942-5671. p. 2760

Walker, Robin, Librn, International Longshore & Warehouse Union, 1188 Franklin St, 4th Flr, San Francisco, CA, 94109. Tel: 415-775-0533. Fax: 415-775-1302. p. 243

Walker, Sally, Dir, Cannelton Public Library, 210 S Eighth, Cannelton, IN, 47520. Tel: 812-547-6028. p. 731

Walker, Scharnae, Br Mgr, Rockford Public Library, Lewis Lemon Branch, 1988 W Jefferson St, Rockford, IL, 61101-5671. Tel: 815-965-4767. Fax: 815-962-4863. p. 697

Walker, Scharnae, Br Mgr, Rockford Public Library, Montague, 1238 S Winnebago St, Rockford, IL, 61102-2944. Tel: 815-965-7606, Ext739. Fax: 815-986-0924. p. 698

Walker, Sharon, Asst Dir, Elizabethton-Carter County Public Library, 201 N Sycamore St, Elizabethton, TN, 37643. Tel: 423-547-6360. Fax: 423-542-1510. p. 2233

Walker, Sharon, Libr Mgr, Vancouver Island Regional Library, Sidney Branch, 10091 Resthaven Dr, Sidney, BC, V8L 3G3, CANADA. Tel: 250-656-0944. Fax: 250-656-6400. p. 2733

Walker, Shaundra, Sr Librn, Fort Valley State University, 1005 State University Dr, Fort Valley, GA, 31030-4313. Tel: 478-825-6281. Fax: 478-825-6663, 478-825-6916. p. 533

Walker, Sheila, Cat Librn, Jenkins Law Library, 833 Chestnut St, Ste 1220, Philadelphia, PA, 19107-4429. Tel: 215-574-7957. Fax: 215-574-7920. p. 2111

Walker Smalley, Ann, Exec Dir, Metronet, 1619 Dayton Ave, Ste 314, Saint Paul, MN, 55104. Tel: 651-646-0475. Fax: 651-649-3169. p. 2947

Walker, Sonia, Librn, Callahan County Library, 100 W Fourth St, B-1, Baird, TX, 79504-5305. Tel: 325-854-5875. Fax: 325-854-5841. p. 2285

Walker, Stephanie, Chief Librn, Info Tech, Brooklyn College Library, 2900 Bedford Ave, Brooklyn, NY, 11210-2889. Tel: 718-951-5336. Fax: 718-951-4540. p. 1589

Walker, Steve, Dr, Pres, Seminole Nation Museum Library, 524 S Wewoka, Wewoka, OK, 74884. Tel: 405-257-5580. p. 1986

Walker, Steven, IT Support, Tech Serv, Andover Newton Theological School, 169 Herrick Rd, Newton Centre, MA, 02459. Tel: 617-831-2418. Fax: 617-831-1643. p. 1110

Walker, Susan, Librn, Genoa Public Library District, 232 W Main St, Genoa, IL, 60135. Tel: 815-784-2627. Fax: 815-784-2627. p. 649

Walker, Susan Odell, Head, Pub Serv, Yale University Library, Lewis Walpole Library, 154 Main St, Farmington, CT, 06032. Tel: 860-677-2140. Fax: 860-677-6369. p. 359

Walker, Suzanne, Youth Serv Librn, Mooresville Public Library, 220 W Harrison St, Mooresville, IN, 46158-1633. Tel: 317-831-7323. Fax: 317-831-7383. p. 766

Walker, Tami, Cat, Circ, Tech Serv, Ohio University-Lancaster Library, 1570 Granville Pike, Lancaster, OH, 43130-1097. Tel: 740-654-6711, Ext 220. Fax: 740-687-9497. p. 1909

Walker, Thomas, Music & Digital Serv Librn, Marshall University Libraries, One John Marshall Dr, Huntington, WV, 25755-2060. Tel: 304-696-2309. Fax: 304-696-5858. p. 2561

Walker, Thomas Paul, Dir, New York College of Podiatric Medicine, 53 E 124th St, New York, NY, 10035. Tel: 212-410-8020. Fax: 212-876-9426. p. 1689

Walker, Tim, Br Mgr, Montgomery County Memorial Library System, George & Cynthia Woods Mitchell Library, 8125 Ashlane Way, The Woodlands, TX, 77382. Tel: 936-442-7728, Ext 307. Fax: 281-362-0772. p. 2300

Walker, Tracy, VPres, Bay Ridge Christian College Library, 3626 FM 2919, PO Box 726, Kendleton, TX, 77451-0726. Tel: 979-532-3982. Fax: 979-532-4352. p. 2349

Walker, Trina, Dir, Communications & Creative Serv, Carnegie Library of Pittsburgh, 4400 Forbes Ave, Pittsburgh, PA, 15213-4080. Tel: 412-578-2483. Fax: 412-688-8617. p. 2122

Walker, Veronica, Ch, Ref, Washington District Library, 380 N Wilmor Rd, Washington, IL, 61571. Tel: 309-444-2241. Fax: 309-444-4711. p. 715

Walker, Virginia, Asst Librn, Invermere Public Library, 201 Seventh Ave, Invermere, BC, V0A 1K0, CANADA. Tel: 250-342-6416. Fax: 250-342-6416. p. 2729

Walker, Walt, Head, Cat, Loyola Marymount University, One LMU Dr, MS 8200, Los Angeles, CA, 90045-2659. Tel: 310-338-7687. Fax: 310-338-4366. p. 175

Walker, Wendy, Asst Dir, Park Hills Public Library, 16 S Coffman St, Park Hills, MO, 63601. Tel: 573-431-4842. Fax: 573-431-2110. p. 1349

Walker, William D, Dean & Univ Librn, University of Miami Libraries, 1300 Memorial Dr, Coral Gables, FL, 33146. Tel: 305-284-3233. Fax: 305-284-4027. p. 434

Walker, William M, Acq, Vanderbilt University, Alyne Queener Massey Law Library, 131 21st Ave S, Nashville, TN, 37203. Tel: 615-343-4079. Fax: 615-343-1265. p. 2261

Walker, Willis C, Librn, Bard College, Levy Economics Institute Library, Blithewood Ave, Annandale-on-Hudson, NY, 12504. Tel: 845-758-7729. Fax: 845-758-1149. p. 1574

Walker-Hitt, Sarah, Dir, Lyndon Carnegie Library, 127 E Sixth, Lyndon, KS, 66451. Tel: 785-828-4520. Fax: 785-828-4565. p. 880

Walker-Lowitz, Bonnie, Cat, Valparaiso Community Library, 459 Valparaiso Pkwy, Valparaiso, FL, 32580. Tel: 850-729-5406. Fax: 850-729-1120. p. 501

Walker-Sokola, Karla, Children's Prog Coordr, Covington-Veedersburg Public Library, 622 Fifth St, Covington, IN, 47932. Tel: 765-793-2572. Fax: 765-793-2621. p. 734

Walkling, Lee, Librn, Washington State Department of Natural Resources, 1111 Washington St SE, Rm 173, MS 47007, Olympia, WA, 98504-7007. Tel: 360-902-1473. Fax: 360-902-1785. p. 2523

Walko, Susan, Circ, Coll Develop, Mercy Hospital of Pittsburgh, 1400 Locust St, Pittsburgh, PA, 15219. Tel: 412-232-7520. Fax: 412-232-8422. p. 2126

Walkowiak, Julie, Acq Spec, College of Saint Scholastica Library, 1200 Kenwood Ave, Duluth, MN, 55811-4199. Tel: 218-723-6649. Fax: 218-723-5948. p. 1247

Walkowiak, Louise, Librn, Dufur School-Community Library, 802 NE Fifth St, Dufur, OR, 97021-3034. Tel: 541-467-2588. Fax: 541-467-2589. p. 1995

Walkowicz, Evelyn, Br Mgr, Henderson District Public Libraries, Galleria Library, Galleria at Sunset, 1300 W Sunset Rd, Ste 1121, Henderson, NV, 89014. Tel: 702-207-4259. p. 1428

Wall, Cindy, Ch, Southington Public Library & Museum, 255 Main St, Southington, CT, 06489. Tel: 860-628-0947. Fax: 860-628-0488. p. 368

Wall, Deborah, Dir, Pembroke Public Library, 142 Center St, Pembroke, MA, 02359-2613. Tel: 781-293-6771, Ext 13. Fax: 781-294-0742. p. 1117

Wall, Diane R, Asst Dir, Tech Serv Librn, Melrose Public Library, 69 W Emerson St, Melrose, MA, 02176. Tel: 781-665-2313. Fax: 781-662-4229. p. 1105

Wall, Donna M, Asst Dir, Ashtabula County District Library, 335 W 44th St, Ashtabula, OH, 44004-6897. Tel: 440-997-9341, Ext 222. Fax: 440-992-7714. p. 1855

Wall, Jamie, Librn, Northeast Regional Library, Walnut Public Library, 102 S Main St, Walnut, MS, 38683-9312. Tel: 662-223-6768. Fax: 662-223-6768. p. 1298

Wall, Jancie, Asst Librn, Red Bud Public Library, 925 S Main St, Red Bud, IL, 62278. Tel: 618-282-2255. Fax: 618-282-4055. p. 694

Wall, Jenna, Libr Mgr, Piedmont Regional Library, Talmo Public, 45 A J Irvin Rd, Talmo, GA, 30575. Tel: 706-693-1905. p. 557

Wall, Karen, Sr Br Librn, OC Public Libraries, San Clemente Branch, 242 Avenida Del Mar, San Clemente, CA, 92672-4005. Tel: 949-492-3493. Fax: 949-498-5749. p. 258

Wall, Karen, Ref, Killingly Public Library, 25 Westcott Rd, Danielson, CT, 06239. Tel: 860-779-5383. Fax: 860-779-1823. p. 335

Wall, Kay L, Dean, Clemson University Libraries, Box 343001, Clemson, SC, 29634-3001. Tel: 864-656-5169. Fax: 864-656-0758. p. 2186

Wall, Nancy, Asst Librn, Albemarle Regional Library, Hertford County Library, 303 W Tryon St, Winton, NC, 27986. Tel: 252-358-7855. Fax: 252-358-0368. p. 1835

Wall, Patricia A, Librn, San Bernardino Valley College Library, 701 S Mount Vernon Ave, San Bernardino, CA, 92410. Tel: 909-384-8577. p. 229

Wall, Patrick, Dir, University City Public Library, 6701 Delmar Blvd, University City, MO, 63130. Tel: 314-727-3150. Fax: 314-727-6005. p. 1370

Wall, Richard, Coll Develop, Queens College, Benjamin S Rosenthal Library, 65-30 Kissena Blvd, Flushing, NY, 11367-0904. Tel: 718-997-3700. Fax: 718-997-3753. p. 1623

Wall, Thomas, Univ Librn, Boston College Libraries, Thomas P O'Neill Jr Library (Central Library), 140 Commonwealth Ave, Chestnut Hill, MA, 02467. Tel: 617-552-4470. Fax: 617-552-0599. p. 1081

Wallace, April, Mgr, Charlotte Mecklenburg Library, Hickory Grove Branch, 5935 Hickory Grove Rd, Charlotte, NC, 28215. Tel: 704-416-4400. p. 1782

Wallace, Barbara, Libr Tech, Sacramento Location, Alliant International University, 5130 E Clinton Way, Fresno, CA, 93727. Tel: 916-561-3202. Fax: 559-253-2223. p. 150

Wallace, Christine, Ch, Woonsocket Harris Public Library, 303 Clinton St, Woonsocket, RI, 02895. Tel: 401-769-9044. Fax: 401-767-4120. p. 2178

Wallace, Christy, Computer Tech, Jacksonville Public Library, 200 Pelham Rd S, Jacksonville, AL, 36265. Tel: 256-435-6332. Fax: 256-435-4459. p. 22

Wallace, Danny, Prof, University of Alabama, 514 Main Library, Tuscaloosa, AL, 35487. Tel: 205-348-4610. Fax: 205-348-3746. p. 2961

Wallace, Darby B, Dir, Jackson County Library, 213 Walnut St, Newport, AR, 72112-3325. Tel: 870-523-2952. Fax: 870-523-5218. p. 111

Wallace, Deb, Exec Dir, Harvard Library, Knowledge & Library Services, Harvard Business School, Ten Soldiers Field Rd, Boston, MA, 02163. Tel: 617-495-6040, 617-495-6397. Fax: 617-496-6909. p. 1076

Wallace, Debra, Asst City Librn, Roanoke Public Library, 308 S Walnut St, Roanoke, TX, 76262. Tel: 817-491-2691. Fax: 817-491-2729. p. 2376

Wallace, Edward, ILL, Department of Veterans Affairs, 130 W Kingsbridge Rd, Bronx, NY, 10468. Tel: 718-584-9000, Ext 6924. Fax: 718-741-4608. p. 1586

Wallace, Edwin, Head, Per, Lehman College, City University of New York, 250 Bedford Park Blvd W, Bronx, NY, 10468-1589. Tel: 718-960-8577. Fax: 718-960-8952. p. 1587

Wallace, Erik, Circ, Whatcom Community College Library, 237 W Kellogg Rd, Bellingham, WA, 98226. Tel: 360-383-3300. p. 2509

Wallace, Grace, Cat, North Carolina Wesleyan College, 3400 N Wesleyan Blvd, Rocky Mount, NC, 27804. Tel: 252-985-5350. Fax: 252-985-5235. p. 1821

Wallace, Greg, Instrul Serv Librn, Ref Librn, Massachusetts College of Art & Design, 621 Huntington Ave, Boston, MA, 02115-5882. Tel: 617-879-7150. Fax: 617-879-7110. p. 1063

Wallace, Irena, Cat, Plain City Public Library, 305 W Main St, Plain City, OH, 43064-1148. Tel: 614-873-4912, Ext 27. Fax: 614-873-8364. p. 1930

Wallace, Isaac, Head, Univ Rec Mgt, Clemson University Libraries, Box 343001, Clemson, SC, 29634-3001. Tel: 864-656-4336. Fax: 864-656-0758. p. 2186

Wallace, J, Libr Assoc, Centralia Correctional Center Library, 9330 Shattuc Rd, Centralia, IL, 62801. Tel: 618-533-4111, Ext 2710. p. 602

Wallace, Jan, Head Librn, University of British Columbia Library, David Lam Management Research Library, 2033 Main Mall, Vancouver, BC, V6T 1Z2, CANADA. Tel: 604-822-9392. Fax: 604-822-9398. p. 2743

Wallace, Jane, Br Mgr, Monterey County Free Libraries, Buena Vista, 18250 Tara Dr, Salinas, CA, 93908. Tel: 831-455-9699. Fax: 831-455-0369. p. 183

Wallace, Janet, Dir, Shelby County Public Library, 57 W Broadway, Shelbyville, IN, 46176. Tel: 317-398-7121, 317-835-2653. Fax: 317-398-4430. p. 778

Wallace, Joshua, Librn, South Texas College Library, 3201 W Pecan Blvd, McAllen, TX, 78501-6661. Tel: 956-872-2623. Fax: 956-872-7202. p. 2361

Wallace, Judith E, Dir, Mattapoisett Free Public Library, Seven Barstow St, Mattapoisett, MA, 02739-0475. Tel: 508-758-4171. Fax: 508-758-4783. p. 1103

Wallace, Judy, Asst Librn, Van Horne Public Library, 114 Main St, Van Horne, IA, 52346. Tel: 319-228-8744. Fax: 319-228-8744. p. 848

Wallace, Karen, Circ, Drake University, Drake Law Library, Opperman Hall, 2615 Carpenter Ave, Des Moines, IA, 50311-4505. Tel: 515-271-2989. Fax: 515-271-2530. p. 809

Wallace, Karen, Dir, Osborne Public Library, 325 W Main St, Osborne, KS, 67473-2425. Tel: 785-346-5486. Fax: 785-346-2888. p. 886

Wallace, Karen, Dir, Fontana Regional Library, 33 Fryemont St, Bryson City, NC, 28713. Tel: 828-488-2382. Fax: 828-488-2638. p. 1778

Wallace, Karen, Dir, Macon County Public Library, 149 Siler Farm Rd, Franklin, NC, 28734. Tel: 828-524-3600, 828-524-3700. Fax: 828-524-9550. p. 1794

Wallace, Kristy L, Dir, Libr Serv, Youngsville Public Library, 100 Broad St, Youngsville, PA, 16371-1421. Tel: 814-563-7670. Fax: 814-563-7670. p. 2160

Wallace, Linda, Circ Supvr, Groton Public Library, 52 Newtown Rd, Groton, CT, 06340. Tel: 860-441-6750. Fax: 860-448-0363. p. 342

Wallace, Linda, Circ, Oak Hill Public Library, 226 S Front St, Oak Hill, OH, 45656. Tel: 740-682-6457. Fax: 740-682-3522. p. 1924

Wallace, Louise, Dir, Orem Public Library, 58 N State St, Orem, UT, 84057-5596. Tel: 801-229-7050. Fax: 801-229-7130. p. 2409

Wallace, Lucille, Circ Mgr, University of Calgary Library, 2500 University Dr NW, Calgary, AB, T2N 1N4, CANADA. Tel: 403-220-3758. Fax: 403-282-1218. p. 2693

Wallace, Lynn, Access Serv Librn, Coll Develop Coordr, Oklahoma State University - Tulsa Library, 700 N Greenwood Ave, Tulsa, OK, 74106-0700. Tel: 918-594-8451. Fax: 918-594-8145. p. 1981

Wallace, Mary Kay, Dir, Brooke County Public Library, 945 Main St, Wellsburg, WV, 26070. Tel: 304-737-1551. Fax: 304-737-1010. p. 2574

Wallace, Mary Kay, Dir, Brooke County Public Library, Follansbee Branch, 844 Main St, Follansbee, WV, 26037. Tel: 304-527-0860. p. 2574

Wallace, Meghan, Info Serv Coordr, Georgetown University, Dahlgren Memorial Library, Preclinical Science Bldg GM-7, 3900 Reservoir Rd NW, Washington, DC, 20007. Tel: 202-687-1173. Fax: 202-687-1862. p. 402

Wallace, Mike, Libr Spec, HACC Central Pennsylvania's Community College, 731 Old Harrisburg Rd, Gettysburg, PA, 17325. Tel: 717-337-1644. Fax: 717-337-2329. p. 2060

Wallace, Milda, Tech Serv Coordr, Holy Family University Library, 9801 Frankford Ave, Philadelphia, PA, 19114. Tel: 267-341-3315, 267-341-3316. Fax: 215-632-8067. p. 2111

Wallace, Nancy, Asst Librn, Anne Arundel County Circuit Court, Seven Church Circle, Ste 303, Annapolis, MD, 21401. Tel: 410-222-1387. Fax: 410-268-9762. p. 1009

Wallace, Olivia, Chief Librn, Evening Post Publishing Co, 134 Columbus St, Charleston, SC, 29403. Tel: 843-937-5698. Fax: 843-937-5696. p. 2184

Wallace, Patricia, Ch, Middlesex County Library, 34B Frank St, Strathroy, ON, N7G 2R4, CANADA. Tel: 519-245-8237. Fax: 519-245-8238. p. 2845

Wallace, Paul, Libr Syst Mgr, United States Court of Appeals, 600 Camp St, Rm 106, New Orleans, LA, 70130. Tel: 504-310-7797. Fax: 504-310-7578. p. 964

Wallace, Rachel, Coordr, Ch Serv, West Florida Public Library, 200 W Gregory, Pensacola, FL, 32502. Tel: 850-436-5060. p. 482

Wallace, Rebecca, Acq, Franklin College, 101 Branigin Blvd, Franklin, IN, 46131-2623. Tel: 317-738-8164. Fax: 317-738-8787. p. 743

Wallace, Rebecca, Br Assoc, Las Vegas-Clark County Library District, Searchlight Library, 200 Michael Wendell Way, Searchlight, NV, 89046. Tel: 702-297-1442. Fax: 702-297-1782. p. 1430

Wallace, Richard, Pub Serv Mgr, East Tennessee State University, James H Quillen College of Medicine Library, Maple St, Bldg 4, Johnson City, TN, 37614. Tel: 423-439-8071. Fax: 423-439-7025. p. 2239

Wallace, Rita, Archivist, US Court of Appeals for the Sixth Circuit Library, 312 Potter Stewart US Courthouse, Cincinnati, OH, 45202. Tel: 513-564-7304. Fax: 513-564-7329. p. 1873

Wallace, Robin H, Ref Archivist/Librn, Alberta Culture, 8555 Roper Rd, Edmonton, AB, T6E 5W1, CANADA. Tel: 780-415-8451. Fax: 780-427-4646. p. 2697

Wallace, Sandy, Coordr, Instrul Serv, Carl Sandburg College, 2400 Tom L Wilson Blvd, Galesburg, IL, 61401. Tel: 309-341-5207. Fax: 309-344-3526. p. 647

Wallace, Sandy, In Charge, Brooklyn Museum of Art, Wilbour Library of Egyptology, 200 Eastern Pkwy, Brooklyn, NY, 11238. Tel: 718-501-6215. Fax: 718-501-6125. p. 1590

Wallace, Scottie, Mgr, Washoe County Library System, Downtown Reno Library, 301 S Center St, Reno, NV, 89501. Tel: 775-327-8300. Fax: 775-327-8390. p. 1434

Wallace, Sheila, Dir, Emily Carr Institute of Art & Design Library, 1399 Johnston St, Granville Island, Vancouver, BC, V6H 3R9, CANADA. Tel: 604-844-3840. Fax: 604-844-3801. p. 2740

Wallace, Sherman, Fac Mgr, Upper Arlington Public Library, 2800 Tremont Rd, Columbus, OH, 43221. Tel: 614-486-9621. Fax: 614-486-4530. p. 1891

Wallace, Sherrie, Librn, Tulsa City-County Library, Suburban Acres, 4606 N Garrison Ave, Tulsa, OK, 74126. Tel: 918-591-4004. Fax: 918-591-4005. p. 1983

Wallace, Shirley, Br Mgr, Chicago Public Library, West Chicago Avenue, 4856 W Chicago Ave, Chicago, IL, 60651. Tel: 312-743-0260. Fax: 312-743-0272. p. 610

Wallace, Stephanie, Pub Serv Librn, Belen Public Library, 333 Becker Ave, Belen, NM, 87002. Tel: 505-864-7522. p. 1552

Wallace, Teri-Ann, Ref, St Louis College of Pharmacy, 4588 Parkview Pl, Saint Louis, MO, 63110. Tel: 314-446-8367. Fax: 314-446-8360. p. 1357

Wallace, Tim, Coll & Ref Serv Mgr, San Bruno Public Library, 701 Angus Ave W, San Bruno, CA, 94066-3490. Tel: 650-616-7078. Fax: 650-876-0848. p. 230

Wallace, Valeri, Dir, Libr Serv, Lincoln College of New England, 2279 Mount Vernon Rd, Southington, CT, 06489-1057. Tel: 860-628-4751, Ext 148. Fax: 860-628-6444. p. 368

Wallace, Vicki, Br Mgr, Antigo Public Library, White Lake Branch, White Lake Village Hall, 615 School St, White Lake, WI, 54491. Tel: 715-882-8501. p. 2578

Wallace, Vicki Lynn, Dir, Tawakoni Area Public Library, 340 W Hwy 276, West Tawakoni, TX, 75474-2644. Tel: 903-447-3445. Fax: 903-447-3445. p. 2399

Wallace, William D, Exec Dir, Worcester Historical Museum, 30 Elm St, Worcester, MA, 01605. Tel: 508-753-8278, Ext 106. Fax: 508-753-9070. p. 1145

Wallach, William K, Assoc Dir, University of Michigan, Bentley Historical Library, 1150 Beal Ave, Ann Arbor, MI, 48109-2113. Tel: 734-764-3482. Fax: 734-936-1333. p. 1151

Wallen, Regina, Interim Head, Access Serv, Stanford University Libraries, Stanford Auxiliary Library, 691 Pampas Lane, Stanford, CA, 94305. Tel: 650-723-9201. p. 271

Wallenius, Leila, Univ Librn, Laurentian University, 935 Ramsey Lake Rd, Sudbury, ON, P3E 2C6, CANADA. Tel: 705-675-4841. Fax: 705-675-4877. p. 2846

Waller, Carolyn, Acq, Librn, Shackelford County Library, 402 N Second St, Albany, TX, 76430. Tel: 325-762-2672. Fax: 325-762-2672. p. 2272

Waller, Deborah, Librn, Central Alabama Community College, Childersburg Campus Library, 34091 US Hwy 280, Childersburg, AL, 35044. Tel: 256-378-5576, Ext 2041. Fax: 256-378-2040. p. 3

Waller, Erin, Dir, Saline County Public Library, 1800 Smithers Dr, Benton, AR, 72015. Tel: 501-778-4766. Fax: 501-778-0536. p. 94

Waller, Lee, Dr, Dir, Texas A & M University - Commerce, 2600 S Neal St, Commerce, TX, 75428. Tel: 903-886-5500, 903-886-5607. Fax: 903-886-5507. p. 2974

Waller, Michael, Cat/Presv Librn, St John's College Library, 60 College Ave, Annapolis, MD, 21401. Tel: 410-626-2549. Fax: 410-295-6936. p. 1011

Waller, Richard, Dir, Saint John's University Library, Kathryn & Shelby Cullom Davis Library, 101 Murray St, 3rd Flr, New York, NY, 10007. Tel: 212-277-5135. Fax: 212-277-5140. p. 1725

Waller, Rosalie, Info Serv, Libr Instruction, Seneca College of Applied Arts & Technology, Newnham Campus (Main), 1750 Finch Ave E, North York, ON, M2J 2X5, CANADA. Tel: 416-491-5050, Ext 22072. Fax: 416-492-7184. p. 2813

Waller, Ted, Head, Archives, Head, Tech Serv, Meredith College, 3800 Hillsborough St, Raleigh, NC, 27607-5298. Tel: 919-760-8531. Fax: 919-760-2830. p. 1815

Wallerich, Andi, Dir, Sigourney Public Library, 720 E Jackson, Sigourney, IA, 52591-1505. Tel: 641-622-2890. Fax: 641-622-3391. p. 843

Wallin, Inger, Librn, Chester County Hospital Library, 701 E Marshall St, West Chester, PA, 19380. Tel: 610-431-5204. Fax: 610-696-8411. p. 2153

Wallin, Irene H, Librn, Mary M Campbell Public Library, Tenth & Green Sts, Marcus Hook, PA, 19061-4592. Tel: 610-485-6519. p. 2084

Wallin, Sam, Commun Librn, Fort Vancouver Regional Library District, Woodland Community Library, 770 Park St, Woodland, WA, 98674. Tel: 360-225-2115. Fax: 360-225-6344. p. 2546

Walling, Bobbette, Dir, Mulliken District Library, 135 Main St, Mulliken, MI, 48861. Tel: 517-649-8611. Fax: 517-649-2207. p. 1212

Walling, Ray, Electronic Serv, Govt Doc, Baker University, 518 Eighth St, Baldwin City, KS, 66006-0065. Tel: 785-594-8389. Fax: 785-594-6721. p. 857

Wallis, Katherine, Dir, Georgian College, One Georgian Dr, Barrie, ON, L4M 3X9, CANADA. Tel: 705-728-1968, Ext 1684. Fax: 705-722-1584. p. 2794

Wallis, Lisa, Web Serv Librn, Northeastern Illinois University, 5500 N Saint Louis Ave, Chicago, IL, 60625-4699. Tel: 773-442-4571. Fax: 773-442-4531. p. 621

Wallis-Halberstadt, Jonnie, Dir, Clayton-Liberty Township Public Library, 5199 Iowa St, Clayton, IN, 46118-9174. Tel: 317-539-2991, 317-539-7052. Fax: 317-539-2050. p. 732

Wallman, Kaela, Librn, Schenectady County Public Library, Mont Pleasant, 1026 Crane St, Schenectady, NY, 12303. Tel: 518-386-2245. Fax: 518-386-2245. p. 1741

Wallmann, Christine, Libr Tech, Canadian Grain Commission Library, 801-303 Main St, Winnipeg, MB, R3C 3G8, CANADA. Tel: 204-984-6336. Fax: 204-983-6098. p. 2754

Wallner, Peter, Libr Dir, New Hampshire Historical Society Library, 30 Park St, Concord, NH, 03301-6384. Tel: 603-228-6688. Fax: 603-224-0463. p. 1442

Walls, Anna, Curator, Proverbs Heritage Organization, 932 Lakeshore Rd 107, RR 3, Essex, ON, N8M 2X7, CANADA. Tel: 519-727-6555. Fax: 519-727-5793. p. 2804

Walls, Bryan, Dr, Curator, Proverbs Heritage Organization, 932 Lakeshore Rd 107, RR 3, Essex, ON, N8M 2X7, CANADA. Tel: 519-727-4866. Fax: 519-727-5793. p. 2804

Walls, Carolyn, Circ Supvr, Hickory Public Library, 375 Third St NE, Hickory, NC, 28601-5126. Tel: 828-304-0500, Ext 7265. Fax: 828-304-0023. p. 1801

Walls, Heather, Cat Asst, Clayton State University, 2000 Clayton State Blvd, Morrow, GA, 30260. Tel: 678-466-4341. Fax: 678-466-4349. p. 545

Walls, Lucinda, Pub Serv Librn, Queen's University, W D Jordan Special Collections - Music, Douglas Library, 6th Level, Kingston, ON, K7L 5C4, CANADA. Tel: 613-533-2839. Fax: 613-533-2584. p. 2814

Walls, Peggy, Dir, Bienville Parish Library, 2768 Maple St, Arcadia, LA, 71001-3699. Tel: 318-263-7410. Fax: 318-263-7428. p. 941

Walls, Susan, Dir, New Castle Public Library, 207 E North St, New Castle, PA, 16101-3691. Tel: 724-658-6659. Fax: 724-658-7209. p. 2096

Walls, Susan E, Dir, Lawrence County Federated Library System, 207 E North St, New Castle, PA, 16101-3691. Tel: 724-658-6659. Fax: 724-658-7209. p. 2096

Wallsteadt, John A, Dir, Michigan Masonic Museum & Library, 233 E Fulton St, Ste 10, Grand Rapids, MI, 49503-3270. Tel: 616-459-9336. Fax: 616-459-9436. p. 1185

Wally, Vickie, Ref Librn, La Crosse County Library, Onalaska Public, 741 Oak Ave S, Onalaska, WI, 54650. Tel: 608-781-9568. Fax: 608-781-9594. p. 2598

Walmsley, Gina, Supvr, Tech Serv, Tecumseh District Library, 215 N Ottawa St, Tecumseh, MI, 49286-1564. Tel: 517-423-2238. Fax: 517-423-5519. p. 1230

Walpole, Becky, Ch, Park Rapids Area Library, 210 W First St, Park Rapids, MN, 56470-8925. Tel: 218-732-4966. Fax: 218-732-4966. p. 1270

Walrath, Gary, Exec Dir, Rocky Mount Historical Association Library, 200 Hyder Hill Rd, Piney Flats, TN, 37686-4630. Tel: 423-538-7396. Fax: 423-538-1086. p. 2263

Walraven, Eileen, Head, Tech Serv, Biola University Library, 13800 Biola Ave, La Mirada, CA, 90639. Tel: 562-944-0351, Ext 3653. Fax: 562-903-4840. p. 162

Walraven, Elizabeth, Libr Spec, Pub Serv, Eastern Shore Community College, 29300 Lankford Hwy, Melfa, VA, 23410. Tel: 757-789-1721. Fax: 757-789-1739. p. 2478

Walser, Pat, Librn, Hazleton Area Public Library, Valley, 211 Main St, Conyngham, PA, 18219. Tel: 570-788-1339. p. 2068

Walsh, Angie, Tech Serv, Ozark-Dale County Public Library, Inc, 416 James St, Ozark, AL, 36360. Tel: 334-774-2399, 334-774-5480. p. 33

Walsh, Ardena, Ref & ILL Librn, Thomas M Cooley Law School Libraries, 300 S Capitol Ave, Lansing, MI, 48901. Tel: 517-371-5140, Ext 3304. Fax: 517-334-5715, 517-334-5717. p. 1202

Walsh, Barbara, Assoc Librn, Per/Acq, State University of New York, 223 Store Hill Rd, Old Westbury, NY, 11568. Tel: 516-876-3164. Fax: 516-876-3325. p. 1710

Walsh, Brian, Ref Librn, Dartmouth Public Libraries, 732 Dartmouth St, Dartmouth, MA, 02748. Tel: 508-999-0726. Fax: 508-992-9914. p. 1084

Walsh, Caitlyn, Actg Head, Youth Serv, Fayetteville Public Library, 401 W Mountain St, Fayetteville, AR, 72701. Tel: 479-856-7000. Fax: 479-571-0222. p. 99

Walsh, Carrie, Librn, Kaiser-Permanente Medical Center, 99 Montecillo Rd, San Rafael, CA, 94903. Tel: 415-444-2058. Fax: 415-444-2492. p. 257

Walsh, Christine, Asst Libr Dir, Kearney Public Library, 2020 First Ave, Kearney, NE, 68847. Tel: 308-233-3283. Fax: 308-233-3291. p. 1403

Walsh, Connie, Chief Financial Officer, Bus & Finance Serv, Consortium of Academic & Research Libraries in Illinois, 100 Trade Ctr Dr, Ste 303, Champaign, IL, 61820. Tel: 217-333-4802. Fax: 217-244-7596. p. 2942

Walsh, Daniel, Librn, International Copper Association Ltd Library, 260 Madison Ave, 16th Flr, New York, NY, 10016. Tel: 212-251-7240, 212-251-7250. Fax: 212-251-7245. p. 1683

Walsh, Debbie, Head, Adult Serv, Geneva Public Library District, 127 James St, Geneva, IL, 60134. Tel: 630-232-0780. Fax: 630-232-0881. p. 649

Walsh, Deidre, Head, Ch, Louis B Goodall Memorial Library, 952 Main St, Sanford, ME, 04073. Tel: 207-324-4714. Fax: 207-324-5982. p. 999

Walsh, Elizabeth, Head, Reader Serv, Folger Shakespeare Library, 201 E Capitol St SE, Washington, DC, 20003-1094. Tel: 202-544-4600. Fax: 202-544-4623. p. 400

Walsh, Elizabeth, Ch, Bayport-Blue Point Public Library, 203 Blue Point Ave, Blue Point, NY, 11715-1217. Tel: 631-363-6133. Fax: 631-363-6133. p. 1583

Walsh, Eric, Ref Librn, Great Basin College Library, 1500 College Pkwy, Elko, NV, 89801. Tel: 775-753-2222. Fax: 775-753-2296. p. 1427

Walsh, Felicity, Circ, Emory University School of Law, 1301 Clifton Rd, Atlanta, GA, 30322. Tel: 404-727-8211. Fax: 404-727-2202. p. 514

Walsh, Gayle, Ref Librn, Paul Pratt Memorial Library, 35 Ripley Rd, Cohasset, MA, 02025-2097. Tel: 781-383-1348. Fax: 781-383-1698. p. 1082

Walsh, Greg, Librn/Scripts/Festivals & Awards, Academy of Motion Picture Arts & Sciences, 333 S La Cienega Blvd, Beverly Hills, CA, 90211. Tel: 310-247-3000, Ext 2209. Fax: 310-657-5193. p. 129

Walsh, James, Network Adminr, Carthage College, 2001 Alford Park Dr, Kenosha, WI, 53140-1900. Tel: 262-551-5900. Fax: 262-551-5904. p. 2601

Walsh, James P, Ref, Mercer University, Walter F George School of Law, Furman Smith Law Library, 1021 Georgia Ave, Macon, GA, 31201-1001. Tel: 478-301-2625. Fax: 478-301-2284. p. 540

Walsh, Jane, Ref, Salem Public Library, 370 Essex St, Salem, MA, 01970-3298. Tel: 978-744-0860. Fax: 978-745-8616. p. 1122

Walsh, Janet, Dir of Libr Serv, American Baptist College of the American Baptist Theological Seminary, 1800 Baptist World Center Dr, Nashville, TN, 37207-4952. Tel: 615-687-6904. Fax: 615-226-7855. p. 2255

Walsh, Jeanne, ILL, Ref, Brooks Memorial Library, 224 Main St, Brattleboro, VT, 05301. Tel: 802-254-5290. Fax: 802-257-2309. p. 2420

Walsh, Jim, Mgr, Info Tech, Surrey Public Library, 10350 University Dr, Surrey, BC, V3T 4B8, CANADA. Tel: 604-598-7309. Fax: 604-598-7310. p. 2739

Walsh, John, Tech Serv & Info Technology Librn, Cochise College Library, Andrea Cracchiolo Library, 901 N Colombo Ave, Sierra Vista, AZ, 85635. Tel: 520-417-4081. Fax: 520-515-5464. p. 61

Walsh, John, Assoc Univ Librn, George Mason University Libraries, 4400 University Dr, MSN 2FL, Fairfax, VA, 22030-4444. Tel: 703-993-3711. Fax: 703-993-2200. p. 2462

Walsh, Kathleen, Dean, Libr & Learning Support, National Louis University Library & Learning Support, 122 S Michigan Ave, Chicago, IL, 60603. Tel: 312-261-3828. Fax: 312-261-3828. p. 619

Walsh, Kathryn, Sr Dir, Libr & Info Serv, Purdue Pharma LP & Associated Companies, One Stamford Forum, 201 Tresser Blvd, Stamford, CT, 06901. Tel: 203-588-7265. Fax: 203-588-6212. p. 369

Walsh, Kathy, Librn, Peabody Institute Library, West, 603 Lowell St, Peabody, MA, 01960. Tel: 978-535-3354. Fax: 978-535-0147. p. 1117

Walsh, Kirsten, Head of Libr, University of British Columbia Library, Music, 6361 Memorial Rd, Vancouver, BC, V6T 1Z2, CANADA. Tel: 604-822-1408. Fax: 604-822-1966. p. 2743

Walsh, Leatha, Dir, Putnam County Public Library, 115 S 16th St, Unionville, MO, 63565-1624. Tel: 660-947-3192. Fax: 660-947-7039. p. 1370

Walsh, Linda C, Dir, Melrose Public Library, 69 W Emerson St, Melrose, MA, 02176. Tel: 781-665-2313. Fax: 781-662-4229. p. 1105

Walsh, Liza, Youth Serv, Rockport Public Library, One Limerock St, Rockport, ME, 04856-6141. Tel: 207-236-3642. Fax: 207-236-3642. p. 999

Walsh, Lynne, Br Mgr, Chesterfield County Library, Matheson Library, 227 Huger St, Cheraw, SC, 29520. Tel: 843-537-3571. Fax: 843-537-1248. p. 2186

Walsh, Margy, Librn, Chevron Global Library Houston, 3901 Briarpark Dr, Houston, TX, 77042. Tel: 713-954-6007. Fax: 713-954-6907. p. 2334

Walsh, Marian, Libr Mgr, Consort Municipal Library, Box 456, Consort, AB, T0C 1B0, CANADA. Tel: 403-577-2501. p. 2695

Walsh, Mary, Tech Serv Librn, Adams State University, 208 Edgemont Ave, Alamosa, CO, 81101-2373. Tel: 719-587-7781. Fax: 719-587-7590. p. 287

Walsh, Mary Jane, Head, Govt Doc, Colgate University, 13 Oak Dr, Hamilton, NY, 13346-1398. Tel: 315-228-7300. Fax: 315-228-7934. p. 1633

Walsh, Mary Lou, Head, Circ, Evergreen Park Public Library, 9400 S Troy Ave, Evergreen Park, IL, 60805-2383. Tel: 708-422-8522. Fax: 708-422-8665. p. 645

Walsh, Michael, Admin Mgr, University of Detroit Mercy Library, Kresge Law Library, 651 E Jefferson, Detroit, MI, 48226. Tel: 313-596-0239. Fax: 313-596-0245. p. 1172

Walsh, Nadine, Circ Mgr, Downers Grove Public Library, 1050 Curtiss St, Downers Grove, IL, 60515. Tel: 630-960-1200. Fax: 630-960-9374. p. 637

Walsh, Sandra, Br Mgr, Ramsey County Library, Maplewood Branch, 3025 Southlawn Dr, Maplewood, MN, 55109. Tel: 651-704-2033. Fax: 651-704-2038. p. 1284

Walsh, Susan, Dr, Dir, Merced College, 3600 M St, Merced, CA, 95348. Tel: 209-384-6082. Fax: 209-384-6084. p. 185

Walsh, William, Head, Tech Serv, Georgia State University Library, 100 Decatur St SE, Atlanta, GA, 30303-3202. Tel: 404-413-2731. Fax: 404-413-2751. p. 516

Walshire, Shannon, Asst Dir, Mechanicsville Public Library, 218 E First St, Mechanicsville, IA, 52306. Tel: 563-432-7135. Fax: 563-432-7135. p. 831

Walster, Dian E, Dr, Prof, Wayne State University, 106 Kresge Library, Detroit, MI, 48202. Tel: 313-577-1825. Fax: 313-577-7563. p. 2967

Walston, Loraine, Supvr, ILL, Dallas Baptist University, 3000 Mountain Creek Pkwy, Dallas, TX, 75211-9299. Tel: 214-333-5213. Fax: 214-333-5323. p. 2305

Walstrom, Leslie, Dir, East Parker County Library, 201 FM 1187 N, Aledo, TX, 76008. Tel: 817-441-6545. Fax: 817-441-5787. p. 2273

Walstrum, Marisa, Librn, National Louis University Library & Learning Support, 122 S Michigan Ave, Chicago, IL, 60603. Tel: 312-261-3439. Fax: 312-261-3439. p. 619

Walter, Blake, Dir, Northern Baptist Theological Seminary, 680 E Butterfield Rd, Lombard, IL, 60148. Tel: 630-620-2104. Fax: 630-620-2170. p. 667

Walter, Bobby, Educ & Ref Librn, Kentucky State University, 400 E Main St, Frankfort, KY, 40601-2355. Tel: 502-597-6824. Fax: 502-597-5068. p. 914

Walter, Canduce, Circ, Southern Illinois University Edwardsville, Campus Box 1063, 30 Hairpin Circle, Edwardsville, IL, 62026-1063. Tel: 618-650-2277. Fax: 618-650-2717. p. 639

Walter, Catherine, Curator, Chancellor Robert R Livingston Masonic Library of Grand Lodge, 71 W 23rd St, 14th Flr, New York, NY, 10010-4171. Tel: 212-337-6620. Fax: 212-633-2639. p. 1672

Walter, Christopher S, Dir, Haddon Heights Public Library, 608 Station Ave, Haddon Heights, NJ, 08035-1907. Tel: 856-547-7132. Fax: 856-547-2867. p. 1489

Walter, Donald, Syst Coordr, Jacksonville State University Library, 700 Pelham Rd N, Jacksonville, AL, 36265. Tel: 256-782-5255. Fax: 256-782-5872. p. 22

Walter, Ed, Acq & Cat Librn, Washington University Libraries, Bernard Becker Medical Library, 660 S Euclid Ave, Campus Box 8132, Saint Louis, MO, 63110. Tel: 314-362-2797. Fax: 314-454-6606. p. 1362

Walter, James, Ref Librn, Stephens College, 1200 E Broadway, Columbia, MO, 65215. Tel: 573-876-7182. Fax: 573-876-7264. p. 1325

Walter, Katherine, Chair, Digital Initiatives & Spec Coll, University of Nebraska-Lincoln, 1248 R St, Lincoln, NE, 68588-4100. Tel: 402-472-2526. p. 1407

Walter, Kelly, Dir, Jane I & Annetta M Herr Memorial Library, 500 Market St, Mifflinburg, PA, 17844. Tel: 570-966-0831. Fax: 570-966-0106. p. 2089

Walter, Leisa, Pub Serv Asst/Doc Delivery & Media Serv, A T Still University of Health Sciences, Kirksville Campus, 800 W Jefferson St, Kirksville, MO, 63501. Tel: 660-626-2679. Fax: 660-626-2031, 660-626-2333. p. 1342

Walter, Lisa, Dir, Fort Scott Public Library, 201 S National, Fort Scott, KS, 66701. Tel: 620-223-2882. p. 867

Walter, Marlene, Asst Librn, Dominy Memorial Library, 201 S Third St, Fairbury, IL, 61739. Tel: 815-692-3231. Fax: 815-692-3503. p. 645

Walter, Nancy, Dir, John Wesley Powell Memorial Museum Library, Six N Lake Powell Blvd, Page, AZ, 86040. Tel: 928-645-9496. Fax: 928-645-3412. p. 70

Walter, Nancy, Superintendent, National Park Service, 900 Kennesaw Mountain Dr, Kennesaw, GA, 30152. Tel: 770-427-4686. Fax: 770-528-8398. p. 537

Walter, Pat, Ch, Ida Public Library, 320 N State St, Belvidere, IL, 61008-3299. Tel: 815-544-3838. Fax: 815-544-8909. p. 594

Walter, Robert A, Dean, Pittsburg State University, 1605 S Joplin St, Pittsburg, KS, 66762-5889. Tel: 620-235-4878. Fax: 620-235-4090. p. 890

Walter, Rose Marie, Archivist, Willamette University, 900 State St, Salem, OR, 97301. Tel: 503-370-6845. Fax: 503-370-6141. p. 2019

Walter, Ruth, Dir, Pittsburgh Technical Institute, 1111 McKee Rd, Oakdale, PA, 15071. Tel: 412-809-5223. Fax: 412-809-5219. p. 2100

Walter, Scott, Univ Librn, DePaul University Libraries, 2350 N Kenmore, Chicago, IL, 60614. Tel: 773-325-3725, 773-325-7862. Fax: 773-325-7870. p. 612

Walter, Thomas B, Computer Librn, Ref Librn, Mississippi College, 151 E Griffith St, Jackson, MS, 39201-1391. Tel: 601-925-7120. Fax: 601-925-7112. p. 1304

Walter, Valero, Instr, Queens College of the City University of New York, Benjamin Rosenthal Library, Rm 254, 65-30 Kissena Blvd, Flushing, NY, 11367. Tel: 718-997-3790. Fax: 718-997-3797. p. 2970

Walter-Smith, Lily, Libr Tech, Regina-Qu'Appelle Health Region, Pasqua Hospital Library, 4101 Dewdney Ave, Regina, SK, S4T 1A5, CANADA. Tel: 306-766-2370. Fax: 306-766-2565. p. 2923

Waltermire, Kyla, Dir, Morris Area Public Library District, 604 Liberty St, Morris, IL, 60450. Tel: 815-942-6880. Fax: 815-942-6415. p. 675

Walters, Anita, Dir, Sherman Public Library District, 2100 E Andrew Rd, Sherman, IL, 62684-9780. Tel: 217-496-2496. Fax: 217-496-2357. p. 702

Walters, Barbara, Automation Syst Coordr, North Central Regional Library, 16 N Columbia St, Wenatchee, WA, 98801-8103. Tel: 509-663-1117, Ext 129. Fax: 509-662-8060. p. 2548

Walters, Carolyn, Interim Dean, Indiana University Bloomington, Herman B Wells Library 234, 1320 E Tenth St, Bloomington, IN, 47405-1801. Tel: 812-855-0100. Fax: 812-855-2576. p. 727

Walters, Cheryl, Head, Digital Libr Serv, Utah State University, 3000 Old Main Hill, Logan, UT, 84322-3000. Tel: 435-797-2623. Fax: 435-797-2880. p. 2407

Walters, Gladys, Br Mgr, Roanoke County Public Library, Bent Mountain Branch, Brent Mountain Elementary School, PO Box L, Bent Mountain, VA, 24059. Tel: 540-929-4700. Fax: 540-929-4700. p. 2494

Walters, Jane, Div Dir, Bus Serv, Gwinnett County Public Library, 1001 Lawrenceville Hwy NW, Lawrenceville, GA, 30046-4707. Tel: 770-822-5324. p. 538

Walters, Janine, Tech Librn, Center Point Public Library, 720 Main St, Center Point, IA, 52213. Tel: 319-849-1509. Fax: 319-849-1509. p. 801

Walters, Jennifer, Dir, Aitkin Memorial District Library, 111 N Howard Ave, Croswell, MI, 48422-1225. Tel: 810-679-3627. Fax: 810-679-3392. p. 1167

Walters, John, Head, Doc Serv, Utah State University, Regional Depository Collection of US Government Documents, 3000 Old Main Hill, Logan, UT, 84322-3000. Tel: 435-797-2683. p. 2407

Walters, John, Head, Govt Doc, Utah State University, 3000 Old Main Hill, Logan, UT, 84322-3000. Tel: 435-797-2683. Fax: 435-797-2880. p. 2407

Walters, Kim, Dir, Autry National Center, Braun Research Library, 234 Museum Dr, Los Angeles, CA, 90065. Tel: 323-221-2164, Ext 255. Fax: 322-221-8223. p. 168

Walters, Laura, Assoc Dir of Teaching, Res & Info Resources, Tufts University, 35 Professors Row, Medford, MA, 02155-5816. Tel: 617-627-2098. Fax: 617-627-3002. p. 1104

Walters, Lee, Librn, Eleanor Daggett Public Library, 299 W Fourth St, Chama, NM, 87520-0786. Tel: 575-756-2184, Ext 225. Fax: 575-756-2412. p. 1553

Walters, Lowell A, Assoc Dean, Liberty University Library, 1971 University Blvd, Lynchburg, VA, 24502. Tel: 434-592-3294. Fax: 434-582-2728. p. 2476

Walters, Michael Eugene, Dean of Libr, Carl Sandburg College, 2400 Tom L Wilson Blvd, Galesburg, IL, 61401. Tel: 309-341-5290. Fax: 309-344-3526. p. 647

Walters, Nancy, ILL, University of Maine at Farmington, 116 South St, Farmington, ME, 04938-1990. Tel: 207-778-7210. Fax: 207-778-7223. p. 985

Walters, Peggy, Dir, Southern Arkansas University, 100 E University, Magnolia, AR, 71753-5000. Tel: 870-235-4171. Fax: 870-235-5018. p. 108

Walters, Rita, Br Mgr, Lonesome Pine Regional Library, Scott County Public, 297 W Jackson St, Gate City, VA, 24251. Tel: 276-386-3302. Fax: 276-386-2977. p. 2504

Walters, Sharon, Head, Access Serv, Saint Mary's College Library, 1928 Saint Mary's Rd, Moraga, CA, 94575. Tel: 925-631-4229. Fax: 925-376-6097. p. 191

Walters, Sharon, Libr Asst, New Hanover County Public Library, Carolina Beach Branch, 300 Cape Fear Blvd, Carolina Beach, NC, 28428. Tel: 910-798-6385. Fax: 910-458-9422. p. 1830

Walters, Sheryl, Electronic Res Librn, Ref Librn, Logan University/College of Chiropractic Library, 1851 Schoettler Rd, Chesterfield, MO, 63006. Tel: 636-227-2100. Fax: 636-207-2448. p. 1323

Walters, Susan, Dir, Vinita Public Library, 215 W Illinois Ave, Vinita, OK, 74301. Tel: 918-256-2115. Fax: 918-256-2309. p. 1984

Walters, Susan, Br Mgr, Richmond Public Library, Steveston Branch, 4111 Moncton St, Richmond, BC, V7E 3A8, CANADA. Tel: 604-274-2012. p. 2736

Walters, William H, PhD, Dean of Libr Serv, Menlo College, 1000 El Camino Real, Atherton, CA, 94027-4300. Tel: 650-543-3826. Fax: 650-543-3833. p. 122

Walters, Winifred, Mgr, Grants & Develop, Oakland Public Library, Main Library, 125 14th St, Oakland, CA, 94612. Tel: 510-238-3134. Fax: 510-238-2232. p. 198

Walterscheid, Sybil, Asst Dir, Carlsbad Public Library, 101 S Halagueno St, Carlsbad, NM, 88220. Tel: 575-885-6776. Fax: 575-887-7706. p. 1552

Walthart, Carol, Libr Dir, Colesburg Public Library, 220 Main St, Colesburg, IA, 52035. Tel: 563-856-5800. Fax: 563-856-5800. p. 803

Waltman, Colleen, Head, Adult Serv, New Lenox Public Library District, 120 Veterans Pkwy, New Lenox, IL, 60451. Tel: 815-485-2605. Fax: 815-485-2548. p. 680

Waltman, Heather, ILL, Ref Serv, South Texas College of Law, 1303 San Jacinto St, Houston, TX, 77002-7000. Tel: 713-646-1711. Fax: 713-659-2217. p. 2342

Waltman, Leslie R, Jr, Librn, United States Army, Aviation Center Library, Bldg 212,Fifth Ave & Novosal, Fort Rucker, AL, 36362-5000. Tel: 334-255-3695. Fax: 334-255-1567. p. 18

Waltmire, Jonathan, Librn, Fresno County Public Library, Reedley Branch, 1027 E St, Reedley, CA, 93654-2982. Tel: 559-638-2818. p. 152

Waltmire, Ted, Tech Coordr, Downers Grove Public Library, 1050 Curtiss St, Downers Grove, IL, 60515. Tel: 630-960-1200. Fax: 630-960-9374. p. 637

Waltner, Robb, Head, Access Serv, University of North Florida, Bldg 12-Library, One UNF Dr, Jacksonville, FL, 32224-2645. Tel: 904-620-1515. Fax: 904-620-2719. p. 455

Walton, Ann, Exec Dir, American Camellia Society Library, 100 Massee Lane, Fort Valley, GA, 31030. Tel: 478-967-2358, 478-967-2722. Fax: 478-967-2083. p. 533

Walton, Charles W, Libr Dir, State Services Organization Library, Hall of the States, Ste 237, 444 North Capital St NW, Washington, DC, 20001. Tel: 202-624-5485. p. 416

Walton, Cris, Youth Serv, Elsie Quirk Public Library of Englewood, 100 W Dearborn St, Englewood, FL, 34223-3309. Tel: 941-861-1214. p. 439

Walton, Dean, Ref Librn, University of Oregon Libraries, Science, Onyx Bridge, Lower Level, University of Oregon, Eugene, OR, 97403. Tel: 541-346-2871. Fax: 541-346-3012. p. 1998

Walton, Earlene, Dir, Daingerfield Public Library, 207 Jefferson St, Daingerfield, TX, 75638. Tel: 903-645-2823. Fax: 903-645-7478. p. 2304

Walton, Edward W, Dean, Southwest Baptist University Libraries, 1600 University Ave, Bolivar, MO, 65613. Tel: 417-328-1619. Fax: 417-328-1652. p. 1320

Walton, Jennifer, Coordr, Libr Serv, Marine Biological Laboratory Woods Hole Oceanographic Institution Library, Seven MBL St, Woods Hole, MA, 02543. Tel: 508-289-7452. Fax: 508-540-6902. p. 1142

Walton, Jennifer, Ref Librn, Bob Jones University, 1700 Wade Hampton Blvd, Greenville, SC, 29614. Tel: 864-242-5100, Ext 6000. Fax: 864-232-1729. p. 2195

Walton, Kate, Cat, East Bonner County Free Library District, 1407 Cedar St, Sandpoint, ID, 83864-2052. Tel: 208-263-6930, Ext 216. Fax: 208-263-8320. p. 583

Walton, Leslie, Libr Dir, Winter Harbor Public Library, 18 Chapel Lane, Winter Harbor, ME, 04693. Tel: 207-963-7556. p. 1007

Walton, Linda, Assoc Univ Librn, Dir, University of Iowa Libraries, Hardin Library for the Health Sciences, 600 Newton Rd, Iowa City, IA, 52242. Tel: 319-335-9871. Fax: 319-353-3752. p. 823

Walton, Peggy, Dir, Marengo Public Library, 235 E Hilton St, Marengo, IA, 52301. Tel: 319-741-3825. Fax: 319-741-3825. p. 830

Walton, Robert, Chief Exec Officer, Claremont University Consortium, 150 E Eighth St, Claremont, CA, 91711. Tel: 909-621-8026, 909-621-8150. Fax: 909-621-8681. p. 2938

Walton, Rosemary, Librn, Law Library of Wolff & Samson, One Boland Dr, West Orange, NJ, 07052. Tel: 973-530-2146. Fax: 973-530-2346. p. 1541

Walton, Sean, Cat Librn, Holy Cross College, 54515 State Rd 933 N, Box 308, Notre Dame, IN, 46556-0308. Tel: 574-239-8391. Fax: 574-239-8324. p. 771

Walton, Wendi, Br Mgr, Lincoln County Library, Alpine Branch, 243 River Circle, Alpine, WY, 83126. Tel: 307-654-7323. Fax: 307-654-2158. p. 2656

Walton, Yvette, Mgr, New York Downtown Hospital, 170 William St, New York, NY, 10038. Tel: 212-312-5000, 212-312-5229. Fax: 212-312-5929. p. 1689

Walton-Cagle, Lisa, Br Mgr, West Georgia Regional Library, Warren P Sewell Memorial Library, 315 Hamilton Ave, Bremen, GA, 30110. Tel: 770-537-3937. Fax: 770-537-1660. p. 524

Walton-Hadlock, Maddy, Sr Librn, San Jose Public Library, Dr Roberto Cruz - Alum Rock, 3090 Alum Rock Ave, San Jose, CA, 95127. Tel: 408-808-3090. Fax: 408-928-5628. p. 251

Walton-Hadlock, Maddy, Sr Librn, San Jose Public Library, Hillview, 1600 Hopkins Dr, San Jose, CA, 95122-1199. Tel: 408-808-3033. Fax: 408-729-9518. p. 251

Waltonbaugh, Ruth, Dir, Eagle Lake Public Library, 75 N Seventh St, Eagle Lake, FL, 33839-3430. Tel: 863-293-2914. Fax: 863-292-0210. p. 438

Waltz, Erin, Pub Serv Mgr, Supreme Court of Ohio, 65 S Front St, 11th Flr, Columbus, OH, 43215-3431. Tel: 614-387-9668. Fax: 614-387-9689. p. 1890

Waltz, Marian, Librn, Friends of the Third World, Inc, 611 W Wayne St, Fort Wayne, IN, 46802-2167. Tel: 260-422-6821. Fax: 260-422-1650. p. 741

Waltz, Rodney, Dir, The S W Hayes Research Foundation, 801 Elks Rd, Richmond, IN, 47374. Tel: 765-962-3745. Fax: 765-966-1931. p. 775

Walvoord, Chantal, Ref Librn, Rockwall County Library, 1215 E Yellowjacket Lane, Rockwall, TX, 75087. Tel: 972-204-7700. Fax: 972-204-7709. p. 2377

Walz, Greg, Librn, Utah State Historical Society, 300 Rio Grande, Salt Lake City, UT, 84101-1182. Tel: 801-533-3535. Fax: 801-533-3504. p. 2415

Walz, Jennifer, Head, Res & Distance Serv, Asbury University, One Macklem Dr, Wilmore, KY, 40390-1198. Tel: 859-858-3511, Ext 2269. Fax: 859-858-3921. p. 938

Walz, Leslie, Br Mgr, Great River Regional Library, Rockford Public Library, 8220 Cedar St, Rockford, MN, 55373. Tel: 763-477-4216. Fax: 763-477-4216. p. 1275

Walz, Missy, Asst Librn, ILL, Samson Memorial Library, 107 Second St, Granton, WI, 54436. Tel: 715-238-5250. Fax: 715-238-8605. p. 2594

Walzer, Barbara, Music, Sarah Lawrence College, One Mead Way, Bronxville, NY, 10708. Tel: 914-395-2375. Fax: 914-395-2473. p. 1588

Walzer, Barbara R, Music Librn, Sarah Lawrence College, William Schuman Music Library, One Mead Way, Bronxville, NY, 10708. Tel: 914-395-2375. Fax: 914-395-2507. p. 1589

Wambach, Andrea, Librn, US Courts Library, 512 Federal Court Bldg, 316 N Robert St, Saint Paul, MN, 55101. Tel: 651-848-1320. Fax: 651-848-1325. p. 1282

Wambold, Sally H, Tech Serv, University of Richmond, William T Muse Law Library, 28 Westhampton Way, Richmond, VA, 23173. Tel: 804-289-8226. Fax: 804-289-8683. p. 2491

Wamer, Tam, Br Mgr, Washington County Public Library, Belpre Branch, 2012 Washington Blvd, Belpre, OH, 45714. Tel: 740-423-8381. Fax: 740-423-8305. p. 1914

Wamsley, Gregg, Dir, Hutchinson Public Library, 901 N Main, Hutchinson, KS, 67501-4492. Tel: 620-663-5441. Fax: 620-663-9506. p. 873

Wan, Fang, Asst Librn, Alfred University, Scholes Library of Ceramics, New York State College of Ceramics at Alfred University, Two Pine St, Alfred, NY, 14802-1297. p. 1572

Wanamaker, Becky, Dir, Lehighton Area Memorial Library, 124 North St, Lehighton, PA, 18235-1589. Tel: 610-377-2750. Fax: 610-377-5803. p. 2080

Wanamaker, Karen, Curric Mats Ctr, Kutztown University, 15200 Kutztown Rd, Bldg 5, Kutztown, PA, 19530-0735. Tel: 610-683-4484. Fax: 610-683-4747. p. 2075

Wanamaker, Karma, Teen Librn, Altoona Public Library, 700 Eighth St SW, Altoona, IA, 50009. Tel: 515-967-3881. Fax: 515-967-6934. p. 792

Wand, Alice, Asst Librn, Paine Memorial Free Library, Two Gilliland Ln, Willsboro, NY, 12996. Tel: 518-963-4478. p. 1770

Wanda, Quoika-Stanka, Librn, University of Alberta, John Alexander Weir Memorial Law Library, Law Centre, 111 St & 89 Ave, Edmonton, AB, T6G 2H5, CANADA. Tel: 780-492-3371. Fax: 780-492-7546. p. 2703

Wanderman, Sandy, Image Cataloger, Art Center College of Design, 1700 Lida St, Pasadena, CA, 91103. Tel: 626-396-2234. Fax: 626-568-0428. p. 205

Wandrey, Joy, Dir, Washington County Public Library, 210 E Main St, Springfield, KY, 40069. Tel: 859-336-7655. Fax: 859-336-0256. p. 935

Wang, Alison, Syst Librn, Tech Serv, Naugatuck Valley Community College, 750 Chase Pkwy, Waterbury, CT, 06708. Tel: 203-575-8024. Fax: 203-575-8062. p. 375

Wang, Bing, Interim Head, Res, Instruction & Outreach Serv, Georgia Institute of Technology Library, 704 Cherry St, Atlanta, GA, 30332-0900. Tel: 404-894-4501. Fax: 404-894-6084. p. 515

Wang, Cathy, Br Head, Vancouver Public Library, Britannia, 1661 Napier St, Vancouver, BC, V5L 4X4, CANADA. Tel: 604-665-2222. Fax: 604-665-3523. p. 2744

Wang, Chengzhi, Coll Develop/Ref Librn, Columbia University, C V Starr East Asian Library, 300 Kent Hall, MC 3901, 1140 Amsterdam Ave, New York, NY, 10027. Tel: 212-854-4318. Fax: 212-662-6286. p. 1675

Wang, Christine, Ref, United States Merchant Marine Academy, 300 Steamboat Rd, Kings Point, NY, 11024-1699. Tel: 516-726-5747. Fax: 516-726-5900. p. 1649

Wang, Dave, Commun Libr Mgr, Queens Borough Public Library, Hollis Community Library, 202-05 Hillside Ave, Hollis, NY, 11423. Tel: 718-465-7355. Fax: 718-264-3248. p. 1644

Wang, Guiyun, Electronic Res & Ref Librn, Instrul Librn, Webmaster, Roosevelt University, 430 S Michigan Ave, Chicago, IL, 60605. Tel: 312-341-2406. Fax: 312-341-2425. p. 623

Wang, Hailan, Librn, North Shore University Health System-Glenbrook Hospital, 2100 Pfingsten Rd, Glenview, IL, 60026-1301. Tel: 847-657-5618. Fax: 847-657-5995. p. 651

Wang, Hanrong, Ref Librn, Jacksonville State University Library, 700 Pelham Rd N, Jacksonville, AL, 36265. Tel: 256-782-5255. Fax: 256-782-5872. p. 22

Wang, Helen, Asst Libr Serv Dir, Burbank Public Library, 110 N Glenoaks Blvd, Burbank, CA, 91502-1203. Tel: 818-238-5600. Fax: 818-238-5553. p. 130

Wang, Henry, Dr, Asst Dir, Weatherford College Library, 225 College Park Dr, Weatherford, TX, 76086. Tel: 817-594-5471, 817-598-6252. Fax: 817 598-9005. p. 2399

Wang, Hongjie, Bibliog Instr, Ref, University of Connecticut Health Center, 263 Farmington Ave, Farmington, CT, 06034. Tel: 860-679-3808. Fax: 860-679-4046. p. 340

Wang, Jenny, Cat, ACA Library of Savannah College of Art & Design, 1600 Peachtree St NW, Atlanta, GA, 30309. Tel: 404-253-3196. Fax: 404-253-3278. p. 510

Wang, Jian, Head, Electronic & Continuing Res, Portland State University Library, 1875 SW Park Ave, Portland, OR, 97201-3220. Tel: 503-725-4574. Fax: 503-725-4524. p. 2014

Wang, Jiangiang, Dr, Asst Prof, University at Buffalo, State University of New York, 534 Baldy Hall, Buffalo, NY, 14260. Tel: 716-645-2412. Fax: 716-645-3775. p. 2971

Wang, Jue, Tech Serv Librn, Leeward Community College Library, 96-045 Ala Ike, Pearl City, HI, 96782-3393. Tel: 808-455-0672. Fax: 808-453-6729. p. 567

Wang, Julia, Acq/Ser Librn, Rockhurst University, 1100 Rockhurst Rd, Kansas City, MO, 64110-2561. Tel: 816-501-4143. Fax: 816-501-4666. p. 1340

Wang, Jun, Dr, Bibliog Instr, San Joaquin Delta College, 5151 Pacific Ave, Stockton, CA, 95207-6370. Tel: 209-954-5146. Fax: 209-954-5691. p. 272

Wang, Lan, Head Librn, Lane College Library, 545 Lane Ave, Jackson, TN, 38301-4598. Tel: 731-426-7593. Fax: 731-426-7591. p. 2238

Wang, Lei, Instrul Design Librn, Yale University Library, Harvey Cushing/John Hay Whitney Medical Library, Sterling Hall of Medicine, 333 Cedar St, L110 SHM, New Haven, CT, 06520. Tel: 203-785-6485. Fax: 203-785-5636. p. 358

Wang, Liping, Cat, Touro College Libraries, 43 W 23rd St, Fifth Fl, New York, NY, 10010. Tel: 212-463-0400, Ext 5321. Fax: 212-627-3696. p. 1701

Wang, Maggie, Adult Ref, AV, Monterey Park Bruggemeyer Library, 318 S Ramona Ave, Monterey Park, CA, 91754-3399. Tel: 626-307-1368. Fax: 626-288-4251. p. 190

Wang, Peiling, Assoc Prof, University of Tennessee, Knoxville, 451 Communications Bldg, 1345 Circle Park Dr, Knoxville, TN, 37996-0341. Tel: 865-974-2148. Fax: 865-974-4967. p. 2974

Wang, Peiming, Librn, Per, OLI Systems, Inc Library, 108 American Rd, Morris Plains, NJ, 07950. Tel: 973-539-4996. Fax: 973-539-5922. p. 1504

Wang, Ray, Dr, Dean, California State Polytechnic University Library, 3801 W Temple Ave, Bldg 15, Pomona, CA, 91768. Tel: 909-869-5250. Fax: 909-869-6922. p. 211

Wang, Rong, Asst Dir, Syst & Tech, Bergen Community College, 400 Paramus Rd, Paramus, NJ, 07652-1595. Tel: 201-612-5563. Fax: 201-493-8167. p. 1517

Wang, Sharon, Ref Librn, York University Libraries, Osgoode Hall Law School Library, One Scholar's Walk, York University, Toronto, ON, M3J 1P3, CANADA. Tel: 416-736-5893. Fax: 416-736-5298. p. 2868

Wang, Wen Qi, Sr Cataloger/Database Librn, Recording for the Blind & Dyslexic, 20 Roszel Rd, Princeton, NJ, 08540. Tel: 609-452-0606. Fax: 609-520-7990, 609-987-8116. p. 1524

Wang, Wendy, In Charge, Metron Inc, 1818 Library St, Ste 600, Reston, VA, 20190-5602. Tel: 703-787-8700. Fax: 703-787-3518. p. 2487

Wang, Wenliang, Libr Tech, Northern College of Applied Arts & Technology Library, 140 Government Rd E, Kirkland Lake, ON, P2N 3L8, CANADA. Tel: 705-567-9291, Ext 3700. Fax: 705-567-3350. p. 2814

Wang, Xiaocan "Lucy", Digital Repository Librn, Indiana State University, 510 North 6 1/2 St, Terre Haute, IN, 47809. Tel: 812-237-3052. Fax: 812-237-3376. p. 781

Wang, Xuemao, Assoc Vice-Provost, Emory University Libraries, Robert W Woodruff Library, 540 Asbury Circle, Atlanta, GA, 30322-2870. Tel: 404-727-6861. Fax: 404-727-0805. p. 514

Wang, Xuemao, Dean & Univ Librn, University of Cincinnati Libraries, PO Box 210033, Cincinnati, OH, 45221-0033. Tel: 513-556-1515. Fax: 513-556-0325. p. 1874

Wang, Yan, Digital Res/Presv Librn, University of Alabama at Birmingham, Mervyn H Sterne Library, 917 13th St S, Birmingham, AL, 35205. Tel: 205-934-6364. p. 10

Wang, Yan, Sr Librn, Central Piedmont Community College Library, 1201 Elizabeth Ave, Charlotte, NC, 28235. Tel: 704-330-6041. Fax: 704-330-6887. p. 1781

Wang, Yan, Syst Librn, North Carolina Central University, 1801 Fayetteville St, Durham, NC, 27707-3129. Tel: 919-530-5240. Fax: 919-530-7612. p. 1789

Wang, Yanhong, Syst Coordr, Shepherd University, 301 N King St, Shepherdstown, WV, 25443. Fax: 304-876-0731. p. 2571

Wang, Yongming, Syst Librn, The College of New Jersey Library, 2000 Pennington Rd, Ewing, NJ, 08628-0718. Tel: 609-771-2311, 609-771-2332. Fax: 609-637-5177. p. 1484

Wang, Youbo, Syst Librn, Fairleigh Dickinson University, 285 Madison Ave, M-LAO-03, Madison, NJ, 07940. Tel: 973-443-8515. Fax: 973-443-8525. p. 1497

Wang, Zheng, Assoc Librn, Hesburgh Libraries, 221 Hesburgh Library, University of Notre Dame, Notre Dame, IN, 46556. Tel: 574-631-5252. Fax: 574-631-6772. p. 770

Wang, Ziyan, Circ Supvr, Somerset County Library System, Hillsborough Public, Hillsborough Municipal Complex, 379 S Branch Rd, Hillsborough, NJ, 08844. Tel: 908-369-2200. Fax: 908-369-8242. p. 1475

Wangsgard, Lynnda, Dir, Weber County Library System, 2464 Jefferson Ave, Ogden, UT, 84401-2464. Tel: 801-337-2617. Fax: 801-337-2615. p. 2408

Wanser, Jeffery, Doc, Ref, Hiram College Library, 11694 Hayden St, Hiram, OH, 44234. Tel: 330-569-5358. Fax: 330-569-5491. p. 1905

Wanser, Margaret, Tech Serv, Oyster Bay-East Norwich Public Library, 89 E Main St, Oyster Bay, NY, 11771. Tel: 516-922-1212. Fax: 516-922-6453. p. 1714

Wanta, Christine, Ref Librn, NHTI, Concord's Community College, 31 College Dr, Concord, NH, 03301-7425. Tel: 603-271-7187. Fax: 603-271-7189. p. 1443

Wantrobski, Mary, Tech Serv, VSE Corporation Library-BAV Division, 2550 Huntington Ave, Alexandria, VA, 22303-1499. Tel: 703-317-5259. Fax: 703-960-6599. p. 2446

Wantuch, Dana, Sr Librn, Joseph F Egan Memorial Supreme Court Library, Schenectady County Judicial Bldg, 612 State St, Schenectady, NY, 12305. Tel: 518-285-8518. Fax: 518-377-5909. p. 1740

Wantz, Michael R, Dir, Perry County District Library, 117 S Jackson St, New Lexington, OH, 43764-1330. Tel: 740-342-4194. Fax: 740-342-4204. p. 1920

Wanza, Mary, Dir, Coppin State College, 2500 W North Ave, Baltimore, MD, 21216-3698. Tel: 410-951-3400. Fax: 410-951-3430. p. 1012

Wanzer, David, Asst Librn, Starr Library, 68 W Market St, Rhinebeck, NY, 12572. Tel: 845-876-4030. Fax: 845-876-4030. p. 1727

Warberg, Dennetta, Asst Librn, Chinook Regional Library, Consul Branch, PO Box 121, Consul, SK, S0N 0P0, CANADA. Tel: 306-299-2118. p. 2928

Warburton, Sally, Libr Dir, Pulaski County Public Library System, 60 W Third St, Pulaski, VA, 24301. Tel: 540-980-7770. Fax: 540-980-7775. p. 2486

Warburtono, Christiane, Commun Libr Mgr, County of Los Angeles Public Library, Clifton M Brakensiek Library, 9945 E Flower St, Bellflower, CA, 90706-5486. Tel: 562-925-5543. Fax: 562-920-9249. p. 141

Warby, Laraine, ILL, Framingham Public Library, 49 Lexington St, Framingham, MA, 01702-8278. Tel: 508-879-3570, Ext 224. Fax: 508-820-7210. p. 1090

Warczak, Jim, Dir, Bloomington Public Library, 453 Canal St, Bloomington, WI, 53804. Tel: 608-994-2531. p. 2582

Ward, Andy, Co-Dir, Tacoma Family History Center, 5915 S 12th, Tacoma, WA, 98465. Tel: 253-564-1103. p. 2540

Ward, Annette, Mgr, Satilla Regional Library, Broxton Public Library, 105 Church St, Broxton, GA, 31519. Tel: 912-359-3887. Fax: 912-359-3887. p. 530

Ward, Antonella, Multimedia Support Librn, Angelo State University Library, 2025 S Johnson, San Angelo, TX, 76904-5079. Tel: 325-486-6540. Fax: 325-942-2198. p. 2378

Ward, Betty, Librn, Westmoreland County Law Library, Two N Main St, Ste 202, Greensburg, PA, 15601. Tel: 724-830-3266. Fax: 724-830-3042. p. 2063

Ward, Brad, Exec Dir, Northeast Florida Library Information Network, 2233 Park Ave, Ste 402, Orange Park, FL, 32073. Tel: 904-278-5620. Fax: 904-278-5625. p. 2940

Ward, Brooke, Archives, Ser Librn, Florida College, 119 N Glen Arven Ave, Temple Terrace, FL, 33617-5578. Tel: 813-988-5131, Ext 212. p. 500

Ward, Caroline, Youth Serv Coordr, The Ferguson Library, One Public Library Plaza, 96 Broad St, Stamford, CT, 06904. Tel: 203-964-1000, Ext 8240. Fax: 203-359-6750. p. 369

Ward, Dane, Assoc Dean, Pub Serv, Illinois State University, 201 N School St, Normal, IL, 61790-8900. Tel: 309-438-3451. Fax: 309-438-3676. p. 681

Ward, Dane, Interim Dean of Libr, Illinois State University, 201 N School St, Normal, IL, 61790-8900. Tel: 309-438-3451. Fax: 309-438-3676. p. 681

Ward, Daniel, Curator, Erie Canal Museum Research Library, 318 Erie Blvd E, Syracuse, NY, 13202. Tel: 315-471-0593. Fax: 315-471-7220. p. 1751

Ward, Darlene, Ser Librn, Illinois College of Optometry Library, 3241 S Michigan Ave, Chicago, IL, 60616-3878. Tel: 312-949-7151. Fax: 312-949-7337. p. 614

Ward, Deborah, Dir, University of Missouri-Columbia, J Otto Lottes Health Sciences Library, One Hospital Dr, Columbia, MO, 65212. Tel: 573-882-0471. Fax: 573-882-5574. p. 1326

Ward, Deborah L, Librn, Hancock County Law Library Association, 300 S Main St, 4th Flr, Findlay, OH, 45840. Tel: 419-424-7077. Fax: 419-425-4136. p. 1899

Ward, Denise, Doc Delivery, Marshall University Libraries, Joan C Edwards School of Medicine Health Science Libraries, 1600 Medical Center Dr, Ste 2400, Huntington, WV, 25701-3655. Tel: 304-691-1750. Fax: 304-691-1766. p. 2562

Ward, Diva, Supvr, Learning Res Ctr, Oxnard College Library, 4000 S Rose Ave, Oxnard, CA, 93033-6699. Tel: 805-986-5949. Fax: 805-986-5888. p. 202

Ward, Doreen, Librn, St John's Medical Center, PO Box 428, Jackson, WY, 83001-0428. Tel: 307-739-7371. Fax: 307-739-7372. p. 2656

Ward, Ellie, Libr & Archives Mgr, Akron Art Museum, One S High, Akron, OH, 44308-1801. Tel: 330-376-9186, Ext 221. Fax: 330-376-1180. p. 1851

Ward, Francis, Dir, Richards Memorial Library, 118 N Washington St, North Attleboro, MA, 02760. Tel: 508-699-0122. Fax: 508-699-8075. p. 1112

Ward, Fred, Mgr, Municipal Research & Services Center of Washington Library, 2601 Fourth Ave, Ste 800, Seattle, WA, 98121-1280. Tel: 206-625-1300. Fax: 206-625-1220. p. 2528

Ward, Jane, Librn, Woodbourne Correctional Facility Library, 99 Prison Rd, Woodbourne, NY, 12788-1000. Tel: 845-434-7730. Fax: 845-434-7730, Ext 2099. p. 1770

Ward, Jane M, Genealogy Librn, Local Hist Librn, Three Oaks Township Public Library, Three N Elm St, Three Oaks, MI, 49128-1303. Tel: 269-756-5621. Fax: 269-756-3004. p. 1230

Ward, Joan, Librn, McKellar Township Public Library, 701 Hwy 124, McKellar, ON, P0G 1C0, CANADA. Tel: 705-389-2611. Fax: 705-389-2611. p. 2821

Ward, Joyce, Head, Ref (Info Serv), Winter Park Public Library, 460 E New England Ave, Winter Park, FL, 32789-4493. Tel: 407-623-3300. Fax: 407-623-3489. p. 505

Ward, Judit, Dir, Info Serv, Rutgers University Libraries, Center of Alcohol Studies, Brinkley & Adele Smithers Hall, 607 Allison Rd, Piscataway, NJ, 08854-8001. Tel: 732-445-3527. Fax: 732-445-5944. p. 1508

Ward, Kay, Co-Dir, Tacoma Family History Center, 5915 S 12th, Tacoma, WA, 98465. Tel: 253-564-1103. p. 2540

Ward, Kelly, Dir, Putnam County District Library, The Educational Service Ctr, 124 Putnam Pkwy, Ottawa, OH, 45875-1471. Tel: 419-523-3747. Fax: 419-523-6477. p. 1925

Ward, Kim, Dir, Pierce District Library, 208 S Main St, Pierce, ID, 83546. Tel: 208-464-2823. Fax: 208-464-2823. p. 581

Ward, Linda, In Charge, Klamath County Library Services District, Keno Branch, Keno Plaza, Unit 8, 15555 Hwy 66, Keno, OR, 97627. Tel: 541-273-0750. Fax: 541-273-0750. p. 2002

Ward, Luciano, Circ Serv, Wilmette Public Library District, 1242 Wilmette Ave, Wilmette, IL, 60091-2558. Tel: 847-256-6950. Fax: 847-256-6933. p. 720

Ward, Lynnette, Librn, Lonoke Prairie County Regional Library Headquarters, Carlisle Public, 105 E Fifth, Carlisle, AR, 72024. Tel: 870-552-3976. Fax: 870-552-9306. p. 108

Ward, Mary, Librn, Westville Public Library, 1035 Broadway, Westville, NJ, 08093. Tel: 856-456-0357. Fax: 856-742-8190. p. 1543

Ward, Michelle, Pub Serv, Okanagan College Library, 1000 KLO Rd, Kelowna, BC, V1Y 4X8, CANADA. p. 2730

Ward, Peter, Dir, Lindenhurst Memorial Library, One Lee Ave, Lindenhurst, NY, 11757-5399. Tel: 631-957-7755. Fax: 631-957-7114. p. 1652

Ward, Priscilla Renee, Youth Serv, Bessemer Public Library, 701 Ninth Ave N, Bessemer, AL, 35020-5305. Tel: 205-428-7882. Fax: 205-428-7885. p. 6

Ward, Rick, Br Librn, Blue Ridge Regional Library, Patrick County, 116 W Blue Ridge St, Stuart, VA, 24171. Tel: 276-694-3352, 276-694-5427. Fax: 276-694-6744. p. 2478

Ward, Rosaleen, Asst Librn, Hudson's Hope Public Library, 9905 Dudley Dr, Hudson's Hope, BC, V0C 1V0, CANADA. Tel: 250-783-9414. Fax: 250-783-5272. p. 2729

Ward, Rose, Librn, Wapiti Regional Library, Humboldt Reid-Thompson Public Library, 705 Main St, Humboldt, SK, S0K 2A0, CANADA. Tel: 306-682-2034. Fax: 306-682-3035. p. 2921

Ward, Sandra, Librn, Clive Public Library, 5115 50th St, Clive, AB, T0C 0Y0, CANADA. Tel: 403-784-3131. Fax: 403-784-3131. p. 2695

Ward, Sarah Laleman, Ref/Outreach Librn, Hunter College Libraries, 695 Park Ave, New York, NY, 10065. Tel: 212-772-4108. Fax: 212-772-4142. p. 1682

Ward, Suzanne, ILL & Reserves Coordr, Loras College Library, 1450 Alta Vista St, Dubuque, IA, 52004-4327. Tel: 563-588-7189. Fax: 563-588-7147. p. 812

Ward, Thelma, Librn, Sylvia Public Library, 121 S Main St, Sylvia, KS, 67581-9700. Tel: 620-486-2472. Fax: 620-486-2070. p. 895

Ward, Tyrone, Dir, Carnegie Library of Homestead, 510 E Tenth Ave, Munhall, PA, 15120-1910. Tel: 412-462-3444. Fax: 412-462-4669. p. 2093

Ward, Vanessa, Libr Mgr, Cottonwood Public Library, 100 S Sixth St, Cottonwood, AZ, 86326. Tel: 928-634-7559. Fax: 928-634-0253. p. 61

Ward, Vernell, Acq of New Ser, Oklahoma Baptist University, 500 W University, OBU Box 61310, Shawnee, OK, 74804-2504. Tel: 405-878-2255. Fax: 405-878-2256. p. 1977

Ward, Violet, Asst Librn, Oscoda County Library, 430 W Eighth St, Mio, MI, 48647. Tel: 989-826-3613. Fax: 989-826-5461. p. 1209

Ward, Wendy, Ch, Ventress Memorial Library, 15 Library Plaza, Marshfield, MA, 02050. Tel: 781-834-5535. Fax: 781-837-8362. p. 1103

Ward-Callaghan, Linda, Youth Serv, Joliet Public Library, 150 N Ottawa St, Joliet, IL, 60432-4102. Tel: 815-740-2660. Fax: 815-740-6161. p. 660

Ward-Crixell, Kit, Youth Serv, New Braunfels Public Library, 700 E Common St, New Braunfels, TX, 78130-5689. Tel: 830-221-4319. Fax: 830-608-2151. p. 2365

Ward-Smith, Angela, Librn, Environment Canada, Queen Sq, 5th Flr, 45 Alderny Dr, Dartmouth, NS, B2Y 2N6, CANADA. Tel: 902-426-7232. Fax: 902-426-6143. p. 2779

Wardell, Sarah, Asst Dir, Info Tech Serv, Duke University Libraries, Medical Center Library, DUMC Box 3702, Ten Bryan-Searle Dr, Durham, NC, 27710-0001. Tel: 919-660-1195. Fax: 919-681-7599. p. 1788

Warden, Anise, Dir, Todd County Public Library, 302 E Main St, Elkton, KY, 42220. Tel: 270-265-9071. Fax: 270-265-2599. p. 912

Warden, Carolyn, Tech Info Spec, General Electric Global Research, One Research Circle, Niskayuna, NY, 12309. Tel: 518-387-4952, 518-387-5000. p. 1706

Warden, Donna, Acq, Volunteer State Community College Library, 1480 Nashville Pike, Gallatin, TN, 37066-3188. Tel: 615-230-3400, Ext 3407. Fax: 615-230-3410. p. 2235

Warden, Pam, Librn, Mingo County Library, Main St, Delbarton, WV, 25670. Tel: 304-475-2749. Fax: 304-475-3970. p. 2558

Wardenburg, Jane, Librn, Williamsburg Public Library, 214 W State St, Williamsburg, IA, 52361. Tel: 319-668-1195. Fax: 319-668-9621. p. 853

Wardlaw, Janet, Dir, Sutter Coast Hospital Library, 800 E Washington Blvd, Crescent City, CA, 95531-3699. Tel: 707-464-8880. Fax: 707-464-8886. p. 138

Wardlaw, Tricia, Coll Mgr, Santa Barbara Botanic Garden Library, 1212 Mission Canyon Rd, Santa Barbara, CA, 93105-2199. Tel: 805-682-4726, Ext 103, 805-682-4726, Ext 107. Fax: 805-563-0352. p. 260

Wardle, Amy, Ref, Free Library of Northampton Township, 25 Upper Holland Rd, Richboro, PA, 18954-1514. Tel: 215-357-3050. p. 2134

Wardley, Lisa, Chairperson, Zama Community Library, PO Box 14, Zama City, AB, T0H 4E0, CANADA. Tel: 780-683-2888. p. 2722

Wardlow, Karla, Instrul Res Ctr Librn, Trevecca Nazarene University, 73 Lester Ave, Nashville, TN, 37210-4227. Tel: 615-248-1548. Fax: 615-248-1452. p. 2259

Wardroper, Lawrence, Head, Libr Syst & Cat, Government of Canada, Federal Courts & Tax Court of Canada, Courts Administration Service-Library Services, 90 Sparks St, Ottawa, ON, K1A 0H9, CANADA. Tel: 613-996-8735. Fax: 613-943-5303. p. 2831

Wardzinski, Carrie, Asst Librn, Trinity Episcopal School for Ministry Library, 311 11th St, Ambridge, PA, 15003. Tel: 724-266-3838, Ext 265. Fax: 724-266-4617. p. 2029

Ware, Fran, Mgr, Montgomery County Public Libraries, Silver Spring Library, 8901 Colesville Rd, Silver Spring, MD, 20910-4339. Tel: 240-773-9420. p. 1039

Ware, Jennifer, Head, Acq, California State University, Sacramento Library, 2000 State University Dr E, Sacramento, CA, 95819-6039. Tel: 916-278-7223. Fax: 916-278-5917. p. 223

Ware, Margaret, ILL, McCowan Memorial Library, 15 Pitman Ave, Pitman, NJ, 08071. Tel: 856-589-1656. Fax: 856-582-4982. p. 1520

Ware, Paige, Br Mgr, Botetourt County Library, Fincastle Branch, 11 Academy St, Fincastle, VA, 24090-3316. Tel: 540-473-8339. Fax: 540-473-1107. p. 2493

Ware, Paula J, Libr Dir, Oskaloosa Public Library, 315 Jefferson St, Oskaloosa, KS, 66066. Tel: 785-863-2475. Fax: 785-863-2088. p. 887

Ware, Roxanne, Librn, Chase Township Public Library, 8400 E North St, Chase, MI, 49623. Tel: 231-832-9511. Fax: 231-832-9511. p. 1162

Ware, Susan, Ref, Pennsylvania State University, Brandywine Campus, 25 Yearsley Mill Rd, Media, PA, 19063-5596. Tel: 610-892-1386. Fax: 610-892-1359. p. 2088

Wareham, Wendy, Mgr, Libr Serv, Brandon Regional Health Authority, 150 McTavish Ave E, Brandon, MB, R7A 2B3, CANADA. Tel: 204-578-4080. Fax: 204-578-4984. p. 2747

Wares, Michael, Assoc Dir, Tech Serv, Fordham University Libraries, 441 E Fordham Rd, Bronx, NY, 10458-5151. Tel: 718-817-3570. Fax: 718-817-3582. p. 1586

Warfield, Jenny, Librn, Federal Correctional Institution Library, 501 Capital Circle NE, Tallahassee, FL, 32301-3572. Tel: 850-878-2173, Ext 1345. Fax: 850-671-6121. p. 492

Warfield, Marsha, Pub Serv Mgr, West Palm Beach Public Library, 411 Clematis St, West Palm Beach, FL, 33401. Tel: 561-868-7719. Fax: 561-868-7706. p. 504

Warga, Sharon, Dir, Minot-Sleeper Library, 35 Pleasant St, Bristol, NH, 03222-1407. Tel: 603-744-3352. p. 1439

Warga, Sharon, Supvr, Ser, University of New Hampshire School of Law, Two White St, Concord, NH, 03301. Tel: 603-228-1541, Ext 1130. Fax: 603-228-0388. p. 1443

Wargo, Diane, Ad, Churchill County Library, 553 S Maine St, Fallon, NV, 89406-3387. Tel: 775-423-7581. Fax: 775-423-7766. p. 1427

Wargo, Nanette Festa, Dir, Nancy L McConathy Public Library, 21737 Jeffery Ave, Sauk Village, IL, 60411. Tel: 708-757-4771. Fax: 708-757-3580. p. 700

Wargo, Terri, Dir, West Lebanon-Pike Township Public Library, 200 N High St, West Lebanon, IN, 47991. Tel: 765-893-4605. Fax: 765-893-4605. p. 787

Warholm-Wohlenhaus, Cassie, Archivist, Librn, American Swedish Institute, 2600 Park Ave, Minneapolis, MN, 55407. Tel: 612-870-3348. Fax: 612-871-8682. p. 1258

Waring, Margaret T, Dir, Comanche Public Library, 311 N Austin St, Comanche, TX, 76442. Tel: 325-356-2122. Fax: 325-356-2122 (Must call first). p. 2299

Wark, Jennifer, Head, Circ, Ludington Public Library, Five S Bryn Mawr Ave, Bryn Mawr, PA, 19010-3471. Tel: 610-525-1776. Fax: 610-525-1783. p. 2039

Wark, Jonathan, Librn, East Albemarle Regional Library, 100 E Colonial Ave, Elizabeth City, NC, 27909-0303. Tel: 252-335-2511. Fax: 252-335-2386. p. 1790

Wark, Jonathan, Dir, Dare County Library, 700 N Hwy 64-264, Manteo, NC, 27954. Tel: 252-473-2372. Fax: 252-473-6034. p. 1808

Wark, Laura, Mgr, Pub Serv, Essa Public Library, 8505 County Rd 10, Unit 1, Angus, ON, L0M 1B1, CANADA. Tel: 705-424-6531. Fax: 705-424-5521. p. 2792

Wark, Meighan, County Librn, Huron County Library, Administration Office, 77722B London Rd, Clinton, ON, N0M 1L0, CANADA. Tel: 519-482-5457. Fax: 519-482-7820. p. 2799

Warkentin, Cheryl, Access & Tech Serv Librn, Hutchinson Community College, 1300 N Plum St, Hutchinson, KS, 67501. Tel: 620-665-3489. Fax: 620-665-3392. p. 873

Warmack, Judy, Mgr, Thomas County Public Library System, Coolidge Public Library, 1029 E Verbena St, Coolidge, GA, 31738. Tel: 229-346-3463. Fax: 229-346-3463. p. 553

Warminski, Beverly, Br Librn, Carson County Public Library, White Deer Branch, 200 Fourth St, White Deer, TX, 79097. Tel: 806-883-7121. Fax: 806-883-7121. p. 2368

Warmka, Sarah, Archivist, Ref, Stearns History Museum, 235 33rd Ave S, Saint Cloud, MN, 56301-3752. Tel: 320-253-8424. Fax: 320-253-2172. p. 1276

Warmkessel, Joann, AV, Lehigh Carbon Community College Library, 4525 Education Park Dr, Schnecksville, PA, 18078-9372. Tel: 610-799-1124. Fax: 610-779-1159. p. 2136

Warmkessel, Marjorie, Dr, Interim Dir, Millersville University, Nine N George St, Millersville, PA, 17551. Tel: 717-872-3618. Fax: 717-872-3854. p. 2090

Warne, Melissa, Asst Librn, Brook-Iroquois-Washington Public Library, 100 W Main St, Brook, IN, 47922. Tel: 219-275-2471. Fax: 219-275-8471. p. 730

Warner, A I, Exec Dir, American Institute of Parliamentarians Library, PO Box 2173, Wilmington, DE, 19899. Tel: 302-762-1811. Fax: 302-762-2170. p. 387

Warner, Barbara, Librn, Public Library of Brookline, Putterham, 959 W Roxbury Pkwy, Chestnut Hill, MA, 02467. Tel: 617-730-2385. Fax: 617-469-3947. p. 1072

Warner, Barbaranne, Dir, Sprague Public Library, One Main St, Baltic, CT, 06330-1320. Tel: 860-822-3012. Fax: 860-822-3013. p. 330

Warner, Blanche, Dir, Naples Library, 118 S Main, Naples, NY, 14512. Tel: 585-374-2757. Fax: 585-374-6493. p. 1664

Warner, Carol, Mgr, Washington County Library, Park Grove Branch, 7900 Hemingway Ave S, Cottage Grove, MN, 55016-1833. Tel: 651-459-2040. Fax: 651-275-8581. p. 1290

Warner, Carol, Librn, Perkins Coie Library, 1201 Third Ave, Ste 4900, Seattle, WA, 98101. Tel: 206-359-8444. Fax: 206-359-9444. p. 2529

Warner, Earleen, Instrul Serv Librn, Bethel University Library, 3900 Bethel Dr, Saint Paul, MN, 55112. Tel: 651-638-6222. Fax: 651-638-6001. p. 1277

Warner, Elizabeth, Evening Supvr, Drexel University Health Sciences Libraries, 245 N 15th St MS 449, Philadelphia, PA, 19102-1192. Fax: 215-762-8180. p. 2105

Warner, Jan, Exec Dir, Charles A Weyerhaeuser Memorial Museum, 2151 Lindbergh Dr S, Little Falls, MN, 56345. Tel: 320-632-4007. p. 1256

Warner, Jennifer, Asst Dir, Weston Public Library, 87 School St, Weston, MA, 02493. Tel: 781-893-3312. Fax: 781-529-0174. p. 1139

Warner, Kathleen, Libr Mgr, Hennepin County Medical Center, Mail Code R2, 701 Park Ave, Minneapolis, MN, 55415. Tel: 612-873-2710. Fax: 612-904-4248. p. 1260

Warner, Ken, Tech Consult, South Central Kansas Library System, 321 N Main St, South Hutchinson, KS, 67505-1146. Tel: 620-663-3211. Fax: 620-663-9797. p. 895

Warner, Linda, Libr Tech, NIH, National Institute of Allergy & Infectious Diseases, 903 S Fourth St, Hamilton, MT, 59840-2932. Tel: 406-363-9212. Fax: 406-363-9336. p. 1381

Warner, Lynn, Br Mgr, Martin County Library System, Hobe Sound Branch, 10595 SE Federal Hwy, Hobe Sound, FL, 33455. Tel: 772-546-2257. Fax: 772-546-3816. p. 492

Warner, Marcia A, Dir, Grand Rapids Public Library, 111 Library St NE, Grand Rapids, MI, 49503-3268. Tel: 616-988-5402, Ext 5431. Fax: 616-988-5429. p. 1185

Warner, Margaret, Head, Pub Serv, Saint Edwards University, 3001 S Congress Ave, Austin, TX, 78704-6489. Tel: 512-428-1024. Fax: 512-448-8737. p. 2281

Warner, Marnie, Coordr, New Bedford Law Library, Superior Courthouse, 441 County St, New Bedford, MA, 02740. Tel: 617-878-0338. Fax: 617-723-8821. p. 1108

Warner, Mary Ann, Head, Ref, Schenectady County Public Library, 99 Clinton St, Schenectady, NY, 12305-2083. Tel: 518-388-4573. Fax: 518-386-2241. p. 1740

Warner, Nancy, Tech Serv Librn, Martin County Library, 110 N Park St, Fairmont, MN, 56031-2822. Tel: 507-238-4207. Fax: 507-238-4208. p. 1250

Warner, Susan, Head, Youth & Neighborhood Serv, Kalamazoo Public Library, 315 S Rose St, Kalamazoo, MI, 49007-5264. Tel: 269-553-7876. Fax: 269-553-7940. p. 1197

Warner, Susan, Dir, Wolverine Community Library, 5716 W Main St, Wolverine, MI, 49799-9403. Tel: 231-525-8800. Fax: 231-525-8713. p. 1237

Warner, Susan, Med Librn, Covenant Health System, 3615 19th St, Lubbock, TX, 79410. Tel: 806-725-0602. Fax: 806-723-7363. p. 2357

Warner, Thea, Librn, Niles, Barton & Wilmer Law Library, 111 S Calvert St, Ste 1400, Baltimore, MD, 21202. Tel: 410-783-6386. Fax: 410-783-6363. p. 1017

Warnick, Mark, Dir, Crowley's Ridge College Library, 100 College Dr, Paragould, AR, 72450. Tel: 870-236-6901. Fax: 870-236-7748. p. 111

Warnick, Walter L, Dir, United States Department of Energy, One Science.gov Way, Oak Ridge, TN, 37830. Tel: 865-576-1188. Fax: 865-576-3609. p. 2262

Warnickl, Shirley S, Dir, Gallatin County Public Library, 209 W Market St, Warsaw, KY, 41095. Tel: 859-567-8333. Fax: 859-567-4750. p. 936

Warnke, Janet, Asst Univ Librn, Syst, Idaho State University, Idaho State University, 850 S Ninth Ave, Pocatello, ID, 83209-8089. Tel: 208-282-2697. Fax: 208-282-5847. p. 581

Warnock, Peggy, Ch, Deer Park Public Library, 3009 Center St, Deer Park, TX, 77536-5099. Tel: 281-478-7208. Fax: 281-478-7212. p. 2311

Warns, Evie, In Charge, Sacred Heart Hospital, 900 W Clairemont Ave, Eau Claire, WI, 54701. Tel: 715-717-4330. Fax: 715-717-6576. p. 2590

Warren, Bradly, Head, Access Serv, Yale University Library, Sterling Memorial Library, 120 High St, New Haven, CT, 06520. Tel: 203-432-3597. Fax: 203-432-1294. p. 359

Warren, Carolyn, Librn, City of Kawartha Lakes Public Library, Bobcaygeon Branch, 21 Canal St, Bobcaygeon, ON, K0M 1A0, CANADA. Tel: 705-738-2088. Fax: 705-738-0918. p. 2816

Warren, Cheryl, Coordr, Las Positas College Library, 3000 Campus Hill Dr, Livermore, CA, 94551-7623. Tel: 925-424-1150. Fax: 925-606-7249. p. 164

Warren, Christa, Mgr, Salt Lake County Library Services, Riverton Branch, 12877 S 1830 West, Riverton, UT, 84065-3204. Tel: 801-944-7677. Fax: 801-466-8601. p. 2414

Warren, Christine, Ref & Info Serv, Maury Loontjens Memorial Library, 35 Kingstown Rd, Narragansett, RI, 02882. Tel: 401-789-9507. Fax: 401-782-0677. p. 2168

Warren, Christopher, Br Mgr, Chattahoochee Valley Libraries, South Columbus Branch, 2034 S Lumpkin Rd, Columbus, GA, 31903-2728. Tel: 706-683-8805. Fax: 706-683-8809. p. 526

Warren, Elizabeth, Circ Librn, Pineville-Bell County Public Library, 214 Walnut St, Pineville, KY, 40977. Tel: 606-337-3422. Fax: 606-337-9862. p. 933

Warren, Elliot, Mgr, Coll Develop/Tech Serv, Contra Costa County Library, 1750 Oak Park Blvd, Pleasant Hill, CA, 94523-4497. Tel: 925-646-6434. Fax: 925-646-6461. p. 208

Warren, Eric, Syst Coordr, Springfield Technical Community College Library, One Armory Sq, Ste 1, Springfield, MA, 01105-1685. Tel: 413-755-4555. Fax: 413-755-6315. p. 1128

Warren, Evelyn, Mgr, NASA Ames Research Center, Technical Library, Bldg 202, Mail Stop 202-3, Moffett Field, CA, 94035-1000. Tel: 650-604-5681. Fax: 650-604-4988. p. 189

Warren, Gail, State Law Librn, Virginia State Law Library, Supreme Court Bldg, 2nd Flr, 100 N Ninth St, Richmond, VA, 23219-2335. Tel: 804-786-2075. Fax: 804-786-4542. p. 2493

Warren, Jalyn, Electronic Res, Community College of Philadelphia Library, 1700 Spring Garden St, Philadelphia, PA, 19130. Tel: 215-751-8000. Fax: 215-751-8762. p. 2104

Warren, Janet, Dir, Ririe City Library, 464 Main St, Ririe, ID, 83443. Tel: 208-538-7974. Fax: 208-538-7974. p. 583

Warren, Jill, Mgr, Elyria Public Library System, Keystone-LaGrange Branch, 101 West St, LaGrange, OH, 44050. Tel: 440-355-6323. Fax: 440-355-8082. p. 1898

Warren, Jill, Librn, Smith-Ennismore-Lakefield Library, 836 Charles St, Bridgenorth, ON, K0L 1H0, CANADA. Tel: 705-652-8623. Fax: 705-652-8878. p. 2797

Warren, Jonathan, Media Serv, Marymount Manhattan College, 221 E 71st St, New York, NY, 10021. Tel: 212-774-4806. Fax: 212-458-8207. p. 1685

Warren, Julie, Libr Serv & Pub Relations Mgr, Palm Springs Public Library, 300 S Sunrise Way, Palm Springs, CA, 92262-7699. Tel: 760-416-6731. Fax: 760-320-9834. p. 203

Warren, Lee, Br Librn, Community District Library, Lennon-Venice Township, 11904 Lennon Rd, Lennon, MI, 48449. Tel: 810-621-3202. Fax: 810-621-3202. p. 1166

Warren, Len, Dir, Park City Community Public Library, 2107 E 61st St N, Park City, KS, 67219. Tel: 316-744-6318. Fax: 316-744-6319. p. 889

Warren, Lynne, In Charge, Museum of Contemporary Art Library, 220 E Chicago Ave, Chicago, IL, 60611-2604. Tel: 312-280-2660. Fax: 312-397-4099. p. 619

Warren, Mark, Librn, Upshur County Library, 702 W Tyler St, Gilmer, TX, 75644. Tel: 903-843-5001. Fax: 903-843-3995. p. 2328

Warren, Nancy, Syst Librn, Fredrikson & Bryon, 200 S Sixth St, Ste 4000, Minneapolis, MN, 55402. Tel: 612-492-7852. Fax: 612-492-7077. p. 1259

Warren, Nina T, Dir of Libr Serv, Genesee Community College, One College Rd, Batavia, NY, 14020-9704. Tel: 585-343-0055, Ext 6256. Fax: 585-345-6933. p. 1578

Warren, Rebecca, Head of Libr, Masonic Medical Research Laboratory Library, 2150 Bleecker St, Utica, NY, 13501-1787. Tel: 315-735-2217, Ext 135. Fax: 315-724-0963. p. 1583

Warren, Richard, In Charge, Progress Energy Corp, 410 S Wilmington St, Raleigh, NC, 27601-1849. Tel: 919-546-7573. Fax: 919-546-5365. p. 1816

Warren, Sandy, Ch, Wilton Free Public Library, Six Goodspeed St, Wilton, ME, 04294. Tel: 207-645-4831. Fax: 207-645-9417. p. 1007

Warren, Sherry, Mgr, Pub Serv, Tempe Public Library, 3500 S Rural Rd, Tempe, AZ, 85282. Tel: 480-350-5554. Fax: 480-350-5544. p. 84

Warren, Stephen, Libr Mgr, Vancouver Island Regional Library, Bella Coola Branch, 450 MacKenzie St, Bella Coola, BC, V0T 1C0, CANADA. Tel: 250-799-5330. Fax: 250-799-5330. p. 2732

Warren, Stephen, Libr Mgr, Vancouver Island Regional Library, Ladysmith Branch, 740 First Ave, No 3, Ladysmith, BC, V9G 1A3, CANADA. Tel: 250-245-2322. Fax: 250-245-2393. p. 2732

Warren, Sue, Coordr, Rideau Lakes Public Library, Halladay St, Elgin, ON, K0G 1E0, CANADA. Tel: 613-359-5334. Fax: 613-359-5418. p. 2803

Warren, Susan, Libr Serv Mgr, Newport Beach Public Library, 1000 Avocado Ave, Newport Beach, CA, 92660-6301. Tel: 949-717-3828. Fax: 949-640-5681. p. 194

Warren, Susanne, Libr Dir, John G McCullough Free Library Inc, Two Main St, North Bennington, VT, 05257. Tel: 802-447-7121. Fax: 802-445-1080. p. 2430

Warrene, Carl, Syst Adminr, University of North Dakota, 215 Centennial Dr, Grand Forks, ND, 58202. Tel: 701-777-2204. Fax: 701-777-2217. p. 1843

Warrick, Beverly, Br Mgr, Albemarle Regional Library, Elizabeth Sewell Parker Memorial Library, 213 E Main, Murfreesboro, NC, 27855. Tel: 252-398-4494. Fax: 252-398-5724. p. 1835

Warrick, Debby, Librn, Johnston Community College Library, Learning Resource Ctr, 245 College Rd, Smithfield, NC, 27577. Tel: 919-464-2251. p. 1824

Warrick, Dianne, Br Supvr, Burlington Public Library, Kilbride, 6611 Panton St, Burlington, ON, L0P 1G0, CANADA. Tel: 905-335-4011. p. 2798

Warrick, Dianne, Br Supvr, Burlington Public Library, New Appleby, 676 Appleby Line, Burlington, ON, L7L 5Y1, CANADA. Tel: 905-639-6373. p. 2798

Warshenbrot, Amalia, Dir, Levine-Sklut Judaic Library & Resource Center, 5007 Providence Rd, Ste 107, Charlotte, NC, 28226. Tel: 704-944-6763. Fax: 704-362-4171. p. 1783

Warthen, Lee, Asst Dir, Head, Coll Develop, University of Utah, S J Quinney Law Library, 332 S 1400 East, Salt Lake City, UT, 84112-0731. Tel: 801-581-5344. Fax: 801-585-3033. p. 2415

Warthman, Susan A, Dir, New England Institute of Technology Library, 1408 Division Rd, East Greenwich, RI, 02818-1205. Tel: 401-739-5000. Fax: 401-886-0861. p. 2166

Wartzok, Sue, Head, Cat, Florida International University, 11200 SW Eighth St, Miami, FL, 33199. Tel: 305-348-6269. Fax: 305-348-1798. p. 465

Wartzok, Sue, Head, Cat, Florida International University, 3000 NE 151st St, North Miami, FL, 33181-3600. Tel: 305-348-6269. Fax: 305-348-3408. p. 472

Warwick, James F, Dir, Saint Clair County Library System, 210 McMorran Blvd, Port Huron, MI, 48060-4098. Tel: 810-987-7323, Ext 139. Fax: 810-987-7874. p. 1219

Warwick, Travis, Head of Libr, University of Wisconsin-Madison, Stephen Cole Kleene Mathematics Library, 480 Lincoln Dr, Madison, WI, 53706. Tel: 608-263-2274. Fax: 608-263-8891. p. 2609

Warzala, Erin, Ch, Wichita Falls Public Library, 600 11th St, Wichita Falls, TX, 76301-4604. Tel: 940-767-0868, Ext 244. Fax: 940-720-6672. p. 2401

Wasch, Marianne, Libr Coordr, Alberta Law Libraries - Canmore, Provincial Bldg, 314, 800 Railway Ave, Canmore, AB, T1W 1P1, CANADA. Tel: 403-678-5915. Fax: 403-678-4936. p. 2694

Waschevski, Sharon L, Dir, Deer Lodge Public Library, 110 Corrine Ave, Deer Lodge, TN, 37726-4239. Tel: 423-965-3029. p. 2233

Wasdin, Gary, Libr Dir, Omaha Public Library, 215 S 15th St, Omaha, NE, 68102-1629. Tel: 402-444-4800. Fax: 402-444-4504. p. 1413

Waseleski, Carol, Librn, Pettee Memorial Library, 16 S Main St, Wilmington, VT, 05363. Tel: 802-464-8557. p. 2440

Wasemiller, Monica, Ch, Hustisford Community Library, 609 W Juneau St, Hustisford, WI, 53034. Tel: 920-349-3463. Fax: 920-349-4540. p. 2599

Washam, Linda, Br Mgr, Trails Regional Library, Odessa Branch, 107 W Mason, Odessa, MO, 64076. Tel: 816-633-4089. p. 1371

Washburn, Anne, Mgr, Libr Serv, Smith Moore, LLP, 300 N Greene St, Greensboro, NC, 27401. Tel: 336-378-5272. Fax: 336-433-7566. p. 1797

Washburn, Elizabeth, Br Mgr, Fall River Public Library, South, 1310 S Main St, Fall River, MA, 02724. Tel: 508-324-2708. Fax: 508-324-2708. p. 1088

Washburn, Elizabeth, Circ, Comsewogue Public Library, 170 Terryville Rd, Port Jefferson Station, NY, 11776. Tel: 631-928-1212. Fax: 631-928-6307. p. 1721

Washburn, George, Ref, Judson College, 306 E Dekalb, Marion, AL, 36756. Tel: 334-683-5281. Fax: 334-683-5188. p. 24

Washburn, Jenny, Dir, Plymouth Library, 103 N Jefferson Ave, Plymouth, NE, 68424-0378. Tel: 402-656-4335. p. 1417

Washburn, Keith E, Dean, Lorain County Community College, 1005 Abbe Rd N, North Elyria, OH, 44035-1691. Tel: 440-366-4795. Fax: 440-366-4127. p. 1924

Washburn, Lesley, Teen Librn, Sterling Municipal Library, Mary Elizabeth Wilbanks Ave, Baytown, TX, 77520. Tel: 281-427-7331. Fax: 281-420-5347. p. 2286

Washburn, Michael, Automation Syst Coordr, Missouri River Regional Library, 214 Adams St, Jefferson City, MO, 65101-3244. Tel: 573-634-6064, Ext 241. p. 1335

Washburn, Paulita, YA Librn, Lawrence Memorial Library, 40 North St, Bristol, VT, 05443. Tel: 802-453-2366. p. 2420

Washburn, Terri Lynn, Dir, La Grande Public LIbrary, 2006 Fourth St, La Grande, OR, 97850-2496. Tel: 541-962-1335. Fax: 541-962-1338. p. 2003

Washecka, Barbara, Head, Cat, University of Texas Libraries, Jamail Center for Legal Research, University of Texas School of Law, 727 E Dean Keeton St, Austin, TX, 78705-3224. Tel: 512-471-7726. Fax: 512-471-0243. p. 2284

Washington, Ana, Circ Spec, Washtenaw Community College, 4800 E Huron River Dr, Ann Arbor, MI, 48105-4800. Tel: 734-477-8710. Fax: 734-973-3446. p. 1153

Washington, Betty, Acq Librn, Fayetteville State University, 1200 Murchison Rd, Fayetteville, NC, 28301-4298. Tel: 910-672-1642. Fax: 910-672-1746. p. 1793

Washington, Carolyn, Br Mgr, Winn Parish Library, Atlanta Branch, 110 School Rd, Atlanta, LA, 71404. Tel: 318-628-7657. p. 972

Washington, Danielle, Librn, South Cook ISC4 Library, 253 W Joe Orr Rd, Chicago Heights, IL, 60411. Tel: 708-754-6600. Fax: 708-754-8687. p. 628

Washington, Dawn, Librn, Western Plains Library System, Seiling Public Library, PO Box 116, Seiling, OK, 73663-0116. Tel: 580-922-4259. Fax: 580-922-4259. p. 1961

Washington, Kelly, Br Mgr, Southeast Arkansas Regional Library, Dermott Branch, 117 S Freeman St, Dermott, AR, 71638. Tel: 870-538-3514. Fax: 870-538-3514. p. 109

Washington, Linda, ILL, Ser, Phillips Community College of the University of Arkansas, 1000 Campus Dr, Helena, AR, 72342. Tel: 870-338-6474. Fax: 870-338-2783. p. 103

Washington, Marquita, Br Mgr, Atlanta-Fulton Public Library System, Martin Luther King Jr Library, 409 John Wesley Dobbs Ave, Atlanta, GA, 30312-1342. Tel: 404-730-1185. p. 512

Washington, Mary, Dir, Darton College, 2400 Gillionville Rd, Albany, GA, 31707. Tel: 229-317-6761. Fax: 229-317-6652. p. 507

Washington, Michelle, Pub Serv, Medical College of Wisconsin Libraries, Health Research Ctr, 3rd Flr, 8701 Watertown Plank Rd, Milwaukee, WI, 53226-0509. Tel: 414-955-8305. Fax: 414-955-6532. p. 2619

Washington, Robyn, ILL, Department of Veterans Affairs, Central Office Library, 810 Vermont Ave NW, Washington, DC, 20420. Tel: 202-273-8520. Fax: 202-273-9125. p. 397

Washington, Roy, Syst Programmer, Jackson State University, 1325 J R Lynch St, Jackson, MS, 39217. Tel: 601-979-2123. Fax: 601-979-2239. p. 1303

Washington, Sharon D, Br Mgr, Atlanta-Fulton Public Library System, Washington Park-Annie McPheeters Library, 1116 Martin Luther King Jr Dr, Atlanta, GA, 30314. Tel: 404-752-8760. Fax: 404-752-8762. p. 513

Washy, Kathleen, Archivist, Doc Delivery, Mercy Hospital of Pittsburgh, 1400 Locust St, Pittsburgh, PA, 15219. Tel: 412-232-7520. Fax: 412-232-8422. p. 2126

Wasielewski, Terrance, Archivist, Tech Serv, The Sage Colleges, 140 New Scotland Ave, Albany, NY, 12208. Tel: 518-244-2435. Fax: 518-292-1904. p. 1570

Wasielewski, Terrance, Archivist, Tech Serv Librn, The Sage Colleges, 45 Ferry St, Troy, NY, 12180. Tel: 518-224-2435. Fax: 518-244-2400. p. 1756

Wasilick, Michael, Dir, Wake County Public Library System, 4020 Carya Dr, Raleigh, NC, 27610-2900. Tel: 919-250-4532. p. 1817

Wasley, Patrick, PhD, Archivist, Ser, Averett University Library, 344 W Main St, Danville, VA, 24541-2849. Tel: 434-791-5690. Fax: 434-791-5637. p. 2459

Wasman, Wendy, Librn, Cleveland Museum of Natural History, One Wade Oval Dr, University Circle, Cleveland, OH, 44106-1767. Tel: 216-231-4600, Ext 3222. Fax: 216-231-5919. p. 1877

Wassberg, Linda A, Libr Tech, United States Courts, 624 US Courthouse, 500 State Ave, Kansas City, KS, 66101-2448. Tel: 913-551-6546. p. 875

Wassenich, Red, Ref Librn, Austin Community College, Rio Grande Campus Library, 1212 Rio Grande, Austin, TX, 78701. Tel: 512-223-3074. Fax: 512-223-3430. p. 2278

Wasserberg, Sharon B, Dir of Educ, Adath Israel Congregation, 3201 E Galbraith Rd, Cincinnati, OH, 45236. Tel: 513-793-1800. Fax: 513-792-5085. p. 1868

Wasserburger, Kathryn, Tech Serv Librn, Gering Public Library, 1055 P St, Gering, NE, 69341. Tel: 308-436-7433. Fax: 308-436-6869. p. 1399

Wasserman, Janet, Ch, North Merrick Public Library, 1691 Meadowbrook Rd, North Merrick, NY, 11566. Tel: 516-378-7474. Fax: 516-378-0876. p. 1706

Wasserman, Mona, Asst Dir, St Francis College Library, 180 Remsen St, Brooklyn, NY, 11201. Tel: 718-489-5305. Fax: 718-489-3402. p. 1594

Wassermann, Mary, Coll Develop Librn, Philadelphia Museum of Art Library, Ruth & Raymond G Perelman Bldg, 2525 Pennsylvania Ave, Philadelphia, PA, 19130. Tel: 215-684-7654. Fax: 215-236-0534. p. 2114

Wassink, Elaine, Tech Serv, Dordt College, 498 Fourth Ave NE, Sioux Center, IA, 51250. Tel: 712-722-6046. Fax: 712-722-1198. p. 843

Wasson, Julie Harte, Dir, Somonauk Public Library District, 115 E Dekalb St, Somonauk, IL, 60552-0307. Tel: 815-498-2440. Fax: 815-498-2135. p. 703

Wasti, Helen, Dir, Morris Public Library, Four North St, Morris, CT, 06763-1415. Tel: 860-567-7440. Fax: 860-567-7432. p. 353

Watahomigie, Lucille, Dir, Edward McElwain Memorial Library, 460 Hualapai Way, Peach Springs, AZ, 86434. Tel: 928-769-2200. Fax: 928-769-2250. p. 71

Watanabe, Cynthia, Br Head, East Baton Rouge Parish Library, Carver, 720 Terrace St, Baton Rouge, LA, 70802. Tel: 225-389-7480. Fax: 225-389-7449. p. 943

Watanuki, Liane, Actg Br Mgr, Hawaii State Public Library System, Kapolei Public Library, 1020 Manawai St, Kapolei, HI, 96707. Tel: 808-693-7050. Fax: 808-693-7062. p. 562

Watch, Charlyn, Youth Serv Librn, Southgate Veterans Memorial Library, 14680 Dix-Toledo Rd, Southgate, MI, 48195. Tel: 734-258-3002. Fax: 734-284-9477. p. 1229

Waterbury, Cristin J, Coll Mgr, Wisconsin Maritime Museum, 75 Maritime Dr, Manitowoc, WI, 54220. Tel: 920-684-0218. Fax: 920-684-0219. p. 2612

Waterhouse, AnnMarie, Circ Asst, Josiah Carpenter Library, 41 Main St, Pittsfield, NH, 03263. Tel: 603-435-8406. p. 1462

Waterhouse, Jan, Dir, Info Syst & Tech Serv, University of Illinois at Springfield, One University Plaza, MS BRK-140, Springfield, IL, 62703-5407. Tel: 217-206-7114. Fax: 217-206-6354. p. 707

Waterhouse, Langhorne, Mgr, Erlanger Health System Library, 975 E Third St, Chattanooga, TN, 37403. Tel: 423-778-7246. Fax: 423-778-7247. p. 2227

Waterhouse, Mary, Dir, Acton Public Library, 33 H Rd, Acton, ME, 04001. Tel: 207-636-2781. p. 973

Waterhouse, Richard, Dir, Cahoon Museum of American Art, 4676 Falmouth Rd, Cotuit, MA, 02635-2521. Tel: 508-428-7581. Fax: 508-420-3709. p. 1083

Waterman, Edra, Dir, Plainfield-Guilford Township Public Library, 1120 Stafford Rd, Plainfield, IN, 46168-2230. Tel: 317-839-6602. Fax: 317-838-3805. p. 773

Waterman, Margaret, Ch, Wilton Public & Gregg Free Library, Seven Forest Rd, Wilton, NH, 03086. Tel: 603-654-2581. Fax: 603-654-3674. p. 1468

Waterman, Phil, Ref & Info Literacy Librn, Assumption College, 500 Salisbury St, Worcester, MA, 01609. Tel: 508-767-7375. Fax: 508-767-7374. p. 1143

Waterman, Robert, Archivist, The Philatelic Foundation, 70 W 40th St, 15th Flr, New York, NY, 10018-2615. Tel: 212-221-6555. Fax: 212-867-6208. p. 1697

Waters, Amy, Ref Spec, State Historical Society of Missouri Library, 1020 Lowry St, Columbia, MO, 65201-7298. Tel: 573-882-7083. Fax: 573-884-4950. p. 1324

Waters, Andrew, Dir, Goshen Public Library, 601 S Fifth St, Goshen, IN, 46526-3994. Tel: 574-533-9531. Fax: 574-533-5211. p. 746

Waters, Carolyn, Asst Head Librn, The New York Society Library, 53 E 79th St, New York, NY, 10075. Tel: 212-288-6900, Ext 244. Fax: 212-744-5832. p. 1694

Waters, Cindy, Adult Prog Coordr, Vols Serv Coordr, Mark Skinner Library, 48 West Rd, Manchester, VT, 05254. Tel: 802-362-2607. p. 2427

Waters, David, Ser, Charlotte Mecklenburg Library, 310 N Tryon St, Charlotte, NC, 28202-2176. Tel: 704-416-0101. Fax: 704-416-0130. p. 1782

Waters, Lorie, Dir, Etowah Carnegie Public Library, 723 Ohio Ave, Etowah, TN, 37331. Tel: 423-263-9475. Fax: 423-263-4271. p. 2234

Waters, Marion, Head, Tech Serv, Wayne County Public Library, 1001 E Ash St, Goldsboro, NC, 27530. Tel: 919-735-1824. Fax: 919-731-2889. p. 1795

Waters, Natalie, Head Librn, McGill University Libraries, Macdonald Campus, 21111 Lakeshore Rd, Sainte Anne de Bellevue, QC, H9X 3V9, CANADA. Tel: 514-398-7876. Fax: 514-398-7960. p. 2899

Waters, Ricci, In Charge, First Presbyterian Church of Arlington Library, 601 N Vermont St, Arlington, VA, 22203. Tel: 703-527-4766. Fax: 703-527-2262. p. 2449

Waters, Vernon, Librn, Weber County Library System, Southwest Branch, 1950 W 4800 South, Roy, UT, 84067-2627. Tel: 801-773-2556. Fax: 801-773-2557. p. 2409

Waters, Vicki, Asst Librn, Grant County Library, 507 S Canyon Blvd, John Day, OR, 97845-1050. Tel: 541-575-1992. p. 2001

Waters, Victoria M, Assoc Librn, Goshen College, Mennonite Historical Library, 1700 S Main, Goshen, IN, 46526. Tel: 574-535-7418. Fax: 574-535-7438. p. 746

Waters, W Robin, Med Librn, Swedish Medical Center Library, 501 E Hampden Ave, Englewood, CO, 80113. Tel: 303-788-6669. Fax: 303-788-6840. p. 306

Waterstone, Marek, Head, Acq & Coll Serv, University of Houston, The O'Quinn Law Library, 12 Law Library, Houston, TX, 77204-6054. Tel: 713-743-2300. Fax: 713-743-2296. p. 2343

Wathen, Charlotte, Librn, Tombigbee Regional Library System, Wren Public Library, 32655 Hwy 45 N, Aberdeen, MS, 39730-9796. Tel: 662-256-4957. Fax: 662-256-4950. p. 1318

Watkins, Ann, Ref, Rutgers University Libraries, John Cotton Dana Library, 185 University Ave, Newark, NJ, 07102. Tel: 973-353-5222. Fax: 973-353-1133. p. 1512

Watkins, Carla, Librn, Library District Number One, Doniphan County, Elwood Branch, 410 N Ninth, Elwood, KS, 66024. Tel: 913-365-2409. p. 898

Watkins, Dan, Ref Serv, Syst Librn, Zula Bryant Wylie Public Library, 225 Cedar St, Cedar Hill, TX, 75104-2655. Tel: 972-291-7323, Ext 1311. Fax: 972-291-5361. p. 2296

Watkins, Diana, Dir, Gaston Community Library, 116 Front St, Gaston, OR, 97119. Tel: 503-985-3464. Fax: 503-985-1014. p. 1998

Watkins, Donna, Br Mgr, OC Public Libraries, Laguna Hills Technology, Laguna Hills Community Ctr, 25555 Alicia Pkwy, Laguna Hills, CA, 92653. Tel: 949-707-2699. Fax: 949-707-2698. p. 258

Watkins, Faye, Dir, Hampton University, 130 E Tyler St, Hampton, VA, 23668. Tel: 757-727-5371. Fax: 757-727-5952. p. 2468

Watkins, Jan, Ch, Skokie Public Library, 5215 Oakton St, Skokie, IL, 60077-3680. Tel: 847-673-7774. Fax: 847-673-7797. p. 703

Watkins, Jane, Chief Librn, North Vancouver City Library, 120 West 14th St, North Vancouver, BC, V7M 1N9, CANADA. Tel: 604-998-3450. Fax: 604-983-3624. p. 2734

Watkins, Jessica, Ref Serv Mgr, Massillon Public Library, 208 Lincoln Way E, Massillon, OH, 44646-8416. Tel: 330-832-9831, Ext 307. Fax: 330-830-2182. p. 1915

Watkins, Jim, Dir, Charlotte County Library, Phenix Branch, Charlotte St, Phenix, VA, 23959. Tel: 434-542-4654. p. 2453

Watkins, Jim, Librn, Charlotte County Library, 112-116 Legrande Ave, Charlotte Court House, VA, 23923. Tel: 434-542-5247. p. 2453

Watkins, Larissa, Asst Librn, Scottish Rite Library, 1733 16th St NW, Washington, DC, 20009-3103. Tel: 202-777-3127. Fax: 202-464-0487. p. 413

Watkins, Melinda, Ch, Valley Cottage Free Library, 110 Rte 303, Valley Cottage, NY, 10989. Tel: 845-268-7700. Fax: 845-268-7760. p. 1760

Watkins, Michael, Head, Govt Info, University of Wisconsin Oshkosh, 801 Elmwood Ave, Oshkosh, WI, 54901. Tel: 920-424-7305. Fax: 920-424-7338. p. 2628

Watkins, Nancy, Dep Dir, Finance, Topeka & Shawnee County Public Library, 1515 SW Tenth Ave, Topeka, KS, 66604-1374. Tel: 785-580-4400. Fax: 785-580-4496. p. 897

Watkins, Patricia, Res & Instruction Librn, Embry-Riddle Aeronautical University, 3700 Willow Creek Rd, Prescott, AZ, 86301-3720. Tel: 928-777-3920. p. 78

Watkins, Rick, Br Head, Winnipeg Public Library, Cornish, 20 West Gate, Winnipeg, MB, R3C 2E1, CANADA. Tel: 204-986-4679. Fax: 204-986-7126. p. 2760

Watkins, Steve, Tech Coordr, California State University-Monterey Bay, 100 Campus Ctr, Seaside, CA, 93955-8001. Tel: 831-582-3793. Fax: 831-582-3875. p. 268

Watkins, Susan J, Dir, Eastern Nazarene College, 23 E Elm Ave, Quincy, MA, 02170. Tel: 617-745-3850. Fax: 617-745-3913. p. 1119

Watkins, Vicki, Electronic Serv, United States Air Force, Air University - Muir S Fairchild Research Information Center, 600 Chennault Circle, Maxwell AFB, AL, 36112-6010. Tel: 334-953-8301. p. 24

Watkis, Errol S, Head, Multimedia, Howard University Libraries, 500 Howard Pl NW, Washington, DC, 20059. Tel: 202-806-7234. Fax: 202-806-5903. p. 403

Watley, Georgia, Assoc Dir, Coordr, Spec Coll & Libr Develop, University of Arkansas-Pine Bluff, 1200 N University Dr, Pine Bluff, AR, 71601. Tel: 870-575-8411. Fax: 870-575-4651. p. 112

Watman, Celeste, Dir, Levittown Public Library, One Bluegrass Lane, Levittown, NY, 11756-1292. Tel: 516-731-5728. Fax: 516-735-3168. p. 1652

Watner, Carl, Librn, Rentaw Foundation, Inc Library, Hwy 176, Gramling, SC, 29348. Tel: 864-472-2750. p. 2195

Watson, Alisa, Br Mgr, Huntsville-Madison Public Library, Gurley Public Library, 225 Walker St, Gurley, AL, 35748. Tel: 256-776-2102. p. 21

Watson, Amanda, Coordr, Spec Projects, Res Support & Instruction Librn, Connecticut College, 270 Mohegan Ave, New London, CT, 06320-4196. Tel: 860-439-2272. Fax: 860-439-2871. p. 359

Watson, Amanda, Access Serv Librn, Tulane University, Law Library, 6329 Freret St, New Orleans, LA, 70118-6231. Tel: 504-865-5955. Fax: 504-865-5917. p. 963

Watson, Amy, Circ/Reserves, Centre College of Kentucky, 600 W Walnut St, Danville, KY, 40422. Tel: 859-238-5272. Fax: 859-236-7925. p. 911

Watson, Amy, Info Spec, PPG Industries, Inc, Glass Technology Center, Guys Run Rd, Harmar Township, PA, 15238. Tel: 412-820-8568. Fax: 412-820-8696. p. 2128

Watson, Ann, Dir, Libr Serv, Ohio University-Lancaster Library, 1570 Granville Pike, Lancaster, OH, 43130-1097. Tel: 740-654-6711, Ext 236. Fax: 740-687-9497. p. 1909

Watson, Ann, Dean, Shepherd University, 301 N King St, Shepherdstown, WV, 25443. Fax: 304-876-0731. p. 2571

Watson, Azusa, Asst Librn, Coronation Memorial Library, 5001 Royal St, Coronation, AB, T0C 1C0, CANADA. Tel: 403-578-3445. p. 2695

Watson, Becky, Librn, Dora Bee Woodyard Memorial Library, Mulberry St, Elizabeth, WV, 26143. Tel: 304-275-4295. Fax: 304-275-4295. p. 2558

Watson, Benjamin, Cat, University of San Francisco, 2130 Fulton St, San Francisco, CA, 94117-1080. Tel: 415-422-5633. Fax: 415-422-5949. p. 248

Watson, Berrie, Head, Syst & Digital Tech, University of South Florida Saint Petersburg, 140 Seventh Ave S, POY118, Saint Petersburg, FL, 33701. Tel: 727-873-4401. Fax: 727-873-4196. p. 489

Watson, Brian, In Charge, Western Canada Aviation Museum Library-Archives, Hangar T-2, 958 Ferry Rd, Winnipeg, MB, R3H 0Y8, CANADA. Tel: 204-786-5503. Fax: 204-775-4761. p. 2759

Watson, Carl, Head, Circ, Tipton County Public Library, 127 E Madison St, Tipton, IN, 46072-1993. Tel: 765-675-8761. Fax: 765-675-4475. p. 782

Watson, Carol A, Dir, University of Georgia, 225 Herty Dr, Athens, GA, 30602-6018. Tel: 706-542-1922. Fax: 706-542-5001. p. 510

Watson, Carole, Tech Serv, Free Public Library of the Borough of Fort Lee, 320 Main St, Fort Lee, NJ, 07024. Tel: 201-592-3614. Fax: 201-585-0375. p. 1486

Watson, Chris, Dir of Libr Serv, Wright State University Libraries, 126 Dunbar Library, 3640 Colonel Glenn Hwy, Dayton, OH, 45435-0001. Tel: 937-775-2608. Fax: 937-775-4109. p. 1894

Watson, Christina N M, Actg Dir, Guam Public Library, 254 Martyr St, Hagatna, GU, 96910. Tel: 671-475-4753, 671-475-4754. Fax: 671-477-9777. p. 2667

Watson, Cory, Librn, Richards, Watson & Gershon, 355 S Grand Ave, 40th Flr, Los Angeles, CA, 90071-3101. Tel: 213-626-8484. Fax: 213-626-0078. p. 177

Watson, Deborah, Ref, University of New Hampshire Library, 18 Library Way, Durham, NH, 03824. Tel: 603-862-3800. Fax: 603-862-2637. p. 1445

Watson, Diana, Supvr, Middlesex County Library, Newbury Branch, 22894 Hagerty St, Newbury, ON, N0L 1Z0, CANADA. Tel: 519-693-4275. Fax: 519-693-4493. p. 2845

Watson, Donna, Librn, Brighton Memorial Library, 110 N Main, Brighton, IL, 62012. Tel: 618-372-8450. Fax: 618-372-7450. p. 597

Watson, Dwight C, Dr, Chair, University of Wisconsin-Eau Claire, 105 Garfield Ave, Eau Claire, WI, 54702. Tel: 715-836-2635. Fax: 715-836-5099. p. 2976

Watson, Elizabeth, Bus Librn, University of Calgary Library, Business Library, Haskayne School of Business, Scurfield Hall, Rm 301, Calgary, AB, T2N 1N4, CANADA. Tel: 403-220-7223. Fax: 403-220-0120. p. 2693

Watson, Elizabeth, Head Librn, York University Libraries, Peter F Bronfman Business Library, Schulich School of Business, Seymour Schulich Bldg, Rm S237, 4700 Keele St, Toronto, ON, M3J 1P3, CANADA. Tel: 416-736-5139. Fax: 416-736-5687. p. 2868

Watson, Fern, Dir, Pottsboro Area Public Library, 104 N Main, Pottsboro, TX, 75076. Tel: 903-786-8274. Fax: 903-786-8274. p. 2372

Watson, Gladys, Dir, Centennial College of Applied Arts & Technology, 941 Progress Ave, Scarborough, ON, M1G 3T8, CANADA. Tel: 416-289-5000, Ext 2601. Fax: 416-289-5228. p. 2840

Watson, Gladys, Dir, Centennial College of Applied Arts & Technology, Ashtonbee Campus Library, 75 Ashtonbee Rd, Scarborough, ON, M1L 4N4, CANADA. Tel: 416-289-5000, Ext 7000. Fax: 416-289-5017. p. 2840

Watson, Gladys, Dir, Centennial College of Applied Arts & Technology, Centre for Creative Communications Library, 951 Carlaw Ave, Toronto, ON, M4K 3M2, CANADA. Tel: 416-289-5000, Ext 8600. Fax: 416-289-5118. p. 2840

Watson, Gladys, Dir, Centennial College of Applied Arts & Technology, Morningside Campus Library, 755 Morningside Ave, Rm 160, Scarborough, ON, M1C 5J9, CANADA. Tel: 416-289-5000, Ext 8000. Fax: 416-289-5156. p. 2840

Watson, Gladys, Dir, Centennial College of Applied Arts & Technology, Progress Campus Library, 941 Progress Ave, Scarborough, ON, M1G 3T8, CANADA. Tel: 416-289-5000, Ext 2600. Fax: 416-289-5242. p. 2840

Watson Hall, Brenda, Mgr, Durham County Library, McDougald Terrace, 1101 Lawson St, Durham, NC, 27701. Tel: 919-560-0274. Fax: 919-560-0283. p. 1788

Watson Hall, Brenda, Mgr, Durham County Library, Stanford L Warren Branch, 1201 Fayetteville St, Durham, NC, 27707. Tel: 919-560-0274. Fax: 919-560-0283. p. 1788

Watson, Jeff, Head Librn, Roanoke Rapids Public Library, 319 Roanoke Ave, Roanoke Rapids, NC, 27870. Tel: 252-533-2890. Fax: 252-533-2892. p. 1820

Watson, Jerry, In Charge, Fairbanks Correctional Center Library, 1931 Eagan St, Fairbanks, AK, 99701. Tel: 907-458-6700. Fax: 907-458-6751. p. 47

Watson, Jessica, Tech Serv Librn, Scholastic Inc Library, 557 Broadway, New York, NY, 10012. Tel: 212-343-6171. Fax: 212-389-3317. p. 1699

Watson, Jinx Stapleton, Assoc Prof, University of Tennessee, Knoxville, 451 Communications Bldg, 1345 Circle Park Dr, Knoxville, TN, 37996-0341. Tel: 865-974-2148. Fax: 865-974-4967. p. 2974

Watson, JoAnn, Prog Coordr, Dalhousie University, 6100 University Ave, Halifax, NS, B3H 3J5, CANADA. Tel: 902-494-2471. Fax: 902-494-2451. p. 2978

Watson, Jonathan, Librn, Solano County Library, Law Library, Hall of Justice, 600 Union Ave, Fairfield, CA, 94533. Tel: 707-421-6520. Fax: 707-421-6516. p. 148

Watson, Julie, Res Librn, Marywood University Library, 2300 Adams Ave, Scranton, PA, 18509-1598. Tel: 570-961-4707. Fax: 570-961-4769. p. 2137

Watson, Julie, Pub Serv Librn, Upper Moreland Free Public Library, 109 Park Ave, Willow Grove, PA, 19090-3277. Tel: 215-659-0741. Fax: 215-830-1223. p. 2157

Watson, Karen, Per, NASA, 21000 Brookpark Rd, MS 60-3, Cleveland, OH, 44135. Fax: 216-433-5777. p. 1880

Watson, Kathryn, Br Head, Toronto Public Library, Woodview Park, 16 Bradstock Rd, Toronto, ON, M9M 1M8, CANADA. Tel: 416-395-5960. Fax: 416-395-5417. p. 2863

Watson, Kathy, Br Supvr, Southside Regional Library, Victoria Public, 1417 Seventh St, Victoria, VA, 23974. Tel: 434-696-3416. Fax: 434-696-2895. p. 2452

Watson, Kelly, Youth Serv Coordr, Bensenville Community Public Library, 200 S Church Rd, Bensenville, IL, 60106. Tel: 630-766-4642. Fax: 630-766-0788. p. 594

Watson, Ken, Pub Serv, Eastern Oregon University, One University Blvd, La Grande, OR, 97850. Tel: 541-962-3546. Fax: 541-962-3335. p. 2003

Watson, Kimberly, Cat, Tech Serv, Bay Minette Public Library, 205 W Second St, Bay Minette, AL, 36507. Tel: 251-580-1648. Fax: 251-937-0339. p. 6

Watson, Laura, Ref Serv, Highland Community College Library, 2998 W Pearl City Rd, Freeport, IL, 61032-9341. Tel: 815-599-3539. Fax: 815-235-1366. p. 647

Watson, Linda, Automation Syst Coordr, Marion County Public Library System, 2720 E Silver Springs Blvd, Ocala, FL, 34470. Tel: 352-671-8551. Fax: 352-368-4545. p. 474

Watson, Lisa, Ch, YA Serv, Flat River Community Library, 200 W Judd St, Greenville, MI, 48838-2225. Tel: 616-754-6359. Fax: 616-754-1398. p. 1186

Watson, Lisa, Librn, Lincoln Family Medicine Program Library, 4600 Valley Rd, Ste 210, Lincoln, NE, 68510-4892. Tel: 402-483-4591. Fax: 402-483-5079. p. 1405

Watson, Lois, Librn, Department of Veterans Affairs, 200 Veterans Ave, Beckley, WV, 25801. Tel: 304-255-2121, Ext 4342. Fax: 304-255-2431. p. 2553

Watson, Margaret, Head, Pub Serv, Alameda County Library, 2450 Stevenson Blvd, Fremont, CA, 94538-2326. Tel: 510-745-1500. Fax: 510-793-2987. p. 149

Watson, Mark R, Assoc Univ Librn, University of Oregon Libraries, 1501 Kincaid St, Eugene, OR, 97403-1299. Tel: 541-346-3056. Fax: 541-346-3485. p. 1997

Watson, Marsha, Dir, Fred & Harriett Taylor Memorial Library, 21 William St, Hammondsport, NY, 14840. Tel: 607-569-2045. Fax: 607-569-3340. p. 1633

Watson, Merla, Librn, Dickens County-Spur Public Library, 415 E Hill St, Spur, TX, 79370-2511. Tel: 806-271-3714. Fax: 806-271-4341. p. 2388

Watson, Natalie, Res, Times Publishing Co, 490 First Ave S, Saint Petersburg, FL, 33701-4223. Tel: 727-893-8111. Fax: 727-893-8107. p. 488

Watson, Pat, Head, Adult Serv, New Britain Public Library, 20 High St, New Britain, CT, 06051-4226. Tel: 860-224-3155. Fax: 860-223-6729. p. 354

Watson, Patricia, Br Mgr, Louisville Free Public Library, Shively-Newman, 3920 Dixie Hwy, Louisville, KY, 40216. Tel: 502-574-1730. Fax: 502-449-3886. p. 925

Watson, Patricia, Tech Serv Librn, Providence Athenaeum, 251 Benefit St, Providence, RI, 02903-2799. Tel: 401-421-6970. Fax: 401-421-2860. p. 2173

Watson, Paul, Libr Tech, First Baptist Church of West Terre Haute Library, 205 S Fifth, West Terre Haute, IN, 47885. Tel: 812-533-2016. p. 787

Watson, Peggy, Head, Br Libr, Alameda County Library, 2450 Stevenson Blvd, Fremont, CA, 94538-2326. Tel: 510-745-1512. Fax: 510-793-2987. p. 149

Watson, Rebecca, Ch, YA Serv, Woodford County Library, 115 N Main St, Versailles, KY, 40383-1289. Tel: 859-873-5191. Fax: 859-873-1542. p. 936

Watson, Rhonda Holman, Librn, Mississippi State University Agricultural & Forestry Experiment Station, Bldg 1532, 82 Stoneville Rd, Stoneville, MS, 38776. Tel: 662-686-3261. Fax: 662-686-3342. p. 1315

Watson, Robert, Dir, Lake Villa District Library, 1001 E Grand Ave, Lake Villa, IL, 60046. Tel: 847-356-7711, Ext 210. Fax: 847-265-9595. p. 663

Watson, Sheila, Dir, Avon Public Library, Garfield & Fifth Ave, Avon By The Sea, NJ, 07717. Tel: 732-502-4525. Fax: 732-775-8430. p. 1470

Watson, Sherry, Asst Librn, Leon Valley Public Library, 6425 Evers Rd, Leon Valley, TX, 78238-1453. Tel: 210-684-0720. Fax: 210-684-2088. p. 2355

Watson, Stacey, Mgr, Website & ILL, Denver Public Library, Ten W 14th Ave Pkwy, Denver, CO, 80204-2731. Tel: 720-865-1111. Fax: 720-865-2087. p. 300

Watson, Stardust, Librn, First Baptist Church of West Terre Haute Library, 205 S Fifth, West Terre Haute, IN, 47885. Tel: 812-533-2016. p. 787

Watson, Sue, Librn, Forest County Library, 106 Pine St, Marienville, PA, 16239. Tel: 814-927-8552. Fax: 814-927-8552. p. 2084

Watson, Susan, Br Head, Vancouver Public Library, Champlain Heights, 7110 Kerr St, Vancouver, BC, V5S 4W2, CANADA. Tel: 604-665-3955. Fax: 604-665-3929. p. 2744

Watson, Thelma, Librn, Pasadena Public Library, Hastings, 3325 E Orange Grove Blvd, Pasadena, CA, 91107. Tel: 626-744-7262. Fax: 626-440-0222. p. 207

Watson, Theresa, Br Mgr, Calcasieu Parish Public Library, Fontenot Memorial, 1402 Center St, Vinton, LA, 70668. Tel: 337-721-7095. Fax: 337-589-3336. p. 954

Watson, Tom, Tech Coordr, Westbank Community Library District, 1309 Westbank Dr, Austin, TX, 78746. Tel: 512-314-3584. Fax: 512-327-3074. p. 2285

Watson, Virginia Faye, Curator, Chatsworth Historical Society, 10385 Shadow Oak Dr, Chatsworth, CA, 91311. Tel: 818-341-3053. Fax: 818-341-3053. p. 133

Watson, Yort, ILL, Ref Serv, Eckerd College, 4200 54th Ave S, Saint Petersburg, FL, 33711. Tel: 727-864-8337. Fax: 727-864-8997. p. 488

Watson-Lakamp, Paula, Communications Mgr, Poudre River Public Library District, 201 Peterson St, Fort Collins, CO, 80524-2990. Tel: 970-221-6740. Fax: 970-221-6398. p. 308

Watson-Mauro, Sharon, Cat, Dir, Moore College of Art & Design, 20th St & The Parkway, Philadelphia, PA, 19103-1179. Tel: 215-965-8582. Fax: 215-965-8544. p. 2112

Watstein, Sarah Barbara, Univ Librn, William Madison Randall Library, 601 S College Rd, Wilmington, NC, 28403-5616. Tel: 910-962-3000. Fax: 910-962-3078. p. 1831

Watt, Michelle, Ch, Swan Library, Four N Main St, Albion, NY, 14411. Tel: 585-589-4246. Fax: 585-589-2473. p. 1571

Watt, Nancy, Head Librn, Gaston Community Library, 116 Front St, Gaston, OR, 97119. Tel: 503-639-8458. Fax: 503-985-1014. p. 1999

Watt, Nancy J, I, Dir, Swaledale Public Library, 504 Main St, Swaledale, IA, 50477. Tel: 641-995-2352. Fax: 641-995-2352. p. 847

Watt, Nicholas, Mgr, Libr Serv, Torys LLP Library, 79 Wellington St W, Ste 3000, Toronto, ON, M5K 1N2, CANADA. Tel: 416-865-7626. Fax: 416-865-7380. p. 2864

Watt, Nona, Head, Tech Serv, Indiana University, School of Law Library, Maurer School of Law, 211 S Indiana Ave, Bloomington, IN, 47405. Tel: 812-855-9666. Fax: 812-855-7099. p. 727

Watters, Gayle, Librn, Head, Clara, & Maria Township Public Library, 15 Township Hall Rd, Stonecliffe, ON, K0J 2K0, CANADA. Tel: 613-586-2526. Fax: 613-586-2596. p. 2845

Watters, Tim, Cat, Library of Michigan, 702 W Kalamazoo St, Lansing, MI, 48915. Tel: 517-373-3071. Fax: 517-373-5700. p. 1201

Watters, Timothy, Ref Librn, Library of Michigan, 702 W Kalamazoo, Lansing, MI, 48909. Tel: 517-373-0630. Fax: 517-373-3915. p. 1201

Watterworth, Jan, Librn, Mathematica Policy Research Inc Library, 600 Alexander Park, Princeton, NJ, 08543. Tel: 609-275-2334. Fax: 609-799-1654. p. 1522

Watts, Adam, Tech Mgr, Westmont Public Library, 428 N Cass, Westmont, IL, 60559-1502. Tel: 630-969-5625. Fax: 630-969-6490. p. 717

Watts, Angela, Libr Asst I, Montgomery City-County Public Library System, Juliette Hampton Morgan Memorial Library (Main Library), 245 High St, Montgomery, AL, 36104. Tel: 334-240-4999. Fax: 334-240-4980. p. 30

Watts, Anne, Asst Libr Dir, Boynton Beach City Library, 208 S Seacrest Blvd, Boynton Beach, FL, 33435. Tel: 561-742-6390. Fax: 561-742-6381. p. 429

Watts, Cammy, Librn, Tulane University, A H Clifford Mathematics Research Library, 430 Gibson Hall, 6823 St Charles Ave, New Orleans, LA, 70118. Tel: 504-862-3455. Fax: 504-865-5063. p. 963

Watts, Carrie, Br Mgr, Ramsey County Library, Mounds View Branch, 2576 County Rd 10, Mounds View, MN, 55112-4032. Tel: 763-717-3272. Fax: 763-717-3275. p. 1284

Watts, Jama, Genealogy Librn, Ref Librn, Marion County Public Library, 201 E Main St, Lebanon, KY, 40033-1133. Tel: 270-692-4698. Fax: 270-692-9555. p. 920

Watts, Jennifer, Curator, Huntington Library, 1151 Oxford Rd, San Marino, CA, 91108. Tel: 626-405-2180. Fax: 626-449-5720. p. 255

Watts, Judy, Dir, Methodist Healthcare, 1265 Union Ave, Memphis, TN, 38104-3499. Tel: 901-726-7899. Fax: 901-726-8254. p. 2250

Watts, Liz, In Charge, Contra Costa County Library, Crockett Library, 991 Loring Ave, Crockett, CA, 94525-1168. Tel: 510-787-2345. Fax: 510-787-7275. p. 209

Watts, Melody, Dir, Spartan College of Aeronautics & Technology Library, 8820 E Pine St, Tulsa, OK, 74115. Tel: 918-836-6886. Fax: 918-831-5245. p. 1982

Watts, Nancy, Adult Serv, Lewistown Public Library, 701 W Main St, Lewistown, MT, 59457. Tel: 406-538-5212. Fax: 406-538-3920. p. 1384

Watts, Natalie Cox, Tech Serv Coordr, Mercer County Public Library, 109 W Lexington St, Harrodsburg, KY, 40330-1542. Tel: 859-734-3680. Fax: 859-734-7524. p. 916

Watts, Randall, Asst Dir, Res Mgt Serv, Medical University of South Carolina Library, 171 Ashley Ave, Ste 300, Charleston, SC, 29425-0001. Tel: 843-792-9211. Fax: 843-792-7947. p. 2184

Watts, Rebecca, Ch, Brazoria County Library System, Freeport Branch, 410 Brazosport Blvd, Freeport, TX, 77541. Tel: 979-233-3622. Fax: 979-233-4300. p. 2275

Watts, Spencer, Dir, East Baton Rouge Parish Library, 7711 Goodwood Blvd, Baton Rouge, LA, 70806-7625. Tel: 225-231-3700. Fax: 225-231-3759. p. 942

Watts, Tania, YA Serv, Northwest Regional Library System, 898 W 11 St, Panama City, FL, 32401. Tel: 850-522-2100. Fax: 850-522-2138. p. 480

Watts, Tas, Br Mgr, Anaheim Public Library, Euclid, 1340 S Euclid St, Anaheim, CA, 92802-2008. Tel: 714-765-3625. Fax: 714-765-3624. p. 120

Watts, Teresa, Librn, Wheeler Public Library, 306 S Canadian St, Wheeler, TX, 79096. Tel: 806-826-5977. Fax: 806-826-5977. p. 2400

Watwood, Carol, Health Sci Librn, Western Kentucky University Libraries, Helm-Cravens Library Complex, 1906 College Heights Blvd, No 11067, Bowling Green, KY, 42101-1067. Tel: 270-745-2905. Fax: 270-745-6422. p. 908

Waugaman, Cynthia, Librn, Birchard Public Library of Sandusky County, Green Springs Memorial, 217 N Broadway, Green Springs, OH, 44836. Tel: 419-639-2014. p. 1900

Waugerman, Carol, Tech Serv Coordr, Allegany County Library System, LaVale Branch, 815 National Hwy, LaVale, MD, 21502. Tel: 301-729-0855. Fax: 301-729-3490. p. 1026

Waugh, Charles, Br Mgr, Palm Beach County Library System, Okeechobee Boulevard, 5689 Okeechobee Blvd, West Palm Beach, FL, 33417. Tel: 561-233-1880. Fax: 561-233-1889. p. 503

Waugh, Joyce H, Librn, Pike-Amite-Walthall Library System, Gloster Branch, 229 E Main, Gloster, MS, 39638. Tel: 601-225-5147. Fax: 601-225-4341. p. 1308

Wavle, Elizabeth, Dean, Libr & Info Tech, Elmira College, One Park Pl, Elmira, NY, 14901. Tel: 607-735-1865. Fax: 607-735-1158. p. 1619

Wawrzaszek, Susan V, Assoc VPres, Libr & Info Serv, Wheaton College Library, 26 E Main St, Norton, MA, 02766-2322. p. 1115

Wax, Denise, Head, Circ, Fayetteville Public Library, 401 W Mountain St, Fayetteville, AR, 72701. Tel: 479-856-7000. Fax: 479-571-0222. p. 99

Waxman, Carol, Ch, West Hartford Public Library, 20 S Main St, West Hartford, CT, 06107-2432. Tel: 860-561-6950. Fax: 860-561-6976. p. 376

Waxman, Sandra, Archivist, Librn, Dedham Historical Society Library, 612 High St, Dedham, MA, 02027. Tel: 781-326-1385. Fax: 781-326-5762. p. 1084

Way, Catherine A, Dir, Chautauqua-Cattaraugus Library System, 106 W Fifth St, Jamestown, NY, 14701. Tel: 716-484-7136. p. 1646

Way, Catherine A, Dir, James Prendergast Library Association, 509 Cherry St, Jamestown, NY, 14701. Tel: 716-484-7135. Fax: 716-487-1148. p. 1647

Waybright, Joyce, Librn, United States Army, Bruce C Clarke Library Community Services Division, Bldg 3202, 597 Manscen Loop, Ste 100, Fort Leonard Wood, MO, 65473-8928. Tel: 573-563-4113. Fax: 573-563-4118. p. 1328

Wayland, Sharon, Dir, Tarrant County Law Library, 100 W Weatherford, Rm 420, Fort Worth, TX, 76196-0800. Tel: 817-884-1481. Fax: 817-884-1509. p. 2323

Wayman, Mathew, Assoc Librn, Pennsylvania State University, 1600 Woodland Rd, Abington, PA, 19001. Tel: 215-881-7497. Fax: 215-881-7423. p. 2025

Waymark, Judy, Libr Coordr, Alberta Law Libraries - Hinton, Courthouse, 237 Jasper St, West & Pembina Ave, Hinton, AB, T7V 1X7, CANADA. Tel: 780-865-8268. Fax: 780-865-8253. p. 2707

Wayne, Jeffrey, Acq, Linden Free Public Library, 31 E Henry St, Linden, NJ, 07036. Tel: 908-298-3830. Fax: 908-486-2636. p. 1495

Wayne, Judith, Coll Develop, Eastfield College Library, 3737 Motley Dr, Mesquite, TX, 75150-2033. Tel: 972-860-7176. p. 2362

Wayne, Kathryn, Librn, University of California, Berkeley, Art History/Classics, 308 Doe Library, Berkeley, CA, 94720-6000. Tel: 510-642-5358. Fax: 510-643-6650. p. 127

Wayne, Michael, Coll Mgr, DC Regional Library for the Blind & Physically Handicapped, Adaptive Services Division, Rm 215, 901 G St NW, Washington, DC, 20001. Tel: 202-559-5368 (videophone), 202-727-2142. Fax: 202-727-0322. p. 397

Wayne, Mike, Circ, ILL, Canadian Museum of Nature Library & Archives, PO Box 3443, Sta D, Ottawa, ON, K1P 6P4, CANADA. Tel: 613-364-4042. Fax: 613-364-4026. p. 2829

Wayte, Ashley, Chief Librn, Fresno Bee, 1626 E St, Fresno, CA, 93786-0001. Tel: 559-441-6381. Fax: 559-495-6803. p. 151

Waytuck, Brett, Prov Librn, Saskatchewan Provincial Library & Literacy Office, 409A Park St, Regina, SK, S4N 5B2, CANADA. Tel: 306-787-2973. p. 2924

Waznis, Betty, Libr Dir, Chula Vista Public Library, 365 F St, Chula Vista, CA, 91910-2697. Tel: 619-691-5170. Fax: 619-427-4246. p. 134

Wazny, Katelyn, Head, Circ, Grimes Public Library, 200 N James, Grimes, IA, 50111. Tel: 515-986-3551. Fax: 515-986-9553. p. 819

Weakland, Deborah, Dir, Altoona Area Public Library, 1600 Fifth Ave, Altoona, PA, 16602-3693. Tel: 814-946-0417. Fax: 814-946-3230. p. 2028

Wealand, Chieko, Br Mgr, San Francisco Public Library, Marina Branch Library, 1890 Chestnut St, San Francisco, CA, 94123-2804. Tel: 415-355-2823. Fax: 415-447-9308. p. 246

Weale, Joy, Libr Supvr, Dartmouth College Library, Paddock Music Library, 6245 Hopkins Ctr, Hanover, NH, 03755. Tel: 603-646-3234. Fax: 603-646-1219. p. 1450

Wear, Lori, Chief Curator, Kern County Museum, 3801 Chester Ave, Bakersfield, CA, 93301-1395. Tel: 661-868-8400. Fax: 661-322-6415. p. 125

Wearly, Jason, Circ Spec, Clark State Community College Library, 570 E Leffel Lane, Springfield, OH, 45505. Tel: 937-328-6022. Fax: 937-328-6133. p. 1935

Weatheral, Linda, Mgr, Grey Highlands Public Library, Kimberley Library, Kimberley Memorial Hall, Grey Rd 13, Kimberley, ON, N0C 1G0, CANADA. Tel: 519-599-6146. Fax: 519-599-6990. p. 2805

Weatherbee, Sue, Head, Access Serv, Texas A&M University-Commerce, 2600 S Neal St, Commerce, TX, 75429. Tel: 903-886-5414. Fax: 903-886-5434. p. 2300

Weatherford, Coni, Managing Librn, Pima County Public Library, Woods Memorial Branch, 3455 N First Ave, Tucson, AZ, 85719. Tel: 520-594-5445. Fax: 520-594-5446. p. 87

Weatherford, David L, Dir, Valparaiso Community Library, 459 Valparaiso Pkwy, Valparaiso, FL, 32580. Tel: 850-729-5406. Fax: 850-729-1120. p. 501

Weatherholt, Jennie, Br Mgr, Spencer County Public Library, Grandview Branch, 403 Main St, Grandview, IN, 47615-0717. Tel: 812-649-9732. p. 776

Weatherly, Carolyn, Br Mgr, Brazoria County Library System, Clute Branch, 215 N Shanks, Clute, TX, 77531-4122. Tel: 979-265-4582. Fax: 979-265-8496. p. 2275

Weathers, Linda, ILL & Distance Libr Serv Spec, Reserves, California Western School of Law Library, 290 Cedar St, San Diego, CA, 92101. Tel: 619-525-1418. Fax: 619-685-2918. p. 231

Weathers, Marganne, Tech Serv, United States Army, Bldg 2109, Joint Base Lewis McChord, WA, 98433-9500. Tel: 253-966-1321. Fax: 253-967-3922. p. 2518

Weathers, Pat, Tech Serv, Pike County Public Library, 1104 Main St, Petersburg, IN, 47567. Tel: 812-354-6257. Fax: 812-354-6259. p. 773

Weatherson, Peggy, Campus Librn, Annapolis Valley Regional Library, Lawrencetown Branch, 50 Elliot Rd, Lawrencetown, NS, B0S 1M0, CANADA. Tel: 902-584-2102. Fax: 902-584-2085. p. 2778

Weaver, Angela, Actg Head, University of Washington Libraries, Art, 101 Art Bldg, Box 353440, Seattle, WA, 98195. Tel: 206-543-0648. p. 2533

Weaver, Angela, Head Librn, University of Washington Libraries, Drama, Hutchinson Hall, Rm 145, Box 353950, Seattle, WA, 98195-3950. Tel: 206-685-3693. Fax: 206-543-8512. p. 2533

Weaver, Ann, Ref, Westchester Public Library, 10700 Canterbury St, Westchester, IL, 60154. Tel: 708-562-3573. Fax: 708-562-1298. p. 717

Weaver, Barbara, In Charge, Merced County Library, South Dos Palos Branch, 21961 S Reynolds Ave, South Dos Palos, CA, 93665. Tel: 209-392-6354. p. 186

Weaver, Barbara K, Regional Dir, Ivy Tech State Community College-Northwest, 1440 E 35th Ave, Gary, IN, 46409-1499. Tel: 219-981-4410. Fax: 219-981-4415. p. 745

Weaver, Betty, Chief Librn, Lillooet Area Library Association, 930 Main St, Lillooet, BC, V0K 1V0, CANADA. Tel: 250-256-7944. Fax: 250-256-7924. p. 2731

Weaver, Bobbi, Foreign & Intl Law Ref, California Western School of Law Library, 290 Cedar St, San Diego, CA, 92101. Tel: 619-525-1497. Fax: 619-685-2918. p. 231

Weaver, Brian, Actg Br Mgr, San Francisco Public Library, Presidio Branch Library, 3150 Sacramento St, San Francisco, CA, 94115-2006. Tel: 415-355-2880. Fax: 415-563-3299. p. 246

Weaver, Bruce, Dir, DeVry University Library, 1350 Alum Creek Dr, Columbus, OH, 43209. Tel: 614-253-7291, Ext 1387. Fax: 614-252-4108. p. 1885

Weaver, Catherine, Librn, Burlington Library, Patterson Creek Rd, Burlington, WV, 26710. Tel: 304-289-3690. Fax: 304-289-3233. p. 2555

Weaver, Catherine, Br Mgr, Keyser-Mineral County Public Library, Burlington Public, PO Box 61, Burlington, WV, 26710-0061. Tel: 304-289-3690. Fax: 304-289-3233. p. 2563

Weaver, Connie, ILL, Ref, Bosler Free Library, 158 W High St, Carlisle, PA, 17013-2988. Tel: 717-243-4642. Fax: 717-243-8281. p. 2041

Weaver, Deb, Mgr, Children's Hospital, Clinical & Research Library, 13123 E 16th Ave, B180, Aurora, CO, 80045. Tel: 720-777-6400. Fax: 720-777-7152. p. 299

Weaver, Denise A, Dir, Mary S Biesecker Public Library, 230 S Rosina Ave, Somerset, PA, 15501. Tel: 814-445-4011. Fax: 814-443-0725. p. 2141

Weaver, Diana, Dir, Basehor Community Library District 2, 1400 158th St, Basehor, KS, 66007. Tel: 913-724-2828. Fax: 913-724-2898. p. 857

Weaver, Elizabeth, Asst Librn, New Brunswick Community College, 950 Grandview Ave, Saint John, NB, E2L 3V1, CANADA. Tel: 506-658-6726. Fax: 506-643-2853. p. 2767

Weaver, Emily, Dir, Perry Public Library, 1101 Willis Ave, Perry, IA, 50220-1649. Tel: 515-465-3569. Fax: 515-465-9881. p. 838

Weaver, Emily Erwin, Archivist, Delta State University, Laflore Circle at Fifth Ave, Cleveland, MS, 38733-2599. Tel: 662-846-4780. Fax: 662-846-4443. p. 1296

Weaver, Jeri, Dir, Fourth Presbyterian Church, 5500 River Rd, Bethesda, MD, 20816-3399. Tel: 301-320-3434. Fax: 301-320-6315. p. 1021

Weaver, Jo Ann, Coordr, Youth Serv, Milan-Berlin Township Public Library, Berlin Township Public, Four E Main St, Berlin Heights, OH, 44814-9602. Tel: 419-588-2250. Fax: 419-588-0025. p. 1918

Weaver, Joan, Dir, Kinsley Public Library, 208 E Eighth St, Kinsley, KS, 67547-1422. Tel: 620-659-3341. p. 876

Weaver, Joyce, Librn, Mint Museum Library, 2730 Randolph Rd, Charlotte, NC, 28207. Tel: 704-337-2000, 704-337-2023. Fax: 704-337-2101. p. 1783

Weaver, Kari D, Coordr, Libr Instruction, University of South Carolina Aiken, 471 University Pkwy, Aiken, SC, 29801. Tel: 803-641-3261. Fax: 803-641-3302. p. 2180

Weaver, Linza, Dir, Learning Res, Paul D Camp Community College Library, Hobbs Suffolk Campus, 271 Kenyon Rd, Suffolk, VA, 23434. Tel: 757-925-6300, 757-925-6345. Fax: 757-925-6374. p. 2465

Weaver, Linza M, Dir, Learning Res, Paul D Camp Community College Library, 100 N College Dr, Franklin, VA, 23851-2422. Tel: 757-569-6735. Fax: 757-569-6736. p. 2465

Weaver, Lori, Dir, Weldon Public Library District, 505 Maple St, Weldon, IL, 61882. Tel: 217-736-2215. Fax: 217-736-2215. p. 717

Weaver, Lori, Dir, Montmorency County Public Libraries, 11901 Haymeadow Rd, Atlanta, MI, 49709. Tel: 989-785-3941. Fax: 989-785-3941. p. 1154

Weaver, Lynne N, Ser, Randolph College, 2500 Rivermont Ave, Lynchburg, VA, 24503. Tel: 434-947-8133. Fax: 434-947-8134. p. 2476

Weaver, Marvin, Assoc Dir, Syst & Tech, Saint Joseph's University, Francis A Drexel Library, 5600 City Ave, Philadelphia, PA, 19131-1395. Tel: 610-660-1905. Fax: 610-660-1916. p. 2116

Weaver, Mary M, Librn, East Woodstock Library Association, 15 Prospect St, East Woodstock, CT, 06244. Tel: 860-928-0284. p. 338

Weaver, Paul, Ref Librn, Bluffton University, One University Dr, Bluffton, OH, 45817-2104. Tel: 419-358-3448. Fax: 419-358-3384. p. 1860

Weaver, Roger, Institutional Repository/Digital Coll Librn, Curtis Laws Wilson Library, 400 W 14th St, Rolla, MO, 65409-0060. Tel: 573-341-4221. Fax: 573-341-4233. p. 1351

Weaver, Sherrill, Dr, Cat Serv Librn, Oakton Community College Library, 1600 E Golf Rd, Rm 1410, Des Plaines, IL, 60016. Tel: 847-635-1642, 847-635-1644. Fax: 847-635-1987. p. 636

Weaver, Steve, Va Region Librn, Saint Leo University, 33701 State Rd 52, Saint Leo, FL, 33574. Tel: 757-766-1468. Fax: 352-588-8484. p. 487

Weaver, Susan, Dir, Harrisville Public Library, Seven Canal St, Harrisville, NH, 03450. Tel: 603-827-2918. Fax: 603-827-2917. p. 1451

Weaver, Susan, Dir, Kent State University, 400 E Fourth St, Rm 216, East Liverpool, OH, 43920-5769. Tel: 330-382-7401, 330-382-7421. Fax: 330-382-7561. p. 1897

Weaver, Suzanne, Adult Serv, Cobb County Public Library System, 266 Roswell St, Marietta, GA, 30060-2004. Tel: 770-528-2320. Fax: 770-528-2349. p. 542

Weaver, Terry, Asst Dir, Access Serv, Missouri Western State University, 4525 Downs Dr, Saint Joseph, MO, 64507-2294. Tel: 816-271-4368. Fax: 816-271-4574. p. 1352

Weaver, Terry, Per, Missouri Western State University, 4525 Downs Dr, Saint Joseph, MO, 64507-2294. Tel: 816-271-4368. Fax: 816-271-4574. p. 1352

Weaver, Theresa, Librn, Henderson County Public Library, Edneyville Branch, Two Firehouse Lane, Hendersonville, NC, 28792. Tel: 828-685-0110. Fax: 828-685-0110. p. 1801

Weaver-Meyers, Pat, Dir of Libr, Samuel Roberts Noble Foundation, Inc, 2510 Sam Noble Pkwy, Ardmore, OK, 73401. Tel: 580-224-6260. Fax: 580-224-6265. p. 1957

Weavil, Vicki, Dir of Libr Serv, University of North Carolina School of the Arts, 1533 S Main St, Winston-Salem, NC, 27127. Tel: 336-770-3270. Fax: 336-770-3271. p. 1833

Webb, Alice, Librn, New Braintree Public Library, 45 Memorial Dr, New Braintree, MA, 01531. Tel: 508-867-7650. Fax: 508-867-7650. p. 1109

Webb, Alisha, Ref Serv, Guilford Technical Community College, 601 High Point Rd, Jamestown, NC, 27282. Tel: 336-334-4822, Ext 2287. Fax: 336-841-4350. p. 1803

Webb, Augie, Librn, Sausalito Public Library, 420 Litho St, Sausalito, CA, 94965-1933. Tel: 415-289-4121. Fax: 415-331-7943. p. 268

Webb, Brian, Ref, Troy University Library, 309 Wallace Hall, 501 University Ave, Troy, AL, 36082. Tel: 334-670-3198. Fax: 334-670-3694. p. 37

Webb, Caroline, Dir, Texas Chiropractic College, 5912 Spencer Hwy, Pasadena, TX, 77505. Tel: 281-998-6049. Fax: 281-487-4168. p. 2369

Webb, Cathy, Asst Librn, Spindale Public Library, 131 Tanner St, Spindale, NC, 28160. Tel: 828-286-3879. Fax: 828-286-8338. p. 1825

Webb, Dana, Interim Dir, Auglaize County Public District Library, 203 S Perry St, Wapakoneta, OH, 45895-1999. Tel: 419-738-2921. Fax: 419-738-5168. p. 1944

Webb, David, Head, Ref, Roanoke County Public Library, 3131 Electric Rd SW, Roanoke, VA, 24018-6496. Tel: 540-772-7507. Fax: 540-989-3129. p. 2494

Webb, Deborah, Br Mgr, Hesburgh Libraries, Architecture, 117 Bond Hall, Notre Dame, IN, 46556-5652. Tel: 574-631-6654. Fax: 574-631-9662. p. 770

Webb, Diane, Librn, Border Regional Library, McAuley Branch, 207 Qu'Appelle St, McAuley, MB, R0M 1H0, CANADA. Tel: 204-722-2221. p. 2753

Webb, Frances, Ref, Randolph College, 2500 Rivermont Ave, Lynchburg, VA, 24503. Tel: 434-947-8133. Fax: 434-947-8134. p. 2476

Webb, Gary, Circ, Stone County Library, Crane Area Branch, 111 Main St, Crane, MO, 65633. Tel: 417-723-8261. Fax: 417-723-8851. p. 1329

Webb, Jonathan T, Dir, Frankenmuth Historical Association, 613 S Main St, Frankenmuth, MI, 48734. Tel: 989-652-9701. Fax: 989-652-9390. p. 1181

Webb, Kathy, Tech Serv, Elyria Public Library System, 320 Washington Ave, Elyria, OH, 44035-5199. Tel: 440-323-5747. Fax: 440-323-5788. p. 1898

Webb, Kevin, Access Serv, Folsom Lake College Library, Ten College Pkwy, Folsom, CA, 95630. Tel: 916-608-6703. Fax: 916-608-6533. p. 148

Webb, Kim Huskins, Dir, United States Air Force, 4FSS/FSDL, 1520 Goodson St, Bldg 3660, Seymour Johnson AFB, NC, 27531. Tel: 919-722-5825. Fax: 919-722-5835. p. 1823

Webb, Lee, Theol & Ref LIbrn, Oklahoma City University, Dulaney-Browne Library, 2501 N Blackwelder, Oklahoma City, OK, 73106. Tel: 405-208-5068. Fax: 405-208-5291. p. 1974

Webb, Lester, Dir, Outreach & Tech, Kingston Frontenac Public Library, 130 Johnson St, Kingston, ON, K7L 1X8, CANADA. Tel: 613-549-8888, Ext 1290. Fax: 613-549-8476. p. 2813

Webb, Linda, ILL, Chelmsford Public Library, 25 Boston Rd, Chelmsford, MA, 01824-3088. Tel: 978-256-5521. Fax: 978-256-8511. p. 1080

Webb, Linda, Circ & ILL, Missouri Baptist University, One College Park Dr, Saint Louis, MO, 63141-8698. Tel: 314-434-1115. Fax: 314-392-2343. p. 1356

Webb, Linda, Circ/Reserves, Missouri Baptist University, One College Park Dr, Saint Louis, MO, 63141-8698. Tel: 314-434-1115. Fax: 314-392-2343. p. 1356

Webb, Lisa, Asst Dir, West Palm Beach Public Library, 411 Clematis St, West Palm Beach, FL, 33401. Tel: 561-868-7787. Fax: 561-868-7706. p. 504

Webb, Maria, Assoc Univ Librn, Dir, Pub Serv, Fairleigh Dickinson University, 285 Madison Ave, M-LAO-03, Madison, NJ, 07940. Tel: 973-443-8533. Fax: 973-443-8525. p. 1497

Webb, Mary, Ser, Saint Luke's Hospital, 4141 Mill St, Kansas City, MO, 64111. Tel: 816-531-0560. Fax: 816-531-6316. p. 1340

Webb, Michael, Head, Tech Serv, Harrison County Library System, 2600 24th Ave, No 6, Gulfport, MS, 39501-2081. Tel: 228-868-1383. Fax: 228-863-7433. p. 1299

Webb, Nancy, Librn, New England Wild Flower Society, Inc, 180 Hemenway Rd, Framingham, MA, 01701-2699. Tel: 508-877-7630. Fax: 508-877-3658. p. 1090

Webb, Nikeda F, Asst Dir, Wilmington Public Library District, 201 S Kankakee St, Wilmington, IL, 60481-1338. Tel: 815-476-2834. Fax: 815-476-7805. p. 720

Webb, Paris E, Digital Res & Syst Support Librn, Marshall University Libraries, One John Marshall Dr, Huntington, WV, 25755-2060. Tel: 304-696-3511. Fax: 304-696-5858. p. 2561

Webb, Paula, Ser, Delta State University, Laflore Circle at Fifth Ave, Cleveland, MS, 38733-2599. Tel: 662-846-4456. Fax: 662-846-4443. p. 1296

Webb, Phyllis, Asst Librn, Robert R Jones Public Library, 900 First St, Coal Valley, IL, 61240. Tel: 309-799-3047. Fax: 309-799-5528. p. 630

Webb, Rebecca, Law Info Spec, Danville Public Library, 511 Patton St, Danville, VA, 24541. Tel: 434-799-5195. Fax: 434-792-5172. p. 2459

Webb, Rebecca, Law Librn, Supvr, Danville Public Library, Law, 511 Patton St, Danville, VA, 24541. Tel: 434-799-5118. Fax: 434-799-5118. p. 2459

Webb, Robb, Br Mgr, Livingston Parish Library, South, 23477 Louisiana Hwy 444, Livingston, LA, 70754. Tel: 225-698-3015. Fax: 225-686-9979. p. 955

Webb, Rodney, Govt Doc Librn, Texas A&M International University, 5201 University Blvd, Laredo, TX, 78041-1900. Tel: 956-326-2119. Fax: 956-326-2399. p. 2354

Webb, Sandra K, Doc Delivery, ILL, Hillcrest Medical Center Library, 1120 S Utica Ave, Tulsa, OK, 74104-4090. Tel: 918-579-8356. Fax: 918-579-8388. p. 1981

Webb, Susan, Librn, Anoka County Library, North Central, 17565 Central Ave NE, Ham Lake, MN, 55304-4302. Tel: 763-434-6542. Fax: 763-434-6542. p. 1241

Webb, Susan, Cat Librn, Circ Librn, Coll Develop Librn, Southeastern Oklahoma State University, 1405 N Fourth Ave, PMB 4105, Durant, OK, 74701-0609. Tel: 580-745-2934. Fax: 580-745-7463. p. 1961

Webb, Tyrone, Dir, Bevill State Community College, 101 S State St, Sumiton, AL, 35148. Tel: 205-648-3271. Fax: 205-648-7152. p. 36

Webb, Virginia E, Mgr, American College, 270 S Bryn Mawr Ave, Bryn Mawr, PA, 19010-2196. Tel: 610-526-1305, 610-526-1307. Fax: 610-526-1322. p. 2038

Webb-Metz, Gina, Asst Dir, Leonia Public Library, 227 Fort Lee Rd, Leonia, NJ, 07605. Tel: 201-592-5774. Fax: 201-592-5775. p. 1495

Webb-Metz, Gina, Dir, Tenafly Public Library, 100 Riveredge Rd, Tenafly, NJ, 07670-2087. Tel: 201-568-8680. Fax: 201-568-5475. p. 1533

Webber, Adrienne, Dean of Libr & Info Serv, South Carolina State University, 300 College St NE, Orangeburg, SC, 29115-4427. Tel: 803-536-7045. Fax: 803-536-8902. p. 2202

Webber, Bob, Historian, Illinois Railway Museum, 7000 Olson Rd, Union, IL, 60180. Tel: 815-923-2020. Fax: 815-923-2006. p. 711

Webber, Desiree, Dir, Mustang Public Library, 1201 N Mustang Rd, Mustang, OK, 73064. Tel: 405-376-2226. Fax: 405-376-9925. p. 1969

Webber, Donna, Archivist, Simmons College, 300 The Fenway, Boston, MA, 02115-5898. p. 1066

Webber, Donna, Assoc Prof of Practice, Simmons College, 300 The Fenway, Boston, MA, 02115. Tel: 617-521-2800. Fax: 617-521-3192. p. 2967

Webber, Kathryn, Head, Tech Serv, Charlton Public Library, 40 Main St, Charlton, MA, 01507. Tel: 508-248-0452. Fax: 508-248-0456. p. 1079

Webber, Mary, Ch, Lake Forest Library, 360 E Deerpath Ave, Lake Forest, IL, 60045-2252. Tel: 847-810-4630. Fax: 847-234-1453. p. 663

Webber, Priscilla J, Ch, Adams Public Library System, 128 S Third St, Decatur, IN, 46733-1691. Tel: 260-724-2605. Fax: 260-724-2877. p. 735

Webber, Ruth A, Assoc Librn, Cat, Worcester State College, 486 Chandler St, Worcester, MA, 01602-2597. Tel: 508-929-8676. Fax: 508-929-8198. p. 1145

Weber, Annette, Youth Serv Librn, Mansfield Public Library, 104 S Wisteria St, Mansfield, TX, 76063. Tel: 817-473-4391. Fax: 817-453-4975. p. 2359

Weber, Barbara, YA Serv, Bedford Park Public Library District, 7816 W 65th Pl, Bedford Park, IL, 60501. Tel: 708-458-6826. Fax: 708-458-9827. p. 593

Weber, Barbara, Teen Librn/Ref, Wyckoff Public Library, 200 Woodland Ave, Wyckoff, NJ, 07481. Tel: 201-891-4866. Fax: 201-891-3892. p. 1546

Weber, Barbara A, Dir, New Holstein Public Library, 2115 Washington St, New Holstein, WI, 53061-1098. Tel: 920-898-5165. Fax: 920-898-9022. p. 2625

Weber, Bonnie, Mgr, Libr Serv, Whittier Public Library, 7344 S Washington Ave, Whittier, CA, 90602. Tel: 562-567-9900. Fax: 562-567-2880. p. 283

Weber, Charlette, Web Serv Mgr, Black & Veatch, 11401 Lamar, Overland Park, KS, 66211. Tel: 913-458-7884. Fax: 913-458-2934. p. 887

Weber, Christine, Financial Mgr, Hamburg Township Library, 10411 Merrill Rd, Hamburg, MI, 48139. Tel: 810-231-1771. Fax: 810-231-1520. p. 1187

Weber, Christine A, Libr Dir, Illinois College of Optometry Library, 3241 S Michigan Ave, Chicago, IL, 60616-3878. Tel: 312-949-7153. Fax: 312-949-7374. p. 614

Weber, Cindy, Head, Tech Serv, Dorothy Alling Memorial Library, 21 Library Lane, Williston, VT, 05495. Tel: 802-878-4918. Fax: 802-878-3964. p. 2440

Weber, Connie A, Dir, Richmond Public Library, 107 E Central, Richmond, KS, 66080-4035. Tel: 785-835-6163. Fax: 785-835-6163. p. 891

Weber, Darlene, Managing Librn I, Sno-Isle Libraries, Mill Creek Community Library, 15429 Bothell Everett Hwy, Mill Creek, WA, 98012. Tel: 425-337-4822. Fax: 425-337-3567. p. 2542

Weber, David, Dir, Rec Mgt, National Archives & Records Administration, 900 Market St, Philadelphia, PA, 19107-4292. Tel: 215-606-0100. Fax: 215-606-0116. p. 2113

Weber, Dawn, Asst Librn, Gordon City Library, 101 W Fifth St, Gordon, NE, 69343. Tel: 308-282-1198. Fax: 308-282-0417. p. 1400

Weber, Debbi, Asst Dir, Chestermere Public Library, Chestermere Town Hall, 105B Marina Rd, Chestermere, AB, T1X 1V7, CANADA. Tel: 403-272-9025. Fax: 403-272-9036. p. 2695

Weber, Diane, Exec Dir, Librn, Society for Academic Achievement Library, WCU Bldg, 510 Maine St, Quincy, IL, 62301. Tel: 217-224-0570. p. 693

Weber, Ellenjoy, Head, Ch, Coronado Public Library, 640 Orange Ave, Coronado, CA, 92118-1526. Tel: 619-522-2471. Fax: 619-435-4205. p. 137

Weber, Francis J, Archivist, Roman Catholic Archdiocese of Los Angeles, 15151 San Fernando Mission Blvd, Mission Hills, CA, 91345. Tel: 818-365-1501. Fax: 818-361-3276. p. 187

Weber, Gary, Head Librn, Alberta Government Library, Capital Blvd, 11th Flr, 10044 - 108 St, Edmonton, AB, T5J 5E6, CANADA. Tel: 780-427-2985. Fax: 780-427-5927. p. 2698

Weber, Jean, Tech Serv, Cincinnati Christian University, 2700 Glenway Ave, Cincinnati, OH, 45204-3200. Tel: 513-244-8139. Fax: 513-244-8434. p. 1869

Weber, Jennifer, Head Librn, Austin Community College, Riverside Campus Library, 1020 Grove Blvd, Austin, TX, 78741. Tel: 512-223-6603. Fax: 512-223-6703. p. 2278

Weber, Joan L, Dir, Libr & Media Serv, Yakima Valley Community College, S 16th Ave at Nob Hill Blvd, Yakima, WA, 98907. Tel: 509-574-4991. Fax: 509-574-4989. p. 2550

Weber, Joe, Dir, Libr Serv, Austin Peay State University, 601 E College St, Clarksville, TN, 37044. Tel: 931-221-7618. Fax: 931-221-7296. p. 2228

Weber, Kathleen, Tech Asst II - Acq & Tech Serv, Potomac State College of West Virginia University, 101 Fort Ave, Keyser, WV, 26726. Tel: 304-788-6907. Fax: 304-788-6946. p. 2563

Weber, Kathleen A, Chief, Classified Libr, United States Naval War College Library, 686 Cushing Rd, Newport, RI, 02841-1207. Tel: 401-841-6504. Fax: 401-841-6491. p. 2169

Weber, Kathy, Circ Supvr, Reserves, Briar Cliff University, 3303 Rebecca St, Sioux City, IA, 51104-2324. Tel: 712-279-5449. Fax: 712-279-1723. p. 843

Weber, Kelley, Sch of Bus Librn, Washburn University, 1700 SW College Ave, Topeka, KS, 66621. Tel: 785-670-1503. Fax: 785-670-3223. p. 897

Weber, Kristin, ILL, Colorado Mountain College, 1330 Bob Adams Dr, Steamboat Springs, CO, 80487. Tel: 970-870-4449. Fax: 970-870-4490. p. 322

Weber, Leon, Instrul & Ref Librn, Alvernia University, 400 St Bernardine St, Reading, PA, 19607-1737. Tel: 610-796-8352. Fax: 610-796-8347. p. 2132

Weber, Lester, Archivist, Library at the Mariners' Museum, 100 Museum Dr, Newport News, VA, 23606-3759. Tel: 757-591-7779. Fax: 757-591-7310. p. 2480

Weber, Linda, Asst Librn, Elmwood Public Library, 111 N Main St, Elmwood, WI, 54740. Tel: 715-639-2615. Fax: 715-639-2615. p. 2591

Weber, Lynne, Access Serv Librn, Minnesota State University, Mankato, ML3097, Mankato, MN, 56001. Tel: 507-389-5952. Fax: 507-389-5155. p. 1257

Weber, Marian, ILL, Pennsylvania College of Optometry, 8360 Old York Rd, Elkins Park, PA, 19027. Tel: 215-780-1261. Fax: 215-780-1263. p. 2054

Weber, Mayreta, Chief Librn, Chenoa Public Library District, 211 S Division, Chenoa, IL, 61726. Tel: 815-945-4253. Fax: 815-945-4203. p. 604

Weber, Melanie, Adult Serv, Public Library for Union County, 255 Reitz Blvd, Lewisburg, PA, 17837-9211. Tel: 570-523-1172. Fax: 570-524-7771. p. 2081

Weber, Melissa, Libr Tech, Wisconsin Indianhead Technical College, 2100 Beaser Ave, Ashland, WI, 54806. Tel: 715-682-4591, Ext 3108. Fax: 715-682-8040. p. 2579

Weber, Michael, Cat, Kutztown University, 15200 Kutztown Rd, Bldg 5, Kutztown, PA, 19530-0735. Tel: 610-683-4484. Fax: 610-683-4747. p. 2075

Weber, Nicholas, Archivist, Ref & Instruction Librn, University of Wisconsin-Parkside Library, 900 Wood Rd, Kenosha, WI, 53141. Tel: 262-595-2077. Fax: 262-595-2545. p. 2602

Weber, Norm, Librn, Attica Correctional Facility School Library, Exchange St, Attica, NY, 14011. Tel: 585-591-2000. p. 1575

Weber, Pamela W, Circ Serv Coordr, Batavia Public Library District, Ten S Batavia Ave, Batavia, IL, 60510-2793. Tel: 630-879-1393. Fax: 630-879-9118. p. 593

Weber, Roberta L, Dir, Oldsmar Library, 400 St Petersburg Dr E, Oldsmar, FL, 34677. Tel: 813-749-1178. Fax: 813-854-1881. p. 474

Weber, Rosina, PhD, Assoc Prof, Drexel University, Rush Bldg, Rm 306, 30 N 33rd St, Philadelphia, PA, 19104-2875. Tel: 215-895-2474. Fax: 215-895-2494. p. 2972

Weber, Sharon, Ch, Jefferson Public Library, 321 S Main St, Jefferson, WI, 53549-1772. Tel: 920-674-7733. Fax: 920-674-7735. p. 2600

Weber, Tina, YA Serv, Milton-Union Public Library, 560 S Main St, West Milton, OH, 45383. Tel: 937-698-5515. Fax: 937-698-3774. p. 1946

Weber-Mendham, Karen, Youth Serv, Land O'Lakes Public Library, 4242 County Hwy B, Land O'Lakes, WI, 54540. Tel: 715-547-6006. Fax: 715-547-6004. p. 2605

Weberg, Lorraine, Syst, Fashion Institute of Technology-SUNY, Seventh Ave at 27th St, New York, NY, 10001-5992. Tel: 212-217-4398. Fax: 212-217-4371. p. 1678

Webster, Ann, Outreach Librn/Circ, Gallatin County Public Library, 209 W Market St, Warsaw, KY, 41095. Tel: 859-567-2786. Fax: 859-567-4750. p. 936

Webster, Bethany, Libr Tech, McCarthy Tetrault Library, 777 Dunsmuir St, No 1300, Vancouver, BC, V7Y 1K2, CANADA. Tel: 604-643-7112. Fax: 604-643-7900. p. 2741

Webster, Donna-Jo, Br Mgr, Pamunkey Regional Library, Cochrane Rockville Branch, 16600 Pouncey Tract Rd, Rockville, VA, 23146. Tel: 804-749-3146. Fax: 804-749-3631. p. 2469

Webster, Eva, Supvr, San Bernardino County Library, Summit Branch Library, 15551 Summit Ave, Fontana, CA, 92336. Tel: 909-357-5950, Ext 3024. Fax: 909-854-6398. p. 229

Webster, Frank M, Assoc Dir, Tech Serv, Teachers College, Columbia University, 525 W 120th St, New York, NY, 10027-6696. Tel: 212-678-3039. p. 1701

Webster, Heidi, Libr Dir, Lebanon College Library, 15 Hanover St, Lebanon, NH, 03766. Tel: 603-448-2445, Ext 110. Fax: 603-448-2491. p. 1453

Webster, Jackie, Librn, Collins College Libraries, 1140 S Priest Dr, Tempe, AZ, 85281. Tel: 480-446-1185. Fax: 480-902-0663. p. 84

Webster, Jackie, Dir, Jensen Memorial Library, 443 N Kearney, Minden, NE, 68959. Tel: 308-832-2648. Fax: 308-832-1642. p. 1408

Webster, Janet, Head, Guin & Cascades Campus Libr, Oregon State University Libraries, 121 The Valley Library, Corvallis, OR, 97331-4501. Tel: 541-867-0108. Fax: 541-867-0105. p. 1994

Webster, Janet G, Head of Libr, Oregon State University, 2030 Marine Science Dr, Newport, OR, 97365. Tel: 541-867-0108. Fax: 541-867-0105. p. 2008

Webster, Jefferson, Coll Develop Librn, Dallas Theological Seminary, 3909 Swiss Ave, Dallas, TX, 75204. Tel: 214-841-3748. Fax: 214-841-3745. p. 2307

Webster, Kay, Outreach Serv Librn, Youth Serv, Greene County Public Library, 76 E Market St, Xenia, OH, 45385-3100. Tel: 937-352-4000, Ext 1231. Fax: 937-372-4673. p. 1951

Webster, Mark, Adminr, Claxton-Hepburn Medical Center Library, 214 King St, Ogdensburg, NY, 13669. Tel: 315-393-3600, Ext 5632. Fax: 315-393-8506. p. 1709

Webster, Miranda, Pub Serv, Albany County Public Library, 310 S Eighth St, Laramie, WY, 82070-3969. Tel: 307-721-2580. Fax: 307-721-2584. p. 2657

Webster, Nancy, Ch, Northumberland Public Library, Inc, 7204 Northumberland Hwy, Heathsville, VA, 22473. Tel: 804-580-5051. Fax: 804-580-5202. p. 2471

Webster, Nevin B, Librn, Waupun Correctional Institution Library, 200 S Madison St, Waupun, WI, 53963-2069. Tel: 920-324-5571. Fax: 920-324-7250. p. 2646

Webster, Peter, Assoc Univ Librn, Info Syst, Saint Mary's University, 5429 Inglis St, Halifax, NS, B3H 3C3, CANADA. Tel: 902-420-5507. Fax: 902-420-5561. p. 2782

Webster, Priscilla, Mgr, Portland Public Library, Peaks Island Branch, 129 Island Ave, Peaks Island, ME, 04108. Tel: 207-766-5540. Fax: 207-766-5540. p. 997

Webster, Susan, Librn, Georgia Public Library, 1697 Ethan Allen Hwy, Fairfax, VT, 05454. Tel: 802-524-4643. Fax: 802-524-7426. p. 2424

Webster, Trish, Mgr, Honigman Miller Schwartz & Cohn LLP, 2290 First National Bldg, 660 Woodward Ave, Detroit, MI, 48226-3583. Tel: 313-465-7169. Fax: 313-465-8000. p. 1171

Webster, Winnifred, Br Mgr, Beaufort, Hyde & Martin County Regional Library, Bath Community, Main & Carteret Sts, Bath, NC, 27808. Tel: 252-923-6371. Fax: 252-923-0497. p. 1828

Webster, Wynell, Br Mgr, Mesa County Public Library District, Clifton Branch, 590 32 Rd, Ste F, Clifton, CO, 81520-7608. Tel: 970-434-6936. p. 311

Weckbacher, Kat, Tech Mgr, Massillon Public Library, 208 Lincoln Way E, Massillon, OH, 44646-8416. Tel: 330-832-9831, Ext 336. Fax: 330-830-2182. p. 1915

Weckwerth, Pam, Dir, Med Health Info, Brookings Health System, 300 22nd Ave, Brookings, SD, 57006-2496. Tel: 605-696-9000. Fax: 605-697-7380. p. 2210

Wedding, Jeff, Training Dir, Evansville State Hospital, 3400 Lincoln Ave, Evansville, IN, 47714. Tel: 812-469-6800. Fax: 812-469-6801. p. 738

Weddle, Andrea, Head, Spec Coll & Archives, Texas A&M University-Commerce, 2600 S Neal St, Commerce, TX, 75429. Tel: 903-886-5463. Fax: 903-886-5434. p. 2300

Weddle, Jackie, Librn, Maine Department of Corrections, Maine State Prison Library, 807 Cushing Rd, Warren, ME, 04864. Tel: 207-273-5300. p. 1004

Weddle, Jeff, Asst Prof, University of Alabama, 514 Main Library, Tuscaloosa, AL, 35487. Tel: 205-348-4610. Fax: 205-348-3746. p. 2961

Wedell, Sara, Ad, Delta Township District Library, 5130 Davenport Dr, Lansing, MI, 48917-2040. Tel: 517-321-4014. Fax: 517-321-2080. p. 1200

Wedergren, Ruth, Pub Awareness Coordr, Texas State Library & Archives Commission, 1201 Brazos, Austin, TX, 78711. Tel: 512-463-5452. Fax: 512-936-0685. p. 2283

Wedes, Lloyd, Libr Dir, DeVry University, 11125 Equity Dr, Houston, TX, 77041. Tel: 713-973-3137. Fax: 713-896-7650. p. 2334

Wedig, Eric, Bibliographer, Tulane University, 7001 Freret St, New Orleans, LA, 70118-5682. Tel: 504-865-5644. Fax: 504-865-6773. p. 963

Wedig, Lori, ILL, University of Wisconsin - Platteville, One University Plaza, Platteville, WI, 53818. Fax: 608-342-1645. p. 2630

Wedman, John, Dir, University of Missouri-Columbia, 303 Townsend Hall, Columbia, MO, 65211. Tel: 573-882-4546. Fax: 573-884-2917. p. 2968

Wedyke, Kathy, Web Serv, Deckerville Public Library, 3542 N Main St, Deckerville, MI, 48427-9638. Tel: 810-376-8015. Fax: 810-376-8593. p. 1168

Wee, Sandy, Mgr, San Mateo County Library, Millbrae Library, One Library Ave, Millbrae, CA, 94030. Tel: 650-697-7607. Fax: 650-692-4747. p. 256

Weeber, Jodi, Archivist, Oregon Coast History Center Library, 545 SW Ninth St, Newport, OR, 97365. Tel: 541-265-7509. Fax: 541-265-3992. p. 2008

Weech, Terry, Assoc Prof, University of Illinois at Urbana-Champaign, Library & Information Science Bldg, 501 E Daniel St, Champaign, IL, 61820-6211. Tel: 217-333-3280. Fax: 217-244-3302. p. 2965

Weed, Ellen, Librn, Norfolk Regional Center, 1700 N Victory Rd, Norfolk, NE, 68701. Tel: 402-370-3290, 402-370-3401. Fax: 402-370-3194. p. 1410

Weed, John, Head, Coll Res, University of Texas Health Science Center at San Antonio Libraries, 7703 Floyd Curl Dr, MSC 7940, San Antonio, TX, 78229-3900. Tel: 210-567-2400. Fax: 210-567-2490. p. 2383

Weed, Kathryn, Librn, West Burke Public Library, 135 Main St, West Burke, VT, 05871. Tel: 802-467-3328. p. 2439

Weed, Virginia, Librn, Mid-Mississippi Regional Library System, Winona-Montgomery County, 115 N Quitman St, Winona, MS, 38967-2228. Tel: 662-283-3443. Fax: 662-283-2642. p. 1306

Weed-Brown, Robin, Dir, Glendora Public Library & Cultural Center, 140 S Glendora Ave, Glendora, CA, 91741. Tel: 626-852-4892. Fax: 626-852-4899. p. 156

Weeden, Heather, Librn, Mississippi Baptist Historical Commission Library, 200 S Capitol St, Clinton, MS, 39058. Tel: 601-925-3434. Fax: 601-925-3435. p. 1296

Weeden, Megan, Youth Serv Librn, Cranston Public Library, William H Hall Free Library, 1825 Broad St, Cranston, RI, 02905-3599. Tel: 401-781-2450. Fax: 401-781-2494. p. 2165

Weedman, Barbara F, Pub Serv Adminr, Henrico County Public Library, 1001 N Laburnum Ave, Henrico, VA, 23223-2705. Tel: 804-290-9000. Fax: 804-222-5566. p. 2471

Weedman, Carol, Librn, Victoria Public Library District, 227 E Main St, Victoria, IL, 61485. Tel: 309-879-2295. Fax: 309-879-2295. p. 714

Weeg, Barbara, Bibliographer, Ref Serv, University of Northern Iowa Library, 1227 W 27th St, Cedar Falls, IA, 50613-3675. Tel: 319-273-3705. Fax: 319-273-2913. p. 799

Weekley, Heather Diane, Dir, Sistersville Public Library, 518 Wells St, Sistersville, WV, 26175. Tel: 304-652-6701. Fax: 304-652-6701. p. 2572

Weekly, Nancy, Curator, Burchfield Penney Art Center, Buffalo State College, 1300 Elmwood Ave, Buffalo, NY, 14222. Tel: 716-878-3244, 716-878-4756. Fax: 716-878-6003. p. 1597

Weeks, Art, Dir, Ames Public Library, 515 Douglas Ave, Ames, IA, 50010. Tel: 515-239-5632. Fax: 515-233-9001. p. 792

Weeks, Carolyn, Assoc Dir, Cent Libr Serv, Johnson County Library, 9875 W 87th St, Overland Park, KS, 66212. Tel: 913-495-2467. Fax: 913-495-2460. p. 888

Weeks, Carolyn, Assoc Dir, Cent Libr Serv, Johnson County Library, Central Resource, 9875 W 87th St, Overland Park, KS, 66212. Tel: 913-826-4600. Fax: 913-495-2480. p. 888

Weeks, Cindy, Asst Dir, Tech Serv, Bradford County Public Library, 456 W Pratt St, Starke, FL, 32091-3396. Tel: 904-368-3911. Fax: 904-964-2164. p. 491

Weeks, Clarice, Dir, Paul Quinn College, 3837 Simpson Stuart Rd, Dallas, TX, 75241. Tel: 214-379-5565. Fax: 214-379-5456. p. 2309

Weeks, David, Libr Instruction, Winthrop University, 824 Oakland Ave, Rock Hill, SC, 29733. Tel: 803-323-2319. Fax: 803-323-2215. p. 2203

Weeks, Dennis, Dr, Dir, Valencia Community College, East Campus, 701 N Econlockhatchee Trail, Orlando, FL, 32825. Tel: 407-582-2467. Fax: 407-582-8914. p. 478

Weeks, Dustin, Head, Tech Serv, Daytona Beach College Library, 1200 W International Speedway Blvd, Daytona Beach, FL, 32114. Tel: 386-506-3593. Fax: 386-506-3008. p. 435

Weeks, Eddie, Assoc Librn, Tennessee General Assembly, Office of Legal Services, G-12 War Memorial Bldg, Nashville, TN, 37243-0059. Tel: 615-741-5816. Fax: 615-741-1146. p. 2258

Weeks, Frances, ILL, University of Houston - Clear Lake, 2700 Bay Area Blvd, Houston, TX, 77058-1098. Tel: 281-283-3930. Fax: 281-283-3937. p. 2343

Weeks, Ginny, Dir, Libr Serv, Blackfeet Community College, US Hwy Two & 89, Browning, MT, 59417. Tel: 406-338-5441. Fax: 406-338-5454. p. 1376

Weeks, Jeaneal C, Dir, Hiawatha Public Library, 150 W Willman St, Hiawatha, IA, 52233. Tel: 319-393-1414. Fax: 319-393-6005. p. 821

Weeks, John, Librn, University of Pennsylvania Libraries, Museum, 3260 South St, Philadelphia, PA, 19104-6324. Tel: 215-898-4021. Fax: 215-573-2008. p. 2119

Weeks, Kate, Dir, Town of Tonawanda Public Library, 160 Delaware Rd, Kenmore, NY, 14217. Tel: 716-873-2842. Fax: 716-873-8416. p. 1649

Weeks, Kate, Dir, Town of Tonawanda Public Library, Kenilworth, 318 Montrose Ave, Buffalo, NY, 14223. Tel: 716-834-7657. Fax: 716-834-4695. p. 1649

Weeks, Mandy, Coll Develop, Librn, Saint Vincent Health Systems Library, Two Saint Vincent Circle, Little Rock, AR, 72205. Tel: 501-552-3231. Fax: 501-552-4311. p. 107

Weeks, Meghan, Syst Librn, Loyola Marymount University, One LMU Dr, MS 8200, Los Angeles, CA, 90045-2659, Tel: 310-338-5929. Fax: 310-338-4366. p. 175

Weeks, Olivia L, Dir, Law Libr, Campbell University, Norman Adrian Wiggins School of Law Library, 225 Hillsborough St, Ste 203, Raleigh, NC, 27603. Tel: 919-865-5869. Fax: 919-865-5995. p. 1778

Weeks, Roosevelt, Dep Dir, Admin, Houston Public Library, 500 McKinney Ave, Houston, TX, 77002-2534. Tel: 832-393-1327. Fax: 832-393-1324. p. 2338

Weeks, Ruth, Asst Dir, University of Alabama, School of Law Library, 101 Paul Bryant Dr, Tuscaloosa, AL, 35487. Tel: 205-348-5925. Fax: 205-348-1112. p. 38

Weeks, William, Libr Tech, Gulf Correctional Institution Library, Annex Branch, 699 Ike Steel Rd, Wewahitchka, FL, 32465. Tel: 850-639-1780. p. 504

Weeks-Wegner, Kathy, Br Mgr, Jackson County Library, Lakefield Branch, 410 Main St, Lakefield, MN, 56150-1201. Tel: 507-662-5782. Fax: 507-662-5782. p. 1255

Weeldreyer, Pat, Ch, Rawlins Municipal Library, 1000 E Church St, Pierre, SD, 57501. Tel: 605-773-7421. Fax: 605-773-7423. p. 2216

Weems, Cheryl, Ch, Deschutes Public Library District, 507 NW Wall St, Bend, OR, 97701-2698. Tel: 541-312-1021. Fax: 541-389-2982. p. 1992

Weerasinghe, Jean, Dir, Libr & Info Serv, Government of Canada, Federal Courts & Tax Court of Canada, Courts Administration Service-Library Services, 90 Sparks St, Ottawa, ON, K1A 0H9, CANADA. Tel: 613-995-1382. Fax: 613-943-5303. p. 2831

Wees, Eric, Mgr, Libr Serv, Department of Canadian Heritage, 15 Eddy St, 2nd Flr, Gatineau, QC, K1A 0M5, CANADA. Tel: 819-994-5724. Fax: 819-953-7988. p. 2883

Weese, Denise, Librn, Charles W Gibson Public Library, 105 E Main St, Buckhannon, WV, 26201. Tel: 304-472-2339. Fax: 304-472-2339. p. 2555

Weessies, Kathleen, Librn, Michigan State University Library, Map Library, W 308 Library, East Lansing, MI, 48824. Tel: 517-884-6467. Fax: 517-432-3532. p. 1175

Weessies, Ralph, Dir, Lawrence Memorial Public Library, 107 N Main St, Climax, MI, 49034-9638. Tel: 269-746-4125. Fax: 269-746-4125. p. 1163

Wegemer, Joel, Assoc Dir, University of Oklahoma, Donald E Pray Law Library, 300 Timberdell Rd, Norman, OK, 73019. Tel: 405-325-4311. Fax: 405-325-6282. p. 1971

Wegener, Brenda, Head of Libr, Center for Fiction, 17 E 47th St, New York, NY, 10017. Tel: 212-755-6710. Fax: 212-824-0831. p. 1671

Wegener, Darla, Mgr, Main Libr, Long Beach Public Library, 101 Pacific Ave, Long Beach, CA, 90822-1097. Tel: 562-570-7500. Fax: 562-570-7408. p. 166

Weglarz, Cathy, Access Serv Librn, Health Sci Librn, Lock Haven University of Pennsylvania, 401 N Fairview Ave, Lock Haven, PA, 17745-2390. Tel: 570-484-2489. Fax: 570-484-2506. p. 2082

Wegner, Lacey, Circ, Fort Hays State University, 600 Park St, Hays, KS, 67601-4099. Tel: 785-628-5837. Fax: 785-628-4096. p. 871

Wegner, Lisa, Youth Serv Dir, Waunakee Public Library, 710 South St, Waunakee, WI, 53597-1638. Tel: 608-849-4217. Fax: 608-849-7817. p. 2645

Wegner, Lucy S, Dir, RAND Corporation Library, 1776 Main St, M1LIB, Santa Monica, CA, 90407. Tel: 310-393-0411, Ext 6940. Fax: 310-451-7029. p. 266

Wegner, Mary, State Librn, State Library of Iowa, 1112 E Grand Ave, Des Moines, IA, 50319. Tel: 515-281-4105. Fax: 515-281-6191. p. 810

Wegner, Mary, State Librn, State of Iowa Libraries Online, State Library of Iowa, 1112 E Grand, Des Moines, IA, 50319. Tel: 515-281-4105. Fax: 515-281-6191. p. 2943

Wegrzyn, Margie, Youth Serv, Flossmoor Public Library, 1000 Sterling Ave, Flossmoor, IL, 60422-1295. Tel: 708-798-3600. Fax: 708-798-3603. p. 646

Wehking, Tracey, Youth Serv Librn, Sumter County Library System, 7375 Powell Rd, Ste 150, Wildwood, FL, 34785. Tel: 352-689-4560. Fax: 352-689-4561. p. 504

Wehmeyer, Susan, Head, Info Serv, Wright State University Libraries, 126 Dunbar Library, 3640 Colonel Glenn Hwy, Dayton, OH, 45435-0001. Tel: 937-775-3565. Fax: 937-775-4109. p. 1895

Wehmeyer, Yancy, Librn, Celeste Public Library, 400 E Cockrell St, Celeste, TX, 75423-9669. Tel: 903-568-0556. p. 2296

Wehr, Peggy, Br Mgr, Indianapolis-Marion County Public Library, Fountain Square, 1066 Virginia Ave, Indianapolis, IN, 46203. Tel: 317-275-4390. p. 754

Wehrheim, Jill, YA Librn, Morton Grove Public Library, 6140 Lincoln Ave, Morton Grove, IL, 60053-2989. Tel: 847-929-5119. Fax: 847-965-7903. p. 676

Wei, Iping, Head, Tech Serv, Princeton University, East Asian Library & The Gest Collection, 33 Frist Campus Ctr, Rm 317, Princeton, NJ, 08544-. Tel: 609-258-3259. Fax: 609-258-4573. p. 1523

Wei, Karen, Head Librn, University of Illinois Library at Urbana-Champaign, Asian, 325 Main Library, 1408 W Gregory Dr, Urbana, IL, 61801. Tel: 217-244-2046. Fax: 217-333-2214. p. 711

Weibel, Marguerite Crowley, Librn, Ohio State University LIBRARIES, John A Prior Health Sciences Library, 376 W Tenth Ave, Columbus, OH, 43210-1240. Tel: 614-292-2538. Fax: 614-292-1920. p. 1889

Weible, Sue, Br Mgr, Jackson District Library, Grass Lake Branch, 130 W Michigan Ave, Grass Lake, MI, 49240. Tel: 517-522-8211. Fax: 517-522-8215. p. 1196

Weich, Elaine, Cat Spec, Fraser Milner Casgrain LLP, Bankers Ct, 15th Flr, 850 Second St SW, Calgary, AB, T2P 0R8, CANADA. Tel: 403-268-7000. Fax: 403-268-3100. p. 2691

Weichert, Nancy, Instrul Serv, University of Illinois at Springfield, One University Plaza, MS BRK-140, Springfield, IL, 62703-5407. Tel: 217-206-6644. Fax: 217-206-6354. p. 707

Weick, Marianne, YA Librn, St Charles Public Library District, One S Sixth Ave, Saint Charles, IL, 60174-2105. Tel: 630-584-0076, Ext 223, Fax: 630-584-3448. p. 699

Weida, Wendy S, Exec Dir, The Moravian Historical Society, 214 E Center St, Nazareth, PA, 18064. Tel: 610-759-5070. Fax: 610-759-2461. p. 2095

Weide, Deb, Ch, Jesse F Hallett Memorial Library, 101 First St SE, Crosby, MN, 56441. Tel: 218-546-8005. Fax: 218-546-7287. p. 1247

Weidner, Amy, Digital Res Librn, Benedictine University Library, 5700 College Rd, Lisle, IL, 60532-0900. Tel: 630-829-6050. Fax: 630-960-9451. p. 666

Weidner, Cheryl, ILL, Pub Serv, United States Department of Justice, MCB No 4, Quantico, VA, 22135. Tel: 703-632-3204. Fax: 703-632-3214. p. 2487

Weidner, Jolisa, Ch, Washington Public Library, 115 W Washington St, Washington, IA, 52353. Tel: 319-653-2726. Fax: 319-653-3095. p. 849

Weidner, Kate, Dir, New Brighton Public Library, 1021 Third Ave, New Brighton, PA, 15066-3011. Tel: 724-846-7991. Fax: 724-846-0717. p. 2095

Weidner, Timothy, Exec Dir, Glens Falls-Queensbury Historical Association, 348 Glen St, Glens Falls, NY, 12801. Tel: 518-793-2826. Fax: 518-793-2831. p. 1629

Weiers, Bernadette, ILL, Clearwater Public Library System, 100 N Osceola Ave, Clearwater, FL, 33755. Tel: 727-562-4970. Fax: 727-562-4977. p. 432

Weigand, Laura, Br Mgr, Forsyth County Public Library, Reynolda Manor, 2839 Fairlawn Dr, Winston-Salem, NC, 27106. Tel: 336-703-2960. Fax: 336-748-3318. p. 1832

Weigard, Lisa J, Fac Librn, Harrisburg Area Community College, 1641 Old Philadelphia Pike, Lancaster, PA, 17602. Tel: 717-358-2226. Fax: 717-358-2952. p. 2076

Weigel, Carolyn, Acq/Res Mgt Asst, Archivist, Ursinus College Library, 601 E Main St, Collegeville, PA, 19426. Tel: 610-409-3000, Ext 2877. Fax: 610-489-0634. p. 2046

Weigel, Judy, Commun Libr Mgr, County of Los Angeles Public Library, A C Bilbrew Library, 150 E El Segundo Blvd, Los Angeles, CA, 90061-2356. Tel: 310-538-3350. Fax: 310-327-0824. p. 141

Weigel, Margaret, Dir, Pulaski Public Library, 4917 N Jefferson St, Pulaski, NY, 13142. Tel: 315-298-2717. Fax: 315-298-2717. p. 1724

Weigel, Susan, Youth Serv Mgr, Cumberland County Public Library & Information Center, North Regional, 855 McArthur Rd, Fayetteville, NC, 28311-1961. Tel: 910-822-1998. Fax: 910-480-0030. p. 1793

Weigert, Kathy, Librn, Olympic College, Poulsbo Campus, 1000 Olympic College Pl NW, Poulsbo, WA, 98370. Tel: 360-394-2720. Fax: 360-394-2721. p. 2511

Weighlhofer, Mary Ann, Libr Dir, Clinton Community College, 136 Clinton Point Dr, Plattsburgh, NY, 12901-5690. Tel: 518-562-4241. Fax: 518-562-4116. p. 1718

Weight, Linda, Tech Coordr, Siuslaw Public Library District, 1460 Ninth St, Florence, OR, 97439-0022. Tel: 541-997-3132. Fax: 541-997-6473. p. 1998

Weigle, Steven, Mgr, Portland Public Library, Riverton, 1600 Forest Ave, Portland, ME, 04103-1399. Tel: 207-797-2915. Fax: 207-756-8864. p. 997

Weigman, Dana, Adult Serv, Columbia Heights Public Library, 820 40th Ave NE, Columbia Heights, MN, 55421. Tel: 763-706-3690. Fax: 763-706-3691. p. 1246

Weigmann, Stefanie, Asst Dir, Boston University Libraries, Pappas Law Library, 765 Commonwealth Ave, Boston, MA, 02215. Tel: 617-358-4997. Fax: 617-353-5995. p. 1058

Weikal, Myrna, Dir, Midvale District Library, 70 E Bridge St, Midvale, ID, 83645-2012. Tel: 208-355-2213. p. 579

Weikel, Lisa, Access Serv, University of Wisconsin-Milwaukee Libraries, 2311 E Hartford Ave, Milwaukee, WI, 53211. Tel: 414-229-4785, 414-229-6202. Fax: 414-229-6766. p. 2622

Weikle, Dawnette, Dir, Maroa Public Library District, 305 E Garfield St, Maroa, IL, 61756. Tel: 217-794-5111. Fax: 217-794-3005. p. 670

Weikum, Jim, Dir, Arrowhead Library System, 5528 Emerald Ave, Mountain Iron, MN, 55768-2069. Tel: 218-741-3840. Fax: 218-748-2171. p. 1267

Weil, Beth, Librn, University of California, Berkeley, Marian Koshland Bioscience & Natural Resources Library, 2101 VLSB, No 6500, Berkeley, CA, 94720-6500. Tel: 510-642-2531. p. 128

Weil, Norman, Ref Librn, Molloy College, 1000 Hempstead Ave, Rockville Centre, NY, 11571. Tel: 516-678-5000, Ext 6567. Fax: 516-678-8908. p. 1734

Weiland, Nancy Jamerson, Res, George M Jones Library Association, 2311 Memorial Ave, Lynchburg, VA, 24501. Tel: 434-846-0501. Fax: 434-846-1572. p. 2475

Weiler, Angela, Per, Pub Serv, Onondaga Community College, 4585 W Seneca Tpk, Syracuse, NY, 13215-4585. Tel: 315-498-2334. Fax: 315-498-7213. p. 1752

Weiman, Dawn, Libr Mgr, Dauphin County Library System, McCormick Riverfront Library, 101 Walnut St, Harrisburg, PA, 17101. Tel: 717-234-4976. Fax: 717-234-7479. p. 2064

Weiman, Dawn, Libr Mgr, Dauphin County Library System, Madeline L Olewine Memorial Library, 2410 N Third St, Harrisburg, PA, 17110. Tel: 717-232-7286. Fax: 717-232-9707. p. 2065

Weimar, Holly A, Asst Prof, Sam Houston State University, 1921 Ave J, Huntsville, TX, 77340. Tel: 936-294-3158. Fax: 936-294-1153. p. 2974

Weimar, Mary, Dir, Orland Park Public Library, 14921 Ravinia Ave, Orland Park, IL, 60462. Tel: 708-428-5100. Fax: 708-349-8322. p. 686

Weimer, Ferne, Acq of New Ser, Dir, Graduate Institute of Applied Linguistics Library, 7500 W Camp Wisdom Rd, Dallas, TX, 75236-5699. Tel: 972-708-7416. Fax: 972-708-7292. p. 2308

Weimer, Jane, Regional Librn, Volusia County Public Library, Port Orange Public, 1005 City Center Circle, Port Orange, FL, 32119. Tel: 386-322-5152. Fax: 386-322-5155. p. 436

Wein, Stacy, Librn, Copley Hospital Medical Library, 528 Washington Hwy, Morrisville, VT, 05661. Tel: 802-888-8347. Fax: 802-888-8361. p. 2430

Weinberg, Linda, Cat Librn, Coordr, Cat, Adelphi University Libraries, One South Ave, Garden City, NY, 11530. Tel: 516-877-3526. Fax: 516-877-3592. p. 1625

Weinberg, Michael, Ref Librn, Northeastern Illinois University, 5500 N Saint Louis Ave, Chicago, IL, 60625-4699. Tel: 773-442-4455. Fax: 773-442-4531. p. 621

Weinberg, Myra Engers, Sr Dir, National Restaurant Association, 1200 17th St NW, Washington, DC, 20036. Tel: 202-331-5960. Fax: 202-331-5950. p. 411

Weinberg, Sara, Dir, Ashland Town Library, 42 Main St, Ashland, NH, 03217. Tel: 603-968-7928. Fax: 603-968-7928. p. 1438

Weinberg, Wanda, Actg Asst Dean, Pub Serv, Ohio University Libraries, 30 Park Pl, Athens, OH, 45701-2978. Tel: 740-593-9685. Fax: 740-593-2708. p. 1856

Weinberg-Kinsey, David, Dir, Cardinal Stritch University Library, 6801 N Yates Rd, Milwaukee, WI, 53207-3985. Tel: 414-410-4263. Fax: 414-410-4268. p. 2617

Weinberger, James, Curator, Princeton University, One Washington Rd, Princeton, NJ, 08544-2098. Tel: 609-258-3279. Fax: 609-258-0441. p. 1523

Weinberger, Paul, Mgr, Pembroke Public Library, 1018 Camelia Dr, Pembroke, GA, 31321-0430. Tel: 912-653-2822. Fax: 912-653-2802. p. 547

Weinberger, Wendy, Dir, Screven-Jenkins Regional Library, 106 S Community Dr, Sylvania, GA, 30467. Tel: 912-564-7526. Fax: 912-564-7580. p. 553

Weinbrom, Laura, Ch, Joint Free Public Library of the Chathams, 214 Main St, Chatham, NJ, 07928. Tel: 973-635-0603. Fax: 973-635-7827. p. 1478

Weineaub, Evviva, Assoc Librn, Info Tech Mgr, Tufts University, Edwin Ginn Library, Mugar Bldg, 1st Flr, 160 Packard St, Medford, MA, 02155-7082. Tel: 617-627-3023. Fax: 617-627-3736. p. 1104

Weiner, Amy, Ref Librn, Sidley, Austin, Brown & Wood LLP, 787 Seventh Ave, 24th Flr, New York, NY, 10019. Tel: 212-839-5300. Fax: 212-839-5599. p. 1700

Weiner, Barbara, Librn, Mgr, Hazelden Foundation Library CO-4, 15251 Pleasant Valley Rd, Center City, MN, 55012-0011. Tel: 651-213-4093. Fax: 651-213-4411. p. 1245

Weiner, Brien, Cat, Juilliard School, 60 Lincoln Center Plaza, New York, NY, 10023-6588. Tel: 212-799-5000, Ext 265. Fax: 212-769-6421. p. 1684

Weiner, Carole, Assoc Dir, Southwestern Law School, 3050 Wilshire Blvd, Los Angeles, CA, 90010. Tel: 213-738-5771. Fax: 213-738-5792. p. 177

Weiner, David, Circ Mgr, Stony Brook University, W-1502 Melville Library, John S Toll Rd, Stony Brook, NY, 11794-3300. Tel: 631-632-7100. Fax: 631-632-7116. p. 1749

Weiner, Deb, Dr, Spec Coll & Archives Librn, Jewish Museum of Maryland, 15 Lloyd St, Baltimore, MD, 21202. Tel: 410-732-6400, Ext 18. Fax: 410-732-6451. p. 1014

Weiner, Gretchen Young, Instruction Librn, Ref Librn, Ser, Lawrence Technological University Library, 21000 W Ten Mile Rd, Southfield, MI, 48075-1058. Tel: 248-204-3000. Fax: 248-204-3005. p. 1228

Weiner, Irene, Ref Serv, Baker University, 518 Eighth St, Baldwin City, KS, 66006-0065. Tel: 785-594-8445. Fax: 785-594-6721. p. 857

Weiner, Jo, Librn, Forney Public Library, 800 FM 741 S, Forney, TX, 75126. Tel: 972-564-7027. Fax: 972-564-5616. p. 2320

Weiner, Nancy, Ref & Instrul Serv, Instr Coordr, William Paterson University of New Jersey, 300 Pompton Rd, Wayne, NJ, 07470. Tel: 973-720-2161. Fax: 973-720-3171. p. 1540

Weiner, Sharon, Dean, Libr Serv, University of Massachusetts Dartmouth Library, 285 Old Westport Rd, North Dartmouth, MA, 02747-2300. Tel: 508-999-8664. Fax: 508-999-8987. p. 1112

Weiner, Stephen, Dir, Maynard Public Library, 77 Nason St, Maynard, MA, 01754-2316. Tel: 978-897-1010. Fax: 978-897-9884. p. 1103

Weinert, Stephanie, Circ, NHTI, Concord's Community College, 31 College Dr, Concord, NH, 03301-7425. Tel: 603-271-7186. Fax: 603-271-7189. p. 1443

Weingard, Alice, Librn, Allegheny Wesleyan College Library, 2161 Woodsdale Rd, Salem, OH, 44460. Tel: 330-337-6403. Fax: 330-337-6255. p. 1933

Weingartz, Emily, Librn, Michigan State Department of Natural Resources & Environment Library, Constitution Hall, 525 W Allegan, Lansing, MI, 48913. Tel: 517-241-9536. Fax: 517-241-2915. p. 1202

Weingram, Ida, Asst Dir, Bus Serv, Jenkins Law Library, 833 Chestnut St, Ste 1220, Philadelphia, PA, 19107-4429. Tel: 215-574-7935. Fax: 215-574-7920. p. 2111

Weinhardt, Beth, Librn, Westerville Public Library, Anti Saloon League Museum & Local History Resource Center, 126 S State St, Westerville, OH, 43081. Tel: 614-882-7277, Ext 160. Fax: 614-882-5369. p. 1947

Weinhold, David J, Dir, Eastern Shores Library System, 4632 S Taylor Dr, Sheboygan, WI, 53081-1107. Tel: 920-208-4900. Fax: 920-208-4901. p. 2637

Weininger, Christie, Exec Dir, Rutherford B Hayes Presidential Center Library, Spiegel Grove, Fremont, OH, 43420-2796. Tel: 419-332-2081, Ext 220. Fax: 419-332-4952. p. 1900

Weinmann, Linda, Tech Serv Librn, Winona Public Library, 151 W Fifth St, Winona, MN, 55987-3170. Tel: 507-452-4582. Fax: 507-452-5842. p. 1290

Weinraub, Evviva, Head, Emerging Tech & Serv, Oregon State University Libraries, 121 The Valley Library, Corvallis, OR, 97331-4501. Tel: 541-737-2458. Fax: 541-737-3453. p. 1994

Weinrauch, Tracy, Libr Mgr, Redcliff Public Library, 131 Main St S, Redcliff, AB, T0J 2P0, CANADA. Tel: 403-548-3335. Fax: 403-548-6295. p. 2715

Weinreb, Allan, Curator, New York State Office of Parks, Recreation & Historic Preservation, 400 Rte 22, Katonah, NY, 10536. Tel: 914-232-5651. Fax: 914-232-8085. p. 1648

Weinreich, K Suzanne, Circ/ILL Librn, Seabrook Library, 25 Liberty Lane, Seabrook, NH, 03874-4506. Tel: 603-474-2044. Fax: 603-474-1835. p. 1465

Weinrich, Linnae, Circ, University of Saint Thomas, Charles J Keffer Library, 1000 LaSalle Ave, MOH 206, Minneapolis, MN, 55403. Tel: 651-962-4644. Fax: 651-962-4648. p. 1282

Weinstein, Robin, Br Mgr, Greene County Public Library, Fairborn Community Library, One E Main St, Fairborn, OH, 45324-4798. Tel: 937-878-9383. Fax: 937-878-0374. p. 1951

Weinstein, Shelly, Librn, Temple B'Rith Kodesh Library, 2131 Elmwood Ave, Rochester, NY, 14618-1021. Tel: 585-244-7060. Fax: 585-244-0557. p. 1733

Weinstein, Tatiana, Dir, Adult Serv, Lisle Library District, 777 Front St, Lisle, IL, 60532-3599. Tel: 630-971-1675. Fax: 630-971-1701. p. 666

Weintraub, Aviva, Assoc Curator, The Jewish Museum, 1109 Fifth Ave, New York, NY, 10128. Tel: 212-423-3234. Fax: 212-423-3232. p. 1683

Weintraub, Tamera, Ser Librn, Palomar College Library - Media Center, 1140 W Mission Rd, San Marcos, CA, 92069-1487. Tel: 760-744-1150, Ext 2848. Fax: 760-761-3500. p. 254

Weintrop, Jane, Electronic Res Librn, Columbia University, Lehman Library, 420 W 118th St, New York, NY, 10027. Tel: 212-854-3794. Fax: 212-854-2495. p. 1675

Weir, Barb, Assoc Col Librn, Tech Serv & Digital Initiatives, Swarthmore College, 500 College Ave, Swarthmore, PA, 19081-1081. Tel: 610-328-8443. Fax: 610-328-7329. p. 2145

Weir, Cindy, Chief Librn/CEO, Owen Sound & North Grey Union Public Library, 824 First Ave W, Owen Sound, ON, N4K 4K4, CANADA. Tel: 519-376-6623, Ext 201. Fax: 519-376-7170. p. 2834

Weir, Dee, Dir, Stanhope Public Library, 665 Iowa St, Stanhope, IA, 50246. Tel: 515-826-3211. Fax: 515-826-3211. p. 845

Weir, Elsa, Asst Librn, Brown Memorial Library, 78 W Main St, Bradford, NH, 03221-3308. Tel: 603-938-5562. p. 1439

Weir, Karen, Tech Serv, Maynard Public Library, 77 Nason St, Maynard, MA, 01754-2316. Tel: 978-897-1010. Fax: 978-897-9884. p. 1103

Weir, Laura, Asst Dir, Head, Tech Serv, Great Neck Library, 159 Bayview Ave, Great Neck, NY, 11023-1938. Tel: 516-466-8055, Ext 228. Fax: 516-829-8297. p. 1630

Weir, Leslie, Chief Librn, University of Ottawa Libraries, 65 University, Ottawa, ON, K1N 6N5, CANADA. Tel: 613-562-5800, 613-562-5883, 613-562-5934. Fax: 613-562-5195. p. 2834

Weir, Linda, Head, Pub Serv, University of California, 200 McAllister St, San Francisco, CA, 94102-4978. Tel: 415-565-4757. Fax: 415-581-8849. p. 248

Weir, RosaLee, Asst Librn, Union Hospital, 1606 N Seventh St, Terre Haute, IN, 47804. Tel: 812-238-7641. Fax: 812-238-7595. p. 781

Weir, Ryan, Dir, Tech Serv & e-Res, Murray State University, 205 Waterfield Library, Dean's Office, Murray, KY, 42071-3307. Tel: 270-809-5607. Fax: 270-809-3736. p. 930

Weis, Ann Marie, Online Serv, Sanofi Aventis, Nine Great Valley Pkwy, Malvern, PA, 19355. Tel: 610-889-8655. Fax: 610-889-8988. p. 2083

Weis, Charlene, Dir, United Tribes Technical College Library, Education Bldg, 3315 University Dr, Bismarck, ND, 58504-7565. Tel: 701-255-3285 , Ext 1282. Fax: 701-530-0625. p. 1838

Weis, Helene H, Ref Serv, Willet Hauser Architectural Glass Library, Ten E Moreland Ave, Philadelphia, PA, 19118-3597. Tel: 215-247-5721. Fax: 215-247-2951. p. 2110

Weis, Judy, Br Mgr, Great River Regional Library, Foley Library, 251 N Fourth Ave, Foley, MN, 56329. Tel: 320-968-6612. p. 1275

Weis, Laura, Circ, Champaign Public Library, 200 W Green St, Champaign, IL, 61820-5193. Tel: 217-403-2050. Fax: 217-403-2053. p. 602

Weis, Valerie, Res & Knowledge Serv Librn, Harvard Library, John F Kennedy School of Government Library, 79 John F Kennedy St, Cambridge, MA, 02138. Tel: 617-495-1300. Fax: 617-495-1972. p. 1075

Weischedel, Elaine, Ch, Milton Public Library, 476 Canton Ave, Milton, MA, 02186-3299. Tel: 617-698-5757. Fax: 617-698-0441. p. 1106

Weischedel, Elaine Fort, Ch, Franklin Public Library, 118 Main St, Franklin, MA, 02038. Tel: 508-520-4940. p. 1090

Weise, Bonnie, Librn, Wollaston & Limerick Public Library, Main St, Coe Hill, ON, K0L 1P0, CANADA. Tel: 613-337-5183. Fax: 613-337-5183. p. 2800

Weisenbeck, Dea, Circ Serv, Clifton Public Library, 150 E Fourth Ave, Clifton, IL, 60927. Tel: 815-694-2069. Fax: 815-694-3179. p. 630

Weisenberger, Susan, Dir, Neosho County Community College, 800 W 14th St, Chanute, KS, 66720-2699. Tel: 620-431-2820, Ext 246. Fax: 620-432-9841. p. 860

Weisenstein, Emily, Youth Serv Librn, Boonton Holmes Public Library, 621 Main St, Boonton, NJ, 07005. Tel: 973-334-2980. Fax: 973-334-3917. p. 1473

Weiser, Lisa, Br Mgr, Akron-Summit County Public Library, North Hill, 183 E Cuyahoga Falls Ave, Akron, OH, 44310-3078. Tel: 330-535-9423. Fax: 330-376-5661. p. 1852

Weisheit, Anita, Info Serv Librn, Sheridan County Public Library System, 335 W Alger St, Sheridan, WY, 82801-3899. Tel: 307-674-8585, Ext 5. p. 2660

Weiskittel, Karen, Tech Serv, Northwest Vista College, Redbud Hall, 3535 N Ellison Dr, San Antonio, TX, 78251. Tel: 210-486-4558. Fax: 210-486-9105. p. 2380

Weisman, Sarah, Dir, Corning Community College, One Academic Dr, Corning, NY, 14830. Tel: 607-962-9251. Fax: 607-962-9466. p. 1610

Weisman, Yaffa, Dr, Dir, Hebrew Union College-Jewish Institute of Religion, 3077 University Ave, Los Angeles, CA, 90007. Tel: 213-749-3424. Fax: 213-749-1937. p. 170

Weismantel, Arlene, Asst Dir, Pub Serv, Michigan State University Library, 100 Library, East Lansing, MI, 48824-1048. Tel: 517-884-6447. Fax: 517-432-3532. p. 1175

Weispfenning, John, Dr, Dean, Santiago Canyon College, 8045 E Chapman Ave, Orange, CA, 92869. Tel: 714-628-5000. Fax: 714-633-2842. p. 201

Weisrock, Tom, Acq, Saddleback College, 28000 Marguerite Pkwy, Mission Viejo, CA, 92692. Tel: 949-528-4921. Fax: 949-364-0284. p. 187

Weiss, Al, Dir, Educ Tech & Curricular Innovation, Pacific University Library, 2043 College Way, Forest Grove, OR, 97116. Tel: 503-352-1417. Fax: 503-352-1416. p. 1998

Weiss, Amy, Assoc Dean, Tech Serv, Florida State University Libraries, Strozier Library Bldg, 116 Honors Way, Tallahassee, FL, 32306-0001. Tel: 850-644-2706. p. 494

Weiss, Amy, Head, Tech Serv, Woodridge Public Library, Three Plaza Dr, Woodridge, IL, 60517-5014. Tel: 630-964-7899. Fax: 630-964-0175. p. 721

Weiss, Andrew, Acq, Troutman Sanders LLP, 600 Peachtree St NE, Ste 5200, Atlanta, GA, 30308-2216. Tel: 404-885-3777. Fax: 404-962-6783. p. 518

Weiss, Ardis, Librn, San Antonio Community Hospital, 999 San Bernardino Rd, Upland, CA, 91786. Tel: 909-920-4972. Fax: 909-931-0102. p. 278

Weiss, Carla, Head, Coll Develop, Rhode Island College, 600 Mt Pleasant Ave, Providence, RI, 02908-1924. Tel: 401-456-8126. Fax: 401-456-9646. p. 2174

Weiss, Charlis, Dir, Morton Memorial Library, 22 Elm St, Pine Hill, NY, 12465. Tel: 845-254-4222. Fax: 845-254-4222. p. 1718

Weiss, Chris, Tech Serv, Petersburg Public Library, 12 Nordic Dr, Petersburg, AK, 99833. Tel: 907-772-3349. Fax: 907-772-3759. p. 52

Weiss, Dan, Dir, Fanwood Memorial Library, 14 Tillotson Rd, Fanwood, NJ, 07023-1399. Tel: 908-322-6400. Fax: 908-322-5590. p. 1485

Weiss, Emily, Head, Ref Serv, Bedford Public Library, Three Meetinghouse Rd, Bedford, NH, 03110-5406. Tel: 603-472-2300, 603-472-3023. Fax: 603-472-2978. p. 1438

Weiss, Jeff, Tech Serv, Muncie Center Township Public Library, 2005 S High St, Muncie, IN, 47302. Tel: 765-747-8220. Fax: 765-747-8220. p. 767

Weiss, Jordana S, Librn, Museum of Fine Arts, 255 Beach Dr NE, Saint Petersburg, FL, 33701-3498. Tel: 727-896-2667. Fax: 727-894-4638. p. 488

Weiss, Judith M, Libr Mgr, Pension Benefit Guaranty Corporation, 1200 K St NW, Ste 360, Washington, DC, 20005-4026. Tel: 202-326-4000, Ext 3091. Fax: 202-326-4011. p. 412

Weiss, Linda, Dir, Niles Public Library District, 6960 Oakton St, Niles, IL, 60714. Tel: 847-663-1234. Fax: 847-663-1350. p. 680

Weiss, Lori, Dir, Shook, Hardy & Bacon, 2555 Grand Blvd, 3rd Flr, Kansas City, MO, 64108-2613. Tel: 816-474-6550. Fax: 816-421-5547. p. 1341

Weiss, Lynn, Asst Br Supvr, Region of Waterloo Library, New Dundee Branch, 136 Main St, New Dundee, ON, N0B 2E0, CANADA. Tel: 519-696-3041. p. 2793

Weiss, Martin, Prof, University of Pittsburgh, 135 N Bellefield Ave, Pittsburgh, PA, 15260. Tel: 412-624-5230. Fax: 412-624-5231. p. 2973

Weiss, Martin B H, Assoc Prof, University of Pittsburgh, 135 N Bellefield Ave, Pittsburgh, PA, 15260. Tel: 412-624-5230. Fax: 412-624-5231. p. 2973

Weiss, Mitch, Asst Univ Librn, Ref/Electronic Serv Librn, Fairleigh Dickinson University, 1000 River Rd, Teaneck, NJ, 07666-1914. Tel: 201-692-2139. Fax: 201-692-9815. p. 1532

Weiss, Nancy, Law Librn, Washington County Law Library, One S Main St, Ste G004, Washington, PA, 15301-6813. Tel: 724-228-6747. p. 2151

Weiss, Nicholas, Dir, Naropa University Library, 2130 Arapahoe Ave, Boulder, CO, 80302. Tel: 305-546-3505. Fax: 303-245-4636. p. 290

Weiss, Patricia, Dir, National American University, 321 Kansas City St, Rapid City, SD, 57701-3692. Tel: 605-394-4943. Fax: 605-394-4871. p. 2217

Weiss, Sarah, Ch, Rockwell City Public Library, 424 Main St, Rockwell City, IA, 50579-1415. Tel: 712-297-8422. Fax: 712-297-8422. p. 841

Weiss, Sarah, Br Mgr, Brooklyn Public Library, Borough Park, 1265 43rd St, Brooklyn, NY, 11219. Tel: 718-437-4085. Fax: 718-437-3021. p. 1591

Weiss, Stephen, Librn, Utah State University, Regional Depository Collection of US Government Documents, 3000 Old Main Hill, Logan, UT, 84322-3000. Tel: 435-797-3661. p. 2407

Weiss, Steven, Exec Dir, Congregation Beth Shalom, 14601 W Lincoln Rd, Oak Park, MI, 48237-1391. Tel: 248-547-7970. Fax: 248-547-0421. p. 1215

Weiss, Susan, Ref Librn, Florida International University, 3000 NE 151st St, North Miami, FL, 33181-3600. Tel: 305-919-5725. Fax: 305-919-5914. p. 472

Weiss, Tina, Pub Serv, Ref Serv, Hebrew Union College-Jewish Institute of Religion, One W Fourth St, New York, NY, 10012-1186. Tel: 212-674-5300. Fax: 212-388-1720. p. 1681

Weiss, William B, Librn, Wayne County Law Library Association, Wayne County Courthouse, 107 W Liberty St, Wooster, OH, 44691-4850. Tel: 330-287-7721. p. 1950

Weiss, Wynne, Br Mgr, San Diego County Library, Vista Branch, 700 Eucalyptus Ave, Vista, CA, 92084-6245. Tel: 760-643-5117. Fax: 760-643-5127. p. 234

Weissenbach, Karl, Dir, National Archives & Records Administration, 200 SE Fourth St, Abilene, KS, 67410-2900. Tel: 785-263-6700. Fax: 785-263-6715, 785-263-6718. p. 855

Weissenburger, Ann, Adult Serv, Rockaway Township Free Public Library, 61 Mount Hope Rd, Rockaway, NJ, 07866. Tel: 973-627-2344. Fax: 973-627-7658. p. 1527

Weisser, Alice, Circ, Maurice M Pine Free Public Library, 10-01 Fair Lawn Ave, Fair Lawn, NJ, 07410. Tel: 201-796-3400. Fax: 201-794-6344. p. 1485

Weisser, Teresa, Cat, Millersville University, Nine N George St, Millersville, PA, 17551. Tel: 717-872-3604. Fax: 717-872-3854. p. 2090

Weissinger, Alison, Dir, DeKalb County Public Library, Administrative Office, 215 Sycamore St, 4th Flr, Decatur, GA, 30030. Tel: 404-370-8450. Fax: 404-370-8469. p. 529

Weisskopf, Vera J, Dir, Georgia Southwestern State University, 800 Georgia Southwestern State University Dr, Americus, GA, 31709. Tel: 229-931-2259. Fax: 229-931-2265. p. 508

Weissler, Edye, Librn, Knoedler Art Library, 19 E 70th St, New York, NY, 10021. Tel: 212-794-0567. Fax: 212-772-6932. p. 1684

Weissman, Sara, Head, Ref Serv, Morris County Library, 30 E Hanover Ave, Whippany, NJ, 07981. Tel: 973-285-6964. p. 1544

Weistling, Ripple, Electronic & Ref Serv, American University, 4801 Massachusetts Ave NW, Washington, DC, 20016-8182. Tel: 202-274-4382. Fax: 202-274-4365. p. 393

Weiter, Stephen P, Dir, State University of New York, College of Environmental Science & Forestry, One Forestry Dr, Syracuse, NY, 13210. Tel: 315-470-6711. Fax: 315-470-4766. p. 1753

Weitz, Anne, Asst Librn, Priest Lake Public Library, 28769 N Hwy 57, Priest Lake, ID, 83856. Tel: 208-443-2454. Fax: 208-443-2454. p. 582

Weitz, Pam, Libr Tech, Montana Legislative Reference Center, State Capitol, Rm 10, Helena, MT, 59620. Tel: 406-444-3588. Fax: 406-444-2588. p. 1382

Weitzel, Sandra, Chief Exec Officer, Dryden Public Library, 36 Van Horne Ave, Dryden, ON, P8N 2A7, CANADA. Tel: 807-223-1475. Fax: 807-223-4312. p. 2802

Weitzenfeld, Ruth, Librn, Siemens Corporate Research, Inc, 755 College Rd E, Princeton, NJ, 08540. Tel: 609-734-6506. Fax: 609-734-6565. p. 1524

Weklar, Patrick, Sr Librn/Cat, New York State Department of Law Library, The Capitol, Albany, NY, 12224. Tel: 518-474-3840. Fax: 518-473-1822. p. 1569

Welborn, Jordan, Adult Serv, Wilkes County Public Library, 215 Tenth St, North Wilkesboro, NC, 28659. Tel: 336-838-2818. Fax: 336-667-2638. p. 1813

Welborn, Jordan, Tech Serv, Campbell County Public Library, 684 Village Hwy, Lower Level, Rustburg, VA, 24588. Tel: 434-332-9657. Fax: 434-332-9697. p. 2495

Welburn, Janice, Dean, Univ Libr, Marquette University Libraries, 1355 W Wisconsin Ave, Milwaukee, WI, 53233. Tel: 414-288-7214. Fax: 414-288-7813. p. 2618

Welch, Andrew, ILS LIbrn, Drake University, 2725 University Ave, Des Moines, IA, 50311. Tel: 515-271-2862. Fax: 515-271-3933. p. 809

Welch, Barbara, Circ Supvr, Willoughby Wallace Memorial Library, 146 Thimble Islands Rd, Stony Creek, CT, 06405. Tel: 203-488-8702. Fax: 203-315-3347. p. 370

Welch, Brigid, Dean, University of the Pacific Library, 3601 Pacific Ave, Stockton, CA, 95211. Tel: 209-946-2434. Fax: 209-946-2805. p. 273

Welch, Carol, ILL, Chester County Library System, 450 Exton Square Pkwy, Exton, PA, 19341-2496. Tel: 610-280-2600. Fax: 610-280-2688. p. 2056

Welch, Carol, Assoc Librn, Lord Corporation, 2000 W Grandview Blvd, Erie, PA, 16514. Tel: 814-868-0924, Ext 3563. Fax: 814-866-6323, p. 2056

Welch, Casey, Librn, Mgr, Penrose-St Francis Health Services, 2222 N Nevada Ave, Colorado Springs, CO, 80907-0736. Tel: 719-776-5288. Fax: 719-776-5028. p. 296

Welch, Celeste L, Librn, Nielsen Engineering & Research, Inc Library, 2700 Augustine Dr, Ste 200, Santa Clara, CA, 95054. Tel: 408-727-9457, Ext 236. Fax: 408-727-1428. p. 262

Welch, Cindy, Dr, Asst Prof, University of Tennessee, Knoxville, 451 Communications Bldg, 1345 Circle Park Dr, Knoxville, TN, 37996-0341. Tel: 865-974-7918. Fax: 865-974-4967. p. 2974

Welch, Claudette, Circ Supvr, NHTI, Concord's Community College, 31 College Dr, Concord, NH, 03301-7425. Tel: 603-271-7186. Fax: 603-271-7189. p. 1443

Welch, Daniel, Dir, Lake Erie College of Osteopathic Medicine, 1858 W Grandview Blvd, Erie, PA, 16509-1025. Tel: 814-866-8451. Fax: 814-868-6911. p. 2055

Welch, Donald A, Sr Librn, Bell Helicopter Textron, Inc, 600 E Hurst Blvd, Fort Worth, TX, 76053. Tel: 817-280-3608. Fax: 817-278-3608. p. 2321

Welch, Erika, Librn, Waubay Public Library, 94 N Main St, Waubay, SD, 57273. Tel: 605-947-4748. Fax: 605-947-4748. p. 2221

Welch, Grace, Access Serv & Syst, University of Ottawa Libraries, 65 University, Ottawa, ON, K1N 6N5, CANADA. Tel: 613-562-5228. Fax: 613-562-5195. p. 2834

Welch, Jacqueline, Dir, Ruby M Sisson Memorial Library, 811 San Juan St, Pagosa Springs, CO, 81147. Tel: 970-264-2209. Fax: 970-264-4764. p. 319

Welch, Jane, Mgr, Okefenokee Regional Library, Clinch County Public, 478 W Dame St, Homerville, GA, 31634. Tel: 912-487-3200. Fax: 912-487-3304. p. 557

Welch, Janet, Ch, Carroll County Library, 625 High St, Ste 102, Huntingdon, TN, 38344-3903. Tel: 731-986-1919. Fax: 731-986-1335. p. 2237

Welch, Jennifer, Archivist, Medical University of South Carolina Library, 171 Ashley Ave, Ste 300, Charleston, SC, 29425-0001. Tel: 843-792-9211. Fax: 843-792-7947. p. 2184

Welch, Jennifer M, Digital Archivist, Medical University of South Carolina Library, Waring Historical Library, 175 Ashley Ave, Charleston, SC, 29425-0001. Tel: 843-792-2288. Fax: 843-792-8619. p. 2185

Welch, Jim, Dep Exec Dir, Tech, Metropolitan Library System in Oklahoma County, 300 Park Ave, Oklahoma City, OK, 73102. Tel: 405-606-3725. Fax: 405-606-3722. p. 1972

Welch, Johanna Julie, Ref Law Librn, University of Maine School of Law, 246 Deering Ave, Portland, ME, 04102. Tel: 207-780-4829. Fax: 207-780-4913. p. 997

Welch, John, Br Mgr, East Central Georgia Regional Library, Euchee Creek Library, 5907 Euchee Creek Dr, Grovetown, GA, 30813. Tel: 706-556-0594. Fax: 706-556-2585. p. 519

Welch, K, YA Serv, North Shore Public Library, 250 Rte 25A, Shoreham, NY, 11786-9677. Tel: 631-929-4488. Fax: 631-929-4551. p. 1743

Welch, Kara, Ch, Westfield Athenaeum, Six Elm St, Westfield, MA, 01085-2997. Tel: 413-568-7833. Fax: 413-568-0988. p. 1138

Welch, Karla, Head, Adult Serv, Coal City Public Library District, 85 N Garfield St, Coal City, IL, 60416. Tel: 815-634-4552. Fax: 815-634-2950. p. 630

Welch, Kata, Librn, Cavendish-Fletcher Community Library, 573 Main St, Proctorsville, VT, 05153. Tel: 802-226-7503. Fax: 802-226-7858. p. 2432

Welch, Kjersten, Admin Serv, Sioux City Art Center, 225 Nebraska St, Sioux City, IA, 51101. Tel: 712-279-6272. Fax: 712-255-2921. p. 844

Welch, Lavinia, Access Serv Librn, California Institute of the Arts, 24700 McBean Pkwy, Valencia, CA, 91355. Tel: 661-253-7885. Fax: 661-254-4561. p. 278

Welch, Lynne, Adult Serv, Herrick Memorial Library, 101 Willard Memorial Sq, Wellington, OH, 44090-1342. Tel: 440-647-2120. Fax: 440-647-2103. p. 1945

Welch, Mindy, Res, Kirkland & Ellis LLP Library, 300 N LaSalle St, 11th Flr, Chicago, IL, 60654. Tel: 312-862-2492. Fax: 312-862-2200. p. 616

Welch, Pamela, Asst Librn, Oscar Foss Memorial Library, 111 S Barnstead Rd, Center Barnstead, NH, 03225. Tel: 603-269-3900. Fax: 603-269-3900. p. 1440

Welch, Parks, Dir, Wake Forest University, Coy C Carpenter School of Medicine Library, Medical Center Blvd, Winston-Salem, NC, 27157-1069. Tel: 336-716-2299. Fax: 336-716-2186. p. 1834

Welch, Patricia, In Charge, Multnomah County Library, North Portland, 512 N Killingsworth St, Portland, OR, 97217-2330. Tel: 503-988-5394. Fax: 503-988-5187. p. 2012

Welch, Paula, Head, Circ, Morse Institute Library, 14 E Central St, Natick, MA, 01760. Tel: 508-647-6520. Fax: 508-647-6527. p. 1107

Welch, Tammy, Div Dean, Dona Ana Community College Library, East Mesa Campus, 2800 N Sonoma Ranch Blvd, Las Cruces, NM, 88011. Tel: 575-527-7675. Fax: 575-528-7422. p. 1558

Welch, Tina, Dir, Harper Public Library, 1002 Oak St, Harper, KS, 67058-1233. Tel: 620-896-2959. Fax: 620-896-7832. p. 870

Welcoizus, Mary, Librn, Pedersen & Houpt Library, 161 N Clark St, Ste 3100, Chicago, IL, 60601-3242. Tel: 312-641-6888. Fax: 312-641-6895. p. 622

Weld, Laura, Br Mgr, Kent District Library, Alpine Township Branch, 5255 Alpine Ave NW, Comstock Park, MI, 49321. Tel: 616-784-2007. Fax: 616-647-3814. p. 1165

Weldin, Pepper, Br Mgr, Chattahoochee Valley Libraries, Parks Memorial Public Library, 890 Wall St, Richland, GA, 31825-0112. Tel: 229-887-2103. Fax: 229-887-2103. p. 526

Weldon, Joan, Asst Regional Dir, Wapiti Regional Library, 145 12th St E, Prince Albert, SK, S6V 1B7, CANADA. Tel: 306-764-0712. Fax: 306-922-1516. p. 2921

Weldon, Lori, Librn, Scott County Library System, New Prague Public Library, 400 E Main St, New Prague, MN, 56071-2429. Tel: 952-758-2391. Fax: 952-758-2391. p. 1284

Weldon, Sharon, Circ, Monterey-Tippecanoe Township Public Library, 6260 E Main St, Monterey, IN, 46960. Tel: 574-542-2171. Fax: 574-542-2171. p. 765

Weldy, Gwendolyn P H, Asst Dir, Albany College of Pharmacy & Health Sciences, 106 New Scotland Ave, Albany, NY, 12208. Tel: 518-694-7274. Fax: 518-694-7300. p. 1567

Welfare, Vicky, Br Mgr 1, Sno-Isle Libraries, Langley Community Library, 104 Second St, Langley, WA, 98260. Tel: 360-221-4383. Fax: 360-221-3067. p. 2542

Welge, William D, Dir, Oklahoma Historical Society, 2401 N Laird Ave, Oklahoma City, OK, 73105-4997. Tel: 405-522-5206. Fax: 405-522-0644. p. 1974

Weliver, Evelyn R, Dir, Interlochen Center for the Arts, John W & Charlene B Seabury Academic Library, 4000 M-137, Interlochen, MI, 49643. Tel: 231-276-7420. Fax: 231-276-5232. p. 1193

Welker, Wendy, Archivist, California Historical Society, 678 Mission St, San Francisco, CA, 94105. Tel: 415-357-1848, Ext 20. Fax: 415-357-1850. p. 240

Welkie, Joyce, Ch, Plainfield-Guilford Township Public Library, 1120 Stafford Rd, Plainfield, IN, 46168-2230. Tel: 317-839-6602. Fax: 317-838-3805. p. 773

Well, Maureen, Dep Dir, Connecticut Judicial Branch Law Libraries, 90 Washington St, Third Flr, Hartford, CT, 06106. Tel: 860-706-5145. Fax: 860-706-5086. p. 344

Wellborn, Renee, Dir, Central Citizens' Library District, 1134 E 3100 North Rd, Ste C, Clifton, IL, 60927-7088. Tel: 815-694-2800. Fax: 815-694-3200. p. 630

Weller, Bridget, Librn, Auglaize County Law Library, County Courthouse, 201 Willipie St, Ste 207, Wapakoneta, OH, 45895. Tel: 419-738-3124. Fax: 419-738-4713. p. 1944

Weller, Cindy Beck, Mgr, Libr Serv, Cooper, White & Cooper, 201 California St, 17th Flr, San Francisco, CA, 94111-5002. Tel: 415-433-1900. Fax: 415-433-5530. p. 241

Weller, Leann, Pub Serv, University of New Mexico, Valencia Campus, 280 La Entrada, Los Lunas, NM, 87031. Tel: 505-925-8993. Fax: 505-925-8994. p. 1551

Weller, Marta, Operations Dir, Tech Coordr, Boyertown Community Library, 29 E Philadelphia Ave, Boyertown, PA, 19512-1124. Tel: 610-369-0496. Fax: 610-369-0542. p. 2036

Weller, Mary P, Dir, George H & Ella M Rodgers Memorial Library, 194 Derry Rd, Hudson, NH, 03051. Tel: 603-886-6030. Fax: 603-816-4501. p. 1452

Welles, Janice, Br Mgr, Latah County Library District, Juliaetta Branch, 205 Main St, Juliaetta, ID, 83535. Tel: 208-276-7071. Fax: 208-276-7071. p. 579

Wellik, Kay, Dir, Mayo Clinic Scottsdale Libraries, 13400 E Shea Blvd, Scottsdale, AZ, 85259. Tel: 480-301-8443. Fax: 480-301-7005. p. 80

Wellikson, McKay, Librn, Central Arizona College, 8470 N Overfield Rd, Coolidge, AZ, 85128. Tel: 520-494-5286. Fax: 520-494-5284. p. 60

Welling, Penny, Dir, Stanly County Public Library, 133 E Main St, Albemarle, NC, 28001. Tel: 704-986-3766. Fax: 704-983-6713. p. 1773

Wellinger, Patty, Ref Serv Coordr, University of Denver, Westminster Law Library, 2255 E Evans Ave, Denver, CO, 80208. Tel: 303-871-6188. Fax: 303-871-6999. p. 304

Wellington, Carol S, Info Res Spec, Day Pitney LLP, One International Pl, Boston, MA, 02110. Tel: 617-345-4600. Fax: 617-345-4745. p. 1060

Wellington, Claudette, Asst Librn, Torys Law Library, 237 Park Ave, 20th Flr, New York, NY, 10017. Tel: 212-880-6177. Fax: 212-682-0200. p. 1701

Wellington, Laurel, Libr Mgr, Brooklyn Hospital Center, 121 DeKalb Ave, 3rd Flr, Brooklyn, NY, 11201. Tel: 718-250-6943, 718-250-6944. Fax: 718-250-6428. p. 1590

Wellington-Nassios, Kathy, Pres, South Suburban Genealogical & Historical Society Library, 3000 W 170th Pl, Hazel Crest, IL, 60429-1174. Tel: 708-335-3340. p. 654

Welliver, Hilary, Asst Dir, Kent County Public Library, 497 S Red Haven Ln, Dover, DE, 19901. Tel: 302-698-6440. Fax: 302-698-6441. p. 382

Wellman, Debbie, Dir, Chouteau County Library, 1518 Main St, Fort Benton, MT, 59442. Tel: 406-622-5222. Fax: 406-622-5294. p. 1379

Wellman, Jared, Dir, Tech Serv & e-Res, Lincoln Land Community College Library, 5250 Shepherd Rd, Springfield, IL, 62794. Tel: 217-786-2354. Fax: 217-786-2251. p. 705

Wellnitz, Julie, Dir, Nobles County Library, 407 12th St, Worthington, MN, 56187. Tel: 507-372-2981. Fax: 507-372-2982. p. 1291

Wellnitz, Kirsten, Managing Libn, Bay County Library System, Auburn Area Branch Library, 235 W Midland Rd, Auburn, MI, 48611. Tel: 989-662-2381. Fax: 989-662-2647. p. 1156

Wellnitz, Kirsten, Managing Libn, Bay County Library System, Pinconning Branch Library, 218 S Kaiser St, Pinconning, MI, 48650-0477. Tel: 989-879-3283. Fax: 989-879-5669. p. 1156

Wells, Brendle, Br Mgr, Sacramento Public Library, Fair Oaks-Orangevale Community Library, 11601 Fair Oaks Blvd, Fair Oaks, CA, 95628. p. 225

Wells, Brittany, Pub Relations, Sweetwater County Library System, 300 N First East, Green River, WY, 82935. Tel: 307-875-3615, Ext 5300. Fax: 307-872-3203. p. 2655

Wells, Carole, Asst Libn, Roodhouse Public Library, 220 W Franklin St, Roodhouse, IL, 62082-1412. Tel: 217-589-5123. p. 698

Wells, Catherine, Asst Dir, Pub Serv, Case Western Reserve University, 11055 Euclid Ave, Cleveland, OH, 44106. Tel: 216-368-5201. Fax: 216-368-6950. p. 1876

Wells, Cindy, Media Spec, Missouri Western State University, 4525 Downs Dr, Saint Joseph, MO, 64507-2294. Tel: 816-271-4368. Fax: 816-271-4574. p. 1352

Wells, Connie, Tech Serv, Eastham Public Library, 190 Samoset Rd, Eastham, MA, 02642. Tel: 508-240-5950. Fax: 508-240-0786. p. 1086

Wells, Deborah Jean, Syst Libn, West Virginia State University, Campus Box L17, Institute, WV, 25112. Tel: 304-766-3150. Fax: 304-766-4103. p. 2562

Wells, Donna, Cat, Southeastern Baptist Theological Seminary Library, 114 N Wingate St, Wake Forest, NC, 27587. Tel: 919-556-3104. Fax: 919-863-8150. p. 1827

Wells, Dorian, Dir of Develop, Phoenixville Public Library, 183 Second Ave, Phoenixville, PA, 19460-3420. Tel: 610-933-3013, Ext 31. Fax: 610-933-4338. p. 2120

Wells, Elaine, Dir, State University of New York, State College of Optometry, 33 W 42nd St, New York, NY, 10036-8003. Tel: 212-938-5690. Fax: 212-938-5696. p. 1700

Wells, Elizabeth, Chair, Spec Coll, Libn, Samford University Library, 800 Lakeshore Dr, Birmingham, AL, 35229. Tel: 205-726-4103. Fax: 205-726-4009. p. 9

Wells, Ellen, Ch, Murray Public Library, 166 E 5300 South, Murray, UT, 84107-6075. Tel: 801-264-2580. Fax: 801-264-2586. p. 2408

Wells, Eunice F, Tech Coordr, Lipscomb University, One University Park Dr, Nashville, TN, 37204-3951. Tel: 615-966-5836. Fax: 615-966-5874. p. 2257

Wells, Geraldine, Ch, Tomah Public Library, 716 Superior Ave, Tomah, WI, 54660-2098. Tel: 608-374-7470. Fax: 608-374-7471. p. 2642

Wells, Janet, Dir, M-C River Valley Public Library District, 304 Main St, Meredosia, IL, 62665. Tel: 217-584-1571. Fax: 217-584-1571. p. 673

Wells, Jean, Access Serv, Winthrop University, 824 Oakland Ave, Rock Hill, SC, 29733. Tel: 803-323-2330. Fax: 803-323-2215. p. 2203

Wells, Jerry, Libn, Florida Department of Corrections, 8515 Hampton Springs Rd, Perry, FL, 32348. Tel: 850-838-4080. Fax: 850-838-4024. p. 483

Wells, John, Mgr, Morgan County Bar Association Library, Court House, 19 E Main St, McConnelsville, OH, 43756. Tel: 740-962-2262. Fax: 740-962-4522. p. 1916

Wells, John W, Dir, Garland County Library, 1427 Malvern Ave, Hot Springs, AR, 71901. Tel: 501-623-4161. Fax: 501-623-5647. p. 104

Wells, Julie, Dir, Urbandale Public Library, 3520 86th St, Urbandale, IA, 50322-4056. Tel: 515-278-3945. Fax: 515-278-3918. p. 848

Wells, Karen, Mgr, Libr Serv, Exempla Lutheran Medical Center, 8300 W 38th Ave, Wheat Ridge, CO, 80033-8270. Tel: 303-425-8662. Fax: 303-467-8794. p. 326

Wells, Karen, Bus Mgr, Jackson-George Regional Library System, 3214 Pascagoula St, Pascagoula, MS, 39567. Tel: 228-769-3092. Fax: 228-769-3146. p. 1310

Wells, Keith, Libr Dir, Denver Seminary, 6399 S Santa Fe Dr, Littleton, CO, 80120-2912. Tel: 303-762-6963. Fax: 303-762-6950. p. 317

Wells, Kimberly, Br Head, Denton Public Library, North Branch, 3020 N Locust, Denton, TX, 76209. Tel: 940-349-8796. Fax: 940-387-5367. p. 2312

Wells, Kyoko, Libr Mgr, New York Public Library - Astor, Lenox & Tilden Foundations, Dongan Hills Branch, 1617 Richmond Rd, (Between Seaview & Liberty Aves), Staten Island, NY, 10304. Tel: 718-980-4770. Fax: 718-987-6883. p. 1691

Wells, Linda, Dir, Craftsbury Public Library, 12 Church St, Craftsbury Common, VT, 05827-9696. Tel: 802-533-2346. Fax: 802-586-9683. p. 2422

Wells, Lisa, Asst Dir, Libr Serv, Pioneer Library System, 225 N Webster Ave, Norman, OK, 73069-7133. Tel: 405-701-2686. Fax: 405-701-2649. p. 1970

Wells, Lori, Dir, Gladstone Area School & Public Library, 300 S Tenth St, Gladstone, MI, 49837-1518. Tel: 906-428-4224. Fax: 906-789-8452. p. 1183

Wells, Marilyn, Libn, South Suburban College Library, 15800 S State St, Rm 1249, South Holland, IL, 60473-1200. Tel: 708-596-2000, Ext 2239. Fax: 708-210-5755. p. 704

Wells, Melissa, Dir, Menifee County Public Library, 1585 Main St, Frenchburg, KY, 40322. Tel: 606-768-2212. Fax: 606-768-9676. p. 914

Wells, Michael David, Dir, Libr & Info Tech, Cincinnati College of Mortuary Science Library, 645 W North Bend Rd, Cincinnati, OH, 45224-1428. Tel: 513-761-2020. Fax: 513-761-3333. p. 1869

Wells, Mickey, Electronic Res, Ref, University of Tampa, 401 W Kennedy Blvd, Tampa, FL, 33606-1490. Tel: 813-253-6231. Fax: 813-258-7426. p. 499

Wells, Pamela, Webmaster Libn, Lindenhurst Memorial Library, One Lee Ave, Lindenhurst, NY, 11757-5399. Tel: 631-957-7755. Fax: 631-957-7114. p. 1652

Wells, Patricia, Libn, Shilo Community Library, PO Box 177, Shilo, MB, R0K 2A0, CANADA. p. 2752

Wells, Paul, Dir, Middle Tennessee State University, Center for Popular Music, John Bragg Mass Communication Bldg, Rm 140, 1301 E Main St, Murfreesboro, TN, 37132. Tel: 615-898-2449. Fax: 615-898-5829. p. 2254

Wells, Paula, Ch, Forest Public Library, 210 S Raleigh St, Forest, MS, 39074. Tel: 601-469-1481. Fax: 601-469-5903. p. 1298

Wells, Rebecca, Dir, Brimfield Public Library, 25 Main St, Brimfield, MA, 01010-9701. Tel: 413-245-3518. Fax: 413-245-3468. p. 1070

Wells, Regina, Dir, Delaware Technical & Community College, 400 Stanton-Christiana Rd, Newark, DE, 19713-2197. Tel: 302-454-3939. Fax: 302-453-3079. p. 385

Wells, Sabrina, Libr Asst II, Montgomery City-County Public Library System, 245 High St, Montgomery, AL, 36104. Tel: 334-240-4300. Fax: 334-240-4977. p. 29

Wells, Sabrina, Libr Asst II, Montgomery City-County Public Library System, Pine Level Branch Library, 20 Kohn Dr, Pine Level, AL, 36065. Tel: 334-584-7144. p. 30

Wells, Shannon, Br Mgr, Robinson Public Library District, Hutsonville Branch, 104 S Main St, Hutsonville, IL, 62433. Tel: 618-563-9603. Fax: 618-563-9603. p. 695

Wells, Stephanie, Libn, Rio Hondo Community College Library, 3600 Workman Mill Rd, Whittier, CA, 90601. Tel: 562-908-3417. Fax: 562-463-4642. p. 283

Wells, Susan, Law Libn, Massachusetts Trial Court Law Libraries, Court House, 425 Main St, Greenfield, MA, 01301. Tel: 413-772-6580. Fax: 413-772-0743. p. 1092

Wells, Tanya, Libr Tech II, College of the North Atlantic, Port aux Basques Campus, 59 Grand Bay Rd, Port aux Basques, NL, A0M 1C0, CANADA. Tel: 709-695-3343. Fax: 709-695-2963. p. 2771

Wells, Tina, Dir, Church of Jesus Christ of Latter-Day Saints, 3100 Old Cheney Rd, Lincoln, NE, 68516-2775. Tel: 402-423-4561. p. 1404

Wells, Tish, Libn, McClatchy Washington Bureau Library, 700 12th St NW, Ste 1000, Washington, DC, 20005. Tel: 202-383-6032. p. 408

Wellspeak, Debra, Access Serv, Albany Medical College, 47 New Scotland Ave, MC 63, Albany, NY, 12208. Tel: 518-262-6460. Fax: 518-262-5820. p. 1568

Welmaker, Roland, Libn, Morehouse School of Medicine Library, 720 Westview Dr SW, Atlanta, GA, 30310-1495. Tel: 404-752-1534. Fax: 404-752-1049. p. 517

Welsh, Donald J, Head, Ref, College of William & Mary in Virginia, Earl Gregg Swem Library, One Landrum Dr, Williamsburg, VA, 23187. Tel: 757-221-3068. Fax: 757-221-2635. p. 2502

Welsh, Eric, Head, Res Serv, Regent University, 1000 Regent University Dr, Virginia Beach, VA, 23464-9800. Tel: 757-352-4454. Fax: 757-352-4451. p. 2499

Welsh, Evelyn, Bus Mgr, Tombigbee Regional Library System, 338 Commerce, West Point, MS, 39773. Tel: 662-494-4872. Fax: 662-494-0300. p. 1317

Welsh, Jennifer, Br Mgr, Stark County District Library, Lake Community Branch, 11955 Market Ave N, Uniontown, OH, 44685. Tel: 330-877-9975. Fax: 330-877-7568. p. 1864

Welsh, Lorraine, Dir, John Curtis Free Library, 534 Hanover St, Hanover, MA, 02339-2228. Tel: 781-826-2972. Fax: 781-826-3130. p. 1093

Welsh, Megan, Instruction & Ref Libn, State University of New York College of Technology, Bush Hall, Two Main St, Delhi, NY, 13753. Tel: 607-746-4635. Fax: 607-746-4327. p. 1613

Welsh, Sandy, In Charge, McKercher LLP, 374 Third Ave S, Saskatoon, SK, S7K 1M5, CANADA. Tel: 306-653-2000. Fax: 306-653-2699. p. 2925

Welsh, Sharon, Head, Circ Serv, Community Library, 24615 89th St, Salem, WI, 53168. Tel: 262-843-3348. Fax: 262-843-3144. p. 2636

Welsh, Sharon Llewellyn, Tech Serv, SEAHEC Medical Library, 2131 S 17th St, Box 9025, Wilmington, NC, 28402-9025. Tel: 910-343-2180. Fax: 910-762-7600. p. 1831

Welsh, Sylvia, Col Libn, Montserrat College of Art, 23 Essex St, Beverly, MA, 01915. Tel: 978-921-4242, Ext 1208. Fax: 978-922-4268. p. 1054

Welsing, Michele, Dir, Communications, Southern California Library for Social Studies & Research, 6120 S Vermont Ave, Los Angeles, CA, 90044. Tel: 323-759-6063. Fax: 323-759-2252. p. 177

Welter, Donna, Coordr, Ser, Loras College Library, 1450 Alta Vista St, Dubuque, IA, 52004-4327. Tel: 563-588-7654. Fax: 563-588-7147. p. 812

Welter, Linda, Librn, Somers Public Library, 502 Sixth St, Somers, IA, 50586. Tel: 515-467-5522. Fax: 515-467-5603. p. 845

Weltin, Heather, ILL, University of Wisconsin-Madison, 728 State St, Madison, WI, 53706. Tel: 608-262-3193. Fax: 608-265-2754. p. 2608

Welton, Eleanor, Librn, University of Manitoba Faculty of Social Work, Three Station Rd, Thompson, MB, R8N 0N3, CANADA. Tel: 204-677-1462. Fax: 204-677-4110. p. 2753

Welton, Nanette, Assoc Dir, University of Washington Libraries, Health Sciences Library, T-334 Health Sciences Bldg, Box 357155, 1959 NE Pacific St, Seattle, WA, 98195-7155. Tel: 206-543-5112. Fax: 206-543-3389. p. 2534

Welty, Ellen, Assoc Librn, Arizona State University Libraries, Library at the Polytechnic Campus, Academic Ctr, Bldg 20, 5988 S Backus Mall, Mesa, AZ, 85212. Tel: 480-727-1157. Fax: 480-727-1077. p. 84

Welzen, Julia, Dir, Argenta-Oreana Public Library District, 100 E Water, Argenta, IL, 62501. Tel: 217-795-2144. Fax: 217-795-4763. p. 589

Welzen, Julia, Dir, Argenta-Oreana Public Library District, 100 S Rte 48, Oreana, IL, 62554-7901. Tel: 217-468-2340. Fax: 217-468-2467. p. 685

Welzenbach, Kristen, Digital Syst & Serv Librn, Goucher College Library, 1021 Dulaney Valley Rd, Baltimore, MD, 21204. Tel: 410-337-6360. Fax: 410-337-6419. p. 1014

Wemer, Joyce, Br Mgr, Harford County Public Library, Fallston Branch, 1461 Fallston Rd, Fallston, MD, 21047-1699. Tel: 410-638-3003. Fax: 410-638-3005. p. 1020

Wemmlinger, Raymond, Librn, The Hampden-Booth Theatre Library at the Players, 16 Gramercy Park S, New York, NY, 10003. Tel: 212-228-1861. Fax: 212-253-6473. p. 1680

Wen, Linda, Head, Info Tech, University of Arkansas at Little Rock, 2801 S University Ave, Little Rock, AR, 72204. Tel: 501-569-3123. Fax: 501-569-3017. p. 107

Wen, Shixing, Tech Serv-Section Head, University of Minnesota Duluth Library, 416 Library Dr, Duluth, MN, 55812. Tel: 218-276-8498. Fax: 218-726-8019. p. 1248

Wen, Yan, Access Serv & Syst, Los Angeles Public Library System, Vermont Square, 1201 W 48th St, Los Angeles, CA, 90037-3787. Tel: 323-290-7406. Fax: 323-290-7408. p. 174

Wenderoth, Christine, Dr, Dir, Lutheran School of Theology at Chicago & McCormick Theological Seminary, 1100 E 55th St, Chicago, IL, 60615-5199. Tel: 773-256-0735. Fax: 773-256-0737. p. 618

Wendorf, Richard, Dir, Boston Athenaeum, 10 1/2 Beacon St, Boston, MA, 02108-3777. Tel: 617-227-0270. Fax: 617-227-5266. p. 1056

Wendt, Julie, Circ Supvr, Edgewood College Library, 1000 Edgewood College Dr, Madison, WI, 53711-1997. Tel: 608-663-3300. Fax: 608-663-6778. p. 2606

Wendt, Karen, Youth Serv Coordr, Monona Public Library, 1000 Nichols Rd, Monona, WI, 53716-2531. Tel: 608-222-6127. Fax: 608-222-8590. p. 2623

Wendt, Mari-Clare, Librn, Centegra Health System, 4201 Medical Center Dr, McHenry, IL, 60050-8499. Tel: 815-759-4076. Fax: 815-759-8088. p. 672

Wendt, Mark, Bus & Tech Mgr, Allen County Public Library, 900 Library Plaza, Fort Wayne, IN, 46802. Tel: 260-421-1216. Fax: 260-421-1386. p. 740

Wendt, Mike, Ref Librn, Washington State Library, Department of Transportation, Department of Transportation, Olympia, WA, 98504. Tel: 360-705-7710. Fax: 360-705-6831. p. 2545

Wendt, Nancy, Mgr, Circ Serv, Suffern Free Library, 210 Lafayette Ave, Suffern, NY, 10901. Tel: 845-357-1237. Fax: 845-357-3156. p. 1750

Wendt, Wendy, Dir, Grand Forks Public Library, 2110 Library Circle, Grand Forks, ND, 58201-6324. Tel: 701-772-8116. Fax: 701-772-1379. p. 1842

Wendtland, Fran, Br Mgr, Maricopa County Library District, Goodyear Branch Library, 250 N Litchfield Park Rd, Ste 185, Goodyear, AZ, 85338. Tel: 602-652-3472. Fax: 602-652-3475. p. 74

Wendy, Ziechner, Pres, Origami USA Library, 15 W 77th St, New York, NY, 10024-5192. Tel: 212-769-5635. Fax: 212-769-5668. p. 1696

Weng, Cathy, Head, Cat, The College of New Jersey Library, 2000 Pennington Rd, Ewing, NJ, 08628-0718. Tel: 609-771-2311, 609-771-2332. Fax: 609-637-5177. p. 1484

Weng, Matthew, In Charge, New Jersey State League of Municipalities, 222 W State St, Trenton, NJ, 08608. Tel: 609-695-3481, Ext 37. Fax: 609-695-5156. p. 1535

Wenger, Carolyn, Archivist, Curator, Lancaster Mennonite Historical Society Library, 2215 Millstream Rd, Lancaster, PA, 17602-1499. Tel: 717-393-9745. Fax: 717-393-8751. p. 2077

Wenger, Charles, Ref Librn, United States Geological Survey Library, 345 Middlefield Rd, Bldg 15 (MS-955), Menlo Park, CA, 94025-3591. Tel: 650-329-5427. Fax: 650-329-5132. p. 185

Wenger, Cynthia, Dir, Reed Memorial Library, 167 E Main St, Ravenna, OH, 44266-3197. Tel: 330-296-2827. Fax: 330-296-3780. p. 1931

Wenger, Dorena, Br Mgr, Chicago Public Library, Jefferson Park, 5363 W Lawrence Ave, Chicago, IL, 60630. Tel: 312-744-1998. Fax: 312-744-3811. p. 609

Wenger, Jean, Intl Law Librn, Cook County Law Library, 2900 Richard J Daley Ctr, 50 W Washington, Chicago, IL, 60602. Tel: 312-603-5423. Fax: 312-603-4716. p. 611

Wenger, Levi, Librn, The Frances Kibble Kenny Lake Public Library, Mile 5 Edgerton Hwy, Copper Center, AK, 99573-9703. Tel: 907-822-3015. Fax: 907-822-3015. p. 46

Wenger, Martha, Asst Librn, Barton Rees Pogue Memorial Library, 29 W Washington St, Upland, IN, 46989. Tel: 765-998-2971. Fax: 765-998-2961. p. 782

Wenner, Lisa, Dir, Haydenville Public Library, Main St, Haydenville, MA, 01039-0516. Tel: 413-268-8406. Fax: 413-268-8406. p. 1095

Wenner, Lisa, Librn, Meekins Library, Two Williams St, Williamsburg, MA, 01096. Tel: 413-268-7472. Fax: 413-268-7488. p. 1140

Wenner, Marylou, Librn, Pipersville Free Library, 7114 Durham Rd, Pipersville, PA, 18947-9998. Tel: 215-766-7880. p. 2121

Wenner, Sandra, Asst Dir, Content Mgt, Library of Rush University Medical Center, Armour Academic Ctr, 600 S Paulina St, 5th Flr, Chicago, IL, 60612-3874. Tel: 312-942-2282. Fax: 312-942-3143. p. 617

Wenning, Kim, ILL, University of Indianapolis, 1400 E Hanna Ave, Indianapolis, IN, 46227-3697. Tel: 317-788-3268. Fax: 317-788-3275. p. 755

Wenning, Sarah, Mgr, Halifax Public Libraries, Keshen Goodman Branch, 330 Lacewood Dr, Halifax, NS, B3M 4G2, CANADA. Tel: 902-490-5738. Fax: 902-490-5739. p. 2779

Wennstrom, Jana, Training Coordr, Tacoma Art Museum, 1701 Pacific Ave, Tacoma, WA, 98402. Tel: 253-272-4258, Ext 3030. Fax: 253-627-1898. p. 2540

Wenrich, Carolyn, Br Mgr, Caroline Library Inc, Ladysmith, Ladysmith Village, 7199 Clara Smith Dr, Ruther Glen, VA, 22546. Tel: 804-448-0357. Fax: 804-448-3124. p. 2479

Wensink, Debra, Br Mgr, Patrick Henry School District Public Library, 208 NE Ave, Deshler, OH, 43516. Tel: 419-278-3616. Fax: 419-278-3616. p. 1896

Wenslauskis, Matthew, Ref Librn, Thomas Ford Memorial Library, 800 Chestnut Ave, Western Springs, IL, 60558. Tel: 708-246-0520. Fax: 708-246-0403. p. 717

Wentink, Andrew, Spec Coll Librn, Middlebury College Library, 110 Storrs Ave, Middlebury, VT, 05753-6007. Tel: 802-443-5501. Fax: 802-443-2074, 802-443-5698. p. 2428

Wentworth, Linda, Head, Coll, Jones Library, Inc, 43 Amity St, Amherst, MA, 01002-2285. Tel: 413-259-3168. Fax: 413-256-4096. p. 1048

Wentworth, Linda, Librn, Leverett Library, 75 Montague Rd, Leverett, MA, 01054-9701. Tel: 413-548-9220. Fax: 413-548-9034. p. 1099

Wentworth, Van, Librn, Monson Free Public Library, Ten Tenney Hill Rd, Monson, ME, 04464-6432. Tel: 207-997-3641. Fax: 207-997-3785. p. 992

Wentz, Jean, Archives Asst, University of Wisconsin-Green Bay, 2420 Nicolet Dr, Green Bay, WI, 54311-7001. Tel: 920-465-2539. Fax: 920-465-2136. p. 2596

Wentz, Julia, Dir, Loyola University Chicago Libraries, Law School Library, 25 E Pearson St, 3rd Flr, Chicago, IL, 60611. Tel: 312-915-7199. Fax: 312-915-6797. p. 617

Wentz, Stephanie, Librn, Mayo Clinic Libraries, 1216 Second St SW, Rochester, MN, 55902. Tel: 507-255-6925. Fax: 507-255-5254. p. 1272

Wentzel, Barbara, Dir, Kimberly Public Library, Gerard H Van Hoof Library, 625 Grand Ave, Little Chute, WI, 54140. Tel: 920-788-7825. Fax: 920-788-7827. p. 2602

Wenzel, Allen, Automation Syst Coordr, Wisconsin Library Services, 728 State St, Rm 464, Madison, WI, 53706-1494. Tel: 608-265-4167. Fax: 608-262-6067. p. 2958

Wenzel, Debbie, Tech Serv, Alpha Park Public Library District, 3527 S Airport Rd, Bartonville, IL, 61607-1799. Tel: 309-697-3822, Ext 16. Fax: 309-697-9681. p. 592

Wenzel, Duane, Br Mgr, Hawaii State Public Library System, Salt Lake-Moanalua Public Library, 3225 Salt Lake Blvd, Honolulu, HI, 96818. Tel: 808-831-6831. Fax: 808-831-6834. p. 563

Wenzler, John, Assoc Dean, Digital Futures, Tech Serv & IT, San Jose State University, One Washington Sq, San Jose, CA, 95192-0028. Tel: 408-808-2065. Fax: 408-808-2141. p. 251

Weppler-Selear, Mary, Libr Serv Mgr, University of California, Merced Library, 5200 N Lake Rd, Merced, CA, 95343-5001. Tel: 209-205-8628. Fax: 209-228-4271. p. 186

Werbach, John, Financial Mgr, Maricopa County Library District, 2700 N Central Ave, Ste 700, Phoenix, AZ, 85004. Tel: 602-652-3051. Fax: 602-652-3071. p. 74

Werbeloff, Marina D, Librn, Harvard Library, Physics Research Library, 450 Jefferson Laboratory, 17 Oxford St, Cambridge, MA, 02138. Tel: 617-495-2878. Fax: 617-495-0416. p. 1076

Werchan, Gary, Syst Coordr, Frisco Public Library, 6101 Frisco Square Blvd, Ste 3000, Frisco, TX, 75034-3000. Tel: 972-292-5669. Fax: 972-292-5699. p. 2325

Werden, Rose, Librn, Walpole Town Library, North Walpole, Ten Church St, North Walpole, NH, 03609. Tel: 603-445-5153. Fax: 603-445-5153. p. 1467

Wereley, Eileen, Librn, Ontario Police College Library, 10716 Hacienda Rd, Aylmer, ON, N5H 2T2, CANADA. Tel: 519-773-4264, 519-773-4266. Fax: 519-773-8225. p. 2793

Wergeland, Kari, Librn, Cuyamaca College Library, 900 Rancho San Diego Pkwy, El Cajon, CA, 92019-4304. Tel: 619-660-4412. Fax: 619-660-4493. p. 145

Werhane, Amanda, Interim Librn, University of Wisconsin-Madison, Biology Library, 430 Lincoln Dr, Madison, WI, 53706. Tel: 608-262-2740. Fax: 608-262-9003. p. 2608

Werking, Albert, Genealogist, Washington County Historical Society, 135 W Washington St, Hagerstown, MD, 21740. Tel: 301-797-8782. Fax: 240-625-9498. p. 1031

Werley, Tom, Ch, South Portland Public Library, 482 Broadway, South Portland, ME, 04106. Tel: 207-767-7660. Fax: 207-767-7626. p. 1002

Werlinger, Elaine, Supvr, Circ, Carson City Library, 900 N Roop St, Carson City, NV, 89701. Tel: 775-887-2244. Fax: 775-887-2273. p. 1425

Werlink, Joy, Curator, Washington State Historical Society Research Center, 315 N Stadium Way, Tacoma, WA, 98403. Tel: 253-798-5916. Fax: 253-597-4186. p. 2541

Werne, Ken, Mgr, Johnson County Library, Antioch, 8700 Shawnee Mission Pkwy, Merriam, KS, 66202. Tel: 913-261-2328. Fax: 913-261-2320. p. 888

Werner, Barb, ILL Spec, College of Saint Scholastica Library, 1200 Kenwood Ave, Duluth, MN, 55811-4199. Tel: 218-723-6140. Fax: 218-723-5948. p. 1247

Werner, Debra, Ref & Instruction Librn, University of Chicago Library, John Crerar Library, 5730 S Ellis Ave, Chicago, IL, 60637. Tel: 773-702-8552. p. 626

Werner, Edward, Dr, Mgr, Info Sys, Saint Lucie County Library System, 101 Melody Lane, Fort Pierce, FL, 34950-4402. Tel: 772-462-1802. Fax: 772-462-2750. p. 447

Werner, Elizabeth, Dir, Clearwater Christian College, 3400 Gulf-to-Bay Blvd, Clearwater, FL, 33759-4595. Tel: 727-726-1153, Ext 218. Fax: 727-723-8566. p. 431

Werner, Lance M, Dir, Kent District Library, 814 West River Center Dr NE, Comstock Park, MI, 49321. Tel: 616-784-2007. Fax: 616-647-3828. p. 1165

Werner, Linda, Dir, Columbus Village Public Library, 222 W Broadway Ave, Columbus, NM, 88029. Tel: 575-531-2612. p. 1554

Werner, Linda, In Charge, Tillamook County Library, Rockaway Beach Branch, 120 N Coral, Rockaway Beach, OR, 97136. Tel: 503-355-2665. Fax: 503-355-2665. p. 2021

Werner, Linda Elaine, Dir, Lamberton Public Library, 101 E Second Ave, Lamberton, MN, 56152-1047. Tel: 507-752-7220. Fax: 507-752-7220. p. 1256

Werner, Peg, Dir, Viking Library System, 204 N Cascade St, Fergus Falls, MN, 56537. Tel: 218-739-5286. Fax: 218-739-5287. p. 1251

Werner, Roye, Bus & Econ Librn, Carnegie Mellon University, Hunt Library, 4909 Frew St, Pittsburgh, PA, 15213-3890. Tel: 412-268-2446. Fax: 412-268-2793. p. 2123

Werner, Sherley, Librn, Congregational Church of Patchogue, 95 E Main St, Patchogue, NY, 11772. Tel: 631-475-1235. Fax: 631-207-9470. p. 1715

Werner, Stacy, Ch, Joslin Memorial Library, 4391 Main St, Waitsfield, VT, 05673-6155. Tel: 802-496-4205. p. 2438

Werner, Susan, Br Mgr, Hawaii State Public Library System, Wailuku Public Library, 251 High St, Wailuku, HI, 96793. Tel: 808-243-5766. Fax: 808-243-5768. p. 563

Werner, Tracy, Libr Assoc, Colville Confederated Tribe Library, Inchelium Resource Center, 12 Community Loop Rd, Inchelium, WA, 99138. Tel: 509-722-7037. Fax: 509-533-7040. p. 2521

Wernet, Bill, Tech Serv, Lee Ola Roberts Public Library, 140 W Main St, Whiteville, TN, 38075. Tel: 731-254-8834. Fax: 731-254-8805. p. 2269

Wernet, Mary Linn, Head Archivist, Northwestern State University Libraries, 913 University Pkwy, Natchitoches, LA, 71497. Tel: 318-357-4585. Fax: 318-357-4470. p. 958

Wernette, Jan, Asst Head, Adult Serv, Villa Park Public Library, 305 S Ardmore Ave, Villa Park, IL, 60181-2698. Tel: 630-834-1164. Fax: 630-834-0489. p. 714

Werre, Debbie, Tech Serv, Alexander Mitchell Public Library, 519 S Kline St, Aberdeen, SD, 57401-4495. Tel: 605-626-7097. Fax: 605-626-3506. p. 2209

Werre, Pam, Pub Serv, Minnesota State University Moorhead, 1104 Seventh Ave S, Moorhead, MN, 56563. Tel: 218-477-2922. Fax: 218-477-5924. p. 1266

Wersching, Yolande, Head of Libr, Loyola University Chicago Libraries, Lewis Library, 25 E Pearson St, 6th Flr, Chicago, IL, 60611. Tel: 312-915-6623. Fax: 312-915-6637. p. 617

Wertheim, Jan, Librn, Sweetser Children's Services, 50 Moody St, Saco, ME, 04072-0892. Tel: 207-294-4945. Fax: 207-294-4940. p. 999

Wertheimer, Andrew B, Dr, Assoc Prof, Chair, University of Hawaii, 2550 The Mall, Honolulu, HI, 96822. Tel: 808-956-7321. Fax: 808-956-5835. p. 2964

Wertheimer, Donna, Ref Serv, Rutgers University Libraries, Paul Robeson Library, Camden, 300 N Fourth St, Camden, NJ, 08102-1404. Tel: 856-225-6033. Fax: 856-225-6428. p. 1477

Werthman-Gizdich, Kathleen, Mgr, Kootenai-Shoshone Area Libraries, Spirit Lake Branch, 32575 N Fifth Ave, Spirit Lake, ID, 83869. Tel: 208-623-5353. Fax: 208-623-5353. p. 575

Werthmann, Eric, Dir, Acorn Public Library District, 15624 S Central Ave, Oak Forest, IL, 60452-3204. Tel: 708-687-3700. Fax: 708-687-3712. p. 683

Wertime, Sam, Ref Librn, Dykema Gossett PLLC, Ten S Wacker Dr, Ste 2300, Chicago, IL, 60606. Tel: 312-876-1700. Fax: 312-876-1155. p. 613

Wertin, Libby, Librn/Acad Files, Academy of Motion Picture Arts & Sciences, 333 S La Cienega Blvd, Beverly Hills, CA, 90211. Tel: 310-247-3000, Ext 2208. Fax: 310-657-5193. p. 128

Wertkin, Jennifer, Ref Librn, Columbia University, Arthur W Diamond Law Library, 435 W 116th St, New York, NY, 10027. Tel: 212-854-3922. Fax: 212-854-3295. p. 1674

Wertz, Jolene, Ref Serv, Historical Society of Western Pennsylvania, 1212 Smallman St, Pittsburgh, PA, 15222. Tel: 412-454-6365. Fax: 412-454-6028. p. 2125

Wertzberger, Janelle, Head, Ref, Gettysburg College, 300 N Washington St, Gettysburg, PA, 17325. Tel: 717-337-7010. Fax: 717-337-7001. p. 2059

Wesby, Pamela, Dir, Middleton Public Library, 7425 Hubbard Ave, Middleton, WI, 53562-3117. Tel: 608-831-5564. Fax: 608-836-5724. p. 2616

Wesdyk, Jennifer, Librn, Wapiti Regional Library, Prud'homme Public Library, 45 Government Rd, Prud'homme, SK, S0K 3K0, CANADA. Tel: 306-654-2221. Fax: 306-654-4411. p. 2922

Wesdyk, Jennifer, Librn, Wapiti Regional Library, Vonda Public Library, 204 Main St, Vonda, SK, S0K 4N0, CANADA. Tel: 306-258-2035. p. 2922

Weseloh, Benjamin R, Adult Serv Mgr, West Chicago Public Library District, 118 W Washington St, West Chicago, IL, 60185. Tel: 630-231-1552. Fax: 630-231-1709. p. 717

Wesley, Crystal, Acq, Centre College of Kentucky, 600 W Walnut St, Danville, KY, 40422. Tel: 859-238-5273. Fax: 859-236-7925. p. 911

Wesley, Holley, Ref, Emmet O'Neal Library, 50 Oak St, Mountain Brook, AL, 35213. Tel: 205-879-0459. Fax: 205-879-5388. p. 32

Wesley, Susan, Ref Serv, Ser, Kenai Community Library, 163 Main St Loop, Kenai, AK, 99611-7723. Tel: 907-283-4378. Fax: 907-283-2266. p. 50

Wesley, Threasa, Head, Res & Instrul Serv, Northern Kentucky University, University Dr, Highland Heights, KY, 41099. Tel: 859-572-5721. Fax: 859-572-5390. p. 917

Wesley, Yvonne, Librn, Sr Adminr, Parkland Health & Hospital System, 5201 Harry Hines Blvd, Dallas, TX, 75235. Tel: 214-590-0066. Fax: 214-590-2720. p. 2309

Wesman, Evelyn, Mgr, Circ Serv, Erie County Public Library, 160 E Front St, Erie, PA, 16507. Tel: 814-451-6908. Fax: 814-451-6907. p. 2055

Wesner, Kendra, Ch, Redford Township District Library, 25320 W Six Mile, Redford, MI, 48240. Tel: 313-531-5960. Fax: 313-531-1721. p. 1220

Wesolek, Mary, Ch, Peoples Library, 880 Barnes St, New Kensington, PA, 15068. Tel: 724-339-1021, Ext 15. Fax: 724-339-2027. p. 2097

Wesolowski, Paul G, Dir, Ref, The Freedonia Gazette, 335 Fieldstone Dr, New Hope, PA, 18938-1012. Tel: 215-862-9734. p. 2097

Wess, Susan, Dir, Milan Public Library, 151 Wabash St, Milan, MI, 48160. Tel: 734-439-1240. Fax: 734-439-5625. p. 1209

Wessale, Lois, Head, Tech Serv, Lake Villa District Library, 1001 E Grand Ave, Lake Villa, IL, 60046. Tel: 847-356-7711, Ext 233. Fax: 847-265-9595. p. 663

Wessel, Dodie, Dir, Greater West Central Public Library District, 202 Center St, Augusta, IL, 62311. Tel: 217-392-2211. Fax: 217-392-2211. p. 591

Wessells, Mike, Br Mgr, Timberland Regional Library, Yelm Branch, 210 Prairie Park St, Yelm, WA, 98597. Tel: 360-458-3374. Fax: 360-458-5172. p. 2544

Wessells, Robert S, Asst Librn, United States Navy, Academic Resources Information Center (ARIC), 440 Meyerkord Rd, Newport, RI, 02841. Tel: 401-841-4352, 401-841-6631. Fax: 401-841-2805. p. 2170

Wesselowski, Jean, Supvr, Acq, Fort Hays State University, 600 Park St, Hays, KS, 67601-4099. Tel: 785-628-4343. Fax: 785-628-4096. p. 871

Wessels, Joanne, IT Mgr, Webmaster, Sanibel Public Library District, 770 Dunlop Rd, Sanibel, FL, 33957. Tel: 239-472-2483. Fax: 239-472-9524. p. 489

Wessels, Michelle, Dir, East Dubuque District Library, 350 Wall St, East Dubuque, IL, 61025-1222. Tel: 815-747-3052. Fax: 815-747-6062. p. 638

Wessenberg, Kristi, Ref Serv, Samuel Merritt College, 400 Hawthorne Ave, Oakland, CA, 94609. Tel: 510-869-6833. Fax: 510-869-6633. p. 199

Wessling, Jean, Asst Librn, Fisher-Whiting Memorial Library, 609 Courtright St, Mapleton, IA, 51034. Tel: 712-881-1312. Fax: 712-881-1312. p. 829

Wessner, Lela, In Charge, United States Navy, Resource Center, Naval Station Bremerton Base-MWR, 120 S Dewey St, Bldg 502, Bremerton, WA, 98314-5000. Tel: 360-535-5932. Fax: 360-476-2908. p. 2511

Wesson, Lindsey, Ch, Nashville Public Library, 615 Church St, Nashville, TN, 37219-2314. Tel: 615-862-5760. Fax: 615-862-5771. p. 2257

Wesson, Ruby, Libr Dir, Henryetta Public Library, 518 W Main, Henryetta, OK, 74437. Tel: 918-652-7377. Fax: 918-652-2796. p. 1965

West, Amy, Archivist, University of Minnesota Libraries-Twin Cities, Charles Babbage Institute, 211 Elmer L Andersen Library, 222 21st Ave S, Minneapolis, MN, 55455. Tel: 612-624-5050. Fax: 612-625-8054. p. 1262

West, Anna, Access Serv, Monterey Institute of International Studies, 425 Van Buren St, Monterey, CA, 93940. Tel: 831-647-4133. Fax: 831-647-3518. p. 190

West, Betsy, Librn, Grove Hill Public Library, 108 Dubose Ave, Grove Hill, AL, 36451-9502. Tel: 251-275-8157. Fax: 251-275-8157. p. 19

West, Brenda, Br Mgr, Tuscarawas County Public Library, Emma Huber Memorial Library, 356 Fifth St SW, Strasburg, OH, 44680. Tel: 330-878-5711. Fax: 330-878-5711. p. 1921

West, C Quill, Circ Mgr, Marylhurst University, 17600 Pacific Hwy (Hwy 43), Marylhurst, OR, 97036-7036. Tel: 503-699-6261, Ext 4435. Fax: 503-636-1957. p. 2004

West, C Quill, Instrul & Electronic Res Librn, Walla Walla Community College Library, 500 Tausick Way, Walla Walla, WA, 99362-9267. Tel: 509-527-4294. Fax: 509-527-4480. p. 2547

West, Carol, Electronic Res, Southern New Hampshire University, 2500 N River Rd, Manchester, NH, 03106-1045. Tel: 603-645-9605, Ext 2159. Fax: 603-645-9685. p. 1456

West, Cheri, Libr Tech, New Mexico Junior College, One Thunderbird Circle, Hobbs, NM, 88240. Tel: 575-492-2870. Fax: 575-492-2883. p. 1557

West, Cheryl, Ch, Muskingum County Library System, 220 N Fifth St, Zanesville, OH, 43701-3587. Tel: 740-453-0391, Ext 115. Fax: 740-455-6937. p. 1953

West, Debbie, Coll Develop/Ref Librn, Troy University, Montgomery Campus, 252 Montgomery St, Montgomery, AL, 36104-3425. Tel: 334-241-5820. Fax: 334-241-9590. p. 31

West, Debby, Electronic Res, Midland College, 3600 N Garfield, Midland, TX, 79705. Tel: 432-685-4560. Fax: 432-685-6710. p. 2363

West, Deborah, Ref & Instruction, Gannon University, 109 University Sq, Erie, PA, 16541. Tel: 814-871-7557. Fax: 814-871-5666. p. 2055

West, Deborah, Chair, Erie Area Health Information Library Cooperative, Gannon University, Nash Library, 109 University Sq, Erie, PA, 16541. Tel: 814-871-7667. Fax: 814-871-5666. p. 2954

West, Elaine, Dir, Smith County Public Library, 215 Main St N, Carthage, TN, 37030. Tel: 615-735-1326. Fax: 615-735-2317. p. 2226

West, George, Dir of Tech, Knox County Public Library, 206 Knox St, Barbourville, KY, 40906. Tel: 606-546-5339, Ext 4. Fax: 606-546-3602. p. 906

West, Heather, Dir, Libr Serv, SIAST-Saskatchewan Institute of Applied Science & Technology, 600 Saskatchewan St W, Moose Jaw, SK, S6H 4R4, CANADA. Tel: 306-691-8233. Fax: 306-694-3427. p. 2919

West, J Thomas, Chief Exec Officer, US National Ski Hall of Fame, 610 Palms Ave, Ishpeming, MI, 49849. Tel: 906-485-6323. Fax: 906-486-4570. p. 1194

West, Jaci, Adult Serv, Paul Sawyier Public Library, 319 Wapping St, Frankfort, KY, 40601-2605. Tel: 502-352-2665. Fax: 502-227-2250. p. 914

West, Janet, Ref Serv, Port Washington Public Library, One Library Dr, Port Washington, NY, 11050. Tel: 516-883-4400. Fax: 516-883-7927. p. 1721

West, Jannie, Dir, Libr Serv, Eleanor London Cote Saint Luc Public Library, 5851 Blvd Cavendish, Cote Saint-Luc, QC, H4W 2X8, CANADA. Tel: 514-485-6900. Fax: 514-485-6966. p. 2881

West, Jennifer, Dir, Highland County District Library, Ten Willettsville Pike, Hillsboro, OH, 45133. Tel: 937-393-3114. Fax: 937-393-2985. p. 1904

West, John R, Dir, Austin College, 900 N Grand Ave, Ste 6L, Sherman, TX, 75090-4402. Tel: 903-813-2490. Fax: 903-813-2297. p. 2387

West, Joyce, Adult Serv Sr Libr Mgr, Alachua County Library District, 401 E University Ave, Gainesville, FL, 32601-5453. Tel: 352-334-3930. Fax: 352-334-3918. p. 448

West, Karen, Asst Librn, Fairfield/Teton Public Library, 14 North Fourth St, Fairfield, MT, 59436. Tel: 406-467-2477. Fax: 406-467-2477. p. 1378

West, Kim, AV Coordr, Laramie County Library System, 2200 Pioneer Ave, Cheyenne, WY, 82001-3610. Tel: 307-773-7212. Fax: 307-634-2082. p. 2652

West, Leslie Cost, Adult Serv, Bessemer Public Library, 701 Ninth Ave N, Bessemer, AL, 35020-5305. Tel: 205-428-7868. Fax: 205-428-7885. p. 6

West, Linda, Libr Spec, Northwestern State University Libraries, 3329 University Pkwy, Leesville, LA, 71446. Tel: 337-392-3126. Fax: 337-392-3184. p. 955

West, Linda, Dir of Tech Serv, Northeastern State University, 711 N Grand Ave, Tahlequah, OK, 74464-2333. Tel: 918-456-5511, Ext 3200. Fax: 918-458-2197. p. 1979

West, Lori, Br Mgr, Fargo Public Library, Northport, 2714 Broadway, Fargo, ND, 58102. Tel: 701-476-4026. p. 1841

West, Lori, Mgr, Br Serv, Fargo Public Library, 102 N Third St, Fargo, ND, 58102. Tel: 701-476-4040. Fax: 701-241-8581. p. 1841

West, Lori K, Br Mgr, Fargo Public Library, Dr James Carlson Branch, 2801 32nd Ave S, Fargo, ND, 58103. Tel: 701-476-4040. Fax: 701-364-2852. p. 1841

West, Lynda, Br Librn, Duplin County Library, Warsaw-Kornegay Library, 117 E College St, Warsaw, NC, 28398. Tel: 910-293-4664. Fax: 910-293-4664. p. 1804

West, Marlene, Cat, Govt Doc, University of Puget Sound, 1500 N Warner St, Campus Mail Box 1021, Tacoma, WA, 98416-1021. Tel: 253-879-8617. Fax: 253-879-3670. p. 2541

West, Mary, Librn, Morristown Centennial Library, Seven Richmond St, Morrisville, VT, 05661. Tel: 802-888-3853. p. 2430

West, Melanie, Assoc Dir, Circ/Media Serv, Embry-Riddle Aeronautical University, 600 S Clyde Morris Blvd, Daytona Beach, FL, 32114-3900. Tel: 386-226-6591. Fax: 386-226-6368. p. 436

West, Polly, Asst Librn, Colfax Public Library, 207 S Clark St, Colfax, IN, 46035. Tel: 765-324-2915, Ext 100. Fax: 765-324-2689. p. 732

West, Rex, ILL, Ser, Lambuth University, 705 Lambuth Blvd, Jackson, TN, 38301. Tel: 731-425-3270. Fax: 731-425-3200. p. 2238

West, Richard, Res Sharing Librn, University of Wisconsin-Madison, Kurt Wendt Engineering Library, 215 N Randall Ave, Madison, WI, 53706. Tel: 608-262-3493. Fax: 608-262-4739, 608-265-8751. p. 2610

West, Richard, Ser Tech Serv Librn, University of Wisconsin-Madison, Kurt Wendt Engineering Library, 215 N Randall Ave, Madison, WI, 53706. Tel: 608-262-3493. Fax: 608-262-4739, 608-265-8751. p. 2610

West, Sally, Circ, Croton Free Library, 171 Cleveland Dr, Croton-on-Hudson, NY, 10520. Tel: 914-271-6612. Fax: 914-271-0931. p. 1612

West, Sandy, Coordr, Tech Serv, Rend Lake College, 468 N Ken Gray Pkwy, Ina, IL, 62846. Tel: 618-437-5321. Fax: 618-437-5677. p. 658

West, Sandy, Dir, Mount Hope Library, 109 S Ohio, Mount Hope, KS, 67108. Tel: 316-667-2665. p. 884

West, Sharon, Coordr, Libr Serv, Charles C Tandy MD Health Sciences Library, 1441 N Beckley Ave, Dallas, TX, 75203. Tel: 214-947-2341. Fax: 214-947-2343. p. 2310

West, Sharon, Mgr, Saskatchewan Justice, Court of the Queen's Bench, Court House, 2425 Victoria Ave, Regina, SK, S4P 3V7, CANADA. Tel: 306-787-7809. Fax: 306-787-7160. p. 2924

West, Sheree, Med Librn, Kalispell Regional Medical Center, 310 Sunnyview Lane, Kalispell, MT, 59901. Tel: 406-752-1739. Fax: 406-752-8771. p. 1384

West, Tammy, Br Mgr, Wayne County Public Library, Collinwood Depot, 101 E Depot St, Collinwood, TN, 38450. Tel: 931-724-2498. Fax: 931-724-2498. p. 2268

West, Thomas, Adult Coordr, Brazoria County Library System, 451 N Velasco, Ste 250, Angleton, TX, 77515. Tel: 979-864-1507. Fax: 979-864-1298. p. 2275

West, Timothy J, Ref/Tech Serv, Flat River Community Library, 200 W Judd St, Greenville, MI, 48838-2225. Tel: 616-754-6359. Fax: 616-754-1398. p. 1186

Westall, Marta, Exec Dir, Central Florida Library Cooperative, 431 E Horatio Ave, Ste 230, Maitland, FL, 32751. Tel: 407-644-9050. Fax: 407-644-7023. p. 2940

Westbay, Karen, Cat, Northwest Community College Library, 5331 McConnell Ave, Terrace, BC, V8G 4X2, CANADA. Tel: 250-638-5407. Fax: 250-635-1594. p. 2739

Westbroks, Lainey, Tech Mgr, East Cleveland Public Library, 14101 Euclid Ave, East Cleveland, OH, 44112-3891. Tel: 216-541-4128. Fax: 216-541-1790. p. 1897

Westbrook, Gail Lee, Dir, Glenville State College, 100 High St, Glenville, WV, 26351. Tel: 304-462-4109, Ext 6161. Fax: 304-462-4049. p. 2559

Westbrook, Hugh M, Dir, Greenville Public Library, 414 W Main St, Greenville, IL, 62246-1615. Tel: 618-664-3115. Fax: 618-664-9442. p. 652

Westbrook, Janet, Web Adminr, Maturango Museum, 100 E Las Flores Ave, Ridgecrest, CA, 93555. Tel: 760-375-6900. Fax: 760-375-0479. p. 216

Westbrook, Josh, Automation Syst Coordr, Walla Walla County Rural Library District, 37 Jade Ave, Walla Walla, WA, 99362-1628. Tel: 509-527-3284. Fax: 509-527-3740. p. 2547

Westbrook, Lydia, Dir, American Hotel & Lodging Association, 229 C N Hilton Hotel & College, University of Houston, Houston, TX, 77204-3028. Tel: 713-743-2515. p. 2334

Westbrook, Lynn, Asst Prof, University of Texas at Austin, One University Sta, D7000, Austin, TX, 78712-0390. Tel: 512-471-3821. Fax: 512-471-3971. p. 2975

Westbrook, Mary, Cat, Central Rappahannock Regional Library, 1201 Caroline St, Fredericksburg, VA, 22401-3761. Tel: 540-372-1144. Fax: 540-373-9411. p. 2465

Westbrook, Miriam, Libr Tech, Colorado Department of Corrections, 21000 Hwy 350, Model, CO, 81059. Tel: 719-845-3212. p. 318

Westbrook, Sandy, Ch, South Windsor Public Library, 1550 Sullivan Ave, South Windsor, CT, 06074. Tel: 860-644-1541. Fax: 860-644-7645. p. 368

Westbrook, Sondra, Dir, Sinking Spring Public Library, 3940 Penn Ave, Sinking Spring, PA, 19608. Tel: 610-678-4311. Fax: 610-670-4826. p. 2140

Westbrook, W Michael, Bibliog Instruction/Ref, Illinois College, 245 Park St, Jacksonville, IL, 62650. Tel: 217-245-3020. Fax: 217-245-3082. p. 658

Westbrooks, Elaine, Assoc Univ Librn, Res, University of Michigan, 818 Hatcher Graduate Library, Ann Arbor, MI, 48109-1205. Tel: 734-764-9356. Fax: 734-763-5080. p. 1152

Westbrooks, Elaine, Assoc Dean, University of Nebraska-Lincoln, 1248 R St, Lincoln, NE, 68588-4100. Tel: 402-472-2526. p. 1407

Westby, Carole, Pres, Bella Vista Historical Society Museum Library, 1885 Bella Vista Way, Bella Vista, AR, 72714. Tel: 479-855-2335. p. 94

Westby, Pamela, Dir, Sparta Free Library, 124 W Main St, Sparta, WI, 54656. Tel: 608-269-2010. Fax: 608-269-1542. p. 2639

Westcott, Anita, Dir, Americus Township Library, 710 Main St, Americus, KS, 66835. Tel: 620-443-5503. Fax: 620-443-5218. p. 855

Westcott, Darlene J, Ch, Chino Valley Public Library, 1020 W Palomino Rd, Chino Valley, AZ, 86323-5500. Tel: 928-636-2687. Fax: 928-636-9129. p. 60

Westcott, Denise, Libr Dir, Art Institute of California, Inland Empire Library, 674 E Brier Rd, Ste 102, San Bernardino, CA, 92408. Tel: 909-915-2146. p. 227

Westendorp, Jacob, Res Librn, Cargill, Inc, 15407 McGinty Rd W, Wayzata, MN, 55391. Tel: 952-742-6498. Fax: 952-742-6062. p. 1287

Westenfeld, Jane, Ref, Spec Coll Librn, Allegheny College Library, 555 N Main St, Meadville, PA, 16335. Tel: 814-332-3789. Fax: 814-337-5673. p. 2086

Wester, Candle, Asst Dir, Fac Serv, University of South Carolina, Coleman Karesh Law Library, USC Law Ctr, 701 Main St, Columbia, SC, 29208. Tel: 803-777-5942. Fax: 803-777-9405. p. 2190

Wester, Jane, Circ Supvr, Duluth Public Library, 520 W Superior St, Duluth, MN, 55802. Tel: 218-730-4242. Fax: 218-723-3815, 218-723-3822. p. 1247

Wester, Peggy, Circ, Oneonta Public Library, 221 Second St S, Oneonta, AL, 35121. Tel: 205-274-7641. Fax: 205-274-7643. p. 32

Wester, Randy, Park Supvr, US National Park Service, 2916 E South St, Lincoln City, IN, 47552. Tel: 812-937-4541. Fax: 812-937-9929. p. 761

Wester-Mittan, Candle M, Access Serv Librn, Southern Illinois University Carbondale, Law Library, Lesar Law Bldg, 1150 Douglas Dr, Carbondale, IL, 62901. Tel: 618-453-8780. Fax: 618-453-8728. p. 600

Westercamp, Darlea, Ch, Keosauqua Public Library, 608 First St, Keosauqua, IA, 52565. Tel: 319-293-3766. Fax: 319-293-3766. p. 825

Westerhaus, Rochelle A, Libr Dir, Pratt Public Library, 401 S Jackson St, Pratt, KS, 67124. Tel: 620-672-3041, 620-672-5842. Fax: 620-672-5151. p. 891

Westerhoff, Donna J, Internal Operations Mgr, Library System of Lancaster County, 1866 Colonial Village Lane, Ste 107, Lancaster, PA, 17601. Tel: 717-207-0500. Fax: 717-207-0504. p. 2077

Westerhold, Mary, Operations Mgr, Madison County Historical Museum & Archival Library, 715 N Main St, Edwardsville, IL, 62025-1111. Tel: 618-656-7562, 618-656-7569. Fax: 618-659-3457. p. 639

Westerman, Myrna, Mgr, Delta County Libraries, Paonia Public, Two Third St, Paonia, CO, 81428. Tel: 970-527-3470. Fax: 970-527-3871. p. 313

Westerman, Stephen, In Charge, Eleanor Slator Hospital, 2090 Wallam Lake Rd, Pascoag, RI, 02859. Tel: 401-567-5488. Fax: 401-567-4001. p. 2170

Westermann, Mary, Dr, Assoc Prof, Long Island University, C W Post Campus, 720 Northern Blvd, Brookville, NY, 11548-1300. Tel: 516-299-2178. Fax: 516-299-4168. p. 2970

Westermann-Cicio, Mary, Chair, Medical & Scientific Libraries of Long Island, c/o Palmer Sch of Libr & Info Sci, C W Post Campus, Long Island Univ, Brookville, NY, 11548. Tel: 516-299-2866. Fax: 516-299-4168. p. 2950

Westermeyer, Beverly, Librn, Florida Keys Community College Library, Bldg A, 2nd Fl, 5901 College Rd, Key West, FL, 33040. Tel: 305-809-3194. Fax: 305-292-5162. p. 456

Westervelt, Jan, Br Mgr, Enoch Pratt Free Library, Govans, 5714 Bellona Ave, Baltimore, MD, 21212-3508. Tel: 410-396-6098. Fax: 410-396-6291. p. 1013

Westfall, Becky, Ref, Patrick Henry Community College, 645 Patriot Ave, Martinsville, VA, 24115. Tel: 276-656-0226. Fax: 276-656-0327. p. 2478

Westfall, Marsha, Dir, Peoria Heights Public Library, 816 E Glen Ave, Peoria Heights, IL, 61616. Tel: 309-682-5578. Fax: 309-682-4457. p. 690

Westfall, Rebecca S, Br Mgr, Dorchester County Library, Summerville Branch, 76 Old Trolley Rd, Summerville, SC, 29485. Tel: 843-871-5075. Fax: 843-875-4811. p. 2204

Westfall, Ruth, Tech Serv, Suffolk Cooperative Library System, 627 N Sunrise Service Rd, Bellport, NY, 11713. Tel: 631-286-1600. Fax: 631-286-1647. p. 1580

Westgate, Izak, Asst Curator, Mgr, Hockey Hall of Fame, 400 Kipling Ave, Toronto, ON, M8V 3L1, CANADA. Tel: 416-360-7735. Fax: 416-251-5770. p. 2854

Westgate, Susan, Asst Dir, Bartlett Public Library District, 800 S Bartlett Rd, Bartlett, IL, 60103. Tel: 630-837-2855. Fax: 630-837-2669. p. 592

Westin, Susan, Prog Mgr, Talking Bks, Oregon State Library, 250 Winter St NE, Salem, OR, 97301-3950. Tel: 503-378-5435. Fax: 503-585-8059. p. 2018

Westley, David, Librn, Boston University Libraries, African Studies Library, 771 Commonwealth Ave, Boston, MA, 02215. Tel: 617-353-3726. Fax: 617-358-1729. p. 1058

Westmoreland, Donald, Dir, Saint Tammany Parish Library, 310 W 21st Ave, Covington, LA, 70433. Tel: 985-871-1219. Fax: 985-871-1224. p. 947

Westmoreland, Patricia, Librn, Marshall County Library System, Potts Camp Public, 20 S Center St, Potts Camp, MS, 38659. Tel: 601-333-7068. Fax: 601-333-7096. p. 1302

Weston, Ann, Circ Mgr, Northbrook Public Library, 1201 Cedar Lane, Northbrook, IL, 60062-4581. Tel: 847-272-6224. Fax: 847-272-5362. p. 682

Weston, Barbara, Ch, Coquitlam Public Library, City Centre, 3001 Burlington Dr, Coquitlam, BC, V3B 6X1, CANADA. Tel: 604-927-3561. Fax: 604-927-3570. p. 2727

Weston, Barbara, Commun Serv, Coquitlam Public Library, 575 Poirier St, Coquitlam, BC, V3J 6A9, CANADA. Tel: 604-937-4140. Fax: 604-931-6739. p. 2727

Weston, Beverly, Tech Serv, PPG Industries, Inc, Glass Technology Center, Guys Run Rd, Harmar Township, PA, 15238. Tel: 412-820-4936. Fax: 412-820-8696. p. 2128

Weston, Charles, Head, Coll Develop, San Diego State University Library & Information Access, 5500 Campanile Dr, San Diego, CA, 92182-8050. Tel: 619-594-6988. Fax: 619-594-3270. p. 237

Weston, Claudia, Govt Info Librn, Portland State University Library, 1875 SW Park Ave, Portland, OR, 97201-3220. Tel: 503-725-4542. Fax: 503-725-4524. p. 2014

Weston, Karen, Archivist, University of Wisconsin-Whitewater Library, 800 W Main St, Whitewater, WI, 53190. Tel: 262-472-5520. Fax: 262-472-5727. p. 2649

Weston, Kim, Tech Serv, Rockland Community College Library, 145 College Rd, Suffern, NY, 10901. Tel: 845-574-4407. Fax: 845-574-4424. p. 1750

Weston, Laura, Dir, Elliott Public Library, 401 Main St, Elliott, IA, 51532. Tel: 712-767-2355. Fax: 712-767-2355. p. 814

Weston, Matt, Br Serv Coordr, Van Buren District Library, 200 N Phelps St, Decatur, MI, 49045-1086. Tel: 269-423-4771. Fax: 269-423-8373. p. 1168

Weston, Priscilla, Asst Dir, Mansfield Public Library, Five Main St, Temple, NH, 03084. Tel: 603-878-3100. Fax: 603-878-0654. p. 1466

Weston, Richard, Assoc Libr Dir, Saul Ewing LLP, Centre Sq W, 1500 Market St, 38th Flr, Philadelphia, PA, 19102. Tel: 215-972-7873. Fax: 215-972-1945. p. 2116

Weston-Elchert, Laura, Mgr, Fort Wayne News-Sentinel Library, 600 W Main St, Fort Wayne, IN, 46802. Tel: 260-461-8468. Fax: 260-461-8817. p. 741

Westphal, Kim, Dir, Casey Public Library, 604 Antique Country Dr, Casey, IA, 50048. Tel: 641-746-2670. Fax: 641-746-2670. p. 799

Westphal, Kristine, In Charge, Phillips, Lytle LLP Library, 3400 HSBC Ctr, Buffalo, NY, 14203. Tel: 716-847-5470. Fax: 716-852-6100. p. 1598

Westphal, Renee, Ref, Arizona Western College & NAU Yuma Branch Campus, 2020 S Ave 8E, Yuma, AZ, 85366. Tel: 928-344-7777. Fax: 928-344-7751. p. 90

Westphal, Robin S, Dir, Livingston County Library, 450 Locust St, Chillicothe, MO, 64601-2597. Tel: 660-646-0547. Fax: 660-646-5504. p. 1323

Westphalen, Peg, Cat Mgr, Robert L Powell Library (The Master's College), 21726 W Placerita Canyon Rd, Santa Clarita, CA, 91321-1200. Tel: 661-259-3540. Fax: 661-362-2719. p. 263

Westra, Brian, Data Serv Librn, University of Oregon Libraries, Science, Onyx Bridge, Lower Level, University of Oregon, Eugene, OR, 97403. Tel: 541-346-2654. Fax: 541-346-3012. p. 1998

Westra, Brian, Librn, Web Serv, King County Hazardous Waste Library, 130 Nickerson St, Ste 100, Seattle, WA, 98109-1658. Tel: 206-263-3051. Fax: 206-263-3070. p. 2528

Westrich, Patty, Librn, United Hospital System, 6308 Eighth Ave, Kenosha, WI, 53143. Tel: 262-656-2120. Fax: 262-653-5780. p. 2601

Westwood, Glenna, Librn, Southern Alberta Art Gallery Library, 601 Third Ave S, Lethbridge, AB, T1J 0H4, CANADA. Tel: 403-327-8770. Fax: 403-328-3913. p. 2710

Westwood, Karen, Head, Ref, William Mitchell College of Law, 871 Summit Ave, Saint Paul, MN, 55105. Tel: 651-290-7618. Fax: 651-290-6318. p. 1283

Westwood, Katharine, Dir, Cheshire Public Library, 23 Depot St, Cheshire, MA, 01225. Tel: 413-743-4746. p. 1080

Wetherall, Robert, Commun Librn, Dover Public Library, 45 S State St, Dover, DE, 19901. Tel: 302-736-7030. Fax: 302-736-5087. p. 382

Wetherbee, Jimm, Info Serv, Ref Serv, Syst Adminr, Wingate University, PO Box 219, Wingate, NC, 28174-1202. Tel: 704-233-8089. Fax: 704-233-8254. p. 1832

Wetherby, Julie, Asst Librn, Cambridge Public Library, 21 W Main St, Cambridge, NY, 12816. Tel: 518-677-2443. Fax: 518-677-2443. p. 1600

Wetherington, Elsie, Dean of Libr, Virginia State University, One Hayden Dr, Petersburg, VA, 23806-0001. Tel: 804-524-5040. Fax: 804-524-6959. p. 2484

Wetherington, Janice, Circ, Northern Wyoming Community College District, 3059 Coffeen Ave, Sheridan, WY, 82801-1500. Tel: 307-674-6446. Fax: 307-674-3350. p. 2660

Wetherington, Mark V, Dr, Exec Dir, Filson Historical Society Library, 1310 S Third St, Louisville, KY, 40208. Tel: 502-635-5083. Fax: 502-635-5086. p. 923

Wethington, Betty, Tech Serv, Pekin Public Library, 301 S Fourth St, Pekin, IL, 61554-4284. Tel: 309-347-7111. Fax: 309-347-6587. p. 689

Wetjen, Susan, Commun Libr Mgr, Queens Borough Public Library, Kew Gardens Hills Community Library, 72-33 Vleigh Pl, Flushing, NY, 11367. Tel: 718-261-6654. p. 1645

Wetmore, Gayle, Supvr, Haliburton County Public Library, Stanhope Branch, 1109 N Shore Rd, Algonquin Highlands, ON, K0M 1J1, CANADA. Tel: 705-489-2402. p. 2808

Wetmore, Jeannette, Pub Serv, Union College Library, 3800 S 48th St, Lincoln, NE, 68506-4386. Tel: 402-486-2514. Fax: 402-486-2678. p. 1406

Wetmore, Lisa, ILL & Ser, Fremont County Library System, Dubois Branch, 202 N First, Dubois, WY, 82513. Tel: 307-455-2992. Fax: 307-455-2032. p. 2657

Wetnight, Jill, Br Mgr, Indianapolis-Marion County Public Library, Franklin Road, 5550 S Franklin Rd, Indianapolis, IN, 46239. Tel: 317-275-4380. p. 754

Wetteland, Annette, Info Spec, State Library of Iowa, 1112 E Grand Ave, Des Moines, IA, 50319. Tel: 515-281-4105. Fax: 515-281-6191. p. 810

Wetter, Susan, Dir, Teen Serv, Spartanburg County Public Libraries, 151 S Church St, Spartanburg, SC, 29306-3241. Tel: 864-596-3500. Fax: 864-596-3518. p. 2205

Wettergreen, Brenda, Librn, Beverly Public Library, Beverly Farms, 24 Vine St, Beverly, MA, 01915-2208. Tel: 978-921-6066. Fax: 978-927-9239. p. 1053

Wettergreen, Brenda, Ch, Reading Public Library, 64 Middlesex Ave, Reading, MA, 01867-2550. Tel: 781-944-0840. Fax: 781-942-9106. p. 1120

Wettleson, Lisa, Interim Head of Libr, University of Wisconsin-Madison, Steenbock Memorial Agricultural Library, 550 Babcock Dr, Madison, WI, 53706. Tel: 608-263-7574. Fax: 608-263-3221. p. 2610

Wettstein, Chris, Ref Serv, Valencia Community College, East Campus, 701 N Econlockhatchee Trail, Orlando, FL, 32825. Tel: 407-582-2467. Fax: 407-582-8914. p. 478

Wetzel, Barbara, Media Serv, Villa Maria College Library, 240 Pine Ridge Rd, Buffalo, NY, 14225-3999. Tel: 716-961-1864. Fax: 716-896-0705. p. 1599

Wetzel, Lynn, Adult Serv, Lee County Library System, East County Regional, 881 Gunnery Rd N, Lehigh Acres, FL, 33971. Tel: 239-461-7306. Fax: 239-461-7321. p. 445

Wever, Julie, Outreach & Youth Serv Librn, Clinton-Essex-Franklin Library System, 33 Oak St, Plattsburgh, NY, 12901-2810. Tel: 518-563-5190, Ext 18. Fax: 518-563-0421. p. 1718

Wey, Carolyn, Youth Serv Librn, L D Fargo Public Library, 120 E Madison St, Lake Mills, WI, 53551-1644. Tel: 920-648-2166. Fax: 920-648-5561. p. 2604

Weybright, Chris, Tech Serv, Bourbonnais Public Library District, 250 W John Casey Rd, Bourbonnais, IL, 60914. Tel: 815-933-1727. Fax: 815-933-1961. p. 596

Weyer, Mary, Librn, Salmon Falls Library, 322 Old Alfred Rd, Hollis, ME, 04042. Tel: 207-929-3990. Fax: 207-929-3990. p. 988

Weymouth, Gail, Dir, Sherburne Memorial Library, PO Box 73, Killington, VT, 05751. Tel: 802-422-4251, 802-422-9765. Fax: 802-422-4323. p. 2427

Weys, Karla, Mgr, Info Mgt, Canadian Radio-Television & Telecommunications Commission Information Resource Centre, One Promenade du Portage, Ottawa, ON, K1A 0N2, CANADA. Tel: 819-997-4484. Fax: 819-994-6337. p. 2830

Whalen, Bernadette, Head, ILL, Martinsburg-Berkeley County Public Library, 101 W King St, Martinsburg, WV, 25401. Tel: 304-267-8933, Fax: 304-267-9720. p. 2565

Whalen, Kimberly, Sci & Bus Librn, Purdue University, 2200 169th St, Hammond, IN, 46323-2094. Tel: 219-989-2947. Fax: 219-989-2070. p. 747

Whalen, Kimberly, Res Serv Librn, Valparaiso University, 1410 Chapel Dr, Valparaiso, IN, 46383-6493. Tel: 219-464-5754. p. 783

Whalen, Marg, Doc, University of Wisconsin-Stevens Point, 900 Reserve St, Stevens Point, WI, 54481-1985. Tel: 715-346-3726. Fax: 715-346-3857. p. 2640

Whalen Smith, Heather, Coll Develop, State University of New York College at New Paltz, 300 Hawk Dr, New Paltz, NY, 12561-2493. Tel: 845-257-3731. p. 1666

Whalen, Tomi, Br Mgr, Kitsap Regional Library, Kingston Branch, Community Ctr, 11212 NE State Hwy 104, Kingston, WA, 98346-0519. Tel: 360-297-3330, Ext 9902. Fax: 360-297-2911. p. 2510

Whalen, Tomi, Br Mgr, Kitsap Regional Library, Little Boston, 31980 Little Boston Rd NE, Kingston, WA, 98346-9700. Tel: 360-297-2670, Ext 9601. Fax: 360-297-2011. p. 2510

Whalen-Nevin, Bridget, Dir, Morristown Public Library, 200 Main St, Morristown, NY, 13664. Tel: 315-375-8833. Fax: 315-375-8266. p. 1663

Whaley, Frances, Coll Develop Librn, Illinois Valley Community College, 815 N Orlando Smith Ave, Oglesby, IL, 61348-9692. Tel: 815-224-0263. Fax: 815-224-9147. p. 684

Whaley, Joyce K, Dir, Brook-Iroquois-Washington Public Library, 100 W Main St, Brook, IN, 47922. Tel: 219-275-2471. Fax: 219-275-8471. p. 730

Whaley, Laura, Br Mgr, Santa Cruz City-County Library System Headquarters, Boulder Creek Branch, 13390 W Park Ave, Boulder Creek, CA, 95006-9301. Tel: 831-427-7703. Fax: 831-427-7723. p. 264

Whaley, Laura, Br Mgr, Santa Cruz City-County Library System Headquarters, Felton Branch, 6299 Gushee St, Felton, CA, 95018-9140. Tel: 831-427-7706, Ext 7734. Fax: 831-427-7728. p. 264

Whaley, Margaret, Librn, Lebanon Public Library, 314 W Saint Louis St, Lebanon, IL, 62254. Tel: 618-537-4504. Fax: 618-537-4399. p. 664

Whaley, Martha, Res Mgr, East Tennessee State University, James H Quillen College of Medicine Library, Maple St, Bldg 4, Johnson City, TN, 37614. Tel: 423-439-8069. Fax: 423-439-7025. p. 2239

Whaley, Michelle, Librn, Alberta Law Libraries, Office of the Chief Medical Examiner Information Centre, 7007 116th St, Edmonton, AB, T6H 5R8, CANADA. Tel: 780-427-4987. Fax: 780-422-1265. p. 2699

Whalin, Kathleen, Ch, York Public Library, 15 Long Sands Rd, York, ME, 03909. Tel: 207-363-2818. Fax: 207-363-7250. p. 1008

Wharton, Amy, Res/Emerging Tech Librn, University of Virginia, Arthur J Morris Law Library, 580 Massie Rd, Charlottesville, VA, 22903-1789. Tel: 434-924-1816. Fax: 434-982-2232. p. 2455

Wharton, Jennifer, Youth Serv Librn, Matheson Memorial Library, 101 N Wisconsin, Elkhorn, WI, 53121. Tel: 262-723-2678. Fax: 262-723-2870. p. 2590

Wharton, Mary, Circ, Starke County Public Library System, 152 W Culver Rd, Knox, IN, 46534-2220. Tel: 574-772-7323. p. 757

Wharton, Maureen, Pub Serv, Brockville Public Library, 23 Buell St, Brockville, ON, K6V 5T7, CANADA. Tel: 613-342-3936. Fax: 613-342-9598. p. 2797

Wharton, Wuanita, Br Mgr, Mansfield-Richland County Public Library, Lexington Branch, 25 Lutz Ave, Lexington, OH, 44904. Tel: 419-884-2500. Fax: 419-884-3695. p. 1913

Wharton-Lake, Beverly, Chief Librn, Organization of American States, 19th & Constitution Ave NW, Washington, DC, 20006-4499. Tel: 202-458-3849. Fax: 202-458-3914. p. 412

Whatford, Mark, Librn & Archivist, Gunston Hall Plantation Library & Archives, 10709 Gunston Rd, Mason Neck, VA, 22079-3901. Tel: 703-550-9220. Fax: 703-550-9480. p. 2478

Whatley, Adrian, Ref Librn, Austin Community College, South Austin Campus Library, 1820 W Stassney Lane, Austin, TX, 78745. Tel: 512-223-9179. Fax: 512-223-9190. p. 2278

Whatley, Angelia, Librn, Naval Surface Warfare Center, 110 Vernon Ave, Panama City, FL, 32407-7001. Tel: 850-234-4848. Fax: 850-234-4844. p. 480

Whatley, Edward, Instruction & Ref Librn, Georgia College & State University, 320 N Wayne St, Milledgeville, GA, 31061-3397. Tel: 478-445-4047. Fax: 478-445-6847. p. 544

Whatley, Joy, Br Mgr, Chula Vista Public Library, South Chula Vista, 389 Orange Ave, Chula Vista, CA, 91911-4116. Tel: 619-585-5786. Fax: 619-420-1591. p. 134

Whatley, Renee, Dir, East Carroll Parish Library, 109 Sparrow St, Lake Providence, LA, 71254-2645. Tel: 318-559-2615. Fax: 318-559-4635. p. 954

Wheat, Curtis, Librn, Reform Public Library, 302 First St S, Reform, AL, 35481. Tel: 205-375-6240. Fax: 205-375-6240. p. 35

Wheat, Maxine, Dir, Parsons Public Library, 105 Kentucky Ave S, Parsons, TN, 38363-2517. Tel: 731-847-6988. Fax: 731-847-3476. p. 2263

Wheatley, Jessica, Fed Libr Mgr, United States Environmental Protection Agency, 77 W Jackson Blvd (PL-16J), Chicago, IL, 60604. Tel: 312-886-6822. Fax: 312-886-1492. p. 626

Wheatley, Pam, Librn, Prince Edward Island Public Library Service, Cornwall Public, 39 Lowther Dr, Cornwall, PE, C0A 1H0, CANADA. Tel: 902-629-8415. p. 2876

Wheatley, Pam, Librn, Prince Edward Island Public Library Service, Hunter River Public, 19816 Rte 2, Hunter River, PE, C0A 1N0, CANADA. Tel: 902-964-2800. p. 2876

Wheaton, Ken, Syst Librn, Alaska State Court Law Library, 303 K St, Anchorage, AK, 99501. Tel: 907-264-0585. Fax: 907-264-0733. p. 44

Wheaton, Nathalie, Asst Archivist, Librn, Library of Rush University Medical Center, Armour Academic Ctr, 600 S Paulina St, 5th Flr, Chicago, IL, 60612-3874. Tel: 312-942-6358. Fax: 312-942-3342. p. 617

Wheatwind, Mimi, Ref/Instruction Librn, Fort Lewis College Library, 1000 Rim Dr, Durango, CO, 81301-3999. Tel: 970-247-7250. Fax: 970-247-7149. p. 305

Wheeldon, Raymond, Asst Dir, Germantown Community Library, 1925 Exeter Rd, Germantown, TN, 38138-2815. Tel: 901-757-7323, Ext 7479. Fax: 901-756-9940. p. 2235

Wheeler, Alan, Computer Support Spec, University of Cincinnati, 2540 Clifton Ave, Cincinnati, OH, 45219. Tel: 513-556-4419. Fax: 513-556-6265. p. 1874

Wheeler, Alice, Asst Librn, Robert L Williams Public Library, 323 W Beech, Durant, OK, 74701. Tel: 580-924-3486. Fax: 580-924-8843. p. 1962

Wheeler, Andrea, Youth Serv Coordr, Penn Yan Public Library, 214 Main St, Penn Yan, NY, 14527. Tel: 315-536-6114. Fax: 315-536-0131. p. 1716

Wheeler, Angela, Librn, Oregon State Penitentiary Library, Coffee Creek Correctional Facility, 24499 SW Grahams Ferry Rd, Wilsonville, OR, 97070. Tel: 503-570-6783. Fax: 503-570-6786. p. 2018

Wheeler, Ann, Br Mgr, Hightower Sara Regional Library, Rockmart Branch, 134 W Elm St, Rockmart, GA, 30153-2938. Tel: 770-684-3022. Fax: 770-684-7876. p. 549

Wheeler, Ann, Dir, Maryland Department of Natural Resources, 580 Taylor Ave, B-3, Annapolis, MD, 21401. Tel: 410-260-8830. Fax: 410-260-8951. p. 1010

Wheeler, Arlene, Librn, Sutter County Free Library, Barber, 10321 Live Oak Blvd, Live Oak, CA, 95953. Tel: 530-695-2021. p. 286

Wheeler, Barbara, Head, Cat, University of New Brunswick Libraries, Five Macaulay Dr, Fredericton, NB, E3B 5H5, CANADA. Tel: 506-458-7412. Fax: 506-453-4595. p. 2763

Wheeler, Barbara J, Dir, Roswell P Flower Memorial Library, 229 Washington St, Watertown, NY, 13601-3388. Tel: 315-785-7705. Fax: 315-788-2584. p. 1763

Wheeler, Carol, Govt Doc, University of Georgia Libraries, Athens, GA, 30602-1641. Tel: 706-542-4108. Fax: 706-542-4144. p. 510

Wheeler, Carolyn A, Librn, Frankston Depot Library & Museum, 159 W Railroad St, Frankston, TX, 75763. Tel: 903-876-4463. Fax: 903-876-3226. p. 2325

Wheeler, Claire, ILL, Holyoke Community College Library, Donahue Bldg, 2nd Flr, 303 Homestead Ave, Holyoke, MA, 01040-1099. Tel: 413-552-2187. Fax: 413-552-2729. p. 1095

Wheeler, Craig, Br Mgr, Texas A&M University-Commerce, Metroplex Commuter Facility Library, 2600 Motley Dr, Mesquite, TX, 75150. Tel: 972-882-7535, 972-882-7537. Fax: 972-882-7536. p. 2300

Wheeler, David, Dean, Dalhousie University, 6100 University Ave, Halifax, NS, B3H 3J5, CANADA. Tel: 902-494-3656. Fax: 902-494-2451. p. 2978

Wheeler, Deanna, Dir, Milltown Public Library, 61 W Main St, Milltown, WI, 54858. Tel: 715-825-2313. Fax: 715-825-4422. p. 2616

Wheeler, Diana, Instruction Coordr, University of Wisconsin-Madison, Kurt Wendt Engineering Library, 215 N Randall Ave, Madison, WI, 53706. Tel: 608-262-3493. Fax: 608-262-4739, 608-265-8751. p. 2610

Wheeler, Don, Acq, Coll Develop Mgr, The LuEsther T Mertz Library, The New York Botanical Garden, 2900 Southern Blvd, Bronx, NY, 10458-5126. Tel: 718-817-8752. Fax: 718-817-8956. p. 1587

Wheeler, Elizabeth, Acq, Taunton Public Library, 12 Pleasant St, Taunton, MA, 02780. Tel: 508-821-1410. Fax: 508-821-1414. p. 1130

Wheeler, Eric, Reader & Digital Serv Librn, Simpson University, 2211 College View Dr, Redding, CA, 96003-8606. Tel: 530-226-4117. Fax: 530-226-4858. p. 214

Wheeler, Evelyn, YA Serv, Holly Township Library, 1116 N Saginaw St, Holly, MI, 48442-1395. Tel: 248-634-1754. Fax: 248-634-8088. p. 1191

Wheeler, Joanne, Mgr, Mercer Human Resource Consulting, 161 Bay St, Toronto, ON, M5J 2S5, CANADA. Tel: 416-868-7697. Fax: 416-868-7171. p. 2855

Wheeler, John Mark, In Charge, Arkansas Department of Correction, Pine Bluff Work Complex Chapel Library, 890 Freeline Dr, Pine Bluff, AR, 71603-1498. Tel: 870-267-6510. Fax: 870-267-6529. p. 112

Wheeler, Justine, Libr Dir, University of Calgary Library, Business Library, Haskayne School of Business, Scurfield Hall, Rm 301, Calgary, AB, T2N 1N4, CANADA. Tel: 403-220-5084. Fax: 403-220-0120. p. 2693

Wheeler, K Lynn, Dir, Carroll County Public Library, 115 Airport Dr, Westminster, MD, 21157. Tel: 410-386-4500, Ext 136. Fax: 410-386-4509. p. 1045

Wheeler, Karen, Supvr, Outreach Serv, Pickaway County District Public Library, 1160 N Court St, Circleville, OH, 43113-1725. Tel: 740-477-1644, Ext 226. Fax: 740-474-2855. p. 1875

Wheeler, Kathy, Ref/Clinical Librn, Eastern Virginia Medical School, 740 W Olney Rd, Norfolk, VA, 23501. Tel: 757-446-5840. Fax: 757-446-5134. p. 2481

Wheeler, Katie, Ch, Exira Public Library, 114 W Washington St, Exira, IA, 50076. Tel: 712-268-5489. Fax: 712-268-5489. p. 815

Wheeler, Laurie, Dir, Arms Library Association, Bridge & Main St, Shelburne Falls, MA, 01370. Tel: 413-625-0306. p. 1123

Wheeler, Maurice, Dr, Assoc Prof, University of North Texas, 1155 Union Circle, Denton, TX, 76203-5017. Tel: 940-565-2445. Fax: 940-565-3101. p. 2975

Wheeler, Michelle, Dir, Dunkerton Public Library, 203 E Tower St, Dunkerton, IA, 50626. Tel: 319-822-4610. Fax: 319-822-4664. p. 812

Wheeler, Millie, Br Support, Stormont, Dundas & Glengarry County Library, St Andrews Branch, 17283 Raisin River Heritage Centre, County Rd 18, Saint Andrews, ON, K0C 2A0, CANADA. Tel: 613-932-6012. p. 2802

Wheeler, Ramon, Syst Adminr, Tangipahoa Parish Library, Administration Office, 200 E Mulberry St, Amite, LA, 70422. Tel: 985-748-7559. Fax: 985-748-2812. p. 941

Wheeler, Rebecca, Librn, Jackson-George Regional Library System, Lucedale-George County Public Library, 507 Oak St, Lucedale, MS, 39452. Tel: 601-947-2123. Fax: 601-766-3360. p. 1310

Wheeler, Susan, Electronic Res, University of Baltimore, 1420 Maryland Ave, Baltimore, MD, 21201. Tel: 410-837-4299. Fax: 410-837-4330. p. 1018

Wheeler, Susan, Asst Br Librn, Ref Librn, Brazoria County Library System, Lake Jackson Branch, 250 Circle Way, Lake Jackson, TX, 77566. Tel: 979-415-2590. Fax: 979-415-2993. p. 2275

Wheeler, Terrie, Br Chief, National Institutes of Health Library, 10 Center Dr, Rm 1L25A, Bethesda, MD, 20892. Tel: 301-496-1157. Fax: 301-402-0254. p. 1021

Wheeler, Verna Anne, Dir, Crosby County Pioneer Memorial Museum Library, 101 W Main St, Crosbyton, TX, 79322. Tel: 806-675-2331. p. 2303

Wheeler, Walker, Libr Syst Mgr, University of Alaska Fairbanks, 310 Tanana Dr, Fairbanks, AK, 99775. Tel: 907-474-7173. Fax: 907-474-6841. p. 48

Wheeler, William, Head, Res & Instruction, Georgetown University, 37th & N St NW, Washington, DC, 20057-1174. Tel: 202-687-6818. Fax: 202-687-7501. p. 402

Wheeler, Woods, Asst Dir, Oklahoma State University-Oklahoma City Library, 900 N Portland, Oklahoma City, OK, 73107-6195. Tel: 405-945-9104. Fax: 405-945-3289. p. 1975

Wheelin, Rebecca, Tech Serv, United States Air Force, 45th Space Wing Technical Library FL2513, Bldg 989, Rm A1-S3, 1030 S Hwy A1A, Patrick AFB, FL, 32925-3002. Tel: 321-494-6638, 321-494-7220. Fax: 321-494-6636. p. 481

Wheelock, Melissa, YA Serv, Kokomo-Howard County Public Library, 220 N Union St, Kokomo, IN, 46901-4614. Tel: 765-457-3242. Fax: 765-457-3683. p. 758

Whelan, David, Mgr, Law Society of Upper Canada, Osgoode Hall, 130 Queen St W, Toronto, ON, M5H 2N6, CANADA. Tel: 416-947-3438. Fax: 416-869-0331. p. 2855

Whelan, John L, Col Librn, College of the North Atlantic, Grand Falls-Windsor Campus, Five Cromer Ave, Grand Falls-Windsor, NL, A2A 1X3, CANADA. Tel: 709-292-5637. Fax: 709-489-5765. p. 2771

Whelchel, Angela, Ch, Atlanta-Fulton Public Library System, Roswell Regional Library, 115 Norcross St, Roswell, GA, 30075. Tel: 770-640-3075. Fax: 770-640-3077. p. 512

Wherry, Timothy, Head Librn, Pennsylvania State University, Altoona College, 3000 Ivyside Park, Altoona, PA, 16601-3760. Tel: 814-949-5255. Fax: 814-949-5246, 814-949-5520. p. 2028

Whetsel, Charlotte, Pres, Wheat Ridge Historical Society Library, 4610 Robb St, Wheat Ridge, CO, 80033. Tel: 303-467-0023. Fax: 303-467-2539. p. 326

Whetzel, Sheila, Mgr, Loudoun County Public Library, Middleburg Branch, 101 Reed St, Middleburg, VA, 20117. Tel: 540-687-5730. Fax: 540-687-3630. p. 2474

Whichard, Mitchell, Head, Circ, University of North Carolina at Chapel Hill, Davis Library, 208 Raleigh St, Campus Box 3900, Chapel Hill, NC, 27514-8890. p. 1780

Whidden, Linda M, Assoc Librn, Head, Tech & Info Res, King's University College at the University of Western Ontario, 266 Epworth Ave, London, ON, N6A 2M3, CANADA. Tel: 519-433-3491, Ext 4506. Fax: 519-963-0307. p. 2817

Whiffen, Bride, Librn, Southern Harbour Public Library, One Municipal Dr, Southern Harbour, NL, A0B 3H0, CANADA. Tel: 709-463-8814. Fax: 709-463-8814. p. 2770

Whildin, Sara Lou, Librn, Pennsylvania State University, Brandywine Campus, 25 Yearsley Mill Rd, Media, PA, 19063-5596. Tel: 610-892-1386. Fax: 610-892-1359. p. 2088

Whinihan, Jacqueline, Adult Serv, Taylor Community Library, 12303 Pardee Rd, Taylor, MI, 48180-4219. Tel: 734-287-4840. Fax: 734-287-4141. p. 1230

Whinnery, Jennifer, Libr Asst, Wiregrass Georgia Technical College Library, 4089 Val Tech Rd, Valdosta, GA, 31602. Tel: 229-259-5177. Fax: 229-259-5179. p. 555

Whipple, Amy, Asst Dir, Terrebonne Parish Library, 151 Library Dr, Houma, LA, 70360. Tel: 985-876-5861. Fax: 985-917-0582. p. 951

Whipple, Jona, Digital Res Librn, Illinois Institute of Technology, Chicago-Kent College of Law Library, 565 W Adams St, Chicago, IL, 60661. Tel: 312-906-5600. Fax: 312-906-5679. p. 615

Whipple, Margaret, Br Mgr, Clay County Public Library System, Keystone Heights Branch, 175 Oriole, Keystone Heights, FL, 32656. Tel: 352-473-4286. Fax: 352-473-5123. p. 475

Whipple, Nancy, Fiscal Officer, Kaubisch Memorial Public Library, 205 Perry St, Fostoria, OH, 44830-2265. Tel: 419-435-2813. Fax: 419-435-5350. p. 1900

Whipple, P Michael, Dir, Loyola University New Orleans, Loyola Law Library, School of Law, 7214 St Charles Ave, New Orleans, LA, 70118. Tel: 504-861-5539. Fax: 504-861-5895. p. 961

Whipple, Rebecca, Br Mgr, Nashville Public Library, Edgehill, 1409 12th Ave S, Nashville, TN, 37203-4903. Tel: 615-862-5861. Fax: 615-862-5840. p. 2257

Whipple, Roberta L, Dir, St Pete Beach Public Library, 365 73rd Ave, Saint Pete Beach, FL, 33706-1996. Tel: 727-363-9238. Fax: 727-552-1760. p. 487

Whipple, Sandra, Adult Serv & Outreach Coordr, Goffstown Public Library, Two High St, Goffstown, NH, 03045-1910. Tel: 603-497-2102. Fax: 603-497-8437. p. 1448

Whipple, Teri, Libr Dir, Rushville Public Library, 207 Sprague St, Rushville, NE, 69360. Tel: 308-327-2740. Fax: 308-327-2740. p. 1418

Whirl, LuAnn, Dir, Tappan-Spaulding Memorial Library, Six Rock St, Newark Valley, NY, 13811-3160. Tel: 607-642-9960. Fax: 607-642-9960. p. 1704

Whisenhunt, Joann, Librn, Montgomery County Library, 145A Whittington St, Mount Ida, AR, 71957-9404. Tel: 870-867-3812. Fax: 870-867-3812. p. 110

Whisler, Debora, Dir, Mkt & Communications, Arlington Heights Memorial Library, 500 N Dunton Ave, Arlington Heights, IL, 60004-5966. Tel: 847-506-2613. Fax: 847-506-2650. p. 589

Whisler, John, Head, Cat, Eastern Illinois University, 600 Lincoln Ave, Charleston, IL, 61920. Tel: 217-581-7561. p. 603

Whisler, Karen, Electronic Res, Head, Coll Develop, Eastern Illinois University, 600 Lincoln Ave, Charleston, IL, 61920. Tel: 217-581-7551. p. 603

Whisler, Laurel, Dir, Cornell College, 620 Third St SW, Mount Vernon, IA, 52314-1012. Tel: 319-895-4260, 895-4271. Fax: 319-895-5936. p. 834

Whisler, Rose, Asst Librn, East Dubuque District Library, 350 Wall St, East Dubuque, IL, 61025-1222. Tel: 815-747-3052. Fax: 815-747-6062. p. 638

Whisman, Linda A, Assoc Dean, Libr Serv, Southwestern Law School, 3050 Wilshire Blvd, Los Angeles, CA, 90010. Tel: 213-738-5771. Fax: 213-738-5792. p. 177

Whisman, Thomas, Bus Librn, Ref Librn, Knox County Public Library System, 500 W Church Ave, Knoxville, TN, 37902-2505. Tel: 865-215-8750. Fax: 865-215-8742. p. 2241

Whisner, Mary, Ref Librn, University of Washington Libraries, Marian Gould Gallagher Law Library, William H Gates Hall, Box 353025, Seattle, WA, 98195-3025. Tel: 206-543-7672. Fax: 206-685-2165. p. 2534

Whistance-Smith, Doug, Dir, Westlock Municipal Library, 10007 100 Ave, No 1, Westlock, AB, T7P 2H5, CANADA. Tel: 780-349-3060. Fax: 780-349-5291. p. 2721

Whitaker, Christine, Coll Develop Librn, University of South Carolina, School of Medicine, 6311 Garners Ferry Rd, Columbia, SC, 29209. Tel: 803-733-3346. Fax: 803-733-1509. p. 2190

Whitaker, Diane, Exec Dir, Annie Halenbake Ross Library, 232 W Main St, Lock Haven, PA, 17745-1241. Tel: 570-748-3321. Fax: 570-748-1050. p. 2082

Whitaker, Dianne, Mgr, Montgomery County Public Libraries, Wheaton Library, 11701 Georgia Ave, Wheaton, MD, 20902-1997. Tel: 240-777-0686. Fax: 301-929-5525. p. 1039

Whitaker, Elizabeth, Outreach/Pub Serv Librn, Bethel University, 325 Cherry Ave, McKenzie, TN, 38201. Tel: 731-352-4083. Fax: 731-352-4070. p. 2247

Whitaker, Evans, Med Librn, Dominican Hospital, 1555 Soquel Dr, Santa Cruz, CA, 95065. Tel: 831-462-7738. Fax: 831-465-7998. p. 264

Whitaker, Evans, Dr, Clinical Librn, University of Southern California Libraries, Norris Medical Library, 2003 Zonal Ave, Los Angeles, CA, 90089-9130. Tel: 323-442-1128. Fax: 323-221-1235. p. 179

Whitaker, J Noelene, Librn, Pulaski County Public Library, Nancy Branch, Mills Springs Plaza, Nancy, KY, 42544. Tel: 606-636-4241. Fax: 606-636-4241. p. 935

Whitaker, Judy, Dir, Olney Public Library, 400 W Main St, Olney, IL, 62450. Tel: 618-392-3711. Fax: 618-392-3139. p. 685

Whitaker, Kellie, Dir, Gardere & Wynne, 1601 Elm St, Ste 3000, Dallas, TX, 75201. Tel: 214-999-4738. Fax: 214-999-3738. p. 2308

Whitaker, Linda, Chief Archivist, Arizona Historical Foundation, Arizona State University, Rm 412, Box 871006, Tempe, AZ, 85287-1006. Tel: 480-965-3283. Fax: 480-966-1077. p. 83

Whitaker, Paula, Ref Serv, Miami University-Hamilton Campus, 1601 University Blvd, Hamilton, OH, 45011. Tel: 513-785-3235. Fax: 513-785-3231. p. 1904

Whitaker, Rick, Asst Dir, Port Arthur Public Library, 4615 Ninth Ave, Port Arthur, TX, 77642. Tel: 409-985-8838, Ext 2241. Fax: 409-985-5969. p. 2371

Whitaker, Robert, Librn, Tolstoy Foundation, Inc, 104 Lake Rd, Valley Cottage, NY, 10989-2339. Tel: 845-268-6722. Fax: 845-268-6937. p. 1760

Whitchurch, Michael, Info Res, Brigham Young University, Harold B Lee Library, 2060 HBLL, Provo, UT, 84602. Tel: 801-422-2927. Fax: 801-422-0466. p. 2411

Whitcomb, Janine, Archives Mgr, University of Massachusetts Lowell Libraries, Center for Lowell History, Patrick J Mogan Cultural Ctr, 40 French St, Lowell, MA, 01852. Tel: 978-934-4997. Fax: 978-934-4995. p. 1101

Whitcomb, Katherine Raveling, Librn, Albion Municipal Library, 107 S Main St, Albion, IA, 50005. Tel: 641-488-2226. Fax: 641-488-2272. p. 792

Whitcraft, Daniel, Fac/Safety Serv Adminr, Alachua County Library District, 401 E University Ave, Gainesville, FL, 32601-5453. Tel: 352-334-3915. Fax: 352-334-3918. p. 448

White, Alica Lisa, Head Librn, Pennsylvania State University, One Campus Dr, Mont Alto, PA, 17237-9703. Tel: 717-749-6044. Fax: 717-749-6059. p. 2091

White, Alice, Br Coordr, Midland County Public Library, 301 W Missouri, Midland, TX, 79701. Tel: 432-688-4320. Fax: 432-688-4939. p. 2363

White, Alice, Librn, Midland County Public Library, Midland Centennial, Imperial Shopping Ctr, 3211 W Wadley, Ste 4B, Midland, TX, 79705-6232. Tel: 432-699-0629. p. 2363

White, Allison, Teen & Adult Prog, Bullitt County Public Library, 127 N Walnut St, Shepherdsville, KY, 40165-6083. Tel: 502-543-7675, Ext 5. Fax: 502-543-5487. p. 935

White, Amy, Dir, Lisbon Public Library, 101 E Main St, Lisbon, IA, 52253. Tel: 319-455-2800. Fax: 319-455-2800. p. 828

White, Andrew, Interim Dean of Libr, Stony Brook University, Health Sciences Library, HST Level 3, Rm 136, 8034 SUNY Stony Brook, Stony Brook, NY, 11794-8034. Tel: 631-444-3101. Fax: 631-444-6649. p. 1750

White, Andy, Dir of Libr Serv, Durango Public Library, 1900 E Third Ave, Durango, CO, 81301. Tel: 97-37-334. Fax: 970-375-3398. p. 304

White, Ann, Ref Serv, Columbus County Public Library, 407 N Powell Blvd, Whiteville, NC, 28472. Tel: 910-642-3116. Fax: 910-642-3839. p. 1829

White, Ann, Bus Mgr, Handley Regional Library, 100 W Piccadilly St, Winchester, VA, 22601. Tel: 540-662-9041, Ext 25. Fax: 540-722-4769. p. 2503

White, Ann Marie, Dir, Oliver Wolcott Library, 160 South St, Litchfield, CT, 06759-0187. Tel: 860-567-8030. Fax: 860-567-4784. p. 349

White, Anne, Asst Dir, Pub Serv, Natchez Adams Wilkinson Library Service, 220 S Commerce St, Natchez, MS, 39120-3502. Tel: 601-445-8862. Fax: 601-446-7795. p. 1309

White, Anthony, Libr Dir, Maryland Institute College of Art, 1401 Mount Royal Ave, Baltimore, MD, 21217. Tel: 410-225-2304, 410-225-2311. Fax: 410-225-2316. p. 1015

White, Barbara, Archivist, Winter Park Public Library, 460 E New England Ave, Winter Park, FL, 32789-4493. Tel: 407-623-3300. Fax: 407-623-3489. p. 505

White, Barbara, Head Librn, Richard A Mautino Memorial Library, 215 E Cleveland St, Spring Valley, IL, 61362. Tel: 815-663-4741. Fax: 815-663-1040. p. 704

White, Barbara, Br Mgr, Akron-Summit County Public Library, Highland Square, 807 W Market St, Akron, OH, 44303-1010. Tel: 330-376-2927. Fax: 330-376-9025. p. 1852

White, Barbara, Dir, Br Serv, Akron-Summit County Public Library, 60 S High St, Akron, OH, 44326. Tel: 330-643-9082. Fax: 330-643-9167. p. 1852

White, Barbara B, Admin Mgr, University of Texas at Austin Center for American History, 3738 FM 2714, Round Top, TX, 78954. Tel: 979-278-3530. Fax: 979-278-3531. p. 2377

White, Becki, Ref, Pottsville Free Public Library, 215 W Market St, Pottsville, PA, 17901-4304. Tel: 570-622-8105, 570-622-8880. Fax: 570-622-2157. p. 2131

White, Belverly, Cat Mgr, Shreve Memorial Library, 424 Texas St, Shreveport, LA, 71101. Tel: 318-226-5897. Fax: 318-226-4780. p. 969

White, Bonny, Br Mgr, Marin County Free Library, Stinson Beach Branch, 3521 Shoreline Hwy, Stinson Beach, CA, 94970. Tel: 415-868-0252. Fax: 415-868-2041. p. 257

White, Bonny, Access Serv Spec, Marlboro College, 64 Dalrymple Rd, Marlboro, VT, 05344-0300. Tel: 802-258-9221. Fax: 802-451-7550. p. 2428

White, Brandon, Computer Lab Asst, Piedmont Technical College Library, 620 N Emerald Rd, Bldg K, Greenwood, SC, 29646. Tel: 864-941-8792. Fax: 864-941-8558. p. 2197

White, Brook, Regional Libran, Volusia County Public Library, Daytona Beach Regional, City Island, Daytona Beach, FL, 32114. Tel: 386-257-6036. Fax: 386-257-6026. p. 436

White Butterfly, Karen, Dir, Oglala Lakota College, Wounded Knee College Center, PO Box 230, Manderson, SD, 57756. Tel: 605-867-5352. Fax: 605-867-1245. p. 2214

White, Caitlin, Pub Relations Coordr, Albany County Public Library, 310 S Eighth St, Laramie, WY, 82070-3969. Tel: 307-721-2580, Ext 5456. Fax: 307-721-2584. p. 2657

White, Cara, Ref Librn, Clark County Public Library, 370 S Burns Ave, Winchester, KY, 40391-1876. Tel: 859-744-5661. Fax: 859-744-5993. p. 938

White, Carolyn, Ref Librn, University of New Hampshire at Manchester Library, 400 Commercial St, Manchester, NH, 03101. Tel: 603-641-4172. Fax: 603-641-4124. p. 1456

White, Charlotte, Librn, Federal Maritime Commission Library, 800 N Capitol St NW, Washington, DC, 20573. Tel: 202-523-5762. Fax: 202-523-5738. p. 400

White, Cheryl, Libr Assoc II, Quinebaug Valley Community College Library, 742 Upper Maple St, Danielson, CT, 06239. Tel: 860-412-7272. Fax: 860-412-7277. p. 335

White, Christine, Circ Serv Dir, Williamsburg Regional Library, 7770 Croaker Rd, Williamsburg, VA, 23188-7064. Tel: 757-259-4063. Fax: 757-259-4079, 757-259-7798. p. 2503

White, Christopher, Syst Librn, The Sage Colleges, 140 New Scotland Ave, Albany, NY, 12208. Tel: 518-244-4521. Fax: 518-292-1904. p. 1570

White, Christopher, Syst Librn, The Sage Colleges, 45 Ferry St, Troy, NY, 12180. Tel: 518-244-4521. Fax: 518-244-2400. p. 1756

White, Christopher C, Coordr, Libr Serv, Saint Louis Community College, Florissant Valley Campus Library, 3400 Pershall Rd, Ferguson, MO, 63135-1408. Tel: 314-513-4484. Fax: 314-513-4053. p. 1357

White, Curtis, In Charge, National Park Service Department of Interior, 244 Central St, Saugus, MA, 01906. Tel: 781-233-0050. Fax: 781-231-7345. p. 1122

White, Dan, Libr Dir, Scappoose Public Library, 52469 SE Second St, Scappoose, OR, 97056. Tel: 503-543-7123. Fax: 503-543-7161. p. 2019

White, Delo, ILL, Ref, Rosenberg Library, 2310 Sealy Ave, Galveston, TX, 77550. Tel: 409-763-8854. Fax: 409-763-0275. p. 2326

White, Dottie, Dir, Nutter Fort Library, 1300 Buckhannon Pike, Nutter Fort, WV, 26301-4406. Tel: 304-622-7563. Fax: 304-622-7563. p. 2567

White, Eddie, Ref, Shook, Hardy & Bacon, 2555 Grand Blvd, 3rd Flr, Kansas City, MO, 64108-2613. Tel: 816-474-6550. Fax: 816-421-5547. p. 1341

White, Edna, Assoc Dean, Cedar Valley College Library, 3030 N Dallas Ave, Lancaster, TX, 75134-3799. Tel: 972-860-8152. Fax: 972-860-8221. p. 2353

White, Elizabeth, Adult Serv, Dunedin Public Library, 223 Douglas Ave, Dunedin, FL, 34698. Tel: 727-298-3080, Ext 224. Fax: 727-298-3088. p. 438

White, Ellen, Asst Librn, Caldwell-Lake George Library, 336 Canada St, Lake George, NY, 12845-1118. Tel: 518-668-2528. Fax: 518-668-2528. p. 1650

White, Gina P, Spec Coll & Archives Librn, Winthrop University, 824 Oakland Ave, Rock Hill, SC, 29733. Tel: 803-323-2131, 803-323-2274, 803-323-2311. Fax: 803-323-2215. p. 2203

White, Gregg, Supvr, Nevada Department of Corrections, PO Box 7007, Carson City, NV, 89702. Tel: 775-684-3005, Ext 3063. Fax: 775-684-3051. p. 1426

White, Harlan, Network Serv Dir, West Virginia Library Commission, State Capitol Complex, 1900 Kanawha Blvd E, Charleston, WV, 25305-0620. Tel: 304-558-3577. Fax: 304-558-3693. p. 2557

White, J'Nevelyn, Asst Dir, Midland County Public Library, 301 W Missouri, Midland, TX, 79701. Tel: 432-688-4320. Fax: 432-688-4939. p. 2363

White, Janel, Broadcast Librn, NPR Library, 635 Massachusetts Ave NW, Washington, DC, 20001. Fax: 202-513-3056. p. 412

White, Janet, Br Mgr, Boone-Madison Public Library, Barrett-Wharton Branch, 38487 Pond Fork Rd, Wharton, WV, 25208. Tel: 304-247-6530. Fax: 304-247-6530. p. 2564

White, Janet Laura, Librn, Blackhawk Technical College Library, 6004 S County Rd G, Janesville, WI, 53547. Tel: 608-757-7705. Fax: 608-743-4518. p. 2599

White, Janet Laura, Mgr, Libr Serv, Blackhawk Technical College Library, Aviation Center, 4618 S Columbia Dr, Janesville, WI, 53546. Tel: 608-757-7743. Fax: 608-758-6950. p. 2599

White, Jeff, Chief Librn, United States Department of Justice, 11900 E Cornell Ave, Unit C, Aurora, CO, 80014. Tel: 303-338-6644. p. 288

White, Jim, IT Serv Mgr, Tech Mgr, Baker County Public Library, 2400 Resort St, Baker City, OR, 97814-2798. Tel: 541-523-6419. Fax: 541-523-9088. p. 1990

White, Jo Nita, Extn Spec, Metropolitan Library System in Oklahoma County, Harrah Extension Library, 1930 N Church Ave, Harrah, OK, 73045-9085. Tel: 405-454-2001. Fax: 405-454-0322. p. 1972

White, Johannah, Ref Librn, Tulane University, 7001 Freret St, New Orleans, LA, 70118-5682. Tel: 504-314-7823. Fax: 504-865-6773. p. 963

White, Joseph, Syst & Cat Librn, Ector County Library, 321 W Fifth St, Odessa, TX, 79761-5066. Tel: 432-332-0633. Fax: 432-377-6502. p. 2366

White, Joyce, Ch, Goodwin Library, 422 Main St, Farmington, NH, 03835-1519. Tel: 603-755-2944. Fax: 603-755-2944. p. 1447

White, Joyce H, Dir, Elizabethton-Carter County Public Library, 201 N Sycamore St, Elizabethton, TN, 37643. Tel: 423-547-6360. Fax: 423-542-1510. p. 2233

White, Joyce L, Librn, Saint John's Cathedral Library, 1350 Washington St, Denver, CO, 80203. Tel: 303-744-0813. Fax: 303-831-7119. p. 303

White, Karen, Sr Librn, United States Agency for International Development, 1300 Pennsylvania Ave NW, Rm M01-010, Washington, DC, 20523-1000. Tel: 202-712-0579. Fax: 202-216-3515. p. 417

White, Karen, Circ Mgr, Obion County Public Library, 1221 E Reelfoot Ave, Union City, TN, 38261-5097. Tel: 731-885-7000, 731-885-9411. Fax: 731-885-9638. p. 2268

White, Karen P, Dir, Elbridge Free Library, 241 E Main St, Elbridge, NY, 13060. Tel: 315-689-7111. Fax: 315-689-9448. p. 1618

White, Kashawna, Mgr, Circ & Br Serv, Laramie County Library System, 2200 Pioneer Ave, Cheyenne, WY, 82001-3610. Tel: 307-773-7210. Fax: 307-634-2082. p. 2652

White, Katharine, Curator of Manuscripts, Northern Illinois University Libraries, Regional History Center, Founders Library, DeKalb, IL, 60115. Tel: 815-753-9394. p. 635

White, Kelvin, PhD, Dr, Asst Prof, University of Oklahoma, Bizzell Memorial Library, 401 W Brooks, Rm 120, Norman, OK, 73019-6032. Tel: 405-325-3921. Fax: 405-325-7648. p. 2972

White, Kimberly, Dir, Public Libraries of Saginaw, 505 Janes Ave, Saginaw, MI, 48607. Tel: 989-755-0904. Fax: 989-755-9829. p. 1223

White, Laurel, Neighborhood Serv Mgr, Boise Public Library, 715 S Capitol Blvd, Boise, ID, 83702. Tel: 208-384-4485. p. 570

White, Leah, Ch, Madrid Public Library, 100 W Third St, Madrid, IA, 50156. Tel: 515-795-3846. Fax: 515-795-3697. p. 828

White, Leah, Dir, Minburn Public Library, 315 Baker St, Minburn, IA, 50167. Tel: 515-677-2712. Fax: 515-677-2245. p. 832

White, Lely, Head, Cat, University of Dallas, 1845 E Northgate Dr, Irving, TX, 75062-4736. Tel: 972-721-5310. Fax: 972-721-4010. p. 2347

White, Lena, Dir, Buna Public Library, 1042 Texas Hwy 62 S, Buna, TX, 77612. Tel: 409-994-5501. Fax: 409-994-4737. p. 2293

White, Linda, Asst Dir, Ref, Perrot Memorial Library, 90 Sound Beach Ave, Old Greenwich, CT, 06870. Tel: 203-637-1066. Fax: 203-698-2620. p. 363

White, Linda, Head, Tech Serv, Thorntown Public Library, 124 N Market St, Thorntown, IN, 46071-1144. Tel: 765-436-7348. Fax: 765-436-7011. p. 782

White, Linda, ILL, Ref, Carnegie Public Library, 114 Delta Ave, Clarksdale, MS, 38614-4212. Tel: 662-624-4461. Fax: 662-627-4344. p. 1295

White, Lindy, Pub Serv, University of Mobile, 5735 College Pkwy, Mobile, AL, 36613-2842. Tel: 251-442-2242. Fax: 251-442-2515. p. 26

White, Lisa, In Charge, Multnomah County Library, Albina, 3605 NE 15th Ave, Portland, OR, 97212-2358. Tel: 503-988-5362. Fax: 503-988-5482. p. 2012

White, Liz, Librn, Animal Alliance of Canada Library, 221 Broadview Ave, No 101, Toronto, ON, M4M 2G3, CANADA. Tel: 416-462-9541. Fax: 416-462-9647. p. 2849

White, Lucinda, Dir, Eastern Maine Medical Center, 489 State St, Bangor, ME, 04402. Tel: 207-973-8228. Fax: 207-973-8233. p. 976

White, Lynda, Asst Dir, University of Virginia, Charles L Brown Science & Engineering Library, Clark Hall, Charlottesville, VA, 22903-3188. Tel: 434-924-3628. Fax: 434-924-4338. p. 2454

White, Lynn, Dir, Terryville Public Library, 238 Main St, Terryville, CT, 06786. Tel: 860-582-3121. Fax: 860-585-4068. p. 372

White, Lynnda, Access Serv & Syst, Lake City Community College, 149 SE College Pl, Lake City, FL, 32025-2006. Tel: 386-754-4400. Fax: 386-754-4900. p. 457

White, Margaret, Dir, Copper Queen Library, Six Main St, Bisbee, AZ, 85603. Tel: 520-432-4232. Fax: 520-432-7061. p. 58

White, Margaret, Mgr, Tech Serv, Willard Memorial Library, Six W Emerald St, Willard, OH, 44890-1498. Tel: 419-933-8564. Fax: 419-933-4783. p. 1948

White, Margaret, Coordr, Metropolitan Consortium of Chicago, Chicago School of Professional Psychology, 325 N Wells St, Chicago, IL, 60610. Tel: 312-329-6633. Fax: 312-644-6075. p. 2942

White, Marie, Dir, Ivy Tech Community College, 8204 Hwy 311, Sellersburg, IN, 47172-1897. Tel: 812-246-3301, Ext 4225. Fax: 812-246-9905. p. 777

White, Marilyn, Asst Dir, Tillamook County Library, 1716 Third St, Tillamook, OR, 97141. Tel: 503-842-4792. Fax: 503-815-8194. p. 2021

White, Marsha, Asst Librn, United States Department of Veterans Affairs, 1601 SW Archer Rd, Gainesville, FL, 32608-1197. Tel: 352-376-1611, Ext 6313. Fax: 352-374-6148. p. 449

White, Mary, Librn, Broad Brook Public Library, 81 Main St, Broad Brook, CT, 06016. Tel: 860-623-1334. Fax: 860-627-0493. p. 332

White, Mary, Asst Dir, Libr Serv, Upper Iowa University, 605 Washington St, Fayette, IA, 52142. Tel: 563-425-5270. Fax: 563-425-5271. p. 816

White, Mary H, Dir, Howe Library, 13 South St, Hanover, NH, 03755. Tel: 603-643-0725, Ext 116. Fax: 603-643-0725. p. 1450

White, Mary Jo, Librn, Utah School for the Deaf & Blind, 742 Harrison Blvd, Ogden, UT, 84404. Tel: 801-629-4817. Fax: 801-629-4896. p. 2408

White, Mary Jo, Dean, Instrul Res, South Seattle Community College, 6000 16th Ave SW, Seattle, WA, 98106-1499. Tel: 206-768-6400. Fax: 206-763-5155. p. 2532

White, Mary Lu H, Managing Librn, Washington State Library, Utilities & Transportation Commission, 1300 S Evergreen Pk Dr SW, Olympia, WA, 98504. Tel: 360-664-1203. Fax: 360-586-1145. p. 2545

White, Mary Lucia, Asst Dir, Cat, Kenai Community Library, 163 Main St Loop, Kenai, AK, 99611-7723. Tel: 907-283-4378. Fax: 907-283-2266. p. 50

White, Maureen, Assoc Prof, University of Houston-Clear Lake, 2700 Bay Area Blvd, Houston, TX, 77058-1098. Tel: 281-283-3577. Fax: 281-283-3630. p. 2974

White, Mindy, Dir, Colorado Mountain College, 3000 County Rd 114, Glenwood Springs, CO, 81601. Tel: 970-947-8268. Fax: 970-947-8288. p. 309

White, Miranda, Br Mgr, Anderson County Library, Piedmont Branch, 1407 Hwy 86, Piedmont, SC, 29673. Tel: 864-845-6534. Fax: 864-845-6534. p. 2181

White, Molly, Librn, University of Texas Libraries, Physics-Mathematics-Astronomy, Robert L Moore Hall 4-200, Austin, TX, 78713. Tel: 512-495-4610. Fax: 512-495-4611. p. 2284

White, Nadine, Pub Serv Librn, Whistler Public Library, 4329 Main St, Whistler, BC, V0N 1B4, CANADA. Tel: 604-935-8433. Fax: 604-935-8434. p. 2746

White, Nancy, Head, Circ, Winthrop University, 824 Oakland Ave, Rock Hill, SC, 29733. Tel: 803-323-2335. Fax: 803-323-2215. p. 2203

White, Naomi, Asst Librn, Shepard-Pruden Memorial Library, 106 W Water St, Edenton, NC, 27932. Tel: 252-482-4112. Fax: 252-482-5451. p. 1790

White, Naomi, Prog Coordr, Global Issues Resource Center Library, Cuyahoga Community College, Education Ctr Bldg, Rm 115, 4250 Richmond Rd, Highland Hills, OH, 44122. Tel: 216-987-2582. Fax: 216-987-2133. p. 1904

White, Naomi E, Info Serv, Norfolk State University Library, 700 Park Ave, Norfolk, VA, 23504-8010. Tel: 757-823-2438. Fax: 757-823-2431. p. 2482

White, Pamela, Librn, Killen Public Library, 325 J C Malden Hwy, Killen, AL, 35645. Tel: 256-757-5471. Fax: 256-757-5471. p. 23

White, Pamela, Sr Admin Assoc, Parkland Health & Hospital System, 5201 Harry Hines Blvd, Dallas, TX, 75235. Tel: 214-590-0066. Fax: 214-590-2720. p. 2309

White, Pat, Librn, Coldwater-Wilmore Regional Library, Wilmore Branch, 100 Taft St, Wilmore, KS, 67155. Tel: 620-738-4464. p. 861

White, Patricia A, Dir, United States Department of Defense, 2475 K St, Rm 315, Bldg 52, Wright-Patterson AFB, OH, 45433-8258. Tel: 937-255-9211. Fax: 937-255-8258. p. 1951

White, Paula, Dir, New Mexico State Library, 423 W Nobles, Tucumcari, NM, 88401. Tel: 575-461-1206. Fax: 575-461-1824. p. 1566

White, Rachel, Dept Head, Tech Serv, State Historical Society of North Dakota, North Dakota Heritage Ctr, 612 E Boulevard Ave, Bismarck, ND, 58505-0830. Tel: 701-328-3571. Fax: 701-328-2650. p. 1838

White, Robert, Exec Dir, Canadian Paraplegic Association Library, 230-1101 Prince of Wales Dr, Ottawa, ON, K2C 3W7, CANADA. Tel: 613-723-1033. Fax: 613-723-1060. p. 2829

White, Robert William, Exec Dir, Bergen County Cooperative Library System, 810 Main St, Hackensack, NJ, 07601. Tel: 201-489-1904. Fax: 201-489-4215. p. 2948

White, Roberta, Spec Projects Librn, New River Community College, 226 Martin Hall, Dublin, VA, 24084. Tel: 540-674-3600, Ext 4339. Fax: 540-676-3626. p. 2460

White, Ronnie, Mgr, Kootenai-Shoshone Area Libraries, Pinehurst-Kingston Branch, 107 Main St, Pinehurst, ID, 83850. Tel: 208-682-3483. Fax: 208-682-3483. p. 575

White, Rosie, Librn, Charlotte E Hobbs Memorial Library, 227 Main St, Lovell, ME, 04051. Tel: 207-925-3177. Fax: 207-925-3177. p. 991

White, Ruth, Librn, Southwest Arkansas Regional Library, Dierks Branch, 202 W Third St, Dierks, AR, 71833. Tel: 870-286-3228. Fax: 870-286-2570. p. 103

White, Scott, Access Serv, Fiorello H LaGuardia Community College Library, 31-10 Thomson Ave, Long Island City, NY, 11101. Tel: 718-482-5421. Fax: 718-482-5444, 718-609-2011. p. 1654

White, Shelley, Librn, Saint John's Health System, Van K Smith Community Health Library, St John's Cancer Ctr, 2055 S Fremont, Springfield, MO, 65804-2263. Tel: 417-820-2539. Fax: 417-820-2587. p. 1367

White, Shelley, Librn, St John's Health System, 1235 E Cherokee St, Springfield, MO, 65804-2263. Tel: 417-820-2539. Fax: 417-820-8761. p. 1367

White, Susan, Dir, Sequoyah Regional Library System, 116 Brown Industrial Pkwy, Canton, GA, 30114-2899. Tel: 770-479-3090, Ext 221. Fax: 770-479-3069. p. 523

White, Susan, Asst City Librn, Eagle Mountain Public Library, 1650 E Stagecoach Run, Eagle Mountain, UT, 84005. Tel: 801-789-6623. Fax: 801-789-6653. p. 2405

White, Suzanne, Customer Serv Mgr, Rowan Public Library, 201 W Fisher St, Salisbury, NC, 28144-4935. Tel: 704-216-7732. Fax: 704-216-8237. p. 1822

White, Tim, Head, Adult Serv, Worth Public Library District, 6917 W 111th St, Worth, IL, 60482. Tel: 708-448-2855. Fax: 708-448-9174. p. 721

White, Todd A, Electronic Res & Ref Librn, College of Saint Scholastica Library, 1200 Kenwood Ave, Duluth, MN, 55811-4199. Tel: 218-723-6140. Fax: 218-723-5948. p. 1247

White, Toni, Br Mgr, Greene County Public Library, Beavercreek Community Library, 3618 Dayton-Xenia Rd, Beavercreek, OH, 45432-2884. Tel: 937-352-4001. Fax: 937-426-0481. p. 1951

White, Tony, Head of Libr, Indiana University Bloomington, Fine Arts Library, Fine Arts Museum, 1133 E Seventh St, Bloomington, IN, 47405. Tel: 812-855-3314. Fax: 812-855-3443. p. 727

White, Trenita, Tech Serv Librn, Santa Fe Community College, 3000 NW 83rd St, Bldg Y-100, Gainesville, FL, 32606. Tel: 352-395-5406. Fax: 352-395-5102. p. 449

White, Valerie, Youth Serv Coordr, Canton Free Library, Eight Park St, Canton, NY, 13617. Tel: 315-386-3712. Fax: 315-386-4131. p. 1602

White, Vivian B, Asst Libr Dir, Montgomery City-County Public Library System, 245 High St, Montgomery, AL, 36104. Tel: 334-240-4922. Fax: 334-240-4977. p. 29

White, William, Dir, Troy Public Library, 300 N Three Notch St, Troy, AL, 36081. Tel: 334-566-1314. Fax: 334-566-4392. p. 37

White-Williams, Patricia, Br Coordr, Fairfax County Public Library, 12000 Government Center Pkwy, Ste 324, Fairfax, VA, 22035-0012. Tel: 703-324-3100. Fax: 703-324-8365. p. 2461

Whitebear, Robin, Admin Librn, United States Bureau of Land Management, 2909 W Second St, Roswell, NM, 88201-2019. Tel: 575-627-0272. p. 1561

Whited, Sarah, Pub Serv Librn, Cedar Park Public Library, 550 Discovery Blvd, Cedar Park, TX, 78613. Tel: 512-401-5600. Fax: 512-259-5236. p. 2296

Whitehead, Amelia, Access Serv Librn, Meharry Medical College Library, 1005 Dr D B Todd Jr Blvd, Nashville, TN, 37208. Tel: 615-327-6326. Fax: 615-327-6448. p. 2257

Whitehead, Beck, Librn, Southwest School of Arts Library, 300 Augusta, San Antonio, TX, 78205. Tel: 210-224-1848. Fax: 210-224-9337. p. 2383

Whitehead, Gloria, In Charge, First Congregational Church Library, 128 Central St, Auburn, MA, 01501. Tel: 508-832-2845. Fax: 508-721-2539. p. 1051

Whitehead, Heather, Acq Librn, Colorado School of Mines, 1400 Illinois St, Golden, CO, 80401-1887. Tel: 303-273-3540. Fax: 303-273-3199. p. 309

Whitehead, Jennifer, Head, Ch, Clapp Memorial Library, 19 S Main St, Belchertown, MA, 01007-0627. Tel: 413-323-0417. Fax: 413-323-0453. p. 1052

Whitehead, Joyce Ellen, Dir, National University of Health Sciences Learning Resource Center, 200 E Roosevelt Rd, Bldg C, Lombard, IL, 60148-4583. Tel: 630-889-6612. Fax: 630-495-6658. p. 667

Whitehead, Leslie, YA Serv, Lost Rivers District Library, 126 S Front St, Arco, ID, 83213. Tel: 208-527-8511. p. 569

Whitehead, Marcia, Librn, Humanities & Soc Sci, University of Richmond, 28 Westhampton Way, Richmond, VA, 23173. Tel: 804-289-8823. Fax: 804-289-8757. p. 2491

Whitehead, Martha, Univ Librn, Queen's University, 101 Union St, Kingston, ON, K7L 5C4, CANADA. Fax: 613-533-6362. p. 2814

Whitehead, Michele, Instruction Librn, University of North Texas Health Science Center at Fort Worth, 3500 Camp Bowie Blvd, Fort Worth, TX, 76107-2699. Tel: 817-735-2070. Fax: 817-763-0325. p. 2324

Whitehead, Pat, Chief Librn Br Serv, Monmouth County Library, 125 Symmes Dr, Manalapan, NJ, 07726. Tel: 732-431-7220. Fax: 732-308-2955. p. 1498

Whitehead, Sue, Spec Coll & Archives Librn, Syst Librn, Biola University Library, 13800 Biola Ave, La Mirada, CA, 90639. Tel: 562-944-0351, Ext 5611. Fax: 562-903-4840. p. 162

Whitehead, Susan, Ref Librn, Union Institute & University, 62 Ridge St, Ste 2, Montpelier, VT, 05602. Tel: 802-828-8747. Fax: 802-828-8748. p. 2429

Whitehead, Tara, Head, Circ, York County Public Library, 100 Long Green Blvd, Yorktown, VA, 23693. Tel: 757-890-5135. Fax: 757-890-5127. p. 2505

Whitehead, Thomas, Spec Coll Librn, Temple University Libraries, 1210 W Berks St, Philadelphia, PA, 19122-6088. Tel: 215-204-4371. Fax: 215-204-5201. p. 2117

Whitehill, Barbara J, Dir, Dailey Memorial Library, 101 Junior High Dr, Derby, VT, 05829. Tel: 802-766-5063. Fax: 802-766-5063. p. 2423

Whitehill, Diana, Assoc Librn, State Education Resource Center Library, 25 Industrial Park Rd, Middletown, CT, 06457-1516. Tel: 860-632-1485, Ext 271. Fax: 860-632-0438. p. 352

Whitehorn, Stanley, Operations Mgr, University of Mississippi, One Library Loop, University, MS, 38677. Tel: 662-915-7935. Fax: 662-915-5734. p. 1316

Whitehouse, Dina, Circ, University of Pittsburgh at Bradford, 300 Campus Dr, Bradford, PA, 16701. Tel: 814-362-7610. Fax: 814-362-7688. p. 2037

Whitehouse, Nick, Librn, National Railway Historical Society, Atlanta Chapter, 3595 Peachtree Rd, Duluth, GA, 30096. Tel: 770-476-2013. p. 531

Whitehurst, Ann N, Ser, Pitt Community College, Hwy 11 S, Greenville, NC, 27835. Tel: 252-321-4362. Fax: 252-321-4404. p. 1799

Whitehurst, Dolores A, Mgr, PQ Corp, 280 Cedar Grove Rd, Conshohocken, PA, 19428-2240. Tel: 610-651-4629. Fax: 610-832-2931. p. 2047

Whiteing, Dhana, Regional Librn, Providence Community Library, Mt Pleasant Library, 315 Academy Ave, Providence, RI, 02908. Tel: 401-272-0106. p. 2173

Whiteley, Elizabeth, Dir, Christian Educ, First Presbyterian Church Library, 215 Locust NE, Albuquerque, NM, 87102. Tel: 505-764-2900. Fax: 505-764-2940. p. 1549

Whiteman, Anna, Librn, Grainfield City Library, 242 Main, Grainfield, KS, 67737. Tel: 785-673-4770. p. 869

Whiteman, Bruce, Librn, University of California Los Angeles Library, William Andrews Clark Memorial Library, 2520 Cimarron St, Los Angeles, CA, 90018. Tel: 323-731-8529. Fax: 323-731-8617. p. 178

Whiteman, Catherine, Librn, Waterloo Law Association, Court House, 20 Weber St E, Kitchener, ON, N2H 1C3, CANADA. Tel: 519-742-0872. Fax: 519-742-4102. p. 2815

Whiteman, Michael, Assoc Dean, Law Libr Serv & Info Tech, Northern Kentucky University, Nunn Dr, Highland Heights, KY, 41099. Tel: 859-572-5717. Fax: 859-572-6529, 859-572-6664. p. 917

Whitener, Sherrill, Asst Librn, Nashville Public Library, 219 E Elm St, Nashville, IL, 62263-1711. Tel: 618-327-3827. Fax: 618-327-4820. p. 679

Whitesell, Brandi, Dir, Media-Upper Providence Free Library, One E Front St, Media, PA, 19063. Tel: 610-566-1918. Fax: 610-566-9056. p. 2087

Whitesell, Melissa, Ref/Instruction Librn, Dalton State College, 650 College Dr, Dalton, GA, 30720-3778. Tel: 706-272-4585. Fax: 706-272-4511. p. 528

Whiteside, Ann, Librn/Asst Dean, Info Res, Harvard Library, Frances Loeb Library, Harvard Graduate School of Design, 48 Quincy St, Gund Hall, Cambridge, MA, 02138. Tel: 617-495-9163. p. 1076

Whiteside, Thomas, Med Media, Department of Veterans Affairs, 1100 Tunnel Rd, Asheville, NC, 28805. Tel: 828-299-5360. Fax: 828-299-2500. p. 1774

Whitesides, Robert, Dir, Shenandoah County Library, 514 Stoney Creek Blvd, Edinburg, VA, 22824. Tel: 540-984-8200. Fax: 540-984-8207. p. 2460

Whitfield, Debra, Acq, Asst Dir, Cat, Fort Stockton Public Library, 500 N Water St, Fort Stockton, TX, 79735. Tel: 432-336-3374. Fax: 432-336-6648. p. 2321

Whitfield, Jan, Head, Pub Serv, Head, Ref Serv, Fayetteville State University, 1200 Murchison Rd, Fayetteville, NC, 28301-4298. Tel: 910-672-1750. Fax: 910-672-1746. p. 1793

Whitfield, Kevin, Cat Librn/Interim Head Coll Serv, Youngstown State University, One University Plaza, Youngstown, OH, 44555-0001. Tel: 330-941-2922. Fax: 330-941-3734. p. 1953

Whitfield, Rosanna, Librn, First United Methodist Church Library, 503 N Central Expressway, Richardson, TX, 75080. Tel: 972-301-0143. Fax: 972-341-0140. p. 2374

Whitfill, Jill, Dir, Bethel University, 325 Cherry Ave, McKenzie, TN, 38201. Tel: 731-352-6913. Fax: 731-352-4070. p. 2247

Whitford, Phillip, Assoc Dir, Support Serv, Braswell Memorial Public Library, 727 N Grace St, Rocky Mount, NC, 27804-4842. Tel: 252-442-1951. Fax: 252-442-7366. p. 1820

Whitford, Susan, Dir, Info Tech & Fac Div, Kitsap Regional Library, 1301 Sylvan Way, Bremerton, WA, 98310-3498. Tel: 360-475-9176. Fax: 360-405-9128. p. 2510

Whitham, Bruce Alan, Dean of Libr, Rowan University Library, 201 Mullica Hill Rd, Glassboro, NJ, 08029. Tel: 856-256-4981. Fax: 856-256-4924. p. 1488

Whithaus, Rhonda, Electronic Res, University of Missouri-Columbia, Elmer Ellis Library, Ellis Library Bldg, Rm 104, Columbia, MO, 65201-5149. Tel: 573-882-9164. Fax: 573-882-8044. p. 1325

Whiting, Elaine, Br Mgr, Somerset County Library System, Warren Township Branch, 42 Mountain Blvd, Warren, NJ, 07059. Tel: 908-754-5554. Fax: 908-754-2899. p. 1475

Whiting, Peter, Ser Tech Serv Librn, University of Southern Indiana, 8600 University Blvd, Evansville, IN, 47712. Tel: 812-465-1280. Fax: 812-465-1693. p. 739

Whiting, Scott, Libr Dir, Concordia College, 1804 Green St, Selma, AL, 36703-3323. Tel: 334-874-5700, Ext 19739. Fax: 334-874-5755. p. 35

Whiting, Thomas, Ref Serv, Central New Mexico Community College Libraries, Montoya Campus Library, J Bldg, Rm 123, 4700 Morris NE, Albuquerque, NM, 87111. Fax: 505-224-5727. p. 1548

Whitis, Andrew, Dir, The University of Findlay, 1000 N Main St, Findlay, OH, 45840-3695. Tel: 419-434-5735. p. 1899

Whitis, Jan, Libr Mgr, Banner & Witcoff, Ltd Library, Ten S Wacker Dr, Ste 3000, Chicago, IL, 60606. Tel: 312-463-5455. Fax: 312-463-5001. p. 606

Whitley, Alisa, Archivist, Library of the Marine Corps, Gray Research Ctr, 2040 Broadway St, Quantico, VA, 22134-5107. Tel: 703-784-4685. Fax: 703-784-4306. p. 2486

Whitley, Peggy, Dean, Lone Star College System, Kingwood College Library, 20000 Kingwood Dr, Kingwood, TX, 77339. Tel: 281-312-1493. Fax: 281-312-1456. p. 2340

Whitlock, Brandy, Instrul Serv Librn, Anne Arundel Community College, 101 College Pkwy, Arnold, MD, 21012-1895. Tel: 410-777-2211. Fax: 410-777-2652. p. 1011

Whitlock, Jennifer, Archivist, Indianapolis Museum of Art, 4000 Michigan Rd, Indianapolis, IN, 46208-3326. Tel: 317-920-2647. Fax: 317-926-8931. p. 754

Whitlow, Tammy, Librn, Southwest Arkansas Regional Library, Foreman Branch, 216 Schuman St, Foreman, AR, 71836. Tel: 870-542-7409. Fax: 870-542-7409. p. 103

Whitman, Mark, Br Mgr, Juneau Public Libraries, Mendenhall Valley, 9105 Mendenhall Mall Rd, Ste 350, Juneau, AK, 99801. Tel: 907-789-0125. Fax: 907-790-2213. p. 50

Whitman, Mark, Circ, Juneau Public Libraries, 292 Marine Way, Juneau, AK, 99801. Tel: 907-586-5324. Fax: 907-586-3419. p. 50

Whitman, Roger A, Interim Librn, The River Christian Reformed Church Library, 459 E Highland Ave, Redlands, CA, 92373. Tel: 909-793-6801. Fax: 909-798-4133. p. 214

Whitmar, Jacqueline A, Dir, Argyle Public Library, 401 E Milwaukee, Argyle, WI, 53504. Tel: 608-543-3193. p. 2579

Whitmell, Vicki, Exec Dir, Legis Librn, Ontario Legislative Library, Legislative Bldg, Queen's Park, Toronto, ON, M7A 1A9, CANADA. Tel: 416-325-3939. Fax: 416-325-3909. p. 2856

Whitmer, Judy Lynn, Dir, Galva Public Library, 203 S Main St, Galva, IA, 51020. Tel: 712-282-4400. Fax: 712-282-4400. p. 817

Whitmer, Kerri, Asst Br Mgr, Dallas Public Library, Lakewood, 6121 Worth St, Dallas, TX, 75214-4497. Tel: 214-670-1376. Fax: 214-670-5701. p. 2307

Whitmer, Sandra, Dir, Warrenville Public Library District, 28 W 751 Stafford Pl, Warrenville, IL, 60555. Tel: 630-393-1171. Fax: 630-393-1688. p. 715

Whitmill, Linda, Syst Adminr, Aurora Public Library, One E Benton St, Aurora, IL, 60505-4299. Tel: 630-264-4100. Fax: 630-896-3209. p. 591

Whitmire, Dana, Electronic Res/Ser Librn, University of Texas Health Science Center at San Antonio Libraries, 7703 Floyd Curl Dr, MSC 7940, San Antonio, TX, 78229-3900. Tel: 210-567-2400. Fax: 210-567-2490. p. 2383

Whitmire, Darla, Asst Dir, Beaman Community Memorial Library, 223 Main St, Beaman, IA, 50609. Tel: 641-366-2912. Fax: 641-366-2912. p. 796

Whitmore, Gregg, Libr Tech, Department of Veterans Affairs, 500 W Fort St, 531/142D, Boise, ID, 83702-4598. Tel: 208-422-1306. Fax: 208-422-1390. p. 570

Whitmore, Keri, Ref Serv, YA, Franklin Public Library, 9151 W Loomis Rd, Franklin, WI, 53132. Tel: 414-425-8214. Fax: 414-425-9498. p. 2593

Whitmore, Tiffany, Br Mgr, Riverside Regional Library, Oran Branch, 120 Mountain St, Oran, MO, 63771. Tel: 573-262-3745. Fax: 573-262-3745. p. 1334

Whitmoyer, Cindy, Pub Serv, Susquehanna University, 514 University Ave, Selinsgrove, PA, 17870-1050. Tel: 570-372-4459. Fax: 570-372-4310. p. 2138

Whitney, Amy, Br Mgr, Frederick County Public Libraries, Urbana, 9020 Amelung St, Frederick, MD, 21704. Tel: 301-600-7000. p. 1029

Whitney, Ann, Cat, Nevada Supreme Court Library, Supreme Court Bldg, 201 S Carson St, Ste 100, Carson City, NV, 89701-4702. Tel: 775-684-1640. Fax: 775-684-1662. p. 1426

Whitney, Greg, Head, Syst Serv, Ecole Polytechnique de Montreal Bibliotheque, 2500, chemin de Polytechnique, Montreal, QC, H3T 1J4, CANADA. Tel: 514-340-4666. Fax: 514-340-4026. p. 2895

Whitney, Gretchen, Assoc Prof, University of Tennessee, Knoxville, 451 Communications Bldg, 1345 Circle Park Dr, Knoxville, TN, 37996-0341. Tel: 865-974-2148. Fax: 865-974-4967. p. 2974

Whitney, Irene, Ref, Ellsworth Public Library, 20 State St, Ellsworth, ME, 04605. Tel: 207-667-6363. Fax: 207-667-4901. p. 984

Whitney, John, Syst Coordr, United States Air Force, 2511 Kennedy Circle, No 155, Brooks AFB, TX, 78235-5116. Tel: 210-536-3323. Fax: 210-536-3239. p. 2292

Whitney, Kathryn, Cent Libr Mgr, Onondaga County Public Library, The Galleries of Syracuse, 447 S Salina St, Syracuse, NY, 13202-2494. Fax: 315-435-8533. p. 1752

Whitney, Loralyn, Acq, Edinboro University of Pennsylvania, 200 Tartan Ave, Edinboro, PA, 16444. Tel: 814-732-2779. Fax: 814-732-2883. p. 2053

Whitney, Toni, Asst Dir, Lorain Public Library System, 351 Sixth St, Lorain, OH, 44052. Tel: 440-244-1192, Ext 225. Fax: 440-244-1733. p. 1911

Whitney, Tracy, Dir, Marion Public Library, 4036 Maple Ave, Marion, NY, 14505. Tel: 315-926-4933. Fax: 315-926-7038. p. 1658

Whitney, Wilma, Asst Librn, Sharon Springs Public Library, 113 W Second St, Sharon Springs, KS, 67758. Tel: 785-852-4685. Fax: 785-852-4687. p. 894

Whiton, Jane, Circ Mgr, Franklin Public Library, 118 Main St, Franklin, MA, 02038. Tel: 508-520-4940. p. 1090

Whitsitt, Kathleen, Authority Control Librn, Lone Star College System, 20515 State Hwy 249, Bldg 11, Rm 11437, Houston, TX, 77070-2607. Tel: 281-290-2842. Fax: 281-290-2979. p. 2340

Whitson, Cindy, Br Mgr, Mulberry Public Library, 220 N Main St, Mulberry, AR, 72947. Tel: 479-997-1226. Fax: 479-997-1226. p. 111

Whitt, Alisa, Acad Res Coordr, Partnership Among South Carolina Academic Libraries, 1333 Main St, Ste 305, Columbia, SC, 29201. Tel: 803-734-0912. Fax: 803-734-0901. p. 2955

Whitt, Connie, Br Mgr, Rockingham County Public Library, Eden Branch, 598 S Pierce St, Eden, NC, 27288. Tel: 336-623-3168. Fax: 336-623-1171. p. 1790

Whitt, Julie, Human Res Mgr, Upper Arlington Public Library, 2800 Tremont Rd, Columbus, OH, 43221. Tel: 614-486-9621. Fax: 614-486-4530. p. 1891

Whitt, Nancy, Adult Prog Coordr, Riverhead Free Library, 330 Court St, Riverhead, NY, 11901-2885. Tel: 631-727-3228. Fax: 631-727-4762. p. 1728

Whitt, Shirley, Librn, Van Buren District Library, Gobles Branch, 105 E Main St, Gobles, MI, 49055. Tel: 269-628-4537. Fax: 269-628-4537. p. 1168

Whitt, Shirley, Ch, Oak Hill Public Library, 226 S Front St, Oak Hill, OH, 45656. Tel: 740-682-6457. Fax: 740-682-3522. p. 1924

Whitt, Susan, Assoc Dean Coll Mgt, University of North Carolina at Pembroke, Faculty Row, Pembroke, NC, 28372. Tel: 910-521-6516. Fax: 910-521-6547. p. 1814

Whittaker, Carol, Archivist, The Henry Ford, 20900 Oakwood Blvd, Dearborn, MI, 48124-5029. Tel: 313-982-6100, Ext 2295. Fax: 313-982-6244. p. 1167

Whittaker, Charles, ILL Librn, Miami-Dade Public Library System, 101 W Flagler St, Miami, FL, 33130-1523. Tel: 305-375-4068. Fax: 305-375-3048. p. 466

Whittaker, Helen, Mgr, Kingsport Public Library & Archives, 400 Broad St, Kingsport, TN, 37660-4292. Tel: 423-229-9488. Fax: 423-224-2558. p. 2240

Whittaker, Jennifer, Asst Librn, State University of New York College of Technology, 34 Cornell Dr, Canton, NY, 13617-1098. Tel: 315-386-7057. Fax: 315-386-7931. p. 1602

Whittaker, Joan, Dir, Irvington Public Library, Civic Sq, Irvington, NJ, 07111-2498. Tel: 973-372-6400. Fax: 973-372-6860. p. 1491

Whittborn, Kim, Coordr, Areawide Hospital Library Consortium of Southwestern Illinois, c/o St Elizabeth Hosp Health Sci Libr, 211 S Third St, Belleville, IL, 62222. Tel: 618-234-2120, Ext 2011. Fax: 618-222-4614. p. 2942

Whitted, John P, Asst Prof, Ref & Info Spec, South Carolina State University, 300 College St NE, Orangeburg, SC, 29115-4427. Tel: 803-536-7045. Fax: 803-536-8902. p. 2202

Whittemore, Gail, Ref Librn, Spec Coll Librn, Pace University, 78 N Broadway, White Plains, NY, 10603. Tel: 914-422-4649. Fax: 914-422-4139. p. 1769

Whittemore, Lori, Br Mgr, New Tecumseth Public Library, D A Jones Branch, 42 Main St W, Beeton, ON, L0G 1A0, CANADA. Tel: 905-729-3726. p. 2792

Whittemore, Lori, Br Mgr, New Tecumseth Public Library, Pam Kirkpatrick Branch, Tottenham Mall, 5-55 Queen St S, Tottenham, ON, L0G 1W0, CANADA. Tel: 905-936-2291. p. 2792

Whitten, Cathy, Br Supvr, Montgomery-Floyd Regional Library System, Jessie Peterman Memorial, 321 W Main St, Floyd, VA, 24091. Tel: 540-745-2947. Fax: 540-745-4750. p. 2457

Whitten, Jamie, Librn, West Georgia Technical College, Carroll Campus-Roger Schoerner Technical Library, 997 S Hwy 16, Carrollton, GA, 30116. Tel: 770-836-4711. Fax: 770-836-6807. p. 556

Whitten, May, Evening Circ, Panola College, 1109 W Panola St, Carthage, TX, 75633. Tel: 903-693-1119. Fax: 903-693-1115. p. 2295

Whitten, Sharon, Bus Mgr, Columbus-Lowndes Public Library, 314 N Seventh St, Columbus, MS, 39701. Tel: 662-329-5300. Fax: 662-329-5156. p. 1297

Whitten, Sherry, Ref Serv, Madison County Library System, Ridgeland Public Library, 397 Hwy 51 N, Ridgeland, MS, 39157. Tel: 601-856-4536. Fax: 601-856-3748. p. 1295

Whittenborne, Lisa, Librn II, Chester Public Library, 733 State St, Chester, IL, 62233. Tel: 618-826-3711. Fax: 618-826-2733. p. 604

Whittenton, Kathy, ILL, Lyon College, 2300 Highland Rd, Batesville, AR, 72501-3699. Tel: 870-307-7205. Fax: 870-307-7279. p. 93

Whittier, David, Coordr, Boston University, School of Education, No 2 Sherborn St, Boston, MA, 02215. Tel: 617-353-3181, 617-353-3182. Fax: 617-353-3924. p. 2967

Whittingham, Rachel, Asst Librn, Central Baptist College, 1501 College Ave, Conway, AR, 72034. Tel: 501-329-6872. Fax: 501-329-2941. p. 96

Whittington, Blair, Librn Spec, Glendale Public Library, Brand Library & Art Center, 1601 W Mountain St, Glendale, CA, 91201-1209. Tel: 818-548-2050. Fax: 818-548-5079. p. 155

Whittington, Christi, Br Mgr, Harris County Public Library, Kingwood Branch, 4400 Bens View Lane, Kingwood, TX, 77339. Tel: 281-360-6804. Fax: 281-360-2093. p. 2336

Whittington, Christine A, Libr Dir, Greensboro College, 815 W Market St, Greensboro, NC, 27401. Tel: 336-272-7102, Ext 315. Fax: 336-217-7233. p. 1796

Whittington, Lea, Ser, Academy of Motion Picture Arts & Sciences, 333 S La Cienega Blvd, Beverly Hills, CA, 90211. Tel: 310-247-3000, Ext 2223. Fax: 310-657-5193. p. 129

Whittington, Margaret, Head, Adult Serv, Rockbridge Regional Library, 138 S Main St, Lexington, VA, 24450-2316. Tel: 540-463-4324. Fax: 540-464-4824. p. 2474

Whittington, Margaret T, Archivist, Chesapeake & Ohio Historical Society Archives, 312 E Ridgeway St, Clifton Forge, VA, 24422-1325. Tel: 540-862-2210. Fax: 540-863-9159. p. 2457

Whittle, Susan, Dir, Southwest Georgia Regional Library, 301 S Monroe St, Bainbridge, GA, 39819. Tel: 229-248-2665. Fax: 229-248-2670. p. 521

Whittle, Susan, Librn, Southwest Georgia Regional Library, Bainbridge Subregional Library for the Blind & Physically Handicapped-Talking Book Center, 301 S Monroe St, Bainbridge, GA, 39819. Tel: 229-248-2680. Fax: 229-248-2670. p. 521

Whitworth, Gail Oquin, Asst Librn, Circ, Inola Public Library, 15 North Broadway, Inola, OK, 74036. Tel: 918-543-8862. Fax: 918-543-3999. p. 1966

Whitworth, Kent, Exec Dir, Kentucky Historical Society, 100 W Broadway, Frankfort, KY, 40601. Tel: 502-564-1792. Fax: 502-564-4701. p. 913

Whorton, Billie, Librn, Madison County Public Library, Hwy 412 & Gaskill, Huntsville, AR, 72740. Tel: 479-738-2754. Fax: 479-738-2754. p. 104

Whynot, Christine, ILL, Dalhousie University, Sexton Design & Technology Library, 1360 Barrington St, Halifax, NS, B3J 2X4, CANADA. Tel: 902-494-3240. Fax: 902-494-6089. p. 2781

Whyte, Susan Barnes, Dir, Libr Serv, Linfield College, 900 S Baker St, McMinnville, OR, 97128. Tel: 503-883-2517. Fax: 503-883-2566. p. 2005

Wiandt, Lynn, Librn, Medina County District Library, Seville Community, N Center St, Seville, OH, 44273. Tel: 330-769-2852. Fax: 330-769-1774. p. 1916

Wiant, Michael, Dr, Dir, Dickson Mounds Museum Library, 10956 N Dickson Mounds Rd, Lewistown, IL, 61542. Tel: 309-547-3721. Fax: 309-547-3189. p. 665

Wibbing, William, Head, Coll & Acq, Washington University Libraries, One Brookings Dr, Campus Box 1061, Saint Louis, MO, 63130-4862. Tel: 314-935-4551. Fax: 314-935-4045. p. 1362

Wible, Joseph G, Bibliographer, Head Librn, Stanford University Libraries, Harold A Miller Marine Biology Library, Hopkins Marine Sta, Pacific Grove, CA, 93950-3094. Tel: 831-655-6228, 831-655-6229. Fax: 831-373-7859. p. 271

Wical, Stephanie, Electronic Res Librn, University of Wisconsin-Eau Claire, 105 Garfield Ave, Eau Claire, WI, 54702-4004. Tel: 715-836-3508. Fax: 715-836-2949. p. 2590

Wicher, Linda, Ch, Highland Park Public Library, 494 Laurel Ave, Highland Park, IL, 60035-2690. Tel: 847-432-0216. Fax: 847-432-9139. p. 655

Wichman, Terri, Tech Serv Mgr, Jackson County Public Library, 303 W Second St, Seymour, IN, 47274-2147. Tel: 812-522-3412, Ext 226. Fax: 812-522-5456. p. 777

Wick, Artis, Asst Librn, John & Mable Ringling Museum of Art Library, 5401 Bayshore Rd, Sarasota, FL, 34243. Tel: 941-359-5700, Ext 2701. Fax: 941-360-7370. p. 490

Wick, Charles Harrison, Archivist, College of Misericordia, 301 Lake St, Dallas, PA, 18612-1098. Tel: 570-674-6231. Fax: 570-674-6342. p. 2048

Wick, Chris, Br Mgr, Clermont County Public Library, New Richmond Branch, 103 River Valley Blvd, New Richmond, OH, 45157. Tel: 513-553-0570. Fax: 513-553-0574. p. 1858

Wick, Melanie, Col Librn, Interim Dean, Rappahannock Community College, 52 Campus Dr, Warsaw, VA, 22572. Tel: 804-333-6714. Fax: 804-333-0589. p. 2501

Wick, Melanie, Col Librn, Richmond County Public Library, Rappahannock Community College Library Ctr, 52 Campus Dr, Warsaw, VA, 22572. Tel: 804-333-6710. Fax: 804-333-0589. p. 2501

Wick, Ryan, Info Tech, Oregon State University Libraries, University Archives & Special Collections, 121 Valley Library, Corvallis, OR, 97331-4501. Tel: 541-737-2075. Fax: 541-737-3453. p. 1995

Wick, Tiffanie, Pub Serv Librn, Ref, Western State College, 600 N Adams St, Gunnison, CO, 81231. Tel: 970-943-2103. Fax: 970-943-2042. p. 312

Wick-Brink, Renee, Patron Serv Mgr, Park Forest Public Library, 400 Lakewood Blvd, Park Forest, IL, 60466. Tel: 708-748-3731. Fax: 708-748-8127. p. 688

Wickam, Carmen, ILL, Baker County Public Library, 2400 Resort St, Baker City, OR, 97814-2798. Tel: 541-523-6419. Fax: 541-523-9088. p. 1990

Wicke, Kim, Asst Librn, Tech Serv, Spalding University Library, 853 Library Lane, Louisville, KY, 40203-9986. Tel: 502-585-7130. Fax: 502-585-7156. p. 925

Wickenheiser, Diane, Librn, Hays Public Library, Box 36, Hays, AB, T0K 1B0, CANADA. Tel: 403-725-3744. Fax: 403-725-3744. p. 2706

Wickens, Joe, Head of Doc Delivery, Dalhousie University, W K Kellogg Health Sciences Library, Tupper Medical Bldg, 5850 College St, Halifax, NS, B3H 1X5, CANADA. p. 2780

Wicker, Janette, Sister, Librn, The Mound Center Library, 585 County Rd Z, Sinsinawa, WI, 53824. Tel: 608-748-4411. Fax: 608-748-4491. p. 2638

Wickers, Donna, Head, Circ, Harborfields Public Library, 31 Broadway, Greenlawn, NY, 11740-1382. Tel: 631-757-4200. Fax: 631-757-7216. p. 1631

Wickham, Donna, Dir, Elizabeth B Pert Library, Valois-Logan-Hector Fire House, Rte 414, Hector, NY, 14841. Tel: 607-546-2605. p. 1634

Wickham, Meredith, Br Mgr, Oconee County Public Library, Salem Branch, 5-B Park Ave, Salem, SC, 29676. Tel: 864-944-0912. p. 2207

Wickline, Mary, Instruction & Outreach Librn, University of California, San Diego, Biomedical Library, 9500 Gilman Dr, 0699, La Jolla, CA, 92093-0699. Tel: 858-534-3418. Fax: 858-822-2219. p. 162

Wicklund, Nancy, Head, Ref, Spec Coll Librn, Rider University, Katharine Houk Talbott Library, Westminster Choir College, 101 Walnut Lane, Princeton, NJ, 08540-3899. Tel: 609-921-7100, Ext 8236. Fax: 609-497-0243. p. 1494

Wickramasekara, Mica, Ref Librn, Alberta Government Library, Capital Blvd, 11th Flr, 10044 - 108 St, Edmonton, AB, T5J 5E6, CANADA. Tel: 780-427-2985. Fax: 780-427-5927. p. 2698

Wicks, Colleen, Librn, Lakeland Library Region, Speers Branch, Main St, Speers, SK, S0M 2V0, CANADA. Tel: 306-246-4866. p. 2920

Wicks, Donald, Dr, Assoc Prof, Kent State University, 314 Library, Kent, OH, 44242-0001. Tel: 330-672-2782. Fax: 330-672-7965. p. 2972

Wicks, Kathryn, Assoc Dir, The Urbana Free Library, 210 W Green St, Urbana, IL, 61801-5326. Tel: 217-367-4057. Fax: 217-367-4061. p. 713

Wickstrom, Kaye, Asst Librn, Southeastern Technical College Library, 346 Kite Rd, Swainsboro, GA, 30401. Tel: 478-289-2322. Fax: 478-289-2322. p. 553

Wickwire, Karen Gilson, Mgr, ILL, Mid-Continent Public Library, 15616 E US Hwy 24, Independence, MO, 64050-2098. Tel: 816-836-5200. Fax: 816-521-7253. p. 1332

Wickwire, Peggy, Ch, Canby Public Library, 292 N Holly St, Canby, OR, 97013-3732. Tel: 503-266-3394. Fax: 503-266-1709. p. 1993

Widder, Kathleen, Cat, United States Merchant Marine Academy, 300 Steamboat Rd, Kings Point, NY, 11024-1699. Tel: 516-726-5750. Fax: 516-726-5900. p. 1649

Widdoes, Sherry, Coll Mgr, University of Texas, M D Anderson Cancer Center Research Medical Library, 1400 Pressler St, Houston, TX, 77030-3722. Tel: 713-792-2812. Fax: 713-563-3650. p. 2344

Widener, Michael, Head, Spec Coll, University of Texas Libraries, Jamail Center for Legal Research, University of Texas School of Law, 727 E Dean Keeton St, Austin, TX, 78705-3224. Tel: 512-471-7726. Fax: 512-471-0243. p. 2284

Widener, Mike, Rare Bks, Yale University Library, Lillian Goldman Library Yale Law School, 127 Wall St, New Haven, CT, 06511. Tel: 203-432-1600. Fax: 203-432-2112. p. 358

Widener, Pamela, Br Mgr, Washington County Public Library, Glade Spring Branch, 212 Grace St, Glade Spring, VA, 24340. Tel: 276-429-5626. Fax: 276-429-2740. p. 2443

Widener, Scott, Librn, New York Daily News Library, 450 W 33rd St, New York, NY, 10001. Tel: 212-210-1509. Fax: 212-244-4033. p. 1689

Wider, Eve, Librn, University of Pittsburgh, Business, 118 Mervis Hall, Pittsburgh, PA, 15260. Tel: 412-648-3356. Fax: 412-648-1586. p. 2128

Wider, Eve, Librn, University of Pittsburgh, Graduate School of Public & International Affairs Economics Library, 1G12 Wesley W Posvar Hall, Pittsburgh, PA, 15260. Tel: 412-648-7574. Fax: 412-648-7569. p. 2129

Widger, Julie, Dir, Lamont Memorial Free Library, Five Main St, McGraw, NY, 13101. Tel: 607-836-6767. Fax: 607-836-8866. p. 1659

Widi, Karen, Mgr, Skidmore, Owings & Merrill Library, 224 S Michigan Ave, Ste 1000, Chicago, IL, 60604. Tel: 312-554-9090. Fax: 312-360-4545. p. 625

Widjeskog, Susan, In Charge, Cumberland County Juvenile Detention Center Library, 135 Sunny Slope Dr, Bridgeton, NJ, 08302. Tel: 856-455-0717, Ext 30. Fax: 856-455-4927. p. 1474

Widman, Nancy, Cat, Henry Ford Community College, 5101 Evergreen Rd, Dearborn, MI, 48128-1495. Tel: 313-845-9786. Fax: 313-845-9795. p. 1167

Widmar, Suzanne, Dir, Drummond Public Library, 14990 Superior St, Drummond, WI, 54832. Tel: 715-739-6290. p. 2588

Widmer, Barbara, Ch, Wolfeboro Public Library, 259 S Main St, Wolfeboro, NH, 03894. Tel: 603-569-2428. Fax: 603-569-8180. p. 1468

Widmer, Susan, Bibliographer, Vanderbilt University, Central Library, 419 21st Ave S, Nashville, TN, 37203-2427. Tel: 615-322-2800. Fax: 615-343-7451. p. 2260

Widmer, Ted, Dir, John Carter Brown Library, Brown University, George & Brown Sts, Providence, RI, 02912. Tel: 401-863-2725. Fax: 401-863-3477. p. 2171

Widner, Jack, Ref, Edinboro University of Pennsylvania, 200 Tartan Ave, Edinboro, PA, 16444. Tel: 814-732-2779. Fax: 814-732-2883. p. 2053

Widner, Melissa, Webmaster, Jasper County Public Library, 208 W Susan St, Rensselaer, IN, 47978. Tel: 219-866-5881. Fax: 219-866-7378. p. 774

Widner, Michael, Syst Coordr, Collier County Public Library, 2385 Orange Blossom Dr, Naples, FL, 34109. Tel: 239-593-0334. Fax: 239-254-8167. p. 471

Widney, Connie, Ch, Farmville Public Library, 4276 W Church St, Farmville, NC, 27828. Tel: 252-753-3355. Fax: 252-753-2855. p. 1792

Widrich, Marlene, Asst Regional Libr Mgr, Broward County Division of Libraries, West Regional, 8601 W Broward Blvd, Plantation, FL, 33324. Tel: 954-382-5860, Ext 262. Fax: 954-382-5873. p. 442

Widrick, Melissa, Educ Curator, Jefferson County Historical Society Library, 228 Washington St, Watertown, NY, 13601. Tel: 315-782-3491. Fax: 315-782-2913. p. 1763

Wiebe, David, Mgr, Access Serv, The College of Wooster Libraries, 1140 Beall Ave, Wooster, OH, 44691-2364. Tel: 330-263-2442. Fax: 330-263-2253. p. 1949

Wiebe, Elaine, Asst Librn, Burns Lake Public Library, 585 Government St, Burns Lake, BC, V0J 1E0, CANADA. Tel: 250-692-3192. Fax: 250-692-7488. p. 2726

Wiebe, Helen, Librn, La Crete Community Library, 10001 99th Ave, La Crete, AB, T0H 2H0, CANADA. Tel: 780-928-3166. Fax: 780-928-3166. p. 2708

Wiebe, Mallory, Libr Tech, Saint Andrew's College Library, 1121 College Dr, Saskatoon, SK, S7N 0W3, CANADA. Tel: 306-966-8983. Fax: 306-966-8981. p. 2926

Wiebe, Margaret, Dir, Hesston College, PO Box 3000, Hesston, KS, 67062-3000. Tel: 620-327-8245. Fax: 620-327-8300. p. 871

Wiebe, Todd, Ref & Instrul Serv Librn, Hope College, Van Wylen Library, 53 Graves Pl, Holland, MI, 49422. Tel: 616-395-7286. Fax: 616-395-7965. p. 1190

Wiebelhaus, Richard, Librn, Cargill, Inc, Law Library, 15407 McGinty Rd W, Wayzata, MN, 55391-2399. Tel: 952-742-6235, 952-742-6334. Fax: 952-742-6349. p. 1288

Wieben, Mary, Librn, St Alexius Medical Center Library, 900 E Broadway, Bismarck, ND, 58506. Tel: 701-530-7718. Fax: 701-530-7701. p. 1838

Wiebenshon, Scott, Dir, East Saint Louis Community College Center, 601 James R Thompson Blvd, East Saint Louis, IL, 62201. Tel: 618-874-8718. Fax: 618-874-6383. p. 639

Wieber, Ryan S, Dir, Van Buren District Library, 200 N Phelps St, Decatur, MI, 49045-1086. Tel: 269-423-4771. Fax: 269-423-8373. p. 1168

Wieber, Ryan S, Dir, Otsego District Public Library, 219 S Farmer St, Otsego, MI, 49078-1313. Tel: 269-694-6455. Fax: 269-694-9129. p. 1216

Wieberg, Jessica, Circ, Missouri River Regional Library, 214 Adams St, Jefferson City, MO, 65101-3244. Tel: 573-634-6064, Ext 223. p. 1335

Wiechelman, Kathleen, Librn, Supv Librn-Tech, Outreach, Delivery Serv, University of Alaska Southeast, 2600 Seventh Ave, Ketchikan, AK, 99901. Tel: 907-228-4517. Fax: 907-228-4520. p. 51

Wiechert, Raegan, Asst Prof, Missouri State University, Duane G Meyer Library, 901 S National Ave, Springfield, MO, 65897. Tel: 417-836-4525. Fax: 417-836-4764. p. 2968

Wiechman, Marie, Dep Dir, Nebraska State Library, State Capitol, 3rd Flr S, Lincoln, NE, 68509. Tel: 402-471-3189. Fax: 402-471-1011. p. 1406

Wiechmann, Karen, Youth Serv Librn, Siouxland Libraries, 200 N Dakota Ave, Sioux Falls, SD, 57104. Tel: 605-367-8708. Fax: 605-367-4312. p. 2218

Wiecki, Lisa, Continuing Res & Cat, Lander University, 320 Stanley Ave, Greenwood, SC, 29649-2099. Tel: 864-388-8043. Fax: 864-388-8816. p. 2197

Wieczorek, Tony, Bus Mgr, Appleton Public Library, 225 N Oneida St, Appleton, WI, 54911-4780. Tel: 920-832-6170. Fax: 920-832-6182. p. 2578

Wiedemann, Diane, ILL, Harrisburg Area Community College, 735 Cumberland St, Lebanon, PA, 17042. Tel: 717-270-6328. p. 2079

Wiedenbeck, Pam, Pres, Southern California Genealogical Society, 417 Irving Dr, Burbank, CA, 91504-2408. Tel: 818-843-7247. Fax: 818-843-7262. p. 130

Wiedenbeck, Susan, PhD, PhD Prog Dir, Prof, Drexel University, Rush Bldg, Rm 306, 30 N 33rd St, Philadelphia, PA, 19104-2875. Tel: 215-895-2474. Fax: 215-895-2494. p. 2972

Wiederaenders, Karen, Dir, Saint Luke's Hospital, 4141 Mill St, Kansas City, MO, 64111. Tel: 816-531-0560. Fax: 816-531-6316. p. 1340

Wiederkehr, James, Libr Mgr, K&L Gates LLP, 70 W Madison, Ste 3100, Chicago, IL, 60602-4207. Tel: 312-372-1121. Fax: 312-827-8000. p. 616

Wiegand, Ann, Dir, Lewisville Public Library System, 1197 W Main at Civic Circle, Lewisville, TX, 75067. Tel: 972-219-3571. Fax: 972-219-5094. p. 2355

Wiegand, Lyn, Librn, Illinois Prairie District Public Library, Springbay Branch, 411 Illinois St, Springbay, IL, 61611. Tel: 309-822-0444. Fax: 309-822-0444. p. 673

Wiegand, Sue, Periodicals Librn, Saint Mary's College, Notre Dame, IN, 46556-5001. Tel: 574-284-4789. Fax: 574-284-4791. p. 771

Wiegard, Chris, Ref, Appomattox Regional Library, 209 E Cawson St, Hopewell, VA, 23860. Tel: 804-458-6329, 804-861-0322. Fax: 804-458-4349. p. 2472

Wiegel, Connie, Librn, Charter Oak Public Library, 461 Railroad, Charter Oak, IA, 51439. Tel: 712-678-3425. p. 801

Wiegel, Sylvia, Libr Tech, Clarion University of Pennsylvania, 1801 W First St, Oil City, PA, 16301. Tel: 814-676-6591, Ext 1246. Fax: 814-677-3987. p. 2100

Wiegleb, Stacey, Learning Res Ctr Adminr, ITT Technical Institute, 7011 A C Skinner Pkwy, Ste 140, Jacksonville, FL, 32256. Tel: 904-573-9100, Ext 135. Fax: 904-573-0512. p. 453

Wiegmann, Rachel, Ad, Comstock Township Library, 6130 King Hwy, Comstock, MI, 49041. Tel: 269-345-0136. Fax: 269-345-0138. p. 1165

Wielgus, Sharon, Acq, Ripon College, 300 Seward St, Ripon, WI, 54971. Tel: 920-748-8330. Fax: 920-748-7243. p. 2634

Wielhorski, Karen, Exec Dir, University of Houston - Clear Lake, 2700 Bay Area Blvd, Houston, TX, 77058-1098. Tel: 281-283-3930. Fax: 281-283-3937. p. 2343

Wiellette, Molly, YA Serv, Winchester Public Library, 80 Washington St, Winchester, MA, 01890. Tel: 781-721-7171, Ext 20. Fax: 781-721-7170. p. 1142

Wiemann, Barbara, Automation Syst Coordr, Cat, Tech Serv, Easton Area Public Library & District Center, 515 Church St, Easton, PA, 18042-3587. Tel: 610-258-2917. Fax: 610-253-2231. p. 2052

Wiemers, Eugene L, Col Librn, VPres, Info & Libr Serv, Bates College, 48 Campus Ave, Lewiston, ME, 04240. Tel: 207-786-6264. Fax: 207-786-6055. p. 989

Wiener, Jonathan, Cat, Case Memorial Library, 176 Tyler City Rd, Orange, CT, 06477-2498. Tel: 203-891-2170. Fax: 203-891-2190. p. 364

Wiener, Judith A, Curator, Ohio State University LIBRARIES, John A Prior Health Sciences Library, 376 W Tenth Ave, Columbus, OH, 43210-1240. Tel: 614-292-9273. Fax: 614-292-9919. p. 1889

Wienhold, Elaine, Asst Dir, Will Rogers Library, 1515 N Florence Ave, Claremore, OK, 74017. Tel: 918-341-1564. Fax: 918-342-0362. p. 1960

Wienke, Sandra, Librn, Ogden Rose Public Library, 103 W Main, Ogden, IL, 61859. Tel: 217-582-2411. Fax: 217-582-2411. p. 684

Wiens, Carol, Chief Librn, Montreal Neurological Institute Hospital Library, 3801 University St, Rm 285, Montreal, QC, H3A 2B4, CANADA. Tel: 514-398-1980. Fax: 514-398-5077. p. 2900

Wiens, Kim, Dir, Wellington Public Library, 121 W Seventh St, Wellington, KS, 67152-3898. Tel: 620-326-2011. Fax: 620-326-8193. p. 899

Wier, Nancy, Head, Support Serv, Oxford Public Library, 530 Pontiac Rd, Oxford, MI, 48371-4844. Tel: 248-628-3034. Fax: 248-628-5008. p. 1216

Wierenga, Suanne, Dir, Dorr Township Library, 1804 Sunset Dr, Dorr, MI, 49323. Tel: 616-681-9678. Fax: 616-681-5650. p. 1174

Wiersma, Gabrielle, Head, Coll Develop & Assessment, University of Colorado Boulder, 1720 Pleasant St, 184 UCB, Boulder, CO, 80309-0184. Tel: 303-492-4316. Fax: 303-492-3340. p. 291

Wierzba, Christine M, Mgr, Libr Serv, Bryan Cave LLP, 1290 Avenue of the Americas, New York, NY, 10104. Tel: 212-541-2165. Fax: 212-541-1465. p. 1671

Wierzbicki, Jan, Principal Librn, Pub Serv, Torrance Public Library, 3301 Torrance Blvd, Torrance, CA, 90503. Tel: 310-618-5950. Fax: 310-618-5952. p. 276

Wierzbicki, Janice, Sr Librn, Torrance Public Library, Isabel Henderson Branch, 4805 Emerald St, Torrance, CA, 90503-2899. Tel: 310-371-2075. Fax: 310-371-5025. p. 276

Wiese, Gail, Asst Univ Archivist, Norwich University, 23 Harmon Dr, Northfield, VT, 05663. Tel: 802-485-2924. Fax: 802-485-2173. p. 2431

Wiese, Glenda, PhD, Spec Serv Librn, Palmer College of Chiropractic-Davenport Campus, 1000 Brady St, Davenport, IA, 52803-5287. Tel: 563-884-5894. Fax: 563-884-5897. p. 806

Wiese, Jason, Asst Dir, Historic New Orleans Collection, 410 Chartres St, New Orleans, LA, 70130-2102. Tel: 504-598-7183. Fax: 504-598-7168. p. 960

Wiese, Joyce, Pres, Tama County Historical Society, 200 N Broadway, Toledo, IA, 52342. Tel: 641-484-6767. Fax: 641-484-7677. p. 848

Wiese, Kathy, Mgr, Acq & Coll Develop, Saint Louis County Library, 1640 S Lindbergh Blvd, Saint Louis, MO, 63131-3598. Tel: 314-994-3300, Ext 2370. Fax: 314-997-7602. p. 1358

Wiesehan, Melessa, Head, Youth Serv, Jackson County Public Library, 303 W Second St, Seymour, IN, 47274-2147. Tel: 812-522-3412, Ext 231. Fax: 812-522-5456. p. 777

Wiesner, Patricia, Ref Librn, Henderson District Public Libraries, 280 S Green Valley Pkwy, Henderson, NV, 89012. Tel: 702-492-7252. Fax: 702-492-1711. p. 1428

Wiest, Colleen, Librn, McLean-Mercer Regional Library, Beulah Branch, 116 N Central Ave, Beulah, ND, 58523-6964. Tel: 701-873-2884. p. 1847

Wiest, Natalie H, Digital Initiatives Librn, Texas A&M University at Galveston, 200 Seawolf Pkwy, Galveston, TX, 77553. Tel: 409-740-4567. Fax: 409-740-4702. p. 2326

Wiethe, Louis, Doc Delivery & ILL Mgr/Access Serv, Duke University Libraries, Medical Center Library, DUMC Box 3702, Ten Bryan-Searle Dr, Durham, NC, 27710-0001. Tel: 919-660-1179. Fax: 919-681-7599. p. 1788

Wigersma, Helen, Assoc Dir, Interim Dean, University of West Florida, 11000 University Pkwy, Pensacola, FL, 32514-5750. Tel: 850-474-3135. Fax: 850-474-3338. p. 482

Wigfall, Kathy, Librn, Waco Tribune-Herald Library, 900 Franklin, Waco, TX, 76701. Tel: 254-757-5757. Fax: 254-757-0302. p. 2398

Wigg, Ristiina, Dir, Southern Tier Library System, 9424 Scott Rd, Painted Post, NY, 14870-9598. Tel: 607-962-3141. Fax: 607-962-5356. p. 1714

Wiggers, Namita Gupta, Curator, Museum of Contemporary Craft Library, 724 NW Davis St, Portland, OR, 97209. Tel: 503-223-2654. Fax: 503-223-0190. p. 2012

Wiggin, Kendall, State Librn, Connecticut State Library, 231 Capitol Ave, Hartford, CT, 06106. Tel: 860-757-6500. Fax: 860-757-6503. p. 345

Wiggins, Beacher, Dir, Library of Congress, Acquisitions & Bibliographic Access, Madison Memorial Bldg, LM Rm 642, 101 Independence Ave SE, Washington, DC, 20540. Tel: 202-707-5325. Fax: 202-707-6269. p. 406

Wiggins, Charles P, Dir of Libr Serv, Isothermal Community College Library, 286 ICC Loop Rd, Spindale, NC, 28160. Tel: 828-286-3636, Ext 216. Fax: 828-286-8208. p. 1825

Wiggins, David, Acq, Ser, La Grange College, 601 Broad St, La Grange, GA, 30240-2999. Tel: 706-880-8233. Fax: 706-880-8040. p. 537

Wiggins, John W, Dir, Libr Serv & Quality Improvement, Drexel University Libraries, Hagerty Library, 33rd & Market Sts, Philadelphia, PA, 19104-2875. Tel: 215-895-2773. Fax: 215-895-2070. p. 2105

Wiggins, Karen, Br Mgr, Toledo-Lucas County Public Library, Waterville Branch, 800 Michigan Ave, Waterville, OH, 43566. Tel: 419-878-3055. Fax: 419-878-4688. p. 1940

Wiggins, Marta, Commun Libr Mgr, County of Los Angeles Public Library, La Crescenta Library, 2809 Foothill Blvd, La Crescenta, CA, 91214-2999. Tel: 818-248-5313. Fax: 818-248-1289. p. 142

Wiggins, Martha, Tech Serv, United States Air Force, 437 SVS/SVMG, 106 W McCaw St, Bldg 215, Charleston AFB, SC, 29404-4700. Tel: 843-963-3320. Fax: 843-963-3840. p. 2185

Wiggins, Marvin, Librn, Brigham Young University, Harold B Lee Library, 2060 HBLL, Provo, UT, 84602. Tel: 801-422-2927. Fax: 801-422-0466. p. 2411

Wiggins, Sarah, Dir, Guernsey Memorial Library, Three Court St, Norwich, NY, 13815. Tel: 607-334-4034. Fax: 607-336-3901. p. 1708

Wiggins, Steve, Dir, Western State Hospital, 2400 Russellville Rd, Hopkinsville, KY, 42241. Tel: 270-889-6025, Ext 436. Fax: 270-885-5257. p. 918

Wiggins, Tanya Steed, Dir, Environmental Protection Agency - R S Kerr Environmental Research Center, 919 Kerr Lab Research Dr, Ada, OK, 74820. Tel: 580-436-8800. Fax: 580-436-8503. p. 1955

Wiggins, Wilbert, Circ/Reserves, Norfolk State University Library, 700 Park Ave, Norfolk, VA, 23504-8010. Tel: 757-823-8517. Fax: 757-823-2431. p. 2482

Wight, Laura M, Dir, eLearning & Libr Serv, Montana State University - Great Falls College of Technology, 2100 16th Ave S, Great Falls, MT, 59405. Tel: 406-771-4398. Fax: 406-771-4317. p. 1380

Wightman, Doris S, Librn, Norborne Public Library, 109 E Second St, Norborne, MO, 64668. Tel: 660-593-3514. Fax: 660-593-3514. p. 1348

Wigley, Lisa, Dir, Hopkins County-Madisonville Public Library, 31 S Main St, Madisonville, KY, 42431. Tel: 270-825-2680. Fax: 270-825-2777. p. 927

Wigmore, Nancy, Ch, Public Library of Johnston County & Smithfield, 305 E Market St, Smithfield, NC, 27577-3919. Tel: 919-934-8146. Fax: 919-934-8084. p. 1824

Wigner, Dann, Distance Serv Librn, Wayland Baptist University, 1900 W Seventh, Plainview, TX, 79072-6957. Tel: 806-291-3701. Fax: 806-291-1964. p. 2370

Wike, Ken, ILL, Sinte Gleska University Library, E Hwy 18, Mission, SD, 57555. Tel: 605-856-8100, 605-856-8112. Fax: 605-856-2011. p. 2215

Wike, Pat, Building Serv Mgr/Acq, Winter Haven Public Library, 325 Ave A NW, Winter Haven, FL, 33881. Tel: 863-291-5880. Fax: 863-298-7708. p. 505

Wikoff, Ann, Archivist, St Petersburg Museum of History Library, 335 Second Ave NE, Saint Petersburg, FL, 33701-3501. Tel: 727-894-1052. Fax: 727-823-7276. p. 488

Wikoff, Karin, Electronic Serv, Tech Serv Dir, Ithaca College Library, 953 Danby Rd, Ithaca, NY, 14850-7060. Tel: 607-274-1364. Fax: 607-274-1539. p. 1643

Wikstrom, Alicia, Asst City Librn, Marble Public Library, 302 Alice Ave, Marble, MN, 55764. Tel: 218-247-7676. Fax: 218-247-7676. p. 1258

Wilbanks, Kellie D, YA Serv, Latt Maxcy Memorial Library, 15 N Magnolia Ave, Frostproof, FL, 33843. Tel: 863-635-7857. Fax: 863-635-8502. p. 447

Wilbarger, Jeannine, Dir, Rossford Public Library, 720 Dixie Hwy, Rossford, OH, 43460-1289. Tel: 419-666-0924. Fax: 419-666-1989. p. 1932

Wilber, Bradley, Ref & Instruction Coordr, Houghton College, One Willard Ave, Houghton, NY, 14744. Tel: 585-567-9607. Fax: 585-567-9248. p. 1638

Wilber, Dorothy, Librn, Harris Memorial Library, 334 Main St, Otego, NY, 13825. Tel: 607-988-6661. Fax: 607-988-6661. p. 1713

Wilber, Michael, Dir, Menominee Tribal County Library, W2760 Chief Little Wave Rd, Keshena, WI, 54135. Tel: 715-799-5212. Fax: 715-799-6516. p. 2602

Wilberscheid, Teresa, Dir, La Vergne Public Library, 5063 Murfreesboro Rd, La Vergne, TN, 37086-0177. Tel: 615-793-7303. Fax: 615-793-7307. p. 2244

Wilberton, Ann, Head, Access Serv, Pace University Library, New York Civic Ctr, One Pace Plaza, New York, NY, 10038-1502. Tel: 212-346-1331. Fax: 212-346-1615. p. 1696

Wilbur, Joseph, In Charge, ITT Technical Institute, 10999 Stahl Rd, Newburgh, IN, 47630. Tel: 812-858-1600. p. 768

Wilburn, Erin, Syst Librn, Mercyhurst College, 501 E 38th St, Erie, PA, 16546. Tel: 814-824-3305. Fax: 814-824-2219. p. 2056

Wilburn, Maria, Coordr, Tech Support, Carnegie Public Library, 127 S North St, Washington Court House, OH, 43160. Tel: 740-335-2540. Fax: 740-335-8409. p. 1945

Wilby, Joyce, Archivist, Alert Bay Public Library & Museum, 118 Fir St, Alert Bay, BC, V0N 1A0, CANADA. Tel: 250-974-5721. Fax: 250-974-5026. p. 2724

Wilcher, Easter, Asst Regional Libr Mgr, Broward County Division of Libraries, South Regional/BC, 7300 Pines Blvd, Pembroke Pines, FL, 33024. Tel: 954-201-8840. Fax: 954-964-0282. p. 442

Wilcox, Brenda K, Librn, Blackfoot Public Library, 129 N Broadway, Blackfoot, ID, 83221-2204. Tel: 208-785-8628. Fax: 208-782-9688. p. 569

Wilcox, Carolyn, Librn, Lincoln County Library, Caliente Branch, 100 Depot Ave, Caliente, NV, 89008-0306. Tel: 775-726-3104. p. 1432

Wilcox, Craig, Cat, United States Army, Brooke Army Medical Center Library, Medical Library MCHE-EDL, 3551 Roger Brooke Dr, Bldg 3600, Rm 371-17, Fort Sam Houston, TX, 78234-6200. Tel: 210-916-1119. Fax: 210-916-5709. p. 2320

Wilcox, Inza E, Librn, Mountaintop Library, Grant St, Thomas, WV, 26292. Tel: 304-463-4582. Fax: 304-463-4582. p. 2573

Wilcox, James, Info Serv Spec, King College, 1350 King College Rd, Bristol, TN, 37620. Tel: 423-224-3379. Fax: 423-652-4871. p. 2225

Wilcox, Janet M, Actg Adminr, First Presbyterian Church, 219 E Bijou St, Colorado Springs, CO, 80903. Tel: 719-884-6121. Fax: 719-884-6200. p. 295

Wilcox, Jennifer, Actg Libr Dir, York Library Region, Chatham Public Library, 24 King St, Miramichi, NB, E1N 2N1, CANADA. Tel: 506-773-6274. Fax: 506-773-6963. p. 2764

Wilcox, Linda, Librn, Shared Library Services, South Huron Hospital, Shared Library Services, 24 Huron St W, Exeter, ON, N0M 1S2, CANADA. Tel: 519-235-5168. Fax: 519-235-2742. p. 2960

Wilcox, Lynn, Tech Serv, University of Maine School of Law, 246 Deering Ave, Portland, ME, 04102. Tel: 207-780-4829. Fax: 207-780-4913. p. 997

Wilcox, Matthew, Librn, Yale University Library, Epidemiology & Public Health, Epidemiology & Public Health, 60 College St, New Haven, CT, 06520. Tel: 203-785-5680. Fax: 203-785-4998. p. 357

Wilcox, Michelle, Asst Librn, Island Pond Public Library, 49 Mill St Extension, Island Pond, VT, 05846. Tel: 802-723-6134. Fax: 802-723-6134. p. 2426

Wilcox, Nancy, Dir, Oxford Memorial Library, Eight Fort Hill Park, Oxford, NY, 13830. Tel: 607-843-6146. Fax: 607-843-9157. p. 1714

Wilcox, Pat, Evening Ref Librn, Southern New Hampshire University, 2500 N River Rd, Manchester, NH, 03106-1045. Tel: 603-645-9605. Fax: 603-645-9685. p. 1456

Wilcox, Randall, Mgr, Xerox Corp, 45 Glover Ave, Norwalk, CT, 06856. Tel: 203-849-2405. Fax: 203-849-2352. p. 362

Wilcox, Sandy, Bus & Human Res Mgr, Salina Public Library, 301 W Elm St, Salina, KS, 67401. Tel: 785-825-4624. Fax: 785-823-0706. p. 893

Wilcox, Susan, Curator, Arizona Historical Society Library, 2340 N Fort Valley Rd, Flagstaff, AZ, 86001. Tel: 928-774-6272. Fax: 928-774-1596. p. 62

Wilcox, Tom, Adult Ref Librn, Leesburg Public Library, 100 E Main St, Leesburg, FL, 34748. Tel: 352-728-9790. Fax: 352-728-9794. p. 461

Wilczek, Keely, Res & Instruction Librn, Harvard Library, John F Kennedy School of Government Library, 79 John F Kennedy St, Cambridge, MA, 02138. Tel: 617-495-1300. Fax: 617-495-1972. p. 1075

Wilczek, Nick, Librn II, Humboldt County Library, 1313 Third St, Eureka, CA, 95501-0553. Tel: 707-269-1918. p. 147

Wilczek, Nicolas, Br Mgr, Humboldt County Library, Arcata Branch, 500 Seventh St, Arcata, CA, 95521-6315. Tel: 707-822-5954. p. 147

Wild, Elizabeth, Dir, Henry Public Library, 702 Front St, Henry, IL, 61537. Tel: 309-364-2516. Fax: 309-364-2717. p. 655

Wild, Judith, Assoc Librn, Tech Serv, Brooklyn College Library, 2900 Bedford Ave, Brooklyn, NY, 11210-2889. Tel: 718-951-5426. Fax: 718-951-4540. p. 1589

Wild, Karline, Circ, Dean College, 99 Main St, Franklin, MA, 02038-1994. Tel: 508-541-1771. Fax: 508-541-1918. p. 1090

Wild, Kimberley, Adult Serv, Circ Librn, Herrin City Library, 120 N 13th St, Herrin, IL, 62948-3233. Tel: 618-942-6109. Fax: 618-942-4165. p. 655

Wild, Larry C, Dir, Judson University, 1151 N State St, Elgin, IL, 60123. Tel: 847-628-2030. Fax: 847-625-2045. p. 641

Wild, Susan, Dir, Dorchester Public Library, 155 N Second St, Dorchester, WI, 54425-9700. Tel: 715-654-5959. Fax: 715-654-5802. p. 2588

Wilde, Amber, Dir, Grace Balloch Memorial Library, 625 N Fifth St, Spearfish, SD, 57783-2311. Tel: 605-642-1330. p. 2220

Wilde, Amber, Circ, Black Hills State University, 1200 University St, Unit 9676, Spearfish, SD, 57799-9676. Tel: 605-642-6834. Fax: 605-642-6298. p. 2220

Wilde, Candace, Dir, Brownville-Glen Park Library, 216 Brown Blvd, Brownville, NY, 13615. Tel: 315-788-7889. Fax: 315-786-1178. p. 1596

Wilde, Deanna, Circ Supvr, Northwest Nazarene University, 623 University Blvd, Nampa, ID, 83686. Tel: 208-467-8614. Fax: 208-467-8610. p. 580

Wilde, Mary Louise, Circ Mgr, Piedmont Technical College Library, 620 N Emerald Rd, Bldg K, Greenwood, SC, 29646. Tel: 864-941-8441. Fax: 864-941-8558. p. 2197

Wildeboer, Billi-Jo, Librn, Hardisty & District Public Library, 5027 - 50 St, Hardisty, AB, T0B 1V0, CANADA. Tel: 780-888-3947. Fax: 780-888-3947. p. 2706

Wildemuth, Barbara M, Assoc Dean, Acad Affairs, University of North Carolina at Chapel Hill, CB No 3360, 100 Manning Hall, Chapel Hill, NC, 27599-3360. Tel: 919-962-8366. Fax: 919-962-8071. p. 2971

Wilder, Betty, Libr Assoc/ILL Section, New Mexico Highlands University, Ninth & National Ave, Las Vegas, NM, 87701. Tel: 505-454-3401. Fax: 505-454-0026. p. 1559

Wilder, Derek, Librn, Georgia Department of Corrections, Office of Library Services, 1000 Indian Springs Dr, Forsyth, GA, 31029. Tel: 478-994-7511. Fax: 478-994-7561. p. 532

Wilder, Dustin, Teen Serv, Guilderland Public Library, 2228 Western Ave, Guilderland, NY, 12084-9701. Tel: 518-456-2400. Fax: 518-456-0923. p. 1632

Wilder, Joni, Asst Dir, La Vista Public Library, 9110 Giles Rd, La Vista, NE, 68128. Tel: 402-537-3900. Fax: 402-537-3902. p. 1403

Wilder, Kelli, Librn, St Philip's College, 1801 Martin Luther King Dr, San Antonio, TX, 78203-2098. Tel: 210-486-2330. Fax: 210-486-2335. p. 2381

Wilder, Kimberly, Librn, Arkansas River Valley Regional Library System, Charleston Branch, 12 S School St, Charleston, AR, 72933-0338. Tel: 479-965-2605. Fax: 479-965-2755. p. 97

Wilder, Michelle, Archivist, University of Toronto Libraries, Media Commons, 130 St George St, Toronto, ON, M5S 1A5, CANADA. Tel: 416-978-4601. Fax: 416-978-8707. p. 2866

Wilder, Paul, Mgr, North Jersey Media Group Library, 150 River St, Hackensack, NJ, 07601. Tel: 201-646-4000. Fax: 201-646-4737. p. 1489

Wilder, Roberta, Head, Tech Serv, East Central Georgia Regional Library, 902 Greene St, Augusta, GA, 30901. Tel: 706-821-2600. Fax: 706-724-6762. p. 519

Wilder, Stanley, Info Serv, University of Rochester, River Campus Libraries, 755 Library Rd, Rochester, NY, 14627-0055. Tel: 585-275-4461. Fax: 585-273-5309. p. 1733

Wilder, Stanley, Univ Librn, University of North Carolina at Charlotte, 9201 University City Blvd, Charlotte, NC, 28223-0001. Tel: 704-687-3110. Fax: 704-687-3050. p. 1784

Wilderdijk, Hetty, Librn, Hinton Municipal Library, 803 Switzer Dr, Hinton, AB, T7V 1V1, CANADA. Tel: 780-865-2363. Fax: 780-865-4292. p. 2707

Wildermuth, Jane, Dept Head, Digital Serv, Wright State University Libraries, 126 Dunbar Library, 3640 Colonel Glenn Hwy, Dayton, OH, 45435-0001. Tel: 937-775-3927. Fax: 937-775-4109. p. 1895

Wildman, Marc, Dir, Cayuga County Community College, 197 Franklin St, Auburn, NY, 13021. Tel: 315-294-8596. Fax: 315-255-2050. p. 1576

Wilds, Angela, YA Serv, Marshall Memorial Library, 110 S Diamond St, Deming, NM, 88030-3698. Tel: 505-546-9202. Fax: 505-546-9649. p. 1554

Wildsmith, Snow, Youth Serv, Mooresville Public Library, 304 S Main St, Mooresville, NC, 28115. Tel: 704-664-2927. Fax: 704-660-3292. p. 1810

Wilen, Kristen, Dir, Correctionville Public Library, 532 Driftwood, Correctionville, IA, 51016. Tel: 712-342-4203. Fax: 712-342-4203. p. 804

Wilensky, Sharon, Br Mgr, San Francisco Public Library, Richmond/Senator Milton Marks Branch Library, 351 Ninth Ave, San Francisco, CA, 94118-2210. Tel: 415-355-5600. Fax: 415-752-7785. p. 246

Wiles, Florenceia M, In Charge, US National Park Service, 151 Hwy 76, Harpers Ferry, IA, 52146-7519. Tel: 563-873-3491. Fax: 563-873-3743. p. 820

Wiles, Sue, Mgr, Lynn Haven Public Library, 901 Ohio Ave, Lynn Haven, FL, 32444. Tel: 850-265-2781. Fax: 850-265-7311. p. 461

Wiles, Tim, Ref, National Baseball Hall of Fame & Museum, Inc, 25 Main St, Cooperstown, NY, 13326-0590. Tel: 607-547-0330. Fax: 607-547-4094. p. 1610

Wiley, Allan, Tech Info Spec, United States Army, 110 Casey Bldg, 7701 Telegraph Rd, Alexandria, VA, 22315-3864. Tel: 703-428-6831. Fax: 703-428-6772. p. 2446

Wiley, Annabelle, Mgr, Cornelia-Habersham County Library, 301 Main St N, Cornelia, GA, 30531. Tel: 706-778-2635. Fax: 706-778-2635. p. 527

Wiley, Ardis, Coord Librn, Fac/Staff/Circ/Mat Handling & Libr Mgt, Hennepin County Library, Brooklyn Park, 8600 Zane Ave N, Brooklyn Park, MN, 55443-1897. Tel: 612-543-8506. Fax: 612-543-6247. p. 1263

Wiley, Ardis, Coord Librn, Fac/Staff/Circ/Mat Handling & Libr Mgt, Hennepin County Library, Champlin, 12154 Ensign Ave N, Champlin, MN, 55316-9998. Tel: 612-543-8506. Fax: 612-543-6252. p. 1263

Wiley, Ardis, Coord Librn, Fac/Staff/Circ/Mat Handling & Libr Mgt, Hennepin County Library, Golden Valley, 830 Winnetka Ave N, Golden Valley, MN, 55427-4532. Tel: 612-543-8506. Fax: 612-543-6377. p. 1263

Wiley, Ardis, Coord Librn, Fac/Staff/Circ/Mat Handling & Libr Mgt, Hennepin County Library, Long Lake, 1865 Wayzata Blvd W, Long Lake, MN, 55356-9587. Tel: 612-543-8506. Fax: 612-543-6427. p. 1264

Wiley, Ardis, Coord Librn, Fac/Staff/Circ/Mat Handling & Libr Mgt, Hennepin County Library, Maple Plain, 5184 Main St E, Maple Plain, MN, 55359-9648. Tel: 612-543-8506. Fax: 612-543-5702. p. 1264

Wiley, Ardis, Coord Librn, Fac/Staff/Circ/Mat Handling & Libr Mgt, Hennepin County Library, Oxboro, 8801 Portland Ave S, Bloomington, MN, 55420-2997. Tel: 612-543-8506. Fax: 612-543-5777. p. 1264

Wiley, Ardis, Coord Librn, Fac/Staff/Circ/Mat Handling & Libr Mgt, Hennepin County Library, Penn Lake, 8800 Penn Ave S, Bloomington, MN, 55431-2022. Tel: 612-543-8506. Fax: 612-543-5802. p. 1264

Wiley, Ardis, Coord Librn, Fac/Staff/Circ/Mat Handling & Libr Mgt, Hennepin County Library, Rogers, 21300 John Milless Dr, Rogers, MN, 55374-9998. Tel: 612-543-8506. Fax: 612-543-6052. p. 1264

Wiley, Ardis, Coord Librn, Fac/Staff/Circ/Mat Handling & Libr Mgt, Hennepin County Library, Saint Bonifacius, 8624 Kennedy Memorial Dr, Saint Bonifacius, MN, 55375-9998. Tel: 612-543-8506. Fax: 612-543-6102. p. 1264

Wiley, Ardis, Coord Librn, Fac/Staff/Circ/Mat Handling & Libr Mgt, Hennepin County Library, Washburn, 5244 Lyndale Ave S, Minneapolis, MN, 55419-1222. Tel: 612-543-8506. Fax: 612-543-8377. p. 1265

Wiley, Ardis, Coord Librn, Fac/Staff/Circ/Mat Handling & Libr Mgt, Hennepin County Library, Wayzata, 620 Rice St, Wayzata, MN, 55391-1734. Tel: 612-543-8506. Fax: 612-543-6152. p. 1265

Wiley, Ardis, Coord Librn, Fac/Staff/Circ/Mat Handling & Libr Mgt, Hennepin County Library, Westonka, 2079 Commerce Blvd, Mound, MN, 55364-1594. Tel: 612-543-8506. Fax: 612-543-6184. p. 1265

Wiley, Brendan, Dir, Topeka Zoological Park Library, 635 SW Gage Blvd, Topeka, KS, 66606-2079. Tel: 785-368-9180. Fax: 785-368-9152. p. 897

Wiley, Christie, Librn, National Oceanic & Atmospheric Administration, 4301 Rickenbacker Causeway, Miami, FL, 33149. Tel: 305-361-4428. Fax: 305-361-4448. p. 468

Wiley, Connie J, Dir, United States Department of the Army, CEHEC-ZL Casey Bldg, 7701 Telegraph Rd, Alexandria, VA, 22315-3860. Tel: 703-428-7430. Fax: 703-428-6310. p. 2446

Wiley, Corona, Coordr, Indiana University School of Medicine-Northwest Center for Medical Education, 3400 Broadway, Gary, IN, 46408-1197. Tel: 219-980-6709, 219-980-6852. Fax: 219-980-6524. p. 745

Wiley, Dixie, Communications Coordr, Coal City Public Library District, 85 N Garfield St, Coal City, IL, 60416. Tel: 815-634-4552. Fax: 815-634-2950. p. 630

Wiley, Douchelle, Educ Coordr, North Shore Medical Center, 1100 NW 95th St, Miami, FL, 33150. Tel: 305-694-3640. Fax: 305-694-4810. p. 468

Wiley, Harmie E, Librn, Bland Correctional Center, 256 Bland Farm, Bland, VA, 24315-9615. Tel: 276-688-3341, Ext 5162. p. 2451

Wiley, Helen, In Charge, Centinela Hospital Medical Center, 555 E Hardy St, Inglewood, CA, 90301-4011. Tel: 310-673-4660, Ext 7266. Fax: 310-419-8275. p. 159

Wiley, Jennie, Dir, Cotuit Library, 871 Main St, Cotuit, MA, 02635. Tel: 508-428-8141. Fax: 508-428-4636. p. 1083

Wiley, Martha Evans, Historian, Cumberland Gap National Historical Park Library, 91 Bartlett Park Rd, Middlesboro, KY, 40965-1848. Tel: 606-246-1051. Fax: 606-248-7276. p. 929

Wiley, Theresa, Libr Mgr, University of Kentucky, 2540 Research Park Dr, Lexington, KY, 40511-8410. Tel: 859-257-0309. Fax: 859-257-0302. p. 921

Wilfer, Mary, Librn, Anamosa State Penitentiary, 406 N High St, Anamosa, IA, 52205. Tel: 319-462-3504, Ext 2237. Fax: 319-462-3013. p. 793

Wilford, Katherine, Libr Asst, Smithers Public Library, 3817 Alfred Ave, Box 55, Smithers, BC, V0J 2N0, CANADA. Tel: 250-847-3043. Fax: 250-847-1533. p. 2737

Wilford, Lisa, Librn, Harvard Public Library, 309 N Clay Ave, Harvard, NE, 68944. Tel: 402-772-7201. p. 1401

Wilgus, Geraldine, Ch, Gloucester County Library System, Glassboro Public, Two Center St, Glassboro, NJ, 08028-1995. Tel: 856-881-0001, 856-881-5571. Fax: 856-881-9338. p. 1507

Wilhelm, Cara, Dir, Libr Serv, West Suburban Hospital Medical Center, Three Erie Court, Oak Park, IL, 60302. Tel: 708-763-6472. Fax: 708-383-8783. p. 684

Wilhelm, Gia, Tech Adminr, Harford County Public Library, 1221-A Brass Mill Rd, Belcamp, MD, 21017-1209. Tel: 410-273-5600, Ext 2248. Fax: 410-273-5606. p. 1020

Wilhelm, Janice, Librn IV, San Diego Public Library, 820 E St, San Diego, CA, 92101-6478. Tel: 619-236-5830. Fax: 619-238-6639. p. 235

Wilhelm, Linda, Dir of Educ, Floyd Medical Center Library, 304 Turner McCall Blvd, Rome, GA, 30162. Tel: 706-509-5789. p. 548

Wilhelm, Ruth, Local Hist Librn, Putnam County District Library, The Educational Service Ctr, 124 Putnam Pkwy, Ottawa, OH, 45875-1471. Tel: 419-523-3747. Fax: 419-523-6477. p. 1926

Wilhelmsen, Shirley, Dir, Hinckley Public Library District, 100 N Maple St, Hinckley, IL, 60520. Tel: 815-286-3220. Fax: 815-286-3664. p. 656

Wilhoit, Karen, Assoc Univ Librn, Coll Serv, Wright State University Libraries, 126 Dunbar Library, 3640 Colonel Glenn Hwy, Dayton, OH, 45435-0001. Tel: 937-775-3039. Fax: 937-775-4109. p. 1895

Wilhoite, Mary B, Librn II, Ref Librn, Montgomery City-County Public Library System, Juliette Hampton Morgan Memorial Library (Main Library), 245 High St, Montgomery, AL, 36104. Tel: 334-240-4999. Fax: 334-240-4980. p. 30

Wilinski, Edwina, Asst Libr Dir, Atlantic County Library System, 40 Farragut Ave, Mays Landing, NJ, 08330-1750. Tel: 609-625-2776. Fax: 609-625-8143. p. 1500

Wilinski, Grant, Dir, Atlantic Cape Community College, 5100 Black Horse Pike, Mays Landing, NJ, 08330. Tel: 609-343-4952. p. 1500

Wiljer, Christopher, Librn, Allen County Public Library, Monroeville Branch, 115 Main St, Monroeville, IN, 46773. Tel: 260-421-1340. Fax: 260-623-6321. p. 741

Wilk, Jocelyn K, Pub Serv Archivist, Columbia University, Archives, Butler Library, 6th Flr, 114th St, MC 1127, New York, NY, 10027. Tel: 212-854-1338. Fax: 212-854-1365. p. 1674

Wilke, Helen, Sister, Coordr, Acq, Thomas More College Library, 333 Thomas More Pkwy, Crestview Hills, KY, 41017-2599. Tel: 859-344-3300. Fax: 859-344-3342. p. 910

Wilke, Janet Stoeger, Dean, University of Nebraska at Kearney, 2508 11th Ave, Kearney, NE, 68849-2240. Tel: 308-865-8546. Fax: 308-865-8722. p. 1403

Wilke, Margaret, Managing Librn, Pima County Public Library, Kirk Bear Canyon, 8959 E Tanque Verde Rd, Tucson, AZ, 85749. Tel: 520-594-5275. Fax: 520-594-5276. p. 87

Wilke, Melanie, Coordr, Northwest Community College Library, 5331 McConnell Ave, Terrace, BC, V8G 4X2, CANADA. Tel: 250-638-5407. Fax: 250-635-1594. p. 2739

Wilke, Melanie, Ch, Terrace Public Library, 4610 Park Ave, Terrace, BC, V8G 1V6, CANADA. Tel: 250-638-8177. Fax: 250-635-6207. p. 2739

Wilke, Trinitie, Dir, Marion Public Library, 120 N Main, Marion, WI, 54950. Tel: 715-754-5368. Fax: 715-754-4610. p. 2613

Wilken, Arin Christopher, Dir, Mondovi Public Library, 146 W Hudson St, Mondovi, WI, 54755. Tel: 715-926-4403. p. 2623

Wilken, Cathi, Librn, Guilford Free Library, 4024 Guilford Center Rd, Guilford, VT, 05301. Tel: 802-257-4603. Fax: 802-257-4603. p. 2425

Wilken, Susan, Librn, Sterling Public Library, 150 Broadway St, Sterling, NE, 68443. Tel: 402-866-2056. Fax: 402-866-2056. p. 1420

Wilkenfeld, Polly, Head, Patron Serv & Instruction, Ursuline College, 2550 Lander Rd, Pepper Pike, OH, 44124-4398. Tel: 440-449-4202. Fax: 440-449-3180. p. 1929

Wilkening, Mary, Librn, Grant Park Public Library, 107 W Taylor St, Grant Park, IL, 60940. Tel: 815-465-6047. p. 652

Wilker, Mary Lou, Dir, Libr Serv, Warner, Norcross & Judd, LLP Library, 900 Fifth Third Ctr, 111 Lyon St NW, Grand Rapids, MI, 49503-2487. Tel: 616-752-2236. Fax: 616-752-2236. p. 1186

Wilkerson, Clarissa, Circ, ILL, Wakulla County Public Library, 4330 Crawfordville Hwy, Crawfordville, FL, 32327. Tel: 850-926-7415. Fax: 850-926-4513. p. 434

Wilkerson, Gail, Chief Librn, Veterans Administration Center, 3687 Veterans Dr, Fort Harrison, MT, 59636. Tel: 406-814-5615. Fax: 406-447-7992. p. 1379

Wilkerson, Jennifer, Dir, Libr Develop, Portland State University Library, 1875 SW Park Ave, Portland, OR, 97201-3220. Tel: 503-725-4509. Fax: 503-725-4524. p. 2014

Wilkerson, Matthew, Syst Adminr, Decatur Public Library, 130 N Franklin St, Decatur, IL, 62523-1327. Tel: 217-424-2900. Fax: 217-233-4071. p. 634

Wilkerson, MJ, Dir, Alamance County Public Libraries, 342 S Spring St, Burlington, NC, 27215. Tel: 336-229-3588. Fax: 336-229-3592. p. 1778

Wilkerson, Sandy, Youth Serv Consult, Southeast Kansas Library System, 218 E Madison Ave, Iola, KS, 66749. Tel: 620-365-5136. Fax: 620-365-5137. p. 874

Wilkes, Faye, Librn, Florida Department of Elder Affairs, 4040 Esplanade Way, Ste 360, Tallahassee, FL, 32399-7000. Tel: 850-414-2000. Fax: 850-414-2364. p. 493

Wilkes, Jamey, Cat, Toccoa Falls College, PO Box 800749, Toccoa Falls, GA, 30598. Tel: 706-886-6831, Ext 5300. Fax: 706-282-6010. p. 554

Wilkes, Linda, Br Mgr, Wake County Public Library System, Wendell Community Library, 207 S Hollybrook Rd, Wendell, NC, 27591. Tel: 919-365-2601. Fax: 919-365-2602. p. 1818

Wilkes, Pam, Librn, Foothill College, 12345 El Monte Rd, Los Altos Hills, CA, 94022-4599. Tel: 650-949-7390. Fax: 650-949-7123. p. 167

Wilkes, Pam, Librn, Foothill College, 12345 El Monte Rd, Los Altos Hills, CA, 94022-4599. Tel: 650-949-7086. Fax: 650-949-7123. p. 2962

Wilkes, Stephanie, Young Adult Serv Coordr, Ouachita Parish Public Library, 1800 Stubbs Ave, Monroe, LA, 71201. Tel: 318-327-1490. Fax: 318-327-1373. p. 957

Wilkes, Susan, Head, Circ, State University of New York at Fredonia, 280 Central Ave, Fredonia, NY, 14063. Tel: 716-673-3191. Fax: 716-673-3185. p. 1624

Wilkin, Donna, Asst Librn, Massachusetts Trial Court, Superior Court House, 84 Elm St, Fitchburg, MA, 01420-3296. Tel: 978-345-6726. Fax: 978-345-7334. p. 1089

Wilkin, John P, Assoc Univ Librn, Info Tech, University of Michigan, 818 Hatcher Graduate Library, Ann Arbor, MI, 48109-1205. Tel: 734-764-9356. Fax: 734-763-5080. p. 1152

Wilkin, Lucia, Librn, Piatt County Historical & Genealogical Society Library, Courthouse Annex, 301 S Charter, Monticello, IL, 61856-1856. Tel: 217-649-1766. p. 675

Wilkins, Alice, Librn, Sandhills Community College, 3395 Airport Rd, Pinehurst, NC, 28374. Tel: 910-695-3822. Fax: 910-695-3947. p. 1814

Wilkins, Catherine, Dr, Asst Univ Librn, Western University - Libraries, The D B Weldon Library, 1151 Richmond St, Ste 2, London, ON, N6A 3K7, CANADA. Tel: 519-661-2111, Ext 84772. p. 2819

Wilkins, James, Dir, Bucyrus Public Library, 200 E Mansfield St, Bucyrus, OH, 44820-2381. Tel: 419-562-7327. Fax: 419-562-7437. p. 1862

Wilkins, James, Dir, Warren-Trumbull County Public Library, 444 Mahoning Ave NW, Warren, OH, 44483. Tel: 330-399-8807. Fax: 330-395-3988. p. 1944

Wilkins, Jean, Head, Circ, Chesterfield Township Library, 50560 Patricia Ave, Chesterfield, MI, 48051-3804. Tel: 586-598-4900. Fax: 586-598-7900. p. 1163

Wilkins, Jennifer, Librn, Collinsville Public Library, 4299 Alabama Hwy 68, Collinsville, AL, 35961. Tel: 256-524-2323. Fax: 256-524-2323. p. 12

Wilkins, Jim, Develop Dir, Auburn Public Library, 49 Spring St, Auburn, ME, 04210. Tel: 207-333-6640. Fax: 207-333-6644. p. 974

Wilkins, Mary, Supvr, Illinois Agricultural Association, 1701 N Towanda Ave, Bloomington, IL, 61701. Tel: 309-557-2552. Fax: 309-557-3185. p. 595

Wilkins, Pamela, Librn, Fisheries & Oceans Canada, 9860 W Saanich Rd, Sidney, BC, V8L 3S1, CANADA. Tel: 250-363-6392. Fax: 250-363-6749. p. 2737

Wilkins, Patricia A, Dir, Houston-Tillotson University, 900 Chicon St, Austin, TX, 78702-3430. Tel: 512-505-3081. Fax: 512-505-3190. p. 2280

Wilkins, Sandra, Head of Libr, University of British Columbia Library, Law, 1822 East Mall, Vancouver, BC, V6T 1Z1, CANADA. Tel: 604-822-2396. Fax: 604-822-6864. p. 2743

Wilkins, Stella, Librn, Monsignor James C Turro Seminary Library, Seton Hall University, 400 S Orange Ave, South Orange, NJ, 07079. Tel: 973-761-9198, 973-761-9336, 973-761-9584. Fax: 973-275-2074. p. 1530

Wilkins, Teresa, Dir, Buck Consultants LLC, 500 Plaza Dr, Secaucus, NJ, 07096. Tel: 201-902-2575. Fax: 201-902-2726. p. 1529

Wilkins, Teresa, Ref, United States Merchant Marine Academy, 300 Steamboat Rd, Kings Point, NY, 11024-1699. Tel: 516-726-5747. Fax: 516-726-5900. p. 1649

Wilkins, Tracie, Ch, Harvey Mitchell Memorial Library, 151 Main St, Epping, NH, 03042. Tel: 603-679-5944. Fax: 603-679-5884. p. 1446

Wilkins, Vercie, Librn, New York City Police Department, 235 E 20th St, Rm 639, New York, NY, 10003. Tel: 212-477-7508. Fax: 212-477-9734. p. 1689

Wilkins-Jordan, Mary, Asst Prof, Simmons College, 300 The Fenway, Boston, MA, 02115. Tel: 617-521-2800. Fax: 617-521-3192. p. 2967

Wilkinson, Belinda, Dir, Trail & District Public Library, 1051 Victoria St, Trail, BC, V1R 3T3, CANADA. Tel: 250-364-1731. Fax: 250-364-2176. p. 2739

Wilkinson, Carol, Br Mgr, Hamilton Public Library, Turner Park, 352 Rymal Rd E, Hamilton, ON, L9B 1C2, CANADA. Tel: 905-546-3200, Ext 4224. p. 2809

Wilkinson, Carolyn, Dir, Hutchinson County Library, 625 N Weatherly Ave, Borger, TX, 79007-3621. Tel: 806-273-0126. Fax: 806-273-0128. p. 2290

Wilkinson, Carroll, Dir, Info Literacy, West Virginia University Libraries, WVU Libraries, 1549 University Ave, Morgantown, WV, 26506. Tel: 304-293-4040. Fax: 304-293-6638. p. 2566

Wilkinson, Catherine, Coordr, Access Serv, ILL, Appalachian State University, 218 College St, Boone, NC, 28608. Tel: 828-262-2774. Fax: 828-262-3001. p. 1777

Wilkinson, Catherine, Librn, Western North Carolina Library Network, c/o Appalachian State University, 218 College St, Boone, NC, 28608. Tel: 828-262-2774. Fax: 828-262-3001. p. 2951

Wilkinson, Claudia W, Br Mgr, Putnam County Library System, Bostwick Public, 125 Tillman St, Palatka, FL, 32177. Tel: 386-326-2750. Fax: 386-326-2733. p. 478

Wilkinson, David, Assoc Dir, Dallas County Law Library, George Allen Courts Bldg, 600 Commerce St, Ste 292, Dallas, TX, 75202-4606. Tel: 214-653-7481. Fax: 214-653-6103. p. 2305

Wilkinson, Diana, Dir, Shepherd Public Library, 30 N Liberty St, Shepherd, TX, 77371-2460. Tel: 936-628-3515. Fax: 936-628-6608. p. 2386

Wilkinson, Elaine, Br Mgr, Cuyahoga County Public Library, Fairview Park Branch, 21255 Lorain Rd, Fairview Park, OH, 44126-2120. Tel: 440-333-4700. Fax: 440-333-0697. p. 1927

Wilkinson, Frances C, Dep Dean, University of New Mexico-University Libraries, 1900 Roma NE, Albuquerque, NM, 87131-0001. p. 1550

Wilkinson, Gail, Br Mgr, Great River Regional Library, Becker Library, 11500 Sherburne Ave, Becker, MN, 55308. Tel: 763-261-4454. Fax: 763-261-4454. p. 1274

Wilkinson, Gina, Head, ILL, Chapman University, One University Dr, Orange, CA, 92866-1099. Tel: 714-532-7756. Fax: 714-532-7743. p. 200

Wilkinson, Heather, Youth Serv, Sargent Memorial Library, 427 Massachusetts Ave, Boxborough, MA, 01719. Tel: 978-263-4680. Fax: 978-263-1275. p. 1069

Wilkinson, Heather, Ch, Goodnow Library, 21 Concord Rd, Sudbury, MA, 01776-2383. Tel: 978-443-1035, Ext 3. Fax: 978-443-1047. p. 1129

Wilkinson, Janelle, Librn, Northwest Arkansas Community College Library, One College Dr, Bentonville, AR, 72712-5091. Tel: 479-619-4244. Fax: 479-619-4115. p. 95

Wilkinson, Janet, Asst Librn, Chinook Regional Library, Frontier Branch, First St W, Frontier, SK, S0N 0W0, CANADA. Tel: 306-296-4667. p. 2928

Wilkinson, Josh, Circ, South Dakota School of Mines & Technology, 501 E Saint Joseph St, Rapid City, SD, 57701-3995. Tel: 605-394-2418. Fax: 605-394-1256. p. 2217

Wilkinson, Judith, Dir, North General Hospital, 1879 Madison Ave, New York, NY, 10035. Tel: 212-423-4476. p. 1696

Wilkinson, Lane, Ref & Instruction Librn, University of Tennessee at Chattanooga Library, 615 McCallie Ave, Dept 6456, Chattanooga, TN, 37403-2598. Tel: 423-425-4501. Fax: 423-425-4775. p. 2228

Wilkinson, Linda, Dir, Head, Pub Serv, Roosevelt University, Robert R McCormick Tribune Foundation Library, 1400 N Roosevelt Blvd, Schaumburg, IL, 60173. Tel: 312-341-3659. Fax: 847-619-7983. p. 623

Wilkinson, Linda, Head, Pub Serv, Roosevelt University, 430 S Michigan Ave, Chicago, IL, 60605. Tel: 312-341-3659. Fax: 312-341-2425. p. 623

Wilkinson, Mary Pat, Pres, Genealogical Society of Linn County Iowa, 813 First Ave SE, Cedar Rapids, IA, 52402. Tel: 319-369-0022. p. 800

Wilkinson, Monica, Circ Mgr, Pike-Amite-Walthall Library System, 1022 Virginia Ave, McComb, MS, 39648. Tel: 601-684-2661. Fax: 601-250-1213. p. 1308

Wilkinson, Patrick J, Dir, University of Wisconsin Oshkosh, 801 Elmwood Ave, Oshkosh, WI, 54901. Tel: 920-424-2147. Fax: 920-424-7338. p. 2628

Wilkinson, Susan, Acq, Alabama Supreme Court & State Law Library, Heflin-Torbert Judicial Bldg, 300 Dexter Ave, Montgomery, AL, 36104. Tel: 334-229-0578. Fax: 334-229-0543. p. 28

Wilkinson, Susan C, In Charge, Food Marketing Institute, 2345 Crystal Dr, Ste 800, Arlington, VA, 22202. Tel: 202-452-8444. Fax: 202-429-4519. p. 2449

Wilkinson, William, Librn, American Federation of State, County & Municipal Employees, 1625 L St NW, Washington, DC, 20036. Tel: 202-429-1060. Fax: 202-223-3255. p. 392

Wilks, Melany A, Dir, Pioneer Memorial Library, 375 W Fourth St, Colby, KS, 67701-2197. Tel: 785-460-4470. Fax: 785-460-4472. p. 861

Will, Carol, Coordr, Learning Commons, University of Massachusetts Amherst, 154 Hicks Way, Amherst, MA, 01003-9275. Tel: 413-545-6795. Fax: 413-545-6873. p. 1049

Will, Christina, Librn, Saint John's River State College, Saint Augustine Center Library, 2990 College Dr, Saint Augustine, FL, 32084. Tel: 904-808-7474. Fax: 904-808-7478. p. 479

Will, Christine, Syst, Wells County Public Library, 200 W Washington St, Bluffton, IN, 46714-1999. Tel: 260-824-1612. Fax: 260-824-3129. p. 728

Will, Jeremy, Admin Assoc, Northern Great Plains Research Laboratory Library, PO Box 459, Mandan, ND, 58554-0459. Tel: 701-667-3000. Fax: 701-667-3054. p. 1846

Will, Katherine Haley, Pres, Central Pennsylvania Consortium, Dickinson College, 249 W Louther St, Carlisle, PA, 17013. Tel: 717-245-1984. Fax: 717-245-1807. p. 2953

Will, Lee, Librn, Arizona Department of Corrections - Adult Institutions, 2014 N Citrus Rd, Goodyear, AZ, 85338. Tel: 623-853-0304, Ext 24480. Fax: 623-853-0304. p. 65

Will, Linda, Dir, Dorsey & Whitney, 50 S Sixth St, Minneapolis, MN, 55402. Tel: 612-492-5522. Fax: 612-492-2868. p. 1259

Will, Linda, Mgr, Libr Res, Thompson & Knight, 1722 Routh St, Ste 1500, Dallas, TX, 75201. Tel: 214-969-1350. Fax: 214-969-1751. p. 2311

Willard, Christine, Ref & Digital Librn, Southern Methodist University, Bridwell Library-Perkins School of Theology, 6005 Bishop Blvd, Dallas, TX, 75205. Tel: 214-768-3483. Fax: 214-768-4295. p. 2310

Willard, Danielle, Acq & Ser Coordr, Westmont College, 955 La Paz Rd, Santa Barbara, CA, 93108-1099. Tel: 805-565-6000, 805-565-6147. Fax: 805-565-6220. p. 262

Willard, Gayle, Dir, Kansas State University Libraries, Veterinary Medical Library, Veterinary Medical Complex, 408 Trotter Hall, Manhattan, KS, 66506-5614. Tel: 785-532-6006. Fax: 785-532-2838. p. 881

Willbanks, Kent, Ref Serv, Belleville Public Library, 121 E Washington St, Belleville, IL, 62220. Tel: 618-234-0441, Ext 19. Fax: 618-234-9474. p. 593

Willeford, Sarah, Dir, Kirkendall Public Library, 1210 NW Prairie Ridge Dr, Ankeny, IA, 50021. Tel: 515-965-6460. Fax: 515-965-6474. p. 794

Willeke, Linda, Coordr, Charles H MacNider Museum Library, 303 Second St SE, Mason City, IA, 50401-3925. Tel: 641-421-3666. Fax: 641-422-9612. p. 830

Willems, Harry, Dir, Central Kansas Library System, 1409 Williams St, Great Bend, KS, 67530-4020. Tel: 620-792-4865. Fax: 620-792-5495. p. 869

Willems, Harry A, Dir, Great Bend Public Library, 1409 Williams St, Great Bend, KS, 67530-4090. Tel: 620-792-2409. Fax: 620-792-5495, 620-793-7270. p. 869

Willemsen, Rebecca, Libr Tech, Madison Heights Public Library, 240 W 13 Mile Rd, Madison Heights, MI, 48071-1894. Tel: 248-588-7763. Fax: 248-588-2470. p. 1205

Willenbrecht, Linda, Ch, Fremont County Library System, 451 N Second St, Lander, WY, 82520-2316. Tel: 307-332-5194. Fax: 307-332-1504, 307-332-3909. p. 2656

Willens, Michael, Librn, Nixon Peabody LLP, 401 Ninth St NW, Ste 900, Washington, DC, 20004. Tel: 202-585-8000, Ext 8320. Fax: 202-585-8080. p. 411

Willer, Kenneth H, Mgr, Libr Serv, Good Samaritan Regional Medical Center, 3600 NW Samaritan Dr, Corvallis, OR, 97330. Tel: 541-768-6200. Fax: 541-768-5087. p. 1994

Willetts, Martin, Jr, Sr Librn, Mohawk Correctional Facility Library, 6100 School Rd, Rome, NY, 13440. Tel: 315-339-5232. Fax: 315-339-5232, Ext 2099. p. 1735

Willey, Cassie, Librn, W E Sears Youth Center, 9400 Sears Lane, Poplar Bluff, MO, 63901-9716. Tel: 573-840-9280. Fax: 573-840-9352. p. 1349

Willey, Charlene, Govt Doc, Ref Librn, Malone University, 2600 Cleveland Ave NW, Canton, OH, 44709-3897. Tel: 330-471-8324. Fax: 330-454-6977. p. 1863

Willhite, Irene, Archivist, Curator, US Space & Rocket Center, One Tranquility Base, Huntsville, AL, 35805-3399. Tel: 256-721-7148. Fax: 256-722-5600. p. 22

Willhite, Rebecca, Ch, Rogers Public Library, 711 S Dixieland Rd, Rogers, AR, 72758. Tel: 479-621-1152, Ext 31. Fax: 479-621-1165. p. 113

Willi Hooper, Michaela, Ref & Instruction Librn, Prescott College Library, 217 Garden St, Prescott, AZ, 86301. Tel: 928-350-1300. p. 78

William, Bryant Chris, Librn, North Georgia Technical College Library, 121 Meeks Ave, Blairsville, GA, 30512. Tel: 706-439-6320, 706-439-6326. Fax: 706-439-6301. p. 521

William, Sheryl L, Ser, University of Nebraska Medical Center, 600 S 42nd St, Omaha, NE, 68198-6705. Tel: 402-559-7098. Fax: 402-559-5498. p. 1415

Williams, Adam, Res & Instruction Librn, Wheelock College Library, 132 The Riverway, Boston, MA, 02215-4815. Tel: 617-879-2279. Fax: 617-879-2408. p. 1068

Williams, Al, Pres, San Francisco African-American Historical & Cultural Society, 762 Fulton St, 2nd Flr, San Francisco, CA, 94102. Tel: 415-292-6172. Fax: 415-440-4231. p. 244

Williams, Alan T, Asst Dir, Charlotte AHEC Library, Medical Education Bldg, 1000 Blythe Blvd, Charlotte, NC, 28203. Tel: 704-355-3129. Fax: 704-355-7138. p. 1781

Williams, Alison, Br Mgr, Jefferson Parish Library, Lakeshore, 1100 W Esplanade, Metairie, LA, 70005. Tel: 504-838-4375. Fax: 504-838-4379. p. 956

Williams, Alissa, Asst Dir, Pekin Public Library, 301 S Fourth St, Pekin, IL, 61554-4284. Tel: 309-347-7111, Ext 226. Fax: 309-347-6587. p. 689

Williams, Allison, Br Mgr, Jefferson Parish Library, North Kenner, 630 W Esplanade Ave, Kenner, LA, 70065. Tel: 504-736-8730. Fax: 504-736-8732. p. 957

Williams, Amanda, Librn, Washburn Public Library, Hwy 131, Washburn, TN, 37888-9708. Tel: 865-497-2506. Fax: 865-497-2506. p. 2268

Williams, Amy, Dir, North Bend Public Library, 140 E Eighth St, North Bend, NE, 68649. Tel: 402-652-8356. Fax: 402-652-8356. p. 1410

Williams, Amy L, Dep Dir, National Archives & Records Administration, 500 W US Hwy 24, Independence, MO, 64050-1798. Tel: 816-268-8200. Fax: 816-268-8295. p. 1333

Williams, Andre, Supv Librn, North Carolina Department of Correction, 527 Commerce Dr, Caller No 5005, Elizabeth City, NC, 27906-5005. Tel: 252-331-4881. Fax: 252-331-4867. p. 1791

Williams, Andrea G, Coll Develop, Jefferson-Madison Regional Library, 201 E Market St, Charlottesville, VA, 22902-5287. Tel: 434-979-7151, Ext 206, 434-979-7151, Ext 207. Fax: 434-971-7035. p. 2453

Williams, Andrea L, Ch, Midwestern State University, 3410 Taft Ave, Wichita Falls, TX, 76308-2099. Tel: 940-397-4698. Fax: 940-397-4689. p. 2400

Williams, Ann, Cat, Saint Joseph College, 1678 Asylum Ave, West Hartford, CT, 06117-2791. Tel: 860-231-5207. Fax: 860-523-4356. p. 376

Williams, Ann L, Librn, Highland Park United Methodist Church Library, 3300 Mockingbird Lane, Dallas, TX, 75205. Tel: 214-521-3111, Ext 273. Fax: 214-520-6451. p. 2308

Williams, Ann M, Head, Adult Serv, Bloomfield Township Public Library, 1099 Lone Pine Rd, Bloomfield Township, MI, 48302-2410. Tel: 248-642-5800. Fax: 248-258-2555. p. 1159

Williams, Anne, Asst Librn, Tuolumne County Genealogical Society Library, 158 W Bradford St, Sonora, CA, 95370-4920. Tel: 209-532-1317. p. 269

Williams, Annette, Assoc Dir for Operations, Vanderbilt University, Annette & Irwin Eskind Biomedical Library, 2209 Garland Ave, Nashville, TN, 37232-8340. Tel: 615-936-3931. Fax: 615-936-1384. p. 2260

Williams, Arthur, ILL Coordr, Maywood Public Library District, 121 S Fifth Ave, Maywood, IL, 60153. Tel: 703-343-1847, Ext 19. Fax: 708-343-2115. p. 672

Williams, Ashlee, Ch, Elizabethton-Carter County Public Library, 201 N Sycamore St, Elizabethton, TN, 37643. Tel: 423-547-6360. Fax: 423-542-1510. p. 2234

Williams, Audrey, Circ Mgr, Williamsburg County Library, 215 N Jackson, Kingstree, SC, 29556-3319. Tel: 843-355-9486. Fax: 843-355-9991. p. 2198

Williams, Audrey, Tech Serv, Regent College, 5800 University Blvd, Vancouver, BC, V6T 2E4, CANADA. Tel: 604-221-3364. Fax: 604-224-3097. p. 2742

Williams, Barbara, Librn, Massachusetts Institute of Technology Libraries, Aeronautics & Astronautics, Bldg 33-111, 77 Massachusetts Ave, Cambridge, MA, 02139-4307. Tel: 617-253-5666. Fax: 617-253-3256. p. 1077

Williams, Barbara, Circ Mgr, Long Branch Free Public Library, 328 Broadway, Long Branch, NJ, 07740. Tel: 732-222-3900. Fax: 732-222-3799. p. 1496

Williams, Barbara, Tech Serv, Canal Fulton Public Library, 154 Market St NE, Canal Fulton, OH, 44614-1196. Tel: 330-854-4148. Fax: 330-854-9520. p. 1863

Williams, Barbara, Sister, Archivist/Librn, Georgian Court University, 900 Lakewood Ave, Lakewood, NJ, 08701-2697. Tel: 732-987-2441. Fax: 732-987-2017. p. 1493

Williams, Becky, Ch, Fulton County Public Library, 320 W Seventh St, Rochester, IN, 46975-1332. Tel: 574-223-2713. Fax: 574-223-5102. p. 776

Williams, Becky, Asst Librn, ILL & Distance Libr Serv Spec, Broken Bow Public Library, 404 Broadway, Broken Bow, OK, 74728. Tel: 580-584-2815. Fax: 580-584-9449. p. 1959

Williams, Benjamin, Assoc Vice Chancellor, Univ Libr Syst, Keiser University Library System, 1500 NW 49th St, Fort Lauderdale, FL, 33309. Tel: 954-351-4035. Fax: 954-351-4051. p. 443

Williams, Beth, Dir, Nevada Public Library, 631 K Ave, Nevada, IA, 50201. Tel: 515-382-2628. Fax: 515-382-3552. p. 834

Williams, Beth, Libr Dir, Louisiana State University Libraries, Paul M Hebert Law Center, One E Campus Dr, Baton Rouge, LA, 70803-1000. Tel: 225-578-5770. Fax: 225-578-5773. p. 944

Williams, Betsy, Coord Libr, Specialized Serv & Librn Mgt, Hennepin County Library, Minneapolis Central, 300 Nicollet Mall, Minneapolis, MN, 55401. Tel: 612- 543-8168. Fax: 612-543-8173. p. 1264

Williams, Betsy, Coord Libr, Specialized Serv & Librn Mgt, Hennepin County Library, Ridgedale, 12601 Ridgedale Dr, Minnetonka, MN, 55305-1909. Tel: 612-543-8168. Fax: 612-543-8819. p. 1264

Williams, Betsy, Coord Libr, Specialized Serv & Librn Mgt, Hennepin County Library, Southdale, 7001 York Ave S, Edina, MN, 55435-4287. Tel: 612-543-8168. Fax: 612-543-5976. p. 1264

Williams, Betty, Br Mgr, Avoyelles Parish Library, Bunkie Branch, 107 W Oak St, Bunkie, LA, 71322-1782. Tel: 318-346-6122. Fax: 318-346-4301. p. 956

Williams, Beverly, Mgr, Georgia Library for Accessible State-wide Services, 1800 Century Place, Ste 150, Atlanta, GA, 30345. Tel: 404-756-4619. Fax: 404-756-4618. p. 515

Williams, Bina, Ch, Bridgeport Public Library, 925 Broad St, Bridgeport, CT, 06604. Tel: 203-576-7408. Fax: 203-576-8255. p. 331

Williams, Bonnie, Dir, United States Air Force, Nine SVS/SVMG, 17849 16th St, Bldg 25219, Beale AFB, CA, 95903-1611. Tel: 530-634-2314. Fax: 530-634-2032. p. 125

Williams, Brandon, Tech Adminr, Mesa Public Library, 64 E First St, Mesa, AZ, 85201-6768. Tel: 480-644-2472. Fax: 480-644-2991. p. 69

Williams, Brenda, Dir, Princeton Public Library, 124 S Hart St, Princeton, IN, 47670. Tel: 812-385-4464. Fax: 812-386-1662. p. 774

Williams, Brenda, Asst Dir, Bus Mgr, Kemper-Newton Regional Library System, 101 Peachtree St, Union, MS, 39365-2617. Tel: 601-774-5096. Fax: 601-774-5096. p. 1316

Williams, Brett, Instr, Libr Sci & Circ Librn, Valdosta State University, 1500 N Patterson St, Valdosta, GA, 31698-0150. Tel: 229-333-5860. Fax: 229-259-5055. p. 555

Williams, Calvin, Dept Chair, Ref Serv, Oakland Community College, Auburn Hills Campus Library, 2900 Featherstone Rd, Bldg D, Auburn Hills, MI, 48326. Tel: 248-232-4125. Fax: 248-232-4136. p. 1154

Williams, Carole, Acq, Dixie State College of Utah, 225 S 700 E, Saint George, UT, 84770. Tel: 435-652-7715. Fax: 435-656-4169. p. 2411

Williams, Carolyn, Dep Dir, Jacksonville Public Library, 303 N Laura St, Jacksonville, FL, 32202-3505. Tel: 904-630-1636. Fax: 904-630-2431. p. 453

Williams, Carolyn, Head, Circ, Rosenberg Library, 2310 Sealy Ave, Galveston, TX, 77550. Tel: 409-763-8854, Ext 141. Fax: 409-763-0275. p. 2326

Williams, Catherine, Br Mgr, Nelson County Public Library, New Haven Branch, 318 Center St, New Haven, KY, 40051. Tel: 502-549-6735. Fax: 502-549-5668. p. 906

Williams, Cathy, Dir, Derby Public Library, 313 Elizabeth St, Derby, CT, 06418. Tel: 203-736-1482. Fax: 203-736-1419. p. 336

Williams, Ceabron D, Head, Tech, Flint River Regional Library, 800 Memorial Dr, Griffin, GA, 30223. Tel: 770-412-4770. p. 535

Williams, Cecilia, ILL, Mercer University, Jack Tarver Library, 1300 Edgewood Ave, Macon, GA, 31207. Tel: 478-301-2102. Fax: 478-301-2111. p. 540

Williams, Chad A, Asst Dir, Oklahoma Historical Society, 2401 N Laird Ave, Oklahoma City, OK, 73105-4997. Tel: 405-522-5205. Fax: 405-522-0644. p. 1974

Williams, Charles Matthew, Asst Br Mgr, Ch, Librn I, Montgomery City-County Public Library System, Pike Road Branch Library, 9585 Vaughn Rd, Pike Road, AL, 36064. Tel: 334-244-8679. Fax: 334-240-4887. p. 30

Williams, Cherri, In Charge, John H Lilley Correctional Center, PO Box 1908, Boley, OK, 74829-1908. Tel: 918-667-4246. Fax: 918-667-4245. p. 1958

Williams, Cheryl, Br Supvr, Barry-Lawrence Regional Library, Cassville Branch, 301 W 17th St, Cassville, MO, 65625-1044. Tel: 417-847-2121. Fax: 417-847-4679. p. 1346

Williams, Chris, Ref Librn, Horry-Georgetown Technical College, 2050 Hwy 501 E, Conway, SC, 29526-9521. Tel: 843-349-5268. Fax: 843-347-0552. p. 2191

Williams, Christina, Tech Serv, Pasquotank-Camden Library, 100 E Colonial Ave, Elizabeth City, NC, 27909. Tel: 252-335-2473, 252-335-7536. Fax: 252-331-7449. p. 1791

Williams, Christine, Librn, Lonoke Prairie County Regional Library Headquarters, Arlene Cherry Memorial, 506 N Grant St, Cabot, AR, 72023. Tel: 501-843-7661. Fax: 501-843-6316. p. 108

Williams, Christy, Dir, Admin Serv Bur, Mississippi Library Commission, 3881 Eastwood Dr, Jackson, MS, 39211. Tel: 601-432-4098. Fax: 601-432-4480. p. 1304

Williams, Cindy, Mgr, Albuquerque-Bernalillo County Library System, Juan Tabo Branch, 3407 Juan Tabo Blvd NE, Albuquerque, NM, 87111. Tel: 505-291-6260. Fax: 505-291-6225. p. 1548

Williams, Cindy, Acq, San Juan College Library, 4601 College Blvd, Farmington, NM, 87402. Tel: 505-566-3248. Fax: 505-566-3381. p. 1555

Williams, Cindy, Libr Asst, Central Square Library, 637 S Main St, Central Square, NY, 13036. Tel: 315-668-6104. Fax: 315-668-6104. p. 1605

Williams, Claire, Circ Mgr, Westchester Public Library, 200 W Indiana Ave, Chesterton, IN, 46304-3122. Tel: 219-926-7696. Fax: 219-926-6424. p. 732

Williams, Clay, Bibliog Instr, Hunter College Libraries, 695 Park Ave, New York, NY, 10065. Tel: 212-772-4137. Fax: 212-772-4142. p. 1682

Williams, Constance, Col Archivist, Coordr, Circ, Queensborough Community College, City University of New York, 222-05 56th Ave, Bayside, NY, 11364-1497. Tel: 718-631-6567. Fax: 718-281-5012. p. 1579

Williams, Craig, Info Tech Coordr, Syst Coordr, Charleston County Public Library, 68 Calhoun St, Charleston, SC, 29401. Tel: 843-805-6850. p. 2183

Williams, Cynthia, YA Serv, Gloucester, Lyceum & Sawyer Free Library, Two Dale Ave, Gloucester, MA, 01930-5906. Tel: 978-281-9763. Fax: 978-281-9770. p. 1091

Williams, Danielle, Periodicals Librn, University of Evansville, 1800 Lincoln Ave, Evansville, IN, 47722. Tel: 812-488-2732. Fax: 812-488-6996. p. 739

Williams, Dean, Libr Spec, Appalachian State University, William Leonard Eury Appalachian Collection, Belk Library, 4th Flr, 218 College St, Boone, NC, 28608. Tel: 828-262-4041. Fax: 828-262-2553. p. 1777

Williams, DeAnza, Br Mgr, Nashville Public Library, Madison Branch, 610 Gallatin Pike S, Madison, TN, 37115-4013. Tel: 615-862-5868. Fax: 615-862-5889. p. 2257

Williams, Deborah, Librn, Jacksonville Campus, Keiser University Library System, 1500 NW 49th St, Fort Lauderdale, FL, 33309. Tel: 954-351-4035. Fax: 954-351-4051. p. 443

Williams, Denise, Acq, Coll Develop, North Suburban Library District, 6340 N Second St, Loves Park, IL, 61111. Tel: 815-633-4247. Fax: 815-633-4249. p. 668

Williams, Denise, Ch, Willamina Public Library, 385 NE C St, Willamina, OR, 97396. Tel: 503-876-6182. Fax: 503-876-1121. p. 2023

Williams, Diane, Ch, York County Library, 138 E Black St, Rock Hill, SC, 29731. Tel: 803-981-5840. Fax: 803-981-5866. p. 2203

Williams, Elaine, Mgr, Highland County District Library, Lynchburg Branch, 102 S Main St, Lynchburg, OH, 45142. Tel: 937-364-2511. Fax: 937-364-2511. p. 1904

Williams, Elizabeth, Curator, Mississippi Museum of Art, 201 E Pascagoula, Jackson, MS, 39201. Tel: 601-960-1515. Fax: 601-960-1505. p. 1305

Williams, Ellen, Librn, Knoxville Public Library, 112 E Main St, Knoxville, PA, 16928. Tel: 814-326-4448. Fax: 814-326-4448. p. 2075

Williams, Ethel J, Dir, White Hall Public Library, 643 Freedom, Whitehall, AL, 36040. Tel: 334-874-7323. Fax: 334-874-7323. p. 40

Williams, Evelyn, Mgr, Apache County Library District, Alpine Public, 17 County Rd 2061, Alpine, AZ, 85920. Tel: 928-339-4925. Fax: 928-339-4925. p. 80

Williams, Faye, Circ Mgr, Lees-McRae College, 191 Main St W, Banner Elk, NC, 28604-9238. Tel: 828-898-8727. Fax: 828-898-8710. p. 1775

Williams, Fredda, Br Mgr, Ch, Knox County Public Library System, South Knoxville Branch, 4500 Chapman Hwy, Knoxville, TN, 37920-4359. Tel: 865-573-1772. Fax: 865-579-4912. p. 2242

Williams, Gary, Info Tech, Pub Serv Spec, George Washington University, Eckles Library, 2100 Foxhall Rd NW, Washington, DC, 20007-1199. Tel: 202-242-6631. Fax: 202-242-6632. p. 402

Williams, Gayle, Dir, Henry Ford Hospital, 2799 W Grand Blvd, Detroit, MI, 48202. Tel: 313-916-2550. Fax: 313-874-4730. p. 1171

Williams, Gayle, Dir, Henry Ford Bi-County Hospital, 13355 E Ten Mile Rd, Warren, MI, 48089. Tel: 586-759-7345. Fax: 586-759-1490. p. 1234

Williams, George, Mgr, Access Serv, Latah County Library District, 110 S Jefferson, Moscow, ID, 83843-2833. Tel: 208-882-3925. Fax: 208-882-5098. p. 579

Williams, George, Asst Dir, Develop, Newark Public Library, Five Washington St, Newark, NJ, 07101. Tel: 973-733-7793. Fax: 973-733-8539. p. 1511

Williams, Georgia E, Dir, Libr Serv, Chowan University, One University Pl, Murfreesboro, NC, 27855. Tel: 252-398-6439. Fax: 252-398-1301. p. 1811

Williams, Ginger, Acq Librn, Wichita State University Libraries, 1845 Fairmount, Wichita, KS, 67260-0068. Tel: 316-978-6442. Fax: 316-978-3048. p. 902

Williams, Glenda, Dir, Long Beach Public Library, 101 Pacific Ave, Long Beach, CA, 90822-1097. Tel: 562-570-7500. Fax: 562-570-7408. p. 166

Williams, Gloria, Br Mgr, Mobile Public Library, Toulminville, 601 Stanton Rd, Mobile, AL, 36617-2209. Tel: 251-438-7075. Fax: 251-438-7058. p. 26

Williams, Gloria, Circ Spec, Central New Mexico Community College Libraries, 525 Buena Vista SE, Albuquerque, NM, 87106-4023. Tel: 505-224-3292. Fax: 505-224-3321. p. 1548

Williams, Gregory, Dir, Archives & Spec Coll, California State University Dominguez Hills, 1000 E Victoria St, Carson, CA, 90747. Tel: 310-243-3013. Fax: 310-516-4219. p. 132

Williams, Hank, Circ Supvr, Linebaugh Public Library System of Rutherford County, 105 W Vine St, Murfreesboro, TN, 37130-3673. Tel: 615-893-4131. Fax: 615-848-5038. p. 2254

Williams, Heather, Tech Serv, Whatcom Community College Library, 237 W Kellogg Rd, Bellingham, WA, 98226. Tel: 360-383-3300. p. 2509

Williams, Helen E, Dir, Rowan County Public Library, 175 Beacon Hill Dr, Morehead, KY, 40351. Tel: 606-784-3528. Fax: 606-784-2130. p. 929

Williams, Holly, Libr Dir, Levant Heritage Library, 1132 Union St, Levant, ME, 04456. Tel: 207-884-8988. p. 989

Williams, Hope, Librn, Nevada State Library & Archives, 100 N Stewart St, Carson City, NV, 89701-4285. Tel: 775-684-3354. Fax: 775-684-3355. p. 1426

Williams, Hope, ILL Librn, Information Nevada, Interlibrary Loan Dept, Nevada State Library & Archives, 100 N Stewart St, Carson City, NV, 89701-4285. Tel: 775-684-3381. Fax: 775-684-3355. p. 2948

Williams, Howell, Asst Br Mgr, Atlanta-Fulton Public Library System, Northside Library, 3295 Northside Pkwy NW, Atlanta, GA, 30327. Tel: 404-814-3508. Fax: 404-814-3511. p. 512

Williams, James F, II, Dean, Dir of Libr, University of Colorado Boulder, 1720 Pleasant St, 184 UCB, Boulder, CO, 80309-0184. Tel: 303-492-7512. Fax: 303-492-3340. p. 291

Williams, Jan, Dir, Russell Public Library, 126 E Sixth St, Russell, KS, 67665-2041. Tel: 785-483-2742. Fax: 785-483-6254. p. 892

Williams, Janene, Librn, Lost Rivers District Library, Howe Branch, 1523 Hwy 22, Howe, ID, 83244. Tel: 208-767-3018. p. 569

Williams, Janet, Librn, Porter Adventist Hospital, 2525 S Downing St, Denver, CO, 80210-5241. Tel: 303-778-5656. Fax: 303-778-5608. p. 303

Williams, Janet D, Assoc Dean, University of New Orleans, College of Education, Rm 342, New Orleans, LA, 70148. Tel: 504-280-6251, 504-280-6528. Fax: 504-280-1120. p. 2967

Williams, Janet L, Coordr, On Campus User Serv, Piedmont College, 165 Central Ave, Demorest, GA, 30535. Tel: 706-776-0111. Fax: 706-776-3338. p. 530

Williams, Janice, Ref Librn, Waycross College Library, 2001 S Georgia Pkwy, Waycross, GA, 31503. Tel: 912-449-7519. Fax: 912-449-7611. p. 557

Williams, Janice, Acq, Southern University, Oliver B Spellman Law Library, 56 Roosevelt Steptoe, Baton Rouge, LA, 70813. Tel: 225-771-2189. Fax: 225-771-6254. p. 944

Williams, Janice, Dir, Timothy C Hauenstein Reynolds Township Library, 117 W Williams St, Howard City, MI, 49329. Tel: 231-937-5575. Fax: 231-937-9240. p. 1192

Williams, Janice, Circ, Carnegie Public Library, 114 Delta Ave, Clarksdale, MS, 38614-4212. Tel: 662-624-4461. Fax: 662-627-4344. p. 1295

Williams, Jean, Cat Librn, Hamilton College, 198 College Hill Rd, Clinton, NY, 13323-1299. Tel: 315-859-4383. Fax: 315-859-4578. p. 1607

Williams, Jean, Head, Pub Serv, North Carolina Agricultural & Technical State University, 1601 E Market St, Greensboro, NC, 27411-0002. Tel: 336-334-7618, Ext 3211. Fax: 336-334-7783. p. 1797

Williams, Jeffrey, Access Serv, Central Florida Community College, 3001 SW College Rd, Ocala, FL, 34474-4415. Tel: 352-237-2111, Ext 1344. Fax: 352-873-5818. p. 473

Williams, Jeneice S, Bibliographer, Florida Agricultural & Mechanical University Libraries, 1500 S Martin Luther King Blvd, Tallahassee, FL, 32307-4700. Tel: 850-599-8770. Fax: 850-599-3436. p. 492

Williams, Jennifer, Electronic Res Librn, Horry-Georgetown Technical College, Elizabeth Mattocks Chapin Memorial Library on the Grand Strand Campus, 3639 Pampas Dr, Myrtle Beach, SC, 29577. Tel: 843-477-2100. Fax: 843-477-2153. p. 2192

Williams, Jennifer, Circ, Whitefish Bay Public Library, 5420 N Marlborough Dr, Whitefish Bay, WI, 53217. Tel: 414-964-4380. Fax: 414-964-5733. p. 2648

Williams, Jerilynn A, Dir, Montgomery County Memorial Library System, 104 I-45 N, Conroe, TX, 77301-2720. Tel: 936-788-8377, Ext 237. Fax: 936-788-8398. p. 2300

Williams, Joan, Dir, Bennett College, 900 E Washington St, Campus Box M, Greensboro, NC, 27401-3239. Tel: 336-517-2139. Fax: 336-517-2144. p. 1795

Williams, Joan, Per, Midland College, 3600 N Garfield, Midland, TX, 79705. Tel: 432-685-4560. Fax: 432-685-6710. p. 2363

Williams, Joe, Head, Access Serv, University of North Carolina at Greensboro, 320 Spring Garden St, Greensboro, NC, 27402. Tel: 336-334-5452. Fax: 336-334-5399. p. 1798

Williams, John, Head, Cat, Fordham University Libraries, 441 E Fordham Rd, Bronx, NY, 10458-5151. Tel: 718-817-3570. Fax: 718-817-3582. p. 1586

Williams, Jon, Libr Asst, Maine State Law & Legislative Reference Library, 43 State House Sta, Augusta, ME, 04333-0043. Tel: 207-287-1600. Fax: 207-287-6467. p. 974

Williams, Jon M, Curator, Hagley Museum & Library, 298 Buck Rd E, Wilmington, DE, 19807. Tel: 302-658-2400. Fax: 302-658-0568. p. 388

Williams, Joseph, Head, Tech Serv, State University of New York Maritime College, Six Pennyfield Ave, Fort Schuyler, Bronx, NY, 10465. Tel: 718-409-7229. Fax: 718-409-7256. p. 1588

Williams, Joyce, Librn, Virgil & Josephine Gordon Memorial Library, 917 N Circle Dr, Sealy, TX, 77474. Tel: 979-885-7469. Fax: 979-885-7469. p. 2385

Williams, Judith, Chmn, Streeter Centennial Library, 5280 50th Ave SE, Streeter, ND, 58483. Tel: 701-424-3602. p. 1848

Williams, Judy, Head Librn, Broken Bow Public Library, 404 Broadway, Broken Bow, OK, 74728. Tel: 580-584-2815. Fax: 580-584-9449. p. 1959

Williams, Judy, Libr Dir, Saxton Community Library, 315 Front St, Saxton, PA, 16678-8612. Tel: 814-635-3533. Fax: 814-635-3001. p. 2136

Williams, Judy, Ref Librn, Belmont University, 1900 Belmont Blvd, Nashville, TN, 37212-3757. Tel: 615-460-6610. Fax: 615-460-5641. p. 2255

Williams, Judy, Dir, Wartburg Public Library, 514 Spring St, Wartburg, TN, 37887. Tel: 423-346-2479. Fax: 423-346-2479. p. 2268

Williams, Judy, Tech Serv, LeTourneau University, 2100 S Mobberly Ave, Longview, TX, 75602-3524. Tel: 903-233-3269. Fax: 903-233-3263. p. 2357

Williams, Julie, Libr Spec III, River Parishes Community College Library, 7384 John LeBlanc Blvd (Hwy 22), Sorrento, LA, 70778. Tel: 226-675-0201. Fax: 225-675-8595. p. 970

Williams, Julie, Libr Tech, Minnesota West Community & Technical College, Granite Falls Campus, 1593 11th Ave, Granite Falls, MN, 56241. Tel: 320-564-4511. Fax: 320-564-2318. p. 1291

Williams, June, Head, Cat, Blue Ridge Community College, One College Lane, Weyers Cave, VA, 24486. Tel: 540-453-2247. Fax: 540-234-9598. p. 2502

Williams, June S, Libr Mgr, Saint Louis Community College, Forest Park Campus Library, 5600 Oakland Ave, Saint Louis, MO, 63110-1316. Tel: 314-644-9209. Fax: 314-644-9240. p. 1357

Williams, Karen, Access Serv/ILL Librn, Auburn University, 7440 East Dr, Montgomery, AL, 36117. Tel: 334-244-3200. Fax: 334-244-3720. p. 28

Williams, Karen, Assoc Univ Librn, Acad Prog, University of Minnesota Libraries-Twin Cities, 499 O Meredith Wilson Library, 309 19th Ave S, Minneapolis, MN, 55455-0414. Tel: 612-625-9148. Fax: 612-626-9353. p. 1262

Williams, Karen, Circ Desk Supvr/Stack Mgr, Northern Virginia Community College Libraries, Woodbridge Library, 15200 Neabsco Mills Rd, Seefeldt 427, Woodbridge, VA, 22191. Tel: 703-878-5727. Fax: 703-670-8433. p. 2448

Williams, Karlan E K, Dir, Forest Lodge Library, 13450 County Hwy M, Cable, WI, 54821. Tel: 715-798-3189. p. 2584

Williams, Kate, Asst Prof, University of Illinois at Urbana-Champaign, Library & Information Science Bldg, 501 E Daniel St, Champaign, IL, 61820-6211. Tel: 217-333-3280. Fax: 217-244-3302. p. 2965

Williams, Kathleen, Dir, Libr & Media, Griffin Technical College Library, 501 Varsity Rd, Griffin, GA, 30223. Tel: 770-412-4755. Fax: 770-229-3006. p. 535

Williams, Kathleen, Librn, Legislative Reference Bureau, City Hall, Rm B-11, 200 E Wells St, Milwaukee, WI, 53202-3567. Tel: 414-286-2299. Fax: 414-286-3004. p. 2618

Williams, Kathy, Ch, East Dubuque District Library, 350 Wall St, East Dubuque, IL, 61025-1222. Tel: 815-747-3052. Fax: 815-747-6062. p. 638

Williams, Kaurri C, Dir, Sevier County Public Library System, 321 Court Ave, Sevierville, TN, 37862. Tel: 865-453-3532. Fax: 865-908-6108. p. 2265

Williams, Kayla, YA Librn, Spencer Public Library, 21 E Third St, Spencer, IA, 51301-4188. Tel: 712-580-7290. Fax: 712-580-7468. p. 845

Williams, Kelli, Ref & Instruction Librn, Carson-Newman College, 1634 Russell Ave, Jefferson City, TN, 37760. Tel: 865-471-3338. Fax: 865-471-3450. p. 2239

Williams, Kevin, Dir, Colorado Mountain College, 1330 Bob Adams Dr, Steamboat Springs, CO, 80487. Tel: 970-870-4493. Fax: 970-870-4490. p. 322

Williams, Kreg, Mgr, Info Tech, American Occupational Therapy Foundation, 4720 Montgomery Lane, Bethesda, MD, 20814-5385. Tel: 301-652-6611, Ext 2557. Fax: 301-656-3620. p. 1021

Williams, Kristin, Coordr, Planning & Develop, Saint Charles City County Library District, 77 Boone Hills Dr, Saint Peters, MO, 63376-0529. Tel: 636-441-2300. Fax: 636-441-3132. p. 1363

Williams, La-Nita, Circ Serv, High Point University, 833 Montlieu Ave, High Point, NC, 27262-4221. Tel: 336-841-9102. Fax: 336-841-5123. p. 1802

Williams, Laine, Automation Syst Coordr, Rochester Public Library, 115 South Ave, Rochester, NY, 14604-1896. Tel: 585-428-7300. Fax: 585-428-8353. p. 1732

Williams, Lanette, Asst Librn, Evelyn Thornton-Warrior Public Library, Ten First St, Warrior, AL, 35180-1501. Tel: 205-647-3006. Fax: 205-647-9280. p. 40

Williams, Laura, Adult Serv, Sunderland Public Library, 20 School St, Sunderland, MA, 01375. Tel: 413-665-2642. Fax: 413-665-1435. p. 1130

Williams, Laura, Mgr, Ch Serv, Burlington Public Library, 2331 New St, Burlington, ON, L7R 1J4, CANADA. Tel: 905-639-3611, Ext 135. Fax: 905-681-7277. p. 2797

Williams, Lauren J, Librn/Communications Spec, PSP Metrics Library, The Frick Bldg, 437 Grant St, Ste 1900, Pittsburgh, PA, 15219-6110. Tel: 412-261-1333. Fax: 412-261-5014. p. 2128

Williams, Laurie, Access Serv Librn, North Carolina Central University, School of Law Library, 1512 S Alston Ave, Durham, NC, 27707. Tel: 919-530-6608. Fax: 919-530-7926. p. 1789

Williams, Lavaine, Librn, Calhoun County Public Library, Altha Branch, PO Box 241, Altha, FL, 32421. Tel: 850-762-8280. Fax: 850-762-4547. p. 427

Williams, Leathea, Coordr, Coll Mgt, Chicago State University, 9501 S Martin Luther King Jr Dr, LIB 440, Chicago, IL, 60628-1598. Tel: 773-995-2251. Fax: 773-995-3772. p. 610

Williams, Leon, Tech Serv, Fort Richardson Post Library, IMPA-FRA-HRE PL, Bldg 7, Chilkoot Ave, Fort Richardson, AK, 99505-0055. Tel: 907-384-1648. Fax: 907-384-7534. p. 48

Williams, Leonette, Assoc Dir, Coll Serv, Assoc Dir, Tech Serv, University of Southern California Libraries, Asa V Call Law Library, 699 Exposition Blvd, LAW 202, MC 0072, Los Angeles, CA, 90089-0072. Tel: 213-740-6482. Fax: 213-740-7179. p. 179

Williams, Lesley, Adult Serv, Evanston Public Library, 1703 Orrington, Evanston, IL, 60201. Tel: 847-448-8600, 847-866-0300. Fax: 847-866-0313. p. 643

Williams, Leslie, Acq & Assessments Librn, Auraria Library, 1100 Lawrence St, Denver, CO, 80204-2095. Tel: 303-556-5807. Fax: 303-556-3528. p. 298

Williams, Leslie, Br Mgr, Denver Public Library, Byers, 675 Santa Fe Dr, Denver, CO, 80204-4426. Tel: 303-571-1665. Fax: 303-572-4787. p. 301

Williams, Lila, Head, Cat, First Baptist Church Library, 2709 Monument Ave, Richmond, VA, 23220. Tel: 804-355-8637, Ext 20. Fax: 804-359-4000. p. 2488

Williams, Lillian Hoggard, Dr, Coordr, Libr Serv, J Sargeant Reynolds Community College Library, Downtown Campus-Library & Information Services, 700 E Jackson St, 2nd Flr, Richmond, VA, 23219-1543. Tel: 804-523-5211. Fax: 804-786-6200. p. 2488

Williams, Linda, Children's & Youth Serv, Connecticut State Library, 231 Capitol Ave, Hartford, CT, 06106. Tel: 860-757-6500. Fax: 860-757-6503. p. 345

Williams, Linda, Librn, Village of Avon Public Library, 105 S Main St, Avon, IL, 61415. Tel: 309-465-3933. Fax: 309-465-3933. p. 592

Williams, Linda, Acq, Tech Serv, Greenwood-Leflore Public Library System, 405 W Washington St, Greenwood, MS, 38930-4297. Tel: 662-453-3634. Fax: 662-453-0683. p. 1299

Williams, Linda, Mgr, Circ Serv, Bucks County Free Library, Levittown Branch, 7311 New Falls Rd, Levittown, PA, 19055-1006. Tel: 215-949-2324. Fax: 215-949-0643. p. 2050

Williams, Lisa, Head, Ref, William Madison Randall Library, 601 S College Rd, Wilmington, NC, 28403-5616. Tel: 910-962-3000. Fax: 910-962-3078. p. 1831

Williams, Lisa W, Dir, Libr & Res Serv, Parker, Poe, Adams & Bernstein, LLP, Wachovia Capitol Ctr, 150 Fayetteville St, Ste 1400, Raleigh, NC, 27601. Tel: 919-828-0564. Fax: 919-834-4564. p. 1816

Williams, Lois, Mgr, Marion County Library, Nichols Branch, 208 Floyd St, Nichols, SC, 29581. Tel: 843-526-2641. Fax: 843-526-2641. p. 2200

Williams, Lori, Libr Supvr, Inglewood Public Library, 101 W Manchester Blvd, Inglewood, CA, 90301-1771. Tel: 310-412-5397. Fax: 310-412-8848. p. 159

Williams, Lou, Dir, Oneida Community Library, 201 Elm St, Oneida, WI, 54155. Tel: 920-869-2210. Fax: 920-869-1299. p. 2627

Williams, Lydia, Archives & Rec Mgr, Longwood University, Redford & Race St, Farmville, VA, 23909. Tel: 434-395-2432. Fax: 434-395-2453. p. 2463

Williams, Lynda, Sr Librn, Alameda Free Library, Bay Farm Island, 3221 Mecartney Rd, Alameda, CA, 94502. Tel: 510-747-7787. Fax: 510-337-1426. p. 119

Williams, Lynn, Reader Serv, Lewis & Clark College, Paul L Boley Law Library, Lewis & Clark Law School, 10015 SW Terwilliger Blvd, Portland, OR, 97219. Tel: 503-768-6776. Fax: 503-768-6760. p. 2011

Williams, Lynne, Dep Dir, Support Serv, Solano County Library, 1150 Kentucky St, Fairfield, CA, 94533-5799. Fax: 707-421-7474. p. 148

Williams, Mable, Br Mgr, Newark Public Library, Roseville, 99 N Fifth St, Newark, NJ, 07107. Tel: 973-733-7770. p. 1512

Williams, Marcia, Librn, North Texas State Hospital, 4730 College Dr, Vernon, TX, 76384. Tel: 940-552-4117. Fax: 940-553-2515. p. 2395

Williams, Maren, Ref Librn, University of Louisiana at Monroe Library, 700 University Ave, Monroe, LA, 71209-0720. Tel: 318-342-1065. Fax: 318-342-1075. p. 958

Williams, Marilyn, Acq, Warren County Public Library, 1225 State St, Bowling Green, KY, 42101. Tel: 270-781-4882. Fax: 270-781-7323. p. 907

Williams, Mark, Librn, University of Texas at Brownsville & Texas Southmost College Library, 80 Fort Brown St, Brownsville, TX, 78521. Tel: 956-882-7108. Fax: 956-882-5495. p. 2292

Williams, Marvin, Ser Tech, University of the District of Columbia, David A Clarke School of Law, Charles N & Hilda H M Mason Law Library, Bldg 39, Rm B-16, 4200 Connecticut Ave NW, Washington, DC, 20008. Tel: 202-274-7310. Fax: 202-274-7311. p. 421

Williams, Mary, Br Mgr, Chicago Public Library, Avalon, 8148 S Stony Island, Chicago, IL, 60617. Tel: 312-747-5234. Fax: 312-747-0590. p. 608

Williams, Mary, Asst Librn, Henry Public Library, 702 Front St, Henry, IL, 61537. Tel: 309-364-2516. Fax: 309-364-2717. p. 655

Williams, Mary, Dir, Laurie Hill Library, PO Box 128, Heron, MT, 59844-0128. Tel: 406-847-2520. p. 1383

Williams, Mary Ann, Dir, Admin Serv, Lehigh Valley Association of Independent Colleges, 130 W Greenwich St, Bethlehem, PA, 18018. Tel: 610-625-7889. Fax: 610-625-7891. p. 2954

Williams, Mary Ellen, Librn, Autauga-Prattville Public Library, Billingsley Public, 2021 Office St, Billingsley, AL, 36006. Tel: 205-755-9809. p. 34

Williams, Mary Pasek, Pub Serv, Oak Lawn Public Library, 9427 S Raymond Ave, Oak Lawn, IL, 60453-2434. Tel: 708-422-4990. Fax: 708-422-5061. p. 683

Williams, Maureen, Ref Librn, Neumann College Library, One Neumann Dr, Aston, PA, 19014-1298. Tel: 610-558-5541. Fax: 610-459-1370. p. 2030

Williams, Maureen, Spec Coll Librn, Saint Francis Xavier University, West St, Antigonish, NS, B2G 2W5, CANADA. Tel: 902-867-5328. Fax: 902-867-5153. p. 2777

Williams, Megan, Tech Serv, Shenandoah University, 1460 University Dr, Winchester, VA, 22601. Tel: 540-665-4638. Fax: 540-665-4609. p. 2503

Williams, Megan, Chair, Department of Community Services, Government of Yukon, Old Crow Community, Chief Zzeh Gittlit School, Old Crow, YT, Y0B 1N0, CANADA. Tel: 867-966-3031. p. 2933

Williams, Melanie, Syst Adminr, Bolivar County Library System, 104 S Leflore Ave, Cleveland, MS, 38732. Tel: 662-843-2774. Fax: 662-843-4701. p. 1295

Williams, Melisa, Br Mgr, Forsyth County Public Library, Carver School Road Branch, 4915 Lansing Dr W, Winston-Salem, NC, 27105. Tel: 336-703-2910. Fax: 336-661-4919. p. 1832

Williams, Merlyn, Dir, Lyons Depot Library, 430 Fifth Ave, Lyons, CO, 80540. Tel: 303-823-5165. Fax: 303-823-9532. p. 318

Williams, Michael, Area Res Mgr, S Region, Indianapolis-Marion County Public Library, 2450 N Meridian St, Indianapolis, IN, 46208. Tel: 317-275-4302. Fax: 317-269-5300. p. 753

Williams, Michael, Sr Libr Tech, Georgetown Peabody Library, Lincoln Park, Georgetown, MA, 01833. Tel: 978-352-5728. Fax: 978-352-7415. p. 1091

Williams, Michael, Circ, ILL, Lee County Library, 107 Hawkins Ave, Sanford, NC, 27331-4399. Tel: 919-718-4665. Fax: 919-775-1832. p. 1823

Williams, Michael B, Dir, Harnett County Public Library, Dunn Public, 110 E Divine St, Dunn, NC, 28334. Tel: 910-892-2899. Fax: 910-892-8385. p. 1807

Williams, Mick, Ref Serv & Ser Librn, Nyack College Library, One South Blvd, Nyack, NY, 10960-3698. Fax: 845-353-0817. p. 1708

Williams, Mike, Br Mgr, Indianapolis-Marion County Public Library, Southport, 2630 E Stop 11 Rd, Indianapolis, IN, 46227-8899. Tel: 317-275-4510. p. 754

Williams, Mondretta, Dir, Leeds Jane Culbreth Public Library, 8104 Parkway Dr, Leeds, AL, 35094-2225. Tel: 205-699-5962. Fax: 205-699-6843. p. 23

Williams, Monica, Br Mgr, Brooklyn Public Library, Saratoga, Eight Thomas S Boyland St, @ Macon St, Brooklyn, NY, 11233. Tel: 718-573-5224. Fax: 718-573-5402. p. 1592

Williams, Nancy, Ref Serv, Ad, Temple Public Library, 100 W Adams Ave, Temple, TX, 76501-7641. Tel: 254-298-5333. Fax: 254-298-5328. p. 2391

Williams, Nelle, Dir, University of Alabama, University Medical Center, 850 Fifth Ave E, Tuscaloosa, AL, 35401. Tel: 205-348-1360. Fax: 205-348-9563. p. 39

Williams, Nicole, Ref Librn, Englewood Public Library, 31 Engle St, Englewood, NJ, 07631. Tel: 201-568-2215. Fax: 201-568-6895. p. 1484

Williams, Nina, Supvr, Shapiro Developmental Center, 100 E Jeffery St, Kankakee, IL, 60901. Tel: 815-939-8011, 815-939-8505. Fax: 815-939-8414. p. 661

Williams, Norma, Libr Assoc for Coll & Access Serv, Barton College, 400 Atlantic Christian College Dr NE, Wilson, NC, 27893. Tel: 252-399-6506. Fax: 252-399-6571. p. 1831

Williams, Owen, Dir, UMC Library, 2900 University Ave, Crookston, MN, 56716-0801. Tel: 218-281-8399. Fax: 218-281-8080. p. 1246

Williams, P J, Syst Coordr, Fort Smith Public Library, 3201 Rogers Ave, Fort Smith, AR, 72903. Tel: 479-783-0229. Fax: 479-782-8571. p. 100

Williams, Paige, Asst Dir, Portsmouth Public Library, 1220 Gallia St, Portsmouth, OH, 45662-4185. Tel: 740-354-5263. Fax: 740-353-1249. p. 1930

Williams, Pam, Ref & Instruction Librn, Three Rivers Community College, 574 New London Tpk, Norwich, CT, 06360-6598. Tel: 860-892-5713. Fax: 860-886-0691. p. 363

Williams, Pam, Librn, Central Florida Community College, 3001 SW College Rd, Ocala, FL, 34474-4415. Tel: 352-237-2111, Ext 1344. Fax: 352-873-5818. p. 473

Williams, Pam, Acq, Orange Public Library, 220 N Fifth St, Orange, TX, 77630. Tel: 409-883-1086. Fax: 409-883-1057. p. 2367

Williams, Pamela, Ref Serv, All Childrens' Hospital, 501 Sixth Ave S, Saint Petersburg, FL, 33701. Tel: 727-767-4278. Fax: 727-767-8557. p. 487

Williams, Pamela S, Assoc Dir, Frostburg State University, One Stadium Dr, Frostburg, MD, 21532. Tel: 301-687-4887. Fax: 301-687-7069. p. 1029

Williams, Patricia, Info Spec, Danville Public Library, Westover, 94 Clifton St, Danville, VA, 24541. Tel: 434-799-5152. p. 2460

Williams, Patrick, Head, Info Tech, Middleton Public Library, 7425 Hubbard Ave, Middleton, WI, 53562-3117. Tel: 608-827-7422. Fax: 608-836-5724. p. 2616

Williams, Patsy, Br Mgr, Orange County Library District, Washington Park, 5151 Raleigh St, Ste A, Orlando, FL, 32811. Fax: 407-521-2468. p. 476

Williams, Patty, Tech Serv, YA Serv, Jackson-Madison County Library, 433 E Lafayette St, Jackson, TN, 38301-6386. Tel: 731-425-8600. Fax: 731-425-8609. p. 2238

Williams, Paul, Librn, Marjorie Mews Public Library, 12 Highland Dr, St. John's, NL, A1A 3C4, CANADA. Tel: 709-737-3020. p. 2772

Williams, Paula, Ref, Bergen Community College, 400 Paramus Rd, Paramus, NJ, 07652-1595. Tel: 201-612-5299. Fax: 201-493-8167. p. 1517

Williams, Peggy, Head, Ch, Frankfort Community Public Library, 208 W Clinton St, Frankfort, IN, 46041. Tel: 765-654-8746. Fax: 765-654-8747. p. 743

Williams, Peggy, Librn, Potter County Free Public Library, 106 E Commercial Ave, Gettysburg, SD, 57442-1507. Tel: 605-765-9518. p. 2212

Williams, Phil, Automation Syst Coordr, Tech Serv, Jefferson-Madison Regional Library, 201 E Market St, Charlottesville, VA, 22902-5287. Tel: 434-979-7151, Ext 206, 434-979-7151, Ext 207. Fax: 434-971-7035. p. 2453

Williams, Phillips, Br Mgr, Memphis Public Library, Cordova Branch, 8457 Trinity Rd, Cordova, TN, 38018. Tel: 901-754-8443. Fax: 901-754-6874. p. 2249

Williams, Phyllis, Circ/Reserves, Norfolk State University Library, 700 Park Ave, Norfolk, VA, 23504-8010. Tel: 757-823-8517. Fax: 757-823-2431. p. 2482

Williams, Rebecca, Librn, Richland Correctional Institution Library, 1001 Olivesburg Rd, Mansfield, OH, 44905-1228. Tel: 419-526-2100, Ext 2215. Fax: 419-521-2814. p. 1913

Williams, Rebecca J, Dir, Fulton County Public Library, 320 W Seventh St, Rochester, IN, 46975-1332. Tel: 574-223-2713. Fax: 574-223-5102. p. 776

Williams, Rhonda, In Charge, Alabama Department of Corrections, PO Box 1107, Elmore, AL, 36025-9900. Tel: 334-567-2221, Ext 260. Fax: 334-567-1519. p. 15

Williams, Rita B, Acq, Pitt Community College, Hwy 11 S, Greenville, NC, 27835. Tel: 252-321-4357. Fax: 252-321-4404. p. 1799

Williams, Robert, Ref, Marshall University Libraries, Joan C Edwards School of Medicine Health Science Libraries, 1600 Medical Center Dr, Ste 2400, Huntington, WV, 25701-3655. Tel: 304-691-1750. Fax: 304-691-1766. p. 2562

Williams, Robyn, Acq of New Ser, Lincoln Memorial University, Cumberland Gap Pkwy, Box 2012, Harrogate, TN, 37752. Tel: 423-869-6218. Fax: 423-869-6426. p. 2236

Williams, Robyn, Cataloger, Lynchburg College, 1501 Lakeside Dr, Lynchburg, VA, 24501-3199. Tel: 434-544-8204. Fax: 434-544-8499. p. 2476

Williams, Rochelle, Asst Librn, Milo Free Public Library, Four Pleasant St, Milo, ME, 04463-1327. Tel: 207-943-2612. Fax: 207-943-2785. p. 992

Williams, Roseline, Online Serv, Scottsdale Community College Library, 9000 E Chaparral Rd, Scottsdale, AZ, 85256. Tel: 480-425-6714. Fax: 480-423-6666. p. 80

Williams, Roxann, Spec Projects Librn, Florida State University Libraries, Charlotte Edwards Maguire Medical Library, 1115 W Call St, Tallahassee, FL, 32304-3556. Tel: 850-645-9398. Fax: 850-644-9942. p. 495

Williams, Ryan, Info Serv Librn, North Central College, 320 E School St, Naperville, IL, 60540. Tel: 630-637-5708. Fax: 630-637-5716. p. 679

Williams, Ryan, Libr Mgr, Timberland Regional Library, Tenino Branch, 172 Central Ave W, Tenino, WA, 98589. Tel: 360-264-2369. Fax: 360-264-6846. p. 2544

Williams, Sabrina, Librn, Berkeley Planning Associates Library, 440 Grand Ave, Ste 500, Oakland, CA, 94610. Tel: 510-465-7884. Fax: 510-465-7885. p. 196

Williams, Sandra, Ref Librn, Belmont Abbey College, 100 Belmont-Mt Holly Rd, Belmont, NC, 28012. Tel: 704-461-6748. Fax: 704-461-6743. p. 1776

Williams, Sandra, Assoc Prof, University of Montana, 32 Campus Dr, Missoula, MT, 59812-6346. Tel: 406-243-4073. Fax: 406-243-4908. p. 2969

Williams, Sara, Dir, College of Saint Mary Library, 7000 Mercy Rd, Omaha, NE, 68106-2606. Tel: 402-399-2467. Fax: 402-399-2686. p. 1411

Williams, Sarah C, Mgr, Merck & Co, Inc, 770 Sumneytown Pike, West Point, PA, 19486. Tel: 215-652-6026. Fax: 215-652-0721. p. 2154

Williams, Sharon, Tech Serv, Waycross College Library, 2001 S Georgia Pkwy, Waycross, GA, 31503. Tel: 912-449-7514. Fax: 912-449-7611. p. 557

Williams, Sharon, Libr Dir, Hurley Medical Center, One Hurley Plaza, Flint, MI, 48503. Tel: 810-257-9427. Fax: 810-762-7107. p. 1180

Williams, Sharon, Circ Supvr, Murray Public Library, 166 E 5300 South, Murray, UT, 84107-6075. Tel: 801-264-2580. Fax: 801-264-2586. p. 2408

Williams, Sharon, Chief Exec Officer, Englehart Public Library, 71 Fourth Ave, Englehart, ON, P0J 1H0, CANADA. Tel: 705-544-2100. Fax: 705-544-2238. p. 2804

Williams, Sheila, AV Serv Librn, Keene Public Library, 60 Winter St, Keene, NH, 03431-3360. Tel: 603-352-0157. Fax: 866-743-0446. p. 1452

Williams, Shelley, Dir, White Lake Community Library, 3900 White Lake Dr, Whitehall, MI, 49461-9257. Tel: 231-894-9531. Fax: 231-893-8821. p. 1237

Williams, Shellie, Librn, Minerva Free Library, 116 Miller St, Sherman, NY, 14781-9783. Tel: 716-761-6378. Fax: 716-761-6335. p. 1743

Williams, Sheree Huber, Dir, Libr Serv, Jefferson Community & Technical College, 109 E Broadway, Louisville, KY, 40202. Tel: 502-213-2156. p. 924

Williams, Sherry, Dir, Alma M Carpenter Public Library, 300 S Ann, Sourlake, TX, 77659. Tel: 409-287-3592. Fax: 409-287-4777. p. 2388

Williams, Sheryl, Librn, University of Kansas Libraries, Spencer Research Library, 1450 Poplar Lane, Lawrence, KS, 66045-7616. Tel: 785-864-4334. Fax: 785-864-5803. p. 878

Williams, Sheryl, Br Mgr, Mid-Continent Public Library, North Oak Branch, 8700 N Oak Trafficway, Kansas City, MO, 64155-2437. Tel: 816-436-4385. Fax: 816-436-1946. p. 1333

Williams, Shirley, Tech Serv, Harding University, 915 E Market St, Searcy, AR, 72149-2267. Tel: 501-279-4376. p. 114

Williams, Shirley, Mgr, University Hospital, 1350 Walton Way, Augusta, GA, 30901-2629. Tel: 706-774-2944. Fax: 706-774-4370. p. 520

Williams, Shirley, Librn, Lyon County, Library District One, 421 Main St, Allen, KS, 66833. Tel: 620-528-3451. Fax: 620-528-3451. p. 855

Williams, Simone, Interim Dir, Libr Serv, Art Institute of Fort Lauderdale, 1600 SE 17th St, 3rd Flr, Fort Lauderdale, FL, 33316. Tel: 954-308-2631. Fax: 954-463-3393. p. 440

Williams, Stacie, Asst Br Mgr, Ch, Librn I, Montgomery City-County Library System, E L Lowder Regional Branch Library, 2590 Bell Rd, Montgomery, AL, 36117. Tel: 334-244-5717. Fax: 334-240-4893. p. 30

Williams, Stephanie, Asst Dir, Pioneerland Library System, 410 Fifth St SW, Willmar, MN, 56201. Tel: 320-235-6106, Ext 28. Fax: 320-214-0187. p. 1288

Williams, Stephanie D, Dir, Robesonia Community Library, 75-A S Brooke St, Robesonia, PA, 19551-1500. Tel: 610-693-3264. Fax: 610-693-6864. p. 2135

Williams, Steven, Circ Supvr, Port Arthur Public Library, 4615 Ninth Ave, Port Arthur, TX, 77642. Tel: 409-985-8838. Fax: 409-985-5969. p. 2371

Williams, Susan D, Dir, Blue Ridge Community College Library, 180 W Campus Dr, Flat Rock, NC, 28731. Tel: 828-694-1824. Fax: 828-694-1692. p. 1793

Williams, Suzanne P, Librn, Alberta Distance Learning Centre Building Library, 4601 63rd Ave, Barrhead, AB, T7N 1P4, CANADA. Tel: 780-674-8756. Fax: 780-674-6561. p. 2684

Williams, Sylvia, Coll Res Mgr, Medina County District Library, 210 S Broadway, Medina, OH, 44256. Tel: 330-722-6235. Fax: 330-725-2053. p. 1916

Williams, Tanya, Libr Asst, Shaw University, 118 E South St, Raleigh, NC, 27601. Tel: 919-546-8407. Fax: 919-831-1161. p. 1817

Williams, Ted, Dir, South Dakota Developmental Center, 17267 W Third St, Redfield, SD, 57469-1001. Tel: 605-472-2400. Fax: 605-472-4457. p. 2218

Williams, Teressa, Librn, Res Ctr Mgr, Anchorage Museum, 625 C St, Anchorage, AK, 99501. Tel: 907-929-9235. Fax: 907-929-9233. p. 44

Williams, Thalia, Asst Dir, Union Parish Library, 202 W Jackson St, Farmerville, LA, 71241-2799. Tel: 318-368-9226, 318-368-9288. Fax: 318-368-9224. p. 949

Williams, Theresa, Br Mgr, Saint Martin Parish Library, 201 Porter St, Saint Martinville, LA, 70582. Tel: 337-394-2207, Ext 23. Fax: 337-394-2248. p. 967

Williams, Tim, Ref Serv, Athens State University Library, 407 E Pryor St, Athens, AL, 35611. Tel: 256-233-8218. Fax: 256-233-6547. p. 5

Williams, Tina, Asst Dir, Perry County Public Library, 289 Black Gold Blvd, Hazard, KY, 41701. Tel: 606-436-2475, 606-436-4747. Fax: 606-436-0191. p. 916

Williams, Tina, Dir, Helix Public Library, 119 Columbia St, Helix, OR, 97835. Tel: 541-457-6130. Fax: 541-457-6130. p. 2000

Williams, Tina, Librn, Mgr, Cleburne Public Library, 302 W Henderson St, Cleburne, TX, 76033. Tel: 817-645-0936. Fax: 817-556-8816. p. 2298

Williams, Todd, Data Spec, Librn, Knox Community Hospital, 1330 Coshocton Rd, Mount Vernon, OH, 43050. Tel: 740-393-9616. Fax: 740-399-3113. p. 1919

Williams, Tonya, Asst Br Mgr, Troup-Harris Regional Library System, Harris County Public Library, 138 N College St, Hamilton, GA, 31811-6031. Tel: 706-628-4685. Fax: 706-628-4685. p. 538

Williams, Tonya, Dir, Venice Public Library, 325 Broadway, Venice, IL, 62090. Tel: 618-877-1330. Fax: 618-877-0633. p. 714

Williams, Trudy, Br Mgr, Saint Louis County Library, Bridgeton Trails Branch, 3455 McKelvey Rd, Bridgeton, MO, 63044. Tel: 314-994-3300. Fax: 314-291-7593. p. 1358

Williams, Valerie, Cat, Circ, Naval Surface Warfare Center, 110 Vernon Ave, Panama City, FL, 32407-7001. Tel: 850-234-4848. Fax: 850-234-4844. p. 480

Williams, Valerie, Dir, Coffey County Library, 410 Juniatta St, Burlington, KS, 66839. Tel: 620-364-2010. Fax: 620-364-2603. p. 859

Williams, Valerie, Dir, Coffey County Library, Burlington Branch, 410 Juniatta, Burlington, KS, 66839. Tel: 620-364-5333. Fax: 620-364-2603. p. 859

Williams, Velma, Circ Asst, Shaw University, 118 E South St, Raleigh, NC, 27601. Tel: 919-546-8438. Fax: 919-831-1161. p. 1817

Williams, Veronica, Librn, Pike-Amite-Walthall Library System, Walthall, 707 Union Rd, Tylertown, MS, 39667. Tel: 601-876-4348. Fax: 601-876-4348. p. 1308

Williams, Veronica, Ref & ILL Librn, Pike-Amite-Walthall Library System, 1022 Virginia Ave, McComb, MS, 39648. Tel: 601-684-2661. Fax: 601-250-1213. p. 1308

Williams, Vicki, Adult Serv, West Melbourne Public Library, 2755 Wingate Blvd, West Melbourne, FL, 32904. Tel: 321-952-4508. Fax: 321-952-4510. p. 502

Williams, Violene, Digital Media Librn, Ref Librn, Mississippi Valley State University, 14000 Hwy 82 W, Itta Bena, MS, 38941. Tel: 662-254-3494. Fax: 662-254-3499. p. 1302

Williams, Virginia, Cat, Frostburg State University, One Stadium Dr, Frostburg, MD, 21532. Tel: 301-687-4884. Fax: 301-687-7069. p. 1029

Williams, Wanda, Dir, Student Serv, St Lawrence College Library, 100 Portsmouth Ave, Kingston, ON, K7L 5A6, CANADA. Tel: 613-544-5400, Ext 1705. Fax: 613-545-3914. p. 2814

Williams, Williams R, Dir, Kearney Public Library, 2020 First Ave, Kearney, NE, 68847. Tel: 308-233-3280. Fax: 308-233-3291. p. 1403

Williams, Yvonne, Cat, Huntingdon College, 1500 E Fairview Ave, Montgomery, AL, 36106. Tel: 334-833-4421. Fax: 334-263-4465. p. 29

Williams, Yvonne, Youth Serv, Auburndale Public Library, 100 W Bridgers Ave, Auburndale, FL, 33823. Tel: 863-965-5548. Fax: 863-965-5554. p. 425

Williams-Bergen, Eric, Sci Librn, Saint Lawrence University, Launders Science Library, Park St, Canton, NY, 13617. Tel: 315-229-5405. Fax: 315-229-7291. p. 1602

Williams-Bergen, Eric R, Sci Librn, St Lawrence University, 23 Romoda Dr, Canton, NY, 13617. Tel: 315-229-5405. Fax: 315-229-5729. p. 1602

Williams-Capone, Dayna, Dir, Victoria Public Library, 302 N Main, Victoria, TX, 77901-6592. Tel: 361-485-3304. Fax: 361-485-3295. p. 2395

Williams-Smith, Jeneice, Assoc Univ Librn, Florida Agricultural & Mechanical University Libraries, Architecture Library, 1938 S Martin Luther King Jr Blvd, Tallahassee, FL, 32307. Tel: 850-599-8770. Fax: 850-599-3535. p. 493

Williams-Vanklooster, Brian, Br Mgr, Milwaukee Public Library, Villard Avenue, 3310 W Villard Ave, Milwaukee, WI, 53209. Tel: 414-286-3079. Fax: 414-286-8473. p. 2620

Williamsen, Julie, Humanities & Soc Sci Librn, Brigham Young University, Harold B Lee Library, 2060 HBLL, Provo, UT, 84602. Tel: 801-422-2927. Fax: 801-422-0466. p. 2411

Williamson, Alice, Libr Tech, Allen Community College Library, 1801 N Cottonwood, Iola, KS, 66749-1648. Tel: 620-365-5116, Ext 208. Fax: 620-365-3284. p. 873

Williamson, Bonnie, Dir, Havre Hill County Library, 402 Third St, Havre, MT, 59501. Tel: 406-265-2123. Fax: 406-262-1091. p. 1381

Williamson, Carla, Circ, The Parrott Centre, 376 Wallbridge-Loyalist Rd, Belleville, ON, K8N 5B9, CANADA. Tel: 613-969-1913, Ext 2339. Fax: 613-969-5183. p. 2795

Williamson, Cathy, Pub Serv, Library at the Mariners' Museum, 100 Museum Dr, Newport News, VA, 23606-3759. Tel: 757-591-7784. Fax: 757-591-7310. p. 2480

Williamson, Clara, Librn, Phillips-Lee-Monroe Regional Library, Elaine Library, 126 Main St, Elaine, AR, 72333. Tel: 870-827-6628. p. 103

Williamson, Cynthia, Coll & Access Mgt Librn, Mohawk College Library, 135 Fennell Ave W, Hamilton, ON, L9C 1E9, CANADA. Tel: 905-575-1212, Ext 3129. Fax: 905-575-2011. p. 2810

Williamson, Darin, ILL, Carlsbad City Library, 1775 Dove Lane, Carlsbad, CA, 92011-4048. Tel: 760-602-2058. Fax: 760-602-7942. p. 132

Williamson, Darlene, Librn, Wilcox County Library, Pine Hill Branch, 530 Oak Grove St, Pine Hill, AL, 36769. Tel: 334-963-4351. Fax: 334-963-4352. p. 11

Williamson, Delicia, Ch, Atlanta-Fulton Public Library System, Hapeville Library, 525 King Arnold St, Hapeville, GA, 30354. Tel: 404-762-4065. Fax: 404-762-4067. p. 512

Williamson, Delicia, Librn, Fulton County Law Library, Justice Center Tower, Ste 7000, 185 Central Ave, Atlanta, GA, 30303. Tel: 404-730-4544. Fax: 404-730-4565. p. 515

Williamson, Elizabeth, Dir, Estill County Public Library, 246 Main St, Irvine, KY, 40336-1099. Tel: 606-723-3030. Fax: 606-726-9971. p. 918

Williamson, Gregg, Genealogy Mgr, Eckhart Public Library, 603 S Jackson St, Auburn, IN, 46706-2298. Tel: 260-925-2414. Fax: 260-925-9376. p. 725

Williamson, Halle, Asst Librn, Phillips County Library, Ten S Fourth St E, Malta, MT, 59538. Tel: 406-654-2407. Fax: 406-654-2407. p. 1385

Williamson, Heather, Dir, Libr Serv, Cisco College, 101 College Heights, Cisco, TX, 76437. Tel: 254-442-5026. Fax: 254-442-5100. p. 2297

Williamson, Jacqueline J, Curator, Thayer County Museum, 311 Seventh St, Belvidere, NE, 68315. Tel: 402-768-2147. p. 1394

Williamson, James, ILL, State University of New York, College of Environmental Science & Forestry, One Forestry Dr, Syracuse, NY, 13210. Tel: 315-470-6711. Fax: 315-470-4766. p. 1753

Williamson, Jane, Asst Dir, Memphis Theological Seminary Library, 168 E Parkway S, Memphis, TN, 38104. Tel: 901-458-8232. Fax: 901-452-4051. p. 2250

Williamson, Jane, Dir, Rokeby Museum, 4334 Rte 7, Ferrisburg, VT, 05456-9711. Tel: 802-877-3406. Fax: 802-877-3406. p. 2424

Williamson, Jay, Curator, Historical Society of Old Newbury Library, Cushing House Museum, 98 High St, Newburyport, MA, 01950. Tel: 978-462-2681. Fax: 978-462-0134. p. 1109

Williamson, Jeanne, Dir, Leon-Saxeville Township Library, N4715 Main St, Pine River, WI, 54965. Tel: 920-987-5110. Fax: 920-987-5110. p. 2630

Williamson, JoEllen, Br Supvr, Boonslick Regional Library, Pettis County, 219 W Third St, Sedalia, MO, 65301. Tel: 660-827-7323. Fax: 660-827-4668. p. 1365

Williamson, Julie, Circ, Arizona Western College & NAU Yuma Branch Campus, 2020 S Ave 8E, Yuma, AZ, 85366. Tel: 928-344-7777. Fax: 928-344-7751. p. 90

Williamson, Lori, Distance Educ, University of Houston, 2602 N Ben Jordan St, Victoria, TX, 77901-5699. Tel: 361-570-4177. Fax: 361-570-4155. p. 2395

Williamson, Lynn, Pub Serv, Free Library of Philadelphia, Government Publications, 1901 Vine St, Philadelphia, PA, 19103-1189. Tel: 215-686-5330. p. 2107

Williamson, Mary, Head, Adult Serv, Oak Brook Public Library, 600 Oak Brook Rd, Oak Brook, IL, 60523. Tel: 630-368-7722. Fax: 630-368-7704, 630-990-4509. p. 683

Williamson, Megan, Tech Serv Mgr, Eagle Public Library, 100 N Stierman Way, Eagle, ID, 83616-5162. Tel: 208-939-6814. Fax: 208-939-1359. p. 574

Williamson, Nan, Librn, Bolivar County Library System, Benoit Public Library, 109 W Preston St, Benoit, MS, 38725. Tel: 662-742-3112. Fax: 662-742-3112. p. 1296

Williamson, Nan, Br Coordr, Haywood County Public Library, 678 S Haywood St, Waynesville, NC, 28786-4398. Tel: 828-452-5169. Fax: 828-452-6746. p. 1828

Williamson, Nancy, Chair, Nassau Community College, One Education Dr, Garden City, NY, 11530-6793. Tel: 516-572-7400, Ext 4206. Fax: 516-572-7846. p. 1626

Williamson, Onagh, Librn, Reston District Library, 220 Fourth St, Reston, MB, R0M 1X0, CANADA. Tel: 204-877-3673. p. 2750

Williamson, Sharon, Circ Mgr, Bolivar County Library System, 104 S Leflore Ave, Cleveland, MS, 38732. Tel: 662-843-2774. Fax: 662-843-4701. p. 1295

Williamson, Sherry, Librn, Texas State Court of Appeals, County Courthouse, 100 W Main St, Ste 300, Eastland, TX, 76448. Tel: 254-629-2638. Fax: 254-629-2191. p. 2315

Williamson, Vanessa, Libr Tech, United States Commission on Civil Rights, 624 Ninth St NW, Ste 600, Washington, DC, 20425. Tel: 202-376-8110. Fax: 202-376-7597. p. 417

Williamson, Vicki, Dean of Libr, University of Saskatchewan Libraries, Murray Library, Three Campus Dr, Saskatoon, SK, S7N 5A4, CANADA. Tel: 306-966-5942. Fax: 306-966-6040. p. 2927

Williard, Nicole, Dir, Archives & Spec Coll, University of Central Oklahoma, 100 N University Dr, Edmond, OK, 73034. Tel: 405-974-2885. Fax: 405-974-3806, 405-974-3874. p. 1962

Williford, Anna Mary, Pub Serv/Instruction Librn, University of Pittsburgh at Greensburg, 150 Finoli Dr, Greensburg, PA, 15601-5898. Tel: 724-836-9687. Fax: 724-836-7043. p. 2062

Williford, Paul, Librn, University of West Florida, 1170 Martin Luther King Jr Blvd, Fort Walton Beach, FL, 32547. Tel: 850-863-6578. Fax: 850-863-6562. p. 447

Willis, Alfred, Coll Develop, Hampton University, 130 E Tyler St, Hampton, VA, 23668. Tel: 757-727-5371. Fax: 757-727-5952. p. 2468

Willis, Alfred, Coll Develop, Hampton University, Architecture, 130 E Tyler St, Hampton, VA, 23668. Tel: 757-727-5443. p. 2468

Willis, Audrey, Head, Automation, Head, Circ, Grinnell Library Association, 2642 E Main St, Wappingers Falls, NY, 12590. Tel: 845-297-3428. Fax: 845-297-1506. p. 1762

Willis, Carrie, Youth Serv Librn, Cheltenham Township Library System, Glenside Free Library, 215 S Keswick Ave, Glenside, PA, 19038-4420. Tel: 215-885-0455. Fax: 215-885-1019. p. 2061

Willis, Catherine, Tech Serv Mgr, Boston Public Library, 700 Boylston St, Boston, MA, 02117-0286. Tel: 617-536-5400. Fax: 617-236-4306. p. 1056

Willis, Cheryl, Admin Coordr, Allegany County Library System, 31 Washington St, Cumberland, MD, 21502. Tel: 301-777-1200. Fax: 301-777-7299. p. 1026

Willis, Clare, Res/Fac Serv Librn, Illinois Institute of Technology, Chicago-Kent College of Law Library, 565 W Adams St, Chicago, IL, 60661. Tel: 312-906-5600. Fax: 312-906-5679. p. 615

Willis, David, Chief Librn, Land Force Concepts & Design, 317 Ontario St, Kingston, ON, K7K 7B4, CANADA. Tel: 613-541-5010, Ext 5829. Fax: 613-546-0589. p. 2814

Willis, Debby, Asst Librn, Saint Augustine Historical Society, Six Artillery Lane, 2nd Flr, Saint Augustine, FL, 32084. Tel: 904-825-2333. p. 486

Willis, Evelyn, Circ Mgr, ILL, Columbus Technical College Library, 928 Manchester Expressway, Columbus, GA, 31904-6577. Tel: 706-649-1852. Fax: 706-649-1885. p. 526

Willis, Fern, Librn, Pratt & Whitney Rocketdyne, Inc, 6633 Canoga Ave, Canoga Park, CA, 91309. Tel: 818-586-2575. Fax: 818-586-9150. p. 131

Willis, Holly, Dir, Libr Serv, McGlannan Health Sciences Library, Mercy Medical Ctr, 301 Saint Paul Pl, Baltimore, MD, 21202. Tel: 410-332-9189. Fax: 410-332-0324. p. 1016

Willis, Jan, Dir, Lee County Library, 219 N Madison St, Tupelo, MS, 38804-3899. Tel: 662-841-9027. Fax: 662-840-7615. p. 1316

Willis, Jean, Asst Dir, Support Serv, Sacramento County Public Law Library, 813 Sixth St, 1st Flr, Sacramento, CA, 95814-2403. Tel: 916-874-6011. Fax: 916-874-5691. p. 224

Willis, Jeffrey, Dr, Dir, Archives & Spec Coll, Converse College, 580 E Main St, Spartanburg, SC, 29302. Tel: 864-596-9216. Fax: 864-596-9075. p. 2204

Willis, Judy, Doc Delivery, Ohio State University LIBRARIES, John A Prior Health Sciences Library, 376 W Tenth Ave, Columbus, OH, 43210-1240. Tel: 614-292-4894. Fax: 614-292-1920. p. 1889

Willis, Laurie, Adult Serv, Electronic Serv Mgr, Hayward Public Library, 835 C St, Hayward, CA, 94541-5120. Tel: 510-881-7936. p. 157

Willis, Mark, Commun Relations Librn, Dayton Metro Library, 215 E Third St, Dayton, OH, 45402-2103. Tel: 937-463-2665. Fax: 937-496-4300. p. 1892

Willis, Michelle, Head, Ch, Scotch Plains Public Library, 1927 Bartle Ave, Scotch Plains, NJ, 07076-1212. Tel: 908-322-5007. Fax: 908-322-0490. p. 1528

Willis, Raydine, Cat, Calaveras County Library, 891 Mountain Ranch Rd, San Andreas, CA, 95249. Tel: 209-754-6510. Fax: 209-754-6512. p. 226

Willis, Rita, Circ, Essex County College Library, 303 University Ave, Newark, NJ, 07102. Tel: 973-877-3238. Fax: 973-877-1887. p. 1510

Willis, Sammie, Librn, Oklahoma Library for the Blind & Physically Handicapped, 300 NE 18th St, Oklahoma City, OK, 73105. Tel: 405-521-3514. Fax: 405-521-4582. p. 1975

Willis, Shamona L, Br Mgr, Pine Mountain Regional Library, Talbot County, 75 N Jefferson St, Talbotton, GA, 31827-9732. Tel: 706-665-3134. Fax: 706-665-8777. p. 542

Willis, Susan, Dir, Chanute Public Library, 111 N Lincoln, Chanute, KS, 66720-1819. Tel: 620-431-3820. Fax: 620-431-3848. p. 860

Willis, Tamie Lyn, Dir, Oklahoma Christian University, 2501 E Memorial Rd, Edmond, OK, 73013. Tel: 405-425-5312. Fax: 405-425-5313. p. 1962

Willits, Pam, In Charge, University of Kansas Life Span Institute, 1000 Sunnyside Dr, Rm 4089, Lawrence, KS, 66045-7555. Tel: 785-864-4095. Fax: 785-864-5063. p. 878

Willman, Eric, Syst Librn, University of Texas Health Science Center at San Antonio Libraries, 7703 Floyd Curl Dr, MSC 7940, San Antonio, TX, 78229-3900. Tel: 210-567-2400. Fax: 210-567-2490. p. 2383

Willmarth, Jack, Bus Mgr, Wyoming State Library, 2800 Central Ave, Cheyenne, WY, 82002. Tel: 307-777-5917. Fax: 307-777-6289. p. 2653

Willmore, Laurie, Dir, Jefferson County District Library, 623A N 3500 E, Menan, ID, 83434. Tel: 208-754-0021. p. 578

Willms, Bruce, Tech Serv Dir, Metropolitan State University, 645 E Seventh St, Saint Paul, MN, 55106. Tel: 651-793-1618. Fax: 651-793-1615. p. 1279

Willms, Marianne R, Dir, John F Kennedy Memorial Library, 92 Hathaway St, Wallington, NJ, 07057. Tel: 973-471-1692. Fax: 973-471-1387. p. 1539

Willner, Heather, Circ, Grande Prairie Public Library, 101-9839 103 Ave, Grande Prairie, AB, T8V 6M7, CANADA. Tel: 780-532-3580. Fax: 780-538-4983. p. 2705

Willner, Judith M, Dir, Sachem Public Library, 150 Holbrook Rd, Holbrook, NY, 11741. Tel: 631-588-5024. Fax: 631-588-3475. p. 1637

Willnerd, Glenda, Pres, Southeast Nebraska Library System, 5730 R St, Ste C-1, Lincoln, NE, 68505. Tel: 402-467-6188. Fax: 402-467-6196. p. 2948

Willoughby, Darrel, Librn, Veterans Affairs Medical Library, 4101 Woolworth Ave, Omaha, NE, 68105. Tel: 402-346-8800, Ext 3531. Fax: 402-449-0692. p. 1415

Willows, Arlene, Asst Librn, Chinook Regional Library, Tompkins Branch, Main St, Tompkins, SK, S0N 2S0, CANADA. Tel: 306-622-2255. p. 2929

Wills, Ann, Br Mgr, Metropolitan Community College Library, Fort Omaha Campus, 30th & Fort Sts, Omaha, NE, 68111. Tel: 402-457-2306. Fax: 402-457-2859. p. 1413

Wills, Deborah, Head, Ref, Wilfrid Laurier University Library, 75 University Ave W, Waterloo, ON, N2L 3C5, CANADA. Tel: 519-884-0710, Ext 3384. Fax: 519-884-3209. p. 2869

Wills, Ellen, Lead Librn, Aims Community College, College Ctr, 5401 W 20th St, 750.1, Greeley, CO, 80634-3002. Tel: 970-339-6347. Fax: 970-506-6937. p. 311

Wills, John, Librn, World Book Publishing, 233 N Michigan Ave, 20th Flr, Chicago, IL, 60601. Tel: 312-729-5581. Fax: 312-729-5600. p. 628

Wills, Linda, Bus Mgr, Acadia Parish Library, Church Point Branch, 311 N Vista St, Church Point, LA, 70525. Tel: 337-684-5774. Fax: 337-684-1593. p. 948

Willson, Doris, Librn, Louisville Science Center, 727 W Main St, Louisville, KY, 40202. Tel: 502-561-6100, Ext 6571. Fax: 502-561-6145. p. 925

Willson, Paula, Ref & Instrul Serv Librn, Kalamazoo Valley Community College Libraries, 6767 West O Ave, Kalamazoo, MI, 49003. Tel: 269-488-4328, 269-488-4380. Fax: 269-488-4488. p. 1197

Willson-Metzger, Alicia, Dr, Coll Mgt Librn, Christopher Newport University, One Avenue of the Arts, Newport News, VA, 23606. Tel: 757-594-8948. Fax: 757-594-7717. p. 2479

Willson-St Clair, Kimberly, Ref & Instruction Librn, Portland State University Library, 1875 SW Park Ave, Portland, OR, 97201-3220. Tel: 503-725-4552. Fax: 503-725-4524. p. 2014

Willumeit, Jenine, Librn, Lakeland Library Region, Glaslyn Branch, Box 501, Glaslyn, SK, S0M 0Y0, CANADA. Tel: 306-342-4748. p. 2920

Wilm, Angela, Chair, Lakeland College Library, 5707 College Dr, Vermilion, AB, T9X 1K5, CANADA. Tel: 780-853-8460. Fax: 780-853-8662. p. 2720

Wilmes, Nancy, Info Serv Librn, Wayne State University Libraries, Science & Engineering, 5048 Gullen Mall, Detroit, MI, 48202-3918. Tel: 313-577-4063. Fax: 313-577-3613. p. 1173

Wilmes, Teresa, Coordr, Libr Serv/Libr Instruction/Ref, Allegany College of Maryland Library, 12401 Willowbrook Rd SE, Cumberland, MD, 21502-2596. Tel: 301-784-5294. Fax: 301-784-5017. p. 1026

Wilmesherr, Jon, Dean, Mayland Community College, 200 Mayland Dr, Spruce Pine, NC, 28777. Tel: 828-765-7351, Ext 243. Fax: 828-765-0728. p. 1825

Wilmeth, Linda, Libr Coordr, Maricopa Community Library, 44240 W Maricopa, Casa Grande Hwy, Maricopa, AZ, 85239. Tel: 520-568-2926. Fax: 520-568-2680. p. 68

Wilmore, Diane, Children & Teen Librn, East Cleveland Public Library, 14101 Euclid Ave, East Cleveland, OH, 44112-3891. Tel: 216-541-4128. Fax: 216-541-1790. p. 1897

Wilmot, April, Asst Librn, Beaver Valley Public Library, 1847 First St, Fruitvale, BC, V0G 1L0, CANADA. Tel: 250-367-7114. Fax: 250-367-7130. p. 2728

Wilmot, Edwin, Librn, Connecticut Correctional Institution, 289 Shaker Rd, Enfield, CT, 06083. Tel: 860-763-7383. Fax: 860-763-7350. p. 338

Wilmot, Joney, Curator, Laramie Plains Museum Association Inc Library, 603 Ivinson Ave, Laramie, WY, 82070-3299. Tel: 307-742-4448. p. 2657

Wilsbach, Robert, Brother, Coll Develop Librn, Lewis University Library, One University Pkwy, Unit 300, Romeoville, IL, 60446-2200. Tel: 815-836-5307. Fax: 815-838-9456. p. 698

Wilsbacher, Greg, Curator, Movietone News, University of South Carolina, Moving Image Research Collections, 707 Catawba St, Columbia, SC, 29201-4305. Tel: 803-777-6841. p. 2190

Wilson, Alice Harrington, Res & Instruction Librn, Monroe Community College, LeRoy V Good Library, 1000 E Henrietta Rd, Rochester, NY, 14692. Tel: 585-292-2304. p. 1730

Wilson, Alicia, Br Mgr, Whitman County Rural Library District, Tekoa Branch, S 139 Crosby, Tekoa, WA, 99033. Tel: 509-284-3121. p. 2513

Wilson, Allan, Chief Librn, Prince George Public Library, 887 Dominion St, Prince George, BC, V2L 5L1, CANADA. Tel: 250-563-9251. Fax: 250-563-0892. p. 2736

Wilson, Amy, Ad, Oro Valley Public Library, 1305 W Naranja Dr, Oro Valley, AZ, 85737-9762. Tel: 520-229-5300. Fax: 520-229-5319. p. 70

Wilson, Amy, Outreach Serv Librn, University of Rio Grande, 218 N College Ave, Rio Grande, OH, 45674. Tel: 740-245-7005. Fax: 740-245-7096. p. 1931

Wilson, Andrea, Br Mgr, Plumas County Library, Greenville Branch, 204 Ann St, Greenville, CA, 95947. Tel: 530-284-7416. p. 212

Wilson, Andrea, Ser Tech, Alberta Government Library, 10025 Jasper Ave, 15th Flr, Edmonton, AB, T5J 2N3, CANADA. Tel: 780-415-0222. Fax: 780-422-9694. p. 2698

Wilson, Andrew, Access Serv Librn, Harvard Library, Eda Kuhn Loeb Music Library, Music Bldg, Harvard University, Cambridge, MA, 02138. Tel: 617-495-2794. Fax: 617-496-4636. p. 1076

Wilson, Barbara, Dir, Minneola City Library, 112 Main St, Minneola, KS, 67865-8544. Tel: 620-885-4749. Fax: 620-885-4278. p. 883

Wilson, Barbara, Dir, Absecon Public Library, 305 New Jersey Ave, Absecon, NJ, 08201. Tel: 609-646-2228. Fax: 609-383-8992. p. 1469

Wilson, Becky, Librn, Herrick Township Public Library, 303 N Broadway, Herrick, IL, 62431. Tel: 618-428-5223. Fax: 618-428-5222. p. 655

Wilson, Benjamin, Bibliog Instr, Utah Valley University Library, 800 W University Pkwy, Orem, UT, 84058-5999. Tel: 801-863-8423. Fax: 801-863-7065. p. 2409

Wilson, Bettina, Br Mgr, Washington County Library System, Arcola Library, 106 Martin Luther King Dr, Arcola, MS, 38722. Tel: 662-827-5262. Fax: 662-827-5262. p. 1298

Wilson, Brenda, Librn, Tombigbee Regional Library System, Amory Municipal Library, 401 Second Ave N at Fourth St, Amory, MS, 38821. Tel: 662-256-5261. Fax: 662-256-6321. p. 1318

Wilson, Brenton, Assoc Dir, Point Park University Library, 414 Wood St, Pittsburgh, PA, 15222. Tel: 412-392-3163. Fax: 412-392-3168. p. 2127

Wilson, Carol H, Dir, Cleveland County Library System, 104 Howie Dr, Shelby, NC, 28150. Tel: 704-487-9069. Fax: 704-487-4856. p. 1823

Wilson, Carolyn, Asst Librn, Ely Public Library, 1595 Dows St, Ely, IA, 52227. Tel: 319-848-7616. Fax: 319-848-4056. p. 814

Wilson, Carolyn, Ch, Hopkinton Public Library, 110 First St SE, Hopkinton, IA, 52237. Tel: 563-926-2514. Fax: 563-926-2065. p. 821

Wilson, Carolyn T, Dir, Lipscomb University, One University Park Dr, Nashville, TN, 37204-3951. Tel: 615-966-1793. Fax: 615-966-5874. p. 2256

Wilson, Carrie, Ch, Havre Hill County Library, 402 Third St, Havre, MT, 59501. Tel: 406-265-2123. Fax: 406-262-1091. p. 1381

Wilson, Catharine, Br Mgr, Chicago Public Library, Northtown, 6435 N California Ave, Chicago, IL, 60645. Tel: 312-744-2292. Fax: 312-744-8221. p. 609

Wilson, Christie, Br Mgr, Librn, Prairie-River Library District, Culdesac Community, 714 Main St, Culdesac, ID, 83524-7806. Tel: 208-843-5215. Fax: 208-843-5215. p. 577

Wilson, Christie, Dir, Arma City Library, 508 E Washington, Arma, KS, 66712. Tel: 620-347-4811. Fax: 620-347-4977. p. 856

Wilson, Christina, Dir, Bibliotheque de Beaumont Library, 5700 49 St, Beaumont, AB, T4X 1S7, CANADA. Tel: 780-929-2665. Fax: 780-929-1291. p. 2685

Wilson, Cindy, Cataloger, Ref Librn, Butler Public Library, 340 S Broadway, Butler, IN, 46721. Tel: 260-868-2351. Fax: 260-868-5491. p. 730

Wilson, Clara, Br Mgr, Newark Public Library, Springfield, 50 Hayes St, Newark, NJ, 07103. Tel: 973-733-7736. p. 1512

Wilson, Cleo, Circ, College of Southern Nevada, Henderson Campus, 700 S College Dr, H1A, Henderson, NV, 89002. Tel: 702-651-3066. Fax: 702-651-3513. p. 1429

Wilson, Cliff, Pres, Ashland Historical Society Library, Two Myrtle St, Ashland, MA, 01721. Tel: 508-881-8183. p. 1050

Wilson, Constance, Children's Coordr, Allegany County Library System, Frostburg Public, 65 E Main St, Frostburg, MD, 21532. Tel: 301-687-0790. Fax: 301-687-0791. p. 1026

Wilson, Craig, Librn, National Marine Fisheries Service, 2725 Montlake Blvd E, Seattle, WA, 98112. Tel: 206-860-3210. Fax: 206-860-3442. p. 2529

Wilson, Cris, Ad, Port Townsend Public Library, 1220 Lawrence St, Port Townsend, WA, 98368-6527. Tel: 360-379-4441. Fax: 360-385-5805. p. 2524

Wilson, Cynthia, Commun Librn, Santa Clara County Library District, Los Altos Main Library, 13 S San Antonio Rd, Los Altos, CA, 94022-3049. Tel: 650-948-7683. Fax: 650-941-6308. p. 181

Wilson, Danna Kay, Br Head, Brazoria County Library System, Alvin Branch, 105 S Gordon, Alvin, TX, 77511. Tel: 281-388-4301. Fax: 281-388-4305. p. 2275

Wilson, Dave, Ref Librn, Austin Community College, South Austin Campus Library, 1820 W Stassney Lane, Austin, TX, 78745. Tel: 512-223-9185. Fax: 512-223-9190. p. 2278

Wilson, Debbie, In Charge, Schreeder, Wheeler & Flint LLP, 1100 Peachtree St NE, Ste 800, Atlanta, GA, 30309-1845. Tel: 404-681-3450. Fax: 404-681-1046. p. 518

Wilson, Debbie, Cat, Harvin Clarendon County Library, 215 N Brooks St, Manning, SC, 29102. Tel: 803-435-8633. Fax: 803-435-8101. p. 2199

Wilson, Denise, Tech Serv Librn, Saint Charles Parish Library, 160 W Campus Dr, Destrehan, LA, 70047. Tel: 985-764-2366. Fax: 985-764-0447. p. 948

Wilson, Dennis, Dir, United States Air Force, 509 FSS/FSDL, 511 Spirit Blvd, Bldg 515, Whiteman AFB, MO, 65305-5019. Tel: 660-687-5614. Fax: 660-687-6240. p. 1372

Wilson, Derek, YA Serv, Atlanta-Fulton Public Library System, East Point Library, 2757 Main St, East Point, GA, 30344. Tel: 404-762-4842. Fax: 404-762-4844. p. 512

Wilson, Dewi, Librn/Head, Ref Coll Develop, Kennesaw State University, 1000 Chastain Rd, Kennesaw, GA, 30144. Tel: 770-423-6661. Fax: 770-423-6185. p. 537

Wilson, Durell, Librn, Anson Public Library, 1137 12th St, Anson, TX, 79501. Tel: 325-823-2711. Fax: 325-823-2711. p. 2276

Wilson, Elaine, Acq, University of Texas, School of Public Health Library, 1200 Herman Pressler Blvd, Houston, TX, 77030-3900. Tel: 713-500-9121. Fax: 713-500-9125. p. 2344

Wilson, Emmett, Librn, North Idaho Correctional Institution Library, 236 Radar Rd, Cottonwood, ID, 83522. Tel: 208-962-3276, Ext 174. Fax: 208-962-5354. p. 573

Wilson, Fran, Chair, Oakland County Pioneer & Historical Society, 405 Cesar E Chavez Ave, Pontiac, MI, 48342-1068. Tel: 248-338-6732. Fax: 248-338-6731. p. 1218

Wilson, Gail S, Circ, Lewis & Clark Library, 120 S Last Chance Gulch, Helena, MT, 59601. Tel: 406-447-1690, Ext 122. Fax: 406-447-1687. p. 1382

Wilson, Gay, Planning & Develop Librn, Springfield-Greene County Library District, 4653 S Campbell, Springfield, MO, 65810-1723. Tel: 417-882-0714. Fax: 417-883-9348. p. 1367

Wilson, Gina, Tech Serv & Automation, Thomasville Public Library, 1401 Mosley Dr, Thomasville, AL, 36784. Tel: 334-636-5343. Fax: 334-636-5343. p. 37

Wilson, Ginger, Asst Librn, Yoakum County Library, 205 W Fourth St, Denver City, TX, 79323. Tel: 806-592-2754. Fax: 806-592-2439. p. 2313

Wilson, Glenda, Asst Dir, Brimfield Public Library, 111 S Galena St, Brimfield, IL, 61517. Tel: 309-446-9575. Fax: 309-446-9357. p. 597

Wilson, Gloria, Librn, Mayerthorpe Public Library, 4911 52nd St, Mayerthorpe, AB, T0E 1N0, CANADA. Tel: 780-786-2404. Fax: 780-786-4590. p. 2711

Wilson, Gwen, Health Sci Librn, Washburn University, 1700 SW College Ave, Topeka, KS, 66621. Tel: 785-670-2609. Fax: 785-670-3223. p. 897

Wilson, Harold, Media Spec, Brooklyn College Library, 2900 Bedford Ave, Brooklyn, NY, 11210-2889. Tel: 718-951-5336. Fax: 718-951-4540. p. 1589

Wilson, Holly, Sr Res Librn, Team Leader, United States Equal Employment Opportunity Commission Library, 131 M St NE, Rm 4SW16N, Washington, DC, 20507. Tel: 202-663-4630. Fax: 202-663-4629. p. 420

Wilson, Hope, Dir, Fremont Public Library, 1004 W Toledo St, Fremont, IN, 46737. Tel: 260-495-7157. Fax: 260-495-7127. p. 744

Wilson, Jacquelyn T, Archivist, Pensacola Historical Society, 110 E Church St, Pensacola, FL, 32502. Tel: 850-595-5840, Ext 100. Fax: 850-595-5989. p. 481

Wilson, Jamie, Acq Librn, Millsaps College, 1701 N State St, Jackson, MS, 39210-0001. Tel: 601-974-1083. Fax: 601-974-1082. p. 1304

Wilson, Jan, Mgr, League of American Orchestras, 33 W 60th St, 5th Flr, New York, NY, 10023. Tel: 212-262-5161, Ext 204. Fax: 212-262-5198. p. 1685

Wilson, Jana, Librn, Stockmen's Memorial Foundation Library, 101 RancheHouse Rd, Cochrane, AB, T4C 1A7, CANADA. Tel: 403-932-3782. Fax: 403-851-1324. p. 2695

Wilson, Janet, Circ, Cerro Coso Community College Library, 3000 College Heights Blvd, Ridgecrest, CA, 93555-9571. Tel: 760-384-6137. Fax: 760-384-6139. p. 216

Wilson, Janet, Libr Dir, Rangeley Public Library, Seven Lake St, Rangeley, ME, 04970. Tel: 207-864-5529. Fax: 207-864-2523. p. 998

Wilson, Janet, In Charge, United States Army, B-202 Clifford Davis Federal Bldg, 167 N Main St, Memphis, TN, 38103-1899. Tel: 901-544-3134. Fax: 901-544-3792. p. 2252

Wilson, Janice, Ref/Govt Doc Librn, Eastern Connecticut State University, 83 Windham St, Willimantic, CT, 06226-2295. Tel: 860-465-5550. Fax: 860-465-5521. p. 378

Wilson, Janice, Ref, Immaculata University, 1145 King Rd, Immaculata, PA, 19345-0705. Tel: 610-647-4400, Ext 3831. Fax: 610-640-5828. p. 2071

Wilson, Janice E, Dir of Libr Serv, Truett-McConnell College, 100 Alumni Dr, Cleveland, GA, 30528-9799. Tel: 706-865-2134, Ext 153. Fax: 706-865-5130. p. 525

Wilson, Janie, Dir, Wagoner City Public Library, 302 N Main, Wagoner, OK, 74467-3834. Tel: 918-485-2126. Fax: 918-485-0179. p. 1985

Wilson, Jennifer, Libr Mgr, Illinois Department of Corrections, 251 N Illinois Hwy 37, Ina, IL, 62846-2419. Tel: 618-437-5300, Ext 467. Fax: 618-437-5627. p. 658

Wilson, Jerry, Cat, Fort Hays State University, 600 Park St, Hays, KS, 67601-4099. Tel: 785-628-5282. Fax: 785-628-4096. p. 871

Wilson, Jessica, Ref Librn, South Kingstown Public Library, 1057 Kingstown Rd, Peace Dale, RI, 02879-2434. Tel: 401-783-4085, 401-789-1555. Fax: 401-782-6370. p. 2171

Wilson, Jill, Outreach Coordr & Coll Spec, Cornell University Library, Physical Sciences Library, Virtual Library, 283 Clark Hall, Ithaca, NY, 14853. Tel: 607-255-1577. Fax: 607-255-5288. p. 1642

Wilson, Jim, Asst Dir, Burke County Public Library, 204 S King St, Morganton, NC, 28655-3535. Tel: 828-437-5638, Ext 219. Fax: 828-433-1914. p. 1811

Wilson, Jim, Dir, Human Res, Kitsap Regional Library, 1301 Sylvan Way, Bremerton, WA, 98310-3498. Tel: 360-475-9164. Fax: 360-405-9128. p. 2510

Wilson, Joan, Libr Mgr, Kootenai Medical Center, 2003 Kootenai Health Way, Coeur d'Alene, ID, 83814. Tel: 208-666-2480. Fax: 208-666-2854. p. 573

Wilson, Jody, Ch, South Fayette Township Library, 515 Millers Run Rd, Morgan, PA, 15064. Tel: 412-257-8660. Fax: 412-257-8682. p. 2092

Wilson, John, Law Librn, University of California Los Angeles Library, Hugh & Hazel Darling Law Library, 112 Law Bldg, Box 951458, 385 Charles E Young Dr E, Los Angeles, CA, 90095-1458. Tel: 310-825-7826. Fax: 310-825-1372. p. 178

Wilson, John, Tech Coordr, Freed-Hardeman University, 158 E Main St, Henderson, TN, 38340-2399. Tel: 731-989-6067. Fax: 731-989-6065. p. 2237

Wilson, John, Dir, Baylor University Libraries, Texas Collection, 1429 S Fifth St, Waco, TX, 76706. Tel: 254-710-1268. Fax: 254-710-1368. p. 2397

Wilson, Judy, Circ, Edinboro University of Pennsylvania, 200 Tartan Ave, Edinboro, PA, 16444. Tel: 814-732-2779. Fax: 814-732-2883. p. 2053

Wilson, Judy, Libr Mgr, Vancouver Island Regional Library, Nanaimo Harbourfront Branch, 90 Commercial St, Nanaimo, BC, V9R 5G4, CANADA. Tel: 250-753-1154. Fax: 250-754-1483. p. 2733

Wilson, Kara, Adult Prog Coordr, Somerville Library, 35 West End Ave, Somerville, NJ, 08876. Tel: 908-725-1336. Fax: 908-231-0608. p. 1530

Wilson, Karen, Exec Dir, WildCare, 76 Albert Park Lane, San Rafael, CA, 94901. Tel: 415-453-1000, Ext 15. Fax: 415-456-0594. p. 257

Wilson, Kathe, Adult Serv, Oregon Public Library District, 300 Jefferson St, Oregon, IL, 61061. Tel: 815-732-2724. Fax: 815-732-6643. p. 686

Wilson, Kathleen, Br Mgr, Kitsap Regional Library, Port Orchard Branch, 87 Sidney Ave, Port Orchard, WA, 98366-5249. Tel: 360-876-2224. Fax: 360-876-9588. p. 2510

Wilson, Kathy, Head, Circ, Derby Public Library, 313 Elizabeth St, Derby, CT, 06418. Tel: 203-736-1482. Fax: 203-736-1419. p. 336

Wilson, Kathy, Br Coordr, Bibliotheque de Publique de Pointe-Claire, Valois Branch, 68 av Prince-Edward, Pointe-Claire, QC, H9R 4C7, CANADA. Tel: 514-630-1219. Fax: 514-695-9924. p. 2903

Wilson, Kathy A, Acq/Res Mgt Asst, Brevard College, One Brevard College Dr, Brevard, NC, 28712-4283. Tel: 828-884-8298. p. 1777

Wilson, Kay, Dir, Elba Public Library, 406 Simmons St, Elba, AL, 36323. Tel: 334-897-6921. Fax: 334-897-6921. p. 15

Wilson, Kitty, Br Coordr, DeKalb County Public Library, Administrative Office, 215 Sycamore St, 4th Flr, Decatur, GA, 30030. Tel: 404-370-8450. Fax: 404-370-8469. p. 529

Wilson, Kristie, Dir, Shawano City-County Library, 128 S Sawyer St, Shawano, WI, 54166-2496. Tel: 715-526-3829, Ext 123. Fax: 715-526-6772. p. 2636

Wilson, Lana J, Ref Librn, Taylor University, 236 W Reade Ave, Upland, IN, 46989-1001. Tel: 765-998-5297. Fax: 765-998-5569. p. 783

Wilson, Lara C, Librn, Madison County Law Library, One N Main, Rm 205, London, OH, 43140-1068. Tel: 740-852-9515. Fax: 740-852-7144. p. 1911

Wilson, Laura, Info & Instruction Librn, Ref Librn, Westfield State University, 577 Western Ave, Westfield, MA, 01085-2580. Tel: 413-572-5251. Fax: 413-572-5520. p. 1138

Wilson, Laura Lee, Ch, Holmes County District Public Library, 3102 Glen Dr, Millersburg, OH, 44654. Tel: 330-674-5972, Ext 210. Fax: 330-674-1938. p. 1918

Wilson, Lauri, Tech Serv, South Arkansas Community College, 300 Summit, El Dorado, AR, 71730. Tel: 870-864-7115. Fax: 870-864-7134. p. 98

Wilson, Laurie, Tech Serv, Davis Polk & Wardwell Library, 450 Lexington Ave, New York, NY, 10017. Tel: 212-450-4266. Fax: 212-450-5522. p. 1677

Wilson, Laverne, Chairperson, Elk Point Public Library, 5123 - 50 Ave, Elk Point, AB, T0A 1A0, CANADA. Tel: 780-724-3737. Fax: 780-724-3739. p. 2703

Wilson, Lesley, Cat & Govt Doc Librn, Baylor University Libraries, Sheridan & John Eddie Williams Legal Research & Technology Center, 1114 S University Parks Dr, One Bear Pl, No 97128, Waco, TX, 76798-7128. Tel: 254-710-2168. Fax: 254-710-2294. p. 2397

Wilson, Leslie, Curator, Spec Coll Librn, Concord Free Public Library, 129 Main St, Concord, MA, 01742-2494. Tel: 978-318-3342. Fax: 978-318-3344. p. 1082

Wilson, Letitia, Asst Dir, Dayton Metro Library, 215 E Third St, Dayton, OH, 45402-2103. Tel: 937-463-2665. Fax: 937-496-4300. p. 1892

Wilson, Linda, Pub Relations Coordr, Birmingham Public Library, 2100 Park Pl, Birmingham, AL, 35203. Tel: 205-226-3746. Fax: 205-226-3743. p. 7

Wilson, Linda, Asst Librn, Martha's Vineyard Museum, Pease House, 59 School St, Edgartown, MA, 02539. Tel: 508-627-4441, Ext 115. Fax: 508-627-4436. p. 1087

Wilson, Linda, Coordr, Libr Serv, Douglas County Public Library, 1625 Library Lane, Minden, NV, 89423-4420. Tel: 775-782-6841. Fax: 775-782-5754. p. 1431

Wilson, Linda, Dir, Bloomfield Public Library, 19 E McClure St, Borough Bldg, New Bloomfield, PA, 17068. Tel: 717-582-7426. Fax: 717-582-0051. p. 2095

Wilson, Lisa, Br Mgr, Saint Mary Parish Library, Patterson Branch, 529 Catherine St, Patterson, LA, 70392. Tel: 985-395-2777. Fax: 985-399-4469. p. 950

Wilson, Lizabeth A, Dean, Univ Libr, University of Washington Libraries, Allen Library, 4th Flr, Rm 482, Box 352900, Seattle, WA, 98195-2900. Tel: 206-543-1763. Fax: 206-685-8727. p. 2533

Wilson, Lucinda, Br Mgr, Sonoma County Library, Cloverdale Regional, 401 N Cloverdale Blvd, Cloverdale, CA, 95425. Tel: 707-894-5271. Fax: 707-894-1861. p. 267

Wilson, Luellen, Mgr, Dayton Metro Library, Trotwood Branch, 651 E Main St, Trotwood, OH, 45426. Tel: 937-496-8958. Fax: 937-496-4358. p. 1893

Wilson, Lyn, Cataloger, Adams Free Library, 92 Park St, Adams, MA, 01220-2096. Tel: 413-743-8345. Fax: 413-743-8344. p. 1047

Wilson, Lynn, Br Mgr, Bay City Public Library, Sargent Branch, FM 457, Sargent, TX, 77414. Tel: 979-245-3032. Fax: 979-245-7297. p. 2286

Wilson, Madelyn M, Dir, Irondale Public Library, 105 20th St S, Irondale, AL, 35210. Tel: 205-951-1415. Fax: 205-951-7715. p. 22

Wilson, Margaret, Librn, Plainville Memorial Library, 200 SW First St, Plainville, KS, 67663. Tel: 785-434-2786. Fax: 785-434-2786. p. 890

Wilson, Margaret, Mem Serv Librn, Manitoba Department of Culture, Heritage & Tourism, 450 Broadway Ave, Rm 260, Winnipeg, MB, R3C 0V8, CANADA. Tel: 204-945-4243. Fax: 204-948-2167. p. 2756

Wilson, Margery, Br Mgr, Waterville Public Library, Deansboro Branch, Marshall Community Ctr, Deansboro, NY, 13328. Tel: 315-841-4888. p. 1764

Wilson, Margo, Dir, Ch Serv, Spartanburg County Public Libraries, 151 S Church St, Spartanburg, SC, 29306-3241. Tel: 864-596-3500. Fax: 864-596-3518. p. 2205

Wilson, Maria, Exec Dir, Waverly Memorial Library, 1115 N Abington Rd, Waverly, PA, 18471. Tel: 570-586-8191. Fax: 570-586-0185. p. 2152

Wilson, Mark, Head, Ref, Cumberland County Public Library & Information Center, North Regional, 855 McArthur Rd, Fayetteville, NC, 28311-1961. Tel: 910-822-1998. Fax: 910-480-0030. p. 1792

Wilson, Martha, Librn, Hamilton County Governmental Law Library, City County Courts Bldg, 600 Market St, Rm 305, Chattanooga, TN, 37402. Tel: 423-209-7595. Fax: 423-209-7596. p. 2227

Wilson, Martha H, Extn Serv, Gaston-Lincoln Regional Library, 1555 E Garrison Blvd, Gastonia, NC, 28054. Tel: 704-868-2164. Fax: 704-853-6012. p. 1794

Wilson, Mary, Cat, Ref, Vanguard University of Southern California, 55 Fair Dr, Costa Mesa, CA, 92626. Tel: 714-556-3610, Ext 2400. Fax: 714-966-5478. p. 137

Wilson, Mary, Principal Librn, Huntington Beach Public Library System, 7111 Talbert Ave, Huntington Beach, CA, 92648. Tel: 714-842-4481. Fax: 714-375-5180. p. 158

Wilson, Mary, ILS Coordr, Tech Serv Coordr, McDaniel College, Two College Hill, Westminster, MD, 21157-4390. Tel: 410-857-2284. Fax: 410-857-2748. p. 1046

Wilson, Mary, Dir, Harvard Public Library, Four Pond Rd, Harvard, MA, 01451-1647. Tel: 978-456-4114. Fax: 978-456-4115. p. 1094

Wilson, Mary, Asst Dir, Paterson Free Public Library, 250 Broadway, Paterson, NJ, 07501. Tel: 973-321-1223, Ext 2294. Fax: 973-321-1205. p. 1518

Wilson, Meada, Br Librn, Wapiti Regional Library, Big River Public Library, 606 First St N, Big River, SK, S0J 0E0, CANADA. Tel: 306-469-2152. p. 2921

Wilson, Megan, Libr Asst, Edmonton Public Library, Strathcona, 8331 104th St, Edmonton, AB, T6E 4E9, CANADA. Tel: 780-496-1828. Fax: 780-496-1451. p. 2700

Wilson, Mia, Admin Serv, South Central Kansas Library System, 321 N Main St, South Hutchinson, KS, 67505-1146. Tel: 620-663-3211. Fax: 620-663-9797. p. 895

Wilson, Michael, Tech Info Spec, United States Air Force, 99 FSS/FSDL, 4311 N Washington Blvd, Bldg 312, Ste 101, Nellis AFB, NV, 89191-7064. Tel: 702-652-4484. p. 1431

Wilson, Mona, Br Mgr, Salinas Alicia City of Alice Public Library, Premont Public Library, 115 S Agnes St, Premont, TX, 78375. Tel: 361-348-3815. p. 2273

Wilson, Monica, Libr Mgr, Nelson, Mullins, Riley & Scarborough, 1320 Main St, Ste 1700, Columbia, SC, 29201. Tel: 803-255-9367. Fax: 803-255-7500. p. 2188

Wilson, Muriel, Cat, Riley County Kansas Genealogical Society Library, 2005 Claflin, Manhattan, KS, 66502-3415. Tel: 785-565-6495. p. 882

Wilson, Murray, Br Mgr, Dakota County Library System, Heritage, 20085 Heritage Dr, Lakeville, MN, 55044. Tel: 952-891-0373. p. 1249

Wilson, Myra, Br Mgr, Harris County Public Library, LaPorte Branch, 600 S Broadway, LaPorte, TX, 77571. Tel: 281-471-4022. Fax: 281-470-0839. p. 2336

Wilson, Nancy, Curator of Coll, Elmhurst Historical Museum Library, 120 E Park Ave, Elmhurst, IL, 60126. Tel: 630-833-1457. Fax: 630-833-1326. p. 642

Wilson, Nancy, Adult Serv Mgr, Morris Area Public Library District, 604 Liberty St, Morris, IL, 60450. Tel: 815-942-6880. Fax: 815-942-6415. p. 675

Wilson, Nancy, Librn, Becket Athenaeum, Inc Library, 3367 Main St, Becket, MA, 01223. Tel: 413-623-5483. p. 1051

Wilson, Nancy, Librn, Medford Public Library, 123 S Main St, Medford, OK, 73759. Tel: 580-395-2801. Fax: 580-395-2342. p. 1968

Wilson, Nancy, Librn, Lawrence Memorial Library, 40 North St, Bristol, VT, 05443. Tel: 802-453-2366. p. 2420

Wilson, Nellie, ILL Coordr, California Institute of Integral Studies, 1453 Mission St, 2nd Flr, San Francisco, CA, 94103. Tel: 415-575-6180. Fax: 415-575-1264. p. 241

Wilson, Nita, Br Mgr, Bossier Parish Central Library, Koran Station, 5413 Hwy 627, Haughton, LA, 71037. Tel: 318-987-3915. p. 946

Wilson, Oceana, Librn, Bennington College, One College Dr, Bennington, VT, 05201-6001. Tel: 802-440-4610. Fax: 802-440-4580. p. 2418

Wilson, Olivia, Youth Serv, Dunedin Public Library, 223 Douglas Ave, Dunedin, FL, 34698. Tel: 727-298-3080, Ext 238. Fax: 727-298-3088. p. 438

Wilson, P J, ILL, Music Librn, Tech Coordr, Allegan District Library, 331 Hubbard St, Allegan, MI, 49010. Tel: 269-673-4625. Fax: 269-673-8661. p. 1148

Wilson, Pam, Asst Librn, Garland Smith Public Library, 407 W Seminole, Marlow, OK, 73055. Tel: 580-658-5354. Fax: 580-658-9110. p. 1967

Wilson, Pam, Coordr, ILL, West Texas A&M University, University Dr & 26th St, Canyon, TX, 79016. Tel: 806-651-2211. Fax: 806-651-2213. p. 2294

Wilson, Pat, Librn, Clarks Public Library, 101 W Amity, Clarks, NE, 68628. Tel: 308-548-2864. p. 1396

Wilson, Patti, Cat, Holmes County Public Library, 303 N J Harvey Etheridge, Bonifay, FL, 32425. Tel: 850-547-3573. Fax: 850-547-2801. p. 429

Wilson, Patti, Coll Librn, University of the Fraser Valley, 33844 King Rd, Abbotsford, BC, V2S 7M8, CANADA. Tel: 604-504-7441, Ext 4277. Fax: 604-853-8055. p. 2724

Wilson, Patty R, Br Mgr, Ohoopee Regional Library System, Glennville Public, 408 E Barnard St, Glennville, GA, 30427. Tel: 912-654-3812. Fax: 912-654-3812. p. 556

Wilson, Paula, Asst Librn, Lake View Public Library, 202 Main St, Lake View, IA, 51450. Tel: 712-657-2310. Fax: 712-657-2310. p. 826

Wilson, Paulette, Dir of Educ, Department of Veterans Affairs Medical Center, 2002 Holcombe Blvd, Houston, TX, 77030. Tel: 713-794-7856. Fax: 713-794-7456. p. 2334

Wilson, Peg, ILL, Indian River County Library System, 1600 21st St, Vero Beach, FL, 32960. Tel: 772-770-5060. Fax: 772-770-5066. p. 501

Wilson, Phil, Chief, Res Mgt, National Park Service, Corner of Broadway & Ripley, PO Box 517, Mountainair, NM, 87036-0517. Tel: 505-847-2585. Fax: 505-847-2441. p. 1560

Wilson, Phyllis, Libr Tech, Colorado Department of Corrections, Limon Correctional Facility Library-General, 49030 State Hwy 71, Limon, CO, 80826. Tel: 719-775-9221, Ext 3240. Fax: 719-775-7676. p. 316

Wilson, Randy, Dir, Parlin Ingersoll Public Library, 205 W Chestnut St, Canton, IL, 61520. Tel: 309-647-0328. Fax: 309-647-8117. p. 599

Wilson, Rebecca, Librn, Edward Chipman Public Library, 126 N Locust St, Momence, IL, 60954. Tel: 815-472-2581. Fax: 815-472-2581. p. 675

Wilson, Rebecca, Adult Serv, Dakota County Library System, 1340 Wescott Rd, Eagan, MN, 55123-1099. Tel: 651-450-2939. Fax: 651-450-2915. p. 1249

Wilson, Rebecca, Assoc Dir, Susquehanna University, 514 University Ave, Selinsgrove, PA, 17870-1050. Tel: 570-372-4321. Fax: 570-372-4310. p. 2138

Wilson, Reginald, Mgr, Springfield City Library, East Forest Park Branch, 122-124 Island Pond Rd, Springfield, MA, 01118. Tel: 413-263-6836. Fax: 413-263-6838. p. 1127

Wilson, Reginald, Mgr, Springfield City Library, Forest Park Branch, 380 Belmont Ave, Springfield, MA, 01108. Tel: 413-263-6843. Fax: 413-263-6845. p. 1127

Wilson, Reginald, Mgr, Springfield City Library, Mason Square Branch, 765 State St, Springfield, MA, 01109. Tel: 413-263-6853. Fax: 413-263-6854. p. 1127

Wilson, Rhea, Asst Librn, Tech Serv & Automation, Covington & Burling LLP, 1201 Pennslyvania Ave NW, 11th Flr, Washington, DC, 20004-2401. Tel: 202-662-6169. Fax: 202-778-6658. p. 397

Wilson, Rich, Librn, Illinois Institute of Art, 1000 Plaza Dr, Ste 100, Schaumburg, IL, 60173-4990. Tel: 847-619-3450. Fax: 847-619-3064. p. 700

Wilson, Richard, Dean of Libr, Eastern Washington University, 816 F St, 100 LIB, Cheney, WA, 99004-2453. Tel: 509-359-2264. Fax: 509-359-6456. p. 2512

Wilson, Rose, Ref Librn, Baker College of Muskegon Library, 1903 Marquette Ave, Muskegon, MI, 49442-3404. Tel: 231-777-5330. Fax: 231-777-5334. p. 1212

Wilson, Rosemary, Circ Serv, Lighthouse Point Library, 2200 NE 38th St, Lighthouse Point, FL, 33064-3913. Tel: 954-946-6398. Fax: 954-781-1950. p. 461

Wilson, Rosemary, Youth Serv, Peotone Public Library District, 515 N First St, Peotone, IL, 60468. Tel: 708-258-3436. Fax: 708-258-9796. p. 690

Wilson, Sally, Circ, Carroll County Library, 625 High St, Ste 102, Huntingdon, TN, 38344-3903. Tel: 731-986-1919. Fax: 731-986-1335. p. 2237

Wilson, Sandra, Head, ILL, University of Detroit Mercy Library, 4001 W McNichols Rd, Detroit, MI, 48221-3038. Tel: 313-993-1071. Fax: 313-993-1780. p. 1172

Wilson, Sandra, Dir, Lakeland Library Cooperative, 4138 Three Mile Rd NW, Grand Rapids, MI, 49534-1134. Tel: 616-559-5253, Ext 201. Fax: 616-559-4329. p. 2946

Wilson, Sara, Dir, Mill Pond Public Library, 140 N South St, Kingston, WI, 53939. Tel: 920-394-3281. Fax: 920-394-3281. p. 2602

Wilson, Scott, Librn, Los Angeles Times, 202 W First St, Los Angeles, CA, 90012-0267. Tel: 213-237-7181. p. 174

Wilson, Serena A, Librn, Quoddy Tides Foundation Marine Library, 123 Water St, Eastport, ME, 04631-1333. Tel: 207-853-2366, 207-853-4806. Fax: 207-853-4095. p. 984

Wilson, Shannon H, Head, Spec Coll & Archives, Berea College, 100 Campus Dr, Berea, KY, 40404. Tel: 859-985-3259. Fax: 859-985-3912. p. 907

Wilson, Sharon, Br Mgr, Caledon Public Library, 150 Queen St S, Bolton, ON, L7E 1E3, CANADA. Tel: 905-857-1400. Fax: 905-857-8280. p. 2795

Wilson, Shatisha, Librn, Georgia Department of Corrections, Office of Library Services, 13262 Hwy 24 E, Davisboro, GA, 31018. Tel: 478-348-5814. Fax: 478-348-5613. p. 528

Wilson, Shelley, Librn, Henry Henley Public Library, 102 N Main St, Carthage, IN, 46115. Tel: 765-565-6631. p. 731

Wilson, Shirley, Dir, CDI Marine Systems Development Division, 6960 Aviation Blvd, No A, Glen Burnie, MD, 21061-2531. Tel: 410-544-2800. Fax: 410-647-3411. p. 1030

Wilson, Stephanie, Ref, Seattle University, School of Law Library, Sullivan Hall, 901 12th Ave, Seattle, WA, 98122-4411. Tel: 206-398-4221. Fax: 206-398-4194. p. 2532

Wilson, Steven P, Coordr, Ctr for Disability Res Libr, University of South Carolina, School of Medicine, 6311 Garners Ferry Rd, Columbia, SC, 29209. Tel: 803-733-1501. Fax: 803-733-1509. p. 2190

Wilson, Sue Ellen, Ch, Chapin Memorial Library, 400 14th Ave N, Myrtle Beach, SC, 29577-3612. Tel: 843-918-1275. Fax: 843-918-1288. p. 2201

Wilson, Susan, Ref Serv, Kilgore College, 1100 Broadway, Kilgore, TX, 75662. Tel: 903-983-8239. Fax: 903-983-8638. p. 2350

Wilson, Susan W, Mgr, National Cancer Institute at Frederick Scientific Library, Bldg 549, Sultan St, Frederick, MD, 21702-8255. Tel: 301-846-1093. Fax: 301-846-6332. p. 1029

Wilson, Suzanne, Libr Tech & Res Dir, Illinois Wesleyan University, One Ames Plaza, Bloomington, IL, 61701-7188. Tel: 309-556-3350. Fax: 309-556-3706. p. 595

Wilson, Suzanne, Circ Supvr, Catawba College, 2300 W Innes St, Salisbury, NC, 28144-2488. Tel: 704-637-4448. Fax: 704-637-4304. p. 1822

Wilson, Tamara L B, Syst Librn, US Customs & Border Protection Library, 90 K St NE, 9th Flr, Washington, DC, 20004. Tel: 202-325-0130. Fax: 202-325-0170. p. 418

Wilson, Tena, Exec Dir, Stark County District Library, 715 Market Ave N, Canton, OH, 44702-1018. Tel: 330-452-0665. Fax: 330-455-9596. p. 1864

Wilson, Terri, Dir, McKenzie Memorial Library, 15 N Broadway, McKenzie, TN, 38201-2101. Tel: 731-352-5741. Fax: 731-352-5741. p. 2247

Wilson, Terri, Asst Dir, Texas Tech University Health Sciences Center at Amarillo, 1400 Wallace Blvd, Amarillo, TX, 79106. Tel: 806-354-5448. Fax: 806-354-5430. p. 2274

Wilson, Terrie, Librn, Michigan State University Library, Fine Arts-Art, W 403 Library, East Lansing, MI, 48824. Tel: 517-884-6469. Fax: 517-432-3532. p. 1175

Wilson, Tiffany, Br Mgr, Johnson County Public Library, Clark Pleasant Library, 530 Tracy Rd, Ste 250, New Whiteland, IN, 46184-9699. Tel: 317-535-6206. Fax: 317-535-6018. p. 744

Wilson, Tiffany, Cat Librn, University of Maryland, Baltimore County, 1000 Hilltop Circle, Baltimore, MD, 21250. Tel: 410-455-2356. Fax: 410-455-1598. p. 1018

Wilson, Vance Joel, Circ Mgr, Belmont University, 1900 Belmont Blvd, Nashville, TN, 37212-3757. Tel: 615-460-5596. Fax: 615-460-5641. p. 2255

Wilson, Vicky, Librn, Parkland Regional Library, Govan Branch, PO Box 40, Govan, SK, S0G 1Z0, CANADA. Tel: 306-484-2122. p. 2932

Wilson, Virginia, Dir, William Paton Public Library, 105 Main St, Paton, IA, 50217. Tel: 515-968-4559. p. 838

Wilson, W Blake, Instrul Serv Librn, University of Kansas Libraries, Wheat Law Library, Green Hall, Rm 200, 1535 W 15th St, Lawrence, KS, 66045-7608. Tel: 785-864-3025. Fax: 785-864-3680. p. 878

Wilson, Wanda, Tech Serv, Brewton Public Library, 206 W Jackson St, Brewton, AL, 36426. Tel: 251-867-4626. Fax: 251-809-1749. p. 10

Wilson, Warren, Dir, South Dakota Library Network, 1200 University, Unit 9672, Spearfish, SD, 57799-9672. Tel: 605-642-6930. Fax: 605-642-6472. p. 2955

Wilson, Wayne V, Dr, VPres, Communications & Educ, LA84 Foundation, 2141 W Adams Blvd, Los Angeles, CA, 90018. Tel: 323-730-4646. Fax: 323-730-0546. p. 171

Wilson, Wesley, Archivist, Spec Coll Librn, DePauw University, 11 E Larrabee St, Greencastle, IN, 46135. Tel: 765-658-4420. Fax: 765-658-4017. p. 746

Wilson, Wesley, Chief, State Libr Res Ctr, Enoch Pratt Free Library, 400 Cathedral St, Baltimore, MD, 21201-4484. Tel: 410-396-5430. Fax: 410-396-1441. p. 1012

Wilson, Whitney Erin, Dir, Webster County Public Library, 101 State Rte 132 E, Dixon, KY, 42409. Tel: 270-639-9171. Fax: 270-639-6207. p. 911

Wilson, William, Br Head, United States Navy, Naval Explosive Ordnance Disposal Technology Division Technical Library, 2008 Stump Neck Rd, Code 2011, Indian Head, MD, 20640-5070. Tel: 301-744-6817. Fax: 301-744-6902. p. 1033

Wilsted, Tom, Spec Coll & Archives Librn, University of Connecticut Library, 369 Fairfield Rd, Storrs, CT, 06269-1005. Tel: 860-486-2219. Fax: 860-486-0584. p. 370

Wilt, Larry, Dr, Dir, University of Maryland, Baltimore County, 1000 Hilltop Circle, Baltimore, MD, 21250. Tel: 410-455-2356. p. 1018

Wilt, Laura, Librn, Oregon Department of Transportation Library, 355 Capitol St NE, Rm 22, Salem, OR, 97301-3871. Tel: 503-986-3280. Fax: 503-986-4025. p. 2017

Wilterding, Cathy, Coordr, Instruction & Outreach, Tarleton State University Library, 201 Saint Felix, Stephenville, TX, 76401. Tel: 254-968-9456. Fax: 254-968-9467. p. 2389

Wilton, Brenda, Librn, Bonavista Public Library, Church St, Bonavista, NL, A0C 1B0, CANADA. Tel: 709-468-2185. p. 2769

Wilton, Karen, Circ Mgr, Upper Moreland Free Public Library, 109 Park Ave, Willow Grove, PA, 19090-3277. Tel: 215-659-0741. Fax: 215-830-1223. p. 2157

Wiltrout, Richard, Mgr, Info Tech, Tuscarawas County Public Library, 121 Fair Ave NW, New Philadelphia, OH, 44663-2600. Tel: 330-364-4474. Fax: 330-364-8217. p. 1921

Wiltzius, Cecilia, Dir, Karl Junginger Memorial Library, 625 N Monroe St, Waterloo, WI, 53594-1183. Tel: 920-478-3344. Fax: 920-478-2351. p. 2644

Wimberley, Bernadette, Dean of Libr, Goldey Beacom College, 4701 Limestone Rd, Wilmington, DE, 19808. Tel: 302-225-6332. Fax: 302-998-6189. p. 388

Wimberly, Linda, Libr Serv Tech, Kaskaskia College Library, 27210 College Rd, Centralia, IL, 62801. Tel: 618-545-3135. Fax: 618-532-9241. p. 602

Wimberly, Ware W, III, Dir, Wabash Carnegie Public Library, 188 W Hill St, Wabash, IN, 46992-3048. Tel: 260-563-2972. Fax: 260-563-0222. p. 785

Wimer, Jessica, Head, Res Serv, University of Southern California Libraries, Asa V Call Law Library, 699 Exposition Blvd, LAW 202, MC 0072, Los Angeles, CA, 90089-0072. Tel: 213-740-6482. Fax: 213-740-7179. p. 179

Wimmer, Helen, Librn, Melvin Public Library, 232 Main St, Melvin, IA, 51350. Tel: 712-736-2107. p. 831

Wimmer, Laura, Mgr, Libr Serv, Resurrection Medical Center Library, 7435 W Talcott Ave, Chicago, IL, 60631-3746. Tel: 773-990-7638. p. 622

Winandy, Maria, Librn, University Park Public Library District, 1100 Blackhawk Dr, University Park, IL, 60466. Tel: 708-534-2580. Fax: 708-534-2583. p. 711

Winant, Richard M, Dean, Acad Info Access, Dir of Libr, State University of New York Downstate Medical Center, 395 Lenox Rd, Brooklyn, NY, 11203. Tel: 718-270-7400. Fax: 718-270-7413, 718-270-7468. p. 1595

Winberry, Jennifer, Asst Libr Dir, Hunterdon County Library, South County, 1108-A Old York Rd, Ringoes, NJ, 08851. Tel: 908-788-1444. Fax: 908-782-0846. p. 1486

Winborne, Norberta, Mgr, District of Columbia Public Library, Lamond Riggs, 5401 S Dakota Ave NE, Washington, DC, 20011. Tel: 202-541-6255. p. 398

Winch, Elsa W, Instruction Librn, Ref Librn, Lock Haven University of Pennsylvania, 401 N Fairview Ave, Lock Haven, PA, 17745-2390. Tel: 570-484-2652. Fax: 570-484-2506. p. 2082

Winch, Susan L, Asst Dir, Scarborough Public Library, 48 Gorham Rd, Scarborough, ME, 04074. Tel: 207-883-4723. Fax: 207-883-9728. p. 1000

Winchcombe, Terri, Mgr, Acq Serv, Saint Mary's University, 5429 Inglis St, Halifax, NS, B3H 3C3, CANADA. Tel: 902-420-5535. Fax: 902-420-5561. p. 2782

Winchel, Lorena, Br Librn, Crawford County Library System, Beaver Creek Township Library, 8888 S Grayling Rd, Grayling, MI, 49738. Tel: 989-275-2808. p. 1186

Winchell, Lyn, Asst Librn, Journal Gazette Library, 600 W Main St, Fort Wayne, IN, 46802. Tel: 260-461-8258. Fax: 260-461-8648. p. 742

Winchester, David, Ser Librn, Washburn University, 1700 SW College Ave, Topeka, KS, 66621. Tel: 785-670-1193. Fax: 785-670-3223. p. 897

Winchester, Stacy, Librn, Northwest Arkansas Community College Library, One College Dr, Bentonville, AR, 72712-5091. Tel: 479-619-4244. Fax: 479-619-4115. p. 95

Winder, Sylvia, Ref Serv, Cabrillo College, 6500 Soquel Dr, Aptos, CA, 95003-3198. Tel: 831-479-6537. Fax: 831-479-6500. p. 121

Windham, Beverly, Librn, Lexington County Public Library System, Batesburg-Leesville Branch, 203 Armory St, Batesburg, SC, 29006. Tel: 803-532-9223. Fax: 803-532-2232. p. 2199

Windham, Beverly, Sr Br Librn, Lexington County Public Library System, Irmo Branch, 6251 St Andrews Rd, Columbia, SC, 29212-3152. Tel: 803-798-7880. Fax: 803-798-8570. p. 2199

Windham, Daphne, Asst Librn, Briceville Public Library, 921 Andy's Ridge Rd, Briceville, TN, 37710. Tel: 865-426-6220. Fax: 865-426-6220. p. 2225

Windham, Donna, Librn, Glankler Brown, One Commerce Sq, Ste 1700, Memphis, TN, 38103. Tel: 901-576-1806. Fax: 901-525-2389. p. 2248

Windham, Nancy, Br Mgr, Webster Parish Library, Cotton Valley Branch, 256 Main St, Cotton Valley, LA, 71018. Tel: 318-832-4290. Fax: 318-832-5335. p. 957

Windham, Sharon, Youth & Young Adult Mgr, Hayner Public Library District, 326 Belle St, Alton, IL, 62002. Tel: 618-462-0677. Fax: 618-462-0665. p. 588

Windham, Teresa, Chief, Main Libr Serv, Richland County Public Library, 1431 Assembly St, Columbia, SC, 29201-3101. Tel: 803-799-9084. Fax: 803-929-3448. p. 2188

Windhorst, Colin, Dr, Dir, Dennysville-Lincoln Memorial Library, 17 King St, Dennysville, ME, 04628. Tel: 207-726-4750. p. 983

Windish, Donna, Instrul Serv Librn, Randolph Community College, 629 Industrial Park Ave, Asheboro, NC, 27205-7333. Tel: 336-633-0204. Fax: 336-629-4695. p. 1773

Windle, Christy, Br Mgr, Shasta Public Libraries, Anderson Branch, 3200 W Center St, Anderson, CA, 96007. Tel: 530-365-7685. Fax: 530-365-7685. p. 214

Windle, Russell, Dir, Res, American Ivy Society Library, PO Box 2123, Naples, FL, 34106-2123. Tel: 845-688-5318. Fax: 845-688-5318. p. 471

Windsor, Lynn, Acq & Cat, Somerset County Library System, 11767 Beechwood St, Princess Anne, MD, 21853. Tel: 410-651-0852, Ext 11. Fax: 410-651-1388. p. 1036

Windsor, Matthew, Syst/Tech Serv, Hendrix College, 1600 Washington Ave, Conway, AR, 72032. Tel: 501-450-1287. Fax: 501-450-3800. p. 97

Windyboy, Helen, Dir, Stone Child College, 8294 Upper Box Elder Rd, Box Elder, MT, 59521. Tel: 406-395-4875. p. 1375

Windyga, Jadwiga, Libr Tech, Alberta Government Library, 10025 Jasper Ave, 15th Flr, Edmonton, AB, T5J 2N3, CANADA. Tel: 780-427-0403. Fax: 780-422-9694. p. 2698

Wine, Jeanine, Archivist, Manchester College, 604 E College Ave, North Manchester, IN, 46962. Tel: 260-982-5361. Fax: 260-982-5362. p. 769

Winecoff, Debra, Libr Serv Adminr, Chesterfield County Public Library, 9501 Lori Rd, Chesterfield, VA, 23832. Tel: 804-751-4475. Fax: 804-751-4679. p. 2457

Winecoff, Judith, Youth Serv Librn, Watauga County Public Library, 140 Queen St, Boone, NC, 28607. Tel: 828-264-8784. Fax: 828-264-1794. p. 1777

Winecoff, Michael, Info Tech, University of North Carolina at Charlotte, 9201 University City Blvd, Charlotte, NC, 28223-0001. Tel: 704-687-2072. Fax: 704-687-3050. p. 1784

Wineland, Terry, Librn, White River Regional Library, Fulton County - Viola Branch, 199 Hwy 223, Viola, AR, 72583. Tel: 870-458-3070. p. 94

Wines, Bill, Asst Dir, Walled Lake City Library, 1499 E West Maple Rd, Walled Lake, MI, 48390. Tel: 248-624-3772. Fax: 248-624-0041. p. 1233

Wines, Judith, Librn, Altamont Free Library, 105 Park St, Altamont, NY, 12009. Tel: 518-861-7239. Fax: 518-861-7239. p. 1572

Wines, Randi, Librn, Roanoke Public Libraries, Gainsboro, 15 Patton Ave NW, Roanoke, VA, 24016. Tel: 540-853-2540. Fax: 540-853-1155. p. 2494

Winfield, Kathleen, Ref & Info Spec, Town of Vail Public Library, 292 W Meadow Dr, Vail, CO, 81657. Tel: 970-479-2182. Fax: 970-479-2192. p. 325

Winfield, Lesley, Libr Mgr, Olds & District Municipal Library, 5217 52nd St, Olds, AB, T4H 1S8, CANADA. Tel: 403-556-6460. Fax: 403-556-6692. p. 2713

Winfield, Sue, Chief Exec Officer, Head Librn, Stirling-Randon Public Library, 43 Front St W, Stirling, ON, K0K 3E0, CANADA. Tel: 613-395-2837. p. 2845

Winfrey, Laura, Dir, Somerville-Fayette County Library, 216 W Market St, Somerville, TN, 38068-1592. Tel: 901-465-5248. Fax: 901-465-5271. p. 2266

Wing, Carol Moen, Res, Lucasfilm Research Library, PO Box 2009, San Rafael, CA, 94912. Tel: 415-662-1912. p. 257

Wing, Justin, Head, Libr Info Tech User Support, University of Delaware Library, 181 S College Ave, Newark, DE, 19717-5267. Tel: 302-831-2231. Fax: 302-831-1046. p. 386

Wing, Kelly, Dir, Communications, Audubon Society of New Hampshire, 84 Silk Farm Rd, Concord, NH, 03301-8200. Tel: 603-224-9909. Fax: 603-226-0902. p. 1442

Wing, Marje, Mgr, Calgary Public Library, Alexander Calhoun Branch, 3223 14th St SW, Calgary, AB, T2T 3V8, CANADA. p. 2689

Wing, Marje, Mgr, Calgary Public Library, Memorial Park, 1221 Second St SW, Calgary, AB, T2R 0W5, CANADA. p. 2690

Wing, Robert, Cat, Librn, Tech Serv, San Jose City College Library, 2100 Moorpark Ave, San Jose, CA, 95128-2799. Tel: 408-298-2181, Ext 3945. Fax: 408-293-4728. p. 250

Wingate, Eliza, Ref Librn, Mendocino College Library, 1000 Hensley Creek Rd, Ukiah, CA, 95482-7821. Tel: 707-468-3053. Fax: 707-468-3056. p. 277

Wingate, Eliza, Br Librn, Mendocino County Library District, Ukiah Main Library, 105 N Main St, Ukiah, CA, 95482. Tel: 707-463-4493. Fax: 707-463-5470. p. 278

Wingate, Terry, Staff Develop Coordr, Omaha Public Library, 215 S 15th St, Omaha, NE, 68102-1629. Tel: 402-444-4835. Fax: 402-444-4504. p. 1414

Winge, Barbara, Librn, Department of Veterans Affairs, One Veterans Dr, 142 D, Minneapolis, MN, 55417. Tel: 612-467-4200. Fax: 612-725-2046. p. 1259

Winger, Jennifer, Asst Librn, Cochranton Area Public Library, 107 W Pine St, Cochranton, PA, 16314-0296. Tel: 814-425-3996. Fax: 814-425-3996. p. 2046

Wingerroth, Janet, Instrul Serv/Ref Librn, Spokane Falls Community College, 3410 Ft George Wright Dr, MS 3020, Spokane, WA, 99224-5288. Tel: 509-533-3224. Fax: 509-533-3144. p. 2537

Wingfield, Debra, Mgr, Hamilton Health Sciences, 286 Victoria Ave N, Hamilton, ON, L8L 5G4, CANADA. Tel: 905-527-4322, Ext 44247, 905-527-4322, Ext 44248. Fax: 905-577-1453. p. 2808

Wingfield, Selena, Ch, Dougherty County Public Library, 300 Pine Ave, Albany, GA, 31701-2533. Tel: 229-420-3200. Fax: 229-420-3215. p. 507

Wingler, Jodi, Youth Serv, Danville-Center Township Public Library, 101 S Indiana St, Danville, IN, 46122-1809. Tel: 317-718-8008, Ext 15. Fax: 317-745-0756. p. 735

Wingreen-Mason, Daria, Libr Tech, Smithsonian Libraries, Joseph F Cullman 3rd, Library of Natural History, Nat Museum of Natural Hist, Rm CE-G15, MRC 154, Tenth St & Constitution Ave NW, Washington, DC, 20560. Tel: 202-633-1184. Fax: 202-633-0219. p. 414

Wingrove, Karen, ILL, Northland Public Library, 300 Cumberland Rd, Pittsburgh, PA, 15237-5455. Tel: 412-366-8100, Ext 119. Fax: 412-366-2064. p. 2126

Wings, Arron, Dir, Kirkwood Community College Library, Benton Hall, 6301 Kirkwood Blvd SW, Cedar Rapids, IA, 52404-5260. Tel: 319-398-5403. Fax: 319-398-4908. p. 800

Winingear, Sara, Asst Dir, Westminster College, National Churchill Museum, 501 Westminster Ave, Fulton, MO, 65251-1299. Tel: 573-592-5234. Fax: 573-592-5222. p. 1328

Winistorfer, Judy, Ref Librn, Marion Public Library, 1095 Sixth Ave, Marion, IA, 52302. Tel: 319-377-3412. Fax: 319-377-0113. p. 830

Winjum, Roberta, Assoc Dean, Tech Serv, Vanderbilt University, 419 21st Ave S, Nashville, TN, 37203-2427. Tel: 615-322-7100. Fax: 615-343-8279. p. 2260

Wink, Ann, Librn, Putnam County Public Library District, Granville Branch, 212 S McCoy St, Granville, IL, 61326. Tel: 815-339-2038. Fax: 815-339-2038, 815-339-2480. p. 655

Wink, Tara, Rare Bks, Spec Coll Librn, West Chester University, 25 W Rosedale Ave, West Chester, PA, 19383. Tel: 610-436-3456. p. 2153

Winke, R Conrad, Assoc Dean of Libr, Columbia College Chicago Library, 624 S Michigan Ave, Chicago, IL, 60605-1996. Tel: 312-369-7165. Fax: 312-344-8062. p. 611

Winkel, Andrew, Head, Circ, Clifton Public Library, 150 E Fourth Ave, Clifton, IL, 60927. Tel: 815-694-2069. Fax: 815-694-3179. p. 630

Winkel, Kathy, Supvr, Ch Serv, Mishawaka-Penn-Harris Public Library, Harris, 51446 Elm Rd, Granger, IN, 46530-7171. Tel: 574-271-3179, Ext 310. Fax: 574-271-3183. p. 765

Winkel, Martha, Dir, Warren Public Library, 15 Sackett Hill Rd, Warren, CT, 06754. Tel: 860-868-2195. p. 374

Winkle, Jeff, Dir, Findlay-Hancock County District Public Library, 206 Broadway, Findlay, OH, 45840-3382. Tel: 419-422-1712. Fax: 419-422-0638. p. 1899

Winkle, Sharon L, Dir, Libr Serv, Mead Public Library, 710 N Eighth St, Sheboygan, WI, 53081-4563. Tel: 920-459-3400, Ext 3414. Fax: 920-459-0204. p. 2637

Winkleblack, Norma, Spec Coll, Coles County Historical Society, 895 Seventh St, Charleston, IL, 61920. Tel: 217-235-6744. p. 603

Winkler, Joy A, Librn, Immanuel Medical Center, 6901 N 72nd St, Omaha, NE, 68122. Tel: 402-572-2121, 402-572-2345. Fax: 402-572-2797. p. 1413

Winkler, Kevin, Dep Dir, Libr Sites & Serv, The New York Public Library - Astor, Lenox & Tilden Foundations, 476 Fifth Ave, (@ 42nd St), New York, NY, 10018-2788. Tel: 212-930-0720. Fax: 212-930-0769. p. 1690

Winkler, Lisa, Br Librn, Wisconsin State Law Library, Dane County Legal Resource Center, Courthouse Rm L1007, 215 S Hamilton St, Madison, WI, 53703. Tel: 608-266-6316. Fax: 608-266-5988. p. 2611

Winkler, Matthew, In Charge, Hudson Area Joint Library, 700 First St, Hudson, WI, 54016. Tel: 715-386-3101. Fax: 715-381-0468. p. 2598

Winkler, Michael, Info Syst, University of Pennsylvania Libraries, 3420 Walnut St, Philadelphia, PA, 19104-6206. Tel: 215-898-2199. Fax: 215-898-0559. p. 2118

Winkler-Peizer, Sharon, Dir, United States Navy, Officer Indoctrination School Library, 291 Kollmeyer St, Newport, RI, 02841-1524. Tel: 401-841-4310. Fax: 401-841-3323. p. 2170

Winks, Amy, ILL, Purdue University Libraries, 504 W State St, West Lafayette, IN, 47907-2058. Tel: 765-494-2900. Fax: 765-494-0156. p. 786

Winks, Kristie, Youth Serv Librn, Burlington County Library, Cinnaminson Branch, 1619 Riverton Rd, Cinnaminson, NJ, 08077. Tel: 856-829-9340. Fax: 856-829-2912. p. 1543

Winlock, Debbie, Libr Dir, Page Public Library, 479 S Lake Powell Blvd, Page, AZ, 86040. Tel: 928-645-4272. Fax: 928-645-5804. p. 70

Winn, Beverly, Head, Tech Serv, Nevins Memorial Library, 305 Broadway, Methuen, MA, 01844-6898. Tel: 978-686-4080. Fax: 978-686-8669. p. 1105

Winn, Cynthia, Asst Dir, Pub Serv, Siouxland Libraries, 200 N Dakota Ave, Sioux Falls, SD, 57104. Tel: 605-367-8725. Fax: 605-367-4312. p. 2218

Winn, Jade, Outreach Librn, University of San Diego, Helen K & James S Copley Library, 5998 Alcala Park, San Diego, CA, 92110. Fax: 619-260-4617. p. 239

Winn, Joyce, ILL, National Sea Grant Library, Ocean Science & Exploration Ctr, URI-Bay Campus, Narragansett, RI, 02882-1197. Tel: 401-874-6114. p. 2168

Winn, Kenneth, Dir, Libr & Pub Serv, Missouri Supreme Court Library, Supreme Court Bldg, 207 W High St, Jefferson City, MO, 65101. Tel: 573-751-7330. Fax: 573-751-2573. p. 1335

Winn, Sharon, Ch, Shelbina Carnegie Public Library, 102 N Center, Shelbina, MO, 63468. Tel: 573-588-2271. Fax: 573-588-2271. p. 1365

Winn, Trevor, Bus Librn, Genesee District Library, Grand Blanc Area (McFarlen Public Library), 515 Perry Rd, Grand Blanc, MI, 48439. Tel: 810-694-5310. Fax: 810-694-5313. p. 1180

Winner, Cristina, Dir, Crowley Public Library, 409 S Oak St, Crowley, TX, 76036. Tel: 817-297-6707. Fax: 817-297-1554. p. 2304

Winnicki, Debbie, Librn, Brokenhead River Regional Library, 427 Park Ave, Beausejour, MB, R0E 0C0, CANADA. Tel: 204-268-7570. Fax: 204-268-7570. p. 2747

Winningham, Laura, Dir, Pickett County Public Library, 79 Pickett Square Annex, Byrdstown, TN, 38549. Tel: 931-864-6281. Fax: 931-864-7078. p. 2225

Winningham, Laura, Assoc Librn, Mount San Jacinto College, 1499 N State St, San Jacinto, CA, 92583-2399. Tel: 951-487-6752, Ext 1580. Fax: 951-654-8387. p. 249

Winningham, Laura, Chief Librn, Crafton Hills College Library, 11711 Sand Canyon Rd, Yucaipa, CA, 92399. Tel: 909-389-3323, 909-794-2161. Fax: 909-794-9524. p. 286

Winningham, Marcia, Evening Librn, Copiah-Lincoln Community College, 151 Colin Dr, Mendenhall, MS, 39111. Tel: 601-849-0116. Fax: 601-849-0160. p. 1308

Winograd, Catherine, Res Librn, Russell Sage Foundation Library, 112 E 64th St, New York, NY, 10065. Tel: 212-752-8640. Fax: 212-688-2684. p. 1698

Winograd, Mary Beth, Circ, Fort Bend County Libraries, 1001 Golfview Dr, Richmond, TX, 77469-5199. Tel: 281-341-2695. Fax: 281-341-2688. p. 2374

Winrich, Carole, Circ, Carroll College, 100 N East Ave, Waukesha, WI, 53186. Tel: 262-524-7307. Fax: 262-524-7377. p. 2644

Winschel, Terrence, Librn, Vicksburg National Military Park Library, 3201 Clay St, Vicksburg, MS, 39183-3495. Tel: 601-619-2908, 601-636-0583. Fax: 601-636-9497. p. 1317

Winship, Andrea, Col Librn, Dine College, PO Box 1000, Tsaile, AZ, 86556. Tel: 928-724-6758. p. 85

Winslow, Dan, Coll Develop, Midwestern State University, 3410 Taft Ave, Wichita Falls, TX, 76308-2099. Tel: 940-397-4169. Fax: 940-397-4689. p. 2400

Winslow, Katherine R, Dir, North Carolina Wesleyan College, 3400 N Wesleyan Blvd, Rocky Mount, NC, 27804. Tel: 252-985-5134. Fax: 252-985-5235. p. 1821

Winslow, Lisa, Head of Libr, Proskauer Rose LLP, 2049 Century Park E, Ste 3200, Los Angeles, CA, 90067. Tel: 310-284-5683, 310-557-2900. Fax: 310-557-2193. p. 177

Winson, Gail, Assoc Dean, Libr & Info Serv, Roger Williams University, Ten Metacom Ave, Bristol, RI, 02809-5171. Tel: 401-254-4530. Fax: 401-254-4543. p. 2163

Winsor, John, Tech Serv, Mills College, 5000 MacArthur Blvd, Oakland, CA, 94613. Tel: 510-430-2466. Fax: 510-430-2278. p. 197

Winstead, Beth, Copyright Officer, East Carolina University, J Y Joyner Library, E Fifth St, Greenville, NC, 27858-4353. Tel: 252-328-0247. Fax: 252-328-6892. p. 1798

Winstead, Tina, Librn, Newfield Public Library, 198 Main St, Newfield, NY, 14867. Tel: 607-564-3594. Fax: 607-564-3594. p. 1705

Winston, Catherine, Digital Res Librn, Amherst College, Amherst, MA, 01002. Fax: 413-542-2662. p. 1048

Winston, Cornell, Librn, United States Department of Justice, 1214 US Courthouse, 312 N Spring St, Los Angeles, CA, 90012. Tel: 213-894-2419. Fax: 213-894-1381. p. 178

Winston, Heidi, Res & Instruction Librn, Barnard College, 3009 Broadway, New York, NY, 10027-6598. Tel: 212-854-9096. p. 1670

Winston, Mark, Dir, Rutgers University Libraries, John Cotton Dana Library, 185 University Ave, Newark, NJ, 07102. Tel: 973-353-5222. Fax: 973-353-1133. p. 1512

Winston, Mark, Asst Prof, Rutgers, The State University of New Jersey, Four Huntington St, New Brunswick, NJ, 08901-1071. Tel: 732-932-7500, Ext 8955. Fax: 732-932-2644. p. 2969

Winter, Arn Ellsworth, Dir, James H Johnson Memorial Library, 670 Ward Dr, Deptford, NJ, 08096. Tel: 856-848-9149. Fax: 856-848-1813. p. 1481

Winter, David, ILL, University of British Columbia Library, 1961 East Mall, Vancouver, BC, V6T 1Z1, CANADA. Tel: 604-822-6721. Fax: 604-822-6465. p. 2742

Winter, Evelyn, Media Spec, Southside Baptist Church, 310 McDonald St, Lakeland, FL, 33803. Tel: 863-682-8764. Fax: 863-682-5849. p. 460

Winter, Heather Lynn, Archivist, Art Librn, Milwaukee Art Museum Library, Milwaukee Art Museum, 700 N Art Museum Dr, Milwaukee, WI, 53202. Tel: 414-224-3270. Fax: 414-271-7588. p. 2619

Winter, Kathy, ILL, Garden City Community College, 801 Campus Dr, Garden City, KS, 67846. Tel: 620-276-9656. Fax: 620-276-9630. p. 868

Winter, Ken, Librn, Virginia Transportation Research Council Library, 530 Edgemont Rd, Charlottesville, VA, 22903. Tel: 434-293-1959. Fax: 434-293-4196. p. 2455

Winter, Kimberlee, Adminr, Elizabeth Township Library, 210 E Myrtle St, Elizabeth, IL, 61028-9785. Tel: 815-858-2212. Fax: 815-858-3475. p. 641

Winter, Pat Quinn, Dir of Develop, Carnegie Library of Pittsburgh, 4400 Forbes Ave, Pittsburgh, PA, 15213-4080. Tel: 412-622-8873. Fax: 412-622-6278. p. 2122

Winter, Paula, Br Mgr, Latah County Library District, Bovill Branch, 310 First Ave, Bovill, ID, 83806. Tel: 208-826-3451. Fax: 208-826-3451. p. 579

Winter, Priscilla, Mgr, Jefferson County Public Library, Evergreen Branch, 5000 State Hwy 73, Evergreen, CO, 80439. p. 315

Winter, Susan, Dir, Hubbard Public Library, 323 E Maple St, Hubbard, IA, 50122. Tel: 641-864-2771. Fax: 641-864-3379. p. 821

Winterbauer, Theresa, Ch, DeKalb Public Library, 309 Oak St, DeKalb, IL, 60115-3369. Tel: 815-756-9568. Fax: 815-756-7837. p. 635

Winterbottom, Marcia, Electronic Res, Toronto Rehab, 550 University Ave, Toronto, ON, M5G 2A2, CANADA. Tel: 416-597-3422, Ext 3050. Fax: 416-591-6515. p. 2864

Winteregg, Candy, Dir, Good Samaritan Hospital Library, 2222 Philadelphia Dr, Dayton, OH, 45406-1891. Tel: 937-734-2141. Fax: 937-734-2634. p. 1893

Winterfeldt, Henry, Dr, Assoc Prof, University of Wisconsin Oshkosh, 800 Algoma Blvd, Oshkosh, WI, 54901. Tel: 920-424-0881. Fax: 920-424-0858. p. 2977

Winterfeldt, Lori, Chief Librn, Department of Veterans Affairs, New York Harbor Healthcare System, 423 E 23rd St, New York, NY, 10010. Tel: 212-686-7500, Ext 7675. Fax: 212-951-3367. p. 1677

Winterman, Brian, Head of Libr, Indiana University Bloomington, Geography & Map Library, Student Bldg 015, 701 E Kirkwood Ave, Bloomington, IN, 47405. Tel: 812-855-1108. Fax: 812-855-4919. p. 727

Winters, Colleen, Dir, Forest Grove City Library, 2114 Pacific Ave, Forest Grove, OR, 97116-9019. Tel: 503-992-3246. Fax: 503-992-3333. p. 1998

Winters, Dale, Librn, Wilcox County Library, Pine Apple Branch, 124 County Rd 59, Pine Apple, AL, 36768. Tel: 251-746-2698. p. 11

Winters, Dennis, Head, Tech & Automation Serv, Geneva Public Library District, 127 James St, Geneva, IL, 60134. Tel: 630-232-0780. Fax: 630-232-0881. p. 649

Winters, Kendra, Br Mgr, West Georgia Regional Library, New Georgia Public Library, 94 Ridge Rd, Dallas, GA, 30157. Tel: 770-459-8163. Fax: 770-459-9343. p. 524

Winters, Lisa, Dir, Allerton Public Library District, 201 N State St, Monticello, IL, 61856. Tel: 217-762-4676. Fax: 217-762-2021. p. 675

Winters, Murl, Ref Librn, Evangel University, 1111 N Glenstone Ave, Springfield, MO, 65802. Tel: 417-865-2815, Ext 7268. p. 1366

Winters Palacio, CM!, Chairperson, Malcolm X College Library, City Colleges of Chicago, 1900 W Van Buren St, Chicago, IL, 60612. Tel: 312-850-7250. Fax: 312-850-7249. p. 618

Winterstein, Jeff, Ref, Elk Grove Village Public Library, 1001 Wellington Ave, Elk Grove Village, IL, 60007-3391. Tel: 847-439-0447. Fax: 847-439-0475. p. 641

Winther, Connie, Librn, Grey Nuns Community Hospital-Caritas Health Group, 1100 Youville Dr W, Edmonton, AB, T6L 5X8, CANADA. Tel: 780-735-7251. Fax: 780-735-7202. p. 2701

Winzenburger, Janet, Acq, Cleveland Institute of Music, 11021 East Blvd, Cleveland, OH, 44106-1776. Tel: 216-795-3114. Fax: 216-791-3063. p. 1877

Wiper, Karen, Br Mgr, Akron-Summit County Public Library, Tallmadge Branch, 90 Community Rd, Tallmadge, OH, 44278. Tel: 330-633-4345. Fax: 330-633-6324. p. 1852

Wipf, Jean, Dir, Woodbury Public Library, 33 Delaware St, Woodbury, NJ, 08096. Tel: 856-845-2611. p. 1545

Wirkkala, Anne, Asst Dir, Learning Res, ILL Librn, NHTI, Concord's Community College, 31 College Dr, Concord, NH, 03301-7425. Tel: 603-271-7720. Fax: 603-271-7189. p. 1443

Wirszyla, Greg, Dir, Mamakating Library, 156-158 Sullivan St, Wurtsboro, NY, 12790. Tel: 845-888-8004. Fax: 845-888-8008. p. 1771

Wirtanen, Ann, Dir, Winchester Public Library, 80 Washington St, Winchester, MA, 01890. Tel: 781-721-7171, Ext 10. Fax: 781-721-7170. p. 1141

Wirth, Amelia, Libr Tech, Colorado Department of Corrections, Sterling Correctional Facility Library-East Side, 12101 Hwy 61, Sterling, CO, 80751. Tel: 970-521-3825. Fax: 970-521-8905. p. 323

Wirth, Wes, Chair, Department of Community Services, Government of Yukon, Teslin Community, Teslin Community Bldg, Teslin, YT, Y0A 1B0, CANADA. Tel: 867-390-2802. p. 2933

Wirtley, Cheryl C, Mgr, Dayton Metro Library, Miami Township, 2718 Lyons Rd, Miamisburg, OH, 45342. Tel: 937-496-8944. Fax: 937-496-4344. p. 1893

Wirtz, Ronald, Coordr, User Serv/Instruction, University of Nebraska at Kearney, 2508 11th Ave, Kearney, NE, 68849-2240. Tel: 308-865-8592. Fax: 308-865-8722. p. 1403

Wirtz, Shelly, Librn, Herington Public Library, 102 S Broadway, Herington, KS, 67449-2634. Tel: 785-258-2011. Fax: 785-258-2011. p. 871

Wirzba, Sharon, Mgr, Calgary Public Library, Signal Hill, 5994 Signal Hill Centre SW, Calgary, AB, T3H 3P8, CANADA. p. 2690

Wisbar, Gloria, Circ, Elkins-Randolph County Public Library, 416 Davis Ave, Elkins, WV, 26241. Tel: 304-637-0287. Fax: 304-637-0288. p. 2558

Wisbey, Peter, Exec Dir, The Seward House Museum, 33 South St, Auburn, NY, 13021-3929. Tel: 315-252-1283. Fax: 315-253-3351. p. 1576

Wiscombe, Shirleen, Site Mgr, Davis County Library, 38 S 100 East, Farmington, UT, 84025. Tel: 801-451-2322. Fax: 801-451-9561. p. 2405

Wiscount, Bonnie, Librn, Tremont Area Free Public Library, 19 N Pine St, Tremont, PA, 17981-1410. Tel: 570-695-3325. p. 2146

Wisdom, Anita, Br Librn, Reynolds County Library District, Oates Branch, 8490 Hwy J, Black, MO, 63625. Tel: 573-269-1117. Fax: 573-269-1117. p. 1323

Wisdom, Sarah, Commun Relations Mgr, Yuma County Library District, 2951 S 21st Dr, Yuma, AZ, 85364. Tel: 928-373-6483. Fax: 928-782-9420. p. 91

Wisdorf, Leesa, Ref & Youth Serv Mgr, Northfield Public Library, 210 Washington St, Northfield, MN, 55057. Tel: 507-645-1804. Fax: 507-645-1820. p. 1269

Wise, Bellinda, Ref, Nassau Community College, One Education Dr, Garden City, NY, 11530-6793. Tel: 516-572-7400. Fax: 516-572-7846. p. 1626

Wise, Betty, Asst Librn, Wallace Public Library, 415 River St, Wallace, ID, 83873-2260. Tel: 208-752-4571. Fax: 208-752-4571. p. 585

Wise, Brianna, Asst Circ/ILL Mgr, Giles County Public Library, 122 S Second St, Pulaski, TN, 38478-3285. Tel: 931-363-2720. Fax: 931-424-7032. p. 2264

Wise, Eliezer M, Dir, Gratz College, 7605 Old York Rd, Melrose Park, PA, 19027. Tel: 215-635-7300, Ext 159. Fax: 215-635-7320. p. 2088

Wise, Eliezer M, Dir, Gratz College, Abner & Mary Schreiber Jewish Music Library, 7605 Old York Rd, Melrose Park, PA, 19027. Tel: 215-635-7300. Fax: 215-635-7320. p. 2088

Wise, Jay, Ref Librn, Indiana Wesleyan University, 4201 S Washington St, Marion, IN, 46953. Tel: 614-529-7563. Fax: 765-677-2676. p. 762

Wise, Jay, Youth Serv, Chillicothe & Ross County Public Library, 140 S Paint St, Chillicothe, OH, 45601. Tel: 740-702-4145. Fax: 740-702-4153. p. 1867

Wise, Julie, Fiscal Officer, Sequoyah Regional Library System, 116 Brown Industrial Pkwy, Canton, GA, 30114-2899. Tel: 770-479-3090, Ext 221. Fax: 770-479-3069. p. 523

Wise, Kenneth, Bus Mgr, University of Tennessee, Knoxville, 1015 Volunteer Blvd, Knoxville, TN, 37996-1000. Tel: 865-974-2359. Fax: 865-974-4259. p. 2243

Wise, Lisa, Dir, Broome County Historical Society Library, Broome County Public Library, 185 Court St, Binghamton, NY, 13901. Tel: 607-778-3572. Fax: 607-778-6429. p. 1582

Wise, Lisa, Dir, Broome County Public Library, 185 Court St, Binghamton, NY, 13901-3503. Tel: 607-778-6407. Fax: 607-778-6429. p. 1582

Wise, Margaret, In Charge, Merced County Library, Snelling Branch, 15916 N Hwy 59, Snelling, CA, 95369-9728. Tel: 209-563-6616. p. 186

Wise, Mary, Cat, Central Washington University, 400 E University Way, Ellensburg, WA, 98926-7548. Tel: 509-963-1901. Fax: 509-963-3684. p. 2514

Wise, Norma, Dir, James J Lunsford (Hillsborough County) Law Library, 701 E Twiggs St, Tampa, FL, 33602. Tel: 813-272-5818. Fax: 813-272-5226. p. 497

Wise, Penny, Ser Librn, Mercyhurst College, 501 E 38th St, Erie, PA, 16546. Tel: 814-824-3309. Fax: 814-824-2219. p. 2056

Wise, Sally H, Dir, University of Miami, 1311 Miller Dr, Coral Gables, FL, 33146. Tel: 305-284-2755. Fax: 305-284-3554. p. 434

Wise, Sharon L, Circ Librn, ILL, Hobbs Public Library, 509 N Shipp, Hobbs, NM, 88240. Tel: 575-397-9328. Fax: 575-397-1508. p. 1556

Wise, Shirley, In Charge, Kern Hospital, 21230 Dequindre Rd, Warren, MI, 48091. Tel: 586-427-1000. Fax: 586-759-0237. p. 1234

Wise, Susan, Acq, Shreve Memorial Library, 424 Texas St, Shreveport, LA, 71101. Tel: 318-226-4980. Fax: 318-226-4780. p. 969

Wise, Susan, Br Head, Toronto Public Library, Elmbrook Park, Two Elmbrook Crescent, Toronto, ON, M9C 5B4, CANADA. Tel: 416-394-5290. Fax: 416-394-5295. p. 2861

Wisehart, Amy, Asst Librn, University of Maine at Machias, 116 O'Brien Ave, Machias, ME, 04654-1397. Tel: 207-255-1256. Fax: 207-255-1356. p. 991

Wisel, Lee Marie, Dir, Ref, Washington Adventist University, 7600 Flower Ave, Takoma Park, MD, 20912-7796. Tel: 301-891-4217. Fax: 301-891-4204. p. 1043

Wisely, Terri, Circ Supvr, Ardmore Public Library, 320 E St NW, Ardmore, OK, 73401. Tel: 580-223-8290. Fax: 580-221-3240. p. 1956

Wiseman, Bryce, Ser Spec, University of Saint Francis, 201 Pope John Paul II Ctr, 2701 Spring St, Fort Wayne, IN, 46808. Tel: 260-399-7700, Ext 6068. Fax: 260-399-8166. p. 743

Wiseman, Carol, ILL, Providence College, One Cunningham Sq, Providence, RI, 02918-0001. Tel: 401-865-2242. Fax: 401-865-2823. p. 2173

Wiseman, Dave, Mgr, Info Sys, Roanoke College, 220 High St, Salem, VA, 24153. Tel: 540-375-2295. p. 2495

Wiseman, Kara, Youth Serv, Lake Wales Public Library, 290 Cypress Garden Lane, Lake Wales, FL, 33853. Tel: 863-678-4004. Fax: 863-678-4051. p. 458

Wiseman, Rhonda, Tech Serv Assoc, University of Cincinnati, 2540 Clifton Ave, Cincinnati, OH, 45219. Tel: 513-556-0165. Fax: 513-556-6265. p. 1874

Wiseman, Robert, Dr, Archivist, Eastern Illinois University, 600 Lincoln Ave, Charleston, IL, 61920. Tel: 217-581-8454. p. 603

Wiseman, Sharon, Dir, Staff & Organization Develop, Gail Borden Public Library District, 270 N Grove Ave, Elgin, IL, 60120-5596. Tel: 847-289-5801. Fax: 847-742-0485. p. 640

Wishard, Leslie A, Dir, Green Free Library, 134 Main St, Wellsboro, PA, 16901-1412. Tel: 570-724-4876. Fax: 570-724-7605. p. 2152

Wishard, Patricia, Head, Prog & PR, Washington County Free Library, 100 S Potomac St, Hagerstown, MD, 21740. Tel: 301-739-3250. Fax: 301-739-7603. p. 1031

Wishart, Angie, Coordr, Support Serv, Essa Public Library, 8505 County Rd 10, Unit 1, Angus, ON, L0M 1B1, CANADA. Tel: 705-424-6531. Fax: 705-424-5521. p. 2792

Wishart, K, Ref Librn, University of Toronto Libraries, Victoria University Library, 71 Queens Park Crescent E, Toronto, ON, M5S 1K7, CANADA. Tel: 416-585-4551, Ext 316. Fax: 416-585-4591. p. 2867

Wishart, Lynn, Dir, Yeshiva University Libraries, Dr Lillian & Dr Rebecca Chutick Law Library, Benjamin N Cardozo School of Law, 55 Fifth Ave, New York, NY, 10003-4301. Tel: 212-790-0223. Fax: 212-790-0236. p. 1703

Wishart, Pat, Circ Librn, Lincoln Public Library, 22 Church St, Lincoln, NH, 03251. Tel: 603-745-8159. Fax: 603-745-2037. p. 1454

Wiskoski, Barbara, Librn, West Rutland Free Library Corp, 595 Main St, West Rutland, VT, 05777. Tel: 802-438-2964. p. 2439

Wismer, Becky, Acq, Tyndale University College & Seminary, 25 Ballyconnor Ct, Toronto, ON, M2M 4B3, CANADA. Tel: 416-226-6620, Ext 2128. Fax: 416-218-6765. p. 2864

Wisner, Betty, Librn, Saint Clair County Public Library, Springville Branch, 6496 US Hwy 11, Springville, AL, 35146. Tel: 205-467-2339. Fax: 205-467-2339. p. 5

Wisner, William H, Ref & ILL Librn, Laredo Community College, West End Washington St, Laredo, TX, 78040. Tel: 956-721-5281. Fax: 956-721-5447. p. 2353

Wisneski, John, Circ, University of Wisconsin-Fox Valley Library, 1478 Midway Rd, Menasha, WI, 54952-1297. Tel: 920-832-2672. Fax: 920-832-2874. p. 2614

Wisneski, Martin, Asst Dir, Head, Tech Serv, Washburn University, School of Law Library, 1700 SW College Ave, Topeka, KS, 66621. Tel: 785-670-1788. Fax: 785-670-3194. p. 897

Wisneski, Richard, Head, Bibliog & Metadata Serv, Case Western Reserve University, 11055 Euclid Ave, Cleveland, OH, 44106. Tel: 216-368-6599. Fax: 216-368-6950. p. 1876

Wisniewski, Chris, Tech Adminr, Hubbard Public Library, 436 W Liberty St, Hubbard, OH, 44425. Tel: 330-534-3512. Fax: 330-534-7836. p. 1905

Wisniewski, Lynn, Mgr, Instrul Media, Halton District School Board, 2050 Guelph Line, Burlington, ON, L7P 5A8, CANADA. Tel: 905-335-3665. Fax: 905-335-9802. p. 2798

Wisofsky, Tami, Dir, Brazosport College Library, 500 College Dr, Lake Jackson, TX, 77566. Tel: 979-230-3308. Fax: 979-230-3185. p. 2352

Wisotzke, Tania, Cat, ILL, Libr Asst, University of Western States, 2900 NE 132nd Ave, Portland, OR, 97230-3099. Tel: 503-251-5752. Fax: 503-251-5759. p. 2015

Wisotzki, Lila, Coordr, Coll Develop, Baltimore County Public Library, 320 York Rd, Towson, MD, 21204-5179. Tel: 410-887-6137. Fax: 410-887-6103. p. 1044

Wisser, Kathy, Asst Prof, Simmons College, 300 The Fenway, Boston, MA, 02115. Tel: 617-521-2800. Fax: 617-521-3192. p. 2967

Wissink, Linda, Asst Librn, Rock Valley Public Library, 1531 Main St, Rock Valley, IA, 51247-1127. Tel: 712-476-5651. Fax: 712-476-5261. p. 841

Wisuri, Marlene, Dir, Carlton County History & Heritage Center, 406 Cloquet Ave, Cloquet, MN, 55720. Tel: 218-879-1938. Fax: 218-879-1938. p. 1245

Witcher, Curt, Mgr, Genealogy Ctr, Allen County Public Library, 900 Library Plaza, Fort Wayne, IN, 46802. Tel: 260-421-1226. Fax: 260-421-1386. p. 740

Witek, Donna, Pub Serv, Virtual Ref, University of Scranton, Monroe & Linden, Scranton, PA, 18510-4634. Tel: 570-941-4000, 570-941-4008. Fax: 570-941-7817. p. 2138

Witham, Suzanne, YA Serv, Grafton Public Library, 35 Grafton Common, Grafton, MA, 01519. Tel: 508-839-4649. Fax: 508-839-7726. p. 1091

Withee, Susan, Adult Serv Mgr, Manhattan Public Library, 629 Poyntz Ave, Manhattan, KS, 66502-6086. Tel: 785-776-4741. Fax: 785-776-1545. p. 881

Witherell, Mary, Dir, Wyckoff Public Library, 200 Woodland Ave, Wyckoff, NJ, 07481. Tel: 201-891-4866. Fax: 201-891-3892. p. 1546

Witherow, Heather, Circ Supvr, Ontario City Library, 215 East C St, Ontario, CA, 91764. Tel: 909-395-2238. Fax: 909-395-2043. p. 200

Withers, Allyson D, Dir, Libr Serv, Sidley Austin LLP Library, One S Dearborn St, Chicago, IL, 60603. Tel: 312-853-7475. Fax: 312-853-7036. p. 624

Withers, Carol, Instrul Serv Librn, San Diego City College, 1313 Park Blvd, San Diego, CA, 92101-4712. Tel: 619-388-3421. Fax: 619-388-3410. p. 232

Withers, Pam, Dir, Grant County Library, 210 N Oak St, Sheridan, AR, 72150-2495. Tel: 870-942-4436. Fax: 870-942-7500. p. 115

Withers, Rob, Head, Access Serv, Miami University Libraries, 225 King Library, Oxford, OH, 45056. Tel: 513-529-6148. Fax: 513-529-3110. p. 1926

Withoff, Alan, Asst Dir, Libr Serv, Central Texas College, Bld 102, 6200 W Central Texas Expressway, Killeen, TX, 76549. Tel: 254-526-1872. Fax: 254-526-1878. p. 2350

Withrow, Alice, Br Mgr, Chickasaw Regional Library System, Atoka County Library, 215 East A St, Atoka, OK, 74525. Tel: 580-889-3555. Fax: 580-889-8860. p. 1957

Withrow, Anita, Mgr, Pearl S Buck Birthplace Foundation, Rt 219, Hillsboro, WV, 24946. Tel: 304-653-4430. p. 2560

Withrow, Kelly, Tech Serv Librn, Texas State Technical College, 1902 N Loop 499, Harlingen, TX, 78550. Tel: 956-364-4612. Fax: 956-364-5149. p. 2331

Withrow, Lil, Pub Serv, Amarillo College Library, 2201 S Washington, Amarillo, TX, 79109. Tel: 806-371-5400. Fax: 806-371-5470. p. 2274

Witiak, Joanne L, Online Serv, Rohm & Haas Co, 727 Norristown Rd, Spring House, PA, 19477-0439. Fax: 215-641-7811. p. 2142

Witkovic, Billie, Cataloger, Southington Public Library & Museum, 255 Main St, Southington, CT, 06489. Tel: 860-628-0947. Fax: 860-628-0488. p. 368

Witkowski, Mary, Head, Historical Coll, Bridgeport Public Library, 925 Broad St, Bridgeport, CT, 06604. Tel: 203-576-7417. Fax: 203-576-8255. p. 331

Witkowski, Sandy, Dir, Worth Pinkham Memorial Library, 91 Warren Ave, Ho-Ho-Kus, NJ, 07423. Tel: 201-445-8078. p. 1491

Witmer, Linda Franklin, Dir, Cumberland County Historical Society, 21 N Pitt, Carlisle, PA, 17013-2945. Tel: 717-249-7610. Fax: 717-258-9332. p. 2041

Witmore, Michael, Dr, Dir, Folger Shakespeare Library, 201 E Capitol St SE, Washington, DC, 20003-1094. Tel: 202-544-4600. Fax: 202-544-4623. p. 400

Witowski, Ed, Librn, Saint Louis Public Library, Central Express, 815 Olive St, Saint Louis, MO, 63101. Tel: 314-206-6755. Fax: 314-621-0215. p. 1360

Witsell, Emily, Ref Serv, Texas A&M University-Commerce, 2600 S Neal St, Commerce, TX, 75429. Tel: 903-886-5717. Fax: 903-886-5434. p. 2300

Witt, Gretchen, Hist Coll Librn, Rowan Public Library, 201 W Fisher St, Salisbury, NC, 28144-4935. Tel: 704-216-8232. Fax: 704-216-8237. p. 1822

Witt, Thomas, Dir, North Merrick Public Library, 1691 Meadowbrook Rd, North Merrick, NY, 11566. Tel: 516-378-7474. Fax: 516-378-0876. p. 1706

Witte, Barbara, Vols Serv Coordr, Fremont Public Library District, 1170 N Midlothian Rd, Mundelein, IL, 60060. Tel: 847-566-8702. Fax: 847-566-0204. p. 678

Witte, Dianne, Head, Tech Serv, University of Wisconsin-Whitewater Library, 800 W Main St, Whitewater, WI, 53190. Tel: 262-472-1022. Fax: 262-472-5727. p. 2649

Witte, Pamela, Br Mgr, Public Library of Youngstown & Mahoning County, East, 430 Early Rd, Youngstown, OH, 44503. Tel: 330-259-3320. p. 1952

Witte, Pamela, Mgr, Public Library of Youngstown & Mahoning County, Brownlee Woods, 4010 Sheridan Rd, Youngstown, OH, 44514. p. 1952

Witte, Pamela, Mgr, Public Library of Youngstown & Mahoning County, Campbell Branch, 374 Sanderson Ave, Campbell, OH, 44405. p. 1952

Witte, Pamela, Br Mgr, Public Library of Youngstown & Mahoning County, Newport, 3730 Market St, Youngstown, OH, 44507. p. 1953

Witte, Pamela, Br Mgr, Public Library of Youngstown & Mahoning County, West, 2815 Mahoning Ave, Youngstown, OH, 44509. p. 1953

Witte, Pamela, Mgr, Public Library of Youngstown & Mahoning County, Struthers, 95 Poland Ave, Youngstown, OH, 44471. p. 1953

Witte-Walker, Deanna, Adminr, Southold Historical Society Museum Library, 54325 Main Rd, Southold, NY, 11971. Tel: 631-765-5500. Fax: 631-765-8510. p. 1746

Witten, Shelle, Chair, Paradise Valley Community College Library, 18401 N 32nd St, Phoenix, AZ, 85032-1200. Tel: 602-787-7203. Fax: 602-787-7205. p. 75

Wittenberg, Ronda, Div Mgr, Circ Serv, Humboldt County Library, 1313 Third St, Eureka, CA, 95501-0553. Tel: 707-269-1918. p. 147

Wittenborg, Karin, Univ Librn, University of Virginia, PO Box 400114, Charlottesville, VA, 22904-4114. Tel: 434-924-3021. Fax: 434-924-1431. p. 2454

Wittenbreer, Mary, Head Librn, Regions Hospital, 640 Jackson St, Saint Paul, MN, 55101. Tel: 651-254-3607. Fax: 651-254-3427. p. 1281

Wittenbreer, William, Pub Serv, Augsburg College, 2211 Riverside Ave, Minneapolis, MN, 55454. Tel: 612-330-1604. Fax: 612-330-1436. p. 1259

Wittenmyer, Eve, Mgr, Circ & Customer Serv, Palos Verdes Library District, 701 Silver Spur Rd, Rolling Hills Estates, CA, 90274. Tel: 310-377-9584, Ext 262. Fax: 310-541-6807. p. 219

Witthar, Karol, Archivist, Blue Springs Historical Society, 101 SW 15th St, Blue Springs, MO, 64015. Tel: 816-224-8979, 816-229-1671. p. 1319

Witthuhn, Nancy, Asst Librn, ILL, Ness City Public Library, 113 S Iowa Ave, Ness City, KS, 67560-1992. Tel: 785-798-3415. Fax: 785-798-2313. p. 884

Wittig, Glenn, Dr, Acq, Southwestern Baptist Theological Seminary Libraries, 2001 W Seminary Dr, Fort Worth, TX, 76115-2157. Tel: 817-923-1921, Ext 4000. Fax: 817-921-8765. p. 2323

Wittig, Nancy, Circ, Ledding Library of Milwaukie, 10660 SE 21st Ave, Milwaukie, OR, 97222. Tel: 503-786-7582. Fax: 503-659-9497. p. 2006

Wittke, David, Circ Supvr, Front Range Community College, 3705 W 112th Ave, Westminster, CO, 80031-2140. Tel: 303-404-5372. Fax: 303-404-5144. p. 326

Wittkop, Debra, Circ Serv, Southwest Public Libraries, SPL Admin, 3359 Park St, Grove City, OH, 43123. Tel: 614-875-6716. Fax: 614-875-2219. p. 1903

Wittkopf, Frances, Mgr, Northwest Regional Library System, Springfield Public Library, 408 School Ave, Springfield, FL, 32401. Tel: 850-872-7510. Fax: 850-747-5758. p. 481

Wittkopp, Michele, Youth Serv Coordr, Muskegon Area District Library, 4845 Airline Rd, Unit 5, Muskegon, MI, 49444-4503. Tel: 231-737-6248. Fax: 231-737-6307. p. 1212

Wittman, Dawn, Dir, Lewiston City Library, 428 Thain Rd, Lewiston, ID, 83501-5399. Tel: 208-743-6519. Fax: 208-798-4446. p. 578

Wittman, Diane, Asst Dir, Kaukauna Public Library, 111 Main Ave, Kaukauna, WI, 54130-2436. Tel: 920-766-6340. Fax: 920-766-6343. p. 2600

Wittman, Jessica, Asst Dir, Acad Tech, The John Marshall Law School, 315 S Plymouth Ct, Chicago, IL, 60604. Tel: 312-427-2737. Fax: 312-427-8307. p. 618

Wittmann, Amy, Br Mgr, Great River Regional Library, Buffalo Library, 18 NW Lake Blvd, Buffalo, MN, 55313. Tel: 763-682-2753. Fax: 763-682-9290. p. 1274

Wittmann, Stacy Ann, Head, Ad Ref Serv, Eisenhower Public Library District, 4613 N Oketo Ave, Harwood Heights, IL, 60706. Tel: 708-867-7828. Fax: 708-867-1535. p. 654

Wittner, Mickey, Commun Libr Supvr, Yakima Valley Libraries, Wapato Library, 119 E Third St, Wapato, WA, 98951. Tel: 509-877-2882. Fax: 509-877-2882. p. 2551

Witty, Cheryl, Coordr, Doc, Saint Joseph's College, Hwy 231 S, Rensselaer, IN, 47978. Tel: 219-866-6209. Fax: 219-866-6135. p. 774

Witwer, Kathy, Bibliographer, Allen County Public Library, 900 Library Plaza, Fort Wayne, IN, 46802. Tel: 260-421-1207. Fax: 260-421-1386. p. 740

Wityk, Brenda, Pres, Ocean Township Historical Museum Library, 703 Deal Rd, Ocean, NJ, 07712. Tel: 732-531-2136. p. 1515

Witzel, Nancy, Librn, Selover Public Library, 31 State Rte 95, Chesterville, OH, 43317-0025. Tel: 419-768-3431. Fax: 419-768-2249. p. 1867

Witzki, Patricia, In Charge, Long Beach Public Library, West End, 810 W Beech St, Long Beach, NY, 11561. Tel: 516-432-2704. p. 1654

Wixom, Jill, Circ Mgr, Franklin Pierce University Library, 40 University Dr, Rindge, NH, 03461-3114. Tel: 603-899-4144. Fax: 603-899-4375. p. 1463

Wixon, Angie, Acq, Per, University of Sioux Falls, 1101 W 22nd St, Sioux Falls, SD, 57105-1699. Tel: 605-331-6614. p. 2219

Wixson, Emily, Co-Dir, University of Wisconsin-Madison, Chemistry Library, 1101 University Ave, Madison, WI, 53706. Tel: 608-262-2942. Fax: 608-262-9002. p. 2608

Wladysiuk, Stefan, Librn, The Polish Library, McGill University, 3479 Peel St, Montreal, QC, H3A 1W7, CANADA. Tel: 514-398-6978. p. 2900

Wlodarczyk, MaryBeth, Ser, Concordia College, 171 White Plains Rd, Bronxville, NY, 10708. Tel: 914-337-9300, Ext 2202. Fax: 914-395-4893. p. 1588

Wobbe, Dottie, Br Mgr, Saint Louis County Library, Eureka Hills Branch, 103 Hilltop Village Ctr, Eureka, MO, 63025. Tel: 636-938-4520. p. 1358

Wobbe, Linda, Head, Coll Mgt, Saint Mary's College Library, 1928 Saint Mary's Rd, Moraga, CA, 94575. Tel: 925-631-4229. Fax: 925-376-6097. p. 191

Wobbrock, Jacob, Asst Prof, University of Washington, Mary Gates Hall, Ste 370, Campus Box 352840, Seattle, WA, 98195-2840. Tel: 206-685-9937. Fax: 206-616-3152. p. 2976

Wobig, Nyla L, Cent Libr Mgr, Des Moines Public Library, 1000 Grand Ave, Des Moines, IA, 50309. Tel: 515-283-4265. Fax: 515-237-1654. p. 808

Wochos, Sharon, Mgr, Libr Serv, Columbia College of Nursing Library, 4425 N Port Washington Rd, Glendale, WI, 53212. Tel: 414-291-1626. Fax: 414-326-2331. p. 2594

Wochos, Sharon, Librn, Saint Mary's Hospital, 2323 N Lake Dr, Milwaukee, WI, 53201. Tel: 414-291-1278. Fax: 414-291-1281. p. 2621

Wodehouse, Kate, Coll Mgt Librn, Providence Athenaeum, 251 Benefit St, Providence, RI, 02903-2799. Tel: 401-421-6970. Fax: 401-421-2860. p. 2173

Wodell, Yvonne, Dir, Human Res, Thunder Bay Public Library, 285 Red River Rd, Thunder Bay, ON, P7B 1A9, CANADA. Tel: 807-684-6806. Fax: 807-345-8727. p. 2849

Wodnick, Anne, Dir, Gloucester County Library System, Glassboro Public, Two Center St, Glassboro, NJ, 08028-1995. Tel: 856-223-6010. Fax: 856-223-6039. p. 1507

Wodnick, Anne, Dir, Gloucester County Library System, Greenwich Township, 411 Swedesboro Rd, Gibbstown, NJ, 08027. Tel: 856-223-6010. Fax: 856-223-6039. p. 1507

Wodnick, Anne, Dir, Gloucester County Library System, Logan Township, 498 Beckett Rd, Logan Township, NJ, 08085. Tel: 856-223-6010. Fax: 856-223-6039. p. 1507

Wodnick, Anne, Dir, Gloucester County Library System, Mullica Hill (Headquarters), 389 Wolfert Station Rd, Mullica Hill, NJ, 08062. Tel: 856-223-6010. p. 1507

Wodnick, Anne S, Dir, Gloucester County Library System, 389 Wolfert Station Rd, Mullica Hill, NJ, 08062. Tel: 856-223-6010. Fax: 856-223-6039. p. 1507

Woelfl, Nancy N, Dir, University of Nebraska Medical Center, 600 S 42nd St, Omaha, NE, 68198-6705. Tel: 402-559-7079. Fax: 402-559-5498. p. 1415

Woell, Yvette N, Libr Mgr, Argonne National Laboratory, 9700 S Cass Ave, Bldg 240, Argonne, IL, 60439-4801. Tel: 630-252-0007. Fax: 630-252-5024. p. 589

Woessner, Jeanette, Tech Serv Mgr, Faegre & Benson, LLP, 2200 Wells Fargo Ctr, 90 South Seventh St, Minneapolis, MN, 55402-3901. Tel: 612-766-7000. Fax: 612-766-1600. p. 1259

Woetzel, Mary Denise, Ref Librn, J Sargeant Reynolds Community College Library, Parham Campus-Library & Information Services, 1651 E Parham Rd, Richmond, VA, 23228. Tel: 804-523-5325. Fax: 804-371-3086. p. 2489

Wofford, Glenda, Dir, Salem Public Library, 102 N Jackson, Salem, MO, 65560. Tel: 573-729-4331. Fax: 573-729-2123. p. 1364

Wofsey, Tammy, ILL, Marymount Manhattan College, 221 E 71st St, New York, NY, 10021. Tel: 212-774-4803. Fax: 212-458-8207. p. 1685

Wofsey, Tammy, Ref, Marymount Manhattan College, 221 E 71st St, New York, NY, 10021. Tel: 212-774-4806. Fax: 212-458-8207. p. 1685

Wofter, Babette, Dir, Licking County Library, 101 W Main St, Newark, OH, 43055-5054. Tel: 740-349-5503. Fax: 740-349-5535. p. 1922

Wogen, Peggy, Librn, Malta Township Public Library, 203 E Adams, Malta, IL, 60150. Tel: 815-825-2525. Fax: 815-825-1525. p. 669

Wogoman, Rebecca, Cat, Clearwater Public Library System, 100 N Osceola Ave, Clearwater, FL, 33755. Tel: 727-562-4970. Fax: 727-562-4977. p. 432

Wohl, Helen, Head, Acq & Coll Develop, University of Miami, 1311 Miller Dr, Coral Gables, FL, 33146. Tel: 305-284-2251. Fax: 305-284-3554. p. 434

Wohleber, Barbara, Chief Librn, Britt Area Library, 841 Riverside Dr, Britt, ON, P0G 1A0, CANADA. Tel: 705-383-2292. Fax: 705-383-0077. p. 2797

Wohlers, John, Tech Coordr, Waubonsee Community College, State Rte 47 at Waubonsee Dr, Sugar Grove, IL, 60554. Tel: 630-466-2587. Fax: 630-466-7799. p. 708

Wohlers, Richard L, Dir, Concordia University Wisconsin, 12800 N Lake Shore Dr, Mequon, WI, 53097-2402. Tel: 262-243-4330, 262-243-4403. Fax: 262-243-4424. p. 2615

Wohlford, Carol, Dir, Andover Public Library, 1511 E Central Ave, Andover, KS, 67002. Tel: 316-558-3500. Fax: 316-558-3503. p. 856

Wohlford, Carol, Dir, Eudora Public Library, 14 E Ninth St, Eudora, KS, 66025-9478. Tel: 785-542-2496. Fax: 785-542-2496. p. 866

Wohlforth, Linda, Asst Librn, Shaw Public Library, Nine Lily Bay Rd, Greenville, ME, 04441. Tel: 207-695-3579. Fax: 207-695-0310. p. 987

Wohlgemut, Jennifer, Libr Dir, Emmanuel Bible College, 100 Fergus Ave, Kitchener, ON, N2A 2H2, CANADA. Tel: 519-894-8900, Ext 232, 519-894-8900, Ext 273. Fax: 519-894-5331. p. 2815

Wohlgemuth, Beth, Inst Librn, University of Illinois Library at Urbana-Champaign, Prairie Research Institute Library, 1816 S Oak St, Champaign, IL, 61820. Tel: 217-244-4907. Fax: 217-244-0802. p. 713

Wohlgemuth, Jill, Info Literacy Librn, Wartburg College Library, 100 Wartburg Blvd, Waverly, IA, 50677-0903. Tel: 319-352-8348. Fax: 319-352-8312. p. 850

Wohlschlag, Sarah, Managing Librn, Bay County Library System, Sage Branch Library, 100 E Midland St, Bay City, MI, 48706. Tel: 989-892-8555. Fax: 989-892-1516. p. 1156

Wohnoutka, Jill, Exec Dir, Kandiyohi County Historical Society, 610 NE Hwy 71, Willmar, MN, 56201. Tel: 320-235-1881. Fax: 320-235-1881. p. 1288

Wojcik, Lisa, Librn, Maine Department of Corrections, 675 Westbrook St, South Portland, ME, 04106. Tel: 207-822-2679. Fax: 207-822-2775. p. 1001

Wojewodsk, Cathy, Mgr, University of Delaware Library, Physics, Sharp Laboratory, Rm 221, Newark, DE, 19717. Tel: 302-831-2323. p. 386

Wojkowski, Suhad, Librn, United States Department of Agriculture, 1100 Robert E Lee Blvd, New Orleans, LA, 70124. Tel: 504-286-4288. Fax: 504-286-4396. p. 964

Wojonowski, Bonnie, Head, Youth Serv, Tompkins County Public Library, 101 E Green St, Ithaca, NY, 14850-5613. Tel: 607-272-4557, Ext 271. Fax: 607-272-8111. p. 1643

Wolak, Jody, Youth Serv Librn, Wayne Public Library, 3737 S Wayne Rd, Wayne, MI, 48184. Tel: 734-721-7832. Fax: 734-721-0341. p. 1235

Wolboldt, Penelope, Ref, Warren Library Association, 205 Market St, Warren, PA, 16365. Tel: 814-723-4650. Fax: 814-723-4521. p. 2151

Wolcott, Laurie, Coll Develop Librn, Tech Serv, Taylor University, 236 W Reade Ave, Upland, IN, 46989-1001. Tel: 765-998-5242. Fax: 765-998-5569. p. 783

Wold, Deb, Pub Serv Mgr, Principia College, One Maybeck Pl, Elsah, IL, 62028-9703. Tel: 618-374-5235. Fax: 618-374-5107. p. 643

Wold, Paula, Tech Serv, Earlville Library District, 205 Winthrop St, Earlville, IL, 60518. Tel: 815-246-9543. Fax: 815-246-6391. p. 638

Woldow, Jane, Librn, Vermont Law School, 68 North Windsor, South Royalton, VT, 05068. Tel: 802-831-1449. Fax: 802-763-7159. p. 2436

Wolf, Cele, Dir, Soldiers Grove Public Library, Solar Town Ctr, 102 Passive Sun Dr, Soldiers Grove, WI, 54655. Tel: 608-624-5815. p. 2638

Wolf, Christina, Archivist, Spec Coll Librn, Oklahoma City University, Dulaney-Browne Library, 2501 N Blackwelder, Oklahoma City, OK, 73106. Tel: 405-208-5068. Fax: 405-208-5291. p. 1974

Wolf, Colleen, Electronic Res, Pawtucket Public Library, 13 Summer St, Pawtucket, RI, 02860. Tel: 401-725-3714. Fax: 401-728-2170. p. 2171

Wolf, Eric, Dir, Menil Foundation, 1500 Branard St, Houston, TX, 77006. Tel: 713-525-9420. Fax: 713-525-9444. p. 2341

Wolf, Eric, PhD, Dr, Dir of Libr, New York School of Interior Design Library, 170 E 70th St, New York, NY, 10021. Tel: 212-472-1500, Ext 214. Fax: 212-472-8175. p. 1694

Wolf, Erin, Dir, Glidden Public Library, 110 Idaho St, Glidden, IA, 51443. Tel: 712-659-3781. Fax: 712-659-3805. p. 818

Wolf, Frances, Librn, Beth Shalom Congregation, 14200 Lamar, Overland Park, KS, 66223. Tel: 913-647-7284. Fax: 913-647-7277. p. 887

Wolf, Heather, Dir, Mesa Public Library, 64 E First St, Mesa, AZ, 85201-6768. Tel: 480-644-2712. Fax: 480-644-2991. p. 69

Wolf, Holly, Adult Serv, Fairport Public Library, One Fairport Village Landing, Fairport, NY, 14450. Tel: 585-223-9091. Fax: 585-223-3998. p. 1621

Wolf, Jay, Media Serv, Vincennes University, Shake Learning Resources Center, 1002 N First St, Vincennes, IN, 47591. Tel: 812-888-4172. Fax: 812-888-5471. p. 784

Wolf, Jay, Head, Tech Serv, Englewood Public Library, 31 Engle St, Englewood, NJ, 07631. Tel: 201-568-2215. Fax: 201-568-6895. p. 1484

Wolf, Jerry, Libr Assoc, Mississippi State University, Veterinary Medicine, PO Box 9825, Mississippi State, MS, 39762. Tel: 662-325-1141. Fax: 662-325-1144. p. 1309

Wolf, Josh, Libr Assoc, Desoto Parish Library, Logansport Branch, 203 Hwy 5, Logansport, LA, 71049. Tel: 318-697-2311. Fax: 318-697-4081. p. 955

Wolf, Joshua, Mgr, Ch Serv, Monroe County Public Library, 303 E Kirkwood Ave, Bloomington, IN, 47408. Tel: 812-349-3050. Fax: 812-349-3051. p. 728

Wolf, Joy, Dir, Sea World Library, 500 Sea World Dr, San Diego, CA, 92109-7995. Tel: 619-226-3834. Fax: 619-226-3634. p. 238

Wolf, Judy, Admin Supvr, Marion Carnegie Library, 206 S Market St, Marion, IL, 62959-2519. Tel: 618-993-5935. Fax: 618-997-6485. p. 670

Wolf, Lucille H, Librn, Blair County Law Library, Blair County Courthouse, Ste 227, 423 Allegheny St, Hollidaysburg, PA, 16648. Tel: 814-693-3090. Fax: 814-693-3289. p. 2069

Wolf, Milton, Dir of Libr Serv, Chadron State College, 300 E 12th St, Chadron, NE, 69337. Tel: 308-432-6271. p. 1395

Wolf, Rachel, Br Mgr 1, Yolo County Library, Arthur F Turner Community Library, 1212 Merkley Ave, West Sacramento, CA, 95691. Tel: 916-375-6464. Fax: 916-371-5612. p. 285

Wolf, Rebecca, Head, Automation, Deerfield Public Library, 920 Waukegan Rd, Deerfield, IL, 60015. Tel: 847-945-3311. Fax: 847-945-3402. p. 634

Wolf, Robert, Ser & Digital Operations Coordr, University of North Carolina at Pembroke, Faculty Row, Pembroke, NC, 28372. Tel: 910-521-6516. Fax: 910-521-6547. p. 1814

Wolf, Ruth, Br Mgr, Mansfield-Richland County Public Library, Ontario Branch, 2221 Village Mall Dr, Mansfield, OH, 44906. Tel: 419-529-4912. Fax: 419-529-3693. p. 1913

Wolfcale, Lidia, Circ Supvr, Saint Johns County Public Library System, Ponte Vedra Beach Branch, 101 Library Blvd, Ponte Vedra Beach, FL, 32082. Tel: 904-827-6956. Fax: 904-827-6955. p. 487

Wolfe, Amy, Tech Serv, LIM College Library, 216 E 45th St, 2nd Flr, New York, NY, 10017. Tel: 646-218-4126. Fax: 212-750-3453. p. 1685

Wolfe, Betty, Librn, Northwest Kansas Heritage Center, 401 Kansas Ave, Brewster, KS, 67732. Tel: 785-694-2891. p. 858

Wolfe, Carin, Librn, International Federation of Flyfishers, 215 E Lewis, Livingston, MT, 59047. Tel: 406-222-9369. Fax: 406-222-9369. p. 1385

Wolfe, Carl, Info Spec, Dow Chemical Library, Business Intelligence Ctr, B-1210, 2301 Brazosport Blvd, Freeport, TX, 77541. Tel: 979-238-2011, 979-238-4854. p. 2325

Wolfe, Cynthia, Ref, West Florida Public Library, 200 W Gregory, Pensacola, FL, 32502. Tel: 850-436-5060. p. 482

Wolfe, David, Dir, Academy for Educational Development, 1825 Connecticut Ave NW, Washington, DC, 20009-5721. Tel: 202-884-8000, 202-884-8118. Fax: 202-884-8491. p. 391

Wolfe, Deana, Librn, Saint Joseph's Hospital, 1824 Murdoch Ave, Parkersburg, WV, 26102. Tel: 304-424-4607. Fax: 304-424-4635. p. 2568

Wolfe, Deanna, Br Mgr, Washington County Public Library, Damascus Branch, 126 E Laurel Ave, Damascus, VA, 24236. Tel: 276-475-3820. Fax: 276-475-5081. p. 2443

Wolfe, Diane, Outreach Serv Librn, Temple Public Library, 100 W Adams Ave, Temple, TX, 76501-7641. Tel: 254-298-5288. Fax: 254-298-5328. p. 2391

Wolfe, Doug, Head Librn, Saint Peter Public Library, 601 S Washington Ave, Saint Peter, MN, 56082-1447. Tel: 507-934-7420. Fax: 507-934-1204. p. 1283

Wolfe, Fran, Info Serv, Mgr, Monterey Bay Aquarium Library, 886 Cannery Row, Monterey, CA, 93940-1085. Tel: 831-648-4849. Fax: 831-648-4884. p. 189

Wolfe, Jean, Librn, Tunbridge Public Library, 289 Vt Rte 110, Tunbridge, VT, 05077. Tel: 802-889-9404. p. 2437

Wolfe, Jennifer, E-Learning & Instruction, Athens State University Library, 407 E Pryor St, Athens, AL, 35611. Tel: 256-233-8218. Fax: 256-233-6547. p. 5

Wolfe, Judith, Dir, Massachusetts School of Law Library, 500 Federal St, Andover, MA, 01810. Tel: 978-681-0800. Fax: 978-681-6330. p. 1049

Wolfe, Katja, Librn, Kasilof Public Library, 5800 Sterling Hwy, Kasilof, AK, 99610. Tel: 907-260-3959. Fax: 907-262-8477. p. 50

Wolfe, Kim, Cent Libr Mgr, Jackson County Library Services, 205 S Central Ave, Medford, OR, 97501-2730. Tel: 541774-6980. Fax: 541 535 7090. p. 2005

Wolfe, Lacy S, Circ, Ref Librn, Ouachita Baptist University, 410 Ouachita, OBU Box 3742, Arkadelphia, AR, 71998-0001. Tel: 870-245-5119. Fax: 870-245-5245. p. 93

Wolfe, Laura, ILL, University of Tennessee Graduate School of Medicine, 1924 Alcoa Hwy, Box U-111, Knoxville, TN, 37920. Tel: 865-305-9525. Fax: 865-305-9527. p. 2243

Wolfe, Leone, Librn, Lewellen Public Library, 208 Main St, Lewellen, NE, 69147. Tel: 308-778-5428. Fax: 308-778-5427. p. 1404

Wolfe, Lindsay, Librn, Brickfield, Burchette, Ritts & Stone Law Library, 1025 Thomas Jefferson St NW, Ste 800 West, Washington, DC, 20007. Tel: 202-342-0800. Fax: 202-342-0807. p. 394

Wolfe, Lisa, Mgr, Three Rivers Regional Library System, Long County Library, 28 S Main St, Ludowici, GA, 31316. Tel: 912-545-2521. Fax: 912-545-8887. p. 522

Wolfe, Lisa, Dir of Libr Serv, Jefferson College Library, 1000 Viking Dr, Hillsboro, MO, 63050. Tel: 636-797-3000, 636-942-3000. Fax: 636-789-3954. p. 1331

Wolfe, Mark, Head of Libr, Free Library of Philadelphia, Widener Branch, 2808 W Lehigh Ave, Philadelphia, PA, 19132-3296. Tel: 215-685-9798, 215-685-9799. Fax: 215-685-9716. p. 2109

Wolfe, Mary Ellen, Dir, Sharon Springs Free Library, Main St, Rte 10, Sharon Springs, NY, 13459. Tel: 518-284-2625. Fax: 518-284-3126. p. 1742

Wolfe, NJ, Dir, Fashion Institute of Technology-SUNY, Seventh Ave at 27th St, New York, NY, 10001-5992. Tel: 212-217-4340. Fax: 212-217-4371. p. 1678

Wolfe, Rebecca, Librn, Allen County Public Library, Dupont, 536 E Dupont Rd, Fort Wayne, IN, 46825. Tel: 260-421-1315. Fax: 260-489-7756. p. 740

Wolfe, Sue, Br Head, Toronto Public Library, Brentwood, 36 Brentwood Rd N, Toronto, ON, M8X 2B5, CANADA. Tel: 416-394-5240. Fax: 416-394-5257. p. 2860

Wolfe, Susan, Librn, Allen F Pierce Free Library, 115 Center St, Troy, PA, 16947-1125. Tel: 570-297-2745. Fax: 570-297-2745. p. 2147

Wolfe, Susan, Br Mgr, Bristol Public Library, Avoca, 1550 Volunteer Pkwy, Bristol, VA, 37620-6000. Tel: 423-968-9663. Fax: 276-645-8795. p. 2453

Wolfe, Susan J, Exec Dir, St Mary's County Historical Society, 41680 Tudor Pl, Leonardtown, MD, 20650-0212. Tel: 301-475-2467. Fax: 301-475-2467. p. 1035

Wolfer, Barbara, Circ Mgr, Woodbridge Town Library, Ten Newton Rd, Woodbridge, CT, 06525. Tel: 203-389-3433. Fax: 203-389-3457. p. 380

Wolff, Joan, Sr Assoc, Info Res N Am, National Economic Research Associates, Inc, 360 Hamilton Ave, 10th Flr, White Plains, NY, 10601. Tel: 213-346-3028. Fax: 914-448-4040. p. 1768

Wolff, Joan, Med Librn, Bryn Mawr Hospital Library, 130 S Bryn Mawr Ave, Bryn Mawr, PA, 19010. Tel: 484-337-3160. Fax: 610-525-5931. p. 2039

Wolff, Kim, Head Librn/Prog Dir II, Saint Petersburg College, Clearwater Campus Library, 2465 Drew St, Clearwater, FL, 33765. Tel: 727-791-2417. Fax: 727-791-2601. p. 483

Wolff, Necia, Bibliog Instr, Ref, Saint Mary's University, Louis J Blume Library, One Camino Santa Maria, San Antonio, TX, 78228-8608. Tel: 210-436-3441. Fax: 210-436-3782. p. 2381

Wolff, Rich, Adminr, Tinley Park Public Library, 7851 Timber Dr, Tinley Park, IL, 60477-3398. Tel: 708-532-0160, Ext 8. Fax: 708-532-2981. p. 709

Wolffe, Linda, Librn/Standards Adminr, ISA - The International Society of Automation, 67 Alexander Dr, Research Triangle Park, NC, 27709. Tel: 910-990-9257. Fax: 919-549-8288. p. 1819

Wolffing, Libby, Res, Riley County Kansas Genealogical Society Library, 2005 Claflin, Manhattan, KS, 66502-3415. Tel: 785-565-6495. p. 882

Wolfgram, Derek, Dep County Librn, Commun Libr & Human Res, Santa Clara County Library District, 14600 Winchester Blvd, Los Gatos, CA, 95032. Tel: 408-293-2326, Ext 3002. Fax: 408-364-0161. p. 180

Wolfgram, Patricia, Mgr, MidMichigan Medical Center, 4005 Orchard Dr, Midland, MI, 48670. Tel: 989-839-3262. Fax: 989-631-1401. p. 1208

Wolfinger, Debra, Cat, Logan-Hocking County District Library, 230 E Main St, Logan, OH, 43138. Tel: 740-385-2348. Fax: 740-385-9093. p. 1910

Wolford, Cathy, Head, Tech Serv, The Henry Ford, 20900 Oakwood Blvd, Dearborn, MI, 48124-5029. Tel: 313-982-6100, Ext 2509. Fax: 313-982-6244. p. 1167

Wolford, Joanne, Librn, Ohio Christian University, 1476 Lancaster Pike, Circleville, OH, 43113. Tel: 740-477-7737, 740-477-7858. Fax: 740-477-7855. p. 1875

Wolford, Linda, Br Mgr, Kansas City, Kansas Public Library, Main Branch, 625 Minnesota Ave, Kansas City, KS, 66101. Tel: 913-279-2202. Fax: 913-279-2032. p. 875

Wolford, Susan, Electronic Serv, Ref Serv, West Virginia University Libraries, George R Farmer, Jr College of Law Library, One Law Center Dr, Morgantown, WV, 26506. Tel: 304-293-6830. Fax: 304-293-6020. p. 2566

Wolfrom, Connie, Tech Consult, Automation System Colorado Consortium, c/o Delta Public Library, 211 W Sixth St, Delta, CO, 81416. Tel: 970-872-4317. p. 2939

Wolfrom, Katelyn, Evening/Weekend Ref Librn, Drexel University Libraries, Hagerty Library, 33rd & Market Sts, Philadelphia, PA, 19104-2875. Tel: 215-895-2750. Fax: 215-895-2070. p. 2105

Wolfson, Gail, Sr Assoc, General Mills, Inc, Business Information Center, One General Mills Blvd, Minneapolis, MN, 55426-1347. Tel: 763-764-5461. p. 1260

Wolfson, Laurel S, Admin Librn, Hebrew Union College-Jewish Institute of Religion, HUC-JIR, 3101 Clifton Ave, Cincinnati, OH, 45220-2488. Tel: 513-487-3274. Fax: 513-221-0519. p. 1870

Wolinsky, Judi, Adult Serv, Mgr, Homewood Public Library, 17917 Dixie Hwy, Homewood, IL, 60430-1703. Tel: 708-798-0121. Fax: 708-798-0662. p. 657

Wolk, Robert, Ref, Spec Coll Librn, William Paterson University of New Jersey, 300 Pompton Rd, Wayne, NJ, 07470. Tel: 973-720-2289. Fax: 973-720-3171. p. 1540

Wolke, Johanna, Asst Dir, Clark Memorial Library, Seven Pinehurst Dr, Carolina, RI, 02812. Tel: 401-364-6100. Fax: 401-364-7675. p. 2164

Woll, Gail, Admin Dir, Dorset Village Library, Rte 30 & Church St, Dorset, VT, 05251. Tel: 802-867-5774. p. 2423

Wollam, Angela, Dir, Brazoria County Law Library, 111 E Locust St, Ste 315-A, Angleton, TX, 77515. Tel: 979-864-1225. Fax: 979-864-1226. p. 2275

Wollenberg, Harriet, Coll Develop Librn, New City Free Library, 220 N Main St, New City, NY, 10956. Tel: 845-634-4997. p. 1665

Wollenberg, Yvonne, Circ, Enfield Public Library, 104 Middle Rd, Enfield, CT, 06082. Tel: 860-763-7510. Fax: 860-763-7514. p. 338

Wollersheim, Sharon, Librn, Coutts Municipal Library, 218 First Ave S, Coutts, AB, T0K 0N0, CANADA. Tel: 403-344-3804. p. 2695

Wollny, Victoria, Evening/Weekend Librn, College of Saint Elizabeth, Two Convent Rd, Morristown, NJ, 07960-6989. Tel: 973-290-4237. Fax: 973-290-4226. p. 1504

Wollon, Gregory, Mrs, Br Mgr, Harford County Public Library, Darlington Branch, 1134 Main St, Darlington, MD, 21034-1418. Tel: 410-638-3750. Fax: 410-638-3752. p. 1020

Wolner, Theresa, Coll Develop, Planned Parenthood of Minnesota & South Dakota, 1200 Lagoon Ave S, Minneapolis, MN, 55408. Tel: 612-823-6568. Fax: 612-825-3522. p. 1261

Wolosinka, Maryann, Librn, Viking Municipal Library, PO Box 300, Viking, AB, T0B 4N0, CANADA. Tel: 780-336-4992. Fax: 780-336-4992. p. 2720

Woloski, Jason, Head, Coll Develop, Legislative Library of Manitoba, 200 Vaughan St, Rm 100, Winnipeg, MB, R3C 1T5, CANADA. Tel: 204-945-1582. Fax: 204-948-1312. p. 2756

Wolotira, Alena, Ref Librn, University of Washington Libraries, Marian Gould Gallagher Law Library, William H Gates Hall, Box 353025, Seattle, WA, 98195-3025. Tel: 206-685-4812. Fax: 206-685-2165. p. 2534

Wolpert, Ann, Dir of Libr, Massachusetts Institute of Technology Libraries, Office of the Director, 160 Memorial Dr, Cambridge, MA, 02142. Tel: 617-253-5297. Fax: 617-253-8894. p. 1077

Wolpert, Louise A, Adult Serv, Adams Public Library System, 128 S Third St, Decatur, IN, 46733-1691. Tel: 260-724-2605. Fax: 260-724-2877. p. 735

Wolpert, Susanne V, Dir, Mason Public Library, 16 Darling Hill Rd, Mason, NH, 03048. Tel: 603-878-3867. Fax: 603-878-6146. p. 1457

Wolstencroft, Lynn, Tech Serv Librn, Jacob Edwards Library, 236 Main St, Southbridge, MA, 01550-2598. Tel: 508-764-5426. Fax: 508-764-5428. p. 1126

Wolstencroft, Pauline, Sr Librn, Los Angeles County Museum of Art, 5905 Wilshire Blvd, Los Angeles, CA, 90036-4597. Tel: 323-857-6121. Fax: 323-857-4790. p. 172

Wolstenholme, Gayle, Dir, Glocester Manton Free Public Library, 1137 Putnam Pike, Chepachet, RI, 02814. Tel: 401-568-6077. Fax: 401-567-0140. p. 2164

Wolstenholme, Gayle, Dir, Harmony Library, 195 Putnam Pike, Harmony, RI, 02829. Tel: 401-949-2850. Fax: 401-949-2868. p. 2167

Wolstenholme, Shirley, Ch, North Indian River County Library, 1001 Sebastian Blvd, CR 512, Sebastian, FL, 32958. Tel: 772-589-1355. Fax: 772-388-3697. p. 491

Wolter, Audrey, Ch, Hartford Public Library, 115 N Main St, Hartford, WI, 53027-1596. Tel: 262-673-8242. Fax: 262-673-8300. p. 2597

Wolter, Barbara, Mgr, Bartram Trail Regional Library, Taliaferro County, 117 Askin St, Crawfordville, GA, 30631. Tel: 706-456-2531. Fax: 706-456-2531. p. 556

Wolter, Helen, Librn, Aldersgate United Methodist Church Library, 4115 Dewey Ave, Rochester, NY, 14616. Tel: 585-663-3665. Fax: 585-865-8442. p. 1728

Wolter, June, Asst Librn, Garnavillo Public Library, 122 Main St, Garnavillo, IA, 52049. Tel: 563-964-2119. Fax: 563-964-2119. p. 817

Wolterstorff, Robert, Dir, Victoria Mansion Library, 109 Danforth St, Portland, ME, 04101. Tel: 207-772-4841, Ext 11. Fax: 207-772-6290. p. 998

Woltz, Jonathan, Syst & Web Mgt Librn, Southwestern Oklahoma State University, 100 Campus Dr, Weatherford, OK, 73096-3002. Tel: 580-774-7023. Fax: 580-774-3112. p. 1985

Wolven, Laura, YA Serv, Finkelstein Memorial Library, 24 Chestnut St, Spring Valley, NY, 10977-5594. Tel: 845-352-5700. Fax: 845-352-2319. p. 1746

Wolverine, Priscilla, Librn, Dave O'Hara Community Library, Bag Service, No 4, La Loche, SK, S0M 1G0, CANADA. Tel: 306-822-2151. Fax: 306-822-2280. p. 2918

Wolverton, Catherine, Dir, Bloomfield Public Library, 90 Broad St, Bloomfield, NJ, 07003. Tel: 973-566-6200, Ext 203. Fax: 973-566-6217. p. 1473

Wolynska, Ewa, Spec Coll, Central Connecticut State University, 1615 Stanley St, New Britain, CT, 06050. Tel: 860-832-2086. Fax: 860-832-3409. p. 353

Wolz, Lyn, Dir, University of Kansas Libraries, Regents Center Library, Edwards Campus, 12600 Quivira Rd, Overland Park, KS, 66213-2402. Tel: 913-897-8572. Fax: 785-864-8573, 913-897-8573. p. 878

Womack, Carol, Bibliog Instr, Santa Monica College Library, 1900 Pico Blvd, Santa Monica, CA, 90405-1628. Tel: 310-434-4334, 310-434-4692. Fax: 310-434-4387. p. 266

Womack, Deb, Br Mgr, Rutherford County Library, Haynes Branch, 141 N Main St, Ste 110, Henrietta, NC, 28076. Tel: 828-657-5278, 828-657-9110. Fax: 828-657-5278. p. 1825

Womack, Jim, Coll Develop, Faulkner University, 5345 Atlanta Hwy, Montgomery, AL, 36109-3398. Tel: 334-386-7207. Fax: 334-386-7481. p. 28

Womack, Kathy, Mgr, Tonto Basin Public Library, 415 Old Hwy 188, Tonto Basin, AZ, 85553. Tel: 928-479-2355. Fax: 928-479-2355. p. 85

Womack, Kirk JD, Supvr, Trinity International University, 2200 N Grand Ave, Santa Ana, CA, 92705-7016. Tel: 714-796-7172. Fax: 714-796-7190. p. 260

Womack, Lorie, Br Mgr, Duchesne Library, Roosevelt Branch, 70 W Lagoon 44-4, Roosevelt, UT, 84066-2841. Tel: 435-722-4441. Fax: 435-722-3386. p. 2404

Womack, Matt, Dir, Ela Area Public Library District, 275 Mohawk Trail, Lake Zurich, IL, 60047. Tel: 847-438-3433. Fax: 847-438-9290. p. 663

Wonderly, Susan, Dir, Pahrump Community Library, 701 E St, Pahrump, NV, 89048-2164. Tel: 775-727-5930. Fax: 775-727-6209. p. 1432

Wondra, Judy, Dir, Independent Township Library, 108 Main St, Claflin, KS, 67525. Tel: 316-587-3488. Fax: 620-587-3488. p. 860

Wones, Suzanne, Actg Exec Dir, Harvard Library, Harvard Law School Library, Langdell Hall, 1545 Massachusetts Ave, Cambridge, MA, 02138. Tel: 617-495-3170. Fax: 617-495-4449. p. 1075

Wong, Anna, Campus Librn, National American University, 10310 Mastin, Overland Park, KS, 66212-5451. Tel: 913-981-8700. p. 889

Wong, Barbara, Librn, Bruce County Public Library, Hepworth Branch, 465 Bruce St, Hepworth, ON, N0H 1P0, CANADA. Tel: 519-935-2030. p. 2837

Wong, Brenda, Librn, Johnson Memorial Hospital, 201 Chestnut Hill Rd, Stafford Springs, CT, 06076. Tel: 860-684-8166. Fax: 860-684-8129. p. 369

Wong, Cecilia, Dean of Libr, Riverside Community College District, 4800 Magnolia Ave, Riverside, CA, 92506-1299. Tel: 951-222-8038. Fax: 951-328-3679. p. 217

Wong, Cindy, Libr Tech, IBI Group Library, 230 Richmond St W, 5th Flr, Toronto, ON, M5V 1V6, CANADA. Tel: 416-596-1930, Ext 1250. Fax: 416-596-0644. p. 2854

Wong, Connie, ILL Coordr, Tufts University, 145 Harrison Ave, Boston, MA, 02111-1843. Tel: 617-636-3787. Fax: 617-636-4039. p. 1068

Wong, Daniel, Admin Coordr for Andrew W Mellon Dir, The New York Public Library - Astor, Lenox & Tilden Foundations, 476 Fifth Ave, (@ 42nd St), New York, NY, 10018-2788. Tel: 212-930-0800. Fax: 212-592-7440. p. 1690

Wong, Dora, Sci Librn, Haverford College, 370 Lancaster Ave, Haverford, PA, 19041-1392. Tel: 610-896-1175. Fax: 610-896-1102. p. 2067

Wong, Dora, Sci, Haverford College, Astronomy, Observatory, 370 W Lancaster Ave, Haverford, PA, 19041. Tel: 610-896-1416. Fax: 610-896-1102. p. 2067

Wong, Dora, Sci, Haverford College, White Science, 370 W Lancaster Ave, Haversford, PA, 19041. Tel: 610-896-1416. Fax: 610-896-1102. p. 2067

Wong, Elaine, Ref & Info Serv, Team Leader, Mission College Library, 3000 Mission College Blvd, Santa Clara, CA, 95054-1897. Tel: 408-855-5162. Fax: 408-855-5462. p. 262

Wong, Elise, Ref/Cat Librn, Saint Mary's College Library, 1928 Saint Mary's Rd, Moraga, CA, 94575. Tel: 925-631-4229. Fax: 925-376-6097. p. 191

Wong, Frances, Mgr, Borden Ladner Gervais LLP Library, Scotia Plaza, 40 King St W, Toronto, ON, M5H 3Y4, CANADA. Tel: 416-367-6000. Fax: 416-361-2752. p. 2850

Wong, Jenny, Cat Librn, Baton Rouge Community College, 201 Community College Dr, Baton Rouge, LA, 70806. Tel: 225-216-8590. Fax: 225-216-8712. p. 942

Wong, Jenny, Acq, East Baton Rouge Parish Library, 7711 Goodwood Blvd, Baton Rouge, LA, 70806-7625. Tel: 225-231-3700. Fax: 225-231-3788. p. 942

Wong, Katherine, Head, Cat, University of Oklahoma, 401 W Brooks, Norman, OK, 73019. Tel: 405-325-4081. Fax: 405-325-7550. p. 1971

Wong, Len, Br Mgr, Richmond Hill Public Library, Richmond Green Library, One William F Bell Pkwy, Richmond Hill, ON, L4S 2T9, CANADA. Tel: 905-780-0711. Fax: 905-780-1155. p. 2839

Wong, Leo, Br Head, Toronto Public Library, Bridlewood, Bridlewood Mall, 2900 Warden Ave, Toronto, ON, M1W 2S8, CANADA. Tel: 416-396-8960. Fax: 416-396-3604. p. 2860

Wong, Leslie, Ref, Touro College, 225 Eastview Dr, Central Islip, NY, 11722-4539. Tel: 631-761-7000, 631-761-7150. Fax: 631-761-7159. p. 1605

Wong, Marilynn Mei Lin, Dir, Maui Memorial Medical Center, 221 Mahalani St, Wailuku, HI, 96793-2526. Tel: 808-242-2337. Fax: 808-242-2340. p. 567

Wong, Marlene M, Head Librn, Smith College Libraries, Werner Josten Performing Arts Library, Mendenhall Ctr for the Performing Arts, Northampton, MA, 01063. Tel: 413-585-2931. Fax: 413-585-3930. p. 1114

Wong, Melinda, In Charge, California Regional Water Quality Control Board, 1515 Clay St, Ste 1400, Oakland, CA, 94612. Tel: 510-622-2300. Fax: 510-622-2460. p. 196

Wong, Monica, Head Librn, El Paso Community College Library, Northwest Campus-Jenna Welch & Laura Busch Community Library, 6701 S Desert Blvd, El Paso, TX, 79932. Tel: 915-831-8840. Fax: 915-831-8816. p. 2316

Wong, Oi-May, Libr Mgr, Seyfarth & Shaw New York Library, 620 Eighth Ave Flr 32, New York, NY, 10018-1405. Tel: 212-218-5500. Fax: 212-218-5526. p. 1699

Wong, Patricia, County Librn, Yolo County Library, Admin Off, 226 Buckeye St, Woodland, CA, 95695-2600. Tel: 530-666-8005. Fax: 530-666-8006. p. 284

Wong, Pui, Tech Serv Mgr, Midwestern University Library, 555 31st St, Downers Grove, IL, 60515. Tel: 630-515-6182. Fax: 630-515-6195. p. 637

Wong, Pui-Ying, Mgr, Health Sci Libr & Archives, Holland Bloorview Kids Rehabilitaion Hospital, 150 Kilgour Rd, Toronto, ON, M4G 1R8, CANADA. Tel: 416-425-6220, Ext 3517. Fax: 416-425-6376. p. 2854

Wong, Siu-Ki, Head, Tech Serv, Campbell University, 113 Main St, Buies Creek, NC, 27506. Tel: 910-893-1460. Fax: 910-893-1470. p. 1778

Wong, Steven, Commun Librn, Alert Bay Public Library & Museum, 118 Fir St, Alert Bay, BC, V0N 1A0, CANADA. Tel: 250-974-5721. Fax: 250-974-5026. p. 2724

Wong-Cross, Philip, Head of Libr, DC Regional Library for the Blind & Physically Handicapped, Adaptive Services Division, Rm 215, 901 G St NW, Washington, DC, 20001. Tel: 202-559-5368 (videophone), 202-727-2142. Fax: 202-727-0322. p. 397

Woo, Janice, Dir of Libr, California College of the Arts Libraries, 5212 Broadway, Oakland, CA, 94618. p. 196

Woo, Janice, Dir of Libr, California College of the Arts Libraries, Simpson Library, 1111 Eighth St, San Francisco, CA, 94107. p. 196

Woo, Kathy, Head, Acq, University of San Francisco, 2130 Fulton St, San Francisco, CA, 94117-1080. Tel: 415-422-6417. Fax: 415-422-5949. p. 248

Woo, Vivian J, Acq, Circ, Western Seminary, 5511 SE Hawthorne Blvd, Portland, OR, 97215-3367. Tel: 503-517-1843. Fax: 503-517-1801. p. 2015

Wood, Anita, Br Mgr, Wythe-Grayson Regional Library, Wythe County Public, 300 E Monroe St, Wytheville, VA, 24382-2367. Tel: 276-228-4951. Fax: 276-228-6034. p. 2472

Wood, Ann, Pub Serv, Kitchener Public Library, 85 Queen St N, Kitchener, ON, N2H 2H1, CANADA. Tel: 519-743-0271. Fax: 519-743-1261. p. 2815

Wood, Anne M, Br Mgr, Porter County Public Library System, Portage Public, 2665 Irving St, Portage, IN, 46368-3504. Tel: 219-763-1508. Fax: 219-762-0101. p. 783

Wood, Arlene, Ref, Escanaba Public Library, 400 Ludington St, Escanaba, MI, 49829. Tel: 906-789-7323. Fax: 906-786-0942. p. 1177

Wood, Barbara, Libr Asst, Central Carolina Community College, Lillington Campus, 1075 E Cornelius Harnett Blvd, Lillington, NC, 27546. Tel: 910-814-8843. p. 1823

Wood, Bill, Dir, Jefferson County Historical Society Library, 228 Washington St, Watertown, NY, 13601. Tel: 315-782-3491. Fax: 315-782-2913. p. 1763

Wood, Bonnie, Cataloger, Shelbina Carnegie Public Library, 102 N Center, Shelbina, MO, 63468. Tel: 573-588-2271. Fax: 573-588-2271. p. 1365

Wood, Bonnie Bess, Dir, Saint Joseph Seminary College, 75376 River Rd, Saint Benedict, LA, 70457-9900. Tel: 985-867-2237. Fax: 985-867-2270. p. 966

Wood, Brian, Chairperson, Bonnyville Municipal Library, 4804 49th Ave, Bonnyville, AB, T9N 2J3, CANADA. Tel: 780-826-3071. Fax: 780-826-2058. p. 2686

Wood, Bryan A, Asst Dir, St Charles Public Library District, One S Sixth Ave, Saint Charles, IL, 60174-2105. Tel: 630-584-0076, Ext 227. Fax: 630-584-3448. p. 699

Wood, Camille, Dir, Crook County Library, 175 NW Meadow Lakes Dr, Prineville, OR, 97754-1997. Tel: 541-447-7978, Ext 301. Fax: 541-447-1308. p. 2016

Wood, Carol, Archivist, Rosenberg Library, 2310 Sealy Ave, Galveston, TX, 77550. Tel: 409-763-8854. Fax: 409-763-0275. p. 2326

Wood, Charles V, Mgr, Loudoun County Public Library, Lovettsville Branch, 12 N Light St, Lovettsville, VA, 20180. Tel: 540-822-5824. Fax: 540-822-5998. p. 2474

Wood, Charlotte, Asst Libr Dir, Wilmington Memorial Library, 175 Middlesex Ave, Wilmington, MA, 01887-2779. Tel: 978-658-2967. Fax: 978-658-9699. p. 1141

Wood, Chequita, Media Res Ed, Air Force Association, 1501 Lee Hwy, Arlington, VA, 22209-1198. Tel: 703-247-5800. Fax: 703-247-5855. p. 2448

Wood, Christopher, Tech Librn, Salisbury University, 1101 Camden Ave, Salisbury, MD, 21801-6863. Tel: 410-543-6130. Fax: 410-543-6203. p. 1040

Wood, Cindy, Asst Dir, Big Horn County Library, 430 West C St, Basin, WY, 82410. Tel: 307-568-2388. Fax: 307-568-2011. p. 2651

Wood, Darrow, Chief Librn, New York City Technical College, 300 Jay St, Brooklyn, NY, 11201. Fax: 718-260-5631. p. 1594

Wood, David, Curator, Concord Museum Library, 200 Lexington Rd, Concord, MA, 01742. Tel: 978-369-9763. Fax: 978-369-9660. p. 1082

Wood, Debi, Libr Serv Mgr, Arlington Public Library System, 101 E Abram St, MS 10-0100, Arlington, TX, 76010-1183. Tel: 817-459-6900. Fax: 817-459-6936. p. 2276

Wood, Dianne, Curatorial Asst, Museum of American Glass, Wheaton Arts & Cultural Ctr, 1501 Glasstown Rd, Millville, NJ, 08332. Tel: 856-825-6800, Ext 141. Fax: 856-825-2410. p. 1502

Wood, Dolores, Dir, Olin Public Library, 301 Parkway St, Olin, IA, 52320. Tel: 319-484-2944. Fax: 319-484-2944. p. 836

Wood, Edna Mae, Dir, Valley Head Public Library, US Rt 219 S, Valley Head, WV, 26294. Tel: 304-339-6071. Fax: 304-339-6071. p. 2573

Wood, Eileen, AV, Circ, Gwynedd-Mercy College, 1325 Sumneytown Pike, Gwynedd Valley, PA, 19437. Tel: 215-646-7300, Ext 493. Fax: 215-641-5596. p. 2063

Wood, Elaine, Pub Serv Librn, Queens University of Charlotte, 1900 Selwyn Ave, Charlotte, NC, 28274-0001. Tel: 704-337-2401. Fax: 704-337-2517. p. 1784

Wood, Ellen, Web Coordr, Maine State Library, LMA Bldg, 230 State St, Augusta, ME, 04333. Tel: 207-287-5629. Fax: 207-287-5615. p. 974

Wood, Emily, Instrul Serv Librn, Ref, Pierce College Library, 9401 Farwest Dr SW, Lakewood, WA, 98498. Tel: 253-964-6302. Fax: 253-964-6713. p. 2519

Wood, Gail, Asst Librn, East Central Community College, 275 E Broad St, Decatur, MS, 39327. Tel: 601-635-2111, Ext 219, 601-635-2111, Ext 220, 601-635-6219. Fax: 601-635-2150. p. 1298

Wood, Gail, Dir, SUNY Cortland, 81 Prospect Terrace, Cortland, NY, 13045. Tel: 607-753-2525. Fax: 607-753-5669. p. 1611

Wood, Greta, Bibliog Instr, Cat, Ref Serv, Wingate University, PO Box 219, Wingate, NC, 28174-1202. Tel: 704-233-8089. Fax: 704-233-8254. p. 1832

Wood, Hannah, Circ Librn, Harding University, 915 E Market St, Searcy, AR, 72149-2267. Tel: 501-279-4205. p. 114

Wood, Holly J, Chairperson, Sterling Public Library, 1183 Plainfield Pike, Oneco, CT, 06373. Tel: 860-564-2692. Fax: 860-564-0789. p. 363

Wood, Jack Darrell, Spec Coll Librn, Jackson-Madison County Library, 433 E Lafayette St, Jackson, TN, 38301-6386. Tel: 731-425-8600. Fax: 731-425-8609. p. 2238

Wood, Jack G, Dir, Delta College Library, 1961 Delta Rd, University Center, MI, 48710. Tel: 989-686-9822. Fax: 989-686-4131. p. 1232

Wood, Jackie, Acq, Archivist, Lambuth University, 705 Lambuth Blvd, Jackson, TN, 38301. Tel: 731-425-3290. Fax: 731-425-3200. p. 2238

Wood, Jennifer, Circ & Tech Serv Librn, Wilton Public & Gregg Free Library, Seven Forest Rd, Wilton, NH, 03086. Tel: 603-654-2581. Fax: 603-654-3674. p. 1468

Wood, Jennifer, Tech Coordr, Henrico County Public Library, 1001 N Laburnum Ave, Henrico, VA, 23223-2705. Tel: 804-290-9000. Fax: 804-222-5566. p. 2471

Wood, Judy, Dir, Deering Public Library, 762 Deering Center Rd, Deering, NH, 03244. Tel: 603-464-5108. Fax: 603-464-3804. p. 1444

Wood, Julie, Coordr, Cat, Illinois Wesleyan University, One Ames Plaza, Bloomington, IL, 61701-7188. Tel: 309-556-3350. Fax: 309-556-3706. p. 595

Wood, Julie, Network Adminr, Southern Utah University, 351 W University Blvd, Cedar City, UT, 84720. Tel: 435-586-8052. Fax: 435-865-8152. p. 2404

Wood, Julienne, Dr, Head, Res Serv, Louisiana State University, One University Pl, Shreveport, LA, 71115-2399. Tel: 318-797-5072. Fax: 318-797-5156. p. 968

Wood, Katrina, Asst Dir, Mountain View Public Library, 125 S Oak St, Mountain View, MO, 65548. Tel: 417-934-6154. Fax: 417-934-5100. p. 1347

Wood, Kelly, Ch, Weston Public Library, 87 School St, Weston, MA, 02493. Tel: 781-893-3312. Fax: 781-529-0174. p. 1139

Wood, Kitty, Br Mgr, Iberville Parish Library, White Castle Branch, 32835 Bowie St, White Castle, LA, 70788. Tel: 225-545-8424. Fax: 225-545-4536. p. 966

Wood, Laura, Dir, Tufts University, 35 Professors Row, Medford, MA, 02155-5816. Tel: 617-627-3345. Fax: 617-627-3002. p. 1104

Wood, Lisa, Br Mgr, Branch District Library, Quincy Branch, 11 N Main St, Quincy, MI, 49082-1163. Tel: 517-639-4001. Fax: 517-639-4001. p. 1164

Wood, Luz, Br Mgr, Riverside County Library System, Norco Library, 3954 Old Hamner Rd, Norco, CA, 92860. Tel: 951-735-5329. Fax: 951-735-0263. p. 218

Wood, Malinda, Librn, Cherokee County Public Library, 310 Mary St, Centre, AL, 35960. Tel: 256-927-5838. Fax: 256-927-2800. p. 11

Wood, Marilyn, Assoc Dir, Monroe County Public Library, 303 E Kirkwood Ave, Bloomington, IN, 47408. Tel: 812-349-3050. Fax: 812-349-3051. p. 728

Wood, Martha, Br Mgr, Pamunkey Regional Library, West Point Branch, 721 Main St, West Point, VA, 23181. Tel: 804-843-3244. Fax: 804-843-4158. p. 2470

Wood, Martin, Head, E-Res & Tech Serv, Florida State University Libraries, Charlotte Edwards Maguire Medical Library, 1115 W Call St, Tallahassee, FL, 32304-3556. Tel: 850-645-7304. Fax: 850-644-9942. p. 495

Wood, Mary, Ref Librn, University of California, Davis, Loren D Carlson Health Sciences Library, Med Sci 1B, One Shields Ave, Davis, CA, 95616-5291. Tel: 530-754-9122. Fax: 530-752-4718. p. 139

Wood, Mary, Circ, ILL, Pub Serv, Albany Law School, 80 New Scotland Ave, Albany, NY, 12208. Tel: 518-445-2340. Fax: 518-472-5842. p. 1568

Wood, Mary, Ref Librn, Washington State University, 600 N Riverpoint Blvd, Spokane, WA, 99202. Tel: 509-358-7930. Fax: 509-358-7928. p. 2538

Wood, Mary, Librn, Taycheedah Correctional Institution Library, 751 Hwy K, Fond du Lac, WI, 54935-9099. Tel: 920-929-3800, Ext 3899. Fax: 920-929-7899. p. 2592

Wood, Mary Anne, Youth Serv Coordr, London Public Library, 20 E First St, London, OH, 43140. Tel: 740-852-9543. Fax: 740-852-3691. p. 1911

Wood, Melanie, Dir, Pickens County Cooperative Library, Service Ctr Bldg, 155 Reform St, Carrollton, AL, 35447. Tel: 205-367-8407. p. 11

Wood, Melanie, Librn, Central Piedmont Community College Library, 1201 Elizabeth Ave, Charlotte, NC, 28235. Tel: 704-330-7695. Fax: 704-330-6887. p. 1781

Wood, Melanie, Ref Librn, Johnson & Wales University, 801 W Trade St, Charlotte, NC, 28202. Tel: 980-598-1604. p. 1783

Wood, Melody Maye, Mgr, Pub Serv, Parkland Regional Library, Yorkton Branch, 93 W Broadway St, Yorkton, SK, S3N 0L9, CANADA. Tel: 306-783-3523. Fax: 306-782-5524. p. 2932

Wood, Merrillene, Learning Res Ctr Dir, Western Nebraska Community College Library, Sidney Campus, 371 College Dr, Sidney, NE, 69162. Tel: 308-254-7451. p. 1419

Wood, Michele, ILL/Distance Educ Librn, Eastern New Mexico University, 1300 S Ave K, Sta 32, Portales, NM, 88130-7402. Tel: 575-562-2644. Fax: 575-562-2647. p. 1560

Wood, Monica, Sister, Dir, Saint Joseph's Seminary, 201 Seminary Ave, Yonkers, NY, 10704. Tel: 914-367-8256. Fax: 914-968-8787. p. 1771

Wood, Nancy M, Dir, Richmond Memorial Library, 15 School Dr, Marlborough, CT, 06447-1582. Tel: 860-295-6210. Fax: 860-295-6212. p. 350

Wood, Neva, Coordr, Coll Serv, Mason County Historical Society, 1687 S Lakeshore Dr, Ludington, MI, 49431. Tel: 231-843-4808. Fax: 231-843-7089. p. 1204

Wood, Pamela, Librn, Oxnard Public Library, Colonia, 1500 Camino del Sol, No 26, Oxnard, CA, 93030. Tel: 805-385-7984. Fax: 805-385-8323. p. 202

Wood, Pamela R, Dir, Libr Serv, Mount Olive College, 634 Henderson St, Mount Olive, NC, 28365-1699. Tel: 919-658-7753. Fax: 919-658-8934. p. 1811

Wood, Pat, Dir, Libr Serv, Association of Governing Boards of Universities & Colleges, 1133 20th St NW, Ste 300, Washington, DC, 20036. Tel: 202-776-0818. Fax: 202-223-7053. p. 394

Wood, Patricia, Circ, Tech Serv, Ohio State University LIBRARIES, Marion Campus Library, 1469 Mount Vernon Ave, Marion, OH, 43302. Tel: 740-725-6335. Fax: 740-725-6309. p. 1888

Wood, Renee, Librn, Peabody Institute Library, South, 78 Lynn St, Peabody, MA, 01960. Tel: 978-531-3380. Fax: 978-531-9113. p. 1117

Wood, Richard C, Exec Dir, Texas Tech University Health Sciences Center, 3601 Fourth St, Lubbock, TX, 79430-7781. Tel: 806-743-2200. Fax: 806-743-2218. p. 2357

Wood, Richard, Dr, Dean, University of South Alabama, 5901 USA Drive N, Rm 145, Mobile, AL, 36688. Tel: 251-460-7021. Fax: 251-460-7181. p. 26

Wood, Robin, Dir, Amherst Public Library, 221 Spring St, Amherst, OH, 44001. Tel: 440-988-4230. Fax: 440-988-4115. p. 1854

Wood, Robin, Adult Serv, San Marcos Public Library, 625 E Hopkins, San Marcos, TX, 78666. Tel: 512-393-8200. p. 2384

Wood, Ronald M, Exec Dir, Mason County Historical Society, 1687 S Lakeshore Dr, Ludington, MI, 49431. Tel: 231-843-4808. Fax: 231-843-7089. p. 1204

Wood, Ross, Acq Mgr, Cat Mgr, Wellesley College, 106 Central St, Wellesley, MA, 02481-8275. Tel: 781-283-2104. Fax: 781-283-3690. p. 1135

Wood, Sharon, Librn, Gabriel Dumont Institute of Metis Studies & Applied Research Library, 48 12th St E, Prince Albert, SK, S6V 1B2, CANADA. Tel: 306-922-6466. Fax: 306-763-4834. p. 2920

Wood, Sherri, Br Mgr, Lewis & Clark Library, Lincoln Branch, 102 Ninth Ave S, Lincoln, MT, 59639. Tel: 406-362-4300. Fax: 406-362-4039. p. 1382

Wood, Shirley K, Dir, Brown City Public Library, 4207 Main St, Brown City, MI, 48416. Tel: 810-346-2511. Fax: 810-346-2511. p. 1160

Wood, Sinai, Govt Doc Librn, Ref & Libr Instruction Unit Leader, Baylor University Libraries, Jesse H Jones Library, 1312 S Third, Waco, TX, 76798. Tel: 254-710-4606. p. 2396

Wood, Susan, Asst Dir, Sullivan City Public Library, Two W Water St, Sullivan, IL, 61951. Tel: 217-728-7221. Fax: 217-728-2215. p. 708

Wood, Susan, Librn, New Hanover County Public Library, 201 Chestnut St, Wilmington, NC, 28401. Tel: 910-798-6300. Fax: 910-798-6312. p. 1830

Wood, Susan, ILL Librn, University Libraries, University of Memphis, 126 Ned R McWherter Library, Memphis, TN, 38152-3250. Tel: 901-678-8223. p. 2252

Wood, Sylvia, Asst Librn, Delta County Public Library, 300 W Dallas Ave, Cooper, TX, 75432-1632. Tel: 903-395-4575. Fax: 903-395-4556. p. 2301

Wood, Thomas, Archivist, University of Illinois at Springfield, One University Plaza, MS BRK-140, Springfield, IL, 62703-5407. Tel: 217-206-6520. Fax: 217-206-6354. p. 707

Wood, Vicki, Dir, Tallahatchie County Library System, 102 N Walnut, Charleston, MS, 38921. Tel: 662-647-2638. Fax: 662-647-0975. p. 1295

Wood, Vicki, Coordr, Youth Serv, Lincoln City Libraries, 136 S 14th St, Lincoln, NE, 68508-1899. Tel: 402-441-8565. Fax: 402-441-8586. p. 1404

Wood, Wendy, Cat Librn, Northern Kentucky University, University Dr, Highland Heights, KY, 41099. Tel: 859-572-5480. Fax: 859-572-5390. p. 917

Wood, Wendy, Tech Serv, Somerville Public Library, 79 Highland Ave, Somerville, MA, 02143. Tel: 617-623-5000, Ext 2945. Fax: 617-628-4052. p. 1124

Woodall, Jennifer, Cataloger/Distribution Librn, Emmanuel College, 400 The Fenway, Boston, MA, 02115. Tel: 617-264-7653. Fax: 617-735-9763. p. 1060

Woodall, Kelly, ILL, Saint Luke's Health System Libraries, 190 E Bannock St, Boise, ID, 83712-6297. Tel: 208-381-2276. Fax: 208-381-4317. p. 572

Woodall, Nancy, Head, Libr Syst, University of Richmond, 28 Westhampton Way, Richmond, VA, 23173. Tel: 804-289-8853. Fax: 804-289-8757. p. 2491

Woodard, Amber, Ref & Instruction Librn, Cumberland University, One Cumberland Sq, Lebanon, TN, 37087. Tel: 615-547-1354. Fax: 615-444-2569. p. 2244

Woodard, Gracie, Br Coordr, Oakland Public Library, 125 14th St, Oakland, CA, 94612. Tel: 510-238-3479. Fax: 510-238-2232. p. 197

Woodard, Patricia, Coordr, Ref Serv (Acting), Hunter College Libraries, 695 Park Ave, New York, NY, 10065. Tel: 212-650-3653. Fax: 212-772-4142. p. 1682

Woodard, Rose, In Charge, Chemung County Library District, West Elmira Library, 1231 W Water St, Elmira, NY, 14905-1996. Tel: 607-733-0541. p. 1619

Woodard, Susan, Dir, Cheney Public Library, 203 N Main St, Cheney, KS, 67025. Tel: 316-542-3331. p. 860

Woodard, Tom, Pres, Monroe County Genealogical Society, c/o Albia Public Library, 203 Benton Ave E, Albia, IA, 52531. Tel: 641-932-2469. p. 791

Woodard, Tracy, Mgr, Suwannee River Regional Library, White Springs Public Library, 12797 Roberts St, White Springs, FL, 32096. Tel: 386-397-1389. Fax: 386-397-4460. p. 461

Woodard-Latin, Ivy, Pub Relations, Shreve Memorial Library, 424 Texas St, Shreveport, LA, 71101. Tel: 318-226-4976. Fax: 318-226-4780. p. 969

Woodbridge, Janet A, Chief Exec Officer, Chief Librn, Essex County Library, 360 Fairview Ave W, Ste 101, Essex, ON, N8M 1Y3, CANADA. Tel: 519-776-5241. Fax: 519-776-6851. p. 2804

Woodbridge, Ross, Libr Mgr, Alachua County Library District, Alachua Public Library, 14913 NW 140 St, Alachua, FL, 32615. Tel: 386-462-2592. Fax: 386-462-5537. p. 448

Woodburn, Chris C, Asst Dir, Oconee Regional Library, 801 Bellevue Ave, Dublin, GA, 31021. Tel: 478-272-5710. Fax: 478-275-5381. p. 531

Woodburn, Chris Campbell, Dep Dir, Ocmulgee Regional Library System, 535 Second Ave, Eastman, GA, 31023. Tel: 478-374-4711. Fax: 478-374-5646. p. 531

Woodburn, Judy, Coordr, Southern Maryland Hospital Center Library, 7503 Surratts Rd, Clinton, MD, 20735. Tel: 301-877-4536. Fax: 301-856-0911. p. 1024

Woodbury, Sara, Dir, Tilton Library, 75 N Main St, South Deerfield, MA, 01373. Tel: 413-665-4683. Fax: 413-665-9118. p. 1124

Woodcock, Linda, Tech Serv & Pub Serv Librn, Kwantlen Polytechnic University Library, 12666 72 Ave., Surrey, BC, V3W 2M8, CANADA. Tel: 604-599-2591. Fax: 604-599-2106. p. 2738

Woodcox, Laura, Br Mgr, Paulding County Carnegie Library, Antwerp Branch, 205 N Madison St, Antwerp, OH, 45813-8411. Tel: 419-258-2855. Fax: 419-258-2855. p. 1928

Wooddell, Michelle, Chief of Operations, Dossin Great Lakes Museum, 100 Strand Dr on Belle Isle, Detroit, MI, 48207. Tel: 313-852-4051. Fax: 313-833-5342. p. 1171

Wooden, Anne, Librn, Delta College Library, 1961 Delta Rd, University Center, MI, 48710. Tel: 989-686-9822. Fax: 989-686-4131. p. 1232

Wooden, Janet, Circ Librn, Benton County Public Library, 121 S Forrest Ave, Camden, TN, 38320-2055. Tel: 731-584-4772. Fax: 731-584-1098. p. 2226

Woodfill, Roger, Adminr, Surveyors Historical Society Library, 628 Ridge Ave, Lawrenceburg, IN, 47025-1912. Tel: 812-537-2000. Fax: 812-537-2000. p. 761

Woodfin, Elizabeth, Libr Asst I, Montgomery City-County Public Library System, E L Lowder Regional Branch Library, 2590 Bell Rd, Montgomery, AL, 36117. Tel: 334-244-5717. Fax: 334-240-4893. p. 30

Woodford, Arthur M, Interim Dir, Suburban Library Cooperative, 44750 Delco Blvd, Sterling Heights, MI, 48313. Tel: 586-685-5750. Fax: 586-685-3010. p. 2946

Woodford, Julie, Dir, Burley Public Library, 1300 Miller Ave, Burley, ID, 83318-1729. Tel: 208-878-7708. Fax: 208-878-7018. p. 572

Woodham, Aris, Dir, Web Serv, Washington University Libraries, Law Library, Washington Univ Sch Law, Anheuser-Busch Hall, One Brookings Dr, Campus Box 1171, Saint Louis, MO, 63130. Tel: 314-935-9897. Fax: 314-935-7125. p. 1363

Woodham, Lamar, Dr, Assoc Prof, University of Louisiana at Monroe, 306 Strauss Hall, 700 University Ave, Monroe, LA, 71209. Tel: 318-362-3008. Fax: 318-342-1213. p. 2966

Woodhouse, Mark, Archivist, Head, Tech Serv, Elmira College, One Park Pl, Elmira, NY, 14901. Tel: 607-735-1869. Fax: 607-735-1158. p. 1620

Woodhull, Rebecca, Dir, Illinois Office of Educational Services, 2450 Foundation Dr, Ste 100, Springfield, IL, 62703-5464. Tel: 217-786-3010, Ext 231. Fax: 217-786-3020. p. 2942

Woodley, Victoria, Dir, Pollard Memorial Library, Senior Center Branch, 276 Broadway St, Lowell, MA, 01854. p. 1100

Woodley, Victoria B, Dir, Pollard Memorial Library, 401 Merrimack St, Lowell, MA, 01852. Tel: 978-970-4120. Fax: 978-970-4117. p. 1100

Woodling, Julie, Instrul Serv Librn, Juniata College, 1815 Moore St, Huntingdon, PA, 16652-2120. Tel: 814-641-3450. Fax: 814-641-3435. p. 2070

Woodman, Ann, Ch, Canton Public Library, 786 Washington St, Canton, MA, 02021-3029. Tel: 781-821-5027. Fax: 781-821-5029. p. 1079

Woodrich, Vicki, ILL, Lenoir-Rhyne University Library, 625 7th Ave NE, Hickory, NC, 28601. Tel: 828-328-7236. Fax: 828-328-7338. p. 1801

Woodrow, Christine, Dir, New Boston Public Library, 127 N Ellis St, New Boston, TX, 75570-2905. Tel: 903-628-5414. Fax: 903-628-9739. p. 2365

Woodrow, Mary Beth, Librn, East Central Regional Library, Aitkin Public Library, 110 First Ave NE, Aitkin, MN, 56431-1319. Tel: 218-927-2339. Fax: 218-927-2339. p. 1243

Woodrow, Sharon, Asst Dir, Haywood County Public Library, 678 S Haywood St, Waynesville, NC, 28786-4398. Tel: 828-452-5169, Ext 2504. Fax: 828-452-6746. p. 1828

Woodrow, Teresa, Tech Serv, Timmins Public Library, 320 Second Ave, Timmins, ON, P4N 4A8, CANADA. Tel: 705-360-2623. Fax: 705-360-2688. p. 2849

Woodruff, Andrea D, Libr Serv Mgr, Lodi Public Library, 201 W Locust St, Lodi, CA, 95240. Tel: 209-333-5505. Fax: 209-367-5944. p. 165

Woodruff, Cathy, Fiscal Officer, Fairfield County District Library, 219 N Broad St, Lancaster, OH, 43130-3098. Tel: 740-653-2745. Fax: 740-653-4199. p. 1908

Woodruff, Debi, Bus Mgr, Ella M Everhard Public Library, 132 Broad St, Wadsworth, OH, 44281-1897. Tel: 330-334-5761. Fax: 330-334-6605. p. 1943

Woodruff, Evelina, ILL, University of New Haven, 300 Boston Post Rd, West Haven, CT, 06516. Tel: 203-932-7190. Fax: 203-932-1469. p. 377

Woodruff, Julie, Tech Serv, Chippewa Falls Public Library, 105 W Central, Chippewa Falls, WI, 54729-2397. Tel: 715-723-1146. Fax: 715-720-6922. p. 2585

Woodruff, Kevin Wayne, Dir, ILL Librn, Ref Librn, Tennessee Temple University, 1815 Union Ave, Chattanooga, TN, 37404. Tel: 423-493-4250. Fax: 423-493-4497. p. 2228

Woodruff, Margaret, Libr Dir, Charlotte Library, 115 Ferry Rd, Charlotte, VT, 05445. Tel: 802-425-3864. p. 2421

Woodruff, Patricia, Asst Br Mgr, Gloucester County Library System, Greenwich Township, 411 Swedesboro Rd, Gibbstown, NJ, 08027. Tel: 856-423-0684. Fax: 856-423-1201. p. 1507

Woodrum, Janet, Adult Serv Mgr, Danville-Center Township Public Library, 101 S Indiana St, Danville, IN, 46122-1809. Tel: 317-718-8008, Ext 12. Fax: 317-745-0756. p. 735

Woods, Alan, Dir, Ohio State University LIBRARIES, Jerome Lawrence & Robert E Lee Theatre Research Institute Library, 1430 Lincoln Tower, 1800 Cannon Dr, Columbus, OH, 43210-1230. Tel: 614-292-6614. Fax: 614-688-8417. p. 1888

Woods, Andrew, Res, Colonel Robert R McCormick Research Center, One S 151 Winfield Rd, Wheaton, IL, 60189-6097. Tel: 630-260-8186. Fax: 630-260-9298. p. 718

Woods, Anita, Asst Dir, Support Serv, Westlake Porter Public Library, 27333 Center Ridge Rd, Westlake, OH, 44145-3925. Tel: 440-871-2600. Fax: 440-871-6969. p. 1947

Woods, Carolyn, Br Mgr, Forsyth County Public Library, Kernersville Branch, 130 E Mountain St, Kernersville, NC, 27284. Tel: 336-703-2930. Fax: 336-993-5216. p. 1832

Woods, Christine, Ref, Ventress Memorial Library, 15 Library Plaza, Marshfield, MA, 02050. Tel: 781-834-5535. Fax: 781-837-8362. p. 1103

Woods, Dana, Br Mgr, Jackson-George Regional Library System, Vancleave Public Library, 12604 Hwy 57, Vancleave, MS, 39565. Tel: 228-826-5857. Fax: 228-826-5893. p. 1311

Woods, Debora, Youth Serv, Calumet Park Public Library, 1500 W 127th St, Calumet Park, IL, 60827. Tel: 708-385-5768. Fax: 708-385-8816. p. 599

Woods, Donna, Cat/Ref Librn, Westbank Community Library District, 1309 Westbank Dr, Austin, TX, 78746. Tel: 512-314-3583. Fax: 512-327-3074. p. 2285

Woods, Doreen M, Asst Dep Dir-Human Res/Workforce Develop Officer, Buffalo & Erie County Public Library System, One Lafayette Sq, Buffalo, NY, 14203-1887. Tel: 716-858-8900. Fax: 716-858-6211. p. 1596

Woods, Doug, Ch, Anacortes Public Library, 1220 Tenth St, Anacortes, WA, 98221-1922. Tel: 360-293-1910. Fax: 360-293-1929. p. 2507

Woods, Janice, Librn, Fayette County Public Libraries, Ansted Public, 102 Oak St, Ansted, WV, 25812. Tel: 304-658-5472. Fax: 304-658-5472. p. 2568

Woods, Jean, Dr, Curator, Delaware Museum of Natural History Library, 4840 Kennett Pike, Wilmington, DE, 19807. Tel: 302-658-9111, Ext 314. Fax: 302-658-2610. p. 387

Woods, Johnny, Librn, Virtual Serv, Kennesaw State University, 1000 Chastain Rd, Kennesaw, GA, 30144. Tel: 678-797-2560. Fax: 770-423-6185. p. 537

Woods, Julie, Asst Librn, Idabel Public Library, Two SE Ave D, Idabel, OK, 74745. Tel: 580-286-1074, 580-286-6406. Fax: 580-286-3708. p. 1966

Woods, Lynette, Operations Mgr, Bagaduce Music Lending Library, Five Music Library Lane, Blue Hill, ME, 04614. Tel: 207-374-5454. Fax: 207-374-2733. p. 978

Woods, Marilyn, Dir, Carnegie-Evans Public Library, 203 Benton Ave E, Albia, IA, 52531-2036. Tel: 641-932-2469. Fax: 641-932-2469. p. 791

Woods, Maureen, Dir, Coquitlam Public Library, 575 Poirier St, Coquitlam, BC, V3J 6A9, CANADA. Tel: 604-937-4131. Fax: 604-931-6739. p. 2727

Woods, Maureen, Chief Exec Officer, The Alberta Library, 6-14, Seven Sir Winston Churchill Sq, Edmonton, AB, T5J 2V5, CANADA. Tel: 780-414-0805, Ext 224. Fax: 780-414-0806. p. 2959

Woods, Mayris, Doc Delivery, Saint John's Mercy Medical Center, Tower B, 621 S New Ballas Rd, Ste 1000, Saint Louis, MO, 63141. Tel: 314-251-6340. Fax: 314-251-4299. p. 1357

Woods, Michele, Ref Outreach Librn, Xavier University of Louisiana, One Drexel Dr, New Orleans, LA, 70125-1098. Tel: 504-520-7584. Fax: 504-520-7940. p. 964

Woods, Pamela, ILL Librn, Rye Public Library, 581 Washington Rd, Rye, NH, 03870. Tel: 603-964-8401. Fax: 603-964-7065. p. 1464

Woods, Peggy, Librn, Gypsum Community Library, 521 Maple, Gypsum, KS, 67448-9783. Tel: 785-536-4319. Fax: 785-536-4296. p. 870

Woods, Sonja A, Dir, Miles City Public Library, One S Tenth St, Miles City, MT, 59301-3398. Tel: 406-234-1496. Fax: 406-234-2095. p. 1386

Woods, Stephen, US Govt Doc Librn, Pennsylvania State University Libraries, Social Sciences, 201 Paterno Library, University Park, PA, 16802-1809. Tel: 814-865-0665. Fax: 814-865-1403. p. 2148

Woods, Steve, Tech Spec, Tulare County Office of Education, 7000 Doe Ave, Ste A, Visalia, CA, 93291. Tel: 559-651-3031. Fax: 559-651-1012. p. 281

Woods, Tymmi, Acq Librn, Arizona Western College & NAU Yuma Branch Campus, 2020 S Ave 8E, Yuma, AZ, 85366. Tel: 928-344-7777. Fax: 928-344-7751. p. 90

Woods, Vicki, Dir, Brentwood Public Library, 8765 Eulalie Ave, Brentwood, MO, 63144. Tel: 314-963-8630. Fax: 314-962-8675. p. 1320

Woods, Vicky, Coordr, Cabell County Public Library, Services for the Blind & Physically Handicapped, 455 Ninth St, Huntington, WV, 25701. Tel: 304-528-5700. p. 2561

Woods-Hindson, Christian, Chair, Department of Community Services, Government of Yukon, Carmacks Community, Tantalus School, One Tantalus Crescent, Carmacks, YT, Y0B 1C0, CANADA. Tel: 867-863-5901. Fax: 867-863-5814. p. 2933

Woodside, Cathy, Regional Librn, Canada Department of Justice, Epcont Tower, 300 10423 101 St, Edmonton, AB, T5J 3Y4, CANADA. Tel: 780-495-2973. Fax: 780-495-2854. p. 2699

Woodside, Kelly Jo, Head, Ref & Info Literacy Serv, Assumption College, 500 Salisbury St, Worcester, MA, 01609. Tel: 508 767-7020. Fax: 508-767-7374. p. 1143

Woodside, Maryellen, Sr Librn, Lee County Library System, North Fort Myers Branch, 2001 N Tamiami Trail NE, North Fort Myers, FL, 33903-2802. Tel: 239-997-0320. Fax: 239-656-7949. p. 445

Woodson, Dorothy, Curator, Yale University Library, Sterling Memorial Library, 120 High St, New Haven, CT, 06520. Tel: 203-432-1883. Fax: 203-432-1294. p. 359

Woodson, Samantha, Librn, American Institute for Economic Research, 250 Division St, Great Barrington, MA, 01230-1119. Tel: 413-528-1216. Fax: 413-528-0103. p. 1092

Woodstrom, Roy, Sr Librn, Hennepin County Library, Hosmer, 347 E 36th St, Minneapolis, MN, 55408-4567. Tel: 612-543-6903. Fax: 612-543-6902. p. 1263

Woodstrup, Wendi, Br Mgr, Hawaii State Public Library System, Mililani Public Library, 95-450 Makaimoimo St, Mililani, HI, 96789-3018. Tel: 808-627-7470. Fax: 808-627-7309. p. 563

Woodward, Elaine, Actg Circuit Librn, United States Court of Appeals, United States Courthouse, 1000 E Main St, Richmond, VA, 23219-3517. Tel: 804-916-2323. p. 2491

Woodward, Ethel, Asst Librn, Patten-North Haverhill Library, 2885 Dartmouth College Hwy, North Haverhill, NH, 03774-4533. Tel: 603-787-2542. p. 1461

Woodward, Gail, Online Serv Librn, McLennan Community College Library, 1400 College Dr, Waco, TX, 76708-1498. Tel: 254-299-8000. Fax: 254-299-8026. p. 2397

Woodward, Janice, Dir, United States Marine Corps, 1401 West Rd, Bldg 1220, Camp Lejeune, NC, 28547-2539. Tel: 910-451-5724. Fax: 910-451-1871. p. 1779

Woodward Johnson, Patricia Ann, Dir, Libr Serv, Stewartville Public Library, 110 Second St SE, Stewartville, MN, 55976-1306. Tel: 507-533-4902. Fax: 507-533-4746. p. 1285

Woodward, Julia, Access Serv, Anne Arundel Community College, 101 College Pkwy, Arnold, MD, 21012-1895. Tel: 410-777-2211. Fax: 410-777-2652. p. 1011

Woodward, Pat, Br Mgr, Saint Louis County Library, Tesson Ferry Branch, 9920 Lin-Ferry Dr, Saint Louis, MO, 63123. Tel: 314-843-0560. p. 1359

Woodward, Sue, Supvr, Circ, Sterling Heights Public Library, 40255 Dodge Park Rd, Sterling Heights, MI, 48313-4140. Tel: 586-446-2640. Fax: 586-276-4067. p. 1229

Woodward, Susie, In Charge, Multnomah County Library, Hollywood, 4040 NE Tillamook St, Portland, OR, 97212. Tel: 503-988-5391. Fax: 503-988-5192. p. 2012

Woodward, Wade, Libr Dir, Converse College, 580 E Main St, Spartanburg, SC, 29302. Tel: 864-596-9020, 864-596-9071. Fax: 864-596-9075. p. 2204

Woodworth, Katheryn, Ref Librn, Burlington County Library, Evesham Branch, Evesham Municipal Complex, 984 Tuckerton Rd, Marlton, NJ, 08053. Tel: 856-983-1444. Fax: 856-983-4939. p. 1543

Woodworth, Lee, Ch, Libr Asst, Paul Memorial Library, 76 Main St, Newfields, NH, 03856-8312. Tel: 603-778-8169. Fax: 603-772-9004. p. 1460

Woodworth, Patricia, Sr Serv, Quincy Public Library, 526 Jersey St, Quincy, IL, 62301-3996. Tel: 217-223-1309, Ext 306. Fax: 217-222-5672. p. 693

Woody, Gloria T, Bibliographer, Florida Agricultural & Mechanical University Libraries, 1500 S Martin Luther King Blvd, Tallahassee, FL, 32307-4700. Tel: 850-599-3704. Fax: 850-561-2648. p. 492

Woody, Pamela, Dir, Universal City Public Library, 100 Northview Dr, Universal City, TX, 78148-4150. Tel: 210-659-7048. Fax: 210-945-9221. p. 2394

Woody, Sue, Br Mgr, Des Moines Public Library, Forest Avenue, 1326 Forest Ave, Des Moines, IA, 50314. Tel: 515-283-4152. Fax: 515-242-2853. p. 808

Woody, Sue, Br Mgr, Des Moines Public Library, South Side, 1111 Porter Ave, Des Moines, IA, 50315. Tel: 515-283-4152. Fax: 515-256-2567. p. 808

Wool, Susan, Dir, Wead Library, 64 Elm St, Malone, NY, 12953-1594. Tel: 518-483-5251. Fax: 581-483-5255. p. 1656

Woolbright, Jacalyn, Librn, Lapeer District Library, Hadley Branch, 3556 Hadley Rd, Hadley, MI, 48440. Tel: 810-797-4101. Fax: 810-797-2912. p. 1202

Wooldridge, Debra, Coll Develop, Florida Institute of Technology, 150 W University Blvd, Melbourne, FL, 32901-6988. Tel: 321-674-8021. Fax: 321-724-2559. p. 463

Woolery, Emily, Ref Serv, Mt San Antonio College Library, 1100 N Grand Ave, Walnut, CA, 91789. Tel: 909-274-4260. Fax: 909-468-4011. p. 282

Woolever, Jennifer, Circ Serv Coordr, University of Saint Francis, 201 Pope John Paul II Ctr, 2701 Spring St, Fort Wayne, IN, 46808. Tel: 260-399-7700, Ext 6069. Fax: 260-399-8166. p. 742

Woolever, Mary, Spec Coll & Archives Librn, Art Institute of Chicago, 111 S Michigan Ave, Chicago, IL, 60603. Tel: 312-443-3671. Fax: 312-443-0849. p. 606

Woolf, Monica, Librn, Congregation Beth Yeshurun, 4525 Beechnut Blvd, Houston, TX, 77096. Tel: 713-666-1884. Fax: 713-666-2924. p. 2334

Woolf, Sarah, Asst Dir, Head, Res & Instrul Serv, Pine Manor College, 400 Heath St, Chestnut Hill, MA, 02467. Tel: 617-731-7080. Fax: 617-731-7045. p. 1081

Woolf-Ivory, Jonalyn, Libr Dir, Sno-Isle Libraries, 7312 35th Ave NE, Tulalip, WA, 98271-7417. Tel: 360-651-7008. Fax: 360-651-7151. p. 2541

Woollett, Raymond, Br Mgr, West Haven Public Library, Louis J Piantino Branch, Allingtown Community Ctr, One Forest Rd, West Haven, CT, 06516-1698. Tel: 203-933-9335. p. 377

Woolman, Kathleen, Curator, Canton Historical Society Library, 11 Front St, Collinsville, CT, 06019. Tel: 860-693-8893. p. 334

Woolridge, E T, Mgr, The Naval Institute, 291 Wood Rd, Annapolis, MD, 21402-5035. Tel: 410-295-1024. Fax: 410-269-7940. p. 1010

Woolson, Sara, Youth Serv Spec, First Regional Library, B J Chain Public Library, 6619 Hwy 305 N, Olive Branch, MS, 38654. Tel: 662-895-5900. Fax: 662-895-9171. p. 1301

Woolums, Jill L, Librn, University of California, Berkeley, Education Psychology, 2600 Tolman Hall, Berkeley, CA, 94720-6000. Tel: 510-642-4209. Fax: 510-642-8224. p. 127

Wooster, Martha F, Librn, Harvard Library, Blue Hill Meteorological Observatory Library, Pierce Hall, 29 Oxford St, Cambridge, MA, 02138. Tel: 617-495-2836. Fax: 617-495-9837. p. 1074

Wooster, Martha F, Librn, Harvard Library, Gordon McKay Library, School of Engineering & Applied Sciences, Pierce Hall, 29 Oxford St, Cambridge, MA, 02138. Tel: 617-495-2836. Fax: 617-495-9837. p. 1076

Wooten, Carolyn, Asst Dir, Ch, Rainsville Public Library, 941 E Main St, Rainsville, AL, 35986. Tel: 256-638-3311. Fax: 256-638-3314. p. 34

Wooten, Jimmi, Dir, Bellwood Public Library, 600 Bohland Ave, Bellwood, IL, 60104-1896. Tel: 708-547-7393. Fax: 708-547-9352. p. 593

Wooton, Melissa, Br Mgr, Indianapolis-Marion County Public Library, Glendale, Glendale Mall, Upper Level South, 6101 N Keystone Ave, Indianapolis, IN, 46220. Tel: 317-275-4410. p. 754

Woppert, Joy, In Charge, Colonial Pennsylvania Plantation, Ridley Creek State Park, Media, PA, 19063. Tel: 610-566-1725. p. 2087

Worcester, Barbara, Dir, Liberty Library, 59 Main St, Liberty, ME, 04949. Tel: 207-589-3161. Fax: 207-589-3161. p. 990

Worden, Christina, Br Mgr, Dallas Public Library, Lakewood, 6121 Worth St, Dallas, TX, 75214-4497. Tel: 214-670-1376. Fax: 214-670-5701. p. 2307

Worden, Christina, Br Mgr, Dallas Public Library, Oak Lawn, 4100 Cedar Springs Rd, Dallas, TX, 75219-3522. Tel: 214-670-1359. Fax: 214-670-5703. p. 2307

Worden, Lori, Ch, Placentia Library District, 411 E Chapman Ave, Placentia, CA, 92870. Tel: 714-528-1906. Fax: 714-528-8236. p. 208

Worden, Melissa, Librn, Lydia Taft Pratt Library, 156 West St, West Dummerston, VT, 05357-0070. Tel: 802-258-9878. p. 2439

Worden, Patti, Tech Serv, New Tecumseth Public Library, Memorial Branch, 17 Victoria St E, Alliston, ON, L9R 1V6, CANADA. Tel: 705-435-5651. Fax: 705-435-0750. p. 2792

Wordinger, Debra, Adult Serv, Indian Prairie Public Library District, 401 Plainfield Rd, Darien, IL, 60561-4207. Tel: 630-887-8760. Fax: 630-887-8801. p. 633

Worford, Darlene, Librn, Birmingham Public Library, Titusville, Two Sixth Ave SW, Birmingham, AL, 35211. Tel: 205-322-1140. Fax: 205-328-2149. p. 8

Work-Makinne, Dawn E, Supv Librn, Tech Serv, Des Moines Public Library, 1000 Grand Ave, Des Moines, IA, 50309. Tel: 515-283-4155. Fax: 515-237-1654. p. 808

Workinger, Doug, Extn Serv, Kokomo-Howard County Public Library, 220 N Union St, Kokomo, IN, 46901-4614. Tel: 765-457-3242. Fax: 765-457-3683. p. 758

Workman, Clay, Libr Operations Mgr, Tempe Public Library, 3500 S Rural Rd, Tempe, AZ, 85282. Tel: 480-350-5540. Fax: 480-350-5544. p. 84

Workman, Darlene, Br Mgr, Mentor Public Library, Mentor-on-the-Lake, 5642 Andrews Rd, Mentor, OH, 44060. Tel: 440-257-2512. Fax: 440-257-6886. p. 1917

Workman, Jean, Librn, Frank D Campbell Memorial Library, 17 S Main St, Bessemer, PA, 16112-2535. Tel: 724-667-7939. Fax: 724-667-0898. p. 2033

Workman, Lisa, Access Serv, ILL, Georgia Health Sciences University, 1459 Laney-Walker Blvd, Augusta, GA, 30912-4400. Tel: 706-721-3441. Fax: 706-721-2018. p. 520

Worku, Adu, Dir, Pacific Union College, One Angwin Ave, Angwin, CA, 94508-9705. Tel: 707-965-6241, 707-965-6311. Fax: 707-965-6504. p. 121

Worland, Joy, Libr Dir, Joslin Memorial Library, 4391 Main St, Waitsfield, VT, 05673-6155. Tel: 802-496-4205. p. 2438

Worley, Betty, Dir, Sequatchie County Public Library, 227 Cherry St W, Dunlap, TN, 37327-5207. Tel: 423-949-2357. Fax: 423-949-6619. p. 2233

Worley, Diane, Ser, Columbus County Public Library, 407 N Powell Blvd, Whiteville, NC, 28472. Tel: 910-642-3116. Fax: 910-642-3839. p. 1829

Worley, Elizabeth, Assoc Dir, Ref, Hardin-Simmons University, 2341 Hickory St, Abilene, TX, 79698. Tel: 325-670-1237. Fax: 325-677-8351. p. 2272

Worley, Mary Lou, Librn, Macon County Public Library, Hudson Library, 554 Main St, Highlands, NC, 28741. Tel: 828-526-3031. Fax: 828-526-5278. p. 1794

Worley, Wynita, Pub Serv Librn, Grant County Public Library District, 201 Barnes Rd, Williamstown, KY, 41097-9482. Tel: 859-824-2080. Fax: 859-824-2083. p. 937

Worlsey, Catherine, Dir, Mercer Carnegie Library, 200 N College Ave, Aledo, IL, 61231. Tel: 309-582-2032, Fax: 309-582-5155. p. 588

Worman, Kelley, Assoc County Librn, Fresno County Public Library, 2420 Mariposa St, Fresno, CA, 93721-2285. Tel: 559-600-7323. p. 151

Wormell, Gayle, Coordr, Braille Institute Library Services, Desert Center, 70-251 Ramon Rd, Rancho Mirage, CA, 92270. Tel: 760-321-1111. Fax: 760-321-9715. p. 168

Wormington, Jeannine, Dir, Sarcoxie Public Library, 506 Center St, Sarcoxie, MO, 64862. Tel: 417-548-2736. Fax: 417-548-3104. p. 1364

Wornek, Lawral, Syst & Emerging Tech Librn, Cabrini College Library, 610 King of Prussia Rd, Radnor, PA, 19087-3698. Tel: 610-902-8568. Fax: 610-902-8539. p. 2132

Woron, Mykola, Librn, St Vladimir's Library & Archives, 404 Meredith Rd NE, Calgary, AB, T2E 5A6, CANADA. Tel: 403-264-3437. Fax: 403-264-3438. p. 2692

Worrall, Karen, Dir, Torrington Library, 12 Daycoeton Pl, Torrington, CT, 06790-6399. Tel: 860-489-6684. Fax: 860-482-4664. p. 372

Worrall, Lisa, In Charge, Hampton Public Library, George Wythe Law Library, 101 Kings Way, 2nd Flr, Hampton, VA, 23669. Tel: 757-728-2065. Fax: www.hamptonpubliclibrary.org/locations/law.html. p. 2468

Worrell, Deena, Ref, Gloucester City Library, 50 N Railroad Ave, Gloucester City, NJ, 08030. Tel: 856-456-4181. Fax: 856-456-6724. p. 1488

Worrell, Diane, Ark Spec Projects Librn, University of Arkansas Libraries, 365 N McIlroy Ave, Fayetteville, AR, 72701-4002. Tel: 479-575-5330. Fax: 479-575-6656. p. 99

Worrell, Donald E, Jr, Dir, Mount Clemens Public Library, 150 Cass Ave, Mount Clemens, MI, 48043. Tel: 586-469-6200. Fax: 586-469-6668. p. 1210

Worrell, Lisa, Librn, Allen County Public Library, Pontiac, 2215 S Hanna St, Fort Wayne, IN, 46803. Tel: 260-421-1350. Fax: 260-744-5372. p. 741

Worringer, Jennifer, Br Mgr, Mercer County Library System, Hickory Corner Branch, 138 Hickory Corner Rd, East Windsor, NJ, 08520. Tel: 609-448-1330. Fax: 609-490-0189. p. 1494

Worsham, Doug, AV, University of Wisconsin-Madison, L & S Learning Support Services, Van Hise Hall, 1220 Linden Dr, Madison, WI, 53706. Tel: 608-262-1408. Fax: 608-262-7579. p. 2609

Worsham, Jeremy, Tech Serv Librn, Berry College, 2277 Martha Berry Hwy, Mount Berry, GA, 30149. Tel: 706-368-6707. p. 546

Worst, Kassia, YA Librn, East Islip Public Library, 381 E Main St, East Islip, NY, 11730-2896. Tel: 631-581-9200. Fax: 631-581-2245. p. 1617

Worster, Carol, Supvr, Gas Technology Institute, 1700 S Mount Prospect Rd, Des Plaines, IL, 60018-1804. Tel: 847-768-0664. Fax: 847-768-0669. p. 636

Worth, Claudia, Presv Spec, Wheat Ridge Historical Society Library, 4610 Robb St, Wheat Ridge, CO, 80033. Tel: 303-467-0023. Fax: 303-467-2539. p. 326

Worth, Donna, Librn, Jefferson County Library System, Whitehall Community Library, 110 First St W, Whitehall, MT, 59759. Tel: 406-287-3763. Fax: 406-287-3763. p. 1375

Worth, Shanna, Librn, Lake Benton Public Library, 110 E Benton, Lake Benton, MN, 56149. Tel: 507-368-4641. p. 1255

Worthen, Claudia, Br Supvr, Jackson/Hinds Library System, Raymond Library, 126 W Court St, Raymond, MS, 39154. Tel: 601-857-8721. Fax: 601-857-4281. p. 1303

Worthen, Isabella P, Dir, Old Forge Library, 220 Crosby Blvd, Old Forge, NY, 13420. Tel: 315-369-6008. Fax: 315-369-2754. p. 1710

Worthen, Jennifer, ILL, Yuma County Library District, 2951 S 21st Dr, Yuma, AZ, 85364. Tel: 928-782-1871. Fax: 928-782-9420. p. 91

Worthen, Melinda, Librn, Champaign County Law Library Association, Champaign County Court House, 200 N Main St, Urbana, OH, 43078. Tel: 937-653-2709. Fax: 937-653-3538. p. 1942

Worthen, Susan, Br Mgr, Uinta County Library, Lyman Branch, 204 E Sage, Lyman, WY, 82937. Tel: 307-787-6556. Fax: 307-787-6339. p. 2655

Worthen, Tina, Br Librn, City College - Gainesville Library, 2400 SW 13th St, Gainesville, FL, 32608. Tel: 352-335-4000, Ext 29. Fax: 352-335-4303. p. 449

Worthen, William B, Exec Dir, Historic Arkansas Museum Library, 200 E Third St, Little Rock, AR, 72201-1608. Tel: 501-324-9308. Fax: 501-324-9345. p. 106

Worthington, Mary, Asst Dir, Pub Serv, Westlake Porter Public Library, 27333 Center Ridge Rd, Westlake, OH, 44145-3925. Tel: 440-871-2600. Fax: 440-871-6969. p. 1947

Worthington, Myrna, Chairperson, Crossfield Municipal Library, 1026 Chisholm Ave, Crossfield, AB, T0M 0S0, CANADA. Tel: 403-946-4232. Fax: 403-946-4212. p. 2696

Worthington, Nancy, Librn, Worthington Biochemical Corp Library, 730 Vassar Ave, Lakewood, NJ, 08701. Tel: 732-942-1660. Fax: 732-942-9270. p. 1494

Worthington-Cady, Amy, Dir, Cornwall Free Library, 30 Pine St, Cornwall, CT, 06753. Tel: 860-672-6874. Fax: 860-672-6398. p. 334

Worthy, Ann, Br Supvr, Gaston County Public Library, Ferguson-Erwin Center, 913 N Pryor St, Gastonia, NC, 28052. Tel: 704-868-8046. Fax: 704-868-8046. p. 1794

Worthy, Elliott, Circ, York County Library, 138 E Black St, Rock Hill, SC, 29731. Tel: 803-981-5860. Fax: 803-981-5866. p. 2203

Worthy, Ryda, Ch, South Mississippi Regional Library, 900 Broad St, Columbia, MS, 39429. Tel: 601-736-5516. Fax: 601-736-1379. p. 1296

Wortman, Marcia, Dir, Klyte Burt Memorial Public Library, 316 Center Ave, Curtis, NE, 69025. Tel: 308-367-4148. p. 1397

Wortman, Mare, Circ, Walsh College, 3838 Livernois Rd, Troy, MI, 48083-5066. Tel: 248-823-1257. Fax: 248-689-9066. p. 1232

Worwa, Amy, Mgr, Forest Lake Library, 220 N Lake St, Forest Lake, MN, 55025. Tel: 651-464-4296. Fax: 651-464-4088. p. 1251

Worwa, Amy, Mgr, Washington County Library, Hardwood Creek Branch, 19955 Forest Rd N, Forest Lake, MN, 55025. Tel: 651-275-7300. Fax: 651-275-7301. p. 1290

Worwa, Amy, Mgr, Washington County Library, Marine Branch, 121 Judd St, Marine-on-St Croix, MN, 55047-0042. Tel: 651-433-2820. Fax: 651-433-2820. p. 1290

Wos, Cathy, Librn, Tampa-Hillsborough County Public Library System, Port Tampa City Library, 4902 W Commerce St, Tampa, FL, 33616-2704. Fax: 813-301-7008. p. 498

Wotherspoon, Maureen, Supv Librn, Mineral Springs Hospital, 305 Lynx St, Banff, AB, T1L 1H7, CANADA. Tel: 403-762-2222. Fax: 403-762-4193. p. 2684

Wotschell, Roxanna, Libr Mgr, Bodo Public Library, PO Box 93, Bodo, AB, T0B 0M0, CANADA. Tel: 780-753-6323. Fax: 780-753-8195. p. 2685

Woycik, Janet, Dir, Cyrenius H Booth Library, 25 Main St, Newtown, CT, 06470. Tel: 203-426-4533. Fax: 203-426-2196. p. 361

Woyner, Linda, Bus Mgr, Eisenhower Public Library District, 4613 N Oketo Ave, Harwood Heights, IL, 60706. Tel: 708-867-7828. Fax: 708-867-1535. p. 654

Wozniak, Linda, Media Spec, Ref Serv, DeWitt Community Library, Shoppingtown Mall, 3649 Erie Blvd E, DeWitt, NY, 13214. Tel: 315-446-3578. Fax: 315-446-1955. p. 1614

Wraight, Jamie, Dr, Curator, University of Michigan-Dearborn, 4901 Evergreen Rd, Dearborn, MI, 48128-2406. Tel: 313-583-6300. Fax: 313-593-5478. p. 1168

Wray, Christina, Librn, Indiana University, Indiana Institute on Disability & Community, 2853 E Tenth St, Bloomington, IN, 47408-2601. Tel: 812-855-0077. Fax: 812-855-9630. p. 727

Wray, Douglas, Mgr, Cat Serv, Westchester Library System, 540 White Plains Rd, Ste 200, Tarrytown, NY, 10591-5110. Tel: 914-231-3243. Fax: 914-674-4186. p. 1755

Wray, Susan, Asst Dir, Mid-Continent Public Library, 15616 E US Hwy 24, Independence, MO, 64050-2098. Tel: 816-521-7220. Fax: 816-521-7253. p. 1332

Wray, Valorie A, Librn, Southwestern Manitoba Regional Library, 149 Main St, Melita, MB, R0M 1L0, CANADA. Tel: 204-522-3923. Fax: 204-522-3923. p. 2749

Wrede, Clint, Bibliographer, Cat, University of Northern Iowa Library, 1227 W 27th St, Cedar Falls, IA, 50613-3675. Tel: 319-273-3654. Fax: 319-273-2913. p. 799

Wren, Daniel, Curator, University of Oklahoma, 401 W Brooks, Norman, OK, 73019. Tel: 405-325-2611. Fax: 405-325-7550. p. 1971

Wren, Daniel, Curator, University of Oklahoma, Bass Business History Collection, Bass Collection, 507 NW, 401 W Brooks St, Norman, OK, 73019. Tel: 405-325-3941. p. 1971

Wren, Jan, Assoc Univ Librn, Digital Serv, Dir, University of the Cumberlands/Cumberland College, 821 Walnut St, Williamsburg, KY, 40769. Tel: 606-539-4329. Fax: 606-539-4317. p. 937

Wrenick, Elaine V, Librn, AMC Rambler Club, Inc Library, 2628 Queenston Rd, Cleveland Heights, OH, 44118. Tel: 216-371-0226. p. 1882

Wrenick, Frank E, Librn, AMC Rambler Club, Inc Library, 2628 Queenston Rd, Cleveland Heights, OH, 44118. Tel: 216-371-0226. p. 1882

Wrenn, Christy Jordan, Dir of Libr Serv, Centenary College of Louisiana, 2834 Woodlawn St, Shreveport, LA, 71104-3335. Tel: 318-869-5047. Fax: 318-869-5004. p. 967

Wrenn, George, Cat, Humboldt State University Library, One Harpst St, Arcata, CA, 95521-8299. Tel: 707-826-3412. Fax: 707-826-3440. p. 122

Wrenn, Jenny, Commun Libr Mgr, County of Los Angeles Public Library, Hollydale Library, 12000 S Garfield Ave, South Gate, CA, 90280-7894. Tel: 562-634-0156. Fax: 562-531-9530. p. 142

Wrigg, Annie M, Dir, Pelican Rapids Public Library, 25 W Mill Ave, Pelican Rapids, MN, 56572. Tel: 218-863-7055. Fax: 218-863-7056. p. 1270

Wright, A J, Librn, University of Alabama at Birmingham, Department of Anesthesiology Library, 619 19th St S, J965, Birmingham, AL, 35249-6810. Tel: 205-975-0158. Fax: 205-975-5963. p. 9

Wright, Amie, Ch, Madison Public Library, 39 Keep St, Madison, NJ, 07940. Tel: 973-377-0722. Fax: 973-377-3142. p. 1498

Wright, Andrea, Sci, Furman University Libraries, Science Library, Plyler Hall of Science, 3300 Poinsett Hwy, Greenville, SC, 29613. Tel: 864-294-2342. p. 2196

Wright, Andrew, Cat Mgr, Dallas Public Library, 1515 Young St, Dallas, TX, 75201-5499. Tel: 214-670-1400. Fax: 214-670-7839. p. 2306

Wright, Ann, Curator, Atascadero Historical Society Museum Library, 6600 Lewis Ave, Atascadero, CA, 93423. Tel: 805-466-8341. p. 122

Wright, Ann, Spec Coll Librn, Buncombe County Public Libraries, 67 Haywood St, Asheville, NC, 28801. Tel: 828-250-4700. Fax: 828-250-4746. p. 1774

Wright, Arthuree, Dr, Dir, Info Resources & Res, Howard University Libraries, Founders & Undergraduate Library, 500 Howard Pl NW, Washington, DC, 20059. Tel: 202-806-7926. p. 404

Wright, Arthuree R, PhD, Assoc Dir, Howard University Libraries, 500 Howard Pl NW, Washington, DC, 20059. Tel: 202-806-7234. Fax: 202-806-5903. p. 403

Wright, Ashlee, Head Archivist, Harrison Memorial Library, Ocean Ave & Lincoln St, Carmel, CA, 93921. Tel: 831-624-1615. Fax: 831-624-0407. p. 132

Wright, Barbara, Circ, Meridian District Library, 1326 W Cherry Lane, Meridian, ID, 83646. Tel: 208-888-4451. Fax: 208-884-0745. p. 579

Wright, Barbara, Evening Supvr, William Jewell College, 500 College Hill, Liberty, MO, 64068-1843. Tel: 816-415-7609. Fax: 816-415-5021. p. 1343

Wright, Bonnie, Circ, Winter Park Public Library, 460 E New England Ave, Winter Park, FL, 32789-4493. Tel: 407-623-3300. Fax: 407-623-3489. p. 505

Wright, Brenda, Asst Dir, Coll Develop, Florida Agricultural & Mechanical University Libraries, 1500 S Martin Luther King Blvd, Tallahassee, FL, 32307-4700. Tel: 850-599-3370. Fax: 850-561-2293. p. 492

Wright, Brenda, Br Mgr, Atlanta-Fulton Public Library System, Hapeville Library, 525 King Arnold St, Hapeville, GA, 30354. Tel: 404-762-4065. Fax: 404-762-4067. p. 512

Wright, Brianne, Archivist, Kingsport Public Library & Archives, 400 Broad St, Kingsport, TN, 37660-4292. Tel: 423-224-2559. Fax: 423-224-2558. p. 2240

Wright, Carol, Cat, Fullerton Public Library, 353 W Commonwealth Ave, Fullerton, CA, 92832-1796. Tel: 714-738-6395. Fax: 714-447-3280. p. 154

Wright, Carol, Access Serv, Algoma University College, 1520 Queen St E, Sault Ste. Marie, ON, P6A 2G4, CANADA. Tel: 705-949-2101. Fax: 705-949-6583. p. 2840

Wright, Carolyn, Dir, Hueytown Public Library, 1372 Hueytown Rd, Hueytown, AL, 35023. Tel: 205-491-1443. Fax: 205-491-6319. p. 20

Wright, Carrie, Educ Dir, Western Fairs Association Library, 1776 Tribute Rd, Ste 210, Sacramento, CA, 95815-4410. Tel: 916-927-3100. Fax: 916-927-6397. p. 226

Wright, Cedric, Librn, Taunton State Hospital, 60 Hodges Ave, Taunton, MA, 02780. Tel: 508-977-3000. p. 1131

Wright, Cherie, Dir, McHenry Nunda Public Library District, 813 W Rte 120, McHenry, IL, 60051. Tel: 815-385-6303. Fax: 815-385-6337. p. 672

Wright, Cheryl, Area Res Mgr, Cent Libr, Indianapolis-Marion County Public Library, 2450 N Meridian St, Indianapolis, IN, 46208. Tel: 317-275-4808. Fax: 317-269-5300. p. 753

Wright, Claudia, Librn, Prosser Public Library, Wintonbury, 1015 Blue Hills Ave, Bloomfield, CT, 06002. Tel: 860-242-0041. p. 331

Wright, Connie, Acq, Chesapeake Public Library, 298 Cedar Rd, Chesapeake, VA, 23322-5512. Tel: 757-926-5753. Fax: 757-410-7112. p. 2456

Wright, Crystal, In Charge, Saint Claire Regional Medical Center Library, 222 Medical Circle, Morehead, KY, 40351. Tel: 606-783-6861. Fax: 606-784-2178. p. 930

Wright, Crystal J, Libr Tech, Eastern Kentucky Health Science Information Network, c/o Camden-Carroll Library, Morehead State University, Morehead, KY, 40351. Tel: 606-783-6861. Fax: 606-784-2178. p. 2944

Wright, Cynthia R, Mgr, Circ & Tech Serv, Groton Public Library, 52 Newtown Rd, Groton, CT, 06340. Tel: 860-441-6750. Fax: 860-448-0363. p. 342

Wright, David, Dr, Libr Dir, Surry Community College, 630 S Main St, Dobson, NC, 27017-8432. Tel: 336-386-8121. Fax: 336-386-3692. p. 1787

Wright, Deborah, Tech Serv, South Carolina School for the Deaf & the Blind, 355 Cedar Springs Rd, Spartanburg, SC, 29302-4699. Tel: 864-577-7642, 864-585-7711. Fax: 864-577-7649. p. 2204

Wright, Deborah L, Chief Librn, Newport News Public Library System, Virgil I Grissom Branch, 366 DeShazor Dr, Newport News, VA, 23608. Tel: 757-369-3190. Fax: 757-369-3198. p. 2480

Wright, Deidre Jean, Ref Serv, Flagler County Public Library, 2500 Palm Coast Pkwy NW, Palm Coast, FL, 32137. Tel: 386-446-6763. Fax: 386-446-6773. p. 479

Wright, Denise, Circ Mgr, Mentor Public Library, 8215 Mentor Ave, Mentor, OH, 44060. Tel: 440-255-8811. Fax: 440-255-0520. p. 1917

Wright, Denise Anton, Dir, New Glarus Public Library, 319 Second St, New Glarus, WI, 53574. Tel: 608-527-2003. Fax: 608-527-5126. p. 2625

Wright, Diane, Dir, Humboldt Public Library, 115 S 16th Ave, Humboldt, TN, 38343-3403. Tel: 731-784-2383. Fax: 731-784-0582. p. 2237

Wright, Doreen, Tech Supvr, Liberal Memorial Library, 519 N Kansas, Liberal, KS, 67901-3345. Tel: 620-626-0180. Fax: 620-626-0182. p. 879

Wright, Dorothy, Librn, Missouri Department of Corrections, Southeast Correctional Center, Hwy 105, Charleston, MO, 63834. Tel: 573-683-4409. Fax: 573-683-7022. p. 1335

Wright, Drew, Res Serv Librn, Cornell University Library, The Samuel J Wood Library & The C V Starr Biomedical Information Center, 1300 York Ave, C115, Box 67, New York, NY, 10065-4896. Tel: 212-746-6050. Fax: 212-746-6494. p. 1642

Wright, Eileen, Archivist, Ref Librn, Montana State University, 1500 University Dr, Billings, MT, 59101-0298. Tel: 406-657-1656. Fax: 406-657-2037. p. 1374

Wright, Holly, Archivist, Nelson-Atkins Museum of Art, 4525 Oak St, Kansas City, MO, 64111-1873. Tel: 816-751-1354. Fax: 816-751-0498. p. 1340

Wright, Irene, Head Librn, Free Library of Philadelphia, Central Children's Department, 1901 Vine St, Philadelphia, PA, 19103-1189. Tel: 215-686-5369. p. 2107

Wright, Jackie, Digital Serv Mgr, Citizens Library, 55 S College St, Washington, PA, 15301. Tel: 724-222-2400. Fax: 724-222-2606. p. 2151

Wright, Jamie, Dir, Haskell Township Library, 700 Choteau St, Sublette, KS, 67877. Tel: 620-675-2771. Fax: 620-675-2771. p. 895

Wright, Jeanette, Librn, Dunklin County Library, Malden Branch, 113 N Madison, Malden, MO, 63863. Tel: 573-276-3674. p. 1342

Wright, Jeanne, Circ Mgr, Tarrant County College, Jenkins Garrett Library-South Campus, 5301 Campus Dr, Fort Worth, TX, 76119. Tel: 817-515-4524. Fax: 817-515-4436. p. 2323

Wright, Jeanne, Exec Dir, Norwegian American Genealogical Center & Naeseth Library, 415 W Main St, Madison, WI, 53703-3116. Tel: 608-255-2224. Fax: 608-255-6842. p. 2607

Wright, Jennifer, Pub Serv, Garnet A Wilson Public Library of Pike County, 207 N Market St, Waverly, OH, 45690-1176. Tel: 740-947-4921. Fax: 740-947-2918. p. 1945

Wright, Jessie, Ch, Meredith Public Library, 91 Main St, Meredith, NH, 03253. Tel: 603-279-4303. Fax: 603-279-5352. p. 1457

Wright, Jo Ellen, Dir, Shedd Free Library, 46 N Main, Washington, NH, 03280. Tel: 603-495-0410. Fax: 603-495-3592. p. 1467

Wright, JoLynn, Librn, Woodbury County Library, Danbury Branch - Cord Memorial Library, 215 Main St, Danbury, IA, 51019. Tel: 712-883-2207. p. 834

Wright, Joseph, Visual Arts Info Spec, Dartmouth College Library, Sherman Art Library, Carpentar Hall, Hinman Box 6025, Hanover, NH, 03755-3570. Tel: 603-646-6467. Fax: 603-646-1218. p. 1450

Wright, Joy, Archivist, Librn, Laumeier Sculpture Park Library & Archive, 12580 Rott Rd, Saint Louis, MO, 63127. Tel: 314-615-5280. Fax: 314-615-5283. p. 1355

Wright, Judith, Assoc Dean of Libr, University of Chicago Library, D'Angelo Law Library, 1121 E 60th St, Chicago, IL, 60637-2786. Tel: 773-702-9615. Fax: 773-702-2889. p. 626

Wright, Judith, Assoc Dean, Law Libr & Info Serv, University of Chicago Library, 1100 E 57th St, Chicago, IL, 60637-1502. Tel: 773-702-9616. Fax: 773-702-2889. p. 626

Wright, Julie, Media Coordr, Culver-Stockton College, One College Hill, Canton, MO, 63435. Tel: 573-288-6640. Fax: 573-288-6615. p. 1321

Wright, Kathleen, Circ, Per, Woodford County Library, 115 N Main St, Versailles, KY, 40383-1289. Tel: 859-873-5191. Fax: 859-873-1542. p. 936

Wright, Kathryn, Dir, Dallas County Library, 501 E Fourth St, Fordyce, AR, 71742. Tel: 870-352-3592. Fax: 870-352-3508. p. 100

Wright, Lacey, Dir, Barclay Public Library District, 220 S Main St, Warrensburg, IL, 62573-9657. Tel: 217-672-3621. Fax: 217-672-8404. p. 715

Wright, Laura, Web Coordr, Youth Serv Librn, Portage District Library, 300 Library Lane, Portage, MI, 49002. Tel: 269-329-4544. Fax: 269-324-9222. p. 1220

Wright, Laura, ILL, Fayetteville State University, 1200 Murchison Rd, Fayetteville, NC, 28301-4298. Tel: 910-672-1231. Fax: 910-672-1746. p. 1793

Wright, Logan S, Dir, Libr & Info Serv, Saint Paul School of Theology, 5123 E Truman Rd, Kansas City, MO, 64127. p. 1341

Wright, Lonnie, Dir, Central Baptist Hospital Library, 1740 Nicholasville Rd, Lexington, KY, 40503. Tel: 859-260-6297. Fax: 859-260-6442. p. 920

Wright, Lorna, Tech Serv, University of Connecticut Health Center, 263 Farmington Ave, Farmington, CT, 06034. Tel: 860-679-4058. Fax: 860-679-4046. p. 340

Wright, Mareda, Cat, Tech Serv Supvr, Twin Falls Public Library, 201 Fourth Ave E, Twin Falls, ID, 83301-6397. Tel: 208-733-2964. Fax: 208-733-2965. p. 584

Wright, MaryAnn, Br Coordr, Chatham-Kent Public Library, , 780 Ross Line, Erieau, ON, N0P 1N0, CANADA. Tel: 519-676-3945. p. 2799

Wright, Matthew, Head, Coll Develop & Instrul Serv, University of Nevada, Las Vegas Libraries, Wiener-Rogers Law Library, William S Boyd School of Law, 4505 Maryland Pkwy, Las Vegas, NV, 89154-1080. Tel: 702-895-2400. Fax: 702-895-2410. p. 1431

Wright, Matthew, Coll Develop Librn, Desert States Law Library Consortium, Wiener-Rogers Law Libr, William S Boyd Sch Law, 4505 Maryland Pkwy, Las Vegas, NV, 89154-1080. Tel: 702-895-2409. Fax: 702-895-2416. p. 2948

Wright, Michele, Br Mgr, Whitman County Rural Library District, Oakesdale Branch, 101 E Steptoe, Oakesdale, WA, 99158. Tel: 509-285-4310. p. 2513

Wright, Nancy, Asst Libr Dir, DeKalb County Public Library, Administrative Office, 215 Sycamore St, 4th Flr, Decatur, GA, 30030. Tel: 404-370-8450. Fax: 404-370-8469. p. 529

Wright, Nancy, Staff Educ Coordr, Riverton Memorial Hospital, 2100 W Sunset, Riverton, WY, 82501. Tel: 307-856-4161. Fax: 307-857-3586. p. 2659

Wright, Nina, Librn, Westerly Hospital, 25 Wells St, Westerly, RI, 02891. Tel: 401-348-3260. Fax: 401-348-3802. p. 2178

Wright, Nova, Dir, Dabney S Lancaster Community College Library-LRC, 1000 Dabney Dr, Clifton Forge, VA, 24422. Tel: 540-863-2800. Fax: 540-863-2916. p. 2457

Wright, Parri, Tech Serv, Aiken Technical College Library, 2276 Jefferson Davis Hwy, Graniteville, SC, 29829. Tel: 803-593-9954, Ext 1335. Fax: 803-593-2169. p. 2195

Wright, Pat, Coordr, New Center for Psychoanalysis Library, 2014 Sawtelle Blvd, Los Angeles, CA, 90025. Tel: 310-478-6541. Fax: 310-477-5968. p. 176

Wright, Raymond S, III, Dir, Church of Jesus Christ of Latter-Day Saints, Family History Library, 35 N West Temple St, Rm 344, Salt Lake City, UT, 84150-3440. Tel: 801-240-2584. Fax: 801-240-3718. p. 2412

Wright, Robert, Dir, Idaho Falls Public Library, 457 W Broadway, Idaho Falls, ID, 83402. Tel: 208-612-8460. Fax: 208-612-8467. p. 576

Wright, Roberta, Tech Serv, Bridgewater College, 402 E College St, Bridgewater, VA, 22812. Tel: 540-828-5740. Fax: 540-828-5482. p. 2452

Wright, Roxie, Mgr, Southeast Arkansas Regional Library, Warren Branch, 115 W Cypress, Warren, AR, 71671. Tel: 870-226-2536. Fax: 870-226-2536. p. 110

Wright, Scott, Tech Librn, Dexter District Library, 3255 Alpine St, Dexter, MI, 48130. Tel: 734-426-4477. Fax: 734-426-1217. p. 1174

Wright, Stephanie, Dir, Muenster Public Library, 418 N Elm St, Muenster, TX, 76252. Tel: 940-759-4291. Fax: 940-759-2250. p. 2364

Wright, Sue, Sr Law Librn, Maine State Law & Legislative Reference Library, 43 State House Sta, Augusta, ME, 04333-0043. Tel: 207-287-1600. Fax: 207-287-6467. p. 974

Wright, Susan, Mgr, Durham County Library, North Regional, 221 Milton Rd, Durham, NC, 27712-2223. Tel: 919-560-0243. Fax: 919-560-0246. p. 1788

Wright, Susan B, Librn, United States Bureau of Alcohol, Tobacco, Firearms & Explosives, 6000 Ammendale Rd, Beltsville, MD, 20705-1250. Tel: 202-648-6074. Fax: 202-648-6073. p. 1020

Wright, Tammie, Libr Mgr, Haut-Saint-Jean Regional Library, Perth-Andover Public Library, 642 E Riverside Dr, Perth-Andover, NB, E7H 1Z6, CANADA. Tel: 506-273-2843. Fax: 506-273-1913. p. 2762

Wright, Terrie, Br Mgr, Ouachita Parish Public Library, Anna Meyer Branch, 1808 Hwy 165 S, Monroe, LA, 71202. Tel: 318-327-1351. Fax: 318-329-4059. p. 957

Wright, Thayla, Librn, Arthur Johnson Memorial Library, 244 Cook Ave, Raton, NM, 87740. Tel: 575-445-9711. p. 1560

Wright, Thomas Temple, Acq, Ref Serv, Harvard Library, Center for Hellenic Studies Library, 3100 Whitehaven St NW, Washington, MA, 20008. Tel: 202-745-4414. Fax: 202-797-1540. p. 1074

Wright, Tom, Coll Develop, Librn, Brigham Young University, Harold B Lee Library, 2060 HBLL, Provo, UT, 84602. Tel: 801-422-2927. Fax: 801-422-0466. p. 2411

Wright, Tommye, Asst Dir, Mickey Reily Public Library, 604 S Mathews St, Corrigan, TX, 75939. Tel: 936-398-4156. Fax: 936-398-5113. p. 2302

Wright, Tonya, Br Mgr, Akron-Summit County Public Library, Maple Valley, 1187 Copley Rd, Akron, OH, 44320-2766. Tel: 330-864-5721. Fax: 330-864-8971. p. 1852

Wright, Tracy, Dir, Eastchester Public Library, 11 Oak Ridge Pl, Eastchester, NY, 10709. Tel: 914-793-5055. Fax: 914-793-7862. p. 1618

Wright, Wayne, Assoc Dir, Pub Serv, New York State Historical Association, 5798 State Hwy 80, Cooperstown, NY, 13326. Tel: 607-547-1474. Fax: 607-547-1405. p. 1610

Wright-Sackett, Angel, Dir, Town of Gainesville Public Library, Ten Church St, Silver Springs, NY, 14550. Tel: 585-493-2970. Fax: 585-493-2970. p. 1744

Wrightington, Lucy, Ref, New York State Department of Health, Empire State Plaza, Albany, NY, 12201. Tel: 518-474-6172. Fax: 518-474-3933. p. 1569

Wrigley, Kathryn, Dir, St John's Hospital, 800 E Carpenter, Springfield, IL, 62769. Tel: 217-544-6464, Ext 44566. Fax: 217-525-2895. p. 706

Wrobel, Assumpta, Sister, In Charge, Missionary Sisters of Saint Benedict Library, 5900 W 147th St, Oak Forest, IL, 60452-1104. Tel: 708-535-9623. p. 683

Wroblewski, Julie, Archives & Spec Coll Librn, Benedictine University Library, 5700 College Rd, Lisle, IL, 60532-0900. Tel: 630-829-6050. Fax: 630-960-9451. p. 666

Wrona, Michael, Supv Librn, Dearborn Heights City Libraries, John F Kennedy Jr Library, 24602 Van Born Rd, Dearborn Heights, MI, 48125. Tel: 313-791-6053. Fax: 313-791-6051. p. 1168

Wronski, Brad, Libr Tech, Minnesota Department of Corrections, 1079 Hwy 292, Red Wing, MN, 55066. Tel: 651-267-3644. Fax: 651-385-6425. p. 1271

Wroten, Karla, Br Mgr, Winn Parish Library, Sikes Branch, 125 Fifth St, Sikes, LA, 71473-0125. Tel: 318-628-2824. p. 972

Wrubel, Roger, Dir, Massachusetts Audubon Society, Ten Juniper Rd, Belmont, MA, 02478. Tel: 617-489-5050. Fax: 617-484-5664. p. 1053

Wrubel, Wayne, Web Coordr, Wilbraham Public Library, 25 Crane Park Dr, Wilbraham, MA, 01095-1799. Tel: 413-596-6141. Fax: 413-596-5090. p. 1140

Wsiaki, Bill, Circ Supvr, University of Manitoba Libraries, Father Harold Drake Library - St Pauls College, 70 Dysart Rd, Winnipeg, MB, R3T 2M6, CANADA. Tel: 204-474-8585. Fax: 204-474-7615. p. 2758

Wu, Anping, Tech Serv, Ouachita Baptist University, 410 Ouachita, OBU Box 3742, Arkadelphia, AR, 71998-0001. Tel: 870-245-5115. Fax: 870-245-5245. p. 93

Wu, Christina, Librn, Vale Inco Ltd, South Tower, Ste 1600, Royal Bank Plaza, 200 Bay St, Toronto, ON, M5J 2K2, CANADA. Tel: 416-361-7518. Fax: 416-361-7781. p. 2867

Wu, David R, Instrul Tech, Allen College, 1825 Logan Ave, Waterloo, IA, 50703. Tel: 319-226-2054. Fax: 319-226-2020, 319-226-2053. p. 849

Wu, Gideon, Circ, Harvard Library, Blue Hill Meteorological Observatory Library, Pierce Hall, 29 Oxford St, Cambridge, MA, 02138. Tel: 617-495-2836. Fax: 617-495-9837. p. 1074

Wu, Hong, Coordr, Electronic Res, Coordr, Info Serv, J Sargeant Reynolds Community College Library, Parham Campus-Library & Information Services, 1651 E Parham Rd, Richmond, VA, 23228. Tel: 804-523-5220. Fax: 804-371-3086. p. 2489

Wu, Jack, Tech Serv, Franciscan University of Steubenville, 1235 University Blvd, Steubenville, OH, 43952-1763. Tel: 740-283-6208. Fax: 740-284-7239. p. 1936

Wu, Jane, Automation Syst Coordr, Govt Doc, Otterbein University, 138 W Main St, Westerville, OH, 43081. Tel: 614-823-1027. Fax: 614-823-1921. p. 1946

Wu, Joan, Head, Syst, Bloomfield Township Public Library, 1099 Lone Pine Rd, Bloomfield Township, MI, 48302-2410. Tel: 248-642-5800. Fax: 248-258-2555. p. 1159

Wu, Kerry, Bus Librn, Portland State University Library, 1875 SW Park Ave, Portland, OR, 97201-3220. Tel: 503-725-4124. Fax: 503-725-4524. p. 2014

Wu, Magdalen, Head, Circ, Berkeley Heights Public Library, 290 Plainfield Ave, Berkeley Heights, NJ, 07922. Tel: 908-464-9333. Fax: 908-464-7098. p. 1472

Wu, Mary, Cat/Database Mgt Librn, Roger Williams University Library, One Old Ferry Rd, Bristol, RI, 02809. Tel: 401-254-3053. Fax: 401-254-3631. p. 2164

Wu, Michelle, Dir of Libr, Georgetown University, Georgetown Law Library (John Wolff & Edward Bennett Williams Libraries), 111 G St NW, Washington, DC, 20001. Fax: 202-662-9168. p. 403

Wu, Michelle M, Dir, Law Libr & Assoc Prof of Law, Hofstra University Law Library, 122 Hofstra University, Hempstead, NY, 11549-1220. Tel: 516-463-5898. Fax: 516-463-5129. p. 1635

Wu, Sara, Dir, World Forestry Center, 4033 SW Canyon Rd, Portland, OR, 97221. Tel: 503-228-1367. Fax: 503-228-4608. p. 2015

Wu, Tonia, Libr Assoc, New Jersey Department of Environmental Protection, 432 E State St, 1st Flr, Trenton, NJ, 08608. Tel: 609-984-2249. Fax: 609-292-3298. p. 1535

Wu, Wendy Gang, Librn III, Wayne State University Libraries, Vera P Shiffman Medical Library & Learning Resources Centers, Rackham Bldg Rm 044, 60 Farnsworth, Detroit, MI, 48202. Tel: 313-577-0586. Fax: 313-577-6668. p. 1173

Wu, Xian, Librn, Michigan State University Library, Area Studies, 100 Library, East Lansing, MI, 48824. Tel: 517-884-6392. Fax: 517-432-3532. p. 1175

Wu, Ya Lan, Tech Serv Dir, Miami University-Hamilton Campus, 1601 University Blvd, Hamilton, OH, 45011. Tel: 513-785-3235. Fax: 513-785-3231. p. 1904

Wu, Yanping, Ref Librn, Hamilton Township Public Library, One Justice Samuel A Alito, Jr Way, Hamilton, NJ, 08619. Tel: 609-581-4060. Fax: 609-581-4067. p. 1490

Wu, Yejun, Dr, Asst Prof, Louisiana State University, 267 Coates Hall, Baton Rouge, LA, 70803. Tel: 225-578-3158. Fax: 225-578-4581. p. 2966

Wu, Ziping, Cat, Bentley College, 175 Forest St, Waltham, MA, 02452-4705. Tel: 781-891-2168. Fax: 781-891-2830. p. 1132

Wubbena, Carol, Ref Librn, Kishwaukee College Library, 21193 Malta Rd, Malta, IL, 60150-9699. Tel: 815-825-2086, Ext 5670. Fax: 815-825-2072. p. 669

Wubbenhorst, Jill, Managing Librn I, Sno-Isle Libraries, Stanwood Community Library, 9701 271st St NW, Stanwood, WA, 98292-8097. Tel: 360-629-3132. Fax: 360-629-3516. p. 2542

Wuepper, Jon, Br Mgr, Cass District Library, Local History, 145 N Broadway St, Cassopolis, MI, 49031. Tel: 269-445-0412. Fax: 269-445-8795. p. 1161

Wuertz, Ron, Librn, Argus Leader Library, 200 S Minnesota Ave, Sioux Falls, SD, 57104. Tel: 605-331-2200. Fax: 605-331-2294. p. 2218

Wukovitz, Laura, Info Literacy Librn, Holy Family University Library, 9801 Frankford Ave, Philadelphia, PA, 19114. Tel: 267-341-3654. Fax: 215-632-8067. p. 2111

Wulff, Warren, Librn, Environment Canada Library, National Hydrology Research Ctr, 11 Innovation Blvd, Saskatoon, SK, S7N 3H5, CANADA. Tel: 306-975-4096. Fax: 306-975-5513. p. 2925

Wulfkuhle, Brad, Dir, FOR Sto-Rox Library, 500 Chartiers Ave, McKees Rocks, PA, 15136. Tel: 412-771-1222. Fax: 412-771-2340. p. 2085

Wunderlich, Molly, Bus Mgr, Van Buren District Library, 200 N Phelps St, Decatur, MI, 49045-1086. Tel: 269-423-4771. Fax: 269-423-8373. p. 1168

Wunsch, Charmaine, Cat, Towers Perrin Information Centre, South Tower, Ste 1501, 175 Bloor St E, Toronto, ON, M4W 3T6, CANADA. Tel: 416-960-2842. Fax: 416-960-2819. p. 2864

Wuolu, David, Coll Develop Librn, Saint John's University, 2835 Abbey Plaza, Collegeville, MN, 56321. Tel: 320-363-2128. Fax: 320-363-2126. p. 1246

Wuolu, David, Coll Develop Librn, College of Saint Benedict, 37 S College Ave, Saint Joseph, MN, 56374. Tel: 320-363-2128. Fax: 320-363-5197. p. 1277

Wuorinen, Louise, Head, Coll Develop, Lakehead University Library, 955 Oliver Rd, Thunder Bay, ON, P7B 5E1, CANADA. Tel: 807-343-8856. Fax: 807-343-8007. p. 2848

Wurangian, Nelia, Tech Serv, Loma Linda University, 11072 Anderson St, Loma Linda, CA, 92350-0001. Tel: 909-558-4581. Fax: 909-558-4121. p. 165

Wurster, Jean, Info Serv, ILL, Catawba College, 2300 W Innes St, Salisbury, NC, 28144-2488. Tel: 704-637-4448. Fax: 704-637-4304. p. 1822

Wurster, Mark, Info Serv, Tech Serv, Catawba College, 2300 W Innes St, Salisbury, NC, 28144-2488. Tel: 704-637-4783. Fax: 704-637-4304. p. 1822

Wurtzel, Barbara S, Coordr, Ref (Info Serv), Springfield Technical Community College Library, One Armory Sq, Ste 1, Springfield, MA, 01105-1685. Tel: 413-755-4816. Fax: 413-755-6315. p. 1128

Wurtzler, Judith, Head, Acq & Coll Develop, University of Wisconsin - Platteville, One University Plaza, Platteville, WI, 53818. Tel: 608-342-1077. Fax: 608-342-1645. p. 2630

Wurz, JoAnn, Ch, Maud Preston Palenske Memorial Library, 500 Market St, Saint Joseph, MI, 49085. Tel: 269-983-7167. Fax: 269-983-5804. p. 1225

Wurzel, Linda, Br Mgr, Ch Mgr, Long Branch Free Public Library, 328 Broadway, Long Branch, NJ, 07740. Tel: 732-222-3900. Fax: 732-222-3799. p. 1496

Wurzel, Linda, Br Mgr, Long Branch Free Public Library, Elberon Branch, 168 Lincoln Ave, Elberon, NJ, 07740. Tel: 732-870-1776. p. 1497

Wurzer, Greg, Librn, University of Saskatchewan Libraries, Law, Law Bldg, Rm 8, 15 Campus Dr, Saskatoon, SK, S7N 5A6, CANADA. Tel: 306-966-5999, 306-966-6053. Fax: 306-966-6162. p. 2927

Wussow, Mary, Br Mgr, Dakota County Library System, Wescott, 1340 Wescott Rd, Eagan, MN, 55123. Tel: 651-450-2900. Fax: 651-450-2955. p. 1249

Wuthenow, Josephine, Adult Serv, Ref, Mastics-Moriches-Shirley Community Library, 407 William Floyd Pkwy, Shirley, NY, 11967. Tel: 631-399-1511. Fax: 631-281-4442. p. 1743

Wuthrich, Antonina, In Charge, Merced County Library, Santa Nella Branch, 29188 W Centinella Ave, Santa Nella, CA, 95322-9600. Tel: 209-826-6059. p. 186

Wuthrich, Antonina, In Charge, Merced County Library, Stevinson Branch, 20314 W Third Ave, Stevinson, CA, 95374. Tel: 209-634-5796. p. 186

Wyant, Curtis, Tech Librn, Wilmington Memorial Library, 175 Middlesex Ave, Wilmington, MA, 01887-2779. Tel: 978-658-2967. Fax: 978-658-9699. p. 1141

Wyant, Judy, Acctg & Acq Supvr, Smyth-Bland Regional Library, 118 S Sheffey St, Marion, VA, 24354. Tel: 276-783-2323, Ext 224. Fax: 276-783-5279. p. 2477

Wyant, Nicholas, Res & Info Serv Librn, Wichita State University Libraries, 1845 Fairmount, Wichita, KS, 67260-0068. Tel: 316-978-5083. Fax: 316-978-3048. p. 902

Wyatt, Carma, Co-Dir, Pine Grove Public Library, Main St, Pine Grove, WV, 26419. Tel: 304-889-3288. Fax: 304-889-3288. p. 2569

Wyatt, Dina, Mgr, Salt Lake County Library Services, South Jordan Branch, 10673 S Redwood Rd, South Jordan, UT, 84095-2481. Tel: 801-943-4636. Fax: 801-254-9047. p. 2414

Wyatt, Jennifer, Pub Serv Librn, Jeffersonville Township Public Library, 211 E Court Ave, Jeffersonville, IN, 47130. Tel: 812-285-5640. Fax: 812-285-5642. p. 756

Wyatt, Jennifer, Pub Serv Librn, Jeffersonville Township Public Library, Clarksville Branch, 1312 Eastern Blvd, Clarksville, IN, 47129-1704. Tel: 812-285-5640. Fax: 812-285-5642. p. 756

Wyatt, Karen, Asst Dir, Blue Hill Public Library, Five Parker Point Rd, Blue Hill, ME, 04614-0821. Tel: 207-374-5515. Fax: 207-374-5254. p. 978

Wyatt, Linda, Tech/Cat Librn, Benton County Public Library, 121 S Forrest Ave, Camden, TN, 38320-2055. Tel: 731-584-4772. Fax: 731-584-1098. p. 2226

Wyatt, Lindsay, Electronic Res Librn, Boise Public Library, 715 S Capitol Blvd, Boise, ID, 83702. Tel: 208-384-4442. p. 570

Wyatt, Margaret, Dir, Republic Community Library, 13 DeGregory Circle, Republic, PA, 15475. Tel: 724-246-0404. Fax: 724-246-0404. p. 2134

Wyatt, Pat, Ref Spec, Northwest Missouri State University, 800 University Dr, Maryville, MO, 64468-6001. Tel: 660-562-1192. Fax: 660-562-1049. p. 1344

Wyatt, Patty, Circ, Decatur County Library, Court Sq, 20 W Market St, Decaturville, TN, 38329. Tel: 731-852-3325. Fax: 731-852-2351. p. 2232

Wyatt, Tony, Coordr, Acq, Spec Coll Librn, Greensboro College, 815 W Market St, Greensboro, NC, 27401. Tel: 336-272-7102, Ext 394. Fax: 336-217-7233. p. 1796

Wyatt, William F, Pres, Westport Historical Society, 25 Drift Rd, Westport, MA, 02790-1203. Tel: 508-636-6011. Fax: 508-636-6011. p. 1139

Wybenga, Fred, Pres, Tallmadge Historical Society Library, PO Box 25, Tallmadge, OH, 44278-0025. Tel: 330-630-9760. p. 1938

Wych, Ruby, Dir, Washta Public Library, 100 S Fifth Ave, Washta, IA, 51061. Tel: 712-447-6546. Fax: 712-447-6158. p. 849

Wyche, Beverley, Head, Circ, Johnson Free Public Library, 274 Main St, Hackensack, NJ, 07601-5797. Tel: 201-343-4169. Fax: 201-343-1395. p. 1489

Wyche, Floyd, Circ Supvr, Bristol Public Library, Five High St, Bristol, CT, 06010. Tel: 860-584-7787. Fax: 860-584-7696. p. 332

Wyche, Stardina, Librn, Georgia Department of Transportation, 15 Kennedy Dr, Forest Park, GA, 30297-2599. Tel: 404-363-7540. Fax: 404-363-7684. p. 532

Wycisk, Kristine, Bibliog Instr, Mercy College Libraries, 555 Broadway, Dobbs Ferry, NY, 10522. Tel: 914-674-7293. Fax: 914-674-7581. p. 1615

Wyckoff, Cammie, Admin Supvr, Cornell University Library, Library Annex, Palm Rd, Ithaca, NY, 14853. Tel: 607-253-3514. Fax: 607-253-4280. p. 1642

Wyckoff, Lindsey, Archivist, Spec Coll Librn, Bank Street College of Education Library, 610 W 112th St, 5th Flr, New York, NY, 10025. Tel: 212-875-4455. Fax: 212-875-4558. p. 1669

Wyckoff, Wade, Assoc Univ Librn, McMaster University Library, 1280 Main St W, Hamilton, ON, L8S 4L6, CANADA. Tel: 905-524-9140, Ext 26557. Fax: 905-524-9850. p. 2810

Wydert, Greg, Dir, Creve Coeur Public Library District, 311 N Highland Ave, Creve Coeur, IL, 61610. Tel: 309-699-7921. Fax: 309-699-0949. p. 632

Wygmans, Peggy, Tech Serv Librn, Essex Free Library, Two Browns River Rd, Essex, VT, 05451. Tel: 802-879-0313. p. 2423

Wykes, Pat, In Charge, City of Kawartha Lakes Public Library, Bethany Branch, 1474 Hwy 7A, Bethany, ON, L0A 1K0, CANADA. Tel: 705-277-2321. Fax: 705-277-1580. p. 2816

Wykle, Helen, Spec Coll Librn, University of North Carolina at Asheville, One University Heights, CPO 1500, Asheville, NC, 28804-8504. Tel: 828-251-6645. p. 1775

Wykoff, Leslie, Libr Dir, Washington State University Libraries, 14204 NE Salmon Creek Ave, Vancouver, WA, 98686. Tel: 360-546-9682. Fax: 360-546-9039. p. 2546

Wylder, John, ILL Librn, Decatur Public Library, 130 N Franklin St, Decatur, IL, 62523-1327. Tel: 217-424-2900. Fax: 217-233-4071. p. 634

Wylie, Lori, Mgr, Libr Develop, University of Central Oklahoma, 100 N University Dr, Edmond, OK, 73034. Tel: 405-974-2877. Fax: 405-974-3806, 405-974-3874. p. 1962

Wylie, Micky, Librn, Dale & Lessmann Library, 181 University Ave, Ste 2100, Toronto, ON, M5H 3M7, CANADA. Tel: 416-863-1010. Fax: 416-863-1009. p. 2852

Wylie, Micky, Librn, Dickinson Wright LLP Library, Ernst & Young Tower, Toronto-Dominion Centre, 222 Bay St, 18th Flr, Toronto, ON, M5K 1H1, CANADA. Tel: 416-777-0101. Fax: 416-865-1398. p. 2853

Wylie, Reina, Librn, Saskatchewan Government Insurance, Government Insurance, 2260 11th Ave, 14th Flr, Regina, SK, S4P 0J9, CANADA. Tel: 306-751-1219. Fax: 306-352-0933. p. 2924

Wyly, Ronald D, Tech Serv, College of the Ozarks, Lyons Memorial Library, One Opportunity Ave, Point Lookout, MO, 65726. Tel: 417-690-3411. Fax: 417-334-3085. p. 1349

Wyma, Heidi, Coordr, Libr Serv, Towers Perrin Information Centre, South Tower, Ste 1501, 175 Bloor St E, Toronto, ON, M4W 3T6, CANADA. Tel: 416-960-2790. Fax: 416-960-2819. p. 2864

Wyman, Andrea, Dr, Curric Center Librn, Edinboro University of Pennsylvania, 200 Tartan Ave, Edinboro, PA, 16444. Tel: 814-732-2779. Fax: 814-732-2883. p. 2053

Wyman, Lance, Librn, Big Bend Community College Library, 7662 Chanute St, Moses Lake, WA, 98837. Tel: 509-793-2350. Fax: 509-762-2402. p. 2521

Wyman, Lisa, Ch, Marion County Public Library, 201 E Main St, Lebanon, KY, 40033-1133. Tel: 270-692-4698. Fax: 270-692-9555. p. 920

Wyman, Lynn, Br Mgr, Ramsey County Library, Headquarters Library, 2180 N Hamline Ave, Roseville, MN, 55113-4241. Tel: 651-628-6803. Fax: 651-628-6818. p. 1284

Wyman, Nick, Res Serv Spec, University of Tennessee, Knoxville, Special Collections, 121 Hodges Library, 1015 Volunteer Blvd, Knoxville, TN, 37996-1000. Tel: 865-974-4480. p. 2244

Wymer, Becky, Syst Librn, Bellevue University, 1000 Galvin Rd S, Bellevue, NE, 68005. Tel: 402-557-7317. Fax: 402-557-5427. p. 1393

Wymer, Suanne, Dep Dir, Tulsa City-County Library, 400 Civic Ctr, Tulsa, OK, 74103. Tel: 918-596-7977. Fax: 918-596-7964. p. 1982

Wymer, Suanne, Dep Dir, Tulsa City-County Library, Central Library, 400 Civic Ctr, Tulsa, OK, 74103. Tel: 918-549-7323. p. 1982

Wynn, Bobby C, Dir, Fayetteville State University, 1200 Murchison Rd, Fayetteville, NC, 28301-4298. Tel: 910-672-1232. Fax: 910-672-1746. p. 1793

Wynn, Lori, Bus Mgr, Omaha Public Library, 215 S 15th St, Omaha, NE, 68102-1629. Tel: 402-444-4815. Fax: 402-444-4504. p. 1413

Wynn, Marian, Dir, Geneva Public Library, 312 S Commerce St, Geneva, AL, 36340. Tel: 334-684-2459. Fax: 334-219-4223. p. 18

Wynn, Stephen, Head, Tech Serv, Truman State University, 100 E Normal, Kirksville, MO, 63501-4211. Tel: 660-785-4535. p. 1342

Wynne, Avera, Tampa Bay Regional Planning Council, 4000 Gateway Center Blvd, Ste 100, Pinellas Park, FL, 33782. Tel: 727-570-5151. Fax: 727-570-5118. p. 483

Wynne, Elizabeth, Ch, Dudley-Tucker Library, Six Epping St, Raymond, NH, 03077. Tel: 603-895-2633. Fax: 603-895-0904. p. 1463

Wynne, Joan, Chairperson, Calmar Public Library, 4705 50th Ave, Calmar, AB, T0C 0V0, CANADA. Tel: 780-985-3472. Fax: 780-985-2859. p. 2694

Wynne, Joe, Syst Librn, University of Virginia, Arthur J Morris Law Library, 580 Massie Rd, Charlottesville, VA, 22903-1789. Tel: 434-924-4736. Fax: 434-982-2232. p. 2455

Wynne, Lewis N, Exec Dir, Florida Historical Society, 435 Brevard Ave, Cocoa, FL, 32922. Tel: 321-690-1971, Ext 211. Fax: 321-690-4388. p. 433

Wynot, Debbie, Librn, Lemle & Kelleher, Pan Am Life Ctr, 21st Flr, 601 Poydras St, New Orleans, LA, 70130. Tel: 504-586-1241. Fax: 504-584-9142. p. 960

Wynstra, John, Info Tech, University of Northern Iowa Library, 1227 W 27th St, Cedar Falls, IA, 50613-3675. Tel: 319-273-3619. Fax: 319-273-2913. p. 799

Wyrick, Lora, Librn, McKinley Public Library, 5454 Grand Ave, McKinley, MN, 55741-9502. Tel: 218-749-5313. Fax: 218-749-5313. p. 1258

Wyrwa, Diana, Dir, Richmond Memorial Library, 19 Ross St, Batavia, NY, 14020. Tel: 585-343-9550. Fax: 585-344-4651. p. 1578

Wysk, Susan C, Dir, Randall Library, 19 Crescent St, Stow, MA, 01775. Tel: 978-897-8572. Fax: 978-897-7379. p. 1129

Wyskochil, Linda, Coordr, Access Serv, Grand Rapids Community College, 140 Ransom NE Ave, Grand Rapids, MI, 49503. Tel: 616-234-3879. Fax: 616-234-3878. p. 1185

Wysocki, Christine, Col Archivist, Flagler College, 44 Sevilla St, Saint Augustine, FL, 32084-4302. Tel: 904-819-6206. Fax: 904-823-8511. p. 486

Wyss, Michele, Ch, Forman Valley Public Library District, 404 1/2 S Harrison, Manito, IL, 61546. Tel: 309-968-6093. Fax: 309-968-7120. p. 670

Wysuph, Michelle, Librn, South Dakota State Penitentiary, 1600 N Dr, Sioux Falls, SD, 57104-0915. Tel: 605-367-5170, 605-367-5171. p. 2219

Wyszynski, Terry, Syst Librn, Asheville-Buncombe Technical Community College, 340 Victoria Rd, Asheville, NC, 28801. Tel: 828-254-1921, Ext 301. Fax: 828-251-6074. p. 1774

Xander, Stephanie, Coll Mgt Librn, United States Army, Van Noy Library, 5966 12th St, Bldg 1024, Fort Belvoir, VA, 22060-5554. Tel: 703-806-3273. p. 2464

Xanders, Charlotte, Head, Bibliog Serv, California State University, Sacramento Library, 2000 State University Dr E, Sacramento, CA, 95819-6039. Tel: 916-278-5679. Fax: 916-278-5917. p. 223

Xavier, Patrick, Br Mgr, Los Angeles Public Library System, Cypress Park, 1150 Cypress Ave, Los Angeles, CA, 90065-1605. Tel: 323-224-0039. Fax: 323-224-0454. p. 173

Xi, Jack, Tech Serv, Piscataway Township Free Public Library, 500 Hoes Lane, Piscataway, NJ, 08854. Tel: 732-752-1166. Fax: 732-463-9022. p. 1520

Xiao, Anna, Cat, Federal Reserve Bank of Saint Louis, One Federal Reserve Bank Plaza, Saint Louis, MO, 63102-2005. Tel: 314-444-8551. Fax: 314-444-8694. p. 1354

Xie, Hongbo, Cat, Tech Serv, Coe College, 1220 First Ave NE, Cedar Rapids, IA, 52402-5092. Tel: 319-399-8026. Fax: 319-399-8019. p. 800

Xie, Susan, Commun Libr Mgr, Queens Borough Public Library, McGoldrick Community Library, 155-06 Roosevelt Ave, Flushing, NY, 11354. Tel: 718-461-1616. p. 1645

Xie, Zhiwu, Virginia Polytechnic Institute & State University Libraries, Drill Field Dr, Blacksburg, VA, 24062-9001. Tel: 540-231-6170. Fax: 540-231-3946. p. 2451

Xing, Sunan, Asst Librn, Mitchell Silberberg & Knupp LLP, 11377 W Olympic Blvd, Los Angeles, CA, 90064-1683. Tel: 310-312-2000. Fax: 310-312-3100. p. 175

Xu, Fei, Syst, South Dakota State University, 1300 N Campus Dr, Box 2115, Brookings, SD, 57007-1098. Tel: 605-688-5560. Fax: 605-688-6133. p. 2211

Xu, Helen, Cat, California Baptist University, 8432 Magnolia Ave, Riverside, CA, 92504. Tel: 951-343-4354. p. 216

Xu, Joe, Librn, Watkins, Ludlam, Winter & Stennis, 190 E Capital St, Ste 800, Jackson, MS, 39201. Tel: 601-949-4792. Fax: 601-949-4804. p. 1305

Xu, Peng, Electronic Serv & Res Librn, Columbia University, Thomas J Watson Library of Business & Economics, 130 Uris Hall, 3022 Broadway, MC 9163, New York, NY, 10027. Tel: 212-854-7804. Fax: 212-854-5723. p. 1675

Xu, Yan, Adult Serv Supvr, Naperville Public Library, Naper Boulevard, 2035 S Naper Blvd, Naperville, IL, 60565-3353. Tel: 630-961-4100, Ext 2232. Fax: 630-961-4119. p. 679

Xu, Yue, Web Serv Librn, University Libraries, University of Memphis, 126 Ned R McWherter Library, Memphis, TN, 38152-3250. Tel: 901-678-4465. p. 2252

Xueying, Chen, Dir, Chattahoochee Valley Community College, 2602 College Dr, Phenix City, AL, 36869-7960. Tel: 334-291-4979. Fax: 334-291-4980. p. 33

Yachnes, Paul, Mgr, Newspaper Association of America, 1921 Gallows Rd, Ste 600, Vienna, VA, 22182. Tel: 703-902-1694. Fax: 703-902-1691. p. 2498

Yackel, Andrew, Computer Serv, Saint Joseph's Hospital Health Center, 206 Prospect Ave, Syracuse, NY, 13203. Tel: 315-448-5053. Fax: 315-423-6804. p. 1753

Yackel, Lynne, Mgr, Northern Onondaga Public Library, 100 Trolley Barn Lane, North Syracuse, NY, 13212. Tel: 315-458-6184. Fax: 315-458-7026. p. 1707

Yackley-Franken, Nicki, Librn, Lake Area Technical Institute Library, PO Box 730, Watertown, SD, 57201-0730. Tel: 605-882-5284, Ext 231. Fax: 605-882-6299. p. 2221

Yaco, Sonia, Head, Spec Coll, Old Dominion University Libraries, 4427 Hampton Blvd, Norfolk, VA, 23529-0256. Tel: 757-683-4483. Fax: 757-683-5767. p. 2482

Yacobucci Farquhar, Kelly, County Historian, Montgomery County Department of History & Archives, Nine Park St, Fonda, NY, 12068. Tel: 518-853-8186. Fax: 518-853-8392. p. 1623

Yacovone, Maria, ILL, Agawam Public Library, 750 Cooper St, Agawam, MA, 01001. Tel: 413-789-1550. Fax: 413-789-1552. p. 1048

Yacyshyn, Joanne, Librn, Wapiti Regional Library, Porcupine Plain Public Library, 310 Elm St, Porcupine Plain, SK, S0E 1H0, CANADA. Tel: 306-278-2488. p. 2921

Yadon, Ann, Librn, Talkeetna Public Library, 23151 S Talkeetna Spur Rd, Talkeetna, AK, 99676-0768. Tel: 907-733-2359. Fax: 907-733-3017. p. 54

Yaeger, Dixie, Librn, Saint John's River State College, Orange Park Center Library, 283 College Dr, Orange Park, FL, 32065-6751. Tel: 904-276-6840. Fax: 904-276-6796. p. 479

Yaeger, Lauren, Mgr, Libr Serv, Saint Louis Children's Hospital, One Children's Pl, Saint Louis, MO, 63110. Tel: 314-454-2768. Fax: 314-454-2340. p. 1357

Yaegle, Sandra, Head, Pub Serv, Regent University Library, 1000 Regent University Dr, Virginia Beach, VA, 23464. Tel: 757-352-4165. Fax: 757-352-4167. p. 2499

Yaek, Larry, Librn, Monroe County Community College, 1555 S Raisinville Rd, Monroe, MI, 48161. Tel: 734-384-4204. Fax: 734-384-4160. p. 1209

Yaek, Larry, Pub Serv, Saint Clair County Community College, 323 Erie St, Port Huron, MI, 48060. Tel: 810-984-3881, 810-989-5640. Fax: 810-984-2852. p. 1219

Yaffee, Rachel, Ch, YA Serv, Kesher Zion Synagogue Sisterhood Library, 1245 Perkiomen Ave, Reading, PA, 19602-1318. Tel: 610-374-1763. Fax: 610-375-1352. p. 2133

Yagerhofer, Jane, Cat, Lehigh Carbon Community College Library, 4525 Education Park Dr, Schnecksville, PA, 18078-9372. Tel: 610-799-1160. Fax: 610-779-1159. p. 2136

Yahne, Jyll, Head, Tech Serv, Fort Richardson Post Library, IMPA-FRA-HRE PL, Bldg 7, Chilkoot Ave, Fort Richardson, AK, 99505-0055. Tel: 907-384-1648. Fax: 907-384-7534. p. 48

Yahnke, Greg, Assoc Warden of Prog, Northern Regional Jail Correctional Facility, RD 2, Box 1, Moundsville, WV, 26041-0001. Tel: 304-843-4067, Ext 106. Fax: 304-843-4089. p. 2567

Yahraus, Jeffrey A, Dir, Williams County Public Library, 107 E High St, Bryan, OH, 43506-1702. Tel: 419-636-6734. Fax: 419-636-3970. p. 1862

Yake, Matthew, In Charge, Multnomah County Library, Belmont, 1038 SE 39th Ave, Portland, OR, 97214-4318. Tel: 503-988-5382. Fax: 503-988-5481. p. 2012

Yakel, Elizabeth, Assoc Prof, University of Michigan, 304 West Hall, 1085 S University, Ann Arbor, MI, 48109-1107. Tel: 734-763-2285. Fax: 734-764-2475. p. 2967

Yakovich, Roberta, Youth Serv Mgr, Bucks County Free Library, Library Center at Doylestown, 150 S Pine St, Doylestown, PA, 18901-4932. Tel: 215-348-0332, Ext 1240. Fax: 215-348-9489. p. 2050

Yam, Helen K, Cat, University of Nebraska Medical Center, 600 S 42nd St, Omaha, NE, 68198-6705. Tel: 402-559-7091. Fax: 402-559-5498. p. 1415

Yamada, Grace, Asst Librn, Carlsmith Ball LLP Library, ASB Tower, Ste 2200, 1001 Bishop St, Honolulu, HI, 96813. Tel: 808-523-2500. Fax: 808-523-0842. p. 560

Yamakawa, Linda, Tech Librn, College of the Sequoias Library, 915 S Mooney Blvd, Visalia, CA, 93277. Tel: 559-730-3824. Fax: 559-737-4835. p. 280

Yamamoto, Linda, Bibliographer, Head Librn, Stanford University Libraries, Mathematics & Computer Sciences, Sloan Mathematics Ctr, Bldg 380, 4th Flr, Stanford, CA, 94305-2125. Tel: 650-723-4672. Fax: 650-725-8998. p. 271

Yamamoto, Sue, Commun Libr Mgr, County of Los Angeles Public Library, Rosemead Library, 8800 Valley Blvd, Rosemead, CA, 91770-1788. Tel: 626-573-5220. Fax: 626-280-8523. p. 143

Yamkowy, Brenda, Exec Dir, HIV North Society, 3039804 100 Ave, Ste 303, Grande Prairie, AB, T8V 0T8, CANADA. Tel: 780-538-3388. Fax: 780-538-3368. p. 2705

Yan, Louise, Ref Serv, Belleville Public Library & Information Center, 221 Washington Ave, Belleville, NJ, 07109-3189. Tel: 973-450-3434. Fax: 973-450-9518, 973-759-6731. p. 1471

Yan, Phil, Webmaster, Tennessee State University, 3500 John A Merritt Blvd, Nashville, TN, 37209. Tel: 615-963-5213. Fax: 615-963-5216. p. 2259

Yan, Ruth, Dr, Librn, Allen College, 1825 Logan Ave, Waterloo, IA, 50703. Tel: 319-226-2080. Fax: 319-226-2020, 319-226-2053. p. 849

Yanakakus, Ada, Asst Librn, Lynn Museum & Historical Society Library, 590 Washington St, Lynn, MA, 01901. Tel: 781-581-6200. Fax: 781-581-6202. p. 1101

Yancey, James, Archivist, National Archives & Records Administration, 441 Freedom Pkwy, Atlanta, GA, 30307. Tel: 404-865-7132. Fax: 404-865-7102. p. 517

Yancey, Susan, Librn, Vinson & Elkins, 3055 First City Tower, 1001 Fannin, Houston, TX, 77002-6760. Tel: 713-758-2678. Fax: 713-615-5211. p. 2345

Yancheff, Kitty, Div Mgr, Pub Serv, Humboldt County Library, 1313 Third St, Eureka, CA, 95501-0553. Tel: 707-269-1918. p. 147

Yandell, Lynn, Mgr, Info Tech, Fayetteville Public Library, 401 W Mountain St, Fayetteville, AR, 72701. Tel: 479-856-7000. Fax: 479-571-0222. p. 99

Yandle, Virginia, Libr Tech, Stanly Community College, Snyder Bldg, Albemarle, NC, 28001. Tel: 704-991-0259. Fax: 704-991-0112. p. 1773

Yang, Alice, Librn, Hagerstown Community College Library, 11400 Robinwood Dr, Hagerstown, MD, 21742-6590. Tel: 301-790-2800, Ext 237. Fax: 301-393-3681. p. 1031

Yang, Andrea, Coll Develop Coordr, Montgomery County Memorial Library System, 104 I-45 N, Conroe, TX, 77301-2720. Tel: 936-538-8130. Fax: 936-788-8398. p. 2300

Yang, Cha Mee, Cataloger, Libr Tech, Willows Public Library, 201 N Lassen St, Willows, CA, 95988-3010. Tel: 530-934-5156. Fax: 530-934-2225. p. 284

Yang, Christine, Ref Librn, Edison Township Free Public Library, North Edison Branch, 777 Grove Ave, Edison, NJ, 08820. Tel: 732-548-3045. Fax: 732-549-5171. p. 1483

Yang, Christine, Ref Serv, Edison Township Free Public Library, 340 Plainfield Ave, Edison, NJ, 08817. Tel: 732-287-2298. Fax: 732-819-9134. p. 1483

Yang, Christopher C, PhD, Assoc Prof, Drexel University, Rush Bldg, Rm 306, 30 N 33rd St, Philadelphia, PA, 19104-2875. Tel: 215-895-2474. Fax: 215-895-2494. p. 2972

Yang, Gigi, Mgr, YA Serv, Mamie Doud Eisenhower Public Library, Three Community Park Rd, Broomfield, CO, 80020-3781. Tel: 720-887-2366. Fax: 720-887-1384. p. 292

Yang, Jainxin, Info Literacy Librn, Gateway Community College, 20 Church St, New Haven, CT, 06510. Tel: 203-285-2158. Fax: 203-285-2055. p. 355

Yang, Jennie, Cat, Tech Serv, Harrison Public Library, Bruce Ave, Harrison, NY, 10528. Tel: 914-835-0324. Fax: 914-835-1564. p. 1634

Yang, Jidong, Dr, Head of Libr, University of Michigan, Asia, Hatcher Library, 920 N University St, Rm 418, Ann Arbor, MI, 48109-1205. Tel: 734-936-2354. Fax: 734-647-2885. p. 1152

Yang, Julie, Info Officer, Toronto Public Health Library, 277 Victoria St, 6th Flr, Toronto, ON, M5B 1W2, CANADA. Tel: 416-338-0049. Fax: 416-338-0489. p. 2859

Yang, Lan, Doc Delivery, ILL, Texas A&M University Libraries, 5000 TAMU, College Station, TX, 77843-5000. Tel: 978-862-1904. Fax: 979-845-6238. p. 2298

Yang, Lucy, Circ Serv Coordr, Tompkins Cortland Community College, 170 North St, Dryden, NY, 13053-8504. Tel: 607-844-8222, Ext 4361. Fax: 607-844-6540. p. 1615

Yang, Mai, Librn, Fresno City College Library, 1101 E University Ave, Fresno, CA, 93741. Tel: 559-442-8204. Fax: 559-265-5758. p. 151

Yang, Patsy, Campus Librn, Golden Gate Baptist Theological Seminary Library, 3200 NE 109th Ave, Vancouver, WA, 98682-7749. Tel: 360-882-2179. Fax: 360-882-2275. p. 2546

Yang, Sharon-Lishiuan, Head, Access Serv, Harvard Library, Harvard-Yenching Library, Two Divinity Ave, Cambridge, MA, 02138. Tel: 617-495-2756. Fax: 617-496-6008. p. 1075

Yang, Tao, Librn, Rutgers University Libraries, East Asian Library, Alexander Library, 169 College Ave, New Brunswick, NJ, 08901-1163. Tel: 732-932-7129, Ext 230. Fax: 732-932-6808. p. 1509

Yang, Xiao Hua, Acq Librn, Western Connecticut State University, 181 White St, Danbury, CT, 06810. Tel: 203-837-9105. Fax: 203-837-9103. p. 335

Yang, Yuezeng Shen, Cat Librn, Cleveland State University, University Library, Rhodes Tower, 2121 Euclid Ave, Cleveland, OH, 44115-2214. Tel: 216-687-5274. Fax: 216-687-2383. p. 1879

Yangarber, Inna, Commun Libr Mgr, Queens Borough Public Library, Rego Park Community Library, 91-41 63rd Dr, Rego Park, NY, 11374. Tel: 718-459-5140. p. 1645

Yangarber, Inna, Commun Libr Mgr, Queens Borough Public Library, Steinway Community Library, 21-45 31st St, Long Island City, NY, 11105. Tel: 718-728-1965. Fax: 718-956-3575. p. 1645

Yanicke, Joan, Mgr, Saint Vincent Hospital, Worcester Medical Ctr, 123 Summer St, Worcester, MA, 01608. Tel: 508-363-6117. Fax: 508-363-9118. p. 1144

Yanikoski, Catherine, Br Mgr, White Oak Library District, Crest Hill Branch, 1298 Theodore St, Crest Hill, IL, 60403. Tel: 815-725-0234. p. 667

Yankauskas, Raye, Libr Asst, Lesley University, 700 Beacon St, Boston, MA, 02215-2598. Tel: 617-585-6672. Fax: 617-585-6655. p. 1062

Yanko, Linda, Mgr, Geauga County Public Library, Geauga West Library, 13455 Chillicothe Rd, Chesterland, OH, 44026. Tel: 440-729-4250. Fax: 440-729-7517. p. 1867

Yankura, Ethan, Librn, Owls Head Transportation Museum Library, PO Box 277, Owls Head, ME, 04854-0277. Tel: 207-594-4418. Fax: 207-594-4410. p. 995

Yannarella, Phil, Librn, Cincinnati Museum Center At Union Terminal, Geier Science Library, 760 W Fifth St, Cincinnati, OH, 45203. Tel: 513-455-7183. Fax: 513-455-7169. p. 1869

Yannarella, Philip, Govt Doc Librn, Northern Kentucky University, University Dr, Highland Heights, KY, 41099. Tel: 859-572-5455. Fax: 859-572-5390. p. 917

Yannotta, Lauren, Ref & Instrul Design Librn, Hunter College Libraries, 695 Park Ave, New York, NY, 10065. Tel: 212-650-3936. Fax: 212-772-4142. p. 1682

Yao, Hong, Coll Develop Coordr, Queens Borough Public Library, 89-11 Merrick Blvd, Jamaica, NY, 11432. p. 1643

Yao, Jennifer, Ref & Instrul Serv Librn, New School, Adam & Sophie Gimbel Design Library, Two W 13th St, 2nd Flr, New York, NY, 10011. Tel: 212-229-8914, Ext 4285. Fax: 212-229-2806. p. 1688

Yap, Derek, Cat/Syst Librn, Yukon College Library, 500 College Dr, Whitehorse, YT, Y1A 5K4, CANADA. Tel: 867-668-8870. Fax: 867-668-8808. p. 2934

Yarbrough, Dorothy, Asst Librn, Blountsville Public Library, 65 Chestnut St, Blountsville, AL, 35031. Tel: 205-429-3156. Fax: 205-429-4806. p. 10

Yarbrough, Felita, Librn, Birmingham Public Library, East Lake, Five Oporto-Madrid Blvd, Birmingham, AL, 35206. Tel: 205-836-3341. Fax: 205-833-8055. p. 7

Yarbrough, Sue, Librn, Carrollton Public Library, 225 Commerce Ave, Carrollton, AL, 35447. Tel: 205-367-2142. Fax: 205-367-2142. p. 11

Yarbrough, Victoria, Dir, Douglas Public Library, 560 Tenth St, Douglas, AZ, 85607. Tel: 520-364-3851. Fax: 520-805-5503. p. 61

Yarchever, Edythe Katz, Chair, JFSA Holocaust Resource Center, 4794 S Eastern Ave, Ste A, Las Vegas, NV, 89119. Tel: 702-433-0005. p. 1429

Yardley, Sherri, Librn, Milford Public Library, 400 S 100 West, Milford, UT, 84751. Tel: 435-387-5039. Fax: 435-387-5027. p. 2407

Yarman, Donald, Dep Dir, Delaware County District Library, 84 E Winter St, Delaware, OH, 43015. Tel: 740-362-3861. Fax: 740-369-0196. p. 1895

Yarman, Violet S, Circ, Public Library of Mount Vernon & Knox County, 201 N Mulberry St, Mount Vernon, OH, 43050-2413. Tel: 740-392-2665. Fax: 740-397-3866. p. 1919

Yarmey, Kristen, Digital Serv & Emerging Tech, University of Scranton, Monroe & Linden, Scranton, PA, 18510-4634. Tel: 570-941-4000, 570-941-4008. Fax: 570-941-7817. p. 2138

Yarnall, Lisa, Human Res, Cecil County Public Library, 301 Newark Ave, Elkton, MD, 21921-5441. Tel: 410-996-5600. Fax: 410-996-5604. p. 1027

Yater, Kara, Tech Serv Librn, Genesee District Library, Headquarters, G-4195 W Pasadena Ave, Flint, MI, 48504. Tel: 810-732-0110. Fax: 810-732-3146. p. 1180

Yates, Barbara, Exec Dir, Debra S Fish Early Childhood Resource Library, Ten Yorkton Ct, Saint Paul, MN, 55117-1065. Tel: 651-641-3544. Fax: 651-645-0990. p. 1278

Yates, Christopher, Coll Develop, South Carolina State Library, 1430 Senate St, Columbia, SC, 29201-3710. Tel: 803-734-4611. Fax: 803-734-4610. p. 2189

Yates, Christopher, Coll Develop, South Carolina State Library, 1430-1500 Senate St, Columbia, SC, 29201. Tel: 803-734-4618. Fax: 803-734-8676. p. 2189

Yates, Doris, Libr Tech, Mount Hope-Funks Grove Townships Library District, 111 S Hamilton St, McLean, IL, 61754-7624. Tel: 309-874-2291. Fax: 309-874-2291. p. 672

Yates, Molly, Librn, Big Horn County Library, Deaver Branch, 180 W First St, Deaver, WY, 82421. Tel: 307-664-2736. p. 2651

Yates, Molly, Librn, Big Horn County Library, Frannie Branch, 311 Fourth St, Frannie, WY, 82423. Tel: 307-664-2323. p. 2651

Yates, Rochelle, Librn, United Hospital Fund of New York, 350 Fifth Ave, 23rd Flr, New York, NY, 10118. Tel: 212-494-0720. Fax: 212-494-0800. p. 1702

Yates, Sheila, Br Head, Toronto Public Library, Morningside, Morningside Mall, 255 Morningside Ave, Toronto, ON, M1E 3E6, CANADA. Tel: 416-396-8881. Fax: 416-396-3606. p. 2862

Yates, Susan, Libr Mgr, Vancouver Island Regional Library, Cortes Island, Sutil Point Rd, Mansons Landing, BC, V0P 1K0, CANADA. Tel: 250-935-6566. Fax: 250-935-6522. p. 2732

Yates, Susan, Libr Mgr, Vancouver Island Regional Library, Gabriola Island Branch, Folklife Village, 5-575 North Rd, Gabriola Island, BC, V0R 1X5, CANADA. Tel: 250-247-7878. Fax: 250-247-7892. p. 2732

Yates, Susan, Libr Mgr, Vancouver Island Regional Library, Hornby Island Branch, New Horizons Ctr, 1765 Sollans Rd, Hornby Island, BC, V0R 1Z0, CANADA. Tel: 250-335-0044. Fax: 250-335-0134. p. 2732

Yates, Susan, Libr Mgr, Vancouver Island Regional Library, Quadra Island, 712 Cramer Rd, Heriot Bay, BC, V0P 1H0, CANADA. Tel: 250-285-2216. Fax: 250-285-2248. p. 2733

Yates, Vickie, Outreach Serv Mgr, Jackson Parish Library, 614 S Polk Ave, Jonesboro, LA, 71251-3442. Tel: 318-259-5697, 318-259-5698. Fax: 318-259-8984. p. 952

Yaughn, Valerie E, Head Librn, South University Library, 709 Mall Blvd, Savannah, GA, 31406. Tel: 912-201-8047. Fax: 912-201-8070. p. 551

Yavarkovsky, Jerome, Univ Librn, Boston College Libraries, 140 Commonwealth Ave, Chestnut Hill, MA, 02467. Tel: 617-552-3195. Fax: 617-552-8828. p. 1080

Yavornitzky, Jackie, In Charge, Baldwin Wallace University, Chemistry Reading Room, Wilker Hall, 320 Front St, Berea, OH, 44017-1732. Tel: 440-826-2312. Fax: 440-826-2399. p. 1859

Yaw, Carol, Asst Dir, Rock County Public Library, 400 State St, Bassett, NE, 68714. Tel: 402-684-3800. Fax: 402-684-3930. p. 1392

Yawger, Tracee, Ch, Spring Township Library, 78C Commerce Dr, Wyomissing, PA, 19610. Tel: 610-373-9888. Fax: 610-373-0334. p. 2159

Yawn, Amy E, Librn, Kelly, Hart & Hallman, Chase Bldg, 201 Main St, Ste 2500, Fort Worth, TX, 76102. Tel: 817-332-2500. Fax: 817-878-9822. p. 2322

Yaws, Renee, Mgr, Westwood College of Technology, 3150 S Sheridan Blvd, Denver, CO, 80227-5548. Tel: 303-934-1122, Ext 665. Fax: 303-934-2583. p. 304

Yazdani, Danesh, Chief Librn, Medgar Evers College, 1650 Bedford Ave, Brooklyn, NY, 11225-2010. Tel: 718-270-4883. Fax: 718-270-5182. p. 1593

Ybarra, Schiree, Librn, North Central Regional Library, Quincy Community, 108 B St SW, Quincy, WA, 98848-1203. Tel: 509-787-2359. p. 2549

Yeado, Diana, Librn, Walhalla Public Library, 1010 Central Ave, Walhalla, ND, 58282-4015. Tel: 701-549-3794. Fax: 701-549-3794. p. 1849

Yeager, Andrew, Info Literacy, Medaille College Library, 18 Agassiz Circle, Buffalo, NY, 14214. Tel: 716-880-2283. Fax: 716-884-9638. p. 1598

Yeager, Cindy, Librn, Pottstown Memorial Medical Center, 1600 E High St, Pottstown, PA, 19464. Tel: 610-327-7468. Fax: 610-705-6903. p. 2131

Yeager, Clara, Per, Yakima Valley Genealogical Society Library, 1901 S 12th Ave, Union Gap, WA, 98903. Tel: 509-248-1328. p. 2545

Yeager, Constance, ILL Librn, Ansonia Library, 53 S Cliff St, Ansonia, CT, 06401-1909. Tel: 203-734-6275. Fax: 203-732-4551. p. 329

Yeager, Jamane, Ref/Electronic Serv Librn, Elon University, 308 N O'Kelly Ave, Elon, NC, 27244-0187. Tel: 336-278-6576. Fax: 336-278-6637. p. 1791

Yeager, Kathleen, Ch, Herrick Memorial Library, 101 Willard Memorial Sq, Wellington, OH, 44090-1342. Tel: 440-647-2120. Fax: 440-647-2103. p. 1945

Yeager, Lynn, Coordr of Educ & Outreach, University of Oklahoma, Schusterman Ctr, 4502 E 41st St, Tulsa, OK, 74135. Tel: 918-660-3216. Fax: 918-660-3215. p. 1984

Yeager, Michelle, YA Supvr, Youth Serv Coordr, Cherry Hill Public Library, 1100 Kings Hwy N, Cherry Hill, NJ, 08034-1911. Tel: 856-903-1232. Fax: 856-667-9503. p. 1478

Yeager, Miriam, Educ Coordr, Cook Inlet Pre-Trial Facility Library, 1300 E Fourth Ave, Anchorage, AK, 99501. Tel: 907-269-0943. Fax: 907-269-0905. p. 45

Yeager, Rhonda, Dir, Laurel Highlands Health Science Library Consortium, 361 Sunrise Rd, Dayton, PA, 16222. Tel: 814-341-0242. Fax: 814-266-8230. p. 2954

Yeager, Virginia Beatrice, Ref, Staff Librn, Glenville State College, 100 High St, Glenville, WV, 26351. Tel: 304-462-4109, Ext 6164. Fax: 304-462-4049. p. 2559

Yeatman, Jill, Chairperson, Elizabethtown-Kitley Township Public Library, 6544 New Dublin Rd, Addison, ON, K0E 1A0, CANADA. Tel: 613-498-3338. p. 2791

Yeats, Evelyn, Coordr, Spec Serv, University of Arkansas-Pine Bluff, 1200 N University Dr, Pine Bluff, AR, 71601. Tel: 870-575-8411. Fax: 870-575-4651. p. 112

Yecies, Carol, Assoc Dir, Ref & Outreach, Nova Southeastern University Libraries, Shepard Broad Law Center Library, 3305 College Ave, Fort Lauderdale, FL, 33314. Tel: 954-262-6100. p. 444

Yeckley, Pauline, Librn, De Anza College, 21250 Stevens Creek Blvd, Cupertino, CA, 95014-5793. Tel: 408-864-8303. Fax: 408-864-8603. p. 138

Yee, B, Tech Serv, College of New Caledonia Library, 3330 22nd Ave, Prince George, BC, V2N 1P8, CANADA. Tel: 250-562-2131, Ext 298. Fax: 250-561-5845. p. 2736

Yee, Karl, Syst Coordr, Northeastern University Libraries, Snell Library, 360 Huntington Ave, Boston, MA, 02115. Tel: 617-373-4904. p. 1065

Yee, Sandra, Dr, Dean of Libr, Wayne State University Libraries, David Adamany Undergraduate Library, 5150 Anthony Wayne, Detroit, MI, 48202. Tel: 313-577-5121. Fax: 313-577-5265. p. 1173

Yee, Sandra G, Dean of Libr, Wayne State University Libraries, Office of the Dean, 3100 Undergraduate Library, 5155 Gullen Mall, Detroit, MI, 48202. Tel: 313-577-4020. Fax: 313-577-5525. p. 1173

Yee, Sandra G, Dr, Dean, Wayne State University, 106 Kresge Library, Detroit, MI, 48202. Tel: 313-577-4020. Fax: 313-577-7563. p. 2967

Yee, Shirley, Br Mgr, Chicago Public Library, Logan Square, 3030 W Fullerton Ave, Chicago, IL, 60647. Tel: 312-744-5295. Fax: 312-744-5551. p. 609

Yee, Warren, Supvr, Access Serv, Northeastern University School of Law Library, 400 Huntington Ave, Boston, MA, 02115. Tel: 617-373-3350. Fax: 617-373-8705. p. 1066

Yeh, Felicia, Asst Dir, Coll Mgt, University of South Carolina, School of Medicine, 6311 Garners Ferry Rd, Columbia, SC, 29209. Tel: 803-733-3344. Fax: 803-733-1509. p. 2190

Yeh, Helen, Asst Dir, Tech Serv, Prairie View A&M University, PO Box 519, MS 1040, Prairie View, TX, 77446-0519. Tel: 936-261-1533. Fax: 936-261-1539. p. 2372

Yeh, Peggy, Head Librn, Alberta Government Library, 10025 Jasper Ave, 15th Flr, Edmonton, AB, T5J 2N3, CANADA. Tel: 780-415-0228. Fax: 780-422-9694. p. 2698

Yehl, Robert, Dir, Henderson State University, 1100 Henderson, Arkadelphia, AR, 71999-0001. Tel: 870-230-5258. Fax: 870-230-5365. p. 93

Yeilding, Howard, Info Tech Serv, San Jose Public Library, 150 E San Fernando St, San Jose, CA, 95112-3580. Tel: 408-808-2420. Fax: 408-808-2401. p. 250

Yela, Max, Spec Coll, University of Wisconsin-Milwaukee Libraries, 2311 E Hartford Ave, Milwaukee, WI, 53211. Tel: 414-229-4785, 414-229-6202. Fax: 414-229-6766. p. 2622

Yelich, Leea, Br Librn, Westchester Public Library, 200 W Indiana Ave, Chesterton, IN, 46304-3122. Tel: 219-926-7696. Fax: 219-926-6424. p. 732

Yelinek, Kathryn, Res Librn, Bloomsburg University of Pennsylvania, 400 E Second St, Bloomsburg, PA, 17815-1301. Tel: 570-389-4224. Fax: 570-389-3066. p. 2035

Yell, Cindy, Br Librn, Brazoria County Library System, Freeport Branch, 410 Brazosport Blvd, Freeport, TX, 77541. Tel: 979-233-3622. Fax: 979-233-4300. p. 2275

Yelle, Joanne, ILL, Tech Serv, Township of Russell Public Library, 1053 Concession St, Box 280, Russell, ON, K4R 1E1, CANADA. Tel: 613-445-5331. Fax: 613-445-8014. p. 2839

Yellman, Abby, Dir, Lied Scottsbluff Public Library, 1809 Third Ave, Scottsbluff, NE, 69361-2493. Tel: 308-630-6251. Fax: 308-630-6293. p. 1418

Yellock, Belinda, Br Mgr, Atlanta-Fulton Public Library System, Thomasville Heights Library, 1700 Thomasville Dr SE, Atlanta, GA, 30315. Tel: 404-624-0620. Fax: 404-624-0622. p. 513

Yelovich, Bruce, Syst Coordr, Mount Saint Mary's University, 16300 Old Emmitsburg Rd, Emmitsburg, MD, 21727-7799. Tel: 301-447-5244. Fax: 301-447-5099. p. 1028

Yeltema, Karen, Librn, Connecticut Judicial Branch Law Libraries, Bridgeport Law Library, Bridgeport Courthouse, 1061 Main St, Bridgeport, CT, 06604. Tel: 203-579-7244. Fax: 203-579-7298. p. 344

Yelverton, Randall, Exec Dir, Washington District Library, 380 N Wilmor Rd, Washington, IL, 61571. Tel: 309-444-2241. Fax: 309-444-4711. p. 715

Yen, Ellen, Sr Ref Librn, Suffolk University, 73 Tremont St, Boston, MA, 02108. Tel: 617-573-8535. Fax: 617-573-8756. p. 1067

Yen, Julie, Ad, Casa Grande Public Library, 449 N Dry Lake, Casa Grande, AZ, 85222. Tel: 520-421-8710, Ext 5240. Fax: 520-421-8701. p. 59

Yencho, Patricia, Asst Librn, Patton Public Library, 444 Magee Ave, Patton, PA, 16668-1210. Tel: 814-674-8231. Fax: 814-674-6188. p. 2101

Yeo, Sandra, Librn, Boyne Regional Library, 15 First Ave SW, Carman, MB, R0G 0J0, CANADA. Tel: 204-745-3504. p. 2748

Yeoman, Brenda, Dir, E J Cottrell Memorial Library, 30 Main St, Atlanta, NY, 14808-0192. Tel: 585-534-5030. Fax: 585-534-9316. p. 1575

Yeoman, Diane, Dir, Mason City Public Library District, 820 W Chestnut St, Mason City, IL, 62664-9768. Tel: 217-482-3799. Fax: 217-482-3799. p. 671

Yeomans, Debra, Pub Serv Asst, Indian Hills Community College, 721 N First St, Bldg CV06, Centerville, IA, 52544. Tel: 641-856-2143, Ext 2237. Fax: 641-856-5527. p. 801

Yerger, Maura, Tech Serv, Woodbury Public Library, 269 Main St S, Woodbury, CT, 06798. Tel: 203-263-3502. Fax: 203-263-0571. p. 380

Yeries, Shirley, Dir, Springmier Community Library, 311 W Marengo Rd, Tiffin, IA, 52340-9308. Tel: 319-545-2960. Fax: 319-545-2863. p. 847

Yerk, Becky, Teen Serv, Cherry Valley Public Library District, 755 E State St, Cherry Valley, IL, 61016-9699. Tel: 815-332-5161, Ext 34. Fax: 815-332-2441. p. 604

Yerkey, Bob, Mgr, Auburn University, Ralph Brown Draughon Library, 231 Mell St, Auburn, AL, 36849. Tel: 334-844-2704. Fax: 334-844-4424. p. 5

Yerman, Roslyn, Libr Dir, Madison Heights Public Library, 240 W 13 Mile Rd, Madison Heights, MI, 48071-1894. Tel: 248-588-7763. Fax: 248-588-2470. p. 1205

Yersavich, Joe, Managing Librn, Columbus Metropolitan Library, New Albany Branch, 200 Market St, New Albany, OH, 43054. Tel: 614-645-2275. Fax: 614-479-4549. p. 1885

Yersin, Della, Dir, Burlington Public Library, 321 14th St, Burlington, CO, 80807-1607. Tel: 719-346-8109. Fax: 719-346-8672. p. 293

Yerxa, Rusty, Coll/Libr Mgr, National Park Service, PO Box 140, Gustavus, AK, 99826-0140. Tel: 907-697-2675. Fax: 907-697-2654. p. 49

Yesnick, Susane, Res Librn, Drinker, Biddle & Reath, 191 N Wacker Dr, Ste 3700, Chicago, IL, 60606-1698. Tel: 312-569-1860. Fax: 312-569-3860. p. 613

Yess, Scott, Coordr, Upper Mississippi River Conservation Committee Library, 555 Lester Ave, Onalaska, WI, 54650. Tel: 608-783-8432. Fax: 608-783-8450. p. 2627

Yetter, George, Archit Librn, Colonial Williamsburg Foundation, John D Rockefeller Jr Library-Special Collections, 313 First St, Williamsburg, VA, 23185-4306. Tel: 757-565-8522. Fax: 757-565-8528. p. 2502

Yeung, Samantha, Div Mgr, Thousand Oaks Library, 1401 E Janss Rd, Thousand Oaks, CA, 91362-2199. Tel: 805-449-2660, Ext 7332. Fax: 805-373-6858. p. 275

Yevropina, Anna, Archivist/Librn, National Endowment for Democracy Library, 1025 F St NW, Ste 800, Washington, DC, 20004. Tel: 202-378-9700. Fax: 202-378-9407. p. 409

Yi, Hua, Coordr, Coll Develop, California State University, 333 S Twin Oaks Valley Rd, San Marcos, CA, 92096-0001. Tel: 760-750-4368. Fax: 760-750-3287. p. 254

Yi, Ju Sun, Archivist, Hawaii State Archives, Iolani Palace Grounds, 364 S King St, Honolulu, HI, 96813. Tel: 808-586-0329. Fax: 808-586-0330. p. 561

Yip, Monyee, Tech Serv Mgr, Weber County Library System, 2464 Jefferson Ave, Ogden, UT, 84401-2464. Tel: 801-337-2617. Fax: 801-337-2615. p. 2408

Yip, Teresa, Cataloger, Marymount Manhattan College, 221 E 71st St, New York, NY, 10021. Tel: 212-774-4818. Fax: 212-458-8207. p. 1685

Yirka, Carl A, Dir, Vermont Law School, 68 North Windsor, South Royalton, VT, 05068. Tel: 802-831-1441. Fax: 802-763-7159. p. 2436

Ylarraz, Alice, Librn, McKee Medical Center, 2000 Boise Ave, Loveland, CO, 80538-0830. Tel: 970-635-4048. Fax: 970-593-6006. p. 318

Yoak, Janice, Librn, Michigan Department of Corrections, N6141 Industrial Park Dr, Munising, MI, 49862. Tel: 906-387-5000, Ext 1302. Fax: 906-387-5033. p. 1212

Yoak, Janice, Librn, Newberry Correctional Facility Library, 3001 Newberry Ave, Newberry, MI, 49868. Tel: 906-293-6200. Fax: 906-293-6323. p. 1214

Yob, Nancy, Br Mgr, Enoch Pratt Free Library, Hamilton, 5910 Harford Rd, Baltimore, MD, 21214-1845. Tel: 410-396-6088. Fax: 410-396-6097. p. 1013

Younce, Eldon, Dir, Anthony Public Library, 624 E Main, Anthony, KS, 67003-2738. Tel: 620-842-5344. Fax: 620-842-5684. p. 856

Young, Anita, Pub Serv Librn, Wake Technical Community College, Northern Wake Library, 6600 Louisburg Rd, Bldg B, Rm 239, Raleigh, NC, 27616. Tel: 919-532-5550. p. 1818

Young, Anne H, Curator, Historical Society of the Town of Greenwich, 39 Strickland Rd, Cos Cob, CT, 06807. Tel: 203-869-6899. Fax: 203-861-9720. p. 334

Young, Annie, Sr Ref Librn, United States Senate Library, SRB-15 Senate Russell Bldg, Washington, DC, 20510-7112. Tel: 202-224-7106. Fax: 202-224-0879. p. 421

Young, April, Br Librn, Rutherford County Library, Mountains Branch, 150 Bills Creek Rd, Lake Lure, NC, 28746. Tel: 828-625-0456. Fax: 828-625-0453. p. 1825

Young, Audrey, Head, Ref, Easttown Library & Information Center, 720 First Ave, Berwyn, PA, 19312-1769. Tel: 610-644-0138. Fax: 610-251-9739. p. 2033

Young, Belle, Libr Tech, First Nations University of Canada, One First Nations Way, Regina, SK, S4S 7K2, CANADA. Tel: 306-790-5950, Ext 3427. Fax: 306-790-5990. p. 2922

Young, Beth, Access Serv, Christopher Newport University, One Avenue of the Arts, Newport News, VA, 23606. Tel: 757-594-7134. Fax: 757-594-7717. p. 2479

Young, Betsy, Ref Librn, Austin Community College, Round Rock Campus Library, 4400 College Park Dr, Round Rock, TX, 78665. Tel: 512-223-0119. Fax: 512-223-0903. p. 2278

Young, Betty, ILL, Ames Public Library, 515 Douglas Ave, Ames, IA, 50010. Tel: 515-239-5656. Fax: 515-233-9001. p. 792

Young, Bill, Pub Info Officer, Oklahoma Department of Libraries, 200 NE 18th St, Oklahoma City, OK, 73105. Tel: 405-521-2502. Fax: 405-525-7804. p. 1974

Young, Carol, In Charge, McNamee, Lochner, Titus & Williams, PC, 677 Broadway, Albany, NY, 12207. Tel: 518-447-3200. Fax: 518-426-4260. p. 1569

Young, Caroline, Ref & Tech Librn, Rutgers University Library for the Center for Law & Justice, 123 Washington St, Newark, NJ, 07102-3094. Tel: 973-353-3146. Fax: 973-353-1356. p. 1513

Young, Cecilia, Fund Develop Officer, Yuma County Library District, 2951 S 21st Dr, Yuma, AZ, 85364. Tel: 928-373-6495. Fax: 928-782-9420. p. 91

Young, Courtney L, Ref Librn, Pennsylvania State University, 100 University Dr, Monaca, PA, 15061. Tel: 724-773-3796. Fax: 724-773-3793. p. 2091

Young, Cynthia, Dir, Amagansett Free Library, 215 Main St, Amagansett, NY, 11930. Tel: 631-267-3810. Fax: 631-267-0087. p. 1573

Young, Cynthia Sue, Br Librn, Eastern Monroe Public Library, Pocono Township Branch, Municipal Bldg, Rte 611, Tannersville, PA, 18372. Tel: 570-629-5858. p. 2144

Young, Dana, Ref, Gavilan College Library, 5055 Santa Teresa Blvd, Gilroy, CA, 95020. Tel: 408-848-4812. Fax: 408-846-4927. p. 154

Young, David Colby, Pres, Androscoggin Historical Society, Two Turner St, Unit 8, Auburn, ME, 04210-5978. Tel: 207-784-0586, 207-784-2129. p. 973

Young, David W, Cat Librn, University of North Carolina at Pembroke, Faculty Row, Pembroke, NC, 28372. Tel: 910-521-6516. Fax: 910-521-6547. p. 1384

Young, Debra, Librn, Butler Memorial Library, 621 Penn St, Cambridge, NE, 69022. Tel: 308-697-3836. Fax: 308-697-3173. p. 1395

Young, Debra J, Asst Dir, Head, Ch, Uxbridge Free Public Library, 15 N Main St, Uxbridge, MA, 01569-1822. Tel: 508-278-8621. Fax: 508-278-8618. p. 1132

Young, Denese, Librn, Missouri Department of Corrections, South Central Correctional Center, 255 W Hwy 32, Licking, MO, 65542-9069. Tel: 573-674-4470. Fax: 573-674-4428. p. 1335

Young, Diane, Dir, Beth Israel Deaconess Medical Center-Needham Campus, 148 Chestnut St, Needham, MA, 02492. Tel: 781-453-5419. Fax: 617-832-8312. p. 1108

Young, Dillon, Sr Librn, Hennepin County Library, Eden Prairie, 565 Prairie Center Dr, Eden Prairie, MN, 55344-5319. Tel: 612-543-6281. Fax: 612-543-6277. p. 1263

Young, Doris, Circ, Emmet O'Neal Library, 50 Oak St, Mountain Brook, AL, 35213. Tel: 205-879-0459. Fax: 205-879-5388. p. 32

Young, Eddiemae, Dr, Ser Librn, Mississippi Valley State University, 14000 Hwy 82 W, Itta Bena, MS, 38941. Tel: 662-254-3494. Fax: 662-254-3499. p. 1302

Young, Eileen, Circ, Dundee Public Library, 202 E Main St, Dundee, FL, 33838. Tel: 863-439-9424. Fax: 863-439-9426. p. 438

Young, Eldon, Dr, Dean of Libr, Cypress College Library, 9200 Valley View St, Cypress, CA, 90630-5897. Tel: 714-484-7302. Fax: 714-826-6723. p. 138

Young, Elizabeth, Br Mgr, Humboldt County Library, Willow Creek Branch, Hwy 299 & Hwy 96, Willow Creek, CA, 95573-0466. Tel: 530-629-2146. p. 147

Young, Elizabeth, Archives & Spec Coll Librn, State University of New York at Oswego, SUNY Oswego, 7060 State Rte 104, Oswego, NY, 13126-3514. Tel: 315-312-3537. Fax: 315-312-3194. p. 1713

Young, Elizabeth, Head, Reader Serv, Elizabethtown College, One Alpha Dr, Elizabethtown, PA, 17022-2227. Tel: 717-361-1456. Fax: 717-361-1167. p. 2053

Young, Emily, Sr Libr Mgr, Alachua County Library District, Millhopper Branch, 3145 NW 43rd St, Gainesville, FL, 32606-6107. Tel: 352-334-1272. Fax: 352-334-1280. p. 448

Young, Eric, Dir, Tech & Info Serv, Nova Southeastern University Libraries, Shepard Broad Law Center Library, 3305 College Ave, Fort Lauderdale, FL, 33314. Tel: 954-262-6100. p. 444

Young, Grace, Univ Archivist, Carlow University, 3333 Fifth Ave, Pittsburgh, PA, 15213. Tel: 412-578-6244. Fax: 412-578-6242. p. 2122

Young, Ian, Ref Serv, John Abbott College, 21,275 Lakeshore Rd, Sainte-Anne-de-Bellevue, QC, H9X 3L9, CANADA. Tel: 514-457-6610, Ext 5335. p. 2910

Young, Irene, Asst Librn, Boynton Public Library, 27 Boynton Rd, Templeton, MA, 01468-1412. Tel: 978-939-5582. Fax: 978-939-8755. p. 1131

Young, J Chris, Assoc Dir, Info Tech, Houston Academy of Medicine, 1133 John Freeman Blvd, Houston, TX, 77030. Tel: 713-799-7803. Fax: 713-790-7052. p. 2337

Young, Jackie, Archivist, Libr Dir, Spalding University Library, 853 Library Lane, Louisville, KY, 40203-9986. Tel: 502-585-7130. Fax: 502-585-7156. p. 925

Young, Jacquelyn, Media Spec, State University of New York - Jefferson Community College, 1220 Coffeen St, Watertown, NY, 13601-1897. Tel: 315-786-2413. Fax: 315-788-0716. p. 1764

Young, James, Admin Dir, Lehigh University, Fairchild-Martindale Library, Eight A E Packer Ave, Bethlehem, PA, 18015-3170. Tel: 610-758-4645. Fax: 610-758-3004. p. 2034

Young, Jane, Acq, Circ, Tech Serv, Century College Library, 3300 N Century Ave, White Bear Lake, MN, 55110. Tel: 651-779-3264. Fax: 651-779-3963. p. 1288

Young, Janet, Tech Serv, Hurst Public Library, 901 Precinct Line Rd, Hurst, TX, 76053. Tel: 817-788-7300. Fax: 817-590-9515. p. 2345

Young, Janice, Law Librn, Clark County Law Library, 309 S Third St, Ste 400, Las Vegas, NV, 89155. Tel: 702-455-4696. Fax: 702-455-5120. p. 1428

Young, Jason, Librn, Genesis Medical Center, 1227 E Rusholme St, Davenport, IA, 52803. Tel: 563-421-7150. Fax: 563-421-2288, 563-421-7152. p. 806

Young, Jason, Librn, Ottumwa Regional Health Center Medical Library, 1003 Pennsylvania Ave, Ottumwa, IA, 52501. Tel: 641-684-2450. Fax: 641-684-2455. p. 837

Young, Jean, Ch, Rockland Public Library, 80 Union St, Rockland, ME, 04841. Tel: 207-594-0310. Fax: 207-594-0333. p. 999

Young, Jennifer, Ch, Perry County Public Library, 289 Black Gold Blvd, Hazard, KY, 41701. Tel: 606-436-2475, 606-436-4747. Fax: 606-436-0191. p. 917

Young, Jessica, Teen Librn, Johnston Public Library, 6700 Merle Hay Rd, Johnston, IA, 50131-0327. Tel: 515-278-5233. Fax: 515-278-4975. p. 824

Young, Jessica, Ch, Council Grove Public Library, 829 W Main St, Council Grove, KS, 66846. Tel: 620-767-5716. Fax: 620-767-7312. p. 862

Young, Jim B, Ch, Greensboro Public Library, 219 N Church St, Greensboro, NC, 27402-3178. Tel: 336-373-4103. Fax: 336-335-5415. p. 1796

Young, Jo Ella, ILL, University of South Florida, Hinks & Elaine Shimberg Health Sciences Library, 12901 Bruce B Downs Blvd, MDC Box 31, Tampa, FL, 33612-4799. Tel: 813-974-2399. Fax: 813-974-3605, 813-974-4930. p. 498

Young, Joan, Librn, Germantown Public Library District, 403 Munster St, Germantown, IL, 62245. Tel: 618-523-4820. Fax: 618-523-4599. p. 649

Young, John, Librn, Georgia Department of Corrections, Office of Library Services, Hwy 36 W, Jackson, GA, 30233. Tel: 770-504-2125. Fax: 770-504-2006. p. 536

Young, Juana R, Assoc Dean, University of Arkansas Libraries, 365 N McIlroy Ave, Fayetteville, AR, 72701-4002. Tel: 479-575-3079. Fax: 479-575-6656. p. 99

Young, Judy, Dir, Hodgkins Public Library District, 6500 Wenz Ave, Hodgkins, IL, 60525. Tel: 708-579-1844. Fax: 708-579-1896. p. 657

Young, Julia Marks, Div Head, Mississippi Department of Archives & History, 200 North St, Jackson, MS, 39201. Tel: 601-576-6876. Fax: 601-576-6964. p. 1304

Young, Kara, Head, Libr Syst, Keene State College, 229 Main St, Keene, NH, 03435-3201. Tel: 603-358-2716. Fax: 603-358-2745. p. 1453

Young, Kay, Ref, University of Wisconsin - Platteville, One University Plaza, Platteville, WI, 53818. Tel: 608-342-1134. Fax: 608-342-1645. p. 2630

Young, Kenneth, Computer Serv, Cumberland County Public Library & Information Center, 300 Maiden Lane, Fayetteville, NC, 28301-5000. Tel: 910-483-7727. Fax: 910-486-5372. p. 1792

Young, Laureen, Ch, Louttit Library, 274 Victory Hwy, West Greenwich, RI, 02817. Tel: 401-397-3434. Fax: 401-397-3837. p. 2177

Young, Lee, Librn, American Truck Historical Society, 10380 N Ambassador Dr, Ste 101, Kansas City, MO, 64153-1378. Tel: 816-891-9900. Fax: 816-891-9903. p. 1336

Young, Libby, Govt Doc, Furman University Libraries, 3300 Poinsett Hwy, Greenville, SC, 29613-4100. Tel: 864-294-2260. Fax: 864-294-3004. p. 2195

Young, Linda, Libr Tech, Charlie Norwood VA Medical Center Library, One Freedom Way, Augusta, GA, 30904-6285. Tel: 706-733-0188, Ext 2813. Fax: 706-823-3920. p. 520

Young, Lisa, Circ Supvr, Lindenwood University, 209 S Kingshighway, Saint Charles, MO, 63301. Tel: 636-949-4820. Fax: 636-949-4822. p. 1351

Young, Lyn, Librn, Central Georgia Technical College Library, 3300 Macon Tech Dr, Macon, GA, 31206-3628. Tel: 478-757-3549. Fax: 478-757-3545. p. 540

Young, Lynne, Dir, Northfield Public Library, 210 Washington St, Northfield, MN, 55057. Tel: 507-645-1801. Fax: 507-645-1820. p. 1269

Young, Marleena, Asst Dir, Ch, Harrington Public Library, 110 Center St, Harrington, DE, 19952. Tel: 302-398-4647. Fax: 302-398-3847. p. 383

Young, Martha, Librn, Margaret Carder Public Library, 201 W Lincoln, Mangum, OK, 73554. Tel: 580-782-3185. Fax: 580-782-5308. p. 1967

Young, Mary, Asst Librn, De Leon City County Library, 125 E Reynosa St, De Leon, TX, 76444-1862. Tel: 254-893-2417. Fax: 254-893-4915. p. 2311

Young, Mary, Acq, Texarkana College, 2500 N Robison Rd, Texarkana, TX, 75599. Tel: 903-832-5565, Ext 3115. Fax: 903-831-7429. p. 2391

Young, Mary Ann, Sr Librn, Palo Alto City Library, Mitchell Park, 3700 Middlefield Rd, Palo Alto, CA, 94303. Fax: 650-856-7925. p. 204

Young, Michelle, Br Mgr, Hawaii State Public Library System, Princeville Public Library, 4343 Emmalani Dr, Princeville, HI, 96722. Tel: 808-826-4310. Fax: 808-826-4311. p. 563

Young, Michelle L, Dir of Libr, Clarkson University Libraries, Andrew S Schuler Educational Resources Center, CU Box 5590, Eight Clarkson Ave, Potsdam, NY, 13699-5590. Tel: 315-268-4268. Fax: 315-268-7655. p. 1721

Young, Michelle L, Dir of Libr, Clarkson University Library, Health Sciences Library, Clarkson Hall - 2nd Flr, CU Box 5880, Eight Clarkson Ave, Potsdam, NY, 13699-5880. Tel: 315-268-4268. Fax: 315-268-7655. p. 1722

Young, Monica Williamson, Librn, Moses Cone Health System, Women's Hospital of Greensboro Library, 801 Green Valley, Greensboro, NC, 27408. Tel: 336-832-6878. Fax: 336-832-6893. p. 1797

Young, Nanci, Archivist, Smith College Libraries, College Archives, Seven Neilson Dr, Northampton, MA, 01063. Tel: 413-585-2976. p. 1114

Young, Pat, Ad, Mansfield Public Library, 104 S Wisteria St, Mansfield, TX, 76063. Tel: 817-473-4391. Fax: 817-453-4975. p. 2359

Young, Patricia, Asst Librn, Butler Memorial Library, 621 Penn St, Cambridge, NE, 69022. Tel: 308-697-3836. Fax: 308-697-3173. p. 1395

Young, Penny, Librn, West Hill Collegiate Institute, 350 Morningside Ave, West Hill, ON, M1E 3G3, CANADA. Tel: 416-396-6864. Fax: 416-396-8300. p. 2870

Young, Rachel Muchin, Coordr, Pub Serv, Manitowoc Public Library, 707 Quay St, Manitowoc, WI, 54220. Tel: 920-686-3000. p. 2612

Young, Richard J, Librn, Seminole Community College, 2505 Lockwood Blvd, Oviedo, FL, 32765-9189. Tel: 407-971-5051. Fax: 407-971-3543. p. 478

Young, Robert H, Dr, Dir, Massachusetts General Hospital, Tracy Burr Mallory Memorial Library, Dept of Pathology, 55 Fruit St, Boston, MA, 02114. Tel: 617-726-8892. Fax: 617-726-7474. p. 1063

Young, Roger O, Tech Coordr, Washington County Public Library, 615 Fifth St, Marietta, OH, 45750-1973. Tel: 740-373-1057, Ext 224. p. 1913

Young, Rosemary, Dir, University of Cincinnati, 4200 Clermont College Dr, Batavia, OH, 45103-1785. Tel: 513-732-5232. Fax: 513-732-5237. p. 1858

Young, Ruth E, Head Librn, Flagler Beach Library, 315 S Seventh St, Flagler Beach, FL, 32136-3524. Tel: 386-517-2030. Fax: 386-517-2234. p. 440

Young, Stephanie, Sr Info Analyst, The National Academies, 500 Fifth St NW, Keck 304, Washington, DC, 20001-2721. Tel: 202-334-2125. Fax: 202-334-1651. p. 409

Young, Stephanie, Dir, Woods Memorial Library, 19 Pleasant St, Barre, MA, 01005. Tel: 978-355-2533. Fax: 978-355-2511. p. 1051

Young, Stephanie, Adult Serv, Ogdensburg Public Library, 312 Washington St, Ogdensburg, NY, 13669-1518. Tel: 315-393-4325. Fax: 315-393-4344. p. 1709

Young, Sue, Br Mgr, Wilson County Public Library, Elm City Branch, 114 N Railroad St, Elm City, NC, 27822-0717. Tel: 252-236-4269. Fax: 252-236-4269. p. 1831

Young, Susan, In Charge, Arkansas Geological Survey Library, 3815 W Roosevelt Rd, Little Rock, AR, 72204-6369. Tel: 501-296-1877. Fax: 501-663-7360. p. 105

Young, Susanne, Br Mgr, Davis Jefferson Parish Library, Jennings Headquarter Branch, 118 W Plaquemine, Jennings, LA, 70546-0356. Tel: 318-824-1210. Fax: 318-824-5444. p. 952

Young, Suzanne, Br Mgr, Jefferson Davis Parish Library, 118 W Plaquemine St, Jennings, LA, 70546-5856. Tel: 337-824-1210. Fax: 337-824-5444. p. 952

Young, Suzanne, Libr Serv Mgr, Jones Day, 901 Lakeside Ave, Cleveland, OH, 44114. Tel: 216-586-3939. Fax: 216-579-0212. p. 1880

Young, Terry S, Dir, McMurry University, Sayles Blvd & S 14th, Abilene, TX, 79605. Tel: 325-793-4690. Fax: 325-793-4930. p. 2272

Young, Thomas Elton, Librn, Philbrook Museum of Art, 2727 S Rockford Rd, Tulsa, OK, 74114-4104. Tel: 918-748-5306. Fax: 918-748-5303. p. 1982

Young, Tonja, Libr Dir, Daphne Public Library, 2607 US Hwy 98, Daphne, AL, 36526. Tel: 251-621-2818. Fax: 251-621-3086. p. 14

Young, Tonja, Librn, Oscar Johnson Memorial Library, 21967 Sixth St, Silverhill, AL, 36576. Tel: 251-945-5201. p. 36

Young, Trevor, Media Spec, Utah Valley University Library, 800 W University Pkwy, Orem, UT, 84058-5999. Tel: 801-863-6846. Fax: 801-863-7065. p. 2409

Young, Vicki, Br Mgr, De Soto Trail Regional Library, Margaret Jones Public, 205 E Pope St, Sylvester, GA, 31791. Tel: 229-776-2096. Fax: 229-776-0079. p. 522

Young, Virginia, Ref Librn, SUNY Upstate Medical University, 766 Irving Ave, Syracuse, NY, 13210-1602. Tel: 315-464-7084. Fax: 315-464-4584. p. 1753

Young, Virginia E, Dr, Dir, Randolph-Macon College, 204 Henry St, Ashland, VA, 23005. Tel: 804-752-7256. Fax: 804-752-3135. p. 2450

Youngberg, Robert, Dir, Ainsworth Public Library, 2338 VT Rte 14, Williamstown, VT, 05679. Tel: 802-433-5887. Fax: 802-433-2161. p. 2440

Youngberg, Sharon, Cat Librn, Syst Adminr, Northland College, 1411 Ellis Ave, Ashland, WI, 54806-3999. Tel: 715-682-1298. Fax: 715-682-1693. p. 2579

Youngblood, Barbara, Dir, San Miguel Library District 2, 1110 Lucerne St, Norwood, CO, 81423. Tel: 970-327-4833. Fax: 970-327-4129. p. 319

Youngblood, Carla, Asst Librn, Berryville Public Library, 104 Spring St, Berryville, AR, 72616. Tel: 870-423-2323. Fax: 870-423-2432. p. 95

Youngblood, Cindy, Dir, Saint Clair County Library, 115 Chestnut St, Osceola, MO, 64776-2502. Tel: 417-646-2214. Fax: 417-646-8643. p. 1348

Youngblood, Joshua, Spec Coll Res & Outreach Serv Librn, University of Arkansas Libraries, 365 N McIlroy Ave, Fayetteville, AR, 72701-4002. Tel: 479-575-7251. Fax: 479-575-6656. p. 99

Youngblood, Lisa D, Dir, Harker Heights Public Library, 400 Indian Trail, Harker Heights, TX, 76548. Tel: 254-699-1776. Fax: 254-699-4772. p. 2331

Youngblood, Merna, Librn, Illinois Eastern Community College, Two Frontier Dr, Fairfield, IL, 62837-9705. Tel: 618-842-3711. Fax: 618-842-4425. p. 645

Youngblood, Suzanne, Dir, Plymouth Public Library, 107 W Main St, Plymouth, PA, 18651-2919. Tel: 570-779-4775. Fax: 570-779-5616. p. 2130

Younge, Val, Prog Head, Emergent Technologies Librn, SIAST-Saskatchewan Institute of Applied Science & Technology, 4500 Wascana Pkwy, Regina, SK, S4P 3S7, CANADA. Tel: 306-775-7411. Fax: 306-798-0560. p. 2924

Younger, Patricia, Dir, Meridian District Library, 1326 W Cherry Lane, Meridian, ID, 83646. Tel: 208-888-4451. Fax: 208-884-0745. p. 579

Youngken, Jill, Curator, Dir, Libr & Archives, Lehigh County Historical Society, Lehigh Valley Heritage Museum, 432 W Walnut St, Allentown, PA, 18102-5428. Tel: 610-435-1074, Ext 20. Fax: 610-435-9812. p. 2026

Youngkin, Molly, Outreach Serv Librn, Wegner Health Science Information Center, 1400 W 22nd St, Ste 100, Sioux Falls, SD, 57105. Tel: 605-357-1400. Fax: 605-357-1490. p. 2219

Younglove, April, Libr Tech Spec, Linfield College, Portland Campus, 2255 NW Northrup, Portland, OR, 97210. Tel: 503-413-7335. Fax: 503-413-8016. p. 2005

Younglove, April, Librn, Rochester Regional Library Council, 390 Packetts Landing, Fairport, NY, 14450. Tel: 585-223-7570. Fax: 585-223-7712. p. 2950

Younglove, Erica, ILL, Perry Public Library, 3753 Main St, Perry, OH, 44081-9501. Tel: 440-259-3300. Fax: 440-259-3977. p. 1929

Youngman, Becky, Cataloger, Anderson University, Robert A Nicholson Library, 1100 E Fifth St, Anderson, IN, 46012-3495. Tel: 765-641-4276. Fax: 765-641-3850. p. 724

Youngmark, Bill, Ref, Southeastern Baptist Theological Seminary Library, 114 N Wingate St, Wake Forest, NC, 27587. Tel: 919-556-3104. Fax: 919-863-8150. p. 1827

Youngmark, Fay, Circ Mgr, Pennsylvania State University-Harrisburg Library, 351 Olmsted Dr, Middletown, PA, 17057-4850. Tel: 717-948-6070. Fax: 717-948-6757. p. 2089

Youngquist, Holly, Pub Serv, Newton Public Library, 100 N Third Ave W, Newton, IA, 50208. Tel: 641-792-4108. Fax: 641-791-0729. p. 835

Youngquist, Mary, Asst Librn, Beaver City Public Library, 408 Tenth St, Beaver City, NE, 68926. Tel: 308-268-4115. p. 1393

Youngs, Lila M, Libr Mgr, Richville Free Library, 87 Main St, Richville, NY, 13681-3102. Tel: 315-287-1481. Fax: 315-287-1481. p. 1727

Youngstrom, Jason, Librn, Syst & Tech Planning, National Renewable Energy Laboratory Library, 15013 Denver West Pkwy, Golden, CO, 80401-3305. Tel: 303-275-4026. Fax: 303-275-4222. p. 310

Younker, Nancy, Pres, Weatherly Area Community Library, 20 Carbon St, Unit 1, Weatherly, PA, 18255. Tel: 570-427-5085. p. 2152

Yount, Anna, Libr Dir, Transylvania County Library, 212 S Gaston, Brevard, NC, 28712. Tel: 828-884-3151, Ext 239. Fax: 828-877-4230. p. 1777

Yount, Diana, Co-Dir, Pub Serv, Spec Coll Librn, Andover Newton Theological School, 169 Herrick Rd, Newton Centre, MA, 02459. Tel: 617-831-2415. Fax: 617-831-1643. p. 1110

Yount, Sue, Librn, Mountainburg Public Library, 1300 Hwy 71 N, Mountainburg, AR, 72946. Tel: 479-369-1600. Fax: 479-369-1600. p. 111

Younts, Wei, Ser, University of Puget Sound, 1500 N Warner St, Campus Mail Box 1021, Tacoma, WA, 98416-1021. Tel: 253-879-3617. Fax: 253-879-3670. p. 2541

Yourist, Laurie, Librn, Memorial Hospital Library, 325 S Belmont St, York, PA, 17403-2609. Tel: 717-849-5305. Fax: 717-849-5489. p. 2159

Yourst, Lora, Info Serv, Martin Memorial Library, 159 E Market St, York, PA, 17401-1269. Tel: 717-846-5300. Fax: 717-848-2330. p. 2159

Youssef, Sherry, Res & Instruction Librn, Alliant International University, 1000 S Fremont Ave, Unit 5, Alhambra, CA, 91803. Tel: 626-270-3272. Fax: 626-284-1682. p. 120

Yowell, Linda, Support Serv Mgr, Fauquier County Public Library, 11 Winchester St, Warrenton, VA, 20186-2825. Tel: 540-349-1327. Fax: 540-349-3278. p. 2500

Yoxall, Connie, Pub Serv, Liberal Memorial Library, 519 N Kansas, Liberal, KS, 67901-3345. Tel: 620-626-0180. Fax: 620-626-0182. p. 879

Yu, Aiju, Ref, Fasken Martineau DuMoulin LLP, Bay Adelaide Centre, Box 20, 333 Bay St, Ste 2400, Toronto, ON, M5H 2T6, CANADA. Tel: 416-865-5143. Fax: 416-364-7813. p. 2853

Yu, Chilin, Dir, Columbus College of Art & Design, 107 N Ninth St, Columbus, OH, 43215-3875. Tel: 614-222-3273, 614-224-9101. Fax: 614-222-6193. p. 1884

Yu, Cristina, ILL, Wake Forest University, PO Box 7777, Winston-Salem, NC, 27109-7777. Tel: 336-758-5675. Fax: 336-758-3694, 336-758-8831. p. 1834

Yu, Emma Lee, Info Serv, Brooklyn College Library, 2900 Bedford Ave, Brooklyn, NY, 11210-2889. Tel: 718-951-5336. Fax: 718-951-4540. p. 1589

Yu, Hainan, Info Tech, Syst Librn, Brooklyn Law School Library, 250 Joralemon St, Brooklyn, NY, 11201. Tel: 718-780-7910. Fax: 718-780-0369. p. 1590

Yu, Hong, Head, Cat, Southwestern University, 1100 E University Ave, Georgetown, TX, 78626. Tel: 512-863-1561. Fax: 512-863-8198. p. 2327

Yu, Lifeng, Tallahassee Campus Libr Dir, Keiser University Library System, 1500 NW 49th St, Fort Lauderdale, FL, 33309. Tel: 954-351-4035. Fax: 954-351-4051. p. 443

Yu, May, Instrul Media, Alcorn State University, 1000 ASU Dr, Alcorn State, MS, 39096-7500. Tel: 601-877-6359. Fax: 601-877-3885. p. 1293

Yu, Miranda, Libr Coordr, Vaughan Public Libraries, Dufferin Clark Library, 1441 Clark Ave W, Thornhill, ON, L4J 7R4, CANADA. Tel: 905-653-7323. Fax: 905-660-7202. p. 2848

Yu, Nancy, Cat, Southeastern Baptist Theological Seminary Library, 114 N Wingate St, Wake Forest, NC, 27587. Tel: 919-556-3104. Fax: 919-863-8150. p. 1827

Yu, Ning, Dr, Asst Prof, University of Kentucky, 320 Little Library Bldg, Lexington, KY, 40506-0224. Tel: 859-257-4109. Fax: 859-257-4205. p. 2966

Yu, Tricia, Librn, University of British Columbia Library, Eric Hamber Library, Children's & Women's Health Ctr, 4480 Oak St, Vancouver, BC, V6H 3V4, CANADA. Fax: 604-875-2195. p. 2743

Yu, Yi, Digital Projects Librn, University of Alaska Fairbanks, 310 Tanana Dr, Fairbanks, AK, 99775. Tel: 907-474-5364. Fax: 907-474-6841. p. 48

Yu, Ying, Ref Serv, Columbia Basin College Library, 2600 N 20th Ave, Pasco, WA, 99301. Tel: 509-542-4690. Fax: 509-546-0401. p. 2523

Yuan, Barbara, Asst Dir, Winchester Public Library, 80 Washington St, Winchester, MA, 01890. Tel: 781-721-7171, Ext 18. Fax: 781-721-7170. p. 1142

Yuan, Haiwang, Webmaster, Western Kentucky University Libraries, Helm-Cravens Library Complex, 1906 College Heights Blvd, No 11067, Bowling Green, KY, 42101-1067. Tel: 270-745-2905. Fax: 270-745-6422. p. 908

Yuan, Xiaojun, Dr, Asst Prof, University at Albany, State University of New York, Draper 116, 135 Western Ave, Albany, NY, 12222. Tel: 518-591-8746. Fax: 518-442-5367. p. 2970

Yue, Kathy, Mgr, Supv Librn, Alameda County Medical Center, 1411 E 31st St, Oakland, CA, 94602. Tel: 510-437-4701. Fax: 510-537-7592. p. 196

Yue, Paoshan, Tech Serv, University of Nevada-Reno, 1664 N Virginia St, Mailstop 0322, Reno, NV, 89557-0322. Tel: 775-682-5599. Fax: 775-784-1328. p. 1433

Yueh, Christina, Mgr, Ch Serv, Sr Librn, Monterey Park Bruggemeyer Library, 318 S Ramona Ave, Monterey Park, CA, 91754-3399. Tel: 626-307-1412. Fax: 626-288-4251. p. 190

Yuen, Debra Wong, Actg Br Mgr, Libr Tech VIII, Hawaii State Public Library System, Naalehu Public Library, 95-5669 Mamalahoa Hwy, Naalehu, HI, 96772. Tel: 808-939-2442. Fax: 808-939-2443. p. 563

Yuen, Debra Wong, Libr Tech VII, Hawaii State Public Library System, Pahala Public & School Library, 96-3150 Pikake St, Pahala, HI, 96777. Tel: 808-928-2015. Fax: 808-928-2016. p. 563

Yuen, Eleanor, Head Librn, University of British Columbia Library, Asian, 1871 West Mall, Vancouver, BC, V6T 1Z2, CANADA. Tel: 604-822-5905. Fax: 604-822-0650. p. 2743

Yuen, Kandace, Med Librn, Connecticut Valley Hospital, Willis Royle Library, Silver St, Middletown, CT, 06457. Tel: 860-262-5520. Fax: 860-262-5049. p. 351

Yuen, Kandace, Librn, Waterbury Hospital, 64 Robbins St, Waterbury, CT, 06721. Tel: 203-573-6136. Fax: 203-573-6706. p. 375

Yuen, Patricia, Tech Serv, Alzheimer's Association, 225 N Michigan Ave, 17th Flr, Chicago, IL, 60601. Tel: 312-604-2456. p. 605

Yuen, Patrivan, Tech Serv & Syst Librn, William Carey University Libraries, 498 Tuscan Ave, Box 5, Hattiesburg, MS, 39401. Tel: 601-318-6169. Fax: 601-318-6171. p. 1301

Yuhas, Stephanie, Dr, Archives Project Mgr, University of Colorado Boulder, Archives & Special Collections, 1720 Pleasant St, Boulder, CO, 80309-0184. Tel: 303-492-3797. Fax: 303-492-1881. p. 291

Yuill, Jo Ann, Tech Librn, United States Department of Energy, 3610 Collins Ferry Rd, Morgantown, WV, 26507. Tel: 304-285-4184. p. 2566

Yukawa, Joyce, PhD, Asst Prof, Saint Catherine University, 2004 Randolph Ave, Mailstop No 4125, Saint Paul, MN, 55105. Tel: 651-690-6802. Fax: 651-690-8724. p. 2968

Yulfososa, Monserrate, Dir, Inter-American University of Puerto Rico, PO Box 20000, Aguadilla, PR, 00905. Tel: 787-891-0925. Fax: 787-882-3020. p. 2671

Yundt Silver, Hallie, Dir, Hannibal Free Public Library, 200 S Fifth St, Hannibal, MO, 63401. Tel: 573-221-0222. Fax: 573-221-0369. p. 1329

Yunker, Beverly, Ref Librn, Mesquite Public Library, North Branch, 2600 Oates Dr, Mesquite, TX, 75150. Tel: 972-681-0465. Fax: 972-681-0467. p. 2362

Yunko, Paula, Access & Ser Librn, Keystone College, One College Green, La Plume, PA, 18440-0200. Tel: 570-945-8332. Fax: 570-945-8969. p. 2075

Yuran, Robin, Dir, Norfolk Library, Nine Greenwoods Rd E, Norfolk, CT, 06058-1320. Tel: 860-542-5075. Fax: 860-542-1795. p. 361

Yurchick, Lann, Dir, Ridgway Public Library, 329 Center St, Ridgway, PA, 15853. Tel: 814-773-7573. Fax: 814-776-1093. p. 2134

Yurgelonis, Christine, Admin Librn, Ridgewood Public Library, 125 N Maple Ave, Ridgewood, NJ, 07450-3288. Tel: 201-670-5600. Fax: 201-670-0293. p. 1526

Yurgil, Gary, Dir, Poynette Public Library, 118 N Main, Poynette, WI, 53955. Tel: 608-635-7577. Fax: 608-635-7577. p. 2631

Yves, Jobin, Dir, Content Prog, Canadian Research Knowledge Network, Preston Sq, Tower 2, 200 343 Preston St, Ottawa, ON, K1S 1N4, CANADA. Tel: 613-907-7033. Fax: 866-903-9094. p. 2959

Zaabel, Josephine, Bus Mgr, Maywood Public Library District, 121 S Fifth Ave, Maywood, IL, 60153. Tel: 708-343-1847, Ext 29. Fax: 708-343-2115. p. 672

Zabel, Diane W, Actg Head Librn, Pennsylvania State University Libraries, William & Joan Schreyer Business Library, 301 Paterno Library, University Park, PA, 16802-1810. Tel: 814-865-1013. Fax: 814-863-6370. p. 2148

Zabelski, Lauren, Image Librn, Historical Society of Western Pennsylvania, 1212 Smallman St, Pittsburgh, PA, 15222. Tel: 412-454-6402. Fax: 412-454-6028. p. 2125

Zabihi, Zoha, Librn, Western Medical Center, 1001 N Tustin Ave, Santa Ana, CA, 92705. Tel: 714-953-3484. Fax: 714-953-2388. p. 260

Zabkowicz, Bob, Sr Librn, Fox Lake Correctional Institution Library, PO Box 147, Fox Lake, WI, 53933-0147. Tel: 920-928-3151, Ext 6240. Fax: 920-928-6229. p. 2593

Zaborowski, Barbara A, Dr, Assoc Dean, Pennsylvania Highlands Community College Library, 101 Community College Way, Johnstown, PA, 15904. Tel: 814-262-6425. Fax: 814-269-9744. p. 2073

Zaborowski, Lindsay, Project Mgr - Wash County Hist Online, Pacific University Library, 2043 College Way, Forest Grove, OR, 97116. Tel: 503-352-1400. Fax: 503-352-1416. p. 1998

Zabriskie, Stephanie, Acq, Cambridge Public Library, 449 Broadway, Cambridge, MA, 02138. Tel: 617-349-4040. Fax: 617-349-4028. p. 1073

Zaccagnino, Nancy, Cat, Kinnelon Public Library, 132 Kinnelon Rd, Kinnelon, NJ, 07405-2393. Tel: 973-838-1321. Fax: 973-838-0741. p. 1493

Zaccaria, Mary G, Dir, Butler Public Library, One Ace Rd, Butler, NJ, 07405. Tel: 973-838-3262. Fax: 973-838-9436. p. 1476

Zaccone, Marie Ann, Dir, Carbondale Public Library, Five N Main St, Carbondale, PA, 18407-2303. Tel: 570-282-4281. Fax: 570-282-7031. p. 2041

Zaccone, Marsha, Dir, Oregon Public Library District, 300 Jefferson St, Oregon, IL, 61061. Tel: 815-732-2724. Fax: 815-732-6643. p. 686

Zach, Lisl, PhD, Asst Prof, Drexel University, Rush Bldg, Rm 306, 30 N 33rd St, Philadelphia, PA, 19104-2875. Tel: 215-895-2474. Fax: 215-895-2494. p. 2972

Zachariah, Gail, Ch, Keene Public Library, 60 Winter St, Keene, NH, 03431-3360. Tel: 603-352-0157. Fax: 866-743-0446. p. 1452

Zachary, Mary Beth, Chair, Access Serv, Bowling Green State University Libraries, 204 Wm T Jerome Library, Bowling Green, OH, 43403-0170. p. 1861

Zachary, Nancy, Reader Serv, YA Serv, Scarsdale Public Library, 54 Olmsted Rd, Scarsdale, NY, 10583. Tel: 914-722-1300. Fax: 914-722-1305. p. 1739

Zachery, Angela, Br Mgr, Opelousas-Eunice Public Library, 212 E Grolee St, Opelousas, LA, 70570. Tel: 337-948-3693. Fax: 337-948-5200. p. 965

Zachery, Imogene, Electronic Res, Prince George's Community College Library, 301 Largo Rd, Largo, MD, 20774-2199. Tel: 301-322-0138. Fax: 301-808-8847. p. 1034

Zachkrewich, Lori, Librn, Grassland Public Library, PO Box 150, Grassland, AB, T0A 1V0, CANADA. Tel: 780-525-3733. Fax: 780-525-3750. p. 2706

Zachman, Cindy, Dir, Ridgemont Public Library, 124 E Taylor St, Mount Victory, OH, 43340-8811. Tel: 937-354-4445. Fax: 937-354-4445. p. 1919

Zachman, Jon, Curator of Coll, Greensboro Historical Museum Archives Library, 130 Summit Ave, Greensboro, NC, 27401-3004. Tel: 336-373-4589. Fax: 336-373-2204. p. 1796

Zachwieja, Jeffrey, Coordr, Electronic Res, Oakland Community College, Library Systems, 2900 Featherstone Rd, MTEC A210, Auburn Hills, MI, 48326. Tel: 248-522-3488. Fax: 248-232-4089. p. 1154

Zackmann, Kelly, ILL, Ontario City Library, 215 East C St, Ontario, CA, 91764. Tel: 909-395-2239. Fax: 909-395-2043. p. 200

Zadek, Susan, Br Head, Toronto Public Library, Albert Campbell, 496 Birchmount Rd, Toronto, ON, M1K 1N8, CANADA. Tel: 416-396-8890. Fax: 416-396-8901. p. 2860

Zadorozhny, Vladimir, Asst Prof, University of Pittsburgh, 135 N Bellefield Ave, Pittsburgh, PA, 15260. Tel: 412-624-5230. Fax: 412-624-5231. p. 2973

Zaenger, Kathleen, Dir, Howell Carnegie District Library, 314 W Grand River Ave, Howell, MI, 48843. Tel: 517-546-0720. Fax: 517-546-1494. p. 1192

Zaffarano, Sandra, Managing Librn, Middleville Free Library, One S Main St, Middleville, NY, 13406. Tel: 315-891-3655. Fax: 315-891-3655. p. 1661

Zafrin, Vika, Institutional Repository Librn, Boston University Libraries, Mugar Memorial Library, 771 Commonwealth Ave, Boston, MA, 02215. Tel: 617-353-3710. Fax: 617-353-2084. p. 1058

Zagan, Beverly, Cat, Hartford Public Library District, 143 W Hawthorne, Hartford, IL, 62048. Tel: 618-254-9394. Fax: 618-254-6522. p. 653

Zagar, Christopher, Librn, Estrella Mountain Community College Library, 3000 N Dysart Rd, Avondale, AZ, 85323-1000. Tel: 623-935-8191. Fax: 623-935-8060. p. 57

Zager, Daniel, Assoc Dean, University of Rochester, Sibley Music Library, 27 Gibbs St, Rochester, NY, 14604-2596. Tel: 585-274-1350. Fax: 585-274-1380. p. 1733

Zago, Susan D., Assoc Dir, Northeastern University School of Law Library, 400 Huntington Ave, Boston, MA, 02115. Tel: 617-373-3331. Fax: 617-373-8705. p. 1066

Zagon, Eileen, Cat Librn, Pennsylvania State University-Harrisburg Library, 351 Olmsted Dr, Middletown, PA, 17057-4850. Tel: 717-948-6070. Fax: 717-948-6757. p. 2089

Zaharek, Rose Marie, Head, Ch, New Canaan Library, 151 Main St, New Canaan, CT, 06840. Tel: 203-594-5000. Fax: 203-594-5026. p. 354

Zaharevich, Thomas, Head Librn, Tech Serv, Trinity College Library, 300 Summit St, Hartford, CT, 06106. Tel: 860-297-2244. Fax: 860-297-2251. p. 347

Zaharis, Kay, Dir, Cortland Free Library, 32 Church St, Cortland, NY, 13045. Tel: 607-753-1042. Fax: 607-758-7329. p. 1611

Zahayko, Michelle, Librn, Saskatchewan Cancer Agency, 4101 Dewdney Ave, Regina, SK, S4T 7T1, CANADA. Tel: 306-766-2203. Fax: 306-766-6222. p. 2923

Zahn, Sally, Tech Serv, Chadron State College, 300 E 12th St, Chadron, NE, 69337. Tel: 308-432-6271. p. 1395

Zahrt, Chad, Asst Dean, University of Wisconsin-Milwaukee, 510 Bolton Hall, 3120 N Maryland Ave, Milwaukee, WI, 53211. Tel: 414-229-4707. Fax: 414-229-6699. p. 2976

Zaikoski, Alice, Dir of Circ, McBride Memorial Library, 500 Market St, Berwick, PA, 18603. Tel: 570-752-2241. Fax: 570-752-8893. p. 2033

Zaino, Jeff, Syst Librn, New Canaan Library, 151 Main St, New Canaan, CT, 06840. Tel: 203-594-5000. Fax: 203-594-5026. p. 354

Zaitz, Mary, Libr Supvr-Popular Libr, Chisholm Public Library, 300 W Lake, Chisholm, MN, 55719-1718. Tel: 218-254-7913. Fax: 218-254-7952. p. 1245

Zajac, Ronnie, Ch, William D Weeks Memorial Library, 128 Main St, Lancaster, NH, 03584-3031. Tel: 603-788-3352. Fax: 603-788-3203. p. 1453

Zajac, Sandra, Mgr, Saint Joseph's Hospital Health Center, 206 Prospect Ave, Syracuse, NY, 13203. Tel: 315-448-5053. Fax: 315-423-6804. p. 1753

Zajackowski, Aleksandra M, Librn, Army & Navy Club Library, 901 17th St NW, Washington, DC, 20006-2503. Tel: 202-628-8400, Ext 386, 202-721-2096. Fax: 202-296-8787. p. 393

Zakar, Kate, Asst Dir, Eureka Springs Carnegie Public Library, 194 Spring St, Eureka Springs, AR, 72632. Tel: 479-253-8754. Fax: 479-253-7807. p. 98

Zakaria, Imad, Cat, Bibliotheque du College Dominicain de Philosophie et de Theologie, 96 Empress Ave, Ottawa, ON, K1R 7G3, CANADA. Tel: 613-233-5696, Ext 216. Fax: 613-233-6064. p. 2828

Zakiene, Larisa, Res Serv Librn, Wilson Elser Moskowitz Edelman & Dicker LLP, 150 E 42nd St, New York, NY, 10017. Tel: 212-490-3000. Fax: 212-490-3038. p. 1703

Zald, Anne, Head of Instruction, University of Nevada, Las Vegas Libraries, 4505 Maryland Pkwy, Box 457001, Las Vegas, NV, 89154-7001. Tel: 702-895-2286. Fax: 702-895-2287. p. 1431

Zald, Anne, Librn, University of Washington Libraries, Map Collection & Cartographic Information Services, Suzzallo/Allen Library, Basement, Universtiy of Washington, Box 352900, Seattle, WA, 98195-2900. Tel: 206-543-2725. Fax: 206-685-8049. p. 2534

Zaldivar, Nora B, Dir, Payette Associates, 285 Summer St, Boston, MA, 02210. Tel: 617-895-1000. Fax: 617-895-1002. p. 1066

Zalduendo, Ines, Archivist, Harvard Library, Frances Loeb Library, Harvard Graduate School of Design, 48 Quincy St, Gund Hall, Cambridge, MA, 02138. Tel: 617-495-9163. p. 1076

Zaleski, Raymond, Ref Librn, Free Public Library of Bayonne, 697 Avenue C, Bayonne, NJ, 07002. Tel: 201-858-6970. Fax: 201-437-6928. p. 1470

Zaletel, Hank, Librn, Iowa Department of Transportation Library, 800 Lincoln Way, Ames, IA, 50010-6915. Tel: 515-239-1200. Fax: 515-233-7840. p. 793

Zalewski, Laura, Libr Dir, Reuben Hoar Library, 41 Shattuck St, Littleton, MA, 01460-4506. Tel: 978-486-4046. Fax: 978-952-2323. p. 1099

Zalewski, Laura, Dir, Topsfield Town Library, One S Common St, Topsfield, MA, 01983-1496. Tel: 978-887-1528. Fax: 978-887-0185. p. 1131

Zalezsak, Ella-Fay, Coordr, Tech Serv, Vancouver Community College, 250 W Pender St, Vancouver, BC, V6B 1S9, CANADA. Tel: 604-871-7385. Fax: 604-871-7446. p. 2743

Zambella, BethAnn, Mgr, Res, Wellesley College, 106 Central St, Wellesley, MA, 02481-8275. Tel: 781-283-3512. Fax: 781-283-3690. p. 1135

Zambella, BethAnn, Col Librn, Dir, Elizabethtown College, One Alpha Dr, Elizabethtown, PA, 17022-2227. Tel: 717-361-1428. Fax: 717-361-1167. p. 2053

Zambrano-Esparza, Marivel, Librn, Santa Barbara Public Library, Eastside, 1102 E Montecito St, Santa Barbara, CA, 93103. Tel: 805-963-3727. p. 261

Zamin, Fatima, Cat Librn, Our Lady of the Lake College Library, 5329 Didesse St, Baton Rouge, LA, 70808. Tel: 225-768-1730. Fax: 225-761-7303. p. 944

Zammerelli, Mary F, Dir, Libr Serv, Saint Joseph Hospital, 200 High Service Ave, North Providence, RI, 02904. Tel: 401-456-3036. Fax: 401-456-3702. p. 2170

Zamon, Christina, Head, Archives & Spec Coll, Emerson College Library, 120 Boylston St, Boston, MA, 02116-4624. Tel: 617-824-8679. Fax: 617-824-7817. p. 1060

Zamora, Evis, Circ, Plattsmouth Public Library, 401 Ave A, Plattsmouth, NE, 68048. Tel: 402-296-4154. Fax: 402-296-4712. p. 1417

Zamora, Larry, Librn, Troy & Gould, 1801 Century Park E, 16th Flr, Los Angeles, CA, 90067. Tel: 310-553-4441. Fax: 310-201-4746. p. 178

Zamora, Olga, Asst Librn, El Progreso Memorial Library, 301 W Main St, Uvalde, TX, 78801. Tel: 830-278-2017. Fax: 830-278-4940. p. 2394

Zamostny, Julie, Ref & Instruction Librn, Hood College, 401 Rosemont Ave, Frederick, MD, 21701. Tel: 301-696-3975. Fax: 301-696-3796. p. 1029

Zampaglione, Tracy, Commun Relations Adminr, Orange County Library District, 101 E Central Blvd, Orlando, FL, 32801. Tel: 407-835-7323. Fax: 407-835-7643. p. 476

Zampini, Carmen, Dir, Kent Free Library, 312 W Main, Kent, OH, 44240-2493. Tel: 330-673-4414. Fax: 330-673-0226. p. 1906

Zampini, Louise, Chef de Div, Bibliothèques de Montrèal, Pierrefonds, 13555, boulevard Pierrefonds, Montreal, QC, H9A 1A6, CANADA. Tel: 514-620-4181, Ext 2210. Fax: 514-620-5503. p. 2891

Zampini, Louise, Chef de Div, Bibliothèques de Montrèal, Roxboro, 110, rue Cartier, Montreal, QC, H8Y 1G8, CANADA. Tel: 514-620-4181, Ext 2210. Fax: 514-684-8563. p. 2891

Zamudio, Dan, Access Serv Librn, ILL, Concordia University, 7400 Augusta St, River Forest, IL, 60305-1499. Tel: 708-209-3057. Fax: 708-209-3175. p. 694

Zandbergen, Dianne, Dir, Libr Serv, Kuyper College, 3333 E Beltline NE, Grand Rapids, MI, 49525. Tel: 616-988-3635. Fax: 616-222-3045, 616-988-3608. p. 1185

Zande, Jane, Librn, Congregation Beth Israel, 701 Farmington Ave, West Hartford, CT, 06119. Tel: 860-233-8215. Fax: 860-523-0223. p. 375

Zander, Ellen, Ref Librn, Berkeley Heights Public Library, 290 Plainfield Ave, Berkeley Heights, NJ, 07922. Tel: 908-464-9333. Fax: 908-464-7098. p. 1472

Zanditon, Rebekah, Librn, Westat, Inc Library, 1650 Research Blvd, Rockville, MD, 20850. Tel: 301-251-1500. Fax: 301-294-2034. p. 1040

Zane, Lawrence, Dir, University of Hawaii-College of Education, 1776 University Ave UA2-7, Honolulu, HI, 96822. Tel: 808-956-6496, 808-956-7834. Fax: 808-956-3374. p. 566

Zanger, Karen, Vols Librn, Rockdale Temple, 8501 Ridge Rd, Cincinnati, OH, 45236. Tel: 513-891-9900. Fax: 513-891-0515. p. 1873

Zangerle, Mary G, Dir, Lee-Whedon Memorial Library, 620 West Ave, Medina, NY, 14103. Tel: 585-798-3430. Fax: 585-798-4398. p. 1659

Zanin-Yost, Alessia, Ref Librn/Visual & Performing Arts Liaison, Western Carolina University, 176 Central Dr, Cullowhee, NC, 28723. Tel: 828-227-3398. Fax: 828-227-7015. p. 1786

Zanis, Alexis, Tech Serv Mgr, Kendall College Library, 900 N North Branch St, 6th Flr, Rm 620, Chicago, IL, 60642. Tel: 312-752-2532. Fax: 312-752-2541. p. 616

Zanish-Belcher, Tanya, Spec Coll Librn, Iowa State University Library, 302 Parks Library, Ames, IA, 50011-2140. Tel: 515-294-1442, 515-294-1443. Fax: 515-294-5525. p. 793

Zanjani, Nina, Asst Dir, Caldwell County Public Library, 120 Hospital Ave, Lenoir, NC, 28645-4454. Tel: 828-757-1270. Fax: 828-757-1413. p. 1806

Zanjani, Nina, Asst Dir, Union County Public Library, 316 E Windsor St, Monroe, NC, 28112. Tel: 704-283-8184. Fax: 704-282-0657. p. 1810

Zanke, Anita, Libr Develop Coordr, Westmoreland County Historical Society, 362 Sand Hill Rd, Ste 1, Greensburg, PA, 15601. Tel: 724-532-1935. Fax: 724-532-1938. p. 2063

Zanoni, Jean, Assoc Dean, Marquette University Libraries, 1355 W Wisconsin Ave, Milwaukee, WI, 53233. Tel: 414-288-5979. Fax: 414-288-7813. p. 2618

Zantow, Thomas, Head, Access Serv, Saginaw Valley State University, 7400 Bay Rd, University Center, MI, 48710. Tel: 989-964-4238. Fax: 989-964-4383. p. 1232

Zapala, Leonard J, Dir, Menands Public Library, Four N Lyons Ave, Menands, NY, 12204. Tel: 518-463-4035. Fax: 518-449-3863. p. 1659

Zapata, Roberto, Mgr, San Antonio Public Library, Great Northwest, 9050 Wellwood, San Antonio, TX, 78251. Tel: 210-684-5251. Fax: 210-543-9025. p. 2382

Zapolski, Debbie, Mgr, Department of Veterans Affairs, 1500 Weiss St, Saginaw, MI, 48602. Tel: 989-497-2500, Ext 3302. Fax: 989-791-2224. p. 1223

Zaporozhetz, Laurence E, Dir, United States Air Force, Air Force Institute of Technology Academic Library FL3319, AFIT/ENWL, 2950 Hobson Way, Bldg 642, Wright-Patterson AFB, OH, 45433-7765. Tel: 937-255-6565, Ext 4216. Fax: 937-656-7746. p. 1951

Zappacosta, Joseph, Exec Dir, Ephrata Public Library, 550 S Reading Rd, Ephrata, PA, 17522. Tel: 717-738-9291. Fax: 717-721-3003. p. 2054

Zappacosta, Joseph, Asst Dir, Reading Public Library, 100 S Fifth St, Reading, PA, 19602. Tel: 610-655-6350. p. 2133

Zappen, Susan, Assoc Col Librn, Skidmore College, 815 N Broadway, Saratoga Springs, NY, 12866. Tel: 518-580-5000. Fax: 518-580-5541. p. 1738

Zappitello, Joseph, Dir, Harbor-Topky Memorial Library, 1633 Walnut Blvd, Ashtabula, OH, 44004. Tel: 440-964-9645. Fax: 440-964-6701. p. 1856

Zaragoza, Aide, Circ, California State University, 9001 Stockdale Hwy, Bakersfield, CA, 93311-1022. Tel: 661-654-3234. Fax: 661-654-3238. p. 123

Zaragoza, Juan, Libr Serv Mgr, Carlos Albizu University Library, 2173 NW 99 Ave, Miami, FL, 33172. Tel: 305-593-1223, Ext 131. Fax: 305-593-8318. p. 464

Zarate, Terri, Supvr, Pub Serv, El Paso Community College Library, Northwest Campus-Jenna Welch & Laura Busch Community Library, 6701 S Desert Blvd, El Paso, TX, 79932. Tel: 915-831-8840. Fax: 915-831-8816. p. 2316

Zaremba, Susan, Adult Ref Librn, Gold Coast Public Library, 50 Railroad Ave, Glen Head, NY, 11545. Tel: 516-759-8300. Fax: 516-759-8308. p. 1628

Zarft, Kathy, Libr Syst Coordr, NorQuest College, 10215-108th St, 5th Flr, Edmonton, AB, T5J 1L6, CANADA. Tel: 708-644-6070. Fax: 780-644-6082. p. 2701

Zarin, Jason, Ref Librn, Georgetown University, Georgetown Law Library (John Wolff & Edward Bennett Williams Libraries), 111 G St NW, Washington, DC, 20001. Fax: 202-662-9168. p. 403

Zarinejad, Shahla, Ch, Rockville Public Library, Inc, 52 Union St, Vernon, CT, 06066-3155. Tel: 860-875-5892. Fax: 860-875-9795. p. 373

Zarinnia, E Anne, Assoc Prof, University of Wisconsin-Whitewater, 800 W Main St, Whitewater, WI, 53190. Tel: 262-472-1380. Fax: 262-472-2841. p. 2977

Zarinnia, E Anne, Dr, Co-Dir, University of Wisconsin System School Library Education Consortium, Grad & Continuing Educ, Univ Wisconsin-Whitewater, 800 W Main St, Whitewater, WI, 53190. Tel: 262-472-1463. Fax: 262-472-5210. p. 2958

Zarka, Wynn, Librn, Women's Club of Welaka Library, Hwy 309, Welaka, FL, 32193. Tel: 386-467-9706. p. 502

Zarnick, Gene, Librn, State Correctional Institution, 10745 Rte 18, Albion, PA, 16475-0001. Tel: 814-756-5778. Fax: 814-756-9735. p. 2026

Zaros, Christa, Coll Mgr, Long Island Museum of American Art, History & Carriages, Gerstenburg Carriage Reference Library, 1200 Rte 25A, Stony Brook, NY, 11790-1992. Tel: 631-751-0066, Ext 232. Fax: 631-751-0353. p. 1749

Zaros, Christa, Librn, Long Island Museum of American Art, History & Carriages, Kate Strong Historical Library, 1200 Rte 25A, Stony Brook, NY, 11790. Tel: 631-751-0066. Fax: 631-751-0353. p. 1749

Zaruba, Barbara M, Dir, San Joaquin County Law Library, Kress Legal Center, 20 N Sutter St, Stockton, CA, 95202. Tel: 209-468-3920. Fax: 209-468-9968. p. 272

Zaryczny, Wlodek, Libr Dir, Beaufort County Library, 311 Scott St, Beaufort, SC, 29902. Tel: 843-255-6471. p. 2181

Zaslav, Stephanie, Youth Serv, Rio Rancho Public Library, 755 Loma Colorado Dr NE, Rio Rancho, NM, 87124. Tel: 505-891-5013. Fax: 502-892-4782. p. 1561

Zaslow, Barry, Music Librn, Miami University Libraries, 225 King Library, Oxford, OH, 45056. Tel: 513-529-2299. Fax: 513-529-1378. p. 1926

Zaslow, Barry, Music Librn, Miami University Libraries, Amos Music Library, Center for Performing Arts, Oxford, OH, 45056. Tel: 513-529-2299. Fax: 513-529-1378. p. 1926

Zaste, Kathy, Asst Librn, Turtle Mountain Community College Library, PO Box 340, Belcourt, ND, 58316-0340. Tel: 701-477-7862, Ext 2081. Fax: 701-477-7805. p. 1837

Zavac, Nancy C, Librn, University of Miami Libraries, Marta & Austin Weeks Music Library, PO Box 248165, Coral Gables, FL, 33124-7610. Tel: 305-284-2429. Fax: 305-284-1041. p. 434

Zavacky, Susan K, Librn, Pennsylvania Legislative Reference Bureau Library, Main Capitol, Rm 641, Harrisburg, PA, 17120-0033. Tel: 717-787-4816. Fax: 717-783-2396. p. 2066

Zavala-Colon, Maria de los Angeles, Libr Dir, University of Puerto Rico, Minillas Park, 170, 174 Rd, Bayamon, PR, 00959-1919. Tel: 787-993-0000, Ext 3222, 787-993-8857. Fax: 787-993-8914. p. 2672

Zavalina, Oksana, Dr, Asst Prof, University of North Texas, 1155 Union Circle, Denton, TX, 76203-5017. Tel: 940-565-2445. Fax: 940-565-3101. p. 2975

Zavar, Albert, Dir, Cuyahoga Community College, Western Campus Library, 11000 Pleasant Valley Rd, Parma, OH, 44130-5199. Tel: 216-987-5403. Fax: 216-987-5050. p. 1879

Zavednak, Steven, Hist Coll Librn, Derby Public Library, 313 Elizabeth St, Derby, CT, 06418. Tel: 203-736-1482. Fax: 203-736-1419. p. 336

Zaveson, Georgia Lee, Librn, North Country Health System, 189 Prouty Dr, Newport, VT, 05855. Tel: 802-334-3256. Fax: 802-334-3240. p. 2430

Zavortink, David, Dir, Camas Public Library, 625 NE Fourth Ave, Camas, WA, 98607. Tel: 360-834-4692. Fax: 360-834-0199. p. 2511

Zawacki, Maria, Dir, Johnsburg Public Library District, 3000 N Johnsburg Rd, Johnsburg, IL, 60051. Tel: 815-344-0077. Fax: 815-344-3524. p. 659

Zawadzki, Danuta, Pres, Poland's Millennium Library in Los Angeles, 3424 W Adams Blvd, Los Angeles, CA, 90018. Tel: 310-234-0279. p. 177

Zawrucha, Corinne, Librn, Parkland Regional Library, Annaheim Branch, PO Box 15, Annaheim, SK, S0K 0G0, CANADA. Tel: 306-598-2155. p. 2931

Zazelenchuk, Mary, Head Librn, Stettler Public Library, 6202 44th Ave, 2nd Flr, Stettler, AB, T0C 2L1, CANADA. Tel: 403-742-2292. Fax: 403-742-5481. p. 2718

Zazueta, Cathy, Lead Librn, Imperial Valley College, 380 E Ira Aten Rd, Imperial, CA, 92251. Tel: 760-355-6378. Fax: 760-355-1090. p. 159

Zazueta, Victor, Br Mgr, Humboldt County Library, Eureka (Main Library), 1313 Third St, Eureka, CA, 95501. Tel: 707-269-1900. p. 147

Zazueta, Victor, County Librn, Humboldt County Library, 1313 Third St, Eureka, CA, 95501-0553. Tel: 707-269-1918. p. 147

Zdenek, Kate, Adult Serv, La Grange Park Public Library District, 555 N LaGrange Rd, La Grange Park, IL, 60526-5644. Tel: 708-352-0100. Fax: 708-352-1606. p. 662

Zdravkovska, Nevenka, Head of Libr, University of Maryland Libraries, Engineering & Physical Sciences Library, College Park, MD, 20742-7011. Tel: 301-405-9144. p. 1025

Zeak, Mary Ann, Librn, William E Anderson Library of Penn Hills, 1037 Stotler Rd, Pittsburgh, PA, 15235-2099. Tel: 412-795-3507. Fax: 412-798-2186. p. 2121

Zebrowski, Cheryl, Head, Cat/Syst Div, New Mexico Highlands University, Ninth & National Ave, Las Vegas, NM, 87701. Tel: 505-454-3401. Fax: 505-454-0026. p. 1559

Zebula, Natalie, Ref & Instruction Librn, Lawrence Technological University Library, 21000 W Ten Mile Rd, Southfield, MI, 48075-1058. Tel: 248-204-3000. Fax: 248-204-3005. p. 1228

Zec, Vedranka, Circ, Tech Serv, Canadian International Trade Tribunal Library, 333 Laurier Ave W, Ottawa, ON, K1A 0G7, CANADA. Tel: 613-990-8715. Fax: 613-990-2431. p. 2829

Zecher, Julie, Acq Librn, United States Naval War College Library, 686 Cushing Rd, Newport, RI, 02841-1207. Tel: 401-841-1082. Fax: 401-841-6491. p. 2169

Zeff, Oliver, Coordr, Info Serv, Coordr, Instruction, Westfield State University, 577 Western Ave, Westfield, MA, 01085-2580. Tel: 413-572-5251. Fax: 413-572-5520. p. 1138

Zegel, Kay, Dir, Mattituck-Laurel Library, 13900 Main Rd, Mattituck, NY, 11952. Tel: 631-298-4134. Fax: 631-298-4764. p. 1658

Zehery, Mohamed, Dr, Dir, Ohio State University LIBRARIES, Lima Campus Library, 4240 Campus Dr, Lima, OH, 45804. Tel: 419-995-8210. Fax: 419-995-8138. p. 1888

Zehfus, Mark J, Dep Dir, Mead Public Library, 710 N Eighth St, Sheboygan, WI, 53081-4563. Tel: 920-459-3400, Ext 3410. Fax: 920-459-0204. p. 2637

Zehnder, Karen, Circ, Carnegie Public Library, 219 E Fourth St, East Liverpool, OH, 43920-3143. Tel: 330-385-2048. Fax: 330-385-7600. p. 1897

Zehner, Donna E, Dir, Dallas Public Library, 950 Main St, Dallas, OR, 97338-2802. Tel: 503-623-2633. Fax: 503-623-7357. p. 1995

Zehnpfennig, Diane, Dir, United States Armed Forces Medical Library, Skyline 6, Rm 670, 5109 Leesburg Pike, Falls Church, VA, 22041-3258. Tel: 703-681-8028. Fax: 703-681-8034. p. 2463

Zehr, Brad, Tech Spec, William C Beck Health Science Library & Resource Center, One Guthrie Sq, Sayre, PA, 18840. Tel: 570-882-4700. Fax: 570-882-4703. p. 2136

Zehr, Mary, Dir, Manor Public Library, 57 Race St, Manor, PA, 15665. Tel: 724-864-6850. Fax: 724-864-6850. p. 2084

Zeiba, Gail, Ch, Willimantic Public Library, 905 Main St, Willimantic, CT, 06226. Tel: 860-465-3081. Fax: 860-465-3083. p. 378

Zeibak, Karen, Head, Circ, Wilton Library Association, 137 Old Ridgefield Rd, Wilton, CT, 06897-3019. Tel: 203-762-3950. Fax: 203-834-1166. p. 378

Zeichner, Elva, Head, Tech Serv, Riverhead Free Library, 330 Court St, Riverhead, NY, 11901-2885. Tel: 631-727-3228. Fax: 631-727-4762. p. 1728

Zeidberg, David S, Dir, Huntington Library, 1151 Oxford Rd, San Marino, CA, 91108. Tel: 626-405-2176. Fax: 626-449-5720. p. 255

Zeider, Patricia, Sr Libr Supvr, Glendale Public Library, Brand Library & Art Center, 1601 W Mountain St, Glendale, CA, 91201-1209. Tel: 818-548-2010. Fax: 818-548-5079. p. 155

Zeidman-Karpinski, Ann, Coll Develop, Ref & Instrul Serv Librn, University of Oregon Libraries, Mathematics, 210 Fenton Hall, University of Oregon, Eugene, OR, 97403. Tel: 541-346-2663. Fax: 541-346-3012. p. 1997

Zeidman-Karpinski, Ann, Librn, University of Oregon Libraries, Science, Onyx Bridge, Lower Level, University of Oregon, Eugene, OR, 97403. Tel: 541-346-2663. Fax: 541-346-3012. p. 1998

Zeigen, Laura, Syst Librn, Web Develop Librn, Oregon Health & Science University Library, 3181 SW Sam Jackson Park Rd, Portland, OR, 97239-3098. Tel: 503-494-3460. Fax: 503-494-3227. p. 2013

Zeiger, Carrie C, Exec Dir, Flint River Regional Library, 800 Memorial Dr, Griffin, GA, 30223. Tel: 770-412-4770. p. 535

Zeiger, Carrie C, Exec Dir, Flint River Regional Library, Griffin-Spalding County Library, 800 Memorial Dr, Griffin, GA, 30223. Tel: 770-412-4770. p. 535

Zeiger, Carrie C, Dir, Coastal Plain Regional Library, 2014 Chestnut Ave, Tifton, GA, 31794. Tel: 229-386-3400. Fax: 229-386-7007. p. 554

Zeigler, Dimmie, Educ & Prog Mgr, Teton County Library, 125 Virginian Lane, Jackson, WY, 83001. Tel: 307-733-2164, Ext 229. Fax: 307-733-4568. p. 2656

Zeigler, Shellie, Blind & Physically Handicapped Libr Dir, Mississippi Library Commission, 3881 Eastwood Dr, Jackson, MS, 39211-6473. Tel: 601-432-4123. Fax: 601-432-4476. p. 1304

Zeigler-Hill, Shellie, Youth Serv, The Library of Hattiesburg, Petal, Forrest County, 329 Hardy St, Hattiesburg, MS, 39401-3496. Tel: 601-582-4461. Fax: 601-582-5338. p. 1300

Zeiher, Lynne, Managing Librn, Pierce County Library System, Bonney Lake Branch, 18501 90th St E, Bonney Lake, WA, 98390. Tel: 253-548-3308. Fax: 253-863-6016. p. 2539

Zeiher, Lynne, Managing Librn, Pierce County Library System, Graham Branch, 9202 224th St E, Graham, WA, 98338. Tel: 253-548-3322. Fax: 253-846-5174. p. 2539

Zeiher, Lynne, Managing Librn, Pierce County Library System, Summit, 5107 112th St E, Tacoma, WA, 98446. Tel: 253-548-3321. Fax: 253-536-6009. p. 2540

Zeiher, Lynne, Managing Librn, Pierce County Library System, Sumner Branch, 1116 Fryar Ave, Sumner, WA, 98390. Tel: 253-548-3306. Fax: 253-863-0650. p. 2540

Zeik, Travis, Curator, The Museums of Oglebay Institute Library, Oglebay Institute, The Burton Center, Wheeling, WV, 26003. Tel: 304-242-7272. Fax: 304-242-7287. p. 2574

Zeile, Carol A, Dir, Alma College Library, 614 W Superior St, Alma, MI, 48801. Tel: 989-463-7342. Fax: 989-463-8694. p. 1149

Zeiter, Lisa, Dir, Garden City Library, 6015 Glenwood St, Garden City, ID, 83714. Tel: 208-472-2941. p. 574

Zeitlin, Richard H, Dir, Wisconsin Department of Veterans Affairs, 30 W Mifflin St, Ste 300, Madison, WI, 53703. Tel: 608-267-1790. Fax: 608-264-7615. p. 2610

Zeitz, Elizabeth, Acq Mgr, Otterbein University, 138 W Main St, Westerville, OH, 43081. Tel: 614-823-1938. Fax: 614-823-1921. p. 1946

Zeitz, Robin, Librn, Beth-El Temple Center, Two Concord Ave, Belmont, MA, 02478-4075. Tel: 617-484-6668. Fax: 617-484-6020. p. 1053

Zelasko, Theresa, Cat Librn, Southwestern University, 1100 E University Ave, Georgetown, TX, 78626. Tel: 512-863-1561. Fax: 512-863-8198. p. 2327

Zelazny, Ilan, Head, Syst, Hunter College Libraries, 695 Park Ave, New York, NY, 10065. Tel: 212-772-4171. Fax: 212-772-4142. p. 1682

Zelazo, Cheryl, Adult Serv, Joshua Hyde Public Library, 306 Main St, Sturbridge, MA, 01566-1242. Tel: 508-347-2512. Fax: 508-347-2872. p. 1129

Zelbovitz, Karyn, Lakeland Campus Libr Dir, Keiser University Library System, 1500 NW 49th St, Fort Lauderdale, FL, 33309. Tel: 954-351-4035. Fax: 954-351-4051. p. 443

Zelechoski, Moira E, Libr Team Lead, United States Navy, 22269 Cedar Point Rd B407, Patuxent River, MD, 20670-1120. Tel: 301-342-1927. Fax: 301-342-1933. p. 1036

Zelenka, Diane, Libr Mgr, Taber Public Library, 5415 50 Ave, Taber, AB, T1G 1V2, CANADA. Tel: 403-223-4343. Fax: 403-223-4314. p. 2719

Zelinka, Kari, Tech Serv Librn, St Mary's Hospital Medical Center, 700 S Park St, Madison, WI, 53715. Tel: 608-258-6161. Fax: 608-258-6119. p. 2607

Zeller, Kevin, Br Mgr, Mid-Continent Public Library, Red Bridge Branch, 11140 Locust St, Kansas City, MO, 64131-3628. Tel: 816-942-1780. Fax: 816-942-2657. p. 1333

Zellers, Paula, ILL, New Albany-Floyd County Public Library, 180 W Spring St, New Albany, IN, 47150-3692. Tel: 812-944-8464. Fax: 812-949-3532. p. 768

Zellmann, Diane, Ch, New Ulm Public Library, 17 N Broadway, New Ulm, MN, 56073-1786. Tel: 507-359-8336. Fax: 507-354-3255. p. 1268

Zelman, Julie, Dir, Brunswick Community Library, 4118 State Hwy 2, Troy, NY, 12180-9029. Tel: 518-279-4023. Fax: 518-279-0527. p. 1756

Zelnick, Vicki, Librn, Stonington Public Library, Main St, Stonington, ME, 04681. Tel: 207-367-5926. p. 1003

Zelten, Julie, Dir, Land O'Lakes Public Library, 4242 County Hwy B, Land O'Lakes, WI, 54540. Tel: 715-547-6006. Fax: 715-547-6004. p. 2605

Zeltzer, Abbie, Librn, Patagonia Public Library, 346 Duquesne, Patagonia, AZ, 85624. Tel: 520-394-2010. Fax: 520-394-2113. p. 70

Zelwietro, Joe, Dep Librn, Prince Rupert Library, 101 Sixth Ave W, Prince Rupert, BC, V8J 1Y9, CANADA. Tel: 250-627-1345. Fax: 250-627-7743. p. 2736

Zeman, Anne, Dir, Hopewell Public Library, 13 E Broad St, Hopewell, NJ, 08525. Tel: 609-466-1625. Fax: 609-466-1996. p. 1491

Zemke, Stacy, Instr, University of Oklahoma, Bizzell Memorial Library, 401 W Brooks, Rm 120, Norman, OK, 73019-6032. Tel: 405-325-3921. Fax: 405-325-7648. p. 2972

Zempter, Valerie, Dir, Mason County Public Library, 218 E Third St, Maysville, KY, 41056. Tel: 606-564-3286. Fax: 606-564-5408. p. 928

Zemrock, Joy, Adult Serv, Ref, Loudonville Public Library, 122 E Main St, Loudonville, OH, 44842-1267. Tel: 419-994-5531. Fax: 419-994-4321. p. 1911

Zenelis, John G, Univ Librn, George Mason University Libraries, 4400 University Dr, MSN 2FL, Fairfax, VA, 22030-4444. Tel: 703-993-2250. Fax: 703-993-2200. p. 2462

Zenert, Jack, Chairperson, Innisfail Public Library, 5300A 55th St Close, Innisfail, AB, T4G 1R6, CANADA. Tel: 403-227-4407. Fax: 403-227-3122. p. 2707

Zeng, Yang, Commun Libr Mgr, Queens Borough Public Library, Peninsula Community Library, 92-25 Rockaway Beach Blvd, Rockaway Beach, NY, 11693. Tel: 718-634-1110. Fax: 718-318-5253. p. 1645

Zenker, Mary, Youth Serv, Sauk City Public Library, 515 Water St, Sauk City, WI, 53583-1159. Tel: 608-643-8346. p. 2636

Zens, Adam, Dir, Turtle Lake Public Library, 114 E Martin Ave, Turtle Lake, WI, 54889. Tel: 715-986-4618. Fax: 715-986-4618. p. 2642

Zens, Lois, Ser, South Dakota School of Mines & Technology, 501 E Saint Joseph St, Rapid City, SD, 57701-3995. Tel: 605-394-2418. Fax: 605-394-1256. p. 2217

Zentichko, Mary Jane, Asst Dir, Newport Public Library, 316 N Fourth St, Newport, PA, 17074-1203. Tel: 717-567-6860. Fax: 717-567-3373. p. 2097

Zentner, Krystal, Libr Dir, Bridger Public Library, 119 W Broadway Ave, Bridger, MT, 59014. Tel: 406-662-3598. Fax: 406-662-3598. p. 1375

Zera, Mark, ILL, Milwaukee Area Technical College, 700 W State St, Milwaukee, WI, 53233-1443. Tel: 414-297-7030. Fax: 414-297-6798. p. 2619

Zeranski, Bill, Ref & Tech Librn, Keystone College, One College Green, La Plume, PA, 18440-0200. Tel: 570-945-8332. Fax: 570-945-8969. p. 2075

Zero, Marie, Tech Serv, Lake Wales Public Library, 290 Cypress Garden Lane, Lake Wales, FL, 33853. Tel: 863-678-4004. Fax: 863-678-4051. p. 458

Zerr, Phyllis, Br Mgr, Jackson County Library Services, Applegate Branch, 18485 N Applegate Rd, Applegate, OR, 97530. Tel: 541-846-7346. Fax: 541-846-7346. p. 2005

Zerr, Phyllis, Br Mgr, Jackson County Library Services, Jacksonville Branch, 340 West C St, Jacksonville, OR, 97530. Tel: 541-899-1665. Fax: 541-899-1665. p. 2005

Zessin, Jan, Media Serv, Hope College, Van Wylen Library, 53 Graves Pl, Holland, MI, 49422. Tel: 616-395-7463. Fax: 616-395-7965. p. 1191

Zeter, Mary Jo, Coordr, Area Studies, Michigan State University Library, Area Studies, 100 Library, East Lansing, MI, 48824. Tel: 517-884-6392. Fax: 517-432-3532. p. 1175

Zethmayr, Noel, YA Serv, La Grange Public Library, Ten W Cossitt Ave, La Grange, IL, 60525. Tel: 708-352-0576, Ext 35. p. 662

Zettl, Marie, Librn, Beaver Valley Public Library, 1847 First St, Fruitvale, BC, V0G 1L0, CANADA. Tel: 250-367-7114. Fax: 250-367-7130. p. 2728

Zettwoch, Mary, ILL, University of Missouri-Saint Louis Libraries, One University Blvd, Saint Louis, MO, 63121. Tel: 314-516-5060. Fax: 314-516-5853. p. 1362

Zevenbergen, Amy, Dir, Doon Public Library, 207 Barton Ave, Doon, IA, 51235. Tel: 712-726-3526. Fax: 712-726-3526. p. 811

Zevenbergen, Leigh, Br Mgr, Lyon County Library System, Silver-Stage Branch, 3905 Hwy 50 W, Silver Springs, NV, 89429. Tel: 775-577-5015. Fax: 775-577-5013. p. 1435

Zeysing, Matt, Librn, Naismith Memorial Basketball Hall of Fame, 1000 W Columbus Ave, Springfield, MA, 01105. Tel: 413-781-6500. Fax: 413-781-1939. p. 1127

Zglinicki, Ann Marie, Mgr, Libr Serv, Mercy Hospital of Philadelphia, 501 S 54th St, Philadelphia, PA, 19143. Tel: 215-748-9415. Fax: 215-748-9341. p. 2112

Zgraggen, Cathy, Supvr, Deschutes Public Library District, La Pine Branch, 16425 First St, La Pine, OR, 97739. Tel: 541-312-1090. Fax: 541-536-0752. p. 1992

Zhang, Hong, Dr, Asst Prof, University of Kentucky, 320 Little Library Bldg, Lexington, KY, 40506-0224. Tel: 859-257-4136. Fax: 859-257-4205. p. 2966

Zhang, Jessica, Acq, Nelson-Atkins Museum of Art, 4525 Oak St, Kansas City, MO, 64111-1873. Tel: 816-751-0407. Fax: 816-751-0498. p. 1340

Zhang, Jian, Access Serv, Cat, Alabama State University, 915 S Jackson St, Montgomery, AL, 36104. Tel: 334-229-4106, 334-229-6890. Fax: 334-229-4911, 334-229-4940. p. 28

Zhang, Jindi, Head, Cat, Pace University, 78 N Broadway, White Plains, NY, 10603. Tel: 914 422-4649. Fax: 914-422-4139. p. 1769

Zhang, Jingping, Dir of Libr Operations, Univ Librn, Marshall University Libraries, One John Marshall Dr, Huntington, WV, 25755-2060. Tel: 304-696-2326. Fax: 304-696-5858. p. 2561

Zhang, Peng, Ref, Oregon Health & Science University, OGI School of Science & Engineering, 20000 NW Walker Rd, Beaverton, OR, 97006-8921. Tel: 503-748-7311. Fax: 503-748-1029. p. 1991

Zhang, Qiping, Dr, Asst Prof, Long Island University, C W Post Campus, 720 Northern Blvd, Brookville, NY, 11548-1300. Tel: 516-299-2180. Fax: 516-299-4168. p. 2970

Zhang, Rongxiang, Evening/Weekend Librn, Columbia University, C V Starr East Asian Library, 300 Kent Hall, MC 3901, 1140 Amsterdam Ave, New York, NY, 10027. Tel: 212-854-4318. Fax: 212-662-6286. p. 1675

Zhang, Sam, In Charge, PerkinElmer Optoelectronics Library, 22001 Dumberry, Vaudreuil-Dorion, QC, J7V 8P7, CANADA. Tel: 450-424-2510, Ext 3370. Fax: 450-424-3413. p. 2914

Zhang, Tian, Ser, Saint John's University Library, 8000 Utopia Pkwy, Queens, NY, 11439. Tel: 718-990-6735. Fax: 718-380-0353. p. 1725

Zhang, Wei, Metadata Librn, Georgetown University, 37th & N St NW, Washington, DC, 20057-1174. Tel: 202-687-7425. Fax: 202-687-7501. p. 402

Zhang, Wen Wen, Commun Libr Mgr, County of Los Angeles Public Library, West Covina Library, 1601 W Covina Pkwy, West Covina, CA, 91790-2786. Tel: 626-962-3541. Fax: 626-962-1507. p. 143

Zhang, Wenxian, Archivist, Rollins College, 1000 Holt Ave, Campus Box 2744, Winter Park, FL, 32789-2744. Tel: 407-646-2231. Fax: 407-646-2122. p. 505

Zhang, Xiangmin, Asst Prof, Rutgers, The State University of New Jersey, Four Huntington St, New Brunswick, NJ, 08901-1071. Tel: 732-932-7500, Ext 8955. Fax: 732-932-2644. p. 2969

Zhang, Xiangmin E, Dr, Asst Prof, Wayne State University, 106 Kresge Library, Detroit, MI, 48202. Tel: 313-577-1825. Fax: 313-577-7563. p. 2968

Zhang, Xiwen, Ref Librn, California State University, San Bernardino, 5500 University Pkwy, San Bernardino, CA, 92407-2318. Tel: 909-537-5106. Fax: 909-537-7048. p. 227

Zhang, Yin, Dr, Assoc Prof, Kent State University, 314 Library, Kent, OH, 44242-0001. Tel: 330-672-2782. Fax: 330-672-7965. p. 2972

Zhang, Yingting, Ref, University of Medicine & Dentistry of New Jersey, PO Box 19, New Brunswick, NJ, 08903. Tel: 732-235-7610. Fax: 732-235-7826. p. 1509

Zhang, Yuqing, Head, Digital Serv & Tech Serv, Fairfield University, 1073 N Benson Rd, Fairfield, CT, 06430-5195. Tel: 203-254-4044. Fax: 203-254-4135. p. 339

Zhang, Yvonne, Cat, California State Polytechnic University Library, 3801 W Temple Ave, Bldg 15, Pomona, CA, 91768. Tel: 909-869-5250. Fax: 909-869-6922. p. 211

Zhang, Zhijiang, Acq & Cat, Manchester Community College Library, Great Path, Manchester, CT, 06040. Tel: 860-512-2875. Fax: 860-512-2871. p. 350

Zhao, Bin, Tech Serv, Highland Park Public Library, 494 Laurel Ave, Highland Park, IL, 60035-2690. Tel: 847-432-0216. Fax: 847-432-9139. p. 655

Zhao, Dangzhi, Dr, Assoc Prof, University of Alberta, 3-20 Rutherford S, Edmonton, AB, T6G 2J4, CANADA. Tel: 780-492-4578. Fax: 780-492-2430. p. 2977

Zhao, Lixia, Cataloger, University of Arkansas at Little Rock, 2801 S University Ave, Little Rock, AR, 72204. Tel: 501-569-3454. Fax: 501-569-3017. p. 107

Zhao, Shuzhen, Head, Acq, University of Windsor, 401 Sunset Ave, Windsor, ON, N9B 3P4, CANADA. Tel: 519-253-3000, Ext 3162. p. 2871

Zhao, Taian, Head, Tech Serv, Borough of Manhattan Community College Library, 199 Chambers St, New York, NY, 10007. Tel: 212-220-1452. Fax: 212-748-7466. p. 1671

Zhe-Heimerman, Karen, Ref Librn, Le Moyne College, 1419 Salt Springs Rd, Syracuse, NY, 13214-1301. Tel: 315-445-4627. Fax: 315-445-4642. p. 1751

Zhong, Jessie, Dir of Tech Serv, Dallas Theological Seminary, 3909 Swiss Ave, Dallas, TX, 75204. Tel: 214-841-3746. Fax: 214-841-3745. p. 2307

Zhong, Lizhu, Librn, State Correctional Institution, PO Box 8837, Camp Hill, PA, 17011-8837. Tel: 717-737-4531. Fax: 717-737-2202. p. 2041

Zhong, Ying, Sr Asst Librn, California State University, 9001 Stockdale Hwy, Bakersfield, CA, 93311-1022. Tel: 661-654-3119. Fax: 661-654-3238. p. 123

Zhorne, Mona, Adult Serv, Pocahontas Public Library, 14 Second Ave NW, Pocahontas, IA, 50574. Tel: 712-335-4471. Fax: 712-335-4471. p. 839

Zhou, June, Br Mgr, San Diego County Library, 4S Ranch, 10433 Reserve Dr, San Diego, CA, 92127. Tel: 858-673-4697. Fax: 858-673-1629. p. 233

Zhou, Peter, Dir, University of California, Berkeley, C V Starr East Asian Library, Berkeley, CA, 94720-6000. Tel: 510-643-6579. Fax: 510-642-3817. p. 128

Zhou, Song, Cat, Western Connecticut State University, 181 White St, Danbury, CT, 06810. Tel: 203-837-8296. Fax: 203-837-9108. p. 335

Zhou, Xiaoyan, Br Mgr, Brooklyn Public Library, Bay Ridge, 7223 Ridge Blvd, Brooklyn, NY, 11209. Tel: 718-748-5709. Fax: 718-748-7095. p. 1590

Zhou, Xigang, Asst Dir, Vaughn College Library, 8601 23rd Ave, Flushing, NY, 11369. Tel: 718-429-6600, Ext 184. Fax: 718-478-7066. p. 1623

Zhou, Zehao, Info Serv, York College of Pennsylvania, 441 Country Club Rd, York, PA, 17403-3651. Tel: 717-815-1518. Fax: 717-849-1608. p. 2160

Zhow, Yvonne, Bus Mgr, Brooklyn Public Library, Dyker, 8202 13th Ave, Brooklyn, NY, 11228. Tel: 718-748-6261. Fax: 718-748-6370. p. 1591

Zhu, Lihong, Head, Tech Serv, Washington State University Libraries, 100 Dairy Rd, Pullman, WA, 99164. Tel: 509-335-7769. Fax: 509-335-6721. p. 2525

Zhu, Yin, Acq, ILL Librn, Board of Governors of The Federal Reserve System, Research Library, 20th & C St NW, MS 102, Washington, DC, 20551. Tel: 202-452-3333. Fax: 202-530-6222. p. 394

Ziarko, Lauren, Spec Coll Librn, Manhattanville College Library, 2900 Purchase St, Purchase, NY, 10577. Tel: 914-323-5422. Fax: 914-323-8139. p. 1724

Ziarnik, Natalie, Head, Youth Serv, Ela Area Public Library District, 275 Mohawk Trail, Lake Zurich, IL, 60047. Tel: 847-438-3433. Fax: 847-438-9290. p. 663

Ziaya, Alana, Mgr, Marshfield Clinic, 1000 N Oak Ave, Marshfield, WI, 54449-5777. Tel: 715-387-5184. Fax: 715-389-5366. p. 2613

Zibell, Joel, Assoc Dir, Karl Junginger Memorial Library, 625 N Monroe St, Waterloo, WI, 53594-1183. Tel: 920-478-3344. Fax: 920-478-2351. p. 2644

Zick, Medina, Youth/Teen Serv Coordr, Scottsdale Public Library, 3839 N Drinkwater Blvd, Scottsdale, AZ, 85251-4467. Tel: 480-312-7323. Fax: 480-312-7993. p. 81

Ziebell, Carl, Cat, ILL, Ripon College, 300 Seward St, Ripon, WI, 54971. Tel: 920-748-8746. Fax: 920-748-7243. p. 2634

Ziegler, Anne, Assoc Dir, Libr Serv, Arcadia University, 450 S Easton Rd, Glenside, PA, 19038-3295. Tel: 215-572-2813. Fax: 215-572-0240. p. 2061

Ziegler, Annette, Circ Mgr, Medicine Hat Public Library, 414 First St SE, Medicine Hat, AB, T1A 0A8, CANADA. Tel: 403-502-8527. Fax: 403-502-8529. p. 2711

Ziegler, Catherine, Circ Mgr, Art Institute of Fort Lauderdale, 1600 SE 17th St, 3rd Flr, Fort Lauderdale, FL, 33316. Tel: 954-308-2631. Fax: 954-463-3393. p. 440

Ziegler, Cathy, Dir, Plano Public Library System, Library Administration, 2501 Coit Rd, Plano, TX, 75075. Tel: 972-769-4208. Fax: 972-769-4269. p. 2370

Ziegler, Georgianna, Dr, Head, Ref, Folger Shakespeare Library, 201 E Capitol St SE, Washington, DC, 20003-1094. Tel: 202-544-4600. Fax: 202-544-4623. p. 400

Ziegler, Judith, Librn, Springfield Hospital Medical Library, 190 W Sproul Rd, Springfield, PA, 19064-2097. Tel: 610-328-8700, 610-328-8749. p. 2142

Ziegler, Judy, Dir, Taylor Hospital, 175 E Chester Pike, Ridley Park, PA, 19078. Tel: 610-595-6000, 610-595-6027. p. 2134

Ziegler, Kathy, Circ, Millbrook Public Library, 3650 Grandview Rd, Millbrook, AL, 36054. Tel: 334-285-6688, Ext 23. Fax: 334-285-0152. p. 25

Ziegler, Myra, Dir, Summers County Public Library, 201 Temple St, Hinton, WV, 25951. Tel: 304-466-4490. Fax: 304-466-5260. p. 2560

Ziegler, Nancy, Dir, Elmore Public Library, 107 E Willis St, Elmore, MN, 56027. Tel: 507-943-3150. Fax: 507-943-3434. p. 1250

Ziegler, Roy, Assoc Dean, Coll Develop, Florida State University Libraries, Strozier Library Bldg, 116 Honors Way, Tallahassee, FL, 32306-0001. Tel: 850-644-0468. p. 494

Ziegler, Susan, Pub Serv Dir, Bucks County Free Library, 150 S Pine St, Doylestown, PA, 18901-4932. Tel: 215-348-0332, Ext 1102. Fax: 215-348-4760. p. 2050

Zielinski, Karen, Head, Ch, Scarsdale Public Library, 54 Olmsted Rd, Scarsdale, NY, 10583. Tel: 914-722-1300. Fax: 914-722-1305. p. 1739

Zielinski, Marilyn, Automation Serv, Tech Serv, Toledo-Lucas County Public Library, 325 N Michigan St, Toledo, OH, 43604-6614. Tel: 419-259-5388. Fax: 419-259-5119. p. 1939

Zielinski, Tamara, Cataloger, Feleti Barstow Public Library, PO Box 997687, Pago Pago, AS, 96799. Tel: 684-633-5816. Fax: 684-633-5823. p. 2666

Zielke, David, Head, Cat, Dixie State College of Utah, 225 S 700 E, Saint George, UT, 84770. Tel: 435-652-7716. Fax: 435-656-4169. p. 2411

Ziemer, Heidi, Evening/Weekend Librn, Alvernia University, 400 St Bernardine St, Reading, PA, 19607-1737. Tel: 610-796-8355. Fax: 610-796-8347. p. 2132

Zienta, Cyndi, Librn, Sandusky County Law Library, Court House, 100 N Park Ave, No 106, Fremont, OH, 43420-2493. Tel: 419-334-6165. Fax: 419-334-6156. p. 1900

Zientara, Jerry, Dr, Librn, Institute for Advanced Study of Human Sexuality, 1523 Franklin St, San Francisco, CA, 94109. Tel: 415-928-1133. Fax: 415-928-8061. p. 242

Zieper, Linda, Head, Info Serv, University of Massachusetts Dartmouth Library, 285 Old Westport Rd, North Dartmouth, MA, 02747-2300. Tel: 508-999-8526. Fax: 508-999-8987. p. 1112

Zierke, Lisa, Acq, Cat, ILL, Prescott Public Library, 215 E Goodwin St, Prescott, AZ, 86303. Tel: 928-777-1507. Fax: 928-771-5829. p. 78

Zietlow, Ruth, Interim Dean, Saint Cloud State University, 112 Miller Ctr, 720 Fourth Ave S, Saint Cloud, MN, 56301-4498. Tel: 320-308-2022. Fax: 320-308-4778. p. 1276

Zietlow, Ruth, Interim Dean, Saint Cloud State University, Learning Resources & Technology Services, 720 Fourth Ave S, Saint Cloud, MN, 56301-4498. Tel: 320-308-2084. Fax: 320-308-4778. p. 2968

Zietz, Stephen, Head, Spec Coll, Georgia State University Library, 100 Decatur St SE, Atlanta, GA, 30303-3202. Tel: 404-413-2889. Fax: 404-413-2881. p. 516

Zigelbaum, Liva, Dir, Med Libr, Kingsbrook Jewish Medical Center, 585 Schenectady Ave, Brooklyn, NY, 11203. Tel: 718-604-5689. Fax: 718-604-5539. p. 1592

Zignego, Terry, Dir, Delafield Public Library, 500 Genessee St, Delafield, WI, 53018-1895. Tel: 262-646-6230. Fax: 262-646-6232. p. 2588

Zilavy, Julie, Mgr, American Association of Advertising Agencies, 405 Lexington Ave, 18th Flr, New York, NY, 10174. Tel: 212-682-2500. p. 1667

Ziliotto, Diane, Col Archivist, Ref & Instruction Librn, Westmont College, 955 La Paz Rd, Santa Barbara, CA, 93108-1099. Tel: 805-565-6000, 805-565-6147. Fax: 805-565-6220. p. 262

Zilka, David, Actg Dir, Monessen Public Library & District Center, 326 Donner Ave, Monessen, PA, 15062-1182. Tel: 724-684-4750. Fax: 724-684-7077. p. 2091

Zilli, Michelle, Br Mgr, Timberland Regional Library, Naselle Branch, Four Parpala Rd, Naselle, WA, 98638. Tel: 360-484-3877. Fax: 360-484-3445. p. 2543

Zillman, Joanne C, Dep Dir, Head, Youth Serv, Batavia Public Library District, Ten S Batavia Ave, Batavia, IL, 60510-2793. Tel: 630-879-1393. Fax: 630-879-9118. p. 592

Zillner, Tom, Coordr of Res Serv, Wisconsin Library Services, 728 State St, Rm 464, Madison, WI, 53706-1494. Tel: 608-265-4167. Fax: 608-262-6067. p. 2958

Zilonis, Mary F, Dir, Sch Libr Teacher Prog & Prof of Practice, Simmons College, 300 The Fenway, Boston, MA, 02115. Tel: 617-521-2800. Fax: 617-521-3192. p. 2967

Zimble, Stephanie, Archivist/Ref Librn, Oakmont Carnegie Library, 700 Allegheny River Blvd, Oakmont, PA, 15139. Tel: 412-828-9532. Fax: 412-828-5979. p. 2100

Zimbleman, Laura, Cataloger, Washtenaw Community College, 4800 E Huron River Dr, Ann Arbor, MI, 48105-4800. Tel: 734-973-3401. Fax: 734-973-3446. p. 1153

Zimerman, Louise, Librn, United Hebrew Congregation Library, 13788 Conway Rd, Saint Louis, MO, 63141. Tel: 314-469-0700. Fax: 314-434-7821. p. 1361

Zimkus, John J, Asst Dir, Historian, Warren County Historical Society, 105 S Broadway, Lebanon, OH, 45036. Tel: 513-932-1817. Fax: 513-932-8560. p. 1909

Zimmelman Lenoil, Nancy, State Archivist, California State Archives, 1020 O St, Sacramento, CA, 95814. Tel: 916-653-7715. Fax: 916-653-7363. p. 222

Zimmer, Annik, Pub Serv, Ref Serv, Tech Serv, Commission des Valeurs Mobilieres du Quebec Bibliotheque, 800 Square Victoria, 22nd Flr, CP 246, Montreal, QC, H4Z 1G3, CANADA. Tel: 514-940-2199, Ext 4494. Fax: 514-873-3090. p. 2894

Zimmer, Delycia, Librn, Kansas Department of Corrections, 1720 N Hersey, Beloit, KS, 67420. Tel: 785-738-5735, Ext 245. Fax: 785-738-6483. p. 857

Zimmer, Jennifer Lammers, Digital Serv, University of Michigan, Kresge Business Administration Library, Stephen M Ross School of Business, 701 Tappan St, K3330, Ann Arbor, MI, 48109-1234. Tel: 734-764-6845. Fax: 734-764-3839. p. 1152

Zimmer, Marvis, Librn, Heisler Municipal Library, 100 Haultain Ave, Heisler, AB, T0B 2A0, CANADA. Tel: 780-889-3925. Fax: 780-889-3925. p. 2706

Zimmer, Norma, Asst Dir, Judith Basin County Free Library, 19 Third N, Stanford, MT, 59479. Tel: 406-566-2277, Ext 123. Fax: 406-566-2211. p. 1388

Zimmer, Scott, Dir of Libr Serv, Univ Librn, Alliant International University, 10455 Pomerado Rd, San Diego, CA, 92131-1799. Tel: 858-635-4553. Fax: 858-635-4599. p. 230

Zimmer, Terri, Supvr, Info Mgt, R V Anderson Associates Ltd Library, 2001 Sheppard Ave E, Ste 400, Toronto, ON, M2J 4Z8, CANADA. Tel: 416-497-8600, Ext 212. Fax: 416-497-0342. p. 2849

Zimmerman, Andy, Dir, Libr & Info Serv, Gordon, Feinblatt, Rothman, Hoffberger & Hollander, 233 E Redwood St, Baltimore, MD, 21202. Tel: 410-576-4255. Fax: 410-576-4246. p. 1013

Zimmerman, Carolyn, Librn, Hatboro Baptist Church Library, 32 N York Rd, Hatboro, PA, 19040. Tel: 215-675-8400. Fax: 215-675-4697. p. 2067

Zimmerman, Debbie, Libr Mgr, Worthington Libraries, 820 High St, Worthington, OH, 43085. Tel: 614-807-2622. Fax: 614-807-2659. p. 1950

Zimmerman, H Neil, Librn, Population Council Library, One Dag Hammarskjold Plaza, New York, NY, 10017. Tel: 212-339-0533. Fax: 212-755-6052. p. 1697

Zimmerman, Jane, Mgr, Geauga County Public Library, Newbury Public Library Station, 14775 Auburn Rd, Newbury, OH, 44065. Tel: 440-564-7552. Fax: 440-564-7117. p. 1867

Zimmerman, Janet, Dir, William Beaumont Hospital, 3601 W 13 Mile Rd, Royal Oak, MI, 48073-6769. Tel: 248-898-1750. Fax: 248-898-1060. p. 1223

Zimmerman, Jason, Pub Serv, Alpha Park Public Library District, 3527 S Airport Rd, Bartonville, IL, 61607-1799. Tel: 309-697-3822, Ext 25. Fax: 309-697-9681. p. 592

Zimmerman, Jennifer, Br Mgr, La Porte County Public Library, Hanna Branch, 202 N Thompson, Hanna, IN, 46340. Tel: 219-797-4735. Fax: 219-797-4735. p. 759

Zimmerman, Jessica, Br Mgr, Enlow Ruth Library of Garrett County, Accident Branch, 106 S North St, Accident, MD, 21520-0154. Tel: 301-746-8792. Fax: 301-746-8399. p. 1035

Zimmerman, Jill M, Automation Syst Coordr, St Philip's College, 1801 Martin Luther King Dr, San Antonio, TX, 78203-2098. Tel: 210-486-2330. Fax: 210-486-2335. p. 2381

Zimmerman, Jonathan, Head, ILL, New Mexico Institute of Mining & Technology, 801 Leroy Pl, Socorro, NM, 87801. Tel: 575-835-5614. Fax: 575-835-5754. p. 1565

Zimmerman, Julia A, Dean, Florida State University Libraries, Strozier Library Bldg, 116 Honors Way, Tallahassee, FL, 32306-0001. Tel: 850-644-2706. p. 494

Zimmerman, Karen, In Charge, SUNY Cortland, Performing Arts, Dowd Fine Arts Ctr, Cortland, NY, 13045. Tel: 607-756-1200. p. 1612

Zimmerman, Kathryn, Sr Librn, Hennepin County Library, Maple Grove, 8001 Main St N, Maple Grove, MN, 55369-4617. Tel: 612-543-6456. Fax: 612-543-6452. p. 1264

Zimmerman, Kathryn, Sr Librn, Hennepin County Library, Osseo, 415 Central Ave, Osseo, MN, 55369-1194. Tel: 612-543-6456. Fax: 612-543-5752. p. 1264

Zimmerman, Linda, Dir, Gridley Public Library District, 320 Center St, Gridley, IL, 61744. Tel: 309-747-2284. Fax: 309-747-3195. p. 653

Zimmerman, Lynn, Circ Librn, Lincoln County Public Libraries, 220 W Sixth St, Libby, MT, 59923-1898. Tel: 406-293-2778. Fax: 406-293-4235. p. 1385

Zimmerman, Martha, Youth Serv, Niceville Public Library, 206 N Partin Dr, Niceville, FL, 32578. Tel: 850-729-4070. Fax: 850-729-4053. p. 472

Zimmerman, Martha, Assoc Dean, Dir of Tech Serv, Salisbury University, 1101 Camden Ave, Salisbury, MD, 21801-6863. Tel: 410-543-6130. Fax: 410-543-6203. p. 1040

Zimmerman, Martin, Electronic Serv Librn, Long Island University, One University Plaza, Brooklyn, NY, 11201-9926. Tel: 718-488-1081. Fax: 718-780-4057. p. 1593

Zimmerman, Michelle, Ch, North Mankato Taylor Library, 1001 Belgrade Ave, North Mankato, MN, 56003. Tel: 507-345-5120. Fax: 507-345-1861. p. 1268

Zimmerman, Nancy P, Assoc Prof, University of South Carolina, 1501 Greene St, Columbia, SC, 29208. Tel: 803-777-3858. Fax: 803-777-7938. p. 2973

Zimmerman, Peter, Info Serv, University of Windsor, 401 Sunset Ave, Windsor, ON, N9B 3P4, CANADA. Tel: 519-253-3000, Ext 3180. p. 2871

Zimmerman, Rochelle, Ref, Northwood University, 4000 Whiting Dr, Midland, MI, 48640-2398. Tel: 989-837-4275. Fax: 989-832-5031. p. 1208

Zimmerman, Sara, Exec Dir, The Louisiana Library Network, Information Technology Services, 200 Frey Computing Services Ctr, Baton Rouge, LA, 70803. p. 2944

Zimmerman, Stephanie, Training & Develop Coordr, Library System of Lancaster County, 1866 Colonial Village Lane, Ste 107, Lancaster, PA, 17601. Tel: 717-207-0500. Fax: 717-207-0504. p. 2077

Zimmerman, Tara, Grants Coordr/Fla Ctr of the Bk, Broward County Division of Libraries, 100 S Andrews Ave, Fort Lauderdale, FL, 33301. Tel: 954-357-7368. Fax: 954-357-5733. p. 441

Zimmerman, Tess, Asst Librn, ILL, Union Institute & University, 62 Ridge St, Ste 2, Montpelier, VT, 05602. Tel: 802-828-8747. Fax: 802-828-8748. p. 2429

Zimmermann, Mary, Ch, Somerset County Library System, 11767 Beechwood St, Princess Anne, MD, 21853. Tel: 410-651-0852, Ext 11. Fax: 410-651-1388. p. 1036

Zimmett, Joan, Dir of Develop, The New York Society Library, 53 E 79th St, New York, NY, 10075. Tel: 212-288-6900, Ext 202. Fax: 212-744-5832. p. 1694

Zimnicki, Linda, Info Spec, Tetra-Tech Em Inc, One S Wacker Dr 37th Flr, Chicago, IL, 60606. Tel: 312-201-7718. Fax: 312-938-0118. p. 625

Zimpelmann, Meagan, Asst Librn, Kenai Peninsula College Library, 156 College Rd, Soldotna, AK, 99669. Tel: 907-262-0384. Fax: 907-262-0386. p. 53

Zimprich, Vanessa, Curator, Waseca County Historical Society Library, 315 Second Ave NE, Waseca, MN, 56093. Tel: 507-835-7700. p. 1287

Zinaman, Sandy, Asst Dir, Stone Ridge Public Library, Rte 209, Stone Ridge, NY, 12484. Tel: 845-687-7023. Fax: 845-687-0094. p. 1749

Zinfon, Lissa, Libr Instruction, Plymouth State University, Highland St, Plymouth, NH, 03264-1595. Tel: 603-535-2258. Fax: 603-535-2445. p. 1462

Zink, Chris, Asst Dir, Onawa Public Library, 707 Iowa Ave, Onawa, IA, 51040. Tel: 712-423-1733. Fax: 712-433-4622. p. 836

Zink, Steven D, Dean of Libr, VPres, Info Tech, University of Nevada-Reno, 1664 N Virginia St, Mailstop 0322, Reno, NV, 89557-0322. Tel: 775-682-5684. Fax: 775-784-4529. p. 1433

Zinkham, Helena, Div Chief, Library of Congress, Prints & Photographs Division, 101 Independence Ave SE, Rm LM 337, Washington, DC, 20540-4730. Tel: 202-707-6394. Fax: 202-707-6647. p. 407

Zinkl, Charlene, Br Mgr, Saint Louis County Library, Meramec Valley Branch, 625 New Smizer Mill Rd, Fenton, MO, 63026. Tel: 636-349-4981. p. 1359

Zinky, Gloria, Head, Tech Serv, University of South Carolina, Coleman Karesh Law Library, USC Law Ctr, 701 Main St, Columbia, SC, 29208. Tel: 803-777-5898. Fax: 803-777-9405. p. 2190

Zinn, Donna Heller, Librn, Perry Historians Library, 763 Dix Hill Rd, New Bloomfield, PA, 17068. Tel: 717-582-4896. p. 2095

Zinn, Heather, Libr Tech, Capital Health/Nova Scotia Hospital, Hugh Bell Bldg, Rm 200, 300 Pleasant St, Dartmouth, NS, B2Y 3Z9, CANADA. Tel: 902-464-3254. Fax: 902-464-4804. p. 2779

Zinnerman-Bethea, Darlene, Dir, Benedict College Library, 1600 Harden St, Columbia, SC, 29204. Tel: 803-705-4773. Fax: 803-748-7539. p. 2186

Zins, Tina, Chief Librn, Apollo Memorial Library, 219 N Pennsylvania Ave, Apollo, PA, 15613. Tel: 724-478-4214. Fax: 724-478-1693. p. 2029

Ziolko, Jay, Dir, Mississippi County Library System, Blytheville Public, 200 N Fifth St, Blytheville, AR, 72315. Tel: 870-762-2431. Fax: 870-762-2442. p. 95

Ziolko, Joseph F, Dir, Mississippi County Library System, 200 N Fifth St, Blytheville, AR, 72315-2791. Tel: 870-762-2431. Fax: 870-762-2442. p. 95

Ziomek, Mark, Actg Dir, United States Government Accountability Office, 441 G St NW, Rm 7158, Washington, DC, 20548. Tel: 202-512-2396. p. 420

Ziorli, Jennifer, Br Head, Toronto Public Library, Beaches, 2161 Queen St E, Toronto, ON, M4L 1J1, CANADA. Tel: 416-393-7703. Fax: 416-393-7422. p. 2860

Ziorli, Severino, Br Head, Toronto Public Library, Gerrard/Ashdale, 1432 Gerrard St E, Toronto, ON, M4L 1Z6, CANADA. Tel: 416-393-7717. Fax: 416-393-7779. p. 2861

Zipfel, Harriett, Dir, Galesburg Public Library, 40 E Simmons St, Galesburg, IL, 61401-4591. Tel: 309-343-6118. Fax: 309-343-4877. p. 648

Zipfel, Joanne, Coordr, Southern Ocean Medical Center, 1140 Rte 72 W, Manahawkin, NJ, 08050. Tel: 609-597-6011. Fax: 609-978-8920. p. 1498

Ziph, Sally, Instrul Serv Librn, University of Michigan, Kresge Business Administration Library, Stephen M Ross School of Business,

701 Tappan St, K3330, Ann Arbor, MI, 48109-1234. Tel: 734-764-5532. Fax: 734-764-3839. p. 1152

Zipkin, Laura, Adult Serv, Killingly Public Library, 25 Westcott Rd, Danielson, CT, 06239. Tel: 860-779-5383. Fax: 860-779-1823. p. 335

Zippay, Vickie, Ch, Williams County Public Library, 107 E High St, Bryan, OH, 43506-1702. Tel: 419-636-6734. Fax: 419-636-3970. p. 1862

Zirpoli, Alexis, Tech Serv Librn, Central New Mexico Community College Libraries, 525 Buena Vista SE, Albuquerque, NM, 87106-4023. Tel: 505-224-3292. Fax: 505-224-3321. p. 1548

Zittrain, Jonathan, Vice Dean, Libr & Info Res, Harvard Library, Harvard Law School Library, Langdell Hall, 1545 Massachusetts Ave, Cambridge, MA, 02138. Tel: 617-495-3170. Fax: 617-495-4449. p. 1075

Zivkovich, Krista, Ref Serv, Ad, YA Serv, Morley Library, 184 Phelps St, Painesville, OH, 44077-3926. Tel: 440-352-3383. Fax: 440-352-9097. p. 1927

Zmaczynski, Mary Anne, Ref & Instruction Librn, DeVry University, 3300 N Campbell Ave, Chicago, IL, 60618. Tel: 773-697-2236. Fax: 773-697-2714. p. 612

Zmola, John F, Ref, North Riverside Public Library District, 2400 S DesPlaines Ave, North Riverside, IL, 60546. Tel: 708-447-0869, Ext 227. Fax: 708-447-0526. p. 682

Zmyewski, Stephen, Coordr, Minnesota State College-Southeast Technical, 1250 Homer Rd, Winona, MN, 55987. Tel: 507-453-1413. Fax: 507-453-1450. p. 1289

Znamirowski, Barbara, Govt Doc, Maps Librn, Trent University, 1600 West Bank Dr, Peterborough, ON, K9J 7B8, CANADA. Tel: 705-748-1011, Ext 1278. Fax: 705-748-1126. p. 2836

Znati, Taieb, Prof, University of Pittsburgh, 135 N Bellefield Ave, Pittsburgh, PA, 15260. Tel: 412-624-5230. Fax: 412-624-5231. p. 2973

Zobel, James W, Archivist, MacArthur Memorial Library & Archives, MacArthur Sq, Norfolk, VA, 23510. Tel: 757-441-2965, 757-441-2968. Fax: 757-441-5389. p. 2481

Zobin, Chris, Librn, La Crosse Tribune Library, 401 N Third St, La Crosse, WI, 54601. Tel: 608-791-8256. Fax: 608-782-9723. p. 2603

Zoccali, Tina, Ref Librn, Alston & Bird, LLP Library, 90 Park Ave, 12th Flr, New York, NY, 10016. Tel: 212-210-9526. Fax: 212-210-9444. p. 1667

Zoe, Butler, Asst Dir, William F Laman Public Library, 2801 Orange St, North Little Rock, AR, 72114-2296. Tel: 501-758-1720. Fax: 501-758-3539. p. 111

Zoellner, Alan F, Dr, Ref/Govt Doc Librn, College of William & Mary in Virginia, Earl Gregg Swem Library, One Landrum Dr, Williamsburg, VA, 23187. Tel: 757-221-3065. Fax: 757-221-2635. p. 2502

Zoet, Char, Librn, Muskegon Area District Library, North Muskegon Walker Branch, 1522 Ruddiman Dr, North Muskegon, MI, 49445-3038. Tel: 231-744-6080. Fax: 231-719-8056. p. 1213

Zola, Jim, Div Mgr, Children's Serv, High Point Public Library, 901 N Main St, High Point, NC, 27262. Tel: 336-883-3668. Fax: 336-883-3636. p. 1802

Zoli, Suzanne, Dir, Richfield Township Public Library, 1410 Saint Helen Rd, Saint Helen, MI, 48656. Tel: 989-389-7630. Fax: 989-389-7795. p. 1224

Zolinski, Élise, Adminr, Bibliothèque Allard Regional Library, 104086 PTH 11, Saint Georges, MB, R0E 1V0, CANADA. Tel: 204-367-8443. Fax: 204-367-1780. p. 2751

Zoll, August H, Sr Librn, Aviation Hall of Fame & Museum Library of New Jersey, Teterboro Airport, 400 Fred Wehran Dr, Teterboro, NJ, 07608. Tel: 201-288-6344. Fax: 201-288-5666. p. 1533

Zollars, Scotty M, Dir, Labette Community College Library, 200 S 14th St, Parsons, KS, 67357. Tel: 620-820-1167. Fax: 620-421-1469. p. 889

Zoller, Danielle, Librn, District of Columbia Department of Corrections, 1901 E St SE, Washington, DC, 20003. Tel: 202-698-3000, Ext 72263. Fax: 202-698-3301. p. 398

Zoller, Gabriela, Cataloger, Albright-Knox Art Gallery, 1285 Elmwood Ave, Buffalo, NY, 14222-1096. Tel: 716-270-8240. Fax: 716-882-6213. p. 1596

Zoller, Karen, Dir, Notre Dame College, 4545 College Rd, South Euclid, OH, 44121. Tel: 216-373-5266. Fax: 216-381-3227. p. 1935

Zoller, Terry, Librn, Park Rapids Area Library, 210 W First St, Park Rapids, MN, 56470-8925. Tel: 218-732-4966. Fax: 218-732-4966. p. 1270

Zolli, Barbara, Dir, Pennsylvania Historical & Museum Commission, 202 Museum Lane, Titusville, PA, 16354-8902. Tel: 814-827-2797. Fax: 814-827-4888. p. 2146

Zollinger, Carla, Mgr, Ad Serv, Provo City Library, 550 N University Ave, Provo, UT, 84601-1618. Tel: 801-852-6673. Fax: 801-852-6688. p. 2411

Zoltai, Steve, Archivist, Coll Develop, Canadian Memorial Chiropractic College, 6100 Leslie St, Toronto, ON, M2H 3J1, CANADA. Tel: 416-482-2340, Ext 206. Fax: 416-482-4816. p. 2851

Zompanti, Eliseo, Br Head, Toronto Public Library, Rexdale, 2243 Kipling Ave, Toronto, ON, M9W 4L5, CANADA. Tel: 416-394-5200. Fax: 416-394-5205. p. 2863

Zonderwyk, Gary, CUL Adminr, New Jersey State Library, Talking Book & Braille Center, 2300 Stuyvesant Ave, Trenton, NJ, 08618. Tel: 609-406-7179, Ext 825. Fax: 609-406-7181. p. 1536

Zonker, Debbie, Librn, Loxley Public Library, 1001 Loxley Ave, Loxley, AL, 36551. Tel: 251-964-5695. p. 24

Zook, Christina L, Court Adminr, Perry County Law Library, Perry County Courthouse, Center Sq, Two E Main St, New Bloomfield, PA, 17068. Tel: 717-582-5143. Fax: 717-582-5144. p. 2095

Zoppel, Carol, Soc Sci Librn, Salem State University Library, 352 Lafayette St, Salem, MA, 01970-5353. Tel: 978-542-6811. Fax: 978-542-6596. p. 1122

Zorbas, John A, Dir, Butte County Public Law Library, 1675 Montgomery St, Oroville, CA, 95965. Tel: 530-538-7122. Fax: 530-534-1499. p. 202

Zorich, Phillip, Dean of Libr, Indiana University of Pennsylvania, Northpointe Regional Campus Library, 167 Northpointe Blvd, Freeport, PA, 16229. Tel: 724-294-3306. Fax: 724-294-3307. p. 2071

Zorich, Phillip, Dr, Dean, Univ Libr, Indiana University of Pennsylvania, 431 S 11th St, Indiana, PA, 15705-1096. Tel: 724-357-2330. Fax: 724-357-4891. p. 2071

Zorn, Marcia, Ref Serv, Web Serv, National Library of Medicine, Bldg 38, Rm 2E-17B, 8600 Rockville Pike, Bethesda, MD, 20894. Tel: 301-496-6308. Fax: 301-496-4450. p. 1022

Zornes, Gabrielle, Ch, Show Low Public Library, 180 N Ninth St, Show Low, AZ, 85901. Tel: 928-532-4074. Fax: 928-532-4079. p. 82

Zornow, Diana, Asst Dir, Elkhart County Historical Society, Inc, 304 W Vistula, Bristol, IN, 46507. Tel: 574-848-4322. Fax: 574-848-5703. p. 729

Zou, Qing (Jason), Librn, Lakehead University Library, 955 Oliver Rd, Thunder Bay, ON, P7B 5E1, CANADA. Tel: 807-343-8251. Fax: 807-343-8007. p. 2848

Zou, Qiong, Librn, Asnuntuck Community College, 170 Elm St, Enfield, CT, 06082-0068. Tel: 860-253-3172. Fax: 860-253-9310. p. 338

Zou, Tim, Head, Access Serv, University of Arkansas Libraries, 365 N McIlroy Ave, Fayetteville, AR, 72701-4002. Tel: 479-575-3201. Fax: 479-575-6656. p. 99

Zrostlik, Cole, Youth Serv, Milltown Public Library, 61 W Main St, Milltown, WI, 54858. Tel: 715-825-2313. Fax: 715-825-4422. p. 2616

Zsulya, Carol, Head, Coll Develop, Cleveland State University, University Library, Rhodes Tower, 2121 Euclid Ave, Cleveland, OH, 44115-2214. Tel: 216-523-7373. Fax: 216-687-9380. p. 1879

Zu, Xiaojing, ILL, Ref Librn, Berry College, 2277 Martha Berry Hwy, Mount Berry, GA, 30149. Tel: 706-236-2221. p. 546

Zubal, John T, Pres, United States Book Exchange Library, 2969 W 25th St, Cleveland, OH, 44113-5393. Tel: 216-241-6960. Fax: 216-241-6966. p. 1881

Zubal, Marilyn, ILL, Per, United States Book Exchange Library, 2969 W 25th St, Cleveland, OH, 44113-5393. Tel: 216-241-6960. Fax: 216-241-6966. p. 1881

Zubal, Thomas A, Librn, United States Book Exchange Library, 2969 W 25th St, Cleveland, OH, 44113-5393. Tel: 216-241-6960. Fax: 216-241-6966. p. 1881

Zuber, Anne, Dir, Wenonah Free Public Library, 101 E Mantua Ave, Wenonah, NJ, 08090-1950. Tel: 856-468-6323. p. 1540

Zuber, Reesa, Dir, Heritage University, 3240 Fort Rd, Toppenish, WA, 98948. Tel: 509-865-8500, Ext 3436. Fax: 509-865-4144. p. 2541

Zubrod, Nancy, Libr Assoc, St Luke's College Library, 2620 Pierce St, Sioux City, IA, 51104. Tel: 712-279-3156. p. 844

Zuccaro, Jennifer, Ser/Govt Doc Librn, West Virginia State University, Campus Box L17, Institute, WV, 25112. Tel: 304-766-5222. Fax: 304-766-4103. p. 2562

Zuckerman, Jane, YA Serv, Floral Park Public Library, 17 Caroline Pl, Floral Park, NY, 11001. Tel: 516-326-6330. Fax: 516-437-6959. p. 1622

Zuckerman, Louise, Coordr, Braille Institute Library Services, San Diego Center, 4555 Executive Dr, San Diego, CA, 92121-3021. Tel: 858-452-1111, Ext 5011. Fax: 858-452-1688. p. 169

Zuckert, Curt, Mgr, Chicago Mercantile Exchange Library, 20 S Wacker Dr, Chicago, IL, 60606. Tel: 312-604-6552. p. 607

Zuehlke, Sandy, Dir, Coloma Public Library, 155 Front St, Coloma, WI, 54930-9670. Tel: 715-228-2530. Fax: 715-228-2532. p. 2586

Zuelke, Elizabeth, Mgr, Public Library of Cincinnati & Hamilton County, Outreach Services, 800 Vine St, Cincinnati, OH, 45202-2009. Tel: 513-369-6963. Fax: 513-369-4586. p. 1872

Zuger, Christine, Assoc Dir, Tech Serv, Georgia College & State University, 320 N Wayne St, Milledgeville, GA, 31061-3397. Tel: 478-445-0983. Fax: 478-445-6847. p. 544

Zuhlke, Helen, Dir, Kendall Public Library, 110 E South Railroad St, Kendall, WI, 54638-9999. Tel: 608-463-7103. p. 2601

Zuichkovski, Cortina, Ch, Putnam County Public Library, 103 E Poplar St, Greencastle, IN, 46135-1655. Tel: 765-653-2755. Fax: 765-653-2756. p. 746

Zuke, Jan, PhD, Librn, Southwestern Illinois College, 4950 Maryville Rd, Granite City, IL, 62040. Tel: 618-641-6653. p. 651

Zukosky, Karen, Br Mgr, Blackwater Regional Library, Isle of Wight County Library/Smithfield Branch, 255 James St, Smithfield, VA, 23430. Tel: 757-357-4856. Fax: 757-357-0883. p. 2458

Zula, Floyd, Acq, Paulina June & George Pollak Library, 800 N State College Blvd, Fullerton, CA, 92834. Tel: 714-278-2714. Fax: 714-278-2439. p. 154

Zuleani, Claire, Mgr, Libr Heritage Res, Greater Sudbury Public Library, 74 MacKenzie St, Sudbury, ON, P3C 4X8, CANADA. Tel: 705-673-1155. Fax: 705-673-6145. p. 2846

Zuleeg, Janis, Br Mgr, Librn II, Jackson-George Regional Library System, St Martin Public Library, 15004 LeMoyne Blvd, Biloxi, MS, 39532-5205. Tel: 228-392-3250. Fax: 228-392-0522. p. 1310